S0-DUU-724

AMERICAN MEN & WOMEN OF SCIENCE

AMERICAN MEN & WOMEN OF SCIENCE

PHYSICAL AND BIOLOGICAL SCIENCES

15TH EDITION
VOLUME V
M-P

EDITED BY
JAQUES CATTELL PRESS

R. R. BOWKER COMPANY
NEW YORK & LONDON 1982

Published by R.R. Bowker Co.
1180 Avenue of the Americas, New York, N.Y. 10036

International Standard Book Number
Set: 0-8352-1413-3
Volume I: 0-8352-1414-1
Volume II: 0-8352-1416-8
Volume III: 0-8352-1417-6
Volume IV: 0-8352-1418-4
Volume V: 0-8352-1419-2
Volume VI: 0-8352-1420-6
Volume VII: 0-8352-1421-4
International Standard Serial Number: 0192-8570
Library of Congress Catalog Card Number: 6-7326

Printed and bound in the United States of America.

CONTENTS

ADVISORY COMMITTEE

Dr. Dael L. Wolfle, Committee Chairman
Professor Emeritus,
Graduate School of Public Affairs
University of Washington

Dr. Carl D. Douglass
Director,
Division of Research Grants
National Institutes of Health

Mr. Alan Fechter
Head,
Scientific and Technical Personnel Studies
National Science Foundation

Dr. Harold S. Ginsberg
Professor & Chairman,
Department of Microbiology
College of Physicians and Surgeons
Columbia University

Dr. Allen L. Hammond
Editor, *Science '81,*
American Association for the Advancement of Science

Dr. Anna J. Harrison
Professor,
Department of Chemistry
Mt. Holyoke College

Dr. William C. Kelly
Executive Director,
Office of Scientific and Engineering Personnel
National Research Council

Dr. H. William Koch
Director,
American Institute of Physics

Dr. Robert Krauss
Executive Director,
Federation of American Societies for Experimental Biology

Dr. William J. LeVeque
Executive Director,
American Mathematical Society

Dr. Raymond P. Mariella
Executive Director,
American Chemical Society

Dr. James H. Mulligan, Jr.
Professor,
Department of Electrical Engineering
University of California, Irvine

Dr. Kenneth Prewitt
President,
Social Science Research Council

Dr. Helen M. Ranney
Professor & Chairman,
Department of Medicine
University of California, San Diego

Dr. Matthias Stelly
Executive Vice President,
American Society of Agronomy

Mr. William E. Zimmie
President,
Zimmite Corporation

PREFACE

American Men and Women of Science is without peer as a chronicle of North American scientific endeavor and achievement. It has recorded the careers of over 280,000 scientists and engineers since the first edition appeared in 1906, and continues to provide current information on the leaders in America's research and academic communities.

The Fifteenth Edition contains the biographies of 130,000 women and men; 7,500 appear for the first time. The names of new entrants were submitted for consideration at the editors' request by current entrants and by persons in charge of academic, government and private research programs. All of those included meet the following criteria:

1. Achievement, by reason of experience and training of a stature in scientific work equivalent to that associated with the doctoral degree, coupled with presently continued activity in such work;

or

2. Research activity of high quality in science as evidenced by publication in reputable scientific journals; or, for those whose work cannot be published because of governmental or industrial security, research activity of high quality in science as evidenced by the judgment of the individual's peers;

or

3. Attainment of a position of substantial responsibility requiring scientific training and experience to the extent described for (1) and (2).

This edition profiles living scientists in the physical and biological fields as well as public health scientists, engineers, mathematicians, statisticians, and computer scientists. The information is collected by means of direct communication whenever possible. Forms are sent to all entrants for corroboration and updating, and those whose biographies are appearing for the first time receive verification proofs before publication. The information submitted by entrants is included as completely as possible within the boundaries of editorial and space restrictions. Full entries are repeated for former listees who do not return forms but whose current location can be verified in secondary sources. References to the previous edition are given for those who do not return forms and cannot be located, but who are presumed to be still active in science or engineering. A notation is made when an entrant from the previous edition is known to be deceased. Non-citizens of the Americas are included if working in the United States or Canada for a reasonable duration. Information on former entrants who have entered fields other than science and engineering, or who have been retired for ten years and are no longer professionally active has been omitted.

American Men and Women of Science has experienced many changes in its long history, and this edition is no exception. Following the suggestion of the advisory committee, and based on the recommendation of a user survey, the geographic and discipline indexes have been discontinued in printed form. The Fifteenth Edition will be available for on-line searching, however, through BRS, DIALOG and the Jaques Cattell Press. All elements of an entry, including field of interest, experience and location, can be accessed by the use of key words. Although *American Men and Women of Science* is on a three year publication cycle, the on-line database will be updated at more frequent intervals. Previous users of the directory will be pleased to find that the type size has been enlarged in response to many requests.

The Social and Behavioral Sciences section of *American Men and Women of Science* was last published in 1978. The limited acceptance of this section caused the postponement of subsequent editions. Realizing the importance of maintaining current data on the disciplines, the publishers are considering several possibilities for the future. One is the inclusion of selected, appropriate fields in the *Directory of American Scholars,* also a Bowker/Cattell publication. Another plan under consideration is the systematic addition of social and behavioral scientists to the on-line database for eventual publication in an all-inclusive *American Men and Women of Science.*

The editors take this opportunity to thank the Fifteenth Edition advisory committee for their guidance, encouragement and support. Appreciation is expressed to the many scientific societies who provided their membership lists for the purpose of locating former entrants whose addresses had changed.

Comments and suggestions on any aspect of the Fifteenth Edition are encouraged and should be directed to The Editors, *American Men and Women of Science,* P.O. Box 25001, Tempe, Arizona 85282.

Martha Cargill, *Editor*
Renee Lautenbach, *Managing Editor*
Terence Basom, *General Manager*
JAQUES CATTELL PRESS

August, 1982

ABBREVIATIONS

AAAS—American Association for the Advancement of Science
abnorm—abnormal
abstr—abstract(s)
acad—academic, academy
acct—account, accountant, accounting
acoust—acoustic(s), acoustical
ACTH—adrenocorticotrophic hormone
actg—acting
activ—activities, activity
addn—addition(s), additional
Add—Address
adj—adjunct, adjutant
adjust—adjustment
Adm—Admiral
admin—administration, administrative
adminr—administrator(s)
admis—admission(s)
adv—adviser(s), advisory
advan—advance(d), advancement
advert—advertisement, advertising
AEC—Atomic Energy Commission
aerodyn—aerodynamic(s)
aeronaut—aeronautic(s), aeronautical
aerophys—aerophysical, aerophysics
aesthet—aesthetic(s)
AFB—Air Force Base
affil—affiliate(s), affiliation
agr—agricultural, agriculture
agron—agronomic, agronomical, agronomy
agrost—agrostologic, agrostological, agrostology
agt—agent
AID—Agency for International Development
Ala-Alabama
allergol—allergological, allergology
alt—alternate
Alta—Alberta
Am—America, American
AMA—American Medical Association
anal—analysis, analytic, analytical
analog—analogue
anat—anatomic, anatomical, anatomy
anesthesiol—anesthesiology
angiol—angiology
Ann—Annal(s)
ann—annual
anthrop—anthropological, anthropology
anthropom—anthropometric, anthropometrical, anthropometry
antiq—antiquary, antiquities, antiquity
antiqn—antiquarian
apicult—apicultural, apiculture
APO—Army Post Office
app—appoint, appointed
appl—applied
appln—application
approx—approximate(ly)
Apr—April
apt—apartment(s)
aquacult—aquaculture
arbit—arbitration
arch—archives
archaeol—archaeological, archaeology
archit—architectural, architecture
Arg—Argentina, Argentine
Ariz—Arizona
Ark—Arkansas
artil—artillery
asn—association
assoc(s)—associate(s), associated
asst(s)—assistant(s), assistantship(s)
Assyriol—Assyriology
astrodyn—astrodynamics
astron—astronomical, astronomy
astronaut—astronautical, astronautics
astronr—astronomer
astrophys—astrophysical, astrophysics
attend—attendant, attending
atty—attorney
audiol—audiology
Aug—August
auth—author
AV—audiovisual
Ave—Avenue
avicult—avicultural, aviculture

b—born
bact—bacterial, bacteriologic, bacteriological, bacteriology
BC—British Columbia
bd—board
behav—behavior(al)
Belg—Belgian, Belgium
bibl—biblical
bibliog—bibliographic, bibliographical, bibliography
bibliogr—bibliographer
biochem—biochemical, biochemistry
biog—biographical, biography
biol—biological, biology
biomed—biomedical, biomedicine
biomet—biometric(s), biometrical, biometry
biophys—biophysical, biophysics
bk(s)—book(s)
bldg—building
Blvd—Boulevard
Bor—Borough
bot—botanical, botany
br—branch(es)
Brig—Brigadier
Brit—Britain, British
Bro(s)—Brother(s)
byrol—byrology
Bull—Bulletin
bur—bureau
bus—business
BWI—British West Indies

c—children
Calif—California
Can—Canada, Canadian
cand—candidate
Capt—Captain
cardiol—cardiology
cardiovasc—cardiovascular
cartog—cartographic, cartographical, cartography
cartogr—cartographer
Cath—Catholic
CEngr—Corps of Engineers
cent—central
Cent Am—Central America
cert—certificate(s), certification, certified
chap—chapter
chem—chemical(s), chemistry
chemother—chemotherapy
chmn—chairman
citricult—citriculture
class—classical
climat—climatological, climatology
clin(s)—clinic(s), clinical
cmndg—commanding
Co—Companies, Company
coauth— coauthor
co-dir—co-director
co-ed—co-editor
coeduc—coeducation, coeducational
col(s)—college(s), collegiate, colonel
collab—collaboration, coloborative
collabr—collaborator
Colo—Colorado
com—commerce, commercial

Comdr—Commander
commun—communicable, communication(s)
comn(s)—commission(s), commissioned
comnr—commissioner
comp—comparative
compos—composition
comput—computation, computer(s), computing
comt(s)—committee(s)
conchol—conchology
conf—conference
cong—congress, congressional
Conn—Connecticut
conserv—conservation, conservatory
consol—consolidated, consolidation
const—constitution, constitutional
construct—construction, constructive
consult(s)—consult, consultant(s) consultantship(s), consultation, consulting
contemp—contemporary
contrib—contribute, contributing, contribution(s)
contribr—contributor
conv—convention
coop—cooperating, cooperation, cooperative
coord—coordinate(d), coordinating, coordination
coordr—coordinator
corp—corporate, corporation(s)
corresp—correspondence, correspondent, corresponding
coun—council, counsel, counseling
counr—councilor, counselor
criminol—criminological, criminology
cryog—cryogenic(s)
crystallog—crystallographic, crystallograpi-ical, crystallography
crystallogr—crystallographer
Ct—Court
Ctr—Center
cult—cultural, culture
cur—curator
curric—curriculum
cybernet—cybernetic(s)
cytol—cytological, cytology
Czech—Czechoslovakia

DC—District of Columbia
Dec—December
Del—Delaware
deleg—delegate, delegation
delinq—delinquency, delinquent
dem—democrat(s), democratic
demog—demographic, demography
demogr—demographer
demonstr—demonstrator
dendrol—dendrologic, dendrological, dendrology
dent—dental, dentistry
dep—deputy
dept—department(al)
dermat—dermatologic, dermatological, dermatology
develop—developed, developing, development, developmental
diag—diagnosis, diagnostic
dialectol—dialectological, dialectology
dict—dictionaries, dictionary
Dig—Digest
dipl—diploma, diplomate
dir(s)—director(s), directories, directory
dis—disease(s), disorders
Diss Abstr—Dissertation Abstracts
dist—district
distrib—distributed, distribution, distributive
distribr—distributor(s)
div—division, divisional, divorced
DNA—deoxyribonucleic acid
doc—document(s), documentary, documentation
Dom—Dominion
Dr—Drive

e—east
ecol—ecological, ecology
econ(s)—economic(s), economical, economy
economet—econometric(s)
ECT—electroconvulsive or electroshock therapy
ed—edition(s), editor(s), editorial
ed bd—editorial board
educ—education, educational
educr—educator(s)
EEG—electroencephalogram, electroencephalographic, electroencephalography
Egyptol—Egyptology
EKG—electrocardiogram
elec—electric, electrical, electricity
electrochem—electrochemical, electrochemistry
electrophys—electrophysical, electrophysics
elem—elementary
embryol—embryologic, embryological, embryology
emer—emeriti, emiritus
employ—employment
encour—encouragement
encycl—encyclopedia
endocrinol—endocrinologic, endocrinology
eng—engineering
Eng—England, English
engr(s)—engineer(s)
enol—enology
Ens—Ensign
entom—entomological, entomology
environ—environment(s), environmental
enzym—enzymology
epidemiol—epidemiologic, epidemiological, epidemiology
equip—equipment
ESEA—Elementary & Secondary Education Act
espec—especially
estab—established, establishment(s)
ethnog—ethnographic, ethnographical, ethnography
ethnogr—ethnographer
ethnol—ethnologic, ethnological, ethnology
Europ—European
eval—evaluation
evangel—evangelical
eve—evening
exam—examination(s), examining
examr—examiner
except—exceptional
exec(s)—executive(s)
exeg—exegeses, exegesis, exegetic, exegetical
exhib(s)—exhibition(s), exhibit(s)
exp—experiment, experimental
exped(s)—expedition(s)
explor—exploration(s), exploratory
expos—exposition
exten—extension

fac—faculty
facil—facilities, facility
Feb—February
fed—federal
fedn—federation
fel(s)—fellow(s), fellowship(s)
fermentol—fermentology
fertil—fertility, fertilization
Fla—Florida
floricult—floricultural, floriculture
found—foundation
FPO—Fleet Post Office
Fr—French
Ft—Fort

Ga—Georgia
gastroenterol—gastroenterological, gastroenterology
gen—general
geneal—genealogical, genealogy
geod—geodesy, geodetic
geog—geographic, geographical, geography
geogr—geographer
geol—geologic, geological, geology
geom—geometric, geometrical, geometry
geomorphol—geomorphologic, geomorphology
geophys—geophysical, geophysics
Ger—German, Germanic, Germany
geriat—geriatric(s)
geront—gerontological, gerontology
glaciol—glaciology
gov—governing, governor(s)
govt—government, governmental
grad—graduate(d)
Gt Brit—Great Britain
guid—guidance
gym—gymnasium
gynec—gynecologic, gynecological, gynecology

handbk(s)—handbook(s)
helminth—helminthology
hemat—hematologic, hematological, hematology
herpet—herpetologic, herpetological, herpetology
Hisp—Hispanic, Hispania
hist—historic, historical, history
histol—histological, histology
HM—Her Majesty
hochsch—hochschule
homeop—homeopathic, homeopathy
hon(s)—honor(s), honorable, honorary
hort—horticultural, horticulture
hosp(s)—hospital(s), hospitalization
hq—headquarters
HumRRO—Human Resources Research Office
husb—husbandry
Hwy—Highway
hydraul—hydraulic(s)
hydrodyn—hydrodynamic(s)
hydrol—hydrologic, hydrological, hydrology
hyg—hygiene, hygienic(s)
hypn—hypnosis

ichthyol—ichthyological, ichthyology
Ill—Illinois
illum—illuminating, illumination
illus—illustrate, illustrated, illustration
illusr—illustrator
immunol—immunologic, immunological, immunology

Imp—Imperial
improv—improvement
Inc—Incorporated
in-chg—in charge
incl—include(s), including
Ind—Indiana
indust(s)—industrial, industries, industry
inf—infantry
info—information
inorg—inorganic
ins—insurance
inst(s)—institute(s), institution(s)
instnl—institutional(ized)
instr(s)—instruct, instruction, instructor(s)
instrnl—instructional
int—international
intel—intelligence
introd—introduction
invert—invertebrate
invest(s)—investigation(s)
investr—investigator
irrig—irrigation
Ital—Italian

J—Journal
Jan—January
Jct—Junction
jour—journal, journalism
jr—junior
jurisp—jurisprudence
juv—juvenile

Kans—Kansas
Ky—Kentucky

La—Louisiana
lab(s)—laboratories, laboratory
lang—language(s)
laryngol—laryngological, laryngology
lect—lecture(s)
lectr—lecturer(s)
legis—legislation, legislative, legislature
lett—letter(s)
lib—liberal
libr—libraries, library
librn—librarian
lic—license(d)
limnol—limnological, limnology
ling—linguistic(s), linguistical
lit—literary, literature
lithol—lithologic, lithological, lithology
Lt—Lieutenant
Ltd—Limited

m—married
mach—machine(s), machinery
mag—magazine(s)
maj—major
malacol—malacology
mammal—mammalogy
Man—Manitoba
Mar—March
Mariol—Mariology
Mass—Massachusetts
mat—material(s)
mat med—materia medica
math—mathematic(s), mathematical
Md—Maryland
mech—mechanic(s), mechanical
med—medical, medicinal, medicine
Mediter—Mediterranean
Mem—Memorial
mem—member(s), membership(s)
ment—mental(ly)
metab—metabolic, metabolism
metall—metallurgic, metallurgical, metallurgy
metallog—metallographic, metallography
metallogr—metallographer
metaphys—metaphysical, metaphysics
meteorol—meteorological, meteorology
metrol—metrological, metrology
metrop—metropolitan
Mex—Mexican, Mexico
mfg—manufacturing
mfr(s)—manufacture(s), manufacturer(s)
mgr—manager
mgt—management
Mich—Michigan
microbiol—microbiological, microbiology
micros—microscopic, microscopical, microscopy
mid—middle
mil—military
mineral—mineralogical, mineralogy
Minn—Minnesota
Miss—Mississippi
mkt—market, marketing
Mo—Missouri
mod—modern
monogr—monograph
Mont—Montana
morphol—morphological, morphology
Mt—Mount
mult—multiple
munic—municipal, municipalities
mus—museum(s)
musicol—musicological, musicology
mycol—mycologic, mycology

n—north
NASA—National Aeronautics & Space Administration
nat—national, naturalized
NATO—North Atlantic Treaty Organization
navig—navigation(al)
NB—New Brunswick
NC—North Carolina
NDak—North Dakota
NDEA—National Defense Education Act
Nebr—Nebraska
nematol—nematological, nematology
nerv—nervous
Neth—Netherlands
neurol—neurological, neurology
neuropath—neuropathological, neuropathology
neuropsychiat—neuropsychiatric, neuropsychiatry
neurosurg—neurosurgical, neurosurgery
Nev—Nevada
New Eng—New England
New York—New York City
Nfld—Newfoundland
NH—New Hampshire
NIH—National Institutes of Health
NIMH—National Institute of Mental Health
NJ—New Jersey
NMex—New Mexico
nonres—nonresident
norm—normal
Norweg—Norwegian
Nov—November
NS—Nova Scotia
NSF—National Science Foundation
NSW—New South Wales
numis—numismatic(s)
nutrit—nutrition, nutritional
NY—New York State
NZ—New Zealand

observ—observatories, observatory
obstet—obstetric(s), obstetrical
occas—occasional(ly)
occup—occupation, occupational
oceanog—oceanographic, oceanographical, oceanography
oceanogr—oceanographer
Oct—October
odontol—odontology
OEEC—Organization for European Economic Cooperation
off—office, official
Okla—Oklahoma
olericult—olericulture
oncol—oncologic, oncology
Ont—Ontario
oper(s)—operation(s), operational, operative
ophthal—ophthalmologic, ophthalmological, ophthalmology
optom—optometric, optometrical, optometry
ord—ordnance
Ore—Oregon
org—organic
orgn—organization(s), organizational
orient—oriental
ornith—ornithological, ornithology
orthod—orthodontia, orthodontic(s)
orthop—orthopedic(s)
osteop—osteopathic, osteopathy
otol—otological, otology
otolaryngol—otolaryngological, otolaryngology
otorhinol—otorhinologic, otorhinology

Pa—Pennsylvania
Pac—Pacific
paleobot—paleobotanical, paleobotany
paleont—paleontological, paleontology
Pan-Am—Pan-American
parasitol—parasitology
partic—participant, participating
path—pathologic, pathological, pathology
pedag—pedagogic(s), pedagogical, pedagogy
pediat—pediatric(s)
PEI—Prince Edward Islands
penol—penological, penology
periodont—periodontal, periodontic(s), periodontology
petrog—petrographic, petrographical, petrography
petrogr—petrographer
petrol—petroleum, petrologic, petrological, petrology
pharm—pharmacy
pharmaceut—pharmaceutic(s), pharmaceutical(s)
pharmacog—pharmacognosy
pharamacol—pharmacologic, pharmacological, pharmacology
phenomenol—phenomenologic(al), phenomenology
philol—philological, philology
philos—philosophic, philosophical, philosophy
photog—photographic, photography
photogeog—photogeographic, photogeography

photogr—photographer(s)
photogram—photogrammetric, photogrammetry
photom—photometric, photometrical, photometry
phycol—phycology
phys—physical
physiog—physiographic, physiographical, physiography
physiol—physiological, physiology
Pkwy—Parkway
Pl—Place
polit—political, politics
polytech—polytechnic(al)
pomol—pomological, pomology
pontif—pontifical
pop—population
Port—Portugal, Portuguese
postgrad—postgraduate
PQ—Province of Quebec
PR—Puerto Rico
pract—practice
practr—practitioner
prehist—prehistoric, prehistory
prep—preparation, preparative, preparatory
pres—president
Presby—Presbyterian
preserv—preservation
prev—prevention, preventive
prin—principal
prob(s)—problem(s)
proc—proceedings
proctol—proctologic, proctological, proctology
prod—product(s), production, productive
prof—professional, professor, professorial
Prof Exp—Professional Experience
prog(s)—program(s), programmed, programming
proj—project(s), projection(al), projective
prom—promotion
protozool—protozoology
prov—province, provincial
psychiat—psychiatric, psychiatry
psychoanal—psychoanalysis, psychoanalytic, psychoanalytical
psychol—psychological, psychology
psychomet—psychometric(s)
psychopath—psychopathologic, psychopathology
psychophys—psychophysical, psychophysics
psychophysiol—psychophysiological, psychophysiology
psychosom—psychosomatic(s)
psychother—psychotherapeutic(s), psychotherapy
Pt—Point
pub—public
publ—publication(s), publish(ed), publisher, publishing
pvt—private

Qm—Quartermaster
Qm Gen—Quartermaster General
qual—qualitative, quality
quant—quantitative
quart—quarterly

radiol—radiological, radiology
RAF—Royal Air Force
RAFVR—Royal Air Force Volunteer Reserve
RAMC—Royal Army Medical Corps
RAMCR—Royal Army Medical Corps Reserve
RAOC—Royal Army Ordnance Corps
RASC—Royal Army Service Corps
RASCR—Royal Army Service Corps Reserve
RCAF—Royal Canadian Air Force
RCAFR—Royal Canadian Air Force Reserve
RCAFVR—Royal Canadian Air Force Volunteer Reserve
RCAMC—Royal Canadian Army Medical Corps
RCAMCR—Royal Canadian Army Medical Corps Reserve
RCASC—Royal Canadian Army Service Corps
RCASCR—Royal Canadian Army Service Corps Reserve
RCEME—Royal Canadian Electrical & Mechanical Engineers
RCN—Royal Canadian Navy
RCNR—Royal Canadian Naval Reserve
RCNVR—Royal Canadian Naval Volunteer Reserve
Rd—Road
RD—Rural Delivery
rec—record(s), recording
redevelop—redevelopment
ref—reference(s)
refrig—refrigeration
regist—register(ed), registration
registr—registrar
regt—regiment(al)
rehab—rehabilitation
rel(s)—relation(s), relative
relig—religion, religious
REME—Royal Electrical & Mechanical Engineers
rep—represent, representative
repub—republic
req—requirements
res—research, reserve
rev—review, revised, revision
RFD—Rural Free Delivery
rhet—rhetoric, rhetorical
RI—Rhode Island
Rm—Room
RM—Royal Marines
RN—Royal Navy
RNA—ribonucleic acid
RNR—Royal Naval Reserve
RNVR—Royal Naval Volunteer Reserve
roentgenol—roentgenologic, roentgenological, roentgenology
RR—Railroad, Rural Route
rte—route
Russ—Russian
rwy—railway

s—south
SAfrica—South Africa
SAm—South America, South American
sanit—sanitary, sanitation
Sask—Saskatchewan
SC—South Carolina
Scand—Scandinavia(n)
sch(s)—school(s)
scholar—scholarship
sci—science(s), scientific
SDak—South Dakota
SEATO—Southeast Asia Treaty Organization
sec—secondary
sect—section
secy—secretary
seismog—seismograph, seismographic, seismography
seismogr—seismographer
seismol—seismological, seismology
sem—seminar, seminary
sen—senator, senatorial
Sept—September
ser—serial, series
serol—serologic, serological, serology
serv—service(s), serving
silvicult—silvicultural, silviculture
soc(s)—societies, society
soc sci—social science
sociol—sociologic, sociological, sociology
Span—Spanish
spec—special
specif—specification(s)
spectrog—spectrograph, spectrographic, spectography
spectrogr—spectrographer
spectrophotom—spectrophotometer, spectrophotometric, spectrophotometry
spectros—spectroscopic, spectroscopy
speleol—speleological, speleology
Sq—Square
sr—senior
St—Saint, Street(s)
sta(s)—station(s)
stand—standard(s), standardization
statist—statistical, statistics
Ste—Sainte
steril—sterility
stomatol—stomatology
stratig—stratigraphic, stratigraphy
stratigr—stratigrapher
struct—structural, structure(s)
stud—student(ship)
subcomt—subcommittee
subj—subject
subsid—subsidiary
substa—substation
super—superior
suppl—supplement(s), supplemental, supplementary
supt—superintendent
supv—supervising, supervision
supvr—supervisor
supvry—supervisory
surg—surgery, surgical
surv—survey, surveying
survr—surveyor
Swed—Swedish
Switz—Switzerland
symp—symposia, symposium(s)
syphil—syphilology
syst(s)—system(s), systematic(s), systematical

taxon—taxonomic, taxonomy
tech—technical, technique(s)
technol—technologic(al), technology
tel—telegraph(y), telephone
temp—temporary
Tenn—Tennessee
Terr—Terrace
Tex—Texas
textbk(s)—textbook(s)
text ed—text edition
theol—theological, theology
theoret—theoretic(al)
ther—therapy
therapeut—therapeutic(s)

thermodyn—thermodynamic(s)
topog—topographic, topographical, topography
topogr—topographer
toxicol—toxicologic, toxicological, toxicology
trans—transactions
transl—translated, translation(s)
translr—translator(s)
transp—transport, transportation
treas—treasurer, treasury
treat—treatment
trop—tropical
tuberc—tuberculosis
TV—television
Twp—Township

UAR—United Arab Republic
UK—United Kingdom
UN—United Nations
undergrad—undergraduate
unemploy—unemployment
UNESCO—United Nations Educational Scientific & Cultural Organization
UNICEF—United Nations International Childrens Fund
univ(s)—universities, university
UNRRA—United Nations Relief & Rehabilitation Administration
UNRWA—United Nations Relief & Works Agency
urol—urologic, urological, urology
US—United States
USA—US Army
USAAF—US Army Air Force
USAAFR—US Army Air Force Reserve
USAF—US Air Force
USAFR—US Air Force Reserve
USAR—US Army Reserve
USCG—US Coast Guard
USCGR—US Coast Guard Reserve
USDA—US Department of Agriculture
USMC—US Marine Corps
USMCR—US Marine Corps Reserve
USN—US Navy
USNAF—US Naval Air Force
USNAFR—US Naval Air Force Reserve
USNR—US Naval Reserve
USPHS—US Public Health Service
USPHSR—US Public Health Service Reserve
USSR—Union of Soviet Socialist Republics
USWMC—US Women's Marine Corps
USWMCR—US Women's Marine Corps Reserve

Va—Virginia
var—various
veg—vegetable(s), vegetation
vent—ventilating, ventilation
vert—vertebrate
vet—veteran(s), veterinarian, veterinary
VI—Virgin Islands
vinicult—viniculture
virol—virological, virology
vis—visiting
voc—vocational
vocab—vocabulary
vol(s)—voluntary, volunteer(s), volume(s)
vpres—vice president
vs—versus
Vt—Vermont

w—west
WAC—Women's Army Corps
Wash—Washington
WAVES—Women Accepted for Voluntary Emergency Service
WHO—World Health Organization
WI—West Indies
wid—widow, widowed, widower
Wis—Wisconsin
WRCNS—Women's Royal Canadian Naval Service
WRNS—Women's Royal Naval Service
WVa—West Virginia
Wyo—Wyoming

yearbk(s)—yearbook(s)
YMCA—Young Men's Christian Association
YMHA—Young Men's Hebrew Association
yr(s)—year(s)
YWCA—Young Women's Christian Association
YWHA—Young Women's Hebrew Association

zool—zoological, zoology

AMERICAN MEN & WOMEN OF SCIENCE

M

MA, BENJAMIN MINGLI, b Nanking, China, Feb 2, 24; nat US; m 58; c 1. AERONAUTICAL ENGINEERING. *Educ:* Nat Cent Univ, China, BS, 45; Stanford Univ, MS, 47, EngD(aeronaut & astronaut eng), 49; Iowa State Univ, PhD(nuclear sci & eng), 62. *Prof Exp:* Asst, Stanford Univ, 47-49, res assoc, 49-51; asst prof mech eng, Ohio Northern Univ, 55-56; assoc prof, SDak State Univ, 56-60; assoc prof, Univ Mich, 60-61; from asst prof to assoc prof, 61-80, PROF NUCLEAR ENG, IOWA STATE UNIV, 80- *Concurrent Pos:* Consult, Argonne Nat Lab, Hanford Eng Develop Lab; invited lectr, Univ Istanbul, Israel Inst Technol, Univ Stockholm, Univ Copenhagen, Athens Tech Univ & Cambridge Univ. *Mem:* Am Nuclear Soc; Am Inst Aeronaut & Astronaut; Am Soc Mech Eng; Am Soc Eng Educ; Am Phys Soc. *Res:* Materials and strength at elevated temperature; heat transfer; radiation effects; reactor fuel elements; nuclear energy conversion systems; nuclear fusion theory and technology. *Mailing Add:* Dept Nuclear Eng Iowa State Univ Ames IA 50010

MA, CYNTHIA SANMAN, b Hong Kong, May 16, 40; US citizen; m 66; c 2. STATISTICS, COMPUTER SCIENCE. *Educ:* Siena Col, BS, 62; Fla State Univ, MS, 66, PhD(systs anal), 69. *Prof Exp:* Statistician, Community Studies Inst, Kansas City, Mo, 62-63; res asst statist, Fla State Univ, 63-66, comput programmer & analyst, Dept Physics, 66-67, systs design analyst, Systs Planning & Develop Ctr, 67-69; ASSOC PROF DATA PROCESSING & STATIST, BALL STATE UNIV, 69- *Concurrent Pos:* Consult, 70- *Mem:* Am Statist Asn; Asn Systs Mgt; Asn Comput Mach. *Res:* Design of computer-based systems for finance analysis and teaching; design and alocation resource model for planning; use of graphics for information systems. *Mailing Add:* Dept of Finance & Mgt Ball State Univ Muncie IN 47304

MA, ER-CHIEH, b Jukao, China, Dec 8, 22; m 46; c 3. ENGINEERING MECHANICS, APPLIED MATHEMATICS. *Educ:* Chiao-Tung Univ, BS, 46; Kans State Univ, MS, 59, PhD(appl mech), 62. *Prof Exp:* Res assoc design, Ord Res Inst, 47-55; sr expert sci educ, Ministry Educ, 55-58; res assoc appl mech, Kans State Univ, 60-62; assoc prof, Wichita State Univ, 62-64; from assoc prof to prof eng, 64-81, PROF MATH, UNIV ARK, LITTLE ROCK, 81- *Concurrent Pos:* Chinese del, Study Conf Sci Teaching, UNESCO, 56. *Mem:* Am Soc Eng Educ; Am Soc Mech Engrs. *Res:* Elasticity; viscoelasticity; vibrations; celestial mechanics; applied analysis. *Mailing Add:* Dept Math & Comput Sci Univ Ark Little Rock AR 72204

MA, JAMES JU LUAN, chemical engineering, see previous edition

MA, MARK T, b Kiangsu, China, Mar 21, 33; m 58; c 2. ELECTROMAGNETISM, TELECOMMUNICATION. *Educ:* Nat Taiwan Univ, BS, 55; Univ Ill, MS, 57; Syracuse Univ, PhD(elec eng), 61. *Prof Exp:* Lectr elec eng, Nat Taiwan Univ, 55-56; engr electronics, Int Bus Mach Corp, 57-58 & Gen Elec Co, 61-64; RES SCIENTIST, NAT BUR STAND, US DEPT COMMERCE, 64- *Concurrent Pos:* Prof adj, Univ Colo, 64-; assoc ed, Radio Sci, 66-67. *Honors & Awards:* Best Original Paper, Nat Electronics Conf, 60; Commerce Sci & Tech Fel, US Dept Commerce, 71. *Mem:* Inst Elec & Electronics Engrs. *Res:* Electromagnetic theory; electromagnetic interference; antenna theory; telecommunications. *Mailing Add:* Nat Bur of Stand US Dept of Commerce Boulder CO 80302

MA, MAW-SUEN, b Peking, China, July 18, 47; c 1. RADIO ANALYTICAL CHEMISTRY, GEOCHEMISTRY. *Educ:* Cheng Kung Univ, Taiwan, BS, 68; Univ Ky, PhD(radio anal chem), 75. *Prof Exp:* Teaching asst chem, Cent Univ, Taiwan, 70-71; teaching asst, Univ Ky, 71-72, res fel, 72-75; co-investr NASA lunar prog geochem, Ore State Univ, 75-81, res asst prof, 81; RES SCIENTIST, US TESTING CO, INC, 81- *Mem:* Geochem Soc; Meteoritical Soc; Am Nuclear Soc; Health Phys Soc. *Res:* Applications of analytical chemistry; radio chemical methods of analysis; neutron activation analysis to samples of geological, environmental and industrial interests; trace element geochemistry. *Mailing Add:* US Testing Co Inc 2800 George Washington Way Richland WA 99352

MA, NANCY SHUI FONG, Hong Kong citizen. CYTOGENETICS. *Educ:* Mt St Vincent Col, Can, BSc, 64; Northeastern Univ, MS, 68; Boston Col, PhD(biol), 73. *Prof Exp:* ASSOC PATH, NEW ENGLAND REGIONAL PRIMATE RES CTR, HARVARD UNIV, 73- *Concurrent Pos:* Cytogenetics consult, Pathobiol Inc, 75- *Res:* Cytogenetic studies of the New World monkeys. *Mailing Add:* New Eng Regional Primate Res Ctr Harvard Med Sch Southborough MA 01772

MA, SHANG-KENG, b Chungkin, China, Sept 24, 40. PHYSICS. *Educ:* Univ Calif, Berkeley, BA, 62, PhD(physics), 66. *Prof Exp:* Asst res physicist, 66-67, from asst prof to assoc prof, 67-75, PROF PHYSICS, UNIV CALIF, SAN DIEGO, 75- *Concurrent Pos:* Mem, Inst Advan Study, 68-69 & 70-; Sloan fel, 71- *Mem:* Am Phys Soc. *Res:* Statistical mechanics; many body theory. *Mailing Add:* Dept of Physics Univ of Calif at San Diego La Jolla CA 92037

MA, TE HSIU, b Hopei, China, Aug 24, 24; nat US; m 60; c 2. CYTOGENETICS. *Educ:* Cath Univ Peking, BS, 48; Nat Taiwan Univ, MS, 50; Univ Va, PhD(biol), 59. *Prof Exp:* Asst cytologist, Sugarcane Cytol, Taiwan Sugar Exp Sta, 50-55; from asst prof to assoc prof biol, Emory & Henry Col, 59-64; asst prof, Western Ill Univ, 64-66; geneticist, Radiation Biol Lab, Smithsonian Inst, Wash, DC, 66-69; assoc prof, 69-73, PROF BIOL SCI, WESTERN ILL UNIV, 73- *Concurrent Pos:* Res partic, Oak Ridge Nat Lab, 63-64; res consult, Oak Ridge Inst Nuclear Studies, 63-; Atomic Energy Comn res grant, 65; Environ Protection Agency res grant, 71-73; radiation safety officer, Western Ill Univ, 71- *Mem:* AAAS; Am Genetics Soc; Am Soc Cell Biol; NY Acad Sci. *Res:* Cytogenetics of sugarcane, corn and Tradescantia; radiation effects on chromosomes of Tradescantia and Vicia; air pollutant effects on chromosomes of Tradescantia; radioactive pollutant effect on fish. *Mailing Add:* Dept of Biol Sci Western Ill Univ Macomb IL 61455

MA, TSU SHENG, b Canton, China, Oct 15, 11; nat US; m 42; c 2. MICROCHEMISTRY, ORGANIC CHEMISTRY. *Educ:* Tsing Hua Univ, China, BS, 31; Univ Chicago, PhD(chem), 38. *Prof Exp:* Instr in charge microchem lab, Univ Chicago, 38-46; prof, Peking Univ, 46-49; sr lectr microchem, Univ Otago, NZ, 49-51; asst prof chem, NY Univ, 51-54; assoc prof, 54-58, PROF CHEM, CITY UNIV NEW YORK, 58- *Concurrent Pos:* Vis prof, Tsinghua Univ, Peking, 47, Lingnan Univ, 49, NY Univ, 54-60, Univ Singapore, 75-76; Fulbright-Hays lectr, China, Japan, Hong Kong, India, Malaya, Australia & NZ, 61-62, Korea, Thailand, Hong Kong & Iran, 68-69; Am specialist, Bur Educ & Cult Affairs, US State Dept, Ceylon, Burma, Thailand, Hong Kong & Philippines, 64; mem comn reagents & reactions, Int Union Pure & Appl Chem, 64-69; ed, Mikrochimica Acta, 65- *Honors & Awards:* Benedetti-Pichler Award in Microchem, 76. *Mem:* AAAS; Am Inst Chem; Am Chem Soc; Royal Soc Chem; NY Acad Sci. *Res:* Synthetic drugs; medicinal plants; microchemical analysis; microtechniques in organic chemistry; small scale experiments for teaching general and organic chemistry. *Mailing Add:* 160 Ridge Trail Chapel Hill NC 27514

MA, WAI-SAI, b Canton, China, Sept 13, 43; m 72; c 2. IMMUNOCHEMISTRY. *Educ:* Univ Cincinnati, BS, 66; State Univ NY Albany, PhD(biochem), 71. *Prof Exp:* Fel immunochem, Kidney Dis Inst, NY State Dept Health, 71-73; res scientist immunochem, Dome Labs Div, Miles Labs, 74-76; proj leader, Abbott Diagnostics, Abbott Labs, 77-78; MGR RES & DEVELOP IMMUNOCHEM, NUCLEAR MED LABS DIV, WARNER-LAMBERT CO, 78- *Mem:* Am Chem Soc; AAAS; Am Chem Soc. *Res:* Process development and system optimization of diagnostic test, using enzyme multiplied immunoassay technique, enzyme linked immunosorbent blocking assay and radioimmunoassay methods in the infectious disease area, particularly hepatitis, cancer and allergy. *Mailing Add:* Nuclear Med Labs 8700 N Stemmons Dallas TX 75247

MA, WILLIAM HSIOH-LIEN, b China, Jan 31, 47; US citizen; m 70; c 1. ELECTRICAL ENGINEERING, PHYSICAL SCIENCE. *Educ:* Univ Ark, BSEE, 70; Ga Inst Technol, MSEE, 70; Purdue Univ, PhD(elec eng), 74. *Prof Exp:* ENGR RES & DEVELOP, IBM CORP, 74- *Mem:* Inst Elec & Electronics Engrs; Am Phys Soc; Am Vacuum Soc. *Res:* Research and development in semiconductor device fabrication process; dry etching, plasma etching, reactive ion etching and device processing development. *Mailing Add:* 3 Cameron Ln Wappingers Falls NY 12590

MA, YI HUA, b Nanking, China, Nov 7, 36; m 63; c 3. CHEMICAL ENGINEERING. *Educ:* Nat Taiwan Univ, BS, 59; Univ Notre Dame, MS, 63; Mass Inst Technol, ScD(chem eng), 67. *Prof Exp:* From asst prof to assoc prof, 67-76, PROF CHEM ENG, WORCESTER POLYTECH INST, 76-, DEPT HEAD, 79- *Concurrent Pos:* Consultant. *Mem:* Am Chem Soc; Am Inst Chem Engrs. *Res:* Heterogeneous catalyst and chemical kinetics; transport phenomena on porous catalyst; applied mathematics in chemical engineering; drying. *Mailing Add:* Dept Chem Eng Worcester Polytech Inst Worcester MA 01609

MA, ZEE-MING, b Shanghai, China, Feb 4, 42; m 64; c 2. HIGH ENERGY PHYSICS. *Educ:* Southwestern Univ, Tex, BS, 62; Duke Univ, PhD(physics), 67. *Prof Exp:* From instr to asst prof physics, Mich State Univ, 67-74, assoc prof, 74-80; MEM STAFF, BELL LABS, 80- *Concurrent Pos:* Prin investr, US Dept Energy. *Mem:* Am Phys Soc. *Res:* Experimental high energy physics. *Mailing Add:* Bell Labs 5-B 101 600 Mountain Ave Murray Hill NJ 07974

MAA, JER-SHEN, b Shanghai, July 6, 44; m; C 2. THIN FILM SCIENCE, MATERIALS CHARACTERIZATION. *Educ:* Nat Cheng Kung Univ, Taiwan, BS, 68; Univ Minn, PhD(mat sci), 74. *Prof Exp:* Res asst, Mat Sci Dept, Univ Minn, 69-74; res assoc, Phys Div, Argonne Nat Lab, 74-75; assoc prof, Mat Sci Dept, Nat Tsing Hua Univ, Taiwan, 75-79; mem tech staff, Solid State Technol Ctr, Solid State Div, 79-81, MEM TECH STAFF, RCA LABS, PRINCETON, 81- *Concurrent Pos:* Mem staff, Thin Film Technol Group, RCA Labs, 79. *Mem:* Am Vacuum Soc; Electrochem Soc Am. *Res:* Deposition, oxidation, heat treatment, plasma etching, reaction and characterization of thin film materials; refractory metal silicide films and aluminum films for semiconductor device applications. *Mailing Add:* RCA Labs Princeton NJ 08540

MAAG, URS RICHARD, b Winterthur, Switz, Jan 20, 38; m 65; c 3. STATISTICS. *Educ:* Swiss Fed Inst Technol, Dipl Math, 61; Univ Toronto, MA, 62, PhD, 65. *Prof Exp:* From lectr to assoc prof math, 64-73, assoc prof info sci, 73-76, PROF COMPUT SCI & OPERS RES, UNIV MONTREAL, 76- *Concurrent Pos:* Statist consult. *Mem:* Am Statist Asn; Inst Math Statist; Statist Soc Can (pres, 80). *Res:* Nonparametric statistics, robust methods in multivariate analysis; applications to genetics; data analysis. *Mailing Add:* Dept of Comput Sci & Opers Res Univ of Montreal Box 6128 Montreal PQ H3C 3J7 Can

MAAHS, HOWARD GORDON, b Los Angeles, Calif, May 16, 39; m 62; c 4. KINETICS, PHYSICAL CHEMISTRY. *Educ:* Stanford Univ, BS, 59; Univ Wash, PhD(chem eng), 64. *Prof Exp:* Chem engr, Univ Wash, 60-61; AEROSPACE TECHNOLOGIST, LANGLEY RES CTR, NASA, 64- *Mem:* Am Chem Soc; Am Inst Chem Engrs. *Res:* Coatings and aerospace materials; chemical kinetics and catalysis; aqueous chemistry of tropospheric cloud droplets; combustion kinetics and pollution formation; heat transfer; graphite ablation and sublimation. *Mailing Add:* Langley Res Ctr NASA Hampton VA 23665

MAAR, JAMES RICHARD, b Wellsville, NY, Oct 7, 43; m 68. MATHEMATICAL STATISTICS, STATISTICAL ANALYSIS. *Educ:* Eckerd Col, BS, 65; Brown Univ, ScM, 67; George Washington Univ, PhD(math statist), 73. *Prof Exp:* MATHEMATICIAN, US DEPT DEFENSE, FT GEORGE G MEADE, 67- *Concurrent Pos:* Assoc prof lectr mgt sci, Col Gen Studies, George Washington Univ, 73-78; lectr math, Univ Md, 79- *Mem:* Sigma Xi; Inst Math Statist; Am Statist Asn; Math Asn Am. *Res:* Multivariate data analysis, including cluster analysis, discriminant analysis, statistical computing and graphical data analysis; new counterexamples to plausible but false statements in probability theory and mathematical statistics. *Mailing Add:* 3906 Walt Ann Dr Ellicott City MD 21043

MAAS, EUGENE VERNON, b Jamestown, NDak, Dec 18, 36; m 61; c 3. PLANT PHYSIOLOGY. *Educ:* Jamestown Col, BS, 58; Univ Ariz, MS, 61; Ore State Univ, PhD(soils), 66. *Prof Exp:* Res assoc soil physics, Univ Ariz, 61; asst soils, Ore State Univ, 61-66; plant physiologist, Mineral Nutrit Lab, USDA, 66-68, PLANT PHYSIOLOGIST, AGR RES SERV, US DEPT AGR, US SALINITY LAB, 68- *Concurrent Pos:* Nat Acad Sci-Nat Res Coun resident res associateship, 66-68. *Mem:* Am Soc Plant Physiol; Am Soc Agron. *Res:* Ion absorption and transport in plants; environmental physiology of plants; tolerance to salts and air pollution. *Mailing Add:* US Salinity Lab 4500 Glenwood Dr Riverside CA 92501

MAAS, JAMES WELDON, b St Louis, Mo, Oct 26, 29; m 53; c 3. PSYCHIATRY. *Educ:* Wash Univ, BA, 50, MD, 54. *Prof Exp:* Intern med, Grady Mem Hosp, Atlanta, Ga, 54-55; resident psychiat, Cincinnati Gen Hosp, Ohio, 55-56 & 58-60; chief sect psychosom med, NIMH, 60-66; prof psychiat, Univ Ill Col Med, 66-72, PROF PSYCHIAT, SCH MED, YALE UNIV, 72- *Concurrent Pos:* Dir res, Ill State Psychiat Inst, 66-72. *Mem:* AAAS; Am Psychiat Asn; Am Psychosom Soc; fel Am Col Neuropsychopharmacology; Am Soc Pharmacol & Exp Therapeut. *Res:* Relationship between biology and behavior; brain chemistry and behavior; biochemistry of synapse; biogenic amines in brain; neurochemistry. *Mailing Add:* Dept Psychiat Yale Univ Sch Med New Haven CT 06510

MAAS, JOHN LEWIS, b Detroit, Mich, Aug 13, 40; m 62; c 3. PLANT PATHOLOGY. *Educ:* Mich State Univ, BS, 62; Univ Wash, MS, 64; Ore State Univ, PhD(plant path), 68. *Prof Exp:* RES PLANT PATHOLOGIST, FRUIT LAB, HORT SCI INST, AGR RES CTR, NORTHEAST REGION, USDA, 68- *Mem:* Am Phytopath Soc; Mycol Soc Am. *Res:* Fungus diseases of small fruit crops; etiology and control of Phytophthora fragariae root rot and Botrytis cinerea fruit rot of strawberry. *Mailing Add:* Hort Sci Inst Agr Res Ctr NE Region US Dept of Agr Beltsville MD 20705

MAAS, KEITH ALLAN, b Burlington, Wis, Apr 7, 36; div; c 2. PHOTOGRAPHIC CHEMISTRY. *Educ:* Mass Inst Technol, SB, 58; Univ Vt, MS, 60; Univ Calif, Davis, PhD(chem), 63. *Prof Exp:* Res chemist, tech rep & col rels rep, E I du Pont de Nemours & Co, Inc, 63-71; SR STAFF SCIENTIST, PHOTOGRAPHIC SYSTS, TECHNICOLOR GRAPHIC SERVS, INC, 72- *Mem:* Am Chem Soc; Soc Photog Scientists & Engrs. *Res:* Photographic materials and processes; techniques of image presentation. *Mailing Add:* PO Box 58863 Houston TX 77058

MAAS, PETER, b Evanston, Ill, Apr 9, 39; m 64; c 2. SOLID STATE PHYSICS, BIOPHYSICS. *Educ:* Mass Inst Tech, BS, 62; Stanford Univ, MS, 64; Univ Colo, PhD(physics), 69. *Prof Exp:* Asst engr, Lockheed Missile & Space Co, 62-63, grad study scientist, 63-65, scientist, 64-65; asst physics, Univ Colo, Boulder, 65-67, solid state physics, 67-69, res assoc & instr biophys, Med Ctr, 69-70; lectr appl physics, 70-76, SR LECTR APPL PHYSICS, UNIV STRATHCLYDE, 76- *Mem:* Asn Comput Mach; Am Asn Physics Teachers. *Res:* Physics applications in biology; experimental population biology; computer uses in science. *Mailing Add:* Dept of Appl Physics Univ of Strathclyde 107 Rottenrow Glasgow Scotland

MAAS, WERNER KARL, b Kaiserslautern, Ger, Apr 27, 21; nat US; m 60; c 3. MOLECULAR GENETICS. *Educ:* Harvard Univ, BA, 43; Columbia Univ, PhD(zool), 48. *Prof Exp:* Asst zool, Columbia Univ, 43-45; mem staff, Med Col, Cornell Univ, 49-54; from asst prof pharmacol to assoc prof microbiol, 54-63, adv, Grad Dept, 64-70, chmn, Dept Basic Med Sci, 75-80, PROF MICROBIOL, SCH MED, NY UNIV, 63- *Concurrent Pos:* Vis investr, Mass Gen Hosp, 52-53; dir honors prog, Sch Med, NY Univ, 58-61, co-dir, USPHS Genetics Training Grant, 61-68, dir, 68-75, dir, Microbiol Training Grant, 64-69; mem, NIH Genetics Training Grants Comt, 61-65, mem study sect microbial chem, 68-72, chmn, 70-72; mem staff, Univ Brussels, 63; mem test comt microbiol, Nat Bd Med Exam, 71-75. *Mem:* Am Soc Microbiol; Am Soc Biol Chem; Genetics Soc Am. *Res:* Microbial genetics and physiology, with emphasis on regulatory mechanisms, especially of protein synthesis; amino acid permeases; polyamine metabolism; genetics of extrachromosomal elements. *Mailing Add:* Dept of Microbiol NY Univ Sch of Med New York NY 10016

MAASBERG, ALBERT THOMAS, b Bronx, NY, Feb 10, 15; m 41; c 2. CHEMISTRY, CHEMICAL ENGINEERING. *Educ:* State Univ NY, BS, 36. *Prof Exp:* Res dir cellulose prod dept, Dow Chem USA, 46-50, asst prod mgr, 50-52, mgr, 52-54, tech dir plastics prod dept, 54-56, dir res & develop, Midland Div, 56-63, dir contract res, develop & eng, 63-79. *Mem:* Am Chem Soc; Sigma Xi; Tech Asn Pulp & Paper Indust; fel Am Inst Chem Eng. *Res:* Pulp and paper manufacturing; cellulose ethers; water soluble polymers; chemicals and plastics process and product; government and industrial contract research and development administration. *Mailing Add:* 3220 Noeske Midland MI 48640

MAASEIDVAAG, FRODE, bioengineering, electrophysiology, see previous edition

MAASS, ALFRED ROLAND, b Plymouth, Wis, Apr 14, 18; m 47; c 3. BIOCHEMISTRY. *Educ:* Antioch Col, BS, 42; Univ Wis, MS, 47, PhD(biochem), 50. *Prof Exp:* Consult, Argonne Nat Labs, 51; sr res biochemist, 51-56, group leader, Biochem Sect, 56-57, asst sect head, 57-62, sect head, 62-67, assoc dir biochem, 67-74, dir develop proj, 74-78, dir anal biochem res, 78-81, DIR SCI ADMIN PRE-CLIN DEVELOP, SMITH, KLINE & FRENCH LABS, 81- *Concurrent Pos:* Chmn civilian adv comt radiation safety, City Philadelphia, 64-73. *Mem:* Fel AAAS; Health Physics Soc; Am Chem Soc; Am Acad Neurol; NY Acad Sci. *Res:* Isotope tracers; drug metabolism; enzymes; neurobiochemistry; gastric and renal physiology; anti-hypertensive, diuretic, uricosuric and anti-lipemic agents. *Mailing Add:* 415 Cornell Ave Swarthmore PA 19081

MAASS, GEORGE JOSEPH, b New York, NY, Jan 6, 38; m 61; c 2. PHYSICAL CHEMISTRY. *Educ:* Fordham Univ, BS, 61; Iowa State Univ, PhD(phys chem), 67. *Prof Exp:* Res scientist paper chem, Union-Camp Res Labs, 67-70; RES SCIENTIST, SCOTT PAPER CO, 70- *Mem:* Am Chem Soc. *Res:* Low temperature magnetic properties; molecular quantum mechanics; thermodynamic and surface properties of fibers; penetration and structure of porous media. *Mailing Add:* Scott Paper Co Scott Plaza Philadelphia PA 19113

MAASS, WOLFGANG SIEGFRIED GUNTHER, b Helsinki, Finland, Oct 23, 29; m 60; c 2. PLANT PHYSIOLOGY, PLANT BIOCHEMISTRY. *Educ:* Univ Tübingen, Dr rer nat, 57. *Prof Exp:* Asst bot, Univ Tübingen, 57; sci collabr, Max-Planck Inst Protein & Leather Res, 58-60; fel biol, Dalhousie Univ, 60-62; asst res officer, 62-65, ASSOC RES OFFICER, ATLANTIC REGIONAL LAB, NAT RES COUN CAN, 66- *Concurrent Pos:* Mem, Plant Phenolics Group NAm. *Mem:* Can Soc Plant Physiol; Ger Bot Soc. *Res:* Taxonomy and distribution of Sphagnum; chemical taxonomy; biochemical aspects of cellular development; biosynthesis of pulvinic acid derivatives and phenolic compounds in general. *Mailing Add:* 53 Albion Rd Halifax NS B3P 1P8 Can

MAASSAB, HUNEIN FADLO, b Damascus, Syria, June 11, 28; nat US; m 59; c 2. EPIDEMIOLOGY, VIROLOGY. *Educ:* Univ Mo, BA, 50, MA, 52; Univ Mich, MPH, 55, PhD(epidemiol sci), 56; Am Bd Med Microbiol, dipl. *Prof Exp:* Res assoc, 57-60, from asst prof to assoc prof, 60-72, PROF

EPIDEMIOL, UNIV MICH, ANN ARBOR, 72- *Mem:* AAAS; Am Asn Immunol; Brit Soc Gen Microbiol; Tissue Cult Asn; Soc Exp Biol & Med. *Res:* Metabolism of infection; host-virus interaction; immunology; tissue culture; tumors; biology of myxoviruses. *Mailing Add:* Dept of Epidemiol Univ of Mich Sch of Pub Health Ann Arbor MI 48109

MAATMAN, RUSSELL WAYNE, b Chicago, Ill, Nov 7, 23; m 48; c 5. PHYSICAL CHEMISTRY. *Educ:* Calvin Col, AB, 46; Mich State Col, PhD(chem), 50. *Prof Exp:* Asst prof chem, DePauw Univ, 49-51; sr technologist, Socony-Mobil Oil Co, 51-58; assoc prof chem, Univ Miss, 58-63; PROF CHEM, DORDT COL, 63- *Mem:* Am Chem Soc; Am Sci Affiliation. *Res:* Catalysis; solution-solid reactions; ion solvation. *Mailing Add:* Dept of Chem Dordt Col Sioux Center IA 51250

MABEY, WILLIAM RAY, b Los Angeles, Calif, Oct 16, 41; m 81. PHYSICAL ORGANIC CHEMISTRY. *Educ:* Univ Calif, Riverside, BA, 65; San Diego State Univ, MS, 68; Univ Ore, PhD(chem), 72. *Prof Exp:* PHYS ORG CHEMIST, SRI INT, 72- *Mem:* Am Chem Soc; AAAS; Soc Environ Toxicol Chem. *Res:* Environmental chemistry; kinetics and mechanisms of hydrolysis, oxidation and photochemistry in environment; persistence and fate of chemicals in environment. *Mailing Add:* SRI Int 333 Ravenswood Menlo Park CA 94025

MABIE, CURTIS PARSONS, b Memphis, Tenn, Feb 26, 32; m 59; c 1. DENTAL MATERIALS, MICROSCOPY. *Educ:* Western Reserve Univ, BA, 54; Univ Mich, MS, 58. *Prof Exp:* Res geologist, US Bur Mines, 58-61; anthracologist, Appl Res Ctr, US Steel Corp, 61-63; res microscopist, IRC, 63-65; res engr, Norton Co, 65-66; ceramic technologist, NL Indust Inc, 66-67; CHIEF SCIENTIST, CERAMICS DIV, AM DENT ASN, NAT BUR STANDARDS, 68- *Mem:* Am Ceramic Soc; Am Soc Testing & Mat. *Res:* Dental porcelains, investments, fillers, and cements; microscopy of dental materials and biological calcifications. *Mailing Add:* Bldg 224 Rm A164 Nat Bur of Standards Washington DC 20234

MABIE, HAMILTON HORTH, b Rochester, NY, Oct 21, 14; m 41; c 3. MECHANICAL ENGINEERING. *Educ:* Univ Rochester, BS, 40; Cornell Univ, MS, 43; Pa State Univ, PhD(mech eng), 54. *Prof Exp:* From instr to assoc prof mech eng, Cornell Univ, 41-60; res & develop engr, Sandia Corp, NMex, 60-64; PROF MECH ENG, VA POLYTECH INST & STATE UNIV, 64- *Concurrent Pos:* Consult, Sandia Corp, NMex, 58-59 & 64-67 & Westinghouse Elec Corp, Va, 69-70. *Mem:* Fel Am Soc Mech Engrs; Am Soc Lubrication Engrs; Am Soc Eng Educ; Soc Exp Stress Anal. *Res:* Mechanisms and kinematics; fatigue of mechanical components; instrument bearings and lubrication. *Mailing Add:* Dept of Mech Eng Va Polytech Inst & State Univ Blacksburg VA 24061

MABLEKOS, VAN ELIAS, electrical engineering, see previous edition

MABROUK, AHMED FAHMY, b Cairo, UAR, Sept 30, 23; m 54; c 3. AGRICULTURAL CHEMISTRY. *Educ:* Univ Cairo, BSc, 45, MSc, 50; Ohio State Univ, PhD(lipid chem), 54. *Prof Exp:* Chemist, Ministry Agr, Egypt, 45-46; instr chem, Fac Agr, Univ Cairo, 46-48, instr agr indust, 48-51; fel agr chem, Ohio State Univ, 54-55; lectr & asst prof chem, Univ Cairo, 55-58, lectr, Grad Sch, 56-58; res org chemist, Am Meat Inst Found, Univ Chicago, 58-61; prin org chemist, Northern Utilization Res & Develop Div, USDA, 61-65; sr res chemist, Food Sci Lab, 65-80, SR RES CHEMIST, SCI & ADVAN TECHNOL LAB, US ARMY NATICK RES & DEVELOP LABS, 80- *Concurrent Pos:* Fel physiol chem, Ohio State Univ, 56; lectr to postgrads, Agr Schs, Egypt. Consult, Tahreer Prov Authority, Egypt, 55-57 & Nat Serv Coun, 56-57. Abstractor, Chem Abstr, 55-65. *Honors & Awards:* Sci Dir Silver Key Res Award, 68. *Mem:* Am Oil Chemists Soc; Am Chem Soc; Inst Food Technologists; Royal Soc Chem; Brit Soc Chem Indust. *Res:* Chromatography of organic compounds; gel permeation chromatography; gas chromatography; ultrafiltration; fat and flavor chemistry; heterogeneous and homogenous hydrogenation of fats and organic compounds; chemical kinetics of oxidative rancidity; antioxidants; isolation and synthesis of naturally occurring compounds. *Mailing Add:* 9 Wildewood Terr Framingham MA 01701

MABRY, JOHN WILLIAM, b Batesville, Ark, Oct 17, 50. ANIMAL BREEDING, SWINE MANAGEMENT. *Educ:* Okla State Univ, BS, 72; Iowa State Univ, MS, 74, PhD(animal breeding), 76. *Prof Exp:* Grad asst animal breeding, Iowa State Univ, 72-76; asst prof, Univ Wis, River Falls, 76-79; ASST PROF ANIMAL BREEDING, UNIV GA, 79- *Mem:* Am Soc Animal Sci; Nat Asn Col Teachers Agr. *Res:* Effects of photoperiod, breeding herd management and the relationships between compositional and sexual maturity. *Mailing Add:* 208 Livestock-Poultry Univ Ga Athens GA 30602

MABRY, TOM JOE, b Commerce, Tex, June 6, 32; m 54, 71; c 1. ORGANIC CHEMISTRY, PHYTOCHEMISTRY. *Educ:* ETex State Univ, BS & MS, 53; Rice Univ, PhD(chem), 60. *Prof Exp:* NIH fel chem, Org Chem Inst, Univ Zurich, 60-61; res scientist, 62, from asst prof to prof phytochem, 63-73, PROF BOT, UNIV TEX, AUSTIN, 73- *Concurrent Pos:* Guggenheim fel, Univ Freiburg, 71. *Mem:* Am Chem Soc; Royal Soc Chem; Bot Soc Am; Phytochem Soc NAm (vpres, 65, pres, 66-67). *Res:* Natural products chemistry; biochemical systematics; molecular evolution. *Mailing Add:* Dept of Bot Univ of Tex Austin TX 78712

MACADAM, DAVID LEWIS, b Philadelphia, Pa, July 1, 10; m 38; c 4. PHYSICS. *Educ:* Lehigh Univ, BS, 32; Mass Inst Technol, PhD, 36. *Prof Exp:* Sr res assoc, Res Labs, Eastman Kodak Co, 36-75; PROF OPTICS, UNIV ROCHESTER, 76- *Concurrent Pos:* Mattiello mem lectr, Fedn Socs Paint Technol, 65; Hurter & Driffield mem lectr, Royal Photog Soc, 66; hon mem, Inter-Soc Color Coun; ed jour, Optical Soc Am, 64-75; chmn, Color Measurement Comt, Mil Personnel Supplies Adv Bd, Nat Res Coun, 78-82. *Honors & Awards:* Godlove Award, Inter-Soc Color Coun, 63; Lomb Medal, Optical Soc Am, 40, Ives Medal, 74. *Mem:* Fel Optical Soc Am (pres, 62); Int Comn Illum. *Res:* Optics; color photography; influence of color contrast on visual acuity; spectroradiometry; color television; photographic image structure. *Mailing Add:* 68 Hammond St Rochester NY 14615

MCADAM, WILL, b Wheeling, WVa, Oct 22, 21; m 45; c 2. ELECTRICAL ENGINEERING. *Educ:* Case Inst Technol, BS, 42; Univ Pa, MS, 59. *Prof Exp:* Asst, 45-49, res technologist, 49-51, sr res technologist, 51-57, head elec sect,Res Div, 57-68, assoc dir res opers, Tech Ctr, 68-80, MGR CHEM INST RES & DEVELOP, LEEDS & NORTHRUP CO, 80- *Mem:* Instrument Soc Am; Inst Elec & Electronics Engrs. *Res:* Electrical instruments for measurement and process control. *Mailing Add:* Tech Ctr Leeds & Northrup Co Sunneytown Park PA 19454

MCADAMS, ARTHUR JAMES, b Santa Barbara, Calif, July 16, 23; m 46; c 4. PEDIATRICS, PATHOLOGY. *Educ:* Johns Hopkins Univ, MD, 48. *Prof Exp:* Instr pediat path, Col Med, Univ Cincinnati, 56-58; dir labs, Children's Hosp East Bay, Oakland, Calif, 58-63; assoc prof, 63-69, PROF PEDIAT & PATH, COL MED, UNIV CINCINNATI, 69-; DIRECTING PATHOLOGIST, CHILDREN'S HOSP & RES FOUND, 63- *Concurrent Pos:* Asst pathologist, Cincinnati Children's Hosp, 56-58; clin asst prof, Sch Med, Univ Calif, 62-63. *Mem:* AAAS; Am Asn Path & Bact; Soc Pediat Res; Int Acad Path; Am Pediat Soc. *Res:* Role of complement in nephritis; pulmonary disease in the newborn; anoxic brain damage. *Mailing Add:* Dept of Path Children's Hosp Res Found Cincinnati OH 45229

MCADAMS, ROBERT ELI, b Hudson, Colo, Jan 2, 29; m 50. NUCLEAR PHYSICS. *Educ:* Colo State Univ, BS, 57; Iowa State Univ, PhD(physics), 64. *Prof Exp:* Fel physics, Iowa State Univ, 64-65; asst prof, 65-73, ASSOC PROF PHYSICS, UTAH STATE UNIV, 73- *Mem:* Am Phys Soc. *Res:* Intermediate-energy physics. *Mailing Add:* Dept Physics Utah State Univ Logan UT 84322

MCADIE, HENRY GEORGE, b Montreal, Que, May 12, 30; m 56; c 4. ENVIRONMENTAL CHEMISTRY, ANALYTICAL CHEMISTRY. *Educ:* McGill Univ, BSc, 51; Queen's Univ, Ont, MA, 53, PhD(phys chem), 56. *Prof Exp:* Res fel, 56-63, sr res scientist, 64-67, prin res scientist, 67-70, from asst dir to actg dir dept phys chem, 70-71, DIR DEPT ENVIRON CHEM, ONT RES FOUND, 72- *Concurrent Pos:* Chmn, Can Adv Comt, Int Stand Orgn/Tech Comt-146 Air Qual, 74-77. *Honors & Awards:* J Charles Honey Award, 78. *Mem:* Fel Chem Inst Can; Int Conf Thermal Anal (vpres, 74-77, pres, 77-80); Am Chem Soc; Air Pollution Control Asn; fel Royal Soc Chem. *Res:* Thermoanalytical methods and applications; heterogeneous processes; air pollution instrumentation; ambient and work-room monitoring; emissions testing; emission control processes; long-range transport. *Mailing Add:* Dept of Environ Chem Ont Res Found Sheridan Park Mississauga ON L5K 1B3 Can

MCADOO, DAVID JOHN, neurobiology, analytical chemistry, see previous edition

MCADOO, JOHN HART, b Baltimore, Md, Mar 16, 45; m 76. OPTICS. *Educ:* Princeton Univ, BSE, 67; Univ Rochester, MS, 76, PhD(plasma physics), 81. *Prof Exp:* RES PHYSICIST OPTICS, SACHS/FREEMAN ASSOC, INC, 81- *Mem:* Am Phys Soc; AAAS; Astron Soc Pac. *Res:* Development of the optical system for a compton regime free-electron laser, with an output wavelength tunable through 16 micrometers, using a regenerative wave-guide free electron amplifier as the heart of the optical system. *Mailing Add:* Code 4740 Naval Res Lab Washington DC 20375

MCAFEE, JERRY, b Port Arthur, Tex, Nov 3, 16; m 40; c 4. CHEMICAL ENGINEERING. *Educ:* Univ Tex, BS, 37; Mass Inst Technol, ScD(chem eng), 40. *Prof Exp:* Res chem engr, Universal Oil Prod Co, Ill, 40-45; tech specialist, Gulf Oil Corp, 45-50, dir chem div, Gulf Res & Develop Co, 50-51, asst dir res, 51-54, vpres & assoc dir res, 54-55; vpres eng, Gulf Oil Corp, 55-60, vpres & exec tech adv, 60-62, vpres & dir planning & econs, 62-64, sr vpres, 64-67; exec vpres, Brit Am Oil Co Ltd, 67-69; pres, Gulf Oil Can Ltd, 69-76; chmn bd, Gulf Oil Corp, 76-81. *Mem:* Nat Acad Eng; Am Chem Soc; Am Inst Chem Engrs (vpres, 59, pres, 60). *Res:* Products; crude oil, refined oil products, and natural gas. *Mailing Add:* Gulf Bldg Pittsburgh PA 15230

MCAFEE, JOHN GILMOUR, b Toronto, Ont, June 11, 26; nat US; wid; c 3. RADIOLOGY. *Educ:* Univ Toronto, MD, 48. *Prof Exp:* Jr intern, Victoria Hosp, London, Ont, 48-49, asst resident radiol, 50-51; sr intern, Westminster Hosp, 49-50; resident radiol, Johns Hopkins Hosp, 51-52; from instr to assoc prof, Johns Hopkins Univ, 53-65; fac scholar, 75, PROF RADIOL, STATE UNIV NY UPSTATE MED CTR, 65- *Concurrent Pos:* Fel radiol, Johns Hopkins Univ, 52-53. *Honors & Awards:* John G McAlee lectr, 78; Paul C Aebersold Award, Soc Nuclear Med, 79. *Mem:* Soc Nuclear Med; Radiol Soc NAm; AMA; Royal Col Physicians & Surgeons Can; Asn Univ Radiologists. *Res:* Use of radioactive tracers in clinical diagnosis; nuclear instrumentation and radiochemistry. *Mailing Add:* Dept Radiol State Univ NY Upstate Med Ctr Syracuse NY 13210

MCAFEE, KENNETH BAILEY, JR, b Chicago, Ill, June 22, 24; m 59; c 2. CHEMICAL PHYSICS, ATMOSPHERIC CHEMISTRY. *Educ:* Harvard Univ, BS, 46, MA, 47, PhD(chem physics), 50. *Prof Exp:* Mem tech staff, 50-66, HEAD ATMOSPHERIC RES DEPT, BELL LABS, 66- *Concurrent Pos:* Mem exec comt, Gaseous Electronics Conf, 65; vis fel, Joint Inst Lab Astrophys, Univ Colo, 65-66; mem, Defense Sci Bd, 66-; mem, New York Health Res Coun, 71-75; mem & consult, US Environ Protection Agency Delphi Panel on Sulfur Oxides Control Technol Forecasting, 72-74; chmn panel status of sulfur oxides technol, Comn on Sociotech Systs, Nat Res Coun, 75-79. *Mem:* Fel Am Phys Soc; Am Chem Soc; Sigma Xi. *Res:* Semiconductors; gaseous diffusion and separation; atomic collision processes; reentry physics; upper atmosphere; atmospheric reactions and dispersion of contaminants; environmental physics and chemistry; halogen photochemistry and excited state reactions. *Mailing Add:* Bell Labs Murray Hill NJ 07974

MCAFEE, ROBERT DIXON, b Zamboanga City, Philippines, Sept 9, 25; US citizen; m 53. PHYSIOLOGY, BIOPHYSICS. *Educ:* Cent Col, AB, 48; Univ Tenn, MS, 51; Tulane Univ, PhD(physiol), 53. *Prof Exp:* Res physiologist, 54-59, ASSOC PHYSIOL, SCH MED, TULANE UNIV, 59-; SR SCIENTIST,

VET ADMIN HOSP, NEW ORLEANS, 59- *Concurrent Pos:* Consult prof, Col Eng, Univ New Orleans, 72-; adj prof, Delta Regional Primate Res Ctr, Covington La, 75-, adj prof, Dept Ophthal, Sch Med, Tulane Univ, 76- *Mem:* Am Physiol Soc; Biophysics Soc. *Res:* Physiological and behavioral effects of microwave irradiation and physiological correlates of operant blood pressure conditioning; biomedical engineering. *Mailing Add:* Col Eng Univ New Orleans Lakefront New Orleans LA 70148

MCAFEE, SIGRID RENEE, b New York, NY. SEMICONDUCTOR PHYSICS. *Educ:* Vassar Col, BA, 71; MS, Polytech Inst NY, 74, PhD(physics), 76. *Prof Exp:* MEM TECH STAFF PHYSICS, BELL LABS, 76- *Mem:* NY Acad Sci; Optical Soc Am; Am Phys Soc. *Res:* Study and characterization of deep level defects in semiconductor, bulk-grown and epitaxially-grown films for microwave and optoelectronic applications as well as fundamental research on their properties; the study of semiconductor processes on a picosecond time scale. *Mailing Add:* Bell Labs 600 Mountain Ave Murray Hill NJ 07974

MCAFEE, WALTER SAMUEL, b Ore City, Tex, Sept 2, 14; m 41; c 2. THEORETICAL PHYSICS. *Educ:* Wiley Col, BS, 34; Ohio State Univ, MS, 37; Cornell Univ, PhD(physics), 49. *Prof Exp:* Teacher jr high sch, 37-42; physicist theoret studies unit, Eng Labs, US Army Electronics Command, 42-45, physicist & supvr, 45-46, physicist radiation physics, 48-53, chief sect electro-magnetic wave propagation, 53-57, consult physicist, Appl Physics Div, 58-65, tech dir, Passive Sensing Tech Area, 65-71, sci adv to dir res, Develop & Eng, Eng Labs, 71-78, SCI ADV, US ARMY ELECTRONICS RES & DEVELOP COMMAND, 78- *Concurrent Pos:* Secy of Army fel, Harvard Univ, 57-58; lectr, West Long Br, Monmouth Col, NJ, 58-75. *Mem:* AAAS; Am Astron Soc; Am Phys Soc; Am Asn Physics Teachers; sr mem Inst Elec & Electronics Engrs. *Res:* Theoretical nuclear physics; electromagnetic theory. *Mailing Add:* DRDEL-SA Ft Monmouth NJ 07703

MCALACK, ROBERT FRANCIS, microbiology, immunology, see previous edition

MACALADY, DONALD LEE, b Shamokin, Pa, Apr 19, 41; m 64; c 2. PHYSICAL INORGANIC CHEMISTRY, ENVIRONMENTAL CHEMISTRY. *Educ:* Pa State Univ, BS, 63; Univ Wis-Madison, PhD(chem), 69. *Prof Exp:* Jr engr, H R B Singer, Inc, 63; asst prof chem, Grinnell Col, 68-70; asst prof, 70-74, ASSOC PROF CHEM, NORTHERN MICH UNIV, 74- *Concurrent Pos:* NSF Fac fel sci, Rosenstiel Sch of Marine & Atmospheric Sci, Univ Miami, 75-76. *Mem:* AAAS; Am Chem Soc; Water Pollution Control Fedn. *Res:* Aquatic chemistry. *Mailing Add:* Dept of Chem Northern Mich Univ Marquette MI 49855

MCALDUFF, EDWARD J, b Alberton, PEI, Dec 3, 39. SPECTROCHEMISTRY. *Educ:* St Francis Xavier Univ, BSc, 61; Univ Toronto, PhD(phys chem), 65. *Prof Exp:* Demonstr, Univ Toronto, 61-65; res fel, Univ Wash, 66-67; asst prof, 67-72, assoc dean, 80-81, ASSOC PROF CHEM, ST FRANCIS XAVIER UNIV, 72-, DEAN SCI, 81- *Concurrent Pos:* Nat Res Coun grant, 67-70; res assoc, La State Univ, 75-76; Nat Sci & Eng Res Coun Can grants, 76- *Mem:* Am Chem Soc; Chem Inst Can. *Res:* Gas phase kinetics; electronically excited states of simple molecules; photochemical aspects of air pollution; photoelectron spectroscopy of photochemically significant molecules. *Mailing Add:* Dept of Chem St Francis Xavier Univ Antigonish NS B2G 1E0 Can

MCALEER, WILLIAM JOSEPH, b Philadelphia, Pa, Oct 11, 22; m 55; c 3. ORGANIC CHEMISTRY, BIOCHEMISTRY. *Educ:* Pa State Univ, BS, 46, MS, 47; Yale Univ, PhD(org chem), 53. *Prof Exp:* Sr chemist, Merck & Co, Inc, 50-57, sr chemist & mgr electronic chem res, Merck Sharp & Dohme Res Labs, 57-63, res fel virus & cell biol, Merck Inst Therapeut Res, 64-73, sr dir biol develop, 73-76, DIR BIOTECHNOL, VIROL & CELL BIOL, MERCK INST THERAPEUT RES, 76- *Mem:* Am Inst Chemists; Am Chem Soc. *Res:* Chemistry of natural products; electronic chemicals; vaccine production, delivery and assay. *Mailing Add:* Merck Inst for Therapeut Res West Point PA 19486

MCALESTER, ARCIE LEE, JR, b Dallas, Tex, Feb 3, 33; m 77; c 2. PALEOBIOLOGY. *Educ:* Southern Methodist Univ, BA, 54, BBA, 54; Yale Univ, MS, 57, PhD(geol), 60. *Prof Exp:* From instr to prof geol, Yale Univ, 59-74, from asst cur to cur, Peabody Mus, 59-74; dean, Sch Humanities & Sci, 74-77, PROF GEOL SCI, SOUTHERN METHODIST UNIV, 74- *Concurrent Pos:* Guggenheim fel, Glasgow Univ, 64-65. *Mem:* AAAS; Geol Soc Am; Paleont Soc; Soc Syst Zool. *Res:* Paleozoic geology; marine ecology and paleocology. *Mailing Add:* Dept of Geol Sci Southern Methodist Univ Dallas TX 75275

MCALICE, BERNARD JOHN, b Providence, RI, Apr 20, 30; m 55; c 3. OCEANOGRAPHY. *Educ:* Univ RI, BS, 62, PhD(biol oceanog), 69. *Prof Exp:* Asst prof, 67-75, actg dir, Ira C Darling Ctr, 76-77, assoc prof oceanog & zool, 75-81, ASSOC PROF BOT & OCEANOG, UNIV MAINE, 81- *Mem:* Am Soc Limnol & Oceanog; Estuarine Res Fedn; Crustacean Soc. *Res:* Ecology, distribution and succession of estuarine plankton. *Mailing Add:* Dept Bot & Plant Path Univ of Maine Orono ME 04469

MCALISTER, ARCHIE JOSEPH, b Birmingham, Ala, Aug 13, 32; m 64. SOLID STATE PHYSICS. *Educ:* Cath Univ Am, AB, 54; Univ Md, MS, 64, PhD(physics), 66. *Prof Exp:* Physicist, Naval Med Res Inst, 55-58 & Naval Res Lab, 59-60; Nat Acad Sci-Nat Res Coun res assoc, 65-67, PHYSICIST, NAT BUR STAND, 67- *Mem:* Am Phys Soc. *Res:* Optical properties, soft x-ray and x-ray photoemission, phase stability of metals and alloys. *Mailing Add:* Nat Bur Standards Bldg 223 RB 150 Washington DC 20234

MCALISTER, DEAN FERDINAND, b Logan, Utah, Sept 8, 10; m 32; c 3. AGRONOMY. *Educ:* Utah State Col, BS, 31, MS, 32; Univ Wis, PhD(plant physiol), 36. *Prof Exp:* Field asst agron, Exp Sta, Utah State Col, 30-32; asst plant physiol, Univ Wis, 32-36; asst physiologist, Bur Plant Indust, 36-42, from assoc plant physiologist to physiologist, Regional Soybean Lab, 46-52, agronomist, Agr Exp Sta, USDA, 52-77, asst dir sta, 58-77, EMER PROF AGRON, UNIV ARIZ, 77- *Concurrent Pos:* Prof agron & head dept, Univ Ariz, 52-66, chief of party, Univ Ariz-Univ Ceara, Brazil Proj, US AID, 66-68. *Mem:* Fel AAAS; Am Soc Plant Physiol; fel Am Soc Agron; Sigma Xi. *Res:* Crop physiology and production; agricultural administration. *Mailing Add:* 3428 E 4th Tucson AZ 85705

MCALISTER, HAROLD ALISTER, b Chattanooga, Tenn, July 1, 49; m 72. ASTRONOMY. *Educ:* Univ Tenn, Chattanooga, BA, 71; Univ Va, MA, 74, PhD(astron), 75. *Prof Exp:* Res asst, Dept Astron, Univ Va, 71-75; res assoc astron, Kitt Peak Nat Osberv, 75-77; ASST PROF, DEPT PHYSICS, GA STATE UNIV, 77- *Mem:* Astron Soc Pac; Int Astron Union; Am Astron Soc. *Res:* Astrometry; speckle interferometry of binary stars; astronomical instrumentation; extra-solar planets. *Mailing Add:* Dept of Physics University Plaza Atlanta GA 30303

MCALISTER, JAMES ANDREW, chemical engineering, see previous edition

MCALISTER, ROBERT HARDY, b Quinter, Kans, Sept 17, 31; m 56; c 4. FOREST PRODUCTS. *Educ:* Univ Idaho, BS, 54, MS, 56; Univ Ga, PhD(forest resources), 72. *Prof Exp:* Forest prod technologist, US Forest Prod Lab, Madison, Wis, 54-62; wood technologist, Roundwood Corp Am, 62-63; wood technologist, Moore Dry Kiln Co, 63-66; WOOD SCIENTIST, SOUTHEAST FOREST EXP STA, ASHEVILLE, NC, 66- *Honors & Awards:* Wood Award, Woodworking Dig, 54; Cert of Merit, USDA, 75. *Mem:* Forest Prod Res Soc. *Mailing Add:* Forestry Sci Lab Carlton St Athens GA 30601

MCALISTER, SEAN PATRICK, b Durban, SAfrica, Apr 1, 45; Can citizen; m 70; c 1. SOLID STATE PHYSICS. *Educ:* Univ Natal, BSc, 66, MSc, 68; Univ Cambridge, PhD(physics), 71. *Prof Exp:* Fel exp physics, Simon Fraser Univ, 71-75; res assoc, 75-77, ASST RES OFFICER SOLID STATE PHYSICS, DIV CHEM, NAT RES COUN CAN, 77- *Mem:* Can Asn Physicists. *Res:* Galvanomagnetic properties of metals and alloys; magnetism. *Mailing Add:* Div of Chem Nat Res Coun of Can Ottawa ON K1A 0R6 Can

MCALISTER, WILLIAM BRUCE, b Seattle, Wash, Aug 11, 29. MARINE ECOLOGY. *Educ:* Univ Wash, BS, 49, MS, 58, JD, 80; Ore State Univ, PhD(oceanog), 62. *Prof Exp:* From instr to asst prof oceanog, Ore State Univ, 58-64; proj dir, Bur Com Fisheries, Wash, 64-70; prog dir phys oceanog, NSF, 70-72; dep dir marine fish, Northwest Fisheries Ctr, Nat Marine Fisheries Serv, 72-74, dep dir marine mammal div, 74-80; PARTNER, AQUASCI MARINE RESOURCE CONSULTS, 81- *Concurrent Pos:* Fulbright res fel, Water Res Inst, Oslo, Norway, 63-64; asst prof, Univ Wash, 65-70; attorney, 80- *Mem:* AAAS; Am Inst Fish Res Biologists; Sigma Xi. *Res:* Resource management, including legal problems; ecosystem dynamics, marine mammals and fisheries. *Mailing Add:* 14014 81st Pl NE Bothell WA 98011

MCALISTER, WILLIAM H, medicine, radiology, see previous edition

MCALLISTER, ALAN JACKSON, b Shelbyville, Ky, Aug 19, 45; m 65; c 2. ANIMAL BREEDING. *Educ:* Univ Ky, BS, 67; Ohio State Univ, MS, 70, PhD(animal breeding), 75. *Prof Exp:* Biomet geneticist poultry, DeKalb Agr Res Inc, 72-75; fel poultry genetics, 75-76, RES SCIENTIST & CHMN, DAIRY CATTLE BREEDING PROG, ANIMAL RES CTR, AGR CAN, 76- *Mem:* Am Soc Animal Sci; Am Dairy Sci Asn; Int Biomet Soc; Can Soc Animal Sci. *Res:* Genetic improvement of animal populations through application of optimal genetic evaluation procedures; where performance includes both directly observable economic traits and basic physiological measurements. *Mailing Add:* Animal Res Ctr Agr Can Genetics Bldg Ottawa ON K1A 0C6 Can

MCALLISTER, ARNOLD LLOYD, b Petitcodiac, NB, Dec 24, 21. GEOLOGY. *Educ:* Univ NB, BSc, 43; McGill Univ, MSc, 48, PhD, 50. *Prof Exp:* Res geologist, Int Nickel Co, 50-52; assoc prof, 52-62, head dept, 62-74, PROF GEOL, UNIV NB, 62- *Mem:* Royal Soc Can; Geol Asn Can; Can Inst Mining & Metall. *Res:* Economic and structural geology. *Mailing Add:* Dept of Geol Univ of NB Fredericton MB E3B 5A3 Can

MCALLISTER, BYRON LEON, b Midvale, Utah, Apr 29, 29; m 57; c 3. GENERAL TOPOLOGY, HISTORY MATHEMATICS. *Educ:* Univ Utah, BA, 51, MA, 55; Univ Wis, PhD(math), 66. *Prof Exp:* From asst prof to assoc prof math, SDak Sch Mines & Technol, 58-67; assoc prof, 67-71, PROF MATH, MONT STATE UNIV, 71- *Concurrent Pos:* Instr, Fox Valley Ctr, Univ Wis, 61-62. *Mem:* Am Math Soc; Math Asn Am; Asn Women Math; Women & Math Educ. *Res:* General topology, particularly Whyburn cyclic element theory and extensions, multifunctions and hyperspaces. *Mailing Add:* Dept of Math Mont State Univ Bozeman MT 59717

MCALLISTER, CRAIG J, physical organic chemistry, see previous edition

MCALLISTER, CYRUS RAY, b Portland, Ore, Apr 22, 22; m 53; c 3. MATHEMATICS. *Educ:* Univ Minn, BA, 48; Univ Ore, MA, 51. *Prof Exp:* Instr math, Univ Idaho, 48-50; analyst, US Dept Defense, 52; mathematician, Sandia Corp, 52-57, consult, 57; sr res scientist & maj proj supvr nuclear div, Kaman Aircraft Corp, 57-59, consult, 59; pres & tech dir, McAllister & Assocs, Inc, 59-63; res dir, Booz, Allen Appl Res, Inc, 63-66; dir sci & consult div, Genge Industs, Inc, 66-68; staff engr, Advan Concepts Off, Aerospace Corp, Calif, 68-72; CONSULT, 72- *Mem:* Am Meteorol Soc. *Res:* Applied mathematics; mathematical statistics; dynamic climatology; weapons systems analysis. *Mailing Add:* 4729 Libbit Ave Encino CA 91436

MCALLISTER, DAVID FRANKLIN, b Richmond, Va, July 2, 41; c 1. GRAPHICS, PERFORMANCE EVALUATION. *Educ:* Univ NC, Chapel Hill, BS, 63, PhD(comput sci), 72; Purdue Univ, MS, 67. *Prof Exp:* Luitenant, US Navy, 63-65; asst math, Purdue Univ, 65-67; instr, Univ NC, Greensboro,

67-72; asst prof, 72-76, ASSOC PROF COMPUT SCI, NC STATE UNIV, 76- *Concurrent Pos:* Consult, Environ Protection Agency, 74-81, Monsanto Corp, 80-81, Boeing Computer Serv, 82- & Pohers Indust, 81-82; prin investr, NASA, 78-, NSF, 79- *Res:* Computer performance evaluation; software reliability modeling; shape preserving spline approximation; large scale linear programming. *Mailing Add:* Dept Comput Sci NC State Univ Raleigh NC 27650

MCALLISTER, DONALD EVAN, b Victoria, BC, Aug 23, 34; m 56; c 5. SYSTEMATIC ICHTHYOLOGY. *Educ:* Univ BC, BA, 55, MA, 57, PhD(ichthyol), 64. *Prof Exp:* CUR FISHES, NAT MUS NATURAL SCI, NAT MUS CAN, 58- *Concurrent Pos:* Lectr, Univ Ottawa, 64-; adj prof, Carleton Univ, 81- *Mem:* Am Soc Ichthyol & Herpet; Can Soc Zool; Can Soc Wildlife & Fishery Biol; Japanese Soc Ichthyol; Soc Syst Zool. *Res:* Fish systematics, evolution, arctic, Canada and world; biogeography; osmeridae; cottidae; endangered ichthoyfauna. *Mailing Add:* Nat Mus Natural Sci Ottawa ON K1A 0M8 Can

MCALLISTER, GREGORY THOMAS, JR, b Boston, Mass, July 6, 34; m 61; c 3. MATHEMATICS. *Educ:* St Peters Col, NJ, BS, 56; Univ Calif, Berkeley, PhD(math), 62. *Prof Exp:* Res mathematician, US Army Ballistic Res Labs, 63-65; PROF MATH, CTR APPLN MATH, LEHIGH UNIV, 65- *Mem:* Am Math Soc; Soc Indust & Appl Math. *Res:* Calculus of variations; partial differential equations; numerical methods. *Mailing Add:* Ctr for Appln of Math Lehigh Univ Bethlehem PA 18015

MCALLISTER, HARMON CARLYLE, JR, biochemistry, see previous edition

MCALLISTER, HOWARD CONLEE, b Cheyenne, Wyo, Mar 14, 24; m 44; c 4. PHYSICS. *Educ:* Univ Wyo, BS, 48, MS, 50; Univ Colo, PhD(physics), 59. *Prof Exp:* From asst prof to assoc prof, 59-70, PROF PHYSICS, UNIV HAWAII, 70-; PRIN INVESTR, INST ASTRON, 69- *Concurrent Pos:* Consult, Univ Colo, 61 & Lincoln Lab, Mass Inst Technol, 63-64; Nat Acad Sci-Nat Res Coun sr resident res assoc, Goddard Space Flight Ctr, 65-66. *Mem:* Am Phys Soc; Optical Soc Am. *Res:* Solar ultraviolet spectroscopy and upper atmospheric physics; atomic and molecular spectroscopy; spectroscopic instrumentation for space research. *Mailing Add:* Dept of Physics & Astron Univ of Hawaii Honolulu HI 96822

MCALLISTER, JEROME WATT, b Bay City, Tex, Mar 19, 44; m 67. PHYSICAL CHEMISTRY. *Educ:* Tex Christian Univ, BS, 67; Univ Tex, Austin, PhD(chem physics), 71. *Prof Exp:* Res assoc phys chem, Iowa State Univ, 71-72; sr res chemist, 72-75, develop specialist, 75-77, supvr, 77-79, MGR RES & DEVELOP, 3M CO, 79- *Mem:* Am Chem Soc; Am Indust Hyg Asn. *Res:* Development of adsorbents and indicating chemistries for use in respirators and personal monitors for gases and vapors. *Mailing Add:* 3M Ctr-230 3M Co St Paul MN 55144

MCALLISTER, MARIALUISA N, b Milan, Italy, Aug 22, 33; US citizen; m 61; c 3. MATHEMATICS, COMPUTER SCIENCES. *Educ:* Univ Rome, PhD(math), 57. *Prof Exp:* NSF fel, 60-61; asst prof math, Univ Dela, 62-64; assoc prof, Towson State Col, 64-65; asst prof, 65-73, ASSOC PROF MATH, MORAVIAN COL, 73- *Mem:* Math Asn Am; Asn Comput Mach; Int Asn Math Modeling. *Res:* Algebraic geometry; numerical analysis; operations research. *Mailing Add:* Dept of Math Moravian Col Bethlehem PA 18018

MCALLISTER, RAYMOND FRANCIS, b Ithaca, NY, June 26, 23; div; c 3. OCEANOGRAPHY, OCEAN ENGINEERING. *Educ:* Cornell Univ, BS, 50; Univ Ill, MS, 51; Agr & Mech Col, Tex, PhD(geol oceanog), 58. *Prof Exp:* Instr geol, Univ Ill, 50-51; res oceanogr, Scripps Inst, Univ Calif, 51-54; marine res geologist & instr geol, Agr & Mech Col, Tex, 54-58; sr oceanogr, Bermuda Sound Fixing & Ranging Sta, Columbia Univ, 58-63; asst dir marine technol group, NAm Aviation Inc, Miami, 64-65; PROF OCEAN ENG, FLA ATLANTIC UNIV, 65-; PRES, MCALLISTER MARINE, DEERFIELD BR, 75- *Concurrent Pos:* mem, Man in the Sea Panel, Nat Acad Eng, 71- *Res:* Marine geology and surveys; bottom photography and sampling; scuba diving as a scientific tool; environmental surveys; artificial reef construction; ocean outfall studies. *Mailing Add:* Dept Ocean Eng Fla Atlantic Univ Boca Raton FL 33431

MCALLISTER, ROBERT MILTON, b Philadelphia, Pa, June 10, 22; m 49; c 6. PEDIATRICS. *Educ:* Ursinus Col, BS, 42; Univ Pa, MD, 45, MS, 55; Am Bd Pediat, dipl, 53. *Prof Exp:* From instr to asst prof pediat, Sch Med, Univ Pa, 51-59; assoc prof, 59-64, PROF PEDIAT, CHILDREN'S HOSP LOS ANGELES, SCH MED, UNIV SOUTHERN CALIF, 64-, DIR RES, 75- *Mem:* Am Pediat Soc; Soc Pediat Res; Am Asn Cancer Res; fel Am Acad Pediat; AMA. *Res:* Microbiology and oncology in the pediatric age group; tissue culture. *Mailing Add:* Children's Hosp of Los Angeles PO Box 54700 Terminal Annex Los Angeles CA 90054

MCALLISTER, ROBERT WALLACE, b Hermosa Beach, Calif, Feb 16, 29; div; c 4. PHYSICS, INSTRUMENTATION. *Educ:* Occidental Col, BA, 51; Stanford Univ, PhD(physics), 60. *Prof Exp:* Asst physics, Univ Zurich, 56-60; instr, Cornell Univ, 60-64; asst prof, 64-66, ASSOC PROF PHYSICS, COLO SCH MINES, 66- *Res:* application and interfacing of microcomputers to control experiments and record data. *Mailing Add:* Dept Physics Colo Sch Mines Golden CO 80401

MCALLISTER, WARREN ALEXANDER, b Augusta, Ga, Mar 12, 41; m 62. INORGANIC CHEMISTRY. *Educ:* Mercer Univ, BA, 63; Univ SC, PhD(inorg chem), 67. *Prof Exp:* Res assoc, Vanderbilt Univ, 66-67; from asst prof to assoc prof chem, East Carolina Univ, 67-75, prof, 75-80. *Concurrent Pos:* Grants, USPHS, Environ Protection Agency & NC Bd Sci & Technol; res assoc, Brown Univ, 73; adj prof, East Carolina Univ, 80- *Mem:* Am Chem Soc. *Res:* Infrared and Raman studies of inorganic compounds. *Mailing Add:* Dept of Chem ECarolina Univ Greenville NC 27834

MCALLISTER, WILLIAM ALBERT, b Youngstown, Ohio, Oct 22, 23; m 47; c 6. PHYSICAL CHEMISTRY. *Educ:* Bowling Green State Univ, BS, 49; Mich State Univ, PhD(phys chem), 54. *Prof Exp:* Res chemist, Celanese Corp Am, 53-55; from scientist to sr scientist, Atomic Power Div, 55-59, sr scientist, Lamp Div, 59-61, phosphor sect mgr, 61-65, RES CONSULT PHOSPHORS, ADVAN DEVELOP DEPT, LAMP DIV, WESTINGHOUSE ELEC CORP, 65- *Concurrent Pos:* Adj prof, NJ Inst Technol, 70, 75-77. *Mem:* Am Chem Soc; Am Phys Soc; Electrochem Soc. *Res:* Luminescent inorganic materials, structure and spectra, especially rare earths; metal halide vapor discharges. *Mailing Add:* Advan Develop Dept Lamp Div Westinghouse Elec Corp Bloomfield NJ 07003

MCALLISTER, WILLIAM TURNER, molecular biology, see previous edition

MCALPINE, GEORGE ALBERT, b Tampa, Fla, Dec 11, 33; m 52; c 4. ELECTRICAL ENGINEERING, RESEARCH ADMINISTRATION. *Educ:* Univ Va, BEE, 57; Stanford Univ, MS, 61; Univ Va, DSc, 67. *Prof Exp:* Sr engr, Martin Co, Fla, 57-59, Sylvania Electronic Defense Labs, Calif, 59-61 & Martin Co, Fla, 61-62; proj engr, Sperry, Piedmont, Va, 62-64; ASSOC PROF ELEC ENG, UNIV VA, 68-, EXEC DIR INDUST RES & DEVELOP CTR, 64-, DIR RES LABS ENG SCI, 67- *Concurrent Pos:* Consult, Sperry Marine Systs Div, Sperry Rand Corp, 64, Radio Corp Am, 65-66, Bio-Space Technol Training Prog, 65-70, Deco Electronics, Inc, Va, 65- & Electronic Commun, Inc, 68; actg assoc provost res, Univ Va, 76-77. *Mem:* Inst Elec & Electronics Engrs; Sigma Xi; Am Soc Eng Educ. *Res:* Communications and systems theory; digital filters; stochastic processes. *Mailing Add:* Res Labs for the Eng Sci Univ of Va Charlottesville VA 22901

MACALPINE, GORDON MADEIRA, b Bozeman, Mont, Feb 23, 45; m 67. ASTROPHYSICS. *Educ:* Earlham Col, AB, 67; Univ Wis, PhD(astron), 71. *Prof Exp:* Mem, Inst Advan Study, 71-72; asst prof, 72-78, ASSOC PROF ASTRON, UNIV MICH, ANN ARBOR, 78- *Mem:* Am Astron Soc. *Res:* Detailed theoretical and observational investigation of the emission-line regions in quasi-stellar objects and Seyfert galaxies. *Mailing Add:* Dept of Astron Univ of Mich Ann Arbor MI 48109

MCALPINE, JAMES BRUCE, b Ingham, Queensland, Australia, Dec 26, 39; m 68; c 2. ORGANIC CHEMISTRY. *Educ:* Univ New Eng, Australia, BSc, 62, MSc, 64, PhD(org chem), 69. *Prof Exp:* Fel biochem, Med Sch, Northwestern Univ, 69-71, asst prof biochem, 71-72; sr res chemist, 72-75, PROJ LEADER ANTIBIOTICS MODIFICATION, ABBOTT LABS, 75- *Mem:* Royal Soc Chem; Am Chem Soc; Sigma Xi. *Res:* The chemistry, mode of action and toxicity of antimicrobial agents. *Mailing Add:* Abbott Labs Dept 482 North Chicago IL 60064

MCALPINE, JAMES FRANCIS, b Maynooth, Ont, Sept 25, 22; m 50. ENTOMOLOGY. *Educ:* Univ Toronto, BSA, 50; Univ Ill, MSc, 54, PhD(entom), 62. *Prof Exp:* Tech officer, 50-53, res officer, 53-63, RES SCIENTIST, BIOSYSTS RES INST, AGR CAN, 63- *Mem:* Entom Soc Can. *Res:* Systematics of two-winged flies. *Mailing Add:* Biosysts Res Inst Agr Can Ottawa ON K1A 0C6 Can

MCALPINE, PHYLLIS JEAN, b Petrolia, Ont, Aug 29, 41. HUMAN GENETICS, MEDICAL GENETICS. *Educ:* Univ Western Ont, BSc, 63; Univ Toronto, MA, 66; Univ London, PhD(human genetics), 70. *Prof Exp:* Med Res Coun Can fel, Queen's Univ, 70-72; res assoc human genetics, Health Sci Children's Ctr, 72-74; ASST PROF PEDIAT, UNIV MAN, 74-; SCI STAFF, HEALTH SCI CHILDREN'S CTR, 75- *Mem:* Genetics Soc Can; Am Soc Human Genetics. *Res:* Mapping the human genome by use of somatic cell hybrids and family studies; expression of genes in human tissues. *Mailing Add:* Dept of Genetics 700 William Ave Winnipeg MB R3T 2N2 Can

MACALUSO, ANTHONY, SR, b New Orleans, La, Oct 4, 39; m 61; c 3. CHEMISTRY. *Educ:* Loyola Univ, BS, 61; Tulane Univ, MS, 63, PhD(chem), 65. *Prof Exp:* SR CHEMIST, RES & TECH DEPT, TEXACO INC, 67- *Mem:* Am Chem Soc. *Res:* Exploratory research in organic and petroleum chemistry. *Mailing Add:* 4135 42nd St Port Arthur TX 77640

MACALUSO, MARY CHRISTELLE, b Lincoln, Nebr, July 9, 31. ANATOMY. *Educ:* Col St Mary, Nebr, BS, 56; Univ Notre Dame, MS, 61; Univ Nebr, PhD(anat), 66. *Prof Exp:* From instr to assoc prof, 61-73, chmn dept, 67-73, PROF BIOL, COL ST MARY, NEBR, 73- *Res:* Sex education; ultrastructure of the corpus luteum of pregnancy and the corpus luteum of lactation in Swiss mice during the first nineteen days postpartum; human development. *Mailing Add:* Dept of Biol Col of St Mary Omaha NE 68124

MACALUSO, PAT, b New York, NY, Aug 29, 16; m 41; c 2. PHYSICAL CHEMISTRY, COMPUTER SCIENCE. *Educ:* City Col NY, BS, 39; Polytech Inst Brooklyn, MS, 46, 78. *Prof Exp:* Chemist indust & consumer specialties, Foster D Snell, Inc, 40-42, group leader, 42-45, acct exec, 45-47; group leader agr chem formulations, 47-54, head prod develop & res sect, 54-65, head polymer prod sect, 65-67, mgr info serv, 67-80, MGR COMPUT SERV, EASTERN RES CTR, STAUFFER CHEM CO, 80- *Mem:* Am Chem Soc; Am Soc Testing & Mat; NY Acad Sci; Asn Comput Mach. *Res:* Polymers, elastomers; polyvinyl chloride; industrial chemical applications; chemical specialties; chemistry of sulfur; physical chemistry of proteins; computer applications in chemical research. *Mailing Add:* Stauffer Chem Co Eastern Res Ctr Dobbs Ferry NY 10522

MCANALLY, JOHN SACKETT, b Indianapolis, Ind, Apr 15, 18; m 43; c 2. ANALYTICAL BIOCHEMISTRY. *Educ:* Ind Univ, BS, 38, AM, 40, PhD(chem), 50. *Prof Exp:* Res asst prof biochem, Med Res Unit, Univ Miami, 50-52, asst prof, Med Sch, 52-57; from asst prof to prof biochem, Occidental Col, 57-82, dean students, 65-68; RETIRED. *Mem:* AAAS; Am Chem Soc; NY Acad Sci. *Res:* Vitamin A; urinary estrogens and androgens; trace element analysis; seawater and marine organisms. *Mailing Add:* Dept Chem Occidental Col Los Angeles CA 90041

MCANDREWS, JOHN HENRY, b Minneapolis, Minn, Jan 16, 33; Can citizen; m 58, 77; c 5. BOTANY, PLANT ECOLOGY. *Educ:* Col St Thomas, BS, 57; Univ Minn, MS, 59, PhD(bot), 64. *Prof Exp:* Res assoc paleoecol, Inst Bio-Archeol, Groningen, Neth, 63-64; asst prof biol, Jamestown Col, 64-66 & Cornell Col, 66-67; cur geol, 67-78, CUR BOT ROYAL ONT MUS, 78-; ASSOC PROF BOT, UNIV TORONTO, 68-, ASSOC PROF GEOL, 80- *Concurrent Pos:* Vis prof ecol, Univ Minn, 74; vis lectr anthrop, Univ Man, 75. *Res:* Vegetation history; climatic change; pollen analysis; pollen morphology. *Mailing Add:* Univ of Toronto St George Campus Toronto ON M5S 1A3 Can

MCANELLY, JOHN KITCHEL, b Logansport, Ind, June 22, 31; m 53; c 2. FOOD MICROBIOLOGY, QUALITY ASSURANCE. *Educ:* Iowa State Univ, BS, 53; NC State Univ, MS, 56; Univ Wis, PhD(bact), 60. *Prof Exp:* Res biochemist, Res & Develop Ctr, Swift & Co, Ill, 59-61, head biochem div, 61-66; dir res & develop, Rival Pet Foods, 66-68, vpres tech develop, 68-75; dir corp qual assurance, 75-78, DIR FOOD PROTECTION, NABISCO, INC, 78- *Mem:* Am Chem Soc; Am Soc Microbiol; Inst Food Technol; fel Am Inst Chemists. *Res:* Biochemistry and microbiology of food products and processes; thermal processing of foods; utilization of proteins. *Mailing Add:* Nabisco Inc Res Ctr Fairlawn NJ 07410

MCANENY, LAURENCE RAYMOND, b Seattle, Wash, Apr 12, 26; m 46; c 3. PHYSICS. *Educ:* Univ Kans, BS, 46, PhD(physics), 57; Univ Calif, MA, 48. *Prof Exp:* Asst prof physics, Park Col, 51-57; from asst prof to assoc prof physics, 57-67, asst dean acad affairs, 63-67, dean div sci & technol, 67-73, PROF PHYSICS, SOUTHERN ILL UNIV, EDWARDSVILLE, 67- *Concurrent Pos:* Pres bd dirs, Cent States Univs, Inc, 75. *Mem:* Am Phys Soc; Am Asn Physics Teachers. *Res:* Theoretical physics; statistical mechanics. *Mailing Add:* Sch Sci & Eng Southern Ill Univ Edwardsville IL 62026

MCANINCH, LLOYD NEALSON, b Guelph, Ont, June 6, 20; m 44; c 3. UROLOGY. *Educ:* Univ Western Ont, MD, 45; FRCPS(C), 53. *Prof Exp:* Intern, Victoria Hosp, London, Ont, 45-46; asst to Dr E D Busby, 46-49; instr anat, Fac Med, Univ Western Ont, 49-50; asst resident surg, Westminster Vet Hosp, Ont, 50-51; resident urol, Toronto Gen Hosp, 51-52; resident, Sunnybrook Hosp, 52-53; asst resident path, Westminster Hosp, 53; from instr to asst prof surg, Univ Western Ont, 53-63, from clin assoc prof to clin prof urol, 63-70, chief urol, 70-73, prof surg, Fac Med, 70-75, chief urol, Univ Hosp, 73-75; RETIRED. *Concurrent Pos:* Consult, Westminster Vet Hosp, 54-; chief urol, Victoria Hosp, Ont, 56-73, consult; attend urologist & consult, St Joseph's Hosp, Ont. *Mem:* Fel Am Col Surg; Can Med Asn; Can Urol Asn (pres, 74-75); fel Can Asn Clin Surg; Can Acad Urol Surg (treas, 60-65, pres, 66). *Res:* Vesico-ureteral reflux; renal trauma; retroperitoneal tumors; urological emergencies; chemotherapy in urology; ureteral substitutions; external meatotomy. *Mailing Add:* 1 Grosvenor St Apt 1423 London ON N6A 1Y2 Can

MCARDLE, EUGENE W, zoology, see previous edition

MCARDLE, JOSEPH JOHN, b Wilmington, Del, July 21, 45. NEUROPHYSIOLOGY, NEUROPHARMACOLOGY. *Educ:* Univ Del, BA, 67; State Univ NY Buffalo, PhD(pharmacol), 71. *Prof Exp:* Vis asst prof pharmacol, Sch Med & Dent, State Univ NY Buffalo, 71-72; asst prof, 72-77, ASSOC PROF PHARMACOL, COL MED & DENT NJ, 77- *Concurrent Pos:* Nat Inst Neurol Comn Dis & Stroke grant, Col Med & Dent NJ, 73-82; vis scientist, Lab de Neurbiol, Grif-sur-Yvette, France, 79-80; fel, La Found de L'Indust Pharmaceut Pour La Recherche, France. *Mem:* Am Soc Pharmacol & Exp Therapeut; Soc Neurosci; Biophys Soc. *Res:* Trophic influences of nerve upon muscle and the effects of drugs upon these phenomena; neuro-muscular regeneration; axoplasmic flow; neuro-muscular development; excitation-secretion coupling; excitation-contraction coupling; neural plasticity; hormonal effects on excitable membranes; human neuro-muscular disorders; genetically mediated neuro-muscular disorders; neuro-toxicology; uses of computers in the study of neurobiological problems; cardiac toxicology; electrophysiology of the mammalian brain slice; direct recording of single channel conductance. *Mailing Add:* Dept of Pharmacol Col Med & Dent of NJ Newark NJ 07103

MCARDLE, RICHARD EDWIN, b Lexington, Ky, Feb 25, 99; m 27; c 3. FORESTRY. *Educ:* Univ Mich, BS, 23, MS, 24, PhD, 30. *Hon Degrees:* ScD, Univ Mich, 53 & Univ Maine, 62; LLD, Syracuse Univ, 61. *Prof Exp:* Jr forester, US Forest Serv, 24-27, from asst silviculturist to assoc silviculturist, 26-34; dean sch forestry, Univ Idaho, 34-35; dir, Rocky Mountain Forest & Range Exp Sta, US Forest Serv, 35-38 & Appalachian Forest Exp Sta, 38-44, asst chief, 44-52, chief serv, 52-62; exec dir, Nat Inst Pub Affairs, 62-64; consult, 65-66; mem bd dirs, Olinkraft, Inc, 67-78; RETIRED. *Concurrent Pos:* Mem, Royal Comn Forestry, Nfld & Labrador, 67-71; resources consult, Nat Wildlife Fedn, 67-; pres, Fifth World Forestry Cong. *Honors & Awards:* Distinguished Serv Award, USDA, 57; Awards, Nat Civil Serv League, 58, Am Forestry Asn, 58 & Pub Personnel Asn, 59; Distinguished Serv Award, NY State Col Forestry, Syracuse Univ; Rockefeller Pub Serv Award; President's Gold Medal & Order Merit Forestry of Miguel Angel de Quevedo, Mex, 61; Knight Comdr, Order Merit, Ger, 62; Sir William Schlich Mem Medal, Soc Am Foresters, 62; Rockefeller Forester-in-Residence, Univ Maine, 65; John Aston Warder Forestry Award, 78. *Mem:* Fel Soil Conserv Soc Am; fel Soc Am Foresters; Royal Swedish Acad Agr & Forestry. *Res:* Executive development; forest administration. *Mailing Add:* 5110 River Hill Rd Bethesda MD 20816

MCARTHUR, CHARLES STEWART, b Stratford, Ont, Apr ll, 08; m 35; c 3. BIOCHEMISTRY. *Educ:* Univ Western Ont, BA, 35, MSc, 38; Univ Toronto, PhD(path chem), 43. *Prof Exp:* Res assoc med res, Univ Toronto, 39-41, demonstr path chem, 40-46, asst prof med res, 47-49; prof biochem, 49-75, EMER PROF BIOCHEM, UNIV SASK, 75- *Res:* Biochemistry of lipids. *Mailing Add:* 1035 Univ Dr Saskatoon SK S7N 0K4 Can

MCARTHUR, CHARLES WILSON, b New Orleans, La, Nov 4, 21; m 43; c 6. MATHEMATICS. *Educ:* La State Univ, BS, 47; Brown Univ, MS, 50; Tulane Univ, PhD(math), 54. *Prof Exp:* Instr math, Univ Md, 52-53; asst prof, Ala Polytech Inst, 53-56; assoc prof, 56-64, chmn dept, 74-80, PROF MATH, FLA STATE UNIV, 64- *Mem:* AAAS; Am Math Soc; Math Asn Am. *Res:* Functional analysis, particularly biorthogonal systems and Schauder bases; ordered topological vector spaces. *Mailing Add:* Dept Math Fla State Univ Tallahassee FL 32306

MCARTHUR, COLIN RICHARD, b Beamsville, Ont, July 18, 35; m 59; c 2. ORGANIC CHEMISTRY. *Educ:* Univ Western Ont, BSc, 57, MSc, 58; Univ Ill, PhD(org chem), 61. *Prof Exp:* Sr res chemist, Allied Chem Corp, NY, 61-67; asst prof natural sci, 67-70 & chem, 70-71, ASSOC PROF CHEM, YORK UNIV, 71-, DIR, LIBERAL SCI PROG, 77- *Mem:* Am Chem Soc; Chem Inst Can. *Res:* Organic halogen compounds; organometallic reagents; asymmetric syntheses; syntheses on polymer supports; carbenes; azomethines; heterocycles. *Mailing Add:* Dept Chem York Univ 4700 Keele St Toronto ON M3J 1P3 Can

MCARTHUR, DAVID SAMUEL, b Nelson, NZ, May 3, 41. PHYSICAL GEOGRAPHY. *Educ:* Univ NZ, BSc, 62; Univ Canterbury, MSc, 64; Christchurch Teachers' Col, dipl, 64; La State Univ, PhD(geog), 69. *Prof Exp:* Res instr coastal geomorphol, Coastal Studies Inst, La State Univ, 68; vis asst prof geol, Mich State Univ, 69; vis asst prof geog, La State Univ, 69-70; asst prof, Univ Calif, Davis, 70-73; ASSOC PROF GEOG, SAN DIEGO STATE UNIV, 73- *Mem:* Asn Am Geog; Coastal Soc. *Res:* Coastal geomorphology, especially beach sedimentation and morphology. *Mailing Add:* Dept of Geog San Diego State Univ San Diego CA 92182

MACARTHUR, DONALD M, b Detroit, Mich, Jan 7, 31; m 62; c 2. ENVIRONMENTAL MANAGEMENT, HEALTH SCIENCES. *Educ:* Univ St Andrews, BSc, 54; Univ Edinburgh, PhD(x-ray crystallog), 57. *Prof Exp:* Lectr chem, Univ Conn, 57-58; from sr scientist to mgr chem & life sci res ctr, Melpar Inc, 58-66; dep dir chem & mat, Off Secy of Defense, 66, dep dir res & technol, 66-70; pres & chief exec officer, Enviro Control, Inc, 70-81; PRES & CHIEF EXEC OFFICER, DYNAMAC INT, 81- *Concurrent Pos:* Consult, Off Water Resources, Dept of Interior, DC, 65-66; contrib ed, Am Ord Mag, 65-66; consult, Off Dir Defense Res & Eng; mem bd, Diversitron, Inc; Module Systs & Develop, Inc; pres, Dynamac Inc, 75- *Mem:* AAAS; Am Chem Soc; Am Water Works Asn; Nat Asn Life Sci (pres, 81-83). *Res:* Air quality and water quality trends; health effects of air pollution; hazardous materials transportation and associated risk analysis; health research in cancer and relationship of nutrition to cancer. *Mailing Add:* Dynamac Corp 11140 Rockville Pike Washington DC 20016

MCARTHUR, ELDON DURANT, b Hurricane, Utah, Mar 12, 41; m 63; c 4. PLANT GENETICS. *Educ:* Univ Utah, BS, 65, MS, 67, PhD(biol), 70. *Prof Exp:* Teaching asst biol, Univ Utah, 66-70; Agr Res Coun Gt Brit fel, Sigma Xi grant & demonstr, Univ Leeds, 70-71; teaching fel biol, Univ Utah, 71; res geneticist, Great Basin Exp Area, 72-75, RES GENETICIST, SHRUB SCI LAB, INTERMOUNTAIN FOREST & RANGE EXP STA, FOREST SERV, USDA, 75- *Concurrent Pos:* Adj fac mem bot & range sci, Brigham Young Univ, 75- *Mem:* Soc Range Mgt; Bot Soc Am; Soc Study Evolution. *Res:* Genetics and cytology of Mimulus; cytology of Brassiceae; genetics, cytology, breeding and selection of intermountain shrubs. *Mailing Add:* Shrub Sci Lab USDA 735 North 500 East Provo UT 84601

MCARTHUR, JANET W, b Bellingham, Wash, June 25, 14. ENDOCRINOLOGY. *Educ:* Univ Wash, AB, 35, MS, 37; Northwestern Univ, MD, 42; Am Bd Internal Med, dipl, 48. *Hon Degrees:* DSc, Mt Holyoke Col, 62. *Prof Exp:* Res fel pediat, 48-50, instr, 50-51, instr gynec, 51-57, clin assoc med, 57-60, from asst clin prof to assoc clin prof, 60-71, assoc prof, 71-73, prof obstet, 73-77, PROF GYNEC, HARVARD MED SCH, 73- *Concurrent Pos:* Asst, Children's Med Serv, Mass Gen Hosp, 48-50, asst med, 50-51, asst physician, 51-60, assoc physician, 60-; consult physician, Mass Eye & Ear Infirmary, 52; mem, Ctr Pop Studies, Sch Pub Health, Harvard Univ; mem comt pop res, NIH, 80- *Mem:* AAAS; Am Fertil Soc; Endocrine Soc; AMA; Am Col Physicians. *Res:* Bioassay of pituitary hormones; identification of pituitary hormones in human plasma; reproductive endocrinology; effects of exercise on female reproductive system. *Mailing Add:* Mass Gen Hosp 32 Fruit St Boston MA 02114

MACARTHUR, JOHN DUNCAN, b Toronto, Ont, Apr 13, 36; m 59; c 2. NUCLEAR PHYSICS. *Educ:* Univ Western Ont, BSc, 58; McMaster Univ, PhD(nuclear physics), 62. *Prof Exp:* Asst prof, 62-67, ASSOC PROF PHYSICS, QUEEN'S UNIV, ONT, 67- *Mem:* Can Asn Physicists; Am Asn Physics Teachers. *Res:* Low energy nuclear physics. *Mailing Add:* Dept of Physics Queen's Univ Kingston ON K7L 3N6 Can

MACARTHUR, JOHN WOOD, b Chicago, Ill, Sept 1, 22; m 47; c 5. PHYSICS. *Educ:* Univ Toronto, BA, 45; Rensselaer Polytech Inst, PhD(physics), 53. *Prof Exp:* MEM FAC PHYSICS, MARLBORO COL, 48- *Concurrent Pos:* With res div, Mass Inst Technol, 57-58; with lunar & planetary lab, Univ Ariz, 66-67. *Mem:* Am Phys Soc; Am Asn Physics Teachers; Am Geophys Union. *Res:* Astronomy; geophysics; population biology. *Mailing Add:* Dept of Physics Marlboro Col Marlboro VT 05344

MCARTHUR, RICHARD EDWARD, b Bradford, Pa, Dec 29, 15; m 42; c 3. ORGANIC CHEMISTRY. *Educ:* Temple Univ, AB, 37; Pa State Col, MS, 39, PhD(org chem), 41. *Prof Exp:* Instr chem, Exten Sch, Temple Univ, 36-37; chem operator, Pa State Univ, 39; res chemist, Niagara Alkali Co, NY, 40; res chemist, Sherwood Refining Co, Pa, 41-45, chief chemist & operating supt, 45-46; res chemist, Olin Corp, Conn, 46-52, sect head chem res, 52-56, mgr, 56-60, assoc dir, 60-64, planning scientist, 65-69, sect mgr customer serv-urethanes, 69-74; CHEM CONSULT, 74- *Mem:* Am Chem Soc; Sigma Xi. *Res:* Organic fluorine compounds; laboratory process development; high pressure reactions; economic analyses and chemical feasibility studies; flexible and rigid urethane foams; polyether and isocyanate synthesis and process development. *Mailing Add:* 104 Walter Lane Hamden CT 06514

MCARTHUR, WILLIAM GEORGE, b Kearney, NJ, July 1, 40; m 66; c 3. COMPUTER SCIENCE. *Educ:* Villanova Univ, BS, 66; Pa State Univ, PhD(math), 69. *Prof Exp:* From asst prof to assoc prof math, 69-74, PROF MATH & COMPUT SCI, SHIPPENSBURG STATE COL, 74- *Mem:* Asn Comput Mach; Math Asn Am; Sigma Xi. *Res:* Use of microcomputers in education. *Mailing Add:* Dept of Math & Comput Sci Shippensburg State Col Shippensburg PA 17257

MCARTHUR, WILLIAM HENRY, b Selma, Ala, Oct 15, 22; m 57; c 1. ZOOLOGY. *Educ:* Morehouse Col, BS, 47; Atlanta Univ, MS, 48; Iowa Univ, PhD, 55. *Prof Exp:* Instr zool, Morehouse Col, 48-51; asst prof, 52-55, PROF ZOOL & CHMN DIV NAT SCI & MATH, KNOXVILLE COL, 55- *Mem:* Nat Inst Sci. *Res:* Parasitology; protozoology. *Mailing Add:* Dept of Biol Knoxville Col Box 173 Knoxville TN 37921

MCASSEY, EDWARD V, JR, b New York, NY, Sept 17, 35; m 58; c 3. MECHANICAL ENGINEERING. *Educ:* Polytech Inst Brooklyn, BME, 56, MME, 59; Univ Pa, PhD(mech eng), 68. *Prof Exp:* Engr, Grumman Aircraft Corp, 59-60 & RCA-Astro Electronic Div, 60-65; from asst prof to assoc prof, 67-75, PROF MECH ENG, VILLANOVA UNIV, 75- *Concurrent Pos:* Consult, Perkin Elmer Co, 68-; NSF fac fel, 75-76. *Mem:* Am Inst Aeronaut & Astronaut; Am Soc Mech Engrs; Am Soc Eng Educ. *Res:* Fluid mechanics, thermodynamics and heat transfer; nuclear heat transfer and two phase flow; computer aided design. *Mailing Add:* Dept of Mech Eng Villanova Univ Villanova PA 19085

MCATEE, JAMES LEE, JR, b Waco, Tex, Aug 29, 24; m 47; c 4. COLLOID CHEMISTRY. *Educ:* Tex A&M Univ, BS, 47; Rice Univ, MS, 49, PhD, 51. *Prof Exp:* Supvr tech serv labs, Baroid Div, Nat Lead Co, 51-59; from asst prof to assoc prof, 59-71, PROF CHEM, BAYLOR UNIV, 71- *Concurrent Pos:* Consult, NL Indust. *Mem:* Am Crystallog Asn; Am Chem Soc; Mineral Soc Am; NAm Thermal Anal Soc; Clay Minerals Soc. *Res:* Clay minerals, especially montmorillonite; crystal structure of montmorillonite and organic and metal-ligand-montmorillonite complexes by means of x-ray diffraction, differential thermal techniques and electron microscopy; use of thermoluminescence for dating pottery and ceramic archaeological artifacts. *Mailing Add:* Dept Chem Baylor Univ Waco TX 76703

MCATEE, LLOYD THOMAS, b Lexington, Ky, July 4, 39; m 66; c 1. CELL BIOLOGY, ZOOLOGY. *Educ:* Hanover Col, BA, 61; Drake Univ, MA, 63; Univ Md, PhD, 69. *Prof Exp:* Assoc prof, 68-75, chmn dept biol sci, 74-81, PROF MICROBIOL, PRINCE GEORGE'S COMMUNITY COL, 75-, ASSOC DEAN SCI/MATH/ENG, 82- *Mem:* AAAS; Am Inst Biol Sci; Am Soc Microbiol. *Res:* Cytogenetic and kinetic effects of sublethal heat shocks on cell suspension cultures. *Mailing Add:* Dept of Biol Sci Prince George's Community Col Upper Marlboro MD 20870

MACAULAY, ANDREW JAMES, b Cazenovia, NY, Oct 31, 37; m 60; c 3. NUCLEAR ENGINEERING, WATER CHEMISTRY. *Educ:* Univ Mo, BS, 60. *Prof Exp:* Design engr, Bettis Lab, 63-67, engr, Plant Opers & Training, Naval Reactor Facil, 67-69, supvr & mgr, 69-74, mgr testing, Bettis Lab, 74-77, DIR SR OFFICER TRAINING, NAVAL REACTOR FACIL, WESTINGHOUSE ELEC CORP, 77- *Mailing Add:* 430 Gustafson Dr Idaho Falls ID 83402

MCAULAY, ROBERT J, b Toronto, Ont, Oct 23, 39; m 62. ELECTRICAL ENGINEERING. *Educ:* Univ Toronto, BASc, 62; Univ Ill, Urbana, MSc, 63; Univ Calif, Berkeley, PhD, 67. *Prof Exp:* RES ENGR, LINCOLN LAB, MASS INST TECHNOL, 67- *Honors & Awards:* M Barry Carlton Award, 78. *Mem:* Inst Elec & Electronics Engrs. *Res:* Statistical communication theory; optimization techniques; optimal control; radar theory; signal design; monopulse analysis; interferometer design; robust speech processing in noise; low-rate vocoder design. *Mailing Add:* Speech Systs Technol Group Mass Inst Technol Lexington MA 02173

MCAULEY, LOUIS FLOYD, b Travelers Rest, SC, Aug 21, 24; m 65; c 3. MATHEMATICS. *Educ:* Okla State Univ, BS, 49, MS, 50; Univ NC, PhD(math), 54. *Prof Exp:* Asst math, Okla State Univ, 49-50, instr, 50; instr Univ NC, 51-54 & Univ Md, 54-56; from instr to assoc prof, Univ Wis, 56-63; prof, Rutgers Univ, New Brunswick, 63-69; chmn dept, 69-77, LEADING PROF MATH, STATE UNIV NY BINGHAMTON, 69- *Concurrent Pos:* Vis assoc prof, La State Univ, 59-60; Off Naval Res fel, Univ Va, 62-63; mem, Inst Advan Study, 66-67; vis, Inst Advan Study, Princeton Univ, 78-79. *Mem:* Am Math Soc; Math Asn Am. *Res:* Topology; point sets; structure of continua, upper semicontinuous collections; abstract spaces; fiber spaces; mappings equivalent to orbit map of group actions; light open mappings; manifolds; regular mappings and generalizations. *Mailing Add:* Dept of Math Sci State Univ of NY Binghamton NY 13901

MCAULEY, PATRICIA TULLEY, b Middlebury, Vt, May 23, 35; m 65; c 3. TOPOLOGY. *Educ:* Vassar Col, AB, 55; Univ Wis-Madison, MS, 58, PhD(math), 62. *Prof Exp:* Asst prof math, Univ Md, 62-65; asst prof, Rutgers Univ, 65-68, assoc prof & chmn dept, Douglass Col, 68-69; ASSOC PROF MATH, STATE UNIV NY BINGHAMTON, 69- *Concurrent Pos:* Grant-dir undergrad res partic proj, NSF, 73. *Mem:* Am Math Soc. *Res:* Fiber spaces; shape theory; open maps; fixed point problems. *Mailing Add:* Dept of Math State Univ of NY Binghamton NY 13903

MCAULIFFE, CLAYTON DOYLE, b Chappell, Nebr, Aug 18, 18; m 43; c 4. SOIL SCIENCE. *Educ:* Nebr Wesleyan Univ, AB, 41; Univ Minn, MS, 42; Cornell Univ, PhD(soil sci), 48. *Prof Exp:* Res chemist, Div War Res, Columbia Univ, 43-44 & Carbide & Carbon Chem Corp, 44-46; asst soil scientist, Bur Plant Indust, USDA, 47-48; res assoc agron, Cornell Univ, 48-50; res assoc prof, Stable Isotopes Lab, NC State Col, 50-56; sr res chemist, 56-67, SR RES ASSOC, CHEVRON OIL FIELD RES CO, 67- *Concurrent Pos:* Mem ocean sci bd, Nat Acad Sci, 75-78, steering comt petrol marine environ, comt on energy & environ. *Mem:* Fel AAAS; Am Chem Soc; Soil Sci Soc Am; Am Soc Agron; Soc Petrol Eng. *Res:* Environmental studies; analysis methods (trace organics); solubility of hydrocarbons in water; multiphase fluid flow; geochemistry in petroleum exploration; soil chemistry; radio isotopes and stable isotopes in soil-plant investigations; stable isotope in surface area measurements; isotopic analysis of uranium. *Mailing Add:* Chevron Oil Field Res Co Box 446 La Habra CA 90631

MCAULIFFE, WILLIAM GEOFFREY, b Santa Monica, Calif, Aug 9, 48. HISTOCHEMISTRY, ELECTRON MICROSCOPY. *Educ:* Calif State Univ, Long Beach, BS, 71, MA, 75; Univ Cincinnati, PhD(anat), 78. *Prof Exp:* INSTR ANAT, SCH MED & DENT, UNIV LOUISVILLE, 78- *Mem:* AAAS; Sigma Xi. *Res:* Histochemistry and electron microscopy of hormone sensitive epithelia and connective tissue in relation to renal function; cell and tissue biology. *Mailing Add:* Dept of Anat Sch of Med Univ of Louisville Louisville KY 40232

MCAVOY, BRUCE RONALD, b Jamestown, NY, Jan 30, 33. PHYSICS. *Educ:* Univ Rochester, BS, 56. *Prof Exp:* Jr engr, Air Arm Div, 56, assoc engr, 57, res engr, Res Lab, 57-66, sr res engr, 67-78, fel engr, 78-81, GROUP LEADER MICROWAVE ACOUST, RES LAB, WESTINGHOUSE ELEC CORP, 81- *Concurrent Pos:* Lectr, Dept Elec Eng, Carnegie-Mellon Univ, 68-; mem, Nat Patent Coun. *Mem:* Am Phys Soc; sr mem Inst Elec & Electronics Engrs; Int Microwave Power Inst; NY Acad Sci. *Res:* Optical physics; masers and lasers; microwave bulk effects in solids; microwave acoustics. *Mailing Add:* Res Lab Westinghouse Elec Corp Pittsburgh PA 15235

MACAVOY, THOMAS COLEMAN, b Jamaica, NY, Apr 24, 28; m 52; c 4. ORGANIC CHEMISTRY. *Educ:* Queens Col, NY, BS, 50; St Johns Univ, MS, 52; Univ Cincinnati, PhD(chem), 57. *Prof Exp:* Anal chemist, Chas Pfizer & Co, Inc, 53-54; sr chemist, 57-61, mgr electronic res, 61-64, dir phys res, 64-66, gen mgr & vpres, Electronic Prod Div, 66-69, gen mgr tech prod group, 69-71, PRES & DIR, CORNING GLASS WORKS, 71- *Concurrent Pos:* Med bd dirs, Quaker Oats Co, Chicago, Dow Corning Corp, Midland, Mich & Chubb Corp, New York. *Res:* Composition and properties of glass; complex phosphates and phosphate glasses; ion exchange equilibria; high temperature inorganic chemistry; growth of single crystals of refractory compounds. *Mailing Add:* Corning Glass Works Houghton Park Corning NY 14830

MCAVOY, THOMAS JOHN, b New York, NY, Apr 25, 40; m 62; c 3. CHEMICAL ENGINEERING. *Educ:* Polytech Inst Brooklyn, BSChE, 61; Princeton Univ, MA, 63, PhD(chem eng), 64. *Prof Exp:* From asst prof to assoc prof chem eng, Univ Mass, Amherst, 64-74, prof, 74-80; PROF CHEM ENG, UNIV MD, 80- *Concurrent Pos:* NSF res grants, 67-78; res assoc, Dept Appl Physics, Tech Univ Delft, 71-72. *Mem:* Am Inst Chem Engrs; Am Chem Soc. *Res:* Process dynamics and control; applied pharmacokinetics. *Mailing Add:* Dept Chem Eng Univ Md College Park MD 20742

MCBAY, ARTHUR JOHN, b Medford, Mass, Jan 6, 19; m 46; c 2. TOXICOLOGY, CHEMISTRY. *Educ:* Mass Col Pharm, BS, 40, MS, 42; Purdue Univ, PhD(chem), 48. *Prof Exp:* From asst prof to assoc prof chem, Mass Col Pharm, 48-55; supvr chem lab, Mass State Police, 55-63; supvr lab, Mass Dept Pub Safety, 63-69; assoc prof path, Med Sch & assoc prof toxicol, Sch Pharm, 69-74, PROF PATH, MED SCH & PROF PHARM, SCH PHARM, UNIV NC, CHAPEL HILL, 74-, CHIEF TOXICOLOGIST, OFF CHIEF MED EXAMR NC, 69- *Concurrent Pos:* Asst, Harvard Med Sch, 52-63; consult, Mass Col Pharm, 55-69; assoc prof, Law-Med Inst & Med Sch, Boston Univ, 63. *Mem:* Am Pharmaceut Asn; Am Acad Forensic Sci. *Res:* Organic pharmaceutical chemistry; spectrophotometric assays; toxicology-barbiturates and carbon monoxide; analytical chemistry; marihauna, other drugs and driving. *Mailing Add:* Off of Chief Med Examr for NC PO Box 2488 Chapel Hill NC 27514

MCBAY, HENRY CECIL, b Mexia, Tex, May 29, 14; m 54; c 2. CHEMISTRY. *Educ:* Wiley Col, BS, 34; Atlanta Univ, MS, 36; Univ Chicago, PhD(chem), 45. *Prof Exp:* Instr chem, Wiley Col, 36-38 & Western Univ Kansas City, 38-39; from instr to assoc prof, 45-71, PROF CHEM, MOREHOUSE COL, 71-, CHMN DEPT, 60- *Concurrent Pos:* Tech expert, UNESCO, 51. *Mem:* Am Chem Soc. *Res:* Organic and inorganic chemistry; free radicals. *Mailing Add:* Dept of Chem Morehouse Col Atlanta GA 30314

MCBEAN, ROBERT PARKER, b Chilliwack, BC, May 6, 39; m 62; c 3. STRUCTURAL ENGINEERING. *Educ:* Univ BC, BASc, 62, MASc, 65; Stanford Univ, PhD(civil eng), 68. *Prof Exp:* Structural engr, H A Simons, Ltd, Int, Vancouver, Can, 62-63, Phillips, Barratt & Partners, 64-65 & Hooley Eng, 65; res engr, John A Blume & Assocs, Calif, 66; instr civil eng, Stanford Univ, 67; asst prof, Univ Missouri-Columbia, 68-71, assoc prof, 71-74; PROJ ENGR, BLACK & VEATCH, CONSULT ENGRS, 74- *Mem:* Am Soc Civil Engrs; Nat Soc Prof Engrs; Sigma Xi. *Res:* Applied mechanics; computer applications, static and dynamic analysis of complex structures. *Mailing Add:* Black & Veatch 1500 Meadow Lake Pkwy Kansas City MO 64114

MCBEATH, DOUGLAS KAY, soil science, plant nutrition, see previous edition

MCBEE, FRANK W(ILKINS), JR, b Ridley Park, Jan 22, 20; m 43; c 2. MECHANICAL ENGINEERING. *Educ:* Univ Tex, BS, 47, MS, 50. *Prof Exp:* From instr to asst prof mech eng, Univ Tex, 47-53, asst prof, Res Lab, 53-60; mech engr & founder, 55, treas, 62-65, sr vpres fiscal contractual & admin affairs, 65-67, exec vpres, 67-70, PRES, TRACOR, INC, 70-, CHMN BD TRUSTEES, 72- *Concurrent Pos:* Foundry consult, Tex Foundries, 48; vpres & dir, 12 domestic & foreign subsidiaries, Tracor, Inc; mem adv coun, Eng Found & Marine Sci Inst, Univ Tex; vchmn & dir, Tex Independent Col Fund. *Mem:* Nat Soc Prof Engrs; Sigma Xi. *Res:* Resistance welding; rare metals and mechanical design of underwater devices; industrial engineering and relations; management of scientific companies. *Mailing Add:* Tracor Inc 6500 Tracor Lane Austin TX 78721

MCBEE, GEORGE GILBERT, b Eastland, Tex, Aug 15, 29; m 54; c 2. PLANT PHYSIOLOGY. *Educ:* Tex A&M Univ, BS, 51, MS, 56, PhD(plant physiol), 65. *Prof Exp:* Asst county agr agent, Agr Exten Serv, Tex A&M Univ, 53-54, res asst soil chem, 54-56, area agron specialist, Agr Exten Serv, 56-60, state agron specialist, 60-62, res asst plant physiol & biochem, 62-64, asst prof turf physiol, 64-69, resident dir res, Tex Agr Exp Sta, 69-75, PROF SOIL & CROP SCI, TEX A&M UNIV, 75- *Mem:* Am Soc Plant Physiol; Am Soc Agron; Weed Sci Soc Am. *Res:* Metabolic, nutritional and photobiological functions in turfgrasses; adaptive research for fungicides, fertilizers, herbicides and management systems in turfgrasses. *Mailing Add:* Dept of Soil & Crop Sci Tex A&M Univ College Station TX 77843

MCBEE, W(ARREN) D(ALE), b Toledo, Ohio, Mar 18, 25; m 50; c 2. ELECTRICAL ENGINEERING. *Educ:* Marquette Univ, BEE, 45; Univ Mich, MS, 48, PhD(elec eng), 51. *Prof Exp:* Proj engr, Sperry Gyroscope Co, 50-53, sr proj engr, 53-54, sect head, 54-56, eng dept head, 56-61, res staff mem, Sperry Rand Res Ctr, 61-64, head radiation sci dept, 64-67, mgr radiation & info sci lab, 67-70, DIR SYSTS LAB, SPERRY RES CTR, SUDBURY, 70- *Mem:* Fel Inst Elec & Electronics Engrs; Am Phys Soc. *Res:* Research management; electromagnetics; plasma physics. *Mailing Add:* Sperry Res Ctr Sperry Corp 100 N Road Sudbury MA 01776

MCBEE, WILLIAM, JR, b Dewar, Okla, Sept 17, 21; m 42; c 3. GEOLOGY. *Educ:* Univ Tulsa, BS, 42; Univ Kans, MS, 48. *Prof Exp:* Asst instr micropaleont & photog & cur geol mus, Univ Kans, 46-48; explor geologist, Calif Co, La, 48-50, Okla, 50-53; div stratigr, Stand Oil Co Tex, 53-56, div staff geologist, 56-61; gulf coast regional geologist, Monsanto Co, 61-64, western region staff geologist, 64-67; northern Can explor supvr, Sinclair Oil Co Can, 67-69; sr area geologist, Atlantic-Richfield Co, 69-74, Can dist develop geologist, 75-77, geologist, Tulsa, 77-80; EXPLOR MGR & CHIEF GEOLOGIST, RESOURCES DIVERSIFIED, INC, 81- *Concurrent Pos:* Dir, MAC Energy Co, 81- *Mem:* Geol Soc Am; Am Asn Petrol Geologists. *Res:* Stratigraphic geology, particularly clastic depositional patterns and environmental determinations. *Mailing Add:* Resources Diversified Inc 2431 E 51st St Tulsa OK 74105

MACBETH, ROBERT ALEXANDER, b Edmonton, Alta, Aug 26, 20; m 49; c 4. SURGERY. *Educ:* Univ Alta, BA, 42, MD, 44; McGill Univ, MSc, 47, dipl surg, 52; FRCS(C), 52. *Prof Exp:* Assoc prof, Univ Alta, 57-60, prof surg & head dept, 60-75, dir surg serv, Univ Hosp, 60-75; prof surg & assoc dean, Dalhousie Univ, 75-77; exec dir, 77-80, EXEC VPRES NAT CANCER INST CAN & CAN CANCER SOC, 80- *Concurrent Pos:* Res fel endocrinol, McGill Univ, 46-47, teaching fel anat, 47-48; Nuffield Found traveling fel surg, Brit Postgrad Med Sch, 50-51; consult, Dept Vet Affairs, Col Mewburn Pavillion, Edmonton, 57-75; dir med educ, Prov of New Brunswick, 75-77. *Mem:* Am Surg Asn; fel Am Col Surg; Soc Univ Surg; Can Med Asn; Can Soc Clin Invest. *Res:* Metabolic adaption to cold; magnesium metabolism; serum and tissue glycoproteins in relation to malignant and inflammatory disease. *Mailing Add:* Nat Cancer Inst Can 130 Bloor St W Suite 1001 Toronto ON M5S 2V7 Can

MCBIRNEY, ALEXANDER ROBERT, b Sacramento, Calif, July 18, 24; m 47; c 4. GEOLOGY, PETROLOGY. *Educ:* US Mil Acad, BS, 46; Univ Calif, Berkeley, PhD(geol), 61. *Prof Exp:* Asst prof geol, Univ Calif, San Diego & staff mem, Scripps Inst Oceanog, 62-65; dir ctr volcanology, 65-68, assoc prof geol, 65-70, chmn dept, 68-71, PROF GEOL, UNIV ORE, 70- *Mem:* AAAS; Geol Soc Am; Am Geophys Union. *Res:* Geology and igneous petrology of Circum-Pacific orogenic regions; layered intrusions; volcanology. *Mailing Add:* Ctr for Volcanology Univ of Ore Eugene OR 97403

MCBLAIR, WILLIAM, b San Diego, Calif, Apr 19, 17; m 57; c 3. PHYSIOLOGY, OCEANOGRAPHY. *Educ:* San Diego State Univ, BA, 47; Univ Calif, Los Angeles, PhD(zool), 56. *Prof Exp:* Asst instr chem, San Diego State Univ, 47; asst zool, Univ Calif, Berkeley, 47-48; instr biol, 48-51, asst prof zool, 51-62, assoc prof biol, 62-68, PROF BIOL, SAN DIEGO STATE UNIV, 68- *Concurrent Pos:* Asst, Scripps Inst Oceanog, Univ Calif, San Diego, 48-52. *Mem:* AAAS; Am Soc Zool; NY Acad Sci; fel Int Oceanog Found; Nat Audubon Soc. *Res:* Active uptake; marine and environmental physiology; biology of spiders, especially prey-predator relationships. *Mailing Add:* Dept of Biol San Diego State Univ San Diego CA 92182

MCBOYLE, GEOFFREY REID, physical geography, see previous edition

MCBRADY, JOHN J, b St Paul, Minn, Feb 1, 16; m 44. PHYSICAL CHEMISTRY. *Educ:* Univ Minn, Minneapolis, BChem, 38, PhD(phys chem), 44. *Prof Exp:* Res chemist, Donnelley & Sons Co, 46 & Celanese Corp, 47-52; sr chemist, Minn Mining & Mfg Co, 52-65, res specialist, 65-70, sr res specialist, 70-81; RETIRED. *Mem:* Am Chem Soc; Coblentz Soc. *Res:* Molecular spectroscopy; infrared and nuclear magnetic resonance; photochemistry. *Mailing Add:* 1555 Burns Ave St Paul MN 55106

MCBRAYER, JAMES FRANKLIN, b Rowan Co, Ky, July 12, 41; m 67; c 2. ECOLOGY. *Educ:* Miami Univ, BS, 63; Purdue Univ, West Lafayette, MS, 70; Univ Tenn, Knoxville, PhD(ecol), 73. *Prof Exp:* Teacher biol pub schs, Ohio, 63-67; asst res biologist, Lab Nuclear Med, Univ Calif, 73-74; asst prof ecol, Univ Minn, St Paul, 74-76; ECOLOGIST, OAK RIDGE NAT LAB, 76- *Concurrent Pos:* Consult, Desert Biome, US Int Biol Prog, 74-75; mem, Interbiome Specialist Comt Elemental Cycling, 74-75. *Mem:* Am Coun Reclamation Res; AAAS; Am Inst Biol Sci; Ecol Soc Am; Sigma Xi. *Res:* Ecosystem analysis; decompostition and elemental cycling in terrestrial ecosystems; synergistic relationships between microflora and decomposer invertebrates; role of fossorial animals in community development; environmental impact assessment. *Mailing Add:* Environ Sci Div PO Box X Oak Ridge TN 37830

MCBREEN, JAMES, b Cavan, Ireland, Sept 5, 38; US citizen; m 66; c 2. ELECTROCHEMISTRY. *Educ:* Nat Univ Ireland, BSc, 61; Univ Pa, PhD(phys chem), 65. *Prof Exp:* Res chemist, Yardney Elec Corp, 65-68; sr res chemist, Res Labs, Gen Motors Corp, 68-77; assoc chemist, 77-80, CHEMIST, BROOKHAVEN NAT LAB, 80- *Honors & Awards:* Battery Div Res Award, Electrochem Soc, 74. *Mem:* AAAS; Electrochem Soc. *Res:* Ambient-temperature aqueous batteries, including work on the zinc, nickel oxide and manganese dioxide electrodes; sealed zinc-nickel oxide batteries; hydrogen-halogen batteries and zinc-bromine and zinc-chlorine batteries; fuel cells; metal deposition; industrial water electrolysis; organic electrochemistry. *Mailing Add:* Dept of Energy & Environ Brookhaven Nat Lab Upton NY 11973

MCBRIDE, CLIFFORD HOYT, b Massena, Iowa, June 14, 26; m 50; c 6. CHEMISTRY. *Educ:* Iowa State Univ, BS, 48; St Louis Univ, MS, 57. *Prof Exp:* Chemist, Mallinckrodt Chem Works, 49-55, supvr, 55-62; sr res chemist, Armour Agr Chem Co, 62-63, anal res mgr, 63-68; sect head, 68-72, MGR ANAL SERV, USS AGRI-CHEM DIV, US STEEL CORP, 72- *Mem:* Am Chem Soc. *Res:* Analytical chemistry; chromatography; spectrometry. *Mailing Add:* US Steel Corp USS Agri-Chem Div 685 DeKalb Indust Way Decatur GA 30033

MCBRIDE, DUNCAN ELDRIDGE, b Chicago, Ill, Oct 26, 45; m 68. EXPERIMENTAL SOLID STATE PHYSICS, SURFACE PHYSICS. *Educ:* Carleton Col, BA, 67; Univ Calif, Berkeley, MA, 69, PhD(physics), 73. *Prof Exp:* US-France exchange fel physics, Lab Solid State Physics, Univ Paris VII, 73-74; asst prof physics, Swarthmore Col, 74-79; ASST PROF PHYSICS, KENYON COL, 79- *Concurrent Pos:* Vis res physicist, Univ Calif, Santa Barbara, 77-78; vis scientist, IBM Res Lab, San Jose, Calif, 79, 80 & 81. *Mem:* AAAS; Am Phys Soc; Sigma Xi. *Res:* Surface science; electron tunneling; inelastic electron tunneling spectroscopy; catalysis; metal-insulator transitions. *Mailing Add:* Dept Physics Kenyon Col Gambier OH 43022

MCBRIDE, EARLE FRANCIS, b Moline, Ill, May 25, 32; m 56; c 2. SEDIMENTARY PETROGRAPHY. *Educ:* Augustana Col, AB, 54; Univ Mo, MA, 56; Johns Hopkins Univ, PhD(geol), 60. *Prof Exp:* From instr to assoc prof, 59-68, PROF GEOL, UNIV TEX, AUSTIN, 68-, CHMN DEPT, 80- *Mem:* Geol Soc Am; Am Asn Petrol Geol; Soc Econ Paleont & Mineral (pres, 79-80); Int Asn Sedimentol. *Res:* Sedimentary petrology; cretaceous rocks of northern Mexico; Paleozoic rocks of Marathon Region, Texas; origin of sedimentary rocks, chiefly clastic rocks and chert; origin of bedding; sandstone diagenesis; evolution of porosity. *Mailing Add:* Dept Geol Sci Univ Tex Austin TX 78712

MCBRIDE, EDWARD FRANCIS, organic chemistry, see previous edition

MCBRIDE, J(AMES) W(ALLACE), b Winnipeg, Man, Feb 26, 15; nat US; m 46; c 1. AERODYNAMICS. *Educ:* Univ Man, BSc, 38; Mass Inst Technol, SM, 40. *Prof Exp:* Res assoc aerodyn, Mass Inst Technol, 38-43; chief exp engr, TurboRes, Ltd, 43-46, prof aeronaut, Purdue Univ, 47-48; chief res engr, govt & spec prod develop, Carrier Corp, 48-54; pres & gen mgr, J W McBride & Assocs, Tech Consult, 54-56; from mgr component develop to chmn div develop bd & mgr, TENEC prog, 56-65, consult engr & mgr advan propulsion systs & progs, 65-80, CONSULT ENGR & MGR ADVAN ENGINE PROGS, GROUP ENG DIV, GEN ELEC CO, 80- *Concurrent Pos:* Mem aerodyn subcomt, Aeronaut Res Comt, Nat Res Coun Can, 44-47; lectr, Columbia Univ, 52-55 & 71-; vis prof, Univ Tenn Space Inst, Tullahoma. *Mem:* Opers Res Soc Am; Am Inst Aeronaut & Astronaut; Eng Inst Can. *Res:* Aerodynamics of turbomachinery, especially unusual gases and vapors; direction of advanced research and development for effective product development; gas dynamics. *Mailing Add:* 6750 Camaridge Lane Cincinnati OH 45243

MCBRIDE, JAMES MICHAEL, b Lima, Ohio, Feb 25, 40; m 64; c 2. PHYSICAL ORGANIC CHEMISTRY. *Educ:* Harvard Univ, BA, 62, PhD(chem), 67. *Prof Exp:* Asst prof, 66-72, ASSOC PROF CHEM, YALE UNIV, 72- *Mem:* Am Chem Soc. *Res:* Free radical reactions; influence of viscous and rigid media on the course of organic reactions; solid state chemistry; electron paramagnetic resonance; isotope effects. *Mailing Add:* Dept of Chem Yale Univ New Haven CT 06520

MCBRIDE, JOHN BARTON, b Philadelphia, Pa, July 6, 43. PHYSICS. *Educ:* St Joseph's Col, Pa, BS, 65; Dartmouth Col, MA, 67, PhD(physics), 69. *Prof Exp:* Res instr physics, Dartmouth Col, 69; res assoc, Princeton Univ, 69-70; mem staff, US Naval Res Lab, 70-74; MEM STAFF, LAB APPL PLASMA SCI, SCI APPLN INC, 74- *Mem:* Am Phys Soc. *Res:* Theoretical plasma physics. *Mailing Add:* Lab of Appl Plasma Sci Sci Appl Inc 1200 Prospect St Box 2351 La Jolla CA 92037

MCBRIDE, JOHN JOSEPH, physical chemistry, see previous edition

MCBRIDE, JOSEPH JAMES, JR, b Philadelphia, Pa, Dec 10, 22; m 48; c 7. ORGANIC CHEMISTRY. *Educ:* St Joseph's Col, BS, 43; Univ Del, MS, 47, PhD(chem), 50. *Prof Exp:* Res chemist, Tidewater Assoc Oil Co, 49-54 & citrus exp sta, Univ Fla, 54-59; sect head org res, Armour Indust Chem Co, 59-61; DIR DEVELOP, ARIZ CHEM CO, 61- *Mem:* Am Chem Soc; Am Oil Chemist Soc; Pulp Chem Asn. *Res:* Organosilicon compounds; organic chemistry of nitrogen, fatty acids; rosin; terpenes. *Mailing Add:* Ariz Chem Co Develop Lab PO Box 2447 Panama City FL 32401

MCBRIDE, LANDY JAMES, plant physiology, see previous edition

MCBRIDE, LYLE E(RWIN), JR, b Omaha, Nebr, Oct 18, 29; m 52; c 6. AUTOMATIC CONTROL SYSTEMS, ELECTRICAL ENGINEERING. *Educ:* Cornell Univ, BEE, 52; Harvard Univ, AM, 61, PhD(appl physics), 64. *Prof Exp:* Engr, Overseas Div, Procter & Gamble Co, Ohio, 52-59; asst prof elec eng, Princeton Univ, 64-67; engr supvr electronic develop & eng, Control Prod Div, 67-71, mgr systs develop, 71-73, elec appln engr, Metall Mat Div,

73-79, MGR APPLN ENG, METAL SYSTS DIV, TEX INSTRUMENTS, INC, 80- *Mem:* Inst Elec & Electronics Engrs. *Res:* Automatic control theory; multiparameter self-optimizing systems; system identification from operating records; nonlinear system modeling. *Mailing Add:* Tex Instruments Inc MS 10-6 34 Forest St Attleboro MA 02703

MCBRIDE, MOLLIE ELIZABETH, b Montreal, Que, May 7, 29; m 51; c 5. MEDICAL MICROBIOLOGY. *Educ:* Dalhousie Univ, BSc, 55; Bryn Mawr Col, MA, 57; McGill Univ, PhD(bact, immunol), 59. *Prof Exp:* Res fel, McGill Univ, 59-60; bacteriologist, Halifax Children's Hosp, 60-63; asst prof, 64-75, ASSOC PROF MICROBIOL, BAYLOR COL MED, 75- *Mem:* AAAS; Brit Soc Gen Microbiol; Can Soc Microbiol; Am Soc Microbiol; Soc Invest Dermat. *Res:* Microbial ecology of the skin; comparison in health and disease, factors influencing staphylococcal and streptococcal skin infections; gram negative colonization; microbial ecology of cervix and bacterial interference; ocular microflora. *Mailing Add:* Dept of Dermat & Microbiol Baylor Col of Med Houston TX 77030

MCBRIDE, RALPH BOOK, b Slippery Rock, Pa, Feb 1, 28; m 54; c 3. MATHEMATICS EDUCATION. *Educ:* Slippery Rock State Col, BS, 51; Indiana Univ Pa, ME, 65; Univ Mich, PhD(math educ), 70. *Prof Exp:* Teacher math, North Butler County Schs, 51-52, Apollo Area Schs, 54-56 & Kiski Area Schs, 56-65; assoc prof, 65-76, chmn dept, 71-80, PROF MATH, MANCHESTER COL, 76-, ISAAC & ETTA H OPPENHEIM PROF, 71- *Res:* General Mathematics. *Mailing Add:* Dept Math Sci Manchester Col Box 103 North Manchester IN 46962

MCBRIDE, RAYMOND ANDREW, b Houston, Tex, Dec 27, 27; div; c 4. IMMUNOBIOLOGY, PATHOBIOLOGY. *Educ:* Tulane Univ, BS, 52, MD, 56; Am Bd Path, dipl, 61. *Prof Exp:* Intern surg, Baylor Col Med, 56-57; asst resident pathologist, Peter Bent Brigham Hosp, 57-58, asst in path, 58-60, sr resident pathologist, 60-61; asst prof path, Col Physicians & Surgeons, Columbia Univ, 63-65; assoc prof surg & immunogenetics, Mt Sinai Sch Med, 65-68; prof path, New York Med Col, Flower & Fifth Ave Hosps, 68-78; exec dean, NY Med Col, Valhalla, 73-75, prof path, 68-78; PROF PATH, BAYLOR COL MED, TEX MED CTR, 78- *Concurrent Pos:* Teaching fel path, Harvard Med Sch, 58-61; Nat Cancer Inst spec fel, McIndoe Mem Res Unit, East Grinstead, Eng, 61-63; resident pathologist, Free Hosp for Women, 59; asst resident pathologist, Children's Hosp Med Ctr, 60; asst attend pathologist, Presby Hosp, New York, 63-65; career scientist, NY Health Res Coun, 67-73; attend pathologist, New York Med Col, Flower & Fifth Ave Hosps, 68-78 & Metrop Hosp, 68-78; exec dir & chief operating officer, Westchester Med Ctr Develop Bd, Inc, 74-76; mem active staff, Methodist Hosp, Houston, 78-; attending pathologist, Harris County Hosp Dist, 78- *Mem:* AAAS; An Asn Pathologists; Transplantation Soc; Am Asn Immunol; An Asn Clin Pathologists. *Res:* Antigen and antibody interactions in isoimmune systems; population dynamics of antibody forming cells in isoimmune systems; factors involved in the recognition of immunogenicity; immunogenetics; DNA and RNA tumor viruses; tumor immunology; molecular genetics; immunogenetics. *Mailing Add:* Dept Path Baylor Col Med Houston TX 77030

MCBRIDE, RICHARD PHILLIPS, microbiology, ecology, see previous edition

MCBRIDE, ROBERT H, b Bellevue, Pa, Nov 10, 20; m 45; c 3. CHEMICAL ENGINEERING. *Educ:* Carnegie Inst Technol, BS, 42. *Prof Exp:* Field supvr, 42-58, coordr res & develop, Eng Serv Div, 58-60 & Planning Div, Electrochem Dept, 60-61, coordr res & develop, Bus Anal Sect, 61-64, MGR BUS ANAL SECT, ELECTRCHEM, INDUST CHEMICALS & CHEMICALS & PIGMENTS DEPTS, E I DU PONT DE NEMOURS & CO, INC, 64- *Concurrent Pos:* Pres, Del State Bd Educ; pres, Nat Asn State Bd Educ; chmn policy comt, Nat Assessment Educ Progress. *Mem:* Am Inst Chem Engrs. *Res:* Development engineering in fine chemicals; atomic energy; refrigerants; inorganic nitrogen chemicals; vinyl monomers and polymers. *Mailing Add:* Chem & Pigments Dept E I du Pont de Nemours & Co Inc Wilmington DE 19898

MCBRIDE, TOM JOSEPH, bacteriology, see previous edition

MCBRIDE, WILLIAM JOSEPH, b Philadelphia, Pa, Dec 24, 38; m 62; c 4. NEUROCHEMISTRY, NEUROBIOLOGY. *Educ:* Rutgers Univ, BA, 64; State Univ NY Buffalo, PhD(biochem), 68. *Prof Exp:* PROF NEUROBIOL & BIOCHEM, SCH MED, IND UNIV, INDIANAPOLIS, 71- *Concurrent Pos:* NIH fel neurobiol, Ind Univ, Bloomington, 68-71; res scientist develop award, NIMH, 79-83. *Mem:* Int Soc Neurochem; Soc Neurosci; Am Soc Neurochem. *Res:* Study of the mechanisms of how nerve cells communicate with one another and how alterations in this process may have an effect on the behavior of animals and man. *Mailing Add:* Inst of Psychiat Res Ind Univ Med Ctr Indianapolis IN 46223

MCBRIDE, WILLIAM ROBERT, b Topeka, Kans, May 9, 28; m 52; c 3. INORGANIC CHEMISTRY. *Educ:* Univ Calif, Los Angeles, BS, 50; Univ Tex, PhD(inorg chem), 55. *Prof Exp:* Res chemist, US Naval Ord Test Sta, 50-51 & 55-59, head inorg chem br, 59-80, SR RES SCIENTIST, NAVAL WEAPONS CTR, 80- *Mem:* Am Chem Soc; Sigma Xi. *Res:* Chemistry of hydronitrogens and derivatives; nonaqueous solutions and solvents; propellants; absorption spectroscopy of optical materials and filters; crystal growth of inorganic compounds; reaction kinetics. *Mailing Add:* Code 38507 Chem Div Res Dept Naval Weapons Ctr China Lake CA 93555

MCBRIDE, WOODROW H, b Milton, NDak, May 23, 18; m 44; c 1. MATHEMATICS. *Educ:* Jamestown Col, BA, 40; Univ NDak, MS, 47. *Prof Exp:* Teacher & prin, High Schs, NDak, 40-44; prin, High Schs, NDak & Minn, 44-46; from instr to assoc prof, 47-69, ASSOC PROF MATH, UNIV NDAK, 69- *Mem:* Math Asn Am. *Mailing Add:* Dept of Math Univ of NDak Grand Forks ND 58202

MCBRIEN, VINCENT OWEN, b Attleboro, Mass, Apr 21, 16; m 48; c 4. MATHEMATICS. *Educ:* Providence Col, BS, 37; Cath Univ Am, MS, 40, PhD(math), 42. *Prof Exp:* Physicist, David Taylor Model Basin, US Dept Navy, 42 & Off Sci Res & Develop, 42-43; asst prof math, Hamilton Col, 43-44; from asst prof to prof math, Col Holy Cross, 43-78, chmn dept, 60-70. *Concurrent Pos:* Ford Found fel, Harvard Univ, 52-53; NSF fac fel, Univ Calif, Berkeley, 60-61; vis prof, Trinity Col, Dublin, 71-72; res assoc, Univ Calif, Berkeley, 76-77 & Harvard Univ, 78-79 & 79- *Mem:* Am Math Soc; Math Asn Am; Soc Indust & Appl Math. *Res:* Algebraic geometry. *Mailing Add:* 14 Saratoga Rd Auburn MA 01501

MCBROOM, MARVIN JACK, b Cherokee, Okla, Apr 13, 41; m 81; c 1. PHYSIOLOGY. *Educ:* Northwestern State Col, BS, 63; Okla State Univ, MS, 64; Univ Okla, PhD(physiol), 68. *Prof Exp:* From asst prof to assoc prof physiol, Sch Med, Univ SDak, Vermillion, 68-76; ASSOC PROF PHYSIOL & ACTG CHMN DEPT, FAC MED, KUWAIT UNIV, 76- *Mem:* AAAS; fel Geront Soc; Am Physiol Soc. Soc Exp Biol & Med. *Res:* Physiology of aging of soft tissues of mammals as related to fluid and electrolyte metabolism and taurine. *Mailing Add:* Dept of Physiol PO Box 24923 Kuwait Kuwait

MCBRYDE, VERNON E(UGENE), b Palmyra, Ark, Feb 3, 33; m 54; c 2. INDUSTRIAL ENGINEERING, APPLIED STATISTICS. *Educ:* Univ Ark, BSIE, 58, MSIE, 60; Ga Inst Technol, PhD(indust eng), 64. *Prof Exp:* Indust engr, Clary Corp, Ark, 57-58; from instr to assoc prof indust eng, Univ Ark, 58-67; prof indust & mgt eng & head dept, Mont State Univ, 67-70; dean sch systs sci, Ark Polytech Col, 70-71, vpres acad affairs, 71-73; ASSOC DEAN, COL ENG, UNIV ARK, 77- *Concurrent Pos:* Pres, Productivity Int, Mgt Consult, 63-; NIH res assoc drug systs, Med Ctr, Univ Ark, 63-65. *Mem:* Am Inst Indust Engrs; Am Soc Eng Educ; Am Soc Qual Control; Nat Soc Prof Engrs; fel Am Prod & Inventory Control Soc. *Res:* Manufacturing management; quality control; production control; cost control. *Mailing Add:* Deans Off Col of Eng Univ of Ark Fayetteville AR 72701

MCBRYDE, WILLIAM ARTHUR EVELYN, b Ottawa, Ont, Oct 20, 17; m 49; c 2. CHEMISTRY. *Educ:* Univ Toronto, BA, 39, MA, 40; Univ Va, PhD(chem), 47. *Prof Exp:* Asst chem, Univ Toronto, 39-41; chemist, Welland Chem Works, 42-44; asst prof chem, Univ Va, 47-48; from asst prof to assoc prof, Univ Toronto, 48-60; prof & chmn dept, Univ Waterloo, 60-64, dean fac sci, 61-69; vis fel, Australian Nat Univ, 69-70; chmn dept, 71-77, PROF CHEM, UNIV WATERLOO, 71- *Mem:* Chem Inst Can. *Res:* Chemistry of precious metals; colorimetric analysis; coordination chemistry. *Mailing Add:* Dept of Chem Univ of Waterloo Waterloo ON N2L 3G1 Can

MCCAA, CONNIE SMITH, b Lexington, Miss, Dec 6, 37; m 57; c 4. BIOCHEMISTRY. *Educ:* Miss Col, BS, 58; Univ Miss, PhD(biochem), 63. *Prof Exp:* Asst, 59-63. from instr to assoc prof, 63-73, PROF BIOCHEM, MED CTR, UNIV MISS, 73-, ASSOC PROF PHYSIOL & BIOPHYS, 70- *Concurrent Pos:* Nat Heart & Lung Inst res grant, 63-74, spec res fel, 67-70; Miss Heart Asn grant, 63-66; Miss Cancer Soc grant, 65-66; mem cardiovasc & renal study sect, NIH, 74- *Mem:* Am Chem Soc; Am Physiol Soc; Am Heart Asn; Endocrine Soc; Am Soc Nephrology. *Res:* Role of aldosterone in the production of hypertension and congestive heart failure and the mechanism whereby normal animals escape from its sodium-retaining effect. *Mailing Add:* Dept of Biochem Univ of Miss Med Ctr Jackson MS 39216

MCCABE, BARBARA ARNY, b Madison, Wis, June 18, 48. COMPARATIVE ENDOCRINOLOGY. *Educ:* Col Wooster, BA, 71; Univ Wash, PhD(zool), 78. *Prof Exp:* ASST PROF BIOL, KEUKA COL, 78- *Mem:* Am Soc Zoologists. *Res:* The role played by hormones in ion and osmoregulation by lamprey. *Mailing Add:* Dept Biol Kauka Col Keuka Park NY 14478

MCCABE, BRIAN FRANCIS, b Detroit, Mich, June 16, 26; m 51; c 2. OTOLARYNGOLOGY. *Educ:* Univ Detroit, BS, 50; Univ Mich, MD, 54. *Prof Exp:* From instr to assoc prof otolaryngol, Med Sch, Univ Mich, 59-64; PROF OTOLARYNGOL & CHMN DEPT, COL MED, UNIV IOWA, 64- *Concurrent Pos:* Consult to Surgeon Gen, USPHS, 66; mem bd dirs, Am Bd Otolaryngol, 67. *Honors & Awards:* Mosher Award, Am Laryngol, Rhinol & Otol Soc, 65. *Mem:* Am Laryngol Asn; Am Otol Soc; Am Acad Ophthal & Otolaryngol; Am Laryngol, Rhinol & Otol Soc; Col Oto-Rhino-Laryngol Amicitiae Sacrum. *Res:* Maxillofacial surgery; neurphysiology of the vestibular apparatus; mechanism of the quick component of nystagmus; surgery of the major salivary glands, particularly cancer. *Mailing Add:* Dept of Otolaryngol Univ of Iowa Iowa City IA 52240

MCCABE, CHESTER CHARLES, b Shoreham, Vt, May 9, 24; m 58. POLYMER SCIENCE. *Educ:* Univ Chicago, BS, 44; Columbia Univ, MS, 48; Purdue Univ, PhD(physics), 54. *Prof Exp:* Instr physics, Purdue Univ, 54; res physicist, Elastomers Lab, 55-59, head new polymers div, 59-72, HEAD TIRE RES & DEVELOP DIV, ELASTOMERS RES & DEVELOP LAB, E I DU PONT DE NEMOURS & CO, INC, 72- *Mem:* Am Phys Soc; Am Chem Soc. *Res:* Basic characterizations and rheological behaviors of high polymers; rheology of elastomers and plastics. *Mailing Add:* Elastomers Res & Develop Lab E I du Pont de Nemours & Co Inc Wilmington DE 19898

MCCABE, GEORGE PAUL, JR, b Brooklyn, NY, Apr 2, 45; m 67; c 3. STATISTICS. *Educ:* Providence Col, BS, 66; Columbia Univ, PhD(math statist), 70. *Prof Exp:* Asst prof, 70-75, ASSOC PROF STATIST, PURDUE UNIV WEST LAFAYETTE, 75-, HEAD STATIST CONSULT, 70- *Concurrent Pos:* Vis assoc prof statist, Princeton Univ, 76-77. *Mem:* Sigma Xi; Inst Math Statist; Am Statist Asn. *Res:* Mathematical statistics; applied statistics; statistical computing. *Mailing Add:* Dept of Statist Purdue Univ West Lafayette IN 47907

MACCABE, JEFFREY ALLAN, b Oakland, Calif, Jan 30, 43; m 71. DEVELOPMENTAL BIOLOGY. *Educ:* Univ Calif, Davis, BS, 64, PhD(genetics), 69. *Prof Exp:* Res assoc, State Univ NY Albany, 69-71; asst prof, 72-77, ASSOC PROF ZOOL, UNIV TENN, KNOXVILLE, 77- *Concurrent Pos:* Res career develop award, NIH, 78-83. *Mem:* AAAS; Am Genetic Asn; Am Soc Zool; Soc Develop Biol; NY Acad Sci. *Res:* Morphogenesis of the vertebrate limb. *Mailing Add:* Dept of Zool Univ of Tenn Knoxville TN 37916

MCCABE, JOHN PATRICK, b New York, NY, Aug 17, 35. MATHEMATICS. *Educ:* Manhattan Col, BS, 57; Harvard Univ, AM, 58, PhD(math), 68. *Prof Exp:* Systs analyst, Gen Elec Co, 62-66; from instr to asst prof, 66-74, chmn dept, 74-77, ASSOC PROF MATH, MANHATTAN COL, 74- *Mem:* Am Math Soc; Soc Indust & Appl Math. *Res:* Abelian varieties over local fields. *Mailing Add:* Dept of Math Manhattan Col New York NY 10471

MCCABE, ROBERT ALBERT, b Milwaukee, Wis, Jan 11, 14; m 41; c 4. WILDLIFE MANAGEMENT. *Educ:* Carroll Col, BA, 39; Univ Wis, MS, 43, PhD(wildlife mgt, zool), 49. *Prof Exp:* Biologist, Arboretum, 43-46, from instr to assoc prof, 46-56, chmn dept, 52-79, PROF WILDLIFE MGT, UNIV WIS-MADISON, 56- *Concurrent Pos:* Mem res adv comn, Wis Dept Natural Resources, 54-; secy adv comt, Wis Dept Resource Develop, 60-64; mem bd dirs, Wis Expos Dept, 60-68; chmn subcomt vertebrates as pests, Nat Acad Sci, 64-; Fulbright prof, Univ Col, Univ Dublin, 69-70; adv to Irish Nat Parks, 70-81. *Mem:* Wildlife Soc (pres, 76-77); Am Soc Mammal; Wilson Ornith Soc; Cooper Ornith Soc; fel Am Ornith Union. *Res:* Wildlife ecology; techniques in wildlife management; land use in wildlife relationship; ornithology. *Mailing Add:* Dept Wildlife Ecol Col Agr & Life Sci Univ Wis Madison WI 53706

MCCABE, ROBERT LYDEN, b Tarrytown, NY, Mar 5, 36; m 59; c 3. MATHEMATICS. *Educ:* Union Col, NY, BS, 57; San Diego State Col, MA, 60; Boston Univ, PhD(math), 71. *Prof Exp:* Asst prof, 64-68, ASSOC PROF MATH, SOUTHEASTERN MASS UNIV, 68- *Concurrent Pos:* Instr, Upperward Bound, 68. *Res:* Ergodic and dilation theories; Markov processes. *Mailing Add:* Dept Math Southeastern Mass Univ North Dartmouth MA 02747

MCCABE, WILLIAM R, b Hugo, Okla, Sept 13, 28; m 51; c 3. INFECTIOUS DISEASES, MICROBIOLOGY. *Educ:* Univ Okla, BS, 49, MD, 53. *Prof Exp:* Intern med, Univ Okla Hosps, 53-54, resident, 56-58; res asst & chief med resident infectious dis, Col Med, Univ Ill, 58-60, asst prof med, 62-63; from asst prof to assoc prof, Sch Med, 63-71, asst prof microbiol, 63-71, PROF MED & MICROBIOL, MED CTR, BOSTON UNIV, 71-, DIR, DIV INFECTIOUS DIS, 63- *Concurrent Pos:* NIH trainee cardiovasc dis, Univ Okla Hosps, 57-58; res fel infectious dis, Univ Ill Res & Educ Hosp, 58-60; clin investr, West Side Vet Admin Hosp, Chicago, 60-63; asst physician, Boston City Hosp, 68-; consult physician, Vet Admin Hosp, Boston, 68-; mem drug eval panel, Nat Acad Sci-Nat Res Coun, 69-71; mem bact & micol study sect, Nat Inst Allergy & Infectious Dis, 69-73; assoc ed, J Infectious Dis, 69-; dir, Maxwell Finland Lab for Infectious Dis, Boston City Hosp, 77-; head med bact & vis physician, Univ Hosp, 63-77. *Mem:* AAAS; Am Soc Clin Invest; Infectious Dis Soc Am; Am Soc Microbiol; Asn Am Physicians. *Res:* Host defense mechanisms and bacterial virulence factors in clinical infections. *Mailing Add:* Lab for Infectious Dis 774 Albany St Boston MA 02118

MACCABEE, BRUCE SARGENT, b Rutland, Vt, May 6, 42. ELECTRONICS, ELECTROOPTICS. *Educ:* Worcester Polytech Inst, BS, 64; Am Univ, MS, 67, PhD(physics), 70. *Prof Exp:* Res assoc physics, Am Univ, 67-72; RES PHYSICIST, WHITE OAK LAB, NAVAL SURFACE WEAPONS CTR, 72- *Concurrent Pos:* Consult, Nat Invests Comt Aerial Phenomena, 66-, Tracor, Inc, 70-71, Compackager Corp, 70-73, Sci Appln, Inc, 73-74 & Radix II, Inc, 78; mem sci bd, Ctr UFO Studies; chmn, Fund for Unidentified Flying Objects, 79- *Mem:* Am Phys Soc; AAAS; Am Optical Soc. *Res:* High energy lasers; optics; underwater sound; high power laser phenomenology; UFO phenomena and history. *Mailing Add:* 10706 Meadowhill Rd Silver Spring MD 20901

MCCAFFERTY, EDWARD, b Swoyerville, Pa, Nov 28, 37; m 66; c 2. CHEMISTRY. *Educ:* Wilkes Col, BS, 59; Lehigh Univ, MS, 64, PhD(chem), 68. *Prof Exp:* Res engr, Bethlehem Steel Corp, Pa, 59-64; Robert A Welch fel chem, Univ Tex, Austin, 68-70; sci off, Off Naval Res, 81-82, RES CHEMIST MAT SCI & TECH, NAVAL RES LAB, 70- *Honors & Awards:* Victor K LaMer Award, Am Chem Soc, 71. *Mem:* Electrochem Soc; Am Chem Soc. *Res:* Surface chemistry; corrosion science; electrochemistry of corrosion processes, kinetics and inhibition; adsorption on metals and oxides. *Mailing Add:* Eng Mat Div Naval Res Lab 4555 Overlook Ave Washington DC 20375

MCCAFFREY, DAVID SAXER, JR, b Mt Kisco, NY, Oct 23, 42; m 67; c 4. CHEMICAL ENGINEERING. *Educ:* Univ Notre Dame, BS, 64, MS, 66, PhD(chem eng), 67. *Prof Exp:* Eng assoc, 69-80, HEAD SECT, EXXON RES & ENG CO, 80- *Mem:* Am Inst Chem Engrs; Am Chem Soc; Sigma Xi. *Res:* Fluidization; air pollution control technology; atmospheric dispersion modeling; engineering thermodynamics; synthetic fuels. *Mailing Add:* Exxon Res & Eng Co PO Box 101 Florham Park NJ 07932

MCCAFFREY, FRANCIS, solid state physics, see previous edition

MCCAFFREY, JOSEPH PETER, b Providence, RI, Apr 7, 51. BIOLOGICAL WEED CONTROL. *Educ:* Univ RI, BA, 74; Va Polytech Inst & State Univ, MS, 78, PhD(entom), 81. *Prof Exp:* ASST PROF, ENTOM DEPT, UNIV IDAHO, 81- *Mem:* Entom Soc Am; Soc Range Mgt; Weed Sci Soc; Int Orgn Biol Control. *Res:* Introduction, establishment, and evaluation of biological central agents for noxious weed control; development of integrated pest management programs for weeds. *Mailing Add:* Entom Dept Univ Idaho Moscow ID 83843

MCCAIN, ARTHUR HAMILTON, b San Francisco, Calif, Aug 31, 25; m 59; c 1. PLANT PATHOLOGY. *Educ:* Univ Calif, BS, 49, PhD, 59. *Prof Exp:* LECTR PLANT PATH, UNIV CALIF, BERKELEY & AGRICULTURIST & EXTEN PLANT PATHOLOGIST, AGR EXP STA, 59- *Concurrent Pos:* Consult, US Forest Serv. *Mem:* AAAS; Am Phytopath Soc. *Res:* Forest tree diseases; control of plant dieases; ornamental diseases; biological control. *Mailing Add:* Dept of Plant Path Univ of Calif Berkeley CA 94720

MCCAIN, FRANCIS SAXON, b Ashland, Ala, Aug 13, 21; m 50; c 1. PLANT BREEDING. *Educ:* Auburn Univ, BS, 42, MS, 48; Purdue Univ, PhD, 50. *Prof Exp:* Assoc prof agron & soils & assoc plant breeder, Auburn Univ, 50-59, prof agron & soils & plant breeder, 59-66; PROF AGR & CHMN DIV AGR, HOME ECON & FORESTRY, ABRAHAM BALDWIN AGR COL, 66-, ASST DIR RURAL DEVELOP CTR, 69- *Mem:* Am Soc Agron. *Res:* Corn breeding. *Mailing Add:* 2205 Murray Ave Tifton GA 31794

MCCAIN, GEORGE HOWARD, b Flora, Ind, Nov 15, 24; m 48; c 1. ORGANIC CHEMISTRY, POLYMER SYNTHESIS. *Educ:* Franklin Col, AB, 49; Univ Ill, MS, 50, PhD(chem), 53. *Prof Exp:* Res chemist, Electrochem Dept, E I du Pont de Nemours & Co, Inc, 52-55; sr chemist, 55-59, RES ASSOC, DIAMOND SHAMROCK CORP, 59- *Mem:* Am Chem Soc; Sigma Xi. *Res:* Vinyl polymerization; ionogenic polymers; membrane chemistry; biologically active polymers, fluorinated polymers. *Mailing Add:* T R Evans Res Ctr Diamond Shamrock Corp Box 348 Painesville OH 44077

MCCAIN, JAMES HERNDON, b Little Rock, Ark, Sept 18, 41; m 63; c 2. ORGANIC CHEMISTRY. *Educ:* Southwestern at Memphis, BS, 63; Northwestern Univ, PhD(org chem), 67. *Prof Exp:* CHEMIST, UNION CARBIDE CORP, 67- *Mem:* Am Chem Soc. *Res:* Applied research; development; plant problems. *Mailing Add:* 1987 Parkwood Rd Charleston WV 25314

MCCAIN, JOHN CHARLES, b Ft Worth, Tex, Aug 11, 39; m 56; c 2. MARINE BIOLOGY. *Educ:* Tex Christian Univ, BA, 62; Col William & Mary, MA, 64; George Washington Univ, PhD(zool), 67; Univ Hawaii, MPH, 75. *Prof Exp:* Res asst, Va Inst Marine Sci, 62-64; mus technologist syst zool, Smithsonian Inst, 64-65, mus specialist, 65, asst cur, 65-67; res assoc oceanog, NSF Antarctic Prog res grant to Dr Joel W Hedgpeth, Ore State Univ, 67-69; in-chg benthic invert div, Oceanog Sorting Ctr, Smithsonian Inst, Washington, DC, 69-70; aquatic ecologist, TRW/Hazleton Labs, Inc, 70-71; sr marine biologist, Hawaiian Elec Co, 71-77, mgr, Environ Dept, 77-80; PRIN BIOLOGIST, TETRA TECH, INC, 80- *Concurrent Pos:* Res assoc, Bernice P Bishop Mus, 73-; res fel, Smithsonian. *Mem:* Soc Syst Zool; Am Fisheries Soc; Western Soc Naturalists; Biomet Soc; Nat Asn Underwater Instr. *Res:* Taxonomy and ecology of invertebrates, particularly Amphipoda; marine ecology; pollution biology; biostatistics. *Mailing Add:* Tetra Tech Inc 630 N Rosemead Blvd Pasadena CA 91107

MCCALDIN, J(AMES) O(ELAND), b Shreveport, La, Apr 3, 22. SOLID STATE PHYSICS, ELECTRONIC MATERIALS. *Educ:* Univ Tex, BA, 44; Calif Inst Technol, PhD(mech eng), 54. *Prof Exp:* Instr math & physics, San Antonio Col, 46-48; engr telemetering, Arabian-Am Oil Co, 52; sr engr physics & metall, Res Labs, Gen Motors Corp, 54-55; mem tech staff, Res Lab, Hughes Aircraft Co, 56-60; group leader semiconductors, NAm Aviation Sci Ctr, 61-68; assoc prof eng, 68-73, PROF APPL PHYSICS, CALIF INST TECHNOL, 73- *Concurrent Pos:* Lectr, Eng Exten, Univ Calif, Los Angeles, 57-59. *Mem:* Am Phys Soc; Inst Elec & Electronics Engrs; Electrochem Soc. *Res:* Physical chemistry of semiconductors; semiconductor interfaces and thin films. *Mailing Add:* Dept of Appl Physics Calif Inst of Technol Pasadena CA 91125

MCCALDIN, ROY OELAND, sanitary engineering, see previous edition

MCCALEB, KIRTLAND EDWARD, b Brighton, Mass, Sept 10, 26; m 49; c 2. ORGANIC CHEMISTRY. *Educ:* Dartmouth Col, AB, 46; Univ Wis, PhD(org chem), 49. *Prof Exp:* Jr chemist, Eastman Kodak Co, 46; fel, Univ Wis, 49-50; sr org chemist, Res Labs, Gen Mills, Inc, Minn, 50-53, leader nitrogen prod sect, 53-60; mgr tech sales serv, Foremost Chem Prod Co, Calif, 60-65; indust economist, Chem Econ Handbook, 65-68, ed, 68-72, DIR CHEM-ENVIRON PROG, SRI INT, 72- *Mem:* Am Chem Soc; Am Oil Chem Soc. *Res:* Surface-active agents; chemical market research; environmental chemicals. *Mailing Add:* 121 Durazno Way Menlo Park CA 94025

MCCALEB, STANLEY B, b Santa Barbara, Calif, Oct 29, 19; m 52; c 3. CLAY MINERALOGY. *Educ:* Univ Calif, BS, 42; Cornell Univ, MS, 48, PhD(soils), 50. *Prof Exp:* From asst prof to assoc prof soil genesis, NC State Col, 50-56; sr soil correlator, Soil Conserv Serv, USDA, Calif, 56-58; sr res geologist & head clay mineral res sect, 58-70, supvr chem eng, Prod Serv Lab, 70-74, MGR PROD SERV LAB, SUN CO, INC, 74- *Mem:* Clay Minerals Soc (pres, 75-76); Soil Sci Soc Am; Am Soc Agron; Int Soc Soil Sci; Asn Inst Mining, Metall & Petrol Engrs. *Res:* Soil morphology, genesis and classification; mineral weathering; land use and management; analysis labs; pollution evaluation; petroleum exploration and production. *Mailing Add:* 200 Westshore Dr Richardson TX 75080

MCCALL, CHARLES B, b Memphis, Tenn, Nov 2, 28; m 51; c 4. MEDICINE. *Educ:* Vanderbilt Univ, BA, 50, MD, 53. *Prof Exp:* Nat Acad Sci-Nat Res Coun pulmonary fel, 57-58; instr med, Med Col Ala, 58-59; from asst prof to assoc prof, Univ Tenn, 59-69; prof, Univ Tex Med Br, Galveston, 69-72, asst vchancellor & coordr regional med prog, Univ Tex Syst, 69-72; assoc dean clin affairs, Univ Tex Southwestern Med Sch, 72-75; dean col med, Ctr Health Sci, Univ Tenn, Memphis, 75-77; dean, Oral Roberts Univ Sch Med, 77-78; CONSULT IN RESIDENCE, UNIV OKLA, TULSA MED COL, 79- *Mem:* Am Fedn Clin Res; fel Am Col Physicians; fel Am Col Chest Physicians; Am Thoracic Soc. *Res:* Pulmonary physiology and mechanics. *Mailing Add:* Univ of Okla 2727 E 21st Tulsa OK 74114

MCCALL, CHARLES EMORY, b Lenoir, NC, Jan 30, 35; m 57; c 3. INFECTIOUS DISEASES. *Educ:* Wake Forest Col, BS, 57; Bowman Gray Sch Med, MD, 61. *Prof Exp:* From intern to resident, Harvard Med Sch, 61-66, teaching asst, 66-68; from asst prof to assoc prof, 68-75, PROF MED, BOWMAN GRAY SCH MED, 75-, DIR INFECTIOUS DIS, 71-, ASSOC PHARM, 80- *Concurrent Pos:* Bowman Gray Sch Med fac award, 61; NIH fel, Thorndike Res Lab, Harvard Med Sch, 66-68; NIH res career develop award, 74. *Mem:* Fel Royal Soc Med; Infectious Dis Soc Am; Am Fedn Clin Res; Am Asn Immunologists; Am Soc Exp Biol. *Res:* Neutrophil biology and host defense. *Mailing Add:* Dept of Med Bowman Gray Sch Med Winston-Salem NC 27103

MCCALL, CHESTER HAYDEN, JR, b Vandergrift, Pa, Aug 6, 27; m 52, 72; c 2. APPLIED STATISTICS. *Educ:* George Washington Univ, AB, 50, AM, 52, PhD, 57. *Prof Exp:* Asst prof statist, George Washington Univ, 52-56; res dir, Booz-Allen Appl Res, Inc, Md, 59-63, vpres & dir western opers, 63-69, managing vpres, Booz-Allen Appl Res, Inc, 69-71; pres, Int Careers Inst, Inc, 71-74; dept mgr systs eval dept, Caci, Inc, 74-78; SR ASSOC, M/M ASSOCS, 78- *Concurrent Pos:* Consult, Corn Industs Res Found, 53-59; eng res & develop lab & logistics res, US Dept Army, 55-59. *Mem:* Am Statist Asn; Opers Res Soc Am; fel Am Soc Qual Control. *Res:* Evaluation planning; survey sampling; experimental design; systems analysis; operations research; audio-visual and audio-manual education, training, and information transfer; application of basic statistical methods to nationwide survey polling and the evaluation of transporation and health care systems. *Mailing Add:* M/M Assocs 387 Fowling St Playa Del Rey CA 90291

MCCALL, DAVID WARREN, b Omaha, Nebr, Dec 1, 28; m 55; c 2. PHYSICAL CHEMISTRY. *Educ:* Univ Wichita, BS, 50; Univ Ill, MS, 51, PhD(chem), 53. *Prof Exp:* Head phys chem, 61-69, asst chem dir, 69-73, MEM TECH STAFF, BELL TEL LABS, INC, 53-, CHEM DIR, 73- *Concurrent Pos:* Mem bd trustees, Gordon Res Conf, 72-78. *Mem:* Fel AAAS; Am Chem Soc; fel Am Phys Soc; Royal Soc Chem; Am Inst Chem Engrs. *Res:* Nuclear magnetic resonance; diffusion in liquids; polymer relaxation; dielectric properties; materials for communications systems. *Mailing Add:* Bell Tel Labs Inc 600 Mountain Ave Murray Hill NJ 07974

MCCALL, JAMES LODGE, b Morristown, NJ, June 3, 35; m 56; c 2. METALLURGICAL ENGINEERING. *Educ:* Ohio State Univ, BMetE, 58, MS, 61. *Prof Exp:* Assoc div chief, Metallog Div, 65-67, chief, Struct of Metals Div, 67-76, MGR MAT RESOURCES & PROCESS METALL, METALL DEPT, BATTELLE MEM INST, 76- *Mem:* Fel Am Soc Metals; Am Inst Mining, Metall & Petrol Engrs; Electron Micros Soc Am; Inst Microstruct Anal Soc. *Res:* Metallographic research on metals and ceramics; process metallurgical research on minerals processing; primary ferrous and non-ferrous metals processing; recycling, energy and environmental concerns of metallurgical operations. *Mailing Add:* Metall Dept Columbus Labs Battelle Mem Inst 505 King Ave Columbus OH 43201

MCCALL, JOHN MICHAEL, b Dallas, Tex, Jan 11, 44; m 66; c 2. ORGANIC CHEMISTRY, MEDICINAL CHEMISTRY. *Educ:* DePauw Univ, BA, 66; Univ Wis, PhD(chem), 70. *Prof Exp:* Res chemist org chem, Monsanto Co, 65-66; NIH fel, Univ Wis, 67-70; fel chem, Harvard Univ, 70-72; RES CHEMIST, UPJOHN CO, 72- *Mem:* Am Chem Soc. *Res:* Medicinal chemistry in the cardiovascular area; heterocyclic chemistry, particularly of pyrimidines, quinolines and pyridines. *Mailing Add:* Upjohn Co 301 Henrietta St Kalamazoo MI 49001

MCCALL, JOHN T(HOMPSON), civil engineering, see previous edition

MCCALL, JOHN TEMPLE, b Davenport, Iowa, May 1, 21; m 50; c 3. BIOCHEMISTRY. *Educ:* Rollins Col, BS, 48; Univ Fla, MS, 56, PhD(animal nutrit), 58. *Prof Exp:* Lab asst animal husb & nutrit, Univ Fla, 50-51, asst, 51-58, asst chemist, Agr Exp Sta, 58-60; asst prof, Iowa State Univ, 60-64; ASSOC PROF BIOCHEM, MAYO GRAD SCH MED, UNIV MINN & BIOCHEMIST, MAYO CLIN, 65- *Mem:* Am Chem Soc; Am Asn Clin Chemists; Am Inst Nutrit. *Res:* Trace mineral metabolism, especially interactions among trace mineral elements; effects of protein-mineral chelates on mineral metabolism and mechanism of mineral transport. *Mailing Add:* Dept of Lab Med Mayo Clin Rochester MN 55901

MCCALL, KEITH BRADLEY, b Oak Park, Ill, Dec 29, 19; m 42; c 5. BIOCHEMISTRY. *Educ:* Univ Nebr, BSc, 41, MA, 43; Univ Wis, PhD(biochem), 47. *Prof Exp:* Asst biochem, Univ Wis, 43-46; instr chem, Mich State Univ, 47-48, asst prof, 48-51; chief blood derivatives unit, Div Labs, State Dept Health, Mich, 51-62; head biol prods develop, Squibb Inst Med Res, NJ, 62-65; asst chief biol prods div, Bur Labs, 65-76, CHIEF, BIOL PROD DIV, MICH DEPT PUB HEALTH, 76- *Mem:* AAAS; Am Chem Soc. *Res:* Blood plasma protein fractionation; biologic products development. *Mailing Add:* Mich Dept of Public Health PO Box 30035 Lansing MI 48909

MCCALL, MARVIN ANTHONY, b Pitts, Ga, Feb 7, 18; m 45; c 2. ORGANIC CHEMISTRY. *Educ:* Univ Ga, BS, 42, MS, 44; Univ Rochester, PhD(org chem), 51. *Prof Exp:* Instr chem, Univ Ga, 43-44; res chemist, Eastman Kodak Co, 44-51, sr res chemist, Tenn Eastman Co, 51-69, res assoc, 69-81; RETIRED. *Mem:* Am Chem Soc. *Res:* Synthetic organic, polymer and organophosphorus chemistry; organometallic compounds; synthesis of organic polymer intermediates, additives and flame retardants. *Mailing Add:* 1720 Savona Pkwy Cape Coral FL 33904

MCCALL, PETER LAW, b Evanston, Ill, Dec 26, 48; m 78. BENTHIC ECOLOGY, PALEOBIOLOGY. *Educ:* Washington Univ, AB, 70; Yale Univ, MPhil, 72, PhD(geol), 75. *Prof Exp:* ASST PROF EARTH SCI, CASE WESTERN RESERVE UNIV, 75- *Mem:* Paleontol Soc; Int Asn Great Lakes Res. *Res:* Marine ecology; freshwater benthic ecology; paleontology; invertebrate ecology and evolution. *Mailing Add:* Dept of Earth Sci Case Western Reserve Univ Cleveland OH 44106

MCCALL, RICHARD C, b Inavale, Nebr, Sept 13, 29; m 56; c 3. RADIOLOGICAL PHYSICS. *Educ:* Mass Inst Technol, BS, 52, PhD, 57. *Prof Exp:* Physicist, Hanford Atomic Prod Oper, Gen Elec Co, 56-59; NIH fel, Univ Lund, 59-61; sr physicist, Controls Radiation, Inc, Mass, 61-64; head health physics group, 64-76, RADIATION PHYSICS GROUP LEADER & RADIATION SAFETY OFFICER, STANFORD LINEAR ACCELERATOR CTR, 76- *Concurrent Pos:* Consult, Varian Assocs and others. *Mem:* Am Asn Physicists in Med; Health Physics Soc. *Res:* Dosimetry; radiation shielding; electron accelerators; health physics and medical physics instrumentation. *Mailing Add:* Stanford Linear Accelerator Ctr Stanford Univ PO Box 4349 Stanford CA 94305

MCCALL, ROBERT G, b Follansbee, WVa, Dec 20, 13; m 40; c 2. ENVIRONMENTAL HEALTH ENGINEERING. *Educ:* Univ WVa, BSCE, 35; Univ NC, MSSE, 50; Am Acad Environ Engrs Intersoc, dipl. *Prof Exp:* Sanit engr, Brooke County Health Dept, WVa, 35-38; sanit engr, State Health Dept, WVa, 38-43 & 46-48, actg dir, Sanit Eng Div, 48-50; actg dir, Sanit Eng Div, US Army, 43-46 & 50-69, sanit engr, Hq, 5th Army, Ill, 50-52, chief, Sanit Eng Div, Environ Health Lab, Army Chem Ctr, Md, 52-55, consult pub health eng, Hq US Army Europe, Ger, 55-58, chief sanit eng, Off Surg Gen, 58-62, consult, 58-68, chief sanit eng br, Med Field Serv Sch, Ft Sam Houston, Tex, 68-69; state sanit engr & dir, Environ Health Serv, WVa State Health Dept, 69-80; SPEC CONSULT, KELLY, GRIDLEY, BLAIR & WOLFE, CONSULT ENGRS, 81- *Concurrent Pos:* Mem comt food serv equip, Nat Sanit Found, 58-66, swimming pool equip, 63-, plastics, 63-; mem study sect, sanit eng & occup health, NIH, 58-62; secy, Conf Fed Sanit Eng, 58-59, pres, 60; liaison rep, Comt Sanit Eng & Environ, Nat Res Coun, 58-62; alt comnr, Interstate Comn Potomac River Basin, 69-74, mem exec bd, 71-; secy-treas, Conf State Sanit Eng, 71-73, chmn, 74-; mem effluent standards & water qual adv comt, Environ Protection Agency, 72-76, mem nat drinking water adv coun, 77-80; mem, Coun Pub Health Consult, NSF, 75-; dir, Am Water Works Asn, 77-79; trustee, Am Acad Environ Engrs, 77-79. *Honors & Awards:* Bedell Award, Fedn Sewage Works Asn, 50; Fuller Award, Am Water Works, 79. *Mem:* Fel Am Pub Health Asn; Nat Soc Prof Engrs; hon mem Am Water Works Asn. *Res:* Industrial wastes; stream pollution control; food service equipment. *Mailing Add:* Kelly Gidley Blair & Wolfe Consult Engrs 550 Eagan St Charleston WV 25305

MCCALL, SAMUEL LEVERTE, b Panama City, Fla, June 18, 40; c 2. PHYSICS. *Educ:* Fla State Univ, BS, 62; Univ Calif, Berkeley, PhD(physics), 68. *Prof Exp:* Jr engr laser physics, Western Develop Labs, Philco-Ford Corp, 62-63; res asst physics, Univ Calif, Berkeley, 63-68; MEM TECH STAFF PHYSICS, BELL LABS, 68- *Mem:* Am Phys Soc. *Res:* Nonlinear optics; atomic physics; solid state physics; astronomy; astrophysics. *Mailing Add:* Rm 1E-300 Bell Labs 600 Mountain Ave Murray Hill NJ 07974

MCCALL, WADE WILEY, b Day, Fla, Aug 13, 20; m 41; c 3. SOIL FERTILITY. *Educ:* Univ Fla, BS, 42, MA, 47; Mich State Univ, PhD(soil sci), 53. *Prof Exp:* Soil chemist, Agr Exp Sta, Fla, 46-47, asst prof soils, Univ Fla, 47-51; asst prof soil sci, Mich State Univ, 53-62; assoc specialist soil mgt, 62-68, PROF SOIL SCI & SPECIALIST SOIL MGT, UNIV HAWAII, 68- *Concurrent Pos:* Agron & soils adv, Kasetsart Univ, Bangkok & dept agr, Thailand, 65-66; consult, Nat Sch Agr, El Salvador, 70. *Mem:* Soil Sci Soc Am; Int Soc Soil Sci. *Res:* Soil fertility research in floricultural greenhouse crops; fruit, vegetable and ornamental crops; basic soils; fertilizer technology. *Mailing Add:* Dept Agron & Soil Sci Univ Hawaii Honolulu HI 96822

MCCALLA, ARTHUR GILBERT, b St Catharines, Ont, Mar 22, 06; m 31; c 3. PLANT BIOCHEMISTRY, PLANT PHYSIOLOGY. *Educ:* Univ Alta, BSc, 29, MSc, 31; Univ Calif, PhD, 33. *Hon Degrees:* Hon DSc, Univ Alberta, 81. *Prof Exp:* Asst plant biochem, 29-31, assoc comt on grain res, 32-41, prof field crops, 41-44, prof plant sci, 44-71, chmn dept, 44-51, dean agr fac, 51-59, dean fac grad studies, 57-71, EMER PROF PLANT BIOCHEM, UNIV ALTA, 71- *Concurrent Pos:* Researcher, Inst Phys Chem, Uppsala, Sweden, 39-40; mem, Nat Res Coun Can, 50-56; mem, Can Commonwealth Scholar & Fel Comt, 59-72; pres, Can Asn Grad Schs, 62-63. *Mem:* Fel Royal Soc Can; Can Biochem Soc; fel Agr Inst Can. *Res:* Chemistry of plant proteins; biochemistry and quality of cereals. *Mailing Add:* 11455 University Ave Edmonton AB T6G 1Y9 Can

MCCALLA, DENNIS ROBERT, b Edmonton, Alta, July 30, 34; m 57; c 2. BIOCHEMISTRY, MUTAGENESIS. *Educ:* Univ Alta, BSc, 57; Univ Sask, MSc, 58; Calif Inst Technol, PhD(biochem, genetics), 61. *Prof Exp:* From asst prof to assoc prof biochem, 61-71, dean fac sci, 67-75, PROF BIOCHEM, McMASTER UNIV, 71- *Mem:* Can Soc Cell Biol; Can Asn Res Toxicol; Physiol; fel Chem Inst Can; Am Soc Biol Chem. *Res:* Biochemical genetics; mechanism of action of mutagens and carcinogens. *Mailing Add:* Dept of Biochem McMaster Univ Hamilton ON L8S 3Z5 Can

MCCALLA, THOMAS MARK, JR, b Corinth, Miss, May 1, 34; m 63. SYSTEMS & ELECTRICAL ENGINEERING. *Educ:* Univ Nebr, Lincoln, BSEE, 56; NMex State Univ, MSEE, 65; Case Western Reserve Univ, PhD(eng), 69. *Prof Exp:* Electronic engr, White Sands Missile Range, 56-63; asst prof eng, 69-73, ASSOC PROF ENG, SOUTHERN ILL UNIV, CARBONDALE, 73- *Concurrent Pos:* Proj dir integrated avionics, NASA, 76-77; consult, Dynatronics, Columbus, 78- & NASA, 80- *Mem:* Inst Elec & Electronics Engrs; Math Asn Am. *Res:* Systems theory, hybrid computer design and applications to systems simulation. *Mailing Add:* Col Eng & Technol Southern Ill Univ Carbondale IL 62901

MCCALLEY, ROBERT B(RUCE), JR, b Miami, Fla, Dec 17, 22; m 51. MECHANICAL ENGINEERING. *Educ:* Univ SC, BS, 47; Cornell Univ, MCE, 49, PhD(struct, civil eng), 52. *Prof Exp:* Res assoc civil eng, Cornell Univ, 48-51; engr, Sr Staff, Appl Physics Lab, Johns Hopkins Univ, 51-55; struct engr, Knolls Atomic Power Lab, Gen Elec Co, 55-58; reactor containment engr, USAEC, 58-59; consult engr, Knolls Atomic Power Lab, 60-62, mgr stress anal, 63-68, mgr struct mech suboper, Aircraft Engine Group, 68-71, mgr tech opers mach apparatus, 71-76, MGR ENG SUPPORT, MACH APPARATUS OPER, GEN ELEC CO, 76- *Mem:* Am Soc Civil Engrs; fel Am Soc Mech Engrs; NY Acad Sci. *Res:* Elasticity; applied mechanics; numerical analysis. *Mailing Add:* 826 Karenwald Lane Schenectady NY 12309

MCCALLEY, RODERICK CANFIELD, b Portland, Ore, Aug 2, 43. MAGNETIC RESONANCE. *Educ:* Calif Inst Technol, BS, 64; Harvard Univ, PhD(phys chem), 71. *Prof Exp:* NSF fel phys chem, Stanford Univ, 71-72; asst prof chem, Dartmouth Col, 72-79; MEM STAFF, LOCKHEED PALO ALTO RES LAB, 79- *Mem:* Sigma Xi. *Res:* Electron spin resonance; radiation damage in solids; spin-label dynamics in solution; magnetic relaxation; electron structure of free radicals. *Mailing Add:* Dept 52-35 Bldg 204 Lockheed Palo Alto Res Lab 3251 Hanover St Palo Alto CA 94306

MCCALLION, WILLIAM JAMES, b Toronto, Ont, Aug 20, 18; m 44; c 4. MATHEMATICS, ASTRONOMY. *Educ:* McMaster Univ, BA, 43, MA, 46. *Prof Exp:* Lectr math, 43-52, from asst prof to assoc prof, 53-70, asst dir exten, 52-53, dir, 55-70, dir educ servs, 62-70, dean, Sch Adult Educ, 70-78, PROF MATH, McMASTER UNIV, 70- *Mem:* Am Math Soc; Math Asn Am; Royal Astron Soc Can; Can Math Cong. *Res:* Modern algebra; mathematics of business. *Mailing Add:* Sch of Adult Educ McMaster Univ Hamilton ON L8S 4L8 Can

MCCALLISTER, LAWRENCE P, b Chicago, Ill, Mar 27, 43; m 73. MICROSCOPIC ANATOMY. *Educ:* Univ Ill, Champaign, BS, 66; Loyola Univ Chicago, PhD(anat), 71. *Prof Exp:* USPHS fel med & physiol, Pritzker Sch Med, Univ Chicago, 71-72; ASST PROF ANAT, MILTON S HERSHEY MED SCH, PA STATE UNIV, 72- *Concurrent Pos:* Nat Heart & Lung Inst grant, Milton S Hershey Med Sch, Pa State Univ, 72-75 & 76-79, Nat Heart & Lung Inst res career develop award, 76- *Mem:* Am Asn Anatomists; Sigma Xi. *Res:* Ultrastructure and function of muscle and nerve. *Mailing Add:* Dept of Anat Pa State Univ Hershey PA 17033

MCCALLUM, CHARLES ALEXANDER, JR, b North Adams, Mass, Nov 1, 25; m 55; c 4. ORAL SURGERY. *Educ:* Tufts Univ, DMD, 51; Med Col Ala, MD, 57; Am Bd Oral Surg, dipl. *Hon Degrees:* DSc, Univ Ala, 75. *Prof Exp:* Intern oral surg, Univ Hosp, 51-52, resident, 52-54, from instr to assoc prof, Sch Dent, 56-59, intern med, Univ Hosp, 57-58, chmn dept oral surg, Sch Dent, 58-65, chief sect oral surg, Med Col, 65-70, dean, 62-77, PROF ORAL SURG, SCH DENT, UNIV ALA, BIRMINGHAM, 59-, VPRES HEALTH AFFAIRS & DIR, MED CTR, 77- *Concurrent Pos:* Consult, Vet Admin Hosps, Birmingham, Tuscaloosa & Tuskegee, 58-, mem med adv comt, 62-; consult, Ariz Med Study, 60 & Martin Army Hosp, Ft Benning, Ga, 61-; mem oral surg test construct comt, Nat Bd Dent Exam, 62-70; mem adv comt hosps & clins, USPHS, 64-66, mem prev med & dent rev panel, 65; mem bd dirs, Am Bd Oral Surg, 64-71, pres, 71; cent off consult, Dept Med & Surg, Vet Admin, 65-70; mem nat adv dent res, coun, Nat Inst Dent Res, 68-; pres, Am Asn Dent Schs, 70; mem bd comnr, Joint Comn Accreditation Hosp, 79 . *Mem:* Inst Med-Nat Acad Sci; Am Dent Asn; AMA; Am Soc Oral Surg (pres, 75-76); fel Am Col Dent. *Res:* Dental infection and effects of various systemic drugs on control of hemorrhage. *Mailing Add:* Med Ctr Univ of Ala Birmingham AL 35294

MCCALLUM, CHARLES JOHN, JR, b Tacoma, Wash, Apr 26, 43; m 67; c 2. OPERATIONS RESEARCH. *Educ:* Mass Inst Technol, SB, 65; Stanford Univ, MS, 67, PhD(opers res), 70. *Prof Exp:* Mem tech staff opers res, 70-75, supvr opers res appl group, 75-79, supvr opers res methods group, 79-81, SUPVR OPERS RES & NETWORK STUDIES GROUP, BELL LABS, 81- *Mem:* Opers Res Soc Am; Inst Mgt Sci; Math Prog Soc; Sigma Xi. *Res:* Mathematical programming; network flow; the linear complementarity problem; facility location models. *Mailing Add:* Bell Labs Holmdel NJ 07733

MACCALLUM, CRAWFORD JOHN, b New York, NY, May 28, 29; m 51; c 5. GAMMA RAY ASTRONOMY. *Educ:* Princeton Univ, BA, 51; Univ NMex, PhD(physics), 62. *Prof Exp:* STAFF MEM, SANDIA CORP, 57- *Concurrent Pos:* Fulbright lectr, Univ Cairo, 64-65. *Mem:* Am Phys Soc; Am Astron Soc. *Res:* Radiation physics; analytical methods electron penetration in solids; gamma ray astronomy. *Mailing Add:* Sandia Lab 4231 Albuquerque NM 87185

MACCALLUM, DONALD KENNETH, b Los Angeles, Calif, Apr 13, 39; m 62; c 2. ANATOMY, HISTOLOGY. *Educ:* Pomona Col, BA, 61; Univ Southern Calif, MS, 64, PhD(anat), 66. *Prof Exp:* Staff mem exp path, Walter Reed Army Inst Res, 66-68; asst prof anat, Med Sch, 69-74, asst prof oral biol, Dent Sch, 69-72, ASSOC PROF CELL BIOL, MED SCH & RES SCIENTIST, DENT RES INST, UNIV MICH, ANN ARBOR, 69-, ASSOC PROF ORAL BIOL, DENT SCH, 72- *Concurrent Pos:* Nat Inst Dent Res fel, Case Western Reserve Univ, 68-69; asst prof lectr, Sch Med, George Washington Univ, 67-68. *Mem:* Am Asn Anat; Am Soc Cell Biol. *Res:* Oral mucosal ultrastructure; epithelial-connective tissue interaction; experimental cytology; corneal endothelial structure and function. *Mailing Add:* Dept of Anat Univ of Mich Med Sch Ann Arbor MI 48104

MCCALLUM, KEITH STUART, b Fond du Lac, Wis, June 21, 19; m 42; c 2. ANALYTICAL CHEMISTRY. *Educ:* Univ Wis, BS, 42, PhD(chem), 50. *Prof Exp:* Group leader anal chem, Redstone Arsenal Res Div, 50-59, PROJ LEADER, ROHM AND HAAS CO, 59- *Mem:* AAAS; Am Chem Soc. *Res:* Trace analysis of air and water pollutants, and impurities from chemical and biodegradation. *Mailing Add:* Rohm and Haas Co Res Labs Spring House PA 19477

MCCALLUM, KENNETH JAMES, b Scott, Sask, Apr 25, 18; m 50; c 2. PHYSICAL CHEMISTRY. *Educ:* Univ Sask, BSc, 36, MSc, 39; Columbia Univ, PhD(chem), 42. *Prof Exp:* From asst prof to assoc prof chem, 43-52, head dept chem, 59-70, PROF CHEM, UNIV SASK, 52-, DEAN COL GRAD STUDIES & RES, 70- *Concurrent Pos:* Nuffield traveling fel natural sci, Cambridge Univ, 50-51. *Mem:* Fel AAAS; fel Royal Soc Can; Chem Inst Can. *Res:* Chemical effects of nuclear reactions; radiation chemistry; isotopic exchange reactions. *Mailing Add:* Col Grad Studies & Res Univ Sask Saskatoon SK S7N 0W0 Can

MCCALLUM, MALCOLM E, b Springfield, Mass, July 28, 34; m 63; c 2. GEOLOGY. *Educ:* Middlebury Col, AB, 56; Univ Tenn, MS, 58; Univ Wyo, PhD(geol), 64. *Prof Exp:* From asst prof to assoc prof geol, 62-71, PROF GEOL, COLO STATE UNIV, 71-; GEOLOGIST, US GEOL SURV, 56- *Concurrent Pos:* Res grants, Wyo Geol Surv, 59-61, Geol Soc Am, 60 & 70 & NSF, 74- *Mem:* AAAS; fel Geol Soc Am; fel Mineral Soc Am; Geochem Soc; Soc Explor Geochem. *Res:* Petrology, structure, and mineral resources of Precambrian crystalline rocks, northern Colorado and southern Wyoming; Precambrian-Tertiary structure and stratigraphy of disturbed belt in northern Big Belt Mountains, Montana; petrology and chemistry of kimberlite and upper mantle-lower crustal rocks and diamonds included in diatremes of northern Colorado and southern Wyoming. *Mailing Add:* Dept of Earth Resources Colo State Univ Ft Collins CO 80523

MCCALLUM, RODERICK EUGENE, b Denver, Colo, Aug 14, 44; m 67; c 2. MICROBIOLOGY, BACTERIOLOGY. *Educ:* Univ Kans, BA, 67, PhD(microbiol), 70. *Prof Exp:* Instr microbiol, Univ Kans, 70; res assoc, Univ Tex, 70-72, instr, 71; asst prof, 72-75, ASSOC PROF MICROBIOL, UNIV OKLA, 75-, ADJ ASSOC PROF ORAL PATH, 77- *Concurrent Pos:* USPHS trainee, Univ Tex, Austin, 70-72; guest prof, Univ Heidelberg, Germany, 80. *Mem:* Shock Soc; Sigma Xi; Am Soc Microbiol; Reticuloendothelial Soc. *Res:* Metabolism in disease; endotoxin; mixed anaerobic infections. *Mailing Add:* Dept of Microbiol & Immunol Univ of Okla Health Sci Ctr Oklahoma City OK 73190

MCCALLY, MICHAEL, physiology, aerospace medicine, see previous edition

MCCALLY, RUSSELL LEE, b Marion, Ohio, Sept 27, 40; m 61; c 2. PHYSICS, BIOPHYSICS. *Educ:* Ohio State Univ, BSc, 64; Johns Hopkins Univ, MSc, 73. *Prof Exp:* Assoc physicist, 65-76, SR PHYSICIST, JOHNS HOPKINS UNIV APPL PHYSICS LAB, 76- *Concurrent Pos:* Co-prin investr, Nat Heart, Lung & Blood Inst Grant, NIH, 76-79; William S Parsons fel, Johns Hopkins Univ, 79-80. *Mem:* Am Phys Soc; Asn Res Vision & Ophthal. *Res:* Application of light scattering methods to biological structural investigations especially corneal structure; effects of infrared radiation on corneal structure. *Mailing Add:* Johns Hopkins Univ Johns Hopkins Rd Laurel MD 20707

MCCAMAN, MARILYN WALES, b Oak Park, Ill, Oct 10, 28; m 53; c 5. NEUROSCIENCES. *Educ:* Grinnell Col, AB, 50; Wash Univ, PhD(pharmacol), 57. *Prof Exp:* Asst pharmacol, Wash Univ, 56-57; from res assoc to asst prof neurol, Sch Med & Inst Phychiat Res, Ind Univ, Indianapolis, 59-70; ASSOC RES SCIENTIST, CITY OF HOPE MED CTR, 70- *Mem:* Am Soc Mass Spectrometry. *Res:* Biochemistry of muscular dystrophy; metabolism of neurotransmitters in the invertebrate central nervous system. *Mailing Add:* Dept of Neurosci City of Hope Med Ctr Duarte CA 91010

MCCAMAN, RICHARD EUGENE, b Barberton, Ohio, Mar 28, 30; m 53; c 5. BIOCHEMISTRY, PHARMACOLOGY. *Educ:* Wabash Col, AB, 52; Wash Univ, PhD(pharmacol), 57. *Prof Exp:* Res assoc & instr biochem & pharmacol, Inst Psychiat Res, Sch Med, Ind Univ, Indianapolis, 57-62, from asst prof to assoc prof pharmacol, 62-68, prin investr neurochem, 62-68; CHIEF NEUROPHARMACOL, CITY OF HOPE MED CTR, 68- *Mem:* AAAS; Asn Res Nerv & Ment Dis; Am Soc Neurochem; Int Soc Neurochem; Am Soc Biol Chem. *Res:* Biochemistry, physiology and chemical pathology of nervous system; chemistry, pharmacology and physiology of neurotransmitters; invertebrate neurobiology; intracellular electrophysiology. *Mailing Add:* City of Hope Res Inst 1450 E Duarte Rd Duarte CA 91010

MCCAMMON, DAN, b Los Angeles, Calif, Aug 6, 44; m 76. ASTRONOMY. *Educ:* Calif Inst Technol, BS, 66; Univ Wis, PhD(physics), 71. *Prof Exp:* Foreign specialist physics, Prince of Songkla Univ, 74-76; assoc scientist astron, 76-80, ASST PROF PHYSICS, UNIV WIS-MADISON, 80- *Mem:* Am Astron Soc. *Res:* X-ray astronomy. *Mailing Add:* Dept of Physics Univ of Wis Madison WI 53706

MCCAMMON, JAMES ANDREW, b Lafayette, Ind, Feb 8, 47; m 69. STATISTICAL MECHANICS, BIOPOLYMER THEORY. *Educ:* Pomona Col, AB, 69; Harvard Univ, AM, 70, PhD(chem physics), 76. *Prof Exp:* NSF res fel chem, Harvard Univ, 76-77, NIH res fel, 77-78; asst prof, 78-81, CHMN, PHYS CHEM DIV, UNIV HOUSTON, 79-, M D ANDERSON PROF CHEM, 81- *Concurrent Pos:* Alfred P Sloan Found fel, 80; Res Career Develop Award, NIH, 80. *Mem:* Am Phys Soc; Am Chem Soc; Biophys Soc; AAAS. *Res:* Statistical mechanics of macromolecules and liquids; theory of protein structure, dynamics and function; development and application of computer models and simulation methods for molecular systems. *Mailing Add:* Dept Chem Univ Houston Cent Campus Houston TX 77004

MCCAMMON, LEWIS B(ROWN), JR, b Wheeling, WVa, Mar 28, 20; m 42; c 3. STRUCTURAL ENGINEERING. *Educ:* Purdue Univ, BS, 41, MS, 48, PhD(struct eng), 51. *Prof Exp:* Stud engr, Long Lines Dept, Am Telephone & Telegraph Co, 41-42; instr civil eng, Purdue Univ, 46-48, instr struct eng, 50-51; struct designer, CF Braun & Co, 51-53, sr designer, 55-59; assoc prof civil eng, Northwestern Technol Inst, 54-55; mem sr staff, Nat Eng Sci Co, 59-64, chief adminr, 64-66, vpres eng, 66-68; mgr ocean technol, W Offshore Drilling & Explor Co, 68-74; HEAD, STRUCT ENG SECT, CF

BRAUN & CO, 74- *Concurrent Pos:* Reserve instr, US Mil Acad, 52-53; lectr, Univ Calif, Los Angeles, 53 & Univ Southern Calif, 57-58. *Mem:* Am Soc Civil Engrs; Am Soc Eng Educ. *Res:* Buckling of column elements; steel; stress distribution in actual bridge members; bolted structural joints. *Mailing Add:* 105 N Cordova St Alhambra CA 91801

MCCAMMON, MARY, b Eng, Aug 23, 27; m 60. MATHEMATICS. *Educ:* Univ London, BSc, 49, MSc, 50, PhD(math), 53. *Prof Exp:* Res assoc math, Mass Inst Technol, 53-54; asst prof, 54-60, ASSOC PROF MATH & COMPUT SCI, PA STATE UNIV, UNIVERSITY PARK, 60- *Mem:* Am Math Soc; Asn Comput Mach. *Res:* Numerical analysis; uses of digital computers. *Mailing Add:* Dept of Math McAllister Bldg Pa State Univ University Park PA 16802

MCCAMMON, RICHARD B, b Indianapolis, Ind, Dec 3, 32; m 56; c 2. GEOLOGY. *Educ:* Mass Inst Technol, BSc, 55; Univ Mich, MSc, 56; Ind Univ, PhD(geol), 59. *Prof Exp:* Rockefeller fel statist, Univ Chicago, 59-60; asst prof geol, Univ NDak, 60-61; res geologist, Gulf Res & Develop Co, 61-68; assoc prof, Univ Ill, Chicago Circle, 68-70, prof geol, 70-76; GEOLOGIST, OFF RESOURCE ANAL, US GEOL SURV, 76- *Mem:* Geol Soc Am; Am Statist Asn; Soc Econ Paleont & Mineral. *Res:* Statistical application to problems in petroleum exploration; multivariate methods in biostratigraphy and paleoecology; computer applications in geology. *Mailing Add:* Off of Resource Anal Nat Ctr 920 Reston VA 22092

MCCAMMON, ROBERT DESMOND, b Northern Ireland, July 23, 32; m 60, 78. SOLID STATE PHYSICS. *Educ:* Queen's Univ, Ireland, BSc, 53; Oxford Univ, DPhil(physics), 57. *Prof Exp:* Vis res assoc, 57-59, asst prof physics, 59-69, ASSOC PROF PHYSICS, PA STATE UNIV, 69- *Concurrent Pos:* Vis fel nat standards lab, Commonwealth Sci & Indust Res Orgn, Australia, 62-63. *Res:* Plastic deformation of metals at low temperatures; internal friction and dielectric behavior of high polymers at low temperatures; thermal expansion of solids; liquid helium-3 and helium-4 solutions; thermal properties of disordered solids at low temperatures. *Mailing Add:* Dept of Physics Pa State Univ University Park PA 16802

MCCAMMOND, DAVID, b Belfast, UK, Aug 23, 41; m 67. MECHANICAL ENGINEERING, BIOENGINEERING. *Educ:* Queen's Univ Belfast, BSc, 65, PhD(mech eng), 68. *Prof Exp:* Design draftsman, Harland & Wolff Ltd, 56-61; asst lectr mech eng, Queen's Univ Belfast, 67-68, lectr, 68-69; asst prof, 69-73, ASSOC PROF MECH ENG, UNIV TORONTO, 74- *Res:* Mechanical properties of plastics; biomaterials; biomechanics. *Mailing Add:* Dept of Mech Eng Univ of Toronto Toronto ON M5S 1A1 Can

MACCAMY, RICHARD C, b Spokane, Wash, Sept 26, 25; m 49; c 3. MATHEMATICS. *Educ:* Reed Col, AB, 49; Univ Calif, Berkeley, PhD(math), 55. *Prof Exp:* Res engr, Univ Calif, Berkeley, 50-54, res mathematician, 54-56; from asst prof to assoc prof, 56-64, PROF MATH, CARNEGIE-MELLON UNIV, 64-, ASSOC CHMN DEPT, 74- *Concurrent Pos:* Air Force Off Sci Res fel, 56-66; Soc Naval Archit & Marine Engrs fel, 57-63; Boeing Sci Res Lab grant, 63-64. *Mem:* Am Math Soc. *Res:* Partial differential and integral equations; fluid dynamics; elasticity; electromagnetic theory. *Mailing Add:* Dept of Math Carnegie-Mellon Univ Pittsburgh PA 15213

MCCANDLESS, BYRON HOWARD, b Florence, Colo, June 30, 24; m 49; c 2. MATHEMATICS. *Educ:* Colo State Univ, BS, 48; Ind Univ, AM & PhD(math), 53. *Prof Exp:* Instr math, Rutgers Univ, 52-54, from asst prof to assoc prof, 54-65; prof, Western Wash State Col, 65-66; PROF MATH, KENT STATE UNIV, 66- *Mem:* Am Math Soc; Math Asn Am. *Res:* Dimension theory; topology. *Mailing Add:* 1880 Carlton Dr Kent OH 44240

MCCANDLESS, ESTHER LEIB, b Brooklyn, NY, Mar 18, 23. PHYSIOLOGY. *Educ:* Bethany Col, BS, 44; Cornell Univ, MS, 47, PhD(animal physiol), 48. *Prof Exp:* Asst biol, Bethany Col, 43-44; teacher high sch, Pa, 44-45; lab technician, Harrisburg Hosp, Pa, 45; asst human physiol, Cornell Univ, 45-48, physiol chem, NY State Vet Col, 48-49; assoc physiol, Woman's Med Col Pa, 49-53; res assoc med, Jefferson Med Col, 53; asst physiol, Univ Tenn, 54-57, asst prof, 57-59; res physiologist, Chronic Dis Res Inst, Univ Buffalo, 59-64; assoc prof biol, 64-69, PROF BIOL, McMASTER UNIV, 69- *Mem:* AAAS; Am Physiol Soc; Can Physiol Soc; Can Soc Cell Biol; Can Soc Immunologists. *Res:* Polysaccharide immunology; algal polysaccharides; connective tissue metabolism; experimental diabetes; ruminant and phospholipid metabolism. *Mailing Add:* Dept of Biol McMaster Univ Hamilton ON L85 4L8 Can

MCCANDLESS, FRANK PHILIP, b Florence, Colo, Apr 27, 32; m 55; c 2. CHEMICAL ENGINEERING. *Educ:* Univ Colo, BS, 59, MS, 63; Mont State Univ, PhD(chem eng), 66. *Prof Exp:* Process engr, Chevron Res Corp, 59-61 & Marathon Oil Co, 61-62; res engr, 66-68, from asst prof to assoc prof, 68-75, PROF CHEM ENG, MONT STATE UNIV, 75- *Mem:* Am Inst Chem Engrs; Am Chem Soc. *Res:* Kinetics; catalysis; extractive crystallization; membrane separations. *Mailing Add:* Dept Chem Eng Mont State Univ Bozeman MT 59717

MCCANDLISS, RUSSELL JOHN, b Pittsburgh, Pa, Jan 18, 48; m 73; c 2. ENZYMOLOGY. *Educ:* Univ Tenn, Knoxville, BS, 69; Purdue Univ, MS, 72, PhD(biochem), 78. *Prof Exp:* Fel, Roche Inst Molecular Biol, 78-80; sr res scientist, Genex Corp, 81-82; PRIN SCIENTIST, GENETIC RES CORP, 82- *Mem:* Am Chem Soc. *Res:* Production of chemicals and proteins by microorganisms, using biochemical genetics and recombinant DNA technology. *Mailing Add:* Genetic Res Corp 9110 Red Br Rd Columbia MD 21045

MCCANE, DONALD IRWIN, organic chemistry, deceased

MCCANN, DAISY S, b Hamburg, Ger, Mar 8, 27; Can citizen; m 50; c 1. CLINICAL CHEMISTRY. *Educ:* Univ Toronto, BA, 50; Wayne State Univ, MS, 56, PhD(biochem), 58. *Prof Exp:* Teacher, Riverside High Sch, Ont, 50-51; tech asst, John Wyeth & Bros Co Ltd, Ont, 51-54; res fel, Wayne State Univ, 55-58, res assoc, 59-67, adj assoc prof, 67-70; asst prof, 70-77, ASSOC PROF BIOL CHEM, UNIV MICH, 77-; DIR RES LAB, WAYNE COUNTY GEN HOSP, MI, 70- *Concurrent Pos:* A J Boyle fel, Wayne State Univ, 58-59; consult, Wayne State Univ, Detroit, 60-65; consult, Jordan Clin Lab, Detroit, 66-68, assoc dir, 68-72. *Mem:* Am Chem Soc; Soc Advan Sci; Am Asn Clin Chem; Endocrine Soc; Clin Ligand Assay Soc. *Res:* Development of clinical laboratory techniques including radioimmunoassay and high performance liquid chromatography; clinical and physiological prostaglandin and catecholamine studies; tissue culture laboratory work on hybridoma antibody production, liver transplantation problems and hormonal influences on cultured hepatocytes; catecholamine metabolism. *Mailing Add:* Wayne County Gen Hosp Res & Educ PO Box 549 Wayne MI 48184

MCCANN, FRANCES VERONICA, b Manchester, Conn, Jan 15, 27; m 62, 70. PHYSIOLOGY, ELECTROPHYSIOLOGY. *Educ:* Univ Conn, AB, 52, PhD(physiol), 59; Univ Ill, MS, 54. *Prof Exp:* Res assoc, Marine Biol Lab, Woods Hole, 52-58; from instr to assoc prof, 59-73, PROF PHYSIOL, DARTMOUTH MED SCH, 73- . *Concurrent Pos:* Estab investr, Am Heart Asn, 65-70, mem coun basic sci, 72- & New Eng res rev comt, 74-; mem physiol study sect, NIH, 73-75 & Gen Res Suppl Rev Comn, 78-; consult, Hitchcock Hosp, 75. *Mem:* Soc Gen Physiol; Am Physiol Soc; Biophys Soc. *Res:* Electrophysiology of neuro-muscular systems; cardiac electrophysiology, insect flight mechanisms; electrophysiology of cancer and macrophages. *Mailing Add:* Dept Physiol Dartmouth Med Sch Hanover NH 03755

MCCANN, GILBERT DONALD, JR, b Glendale, Calif, Jan 12, 12; m 36; c 2. INFORMATION SCIENCE. *Educ:* Calif Inst Technol, BS, 34, MS, 35, PhD(elec eng), 39. *Prof Exp:* Engr cent sta, Westinghouse Elec Corp, Pa, 38-41, consult transmission engr, 41-46; prof elec eng, 47-65, prof appl sci, 65-80, dir, Willis H Booth Comput Ctr, 61-71, EMER PROF APPL SCI, CALIF INST TECHNOL, 80- *Concurrent Pos:* Westinghouse lectr, Univ Pittsburgh, 40-46; mem adv comt lightning protection, US Army Ord; mem, Int Cong High Tension Transmission, 47. *Mem:* Am Soc Mech Eng; Am Soc Eng Educ; fel Inst Elec & Electronics Eng. *Res:* Electrical transmission and lightning research; large-scale computing devices; fulchronograph; Westinghouse transients analyzer; electric analog computer; bioengineering; biomedical engineering. *Mailing Add:* Dept Info Sci 286-80 Calif Inst Technol Pasadena CA 91125

MCCANN, JAMES ALWYN, b Boston, Mass, May 20, 34; m 57; c 3. FISHERIES ECOLOGY, BIOMETRICS. *Educ:* Univ Mass, BS, 56; Iowa State Univ, MS, 58, PhD(fishery mgt, biomet), 60. *Prof Exp:* Asst, Iowa State Univ, 56-60; marine biologist, US Bur Commercial Fisheries, Mass, 60-63, leader fisheries res, Mass Coop Fishery Unit, US Bur Sport Fisheries & Wildlife, 63-72; chief, Br Fish Ecosyst Res, 72-73, chief, Div Pop Ecol, 73-76, chief div fishery res, 76-77, DIR, NAT FISHERY RES LAB, US FISH & WILDLIFE SERV, 77- *Concurrent Pos:* Assoc prof, Univ Mass, 63-72. *Mem:* Am Soc Ichthyologist & Herpetologist; Am Fisheries Soc; Am Inst Fishery Res Biol. *Res:* Fishery research and biometrics; aquatic ecology; exotic fishes; fishery ecosystems. *Mailing Add:* Nat Fishery Res Lab Univ of Fla Gainesville FL 32611

MCCANN, LESTER J, b Minneapolis, Minn, Sept 16, 15; m 44; c 7. VERTEBRATE ZOOLOGY. *Educ:* Univ Minn, BS, 37, MS, 38; Univ Utah, PhD(vert zool), 55. *Prof Exp:* Instr biol, Boise Col, 49-55; PROF BIOL, COL ST THOMAS, 55- *Concurrent Pos:* NSF res grant, 60-61; head dept natural sci, St Mary's Jr Col, 61-69, assoc dean tech educ, 68-69. *Mem:* AAAS; Am Soc Zool; Sigma Xi. *Res:* Comparative vertebrate anatomy and embryology; human anatomy and physiology; role of predation in wildlife ecology. *Mailing Add:* Dept Biol Col St Thomas St Paul MN 55105

MCCANN, PETER PAUL, b Alexandria, La, Nov 21, 43; m 71. CELL BIOLOGY, CELL PHYSIOLOGY. *Educ:* Columbia Col, Columbia Univ, AB, 65; Syracuse Univ, PhD(molecular biol), 70. *Prof Exp:* Fel molecular biol, Lab Molecular Biol, Nat Inst Arthritis, Metabolism & Digestive Dis, NIH, 70-73; sr scientist biochem, Ctr Rech Merrell Int, Strasbourg, France, 73-79; SR BIOCHEMIST, MERRELL RES CTR, MERRELL DOW PHARMACEUT, CINCINNATI, OHIO, 79- *Concurrent Pos:* Assoc prof, Dept Anat & Cell Biol, Col Med, Univ Cincinnati, 81- *Mem:* Am Soc Cell Biol; Am Soc Tropical Med & Hygiene; Am Soc Biol Chemists. *Res:* Role of the induction of ornithine decarboxylase and putrescine biosynthesis in cell replication and cell differentiation. *Mailing Add:* Merrell Dow Res Ctr 2110 E Galbraith Rd Cincinnati OH 45215

MCCANN, ROGER C, b Lakewood, Ohio, Aug 30, 42. MATHEMATICS. *Educ:* Pomona Col, BA, 64; Case Inst Technol, MS, 66; Case Western Reserve Univ, PhD(math), 68. *Prof Exp:* Asst prof math, Calif State Col, Los Angeles, 68-69; vis asst prof, 69-70, asst prof math, Case Western Reserve Univ, 70-77; asst prof, 77-78, ASSOC PROF MATH, MISS STATE UNIV, 78- *Mem:* Am Math Soc. *Res:* Dynamical systems; ordinary differential equations. *Mailing Add:* Dept of Math Miss State Univ Mississippi State MS 44106

MCCANN, SAMUEL MCDONALD, b Houston, Tex, Sept 8, 25; m 50; c 3. NEUROENDOCRINOLOGY, PHYSIOLOGY. *Educ:* Rice Inst, 42-44; Univ Pa, MD, 48. *Prof Exp:* Intern internal med, Mass Gen Hosp, 48-49, asst resident, 49-50; instr physiol, Sch Med, Univ Pa, 48 & 52-53, assoc, 53-54, from asst prof to prof, 54-64; PROF PHYSIOL & CHMN DEPT, UNIV TEX HEALTH SCI CTR DALLAS, 65- *Concurrent Pos:* Rockefeller Found traveling grant, Royal Vet Col, Sweden, 54-55; sr asst, Royal Vet Col, Sweden, 54-55; consult, Schering Corp, NJ, 58; mem gen med B study sect, NIH, 65-67, mem endocrinol study sect, 67-69, mem corpus luteum panel, 71-74; mem pop res comn, Nat Inst Child Health & Human Develop, 74-76, mem, Reprod

Biol Study Sect, 77-, chmn, 80-82; mem sci adv bd, Wis Regional Primate Ctr, 74- *Honors & Awards:* Oppenheimer Award, Endocrine Soc, 66; Fred Conrad Koch Medal, Endocrine Soc, 79; Harris Mem lectr, Melbourne, 80. *Mem:* Am Physiol Soc; NY Acad Sci; Am Soc Clin Invest; Int Brain Res Orgn; Int Soc Res Reproduction. *Res:* Experimental neurogenic hypertension; hypothalamic regulation of thirst and pituitary function. *Mailing Add:* Dept Physiol Univ Tex Health Sci Ctr Dallas TX 75235

MCCANN, WILLIAM PETER, b Baltimore, Md, Dec 12, 24; m 54; c 2. PHARMACOLOGY, INTERNAL MEDICINE. *Educ:* Princeton Univ, AB, 49; Cornell Univ, MD, 49. *Prof Exp:* Intern internal med, Barnes Hosp, St Louis, Mo, 49-50; instr clin pharmacol & med, Johns Hopkins Univ, 57-58; asst prof pharmacol, Sch Med, Univ Colo, 58-63, asst prof med, 58-63; assoc prof pharmacol, 63-67, asst prof med, 63-71, PROF PHARMACOL, UNIV ALA, BIRMINGHAM, 67-, ASSOC PROF MED, 71- *Concurrent Pos:* Res fel pharmacol, Sch Med, Wash Univ, 52-54; res fel physiol chem, Sch Med, Johns Hopkins Univ, 54-55, res fel clin pharmacol & med, 55-57. *Mem:* AAAS; Am Soc Pharmacol & Exp Therapeut; Am Soc Nephrology; Am Soc Clin Pharmacol & Therapeut. *Res:* Human pharmacology; pharmacokinetics. *Mailing Add:* Dept Pharmacol Univ Ala Univ Sta Birmingham AL 35294

MCCANN, WILLIAM R, b Oceanside, NY, Oct 27, 51. SEISMOLOGY, TECTONICS. *Educ:* State Univ NY, Albany, BS, 73; Columbia Univ, MA, 76, MPhil, 80, PhD(seismol), 80. *Prof Exp:* Res scientist, 80-81, RES ASSOC, LAMONT-DOHERTY GEOL OBSERV, 81- *Mem:* Am Geophys Union; Seismol Soc Am; Sigma Xi. *Res:* Earthquake prediction; Caribbean tectonics and risk analysis; subduction tectonics and seismicity studies. *Mailing Add:* Lamont-Doherty Geol Observ Palisades NY 10964

MACCANNELL, KEITH LEONARD, b Transcona, Man, Jan 8, 34; m 72. CLINICAL PHARMACOLOGY. *Educ:* Univ Man, BSc & MD, 58, PhD(pharmacol), 63; FRCP(C), 65; FACP, 78. *Prof Exp:* Vis asst prof pharmacol & internal med, Sch Med, Emory Univ, 64-66; assoc prof pharmacol & asst prof internal med, Univ BC, 67-69; chmn dept pharmacol & therapeut, 69-74, assoc dean res, 72-75, PROF PHARMACOL, FAC MED, UNIV CALGARY, 69-, PROF INTERNAL MED, 74- *Concurrent Pos:* Can Found for Advan Therapeut fel, Emory Univ, 64-66; Markle scholar & Med Res Coun Can scholar, 66-71. *Mem:* Am Fedn Clin Res; Pharmacol Soc Can; Am Soc Pharmacol & Exp Therapeut; Can Med Asn. *Res:* Cardiovascular physiology-pharmacology. *Mailing Add:* Dept of Pharmacol & Therapeut Univ of Calgary Fac of Med Calgary AB T2N 1N4 Can

MACCANON, DONALD MOORE, b Norwood, Iowa, June 17, 24; m 46; c 2. CARDIOVASCULAR PHYSIOLOGY, PHARMACOLOGY. *Educ:* Drake Univ, BA, 48; Univ Iowa, MS, 51, PhD(physiol), 53. *Prof Exp:* Asst, Drake Univ, 42-43; asst physiol, Univ Iowa, 50-51, res assoc, 53-54; asst prof physiol & pharmacol, Sch Med Sci, Univ SDak, 54-60; asst prof physiol & pharmacol & chief exp cardiol, Chicago Med Sch, 60-61, from assoc prof to prof cardiovasc res, 61-71, assoc dir, 62-71, from assoc prof to prof physiol, 64-71; health scientist adminr, Training Grants & Awards Br, Nat Heart & Lung Inst, 71-72, actg head postdoctoral sect, Fel Br, Nat Inst Gen Med Sci, 72-73; health scientist adminr, Cardiac Functions Br, 73-74, chief, Manpower Br, 74-80, CHIEF, RES TRAINING & DEVELOP BR, DIV HEART & VASCULAR DIS, NAT HEART, LUNG & BLOOD INST, 80- *Concurrent Pos:* Life ins res fel physiol, Univ Iowa, 51-54; NIH career prog awardee, 61-71; consult, Physiol Fels Rev Panel, USPHS, 65-68, Anesthesiol Training Comt, NIH, 68-70, Chicago Heart Res Comt, 69-71 & Career Opportunities Physiol Comt, 79- *Honors & Awards:* Morris L Parker Award Meritorious Res, 64; Res Award, Interstate Postgrad Med Asn, 67. *Mem:* Fel AAAS; fel Am Col Cardiol; Am Physiol Soc; Am Heart Asn. *Res:* Cardiac function; pulmonary circulation; hemodynamics; cardiac vibrations. *Mailing Add:* 401 Nina Pl Rockville MD 20852

MCCANTS, CHARLES BERNARD, b Andrews, SC, Sept 14, 24; m 47; c 2. SOIL SCIENCE. *Educ:* NC State Col, BS, 49, MS, 50; Iowa State Univ, PhD(soils), 55. *Prof Exp:* Instr soils, NC State Col, 50-52; assoc agronomist, Clemson Col, 55-56; from asst prof to assoc prof, 56-63, prof, 63-71, PROF & HEAD DEPT SOIL SCI, NC STATE UNIV, 71- *Mem:* Am Soc Agron; Soil Sci Soc Am. *Res:* Soil fertility; ion absorption; plant nutrition; tobacco production. *Mailing Add:* Dept of Soil Sci NC State Univ Raleigh NC 27607

MCCARDELL, W(ILLIAM) M(ARKHAM), b Houston, Tex, Nov 1, 23; m 49; c 2. CHEMICAL ENGINEERING. *Educ:* Rice Univ, BS, 48; Calif Inst Technol, MS, 49. *Prof Exp:* Res engr, Humble Oil & Refining Co, 49-59, chief res engr, Prod Res Div, 59-61, mgr econ & planning, 61-63, regional mkt mgr, 63-68, mkt vpres, 68-70; mkt vpres, Standard Oil Co NJ, 70-77, vpres mining & synthetic fuels, Exxon Corp, 77-80, PRES, EXXON MINERALS CO, 80- *Concurrent Pos:* Mem adv mgt prog, Harvard Univ, 66; exec vpres, Esso Eastern Inc, 75-77. *Mem:* Am Meteorol Soc; Am Inst Mining, Metall & Petrol Engrs; Am Inst Chem Engrs. *Res:* Management; petroleum and chemical engineering; physical chemistry. *Mailing Add:* Exxon Minerals Co 1251 Ave of the Americas New York NY 10020

MCCARL, RICHARD LAWRENCE, b Grove City, Pa, July 6, 27; m 51; c 3. BIOCHEMISTRY. *Educ:* Grove City Col, BS, 50; Pa State Univ, MS, 58, PhD(biochem), 61. *Prof Exp:* Teacher high sch, Pa, 50-55; asst biochem, 55-57, instr, 57-61, from asst prof to assoc prof, 61-74, PROF BIOCHEM, PA STATE UNIV, 74- *Concurrent Pos:* NIH grants, 66-78. 70-73. *Mem:* Am Chem Soc; Am Soc Biol Chem; Tissue Cult Asn. *Res:* Lipid biosynthesis; animal tissue culture; physiology of cultured heart cells; lipid, RNA, DNA and protein patterns during differentiation and aging. *Mailing Add:* 303 Althouse Lab Pa State Univ University Park PA 16802

MCCARLEY, ROBERT EUGENE, b Denison, Tex, Aug 17, 31; m 52; c 4. INORGANIC CHEMISTRY. *Educ:* Univ Tex, BS, 53, PhD(chem), 56. *Prof Exp:* From instr to assoc prof chem, Univ, 56-70, res assoc, Ames Lab, 56-57, assoc chemist, 57-63, chemist, 63-74, PROF CHEM, IOWA STATE UNIV, 70-, CHMN DEPT, 76-, SR CHEMIST, AMES LAB, 74- *Mem:* Am Chem Soc. *Res:* Chemistry of transition elements; metal halide vaporization equilibria; metal carbonyl compounds; metal-metal bonding. *Mailing Add:* Dept of Chem Iowa State Univ Ames IA 50010

MCCARLEY, ROBERT WILLIAM, b Mayfield, Ky, Aug 17, 37; m 68; c 2. NEUROPHYSIOLOGY. *Educ:* Harvard Col, AB, 59; Harvard Med Sch, MD, 64. *Prof Exp:* Intern, Peter Bent Brigham Hosp, Boston, 64-65; resident psychiat, Ctr, 65-68, from instr to asst prof, Sch & Ctr, 68-78, ASSOC PROF PSYCHIAT, HARVARD MED SCH & MASS MENT HEALTH CTR, 78-, CO-DIR LAB NEUROPHYSIOL, 75-, CO-DIR CLIN RES TRAINING PROG, 80- *Concurrent Pos:* NIH spec fel, 68-71; Nat Ctr Sci Res fel, Univ Paris, 75; investr res grants, Nat Inst Ment Health, 72-, Milton Fund, Harvard Univ, 75-80, NSF, 79 & NIMH res scientist develop award, 80- *Mem:* Asn Psychophysiol Study Sleep; AAAS; Neurosci Soc; Am Psychiat Asn. *Res:* Physiology of sleep; mathematical modeling and computer processing of physiological data. *Mailing Add:* Harvard Med Sch 74 Fenwood Rd Boston MA 02115

MCCARLEY, WARDLOW HOWARD, b Pauls Valley, Okla, May 2, 26; m 50; c 3. VERTEBRATE ZOOLOGY. *Educ:* Austin Col, AB, 48; Univ Tex, MA, 50, PhD(ecol), 53. *Prof Exp:* Instr biol, Austin Col, 48; instr zool, Stephen F Austin State Col, 50-52, from asst prof to assoc prof, 53-55; prof biol & head dept, Southeastern State Col, 59-61; chmn dept, 63-71, PROF BIOL, AUSTIN COL, 61- *Concurrent Pos:* AEC res grant, 54-58; vis prof biol sta, Univ Okla, 58-; NSF res grants, 59-62 & 64-71. *Mem:* AAAS; Am Soc Mammal; Ecol Soc Am. *Res:* Speciation; behavioral ecology, behavior and vocalization of wild canids. *Mailing Add:* Dept of Biol Austin Col Sherman TX 75090

MCCARROLL, BRUCE, PHYSICAL CHEMISTRY. *Educ:* Univ Calif, Los Angeles, BS, 55; Univ Chicago, PhD(phys chem), 58. *Prof Exp:* Asst, AEC, Univ Chicago, 55-56, res assoc, Dept Chem & Enrico Fermi Inst Nuclear Studies, 58-60; phys chemist, Metall & Ceramics Lab, Gen Elec Res & Develop Ctr, NY, 60-71, sr develop engr, 71-74, MGR MAT ANAL & TEST, GEN ELEC CO, 74-, MGR, COMPUT AIDED DESIGN & COMPUT AIDED MANUFACTURING PROJ, 80- *Mem:* Am Phys Soc; Am Chem Soc. *Res:* Advanced development; electro-mechanical systems; food preparation systems; heat transfer; technological forecasting; materials testing; quality control; computer aided manufacturing. *Mailing Add:* 44 Flower House Lane Fairfield CT 06430

MCCARROLL, JAMES RENWICK, b New York, NY, Nov 14, 21; m. MEDICAL RESEARCH. *Educ:* Colby Col, AB, 42; Cornell Univ, MD, 46. *Prof Exp:* Asst prof pub health & dir div epidemiol res, Med Col, Cornell Univ, 57-66; prof prev med & dir environ health div, Sch Med, Univ Wash, 66-70, prof environ health & chmn dept, Sch Pub Health & Community Med, 70-73; clin prof, Community Environ Med, Univ Calif, Irvine, 75-77; CLIN PROF, FAMILY COMMUNITY & PREV MED, STANFORD MED SCH, 77-; PROG MGR HEALTH EFFECTS, ELEC POWER RES INST, 76- *Concurrent Pos:* Dir personnel health serv, New York Hosp, 53-66; asst med dir, City of Los Angeles, 73-76. *Mem:* Am Acad Occup Med; Am Occup Med Asn; AMA; Am Heart Asn; Int Epidemiol Asn. *Res:* Health effects of air pollution. *Mailing Add:* Elec Power Res Inst PO Box 10412 Palo Alto CA 94303

MCCARROLL, WILLIAM HENRY, b Brooklyn, NY, Mar 19, 30; m 58; c 4. INORGANIC CHEMISTRY. *Educ:* Univ Conn, BA, 53, MS, 55, PhD(chem), 57. *Prof Exp:* Asst chem, Univ Conn, 54-56; mem tech staff, RCA Labs, 56-67; asst prof, 67-73, assoc prof, 73-78, chmn dept, 72-80, PROF CHEM, RIDER COL, 79- *Mem:* Am Chem Soc. *Res:* Inorganic solid state; crystal structures; photoelectronic materials; transition metal oxides in low valence states; oxides with metal atom clusters. *Mailing Add:* Dept of Chem Rider Col Lawrenceville NJ 08648

MCCARRON, MARGARET MARY, b Chicago, Ill. INTERNAL MEDICINE, PHARMACY. *Educ:* St Xavier Col, Ill, BA, 50; Loyola Univ Chicago, MD, 54. *Prof Exp:* Asst prof, 60-68, assoc prof pharm, 68-76, ASSOC PROF MED, UNIV SOUTHERN CALIF, 60-; ASST MED DIR, LOS ANGELES COUNTY-UNIV SOUTHERN CALIF MED CTR, 62- *Concurrent Pos:* NIH fel diabetes, Univ Southern Calif, 58-59; consult, Vet Admin & Indian Health Serv; consult task force on prescription drugs, Dept Health, Educ & Welfare, consult rev comt task force on drugs; consult comt rev, US Pharmacopeia; consult task force on role of pharmacist, Nat Ctr Health Serv Res & Develop. *Honors & Awards:* Dart Award, Univ Southern Calif, 70. *Mem:* AMA; Am Col Physicians; Am Soc Clin Pharmacol & Chemother; Am Asn Cols Pharm; Am Pharmaceut Asn. *Mailing Add:* Dept of Med & Pharmacol Univ of Southern Calif Sch of Med Los Angeles CA 90033

MCCART, BRUCE RONALD, b Omaha, Nebr, Dec 21, 38; m 61; c 4. PHYSICS. *Educ:* Carleton Col, BA, 60; Iowa State Univ, PhD(physics), 65. *Prof Exp:* From asst prof to assoc prof, 65-79, assoc dean & dir instnl res, 70-76, PROF PHYSICS, AUGUSTANA COL, ILL, 79- *Mem:* Am Phys Soc; Sigma Xi. *Res:* Nuclear magnetic resonance in solids; x-ray studies of liquid crystals; optimal structural design. *Mailing Add:* Dept of Physics Augustana Col Rock Island IL 61201

MCCARTAN, LUCY, b Miami, Fla, Oct 4, 42. GEOLOGY, SEDIMENTOLOGY. *Educ:* Occidental Col, BA, 65; Lehigh Univ, MS, 67, PhD(geol), 72. *Prof Exp:* GEOLOGIST STRATIG, US GEOL SURV, 75- *Mem:* Soc Econ Mineral & Paleontologists. *Res:* Mapping and environmental interpretation of Southeastern United States coastal plain sediments (Cretaceous to Holocene); mapping and structural interpretation of Triassic and Permian sedimentary rocks in New Zealand. *Mailing Add:* US Geol Surv 926 Reston VA 22092

MCCARTER, JOHN ALEXANDER, b Eng, Jan 25, 18; nat Can; m 41; c 4. VIROLOGY. *Educ:* Univ BC, BA, 39, MA, 41; Univ Toronto, PhD(biochem), 45. *Prof Exp:* Asst res officer, Nat Res Coun Can, 45-48; from assoc prof to prof biochem, Dalhousie Univ, 48-65; prof biochem & dir cancer res, Univ Western Ont, 65-80; PROF BIOCHEM & MICROBIOL, UNIV VICTORIA, 80- *Concurrent Pos:* Brit Empire Cancer Campaign fel, 59-60. *Mem:* Can Biochem Soc; Royal Soc Can. *Res:* Carcinogenesis. *Mailing Add:* Univ Victoria PO Box 1700 Victoria BC V8W 2Y2 Can

MCCARTER, ROGER JOHN MOORE, b Bloemfontein, SAfrica, Feb 18, 41; US citizen; m 70; c 1. PHYSIOLOGY, BIOPHYSICS. *Educ:* Univ Witwatersrand, BSc Hons, 64, MSc, 65; Med Col Va, PhD(physiol), 68. *Prof Exp:* Lectr physiol & physics, Univ Witwatersrand, 70-72; asst prof, 72-76, ASSOC PROF PHYSIOL, UNIV TEX HEALTH SCI CTR, 77- *Concurrent Pos:* Can Med Res fel, Univ Western Ont, 68-69; co-investr NIH grants aging & nutrit, Univ Tex Med Sch, San Antonio, 74-78, prin investr aging of skeletal muscle, 79- *Mem:* Geront Soc; Am Physiol Soc; SAfrican Inst Physics. *Res:* Aging process in skeletal muscle; biophysics of muscular contraction. *Mailing Add:* Dept of Physiol Univ of Tex Health Sci Ctr San Antonio TX 78284

MCCARTER, STATES MARION, b Clover, SC, Sept 30, 37; m 63; c 2. PLANT PATHOLOGY, PHYTOBACTERIOLOGY. *Educ:* Clemson Univ, BS, 59, MS, 61, PhD(plant path), 65. *Prof Exp:* Exten plant pathologist & nematologist, Auburn Univ, 65-66; res plant pathologist, Ga Coastal Plain Exp Sta, Agr Res Serv, USDA, 66-68; asst prof, 68-72, assoc prof, 72-78, PROF PLANT PATH, UNIV GA, 78- *Mem:* Am Phytopath Soc. *Res:* bacterial diseases of plants. *Mailing Add:* Dept Plant Path & Plant Genetics Col Agr Univ Ga Athens GA 30602

MCCARTHY, BRIAN JOHN, b London, Eng, Mar 27, 34; m 58; c 4. MICROBIOLOGY, MOLECULAR BIOLOGY. *Educ:* Oxford Univ, BA, 55, MA & DPhil(chem), 58. *Prof Exp:* Fel microbiol, Carnegie Inst Dept Terrestrial Magnetism, 58-60, staff mem, 60-64; assoc prof microbiol & genetics, Univ Wash, 64-69, prof, 69-72; prof biochem, Univ Calif, San Francisco, 72-81; PROF MOLECULAR BIOL & BIOCHEM, UNIV CALIF, IRVINE, 81- *Honors & Awards:* Eli Lilly Award Microbiol & Immunol, 68. *Res:* Chemistry of biology of nucleic acids; evolution and development at the molecular level. *Mailing Add:* Dept Molecular Biol & Biochem Univ of Calif Irvine CA 92717

MCCARTHY, CHARLES ALAN, b Rochester, NY, Aug 7, 36; m 57; c 3. MATHEMATICAL ANALYSIS. *Educ:* Univ Rochester, BA, 56; Yale Univ, PhD(math), 59. *Prof Exp:* CLE Moore instr math, Mass Inst Technol, 59-61; from asst prof to assoc prof, 61-67, PROF MATH, UNIV MINN, MINNEAPOLIS, 67- *Concurrent Pos:* Alfred P Sloan Res Found fel, 62-64. *Mem:* Am Math Soc; Math Asn Am. *Res:* Functional analysis, especially the theory of operators. *Mailing Add:* Sch Math Univ Minn Minneapolis MN 55455

MCCARTHY, CHARLOTTE MARIE, b Watford City, NDak, Sept 7, 37. MICROBIOLOGY. *Educ:* Idaho State Univ, BS, 58; Ore State Univ, MS, 61; Univ Wash, PhD(microbiol), 67. *Prof Exp:* Res microbiologist, Nat Jewish Hosp & Res Ctr, Denver, 68-71; asst prof, 72-75, ASSOC PROF BIOL, N MEX STATE UNIV, 76- *Concurrent Pos:* NIH res grants, 70-76 & 78-84. *Mem:* Am Soc Microbiol; AAAS. *Res:* Physiology of pathogenic bacteria, particularly mycobacteria which are drug-resistant. *Mailing Add:* Dept Biol Box 3AF NMex State Univ Las Cruces NM 88003

MCCARTHY, DENNIS DEAN, b Oil City, Pa, Sept 22, 42; m 66; c 2. ASTRONOMY. *Educ:* Case Inst Technol, BS, 64; Univ Va, MA, 70, PhD(astron), 72. *Prof Exp:* ASTRONR, US NAVAL OBSERV, WASHINGTON, DC, 65- *Mem:* Am Astron Soc; Am Geophys Union. *Res:* Astronomical research into rotational speed of the Earth; variation of astronomical latitude; precise star positions and proper motions; fundamental astronomical constants. *Mailing Add:* US Naval Observ 34th & Massachusetts Aves NW Washington DC 20390

MCCARTHY, DENNIS JOSEPH, b Syracuse, NY, Oct 10, 53; m 80. BIOLOGY. *Educ:* State Univ NY at Oswego, BA, 75, Syracuse Univ, PhD(biol), 81. *Prof Exp:* RES BIOCHEMIST, SOUTHERN RES INST, 81- *Mem:* Am Chem Soc. *Res:* Isolation and identification of drug metabolites including synthesis of proposed metabolites; identification of organic compounds using mass spectroscopy, infrared spectroscopy, and nuclear magnetic resonance spectroscopy; high-pressure liquid chromatogrphy and gas chromatography. *Mailing Add:* Southern Res Inst PO Box 3307-A Birmingham AL 35255

MCCARTHY, DONALD JOHN, b New York, NY, Dec 22, 38; m 63; c 4. ALGEBRA. *Educ:* Manhattan Col, BS, 61; NY Univ, MS, 63, PhD(math), 65. *Prof Exp:* Asst prof math, Fordham Univ, 65-70; asst prof, 70-72, ASSOC PROF MATH, ST JOHN'S UNIV, NY, 72- *Mem:* Am Math Soc; Soc Indust & Appl Math; NY Acad Sci; Parapsychol Asn; Math Asn Am. *Res:* Group theory; general algebra; parapsychology; combinatorial mathematics. *Mailing Add:* Dept of Math & Comput Sci St John's Univ Jamaica NY 11439

MCCARTHY, DOUGLAS ROBERT, b New York, NY, July 10, 43; m 64; c 1. MATHEMATICS. *Educ:* Rensselaer Polytech Inst, BS, 64; Rutgers Univ, MS, 66, PhD(math), 70. *Prof Exp:* Asst prof math, Purdue Univ, Ft Wayne, 69-75, assoc prof math, 75-80, VIS ASSOC PROF, PURDUE UNIV, WEST LAFAYETTE, 80- *Concurrent Pos:* Res analyst, Boeing Com Airplane Co, 78-79. *Mem:* Am Math Soc; Math Asn Am; Soc Indust & Appl Math. *Res:* Nonlinear existence theory in differential equations; topological degree; optimization; numerical solution of partial differential equations; control theory; differential games. *Mailing Add:* Comput Sci Dept Purdue Univ West Lafayette IN 47907

MCCARTHY, EUGENE GREGORY, b Boston, Mass, Nov 8, 34; m 58; c 3. PUBLIC HEALTH. *Educ:* Boston Col, AB, 56; Yale Univ, MD, 60; Johns Hopkins Univ, MPH, 62. *Hon Degrees:* Dr, Univ Asuncion, Paraguay, 64. *Prof Exp:* Asst prof pub health, Med Sch, Columbia Univ, 65-69; assoc prof, 70-78, CLIN PROF PUB HEALTH, MED SCH, CORNELL UNIV, 78- *Concurrent Pos:* Consult health, AID, Dept State, 64-67, US Social Security Admin, 65-68, Roman Catholic Diocese, Brooklyn, 65-69, Catholic Hosp Asn US & Can, 66-69, Roman Catholic Archdiocese New York, 66-70, Mercy Catholic Med Ctr, 66-78, Tufts Med Sch, 69-70, City New York, 75-78, Gen Motors, Ford, Chrysler and United Auto Workers, 76- & Off Health Serv Res, HEW, 79-; vis prof, Med Sch, Johns Hopkins Univ, 79. *Honors & Awards:* Eisenberg lectr, Peter Bent Brigham Hosp, Harvard Med Sch, 76. *Mem:* Am Fedn Clin Investrs; NY Acad Med; Am Pub Health Asn. *Res:* Delivery of health services; surgical health care; established second opinion elective surgical consultations as a medical care instrument for improvement in quality of care and reduction of in-hospital elective surgery. *Mailing Add:* Dept Pub Health Cornell Univ Med Sch New York NY 10021

MCCARTHY, FRANCIS DAVEY, b Sioux City, Iowa, Apr 30, 43; m 68; c 1. BIOLOGICAL OCEANOGRAPHY. *Educ:* Marquette Univ, BS, 68; Tex A&M Univ, PhD(biol oceanog), 73. *Prof Exp:* Asst prof, 73-78, ASSOC PROF BIOL SCI, CALIF STATE COL, DOMINGUEZ HILLS, 78- *Mailing Add:* Dept Biol Sci Calif State Col 1000 E Victoria St Dominguez Hills CA 90747

MCCARTHY, FRANCIS DESMOND, b Cork, Ireland, Dec 2, 36. ELECTRICAL ENGINEERING. *Educ:* Univ Col Cork, BE, 58; NY Univ, MEE, 63, PhD(elec eng), 66. *Prof Exp:* Grad appt, Gen Elec Co Ltd, 58-60, design standards engr, 60-61; teaching fel & res assoc elec eng, NY Univ, 62-66; staff scientist, Draper Lab, Mass Inst Technol, 66-69; asst prof elec eng, 69-76, ASSOC PROF ELEC ENG, NORTHEASTERN UNIV, 76- *Concurrent Pos:* Adj lectr, Northeastern Univ, 68-69; staff scientist, Draper Lab, Mass Inst Technol, 69- *Mem:* Brit Inst Elec Engrs. *Res:* Statistical analysis; data reduction; control systems; gyrators; mathematical modeling of physical processes. *Mailing Add:* Dept of Elec Eng Northeastern Univ Boston MA 02115

MCCARTHY, FRANK JOHN, b Mt Carmel, Pa, Mar 7, 28; m 51; c 3. MICROBIOLOGY. *Educ:* Mt St Mary's Col, Md, BS, 49; Fordham Univ, MS, 51; Lehigh Univ, PhD(biol), 60. *Prof Exp:* Asst biol, Fordham Univ, 49-51; res assoc, Merck Inst Therapeut Res, 53-63; mgr virus prods, 63-75, ASSOC DIR BIOL PRODS, WYETH LABS, INC, 75- *Mem:* Am Soc Microbiol; Tissue Cult Asn; NY Acad Sci. *Res:* Viral and bacterial vaccines; tissue culture; cytogenetics; anti-viral and anti-tumor agents; purification of virus and bacterial products. *Mailing Add:* Wyeth Labs Inc Marietta PA 17547

MCCARTHY, FRANK MARTIN, b Olean, NY, Aug 27, 24; m 49; c 2. DENTISTRY, ANESTHESIOLOGY. *Educ:* Univ Pittsburgh, BS, 44, DDS, 45, MD, 49; Georgetown Univ, MS, 54. *Hon Degrees:* ScD, St Bonaventure Univ, 56. *Prof Exp:* Instr oral surg, 57-66, clin prof, 66-75, assoc dean admin affairs, 76-80, PROF ANESTHESIA & MED, SCH DENT, UNIV SOUTHERN CALIF, 75-, ASST DEAN HOSP AFFAIRS, 80- *Concurrent Pos:* Am Fire Protection Asn, 72-80; mem ad hoc comt res in pain, Nat Inst Dent Res, 71; active mem sci rev panel, Am Pharmaceut Asn, 71-80; ed anesthesia sect, J Oral Surg, Am Dent Asn, 72-81; consult anesthesiol, Coun Dent Therapeut, 73- & Coun Dent Mat & Devices, 74-80; consult, Calif Select Comt Med Malpract, 73-75; mem comt MD-156, Am Nat Standards Inst, 74- *Honors & Awards:* Heidbrink Award, Am Dent Soc Anesthesiol, 77. *Mem:* Am Soc Oral Surgeons; Am Dent Soc Anesthesiol; fel Int Asn Oral Surgeons; Am Soc Advan Anesthesia Dent; Int Anesthesia Res Soc. *Res:* Pain/anxiety control, physical evaluation and emergency medicine in dentistry. *Mailing Add:* Univ Southern Calif Sch Dent PO Box 77951 Los Angeles CA 90007

MCCARTHY, GERALD T(IMOTHY), b Dover, NJ, May 5, 09; m 35; c 2. CIVIL ENGINEERING. *Educ:* Pa State Univ, BS, 30. *Prof Exp:* Student engr & construct inspector, Standard Oil Co, NJ, 30-31; from jr engr to sr engr flood control, power & navig projs, US Eng Corps, 31-38; spec partner for Latin Am, Parsons, Brinckerhoff, Hogan & MacDonald, NY, 38-47; PARTNER, TIPPETTS-ABBETT-McCARTHY-STRATTON, 47- *Concurrent Pos:* Dir, Far East-Am Coun Commerce & Indust; past pres, Int Comn Large Dams; past chmn, US Comt Large Dams; dir, Int Rd Fedn. *Mem:* Nat Acad Eng; hon mem Am Soc Civil Engrs; Soc Am Mil Engrs; Nat Soc Prof Engrs; Am Inst Consult Engrs (past pres). *Mailing Add:* 94 Colt Rd Summit NJ 07901

MCCARTHY, GREGORY JOSEPH, b Waltham, Mass, Apr 6, 43; m 67; c 2. SOLID STATE CHEMISTRY, X-RAY CRYSTALLOGRAPHY. *Educ:* Boston Col, BS, 64; Pa State Univ, PhD(solid state sci), 69. *Prof Exp:* Asst prof solid state sci, Pa State Univ, 69-74, sr res assoc solid state chem, 74-78, assoc prof mat res, 78-80; MEM FAC CHEM, NDAK STATE UNIV, 80- *Concurrent Pos:* Dir & chmn tech comt, Joint Comt Powder Diffraction Stand, Int Ctr Diffraction Data, 73- *Mem:* Am Chem Soc; Am Crystallog Asn; Am Ceramic Soc; AAAS; Mineral Soc Am. *Res:* Crystal chemistry, phase equilibria and geochemistry of rare earths; transition metal oxide systems; nuclear waste solidification and geologic isolation. *Mailing Add:* Chem Dept NDak State Univ Fargo ND 58102

MCCARTHY, JAMES FRANCIS, b Sharon, Pa, Apr 29, 14; m 47; c 3. ORGANIC CHEMISTRY. *Educ:* Grove City Col, BS, 35. *Prof Exp:* Chemist, Sharon Steel Corp, 35-37; res fel biochem, Mellon Inst, 38-42; dir res spec textile finishes, Treesdale Labs, Inc & Pittsburgh Metals Purifying Co, 42-70, DIR RES & DEVELOP, TREESDALE, INC, PITTSBURGH METALS PURIFYING CO, 70- *Mem:* Am Chem Soc; fel Am Inst Chem; Am Soc Testing & Mat. *Res:* Durable flame proofing; special finishes for textiles; fluxes and exothermic compounds for metals industries; exothermic reactions; high temperature insulation. *Mailing Add:* Treesdale Inc Box 337 Saxonburg PA 16056

MCCARTHY, JAMES JOSEPH, b Ashland, Ore, Jan 25, 44; m 69; c 2. BIOLOGICAL OCEANOGRAPHY. *Educ:* Gonzaga Univ, BS, 66; Scripps Inst Oceanog, Univ Calif, San Diego, PhD(biol oceanog), 71. *Prof Exp:* Res assoc biol oceanog, Chesapeake Bay Inst, Johns Hopkins Univ, 71-72, assoc res scientist, 72-74; asst prof, 74-77, assoc prof, 77-80, PROF BIOL OCEANOG, HARVARD UNIV, 80- *Mem:* AAAS; Phycol Soc Am; Sigma Xi; Am Soc Limnol & Oceanog. *Res:* Investigation of the recycling of aquatic plant nutrients employing isotopic techniques to quantitate the rate of flux of elemental material via various processes within planktonic ecosystems. *Mailing Add:* Mus Comp Zool Harvard Univ Cambridge MA 03138

MCCARTHY, JAMES RAY, b Bronx, NY, Dec 16, 43; m 67, 77; c 2. ORGANIC CHEMISTRY. *Educ:* Ariz State Univ, BS, 65; Univ Utah, PhD(org chem), 69. *Prof Exp:* RES CHEMIST, DOW CHEM USA, 68- *Concurrent Pos:* Adj prof, Dept Chem, Ind Univ-Purdue Univ, Indianapolis. *Mem:* Am Chem Soc. *Res:* Organic synthesis in the area of natural products and biologically active compounds. *Mailing Add:* 1100 Maxwell Lane Zionsville IN 46077

MACCARTHY, JEAN JULIET, b Rathcoole, Ireland. CELL BIOLOGY. *Educ:* Nat Univ, Ireland, BSc, 63, MSc, 64; Univ Md, PhD(plant physiol), 72. *Prof Exp:* Fel plant tissue, Nat Res Coun Can, 73-75; res assoc, Bot Lab, Univ Leicester, Eng, 75-77; res biochemist, Dept Biochem & Biophys, Univ Calif, Davis, 77-80; RES SPECIALIST PLANT TISSUE CULTURES, COL PHARM HEALTH SCI, UNIV MINN, 80- *Mem:* Int Asn Plant Tissue Culture; Sigma Xi. *Res:* Plant cell and tissue culture; lipid biosynthesis and secondary product metabolism; steroidal glycoside production and biosynthesis; algal physiology. *Mailing Add:* Dept Pharmaceut Cell Biol Col Pharm Health Sci Unit F Univ Minn Minneapolis MN 55455

MCCARTHY, JOHN, b Boston, Mass, Sept 4, 27; m 54; c 2. COMPUTER SCIENCE. *Educ:* Calif Inst Technol, BS, 48; Princeton Univ, PhD(math), 51. *Prof Exp:* Res instr math, Princeton Univ, 51-53; actg asst prof, Stanford Univ, 53-55; asst prof, Dartmouth Col, 55-58; from asst prof to assoc prof commun sci, Mass Inst Technol, 58-61; PROF COMPUT SCI, STANFORD UNIV, 62-, DIR ARTIFICIAL INTEL LAB, 66- *Honors & Awards:* A M Turing Award, Asn Comput Mach, 71. *Mem:* Am Math Soc; Asn Comput Mach. *Res:* Programming languages; time-sharing; mathematical theory of computation; artificial intelligence. *Mailing Add:* Dept of Comput Sci Stanford Univ Stanford CA 94305

MCCARTHY, JOHN, b New Orleans, La, July 3, 42. METEOROLOGY. *Educ:* Grinnell Col, BA, 64; Univ Okla, MS, 67; Univ Chicago, PhD(geophys sci), 73. *Prof Exp:* Res meteorologist, Weather Sci, Inc, 66-67 & Cloud Physics Lab, Univ Chicago, 67-68; asst prof meteorol, Univ Okla, 73-78; assoc prof, 78-80, STAFF SCIENTIST, NAT CTR FOR ATMOSPHERIC RES, 80- *Concurrent Pos:* Mem, Univ Rels Comt, Univ Corp Atmospheric Res, 74- *Mem:* Am Meteorol Soc; Sigma Xi. *Res:* Radar and aircraft studies of severe thunderstorms and tornadoes; source of thunderstorm rotation; applied aircraft hazards near thunderstorms; weather modification. *Mailing Add:* Nat Ctr Atmospheric Res PO Box 3000 Balder CO 80307

MCCARTHY, JOHN F(RANCIS), b St Louis, Mo, May 5, 20; m 56; c 4. CIVIL ENGINEERING. *Educ:* Univ Mo-Rolla, BS, 48, MS, 50. *Prof Exp:* Instr civil eng, Mo Sch Mines, 48-51; chief struct engr, Fruin-Colnon Contracting Co, 51-53 & W R Bendy, Cement Engrs, 53-55; from asst prof to prof civil eng, St Louis Univ, 55-69, dir dept, 56-69; supt, Bissell Point, 69-76, TECH COORDR, METROP ST LOUIS SEWER DIST, 76- *Concurrent Pos:* Chmn bldg code rev comt, St Louis County, 62- *Mem:* Am Soc Civil Engrs; Nat Soc Prof Engrs; Am Soc Eng Educ; Water Pollution Control Fedn. *Res:* Structural engineering. *Mailing Add:* Metrop St Louis Sewer Dist 9200 S Broadway St Louis MO 63125

MCCARTHY, JOHN F, b New York, NY, June 16, 47; m 69; c 1. ENVIRONMENTAL SCIENCES. *Educ:* Fordham Univ, NY, BS, 69; Univ RI, PhD(oceanog), 74. *Prof Exp:* Fel, Biol Div, 75-78, res assoc, 78-80, RES ASSOC, ENVIRON SCI DIV, OAK RIDGE NAT LAB, 80- *Mem:* Sigma Xi; Am Soc Zoologists; AAAS. *Res:* Aquatic ecology and toxicology; uptake and metabolism of organic pollutants by aquatic organisms; fate and transport of organic contaminants in water; crustacean endocrinology and development. *Mailing Add:* Environ Sci Div Oak Ridge Nat Lab PO Box X Oak Ridge TN 37830

MCCARTHY, JOHN FRANCIS, JR, b Boston, Mass, Aug 28, 25; m 68; c 3. AEROSPACE SYSTEMS. *Educ:* Mass Inst Technol, SB, 50, SM, 51; Calif Inst Technol, PhD(aeronaut, physics), 62. *Prof Exp:* Supvr air-ground commun, Trans World Airlines, Rome, 46-47; proj mgr, Aeroelastic & Struct Res Lab, Mass Inst Technol, 51-55; opers analyst, hq, Strategic Air Command, Offutt AFB, Nebr, 55-58; res asst & consult aeronaut, Calif Inst Technol, 58-62; asst chief engr, Apollo & dir Apollo technol, N Am Aviation, Inc, Calif, 62-63, dir Apollo control systs, 63-65, div dir aerospace sci & vpres res & eng, 65-67, vpres res, Eng & Test Space Div, N Am Rockwell Corp, 67-68, vpres res & eng, N Am Aviation Div Off, 68-69, exec vpres technol, Los Angeles Div, 69-70, vpres res & eng, 70, vpres systs eng, 70-71; prof aeronaut & astronaut, Mass Inst Technol, 71-78, dir, Ctr Space Res, 74-78; DIR, LEWIS RES CTR, NASA, CLEVELAND, 78- *Concurrent Pos:* Prin scientist, Space & Info Systs Div, N Am Aviation, Inc, 61-62; mem res adv comt space vehicle aerodyn, NASA, 65-67; spec adv, Aeronaut Systs Div, US Air Force, 69-71, chmn, 71-78, mem sci adv bd, 70-; consult, Off Secy Defense, 76-77; mem, Joint Chiefs of Staff, Joint Strategic Planning Staff, Sci Adv Group, 76-; mem, Fed Exec Bd, Cleveland, 78- *Honors & Awards:* Apollo Achievement Award, NASA, 69. *Mem:* Fel Am Inst Aeronaut & Astronaut; assoc fel Royal Aeronaut Soc; Sigma Xi; Am Mgt Asn; Am Soc Eng Educ. *Res:* Aerospace systems; engineering management; entry vehicles; hypersonic wakes; supersonic flutter; aeroelasticity; vehicle dynamics. *Mailing Add:* NASA Lewis Res Ctr 21000 Brookpark Rd Cleveland OH 44135

MCCARTHY, JOHN JOSEPH, b Troy, NY, June 24, 23; m 48; c 1. PHYSICAL METALLURGY. *Educ:* Rensselaer Polytech Inst, BMetE, 48, MMetE, 51, PhD(metall), 58. *Prof Exp:* From instr to asst prof, 48-60, ASSOC PROF METALL ENG, RENSSELAER POLYTECH INST, 60-, EXEC OFFICER, DEPT MAT ENG, 76- *Mem:* Am Soc Metals; Am Welding Soc. *Res:* Welding, brazing and mechanical property determinations. *Mailing Add:* Mat Div Mat Res Ctr Rensselaer Polytech Inst Troy NY 12181

MCCARTHY, JOHN LAWRENCE, JR, b New Haven, Conn, Aug 13, 29; m 55; c 2. PHYSIOLOGICAL CHEMISTRY. *Educ:* Univ Miami, Fla, BS, 51; Purdue Univ, MA, 53, PhD(endocrinol), 58. *Prof Exp:* From asst prof to assoc prof biol, 58-69, PROF BIOL, SOUTHERN METHODIST UNIV, 69- *Concurrent Pos:* NIH fel, 64-65; vis prof biochem, Univ Edinburgh, 72; bd dir, Oak Ridge Assoc Univ, 81-84. *Mem:* AAAS; Am Soc Zool; Soc Exp Biol Med; Am Physiol Soc; Endocrine Soc. *Res:* Physiological and chemical relationship between the thyroid and adrenal glands; adrenal steroid biosynthesis; steroid metabolism. *Mailing Add:* Dept of Biol Southern Methodist Univ Dallas TX 75275

MCCARTHY, JOHN RANDOLPH, b Huntington, WVa, Mar 1, 15; m 49. ORGANIC CHEMISTRY. *Educ:* Columbia Univ, PhD(chem), 49. *Prof Exp:* Anal chemist, Stand Ultramarine Co, 39-41; res chemist, Del, 49-74, SUPVR, MED LAB, CHAMBERS WORKS, E I DU PONT DE NEMOURS & CO, DEEPWATER, NJ, 74- *Mem:* Am Chem Soc. *Res:* Process control; elastomers; petroleum; dyes and intermediates; urine and blood analyses for biological monitoring of workplace exposure. *Mailing Add:* 230 Meredith St Kennett Square PA 19348

MCCARTHY, JOSEPH L(EPAGE), b Spokane, Wash, Oct 19, 13; m 45; c 2. CHEMICAL ENGINEERING, WOOD CHEMISTRY. *Educ:* Univ Wash, Seattle, BS, 34; Univ Idaho, MS, 36; McGill Univ, PhD(chem), 38. *Prof Exp:* Sessional lectr & res fel, McGill Univ, 38-40; dir res, Fraser Cos, Ltd, 40-41; res assoc chem, 41-42, from instr to assoc prof, 42-52, prin investr, Pulp Mills Res, 44-74, dean, Grad Sch, 59-74, PROF CHEM ENG, UNIV WASH, 52-, PROF FOREST RESOURCES, 78-, EMER DEAN, GRAD SCH, 74- *Honors & Awards:* Johan Richter Prize, 78. *Mem:* Am Soc Eng Educ; Tech Asn Pulp & Paper Indust: Am Inst Chem Engrs; Can Pulp & Paper Asn; fel Int Acad Wood Sci. *Res:* Wood chemistry, lignin, cellulose, pulp and paper; chemical engineering thermodynamics; lignin and cellulose chemistry; thermodynamics; biochemical engineering. *Mailing Add:* Dept of Chem Eng BF-10 Univ of Wash Seattle WA 98195

MCCARTHY, KATHRYN AGNES, b Lawrence, Mass, Aug 7, 24. SOLID STATE PHYSICS. *Educ:* Tufts Univ, AB, 44, MS, 46; Radcliffe Col, PhD(appl physics), 57. *Prof Exp:* Asst physics, 45-46, instr, 46-53, from asst prof to assoc prof, 57-62, actg chmn dept, 61-62, dean grad sch arts & sci, 69-73; provost/sr vpres, 73-79, PROF PHYSICS, TUFTS UNIV, 62- *Concurrent Pos:* Res physicist, Baird Assocs, Inc, 47-49 & 51; res fel phys metall, Harvard Univ, 57-59, vis scholar, 79-80; assoc res engr & res consult, Univ Mich, 57-59; dir, Doble Eng Co, 67-70; dir, Mass Elec Co, 73- & State Mutual Assurance, 76- mem exec bd, New Eng Conf Grad Educ, 70-74; mem comn inst higher educ, New Eng Asn Cols & Sec Schs, Inc, 72-77, vchmn, 73-74, chmn, 74-77, mem comt disadvantaged students, Coun Grad Schs, 72-74, mem exec comt, 73-75; mem comn inst affairs, Asn Am Cols, 73-; mem grad adv acad comt, Bd High Educ Mass, 72-74; mem comn admin affairs & educ statist, Am Coun Educ, 73-; trustee, Southern Mass Univ, 72-74, Merrimack Col, 74- & Col Holy Cross, 80-; mem bd dir, Lawrence Mem Hosp, Medford, 77- *Mem:* Fel Am Phys Soc; fel Optical Soc Am; sr mem Soc Women Engrs. *Res:* Low-temperature thermal conductivity; color centers in alkali halides; ultrasonic attenuation in solids. *Mailing Add:* Dept Physics Tufts Univ Medford MA 02155

MCCARTHY, MARTIN, b Lowell, Mass, July 10, 23. ASTRONOMY. *Educ:* Boston Col, AB, 46, MA, 47; Georgetown Univ, PhD(astron), 51; Weston Col, STL, 55. *Prof Exp:* MEM STAFF ASTRON, VATICAN OBSERV, 56- *Concurrent Pos:* Vis prof, Georgetown Univ, 62-63; guest investr, Carnegie Inst, 65-66, 71, 73 & 74; observ consult, Cerro Tololo Interam Observ, Asn Univs Res in Astron, 72 & consult adv, 74; observer for Vatican City State at World Meteorol Orgn, 80. *Mem:* AAAS; Royal Astron Soc; Sigma Xi; Int Astron Union. *Res:* Spectral classification of stars; galactic structure; photoelectric and photographic photometry. *Mailing Add:* Vatican Observ Castle Gandolfo 00040 Rome Italy

MCCARTHY, MARY ANNE, b Tarentum, Pa, May 26, 39; div. NUMERICAL ANALYSIS, SYSTEM ANALYSIS. *Educ:* Wellesley Col, BA, 61; Rice Univ, MA, 66, PhD(math sci), 73. *Prof Exp:* Comput programmer, Bell Tel Labs Inc, 61-63; physicist, Shell Develop Co, Shell Oil Co, 67-69; assoc syst analyst, Lulejian & Assoc Inc, 73-75; researcher, R & D Assoc Inc, 75-81; VPRES, PARAGON SOFTWARE INC, 81- *Mem:* Am Math Soc; Asn for Women in Math; Soc Indust & Appl Math; Sigma Xi. *Res:* Development of a mathematical method which yields closed form solutions to various types of probabilistic problems which previously have required Monte Carlo simulation. *Mailing Add:* 2706 Pine Ave Manhatten Beach CA 90266

MCCARTHY, MILES DUFFIELD, b Camden, NJ, Oct 12, 14; m 59. REPRODUCTIVE BIOLOGY. *Educ:* Pa State Teachers Col, BS, 36; Univ Pa, PhD(zool), 43. *Prof Exp:* Asst, Inst Med Res, Pa, 37-39; instr zool, Univ Pa, 39-42, tech assoc, Med Sch, 42, instr vert anat, Univ, 44-45, genetics, Vet Sch, 45-46; asst prof zool, Pomona Col, 46-49, from assoc prof to prof, 49-59; vpres acad affairs, 70-74, chmn div sci & math, 59-64, dean sch letters, arts & sci, 64-70, actg pres, 81, PROF BIOL, CALIF STATE UNIV, FULLERTON, 59- *Concurrent Pos:* Harrison res fel, Med Sch, Univ Pa, 44-46, vis asst prof, 51-52; responsible investr, US Dept Army contract, Pomona Col, 54-56; NIH fel, 57-61. *Mem:* AAAS; Soc Exp Biol & Med; Am Physiol Soc. *Res:* Growth and development; burn shock and infusion fluids; hemolytic and hematopoietic changes in relation to survival following severe thermal injury; reproduction and human sexuality. *Mailing Add:* Dept of Biol Calif State Univ Fullerton CA 92634

MCCARTHY, NEIL JUSTIN, JR, b Chicago, Ill, Oct 25, 39; m 63; c 2. ORGANIC POLYMER CHEMISTRY. *Educ:* Georgetown Univ, BS, 62; Cornell Univ, PhD(org chem), 69. *Prof Exp:* Res chemist, Res Lab & Develop Lab, Union Carbide Corp, Bound Brook, 66-76, proj scientist org polymer chem, 71-76, financial analyst specialty chem, 76-80, MARKET MGR, EPOXIES & PLASTICIZERS, UNION CARBIDE CORP, 80- *Mem:* Am Chem Soc; Soc Plastics Engrs. *Res:* Physical-organic and physical polymer chemistry and composite science; specialty chemicals. *Mailing Add:* Union Carbide Corp Old Ridgebury Rd Danbury CT 06817

MACCARTHY, PATRICK, b Galway, Ireland, Jan 13, 46; m 72; c 4. ANALYTICAL CHEMISTRY, SOIL CHEMISTRY. *Educ:* Univ Col Galway, Ireland, BSc, 68, MSc, 71; Northwestern Univ, MS, 71; Univ Cincinnati, PhD(anal chem), 75. *Prof Exp:* Vis lectr anal chem, Univ Ga, 75-76; asst prof chem, 76-79, ASSOC PROF CHEM & GEOCHEM, COLO SCH MINES, 79- *Concurrent Pos:* Chmn, Humic Acid Working Group, Int Soc Soil Sci. *Mem:* Int Humic Substances Soc (secy-treas); Am Chem Soc; Soil Sci Soc Am; Int Soc Soil Sci. *Res:* Metal complexation by humic substances; chemistry of humic substances; use of chemically modified peat for removal of pollutants; mathematical modeling and computer simulation of multimetal-multiligand equilibrium; analytical chemistry. *Mailing Add:* Dept of Chem & Geochem Colo Sch of Mines Golden CO 80401

MCCARTHY, PATRICK CHARLES, b Cadillac, Mich, Mar 27, 40; m 66; c 3. GENETICS. *Educ:* Wayne State Univ, BS, 65, MS, 66, PhD(biol), 70. *Prof Exp:* Instr, Wayne State Univ, 68-70; asst prof, 70-76, ASSOC PROF BIOL, WESTMINSTER COL, 76- *Concurrent Pos:* J S Mack Found researcher, Westminster Col, 71-72. *Mem:* AAAS; Inst Soc, Ethics & Life Sci. *Res:* Physiology and genetics of tissue proteins in the Mongolian gerbil, Meriones unguiculatus. *Mailing Add:* Dept of Biol Westminster Col New Wilmington PA 16142

MCCARTHY, PAUL JAMES, b Rochester, NY, June 15, 24. PHYSICAL INORGANIC CHEMISTRY. *Educ:* Spring Hill Col, AB, 5O; Col of Holy Cross, MS, 52; Clark Univ, PhD(chem), 55. *Prof Exp:* Instr high sch, NY, 50-51; instr chem, St Peters Col, 59-60; instr, 60-62, from asst prof to assoc prof, 62-72, PROF CHEM, CANISIUS COL, 72- *Concurrent Pos:* NATO fel, Copenhagen Univ, 66-67. *Mem:* AAAS; Am Chem Soc; The Chem Soc. *Res:* Coordination complexes, especially their preparation, structure and absorption spectra. *Mailing Add:* Dept of Chem Canisius Col 2001 Main St Buffalo NY 14208

MCCARTHY, PAUL JOSEPH, b Chicago, Ill, Oct 23, 28; m 52; c 2. MATHEMATICS. *Educ:* Univ Notre Dame, BS, 50, MS, 52, PhD(math), 55. *Prof Exp:* Instr math, Univ Notre Dame, 54-55; instr, Col Holy Cross, 55-56; from asst prof to assoc prof, Fla State Univ, 56-61; assoc prof, 61-65, PROF MATH, UNIV KANS, 65- *Mem:* Am Math Soc; Math Asn Am. *Res:* Rings; graph theory; number theory. *Mailing Add:* Dept of Math Univ of Kans Lawrence KS 66045

MCCARTHY, PHILIP JOHN, b Friendship, NY, Feb 9, 18; m 42; c 4. STATISTICS. *Educ:* Cornell Univ, AB, 39; Princeton Univ, MA, 41, PhD(math), 47. *Prof Exp:* Res assoc, Columbia Univ, 41-42; opers res, US Dept Navy, 42-43; Princeton Univ, 43-46, Soc Sci Res Coun fel, 46-48; PROF APPL STATIST, STATE UNIV NY SCH INDUST & LABOR RELS, CORNELL UNIV, 47- *Concurrent Pos:* Consult, Nat Ctr Health Statist, 64- & Comt Nat Statist, 74- *Mem:* Fel Am Statist Asn; Inst Math Statist; Int Asn Surv Statisticians. *Res:* Sampling methods; application of statistics in the social sciences. *Mailing Add:* NY State Sch Indust & Labor Rels Cornell Univ Ithaca NY 14850

MCCARTHY, RAYMOND LAWRENCE, b Jersey City, NJ, Sept 6, 20; m 43; c 4. PHYSICS. *Educ:* Fordham Univ, AB, 41, MA, 42; Yale Univ, MS, 47, PhD(physics), 48. *Prof Exp:* Physicist, Naval Ord Lab, 42-44; asst, Yale Univ, 46-48; res physicist, 48-55, res mgr, Radiation Physics Lab, 55-59, asst dir, 59-61, process supt, Org Chem Dept, 61-64, DIR FREON PROD LAB, E I DU PONT DE NEMOURS & CO, INC, 64- *Mem:* Sigma Xi; AAAS. *Res:* fluorocarbon compounds and their environmental effects; atmospheric chemistry and physics; chemical and radiation physics; instrumentation. *Mailing Add:* Freon Prod Lab Chestnut Run E I Du Pont De Nemours & Co Inc Westtown PA 19395

MCCARTHY, ROBERT ELMER, b Washington, DC, May 19, 26; m 49; c 1. IMMUNOLOGY, MICROBIOLOGY. *Educ:* Univ Md, BS, 51, MS, 53; Brown Univ, PhD(biol), 56. *Prof Exp:* Asst poultry, Univ Md, 51-53; asst biol, Brown Univ, 53-55; asst path, Harvard Med Sch, 57-62, res assoc, 62-69, assoc, 69-70; ASSOC PROF MED MICROBIOL & IMMUNOL, UNIV NEBR MED CTR, OMAHA, 70- *Concurrent Pos:* USPHS fel, Inst Cell Res & Genetics, Karolinska Inst, Sweden, 62-63; asst path, Children's Hosp, Boston, 56-59, res assoc, 59-70; asst path, Children's Cancer Res Found, 56-59, res assoc, 59-70, chief lab of immunol, 68-69; assoc oral path, Sch Dent Med, Harvard Univ, 69-70. *Mem:* Am Soc Exp Path; NY Acad Sci; Am Asn Immunol; Am Soc Cancer Res. *Res:* Radiation biology, antigen structure, cytochemistry and cytogenetics of mammalian cells in culture; study of inhibition of allograft rejection by ascites tumors; immunochemistry of synthetic polypeptides; immunoregulators; effect of pesticides on immune response. *Mailing Add:* Dept of Med Microbiol Univ of Nebr Med Ctr Omaha NE 68105

MCCARTHY, SHAUN LEAF, b Berkeley, Calif, Oct 20, 39; m 63; c 2. EXPERIMENTAL SOLID STATE PHYSICS. *Educ:* Univ Calif, Berkeley, BA, 62; Univ Chicago, MS, 63; Univ Calif, San Diego, PhD(physics), 70. *Prof Exp:* Res physicist, Univ Calif, San Diego, 70-71; res physicist, State Univ NY, Stony Brook, 71-73; RES SCIENTIST, FORD MOTOR CO, 73- *Mem:* Am Phys Soc. *Res:* High temperature superconductivity; thin-film Josephson phenomena; optical properties of thin-metal films; electroluminescence anisotropic etching of silicon. *Mailing Add:* 2024 Pauline Blvd 2B Ann Arbor MI 48103

MCCARTHY, VINCENT CORMAC, parasitology, microbiology, see previous edition

MCCARTHY, WALTER CHARLES, b Brooklyn, NY, Oct 25, 22; m 45; c 3. MEDICINAL CHEMISTRY. *Educ:* Mass Inst Technol, BS, 43; Univ Ind, PhD(org chem), 49. *Prof Exp:* From asst prof to assoc prof, 49-65, PROF PHARMACEUT CHEM, UNIV WASH, 65- *Mem:* Am Chem Soc; Am Pharmaceut Asn; The Chem Soc; Swiss Chem Soc. *Res:* Sympathomimetic amines; organic sulfur compounds; thiophene and furan derivatives. *Mailing Add:* Univ of Wash Med Chem BG-210 Seattle WA 98195

MCCARTHY, WILLIAM CHASE, b Kansas City, Mo, Oct 20, 27; m 50; c 2. CHEMICAL ENGINEERING. *Educ:* Univ Kans, BS, 50. *Prof Exp:* Chem engr, Eastman Kodak Co, 50-52; develop engr, 52-57, group leader liquid-liquid separations, 57-61, tech adv, 61-71, sect mgr, 71-79, ASST LICENSING DIR REFINING TECHNOL, PHILLIPS PETROL CO, 79- *Mem:* Am Inst Chem Engrs. *Res:* Separation and petroleum refining process including fractionation, extractive distillation, liquid-liquid extraction, adsorption, crystallization, waste water purification, reforming and heavy oil cracking. *Mailing Add:* Bldg 94-G Phillips Res Ctr Phillips Petrol Co Bartlesville OK 74004

MCCARTHY, WILLIAM JOHN, b Mamaroneck, NY, June 27, 41; m 77; c 2. VIROLOGY, BIOCHEMISTRY. *Educ:* Univ Del, BA, 63; NY Univ, MS, 68, PhD(biol), 70. *Prof Exp:* Fel virol, Boyce Thompson Inst Plant Res, 70-73; assoc res scientist, Pesticide Res Lab, 74-78, ASST PROF PLANT PATH, PA STATE UNIV, 78- *Mem:* Am Soc Microbiol; Soc Invert Path; Tissue Cult Asn. *Res:* Cellular and viral protein and nucleic acid synthesis in lepidoptera and insect tissue cultures; isolation and characterization of insect viruses; proteins and nucleic acids; characterization of nucleic acid and proteins of baculoviruses, entomopoxviruses, and cytoplasmic polyhedrosis viruses; genetics of bawloviruses. *Mailing Add:* Pesticide Res Lab Pa State Univ University Park PA 16802

MCCARTIN, BRIAN JAMES, b Providence, RI, Aug 26, 51; m 71; c 2. NUMERICAL ANALYSIS, COMPUTATIONAL FLUID DYNAMICS. *Educ:* Univ RI, BS, 76, MS, 77; New York Univ, PhD(math), 81. *Prof Exp:* Sci analyst, Pratt & Whitney Aircraft, 77-81; appl mathematician, Gerber Systs Technol, 81; APPL MATHEMATICIAN, UNITED TECHNOL RES CTR, 81- *Concurrent Pos:* Instr math, Manchester Community Col, 80-81. *Mem:* Irish Math Soc; Math Asn; Math Asn Am; Am Math Soc; Soc Indust & Appl Math. *Res:* Numerical solution of partial differential equations, including fluid dynamics and semiconductor physics; computational algorithms in approximation theory, particularly splines. *Mailing Add:* 166 Homestead St Apt N Manchester CT 06040

MCCARTNEY, MICHAEL SCOTT, physical oceanography, fluid dynamics, see previous edition

MCCARTNEY, MORLEY GORDON, b Picton, Ont, Mar 4, 17; nat US; m 46; c 5. GENETICS. *Educ:* Ont Agr Col, BSA, 40; Univ Md, MS, 47, PhD, 49. *Prof Exp:* Poultry specialist, Ont Agr Col, 40-41; asst poultry husb, Univ Md, 46-49; poultry physiologist, USDA, Md, 49; from asst prof to assoc prof poultry, Pa State Univ, 49-55; prof & assoc chmn dept, Agr Exp Sta, Ohio State Univ, 55-64; PROF POULTRY SCI, HEAD DEPT & CHMN DIV POULTRY, UNIV GA, 64- *Honors & Awards:* Award, Nat Turkey Fedn, 59. *Mem:* World's Poultry Sci Asn; Poultry Sci Asn. *Res:* Population genetics and physiology of reproduction of poultry. *Mailing Add:* Dept of Poultry Sci Univ of Ga Athens GA 30601

MCCARTNEY, R(AYMOND) F(RANCIS), b Pittsburgh, Pa, May 7, 24; m 47; c 2. PHYSICAL METALLURGY. *Educ:* Carnegie Inst Technol, BS, 49. *Prof Exp:* Physicist, Physics & Anal Chem Div, 49-59, res metallurgist, Appl Res Lab, 59-69, sect supvr, 69-74, ASSOC RES CONSULT MECH BEHAV METALS, RES LAB, US STEEL CORP, 74- *Mem:* Am Soc Metals. *Res:* Physical metallurgy of steels; relationship of structure to properties; x-ray and electron optics; instrumental analysis; surface physics; correlation of fine structure of steels with physical properties; mechanical behavior and mechanism of hardening; failure analysis of structural components. *Mailing Add:* Mech Behav of Metals Res Lab US Steel Corp Monroeville PA 15146

MCCARTNEY, WILLIAM DOUGLAS, economic geology, see previous edition

MCCARTY, BILLY DEAN, b Wymore, Nebr, Oct 31, 23; m 46; c 2. ANALYTICAL CHEMISTRY. *Educ:* Nebr Wesleyan Univ, AB, 48. *Prof Exp:* Anal chemist oil shale demonstration plant, US Bur Mines, Colo, 50-53; spectrographer, Los Alamos Sci Lab, 53-58 & Union Carbide Nuclear Co, Colo, 58-62; spectrographer, 62-66, anal unit supvr, 66-70, advan scientist, 70-78, sr scientist, 78-81, INSTRUMENTAL ANAL SECT SUPVR, MARATHON OIL CO RES CTR, 81- *Honors & Awards:* Outstanding Serv Award, Rocky Mt Sect, Soc Appl Spectros, 72. *Mem:* Soc Appl Spectros; Sigma Xi. *Res:* Optical emission spectroscopy; x-ray diffraction and spectroscopy; scanning electron microscopy; isotopic ratio mass spectroscopy. *Mailing Add:* Marathon Oil Co PO Box 269 Littleton CO 80160

MCCARTY, CLARK WILLIAM, b Kansas City, Mo, Feb 27, 16; m 40; c 5. PHYSICAL CHEMISTRY. *Educ:* Univ Kans City, AB, 37; Cent Mo State Col, BSE, 40; Univ Nebr, MS, 39; Univ Mo, AM, 47, PhD(chem), 53. *Prof Exp:* Asst chem, Univ Nebr, 37-39; chemist & supvr bact, Cerophyl Labs, Inc, 40-42; instr chem & math, Kemper Mil Sch, 42-43; instr, Jefferson City Jr Col, 46; instr chem, Univ Mo, 46-47; instr chem, Southwest Mo State Col, 47-48; instr math, Univ Mo, 48-49; assoc prof chem & math, 50 & 52-58, prof & chmn, Dept Physics, 58-81, EMER PROF CHEM & PHYSICS, OUACHITA BAPTIST UNIV, 81- *Mem:* Acoust Soc Am; Am Asn Physics Teachers; Nat Weather Asn; Optical Soc Am; Am Meteorol Soc. *Res:* Partial vapor pressures of ternary systems. *Mailing Add:* 1049 Phelps Circle Arkadelphia AR 71923

MACCARTY, COLLIN STEWART, b Rochester, Minn, Sept 20, 15; m 40; c 3. NEUROSURGERY. *Educ:* Dartmouth Col, AB, 37; Johns Hopkins Univ, MD, 40; Univ Minn, MS, 44; Am Bd Neurol Surg, dipl, 47. *Prof Exp:* From instr to prof neurosurt, Mayo Grad Sch Med, Univ Minn, 61-73, prof, 73-80, mem dept neurosurg, Mayo Clin, 46-80, chmn, 63-80; RETIRED. *Concurrent Pos:* Pres-elect med staff, Mayo Clin, 65, pres, 66; secy cong affairs, Liaison & Admin Coun & chmn prog comt, World Fedn Neurosurg Socs, 65-69; nat consult neurol surg, US Air Force, 72- *Mem:* Am Col Surg; Soc Neurol Surg; Neurosurg Soc Am (vpres, 54, pres, 59); Am Asn Neurol Surg (vpres, 6S-66, pres, 70-71). *Mailing Add:* Mayo Clin Dept of Neurol Surg 200 First St SW Rochester MN 55901

MCCARTY, DANIEL J, JR, b Philadelphia, Pa, Oct 31, 28; m 54; c 5. INTERNAL MEDICINE. *Educ:* Villanova Univ, BS, 50; Univ Pa, MD, 54. *Prof Exp:* Intern med, Fitzgerald-Mercy Hosp, Darby, Pa, 54-55; resident internal med, Hosp, Univ Pa, 57-58; resident, Philadelphia Vet Admin Hosp, 58-59; from asst prof to assoc prof internal med, Hahnemann Med Col, 60-67, head sect rheumatol, 60-63; prof internal med, Univ Chicago, 67-74, head sect arthritis & metab dis, 71-74; PROF MED & CHMN DEPT, MED COL WIS, 74-; CHIEF MED, MILWAUKEE COUNTY GEN HOSP, 74- *Concurrent Pos:* Nat Inst Arthritis & Metab Dis fel rheumatol, Hosp, Univ Pa, 59-60; Markle scholar, 62-; attend physician & chief arthritis clin, Div B, Philadelphia Gen Hosp, 60-; consult, Vet Admin Hosp, Philadelphia, 60-; consult arthritis training progs, Surgeon Gen, USPHS, 67-71; mem fel subcomt, Arthritis Found, 67-71, res comt chmn nat reference ctr rheumatol, 69; mem subcomt rheumatol, Am Bd Internal Med, 70-76; chief ed, Arthritis & Rheumatism, Am Rheumatism Asn, 65-70. *Honors & Awards:* Hektoen Silver Medal, AMA, 63; Russell S Cecil Award, Arthritis Found & Gairdner Found Award, 65; Ciba-Geigy Int Rheumatism Award, 81. *Mem:* AAAS; Am Fedn Clin Res; Am Rheumatism Asn (vpres, 78-79, pres, 79-80); Am Soc Clin Pharmacol & Therapeut; NY Acad Sci. *Res:* Rheumatic diseases; crystallography, mechanisms of inflammation; measurement of inflammation, clinical, physiological and biochemical parameters. *Mailing Add:* Dept of Med Med Col Wis Milwaukee WI 53226

MCCARTY, FREDERICK JOSEPH, b Chillicothe, Ohio, May 2, 27; m 61; c 4. ORGANIC CHEMISTRY, MEDICINAL CHEMISTRY. *Educ:* Univ Ohio, BS, 51; Mich State Univ, MS, 53; Univ Mich, PhD(med chem), 59. *Prof Exp:* Asst res chemist, Wm S Merrell Co Div, Richardson-Merrell, Inc, 53-56, proj leader med chem res, 59-64; sect head org res, Aldrich Chem Co, 64-65; group leader med chem res, Nat Drug Co Div, 65-70, SECT HEAD CHEM DEVELOP, MERRELL-NAT LABS DIV, RICHARDSON-MERRELL, INC, 70- *Mem:* Am Chem Soc. *Res:* Mannich reaction. *Mailing Add:* Chem Develop Merrell-Nat Labs 2110 E Galbraith Rd Cincinnati OH 45215

MCCARTY, JOHN EDWARD, b Iowa City, Iowa, Aug 27, 28; m 55; c 2. ORGANIC CHEMISTRY. *Educ:* Univ Iowa, BS, 50; Univ Calif, Los Angeles, PhD, 57. *Prof Exp:* Res fel, Univ Kans, 56-59; from asst prof to assoc prof chem, 59-67, prof, Environ Inst, 72-75, PROF CHEM, MANKATO STATE UNIV, 67- *Mem:* Am Chem Soc. *Res:* Mechanism of organic reactions; heterocyclic compounds; environmental chemistry. *Mailing Add:* Dept Chem Mankato State Univ Mankato MN 56001

MCCARTY, JON GILBERT, b Keokuk, Iowa, Nov 26, 46; m 69; c 1. CHEMICAL ENGINEERING. *Educ:* Iowa State Univ, BS, 69; Stanford Univ, MS, 71, PhD(chem eng), 74. *Prof Exp:* Chem engr process develop, E I du Pont de Nemours & Co, 74-75; CHEM ENGR & CHEMIST, SRI INT, 75- *Mem:* Am Chem Soc; NAm Catalysis Soc; Am Inst Chem Engrs; Am Vacuum Soc. *Res:* Heterogeneous catalysis; chemisorption; surface analysis. *Mailing Add:* 2337 Saint Francis Dr Palo Alto CA 94303

MCCARTY, KENNETH SCOTT, b Dallas, Tex, June 20, 22; m 44; c 2. BIOCHEMISTRY. *Educ:* Georgetown Univ, BS, 44; Columbia Univ, PhD, 58. *Prof Exp:* Res biochemist, US Food & Drug Admin, 44-45; asst to dir cancer res, Hyde Found, Interchem Corp, NY, 45-52; mem staff tissue cult course, NY & Colo, 54-58; instr biochem, bol Physicians & Surgeons, Columbia Univ, 57-59; assoc prof, 59-68, PROF BIOCHEM, SCH MED, DUKE UNIV, 68- *Concurrent Pos:* Electron micros consult, Vet Admin Hosp, NY, 49-54; consult, Organon Corp, NJ, 56-60 & Parke, Davis & Co, Mich, 60-61. *Mem:* Am Chem Soc; Am Soc Biol Chemists; Electron Micros Soc Am; Harvey Soc; Am Asn Cancer Res. *Res:* Molecular mechanisms in the control of RNA transcription, RNA transport and RNA translation; development of procedures to maintain homeostasis in tissue cultures to study malignant transformation, nucleic acid synthesis, amino acid metabolism and hormone induction in tissue culture. *Mailing Add:* Dept of Biochem Duke Med Ctr Durham NC 27710

MCCARTY, LESLIE PAUL, b Detroit, Mich, May 30, 25; m 48; c 4. PHARMACOLOGY. *Educ:* Salem Col, BS, 47; Ohio State Univ, MSc, 49; Univ Wis, PhD(pharmacol), 60. *Prof Exp:* Res chemist, Upjohn Co, 49-55; res pharmacologist, 60-64, sr res pharmacologist, 64-80, RES LEADER, DOW CHEM CO, 80- *Mem:* AAAS; Am Soc Pharmacol & Exp Therapeut; Sigma Xi. *Res:* Cardiovascular, autonomic and neuromuscular pharmacology. *Mailing Add:* Biomed Res Bldg 607 Dow Chem Co Midland MI 48640

MCCARTY, LEWIS VERNON, b Buffalo, NY, June 7, 19; m 46; c 1. CHEMISTRY. *Educ:* Oberlin Col, AB, 41; Univ Rochester, PhD(phys chem), 45. *Prof Exp:* Res chemist, 45-64, mgr feasibility invests, 64-66, RES ADV INORG CHEM, GEN ELEC CO, 66- *Mem:* Am Chem Soc; Electrochem Soc. *Res:* Reaction kinetics and mechanisms; inorganic syntheses; high temperature chemistry. *Mailing Add:* 3354 Rumson Rd Cleveland Heights OH 44118

MCCARTY, MACLYN, b South Bend, Ind, June 9, 11; m 34, 66; c 4. MEDICAL BACTERIOLOGY. *Educ:* Stanford Univ, AB, 33; Johns Hopkins Univ, MD, 37. *Prof Exp:* Asst pediat, Sch Med, Johns Hopkins Univ, 39-40; fel sulfonamide drugs, NY Univ, 40-41; Nat Res Coun fel, 41-42, assoc med, 46-48, assoc mem, 48-50, mem & physician, 50-60, physician-in-chief, Hosp, 60-74, prof bacteriol & immunol, 60-81, vpres, 65-78, EMER PROF BATERIOL & IMMUNOL, ROCKEFELLER UNIV, 81- . *Concurrent Pos:* VPres & chmn sci adv comt, Helen Hay Whitney Found; chmn, Health Res Coun New York, 72-75; chmn res coun & mem bd trustees, Pub Health Res Inst New York. *Honors & Awards:* Eli Lilly Award, 46. *Mem:* Nat Acad Sci; Nat Inst Med; Am Soc Microbiol; Am Soc Clin Invest; Soc Exp Biol & Med (pres, 74-75). *Res:* Transformation of pneumococcal types; biology of hemolytic streptococci; rheumatic fever. *Mailing Add:* Rockefeller Univ York Ave & E 66th St New York NY 10021

MCCARTY, MACLYN, JR, physical chemistry, see previous edition

MCCARTY, MELVIN KNIGHT, b Farmington, NMex, Sept 1, 17; m 43; c 4. WEED SCIENCE. *Educ:* Colo Agr & Mech Col, BSF, 39; Univ Nebr, MS, 51, PhD, 55. *Prof Exp:* Range exam, US Indian Forest Serv, 39-46; work unit conservationist, Soil Conserv Serv, 46-49, assoc agronomist, Weed Invests Sect, Agr Res Serv, 53-58, AGRONOMIST, AGR RES, SCI & EDUC ADMIN, USDA, 58- *Mem:* Fel AAAS; Weed Sci Soc Am; Soc Range Mgt. *Res:* Pasture weed control; life cycles pasture and rangeland weeds; biological control of weeds. *Mailing Add:* 1100 Fall Creek Rd Lincoln NE 68510

MCCARTY, PERRY L(EE), b Grosse Pointe, Mich, Oct 29, 31; m 53; c 4. SANITARY ENGINEERING. *Educ:* Wayne State Univ, BS, 53; Mass Inst Technol, SM, 57, ScD(sanit eng), 59. *Prof Exp:* Instr civil eng, Wayne State Univ, 53-54; from instr to asst prof sanit eng, Mass Inst Technol, 58-62; assoc prof, 62-67, prof, 67-75, SILAS H PALMER PROF CIVIL ENG, STANFORD UNIV, 75-, CHMN DEPT, 80- *Concurrent Pos:* vchmn, Environ Studies Bd, Nat Res Coun, 77-80, mem, Comn on Natural Resources, 77-80, chmn, Comt to Rev Potomac Estuarf Exp Water Treatment Plant, 77-80; consult, Interagency Agr Waste Water Treatment Study, Fed Water Pollution Control Admin, US Bur Reclamation & Calif Dept Water Resources, 66-71; NSF sci fac fel, Harvard Univ, 68-69; fac mem, postgrad course hydrol eng, Ministry Pub Works, Venezuela, 69-; consult, training grants div, Environ Protection Agency, 70-; chmn, Gordon Res Conf on Environ Sci-Water, 72. *Honors & Awards:* Eddy Medal, Water Pollution Control Fedn, 62, 67 & 67, Thomas Camp Award, 75; Huber Res Prize, Am Soc Civil Engrs, 69, Simons W Freese Environ Eng Lectr Award, 79. *Mem:* Am Soc Civil Engrs; Water Pollution Control Fedn; Am Water Works Asn; fel AAAS; hon mem Am Water Works Asn. *Res:* Biological waste treatment processes, treatment and fate of trace contaminants. *Mailing Add:* Dept of Civil Eng Stanford Univ Stanford CA 94305

MCCARTY, RICHARD EARL, b Baltimore, Md, May 3, 38; m 61; c 3. BIOCHEMISTRY. *Educ:* Johns Hopkins Univ, BA, 60, PhD(biochem), 64. *Prof Exp:* NIH fel biochem, Pub Health Res Inst, New York, 64-66; asst prof, 66-71, assoc prof, 71-77, PROF BIOCHEM, CORNELL UNIV, 77-, CHMN SECT BIOCHEM, MOLECULAR & CELL BIOL, 80- *Concurrent Pos:* NIH career develop award, 69. *Mem:* Am Soc Biol Chem; Am Soc Plant Physiol; Am Soc Photobiol. *Res:* Photophosphorylation and electron flow in chloroplasts. *Mailing Add:* Sect of Biochem & Molecular Biol Wing Hall Cornell Univ Ithaca NY 14853

MCCARVILLE, MICHAEL EDWARD, b Moorland, Iowa, Aug 27, 36; m 62; c 3. ENZYMOLOGY. *Educ:* Loras Col, BS, 58; Iowa State Univ, PhD(biophys), 67. *Prof Exp:* Fel chem, La State Univ, Baton Rouge, 67-68; asst prof, 68-76, ASSOC PROF CHEM, WESTERN MICH UNIV, 76- *Concurrent Pos:* Sabbatical leave, Upjohn Co, 75-76. *Mem:* AAAS; Am Chem Soc. *Res:* Purification and characterization of microbial enzymes involved in waste treatment and drug biotransformation. *Mailing Add:* Dept of Chem Western Mich Univ Kalamazoo MI 49008

MCCARY, RICHARD O, b Sherman, Tex, Mar 21, 26; m 47; c 4. ELECTRICAL ENGINEERING. *Educ:* Univ Louisville, BEE, 46; Syracuse Univ, MEE, 57. *Prof Exp:* Test engr, Gen Elec Co, 46-48, develop engr, Electronics Dept, 48-49; instr elec eng, Syracuse Univ, 49-51; develop engr, Adv Electronics Ctr, 53-56, prin engr, Comput Dept, Univ Ariz, 56-61, consult engr, Light Mil Electronics Dept, NY, 61-64, STAFF MEM, RES & DEVELOP CTR, GEN ELEC CO, NY, 64- *Concurrent Pos:* Spec lectr, Ariz State Univ, 57-59. *Mem:* Inst Elec & Electronics Engrs; Magnetic Soc; Comput Soc. *Res:* Nonlinear magnetic devices and circuits; computer memories; magnetic recording; eddy current testing. *Mailing Add:* Res & Develop Ctr Gen Elec Co Schenectady NY 12309

MCCASHLAND, BENJAMIN WILLIAM, b Geneva, Nebr, May 7, 21; m 43; c 4. CELL PHYSIOLOGY. *Educ:* Univ Nebr, Lincoln, AB, 47, MS, 48, PhD(zool, physiol), 55. *Prof Exp:* Instr physiol, Univ Nebr, Lincoln, 47-55, from asst prof to assoc prof, 55-62, prof, 62-70, asst dean grad col, 65-70; PROF BIOL & DEAN GRAD STUDIES, MOORHEAD STATE UNIV, 70- *Mem:* Fel AAAS; Am Soc Cell Biol; Soc Exp Biol & Med; Sigma Xi. *Res:* Protozoan growth and respiration. *Mailing Add:* Moorhead State Univ Moorhead MN 56560

MCCASKEY, A(MBROSE) E(VERETT), b New Martinsville, WVa, Oct 2, 09; m 32; c 1. CIVIL ENGINEERING. *Educ:* Univ WVa, BSCE, 32, MSCE, 36; Univ Wis, PhD(civil eng), 55. *Prof Exp:* From chemist to plant mgr, WVa Water Serv, 32-35; asst prof eng, Marshall Col, 36-42; chief, utilities opers, Mid Atlantic Div Eng, 42-46; utilities oper br, Off Chief Engr, US Dept Army, 46-51; head dept eng, Marshall Univ, 36-60, prof eng, 51-71, dean col appl sci, 60-71; WATER RESOURCES COORDR, HUNTINGTON DIST, CORPS ENGRS, 71- *Concurrent Pos:* Pres, WVa Registr Bd Prof Engrs; mem, Nat Coun Eng Exam & Gov Adv Coun Comprehensive Health Planning. *Mem:* AAAS; fel Am Soc Civil Engrs; Am Water Works Asn; Am Soc Eng Educ; Nat Audubon Soc. *Res:* Flow through sharp edged circular orifices in pipe line; Mendota Basin hydrology. *Mailing Add:* 61 Edgemont Terr Huntington WV 25701

MCCASKEY, THOMAS ANDREW, b Jacksonville, Ohio, Mar 23, 28; m 60; c 1. MICROBIOLOGY. *Educ:* Ohio Univ, BS, 60; Purdue Univ, MS, 63, PhD(dairy microbiol), 66. *Prof Exp:* Teaching asst microbiol, Purdue Univ, 60-62, teaching assoc, 62-63, res asst dairy microbiol, 63-66, res assoc pesticide anal, 66-67; asst prof, 67-74, ASSOC PROF MICROBIOL, AUBURN UNIV, 74- *Mem:* Inst Food Technologists; Am Dairy Sci Asn. *Res:* Pesticide residues in poultry and processed milk; microbial spoilage of milk; prevalence of salmonellae in food; water and soil pollution by dairy farm wastes. *Mailing Add:* Dept of Dairy Sci Auburn Univ Auburn AL 36830

MCCASLIN, BOBBY DUANE, soil fertility, see previous edition

MCCASLIN, JOHN GARFIELD, physics, see previous edition

MCCASLIN, JOHN WEAVER, b Kansas City, Mo, Dec 22, 17; m 43; c 3. HEALTH PHYSICS, SAFETY ENGINEERING. *Educ:* Univ Kans, BS, 40; Am BD Health Physics, dipl, 60; Bd Cert Safety Prof, cert, 71. *Prof Exp:* Assoc res chemist, Phillips Petrol Co, 40-41, 46-47, res & develop safety engr, 47-51, supvr radiation safety, Atomic Energy Div, 51-53, health & safety bd mgr, 53-66; safety standards br mgr, Aerojet Nuclear Corp, 66-76; safety standards br mgr, 76-78, INDUST SAFETY TECH SUPPORT BR MGR, EG&G IDAHO, INC, 78- *Concurrent Pos:* Mem, Am Bd Health Physics, 61-66, secy-treas, 62-66; affil prof, Univ Idaho, 72- *Mem:* Health Physics Soc (secy, 59-61); Am Indust Hyg Asn; Am Soc Safety Eng. *Res:* Radiation protection associated with test and power reactors, critical facilities and chemical separations; industrial hygiene and toxicology; safety engineering and fire protection. *Mailing Add:* EG&G Idaho Inc PO Box 1625 Idaho Falls ID 83415

MCCAUGHAN, DONALD, b Dublin, Ireland, Mar 10, 29; US citizen; c 3. MEDICINE, ELECTROCARDIOLOGY. *Educ:* Dublin Univ, BA, 52, MB, BCh & BAO, 53, MD & MA, 61. *Prof Exp:* Asst chief cardiol, Vet Admin Hosp, West Roxbury, Mass, 63-76; CHIEF MED OFFICER, WORCESTER VET ADMIN CLIN, 76- *Concurrent Pos:* Prin investr coronary drug proj, Vet Admin Hosp, West Roxbury, Mass, 67-75, prin investr persantine aspirin reinfarction study, 75-80; asst prof med, Harvard Med Sch, 73- *Mem:* AAAS. *Res:* Coronary heart disease; hyperlipidemia; hypertension; electrocardiography. *Mailing Add:* Vet Admin Hosp 1400 Vet Foreign Wars Pkwy West Roxbury MA 02132

MCCAUGHEY, JOSEPH M, b Philadelphia, Pa, Nov 23, 21; m 50; c 3. METALLURGY, PHYSICS. *Educ:* Drexel Inst Technol, BSChE, 48. *Prof Exp:* Physicist, Frankford Arsenal, Philadelphia, 64-55, res adv, 55-69, assoc tech dir, 69-73, civilian exec, 73-77; CONSULT, 77- *Honors & Awards:* Eisenman Award, Am Soc Metals, 74. *Mem:* Fel Am Soc Metals. *Res:* Administration of programs in basic and applied research, materials engineering and exploratory development. *Mailing Add:* 719 Oak Terrace Dr Ambler PA 19002

MCCAUGHEY, WILLIAM FRANK, b Chicago, Ill, Oct 1, 21; m 43; c 1. NUTRITIONAL BIOCHEMISTRY. *Educ:* Purdue Univ, BS, 42; Northwestern Univ, MS, 48; Univ Ariz, PhD(agr chem), 51. *Prof Exp:* Asst biochem & nutrit, 51-55, asst agr biochemist, 55-57, from asst prof to assoc prof biochem & nutrit, 57-64, PROF BIOCHEM & NUTRITION, UNIV ARIZ, 64- *Mem:* Am Assoc Univ Prof; AAAS; Sigma Xi. *Res:* Honey bee nutrition; intermediary metabolism of amino acids. *Mailing Add:* Agr Sci 301 Univ of Ariz Tucson AZ 85721

MCCAUGHRAN, DONALD ALISTAIR, b Vancouver, BC, July 9, 32; m 52; c 3. BIOMETRICS, STATISTICS. *Educ:* Univ BC, BSc, 59, MSc, 62; Cornell Univ, PhD(biomet, statist), 70. *Prof Exp:* Regional wildlife biologist, BC Fish & Game Br, 61-65; asst prof statist & biomet, Univ Wash, 69-77; statist consult, 77-78; DIR INT PAC HALIBUT COMN, 78- *Mem:* Am Statist Asn; Biomet Soc. *Res:* Experimental design; mathematical models in biology; estimation problems in fisheries and wildlife. *Mailing Add:* 6148 133 NE Kirkland WA 98033

MCCAULEY, DAVID EVAN, b Baltimore, Md, Aug 4, 50. EVOLUTIONARY BIOLOGY, POPULATION GENETICS. *Educ:* Univ Md, BS, 72; State Univ NY Stony Brook, PhD(ecol, evolution), 76. *Prof Exp:* Teach asst ecol, State Univ NY Stony Brook, 72-74, res asst population biol, 74-76; res assoc population biol, Univ Chicago, 76-80; DEPT BIOL, VANDERBILT UNIV, 80- *Mem:* Soc Study Evolution; Ecol Soc Am. *Res:* Population ecology and genetics of insect populations, especially Tribolium; mating behavior of soldier and milkweed beetles. *Mailing Add:* Dept of Biol Vanderbilt Univ Nashville TN 37235

MCCAULEY, GERALD BRADY, b Missoula, Mont, Apr 18, 35; m 58; c 1. ANALYTICAL CHEMISTRY. *Educ:* Univ Mont, BA, 57; Univ of the Pac, PhD(inorg chem), 67. *Prof Exp:* Physicist, US Naval Ord Lab, Calif, 57-63; res scientist anal chem, Lockheed Aircraft Corp, 67-70, RES SCIENTIST ANAL CHEM, LOCKHEED RES LAB, LOCKHEED MISSILES & SPACE CO, 70- *Mem:* Am Chem Soc. *Res:* Macrocyclic complexes of group eight metals; trace contamination analysis; vacuum degassing analysis using thermogravimetric techniques. *Mailing Add:* 163 Caymus Ct Sunnyvale CA 94086

MCCAULEY, HOWARD W, b Superior, Wis, Nov 27, 19; m 42; c 3. STRUCTURAL & CIVIL ENGINEERING. *Educ:* NDak State Univ, BS, 48; Univ Minn, MS, 49. *Prof Exp:* Assoc prof civil eng, NDak State Univ, 50-56; prof civil eng, 56-77, PROF MAT ENG, UNIV IOWA, 77- *Mem:* Am Soc Civil Engrs; Am Soc Eng Educ. *Res:* Response to reinforced concrete beams to torsional and bending loads. *Mailing Add:* Univ of Iowa 4136 Eng Bldg Iowa City IA 52240

MCCAULEY, JAMES A, b New York, NY, Jan 15, 41; m 68; c 2. PHYSICAL CHEMISTRY. *Educ:* St Vincent Col, BS, 62; Fordham Univ, PhD(chem), 68. *Prof Exp:* Sr res chemist, 67-78, RES FEL, MERCK SHARP & DOHME RES LABS, MERCK & CO, 78- *Mem:* Am Chem Soc. *Res:* Analytical and physical chemistry of immunological polysaccharides; the application of thermodynamics to the evaluation of the purity of biologically active compounds; isolation and identification of impurities in these compounds; polymorphism. *Mailing Add:* Merck Sharp & Dohme Res Labs Merck & Co Rahway NJ 07065

MCCAULEY, JAMES WEYMANN, b Philadelphia, Pa, Mar 21, 40; m 64; c 3. MATERIALS SCIENCE, CRYSTALLOGRAPHY. *Educ:* St Joseph's Col, Ind, BS, 61; Pa State Univ, MS, 65, PhD(solid state sci), 68. *Prof Exp:* Res asst solid state sci, Pa State Univ, 66-68; res chemist, 68-76, SUPVRY MAT RES ENGR, ARMY MAT & MECH RES CTR, 76- *Mem:* Am Crystallog Asn; Am Ceramic Soc; Mineral Soc Am; Am Asn Crystal Growth. *Res:* Microstructural control of material properties; powder characterization; material characterization; oxides; oxynitrides; micas; carbonates. *Mailing Add:* Ceramics Div Army Mat & Mech Res Ctr Watertown MA 02172

MCCAULEY, JOHN CORRAN, JR, b Rochester, Pa, Feb 25, 01; m 39; c 2. ORTHOPEDIC SURGERY. *Educ:* Univ Colo, MD, 27. *Prof Exp:* From instr to asst prof orthop surg, 30-44, assoc prof clin orthop surg, 44-47, from assoc prof to prof, 47-78, EMER PROF ORTHOP SURG, MED SCH, NY UNIV, 78- *Concurrent Pos:* Clin asst vis orthopedist, Bellevue Hosp, 30-33, asst vis surgeon, 33-35, assoc vis surgeon, 35-41, vis surgeon, 41-; attend surgeon, Univ Clin, NY Univ, 30-; consult, Flushing Hosp, 36-; assoc attend surgeon, Neponsit Beach Hosp, 37-43; attend surgeon in charge serv, Seaside Hosp, 38-40; consult, USPHS, 39; asst attend surgeon, NY State Rehab Hosp, 41-42, attend surgeon, 42-43, sr surgeon, 43-47, surgeon-in-chief, 47-; asst attend surgeon in charge club foot clin, NY Orthop Dispensary & Hosp, 41-; attend surgeon, Univ Hosp; consult orthop surgeon, Nyack, Lawrence & St Agnes Hosps. *Mem:* Fel AMA; Am Orthop Asn; fel Am Col Surgeons; fel Am Acad Orthop Surg; fel NY Acad Sci. *Res:* Problems of orthopedic surgery, particularly congenital deformities of the feet; surgical treatment of neurotrophic joints; evaluation of the crippled for proper rehabilitation. *Mailing Add:* 2452 Terry Lane Sarasota FL 33581

MCCAULEY, JOHN FRANCIS, b New York, NY, Apr 2, 32; m 56; c 3. ASTROGEOLOGY. *Educ:* Fordham Univ, BS, 53; Columbia Univ, MA, 57, PhD(geol), 59. *Prof Exp:* Coop geologist, Pa Geol Surv, 56-58; asst prof, Univ SC, 58-62, assoc prof, 62-63; geologist, 63-70, BR CHIEF, BR ASTROGEOL STUDIES, US GEOL SURV, 70- *Concurrent Pos:* Lectr, Columbia Univ, 57-58; proj geologist, Div Geol, SC Develop Bd, 58-63; consult geologist, 58-63; co-investr, Mars Mariner TV Team, 71. *Mem:* Fel Geol Soc Am; Am Astron Soc. *Res:* Uranium occurrences in Pennsylvania; metamorphism, structure and mineral deposits of the Southern Appalachian Piedmont; lunar structure and stratigraphy; use of television systems for planetary exploration; geology of Mars. *Mailing Add:* 60 Wilson Lane Flagstaff AZ 86001

MCCAULEY, JOSEPH LEE, JR, b Lexington, Ky, Feb 22, 43; m 62; c 3. THEORETICAL PHYSICS. *Educ:* Univ Ky, BSS, 65; Yale Univ, MS, 66, MPh, 68, PhD(physics), 72. *Prof Exp:* Asst, 74-80, ASSOC PROF PHYSICS, UNIV HOUSTON, 80- *Mem:* Am Phys Soc. *Res:* Statistical mechanics and fluids, especially the theory of vortices in superfluids. *Mailing Add:* Physics Dept Univ Houston Houston TX 77004

MCCAULEY, ROBERT F(ORRESTELLE), b Reno, Nev, Aug 31, 13; m 45; c 2. CIVIL & SANITARY ENGINEERING. *Educ:* NMex State Col, BS, 39; Mich State Univ, MS, 49; Mass Inst Technol, DSc, 52. *Prof Exp:* Assoc prof civil & sanit eng, 47-74, EMER ASSOC PROF, MICH STATE UNIV, 74-; PRES, WOLVERINE ENGRS & SURVR, 69- *Concurrent Pos:* Vis prof, Sch Pub Health, Hawaii Univ, 66-67; recipient res grants & prin investr, NIH; eng consult, Mich State Univ. *Mem:* Am Water Works Asn; Water Pollution Control Fedn. *Res:* Control of corrosion in water distribution systems; removal of radioactivity and pollution from water. *Mailing Add:* 2803 LaSalle Gardens Lansing MI 48910

MCCAULEY, ROBERT WILLIAM, b Toronto, Ont, July 8, 26; m 56; c 3. FISH BIOLOGY. *Educ:* Univ Toronto, BA, 50, MA, 57; Univ Western Ont, PhD(zool), 62. *Prof Exp:* Res scientist, Fisheries Res Bd, Can, 55-62; biologist in charge fish cultural prog, Ont Dept Lands & Forests, 62-63, res scientist, 63-65; assoc prof, 65-80, PROF BIOL, WILFRID LAURIER UNIV, 80- *Concurrent Pos:* Consult, Ont Hydro-Prov of Ont, 74-76. *Mem:* Am Fisheries Soc; Am Inst Biol Sci; Can Soc Zool. *Res:* Fish physiology; thermal ecology; effects of warm effluents on fish. *Mailing Add:* 118 Forest Hill Dr Kitchener ON N2M 4G3 Can

MCCAULEY, ROY B, JR, b Chicago, Ill, Feb 9, 19; m 41; c 4. ENGINEERING. *Educ:* Cornell Col, BA, 40; Ill Inst Technol, MS, 43. *Prof Exp:* Res metallurgist, 38-39; asst metall, Ill Inst Technol, 40-43, from instr to asst prof, 43-50, actg chmn dept metall eng, 44-46; instr welding eng, 50-54, assoc prof, 54-60, res supvr, Eng Exp Sta, 56-62, chmn dept, 56-79, PROF WELDING ENG, OHIO STATE UNIV, 56-, PROF METALL ENG, 71-, DIR CTR WELDING RES, 79- *Concurrent Pos:* Robert Mehl hon lectr, Soc Nondestructive Testing, 65, lectr, Assembly, 67; vis scientist, Yugoslavia Welding Soc, 65; Nat Acad Sci vis scientist, Romania, 69; consult, govt & various indust concerns; mem comn pres educ, Int Inst Welding, 64-81, sub-comt pres testing, 77- *Honors & Awards:* Award, Am Welding Soc, 59. *Mem:* Am Soc Eng Educ; Am Soc Metals; Soc Nondestructive Testing; Am Welding Soc (vpres, 63-66, pres, 66-67). *Res:* Welding engineering education and metallurgy; development of phosfide alloys; casting metallurgy; industrial radiography with isotopes and x-rays; state of stress; bond mechanisms; discontinuity evaluations of manufactured metals and alloys. *Mailing Add:* Dept of Welding Eng 190 W 19th Ave Columbus OH 43210

MCCAULEY, WILLIAM JOHN, b Ray, Ariz, Aug 11, 20; m 47; c 2. PHYSIOLOGY, ANATOMY. *Educ:* Univ Ariz, BS, 47; Univ Southern Calif, PhD(zool), 55. *Prof Exp:* Res assoc pharmacol, Lederle Labs, Am Cyanamid Co, NY, 47-49; lab assoc zool, Univ Southern Calif, 49-51, instr anat, Sch Dent, 52-54, Sch Med, 54-55; instr zool, 55-56, from asst prof to prof biol, 56-78, assoc dean, Grad Col, 74-78, PROF GEN BIOL, UNIV ARIZ, 78- *Res:* Vertebrate physiology; biological education. *Mailing Add:* Dept Gen Biol Univ of Ariz Tucson AZ 85721

MCCAULLY, RONALD JAMES, b West Reading, Pa, Dec 25, 36; m 60; c 2. ORGANIC CHEMISTRY, MEDICINAL CHEMISTRY. *Educ:* Mass Inst Technol, SB, 58; Harvard Univ, PhD(org chem), 65. *Prof Exp:* Chemist, Arthur D Little, Inc, 60-61; sr res chemist, 63-68, group leader, 68-77, SECT MGR, WYETH LABS, AM HOME PRODS CORP, 77- *Mem:* Am Chem Soc. *Res:* Synthesis of new organic compounds as potential medicinal products; investigation of novel chemical reactions; syntheses of cardiovascular agents, benzodiazepines, antimicrobials and respiratory drugs. *Mailing Add:* Wyeth Labs Inc PO Box 8299 Philadelphia PA 19101

MCCAUSLAND, IAN, b Lisbellaw, Northern Ireland, Apr 10, 29; m 65; c 2. ELECTRICAL ENGINEERING. *Educ:* Queen's Univ Belfast, BSc, 49, MSc, 50; Univ Toronto, PhD(elec eng), 58; Univ Cambridge, PhD(control eng), 64. *Prof Exp:* Design engr, Ferranti Ltd, Eng, 50-52; distribution engr, Elec Supply Bd, Ireland, 52-53; develop engr, Can Gen Elec, Toronto, 53-54 & Guelph, 54-55; demonstr elec eng, Univ Toronto, 55-56, lectr, 58-60, asst prof, 60-61; NATO sci fel, Nat Res Coun Can, Churchill Col, Univ Cambridge, 61-63; from asst prof to assoc prof, 64-71, PROF ELEC ENG, UNIV TORONTO, 71- *Concurrent Pos:* Vis scientist, Univ Cambridge, 71-72; ed, Can Elec Eng J, 79-80. *Mem:* Am Inst Elec & Electronics Engrs. *Res:* Control of systems with distributed parameters; theory of optimal control; adaptation in control systems; special relativity. *Mailing Add:* Dept of Elec Eng Univ of Toronto Toronto ON M5S 1A4 Can

MCCAWLEY, ELTON LEEMAN, b Long Beach, Calif, Nov 1, 15; m 40; c 2. PHARMACOLOGY. *Educ:* Univ Calif, AB, 38, MS, 39, PhD(pharmacol), 42. *Prof Exp:* Asst pharmacol, Sch Med, Univ Calif, 39-42, Int Cancer Res Found fel, lectr & res assoc, 42-43; from instr to asst prof pharmacol, Sch Med, Yale Univ, 43-49; assoc prof, 49-60, PROF PHARMACOL, MED SCH, UNIV ORE, 60- *Concurrent Pos:* Dir, Ore Poison Control Ctr, 57-64; consult, Providence Hosp; trustee, Ore Mus Sci & Indust, 60-66; mem bd dirs, Portland Ctr Speech & Hearing, 63-66; chmn, Gov Adv Comt Methadone Treatment Heroin Addicts, 69-72; inst rev comt drug studies in humans, Ment Health Div, 71-72. *Mem:* Am Soc Pharmacol & Exp Therapeut; AMA; Am Fedn Clin Res. *Res:* Cardiovascular pharmacology; morphine derivatives; drugs in cardiac arrhythmias; anesthetics. *Mailing Add:* Dept of Pharmacol Univ of Ore Med Sch Portland OR 97201

MCCAWLEY, FRANK X(AVIER), b Scranton, Pa, May 18, 24; m 54; c 5. METALLURGY, INORGANIC CHEMISTRY. *Educ:* Scranton Univ, BS, 49. *Prof Exp:* Chemist, Chicago Develop Corp, Md, 49-51, lab supvr, 51-59; metallurgist, 59-61, proj leader electroplating & electrometall, 61-73, proj leader, Corrosion & Electrometall Res Group, College Park, 73-79, SR COORDR, MINERAL LAND ASSESSMENT & FIELD OPER, US BUR MINES, WASHINGTON, DC, 79- *Mem:* Am Soc Metals; Am Inst Mining, Metall & Petrol Engrs; Electrochem Soc; fel Am Inst Chemists; AAAS. *Res:* Electrorefining and electroplating of refractory type metals from fused salts; electroplating of platinum metals from fused salts; electrorefining of copper from sulphate solutions; corrosion studies of construction materials in hypersaline geothermal brine; mineral land assessment management; resourse project management. *Mailing Add:* 2309 Cheverly Ave Cheverly MD 20785

MCCAY, PAUL BAKER, b Tulsa, Okla, June 5, 24. BIOCHEMISTRY. *Educ:* Univ Okla, BS, 48, MS, 50, PhD(physiol, biochem), 55. *Prof Exp:* USPHS fel biochem, Okla Med Res Inst, 56-58, mem biochem sect, 58-71; from asst prof to assoc prof, 59-68, PROF BIOCHEM, SCH MED, UNIV OKLA, 68-; HEAD BIOMEMBRANE RES LAB, OKLA MED RES FOUND, 72- *Concurrent Pos:* NIH grants, 56-; mem nutrit study sect, NIH, 74-78. *Mem:* Am Inst Nutrit; Am Soc Biol Chemists; Brit Biochem Soc; Am Oil Chemists Soc. *Res:* Role of membrane-bound electron transport systems in promoting lipid peroxidation in biological membranes; alterations of membrane function caused by free radicals generated by the activity of oxidoreductases; role of dietary antioxidants and fat in chemical carcinogenesis; influence of dietary states on carcinogen metabolism. *Mailing Add:* Rte 4 Box 441 Oklahoma City OK 73121

MCCHESNEY, JAMES DEWEY, b Hatfield, Mo, Aug 27, 39; m 59; c 7. PLANT SCIENCE, BIO-ORGANIC CHEMISTRY. *Educ:* Iowa State Univ, BS, 61; Ind Univ, MA, 64, PhD(org chem), 65. *Prof Exp:* Chemist, Battelle Mem Inst, summer, 61; from asst prof to prof bot & med chem, Univ Kans, 65-78; PROF & CHMN DEPT PHARMACOGNOSY, UNIV MISS, 78- *Mem:* AAAS; Am Chem Soc; Am Soc Plant Physiol; NY Acad Sci; Am Asn Cols Pharm. *Res:* Chemistry and biochemistry of biologically active secondary plant substances; chemotherapy of tropical diseases. *Mailing Add:* RR #1 Box 340 Etta MS 38627

MACCHESNEY, JOHN BURNETTE, solid state chemistry, see previous edition

MACCHI, I ALDEN, b Bologna, Italy, Feb 21, 22; nat US; m 53; c 1. ENDOCRINOLOGY. *Educ:* Clark Univ, BA, 47, MA, 50; Boston Univ, PhD(endocrinol), 54. *Prof Exp:* Mem res staff, Worcester Found Exp Biol, 50-54; asst prof physiol, Clark Univ, 54-56; from asst prof to assoc prof 56-64, exec asst res, Biol Sci Ctr, 56-67, actg chmn dept biol, 74-76, PROF BIOL, BOSTON UNIV, 64-, ASSOC CHMN DEPT, COL LIB ARTS, 76- *Concurrent Pos:* Lalor Found fel, 55; vis lectr & Dept Sci & Indust Res Eng sr res fel, Univ Sheffield, 62-63. *Mem:* Am Physiol Soc; Am Soc Zool; Endocrine Soc; Soc Exp Biol & Med; fel AAAS. *Res:* Comparative aspects of corticosteroid biogenesis; regulation of adrenocortical and pancreatic endocrine secretion; transplantation of adrenal and endocrine pancreas; pancreatic tissue culture. *Mailing Add:* 52 Roundwood Rd Newton MA 02164

MACCINI, JOHN ANDREW, b Boston, Mass, July 9, 28; m 61; c 4. GEOLOGY. *Educ:* Boston Univ, BA, 52, MA, 54; Ohio State Univ, PhD(earth sci educ), 69. *Prof Exp:* Sr tech officer, Nfld Geol Surv, 53; construct & soils engr, Thompson & Lichtner Co, Brookline, Mass, 54-58; teacher earth sci, Lincoln-Sudbury Regional High Sch, Mass, 58-66; teaching assoc geol, Ohio State Univ, 66-69; assoc prof geol & sci educ, Univ Md, College Park, 69-71; PROG MGR SCI EDUC, NSF, 71- *Concurrent Pos:* Regional dir skylab student proj, NASA, 70-71. *Mem:* Nat Sci Teachers Asn; Nat Asn Geol Teachers; Nat Asn Res Sci Teaching. *Res:* Improvement of undergraduate science instruction with specific focus on audio-visual tutorial laboratory development for undergraduate geology courses. *Mailing Add:* Div of Sci Educ Educ Directorate Resources Improv NSF 1800 G St Washington DC 20550

MCCLAIN, ERNEST PAUL, b Columbus, Ohio, Jan 11, 26; m 51; c 4. METEOROLOGY. *Educ:* Univ Chicago, SM, 50; Fla State Univ, PhD(meteorol), 58. *Prof Exp:* Instr meteorol, Univ Wash, Seattle, 50-54; instr, Fla State Univ, 56-57; instr, Univ Chicago, 57-58, asst prof, 59-62; res meteorologist, US Weather Bur, 62-67, PRIN SCIENTIST, EARTH SCI LAB, NAT EARTH SATELLITE SERV, NAT OCEANIC & ATMOSPHERIC ADMIN, 67- *Concurrent Pos:* NOAA Mem, USA/USSR Joint Working Group Nat Environ, 71- *Mem:* AAAS; Am Meteorol Soc; Am Geophys Union. *Res:* Use of aircraft and satellite data in synoptic meteorology; develop applications of earth satellite data to oceanography and hydrology. *Mailing Add:* Earth Sci Lab WWB S/RE 1 Suitland MD 20233

MCCLAIN, JOHN WILLIAM, b Dayton, Ohio, Nov 3, 28. PHYSICS. *Educ:* Antioch Col, BS, 52; Princeton Univ, MA, 53, PhD(physics), 57. *Prof Exp:* Instr physics, Princeton Univ, 55-56; asst lectr, Univ Manchester, 56-57; from asst prof to prof physics, Am Univ Beirut, 57-76; ASSOC PROF PHYSICS, YARMOUK UNIV, 78- *Concurrent Pos:* Res assoc, Harvard Univ, 67. *Mem:* Am Phys Soc; Sigma Xi; Am Asn Physics Teachers. *Res:* Science education; history of science. *Mailing Add:* Dept of Physics Yarmouk Univ Irbid Jordan

MCCLAIN, PHILIP EDWIN, nutritional biochemistry, see previous edition

MCCLAMROCH, N HARRIS, b Houston, Tex, Oct 7, 42; m 63. APPLIED MATHEMATICS. *Educ:* Univ Tex, Austin, BS, 63, MS, 65, PhD(eng mech), 67. *Prof Exp:* PROF COMPUT INFO & CONTROL ENG, UNIV MICH, ANN ARBOR, 67- *Mem:* Math Asn Am; Inst Elec & Electronics Eng; Soc Indust & Appl Math. *Res:* Optimal control theory; theory of differential equations; stability theory. *Mailing Add:* Dept of Aerospace Univ of Mich Ann Arbor MI 48104

MCCLANAHAN, BEATRICE J, b Buffalo, NY, July 30, 25. RADIOBIOLOGY. *Educ:* Ind Univ, BS, 47, MS, 49; Wash State Univ, PhD(nutrit), 65. *Prof Exp:* Teaching assoc chem, Ind Univ, 47-48; res chemist, Gen Elec Co, Wash, 48-54 & 55-60, biol scientist, 62-65; asst nutrit, Wash State Univ, 60-62; SR BIOL SCIENTIST, PAC NORTHWEST LAB, BATTELLE MEM INST, 65- *Mem:* AAAS. *Res:* Bone metabolism; mammalian mineral metabolism; cytogenetics. *Mailing Add:* Biol Dept Battelle Mem Inst Richland WA 99352

MCCLANAHAN, ROBERT JOSEPH, b Rainy River, Ont, Jan 22, 29; m 56; c 3. VEGETABLE INSECT CONTROL. *Educ:* McMaster Univ, BA, 51; Univ Western Ont, MSc, 54; Mich State Univ, PhD(entom), 62. *Prof Exp:* Asst entomologist, Entom Lab, 54-65, RES SCIENTIST, RES STA, CAN DEPT AGR, 65- *Mem:* Entom Soc Can; Entom Soc Am; Int Orgn Biol Control. *Res:* Integrated control of greenhouse insects. *Mailing Add:* Res Sta Agr Can Harrow ON N0R 1G0 Can

MCCLARD, RONALD WAYNE, b Brawley, Calif, Aug 12, 51. METABOLIC DISEASE. *Educ:* Cent Col, Iowa, BA, 72; Univ Calif, Los Angeles, PhD(biochem), 78. *Prof Exp:* NIH fel, Dept Biochem, Univ NC, 79-82; ASST PROF CHEM, DEPT CHEM, BOSTON COL, 82- *Mem:* Am Chem Soc; AAAS; Sci Res Soc. *Res:* Design of ribosyl-(C1)-phosphonate analog/inhibitors and metabolism of ribosyl phosphates; multifunctional proteins; nucleic acid precursor biosynthesis; regulation of metabolism; inherited metabolic disease. *Mailing Add:* Dept Chem Boston Col Chestnut Hill MA 02167

MCCLAREN, MILTON, JR, b Vancouver, BC, Sept 3, 40; m 63. BOTANY, MYCOLOGY. *Educ:* Univ BC, BEd, 63, PhD(bot), 67. *Prof Exp:* Asst prof biol sci, 67-74, ASSOC PROF BIOL SCI & ASSOC PROF EDUC, SIMON FRASER UNIV, 67- *Concurrent Pos:* Nat Res Coun Can res grants, 67-69. *Mem:* AAAS; Mycol Soc Am; Can Bot Asn. *Res:* Species genetics in Basidiomycetes; fungal ecology and cytology. *Mailing Add:* Dept of Biol Sci Simon Fraser Univ Burnaby BC V5A 1S6 Can

MACCLAREN, ROBERT H, b Scranton, Pa, Aug 24, 13; m 35, 48, 76; c 6. CHEMICAL ENGINEERING. *Educ:* Wayne State Univ, BS, 34; Univ Mich, MS, 35. *Prof Exp:* Admin supvr wood cellulose, Eastman Kodak Co, 35-65; mgr paper technol, Xerox Corp, Webster, 65-76; CHIEF CHEMIST, NAT ARCHIVES & RECORDS SERV, 76- *Mem:* AAAS; Am Inst Chem Engrs; Am Chem Soc; Tech Asn Pulp & Paper Indust; Can Pulp & Paper Asn. *Res:* Cellulose morphology, water relationships and wood analysis; paper, film and image permanence; paper and parchment restoration and conservation. *Mailing Add:* Nat Archives & Records Serv Seventh & Pennsylvania Aves NW Washington DC 20408

MCCLARY, ANDREW, b Chicago, Ill, Apr 15, 27; m 54; c 2. SCIENCE EDUCATION, SCIENCE IN MEDIA. *Educ:* Dartmouth Col, AB, 50; Univ Mich, MA, 54, PhD(zool), 60. *Prof Exp:* Res asst city planning, Chicago Plan Comn, 50-51; shrimp fishery, 51-52; from asst prof to assoc prof zool, Univ Wis-Milwaukee, 59-64; from asst prof to assoc prof natural sci, 64-69, PROF NATURAL SCI, MICH STATE UNIV, 69- *Mem:* AAAS; Am Inst Biol Sci. *Res:* History of hygiene, popular and consumer health and sanitation; science, especially health science education; health sciences and the media. *Mailing Add:* Dept of Natural Sci Mich State Univ East Lansing MI 48824

MCCLARY, CECIL FAY, b Grayson, La, June 22, 13; m 40; c 2. GENETICS. *Educ:* La State Univ, BS, 36, MS, 38; Univ Calif, PhD(genetics), 50. *Prof Exp:* Asst poultryman, Western Wash Exp Sta, Wash State Univ, 38-52, assoc poultry scientist, 52-56; geneticist, Heisdorf & Nelson Farms, Inc, 56-71; dir genetics res, H&N Inc, 72-77; RETIRED. *Concurrent Pos:* Asst prof, Wash State Univ, 46; asst, Univ Calif, 46-49; consult, poultry breeding and prod mgt. *Mem:* Poultry Sci Asn. *Res:* Disease resistance and heredity; genetics of egg quality. *Mailing Add:* 8810-172nd Ave NE Redmond WA 98052

MCCLARY, DANIEL OTHO, b Ft Towson, Okla, Apr 24, 18; m 42; c 2. MICROBIOLOGY. *Educ:* Southeastern State Col, BS, 40; Wash Univ, PhD, 51. *Prof Exp:* From asst prof to assoc prof, 51-70, PROF MICROBIOL, SOUTHERN ILL UNIV, CARBONDALE, 70- *Mem:* AAAS; Am Soc Microbiol; Am Inst Biol Sci; Am Acad Microbiol. *Res:* Physiology and cytology of yeasts. *Mailing Add:* 203 S Tower Rd Carbondale IL 62901

MCCLATCHEY, ROBERT ALAN, b Rockville, Conn, July 26, 38; m 61; c 2. ATMOSPHERIC PHYSICS. *Educ:* Mass Inst Technol, BS, 60, MS, 61; Univ Calif, Los Angeles, PhD(meteorol), 66. *Prof Exp:* Sr scientist, Jet Propulsion Lab, Calif Inst Technol, 63-67; sr scientist, AVCO Space Systs Div, 67-68; res scientist, 68-75, br chief, 75-80, DIR, METEOROL DIV, AIR FORCE GEOPHYSICS LAB, 80- *Honors & Awards:* Losey Award, Am Inst Aeronaut & Astronaut, 78. *Mem:* AAAS; Am Meteorol Soc. *Res:* Atmospheric radiation, the transmission and emission of radiation in the atmosphere; molecular spectroscopy involved in the problem of atmospheric transmission; radiative transfer in the atmosphere and its relationship to meteorology; satellite-based atmospheric remote sensing. *Mailing Add:* Air Force Geophysics Lab (OPI) L G Hanscom Field Bedford MA 01731

MCCLATCHY, JOSEPH KENNETH, b Brownwood, Tex, July 5, 39; m 60; c 4. MEDICAL MICROBIOLOGY. *Educ:* Tex Tech Col, BS, 61; Univ Tex, MA, 63, PhD(microbiol), 66. *Prof Exp:* Fel, Ind Univ, 65-66; fel, 66-67, chief clin labs, 67-77, asst dir prof serv, 77-81, RES SCIENTIST, NAT JEWISH HOSP & RES CTR, 81-; LAB DIR, COLO CLIN LAB, 81- *Concurrent Pos:* Mem adv comt, Trudeau Mycobacterial Cult Collection, 77-80; consult microbiol, US Army, 77-81; vpres, Arvada Mgt Co, 81- *Mem:* AAAS; Am Soc Microbiol; Conf Pub Health Lab Dirs. *Res:* Modes of action of antituberculosis drugs; diagnostic microbiology; resistance to microbial infections; immunotherapy of cancer; mechanisms of drug resistance; gerontology. *Mailing Add:* Arvada Mgt Co 1390 Stuart St Denver CO 80204

MCCLEARY, CHARLES DAVID, b Huntsville, Ohio, Nov 19, 14; m 42; c 4. CHEMISTRY. *Educ:* Wittenberg Col, BA, 36; Ohio State Univ, PhD(org chem), 40. *Prof Exp:* Asst chemist, Ohio State Univ, 36-40; res chemist, Chem Div, US Rubber Co, 40-44, develop chemist synthetic rubber develop, 44-46, mgr plastics process develop, Chem Div, 46-49, mgr process develop, 49-52, mgr basic res, 52-54, mgr, Marvinol Develop, 54-56, asst dir res & develop, 56-61, DIR RES & DEVELOP, UNIROYAL CHEM, DIV UNIROYAL, INC, 61- *Mem:* Fel AAAS; Am Chem Soc. *Res:* Organic synthesis; emulsion polymerization of rubber and plastics; shortstop for synthetic rubber; isomeric esters of the benzoyl benzoic acids. *Mailing Add:* Uniroyal Chem Div of Uniroyal Inc Naugatuck CT 06770

MCCLEARY, HAROLD RUSSELL, b Huntsville, Ohio, Oct 11, 13; m 41; c 3. PHYSICAL CHEMISTRY. *Educ:* Monmouth Col, BS, 37; Columbia Univ, PhD(chem), 41. *Prof Exp:* Asst, Columbia Univ, 37-40; res chemist, 41-45, asst chief chemist, 45-52, asst mgr pigments res, 52-54, mgr, 54-57, dir res serv, 57-64, mgr dyes res & develop, 64-71, mgr dyes & textiles chem res & develop, 71-74, asst dir, Bound Brook Res Lab, Am Cyanamid Co, 75-78; RETIRED. *Mem:* Am Chem Soc. *Res:* Kinetics and mechanism of organic reactions; spectrophotometric methods; dyeing and textile chemistry; analytical methods; pigments. *Mailing Add:* Box 76 Rosemont NJ 08556

MCCLEARY, JAMES A, b Bridgeport, Ohio, Mar 26, 17; m 38; c 4. BOTANY. *Educ:* Asbury Col, AB, 38; Univ Ohio, MS, 46; Univ Mich, PhD, 52. *Prof Exp:* Asst bot, Univ Ohio, 39-40; asst prof, Ariz State Univ, 47-51, from assoc prof to prof, 52-60; prof, Calif State Univ, Fullerton, 60-69; chmn dept biol sci, 69-78, PROF BOT, NORTHERN ILL UNIV, 69- *Concurrent Pos:* Instr, Univ Mich, 51; NSF fac fel, 59-60; assoc prog dir, NSF Undergrad Res Participation Prog, Washington, DC. *Mem:* AAAS; Am Bryol & Lichenological Soc; Ecol Soc Am; Int Soc Plant Taxon; Bot Soc Am. *Res:* Bryophytes; desert plants. *Mailing Add:* Dept of Biol Sci Northern Ill Univ DeKalb IL 60115

MCCLEARY, JEFFERSON RAND, b Reno, Nev, Aug 31, 48; m 68. GEOLOGY, GEOLOGICAL ENGINEERING. *Educ:* Univ Nev, BS, 70, MS, 75. *Prof Exp:* Geologist remote sensing, NASA Earth Res Prog, Univ Nev, 68; geologist eng geol, Nev State Hwy Dept, 69; teaching fel geol, Univ Nev, 71, teaching asst, 71-73; GEOLOGIST, WOODWARD-CLYDE CONSULTS, 73- *Mem:* Geol Soc Am. *Res:* Manifestations of active tectonic processes in areas of low and moderate seismscity as determined from detailed studies of structure and stratigraphy. *Mailing Add:* Woodward-Clyde Consults Suite 700 3 Embarcadero Ctr San Francisco CA 94111

MCCLEARY, STEPHEN HILL, b Houston, Tex, Feb 6, 41; div. ALGEBRA. *Educ:* Rice Univ, BA, 63; Univ Wis, MS, 64, PhD(math), 67. *Prof Exp:* Instr math, Univ Wis, 67; vis asst prof, Tulane Univ, 67-68; ASSOC PROF MATH, UNIV GA, 68- *Mem:* Am Math Soc. *Res:* Ordered groups. *Mailing Add:* Dept of Math Univ of Ga Athens GA 30602

MCCLEAVE, JAMES DAVID, b Atchison, Kans, Dec 17, 39; m 62; c 1. ZOOLOGY. *Educ:* Carleton Col, AB, 61; Mont State Univ, MS, 63, PhD(zool), 67. *Prof Exp:* Instr zool, Mont State Univ, 63-64; asst prof, Western Ill Univ, 67-68; assoc prof, 68-77, PROF ZOOL, UNIV MAINE, ORONO, 77- *Concurrent Pos:* NSF grants, Mont State Univ, 68-70 & Univ Maine, 70-71; Off Naval Res grant, Univ Maine, 71-72. *Mem:* AAAS; Am Soc Zool; Am Fisheries Soc; Animal Behav Soc. *Res:* Orientation of migratory fishes; effects of thermal pollution on ecology of fishes. *Mailing Add:* Dept of Zool Univ of Maine Orono ME 04473

MCCLELLAN, AUBREY LESTER, b Oklahoma City, Okla, Feb 5, 23; m 46; c 2. PHYSICAL CHEMISTRY. *Educ:* Centenary Col, BS, 43; Univ Tex, MS, 46, PhD(phys chem), 49. *Prof Exp:* Res fel, Univ Calif, 48-50; res fel, Mass Inst Technol, 50-51; res chemist, 51-54, staff asst to vpres res, 54-56, mem pres staff, 56-57, sr res chemist, 57-65, sr res assoc, 65-72, GROUP LEADER, MOLECULAR IDENTIFICATION, CHEVRON RES CO, STANDARD OIL CO CALIF, 72- *Mem:* Am Chem Soc. *Res:* Hydrogen bonding; chemical education in secondary schools; dipole moments; spectroscopic analysis, frequency tolerance-nuclear magnetic resonance. *Mailing Add:* Chevron Res Co 576 Standard Ave Richmond CA 94802

MCCLELLAN, BETTY JANE, b Little Rock, Ark, Oct 26, 32. PATHOLOGY. *Educ:* Southern Methodist Univ, BS, 55; Univ Ark, MD, 57; Am Bd Path, dipl, 67. *Prof Exp:* From intern to asst resident path, Mass Gen Hosp, 57-60; from instr to asst prof, Johns Hopkins Univ, 61-64; dir surg path, Health Sci Ctr, 64-75, assoc prof, 64-69, PROF PATH, SCH MED, UNIV OKLA, 69-, PROF CLIN LAB SCI, COL HEALTH 70-, ASSOC DIR SURG PATH, UNIV HOSP & CLINS, 75-, MED DIR, UNIV HOSP & CLINS SCH CYTOTECHNOL, 77-, ACTG DIR SURG PATH & DIR PROG CYTOTECHNOL, COL HEALTH, 78- *Concurrent Pos:* Pathologist, Johns Hopkins Hosp, 62-64, assoc dir, Sch Cytotechnol, 63-64; consult & mem sci adv bd consults, Armed Forces Inst Path, Washington, DC, 78-80. *Mem:* Am Soc Clin Pathologists; Col Am Pathologists; Am Soc Cytol; Int Acad path. *Res:* Anatomic, surgical pathology; cytopathology; cancer detection. *Mailing Add:* Surg Path Okla Mem Hosp PO Box 26307 Oklahoma City OK 73126

MCCLELLAN, BOBBY EWING, b Cayce, Ky, July 5, 37; m 59. ANALYTICAL CHEMISTRY. *Educ:* Murray State Univ, BA, 59; Univ Miss, PhD(anal chem), 63. *Prof Exp:* Res fel, Univ Ariz, 63-64; group leader anal chem, PPG Industs, 64-65; Comt Instnl Studies & Res Grant, 66-67, PROF CHEM, MURRAY STATE UNIV, 65- *Mem:* Am Chem Soc. *Res:* Solvent extraction separations; extraction kinetics; atomic absorption spectrometry; nuclear chemistry as applied to analytical chemistry. *Mailing Add:* Dept of Chem Murray State Univ Murray KY 42072

MCCLELLAN, GENE ELVIN, elementary particle physics, see previous edition

MCCLELLAN, GUERRY HAMRICK, b Gainesville, Fla, Nov 1, 39; m 62; c 2. MINERALOGY, GEOLOGY. *Educ:* Univ Fla, BS, 61, MS, 62; Univ Ill, PhD(geol, clay mineral, chem), 64. *Prof Exp:* Res chemist, Nat Fertilizer Res Ctr, 65-66, proj leader, Nat Fertilizer Develop Ctr, 66-73, sr proj leader, 73-76, RES COORDR, INT FERTILIZER DEVELOP CTR, TENN VALLEY AUTH, 76- *Concurrent Pos:* Fel, Nat Petrol Co of Aquitaine & Univ Bordeaux, France, 64-65. *Mem:* Mineral Soc Am; Clay Mineral Soc; Mineral Soc Gt Brit & Ireland. *Res:* Evaluation of phosphate rocks for industrial and agricultural uses; modification of elemental sulfur melts; sludge from stack gas removal processes; crystallography; geochemistry, inorganic and organic; phosphate rock beneficiation. *Mailing Add:* Box 2040 Muscle Shoals AL 35660

MCCLELLAN, JOHN FORBES, b Pembrook, Ont, Aug 30, 17; nat US; m 50; c 3. PROTOZOOLOGY, SOIL PROTOZOA. *Educ:* Univ Ill, Urbana, BS, 47, MS, 48, PhD(zool), 54. *Prof Exp:* Asst instr zool, Univ Ill, Urbana, 47, asst instr protozool, 47-49; from instr to assoc prof, Univ Detroit, 51-63; ASSOC PROF ZOOL, COLO STATE UNIV, 63- *Concurrent Pos:* Grants, Nat Cancer Inst, Univ Detroit, 57-60, AEC, 62, NSF co-investr, Belowground Ecosyst Processes, 75-83; consult, Wayne County Rd Comnr, Mich, 62; grant consult, NSF Undergrad Sci Equip Prog, 64-65, dir, NSF Summer Insts in Field Biol for Col Teachers, Colo State Univ, Mountain Campus, 68-72, proposal consult, NSF Col Teachers Progs, 69-71; consult, Colo Utility Power Co, 70-71. *Mem:* Fel AAAS; Soc Protozool; Sigma Xi; Am Soc Zool. *Res:* Role of Protozoa in soil; interaction of protozoa with other microbiol soil organisms including the increase in soil mineralization dueto associations of microbiol organisms and plant species; cytology. *Mailing Add:* Dept of Zool & Entom Colo State Univ Ft Collins CO 80523

MCCLELLAN, ROGER ORVILLE, b Tracy, Minn, Jan 5, 37; m 62; c 3. INHALATION TOXICOLOGY, VETERINARY TOXICOLOGY. *Educ:* Wash State Univ, DVM, 60; Am Bd Vet Toxicol, dipl, 67; Am Bd Toxicol, cert, 80. *Prof Exp:* Biol scientist radiobiol, Hanford Labs, Gen Elec Co, Wash, 60-63, sr scientist, 63-65; sr scientist, Pac Northwest Labs, Battelle Mem Inst, 65; scientist div biol & med, US AEC, 65-66; dir fission prod inhalation prog & asst dir res, 66-73, vpres & dir res admin, 73-76, PRES/DIR INHALATION TOXICOL RES INST, LOVELACE BIOMED & ENVIRON RES INST, 76- *Concurrent Pos:* Lectr sch vet med, Wash State Univ, 63; mem div biol & med, Adv Comt Space Nuclear Systs Radiol Safety, 67-73; adv, Lab Animal Biol & Med Training Prog, Univ Calif, Davis, 68-70; consult, Nat Inst Environ Health Sci, NIH, 68-71, mem toxicol study sect, NIH, 69-73; chmn sci comt 30, Nat Coun Radiation Protection & Measurements, 69-79; adj prof sch pharm, Univ Ark, 70-74; pres, Am Bd Vet Toxicol, 70-73; clin assoc sch med, Univ NMex, 71-, adj prof biol, 73-; mem, Transuranium Tech Group, Adv to US AEC Div Biomed & Environ Res, 72-77; mem environ radiation exposure adv comt, Environ Protection Agency, 72-, chmn, 74-77; mem adv bd vet specialities; mem NIH animal res adv comt, 74-78; mem, ad hoc comt on biol effects of ionizing radiations, Nat Res Coun-Nat Acad Sci, 74-76, mem comt animal models for res on aging & chmn, subcomt on carnivores, Inst Lab Animal Res, 77-80, comt on Animal Models for Res on Aging & comt toxicol, Inst Lab Animal Resources, 79-, chmn, 80-, ad hoc mem, Bd Toxicol & Environ Health Hazards, 80-; mem, biomed adv comt on health effects for reactor safety study to Nuclear Regulatory Comt, 75-76; chmn, Ad Hoc Rev Comt, US Environ Protection Agency, 78-80, co-chmn, Health Effects Res Prog, 78-79, mem, Health Effects Comt, 80-, Ad Hoc Clear Air Sci Adv Comt, 80-; chmn, ad hoc review comt on sci criteria for environ lead, Environ Protection Agency, 77-78; mem, Enewetak Atoll cleanup adv group, 77-80; chmn, health effects panel, Environ Impact of Oil Shale Technol Workshop, 77-78; mem, comt legislative assistance, Soc Toxicol, 78- mem sci adv bd, 74-; adj prof, Dept Vet & Comp Anat Pharmacol & Physiol & mem, Grad Fac Prog Vet Sci, Col Vet Med, Wash State Univ, Pullman, 80-; mem, Nat Coun Radiation Protection & Measurements, 71-, Prog Comt, 77-81, chmn, 81, Sci Comt #57, 77-; mem, Dose Assessment Adv Group, Dept Energy, 80- *Honors & Awards:* Elda Anderson Award, Health Physics Soc, 74. *Mem:* Fel AAAS; Am Col Vet Toxicol; Am Vet Med Asn; Health Physics Soc; Sigma Xi. *Res:* Inhalation toxicology; late effects of internally-deposited radionuclides; comparative medicine; occupational and environmental exposure standards. Res: Metabolism and toxicity of radionuclides, especially effects of inhaled radionuclides and late radiation effects of bone-seeking radionuclides on bone and hematopoietic tissue; comparative medicine; health effects of automotive emissions, effects of inhaled radioactivity; radiation toxicology. *Mailing Add:* Inhalation Toxicol Res Inst Lovelace Biomed & Environ Res Inst Box 5890 Albuquerque NM 87115

MCCLELLAN, WILBUR DWIGHT, plant pathology, research administration, deceased

MCCLELLAN, WILLIAM ALAN, b Seattle, Wash, Feb 14, 40. ENVIRONMENTAL GEOLOGY. *Educ:* Univ Ariz, BS, 63; Univ Cincinnati, MS, 65; Univ Wash, Seattle, PhD(geol), 69. *Prof Exp:* Jr geologist, Atlantic Richfield Co, summer, 64, geologist, 65-66; from asst prof to assoc prof geol, Univ Nev, Las Vegas, 69-76; geologist, Amerada Hess Corp, 76-78; sr geologist, Odessa Natural Corp, 78-80; DIST GEOLOGIST, MGF OIL CORP, 80- *Concurrent Pos:* Consult paleontologist, Nev Archeol Soc, 74-75. *Mem:* Paleont Soc; Paleont Res Inst; Am Asn Petrol Geol; Am Forestry Asn. *Res:* Invertebrate paleontology; micropaleontology; biostratigraphy of Paleozoic microfossils. *Mailing Add:* 3943 Greenwood Rd Sedalia CO 80135

MCCLELLAND, ALAN LINDSEY, b Galesburg, Ill, Sept 19, 25; m 47; c 4. INORGANIC CHEMISTRY, RESEARCH ADMINISTRATION. *Educ:* Northwestern Univ, BS, 45; Univ Ill, PhD(chem), 50. *Prof Exp:* Asst, Univ Ill, 47-49; Nat Res Coun fel, Univ Birmingham, 50-51; instr chem, Univ Conn, 51-54; res chemist, Cent Res Dept, E I du Pont de Nemours & Co, Inc, 54-60, col rels rep, Employee Rels Dept, 60-64; vpres eng, Cherry-Burrell Corp, Iowa, 64-67; staff asst personnel div, Employee Rels Dept, 67-69, PERSONNEL ADMINR, CENT RES DEPT, E I DU PONT DE NEMOURS & CO, INC, 69- *Mem:* AAAS; Am Chem Soc. *Res:* Technical personnel administration. *Mailing Add:* Cent Res Dept E I du Pont de Nemours & Co Inc Wilmington DE 19898

MCCLELLAND, BERNARD RILEY, b Denver, Colo, Jan 23, 35. AVIAN ECOLOGY. *Educ:* Colo A&M Col, BS, 56; Colo State Univ, MS, 68; Univ Mont, PhD(habitat mgt), 77. *Prof Exp:* Ranger & naturalist protection interpretation, Nat Park Serv, US Dept Interior, 56-73; instr resource mgt, 73-77, ASST PROF RESOURCE MGT, UNIV MONT, 77- *Mem:* Wildlife Soc; Am Inst Biol Scientists; Sigma Xi. *Res:* Ecology of hole nesting birds; long range movements of bald eagles; fire ecology in the northern Rocky Mountains. *Mailing Add:* Sch of Forestry Univ of Mont Missoula MT 59812

MCCLELLAND, GEORGE ANDERSON HUGH, b Bushey, Eng, May 12, 31; m 58, 75; c 4. MEDICAL ENTOMOLOGY, GENETICS. *Educ:* Univ Cambridge, BA, 55; Univ London, PhD(zool, entom), 62. *Prof Exp:* Sci officer, EAfrican Virus Res Inst, Entebbe, Uganda, 55-59; res assoc entom, London Sch Hyg & Trop Med, 59-62; res assoc, Univ Notre Dame, 62-63; from asst prof to assoc prof, 63-75, PROF ENTOM, UNIV CALIF, DAVIS, 75- *Concurrent Pos:* Proj leader, EAfrican Aedes Res Univ, WHO, Tanzania, 69-70. *Mem:* Entom Soc Am; Am Soc Naturalists; Am Soc Trop Med & Hyg; Royal Entom Soc London; Zool Soc London. *Res:* Biology and ecology of mosquitoes, particularly genetics; yellow fever mosquito Aedes aegypti. *Mailing Add:* Dept of Entom Univ of Calif Davis CA 95616

MCCLELLAND, JOHN FREDERICK, b Elmira, NY, July 22, 41. PHOTOACOUSTIC SPECTROSCOPY, PHOTOACOUSTIC MICROSCOPY. *Educ:* Dickinson Col, BS, 65; Iowa State Univ, PhD(physics), 76. *Prof Exp:* Physicist, Nat Bur Standards, 62-74; res physics, Iowa State Univ, 67-76; res scientist electro-optics, Honeywell Electro-Optics Ctr, 76-77; ASSOC PHYSICIST, AMES LAB, US DEPT OF ENERGY, 77- *Mem:* Am Phys Soc; Optical Soc Am. *Res:* Optical properties of condensed matter including solar energy applications; photothermal and photovoltaic energy conversion; photoacoustic and modulation spectroscopy; solar materials science; solar thermal systems. *Mailing Add:* Ames Lab US Dept Energy Iowa State Univ Ames IA 50011

MCCLELLAND, NINA IRENE, b Columbus, Ohio, Aug 21, 29. ENVIRONMENTAL CHEMISTRY. *Educ:* Univ Toledo, BS, 51, MS, 63; Univ Mich, MPH, 64, PhD(environ chem), 68. *Prof Exp:* Chemist-bacteriologist, City of Toledo, 51-56, from chemist to chief chemist, 56-63; prof dir water, 68-74, VPRES TECH SERV, NAT SANIT FOUND, 74- *Concurrent Pos:* Consult, Ann Arbor Sci Publ, 70-; resident lectr, Univ Mich, 70- *Mem:* Am Chem Soc; Am Pub Health Asn; Am Water Works Asn; Nat Environ Health Asn; Water Pollution Control Fedn. *Res:* Development of electrochemical instrumentation for potable water quality characterization, continuous monitoring in distribution systems and in-plant treatment process control; chemical leaching from plastics pipe and piping systems for potable water applications. *Mailing Add:* Nat Sanit Found PO Box 1468 Ann Arbor MI 48106

MCCLELLAND, ROBERT NELSON, b Gilmer, Tex, Nov 20, 29; m 58; c 3. SURGERY. *Educ:* Univ Tex, BA, 52; Univ Tex Med Br Galveston, MD, 54. *Prof Exp:* Intern, Med Ctr, Univ Kans, 54-55; resident gen surg, Parkland Mem Hosp, Dallas, 57-59; gen practitioner, Neblett Hosp, Canyon, Tex, 59-60; resident gen surg, Parkland Mem Hosp, Dallas, 60-62; from instr to assoc prof, 62-71, PROF GEN SURG, UNIV TEX HEALTH SCI CTR DALLAS, 71- *Concurrent Pos:* Nat Inst Gen Med Sci res grant, Univ Tex Health Sci Ctr Dallas, 65-67, NIH res grant, 67-; surg consult, 4th Army, US Darnall Gen Hosp, 68-; ed, Audio-Jour Rev-Gen Surg, 71-; chmn ad hoc comt study liver injuries in Viet Nam, Vet Admin, 71- *Mem:* Soc Surg Alimentary Tract; Am Gastroenterol Asn; Am Surg Asn; fel Am Col Surg. *Res:* Gastroenterology, especially splanchnic blood flow and gastroduodenal stress ulceration. *Mailing Add:* 5323 Harry Hines Blvd Dallas TX 75235

MCCLELLAND, WILSON MELVILLE, JR, b San Francisco, Calif, Aug 22, 32; m 58; c 2. NUCLEAR PHYSICS. *Educ:* Univ Calif, Berkeley, 54; Cornell Univ, PhD(exp physics), 60. *Prof Exp:* PHYSICIST, LAWRENCE LIVERMORE LAB, UNIV CALIF, 60- *Mem:* AAAS; Am Phys Soc. *Res:* Physics of nuclear weapons and their effects. *Mailing Add:* Lawrence Livermore Lab PO Box 808 Livermore CA 94550

MCCLEMENT, JOHN HENRY, b Watertown, NY, May 6, 18. PULMONARY DISEASES. *Educ:* Univ Rochester, MD, 43. *Prof Exp:* Asst med, Columbia Univ, 47-48, assoc, 49-52; instr, Cornell Univ, 48-49; asst prof, Univ Utah, 52-55; assoc prof, Col Physicians & Surgeons, Columbia Univ, 55-68; PROF MED, NY UNIV, 68- *Concurrent Pos:* Chief tuberc serv, Vet Admin Hosp, Ft Douglas, Salt Lake City, Utah, 52-55; dir chest serv, Bellevue Univ Hosp, 68-; adj assoc prof, Col Physicians & Surgeons, Columbia Univ, 68-72, lectr med, 72-; consult, Vet Admin. *Mem:* Am Thoracic Soc; NY Acad Med. *Res:* Clinical pulmonary physiology; acute and chronic pulmonary disease. *Mailing Add:* Chest Serv Bellevue Hosp New York NY 10016

MCCLENACHAN, ELLSWORTH C, b Chicago, Ill, Mar 13, 34; m 58; c 1. ORGANIC CHEMISTRY. *Educ:* Univ Chicago, BA, 54, SM, 55; Univ Mich, PhD(org chem), 59. *Prof Exp:* Res chemist, Am Cyanamid Co, 59-61; res dir plastics, Miller-Stephenson Chem Co, 61-64; vpres, 64-67, PRES, R H CARLSON CO, 67- *Mem:* Am Chem Soc. *Res:* Organic reaction mechanisms; thermosetting resins to use in electronic and aerospace applications; epoxy resins, polyesters and silicones. *Mailing Add:* 55 North St Greenwich CT 06830

MCCLENAGHAN, LEROY RITTER, JR, b Kansas City, Mo, Nov 10, 48; m 69; c 2. POPULATION ECOLOGY, ECOLOGICAL GENETICS. *Educ:* Colo State Univ, BS, 70; Univ Kans, PhD(biol), 77. *Prof Exp:* ASST PROF BIOL, SAN DIEGO STATE UNIV, 77- *Mem:* Am Soc Mammalogists; AAAS; Ecol Soc Am; Genetics Soc Am; Soc Study Evolution. *Res:* Evolution of small mammals. *Mailing Add:* Dept of Biol San Diego State Univ San Diego CA 92182

MCCLENAHAN, JAMES BRICE, b Des Moines, Iowa, Feb 13, 31; m 55; c 3. MEDICINE. *Educ:* DePauw Univ, BA, 53; Washington Univ, MD, 57. *Prof Exp:* USPHS fel cardiopulmonary physiol, 61-63; mem staff, 63-67, DIR COWELL HEALTH CTR, STANFORD UNIV, 67-, ASST PROF MED, SCH MED, 68-, DIR STUDENT HEALTH SERV, 77- *Concurrent Pos:* Sr res assoc, Palo Alto Med Res Found, 63- *Mem:* Am Fedn Clin Res. *Res:* Internal medicine; cardiology. *Mailing Add:* Cowell Health Ctr Stanford Univ Stanford CA 94305

MCCLENAHAN, WILLIAM ST CLAIR, b Brainerd, Minn, Sept 24, 12; m 41; c 4. ORGANIC CHEMISTRY. *Educ:* Carleton Col, BA, 33; Mass Inst Technol, PhD(org chem), 38. *Prof Exp:* Chemist, Northwest Paper Co, Minn, 33-35; res assoc div chem, NIH, 38-40; indust fel, Mellon Inst, 40-43, sr fel, 43-55; coordr chem & phys res div, Standard Oil Co (Ohio), 55-60, chief spec projs mkt res & prod develop div, Chem Dept, 60-63, sr mkt res analyst, Corp Planning & Develop Dept, 63; assoc, Skeist Labs, 64-65; chief chem resources group, Inst Paper Chem, 65-69, dir, Div Info Serv, 69-81; RETIRED. *Concurrent Pos:* Corn Industs Res Found fel, NIH, 38-40; lectr, Univ Pittsburgh, 47-48. *Mem:* Tech Asn Pulp & Paper Indust; Am Chem Soc; Soc Am Foresters; Chem Mkt Res Asn. *Res:* Oxidation of glycosides with lead tetraacetate; chemistry of starch and dextrins; patents; market research; pulp and paper; information storage and retrieval. *Mailing Add:* 4545-C W Pine St Appleton WI 54911

MCCLENAHEN, JAMES RICHARD, environmental biology, forest ecology, see previous edition

MCCLENDON, JAMES FRED, b Alexandria, La, Jan 1, 38; div; c 3. MATHEMATICS. *Educ:* Tulane Univ, BA, 58; Univ Calif, Berkeley, MS, 63, PhD(math), 66. *Prof Exp:* Instr math, Yale Univ, 66-68; asst prof, 68-72, ASSOC PROF MATH, UNIV KANS, 71- *Mem:* Am Math Soc. *Res:* Algebriac topology. *Mailing Add:* Dept Math Univ Kans Lawrence KS 66044

MCCLENDON, JOHN HADDAWAY, b Minneapolis, Minn, Jan 17, 21; m 47; c 3. PLANT PHYSIOLOGY. *Educ:* Univ Minn, BA, 42; Univ Pa, PhD(bot), 51. *Prof Exp:* Res assoc, Hopkins Marine Sta, Stanford Univ, 51-52; res assoc bot, Univ Minn, 52-53; asst res prof agr biochem & food tech, Univ Del, 53-64, actg chmn dept, 59-64; ASSOC PROF BOT, UNIV NEBR, LINCOLN, 65- *Concurrent Pos:* Civilian with sci & tech div, Supreme Comdr Allied Powers, Tokyo, 46-47. *Mem:* AAAS; Bot Soc Am; Am Soc Plant Physiol. *Res:* Intracellular physiology and biochemistry of plant tissues; plant cell wall enzymology; plant metabolism. *Mailing Add:* Sch of Life Sci Univ of Nebr Lincoln NE 68588

MCCLENON, JOHN R, b Grinnell, Iowa, May 1, 37; m 59; c 3. ORGANIC CHEMISTRY. *Educ:* Grinnell Col, BA, 59; Univ Calif, Los Angeles, PhD(org chem), 64. *Prof Exp:* Asst prof chem, Milton Col, 63-65; asst prof, 65-71, assoc prof, 71-76 PROF CHEM, SWEET BRIAR COL, 76- *Mem:* Am Chem Soc. *Res:* Chemistry of allenes; use of differential thermal analysis for analysis of organic compounds; construction of inexpensive instruments for teaching and research; use of computers in teaching and research. *Mailing Add:* Dept of Chem Sweet Briar Col Sweet Briar VA 24595

MCCLINTIC, JOSEPH ROBERT, b Fayette, Mo, July 13, 28. PHYSIOLOGY. *Educ:* San Diego State Col, BA, 49; Univ Calif, PhD(physiol), 55. *Prof Exp:* Asst instr biol, San Diego State Col, 49-50; res physiologist, Univ Calif, 53-54; from instr to assoc prof biol, 54-70, PROF BIOL, CALIF STATE UNIV, FRESNO, 70- *Res:* Sodium metabolism; endocrinology. *Mailing Add:* Dept of Biol Calif State Univ Fresno CA 93740

MCCLINTOCK, BARBARA, b Hartford, Conn, June 16, 02. GENETICS, CYTOLOGY. *Educ:* Cornell Univ, BS, 23, MA, 25, PhD(bot), 27. *Hon Degrees:* ScD, Univ Rochester, 47, Western Col, 49, Smith Col, 58, Univ Mo, 68, Williams Col, 72. *Prof Exp:* Asst bot, Cornell Univ, 24-27, instr, 27-31; Nat Res Coun fel, Calif Inst Technol, 31-33; Guggenheim Mem Found fel, Bot Inst, Univ Freiburg, 33-34; asst plant breeding, Cornell Univ, 34-36; asst prof bot, Univ Mo, 36-41; staff mem, 41-67, DISTINGUISHED SERV MEM, CARNEGIE INST, 67- *Concurrent Pos:* Andrew D White prof-at-large, Cornell Univ, 65. *Honors & Awards:* Kimber Genetics Award, 67; Nat Medal Sci, 70; Rosenstiel Award, 78. *Mem:* Nat Acad Sci; Am Soc Naturalists; Am Philos Soc; Bot Soc Am; Genetics Soc Am (vpres, 39, pres, 45). *Res:* Cytogenetics of maize. *Mailing Add:* Cold Spring Harbor Lab Cold Spring Harbor NY 11724

MACCLINTOCK, COPELAND, b Princeton, NJ, Dec 3, 30; m 56; c 2. INVERTEBRATE PALEONTOLOGY. *Educ:* Franklin & Marshall Col, BS, 54; Univ Wyo, MA, 57; Univ Calif, Berkeley, PhD(paleont), 64. *Prof Exp:* Field asst, US Geol Surv, 54-55; res asst, 63-65, RES ASSOC, PEABODY MUS, YALE UNIV, 65-, ASST TO DIR, 68- *Concurrent Pos:* NASA res grant, 65-68. *Mem:* Geol Soc Am; Paleont Soc. *Res:* Microstructure and growth of fossil and recent mollusk shells; relationship between shell structures and classification, phylogeny and ecology of mollusks. *Mailing Add:* Peabody Mus Yale Univ New Haven CT 06520

MCCLINTOCK, DAVID K, b Springfield, Ohio, May 1, 38; m 61; c 2. BIOCHEMISTRY. *Educ:* State Univ NY Buffalo, BA, 64, PhD(biochem), 69. *Prof Exp:* Biochemist fibrinolysis, 70-74, group leader atherosclerosis, 74, head dept cardiovasc-renal pharmacol, 74-75, sect dir med prod, 75-78, SECT DIR METAB DIS RES, LEDERLE LABS DIV, AM CYANAMID CO, 78- *Mem:* AAAS. *Res:* New drug discovery; metabolic diseases. *Mailing Add:* Lederle Labs Pearl River NY 10954

MCCLINTOCK, ELIZABETH, b Los Angeles, Calif, July 7, 12. SYSTEMATIC BOTANY. *Educ:* Univ Calif, Los Angeles, BA, 37, MA, 39; Univ Mich, PhD, 56. *Prof Exp:* Herbarium botanist, Univ Calif, Los Angeles, 41-47; assoc cur, 48-69, cur bot, Calif Adac Sci, 69-77; RETIRED. *Concurrent Pos:* Res assoc, Dept Bot, Univ Calif, Berkeley, 78- *Mem:* Am Inst Biol Sci; Bot Soc Am; Am Soc Plant Taxon; Sigma Xi. *Res:* Monographic studies in Labiatae and Hydrangeaceae; taxonomy of woody ornamentals. *Mailing Add:* 1335 Union St San Francisco CA 94109

MCCLINTOCK, FRANK A(MBROSE), b St Paul, Minn, Jan 2, 21; m 44; c 4. MECHANICAL ENGINEERING. *Educ:* Mass Inst Technol, BS & MS, 43; Calif Inst Technol, PhD(mech eng), 50. *Prof Exp:* Asst proj engr, United Aircraft Corp, 43-46; instr mech eng, Calif Inst Technol, 48-49; from asst prof to assoc prof, 49-59, PROF MECH ENG, MASS INST TECHNOL, 59- *Mem:* Am Soc Mech Engrs; Am Soc Testing & Mat; Am Soc Metals; Am Soc Eng Educ; fel Am Acad Arts & Sci. *Res:* Plastic flow and fracture. *Mailing Add:* Rm 1-304C Mass Inst of Technol Cambridge MA 02139

MCCLINTOCK, MICHAEL, b Ft Pierce, Fla, Jan 3, 27. ATOMIC PHYSICS, MOLECULAR PHYSICS. *Educ:* Univ Ariz, BS, 49; Univ Colo, MS, 56, PhD, 67. *Prof Exp:* Mech engr, Reynolds Metals Co, 49-50; mech engr, Cryogenic Eng Lab, Nat Bur Standards, 53-61, proj leader, 58-61, physicist, 62-70; sr scientist & dir global air pollution res prog, Space Sci Ctr, Univ Wis-Madison, 70-73; vis prof physics, Clark Univ, 73-76; assoc dir, Ctr Energy Studies & res prof eng, Boston Univ, 77-78; PRES, MICHAEL MCCLINTOCK & ASSOCS, 78- *Concurrent Pos:* Consult, Technol Consult Group, Boston, 81- *Mailing Add:* 10 Commercial Wharf W Boston MA 02110

MCCLOSKEY, ALLEN LYLE, b Granville, NDak, Aug 25, 22; m 47; c 3. INDUSTRIAL CHEMISTRY. *Educ:* Whittier Col, AB, 46; Univ Wis, PhD(org chem), 51. *Prof Exp:* Instr chem, Univ Calif, Los Angeles, 51-52; instr, Univ Pa, 52-54; res chemist, US Borax & Chem Corp, 55-57, group leader, US Borax Res Corp, 57-59, from assoc dir chem res to dir chem res, 59-69, VPRES & DIR RES, US BORAX RES CORP, 69- *Mem:* Am Chem Soc. *Res:* Steroid synthesis; glyicodnitriles; acyloin reaction in ammonia; mechanism of Stobbe reaction; addition of carboxylic acids to olefins; boron and organoboron chemistry. *Mailing Add:* US Borax Res Corp 412 Crescent Way Anaheim CA 92801

MCCLOSKEY, CHESTER MARTIN, b Fresno, Calif, July 21, 18; m 44; c 2. ORGANIC CHEMISTRY. *Educ:* Whittier Col, BA, 40; Univ Iowa, MS, 42, PhD(org chem), 44. *Prof Exp:* With Nat Defense Res Comt Proj, Iowa, 44-45 & comt med res proj, Calif Inst Technol, 45-46; chief chemist, Alexander H Kerr & Co, Inc, 46-48; phys scientist, Off Naval Res, 48-54, chief scientist, Calif, 55-57; exec dir & sr res fel, Off Indust Assocs, Calif Inst Technol, 57-62; PRES & TECH DIR, NORAC CO, INC, 62- *Honors & Awards:* Bartow Award, Am Chem Soc. *Mem:* Am Chem Soc; Soc Plastics Indust; Nat Fire Protection Asn. *Res:* Organic peroxides; vinyl polymerization; photopolymerization; carbohydrates. *Mailing Add:* Norac Co Inc 405 S Motor Ave Azusa CA 91702

MCCLOSKEY, DAVID J(AMES), engineering science, applied mathematics, see previous edition

MCCLOSKEY, JAMES AUGUSTUS, JR, b San Antonio, Tex, June 25, 36; m 60; c 4. CHEMISTRY. *Educ:* Trinity Univ, Tex, BS, 57; Mass Inst Technol, PhD(chem), 63. *Prof Exp:* Asst prof chem, Baylor Col Med, 64-67, from assoc prof to prof, 67-74; PROF BIOMED CHEM, UNIV UTAH, 74- *Concurrent Pos:* NIH fel, Nat Ctr Sci Res, Ministry Educ, France, 63-64; sabbatical, Nat Cancer Ctr Res Inst, Tokyo, 71 & vis prof, Univ Utah, 72. *Mem:* Am Chem Soc; Am Soc Biol Chem; Am Soc Mass Spectrometry (pres, 78-80). *Res:* Mass spectrometry and its applications to structural problems in organic chemistry and biochemistry. *Mailing Add:* Dept Med Chem Univ of Utah Salt Lake City UT 84112

MCCLOSKEY, JOHN W, b Dayton, Ohio, Mar 2, 38; m 60; c 3. MATHEMATICAL STATISTICS. *Educ:* Univ Dayton, BS, 60; Mich State Univ, MS, 62, PhD(statist), 65. *Prof Exp:* Asst prof math, 65-69, ASSOC PROF MATH, UNIV DAYTON, 69-, CHMN DEPT, 76- *Mem:* Am Statist Asn. *Res:* Computer simulation; error analysis; mathematical modeling; regression techniques. *Mailing Add:* Dept of Math Univ of Dayton Dayton OH 45469

MCCLOSKEY, LAWRENCE RICHARD, b Philadelphia, Pa, May 5, 39; m. ZOOLOGY. *Educ:* Atlantic Union Col, AB, 61; Duke Univ, MA, 65, PhD(zool), 68. *Prof Exp:* Res assoc, Friday Harbor Labs, Univ Wash, 67-68; res fel, Systs-Ecol Prog, Marine Biol Lab, Woods Hole, 69-71; asst prof, 70-76, assoc prof, 76-79, PROF BIOL, WALLA WALLA COL, 79- *Mem:* AAAS; Am Soc Limnol & Oceanog; Ecol Soc Am; Am Inst Biol Sci. *Res:* Marine and community ecology; coral biology; effects of various pollutants on marine animals; coral respiration. *Mailing Add:* Dept Biol Walla Walla Col College Place WA 99324

MCCLOSKEY, RICHARD VENSEL, infectious diseases, see previous edition

M'CLOSKEY, ROBERT THOMAS, b Los Angeles, Calif, Nov 10, 40; m 64; c 2. ECOLOGY. *Educ:* Univ Calif, Los Angeles, BA, 64; Calif State Col, Los Angeles, MA, 66; Univ Calif, Irvine, PhD(pop biol), 70. *Prof Exp:* Asst prof ecol, 70-75, ASSOC PROF BIOL, UNIV WINDSOR, 75- *Concurrent Pos:* Nat Res Coun Can fel, Univ Windsor, 70-; Dept Indian Affairs Nat Parks Br fel, 71-72. *Mem:* AAAS; Am Inst Biol Sci; Ecol Soc Am; Brit Ecol Soc; Am Soc Mammal. *Res:* Species diversity and coexistence; habitat selection. *Mailing Add:* Dept of Biol Univ of Windsor Windsor ON N9B 3P4 Can

MCCLOSKEY, TERESEMARIE, b Toledo, Ohio, July 1, 26. MATHEMATICAL LOGIC. *Educ:* Notre Dame Col, Ohio, BS, 49; John Carroll Univ, MS, 53; Case Western Reserve Univ, PhD(math), 72. *Prof Exp:* Teacher math & sci, St Mary High Sch, Warren, Ohio, 49-50, Notre Dame Acad, Cleveland, 50-53 & Elyria Dist Cath High Sch, 53-58, 60-63; instr math, Notre Dame Col, 63-65; teacher math & chmn dept, Elyria Dist Cath High Sch, 67-68; from instr to asst prof, 68-74, ASSOC PROF MATH & CHMN DEPT, NOTRE DAME COL, 74- *Mem:* Math Asn Am; Asn Comput Mach; Nat Coun Teachers Math. *Res:* Abstract families of languages, leading to more complete treatment of context sensitive languages; computer simulation techniques for small machines. *Mailing Add:* Notre Dame Col 4545 College Rd Cleveland OH 44121

MCCLOUD, DARELL EDISON, b Cass Co, Ind, Mar 7, 20; m 40; c 3. AGRONOMY, AGRICULTURE. *Educ:* Purdue Univ, BSA, 45, MS, 47, PhD(agron), 49. *Prof Exp:* Asst prof agron, Univ Fla, 48-54, assoc agronomist, 54-57; head humid pasture & range res sect, Agr Res Serv, USDA, 57-65; chmn dept, 65-74, PROF AGRON, INST FOOD & AGR SCI, UNIV FLA, 65- *Concurrent Pos:* Consult, Lab Climat, Johns Hopkins Univ, 53; consult bioclimat sect, US Weather Bur, 55. *Mem:* Crop Sci Soc Am (pres); fel Am Soc Agron (pres, 73-74). *Res:* Agricultural administration; agroclimatology; crop ecology; field and forage crop production and management research. *Mailing Add:* 304 Newell Hall Dept of Agron Univ of Fla Gainesville FL 32601

MCCLOUD, HAL EMERSON, JR, b Kansas City, Mo, Feb 15, 38; m 66. SOLID STATE PHYSICS, ELECTRICAL ENGINEERING. *Educ:* Univ Kans, BS, 61; Univ Mo, Rolla, MS, 64, PhD(eng physics), 67. *Prof Exp:* Asst prof, 66-71, ASSOC PROF PHYSICS, ARK STATE UNIV, 71- *Mem:* Am Phys Soc. *Res:* Electromagnetic theory. *Mailing Add:* Dept of Physics Drawer F Ark State Univ State University AR 72467

MACCLUER, JEAN WALTERS, b Columbus, Ohio, Mar 30, 37. HUMAN GENETICS, POPULATION GENETICS. *Educ:* Ohio State Univ, BSc, 59; Univ Mich, MSc, 63, PhD(human genetics), 68. *Prof Exp:* Res asst mech eng, Battelle Mem Inst, 59-60; elec eng, Antenna Lab, Ohio State Univ, 60-62; res assoc human genetics, Univ Mich, 68-71; res assoc anthrop, 71-72, asst prof, 72-74, ASSOC PROF BIOL, PA STATE UNIV, UNIVERSITY PARK, 74- *Concurrent Pos:* Mem, Arteriosclerosis Res Ctrs Adv Comt, Nat Heart & Lung Inst, 72-74. *Mem:* Am Soc Human Genetics; Am Soc Naturalists; Pop Asn Am; Soc Study Evolution; Soc Study Social Biol. *Res:* Population genetics; genetic demography; computer simulation. *Mailing Add:* Dept of Biology Pa State Univ University Park PA 16802

MCCLUER, ROBERT HAMPTON, b San Angelo, Tex, Apr 13, 28; m 49; c 4. BIOCHEMISTRY. *Educ:* Rice Inst, BA, 49; Vanderbilt Univ, PhD(biochem), 55. *Prof Exp:* Res fel biochem, Univ Ill, 55-57; from instr to assoc prof physiol chem & psychiat, Ohio State Univ, 57-68, prof physiol chem, 68-69; asst dir biochem res, 70-75, DIR BIOCHEM RES, EUNICE KENNEDY SHRIVER CTR MENT RETARDATION, 75-; PROF BIOCHEM, BOSTON UNIV, 71- *Mem:* Am Chem Soc; NY Acad Sci; Am Soc Neurochem; Int Soc Neurochem; Soc Neurosci. *Res:* Chemistry and metabolism of gangliosides; chemistry and metabolism of neutral glycolipids; neurochemistry; high performance liquid chromatography of lipids; kidney glycolipids. *Mailing Add:* Eunice Kennedy Shriver Ctr for Ment Retardation Waltham MA 02154

MCCLUGAGE, SAMUEL GARDNER, JR, anatomy, see previous edition

MCCLUNG, ANDREW COLIN, b Morgantown, WVa, Oct 15, 23; m 47; c 2. SOIL FERTILITY. *Educ:* Univ WVa, BS, 47; Cornell Univ, MS, 49, PhD(soils), 50. *Prof Exp:* Res assoc prof agron, NC State Col, 50-56; agronomist, IBEC Res Inst, Sao Paulo, Brazil, 56-60; soil scientist, Rockefeller Found, 60-64; assoc dir, Int Rice Res Inst, Philippines, 64-71; dep dir gen, Int Ctr Trop Agr, 72-73; dep dir agr sci, Rockefeller Found, 73-76; exec officer, 76-80, PRES, INT AGR DEVELOP SERV, 80- *Mem:* Soil Sci Soc Am; Am Soc Agron. *Res:* Mineral nutrition of tree crops; methods of assessing the fertility status of soils; tropical agriculture; rural development; farming systems. *Mailing Add:* Int Agr Develop Serv 1133 Ave of the Americas New York NY 10036

MCCLUNG, LELAND SWINT, b Atlanta, Tex, Aug 4, 10; m 44. MICROBIOLOGY. *Educ:* Univ Tex, AB, 31, AM, 32; Univ Wis, PhD(bact), 34. *Prof Exp:* Res bacteriologist, Res Div, Am Can Co, 34-36; instr fruit prod & jr bacteriologist, Col Agr, Univ Calif, 36-37, instr res med, Hooper Found, Med Sch, 37-39; Guggenheim fel, Harvard Med Sch, 39-40; asst prof in chg dept, 40-44, assoc prof bact, 44-48, chmn dept, 47-66, asst dir div biol sci, 65-68, prof, 48-81, EMER PROF MICROBIOL, IND UNIV, BLOOMINGTON, 81- *Concurrent Pos:* Secy, Pub Health & Nutrit Sect, Pac Sci Cong, 39; mem comt educ, Am Inst Biol Sci, 59-65, bd gov, 67-74; archivist, Am Soc Microbiol, 53- *Mem:* AAAS; Soc Indust Microbiol (vpres, 58); Soc Exp Biol & Med; Nat Asn Biol Teachers (pres, 65); fel Am Acad Microbiol. *Res:* General and applied microbiology; history of microbiology; bacteriophage; Clostridium; science education; microbial food poisoning. *Mailing Add:* Dept of Biol Jordan Hall 138 Ind Univ Bloomington IN 47401

MCCLUNG, MARVIN RICHARD, b Bamboo, WVa, Apr 3, 17; m 43; c 2. ANIMAL BREEDING. *Educ:* Univ WVa, BS, 41; Univ Md, MS, 42; Iowa State Univ, PhD(animal breeding, statist), 53. *Prof Exp:* County agent, Exten Serv, WVa, 42-45; agr counr, Monongahela Power Co, 45-47; asst prof animal indust & vet sci, Univ Ark, 47-52; geneticist & dir poultry div, Southern Farms Asn, 52-57; chmn, Dept Poultry Sci, Univ RI, 57-64; chemn, Dept Animal Indust & Vet Sci, 64-70, prof animal sci & animal scientist, 70-79, EMER PROF ANIMAL SCI, WVA UNIV, 79- *Concurrent Pos:* Dir, Dist E, Southern States Coop, Inc, Richmond, Va, 80- *Mem:* Fel AAAS; Poultry Sci Asn; Am Soc Animal Sci; Genetics Soc Am; Am Genetic Asn. *Res:* Population genetics; selection experiments in poultry and beef cattle and correlated responses. *Mailing Add:* Div Animal Sci WVa Univ Col Agr & Forestry Morgantown WV 26506

MCCLUNG, NORVEL MALCOLM, b Bingham, WVa, June 9, 16; m 45; c 4. MICROBIOLOGY. *Educ:* Glenville State Col, AB, 36; Univ Mich, MS, 40, PhD(bot), 49. *Prof Exp:* Teacher high sch, WVa, 36-41; asst prof bot, Univ Kans, 48-57; assoc prof bact, Univ Ga, 57-66; PROF BIOL, UNIV SOUTH FLA, 66- *Concurrent Pos:* Fulbright res scholar, Japan, 62-63. *Mem:* AAAS; fel Am Acad Microbiol; Am Soc Microbiol; Mycol Soc Am; Bot Soc Am. *Res:* Biology of Actinomycetes, especially the genus Nocardia; ultrastructure of microorganisms; medical mycology. *Mailing Add:* Dept of Biol Univ of S Fla Tampa FL 33620

MCCLUNG, RONALD EDWIN DAWSON, b Victoria, BC, Oct 27, 41; m 64; c 2. CHEMISTRY, PHYSICS. *Educ:* Univ Alta, BSc, 63; Univ Calif, Los Angeles, PhD(chem), 67. *Prof Exp:* Nat Res Coun Can fel, Univ Leeds, 68-69; asst prof, 69-77, assoc prof, 75-81, PROF CHEM, UNIV ALTA, 81- *Mem:* Am Inst Physics; Am Chem Soc; Chem Inst Can. *Res:* Molecular motion in fluids; spectroscopy; magnetic resonance; transition metal chemistry. *Mailing Add:* Dept of Chem Univ of Alta Edmonton AB T6G 2G2 Can

MCCLURE, BENJAMIN THOMPSON, b Rochester, Minn, Oct 14, 25; m 51; c 3. ELECTRONIC PHYSICS. *Educ:* Univ Minn, BA, 45, MA, 47; Harvard Univ, PhD(physics), 51. *Prof Exp:* Physicist, Tracerlab Inc, 48-49; res asst, Harvard Univ, 51; mem tech staff, Bell Tel Labs, Inc, 51-59; staff physicist, Int Bus Mach Corp, 59-60; prin res scientist, 60-64, staff scientist, 64-65, sect head, 65-69, dept mgr, 69-71, SR STAFF SCIENTIST, CORP RES CTR, HONEYWELL INC, 71- *Concurrent Pos:* Instr, Augsburg Col, 62-63 & Macalester Col, 64-65. *Mem:* Am Phys Soc; Am Meteorol Soc. *Res:* Charge transport in dielectrics; conductivity-type atmospheric impurity detection. *Mailing Add:* Res Ctr 10701 Lyndale Ave S Bloomington MN 55420

MCCLURE, CHARLES FREDERICK, b Madison, Wis, July 9, 40. STATISTICAL MECHANICS, OPERATIONS RESEARCH. *Educ:* Johns Hopkins Univ, BA, 62; Univ Md, PhD(physics), 72. *Prof Exp:* PHYSICIST OPERS RES, US NAVAL SURFACE WEAPONS CTR, 63- *Mem:* Am Phys Soc; AAAS. *Res:* Application of non-equilibrium kinetic theory methods to problems involving the flow of dense gases and fluids in the presence of boundaries. *Mailing Add:* US Naval Surface Weapons Ctr White Oak Silver Spring MD 20910

MCCLURE, CLAIR WYLIE, b Greenville, Pa, Oct 17, 27; m 48; c 3. MATHEMATICS. *Educ:* Thiel Col, BS, 50; Ohio State Univ, MA, 62, PhD(math educ), 71. *Prof Exp:* Teacher math, Mercer Area Sch Dist, Pa, 51-63; assoc prof, 63-72, chmn dept, 72-75, PROF MATH, SLIPPERY ROCK STATE COL, 72- *Mem:* Math Asn Am. *Res:* Mathematics laboratories for junior high school students; non-Euclidean geometries for high school students. *Mailing Add:* Dept of Math Slippery Rock State Col Slippery Rock PA 16057

MCCLURE, DAVID WARREN, b Yakima, Wash, Sept 12, 36; m 81; c 2. PHYSICAL CHEMISTRY. *Educ:* Wash State Univ, BS, 58; Univ Wash, PhD(phys chem), 63. *Prof Exp:* Gatty fel, Cambridge Univ, 63-64, Oppenheimer res grant, 64-65; chemist, Shell Develop Co, 65-66; assoc prof, 66-80, PROF CHEM, PORTLAND STATE UNIV, 80-, HEAD DEPT, 77- *Concurrent Pos:* Asst prof, Med Sch, Univ Ore. *Mem:* Am Phys Soc. *Res:* Thermodynamics and statistical mechanics of non-ideal gases and solutions; theory of phase transitions. *Mailing Add:* Dept of Chem Box 751 Portland State Univ Portland OR 97207

MCCLURE, DONALD ERNEST, b Portland, Ore, Oct 22, 44; m 71; c 2. APPLIED MATHEMATICS. *Educ:* Univ Calif, Berkeley, AB, 66; Brown Univ, PhD(appl math), 70. *Prof Exp:* From instr to asst prof, 69-75, ASSOC PROF APPL MATH, BROWN UNIV, 75- *Concurrent Pos:* Consult, Statist Consult Assoc, Inc. *Mem:* Am Math Soc; Inst Math Statist; Soc Indust & Appl Math: Math Asn Am. *Res:* Pattern analysis; approximation theory; mathematical statistics. *Mailing Add:* Div of Appl Math Brown Univ Providence RI 02912

MCCLURE, DONALD STUART, b Yonkers, NY, Aug 27, 20; m 49; c 3. PHYSICAL CHEMISTRY. *Educ:* Univ Minn, BCh, 42; Univ Calif, Berkeley, PhD(phys chem), 48. *Prof Exp:* Res scientist, War Res Div, Columbia Univ, 42-44, SAM Labs & Carbide & Carbon Chem Corp, 44-46; asst chem, Univ Calif, Berkeley, 46-47, from instr to asst prof, 48-55; mem tech staff, RCA Labs, Inc, 55-62; prof chem, Univ Chicago, 62-67; PROF CHEM, PRINCETON UNIV, 67- *Concurrent Pos:* Guggenheim fel, 72 & Humboldt fel, 81. *Honors & Awards:* Angmuir Award chem physics, 79. *Mem:* Am Chem Soc; fel Am Phys Soc; Am Acad Arts & Sci. *Res:* Ultraviolet spectra and triplet states of organic molecules; spectra and electronic processes in molecular crystals; crystal field theory and spectra of inorganic ions and crystals; photochemistry. *Mailing Add:* Dept Chem Princeton Univ Princeton NJ 08540

MCCLURE, ELDON RAY, b Carson, NDak, Dec 31, 33; m 56; c 2. MECHANICAL ENGINEERING. *Educ:* Wash State Univ, BS, 55; Ohio State Univ, MS, 59; Univ Calif, Berkeley, DEng(mech eng), 69. *Prof Exp:* Flight test engr, Boeing Co, Wash, 55-57; res engr, Battelle Mem Inst, Ohio, 57-58; from instr to asst prof mech eng, Ore State Univ, 58-63; mech engr, 65-71, dep head dept mech eng, 71-72, div leader, Energy Systs Eng Div, 72-78, PROG LEADER, PRECISION ENG PROG, LAWRENCE LIVERMORE LAB, 78- *Concurrent Pos:* Consult, Gerlinger Carrier Co, Ore, 61-62 & US Bur Mines, 62-63. *Res:* Machine tool metrology; manufacturing engineering. *Mailing Add:* Lawrence Livermore Nat Lab PO Box 808 L-506 Livermore CA 94550

MCCLURE, GEORGE RICHARD, organic chemistry, pharmaceutical chemistry, see previous edition

MCCLURE, GORDON WALLACE, b Mt Pleasant, Iowa, Mar 22, 23; m 44; c 3. PHYSICS. *Educ:* Univ Ill, BS, 44; Univ Chicago, PhD(physics), 50. *Prof Exp:* Mem staff, Radiation Lab, Mass Inst Technol, 44-45; physicist, Bartol Res Found, Franklin Inst, 49-55; PHYSICIST, SANDIA LABS, 55- *Mem:* Am Phys Soc. *Res:* Gaseous electronics; atomic collisions; physical electronics. *Mailing Add:* Sandia Nat Labs Kirtland AFB East Albuquerque NM 87115

MCCLURE, HAROLD MONROE, b Hayesville, NC, Oct 2, 37; m 58; c 3. VETERINARY PATHOLOGY, COMPARATIVE PATHOLOGY. *Educ:* NC State Col, BS, 63; Univ Ga, DVM, 63. *Prof Exp:* NIH fel exp path, Univ Wis-Madison, 63-66; clin instr path & Emory Univ & pathologist, 66-80, ASST PROF PATH & EMORY UNIV & RES PROF & CHIEF, DIV PATH & IMMUNOL, YERKES PRIMATE CTR, 80- *Concurrent Pos:* Grants, USDA, Emory Univ, 69-72 & Nat Cancer Inst, 71-82, Nat Inst Dent Res, 75-80, Cystic Fibrosis Found, 79-82, NASA, 79-82. *Mem:* Am Soc Primatologists; Am Vet Med Asn; Am Asn Lab Animal Sci; Int Acad Path; Am Soc Vet Clin Pathologists. *Res:* Comparative and clinical pathology; electron microscopy; cytogenetics; cancer research; animal models for human diseases. *Mailing Add:* Yerkes Primate Ctr Emory Univ Atlanta GA 30322

MCCLURE, J DOYLE, b Clayton, NMex, June 23, 35; m 57; c 2. FLUID MECHANICS. *Educ:* Univ Wash, Seattle, BS, 56, MS, 58; Mass Inst Technol, PhD(fluid mech), 62. *Prof Exp:* Res engr, Boeing Airplane Co, 57-58, res specialist, Boeing Sci Res Labs, 62-72, sr res engr laser technol, 72-81, MGR PULSED LASER RES & DEVELOP, BOEING AEROSPACE CO, 81- *Mem:* Am Phys Soc. *Res:* Theoretical and experimental investigations of the interaction kinetics of gas-solid scattering processes; chemical and physical processes in pulsed gas lasers; high power pulsed laser research. *Mailing Add:* Boeing Aerospace Co MS 88-46 PO Box 3999 Seattle WA 98124

MCCLURE, JAMES DOUGLAS, b Glen Cove, NY, May 24, 32; m 64; c 1. ORGANOMETALLIC CHEMISTRY. *Educ:* Polytech Inst Brooklyn, BS, 53; Univ Chicago, PhD(org chem), 57. *Prof Exp:* STAFF RES CHEMIST, SHELL DEVELOP CO, 57- *Mem:* Am Chem Soc. *Res:* Hydrogen peroxide chemistry; chemistry of epichlorohydrin; phosphorus ylid chemistry; catalysis with phosphines; homogeneous catalysis with transition metals; heterogeneous catalysis with supported transition metals. *Mailing Add:* Shell Develop Co Westhollow Res Ctr PO Box 1380 Houston TX 77001

MCCLURE, JAMES HERBERT, b Wooster, Ohio, Aug 9, 22; m 48; c 2. OBSTETRICS & GYNECOLOGY. *Educ:* Ohio State Univ, BA & MD, 50, MMSc, 54. *Prof Exp:* Instr gynec & obstet, Col Med, Ohio State Univ, 53-54; instr, Sch Med, Emory Univ, 54-56, Joseph B Whitehead res fel, 54-55; from asst prof to assoc prof, Univ Ill Col Med, 56-61; prof, Med Col, Univ Ala, 61-63; chmn dept, 63-73, PROF GYNEC & OBSTET, UNIV CALIF, IRVINE-CALIF COL MED, 63- *Honors & Awards:* Centennial Achievement Award, Ohio State Univ, 70. *Mem:* AMA; fel Am Col Obstet & Gynec; Soc Gynec Invest; Sigma Xi. *Res:* Physiology of pregnancy, labor, delivery and the newborn; medical education. *Mailing Add:* Dept of Gynec & Obstet 101 City Dr S Orange CA 92668

MCCLURE, JAMES NATHANIEL, JR, psychiatry, see previous edition

MCCLURE, JERRY WELDON, b Floydada, Tex, May 3, 33; m 54; c 2. PLANT CHEMISTRY. *Educ:* Tex Tech Col, BS, 54, MS, 61; Univ Tex, PhD(bot), 64. *Prof Exp:* From asst prof to assoc prof, 64-73, PROF BOT, MIAMI UNIV, 73- *Concurrent Pos:* NSF grants, 65 & 70; Fulbright hon res fel, WGer, 74-75; Humboldt sr scientist award, WGer Govt, 74-75; mem adv screening comt Life Sci, Coun Int Exchange Scholars, 75-78. *Mem:* AAAS; Bot Soc Am; Phytochem Soc NAm (secy, 71-74, pres elect, 75-76, pres, 76-77); Am Soc Plant Physiol. *Res:* Phytochemistry, especially biochemistry of plant phenolics; physiology and functions of flavonoids. *Mailing Add:* Dept of Bot Miami Univ Oxford OH 45056

MCCLURE, JOEL WILLIAM, JR, b Irvine, Ky, Aug 8, 27; m 53; c 2. THEORETICAL PHYSICS, SOLID STATE PHYSICS. *Educ:* Northwestern Univ, BS, 49, MS, 51; Univ Chicago, PhD, 54. *Prof Exp:* Asst prof physics, Univ Ore, 54-56; res physicist, Nat Carbon Co Div, Union Carbide Corp, 56-61; assoc prof, 61-65, PROF PHYSICS, UNIV ORE, 65- *Mem:* Am Phys Soc. *Res:* Transport and magnetic properties; carbons and graphite. *Mailing Add:* Dept of Physics Univ of Ore Eugene OR 97403

MCCLURE, JOHN ARTHUR, b Belle Center, Ohio, Jan 19, 34; m 60; c 3. MATHEMATICAL ANALYSIS. *Educ:* Geneva Col, BS, 56; Univ Rochester, MS, 57; Va Polytechnic Inst, PhD(physics), 62. *Prof Exp:* Scientist reactor physics, Phillips Petrol Co, 62-69; assoc scientist comput sci, Aerojet Nuclear Corp, 69-73; sr scientist physics, 73-75, PRIN ANALYST PHYSICS, ENERGY INC, 75- *Mem:* Am Phys Soc; Soc Indust & Appl Math. *Res:* Application of numerical methods to problems in science and engineering. *Mailing Add:* Energy Inc 1 Energy Dr Idaho Falls ID 83401

MCCLURE, JOHN HIBBERT, b Truro, NS, Feb 7, 18; nat US; m 43; c 2. ANALYTICAL CHEMISTRY. *Educ:* Mt Allison Univ, BSc, 39, MSc, 41; Iowa State Col, PhD, 51. *Prof Exp:* Control chemist, Can Industs, Ltd, 41-44, supvr prod, 44-45, res chemist, 45-46; res chemist, Polychem Dept, E I Du Pont de Nemours & Co, 51-55, group supvr, Org Chem Dept, 56, chief supvr, 57-60, supvr anal res, 60-62, supvr chem & phys anal, Chem Dyes & Pigments Dept, 62-80; RETIRED. *Res:* General analytical research as applied to organic compounds; colorimetry; gas chromatography; infrared; polarography. *Mailing Add:* 208 Hackney Cir Wilmington DE 19803

MCCLURE, JOHN PHILIP, b Chicago, Ill, Nov 27, 36; Div. ATMOSPHERIC SCIENCES, GENERAL. *Educ:* Univ Ill, BS, 58, MS, 59, PhD(elec eng), 64. *Prof Exp:* Elec eng, Nat Bur Standards, US Dept Com, 64-65, physicist, Nat Oceanic & Atmospheric Admin, 65-69; RES SCIENTIST, UNIV TEX, DALLAS, 69- *Concurrent Pos:* Assoc ed, J Geophys Res, Am Geophys Union, 80- *Mem:* Am Geophys Union; Int Union Radio Sci. *Res:* Physics of the atmosphere; Plasma instabilities in the ionosphere; thermospheric tides, temperatures, drifts and waves; diagnostic techniques including incoherent scatter radar and satellite-born instrumentation. *Mailing Add:* PO Box 688 Stop F023 Richardson TX 75080

MCCLURE, JOSEPH ANDREW, JR, b Sumter, SC, Jan 22, 34; m 57; c 2. THEORETICAL PHYSICS. *Educ:* Univ NC, BS, 56; Vanderbilt Univ, MA, 60, PhD(theoret physics), 63. *Prof Exp:* Res assoc & NSF fel theoret physics, Stanford Univ, 63-64; res assoc, Tufts Univ, 64-67; asst prof, 67-72, ASSOC PROF THEORET PHYSICS, GEORGETOWN UNIV, 72- *Mem:* Am Phys Soc. *Res:* High energy theoretical physics. *Mailing Add:* Dept of Physics Georgetown Univ Washington DC 20007

MCCLURE, JUDSON P, b Longmont, Colo, Feb 7, 34; m 61; c 3. ORGANIC CHEMISTRY. *Educ:* Bob Jones Univ, BS, 55; Univ Colo, PhD(chem), 61. *Prof Exp:* Res chemist, Esso Res & Eng Co, NJ, 61-63; from asst prof to assoc prof chem, Ohio Northern Univ, 63-68; fel, Case Western Reserve Univ, 68-69; assoc prof, Ohio Northern Univ, 69-70; from asst prof to assoc prof, 70-75, PROF CHEM, MERCY COL NY, 75-, CHMN DEPT NAT SCI, 77- *Concurrent Pos:* NSF-Acad Year Exten fel, 64-66. *Mem:* Am Chem Soc. *Res:* Reaction mechanisms; carbene or methylene; additives for lubricating oils; fluorinated organic compounds. *Mailing Add:* Dept of Natural Sci Mercy Col 555 Broadway Dobbs Ferry NY 10522

MCCLURE, MARK STEPHEN, b Northbridge, Mass, Oct 27, 48; m 71; c 1. HOMOPTERA. *Educ:* Univ Mass, Boston, BA, 70; Univ Ill, Urbana, MS, 73, PhD(entom), 75. *Prof Exp:* Med technician, Leonard Morse Hosp, Mass, 70-71; USPHS trainee entom, Univ Ill, Urbana, 71-75, teaching asst insect ecol, 72-73; from asst agr scientist to assoc agr scientist, 75-81, AGR SCIENTIST, CONN AGR EXP STA, 81- *Mem:* AAAS; Ecol Soc Am; Entom Soc Am; Entom Soc Can; Org Trop Studies. *Res:* The biology, ecology and control of Homoptera, expecially Adelgidae, Coccoidea & Cicadellidae; ecology and control of Matsucoccus resinosae and Pineus boerneri on red pine, Fiorinia externa and Tsugaspidietus tsugae on hemlock, and leafhopper vectors of peach X-disease. *Mailing Add:* Box 1106 Dept Entom Conn Agr Exp Sta New Haven CT 06504

MCCLURE, MICHAEL ALLEN, b San Diego, Calif, Jan 19, 38; m 56; c 3. NEMATOLOGY. *Educ:* Univ Calif, Davis, BS, 59, PhD(nematol), 64. *Prof Exp:* Nematologist, Univ Calif, Davis, 64-65; asst prof nematol, Rutgers Univ, 65-68; assoc prof plant path & assoc plant pathologist, 68-74, PROF PLANT PATH, UNIV ARIZ, 74-, RES SCIENTIST PLANT PATH, AGR EXP STA, 76- *Mem:* Soc Nematol. *Res:* Nematode biology and physiology; culture and nutrition of plant parasitic nematodes; physiology of host-parasite relationships. *Mailing Add:* Dept of Plant Path Univ of Ariz Tucson AZ 85721

MCCLURE, MICHAEL EDWARD, cell biology, biochemistry, see previous edition

MCCLURE, POLLEY ANN, b Austin, Tex, Apr 5, 43; div. REPRODUCTION, GROWTH. *Educ:* Univ Tex, Austin, BA, 65, PhD(ecol), 70; Univ Mont, MA, 67. *Prof Exp:* Asst prof zool, 70-76, ASSOC PROF BIOL, IND UNIV, 77- *Mem:* Ecol Soc Am; AAAS; Am Soc Zoologists; Asn Study Animal Behav; Asn Women Sci. *Res:* Physiological mechanisms and functional significance oflife history features; empirical analysis of reproductive costs and reproductive strategies. *Mailing Add:* Dept Biol Ind Univ Bloomington IN 47401

MCCLURE, RICHARD MARK, b Rutland, Pa, May 4, 34; m 56; c 1. CIVIL ENGINEERING. *Educ:* Pa State Univ, BSCE, 58, MSCE, 66, PhD(civil eng), 69. *Prof Exp:* Civil engr, US Forest Serv, 58-63; from instr to asst prof struct, 63-77, ASSOC PROF CIVIL ENG, PA STATE UNIV, 77- *Mem:* Am Soc Civil Engrs; Am Soc Eng Educ. *Res:* Combined bending and torsion in prestressed concrete box beams; computer applications in structural analysis and design. *Mailing Add:* Dept of Civil Eng Pa State Univ University Park PA 16802

MCCLURE, ROBERT CHARLES, b Grinnell, Iowa, Feb 15, 32; m 54; c 2. VETERINARY ANATOMY. *Educ:* Iowa State Univ, DVM, 55; Cornell Univ, PhD(vet anat surg physiol), 64. *Prof Exp:* Instr vet anat, Iowa State Univ, 55-56; instr vet anat, Cornell Univ, 56-60, asst comp neurol, 60; chmn dept, 60-69, PROF VET ANAT, UNIV MO-COLUMBIA, 60-, CHMN DEPT, 81- *Concurrent Pos:* Mem, Int Comt Vet Anat Nomenclature, 64-; Fulbright lectr, Inst Vet Med, Austria, 72-73; chmn, Nomina Embryologia Vet Comt, World Asn Vet Anatomists, 75-80; vis prof anat, Tufts Univ, 79-80. *Mem:* Am Asn Vet Anat (secy-treas, 65-66, pres elect, 66-67, pres, 67-68); Am Asn Anat; World Asn Vet Anat; Am Vet Med Asn; Am Asn Lab Animal Sci. *Res:* Comparative gross veterinary and developmental anatomy; laboratory animal anatomy; tooth development; comparative neuroanatomy; comparative anatomical nomenclature; veterinary medical and anatomical education and history. *Mailing Add:* Dept Vet Anat-Physiol Col Vet Med Univ Mo Columbia MO 65211

MCCLURE, ROBERT D, astronomy, see previous edition

MCCLURE, THEODORE DEAN, b New Virginia, Iowa, Oct 10, 36; m 59; c 3. NEUROANATOMY. *Educ:* Simpson Col, BA, 62; Univ Okla, MS, 65, PhD(med sci), 70. *Prof Exp:* Instr anat, Med Ctr, Univ Okla, 66-70, asst prof anat sci, Health Sci Ctr, 70-74, prof anat, 74-75; PROF ANAT, MED SCH, UNIV MO-KANS CITY, 75- *Mem:* Am Asn Anat; Sigma Xi. *Res:* Gross anatomy; histology; embryology; teratology. *Mailing Add:* Sch Med Univ Mo 2411 Holmes Kansas City MO 64108

MCCLURE, WILLIAM OWEN, b Yakima, Wash, Sept 29, 37; m 80; c 2. NEUROCHEMISTRY. *Educ:* Calif Inst Technol, BSc, 59; Univ Wash, PhD(biochem), 64. *Prof Exp:* Guest investr biochem, Rockefeller Univ, 64-65, res assoc, 65-66, asst prof, 66-68; asst prof biochem, Univ Ill, Urbana, 68-75; assoc prof, 75-78, dir, cellular biol, 77-81, PROF BIOL SCI, UNIV SOUTHERN CALIF, 78-; VPRES, NELSON RES, IRVINE, CALIF, 81- *Concurrent Pos:* USPHS fel, 64-66; fel neurosci, Alfred P Sloan Found, 72-76; mem res coun, Nelson Res & Develop, 72- *Mem:* Am Chem Soc; Am Soc Neurochem; Soc Neurosci; NY Acad Sci; Am Soc Biol Chemists. *Res:* Axoplasmic transport; mechanism of neurotransmitter release; mechanism of action of psychoactive drugs; mechanism of action of neurotoxins. *Mailing Add:* Dept of Biol Sci Univ of Southern Calif Los Angeles CA 90007

MCCLURG, CHARLES ALAN, b Ames, Iowa, Aug 14, 44. HORTICULTURE. *Educ:* Iowa State Univ, BS, 66; Pa State Univ, MS, 68, PhD(hort), 70. *Prof Exp:* Asst prof, 71-78, ASSOC PROF HORT, UNIV MD, 78- *Mem:* Am Soc Hort Sci. *Res:* Vegetable growth, development and processing. *Mailing Add:* Dept of Hort Univ of Md College Park MD 20742

MCCLURG, JAMES EDWARD, b Bassett, Nebr, Mar 23, 45. HUMAN PHARMACOLOGY, CLINICAL RESEARCH. *Educ:* Nebr Wesleyan Univ, BS, 67; Univ Nebr, PhD(biochem), 73. *Prof Exp:* Instr biochem & res instr obstet & gynec, Univ Nebr Med Ctr, Omaha, 73-76; tech dir, 76-78, VPRES, HARRIS LABS, INC, 78- *Mem:* AAAS; Am Chem Soc (secy, Div Small Chem Bus); Am Soc Microbiol; Sigma Xi; Am Asn Clin Chemists. *Res:* Local immune response; biopharmaceutics; normal and malignant cell growth. *Mailing Add:* Lab Inc PO Box 80837 Lincoln NE 68501

MCCLURKIN, ARLAN WILBUR, b Clay Center, Kans, July 8, 17; m 54; c 4. VETERINARY MEDICINE, VIROLOGY. *Educ:* Kans State Univ, DVM, 43; Univ Wis, PhD(virol), 56. *Prof Exp:* Asst vet, Pvt Vet Hosp, 43; vet & prof animal husb, Allahabad Agr Inst, India, 47-51; res asst & instr, Univ Wis, 54-56; VET VIROLOGIST, NAT ANIMAL DIS LAB, SCI & EDUC ADMIN-AGR RES, USDA, 56- *Mem:* Am Vet Med Asn; Conf Res Workers Animal Dis; NY Acad Sci; Sigma Xi. *Res:* Virus diseases of animals; characterization of the virus, epizootiology, pathogenesis and pathology produced in the animal. *Mailing Add:* 1612 Duff Ave Ames IA 50010

MCCLURKIN, IOLA TAYLOR, b Kinston, NC, May 22, 30; m 58; c 3. BIOLOGY. *Educ:* Duke Univ, BA, 52; E Carolina Col, MA, 57; Univ Miss, PhD(physiol), 65. *Prof Exp:* Asst zool, Duke Univ, 52-53; med technologist, Kafer Mem Hosp, New Bern, NC, 53-54; teacher high sch, NC, 54-57; asst zool, Duke Univ, 57-58; from instr to assoc prof biol, 58-74, PROF BIOL, UNIV MISS, 74- *Concurrent Pos:* Fac res grants, Univ Miss, 64-67, 78. *Mem:* AAAS; Histochem Soc; Electron Micros Soc Am; Sigma Xi. *Res:* Cytochemical studies involving transport enzyme locations in cellular membrane systems; histology of avian kidney; histology; histochemistry. *Mailing Add:* Dept of Biol Univ of Miss University MS 38677

MCCLURKIN, JOHN IRVING, JR, b Conway, Ark, Dec 20, 13; m 38; c 2. BIOLOGY. *Educ:* Univ Ark, BS, 34; Univ Colo, MS, 35; Stanford Univ, PhD, 53. *Prof Exp:* Asst biol, Univ Colo, 34-35; asst, Stanford Univ, 35-37; plant quarantine inspector, Bur Entom & Plant Quarantine, USDA, 43-44, entomologist, Div Control Invests, 44-49; prof biol, Lambuth Col, 53-56; assoc prof, Memphis State Univ, 56-59; head dept, 59-71, prof biol, 59-79, EMER PROF RANDOLPH-MACON COL, 79- *Concurrent Pos:* Consult tropical biol, Jamaica. *Res:* Control methods, especially vacuum, atmospheric and soil fumigation; insecticidal dips; plant tolerance; camellias. *Mailing Add:* Dept of Biol Randolph-Macon Col Ashland VA 23005

MCCLUSKEY, EDWARD JOSEPH, b New York, NY, Oct 16, 29; m 81; c 6. COMPUTER SCIENCE, ELECTRICAL ENGINEERING. *Educ:* Bowdoin Col, AB, 53; Mass Inst Technol, BS & MS, 53, ScD(elec eng), 56. *Prof Exp:* Instr, Mass Inst Technol, 55; mem tech staff, Bell Tel Labs, Inc, 55-59; from assoc prof to prof elec eng, Princeton Univ, 59-67; PROF COMPUT SCI & ELEC ENG, STANFORD UNIV, 67- *Concurrent Pos:* Dir, Comput Ctr, Princeton Univ, 61-66; ed, J Asn Comput Mach, 63-69; dir, Digital Systs Lab, Stanford Univ, 69-78; ed, Comput Design & Archit Series, 73-; ed, Annals of Hist Comput, 78-; res fel, Japan Soc Prom Sci, 78; Signetics consult, Digital Equip Corp, Xerox Corp, Gen Precision Co, IBM & Honeywell. *Mem:* Fel AAAS; Inst Elec & Electronics Engrs; Asn Comput Mach. *Res:* Computer reliability; digital design and testing; multiprocessors; computer design automation. *Mailing Add:* Comput Systs Lab Stanford Univ Stanford CA 94305

MCCLUSKEY, ELWOOD STURGES, b Loma Linda, Calif, June 1, 25; m 48; c 4. COMPARATIVE PHYSIOLOGY, CIRCADIAN RHYTHMS. *Educ:* Walla Walla Col, BA, 50, MA, 52; Stanford Univ, PhD(biol), 59. *Prof Exp:* Asst bot, Walla Walla Col, 50-51; asst embryol, Stanford Univ, 51; asst prof biol, Atlantic Union Col, 52-54; asst instr physiol, 54-59, from instr to asst prof, 59-75, ASSOC PROF PHYSIOL & BIOL, LOMA LINDA UNIV, 75- *Concurrent Pos:* NSF fel, Harvard Univ, 59-60. *Mem:* AAAS; Am Soc Zoologists; Ecol Soc Am. *Res:* Comparative physiology, periodicity and ant biology; entomology. *Mailing Add:* 11899 Myrtlewood Colton CA 92324

MCCLUSKEY, GEORGE E, JR, b Hammonton, NJ, Aug 28, 38; m 64. ASTROPHYSICS. *Educ:* Univ Pa, AB, 60, MS, 63, PhD(astron), 65. *Prof Exp:* Asst prof, 65-68, assoc prof, 68-76, PROF ASTRON, LEHIGH UNIV, 76- *Concurrent Pos:* NASA grant, Lehigh Univ, 71-75; guest investr, Copernicus Satellite. *Mem:* AAAS; Am Astron Soc; Int Astron Union. *Res:*

Eclipsing binary stars; double stars; x-ray and gamma-ray generation in close binaries; general relativistic effects in close binary systems containing neutron stars. *Mailing Add:* Dept of Math & Astron Lehigh Univ Bethlehem PA 18015

MCCLUSKEY, ROBERT TIMMONS, b New Haven, Conn, Jan 16, 23; m 57; c 2. PATHOLOGY. *Educ:* Yale Univ, AB, 44; NY Univ, MD, 47. *Prof Exp:* Intern, Kings County Hosp, Brooklyn, NY, 47-49, asst resident path, 49-50; asst, Sch Med, NY Univ, 50-52, from instr to prof & dir univ hosp labs, 52-68; prof path & chmn dept, Sch Med & Dent, State Univ NY Buffalo, 68-71; S Burt Wolbach Prof, 71-74, MALLINCKRODT PROF PATH, HARVARD MED SCH, 75-; CHIEF PATH, MASS GEN HOSP, 74- *Concurrent Pos:* Resident, Bellevue Hosp, NY, 50-52, asst pathologist, 52-53, 55-60, assoc pathologist, 60; consult, Manhattan Vet Admin Hosp, NY, 59-68; pathologist-in-chief, Children's Hosp Med Ctr, 71-74; co-ed, Clin Immunol & Immunopath. *Mem:* Am Soc Exp Path; AMA; Asn Path & Bact; Int Acad Path; Am Soc Nephrology. *Res:* Pathogenesis of glomerulonephritis; pathogenesis of cell mediated reactions; identification of lymphocyte subsets in tissue sections with monoclonal antibodies. *Mailing Add:* Mass Gen Hosp Boston MA 02114

MCCLYMONT, JOHN WILBUR, b Geneseo, NY, Feb 13, 25; m 52; c 1. BOTANY. *Educ:* Syracuse Univ, AB, 49, MS, 50; Univ Mich, PhD(bot), 55. *Prof Exp:* Asst prof biol, Milwaukee-Downer Col, 54-59; assoc prof, Morris Harvey Col, 59-61; prof, Findlay Col, 61-65; PROF BIOL, SOUTHERN CONN STATE COL, 65- *Mem:* Am Bryol & Lichenological Soc; Bot Soc Am. *Res:* Spores of the Bryophyta. *Mailing Add:* Dept of Biol Southern Conn State Col New Haven CT 06515

MCCOART, RICHARD F, JR, mathematics, see previous edition

MCCOLL, DANIEL CLYDE, theoretical physics, elementary particle physics, see previous edition

MCCOLL, JAMES RENFREW, b Albany, NY, Oct 30, 40; m 62; c 3. EXPERIMENTAL SOLID STATE PHYSICS. *Educ:* Univ Rochester, BS, 62; Univ Calif, Berkeley, PhD(physics), 67. *Prof Exp:* NATO fel, Clarendon Lab, Oxford, Eng, 67-68; asst prof physics, Yale Univ, 68-73, assoc prof, 73-76; MEM TECH STAFF, GTE LABS, WALTHAM, MASS, 76- *Res:* Liquid crystals; amorphous solids; phosphors. *Mailing Add:* 40 Sylvan Rd GTE Labs Waltham MA 02254

MCCOLL, JOHN DUNCAN, b London, Ont, Nov 11, 25; m 54; c 3. PHARMACOLOGY. *Educ:* Univ Western Ont, BA, 46, MSc, 50; Univ Toronto, PhD(pharmacol), 53. *Prof Exp:* Asst res chemist, Parke, Davis & Co, Mich, 50-51; dir pharmacol res, Frank W Horner, Ltd, Can, 53-62, asst dir res, 62-69; vpres biol sci, Mead Johnson Res Ctr, 70-75; VPRES & DIR RES & DEVELOP, CHATTEM INC, 75- *Concurrent Pos:* Mem toxicol panel, Defence Res Bd Can, 69-72. *Mem:* Am Soc Pharmacol & Exp Therapeut; Am Soc Clin Pharmacol & Therapeut; NY Acad Sci; Pharmacol Soc Can (secy, 61-63); Can Biochem Soc. *Res:* Toxicology; neuropharmacology; central nervous system agents; biochemistry. *Mailing Add:* Chattem Inc Chattanooga TN 37409

MCCOLL, MALCOLM, b Detroit, Mich, Oct 6, 33; m 54; c 2. ELECTRONICS ENGINEERING. *Educ:* Wayne State Univ, BS, 57; Calif Inst Technol, MS, 58, PhD(elec eng), 64. *Prof Exp:* RES SCIENTIST, IVAN A GETTING LABS, AEROSPACE CORP, 62- *Concurrent Pos:* Res fel, Calif Inst Technol, 64-66. *Mem:* Am Phys Soc; Inst Elec & Electronic Engrs. *Res:* Transport mechanisms in electronic devices; development of millimeter and submillimeter-wave detectors; solid-state device fabrication. *Mailing Add:* Aerospace Corp PO Box 92957 Los Angeles CA 90009

MACCOLL, ROBERT, b Brooklyn, NY, Mar 27, 42; m 63; c 3. PHYSICAL CHEMISTRY, BIOCHEMISTRY. *Educ:* Queens Col, NY, BA, 63; Univ Miss, MS, 67; Adelphi Univ, PhD(phys chem), 69. *Prof Exp:* Fel, 69-70, res scientist, 70-72, SR RES SCIENTIST, DIV LABS & RES, NY STATE DEPT HEALTH, 72- *Concurrent Pos:* Asst prof microbiol, Albany Med Col, 74- *Mem:* Am Chem Soc; Am Soc Photobiol. *Res:* Protein chemistry; photosynthesis; virus assembly; interactions between proteins and chromophores. *Mailing Add:* Div Labs & Res NY State Dept Health Albany NY 12201

MCCOLLESTER, DUNCAN L, b Tyringham, Mass, July 2, 25; m 57; c 1. CANCER. *Educ:* Harvard Univ, BA, 48; Tufts Univ, MD, 53; Univ Cambridge, PhD(biochem), 64. *Prof Exp:* From intern to resident med, Bellevue Hosp, New York, 53-56; clin assoc, Nat Heart Inst, 56-58; RES ASSOC COLUMBIA-PRESBY MED CTR, 65- *Mem:* AAAS; Brit Biochem Soc; Biophys Soc; Am Chem Soc. *Res:* Separation and properties of cell surface membranes; cancer immunology; cancer specific immunotherapy. *Mailing Add:* PS14-402 Columbia-Presby Med Ctr 630 W 168th St New York NY 10032

MCCOLLISTER, ROBERT JOHN, b Iowa City, Iowa, July 27, 28; m 58; c 2. INTERNAL MEDICINE. *Educ:* State Univ Iowa, BA, 49, MD, 52. *Prof Exp:* Instr med, Sch Med, Univ Minn, Minneapolis, 59-61; instr, Duke Univ, 61-62; from instr to asst prof, 62-69, ASSOC PROF MED, SCH MED, UNIV MINN, MINNEAPOLIS, 69-, ASST DEAN SCH, 64- *Mem:* Am Fedn Clin Res; Am Soc Hemat. *Res:* Hematology; medical education. *Mailing Add:* Box 33 Mayo Mem Bldg Univ of Minn Med Ctr Minneapolis MN 55455

MCCOLLOCH, ROBERT JAMES, b Manhattan, Kans, July 26, 20; m 48; c 2. PHYSICAL CHEMISTRY, BIOCHEMISTRY. *Educ:* Kans State Col, BS, 41, PhD(phys biochem), 48. *Prof Exp:* Asst & asst chemist agr biochem, Purdue Univ, 42-44; from investr to res assoc, Plant Biochem, Cornell Univ, 44-48; chemist, Fruit & Veg Chem Lab, USDA, 48-52, unit supvr agr res serv, 52-56; assoc prof agr res chem, 56-58, PROF BIOCHEM & HEAD DIV, UNIV WYO, 58-, DEAN GRAD SCH, 72- *Concurrent Pos:* Instr Kans State Col, 46-47. *Mem:* AAAS; Am Chem Soc; Am Soc Plant Physiol; Am Soc Animal Sci; NY Acad Sci. *Res:* Plant biochemistry; citrus products biochemistry and technology; pectic substances and pectic enzymes; instrumentation. *Mailing Add:* Grad Sch Univ Wyo PO Box 3108 Univ Sta Laramie WY 82070

MACCOLLOM, GEORGE BUTTERICK, b Boston, Mass, June 10, 25; m 53; c 4. ENTOMOLOGY. *Educ:* Univ Mass, BS, 50; Cornell Univ, PhD, 54. *Prof Exp:* Entomologist, Exp Sta, 54-66, PROF ENTOM, UNIV VT, 66- *Mem:* Entom Soc Am. *Res:* Biology and control of apple insects; detection and measurement of environmental contamination by insecticides. *Mailing Add:* Dept Plant & Soil Sci Univ of Vt Burlington VT 05401

MCCOLLOM, KENNETH A(LLEN), b Sentinel, Okla, June 17, 22; m 44; c 2. ELECTRICAL ENGINEERING, NUCLEAR ENGINEERING. *Educ:* Okla State Univ, BS, 48; Univ Ill, MS, 49; Iowa State Univ, PhD(elec eng), 64. *Prof Exp:* Jr engr, Res Div, Phillips Petrol Co, 49-51, group leader nuclear instrumentation design, Atomic Energy Div, 51-54, engr, Res Div, 54-57, br mgr, Instrument Develop Br, Atomic Energy Div, 57-62; assoc nuclear reactor control, Ames Lab, Iowa State Univ, 62-64; assoc prof, 64-67, from asst dean to assoc dean eng, 68-77, PROF ELEC ENG, OKLA STATE UNIV, 67-, DEAN ENG, 77- *Concurrent Pos:* Consult, Ames Lab, Iowa State Univ, 64-65, Babcock & Wilcox Corp, 64-65 & Atlantic Refining Co, 65-68; admin law judge, Atomic Safety & Licensing Bd Panel, US Nuclear Regulatory Comn, 72- *Honors & Awards:* Chester F. Carlson Award, Am Soc Eng Educ, 73. *Mem:* Sr mem Inst Elec & Electronics Engrs; Am Nuclear Soc; Nat Soc Prof Engrs; Am Soc Eng Educ. *Res:* Nuclear reactor instrumentation and control design; design of physical and chemical measuring instrumentation; use of computers in control system design; implementation and design of innovative educational methods. *Mailing Add:* Col Eng 111 Eng North Okla State Univ Stillwater OK 74078

MCCOLLOUGH, FRED, JR, b Crawfordsville, Ind, July 19, 28; m 52; c 2. INORGANIC CHEMISTRY. *Educ:* Wabash Col, AB, 50; Univ Ill, MS, 52, PhD(chem), 55. *Prof Exp:* Sr res chemist, Victor Chem Works, 55-57, supvr inorg res, 57-64; assoc prof, 64-71, PROF CHEM, MacMURRAY COL, 71-, CHMN DEPT, 69- *Mem:* Am Chem Soc. *Res:* Coordination and phosphorus chemistry; computer application to undergraduate teaching. *Mailing Add:* 407 Sandusky St Jacksonville IL 62650

MCCOLLUM, ANTHONY WAYNE, b Macomb, Ill, Sept 3, 44; c 3. ORGANIC CHEMISTRY. *Educ:* Western Ill Univ, BS, 65; Univ Ark, Fayetteville, PhD(org chem), 69. *Prof Exp:* Chemist, 69-74, group leader appl chem res & sr chemist, 74-79, head res & develop planning & serv, 77-79, res assoc, 79, HEAD, CHEM RES DEPT, TEX EASTMAN CO, DIV EASTMAN KODAK CO, 79- *Mem:* Am Chem Soc. *Res:* Organic synthesis; new monomer synthesis; natural products synthesis; aldol chemistry; high solids and water-borne coatings. *Mailing Add:* Tex Eastman Co Box 7444 Longview TX 75601

MCCOLLUM, CLIFFORD GLENN, b Macon Co, Mo, May 12, 19; m 40; c 2. ZOOLOGY, HISTORY OF SCIENCE. *Educ:* Univ Mo, BS, 39, AM, 47, EdD(zool), 49. *Prof Exp:* Instr high schs, Mo, 38-43; asst prof, State Col Iowa, 49-55; prof State Univ NY Col Oneonta, 55-56; assoc prof sci, 56-59, head dept, 57-68, PROF BIOL, UNIV NORTHERN IOWA, 59-, DEAN COL NATURAL SCI, 68- *Concurrent Pos:* Consult, schs & cols sci curricula. *Mem:* AAAS; Nat Sci Teachers Asn; Nat Asn Res Sci Teaching; Nat Asn Biol Teachers; Hist Sci Soc. *Res:* Small mammal populations; science curricula in elementary and secondary schools. *Mailing Add:* Col of Nat Sci Univ of Northern Iowa Cedar Falls IA 50613

MCCOLLUM, DONALD CARRUTH, JR, b Baltimore, Md, Nov 6, 30; m 52; c 1. PHYSICS. *Educ:* Univ Calif, BA, 53, MA, 54, PhD(physics), 60. *Prof Exp:* From instr to assoc prof, 58-72, PROF PHYSICS, UNIV CALIF, RIVERSIDE, 72- *Concurrent Pos:* NSF fac fel, 65. *Mem:* Am Phys Soc; Am Asn Physics Teachers. *Res:* Low temperature physics. *Mailing Add:* Dept of Physics Univ of Calif Riverside CA 92502

MCCOLLUM, DONALD E, b Winston Salem, NC, Dec 7, 27; m 53; c 1. ORTHOPEDIC SURGERY. *Educ:* Wake Forest Col, BS, 49; Bowman Gray Sch Med, MD, 53. *Prof Exp:* Resident orthop surg, 58-62, from asst prof to assoc prof, 62-72, PROF ORTHOP SURG, MED CTR, DUKE UNIV, 72- *Concurrent Pos:* NIH trainee rheumatology, Med Ctr, Duke Univ, 57-58; consult, Vet Admin Hosp, 62-; orthop consult, US Air Force & Voc Rehab, 64- *Mem:* Am Acad Orthop Surg; Am Rheumatism Asn; Am Orthop Asn; Asn Bone & Joint Surgeons. *Res:* Rheumatology. *Mailing Add:* Dept of Orthop Surg Duke Univ Med Ctr Durham NC 27710

MCCOLLUM, GILBERT DEWEY, JR, b Bellingham, Wash, Aug 25, 29. PLANT CYTOGENETICS. *Educ:* Wash State Univ, BS, 51, MS, 53; Univ Calif, PhD(genetics), 58. *Prof Exp:* RES GENETICIST, AGR RES SERV, USDA, 58- *Mem:* Bot Soc Am; Am Genetic Asn. *Res:* Botany; cytology; genetics; species relationships. *Mailing Add:* Hort Sci Inst Veg Lab Agr Res Ctr USDA Beltsville MD 20705

MCCOLLUM, GIN, b Washington, DC. NEUROBIOLOGY. *Educ:* Brandeis Univ, BA, 69; Yeshiva Univ, PhD(physics), 75. *Prof Exp:* MEM STAFF, NEUROL SCI INST, GOOD SAMARITAN HOSP & MED CTR, 81- *Mailing Add:* Good Samaritan Hosp 1015 Northwest 22nd Ave Portland OR 97210

MCCOLLUM, JOHN DAVID, b Evanston, Ill, Jan 8, 29; m 50; c 2. CHEMISTRY. *Educ:* Univ Ill, Urbana, BSc, 49; Harvard Univ, AM, 51, PhD(chem), 57. *Prof Exp:* Sr res scientist, Res & Develop Dept, Am Oil Co, 53-72, RES ASSOC, AMOCO OIL CO, 72- *Mem:* Am Chem Soc; Am Inst Chemists. *Res:* Homogeneous and heterogeneous catalysis of hydrocarbon reactions; organometallic chemistry; photo and radiation chemistry of hydrocarbons; high pressure hydrothermal reactions; fuel technology. *Mailing Add:* Amoco Oil Co Res & Develop Dept PO Box 400 Naperville IL 60540

MCCOLLUM, ROBERT EDMUND, b Reidsville, NC, Jan 3, 22; m 46; c 6. SOILS, PLANT BIOCHEMISTRY. *Educ:* NC State Col, BS, 52, MS, 53; Univ Ill, PhD, 57. *Prof Exp:* Asst, NC State Col, 52-53 & Univ Ill, 53-57; ASSOC PROF SOIL FERTIL, NC STATE UNIV, 57- *Concurrent Pos:* NC State Univ-US Agency Int Develop Proj, Peru, 63-66. *Mem:* Am Soc Agron. *Res:* Soil chemistry and fertility. *Mailing Add:* Dept Soil Sci NC State Univ Raleigh NC 27650

MCCOLLUM, ROBERT WAYNE, b Waco, Tex, Jan 29, 25; m 54; c 2. EPIDEMIOLOGY. *Educ:* Baylor Univ, AB, 45; Johns Hopkins Univ, MD, 48; Univ London, DPH, 58. *Prof Exp:* Asst prev med, 51-52, from asst prof to assoc prof epidemiol & prev med, 54-65, PROF EPIDEMIOL, SCH MED, YALE UNIV, 65-, CHMN DEPT EPIDEMIOL & PUB HEALTH, 69- *Concurrent Pos:* Assoc mem comn viral infections, Armed Forces Epidemiol Bd, 59-61, mem, 61-72; consult, Surgeon Gen, 61- & WHO, 62-63, 70, 72 & 74. *Mem:* Soc Epidemiol Res; Int Epidemiol Asn; Am Epidemiol Soc; Infectious Dis Soc Am; Am Pub Health Asn. *Res:* Infectious diseases; viral hepatitis. *Mailing Add:* Dept of Epidemiol & Pub Health Yale Univ Sch of Med New Haven CT 06510

MCCOLLUM, WILLIAM HOWARD, b Traveller's Rest, Ky, Aug 17, 23. VIROLOGY. *Educ:* Univ Ky, BS, 47, MS, 49; Univ Wis, PhD(bact, biochem), 54. *Prof Exp:* Bacteriologist virol, 54-60, prof animal path, 60, PROF VET SCI, UNIV KY, 63- *Mem:* Am Soc Microbiol; Poultry Sci Asn; Tissue Cult Asn. *Res:* Virus diseases of animals, especially the horse; immunology. *Mailing Add:* Dept of Vet Sci Univ of KY Lexington KY 40506

MCCOLLY, HOWARD F(RANKLIN), b Ames, Iowa, Apr 8, 02; m 26; c 3. AGRICULTURAL ENGINEERING. *Educ:* Iowa State Univ, BS, 25, MS, 26. *Prof Exp:* Mem staff, Deere & Co, Ill, 25-28; asst agr engr, NDak Agr Col, 29-31, head, Agr Eng Dept, 31-39; secy & chief engr, State Water Conserv Comn, NDak, 39-41; construct engr, USDA, Colo, 41-42, chief water facilities eng, 42-46, res agr engr, Comt Agr Eng to China, 46-49; prof, 49-70, EMER PROF AGR ENG, MICH STATE UNIV, 70- *Concurrent Pos:* Foreign assignments, Taiwan, 60-62, Saudi Arabia, 66, Asian studies, 67 & Peru, 69; Div ed, Am Soc Agr Engrs Transactions, 72-80. *Honors & Awards:* McCormick Gold Medal, Am Soc Agr Engrs, 68. *Mem:* Fel Am Soc Agr Engrs. *Mailing Add:* 225 Kensington Rd East Lansing MI 48823

MCCOLM, DOUGLAS WOODRUFF, b Kisaran, Sumatra, Sept 26, 33; US citizen; m 55; c 3. PHYSICS. *Educ:* Oberlin Col, BA, 55; Yale Univ, PhD(physics), 61. *Prof Exp:* Staff physicist, Lawrence Radiation Lab, Univ Calif, Berkeley, 61-66; ASSOC PROF PHYSICS, UNIV CALIF, DAVIS, 66- *Mem:* Am Phys Soc. *Res:* Atomic physics. *Mailing Add:* Dept of Physics Univ Calif 1000 Plum Lane Davis CA 95616

MCCOMAS, STUART T, b Shelbyville, Ind, Apr 23, 32; m 56; c 2. HEAT TRANSFER, FLUID MECHANICS. *Educ:* Marquette Univ, BSME, 56; Univ Minn, MS, 60, PhD, 64. *Prof Exp:* Instr mech eng, Marquette Univ, 56-58 & Univ Minn, 60-63; from asst prof to assoc prof, 63-71, asst dean, 70-76, PROF MECH ENG, UNIV NOTRE DAME, 71- *Concurrent Pos:* Consult, Inc, 66-67 & Miles Lab Inc, 69; vis engr, US Environ Protection Agency, 74-75. *Mem:* Am Soc Mech Engrs; Sigma Xi. *Res:* Thermodynamics and heat transfer; solar energy; energy conservation; energy conversion. *Mailing Add:* Dept Aerospace & Mech Eng Univ of Notre Dame Notre Dame IN 46556

MCCOMBE, BRUCE DOUGLAS, b Sanford, Maine, Mar 2, 38; m 63; c 1. SOLID STATE PHYSICS, SEMICONDUCTOR PHYSICS. *Educ:* Bowdoin Col, AB, 60; Brown Univ, PhD(physics), 66. *Prof Exp:* Nat Res Coun/Naval Res Lab res assoc semiconductor physics, 65-67, res physicist, 67-70, actg head surface & transp sect, 70, head semiconductor & appln sct, 70-73, head optical interactions sect, 73-74, head, Semiconductors Br, 74-80, SUPT, ELECTRONICS TECHNOL DIV, NAVAL RES LAB, 80- *Concurrent Pos:* Mem ad hoc comt elec properties, Nat Res Coun/Nat Acad Sci, 70, mem ad hoc panel high magnetic field res & facil, 77-78; Naval Res Lab sabbatical study prog, Max Planck Inst Solid State Res, Stuttgart, 72-73; Navy mem tech rev comt, Joint Serv Electronics Prog, Dept Defense, 74-; mem var prog comts int conf, 74-; adj prof physics, State Univ NY Buffalo, 78; mem Mat Res adv comt, NSF, 78- *Honors & Awards:* Pure Sci Award, Sci Res Soc Am, 72. *Mem:* Fel Am Phys Soc; Sigma Xi. *Res:* Semiconductors; infrared and far infrared properties of solids; magneto-optical studies of semiconductors; metal-insulator-semiconductor structures; photoluminescence in semiconductors; electronic materials characterization; electron devices. *Mailing Add:* Electronics Technol Div Code 6800 Naval Res Lab Washington DC 20375

MCCOMBS, CHARLES ALLAN, b Oklahoma City, Okla, Aug 28, 48; m 71. ORGANIC CHEMISTRY. *Educ:* Calif State Univ, Long Beach, BS, 73; Univ Calif, Los Angeles, PhD(org chem), 78. *Prof Exp:* RES CHEMIST ORG CHEM, RES LABS, TENN EASTMAN CO, 78- *Mem:* Am Chem Soc. *Res:* Development of new synthetic reagents; new methodology for total synthesis; transition metal catalysis for organic synthesis. *Mailing Add:* Res Labs Bldg 150B Tenn Eastman Co Kingsport TN 37662

MCCOMBS, CLARENCE LESLIE, b Westerville, Ohio, Nov 5, 20; m 42; c 3. PLANT PHYSIOLOGY. *Educ:* Ohio State Univ, BSc, 47, MSc, 48, PhD(hort), 55. *Prof Exp:* Agent horticulturist, Wenatchee Field Sta, USDA, 49-50; from instr to prof hort, NC State Univ, 50-71; prof hort & head dept, 71-81, EXTEN SPECIALIST SMALL FRUIT, VA POLYTECH INST & STATE UNIV, 81- *Mem:* Am Soc Hort Sci. *Res:* Biochemical changes in vegetables during the post-harvest period; mechanism of disease resistance in vegetable varieties. *Mailing Add:* Dept Hort Va Polytech Inst & State Univ Blacksburg VA 24061

MCCOMBS, FREDA SILER, b Asheville, NC, Feb 26, 33; m 62; c 3. SCIENCE EDUCATION. *Educ:* Salem Col, BS, 55; Univ NC, Chapel Hill, MEd, 59, EdD(sci educ), 63. *Prof Exp:* Teacher gen sci & biol city schs, Va, 55-56; teacher biol & chem pub schs, NC, 57-58; instr biol & phys sci, Longwood Col, 61-63; assoc prof biol, Cent Va Community Col, 68-70; asst prof, 70-71, ASSOC PROF SCI EDUC, LONGWOOD COL, 71- *Res:* Curriculum materials; teaching aids and student resource materials for elementary science, particularly kindergarten and primary grades. *Mailing Add:* Dept of Natural Sci Longwood Col Farmville VA 23901

MCCOMIS, WILLIAM T(HOMAS), b Chicago, Ill, Aug 20, 38; m 62; c 1. FOOD SCIENCE, BIOMEDICAL ENGINEERING. *Educ:* Ill Inst Technol, BS, 60; Mass Inst Technol, PhD(food sci), 64. *Prof Exp:* Res food technologist, Div Biochem & Microbiol, 64-67, div chief, Div Microbiol & Environ Biol, 67-69, div chief, 69-71, assoc chief, Div Food & Biol Sci, 71-73, sect mgr, 73-74, assoc mgr, Bioeng-Health Sci Sect, 74-79, PROG MGR, BIOMED SCI SECT, COLUMBUS DIV, BATTELLE MEM INST, 79- *Concurrent Pos:* Jr technician, Post Cereal Div, Gen Foods Corp, 60. *Mem:* AAAS; Inst Food Technol; Soc Rheol. *Res:* Food product and process development; microbiology and public health. *Mailing Add:* Biomed Sci Sect Battelle Mem Inst Columbus Div Columbus OH 43201

MCCONAGHY, JOHN STEAD, JR, b Philadelphia, Pa, Feb 3, 42; m 65; c 2. PHYSICAL ORGANIC CHEMISTRY, CATALYSIS. *Educ:* Haverford Col, BA, 63; Yale Univ, MS, 64, PhD(org chem), 66. *Prof Exp:* Sr res chemist, Cent Res Dept, 66-69 & Petrochem Res Dept, 69-75, res group leader, 76-80, SR RES GROUP LEADER, PETROCHEM RES DEPT, MONSANTO CO, 80- *Mem:* Am Chem Soc; Sigma Xi. *Res:* Mechanism; catalysis; vapor phase reactions; organometallic chemistry. *Mailing Add:* Monsanto Co 800 N Lindbergh Blvd St Louis MO 63166

MCCONAHEY, WILLIAM MCCONNELL, JR, b Pittsburgh, Pa, May 7, 16; m 40; c 3. INTERNAL MEDICINE, ENDOCRINOLOGY. *Educ:* Washington & Jefferson Col, AB, 38; Harvard Med Sch, MD, 42; Univ Minn, MS, 48. *Prof Exp:* Intern, Philadelphia Gen Hosp, 42-43; fel internal med, Mayo Grad Sch Med, 46-48; from instr to prof, Mayo Grad Sch Med, 50-73, chmn dept endocrinol, 67-74, PROF MED, MAYO MED SCH, 73- *Concurrent Pos:* Consult, Mayo Clin & Hosps, 49- *Mem:* Endocrine Soc; Am Diabetes Asn; Am Thyroid Asn (treas, 61-65, secy, 66-70, pres, 75-76); Am Fedn Clin Res; fel Am Col Physicians. *Res:* Diseases of the thyroid gland. *Mailing Add:* Div of Endocrinol Mayo Clin Rochester MN 55901

MCCONATHY, WALTER JAMES, b McAlester, Okla, Nov 3, 41; m 66; c 1. LIPID CHEMISTRY, PROTEIN CHEMISTRY. *Educ:* Univ Okla, Norman, BA, 64, BS, 66; Univ Okla, Oklahoma City, PhD(biochem), 71. *Prof Exp:* Fel, 71-74, staff scientist, 74-75, ASST MEM LIPOPROTEINS, OKLA MED RES FOUND, 75- *Mem:* Am Heart Asn; Sigma Xi; AAAS. *Res:* Investigating the structure, function and interrelations of human plasma lipoproteins in both normal and pathological conditions for potential application as diagnostic or prognostic tools in human disease states. *Mailing Add:* Lipoprotein Lab Okla Med Res Found 825 NE 13th St Oklahoma City OK 73104

MCCONAUGHY, DAVID LESTER, b Pittsburgh, Pa, Nov 7, 21; m 43; c 4. CHEMICAL PHYSICS. *Educ:* Muskingum Col, BS, 43. *Prof Exp:* Sr fel protective coatings, Mellon Inst, 46-60; res chemist, 60-65, prod res chemist, 65-67, DIR RES & DEVELOP, ELEC MAT CO, 67- *Mem:* Am Foundrymen's Soc; Am Soc Metals; Am Inst Mining, Metall & Petrol Eng; Metall Soc. *Res:* Development of processes and materials in producing and fabrication of copper alloys into mill products, forgings, castings and special machinery; development of new materials, alloys and circuits for electric commutators; copper heating and melting equipment. *Mailing Add:* Elec Materials Co Clay & Washington North East PA 16428

MCCONKEY, JOHN WILLIAM, b Portadown, North Ireland. PHYSICS. *Educ:* Queen's Univ Belfast, BSc, 58, PhD(physics), 62. *Prof Exp:* Lectr physics, Queen's Univ Belfast, 63-70; PROF PHYSICS, UNIV WINDSOR, 70- *Mem:* Fel Brit Inst Physics; Am Phys Soc; Can Asn Physicists. *Res:* Electron collisions; atmospheric processes; spectroscopy. *Mailing Add:* Dept of Physics Univ of Windsor Windsor ON N9B 3P4 Can

MACCONNACHIE, HUGH JOHN, b New Glasgow, NS, Dec 29, 20; m 42; c 3. RESTORATIVE DENTISTRY. *Educ:* Dalhousie Univ, DDS, 53; Ind Univ, MSD, 67. *Prof Exp:* PROF OPER DENT, DALHOUSIE UNIV, 65-, CHMN DEPT RESTORATIVE DENT, 69- *Mem:* Int Asn Dent Res; Can Dent Asn. *Res:* Restorative dental materials. *Mailing Add:* Fac of Dent Dalhousie Univ Halifax NS B3H 3J5 Can

MCCONNACHIE, PETER ROSS, b Montreal, Que, Mar 31, 40; m 64; c 2. IMMUNOBIOLOGY. *Educ:* Univ BC, BSc, 62, MSc, 65; Univ Alta, PhD(immunol), 70. *Prof Exp:* Sr scientist tissue typing, Dept Clin Path, Univ Hosp, Edmonton, Alta, 70-74, sr scientist, Transplant Lab, 74-75; DIR TRANSPLANT LAB, MEM MED CTR, 75-; ASSOC PROF MED MICROBIOL & IMMUNOL, SCH MED, SOUTHERN ILL UNIV, 80- *Concurrent Pos:* Immunologist II, Dept Surg, Univ Calif, Los Angeles, 72-73; sessional lectr path, Med Lab Sci, Univ Alta, 73-, prof asst, Med Res Coun Can Transplant Immunol Unit, 74-75. *Mem:* AAAS; Can Soc Clin Invest. *Res:* Transplantation immunology; histo compatibility; reproductive immunology. *Mailing Add:* Transplant Lab Mem Med Ctr Springfield IL 62702

MCCONNAUGHEY, BAYARD HARLOW, b Pittsburgh, Pa, Apr 21, 16; m 49; c 5. MARINE BIOLOGY. *Educ:* Pomona Col, BA, 38; Univ Hawaii, MA, 41; Univ Calif, PhD(zool), 48. *Prof Exp:* Asst zool, Univ Calif, 38-40 & Univ Hawaii, 40-41; asst, Scripps Inst, Univ Calif, 47-48, res assoc, 48; from asst prof to assoc prof, 48-72, PROF BIOL, UNIV ORE, 72- *Concurrent Pos:* Ky Contract Team assoc prof, Inst Agr Sci, Fac Fisheries, Univ Indonesia, 63-66; guest scientist, Coun Sci, Indonesia, 66; mem fac, World Campus Afloat, 75. *Mem:* Fel AAAS; Soc Syst Zool; Am Soc Parasitol; Am Soc Limnol & Oceanog; Sigma Xi. *Res:* Taxonomy and life history of the Mesozoa; microbiology; association analysis; plankton communities; delimiting and characterizing marine biotic communities. *Mailing Add:* Dept of Biol Univ of Ore Eugene OR 97403

MCCONNEL, ROBERT MERRIMAN, b Rochester, Pa, Mar 19, 36; m 62. MATHEMATICS. *Educ:* Washington & Jefferson Col, BA, 58; Duke Univ, PhD(math), 62. *Prof Exp:* Asst prof math, Univ Ariz, 62-64; asst prof, 64-66, assoc prof, 66-76, PROF MATH, UNIV TENN, KNOXVILLE, 76- *Mem:* Am Math Soc; Math Asn Am. *Res:* Number theory; finite field theory; polynomials over finite fields. *Mailing Add:* Dept of Math Univ of Tenn Knoxville TN 37916

MCCONNELL, BRUCE, b Pittsburgh, Pa, Sept 12, 32; m 64; c 1. BIOCHEMISTRY. *Educ:* Grove City Col, BS, 54; Univ Vt, PhD(biochem), 66. *Prof Exp:* Tech rep, Atlas Powder Co, Del, 54-56; pilot plant supvr, Koppers Co, Inc, Pa, 56-59; NIH fel molecular biol, Dartmouth Med Sch, 66 & Univ Ore, 66-69; asst prof, 69-74, ASSOC PROF BIOPHYS, UNIV HAWAII, HONOLULU, 74- *Concurrent Pos:* NSF res grant. *Mem:* Am Chem Soc. *Res:* Physical chemistry and biosynthesis of macromolecules; protein chemistry and isolation; molecular configurations of DNA by hydrogen exchange and physical-chemical; nuclear magnetic resonance-proton exchange. *Mailing Add:* Dept of Biochem & Biophys Univ of Hawaii Honolulu HI 96822

MCCONNELL, C(HARLES) W(ILLIAM), b Salem, Ohio, July 24, 12; m 37; c 2. CHEMICAL ENGINEERING. *Educ:* Carnegie Inst Technol, BS, 34, ChE, 38. *Prof Exp:* Res chem engr, Conewango Refining Co, 34-36, chief chemist, 36-39; chem engr, Linde Air Prod Co, 39-44, patent engr, 44-53, engr, Patent Dept, Union Carbide & Carbon Corp, 53-58, asst div attorney, Union Carbide Corp, 58-61, Prom & Advert Dept, Chem Div, 61-63, ed, Chem Prog, 63-67, publ mgr, Chem & Plastics Div, 67-77; RETIRED. *Res:* Lube oil refining; antifreeze; synthetic lubricants. *Mailing Add:* 17 Ann Dr Tappan NY 10983

MCCONNELL, DAVID GRAHAM, b Bronxville, NY, Dec 3, 26; m 48; c 4. BIOPHYSICS, BIOCHEMISTRY. *Educ:* Columbia Univ, AB & AM, 49; Ind Univ, PhD(exp psychol), 57. *Prof Exp:* Res assoc psychol, Ohio State Univ, 56-61, res assoc chem, 60-61; proj dir med prog, Britannica Ctr, Calif, 61-62; assoc prof physiol optics, Ohio State Univ, 62-65, assoc prof biophys, 65-71, assoc prof biochem, 67-71, prof biochem & biophys, 71-73; PROF BIOCHEM, MICH STATE UNIV, 73- *Concurrent Pos:* Vis assoc prof, Enzyme Inst, Univ Wis, 64-65. *Mem:* Psychonomic Soc; Biophys Soc; Am Soc Cell Biol; Am Soc Biol Chemists; Am Soc Neurochem. *Res:* Neurochemistry; photochemistry; photobiology; learning; electron microscopy of biological membranes; biochemistry of the retina. *Mailing Add:* Biochem Bldg Mich State Univ East Lansing MI 48824

MCCONNELL, DENNIS BROOKS, b Waupun, Wis, Aug 18, 38; m 64; c 2. ORNAMENTAL HORTICULTURE. *Educ:* Wis State Univ, River Falls, 66; Univ Wis-Madison, MS, 67, PhD(bot, hort), 70. *Prof Exp:* Asst prof ornamental hort, Agr Res Ctr, 70-75, ASSOC PROF ORNAMENTAL HORT, UNIV FLA, 75- *Mem:* Am Soc Hort Sci; Am Hort Soc; Bot Soc Am. *Res:* Morphology and anatomy of normal and experimentally modified subtropical and tropical plants. *Mailing Add:* Dept Ornamental Hort Univ Fla Gainesville FL 32601

MCCONNELL, DUNCAN, b Chicago, Ill, Jan 30, 09; m 34; c 3. DENTAL RESEARCH, MATERIALS SCIENCE. *Educ:* Washington & Lee Univ, BS, 31; Cornell Univ, MS, 32; Univ Minn, PhD(mineral), 37. *Prof Exp:* Instr mineral, Univ Tex, Austin, 37-41; chemist-petrographer, US Bur Reclamation, Denver, 41-47; actg asst div chief geol, Gulf Res & Develop Co, 47-50; prof mineral, 50-56 & 64-76, prof dent res, 57-76, EMER PROF DENT RES & GEOL MINERAL, OHIO STATE UNIV, 76- *Concurrent Pos:* USPHS spec res fel, Ohio State Univ, 57-61, USPHS grants, 57-68, US Army Med Res & Develop Command grant, 66-67; consult & site visitor, Nat Inst Dent Res, 73; examr, Dept Orthop Surg, Yale Univ, 73; consult, NSF, 73, Nat Inst Dent Res, 74 & Prev Dent Res Inst, Ind Univ, Ft Wayne, 74. *Mem:* Fel AAAS; Electron Micros Soc Am; fel Mineral Soc Am; Brit Mineral Soc; Soc Econ Geologists. *Res:* Crystal chemistry of inorganic component of teeth and bones, restorative materials, mineralization process and biogeochemistry of phosphate minerals. *Mailing Add:* Dept Chem Ohio State Univ Columbus OH 43210

MCCONNELL, ELLICOTT, b Providence, RI, Mar 4, 24; m 50; c 2. MEDICAL PARASITOLOGY. *Educ:* Univ Conn, BS, 49; Univ Minn, MS, 53, PhD(entom), 57. *Prof Exp:* Asst, Univ Minn, 50-55; entomologist, State Dept Agr, Minn, 56-57; microbiologist, Gorgas Mem Lab, Panama, 57-62; parasitologist, US Naval Med Res Unit 3, Cairo, 62-67, head dept parasitol, 63-67; entomologist, US Naval Med Res Unit 5, Addis Ababa, Ethiopia, 67-72, head med zool, 72-77; IMMUNOPARASITOL, NAVAL MED RES INST, 77- *Mem:* AAAS; Entom Soc Am; Am Soc Trop Med & Hyg; Am Soc Parasitol; Royal Soc Trop Med & Hyg. *Res:* African trypanosomiasis; leishmaniasis transmission; malaria. *Mailing Add:* Dept of Immunoparasitol Naval Med Res Inst Bethesda MD 20014

MCCONNELL, ERNEST EUGENE, b Orville, Ohio, Nov 14, 37; m 58; c 3. PATHOLOGY, VETERINARY MEDICINE. *Educ:* Ohio State Univ, DVM, 61; Mich State Univ, MS, 66; Am Col Vet Pathologists, dipl, 68; Am Bd Toxicol, 80. *Prof Exp:* Base vet, Hill AFB, Utah, 61-64; resident path, Armed Forces Inst Path, 65-67 & Aerospace Path Div, 67-69; researcher, Onderstepoort Vet Inst, S Africa, 69-72 & Inhalation Toxicol Lab, Wright Patterson AFB, 72-74; researcher, 74-80, CHIEF, CHEM PATHOL BR, NAT TOXICOL PROG, NAT INST ENVIRON HEALTH SCI, NIH, 80- *Concurrent Pos:* Mem biohazards safety comt, NIH, 76-79; mem exp design subgroup, Nat Cancer Inst, 77-80; adj asst prof vet sci, NC State Univ, 77-; consult, NC Zool Park, 77-81. *Mem:* Am Col Vet Pathologists; Am Vet Med Asn; AAAS; Wildlife Dis Asn. *Res:* Pathology of toxic chemicals of environmental interest, especially halogenated hydrocarbons; spontaneous diseases of primates. *Mailing Add:* Comp Path Sect PO Box 12233 Research Triangle Park NC 27709

MCCONNELL, FREEMAN ERTON, b West Point, Ind, Apr 20, 14; m 41; c 2. AUDIOLOGY. *Educ:* Univ Ill, BS, 39, MA, 46; Northwestern Univ, PhD(audiol), 50. *Prof Exp:* Instr, Ill High Sch, 39-43; high sch & jr col instr, 46-48; lectr speech correction & audiol, Northwestern Univ, 48-50; asst prof audiol, Inst Logopedics Wichita & Wichita Univ, 50-51; from asst prof to prof, Vanderbilt Univ, 51-60; prof & head dept, Univ Tenn, 60-63; head dept, 63-76, prof audiol & dir, Bill Wilkerson Hearing & Speech Ctr, 63-79, EMER PROF AUDIOL, VANDERBILT UNIV, 79- *Concurrent Pos:* Consult, Arnold Eng Develop Ctr, US Air Force, 53-71 & Bur Res, US Off Educ, 65-73; chmn bd dirs, Educ & Auditory Res Found, Nashville, 78-79; mem, US-Can Adv Comt, Ann Surv Hearing Impaired Children & Youth, 72-78. *Mem:* AAAS; Acoust Soc Am; fel Am Speech-Lang-Hearing Asn; Acad Rehab Audiol (pres, 71). *Res:* Clinical audiology; language impaired children; hereditary deafness. *Mailing Add:* Dept of Hearing & Speech Sci Vanderbilt Univ Med Ctr Nashville TN 37232

MCCONNELL, H(OWARD) M(ARION), b Dallas Co, Iowa, July 18, 24; div; c 4. ELECTRICAL ENGINEERING, ENGINEERING MANAGEMENT. *Educ:* Marquette Univ, BEE, 47; Carnegie Inst Technol, MS, 48, DSc(elec eng), 50. *Prof Exp:* Instr elec eng, Carnegie Inst Technol, 49-50, asst prof, 50-55; mgr res & develop, Jack & Heintz, Inc, 55-58, chief engr, 58-62; dir eng, Power Equip Div, Lear-Siegler, Inc, 62-63; prod mgr, Harris-Intertype Corp, 64-67, chief printing systs res, 67-68, chief elec engr, Harris-Seybold Co, 68-74; consult, 74-78; programmer/analyst, 78-80, STAFF ENGR, AVTRON MFG INC, 80- *Concurrent Pos:* Lectr, Exten Div, Univ Pittsburgh, 50-51; design engr, Westinghouse Elec Corp, 50-51; lectr, Cleveland State Univ, 81- *Res:* Electrical machinery; magnetic amplifiers; magnetic materials; aircraft accessories; graphic arts equipment; food processing machinery; computer programming; aerospace test equipment. *Mailing Add:* 331 Oakmoor Ave Bay Village OH 44140

MCCONNELL, HARDEN MARSDEN, b Richmond, Va, July 18, 27; m 56; c 3. BIOPHYSICAL CHEMISTRY. *Educ:* George Washington Univ, BS, 47; Calif Inst Technol, PhD(chem), 51. *Prof Exp:* Nat Res Coun fel physics, Univ Chicago, 50-52; res chemist, Shell Develop Co, 52-56; from asst prof to prof chem, Calif Inst Technol, 56-65; prof, 65-79, ROBERT ECKLES SWAIN PROF CHEM, STANFORD UNIV, 79- *Concurrent Pos:* Consult, Calif Res Corp, 59-65, Varian Assocs, 64-66 & Syva, 69-76; consult, Exxon, 75-, Becton, Dickinson & Co, 77- & DNAX, 81- *Honors & Awards:* Pure Chem Award, 62, Harrison Howe Award, 68 & Irving Langmuir Award, Am Chem Soc, 71; Harkins lectr, Univ Chicago, 67; Falk-Plaut lectr, Columbia Univ, 67; Debeye lectr, Cornell Univ, 71; Harvey lectr, Rockefeller Univ, 77; A L Patterson lectr, Inst Cancer Res, Univ Pennsylvania, 78. *Mem:* Nat Acad Sci; fel Am Phys Soc; Am Soc Biol Chemists; Biophys Soc; Am Chem Soc. *Res:* Spin distributions and hyperfine interactions in organic radicals, electron and nuclear magnetic resonance spectroscopy; excitons in molecular crystals; spin labels; biological membranes. *Mailing Add:* Dept Chem Stanford Univ Stanford CA 94305

MCCONNELL, JACK BAYLOR, b Crumpler, WVa, Feb 1, 25; m 58. MEDICINE. *Educ:* Univ Tenn, MD, 49. *Prof Exp:* Resident, Baylor Univ, 49-52; assoc dir prof serv, Lederle Labs, Am Cyanamid Co, NY, 53-57, dir clin invest, 57-59, dir clin develop, 59-61; exec dir new prod div, McNeil Labs, Inc, 61-67, vpres com develop, 67-69, CORP DIR COMMERCIAL DEVELOP, JOHNSON & JOHNSON, 69- *Mem:* AAAS; Am Acad Pediat; Am Thoracic Soc; AMA; Am Med Writers' Asn. *Res:* Biomedical instruments and materials in the field of respiratory care, laboratory instruments and patient monitoring. *Mailing Add:* Johnson & Johnson Com Develop 501 George St New Brunswick NJ 08903

MCCONNELL, JAMES FRANCIS, b Syracuse, NY, Dec 15, 36; m 59; c 4. ORGANIC CHEMISTRY. *Educ:* Le Moyne Col, NY, BS, 58; Syracuse Univ, PhD(org chem), 59. *Prof Exp:* Asst prof org chem, Mansfield State Col, 62-64; asst prof, 64-74, ASSOC PROF ORG CHEM, STATE UNIV NY COL CORTLAND, 74- *Mem:* Am Chem Soc. *Res:* Stereochemical approach to the mechanism of the Mannich reaction; rate of loss of optical activity of nitroalkanes compared to the rate in which they form Mannich base products in Mannich reaction. *Mailing Add:* Dept of Chem State Univ of NY Cortland NY 13045

MCCONNELL, JOHN CHARLES, b Belfast, Northern Ireland, Sept 11, 45; m 68; c 2. AERONOMY, SPACE SCIENCE. *Educ:* Queens Univ Belfast, BSc, 66, PhD(quantum mech), 69. *Prof Exp:* Res asst planetary sci, Kitt Peak Nat Observ, 69-70; res asst atmospheric physics, Ctr Earth Planetary Physics, Harvard Univ, 70-72; asst prof, 72-75, assoc prof, 75-80, PROF PHYSICS, YORK UNIV, 81- *Mem:* Am Astron Soc; AAAS; Am Geophys Union; Can Asn Physicists. *Res:* Tropospheric and stratospheric chemistry; auroral physics; planetary atmospheres; ionospheric physics; radiative transfer; atmospheric modelling. *Mailing Add:* Dept of Physics 4700 Keele St Downsview ON M3J 1P3 Can

MACCONNELL, JOHN GRIFFITH, b Chicago, Ill, Oct 14, 42; m 75. AGRICULTURAL PESTICIDE RESEARCH. *Educ:* Univ Ill, Urbana, BS, 64; Univ Mich, Ann Arbor, MS, 68, PhD(org chem), 69. *Prof Exp:* Res assoc org chem, Univ Ga, 69-70, NY State Col Forestry, Syracuse Univ, 70-72 & Univ Ga, 72-73; asst prof chem, Dalton Jr Col, 73-74; instr psychiat & Chem, Emory Univ, 74-75; SR RES CHEMIST, MERCK SHARP & DOHME RES LABS, 75- *Mem:* AAAS; Am Chem Soc. *Res:* Planning and execution of agricultural pesticide research and development programs. *Mailing Add:* Dept Agr Res Merck Sharp & Dohme Res Labs Rahway NJ 07065

MCCONNELL, KENNETH G, b East Ellsworth, Wis, May 11, 34; m 59; c 4. ENGINEERING MECHANICS. *Educ:* Col St Thomas, BA, 57; Univ Notre Dame, BS, 57; Iowa State Univ, MS, 60, PhD(eng mech), 63. *Prof Exp:* From instr to assoc prof eng mech, 57-74, PROF ENG SCI & MECH, IOWA STATE UNIV, 74- *Concurrent Pos:* Consult sound & vibration to local & nat industs. *Mem:* Am Soc Eng Educ; Soc Exp Stress Anal. *Res:* Vibrations; acoustics; dynamic instrumentation. *Mailing Add:* 205 Lab of Mech Iowa State Univ Ames IA 50011

MCCONNELL, KENNETH PAUL, b Rochester, NY, June 19, 11; m 50. BIOCHEMISTRY. *Educ:* Univ Rochester, AB, 35, MS, 37, PhD(biochem, nutrit), 42. *Prof Exp:* Asst, Sch Med & Dent, Univ Rochester, 35-37, instr, Dept Radiation Biol & assoc, Atomic Energy Proj, 48-49; asst, Med Sch, Ohio State Univ, 37-38; asst, Univ Iowa, 38-39; biochemist, USPHS, 46; biochemist, Med Dept, Field Res Lab, Ft Knox, Ky, 46-48; asst prof biochem & nutrit & dir med physics lab, Univ Tex Med Br, 50-52; res assoc, 52-60, from assoc prof to prof, 60-78, EMER PROF BIOCHEM, SCH MED, UNIV LOUISVILLE, 78- *Concurrent Pos:* Asst dir radioisotope serv, Vet Admin Hosp, 52-60, biochemist & prin scientist, 52-78; consult, Oak Ridge Inst Nuclear Studies, 52-59. *Mem:* Fel AAAS; Am Chem Soc; Am Inst Nutrit; Am Soc Biol Chemists; Soc Exp Biol & Med. *Res:* Metabolism of trace elements in the mammalian organism in health and disease; use of isotopes in research and medicine. *Mailing Add:* 705 Victoria Pl Louisville KY 40207

MCCONNELL, ROBERT A, b McKeesport, Pa; m. BIOPHYSICS, PARAPSYCHOLOGY. *Educ:* Carnegie Inst Technol, BS, 35; Univ Pittsburgh, PhD(physics), 47. *Prof Exp:* Asst geophysicist, Gulf Res Develop Co, 37-39; asst physicist, US Naval Aircraft Factory, 39-41; mem staff, Radiation Lab, Mass Inst Technol, 41-44, group leader, 44-46; asst prof physics, 47-53, from asst res prof to assoc res prof, 53-63, RES PROF BIOPHYS, UNIV PITTSBURGH, 64- *Mem:* Inst Elec & Electronics Engrs; Parapsychol Asn (pres, 57-58). *Res:* Radar moving target indication; theory of the iconoscope; ultrasonic microwaves; extrasensory perception; psychokinesis. *Mailing Add:* Dept Biol Sci Univ Pittsburgh Pittsburgh PA 15260

MCCONNELL, ROBERT KENDALL, b Toronto, Ont, Mar 1, 37; m 58; c 2. GEOPHYSICS, GEOLOGY. *Educ:* Princeton Univ, BScE, 58; Univ Toronto, MASc, 60, PhD(physics), 63. *Prof Exp:* Geologist, Invex Corp, Ltd, 57-58; geophysicist, Hunting Surv Corp, 59-60; geophysicist, Arthur D Little, Inc, 63-69; pres, Earth Sci Res, Inc, 70-75; res geophysicist, Boston Col, 75-78; CONSULT, 77- *Concurrent Pos:* Vis prof, Univ RI, 70. *Mem:* Am Geophys Union; Soc Explor Geophys; Europ Asn Explor Geophys; Seismol Soc Am. *Res:* Tectonophysics; planetary evolution; geological and geophysical interpretation. *Mailing Add:* 14 Stevens Terr Arlington MA 02174

MCCONNELL, STEWART, b El Paso, Tex, Apr 25, 23; m 49; c 3. VIROLOGY, IMMUNOLOGY. *Educ:* Ohio State Univ, MS, 60; Tex A&M Univ, DVM, 50. *Prof Exp:* Vet virol & res, Walter Reed Army Inst Res, Vet Corps, US Army, 60-63, adv, US Agency Int Develop, 63-65, vet malaria res, Walter Reed Army Inst Res, 65-66, vet infectious dis res, US Army Med Res Inst Infectious Dis, 66-68; assoc prof, 68-77, PROF VET MICROBIOL, TEX A&M UNIV, 77- *Concurrent Pos:* Mem subcomt fish standards, comt standards, Inst Lab Animal Resources, Nat Res Coun-Nat Acad Sci, foreign animal dis comt, US Animal Health Asn, Western Hemisphere Comt Animal Virus Characterization & bd comp virol, WHO-Food & Agr Orgn. *Honors & Awards:* Medal, Bolivian Ministry Agr, 64; Spec Commendation, Bolivian Hemorrhagic Fever Comn, 65. *Mem:* Am Asn Lab Animal Sci; Am Soc Lab Animal Practitioners; Am Soc Microbiol; fel NY Acad Sci. *Res:* Virus that play a role in respiratory diseases of feedlot cattle; poxvirus of animals; virus diseases of marine fish and shellfish. *Mailing Add:* Dept of Vet Microbiol Tex A&M Univ College Station TX 77843

MCCONNELL, VIRGINIA FENNER, b New Orleans, La, July 22, 05; m 28; c 3. ORGANIC CHEMISTRY. *Educ:* Tulane Univ, BA, 26, MS, 27. *Prof Exp:* Lab instr biochem, Sch Med, Tulane Univ, 27-29, lab instr biochem, Newcomb Col, 42-44, from instr to assoc prof chem, 44-71, head dept, 64-70, EMER ASSOC PROF CHEM, NEWCOMB COL, TULANE UNIV, 71- *Mem:* AAAS; Am Chem Soc; Hist Sci Soc. *Res:* History of organic chemistry; biographical catalogue of chemists; life of Emil Fischer; contributions of women to chemistry. *Mailing Add:* 1731 Calhoun St New Orleans LA 70118

MCCONNELL, WALLACE BEVERLY, b Metiskow, Alta, Sept 24, 16; m 40; c 2. BIOCHEMISTRY. *Educ:* Univ Alta, BSc, 46, MSc, 47; McGill Univ, PhD(phys chem), 49. *Prof Exp:* Jr res officer protein chem, Prairie Regional Lab, Nat Res Coun Can, 49-51, from asst res officer to sr res officer, 51-66; prof chem, Univ Sask, Regina, 66-73, chmn dept, 67-73, assoc dean, Div Natural Sci, 73-74; dean fac sci, Univ Regina, 75-81. *Mem:* Fel Chem Inst Can. *Res:* Plant biochemistry; amino acids and proteins; biosynthesis of selenium and sulphur containing compounds in plants. *Mailing Add:* Fac of Sci Univ of Regina Regina SK S4S 0H2 Can

MCCONNELL, WESLEY JAMES, physical chemistry, chemical engineering, see previous edition

MCCONNELL, WILLIAM A(RTHUR), b Great Falls, Mont, Jan 3, 18; m 41; c 4. MECHANICAL ENGINEERING, COMPUTER SCIENCES. *Educ:* Williams Col, AB; Univ Nebr, AB, 39, BSME, 41, ME, 49. *Hon Degrees:* DrEng, Univ Nebr, 60. *Prof Exp:* Student engr, Res Labs, Gen Motors Corp, 39, proj engr, proving grounds, 41-45; mech engr, Harvard Univ, 45-46; head eng test sect, 46-55, exec asst vehicles testing, 55-58, mgr vehicles testing, 58-60, mgr performance anal, 60-61, exec engr, 61-62, asst dir prod res, 62-64, dir systs res, 64-66, dir opers, eng & res staff, 66-69, dir test opers prod develop group, 69-72, dir emission cert, 72-73, CHIEF ENGR, TEST OPERS & ENG SERV, FORD MOTOR CO, 73- *Concurrent Pos:* Mem exec comt, Hwy Res Bd, Nat Acad Sci-Nat Res Coun, 69-; chmn, Ann Arbor Transportation Authority. *Mem:* Fel Soc Automotive Engrs; Soc Exp Stress Anal; Sigma Xi. *Res:* Automotive testing; experimental stress analysis; instrumentation; design automation; transportation technology. *Mailing Add:* Ford Motor Co Res Eng Ctr 21500 Oakwood Blvd Dearborn MI 48124

MACCONNELL, WILLIAM PRESTON, b NB, Can, June 15, 18; nat US; m 43; c 3. FORESTRY. *Educ:* Univ Mass, BS, 43; Yale Univ, MF, 48. *Prof Exp:* Assoc prof, 48-63, PROF FORESTRY, UNIV MASS, AMHERST, 63- *Mem:* Soc Am Foresters; Am Soc Photogram. *Res:* Forest management; aerial photogrammetry. *Mailing Add:* Dept of Forestry Univ of Mass Amherst MA 01003

MCCONNELL, WILLIAM RAY, b Wise, Va, Oct 15, 43; m 67. PHARMACOLOGY, TOXICOLOGY. *Educ:* Va Polytech Inst & State Univ, BS, 65; Med Col Va, MS, 73, PhD(pharmacol), 76. *Prof Exp:* Res pharmacologist, Southern Res Inst, 76-79; SR RES TOXICOLOGIST, A H ROBINS PHARMACEUT CO, INC, 79- *Concurrent Pos:* Adj asst prof pharmacol, Univ Ala, Birmingham, 77-79. *Mem:* AAAS; Am Soc Pharm & Exp Therapeut. *Res:* Biochemical pharmacology as related to pharmacokinetics and metabolism of anti-cancer and anti-malarial drugs; analytical and biochemical methodology for measuring drugs; toxicology of pharmaceutical drugs. *Mailing Add:* 9720 Tuxford Rd Richmond VA 23235

MCCONVILLE, BRIAN JOHN, b Queenstown, NZ, May 11, 33; m 59; c 3. PSYCHIATRY. *Educ:* Univ Otago, NZ, MB, ChB, 57; Royal Col Physicians Can, cert psychiat, 66, fel psychiat, 72. *Prof Exp:* Lectr psychiat, 65-67, lectr pediat, 65-69, from asst prof to assoc prof psychiat, 67-77, ASST PROF PEDIAT, QUEEN'S UNIV, ONT, 69-, DIR CHILD PSYCHIAT TRAINING, 70-, PROF PSYCHIAT, 77- *Concurrent Pos:* Dir, Regional Children's Centre, Kingston Psychiat Hosp, 67-; liaison off, Can Psychiat Asn-Can Pediat Soc, 70-; chmn child-adolescent comt, Child, Adolescent & Retardate Sect, Can Psychiat Asn, 70-, mem sci coun, 72- *Mem:* Can Psychiat Asn; Can Med Asn; Soc Psychophysiol Res; Am Psychiat Asn; Am Acad Child Psychiat. *Res:* Child psychiatry; measurement of behavioral change in children's inpatient units; phenomena of childhood depression-aggression; family therapy; illness after depression. *Mailing Add:* Dept of Psychiat Queen's Univ Kingston ON K7L 3N6 Can

MCCONVILLE, DAVID RAYMOND, b Benson, Minn, Feb 9, 46. LIMNOLOGY, FISHERIES. *Educ:* St Cloud State Univ, BS, 68, MA, 69; Univ Minn, St Paul, PhD(fisheries), 72. *Prof Exp:* Asst, St Cloud State Univ, 68-70, res assoc, 70-71; instr biol, Univ Minn Tech Col-Waseca, 71-73; ASSOC PROF BIOL & DIR AQUATIC STUDIES, ST MARY'S COL, MINN, 73- *Concurrent Pos:* Consult ecol studies, Northern States Power Co, Minneapolis, 73-75; prin investr, Off Water Resources res grant fisheries studies, St Mary's Col, 73-75, dir, NSF environ equip grant, 75-77, dir, US Fish & Wildlife Serv biol res contract, 75-79, dir, US Army Corps Engrs biol res contract, 75-76; dir, US Environ Protection Agency Res Contract, 76-78; river biologist, US Army Corps, 80-81. *Mem:* Am Fisheries Soc; NAm Benthological Soc; Sigma Xi. *Res:* Current flows and fisheries; use of artificial substrates; emergence studies of insects; relative abundance, age and growth, food habits and selected movement studies of Mississippi River fish; riverine habitat improvement. *Mailing Add:* Dept Aquatic Studies Biol St Mary's Col Terrace Heights Winona MN 55987

MCCONVILLE, GEORGE T, b St Paul, Minn, Sept 23, 34; m 59. PHYSICS. *Educ:* Carleton Col, AB, 56; Purdue Univ, MS, 59; Rutgers Univ, PhD(physics), 64. *Prof Exp:* Tech staff assoc low temperature physics, RCA Labs, 59-61; sr res physics, 64-69, res specialist, 69-75, SR RES SPECIALIST, MONSANTO RES CORP, 75- *Mem:* Am Phys Soc; AAAS. *Res:* Low temperature physics; superconductivity; calorimetry; gas transport. *Mailing Add:* Mound Lab Monsanto Res Corp Miamisburg OH 45342

MCCONVILLE, JOHN THEODORE, b Centerville, Iowa, Nov 15, 27; m 54; c 3. PHYSICAL ANTHROPOLOGY. *Educ:* Univ NMex, BA, 53; Univ Ariz, MA, 59; Univ Minn, PhD, 69. *Prof Exp:* Res analyst, US Army Electronic Proving Grounds, 56-59; assoc dir anthrop res proj, Antioch Col, 59-69; assoc dir anthrop res proj, Webb Assocs, Inc, 70-77; PRES, ANTHROP RES PROJ, INC, 78- *Mem:* Am Asn Phys Anthrop. *Res:* Human biology, particularly man as a component of complex systems; research in body size variability and human physical characteristics such as body strength and composition. *Mailing Add:* Anthrop Res Proj 503 Xenia Ave Yellow Springs OH 45387

MCCOOK, GEORGE PATRICK, b July 23, 37; US citizen; m 61; c 3. ASTRONOMY. *Educ:* Villanova Univ, BS & MA, 61; Univ Pa, MS, 65, PhD(astron), 68. *Prof Exp:* From asst prof to assoc prof, 61-81, PROF ASTRON, VILLANOVA UNIV, 81-, CHMN, DEPT ASTRON, 74- *Mem:* Am Astron Soc. *Res:* Microcomputer based instrumentation and photometric studies of variable stars. *Mailing Add:* Dept of Astron Villanova Univ Villanova PA 19085

MCCOOK, ROBERT DEVON, b Columbus, Ga, Jan 23, 29; m 57. CLINICAL ENGINEERING. *Educ:* La State Univ, BS, 50, MS, 52; Loyola Univ, Ill, PhD(physiol), 64. *Prof Exp:* Instr chem, Concord Col, 53-54; asst biochem, Stritch Sch Med, Loyola Univ Chicago, 54-57, asst physiol, 57-62, from instr to asst prof physiol, 62-74; CHIEF BIOMED ENG, VET ADMIN HOSP, LEXINGTON, 74- *Concurrent Pos:* Res physiologist, Vet Admin Hosp, Hines, Ill, 71-74. *Mem:* AAAS; Am Physiol Soc; Inst Elec & Electronics Engrs; Sigma Xi. *Res:* Central control of temperature regulation; physiological instrumentation; computer applications to medicine and biology. *Mailing Add:* Lexington Vet Admin Hosp Leestown Rd Lexington KY 40507

MCCOOL, D(ONALD) K, b St Joseph, Mo, May 22, 37; m 72; c 3. SOIL & WATER. *Educ:* Univ Mo, BS(agr) & BS(agr eng), 60, MS, 61; Okla State Univ, PhD(agr eng), 65. *Prof Exp:* Agr engr, Water Conserv Struct Lab, Southern Plains Br, Soil & Water Conserv Res Div, Agr Res Serv, 61-71, agr engr, Sci & Educ Admin, Agr Res Western Region, Ore-Wash Area, 71-80, AGR ENGR, WESTERN REGION, PACIFIC NORTHWEST AREA, PALOUSE CONSERV FIELD STA, AGR RES SERV, USDA, 80- *Concurrent Pos:* Asst prof agr eng, Okla State Univ, 66-71; assoc agr engr dept agr eng, Wash State Univ, 71- *Mem:* Am Soc Agr Engrs; Am Soc Civil Engrs; Soil Conserv Soc Am; Sigma Xi. *Res:* Hydrologic conditions leading to runoff and erosion-sedimentation events; effective hydraulic roughness of soil-crop surfaces and their resistance to erosion; prediction model for estimating erosion, sedimentation and downstream water quality for different crop managements under pacific northwest conditions; controlling snow deposition and soil freezing. *Mailing Add:* Dept of Agr Eng Smith Eng Bldg Wash State Univ Pullman WA 99164

MCCOOL, JOHN IGNATIUS, b Philadelphia, Pa, Feb 21, 36; m 58; c 2. MATHEMATICAL STATISTICS, TRIBOLOGY. *Educ:* Drexel Univ, BS, 59, MS, 62. *Prof Exp:* RES SCIENTIST, SKF INDUSTS, INC, 59- *Concurrent Pos:* Lectr, Radnor Grad Ctr, Pa State Univ, 65- *Mem:* Am Statist Asn; Opers Res Soc Am. *Res:* Inference in life testing; stochastic topography of surfaces; operations research. *Mailing Add:* SKF Industs Inc 1100 First Ave King of Prussia PA 19406

MCCOOL, JOHN MACALPINE, b San Mateo, Calif, Apr 24, 30; m 52. ELECTRICAL ENGINEERING, ACOUSTICS. *Educ:* Calif Inst Technol, BS, 52. *Prof Exp:* Physicist, US Naval Ord Test Sta, 52-56, head electronics br, 56-71, head electronics div, US Naval Undersea Ctr, 71-74, CONSULT, NAVAL OCEAN SYSTS CTR, 74- *Mem:* Inst Elec & Electronics Engrs. *Res:* Extension of statistical detection theory to a back scattering medium; research in adaptive systems. *Mailing Add:* 11624 Fuerte Dr El Cajon CA 92020

MCCORD, COLIN WALLACE, b Chicago, Ill, May 15, 28; m 54; c 3. PUBLIC HEALTH, SURGERY. *Educ:* Williams Col, BA, 49; Columbia Univ, MD, 53. *Prof Exp:* Instr & asst prof surg, Sch Med, Univ Ore, 61-65; asst prof & assoc prof, Columbia Univ, 65-71; ASSOC PROF INT HEALTH, SCH HYG, JOHNS HOPKINS UNIV, 71- *Concurrent Pos:* Attend clin surgeon, St Lukes Hosp, NY, 65-71; resident dir, Rural Health Res Ctr, Narangwal, Punjab, India, 71-72; dir, Companiganj Health Proj, Noakhali, Bangladesh, 72-75. *Mem:* Am Col Surgeons; Am Asn Thoracic Surgeons. *Res:* Cost and effectiveness of health programs in developing countries; cost and effectiveness of nutrition interventions. *Mailing Add:* 615 N Wolfe St Baltimore MD 21205

MCCORD, D(AVID) R(OBERT), b Indianapolis, Ind, Mar 11, 19; m 50; c 4. PETROLEUM ENGINEERING, GEOLOGY. *Educ:* Rice Inst, BA, 40. *Prof Exp:* Asst hydrocarbon chem, Magnolia Petrol Co Div, Socony Mobil Oil Co, Inc, 40-42; petrol engr, Creole Petrol Corp, 46-52, chief reservoir engr, 52-54; pres & consult, D R McCord & Assocs, Inc, 54-67; managing dir, Overseas Comput Utility Div & dir, Univ Comput Co, 71-72; organizer & head, Off Energy Data & Anal, US Dept Interior, 73-74; EXEC VPRES, AMM, INC, 77-; PRES, MID CON ENERGY CORP, 79- *Mem:* Soc Petrol Engrs; Am Asn Petrol Geologists. *Res:* Petroleum and reservoir engineering; geology. *Mailing Add:* Rte 2 Box 46 A Mapleton KS 66754

MCCORD, JOE MILTON, b Memphis, Tenn, Mar 3, 45. FREE RADICAL PATHOLOGY. *Educ:* Southwestern at Memphis, BS, 66; Duke Univ, PhD(biochem), 70. *Prof Exp:* Fel biochem, Duke Univ Med Ctr, 70-71, assoc med & biochem, 72-76, res asst prof, 76; assoc prof, 76-80, co-chmn, 80-81, PROF BIOCHEM, UNIV SOUTH ALA, 80-, CHMN DEPT, 81- *Concurrent Pos:* Consult, Diag Data Inc, 71-77 & Pharmacia AB, 80- *Mem:* Am Soc Biol Chemists. *Res:* Biology of superoxide free radical and superoxide dismutase; pathophysiological roles of oxygen-derived metabolites, especially in inflammatory and ischemic disease states. *Mailing Add:* Dept Biochem Univ S Ala Mobile AL 36688

MCCORD, MICHAEL CAMPBELL, b Knoxville, Tenn, Apr 28, 36; m 58; c 3. COMPUTER SCIENCE. *Educ:* Univ Tenn, BA, 58; Univ Tenn, MA, 60; Yale Univ, PhD(math), 63. *Prof Exp:* Actg instr math, Yale Univ, 62-63; asst prof, Univ Wis, 63-64; from asst prof to assoc prof, Univ Ga, 64-69; assoc prof math, 69-75, ASSOC PROF COMPUT SCI, UNIV KY, 75- *Concurrent Pos:* Mem, Inst Advan Study, NJ, 67-68. *Mem:* Asn Comput Mach; Asn Computational Ling. *Res:* Artificial intelligence and logic programming; computational linguistics; syntax and semantics. *Mailing Add:* Dept of Comput Sci Univ of Ky Lexington KY 40506

MCCORD, THOMAS BARD, b Elverson, Pa, Jan 18, 39; m 62. ASTRONOMY. *Educ:* Pa State Univ, BS, 64; Calif Inst Technol, MS, 66, PhD(planetary sci & astron), 68. *Prof Exp:* Res fel planetary sci, Calif Inst Technol, 68; asst prof, Mass Inst Technol, 68-71, assoc prof planetary physics & dir, George R Wallace Astrophys Observ, 71-77; asst dir Inst Artron, 76-79, PROF PLANETARY SCI & HEAD PLANETARY GEOSCI DIV, HAWAII INST GEOPHYSICS, UNIV, HAWAII, 79- *Concurrent Pos:* Vis assoc, Calif Inst Technol, 69-72; sr scientist, Ctr Space Res Mass Inst Technol, 77- *Mem:* Fel AAAS; fel Am Geophys Union; Am Astron Soc; Am Astronomical Soc. *Res:* Composition and structure of surfaces of solar system objects using remote sensing techniques; development of instrumentation with which to make such studies. *Mailing Add:* 2525 Correa Rd Hawaii Inst Geophysics Univ Hawaii Honolulu HI 96822

MCCORD, TOMMY JOE, b Lubbock, Tex, Feb 19, 32; m 51; c 4. BIOCHEMISTRY. *Educ:* Abilene Christian Col, BS, 54; Univ Tex, MA, 58, PhD(biochem, org chem), 59. *Prof Exp:* Asst, Abilene Christian Col, 53-54; res scientist, Biochem Inst, Univ Tex, 56-58; from asst prof to assoc prof chem, 58-64, asst head dept, 65-67, PROF CHEM, ABILENE CHRISTIAN UNIV, 64-, HEAD DEPT, 67- *Concurrent Pos:* Res grants, USPHS, NSF & Welch Found. *Mem:* AAAS; Am Chem Soc. *Res:* Preparation and biological testing of structural analogs of important biological compounds as potential metabolic antagonists. *Mailing Add:* Dept of Chem Abilene Christian Univ Abilene TX 79601

MCCORD, WILLIAM MELLEN, b Durban, SAfrica, Jan 24, 07; m 30; c 2. BIOCHEMISTRY. *Educ:* Oberlin Col, AB, 28; Yale Univ, PhD(org chem), 31; La State Univ, MB, 39, MD, 40. *Prof Exp:* From instr to assoc prof biochem, Sch Med, La State Univ, 31-45; prof, 45-77, EMER PROF BIOCHEM, MED UNIV SC, 77-, PRES, 64- *Concurrent Pos:* Intern, Charity Hosp, New Orleans, 39-40, vis biochemist, 40- *Mem:* AAAS; Am Chem Soc; Am Fedn Clin Res. *Res:* Aldehyde condensations; blood chemistry; pathological chemistry; toxicology; clinical biochemistry; porphyrin determinations; sickle cell anemia. *Mailing Add:* PO Box 4 Lodge SC 29082

MCCORKLE, RICHARD ANTHONY, b Gastonia, NC, Aug 6, 40; m 64; c 1. PLASMA PHYSICS. *Educ:* NC State Univ, BS, 62, PhD(physics), 70. *Prof Exp:* Asst prof physics, ECarolina Univ, 68-73; RES SCIENTIST, IBM, THOMAS J WATSON RES CTR, 73- *Concurrent Pos:* Res dir, NSF grant, 69-70. *Honors & Awards:* Bisplinghoff Award, 72. *Mem:* Am Phys Soc. *Res:* Ion sources; short wavelength sources, x-ray; electron streams. *Mailing Add:* IBM Watson Res Ctr PO Box 218 Yorktown Heights NY 10598

MCCORKLE, WILLIAM C, JR, physics, aerospace sciences, see previous edition

MCCORMAC, BILLY MURRAY, b Zanesville, Ohio, Sept 8, 20; m 48 & 69; c 5. ASTROPHYSICS. *Educ:* Ohio State Univ, BS, 43; Univ Va, MS, 56, PhD(nuclear physics), 57. *Prof Exp:* Physicist, Off Spec Weapons Develop, US Army, 57-60, scientist, Off Chief Staff, 60-61, physicist, Defense Atomic Support Agency, 61-62, chief electromagnetic br, 62-63; sci adv, IIT Res Inst, 63, dir geophys div, 63-68; sr consult scientist, 68-69, mgr, Radiation Physics Lab, 69-74, mgr, Electro-Optics Lab, 74-76, mgr solar physics, 76-80, MGR SOLAR & OPTICAL PHYSICS LAB, LOCKHEED PALO ALTO RES LAB, 80- *Concurrent Pos:* Ed, J Water, Air & Soil Pollution & Geophys & Astrophys Monographs; chmn adv study inst radiation trapped in earth's magnetic field, Norway, 65, aurora & airglow, Eng, 66, Norway, 68, Can, 70, France, 72 & Belg, 74, earth's particles & fields, Ger, 67, Calif, 69, Italy, 71, Eng, 73, Austria, 75 & solar terrestrial influences on weather & climate, Ohio, 78. *Mem:* AAAS; sr mem Am Astronaut Soc; Am Geophys Union; Marine Technol Soc; assoc fel Am Inst Aeronaut & Astronaut. *Res:* Nuclear weapons effects, especially high altitude effect; multidisciplinary research in aeronomy and the earth's magnetosphere; solar physics; electro-optical systems. *Mailing Add:* Lockheed Palo Alto Res Lab Dept 52-13 B202 3251 Hanover St Palo Alto CA 94304

MCCORMAC, JACK CLARK, b Columbia, SC, July 6, 27; m 57; c 2. CIVIL ENGINEERING. *Educ:* The Citadel, BS, 48; Mass Inst Technol, SM, 49. *Prof Exp:* Instr civil eng, Clemson Col, 49-51; civil engr, E I du Pont de Nemours & Co, 51-54 & Finfrock Industs, 54-55; from asst prof to assoc prof civil eng, 55-76, PROF CIVIL ENG, CLEMSON UNIV, 76- *Mem:* Am Soc Civil Engrs. *Res:* Bridge vibrations; prestressed concrete and steel structures. *Mailing Add:* Dept of Civil Eng Clemson Univ Clemson SC 29631

MCCORMACK, CHARLES ELWIN, b Gurnee, Ill, Jan 3, 38; m 61; c 2. PHYSIOLOGY. *Educ:* Carroll Col, Wis, BS, 59; Univ Wis-Madison, PhD(endocrinol), 63. *Prof Exp:* Fel zool, Univ Wis, 63-64; from instr to asst prof physiol, 64-70, assoc prof, 70-76, PROF PHYSIOL, CHICAGO MED SCH, 76- *Mem:* Am Soc Zoologists; Endocrine Soc; Am Physiol Soc; Int Soc Neuroendocrinol; Soc Study Reproduction. *Res:* Influence of the brain and gonadal steroids on ovulation. *Mailing Add:* 3333 Green Bay Rd North Chicago IL 60064

MCCORMACK, DONALD EUGENE, b Chicago, Ill, Apr 22, 30; m 49; c 4. SOIL SCIENCE. *Educ:* Univ Ill, BS, 53, MS, 60; Ohio State Univ, PhD(soil sci), 73. *Prof Exp:* Soil scientist field, 53-60, asst state soil scientist, Mich, 60-63, state soil scientist, Ohio, 63-72, asst dir soil surv interpretations div, 72-76, leader resource & mgt info syst, 76, dir soil surv interpretations div, 76-80, STAFF LEADER, SOIL TECHNOL, US SOIL CONSERV SERV, 80- *Concurrent Pos:* Mem Transportation Res Bd, Nat Acad Sci, 72- *Honors & Awards:* Outstanding Performance Award, US Soil Conserv Serv, 74. *Mem:* Soil Sci Soc Am; Am Soc Agron; Int Soil Sci Soc; Soil Conserv Soc Am. *Res:* Relationship of soil properties used in identifying, characterizing and classifying soils by pedologists; engineering behavior of soils. *Mailing Add:* Soil Conserv Serv S Agr Bldg Rm 6246 Washington DC 20250

MCCORMACK, FRANCIS JOSEPH, b Mobile, Ala, Dec 6, 38; m 67. PLASMA PHYSICS. *Educ:* Spring Hill Col, BS, 60; Fla State Univ, PhD(physics), 64. *Prof Exp:* From asst prof to assoc prof, 67-77, PROF PHYSICS, UNIV NC, GREENSBORO, 77- *Mem:* Am Phys Soc; Am Asn Physics Teachers. *Res:* Kinetic theory of ordinary and ionized gases. *Mailing Add:* Dept of Physics Univ of NC Greensboro NC 27412

MCCORMACK, GRACE, b Rochester, NY, Feb 16, 08. MICROBIOLOGY. *Educ:* Univ Rochester, AB, 41; Univ Md, MS, 51; Nat Registry Microbiologists, regist, 75. *Prof Exp:* Technician endocrinol, Sch Med & Dent, Univ Rochester, 42-48; bacteriologist fish & wildlife serv, US Dept Interior, 48-53; assoc bacteriologist, Md State Dept Health, 53-55; bacteriologist-technologist, Vet Admin Hosp, Canandaigua, NY, 55-66; from asst prof to assoc prof, 66-75, prof, 75-77, EMER PROF BIOL SCI, MONROE COMMUNITY COL, 77- *Concurrent Pos:* Lectr, Univ Md, 50. *Honors & Awards:* Sustained Superior Serv Award, Vet Admin Hosp, 63. *Mem:* AAAS; fel Am Inst Chem; Am Soc Microbiol; Am Chem Soc; Am Pub Health Asn. *Res:* Assays of gonadotropic hormone; enterococci; antibiotic study of preservation of crabmeat; pollution studies of clam and oyster beds; comparative study of various media; cause of discoloration of oysters; collaborating on research problem; testing of viability of brewery yeast. *Mailing Add:* Dept of Biol Sci Monroe Community Col Rochester NY 14534

MCCORMACK, HAROLD ROBERT, b St Louis, Mo, Nov 25, 22; m 46; c 4. GEOPHYSICS. *Educ:* St Louis Univ, BS, 46. *Prof Exp:* Geophysicist, Sun Oil Co, 43-53, dir geophys, 54-67, mgr geophys res, 68-75, mgr geophys data processing, 75-77; MEM STAFF, SUNMARK EXPLOR CO, 77- *Mem:* Europeans Asn Explor Geophysicists; Soc Explor Geophys (secy-treas, 75-76); Seismol Soc Am. *Res:* Geophysical research applied to petroleum exploration. *Mailing Add:* Sun Explor Co PO Box 340180 Dallas TX 75234

MCCORMACK, JOHN JOSEPH, JR, b Boston, Mass, Jan 20, 38; m 62; c 4. ORGANIC CHEMISTRY, PHARMACOLOGY. *Educ:* Boston Col, BS, 59; Yale Univ, PhD(pharmacol), 64. *Prof Exp:* Nat Cancer Inst res fel med chem, Australian Nat Univ, 64-66; asst prof pharmacol, 66-69, assoc prof, 69-77, PROF PHARMACOL, UNIV VT, 77- *Mem:* AAAS; Am Chem Soc; Royal Soc Chem; Am Soc Pharmacol & Exp Therapeut. *Res:* Heterocyclic and medicinal chemistry; chemotherapy of neoplastic and protozoal diseases. *Mailing Add:* Dept Pharmacol Given Med Bldg Univ Vt Burlington VT 05401

MCCORMACK, MICHAEL KEVIN, b South Amboy, NJ, Nov 3, 49. HUMAN GENETICS. *Educ:* Seton Hall Univ, NJ, BA, 71; Univ Minn, Minneapolis, PhD(genetics), 75. *Prof Exp:* ASST PROF GENETICS, RUTGERS UNIV, NEW BRUNSWICK, 75-; RES SCIENTIST GROWTH & DEVELOP, W M KROGMAN CTR RES CHILD GROWTH & DEVELOP, CHILDREN'S HOSP OF PHILADELPHIA, 75- *Concurrent Pos:* Fel pediat hemat, Dept Pediat, Univ Minn Med Ctr, Minneapolis, 75; NIH fel med genetics, 75. *Mem:* Am Soc Human Genetics; Behav Genetics Asn; Am Soc Hemat; Am Soc Cell Biol. *Res:* Biochemical genetics of hemoglobin structure and synthesis; structure-function relationships in mutant human hemoglobins; chemical modification of human hemoglobins; growth and development of children with various hemoglobinopathies. *Mailing Add:* Div Human Genetics Rutgers Univ 32 Bishop St New Brunswick NJ 08903

MCCORMACK, ROBERT MORRIS, b Sheboygan, Wis, June 11, 18; m 44; c 3. PLASTIC SURGERY. *Educ:* Swarthmore Col, BA, 40; Univ Chicago, MD, 43; Am Bd Plastic Surg, dipl. *Prof Exp:* From instr to assoc prof, 50-57, vchmn dept surg, 68-77, PROF PLASTIC SURG, SCH MED, UNIV ROCHESTER, 57-, CHMN, DEPT SURG, 77-; PLASTIC SURGEON-IN-CHIEF, STRONG MEM HOSP, 77- *Concurrent Pos:* Am Soc Plastic & Reconstruct Surg scholar, 53. *Mem:* Am Soc Surg of Hand (pres, 64-65); Am Soc Plastic & Reconstruct Surg; Am Col Surg; Am Asn Plastic Surg (secy, 62-64, pres, 69); Am Burn Asn (pres, 72). *Res:* Transplantation of tissues. *Mailing Add:* Dept of Med Univ of Rochester Sch of Med Rochester NY 14627

MCCORMACK, WILLIAM BREWSTER, b Mirror, Alta, Nov 20, 23; US citizen; m 45; c 2. ORGANIC CHEMISTRY. *Educ:* Univ Alta, BSc, 44; Univ Wis, PhD(chem), 48. *Prof Exp:* Res chemist, 48-53, res supvr, 53-55, RES ASSOC, JACKSON LAB, E I DU PONT DE NEMOURS & CO, INC, 55-, INTERNAL TECH CONSULT, 70- *Mem:* AAAS; Am Chem Soc; Combustion Inst; Royal Soc Chem. *Res:* Phosphorus; fluorine; organometallics; dyes and textile chemicals; nucleophilic and free radical processes; aromatic intermediates; scientific philosophy; combustion; permeation separation. *Mailing Add:* CD&P Dept Jackson Lab E I du Pont de Nemours & Co Inc Wilmington DE 19898

MCCORMICK, ANTHONY WAYNE, b Moline, Ill, Apr 1, 53. MATERIALS SCIENCE, PHYSICS. *Educ:* Northern Ill Univ, BS, 75; Cornell Univ, MEng, 76. *Prof Exp:* SCI ASST MAT SCI, ARGONNE NAT LAB, 77- *Mem:* Electron Micros Soc Am. *Res:* Analytical electron microscopy of metal alloys and ceramics. *Mailing Add:* Argonne Nat Lab 9700 S Cass Ave Argonne IL 60439

MCCORMICK, BAILIE JACK, b Amarillo, Tex, Aug 20, 37; m 58; c 2. INORGANIC CHEMISTRY. *Educ:* West Tex State Univ, BS, 59; Okla State Univ, PhD(chem), 62. *Prof Exp:* Robert A Welch Found fel, Univ Tex, 62-64; from asst prof to assoc prof chem, WVa Univ, 64-73, prof, 73-79; PROF CHEM & CHMN DEPT, WICHITA STATE UNIV, 79- *Mem:* Am Chem Soc. *Res:* Structure, spectra and reactions of coordination compounds; inorganic geochemistry; sulfide minerals; donor properties of sulfur; sulfur-nitrogen compounds; biological aspects of metal binding. *Mailing Add:* Chem Dept Wichita State Univ Wichita KS 67208

MCCORMICK, BARNES W(ARNOCK), JR, b Waycross, Ga, July 15, 26; m 46; c 1. AERONAUTICAL ENGINEERING. *Educ:* Pa State Univ, BS, 48, MS, 49, PhD(aeronaut eng), 54. *Prof Exp:* Assoc prof eng res, Pa State Univ, 54-56; chief aerodyn, Vertol Aircraft Corp, 56-58; assoc prof aeronaut eng & head dept, Univ Wichita, 58-59; assoc prof aeronaut eng, 59-65, PROF AEROSPACE ENG, PA STATE UNIV, 65-, HEAD DEPT, 69-, RESEARCHER, ORD RES LAB, 59- *Concurrent Pos:* Consult, Vertol Div, Boeing Co, 58- & Outboard Marine Corp, 60-; pres, Aero Eng Assocs, Inc, 66-; ed J, Am Helicopter Soc, 71-72. *Honors & Awards:* Educ Achievement Award, Am Soc Eng Educ & Am Inst Aeronaut & Astronaut, 76. *Mem:* Am Inst Aeronaut & Astronaut; Am Helicopter Soc; Am Soc Eng Educ; Soc Automotive Engrs. *Res:* Aerodynamics; hydrodynamics; helicopters; standard and vertical take-off and landing aircraft; hydroballistics. *Mailing Add:* Dept of Aerospace Eng Pa State Univ 233 Hammond Bldg University Park PA 16802

MCCORMICK, CLYDE TRUMAN, b Oblong, Ill, Mar 6, 08; m 37; c 3. APPLIED MATHEMATICS. *Educ:* Univ Ill, AB, 30, AM, 32; Ind Univ, PhD(math physics), 37. *Prof Exp:* Prof math & physics, Greenville Col, 37-38; from asst prof to prof math, Ft Hays State Univ, 38-44, head dept, 41-44; assoc prof, Ill State Univ, 44-48, prof math, 48-54, head dept, 54-71; vis prof, 71-81, DISTINGUISHED VIS PROF, PALM BEACH ATLANTIC COL, 81- *Mem:* Am Math Soc; Math Asn Am. *Res:* Applied mathematics in mechanics and sound. *Mailing Add:* Dept of Math Palm Beach Atlantic Col West Palm Beach FL 33401

MCCORMICK, DONALD BRUCE, b Front Royal, Va, July 15, 32; m 55; c 3. BIOCHEMISTRY. *Educ:* Vanderbilt Univ, BA, 53, PhD(biochem), 58. *Prof Exp:* Asst biochem, Vanderbilt Univ, 53-58; consult biochemist, Interdepartment Comt Nutrit for Nat Defense, Madrid, 58; USPHS res fel, Univ Calif, 58-60; asst prof nutrit, Cornell Univ, 60-65, assoc prof biochem & biol sci, 65-69, prof, 69-78, L H Bailey prof nutrit, Biochem & Molecular Biol, 78-79 ; PROF & CHMN BIOCHEM, EMORY UNIV, 79- *Concurrent Pos:* Guggenheim Mem Found fel, 66-67. *Honors & Awards:* Mead Johnson Award, Am Inst Nutrit, 70; Osborne & Mendel Award, Am Inst Nutrit, 78. *Mem:* AAAS; Am Soc Biol Chemists; Am Inst Nutrit; Am Chem Soc; Am Soc Microbiol. *Res:* Chemistry and biochemistry of cofactors; enzymology; chemistry, metabolism and enzymology of vitamins, coenzymes and metal ions. *Mailing Add:* Dept Biochem Emory Univ Atlanta GA 30322

MCCORMICK, FRANCIS B, b New Concord, Ohio, Apr 2, 16; div. AGRICULTURAL ECONOMICS. *Educ:* Ohio State Univ, BS, 39, MS, 47, PhD(agr econ), 53. *Prof Exp:* County supvr, Farm Security Admin, Jackson, Vinton & Perry Counties, Ohio, USDA, 40-43; asst, 46-49, from instr to assoc prof agr econ, Ohio State Univ, 49-64, staff mem, Dept Agr Econ & Rural Soc, 61-66, actg chmn, Dept Agr Econ, 66-67, prof agr econ, 64-78, assoc chmn dept, 68-78; prog specialist, Agr Stabilization & Conserv Serv, USDA, 78-81; RETIRED. *Mem:* Int Conf Agr Econ; Am Agr Econ Asn; Am Soc Farm Mgrs & Rural Appraisers. *Res:* Agricultural policy and agricultural marketing. *Mailing Add:* 760 Beauty View Ct Columbus OH 43214

MCCORMICK, FRED C(AMPBELL), b Waynesboro, Va, Jan 18, 26; m 54; c 1. CIVIL ENGINEERING. *Educ:* Univ Va, BCE, 51; Univ Mich, MSE, 52, PhD, 64. *Prof Exp:* Construct engr, E I du Pont de Nemours & Co, SC, 52-54; design engr, Polglaze & Basenberg Engrs, Ala, 54-55; from asst prof to assoc prof civil eng, 55-72, PROF CIVIL ENG, UNIV VA, 72- *Concurrent Pos:* Hwy res engr & indust consult, 72- *Mem:* Am Soc Civil Engrs; Soc Plastics Engrs; Struct Plastics Res Coun. *Res:* Experimental stress analysis; materials of construction and composite materials. *Mailing Add:* Dept of Civil Eng Thornton Hall Univ of Va Charlottesville VA 22903

MCCORMICK, GEORGE R, b Columbus, Ohio, Apr 12, 36; m 62; c 2. MINERALOGY, PETROLOGY. *Educ:* Ohio Wesleyan Univ, BA, 58; Ohio State Univ, MSc, 60, PhD(mineral), 64. *Prof Exp:* Geologist, Ohio Div, Geol Surv, 61-62 & Norris Lab, US Bur Mines, 62-65; asst prof geol, Boston Univ, 65-68; PROF GEOL, UNIV IOWA, 68- *Concurrent Pos:* Consult, Kennecott Copper Co, 67- & Humble Minerals, 71-; geologist, US Geol Surv, 72- *Mem:* Clay Minerals Soc; Mineral Soc Am; Mineral Soc Gt Brit & Ireland; Geol Soc Am; AAAS. *Res:* Phase equilibrium studies of silicate and germanate systems; microchemical study of igneous and metamorphic complexes; chemical and mineralogic study of clays; geochemical studies of copper, lead, zinc and silver deposits of Utah, Nevada and Arizona. *Mailing Add:* Dept of Geol Univ of Iowa Iowa City IA 52240

MCCORMICK, J FRANK, b Indianapolis, Ind, Oct 25, 35; m 59; c 3. ECOLOGY. *Educ:* Butler Univ, BS, 58; Emory Univ, MS, 60, PhD(biol), 61. *Prof Exp:* Asst prof biol, Vanderbilt Univ, 61-63; asst prof zool, Univ Ga, 63-64; asst prof bot, Univ NC, Chapel Hill, 64-71, prof bot & ecol, 71-74; PROF & DIR GRAD PROG ECOL, UNIV TENN, 74- *Concurrent Pos:* Grants, NSF, Natural Sci Comt, Vanderbilt Univ, 62; AEC, 64-, radiation ecol training, 66-; Univ NC fac res coun, 65 & 66; USPHS ecol training prog, 66-; consult, Oak Ridge Nat Lab, 62-; PR Nuclear Ctr, 64- *Honors & Awards:* Sigma Xi Res Award, Emory Univ, 61. *Mem:* AAAS; Ecol Soc Am. *Res:* Environmental and radiation biology; evolution and natural selection; environmental assessment; population; pollution studies; natural resource management. *Mailing Add:* Ecol Prog Univ of Tenn Knoxville TN 37916

MCCORMICK, J JUSTIN, b Detroit, Mich, Sept 26, 33. CANCER, MOLECULAR BIOLOGY. *Educ:* St Paul's Col, Washington, DC, BA, 57, MA, 59; Cath Univ Am, MS, 61, PhD(biol), 67. *Prof Exp:* Fel, McArdle Lab Cancer Res, Univ Wis, 67-70, res assoc, 70-71; res scientist, Mich Cancer Found, 71-73, chief, Molecular Biol Lab, 73-76; ASSOC PROF & CO-DIR, CARCINOGENESIS LAB, COL OSTEOP MED, MICH STATE UNIV, 76-, ASSOC PROF MICROBIOL & PUB HEALTH & DEPT BIOCHEM, 78- LAB, MICH CANCER FOUND, 73- *Mem:* Am Asn Cancer Res; Am Soc Cell Biol; Environ Mutagen Soc; Am Soc Photobiol; Sigma Xi. *Res:* Mutagenic and transforming effect of chemical and physical carcinogens on human cells in culture; DNA repair; application of biophysical techniques to the problems of carcinogenesis. *Mailing Add:* Carcinogenesis Lab Fee Hall East Lansing MI 48824

MCCORMICK, J ROBERT D, b St Albans, WVa, Feb 24, 21; m 53; c 1. BIOCHEMISTRY. *Educ:* Rensselaer Polytech Inst, BS, 46; Univ Calif, Los Angeles, PhD(chem), 54. *Prof Exp:* Res chemist, Winthrop Chem Co, 43-46; develop chemist, 49-54, biochem group leader, 54-58, head biochem dept, 58-60, res assoc fermentation biochem, 60-65, RES FEL FERMENTATION BIOCHEM, LEDERLE LABS, AM CYANAMID CO, 65- *Concurrent Pos:* Am Cyanamid award advan study sr res fel, Univ Leicester, 70-71. *Mem:* Fel AAAS; fel Am Inst Chem; Am Chem Soc; NY Acad Sci. *Res:* Natural products isolation and structure. *Mailing Add:* McNamara Rd Spring Valley NY 10977

MCCORMICK, JOHN E, b Manitowoc, Wis, Aug 18, 23; m 58; c 4. CHEMICAL ENGINEERING, MATHEMATICS. *Educ:* Iowa State Univ, BSc, 48; Univ Cincinnati, PhD(chem eng), 57. *Prof Exp:* Jr engr, Linde Air Prod Div, Union Carbide Corp, NY, 48-53; asst, Univ Cincinnati, 53-55, teaching fel quant chem, 55-56; engr, Esso Res & Eng Co, NJ, 57-62; asst prof chem eng, 62-64, ASSOC PROF CHEM ENG, NJ INST TECHNOL, 64-, ASSOC CHMN DEPT, 79- *Concurrent Pos:* Consult, Am Cyanamid Co, NJ, 63-65, Nopco Chem Div, Diamond Shamrock Chem Co, 66-67 & 70- & Merck & Co Inc, 68-70 & 73-78. *Mem:* Am Inst Chem Engrs. *Res:* Molecular sieve preparation; acidic alkylation; mathematics of engineering processes; applications of computers. *Mailing Add:* Dept of Chem Eng 323 High St Newark NJ 07102

MCCORMICK, JOHN PAULING, b Lansing, Mich, May 26, 43; m 68; c 2. BIO-ORGANIC CHEMISTRY. *Educ:* DePauw Univ, BA, 65; Stanford Univ, PhD(chem), 71. *Prof Exp:* Res assoc, Swiss Fed Inst Technol, 70-71; vis prof org chem, State Univ Groningen, 71-72; asst prof, 72-77, ASSOC PROF ORG CHEM, UNIV MO-COLUMBIA, 77- *Mem:* Am Chem Soc; AAAS. *Res:* Terpene synthesis and biosynthesis; mechanism of biochemical reactions; structure of physiologically active natural products; effects of near-UV on biomolecules. *Mailing Add:* 1424 Bradford Dr Columbia MO 65201

MCCORMICK, JON MICHAEL, b Portland, Ore, Feb 8, 41; m 71. MARINE ECOLOGY. *Educ:* Portland State Univ, BS, 63; Ore State Univ, MS, 65, PhD(biol sci), 69. *Prof Exp:* Res asst oceanog, Ore State Univ, 63-65; asst prof biol, Millersville State Col, 68-70; asst prof, 70-76, ASSOC PROF BIOL, MONTCLAIR STATE COL, 76- *Concurrent Pos:* NSF fel, Marine Biol Lab, Woods Hole, 69, partic, NSF instr Sci Equip Prog, Millersville State Col, 69-70; instr, Pa Marine Sci Consortium, 69-70; adj instr, Jersey City State Col, 70-71; instr, NJ Marine Sci Consortium, 71-75. *Mem:* AAAS; Ecol Soc

Am; Am Soc Limnol & Oceanog; Atlantic Estuarine Res Soc. *Res:* Estuarine ecology; marine zooplankton; marine benthos, hydrozoa, population dynamics, trophic ecology and environmental toxicology. *Mailing Add:* Dept of Biol Montclair State Col Upper Montclair NJ 07043

MCCORMICK, KATHLEEN ANN, b Manchester, NH, June 27, 47; m 71. PHYSIOLOGY, NURSING. *Educ:* Univ Wis, PhD(physiol), 78. *Prof Exp:* ASST FOR RES TO THE CHIEF, NURSING DEPT, NIH, 78- *Mem:* Am Thoracic Soc; Am Nurses' Asn. *Res:* Lung pathophysiology; adult respiratory distress syndrome; nursing res; exercise physiology; blood coagulation pathophysiology. *Mailing Add:* 220 Pender Pl Rockville MD 20850

MCCORMICK, KENNETH JAMES, b Toledo, Ohio, Sept 11, 37; m 63; c 3. CANCER. *Educ:* Univ Toledo, BS, 59; Univ Mich, Ann Arbor, MS, 62, PhD(microbiol), 65. *Prof Exp:* From instr to assoc prof exp biol, Dept Surg, Baylor Col Med, 65-75; head sect tumor immunol, Lab Cancer Res, St Joseph Hosp, Houston, 75-76, ASSOC LAB DIR, STEHLIN FOUND CANCER RES, 76- *Concurrent Pos:* Am Cancer Soc instnl grants, Baylor Col Med, 67-68 & 70-71, adj assoc prof exp biol, 75- *Mem:* AAAS; Am Asn Cancer Res; Am Asn Immunologists; Tissue Cult Asn; Am Soc Microbiol. *Res:* Tumor immunology and virology. *Mailing Add:* Stehlin Found for Cancer Res 777 St Joseph Prof Bldg Houston TX 77002

MCCORMICK, MICHAEL EDWARD, b Washington, DC, Sept 11, 36; m; c 2. FLUID MECHANICS, APPLIED MECHANICS. *Educ:* Am Univ, BA, 59; Cath Univ Am, MS, 61, PhD(fluid mech), 66. *Prof Exp:* Physicist, David Taylor Model Basin, 58-61; instr mech eng, Swarthmore Col, 61-62; instr, Cath Univ Am, 62-63, asst prof, 63-64, res engr, 62-64; res mech engr, David Taylor Model Basin, 64-65; asst prof mech, Trinity Col, Conn, 65-68; assoc prof ocean eng, 68-74, dir, Ocean Eng, 68-70, chmn, Naval Syst Eng Dept, 70-72, PROF OCEAN ENG, US NAVAL ACAD, 74-, DIR, OCEAN ENG, 78- *Concurrent Pos:* Vis scholar, Swarthmore Col, 76-77. *Mem:* Am Soc Mech Engrs; Am Soc Eng Educ; Marine Technol Soc; Am Soc Civil Engrs. *Res:* Wave energy; wave mechanics; hydromechanics; drag reduction. *Mailing Add:* Dept of Naval Systs Eng US Naval Acad Annapolis MD 21402

MCCORMICK, MICHAEL PATRICK, b Canonsburg, Pa, Nov 23, 40; m 62; c 2. ATMOSPHERIC PHYSICS. *Educ:* Washington & Jefferson Col, BA, 62; Col William & Mary, MA, 64, PhD(physics), 67. *Hon Degrees:* DSc, Washington & Jefferson Col, 81. *Prof Exp:* Head photoelectronic instrumentation sect, 67-75, CHIEF, AEROSOL MEASUREMENTS RES BR, LANGLEY RES CTR, NASA, 75- *Honors & Awards:* Arthur S Fleming Award, 80. *Mem:* Am Geophys Union. *Res:* Design, development and application of advanced sensors to atmospheric research; light scattering and atmospheric optics; electrooptics; laser radars. *Mailing Add:* Langley Res Ctr M/S 234 NASA Hampton VA 23665

MCCORMICK, NEIL GLENN, b Everett, Wash, Aug 17, 27; m 57; c 3. MICROBIOLOGY. *Educ:* Univ Wash, BS, 51, MS, 57, PhD(microbiol), 60. *Prof Exp:* Anal chemist, Wash State Dept Agr, 51-53; res assoc microbiol, Univ Wash, 60-61; USPHS fel, Univ Wis, 61-63; asst prof, Univ Va, 63-68; RES MICROBIOLOGIST, FOOD SCI LAB, US ARMY NATICK RES & DEVELOP COMMAND, 68- *Concurrent Pos:* Nat Inst Arthritis & Infectious Dis grants, 64-66. *Mem:* AAAS; Am Soc Microbiol. *Res:* Biodegradation and biotransformation of organic nitro-compounds; biotransformation efficiency improvement by selection of radiation-induced mutants. *Mailing Add:* Sci & Advan Technol Lab US Army Natick Res & Develop Labs Natick MA 01760

MCCORMICK, NORMAN JOSEPH, b Hays, Kans, Dec 9, 38; m 61; c 2. NUCLEAR ENGINEERING. *Educ:* Univ Ill, BS, 60, MS, 61; Univ Mich, PhD(nuclear eng), 65. *Prof Exp:* NSF fel, Univ Ljubljana, 65-66; from vis asst prof to assoc prof, 66-75, PROF NUCLEAR ENG, UNIV WASH, 75- *Concurrent Pos:* Nat Acad Sci fel, Univ Ljubljana, 71; consult, Westinghouse Hanford Co, 74-; exec ed, Progress in Nuclear Energy, 80- *Mem:* Am Nuclear Soc; Inst Nuclear Mat Mgt; Soc Risk Analysis. *Res:* Reliability and risk analysis, methods and nuclear and non-nuclear power applications; neutron and photon transport; nuclear materials safeguards. *Mailing Add:* Dept Nuclear Eng BF-10 Univ Wash Seattle WA 98195

MCCORMICK, PATRICK GARY, analytical chemistry, see previous edition

MCCORMICK, PAUL R(ICHARD), b Johnstown, Pa, Aug 5, 25; m 47; c 3. ELECTRICAL ENGINEERING. *Educ:* Cornell Univ, BS, 47; Univ Pittsburgh, MS, 53, PhD, 62. *Prof Exp:* From instr to asst prof, 47-62, assoc chmn dept, 64-66, ASSOC PROF ELEC ENG, UNIV PITTSBURGH, 62-, DIR LOWER DIV PROGS, 69-, ASSOC CHMN DEPT, 81- *Concurrent Pos:* Grants, Danforth Found, 48 & NSF, 59; instr, Duquesne Light Co, 55-58; USAID chief of party & consult, Valparaiso Tech Univ, Chile, 62-64. *Mem:* Inst Elec & Electronics Engrs; Am Soc Eng Educ. *Res:* Power system development and planning; machinery; control; direct energy conversion. *Mailing Add:* 346 Benedum Hall Univ of Pittsburgh Pittsburgh PA 15261

MCCORMICK, PHILIP THOMAS, b Oak Park, Ill, Nov 28, 26; m 57; c 5. THEORETICAL PHYSICS, PLANETARY SCIENCE. *Educ:* Univ Notre Dame, BS, 48, PhD(physics), 54. *Prof Exp:* Instr physics, DePaul Univ, 52-54; head sidewinder simulation sect, Naval Ord Test Sta, 54-57, physicist weapons planning group, 57-58; from asst prof to assoc prof, 58-69, PROF PHYSICS, UNIV SANTA CLARA, 70- *Concurrent Pos:* Sr eng specialist advan progs sect, Philco Corp, 59-61; Fulbright lectr, Univ Sind, Pakistan, 64-65; consult weapons planning group, Naval Weapons Ctr, 67- *Mem:* AAAS; Am Am Geophys Union; Phys Soc; Am Asn Physics Teachers. *Res:* Space science; electromagnetic interactions with nuclei; weapons and communications systems analysis; planetary environments; radio wave investigations of planetary atmospheres and ionospheres; aeronomy; mathematical modeling of planetary atmospheres. *Mailing Add:* Dept of Physics Univ of Santa Clara Santa Clara CA 95053

MCCORMICK, ROBERT BECKER, b Watertown, Wis, May 24, 09; m 36; c 1. GEOLOGY, MINING ENGINEERING. *Educ:* Univ Wis, BA, 30, MS, 32, PhD(geol), 36. *Prof Exp:* Asst, Univ Wis, 31-35; sales engr, E Leitz, Inc, NY, 36-39; asst to lab sales mgr, A S Aloe Co, Mo, 39-42; indust specialist, Miscellaneous Minerals Div, War Prod Bd, 42-45; metals specialist, US Tariff Comn, 45-48; indust specialist, Off Asst Secy Defense, 48-58; coordr chem & ceramic mat, Off Minerals Mobilization, US Dept Interior, 58-62, coordr for minerals, Off Minerals & Solid Fuels, 62-65, spec asst to asst dir for mineral resource develop, US Bur Mines, 65-69, coordr earth resources satellite & wilderness prog, Environ Activities Div, 69-70, liaison officer, SC, 70-72; CONSULT, 72- *Mem:* AAAS; Am Inst Mining, Metall & Petrol Engrs. *Res:* Mineral economics of industrial minerals and non-ferrous metals. *Mailing Add:* 446 Leton Dr Columbia SC 29210

MCCORMICK, ROBERT H(ENRY), b Centre Co, Pa, Apr 28, 14; m 39; c 1. CHEMICAL ENGINEERING, TECHNOLOGY TRANSFER. *Educ:* Pa State Univ, BS, 35, MS, 42. *Prof Exp:* Asst petrol ref, 35-44, from instr to asst prof, 44-49, from asst res prof to assoc res prof, 49-64, mem grad fac, 53-79, prof chem eng, 64-79, EMER PROF CHEM ENG, PA STATE UNIV, 79- *Concurrent Pos:* Tech field specialist, Pa Tech Assistance Prog, 71-79; consult to indust & govt agencies. *Mem:* Fel Am Inst Chem Engrs; Am Chem Soc; fel Am Inst Chem; Am Soc Eng Educ. *Res:* Vapor-liquid and liquid-liquid equilibrium data on multi-component systems; equipment, methods and processes for making separations on multicomponent mixtures; air and water pollution; solid waste disposal. *Mailing Add:* Dept of Chem Eng Pa State Univ 119 Chem Eng Bldg University Park PA 16802

MCCORMICK, ROY L, b Hillsboro, Ind, Feb 8, 29; m 49; c 2. MATHEMATICS. *Educ:* Wabash Col, AB, 50; Wash Univ, MA, 60; Purdue Univ, PhD(math ed), 65. *Prof Exp:* Teacher high schs, Ind, 50-51 & 56-60; instr math ed, Purdue Univ, 60-62; from asst prof to assoc prof, 62-71, PROF MATH, BALL STATE UNIV, 71- *Concurrent Pos:* Dir, NSF Inst, 67-72; chmn state adv coun, Elem & Sec Educ Act Title III, 70-72. *Mem:* Math Asn Am. *Res:* Training of secondary and elementary teachers of mathematics. *Mailing Add:* Dept of Math Sci Ball State Univ Muncie IN 47306

MCCORMICK, STEPHEN FAHRNEY, b Glendale, Calif, Sept 16, 44; m 68. NUMERICAL ANALYSIS. *Educ:* San Diego State Col, BA, 66; Univ Southern Calif, PhD(math), 71. *Prof Exp:* Mem tech staff data anal, Hughes Aircraft Co, 66-68; asst prof math, Pomona Col, 70-72; asst dir, Inst Educ Comput, Claremont Cols, 70-73; asst prof numerical anal, 73-77, ASSOC PROF MATH, COLO STATE UNIV, 77- *Concurrent Pos:* Partner & dir comput, Solar Environ Eng Co, 74- *Mem:* Soc Indust & Appl Math; Am Math Soc; Asn Comput Mach. *Res:* Matrix linear algebra, optimization, approximation theory, and algebraic iterative methods in general. *Mailing Add:* Dept of Math Colo State Univ Ft Collins CO 80521

MCCORMICK, WILLIAM CONNER, b Ft White, Fla, July 24, 20; m 47; c 3. ANIMAL BREEDING. *Educ:* Univ Fla, BS, 42; Kans State Col, MS, 47; Agr & Mech Col, Tex, PhD, 54. *Prof Exp:* Asst animal husbandman, NFla Agr Exp Sta, 42-44; from asst animal husbandman to animal husbandman, 45-67, PROF & HEAD DEPT ANIMAL SCI, COASTAL PLAIN EXP STA, UNIV GA, 67- *Res:* Animal breeding and feeding of cattle and swine. *Mailing Add:* Coastal Plain Exp Sta Univ of Ga Tifton GA 31793

MCCORMICK, WILLIAM DEVLIN, b Tacoma, Wash, May 9, 31; m 70. PHYSICS. *Educ:* Calif Inst Technol, BS, 53; Duke Univ, PhD(physics), 59. *Prof Exp:* Fulbright travel grant, Univ Padua, 59-60; asst prof physics, Univ Wash, 63-68; ASSOC PROF PHYSICS, UNIV TEX, AUSTIN, 68- *Concurrent Pos:* Sloan fel, Univ Wash, 63-65; Richland fac fel, Battelle-Northwest, 67-68. *Mem:* Am Inst Physics. *Res:* Low temperature and solid state physics; liquid helium; phase transitions; nuclear magnetic resonance and calorimetry of molecular solids; surface physics. *Mailing Add:* Dept of Physics Univ of Tex Austin TX 78712

MCCORMICK, WILLIAM F, b Riverton, Va, Sept 9, 33; m 54; c 2. PATHOLOGY, NEUROPATHOLOGY. *Educ:* Univ Chattanooga, BS, 53; Univ Tenn, MD, 55, MS, 57; Am Bd Path, dipl, 60. *Prof Exp:* Asst path, Univ Tenn, 57-60, from instr to asst prof, 60-64; from assoc prof neuropath to prof path, Univ Iowa, 64-71, prof neurol, 71-73; PROF NEUROL & PATH, UNIV TEX MED BR GALVESTON, 73- *Concurrent Pos:* NIH spec fel & instr neuropath, Col Physicians & Surgeons, Columbia Univ, 60-61; scientist, Armed Forces Inst Path, 65; consult, Vet Admin Hosp, Iowa City, 64-73; chief med examiner, Galveston Co, 78- *Mem:* Am Asn Path & Bact; Am Soc Exp Pathologists; Am Soc Human Genetics; Am Asn Neuropath; fel Am Col Pathologists. *Res:* Aneurysms, angiomas and infections of the central nervous system; diseases of muscle, brain death; forensic anthropology; forensic pathology. *Mailing Add:* Div of Neuropath Univ of Tex Med Br Galveston TX 77550

MCCORQUODALE, DONALD JAMES, b Winnipeg, Man, Aug 27, 27; nat US; m 51; c 4. BIOCHEMISTRY. *Educ:* Univ BC, BA, 50; Univ Wis, PhD(cytol, biochem), 55. *Prof Exp:* Am Cancer Soc fels, Dept Oncol, McArdle Mem Inst, Univ Wis, 55-57 & Max Planck Inst Biochem, Munich, 57-58; from asst prof to assoc prof biochem, Emory Univ, 58-67; assoc prof, Southwest Ctr Advan Studies, 68-69, from assoc prof to prof, Univ Tex, Dallas, 69-75; PROF BIOCHEM, MED COL OHIO, 75- *Concurrent Pos:* USPHS res career develop award, 60-67; vis assoc prof, Mass Inst Technol, 65-66. *Mem:* AAAS; Am Chem Soc; Am Soc Biol Chemists; Am Soc Microbiol. *Res:* Biochemical virology; macromolecular biosynthesis; cellular control mechanisms. *Mailing Add:* Dept of Biochem Med Col of Ohio C S 10008 Toledo OH 43699

MCCORQUODALE, JOHN ALEXANDER, b Woodstock, Ont, June 21, 38; m 65; c 4. CIVIL ENGINEERING. *Educ:* Univ Western Ont, BES, 62; Glasgow Univ, MS, 64; Univ Windsor, PhD(civil eng), 70. *Prof Exp:* Hydraul engr, H G Acres & Co Ltd, 64-66; lectr, 66-68, from asst prof to assoc prof, 68-76, PROF HYDROL & HYDRAUL, UNIV WINDSOR, 76- *Concurrent*

Pos: Consult hydraulics. *Honors & Awards:* Galbraith Prize, Eng Inst Can. *Mem:* Eng Inst Can; Am Soc Civil Engrs; Asn Professional Engrs Ont. *Res:* Hydraulics; hydrology; numerical analysis. *Mailing Add:* Dept of Civil Eng Univ of Windsor Windsor ON N9B 3P4 Can

MCCORRISTON, JAMES ROLAND, b Sask, July 27, 19; wid; c 3. SURGERY. *Educ:* Univ Sask, BA, 39; Queen's Univ, Ont, MD & CM, 43; McGill Univ, MSc, 48; FRCPS(C), 50; Am Bd Surg, dipl, 52. *Prof Exp:* Demonstr, McGill Univ, 51-53, lectr, 53-56, Markle scholar med sci, 53-58, from asst prof to assoc prof surg, 56-63; head dept, 63-73, PROF SURG, QUEEN'S UNIV, ONT, 63-; SURGEON, KINGSTON GEN HOSP, 73- *Concurrent Pos:* Clin asst surg, Royal Victoria Hosp, Montreal, 51-53, asst surgeon, 53-59, assoc surgeon, 59-63, hon consult, 63-; surgeon-in-chief, Kingston Gen Hosp, 63-73; consult, Hotel Dieu Hosp, Kingston. *Mem:* Fel Am Col Surgeons; Whipple Surg Soc; Can Med Asn; Can Asn Clin Surg; Can Asn Gastroenterol. *Res:* Clinical, general and experimental surgery; peptic ulcer; blood volume; electrolyte balance; homotransplantation; esophageal physiology. *Mailing Add:* Dept Surg Queen's Univ Kingston ON K7L 3N6 Can

MCCOSKER, JOHN E, b Los Angeles, Calif, Nov 17, 45. AQUATIC BIOLOGY, ICHTHYOLOGY. *Educ:* Occidental Col, BA, 67; Scripps Inst Oceanog, PhD(marine biol), 73. *Prof Exp:* Res fel ichthyol, Smithsonian Trop Res Inst, 70-71; lectr marine biol, Univ Calif, San Diego, 73; DIR, STEINHART AQUARIUM, CALIF ACAD SCI, 73- *Concurrent Pos:* Adj prof, San Francisco State Univ, 75- *Mem:* AAAS; Am Soc Ichthyologists & Herpetologists; Soc Protection Old Fishes; Soc Syst Zool; Am Asn Zool Parks & Aquariums. *Res:* Systematics of marine fishes; aquarium maintenance of mesopelagic animals; behavior of sea snakes; solar energy applications to aquarium design; of the family biology of primitive fishes, particularly the coelacanth. *Mailing Add:* Steinhart Aquarium Cal Acad Sci Golden Gate Park San Francisco CA 94118

MACCOSS, MALCOLM, b Cleator, Eng, June 2, 47; m 71; c 2. BIO-ORGANIC CHEMISTRY. *Educ:* Univ Birmingham, Eng, BSc, 68, PhD(chem), 71. *Prof Exp:* Fel chem, Univ Alta, 72-74, res assoc, 74-76; asst scientist, 76-80, SCIENTIST BIO-ORG CHEM, ARGONNE NAT LAB, 80- *Concurrent Pos:* Adj assoc prof med chem, Dept Med Chem, Col Pharm, Univ Ill Med Ctr, 81- *Mem:* Royal Soc Chem; Am Chem Soc. *Res:* Chemistry and biochemistry of nucleic acids, nucleosides and nucleotides; synthesis of nucleic acid components of potential biological and medicinal interest; design of novel prodrugs. *Mailing Add:* Div of Biol & Med Res Argonne Nat Lab Argonne IL 60439

MCCOUBREY, ARTHUR ORLANDO, b Regina, Sask, Mar 11, 20; nat US; m 42; c 3. PHYSICS, SCIENCE ADMINISTRATION. *Educ:* Calif Inst Technol, BS, 43; Univ Pittsburgh, PhD(physics), 53. *Prof Exp:* Res engr, Res Labs, Westinghouse Elec Corp, 43-47, res physicist, 47-52, adv physicist, 52-57; mgr physics dept, Nat Co, Inc, 57-60; mgr res & adv develop, Bomac Labs, Inc, 60-63; mgr atomic frequency stand, Varian Assocs, Mass, 64-67, mgr res & develop, Quantum Electronics Div, Calif, 67-68, dir cent res labs, 68-72; vpres, Frequency & Time Systs, Inc, Danvers, Mass, 72-74; dir, Inst Basic Stand, 74-78, ASSOC DIR MEASUREMENT SERV, 78- NAT BUR STANDARDS, 78- *Mem:* Am Phys Soc; fel Inst Elec & Electronics Eng; NY Acad Sci. *Res:* Microwaves; resonance physics; atomic frequency standards; quantum devices. *Mailing Add:* 8113 Whirlwind Ct Gaithersburg MD 20879

MCCOURT, A(NDREW) W(AHLERT), b St Louis, Mo, Jan 13, 24; m 49; c 4. AEROSPACE & DEFENSE SYSTEMS. *Educ:* Washington Univ, St Louis, BS, 43; Calif Inst Technol, MS, 47; Univ Pittsburgh, PhD(elec eng), 56. *Prof Exp:* Engr, Spec Prod Div, Westinghouse Elec Corp, 57-51 & Air Arm Div, 52-63, eng sect mgr, Defense & Space Ctr, 63-67, dir syst anal, Ctr Advan Studies & Anal, 67-74, adv engr, Defense & Electronic Syst Ctr, 75-82. *Concurrent Pos:* Adj assoc prof, Univ Pittsburgh, 57-65. *Mem:* Am Inst Aeronaut & Astronaut; Nat Soc Prof Engrs; Inst Elec & Electronics Engrs. *Res:* Weapon system analysis; aircraft dynamics and control; computers. *Mailing Add:* 168 Arundel Beach Rd Severna Park MD 21146

MCCOURT, FREDERICK RICHARD WAYNE, b New Westminster, BC, Jan 16, 40; m 71. MOLECULAR PHYSICS, CHEMICAL PHYSICS. *Educ:* Univ BC, BSc, 63, PhD(chem), 66. *Prof Exp:* Nat Res Coun Can fel, Swiss Fed Inst Technol, 66-67; Nat Res Coun Can fel, Kamerlingh Onnes Lab, Leiden, 67-68, Found Fundamental Res Matter sci co-worker, 68-69; vis asst prof, Inst Physics, Univ Genoa, 69; from asst prof to assoc prof, 70-78, assoc prof appl math, 73-78, PROF CHEM, UNIV WATERLOO, 78-, PROF APPL MATH, 78- *Concurrent Pos:* Alfred P Sloan Found fel, 73-75. *Mem:* Am Phys Soc; Can Asn Physicists. *Res:* Nuclear magnetic relaxation; light scattering; spectral line broadening; kinetic theory of polyatomic gases; molecular collision theory. *Mailing Add:* Dept of Chem Univ of Waterloo Waterloo ON N2L 3G1 Can

MCCOURT, ROBERT PERRY, b Highland Park, Mich, Apr 27, 29; m 50; c 7. VERTEBRATE ZOOLOGY, RADIATION BIOLOGY. *Educ:* Univ Mich, AB, 50; Ohio State Univ, MS, 52, PhD, 54. *Prof Exp:* Asst instr zool, Ohio State Univ, 52-54; from instr to asst prof, 54-62, ASSOC PROF ZOOL, HOFSTRA UNIV, 62- *Concurrent Pos:* Dir, Artemia Bibligraphic Ctr, 80- *Mem:* AAAS; Sigma Xi. *Res:* Radiation biology of artemia; techniques of liquid scintillation counting. *Mailing Add:* Dept of Biol Hofstra Univ Hempstead NY 11550

MCCOWAN, JAMES ROBERT, b Nampa, Idaho, Feb 24, 23; m 46; c 3. PHARMACY. *Educ:* Univ Colo, BS, 48, MS, 49; Univ Fla, PhD(pharm), 54. *Prof Exp:* From instr to asst prof pharm, Loyola Univ La, 49-55; from asst prof to prof, St Louis Col Pharm, 55-68; asst dean, 70-77, PROF PHARMACEUT, COL PHARM, UNIV ARK FOR MED SCI, 68-, ASSOC DEAN ACAD AFFAIRS, 77- *Mem:* Am Pharmaceut Asn. *Res:* Ophthalmic solutions; aerosols. *Mailing Add:* Col Pharm Univ Ark for Med Sci Little Rock AR 72201

MCCOWAN, OTIS BLAKELY, b Monterey, Tenn, June 17, 34. MATHEMATICS. *Educ:* Tenn Technol Univ, BS, 59; La State Univ, MA, 66; George Peabody Col, PhD, 75. *Prof Exp:* Mathematician, Air Force Missile Develop Ctr, Holloman AFB, NMex, 62-63; math teacher, Rhea Cent High Sch, Dayton, Tenn, 63-65; instr math, Kilgore Col, Tex, 66-67; from asst prof to assoc prof math, 67-75, PROF MATH, BELMONT COL, NASHVILLE, 75- *Mem:* Math Asn Am; Am Math Soc; Nat Coun Teachers Math. *Res:* Mathematics in education; mathematics teacher education. *Mailing Add:* Dept Math Belmont Col Nashville TN 37203

MCCOWEN, MAX CREAGER, b Sullivan, Ind, July 4, 15; m 46. PARASITOLOGY. *Educ:* Ind State Univ, BS, 37, MS, 38. *Prof Exp:* Instr high sch, Ind, 38-42; res assoc, Res Labs, Eli Lilly & Co, 46-47, asst chief parasitol res, 47-48, head dept, 48-58, sr parasitologist, 58-65, chief parasitologist, Lilly Res Ctr, Surrey, Eng, 65-68, head parasitol res, 68-71, res scientist aquatic biocides, 71-80, RES SCIENTIST PLANT MGT RES, GREENFIELD LABS, ELI LILLY & CO, 80- *Concurrent Pos:* Lectr, Sch Med, Ind Univ, 60. *Mem:* AAAS; Am Soc Parasitol; Aquatic Plant Mgt Soc; Am Soc Trop Med & Hyg; Sigma Xi. *Res:* Chemotherapy of parasitic diseases; immunology of parasitic infections; diagnosis of protozoan and helminthic diseases; aquatic research; aquatic herbicides, algicides, molluscicides and aquatic larvacides; environmental research. *Mailing Add:* Greenfield Labs Eli Lilly & Co Greenfield IN 46140

MCCOWEN, SARA MOSS, b Washington, NC, Jan 7, 44; m 69. MICROBIAL PHYSIOLOGY. *Educ:* Duke Univ, BA, 66; Univ NC, MAT, 68; Va Commonwealth Univ, MS, 73, PhD(microbiol), 75. *Prof Exp:* ASST PROF BIOL, VA COMMONWEALTH UNIV, 75- *Mem:* Am Soc Microbiol. *Res:* Carbohydrate metabolism in Pseudomonas species. *Mailing Add:* Dept of Biol Va Commonwealth Univ Richmond VA 23284

MCCOWN, BRENT HOWARD, b Chicago, Ill, Feb 21, 43; m 68; c 1. PHYSIOLOGICAL ECOLOGY, HORTICULTURE. *Educ:* Univ Wis-Madison, BS, 65, MS, 67, PhD(bot, hort), 69. *Prof Exp:* Res & develop coordr, US Army Cold Regions, Res & Eng Lab, Hanover, NH, 70-72; asst prof, 72-77, ASSOC PROF HORT, INST ENVIRON STUDIES, UNIV WIS-MADISON, 78- *Concurrent Pos:* Adj asst prof, Inst Arctic Biol, Univ Alaska, 70-72. *Mem:* AAAS; Am Soc Plant Physiol; Am Soc Hort Sci; Nat Parks & Conserv Org; Int Plant Propagations Soc. *Res:* Adaption of plants to environment; plant juvenility; resource analysis and carrying capacity; influence of man's activities on plant growth and survival; petroleum toxicity to terrestrial ecosystems; plant growth regulation; microculture of plant cells and organs. *Mailing Add:* Dept of Hort Univ of Wis Madison WI 53706

MCCOWN, JOHN JOSEPH, b Cleveland, Ohio, Mar 14, 29; m 48, 66, 80; c 5. SODIUM TECHNOLOGY, RADIO CHEMISTRY. *Educ:* Drury Col, BS, 51; Univ Tenn, MS, 55. *Prof Exp:* Jr chemist, USDA, 51-52; from jr chemist to assoc chemist anal chem div, Oak Ridge Nat Lab, 52-56; from asst chemist to assoc chemist chem eng div, Argonne Nat Lab, 56-60, assoc chemist, Idaho Div, 60-63; sr scientist, Nev Test Opers, Westinghouse Astronuclear Lab, 63-65, fel scientist, 65-68; sr res scientist, Pac Northwest Labs, Battelle Mem Inst, 68-70; fel scientist, 70-74, mgr sodium systs anal, 74-76, mgr sodium systs tech, 76-81, MGR CHEM & ANAL, HANFORD ENG DEVELOP LAB, WESTINGHOUSE HANFORD CO, 81- *Mem:* Am Chem Soc; Am Nuclear Soc. *Res:* Remote analyses of highly radioactive materials; remote analytical techniques and equipment; analytical radiochemistry; reactor core analysis by gamma spectrometry methods; sodium systems eng; sodium technology; rector coolant and cover gas characterization and fuel failure monitoring. *Mailing Add:* Westinghouse Hanford Co Dept of Chem Eng Box 1970 Richland WA 99352

MCCOWN, JOSEPH DANA, b Moscow, Idaho, Aug 31, 40. INDUSTRIAL ORGANIC CHEMISTRY, RESEARCH ADMINISTRATION. *Educ:* Univ Idaho, BS, 62, MS, 64; Univ Iowa, PhD(org chem), 68. *Prof Exp:* Sr res chemist, 68-71, info scientist, 71-73, res supvr, Minn Mining & Mfg Co, 73-78; mgr explor imaging & appln, Minn 3M Res Ltd, Harlow, England, 78-81, CHEM RES MGR, CENT RES LABS, 3M CO, ST PAUL, MINN, 81- *Mem:* Am Chem Soc; Sigma Xi. *Res:* Aryl sulfonyl isocyanates; hydroxamic acid esters; beta-diketones; N-nitrosoenamines; thermal rearrangement reactions; fluorocarbon chemistry. *Mailing Add:* 2443 Southcrest Ave St Paul MN 55119

MCCOWN, MALCOLM G, b Prairie Lea, Tex, Aug 14, 19; m 51; c 1. ALGEBRA. *Educ:* Trinity Univ, BS, 41, MEd, 51. *Prof Exp:* Instr, 55-60, ASST PROF MATH, TRINITY UNIV, 60- *Mem:* Am Math Soc; Nat Coun Teachers Math. *Res:* Geometry; theory of equations. *Mailing Add:* 218 Brian Dr Pleasanton TX 78064

MCCOWN, ROBERT BRUCE, b Portland, Ore, Nov 7, 39; m 73. PHYSICS. *Educ:* Hastings Col, BA, 64, MS, 66, PhD(physics), 75. *Prof Exp:* Asst prof physics, Univ South Ala, 76-80; MEM STAFF, INTERMAGNETICS GEN CORP, 80- *Mem:* AAAS; Inst Elec & Electronics Engrs. *Res:* Use of microcomputers in scientific teaching and in devices for the disabled. *Mailing Add:* Intermagnetics Gen Corp PO Box 566 Guilderland NY 36688

MCCOY, BARRY, b Trenton, NJ, Dec 14, 40; m 70. THEORETICAL PHYSICS. *Educ:* Calif Inst Technol, BS, 63; Harvard Univ, PhD(physics), 67. *Prof Exp:* Res assoc, 67-69, asst prof, 69-74, assoc prof, 74-80, PROF PHYSICS, STATE UNIV NY STONY BROOK, 80- *Mem:* Inst Theoret Physics. *Res:* Statistical mechanics. *Mailing Add:* Dept of Physics State Univ of NY Stony Brook NY 11790

MCCOY, BENJAMIN J(OE), b Fairview, WVa, May 9, 41; m 70. CHEMICAL ENGINEERING. *Educ:* Ill Inst Technol, BS, 63; Univ Minn, Minneapolis, MS, 64, PhD(chem eng), 67. *Prof Exp:* assoc prof, 67-80, PROF & CHMN CHEM ENG, UNIV CALIF, DAVIS, 80- *Mem:* Am Inst Chem Engrs; Am Phys Soc. *Res:* Separation processes; transport phenomena. *Mailing Add:* Dept of Chem Eng Univ of Calif Davis CA 95616

MCCOY, CHARLES RALPH, b Freeport, Ill, June 14, 27; m 55; c 1. PHYSICAL CHEMISTRY. *Educ:* Roosevelt Univ, BS, 56; Northwestern Univ, PhD(chem), 60. *Prof Exp:* From instr to asst prof chem, Loyola Univ Chicago, 59-63; prof chem, 63-76, MEM FAC CHEM, UNIV WIS-WHITEWATER, 76- *Mem:* Am Chem Soc; Am Phys Soc. *Res:* Kinetics. *Mailing Add:* Dept of Chem Univ of Wis Whitewater WI 53190

MCCOY, CLARENCE JOHN, b Lubbock, Tex, July 25, 35; m 57; c 2. HERPETOLOGY. *Educ:* Okla State Univ, BS, 57, MS, 60; Univ Colo, PhD(zool), 65. *Prof Exp:* From asst cur to assoc cur, 64-72, CUR AMPHIBIANS & REPTILES, CARNEGIE MUS NATURAL HIST, 72- *Concurrent Pos:* Vis prof, Ariz State Univ, 69-70; adj assoc prof, Univ Pittsburgh, 72-; chmn comt syst resources herpet, 75-77. *Mem:* AAAS; Am Soc Ichthyologists & Herpetologists; Am Soc Mammal; Soc Syst Zool; Soc Study Amphibians & Reptiles. *Res:* Natural history and systematics of reptiles and amphibians; reptilian reproductive cycles; biogeography of Mexico; general vertebrate zoology. *Mailing Add:* Carnegie Mus Natural Hist 4400 Forbes Ave Pittsburgh PA 15213

MCCOY, CLAYTON WILLIAM, b Rochester, Minn, June 22, 38; m 63; c 1. ENTOMOLOGY. *Educ:* Gustavus Adolphus Col, BS, 60; Univ Nebr, MSc, 63; Univ Calif, PhD(entom), 67. *Prof Exp:* Res entomologist, USDA, 67-72; ASSOC ENTOMOLOGIST, AGR RES & EDUC CTR, UNIV FLA, 72- *Mem:* Entom Soc Am; Int Orgn Biol Control; Int Soc Invert Path. *Res:* Biological control of economic pests of citrus. *Mailing Add:* Agr Res & Educ Ctr Univ Fla PO Box 1088 Lake Alfred FL 33850

MACCOY, CLINTON VILES, b Brookline, Mass, Mar 27, 05; m 36; c 2. ECOLOGY. *Educ:* Harvard Univ, AB, 28, AM, 29, PhD(biol), 34. *Prof Exp:* Cur fishes & mammals, Secy & ed, Boston Soc Natural Hist, 29-39; asst prof zool, Mass State Col, 39-44; from assoc prof to prof, 44-70, EMER PROF BIOL, WHEATON COL, MASS, 70-; DIR NORWELL LABS, 70- *Concurrent Pos:* Asst biologist, State Fish & Game Dept, NH, 39; res assoc, Woods Hole Oceanog Inst, 55-64. *Mem:* Am Soc Mammal; Am Soc Ichthyol & Herpet; Am Soc Limnol & Oceanog; Int Soc Limnol. *Res:* Limnology; oceanography, especially estuarine areas; intertidal in-fauna, especially meiofauna. *Mailing Add:* Norwell Labs 77Winter St Norwell MA 02061

MCCOY, DAVID ROSS, b Culver City, Calif, July 21, 42; m 66; c 4. ORGANIC CHEMISTRY. *Educ:* Univ Calif, Los Angeles, BS, 63; Univ Ore, PhD(org chem), 67. *Prof Exp:* From chemist to sr chemist, Texaco, Inc, NY, 67-72, res chemist, 72-76; SR PROJ CHEMIST, TEXACO CHEM CO, 76- *Mem:* Am Chem Soc. *Res:* Chemistry of heterocyclic compounds; organophosphorus chemistry; mechanisms of heterogeneous catalysis; petrochemical synthesis; enhanced oil recovery; demulsifiers. *Mailing Add:* 9202 Parkfield Dr Austin TX 78758

MCCOY, DONALD W, microbiology, biochemistry, see previous edition

MCCOY, DOROTHY, b Waukomis, Okla, Aug 9, 03. MATHEMATICS. *Educ:* Baylor Univ, BA, 25; Univ Iowa, MS, 27, PhD(math), 29. *Prof Exp:* Teacher high sch, Iowa, 25-26; asst, Univ Iowa, 28-29; prof math & head dept, Belhaven Col, 29-40; chmn div phys & biol sci, 49-72, prof math & head dept, 49-75, DISTINGUISHED PROF & EMER MATHEMETICIAN, WAYLAND BAPTIST COL, 75- *Concurrent Pos:* Fulbright prof, Col Sci, Univ Baghdad, 53-54. *Mem:* Am Math Soc; Math Asn Am. *Res:* Geometry; complete existential theory of eight fundamental properties of topological spaces. *Mailing Add:* Dept of Math Wayland Baptist Col Plainview TX 79072

MCCOY, ELBERT JULIUS, physiology, see previous edition

MCCOY, ERNEST E, b Victoria, BC, Sept 3, 23; m 50; c 4. MEDICINE. *Educ:* Univ Alta, BSc, 47, MD, 49. *Prof Exp:* Jr intern med, Royal Alexandria Hosp, Edmonton, Alta, 49-50; sr intern, Col Belcher Hosp, Calgary, 50-51; jr resident pediat, St Louis Children's Hosp, Mo, 51-52, asst resident, 52-53; clin instr, Univ BC, 54-57; res assoc microbiol, Vanderbilt Univ, 57-59, asst prof pediat, 59-61; assoc prof, Univ Mo-Columbia, 61-66; prof, Univ Va, 66-69; PROF PEDIAT & CHMN DEPT, UNIV ALTA, 70- *Concurrent Pos:* Res fel pediat, Washington Univ, 53; Markle scholar, 59. *Res:* Enzymatic abnormalities in congenital metabolic derangements. *Mailing Add:* Dept Pediat Univ Alta Edmonton AB T6G 2G7 Can

MCCOY, HERBERT E, b Fayetteville, WVa, June 4, 35; m 55; c 2. METALLURGY. *Educ:* Univ Tenn, BS, 57, MS, 58, PhD(metall), 64. *Prof Exp:* METALLURGIST, OAK RIDGE NAT LAB, 58- *Concurrent Pos:* Lectr mech, Univ Tenn, Knoxville, 65- *Mem:* Am Soc Metals; Am Inst Mining, Metall & Petrol Engrs. *Res:* Mechanical properties of metals at high temperature; gas metal reactions at elevated temperature; influence of neutron irradiation on mechanical properties of metals. *Mailing Add:* Bldg 4500S Oak Ridge Nat Lab PO Box X Oak Ridge TN 37830

MCCOY, JAMES ERNEST, b Glendale, Calif, May 4, 41; m 62; c 2. MAGNETOSPHERIC PHYSICS. *Educ:* Calif Inst Technol, BS, 63; Rice Univ, PhD(space sci), 69. *Prof Exp:* PHYSICIST, MANNED SPACECRAFT CTR, NASA, 63- *Mem:* Am Geophys Union. *Res:* Geomagnetically trapped radiation; access of solar and cosmic ray radiation to the polar caps; magneto tail electric fields; low energy solar cosmic ray protons; solar cosmic ray physics. *Mailing Add:* TN2 NASA Manned Apacecraft Ctr Houston TX 77058

MCCOY, JEROME DEAN, physics, see previous edition

MCCOY, JIMMY JEWELL, b Corsicana, Tex, Mar 18,43; m 65. MATHEMATICAL PHYSICS, SOLID STATE PHYSICS. *Educ:* Baylor Univ, BS, 65, PhD(physics), 69. *Prof Exp:* AEC grant, Baylor Univ, 69-70; ASST PROF PHYSICS, TARLETON STATE COL, 70- *Res:* Particle size effects in x-ray scattering. *Mailing Add:* Dept of Physics Tarleton State State Col Stephenville TX 76401

MCCOY, JOHN HAROLD, b Conroe, Tex, May 16, 35; m 61; c 3. COMPUTER SCIENCE. *Educ:* Sam Houston State Univ, BS, 63, MA, 64; Ohio State Univ, PhD(elec eng), 68. *Prof Exp:* Exp physicist, United Aircraft Res Labs, 68-70; assoc prof math, 70-72, PROF COMPUT SCI, SAM HOUSTON STATE UNIV, 72-, DIR COMPUT FACIL, 71- *Mem:* Asn Comput Mach; Inst Elec & Electronics Eng. *Mailing Add:* Dept of Comput Sci Sam Houston State Univ Box 2206 Huntsville TX 77340

MCCOY, JOHN J, b New York, NY, Sept 18, 36; m 62; c 3. ENGINEERING MECHANICS. MECHANICS. *Educ:* Cooper Union, BCE, 58; Columbia Univ, MS, 59, ScD(eng mech), 61. *Prof Exp:* Staff engr, Int Bus Mach Corp, 61-63; asst prof appl mech, Univ Pa, 63-69; assoc prof, 69-74, PROF CIVIL ENG, CATH UNIV AM, 74- *Concurrent Pos:* Consult, Naval Res Lab, Washington, DC, 70-; assoc ed, J Appl Mech, 76- *Mem:* Am Soc Mech Engrs; Acoust Soc Am; Am Acad Mech; Am Soc Civil Engrs. *Res:* Stochastic processes; propagation through random media; theory of heterogeneous media; waves in fluids and solids; applied mathematics. *Mailing Add:* Dept Civil Eng Cath Univ Am Washington DC 20064

MCCOY, JOHN J, b Coalton, WVa, July 15, 27; m 49; c 2. ORNITHOLOGY. *Educ:* WVa Wesleyan Col, BS, 50; Univ WVa, MS, 52; Univ Fla, PhD, 60. *Prof Exp:* Asst prof biol, Tenn Wesleyan Col, 56-57; head dept, Jacksonville Univ, 57-63; head dept biol, 63-67, ASSOC PROF BIOL, UNIV NC, ASHEVILLE, 63- *Mem:* Cooper Ornith Soc; Am Ornith Union. *Res:* Paleo-ornithology. *Mailing Add:* Dept Biol Univ NC Asheville NC 28800

MCCOY, JOHN ROGER, b Trenton, NJ, June 11, 16; m 45; c 1. CHEMOTHERAPY, COMPARATIVE PATHOLOGY. *Educ:* Univ Pa, VMD, 40. *Prof Exp:* Res specialist, 50-69, ADJ RES PROF, BUR BIOL RES, RUTGERS UNIV, 70-; PROF COMP PATH & DIR VIVARIUM, RUTGERS MED SCH, COL MED & DENT NJ, 70- *Concurrent Pos:* Consult to govt & var pharmaceut concerns; mem grant adv coun, Seeing Eye Found; mem vet adv coun, Vet Cancer Unit; mem subcomt org contaminants, Safe Drinking Water Comt, Nat Res Coun-Nat Acad Sci; mem comt substances generally recognized as safe, Fedn Am Soc Exp Biol. *Mem:* AAAS; Am Vet Med Asn (pres, 71-72); Soc Toxicol; fel NY Acad Sci; Am Asn Lab Animal Sci. *Res:* Spontaneous canine cancer; pathology of leishmaniasis; food additives; steroids; cancer chemotherapy. *Mailing Add:* 1007 River Rd Piscataway NJ 08854

MCCOY, JOSEPH HAMILTON, b Johnson City, Tenn, May 7, 34. PHYSICAL CHEMISTRY. *Educ:* E Tenn State Univ, BS, 56; Mich State Univ, PhD(chem), 63. *Prof Exp:* Res chemist, E I du Pont de Nemours & Co, 62-64; asst prof, 64-67, ASSOC PROF CHEM, EMORY & HENRY COL, 67- *Mem:* AAAS; Am Chem Soc. *Res:* Polymer solution studies; gas chromatography. *Mailing Add:* Dept of Chem Emory & Henry Col Emory VA 24327

MCCOY, JOSEPH WESLEY, b Eugene, Ore, Jan 20, 30; m 51; c 6. ORGANIC CHEMISTRY. *Educ:* Univ Portland, BS, 52; Univ Notre Dame, PhD(org chem), 59. *Prof Exp:* Res chemist, Calif Res Corp Div, Standard Oil Co, Calif, 55-60; instr chem, 60-65, head div sci & math, 67-69, ASSOC PROF CHEM, UNIV PORTLAND, 65-, DIR GRAD PROG SCI, 69- *Mem:* Am Chem Soc. *Res:* Surface active agents; petrochemicals. *Mailing Add:* Dept of Chem Univ of Portland Portland OR 97203

MCCOY, LAYTON LESLIE, b Seattle, Wash, Mar 11, 27. ORGANIC CHEMISTRY. *Educ:* Univ Wash, BS, 47, PhD(chem), 51. *Prof Exp:* Instr chem, Columbia Univ, 51-53; NSF fel, Univ Wash, 57-58; from instr to asst prof chem, Columbia Univ, 58-62; from asst prof to assoc prof, 62-67, asst chmn dept, 73-75, PROF CHEM, UNIV MO-KANSAS CITY, 67- *Mem:* AAAS; Am Chem Soc. *Res:* Synthesis and reactions of cyclopropanes; stereospecific and stereoselective syntheses and reactions; correlation of structure and relative acidity of acids. *Mailing Add:* Dept Chem Univ Mo Kansas City MO 64110

MCCOY, LOWELL EUGENE, b Hillsboro, Ohio, June 1, 37; m 59; c 4. PHYSIOLOGY, BIOCHEMISTRY. *Educ:* Miami Univ, BA, 60, MA, 61; Wayne State Univ, PhD(physiol), 66. *Prof Exp:* Res asst cancer chemother & toxicol, Christ Hosp Inst Med Res, 61-63; res assoc blood coagulation biochem, 66-67, asst prof, 68-73, ASSOC PROF PHYSIOL, SCH MED, WAYNE STATE UNIV, 73- *Concurrent Pos:* Mem coun thrombosis, Am Heart Asn. *Mem:* Am Inst Chem; Am Chem Soc; Int Soc Thrombosis & Haemostasis; NY Acad Sci. *Res:* Blood coagulation protein biochemistry, including physical and enzymologic properties; hematology; erythropoiesis; peptide synthesis; amino acid sequence. *Mailing Add:* 22175 Thorofare Grosse Ile MI 48138

MCCOY, OLIVER RUFUS, b St Louis, Mo, Aug 1, 05; m 37; c 3. PARASITOLOGY. *Educ:* Wash Univ, AB, 26, MS, 27; Johns Hopkins Univ, ScD, 30; Univ Rochester, MD, 42. *Hon Degrees:* LLD, Keio Univ, Japan, 56. *Prof Exp:* Asst zool, Wash Univ, 26-27; helminth, Sch Hyg & Pub Health, Johns Hopkins Univ, 28-29, instr, 29-30; asst prof parasitol, Sch Med & Dent, Univ Rochester, 30-42; epidemiologist, Douglas Aircraft Co, E Africa, 42-43; field staff, Mem Div, Med & Pub Health, Rockefeller Found, 46-56; from assoc dir to dir, China Med Bd New York, 56-69, pres, 69-73. *Concurrent Pos:* Vis prof, Nat Med Col, Shanghai, 36; consult, Gorgas Mem Lab, 34; mem, State Trichinosis Comn, NY, 40-42; mem bd, Coord Malaria Studies, Nat Res Coun, 43-46. *Honors & Awards:* Third Order Sacred Treasure, Japan. *Mem:* AAAS; Am Soc Parasitol; Am Soc Trop Med & Hyg; Am Pub Health Asn. *Res:* Life histories of trematodes; immunity of helminth parasites; hookworm; trichinosis; filariasis; malaria and tropical disease control. *Mailing Add:* 10085-4 Windstream Dr Columbia MD 21044

MCCOY, RA' PH HINES, b Crowell, Tex, Nov 22, 40; m 74; c 1. WILDLIFE DISEASES, MEDICAL BACTERIOLOGY. *Educ:* Baylor Univ, BS, 63, MS, 65; Ore State Univ, PhD(microbiol), 73. *Prof Exp:* asst prof biol, Tex A&I Univ, 74-76; asst prof, 77-80, ASSOC PROF BIOL, AUSTIN PEAY STATE

UNIV, 80- *Concurrent Pos:* Consult, Garcia & Rangel, Attys, 75-76 & Mem Hosp, Clarksville, Tenn, 77- *Mem:* Wildlife Dis Asn; Am Soc Microbiol; Am Soc Mammalogists; Wildlife Soc. *Res:* Zoonoses; infectious diseases of wild and domestic animals. *Mailing Add:* Dept of Biol Austin Peay State Univ Clarksville TN 37040

MCCOY, RAWLEY D, b Nutley, NJ, Dec 21, 14; m 47; c 3. COMPUTER & SPACE SCIENCE. *Educ:* Stevens Inst Technol, ME, 37. *Prof Exp:* Instr elec eng, Stevens Inst Technol, 37-38; radio engr, Lustron Lights, Inc, 38-40; proj engr, Sperry Gyroscope Co, 41-46; chief engr, Reeves Instrument Corp, 46-58, vpres eng, 58-66, sr vpres, 66-67; vpres, RC-95, Inc, 67-70; CONSULT, 71- *Mem:* Fel Inst Elec & Electronics Engrs. *Res:* Servomechanisms; electronic analogue computers. *Mailing Add:* Ten the Byway Bronxville NY 10708

MCCOY, RAYMOND DUNCAN, b Newberg, Ore, Dec 30, 24; m 51; c 3. PHYSICAL CHEMISTRY, INSTRUMENTATION. *Educ:* Willamette Univ, BS, 50; Univ Ore, PhD(phys chem), 56. *Prof Exp:* Instrument engr, Phillips Petrol Co, Okla, 55-71; MEM STAFF, APPL AUTOMATION, INC, 71- *Mem:* Am Chem Soc. *Res:* Kinetics of gaseous reactions; process instrumentation and automation. *Mailing Add:* Appl Automation Inc Pawhuska Rd RB 2 Bartlesville OK 74004

MCCOY, ROBERT A, b Springfield, Ill, Oct 1, 42; m 64; c 2. TOPOLOGY. *Educ:* Southern Ill Univ, BA, 64; Iowa State Univ, PhD(math), 68. *Prof Exp:* Asst prof, 68-73, assoc prof, 73-79, PROF MATH, VA POLYTECH INST & STATE UNIV, 79- *Mem:* Am Math Soc; Math Asn Am. *Res:* General topology. *Mailing Add:* Dept of Math Va Polytech Inst & State Univ Blacksburg VA 24061

MCCOY, ROGER MICHAEL, b Dewey, Okla, Feb 3, 33; m 55; c 2. PHYSICAL GEOGRAPHY. *Educ:* Univ Okla, BS, 57; Univ Colo, MA, 64; Univ Kans, PhD(geog), 67. *Prof Exp:* Asst prof geog, Univ Ill, Chicago, 67-69; asst prof, Univ Ky, 69-72; assoc prof, 72-80, PROF GEOG & CHMN DEPT, UNIV UTAH, 80- *Concurrent Pos:* Consult remote sensing. *Honors & Awards:* Ford-Bartlett Award, Am Soc Photogram. *Mem:* Am Soc Photogram; Asn Am Geog. *Res:* Fluvial geomorphology; remote sensing. *Mailing Add:* Dept of Geog Univ of Utah Salt Lake City UT 84112

MCCOY, RONALD EUGENE, b Hershey, Pa, May 3, 34; m 52; c 6. MATHEMATICS. *Educ:* Ind Univ Pa, BS, 56; Univ Pittsburgh, MEd, 57; Pa State Univ, DEd(math educ), 71. *Prof Exp:* Teacher pub sch, Pa, 56-57, teacher & dept chmn high sch, Pa, 57-67; ASSOC PROF MATH, IND UNIV PA, 67- *Mem:* Math Asn Am; Nat Coun Teachers Math. *Res:* Mathematics education; theory of construction of deductive proofs in mathematics as applied to teaching. *Mailing Add:* Dept Math Ind Univ Pa Indiana PA 15701

MCCOY, SUE, biochemistry, see previous edition

MCCOY, THOMAS LARUE, b Seville, Ohio, Jan 16, 33; m 57; c 1. MATHEMATICS. *Educ:* Oberlin Col, BA, 54; Univ Wis, MS, 56, PhD(math), 61. *Prof Exp:* Instr math, Ill Inst Technol, 60, asst prof, 64; from asst prof to assoc prof, 64-77, PROF MATH, MICH STATE UNIV, 77- *Mem:* Am Math Soc. *Res:* Functions of a complex variable; differential equation; calculus of variation. *Mailing Add:* Dept of Math Mich State Univ East Lansing MI 48823

MCCOY, V EUGENE, JR, b Chicago, Ill, July 7, 33; m 57; c 3. PHYSICAL ORGANIC CHEMISTRY. *Educ:* Princeton Univ, AB, 55; Harvard Univ, PhD(chem), 65. *Prof Exp:* Res chemist, Pioneering Res Lab, Textile Fibers Dept, 64-67, sr res chemist, 67-68 & 69-73, SR RES CHEMIST, TEXTILE RES LAB, E I DU PONT DE NEMOURS & CO, INC, 73- *Mem:* Am Chem Soc; Sigma Xi; Textured Yarn Asn Am. *Res:* Electron exchange reactions; chemistry of organophosphorus compounds; polymers and chemical reactions for textile fibers; feed yarn and textured yarn development. *Mailing Add:* 2641 Majestic Dr Wilmington DE 19810

MCCOY, WILLIAM HARRISON, b Nelsonville, Ohio, May 28, 25; m 59. PHYSICAL CHEMISTRY. *Educ:* Youngstown Univ, BS, 50; Univ Pittsburgh, PhD(phys chem), 55. *Prof Exp:* Asst prof chem, Washington & Jefferson Col, 55-56 & Tex A&M Univ, 56-57; assoc prof, Youngstown Univ, 57-63; phys chemist, Off Saline Water, 63-64, chief div chem physics, 64-74, phys chemist, 74-78, SR WATER RES SPECIALIST, OFF WATER RES & TECHNOL, US DEPT INTERIOR, 78- *Mem:* Am Chem Soc. *Res:* Thermodynamic properties of liquids and electrolyte solutions; theory of liquids; properties of solutions, with special reference to contaminated water. *Mailing Add:* Div Phys Chem Off Water Res US Dept of Interior Washington DC 20240

MCCRACKEN, ALEXANDER WALKER, b Motherwell, Scotland, Nov 24, 31; m 60; c 2. MEDICAL MICROBIOLOGY. *Educ:* Univ Glasgow, MB, ChB, 55; Univ London, DCP, 62; Univ Liverpool, DTM, 66. *Prof Exp:* Pathologist, Royal Air Force Hosp, Akrotiri, Cyprus, 58-61; chief clin microbiol, Royal Air Force Inst Path & Trop Med, Halton, Eng, 62-68; assoc dir labs, Bexar County Teaching Hosp, 71-72; dir labs, Herman Hosp, Houston, 72-73; chief microbial path, Univ Tex Med Sch San Antonio, 68-71, assoc prof path & microbiol, 68-73, actg chmn dept, 71-73, prof path, 72-73, adj prof microbiol, 73-80, prof allied health sci, 78-80 ; prof & chmn dept path, assoc chief path serv & dir clin microbiol & virol, Baylor Univ Med Ctr, 73-81, PROF PATH, BAYLOR COL DENT, DALLAS, 81. *Concurrent Pos:* chief path serv & dir labs, Methodist Hosps, Dallas, 81- *Mem:* Brit Asn Clin Path; Brit Soc Gen Microbiol; Col Path Eng; Int Acad Path; Am Col Pathologists. *Res:* Rapid diagnostic techniques in clinical microbiology; fluorescent antibody methodology; respiratory virus isolation methods and epidemiology; automation in microbiology; pathogenesis of viral infections. *Mailing Add:* Dept of Path Baylor Univ Med Ctr Dallas TX 75246

MCCRACKEN, CURTIS W, b Vici, Okla, June 7, 34. ASTRONOMY, PHYSICS. *Educ:* Panhandle Agr & Mech Col, BS, 56; Okla State Univ, MS, 59. *Prof Exp:* PHYSICIST & ASTRONOMER, GODDARD SPACE FLIGHT CTR, NASA, 60- *Mem:* AAAS; Am Astron Soc; Am Geophys Union. *Res:* Interplanetary dust particles using rockets and spacecraft; image intensifier studies of comets, galactic II regions, and planetary nebulae. *Mailing Add:* Code 685 NASA Goddard Space Flight Ctr Greenbelt MD 20771

MCCRACKEN, DEREK ALBERT, b Eng, Feb 11, 43; m 63; c 3. PLANT PHYSIOLOGY. *Educ:* McMaster Univ, BA, 63; Univ Toronto, MA, 66, PhD(bot), 69. *Prof Exp:* asst prof, 69-77, ASSOC PROF BIOL SCI, ILL STATE UNIV, 77- *Mem:* AAAS; Am Soc Plant Physiol; Can Soc Plant Physiol; Scand Sco Plant Physiol. *Res:* Starch biosynthesis; interaction between nuclear and cytoplasmic genes. *Mailing Add:* Dept of Biol Sci Ill State Univ Normal IL 61761

MACCRACKEN, ELLIOTT B, b Winnetka, Ill, May 24, 11; m 56; c 3. SCIENCE EDUCATION, MATHEMATICS. *Educ:* Ore State Col, BS, 32; Columbia Univ, MA, 41; Stanford Univ, EdD, 53. *Prof Exp:* Teacher pub schs, Ore, 34-36, high schs, 36-42; engr, Watson Labs, 46; from instr to prof, 46-76, EMER PROF SCI, SOUTHERN ORE STATE COL, 76- *Mem:* Am Asn Physics Teachers; Inst Elec & Electronics Engrs; Am Asn Univ Profs. *Res:* Preparation of teachers. *Mailing Add:* 645 Glenwood Ashland OR 97520

MCCRACKEN, FRANCIS IRVIN, b Bicknell, Ind, Aug 19, 35; m 59; c 2. FOREST PATHOLOGY. *Educ:* Ariz State Univ, BS, 57; Okla State Univ, MS, 59; Wash State Univ, PhD(plant path), 72. *Prof Exp:* Instr bot, Univ Idaho, 62-67; RES PLANT PATH, US FOREST SERV, USDA, 67- *Mem:* Am Phytopath Soc; Sigma Xi. *Res:* Etiology and control of diseases effecting southern bottomland hardwood tree species. *Mailing Add:* US Forest Serv PO Box 227 Stoneville MS 38776

MCCRACKEN, JOHN AITKEN, b Glasgow, Scotland, Aug 16, 34. ENDOCRINOLOGY. *Educ:* Glasgow Univ, BVMS, 58, PhD(endocrinol), 63. *Prof Exp:* House surgeon, Glasgow Univ, 58-59; vis res fel, Cambridge Univ, 60; Agr Res Coun res fel endocrine physiol, Univ Birmingham, 63-64; staff scientist, 64-70, SR SCIENTIST, WORCESTER FOUND EXP BIOL, 70- *Concurrent Pos:* Vis prof, Cornell Univ, 69-70; adj prof physiol, Med Sch, Univ Mass, 78- *Mem:* AAAS; Soc Study Reproduction; NY Acad Sci; Royal Col Vet Surg; Endocrine Soc. *Res:* Steroid biochemistry; physiology and biochemistry of prostaglandins; transplantations of ovary, uterus and adrenal glands in the sheep and their various interrelationships; interrelationships between steroids, prostaglandins and polypeptide hormones; utero-ovarian-pituitary axis. *Mailing Add:* Worcester Found Exp Biol 222 Maple Ave Shrewsbury MA 01545

MCCRACKEN, JOHN DAVID, b Fairfield, Iowa, Sept 17, 39; m 61; c 2. AGRICULTURAL EDUCATION. *Educ:* Iowa State Univ, BS, 61, MS, 62; Ohio State Univ, PhD(agr educ), 70. *Prof Exp:* Teacher voc agr, Charles City Public Schs, 64-68; res assoc voc educ, 68-70, res specialist, 70-73, from asst prof to assoc prof, 73-79, PROF AGR EDUC, OHIO STATE UNIV, 79- *Concurrent Pos:* Res ed, Agr Educ Magazine, 71-74; ed, Summaries res & develop activities Agr Educ, 74-76, Am Asn Teacher Educr Agr, 78 & J Voc Educ Res, Am Voc Educ Res Asn, 79; policy comn, Agr Educ Div, Am Voc Asn, 78-80; vis prof, Kans State Univ, 81; sect ed, Annual Rev Res Voc Educ, Univ Ill, 81. *Mem:* Am Asn Teacher Educr Agr (vpres, 76-77, pres, 79, past pres, 80); Am Voc Asn; Am Voc Educ Res Asn; Am Educ Res Asn. *Res:* Agricultural education; vocational agriculture curriculum and experiential learning; occupational surveys of agricultural occupations. *Mailing Add:* 6641 Millbrae Rd Worthington OH 43085

MCCRACKEN, LESLIE G(UY), JR, b Philadelphia, Pa, June 8, 25; m 47. ELECTRICAL ENGINEERING. *Educ:* Mass Inst Technol, SB, 45; Lehigh Univ, MS, 47; Pa State Univ, PhD(elec eng), 52. *Prof Exp:* Asst elec eng, Lehigh Univ, 46-47; asst ord res lab, Pa State Univ, 47-48, instr elec eng, 49-51; electronic scientist, Naval Res Lab, Wash, 51-56; ASSOC PROF ELEC ENG, LEHIGH UNIV, 56- *Concurrent Pos:* Staff mem, Gen Atronics Corp, Pa, 58-59 & Bell Aerospace Corp, 63; Off Naval Res grant, 60; Int Bus Mach Corp fel, 61; NASA-Am Soc Eng Educ fel, Univ Md, 65. *Mem:* Am Soc Eng Educ; Sigma Xi; sr mem Inst Elec & Electronics Engrs; Soc Eng Sci; NY Acad Sci. *Res:* Electromagnetic boundary value problems with cylindrical symmetry; reflection and scattering of impulse waves by random boundaries; nonlinear control system analysis and synthesis; dynamic and statistical design of multivariable control systems; multivariable stochastic processes; synthesis of sequential machines. *Mailing Add:* Dept of Elec Eng Lehigh Univ Bethlehem PA 18015

MCCRACKEN, MARJORIE, mathematics, see previous edition

MACCRACKEN, MICHAEL CALVIN, b Schenectady, NY, May 20, 42; m 67; c 2. ATMOSPHERIC PHYSICS, AIR POLLUTION. *Educ:* Princeton Univ, BSE, 64; Univ Calif, Davis, MS, 66, PhD(appl sci), 68. *Prof Exp:* PHYSICIST, LAWRENCE LIVERMORE NAT LAB, UNIV CALIF, 68-, DEP DIV LEADER ATMOSPHERIC & GEOPHYS SCI, 74- *Concurrent Pos:* Proj dir, Multistate Atmospheric Power Prod Pollution Study, US Dept Energy, 76-79; sci dir, Climate & Carbon Dioxide Res Prog, US Dept Energy, 79- *Mem:* Am Geophys Union; Am Quaternary Asn; Arctic Inst NAm. *Res:* Numerical simulation of processes governing the global climate and the factors causing climatic change, and regional air quality for land use planning and control strategy assessment. *Mailing Add:* Lawrence Livermore Lab PO Box 808 Livermore CA 94550

MCCRACKEN, MICHAEL DWAYNE, b Terrell, Tex, Feb 15, 41. BOTANY. *Educ:* Tex Tech Univ, BS, 63, MS, 65; Ind Univ, Bloomington, PhD(bot), 69. *Prof Exp:* Asst prof bot, Univ Wis-Madison, 69-71; asst prof, 71-75, ASSOC PROF BIOL, TEX CHRISTIAN UNIV, 75-, CHMN BIOL,

75- *Concurrent Pos:* NSF fel, Univ Wis-Madison, 70-72. *Mem:* Phycol Soc Am; Int Phycol Soc; Am Soc Limnol & Oceanog; Int Soc Theoret & Appl Limnol. *Res:* Algology, differentiation and development in Volvox; algal primary productivity. *Mailing Add:* Dept of Biol Tex Christian Univ Ft Worth TX 76129

MCCRACKEN, PHILIP GLEN, b Santa Cruz, NMex, Feb 11, 28; m 49; c 4. CHEMICAL ENGINEERING. *Educ:* NMex State Univ, BS, 51; Purdue Univ, PhD(chem eng), 56. *Prof Exp:* Mem staff, Com Solvents Corp, 51-52 & Dow Chem Co, 56-61; head develop, Geigy Chem Corp, McIntosh, 61-68, tech mgr, St Gabriel Plant, 68-71, TECH DIR, AGR CHEM DIV, CIBA-GEIGY CORP, 71- *Res:* Research and development of chemical processes; chronological history. *Mailing Add:* Ciba Geigy Corp Agr Chem Div 410 Swing Rd Greensboro NC 27410

MCCRACKEN, RALPH JOSEPH, b Guantanamo, Cuba, July 3, 21; nat US; m 49; c 2. SOIL SCIENCE. *Educ:* Earlham Col, AB, 42; Cornell Univ, MS, 51; Iowa State Univ, PhD(soils), 56. *Prof Exp:* Soil scientist, USDA, 47-49, 51-55; assoc agronomist, Univ Tenn, 55-56; assoc prof, Soil Sci, N C State Univ, 56-62, prof, 62-73, asst dir res, Sch Agr & Life Sci, 70-73; assoc admin, USDA Agr Res Serv, 73-78; actg assoc dir, Sci & Educ Admin, 78-80, DEP CHIEF, SOIL CONSERVATION SERV, USDA, 81- *Mem:* Fel AAAS; fel Soil Sci Soc Am; fel Am Soc Agron; Soil Conserv Soc Am; Int Soc Soil Sci. *Res:* Genesis, classification and mineralogy of soils. *Mailing Add:* US Dept of Agr Sci & Educ Admin Washington DC 20250

MCCRACKEN, RICHARD OWEN, b Racine, Wis, Mar 26, 39; m 65; c 2. PARASITOLOGY. *Educ:* Univ Wis-Whitewater, BS, 65, MST, 67; Iowa State Univ, PhD(zool), 72. *Prof Exp:* Instr natural sci, Milton Col, 67-68; sr res parasitologist, Merck Inst Therapeut Res, Merck & Co, Inc, 74-75; lectr, Tex A&M Univ, 75-77; asst prof, 77-81, ASSOC PROF BIOL, IND UNIV-PURDUE UNIV, INDIANAPOLIS, 81- *Concurrent Pos:* NIH fel, Tulane Univ, 72-74. *Mem:* Am Soc Parasitologists; Am Inst Biol Sci; AAAS; Sigma Xi. *Res:* Biochemistry; physiology and chemotherapy of parasitic helminths; structure and function of parasite surface membranes; membrane transport. *Mailing Add:* Dept of Biol Ind Univ-Purdue Univ Indianapolis IN 46205

MCCRACKEN, WALTER JOHN, b Bucyrus, Ohio, Sept 24, 53. MATERIALS SCIENCE ENGINEERING. *Educ:* Gen Motors Inst, Flint, Mich, BA, 76; Univ Fla, MA, 78, PhD(mat sci), 81. *Prof Exp:* Assoc process develop engr, Frigidaire Div, Gen Motors Corp, 76-77; grad res assoc, Dept Mat, Sci & Eng, Univ Fla, 77-81; ENGR CERAMICS, NEUTRON DEVICES DEPT, GEN ELEC CO, 81- *Concurrent Pos:* Fel, Dept Math Sci & Eng, Univ Fla, 81; pres, Mc-R Consults Inc, Gainesville, Fla, 81- *Mem:* Am Ceramic Soc; Nat Asn Corrosion Engrs; Electron Micros Soc Am. *Res:* Development and characterization of glasses and glass-ceramics for sealing to metals; sol-gel processing of glass films and monoliths; electron beam channeling of single crystal ceramics. *Mailing Add:* Gen Elec Co Neutron Devices Dept PO Box 11508 St Petersburg FL 33733

MCCRADY, EDWARD, embryology, biophysics, deceased

MCCRADY, EDWARD, III, b Trenton, NJ, Sept 24, 33; m 55; c 3. DEVELOPMENTAL BIOLOGY. *Educ:* Univ of the South, BS, 55; Univ Va, MA, 61, PhD(biol), 64. *Prof Exp:* Asst biol, Univ Va, 60-63; asst prof, 64-70, ASSOC PROF BIOL, UNIV N C, GREENSBORO, 70- *Mem:* AAAS; Am Soc Zool; Develop Biol Soc. *Res:* Insect tissue culture; development of imaginal discs. *Mailing Add:* Dept of Biol Univ of N C Greensboro NC 27412

MCCRADY, JAMES DAVID, b Beaumont, Tex, June 26, 30; m 51; c 3. VETERINARY PHYSIOLOGY. *Educ:* Tex A&M Univ, BS, 52, DVM, 58; Baylor Univ, PhD(physiol), 65. *Prof Exp:* From instr to asst prof physiol, Tex A&M Univ, 58-62; fel, instr & dir animal resources, Col Med, Baylor Univ, 62-64; assoc prof physiol, 64-65, PROF VET PHYSIOL & PHARMACOL & HEAD DEPT, TEX A&M UNIV, 65- *Mem:* Am Soc Vet Physiol & Pharmacol; Am Physiol Soc; Am Col Clin Pharmacol. *Res:* Pulmonary hypertension; atrial fibrillation; electrocardiography. *Mailing Add:* Dept of Vet Physiol & Pharmacol Tex A&M Univ College Station TX 77843

MCCRADY, WILLIAM B, b Forreston, Tex, July 25, 33; m 54; c 3. GENETICS. *Educ:* ETex State Col, BS, 54, MS, 58; Univ Nebr, PhD(zool), 61. *Prof Exp:* Asst prof biol, Ark State Col, 61-62; from asst prof to assoc prof, 62-74, PROF BIOL, UNIV TEX, ARLINGTON, 74- *Mem:* Genetics Soc Am. *Res:* Carbon dioxide sensitivity in Drosophila. *Mailing Add:* Dept of Biol Univ of Tex Arlington TX 76010

MCCRANIE, ERASMUS JAMES, b Milan, Ga, July 24, 15; m 45; c 3. PSYCHIATRY. *Educ:* Emory Univ, AB, 37, MS, 38; Univ Mich, PhD(bot), 42, MD, 45. *Prof Exp:* Instr biol, SGa Col, 41-42; from instr to assoc prof psychiat, Univ Tex Southwestern Med Sch, 51-56; chmn dept, 57-79, PROF PSYCHIAT, MED COL GA, 56- *Concurrent Pos:* Consult, Vet Admin Hosp, Augusta, 56- & Ga Regional Hosp, 70- *Mem:* AMA; Am Psychiat Asn. *Res:* Psychosomatic medicine; medical applications of hypnosis; psychodynamics. *Mailing Add:* Dept of Psychiat Med Col of Ga Augusta GA 30902

MCCRARY, ANNE BOWDEN, b Wilmington, NC, Oct 25, 26; m 44; c 2. INVERTEBRATE ZOOLOGY, MARINE BIOLOGY. *Educ:* Univ NC, Chapel Hill, AB, 61, MA, 65, PhD(zool), 69. *Prof Exp:* Asst prof, 70-75, ASSOC PROF BIOL, UNIV N C, WILMINGTON, 75- *Mem:* Am Soc Zool; Am Inst Biol Sci; Estuarine Res Fedn; Am Malacological Union; Crustacean Soc. *Res:* Marine Invertebrate Larvae; zooplankton. *Mailing Add:* Dept of Biol Univ of NC Wilmington NC 28403

MCCRAY, RICHARD ALAN, b Los Angeles, Calif, Nov 24, 37; m 61; c 2. ASTROPHYSICS. *Educ:* Stanford Univ, BS, 59; Univ Calif, Los Angeles, MA, 62, PhD(physics), 67. *Prof Exp:* Res fel physics, Calif Inst Technol, 67-68; asst prof astron, Harvard Col Observ, 68-71; assoc prof, 71-75, PROF PHYSICS & ASTROPHYS, UNIV COLO, BOULDER, 75-, FEL, JOINT INST LAB ASTROPHYS, 72-, CHMN, INST LAB, 81- *Concurrent Pos:* Fel, John Simon Guggenheim Mem Found, 75. *Mem:* Am Astron Soc; Int Astron Union. *Res:* Theoretical astrophysics; interstellar gas dynamics; theory of x-ray stars. *Mailing Add:* Joint Inst Lab Astrophys Univ of Colo Boulder CO 80309

MCCREA, PETER FREDERICK, b Pawtucket, RI, Oct 6, 42; m 66; c 2. INSTRUMENTATION, PROCESS CONTROL. *Educ:* Providence Col, BS, 64, MS, 66; Univ Wales, PhD(chem), 69. *Prof Exp:* Res scientist, 69-72, sr res scientist, 72-75, res coordr, 75-80, MGR RES, RES CTR, THE FOXBORO CO, 81- *Mem:* Am Chem Soc; Indust Res Inst. *Res:* Gas chromatography; liquid chromatography; thermoanalytical techniques and ultrasonics; instrumentation for physical and chemical measurements in industrial environments; management of industrial research relevent to process control instrumentation. *Mailing Add:* Foxboro Co Res Ctr 38 Neponset Ave Foxboro MA 02035

MACCREADY, PAUL BEATTIE, JR, b New Haven, Conn, Sept 29, 25; m 57; c 3. AIR POLLUTION. *Educ:* Yale Univ, BS, 47; Calif Inst Technol, MS, 48, PhD(aeronaut), 52. *Prof Exp:* Meteorol consult, Salt River Valley Water Users' Asn, 50-51; pres, Meteorol Res, Inc, 51-70 & Atmospheric Res Group, 58-70; PRES, AERO VIRONMENT INC, 71- *Concurrent Pos:* Consult, various orgns, 73- *Honors & Awards:* Reed Aeronautical Award, Am Inst Aeronaut & Astronaut, 79; Edward Longstreth Medal, Franklin Inst, 79; Krewer Prize, 79. *Mem:* AAAS; fel Am Inst Aeronaut & Astronaut; Nat Acad Eng; fel Am Meteorol Soc. *Res:* Instrumentation development in aeronautics and atmospheric science; basic and applied studies in turbulence and diffusion; cloud physics, cloud electrification and weather modification; developer of human-forsearch and solar powered aircraft. *Mailing Add:* Aero Vironment Inc 145 Vista Ave Pasadena CA 91107

MCCREADY, RONALD GLEN LANG, b Calgary, Alta, Jan 19, 39; m 72; c 1. MICROBIOLOGY. *Educ:* Univ Alta, BSc, 61, MSc, 63; Univ Calgary, PhD(microbiol), 73. *Prof Exp:* Res assoc microbiol, Univ Calgary Interdisciplinary Sulphur Res, 73-75; staff microbiologist, CANMET, Energy, Mines & Resources, 75-78; MICROBIOLOGIST, LETHBRIDGE RES STA AGR CAN, 78- *Concurrent Pos:* Microbiologist indust biol, Dalhousie Univ, 82. *Mem:* Can Soc Microbiol; Am Soc Microbiol; Soc Indust Microbiol; Can Pharmaceut Asn; Can Col Microbiologists. *Res:* Stable isotope metabolism by microorganisms; microbial sulphur cycle; magnetic effects on plant metabolism. *Mailing Add:* 33 Simon Fraser Blvd Lethbridge AB T1K 4R1 Can

MCCREADY, THOMAS ARTHUR, b Pueblo, Colo, Sept 1, 40; m 65; c 2. MATHEMATICS. *Educ:* Univ Calif, Berkeley, AB, 62; Stanford Univ, PhD(math), 68. *Prof Exp:* Sr assoc programmer, Eng & Sci Comput Lab, Int Bus Mach Corp, Calif, 66-68; assoc prof, 68-73, PROF MATH, CALIF STATE UNIV, CHICO, 73- *Res:* Fluid dynamics; numerical analysis; elliptic partial differential equations. *Mailing Add:* 4 Rosemary Circle Chico CA 95926

MACCREARY, DONALD, b Literberry, Ill, Nov 18, 02; m 32; c 1. ENTOMOLOGY. *Educ:* Iowa Wesleyan Col, BS, 29; Univ Md, MS, 30. *Prof Exp:* Fel, Crop Protection Inst, 30-32, asst entomologist, 32-41, assoc entomologist, 41-50, assoc res prof, 50-58, res prof, 58-71, EMER PROF ENTOM, UNIV DEL, 71- *Mem:* Entom Soc Am; Mosquito Control Asn. *Res:* Bionomics and control of agricultural insects and insects affecting man and animals; general entomology. *Mailing Add:* 126 Winslow Rd Newark DE 19711

MCCREDIE, JOHN A, b Anahilt, Northern Ireland, Sept 8, 23; m 54; c 5. CANCER, SURGERY. *Educ:* Queen's Univ Belfast, MB, 46, MCh, 57; FRCS(E) & FRCS, 51; FRCS(C), 60. *Prof Exp:* Registr surg, Royal Victoria Hosp, Belfast, 49-56; instr, Univ Ill, Chicago, 57-58; lectr, 59-68, Assoc prof, 68-78, PROF SURG & RADIATION ONCOL, UNIV WESTERN ONT, 78-; RES ASSOC, ONT CANCER FOUND, 59- *Honors & Awards:* Jacksonian Prize, Royal Col Surgeons, Eng, 56. *Mem:* Am Asn Cancer Res; fel Am Col Surgeons. *Res:* Immunology of tumors. *Mailing Add:* Dept of Surg Victoria Hosp London ON N6A 4G5 Can

MCCREDIE, KENNETH BLAIR, b Christchurch, New Zealand, July 2, 35; nat US. HEMATOLOGY & ONCOLOGY, LEUKEMIA RESEARCH. *Educ:* Otago Univ, New Zealand, MB & ChB, 60. *Prof Exp:* Intern med, Napier Hosp, New Zealand, 61-62, resident, 62-65; resident med, Prince Henry Hosp, Sydney, Australia, 65-66, sr fel hemat, 66-69; proj investr, 69-70, asst internist & asst prof med, 70-73, asst prof internal med, 73-74, assoc internist & assoc prof med, 73-78, assoc prof oncol, 77-79, ASSOC PROF INTERNAL MED, SCH MED, UNIV TEX, HOUSTON, 74-, PROF MED, INTERNIST & CHIEF LEUKEMIA SERV, DEPT DEVELOP THERAPEUT, M D ANDERSON HOSP, SYST CANCER CTR, 78-, PROF ONCOL, DENT BR, HEALTH SCI CTR, 79- *Mem:* Am Soc Clin Oncol; Asn Cancer Res; Royal Soc Med; Int Soc Exp Hemat; AMA. *Mailing Add:* Dept Develop Therapeut Univ Tex Syst Cancer Ctr Houston TX 77030

MCCREERY, RICHARD LOUIS, b Los Angeles, Calif, Oct 8, 48; m 74. ANALYTICAL CHEMISTRY. *Educ:* Univ Calif, Riverside, BS, 70; Univ Kans, PhD(chem), 74. *Prof Exp:* asst prof, 74-79, ASSOC PROF CHEM, OHIO STATE UNIV, 79- *Mem:* Am Chem Soc; AAAS. *Res:* Electrochemistry; spectroscopy; reactions of electrogenerated species. *Mailing Add:* Chem Dept Ohio State Univ 140 W 18th St Columbus OH 43210

MCCREERY, ROBERT ATKESON, b Columbia, Mo, May 30, 17; m 40; c 7. AGRONOMY, SOILS. *Educ:* Univ Ga, BS, 46, MS, 47; State Col Wash, PhD(soils), 54. *Prof Exp:* Jr soil scientist & instr, State Col Wash, 47-54; soil scientist, Cotton Br, Agr Res Serv, USDA, Costa Rica, 54-57; asst prof agron, Univ Ga, 57-68, assoc prof, 68-80; RETIRED. *Mem:* Am Soc Agron; Soil Sci Soc Am; Am Chem Soc; Mineral Soc Am. *Res:* Soil chemistry and mineralogy; forest soils; reclamation. *Mailing Add:* Dept of Agron Univ of Ga Athens GA 30602

MCCREESH, ARTHUR HUGH, b New York, NY, May 18, 31; m 63; c 3. PHARMACOLOGY, VETERINARY TOXICOLOGY. *Educ:* St John's Univ, NY, BS, 53; Temple Univ, MS, 57, PhD(pharmacol), 60. *Prof Exp:* Instr physiol, Temple Univ, 57-60; res pharmacologist, 60-73, CHIEF, TOXICOL DIV, US ARMY ENVIRON HYG AGENCY, 73- *Mem:* AAAS; Soc Toxicol; An Soc Testing & Mat. *Res:* Testing of chemical compounds for toxic hazard; development of new screening procedures; cutaneous toxicity; inhalation toxicology. *Mailing Add:* Toxicol Div US Army Environ Hyg Agency Aberdeen Proving Ground MD 21010

MCCREIGHT, CHARLES EDWARD, b Camden, SC, Mar 17, 13. ANATOMY. *Educ:* George Washington Univ, BS, 48, MS, 50, PhD(anat), 54. *Prof Exp:* Lab instr zool, George Washington Univ, 48-50, asst anat, 50-52; assoc, 52-53, from instr to asst prof, 53-65, ASSOC PROF ANAT, BOWMAN GRAY SCH MED, 65- *Mem:* Fel Geront Soc; Am Asn Anatomists; Am Asn Univ Prof; Sigma Xi. *Res:* Experimental studies in growth, development and regeneration of the kidney; epidermal cytology; cytology of lung. *Mailing Add:* Dept of Anat Bowman Gray Sch of Med Winston-Salem NC 27103

MCCREIGHT, EDWARD M, US citizen. COMPUTER SCIENCES. *Educ:* Col Wooster, AB, 66; Carnegie-Mellon Univ, PhD(comput sci), 70. *Prof Exp:* Res scientist comput sci, Boeing Sci Res Labs, Wash, 69-71; MEM RES STAFF COMPUT SCI, PALO ALTO RES CTR, XEROX CORP, 71- *Mem:* Asn Comput Mach; Inst Elec & Electronics Engrs. *Res:* Data structures; analysis of algorithms; theory of computing; computer architecture. *Mailing Add:* Xerox Palo Alto Res Ctr 3333 Coyote Hill Rd Palo Alto CA 94304

MCCREIGHT, LOUIS R(ALPH), b Zion, Ill, Nov 26, 22; m 49; c 2. CERAMIC ENGINEERING. *Educ:* Univ Ill, BS, 46, MS, 49. *Prof Exp:* Asst, Manhattan Proj, 44-45 & Air Force Proj, Univ Ill, 45-49; asst & ceramist, Knolls Atomic Power Lab, 49-52, fuel engr, 52-55, mgr mat sci, Space Sci Lab, Missiles & Space Div, Gen Elec Co, 55-69, mgr Mat Res & Develop, Space Sci Lab, 69-81; SR ENG MAT SCI LAB, AEROSPACE CORP, LOS ANGELES, 81- *Concurrent Pos:* Mem panel mat adv bd, Nat Acad Sci-Nat Res Coun, 59- *Mem:* Am Ceramic Soc. *Res:* Refractory materials; nuclear fuel elements; vehicle materials; space processing. *Mailing Add:* Aerospace Corp PO Box 92957 Los Angeles CA 90009

MCCRELESS, THOMAS GRISWOLD, b San Antonio, Tex, Aug 20, 27; m 51; c 2. NUCLEAR ENGINEERING. *Educ:* US Naval Acad, BS, 51; Univ Md, MS, 65, PhD(nuclear eng), 77. *Prof Exp:* Staff engr, US AEC, 60-75; SR STAFF ENGR & BR CHIEF ADV COMT REACTOR SAFEGUARDS, US NUCLEAR REGULATORY COMN, 75-, ASST EXEC DIR, 80- *Mem:* Sigma Xi; Am Nuclear Soc; Soc Comput Simulation. *Res:* Applications of invariant imbedding techniques to classical engineering problems. *Mailing Add:* Adv Comt on Reactor Safeguards US Nuclear Regulatory Comn Washington DC 20555

MCCRIMMON, DONALD ALAN, JR, b Tampa, Fla, Feb 2, 44; m 69; c 2. RESOURCE MANAGEMENT. *Educ:* Univ SFla, BA, 64; Vanderbilt Univ, Nashville, MA, 67; NC State Univ, Raleigh, PhD(zool), 75. *Prof Exp:* Instr psychol, Univ NC, Asheville, 66-70; biologist, 75-79, SR STAFF SCIENTIST, NAT AUDUBON SOC, 79- *Concurrent Pos:* Asst prof, Cornell Univ, 79- *Mem:* Am Ornithologists Union. *Res:* Ecology and reproductive biology of avian species, especially colonially nesting birds; design and management of nature preserves; biostatistics. *Mailing Add:* Coop Res Prog Cornell Lab Ornith 159 Sapsucker Woods Rd Ithaca NY 14850

MCCRONE, ALISTAIR WILLIAM, b Regina, Sask, Oct 7, 31; US citizen; m 58; c 3. GEOLOGY, PALEOECOLOGY. *Educ:* Univ Sask, BA, 53; Univ Nebr, MSc, 55; Univ Kans, PhD(geol), 61. *Prof Exp:* From instr to prof geol, NY Univ, 59-70, chmn dept, 66-69, assoc dean, Grad Sch Arts & Sci, 69-70; prof, Univ of the Pac, 70-74, acad vpres, 70-71, 71-74; PROF GEOL, HUMBOLDT STATE UNIV, 74-, PRES, 74- UNIV, 74- *Concurrent Pos:* Wellsite geologist, Brit Am Oil Co, Sask, 53; field party chief, Shell Oil Co, Can, 56-68; mem fac comt educ policy, NY Univ, 67-69; mem, Pres Search Comt, Calif State Univ, Chico. *Mem:* Fel AAAS; fel Geol Soc Am; Am Asn Petrol Geol; NY Acad Sci; Sigma Xi. *Res:* Paleozoic and subsurface stratigraphy; marine ecology and paleoecology; marine and estuarine sedimentation; aquatic geochemistry; sedimentary facies analysis. *Mailing Add:* Humboldt State Univ Arcata CA 95521

MCCRONE, JOHN DAVID, b Somerville, Mass, Nov 9, 34; m 57; c 2. ZOOLOGY, ADMINISTRATIVE SCIENCES. *Educ:* Univ Fla, BS, 56, PhD(biol), 61. *Prof Exp:* Asst prof biol, Fairleigh Dickinson Univ, 61-62; from asst prof to assoc prof, Fla Presby Col, 62-66; assoc prof zool, Univ Fla, 66-69; assoc dean grad sch, Univ of the Pac, 69-71; dir res, Grad Sch, 71-73, assoc vpres educ develop & res, Univ Iowa, 73-75; DEAN, SCH ARTS & SCI, WESTERN CAROLINA UNIV, 75- *Mem:* Fel AAAS; Soc Syst Zool; Soc Study Evolution; Int Soc Toxinol. *Res:* Arachnology; systematics; ecology; toxinology. *Mailing Add:* Western Carolina Univ Cullowhee NC 28723

MACCRONE, ROBERT K, b Johannesburg, SAfrica; m; c 3. PHYSICS, METALLURGICAL ENGINEERING. *Educ:* Univ Witwatersrand, BSc, 54, Hons, 55, MSc, 56; Oxford Univ, DPhil(physics), 59. *Prof Exp:* Fel metall eng, Univ Pa, 59-62, asst prof, 62-67; PROF MAT SCI, RENSSELAER POLYTECH INST, 67- *Mem:* Am Ceramic Soc; Am Physical Soc; Bot Soc SAfrica. *Res:* Electric and magnetic properties of oxides, glasses and polymers; paramagnetic resonance; protective coatings; ion implantation; super conductivity. *Mailing Add:* Dept of Mat Sci Rensselaer Polytech Inst Troy NY 12181

MCCRONE, WALTER C, b Wilmington, Del, June 9, 16; m 57. CHEMICAL MICROSCOPY. *Educ:* Cornell Univ, BChem, 38, PhD(chem micros), 42. *Prof Exp:* Chem microscopist, Off Sci Res & Develop Proj, Cornell Univ, 42-44; chem microscopist, Armour Res Found, Ill Inst Technol, 44-45, supvr anal chem, 45-46, asst chmn chem & chem eng, 46-52, sr scientist, 52-56; mem staff McCrone Assocs, Inc, 56-79, chmn bd, 67-81, EMER CHMN BD, MCCRONE ASSOCS, INC, 81-, PRES, MCCRONE RES INST, 66- *Concurrent Pos:* Publ & ed, Microscope Publications Ltd, 65-; mem adv bd, J Anal Chem, Am Chem Soc, 75-76. *Honors & Awards:* Benedetti-Pichler Award, 71; Ernst Abbe Award, 77. 71; Anal Chem Award, Am Chem Soc, 81. *Mem:* Am Chem Soc; Am Phys Soc; Am Soc Test & Mat; Am Acad Forensic Sci; Royal Micros Soc. *Res:* Crystallography; chemical microscopy; polymorphism; crystal growth; correlation of solid state properties and performance; ultramicroanalysis. *Mailing Add:* McCrone Res Inst Inc 2508 S Michigan Ave Chicago IL 60616

MCCROREY, HENRY LAWRENCE, b Philadelphia, Pa, Mar 13, 27; m 57; c 4. PHYSIOLOGY. *Educ:* Univ Mich, BS, 49, MS, 50; Univ Ill, MS, 58, PhD(physiol), 63. *Prof Exp:* Res assoc pharmacol, Sharp & Dohme, Pa, 51-55; asst physiol, Col Med, Univ Ill, 56-61, from instr to asst prof, 61-66; from asst prof to assoc prof, 66-73, PROF PHYSIOL & BIOPHYS, COL MED, UNIV VT, 73- *Mem:* Am Physiol Soc. *Res:* Muscle contraction; experimental hypertension; renal physiology. *Mailing Add:* Dept of Physiol & Biophys Univ of Vt Col of Med Burlington VT 05401

MCCRORY, ROBERT LEE, JR, b Lawton, Okla, Apr 30, 46; m 69. PLASMA PHYSICS, HYDRODYNAMICS. *Educ:* Mass Inst Technol, ScB, 68, PhD(plasma physics), 73. *Prof Exp:* Scientist geophys, Pan Am Petrol Res, Standard Oil Ind, 68-73; staff scientist theoret physics, theoret div, Los Alamos Sci Lab, Univ Calif, 73-76; group leader theory & comput group, Lab Laser Energetics, 76-78, DIR, THEORET DIV, UNIV ROCHESTER, 78-, ASSOC PROF PHYSICS & MECH ENG, 80- *Concurrent Pos:* Sr sci programmer, Res Lab Electronics, Mass Inst Technol, 68-73, res assoc, Dept Nuclear Eng/Dept Aerodyn & Astrophys, 72-73; US deleg, Conf Plasma Physics & Controlled Fusion Res, Int Atomic Energy Agency, Vienna, Austria, 74; vis staff mem, theoret div, Los Alamos Sci Lab, Univ Calif, 76-; consult, Cambridge Hydrodynamics, Inc, Boston. *Mem:* Am Phys Soc; Sigma Xi. *Res:* Symmetry-stability studies of laser induced implosions; plasma physics/hydrodynamics of laser-initiated fusion; microinstabilities of magnetically confined plasma; weapons physics; laser-plasma interaction studies; radiation hydrodynamics. *Mailing Add:* 93 Kirklees Rd Pittsford NY 14534

MCCRORY, WALLACE WILLARD, b Racine, Wis, Jan 19, 20; m 43; c 3. PEDIATRICS. *Educ:* Univ Wis, BS, 41, MD, 44. *Prof Exp:* Instr path, Med Sch, Univ Wis, 42-43; from asst prof to assoc prof, Sch Med, Univ Pa, 53-58; prof & head dept, Col Med, Univ Iowa, 58-61; PROF PEDIAT & CHMN DEPT, MED CTR, CORNELL UNIV, 61-; PEDIATRICIAN-IN-CHIEF, NEW YORK HOSP, 61- *Concurrent Pos:* Ledyard fel pediat, Cornell Univ, 49-50; dir, Clin Chem Lab, Children's Hosp, Philadelphia, 53-58. *Mem:* AAAS; Am Pediat Soc; NY Acad Sci; fel Royal Soc Med. *Res:* Renal disease and clinical biochemistry. *Mailing Add:* Dept of Pediat Cornell Univ Med Ctr New York NY 10021

MCCRORY-JOY, CAROLYN, b Natchitoches, La, Nov 23, 48. ELECTROANALYTICAL CHEMISTRY. *Educ:* Northwestern State Univ, BS, 69; Univ New Orleans, PhD(anal chem), 74. *Prof Exp:* MEM TECH STAFF ANAL CHEM, BELL TEL LABS, 75- *Mem:* Am Chem Soc; AAAS; Electrochem Soc. *Res:* Polarography; voltammetry; coulometry; electrochemical reaction mechanisms; on-line analysis; computerized analysis. *Mailing Add:* Bell Tel Labs 600 Mountain Ave Murray Hill NJ 07974

MCCROSKEY, JACK E, animal nutrition, see previous edition

MCCROSKEY, ROBERT LEE, b Richwood, WVa, Feb 22, 24; m 50; c 4. AUDIOLOGY, SPEECH PATHOLOGY. *Educ:* Ohio State Univ, BS, 48, MA, 52, PhD(speech sci), 56. *Prof Exp:* Res assoc speech sci, Ohio State Res Found, Pensacola, Fla, 55-56; prof speech path, Miss Southern Col, 56-59; prof speech & hearing, Emory Univ, 59-67; PROF COMMUN DISORDERS & SCI, WICHITA STATE UNIV, 67- *Concurrent Pos:* Dir, Atlanta Speech Sch, Ga, 59-67; Am Speech & Hearing Asn int travel grant, 63 & 66; consult, Am Hearing Soc, 64-67, Div Voc Rehab, Ga, 66, Bur Educ of Handicapped, US Off Educ, 71- & Glenrose Hosp, Edmonton, Ont, 73-74; dir prof servs, Inst Logopedics, 68-70; reviewer div int activities, Dept Health, Educ & Welfare, 71-75. *Mem:* Speech Commun Asn; fel Am Speech & Hearing Asn; Am Auditory Soc. *Res:* Early diagnosis of hearing impairments; home training programs for deaf; auditory temporal processing for children with learning disabilities; effects of speech expansion upon comprehension; auditory localization. *Mailing Add:* Dept Commun Disorders & Sci Wichita State Univ Wichita KS 67208

MCCROSKEY, WILLIAM JAMES, b San Angelo, Tex, Mar 9, 37; m 60; c 2. FLUID MECHANICS. *Educ:* Univ Tex, BS, 60; von Karman Inst Fluid Dynamics, dipl, 63; Princeton Univ, PhD(aerospace sci), 66. *Prof Exp:* Res assoc, Princeton Univ, 66; res scientist, US Army Aeromech Lab, 66-80, SR STAFF SCIENTIST, AMES RES CTR, US ARMY & NASA, 80- *Concurrent Pos:* Mem, Fluid Dynamics Panel, NATO Adv Group Aerospace Res & Develop. *Honors & Awards:* Freeman Scholar Award, Am Soc Mech Engrs, 76. *Mem:* Am Helicopter Soc; Am Inst Aeronaut & Astronaut; Am Soc Mech Engrs. *Res:* Experimental and theoretical studies of three-dimensional, time-dependent viscous boundary layers; rarefied gas dynamics and low-density boundary layers and shock waves; helicopter aerodynamics; experimental and numerical research in unsteady aerodynamics. *Mailing Add:* Ames Res Ctr N2028-1 NASA Moffett Field CA 94035

MCCROSKY, RICHARD EUGENE, b Akron, Ohio, Apr 28, 24; m 52; c 4. ASTRONOMY. *Educ:* Harvard Univ, BS, 52, PhD(astron), 56. *Prof Exp:* Sr res asst, 56, LECTR ASTRON, HARVARD UNIV, 56-, RES ASSOC, SMITHSONIAN ASTRO OBSERV, 57- *Concurrent Pos:* Astronr, Smithsonian Astrophys Observ, 57-58 & 60-, consult, 58-59; scientist chg, Meteorite Photog & Recovery Proj, 62-; mem, Int Astron Union. *Mem:* Fel AAAS; Meteoritical Soc; Am Astron Soc; Am Geophys Union. *Res:* Physics of meteors; meteor statistics and orbits; optical instrumentation; meteor photography. *Mailing Add:* Smithsonian Astro Observ 60 Garden St Cambridge MA 02138

MCCROSSAN, ROBERT GEORGE, b Vancouver, BC, Mar 27, 24; m 51; c 1. PETROLEUM GEOLOGY. *Educ:* Univ BC, BA, 48; Univ Chicago, SM, 52, PhD(geol), 56. *Prof Exp:* Subsurface geologist, Seaboard Oil Co, 49-58; res geologist, Imperial Oil Ltd, 58-65; head energy subdiv, Geol Surv Can, 65-78; RES ADV, ESSO RESOURCES CAN LTD, 78- *Mem:* Am Asn Petrol Geol; hon mem Can Soc Petrol Geol (pres, 65); Asn Prof Engrs, Geologists & Geophysicists Can. *Res:* Petroleum occurrence and potential; organic geochemistry; regional stratigraphic studies; hydrocarbon assessment; basin evaluation. *Mailing Add:* Esso Resources Can Ltd 237 4th Ave SW Calgary AB T2P 0H6 Can

MCCROSSEN, GARNER, b New York, NY, Feb 22, 23; m 49; c 2. MATHEMATICS. *Educ:* Univ Wyo, BA, 48, MA, 49; Univ Colo, PhD(math), 54. *Prof Exp:* Instr math, Univ Nev, 49-50; programmer digital comput, Holloman AFB, 55-58, chief prog & operating sect, 58-60; programmer, 60-62, applns mgr, 62-68, VPRES, DIGITAL COMPUT, CONTROL DATA CORP, 68-, SR STAFF CONSULT, 75- *Res:* Philosophy; development of digital computer operating systems; development of assemblers for digital computers; development of compilers for digital computers. *Mailing Add:* Box 481 Chippewa Falls WI 54729

MCCROSSON, F JOSEPH, b Brooklyn, NY, June 27, 40; m 65; c 3. REACTOR PHYSICS. *Educ:* Fairfield Univ, BS, 62; Va Inst Technol & State Univ, MS, 65, PhD(physics), 68. *Prof Exp:* Physicist, 65-67, res physicist, 68-72, staff physicist, 72-74, RES SUPVR REACTOR PHYSICS, SAVANNAH RIVER LAB, E I DU PONT DE NEMOURS & CO, 74- *Mem:* Sigma Xi; Am Nuclear Soc. *Res:* Neutron cross-sections; shielding, charge design and accident analysis development. *Mailing Add:* 1171 Aldrich NE Aiken SC 29801

MCCRUM, RICHARD CASWELL, plant pathology, see previous edition

MCCRUM, WILBUR ROSS, anatomy, deceased

MCCRUMM, J(OHN) D(OENCH), b Colorado Springs, Colo, Apr 17, 12; m 38; c 2. ELECTRICAL ENGINEERING. *Educ:* Univ Colo, BS, 33, MS, 34. *Prof Exp:* Test engr, Gen Elec Co, NY, 34-35, res engr, Pa, 38; from instr to asst prof elec eng, Swarthmore Col, 35-44; res engr, Douglas Aircraft Co, Calif, 44-46; from assoc prof elec eng to prof & chmn dept eng, 46-59, Eavenson prof, 59-78, chmn dept elec eng, 70-78, EMER PROF ENG, SWARTHMORE COL, 78- *Concurrent Pos:* Consult to various indust concerns, 46-; asst to vpres, Burroughs Corp, 57-58; NSF fel, Athens, Greece, 65-66. *Mem:* Am Soc Eng Educ; Inst Elec & Electronics Engrs. *Res:* Control theory; systems engineering; research management. *Mailing Add:* Dept of Eng Swarthmore Col Swarthmore PA 19801

MACCUBBIN, ALEXANDER ERNEST, b Putnan, Conn, Aug 2, 47; m 80; c 1. MICROBIAL ECOLOGY, MICROBIAL BIOGEOCHEMISTRY. *Educ:* Rutgers Univ, BS, 69; Western Mich Univ, MA, 76; Va Inst Marine Sci, PhD(marine microbiol), 80. *Prof Exp:* Res assoc, 79-81, ASST RES MICROBIOLOGIST, UNIV GA, 81- *Concurrent Pos:* Mem, Inst Ecol, Univ Ga, 80- *Mem:* Am Soc Microbiol; Soc Environ Toxicol Chem. *Res:* Role of bacteria in the cycling of dissolved and particulate organic matter in aquatic environments; microbial processing of lignocellulosic detritus; transport of dissolved organic compounds by marine bacteria. *Mailing Add:* Dept Microbiol Univ Ga Athens GA 30602

MCCUBBIN, DONALD GENE, b Glencoe, Okla, Oct 24, 30; m 62; c 2. PETROLEUM GEOLOGY, SEDIMENTOLOGY. *Educ:* Okla State Univ, BS, 52; Harvard Univ, MA, 55, PhD(geol), 61. *Prof Exp:* Res geologist, 57-65, adv res geologist, 65-70, SR RES GEOLOGIST, DENVER RES CTR, MARATHON OIL CO, 70- *Mem:* Geol Soc Am; Am Asn Petrol Geol; Soc Econ Paleont & Mineral. *Res:* Sandstone petrology and facies; sedimentary structures; nearshore sediments and processes; sandstone petroleum reservoirs; diagenesis of clay sediments; hydrocarbon generation and migration; thermal history of sedimentary basins. *Mailing Add:* Denver Res Ctr Marathon Oil Co Box 269 Littleton CO 80160

MCCUBBIN, THOMAS KING, JR, b Baltimore, Md, June 1, 25; m 51; c 3. PHYSICS. *Educ:* Univ Louisville, BEE, 46; Johns Hopkins Univ, PhD(physics), 51. *Prof Exp:* Fel physics, Johns Hopkins Univ, 51-53; mem res staff phys chem, Mass Inst Technol, 53-57; from asst prof to assoc prof, 57-64, PROF PHYSICS, PA STATE UNIV, 64- *Mem:* Fel Optical Soc Am; fel Am Phys Soc. *Res:* Optics and spectroscopy; molecular spectra. *Mailing Add:* Dept Physics Davey Lab Pa State Univ University Park PA 16802

MCCUE, CAROLYN M, b Richmond, Va, June 26, 16; m 41; c 2. PEDIATRICS. *Educ:* Stanford Univ, BA, 37; Med Col Va, MD, 41; Am Bd Pediat, dipl, 48, cert pediat cardiol, 59. *Prof Exp:* Instr, 46-49, assoc, 49-52, from asst prof to assoc prof, 52-63, interim chmn dept, 58-61, PROF PEDIAT, MED COL VA, 63- *Concurrent Pos:* Clin dir, Richmond Rheumatic Fever & Congenital Heart Clins, 47- *Mem:* Am Heart Asn; fel Am Col Physicians; fel Am Acad Pediat; fel Am Col Cardiol. *Res:* Pediatric cardiology. *Mailing Add:* Dept Pediat Med Col Va Richmond VA 23298

MCCUE, EDMUND BRADLEY, b Worcester, Mass, Mar 8, 29. MATHEMATICS. *Educ:* Union Col, AB, 50; Univ Mich, MS, 51; Carnegie Inst Technol, PhD(math), 60. *Prof Exp:* Mathematician, US Dept Defense, 51-54; asst prof math, Ohio Univ, 58-63; prof statist, Inter-Am Statist Inst, 63-64; ASSOC PROF MATH & STATIST, AM UNIV, 64- *Mem:* Inst Math Statist; Am Statist Asn; Math Asn Am. *Res:* Mathematical statistics. *Mailing Add:* Dept of Math & Statist American Univ Washington DC 20016

MCCUE, JOHN FRANCIS, b Milford, NH, Nov 22, 33; m 62; c 4. PARASITOLOGY. *Educ:* St John's Univ, Minn, BS, 60; Univ Notre Dame, MS, 62, PhD(biol), 64. *Prof Exp:* NIH fel, Sch Med, Nat Univ Mex, 64-65; res assoc parasitol, Sch Vet Med, Auburn Univ, 65-67; from asst prof to assoc prof, 67-77, PROF BIOL SCI, ST CLOUD STATE UNIV, 77- *Mem:* Am Soc Parasitologists. *Res:* Parasitic immunology; parasite life cycles; host-parasite relationships. *Mailing Add:* Dept of Biol St Cloud State Univ St Cloud MN 56301

MCCUE, ROBERT OWEN, b Kearney, Nebr, May 20, 47; m 70; c 3. BIOLOGY. *Educ:* Nothern Ariz Univ, BS, 70; Tulane Univ, MS, 73, PhD(develop biol), 77. *Prof Exp:* Asst prof, Univ Nev, 77-78; ASST PROF BIOL, WAYNE STATE COL, 78- *Res:* Embryonic development and differentiation and regeneration. *Mailing Add:* Math/Sci Div Wayne State Col Wayne NE 68787

MCCUEN, ROBERT WILLIAM, b Darby, Pa, Apr 14, 40; m 65; c 2. MICROBIOLOGY, GENETIC TOXICOLOGY. *Educ:* Drexel Univ, BS, 63; Temple Univ, MS, 66; Univ Mass, PhD(microbiol), 71. *Prof Exp:* Res fel, Sloan-Kettering Inst Cancer Res, 71-73; res scientist, 73-80, ASSOC SR SCIENTIST BIOL EFFECTS OF SMOKE, PHILIP MORRIS RES CTR, 80- *Mem:* Am Asn Cancer Res; Am Soc Microbiol; Environ Mutagen Soc; Genetic Toxicol Asn. *Res:* In vitro short term bioassays as predictors of chemical carcinogens. *Mailing Add:* Philip Morris Res Ctr 4201 Commerce Rd Richmond VA 23261

MCCUISTION, WILLIS LLOYD, b Fowler, Colo, May 28, 37; m 59; c 2. GENETICS, PLANT BREEDING. *Educ:* Colo State Univ, BS, 59; State Univ-USDA, 59-62; asst plant breeding & genetics, Okla State Univ, 62-67; plant breeder, Rockefeller Found, India, 67-68, dir & plant breeder, Int Maize & Wheat Improv Ctr, Tunisia, 68-71 & Algeria, 71-75; ASSOC PROF, CROP SCI DEPT, ORE STATE UNIV, 75- *Concurrent Pos:* Rockefeller Found fel, All-India Mex Wheat Prog & Tunisia Wheat Prog, 67-69. *Mem:* Am Soc Agron; Crop Sci Soc Am; Am Inst Biol Sci. *Res:* Increasing agricultural production in general, especially in developing countries; training local scientists in applied scientific methods. *Mailing Add:* Crop Sci Dept 138 Agr Hall Ore State Univ Corvallis OR 97331

MCCULLA, WILLIAM HARVEY, b Birmingham, Ala, Sept 19, 41; m 63; c 2. INORGANIC CHEMISTRY. *Educ:* Auburn Univ, BS, 65, MS, 68; Univ Tenn, PhD(inorg chem), 81. *Prof Exp:* Res assoc process chem group, 67-70, res chemist, 70-74, res chemist advan isotope separation group, 74-76, prin investr Laser Isotope Separation Exp Advan Isotope Chem Group, 76-80, GROUP LEADER, LASER SPECTROS GROUP, NUCLEAR DIV, UNION CARBIDE CORP, 80- *Mem:* AAAS; Optical Soc Am. *Res:* Laser isotope separation including uranium enrichment, laser raman spectroscopy and laser induced chemistry. *Mailing Add:* Nuclear Div PO Box P Oak Ridge TN 37830

MCCULLEN, JOHN DOUGLAS, b Sioux Falls, SDak, Oct 4, 32; m 54; c 3. NUCLEAR PHYSICS. *Educ:* Univ Colo, BA, 54, MS, 58, PhD(nuclear physics & spectros), 60. *Prof Exp:* Asst physics, Univ Colo, 56-60; res assoc, Princeton Univ, 60-62, asst prof, 62-65; assoc prof, 65-67, PROF PHYSICS, UNIV ARIZ, 67- *Concurrent Pos:* Sloane Found fel, 66-68. *Mem:* Am Phys Soc. *Res:* Nuclear spectroscopy and structure theory; atomic and polarized beams. *Mailing Add:* Dept of Physics Univ of Ariz Tucson AZ 85721

MCCULLOCH, ARCHIBALD WILSON, b Troon, Scotland, Oct 31, 40; Can citizen; m 71; c 2. ORGANIC CHEMISTRY. *Educ:* Univ Glasgow, BSc, 62, PhD(chem), 65. *Prof Exp:* Fel chem, 65-66, asst res officer, 66-70, assoc res officer, 71-79, SR RES OFFICER CHEM, NAT RES COUN CAN, HALIFAX, 80- *Mem:* Chem Inst Can; Royal Soc Chem. *Res:* Synthetic organic chemistry; heterocyclic chemistry; Lewis acid catalysis; nuclear magnetic resonance; organic photochemistry; chemistry of silicon. *Mailing Add:* Atlantic Regional Lab 1411 Oxford St Halifax NS B3H 3Z1 Can

MCCULLOCH, CLAY YOUNG, JR, ecology, see previous edition

MCCULLOCH, DAVID SEARS, geology, geomorphology, see previous edition

MCCULLOCH, ERNEST ARMSTRONG, b Toronto, Ont, Apr 27, 26; m 53; c 5. MEDICINE. *Educ:* Univ Toronto, MD, 48; FRCP(C), 54. *Prof Exp:* From jr intern to sr intern, Toronto Gen Hosp, 49-52; asst resident, Sunnybrook Hosp, 52-53; clin teacher med, 54-60, assoc, 60-67, from asst prof to assoc prof med, 68-70, from asst prof to assoc prof med biophys, 59-66, PROF MED BIOPHYS, UNIV TORONTO, 66-, PROF MED, 70-, DIR INST MED SCI, 78- *Concurrent Pos:* Ellen Mickle fel, Lister Inst, Eng, 48-49; Nat Res Coun Can res fel path, Univ Toronto, 50-51; Nat Cancer Inst Can fel, 54-57; asst physician, Toronto Gen Hosp, 54-60, physician, 60-67; head subdiv hemat, Div Biol Res, Int Cancer Inst, 57-67; mem grants comt microbiol & path, Med Res Coun Can, 66-67, immunol & transplantation, 67-69; mem panel B, Grants Comt, Nat Cancer Inst Can, 70-74; ed, J Cell Physiol, 69-; sr physician, Princess Margaret Hosp, 70- *Honors & Awards:* Starr Medal, Univ Toronto, 57, Goldie Prize in Med, 64; Gairdner Award, 69. *Mem:* Am Asn Cancer Res; Am Soc Exp Path; Soc Exp Biol & Med; Can Soc Cell Biol; Royal Soc Can. *Res:* Hematology; stem cell functions, especially physiologic and genetic control mechanisms; leukemia research. *Mailing Add:* Dept of Med Univ of Toronto Toronto ON M4X 1K9 Can

MCCULLOCH, JOSEPH HOWARD, b Durham, NC, Feb 17, 46; m 70; c 2. BIOLOGY, BOTANY. *Educ:* Eastern Mich Univ, BS, 68, MS, 71; Mich State Univ, PhD(bot), 77. *Prof Exp:* Instr, Eastern Mich Univ, 70-73 & Mich State Univ, 73-74; PROF BIOL, NORMANDALE COMMUNITY COL, 74- *Mem:* Am Bot Soc; Am Fern Soc; Los Angeles Int Fern Soc; Am Mus Natural Hist. *Res:* Cheilanthoid fern rhizome anatomy; ontogeny of stelar anatomy in the pteridophyta; educational biology. *Mailing Add:* Dept of Bot Normandale Community Col Bloomington MN 55431

MCCULLOCH, PETER BLAIR, b Hamilton, Ont, Mar 7, 39; m 69; c 3. CANCER. *Educ:* Univ Toronto, MD, 64; FRCP(C), 69. *Prof Exp:* Lectr med, McGill Univ, 70-72; ASST PROF MED, MCMASTER UNIV, 72- *Concurrent Pos:* Internist oncol, Ont Cancer Found, 72- *Mem:* Can Med Asn; Can Soc Clin Oncol. *Res:* Cytogenetics of human malignancy; chemotherapy and immunotherapy of human cancer. *Mailing Add:* Hamilton Cancer Clin Henderson Hosp Hamilton ON L8V 1C3 Can

MCCULLOH, THANE H, b Glendale, Calif, July 25, 26; m 49, 63; c 5. PETROLEUM GEOLOGY. *Educ:* Pomona Col, AB, 49; Univ Calif, Los Angeles, PhD(geol), 52. *Prof Exp:* Res assoc geol, Univ Calif, Los Angeles, 52-53; asst prof, Calif Inst Technol, 53-55; from assoc prof to prof, Univ Calif, Riverside, 55-64; geologist, DC, 64-72, chief, Off Energy Res, 72-73, RES GEOLOGIST, US GEOL SURV, 73- *Concurrent Pos:* NSF fel, 52-53; Guggenheim fel, 60; affil prof oceanog, Univ Wash, 73- *Honors & Awards:* PL 313 Position Award, US Geol Surv, 74. *Mem:* Geol Soc Am; Soc Explor Geophys; Am Asn Petrol Geol; Norweg Geol Asn. *Res:* Areal geology of the central Mojave Desert; igneous and metamorphic petrology; gravimetry; structural geology of the Los Angeles Basin; petrophysics; petroleum exploration research and sedimentary basin resource studies. *Mailing Add:* US Geol Surv 1107 NE 45th St Seattle WA 98105

MCCULLOUGH, BENJAMIN FRANKLIN, b Austin, Tex, Mar 25, 34; m 56; c 5. CIVIL ENGINEERING. *Educ:* Univ Tex, BS, 57, MS, 62; Univ Calif, PhD(transp eng), 69. *Prof Exp:* Engr in training, US Bur Reclamation, 56; testing engr, Convair Aircraft Co, 57; supv design & res engr, Tex Hwy Dept, 57-66; sr engr, Mat Res & Develop, Inc, Calif, 66-68; asst prof civil eng, Ctr Hwy Res, Univ Tex, Austin, 68-71; design engr, Dallas-Ft Worth Regional Airport, 71-73; PROF CIVIL ENG, UNIV TEX, AUSTIN, 76- *Concurrent Pos:* Chmn comt A2-B01, Transp Res Bd, Nat Acad Sci-Nat Res Coun, 66-77; proj engr, US Air Force, Palmdale AFB, Calif, 69-70; consult, Bd Consult, Dept Transp, 76-, Fed Aviation Admin, 77- & Area 5-E Zero Maintenance, Transp Res Bd, Fed Hwy Admin, Washington, DC, 77- *Honors & Awards:* Meritorious Tech Paper Award, Am Soc Civil Engrs, 61; Commendation, Mexican Govt, 75. *Mem:* Am Soc Civil Engrs; Am Concrete Inst. *Res:* Highway and airport pavement design; pavement rehabilitation; design of military airport in Saudi Arabia. *Mailing Add:* Dept of Civil Eng 6-10 ECJ Univ of Tex Austin TX 78712

MCCULLOUGH, DALE RICHARD, b Sioux Falls, SDak, Dec 5, 33; m 58; c 3. WILDLIFE MANAGEMENT, ECOLOGY. *Educ:* SDak State Univ, BS, 57; Ore State Univ, MS, 60; Univ Calif, Berkeley, PhD(zool), 66. *Prof Exp:* Instr zool, Univ Calif, Berkeley, 65-66; asst prof wildlife mgt, Univ Mich, Ann Arbor, 66-69, assoc prof wildlife & fisheries, 69-74, chmn resource ecol prog, 71-74, prof natural resources, 74-80; MEM FAC FORESTRY & RES MGT, UNIV CALIF, BERKELEY, 80- *Mem:* Wildlife Soc; Ecol Soc Am. *Res:* Ecology and population dynamics of large herbivores; ecosystem processes. *Mailing Add:* Dept Forestry & Res Mgt Univ Calif Berkeley CA 94720

MCCULLOUGH, EDGAR JOSEPH, JR, b Charleston, WVa, Nov 29, 31; m 81; c 2. STRUCTURAL GEOLOGY. *Educ:* Univ WVa, AB, 53, MS, 55; Univ Ariz, PhD(geol), 63. *Prof Exp:* From instr to assoc prof geol, 58-69, PROF GEOSCI & HEAD DEPT, UNIV ARIZ, 70- *Concurrent Pos:* Acting asst dir geol surv bur & acting state geologist, Ariz Bur Geol & Mineral Technol, 77- *Mem:* AAAS; Nat Asn Geol Teachers; Geol Soc Am. *Res:* Geologic hazards; development of fluid structural features in solid rocks; science education. *Mailing Add:* Dept Geosci Univ Ariz Tucson AZ 85721

MCCULLOUGH, EDWIN CHARLES, b New York, NY, June 2, 42; m 70; c 2. MEDICAL PHYSICS. *Educ:* State Univ NY Stony Brook, BS, 64; Univ Md, MS, 67; Univ Wis-Madison, PhD(radiol physics), 71. *Prof Exp:* Scientist neutron physics, Med Res Coun Cyclotron Unit, Hammersmith Hosp, 71; res scientist radiation physics, Univ Wis-Madison, 71-73; STAFF PHYSICIST, MAYO CLIN, 73- *Mem:* Am Asn Physicists Med; Radiol Soc NAm; Sigma Xi. *Res:* Radiation therapy dosimetry and treatment planning; diagnostic radiology imaging; computer assisted tomography performance evaluation and quality assurance. *Mailing Add:* Mayo Clin 200 First St SW Rochester MN 55901

MCCULLOUGH, ELIZABETH ANN, b Spartanburg, SC, Feb 14, 52; m 81. TEXTILE SCIENCE. *Educ:* Ohio State Univ, BS, 74; Univ Tenn, Knoxville, MS, 75, PhD(textiles), 78. *Prof Exp:* Grad asst clothing & textiles, Univ Tenn, Knoxville, 74-78; ASST PROF TEXTILE SCI & ECON, KANS STATE UNIV, 78- *Concurrent Pos:* Mem, Nat Adv Comt, Flammable Fabrics Act, Consumer Prod Safety Comn, 79-81, educ & rep, 79-80; res assoc, Inst Environ Res, Kans State Univ, 79-; res intern, US Army Res Inst Environ Med, Natick, Maine, 80. *Mem:* Am Soc Testing & Mat; Asn Col Prof Textiles & Clothing; Am Asn Textile Chemists & Clorists; Am Home Economics Asn. *Res:* Measuring the heat transfer characteristics of fabrics using a guarded hot plate and of clothing systems using an electrically heated mannequin; factors which affect the heat exchange permitted by clothing between a person and the environment. *Mailing Add:* Kans State Univ 219 Justin Hall Manhattan KS 66506

MCCULLOUGH, HERBERT ALFRED, b Pittsburgh, Pa, Dec 19, 14; m 43; c 2. BIOLOGY. *Educ:* Univ Pittsburgh, BS, 35, MS, 37, PhD(biol), 39. *Prof Exp:* Asst biol, Univ Pittsburgh, 36-39; prof & head dept, Bessie Tift Col, 39-47; assoc prof, 47-52, prof, 52-79, head dept, 57-79, DISTINGUISHED PROF BIOL, SAMFORD UNIV, 79- *Concurrent Pos:* Ala Acad Sci res grant, 50, 54. *Mem:* Fel AAAS; Am Bryol & Lichenological Soc; Am Inst Biol Sci; Brit Lichen Soc. *Res:* Lichenology; plant ecology; conservation of natural areas. *Mailing Add:* Dept of Biol Samford Univ Birmingham AL 35229

MCCULLOUGH, JACK DENNIS, b San Antonio, Tex, Aug 8, 31; m 53; c 2. LIMNOLOGY. *Educ:* Univ Tex, BS, 55; Stephen F Austin State Univ, MA, 62; Tex A&M Univ, PhD(biol), 70. *Prof Exp:* Teacher pub schs, Tex, 55-63; instr biol, Tex A&M Univ, 63-64; assoc prof, 64-77, PROF BIOL, STEPHEN F AUSTIN STATE UNIV, 77- *Concurrent Pos:* Researcher, US Army Corps Engrs, 71-73 & 75; mem, Tex Gov 2000 planning comt; mem eval panel, NSF. *Mem:* Sigma Xi; Am Soc Limnol & Oceanog; Int Soc Limnol. *Res:* Primary productivity in aquatic environments. *Mailing Add:* Dept of Biol Stephen F Austin State Univ Nacogdoches TX 75962

MCCULLOUGH, JAMES DOUGLAS, JR, b Long Beach, Calif, Nov 28, 38; m 75. ORGANIC CHEMISTRY, PHYSICAL CHEMISTRY. *Educ:* Univ Calif, Los Angeles, BS, 63; San Diego State Col, MS, 65; Univ Ill, Urbana, PhD(chem), 70. *Prof Exp:* SR RES CHEMIST, WESTHOLLOW RES CTR, SHELL DEVELOP CO, HOUSTON, 76- *Mem:* Soc Plastics Engrs; Am Soc Testing & Mat; Am Chem Soc. *Res:* Plastics technology; polymer science; petrochemical additives. *Mailing Add:* Shell Develop Co Westhollow Res Ctr PO Box 1380 Houston TX 77001

MCCULLOUGH, JAMES MATTHEW, b Pittsburgh, Pa, July 6, 25; m 50; c 2. BOTANY, ENVIRONMENTAL BIOLOGY. *Educ:* Pa State Univ, BS, 51, MS, 52; George Washington Univ, PhD(bot), 68. *Prof Exp:* Res technologist mat develop, Bur Ships, Navy Dept, 52-56; chmn dept biol & chem, Wakefield High Sch, Va, 56-63; head biosci div, Navy Sci & Tech Ctr, Navy Dept, 63-68, head dept sci & technol, 68-69; asst chief, 69-79, SR SPECIALIST LIFE SCI & ASST CHIEF, SCI POLICY RES DIV, CONG RES SERV, LIBR OF CONG, 69-, CHIEF, 79- *Concurrent Pos:* Sr consult engr, Packaging Consults, Inc, 59-62; adj prof, Sch Gen Studies, Univ Va, 60-63 & 70-77; adj prof, Va Polytech Inst & State Univ, 73-74. *Mem:* AAAS; Soc Environ Geochem & Health; NY Acad Sci; Am Inst Biol Sci. *Res:* Effects of physical and biological factors on growth and development. *Mailing Add:* Sci Policy Res Div Cong Res Serv Library Congress Washington DC 20540

MCCULLOUGH, JOHN JAMES, b Belfast, Northern Ireland, Sept 27, 37; m 63. ORGANIC CHEMISTRY. *Educ:* Queens Univ, Belfast, BSc, 59, PhD(chem), 62. *Prof Exp:* Dept Sci & Indust Res fel, 62-63; res assoc, Univ Wis, 63-65; from asst prof to assoc prof, 65-75, PROF CHEM, MCMASTER UNIV, 75- *Mem:* Am Chem Soc; Chem Inst Can; Royal Soc Chem. *Res:* Stereochemistry; photochemistry; physical organic chemistry. *Mailing Add:* Dept of Chem McMaster Univ Hamilton ON L8S 4K1 Can

MCCULLOUGH, JOHN MARTIN, b Chicago, Ill, Mar 9, 40; m 71; c 3. PHYSICAL ANTHROPOLOGY. *Educ:* Pa State Univ, BA, 62; Univ Ill, PhD(anthrop), 72. *Prof Exp:* Asst prof, 69-75, ASSOC PROF ANTHROP, UNIV UTAH, 75-, CHMN DEPT, 78- *Concurrent Pos:* Forensic anthropologist, Off Med Examr, Utah State Bd Health, 69- *Mem:* AAAS; Am Asn Phys Anthrop; Am Anthrop Asn; Brit Soc Study Human Biol; Int Asn Human Biol. *Res:* Human biology; adaptability; ecological genetics; ecological demography; Latin America, especially Mexico and Yucatan. *Mailing Add:* Dept of Anthrop Univ of Utah Salt Lake City UT 84112

MCCULLOUGH, JOHN PRICE, b Dallas, Tex, May 10, 25; m 46; c 3. PHYSICAL CHEMISTRY. *Educ:* Univ Okla, BS, 45; Ore State Col, MS, 48, PhD(chem), 49. *Prof Exp:* Phys chemist, Thermodyn Lab, Bartlesville Petrol Res Ctr, US Bur Mines, Okla, 49-56, chief, 56-63; mgr cent res div, Mobil Oil Corp, 63-69, appl res & develop, Mobil Res & Develop Corp, 69-71, gen mgr, res & develop, Mobil Chem Co, 71-78; VPRES, ENVIRON AFFAIRS & TOXICOL, MOBIL RES & DEVELOP CORP, 78- *Concurrent Pos:* Adj Prof, Okla State Univ, 61-63; dir, Mobil Tyco Solar Energy Co, 74- & Chem Indust Inst Toxicol, 79- *Honors & Awards:* Distinguished Serv Award, US Dept Interior, 62; Award in Petrol Chem, Am Chem Soc, 63, Leo Friend Award, 77. *Mem:* AAAS; Am Chem Soc. *Res:* Thermodynamics and molecular structure of hydrocarbons and related substances; research administration. *Mailing Add:* Mobil Res & Develop Corp 150 E 42nd St New York NY 10017

MCCULLOUGH, MARSHALL EDWARD, b Wick, WVa, July 24, 24. DAIRY NUTRITION. *Educ:* Berea Col, BS, 49; Univ Ky, MS, 51. *Prof Exp:* Asst dairy, Univ Ky, 50-51; asst dairy nutritionist, 51-59, ASSOC NUTRITIONIST, AGR EXP STA, UNIV GA, 59-, PROF ANIMAL NUTRIT, 68-, HEAD DEPT ANIMAL SCI, 71- *Honors & Awards:* Zur Craine Medal. *Mem:* AAAS; Soc Range Mgt; Am Soc Animal Sci; Am Dairy Sci Asn. *Res:* Plant and animal complex in grassland utilization; calf nutrition; systems for forage evaluation. *Mailing Add:* 376 E College Griffin GA 30223

MCCULLOUGH, NORMAN B, b Milford, Mich, Feb 23, 09; m 39; c 2. MICROBIOLOGY, INFECTIOUS DISEASES. *Educ:* Mich State Col, BS, 32, MS, 33; Univ Chicago, PhD(bact), 37, MD, 44; Am Bd Microbiol, dipl & cert pub health & med lab microbiol. *Prof Exp:* Asst, Mich State Col, 32-34; asst physiologist, Parke, Davis & Co, 34-36, res bacteriologist, 38-40, res bacteriologist, Tex, 40-42; from intern to asst resident, Univ Chicago Clins, 44-46, asst clin prof med, 47-50; chief brucellosis unit, Lab Infectious Dis, Nat Inst Allergy & Infectious Dis, 51-56, chief lab clin invests & clin dir, 52-58, chief lab bact dis, 58-68; prof, 68-79, EMER PROF MED, MICROBIOL & PUB HEALTH, MICH STATE UNIV, 79- *Concurrent Pos:* Eve instr, Detroit Inst Technol, 38-40; mem comt brucellosis, Nat Res Coun, 51-58; mem expert panel brucellosis, Food & Agr Orgn, WHO, 52-; med dir, USPHS, 52-68; spec lectr, Georgetown Univ, 52-66; instr, USDA Grad Sch, 54-61; mem adv coun, Med Int Coop, 58-60; expert taxon subcomt brucella, Int Comt Bact Nomenclature, 58-; mem, Nat Brucellosis Comt, Inc, 61-69, mem bd dirs, 63-69; instr, Found Adv Educ in Sci, Inc, 61-68, fac chmn microbiol & immunol, 63-68. *Mem:* AAAS; Am Soc Microbiol; Am Acad Microbiol; NY Acad Sci. *Res:* Medical microbiology; infectious and parasitic diseases. *Mailing Add:* Dept of Microbiol & Pub Health Mich State Univ East Lansing MI 48824

MCCULLOUGH, ROBERT WILLIAM, b Washington, DC, Oct 16, 47; m 67; c 1. MECHANICAL ENGINEERING, PHYSICS. *Educ:* Occidental Col, BA, 70; Columbia Univ, BS, 70; Stanford Univ, MS, 71, PhD(mech eng), 75. *Prof Exp:* Res fel high temperature chem kinetics, High Temperature Gas Dynamics Lab, 70-75; proj scientist solar energy, Linde Res, Union Carbide Corp, 75-78; assoc consult radiation transp, 78-81, VPRES AEROPHYSICS, AERONAUT RES ASSOC PRINCETON, 81- *Mem:* Am Soc Mech Engrs; Am Inst Aeronaut & Astronaut; Int Solar Energy Soc; Sigma Xi; Optical Soc Am. *Res:* Thermosciences; heat transfer; thermodynamics; fluid mechanics; molecular physics; chemical kinetics; radiation transport. *Mailing Add:* Aeronaut Res Assoc of Princeton PO Box 2229 50 Washington Rd Princeton NJ 08540

MCCULLOUGH, ROY LYNN, b Hillsboro, Tex, Mar 20, 34; m 58. PHYSICAL CHEMISTRY. *Educ:* Baylor Univ, BS, 55; Univ NMex, PhD(chem), 60. *Prof Exp:* Mem staff, Los Alamos Sci Lab, 58-59; group leader, Chemstrand Corp, Monsanto Co, NC, 59-69; mem staff, Polymer Sci Lab, Boeing Sci Res Lab, Wash, 69-71; PROF CHEM ENG, UNIV DEL, 71- *Mem:* Am Chem Soc; Am Phys Soc; AAAS; fel Am Inst Chem. *Res:* Influence of molecular structure on solid state properties. *Mailing Add:* Dept of Chem Eng Univ of Del Newark DE 19711

MCCULLOUGH, THOMAS F, b Los Angeles, Calif, Nov 12, 22. ORGANIC CHEMISTRY. *Educ:* Univ Notre Dame, BS, 48, MS, 49; Univ Utah, PhD(chem), 55. *Prof Exp:* Anal chemist & chem engr, Union Oil Co, 50-51; instr chem, Long Beach City Col, 55-56; INSTR CHEM, ST EDWARD'S UNIV, 57- *Mem:* Am Chem Soc; Entom Soc Am. *Res:* Analytical organic chemistry in natural products. *Mailing Add:* Dept of Chem St Edward's Univ Austin TX 78704

MCCULLY, JOSEPH C, b Kalamazoo, Mich, Feb 6, 24; m 47; c 4. MATHEMATICS. *Educ:* Western Mich Univ, BA, 47; Univ Mich, MA, 49, PhD(math), 57. *Prof Exp:* Asst prof math, Univ SDak, 53-55; asst prof, Univ RI, 55-56; assoc prof, 56-66, PROF MATH, WESTERN MICH UNIV, 66- *Mem:* Am Math Soc; Math Asn Am. *Res:* Integral transforms; operational calculus. *Mailing Add:* Dept of Math Western Mich Univ Kalamazoo MI 49008

MCCULLY, KILMER SERJUS, b Daykin, Nebr, Dec 23, 33; m 55; c 2. EXPERIMENTAL PATHOLOGY. *Educ:* Harvard Univ, AB, 55; Harvard Med Sch, MD, 59. *Prof Exp:* Intern, Mass Gen Hosp, 59-60; biochemist, NIH, 60-62; USPHS res fel med, Harvard Med Sch, 62-63, res fel biol, Harvard Univ, 63-65, Am Cancer Soc fac res assoc, 63-68, asst path, Harvard Med Sch, 65-68, instr, 68-70; asst pathologist, 68-73, ASSOC PATHOLOGIST, MASS GEN HOSP, 74-; ASST PROF PATH, HARVARD MED SCH, 70- *Concurrent Pos:* Res assoc, Glasgow Univ, 63-64; clin & res fel path, Mass Gen Hosp, 65-68; NIH career develop award, 71-76. *Mem:* AAAS; Am Asn of Pathologists; Am Soc Clin Pathologists; Int Acad Path. *Res:* Nucleic acid structure; protein biosynthesis; microbial genetics; amino acid metabolism; arteriosclerosis; growth hormone; ascorbate; pyridoxine; somatomedin; cancer. *Mailing Add:* Dept of Path Mass Gen Hosp Boston MA 02114

MCCULLY, MARGARET E, b St Marys, Ont, July 25, 34. BIOLOGY. *Educ:* Univ Toronto, BSA, 56, MSA, 60; Harvard Univ, PhD(biol), 66. *Prof Exp:* Res assoc microbiol, Parke Davis Co, 56-57; teacher high sch, Ont, 57-58 & St Felix Sch, Eng, 60-62; from asst prof to assoc prof, 66-78, PROF BIOL, CARLETON UNIV, 78- *Concurrent Pos:* External prof, Univ Ottawa, 77- *Mem:* Soc Develop Biol; Histochem Soc; Soc Exp Biol; Bot Soc Am; Royal Micros Soc. *Res:* Cytology, histology and histochemistry in relation to plant development. *Mailing Add:* Dept of Biol Carleton Univ Ottawa ON K1S 5B6 Can

MCCULLY, WAYNE GUNTER, b New Cambria, Mo, Jan 3, 22; m 44. RANGE SCIENCE. *Educ:* Colo State Univ, BS, 47; Tex A&M Univ, MS, 50, PhD, 58. *Prof Exp:* From asst prof to prof range mgt, 47-73, acting head dept, 71-72, prof & resident dir res, 73-79, RANGE SCIENTIST & HEAD VEG MGT, TEX A&M UNIV, 62- *Concurrent Pos:* Mem roadside maintenance comt, Transp Res Bd, Nat Res Coun, Nat Acad Sci. *Mem:* Soc Range Mgt; Ecol Soc Am; Am Soc Plant Physiol; Weed Sci Soc Am. *Res:* Noxious plant control; range ecology; grassland management; roadside vegetation management. *Mailing Add:* Tex A&M Univ Res & Ext Ctr Box 1658 Vernon TX 76384

MCCUMBER, DEAN EVERETT, b Rochester, NY, Nov 25, 30; m 57. PHYSICS. *Educ:* Yale Univ, BE, 52, ME, 55; Harvard Univ, AM, 56, PhD(physics), 60. *Prof Exp:* Head crystal electronics res dept, 65-69, PHYSICIST, BELL LABS, INC, 61-, DIR, INTERCONNECTION TECHNOL LAB, 69- *Mem:* Sr mem Inst Elec & Electronics Eng; fel Am Phys Soc. *Res:* Lasers; vibrational structure in optical spectra of solids; electrical instabilities in solid-state materials; Gunn effect; electronic interconnection systems. *Mailing Add:* Bell Labs Inc Rm 3137 c 2 295 Maple Ave Basking Ridge NJ 07920

MCCUNE, CONWELL CLAYTON, b Salt Lake City, Sept 8, 32; m 57; c 6. CHEMICAL ENGINEERING, PHYSICAL CHEMISTRY. *Educ:* Univ Utah, BS, 53, MS, 58, PhD(chem eng), 61. *Prof Exp:* Assoc technologist, Appl Res Lab, US Steel Corp, 60-62; res engr, Gulf Res & Develop Co, 62-66; sr chem engr, Houdry Process & Chem Co, Pa, 66-67; res adv engr, Westinghouse Elec Corp, 67-68; res engr, 68-70, sr res engr, 70-77, SR ENG ASSOC, CHEVRON OILFIELD RES CO, 77- *Concurrent Pos:* Eve instr continuing educ prog, Pa State Univ, 64-66; eve instr petrol eng, Univ Southern Calif, 77- *Mem:* AAAS; Am Inst Chem Engrs; Soc Petrol Engrs; Am Asn Physics Teachers. *Res:* High pressure reaction kinetics; shock tube and propellant ignition; refinery process; hydrocarbon oxidation; oil well stimulation processes; oil field water treating. *Mailing Add:* Chevron Oilfield Res Co PO Box 446 La Habra CA 90631

MCCUNE, DELBERT CHARLES, b Los Angeles, Calif, Aug 21, 34. PLANT PHYSIOLOGY. *Educ:* Calif Inst Technol, BS, 56; Yale Univ, MS, 57, PhD(bot), 60. *Prof Exp:* From asst plant physiologist to assoc plant physiologist, 60-68, PLANT PHYSIOLOGIST, BOYCE THOMPSON INST PLANT RES, 68- *Mem:* AAAS; Bot Soc Am; Am Soc Plant Physiol; NY Acad Sci. *Res:* Plant growth regulators; air pollution; effects on vegetation. *Mailing Add:* Boyce Thompson Inst for Plant Res Cornell Univ Tower Rd Ithaca NY 14853

MCCUNE, DUNCAN CHALMERS, b Chicago, Ill, Mar 16, 25; m 47; c 2. STATISTICAL ANALYSIS. *Educ:* Col of Wooster, AB, 48; Purdue Univ, MS, 50. *Prof Exp:* Res assoc, Purdue Univ, 50-52; statistician, Tubular Prods Div, Babcock & Wilcox Co, 52-55; sr statistician, 55-64, supvr appl math, 64-68, asst to dir tech serv, 69-71, MGR QUAL ASSURANCE, JONES & LAUGHLIN STEEL CORP, 71- *Mem:* Am Soc Qual Control; Am Soc Test & Mat; Royal Statist Soc; fel Am Soc Qual Control. *Mailing Add:* Jones & Laughlin Steel Corp #2 Gateway Ctr 9 East Pittsburgh PA 15263

MCCUNE, EMMETT L, b Cuba, Mo, Jan 2, 27; m 54; c 3. VETERINARY MICROBIOLOGY, AVIAN PATHOLOGY. *Educ:* Univ Mo, BS & DVM, 56, MS, 61; Univ Minn, PhD(microbiol), 67. *Prof Exp:* Instr vet bact, 56-61, from asst prof to assoc prof, 61-77, PROF VET MICROBIOL, COL VET MED, UNIV MO-COLUMBIA, 77- *Concurrent Pos:* Consult on com avian health mgt. *Mem:* Am Col Vet Microbiol; Am Vet Med Asn; Am Asn Avian Path; Am Soc Microbiol. *Res:* Microbiology, expecially mycoplasma, Pasteurella and Escherichia coli as related to avian pathology and metabolism; resistance factor in Salmonella and Escherichia coli. *Mailing Add:* 506 High St Columbia MO 65201

MCCUNE, FRANCIS K(IMBER), b Santa Barbara, Calif, Apr 10, 06; m 37, 69; c 2. ENGINEERING. *Educ:* Univ Calif, BS, 28. *Prof Exp:* Engr, Gen Elec Co, 28-45, asst works engr, Mass, 45-46, asst to mgr eng, NY, 46-48, asst gen mgr nucleonics, Wash, 48-51, mgr eng, Apparatus Div, NY, 51, asst mgr, 51-53, gen mgr, Atomics Prod Div, 53-59, vpres atomic bus develop mkt serv, 59-60, vpres eng, 60-65, vpres bus studies serv, 65-67; pres, Am Nat Standards Inst, 66-68 & McCune Realty & Oil Co, 68-75; RETIRED. *Concurrent Pos:* Past pres & hon dir, Atomic Indust Forum; past mem adv bd for residencies in eng, Ford Found; mem, Nat Res Coun, 69-72; hon mem, Woods Hole Oceonog Inst. *Honors & Awards:* Howard Coonley Medal, Am Standards Inst, 69. *Mem:* Nat Acad Eng; fel Inst Elec & Electronics; Am Soc Mech Engrs; Am Nuclear Soc. *Res:* Nuclear, electrical and mechanical engineering. *Mailing Add:* 909 Magellan Dr Sarasota FL 33580

MCCUNE, HOMER WALLACE, b Grove City, Pa, Sept 5, 23; m 49; c 3. CHEMISTRY. *Educ:* Grove City Col, BS, 44; Cornell Univ, PhD(inorg chem), 49. *Prof Exp:* Mem staff, Coal Res Lab, Carnegie Inst Technol, 44-45; res chemist, Chem Div, 49-54, sect head, 54-56, dept head, 56-58, patent div, 58-59, assoc dir, Res Div, 59-71, assoc dir paper & toilet goods technol div, 71-74, assoc dir soap & toilet goods technol div, 74, ASSOC DIR, FOOD, COFFEE & TOILET GOODS TECHNOL DIV, RES & DEVELOP DEPT, PROCTER & GAMBLE CO, 81- *Mem:* AAAS; Am Chem Soc; Am Inst Biol Sci. *Res:* Phosphates; corrosion; phosphorus compounds; surface chemistry; detergency; administration. *Mailing Add:* Procter & Gamble Co PO Box 175 Mt Healthy Sta Cincinnati OH 45239

MCCUNE, LEROY K(ILEY), b Chicago, Ill, June 30, 17; m 42, 68; c 8. CHEMICAL ENGINEERING. *Educ:* Princeton Univ, BS, 40, PhD(chem eng), 50. *Prof Exp:* Res engr, Textile Fibers Dept, E I DuPont de Nemours & Co, Inc, 48-50, res supvr, 50-52, res mgr, 52-53, tech supt, Film Dept, 53-55, lab dir, Textile Fiber Dept, 56-59, plant tech mgr, 59-63, tech dir, 63-65, mfg dir, 65-67, dir nylon mfg div, 67-71, dir, Prod Div & gen dir mfg, 71-79, dir dept plans, Textile Fibers Dept, 79-81; MGT CONSULT, 81- *Mem:* Am Inst Chem Engrs. *Res:* Polymer and fiber manufacture. *Mailing Add:* 3 Barley Mill Dr Greenville DE 19807

MCCUNE, MARY JOAN HUXLEY, b Lewistown, Mont, Jan 14, 32; m 65; c 2. MICROBIOLOGY. *Educ:* Mont State Univ, BS, 53; Wash State Univ, MS, 55; Purdue Univ, PhD(microbiol), 65. *Prof Exp:* Res technician, Vet Admin Hosp, Oakland, Calif, 55-59; bacteriologist, US Naval Radiol Defense Lab, Calif, 59-61; teaching assoc microbiol, Purdue Univ, 61-65, vis asst prof biol, 65-66; asst prof microbiol, Occidental Col, 66-69; fel, Univ Calif, Los Angeles, 69-70; affil asst prof, 70-80, ASST PROF MICROBIOL, IDAHO STATE UNIV, 80- *Mem:* AAAS; Am Soc Microbiol; NY Acad Sci; Sigma Xi. *Res:* Microbial physiology; genetics and taxonomy; microbial regulation of protein synthesis; ethanol production from renewable resources. *Mailing Add:* Dept Microbiol & Biochem Idaho State Univ Pocatello ID 83209

MCCUNE, RONALD WILLIAM, b Glade, Kans, Sept 23, 38; m 65; c 2. BIOCHEMISTRY. *Educ:* Kans State Univ, BS, 61; Purdue Univ, MS, 64, PhD(biochem), 66. *Prof Exp:* Trainee, Univ Calif, Los Angeles, 66-67, res biol chemist, 67-70; asst prof, 70-73, chmn dept microbiol & biochem, 71-77, assoc prof, 73-79, PROF BIOCHEM, IDAHO STATE UNIV, 79- *Concurrent Pos:* Vis assoc res biochemist, Univ Calif, San Diego, 77-78. *Mem:* Am Soc Microbiol; Sigma Xi; AAAS; Am Chem Soc; NY Acad Sci. *Res:* Effect of antibiotics on short-chain fatty acid metabolism by rumen microorganisms; urea-N metabolism in the ruminant animal; metabolic control of adrenal steroid biosynthesis; mechanisms of hormonal action; cAMP and cGMP-dependent protein kinases; mitochondrial metabolism. *Mailing Add:* Dept of Microbiol & Biochem Idaho State Univ Pocatello ID 83209

MCCURDY, DAVID HAROLD, b East Orange, NJ, Apr 28, 30; m 56; c 1. PHARMACOLOGY. *Educ:* Dalhousie Univ, BSc, 53, MSc, 55; Univ Toronto, PhD(pharmacol), 58. *Prof Exp:* Asst pharmacol, Dalhousie Univ, 53-55; asst, Univ Toronto, 55-58; pharmacologist, Chem Res & Develop Labs, US Army Chem Ctr, Md, 58-62; sr res pharmacologist, 62-65, mgr pharmacol sect, 65-75, asst dir drug design & eval, 73-76, DIR RES ADMIN, ICI AMERICAS INC, 76- *Mem:* AAAS; Sigma Xi; NY Acad Sci; Pharmacol Soc Can; Am Soc Pharmacol & Exp Therapeut. *Res:* Basic pharmacology, including the molecular basis of drug action; drug screening and development; central nervous system pharmacology research and management. *Mailing Add:* Biomed Res Dept & Lab Concord Pike & New Murphy Rd Wilmington DE 19897

MCCURDY, DENNIS, veterinary pharmacology, see previous edition

MCCURDY, HOWARD DOUGLAS, JR, b London, Ont, Can, Dec 10, 32; m 56, 78; c 4. MICROBIOLOGY. *Educ:* Western Ontario Univ, BA, 53; Assumption Univ, BSc, 54; Mich State Univ, MSc, 55, PhD(microbiol), 59. *Prof Exp:* Asst, Mich State Univ, 55-59; assoc prof, 59-70, PROF BIOL, UNIV WINDSOR, 70-, DEPT HEAD, 74- *Mem:* AAAS; Am Soc Microbiol; Can Soc Microbiol; Can Asn Univ Teachers (pres, 68-69); Can Col Microbiologists (pres). *Res:* Ecology of prokaryotes; biology of myxobacteria. *Mailing Add:* Dept Biol Univ Windsor Windsor ON N9B 3P4 Can

MCCURDY, JOHN DENNIS, b Irvington, NJ, Aug 17, 42. BIOCHEMISTRY. *Educ:* Fairleigh Dickinson Univ, BSc, 66; Am Univ, MSc, 72, PhD(chem), 74. *Prof Exp:* Lab officer biochem, US Army, 66-69; res asst, Am Univ, 69-74; new drug chemist anal & biochem, 74-80, BIOCHEMIST, ANIMAL FEED SAFETY, BUR VET MED, FOOD & DRUG ADMIN, 80- *Concurrent Pos:* Res scientist chem, Am Univ, 75- *Mem:* Am Chem Soc; NY Acad Sci; AAAS; Asn Off Anal Chemists; fel Am Inst Chemists. *Res:* Biochemistry of pharmacologically active compounds; thymic hormone research. *Mailing Add:* 5531 Green Dory Lane Columbia MD 21044

MCCURDY, JON ALAN, b Lacona, Iowa, Oct 18, 12; m 42; c 3. VETERINARY ANATOMY. *Educ:* Iowa State Univ, BS & DVM, 38. *Prof Exp:* Instr vet anat, Agr & Mech Col, Tex, 38-39; from asst prof to assoc prof, Col Vet Med, Wash State Univ, 46-56, prof vet anat & chmn dept, 56-76; RETIRED. *Mem:* Am Asn Vet Anat (secy, 53, pres, 55); Am Vet Med Asn. *Res:* Microscopic anatomy; embryology. *Mailing Add:* Rte 1 Box 83 Worley ID 83876

MCCURDY, KEITH G, b Lampman, Sask, Can, Dec 4, 37; m 60; c 3. PHYSICAL CHEMISTRY. *Educ:* Univ Sask, BA, 59, MA, 61; Univ Ottawa, PhD(chem), 64. *Prof Exp:* Asst prof chem, Univ Guelph, 63-67; from asst prof to assoc prof, 67-77, PROF CHEM, UNIV LETHBRIDGE, 77- *Res:* Chemical kinetics. *Mailing Add:* Dept of Chem Univ of Lethbridge Lethbridge AB T1K 2V7 Can

MCCURDY, LAYTON, b Florence, SC, Aug 20, 35; m 58; c 2. PSYCHIATRY. *Educ:* Med Univ SC, MD, 60. *Prof Exp:* Rotating intern, Med Col SC, 60-61; resident psychiat, NC Mem Hosp, 61-64; asst prof psychiat, Sch Med, Emory Univ, 66-68; PROF PSYCHIAT & CHMN DEPT, MED UNIV SC, 68- *Concurrent Pos:* Consult, NIMH, 66-67, Clayton County Ment Health Clin, Ga, 66-68, Volunteers in Serv to Am, Washington, DC, 67-68, Charleston Vet Admin Hosp, Va & SC Dept Ment Health, 68- & Va Med Res Rev Bd Behav Sci, NIMH, 74-77; psychoanal trainee, Columbia Univ Psychoanal Clin, Atlanta, Ga, 67-68; mem res rev comt, Appl Res Br, NIMH, 70-74; NIMH res fel, Maudsley Hosp, London, Eng, 74-75; mem, Nat Adv Ment Health Coun, 80-83. *Mem:* Fel Am Col Psychiat; fel Am Psychiat Asn; fel Am Psychosom Soc; Asn Am Med Cols; fel Asn Acad Psychiat (pres, 70-72). *Res:* Behavioral sciences; medical education. *Mailing Add:* Dept of Psychiat Med Univ of SC Charleston SC 29401

MCCURDY, PAUL RANNEY, b Middletown, Conn, Sept 26, 25; m 52; c 5. INTERNAL MEDICINE, HEMATOLOGY. *Educ:* Wesleyan Univ, AB, 46; Harvard Med Sch, MD, 49. *Prof Exp:* Fel med, Sch Med, Georgetown Univ, 54-55; instr, 55-60, assoc prof, 60-72, PROF MED, SCH MED, GEORGETOWN UNIV, 72- *Concurrent Pos:* Consult, NIH & US Naval Hosp, Bethesda, Md, 70-; dir, Am Red Cross Blood Serv, Washington, DC, Region, 75- *Mem:* Am Soc Hemat; Int Soc Hemat; Am Col Physicians; sr mem Am Fedn Clin Res; Am Asn Blood Banks. *Res:* Red blood cell, including enzymes G-6-PD and abnormal hemoglobins. *Mailing Add:* Am Red Cross Regional Blood Prog 2025 E St NW Washington DC 20003

MCCURDY, WALLACE HUTCHINSON, JR, b Pittsburgh, Pa, Nov 16, 26; m 54; c 3. ANALYTICAL CHEMISTRY. *Educ:* Pa State Univ, BS, 47; Univ Ill, MS, 47, PhD(chem), 51. *Prof Exp:* From instr to asst prof chem, Princeton Univ, 51-59; asst prof, 59-64, ASSOC PROF CHEM, UNIV DEL, 64- *Concurrent Pos:* Res chemist, Bell Tel Labs, Inc, NJ, 53; Textile Res Inst, 56; res fel, Nat Bur Standards, 70-71. *Mem:* Am Chem Soc. *Res:* inorganic reaction mechanisms; coordination complexes; nonaqueous solvent systems; electroanalytical instrumentation. *Mailing Add:* Dept of Chem Univ of Del Newark DE 19711

MCCURRY, PATRICK MATTHEW, JR, b Homestead, Pa, Nov 2, 44; m 67. CHEMISTRY. *Educ:* Univ Pittsburgh, BS, 65; Columbia Univ, PhD, 70. *Prof Exp:* Res chemist, US Bur Mines, 65 & 66; NIH fel, Stanford Univ, 70-71; asst prof chem, Mellon Inst Sci, Carnegie-Mellon Univ, 71-76, assoc prof, 76-81; SR RES CHEMIST, A E STALEY CORP, DECATUR, ILL, 81- *Concurrent Pos:* Res fel, Alfred P Sloan Found, 75-78. *Mem:* Am Chem Soc; Royal Soc Chem. *Res:* Natural product synthesis; novel synthetic methods. *Mailing Add:* A E Staley Mfg Co 2200 E Elderado St Decatur IL 62525

MCCUSKER, JANE, b London, Eng, Aug 27, 43; m 67; c 3. EPIDEMIOLOGY. *Educ:* McGill Univ, MD, CM, 67; Columbia Univ, MPH, 69, DrPH(epidemiol), 74. *Prof Exp:* Lectr epidemiol statist, Fac Med, Univ Dar es Salaam, 73-74; asst prof prev med, Sch Med & Dent, Univ Rochester, 75-81; ASSOC PROF, DIV PUB HEALTH, SCH HEALTH SCI, UNIV MASS, AMHERST, 81- *Mem:* Am Pub Health Asn; Soc Epidemiol Res; Int Epidemiol Asn; Asn Teachers Prev Med. *Res:* Epidemiology in health sciences research; graduation of health care of chronically and terminally ill; general epidemiologic research. *Mailing Add:* Div Pub Health Sch Health Sci Univ Mass Amherst MA 01003

MCCUSKEY, ROBERT SCOTT, b Cleveland, Ohio, Sept 8, 38; m 58, 74. ANATOMY. *Educ:* Western Reserve Univ, AB, 60, PhD(anat), 65. *Prof Exp:* From instr to prof anat, Col Med, Univ Cincinnati, 65-78; PROF ANAT & CHMN DEPT, SCH MED, W VA UNIV, 78- *Concurrent Pos:* Consult, Procter & Gamble Co, 66-68, 71-75 & Hoffmann-La Roche, 72-75; NIH res grants, Univ Cincinnati, 66-78, Southwest Ohio Heart Asn res grant, 68-69 & 73-77, Akron Heart Asn res grant, 70-71 & Am Heart Asn res grant, 77-, WVa Univ, 78-; NIH res career develop award, 69-74; assoc ed, Microvascular Res, 74-; vis prof, Univ Heidelberg, 81. *Mem:* Microcirc Soc; Am Asn Anatomists; Am Soc Hemat; Int Soc Exp Hemat; Am Asn Study Liver Dis. *Res:* In vivo microscopic anatomy of living organs; microcirculation; liver structure and function; hematology; endotoxins and host defense mechanisms. *Mailing Add:* Dept of Anat WVa Univ Med Ctr Morgantown WV 26506

MCCUSKEY, SIDNEY WILCOX, astronomy, deceased

MCCUTCHAN, JOSEPH W(ILSON), b Pawnee, Okla, Dec 24, 17; m 42; c 3. CHEMICAL & MECHANICAL ENGINEERING. *Educ:* Univ Ark, BSChE, 39; Univ Calif, Los Angeles, MS, 50. *Prof Exp:* Draftsman, Midwestern Eng & Construct Co, 39-40; engr, Douglas Aircraft Co, 40-46; assoc prof eng, 46-66, PROF CHEM, NUCLEAR & THERMOL ENG, UNIV CALIF, LOS ANGELES, 66- *Concurrent Pos:* Mem staff off saline water, US Dept Interior, DC, 60-61 & 67-68 & Off Water Res & Technol, 75-76. *Mem:* Am Soc Mech Engrs; Am Soc Eng Educ; Am Inst Chem Engrs; Am Water Works Asn; Nat Water Supply Improvement Asn. *Res:* Demineralization of sea water by reverse osmosis and distillation process; human tolerance to extreme heat. *Mailing Add:* Sch of Eng & Appl Sci Univ of Calif 5532 Boelter Hall Los Angeles CA 90024

MCCUTCHAN, ROY T(HOMAS), b Dallas, Tex, Sept 19, 18; m 41. CHEMICAL ENGINEERING, PHYSICAL CHEMISTRY. *Educ:* Univ Tex, BS, 40, MS, 41, PhD(chem eng), 49. *Prof Exp:* Engr, Dow Chem Co, 42-44; mem staff, Los Alamos Sci Lab, 49-52; chem engr, Southwest Res Inst, 52-56, mgr inorg process develop, 56-59; asst prof chem, St Mary's Univ, Tex, 59-62; aerospace technologist, Manned Spacecraft Ctr, NASA, 62-64; supvr process develop, Thiokol Chem Corp, 64-66; assoc prof eng eng, 66-69, PROF ENG, ST MARY'S UNIV, TEX, 69- *Mem:* Am Inst Chem Engrs. *Res:* Solid propellant rocket process development; military pyrotechnics; high energy boron fuel; aromatic mercury compounds; thermodynamics; water quality surveys. *Mailing Add:* Div of Eng St Mary's Univ San Antonio TX 78284

MCCUTCHEN, CHARLES WALTER, b Princeton, NJ, Mar 9, 29. PHYSICS, BIOLOGY. *Educ:* Princeton Univ, BA, 50; Brown Univ, MSc, 52; Cambridge Univ, PhD, 57. *Prof Exp:* Res physicist, Cambridge Univ, 57-62; RES PHYSICIST, LAB EXP PATH, NAT INST ARTHRITIS, METAB & DIGESTIVE DIS, 62- *Mem:* Am Phys Soc; Optical Soc Am. *Res:* Lubrication of animal joints; optical diffraction theory; applied optics; hydrodynamics. *Mailing Add:* Lab of Exp Path Nat Inst Arthritis Metab & Digestive Dis Bethesda MD 20014

MCCUTCHEN, SAMUEL P(ROCTOR), b Corinth, Miss, May 2, 28; m 53, 72; c 6. ELECTRICAL ENGINEERING. *Educ:* Vanderbilt Univ, BE, 50; LaSalle Exten Univ, LLB, 66. *Prof Exp:* Prod engr magnetic head design, Brush Electronics Co, Ohio, 53-55; proj engr infrared syst, Aerojet-Gen Corp, 55-58; design supvr Polaris syst, Lockheed Aircraft Corp, 58-59; supvr electronic systs studies, Sylvania Elec Prod Co, 59-60; mem staff, Inst Defense Anal, 60-63; mgr systs eng dept, NAm Air Defense Combat Opers Ctr Proj, Burroughs Corp, 63-66; sr staff mem, ASW Systs Studies, TRW Systs, Washington, 66-69; DIR, MGT INFO SYSTS, US ARMY MOBILITY EQUIP RES & DEVELOP COMMAND, 69- *Res:* Systems management; computer center management. *Mailing Add:* US Army Mobility Equip Res & Develop Command Ft Belvoir VA 22060

MCCUTCHEON, ERNEST P, b Durham, NC, May 7, 33; m 56; c 3. MEDICAL PHYSIOLOGY, BIOMEDICAL ENGINEERING. *Educ:* Davidson Col, BS, 55; Duke Univ, MD, 59. *Prof Exp:* Intern med, Grady Mem Hosp, Atlanta, Ga, 59-60; res med, Duke Univ, 60-61; head bioinstrumentation & physiol data sect, Launch Site Med Opers, NASA, 61-63; NIH sr res fel physiol & biophys, Univ Wash, 63-66; from asst prof to assoc prof, Univ Ky, 66-74; sr res assoc, Nat Acad Sci-Nat Res Coun, NASA, 73-74, res med officer, Biomed Res Div, Ames Res Ctr, 74-77; ASSOC PROF PHYSIOL, SCH MED, UNIV SC, 77- *Concurrent Pos:* Vis assoc prof, Stanford Univ Med Ctr, 73-74. *Mem:* Am Physiol Soc; AAAS; Inst Elec & Electronics Engrs; Am Heart Asn; Biomed Eng Soc. *Res:* Cardiovascular dynamics; instrumentation; indirect blood pressure determination; ultrasonics. *Mailing Add:* Dept Physiol Sch Med Univ SC Columbia SC 29208

MCCUTCHEON, MARTIN J, b Little Rock, Ark, Dec 23, 41; m 63; c 2. INSTRUMENTATION, MEASUREMENT. *Educ:* Univ Ark, BSEE, 64, MSEE, 65, PhD(elec eng), 67. *Prof Exp:* Asst prof, 67-71, assoc prof, 71-76, PROF ENG, UNIV ALA, BIRMINGHAM, 77-, ASSOC PROF BIOCOMMUN, 75- *Concurrent Pos:* Consult, NIH, 80 & Zurn Air Systs, 81. *Mem:* Inst Elec & Electronics Engrs; Eng Med & Biol Soc; Acoust Soc Am. *Res:* Development of instrumentation for speech research and therapy; applications of computers and microprocessors in engineering in medicine and biology. *Mailing Add:* Sch of Eng Univ of Ala Birmingham AL 35233

MCCUTCHEON, ROB STEWART, b Idaho Falls, Idaho, May 10, 08; m 29; c 3. PHARMACOLOGY. *Educ:* Univ Idaho, BS, 33; Univ Wash, MS, 46, PhD(pharmaceut chem), 48. *Prof Exp:* Prof pharmacol, Ore State Univ, 48-64; scientist admin pharmacol, NIH, 64-65, exec secy, toxicol study sect, div res grants, 65-78; RETIRED. *Concurrent Pos:* Res fel cardiovasc pharmacol, Med Col Ga, 55-56; NIH spec fel, Sch Med, WVa Univ, 62-63; ed, J Toxicol & Environ Health, 78- *Mem:* Fel AAAS; Am Pharmaceut Asn; Am Soc Pharmacol & Exp Therapeut; Soc Toxicol. *Res:* Cardiovascular pharmacology; toxicology. *Mailing Add:* 703 Morgan Creek Rd Chapel Hill NC 27514

MCCUTCHEON, WILLIAM HENRY, b Toronto, Ont, Aug 26, 40; m 65; c 2. RADIO ASTRONOMY. *Educ:* Queen's Univ, Ont, BSc, 62, MSc, 64; Univ Manchester, PhD(radio astron), 69. *Prof Exp:* Res asst radio astron, Nuffield Radio Astron Labs, Jodrell Bank, Eng, 67-69; fel, 69-71, res assoc, 71-72, vis asst prof, 72-73, asst prof, 73-80, ASSOC PROF, DEPT PHYSICS, UNIV BC, 80- *Mem:* Royal Astron Soc; Can Astron Soc (treas, 78-83); Am Astron Soc; Int Astron Union. *Res:* Spectral line studies in radio astronomy; neutral hydrogen studies of external galaxies. *Mailing Add:* Dept of Physics Univ of BC Vancouver BC V6T 1W5 Can

MCDADE, JOSEPH EDWARD, b Cumberland, Md, Feb 4, 40; m 64; c 2. MICROBIOLOGY, RICKETTSIOLOGY. *Educ:* Western Md Col, BA, 62; Univ Del, MA, 65, PhD(microbiol), 67. *Hon Degrees:* DSc, Western Md Col, 77. *Prof Exp:* Captain, US Army Biol Labs, 67-69; dir cell prod dept, Microbiol Assocs, Inc, 69-71; res assoc, Sch Med, Univ Md, 71-75; RES MICROBIOLOGIST, CTR DIS CONTROL, 75- *Honors & Awards:* Secy's Award for Exceptional Achievement, Off Secy, HEW, 78; Richard & Hinda Rosenthal Award, Am Col Physicians, 79. *Mem:* Am Soc Microbiol; AAAS; Am Acad Microbiol; fel Infectious Dis Soc. *Res:* Properties of the agent responsible for Legionnaire's disease; rickettsiae and rickettsial diseases. *Mailing Add:* Bldg 7 Rm B 5 Ctr Dis Control Atlanta GA 30333

MCDANIEL, BENJAMIN THOMAS, b Pickens, SC, Feb 15, 35. ANIMAL GENETICS, ANIMAL BREEDING. *Educ:* Clemson Col, BS, 57; Univ Md, MS, 60; NC State Univ, PhD(animal breeding), 64. *Prof Exp:* Dairy husb, Animal Husb Res Div, USDA, 57-60; fel animal breeding, NC State Univ, 63-64; res dairy scientist, Animal Sci Res Div, USDA, 64-72; PROF ANIMAL SCI & GENETICS, NC STATE UNIV, 72- *Mem:* Am Dairy Sci Asn. *Res:* Genetics and breeding of domestic animals, with emphasis on dairy cattle. *Mailing Add:* Dept Animal Sci NC State Univ Raleigh NC 27650

MCDANIEL, BOYCE DAWKINS, b Brevard, NC, June 11, 17; m 41; c 2. EXPERIMENTAL HIGH ENERGY PHYSICS. *Educ:* Ohio Wesleyan Univ, BS, 38; Case Inst Technol, MS, 40; Cornell Univ, PhD(physics), 43. *Prof Exp:* Asst physics, Case Inst Technol, 38-40; asst & res assoc, Cornell Univ, 40-42; mem staff, Radiation Lab, Mass Inst Technol, 43; physicist, Los Alamos Sci Lab, NMex, 43-45; from asst prof to assoc prof, 45-56, assoc dir, 60-67, PROF PHYSICS, CORNELL UNIV, 56-, DIR LAB NUCLEAR STUDIES, 67- *Concurrent Pos:* Fulbright res award, Australian Nat Univ, 53; Guggenheim & Fulbright award, Univ Rome & Synchrontron Lab, Frascati, Italy, 59; trustee, Assoc Univs, Inc, 63-75; res collabr, Brookhaven Nat Lab, 66; trustee, Univ Res Asn Inc, 71-77. *Mem:* Nat Acad Sci; fel Am Phys Soc. *Res:* Electron diffraction; slow neutron and gamma ray spectroscopy; high energy particle physics; accelerator design, construction and operation. *Mailing Add:* Lab Nuclear Studies Cornell Univ Ithaca NY 14050

MCDANIEL, BURRUSS, JR, b Ft Smith, Ark, Apr 18, 27; m 58; c 2. ENTOMOLOGY. *Educ:* Univ Alaska, BA, 53; Tex A&M Univ, MS, 61, PhD(entom), 65. *Prof Exp:* Consult entomologist, Insect Control & Res, Inc, Md, 57-59; asst prof biol, Tex Col Arts & Indust, 61-66; assoc prof entom, 66-71, PROF ENTOM, SDAK STATE UNIV, 71- *Concurrent Pos:* Consult, Rockefeller Found, Mex, 57-59. *Mem:* Soc Study Evolution; Entom Soc Am; Am Ornith Union. *Res:* Systematic and ecological studies of soil microarthropods; investigation on Entomophaga Grylli, a pathogen of grasshoppers. *Mailing Add:* Dept Entom-Zool SDak State Univ Brookings SD 57006

MCDANIEL, CARL NIMITZ, b Englewood, NJ, June 9, 42; m 67; c 2. DEVELOPMENTAL BIOLOGY, PLANT CELL CULTURE. *Educ:* Oberlin Col, BA, 64; Wesleyan Univ, MS, 66, PhD(biol), 73. *Prof Exp:* Instr biol & chem, US Naval Acad, 69; fel biol, Yale Univ, 73-75; asst prof, 75-80, ASSOC PROF BIOL, RENSSELAER POLYTECH INST, 81- *Concurrent Pos:* Vis assoc res prof, Univ Calif, Davis, 81-82. *Mem:* Soc Develop Biol; Am Soc Plant Physiologists. *Res:* Differentiation of shoot apical meristems and plant somatic cell genetics. *Mailing Add:* Dept Biol Cogswell Lab Rensselaer Polytech Inst Troy NY 12181

MCDANIEL, CARL VANCE, b Grafton, WVa, Dec 4, 29; m 52; c 2. PHYSICAL CHEMISTRY. *Educ:* Univ Pittsburgh, BS, 57; Mass Inst Technol, PhD(phys chem), 62. *Prof Exp:* Res technologist, US Steel Corp, 52-58; asst phys chem, Mass Inst Technol, 58-62; res chemist, 62-65, RES SUPVR PHYS CHEM, W R GRACE & CO, COLUMBIA, 65- *Mem:* Am Chem Soc; AAAS; Catalysis Soc. *Res:* Chemical metallurgy; physicochemical properties of ion exchange systems; physicochemical properties of molecular sieves; hydrocarbon catalysis and catalysts; coal gasification and liquefaction; synthetic fuels. *Mailing Add:* 10725 Crestview Lane Laurel MD 20810

MCDANIEL, EARL WADSWORTH, b Macon, Ga, Apr 15, 26; m 48; c 2. PHYSICS. *Educ:* Ga Inst Technol, BA, 48; Univ Mich, MS, 50, PhD, 54. *Prof Exp:* Asst physics, Univ Mich, 48-54; res physicist, 54-55, from asst prof to prof, 55-70, REGENTS' PROF PHYSICS, GA INST TECHNOL, 70- *Concurrent Pos:* Instr, Ga Power Co, 57-; consult, Union Carbide Nuclear Co, 59-, US Army Missile Command, 70- & United Technol Res Ctr, 76-; Guggenheim fel & Fulbright sr res scholar, Univ Durham, Eng, 66-67. *Mem:* Am Phys Soc. *Res:* Atomic collisions; gaseous electronics; plasma physics. *Mailing Add:* Dept of Physics Ga Inst of Technol Atlanta GA 30332

MCDANIEL, EDGAR LAMAR, JR, b Augusta, Ga, Dec 28, 31; m 54; c 2. INDUSTRIAL ORGANIC CHEMISTRY. *Educ:* Univ Tenn, BS, 53, MS, 54, PhD(chem), 56. *Prof Exp:* Asst chem, Univ Tenn, 52-56; res chemist, 56-59, sr res chemist, 60-68, res assoc, 68-74, div head, Eng Res Div, 74-77, staff asst gen mgt, Tenn Eastman Co, 77-80, coordr appl res, 80-81, ASST DIR DEVELOP, EASTMAN CHEM DIV, EASTMAN KODAK CO, 81- *Mem:* Am Chem Soc; Am Inst Chem. *Res:* Catalytic reactions; petrochemistry; chemical kinetics; chemical reaction engineering. *Mailing Add:* Eastman Chem Div Eastman Kodak Co PO Box 511 Kingsport TN 37662

MCDANIEL, GAYNER RAIFORD, b Milport, Ala, Feb 4, 29; m 48; c 2. GENETICS, PHYSIOLOGY. *Educ:* Auburn Univ, BS, 53, MS, 54; Kans State Univ, PhD(genetics), 60. *Prof Exp:* Exten poultryman, Kans State Univ, 59-61; dir res & develop turkeys, Ralston Purina Co, 61-68; assoc prof reproductive physiol, 68-81, PROF POULTRY SCI, AUBURN UNIV, 81- *Mem:* Artificial insemination of broiler breeders in cages; reproductive performance of breeders; environmental factors related to hatchability. *Mailing Add:* Dept of Poultry Sci Auburn Univ Auburn AL 36830

MCDANIEL, IVAN NOEL, b Martinsville, Ill, Feb 13, 28; m 57; c 3. MEDICAL ENTOMOLOGY. *Educ:* Eastern Ill Univ, BS, 51; Univ Ill, MS, 52, PhD(entom), 58. *Prof Exp:* Asst biol, Univ Ill, 53-57; asst prof, 57-63, ASSOC PROF ENTOM, UNIV MAINE, ORONO, 63- *Concurrent Pos:* Mem sci adv panel, World Health Orgn, 75-80. *Mem:* AAAS; Ecol Soc Am; Entom Soc Am; Entom Soc Can; Am Mosquito Control Asn. *Res:* Identification of attractants and stimulants that influence oviposition of mosquitoes; biological control of mosquitoes and black flies. *Mailing Add:* Dept of Entom 303 Deering Hall Univ of Maine Orono ME 04469

MCDANIEL, JAMES SCOTT, parasitology, deceased

MCDANIEL, LLOYD EVERETT, b Michigan Valley, Kans, Apr 4, 14; m 44; c 3. MICROBIOLOGY. *Educ:* Kans State Univ, BS, 35, MS, 37; Univ Wis, PhD(bact), 41. *Prof Exp:* Res microbiologist, Merck Sharp & Dohme Res Labs Div, Merck & Co, Inc, 40-46, head develop sect, 46-51, mgr microbiol develop, 51-56, asst dir microbiol res, 56-61; assoc prof, 61-76, PROF MICROBIOL, INST MICROBIOL, RUTGERS UNIV, 76- *Mem:* Am Soc Microbiol; Am Chem Soc; Soc Indust Microbiol. *Res:* Fermentation research and technology; polyene macrolide antibiotics; production of chemicals by microorganisms. *Mailing Add:* Waksman Inst of Microbiol Rutgers Univ PO Box 759 Piscataway NJ 08854

MCDANIEL, MAX PAUL, b Ft Worth, Tex, May 11, 47; m 69. SURFACE CHEMISTRY. *Educ:* Southern Ill Univ, BA, 69; Northwestern Univ, MS, 70, PhD(phys chem), 74. *Prof Exp:* Res assoc catalysis, Nat Ctr Sci Res, France, 74; RES CHEMIST, PHILLIPS PETROL CO, 75- *Mem:* Am Chem Soc; Soc Plastics Engrs. *Res:* Modifying and testing the Phillips polymerization catalyst, seeking to improve activity and melt index capability and a better understanding of the mechanism of polymerization. *Mailing Add:* 86-G Phillips Res Ctr Bartlesville OK 74004

MCDANIEL, MILTON EDWARD, b Elk City, Okla, Jan 17, 38; m 60; c 1. PLANT BREEDING, GENETICS. *Educ:* Okla State Univ, BS, 60; Va Polytech Inst, PhD(plant breeding), 65. *Prof Exp:* Assoc prof small grains breeding, 65-77, ASSOC PROF AGRON & GENETICS, TEX A&M UNIV, 77- *Mem:* Am Soc Agron. *Res:* Oat and barley breeding and genetic research. *Mailing Add:* Dept of Soil & Crop Sci Tex A&M Univ College Station TX 77843

MCDANIEL, ROBERT GENE, b Wash, DC, Aug 2, 41; m 76; c 4. GENETICS, PLANT PHYSIOLOGY. *Educ:* Univ WVa, AB, 63, PhD(genetics), 67. *Prof Exp:* Asst agronomist, 67-71, assoc prof agron & plant genetics, 71-75, PROF PLANT SCI, UNIV ARIZ, 75- *Mem:* AAAS; Am Soc Agron; Crop Sci Soc Am; Am Soc Plant Physiol. *Res:* Biochemical and physiological studies of heterosis in eukaryotes; biochemistry of plant hormones; genetics of mitochondria; biochemical studies of aging; genetics and biochemistry of hybrids; mitochondrial DNA; histones and nuclear proteins; genetic engineering. *Mailing Add:* Dept Plant Sci Univ Ariz Tucson AZ 85721

MCDANIEL, ROBERT S(TEPTOE), b Lynchburg, Va, Apr 15, 21; m 46; c 4. PROCESS ENGINEERING, SAFETY ENGINEERING. *Educ:* Univ Va, BChE, 42; Princeton Univ, ChE, 43. *Prof Exp:* Mem staff, Standard Oil Co, Ind, 43, asst proj chem engr, 43-47, group leader, Tech Serv Div, 47-50, asst gen foreman pressure stills, 50-52, supvr light oils planning, Gen Mgrs Mfg Dept, 52-61, asst mgr, Planning Div, Mfg Dept, Am Oil Co, 61-62, mgr financial anal & control div, Admin Dept, 62-70, mgr, Mfg Planning, 70-73; MGR, ENVIRON & QUAL CONTROL, AMOCO OIL CO, 73- *Mailing Add:* Amoco Oil Co PO Box 182 Wood River IL 62095

MCDANIEL, ROBERT STEWART, b June 12, 40; Can citizen; m 65; c 2. CHEMICAL KINETICS, DATA PROCESSING. *Educ:* Univ BC, BSc, 64; Simon Fraser Univ, PhD(chem), 71. *Prof Exp:* Teacher math & sci, Alberni Sch Dist, 64-66; fel photochem, Univ Alta, 71-73, instr chem, 73-75; RES OFFICER, ALTA RES COUN, 75- *Res:* Hydrogen production. *Mailing Add:* Alta Res Coun 11315 87th Ave Edmonton AB T6G 2C2 Can

MCDANIEL, ROGER LANIER, JR, b Suffolk, Va, Dec 29, 52. HERBICIDES. *Educ:* Campbell Univ, BS, 75; NC State Univ, PhD(org chem), 81. *Prof Exp:* SR CHEMIST, UNION CARBIDE AGR PROD CO, 81- *Mem:* Am Chem Soc. *Res:* Synthesis and reactions of spirocyclic enones; synthesis of strained bridgehead olefins; herbicides and plant growth regulators. *Mailing Add:* Union Carbide T W Alexander Dr PO Box 12014 Research Triangle Park NC 27709

MCDANIEL, SUSAN GRIFFITH, b Kansas City, Kans, Dec 3, 38; wid. ZOOLOGY. *Educ:* Kans State Teachers Col, BS, 59, MS, 62; Univ Okla, PhD(zool), 66. *Prof Exp:* Asst prof biol, 67-79, asst provost, 73-77, asst vchancellor 77, ASSOC VCHANCELLOR ACAD AFFAIRS, EAST CAROLINA UNIV, 77-, ASSOC PROF BIOL, 79- *Mem:* Am Mus Natural Hist; Sigma Xi. *Res:* Animal ecology and behavior. *Mailing Add:* Off VChancellor Acad Affairs East Carolina Univ Greenville NC 27834

MCDANIEL, TERRY WAYNE, b Decatur, Ind, Apr 12, 46; m 68; c 2. DISK FILE DEVELOPMENT, APPLIED PHYSICS. *Educ:* Wittenberg Univ, Ohio, BA, 68; Mich State Univ, MS, 70, PhD(physics), 73. *Prof Exp:* Asst physics, Mich State Univ, 68-73, res assoc, 73-74; asst prof physics, Va Commonwealth Univ, 74-78; sr assoc engr, 78-80, STAFF PHYSICIST, IBM

CORP, 80- *Mem:* Am Phys Soc. *Res:* Magnetic recording physics; computer aided simulation of recording systems; electo-magnetism; solid state physics; magneto-optics. *Mailing Add:* IBM Corp 2H3/030-1 Hwy 52 & 37th St NW Rochester MN 55901

MCDANIEL, THOMAS LEE, nuclear chemistry, radiochemistry, see previous edition

MCDANIEL, VAN RICK, b San Antonio, Tex, Oct 29, 45; m 66; c 3. MAMMALOGY, HERPETOLOGY. *Educ:* Tex A&I Univ, BS, 67, MS, 69; Tex Tech Univ, PhD(zool), 73. *Prof Exp:* ASSOC PROF ZOOL, ARK STATE UNIV, 72- *Mem:* Am Soc Mammalogists; Am Soc Ichthyologists & Herpetologists; Soc Study Amphibians & Reptiles; Sigma Xi; Nat Speleol Soc. *Res:* Taxonomy and natural history of mammals and herptiles; natural history of Ozark cave communities. *Mailing Add:* Div of Biol Sci Ark State Univ State University AR 72467

MCDANIEL, WILLARD RICH, b Hammond, Ind, June 9, 34; div; c 2. METEOROLOGY, GEOLOGY. *Educ:* Miami Univ, AB, 56, MS, 57; Tex A&M Univ, PhD(meteorol), 67. *Prof Exp:* Geologist, Lion Oil Co, 57-58; assoc prof, 59-74, PROF & HEAD DEPT EARTH SCI, E TEX STATE UNIV, 74- *Mem:* Am Meteorol Soc. *Res:* Applied climate; air pollution. *Mailing Add:* Dept of Earth Sci East Tex State Univ Commerce TX 73428

MCDANIEL, WILLIAM FRANKLIN, b Washington, DC, Nov 26, 51; m 75. BIOPSYCHOLOGY, NEUROANATOMY. *Educ:* Duke Univ, BS, 73; Appalachian State Univ, MA, 74; Univ Ga, PhD(psychol), 77. *Prof Exp:* ASST PROF PSYCHOL, GA COL, 77- *Concurrent Pos:* Res grants, Fac Res Fund, Ga Col, 77-81, Am Philos Soc, 78-79 & Nat Sci Found, 80-81. *Mem:* Soc Neurosci; Southern Soc Philos & Phychol; Southeastern Psychol Asn. *Res:* Functions of posterior association cortex; aluminum neurotozicity; recovery from brain damage; neocortical mecchanisms of vision. *Mailing Add:* Dept of Psychol Ga Col Milledgeville GA 31061

MCDANIEL, WILLIE L(EE), JR, b Montgomery, Ala, Sept 19, 32. ELECTRICAL ENGINEERING, CONTROL SYSTEMS. *Educ:* Ala Polytech Inst, BEE, 57; Miss State Univ, MSEE, 61; Auburn Univ, PhD(elec eng), 65. *Prof Exp:* Design engr, Bell Tel Labs, Inc, 57-59; asst prof elec eng, Miss State Univ, 59-62; res asst flight dynamics, Boeing Co, 63; instr elec eng, Auburn Univ, 63-65; assoc prof, 65-68, assoc dean eng, 71-78, PROF ELEC ENG, MISS STATE UNIV, 68-, DEAN ENG, 78- *Mem:* Inst Elec & Electronics Engrs; Am Soc Eng Educ. *Res:* Optimization techniques for large scale systems; development of design tool aids using the digital computer in an adaptive mode. *Mailing Add:* Col of Eng Miss State Univ Mississippi State MS 39762

MCDANIELS, DAVID K, b Hoquiam, Wash, May 21, 29; m 53, 66; c 3. NUCLEAR PHYSICS, SOLAR ENERGY. *Educ:* Wash State Univ, BS, 51; Univ Wash, Seattle, MS, 58, PhD(physics), 60. *Prof Exp:* Physicist, Hanford Atomic Prod Oper, Gen Elec Co, 51-54; res instr physics, Univ Wash, Seattle, 60-61; NSF fel, Nuclear Res Ctr, Saclay, France, 62-63; from asst prof to assoc prof, 63-69, PROF PHYSICS, UNIV ORE, 69- *Concurrent Pos:* Vis staff mem, Los Alamos Sci Lab, 70- *Mem:* Int Solar Energy Soc; Am Phys Soc; Am Asn Physics Teachers; Sigma Xi. *Res:* Fast neutron radiative capture; inelastic proton scattering at medium energies; solar radiation; solar energy applications to flat-plate collector systems; giant multipole resonances. *Mailing Add:* Dept of Physics Univ of Ore Eugene OR 97403

MCDAVID, JAMES MICHAEL, b Kingsport, Tenn, Dec 8, 45. MATERIALS SCIENCE, SOLID STATE PHYSICS. *Educ:* Univ Tenn, Knoxville, BSEPhys, 68; Univ Wash, MS, 69, PhD(physics), 75. *Prof Exp:* Process & metall engr, Northwest Div, Davis Walker Corp, 76-77; RES ASSOC MAT SCI, UNIV WASH, 77- *Mem:* Am Phys Soc. *Res:* Auger electron spectroscopy; surface properties of metals and alloys; photoacoustic spectroscopy; optical absorption in highly transparent materials. *Mailing Add:* Dept of Elec Eng FT-10 Univ of Wash Seattle WA 98195

MCDERMED, JOHN DALE, b Alva, Okla, Dec 20, 41; m 65. MEDICINAL CHEMISTRY. *Educ:* Okla State Univ, BA, 63; Univ Tex, Austin, PhD(org chem), 68. *Prof Exp:* NIH fel chem, Ind Univ, 68-69; sr res scientist med chem, 70-79, PRIN SCIENTIST, WELLCOME RES LABS, 79- *Concurrent Pos:* Lectr chem, Eve Col, Univ NC, 74-76. *Mem:* Am Chem Soc; AAAS. *Res:* Neurotransmitters; dopamine receptors, agonists and antagonists; enzyme inhibitors; cardiovascular drugs. *Mailing Add:* Dept of Chem 3030 Cornwallis Rd Research Triangle Park NC 27709

MCDERMOTT, JOHN FRANCIS, JR, b Hartford, Conn, Dec 12, 29; m; c 2. PSYCHIATRY. *Educ:* Cornell Univ, AB, 51; NY Med Col, MD, 55; Am Bd Psychiat, cert psychiat, 62, cert child psychiat, 65. *Prof Exp:* Intern, Henry Ford Hosp, 55-56; resident psychiat, Med Ctr, Univ Mich, 56-58, child psychiatrist, 60-62, from instr to assoc prof, 62-69; PROF PSYCHIAT & CHMN DEPT, SCH MED, UNIV HAWAII, 69- *Concurrent Pos:* Chmn, Comt Cert Child Psychiat, Am Bd Psychiat & Neurol, Inc, 73-78. *Mem:* Fel Am Psychiat Asn; Am Orthopsychiat Asn; Am Col Psychiatrists; Am Acad Child Psychiatrists. *Res:* Child psychiatric practice and training nationally; child custody; assessment of medical and psychiatric competence. *Mailing Add:* Univ of Hawaii Sch of Med 1356 Lusitana St Honolulu HI 96813

MCDERMOTT, JOHN JOSEPH, b Newark, NJ, May 31, 27; m 54; c 2. PARASITOLOGY, MARINE BIOLOGY. *Educ:* Seton Hall, BS, 49; Rutgers Univ, MS, 51, PhD(zool), 54. *Prof Exp:* Asst biol, genetics & parasitol, Rutgers Univ, 51-53, parasitol, Bur Biol Res, 53-54; res assoc oyster invests, Agr Exp Sta, Oyster Res Lab, 54-56, asst res specialist, 56-58; from asst prof to assoc prof, 58-69, chmn dept, 63-73, PROF BIOL, FRANKLIN & MARSHALL COL, 69- *Concurrent Pos:* Vis prof marine sci, Va Inst Marine Sci, 68-74; dir summer course, Bermuda Biol Sta, 77-78. *Mem:* AAAS; Am Soc Parasitol; Ecol Soc Am; Am Soc Zool; Crustacean Soc. *Res:* Larval trematode studies; marine biology and ecology; biology of marine symbiotic relationships; nemertean feeding. *Mailing Add:* Dept of Biol Franklin & Marshall Col Box 3003 Lancaster PA 17604

MCDERMOTT, LILLIAN CHRISTIE, b New York, NY, Feb 9, 31; m 54; c 3. PHYSICS, SCIENCE EDUCATION. *Educ:* Vassar Col, BA, 52; Columbia Univ, MA, 56, PhD(physics), 59. *Prof Exp:* Instr physics, City Univ New York, 61-62; lectr physics, Seattle Univ, 65-69; lectr, 67-73, asst prof, 73-76, assoc prof, 76-80, PROF PHYSICS, UNIV WASH, 80- *Mem:* Sigma Xi; Am Phys Soc; Am Asn Physics Teachers; Nat Sci Teachers Asn. *Res:* Physics education; preparing teachers to teach physics and physical science, investigating conceptual difficulties in physics, developing curriculum for special groups of students. *Mailing Add:* Dept of Physics Univ of Wash Seattle WA 98195

MCDERMOTT, MARK NORDMAN, b Yakima, Wash, Feb 6, 30; m 54; c 3. ATOMIC PHYSICS. *Educ:* Whitman Col, BA, 52; Columbia Univ, MA, 56, PhD(physics), 59. *Prof Exp:* Asst physics, Columbia Univ, 53-59; res assoc, Univ Ill, 59-60; instr, Columbia Univ, 60-62; from asst prof to assoc prof, 62-74, PROF PHYSICS, UNIV WASH, 74- *Mem:* Fel Am Phys Soc. *Res:* Radiofrequency spectroscopy; atomic beams magnetic resonance; optical pumping. *Mailing Add:* Dept of Physics Univ of Wash Seattle WA 98195

MCDERMOTT, RICHARD P, b Weston, WVa, Jan 2, 28; m 54. SPEECH PATHOLOGY, AUDIOLOGY. *Educ:* Univ Mo, BA, 52; Western Mich Univ, BS, 53; Ohio State Univ, MA, 55; Univ Iowa, PhD(speech path, audiol), 62. *Prof Exp:* Instr speech path, Univ Iowa, 58-60; asst prof, St Cloud State Col, 60-62, assoc prof speech path & dir speech & hearing serv, 62-64; asst prof speech path, 64-67, assoc prof, 67-77, PROF SPEECH PATH & AUDIOL, UNIV MINN, MINNEAPOLIS, 77-, ASST DIR SPEECH & HEARING CLIN, 64- *Mem:* Am Speech & Hearing Asn. *Res:* Speech physiology; articulation skills. *Mailing Add:* 481 Laurel Ave W-3 St Paul MN 55102

MCDERMOTT, ROBERT EMMET, b Maywood, Ill, Oct 5, 20; m 43; c 2. FORESTRY. *Educ:* Iowa State Col, BS, 43, MS, 47; Duke Univ, PhD(bot, forestry), 52. *Prof Exp:* Jr forester, Cook County Forest, Ill, 46; instr bot, Iowa State Col, 46-47; forestry, Univ Mo, 48-49; asst bot, Duke Univ, 50-52; from asst prof to assoc prof forestry, Univ Mo, 52-59; prof forestry & head dept forestry & wildlife, Pa State Univ, 59-69, assoc dean grad sch, 66-69, asst dir sch forest resources, 59-65; dean grad sch, Univ Ark, Fayetteville, 69-72; provost, 72-81, ASSOC PROF MGT SCI, PA STATE UNIV, 81-, HEAD DIV PUBLIC AFFAIRS, 81- *Mem:* AAAS; Ecol Soc Am; Soc Am Foresters. *Res:* Forest ecology and physiology; rural land use. *Mailing Add:* Capitol Campus Pa State Univ Middletown PA 17057

MCDERMOTT, WALSH, medicine, deceased

MCDERMOTT, WILLIAM VINCENT, JR, b Salem, Mass, Mar 7, 17; m; c 3. SURGERY. *Educ:* Harvard Univ, AB, 38, MD, 42. *Prof Exp:* Intern surg, Mass Gen Hosp, Boston, 42-43, from asst resident surgeon to resident surgeon, 46-49; instr, 51-54, clin assoc, 54-57, asst clin prof, 57-63, DAVID W & DAVID CHEEVER PROF SURG, HARVARD MED SCH, 63-; dir, Harvard Surg Serv & Sci Dir, Cancer Res Inst, 73-80, CHMN, DEPT SURG, NEW ENG DEACONESS HOSP, 80- *Concurrent Pos:* NIH res fel, 49-50; fel surg, Mass Gen Hosp, 50-51; consult staff & asst surg, Mass Gen Hosp, 51-54, asst surgeon, 54-57, assoc vis, 57-63, vis, 63-; dir, Fifth Surg Serv & Sears Surg Lab, Boston City Hosp, 63-73. *Mem:* Am Surg Asn; Am Acad Arts & Sci; Soc Univ Surg; Am Col Surg; Am Fedn Clin Res. *Res:* Diseases of the liver and portal circulation; endocrine system; gastrointestinal physiology. *Mailing Add:* Harvard Surg Serv New Eng Deaconess Hosp Boston MA 02215

MCDEVIT, WILLIAM FERRIS, b Staten Island, NY, July 28, 20; m 44; c 1. PHYSICAL CHEMISTRY. *Educ:* Haverford Col, AB, 40; Rutgers Univ, MS, 42; Cornell Univ, PhD(chem), 50. *Prof Exp:* Du Pont fel, 50-51; res chemist, Chem Dept, 51-54, res supvr, Nylon Res Div, 54-62, res mgr, Orlon Res Div, 62-64, tech supt lycra, 64-65, tech supt nylon, Tenn, 65-66, dir, Dacron Res Lab, NC, 66-68, res dir, Dacron Tech Div, Del, 68-70, prod mgr, 70-71, mfg dir, Textile Fibers Dept, Orlon-Acetate-Lycra Div, 71-78, EXEC DIR, COMT EDUC AID, E I DU PONT DE NEMOURS & CO INC, 78- *Mem:* Am Chem Soc; Sigma Xi; Am Soc Eng Educ. *Res:* Theory and properties of aqueous solutions; reaction kinetics; electrochemistry; fiber and polymer physics. *Mailing Add:* Comt Educ Aid E I du Pont de Nemours & Co Inc Wilmington DE 19898

MCDEVITT, DANIEL BERNARD, b Pocatello, Idaho, Apr 14, 27; m 52. ENGINEERING, COMPUTER SCIENCE. *Educ:* Univ Idaho, BS, 50. *Hon Degrees:* DSc, Univ Karachi, 76 & Riyadh Univ, 77. *Prof Exp:* Engr, Gen Elec Co, 50-54, systs specialist, 54-56, mgr power, control & commun systs, 56-59; mgr mkt control, commun systs networks, Nelson Elec 59-62; partner, Dan B McDevitt & Assoc, 62-75, EXEC PARTNER, MANHATTAN-McDEVITT-PROGRESS ENG & WALLACE, LTD, 75- *Concurrent Pos:* Pres, Res & Develop Inst US, 63-, Progress Eng, 65-, I-C Comput Corp, 68-69, Saudi-Am Group & Saudi-Am Construct Co, Saudi-Am Concrete Co, Saudi-Am Metal Fabricating & Equip Co, Saudi-Am Transp Co, Saudi-Am Woodworking Co, King Khalid City Develop Co & Saudi-Am Develop Co, 76-; US Agency Int Develop grant, Govt Pakistan, 63-64 & Water & Elec Authority, Iran, 65-66; consult, Ministry Water & Elec, Govt Iran, 64-66; adv, US Small Bus Admin, 65-67; chmn, First Select Acad, Govt & Bus Regional Conf, 66-67; US Econ Develop Admin grant, Off Econ Opportunity Exten Wyo, 67-68; chmn & pres, ICM Comput Corp, 69-; chmn, US Coun Environ, 70-; dir, US Coalition for clean air, 71-; comn mem, King Faisal Air Acad Develop Comn, Kingdom of Saudi Arabia, 74-76. *Honors & Awards:* Citations, US Small Bus Admin & Cong Record, 67; spec commendation, King Faisal Air Acad, 75. *Mem:* AAAS; sr mem Inst Elec & Electronics Engrs; Nat Soc Prof Engrs. *Res:* Highly interactive computer-communications networks for integrated information operating systems and knowledge access automation; control; computer applications; economic dynamic models; logistics. *Mailing Add:* PO Drawer 7220 Tulsa OK 74105

MCDEVITT, DAVID STEPHEN, b Philadelphia, Pa, Nov 15, 40; m 63; c 2. DEVELOPMENTAL BIOLOGY. *Educ:* Villanova Univ, BS, 62; Bryn Mawr Col, MA, 63, PhD(biol), 66. *Prof Exp:* Investr, Biol Div, Oak Ridge Nat Lab, 66-68; asst prof, 68-73, ASSOC PROF ANIMAL BIOL, SCH VET MED, UNIV PA, 73- *Concurrent Pos:* Consult, Biol Div, Oak Ridge Nat Lab, 69-; res fel, Cancer Res Campaign, UK, 74-75. *Mem:* AAAS; Int Soc Develop Biologists; Am Soc Cell Biol; Am Soc Zool; Asn Res Vision & Ophthalmol. *Res:* Lens-specific proteins in lens development and lens regeneration as studied by biochemical and immunological techniques. *Mailing Add:* Dept of Animal Biol Univ of Pa Sch of Vet Med Philadelphia PA 19104

MCDEVITT, HUGH O'NEILL, b Cincinnati, Ohio, 1930. IMMUNOLOGY. *Educ:* Harvard Univ, MD, 55; Am Bd Internal Med, cert med, 68. *Prof Exp:* Intern, Peter Bent Brigham Hosp, Boston, 55-56, sr asst resident med, 61-62; asst resident, Bell, 56-57; res fel, Dept Bact & Immunol, Harvard Univ, 59-61; USPHS spec fel, Nat Inst Med Res, Mill Hill, London, Eng, 62-64; assoc prof med immunol, 69-72, PROF MED IMMUNOL, SCH MED, STANFORD UNIV, 72-, CHIEF DIV IMMUNOL, UNIV HOSP, 70- *Concurrent Pos:* Physician, Stanford Univ Hosp, 66-; consult physician, Vet Admin Hosp, Palo Alto, Calif, 68- *Mem:* Nat Acad Sci; AAAS; Am Fedn Clin Res; Am Soc Clin Invest; Am Asn Immunologists. *Mailing Add:* Dept Med Micros D-345 Fairchild Stanford Univ Hosp Stanford CA 94305

MACDIARMID, ALAN GRAHAM, b Masterton, NZ, Apr 14, 27; m 54; c 4. INORGANIC CHEMISTRY, SOLID STATE CHEMISTRY. *Educ:* Univ NZ, BSc, 48, MSc, 50; Univ Wis, MS, 52, PhD(chem), 53; Cambridge Univ, PhD(chem), 55. *Prof Exp:* Asst lectr chem, St Andrews Univ, 55; from instr to assoc prof, 55-64, PROF CHEM, UNIV PA, 64- *Concurrent Pos:* Sloan fel, Univ Pa, 59-63. *Mem:* Am Chem Soc; Royal Soc Chem. *Res:* Preparation and characterization of organosilicon compounds, derivatives of sulfur nitrides and quasi one-dimensional semiconducting and metallic covalent polymers such as polyacetylene and its derivatives. *Mailing Add:* Dept of Chem Univ of Pa Philadelphia PA 19104

MCDIARMID, DONALD RALPH, b Vancouver, BC, Apr 6, 37; m 71. IONOSPHERIC & MAGNEOSPHERRIC PHYSICS. *Educ:* Univ BC, BASc, 60, MASc, 61, PhD(elec eng), 65. *Prof Exp:* Asst res officer, 65-71, assoc res officer, 71-80, SR RES OFFICER, IONOSPHERIC & MAGNETOSPHERIC PHYSICS, PLANETARY SCI SECT, HERZBERG INST ASTROPHYSICS, NAT RES COUN CAN, 80- *Mem:* Am Geophys Union; Can Asn Physicists; Inst Elec & Electronics Engrs. *Res:* Study of radio aurora; mechanisms and relationships to other auroral and magnetospheric phenomena; theorctical study of geomagnetic pulsaturns. *Mailing Add:* Planetary Sci Sect Nat Res Coun Ottawa ON K1A 0K6 Can

MCDIARMID, IAN BERTRAND, b Carleton Place, Ont, Oct 1, 28; m 51; c 2. SPACE PHYSICS. *Educ:* Queen's Univ, Can, BA, 50, MA, 51; Univ Manchester, PhD(physics), 54. *Prof Exp:* Head cosmic ray sect, 55-69, asst dir div physics, 69-75, asst dir, Herzberg Inst Astrophysics, 75-80, DIR CAN CTR SPACE SCI, NAT RES COUN, CAN, 80- *Concurrent Pos:* Sessional lectr, Univ Ottawa, 56- *Mem:* Royal Soc Can; Am Geophys Union; Can Asn Physicists. *Res:* Cosmic rays; high energy particle physics; space research; rocket borne particle detectors. *Mailing Add:* Herzberg Inst of Astrophysics Nat Res Coun of Can Ottawa ON K1A 0R6 Can

MCDIARMID, ROY WALLACE, b Santa Monica, Calif, Feb 18, 40; m 67. ZOOLOGY, VERTEBRATE ECOLOGY. *Educ:* Univ Southern Calif, AB, 61, MS, 66, PhD(biol), 69. *Prof Exp:* Teaching asst gen biol, Univ Southern Calif, 61-65, teaching assoc, 65-66; instr biol, Univ Chicago, 68-69; asst prof biol, Univ SFla, 69-77, assoc prof, 77-79; RES ZOOLOGIST, NAT MUS NATURAL HIST, US FISH & WILDLIFE SERV, 79- *Concurrent Pos:* Orgn Trop Studies res grant, 64; worker, Los Angeles County Mus Natural Hist, 64-69; coordr advan biol course, Orgn Trop Studies, 71. *Mem:* Am Soc Naturalists; Herpetologists' League (pres, 80-82); Am Soc Ichthyologists & Herpetologists; Asn Trop Biol; Ecol Soc Am. *Res:* Major patterns of evolution in anuran amphibians; systematics of neotropical amphibians and reptiles; biogeography and ecology of neotropical vertebrates; biosystematics of neotropical frogs of families Bufonidae and Centrolenidae. *Mailing Add:* Mus Sect Nat Mus Natural Hist US Fish & Wildlife Serv Washington DC 20560

MACDIARMID, WILLIAM DONALD, b Arcola, Sask, June 22, 26; m 53; c 4. INTERNAL MEDICINE, HUMAN GENETICS. *Educ:* Univ Sask, BA, 47; Univ Toronto, MD, 49; Am Bd Internal Med, dipl, 67; FRCPS(C) & cert, 67 & 77. *Prof Exp:* Instr internal med, Col Med, Univ Utah, 64-66, from asst prof to assoc prof, 66-69; prof med fac med, Univ Man, 69-75; PROF & CHMN MED, FAC MED, MEM UNIV NFLD, 75- *Concurrent Pos:* NIH training grant, Univ Utah, 60-62; Neuromuscular Found fel, Univ London, 62-64; consult, Winnipeg Children's Hosp, 69- & Winnipeg Gen Hosp, 70-; physician-in-chief, St Boniface Gen Hosp; sr consult, Janeway Child Health Ctr, St Clare's Mercy Hosp. *Mem:* AAAS; fel Am Col Physicians; fel Can Col Med Geneticists; Genetics Soc Can; Am Soc Human Genetics. *Mailing Add:* Dept of Med Health Sci Ctr St John's NF A1C 5S7 Can

MCDIFFETT, WAYNE FRANCIS, b Uniontown, Pa, Sept 2, 39; m 65; c 1. ECOLOGY. *Educ:* WVa Univ, AB, 61, MS, 64; Univ Ga, PhD(zool), 70. *Prof Exp:* Instr biol, Frostburg State Col, 63-65; asst prof, 69-74, ASSOC PROF BIOL, BUCKNELL UNIV, 74- *Mem:* Ecol Soc Am; Am Soc Limnol & Oceanog. *Res:* Fresh-water ecology; productivity and energy relationships. *Mailing Add:* Dept of Biol Bucknell Univ Lewisburg PA 17837

MCDIVITT, JAMES FREDERICK, mineral economics, see previous edition

MCDIVITT, MAXINE ESTELLE, b Rosedale, Ind, Aug 16, 12. FOOD SCIENCE, NUTRITION. *Educ:* Univ Ill, BS, 40, MS, 41; Univ Wis, PhD(foods & nutrit), 52. *Prof Exp:* Instr home econ, Univ Mo, 41-44, asst prof, 45-47; instr, Univ Iowa, 47-49; from assoc prof to prof, Univ Wis-Madison, 52-67; prof, 67-77, EMER PROF HOME ECON, UNIV WIS-MILWAUKEE, 77- *Concurrent Pos:* On leave, UN Food & Agr Orgn, India, 64-66; USDA grant, Univ Wis-Milwaukee, 67-77; Danforth Assoc. *Mem:* Am Home Econ Asn; Am Dietetics Asn. *Res:* Bacteriological aspects of food handling procedures; heat resistance of food poisoning organisms; heat transfer in foods; food habits in urban communities; consumer acceptance of dairy products; studies of milk flavor. *Mailing Add:* Sch of Social Welfare-Home Econ Univ of Wis Milwaukee WI 53201

MCDIVITT, ROBERT WILLIAM, b West Sunbury, Pa, Mar 30, 31; m 61; c 2. PATHOLOGY. *Educ:* Harvard Univ, BA, 53; Yale Univ, MD, 56. *Prof Exp:* Attend pathologist, Mem-Sloan Kettering Cancer Ctr, 64-71; assoc prof surg, Med Sch, Cornell Univ, 68-71; PROF PATH, MED SCH, UNIV UTAH, 71- *Concurrent Pos:* Chmn, Southwest Oncol Group, 75-; chmn, DCCR Path Working Group, Nat Cancer Inst, 77-78, DCT Path Working Group, 78 & DCT Path Task Force, 78-; consult, Ctr for Dis Control, Atlanta, 78. *Mem:* Soc Surg Oncol; Int Acad Path; Am Soc Clin Path; Arthur Purdy Stout Soc; Sigma Xi. *Res:* Etiology and epidemiology of human breast cancer. *Mailing Add:* Path Dept Med Ctr Univ Utah Salt Lake City UT 84112

MCDOLE, ROBERT E, b Eugene, Ore, Oct 7, 30; m 65; c 3. SOIL FERTILITY, SOIL GENESIS. *Educ:* Ore State Univ, BS, 52; Univ Idaho, MS, 68, PhD(soils), 69. *Prof Exp:* Soil scientist, Bur Indian Affairs, US Dept Interior, Idaho, Ore & Wash, 52-65; from asst res prof to assoc res prof soils, Aberdeen Br Sta, 69-77, EXTEN SOIL SPECIALIST, DEPT PLANT & SOIL SCI, UNIV IDAHO, 77- *Concurrent Pos:* Vis prof, Wash State Univ, 74-75. *Mem:* Soc Agron; Soil Sci Soc Am; Potato Asn Am. *Res:* Soil surveys of Northwest Indian reservations; study of loess soil materials in Southern Idaho; fertility of potato production. *Mailing Add:* Dept of Plant & Soil Sci Univ of Idaho Moscow ID 83843

MCDONAGH, JAN M, b Wilmington, NC, Nov 9, 42; m 68; c 1. BIOCHEMISTRY, PATHOLOGY. *Educ:* Wake Forest Univ, BS, 64; Univ NC, PhD(biochem), 68. *Prof Exp:* NIH fels, Univ NC, Chapel Hill, 68-69, Med Univ Klinik, Basel, Switz, 69-70 & Karolinska Inst, 70-71; asst prof path, Med Sch, Univ NC, Chapel Hill, 71-76, asst prof biochem, 74-76, assoc prof path & biochem, 76-82; ASSOC PROF PATH, HARVARD MED SCH, BOSTON, MASS, 82- *Concurrent Pos:* Mem coun thrombosis, Am Heart Asn, 72-, estab investr, 77-78. *Mem:* Int Soc Thrombosis & Haemostasis. *Res:* Biochemistry of blood coagulation and fibrinolysis; pathogenesis of thrombosis. *Mailing Add:* Harvard Med Sch Dept Path Beth Isreal Hosp Boston MA 02215

MCDONAGH, RICHARD PATRICK, JR, physiology, experimental pathology, deceased

MACDONALD, ALAN ANGUS, organic chemistry, see previous edition

MCDONALD, ALAN T(AYLOR), b Los Angeles, Calif, Oct 11, 38; m 58; c 4. MECHANICAL ENGINEERING. *Educ:* Purdue Univ, BS, 60, MS, 62, PhD(mech eng), 65. *Prof Exp:* Asst prof mech eng, Univ Calif, Davis, 64-67; assoc prof, 67-74, PROF MECH ENG, SCH MECH ENG, PURDUE UNIV, WEST LAFAYETTE, 74- *Mem:* Am Soc Mech Engrs; Soc Automotive Engrs; Am Inst Aeronaut & Astronaut; Am Soc Eng Educ. *Res:* Fluid mechanics. *Mailing Add:* Sch of Mech Eng Purdue Univ West Lafayette IN 47907

MACDONALD, ALASTAIR DAVID, botany, morphology, see previous edition

MACDONALD, ALEX BRUCE, immunology, biochemistry, see previous edition

MACDONALD, ALEXANDER, JR, b Quincy, Mass, Oct 29, 36; m 62; c 1. ANALYTICAL CHEMISTRY. *Educ:* Northeastern Univ, BS, 59; Univ Iowa, MS & PhD(chem), 63. *Prof Exp:* Asst prof chem, Mich State Univ, 65-67; sr chemist, 67-71, res fel, 71-74, res group chief, 74-75, ASST DIR ANIMAL HEALTH RES, HOFFMAN-LA ROCHE, INC, 76- *Mem:* Am Chem Soc. *Res:* Chromatography; aerosols; automated analysis; residue analysis; veterinary drug metabolism. *Mailing Add:* Hoffman-La Roche Inc Nutley NJ 07110

MACDONALD, ALEXANDER DANIEL, b Sydney, NS, Apr 8, 23; m 46; c 4. PHYSICS. *Educ:* Dalhousie Univ, BSc, 45, MSc, 47; Mass Inst Technol, PhD(physics), 49. *Prof Exp:* Res assoc physics, Mass Inst Technol, 48-49; from asst prof to prof, Dalhousie Univ, 49-60; sr specialist, Microwave Physics Lab, Gen Tel & Electronics Lab, Inc, 60-62; prof appl math & head div, Dalhousie Univ, 62-65; sr mem res labs, Lockheed Missiles & Space Co, 65-73, dir, Electronic & Commun Sci Lab, Palo Alto Labs, 73-78, chief scientist, Space Systs Div, 78-80; PVT CONSULT, 81- *Concurrent Pos:* Res scientist, Defence Res Bd, Can, 49-52; mem nat comn electronics, Int Union Radio Sci, 52-; specialist, Sylvania Elec Prod Co, 56-57. *Mem:* Fel Am Phys Soc. *Res:* Physical electronics; ultrasonics; theoretical physics; computer science. *Mailing Add:* 3056 Greer Rd Palo Alto CA 94303

MCDONALD, ALISON DUNSTAN, b St Albans, Eng, Aug 5, 17; m 42; c 4. EPIDEMIOLOGY. *Educ:* Univ London, MB & BS, 41, DCH, 47, DPH & MD, 50. *Prof Exp:* Lectr prev & social med, London Sch Hyg & Trop Med & Royal Free Hosp, 52-56; res assoc epidemiol, Pediat Res Unit, Guy's Hosp, London, Eng, 58-59, sr lectr, 60-64; from assoc prof to prof epidemiol, 64-78, PROF EPIDEMIOL & HEALTH, MCGILL UNIV, 81- *Concurrent Pos:* Prof & head, Dept Epidemiol, St Mary's Hosp Med Sch, London, Eng, 78-81; prog dir women at work, Inst Res, Health & Occup Safety, Montreal, 81- *Mem:* Int Epidemiol Asn; Soc Social Med. *Res:* Epidemiology of developmental disorders, particularly mental deficiency, congenital malformation, cerebral palsy and very low birth weight; health care research; health effects of asbestos, mesothelioma and mineral type of asbestos. *Mailing Add:* Inst Res Health & Occup Safety 505 Ouest de Maisonnewve 1111 Montreal PQ H3A 3C2 Can

MCDONALD, ALLAN W, b Oakland, Calif, Feb 23, 19; m 50; c 4. PHYSICS. *Educ:* Loyola Univ, BS, 42; Georgetown Univ, MS, 47; La State Univ, PhD(physics), 52. *Prof Exp:* Assoc prof physics, Loyola Univ, 52-56; res physicist, Aeronaut Div, Robertshaw-Fulton Controls Co, 56-57; asst proj mgr missile eval, Automation Electronics, Inc, 57-58; sr res engr, Gen Dynamic/Convair, 58-59 & Tasker Instrument Corp, 59-62; prin scientist, Space & Info Systs Div, NAm Rockwell Corp, 62-70, mem tech staff space navig systs radiation effects, 72-75, MEM TECH STAFF SHUTTLE TRAJECTORY SIMULATION, SPACE TRANSP SYSTS GROUP, ROCKWELL INT, 75- *Res:* Construction simulation models in fields of physics, mathematics and management systems; mechanics; electric and magnetic fields. *Mailing Add:* Space Transp Systs Group FB 95 Rockwell Int 2214 Lakewood Blvd Downey CA 90241

MCDONALD, ARTHUR BRUCE, b Sydney, NS, Aug 29, 43; m 66; c 4. PHYSICS. *Educ:* Dalhousie Univ, BSc, 64, MSc, 65; Calif Inst Technol, PhD(physics), 70. *Prof Exp:* Nat Res Coun Can & Rutherford Mem fels, 70-71, RES PHYSICIST, CHALK RIVER NUCLEAR LABS, ATOMIC ENERGY CAN, LTD, 71- *Concurrent Pos:* Vis scientist, Univ Wash, 77 & Los Alamos Nat Lab, 81. *Mem:* Am Phys Soc; Can Asn Physicists. *Res:* Nuclear physics, especially investigations of structure of nuclei using particle accelerators; parity violation measurements. *Mailing Add:* Chalk River Nuclear Labs Nuclear Physics Br Atomic Energy Can Chalk River ON K0J 1J0 Can

MCDONALD, BARBARA BROWN, b Ray, Ariz, Feb 14, 24; m 52. CYTOLOGY. *Educ:* Simmons Col, BS, 48; Columbia Univ, MA, 55, PhD, 57. *Prof Exp:* From instr to assoc prof, 56-73, PROF BIOL, DICKINSON COL, 73- *Mem:* AAAS; Am Soc Cell Biol; Histochem Soc; Genetics Soc Am; Soc Protozool. *Res:* Cytochemistry; protozoology; nucleic acids in Tetrahymena. *Mailing Add:* Dept of Biol Dickinson Col Carlisle PA 17013

MCDONALD, BERNARD ROBERT, b Kansas City, Kans, Nov 17, 40; m 63; c 2. MATHEMATICS. *Educ:* Park Col, BA, 62; Kans State Univ, MA, 64; Mich State Univ, PhD(math), 68. *Prof Exp:* From asst prof to assoc prof, 68-78, PROF MATH, UNIV OKLA, 78-, CHMN DEPT, 81- *Concurrent Pos:* Vis prof, Pa State Univ, 74-75, Queen's Univ, 79 & Univ Calif, Santa Barbara, 80-81. *Mem:* Am Math Soc; Math Asn Am. *Res:* Algebra; matrix theory; commutative rings; finite rings; combinatorial theory. *Mailing Add:* Dept Math Univ Okla Norman OK 73019

MACDONALD, BRUCE ALAN, b Lakewood, Ohio, June 20, 36; m 65. PHYSICAL METALLURGY. *Educ:* Carnegie Inst Technol, BS, 58; Mass Inst Technol, MS, 61, PhD(metall), 64. *Prof Exp:* Res scientist, Ingersoll-Rand Co, 64-69; METALLURGIST, OFF NAVAL RES, 69- *Mem:* Am Soc Metals; Am Inst Mining, Metall & Petrol Engrs. *Res:* X-ray measurement of residual stresses; role of residual stresses on fatigue life of steel; electron fractography and failure analysis; thermomechanical working of steel and its effect on properties. *Mailing Add:* 11321 French Horn Lane Reston VA 22091

MCDONALD, BRUCE EUGENE, b Mannville, Alta, Apr 30, 33; m 62; c 5. NUTRITION. *Educ:* Univ Alta, BSc, 58, MSc, 60; Univ Wis, PhD(biochem, poultry nutrit), 63. *Prof Exp:* Res assoc, Univ Ill, 63-64; asst prof animal sci, Macdonald Col, McGill Univ, 64-68; from assoc prof to prof nutrit, 68-77, DEAN, FAC HUMAN ECOL, UNIV MAN, 77- *Concurrent Pos:* Vis prof, Inst Nutrit, Univ Uppsala, Sweden, 76-77. *Mem:* Nutrit Soc Can; Am Inst Nutrit; Can Inst Food Sci & Technol; Am Oil Chemists Soc; Can Dietetic Asn. *Res:* Effect of diet on lipid metabolism in the human; plant proteins for human consumption. *Mailing Add:* Fac of Home Econ Univ of Man Winnipeg MB R3T 2N2 Can

MCDONALD, BRUCE JERALD, mathematical statistics, see previous edition

MACDONALD, BURNS, experimental physics, medical imaging, see previous edition

MACDONALD, CAROLYN TROTT, b Iowa City, Iowa, June 23, 41; c 3. APPLIED MATHEMATICS, MATHEMATICS EDUCATION. *Educ:* Univ Minn, BS, 61; Univ Ore, MA, 63 & 65; Brown Univ, PhD(chem), 68. *Prof Exp:* Asst prof chem, Moorhead State Col, 68-71; asst prof phys sci & chmn dept, Univ Mo-Kansas City, 72-76; assoc prof math & physics & chairperson dept, Baptist Col, Charleston, SC, 76-79; SDIP COORDR, ROCKHURST COL, KANSAS CITY, MO, 79- *Concurrent Pos:* Proj Dir, NSF grants, 74-75, 78-79 & 81. *Mem:* AAAS; Am Math Soc; Am Asn Physics Teachers; Math Asn Am. *Res:* Mathematical modeling. *Mailing Add:* 5412 Locust St Kansas City MO 64110

MCDONALD, CHARLES CAMERON, b Wyoming, Ont, Aug 5, 26; m 49; c 4. RESEARCH ADMINISTRATION. *Educ:* Univ Western Ontario, BSc, 49, MSc, 50; Ill Inst Technol, PhD(chem), 54. *Prof Exp:* Res fel chem, Ill Inst Technol, 54-55; res chemist, 55-65, res supvr, Cent Res Dept, 65-78, RES MGR, CENT RES & DEVELOP DEPT, E I DU PONT DE NEMOURS & CO, INC, 65- *Res:* Gas phase reaction kinetics; photochemistry; magnetic resonance; biophysics; structure of proteins; plant science; single cell protein; fermentation microbiology, molecular genetics. *Mailing Add:* Cent Res Dept E I du Pont de Nemours & Co Wilmington DE 19898

MCDONALD, CHARLES JOSEPH, b Cambridge, Mass, Feb 20, 41. POLYMER REACTIONS. *Educ:* Boston Col, BS, 63; Holy Cross Col, MS, 64; Clarkson Col Technol, PhD(polymer chem), 70. *Prof Exp:* Res chemist, Immont Corp, 64-66; fel, Uppsala Univ, Sweden, 70-73; RES LEADER, DOW CHEM CORP, 73- *Mem:* Am Chem Soc; Sigma Xi; AAAS. *Res:* Polymer solution properties; emulsion technology. *Mailing Add:* 1604 Bldg Designed Latenes & Resins Dow Chem Corp Midland MI 48640

MCDONALD, CLARENCE EUGENE, b McPherson, Kans, Oct 10, 1926; m 55; c 3. CEREAL CHEMISTRY. *Educ:* McPherson Col, AB, 50; Kans State Univ, MS, 53; Purdue Univ, PhD(biochem), 57. *Prof Exp:* Asst, Kans State Univ, 52-53; asst, Purdue Univ, 53-56, res fel, 57; chemist, Western Utilization Res & Develop Div, Agr Res Serv, USDA, 57-64; assoc prof, 64-77, PROF CEREAL CHEM & TECHNOL, NDAK STATE UNIV, 77- *Mem:* Am Chem Soc; Am Asn Cereal Chem; Inst Food Technol. *Res:* Isolation and characterization of wheat proteins and enzymes; nutrition of cereal proteins. *Mailing Add:* Dept of Cereal Chem & Technol N Dak State Univ Fargo ND 58105

MCDONALD, CLAUDIE KENNETH, engineering mechanics, structural engineering, see previous edition

MCDONALD, DANIEL JAMES, b New York, NY, Jan 27, 25; m 52. GENETICS. *Educ:* Siena Col, BS, 50; Columbia Univ, MA, 52, PhD(zool), 55. *Prof Exp:* Lectr zool, Columbia Univ, 53-55, instr, 55-56; from asst prof to assoc prof biol, 56-70, PROF BIOL, DICKINSON COL, 70- *Concurrent Pos:* Instr, Long Island Univ, 55-56. *Mem:* AAAS; Am Soc Nat; Ecol Soc Am; Genetics Soc Am; Soc Study Evolution. *Res:* Population genetics; ecology of the flour beetles Tribolium confusum and Tribolium castaneum. *Mailing Add:* Dept of Biol Dickinson Col Carlisle PA 17013

MACDONALD, DAVID HOWARD, b Cleveland, Ohio, Sept 23, 34; m 56; c 3. PLANT NEMATOLOGY, POMOLOGY. *Educ:* Purdue Univ, BS, 56; Cornell Univ, MS, 62, PhD(pomol), 66. *Prof Exp:* From asst prof to assoc prof plant nematol, 66-74, assoc prof plant path, 74-77, PROF PLANT PATH, UNIV MINN, ST PAUL, 77- *Mem:* Am Phytopath Soc; Soc Nematol. *Res:* Chemical and physical factors affecting rate of build-up of plant parasitic nematodes. *Mailing Add:* Dept of Plant Path Univ of Minn St Paul MN 55101

MACDONALD, DAVID J, b San Diego, Calif, May 14, 32; m 62; c 2. PHYSICAL CHEMISTRY, INORGANIC CHEMISTRY. *Educ:* Calif Inst Technol, BS, 53, MS, 54; Univ Calif, Los Angeles, PhD(phys chem), 60. *Prof Exp:* Chem engr, Apache Powder Co, 54-55; res asst, Univ Calif, Los Angeles, 60; asst prof chem, Univ Nev, Reno, 63-68; RES CHEMIST, RENO RES CTR, US BUR MINES, 68- *Mem:* AAAS; Am Chem Soc; Am Inst Mining, Metall & Petrol Engrs. *Res:* Kinetics of substitution reactions in coordination compounds; extractive metallurgy; liquid-liquid extraction. *Mailing Add:* Reno Metall Res Ctr US Bur Mines 1605 Evans Ave Reno NV 89520

MCDONALD, DAVID WILLIAM, b Shreveport, La, Aug 4, 23; m 48; c 4. ORGANIC CHEMISTRY. *Educ:* Southwestern La Univ, BS, 43; Univ Tex, PhD(chem), 51. *Prof Exp:* Jr res chemist, Humble Oil Co, 46-47; res chemist, Monsanto Chem Co, 51-54, asst res group leader, 54-56, res group leader, 56-59, res sect leader, 59-64, mgr polyolefins res, Monsanto Co, Tex, 64-67, prod adminr polyolefins, Mo, 67-69, dir res & develop, Hydrocarbons & Polymers Div, 69-71, dir plastics res, 71-74, dir technol, Polymers & Petrochem Co, 74-78, dir technol, 78-80, DIR TECH PLANS CORP RES & DEVELOP STAFF, MONSANTO PLASTICS & RESINS CO, 80- *Mem:* Am Chem Soc; Soc Plastics Engrs; AAAS; Am Inst Chemists. *Res:* Petrochemicals; monomers; polymer synthesis, properties and applications; polymer combustion properties; safe uses of plastics. *Mailing Add:* Monsanto Plastics & Resins Co 800 N Lindberg Blvd St Louis MO 63166

MACDONALD, DIGBY DONALD, physical chemistry, electrochemistry, see previous edition

MCDONALD, DONALD, b Montgomery, Ala, Oct 16, 30; m 60; c 3. CIVIL ENGINEERING, STRUCTURAL MECHANICS. *Educ:* Auburn Univ, BCE, 52; Univ Ill, MS, 57, PhD(civil eng), 59. *Prof Exp:* Sr res engr, Lockheed Missiles & Space Co, 59-61, res specialist, 61-62; from asst prof to assoc prof civil eng, NC State Univ, 62-67; mgr struct & mech dept, Lockheed Missiles & Space Co, 67-73; assoc head, Civil Eng Dept, 74-79, PROF CIVIL ENG, TEX A&M UNIV, 73-, HEAD, CIVIL ENG DEPT, 79- *Mem:* Am Soc Civil Engrs; Am Inst Aeronaut & Astronaut; Am Soc Eng Educ; Nat Soc Prof Engrs. *Res:* Structural vibrations; numerical analysis. *Mailing Add:* Dept of Civil Eng Tex A&M Univ College Station TX 77843

MCDONALD, DONALD BURT, b Salt Lake City, Utah, Mar 5, 32; m 77. LIMNOLOGY, TOXICOLOGY. *Educ:* Univ Utah, BS, 54, MS, 56, PhD(limnol), 62. *Prof Exp:* Proj leader fisheries, Utah Fish & Game Dept, 58-60; instr biol, Carbon Col, 60-62; PROF ENG, UNIV IOWA, 62- *Concurrent Pos:* Consult, Iowa Elec Co & Commonwealth Edison Co, 71-; dir, D B McDonald Res, Inc, 73- *Mem:* Am Waterworks Asn; Water Pollution Control Fedn. *Res:* Thermal pollution; environmental assessment; environmental toxicology. *Mailing Add:* Dept of Environ Eng Univ of Iowa Iowa City IA 52242

MCDONALD, DONALD C, b Norwood, Ohio, Dec 25, 19; c 2. ENGINEERING. *Educ:* Mass Inst Technol, SB, 41, SM, 42. *Prof Exp:* Res asst, Servo Lab, Mass Inst Technol, 42-45; proj engr, Doelcam Corp, Mass, 46-47; div supvr, Controls & Instrumentation Div, Willow Run Res Ctr, Univ Mich, 48-49; asst dir, Res Labs Div, Cook Elec Co, Ill, 50-56; dir eng, Friez Instrument Div, Bendix Aviation Corp, Md, 56-57; vpres in charge eng, Cook Elec Co, 58-59 & Sola Elec Co, 60-64; dir eng, Int Register Co, 65-67; vpres eng, Electronics Corp Am, 67-70; VPRES ENG, O S WALKER CO, INC, 70- *Res:* Electronics; electromechanical components; subsystems and systems in the instrumentation and control fields; magnetics. *Mailing Add:* O S Walker Co Inc Rockdale Ave Worcester MA 01606

MACDONALD, DONALD LAURIE, b Toronto, Ont , Nov 16, 22; nat US; m 47; c 3. BIOCHEMISTRY. *Educ:* Univ Toronto, BA, 44, MA, 46, PhD(chem), 48. *Prof Exp:* Asst, Univ Calif, 48-50, instr, 50-52, asst prof biochem, 52-57; vis scientist, Nat Inst Arthritis & Metab Dis, 57-60, chemist, 60-61; USPHS fel, Heidelberg, 61-62; prof biochem, 62-67, PROF BIOCHEM & BIOPHYS, ORE STATE UNIV, 67- *Concurrent Pos:* USPHS career develop award, 62-67; fel, Harvard Med Sch, 70-71; vis investr, Fred

Hutchinson Cancer Res Ctr, Univ Wash, Seattle, 78-79. *Mem:* Am Chem Soc; Am Soc Biol Chem. *Res:* Degradation of monosaccharides; sugar phosphates; glycoproteins. *Mailing Add:* Dept of Biochem & Biphysics Ore State Univ Corvallis OR 97331

MACDONALD, DONALD MACKENZIE, b Newark, NJ, July 26, 28; Can citizen; m 60; c 2. CELLULOSE CHEMISTRY. *Educ:* Mt Allison Univ, BSc, 49; Univ NB, Fredericton, MSc, 51, PhD(org chem), 53. *Prof Exp:* Nat Res Coun Can fel, Nat Res Coun Labs, 53-54; defense sci serv officer org & polymer chem, Defense Res Bd Can, 54-60; res assoc cellulose chem, Can Int Paper Res Ltd, 60-69; RES CHEMIST, INT PAPER CO, 69- *Mem:* Am Chem Soc. *Res:* Chemistry of viscose process and cellulose derivatives. *Mailing Add:* Corporate Res Ctr Int Paper Co Box 797 Tuxedo Park NY 10987

MACDONALD, DOUGLAS GORDON, b Dryden, Ont, May 13, 39; m 64; c 3. CHEMICAL ENGINEERING, BIOCHEMICAL ENGINEERING. *Educ:* Queen's Univ, Ont, BSc, 62, MSc, 65, PhD(chem eng), 68. *Prof Exp:* ASSOC PROF CHEM ENG, UNIV SASK, 68- *Mem:* Chem Inst Can; Asn Prof Eng Sask. *Res:* Removal of color from pulp mill effluents; bioconversion of cellulosic materials to protein; acid hydrolysis of cellulose materials. *Mailing Add:* Dept of Chem & Chem Eng Univ of Sask Saskatoon SK S7H 0W0 Can

MACDONALD, DUNCAN ROSS, b Hamilton, Ont, Oct 15, 28; m 59; c 2. FOREST ENTOMOLOGY. *Educ:* Univ Toronto, BScF, 52; Univ Mich, MF, 57. *Prof Exp:* Res off forest entom, Forest Res Lab, Can Dept Forestry, NB, 52-68, head forest entom sect, BC, 68- 69, prog mgr forest protection res, Pac Forest Res Ctr, Dept Environ, 69-77, dept dir, 73-77, DIR FOREST PROTECTION BR, CAN FORESTRY SERV, 77- *Mem:* Can Inst Forestry; Can Entom Soc. *Res:* Aerial spraying against spruce budworm; effects of pesticides on population dynamics of the budworm, associated species and the forest. *Mailing Add:* 3-162 Lebrun Vanier Ottawa ON K1L 5C9 Can

MACDONALD, ETTA MAE, microbiology, see previous edition

MACDONALD, EVE LAPEYROUSE, b Baton Rouge, La, Jan 2, 29; m 50; c 1. DEVELOPMENTAL BIOLOGY, CELL BIOLOGY. *Educ:* Wellesley Col, AB, 50; Bryn Mawr Col, MA, 65, PhD(develop biol), 67. *Prof Exp:* Teaching asst, Bryn Mawr Col, 64-66; from asst prof to assoc prof biol, Wilson Col, 67-76, dir inst electron micros, 75-76; res scientist, Burroughs Wellcome Co, 76-80; MEM STAFF, BRENNAN ASSOCS, 80- *Concurrent Pos:* NSF fel, 66; co-instr develop biol, Marine Biol Lab, Woods Hole, Mass, 76; prog coordr, Marine Lab, Electron Microscope Inst, Duke Univ, 76- *Mem:* AAAS; Am Soc Zool; Sigma Xi; Soc Develop Biol; Electron Microscope Soc Am. *Res:* Development of the amphibian eye at different temperatures; cellular differentiation in Rana pipiens and Xenopus laevis; ultrastructure of differentiating cells; polymerization of microtubules. *Mailing Add:* Brennan Assocs Suite 300 4101 McEwen Rd Dallas TX 75234

MCDONALD, FRANCIS RAYMOND, b Phila, Pa, Sept 28, 24; m 55; c 1. SPECTROSCOPY, ORGANIC CHEMISTRY. *Educ:* Phila Col Textiles & Sci, BS, 54. *Prof Exp:* Asst chief chemist, Niagara Falls Div, Int Minerals & Chem Corp, NY, 55-57; chemist, 57-61, res chemist, 61-75, proj leader, Laramie energy res ctr, US Energy Res & Develop Admin, 75-77, SECT SUPVR, GEN ANAL SECT, DIV RES SUPPORT, US DEPT ENERGY, LARAMIE ENERGY TECHNOL CTR, 77- *Mem:* Soc Appl Spectros; Coblentz Soc. *Res:* Molecular structure of petrochemical compounds found in oil shale and shale oil using nuclear magnetic resonance, infrared and ultraviolet spectroscopy; mass spectroscopy, environmental monitoring; air pollution; stack and process monitoring of in situ retorting of oil shale, tar sands and coal gasification. *Mailing Add:* Laramie Energy Tech Ctr PO Box 3395 Laramie WY 82071

MCDONALD, FRANK ALAN, b Dallas, Tex, Jan 11, 37; m 64; c 2. THEORETICAL PHYSICS, ACOUSTICS. *Educ:* Southern Methodist Univ, BS & BA, 58; Yale Univ, MS, 59, PhD(physics), 65. *Prof Exp:* Asst prof physics, Tex A&M Univ, 64-69; assoc prof, 69-81, PROF, SOUTHERN METHODIST UNIV, 81- *Mem:* Am Phys Soc; Am Asn Physics Teachers; Sigma Xi. *Res:* Photo acoustic spectroscopy; photoacoustics in condensed matter. *Mailing Add:* Dept of Physics Southern Methodist Univ Dallas TX 75275

MCDONALD, FRANK BETHUNE, b Columbus, Ga, May 28, 25; m 51; c 3. PHYSICS. *Educ:* Duke Univ, BS, 48; Univ Minn, MS, 51, PhD, 55. *Prof Exp:* Asst physics, Duke Univ, 47-48; asst, Univ Minn, 48-51; asst prof, Univ Iowa, 53-59; head fields & particles br, 59-70, CHIEF LAB HIGH ENERGY ASTROPHYS, 70-, PROJ SCIENTIST, EXPLORER SATELLITES & HIGH ENERGY ASTRON OBSERV, NASA GODDARD SPACE FLIGHT CTR, 64- *Concurrent Pos:* Prof, Univ Med, 64- *Mem:* Am Phys Soc; Am Geophys Union. *Res:* Study of primary cosmic radiation at high altitudes by means of rockets, balloons and satellites. *Mailing Add:* Code 660 Lab High Energy Astrophys NASA Goddard Space Flight Ctr Greenbelt MD 20771

MCDONALD, GEORGE GORDON, b Chicago, Ill, Feb 20, 44. BIOCHEMISTRY, BIOPHYSICS. *Educ:* Loyola Univ Chicago, BS, 66; Johns Hopkins Univ, PhD(biochem), 70. *Prof Exp:* Fel biochem, 70-74, asst prof, 74-80, RES ASSOC PROF, DEPT BIOCHEM & BIOPHYSICS, UNIV PA, 80- *Concurrent Pos:* Career investr fel, Am Heart Asn, 71-73; dir mid Atlantic Nuclear Magnetic Resonance Facil, 73- *Mem:* AAAS; Am Chem Soc; Am Soc Biol Chemists; Acad Sci. *Res:* Relationship between the structure and function of macromolecules; nuclear magnetic resonance. *Mailing Add:* Dept Biochem & Biophysics Univ Pa Philadelphia PA 19104

MCDONALD, GERAL IRVING, b Wallowa, Ore, Dec 31, 35; m 62; c 3. PLANT PATHOLOGY. *Educ:* Wash State Univ, BS, 63, PhD(plant path), 69. *Prof Exp:* Res plant geneticist, 66-68, RES PLANT PATHOLOGIST, INTERMT FOREST & RANGE EXP STA, US FOREST SERV, 68- *Concurrent Pos:* Affiliate prof, Univ Idaho, 68- *Mem:* Am Phytopath Soc. *Res:* Genetics, computer simulation and evolution of host-pest interaction in forest trees. *Mailing Add:* Intermt Forest & Range Exp Sta Forestry Sci Lab US Forest Serv Moscow ID 83843

MACDONALD, GORDON J, b Staten Island, NY, May 18, 34; m 56; c 2. PHYSIOLOGY, ANATOMY. *Educ:* Rutgers Univ, BS, 55, MS, 58, PhD, 61. *Prof Exp:* Res asst dairy sci, Rutgers Univ, 57-58; trainee endocrinol, Univ Wis, 61-63; res fel physiol, Sch Dent Med, Harvard Univ, 63-64, res asst, 64-68; res assoc anat, New Eng Regional Primate Res Ctr, Harvard Med Sch, 68-, asst prof, Lab Human Reproduction & Reproductive Biol, 69-73; assoc prof, 73-79, PROF ANAT, RUTGERS MED SCH, UNIV MED & DENT NJ, 79- *Mem:* Am Soc Zool; Endocrine Soc; Soc Study Reproduction; NY Acad Sci; Int Soc Res Reprod. *Res:* Role of pituitary gonadotropins in ovarian function; hormonal control of mammary gland growth and lactation; endocrinology reproduction. *Mailing Add:* Dept of Anat Rutgers Med Sch-CMDNJ Piscataway NJ 08854

MACDONALD, GORDON JAMES FRASER, b Mexico City, July 30, 29; US citizen. MATHEMATICAL STATISTICS, THEORETICAL PHYSICS. *Educ:* Harvard Univ, AB, 50, AM, 52, PhD(geophysics), 54. *Prof Exp:* From vpres to exec vpres, Inst Defense Anal, 66-68; prof physics & geophysics, Univ Calif, Santa Barbara, 68-70; mem, Comn Environ Qual, Exec Off Pres, Washington, DC, 70-72; Henry R Lyce Third Century prof & dir, Environ Studies, Dartmouth Col, 72-79; CHIEF SCIENTIST, MITRE CORP, 79- *Concurrent Pos:* Mem, Bd Trustees, Inst Defense Anal, 66-70 & Mass Inst Tech Res Estab, 68-70, 72-77 & Exec Comt, 72-77; vchancellor, Res & Grad Affairs, Univ Calif, Santa Barbara, 68-70; mem, Bd Dir, Inst Congress, 74-78, Environ Law Inst, 75- & Adv Bd, Gas Res Inst, 76-79; distinguished vis scholar, MITRE Corp, 77-79; adj prof, Environ Studies, Darmouth Col, 79- *Honors & Awards:* James B Macelwane Award, Am Geophys Union, 65. *Mem:* Nat Acad Sci; Am Acad Arts & Sci; Am Philos Soc; fel Am Geophys Union; assoc Royal Astron Soc. *Res:* Earth's interior to the upper atmosphere. *Mailing Add:* 1820 Dolley Madison Blvd McLean VA 22102

MCDONALD, H(ENRY) S(TANTON), b Pa, Oct 28, 27; m 54; c 2. ELECTRICAL ENGINEERING. *Educ:* Cath Univ, BEE, 50; Johns Hopkins Univ, MS, 53, DE, 55. *Prof Exp:* Instr elec eng, Johns Hopkins Univ, 53-55, res staff asst, 54-55; mem tech staff, 55-60, head signal processing res dept, 60-67, asst dir commun principles res ctr, 67-72, asst dir, Electronic & Comput Systs Res Lab, 72-76, CONSULT, SYSTS ARCHIT RES, BELL TEL LABS, 76- *Mem:* Fel Inst Elec & Electronics Engrs; Asn Comput Mach; Sigma Xi; AAAS. *Res:* Perception and encoding of visual and acoustic signals; communication theory; computer design and applications; computer graphics. *Mailing Add:* Rm 4D-501 Bell Tel Labs Crawfords Corner Rd Holmdel NJ 07733

MACDONALD, HAROLD CARLETON, b Englishtown, NS, Sept 18, 30; m 55; c 5. GEOLOGY. *Educ:* State Univ NY, Binghamton, BA, 60; Univ Kans, MS, 62, PhD(geol), 69. *Prof Exp:* Explor geologist, Sinclair Oil & Gas Co, 62-65; res assoc geol, Ctr Res, Univ Kans, 69-70; asst prof, Ga Southern Col, 70-71; assoc prof geol, Univ Ark, Fayetteville, 71-73; ASSOC DIR, ARK WATER RESOURCES RES CTR, 73-; PROF GEOL, UNIV ARK, FAYETTEVILLE, 76- *Mem:* Geol Soc Am; Am Asn Petrol Geologists; Sigma Xi; Am Soc Photogram; Am Geophys Union. *Res:* Geoscience evaluation of side-looking airborne imaging radars; geological remote sensing. *Mailing Add:* Dept of Geol Univ of Ark Fayetteville AR 72701

MCDONALD, HARRY SAWYER, b New Orleans, La, Sept 24, 30; m 56; c 2. COMPARATIVE PHYSIOLOGY, HERPETOLOGY. *Educ:* Loyola Univ, La, BS, 54, Univ Notre Dame, PhD(zool), 58. *Prof Exp:* Nat Heart Inst fel zool, Univ Calif, Los Angeles, 58-59, cardiovasc trainee, 59-60; from asst prof to assoc prof biol, St John's Univ, NY, 60-65; from asst prof to assoc prof, 65-68, PROF BIOL, STEPHEN F AUSTIN STATE UNIV, 68- *Mem:* Am Soc Zool; Am Soc Ichthyol & Herpet; Soc Study Amphibians & Reptiles. *Res:* Reptile electrocardiography; breathing in snakes; thermal acclimation; snake anatomy and organ topography. *Mailing Add:* Dept Biol Stephen F Austin State Univ Nacogdoches TX 75962

MCDONALD, HECTOR O, b Casper, Wyo, Sept 4, 30; m 52; c 2. PHYSICAL INORGANIC CHEMISTRY. *Educ:* Cent Methodist Col, AB, 52; Ala Polytech Inst, MS, 54; Univ Ark, PhD(chem), 60. *Prof Exp:* Control chemist, Southern Cotton Oil Co, Ill, 54-55; res asst chem, Univ Ark, 55-59; assoc prof, West Tex State Univ, 59-63; ASSOC PROF CHEM, UNIV MO-ROLLA, 63- *Concurrent Pos:* Res chemist, US Bureau Mines, 72- *Mem:* Am Chem Soc; Royal Soc Chem. *Res:* Chemistry of inorganic complexes; chemical kinetics in aqueous media, non-aqueous solvent systems and mass spectrometry. *Mailing Add:* Dept of Chem Univ of Mo Rolla MO 65401

MACDONALD, HENRY C, b Long Beach, Calif, July 2, 28; m 55; c 3. ENGINEERING. *Educ:* Univ Calif, AB, 52. *Prof Exp:* Proj engr, 60-69, leader, Physics Systs Div, 63-69, dep dept head, 69-72, head, Dept Elec Eng, 72-74, ASSOC DIR ENG, LAWRENCE LIVERMORE NAT LAB, 74- *Mem:* Inst Elec & Electronics Engrs. *Res:* Nuclear engineering. *Mailing Add:* 201 Midland Way Danville CA 94526

MACDONALD, HUBERT C, JR, b Detroit, Mich, Aug 3, 41; m 67; c 4. ANALYTICAL CHEMISTRY, ENVIRONMENTAL SCIENCES. *Educ:* Wheeling Col, BS, 63; Univ Mich, MS, 65, PhD(chem), 69. *Prof Exp:* Res scientist, Koppers Co, Inc, 69-78; dir, Senate Environ Testing Lab, Inc, 78-82; SR ENGR & TECH DIR, INDUST SERV DIV, WESTINGHOUSE ELEC CORP, 82- *Concurrent Pos:* Consult water & waste water industs, 78-82. *Mem:* Am Chem Soc; Spectros Soc. *Res:* Electrochemistry; x-ray spectroscopy; inorganic chemistry; catalyst testing; gas chromatography; atomic absorption spectroscopy; analysis of drinking water by atomic absorption and gas chromatographic methods; analysis of industrial waste streams and other watewater streams. *Mailing Add:* Indust Serv Div Westinghouse Elec 875 Greentree Rd Bldg 8 Pittsburgh PA 15220

MCDONALD, HUGH JOSEPH, b Glen Nevis, Ont, July 27, 13; nat US; m; c 3. BIOCHEMISTRY, PHYSICAL CHEMISTRY. *Educ:* McGill Univ, BSc, 35; Carnegie-Mellon Univ, MS, 36, DSc(phys chem), 39; Am Bd Clin Chem, dipl, 52. *Hon Degrees:* Grad, Univ Rio de Janeiro, 62. *Prof Exp:* Asst chem, Carnegie-Mellon Univ, 36-38, instr, 38-39; from instr to prof, Ill Inst Technol, 39-48; prof biochem & biophys & chmn dept, 48-81, EMER PROF, STRITCH SCH MED, LOYOLA UNIV CHICAGO, 81- *Concurrent Pos:* Res scientist, Manhattan Proj, Columbia Univ, 43; dir corrosion res lab, Ill Inst Technol, 44-48; ed theoret sect, Corrosion & Mat Protection, 45-48; consult, Argonne Nat Lab, 46-, State of Ill Dept Pub Health, 67- *Honors & Awards:* Nat Award Educ & Training, Am Asn Clin Chem, 77. *Mem:* Am Chem Soc; Soc Exp Biol & Med; Am Soc Biol Chemists; Biophys Soc; Am Asn Clin Chemists (vpres, 52, pres, 53). *Res:* Biochemical aspects of diabetes and atherosclerosis; separation processes; electrophoresis; lipoproteins; oral hypoglycemic agents. *Mailing Add:* Dept of Biochem & Biophys Loyola Univ Stritch Sch of Med Maywood IL 60153

MACDONALD, IAN ALASTAIR, b Duncan, BC, July 16, 43; m 70; c 2. GASTROENTEROLOGY. *Educ:* Dalhousie Univ, BSc, 67; Univ Ottawa, PhD(biochem), 71. *Prof Exp:* Fel biochem, 71-72, gel gastroenterol, 72-73, lectr, 73-75, ASST PROF GASTROENTEROL, DALHOUSIE UNIV, 75- *Mem:* Can Biochem Soc; Can Asn Gastroenterol. *Res:* Degradation of bile salts in human intestinal bacteria; activation of cancinogens/mutagens by human fecal bacteria. *Mailing Add:* Clin Res Ctr 5849 University Ave Halifax NS B3H 3J5 Can

MCDONALD, IAN CAMERON CRAWFORD, b Flint, Mich, Feb 20, 39; m 64; c 2. ENTOMOLOGY, GENETICS. *Educ:* Southern Methodist Univ, BS, 62, MS, 65; Va Polytech Inst, PhD(entom), 68. *Prof Exp:* Asst, Va Polytech Inst, 64-67; ENTOMOLOGIST, METAB & RADIATION RES LAB, ENTOM RES DIV, AGR RES SERV, USDA, 68- *Mem:* Genetics Soc Am; Am Genetic Asn. *Res:* Insect and house fly genetics; genetic control measures. *Mailing Add:* Metab & Radiation Res Lab Agr Res Serv USDA State Univ Sta Box 5674 Fargo ND 58102

MACDONALD, IAN FRANCIS, b Montreal, Que, Feb 8, 42; m 63; c 2. RHEOLOGY, CHEMICAL ENGINEERING. *Educ:* NS Tech Col, BE, 63; Univ Wis-Madison, PhD(chem eng), 68. *Prof Exp:* Nat Res Coun Can overseas fel, Inst Sci & Technol, Univ Manchester, 68-69; res engr, Exp Sta, E I du Pont de Nemours & Co, Inc, 69-70; asst prof chem eng, 70-75, ASSOC PROF CHEM ENG, UNIV WATERLOO, 75- *Concurrent Pos:* Vis assoc prof chem eng, Univ Wash, 78-79. *Mem:* Soc Rheol; Can Soc Chem Engrs. *Res:* Rheological behavior of viscoelastic materials; flow in and structure of porous media. *Mailing Add:* Dept of Chem Eng Univ of Waterloo Waterloo ON N2L 3G1 Can

MCDONALD, IAN JOHNSON, b Bangor, NIreland, Feb 23, 21; Can citizen; m 58; c 2. MICROBIAL PHYSIOLOGY. *Educ:* Univ BC, BSA, 43; Univ Wis, MSc, 48, PhD(agr bact), 50. *Prof Exp:* From asst res officer to assoc res officer, Div Biosci, 50-68, SR RES OFFICER, DIV BIOL SCI, NAT RES COUN CAN, 68- *Concurrent Pos:* Vis worker, Nat Inst Res in Dairying, Reading, Eng, 67-68. *Mem:* Am Soc Microbiol; Can Soc Microbiol (2nd vpres, 65-66, 76-77, secy-treas, 80); Can Inst Food Technol; Brit Soc Appl Bacteriol; Brit Soc Gen Microbiol. *Res:* Casein utilization by lactobacilli and lactic streptococci; location in cells and liberation of extracellular bacterial proteinases; chemostat cultivation of streptoccocci and Neisseria; effect of environment on composition and physiology of cells. *Mailing Add:* Div of Biol Sci Nat Res Coun 100 Sussex Dr Ottawa ON K1A 0R6 Can

MCDONALD, IAN MACLAREN, b Regina, Sask, May 20, 28; m 53; c 5. PSYCHIATRY. *Educ:* Univ Man, MD, 53; Royal Col Physicians & Surgeons Can, dipl psychiat, 58. *Prof Exp:* Psychiatrist, Crease Clin Psychol Med, 53-54 & Psychiat Serv, Prov Sask, 54-56; fel neurol, Col Med, Univ Sask, 56; fel psychiat, Med Ctr, Univ Colo, 56-58; lectr, 58, from asst prof to assoc prof, 59-67, PROF PSYCHIAT, UNIV SASK, 67-, HEAD DEPT PSYCHIAT, UNIV & HEAD PSYCHIAT, UNIV HOSP, 71- *Concurrent Pos:* Mem Sask Bd of Review. *Mem:* Am Psychiat Asn. *Res:* Social psychiatry. *Mailing Add:* Dept of Psychiat Univ of Sask Saskatoon SK S7N 0W0 Can

MCDONALD, JACK RAYMOND, b Birmingham, Ala, May 20, 44; m 71; c 3. ELECTROSTATIC PRECIPITATION, GASEOUS DISCHARGE PHYSICS. *Educ:* Samford Univ, BS, 66; Auburn Univ, MS, 68, PhD(physics), 77. *Prof Exp:* Instr physics & math, Jefferson State Jr Col, 72-74; assoc & res physicist, Southern Res Inst, 74, sect head, 77-82; VPRES, PAUL & MCDONALD ASSOCS, INC, 82- *Mem:* Air Pollution Control Asn. *Res:* Fundamental mechanisms in the separation of particles from gas streams by electrostatic precipitation, filtration, and scrubbing; investigate applications to stationary and mobile sources of gas streams. *Mailing Add:* Paul & McDonald Assocs Inc Riverchase Off Plaza Bldg 2 Suite 106 Birmingham AL 35244

MACDONALD, JAMES CAMERON, b Can, Nov 3, 26; m 57. BIOCHEMISTRY. *Educ:* Univ Alta, BSc, 49; Univ Wis, MSc, 51, PhD(physiol chem), 53. *Prof Exp:* Asst, Univ Wis, 49-53; Anna Fuller Fund fel, Univ Sheffield, 53-54 & Oxford Univ, 54-55; Nat Res Coun Can fel, McMaster Univ, 55-56; with Gerber Baby Foods Co, 56-57; from asst res officer to assoc res officer, 57-64, SR RES OFFICER MICROBIOL, PHYSIOL & BIOCHEM, PRAIRIE REGIONAL LAB, NAT RES COUN CAN, 64- *Mem:* Am Chem Soc; Chem Inst Can. *Res:* Microbiology. *Mailing Add:* Prairie Regional Lab Nat Res Coun Can Saskatoon SK S7N 0W9 Can

MCDONALD, JAMES CLIFTON, b Oklahoma City, Okla, Apr 2, 30; m 54; c 3. MYCOLOGY. *Educ:* Wash Univ, St Louis, AB, 52; Univ Mo, MA, 57, PhD(bot), 60. *Prof Exp:* Asst bot, Univ Mo, 59-60; asst prof, 60-65, chmn dept, 71-75, assoc prof, 65-79, PROF BIOL, WAKE FOREST UNIV, 79- *Mem:* AAAS; Am Inst Biol Sci; Mycol Soc Am; Asn Southeastern Biologists (secy, 74-76); Sigma Xi. *Res:* Myxobacteria, nutrition, taxonomy and ecology. *Mailing Add:* Dept of Biol Wake Forest Univ Winston-Salem NC 27109

MACDONALD, JAMES DOUGLAS, b Portland, Ore, July 14, 48; m 67; c 2. PLANT PATHOLOGY, SOIL MICROBIOLOGY. *Educ:* Univ Calif, BS, 73, MS, 75, PhD(plant path), 77. *Prof Exp:* ASST PROF PLANT PATH, UNIV CALIF, DAVIS, 78- *Mem:* Am Phytopath Soc; Am Soc Hort Sci. *Res:* Diseases of ornamental plants; abiotic diseases of plants; environmental stresses as factors in plant disease. *Mailing Add:* Dept of Plant Path Univ of Calif Davis CA 95616

MCDONALD, JAMES E, b Chicago, Ill, Nov 9, 22; m 46; c 3. OPHTHALMOLOGY. *Educ:* Loyola Univ Chicago, MD, 45. *Prof Exp:* From asst prof to assoc prof ophthal, Col Med, Univ Ill, 53-70; CLIN PROF OPHTHAL & CHMN DEPT, STRITCH SCH MED, LOYOLA UNIV CHICAGO, 70- *Mem:* AMA; Am Acad Ophthal & Otolaryngol. *Res:* Effects of radiation on the eye; corneal wound healing. *Mailing Add:* 1046 Chicago Ave Oak Park IL 60301

MCDONALD, JAMES FREDERICK, b Detroit, Mich, Sept 26, 39; m 64. MATHEMATICAL PHYSICS. *Educ:* Wayne State Univ, BS, 61, PhD(physics), 67. *Prof Exp:* Asst prof, 67-71, dept univ affairs grant, 69, assoc prof, 71-76, PROF MATH, UNIV WINDSOR, 76- *Concurrent Pos:* Nat Res Coun Can grant, 67-79. *Mem:* Am Phys Soc; Am Math Soc; Math Asn Am. *Res:* Statistical theory of energy levels of complex quantum mechanical systems; population genetics and applications to fish population. *Mailing Add:* Dept of Math Univ of Windsor Windsor ON 9N3 3P4 Can

MCDONALD, JAMES HOGUE, b Asheville, NC, May 16, 15; m 49; c 1. UROLOGY. *Educ:* NCent Col, Ill, AB, 38; Univ Ill, MD, 42; Am Bd Urol, dipl, 52. *Prof Exp:* From assoc prof to prof urol, Univ Ill Col Med, 58-68, head div, 58-68; secy, Am Bd Urol, 68-74; CHIEF UROL SECT, MARICOPA COUNTY GEN HOSP, 74- *Concurrent Pos:* Trustee, Am Bd Urol, 63-81. *Mem:* Sigma Xi; Am Urol Asn; Am Col Surg; Am Asn Genito-Urinary Surg. *Res:* Carcinogenesis of the urinary tract utilizing 2-acetylamino fluorene, indole and lead; regrowth of the ureter in normal and abnormal state; study of male infertility. *Mailing Add:* Dept of Surg Sect of Urol Maricopa County Gen Hosp Phoenix AZ 85008

MCDONALD, JAMES LEE, JR, b LaGrange, Ky, May 21, 39; m 63; c 2. ORAL BIOLOGY, NUTRITION. *Educ:* Ind Univ, AB, 62, PhD(dent sci), 68. *Prof Exp:* Asst prof, 68-77, ASSOC PROF PREV DENT, SCH DENT, IND UNIV, INDIANAPOLIS, 77- *Mem:* AAAS; assoc Am Dent Asn; Int Asn Dent Res. *Res:* Nutritional control of dental caries. *Mailing Add:* Sch of Dent Ind Univ Bloomington IN 47401

MACDONALD, JAMES REID, b St Helena, Calif, Aug 22, 18; m 41, 57, 69; c 3. VERTEBRATE PALEONTOLOGY, GEOLOGY. *Educ:* Univ Calif, BA, 40, MS, 47, PhD(paleont), 49. *Prof Exp:* Lab asst mus paleont, Univ Calif, 45-46, lab technician, 46-49; from asst prof to assoc prof geol, SDak Sch Mines & Technol, 49-57, cur, 49-57; occup analyst, Idaho Dept Hwy, 57-58; res assoc, Am Mus Natural Hist, 58-60; spec projs technician, Idaho Dept Hwy, 60-61; dep dir admin, State of Idaho, 61-62; assoc prof geol, Univ Idaho, 62; sr cur vert paleont, Los Angeles County Mus Natural Hist, 62-69; instr geog, Calif State Polytech Col, San Luis Obispo, 70; prof geol, Foothill Col, 70-80; CONSULT RES ASSOC, MUS GEOL, SDAK SCH MINES & TECHNOL, RAPID CITY, 80- *Concurrent Pos:* Adj prof, Univ Southern Calif, 65-69. *Mem:* Soc Vert Paleont; Paleont Soc; Am Soc Mammal. *Res:* Pliocene faunas of Nevada, California and South Dakota; Oligocene and Miocene mammals of South Dakota and adjacent regions. *Mailing Add:* Harmony Heights Rapid City SD 57701

MACDONALD, JAMES ROBERT, experimental physics, see previous edition

MACDONALD, JAMES ROSS, b Savannah, Ga, Feb 27, 23; m 46; c 3. SOLID STATE PHYSICS. *Educ:* Williams Col, BA, 44; Mass Inst Technol, SB, 44, SM, 47; Oxford Univ, DPhil(physics), 50, DSc, 67. *Prof Exp:* Asst, Radar & Electronics Lab, Mass Inst Technol, 43-44, asst elec eng, 46-47; physicist, Armour Res Found, Ill Inst Technol, 50-52; assoc physicist, Argonne Nat Lab, 52-53; res physicist semiconductor & solid state physics, Tex Instruments Inc, 53-55, dir solid state physics res, 55-61, dir physics res lab, 61-63, dir cent res labs, 63-72, asst vpres corp res & eng, 67, vpres, 68-74, vpres corp res & develop, 73-74; W R KENAN JR PROF PHYSICS, DEPT PHYSICS & ASTRON, UNIV NC, CHAPEL HILL, 74- *Concurrent Pos:* Adj assoc prof, Southwestern Med Sch, Univ Tex, 54, adj prof, 71-74; chmn, Numerical Data Adv Bd, Nat Acad Sci, 70-74, mem, Comt Motor Vehicle Emissions, 71-73, chmn, 73-74; mem coun, Nat Acad Eng, 71-74. *Honors & Awards:* Achievement Award, Inst Elec & Electronics Engrs, 62, Merit Serv Award, 74; Achievement Award, Inst Radio Engrs. *Mem:* Nat Acad Sci; Nat Acad Eng; fel Am Phys Soc; fel Inst Elec & Electronics Engrs. *Res:* Semiconductors; space-charge; electrolyte double layer; data analysis; equations of state. *Mailing Add:* 308 Laurel Hill Rd Chapel Hill NC 27514

MACDONALD, JAMES SCOTT, b Appleton, Wis, July 4, 48. ENVIRONMENTAL TOXICOLOGY, BIOCHEMISTRY. *Educ:* DePauw Univ BA, 70; Univ Cincinnati, PhD(toxicol), 75; Am Bd Toxicol, dipl, 80. *Prof Exp:* Fel toxicol, Ctr Toxicol, Vanderbilt Univ, 75-77; sr res toxicologist, 77-79, ASSOC DIR TOXICOL, MERCK INST THERAPEUT RES, 79- *Mem:* NY Acad Sci; AAAS. *Res:* Mechanisms of toxicity; carcinogenesis; promotion of tumorigenesis; drug metabolism. *Mailing Add:* Dept of Toxicol Merck Inst for Therapeut Res West Point PA 19486

MCDONALD, JIMMIE REED, b Austin, Tex, Aug 20, 42; m 63; c 2. PHYSICAL CHEMISTRY, MOLECULAR SPECTROSCOPY. *Educ:* Southwestern Univ, Tex, BS, 64; La State Univ, Baton Rouge, PhD(phys chem), 68. *Prof Exp:* Vis asst prof, La State Univ, Baton Rouge, 68-70; RES CHEMIST, NAVAL RES LAB, 70- *Mem:* Am Chem Soc. *Res:* Molecular electronic spectroscopy; photochemistry; dye laser technology. *Mailing Add:* Code 6110 Naval Res Lab Washington DC 20390

MACDONALD, JOHN ALAN, comparative physiology, see previous edition

MACDONALD, JOHN BARFOOT, b Toronto, Ont, Feb 23, 18; m 67; c 5. MICROBIOLOGY. *Educ:* Univ Toronto, DDS, 42; Univ Ill, MS, 48; Columbia Univ, PhD(bact), 53; Univ Man, LLD, 62; Univ BC, DSc, 67. *Prof Exp:* Lectr prev dent, Univ Toronto, 42-44, instr bact, 46-47; res asst, Univ Ill, 47-48; asst prof, Univ Toronto, 49-53, assoc prof bact & chmn div dent res, 53-56, prof, 56; prof microbiol, Sch Dent Med, Harvard Univ, 56-62, dir postdoctoral studies, 60-62; pres, Univ BC, 62-67; prof higher educ, Univ Toronto, 68; exec dir, Coun Ont Univs, 68-76; pres, 76-81, CHMN, ADDICTION RES FOUND, 81- *Concurrent Pos:* Charles Tomes lectr, Royal Col Surgeons, Eng, 62; dir, Forsyth Dent Infirmary, 56-62, consult, 62-; consult, Univ BC, 55-56; consult, Dent Med Sect, Corp Res Div, Colgate-Palmolive Co, 58-62; mem bd, Banff Sch Advan Mgt, 62-67, chmn, 66-67; consult, Donwood Found, Toronto, 67-, Sci Coun Can & Can Coun Support Res in Can Univs, 67-69 & Addiction Res Found, Toronto, 68; mem dent study sect, NIH, 61-65; mem, Ont Coun Health, 81- *Mem:* AAAS; Am Soc Microbiol; NY Acad Sci; Can Ment Health Asn; Int Asn Dent Res (pres, 68). *Res:* Ecology of mucous membranes; mixed anaerobic infections. *Mailing Add:* Addiction Res Found 33 Russell St Toronto ON M5S 2S1 Can

MCDONALD, JOHN C, b Baldwin, Miss; c 3. SURGERY, IMMUNOLOGY. *Educ:* Miss Col, BS, 51; Tulane Univ La, MD, 55. *Prof Exp:* Intern, Confederate Mem Med Ctr, Shreveport, La, 55-56; resident, E J Meyer Mem Hosp, Buffalo, NY, 58-63; Buswell res fel & instr surg, State Univ NY Buffalo, 63-65; assoc dir surg res lab, E J Meyer Mem Hosp, Buffalo, 65-68, head sect transplantation, 66-68; assoc prof surg, 68-72, prof surg & assoc prof microbiol, Sch Med, Tulane Univ La, 72-77, dir surg labs, 68-77, PROF & CHMN DEPT OF SURG, 77-, SURGEON-IN- CHIEF, LA STATE MED CTR, 77- *Concurrent Pos:* Head sect transplantation, State Univ NY Buffalo, 66; attend surgeon, E J Meyer Mem Hosp, Buffalo, 67; attend surgeon & head sect transplantation, Deaconess Hosp, Buffalo, 68; consult, Roswell Park Mem Hosp, 68 & Masten Park Rehab Ctr, 68; dir transplantation, Tulane Univ La & Charity Hosp, New Orleans; consult surgeon, Lallie Kemp Charity Hosp, Keesler AFB, Biloxi, Miss, Pineville Vet Admin Hosp & Huey P Long Charity Hosp; clin asst surgeon, Touro Infirm, Med staff, Southern Baptist Hosp & assoc mem, dept surg, Hotel Dieu Hosp, New Orleans; dir, Tulane Univ Med Ctr Histocompatibility Testing Lab, La Organ Procurement Prog; consult, Northwest La Emergency Med Serv. *Mem:* Am Col Surgeons; Am Surg Asn; Soc Univ Surgeons; Transplantation Soc; Southern Surg Asn. *Res:* Transplantation. *Mailing Add:* Dept of Surg La State Univ Sch Med Shreveport LA 71130

MACDONALD, JOHN CAMPBELL FORRESTER, b Kelowna, BC, Sept 24, 20; m 50; c 3. PHYSICS. *Educ:* Univ BC, BA, 41, MA, 48; Univ Toronto, PhD(exp physics), 51. *Prof Exp:* Physicist radiol physics, Toronto Gen Hosp, 51-57; asst prof, 61-71, PROF RADIATION ONCOL & HON LECTR PHYSICS & DIAG RADIOL, UNIV WESTERN ONT, 71-; sr physicist, 57-78, CHIEF PHYSICIST, ONT CANCER FOUND, VICTORIA HOSP, 79- *Concurrent Pos:* Clin teacher fac med, Univ Toronto, 54-57; mem, Can Sci Mission to USSR, 66. *Mem:* Can Asn Physicists; Am Asn Physicists Med; Brit Inst Radiol; fel Can Col Physicists Med. *Res:* Physics applied to medicine, especially applications of ionizing radiation in treatment of cancer. *Mailing Add:* Ontario Cancer Found Victoria Hosp London ON N6A 4G5 Can

MACDONALD, JOHN CHISHOLM, b Boston, Mass, Mar 17, 33; m 64; c 2. ANALYTICAL CHEMISTRY. *Educ:* Boston Col, BS, 55, MS, 57; Univ Va, PhD(chem), 62. *Prof Exp:* AEC fel & res assoc chem, Pa State Univ, 62-63; sr res chemist, Monsanto Res Corp, Mass, 63-66; from asst prof to assoc prof, 66-75, PROF CHEM, FAIRFIELD UNIV, 75- *Concurrent Pos:* NIH spec res fel, Med Lab, Sch of Med, Yale Univ, 72-73; vis prof, Arrhenius Lab, Univ Stockholm, 79. *Mem:* AAAS; Am Chem Soc; Sigma Xi. *Res:* Chemical analysis and instrumentation; computers in chemistry; science for society; chemometrics; orthomolecular medicine. *Mailing Add:* 250 Strobel Rd Trumbull CT 06611

MCDONALD, JOHN F(RANCIS), b Narberth, Pa, Jan 14, 42. ELECTRICAL ENGINEERING, COMPUTER ENGINEERING. *Educ:* Mass Inst Technol, BSEE, 63; Yale Univ, MEng, 64, PhD(elec eng), 69. *Prof Exp:* Mem tech staff, Bell Telephone Labs, 65; from lectr to asst prof eng & comput sci, Yale Univ, 69-74; ASSOC PROF, DEPT ELEC & SYSTS ENG, RENSSELAER POLYTECH INST, 74- *Concurrent Pos:* Contract co-supvr, US Navy Underwater Sound Lab, Conn, 69-71; consult, CTMS Inc, NY, Argonne Nat Lab, 75, Westinghouse Hanford Eng, Develop Lab, 76-77, Gen Elec Corp Res & Develop Ctr, 78, TV Data Corp, 78, Teledyne Gurley Corp, 79. *Mem:* Sigma Xi; Inst Elec & Electronics Engrs; Asn Comput Mach; Am Inst Physics. *Res:* Computer design; communication; detection estimation systems research; control system studies; information theory and coding; digital test set generation; phased array design; microprocessor systems; medical instrumentation. *Mailing Add:* Dept of Elec & Systs Eng JEC 6026 Rensselaer Polytech Inst Troy NY 12181

MACDONALD, JOHN JAMES, b New Glasgow, NS, Oct 31, 25; m 52; c 7. ELECTROCHEMISTRY. *Educ:* St Francis Xavier Univ, Can, BSc, 45; Univ Toronto, MA, 47, PhD(chem), 51. *Prof Exp:* Demonstr, Univ Toronto, 45-49; assoc prof chem, 49-60, dean sci, 60-70, acad vpres, 70-78, EXEC VPRES, ST FRANCIS XAVIER UNIV, 78- *Concurrent Pos:* Researcher, Ottawa Univ, 59-60; mem, Can Nat Coun, UNESCO, 68-; chmn bd gov, Atlantic Inst Educ, 70; mem, Maritime Prov Higher Educ Comn, 74- & Can Coun, 75-76; mem, Sci Coun Can, 77-, chmn transp study comt, 81; mem, Atlantic Region Adv Comt, Nat Res Coun & Regional Develop Adv Comt, Nat Sci & Eng Res Coun, 81. *Honors & Awards:* Centennial Medal, 67. *Mem:* AAAS; Chem Inst Can; Comp Educ Soc; Can Soc Study Higher Educ. *Res:* Electrochemical kinetics. *Mailing Add:* St Francis Xavier Univ Antigonish NS B2G 1C0 Can

MCDONALD, JOHN KENNELY, b Vancouver, BC, Oct 4, 30; US citizen; m 53; c 3. BIOCHEMISTRY, ENDOCRINOLOGY. *Educ:* Univ BC, BSA, 53; Purdue Univ, MS, 56; Ore State Univ, PhD(chem), 60. *Prof Exp:* Bacteriologist, Defence Res Bd, Can 53; protein chemist, Cutter Labs, Calif, 60-62; res scientist, Biomed Res Div, NASA-Ames Res Ctr, 62-75; vis prof biochem, 74-75, PROF BIOCHEM, MED UNIV S C, 75- *Mem:* AAAS; Am Soc Biol Chem; Endocrine Soc. *Res:* Protein chemistry; enzymology; structure and function of tissue peptidases and proteases. *Mailing Add:* Dept of Biochem Med Univ of S C Charleston SC 29401

MACDONALD, JOHN LAUCHLIN, b Woodstock, NB, Oct 7, 38; US citizen; m 63; c 3. MATHEMATICS. *Educ:* Harvard Univ, AB, 59; Univ Chicago, MS, 61, PhD(math), 65. *Prof Exp:* Humboldt fel math, Math Seminar, Frankfurt, 65-66; asst prof, 66-74, ASSOC PROF MATH, UNIV BC, 74- *Concurrent Pos:* Nat Res Coun grant, 66-78; vis prof math, Res Inst, Swiss Fed Inst Technol, 70-71; Can Coun fel, Swiss Fed Inst Technol & Florence, Italy, 77-78. *Mem:* Am Math Soc; Can Math Cong. *Res:* Category theory; algebraic topology; universal algebra. *Mailing Add:* Dept of Math Univ of BC Vancouver BC V6T 1W5 Can

MACDONALD, JOHN MARSHALL, b Dunedin, NZ, Nov 9, 20; m 52; c 3. PSYCHIATRY, CRIMINOLOGY. *Educ:* Univ Otago, MD, 46; Univ London, dipl, 50. *Prof Exp:* House physician, New Plymouth Gen Hosp, 46; asst physician, Belmont Hosp, London, Eng, 48-49; asst physician, Royal Edinburgh Hosp, 49-51; instr psychiat, 51-54, asst prof, 54-61, assoc prof, 61-71, PROF PSYCHIAT, SCH MED, UNIV COLO MED CTR, DENVER, 71-, DIR FORENSIC PSYCHIAT, MED CTR, 60- *Concurrent Pos:* Med consult, Colo State Hosp, 62- & Fitzsimons Gen Hosp, US Army, 64-77; med adv, Social Security Admin, 64-74. *Mem:* Fel Am Psychiat Asn. *Res:* Crime. *Mailing Add:* 2205 E Dartmouth Circle Englewood CO 80110

MCDONALD, JOHN N, b Bayonne, NJ, Apr 26, 42; c 2. MATHEMATICS. *Educ:* King's Col, AB, 64; Rutgers Univ, MS, 66, PhD(math), 69. *Prof Exp:* Vis assoc prof, Univ Conn, 75-76; asst prof, 69-75, ASSOC PROF MATH, ARIZ STATE UNIV, 76- *Concurrent Pos:* Grant, Ariz State Univ, 78. *Res:* Convex sets; spaces of analytic functions; stochastic processes. *Mailing Add:* Dept of Math Ariz State Univ Tempe AZ 85281

MCDONALD, JOHN STONER, b Mt Hope, Wash, Sept 20, 32; m 63; c 1. VETERINARY MEDICINE, MICROBIOLOGY. *Educ:* Wash State Univ, BA, 54, DVM, 56; Univ Idaho, MS, 58; Iowa State Univ, PhD(vet microbiol), 67. *Prof Exp:* Sta vet, Univ Idaho, 56-58; pvt pract, 58-61; RES VET, NAT ANIMAL DIS CTR, AGR RES SERV, USDA, 61- *Mem:* Am Vet Med Asn; Am Col Vet Microbiol. *Res:* Pathogenesis of udder infection and mastitis. *Mailing Add:* Nat Animal Dis Ctr Box 70 Ames IA 50010

MCDONALD, JOHN WILLIAM, b Decatur, Ill, Mar 29, 45; m 72; c 2. BIOINORGANIC CHEMISTRY. *Educ:* Grinnell Col, BA, 67; Northwestern Univ, PhD(inorg chem), 71. *Prof Exp:* Sr res assoc, 71-73, staff scientist, 73-78, INVESTR, CHARLES F KETTERING RES LAB, 78- *Mem:* Am Chem Soc. *Res:* Synthesis and characterization of metal complexes as probes for the mechanism of action of molybdoenzymes. *Mailing Add:* Charles F Kettering Res Lab Yellow Springs OH 45387

MCDONALD, JOHN WILLIAM DAVID, b Chatham, Ont, Jan 7, 38; m 70; c 2. HEMATOLOGY, INTERNAL MEDICINE. *Educ:* Univ Western Ont, MD, 61, PhD(biochem), 66; FRCP(C), 69. *Prof Exp:* Intern med, Victoria Hosp, London, Ont, 61-62; resident, Montreal Gen Hosp, 66-67; res & clin fel med & hemat, Royal Victoria Hosp, Montreal, 67-70; asst prof path chem & med, Victoria Hosp, Univ Western Ont, 70-72, asst prof med, Univ Hosp, 72-73, asst prof biochem, Univ Western Ont, 72-78, assoc prof med, 73-78, asst dean res, Fac Med, 75-78, HON LECTR, DEPT BIOCHEM & PROF MED, UNIV WESTERN ONT, 78- *Concurrent Pos:* Dir biochem-radioisotope-hemat lab & physician, Dept Med, Victoria Hosp, 70-72; physician & dir biochem-radioisotope-hemat, Hemat Serv, Hosp, Univ Western Ont, 72-; physician, Hemat-Oncol Serv, Dept Med, Univ Hosp, 72- & physician, Gastroenterol Serv, Dept Med, 78- *Mem:* Royal Col Physicians & Surgeons Can; Can Soc Hemat; Can Soc Clin Invest; Am Soc Hemat; Am Fedn Clin Res. *Res:* Effect of drugs on platelet prostaglandin synthesis and platelet function. *Mailing Add:* Dept Med Univ Hosp PO Box 5339 Terminal A London ON N6A 3K7 Can

MCDONALD, JOSEPH KYLE, b Athens, Ala, Oct 31, 42; m 69; c 2. PHYSICAL CHEMISTRY, MOLECULAR SPECTROSCOPY. *Educ:* Athens Col, BS, 64; Vanderbilt Univ, PhD(phys chem), 68. *Prof Exp:* Assoc prof math & chem, 70-77, ASSOC PROF MATH & PHYSICS, ATHENS STATE COL, 77- *Mem:* Am Chem Soc; Optical Soc Am. *Res:* Lifetimes, vibrational, and rotational analysis of electronic states of molecular radicals produced in various discharge systems. *Mailing Add:* Dept of Chem Athens State Col Box 225 Athens AL 35611

MCDONALD, KEITH LEON, b Murray City, Utah, Apr 20, 23; m 56. THEORETICAL PHYSICS. *Educ:* Univ Utah, BS, 50, MS, 51, PhD(physics), 56. *Prof Exp:* Mem staff, Los Alamos Sci Lab, Calif, 56-57; physicist, Dugway Proving Ground, 57-60; physics fac mem, Brigham Young Univ, 60-62 & Univ Utah, 62-63; res physicist, Nat Bur Standards, 63-64; physics fac mem, Idaho State Univ, 65; theoret geophysicist, Inst Earth Sci, Environ Sci Serv Admin-Inst Environ Res, 66-69; consult, Environ Res Labs, Environ Sci Serv Admin, Colo, 69-70 & Nat Oceanic & Atmospheric Admin, 71; CONSULT, 71- *Mem:* Optical Soc Am; Am Phys Soc; Am Astron Soc; Am Geophys Union; Am Asn Physics Teachers. *Res:* Electromagnetic theory and hydromagnetism; theoretical optics; kinetic theory; statistical mechanics; solar-terrestrial relations; geomagnetism; solar atmosphere and interior; planetary interiors; cosmic hydromagnetic dynamos. *Mailing Add:* PO Box 2433 Salt Lake City UT 84110

MACDONALD, KENNETH CRAIG, MARINE GEOPHYSICS. *Educ:* Univ Calif, Berkeley, BS, 70; Mass Inst Technol, PhD(marine geophysics), 75. *Prof Exp:* Green scholar geophysics, Inst Geophysics & Planetary Physics, 75-76; res geophysicist marine geophysics, Scripps Inst Oceanog, 76-79; ASSOC PROF MARINE GEOPHYSICS, UNIV CALIF, SANTA BARBARA, 79- *Concurrent Pos:* Assoc ed, J Geophys Res, 78-81 & Earth & Planetary Sci Letter, 78-; mem, Ocean Sci Bd, Nat Res Coun, 79-, Woods

Hole Oceanog Inst Corp, 79-; assoc res geophysicist, Scripps Inst Oceanog, 79-; co-leader, Riveira Submersible Exp Exped, 78-81. *Honors & Awards:* Newcomb-Cleveland Prize, AAAS, 80. *Mem:* Am Geophys Union; Geol Soc Am. *Res:* Marine magnetics; marine seismology; tectonics of spreading centers and transform faults; fine scale structural geology of submarine plate boundaries. *Mailing Add:* Dept Geol Univ Calif Santa Barbara CA 93106

MCDONALD, KIRK THOMAS, b Vallejo, Calif, Oct 20, 45; m. EXPERIMENTAL HIGH ENERGY PHYSICS. *Educ:* Univ Ariz, BS, 66; Calif Inst Technol, PhD(physics), 72. *Prof Exp:* Res assoc, Europ Coun Nuclear Res, Geneva, 72-74 & Enrico Fermi Inst, Univ Chicago, 75-76; asst prof, 76-81, ASSOC PROF HIGH ENERGY PHYSICS, PRINCETON UNIV, 81- *Res:* Experimental research into the structure of nuclear matter, as probed by high transverse momentum jets and by massive drell-yan muon pairs. *Mailing Add:* Dept of Physics Princeton Univ Princeton NJ 08540

MCDONALD, L(OUIS), organic chemistry, chemical engineering, deceased

MCDONALD, LARRY WILLIAM, b Louisville, Nebr, May 25, 28; m 55; c 3. PATHOLOGY, NEUROPATHOLOGY. *Educ:* Univ Calif, Berkeley, AB, 50; Northwestern Univ, MD, 55. *Prof Exp:* Res pathologist, Pondville State Hosp, Norfolk, Mass, 59-61; res assoc, Univ Calif, Berkeley, 62-68; assoc prof path, Sch Med, Univ Calif, Davis, 68-75; prof path, sch med, Wright State Univ, 75-77; PROF NEUROPATH, UNIV ILL MED CTR, CHICAGO, 78- *Concurrent Pos:* Damon Runyon grant, 60-62; USPHS trainee radiobiol, Cancer Res Inst, New Eng Deaconess Hosp, Boston, 61-62; consult, Vet Admin Hosp, Martinez, Calif, 66-73, chief electron micros in path, 67; consult, Lawrence Berkeley Lab, Univ Calif, 68- & Sacramento County Coroners Off, 71-75; chief lab serv, Vet Admin Ctr, Dayton, Ohio, 75-76. *Mem:* AAAS; Am Asn Neuropath; AMA; Am Asn Pathologists. *Res:* Effects of radiation on the nervous system, particularly the mechanism of production of the delayed effects; vascular disease in the nervous system; mechanisms of induction of tumors in the central nervous system. *Mailing Add:* Dept of Neurosurgery ALSM Univ Ill Med Ctr Chicago IL 60680

MCDONALD, LESLIE ERNEST, b Middletown, Mo, Oct 14, 23; m 46; c 3. PHYSIOLOGY. *Educ:* Mich State Univ, BS, 48, DVM, 49; Univ Wis, MS, 51, PhD(physiol), 52. *Prof Exp:* Practicing vet, 49-50; instr physiol, Univ Ill, 52-53, assoc prof, 53-54; prof & head dept, Okla State Univ, 54-69; assoc dean, Col Vet Med, Univ Ga, 69-71; dean, Col Vet Med, Ohio State Univ, 71-72; PROF PHYSIOL, COL VET MED, UNIV GA, 72- *Concurrent Pos:* Consult, USPHS, 64-; mem, Comt Vet Drug Efficacy, Nat Res Coun, 66- *Mem:* Soc Exp Biol & Med; Am Physiol Soc; Am Vet Med Asn; Brit Soc Study Fertil. *Res:* Endocrinology; reproductive physiology. *Mailing Add:* Dept of Physiol Col of Vet Med Univ of Ga Athens GA 30601

MACDONALD, MALCOLM DUNCAN, b Kimberley, BC, May 23, 27; m 49; c 4. PLANT BREEDING, CYTOGENETICS. *Educ:* Univ Alta, BSc, 50; Univ Minn, PhD(plant genetics), 59. *Prof Exp:* Asst entomologist, 49-51, asst cytogeneticist, 51-59, cytogeneticist, 59-71, CORN BREEDER, AGR CAN RES STA, 71- *Res:* Cytogenetics of winter-wheat; inheritance of resistance to winter injury; corn breeding; developing inbred lines, hybrids and populations for grain corn production in areas with less than 1300 growing degree days. *Mailing Add:* Agr Can Res Sta Lethbridge AB T1J 4B1 Can

MCDONALD, MALCOLM EDWIN, b Ann Arbor, Mich, May 29, 15; m 41; c 2. PARASITOLOGY, ECOLOGY. *Educ:* Parsons Col, BS, 37; Univ Iowa, MS, 39; Univ Mich, PhD(wildlife mgt), 51. *Prof Exp:* Asst prof biol, Parsons Col, 40-42; instr, Beloit Col, 50-51; asst prof, Union Col, NY, 51-56 & Univ Nev, 56-57; wildlife res biologist, US Fish & Wildlife Serv, US Dept Interior, 57-81; RETIRED. *Concurrent Pos:* Parasitologist, Malaria Surv Unit, Sanit Corps, 42-46. *Mem:* Ecol Soc Am; Am Soc Parasitol; Wildlife Soc; Wilson Ornith Soc; Wildlife Dis Asn. *Res:* Animal parasitology and ecology; parasites of waterfowl; wildlife conservation. *Mailing Add:* 1017 Magnolia Lane Madison WI 53713

MACDONALD, NORMAN SCOTT, b Boston, Mass, Jan 16, 17; m 51; c 2. RADIOACTIVE TRACERS. *Educ:* Western Reserve Univ, AB, 38; Ohio State Univ, MSc, 40, PhD(org chem), 42. *Prof Exp:* Asst chem, Ohio State Univ, 38-42; res assoc, Mass Inst Technol, 42-43; asst prof, Occidental Col, 46-48; assoc prof biophys, 49-67, PROF RADIOL, SCH MED, UNIV CALIF, LOS ANGELES, 67-, DIR BIOMED CYCLOTRON FACIL, 71- *Mem:* Am Chem Soc; Am Soc Biol Chem; Am Soc Nuclear Med. *Res:* Cyclotron production of radionuclides and labeling of compounds for applications in nuclear medicine; measurement of radioactivity in human body. *Mailing Add:* 900 Veteran Ave Los Angeles CA 90024

MCDONALD, P(ATRICK) H(ILL), JR, b Carthage, NC, Dec 25, 24; m 51; c 3. MECHANICAL ENGINEERING. *Educ:* NC State Univ, BS, 47; Northwestern Univ, MS, 51, PhD(mech), 53. *Prof Exp:* Instr mech eng, NC State Univ, 47-48; instr mech & hydraul, Clemson Col, 48-50; asst, Northwestern Univ, 51-52; from res assoc prof to res prof mech eng, 53-58, prof & grad adminstr, 58-60, prof & head dept, 60-65, head dept, 65-76, HARRELSON PROF MECH ENG, NC STATE UNIV, 65- *Concurrent Pos:* Exec chmn, 5th Southeastern Conf Theoret & Appl Mech, 68-70. *Honors & Awards:* Award, Am Soc Eng Educ, 59. *Mem:* Am Soc Mech Engrs; Am Soc Eng Educ; Soc Exp Stress Anal. *Res:* Applied and continuum mechanics; stress analysis; vibration; shock and wave motion; engineering cybernetics. *Mailing Add:* Dept of Civil Eng NC State Univ Raleigh NC 27650

MCDONALD, PAUL THOMAS, b Waterbury, Conn, Oct 15, 40; m 68; c 1. GENETICS, ENTOMOLOGY. *Educ:* Yale Univ, BA, 64; Univ Notre Dame, PhD(biol), 70. *Prof Exp:* Fel genetics, Int Ctr Insect Physiol & Ecol, 71-74; fel med entom, 74-76, ENTOMOLOGIST MED ENTOM, UNIV CALIF, BERKELEY, 76- *Mem:* Entom Soc Am. *Res:* Genetic control of insect vectors of disease. *Mailing Add:* 1212 Milvia St Berkeley CA 94709

MCDONALD, PERRY FRANK, b Garner, Tex, July 26, 33; m 59; c 2. SOLID STATE PHYSICS. *Educ:* Tex Christian Univ, BA, 54; NTex State Univ, MA, 60; Univ Ala, Tuscaloosa, PhD(physics), 68. *Prof Exp:* Res asst, Socony Mobil Field Res Lab, Tex, 60-61; res physicist, Brown Eng CoInc, Ala, 61-66 & US Army Missile Command, Redstone Arsenal, 66-68; ASSOC PROF PHYSICS, SAM HOUSTON STATE UNIV, 68- *Mem:* Am Phys Soc; Sigma Xi. *Res:* Acoustic paramagnetic resonance; electron paramagnetic resonance; spin lattice interactions. *Mailing Add:* Dept Physics Sam Houston State Univ Huntsville TX 77340

MCDONALD, PHILIP MICHAEL, b Seattle, Wash, Feb 5, 36; m 60; c 3. FORESTRY, ECOLOGY. *Educ:* Wash State Univ, BS, 60; Duke Univ, MF, 61; Ore State Univ, PhD(forest sci), 78. *Prof Exp:* RES FORESTER, PAC SOUTHWEST FOREST & RANGE EXP STA, 61- *Mem:* Ecol Soc Am. *Res:* Silviculture-ecology; cutting methods; seed production; regeneration; growth, including evaluation of succession; dynamics; biomass of conifers, hardwoods, woody shrubs and lesser vegetation. *Mailing Add:* Pac SW Forest & Range Exp Sta 2400 Washington Plaza Redding CA 96001

MCDONALD, RALPH EARL, b Indianapolis, Ind, May 12, 20; m 42; c 3. DENTISTRY. *Educ:* Ind Univ, BS, 42, DDS, 44, MS, 51; Am Bd Pedodontics, dipl, 52. *Prof Exp:* From instr to assoc prof pedodontics, 46-57, asst dean & secy grad dent educ, 64-68, chmn dept, 53-68, PROF PEDODONTICS, SCH DENT, IND UNIV, INDIANAPOLIS, 57-, DEAN, 69- *Concurrent Pos:* Consult, USPHS, 50-; mem exam bd, Am Bd Pedodontics, 55-62, chmn bd, 60-62. *Honors & Awards:* Distinguished Serv Award, Am Soc Dent for Children. *Mem:* Am Soc Dent for Children (secy-treas, 57-59, vpres, 59, pres, 62); fel Am Col Dent; Am Acad Pedodont (pres, 67; hon mem Brazilian Acad Dent & Am Dent Soc Ireland. *Res:* Clinical dental caries control; pathology of the dental pulp. *Mailing Add:* Sch Dent Ind Univ Indianapolis IN 46202

MCDONALD, RAY LOCKE, b Chula Vista, Calif, Oct 5, 31; m 60; c 2. PHYSICAL CHEMISTRY. *Educ:* San Diego State Col, AB, 55; Ore State Univ, PhD(chem), 60. *Prof Exp:* Res assoc chem, Mass Inst Technol, 60-61; asst prof, NDak State Univ, 61-65; from asst prof to assoc prof, 65-74, assoc chmn dept, 71-74, prof chem & dept chmn, 74-77, assoc dean, Col Arts & sci, 77-81, VCHANCELLOR ACAD PROG, UNIV HAWAII, 82- *Mem:* Am Chem Soc. *Res:* Ionic interactions in nonaqueous solvents; solvent extraction of ions. *Mailing Add:* Dept Chem Univ of Hawaii Honolulu HI 96822

MACDONALD, RICHARD ANNIS, b Manistee, Mich, July 23, 28; m 54; c 3. MEDICINE, PATHOLOGY. *Educ:* Albion Col, AB, 51; Boston Univ, MD, 54. *Prof Exp:* Intern med, Boston City Hosp, Mass, 54-55, resident path, Mallory Inst Path, 56-59; instr, Harvard Med Sch, 59-60, assoc, 60-62, asst prof, 62-65; prof, Sch Med, Univ Colo, 66-69; prof, Sch Med, Boston Univ, 69-71; prof & chmn dept, Sch Med, Univ Mass, 71-73; PROF PATH, SCH MED, BOSTON UNIV, 73- *Concurrent Pos:* Fel path, Harvard Med Sch, 57-59; Am Heart Asn sr res fel, Mallory Inst Path, Boston City Hosp, 58-59; chief path dept, Norwood Hosp. *Mem:* AMA; Am Asn Path & Bact; Soc Exp Biol & Med; Am Soc Exp Path; Int Acad Path. *Res:* Liver and hematological diseases; nutrition. *Mailing Add:* Dept of Path Norwood Hosp Norwood MA 02062

MCDONALD, RICHARD NORMAN, b Detroit, Mich, Feb 26, 31; m 56; c 2. ORGANIC CHEMISTRY. *Educ:* Wayne State Univ, BS, 54, MS, 55; Univ Wash, PhD(org chem), 57. *Prof Exp:* Res chemist, Pioneering Res Div, Textile Fibers Dept, E I du Pont de Nemours & Co, 57-60; from asst prof to assoc prof, 60-68, PROF CHEM, KANS STATE UNIV, 68- *Concurrent Pos:* Hon lectr, Mid Am State Univ Asn, 78-79; mem comt disposal hazardous indust wastes, Nat Res Coun, 81-82. *Mem:* Am Chem Soc; Royal Soc Chem. *Res:* Synthesis and chemistry of non-benzenoid aromatic compounds, small ring compounds and strained polycyclic structures; chemistry of hypovalent radicals; gas phase ion-molecule reactions; structures of gas phase ions; reaction mechanisms. *Mailing Add:* Chem Dept Kans State Univ Manhattan KS 66506

MACDONALD, ROBERT D(UNCAN), b Billings, Mont, Sept 8, 15; m 40; c 6. METALLURGY. *Educ:* Mont Sch Mines, BS, 37; Mass Inst Technol, SM, 40. *Prof Exp:* Res engr, Gen Eng Co, Utah, 40-42 & Battelle Mem Inst, 42-46; chief mineral dressing engr, Watertown Lab, Mass Inst Technol, 46-51; pilot plant supt, Chem Construct Co, Can, 51-52; asst chief, Minerals Beneficiation Div, Battelle Mem Inst, 52-59; vpres, Bonneville, Ltd, 60-64; dir res US Smelting, Ref & Mining Co, Utah, 64-66; DIR METALL, NEWMONT EXPLOR LTD, 66-, VPRES, 79- *Mem:* Am Chem Soc; Am Inst Mining, Metall & Petrol Engrs; Mining & Metall Soc Am; Can Inst Mining & Metall. *Res:* Mineral dressing; extractive metallurgy; flotation; hydrometallurgy. *Mailing Add:* Newmont Exploration Ltd 44 Briar Ridge Rd Box 310 Danbury CT 06810

MCDONALD, ROBERT H, JR, b Cincinnati, Ohio, Nov 15, 33; m 58; c 2. CLINICAL PHARMACOLOGY. *Educ:* Xavier Univ, BS, 55; Stritch Sch Med, MD, 59. *Prof Exp:* Intern, Health Ctr Hosps, Univ Pittsburgh, 59-60; jr resident internal med, Univ Pittsburgh, 60-61; NIH fels clin pharmacol, Emory Univ, 61-63; assoc surgeon, Nat Heart Inst, 63-65; USPHS hon res asst physiol, Univ Col, London, 65-66; from asst prof to assoc prof, 66-77, PROF MED & PHARMACOL, SCH MED, UNIV PITTSBURGH, 77-, CHIEF SECT CLIN PHARM, 71- *Mem:* Am Fedn Clin Res; Am Soc Pharmacol & Exp Therapeut; Royal Soc Med; Am Physiol Soc. *Res:* Human pharmacokinetics; hypertension; adrenergic mechanisms; drug abuse; inotropic modification of myocardial energetics. *Mailing Add:* Dept of Med 488 Scaife Hall Pittsburgh PA 15261

MACDONALD, ROBERT NEAL, b Mansfield, Ohio, Nov 2, 16; m 41; c 3. ORGANIC CHEMISTRY. *Educ:* Oberlin Col, AB, 38; Yale Univ, PhD(org chem), 41. *Prof Exp:* chemist, E I Du Pont de Nemours & Co, Inc, 41-81. *Mem:* Sigma Xi. *Res:* Synthesis of high polymers. *Mailing Add:* 5 Crestfield Rd Wilmington DE 19810

MCDONALD, ROBERT SKILLINGS, b Pittsburgh, Pa, July 19, 18; m 43; c 3. PHYSICAL CHEMISTRY, SPECTROSCOPY. *Educ:* Univ Maine, BS, 41; Mass Inst Technol, PhD(phys chem), 52. *Prof Exp:* Jr engr, Hygrade Sylvania Co, Mass, 51; res physicist, Am Cyanamid Co, Conn, 42-46; res assoc, Mass Inst Technol, 46-50; RES ASSOC, RES & DEVELOP CTR, GEN ELEC CO, 51- *Mem:* Am Chem Soc; Am Phys Soc; Coblentz Soc. *Res:* Infrared spectroscopy; surface chemistry; computer applications in analytical chemistry; mass spectroscopy. *Mailing Add:* Gen Elec Res & Develop Ctr PO Box 8 Knolls 1 Schenectady NY 12301

MACDONALD, RODERICK, JR, b Charleston, SC, Oct 16, 26; m 51; c 5. OPHTHALMOLOGY. *Educ:* Davidson Col, BS, 47; Med Col SC, MD, 50. *Prof Exp:* Resident ophthal, New Orleans Eye, Ear, Nose & Throat Hosp, La, 52-53 & 55-56; instr ophthal, Sch Med, Tulane Univ, 56-57; exec dir, Dept Ophthal, Sch Med, Univ Louisville, 57- 65, from asst prof to prof ophthal, 57-73, actg chmn dept, 65, chmn dept, 65-73, assoc pharmacol, 69, assoc dean, 69-70, vdean, 70-73; prof ophthal & chmn dept, Med Col Va, 73-76; DEAN SCH MED, UNIV SC, 76- *Concurrent Pos:* Mem vision res training comt, NIH, 68-71. *Mem:* AAAS; Am Col Surg; Am Ophthal Soc; Royal Soc Med; Am Acad Opthal. *Res:* External diseases of the eye; ocular immunology. *Mailing Add:* Sch of Med Univ of SC Columbia SC 29208

MACDONALD, RODERICK PATTERSON, b Detroit, Mich, Nov 9, 24. BIOCHEMISTRY. *Educ:* Mich State Univ, BS, 47; Univ Detroit, MS, 49; Wayne State Univ, PhD(physiol chem), 52; Am Bd Clin Chem, dipl; Can Bd Clin Chem, dipl. *Prof Exp:* Asst chem, Univ Detroit, 47-49; spec instr, Mortuary Sch, Wayne State Univ, 49-51; supvr chem lab, 52-59, res assoc, 52-75, dir clin chem, 59-75, CLIN CHEMIST, HARPER HOSP, 75- *Concurrent Pos:* Asst prof path, Wayne State Univ, 64- *Honors & Awards:* McLean Award, 52. *Mem:* Am Chem Soc; Am Asn Clin Chem (secy, 65-68); Can Soc Clin Chem. *Res:* Metabolism and physiology of bone; thyroid diseases and hypometabolism; ultramicro clinical methods; general clinical chemistry; clinical enzymology. *Mailing Add:* Dept of Path 3990 John R St Detroit MI 48201

MACDONALD, RONALD NEIL ANGUS, hematology, oncology, see previous edition

MACDONALD, ROSEMARY A, b Leamington Spa, Eng, Oct 7, 30; m 65; c 2. SOLID STATE PHYSICS. *Educ:* St Andrews Univ, BSc, 54; Oxford Univ, DPhil(solid state physics), 59. *Prof Exp:* Lectr physics, Somerville Col, Oxford Univ, 57-59; res assoc, Univ Md, 59-61; NATO res fel, Bristol Univ, 61-62; lectr, Sheffield Univ, 62-64; PHYSICIST, NAT BUR STAND, 64- *Mem:* Am Phys Soc; Brit Inst Physics. *Res:* Lattice dynamics; point defects; phase transitions; molecular dynamical calculations of nonequilibrium behavior of solids and liquids. *Mailing Add:* Thermophysics Div Nat Bur of Stand Washington DC 20234

MACDONALD, RUSSELL EARL, b NB, Can, Feb 18, 28; m 59; c 3. BACTERIOLOGY. *Educ:* Acadia Univ, BA, 50, MA, 52; Univ Mich, PhD(bact), 57. *Prof Exp:* Asst bact, Acadia Univ, 50-52; asst, Univ Mich, 53-55, instr & res assoc, 56-57; asst prof, 57-62, ASSOC PROF BACT, CORNELL UNIV, 62- *Concurrent Pos:* Jane Coffin Childs Mem Fund Med Res fel, 64-65; vis scientist, Ames Res Ctr, 74-75. *Mem:* Am Soc Microbiol. *Res:* Microbial ecology; molecular biology; control mechanisms; ribosomes; membrane transport. *Mailing Add:* 410 Stocking Hall Cornell Univ Ithaca NY 14853

MCDONALD, SAMUEL GILBERT, III, b Atlanta, Ga, Dec 13, 46; m 68; c 2. METALLURGICAL ENGINEERING. *Educ:* Univ Notre Dame, BS, 68, MS, 70, PhD(metall eng), 73. *Prof Exp:* Sr engr, 72-81, FEL ENGR, RES & DEVELOP CTR, WESTINGHOUSE ELEC CORP, 81- *Mem:* Sigma Xi; Am Soc Testing Mat; Am Nuclear Soc; Am Soc Metals. *Res:* Materials research (corrosion, mechanical properties, performance evaluation) relative to the materials used in light water reactors, particularly zirconium alloys. *Mailing Add:* Res & Develop Ctr Westinghouse Elec Corp 1310 Beulah Rd Pittsburgh PA 15235

MCDONALD, T(HOMAS) W(ILLIAM), b Winnipeg, Man, June 24, 29; m 53; c 3. MECHANICAL ENGINEERING. *Educ:* Queen's Univ, BSc, 52, MSc, 55; Purdue Univ, PhD(convective heat transfer), 65. *Prof Exp:* Spec lectr mech eng, Univ Sask, 54-56, from asst prof to assoc prof, 56-68; PROF MECH ENG, UNIV WINDSOR, 68-, HEAD DEPT, 78- *Mem:* Can Soc Mech Engrs; Am Soc Heating, Refrig & Air-Conditioning Engrs; Int Solar Energy Soc; Solar Energy Soc Can. *Res:* Waste heat recovery systems; simulation of thermal and flow systems; two phase flow thermal systems. *Mailing Add:* Dept of Mech Eng Univ of Windsor Windsor ON N9B 3P4 Can

MCDONALD, TED PAINTER, b Loudon, Tenn, Nov 23, 30; m 55; c 3. BIOCHEMISTRY. *Educ:* Univ Tenn, BS, 55, MS, 58, PhD(animal sci, biochem), 65. *Prof Exp:* Radiobiologist, Oak Ridge Nat Lab, 58-64; res asst blood platelet & mucopolysaccharide chem, Res Lab, AEC, 64-65, res assoc exp hemat, Mem Res Ctr, 65, res instr, 65-68, asst prof, 68-73, assoc prof, 73-77, PROF EXP HEMAT, MEM RES CTR, UNIV TENN, KNOXVILLE, 77- *Concurrent Pos:* Mem coun thrombosis, Am Heart Asn. *Mem:* Am Soc Hemat; Int Soc Hemat; Soc Exp Biol & Med; Soc Exp Hemat; Radiation Res Soc. *Res:* Blood platelet physiology; mucopolysaccharide chemistry; experimental hematology. *Mailing Add:* Univ of Tenn Mem Res Ctr 1924 Alcoa Hwy Knoxville TN 37920

MACDONALD, THOMAS THORNTON, b Glasgow, Scotland, Jan 9, 51. IMMUNOLOGY. *Educ:* Univ Glasgow, BSc Hons, 73, PhD(immunol), 77. *Prof Exp:* Res asst, Univ Glasgow, 73-76; res assoc, Trudeau Inst, Sacanac Lake, NY, 76-78; ASST PROF MICROBIOL, THOMAS JEFFERSON UNIV, 78- *Concurrent Pos:* Fels, Nat Found Ileitis & Colitis Inc, 76-78 & res grant, 78-79; Asn Gnotobiotics fel, 78. *Mem:* Brit Soc Immunol; Am Soc Microbiol; Asn Gnotobiotics. *Res:* The role of cell-mediated immunity in host defenses at mucous surfaces. *Mailing Add:* Dept of Microbiol Jefferson Med Col Philadelphia PA 19107

MACDONALD, TIMOTHY, genetics, biochemistry, see previous edition

MACDONALD, TIMOTHY LEE, b Long Beach, Calif, Mar 12, 48; m 71. ORGANIC CHEMISTRY, BIO-ORGANIC CHEMISTRY. *Educ:* Univ Calif, Los Angeles, BSc, 71; Columbia Univ, PhD(chem), 75. *Prof Exp:* NIH fel chem, Stanford Univ, 75-77; ASST PROF CHEM, VANDERBILT UNIV, 77- *Concurrent Pos:* A P Sloan Found res fel, 81-83. *Mem:* Am Chem Soc. *Res:* Synthesis of natural products, development of new synthetic methods, establishment and study of laboratory chemical models which mimic biological processes, and determination of chemical mechanisms of enzymes with toxicological relevance. *Mailing Add:* Dept of Chem Vanderbilt Univ Box 1822 Sta B Nashville TN 37235

MCDONALD, TIMOTHY SCOTT, b Albuquerque, NMex, Feb 20, 46; m 71; c 2. COMPUTER SCIENCE. *Educ:* Univ NMex, BS, 70, MS, 72, PhD(elec eng), 77. *Prof Exp:* From res asst to res engr, 67-77, PROG MGR MINICOMPUT SYSTS & DATA COMMUN, DIKEWOOD INDUSTS, INC, 77- *Concurrent Pos:* Consult, Equ-A-Ex Corp, 78- *Res:* Digital signal analysis; minicomputer system software development; data communications; computerized mass spectrometry. *Mailing Add:* Dept of Eng 1009 Bradbury SE Albuquerque NM 87106

MCDONALD, W JOHN, b Lethbridge, Alta, Sept 29, 36; m 61; c 61; c 3. NUCLEAR PHYSICS. *Educ:* Univ Sask, BSc, 59, MSc, 61; Univ Ottawa, Ont, PhD(physics), 64. *Prof Exp:* Asst prof, 65-70, assoc prof, 70-75, PROF PHYSICS, UNIV ALTA, 75- *Mem:* Am Asn Physics Teachers; Am Phys Soc; Can Asn Physicists. *Res:* Intermediate energy physics on 500 mev proton cyclotron, especially quasi free scattering and med energy heavy ion physics and biophysics. *Mailing Add:* Fac Sci Univ of Alta Edmonton AB T6G 2E9 Can

MACDONALD, WILLIAM, b Salem, Ohio, Nov 25, 27; m 65; c 2. NUCLEAR PHYSICS. *Educ:* Univ Pittsburgh, BS, 50; Princeton Univ, PhD(physics), 55. *Prof Exp:* Asst, Princeton Univ, 50-54; theoret physicist, Radiation Lab, Univ Calif, 54-55; vis prof physics, Univ Wis, 55-56; from asst prof to assoc prof, 56-63, PROF PHYSICS, UNIV MD, COLLEGE PARK, 63- *Mem:* Am Phys Soc; Sigma Xi. *Res:* Structure of light nuclei; nuclear reaction theory; plasma physics; space physics. *Mailing Add:* Dept Physics & Astron Univ Md College Park MD 20742

MCDONALD, WILLIAM CHARLES, b Chicago, Ill, Feb 14, 33; m 57; c 4. MICROBIOLOGY. *Educ:* Univ Okla, BS, 55; Univ Tex, PhD(bact), 59. *Prof Exp:* Res assoc biochem genetics, Children's Hosp, Buffalo, NY, 59-60; asst prof bact, Wash State Univ, 62-65; from assoc prof to prof biol, Tulane Univ, 65-73; PROF BIOL & CHMN DEPT, UNIV TEX, ARLINGTON, 73- *Concurrent Pos:* State of Wash initiative measure grants, 63-66; NSF res grants, 63-69. *Mem:* AAAS; fel Am Acad Microbiol; Am Soc Microbiol. *Res:* Effects of radiation on bacteria; microbial genetics; temperature sensitivity and resistance in microorganisms; biology of bacteriophages. *Mailing Add:* Dept of Biol Univ of Tex Arlington TX 76019

MCDONALD, WILLIAM CRAIK, plant pathology, see previous edition

MACDONALD, WILLIAM DAVID, b Chatham, Ont, Feb 28, 37; m 70. STRUCTURAL GEOLOGY, TECTONICS. *Educ:* Univ Western Ont, BSc, 59; Princeton Univ, PhD(geol), 65. *Prof Exp:* Asst prof geol, Villanova Univ, 64-65; from asst prof to assoc prof, 65-78, PROF GEOL, STATE UNIV NY BINGHAMTON, 78- *Concurrent Pos:* Vis prof & researcher, Univ Sao Paulo, 71, Cambridge Univ, 72 & Stanford Univ, 78-79. *Mem:* Geol Soc Am; Am Geophys Union; Geol Asn Can. *Res:* Structural geology, tectonics and paleomagnetism of Latin America and Caribbean regions; computer applications in geology and geophysics; orientation analysis. *Mailing Add:* Dept Geol Sci State Univ NY Binghamton NY 13901

MACDONALD, WILLIAM E, JR, b Columbus, Ohio, Nov 21, 16; m 40. PHARMACOLOGY, TOXICOLOGY. *Educ:* Emory Univ, AB, 39; Univ Fla, MS, 51; Univ Miami, PhD(pharmacol), 61; Am Acad Indust Hyg, dipl; Am Bd Toxicol, dipl. *Prof Exp:* Formulator, Biscayne Chem Co, 39-40; spec officer, Seaboard Air Line RR, 40-41; chemist, Fla State Bd Health, 41-46, indust hyg chemist, 46-55; instr, Sch Med, Univ Miami, 55-63, asst prof pharmacol & toxicol, 63-75, assoc dir, Res & Teaching Ctr Toxicol, 73-75; dir sci div, 75-80, PRIN TOXICOLOGIST, TRACOR JITCO, INC, 75-, SCI ADV TO PRES, 81- *Concurrent Pos:* Am Cancer Soc instnl grants, 64-66. *Mem:* Soc Toxicol; Am Chem Soc; Am Conf Govt Indust Hygienists; Am Indust Hyg Asn; Sigma Xi. *Res:* Pharmacology, toxicology and industrial hygiene of silicones, nitroolefins, benzene, food additives including drugs, pesticides and anticorrosives; bladder carcinogens; subliminal toxicology of pesticides; carcinogenesis bioassay. *Mailing Add:* Tracor Jitco Inc 1776 E Jefferson St Rockville MD 20852

MCDONALD, WILLIAM JOHN, b Nunda, SDak, Feb 19, 24; m 49; c 4. PHYSICS, MATHEMATICS. *Educ:* Iowa State Col, BS, 49. *Prof Exp:* Jr physicist, Res Lab, Bendix Aviation Corp, 49-51; physicist, Cent Res Lab, 52-59, physicist abrasive lab, 59-61, phys studies supvr, 61-69, sr res specialist, abrasive lab, 69-77, CORPORATE SCIENTIST, ABRASIVE LAB, MINN MINING & MFG CO, 77- *Res:* Metal cutting; wear of hard minerals; mineral synthesis; instrumentation; geometric optics; electrostatic forces. *Mailing Add:* 3M Ctr Minn Mining & Mfg Co Bldg 251 St Paul MN 55101

MCDONALD, WILLIAM TRUE, b Bellingham, Wash, July 18, 35; m 61; c 3. AEROSPACE SCIENCES. *Educ:* Calif Inst Technol, BS, 57, MS, 58; Mass Inst Technol, ScD(instrumentation), 68. *Prof Exp:* Res engr, Jet Propulsion Lab, 60; supvr, Autonetics Div, NAm Aviation, Inc, 60-62; staff engr, Instrumentation Lab, Mass Inst Technol, 62-64, staff engr, Exp Astron Lab, 64-68; mem tech staff, 68-79, CHIEF SCIENTIST, SENSORS & SIGNAL PROCESS SYSTS, ROCKWELL INT CORP, 79- *Concurrent Pos:* Founder & dir, Dover Instrument Corp, Mass, 64-68; consult, Rockwell Int Corp, 66-67, Med Systs Tech Serv, Inc, 78-79 & Asst Secy Defense, Health Affairs, 79-; consult & auth in field of small arms ballistics, 71- *Honors & Awards:* Engr of Year, Rockwell Int Corp, 76. *Res:* Missile and spacecraft guidance, navigation and control systems engineering; visible and infrared sensor systems. *Mailing Add:* Autonetics Strat Syts Div Rockwell Int Corp 3370 Miraloma Ave Anaheim CA 92803

MCDONEL, EVERETT TIMOTHY, b Lima, Ohio, Oct 6, 33; m 55; c 6. POLYMER CHEMISTRY, CHEMICAL ENGINEERING. *Educ:* Case Inst Technol, BS, 55, MS, 57, PhD(org chem), 60. *Prof Exp:* Res asst polymer chem, Case Inst Technol, 57-59; res chemist, 59-61, sr res chemist tire mat, 61-64, SECT LEADER TIRE MAT, RES CTR, B F GOODRICH CO, 64-, GROUP MGR TIRE RES, TIRE DIV, 72- *Mem:* Am Chem Soc. *Res:* Oxidation and vulcanization of elastomers; relation of polymer structure to performance; new elastomers for tires. *Mailing Add:* Tire Mat B F Goodrich Res Ctr Brecksville OH 44141

MCDONELL, WILLIAM ROBERT, b New Rockford, NDak, Mar 8, 25; m 55; c 2. RADIATION CHEMISTRY. *Educ:* Univ Mich, BS, 47, MS, 48; Univ Calif, PhD(chem), 51. *Prof Exp:* Chemist, Radiation Lab, Univ Calif, 48-51 & Argonne Nat Lab, 51-53; chemist, 53-60, res supvr, 60-70, sr res scientist, 69-70, RES ASSOC, SAVANNAH RIVER LAB, E I DU PONT DE NEMOURS & CO, INC, 70- *Mem:* Am Chem Soc; Am Nuclear Soc. *Res:* Nuclear and radiation chemistry; effects of radiation on materials; reactor fuel behavior; development of radioisotopic heat and radiation sources. *Mailing Add:* 1318 Evans Rd Aiken SC 29801

MCDONNEL, GERALD M, b Salt Lake City, Utah, Feb 13, 19; m 41; c 7. RADIOLOGY, RADIOBIOLOGY. *Educ:* Univ Utah, BA, 40; Temple Univ, MD, 43. *Prof Exp:* Intern, Temple Univ Hosp, 43, resident internal med, 44; assoc prof radiol, ctr health sci, Univ Calif, Los Angeles, 59-67; chancellor, Am Col Radiol, 66-72. *Concurrent Pos:* Mem sci adv bd, US Air Force, 60-76 & Defense Sci Bd, 64-68; mem staff dept radiol, Hosp of the Good Samaritan, Los Angeles, 68- *Mem:* AMA; Am Col Radiol; Radiol Soc NAm. *Res:* Nuclear weapons effects; radiation effects and space radiation effects in humans; megavoltage diagnostic radiology. *Mailing Add:* Hosp of the Good Samaritan 616 S Witmer St Los Angeles CA 90017

MCDONNELL, FRANCIS NICHOLAS, b Ottawa, Ont, Sept 28, 40; m 67; c 3. NUCLEAR ENGINEERING, PHYSICS. *Educ:* Royal Mil Col, BEng, 63; Univ Toronto, MASc, 66; Univ Manchester, PhD, 70. *Prof Exp:* Res officer, Appl Math Br, 70-79, sr adv to vpres res, 79-81, EXEC ASST TO PRES, ATOMIC ENERGY CAN LTD, 82- *Mem:* Am Nuclear Soc. *Res:* Reactor physics; measurement and analysis; reactor dynamics; code development; research and development management. *Mailing Add:* Atomic Energy Can Ltd 275 Slater Ottawa ON K1A 0S4 Can

MCDONNELL, J(AMES) S(MITH), aeronautical engineering, deceased

MACDONNELL, JOHN JOSEPH, b Springfield, Mass, Mar 28, 27. MATHEMATICS. *Educ:* Boston Col, AB, 50, MA, 51; Cath Univ Am, PhD(math), 57. *Prof Exp:* From instr to assoc prof, 60-69, ASSOC PROF MATH, COL OF THE HOLY CROSS, 69- *Mem:* Math Asn Am; Am Math Soc. *Res:* Convergence theorems for Dirichlet type series. *Mailing Add:* Dept of Math Col of the Holy Cross Worcester MA 01610

MACDONNELL, JOSEPH FRANCIS, b Springfield, Mass, May 4, 29. MATHEMATICS. *Educ:* Boston Col, BA, 54, MA, 59 & 62; Fordham Univ, MS, 64; Columbia Univ, EdD, 72. *Prof Exp:* Asst prof, Al Hikma Univ, Baghdad, 64-69; asst prof, 69-78, ASSOC PROF MATH, FAIRFIELD UNIV, 78- *Mem:* Am Math Asn; Am Math Soc; Sigma Xi. *Res:* Ruled surfaces; moebius surfaces of n half twists. *Mailing Add:* Dept of Math Fairfield Univ Fairfield CT 06430

MCDONNELL, LEO F(RANCIS), b Edmonton, Alta, May 10, 26; nat US; m 57; c 5. CHEMICAL ENGINEERING. *Educ:* Univ Alta, BSc, 48; Lawrence Col, MS, 55, PhD(chem eng), 59. *Prof Exp:* Res engr, Minn & Ont Paper Co, 48-53; tech dir, Cup Div, 58-61, tech dir, Marinette Plant, 61-65, brand tech mgr, staff tech servs, 65-73, INT DEVELOP MGR, SCOTT PAPER CO, 73- *Mem:* Tech Asn Pulp & Paper Indust. *Res:* Pulp, paper and fiber insulation board manufacture and conversion; organic protective and decorative coating adhesives. *Mailing Add:* 1999 Kimberwick Rd Media PA 19063

MACDONNELL, WILFRED DONALD, b Boston, Mass, Nov 3, 11; m 37, 71; c 3. METALLURGY. *Educ:* Mass Inst Technol, BS, 34. *Hon Degrees:* LLD, Lawrence Inst Technol, 61. *Prof Exp:* Trainee to gen supt, Bethlehem Steel Co, NY, 34-49, asst gen mgr, Pa, 49-57; vpres opers, Great Lakes Steel Co Div, Nat Steel Corp, Mich, 57-59, pres, 59-62; vpres, Kelsey-Hayes Co, 62, pres, 62-69, pres & chief exec officer, 69-76, chmn & chief exec officer, 76-77; RETIRED. *Concurrent Pos:* Consult, Kelsey-Hayes Co, 78- *Mem:* Nat Acad Engrs; Soc Automotive Engrs. *Res:* Steel industry management; management of supplier to transportation industry. *Mailing Add:* Kelsey-Hayes Co 38481 Huron River Dr Romulus MI 48174

MCDONNELL, WILLIAM VINCENT, b Carbondale, Pa, Oct 28, 22; m 49. PATHOLOGY. *Educ:* Univ Scranton, AB, 43; Jefferson Med Col, MD, 47; Am Bd Path, dipl. *Prof Exp:* From asst prof to assoc prof, 52-69, PROF PATH, JEFFERSON MED COL, 69-; med dir, 69-79, VPRES MED AFFAIRS, WEST JERSEY HEALTH SYST, 72- *Concurrent Pos:* Asst dir clin lab, Methodist Hosp & Jefferson Med Col, 52-61; coordr cancer teaching, Jefferson Med Col, 55-60; dir clin lab, West Jersey Hosp, 61-79. *Mem:* Am Soc Clin Pathologists; AMA; Col Am Pathologists; Am Acad Med Dis; Am Col Physician Execs. *Res:* Human pathology. *Mailing Add:* West Jersey Health Syst Mt Ephriam & Atlantic Ave Camden NJ 08104

MCDONOUGH, EUGENE STOWELL, b Abingdon, Ill, Apr 16, 05; m 30, 75. MYCOPATHOLOGY, GENETICS. *Educ:* Marquette Univ, BS, 28, MS, 31; Iowa State Col, PhD(bot), 36. *Prof Exp:* Asst bot, Marquette Univ, 28-29; instr, Mich State Col, 29-30; from instr to prof, 30-70, EMER PROF BOT, MARQUETTE UNIV, 70- *Concurrent Pos:* Co-dir, Holton & Hunkel Res Award, 44-50; researcher, Mycol Unit, USPHS grant, Commun Dis Ctr, Ga, 58-59. *Mem:* Fel AAAS; Mycol Soc Am; Am Phytopath Soc; Am Soc Microbiol; Med Mycol Soc Americas. *Res:* Cytology and genetics of fungi; polyploidy; human heredity; host-parasite relations of plant diseases; diseases of flowering plants; chromosome structure; antimycotics; phytopathology; medical mycology; soil mycolysis; epidemiology; epidemiological studies on blastomycosis. *Mailing Add:* Dept of Biol Marquette Univ Milwaukee WI 53233

MCDONOUGH, EVERETT GOODRICH, b Birmingham, Ala, Feb 22, 05; m 32; c 3. ORGANIC CHEMISTRY. *Educ:* Howard Col, AB, 26; Columbia Univ, PhD(chem), 32. *Prof Exp:* Mem fac, Howard Col, 26-27; chief chemist, Marinello Co, 28-33; asst tech dir, Inecto, Inc, 33-40; from vpres to exec vpres, Evans Chemetics, Inc, 40-66, dir, 40-78, pres, 66-78; SR VPRES, ZOTOS INT INC, 71- *Concurrent Pos:* Tech dir, Sales Affiliates, Inc, 41-66, vpres, 66-69, dir, 66-, pres, 69-; mem chem indust adv comt, Nat Prod Authority, 51-54; trustee, St John's Riverside Hosp, Yonkers, NY, 52-, vpres, 67-78, hon life trustee; exec vpres, Evans Res & Develop Corp, 56-66, dir, 56-69, pres, 66-69; vpres, Zotos Int, Inc, 69-71, dir, 69- *Honors & Awards:* Cosmetology Hall of Fame; Medal, Soc Cosmetic Chem, 52. *Mem:* Fel AAAS; Am Chem Soc; Soc Chem Indust; Soc Cosmetic Chem (vpres, 48 & 50, pres, 51); Cosmetic, Toiletry & Fragrance Asn (dir, 71, secy, 77). *Res:* Keratin chemistry; cosmetic depilatories and permanent waving containing substituted mercaptans; organic sulfur chemistry; dermatology; medicine. *Mailing Add:* Zotos Int Inc Box 1005 Darien CT 06820

MCDONOUGH, JAMES FRANCIS, b Boston, Mass, June 7, 39. STRUCTURES, COMPUTER APPLICATIONS. *Educ:* Northeastern Univ, BSCE, 62, MSCE, 64; Univ Cincinnati, PhD(civil eng), 68, MBA, 81. *Prof Exp:* Asst prof, 68-74, assoc prof, 74-78, HEAD & PROF CIVIL ENG, UNIV CINCINNATI, 78- *Concurrent Pos:* Prof civil eng, Univ Kabul, Afghanistan, 69-71; vis prof, NC State Univ, 71; consult, Huskey Prod & various firms, 78-; William Thomas Prof Civil Eng, 78. *Honors & Awards:* Western Elec Award, Am Soc Eng Educ, 75 & Dow Award, 77. *Mem:* Am Soc Civil Eng; Am Soc Eng Educ; Nat Soc Prof Engrs. *Mailing Add:* Univ Cincinnati Mail Location 71 Cincinnati OH 45221

MCDONOUGH, ROBERT NEWTON, b Huntingdon, Pa, Feb 3, 35; m 65; c 2. ELECTRICAL ENGINEERING. *Educ:* Johns Hopkins Univ, BEngS, 56, DE(elec eng), 63. *Prof Exp:* Asst prof elec eng, Univ Del, 62-65; mem tech staff, Bell Tel Labs, 65-69; assoc prof elec eng & asst dean, Univ Del, 69-80; SR ENGR, APPLIED PHYSICS LAB, JOHNS HOPKINS UNIV, 80- *Concurrent Pos:* Ed, Scripta Publ Corp, 68- *Mem:* Inst Elec & Electronics Engrs. *Res:* Acoustic array processing; system modeling; estimation and detection theory. *Mailing Add:* Appl Physics Lab Johns Hopkins Rd Laurel MD 20707

MCDONOUGH, THOMAS JOSEPH, b Toronto, Ont, Sept 16, 40. CHEMICAL ENGINEERING, ORGANIC CHEMISTRY. *Educ:* Univ Toronto, BASc, 62, PhD(chem eng), 72. *Prof Exp:* Res engr, Can Int Paper Co, 62-66 & Can Industs Ltd, 72-78; asst prof, 78-80, RES ASSOC, INST PAPER CHEM, 78-, ASSOC PROF, 80- *Honors & Awards:* C Howard Smith Medal, Can Pulp & Paper Asn, 71. *Mem:* Can Pulp & Paper Asn; Tech Asn Pulp & Paper Indust. *Res:* Pulping and bleaching technology; chemistry and kinetics of wood pulping and bleaching reactions. *Mailing Add:* Inst Paper Chem PO Box 1039 Appleton WI 54912

MCDONOUGH, WALTER THOMAS, physiological ecology, see previous edition

MACDORAN, PETER FRANK, b Los Angeles, Calif, Jan 2, 41; m 64; c 2. GEODESY. *Educ:* Calif State Univ, Northridge, BS, 64; Univ Calif, Santa Barbara, MS, 66. *Prof Exp:* ARIES PROJ MGR RADIO GEOD, JET PROPULSION LAB, CALIF INST TECHNOL, 68- *Honors & Awards:* NASA Except Sci Achievement Award, 70. *Mem:* Am Geophys Union; Inst Elec & Electronics Engrs. *Res:* Research and development of radio interferometry for applications to problems of geodesy and earth physics. *Mailing Add:* Calif Inst Technol 4800 Oak Grove Dr Pasadena CA 91103

MCDOUGAL, DAVID BLEAN, JR, b Chicago, Ill, Jan 31, 23; m 47; c 3. PHARMACOLOGY. *Educ:* Princeton Univ, BA, 45; Univ Chicago, MD, 47. *Prof Exp:* Instr anat, Johns Hopkins Univ, 50-53; from instr to assoc prof, 57-71, PROF PHARMACOL, SCH MED, WASH UNIV, 71- *Res:* Neurochemistry. *Mailing Add:* Dept of Pharmacol Wash Univ Sch of Med St Louis MO 63110

MCDOUGAL, ROBERT NELSON, b Breckenridge, Minn, Mar 21, 20; m 45; c 3. MECHANICAL ENGINEERING, MATHEMATICS. *Educ:* NDak State Univ, BS, 61, MS, 64; Univ Nebr, Lincoln, PhD(eng mech), 71. *Prof Exp:* From instr to assoc prof mech eng, 63-77, asst dean sch eng, NDak State Univ, 71-77; asst prof mech eng, 77-81, ASSOC PROF ENG MECH, UNIV NEBR, 81- *Concurrent Pos:* Vpres, Forensic Engrs, Ltd, 70- *Mem:* AM Soc Mech Eng; Am Soc Eng Educ; Soc Exp Stress Anal; Am Soc Testing & Mat. *Res:* Heat transfer through composite materials; stress analysis in structural and machine elements. *Mailing Add:* Dept of Mech Eng Bancroft Hall Rm 309 Lincoln NE 68588

MCDOUGALD, LARRY ROBERT, b Broken Bow, Okla, Dec 31, 41; m 62; c 1. PARASITOLOGY. *Educ:* Southeastern State Col, BS, 62; Kans State Univ, MS, 66, PhD(parasitol), 69. *Prof Exp:* Teacher pub schs, Kans, 62-64; instr biol, Mt St Scholastica Col, 67-68; instr zool, Kans State Univ, 68-69; fel poultry sci, Univ Ga, 69-71; sr parasitologist, Parasitol Res Dept, Eli Lilly & Co, 71-77; ASSOC PROF POULTRY SCI DEPT, UNIV GA, 77- *Mem:* Am Soc Parasitol; Am Micros Soc; Poultry Sci Asn; Am Asn Avian Pathologists. *Res:* Physiological and chemical aspects of host-parasite relationships; chemotherapy of protozoan parasites. *Mailing Add:* Poultry Sci Dept Univ of Ga Athens GA 30602

MACDOUGALL, DUNCAN PECK, b College Station, Tex, Apr 13, 09; m 42; c 1. PHYSICAL CHEMISTRY. *Educ:* Pomona Col, AB, 29; Univ Calif, PhD(chem), 33. *Prof Exp:* Instr chem, Univ Calif, 33-34 & Harvard Univ, 34-37; asst prof, Clark Univ, 37-41; phys chemist, US Bur Mines, Pa, 41-43; assoc dir res, Nat Defense Res Comt, Explosives Res Lab, Carnegie Inst Technol, 43-46; chief explosives div, Naval Ord Lab, 46-48; div leader, 48-70, asst dir weapons, 70-72, assoc dir weapons, 72-76, CONSULT, LOS ALAMOS NAT LAB, 76- *Honors & Awards:* Medal of Merit, 48. *Res:* Cryogenics below one degree absolute; vibrations of polyatomic molecules; high explosives chemistry and physics; nuclear weapons. *Mailing Add:* 1984 Peach St Los Alamos NM 87544

MACDOUGALL, JOHN DOUGLAS, b Toronto, Ont, Mar 9, 44; m 68; c 2. GEOCHEMISTRY, METEORITICS. *Educ:* Univ Toronto, BSc, 67; McMaster Univ, MSc, 68; Univ Calif, San Diego, PhD(earth sci), 72. *Prof Exp:* Asst res geologist, Univ Calif, Berkeley, 72-74; asst prof, 74-80, ASSOC PROF EARTH SCI, SCRIPPS INST OCEANOG, UNIV CALIF, SAN DIEGO, 80- *Mem:* AAAS; Am Geophys Union; Meteoritical Soc; Geochem Soc. *Res:* Isotope geology and geochromology; evolution of earth's mantle; volcanic rocks; evolution of meteorites; particle tracks. Res: Fission track geochronology; chemical exchange. *Mailing Add:* Geol Res Div A-020 Scripps Inst Oceanog La Jolla CA 92093

MCDOUGALL, KENNETH J, b Ashland, Wis, Aug 31, 35; m 65; c 2. MICROBIAL GENETICS. *Educ:* Northland Col, BS, 57; Marquette Univ, MS, 59; Kans State Univ, PhD(genetics), 64. *Prof Exp:* Instr zool, Northland Col, 59-60; res assoc genetics, Rice Univ, 63-64, NIH fel, 64-65, res assoc, 65-66; asst prof, 66-69, assoc prof, 69-77, BIOL, UNIV DAYTON, 69- 77- AAAS; Genetics Soc Am; Am Soc Microbiol. *Res:* Mutagenesis and antimutagenesis. *Mailing Add:* Dept of Biol Univ of Dayton Dayton OH 45469

MACDOUGALL, ROBERT DOUGLAS, b McVille, NDak, Jan 2, 22; m 61; c 2. PETROLEUM GEOLOGY. *Educ:* Univ Mont, BA, 49; Univ Minn, Minneapolis, MS, 52. *Prof Exp:* Field geologist, Arabian Am Oil Co, Saudi Arabia, 52-56, subsurface geologist, 56-59; consult, 59-62; GEOLOGIST, US GEOL SURV, 62- *Mem:* Am Asn Petrol Geol; fel Royal Geog Soc. *Res:* Subsurface geology. *Mailing Add:* 646 Oak St Mandeville LA 70448

MCDOUGLE, PAUL E, b Peru, Ind, May 25, 28. MATHEMATICS. *Educ:* Purdue Univ, MS, 49; Univ Va, PhD(math), 58. *Prof Exp:* Asst prof, 58-67, ASSOC PROF MATH, UNIV MIAMI, 67-, ASSOC CHMN DEPT, 70- *Mem:* Math Asn Am. *Res:* Topology; study of decomposition spaces. *Mailing Add:* Dept of Math Univ of Miami Coral Gables FL 33124

MCDOW, JOHN J(ETT), b Covington, Tenn, Jan 6, 25; m 46; c 2. AGRICULTURAL ENGINEERING. *Educ:* Univ Tenn, BS, 48; Mich State Univ, MS, 49, PhD, 57. *Prof Exp:* Instr, Mich State Univ, 49; instr & asst prof, Okla State Univ, 49-51; prof agr eng & head dept, La Polytech Inst, 51-62; head agr eng dept, 62-73, PROF AGR ENG, UNIV TENN, KNOXVILLE, 62-, DEAN ADMIS & RECORDS, 73- *Concurrent Pos:* Consult, Collaborator, Agr Res Serv, US Dept Agr, 70-76. *Mem:* Am Soc Agr Engrs. *Res:* Chemical and mechanical brush control; solar energy use in agriculture; utilization of solar energy in agriculture; silo structures; electric treatment of plant materials. *Mailing Add:* 2008 Walnut Hills Dr Knoxville TN 37920

MACDOWALL, FERGUS D H, b Victoria, BC, Dec 19, 24; m 49; c 3. PLANT PHYSIOLOGY. *Educ:* McGill Univ, BSc, 46; Univ Minn, MS, 47; Stanford Univ, PhD(biol), 54. *Prof Exp:* Instr plant physiol, Univ Mich, 49-51; RES SCIENTIST, CHEM & BIOL RES INST, CAN DEPT AGR, 52- *Concurrent Pos:* AEC fel, Univ Minn, 63-65, lectr, 65. *Mem:* Am Soc Plant Physiol; Bot Soc Am; Am Inst Biol Sci; Am Soc Photobiol; Int Solar Energy Soc. *Res:* Photobiological mechanisms; chloroplasts; growth; ozone damage; frost resistance; tobacco; wheat. *Mailing Add:* Res Br Can Dept Agr Ottawa ON K1A 0C6 Can

MCDOWELL, CHARLES ALEXANDER, b Belfast, Ireland, Aug 29, 18; m 45; c 3. PHYSICAL CHEMISTRY. *Educ:* Queen's Univ, Belfast, BSc, 41-42, DSc, 55. *Prof Exp:* Asst lectr chem, Queen's Univ, Belfast, 41-42; lectr inorg & phys chem, Univ Liverpool, 45-55; prof chem & head dept, 55-81, UNIV PROF CHEM, UNIV BC, 81- *Concurrent Pos:* Spec lectr & spec sci medal, Univ Liege, 55; Nat Res Coun Can sr res fel, Cambridge Univ, 63-64; vis prof, Kyoto Univ, 65 & 69; Killiam sr fel, 69-70; distinguished vis prof, Univ Fla, Gainesville, 74; fac sci distinguished lectr, Univ Calgary, 78. *Honors & Awards:* Letts Gold Medal Theoret Chem, 41; Centennial Medal, Govt Can, 67; Chem Inst Can Award, 69; Frontiers of Chem lectr, Wayne State Univ, 78; Queen Elizabeth's Silver Jubilee Medal, 78; Montreal Medal, Chem Inst Can, 82. *Mem:* Am Phys Soc; Am Chem Soc; fel Royal Soc Can; fel Chem Inst Can (pres, 78-79); fel Am Inst Physics. *Res:* Mass spectrometry; chemical kinetics; electron and nuclear spin resonance spectroscopy; molecular structure; electronic structures of molecules; photoelectron spectrometry. *Mailing Add:* Dept Chem Univ BC Vancouver BC V6T 1W5 Can

MCDOWELL, DAWSON CLAYBORN, b Chic ;o, Ill, July 19, 13; m 36; c 1. METEOROLOGY. *Educ:* Univ Chicago, BS, 35, MS, 42. *Prof Exp:* Instr, Univ Chicago, 42-45; PROF METEOROL & DIR INST TROP METEOROL, UNIV PR, 45- *Concurrent Pos:* Mem, Nat Adv Comt Educ. *Mem:* Am Meteorol Soc; Am Geophys Union. *Res:* Tropical meteorology. *Mailing Add:* Dept Meteorol Univ PR PO Box 22931 Rio Piedros PR 00931

MACDOWELL, DENIS W H, b Belfast, Northern Ireland, Jan 26, 24; US citizen; m 49; c 4. ORGANIC CHEMISTRY. *Educ:* Queen's Univ, Belfast, BSc, 45, MSc, 47; Mass Inst Technol, PhD(org chem), 55. *Prof Exp:* Res chemist, Linen Indust Res Asn, 45-48; instr, Univ Toronto, 48-51; NIH fel org chem, Ohio State Univ, 55-57; lectr, Univ Toronto, 57-59; PROF CHEM, WVA UNIV, 59- *Mem:* Am Chem Soc. *Res:* Polycyclic aromatic hydrocarbon derivatives; thiophene chemistry. *Mailing Add:* Dept of Chem WVa Univ Morgantown WV 26506

MCDOWELL, ELIZABETH MARY, b Kew Gardens, Eng, Mar 30, 40. PATHOLOGY. *Educ:* Univ London, BVetMed, 64; Univ Cambridge, PhD(path), 71, MA, 72. *Prof Exp:* Vet gen pract, 64-66; instr, 71-73, asst prof, 73-76, assoc prof, 76-80, PROF PATH, UNIV MD, BALTIMORE CITY, 80- *Mem:* Royal Col Vet Surg; Histochem Soc; Int Acad Path; Am Asn Cancer Res; Soc Toxicol Pathologists. *Res:* Cellular and subcellular pathology; pulmonary pathology. *Mailing Add:* Dept of Path 31 S Greene St Univ of Md Sch of Med Baltimore MD 21201

MCDOWELL, FLETCHER HUGHES, b Denver, Colo, Aug 5, 23; m 58; c 3. NEUROLOGY. *Educ:* Dartmouth Col, AB, 43; Cornell Univ, MD, 47. *Prof Exp:* From instr to assoc prof med, 52-68, PROF NEUROL, MED COL, CORNELL UNIV, 68-, ASSOC DEAN MED COL, 70-; MED DIR, BURKE REHAB HOSP, WHITE PLAINS, 73- *Mem:* Am Acad Neurol; Am Neurol Asn; Am Fedn Clin Res. *Res:* Cerebrovascular disease. *Mailing Add:* Cornell Univ Med Col 1300 York Ave New York NY 10021

MCDOWELL, FRANK, surgery, deceased

MCDOWELL, FRED WALLACE, b Abington, Pa, Sept 30, 39; m 64; c 3. GEOCHEMISTRY. *Educ:* Lafayette Col, AB, 61; Columbia Univ, PhD(geochem), 66. *Prof Exp:* Researcher geochronology, Swiss Fed Inst Technol, 66-69; RES SCIENTIST, UNIV TEX, AUSTIN, 69- *Mem:* Fel Geol Soc Am. *Res:* Application of isotopic age determination methods to geologic problems, including volcanism, orogenesis and metallization. *Mailing Add:* Dept of Geol Sci Univ of Tex Austin TX 78712

MCDOWELL, HARDING KEITH, b High Point, NC, Feb 5, 44; m 75. CHEMICAL PHYSICS. *Educ:* Wake Forest Univ, BS, 66; Harvard Univ, PhD(chem physics), 72. *Prof Exp:* Res assoc chem, State Univ NY Stony Brook, 72-74; asst prof, 74-78, ASSOC PROF CHEM, CLEMSON UNIV, 78- *Concurrent Pos:* Alfred P Sloan Res Fel, 78-80. *Mem:* Am Phys Soc; Am Chem Soc; AAAS. *Res:* Study of many-body effects in chemical systems. *Mailing Add:* Dept of Chem & Geol Clemson Univ Clemson SC 29631

MCDOWELL, HERSHEL, b Gaffney, SC, Aug 9, 30; m 56; c 2. PHYSICAL CHEMISTRY. *Educ:* Morgan State Col, BS, 57; Howard Univ, PhD(chem), 67. *Prof Exp:* Res asst immunol, Johns Hopkins Univ, 57-58; res asst, Charlotte Mem Hosp, NC, 58-62; res assoc chem, Am Dent Asn, Nat Bur Standards, DC, 65-69; prof chem & chmn dept, Fed City Col, DC, 69-78, PROF CHEM & ACTG CHMN DEPT, UNIV DC, 78- *Mem:* Am Chem Soc. *Res:* Solubility and thermodynamic properties of the calcium orthophosphates; stability of complexes between calcium and phosphate ions and organic ligands. *Mailing Add:* Dept of Chem Univ DC 1331 H St NW Washington DC 20005

MACDOWELL, JOHN FRASER, b Oct 10, 32; US citizen; m 57; c 5. GEOLOGY, CHEMISTRY. *Educ:* Univ Mich, BS, 58, MS, 59. *Prof Exp:* Chemist, 59-61, sr chemist, 61-64, res mgr glass ceramics, 64-66, DIR CHEM RES, CORNING GLASS WORKS, 66- *Concurrent Pos:* Mem panel ceramic processing, Mat Adv Bd, Nat Acad Sci-Nat Res Coun, 65- *Mem:* Am Chem Soc; fel Am Ceramic Soc; Mineral Soc Am; Brit Soc Glass Technol. *Res:* Devitrification of glass and ceramic materials formed in this manner; controlling nucleation to create unique ceramics. *Mailing Add:* Corning Glass Works Sullivan Park Corning NY 14830

MCDOWELL, JOHN PARMELEE, b Ridgewood, NJ, Feb 13, 31; m 55; c 2. SEDIMENTARY PETROLOGY. *Educ:* Yale Univ, BS, 53; Dartmouth Col, MA, 55; Johns Hopkins Univ, PhD, 63. *Prof Exp:* Geologist, US Geol Surv, 54-58; instr, 58-63, asst dean col arts & sci, 64-67, ASST PROF GEOL, TULANE UNIV LA, 63-, ASSOC DEAN COL ARTS & SCI, 67- *Concurrent Pos:* Spec geologist, Ont Dept Mines, Can, 56-57; fel acad admin, Am Coun Educ. *Mem:* Am Asn Petrol Geol; fel Geol Soc Am; Soc Econ Paleont & Mineral; Mineral Asn Can. *Res:* Sedimentary petrology. *Mailing Add:* Off of Dean Col of Arts & Sci Tulane Univ New Orleans LA 70118

MCDOWELL, JOHN ROBERT, physical chemistry, see previous edition

MCDOWELL, JOHN WILLIS, b Honolulu, Hawaii, Dec 12, 21; m 50; c 2. PARASITOLOGY. *Educ:* Colo State Univ, BS, 47, MS, 48; Univ NC, MPH, 50; Okla State Univ, PhD(zool), 53. *Prof Exp:* Adv parasitol, USPHS, Int Coop Admin, Cambodia, Laos & Vietnam, 51-53, co-dir malaria control, Govt Iran, 54-56, tech adv malaria eradication, US Opers Mission, Philippines, 56-60, regional adv, Western Pac Region, AID, 60-61, spec asst to chief training br, Commun Dis Ctr, 61-62, asst chief vector borne dis sect, 62-64, chief eval unit, Aedes Aegypti Eradication Br, 64-66, asst chief eval sect, Malaria Eradication Br, 66-69; assoc prof, 69-72, PROF BIOL, BERRY COL, 72- *Concurrent Pos:* Mem independent malaria assessment team, US-WHO, Thailand & Iran, 63 & Vietnam, 64; consult, 11th Exper Comt Malaria, WHO, 64; US del, Int Cong Trop Med & Malaria, Lisbon, 58, Asian Malaria Conf, New Delhi, 58, Anti-Malaria Coord Bd, Southeast Asia, 59 & Borneo Conf Malaria Semarang, 60; Lilly Found fel environ educ, Ohio State Univ, 74-75; mem joint WHO/US Task Force on Malaria Training in Asia, 78. *Mem:* Am Soc Parasitol; Am Soc Trop Med & Hyg; Royal Soc Trop Med & Hyg; Am Mosquito Control Asn. *Res:* Field investigation and control of parasitic diseases, especially those which are arthropod borne; eradication and control of vector-borne disease or disease vectors, particularly malaria, filariasis and yellow fever; technical, organizational and administrative evaluation of such programs. *Mailing Add:* 5 Beaver Run Rome GA 30161

MACDOWELL, JOSEPH, b Wallasey, Eng, Aug 14, 26; Can citizen; m 55; c 4. GEOPHYSICS, METEOROLOGY. *Educ:* Cambridge Univ, BA, 51, MA, 55. *Prof Exp:* Sci officer, Meteorol Off, Eng, 51-55, sr sci officer, 55-56; group leader meteorol, Royal Soc Int Geophys Year Antarctic Exped, Halley Bay, 56-58, exped leader geophys, 58-59, group leader, Eng, 59-60; sr scientist, Brit Aircraft Corp Eng, 60-63, chief physicist, 63-66; gen mgr res & develop div, Barringer Res, Ont, 66-69; coordr environ Can, Can Centre Inland Waters, 69-78; COUNR SCI & TECHNOL, CAN EMBASSY, 78- *Concurrent Pos:* Mem assoc comt avionics, Nat Res Coun Can, 66. *Honors & Awards:* Bruce Medal, Royal Soc Edinburgh, 60; Officer Brit Empire, 60; Polar Medal, 61. *Mem:* Inst Elec & Electronics Engrs; Can Aeronaut & Space Inst; Can Meteorol Soc; Royal Meteorol Soc; assoc fel Royal Aeronaut Soc. *Res:* Meteorological instrument development; polar research in meteorology, geomagnetism and glaciology; design of space craft instruments; development of remote sensing techniques for earth resources; research on Laurentian Great Lakes and air-water interactions. *Mailing Add:* Can Embassy 1746 Massachusetts Ave NW Washington DC 20036

MCDOWELL, LEE RUSSELL, b Sodus, NY, Apr 11, 41; m 71; c 3. ANIMAL NUTRITION. *Educ:* Univ Ga, BS, 64, MS, 65; Wash State Univ, PhD(animal nutrit), 71. *Prof Exp:* Res asst animal nutrit, Univ Ga, 64-65; agr vol, Peace Corps, Bolivia, 65-67; res asst animal nutrit & teaching asst animal prod, Wash State Univ, 68-71; asst prof, 71-76, ASSOC PROF ANIMAL NUTRIT, UNIV FLA, 76- *Concurrent Pos:* Mineral res consult, 74. *Mem:* Am Soc Animal Sci; Am Dairy Sci Asn; Latin Am Asn Animal Prod. *Res:* Problems dealing with international animal nutrition and production; chemical composition and feeding value of Latin American feeds; determining the location of mineral deficiencies or toxicities that are inhibiting livestock production in Latin America. *Mailing Add:* Dept of Animal Sci Livestock Pavilion Univ of Fla Gainesville FL 32611

MCDOWELL, MARION EDWARD, b Torrington, Wyo, Nov 4, 21; m 44; c 2. MEDICINE, NUTRITION. *Educ:* Univ Wyo, BS, 42; Univ Rochester, MD, 45; Am Bd Internal Med, dipl, 53, recert, 74. *Prof Exp:* Instr med, Sch Med, Univ Rochester, 45-46 & 48-50, from intern to assoc resident, Sch Med, Univ Rochester & Strong Mem Hosp, 45-50; med res, Walter Reed Army Med Ctr, 50-54, dir med div, Walter Reed Army Inst Res, 54-56, from asst chief to chief dept med, Tokyo Army Hosp, 56-58, chief outpatient dept, US Army Med Hosp, Camp Zama, Japan, 58-59, dep comdr & chief metab div, US Army Med Res & Nutrit Lab, 59-60, cmndg officer, 60-64; DIR MED EDUC, ST JOSEPH HOSP, DENVER, 64-; ASSOC CLIN PROF MED, SCH MED, UNIV COLO, 80- *Concurrent Pos:* Fel renal dis, Peter Bent Brigham Hosp, 50; Army liaison rep, Food & Nutrit Bd, Nat Acad Sci-Nat Res Coun & Nutrit Study Sect, NIH, 61-64; mem subcomt feeding & nutrit space, Nat Res Coun, 62-64; asst clin prof med, Sch Med, Univ Colo, 64-80. *Mem:* Fel Am Col Physicians; Am Soc Internal Med; Am Inst Nutrit; Am Soc Clin Nutrit; Am Fedn Clin Res. *Res:* Internal medicine and clinical research; renal disease; fluid and electrolyte metabolism; hemodialysis in renal failure; clinical nutrition; military medicine; medical education. *Mailing Add:* 7865 E Mississippi Ave Denver CO 80231

MCDOWELL, MAURICE JAMES, b Dannevirke, NZ, Dec 6, 22; nat US; m 57; c 4. AUTOMOTIVE COATINGS, COLLOIDS. *Educ:* Univ Otago, NZ, BSc, 43, MSc, 44; Brown Univ, PhD(chem), 50. *Prof Exp:* Lectr, Univ Otago, NZ, 44-47; chemist, E I du Pont de Nemours & Co, Inc, 50-52; res assoc, Univ Montreal, 52; chem assoc, 53-60, res supvr, 60-63, RES ASSOC, FABRICS & FINISHES DIV, E I DU PONT DE NEMOURS & CO, INC, 64- *Mem:* Am Chem Soc; Fedn Soc Coating Technol. *Res:* Polymer research; colloid chemistry; research on coatings for automobiles. *Mailing Add:* Fabrics & Finishes Div E I du Pont de Nemours & Co Inc PO Box 3886 Philadelphia PA 19146

MCDOWELL, ROBERT CARTER, b Glens Falls, NY, Feb 15, 35; m 63; c 3. GEOLOGY. *Educ:* Va Polytech Inst, BS, 56, MS, 64, PhD(geol), 68. *Prof Exp:* Instr geol, Va Polytech Inst, 65-66; asst prof, Wis State Univ, River Falls, 66-67; GEOLOGIST, US GEOL SURV, 67- *Mem:* Geol Soc Am. *Res:* Structural geology and petrography of the Arvonia slate quarries, Virginia; structural geology and stratigraphy of lower Cambrian quartzites, Pulaski County, Virginia; field geology of northeastern Kentucky. *Mailing Add:* Nat Ctr US Geol Surv 12201 Sunrise Valley Dr MS 928 Reston VA 22092

MCDOWELL, ROBERT E, JR, b Charlotte, NC, June 27, 21; m 45; c 3. ANIMAL SCIENCE, ANIMAL PHYSIOLOGY. *Educ:* NC State Col, BS, 42; Univ Md, MS, 49, PhD(dairy husb), 54. *Prof Exp:* Dist supvr, Vet Training Prog, NC, 46; dairy husbandman, Dairy Husb Res Br, Agr Res Serv, USDA, 46-58, sr res scientist, Dairy Cattle Res Br, Animal Husb Res Div, 58-67; PROF INT ANIMAL SCI, CORNELL UNIV, 67- *Concurrent Pos:* Instr, Johns Hopkins Univ, 53-57; consult to various US agencies & foreign govt, 56-; vis prof, Cornell Univ, 66; prof, Univ PR, 69-80; vis prof, Fac de Agron, Cent Univ, Venezuela, 74, Nat Univ Pedro Henriquez Urena, Dominican Repub, 76; chmn bd trustees, Int Livestock Ctr, Africa, 80- *Honors & Awards:* Superior Serv Award, USDA, 62; Am Soc Animal Sci Award, Int Animal Agr, 79. *Mem:* Am Soc Animal Sci; Am Dairy Sci Asn; Int Soc Biometeorol; AAAS. *Res:* Means of improving contribution of livestock to man's need in developing countries; use of crossbreeding as mating system in animal production; farming systems in developing countries. *Mailing Add:* Dept of Animal Sci Cornell Univ Ithaca NY 14850

MCDOWELL, ROBERT HULL, b Chicago, Ill, Dec 1, 27; m 56; c 3. MATHEMATICS. *Educ:* Univ Chicago, PhB, 47, BS & MS, 50; Purdue Univ, PhD, 59. *Prof Exp:* Asst mathematician, Argonne Nat Lab, 53-54; asst math, Purdue Univ, 54-55; instr & asst prof, Rutgers Univ, 59; asst prof, Purdue Univ, 59-60; from asst prof to assoc prof, 60-72, PROF MATH, WASH UNIV, 72-, CHMN DEPT, 74- *Concurrent Pos:* Dir comt undergrad prog math, NSF, 64-66, mem panel teacher training, mem adv group commun, mem comt teaching undergrad math; Nat Acad Sci interacad sci exchange, Czech, 81. *Mem:* Am Math Soc; Math Asn Am. *Res:* Set theoretic topology and algebra and their interrelationships; mathematical structures; category theory. *Mailing Add:* Dept of Math Wash Univ St Louis MO 63130

MACDOWELL, ROBERT W, b Detroit, Mich, Dec 11, 24; m 44; c 3. MATHEMATICS. *Educ:* Oberlin Col, AB, 48; Univ Mich, AM, 49, PhD(math), 53. *Prof Exp:* From instr to asst prof math, Univ Rochester, 51-57; res assoc, Cornell Univ, 57-58; from assoc prof to prof, Antioch Col, 58-70; vpres & dean, 74-77, PROF MATH, HIRAM COL, 70- *Concurrent Pos:* Sci fac fel, 57-58. *Mem:* Am Math Soc; Math Asn Am; Asn Symbolic Logic. *Res:* Model theory in mathematical logic; logic of quantum mechanics. *Mailing Add:* Dept of Math Hiram Col Hiram OH 44234

MCDOWELL, ROBIN SCOTT, b Greenwich, Conn, Nov 14, 34; m 63; c 2. MOLECULAR SPECTROSCOPY. *Educ:* Haverford Col, BA, 56; Mass Inst Technol, PhD(phys chem), 60. *Prof Exp:* Asst chem, Mass Inst Technol, 56-60; staff mem phys chem, 60-81, ASST GROUP LEADER, LOS ALAMOS NAT LAB, 81- *Mem:* AAAS; Optical Soc Am; Coblentz Soc; Soc Appl Spectros; Laser Inst Am. *Res:* Infrared laser spectroscopy; vibrational spectra of inorganic and isotopically-substituted molecules, especially fluorides; molecular dynamics and force fields; calculated thermodynamic properties of ideal gases; infrared analytical methods; atmospheric optics. *Mailing Add:* 885 Camino Encantado Los Alamos NM 87544

MCDOWELL, SAM BOOKER, b New York, NY, Sept 13, 28; m 52; c 2. HERPETOLOGY. *Educ:* Columbia Univ, AB, 47, PhD(zool), 57. *Prof Exp:* From asst instr to assoc prof biol, 56-68, PROF ZOOL, RUTGERS UNIV, NEWARK, 68- *Mem:* Am Soc Ichthyol & Herpet; Soc Study Evolution; Zool Soc London; Soc Study Amphibians & Reptiles; Linnean Soc London. *Res:* Vertebrate paleontology; teleost and reptilian anatomy; origin of higher taxonomic categories; New Guinea snakes; primitive teleosts. *Mailing Add:* Dept of Zool Rutgers Univ Newark NJ 07102

MACDOWELL, SAMUEL WALLACE, b Recife, Brazil, Mar 24, 29; m 53; c 3. PHYSICS. *Educ:* Univ Recife, BS, 51; Univ Birmingham, PhD(physics), 58. *Prof Exp:* Instr physics, Brazilian Ctr Phys Res, 54-56; instr, Princeton Univ, 59-60; from assoc prof to prof, Brazilian Ctr Phys Res, 60-63; mem, Inst Advan Study, 63-65; assoc prof, 65-67, PROF PHYSICS, YALE UNIV, 67- *Concurrent Pos:* Prof, Cath Univ Rio de Janiero, 62-63, vis prof, 69 & 74-75. *Mem:* Fel Am Phys Soc; Brazilian Acad Sci; NY Acad Sci. *Res:* Strong and weak interactions of elementary particles; s-matrix theory; analytic properties of scattering amplitudes and form factors; group theory and symmetries of interactions; gauge theories; spontaneous symmetry breaking; renormalization group; theory of gravitation and supergravity. *Mailing Add:* Dept of Physics Yale Univ New Haven CT 06520

MCDOWELL, THEODORE C, floriculture, horticulture, see previous edition

MCDOWELL, WILBUR BENEDICT, b Omaha, Nebr, Feb 27, 20; m 47; c 3. ORGANIC CHEMISTRY, PHARMACEUTICAL CHEMISTRY. *Educ:* Ohio State Univ, BSc, 41, MSc, 42, PhD(chem), 44. *Prof Exp:* Asst chem, Ohio State Univ, 42-43; res assoc, Squibb Inst Med Res, 44-52; head synthetic org develop sect, Olin Mathieson Chem Corp, 53-59, sr res chemist, 59-66; assoc mgr, New York, 66-69, SCI MGR PROF SERV, E R SQUIBB & SONS, INC, PRINCETON, 69- *Mem:* fel AAAS; Am Chem Soc; fel Am Inst Chem; Soc Nuclear Med; NY Acad Sci. *Res:* Synthesis and isolation of antibiotics; synthetic organic process development. *Mailing Add:* 4 Fairview Ave East Brunswick NJ 08816

MCDOWELL, WILLIAM H, b Philadelphia, Pa, Apr 26, 53. AQUATIC ECOLOGY. *Educ:* Amherst Col, BA, 75; Cornell Univ, PhD(aquatic ecol), 82. *Prof Exp:* RES ASSOC, ECOSYSTS RES CTR, CORNELL UNIV, 81- *Mem:* Am Soc Limnol & Oceanog; AAAS; Ecol Soc Am; Sigma Xi. *Res:* Biochemistry of dissolved organic carbon in terrestrial and aquatic ecosystems; mechanisms controlling stream water chemistry. *Mailing Add:* Ecosyst Res Ctr Cornell Univ 468 Hollister Hall Ithaca NY 14853

MCDOWELL, WILLIAM JACKSON, b McMinnville, Tenn, July 14, 25; m 51; c 2. SOLVENT EXTRACTION CHEMISTRY. *Educ:* Tenn Technol Univ, BS, 51; Univ Tenn, MS, 54. *Prof Exp:* Jr chemist, 51-52, res chemist, 54-75, RES GROUP LEADER, UNION CARBIDE NUCLEAR, OAK RIDGE NAT LAB, 75- *Honors & Awards:* Indust Res-100 Award, Indust Res, 81. *Mem:* Am Chem Soc; Am Nuclear Soc; Sigma Xi; AAAS. *Res:* Inorganic separations chemistry, primarily liquid-liquid extraction and ion exchange, relating to hydrometallurgical processes and analytical procedures. *Mailing Add:* Oak Ridge Nat Lab Oak Ridge TN 37830

MCDUFF, ODIS P(ELHAM), b Gordo, Ala, May 16, 31; m 53; c 4. ELECTRICAL ENGINEERING. *Educ:* Univ Ala, BS, 52; Mass Inst Technol, SM, 53; Stanford Univ, PhD(quantum electronics), 66. *Prof Exp:* Test engr, Gen Elec Co, 52, circuit develop engr, 56-59, supv engr, 59; mem tech staff elec eng, Bell Tel Lab, 53-54; asst prof microwaves, 59-66, assoc prof quantum electronics, Dept Elec Eng, 66-68, PROF & HEAD DEPT, DEPT ELEC ENG, UNIV ALA, TUSCALOOSA, 68- *Concurrent Pos:* NSF res grant, 67-68; mem laser technol comt, Army Missile Command, Ala, 67-70. *Mem:* Sr mem Inst Elec & Electronics Engrs; Am Soc Eng Educ. *Res:* Quantum electronics; nonlinear optics; microwaves; laser mode coupling; laser modulation. *Mailing Add:* Dept of Elec Eng PO Box 6167 University AL 35486

MCDUFFIE, BRUCE, b Atlanta, Ga, Aug 25, 21; m 50; c 3. CHEMISTRY. *Educ:* Princeton Univ, AB, 42, MA, 46, PhD(chem), 47. *Prof Exp:* Asst chem, Cornell Univ, 42; asst Manhattan Proj, Princeton Univ, 42-47; instr, Emory Univ, 47-51; assoc prof, Washington & Jefferson Col, 51-58; assoc prof, 58-61, PROF CHEM, STATE UNIV NY, BINGHAMTON, HARPER COL, 61- *Honors & Awards:* Spec Award Merit, US Environ Protection Agency, 76. *Mem:* AAAS; Am Chem Soc; Scientists Inst Pub Info. *Res:* Electroanalytical chemistry; trace methods and environmental analysis for toxic metals and organic pollutants; river pollution and sludge disposal studies. *Mailing Add:* Dept of Chem State Univ NY Binghamton NY 13901

MCDUFFIE, FREDERIC CLEMENT, b Lawrence, Mass, Apr 27, 24; m 52; c 4. MEDICINE. *Educ:* Harvard Med Sch, MD, 51. *Prof Exp:* From intern to jr asst resident, Peter Bent Brigham Hosp, Boston, 51-53; fel phys chem, Harvard Univ, 53-54; fel microbiol, Col Physicians & Surgeons, Columbia Univ, 54-56; sr asst resident, Peter Bent Brigham Hosp, 56-57; from asst prof to assoc prof med & microbiol, Sch Med, Univ Miss, 57-65; asst prof, med & microbiol, Mayo Med Sch, Univ Minn, 65-69, assoc prof, Mayo Grad Sch Med, 69-74, prof, 74-79, consult, Mayo Clin, 65-79; SR VPRES MED AFFAIRS, ARTHRITIS FOUND, 79-; PROF MED, EMORY UNIV, 79- *Concurrent Pos:* Vis investr, Ctr Dis Control, 79- *Mem:* Am Asn Immunologists; Am Rheumatism Asn; Am Fedn Clin Res; Am Col Physicians; Soc Exp Biol & Med. *Res:* Complement system in connective tissue diseases; antibody production in chickens. *Mailing Add:* Arthritis Foundation 3400 Peachtree Rd NE Atlanta GA 30326

MCDUFFIE, GEORGE E(ADDY), JR, b Washington, DC, Apr 4, 25; m 50; c 6. ELECTRICAL ENGINEERING. *Educ:* Cath Univ Am, BEE, 49, MEE, 52; Univ Md, PhD, 62. *Prof Exp:* From instr to assoc prof elec eng, 49-63, chmn dept, 69-70, actg dean, 70-71, PROF ELEC ENG, CATH UNIV AM, 63-, DEAN, 76- *Concurrent Pos:* NSF grant, 58-60; physicist, Naval Ord Lab,

Md, 58- *Mem:* Am Soc Eng Educ; Inst Elec & Electronics Engrs. *Res:* Properties of liquid dielectrics and their measurement under varying temperature, pressure and frequency; modern network theory; pattern recognition. *Mailing Add:* Dept of Elec Eng Cath Univ of Am Washington DC 20017

MCDUFFIE, NORTON G(RAHAM), JR, b Beaumont, Tex, Nov 26, 30; m 61; c 2. BIOCHEMISTRY, CHEMICAL ENGINEERING. *Educ:* Tex A&M Univ, BS, 52; Univ Tex, PhD(chem), 62. *Prof Exp:* Process engr, Mobil Oil Co, 52-57; fel biochem, Clayton Found Biochem Inst, 62-63; asst prof chem, Lamar Univ, 63-64; asst prof biochem, Sch Med, Univ Okla, 64-69; ASSOC PROF CHEM ENG, UNIV CALGARY, 69- *Concurrent Pos:* Assoc, Okla Med Res Found, 64-69; vis lectr, Univ Tex, Austin, 67-68; consult, Mobil Chem Co, 68-70. *Mem:* Am Chem Soc; Am Inst Chem Engrs; Am Soc Microbiol. *Res:* Cancer; chemical engineering design; viruses; electron microscopy. *Mailing Add:* Dept of Chem Eng 2920 24th Ave NW Calgary AB T2N 1N4 Can

MCDUGLE, WOODROW GORDON, JR, inorganic chemistry, physical chemistry, see previous edition

MACE, ARNETT C, JR, b Hackers Valley, WVa, Nov 18, 37; m 62; c 2. FOREST HYDROLOGY. *Educ:* WVa Univ, BS, 60; Univ Ariz, MS, 62, PhD(forest hydrol), 68. *Prof Exp:* Res forester forest hydrol, Res Br, US Forest Serv, 62-64; instr, Univ Ariz, 64-67; from asst prof to assoc prof, Univ Minn, 67-74, head forest biol dept, 72-74, prof & head forest resources dept, 74-78; DIR, SCH FOREST RESOURCES & CONSERV, UNIV FLA, 78- *Mem:* Soc Am Foresters; Am Geophys Union; Am Water Resources Asn. *Res:* Applied and basic research related to forest land management practices and policies, with particular emphasis on water resources problems related to forest land management. *Mailing Add:* Sch of Forest Resources & Conserv Univ of Fla Gainesville FL 32611

MACE, JOHN WELDON, b Buena Vista, Va, July 9, 38; m 62; c 3. PEDIATRIC ENDOCRINOLOGY, METABOLISM. *Educ:* Columbia Union Col, BA, 60; Loma Linda Univ, MD, 64. *Prof Exp:* Attend physician pediat, Naval Hosp, San Diego, 68-70; fel endocrinol, Univ Colo Med Ctr, Denver, 70-72; asst prof, 72-75, PROF PEDIAT & DEPT CHMN, SCH MED, LOMA LINDA UNIV, 75- *Concurrent Pos:* Consult, Calif Newborn Screening Comt & Calif Med Asn Pediat Adv Comt, 75- *Mem:* Am Acad Pediat; Lawson Wilkens Pediat Endocrine Soc; Asn Med Sch Pediat Dept Chmn. *Res:* Behavioral factors as related to juvenile diabetes patients and diabetic control; growth promoting effects of oxandrolowe on short stature. *Mailing Add:* Dept Pediat Med Sch Loma Linda Univ Loma Linda CA 92354

MACE, KENNETH DEAN, b Pekin, Ill, Jan 29, 26; m; c 1. MICROBIOLOGY, CELL PHYSIOLOGY. *Educ:* Univ Ark, BS, 51, MS, 57, PhD(plant physiol), 64. *Prof Exp:* Bacteriologist, Pepsi Cola Co, NY, 51-54; asst epidemiol, Univ Ark, 54-55 & bact, 55-57; bact chemist, Pepsi Cola Co, NY, 57-59; asst bot & bact, Univ Ark, 59-64; from asst prof to assoc prof, 64-71, PROF BIOL, STEPHEN F AUSTIN STATE UNIV, 71- *Concurrent Pos:* Dept Health, Educ & Welfare grants, 71-73. *Mem:* AAAS; Sigma Xi; NY Acad Sci; Am Soc Microbiol. *Res:* Cyclic adenosine monophosphate relationships early in infection by New Castle disease virus; humoral and secretory immune response to whole cell and ribosomal preparation of Candida albicans; cyclic adenosine monophosphate levels in liver cells in response to ethyl alcohol intake at two levels of intake; development of certain monoclonal antibodies by the hybridoma technique; immunology. *Mailing Add:* Dept of Biol Stephen F Austin State Univ Nacogdoches TX 75962

MCEACHRAN, JOHN D, b Iron Mountain, Mich, Nov 1, 41; m 72; c 1. ICHTHYOLOGY, TAXONOMY. *Educ:* Mich State Univ, BA, 65; Col William & Mary, MA, 68, PhD(marine biol), 73. *Prof Exp:* Asst prof, 73-78, ASSOC PROF WILDLIFE & FISHERIES SCI, TEX A&M UNIV, 78- *Concurrent Pos:* Prin investr, NSF grant, 78-81. *Mem:* Am Soc Ichthyologists & Herpetologists; Soc for Study Evolution; Soc Syst Zool; AAAS. *Res:* Systematics; evolutionary biology and zoogeography of the flattened elasmobranchs; systematic and ecological interrelationships of fishes. *Mailing Add:* Dept of Wildlife & Fisheries Sci Tex A&M Univ College Station TX 77843

MACEK, ANDREJ, b Zagreb, Yugoslavia, Oct 24, 26; nat US; m 56; c 2. PHYSICAL CHEMISTRY. *Educ:* Georgetown Univ, BS, 50; Cath Univ Am, MS, 51, PhD(phys chem), 53. *Prof Exp:* Asst, Cath Univ Am, 51-53, res assoc, 53-54; asst prof, Lafayette Col, 54-55; res assoc, US Naval Ord Lab, 55-60; phys chemist, Atlantic Res Corp, 60-69, chief kinetics & combustion group, 69-74; proj leader flame & combustion res, Nat Bur Stand, 74-75; chief, Power & Combustion Br, Energy Res & Develop Admin, Dept Energy, 75-78; COMBUSTION SCIENTIST, NAT BUR STANDARDS, 78- *Concurrent Pos:* Adj prof, Am Univ, 58-72. *Mem:* Am Chem Soc; Combustion Inst. *Res:* Combustion; chemical kinetics and thermodynamics. *Mailing Add:* 859 Golden Arrow St Great Falls VA 22066

MACEK, JOSEPH, b Rapid City, SDak, July 4, 37; m 64; c 2. PHYSICS. *Educ:* SDak State Col, BS, 60; Rensselaer Polytech Inst, PhD(physics), 64. *Prof Exp:* Nat Res Coun fel, Nat Bur Stand, 64-66; Oxford-Harwell fel, Atomic Energy Res Estab, UK, 66-68; from asst prof to assoc prof, 68-74, PROF PHYSICS, UNIV NEBR, LINCOLN, 74- *Mem:* Am Phys Soc. *Res:* Atomic physics. *Mailing Add:* Behlen Lab of Physics Univ of Nebr Lincoln NE 68508

MACEK, ROBERT JAMES, b Rapid City, SDak, July 14, 36; m 62; c 2. ELEMENTARY PARTICLE PHYSICS, EXPERIMENTAL NUCLEAR PHYSICS. *Educ:* SDak State Univ, BS, 58; Calif Inst Technol, PhD(physics), 65. *Prof Exp:* Res assoc physics, Univ Pa, 66-69; GROUP LEADER & MEM STAFF MEDIUM ENERGY PHYSICS DIV, LOS ALAMOS SCI LAB, 69- *Mem:* AAAS; Am Phys Soc; Sigma Xi. *Res:* Weak interactions and rare decay modes of mesons; pion production and absorption reactions on nuclei; nuclear instrumentation; particle beam optics and beam instrumentation. *Mailing Add:* MP-13 MS838 Los Alamos Sci Lab Los Alamos NM 87545

MACEK, THOMAS JOSEPH, b Newark, NJ, Oct 25, 17; m 42; c 2. TECHNICAL REGULATORY MANAGEMENT, PHARMACEUTICAL CHEMISTRY. *Educ:* Rutgers Univ, BS, 38, PhD(physiol, biochem), 50; Univ Fla, MS, 40. *Prof Exp:* Control chemist, Burroughs Wellcome & Co, Inc, 40-41; res assoc, Merck & Co, Inc, 42-56, from asst mgr to mgr, 50-56, mgr pharmaceut res, Merck Sharp & Dohme Res Labs, 56-60, dir pharmaceut res & develop, 60-70; dir rev, US Pharmacopeia, 70-72; SR VPRES, REGULATORY AFFAIRS & QUAL ASSURANCE, CHEM MFG, TECHNICON INSTRUMENTS CORP, 72- *Concurrent Pos:* Expert comt on stand for pharmaceuticals, WHO, 71-72. *Mem:* Am Chem Soc; Am Pharmaceut Asn (1st vpres, 64-65); Acad Pharmaceut Sci (pres, 70-71); Int Pharmaceut Fedn. *Res:* Drug extraction; stabilization of pharmaceuticals; drug, diagnostic and safety regulations; vitamins; antibiotics; adrenocortical hormones; narcotics; diuretics; synthetic therapeutics; drug standards; clinical chemistry; hematology; automated analysis; industrial management; quality control and quality assurance. *Mailing Add:* Technicon Instruments Corp Tarrytown NY 10591

MCELANEY, JAMES H, b Boston, Mass, Aug 28, 23. PHYSICS. *Educ:* Boston Col, BA, 47, MA, 48; Weston Col, PhL, 48, STL, 55; Johns Hopkins Univ, PhD(physics), 64. *Prof Exp:* Instr physics & math, Boston Col, 48-50 & Col Holy Cross, 50-51; from asst prof to assoc prof, 63-75, PROF PHYSICS, FAIRFIELD UNIV, 75-, CHMN DEPT, 64- *Mem:* Optical Soc Am; Am Asn Physics Teachers; Am Phys Soc. *Res:* Free-ion spectroscopy; spectroscopy of the middle and far ultraviolet. *Mailing Add:* Dept of Physics Fairfield Univ Fairfield CT 06430

MCELCHERAN, DONALD ELMO, b Hamilton, Ont, Apr 14, 25; m 53; c 4. PHYSICAL CHEMISTRY. *Educ:* McMaster Univ, BSc, 49, MSc, 50; Univ Leeds, PhD(chem), 54. *Prof Exp:* Fel, Nat Res Coun Can, 54-56; res assoc physics, Laval Univ, 56-57; asst prof, 57-67, ASSOC PROF PHYS CHEM, LOYOLA FAC ARTS & SCI, CONCORDIA UNIV, 67- *Mem:* The Chem Soc; Chem Inst Can. *Res:* Gas phase kinetics; mass spectrometry. *Mailing Add:* Dept of Chem Loyola Fac Arts & Sci Concordia Univ 7141 Sherbrooke St W Montreal PQ H4B 1R6 Can

MCELGUNN, JAMES DOUGLAS, b Vancouver, BC, Mar 22, 39; m 61; c 3. FORAGE CROP PRODUCTION, CROP PHYSIOLOGY. *Educ:* Mont State Col, BS, 62, MS, 64; Mich State Univ, PhD(crop prod), 67. *Prof Exp:* RES SCIENTIST FORAGE, AGR CAN RES BR, 67-; DIR, KAMKLOOPS RANGE RES STA, 80- *Concurrent Pos:* Can chmn, Lucerne Weather Data Acquisition, World Meteorol Orgn, UN, 75-; assoc ed, Can J Plant Sci, 75-81; consult, Can-China deleg, 81. *Mem:* Can Soc Agron; Agr Inst Can. *Res:* Forage crop agronomy under dryland and irrigated conditions including establishment, management and harvesting. *Mailing Add:* Agr Can Res Sta 3015 Ord Rd Kamloops BC V2B 8A9 Can

MCELHANEY, JAMES HARRY, b Philadelphia, Pa, Oct 27, 33; m 55; c 3. MECHANICAL ENGINEERING, BIOMECHANICS. *Educ:* Villanova Univ, BSME, 55; Pa State Univ, MSME, 60; WVa Univ, PhD(biomech), 64. *Prof Exp:* Asst prof mech eng, Villanova Univ, 55-61; from assoc prof to prof theoret & appl mech, WVa Univ, 61-69; assoc prof biomech & head dept, Hwy Safety Res Inst, Univ Mich, Ann Arbor, 69-77; PROF BIOMED ENGR, DUKE UNIV, 77- *Res:* Biomechanics of head and neck injuries; protective systems; sensory feedback & protheses. *Mailing Add:* Dept of Biomed Eng Duke Univ Durham NC 27707

MCELHANEY, RONALD NELSON, b Youngstown, Ohio, Jan 5, 42; m 65, 79; c 2. BIOCHEMISTRY, BIOPHYSICS. *Educ:* Wash & Jefferson Col, BA, 64; Univ Conn, PhD(biochem), 69. *Prof Exp:* NIH fel biochem, State Univ Utrecht, 69-70; asst prof, 70-74, assoc prof, 74-79, PROF BIOCHEM, UNIV ALTA, 79- *Concurrent Pos:* Med Res Coun Can res grant, Univ Alta, 70- *Mem:* Biophys Soc; Can Biochem Soc; Am Soc Microbiol; Am Soc Biol Chemists; Am Oil Chem Soc. *Res:* Biological membrane structure and function; role of membrane polar lipids and cholesterol in passive and mediated membrane transport and in membrane enzyme activity; calorimetric and nuclear magnetic resonance studies of model and biomembranes. *Mailing Add:* Dept of Biochem Univ of Alta Edmonton AB T6G 2G7 Can

MCELHENY, GEORGE CLARK, b Tiffin, Ohio, Apr 21, 20; m 45; c 3. ORGANIC CHEMISTRY. *Educ:* Harvard Univ, BS, 42; Wash Univ, PhD(org chem), 50. *Prof Exp:* Res chemist, Mallinckrodt Chem Works, 42-46 & 50-56, group leader org synthesis, 56-67, com develop specialist, 67-70, res assoc, 71-79, SCIENTIST, MALLINCKRODT, INC, 79- *Mem:* Am Chem Soc. *Res:* Organic synthesis; medicinal chemicals; alkaloids of opium. *Mailing Add:* Mallinckrodt Inc 3600 N Second St St Louis MO 63147

MCELHINEY, JOHN EDWARD, chemical & petroleum engineering, see previous edition

MCELHINNEY, JOHN, b Philadelphia, Pa, Mar 25, 21; m 42; c 2. PHYSICS. *Educ:* Ursinus Col, BS, 42; Univ Ill, MS, 43, PhD(physics), 47. *Prof Exp:* Asst physics, Univ Ill, 42-44 & Manhattan Dist, 44-45, spec res assoc, 47-48; assoc scientist, Los Alamos Sci Lab, 48-49; physicist, Nat Bur Standards, 49-55; head, Nuclear Interactions Br, 55-62, assoc supt, Nucleonics Div, 57-66, head, Linac Br, 62-66, supt, Nuclear Sci Div, 66-74, supt, Radiation Tech Div, 74-80, CONSULT, CONDENSED MATTER & RAD SCI DIV, NAVAL RES LAB, 80- *Concurrent Pos:* Partic sabbatical study & res prog, Stanford Univ-Lawrence Livermore Lab, 69-70. *Mem:* Am Phys Soc; Sigma Xi; Am Nuclear Soc; Inst Elec & Electronics Engrs. *Res:* Nuclear physics with betatron, synchrotron, electron linac, Van de Graaff, cyclotron; nuclear and x-ray instrumentation; application of nuclear technology; radiation dosimetry. *Mailing Add:* Condensed Matter & Rad Sci Div 11601 Stephen Rd Silver Spring MD 20904

MCELHINNEY, MARGARET M (COCKLIN), b Grandview, Iowa; div; c 2. BIOLOGY. *Educ:* Iowa Wesleyan Col, BS, 45; Univ Northern Colo, MS, 60; Ball State Univ, EdD(sci educ), 66. *Prof Exp:* Teacher pub schs, Iowa, seven years; assoc prof, 61-74, PROF BIOL, BALL STATE UNIV, 74- *Concurrent Pos:* Nat Sci Teachers Asn; Am Asn Biol Teachers. *Res:* Museum technology; developing instructional materials and preparing exhibits for direct experience learning. *Mailing Add:* Dept of Biol Ball State Univ Muncie IN 47306

MCELHOE, FORREST LESTER, JR, b Carnation, Wash, Feb 15, 23; m 53; c 2. PHYSICAL GEOGRAPHY, ECONOMIC GEOGRAPHY. *Educ:* Univ Wash, BA, 48, MA, 50; Ohio State Univ, PhD(geog), 55. *Prof Exp:* Instr geog, Ohio State Univ, 55-56; asst prof, Univ Ky, 56-68; asst prof, 68-72, ASSOC PROF GEOG, CALIF STATE POLYTECH UNIV, POMONA, 72- *Mem:* Asn Am Geog; AAAS; Nat Coun Geog Educ. *Res:* Climate. *Mailing Add:* Dept of Soc Sci Calif State Polytech Univ Pomona CA 91768

MCELIGOT, DONALD M(ARINUS), b Passaic, NJ, Mar 9, 31; m 57; c 3. FLUID MECHANICS, THERMAL SCIENCE. *Educ:* Yale Univ, BEME, 52; Univ Wash, MSE, 58; Stanford Univ, PhD(mech eng), 63. *Prof Exp:* Engr, Gen Elec Co, 55-57 & Knolls Atomic Power Lab, 57; assoc prof mech eng, 63-68, PROF AEROSPACE & MECH ENG, UNIV ARIZ, 68- *Concurrent Pos:* Consult, Los Alamos Sci Lab, 67-; mem vis staff, Imp Col, Univ London, 69-70; guest prof, Univ Karlsruhe, 75-76. *Mem:* Am Soc Mech Engrs; Am Phys Soc; Am Soc Testing & Mat. *Res:* Turbulent and transitional flow; variable property, internal convective heat transfer experiments and numerical analyses. *Mailing Add:* Col of Eng Univ of Ariz Tucson AZ 85721

MCELIN, THOMAS (WELSH), b Janesville, Wis, Aug 27, 20; m 45; c 2. MEDICINE. *Educ:* Dartmouth Col, AB, 42; Harvard Med Sch, MD, 44; Univ Minn, MS, 48; Am Bd Obstet & Gynec, dipl, 53. *Prof Exp:* Intern, Passavant Mem Hosp, 44-45; resident, Mayo Found, Univ Minn, 45-50, assoc, Mayo Clin, 50; clin asst, 50-53, instr, 53-54, assoc, 54-56, from asst prof to assoc prof, 56-67, PROF OBSTET & GYNEC, NORTHWESTERN UNIV MED SCH, CHICAGO, 67-, ASST CHMN DEPT, 74- *Concurrent Pos:* Mem attend staff, St Mary's Hosp, Rochester, Minn, 50; mem courtesy staff & jr attend physician, Evanston Hosp, 50-52, mem attend staff, 52-, chmn dept obstet & gynec, 65- *Mem:* AMA; Am Asn Obstet & Gynec; fel Am Col Obstetricians & Gynecologists; fel Am Col Surgeons. *Res:* Obstetrics and gynecology. *Mailing Add:* Evanston Hosp 2650 Ridge Ave Evanston IL 60201

MCELLIGOTT, JAMES GEORGE, b New York, NY, June 20, 38; m 67; c 2. NEUROSCIENCE, NEUROPHARMACOLOGY. *Educ:* Fordham Univ, BS, 60; Columbia Univ, MA, 63; McGill Univ, PhD(psychol), 66. *Prof Exp:* NIH fel neuroanat, Univ Calif, Los Angeles, 67-68, asst res anatomist, Sch Med, 68-71; asst prof, 71-76, ASSOC PROF PHARMACOL, SCH MED, TEMPLE UNIV, 76- *Mem:* AAAS; Soc Neurosci. *Res:* Neurophysiology; bioengineering; computer analysis of neuroscientific data. *Mailing Add:* Dept of Pharmacol Temple Univ Sch of Med Philadelphia PA 19140

MCELLIGOTT, PETER EDWARD, b New York, NY, Apr 4, 35; m 62; c 2. SURFACE CHEMISTRY, TRIBOLOGY. *Educ:* NC State Col, BS, 57; Rensselaer Polytech Inst, MS, 61, PhD(metall), 66. *Prof Exp:* Physicist, Alco Prod, Inc, NY, 57-59; physicist, Knolls Atomic Power Lab, 59-62, phys chemist, 62-73, liasion scientist, 73-77, PROJ DEVELOP MGR, RES & DEVELOP CTR, GEN ELEC CO, 77- *Mem:* Fel Am Inst Chem; Am Soc Lubrication Eng. *Res:* Friction, lubrication and wear of materials; electrical contact phenomena; surface chemistry of metals and semiconductors. *Mailing Add:* Res & Develop Ctr Gen Elec Co PO Box 43 Schenectady NY 12301

MCELLISTREM, MARCUS THOMAS, b St Paul, Minn, Apr 19, 26; m 57; c 6. NUCLEAR PHYSICS. *Educ:* Col St Thomas, BA, 50; Univ Wis, MS, 52, PhD, 56. *Prof Exp:* Asst physics, Univ Wis, 50-55; res assoc, Ind Univ, 55-57; from asst prof to assoc prof, 57-65, distinguished prof arts & sci, 81-82, PROF PHYSICS, UNIV KY, 65- *Concurrent Pos:* Pres, Adena Corp, 71-74; prog officer nuclear sci, NSF, 81-82. *Mem:* AAAS; fel Am Phys Soc. *Res:* Analysis of nuclear reactions; measurements of differential cross sections of nuclear reactions; fast neutron physics, neutron induced reaction cross sections; radioisotopes for nuclear medicine. *Mailing Add:* Dept Physics & Astron Univ Ky Lexington KY 40506

MCELRATH, GAYLE W(ILLIAM), b Randolph, Minn, Dec 15, 15; m 46; c 5. QUALITY CONTROL ENGINEERING. *Educ:* Univ Minn, BS, 41, MS, 46. *Prof Exp:* From instr to asst prof math & mech eng, Univ Minn, 43-53, assoc prof med eng, 53-58, head indust eng, 55-70, prof indust eng, 58-70; vpres, 56-78, PRES, MCELRATH & ASSOCS, INC, 78- *Concurrent Pos:* Consult indust & govt, 50-; dir, Coun Int Progress Mgt. *Honors & Awards:* E L Grant Award, Am Soc Qual Control, 69. *Mem:* Fel AAAS; fel Am Soc Qual Control (vpres, 61-65); Opers Res Soc Am; Am Statist Asn; Sigma Xi. *Res:* Industrial statistics; design and analysis of experiments; statistical quality control. *Mailing Add:* McElrath & Assocs Southdale Off Ctr 6700 France Ave S Minneapolis MN 55435

MCELREE, HELEN, b Waxahachie, Tex, Nov 22, 25. IMMUNOBIOLOGY. *Educ:* Col Ozarks, BS, 47; Univ Okla, MS, 54; Univ Kans, PhD, 59. *Prof Exp:* Asst prof bact, Univ Kans, 59-62; assoc prof, 62-68, PROF BIOL, EMPORIA KANS STATE COL, 68- *Mem:* AAAS; Am Soc Microbiol. *Res:* Role of reticulo-endothelial system in viral infections. *Mailing Add:* Dept of Biol Emporia Kans State Col Emporia KS 66801

MCELROY, ALBERT DEAN, b Quinter, Kans, Feb 25, 22; m 55; c 2. INORGANIC CHEMISTRY. *Educ:* Sterling Col, BS, 47; Univ Kans, PhD(inorg chem), 51. *Prof Exp:* Res asst, Univ Ill, Urbana, 51-53; res chemist, Callery Chem Co, Pa, 53-64; RES CHEMIST SUPVR, MIDWEST RES INST, KANSAS CITY, 64- *Mem:* Am Chem Soc; Sigma Xi. *Res:* Synthesis and product research in boron hybride derivatives, perchloro and perfluoramino compounds; water and wastewater treatment processes. *Mailing Add:* Midwest Res Inst 425 Volker Blvd Kansas City MO 64110

MCELROY, DAVID L(OUIS), b Fairfield, Ala, June 16, 30; m 54; c 4. METALLURGY. *Educ:* Univ Ala, BS, 51, MS, 53; Univ Tenn, PhD(metall), 57. *Prof Exp:* Res engr, Eng Exp Sta, Univ Tenn, 56-59; METALLURGIST, OAK RIDGE NAT LAB, 59- *Concurrent Pos:* Nat Acad Sci adv panel mem, Heat Div, Nat Bur Standards, 69-72 & Off Standard Reference Data, 71-73; Ford Found lectr, Univ Tenn, 71-72; foreign assignment, AERE Harwell, UK, 74-75; mem, Dept Commerce Criteria Comt Lab Accreditation, 78; chmn, Int Thermal Conductivity Conf Bd, 81. *Honors & Awards:* Annual Thermal Conductivity Conf Award, 71. *Mem:* Fel Am Soc Metals; Am Soc Testing & Mat. *Res:* Temperature measurement at high temperatures; thermocouple research at 2000 degrees Fahrenheit; adiabatic calorimetry to 950 degrees centigrade on iron-carbon alloys; thermal conductivity of nuclear refractory materials to 2400 degrees centigrade; steel transformation; heat capacity Americium, Pu-C 4 to 300 Kelvin; thermal insulation properties. *Mailing Add:* Metals & Ceramics Div Oak Ridge Nat Lab Oak Ridge TN 37830

MCELROY, FRED DEE, b Seattle, Wash, Oct 3, 34; m 55; c 3. PLANT PATHOLOGY, NEMATOLOGY. *Educ:* Wash State Univ, BS, 60; Univ Calif, Riverside, PhD(plant path), 67. *Prof Exp:* Exp aide nematol, Wash State Univ, 60-63; res scientist, Can Dept Agr, 67-77; nematode diag & consult, 77-80, PEST MGT CONSULT, PENINSU-LAB, 80- *Concurrent Pos:* Hon lectr, Univ BC, 72- *Mem:* Am Phytopath Soc; Am Sci Affiliation; Soc Nematol; Tissue Cult Asn; Soc Europ Nematol. *Res:* Nematode resistance in small fruits; pathogenic effect of nematodes on various crops; nematode-fungus interations affecting forest nursery stock. *Mailing Add:* Peninsu-Lab 23976 Newellhurst Ct Kingston WA 98346

MCELROY, MARY KIERAN, b Philadelphia, Pa, Feb 24, 18. INORGANIC CHEMISTRY, ANALYTICAL CHEMISTRY. *Educ:* Chestnut Hill Col, AB, 56; Univ Pa, PhD(chem), 64. *Prof Exp:* Teacher parochial schs, Pa, 37-54, dept head math & chem, 54-62; lectr, 62-64, from instr to asst prof, 64-70, assoc prof, 70-76, PROF CHEM, CHESTNUT HILL COL, 76-, CHAIRWOMAN DEPT, 75- *Mem:* Am Chem Soc; Sigma Xi; AAAS; fel Am Inst Chemists. *Res:* Electrochemical and spectral studies of the iron-polyphosphate systems. *Mailing Add:* Dept of Chem Chestnut Hill Col Philadelphia PA 19118

MCELROY, MICHAEL BRENDAN, b Shercock Co Cavan, Ireland, May 18, 39; m 63. APPLIED MATHEMATICS, PHYSICS. *Educ:* Queen's Univ, Belfast, BA, 60, PhD(math), 62. *Prof Exp:* Proj assoc, Theoret Chem Inst, Univ Wis, 62-63; from asst physicist to physicist, Kitt Peak Nat Observ, 63-71; PHYSICIST, HARVARD CTR FOR EARTH & PLANETARY PHYSICS, 71- *Concurrent Pos:* Mem Mars panel, Lunar & Planetary Missions Bd, NASA, 68-69, mem, Stratospheric Res Adv Comt, Space & Terrestrial Appl Adv Comt; mem, Comt Atmospheric Sci, Nat Acad Sci, Space Sci Bd, chmn, Comt Planetary & Lunar Explor. *Honors & Awards:* James B Macelwane Award, Am Geophys Union, 68; Newcomb Cleveland Prize, AAAS, 77; Pub Serv Medal, NASA, 78. *Mem:* AAAS; Am Astron Soc; Am Geophys Union. *Res:* Physics and chemistry of planetary atmospheres. *Mailing Add:* Ctr for Earth & Planetary Physics Harvard Univ Cambridge MA 02138

MCELROY, PAUL TUCKER, b Boston, Mass, Sept 25, 31; m 63; c 4. UNDERWATER ACOUSTICS. *Educ:* Harvard Univ, AB, 53, MA, 60, PhD(solid state physics), 68. *Prof Exp:* Asst scientist underwater acoustics, Woods Hole Oceanog Inst, 68-75; SR SCIENTIST, BOLT BERANEK & NEWMAN, INC, 75- *Mem:* AAAS; Sigma Xi. *Res:* Structure-borne vibrations; low noise; sonar arrays; scattering of sound from marine organisms; statistical analysis of relationship of acoustic scattering and biological targets; signal processing; medical ultrasonics; computer control of real-time processes. *Mailing Add:* Bolt Beranek & Newman Inc 50 Moulton St Cambridge MA 02138

MACELROY, ROBERT DAVID, exobiology, see previous edition

MCELROY, WILBUR RENFREW, b Fayetteville, Pa, Aug 20, 14; m 39; c 1. POLYMER CHEMISTRY, POLYMER ENGINEERING. *Educ:* Gettysburg Col, AB, 36; Pa State Univ, MS, 38; Purdue Univ, PhD(chem), 43. *Prof Exp:* Res chemist, Tex Co, NY, 39-40 & 43-45; proj leader, Jefferson Chem Co, 45-49; chem eng consult & owner, Wayne Labs, Pa, 49-78; PRES, ACTION PROD, INC, 69- *Concurrent Pos:* Dir chem technol, Cent Res Labs, Westinghouse Air Brake Co, Va, 52-55; sr group leader, Mobay Chem Co, 55-64; exec vpres, Conap, Inc, 64-69. *Mem:* Am Chem Soc; fel Am Inst Chem; Am Soc Test & Mat; NY Acad Sci; Nat Soc Prof Eng. *Res:* Process and product development in chemical intermediates and urethanes; orthopedic pads, radiation bolus and other health care products; industrial elastomers, sealants, coatings. *Mailing Add:* Admin Action Prods Inc 22 N Mulberry St Hagerstown MD 21740

MCELROY, WILLIAM DAVID, b Rogers, Tex, Jan 22, 17; m 40, 67; c 5. BIOLOGY, BIOCHEMISTRY. *Educ:* Stanford Univ, BA, 39; Reed Col, MA, 41; Princeton Univ, PhD(biol), 43. *Hon Degrees:* DSc, Univ Buffalo, 62, Mich State Univ, Loyola Univ, Chicago & Providence Col, 70, Del State Col & Univ Pittsburgh, 71 & Notre Dame Univ, 75; DPS, Providence Col, 70; LLD, Univ Pittsburgh, 71, Univ Calif, San Diego, 72 & Fla State Univ, 73, Johns Hopkins Univ & Pasadena City Col, 77, Calif Sch Prof Psychol, 78. *Prof Exp:* Asst, Reed Col, 39-41; asst, Princeton Univ, 43-44, res assoc, 44-45; Nat Res Coun fel, Stanford Univ, 45; from instr to prof biol, Johns Hopkins Univ, 45-69, chmn dept, 56-69, dir, McCollum-Pratt Inst, 49-69; dir, NSF, 69-72; chancellor, 72-80, PROF BIOL, UNIV CALIF, SAN DIEGO, 80- *Concurrent Pos:* Trustee, Brookhaven Nat Lab, 54; ex officio mem, Nat Sci Bd, 69-72; co-ed, Anal Biochem. *Honors & Awards:* Barnett Cohen Award, Am Soc Microbiol, 58; Andrew White Medal, Loyola Col, Md, 71; Howard N Potts Medal, Franklin Inst, 71; Rumford Award, Am Acad Arts & Sci. *Mem:* Nat Acad Sci; AAAS (pres, 75-76); Am Chem Soc; Am Acad Arts & Sci; Am Soc Microbiol. *Res:* Bioluminescence; bacterial mutations; biochemical genetics; mechanism of inhibitor action; bacterial and mold metabolism. *Mailing Add:* Univ of Calif San Diego La Jolla CA 92093

MCELROY, WILLIAM NORDELL, b Minneapolis, Minn, Nov 28, 26; m 50; c 4. REACTOR PHYSICS. *Educ:* Univ Southern Calif, BA, 51; Ill Inst Technol, MA, 60, PhD(physics), 65. *Prof Exp:* Sr engr, Atomics Inst, 51-57, sr tech specialist, 65-67; mgr reactor oper, Ill Inst Technol, 57-65; res assoc, Battelle-Northwest, 67-70; MGR & FEL SCIENTIST IRRADIATION CHARACTERIZATION & ANAL, HANFORD ENGR DEVELOP LAB, WESTINGHOUSE HANFORD CO, 70- *Concurrent Pos:* Mem, Nat Acad Sci-Nat Acad Engr-Nat Res Coun Panel For Nat Bur Standards Ctr For Radiation Res, 73- *Mem:* Am Nuclear Soc; AAAS. *Res:* Reactor environmental characterization and fuels and materials data correlation and damage analysis for light water, fast reactor and comtrolled thermonuclear reactors. *Mailing Add:* 113 Thayer Rd Richland WA 99352

MCELROY, WILLIAM TYNDELL, JR, b Shreveport, La, Sept 29, 24. PHYSIOLOGY. *Educ:* La State Univ, BS, 49; Univ Minn, MS, 54; Stanford Univ, PhD, 56. *Prof Exp:* Asst prof physiol, SDak State Col, 56-58; res assoc, Hahnemann Med Col, 59, asst prof, 60-67; PROF PHYSIOL & BIOPHYS & ASST DEAN STUD AFFAIRS, SCH MED, LA STATE UNIV, SHREVEPORT, 67-, ASSOC DEAN, SCH MED, 77- *Mem:* Am Physiol Soc; Am Fedn Clin Res. *Res:* Cardiovascular lipid metabolism; immunology. *Mailing Add:* Dept of Physiol & Biophys La State Univ Sch of Med Shreveport LA 71101

MCELWEE, EDGAR WARREN, b Centreville, Miss, Nov 11, 07; m 34; c 2. ORNAMENTAL HORTICULTURE. *Educ:* Miss State Col, BS, 30; Ala Polytech Inst, MS, 32; Ohio State Univ, PhD, 51. *Prof Exp:* Asst, Ala Polytech Inst, 30-32, lab technician, 32-33, from asst prof to assoc prof hort, 35-47; asst, Ohio State Univ, 33-35; prof floricult, Miss State Col & Agr Exp Sta, 48-52; assoc & prof res, NC Agr Exp Sta, 52-53; prof ornamental hort, 56-73, ornamental horticulturist, Coop Exten Serv, 53-73, chmn dept ornamental hort, 56-67, EMER ORNAMENTAL HORTICULTURIST, UNIV FLA, 73- *Mem:* Am Soc Hort Sci. *Res:* Photoperiodism in flowering plants; nutrition and physiology of greenhouse plants. *Mailing Add:* 1403 NW 14th Ave Gainesville FL 32605

MCELWEE, ROBERT L, b Elkins, WVa, Oct 4, 27; m 51; c 3. FOREST MANAGEMENT, GENETICS. *Educ:* WVa Univ, BSF, 51; NC State Col, MS, 60, NC State Univ, PhD, 70. *Prof Exp:* Mgt forester, Gaylord Container Corp, 51-56; liaison geneticist, NC State Univ, 56-63, dir hardwood res prog, 63-70; PROJ LEADER, EXTEN FORESTRY, WILDLIFE & OUTDOOR RECREATION, VA POLYTECH INST & STATE UNIV, 70- *Concurrent Pos:* Assoc prof, Univ Maine, 70-71. *Mem:* Soc Am Foresters. *Mailing Add:* Ext Forest Wildlife & Outdoor Rec Va Polytech Inst & State Univ Blacksburg VA 24060

MCENALLY, TERENCE ERNEST, JR, b Richmond, Va, Apr 21, 27; m 64; c 2. PHYSICS, ELECTRONIC ENGINEERING. *Educ:* Va Polytech Inst, BS, 50, MS, 55; Mass Inst Technol, PhD(physics), 66. *Prof Exp:* Instr physics, Va Polytech Inst, 52-55; instr elec eng, NC State Univ, 61-63; instr physics, Mass Inst Technol, 66-67; ASST PROF PHYSICS, E CAROLINA UNIV, 67- *Mem:* Am Phys Soc. *Res:* Electron spin resonance of transition metal ions in crystals; exchange coupling of paramagnetic ions in crystals; theory of nuclear magnetic resonance of fluid molecules. *Mailing Add:* Dept of Physics E Carolina Univ Greenville NC 27834

MCENTEE, KENNETH, b Oakfield, NY, Mar 30, 21; m 52; c 2. VETERINARY PATHOLOGY. *Educ:* State Univ NY, DVM, 44. *Hon Degrees:* Dr, Royal Vet Col, Sweden, 75. *Prof Exp:* Asst path, 47-48, from asst prof to assoc prof vet path, 48-55, chmn dept large animal med, obstet & surg, 65-69, assoc dean clin studies, 69-73, PROF VET PATH, NY STATE VET COL, CORNELL UNIV, 55- *Concurrent Pos:* Commonwealth Sci & Indust Res Orgn sr res fel, Univ Melbourne, 65-66; vis lectr & researcher, Royal Vet Col, Sweden, 73, 75 & 77; vis prof, Vet Col, Belo Horizonte, Brazil, 73-74. *Honors & Awards:* Borden Award, Am Vet Med Asn, 71. *Mem:* Am Vet Med Asn; Am Col Vet Path; Int Fertil Asn; Int Acad Path; Am Asn Pathologists. *Res:* Pathology of reproduction in dairy cattle; vibriosis of cattle. *Mailing Add:* Vet Col Cornell Univ Ithaca NY 14853

MCENTEE, THOMAS EDWIN, b San Mateo, Calif, Feb 27, 43; m 63, 74; c 3. ORGANIC CHEMISTRY. *Educ:* Univ Vt, BA, 66; Univ Colo, PhD(chem), 72. *Prof Exp:* Res chemist, 73-78, SR RES CHEMIST, ARAPAHOE CHEM, INC, DIV, SYNTEX CORP, 78- *Mem:* Am Chem Soc. *Res:* Synthesis of organic medicinals; industrial methods for fine organic chemicals synthesis. *Mailing Add:* Arapahoe Chem Inc 2075 N 55th St Boulder CO 80301

MCENTIRE, RICHARD WILLIAN, b Miami, Fla, Sept 10, 42; m 66; c 2. SPACE PHYSICS. *Educ:* Mass Inst Technol, BS, 64; Univ Minn, PhD(physics), 72. *Prof Exp:* Res asst physics, Univ Minn, 65-72; SR STAFF PHYSICIST, APPL PHYSICS LAB, JOHNS HOPKINS UNIV, 72- *Mem:* Am Phys Soc; Am Geophys Union; AAAS. *Res:* Planetary magnetospheric physics; interplanetary phenomena; solar and galactic cosmic rays. *Mailing Add:* Appl Physics Lab Johns Hopkins Univ Laurel MD 20707

MCENTYRE, JOHN G(ERALD), b Topeka, Kans, Nov 3, 20; m 48; c 3. CIVIL ENGINEERING. *Educ:* Kans State Univ, BS, 42, MS, 48; Cornell Univ, PhD(surv, mapping), 54. *Prof Exp:* From instr to prof civil eng, Kans State Univ, 46-65; from assoc prof to prof civil eng technol, 65-71, PROF LAND SURV, PURDUE UNIV, 71- *Concurrent Pos:* Vis prof, Kabul Univ, Afghanistan, 65-67. *Mem:* Fel Am Soc Civil Engrs; Nat Soc Prof Engrs; Am Soc Photogram; fel Am Cong Surv & Mapping. *Res:* Land surveying and precise surveying problems. *Mailing Add:* Sch of Civil Eng Purdue Univ West Lafayette IN 47907

MACERO, DANIEL JOSEPH, b Revere, Mass, Nov 19, 28; m 52; c 2. ANALYTICAL CHEMISTRY. *Educ:* Mass Inst Technol, BS, 51; Univ Vt, MS, 53; Univ Mich, PhD(chem), 58. *Prof Exp:* Instr chem, Univ Mich, 56-57; asst prof, 57-64, actg chmn, 70-71, assoc prof anal chem, 64-77, vchmn chem, 70-79, PROF ANAL CHEM, SYRACUSE UNIV, 77- *Concurrent Pos:* Res assoc, Univ NC, Chapel Hill, 67-68; acad dir, Summer Inst Microcomput, Am Cancer Soc, 80 & 81. *Mem:* AAAS; Am Chem Soc. *Res:* Kinetics of electron transfer; electrochemistry of transition metal complexes; computer assisted instruction; intro of microcomputer technology into the chemistry curriculum; development of analytical instrumentation; the study of electrode processes; development of new electroanalytical probes; use of computer method for experiment control and data enhancement, analysis of second phases in steel. *Mailing Add:* Dept of Chem Syracuse Univ Syracuse NY 13210

MCEUEN, ROBERT BLAIR, geophysics, see previous edition

MCEVILLY, THOMAS V, b East St Louis, Ill, Sept 2, 34; m 55; c 6. GEOPHYSICS, SEISMOLOGY. *Educ:* St Louis Univ, BS, 56, PhD(geophys), 64. *Prof Exp:* Geophysicist, Calif Co, 57-60; res asst, St Louis Univ, 60-64; asst prof seismol, 64-68, assoc prof, 68-74, chmn dept, 76-80, PROF, DEPT GEOL & GEOPHYS, UNIV CALIF, BERKELEY, 74-, ASST DIR, SEISMOL STA, 68- *Concurrent Pos:* Vpres eng, W F Sprengnether Instrument Co, 63-68. *Mem:* AAAS; Seismol Soc Am; Am Geophys Union; Soc Explor Geophys; Royal Astron Soc. *Res:* Structure of the earth as revealed by seismic surface and body wave propagation; nature of earthquake sequences; seismic instrumentation. *Mailing Add:* Dept of Geol & Geophys Univ of Calif Berkeley CA 94720

MCEVILY, ARTHUR JOSEPH, JR, b New York, NY, Dec 20, 24; m 53; c 4. METALLURGY. *Educ:* Columbia Univ, BS, 45, MS, 49, DEngSc(metall), 59. *Prof Exp:* Res scientist, NASA, 49-61; sr res scientist, Sci Lab, Ford Motor Co, 61-67; head dept metall, 67-78, PROF METALL, UNIV CONN, 67- *Concurrent Pos:* Consult, several indust orgn, 67- *Honors & Awards:* Howe Medal, Am Soc Metals, 64. *Mem:* Am Soc Metals; Am Soc Mech Engrs; Am Soc Testing & Mat; Am Inst Mining, Metall & Petrol Engrs. *Res:* Fatigue and fracture of metals; stress corrosion; alloy development; mechanical metallurgy. *Mailing Add:* Dept of Metall U-136 Sch of Eng Univ of Conn Storrs CT 06268

MCEVOY, FRANCIS JOSEPH, b New York, NY, Jan 18, 23; m 57; c 4. CHEMISTRY. *Educ:* Seton Hall Univ, BS, 48; Fordham Univ, MS, 50. *Prof Exp:* SR CHEMIST RES, LEDERLE LABS, DIV AM CYANAMID CO, 50- *Mem:* Am Chem Soc. *Res:* Medicinal chemical research. *Mailing Add:* Lederle Labs Pearl River NY 10965

MCEVOY, JAMES EDWARD, b London, Eng, Aug 5, 20; US citizen; m 41; c 2. GENERAL CHEMISTRY. *Educ:* Temple Univ, BA, 55. *Prof Exp:* Res chemist, Houdry Process & Chem Co, 55-64, proj dir catalyst res, 64-66, sect head explor process res, 66-69, asst dir chem res, Houdry Labs, 69-71, asst dir res & develop, Houdry Div, 71-72, dir contract res & develop, 72-78, mgr govt relations, 76-78, mgr bus develop, 78-80, DIR, ADMIN SCI CTR, AIR PROD & CHEM, INC, 80- *Concurrent Pos:* Mem, Inst Cong Catalysis. *Honors & Awards:* Joseph Stewart Award, Am Chem Soc. *Mem:* Am Chem Soc; Coun Chem Res. *Res:* Applied catalysis; catalytic cracking; hydrogenation; desulfurization; fuel cell catalysts; catalytic oxidation of environmental pollutants; auto emissions control catalysts; synthetic fuels from coal; research administration. *Mailing Add:* Air Prods & Chem Inc PO Box 538 Allentown PA 18105

MCEWAN, ALAN THOMAS, b London, Eng, May 2, 40; m 64; c 4. COMPUTER SCIENCE. *Educ:* Univ Hull, BSc, 61. *Prof Exp:* Res mathematician, English Elec, Luton, Eng, 61-62; data processing mgr, Assoc Newspapers, London Ltd, 62; res asst comput sci, Univ Hull, 62-64; lect numerical anal, Cripps Comput Ctr, Univ Nottingham, 64-66; assoc prof comput sci & dir, Comput Ctr, Lakehead Univ, 66-76; head, comput serv, Bedford Inst Oceanog, 76-80; DIR, COMPUT CTR, ACADIA UNIV, 80- *Mem:* Asn Comput Mach; Brit Comput Soc. *Res:* Compiler writing techniques and operating system organization; image processing. *Mailing Add:* Acadia Univ Wolfville NS B0P 1X0 Can

MACEWAN, DOUGLAS W, b Ottawa, Ont, Nov 11, 24; m; c 4. RADIOLOGY. *Educ:* McGill Univ, BSc, 48, MD, CM, 52; FRCPS(C), 58. *Prof Exp:* Asst radiologist, Montreal Children's Hosp, 58-63; asst prof radiol, McGill Univ, 63-65; PROF RADIOL, UNIV MAN, 66-; CHIEF RADIOLOGIST, HEALTH SCI CENTRE, 66- *Concurrent Pos:* Radiologist, Montreal Gen 63-65. *Honors & Awards:* Queen's Silver Jubilee Medal, 77. *Mem:* Can Med Asn; Can Asn Radiol; fel Am Col Radiol; Radiol Soc NAm. *Res:* Renal disease; standards, administration and costs of radiology. *Mailing Add:* Health Sci Centre 700 William Ave Winnipeg MB R3E 0Z3 Can

MCEWAN, IAN HUGH, b Cardiff, Wales, Aug 13, 33, Can citizen; m 57; c 3. POLYMER CHEMISTRY. *Educ:* Univ Wales, BSc & ARIC, 54, PhD(phys org chem), 58. *Prof Exp:* Tech off oil cracking, Heavy Org Chem Div, Imperial Chem Industs, 57-58; chemist polymers & paints, Can Industs, Ltd, 58-66, group leader, Paints Div, 66-80, RES MGR, CIL PAINTS INC, 80- *Mem:* Fel Chem Inst Can; Royal Soc Chem; Royal Inst Chem. *Res:* Free radical polymerization; design of polymers for use in paints and formulation of paints, especially water-borne systems. *Mailing Add:* Paint Res Lab CIL Paints Inc 1330 Castlefield Ave Toronto ON M6B 4B3 Can

MCEWEN, BRUCE SHERMAN, b Ft Collins, Colo, Jan 17, 38; m 60; c 2. NEUROBIOLOGY. *Educ:* Oberlin Col, AB, 59; Rockefeller Univ, PhD(biol), 64. *Prof Exp:* USPHS fel, Inst Neurobiol, Gothenburg Univ, Sweden, 64-65; asst prof zool, Univ Minn, Minneapolis, 66; asst prof, 66-71, assoc prof, 71-81, PROF NEUROSCI, ROCKEFELLER UNIV, 81- *Mem:* Soc Gen Physiol; Soc Neurosci; Am Soc Neurochem; Endocrine Soc. *Res:* Gene activity in nervous tissue, focusing on steroid hormone action. *Mailing Add:* Dept of Neurosci Rockefeller Univ New York NY 10021

MCEWEN, C(ASSIUS) RICHARD, b Missoula, Mont, Dec 22, 25; m 50; c 2. INSTRUMENTATION. *Educ:* Calif Inst Technol, BS, 46; Mont State Univ, BA, 48; Stanford Univ, MS, 50, PhD(chem eng), 52. *Prof Exp:* Sect leader, Res Dept, Union Oil Co Calif, 52-64; RES DIR, SPINCO DIV, BECKMAN INSTRUMENTS, INC, PALO ALTO, 64- *Mem:* AAAS; Am Chem Soc. *Res:* New product identification, primarily in field of biomedical resarch. *Mailing Add:* Beckman Instruments Inc 1117 California Ave Palo Alto CA 94304

MCEWEN, CHARLES NEHEMIAH, b Matoaca, Va, Feb 9, 42; m 67; c 2. MASS SPECTROMETRY. *Educ:* Col William & Mary, BS, 65; Atlanta Univ, MS, 70; Univ Va, PhD(chem), 73. *Prof Exp:* Teacher chem, Hermitage High Sch, Henrico County, Va, 65-68; SECT SUPVR GAS CHROMATOG & MASS SPECTROMETRY, CENT RES & DEVELOP DEPT, E I DU PONT DE NEMOURS & CO, INC, 73- *Mem:* Am Chem Soc; Am Soc Mass Spectrometry. *Res:* Mass spectrometry of radical and ion structures, field desorption chemical ionization; emphasis on special techniques and new applications such as sputtered ion mass spectrometry of organics. *Mailing Add:* Exp Sta E228 E I du Pont de Nemours & Co Wilmington DE 19898

MCEWEN, CURRIER, b Newark, NJ, Apr 1, 02; m 30; c 4. MEDICINE. *Educ:* Wesleyan Univ, BS, 23; NY Univ, MD, 26. *Hon Degrees:* DSc, Wesleyan Univ, 50; DSc, Marietta Col, 52. *Prof Exp:* Intern, Bellevue Hosp, 26-27, asst res, 27-28; asst med & asst resident physiciatn, Rockefeller Inst, 28-30, assoc med, 30-32; from asst prof to prof, 33-70, asst dean & secy, 32-37, dean, 37-55, EMER PROF MED, SCH MED, NY UNIV, 70- *Concurrent Pos:* Consult physician, Bellevue Hosp Ctr, 32-; consult physician, Goldwater Mem Hosp, 46-70; vis physician, Univ Hosp, 49-70; consult, Vet Admin Hosps, New York, 55-70 & Vet Admin Cent Off, 59-70; consult physician, Maine Med Ctr, Regional Mem Hosp, Cent Maine Med Ctr, Togus Vet Admin Hosps, Mid-Maine Med Ctr, Northern Maine Med Ctr, Cary Med Ctr. *Mem:* Am Soc Clin Invest; Am Rheumatism Asn (pres, 52-53); Asn Am Physicians; master Am Col Physicians. *Res:* Rheumatic and collagen diseases. *Mailing Add:* South Harpswell ME 04079

MCEWEN, DAVID JOHN, b Winnipeg, Man, July 23, 30; m 54; c 4. ANALYTICAL CHEMISTRY. *Educ:* Acadia Univ, BSc, 52; Purdue Univ, MS, 55, PhD(chem), 57. *Prof Exp:* Res chemist, Cent Res Lab, Can Industs, Ltd, Que, 57-60; sr res chemist, Res Labs, 60-81, STAFF RES SCIENTIST, GEN MOTORS CORP, WARREN, 80- *Mem:* Soc Appl Spectros; Coblentz Soc. *Res:* Gas chromatography; mass spectrometry; analysis of vehicle emissions, polymers, solvents, synthesized chemicals; fourier-transform infrared spectroscopy. *Mailing Add:* 3477 Newgate Rd Troy MI 48084

MCEWEN, EVERETT E(DWIN), b Providence, RI, July 15, 32; m 56; c 2. CIVIL ENGINEERING. *Educ:* Univ RI, BS, 54; Univ Ill, MS, 56; Rensselaer Polytech Inst, DEng, 64. *Prof Exp:* Asst struct eng, Univ Ill, 54-56; instr civil eng, 56-57; from instr to asst prof, Rensselaer Polytech Inst, 57-62; asst prof, 62-65, ASSOC PROF CIVIL ENG, UNIV RI, 65- *Mem:* Am Soc Civil Engrs; Am Soc Eng Educ; Am Concrete Inst. *Res:* Structural dynamics; numerical methods; offshore towers; reinforced concrete. *Mailing Add:* Dept of Civil Eng Univ of RI Kingston RI 02881

MCEWEN, FREEMAN LESTER, b Bristol, PEI, Nov 11, 26; m 47; c 3. ENTOMOLOGY. *Educ:* McGill Univ, BS, 50; Univ Wis, MS, 52, PhD(entom), 54. *Prof Exp:* Asst, Univ Wis, 50-54; agr res off, Sci Serv Can, 54; from asst prof to prof entom & head dept, NY State Agr Exp Sta, Cornell Univ, 54-69; prof zool, 69-71, PROF ENVIRON BIOL & CHMN DEPT, UNIV GUELPH, 71- *Mem:* AAAS; fel Entom Soc Can (pres, 78-79); Sigma Xi; Am Inst Biol Sci; Entom Soc Am. *Res:* Vegetable insect control; transmission of plant virus diseases by insects; microbial control of insects. *Mailing Add:* Dept of Environ Biol Graham Hall Univ of Guelph Guelph ON N1G 2W1 Can

MACEWEN, JAMES DOUGLAS, b Detroit, Mich, July 31, 26; m 47; c 1. TOXICOLOGY. *Educ:* Wayne State Univ, BS, 49, PhD(pharmacol, physiol), 62; Univ Mich, Ann Arbor, MPH, 57; Am Bd Indust Hyg, dipl, 64; Am Bd Toxicol, dipl, 80. *Prof Exp:* Chemist, Water Bd, City of Detroit, Mich, 49, asst indust hyg, Bur Indust Hyg, 51-56; chemist, USPHS Hosp, Detroit, 50-51; asst prof & res assoc toxicol, Wayne State Univ, 56-63; dir environ health, Toxic Hazards Res Unit, Systemed Corp, 63-72; DIR ENVIRON HEALTH, TOXIC HAZARDS RES LAB, UNIV CALIF, DAYTON, OHIO, 72- *Mem:* Soc Toxicol; Am Indust Hyg Asn; Am Conf Govt Indust Hyg; NY Acad Sci. *Res:* Inhalation toxicology; environmental analysis and control. *Mailing Add:* 927 Cranbrook Ct Dayton OH 45459

MCEWEN, MILDRED MORSE, b Charlotte, NC, Aug 6, 01; m 29. CHEMISTRY. *Educ:* Queens Col, NC, AB, 22; Univ NC, MA, 24, PhD(biochem), 45. *Prof Exp:* Asst prof chem, Queens Col, NC, 24-42; asst biochem, Univ NC, 42-45, fels asst biochem, Med Sch, 43-45; prof, 45-71, EMER PROF CHEM, QUEENS COL, NC, 71- *Mailing Add:* 2316 Westfield Rd Charlotte NC 28207

MCEWEN, WILLIAM EDWIN, b Oaxaca, Mex, Jan 13, 22; m 45; c 3. ORGANIC CHEMISTRY. *Educ:* Columbia Univ, AB, 43, MA, 45, PhD(chem), 47. *Prof Exp:* Asst chem, Columbia Univ, 43-45; tech engr, Carbide & Carbon Chem Corp, Oak Ridge, 45-46; from asst prof to prof chem, Univ Kans, 47-62; prof chem & head dept, 62-76, COMMONWEALTH PROF, UNIV MASS, AMHERST, 77- *Concurrent Pos:* Res collab, Brookhaven Nat Lab. *Mem:* Fel NY Acad Sci; fel Am Chem Soc. *Res:* Mechanisms of organic reactions; stereochemistry of organophosphorus compounds; heterocyclic, organosulfur and organoantimony chemistry; organometallic compounds. *Mailing Add:* Dept of Chem Univ of Mass Amherst MA 01002

MCEWEN, WILLIAM ROBERT, b Duluth, Minn, Aug 21, 11; m 40; c 6. MATHEMATICS. *Educ:* Minn State Teachers Col, Duluth, BE, 35; Univ Minn, MA, 39, PhD(math), 47. *Prof Exp:* Teacher high schs, Minn, 35-37; asst math, Univ Minn, Minneapolis, 37-39, from instr to asst prof, 39-47, assoc prof, Univ Minn, Duluth, 47-49, head dept, 47-54, chmn div sci & math, 55-77, prof math, 49-81; RETIRED. *Mem:* Am Math Soc; Math Asn Am. *Res:* Orthogonal polynomials; probability; statistics. *Mailing Add:* Dept of Math Univ of Minn Duluth MN 55812

MACEY, JAMES P, b East Chicago, Ind, July 3, 39; m 61; c 3. MECHANICAL SYSTEMS, TRANSMISSIONS. *Educ:* Purdue Univ, BSME, 61, PhD(fluid mech), 75; Univ Mich, MSE, 65. *Prof Exp:* Grad asst design, Univ Mich, 63-65; instr fluid mech, Purdue Univ, 65-69; RES ENGR AUTOMOTIVE, GEN MOTORS RES LABS, 69- *Concurrent Pos:* Mem staff compressor anal, Detroit Diesel Allison Div, 65-67; NSF fel, 69; adj prof, Univ Mich, 78-80; mem fac, Wayne State Univ, 81- *Mem:* Am Soc Mech Engrs; Soc Automotive Engrs. *Res:* Mechanical components of automotive products; novel alternative mechanisms and definition of alternate system configurations. *Mailing Add:* 1052 Chester Birmingham MI 48009

MACEY, ROBERT IRWIN, b Minneapolis, Minn, Sept 22, 26; m 56; c 2. PHYSIOLOGY, BIOPHYSICS. *Educ:* Univ Minn, BA, 47; Univ Chicago, PhD(math biol), 54. *Prof Exp:* Instr chem & physiol, George Williams Col, 49-51; instr math, Ill Inst Technol, 53-54; res assoc physiol, Aeromed Lab, Univ Ill, 55-57, asst prof, Col Med, 57-60; from asst prof to assoc prof, 60-69, PROF PHYSIOL, UNIV CALIF, BERKELEY, 69- *Concurrent Pos:* Asst, Univ Chicago, 53-54; consult, Rand Corp, 63 & NIH, 65. *Mem:* Biophys Soc; Soc Math Biol; Am Physiol Soc. *Res:* Theoretical biophysics; membrane transport; kidney; blood. *Mailing Add:* Dept of Physiol Univ of Calif Berkeley CA 94720

MACEY, WADE THOMAS, b Mt Airy, NC, Jan 13, 36; m 58; c 3. MATHEMATICS. *Educ:* Guilford Col, BS, 60; Fla State Univ, MS, 62, PhD(math educ), 70. *Prof Exp:* Instr math, Oxford Col, Emory Univ, 62-65; ASSOC PROF & HEAD, DEPT MATH, PFEIFFER COL, 67- *Mem:* Math Asn Am. *Res:* Effect of prior instruction of selected topics of logic on the understanding of the limit of a sequence. *Mailing Add:* Dept of Math Pfeiffer Col Misenheimer NC 28109

MCFADDEN, BRUCE ALDEN, b La Grande, Ore, Sept 23, 30; m 58; c 3. BIOCHEMISTRY, MICROBIOLOGY. *Educ:* Whitman Col, AB, 52; Univ Calif, Los Angeles, PhD(chem), 56. *Hon Degrees:* DSc, Whitman Col, 78. *Prof Exp:* Asst chem, Univ Calif, Los Angeles, 52-54; from instr to assoc prof, 56-66, dir develop, Div Sci, 74-78, PROF CHEM, WASH STATE UNIV, 66-, CHMN, DEPT BIOCHEM & BIOPHYS, 78- *Concurrent Pos:* NIH res career develop award, 63-69; vis prof, Univ Ill, Urbana, 66-67, Tech Univ, Munchen, 80-81; Guggenheim fel & vis prof, Univ Leicester, 72-73; NIH spec fel, 73, mem ad hoc rev comt, 78-79; ed, Arch Microbiol, 77-82; Humboldt sr scientist award, 80-81. *Mem:* AAAS; Am Soc Biol Chem; Am Soc Microbiol; Am Chem Soc; Am Soc Plant Physiol. *Res:* Microbial assimilation of one-carbon and two-carbon compounds; nematode and plant biochemistry. *Mailing Add:* Dept of Chem Wash State Univ Pullman WA 99163

MCFADDEN, DAVID LEE, b Orange, Calif, Oct 18, 45; m 70. CHEMICAL PHYSICS. *Educ:* Occidental Col, AB, 67; Mass Inst Technol, PhD(phys chem), 72. *Prof Exp:* Res fel chem, Harvard Univ, 72-73; asst prof, 73-78, ASSOC PROF CHEM, BOSTON COL, 78- *Mem:* Am Phys Soc; Am Chem Soc; AAAS. *Res:* Gas phase reaction dynamics and kinetics. *Mailing Add:* Dept of Chem Boston Col Chestnut Hill MA 02167

MCFADDEN, DENNIS LEE, inorganic chemistry, see previous edition

MACFADDEN, DONALD LEE, b Port Deposit, Md, Dec 12, 26; m 53; c 4. PHYSIOLOGY, BIOLOGY. *Educ:* Univ Del, BS, 53, MS, 55; Univ Kans, PhD(physiol), 59. *Prof Exp:* Asst prof nutrit, Univ Mass, 60-63; prof physiol, 63-73, PROF BIOL, KING COL, 73-, HEAD DEPT, 63- *Concurrent Pos:* Sterling-Winthrop Res Corp res grant, 61-64; res consult, Chevron Res Co, 74-80. *Mem:* AAAS; Am Inst Biol Sci. *Res:* Mode of action of antibiotics in growth stimulation; studies on histological and immunological mechanisms involved in homograft rejections with intent of reducing severity of this response. *Mailing Add:* Dept Biol King Col Bristol TN 37620

MCFADDEN, HARRY WEBBER, JR, b Greenwood, Nebr, Dec 9, 19; m 45; c 2. MEDICAL MICROBIOLOGY, INFECTIOUS DISEASES. *Educ:* Univ Nebr, AB, 41, MD, 43; Am Bd Path, dipl, 51 & 65. *Prof Exp:* From intern to resident path, 43-45, resident clin path & bact, 47-49, fel & instr path & bact, 49-52, asst prof path & microbiol, 52-55, interim chancellor, Med Ctr, 72 & 76-77, interim assoc dean grad studies, Med Ctr, 72-79, PROF MED MICROBIOL & CHMN DEPT, COL MED, UNIV NEBR, OMAHA, 55-, PROF PATH, 68- *Concurrent Pos:* Trustee, Am Bd Path, 70- *Mem:* Col Am Pathologists; Am Soc Microbiol; Am Soc Clin Pathologists; NY Acad Sci; Am Fedn Clin Res. *Res:* Immunology, microbiology and pathology. *Mailing Add:* Dept of Med Microbiol Univ of Nebr Col of Med Omaha NE 68105

MCFADDEN, JAMES DOUGLAS, b Winchester, Va, Feb 19, 34; m 61; c 4. METEOROLOGY, OCEANOGRAPHY. *Educ:* Va Polytech Inst, BS, 56; Univ Wis-Madison, PhD(meteorol), 65. *Prof Exp:* Res meteorologist, NOAA, 65-73, dir, res Flight Facil, 73-75, DIR, FLIGHT OPER, RES FACIL CTR, NAT OCEANIC & ATMOSPHERIC ADMIN, 75- *Mem:* Am Meteorol Sco; Am Geophys Union; Am Geog Soc; Sigma Xi. *Res:* Airborne meteorological and oceanographic research; cloud physics; weather modification; remote sensing of the environment. *Mailing Add:* Nat Oceanic & Atmospheric Admin Box 520197 Miami FL 33152

MCFADDEN, JAMES THOMPSON, population ecology, see previous edition

MACFADDEN, KENNETH ORVILLE, b Philadelphia, Pa, Sept 5, 45; m 68; c 2. ANALYTICAL CHEMISTRY. *Educ:* Juniata Col, BS, 66; Georgetown Univ, PhD(phys chem), 72. *Prof Exp:* Fel kinetics, Univ Calgary, 71-73; asst prof chem, Stockton State Col, 73-75; anal chemist, 75-77, group leader, 77-78, sect mgr, 79-81, MGR ANAL SERV, AIR PROD & CHEM CO, 81- *Mem:* Am Chem Soc; AAAS; Sigma Xi. *Res:* Mass spectrometric analysis and methods development. *Mailing Add:* Air Prod & Chem Co 50 Snowdrift Rd Fogelsville PA 18051

MCFADDEN, LORNE AUSTIN, b Lower Stewiacke, NS, Oct 12, 26; nat US; m 53; c 3. PLANT PATHOLOGY. *Educ:* McGill Univ, BSc, 49; Cornell Univ, MS, 54, PhD(plant path), 56. *Prof Exp:* Plant pathologist, NS Agr Col, 49-50; asst, Cornell Univ, 50-56; asst plant pathologist, Subtrop Exp Sta, Univ Fla, 56-63; assoc prof plant sci, Univ NH, 63-69, prof plant path, 69-72; PROF BIOL & HEAD DEPT, NS AGR COL, 72- *Concurrent Pos:* Exten horticulturist, Agr Exp Sta, Univ NH, 63-69. *Mem:* Am Phytopath Soc; Can Phytopath Soc; Agr Inst Can. *Res:* Bacterial plant pathogens; diseases of ornamental and other crop plants. *Mailing Add:* Dept of Biol NS Agr Col Truro NS B2N 5E3 Can

MCFADDEN, PETER W(ILLIAM), b Stamford, Conn, Aug 2, 32; div; c 3. MECHANICAL ENGINEERING. *Educ:* Univ Conn, BS, 54, MSME, 57; Purdue Univ, PhD(mech eng), 59. *Prof Exp:* Asst instr graphics, Univ Conn, 54-56; instr thermodyn, Purdue Univ, 56-59, asst prof heat transfer, 59-62, assoc prof, 62-65, prof & head sch mech eng, 65-71; PROF MECH ENG & DEAN SCH ENG, UNIV CONN, 71- *Concurrent Pos:* Res fel, Swiss Fed Inst Technol, 60-61. *Mem:* Am Soc Mech Engrs; Am Soc Eng Educ. *Res:* Cryogenic heat transfer; combined heat and mass convection; optical investigations of transport phenomena; interaction of thermal radiation and convection; boiling studies; convection problems. *Mailing Add:* Off of the Dean Sch of Eng Univ of Conn Storrs CT 06268

MCFADDEN, ROBERT, b Belfast, Northern Ireland, Oct 7, 34; m 57; c 2. MATHEMATICS. *Educ:* Queen's Univ Belfast, BA, 55, MA, 59, PhD(math), 62. *Prof Exp:* Lectr math, Queen's Univ Belfast, 62-68; PROF, NORTHERN ILL UNIV, 68- *Concurrent Pos:* Asst prof, Ind Univ, 64-65 & La State Univ, 65-66; NSF res grants, Northern Ill Univ, 69-73; vis prof, Monash Univ, 73-74 & St Andrews Univ, 80-81. *Mem:* London Math Soc; Math Asn Am. *Res:* Theory of partially ordered semigroups; algebraic theory of semigroups. *Mailing Add:* Dept of Math Northern Ill Univ De Kalb IL 60115

MACFADYEN, JOHN ARCHIBALD, JR, b Scranton, Pa, July 10, 22; m 46; c 3. GEOLOGY. *Educ:* Williams Col, BA, 48; Lehigh Univ, MS, 50; Columbia Univ, PhD(geol), 62. *Prof Exp:* Asst geol, Lehigh Univ, 48-50 & Columbia Univ, 50-52; from instr to prof geol, 52-74, Edward Brust prof geol & mineral, 74-75, EDNA McCONNELL CLARK PROF GEOL, WILLIAMS COL, 75-, CHMN DEPT, 68- *Concurrent Pos:* Geologist, Vt Geol Surv, 51-54; res assoc, Mineral Inst, Univ Oslo, 65-66; vis prof geol, Univ Aarhus, 72-73; consult struct geol; vis scientist, Imperial Col London, 79-80. *Mem:* Geol Soc Am. *Res:* Structural geology; deformation and flow of solids; genesis of mylonites and cataclasitese. *Mailing Add:* Dept of Geol Williams Col Williamstown MA 01267

MCFALL, ELIZABETH, b San Diego, Calif, Oct 28, 28. BIOCHEMISTRY. *Educ:* San Diego State Col, BS, 50; Univ Calif, MA, 54, PhD(biochem), 57. *Prof Exp:* Asst resident biochemist, Univ Calif, 57; res assoc microbiol, Mass Inst Technol, 60-61, 62-63; from asst prof to assoc prof, 63-72, PROF MICROBIOL, SCH MED, NY UNIV, 72- *Concurrent Pos:* Res fel bact, Harvard Med Sch, 57-60; Nat Inst Med Res fel, London, 61-62; USPHS career develop award, 63-73. *Mem:* Am Soc Biol Chemists; Am Soc Microbiol. *Res:* Microbial genetics; regulatory mechanisms in microorganisms. *Mailing Add:* Dept of Microbiol NY Univ Sch of Med New York NY 10016

MCFARLAN, EDWARD, JR, b Brooklyn, NY, Mar 24, 21; m 49; c 2. PETROLEUM GEOLOGY, SEDIMENTOLOGY. *Educ:* Williams Col, BA, 43; Univ Tex, MA, 48. *Prof Exp:* Res geologist, Humble Oil & Ref Co, 48-59, area stratigrapher, La, 59-64, area explor geologist, 64-65; div stratigrapher, STex, 65-66, Mgr basin geol div, Esso Prod Res Co, 66-69, mgr stratig geol div, Exxon Prod Res Co, 69-73, explor adv, 73-77, geol scientist, 77-81, SR GEOL SCIENTIST, EXPLORATION DEPT, HQ, EXXON CO USA, 81- *Mem:* Soc Econ Paleont & Mineral; Geol Soc Am; Am Inst Prof Geol; Am Asn Petrol Geol. *Res:* Recent and Pleistocene geology; sedimentation; photogeology; geomorphology; Cenozoic and Mesozoic structure and stratigraphy of the Gulf Coast and adjacent offshore areas; Regional petroleum geology of the Cenozoic and Mesozoic sequences in the US Gulf Coast from Florida to Mexico. *Mailing Add:* Exxon Co USA PO Box 2180 Rm 3993-Exxon Bldg Houston TX 77001

MCFARLAND, CHARLES ELWOOD, b Kirkwood, Mo, June 20, 27; m 50; c 2. PHYSICS. *Educ:* Mo Sch Mines, BS, 49; Wash Univ, PhD(physics), 55. *Prof Exp:* Sr scientist, Bettis Atomic Power Div, Westinghouse Elec Corp, 55-56; nuclear physicist, Internuclear Co, 56-60; ASSOC PROF PHYSICS, UNIV MO-ROLLA, 60- *Mem:* Am Phys Soc. *Res:* Solid state physics; nuclear physics. *Mailing Add:* Dept of Physics Univ of Mo Rolla MO 65401

MCFARLAND, CHARLES MANTER, b Dayton, Ohio, Jan 11, 20; m 42; c 3. CHEMICAL ENGINEERING, EXTRACTIVE METALLURGY. *Educ:* Univ Dayton, BChE, 41. *Prof Exp:* Asst investr metall, NJ Zinc Co, Pa, 41-48, investr, 48-60; mem res staff mat appl & eval, Res Lab, 61-65, group liaison scientist, 65-71, mgr separation technol, Phys Chem Lab, 77-79, MEM STAFF PROCESS DEVELOP, METALL LAB, CORP RES & DEVELOP, GEN ELEC CO, 71- *Mem:* Am Chem Soc; Am Inst Mining, Metall & Petrol Engrs. *Res:* Extractive metallurgy of titanium, copper, zinc, rare earths and other metals. *Mailing Add:* Gen Elec Co PO Box 8 Schenectady NY 12301

MCFARLAND, CHARLES R, b Columbus, Ohio, Aug 26, 27; m 50. MICROBIOLOGY. *Educ:* Otterbein Col, BS, 49; Ohio State Univ, MS, 50; WVa Univ, PhD(microbiol), 68. *Prof Exp:* Clin microbiologist, Clifton Springs Sanitarium & Clin, NY, 55-57, Aultman Hosp, Canton, Ohio, 57-60 & Good Samaritan Hosp, Dayton, 60-65; asst prof, 67-74, ASSOC PROF MICROBIOL, WRIGHT STATE UNIV, 74- *Concurrent Pos:* Consult, Barney's Children's Med Ctr, Dayton, Ohio, 69- *Mem:* AAAS; Am Soc Microbiol. *Res:* Chemistry, metabolism and biological significance of microbial lipids; bacterial endogenous carbon and energy reserves. *Mailing Add:* Dept of Biol Sci Wright State Univ Dayton OH 45431

MACFARLAND, HAROLD NOBLE, b London, Eng, July 30, 17; m 43; c 2. INDUSTRIAL HYGIENE, TOXICOLOGY. *Educ:* Univ Toronto, BA, 41, MA, 42, PhD(physiol hyg), 49; Am Bd Indust Hyg, dipl. *Prof Exp:* Lectr indust hyg, Univ Toronto, 47-49; chief toxicol sect, Defence Res Med Labs, Dept Nat Defence, 49-52; asst chief occup health labs, Dept Nat Health & Welfare, 52-54, head res group, Div Occup Health, 54-59, sr scientist biol unit, 59-62; sr toxicologist, Hazleton Labs, Inc, 62-65; dir inhalation div & vpres & dir, Resources Res, Inc, 65-68; prof natural sci, York Univ, 68-72; vpres, Bio-Res Labs Ltd & Eco-Res Ltd, 72-74; dir toxicol, Med Dept, 75-81, GEN MGR, TOXICOL DEPT, MED DIV, GULF OIL CORP, 81- *Concurrent Pos:* Mem comt on toxic dusts & gases, Am Nat Standards Inst & toxicol res comt, Am Petrol Inst. *Honors & Awards:* Karl Wilhelm Scheele medalist, Stockholm, 73. *Mem:* Am Indust Hyg Asn; Soc Toxicol; Brit Toxicol Soc; Brit Occup Hyg Soc; Soc Ecotoxicol & Environ Safety. *Res:* Experimental toxicology, particularly on air-borne toxicants; research and development on air quality criteria and standards; design of inhalation studies and equipment; related university teaching. *Mailing Add:* Gulf Bldg PO Box 1166 Pittsburgh PA

MCFARLAND, JAMES THOMAS, b Junction City, Kans, Dec 7, 42; m 64; c 2. BIOCHEMISTRY. *Educ:* Col Wooster, BA, 64; Calif Inst Technol, PhD(chem), 68. *Prof Exp:* USPHS fel, Inst Molecular Biol, Univ Ore, 68-70; asst prof, 70-77, ASSOC PROF CHEM, UNIV WIS-MILWAUKEE, 77- *Mem:* Am Chem Soc. *Res:* Elucidation of the mechanism of action of enzymes; the use of rapid kinetic measurements, magnetic resonance and raman spectroscopy to investigate biological systems. *Mailing Add:* Dept of Chem Univ of Wis-Milwaukee Milwaukee WI 53201

MCFARLAND, JAMES WILLIAM, b Sacramento, Calif, Nov 16, 31; m 61; c 3. MEDICINAL CHEMISTRY. *Educ:* Chico State Col, BA, 54; Univ Calif, Berkeley, PhD(org chem), 57. *Prof Exp:* Fulbright fel, Univ Munich, 57-58; res fel org chem, Univ Calif, Berkeley, 58-59; res chemist, 60-68, PROJ LEADER, PFIZER, INC, 68- *Mem:* Am Chem Soc. *Res:* Heterocyclic syntheses; quantitative structure-activity correlations; pesticides; anthelmintic and antibacterial agents. *Mailing Add:* Dept of Chem Res Pfizer Inc Groton CT 06340

MCFARLAND, JOHN WILLIAM, b Elkton, Tenn, Aug 16, 23; m 47; c 4. ORGANIC CHEMISTRY. *Educ:* DePauw Univ, AB, 49; Vanderbilt Univ, PhD(chem), 53. *Prof Exp:* Fel, Mass Inst Technol, 53-55; res chemist, E I du Pont de Nemours & Co, Inc, Del, 55-61; assoc prof, 61-67, PROF CHEM, DEPAUW UNIV, 67- *Concurrent Pos:* Fel, Univ Groningen, 71. *Mem:* Am Chem Soc. *Res:* Organic syntheses and reaction mechanisms; polymerization. *Mailing Add:* Dept of Chem DePauw Univ Greencastle IN 46135

MCFARLAND, KAY FLOWERS, b Daytona Beach, Fla, Jan 27, 42; m 63; c 4. INTERNAL MEDICINE, ENDOCRINOLOGY. *Educ:* Wake Forest Col, BS, 63; Bowman Gray Sch Med, MD, 66. *Prof Exp:* From instr to assoc prof internal med & endocrinol, Med Col Ga, 71-77; PROF OBSTET & GYNEC, UNIV SC SCH MED, 77- *Concurrent Pos:* Endocrinologist, pvt pract, 72-75. *Mem:* Am Diabetes Asn; fel Am Col Physicians; Am Soc Internal Med. *Res:* Clinical research on diabetes and hypertension. *Mailing Add:* 120 Cricket Hill Rd Columbia SC 29206

MCFARLAND, MACK, b Houston, Tex, Sept 9, 47; m 68; c 2. AIR POLLUTION. *Educ:* Univ Tex, Austin, BS, 70; Univ Colo, PhD(chem physics), 73. *Prof Exp:* Chemist, Aeronomy Lab, Nat Oceanic & Atmospheric Admin, US Dept Com, 73-74; proj scientist air pollution, York Univ, 74-75; CHEMIST, AERONOMY LAB, NAT OCEANIC & ATMOSPHERIC ADMIN, US DEPT COM, 75- *Mem:* Am Geophys Union. *Res:* Monitoring trace gas constituents of the troposphere and stratosphere. *Mailing Add:* Aeronomy Lab US Dept Com 325 Broadway 24-2107 Boulder CO 80303

MCFARLAND, RICHARD HERBERT, b Cleveland, Ohio, Jan 20, 29; m 50; c 3. ELECTRICAL ENGINEERING. *Educ:* Univ Ohio, BS, 50; Ohio State Univ, MS, 57, PhD(elec eng), 61. *Prof Exp:* From instr to asst prof elec eng, Ohio State Univ, 57-61; assoc prof, 62-69, PROF ELEC ENG & DIR AVIONICS RES, OHIO UNIV, 69- *Mem:* Inst Elec & Electronics Engrs; Am Soc Eng Educ; Am Inst Navig. *Res:* Air navigation, including systems for permitting aircraft to land under conditions of low ceiling and visibility. *Mailing Add:* Dept of Elec Eng Ohio Univ Athens OH 45701

MCFARLAND, ROBERT HAROLD, b Severy, Kans, Jan 10, 18; m 40; c 2. PHYSICS. *Educ:* Kans State Teachers Col, BS & BA, 40; Univ Wis, PhM, 43, PhD(physics), 47. *Prof Exp:* Instr high sch, Kans, 40-41 & Radio Sch, Univ Wis, 43-44; sr engr, Sylvania Elec Prod, Inc, 44-46; from asst prof to prof physics, Kans State Univ, 47-60, dir nuclear lab, 58-60; physicist, Lawrence Livermore Lab, Univ Calif, 60-69; actg vpres acad affairs, Univ Mo, 74-75; dean grad sch, 69-79, PROF PHYSICS, UNIV MO-ROLLA, 69-, DIR INST ANAL & PLANNING, 79- *Concurrent Pos:* Consult, Well Survs, Inc, Okla, 53-54; mem, Grad Rec Exam Bd, 71-75; Vis prof, Univ Calif, Berkeley, 80-81. *Mem:* Fel Am Phys Soc; Am Asn Physics Teachers. *Res:* Atomic spectra; gaseous electronics; nuclear physics; effect of humidity on low pressure discharges; fluorescent and discharge spectra of mercury with zinc, thallium and indium metals; use of tracers; electron impact ionization of alkali metals; threshold polarization of helium radiation. *Mailing Add:* 204 Parker Hall Univ Mo Rolla MO 65401

MCFARLAND, WILLIAM, b Wilkinsburg, Pa, Nov 4, 19; m 45; c 2. HEMATOLOGY. *Educ:* Washington & Jefferson Col, BS, 41; Univ Pittsburgh, MD, 44; Am Bd Internal Med, dipl, 55. *Prof Exp:* Intern, St Francis Hosp, Pittsburgh, Pa, 44-45; resident internal med, Henry Ford Hosp, Detroit, 45-48; pvt pract, Pa, 48-54; instr med, Univ Louisville, 54-55; res fel hemat, New Eng Ctr Hosp, Boston, 56-58; hematologist, Nat Naval Med Ctr, Bethesda, Md, 58-61; from asst prof to assoc prof med, Georgetown Univ, 61-73; prof med, Univ Calif, Davis, 73-80; RETIRED. *Concurrent Pos:* Consult bone dent res lab, Pa State Univ, 52-54; instr, Sch Med, Tufts Univ, 56-58; mem hemat study sect, NIH, 60-65; consult, Nat Naval Med Ctr, 61-; mem erythropoietin subcomt, Nat Heart Inst, 63-67; chief hemat res sect, Vet Admin Hosp, Washington, DC, 61-73; mem staff, Vet Admin Hosp, Martinez, Calif. *Mem:* AAAS; Am Fedn Clin Res; Am Soc Hemat. *Res:* Relative roles and interactions of blood cells in immunologic reactions. *Mailing Add:* 10 Bella Vista Diable CA 94528

MCFARLAND, WILLIAM D, b Sedalia, Mo, July 4, 45; m 68; c 3. DIGITAL IMAGE ANALYSIS, COMPUTER ENGINEERING. *Educ:* Univ Mo, BSEE, 68, MS, 71, PhD(elec eng), 73. *Prof Exp:* asst prof bioeng, 73-75, assoc prof elec eng, 75-81, ASSOC PROF RADIOL, MED SCH, UNIV MO, 75-, PROF ELEC ENG, 81- *Concurrent Pos:* Coordr, Elec Eng Dept, Comput Eng Div, Univ Mo-Columbia, 79-81; consult, McDonnell-Douglas Astronaut Corp, 81- *Mem:* Inst Elec & Electronics Engrs; Soc Photo-Optical Instrumentation Engrs. *Res:* Digital image analysis specifically in medical imaging and remote sensing; computerized tomography imaging; digital radiography; automated diagnosis from x-ray films; applied image analysis to landsat and digitized aerial photography. *Mailing Add:* Elec Eng 303 Univ Mo Columbia MO 65211

MCFARLAND, WILLIAM NORMAN, b Toronto, Ont, Sept 11, 25; nat US; m 50; c 3. ZOOLOGY. *Educ:* Univ Calif, Los Angeles, BA, 51, MA, 53, PhD(zool), 59. *Prof Exp:* Chemist & biologist, Marineland of Pac, Calif, 54-57; marine biologist, State Game & Fish Comn, Univ Tex, 58; res scientist, Inst Marine Sci & lectr zool, Univ Tex, 58-61; from asst prof to assoc prof, 61-73, PROF ZOOL, CORNELL UNIV, 73- *Mem:* AAAS; Am Soc Ichthyol & Herpet; Am Soc Zool; Am Fisheries Soc; Ecol Soc Am. *Res:* Fish physiology; comparative physiology and ecology. *Mailing Add:* Sect Ecol & Syst Div Biol Sci Cornell Univ Ithaca NY 14850

MACFARLANE, CONSTANCE IDA, b Charlottetown, PEI. BIOLOGY. *Educ:* Dalhousie Univ, BA, 29, MSc, 32. *Hon Degrees:* DSc, Acadia Univ, 75; LLD, Dalhousie Univ, 75 & Univ PEI, 75. *Prof Exp:* Asst bot, Dalhousie Univ, 30-32; head dept sci, High Sch, Can, 32-33 & 39-46; lectr bot & dean women's residence, Univ Alta, 46-48; spec lectr biol, Victoria Col, 48-49; spec lectr, Acadia Univ, 49-61, res assoc, 61-65, assoc prof, 65-70; INDUST CONSULT, 70- *Concurrent Pos:* Vprin, Mt Allison Sch Girls, Can, 42-44, prin, 55-56; marine phycologist & dir seaweeds div, NS Res Found, 49-70; consult, Indust Develop Br, Fisheries Serv, Environ Can, 68-75. *Mem:* Int Phycol Soc; Brit Phycol Soc; Can Bot Asn; Bot Soc Am. *Res:* Field survey methods; ecology; harvesting techniques commercial seaweeds to promote maintenance of productivity of seaweed beds. *Mailing Add:* 1101 Wellington St Halifax NS B3H 3A1 Can

MACFARLANE, DONALD ROBERT, b Oshkosh, Wis, July 10, 30; m 62; c 2. NUCLEAR ENGINEERING, CHEMICAL ENGINEERING. *Educ:* Ill Inst Technol, BS, 52; Purdue Univ, MS, 57, PhD(nuclear eng), 66. *Prof Exp:* Chem engr, Sinclair Res Labs, Ill, 52-54; assoc chem engr, Argonne Nat Lab, 57-73; sr engr, Commonwealth Edison, Co, 73-74; V PRES, ETA ENG, INC, 74- *Concurrent Pos:* Prof, Midwest Col Eng, 71- *Mem:* Am Nuclear Soc; Nat Soc Prof Engrs. *Res:* Environmental impacts of nuclear power; nuclear reactor safety problems; numerical analysis. *Mailing Add:* ETA Eng Inc 415 E Plaza Dr Westmont IL 60559

MCFARLANE, ELLEN SANDRA, b Halifax, NS, May 19, 38. ONCOLOGY. BIOCHEMISTRY. *Educ:* DAlhousie Univ, BSc, 59, MSc, 61, PhD(biochem), 63. *Prof Exp:* Asst prof, 71-80, ASSOC PROF MICROBIOL & LECTR BIOCHEM, DALHOUSIE UNIV, 80- *Concurrent Pos:* Nat Cancer Inst Can fel, Univ Man, 63-64; Med Res Coun Can fel, Harvard Univ, 64 & Dalhousie Univ, 65; Med Res Coun Can scholar microbiol, Dalhousie Univ, 66-71. *Mem:* Can Biochem Soc; Brit Biochem Soc; Can Microbiol Soc. *Res:* The study of viral oncology with particular reference to human tumors. *Mailing Add:* Dept of Microbiol Dalhousie Univ Halifax NS B3H 3J5 Can

MCFARLANE, FINLEY EUGENE, b Atkins, Va, Nov 24, 40; m 64; c 2. POLYMER CHEMISTRY. *Educ:* King Col, AB, 63; Univ NC, PhD(chem), 68. *Prof Exp:* Sr res chemist, 67-75, RES ASSOC, TENN EASTMAN CO, 75- *Mem:* Am Chem Soc. *Res:* Polyester chemistry; catalysis, kinetics and mechanisms of polymerization and degradation reactions; polymer synthesis; preparation and properties of liquid-crystalline polyesters. *Mailing Add:* Bldg 150B Tenn Eastman Co Kingsport TN 37662

MCFARLANE, HAROLD FINLEY, b Hagerstown, Md, Apr 23, 45; m 68; c 1. NUCLEAR ENGINEERING, NEUTRON PHYSICS. *Educ:* Univ Tex, Austin, BS, 67; Calif Inst Technol, MS, 68, PhD(eng sci), 71. *Prof Exp:* Asst prof nuclear eng, NY Univ, 71-72; NUCLEAR ENGR REACTOR PHYSICS, ARGONNE NAT LAB, 72- *Mem:* Am Nuclear Soc. *Res:* Physics of fast breeder reactors. *Mailing Add:* Lower Power Plant Rd Idaho Falls ID 83401

MCFARLANE, HUGH MURRAY, b Winnipeg, Man, Jan 7, 19; m 47; c 3. CHEMISTRY. *Educ:* Univ Man, BSc, 41, MSc, 42; McGill Univ, PhD(chem), 50. *Prof Exp:* Res chemist, Abitibi Power & Paper Co, 50-51; sr res chemist, Bathurst Power & Paper Co, 51-56; supvr, Wastes & By-prod Sect, Cent Res Div, Abitibi Power & Paper Co, 56-64; tech dir, Sandwell & Co, Ltd, BC, 64-71, mgr, PR Sandwell & Co, UK, Ltd, London, 71-72; forestry officer, IBRD Coop Prog, Food & Agr Orgn, 72-78; mgr mill oper, 78-80, VPRES, SANDWELL MGT CONSULTS LTD, 80- *Mem:* Tech Asn Pulp & Paper Indust; Chem Inst Can; Can Pulp & Paper Asn. *Res:* Cellulose chemistry; pulp and paper processes. *Mailing Add:* Sandwell Mgt Consults Ltd 1550 Alberni St Vancouver BC V6G 1A4 Can

MCFARLANE, JOHN ELWOOD, b Tisdale, Sask, Aug 1, 29; m 60; c 3. INSECT PHYSIOLOGY. *Educ:* Univ Sask, BA, 49, MA, 51; Univ Ill, PhD(entom), 55. *Prof Exp:* From asst prof to assoc prof, 55-72, actg chmn, Dept Entom, 80-81, PROF ENTOM, MACDONALD COL, MCGILL UNIV, 73- *Mem:* Entom Soc Can; NY Acad Sci. *Res:* Physiology of development and aging in insects. *Mailing Add:* Fac of Agr Macdonald Campus 21 111 Lakeshore Rd Ste Anne de Bellevue PQ H9X 1C0 Can

MACFARLANE, JOHN O'DONNELL, b Valparaiso, Ind, Apr 16, 20; m 43; c 4. MEDICAL MICROBIOLOGY, ONCOLOGY. *Educ:* Purdue Univ, BS, 41; Univ Cincinnati, PhD(bact), 48. *Prof Exp:* Bacteriologist, Virus Div, E R Squibb & Sons, NJ, 42-43 & Antibiotic Div, Upjohn Co, Mich, 43-46; bacteriologist, Eli Lilly & Co, 48-53, head biol develop, 53-58, asst dir, 58-63; tech assoc, Midwest Res Inst, 63-64, from sr virologist to prin virologist, 64-67, head life sci sect, 67-76; CONSULT, 76- *Concurrent Pos:* Operator, Mac Bac Lab, 78- *Mem:* AAAS; Am Soc Microbiol; NY Acad Sci; Sigma Xi; Am Inst Biol Sci. *Res:* Viral, phage and microbial agents as indicators of pollution and application of enzymes for medicine, toxicology and monitoring. *Mailing Add:* 9220 Roe Ave Prairie Village KS 66207

MCFARLANE, JOHN SPENCER, b Lothair, Mont, Aug 26, 15; m 47. GENETICS. *Educ:* Mont State Col, BS, 38; Univ Wis, PhD(genetics), 43. *Prof Exp:* Asst, Univ Wis, 38-43, instr genetics & entom, 43-44; asst olericulturist, Univ Hawaii, 44-46; assoc geneticist, Curly Top Resistance Breeding Comt, Utah, 46-47; geneticist, Bur Plant Indust Soils & Agr Eng, Calif, 47-53, supt agr res sta, 64-72, leader sugar beet invests, 69-72, GENETICIST, AGR RES SERV, USDA, 53-, LOCATION LEADER, AGR RES STA & RES LEADER SUGARBEET PROD, 72- *Mem:* AAAS; Am Phytopath Soc; Am Genetic Asn; Am Soc Sugar Beet Technol; Int Inst Sugar Beet Res. *Res:* Genetics of sugar beet; breeding for disease resistance; breeding hybrid sugar beet varieties. *Mailing Add:* Agr Res Sta USDA Box 5098 Salinas CA 93915

MACFARLANE, JOHN T, b Hamilton, Ont, Nov 23, 23; m 46; c 5. PHYSICS. *Educ:* McMaster Univ, BA, 44; Univ Montreal, MSc, 53. *Prof Exp:* Asst prof physics, Sir George Williams Univ, 45-51; lectr physics & math, Univ Col, Ethiopia, 51-54; res scientist, Can Armament Res & Develop Estab, Que, 54-58; assoc prof physics, Univ Col, Haile Sellassie, 58-63, dean sci, 59-63, prin, 61-63; prof physics, Univ Libya, 63-64; head dept, Univ Col Sci Educ, Ghana, 64-65; assoc prof, Mt Allison Univ, 65-69; vrector, Nat Univ Rwanda, 69-72; assoc prof, 72-75, PROF PHYSICS, MT ALLISON UNIV, 75- *Concurrent Pos:* Asst lectr, Univ Montreal, 47-49; mem, Nat Comts Educ in Ethiopia, 60-63. *Mem:* Inst Elec & Electronics Engrs; Am Asn Physics Teachers; Fr Phys Soc. *Res:* Systems analysis; gas laser physics. *Mailing Add:* Dept of Physics Mt Allison Univ Sackville NB E0A 3C0 Can

MACFARLANE, MALCOLM DAVID, b Cambridge, Mass, Sept 26, 40. CLINICAL PHARMACOLOGY, MEDICAL RESEARCH. *Educ:* New Eng Col Pharm, BS, 62; Georgetown Univ, PhD(pharmacol), 67. *Prof Exp:* Instr pharmacol, Kirksville Col, 67-69; asst prof, Univ Southern Calif, 69-74; dir res, Inst Res, Meyer Labs, 74-79; vpres professional serv, 79-81, DIR REGULATORY AFFAIRS, GLAXO, INC, NC, 81- *Concurrent Pos:* Consult, Kirksville Osteop Hosp & Still-Hildreth Hosp, 67-69, Rom-Amer Pharmaceuts, Ltd, LAC/USC Med Ctr, 69-74, Calif Dept Consumer Affairs, 72-74 & Superior Court of Calif, 72-74. *Mem:* Fel Am Col Clin Pharmacol; Am Pharmaceut Asn; Am Soc Pharmacol & Exp Therapeut; Am Geriat Soc; NY Acad Sci. *Res:* Pharmacology of the autonomic nervous system; cardiovascular and renal pharmacology; microvascular renal physiology; narcotic analgesics and treatment of addiction; neuropsychopharmacology; clinical nutrition; clinical and geriatric pharmacology. *Mailing Add:* 3306 Chapel Hill-Nelson Hwy GLAXO/NC Research Triangle Park NC 27709

MACFARLANE, MALCOLM HARRIS, b Brechin, Scotland, May 22, 33; m 57; c 4. NUCLEAR PHYSICS, THEORETICAL PHYSICS. *Educ:* Edinburgh Univ, MA, 55; Univ Rochester, PhD(physics), 59. *Prof Exp:* Res assoc physics, Argonne Nat Lab, 59-60, assoc scientist, 61-68, sr scientist physics, 68-80; PROF PHYS, IND UNIV, 80- *Concurrent Pos:* Fel, John Simon Guggenheim Found, 66-67; prof physics, Univ Chicago, 69-80; assoc ed, Phys Review Letters, 72-77. *Mem:* Fel Am Phys Soc. *Res:* Theory of nuclear reactions and nuclear structure. *Mailing Add:* Phys Dept Swain Hall W 226 Ind Univ Bloomington IN 47405

MACFARLANE, ROBERT, JR, b Brooklyn, NY, Aug 26, 30; m 52; c 5. PHYSICAL CHEMISTRY. *Educ:* Brown Univ, ScB, 52; Yale Univ, PhD(phys chem), 56. *Prof Exp:* Sr res chemist, Chem Div, US Rubber Co, 56-65; from res chemist to sr res chemist, Imp Oil Enterprises, Ltd, Esso Res & Eng Co, 65-74; group leader, 74-77, res supvr, 76-77, MGR QUAL ASSURANCE, ALLIED CHEM CORP, 77- *Concurrent Pos:* Lectr grad sch, Brooklyn Polytech Inst, 69-70. *Mem:* Am Chem Soc; Soc Rheol; NY Acad Sci; Soc Plastics Engrs. *Res:* Emulsion stability; controlled aglomeration of colloids; mechanics of liquid-liquid mixing; molecular structure versus physical properties of polymers; polymerization kinetics and mechanisms; thermally stable polymers; techniques of polymer characterization. *Mailing Add:* 25 Linda Pl Fanwood NJ 07023

MACFARLANE, ROGER MORTON, b Dunedin, NZ, Oct 25, 38; m 59; c 2. SOLID STATE PHYSICS. *Educ:* Univ Canterbury, BSc, 59, PhD(solid state physics), 64. *Prof Exp:* Asst lectr physics, Univ Canterbury, 64-65; res assoc, Stanford Univ, 65-68; STAFF MEM, IBM RES LAB, 68- *Concurrent Pos:* Sci Res Coun sr vis fel, Oxford Univ, 74. *Mem:* Am Phys Soc. *Res:* Laser spectroscopy and studies of phase transitions in organic and magnetic solids; biophysics. *Mailing Add:* IBM Res Lab San Jose CA 95193

MACFARLANE, RONALD DUNCAN, b Buffalo, NY, Feb 21, 33; m 56; c 2. BIOPHYSICAL CHEMISTRY. *Educ:* Univ Buffalo, BA, 54; Carnegie Inst Technol, MS, 57, PhD(chem), 59. *Prof Exp:* Res fel nuclear chem, Lawrence Radiation Lab, Univ Calif, Berkeley, 59-62; asst prof chem, McMaster Univ, 62-64, assoc prof, 65-67; PROF CHEM, TEX A&M UNIV, 67- *Concurrent Pos:* Guggenheim fel, 69-70. *Mem:* Am Chem Soc; Am Phys Soc. *Res:* Mass spectroscopy of biomolecules; pattern recognition. *Mailing Add:* Dept of Chem Tex A&M Univ College Station TX 77843

MCFARLANE, ROSS ALEXANDER, b Toronto, Ont, Can, June 10, 31; m 60. PHYSICS. *Educ:* McMaster Univ, BSc, 53; McGill Univ, MSc, 55, PhD, 59. *Prof Exp:* Asst physics, Eaton Electronics Lab, McGill Univ, 59; mem staff, Res Lab Electronics, Mass Inst Technol, 59-61; mem staff, Bell Tel Labs, Inc, 61-69; assoc prof, Cornell Univ, 69-74, prof elec eng, 74-79; HEAD, QUANTUM ELECTRONICS SECT, HUGHES RES LABS, 79- *Mem:* fel Optical Soc Am; Inst Elec & Electronics Eng. *Res:* Microwave physics and frequency standards; noise and signal studies of electron beam type microwave devices; paramagnetic resonance; chemical lasers; reaction kinetics; atomic and molecular spectroscopy; nonlinear optics; photoacoustics. *Mailing Add:* Hughes Res Labs 3011 Malibu Canyon Rd Malibu CA 90265

MCFARLANE, WALTER KENNETH, b Glasgow, Scotland, Mar 7, 37; m 61; c 2. PHYSICS. *Educ:* Glasgow Univ, BSc, 58; Univ Birmingham, PhD(high energy physics), 64. *Prof Exp:* Res investr high energy physics, Univ Pa, 63-66, asst prof, 66-69; assoc prof, 69-75, chmn dept, 70-75, PROF PHYSICS, TEMPLE UNIV, 75- *Mem:* Am Phys Soc; Am Asn Physics Teachers; Am Asn Univ Profs. *Res:* Proton-nucleon scattering and meson production; proton-antiproton interactions; K meson decays; pi meson decays. *Mailing Add:* Dept of Physics Barton Hall Temple Univ Philadelphia PA 19122

MCFARLIN, RICHARD FRANCIS, b Oklahoma City, Okla, Oct 12, 29; m 53; c 4. INORGANIC CHEMISTRY. *Educ:* Va Mil Inst, BS, 51; Purdue Univ, MS, 53, PhD, 56. *Prof Exp:* Sr res chemist, Monsanto Chem Co, Mo, 56-60; supvr inorg chem, Int Minerals & Chem Corp, 60-62; mgr Atlanta Res Ctr, Armour Agr Chem Co, 62-64, tech dir, 64-65; vpres & tech dir, Armour Agr Chem Co, 65-68; vpres com develop, 68-69 & develop & admin, 69-74, VPRES OPERS, USS AGRI-CHEM, INC, US STEEL CORP, 74-, VPRES PLANNING & ADMIN, 82- *Concurrent Pos:* Mem adv mgt prog, Columbia Univ, 67. *Mem:* AAAS; Am Chem Soc. *Res:* Nitrogen and industrial chemicals; industrial explosives; rocket oxidants; fertilizer materials; metal hydrides; inorganic phosphates. *Mailing Add:* 455 Forest Dale Dr NE Atlanta GA 30342

MCFARREN, EARL FRANCIS, b Akron, Ohio, June 30, 19; m 45; c 3. ANALYTICAL CHEMISTRY. *Educ:* Bowling Green State Univ, BA, 41. *Prof Exp:* Asst chem, Bowling Green State Univ, 41-42; chemist, Nat Dairy Res Labs, Inc, Div Nat Dairy Prod Corp, 46-52; chemist, Robert A Taft Sanit Eng Ctr, USPHS, 52-64; with training prog, Environ Control Admin, Environ Protection Agency, 64-69, chief anal qual control, Water Supply Prog Div, 69-72, chief water supply prog support activ, 72-76, chief distrib qual sect, Drinking Water Res Div, 76-78; RETIRED. *Concurrent Pos:* Consult, Dept Interior, Marshall Islands, 57. *Honors & Awards:* USPHS Awards, 58 & 63. *Mem:* Am Chem Soc; Am Water Works Asn; Am Soc Testing & Mat; Sigma Xi. *Res:* Paper chromatography of amino acids and sugars; enzymatic digestion of casein; reactivation of normal alkaline milk phosphatase; bioassay and chemical assay of paralytic shellfish poison and poisonous fishes; gas chromatography of pesticides; chemical analysis of water; statistics. *Mailing Add:* Rte 4 Box 104 Chopin SC 29036

MCFATE, KENNETH L(EVERNE), b LeClaire, Iowa, Feb 5, 24; m 54; c 3. AGRICULTURAL ENGINEERING, COMMUNICATIONS. *Educ:* Iowa State Univ, BS, 50; Univ Mo, MS, 59. *Prof Exp:* Assoc agr engr, Iowa State Univ, 51-53, exten agr engr, 53-56; from asst prof to assoc prof, 56-74, PROF AGR ENG, UNIV MO-COLUMBIA, 74- *Concurrent Pos:* Dir, Farm Elec Utilization Proj, 56-76; vpres, Penreico, Inc, 69-76, treas, 76-78; exec mgr, Nat Farm Elec Coun, 76-77; pres & exec mgr, Nat Food & Elec Coun, 77- *Honors & Awards:* George Kable Elec Award, Am Soc Agr Engrs, 74. *Mem:* Fel Am Soc Agr Engrs. *Mailing Add:* 108 Agr Eng Bldg Univ of Mo Columbia MO 65211

MCFEAT, TOM FARRAR SCOTT, b Montreal, Que, Feb 5, 19; m 47; c 2. ETHNOLOGY. *Educ:* McGill Univ, BA, 50; Harvard Univ, AM, 54, PhD, 57. *Prof Exp:* Assoc prof anthrop, Univ NB, 54-59; sr ethnologist, Nat Mus Can, 59-63; sr ethnologist, Carleton Univ, 63-64; chmn dept, 64-74, PROF ANTHROP, UNIV TORONTO, 64- *Mem:* Fel Am Anthrop Asn; Can Polit Sci Asn. *Res:* Culture process, particularly concepts of growth, evolution and pattern in diachronic analysis; small group culture, especially influence of information on structure of n-generation groups; Canadian Indian and other ethnic communities; certain aspects of mass media analysis. *Mailing Add:* Dept of Anthrop Univ of Toronto 1000 St George St Toronto ON M5S 1A1 Can

MCFEDRIES, ROBERT, JR, b Chicago, Ill, Nov 11, 30; m 52; c 2. CHEMICAL ENGINEERING, POLYMER SCIENCE. *Educ:* Purdue Univ, BS, 52, MS, 56. *Prof Exp:* Develop engr, 55-58, sect head, Plastics & Packaging Div, 58-62, div leader packaging res, 62-65, lab dir flexible packaging, 65-67, tech mgr, 67-72, dir res & develop, Packaging Dept, 72-73, exec vpres, Dow Chem Investment & Finance Co, 73-76, dir res & develop, Designed Prod Dept, 79-81, DIR LICENSING, DOW CHEM CO, 81- *Concurrent Pos:* Bd mem, Hydrosci, Inc, 76- *Mem:* Am Chem Soc; Am Soc Soc Testing & Mat; Soc Plastics Engrs; Am Inst Chem Engrs. *Res:* Epoxy modification of alkyd resins; effects of radiation on polymers; styrene foam systems; ion exchange resins. *Mailing Add:* 2020 Dow Ctr Midland MI 48640

MCFEE, ALFRED FRANK, b Knoxville, Tenn, Aug 19, 31; m 51; c 2. CYTOGENETICS, RADIOBIOLOGY. *Educ:* Univ Tenn, BS, 53, MS, 59; Cornell Univ, PhD(animal breeding), 63. *Prof Exp:* From asst prof to assoc prof, Agr Res Lab, Univ Tenn-AEC, 63-75, prof, comp animal res lab, Univ Tenn-Dept Energy, 75-81; SCIENTIST, OAK RIDGE ASSOC UNIVS, 81- *Mem:* Radiation Res Soc Am; Environ Mutagen Soc. *Res:* Adverse effects of energy-related pollutants on chromosome structure and cell behavior as they relate to embryonic survival. *Mailing Add:* Comp Animal Res Lab 1299 Bethel Valley Rd Oak Ridge TN 37830

MCFEE, ARTHUR STORER, b Portland, Maine, May 1, 32; m 67. SURGERY. *Educ:* Harvard Univ, BA, 53, MD, 57; Univ Minn, MS, 66, PhD(surg), 67; Am Bd Surg, dipl, 67. *Prof Exp:* Intern surg, Univ Minn Hosp, 57-58, spec fel surg, 58-65; from asst prof to assoc prof, 67-73, PROF SURG, UNIV TEX HEALTH SCI CTR SAN ANTONIO, 73- *Concurrent Pos:* Co-dir surg intensive care unit, Bexar County Hosp, San Antonio, 68- *Mem:* Asn Acad Surgeons; Asn Hist Med; AMA; Am Col Surgeons; Soc Surg Alimentary Tract. *Res:* Local gastric hypothermia; gastric physiology; prevention of hepatic metastatic diseases; emergency medicine and transportation. *Mailing Add:* Dept of Surg Univ of Tex Health Sci Ctr San Antonio TX 78284

MCFEE, DONALD RAY, b Union Co, Ind, July 4, 29; m 54; c 3. INDUSTRIAL AND ENVIRONMENTAL HEALTH. *Educ:* Purdue Univ, BSc, 51; Univ Cincinnati, MSc, 60, DrSc(indust health), 62; Am Bd Indust Hyg, cert comprehensive pract indust hyg, 64; Bd Cert Safety Prof, cert, 71. *Prof Exp:* Tool engr, Boeing Airplane Co, Wash, 51-53, facil engr, 53-54, sr facil engr, Pilotless Aircraft Div, 58; assoc indust hygienist, Indust Hyg & Safety Div, Argonne Nat Lab, 61-72, supvr indust hyg group, 71-72; VPRES, OCCUSAFE, INC, WHEELING, 72- *Concurrent Pos:* Lectr, Nat Safety Coun, 63-71. *Mem:* Am Indust Hyg Asn (vpres, 77, pres elect, 78, pres, 79); Am Acad Indust Hyg; Am Indust Hyg Found (treas, 80, vpres, 81). *Res:* Industrial and environmental health and safety engineering and management, including industrial hygiene; air pollution; ventilation, hazard analysis and control; government regulations; product safety; dusts and fume characteristics; sand filtration of fumes; toxicology of organic solvents; noise, air sampling; air cleaning and filtration; combustible gas detection systems. *Mailing Add:* 25 W 210 Highview Dr Naperville IL 60540

MCFEE, RAYMOND HERBERT, b Somerville, Mass, Mar 1, 16; m 38; c 2. PHYSICS. *Educ:* Mass Inst Technol, SB, 37, SM, 38, PhD(physics), 43. *Prof Exp:* Tech asst, Geophys Res Corp, Okla, 38-40; asst physics, Mass Inst Technol, 41-42, physicist, Div Indust Coop, 42-43; chief physicist, White Res Assocs, Boston, 43-45; physicist, Cambridge Thermionic Corp, 45-46; sr elec engr, Submarine Signal Co, 46; res physicist, Electronics Corp of Am, 46-53, dir eng, 53-54, res, 54-56; dir res avionics div, Aerojet-Gen Corp, 56-60 & Azusa Plant, 60-64; sect mgr, Jet Propulsion Lab, Calif Inst Technol, 64-67; assoc dir, Douglas Advan Res Labs, McDonnell Douglas Corp, Calif, 67-70, sr staff engr, McDonnell Douglas Astronaut Co, 70-73, prin engr/scientist, 73-81; CONSULT, 81- *Mem:* AAAS; Am Phys Soc; fel Optical Soc Am; assoc fel Am Inst Aeronaut & Astronaut. *Res:* Solid state physics; semiconductors; spectroscopy; electronics; optical system design; purification of materials by recrystallization from the melt; infrared systems and techniques; space science; optics of solar power systems. *Mailing Add:* 5163 Belmez Laguna Hills CA 92653

MCFEE, RICHARD, b Pittsburgh, Pa, Jan 24, 25. ELECTRICAL ENGINEERING. *Educ:* Yale Univ, BE, 47; Syracuse Univ, MS, 49; Univ Mich, PhD(elec eng), 54. *Prof Exp:* Instr elec eng, Syracuse Univ, 48-49; res assoc, Hosp, Univ Mich, 49-52; mem tech staff, Bell Tel Labs, Inc, 53-57; assoc prof elec eng, 57-63, PROF ELEC ENG, SYRACUSE UNIV, 63- *Mem:* Inst Elec & Electronics Engrs. *Res:* Biophysics; linear and nonlinear systems; device development; cryogenics. *Mailing Add:* RD 1 Union Springs NY 13160

MCFEE, WILLIAM WARREN, b Concord, Tenn, Jan 8, 35; m 57; c 3. FOREST SOILS, SOIL FERTILITY. *Educ:* Univ Tenn, BS, 57; Cornell Univ, MS, 63, PhD(soils), 66. *Prof Exp:* Asst soils, Cornell Univ, 61-65; from asst prof to assoc prof, 65-73, PROF AGRON, PURDUE UNIV, WEST LAFAYETTE, 73-, DIR NATURAL RESOURCE & ENVIRON SCI PROG, 75- *Mem:* Fel Soil Sci Am; fel Am Soc Agron. *Res:* Relationship of soils to plant nutrition; mechanisms of ion uptake; forest tree-site relationships; mined land reclamation; effects of atmospheric deposition on soils; forest tree species; common agricultural plants. *Mailing Add:* Dept of Agron Purdue Univ West Lafayette IN 47906

MCFEELEY, JAMES CALVIN, b Altoona, Pa, Aug 6, 40; m 63; c 2. BOTANY. *Educ:* Otterbein Col, BS, 65; Ohio Univ, MS, 68; Ohio State Univ, PhD(plant path), 71. *Prof Exp:* Teacher, High Sch, Ohio, 65-66; asst prof, 72-77, ASSOC PROF BIOL, EAST TEX STATE UNIV, 77-, ASST DEAN GRAD SCH, 81- *Concurrent Pos:* Res assoc, Purdue Univ, 71-72; consult, Tulsa Dist, US Corps Engrs, 73 & Tex Hwy Dept, 73- *Mem:* Am Phytopath Soc; Am Bot Soc; Mycol Soc Am; Sigma Xi. *Res:* Study of the affect of strong 60- hertz electric fields on biological systems. *Mailing Add:* Dept of Biol ETex State Univ Commerce TX 75428

MCFEELY, RICHARD AUBREY, b Trenton, NJ, Dec 3, 33; div; c 3. VETERINARY MEDICINE, CYTOGENETICS. *Educ:* Pa State Univ, BS, 55; Univ Pa, VMD, 61, MS, 67; Am Col Theriogenologists, dipl, 73. *Prof Exp:* Pvt pract, 61-62; res asst comp cardiol, Sch Vet Med, 62, USPHS fels reprod physiol, 62-63, grad div, Sch Med, 63-65 & cytogenetics, Sch Vet Med, 65-66, from asst prof to assoc prof clin reprod, 66-75, chief, Sect Reprod, 68-73, chief of staff, 73-76, PROF CLIN REPROD, SCH VET MED, UNIV PA, 75-, ASSOC DEAN, 76- *Concurrent Pos:* NIH res grant, 64-; Lalor fel award, 71-72. *Mem:* Am Vet Med Asn; Am Asn Vet Clinicians; Soc Theriogenol. *Res:* Chromosome abnormalities in domestic mammals; especially sex determination and altered reproductive function. *Mailing Add:* New Bolton Ctr Kennett Square PA 19348

MCFERON, D(EAN) E(ARL), b Portland, Ore, Dec 24, 23; m 45; c 4. MECHANICAL ENGINEERING, HEAT TRANSFER. *Educ:* Univ Colo, BSME, 45, MSME, 48; Univ Ill, PhD(mech eng), 56. *Prof Exp:* Instr mech eng, Univ Colo, 46-48; from instr to assoc prof, Univ Ill, 48-58; PROF MECH ENG, UNIV WASH, 58- *Concurrent Pos:* Res fel, NSF-Atomic Energy Comn, Argonne Nat Lab, 56, res assoc, 57-58; NSF fac fel, 67-68. *Mem:* Am Soc Mech Engrs; Am Soc Eng Educ; Am Soc Heating, Refrig & Air Conditioning Engrs; Sigma Xi (pres, 78). *Res:* Heat transfer and fluid flow; power plant cooling systems; thermodynamics. *Mailing Add:* Dept of Mech Eng FU-10 Univ of Wash Seattle WA 98195

MCFETERS, GORDON ALWYN, b Ayer, Mar 28, 39; m 63; c 2. MICROBIAL PHYSIOLOGY, WATER MICROBIOLOGY. *Educ:* Andrews Univ, BA, 61; Loma Linda Univ, MS, 63; Ore State Univ, PhD(microbiol), 67. *Prof Exp:* Asst prof, 67-72, assoc prof, 72-78, PROF MICROBIOL, MONT STATE UNIV, 78- *Concurrent Pos:* Sigma Xi fac res award, Mont State Univ. *Mem:* Am Soc Microbiol; fel Am Acad Microbiol. *Res:* Microbial control mechanisms, enzymology and electron transport mechanisms; water microbiology. *Mailing Add:* Dept Microbiol Mont State Univ Bozeman MT 59717

MCGAHAN, MERRITT WILSON, b Los Angeles, Calif, Mar 8, 20; m 46; c 2. PLANT MORPHOLOGY. *Educ:* Univ Calif, Berkeley, AB, 48; Univ Calif, Davis, PhD(bot), 52; Union Theol Sem, NY, MDiv, 66. *Prof Exp:* Teaching asst bot, Univ Calif, Davis, 49-51; res assoc chem debarking, State Univ NY Col Forestry, Syracuse Univ, 51-52; from instr to asst prof bot, Univ RI, 52-59; anatomist-morphologist, United Fruit Co, Mass, 59-61 & Honduras, 61-63; prof bot, dean grad sch & dir, Inst Sci Res, 66-70, dean acad affairs, 70-74, chmn dept, 74-77, PROF BIOL, NMEX HIGHLANDS UNIV, 74- *Concurrent Pos:* Vis assoc prof, Brandeis Univ, 60-61. *Mem:* AAAS; Bot Soc Am. *Res:* Effects of trace metals on growth of Southwestern range grasses. *Mailing Add:* NMex Highlands Univ Las Vegas NM 87701

MCGAHAN, WALLACE A, b Calif, Mar 3, 26; m 49; c 4. MECHANICAL ENGINEERING. *Educ:* Mass Inst Technol, BS, 47, MS, 63, ScD(mech eng), 65. *Prof Exp:* Engr, Carrier Corp, 47-50; develop engr turbomach, 50-62, DIR RES, INGERSOLL-RAND RES, INC, INGERSOLL-RAND CO, 65- *Mem:* Am Soc Mech Engrs. *Res:* Turbomachinery; compressors; pumps; rock drills; pneumatic and electric tools and industrial machinery development. *Mailing Add:* Ingersoll-Rand Res Inc Box 301 Princeton NJ 08540

MCGAHEN, JOE WINFIELD, microbiology, see previous edition

MCGAHREN, WILLIAM JAMES, b Ballyshannon, Ireland, Feb 16, 24; US citizen; m 58; c 4. ORGANIC CHEMISTRY. *Educ:* Chelsea Polytech Col, BSc, 53; Brooklyn Col, MA, 57; Brooklyn Polytech Inst, PhD(org chem), 66. *Prof Exp:* Chemist, Charles Pfizer Co, 53-63; res fel chem, Brooklyn Polytech Inst, 64-66; SR RES SCIENTIST NATURAL PROD CHEM, LEDERLE LABS, AM CYANAMID CO, PEARL RIVER, NY, 66- *Mem:* Am Chem Soc; Sigma Xi. *Res:* Isolation from microbial sources of novel products that exhibit a specific biological activity; elucidation of structure and sterochemistry of these materials; microbial enzyme transformation of substrates of commercial interest; protein chemistry. *Mailing Add:* 64 Glenwood Ave Demarest NJ 07627

MCGANDY, EDWARD LEWIS, b Washington, DC, Apr 22, 30; m 55; c 2. PHYSICAL CHEMISTRY, COMPUTER AND CONTROL SYSTEMS. *Educ:* George Washington Univ, BS, 51; Boston Univ, PhD(chem), 60. *Prof Exp:* Lab technician, Geophys Lab, Carnegie Inst, 47-51; anal chemist, Nat Bur Stand, Washington, DC, 51-54, phys chemist, 54-55; Am Cancer Soc exchange fel, Med Res Coun Lab, Molecular Biol, Cambridge Univ, 60-63; asst prof biol, Purdue Univ, West Lafayette, 64-67; asst prof biochem & crystallog, Grad Sch Pub Health, Univ Pittsburgh, 67-73; mgr anal instrumentation, Bailey Meter Co, Wickliffe, Ohio, 73-77; consult, 77-78, PROJ LEADER, STANDARD OIL RES LAB, CLEVELAND, 78- *Mem:* Am Chem Soc; Am Crystallog Asn; Am Inst Physics ISA. *Res:* Direct and inferential process control systems with computer automation; automatic analyzers; pollution control systems. *Mailing Add:* Standard Oil Res Lab 4440 Warrensville Center Rd Cleveland OH 44128

MCGANITY, WILLIAM JAMES, b Kitchener, Ont, Sept 21, 23; nat US; m 48; c 3. OBSTETRICS & GYNECOLOGY. *Educ:* Univ Toronto, MD, 46; FRCS(C), 53; Am Bd Nutrit, dipl. *Prof Exp:* Intern, Toronto Gen Hosp, Ont, Can, 46-47; resident obstet & gynec, Univ Toronto & Toronto Gen Hosp, 49-52; from instr to assoc prof, Sch Med, Vanderbilt Univ, 52-59; PROF OBSTET & GYNEC & CHMN DEPT, UNIV TEX MED BR, GALVESTON, 60- *Concurrent Pos:* Res fel nutrit, Univ Toronto, 47-48; res fel, Vanderbilt Univ, 48-49; Lowell M Palmer sr fel, 54-56; part time lectr, Univ Toronto, 49-52; consult, Interdept Comt Nutrit Nat Defense, DC, 56-73, Dept Air Force, 60-, Dept Army, 60-67 & Comt Consider Folic Acid, Food & Drug Admin, 60-63; mem, Comts Dietary Allowances & Int Nutrit, Food & Nutrit Bd, Nat Res Coun, 59-63; dean fac, Univ Tex Med Br, Galveston, 64-67; mem comt maternal nutrit, 66-70; chmn, Comt Maternal Health & Sci Activ, Tex Med Asn, 61-67, Coun Foods & Nutrit, AMA, 63-66, Nutrit Study Sect, NIH, 63-67 & Res Panel Maternal & Child Health, Children's Bur, 64-66; panel mem, White House Conf Nutrit & Health, 69; co-chmn panel nutrit & health, US Senate Select Comt Nutrit & Human Needs, 74. *Honors & Awards:* Hendry Prize, Univ Toronto, 47. *Mem:* Am Col Obstet & Gynec; Am Inst Nutrit; AMA; Am Soc Clin Nutrit (past pres); Asn Prof Gynec & Obstet. *Res:* Nutrition in reproduction; nutrition among underdeveloped populations; physiology of human reproduction. *Mailing Add:* Dept of Obstet & Gynec Univ of Tex Med Br Galveston TX 77550

MCGANN, LOCKSLEY EARL, b Kingston, Jamaica, Aug 11, 46; Can citizen; m 69; c 3. CRYOBIOLOGY. *Educ:* Univ Waterloo, BSc, 69, MSc, 70, PhD(physics), 73. *Prof Exp:* Med Res Coun Can fel, Div Cryobiol, Clin Res Ctr, Harrow, Eng, 73-75; asst prof, 75-79, ASSOC PROF BIOMED ENG, UNIV ALTA, 79- *Concurrent Pos:* Consult comput applications. *Mem:* Soc Cryobiol; Can Inst Food Sci & Technol. *Res:* Interactions of living systems with the environment during cooling to and warming from low temperatures; development of methods for the frozen preservation of cells, tissues and organs; osmotic properties of cells and tissues. *Mailing Add:* Div Biomed Eng & Appl Sci Univ Alta Edmonton AB T6G 2G7 Can

MCGANNON, DONALD E, JR, b Minneapolis, Minn, Oct 12, 29; m 55; c 3. GEOLOGY, GEOCHEMISTRY. *Educ:* Syracuse Univ, BA, 52; Univ Minn, MS, 57, PhD(geol), 60. *Prof Exp:* Assoc prof, 59-71, chmn dept, 59-79, PROF GEOL, TRINITY UNIV, TEX, 71- *Mem:* AAAS; Geol Soc Am; Nat Asn Geol Teachers. *Res:* Petrology; mineralogy. *Mailing Add:* Dept of Geol Trinity Univ 715 Stadium Dr San Antonio TX 78282

MCGARITY, ARTHUR EDWIN, b Chicago, Ill, Apr 2, 51; m 77; c 1. SOLAR ENERGY, OPERATIONS RESEARCH. *Educ:* Trinity Univ, BS, 73; John Hopkins Univ, MSE & PhD(environ eng), 78. *Prof Exp:* Elec engr instrumentation, San Antonio City Pub Serv Bd, 73-74; ASST PROF ENG, SWARTHMORE COL, 78- *Concurrent Pos:* Consult, NSF, 75-76; res assoc, Donnovan, Hammester, Rattien, Inc, Washington, DC, 77-78; vis asst prof, G W C Whiting Sch Eng, Johns Hopkins Univ, 81; scientist in residence, Solar Energy Group, Argonne Nat Lab, 81-82. *Mem:* Int Solar Energy Soc; Inst Mgt Sci; AAAS; Sigma Xi. *Res:* Solar energy engineering and economics; geothermal energy resource assessment; operations research applied to public sector problems involving the supply of energy, water and other natural resources. *Mailing Add:* Dept of Eng Swarthmore Col Swarthmore PA 19081

MCGARITY, WILLIAM CECIL, b Jersey, Ga, Oct 5, 21; m 50; c 3. SURGERY. *Educ:* Emory Univ, BA, 42, MD, 45. *Prof Exp:* Instr, 51-54, assoc, 54-59, from asst prof to assoc prof, 59-76, PROF SURG, SCH MED, EMORY UNIV, 76- *Concurrent Pos:* Mem, Am Bd Surg. *Mem:* AMA; Am Heart Asn; fel Am Col Surg. *Res:* Burns treated with steroids; transminase values in biliary tract and liver pathology; prognosis and course of dogs following litigation of common duct; arterial emboli. *Mailing Add:* Dept of Surg Emory Univ Med Sch Atlanta GA 30322

MCGARR, ARTHUR, b San Francisco, Calif, May 24, 40; m 71. GEOPHYSICS. *Educ:* Calif Inst Technol, BS, 62, MS, 63; Columbia Univ, PhD(geophys), 68. *Prof Exp:* Res asst, Lamont Geol Observ, Columbia Univ, 63-68; sr res fel, Univ Witwatersrand, 68-70, sr res officer geophys, Bernard Price Inst Geophys Res, 70-78; GEOPHYSICIST, US GEOL SURV, 78- *Mem:* Royal Astron Soc; AAAS; Am Geophys Union; Seismol Soc Am. *Res:* Modes of rock deformation in high-stress environments; earthquakes associated with mining and fluid injection; magnitude statistics of earthquakes; seismic near-field measurements of tilt, strain and. *Mailing Add:* Off of Earthquake Studies 345 Middlefield Rd Menlo Park CA 94025

MCGARRITY, GERARD JOHN, b Brooklyn, NY, Oct 10, 40; m 64; c 2. MICROBIOLOGY, CELL BIOLOGY. *Educ:* St Joseph Col, Pa, BS, 62; Jefferson Med Col, MS, 65, PhD(microbiol), 70. *Prof Exp:* Asst prof biol, Glassboro State Col, 64-65; res assoc cell biol, 65-71, HEAD DEPT MICROBIOL, INST MED RES, 71- *Concurrent Pos:* Instr Univ Pa, 71-75; exchange visitor, Czechoslovak Acad Sci, 75; adj fac mem, W Alton Jones Cell Sci Ctr, Lake Placid, 77-; mem recombinant DNA adv comt, NIH, 80-, cellular physiol rev group, 79- *Mem:* AAAS; Am Soc Microbiol; Tissue Culture Asn (vpres, 80-82). *Res:* Mycoplasma infection of cell cultures; detection of environmental mutagens; mutagenicity testing; cell culture facilities. *Mailing Add:* Dept of Microbiol Inst for Med Res Copewood St Camden NJ 08103

MCGARRY, FREDERICK J(EROME), b Rutland, Vt, Aug 22, 27; m 50; c 6. MATERIALS ENGINEERING, POLYMER SCIENCE. *Educ:* Middlebury Col, AB, 50; Mass Inst Technol, SB, 50, SM, 53. *Prof Exp:* Res asst civil eng, 50-51, from instr to assoc prof, 51-65, PROF CIVIL ENG, MASS INST TECHNOL, 65- *Concurrent Pos:* Consult, numerous indust orgn. *Mem:* AAAS; Am Soc Testing & Mat; Am Concrete Inst; Soc Rheol; Am Chem Soc. *Res:* Relationship between the mechanical properties and the structure and composition of polymers; reinforced polymers; adhesion. *Mailing Add:* Rm 8-211 Dept of Mat Sci & Eng Mass Inst of Technol Cambridge MA 02139

MCGARRY, JOHN DENIS, b; m 67; c 3. BIOCHEMISTRY. *Educ:* Victoria Univ, Manchester, BSc, 62, PhD(biochem), 66. *Prof Exp:* From asst prof to assoc prof, 69-77, PROF INTERNAL MED & BIOCHEM, UNIV TEX HEALTH SCI CTR DALLAS, 77- *Concurrent Pos:* Fels, Univs Liverpool & Wales, 65-67; fel, Univ Tex Southwestern Med Sch Dallas, 68-69. *Mem:* Am Diabetes Asn; Brit Biochem Soc; Am Soc Biol Chem. *Res:* Regulation of carbohydrate and lipid metabolism with particular emphasis on the control of ketogenesis in starvation and diabetes. *Mailing Add:* Dept of Internal Med Univ of Tex Health Sci Ctr Dallas TX 75235

MCGARRY, MARGARET, b Boston, Mass, Apr 11, 28. INORGANIC CHEMISTRY, ANALYTICAL CHEMISTRY. *Educ:* Regis Col, Mass, AB, 57; Univ Pa, PhD(chem), 64. *Prof Exp:* From instr to asst prof, 64-70, ASSOC PROF CHEM, REGIS COL, MASS, 70- *Mem:* Am Chem Soc. *Res:* Liability of aqueous solutions of alkali silicates; spectral properties of dyes in colloidal systems; flocculation of colloids; electron microscopy of colloidal substances; ion exchange separations; gas chromatography. *Mailing Add:* Dept of Chem Regis Col Weston MA 02193

MCGARRY, PAUL ANTHONY, b Warren, Pa, Nov 13, 28; m 55; c 3. PATHOLOGY, NEUROPATHOLOGY. *Educ:* Pa State Univ, BS, 50; Temple Univ, MD, 54; Am Bd Path, dipl & cert anat & clin path, 63, cert neuropath, 68. *Prof Exp:* From instr to assoc prof, 63-72, PROF PATH, SCH MED, LA STATE UNIV, 72- *Concurrent Pos:* Asst vis pathologist, Charity Hosp, New Orleans, La, 63-65, vis pathologist, 65-; vis pathologist, New Orleans Vet Admin, La, 68- *Mem:* Am Asn Neuropath. *Res:* Cerebrovascular disease; cervical spondylotic myelopathy; cerebrospinal fluid cytology. *Mailing Add:* Dept Path La State Univ New Orleans LA 70112

MCGARVEY, ALAN R(AYMOND), b Philadelphia, Pa, May 11, 14; m 40. CHEMICAL ENGINEERING. *Educ:* Univ Pa, BS, 36, ChE, 43. *Prof Exp:* Jr chemist, 36-38, asst sect head, 38-46, tech specialist, 46-58, mgr indust insulation res, 58-63, MGR TECH INFO SERV, ARMSTRONG CORK CO, 63- *Mem:* Am Chem Soc; Am Inst Chem Engrs; Am Soc Info Sci. *Res:* Product and process development; low temperature insulants; rubber latex; asphalt; magnesia; mineral wool; adhesives; lamination of felts; method for manufacture of corkboard and mineral wool board; cellular plastics and elastomers; documentation and information retrieval. *Mailing Add:* Armstrong Cork Co Res & Develop Ctr Lancaster PA 17604

MCGARVEY, BRUCE RITCHIE, b Springfield, Mo, Mar 10, 28; m 54; c 3. PHYSICAL CHEMISTRY. *Educ:* Carleton Col, BA, 50; Univ Ill, MA, 51, PhD(chem), 53. *Prof Exp:* From instr to asst prof chem, Univ Calif, 53-57; from asst prof to assoc prof, Kalamazoo Col, 57-62; from assoc prof to prof, Polytech Inst Brooklyn, 62-72, actg head dept, 71-72; PROF CHEM, UNIV WINDSOR, 72- *Concurrent Pos:* Guggenheim fel, Imp Col, Univ London, 67-68. *Mem:* Am Chem Soc; Am Phys Soc; fel Chem Inst Can. *Res:* Nuclear magnetic and electron spin resonance. *Mailing Add:* Dept Chem Univ Windsor Windsor ON N9B 3P4 Can

MCGARVEY, FRANCIS X(AVIER), b Kingston, NY, Mar 16, 19; m 41; c 4. CHEMICAL ENGINEERING. *Educ:* Univ Pa, BS, 41, MS, 44. *Prof Exp:* Engr, US Navy, NJ, 41-44; phys chemist, Manhattan Proj, Los Alamos Sci Lab, 44-45; sr chemist res dept, Rohm & Haas Co, 45-58, tech consult, Foreign Opers Div, 58-65; dir res & develop, Barnstead Still & Sterilizer Co, 65-66; vpres, Hartung Assocs, 66-68; pres, Puricons Inc, 68-76; MGR TECH CTR, IONAC CHEM CO, 76- *Mem:* Am Chem Soc; Electrochem Soc; Am Water Works Asn; Am Inst Chem Engrs. *Res:* Technical development of the use of ion exchange materials in industry, study of their role in nuclear reactor development, uranium recovery, sugar processing, desalination, water treatment and radioactivity waste disposal. *Mailing Add:* Ionac Chem Co Birmingham NJ 08011

MCGARY, CHARLES WESLEY, JR, b New Castle, Pa, Dec 12, 29; m 49; c 5. POLYMER CHEMISTRY. *Educ:* Westminster Col, Pa, BS, 51; Purdue Univ, PhD(phys org chem), 55. *Prof Exp:* Res chemist, Chem Div, Union Carbide Corp, 54-61, group leader, 61-66, asst dir chem & plastics div, 66-73, prod mgr, 73-77, int mkt mgr, 77-80; dir res & develop, Riverain Corp, 80-82; DIR RES & DEVELOP, DESERET POLYMER RES DIV, WARNER-LAMBERT CO, 82- *Mem:* Am Chem Soc. *Res:* Plastics intermediates, epoxy resins, polyesters, plasticizers, vinyl resins, latex paints, coatings and water soluble polymers. *Mailing Add:* Warner-Lambert Co 11125 Yankee St PO Box 1285 Dayton OH 45401

MCGAUGH, JAMES L, b Long Beach, Calif, Dec 17, 31; m 52; c 3. PSYCHOBIOLOGY, NEUROBIOLOGY. *Educ:* San Jose State Univ, BA, 53; Univ Calif, Berkeley, PhD(psychol), 59. *Prof Exp:* From asst prof to assoc prof, San Jose State Univ, 57-61; Nat Res Coun sr fel physiol psychol, Adv Inst Health, Italy, 61-62; assoc prof psychol, Univ Ore, 62-64; prof psychobiol & chmn dept, 64-67, dean, Sch Biol Sci, 67-70, chmn psychobiol dept, 71-74, v chancellor acad affairs, 75-77, PROF PSYCHOBIOL, UNIV CALIF, IRVINE, 66-, EXEC V CHANCELLOR, 78- *Concurrent Pos:* Mem biol sci training rev comt, Nat Inst Ment Health, chmn, 71-72, mem preclin psychopharmacol res rev comt, 75-78, mem, Nat Acad Sci Comt, aging, 78-79, W Clement Stone Found, 79-; consult, Vet Admin; ed, Behav & Neural Biol. *Mem:* Fel AAAS; Int Brain Res Orgn; Soc Neurosci; fel Am Psychol Asn; Am Col Neuropsychopharmacol. *Res:* Biological bases of behavior; neurobiology of learning and memory. *Mailing Add:* Dept of Psychobiol Univ of Calif Irvine CA 92717

MCGAUGH, JOHN WESLEY, b Garden City, Kans, June 26, 38; m 64; c 3. ANIMAL SCIENCE. *Educ:* Colo State Univ, BS, 66; Univ Ky, MS, 68, PhD(reprod physiol), 71. *Prof Exp:* Res asst, Univ Ky, 66-71; dist sales mgr, Am Breeders Serv Inc, 71-75; asst prof, 75-80, ASSOC PROF AGR, FT HAYS STATE UNIV, 80- *Mem:* Am Soc Animal Sci; Sigma Xi. *Mailing Add:* Dept of Agr Ft Hays State Univ Hays KS 67601

MCGAUGHAN, HENRY S(TOCKWELL), b Philadelphia, Pa, Nov 5, 17; m 41; c 3. ELECTRICAL ENGINEERING. *Educ:* Univ Mich, BS, 41; Cornell Univ, MEE, 49. *Prof Exp:* From jr engr to sub-sect chief, US Naval Ord Lab, 41-47; from instr to assoc prof, 47-60, vis prof, Cornell Aeronaut Lab, 57-58, PROF ELEC ENG, CORNELL UNIV, 60- *Concurrent Pos:* Consult, US Naval Ord Lab, 55-56; tech assistance expert, Int Telecommun Union, Inst Electronics, Taiwan, 62-63. *Mem:* Sr mem Inst Elec & Electronics Engrs. *Res:* Underwater sound measurements and analysis; electronic instrumentation in radio astronomy; statistical studies of integrated defense systems; electronic countermeasures in communications and radar. *Mailing Add:* Dept of Elec Eng Cornell Univ Ithaca NY 14850

MCGAUGHEY, CHARLES GILBERT, b San Diego, Calif, Sept 8, 25. BIOCHEMISTRY, DENTAL RESEARCH. *Educ:* Univ Calif, BA, 50; Univ Southern Calif, MA, 52. *Prof Exp:* Asst biochem, Univ Southern Calif, 51-52; radiol biochemist, US Naval Radiol Defense Lab, 52; res biochemist med, 52-63, RES BIOCHEMIST, ORAL DIS RES LAB, VET ADMIN HOSP, LONG BEACH, CALIF, 63- *Mem:* AAAS; Am Chem Soc. *Res:* Mechanism of formation of dental plaque and calculus; biochemistry and physiology of cancer cell; mechanisms of tumor promotion; effects of polyphosphates on parameters related to dental caries; mammalian bioassay for tumor initiation and promotion. *Mailing Add:* Oral Dis Res Lab R-4 Vet Admin Hosp Long Beach CA 90801

MCGAUGHEY, WILLIAM HORTON, entomology, see previous edition

MCGAVIN, MATTHEW DONALD, b Goondiwindi, Australia, July 25, 30; m 61; c 3. VETERINARY PATHOLOGY. *Educ:* Univ Queensland, BVSc, 52, MVSc, 62; Mich State Univ, PhD(path), 64; Am Col Vet Path, dipl, 63. *Prof Exp:* Vet off, Animal Res Inst, Yeerongpilly, Australia, 52-59, sr histopathologist, 59-61 & 64-68; from assoc prof to prof path, Kans State Univ, 68-76; PROF PATH, UNIV TENN, 76- *Mem:* Am Vet Med Asn; Am Col Vet Path; Australian Vet Asn. *Res:* Ovine muscular dystrophy; comparative neuropathology. *Mailing Add:* Dept of Path Univ of Tenn Knoxville TN 37901

MCGAVIN, RAYMOND E, b Youngstown, Ohio, Jan 13, 21; m 50; c 6. PHYSICS. *Educ:* Niagara Univ, BA, 46; Univ Colo, BA, 50. *Prof Exp:* Physicist, Nat Bur Standards, 50-52, electronics scientist, 52-59, supvr elec sci, 59-61, physicist, 61-64, supvry physicist, Environ Sci Serv Admin, 64-69, SUPVRY PHYSICIST, NAT OCEANIC & ATMOSPHERIC ADMIN, 69- *Concurrent Pos:* Mem, Inter-Range Instrumentation Group, 65- *Mem:* Am Geophys Union; Sigma Xi; Inst Elec & Electronics Engrs. *Res:* Radio meteorology; atmospheric turbulence; tropospheric radio wave propagation. *Mailing Add:* Nat Oceanic & Atmospheric Admin 325 Broadway Boulder CO 80302

MCGAVOCK, WALTER DONALD, b Nashville, Tenn, Apr 18, 33. INVERTEBRATE ZOOLOGY, PARASITOLOGY. *Educ:* Mid Tenn State Univ, BS, 56, MA, 58; Univ Tenn, PhD(zool), 67. *Prof Exp:* Chmn dept biol, Limestone Col, 58-62; asst prof, Wofford Col, 62-64; instr & res asst zool, Univ Tenn, 66-67; assoc prof biol, ETenn State Univ, 67-70; from assoc prof to prof biol, Tusculum Col, 70-76, dir div natural sci & math, 70-76; ASSOC PROF BIOL, E TENN STATE UNIV, 76- *Concurrent Pos:* Lectr, Spartanburg Gen Hosp, SC, 62-64. *Mem:* Am Soc Parasitol. *Res:* Chemotherapy of cestodes; taxonomy of helminths; host-parasitic relationships. *Mailing Add:* Dept of Biol E Tenn State Univ Johnson City TN 37601

MCGAVOCK, WILLIAM GILLESPIE, mathematics, deceased

MCGAVRAN, MALCOLM HOWARD, b Harda, India, Oct 18, 29; US citizen; c 5. PATHOLOGY. *Educ:* Bethany Col, WVa, AB, 51; Wash Univ, MD, 54; Am Bd Path, dipl, 59. *Prof Exp:* From instr to assoc prof path, Med Sch, Wash Univ, 57-70; prof path, Hershey Col Med, Pa State Univ & dir anat path, Hershey Med Ctr Hosp, 70-75; PROF PATH & DIR DIV ANAT PATH, BAYLOR COL MED, 75-; CHIEF ANAT PATH, THE METHODIST HOSP, 75- *Concurrent Pos:* Consult, Vet Admin Hosp, Houston. *Mem:* AAAS; Am Asn Path; Int Acad Path. *Res:* Surgical pathology; oncology; electron microscopy. *Mailing Add:* The Methodist Hosp Tex Med Ctr Houston TX 77030

MCGEACHIN, ROBERT LORIMER, b Pasadena, Calif, May 13, 17; m 47; c 2. BIOCHEMISTRY. *Educ:* Univ Nebr, BS, 39, MS, 40; Wash Univ, PhD(org chem), 42. *Prof Exp:* Asst chem, Univ Nebr, 39-40; asst, Univ Ill, 46-47; from asst prof to assoc prof, 47-66, PROF BIOCHEM, SCH MED, UNIV LOUISVILLE, 66- *Concurrent Pos:* USPHS fel, Univ Ill, 46-47; chmn dept biochem, Sch Med, Univ Louisville, 72-76. *Mem:* Am Chem Soc (treas, Div Biol Chem, 63-66); Soc Exp Biol & Med; Am Soc Biol Chem. *Res:* Biochemistry and physiology of mammlian amylases. *Mailing Add:* Univ of Louisville Sch of Med Louisville KY 40292

MCGEADY, LEON JOSEPH, b Freemansburg, Pa, July 5, 21; m 49; c 6. PHYSICAL METALLURGY. *Educ:* Lehigh Univ, BS, 43, MS, 46, PhD, 50. *Prof Exp:* Sci investr, Lehigh Univ, 43-49; from asst prof to assoc prof metall eng, 49-57, PROF METALL ENG, LAFAYETTE COL, 57-, DIR ENG, 75- *Concurrent Pos:* Consult, Naval Res Lab, Washington, DC, 64- *Mem:* Am Soc Metals; Am Welding Soc; Am Soc Eng Educ; Am Inst Mining, Metall & Petrol Engrs. *Res:* Welding; internal friction in metals; fracture and plastic deformation. *Mailing Add:* Dept of Metall Eng Dana Hall of Eng Lafayette Col Easton PA 18042

MCGEARY, DAVID F R, b Bellefonte, Pa, Dec 23, 40; m 67; c 1. GEOLOGY, OCEANOGRAPHY. *Educ:* Williams Col, BA, 62; Univ Ill, Urbana, 64; Scripps Inst Oceanog, PhD(oceanog), 69. *Prof Exp:* Asst prof, 69-74, ASSOC PROF GEOL, CALIF STATE UNIV, SACRAMENTO, 74- *Mem:* AAAS; Geol Soc Am; Am Geophys Union; Am Asn Petrol Geologists. *Res:* Marine geology. *Mailing Add:* Dept of Geol Calif State Univ Sacramento CA 95819

MCGEE, CHARLES E, b Baylor Co, Tex, July 29, 35; m 60; c 1. ANALYTICAL CHEMISTRY, HEALTH PHYSICS. *Educ:* ETex State Univ, BS, 62; Purdue Univ, MS, 66, PhD(bionucleonics), 68. *Prof Exp:* Res asst physiol, Southwestern Med Sch, Univ Tex, 60-62; from asst prof to assoc prof radiochem, Sch Pharm, Temple Univ, 67-74, proj dir, Radiol Health Specialist Training Proj, 68-74; mgr health physics, 74-78, mgr consult & lab serv, 78-80, DIR MKT, RADIATION MGT CORP, 80- *Mem:* Am Chem Soc; Health Physics Soc. Environmental health; health physics, environmental radiochemistry. *Mailing Add:* Radiation Mgt Corp PO Box 7940 Philadelphia PA 19101

MCGEE, HENRY A(LEXANDER), JR, b Atlanta, Ga, Sept 12, 29; m 51; c 3. PHYSICAL CHEMISTRY, CRYOGENICS. *Educ:* Ga Inst Technol, BChE, 51, PhD(chem eng), 55. *Prof Exp:* Res asst, Theoret Chem Lab, & Sch Chem Eng, Univ Wis, 55; instr, Huntsville Ctr, Univ Ala, 56-59; from assoc prof to prof chem eng, Ga Inst Technol, 59-71; PROF CHEM ENG & HEAD DEPT, VA POLYTECH INST & STATE UNIV, 71- *Concurrent Pos:* lectr, US & Europe; res chemist, Army Rocket & Guided Missile Agency, Ala, 56-58; phys scientist, Army Ballistic Missile Agency, 59 & George C Marshall Space Flight, Ctr, NASA, 59. *Mem:* AAAS; Am Chem Soc; Am Inst Chem Engrs; Sigma Xi. *Res:* Cryogenics, especially low temperature chemistry and related techniques; experimental and theoretical kinetics and thermodynamics; chemical and physical properties of matter at extremes of temperature and pressure; chemical lasers. *Mailing Add:* Va Polytech Inst & State Univ Blacksburg VA 24061

MACGEE, JOSEPH, b Edinburgh, Scotland, Nov 24, 25; nat US; m 47, 81; c 1. BIOCHEMISTRY, ANALYTICAL CHEMISTRY. *Educ:* Univ Calif, PhD(comp biochem), 54. *Prof Exp:* Lab technician res & develop, Merck & Co, Inc, 44-50; asst bact, Univ Calif, 52-53; res anal biochemist, Procter & Gamble Co, 55-61; from asst prof to assoc prof exp biol, 61-77, asst prof biol chem, 61-70, ASSOC PROF BIOL CHEM, COL MED, UNIV CINCINNATI, 70-, PROF EXP MED, 77-; RES BIOCHEMIST, VET ADMIN HOSP, 61- *Concurrent Pos:* USPHS fel, Univ Ill, 54-55. *Res:* Analytical biochemistry. *Mailing Add:* Basic Sci Lab Vet Admin Med Ctr 3200 Vine St Cincinnati OH 45220

MCGEE, LAWRENCE RAY, b Salt Lake City, Utah, Oct 29, 52; m 77; c 2. CHEMISTRY. *Educ:* Univ Utah, BA, 74; Calif Inst Technol, PhD(chem), 82. *Prof Exp:* RES CHEMIST, CENT RES & DEVELOP, E I DU PONT DE NEMOURS & CO, INC, 81- *Mem:* Am Chem Soc. *Res:* Natural product synthesis with emphasis on pharmacologically active, novel structural types; development of new synthetic methods; use of organometallic centers for stereo control in organic synthesis. *Mailing Add:* DuPont Exp Sta Wilmington DE 19898

MCGEE, THOMAS DONALD, b Tripoli, Iowa, June 9, 25; m 48, 81; c 4. CERAMIC ENGINEERING. *Educ:* Iowa State Univ, BSc, 48, MSc, 58, PhD(ceramic eng, metall), 61. *Prof Exp:* Res engr, A P Green Refractories Co, Mo, 48-54, res eng supvr, 54-56; from asst prof to assoc prof ceramic eng, 61-65, PROF CERAMIC ENG, IOWA STATE UNIV, 65- *Mem:* Fel Am Ceramic Soc; Nat Inst Ceramic Eng; Am Soc Eng Educ; Brit Soc Glass Technol. *Res:* Refractories; glass; electron microscopy; ceramic bone implants. *Mailing Add:* Dept of Mats Sci & Eng Iowa State Univ Ames IA 50010

MCGEE, THOMAS HOWARD, b New York, NY, Dec 19, 41; m 66; c 3. CHEMICAL KINETICS, PHOTOCHEMISTRY. *Educ:* St John's Univ, NY, BS, 62; Univ Conn, PhD(phys chem), 66. *Prof Exp:* Fel chem, Univ Tex, Austin, 66-67; asst prof, 67-74, ASSOC PROF CHEM, YORK COL, NY, 74-, CHMN DEPT NATURAL SCI, 76- *Concurrent Pos:* NSF acad year award, 68-69; res collabr, Chem Dept, Brookhaven Nat Lab, 75-77. *Mem:* Am Chem Soc. *Res:* Chemical kinetics; photochemistry. *Mailing Add:* Dept of Chem City Univ New York Jamaica NY 11451

MCGEE, WILLIAM F, b Toronto, Ont, Jan 16, 37; m 62; c 5. ELECTRICAL ENGINEERING. *Educ:* Univ Toronto, BASc, 59, MA, 60; Univ Ill, PhD(elec eng), 62. *Prof Exp:* Asst prof elec eng, Univ Waterloo, 63-66; MEM SCI STAFF, BELL NORTHERN RES, 66- *Mem:* Inst Elec & Electronics Engrs. *Res:* Approximation problems in electric network synthesis; theory of pulse transmission. *Mailing Add:* Bell Northern Res Box 3511 Sta C Ottawa ON K1Y 4H7 Can

MCGEE, WILLIAM WALTER, b Toledo, Ohio, June 27, 39; m 63; c 1. ANALYTICAL CHEMISTRY. *Educ:* Univ Toledo, BS, 61, MS, 63; Univ Fla, PhD(chem), 66. *Prof Exp:* Group leader gas chromatography lab, B F Goodrich Co, 66-68; from asst prof to assoc prof anal chem, 68-77, ASSOC PROF FORENSIC SCI, UNIV CENT FLA, 77- *Mem:* Am Chem Soc. *Res:* Fundamental processes which occur in the flame, as used in flame spectroscopy. *Mailing Add:* Dept of Chem Univ Cent Fla PO Box 25000 Orlando FL 32816

MCGEER, EDITH GRAEF, b New York, NY, Nov 18, 23; m 54; c 3. ORGANIC CHEMISTRY. *Educ:* Swarthmore Col, BA, 44; Univ Va, PhD(org chem), 46. *Prof Exp:* Technician, Squibb Inst Med Res, E R Squibb & Sons, 43; res chemist, Exp Sta, E I du Pont de Nemours & Co, Inc, 46-54; res assoc, 54-74, assoc prof, 74-78, PROF, KINSMEN LAB NEUROL RES, UNIV BC, 78- *Mem:* Can Biochem Soc; Int Neurochem Soc; Am Neurochem Soc; Soc Neurosci. *Res:* Synaptic transmission; neurochemistry and anatomy; neurochemisty and pathology. *Mailing Add:* Kinsmen Lab Neurol Res Univ of BC Vancouver BC V6T 1W5 Can

MCGEER, JAMES PETER, b Vancouver, BC, May 14, 22; m 48; c 4. PHYSICAL CHEMISTRY, EXTRACTIVE METALLURGY. *Educ:* Univ BC, BA, 44, MA, 46; Princeton Univ, MA, 48, PhD(chem), 49. *Prof Exp:* Res phys chemist & group leader, Aluminum Labs, Ltd, 49-68; tech supt, Aluminum Co Can Ltd, 68-70, asst mgr reduction div, Arvida Works & mgr reduction technol, Quebec Smelters, Alcan, 70-73, mgr reduction technol, Alcan Smelters Serv, 73-77, DIR RES, ALCAN INT LTD, 77- *Mem:* Am Inst Mining, Metall & Petrol Engrs; Chem Inst Can. *Res:* Electrometallurgy of aluminum; carbon; smelting furnace operation; hydrometallurgy of bauxite. *Mailing Add:* Kingston Res & Develop Ctr Alcan Int Ltd PO Box 8400 Kingston ON K7M 4M2 Can

MCGEER, PATRICK L, b Vancouver, BC, Can, June 29, 27; m 54; c 3. BIOCHEMISTRY. *Educ:* Univ BC, BA, 48, MD, 58; Princeton Univ, PhD(phys chem), 51. *Prof Exp:* Res chemist, Polychem Dept, E I du Pont de Nemours & Co, 51-54; res assoc, 56-58, from asst prof to assoc prof, 59-74, PROF, KINSMEN LAB NEUROL RES, UNIV BC, 74- DIR, 64-, HEAD DEPT, 77- *Concurrent Pos:* Intern Vancouver Gen Hosp, 58-59; dir, BC Hydro, BC Petrol Corp, Discovery Found, Discovery Parks Inc & BC Res Coun; minister educ, BC, 74-77, sci & technol, 77-79 & sci & commun, 79- *Mem:* Fel AAAS; Soc Neurosci; Can Biochem Soc; Am Neurochem Soc; Int Brain Res Orgn. *Res:* Medical biochemistry; neurochemistry; neurophysiology; biogenic amine metabolism. *Mailing Add:* Kinsmen Lab of Neurol Res Univ of BC Vancouver BC V6T 1W8 Can

MCGEE-RUSSELL, SAMUEL M, b Sutton, Eng, Aug 24, 27; m 55; c 3. BIOLOGY, ELECTRON MICROSCOPY. *Educ:* Oxford Univ, BA, 51, MA, 54, DPhil(zool), 55. *Prof Exp:* Asst lectr zool, Birkbeck Col, Univ London, 54-56; vis scientist fel, NIH, 56-57; lectr zool, Birkbeck Col, Univ London, 57-61; lab dir & staff scientist, Virus Res Unit, Med Res Coun, 62-68; sr res assoc & lectr cell biol, 68-72, PROF CELL BIOL & ELECTRON MICROS, STATE UNIV NY ALBANY, 72- *Concurrent Pos:* Dir, Co of Biologists, 67- *Mem:* Fel Zool Soc London; fel Royal Micros Soc; Brit Soc Exp Biol (secy, 62-66); Am Soc Cell Biol; Electron Micros Soc Am. *Res:* Light microscopy; e m; microtechnique and microtomy; cell biology; histochemistry; protozoology; invertebrate zoology especially of mollusca; virology. *Mailing Add:* Dept of Biol Sci State Univ of NY Albany NY 12222

MCGEHEE, OSCAR CARRUTH, b Baton Rouge, La, Nov 29, 39. MATHEMATICS. *Educ:* Rice Univ, BA, 61; Yale Univ, MA, 63, PhD(math), 66. *Prof Exp:* From instr to asst prof math, Univ Calif, Berkeley, 65-71; assoc prof, 71-79, PROF & CHMN, LA STATE UNIV, BATON ROUGE, 79- *Concurrent Pos:* NATO fel, Fac Sci, Orsay, France, 67-68. *Mem:* Am Math Soc; Math Asn Am; Math Soc France; London Math Soc; Sigma Xi. *Res:* Commutative harmonic analysis; functional analysis. *Mailing Add:* Dept Math La State Univ Baton Rouge LA 70803

MCGEHEE, RALPH MARSHALL, b Magnolia, Miss, Apr 23, 21; m 45; c 1. APPLIED MATHEMATICS, NUMERICAL ANALYSIS. *Educ:* La Col, BA, 42; NC State Col, BEE, 49, MS, 50, PhD(elec eng), 53. *Prof Exp:* Staff mem, Sandia Lab, US AEC, 53-61; mem tech staff, Tucson Eng Lab, Hughes Aircraft Co, 61-62; assoc prof math, 62-66, head dept comput sci, 66-67, assoc prof, 66-77, PROF COMPUT SCI, NMEX INST MINING & TECHNOL, 77- *Mem:* Inst Elec & Electronics Eng; Asn Comput Mach; Soc Indust & Appl Math; Opers Res Soc Am; Am Meteorol Soc. *Res:* Applied analysis; numerical analysis of modeling; atmospheric dynamics on thunderstorn scales. *Mailing Add:* Dept of Comput Sci NMex Inst of Mining & Technol Socorro NM 87801

MCGEHEE, RICHARD PAUL, b San Diego, Calif, Sept 20, 43; m 67, 81. MATHEMATICS. *Educ:* Calif Inst Technol, BS, 64; Univ Wis-Madison, MS, 65, PhD(math), 69. *Prof Exp:* Vis mem, Courant Inst Math Sci, NY Univ, 69-70; from asst prof to assoc prof, 70-79, PROF MATH, UNIV MINN, MINNEAPOLIS, 79- *Mem:* Am Math Soc; Math Asn Am. *Res:* Qualitative theory of ordinary differential equations. *Mailing Add:* Sch of Math Univ of Minn Minneapolis MN 55455

MCGEHEE, RICHARD VERNON, b Tyler, Tex, Aug 1, 34; m 58; c 2. GEOLOGY. *Educ:* Univ Tex, BS, 55, PhD(geol), 63; Yale Univ, MS, 56, Tex A&M, MS, 78. *Prof Exp:* Petrol geologist, Phillips Petrol Co, 56-57; instr geol, Univ Kans, 63; asst prof, Western Mich Univ, 63-66 & SDak Sch Mines & Technol, 66-67; assoc prof, Western Mich Univ, 67-72; vis prof geol, Inst Geol, Nat Univ Mex, 72-74; assoc prof, Univ Tex at San Antonio, 74-77, prof geol, Div Earth & Phys Sci, 77-79; assoc prof, 78-81, PROF HEALTH & PHYS EDUC SOUTHEASTERN LA UNIV, 81- *Mem:* Geol Soc Am; Nat Asn Geol Teachers; Am Asn Petrol Geologists. *Res:* Igneous and metamorphic petrology; structural and economic geology. *Mailing Add:* Box 677 Southeastern La Univ Hammond LA 70402

MCGEORGE, A(RTHUR), JR, b Wilmington, Del, July 6, 21; m 52; c 3. CHEMICAL ENGINEERING. *Educ:* Univ Pa, BS, 42, PhD(chem eng), 51. *Prof Exp:* Jr chemist, E I du Pont de Nemours & Co, 42-44; develop engr, B F Goodrich Chem Co, 44-47; asst instr chem eng, Univ Pa, 47-50; res engr nylon res, 51-52, res supvr, 53-57, sr res supvr, Dacron Res Lab, 57-58, tech supvr, 58-65, TECH MGR DEVELOP DEPT, NEWPORT LAB, E I DU PONT DE NEMOURS & CO, INC, 65- *Mem:* Am Chem Soc; Soc Rheol; Sigma Xi; Am Inst Chem Engrs. *Res:* Fluid flow; rheology; heat transfer; molecular structure of polymers; design of experiments. *Mailing Add:* 700 Center Mill Rd Greenville DE 19807

MCGERITY, JOSEPH LOEHR, b New York, NY, Sept 16, 28; m 65; c 2. ALLERGY, IMMUNOLOGY. *Educ:* Duke Univ, BS, 50, MD, 54. *Prof Exp:* Resident internal med, Letterman Gen Hosp, 59-62; fel allergy-immunol, Univ Buffalo, 65-67; ASSOC PROF MED & DIR ALLERGY SERV, CHEST DIV, DEPT MED, UNIV CALIF, SAN FRANCISCO, 75- *Concurrent Pos:* Med mem, US Army Phys Disability Agency, 73-; asst clin prof med, Stanford Univ, 74- *Mem:* Am Acad Allergy; Asn Mil Allergists (pres, 77). *Res:* Detection of clinical allergens by botanical and immunologic investigation; influence of allergic disease and therapy thereof on physiology of pregnancy. *Mailing Add:* Allergy Div Chest Clin 536-A 400 Parnasus Ave San Francisco CA 94143

MCGERVEY, JOHN DONALD, b Pittsburgh, Pa, Aug 9, 31; m 57; c 2. EXPERIMENTAL SOLID STATE PHYSICS. *Educ:* Univ Pittsburgh, BS, 52; Carnegie Inst Technol, MS, 55, PhD(physics), 61. *Prof Exp:* Instr math, Carnegie Inst Technol, 57-60; asst prof, 60-65, ASSOC PROF PHYSICS, CASE WESTERN RESERVE UNIV, 65- *Concurrent Pos:* Vis scientist, Inst Solid State Physics & Nuclear Res, W Ger, 72-73. *Mem:* AAAS; Am Phys Soc; Am Asn Physics Teachers; Am Asn Univ Prof; Sigma Xi. *Res:* Study of solids and liquids by positron annihilation. *Mailing Add:* Dept of Physics Case Western Reserve Univ Cleveland OH 44106

MCGETCHIN, THOMAS R, geology, deceased

MCGHAN, WILLIAM FREDERICK, b Sacramento, Calif, July 6, 46; m 68; c 2. PHARMACY ADMINISTRATION, HEALTH SERVICES RESEARCH. *Educ:* Univ Calif, PharmD, 70; Univ Minn, Minneapolis, PhD(pharm admin), 79. *Prof Exp:* Resident, Med Ctr, Univ Calif, San Francisco, 70-71; pharm coordr, Appalachian Student Health Proj, 69-70; exec secy, Student Am Pharm Asn, 71-74 & Acad Pharmaceut Sci, 74-76; instr pharm, Univ Minn, 76-78; ASST PROF PHARM, SCH PHARM, UNIV SOUTHERN CALIF, 78- *Concurrent Pos:* Dir, Nat Student Drug Educ grant, 71-73; fel, Am Found Pharmaceut Educ, 76-78; consult, Nat Comn Protection Human Subjects, 76-78 & Vet Admin San Diego Pharm Servs, 78-; mem comt, Nat Drug Educ Asn, 74-75; mem pub policy comt, Acad Pharm Sci, 74- *Mem:* Am Pharmaceut Asn; Acad Pharmaceut Sci; Am Pub Health Asn; Am Soc Hosp Pharmacists; Sigma Xi. *Res:* Administrative and social pharmacy; evaluation of health services; drug utilization review; health services research; educational development in the health science. *Mailing Add:* Sch of Pharm 1985 Zonal Ave Los Angeles CA 90033

MCGHEE, CHARLES ROBERT, b Chattanooga, Tenn, July 17, 34; m 64; c 3. SYSTEMATIC ZOOLOGY. *Educ:* Mid Tenn State Univ, BS, 61, MA, 62; Va Polytech Inst, PhD(zool), 70. *Prof Exp:* Asst prof, 68-73, assoc prof, 73-79, PROF BIOL, MID TENN STATE UNIV, 79- *Mem:* Am Arachnol Soc; Sigma Xi. *Res:* Systematics of phalangid genus Leiobunum. *Mailing Add:* Dept of Biol Mid Tenn State Univ Murfreesboro TN 37132

MCGHEE, GEORGE RUFUS, JR, b Henderson, NC, Sept 25, 51; m 71. PALEOECOLOGY, EVOLUTIONARY MORPHOLOGY. *Educ:* NC State Univ, BSc, 73; Univ NC, Chapel Hill, MSc, 75; Univ Rochester, PhD(geol), 78. *Prof Exp:* ASST PROF GEOL & ECOL, RUTGERS UNIV, 78- *Concurrent Pos:* Sci asst, Univ Tübingen, 77; vis scientist, Field Mus Natural Hist, 81; prin investr, NSF Grant, Earthsci Div, 81-; res assoc, Am Mus Natural Hist, 82- *Mem:* Int Paleont Asn; Paleont Soc; Paläonologishe

Ges; Brit Paleont Asn; AAAS. *Res:* Marine community paleoecology; evolution of ecosystems; theorectical morphology; evolutionary theory; phenotypic evolution; animal form and function in nature. *Mailing Add:* Dept Geol Sci Wright Geol Lab Rutgers Univ New Brunswick NJ 08903

MCGHEE, JERRY ROGER, b Knoxville, Tenn, June 25, 41; m 61; c 2. MICROBIOLOGY, IMMUNOLOGY. *Educ:* Univ Tenn, Knoxville, BS, 64; Univ Tenn, Memphis, PhD(microbiol), 69. *Prof Exp:* Res asst prof, Univ Tenn, Memphis, 69; instr microbiol & dent res, 69-71, asst prof microbiol, 72-75, ASSOC PROF MICROBIOL & SCIENTIST INST DENT RES, UNIV ALA, BIRMINGHAM, 75- *Concurrent Pos:* Teaching fel microbiol, Med Units, Univ Tenn, Memphis, 64-66; NIH fel microbiol, Univ Chicago, 71-72; sabbatical, Lab Micro Immunol, Nat Inst Dent Res, NIH, 77-78. *Mem:* Am Soc Microbiol; Am Asn Immunol; Soc Exp Biol & Med; Reticuloendothelial Soc; Tissue Cult Asn. *Res:* Host-parasite interrelationships; cellular rates of synthesis; effective immunity to dental cavities and enteric diseases; local immunity; LPS effects on lymphoid cells. *Mailing Add:* Dept of Microbiol Univ of Ala Med Ctr Birmingham AL 35233

MCGHEE, ROBERT B, b Detroit, Mich, June 6, 29; m 52; c 3. ELECTRICAL ENGINEERING. *Educ:* Univ Mich, BS, 52; Univ Southern Calif, MS, 57, PhD(elec eng), 63. *Prof Exp:* Mem tech staff, Hughes Aircraft Co, 55-63; from asst prof to assoc prof elec eng, Univ Southern Calif, 63-68; PROF ELEC ENG, OHIO STATE UNIV, 68- *Mem:* Inst Elec & Electronics Engrs. *Res:* Control and switching theory; non-linear system identification; statistical analysis; computer design and applications; prosthetics; digital computers; biomedical engineering. *Mailing Add:* Dept of Elec Eng 15th Ave & N High St Columbus OH 43210

MCGHEE, ROBERT BARCLAY, b Cleveland, Tenn, Feb 22, 18; m 46; c 3. PARASITOLOGY. *Educ:* Berea Col, AB, 40; Univ Ga, MS, 42; Univ Chicago, PhD(bact, parasitol), 48. *Prof Exp:* Asst animal path, Rockefeller Inst, 48-51, assoc, 51-54; assoc prof biol, 54-55, head dept zool, 55-64, prof, 59-64, ALUMNI FOUND DISTINGUISHED PROF ZOOL, UNIV GA, 64- *Concurrent Pos:* Vis lectr, Univ Mex, 64-65; mem study sect, Trop Med & Parasitol, NIH, 66-71, chmn, 70-71; mem sci adv bd, Gorgas Mem Inst, 72- *Mem:* AAAS; Am Soc Nat; Am Soc Zool; Am Soc Parasitol; Am Soc Protozool. *Res:* Relationship of host to parasite, as expressed in various species of plasmodia and trypanosomids; innate and acquired immunity; evolution of parasitic organisms; medical bacteriology and parasitology; insects affecting man and animals; invertebrate zoology. *Mailing Add:* Dept of Zool Univ of Ga Athens GA 30602

MCGHEE, TERENCE JOSEPH, b Summit, NJ, July 5, 36; m 69. SANITARY ENGINEERING. *Educ:* Newark Col Eng, BS, 59; Va Polytech Inst, MS, 63; Univ Kans, PhD(civil eng), 68. *Prof Exp:* Ciivl engr, US Forest Serv, 59-62; res engr, Boeing Co, 62-64 & Lord Mfg Co, 64-65; asst prof civil eng, Univ Louisville, 68-70; from asst prof to assoc prof, Univ Nebr, 70-75; assoc prof, 75-79, PROF CIVIL ENG, TULANE UNIV, 79- *Concurrent Pos:* Sr proj adv, N-Y Assocs, Consult Engrs, 76-79 & United Res Serv, 79- *Mem:* Water Pollution Control Fedn; Am Water Works Asn; Am Soc Civil Engrs. *Res:* Water quality; water pollution; wastewater and water treatment. *Mailing Add:* Dept of Civil Eng Tulane Univ New Orleans LA 70118

MCGIBBON, WILLIAM HENRY, genetics, deceased

MCGIBNEY, DONALD JOSEPH, molecular physics, operations research, see previous edition

MCGIFF, JOHN C, b New York, NY, Aug 6, 27; m 58; c 5. PHARMACOLOGY, INTERNAL MEDICINE. *Educ:* Georgetown Univ, BS, 47; Columbia Univ, MD, 51; Am Bd Internal Med, dipl, 64. *Prof Exp:* Res assoc, Sch Med, St Louis Univ, 58-59; from asst instr to instr, Univ Pa, 60-62; assoc med & pharmacol, 62-64, asst prof, 64-65; assoc prof internal med & chief cardiovasc sect, Sch Med, St Louis Univ, 65-70, prof med, 70-71; prof pharmacol & med & dir clin pharm sect, Med Col Wis, 71-75; prof & chmn dept pharmacol, Univ Tenn, Ctr Health Sci, 75-80; MEM FAC, NEW YORK MED COL, 80- *Concurrent Pos:* Fel med, Col Physicians & Surgeons, Columbia Univ, 57-58; Am Heart Asn res fel, 57-59; fel & co-recipient inst grant, USPHS, 63-65; Burroughs Wellcome Fund scholar; estab investr, Am Heart Asn, 64-69; vis prof, Tulane Univ, 69-; mem, Cardiovasc B Study Sect, NIH; mem med adv bd, Coun High Blood Pressure Res. *Mem:* Am Fedn Clin Res; Am Physiol Soc; NY Acad Sci; Am Soc Pharmacol; Am Soc Clin Invest. *Res:* Cardiorenal pharmacology and physiology; clinical pharmacology. *Mailing Add:* c/o New York Med Col Basic Sci Bldg Valhalla NY 10595

MCGILL, DAVID A, b Albany, NY, Sept 18, 30. OCEANOGRAPHY. *Educ:* Bucknell Univ, BSc, 52; Columbia Univ, MA, 56; Yale Univ, PhD(zool), 63. *Prof Exp:* Technician chem oceanog, Woods Hole Oceanog Inst, 56-59, fel, 59-62, asst scientist, 62-66; asst prof, Southeastern Mass Tech Inst, 66-68; PROF OCEAN SCI, US COAST GUARD ACAD, 68- *Concurrent Pos:* Mem, Int Geophys Year Surv Atlantic Ocean, 57-58; Sci Comt Oceanic Res-UNESCO grants, Hawaii, 61 & Australia, 62; mem, Int Indian Ocean Expeds, 62-65. *Mem:* AAAS; Soc Study Evolution; Am Soc Limnol & Oceanog; Marine Biol Asn UK. *Res:* Distribution of nutrient elements in sea water, chiefly inorganic and total phosphorus. *Mailing Add:* Dept Ocean Sci US Coast Guard Acad New London CT 06320

MCGILL, DAVID JOHN, b New Orleans, La, Oct 9, 39; m 61; c 3. ENGINEERING MECHANICS. *Educ:* La State Univ, BS, 61, MS, 63; Univ Kans, PhD(eng mech), 66. *Prof Exp:* asst prof, 66-80, PROF ENG MECH, GA INST TECHNOL, 80- *Mem:* Sigma Xi. *Res:* Dynamics. *Mailing Add:* Dept of Eng Mech Ga Inst of Technol Atlanta GA 30332

MCGILL, DAVID PARK, b Waverly, Nebr, Sept 3, 19; m 44; c 1. AGRONOMY. *Educ:* Univ Nebr, BS, 41, MS, 49; Iowa State Col, PhD(agron), 54. *Prof Exp:* Asst agron, 46-51, from asst agronomist to assoc agronomist, 51-62, PROF AGRON, UNIV NEBR, LINCOLN, 62- *Mem:* Am Soc Agron. *Res:* Genetics teaching. *Mailing Add:* Dept of Agron Univ of Nebr Lincoln NE 68583

MCGILL, DOUGLAS B, b New York, NY, Aug 14, 29; m 53; c 4. GASTROENTEROLOGY. *Educ:* Yale Univ, BA, 51; Tufts Univ, MS, 55; Univ Minn, MS, 61. *Prof Exp:* Intern med, Boston City Hosp, 55-56; resident, Mayo Grad Sch Med, Univ Minn, 58-61; assoc prof med, Med Sch, 73-77, CONSULT MED & GASTROENTEROL, MAYO CLIN, 61-, PROF MED, MAYO MED SCH, 77- *Mem:* AMA; fel Am Col Physicians; Am Gastroenterol Asn; Am Asn Study Liver Dis; Am Fedn Clin Res. *Res:* Liver disease. *Mailing Add:* Div of Gastroenterol Mayo Clin 200 First St SW Rochester MN 55901

MACGILL, ELIZABETH MURIEL GREGORY, aeronautical engineering, deceased

MCGILL, GEORGE EMMERT, b Des Moines, Iowa, June 10, 31; m 55; c 3. STRUCTURAL GEOLOGY, PLANETARY SCIENCE. *Educ:* Carleton Col, BA, 53; Univ Minn, MS, 55; Princeton Univ, PhD(geol), 58. *Prof Exp:* From asst prof to assoc prof, 58-73, PROF GEOL, UNIV MASS, AMHERST, 73-, HEAD DEPT GEOL & GEOG, 77- *Mem:* Am Geophys Union; fel Geol Soc Am; Sigma Xi; Am Astron Soc. *Res:* Structural and regional geology; astrogeology. *Mailing Add:* Dept of Geol & Geog Univ of Mass Amherst MA 01003

MCGILL, HENRY COLEMAN, JR, b Nashville, Tenn, Oct 1, 21; m 45; c 3. PATHOLOGY. *Educ:* Vanderbilt Univ, BA, 43, MD, 46. *Prof Exp:* Intern, Vanderbilt Univ, 46-47; asst, Sch Med, La State Univ, 47-48, from asst prof to prof path, 50-66, head dept, 61-66, chmn dept path, 66-72, PROF PATH, UNIV TEX HEALTH SCI CTR, SAN ANTONIO, 72- *Concurrent Pos:* Mem coun arteriosclerosis, Am Heart Asn. *Mem:* Am Soc Exp Path; Am Asn Path; Int Acad Path. *Res:* Arteriosclerotic heart disease. *Mailing Add:* Dept of Path Univ of Tex Health Sci Ctr San Antonio TX 78284

MCGILL, JAMES ROBERT, chemical data analysis, see previous edition

MCGILL, JOHN THOMAS, b Memphis, Tenn, June 19, 21; m 43; c 2. LANDSLIDES. *Educ:* Univ Calif, Los Angeles, AB, 43, MA, 48, PhD(geol), 51. *Prof Exp:* Lectr geol, Univ Calif, Los Angeles, 48-50 & 51-52, asst res geologist, 52-53; geologist, 53-64, admin geologist & chief, 64-74, GEOLOGIST, ENG GEOL BR, US GEOL SURV, 74- *Mem:* Geol Soc Am; Asn Eng Geol (vpres, 59-60); Sigma Xi. *Res:* Urban engineering geology and environmental geology; landslides, especially southern California; coastal geomorphology; quaternary geology. *Mailing Add:* US Geol Surv Fed Ctr Denver CO 80225

MCGILL, JULIAN EDWARD, b Blacksburg, SC, Oct 22, 32; m 59; c 2. ANALYTICAL CHEMISTRY. *Educ:* Erskine Col, BA, 55; Clemson Univ, MS, 68, PhD(chem), 71. *Prof Exp:* Qual control engr, Celanese Fibers Co, 59-61; asst prof, 70-76, ASSOC PROF PHARM CHEM, COL PHARM, MED UNIV SC, 76- *Mem:* Am Chem Soc. *Res:* Spectrophotometric analysis; pharmaceutical analysis, high performance liquid chromatography. *Mailing Add:* Col of Pharm Med Univ of SC 171 Ashley Ave Charleston SC 29425

MCGILL, LAWRENCE DAVID, b Lincoln, Nebr, Mar 24, 44; m 66. VETERINARY PATHOLOGY. *Educ:* Okla State Univ, BS, 66, DVM, 68; Tex A&M Univ, PhD(vet path), 72; Am Col Vet Pathologists, dipl. *Prof Exp:* NIH fel, Tex A&M Univ, 68-71, teaching asst vet path, 71; asst prof, Univ Minn, St Paul, 71-72; asst prof vet path, Univ Nebr, Lincoln, 72-77; vet pathologist, 77-81, CHIEF PATH, VET REF LAB, SALT LAKE CITY, 81- *Mem:* Int Acad Path; Am Vet Med Asn; Am Col Vet Path; AAAS. *Res:* Immunopathology; pathogenesis of viral infections; ultrastructural pathology; host-virus relationships. *Mailing Add:* PO Box 30633 Salt Lake City UT 84125

MCGILL, LOIS SATHER, b Wilsonville, Ore, July 5, 23; m 69; c 6. FOOD SCIENCE. *Educ:* Ore State Col, BS, 45. *Prof Exp:* Instr food technol, 45-58, from instr to assoc prof food sci, 52-72, PROF FOOD SCI & TECH, ORE STATE UNIV, 72- *Mem:* Fel Inst Food Technol; Am Dairy Sci Asn; Am Home Econ Asn. *Res:* Sensory evaluation of foods and product development. *Mailing Add:* Dept of Food Sci & Technol Ore State Univ Corvallis OR 97331

MCGILL, RALPH NORMAN, mechanical engineering, heat transfer, see previous edition

MCGILL, ROBERT MAYO, b Marianna, Ark, Nov 29, 25. PHYSICAL INORGANIC CHEMISTRY. *Educ:* Univ Ark, BS, 45, MA, 48; Univ Tenn, PhD(phys chem), 55. *Prof Exp:* Chemist, 48-78, SR STAFF CONSULT, RES LAB, K-25 PLANT, UNION CARBIDE CORP, 78- *Mem:* Am Chem Soc; AAAS; fel Am Inst Chemists. *Res:* Molecular weight determination; adsorption of fatty acids on metals; chemistry of uranium and fluorine; kinetics of precipitation; isotope separations. *Mailing Add:* Union Carbide Corp Nuclear Div Oak Ridge TN 37830

MCGILL, SUZANNE, b Port Arthur, Tex, Mar 10, 44. MATHEMATICS. *Educ:* Univ St Thomas, BA, 67; Tex Christian Univ, MS, 70, PhD(math), 72. *Prof Exp:* Instr, Pub Sch, Tex, 67-68; instr math, Tex Christian Univ, 72; PROF MATH, UNIV S ALA, 72- *Mem:* Math Asn Am. *Res:* Research activities are of general nature in the field of abstract algebra. *Mailing Add:* Dept of Math Univ of SAla Mobile AL 36688

MCGILL, THOMAS CONLEY, JR, b Port Arthur, Tex, Mar 20, 42; m 66. PHYSICS, ELECTRICAL ENGINEERING. *Educ:* Lamar State Col, BS, 63 & 64; Calif Inst Technol, MS, 65, PhD(elec eng, physics), 69. *Prof Exp:* Asst prof, 71-74, assoc prof, 74-77, PROF APPL PHYSICS, CALIF INST TECHNOL, 77-; CONSULT, ARCO SOLAR, 81- *Concurrent Pos:* Mem tech staff, Hughes Res Labs, 67-73, consult, 73-; NATO fel theoret physics, Bristol Univ, 69-70; Air Force Nat Res Coun fel, Princeton Univ, 70-71; Alfred P Sloan Found fel, 74-76; mem adv res proj agency, Mat Res Coun. *Mem:* AAAS; Am Inst Physics; Inst Elec & Electronics Eng. *Res:* Solid state physics, particularly semiconductors and insulators. *Mailing Add:* Dept of Appl Physics Calif Inst of Technol Pasadena CA 91125

MCGILL, WILLIAM BRUCE, b Morden, Man, Oct 20, 45; m 66; c 3. SOIL BIOLOGY, BIOCHEMISTRY. *Educ:* Univ Man, BSA Hons, 67, MSc, 69; Univ Sask, PhD(soil biol & biochem), 72. *Prof Exp:* Asst prof, 71-75, assoc prof, 75-81, PROF SOIL BIOCHEM, UNIV ALTA, 81-, CHMN, DEPT SOIL SCI, 79- *Mem:* Can Soc Soil Sci; Can Soc Microbiol; Soil Sci Soc Am; Int Ecol Soc; Int Soc Soil Sci. *Res:* Soil carbon, nitrogen and phosphorous cycling; modelling of organic matter turnover in soil; soil enzymology; land reclamation. *Mailing Add:* Dept of Soil Sci Univ of Alta Edmonton AB T6G 2E3 Can

MCGILLEM, C(LARE) D(UANE), b Clinton, Mich, Oct 9, 23; m 47; c 1. ELECTRICAL ENGINEERING. *Educ:* Univ Mich, BSEE, 47; Purdue Univ, MSE, 49, PhD(elec eng), 55. *Prof Exp:* Res engr, Diamond Chain Co, Inc, Ind, 47-51; proj engr mil electronics, US Naval Avionics Facility, 51-53, div head radar, 53-56; dept head mil & electronic eng, AC Spark Plug Div, Gen Motors Corp, Mich, 56-59, dir electronics & appl res, Wis, 59-60, prog mgr lunar explor, Defense Res Labs, Calif, 60-63; assoc prof elec eng, 63-67, dir electronic systs res lab, 65-68, assoc dean eng & dir eng exp sta, 68-72, PROF ELEC ENG, SCH ELEC ENG, PURDUE UNIV, 67- *Concurrent Pos:* Pres & mem bd dirs, Technol Assocs, Inc, West Lafayette, 76- *Honors & Awards:* Meritorious Civilian Serv Award, US Navy Dept, 54. *Mem:* AAAS; fel Inst Elec & Electronics Engrs; Am Soc Eng Educ; Geosci Electronics Soc (pres, 76). *Res:* Monopulse radar; automatic tracking and firecontrol systems; radar resolution and scattering; microwave radiometry; signal detection and estimation; random signal analysis; bioelectric signal processing; statistical communications theory; information processing. *Mailing Add:* Sch of Elec Eng Purdue Univ West Lafayette IN 47907

MCGILLIARD, A DARE, b Stillwater, Okla, Oct 15, 26; m 51; c 3. ANIMAL NUTRITION. *Educ:* Okla State Univ, BS, 51, MS, 52; Mich State Univ, PhD(animal nutrit), 61. *Prof Exp:* From asst prof to assoc prof, 57-72, PROF ANIMAL SCI, IOWA STATE UNIV, 72- *Concurrent Pos:* Chmn physiol panel, Rumen Function Conf, 69- *Honors & Awards:* Am Feed Mfrs Award, 72. *Mem:* Am Dairy Sci Asn; Am Inst Nutrit; Am Soc Animal Sci. *Res:* Nutritional physiology and biochemistry; experimental surgery of digestive tract; cardiovascular and lymphatic systems. *Mailing Add:* Dept of Animal Sci Iowa State Univ Ames IA 50011

MCGILLIARD, LON DEE, b Manhattan, Kans, Aug 9, 21; c 4. ANIMAL BREEDING, DAIRY SCIENCE. *Educ:* Okla State Univ, BS, 42; Mich State Univ, MS, 47; Iowa State Univ, PhD(animal breeding, dairy husb), 52. *Prof Exp:* Asst dairy prod, Mich State Univ, 46-47; asst animal breeding, Iowa State Univ, 48-49, from res assoc to assoc prof animal breeding & dairy husb, 49-55; assoc prof, 55-62, PROF DAIRY CATTLE BREEDING, MICH STATE UNIV, 62- *Concurrent Pos:* Assoc ed, J Dairy Sci, 69-72, ed, 73- *Mem:* Am Dairy Sci Asn; Sigma Xi; Coun Biol Ed. *Res:* Improving dairy cattle through breeding; population genetics. *Mailing Add:* Dept Animal Sci Mich State Univ East Lansing MI 48824

MCGILLIARD, MICHAEL LON, b Lansing, Mich, Sept 29, 47; m 70. DAIRY SCIENCE, ANIMAL GENETICS. *Educ:* Mich State Univ, BS, 69; Iowa State Univ, MS, 70, PhD(animal breeding), 74. *Prof Exp:* EXTEN SPECIALIST DAIRY SCI, VA POLYTECH INST & STATE UNIV, 75- *Mem:* Am Dairy Sci Asn. *Res:* Determining the influence of quantitative measures on dairy herd management. *Mailing Add:* Dept of Dairy Sci Va Polytech Inst & State Univ Blacksburg VA 24061

MACGILLIVRAY, ARCHIBALD DEAN, b Vancouver, BC, Dec 28, 29; m 57; c 3. APPLIED MATHEMATICS. *Educ:* Univ BC, BASc, 55; Calif Inst Technol, MS, 57, PhD(aeronaut), 60. *Prof Exp:* Instr math, Calif Inst Technol, 60-61; mathematician, Lincoln Lab, Mass Inst Technol, 61-62, instr math, 62-64; asst prof, 64-67, ASSOC PROF MATH, STATE UNIV NY BUFFALO, 67- *Concurrent Pos:* Sr scientist, Jet Propulsion Labs, Calif Inst Technol, 60-61; consult, Lincoln Lab, 62-64. *Mem:* Am Math Soc; Am Phys Soc. *Res:* Asymptotic expansions of solutions of differential equations. *Mailing Add:* Dept of Math State Univ of NY Buffalo NY 14214

MACGILLIVRAY, JEFFREY CHARLES, b Washington, DC, Apr 14, 52. MATHEMATICAL PHYSICS, ELECTRO-OPTICS. *Educ:* Mass Inst Technol, SB(elec eng) & SB(physics), 73, ScD(physics), 78. *Prof Exp:* STAFF ELECTRO-OPTIC SCIENTIST, OPTICAL SYSTS DIV, ITEK CORP, 78- *Res:* Mathematical modeling of electro-optic systems; digital image processing. *Mailing Add:* Optical Systs Div Itek Corp 10 Maguire Rd Lexington MA 02173

MACGILLIVRAY, M ELLEN, b Fredericton, NB, Nov 26, 25; m 48. ENTOMOLOGY. *Educ:* Univ NB, BA, 47; Univ Mich, MSc, 51; State Univ Leiden, DSc, 58. *Hon Degrees:* DSc, Univ NB, 81. *Prof Exp:* Sr agr asst, Div Entom, Can Dept Agr, 47-48, tech officer, 48-54, res officer, 54-59, res scientist, Res Br, 59-80; RETIRED. *Mem:* Entom Soc Can (pres, 76-77); Can Soc Zool; Entom Soc Am. *Res:* Systematics and biology of aphids of the Atlantic provinces of Canada and the New England states; potato pest management. *Mailing Add:* 156 Glengarey Place Fredericton NB E3B 5Z9 Can

MACGILLIVRAY, MARGARET HILDA, b San Fernando, Trinidad, WI, Aug 30, 30; Can citizen; m 57; c 3. ENDOCRINOLOGY, IMMUNOLOGY. *Educ:* Univ Toronto, MD, 56. *Prof Exp:* From lectr to assoc prof pediat endocrinol, 64-76, PROF PEDIAT & CO-DIR DIV ENDOCRINOL, CHILDREN'S HOSP & MED SCH, STATE UNIV NY BUFFALO, 76- *Concurrent Pos:* AEC grant biol, Calif Inst Technol, 60-61; USPHS grants endocrinol & metab, Mass Gen Hosp, 61-64 & juvenile diabetes, 76- *Mem:* Soc Pediat Res; Endocrine Soc; Andrology Soc. *Res:* The role of growth hormone in dwarfism of childhood; hormonal control of carbohydrate metabolism in hypopituitary children and juvenile onset diabetes. *Mailing Add:* Children's Hosp 219 Bryant St Buffalo NY 14222

MCGILVERY, ROBERT WARREN, b Coquille, Ore, Aug 25, 20; m 43; c 4. BIOCHEMISTRY. *Educ:* Ore State Col, BS, 41; Univ Wis, PhD(physiol chem), 47. *Prof Exp:* From asst prof to assoc prof physiol chem, Univ Wis, 48-57; assoc prof, 57-62, PROF BIOCHEM, UNIV VA, 62- *Concurrent Pos:* USPHS sr res fel, Univ Wis, 47-48; vis prof biochem, State Univ NY Buffalo, 71. *Mem:* AAAS; Am Soc Biol Chemists. *Res:* Metabolic economy. *Mailing Add:* PO Box 3852 Charlottesville VA 22903

MCGINN, CLIFFORD, b New York, NY, Aug 22, 22; m 54; c 4. ORGANIC CHEMISTRY. *Educ:* Fordham Univ, BS, 43, MS, 46; Syracuse Univ, PhD(chem), 57. *Prof Exp:* From instr to assoc prof, 49-70, PROF CHEM, LEMOYNE COL, NY, 70- *Mem:* Am Chem Soc. *Res:* Theoretical organic chemistry; chemical bonding. *Mailing Add:* Dept of Chem LeMoyne Col Syracuse NY 13214

MCGINNES, BURD SHELDON, b Pittsburgh, Pa, Aug 10, 21; m 46; c 1. WILDLIFE RESEARCH. *Educ:* Pa State Univ, BS, 48, MS, 49; Va Polytech Inst & State Univ, PhD(biol), 58. *Prof Exp:* Proj leader, Del Game & Fish Comn, 49-51 & 52-55; leader wild turkey invest, Pa Game Comn, 58; LEADER COOP WILDLIFE RES UNIT, VA POLYTECH INST & STATE UNIV, 58- *Mem:* Wildlife Soc (vpres, 75-76); Sigma Xi; Wildlife Dis Asn. *Res:* Animal ecology; wildlife diseases and management techniques. *Mailing Add:* Coop Wildlife Res Unit Va Polytech Inst & State Univ Blacksburg VA 24061

MCGINNES, EDGAR ALLAN, b Chestertown, Md, Feb 15, 26; m 51; c 3. WOOD CHEMISTRY, WOOD TECHNOLOGY. *Educ:* Pa State Univ, BS, 50, MF, 51; State Univ NY Col Forestry, Syracuse Univ, PhD(wood technol), 55. *Prof Exp:* Jr res chemist, Am Viscose Corp, 51-52, res chemist, 55-58, res specialist, 59-60; assoc prof, 60-63, PROF FORESTRY, UNIV MO-COLUMBIA, 63- *Mem:* Fel AAAS; fel Am Inst Chemists; Am Chem Soc; Soc Am Foresters; Forest Prod Res Soc. *Res:* Wood anatomy; influence of environmental stress on wood structure. *Mailing Add:* Sch of Forestry Fisheries & Wildlife Univ of Mo Columbia MO 65201

MCGINNESS, JAMES DONALD, b Evansville, Ind, June 23, 30; m 50; c 5. COATING PLASTICS, SPECTROSCOPY. *Educ:* Univ Evansville, AB, 52. *Prof Exp:* Chemist, Sherwin-Williams Co, 52-55, chemist & group leader spectros, 55-61, dir anal res dept, Ill, 61-70, mgr reliability, Ohio, 70-74, group mgr automotive chem coatings, 74-77; MGR HIGH SOLIDS & BUS MACH COATINGS, RED SPOT PAINT & VARNISH CO, 77- *Mem:* Am Chem Soc; Soc Appl Spectros; Fedn Socs Paint Technol; Soc Plastics Engrs. *Res:* Infrared spectroscopy; gas chromatography; x-ray emission; flame photometry; coatings technology; color science; polymer characterization; nuclear magnetic resonance. *Mailing Add:* Red Spot Paint & Varnish Co Box 418 Evansville IN 47703

MCGINNIES, WILLIAM GROVENOR, b Steamboat Springs, Colo, Aug 14, 99; m 25; c 1. PLANT ECOLOGY. *Educ:* Univ Ariz, BSA, 22; Univ Chicago, PhD(plant ecol), 32. *Prof Exp:* Asst range examr, US Forest Serv, 24-26; asst prof animal husb, univ & range specialist, Exp Sta, Univ Ariz, 27-29, assoc prof & range ecologist, 30-32, actg head dept bot, 32-35; mgr & dir land mgt, Navajo Dist, Soil Conserv Serv, USDA, 35-38, chief div range res, Southwest Forest & Range Exp Sta, US Forest Serv, 38-42; chief div surv & invest, Guayule Emergency Rubber Proj, 42-44; dir, Rocky Mountain Forest & Range Exp Sta, US Forest Serv, 45-53 & Cent States Forest Exp Sta, 54-60; dir lab tree-ring res & coordr arid lands res prog, 60-65, prof dendrochronol & proj mgr, Off Arid Lands Res, 65-70, EMER PROF DENDROCHRONOL & EMER DIR ARID LANDS STUDIES, UNIV ARIZ, 70- *Mem:* Ecol Soc Am; Soc Range Mgt; Tree Ring Soc. *Res:* ecology of desert plants; frequency and abundance of plants; water requirement of Xerophytes. *Mailing Add:* 530 E Cambridge Dr Tucson AZ 85704

MCGINNIES, WILLIAM JOSEPH, b Tucson, Ariz, Jan 2, 27; m 49; c 3. RANGE SCIENCE, PLANT ECOLOGY. *Educ:* Colo State Univ, BS, 48, PhD, 67; Univ Wis, MS, 52. *Prof Exp:* Forester watershed mgt, Forest Serv, Idaho, 48, range conservationist grazing mgt & range reseeding, Utah, 49-53, range conservationist range reseeding, Agr Res Serv, Utah, 54-56 & Colo, 56-66, RANGE SCIENTIST RANGE RESEEDING, AGR RES SERV, USDA, 66- *Concurrent Pos:* Fac affil & mem grad fac, Colo State Univ, 66- *Mem:* AAAS; Soc Range Mgt; Crop Sci Soc Am; Am Soc Agron; Soil Sci Soc Am. *Res:* Adaptability of species for range seeding; methods of establishing seeded grasses on rangeland; techniques for measuring range herbage and environmental requirements of range plants; rehabilitation of strip mines and other disturbed areas; seeding and management of saline (Solonetz or Natrustoll) soils; fertilization of rangeland. *Mailing Add:* Agr Res Serv USDA Colo State Univ Ft Collins CO 80523

MCGINNIS, ARTHUR JAMES, b Edmonton, Alta, Dec 28, 21; m 48; c 4. BIOCHEMISTRY. *Educ:* Univ Alta, BSc, 46; Mont State Univ, MS, 50; Ore State Univ, PhD(biochem), 55. *Prof Exp:* Entomologist, Agr Can, Alta, 55-66, head cereal crop protection sect, Winnipeg, 66-72, dir res sta, Vineland, 72-81; RETIRED. *Mem:* Fel Entom Soc Can; Agr Inst Can. *Res:* Nutrition and biochemistry of insects. *Mailing Add:* Res Sta Agr Can PO Box 185 Vineland Station ON L0R 2E0 Can

MCGINNIS, CHARLES HENRY, JR, b Newark, NJ, Nov 24, 34; m 56; c 2. AVIAN PHYSIOLOGY. *Educ:* Rutgers Univ, New Brunswick, BS, 56; Purdue Univ, MS, 61; Mich State Univ, PhD(poultry physiol), 65. *Prof Exp:* Asst prof physiol, Sch Vet Med, Univ Minn, St Paul, 65-67; avian physiologist, 67-69, head poultry res sect, 69-76, MGR NUTRIT SERV, RHONE POULENC INC, 77- *Mem:* Poultry Sci Asn; World Poultry Sci Asn; Am Physiol Soc; Am Inst Biol Sci; NY Acad Sci. *Res:* Physiology, nutrition and toxicology in poultry. *Mailing Add:* Rhone Poulenc Inc 880 Johnson Ferry Rd Atlanta GA 30342

MCGINNIS, DAVID FRANKLIN, JR, b Baltimore, Md, Nov 10, 44; m 68; c 1. SATELLITE REMOTE SENSING. *Educ:* Univ Del, BS, 65; Pa State Univ, MS, 67, PhD(civil eng), 71. *Prof Exp:* HYDROLOGIST RES, LAND SCI BR, NAT EARTH SATELLITE SERV, NAT OCEANIC & ATMOSPHERIC ADMIN, US DEPT COMMERCE, 71- *Mem:* Am Meteorol Soc; Am Soc Photogrammetry; Am Soc Civil Engrs. *Res:* Use of satellite data to study water resources; agricultural science; anthropogenic effects. *Mailing Add:* S/RE12 Rm 701 World Weather Bldg Nat Oceanic & Atmospheric Admin Washington DC 20233

MCGINNIS, EDGAR LEE, petroleum chemistry, see previous edition

MCGINNIS, ETHELEEN, molecular biology, biochemistry, see previous edition

MCGINNIS, EUGENE A, b Jessup, Pa, May 15, 21; m 41; c 5. PHYSICS. *Educ:* Univ Scranton, BS, 48; NY Univ, MS, 53; Fordham Univ, PhD(physics), 60. *Prof Exp:* Instr, Clarks Summit Sch, 46-48; from instr to assoc prof, 48-63, chmn dept, 67-76, PROF PHYSICS, UNIV SCRANTON, 63- *Mem:* Am Asn Physics Teachers; Soc Appl Spectros. *Res:* Emission and molecular spectroscopy, particularly Raman spectorscopy of gases. *Mailing Add:* Dept Physics Univ Scranton Scranton PA 18510

MCGINNIS, GARY DAVID, b Everett, Wash, Oct 1, 40; m 64; c 3. CARBOHYDRATE CHEMISTRY. *Educ:* Pac Lutheran Univ, BS, 62; Univ Wash, MS, 68; Univ Mont, PhD(org chem), 70. *Prof Exp:* Prod chemist, Am Cyanamid Co, 64-67; fel, Univ Mont, 70-71; asst prof wood chem, Forest Prod Lab, 71-77, ASSOC PROF WOOD SCI & TECHNOL & CHEM & ASSOC TECHNOLOGIST, FOREST PROD UTILIZATION LAB, MISS STATE UNIV, 77- *Mem:* Am Chem Soc (secy carbohydrate div, 75); Forest Prod Res Soc; Sigma Xi. *Res:* Thermal decomposition of wood; high pressure liquid chromatography of natural products; chemical composition of wood barks. *Mailing Add:* Dept of Wood Sci & Technol Miss State Univ Mississippi State MS 39762

MCGINNIS, JAMES, b Cliffside, NC, Apr 10, 18; m 52; c 1. NUTRITION. *Educ:* NC State Col, BS, 40; Cornell Univ, PhD(nutrit), 44. *Prof Exp:* Asst nutrit, Cornell Univ, 40-43, res assoc, 43-44; from asst prof to assoc prof poultry sci, 44-50, PROF POULTRY SCI, POULTRY SCIENTIST & EXTEN POULTRY SCI SPECIALIST, WASH STATE UNIV, 50- *Concurrent Pos:* Asst dir agr develop dept, Chas Pfizer & Co, 52-53. *Mem:* AAAS; Am Chem Soc; Soc Exp Biol & Med; Poultry Sci Asn; Am Inst Nutrit. *Res:* Nutritional requirements of poultry; biochemistry of proteins; nutritional and endocrinological interrelationships; Browning reaction in foods; antibiotics and nutrition. *Mailing Add:* Dept of Animal Sci Wash State Univ Pullman WA 99163

MCGINNIS, JAMES LEE, b Jacksonville, Ill, Nov 28, 45; m 77. ORGANIC CHEMISTRY, CATALYSIS. *Educ:* MacMurray Col, BA, 67; Columbia Univ, PhD(chem), 76. *Prof Exp:* Res assoc chem, Mass Inst Technol, 76-77; res chemist, 77-81, SR RES CHEMIST, CELANESE RES CO, 81- *Mem:* Am Chem Soc. *Res:* Homogeneous catalysis; reaction mechanisms; physical organic chemistry; organometallics. *Mailing Add:* Celanese Res Co 86 Morris Ave Summit NJ 07901

MCGINNIS, JOHN THURLOW, b Mattoon, Ill, July 9, 34; m 56; c 6. ECOLOGY, BIOSTATISTICS. *Educ:* Eastern Ill Univ, BS, 56; Univ Tenn, MS, 58; Emory Univ, PhD(biol), 64. *Prof Exp:* Res assoc biol, Emory Univ, 60-64; asst statistician, Inst Ecol, Univ Ga, 64-69, asst prof bot, 66-69, sr ecologist, 69-70; assoc chief ecol & ecosysts anal sect, 70-72, mgr ecol & ecosysts anal sect, 73-76; RES LEADER, BIOENVIRON SCI SECT, COLUMBUS LABS, BATTELLE MEM INST, 76- *Co..current Pos:* Consult, Off Technol Assessment, 76; fel, Inst Environ Sci, Miami Univ, Ohio, 77. *Mem:* Fel AAAS; Ecol Soc Am; Sigma Xi. *Res:* Environmental effects, assessment and systems ecology for government and industrial projects. *Mailing Add:* Colubus Labs Battelle Mem Inst 505 King Ave Columbus OH 43201

MCGINNIS, LYLE DAVID, b Appleton, Wis, Mar 5, 31; m 59; c 5. GEOPHYSICS. *Educ:* St Norbert Col, BSc, 54; St Louis Univ, MSc, 60; Univ Ill, PhD(geol), 65. *Prof Exp:* Geophys trainee, Carter Oil Co, Okla, 54-55; asst geophysicist, Arctic Inst NAm, 57-59; assoc geophysicist, Ill State Geol Surv, 59-66; tech expert, UN Develop Prog, Afghanistan, 66-67; assoc prof, 67-72, PROF GEOL, NORTHERN ILL UNIV, 72-, CHMN, GEOL DEPT, 80- *Concurrent Pos:* Consult geophysicist, Desert Res Inst, Univ Nev, 61-62; consult, Minn Geol Surv, 70-; NSF coordr, Antarctic Drilling Prog, 71-; geophysicist, US Geol Surv, Woods Hole, Mass, 75-76. *Mem:* AAAS; fel Geol Soc Am; Soc Explor Geophys; Am Geophys Union; Glaciol Soc. *Res:* Polar geology and geophysics gravity field related to and tectonics; geophysical studies applied to ground water. *Mailing Add:* Dept of Geol Northern Ill Univ De Kalb IL 60115

MCGINNIS, MICHAEL RANDY, b Hayward, Calif, Oct 22, 42. MYCOLOGY. *Educ:* Calif State Polytech Col, BS, 61; Iowa State Univ, PhD(mycol), 69. *Prof Exp:* Fel, Ctr Dis Control, USPHS, 71-73; supvr, Mycol Lab, SC Dept Health & Environ Control, 74-75; ASSOC DIR, CLIN MICROBIOL LABS, NC MEM HOSP, UNIV NC, 75- *Mem:* Mycol Soc Am; Am Soc Microbiol; Int Soc Human & Animal Mycol; Paleont Soc. *Res:* Taxonomic relations of the human pathogenic dematiaceous hyphomycetes. *Mailing Add:* Clin Microbiol Labs NC Mem Hosp Univ of NC Chapel Hill NC 27514

MCGINNIS, ROBERT CAMERON, b Edmonton, Alta, Aug 18, 25; m 51; c 3. AGRONOMY. *Educ:* Univ Alta, BSc, 49, MSc, 51; Univ Man, PhD(cytogenetics), 54. *Prof Exp:* Asst, Univ Alta, 49-51; cytologist, Can Dept Agr, 51-60; assoc prof plant sci, Univ Man, 60-65, prof & Head dept, 65-75; assoc dir, Int Crops Res Inst for Semi-Arid Tropics, 75-80; DEAN FAC AGR, UNIV MAN, 80- *Concurrent Pos:* Dir, Plant Breeding Sta, Njoro, Kenya, 73-75. *Honors & Awards:* Centennial Medal, Can Govt, 67. *Mem:* Sigma Xi; NY Acad Sci; Genetics Soc Can; Agr Inst Can. *Res:* Improving crops and farming systems for the semi-arid tropics. *Mailing Add:* Fac Agr Univ Man Winnipeg MB R3T 2N2 Can

MCGINNIS, ROGER NOLAN, inorganic chemistry, heterogeneous catalysis, see previous edition

MCGINNIS, SAMUEL M, herpetology, see previous edition

MCGINNIS, WILLIAM JOSEPH, b St Louis, Mo, Apr 30, 23; m 51; c 4. INORGANIC CHEMISTRY, PHYSICAL CHEMISTRY. *Educ:* Colo Col, BA, 48; Iowa State Col, MS, 51. *Prof Exp:* Chemist, Los Alamos Sci Lab, Univ Calif, 48-49; res asst, Inst Atomic Res, Iowa State Col, 49-51; chemist, Int Minerals & Chem Corp, 51-56; chemist, Pigments Dept, E I du Pont de Nemours & Co, Inc, 56-63, sr res chemist, 63, tech supvr, Tenn, 63-69, prod specialist, Del, 69-70, tech serv supvr, 70-74, TECH SERV CONSULT, CHEM & PIGMENTS DEPT, E I DU PONT DE NEMOURS & CO, INC, 74- *Mem:* Am Chem Soc; Tech Asn Pulp & Paper Indust. *Res:* Rare earth metals; potassium and magnesium compounds; phosphate chemistry; titanium chemistry and compounds, particularly titanium dioxide pigments. *Mailing Add:* Chem & Pigments Dept E I du Pont de Nemours & Co Inc Wilmington DE 19898

MCGINNISS, VINCENT DANIEL, b Philadelphia, Pa, Feb 9, 42; m 68; c 3. POLYMER CHEMISTRY. *Educ:* Univ Fla, BS, 63; Univ Ariz, PhD(phys org chem), 70. *Prof Exp:* Anal chemist agr, Agr Dept, Univ Fla, 62-63; res chemist polymers, Peninsular Chem Res, 64-65; teaching asst org chem, Univ Ariz, 66-68; sr res chemist, Glidden-Durkee, 70-72, scientist polymers, 72-77; SR RES SCIENTIST POLYMERS & COATINGS, COLUMBUS LABS, BATTELLE MEM INST, 77- *Honors & Awards:* Roon Award, Fedn Socs Paint Technol, 73 & 77. *Mem:* Am Chem Soc. *Res:* Kinetics and mechanisms of photopolymerization reactions; photoinitiation and network formation as applied to coatings and films; solar energy applications of polymers and coatings, electrical properties of polymers and coatings, prediction of the chemical, electrical, physical and mechanical properties of polymers and coatings; polymer synthesis and applications. *Mailing Add:* 445 Home Rd Delaware OH 43015

MCGIRK, RICHARD HEATH, b Boonville, Mo, Jan 25, 45; m 66; c 2. ORGANIC POLYMER CHEMISTRY. *Educ:* Tex Christian Univ, BS, 67; Univ Colo, PhD(chem), 71. *Prof Exp:* Fel, Univ Col, Univ London, 71-72 & Johns Hopkins Univ, 72-73; SR RES CHEMIST ORG POLYMER CHEM, POLYMER PROD DEPT, E I DU PONT DE NEMOURS & CO, INC, BEUMONT, 73- *Mem:* Sigma Xi; Am Chem Soc. *Res:* Polymer, vulcanization of elastomers, isocyanate and polyurethane chemistry; polyester elastomers; ethyleene-propylene-diene monomer elastomers. *Mailing Add:* Polymer Prod Dept E I du Pont de Nemours & Co Beaumont TX 77706

MCGIVERN, JAMES F(RED), JR, metallurgical engineering, see previous edition

MCGLAMERY, MARSHAL DEAN, b Mooreland, Okla, July 29, 32; m 57; c 2. AGRONOMY, WEED SCIENCE. *Educ:* Okla Agr & Mech Col, BS, 56; Okla State Univ, MS, 58; Univ Ill, Urbana, PhD, 65. *Prof Exp:* Instr soils, Panhandle Agr & Mech Col, 58-60; agronomist, Agr Bus Co, 60-61; instr soils, 61-63, from res assoc to assoc prof weed control, 64-75, PROF WEED CONTROL, UNIV ILL, URBANA, 75- *Concurrent Pos:* AID weed control consult, India, 67-68; vis assoc prof, Univ Minn, 71-72; vis prof, NC State Univ, 81. *Mem:* Weed Sci Soc Am; Coun Agr Sci & Technol; Am Soc Agron. *Res:* Herbicide residue; weed taxonomy; herbicide selectivity. *Mailing Add:* Weed Control Dept of Agron Univ of Ill Urbana IL 61871

MCGLASSON, ALVIN GARNETT, b Boone Co, Ky, July 27, 25; m 49; c 3. MATHEMATICS. *Educ:* Eastern Ky State Col, BS, 49; Univ Ky, MS, 52. *Prof Exp:* From instr to assoc prof, 50-74, PROF MATH, EASTERN KY UNIV, 74- *Concurrent Pos:* NSF fel, Univ Kans, 59. *Mem:* Math Asn Am; Nat Coun Teachers of Math. *Res:* Geometry and preparation of high school teachers of mathematics; computer science. *Mailing Add:* Dept of Math Eastern Ky Univ Richmond KY 40475

MCGLASSON, ROBERT LEE, metallurgical engineering, see previous edition

MCGLAUCHLIN, LAURENCE D(ONALD), b Beloit, Wis, Apr 6, 20; m 48; c 2. ELECTRONICS, OPTICS. *Educ:* Beloit Col, BS, 48; Mass Inst Technol, SM, 50. *Prof Exp:* Asst phys electronics, Res Lab, Mass Inst Technol, 49; res physicist, Int Tel & Tel Corp, Ind, 50-55; asst dir res, 56-72, SR STAFF SCIENTIST, CORP RES CTR, HONEYWELL, INC, 72- *Mem:* Am Phys Soc. *Res:* Measured spectral emissivity of tantalum; photoemissive cathodes; photoemissive diode of large linear current range; infrared detectors; television camera tube development; research management. *Mailing Add:* Honeywell Inc 10701 Lyndale Ave S Bloomington MN 55420

MCGLINN, WILLIAM DAVID, b Leavenworth, Kans, Feb 15, 30; m 53; c 5. THEORETICAL PHYSICS. *Educ:* Univ Kans, BS, 52, PhD(physics), 59. *Prof Exp:* From instr to asst prof physics, Northwestern Univ, 58-63; physicist, Argonne Nat Lab, 63-65; assoc prof, 65-68, PROF PHYSICS, UNIV NOTRE DAME, 68- *Mem:* Am Phys Soc. *Res:* Particle physics; strong and weak interaction theory. *Mailing Add:* Dept of Physics Univ of Notre Dame Notre Dame IN 46556

MCGLOIN, PAUL ARTHUR, b Woburn, Mass, Jan 15, 23; m 53; c 3. MATHEMATICS, COMPUTER SCIENCE. *Educ:* Boston Univ, AB & AM, 49; Rensselaer Polytech Inst, PhD(math), 68. *Prof Exp:* Instr math, Univ Conn, 49-51 & 53-55; asst prof, 55-65, ASSOC PROF MATH, RENSSELAER POLYTECH INST, 65- *Mem:* Asn Comput Mach. *Res:* Graph theory, non-Hamiltonian graphs. *Mailing Add:* Dept of Math Rensselaer Polytech Inst Troy NY 12181

MCGLONE, ROBERT ERNEST, speech sciences, hearing sciences, see previous edition

MCGLYNN, SEAN PATRICK, b Ireland, Mar 8, 31; nat US; m 55; c 5. PHYSICAL CHEMISTRY. *Educ:* Nat Univ Ireland, BSc, 51, MSc, 52; Fla State Univ, PhD(phys chem), 56. *Prof Exp:* Fel chem, Fla State Univ, 56 & Univ Wash, 56-57; from asst prof to prof, 57-68, BOYD PROF CHEM, LA STATE UNIV, BATON ROUGE, 68-, VCHANCELLOR RES, 81- *Concurrent Pos:* Assoc prof, Yale Univ, 61; NSF lectr, 63 & 64; consult biophys prog, Mich State Univ, 63-65; consult, Am Optical Co & Am Instrument Co, 63- & Bell Tel Labs, 65; Alfred E Sloan Found fel, 64-; US Sr scientist award, Alexander von Humboldt Found, 79. *Honors & Awards:* Southwestern US Award, Am Chem Soc, 67 & Fla Award, 70. *Mem:* AAAS; Am Chem Soc; Am Phys Soc. *Res:* Biophysics; excitons; spectroscopy; fluorescence and phosphorescence; energy transfer; electronic structure of inorganic anions; charge transfer; conductivity of aromatics; spin-orbital perturbation; rotation barriers; vacuum ultraviolet. *Mailing Add:* Dept of Chem La State Univ Baton Rouge LA 70803

MCGONIGAL, WILLIAM E, b Decatur, Ga, Aug 20, 39; m 59; c 1. ORGANIC CHEMISTRY. *Educ:* Ga Inst Technol, BS, 61, PhD(org chem), 65. *Prof Exp:* M A Ferst Sigma Xi res award, 65; res chemist, Indust & Biochem Dept, Del, 65-67, sr res chemist, 67-68, res supvr, 68-69, admin asst, 69-73, tech area supvr, Biochem Dept, Tex, 73-75, biochem prod supt, Biochem Dept, Belle WVa, 75-76, lab dir, Biochem Dept, 76-79, prin consult, Corp Plans Dept, 79-80, MGR NEW BUS DEVELOP, CLIN SYSTS DIV, E I DU PONT DE NEMOURS & CO INC, 80- *Concurrent Pos:* Mem chem abstracts adv comt, 77-80; mem res dirs coun, Nat Agr Chem Asn, 79-80. *Mem:* Am Chem Soc; The Chem Soc. *Res:* Synthetic, organic, carbohydrate, heterocyclic, agricultural, pharmaceutical and diagnostic chemistry. *Mailing Add:* Clin Systs Concord Plaza E I du Pont de Nemours & Co Inc Wilmington DE 19807

MCGONIGLE, EUGENE JOSEPH, analytical chemistry, see previous edition

MCGOOKEY, DONALD PAUL, b Sandusky, Ohio, Sept 19, 28; m 51; c 6. PETROLEUM GEOLOGY. *Educ:* Bowling Green State Univ, BS, 51; Univ Wyo, MA, 52; Ohio State Univ, PhD(geol), 58. *Prof Exp:* Div stratigr, Texaco, Inc, Houston, 52-69, exec producing comnr, Midland Div, Texaco Inc, 69-71, chief geologist, 71-78, asst div mgr explor, 78-79; sr vpres explor, Omni-Explor Inc, 79-80; CONSULT GEOLOGIST, MIDLAND TEX, 80- *Mem:* AAAS; Geol Soc Am; Am Asn Petrol Geologists; Soc Explor Paleontologists & Mineralogists. *Res:* Investigation of sedimentary basins of North America by detailed study of the chronology of structural development and related sedimentary deposits. *Mailing Add:* 228 Western United Life Bldg Midland TX 79701

MCGOUGH, WILLIAM EDWARD, b Union City, NJ, Nov 12, 28. PSYCHIATRY. *Educ:* St Peter's Col, BS, 50; Duke Univ, MD, 56; Am Bd Psychiat & Neurol, dipl, 63. *Prof Exp:* Instr psychiat & med, Sch Med, Univ Rochester, 60; from instr to asst prof psychiat, Sch Med, Duke Univ, 61-64; asst prof, Rutgers Med Sch, 64-66, assoc prof, Col Med & Dent NJ, 66-71, assoc dean, 72-76, PROF PSYCHIAT, RUTGERS MED SCH, COL MED & DENT NJ, 71-, CHIEF PSYCHIAT, MIDDLESEX GEN HOSP, 79- *Concurrent Pos:* NIMH res fel, Sch Med, Duke Univ, 60-62; staff psychiatrist, Duke Hosp, 61-64; consult, Vet Admin Hosp, Durham, NC, 63-64, Fayetteville, NC, 64 & Lyons, NJ, 67-; consult, NJ Rehab Comn, 64-, Family Life & Ment Health Proj, Cornell Univ, 65-66 & Family Life & Ment Health Proj, Harvard Sch Pub Health, Harvard Med Sch, 66-71; dir, Fifth Channel in NJ, Col Med & Dent NJ, 72-77. *Mem:* Am Psychiat Asn; Am Psychosom Asn. *Res:* Culture and psychiatric illness; depression and culture; economic forms of speech therapy for stuttering. *Mailing Add:* Laird Rd Colts Neck NJ 07722

MCGOVERN, JOHN JOSEPH, b Pittsburgh, Pa, June 21, 20; m 47; c 6. CHEMISTRY, ENVIRONMENTAL SCIENCES. *Educ:* Carnegie Inst Technol, BS, 42, MS, 44, ScD(chem), 46. *Prof Exp:* Asst, Carnegie Inst Technol, 43-44, instr, 44-45; fel spectros, Mellon Inst, 45-48, sr fel spectros & chem anal groups, 48-50; asst chief chemist, Kobuta Plant Chem Div, Koppers Co, 50-56, chief chemist, 56-58; head res serv, Mellon Inst, 58-71, dir educ & res serv, Carnegie-Mellon Univ, 71-73; asst dir, Carnegie-Mellon Inst Res, 73-76; info scientist, Univ Pittsburgh, 76-79; EDUC SERV MGR, AIR POLLUTION CONTROL ASN, 79- *Mem:* Am Chem Soc; Air Pollution Control Asn; Am Soc Eng Educ. *Res:* Administration of technical activities. *Mailing Add:* 925 Woodbourne Ave Pittsburgh PA 15226

MCGOVERN, JOHN PHILLIP, b Washington, DC, June 2, 21. ALLERGY. *Educ:* Duke Univ, MD, 45; Am Bd Pediat, dipl, 52. *Hon Degrees:* ScD, Ricker Col, 71, Univ Nebr, 73, Ball State, 77, Huston-Tillotson Col, 77 & John F Kennedy Univ, 78; LLD, Union Col, 72; LHD, Kent State Univ, 73 & Emerson Col, 76; DPM, Ill Col Podiatric Med, 75; LittD, Lincoln Col, 76. *Prof Exp:* Intern pediat, New Haven Gen Hosp, 45-46; asst resident, Sch Med, Duke Univ, 48-49; asst chief resident, Children's Hosp, Washington, DC, 49, chief resident, 50; assoc, Sch Med, George Washington Univ, 50-51, asst prof, 51-54; assoc prof, Sch Med, Tulane Univ, La, 54-56; from assoc clin prof to clin prof allergy, Univ Tex Grad Sch Biomed Sci, 56-59, prof hist med, 69-78; CLIN PROF PEDIAT & MICROBIOL, BAYLOR COL MED, 69-; CLIN PROF MED, SCH MED, UNIV TEX, 78- *Concurrent Pos:* Markle scholar, 50-55; asst, Sch Med, Yale Univ, 45-46; chief outpatient dept, Children's Hosp, Washington, DC, 50-51, asst to pres res found, 51-52, mem assoc attend staff, 51-54, mem attend staff, Allergy Clin, 53-54; assoc, Univ Hosp, George Washington Univ, 50-54; attend physician & chief, George Washington Univ Pediat Div, DC Gen Hosp, 51-54; attend physician, Doctors Hosp, 52-54; chief Tulane pediat allergy clin & vis physician, Charity Hosp, New Orleans, La, 54-55; clin assoc prof, Baylor Col Med, 56-69, clin assoc prof microbiol, 57-69, chief allergy sect, Dept Pediat, 58-78, adj prof allergy, 69-; mem staff, Tex Children's Hosp, Houston, 56-, chief allergy serv & dir allergy clin, 57-; dir, McGovern Allergy Clin, Houston; consult, Episcopal Eye, Ear & Throat Hosp, Washington, DC, 53-54, Huey Long Charity Hosp, La, 54-56 & Lackland AFB, Tex, 59-; regional consult, Children's Asthma Res Inst & Hosp, Denver, 60-78 & Nat Found Asthmatic Children, Sahuaro Sch, Tucson, Ariz, 60. *Mem:* Am Osler Soc (past pres); AMA; Asn Res Nerve & Ment Dis; Am Asn Hist Med; Am Col Allergists (past pres). *Res:* Clinical allergy; immunology of hypersensitivity. *Mailing Add:* McGorcan Allergy Clin 6969 Bromoton Rd Houston TX 77025

MCGOVERN, TERENCE JOSEPH, b New York, NY, Aug 9, 42; m 68; c 3. COMPUTER SYSTEMS. *Educ:* Cooper Union, BE, 65; Northwestern Univ, MS, 68, PhD(chem eng), 70. *Prof Exp:* Proj engr, Chem & Plastics Div, 70-76, SR PROGRAMMER ANALYST, UNION CARBIDE CORP, 76- *Concurrent Pos:* Adj fac mem, WVa Col Grad Studies. *Mem:* Am Inst Chem Engrs; Am Chem Soc. *Res:* Reaction engineering; simulation; modeling; polymerization; kinetics; computer systems for medical records, work history and environmental impact analysis. *Mailing Add:* Union Carbide Corp PO Box 8361 South Charleston WV 25303

MCGOVERN, TERRENCE PHILLIP, b Kenosha, Wis, July 30, 30; m 55; c 3. ORGANIC CHEMISTRY. *Educ:* Univ Md, BS, 59, PhD(org chem), 62. *Prof Exp:* RES ORG CHEMIST, USDA, 62- *Mem:* AAAS; Entom Soc Am; Am Chem Soc. *Res:* Organic synthesis directed toward development of insect attractants, repellents and insect growth regulating chemicals as well as other insect behavior modifying chemicals. *Mailing Add:* Agr Environ Qual Inst Rm 309 Beltsville Agr Res Ctr E Bldg 306 Beltsville MD 20705

MCGOVERN, WAYNE ERNEST, b Orange, NJ, June 3, 37; m 63; c 2. METEOROLOGY. *Educ:* Newark Col Eng, BSME, 59, MS, 64; NY Univ, PhD(meteorol), 67. *Prof Exp:* Aerospace scientist, NASA, 67-68; meteorologist, Nat Meteorol Ctr, 68-69; assoc prof meteorol, Univ Ariz, 69-72; METEOROLOGIST, RES & DEVELOP, NAT OCEANIC & ATMOSPHERIC ADMIN, 72- *Concurrent Pos:* Dept of Com sci fel & prog leader, Global Environ Monitoring Syst Prog, Dept of State, 75-76; US sci coordr, Global Weather Exp. *Mem:* Am Inst Archaeol; Am Meteorol Soc; Royal Numismatic Soc; Am Numismatic Soc. *Res:* Program development. *Mailing Add:* Res & Develop/SP Nat Oceanic & Atmospheric Admin 6010 Exec Blvd Rockville MD 20852

MCGOVREN, JAMES PATRICK, b Washington, Ind, June 12, 47; m 68; c 2. PHARMACOLOGY, PHARMACEUTICS. *Educ:* Purdue Univ, BS, 70; Univ Ky, PhD(pharmaceut sci), 75. *Prof Exp:* RES ASSOC, UPJOHN CO, 75- *Mem:* Am Pharmaceut Asn; Acad Pharmaceut Sci; Am Asn Cancer Res. *Res:* Pharmacology of antitumor agents; drug disposition, drug metabolism and pharmacokinetics; analytical methods for drugs in biofluids; bioavailability of drug products. *Mailing Add:* Cancer Res 7252-25-4 Upjohn Co Kalamazoo MI 49001

MCGOWAN, BLAINE, JR, b San Francisco, Calif, Oct 3, 21; m 49; c 2. VETERINARY MEDICINE. *Educ:* Univ Calif, Davis, BS, 50, DVM, 52. *Prof Exp:* From instr to prof vet med, 52-69, assoc dean sch vet med, 64-69, prof clin sci, 69-74, PROF VET MED, SCH VET MED, UNIV CALIF, DAVIS, 74- *Concurrent Pos:* Vet consult & mem bd dirs, Calif Wool Growers Asn, 53-; chmn, Nat Comt Foot Rot Sheep, 64- *Mem:* Am Vet Med Asn; Am Asn Lab Animal Sci. *Res:* Transmissable diseases of sheep and beef cattle; preventive veterinary medicine; veterinary medical education. *Mailing Add:* Sch of Vet Med Univ of Calif Davis CA 95616

MCGOWAN, CLEMENT LEO, III, computer science, see previous edition

MCGOWAN, ELEANOR BROOKENS, b Santa Barbara, Calif, Oct 7, 44; m 67; c 1. BIOCHEMISTRY. *Educ:* Grinnell Col, BA, 65; Univ Iowa, PhD(biochem), 69. *Prof Exp:* Res assoc biochem, Brandeis Univ, 69-71 & Harvard Med Sch, 71-72; res assoc, 72-74, sr res assoc, 74-77, ASST PROF BIOCHEM, STATE UNIV NY DOWNSTATE MED SCH, 77- *Concurrent Pos:* Muscular Dystrophy Asn fel, 74-75; Young investr, Nat Heart, Lung & Blood Inst, NIH, 77-80. *Mem:* Biophys Soc; Am Soc Cell Biol; NY Acad Sci; Harvey Soc; Sigma Xi. *Res:* Protein structure, function and breakdown; calcium-binding proteins; muscle proteins; chromophores in proteins; muscular dystrophy; platelet function. *Mailing Add:* Dept of Biochem PO Box 8 450 Clarkson Ave Brooklyn NY 11203

MCGOWAN, FRANCIS KEITH, b Baileyville, Kans, May 2, 21; m 44. PHYSICS. *Educ:* Kans State Teachers Col, Emporia, AB, 42; Univ Wis, PhM, 44; Univ Tenn, PhD(physics), 51. *Prof Exp:* Asst physics, Univ Wis, 42-44; res engr, Sylvania Elec Prod, Inc, NY, 44-46; PHYSICIST, OAK RIDGE NAT LAB, 46- *Mem:* Fel Am Phys Soc. *Res:* Short-lived nuclear states; short-lived isomers of nuclei; gamma-ray spectroscopy; coulomb excitation of nuclei; cross sections for charged-particle induced reactions. *Mailing Add:* Oak Ridge Nat Lab PO Box X Oak Ridge TN 37830

MCGOWAN, H CHRISTOPHER, ceramics, ceramic engineering, see previous edition

MCGOWAN, JAMES WILLIAM, b Pittsburgh, Pa, July 5, 31; m 58; c 6. ATOMIC PHYSICS, MOLECULAR PHYSICS. *Educ:* St Francis Xavier Univ, BSc, 53; Carnegie-Mellon Univ, MS, 58; Laval Univ, DSc(physics), 61. *Prof Exp:* Instr physics, St Francis Xavier Univ, 55-56; res asst, Westinghouse Res Labs, 57-58; instr physics, St Lawrence Col, Laval Univ, 58-59; staff mem, Gen Atomic Div, Gen Dynamics Corp, 62-69; chmn dept physics, 69-72, chmn, founding Ctr Interdisciplinary Studies Chem Physics, 73-76, PROF PHYSICS, UNIV WESTERN ONT, 69- *Concurrent Pos:* Fel, Joint Inst Lab Astrophys, Univ Colo, Boulder, 66; adv, NSF, Nat Bur Standards, AEC, Advan Res Proj Agency, US Dept Defense, Defense Atomic Support Agency & Defense Res Bd Can; consult, Vacuum Electronics Corp, 59-61, Bach-Simpson Ltd, 71- & Med Physics Group, Lawrence Berkeley Labs, 78-; vis prof, Centro Atomico, Argentina, 71, Fac Univ Namur, Belg, 76-77 & Univ Cath Louvain, Belg, 78-; mem, Comt Sci & Technol in Developing Nations,

India, 77; mem, Can Pugwash Group, 78-; sr indust fel, Bell Northern Res Co, Ottawa, 81-; founding chmn, Very Large Scale Integration Study Group, 81 & coordr, Can Very Large Scale Integration Implementation Group, 81-; secy comn physics develop, Int Union Pure & Appl Physics, 81-; mem bd dir, Ont Sci Control, 80-; found chmn, Sci Tech & You, London, 78- *Mem:* Fel AAAS; Asn Sci, Eng & Technol Community Can; fel Am Phys Soc; Can Asn Physicists; Am Vacuum Soc. *Res:* Experimental atomic and molecular collision physics; energy deposition studies; positrons and ions in solids; charge transfer lasers; laser interaction with eyes; soft x-ray studies of biologically significant molecules using synchrotron radiation; very large scale integration related studies of polymers; x-ray lithography and surfaces; science policy related to regional and international development. *Mailing Add:* Dept Physics Univ Western Ont London ON N6A 3K7 Can

MCGOWAN, JOHN ARTHUR, b Oshkosh, Wis, Aug 22, 24. BIOLOGICAL OCEANOGRAPHY. *Educ:* Ore State Univ, BS, 50, MS, 51; Univ Calif, San Diego, PhD(oceanog), 60. *Prof Exp:* Marine biologist, Trust Territory of Pac Islands, 56-58; asst res biologist, 60-62, from asst prof to assoc prof, 62-72, PROF OCEANOG, SCRIPPS INST OCEANOG, UNIV CALIF, SAN DIEGO, 72- *Concurrent Pos:* Mem UNESCO consult comt, Indian Ocean Biol Ctr, 63-66. *Mem:* AAAS; Am Soc Limnol & Oceanog. *Res:* Ecology and zoogeography of oceanic plankton; taxonomy of Thecosomata and Heteropoda; biology of squid. *Mailing Add:* Div of Oceanic Res Scripps Inst of Oceanog La Jolla CA 92093

MCGOWAN, JON GERALD, b Lockport, NY, May 3, 39; m 65. MECHANICAL ENGINEERING. *Educ:* Carnegie Inst Technol, BS, 61, PhD(mech eng), 65; Stanford Univ, MS, 62. *Prof Exp:* Develop engr, E I du Pont de Nemours & Co, Inc, 65-67; from asst prof to assoc prof mech & aerospace eng, 67-76, PROF MECH & AEROSPACE ENG, UNIV MASS, AMHERST, 76- *Concurrent Pos:* Consult, Combustion Eng, Inc, Conn, 70- *Mem:* AAAS; Am Soc Mech Engrs; Air Pollution Control Asn; Int Solar Energy Soc. *Res:* Solar and wind energy conversion; thermodynamics; combustion; air pollution control; heat transfer; fluid mechanics. *Mailing Add:* 134 Main St Northfield MA 01360

MCGOWAN, MICHAEL JAMES, b Chicago, Ill, Apr 22, 52; m 80. MEDICAL ENTOMOLOGY, ACAROLOGY. *Educ:* Univ Kans, BA, 74, MA, 78; Okla State Univ, PhD(entom), 80. *Prof Exp:* Fel entom, Okla State Univ, 80; res assoc, Univ Fla, 80; ENTOMOLOGIST IV, WEST FLA ANTHROPOD RES LAB, AGR RES SERV, USDA, 80- *Mem:* AAAS; Entom Soc Am; Sigma Xi; Am Soc Parasitologists. *Res:* Biology, ecology and physiology of insects of medical and veterinary importance, specifically flies and diseases which flies transmit. *Mailing Add:* Agr Res Serv USDA PO Box 14565 Gainesville FL 32604

MCGOWAN, WILLIAM COURTNEY, JR, b Mobile, Ala, Aug 8, 37; m 65; c 2. SOLID STATE PHYSICS. *Educ:* Spring Hill Col, BS, 59; Univ NC, PhD(physics), 65. *Prof Exp:* Electronic engr, White Sands Missile Range, 65-66, asst chief anti-tank div & res engr, 66; assoc prof physics, 66-76, PROF PHYSICS, WESTERN CAROLINA UNIV, 76-, CHMN DEPT, 66- *Mem:* Am Asn Physics Teachers; Am Phys Soc. *Res:* Imperfections in ionic crystals; motion and charge on dislocations in silver chloride; range and velocity measurement accuracy as affected by radar signal design. *Mailing Add:* Dept of Physics Western Carolina Univ Cullowhee NC 28723

MCGOWEN, JOSEPH HOBBS, b Baird, Tex, Jan 15, 32. GEOLOGY. *Educ:* Hardin-Simmons Univ, BA, 60; Baylor Univ, MA, 64; Univ Tex, Austin, PhD(geol), 69. *Prof Exp:* GEOLOGIST, BUR ECON GEOL, UNIV TEX, AUSTIN, 66- *Concurrent Pos:* Geologist, Gen Land Off, State of Tex, 71-72. *Res:* Coastal geology; sedimentary processes and facies of coastal and fluvial environments; utilization of depositional models in mineral exploration; application of geology in solving environmental problems. *Mailing Add:* Bur of Econ Geol Univ of Tex Austin TX 78712

MCGRADY, ANGELE VIAL, b New Rochelle, NY, Dec 31, 41; m 68; c 1. PHYSIOLOGY. *Educ:* Chestnut Hill Col, BS, 63; Mich State Univ, MS, 66; Univ Toledo, PhD(physiol), 72. *Prof Exp:* Instr vet physiol, Wash State Univ, 65-66; res assoc physiol Kresge Eye Inst, Wayne State Univ, 66-68; instr, 68-72, asst prof, 72-80, ASSOC PROF PHYSIOL, MED COL OHIO, 80- *Mem:* AAAS; Soc Neurosci; Biofeedback Res Soc. *Res:* Electrophysiology of spermatozoa; neurosciences, biofeedback for control of hypertension and migraine headache. *Mailing Add:* Dept of Physiol C S 10008 Toledo OH 43699

MCGRAIL, DAVID WAYNE, b Key West, Fla, Apr 30, 44; m 67; c 1. OCEANOGRAPHY, SEDIMENTOLOGY. *Educ:* Col Wooster, BA, 67; Univ RI, MS, 71, PhD(oceanog), 76. *Prof Exp:* Oceanographer, US Coast Guard Oceanog Unit, 70-72; asst prof, 76-81, ASSOC PROF OCEANOG, TEX A&M UNIV, 81-, INTERIM DEP DEPT HEAD, 80- *Mem:* Am Geophys Union; Soc Econ Paleontologists & Mineralogists; Am Meteorol Soc. *Res:* Geophysical fluid dynamics of marine sedimentary processes, with particular emphasis in the realm of oceanic boundary layer dynamics as it pertains to erosion, transport and deposition of sediment; time series analyses. *Mailing Add:* Dept of Oceanog Tex A&M Univ College Station TX 77843

MCGRATH, CHARLES MORRIS, b Seattle, Wash, Sept 17, 43. ONCOLOGY. *Educ:* Univ Portland, BS, 65; Univ Calif, Berkeley, PhD(virol), 70. *Prof Exp:* Cell biologist, Univ Calif, Berkeley, 70-71; viral oncologist, Inst Jules Bordet, Brussels, Belg, 71-72; res scientist viral oncol, 72-83, CHIEF TUMOR BIOL LAB VIRAL ONCOL, MICH CANCER FOUND, 73- *Concurrent Pos:* NIH res grant, Nat Cancer Inst, 75. *Mem:* Tissue Cult Asn; Am Asn Cancer Res. *Res:* Viral and hormonal involvement in malignant conversion of breast epithelial cells. *Mailing Add:* Mich Cancer Found 110 E Warren Detroit MI 48201

MCGRATH, JAMES EDWARD, b Easton, NY, July 11, 34; m 59; c 6. ORGANIC POLYMER CHEMISTRY, POLYMER SCIENCE. *Educ:* Siena Col, BS, 56; Univ Akron, MS, 64, PhD(polymer sci), 67. *Prof Exp:* Res chemist, ITT-Rayonier, 56-59 & Goodyear Tire & Rubber Co, 59-65; fel polymer sci, Univ Akron, 67; res scientist, Union Carbide Corp, 67-75; assoc prof, 75-78, PROF POLYMER SCI, VA POLYTECH INST & STATE UNIV, 78-, CO-DIR, POLYMERIC MAT & INTERFACES LAB, 78- *Concurrent Pos:* Polymer consult; chmn, Gordon Res Conf on Elastomers, 79. Corp, 75- *Mem:* Am Chem Soc (secy, Polymer Div, 78-80); NY Acad Sci. *Res:* Anionic polymerization; block and graft copolymers; reactions of polymers. *Mailing Add:* Dept of Chem Va Polytech Inst & State Univ Blacksburg VA 24061

MCGRATH, JAMES J, b Brooklyn, NY, Oct 30, 31. PLANT ANATOMY. *Educ:* Univ Notre Dame, AB, 55; Univ Calif, Davis, MA, 64, PhD(bot), 66. *Prof Exp:* Asst prof biol & rector, 65-71, ASSOC PROF BIOL, UNIV NOTRE DAME, 71-, ASST CHMN DEPT, 74- *Mem:* Am Forestry Asn; Bot Soc Am; Int Soc Plant Morphol. *Res:* Developmental plant anatomy; seasonal changes in secondary phloem of angiosperms. *Mailing Add:* Box 369 Univ of Notre Dame Notre Dame IN 46556

MCGRATH, JAMES JOSEPH, inhalation toxicology, see previous edition

MCGRATH, JAMES RUSSELL, b Chicago, Ill, Dec 2, 32; m 59; c 4. PHYSICS, AERONAUTICAL ENGINEERING. *Educ:* Cath Univ, BAE, 57, MS, 65, PhD, 71; George Washington Univ, BA, 63. *Prof Exp:* Aeronaut res engr, Res Div, Bur Aeronaut, 57-60, opers res analyst, Bur Naval Weapons, 60-61, res physicist, Naval Res Lab, 62-67 & Maury Ctr Ocean Sci, 67-68, RES PHYSICIST, ACOUST DIV, NAVAL RES LAB, DEPT NAVY, 68- *Mem:* Fel Acoust Soc Am; Sigma Xi; fel Inst Acoust; Brit Inst Physics; Eng & Sci Asn Ireland. *Res:* Preliminary aircraft design and performance; exploding wire phenomena; underwater explosions and acoustics; air-sea interactions. *Mailing Add:* Naval Res Lab Off Naval Res Washington DC 20375

MCGRATH, JOHN F, b New York, NY, Dec 30, 27; m 50; c 3. PHYSICAL CHEMISTRY, INORGANIC CHEMISTRY. *Educ:* Siena Col, NY, BS, 49; State Univ NY, MS, 51; Rensselaer Polytech Inst, MS, 60. *Prof Exp:* Teacher, Colonie Cent High Sch, 53-60; from asst prof to assoc prof phys sci, 61-74, chmn div natural sci, 73-76, PROF PHYS SCI, COL ST ROSE, 74- *Concurrent Pos:* Partic, NSF Summer Inst, Rensselaer Polytech Inst, 55-59; consult geol Lake Superior region res, Mich Technol Univ, 65; partic, Inst Sci, Ithaca Col, 68 & Eastern Regional Inst, 68-71; ed, Bull Sci Teachers Asn NY State, 71-74. *Mem:* Am Chem Soc. *Res:* Instrumental analysis; determination of stability constants of series of esters of some complexes of tripositive cobalt. *Mailing Add:* Dept of Chem Col of St Rose 432 Western Ave Albany NY 12203

MCGRATH, JOHN THOMAS, b Philadelphia, Pa, Sept 27, 18; m 47; c 3. PATHOLOGY. *Educ:* Univ Pa, VMD, 43. *Prof Exp:* Instr path, Vet Sch, 47-48, assoc, 48-50, from asst prof to assoc prof, 50-58, PROF PATH, GRAD SCH MED, UNIV PA, 58- *Mem:* Am Vet Med Asn; Am Asn Neuropath; Am Col Vet Path; Am Acad Neurol. *Res:* Nervous disorders of animals; pathology of central nervous system diseases of animals. *Mailing Add:* Dept of Vet Path Univ of Pa Philadelphia PA 19104

MCGRATH, MICHAEL GLENNON, b St Louis, Mo, Oct 12, 41; m 67. ORGANIC CHEMISTRY. *Educ:* Col Holy Cross, BS, 63; Mass Inst Technol, PhD(chem), 67. *Prof Exp:* Asst prof, 67-72, ASSOC PROF CHEM, COL OF THE HOLY CROSS, 72- *Mem:* Am Chem Soc. *Res:* Synthesis and reactions of small ring carbon compounds; carbon chemistry; synthesis of non-benzenoid aromatic compounds. *Mailing Add:* Dept of Chem Col of the Holy Cross Worcester MA 01610

MCGRATH, ROBERT L, b Iowa City, Iowa, Nov 2, 38; m 60; c 2. NUCLEAR PHYSICS. *Educ:* Oberlin Col, BA, 60; Univ Iowa, MS, 62, PhD(physics), 65. *Prof Exp:* Fel physics, Univ Iowa, 65; res assoc, Lawrence Radiation Lab, Univ Calif, 66-68; asst prof, 68-73, ASSOC PROF PHYSICS, STATE UNIV NY STONY BROOK, 73- *Concurrent Pos:* Alexander von Humboldt Found sr US scientist award, 74-75. *Mem:* Fel Am Phys Soc. *Res:* Low energy nuclear reaction research on the structure of nuclei; heavy ion reactions. *Mailing Add:* Dept Physics State Univ NY Stony Brook NY 11794

MCGRATH, THOMAS FREDERICK, b Braddock, Pa, Jan 4, 29; m 52; c 4. ORGANIC CHEMISTRY. *Educ:* Franklin & Marshall Col, BS, 50; Univ Pittsburgh, PhD(org chem), 55. *Prof Exp:* Res chemist, Reilly Tar & Chem Corp, 54-55 & Am Cyanamid Co, 57-63; assoc prof, 63-69, PROF CHEM, SUSQUEHANNA UNIV, 70- *Mem:* Am Acad Arts & Sci; Sigma Xi. *Res:* Organometallic and organofluorine chemistry. *Mailing Add:* Dept of Chem Susquehanna Univ Selinsgrove PA 17870

MCGRATH, W PATRICK, b Pittsburgh, Pa, Jan 28, 47; m 69. CLINICAL CHEMISTRY. *Educ:* Georgetown Univ, BS, 68, PhD(biochem), 73. *Prof Exp:* Chief clin chem, 10th US Army Med Lab, 73-76; clin chemist, Bio-Sci Lab, 76-80; LAB DIR, BOSTON MED LAB, 80- *Mailing Add:* Boston Med Lab 15 Lunda Waltham MA 02154

MCGRATH, WILLIAM THOMAS, b Lincoln, Nebr, Feb 27, 33. FOREST PATHOLOGY, FOREST FIRE. *Educ:* Mont State Univ, BSF, 60; Univ Wis, PhD(plant path), 67. *Prof Exp:* Tech asst, Australian Forestry & Timber Bur, 61-62; ASSOC PROF FORESTRY, STEPHEN F AUSTIN STATE UNIV, 68- *Mem:* Am Phytopath Soc; Am Inst Biol Sci; Sigma Xi. *Res:* Pine rusts; identification of Western Gulf Coast wood decay fungi; American mistletoe host specificity. *Mailing Add:* Sch of Forestry Stephen F Austin State Univ Nacogdoches TX 75962

MCGRATTAN, ROBERT JOSEPH, b New York, NY, Nov 7, 35; m 61; c 6. SOLID MECHANICS, OCEAN ENGINEERING. *Educ:* Manhattan Col, BCE, 57; Lehigh Univ, MSCE, 59; Univ Conn, PhD(appl mech), 70. *Prof Exp:* Asst appl mech, Lehigh Univ, 57-59; res engr solid mech, Elec Boat Div, 59-64, suprvr stress anal, 64-66, supvr spec proj, 66, chief underwater develop eng, 66-69, chief ocean sci & eng, 69-77, CHIEF NAVAL ARCHIT, ELEC BOAT DIV, GEN DYNAMICS CORP, 77- *Concurrent Pos:* Lectr, Grad Sch, Univ Conn, 61- *Honors & Awards:* Henry Hess Award, Am Soc Mech Engrs, 64. *Mem:* Am Soc Mech Engrs; Marine Technol Soc. *Res:* Structures; static and dynamic analysis of plates and shells. *Mailing Add:* 8 Eagle Ridge Dr Gales Ferry CT 06335

MCGRAW, CHARLES PATRICK, b Sherman, Tex, Feb 17, 42; m 67; c 4. NEUROPHYSIOLOGY, BIOMEDICAL INSTRUMENTATION. *Educ:* Belmont Abbey Col, BCh, 64; ETex State Univ, MS, 67; Baylor Univ, cert biomed eng, 68; Tex A&M Univ, PhD(neurophysiol), 69. *Prof Exp:* Mem fac, ETex State Univ, 65-67; mem fac, Tex A&M Univ, 67-69; mem fac & neurophysiologist, Div Neurosurg & Dept Physiol, Tex Med Br, Galveston, 69-73; mem fac & assoc prof, Dept Neurol, Anat & Physiol, Bowman Gray Sch Med, 73-80; MEM FAC, PROF & ASST DIR NEUROSCI PROGS, DIV NEUROSURG, MED SCH, UNIV LOUISVILLE, 80- *Concurrent Pos:* HEW grant. *Mem:* AAAS; Am Inst Biol Sci; Am Heart Asn; Am Physiol Soc; Am Soc Clin Hypnosis. *Res:* Tritium labeled testosterone locating centers in the rat brain with radioaudiography; neural mechanisms involved in the immobility reflex from phylogenetic ontogenetic, pharmacological and surgical approaches; head injury and stroke; neurological and neurosurgical research; cerebral blood flow; autoregualtion; patient monitoring; monitoring of intracranial pressure. *Mailing Add:* Univ Louisville Med Sch S Third St Louisville KY 40208

MCGRAW, DELFORD ARMSTRONG, b Keyrock, WVa, May 13, 17; m 41; c 2. PHYSICS. *Educ:* Concord Col, AB, 37; WVa Univ, MS, 39. *Prof Exp:* Supvr, Ballistics Lab, Hercules Powder Co, 41-45; res physicist, Owens-Ill Glass Co, 46-55, sr physicist, Owens-Ill, Inc, 55-66, mgr res instrumentation, 66-69, assoc dir res, 69-70, dir eng res, 70-73, mgr process systs, 73-78, CHIEF ENGR, ENG & TECH SERV, OWENS-ILL, INC, 78- *Honors & Awards:* Forrest Award, Am Ceramic Soc, 52 & 59. *Mem:* Fel Am Ceramic Soc; fel Brit Soc Glass Technol. *Res:* Velocity of sound in gases; ballistics of small arms and rocket powders; mechanical and thermal properties of glass and plastics. *Mailing Add:* 3410 Chapel Dr Toledo OH 43615

MCGRAW, GARY EARL, b Wellsville, NY, Sept 26, 40; m 63; c 3. PHYSICAL CHEMISTRY. *Educ:* Univ Mich, BS, 62; Pa State Univ, PhD(phys chem), 65. *Prof Exp:* US Dept Health, Educ & Welfare fel, Div Air Pollution, Univ Calif, Berkeley, 66-67; res chemist, Tenn Eastman Co, 67-68, sr res chemist, 69-74, res assoc, 74-75, actg div head, Phys & Anal Chem Div, 75-76, actg div dir, Anal Sci Div, 76-77, staff asst to exec vpres develop, 77, asst works mgr, 78, asst div supvr, Polymers Div, 78-80, DIR, DEVELOP DIV, TEX EASTMAN CO, EASTMAN KODAK CO, 80- *Mem:* AAAS; Am Chem Soc; NY Acad Sci. *Res:* Spectroscopy; polymer morphology. *Mailing Add:* Tex Eastman Co Longview TX 75607

MCGRAW, GERALD WAYNE, b Tampa, Fla, Apr 30, 43; m 67; c 1. BIOCHEMISTRY, ORGANIC CHEMISTRY. *Educ:* Ouachita Baptist Univ, BS, 65; Fla State Univ, PhD(org chem), 71. *Prof Exp:* Asst prof, 70-74, ASSOC PROF CHEM, LA COL, 74- *Mem:* Am Chem Soc. *Res:* Synthesis and enzymolysis of polypeptides related to collagen. *Mailing Add:* La Col Dept of Chem College Station Pineville LA 71360

MCGRAW, JAMES CARMICHAEL, b Martins Ferry, Ohio, Mar 20, 28; m 51; c 3. ZOOLOGY, PARASITOLOGY. *Educ:* Oberlin Col, AB, 51; Ohio State Univ, MS, 57, PhD(zool, parasitol), 68. *Prof Exp:* ASST PROF BIOL, STATE UNIV NY COL PLATTSBURGH, 64- *Mem:* AAAS; Am Soc Parasitol; Am Inst Biol Sci. *Res:* Nematodes parasitic in amphibians, especially the genus Cosmocercoides. *Mailing Add:* Dept of Biol State Univ of NY Col Plattsburgh NY 12901

MCGRAW, JOHN LEON, JR, b Port Arthur, Tex, June 16, 41; m 57; c 3. CELL BIOLOGY, PARASITOLOGY. *Educ:* Lamar State Col, BS, 62; Tex A&M Univ, MS, 64, PhD(biol), 68. *Prof Exp:* Res grants, Res Ctr, 67-74, asst prof, 67-74, assoc prof, 72-77, PROF BIOL, LAMAR UNIV, 78- *Honors & Awards:* Regents' Merit Award, Lamar Univ, 72; Edwin S Hays Sci Teacher Award, 76. *Mem:* Am Soc Parasitologists; Soc Protozool; Sigma Xi; Bot Soc Am; Electron Micros Soc Am. *Res:* Parasites of fishes; morphology and ecological distribution of Myxomycetes; Tardigrada-taxonomy; ultrastructural studies and toxicology of dimethyl sulfoxide; ultrastructural studies related to vertebral subluxations and nerve damage. *Mailing Add:* Dept of Biol Box 10037 Beaumont TX 77710

MCGRAW, LESLIE DANIEL, b Hutchinson, Minn, Dec 19, 20; m 47; c 2. CHEMISTRY. *Educ:* Col St Thomas, BS, 42; Carnegie Inst Technol, MS, 43, DSc(phys chem), 46. *Prof Exp:* Instr chem, Pa Col Women, 45-46; asst prof, Webster Col, 46-48; from assoc consult chemist to asst div chief, Battelle Mem Inst, 48-63; dir res phys chem, North Star Res & Develop Inst, 63-65; DIV CHIEF CHEM PROCESSES & RES SERV, NAT STEEL CORP, 65- *Mem:* Am Chem Soc; Electrochem Soc; Am Electroplaters Soc. *Res:* Analytical chemistry; electro-mechanical research; operations research; information services; corrosion; electrochemical processes. *Mailing Add:* Nat Steel Corp Res Ctr 3 Springs Dr Weirton WV 26062

MCGRAW, ROBERT LEONARD, b Phillipsburg, NJ, Jan 18, 49. ATMOSPHERIC SCIENCES. *Educ:* Drexel Univ, BS, 72; Univ Chicago, SM, 74, PhD(phys chem), 79. *Prof Exp:* Res assoc, Univ Calif, Los Angeles, 77-80; ASST SCIENTIST, BROOKHAVEN NAT LAB, 81- *Mem:* Am Chem Soc. *Res:* Physical chemistry including the statistical mechanics of phase transitions and nucleation; mechanisms of gas-to-particle conversion in combustion streams and polluted air. *Mailing Add:* Environ Chem Div Bldg 426 Brookhaven Nat Lab Upton NY 11973

MCGRAY, ROBERT JAMES, b Fond du Lac, Wis, June 4, 25; m 47; c 4. ENTOMOLOGY, PUBLIC HEALTH. *Educ:* Marquette Univ, PhB, 50, MS, 52. *Prof Exp:* Bacteriologist, Microbiol Labs, Pabst Brewing Co, 52-53; assoc microbiologist, Froedtert Malt Corp, 53-55; instr biol, Marquette Univ, 56; asst biologist, 57-60, microbiologist, 60-65, sr microbiologist, 65-71, mkt develop supvr, 71-75, mkt develop mgr, 75-79, TECHNOL MGR, S C JOHNSON & SON, INC, 79- *Mem:* Am Pub Health Asn; Am Soc Microbiol. *Res:* Industrial microbiology; preservation of raw materials and finished products; anti-microbial products; public health microbiology; antiseptics and disinfectants; environmental aspects of epidemiology of infectious diseases. *Mailing Add:* SC Johnson & Son Inc Racine WI 53403

MCGREER, DONALD EDWARD, organic chemistry, see previous edition

MACGREGOR, ALEXANDER HAMILTON, medical research, see previous edition

MACGREGOR, ALEXANDER WILLIAM, b Strathpeffer, Scotland, Jan 29, 38; Can citizen; m 67. CEREAL CHEMISTRY, PLANT BIOCHEMISTRY. *Educ:* Univ Edinburgh, BSc Hons, 60, PhD(chem), 64. *Prof Exp:* Asst prof agr biochem, Edinburgh Sch Agr, Univ Edinburgh, 64-68; RES SCIENTIST CEREAL CHEM, GRAIN RES LAB, CAN GRAIN COMN, 68- *Mem:* Royal Soc Chem; Am Asn Cereal Chem; Am Soc Plant Physiol. *Res:* Chemistry and biochemistry of cereal grains during growth, maturation and germination. *Mailing Add:* Grain Res Lab Can Grain Comn 1364-303 Main St Winnipeg MB R3C 3G8 Can

MCGREGOR, BONNIE A, b Fitchburg, Mass, June 13, 42; m 75. OCEANOGRAPHY. *Educ:* Tufts Univ, BS, 64; Univ RI, MS, 67; Univ Miami, PhD(marine sci), 75. *Prof Exp:* Res asst oceanog, Univ RI, 65-70, res assoc, 70-72; oceanogr, Atlantic Oceanog & Meteorol Labs, Nat Oceanog & Atmospheric Admin, 72-78; res assoc, Tex A&M Univ, 78-79; GEOLOGIST, US GEOL SURVEY, 79- *Mem:* Am Geophys Union; Am Geol Inst; Soc Econ Paleontologists & Mineralogists; Am Asn Petrol Geologists. *Res:* Processes responsible for the evolution of the sea floor; sedimentary framework and the processes which determine the sediment stability of a passive continental margin. *Mailing Add:* US Geol Surv Fisher Island Sta Miami FL 33139

MACGREGOR, C(HARLES) W(INTERS), b Dayton, Ohio, May 25, 08; m 51; c 1. MECHANICAL ENGINEERING. *Educ:* Univ Mich, BS, 29; Univ Pittsburgh, MS, 32, PhD(mech), 34. *Prof Exp:* Res engr, Westinghouse Elec & Mfg Co, Pa, 29-34; asst engr, US Bur Reclamation, 34; from instr to prof mech eng, Mass Inst Technol, 34-52; vpres in chg eng & sci studies, Univ Pa, 52-54; private consult, 54-60; eng consult & mgr adv tech, Systs Develop Div Develop Lab, IBM Corp, 60-68, eng consult, 68-71; PRIVATE CONSULT, 71- *Honors & Awards:* Levy Medal, Franklin Inst, 41; Dudley Medal, Am Soc Testing & Mat, 41; Ord Develop Award, US Navy, 45. *Mem:* Am Soc Mech Engrs; Am Soc Metals; Am Soc Testing & Mat; fel Franklin Inst; Am Inst Mining, Metall & Petrol Engrs; fel Am Acad Arts & Sci. *Res:* Plasticity and brittle fracture of materials; elasticity; stress analysis; testing of materials; rolling of metals; applied mechanics. *Mailing Add:* 112 Jerusalem Rd Cohasset MA 02025

MACGREGOR, CAROLYN HARVEY, protein chemistry, see previous edition

MCGREGOR, DENNIS NICHOLAS, b Oelwein, Iowa, Nov 6, 43; m 65; c 2. COMMUNICATIONS, SYSTEMS ENGINEERING. *Educ:* Cath Univ Am, BEE, 65, MEE, 66. *Prof Exp:* Mem tech staff commun syst, Comput Sci Corp, 66-70, sr mem tech staff, 70-71; prin staff, 71-73, assoc prog dir, 73-75, SR SCIENTIST COMMUN SYSTS DIV, ORI INC, 75- *Mem:* Inst Elec & Electronics Engrs; Sigma Xi. *Res:* Satellite and terrestrial communications systems; multiple access; modulation; anti-jam techniques; error control coding; surveillance and navigation techniques; propagation and interference effects; traffic control; data collection and processing; tracking techniques. *Mailing Add:* Commun Systs Div 1400 Spring St Silver Spring MD 20910

MACGREGOR, DONALD MAX, b UK, Oct 2, 49. ELECTRONIC ENGINEERING, APPLIED MATHEMATICS. *Educ:* St Catharine's Col, Cambridge, UK, BA, 70; Univ Col NWales, PhD(electronic eng), 73. *Prof Exp:* STAFF ENGR, ELECTROCON INT, INC, 73- *Res:* Computer-aided simulation and design of electron tubes including cathode-ray tubes, klystrons, traveling-wave tubes, crossed-field tubes and gyroresonant devices; semiconductor device modeling; production costing for electric utilities. *Mailing Add:* Electrocon Int, Inc 611 Church St Ann Arbor MI 48104

MCGREGOR, DONALD NEIL, b Cameron, Tex, Mar 27, 36; m 57; c 1. ORGANIC CHEMISTRY. *Educ:* Rice Univ, BA, 57; Mass Inst Technol, PhD(org chem), 61. *Prof Exp:* Res asst chem, Lever Bros Co, 56 & 57; teaching asst org chem, Mass Inst Technol, 57-58; sr res scientist, 61-69, asst dir org chem res, 69-73, dir antibiotic chem res, 73-77, ASSOC DIR MED CHEM, BRISTOL LABS, 77- *Mem:* Am Chem Soc. *Res:* Chemistry of medicinal agents and antibiotics; amino acid chemistry. *Mailing Add:* 110 Fairfield St Fayetteville NY 13066

MACGREGOR, DOUGLAS, b Fresno, Calif, Dec 5, 25; m 56; c 4. ENGINEERING. *Prof Exp:* Petrol engr, Arabian Am Oil Co, 46-48; engr plant construct, CWI, Stockholm, 49-50; proj engr agr, Pineapple Res Inst, Hawaii, 50-53; proj engr automation, HMRN, Samoa, 53-55; asst plant engr, Kennecott Copper Corp, 55-57; staff engr, US Steel Corp, 57-58; proj engr, Kaiser Eng, 59-61; hazards engr, Exp Gas-Cooled Reactor Proj, Oak Ridge, Tenn, 61-63; VPRES RES & DEVELOP, TERRALAB ENGRS, 63- *Concurrent Pos:* Pres, Energy Bioneers Inc; dir, Unilink Corp; chmn, Intergalactic Corp; dir, Edenglo Corp. *Mem:* Am Soc Testing & Mat; Am Nuclear Soc; AAAS; Am Inst Chem Engrs; Am Chem Soc. *Res:* Agriculture; hydroelectrometallurgy; test methods and procedures; application engineering; safety analysis; consumer safety procedures; failure analysis; nutrition; recipe development; photo engineering; acoustics; mechanics. *Mailing Add:* 972 East 5650 South Salt Lake City UT 84121

MCGREGOR, DOUGLAS D, b Hamilton, Ont, Mar 5, 32; m 63; c 1. EXPERIMENTAL PATHOLOGY. *Educ:* Univ Western Ont, BA, 54, MD, 56; Oxford Univ, DPhil(path), 63. *Prof Exp:* Asst prof path, Case Western Reserve Univ, 63-68; assoc prof, Univ Conn, 68-69; mem, Trudeau Inst, 69-76, PROF IMMUNOL & DIR, JAMES A BAKER INST FOR ANIMAL HEALTH, CORNELL UNIV, 76- *Res:* Development and immunological activity of lymphocytes. *Mailing Add:* J A Baker Inst Animal Health Cornell Univ Snyder Hill Rd Ithaca NY 14850

MCGREGOR, DOUGLAS IAN, b Ottawa, Ont, June 22, 42; m 74; c 1. PLANT BIOCHEMISTRY, PLANT PHYSIOLOGY. *Educ:* Carleton Univ, BSc, 64; Purdue Univ, PhD(biochem, physiol), 69. *Prof Exp:* RES SCIENTIST OIL SEED CROPS, AGR CAN, 70- *Concurrent Pos:* Chmn Can assoc comt, Int Standards Orgn, 77- *Mem:* Agr Inst Can. *Res:* Improvement of the efficiency of production, adaptability and quality of rape seed, mustard and their products through physiological biochemical research. *Mailing Add:* Agr Can Res Sta 107 Sci Crescent Sask SK S7N 0X2 Can

MACGREGOR, DUGAL, b Fernie, BC, Mar 7, 25; m 45; c 4. FOOD SCIENCE. *Educ:* Univ BC, BSA, 50; Ore State Col, MS, 52, PhD(bact), 55. *Prof Exp:* Instr bact, Ore State Col, 52-55; serologist, 55-57, FOOD TECHNOLOGIST, CAN DEPT AGR, 57- *Concurrent Pos:* Prof nutrit & food sci & head dept, Univ Ghana, 71-73. *Mem:* Can Inst Food Technologists; Inst Food Technologists. *Res:* Fruit and vegetable processing; chemistry and product development. *Mailing Add:* Fruit Processing Lab Can Dept of Agr Res Sta Summerland BC V0H 1Z0 Can

MCGREGOR, DUNCAN COLIN, b St Catharines, Ont, Dec 27, 29; m 59; c 3. PALYNOLOGY. *Educ:* McMaster Univ, BA, 51, MSc, 53, PhD(paleobot), 57. *Prof Exp:* Geologist & paleobotanis, 57-65, RES SCIENTIST, GEOL SURV CAN, 65- *Mem:* Am Paleont Soc; Am Asn Stratig Palynologists; Brit Palaeont Asn; Int Comn Palynology; Can Asn Palynologists. *Res:* Plant microfossils, particularly Silurian and Devonian spores and their botanical and geological implications. *Mailing Add:* Geol Surv of Can 601 Booth St Ottawa ON K1A 0E8 Can

MCGREGOR, DUNCAN J, b St Joseph, Mo, Jan 3, 21; m 46; c 3. GEOLOGY. *Educ:* Univ Kans, BS, 43, MS, 48; Univ Mich, PhD(geol), 53. *Prof Exp:* Geologist indust minerals, State Geol Surv, Kans, 47; asst dist geologist petrol geol, Sinclair Oil & Gas Co, 48; asst prof geol & head indust minerals sect, Geol Surv, Ind Univ, 53-63; PROF GEOL & STATE GEOLOGIST, STATE GEOL SURV, UNIV SDAK, 63- *Mem:* AAAS; Asn Am State Geologists; Geol Soc Am; Soc Econ Geologists; Soc Econ Paleontologists & Mineralogists; Am Asn Petrol Geologists. *Res:* Industrial minerals; economic geology. *Mailing Add:* SDak State Geol Surv Univ of SDak Sci Ctr Vermillion SD 57069

MACGREGOR, IAN DUNCAN, b Calcutta, India, Jan 5, 35; Can citizen; m 56; c 4. PETROLOGY, GEOCHEMISTRY. *Educ:* Univ Aberdeen, BSc, 57; Queen's Univ, Ont, MSc, 60; Princeton Univ, PhD(geol), 64. *Prof Exp:* Sr asst, Geol Surv Can, Ottawa, 57, party chief, 58-59; fel exp petrol, Geophys Lab, Washington, DC, 64-65; assoc prof high pressure exp petrol, Southwest Ctr Advan Studies, Tex, 65-69; chmn dept, 69-74, PROF GEOL, UNIV CALIF, DAVIS, 69- *Concurrent Pos:* Chmn petrol panel, Joint Oceanog Insts Deep Earth Sampling, 66- *Mem:* Am Geophys Union; Mineral Soc Am. *Res:* Field geology; experimental petrology. *Mailing Add:* Dept of Geol Univ of Calif Davis CA 95616

MACGREGOR, IAN ROBERTSON, b Andover, Eng, Mar 7, 17; nat US. CHEMISTRY. *Educ:* Univ Cincinnati, AB, 41, PhD(org chem), 45. *Prof Exp:* Lab asst chem, Univ Cincinnati, 41-44, instr, 44-45, 47-48, from asst prof to assoc prof, 48-60, assoc dean admin, 60-61; financial vpres, Univ Akron, 61-65, prof chem, 65-82, vpres planning, 67-82; RETIRED. *Mem:* Am Chem Soc. *Res:* Organic medicinal chemistry; organic synthesis; polynuclear compounds; synthetic organic coatings; fluorene and thiaxanthene derivatives. *Mailing Add:* 3459 Granger Rd Akron OH 44313

MACGREGOR, JAMES GRIERSON, structural engineering, see previous edition

MACGREGOR, MALCOLM HERBERT, b Detroit, Mich, Apr 24, 26; m 49; c 3. PHYSICS. *Educ:* Univ Mich, BA, 49, MS, 50, PhD(physics), 54. *Prof Exp:* PHYSICIST, LAWRENCE LIVERMORE NAT LAB, UNIV CALIF, 53- *Concurrent Pos:* NATO fel, Inst Theoret Physics, Denmark, 60-61; lectr, Univ Calif, 60, 62 & 63; consult, Appl Radiation Corp, 56-73, Gen Atomic Div, Gen Dynamics Corp, 62-69 & Sci Appln, Inc, 69-73. *Mem:* Fel Am Phys Soc. *Res:* Neutron scattering; two-nucleon problem; elementary particle structure. *Mailing Add:* Lawrence Livermore Nat Lab PO Box 808 Livermore CA 94551

MCGREGOR, ROBERT FINLEY, biochemistry, endocrinology, see previous edition

MACGREGOR, RONAL ROY, b Hayward, Calif, July 4, 39; m 65; c 2. BIOCHEMISTRY. *Educ:* Calif State Col, Long Beach, BS, 64; Ind Univ, PhD(biochem), 68. *Prof Exp:* Instr biochem, Sch Dent, Univ Mo, Kansas City, 68-70, res assoc biochem, 68-70, RES CHEMIST, VET ADMIN HOSP, KANS CITY, MO, 70-; ASST PROF BIOCHEM, SCH DENT, UNIV MO, KANS CITY, 70-, ASST PROF MED CTR, 77- *Concurrent Pos:* Instr biochem, Sch Dent, Univ Mo, Kans City, 68-70, asst prof, 70-, asst prof, Med Ctr, 77-81, assoc prof, Med Ctr, 81- *Mem:* Am Soc Biol Chemists; Endocrine Soc. *Res:* The biosynthesis of proparathormone and its conversion to parathormone, the packaging and secretion of parathormone; the mechanisms of these processes and their control. *Mailing Add:* 409 E 70 Terr Kansas City MO 64131

MACGREGOR, RONALD JOHN, b South Bend, Ind, Nov 30, 38; m 60; c 3. ENGINEERING SCIENCES, NEUROPHYSIOLOGY. *Educ:* Purdue Univ, BS, 62, MS, 64, PhD(eng sci), 67. *Prof Exp:* Res asst, Purdue Univ, 62-66; engr bioeng, Rand Corp, Calif, 66-71; asst prof chem eng & eng design, 71-78, ASSOC PROF CHEM ENG, UNIV COLO, 78- *Concurrent Pos:* Consult bioeng, Rand Corp, 65-66; prin investr, NSF grant, 72-77 & NIH grant, 74-77. *Mem:* Am Inst Chem Engrs. *Res:* Neural modeling particular reference to theoretical models for sustained activity in neuronal networks. *Mailing Add:* Dept of Chem Eng Univ of Colo Boulder CO 80302

MCGREGOR, RONALD LEIGHTON, b Manhattan, Kans, Apr 4, 19; m 42. BOTANY. *Educ:* Univ Kans, AB, 41, MA, 47, PhD, 54. *Prof Exp:* Asst instr, 41-42 & 46, from instr to assoc prof, 47-60, chmn dept, 61-69, chmn div biol sci, 69-76, PROF BOT, UNIV KANS, 61-, DIR HERBARIUM & DIR, STATE BIOL SURV, 73- *Mem:* Am Bryol Soc; Bot Soc Am; Am Fern Soc; Am Soc Plant Taxonomists; Brit Bryol Soc. *Res:* Systematic botany; ecology; flora of Kansas and the southwest United States. *Mailing Add:* Dept of Bot Univ of Kans Lawrence KS 66045

MCGREGOR, SANDY, virology, see previous edition

MCGREGOR, STANLEY DANE, b Endicott, NY, Nov 11, 38; m 60; c 2. ORGANIC CHEMISTRY. *Educ:* WVa Wesleyan Col, BS, 60; Univ Wis, MS, 61, PhD(org chem), 66. *Prof Exp:* Instr chem, Davis & Elkins Col, 61-63; fel, Univ Fla, 66-67; res chemist, E C Britton Res Lab, 68-71, RES CHEMIST, AGR SYNTHESIS LAB, DOW CHEM USA, 71- *Mem:* Am Chem Soc; AAAS. *Res:* Synthesis of biologically active organic compounds; heterocyclic synthesis. *Mailing Add:* 3903 Chestnut Hill Dr Midland MI 48640

MACGREGOR, THOMAS HAROLD, b Jersey City, NJ, June 21, 33; m 56; c 1. MATHEMATICS. *Educ:* Lafayette Col, AB, 54; Univ Pa, MA, 56, PhD(math), 61. *Prof Exp:* Instr math, Col South Jersey, Rutgers Univ, 58-59; prof, Lafayette Col, 59-67; chmn dept, 75-78, PROF MATH, STATE UNIV NY ALBANY, 67- *Concurrent Pos:* NSF grants, 62-64, 65-67 & 68-71. *Mem:* Am Math Soc; Math Asn Am. *Res:* Complex analysis; geometric function theory. *Mailing Add:* Dept of Math State Univ of NY Albany NY 12222

MCGREGOR, WHEELER KESEY, JR, b Akron, Ohio, Apr 20, 29; m 48. PHYSICS. *Educ:* Univ Tenn, BS, 51, MS, 61, PhD(physics), 69. *Prof Exp:* Instrument engr controls anal, ARO, Inc, Engine Testing Facil, Instrument Br, 51-56, supvr controls sect, 56-58, res engr measurement tech, Res Br, 58-68, supvr physics sect res, 68-70, res engr, T-Proj Br, 70-75, supvr physics sect res, Technol Appl Br, 75-77; phys scientist, US Air Force Rocket Propulsion Lab, Edwards Air Force Base, 77-78; staff scientist, Advan Diag Br, Aro, Inc, 78-80; SR TECH SPECIALIST, SVERDRUP TECHNOL INC, 81- *Concurrent Pos:* Assoc prof, Univ Tenn Space Inst, Tullahoma, 76- *Honors & Awards:* Gen H H Arnold Award, Am Inst Aeronaut & Astronaut, 62. *Mem:* Am Phys Soc; Am Inst Aeronaut & Astronaut. *Res:* Spectroscopy and radiative transfer in gases (combustion flames and plasmas). *Mailing Add:* Stillwood Dr Rte 6 Manchester TN 37355

MCGREGOR, WILLIAM HENRY DAVIS, b SC, Mar 25, 27; m 50; c 2. PLANT PHYSIOLOGY, FORESTRY. *Educ:* Clemson Col, BS, 51; Univ Mich, BSF & MF, 53; Duke Univ, PhD(physiol), 58. *Prof Exp:* Res forester, Forest Serv, USDA, 53-57, plant physiologist, 57-60; from assoc prof to prof forestry, 60-69, head dept, 69-70, dean, Col Forest & Recreation Resources, 70-78, PROF FORESTRY, CLEMSON UNIV, 78- *Concurrent Pos:* Asst, Duke Univ, 55-57. *Mem:* Sigma Xi; fel Soc Am Foresters. *Res:* Forest influences, forest ecology and tree physiology, particularly vegetation analysis, succession and hydrology. *Mailing Add:* Col of Forest & Recreation Resources Clemson Univ Clemson SC 29631

MCGREW, ELIZABETH ANNE, b Faribault, Minn, Aug 30, 16. PATHOLOGY. *Educ:* Carleton Col, AB, 38; Univ Minn, MB, 44, MD, 45. *Prof Exp:* From instr to asst prof path, Col Med, 46-47, from asst pathologist to assoc pathologist, Res & Educ Hosps, 47-62, PROF PATH, UNIV ILL COL MED, 62-, PATHOLOGIST, UNIV HOSPS, 62- *Mem:* Am Soc Clin Path; Col Am Path; Am Asn Path & Bact; Am Asn Cancer Res; Am Soc Cytol. *Res:* Cytology and cancer. *Mailing Add:* Dept of Path Univ of Ill Col of Med Chicago IL 60612

MCGREW, JOHN ROBERTS, phytopathology, viticulture, see previous edition

MCGREW, LEROY ALBERT, b Galva, Ill, Nov 1, 38; m 63; c 3. ORGANIC CHEMISTRY. *Educ:* Knox Col, BA, 60; Univ Iowa, MS, 63, PhD(chem), 64. *Prof Exp:* Prof chem, Ball State Univ, 64-77; PROF CHEM & HEAD DEPT, UNIV NORTHERN IOWA, 77- *Mem:* Am Chem Soc. *Res:* Mechanisms of organic reactions, especially reactions of isocyanates. *Mailing Add:* Dept Chem Univ Northern Iowa Cedar Falls IA 50613

MCGREW, PAUL ORMAN, b Ottumwa, Iowa, Aug 27, 09; m 34; c 3. GEOLOGY, PALEONTOLOGY. *Educ:* Univ Nebr, AB, 33; Univ Calif, MA, 35; Univ Chicago, PhD(geol paleont), 42. *Prof Exp:* Asst, Mus, Univ Nebr, 29-33; asst paleont, Field Mus Natural Hist, 38-39, asst cur, 40-46; from asst prof to assoc prof, 46-58, prof, 58-75, EMER PROF GEOL, UNIV WYO, 75- *Concurrent Pos:* Mem expeds, Great Plains, 29-37 & 39-40, Honduras, 37-38 & 41-42; ed, J Soc Vert Paleont, 45-47. *Mem:* Soc Study Evolution; Soc Vert Paleont; fel Geol Soc Am. *Res:* Mammalian paleontology; Tertiary stratigraphy. *Mailing Add:* Dept Geol Univ Wyo Laramie WY 82070

MCGRIFF, RICHARD BERNARD, b St Petersburg, Fla, July 15, 35; m 69; c 2. ORGANIC CHEMISTRY, ANALYTICAL CHEMISTRY. *Educ:* Fla A&M Univ, BS, 55; Calif Inst Technol, MS, 59; Univ Wis, PhD(chem), 67. *Prof Exp:* Med chemist, Riker Labs, Inc, 59-61; res chemist org chem, Organics Dept, Hercules, Inc, 67-73; tech specialist, Special Mat Area, 73-75, SR CHEMIST ANAL CHEM, MAT ANAL AREA, XEROX CORP, 75-

Mem: Am Chem Soc. *Res:* Thermal analysis of polymers; structure-property relationships; development of specialty elastomers; water based thermosets; cationic resins; urethanes; acrylics; fluorocarbons; siloxanes; oxidation and electrical conduction in polymers. *Mailing Add:* Xerox Corp 800 Phillips Rd Webster NY 14580

MCGROARTY, ESTELLE JOSEPHINE, b Lafayette, Ind, Sept 14, 45; m 67; c 2. MEMBRANE BIOPHYSICS, MEMBRANE BIOCHEMISTRY. *Educ:* Purdue Univ, BS, 67, PhD(molecular biol), 71. *Prof Exp:* Lectr, Dept Biol, Purdue Univ, 71-72; res assoc biochem, 73-73, asst prof biophysics, 73-78, actg chmn biophys, 75-76, assoc prof, 78-81, ASSOC PROF BIOCHEM, MICH STATE UNIV, 81- *Mem:* Biophys Soc; Am Soc Microbiol. *Res:* Membrane biophysics and biochemistry; interactions of surface active componds with erythrocyte membranes; structure, composition and physical properties of bcterial membranes; biophysical and biochemical changes in cell membranes induced upon transformation. *Mailing Add:* Dept Biochem Mich State Univ East Lansing MI 48824

MCGROARTY, JOSEPH A, b Wilkes-Barre, Pa, May 26, 16; m 47; c 3. INDUSTRIAL CHEMISTRY. *Educ:* Rensselaer Polytech Inst, BS, 41. *Prof Exp:* Supvr process develop, Merck & Co, Inc, 41-49, supvr indust eng, 49-50, supvr commercial develop, 50-56, supvr indust sales, 56-64, sales mgr, Indust & Agr Chem, 64-74; CHEM & MKT CONSULT, 74- *Concurrent Pos:* Chief facilities br, Chem Div, Nat Prod Authority, 51-52; consult, Merck & Co, Inc, 74- & C P Chem, Inc, 75- *Honors & Awards:* Cert, Secy of Com, 52. *Mem:* Am Chem Soc; Commercial Develop Asn; assoc Consult Chemists & Engrs. *Res:* Commercial development; chemical marketing; organic and inorganic chemistry; Environmental Protection Agency pesticide registration; chemical toxicity. *Mailing Add:* 925 Lawrence Ave Westfield NJ 07090

MCGRODDY, JAMES CLEARY, b New York, NY, Apr 6, 37; c 4. SOLID STATE PHYSICS. *Educ:* St Joseph's Col, Pa, BS, 58; Univ Md, PhD(physics), 64. *Prof Exp:* Res assoc physics, Univ Md, 64-65; res scientist, 65-77, dir, Semiconductor Sci & Technol, 77-81, VPRES LOGIC & MEMORY, IBM RES, IBM CORP, 81- *Concurrent Pos:* Vis prof, Tech Univ Denmark, 70-71. *Mem:* Fel Am Phys Soc; fel Inst Elec & Electronics Engrs. *Res:* Semiconductor technology; experimental semiconductor and surface physics. *Mailing Add:* IBM Thomas J Watson Res Ctr Yorktown Heights NY 10598

MCGRORY, JOSEPH BENNETT, b Philadelphia, Pa, Feb 23, 34; m 57; c 2. NUCLEAR PHYSICS. *Educ:* Univ of the South, BA, 55; Vanderbilt Univ, MS, 57, PhD(physics), 64. *Prof Exp:* Sanitarian health physics, USPHS, 57-60; nuclear physicist nuclear theory, 63-76, NUCLEAR THEORY GROUP LEADER, OAK RIDGE NAT LAB, 76- *Mem:* AAAS; Am Phys Soc. *Res:* Microscopic theory of nuclear structure; nuclear shell model. *Mailing Add:* Physics Div Bldg 6003 Oak Ridge Nat Lab Oak Ridge TN 37830

MCGUCKIN, WARREN FRANCIS, clinical chemistry, instrumentation, deceased

MCGUGAN, WESLEY ALEXANDER, b Weyburn, Sask, Oct 31, 20; m 58. FOOD CHEMISTRY. *Educ:* Univ Sask, BSA, 49; Univ Wis, MS, 53, PhD(dairy & food indust, biochem), 54. *Prof Exp:* Agr res officer, Dairy Technol Res Inst, 54-62, RES SCIENTIST, FOOD RES INST, AGR CAN, 62- *Mem:* Am Dairy Sci Asn; Agr Inst Can; Can Inst Food Sci & Technol. *Res:* Dairy chemistry; flavors. *Mailing Add:* Food Res Inst Agr Can Ottawa ON Can

MCGUIGAN, JAMES E, b Paterson, NJ, Aug 20, 31; m 56; c 3. GASTROENTEROLOGY, IMMUNOLOGY. *Educ:* Seattle Univ, BS, 52; St Louis Univ, MD, 56; Am Bd Gastroenterol, dipl. *Prof Exp:* Intern med, Pa Hosp, Philadelphia, 56-57; resident internal med, Sch Med, Univ Wash, 60-62; asst prof med, Wash Univ, 66-69; chief div gastroenterol, 69-78, PROF MED, COL MED, UNIV FLA, 69-, CHMN DEPT MED, 76- *Concurrent Pos:* NIH fel gastroenterol, 62-64; Nat Inst Allergy & Infectious Dis spec fel immunol, Sch Med, Wash Univ, 64-66; NIH res career develop award, 66-69. *Mem:* Asn Am Physicians; Asn Prof Med; AAAS; Am Soc Clin Invest. *Res:* Immunological phenomena associated with gastrointestinal diseases. *Mailing Add:* Col of Med Univ of Fla Gainesville FL 32601

MCGUIGAN, ROBERT ALISTER, JR, b Evanston, Ill, July 21, 42; m 65. MATHEMATICS. *Educ:* Carleton Col, BA, 64; Univ Md, College Park, PhD(math), 68. *Prof Exp:* Asst prof math, Univ Mass, Amherst, 68-74; asst prof, 74-78, chmn dept, 75-81, ASSOC PROF MATH, WESTFIELD STATE COL, 78- *Concurrent Pos:* Res anal, Nat Hwy Traffic Safety Admin, Washington, DC, 79-80; consult, Abt Assocs, Inc, 81. *Mem:* Am Math Soc; Math Asn Am. *Res:* Banach spaces; spaces of continuous functions; non-standard analysis; history of mathematics; theoretical linguistics; graph theory; computer science; data analyses, structures and the theory of computation. *Mailing Add:* Dept of Math Westfield State Col Westfield MA 01085

MCGUINNESS, EUGENE T, b Newark, NJ, Feb 2, 27; m 59; c 2. BIOCHEMISTRY. *Educ:* St Peter's Col, BS, 49; Fordham Univ, MS, 54; Rutgers Univ, PhD(biochem), 61. *Prof Exp:* Anal chemist, Wallace & Tiernan, Inc, 49-50; res asst, Fordham Univ, 51-52; asst lab control supvr, P Ballantine & Sons, 52-55; from instr to assoc prof, 55-79, PROF CHEM, SETON HALL UNIV, 79- *Mem:* AAAS; Am Chem Soc; Am Soc Biol Chemists. *Res:* Mechanisms of enzyme action; biological oxidation; evolution of enzyme function. *Mailing Add:* Dept of Chem Seton Hall Univ South Orange NJ 07079

MCGUINNESS, JAMES ANTHONY, b Staten Island, NY, Nov 4, 41. ORGANIC CHEMISTRY. *Educ:* St Peter's Col, NJ, BS, 63; Columbia Univ, MA, 64, PhD(chem), 68. *Prof Exp:* RES CHEMIST RES & DEVELOP, UNIROYAL INC, 67- *Mem:* Am Chem Soc; Royal Soc Chem. *Res:* Polymer degradation, especially photochemical; polymer modification by organic reactions; synthesis of organic chemicals as agricultural products. *Mailing Add:* Res & Develop Uniroyal Inc Middlebury CT 06749

MCGUIRE, AUSTIN DOLE, b Malden, Mass, Oct 13, 24; m 50; c 1. PARTICLE PHYSICS. *Educ:* Mass Inst Technol, BS, 49; Univ Rochester, PhD(physics), 54. *Prof Exp:* Jr physicist, Univ Rochester, 49; staff mem, Los Alamos Sci Lab, 54-65; prog mgr, Electro-Optical Systs, Inc, 65-66; sr staff mem, TRW Systs, Calif, 66-67; mem staff, EG&G Inc, 67-70; spec proj officer, Los Alamos Sci Lab, 70-79; proj mgr, Los Alamos Tech Assoc, 79-82; TESTING DIR, INESCO INC, 82- *Mem:* Fel Am Phys Soc. *Res:* Fundamental particles; interaction of mesons with nucleii; detection of free neutrino; space radiation; particle accelerator design; nuclear weapon testing. *Mailing Add:* 11077 N Torrey Pines Rd INESCO INC La Jolla CA 92037

MCGUIRE, CHARLES FRANCIS, b Heber City, Utah, May 13, 29; m 52; c 5. AGRONOMY, CEREAL CHEMISTRY. *Educ:* Brigham Young Univ, BS, 54; Utah State Univ, MS, 65; NDak State Univ, PhD(agron), 68. *Prof Exp:* Lab technician & mgr qual control, Pillsbury Co, 55-63; asst prof, 68-71, assoc prof, 71-77, PROF AGRON & CEREAL TECHNOL, MONT STATE UNIV, 77- *Mem:* Am Asn Cereal Chemists; Am Soc Agron. *Res:* Improvement in wheat and barley quality through improved breeding and cultural practices. *Mailing Add:* Dept of Plant & Soil Sci Mont State Univ Bozeman MT 59717

MCGUIRE, DAVID KELTY, b Pittsburgh, Pa, Dec 18, 34; div; c 3. SCIENCE POLICY. *Educ:* St Vincent Col, BS, 57; Univ Pittsburgh, PhD(anal chem), 64. *Prof Exp:* Res assoc, Brookhaven Nat Lab, 64-65; asst prof chem, Rider Col, 65-67; asst prof, 67-70, chmn dept, 71-76, ASSOC PROF CHEM, UPSALA COL, 70-, DIR, TITLE III PROG, 79- *Mem:* AAAS; Am Chem Soc. *Res:* Science, technology, and public policy relationships, with special attention to the energy situation. *Mailing Add:* 94 Christopher St Montclair NJ 07042

MCGUIRE, DONALD CHARLES, b Clearwater, Kans, Sept 20, 15; m 42; c 4. GENETICS. *Educ:* Univ Wash, BS, 46; Univ Calif, PhD(genetics), 50. *Prof Exp:* From asst prof to prof agr, Univ Hawaii, 50-62, asst olericulturist, Agr Exp Sta, 50-54, chmn dept agr, Univ, 56-59, chmn dept trop crop sci, 57-62; assoc prog dir, 62-66, dir undergrad student prog, 66-69, dir pre-serv teaching educ prog, 69-78, prog mgr, local course improvement prog, 78-81, PROG MGR, COMPREHENSIVE ASSISTANCE UNDERGRAD SCI EDUC, NSF, 81- *Mem:* Fel AAAS; Am Inst Biol Sci. *Res:* Self-incompatibility of wild tomato; inheritance of disease resistance in cultivars; science education, particularly at the undergraduate level; development of programs for enhancement of science education. *Mailing Add:* Nat Sci Found 1800 G St NW Washington DC 20550

MCGUIRE, EUGENE J, b New York, NY, May 15, 38; m 65; c 3. ATOMIC PHYSICS. *Educ:* Manhattan Col, BEE, 59; Cornell Univ, PhD, 65. *Prof Exp:* Mem tech staff physics res, 65-74, SUPVR LASER THEORY DIV, SANDIA LABS, 74- *Mem:* Am Phys Soc. *Res:* High power gas laser theory; x-ray lasers; auger transitions and electron spectroscopy; gas discharges; inelastic atomic processes. *Mailing Add:* Sandia Labs Box 5800 Albuquerque NM 87115

MCGUIRE, FRANCIS JOSEPH, b Baltimore, Md, Aug 29, 32; m 63. ORGANIC CHEMISTRY, ANALYTICAL CHEMISTRY. *Educ:* Loyola Col, Md, BS, 54; Johns Hopkins Univ, MA, 56, PhD(org chem), 61. *Prof Exp:* Res chemist, E I du Pont de Nemours & Co, 61-63; from instr to asst prof, 63-67, chmn dept, 65-67, dean studies, 67-77, ASSOC PROF CHEM, LOYOLA COL, MD, 67-, DEAN UNDERGRAD STUDIES & ACAD REC, 77- *Concurrent Pos:* Acad internship prog fel, Am Coun on Educ, 69-70. *Mem:* Am Chem Soc. *Res:* Structure determination and mechanism of cyclization reactions of natural products; synthesis of polymers; problems in chemical education. *Mailing Add:* Off of Dean Studies Day Div Loyola Col 4501 N Charles St Baltimore MD 21210

MCGUIRE, GEORGE, b Edinburgh, Scotland, Apr 25, 40; m 64; c 2. INORGANIC CHEMISTRY. *Educ:* Heriot Watt Univ, BSc, 62; Edinburgh Univ, PhD(inorg chem), 65; FRIC, 73. *Prof Exp:* Lab supvr, Que Iron & Titanium Corp, 65-69; sr chemist, Johnson Matthey Chem, 69-71, develop supt, 71-73; develop supt refining, Matthey Rustenburg Refiners, 73-74; res mgr, Matthey Bishop Inc, 74-78, VPRES RES, JOHNSON MATTHEY INC, 78- *Mem:* Royal Inst Chem; Inst Works Mgrs; AAAS. *Res:* Chemistry and metallurgy of platinum group metals; applications to catalysis, drugs, refining of precious metals, powders and organometallic complexes. *Mailing Add:* Johnson Matthey Inc West Whiteland Lab Malvern PA 19355

MCGUIRE, JAMES B, b Newcastle, Ind, May 7, 34; m 56; c 4. THEORETICAL PHYSICS. *Educ:* Purdue Univ, BSEE, 56; Univ Calif, Los Angeles, MS, 60, PhD(physics), 63. *Prof Exp:* Mem tech staff, Hughes Aircraft Co, 56-57 & Space Technol Labs, 57-63; asst res physicist, Univ Calif, Los Angeles, 63-64; chmn dept, 74-77, from asst prof to assoc prof, 64-77, PROF PHYSICS, FLA ATLANTIC UNIV, 77- *Concurrent Pos:* Vis asst physicist, Brookhaven Nat Lab, 65. *Mem:* Am Phys Soc. *Res:* Scattering theory; many particle systems; one dimensional models. *Mailing Add:* Dept of Physics Fla Atlantic Univ Boca Raton FL 33432

MCGUIRE, JAMES HORTON, b Canandaigua, NY, June 7, 42; c 4. ATOMIC PHYSICS. *Educ:* Rensselaer Polytech Inst, BS, 64; Northeastern Univ, MS, 66, PhD(physics), 69. *Prof Exp:* Asst prof physics, Tex A&M Univ, 69-72; asst prof, 72-76, ASSOC PROF PHYSICS, KANS STATE UNIV, 76- *Concurrent Pos:* US Dept Energy grant; consult, Picatinny Arsenal, 72, Naval Surface Weapons Lab, 78 & Lawrence Livermore Lab, 78. *Mem:* Am Phys Soc. *Res:* Atomic scattering theory; excitation; ionization; charge transfer; electron systems; multi electron excitation by charge particle impact. *Mailing Add:* Dept of Physics Kans State Univ Manhattan KS 66506

MCGUIRE, JAMES MARCUS, b Gassville, Ark, July 30, 35; m 56; c 4. PLANT PATHOLOGY. *Educ:* Univ Ark, BS, 56, MS, 57; NC State Univ, PhD(plant path), 61. *Prof Exp:* Asst prof plant path, SDak State Univ, 61-63; res assoc, 63-65, assoc prof, 65-70, PROF PLANT PATH, UNIV ARK,

FAYETTEVILLE, 70- *Mem:* Am Phytopath Soc; Soc Nematol. *Res:* Nematode transmission of viruses; interactions between nematodes and other plant pathogens; virus diseases of horticultural plants. *Mailing Add:* Dept Plant Path Univ Ark Fayetteville AR 72701

MCGUIRE, JOHN ALBERT, b Banner, Miss, July 31, 31; m 55. ANIMAL BREEDING, ANIMAL GENETICS. *Educ:* Miss State Univ, BS, 51, MS, 57; Auburn Univ, PhD(animal breeding), 69. *Prof Exp:* Instr animal sci, Miss State Univ, 55-56, supt, Natchez Br Exp Sta, 56-65; asst prof, 68-74, ASSOC PROF BIOSTATIST, AUBURN UNIV, 74- *Mem:* Am Soc Animal Sci; Biomet Soc. *Res:* Animal physiology; improvement of important production traits in beef cattle and sheep by selection for genetically superior animals. *Mailing Add:* Res Data Anal Auburn Univ Auburn AL 36849

MCGUIRE, JOHN J, b Mar 19, 30; US citizen; m 54; c 6. ORNAMENTAL HORTICULTURE. *Educ:* Rutgers Univ, BS, 58; Univ RI, MS, 61, PhD(biol sci), 68. *Prof Exp:* Instr hort, Va Polytech Inst & State Univ, 61-62; from instr to assoc prof, 62-77, PROF HORT, UNIV RI, 77- *Mem:* Am Soc Hort Sci; Int Plant Propagators Soc. *Res:* Winter hardiness of woody ornamental plants; marketing technology of container grown ornamental plants; propagation of woody plants. *Mailing Add:* Dept of Plant & Soil Sci Univ of RI Kingston RI 02881

MCGUIRE, JOHN L, b Kittanning, Pa, Nov 3, 42; m 69. PHARMACOLOGY. *Educ:* Butler Univ, BS, 65; Princeton Univ, MS, 68, PhD(physiol, biochem), 69. *Prof Exp:* Pop Coun fel, 69; from assoc scientist pharmacol to scientist pharmacol, 69-72, sect head molecular biol, 72-75, exec dir res, 75-80, VPRES BASIC SCI, ORTHO PHARMACEUT CORP, 80- *Concurrent Pos:* Adj assoc prof, Dept Med, M S Hershey Sch Med, Pa State Univ, 78- *Mem:* Am Soc Pharmacol & Exp Therapeut; Endocrine Soc; Soc Exp Biol & Med; Am Physiol Soc; Am Soc Clin Pharmacol & Therapeut. *Res:* Gastrointestinal and endocrine pharmacology; toxicology; endocrinology. *Mailing Add:* Ortho Pharmaceut Corp Raritan NJ 08869

MCGUIRE, JOHN MURRAY, b New Bedford, Mass, May 15, 29; m 54; c 5. ANALYTICAL CHEMISTRY. *Educ:* Univ Miami, BS, 48, MS, 51; Univ Fla, PhD(phys chem), 55. *Prof Exp:* Prod chemist, Gen Elec Co, 55-57; sr res chemist, Wash Res Ctr, W R Grace & Co, 57-60; sr chemist, Cathode Ray Tube Dept, Gen Elec Co, 60-63, supvr fluid develop eng, TV Receiver Dept, 63-68, supvr fluids eval, Advan Eng Proj Oper, Visual Commun Dept, 68-70, advan mat engr, Audio Prod Dept, 70-71; res chemist, Contaminants Characterization Prog, Southeast Water Lab, 71-73, CHIEF ORG ANAL SECT, ANAL CHEM BR, ENVIRON RES LAB, ENVIRON PROTECTION AGENCY, 73- *Concurrent Pos:* Ed adv, Biomed Mass Spectrometry, 74- *Mem:* Am Chem Soc; Am Soc Mass Spectrometry; Am Soc Testing & Mat. *Res:* Mass spectrometric and gas chromatographic analysis of water contaminants; computer control of analytical instrumentation; computerized spectrum matching. *Mailing Add:* Athens Environ Res Lab College Station Rd Athens GA 30613

MCGUIRE, JOSEPH CLIVE, b Columbus, Ohio, Oct 14, 20; m 43; c 4. PHYSICAL CHEMISTRY, METALLURGY. *Educ:* Franklin Col, AB, 43; Univ NMex, MS, 63. *Prof Exp:* Chemist, Continental Can Co, 43-44 & Sherwin Williams Co, 46-47; staff mem, Argonne Nat Lab, 47-53; consult, 53-54; staff mem, Los Alamos Sci Lab, 54-66; sr lab scientist, Donald W Douglas Labs, McDonnell Douglas Astronaut Co, Richland, 66-73; prin engr, 73-80, FEL ENGR, WESTINGHOUSE-HANFORD CO, 80- *Concurrent Pos:* Nuclear consult, Argentine Atomic Energy Comn, 74. *Mem:* Am Chem Soc; Sigma Xi; fel Am Inst Chemists. *Res:* Gas-metal reactions of refractory and transition metals; high temperature vacuum metallurgy; tritium and helium three production; radioisotope transport in liquid metals; heat pipes; helium venting from radiosiotope capsules; radionuclide traps; sodium technology; tritium permeation. *Mailing Add:* 1637 Mowry Sq Richland WA 99352

MCGUIRE, JOSEPH SMITH, JR, b Logan, WVa, Apr 19, 31; div; c 6. MEDICINE. *Educ:* WVa Univ, AB, 52; Yale Univ, MD, 55. *Prof Exp:* Intern med, Yale-New Haven Med Ctr, 55-56; clin assoc, Nat Inst Arthritis & Metab Dis, 56-58, investr, 58-59; from asst prof to assoc prof med, 61-72, PROF DERMAT, SCH MED, YALE UNIV, 72- *Concurrent Pos:* USPHS spec fel med, Yale Univ, 59-61, USPHS award, Sch Med, 61-63, dir clin res training prog, Yale Univ, 64-69, mem gen med A study sect, 75-79. *Mem:* AAAS; Soc Invest Dermat; Am Dermat Asn; Am Soc Cell Biol; Am Acad Dermat. *Res:* Control of cell division in cultivated malignant and non-malignant cells; control of cell division, differentiation of keratinocytes and structure of keratins. *Mailing Add:* Dept of Dermat Yale Univ Sch of Med New Haven CT 06510

MCGUIRE, ODELL, b Knoxville, Tenn, Apr 19, 27; m 57; c 3. GEOLOGY. *Educ:* Univ Tulsa, BS, 56; Columbia Univ, MA, 58; Univ Ill, PhD(geol), 62. *Prof Exp:* Assoc prof, 62-71, PROF GEOL, WASHINGTON & LEE UNIV, 71- *Concurrent Pos:* Geologist, Va Div Mining Resources. *Res:* Fossil population studies; geology of Appalachian region. *Mailing Add:* Dept of Geol Washington & Lee Univ Lexington VA 24450

MCGUIRE, ROBERT FRANCIS, b Rochester, NY, Mar 3, 38; m 67; c 5. BIOPHYSICS, BIOCHEMISTRY. *Educ:* St John Fischer Col, BA, 60; Univ Ky, MS, 62; Univ Rochester, PhD(biophys), 68. *Prof Exp:* Instr, Univ Ky, 62; fel, Cornell Univ, 68-71; scientist biophys, Worcester Found Exp Biol, 71-74; ASST PROF BIOCHEM, SCH MED, UNIV MASS, WORCESTER, 75- *Mem:* Biophys Soc. *Res:* Physical chemical studies on structure-function relationships in cell membranes; hormone-membrane receptor interactions; hormone binding; activation of membrane enzymes; membrane isolation techniques and characterization; spectroscopy in membranes. *Mailing Add:* Dept of Biochem Univ of Mass Sch of Med Worcester MA 01605

MCGUIRE, ROBERT FRANK, b Greeneville, Tenn, Oct 8, 37; m 62. PHYCOLOGY. *Educ:* Union Col, Ky, BA, 60; Univ Tenn, Knoxville, MS, 64, PhD(bot), 71. *Prof Exp:* Teacher, Pub Schs, Ky, 60-62; instr math & sci, Eastern Ky Univ, 64-67; from teaching asst to instr bot, Univ Tenn, Knoxville, 67-71; asst prof, 71-74, ASSOC PROF BIOL, UNIV MONTEVALLO, 74- *Concurrent Pos:* NDEA fel, Univ Tenn, Knoxville, 70. Mem; Am Inst Biol Sci; Int Phycol Soc; Phycol Soc Am. *Res:* Application of the principles of numerical taxonomy to the algal divisions, especially the Chlorophyta; these procedures have been used with selected species of Chlorococcum and clones of Chara. *Mailing Add:* Dept of Biol Sta 110 Univ of Montevallo Montevallo AL 35115

MCGUIRE, STEPHEN CRAIG, b New Orleans, La, Sept 17, 48; m 71; c 2. NUCLEAR STRUCTURE. *Educ:* Southern Univ & A&M Col, BS, 70; Univ Rochester, MS, 74; Cornell Univ, PhD(nuclear sci), 79. *Prof Exp:* Teaching asst & res asst physics, Univ Rochester, 70-74; res asst, Ward Lab, Cornell Univ, 75-78; DEVELOP ASSOC, CHEM TECHNOL DIV, OAK RIDGE NAT LAB, 78- *Concurrent Pos:* Lectr physics, Stanford Linear Accelerator Ctr, 76. *Mem:* Am Phys Soc; Am Nuclear Soc; AAAS; Sigma Xi. *Res:* Nuclear structure of freezing point-shell and heavy nuclei; transplutonium element production; commercial fuel cycle waste management. *Mailing Add:* Oak Ridge Nat Lab Bldg 3017 Oak Ridge TN 37830

MCGUIRE, STEPHEN EDWARD, b Excelsior Springs, Mo, Mar 25, 42; m 63; c 2. INDUSTRIAL CHEMISTRY. *Educ:* Lamar State Col Technol, BS, 63; Univ Tex, Austin, PhD(org chem), 67. *Prof Exp:* Res chemist, 67-70, sr res chemist, Continental Oil Co, 70-73, RES GROUP LEADER, CONOCO INC, 73- *Mem:* Am Oil Chemists' Soc. *Res:* Friedel-Crafts alkylations; carbonium ions; detergent intermediates. *Mailing Add:* Res & Develop Dept Res Div Conoco Inc Ponca City OK 74601

MCGUIRE, WILLIAM, b Staten Island, NY, Dec 17, 20; m 44; c 2. CIVIL ENGINEERING. *Educ:* Bucknell Univ, BS, 42; Cornell Univ, MCE, 47. *Prof Exp:* Struct engr, Jackson & Moreland, 47-49; from asst prof to assoc prof civil eng, 49-60, PROF CIVIL ENG, CORNELL UNIV, 60- *Concurrent Pos:* Consult engr, 51-; design engr, Pittsburgh-Des Moines Steel Co, 54-56; vis prof, Asian Inst Technol, 68-70; Gledden sr fel, Univ Western Australia, 73; vis scholar, Univ Tokyo, 79. *Honors & Awards:* Norman Medal, Am Soc Civil Engrs, 62. *Mem:* Fel Am Soc Civil Engrs; Int Asn Bridge & Struct Engrs; Am Concrete Inst. *Res:* Structural engineering. *Mailing Add:* Col of Eng Hollister Hall Cornell Univ Ithaca NY 14850

MCGUIRE, WILLIAM SAXON, b Prescott, Ark, Oct 9, 22; m 52; c 3. AGRONOMY. *Educ:* Univ Ark, BS, 47; Univ NZ, MAgSc, 51; Wash State Univ, PhD(agron), 52. *Prof Exp:* Asst prof agron & asst agronomist, Miss State Univ, 52-55; assoc prof agron & assoc agronomist, NMex State Univ, 56; PROF AGRON & AGRONOMIST, ORE STATE UNIV, 57- *Mem:* Am Soc Agron; Crop Sci Soc Am; Am Forage & Grassland Coun. *Res:* Pasture and forage production and management. *Mailing Add:* Dept of Crop Sci Ore State Univ Corvallis OR 97331

MCGURK, DONALD J, b Wichita, Kans, June 2, 40. ORGANIC CHEMISTRY. *Educ:* Univ Nebr, BS, 62; Okla State Univ, PhD(org chem), 68. *Prof Exp:* Asst prof, 68-72, assoc prof, 72-80, PROF CHEM, SOUTHWESTERN STATE COL, OKLA, 80- *Mem:* AAAS. *Res:* Chemistry of natural products; structure of molecules in oil of catnip; identity of volatile compounds produced by ants. *Mailing Add:* Dept of Chem Southwestern State Col Weatherford OK 73096

MACH, GEORGE ROBERT, b Cedar Falls, Iowa, July 23, 28; m 52; c 3. MATHEMATICS. *Educ:* Univ Northern Iowa, BA, 50; Univ Iowa, MS, 51; Purdue Univ, PhD(math), 63. *Prof Exp:* From instr to assoc prof, 54-67, PROF MATH, CALIF POLYTECH STATE UNIV, SAN LUIS OBISPO, 67- *Mem:* Math Asn Am. *Res:* Mathematics education. *Mailing Add:* Dept of Math Calif Polytech State Univ San Luis Obispo CA 93407

MACH, MARTIN HENRY, b New York, NY, Feb 10, 40; div; c 1. ENVIRONMENTAL ANALYSIS, PHYSICAL ORGANIC CHEMISTRY. *Educ:* City Col New York, BS, 61; Clark Univ, MA, 65; Univ Calif, Santa Cruz, PhD(chem), 73. *Prof Exp:* Assoc scientist chem, Polaroid Corp, Mass, 65-69; mem tech staff chem, Aerospace Corp, 73-81; SECT HEAD, TRW CORP, 81- *Concurrent Pos:* Consult, Aerospace Corp, 81- *Mem:* Sigma Xi. *Res:* Analytical organic chemistry using interfaced, computerized gas chromatography-mass spectrometry, including environmental analysis, forensic science, fuel and synfuel synthesis and analysis, and lubrication phenomena. *Mailing Add:* TRW 0-1/2030 1 Space Park Dr Redondo Beach CA 90278

MACH, WILLIAM HOWARD, b Hamilton, Tex, July 16, 45. METEOROLOGY. *Educ:* Univ Wash, BS, 69, MS, 72; Pa State Univ, PhD(meteorol), 78. *Prof Exp:* ASST PROF METEOROL, FLA STATE UNIV, 78- *Mem:* Am Meteorol Soc. *Res:* Atmospheric optics; cloud physics. *Mailing Add:* Dept of Meteorol Fla State Univ Tallahassee FL 32306

MACHA, MILO, b Motycin, Czech, July 18, 18; US citizen; m 50; c 2. SOLID STATE ELECTRONICS, CERAMICS. *Educ:* Prague Tech Univ, dipl eng, 39, PhD(ceramics), 47. *Prof Exp:* Asst to Prof R Barta, Prague Tech Univ, 45-47; mgr, Ceramic Res Inst Gouda, Neth, 47-50; consult ceramics, N V Naga Hidjau, Indonesia, 50-52 & Georgian China Ltd, Can, 52-53; res scientist, Gen Foods Corp, Calif, 54-55; mgr solar cells res, Int Rectifier Corp, 55-60; sr res scientist, Acoustica Assoc Inc, 60-61; proj mgr, Lear Siegler Inc, 61-63; sr res scientist, Librascope Div, Gen Precision Inc, 63-64 & Douglas Aircraft Co, 64-66; head physics sect, Librascope Div, Gen Precision Inc, 66-71; sr res engr, Teledyne Systs Co, 71-75; PRES/OWNER, SOLLOS, INC, 75- *Concurrent Pos:* Translr & abstractor, Am Chem Soc. *Mem:* Electrochem Soc; sr mem Inst Elec & Electronics Engrs; Am Ceramic Soc; Acoust Soc Am. *Res:* Electrooptical devices, including preparation of single crystal materials in bulk form as well as thin films, device construction and application. *Mailing Add:* 1519 Comstock Ave Los Angeles CA 90024

MACHACEK, MARIE ESTHER, b Cedar Rapids, Iowa, Sept 12, 47; m 67; c 3. THEORETICAL HIGH ENERGY PHYSICS. *Educ:* Coe Col, BA, 69; Univ Mich, MS, 70; Univ Iowa, PhD(physics), 73. *Prof Exp:* Teaching asst physics, Univ Iowa, 70-71; hon fel physics, Univ Wis-Madison, 73-74; jr fel, Mich Soc Fellows, Univ Mich, 74-76; hon res fel, Harvard Univ, 76-77, lectr physics, 77-79; ASST PROF PHYSICS, NORTHEASTERN UNIV, 79- *Concurrent Pos:* Lectr physics, Univ Wis-Madison, 74. *Mem:* Am Phys Soc. *Res:* Unified theories of weak, electromagnetic and strong interactions such as nonabelian gauge theories, quark models and applications to new narrow resonance phenomena, perturbative quantum chromodynamics, grand unitied models, proton decay, renormalization group analysis of fermion masses and other predictions of unified theorie. *Mailing Add:* Lyman Lab Physics Harvard Univ Cambridge MA 02138

MACHACEK, MILOS, b Prague, Czech, Sept 11, 32; US citizen; m 52; c 2. ATOMIC PHYSICS. *Educ:* Univ Tex, BS, 58, MA, 60, PhD(physics), 64. *Prof Exp:* Staff res engr, AC Electronics Div, Mass, 64-69, STAFF RES ENGR, DELCO ELECTRONICS, GEN MOTORS CORP, 69- *Concurrent Pos:* Russ physics translr, Consult Bur, Inc, 67- *Mem:* Am Phys Soc. *Res:* Computational atomic and molecular physics; magnetic resonance; quantum electronics; underwater acoustics; electromagnetic wave propagation. *Mailing Add:* 6170 Manzanillo Dr Goleta CA 93117

MACHACEK, OLDRICH, b Nachod, Czech, Arp 3, 30; US citizen; m 54; c 3. CHEMISTRY OF EXPLOSIVES, PROPELLANTS. *Educ:* Univ Chem Technol, Prague, MS, 53, PhD(chem of propellants), 61. *Prof Exp:* Proj leader propellants, Res Inst Indust Chem, Pardubice, Czech, 54-69; res chemist org chem, Universal Oil Prod, 70-72; res scientist explosives, Atlas Powder Co, 72-78; DIR RES & DEVELOP EXPLOSIVES, NIPAK ENERGY CORP, 78- *Mem:* Am Chem Soc. *Res:* Chemistry of modern commerical explosives and propellants; watergels, emulsions, aluminised and permissible explosives; rocket propellants and double based smokeless powders. *Mailing Add:* Nipak Energy Corp 13601 Preston Rd Suite 1007W Dallas TX 75240

MACHADO, EMILIO ALFREDO, b Buenos Aires, Arg, Feb 12, 27. EXPERIMENTAL PATHOLOGY. *Educ:* Mariano Moreno Col, Arg, BD, 44; Univ Buenos Aires, Physician, 52, MD(path), 53. *Prof Exp:* Instr path, Univ Buenos Aires, 53-61, chief lab path, Clin Univ Hosp, 54-60; chief lab exp path, NIH, Inst Gastroenterol, Buenos Aires, 63-70; assoc investr exp path, Univ Buenos Aires, 70-73; res assoc prof exp path, 73-81, PROF, DEPT MED BIOL, COL MED, MEM RES CTR, UNIV TENN, KNOXVILLE, 81- *Mem:* AAAS; Reticuloendothelial Soc; Int Acad Path; NY Acad Sci. *Res:* Cancer research-matastasis. *Mailing Add:* Mem Res Ctr Univ of Tenn 1924 Alcoa Hwy Knoxville TN 37920

MCHAFFEY, DAVID GEORGE, entomology, plant pathology, see previous edition

MCHALE, EDWARD THOMAS, b Hazleton, Pa, Dec 10, 32; m 57; c 3. RESEARCH AND DEVELOPMENT MANAGEMENT. *Educ:* King's Col, Pa, BS, 54; Pa State Univ, PhD(fuel sci), 64. *Prof Exp:* Res chemist, Gen Chem Div, Allied Chem Corp, 54-58; chemist, Reaction Motors Div, Thiokol Chem Corp, 58-60; prin scientist, 64-72, MGR COMBUSTION & PHYS SCI DEPT, ATLANTIC RES CORP, 72- *Mem:* Am Chem Soc; Combustion Inst. *Res:* Fundamental combustion studies, combustion engineering projects, and physical and analytical chemistry. *Mailing Add:* Atlantic Res Corp Alexandria VA 22314

MCHALE, JOHN T, b New York, NY, Nov 2, 33; c 1. BOTANY, CYTOLOGY. *Educ:* Iona Col, BS, 55; Univ Tex, PhD(bot), 65. *Prof Exp:* Asst prof, Loyola Univ, La, 65-69, assoc prof biol, 69-74; BIOL WRITER, 74- *Concurrent Pos:* Sigma Xi grant-in-aid-of res, 67; consult cytol & cytogenetics, Gulf South Res Inst, La, 68-70 & 72-74; NIH training grant, Univ Calif, Berkeley, 70-71, res assoc, 71-72; res physiologist consult, Vet Admin Hosp, Martinez, Calif, 70-72. *Mem:* Am Physiol Soc. *Res:* Mechanisms of aging on the cellular level; bioenergetics of subcellular organelles; ultrastructure of plant cells; plant morphogenesis; cytology and cytogenetics. *Mailing Add:* 725 18th Ave San Francisco CA 94121

MACHALEK, MILTON DAVID, b Oenaville, Tex, July 30, 41; m 63; c 1. PHYSICS. *Educ:* Harvard Univ, AB, 63; Univ Chicago, MS, 68; Univ Tex, Austin, PhD(physics), 72. *Prof Exp:* Res asst nuclear physics, Argonne Nat Lab, 65-68; res scientist plasma physics, Univ Tex, Austin, 72-74; staff scientist plasma physics, Los Alamos Sci Lab, Controlled Thermonuclear Res Div, 74-78; assoc group leader accelerator design, Accelerator Technol Div, Los Alamos Nat Lab, 78-80; HEAD ENG, PRINCETON PLASMA PHYS LAB, 80- *Mem:* Am Phys Soc; Am Vacuum Soc; Inst Elec & Electronics Engrs. *Res:* Plasma physics; controlled thermonuclear research; high current particle accelerators. *Mailing Add:* Princeton Plasma Physics Lab PO Box 451 C-Site Princeton NJ 08544

MACHAMER, HAROLD EUGENE, b Tower City, Pa, Jan 29, 22; m 51; c 3. MICROBIOLOGY. *Educ:* Pa State Univ, BS, 42, MS, 48, PhD(bact, chem), 50. *Prof Exp:* Res microbiologist, Tex Co, 50-52; res microbiologist, 52-54, lab dir antibiotic develop, 54-60, asst dir, Microbiol Res Dept, 60-62, dir, Antibiotic & Microbial Tech Res Dept, 63-66, DIR BIOL RES & DEVELOP, PARKE, DAVIS & CO, 66- *Mem:* AAAS; Am Chem Soc; Am Soc Microbiol; Soc Indust Microbiol; NY Acad Sci. *Res:* Microbiological fermentation; microbial physiology. *Mailing Add:* Biol Res & Develop Dept Parke Davis & Co Detroit MI 48232

MCHARDY, GEORGE GORDON, b New Orleans, La, Mar 7, 10; m; c 3. MEDICINE. *Educ:* Spring Hill Col, BA, 32; Tulane Univ, MD, 36; Am Bd Internal Med, dipl & cert gastroenterol, 43. *Prof Exp:* Asst prof med, Tulane Univ La, 38-51; chief div gastroenterol, 60-71, assoc prof, 51-58, prof, 59-81, EMER PROF MED, SCH MED, LA STATE UNIV, NEW ORLEANS, 81- *Concurrent Pos:* Mem, World Cong Gastroenterol, 58-62; lectr, Univ Brazil, 60; sr vis physician, Charity Hosp. *Honors & Awards:* Rudolf Schindler Mem Award, Am Soc Gastrointestinal Endoscopy, 70. *Mem:* AMA; Am Gastroenterol Asn (treas, 53-59, vpres, 59-62, pres, 62); Am Soc Gastrointestinal Endoscopy (pres, 65); Am Col Physicians; Bockus Inst Soc Gastroenterol. *Res:* Gastroenterology. *Mailing Add:* Med Ctr of New Orleans 3638 St Charles Ave New Orleans LA 70115

MCHARGUE, CARL J(ACK), b Corbin, Ky, Jan 30, 26; m 60; c 3. PHYSICAL METALLURGY. *Educ:* Univ Ky, BS, 49, MS, 51, DrEng(phys metall), 53. *Prof Exp:* Res assoc, Univ Ky, 49-52; res metallurgist, Ky Res Found, 52-53; metallurgist, 53-59, mgr res sect, 59-79, MGR MAT SCI, METALL & CERAMICS DIV, OAK RIDGE NAT LAB, 79-; PROF CHEM & METALL ENG, UNIV TENN, 59- *Concurrent Pos:* Lectr, Univ Ky, 50-53 & Univ Tenn, 56-59. *Mem:* Fel Am Soc Metals; fel Metall Soc; Sigma Xi; Am Inst Mining, Metall & Petrol Engrs; Mat Res Soc. *Res:* plastic deformation of crystalline solids; radiation damage; ion implantation ceramics. *Mailing Add:* Metals & Ceramics Div Oak Ridge Nat Lab Oak Ridge TN 37830

MCHARRIS, WILLIAM CHARLES, b Knoxville, Tenn, Sept 12, 37; m 60; c 1. NUCLEAR CHEMISTRY. *Educ:* Oberlin Col, BA, 59; Univ Calif, Berkeley, PhD(nuclear chem), 65. *Prof Exp:* From asst prof to assoc prof, 65-71, PROF CHEM & PHYSICS, COL NATURAL SCI, MICH STATE UNIV, 71- *Concurrent Pos:* Consult, Heavy Elements Group, Argonne Nat Lab, 66-; sabbatical, Lawrence Berkeley Lab, Univ Calif, 71-72; Sloan fel, 72-76. *Mem:* AAAS; Am Phys Soc; Am Chem Soc; Sigma Xi. *Res:* Nuclear spectroscopy and reactions in actinides, lead region and deformed rare earths; on-line spectroscopy with cyclotron; beta-decay theory. *Mailing Add:* Dept of Chem Mich State Univ East Lansing MI 48823

MACHATTIE, LESLIE BLAKE, b Weihwei, China, Jan 29, 17; m 42; c 2. METEOROLOGY. *Educ:* Dalhousie Univ, BSc, 37, MSc, 39; Univ Toronto, MA, 40. *Prof Exp:* Meteorologist forecasting, Meteorol Serv Can, 41-51; meteorologist, Irish Meteorol Serv, Eire, 52-53; res scientist meteorol, Can Forestry Serv, 54- *Concurrent Pos:* Assoc ed, J Appl Meteorol, Am Meteorol Soc, 62-67; counr, Royal Meteorol Soc, Can Br, 63-66; Rapporteur Agrotopoclimatol, Comn Agr Meteorol World Meteorol Orgn, 67-71, mem, Working Group on appln of meteorol to forestry, 75-78. *Mem:* Can Meteorol Soc; Am Meteorol Soc. *Res:* The meteorology and climatology of forest fire occurrence, behavior and control; cumulus cloud seeding for fire suppression; topoclimatology. *Mailing Add:* 45 Corona Ave Rockcliffe Park Ottawa ON K1M 1K8 Can

MACHATTIE, LLOYD ELLIOT, b Changte, China, Jan 8, 15; m 52; c 3. PHYSICS. *Educ:* Dalhousie Univ, BSc, 36, MSc, 38; Univ Va, PhD(physics), 41. *Prof Exp:* Res physicist, Univ Toronto, 41-43; physicist, Appl Physics Lab, Johns Hopkins Univ, 43-45; res physicist, Univ Toronto, 45-48; physicist, Comput Devices Can, Ltd, Ottawa, 49-51; defence scientist, Defence & Civil Inst Environ Med, 51-79; RETIRED. *Mem:* Can Asn Physicists (secy, 47, treas, 48). *Res:* Electronics; environmental stress instrumentation. *Mailing Add:* Defence & Civil Inst Environ Med PO Box 2000 Downsview ON M3M 3B9 Can

MACHATTIE, LORNE ALLISTER, b Anyang, China, Apr 7, 25; Can citizen; div; c 3. BACTERIAL VIRUSES, PLASMIDS. *Educ:* Univ Toronto, BA, 49; Univ Western Ont, MSc, 55; Univ Buffalo, PhD(physiol), 61. *Prof Exp:* Instr physiol, Sch Med, Univ Buffalo, 61; res assoc, Johns Hopkins Univ, 65-67; lectr biol chem, Harvard Univ, 67-69; assoc prof biophys, Univ Toronto, 69-76; SR RES ASSOC MICROBIOL, UNIV CHICAGO, 76- *Concurrent Pos:* Teaching fel physiol, Sch Med, Univ Buffalo, 53-61; fel biophys, Johns Hopkins Univ, 61-65; Damon Runyon cancer res fel, 62-64; USPHS career develop award, 65-67. *Mem:* Fel AAAS; Biophys Soc; Sigma Xi. *Res:* Electron microscopy; molecular genetics of bacteriophage chromosomes; transposition functions. *Mailing Add:* Dept of Microbiol 920 E 58th St Chicago IL 60637

MACHEL, ALBERT R, b Dallas, Tex, Apr 17, 20; m 60; c 1. ANALYTICAL CHEMISTRY, INORGANIC CHEMISTRY. *Educ:* NTex Teachers Col, BS, 46; Univ Tex, MA, 49; Tex A&M Univ, PhD(chem), 58. *Prof Exp:* Jr chemist, Helium Plant, US Bur Mines, Tex, 42-44; instr chem, Hardin Jr Col, 46-48, asst prof, 50-51; asst prof, Tex Col Arts & Indust, 52-55 & ETex State Col, 57-58; asst prof, 58-64, ASSOC PROF CHEM, STEPHEN F AUSTIN STATE UNIV, 64- *Mem:* Am Chem Soc. *Res:* Organic chemistry; biochemistry. *Mailing Add:* Dept of Chem Stephen F Austin State Univ Box 6164 Nacogdoches TX 75962

MACHELL, GREVILLE, b Blackburn, Eng, Nov 19, 29; m 52; c 4. ORGANIC CHEMIS7RY, TEXTILE CHEMISTRY. *Educ:* Univ London, BSc, 48, Hons, 50, PhD(org chem), 52. *Prof Exp:* Res chemist, Brit Rayon Res Asn, 55-59 & Brit Celanese Ltd, 60-61; res chemist, Deering Milliken Res Corp, 61-64, dept mgr radiation chem, 64-67, mgr tech opers div, 67-69, gen mgr decorative fabrics div, 69-75, dir develop, Decorative Fabrics Div, Deering Milliken Inc, Ga, 75-76, RES ASSOC, MILLIKEN RES CORP, 76- *Mem:* Am Chem Soc. *Res:* Reaction mechanisms; alkaline degradation of carbohydrates; chemical modification of textile fibers; specialty chemicals; radiation-initiated graft polymerization. *Mailing Add:* Milliken Res Corp Iron Ore Rd Spartanburg SC 29304

MACHEMEHL, JERRY LEE, b Bryan, Tex, Jan 8, 38; m 59; c 3. COASTAL ENGINEERING, OCEAN ENGINEERING. *Educ:* Tex A&M Univ, BSCE, 62, MSCE, 68, BSARCO, 70, PhD(civil eng), 70. *Prof Exp:* Eng res assoc, Tex A&M Univ, 65-68, instr civil eng, 69-70; civil engr, Coastal Eng Res Ctr, 68-69; from asst prof to assoc prof civil eng, 70-78, ASSOC PROF MARINE SCI & ENG, NC STATE UNIV, 78- *Concurrent Pos:* Prin investr, Sea Grant Prog, Nat Oceanic & Atmospheric Admin, 73-74 & 78-80, Univ NC Water Resources Inst, 73-74. *Honors & Awards:* Exten Serv Award, NC State Univ, 73. *Mem:* Am Soc Civil Engrs; Sigma Xi. *Mailing Add:* Dept of Marine Sci & Eng NC State Univ Raleigh NC 27650

MACHEMER, PAUL EWERS, b Romney, WVa, Jan 30, 19; m 41; c 3. ANALYTICAL CHEMISTRY. *Educ:* Princeton Univ, AB, 40; Univ Pa, MS, 43, PhD(chem), 49. *Prof Exp:* From chemist to chief chemist, Anal Lab, Warner Co, 41-44; from jr chemist to sr shift supvr, Manhattan Proj, Carbide & Carbon Chem Co, 44-45; from asst prof to assoc prof, Villanova Univ, 49-55; from asst prof to assoc prof, 55-67, PROF CHEM, COLBY COL, 67- *Concurrent Pos:* Vis prof, Rosemont Col, 51-52. *Mem:* AAAS; Am Chem Soc; Electrochem Soc. *Res:* Inorganic analytical chemistry; instrumental analysis. *Mailing Add:* Dept of Chem Colby Col Waterville ME 04901

MCHENRY, HENRY MALCOLM, b Los Angeles, Calif, May 19, 44; m 66. BIOLOGICAL ANTHROPOLOGY. *Educ:* Univ Calif, Davis, BA, 66, MA, 67; Harvard Univ, PhD(anthrop), 72. *Prof Exp:* Asst prof, 71-77, assoc prof, 77-81, PROF ANTHROP, UNIV CALIF, DAVIS, 81- *Mem:* AAAS; Sigma Xi; Am Asn Phys Anthrop; Am Anthrop Asn; Brit Soc Study Human Biol. *Res:* Paleoanthropology; australopithecine postcranial anatomy. *Mailing Add:* Dept of Anthrop Univ of Calif Davis CA 95616

MCHENRY, HUGH LANSDEN, b Baxter, Tenn, Aug 19, 37; m 63; c 2. STATISTICS, MATHEMATICS. *Educ:* Tenn Technol Univ, BS, 60; George Peabody Col, MA, 61, PhD(math), 70. *Prof Exp:* Instr math, Okla Christian Col, 61-63, asst prof, 65-68; from asst prof to assoc prof, 68-78, PROF MATH, MEMPHIS STATE UNIV, 78- *Mem:* Am Statist Asn; Math Asn Am. *Res:* Mathematics and statistics education. *Mailing Add:* Dept of Math Sci Memphis State Univ Memphis TN 38152

MCHENRY, K(EITH) W(ELLES), JR, b Champaign, Ill, Apr 6, 28; m 52; c 2. CHEMICAL ENGINEERING. *Educ:* Univ Ill, BS, 51; Princeton Univ, PhD(chem eng), 58. *Prof Exp:* Chem engr, Whiting Res Labs, Standard Oil Co, Ind, 55-58, group leader, 58-62, proj mgr, Res & Develop Dept, Am Oil Co, 62-66, res assoc, 66-67, asst dir, 67-70, dir process & anal res, Whiting Res Labs, Am Oil Co, 70-74, mgr process res, Naperville, Ill, 74-75, VPRES RES & DEVELOP, AMOCO, NAPERVILLE, ILL, 75- *Honors & Awards:* Charles D Hurd lectr, Northwestern Univ, 81. *Mem:* AAAS; Am Chem Soc; Am Inst Chem Eng. *Res:* Heterogeneous catalysis; cracking; reforming; engineering kinetics; reactor design; research management. *Mailing Add:* PO Box 400 Naperville IL 60566

MCHENRY, KELLY DAVID, b Williamsport, Pa, Feb 24, 52. FERROELECTRICS, COMPOSITES. *Educ:* Pa State Univ, BS, 74, MS, 76, PhD(ceramic sci), 78. *Prof Exp:* Prin res scientist, Honeywell Corp Technol Ctr, 78-81, PRIN DEVELOP ENGR, HONEYWELL CERAMICS CTR, 81- *Mem:* Am Ceramic Soc. *Res:* Processing and development of ferroelectric ceramics & lightweight composite ceramics to enhance mechanical dielectric and optical properties; novel surface finishing techniques for polishing of ceramics. *Mailing Add:* Honeywell Ceramics Ctr 5121 Winnetka Ave N New Hope MN 55428

MCHENRY, WILLIAM EARL, b Camden, Ark, July 22, 50; m 76. ORGANIC CHEMISTRY, PESTICIDE CHEMISTRY. *Educ:* Southern Ark Univ, BS, 72; Miss State Univ, PhD(org chem), 77. *Prof Exp:* Teaching asst, 72-75, res asst, 75-76, teaching asst, 76-77, ASST PROF ORG CHEM, MISS STATE UNIV, 77- *Concurrent Pos:* Prin investr alternative toxicants contract, Miss Dept Agr & Com, 78-79. *Mem:* Am Chem Soc; AAAS. *Res:* Synthesis of organophosphorous compounds; chemical and physical properties of small ring heterocycles. *Mailing Add:* Dept of Org Synthesis Drawer CH Miss State Univ Mississippi State MS 39762

MACHIA, BOLLERA MUDDAPPA, b Coorg, India, Aug 8, 33; US citizen; m 66; c 2. PLANT PHYSIOLOGY. *Educ:* Univ Poona, BSc, 60; Kans State Univ, MS, 62, PhD(plant physiol), 65. *Prof Exp:* Instr food technol, Kans State Univ, 62-65; fel plant nutrit, Univ Calif, Berkeley, 65-67; res plant physiologist, Univ Calif, Riverside, 67-68; PROF BIOCHEM & CELL PHYSIOL, ST MARY'S UNIV, TEX, 68- *Concurrent Pos:* Consult, Wilco Peanut Co, Tex, 72- *Mem:* Am Chem Soc; Am Soc Plant Physiologists; Sigma Xi; Am Inst Biol Sci; AAAS. *Res:* Environmental factors, particularly plant nutrient elements and key enzymes of nitrogen metabolism for increased protein synthesis in rice plants and evaluation of the quality of rice protein as affected by this treatment. *Mailing Add:* Dept of Life Sci St Mary's Univ San Antonio TX 78284

MACHIELE, DELWYN EARL, b Zeeland, Mich, Dec 30, 38; m 62; c 2. ORGANIC CHEMISTRY. *Educ:* Hope Col, AB, 60; Univ Ill, Urbana, PhD(org chem), 64. *Prof Exp:* RES ASSOC, EASTMAN KODAK CO, 64- *Mem:* Am Chem Soc. *Mailing Add:* Res Lab Eastman Kodak Co 1669 Lake Ave Bldg 82A Rochester NY 14650

MACHIN, J, b Herne Bay, Eng, June 29, 37; m 61; c 3. COMPARATIVE PHYSIOLOGY. *Educ:* Univ London, BSc, 59, PhD(zool), 62. *Prof Exp:* From asst prof to assoc prof, 62-78, PROF ZOOL, UNIV TORONTO, 78- *Concurrent Pos:* Vis assoc prof, Univ Wash. *Honors & Awards:* T H Huxley Award, Zool Soc London, 62. *Mem:* AAAS; Am Physiol Soc; Marine Biol Asn UK; Brit Soc Exp Biol; Zool Soc London. *Res:* Comparative physiology of terrestrial moist skinned animals, particularly physics and physiology of evaporation; water transport in insects; osmotic regulation in cells. *Mailing Add:* Dept of Zool Univ of Toronto Toronto ON M5S 1A1 Can

MACHLEDER, WARREN HARVEY, b New York, NY, Aug 2, 43; m 67; c 1. ORGANIC CHEMISTRY. *Educ:* NY Univ, BA, 64; Ind Univ, Bloomington, PhD(chem), 68. *Prof Exp:* res chemist, 68-74, proj leader, 74-78, mem staff mkt res, 78-80, MKT PLANNING MGR, PETROL CHEM, ROHM & HAAS CO, 80- *Mem:* Am Chem Soc. *Res:* Allene oxidations; petroleum additives, antiwear agents and carburetor detergents. *Mailing Add:* Rohm & Haas Co Independence Mall West Philadelphia PA 19105

MACHLIN, E(UGENE) S(OLOMON), b New York, NY, Dec 29, 20; m 43, 60; c 3. MATERIALS SCIENCE. *Educ:* City Col New York, BME, 42; Case Inst Technol, MS, 48; Mass Inst Technol, ScD, 51. *Prof Exp:* Aeronaut res scientist, Nat Adv Comt Aeronaut, 42-48; res assoc metall, Mass Inst Technol, 48-50, asst prof, 51; from asst prof to assoc prof, 51-58, PROF METALL, COLUMBIA UNIV, 58- *Concurrent Pos:* Guggenheim fel and Fulbright lectr, Italy, 65-66. *Honors & Awards:* Mathewson Gold Medal, Am Inst Mining, Metall & Petrol Engrs, 54. *Mem:* Am Soc Metals; Am Inst Mining, Metall & Petrol Engrs. *Res:* Theory of alloy phases; prediction of phase diagrams. *Mailing Add:* 1106 SW Mudd Bldg Columbia Univ 520 W 120th St New York NY 10027

MACHLIN, LAWRENCE JUDAH, b New York, NY, June 24, 27; m 53; c 3. NUTRITIONAL BIOCHEMISTRY. *Educ:* Cornell Univ, BS, 48, MNS, 49; Georgetown Univ, PhD(biochem), 54. *Prof Exp:* Poultry nutritionist, USDA, 49-50, biochemist, 50-53, biochemist, Agr Res Serv, 53-56; biochemist, Monsanto Co, 56-73; SR RES GROUP CHIEF, HOFFMANN-LA ROCHE, 73- *Concurrent Pos:* Lectr, Washington Univ, 69-72; adj prof nutrit, NY Univ, 77- & Cornell Univ Med Col, 79- *Mem:* Am Inst Nutrit; Endocrine Soc; Am Soc Clin Nutrit; Soc Exp Biol & Med; NY Acad Sci. *Res:* Biochemical function and nutritional role of vitamin E, vitamin A, ascorbic acid, carotene, antioxidants and fatty acids and amino acids; regulation and function of growth hormone in farm animals. *Mailing Add:* Hoffmann-La Roche Inc 340 Kingsland St Nutley NJ 07110

MACHLIS, SAMUEL, b New York, NY, May 25, 07; m 39; c 1. TEXTILE CHEMISTRY. *Educ:* NY Univ, BS, 30, MS, 31, PhD(biochem), 35. *Prof Exp:* Asst, Wash Sq Col, NY Univ, 31-35; asst res, Benton & Bowles, 35-36; chief chemist, Sedley Chem Co, 41-71; V PRES, ANSCOTT CHEM INDUST, INC, 71- *Concurrent Pos:* Dir res, O D Chem Corp, 44-46; res dir, Emtec Res Assocs, 47-50; pres, Stamford Chem Co, 50- *Mem:* Assoc Am Chem Soc; assoc Am Oil Chem Soc. *Res:* Synthetic detergents; emulsifiers; anti-caking of synthetics; packaging synthetics; role of glutathiene in the metabolism of yeast. *Mailing Add:* 179 Woodlawn Ave New Rochelle NY 10804

MACHLOWITZ, ROY ALAN, b Brooklyn, NY, Apr 16, 21; m 49; c 2. ANALYTICAL BIOCHEMISTRY, VIROLOGY. *Educ:* Brooklyn Col, AB, 41. *Prof Exp:* Jr chemist, US Naval Boiler & Turbine Lab, 42-45, chemist, Naval Air Exp Sta, 45-51; res assoc antibiotics, 51-56 & virus & tissue cult res, 56-64, SR RES BIOCHEMIST, MERCK SHARP & DOHME RES LABS, 64- *Mem:* AAAS; Am Chem Soc. *Res:* Purification of antibiotics; purification and assay of viruses. *Mailing Add:* 520 Laverock Rd Glenside PA 19038

MACHLUP, STEFAN, b Vienna, Austria, July 1, 27; nat US; m 61, 71; c 2. PHYSICS. *Educ:* Swarthmore Col, BA, 47; Yale Univ, MS, 49, PhD, 52. *Prof Exp:* Asst, Yale Univ, 49-51; mem tech staff, Bell Tel Labs, Inc, 52-53; res assoc physics, Univ Ill, 53-55; mem sci staff, Van der Waals Lab, Amsterdam, 55-56; asst prof, 56-61, ASSOC PROF PHYSICS, CASE WESTERN RESERVE UNIV, 61- *Concurrent Pos:* Consult, Res Ctr, Clevite Corp, 57-62, Educ Serv Inc, Auckland, NZ, 61, Ibadan, Nigeria, 62 & Watertown, Mass, 64-65; NSF sci fac fel, Univ Liverpool, 62-63; consult, Mass Inst Technol, 68, 69. *Mem:* AAAS; Am Phys Soc; Am Asn Physics Teachers. *Res:* Theory of solids; imperfections in metals; polaron mobility; fluctuations and irreversible processes; noise in semiconductors; oscillatory chemical reactions; underwater sound scattering. *Mailing Add:* Dept of Physics Case Western Reserve Univ Cleveland OH 44106

MACHNE, XENIA, b Trieste, Italy, Sept 28, 21. PHYSIOLOGY. *Educ:* Univ Padua, MD, 46. *Prof Exp:* Asst physiol, Univ Parma, 47-48; asst, Univ Bologna, 48-51; res assoc physiol, Univ Ore, 56-58; asst prof pharmacol, Univ Ill, 58-62; assoc prof physiol, Sch Med, Tulane Univ, 62-71; prof pharmacol, Univ Minn, Minneapolis, 71-76; RETIRED. *Concurrent Pos:* Brit Coun scholar, Univ Col, Univ London, 51-53; Fulbright fel, Univ Calif, Los Angeles, 53-55. *Mem:* Am Physiol Soc. *Res:* Neurophysiology; neuropharmacology; electrophysiological methods; microelectrode techniques. *Mailing Add:* Via Celesti 13 Desenzano 25015 Italy

MACHOL, ROBERT E(NGEL), b New York, NY, Oct 16, 17; m 46; c 2. SYSTEMS ANALYSIS. *Educ:* Harvard Univ, BA, 38; Univ Mich, MS, 53, PhD(chem), 57. *Prof Exp:* Tech ed, Opers Eval Group, US Dept Navy, 49-50; sci ed, Am Peoples Encyclop, 50-51; syst engr, Willow Run Res Ctr, Univ Mich, 51-58; prof elec eng, Purdue Univ, 58-61; vpres, Conductron Corp, 61-64; prof systs eng & head dept, Univ Ill, Chicago, 64-67; PROF SYSTS, GRAD SCH MGT, NORTHWESTERN UNIV, EVANSTON, 67- *Concurrent Pos:* Lectr, Waseda Univ, Japan, 57, Univ Mich, 57-58 & Europ Inst Bus Admin, France, 71; consult, indust, govt & educ. *Mem:* Fel AAAS; sr mem Inst Elec & Electronics Engrs; Opers Res Soc Am (pres, 71-72); Inst Mgt Sci. *Res:* Design, analysis and evaluation of large-scale and complex systems. *Mailing Add:* Grad Sch of Mgt Northwestern Univ Evanston IL 60201

MACHONIS, ALVIN A(NTHONY), metallurgy, materials science, see previous edition

MACHOVER, MAURICE, b New York, NY, Dec 5, 31; m 64. MATHEMATICAL ANALYSIS. *Educ:* Brooklyn Col, BS, 56; Columbia Univ, MA, 58; NY Univ, MS, 60, PhD(math), 63. *Prof Exp:* Lectr math & physics, Brooklyn Col, 56-58; asst math, NY Univ, 58-63, asst res scientist, 63; asst prof math, Fairleigh Dickinson Univ, 64-65, assoc prof & chmn dept, 65-67; ASSOC PROF MATH, ST JOHN'S UNIV, NY, 67- *Concurrent Pos:* Asst physics, Columbia Univ, 56-58. *Mem:* Am Math Soc; Math Asn Am; Asn Symbolic Logic; Soc Indust & Appl Math. *Res:* Eigenfunction expansions as applied to self adjoint differential and integral equations and their extentions to non-self adjoint problems. *Mailing Add:* Dept of Math St John's Univ Jamaica NY 11439

MACHT, MARTIN BENZYL, b Baltimore, Md, Aug 31, 18; m 39. PHYSIOLOGY. *Educ:* Johns Hopkins Univ, AB, 39, PhD(neurophysiol), 42, MD, 45. *Prof Exp:* Asst instr psychol, Johns Hopkins Univ, 39-42, instr physiol, Med Sch, 42-45; intern & asst resident med, Jewish Hosp, Cincinnati, Ohio, 45-46; physiologist & sta surgeon, Climatic Res Lab, Mass, 46-48; instr pharmacol, 48-54, asst clin prof med, 54-77, ASST PROF PHYSIOL, COL MED, UNIV CINCINNATI, 54-, PROF MED, 77- *Concurrent Pos:* Chief res, Jewish Hosp, 48-49, dir med educ, 49-50; co-dir internal med, Rollman Receiving Hosp. *Mem:* Am Physiol Soc; assoc Am Psychol Asn; AMA; Am Diabetes Asn; Am Geriat Soc. *Res:* Neurophysiology; localization of function in central nervous system; temperature regulation; peripheral blood flow; frost bite; neural basis of emotion; decerebrate preparations in the chronic state; psychopharmacology; psychosomatic medicine; renal disease. *Mailing Add:* Dept of Physiol Univ of Cincinnati Col of Med Cincinnati OH 45219

MACHTINGER, LAWRENCE ARNOLD, b St Louis, Mo, Mar 11, 36; m 64; c 2. MATHEMATICS EDUCATION, EDUCATIONAL COMPUTERS. *Educ:* Wash Univ, BSChE, 59, AM, 63, PhD(math), 65. *Prof Exp:* Asst prof math, Webster Col, 64-65; asst prof, St Louis Univ, 65-66; asst prof, Ill Inst Technol, 66-72; dir sci & math proj, ASSOC PROF MATH, PURDUE UNIV, N CENT CAMPUS, 72- *Concurrent Pos:* Dir, Curric Improv & Teacher Training Inst Proj; consult, high sch math; consult, Madison Proj, Syracuse Univ & Webster Col, 64-72; mem math adv coun, State of Ind, 74-76. *Mem:* Am Math Soc; Math Asn Am; Nat Coun Teachers Math. *Res:* Group theory and ordered rings. *Mailing Add:* 2930 Alexander Crescent Flossmoor IL 60422

MCHUGH, ALEXANDER E(DWARD), b Goodhue, Minn, Mar 28, 04; m 41; c 3. METALLURGY. *Educ:* Univ Minn, BMetE, 40. *Prof Exp:* Asst, Univ Minn, 40-41; instr metall, State Col Wash, 41-42; carbon plant foreman, Aluminum Co Am, 42-43; res engr, Battelle Mem Inst, 43-47; from assoc prof to prof metall, SDak Sch Mines & Technol, 47-69; mill metallurgist, 69-71; CONSULT, 71- *Concurrent Pos:* Consult metallurgist, US Bur Mines, 58-60; Fulbright lectr, Nat Univ Eng, Peru, 60. *Mem:* Am Soc Eng Educ. *Res:* Thermodynamics of metals in higher temperature ranges; extractive metallurgy. *Mailing Add:* 1911 Red Dale Dr Rapid City SD 57701

MCHUGH, JAMES ANTHONY, JR, b Stockton, Calif, Oct 7, 37; m 57; c 4. SURFACE ANALYSIS, SECONDARY ION MASS SPECTROMETRY. *Educ:* Univ Pac, BS, 59; Univ Calif, Berkeley, PhD(chem), 63. *Prof Exp:* Phys chemist, 63-74, mgr, Mass Spectrometry Res & Develop, 74-75, MGR, CHEM LAB, KNOLLS ATOMIC POWER LAB, GEN ELEC CO, 75- *Mem:* Am Soc Mass Spectrometry; Am Chem Soc; Am Inst Chemists. *Res:* Mass spectrometry; systematics of nuclear fission; medium energy ion-surface interactions and secondary positive ion emission; ionization phenomena; surface analysis; secondary ion mass spectrometry; ion microprobe; microbeam analysis. *Mailing Add:* Chem Lab Knolls Atomic Power Lab Gen Elec Co PO Box 1072 Schenectady NY 12301

MCHUGH, JOHN LAURENCE, b Vancouver, BC, Nov 24, 11; nat US; m 41; c 3. FISHERIES MANAGEMENT. *Educ:* Univ BC, BA, 36, MA, 38; Univ Calif, Los Angeles, PhD(zool), 50. *Prof Exp:* Asst, Univ BC, 36-38; fishery biologist, Pac Biol Sta, BC, 38-41; asst ichthyol, Scripps Inst, Univ Calif, 47-48, res assoc, 48-51; dir, Va Fisheries Lab, 51-59; chief div biol res, Bur Commercial Fisheries, US Fish & Wildlife Serv, 59-63, asst dir biol res, 63-66, dept dir bur, 66-68; actg dir, Off Marine Resources, US Dept Interior, 68-70; head, Off Int Decade Ocean Explor, NSF, 70; PROF MARINE RESOURCES, MARINE SCI RES CTR, STATE UNIV NY STONY BROOK, 70- *Concurrent Pos:* Prof marine biol, Col William & Mary, 51-59; mem, Nat Res Coun, 65-70; adv comn marine resources to dir gen, Food & Agr Orgn, 66-70; mem US nat sect, Int Biol Prog, 67-70; comt int marine sci affairs policy, Nat Acad Sci, 70-74; US comnr, Inter-Am Trop Tuna Comn, 60-70; vchmn, Int Whaling Comn, 68-71, chmn, 71-72; mem hard clam adv comt, Nassau-Suffolk Regional Marine Resources Coun, 73-; consult, Town of Islip, NY & Islip Town Shellfish Mgt Comn, 74-78; mem, Mid Atlantic Fishery Mgt Coun, 76-79. *Mem:* AAAS; Am Inst Biol Sci; Am Fisheries Soc; Inst Fishery Res Biol. *Res:* Oceanography; fishery biology and management; resolution of social-political impediments to application of scientific knowledge in fishery utilization and management. *Mailing Add:* Marine Sci Res Ctr State Univ of NY Stony Brook NY 11794

MCHUGH, KENNETH LAURENCE, b Brooklyn, NY, Mar 22, 27; m 53; c 5. ORGANIC CHEMISTRY. *Educ:* Hofstra Col, BA, 51; Univ Conn, PhD(chem), 59. *Prof Exp:* Jr res chemist, Evans Res & Develop Corp, 51-53; res chemist, Conn Hard Rubber Co, 53-56; asst instr chem, Univ Conn, 56-58; sr res chemist, 58-60, res group leader, Spec Proj Dept, 60-61 & Org Chem Div, 61-64, proj mgr org develop dept, 64-66, sr proj mgr, 66-68, proj mgr commercial develop, Chemstrand Res Ctr, New Enterprises Div, 68-71, mgr commercial develop, New Enterprises Div, 71-77, MGR NEW VENTURES DEVELOP, CORP RES & DEVELOP, MONSANTO CO, 77- *Mem:* Am Chem Soc; Am Soc Lubrication Engrs; Coord Res Coun. *Res:* High temperature stable fluids, principally those derived from organometallic, organophosphorus and polyaromatic ether chemistry for use as turbine lubricants, lubricant additives, power transmission fluids and thermodynamic fluids for Rankine and Brayton power cycles; air pollution control by catalytic processes. *Mailing Add:* G5ED New Ventures Develop Monsanto Co St Louis MO 63166

MCHUGH, PAUL RODNEY, b Lawrence, Mass, May 21, 31; m 59; c 3. NEUROLOGY, PSYCHIATRY. *Educ:* Harvard Univ, AB, 52, MD, 56. *Prof Exp:* Intern med, Peter Bent Brigham Hosp, 56-57; res neurol, Mass Gen Hosp, 57-60; clin asst psychiat, Maudsley Hosp, London, Eng, 60-61; res asst neuroendocrinol, Walter Reed Army Inst Res, 61-64; asst prof neurol & psychiat, Med Col, Cornell Univ, 64-71, prof psychiat, 71-73; prof psychiat & chmn dept, Med Sch, Univ Ore, 73-75; CHMN & PSYCHIATRIST-IN-CHIEF DEPT PSYCHIAT & BEHAV SCI, SCH MED, JOHNS HOPKINS UNIV, 75- *Concurrent Pos:* Clin dir & supvr psychiat educ, Westchester Div, New York Hosp-Cornell Med Ctr, 69-73. *Mem:* Am Psychiat Asn; Am Neurol Asn; Am Physiol Soc; Harvey Soc; Am Psychopath Asn. *Res:* Neural mechanisms of visceral, endocrine and behavioral control. *Mailing Add:* Dept of Psychiat & Behav Sci Johns Hopkins Univ Hosp Baltimore MD 21205

MCHUGH, RICHARD B, b Villard, Minn, Oct 25, 23; m 51; c 5. BIOMETRICS, BIOSTATISTICS. *Educ:* Univ Minn, PhD, 55. *Prof Exp:* Assoc prof psychol statist, Iowa State Univ, 50-56; assoc prof, 56-62, dir biomet, 68-71, PROF BIOMET, UNIV MINN, MINNEAPOLIS, 62- *Concurrent Pos:* Nat Inst Gen Med Sci fel, Univ Calif, Berkeley, 64-65; vis scholar, Univ London, 71-72; consult, Dept Med & Surg, Vet Admin; mem pancreatic cancer study sect, Nat Cancer Inst, 74-78; mem oncol adv comt, Food & Drug Admin, 77-; Int Union Against Cancer res fel, Univ Oxford, 78-79; ed, The Am J Epidemiol, 80- *Mem:* Hon fel AAAS; Pop Asn Am; hon fel Am Statist Asn; hon fel Am Pub Health Asn; Biomet Soc. *Res:* Research design in the health and life sciences; mathematical demography; epidemetrics; biomathematical models in assay; biostatistics in health services research; cancer clinical trials and surveys. *Mailing Add:* Sch of Pub Health Univ of Minn Mayo Box 197 Minneapolis MN 55455

MCHUGH, STUART LAWRENCE, b San Francisco, Calif, Nov 7, 49. GEOPHYSICS, MATERIALS SCIENCE. *Educ:* Univ Nev, Reno, BS, 71, BS, 72; Stanford Univ, MS, 74, MS, 76, PhD(geophys), 77. *Prof Exp:* Geophysicist fracture mech, SRI Int, 77-81; GEOPHYSICIST, LOCKHEED CORP, 81- *Concurrent Pos:* Consult, SRI Int, 81- *Mem:* Am Geophys Union; Am Phys Soc; Int Soc Rock Mech. *Res:* Fracture mechanics. *Mailing Add:* Lockheed 0/52-35 Bldg 204 3251 Hanover St Palo Alto CA 94304

MACHUSKO, ANDREW JOSEPH, JR, b Hiller, Pa, Dec 31, 37; m 62; c 2. MATHEMATICS. *Educ:* Calif State Col, Pa, BS, 59; Univ Ga, MA, 64, PhD(math), 68. *Prof Exp:* Teacher high sch, Ohio, 59-62; instr math, Univ Ga, 67-68; asst prof, Univ Tenn, Knoxville, 68-70; assoc prof, 70-71, PROF MATH, CALIF STATE COL, PA, 71- *Mem:* Math Asn Am. *Res:* Topology; algebra. *Mailing Add:* Dept of Math Calif State Col California PA 15419

MACIAG, THOMAS EDWARD, molecular biology, see previous edition

MACIAG, WILLIAM JOHN, JR, b Rome, NY, May 28, 36; m 58; c 2. MICROBIOLOGY. *Educ:* Univ Buffalo, BS, 57; Syracuse Univ, MS, 59, PhD(microbiol), 63. *Prof Exp:* Asst instr microbiol, Syracuse Univ, 59-63; res microbiologist, 63-72, SR RES MICROBIOLOGIST, STINE LAB, E I DU PONT DE NEMOURS & CO, INC, 72- *Mem:* AAAS; Soc Indust Microbiol; Am Soc Microbiol. *Res:* Pharmaceutical drug research; intermediary metabolism; autotrophic mechanisms. *Mailing Add:* Stine Lab E I du Pont de Nemours & Co Inc Newark DE 19711

MACIAK, GEORGE M, b Poland, Sept 14, 21; nat US; m 47; c 2. MICROCHEMISTRY. *Educ:* Swiss Fed Inst Technol, ChemEng, 45; DSci, Tech Univ Gdansk, Poland, 79. *Prof Exp:* Anal chemist, Exp Labs, Bally Shoe Ltd, Switz, 47-49; microanalyst, Swiss Fed Inst Technol, 49-50 & Micro-Tech Labs, Ill, 50-52; microanalyst, 52-67, SR MICROANAL CHEMIST, LILLY RES LABS, 67- *Mem:* Am Chem Soc; AAAS; Am Microchem Soc; Asn Swiss Microchemists. *Res:* Structure elucidation of natural products, alcaloids and antibiotics; new procedures for microanalysis; automation and computerization of micro analytical procedures. *Mailing Add:* Lilly Res Labs Div Eli Lilly & Co Indianapolis IN 46285

MACIAS, EDWARD S, b Milwaukee, Wis, Feb 21, 44; m 67; c 2. NUCLEAR CHEMISTRY, RADIOCHEMISTRY. *Educ:* Colgate Univ, AB, 66; Mass Inst Technol, PhD(nuclear chem), 70. *Prof Exp:* Asst prof, 70-76, ASSOC PROF CHEM, WASHINGTON UNIV, 76- *Concurrent Pos:* Consult, Argonne Nat Lab, 67, US Dept Transp, 75-76 & Meteorol Res Inc, 75-; vis scientist, Lawrence Livermore Lab, Univ Calif, 71; vis prof, Calif Inst Technol, 78-79. *Mem:* AAAS; Sigma Xi; Am Phys Soc; Am Chem Soc; Air Pollution Control Asn. *Res:* Aerosol chemistry and physics; nuclear structure studies; atomic structure studies via x-ray spectroscopy; atmospheric chemistry; effects of air pollution; visibility and atmospheric optics; air pollution. *Mailing Add:* Dept of Chem Washington Univ St Louis MO 63130

MACIEL, GARY EMMET, b Niles, Calif, Jan 18, 35; m 56; c 2. PHYSICAL CHEMISTRY. *Educ:* Univ Calif, Berkeley, BS, 56; Mass Inst Technol, PhD(chem), 60. *Prof Exp:* Res asst chem, Mass Inst Technol, 59-60, NSF fel, 60-61; from asst prof to prof, Univ Calif, Davis, 61-70; PROF CHEM, COLO STATE UNIV, 71- *Mem:* AAAS; Am Chem Soc; Am Phys Soc. *Res:* Nuclear magnetic resonance and its application to chemical problems, particularly involving solid samples using the less common nuclei; relationships between high magnetic resonance parameters; fossil fuels. *Mailing Add:* Dept of Chem Colo State Univ Ft Collins CO 80521

MCILHENNY, HUGH M, b Gettysburg, Pa, Sept 25, 38; m 62; c 2. DRUG REGULATORY AFFAIRS, DRUG METABOLISM. *Educ:* Pa State Univ, BS, 60; Univ Mich, MS, 64, PhD(pharm, chem), 66. *Prof Exp:* Res asst antibiotics, Parke-Davis & Co, Inc, 60-62; anal chemist, 66-75, res investr, 75-79, REGULATORY AFFAIRS LIAISON, PFIZER, INC, 79- *Mem:* Am Soc Pharmacol & Exp Therapeut. *Res:* Fate of foreign substances in biological systems; factors influencing drug metabolism; drug bioavailability; development of assay methods for the measurement of drugs and their metabolites. *Mailing Add:* Cent Res Dept Clin Res Pfizer Inc Groton CT 06340

MCILHENNY, WILLIAM FRANKLIN, chemical engineering, see previous edition

MCILRATH, THOMAS JAMES, b Dowagiac, Mich, May 10, 38; m 62; c 2. VACUUM ULTRAVIOLET RADIATION PHYSICS. *Educ:* Mich State Univ, BS, 60; Princeton Univ, PhD(physics), 66. *Prof Exp:* Res fel astrophysics, Harvard Col Observ, 67-70, res assoc, 70-73; vis assoc prof, 73-74, assoc prof, 74-81, PROF, INST PHYS SCI & TECHNOL, UNIV MD, 81- *Concurrent Pos:* Lectr, Astron Dept, Harvard Univ, 70-73; staff physicist, Nat Bur Standards, Gaithersberg, Md, 74- *Honors & Awards:* Indust Res-100 Award, Indust Res Mag Inc, 80; Silver Medal, US Dept Com, 80. *Mem:* Optical Soc Am; Am Phys Soc. *Res:* Atomic and molecular structure; high resolution laser spectroscopy; vacuum ultraviolet spectroscopy; non-linear mixing in gases; generation of coherent vacuum ultraviolet radiation; photochemistry and spectroscopy of small molecules; atmospheric remote sensing; optical techniques for study of atomic structure; laser-matter interactions; molecular fluorescense. *Mailing Add:* Inst Phys Sci & Technol Univ Md College Park MD 20742

MCILRATH, WAYNE JACKSON, b Laurel, Iowa, Oct 18, 21; m 42; c 3. PLANT PHYSIOLOGY. *Educ:* Iowa State Teachers Col, BA, 43; Univ Iowa, MS, 47, PhD(plant physiol), 49. *Prof Exp:* From asst to instr bot, Univ Iowa, 46-49; asst prof plant physiol, Agr & Mech Col Tex & Agr Exp Sta, 49-51; from asst prof to prof bot, Univ Chicago, 51-64; dean grad sch, 64-73, PROF BIOL SCI, NORTHERN ILL UNIV, 64- *Concurrent Pos:* Consult, Argonne Nat Lab, 56-; OEEC sr vis fel, Sorbonne, 61; res assoc, Univ Chicago, 64-66; chmn coun, Cent States Univs, Inc, 67-68, bd dirs, 69-80, tres, 71-80; mem comn scholars, Ill Bd Educ, 68-71; mem coun & gov bd, Quad-Cities Grad Study Ctr, 70-73. *Mem:* AAAS; Am Soc Plant Physiologists; Bot Soc Am; Am Inst Biol Sci; Scand Soc Plant Physiol. *Res:* Mineral nutrition of plants; physiology of growth and development. *Mailing Add:* Dept of Biol Sci Northern Ill Univ De Kalb IL 60115

MCILRATH, WILLIAM OLIVER, b Coulterville, Ill, Aug 30, 36; m 63; c 3. PLANT BREEDING, GENETICS. *Educ:* Univ Ill, BS, 59, MS, 64; Okla State Univ, PhD(agron), 67. *Prof Exp:* From asst prof to assoc prof agron, La State Univ, 67-73; RES AGRONOMIST, AGR RES SERV, USDA, 73- *Mem:* Am Soc Agron; Crop Sci Soc Am; Am Genetic Asn; Soc Advan Breedong Res in Asia & Oceania. *Res:* Effects of artificial shading on development and morphology of corn; heterosis; combining ability and quantitative genetics of hexaploid wheat; breeding, genetics of rice. *Mailing Add:* Rte 7 Box 999 Beaumont TX 77706

MCILREATH, FRED J, b Amsterdam, NY, Apr 1, 29; m 52; c 5. PHYSIOLOGY, PHARMACOLOGY. *Educ:* Siena Col, BS, 51; Univ Ky, MS, 55; McGill Univ, PhD(physiol), 59. *Prof Exp:* Sr pharmacologist, Strasenburgh Labs, 59-62; from asst dir to assoc dir clin invest, Riker Labs, 62-71; asst dir, G D Searle & Co, 71-73, dir regulatory affairs, 73-78; vpres clin & regulatory affairs, 78-80, VPRES RES & DEVELOP, REED & CARNRICK LABS, 80- *Concurrent Pos:* Head pulmonary dis sect, Riker Labs, 68-71. *Mem:* AAAS; Am Physiol Soc; Am Soc Clin Pharmacol & Therapeut; NY Acad Sci. *Res:* Clinical pharmacology and drug development; effects of drugs on air flow dynamics. *Mailing Add:* Reed & Carnrick Labs Piscataway NJ 08854

MCILWAIN, CARL EDWIN, b Houston, Tex, Mar 26, 31; m 52; c 2. PHYSICS. *Educ:* NTex State Col, BME, 53; Univ Iowa, MS, 56, PhD(physics), 60. *Prof Exp:* Asst prof physics, Univ Iowa, 60-62; assoc prof, 62-66, PROF PHYSICS, UNIV CALIF, SAN DIEGO, 66- *Concurrent Pos:* Guggenheim fels, Eng, 67-68 & Eng, Ger & Sweden, 72; Alexander von Humboldt US Sr scientist award. *Honors & Awards:* Space Sci Award, Am Inst Aeronaut & Astronaut, 70. *Mem:* Am Phys Soc; Am Geophys Union; Am Astron Soc. *Res:* Energetic particles in solar system. *Mailing Add:* CASS/C-011 Univ of Calif at San Diego La Jolla CA 92093

MCILWAIN, DAVID LEE, b Memphis, Tenn, Jan 7, 38. NEUROCHEMISTRY. *Educ:* Vanderbilt Univ, BA, 60; Wash Univ, MD, 64. *Prof Exp:* Fel biochem, Univ Calif, Berkeley, 64-66; fel neurochem, Col Physicians & Surgeons, Columbia Univ, 68-72; asst prof, 72-78, ASSOC PROF PHYSIOL, UNIV NC, CHAPEL HILL, 78- *Mem:* Soc Neurosci; Am Soc Neurochem. *Res:* Chemistry of spinal motoneurons. *Mailing Add:* Dept of Physiol Sch of Med Univ of NC Chapel Hill NC 27514

MCILWAIN, ROBERT LESLIE, JR, b Lancaster, SC, Apr 16, 29; m 54; c 3. HIGH ENERGY PHYSICS. *Educ:* Carnegie Inst Technol, BS, 53, PhD, 60. *Prof Exp:* Instr physics, Princeton Univ, 59-62; from asst prof to assoc prof, 62-76, PROF PHYSICS, PURDUE UNIV, WEST LAFAYETTE, 76- *Mem:* Am Phys Soc. *Res:* High energy nuclear physics and elementary particles. *Mailing Add:* Dept of Physics Purdue Univ West Lafayette IN 47907

MCINDOE, DARRELL W, b Wilkinsburg, Pa, Sept 28, 30; c 5. ENDOCRINOLOGY, NUCLEAR MEDICINE. *Educ:* Allegheny Col, BS, 52; Temple Univ, MD, 56, MSD, 60. *Prof Exp:* Chief internal med & hosp serv, 7520th US Air Force Hosp, 64-68; Air Force Inst Technol fel, Royal Postgrad Med Sch, London, 68-69; chief & chmn, Endocrinol Serv, Nuclear Med, Keesler AFB, 69-75; dep dir, Armed Forces Radiobiol Inst, Defense Nuclear Agency, 75-77, dir, 77-79; ASST PROF, DEPT RADIOL & NUCLEAR MED, UNIFORMED SERV UNIV HEALTH SCI & STAFF PHYSICIAN, DEPT RADIOL, NUCLEAR MED BR, NAT NAVAL MED CTR, 79- *Concurrent Pos:* Med adv to mgr, Nevada oper, Dept Energy, 80- *Mem:* Uniformed Serv Nuclear Med Asn (pres, 75); Am Col Nuclear Physicians; Soc Nuclear Med; Air Force Soc Physicians; fel Royal Soc Med. *Res:* Nuclear weapons effects; basic science of endocrinology and nuclear medicine; diagnosis and management of thyroid carcinoma. *Mailing Add:* 12405 Borges Ave Silver Spring MD 20904

MCINERNEY, JOHN EDWARD, ichthyology, see previous edition

MACINNES, DAVID FENTON, JR, b Abington, Pa, Mar 19, 43. INORGANIC CHEMISTRY. *Educ:* Earlham Col, BA, 65; Princeton Univ, MA, 70, PhD(chem), 72. *Prof Exp:* Teacher chem, Westtown Sch, Pa, 70-73; ASST PROF CHEM, GUILFORD COL, 73- *Mem:* Am Chem Soc. *Res:* Transition metal complexes; x-ray crystallography; chemical education; computers and chemistry; conducting polymers; organic batteries. *Mailing Add:* Dept of Chem Guilford Col Greensboro NC 27410

MACINNIS, AUSTIN J, b Virginia, Minn, Mar i5, 31; m 57; c 3. PARASITOLOGY, BIOCHEMISTRY. *Educ:* Concordia Col, Moorhead, Minn, BA, 57; Fla State Univ, MS, 59, PhD(parasitol), 63. *Prof Exp:* Asst, Fla State Univ, 57-59; NIH scholar parasitol, Rice Univ, 63-65; from asst prof to prof zool, 65-77, PROF CELL BIOL, UNIV CALIF, 77- *Concurrent Pos:* NSF foreign travel award, 65-; ed, J Parasitol, 79- *Mem:* Fel AAAS; Am Soc Parasitol; Am Soc Trop Med & Hyg; Am Soc Zool; fel Royal Soc Trop Med & Hyg. *Res:* Behavior, physiology and biochemistry of parasitism. *Mailing Add:* Dept of Biol Univ of Calif Los Angeles CA 90024

MACINNIS, CAMERON, b West Bay, NS, Mar 25, 26. CIVIL ENGINEERING. *Educ:* Dalhousie Univ, BSc, 46; NS Tech Col, BE, 48; Durham Univ, PhD(concrete), 62. *Prof Exp:* Res engr, Hydro Elec Power Comn Ont, 48-59; res assoc, Durham Univ, 59-62; assoc prof civil eng, 63-68, PROF CIVIL ENG, UNIV WINDSOR, 68-, HEAD DEPT, 76- *Honors & Awards:* Wason Medal, Am Concrete Inst, 75. *Mem:* Eng Inst Can; Am Concrete Inst; Am Soc Testing & Mat. *Res:* Concrete technology, especially frost durability, high-strength drying, shrinkage and creep. *Mailing Add:* Dept of Civil Eng Univ of Windsor Windsor ON N9B 3P4 Can

MACINNIS, MARTIN BENEDICT, b Big Pond, NS, Aug 16, 25; m 53; c 4. CHEMISTRY, PHYSICS. *Educ:* St Francis Xavier Univ, BSc, 46; Col of the Holy Cross, MS, 53. *Prof Exp:* Prof chem, Loyola Col Montreal, 46-52; from engr to sr engr, Sylvania Elec Prod Inc, 53-60, develop engr, 60-63, advan develop engr, GTE Sylvania Inc, 63-74, head dept chem develop, 69-74, sect head chem develop & process eng, 74-80, ENG MGR CHEM, GTE SYLVANIA INC, 74- *Mem:* Am Chem Soc. *Res:* Chemistry of tungsten, rhenium, molybdenum, rare earths, tantalum and niobium; solvent extraction; pyrometallurgy; hydrometallurgy; chemical vapor deposition; germanium and silicon; sugar chemistry; organic phosphors and fire retardants. *Mailing Add:* Chem & Metall Div GTE Prod Corp Towanda PA 18848

MCINROY, ELMER EASTWOOD, b Ont, Can, Nov 2, 21; m 46; c 3. AGRICULTURAL CHEMISTRY. *Educ:* Ont Agr Col, BSA, 44. *Prof Exp:* Res chemist, Defense Industs, Ltd, Can, 43; metall chemist, Deloro Smelting & Refining Co, 44-46; res biochemist, Cent Res Labs, Gen Foods Corp, NJ, 46-50, lab supvr, Gaines Div, 50-53; dir animal nutrit, Foxbilt, Inc, Iowa, 53-56; dir animal nutrit, 56-65, vpres nutrit & tech serv, 65, DIR, ARBIE MINERAL FEED CO, INC, 65- *Mem:* AAAS; Am Chem Soc; Am Soc Animal Sci; Am Registry Cert Animal Scientists; Am Feed Mfrs Asn. *Res:* Animal, human and dog nutrition; food technology; audio-visual training; technical sales; technical service; public speaking. *Mailing Add:* Arbie Mineral Feed Co Inc 404 S Center St Marshalltown IA 50158

MCINTIRE, CHARLES DAVID, b St Louis, Mo, Sept 20, 32; m 65; c 3. AQUATIC ECOLOGY. *Educ:* Southern Methodist Univ, BBA, 54; Ore State Univ, BS, 58, MS, 60, PhD(bot), 64. *Prof Exp:* Res asst fisheries, 58-60, res asst bot, 61-63, asst prof, 64-69, assoc prof, 69-76, PROF BOT, ORE STATE UNIV, 76- *Concurrent Pos:* Acad Natural Sci Philadelphia McHenry Fund grant, 67; NSF sci fac fel, Ctr Quant Sci, Univ Wash, 70-71. *Mem:* Ecol Soc Am; Am Soc Limnol & Oceanog; Phycol Soc Am. *Res:* Physiological ecology of marine and freshwater algae; trophic ecology of aquatic ecosystems; mathematical ecology and systems analysis; diatom systematics. *Mailing Add:* Dept of Bot Cordley Hall Ore State Univ Corvallis OR 97331

MCINTIRE, JUNIUS MERLIN, b Price, Utah, Jan 27, 18; m 47; c 2. BIOCHEMISTRY. *Educ:* Brigham Young Univ, AB, 40; Univ Wis, MS, 42, PhD(biochem), 44. *Prof Exp:* Res biochemist, Western Condensing Co, Wis, 44-50; chief dairy oil & fat div, Qm Food & Container Inst, 50-55; asst dir res, 55-67, GEN MGR RES, CARNATION CO, 67- *Mem:* AAAS; Am Chem Soc. *Res:* Animal nutrition; vitamin assays; protein chemistry of milk; food processing of milk products; distribution and nutritional significance of certain members of vitamin B complex. *Mailing Add:* Carnation Labs 8015 Van Nuys Blvd Van Nuys CA 91412

MCINTIRE, KENNETH ROBERT, b Portland, Ore, Mar 31, 33; m 54; c 5. BIOLOGY, IMMUNOLOGY. *Educ:* Univ VA, BA, 55, MD, 59. *Prof Exp:* From intern to resident internal med, Univ Hosps of Cleveland, Western Reserve Univ, 59-61; res assoc, 61-63, staff scientist, Lab Biol, 63-70, staff scientist, Lab Cell Biol, 70-75, sr investr, Lab Immunodiag, 75-78, CHIEF DIAG BR, NAT CANCER INST, 78- *Mem:* Am Asn Immunologists; Int Soc Oncodevelop Biol & Med; AAAS; Am Asn Cancer Res. *Res:* Identification and study of circulating tumor associated antigens for the early diagnosis of cancer and for monitoring the effectiveness of therapy. *Mailing Add:* Diag Br Bldg 31 Rm 3A-10 Nat Cancer Inst Bethesda MD 20014

MCINTIRE, LARRY V(ERN), b St Paul, Minn, June 28, 43; m 69. CHEMICAL ENGINEERING. *Educ:* Cornell Univ, BChE & MS, 66; Princeton Univ, MA, 68, PhD(chem eng), 70. *Prof Exp:* From asst prof to assoc prof, 70-78, PROF CHEM ENG, RICE UNIV, 78-, CHMN DEPT, 82- *Concurrent Pos:* NATO-NSF sr postdoctoral fel, Imp Col, London, 76-77; adj prof internal med, Sch of Med, Univ Tex, Houston, 77- *Mem:* AAAS; Soc Rheol; Am Inst Chem Engrs. *Res:* Rheology of nonlinear materials; fluid mechanics; hydrodynamic stability of viscoelastic fluids; red and white blood cell deformability studies; biorheology; biomedical engineering; kinetics of protein polymerizations. *Mailing Add:* Dept of Chem Eng Rice Univ Houston TX 77001

MCINTIRE, LOUIS V(ICTOR), b Lafayette, La, Jan 6, 25; m; c 5. CHEMICAL ENGINEERING. *Educ:* Southwestern La Inst, BS, 44; Ohio State Univ, MSc, 48, PhD(chem eng), 51. *Prof Exp:* Instr chem eng, Southwestern La Inst, 46-47, assoc prof, 53-56; res asst, Mathieson Proj, Res Found, Ohio State Univ, 48-51; chem engr, Mathieson Chem Corp, 51-53; chem engr, E I du Pont de Nemours & Co, Inc, 56-58, supvr, 58-59, sr res engr, 59-72; CONSULT, 72- *Mailing Add:* 1732 Greenbriar Orange TX 77630

MCINTIRE, MATILDA S, b Brooklyn, NY, July 15, 20; c 1. PEDIATRICS. *Educ:* Mt Holyoke Col, BA, 42; Albany Med Col, MD, 46; Am Bd Pediat, dipl. *Prof Exp:* Intern, Flower & Fifth Ave Hosps, New York, 46-47; pediatrician, 8th Army Hq, Japan, 48-49; resident pediat, St Louis Univ Med Sch, 52-53 & Univ Nebr Hosp, 53-54; pvt pract, 54-56; instr pediat, Sch Med, Creighton Univ, 55-61; pediat consult & asst res prof, Col Med, Univ Nebr,

61-66; from assoc clin prof to clin prof pediat, 66-73, CLIN PROF PUB HEALTH & PREV MED, SCH MED, CREIGHTON UNIV, 68-, PROF PEDIAT & DIR COMMUNITY PEDIAT, 73- *Concurrent Pos:* Children's Mem Hosp trainee, 73; dir div prev dis control, Omaha-Douglas County Health Dept, 56-61, dir div maternal & child health, 66-; asst prof pediat, Col Med, Univ Nebr, 61-72, assoc prof, 72-, asst prof food & nutrit, 70-; consult, co-investr & prin investr, USPHS grants, 66-74; consult toxicol info prog, Nat Libr Med; consult fac, Inst Clin Toxicol, Houston, Tex; mem infant stand comt, Nebr Dept Pub Welfare; mem comt accident prev, Am Acad Pediat, 74-; med consult, Omaha Douglas County Health Dept, 79; med dir, Nebr Reg Poison Control Ctr, Childrens Mem Hosp, Omaha, Nebr, 79. *Mem:* AAAS; Am Col Prev Med; AMA; fel Am Pub Health Asn; fel Am Acad Pediat. *Mailing Add:* Dept of Pediat Creighton Univ Sch of Med Omaha NE 68108

MCINTIRE, SUMNER HARMON, b Essex, Mass, July 7, 12; m 36; c 2. PHYSICS, ACADEMIC ADMINISTRATION. *Educ:* Bowdoin Col, AB, 33; NY Univ, MA, 37; Boston Univ, MS, 54. *Hon Degrees:* DSc, 64, DEd, 77, Norwich Univ. *Prof Exp:* Instr, Westbrook Jr Col, 34-36 & Thornton Acad, 37-38; instr chem, 36-37, from instr to assoc prof physics, 38-57, chmn dept, 62-72, prof, 57-77, dean univ, 72-77, EMER PROF PHYSICS, NORWICH UNIV, 77-, EMER DEAN UNIV, 77- *Concurrent Pos:* State exam consult, Vt, 44-46; res worker, Bur Indust Res, Northfield, 47; consult, Vt Dept Pub Safety, 54-; sci adv to Gov, 71-; mem, State Bd Radiologic Technicians, 78- *Mem:* Nat Asn Res Sci Teaching; Am Asn Physics Teachers; Am Asn Higher Educ; Am Conf Acad Deans. *Res:* Wood-machining practices in Vermont. *Mailing Add:* Dean's Off Norwich Univ Northfield VT 05663

MCINTOSH, ALEXANDER OMAR, b Acton, Ont, Oct 27, 13. INDUSTRIAL CHEMISTRY. *Educ:* Univ Toronto, BA, 39; Univ Minn, MS, 40; Univ Glasgow, PhD(phys chem), 51. *Prof Exp:* Asst geol, Univ Minn, 39-40; chemist, Defence Industs, Ltd, 41-44; res chemist, Can Indust, Ltd, 44-48; demonstr, Univ Glasgow, 48-50; res chemist, Can Indust Ltd, 51-56, group leader, Cent Res Lab, 56-62, patent asst, Legal Dept, 62-65, patent agt, Legal Dept, 65-76; consult, 76-81; RETIRED. *Mem:* Fel Chem Inst Can. *Res:* Protection of chemical inventions. *Mailing Add:* 404-120 Edinburgh Rd S Guelph ON N1H 5P7 Can

MCINTOSH, ARTHUR HERBERT, b St Thomas, VI, Apr 2, 34; m 64; c 3. MICROBIOLOGY. *Educ:* McMaster Univ, BA, 59; Univ Guelph, MS, 62; Harvard Univ, DSc(microbiol), 69. *Prof Exp:* NIH fel, Stanford Res Inst, 69-71; staff researcher microbiol, Boyce Thompson Inst, NY, 71-74; asst res prof, Waksman Inst Microbiol, Rutgers Univ, New Brunswick, 74-79; RES MICROBIOLOGIST, CONTROL INSECTS RES LAB, USDA, 79- *Concurrent Pos:* NSF grant, 75. *Mem:* Am Soc Microbiol; Sigma Xi; Soc Invert Path; Tissue Culture Asn. *Res:* Invertebrate and vertebrate tissue culture and virology; in vitro safety testing of viral insecticides; plant and animal mycoplasmas. *Mailing Add:* Biol Control Insects Res Lab USDA PO Box A Columbia MO 65205

MCINTOSH, BRUCE ANDREW, b Walkerton, Ont, Oct 30, 29; m 54; c 4. PHYSICS, ELECTRONICS. *Educ:* Western Ont Univ, BSc, 52, MSc, 53; McGill Univ, PhD(electron beams), 58. *Prof Exp:* Asst res officer, 53-55, assoc res officer, 58-70, secy assoc comt meteorites, 60, SR RES OFFICER, NAT RES COUN CAN, 70- *Mem:* Can Asn Physicists; Meteoritical Soc; Int Astron Union; Can Astron Soc. *Res:* Meteoritics; upper atmosphere physics. *Mailing Add:* Nat Res Coun Can Herzberg Inst Astrophys Ottawa ON K1A 0R6 Can

MCINTOSH, DOUGLAS CARL, b Ottawa, Ont, Aug 30, 21; m 45; c 4. BOTANY, WOOD TECHNOLOGY. *Educ:* Queen's Univ, Ont, BA, 44, MA, 45; State Univ NY Col Forestry, Syracuse Univ, PhD(wood technol), 54. *Prof Exp:* Forest prod engr, Can Forest Prod Lab, Univ Ottawa, 45-54; wood & fiber technologist, Int Cellulose Res, Ltd, Can Int Paper Co, 54-57; sr res engr, Cent Res Lab, Mead Corp, 57-67, res fel wood & fiber technol, 67-69; consult, Arthur D Little, Inc, Mass, 69-71; res scientist, Corp Res Ctr, 72, supvr, microstruct lab, Corp Res & Develop Div, 72-77, MGR, MICROS & TESTING GROUP, INT PAPER CO, 77- *Res:* Wood, fiber and paper structure and properties; microscopy of fibers and paper coatings and pigments. *Mailing Add:* Microstruct Lab Int Paper Co PO Box 797 Tuxedo Park NY 10987

MCINTOSH, ELAINE NELSON, b Webster, SDak, Jan 30, 24; m 55; c 3. PHYSIOLOGICAL BACTERIOLOGY, NUTRITION. *Educ:* Augustana Col, SDak, AB, 45; Univ SDak, Vermillion, MA, 49; Iowa State Univ, PhD(phys bact & biochem), 54. *Prof Exp:* From instr to asst prof chem, Sioux Falls Col, SDak, 45-48; res fel biochem, Univ SDak, Vermillion, 48-49; instr bact, Iowa State Univ, 49-54; res assoc dairy sci, Univ Ill, Urbana, 54-55; res assoc home econ res, Iowa State Univ, 55-62; from asst prof to assoc prof nutrit sci, 68-75, asst to vchancellor, 74-75, spec asst to Chancellor, 75-76, chmn human biol, 75-80, ASSOC PROF NUTRIT SCI, UNIV WIS-GREEN BAY, 72- *Concurrent Pos:* Sigma Xi res grant, 66; pres, Wis Nutrit Coun, 75. *Honors & Awards:* Chancellor's Res Award, Univ Wis-Green Bay, 69. *Mem:* Sigma Xi; Inst Food Technologists; Am Dietetic Asn; Soc Nutrit Educ. *Res:* Food additives and their relationship to human nutrition and food safety; nutrition education research. *Mailing Add:* Environ Sci 301 Univ of Wis Green Bay WI 54302

MACINTOSH, FRANK CAMPBELL, b Baddeck, NS, Dec 24, 09; m 38; c 5. PHYSIOLOGY. *Educ:* Dalhousie Univ, BA, 30, MA, 32; McGill Univ, PhD(physiol), 37. *Hon Degrees:* LLD, Univ Alta, 64, Queen's Univ, Can, 65, Dalhousie Univ, 76; MD, Univ Ottawa, 74; DSc, McGill Univ, 80. *Prof Exp:* Instr biol, Dalhousie Univ, 30-31, biochem, 31-32 & pharmacol, 32-33; demonstr physiol, McGill Univ, 36-37; mem res staff, Med Res Coun Gt Brit, 38-49; Joseph Morley Drake prof physiol, 49-78, EMER PROF PHYSIOL, MCGILL UNIV, 80- *Concurrent Pos:* Treas, Int Union Physiol Sci, 62-68; mem, Sci Coun Can, 66-71; ed, Can J Physiol & Pharmacol, 68-72. *Mem:* Am Physiol Soc; Royal Soc London; Royal Soc Can; Can Physiol Soc (pres, 60-61); Brit Physiol Soc. *Res:* Acetylcholine metabolism. *Mailing Add:* Dept of Physiol McGill Univ 3655 Drummond St Montreal PQ H3G 1Y6 Can

MCINTOSH, HAROLD LEROY, b Fairfax, Mo, Dec 25, 31; m 53; c 3. PHYSICS. *Educ:* Tarkio Col, BA, 53; Univ Colo, MS, 61; Ore State Univ, PhD(physics, chem), 68. *Prof Exp:* Pub sch teacher, Mo, 56-61; acad dean, 74-80, PROF PHYSICS, TARKIO COL, 62-, PRES, 80- *Mem:* Am Asn Physics Teachers. *Res:* Chemistry; mathematics. *Mailing Add:* Dept of Physics Tarkio Col Tarkio MO 64491

MCINTOSH, HENRY DEANE, b Gainesville, Fla, July 19, 21; m 45; c 3. INTERNAL MEDICINE. *Educ:* Davidson Col, BS, 43; Univ Pa, MD, 50; Am Bd Internal Med, dipl, 57; Am Bd Cardiovasc Dis, dipl, 64. *Prof Exp:* Intern med, Duke Univ Hosp, 50-51; asst res, Lawson Vet Admin Hosp, 51-52; from instr to assoc med, Sch Med, Duke Univ, 54-58, from asst prof to prof, 58-70; prof med & chmn dept, Baylor Col Med, 70-77; MEM STAFF, CARDIOL SECT, WATSON CLIN, LAKELAND, 77-; CLIN PROF MED, UNIV FLA, 77- *Concurrent Pos:* Am Heart Asn fel cardiol, Duke Univ Hosp, 52-54; consult, Vet Admin Hosps, Durham, NC, 56-70 & Fayetteville, 57-70, Womack Army Hosp, Ft Bragg, 57-70, Watts Hosp, Durham, 57-70 & Portsmouth Naval Hosp, Va, 57-70; dir cardiovasc lab, Med Ctr, Duke Univ, 56-70, dir cardiovasc div, 66-70; asst ed, Mod Concepts Cardiovasc Dis, 65-68; mem cardiovasc study sect, Nat Heart Inst, 65-69; mem, Subspecialty Bd Cardiovasc Dis, Am Bd Internal Med, 68-76, & Am Bd Emergency Med, 79; chief med serv, Methodist Hosp, Houston, 70-77, Ben Taub Gen Hosp, Jefferson Davis Hosp & Houston Vet Admin Hosp; consult, St Luke's Hosp; ed consult, Am J Cardiol & Circulation, 70-76; chmn coun clin cardiol, Am Heart Asn, 74-76; adj prof med, Baylor Col Med, 77- *Mem:* Am Soc Internal Med; Am Heart Asn; Am Col Physicians; Asn Am Physicians; distinguished fel Am Col Cardiol (pres, 73-74). *Res:* Cardiovascular hemodynamics, especially factors controlling cardiac output. *Mailing Add:* Watson Clin Lakeland FL 33802

MCINTOSH, JERRY LEON, soil chemistry, agronomy, see previous edition

MCINTOSH, JOHN MCLENNAN, b Galt, Ont, Apr 16, 40; m 65; c 2. SYNTHETIC ORGANIC CHEMISTRY. *Educ:* Queen's Univ, Ont, BSc, 62; Mass Inst Technol, PhD(org chem), 66. *Prof Exp:* Fel org chem, Nat Res Coun Can, 66-68; teaching fel, Univ Waterloo, 68; asst prof, 68-73, assoc prof, 73-80, PROF ORG CHEM, UNIV WINDSOR, 80- *Mem:* Am Chem Soc; Chem Inst Can. *Res:* Synthesis of complex molecules; new methods of organic synthesis, especially those utilizing organo-sulfur and organo-phosphorus compounds; phase-transfer catalysis. *Mailing Add:* Dept of Chem Univ of Windsor Windsor ON N9B 3P4 Can

MCINTOSH, JOHN RICHARD, b New York, NY, Sept 25, 39; m 61; c 3. CELL BIOLOGY. *Educ:* Harvard Univ, BA, 61, PhD(biophys), 67. *Prof Exp:* Sch teacher, Mass, 61-63; from instr to asst prof biol, Harvard Univ, 67-70; asst prof, 71-73, assoc prof, 73-77, PROF BIOL, UNIV COLO, BOULDER, 77- *Concurrent Pos:* Consult, Educ Serv Inc, 62-63; NIH fel, Biol Labs, Harvard Univ, 68; ed, J Cell Biol, 77-81; mem, Coun Am Soc Cell Biol, 78-81. *Mem:* Am Soc Cell Biologists; Biophys Soc; Soc Develop Biologists. *Res:* Mitosis and cell motion; control of cell form; structure and biochemistry of the mitotic apparatus in an effort to understand the mechanisms of chromosome movement. *Mailing Add:* Dept of Molecular, Cellular & Develop Biol Univ of Colo Boulder CO 80302

MCINTOSH, JOHN STANTON, b Ford City, Pa, Jan 6, 23. THEORETICAL PHYSICS. *Educ:* Yale Univ, BS, 48, MS, 49, PhD(physics), 52. *Prof Exp:* Res assoc physics, Proj Matterhorn, Princeton Univ, 52-53, instr, Univ, 53-56; from instr to asst prof, Yale Univ, 56-63; assoc prof, 63-65, PROF PHYSICS, WESLEYAN UNIV, 65- *Concurrent Pos:* Consult, Los Alamos Sci Lab & Rand Corp, 53; res assoc, Peabody Mus Natural Hist, Yale Univ, 65-71. *Mem:* Am Phys Soc; Soc Vert Paleont. *Res:* Low energy nuclear and nuclear scattering theories; heavy ion scattering and reactions. *Mailing Add:* Dept of Physics Wesleyan Univ Middletown CT 06457

MCINTOSH, LEE, b Wichita, Kans, June 29, 49. PLANT GENES, PHOTOSYNTHESIS. *Educ:* Univ Calif, Irvine, BSc, 72; Univ Wash, Seattle, PhD(develop bot), 77. *Prof Exp:* Res fel, Biol Lab, Harvard Univ, 77-81; ASST PROF BIOCHEM, DEPT ENERGY PLANT RES LAB, MICH STATE UNIV, 81- *Mem:* Am Soc Plant Physiol; Soc Develop Biol. *Res:* Molecular basis controlling the development of photosynthetic competence in higher plants. *Mailing Add:* Plant Res Lab Mich State Univ East Lansing MI 48824

MCINTOSH, MICHAEL JOSEPH, chemical engineering, see previous edition

MCINTOSH, ROBERT EDWARD, b Hartford, Conn, Jan 19, 40; m 62; c 5. ELECTRICAL ENGINEERING, APPLIED PHYSICS. *Educ:* Worcester Polytech Inst, BSEE, 62; Harvard Univ, SM, 64; Univ Iowa, PhD(elec eng), 67. *Prof Exp:* Mem tech staff microwave eng, Bell Tel Labs, 62-65; teaching asst elec eng, Univ Iowa, 65-66; from asst prof to assoc prof eng, 67-72, PROF ENG, UNIV MASS, AMHERST, 72- *Concurrent Pos:* Guest prof physics, Cath Univ Nijmegen, 73-74; ed, Antennas & Propagation Soc Newsletter, 79- *Mem:* Inst Elec & Electronics Engrs; Int Radio Sci Union; Am Phys Soc; Optical Soc Am. *Res:* Nonlinear electromagnetic pulse transmission in physical media; communication through randomly dispersive media; far infrared propagation. *Mailing Add:* Dept of Elec & Comput Eng Univ of Mass Amherst MA 01003

MCINTOSH, ROBERT PATRICK, b Milwaukee, Wis, Sept 24, 20; m 47; c 2. PLANT ECOLOGY. *Educ:* Lawrence Col, BS, 42; Univ Wis, MS, 48, PhD, 50. *Prof Exp:* Asst bot, Univ Wis, 46-50; from instr to asst prof, Middlebury Col, 50-53; asst prof, Vassar Col, 53-58; asst prof, 58-67, PROF BIOL, UNIV NOTRE DAME, 67- *Concurrent Pos:* Ed, Am Midland Naturalist, 70-; prog dir, Nat Sci Found, 77-78. *Mem:* AAAS; Ecol Soc Am; Brit Ecol Soc; Soc Am Naturalists. *Res:* Forest ecology; history of ecology. *Mailing Add:* Dept of Biol Univ of Notre Dame Notre Dame IN 46556

MCINTOSH, THOMAS HENRY, b Ames, Iowa, July 3, 30; m 55; c 3. ENVIRONMENTAL SCIENCES. *Educ:* Iowa State Univ, BS, 56, MS, 58, PhD(soil microbiol), 62. *Prof Exp:* Instr soils, Iowa State Univ, 60-62; from asst prof to assoc prof, Univ Ariz, 62-68; asst dean col environ sci, 68, assoc prof sci & environ change, 68-71, asst dean cols, 70-73, assoc dean, 73-75, PROF SCI & ENVIRION CHANGE, UNIV WIS-GREEN BAY, 71-, ASST CHANCELLOR STUDENT & ADMIN SERV, 76- *Concurrent Pos:* Vis prof, Iowa State Univ, 67. *Mem:* Am Soc Agron; Soil Sci Soc Am; Am Soc Microbiol; Am Chem Soc; Soil Conserv Soc Am. *Res:* Soil organic matter chemistry; nitrogen; transformations in soil and aquatic systems; biogeochemistry. *Mailing Add:* Asst to Chancellor of Wis Green Bay WI 54302

MCINTOSH, THOMAS JAMES, b Geneva, NY, Feb 4, 47; m 68; c 3. ANATOMY. *Educ:* Univ Rochester, BS, 69; Carnegie-Mellon Univ, MS, 71, PhD(physics), 73. *Prof Exp:* Res assoc, 74-77, ASST PROF ANAT, DUKE UNIV MED CTR, 77- *Mem:* Biophys Soc. *Res:* Structure of biological membranes and the effects of small molecules on lipid bilayer organization. *Mailing Add:* Anat Dept Duke Univ Med Ctr Durham NC 27710

MCINTOSH, WILLIAM DAVID, b Pryor, Okla, Oct 14, 36. MATHEMATICS. *Educ:* Southwestern Col, Kans, BA, 58; Univ Kans, MA, 60, PhD(math), 65. *Prof Exp:* Asst instr math, Univ Kans, 58-63, asst, 63-64, asst instr, 64-65; asst prof, Univ Mo-Columbia, 65-70; PROF MATH & CHMN DEPT, CENTRAL METHODIST COL, 70- *Mem:* Am Math Soc; Math Asn Am. *Res:* Theory of retracts. *Mailing Add:* Dept of Math Cent Methodist Col Fayette MO 65248

MCINTURFF, ALFRED D, b Clinton, Okla, Feb 24, 37; m 60, 64; c 2. HIGH ENERGY PHYSICS, CRYOGENICS. *Educ:* Okla State Univ, BS, 59; Vanderbilt Univ, MS, 60, PhD(physics), 64. *Prof Exp:* Res assoc, Vanderbilt Univ, 64-66, sr res engr, Atomics Int, 66-67; mem staff, Advan Accelerator Design Div, Brookhaven Nat Lab, 67-71, physicist, Accelerator Dept, 71-81; PHYSICIST, CRYOGENIC RES, FERMI NAT ACCELERATOR LAB, 81- *Mem:* Am Phys Soc. *Res:* High field super conductors; photostar research; photosigma production; sigma magnetic moment studies. *Mailing Add:* Fermi Nat Accelerator Lab PO Box 500 Batavia IL 60510

MCINTYRE, ADELBERT, b Providence, RI, Jan 1, 29; m 59; c 3. PHYSICS, SPACE SCIENCES. *Educ:* Univ RI, BSc, 58. *Prof Exp:* Instr physics, Univ RI, 58-61; spec scientist space physics, Off Aerospace Res, US Air Force, 61-63; spec scientist space physics & optics, Air Force Cambridge Res Labs, 63-74, RES PHYSICIST OPTICS & TECH DIR MISSILE SURVEILLANCE TECHNOL, AIR FORCE GEOPHYS LAB, AIR FORCE SYSTS COMMAND, 74- *Concurrent Pos:* Teaching fel, Univ RI, 58-59; prin investr & res physicist physics, Navy Underwater Ord Lab, 59-61; consult, US Comt Space Res, Nat Acad Sci-Nat Res Coun, 65-74 & Off Undersecy Defense for Res & Eng, 74-; consult & mem, Ballistic Missile Defense Working Group, 66-69; consult & dept defense mem, Joint US-Can Res Coun Working Group for Churchill Rocket Range, 69-74; mem & consult, Missile Plume Technol Working Group, US Air Force, 74- *Mem:* Sigma Xi. *Res:* Simultaneous, in situ infrared spectral, spatial, and total radiant emmissivity measurements of a rocket engine plume. *Mailing Add:* 46 Pequot Rd Wayland MA 01778

MCINTYRE, ALAN DAVID, polymer chemistry, see previous edition

MCINTYRE, ANDREW, b Weehawken, NJ, Sept 17, 31; m 67, 78. MARINE GEOLOGY, PALEOCLIMATOLOGY. *Educ:* Columbia Univ, BA, 55, PhD(marine biol), 67. *Prof Exp:* Lectr geol, Barnard Col, Columbia Univ, 61-62; instr, City Col New York, 63-64; res assoc, 62-67, SR VIS RES ASSOC OCEANOG, LAMONT GEOL OBSERV, COLUMBIA UNIV, 67-; PROF GEOL, QUEENS COL, NY, 77- *Concurrent Pos:* NSF res grants, 62-; asst prof geol, Queens Col, NY, 67-69, assoc prof, 69-77. *Mem:* AAAS; Geol Soc Am; NY Acad Sci; Am Geophys Union; Am Quaternary Asn. *Res:* Biogeography and ecology of Coccolithophorida, Pleistocene paleoclimatology and paleooceanography; nanoplankton of the oceans; skeletal ultramicrostructure of nanoplankton and microplankton. *Mailing Add:* Dept of Earth & Environ Sci Queens Col Flushing NY 11367

MACINTYRE, BRUCE ALEXANDER, b Oak Park, Ill, Sept 10, 42; m 65; c 2. PHYSIOLOGY. *Educ:* Carroll Col, Wis, BS, 63; Ind Univ, Bloomington, PhD(physiol), 68. *Prof Exp:* Asst prof, 68-73, ASSOC PROF BIOL, CARROLL COL, WIS, 73- *Mem:* AAAS; Am Inst Biol Sci. *Res:* Human thermoregulatory control mechanisms; cellular enzymology, including carbohydrate metabolism of choriocarcinoma cells. *Mailing Add:* 100 N East Ave Waukesha WI 53186

MCINTYRE, DAVID H, b Yakima, Wash, July 13, 36; m 67. GEOLOGY. *Educ:* Univ Wash, BS, 59, MS, 60; Wash State Univ, PhD(geol), 66. *Prof Exp:* GEOLOGIST, US GEOL SURV, 66- *Mem:* Geol Soc Am. *Res:* Cenozoic volcanic rocks of Southwestern and Central Idaho; geology of Western Puerto Rico. *Mailing Add:* US Geol Surv Bldg 25 Denver Fed Ctr Denver CO 80225

MCINTYRE, DONALD, b Detroit, Mich, Sept 8, 28; m 57; c 4. POLYMER CHEMISTRY. *Educ:* Lafayette Col, BA, 49; Cornell Univ, PhD(chem), 54. *Prof Exp:* Chemist, Monsanto Chem Co, Mass, 53-54; chemist, Nat Bur Standards, 56-62, sect chief macromolecules sect, 62-66; PROF POLYMER SCI & CHEM, UNIV AKRON, 66- *Mem:* Am Chem Soc; Am Phys Soc. *Res:* Physical chemistry of polymers; solution properties; kinetics; phase equilibria of polymers; characterization of polymers; cycloparaffins; structure of polymers. *Mailing Add:* Inst of Polymer Sci Univ of Akron Akron OH 44325

MCINTYRE, DONALD B, b Edinburgh, Scotland, Aug 15, 23; m 57; c 1. GEOLOGY. *Educ:* Univ Edinburgh, BSc, 45, PhD, 47. *Hon Degrees:* DSc, Univ Edinburgh, 51. *Prof Exp:* Lectr econ geol, Univ Edinburgh, 48-52, lectr petrol, 52-54; from assoc prof to prof, 54-75, MINNIE B CAIRNS PROF GEOL, POMONA COL, 75-, CHMN DEPT, 55- *Concurrent Pos:* Res assoc, Univ Calif, 52; Guggenheim Found fel, 69-70; consult, IBM Sci Ctr. *Honors & Awards:* Pigeon Award, Geol Soc London, 52. *Mem:* Geol Soc Am; Geol Soc London; Royal Soc Edinburgh. *Res:* Structural geology of deformed rocks; petro-genesis; sampling methods; computer applications; James Hutton and the foundation of geology. *Mailing Add:* Dept Geol Pomona Col Claremont CA 91711

MCINTYRE, ELDON ATKIN, JR, b Brooklyn, NY, Dec 28, 45. APPLIED MATHEMATICS, PARTIAL DIFFERENTIAL EQUATIONS. *Educ:* Brooklyn Col, BS, 67; NY Univ, MS, 70, PhD(math), 76. *Prof Exp:* Instr math, City Univ New York, 72-76; MEM TECH STAFF MATH, BELL LABS, 77- *Mem:* Soc Indust & Appl Math; Am Math Soc; Asn Comput Mach. *Res:* Computational approaches to partial differential equations; fluid dynamics. *Mailing Add:* Bell Labs 600 Mountain Ave Murray Hill NJ 07974

MCINTYRE, GARY A, b Portland, Ore, July 16, 38; m 63. PLANT PATHOLOGY. *Educ:* Ore State Univ, BS, 60, PhD(plant path), 64. *Prof Exp:* From asst prof to prof plant path, Univ Maine, Orono, 64-75, actg head dept bot & plant path, 68-69, chmn dept, 69-75; CHMN DEPT BOT & PLANT PATH, COLO STATE UNIV, 75- *Concurrent Pos:* Dir, Biol Core Curriculum, Colo State Univ, 76-81. *Mem:* Am Phytopath Soc; Potato Asn Am; Sigma Xi; AAAS. *Res:* Potato diseases; physiology of parasitism. *Mailing Add:* Dept of Bot & Plant Path Colo State Univ Ft Collins CO 80521

MCINTYRE, GEORGE FRANCIS, b Chicago, Ill, Mar 12, 43; m 65; c 2. APPLIED CHEMISTRY. *Educ:* Univ Dayton, BS, 65; Ill Inst Technol, PhD(phys chem), 70. *Prof Exp:* Applns chemist, 69-72, prod specialist, 72-74, mining indust mgr, 74-76, DISTRICT SALES MGR, NALCO CHEM CO, 76- *Mem:* Am Chem Soc; Soc Mining Engrs; Am Mining Cong; Am Inst Metall Engrs. *Res:* Coagulation and flocculation of mineral process slurries; new water and process chemical development for mining and mineral processing industry. *Mailing Add:* Nalco Chem Co 1120 Kanawha Blvd E Charleston WV 25301

MACINTYRE, GILES T, b Bridgeton, NJ, Oct 6, 26; div; c 3. VERTEBRATE ZOOLOGY, VERTEBRATE PALEONTOLOGY. *Educ:* Columbia Univ, BS, 55, MA, 57, PhD(zool), 64. *Prof Exp:* Asst zool, Columbia Univ, 56-57, lectr, 57-59; lectr biol, 62-64, instr, 64-65, asst prof, 66-68, ASSOC PROF BIOL, QUEENS COL, NY, 69- *Concurrent Pos:* Higgins & NIH fel. *Mem:* Am Soc Mammal; Soc Syst Zool; Soc Study Evolution; Soc Vert Paleont; Sigma Xi. *Res:* Mesozoic mammals; quasi-mammals and therapsid reptiles; carnivore evolution and systematics; basicranial osteology and associated anatomy; functional anatomy of teeth and jaws; adaptive radiation. *Mailing Add:* Dept of Biol Queens Col Flushing NY 11367

MCINTYRE, JAMES DOUGLASS EDMONSON, b Toronto, Ont, Feb 16, 34; m 60; c 3. PHYSICAL CHEMISTRY. *Educ:* Univ Toronto, BA, 56, MA, 58; Rensselaer Polytech Inst, PhD(phys chem), 61. *Prof Exp:* Res assoc chem, Princeton Univ, 60-62; MEM TECH STAFF CHEM RES, BELL LABS, 62- *Mem:* Am Chem Soc; Electrochem Soc. *Res:* Electrode kinetics and adsorption; electrodeposition; chemistry and physics of surfaces; catalysis; optical properties of thin films; modulation spectroscopy. *Mailing Add:* Chem Physics Res Dept Bell Labs Murray Hill NJ 07974

MCINTYRE, JOHN ARMIN, b Seattle, Wash, June 2, 20; m 47; c 1. NUCLEAR PHYSICS. *Educ:* Univ Wash, BS, 43; Princeton Univ, MA, 48, PhD(physics), 50. *Prof Exp:* Instr elec eng, Carnegie Inst Technol, 43-44; radio engr, Westinghouse Elec Corp, 44-45; res assoc, Stanford Univ, 50-57; from asst prof to assoc prof physics, Yale Univ, 57-63; assoc dir cyclotron inst, 65-70, PROF PHYSICS, TEX A&M UNIV, 63- *Concurrent Pos:* Consult, Varian Assocs, 55; vis scientist, NSF, 60-65; Oak Ridge Inst Nuclear Studies res partic grant, 63-67; Welch Found grants, 64-66 & 67-70; councilor, Oak Ridge Assoc Univs, 65-71; Am Cancer Soc grant, 80-81. *Mem:* AAAS; fel Am Phys Soc; Soc Nuclear Med; Am Sci Affil. *Res:* Scintillation counters; Compton effect; high energy electron scattering; heavy ion scattering and transfer reactions; gamma ray spectroscopy; three-nucleon scattering; nuclear instrumentation for medicine and technology. *Mailing Add:* Dept of Physics Tex A&M Univ College Station TX 77843

MCINTYRE, JOHN LEE, b Portland, Ore, Jan 31, 47; m 71; c 1. PLANT PATHOLOGY. *Educ:* Ore State Univ, BS, 69, MS, 71; Purdue Univ, PhD(plant path & biochem), 74. *Prof Exp:* assoc plant pathologist, Conn Agr Exp Sta, 74-80; GROUP LEADER AGR RES, ALLIED CHEM CO, 80- *Mem:* Am Phytopath Soc; AAAS. *Res:* Host-parasite interactions between plants and plant pathogenic microorganisms. *Mailing Add:* Syracuse Res Lab Allied Chem Co PO Box 6 Soluay NY 13209

MACINTYRE, JOHN R(ICHARD), b Eng, June 29, 08; nat US; m 34; c 3. ELECTRICAL ENGINEERING. *Educ:* Univ Mich, BSEE, 34. *Prof Exp:* Elec instrument design engr, Gen Elec Co, 36-40, aircraft instrument design engr, 40-44, adv develop engr, Electromech Devices, 44-54, adv develop eng mgr, 54-58, consult engr, 58-64, instrumentation & adv systs engr, 64-73; RETIRED. *Mem:* Soc Prof Engrs; fel Inst Elec & Electronics Engrs; fel Instrument Soc Am. *Res:* Development and design of instrument and control systems and mechanisms. *Mailing Add:* 231 Queensbury Dr Apt 4 Huntsville AL 35802

MCINTYRE, JUDITH WATLAND, b Kansas City, Mo, Aug 19, 30; m 57; c 3. ORNITHOLOGY, ETHOLOGY. *Educ:* Carleton Col, BA, 52; Univ Minn, MA, 70, PhD(zool), 75. *Prof Exp:* Asst prof, 77-80, ASSOC PROF VERT BIOL, UTICA COL, SYRACUSE UNIV, 80- *Concurrent Pos:* Dir, Oikos Res Found, 76-; coordr, Conf on Common Loon Res & Mgt, 77-; res grants, Dept Environ Conserv, Endangered Species Div, NY State, 78-79, Geog Soc, 79-80 & NSF, 81-82. *Mem:* Am Ornithologists Union; AAAS; Cooper Ornith Soc; Wilson Soc; Animal Behav Soc. *Res:* Behavior of common loons; sound transmission over water; vocal communication. *Mailing Add:* Dept Biol Utica Col Syracuse Univ Utica NY 13502

MCINTYRE, LAURENCE COOK, JR, b Knoxville, Tenn, July 9, 34; m 57; c 4. ATOMIC PHYSICS. *Educ:* Stanford Univ, BS, 57; Univ Wis, MS, 61, PhD(physics), 65. *Prof Exp:* Instr physics, Princeton Univ, 65-66; from asst prof to assoc prof, 66-78, PROF PHYSICS, UNIV ARIZ, 78- *Mem:* Am Phys Soc. *Res:* Atomic and molecular physics; beam foil spectroscopy; molecular dissociation. *Mailing Add:* Dept of Physics Univ of Ariz Tucson AZ 85721

MACINTYRE, MALCOLM NEIL, b Honolulu, Hawaii, Aug 12, 19; m 41; c 4. CYTOGENETICS. *Educ:* Univ Mich, BA, 48, MA, 50, PhD(zool), 55. *Prof Exp:* From instr to sr instr, 54-57 & asst prof to assoc prof, 57-67, PROF ANAT, CASE WESTERN RESERVE UNIV, 67- *Concurrent Pos:* Mem anat sci training comt, NIH, 62-, chmn, 65- *Mem:* AAAS; Teratol Soc; Am Asn Anat; Am Soc Zool; Soc Human Genetics. *Res:* Human reproduction and development; human reproductive failure; association of chromosomal abnormalities with congenital malformations; amniotic fluid cultures; prenatal genetic evaluation; genetic counseling. *Mailing Add:* Dept of Anat Case Western Reserve Univ Cleveland OH 44106

MCINTYRE, OSWALD ROSS, b Chicago, Ill, Feb 13, 32; m 57; c 3. HEMATOLOGY. *Educ:* Dartmouth Col, AB, 53; Harvard Med Sch, MD, 57. *Prof Exp:* Intern, Hosp Univ Pa, 57-58; resident med, Dartmouth Affiliated Hosps, 58-60; trainee hemat, Dartmouth Med Sch, 60-61; asst chief clin res sect, Pakistan SEATO Cholera Res Lab, 61-62; mem bact prof, Div Biol Standards, NIH, 62-63; trainee hemat, 63-64, from asst prof med to assoc prof med, 66-76, PROF MED, DARMOUTH MED SCH, 76- *Concurrent Pos:* Markle scholar acad med, 65; counsult, Hitchcock Clin, 64; attend physician, Vet Admin Hosp, White River Junction, Vt, 64. *Mem:* AAAS; Am Fedn Clin Res; Am Soc Hemat; NY Acad Sci. *Res:* Cellular immunology; in vitro lymphocyte culture and chemotherapy of hematologic malignancies; genetic aspects of hematologic illness. *Mailing Add:* Norris Cotton Cancer Ctr Hinman Box 7000 Hanover NH 03755

MCINTYRE, PATRICIA ANN, b Christopher, Ill, Sept 1, 26. MEDICINE. *Educ:* Kalamazoo Col, AB, 48; Johns Hopkins Univ, MD, 52; Am Bd Internal Med, dipl, 62; Am Bd Nuclear Med, dipl, 72. *Prof Exp:* Intern, Mass Gen Hosp, 52-53; asst resident internal med, Johns Hopkins Hosp, 53-55, instr med, 57-58, clin dir dept med, Mem Med Ctr, 58-64; res assoc hemat div, Sch Med, 64-65, instr med, 65-67, instr, Univ, 66-67, asst prof med & radiol sci, 67-71, assoc prof radiol sci, Sch Hyg, 71-73, ASSOC PROF MED & RADIOL, SCH MED, JOHNS HOPKINS UNIV, 71-, ASSOC PROF RADIOL SCI, SCH MED & ASSOC PROF ENVIRON HEALTH, SCH HYG, 73- *Concurrent Pos:* Fels hemat, Sch Med, Johns Hopkins Univ, 55-57; dir med educ, Hosp for Women, 57-58; chmn, panel int comt standardization hemat. *Mem:* Am Fedn Clin Res; Am Soc Hemat; Soc Nuclear Med; fel Am Col Physicians. *Res:* Hematology; nuclear medicine. *Mailing Add:* Rm 2001 Johns Hopkins Med Inst 615 N Wolfe St Baltimore MD 21205

MCINTYRE, ROBERT GERALD, b Cleveland, Okla, Mar 26, 24; m 59; c 3. APPLIED MATHEMATICS, THEORETICAL PHYSICS. *Educ:* US Naval Acad, BS, 45; Univ Okla, PhD(physics), 59. *Prof Exp:* Res mathematician, Sohio Petrol Co, 56-59; asst prof math & physics, Grad Inst Technol, Univ Ark, 57-60; mem tech staff & theoret physicist, Tex Instruments, Inc, 60-63; asst prof math, Okla State Univ, 63-65; from assoc prof to prof physics, 65-69, prof math, 69-74, PROF PHYSICS, UNIV TEX, EL PASO, 74- *Mem:* Am Math Soc; Am Phys Soc. *Mailing Add:* Dept of Physics Univ of Tex El Paso TX 79902

MCINTYRE, ROBERT JOHN, b Bathurst, NB, Dec 19, 28; m 55; c 2. SOLID STATE PHYSICS. *Educ:* St Francis Xavier Univ, Can, BSc, 50; Dalhousie Univ, MSc, 53; Univ Va, PhD(physics), 56. *Prof Exp:* Sr mem sci staff, RCA Victor Co, Ltd, 56-67; dir semiconductor electronics lab, 67-76, MGR, ELECTROOPTICS RES & DEVELOP, RCA INC, 76- *Mem:* Fel Inst Elec & Electronics Engrs; Can Asn Physicists. *Res:* Solid state surface, semiconductor and device physics. *Mailing Add:* RCA Inc Ste Anne de Bellevue PQ H9X 3L3 Can

MCINTYRE, RUSSELL THEODORE, b Alexis, Ill, Mar 20, 25; m 48; c 3. BIOCHEMISTRY. *Educ:* Monmouth Col, BS, 49; Kans State Col, MS, 50, PhD(chem), 52. *Prof Exp:* Asst prof chem, La State Univ, 52-53; asst biochemist agr chem & biochem, 53-56; biochemist, Haynie Prod, Inc, NJ, 56-61; dir qual control, 61-65, DIR SPEC PROD DEVELOP, INDUST PROD GROUP, STOKELY VAN CAMP, INC, COLUMBUS, 65- *Mem:* Am Chem Soc; Inst Food Technologists; Am Oil Chemists Soc. *Res:* Electrophoresis of plant proteins; biochemistry of fishes; lipid chemistry; polyglycerols and their derivatives. *Mailing Add:* 3780 Smiley Rd Hilliard OH 43026

MCINTYRE, THOMAS WILLIAM, b Chicago, Ill, Apr 22, 41; m 60; c 3. ORGANIC CHEMISTRY, RESEARCH ADMINISTRATION. *Educ:* DePauw Univ, BA, 62; Univ Iowa, PhD(org chem), 67. *Prof Exp:* Sr org chemist, Eli Lilly & Co, 67-71, res scientist, 71-73, mgr prod introd & chmn cardiovasc proj teams, 73-77, mgr prod licensing, 77-78; V PRES, KINGSWOOD LABS, INC, 78- *Concurrent Pos:* Consult, chem & pharmaceut res & develop, 78-; mem bd dirs, Kingswood Labs, Telesis Inc, Calida, Inc. *Mem:* AAAS; Am Chem Soc. *Res:* Electrochemical reactions of organic compounds; synthesis, modification and purification of cephalosporin antibiotics; process research on plant fungicides and herbicides. *Mailing Add:* 336 Heather Dr Carmel IN 46032

MCINTYRE, THOMAS WOODFORD, biophysics, computer science, see previous edition

MCINTYRE, WILLIAM ERNEST, JR, b Alvy, WVa, Dec 19, 25; m 50; c 1. CHEMISTRY, ORGANIC CHEMISTRY. *Educ:* Salem Col, WVa, BS, 48; Carnegie Inst Technol, MS, 51, PhD(org chem), 53. *Prof Exp:* Lab instr chem, Carnegie Inst Technol, 48-51; res chemist, E I du Pont de Nemours & Co, 52-69, staff scientist, Film Dept, 66-77, sr res chemist, Polymer Prod Dept, 77-80. *Mem:* AAAS; Am Chem Soc; NY Acad Sci. *Res:* Polymer synthesis, evaluation and chemistry; plastic film manufacture. *Mailing Add:* 610 Plaza Dr Circleville OH 43113

MACINTYRE, WILLIAM JAMES, b Cannan, Conn, Nov 26, 20; m 47; c 2. NUCLEAR MEDICINE, MEDICAL PHYSICS. *Educ:* Western Reserve Univ, BS, 43, MA, 47; Yale Univ, MS, 48, PhD(physics), 50. *Prof Exp:* Res asst, Atomic Energy Med Res Proj, 47, res assoc, 49-51, sect chief radiation physics, 51-58, sr instr radiol, 50-52, asst prof, 52-63, from asst prof to assoc prof biophys, 58-71, PROF BIOPHYS, SCH MED, CASE WESTERN RESERVE UNIV, 71-; PHYSICIST, CLEVELAND CLIN, 72- *Concurrent Pos:* Lectr, Mid East Regional Ctr Arab Countries, Egypt, 64; mem US nat comt med physics, Int Atomic Energy Agency, 66-72; mem coun cardiovasc radiol, Am Heart Asn; chmn, Fed Coun Nuclear Med Orgn, 77-82. *Mem:* Am Col Radiol; Radiol Soc NAm; Am Asn Physicists in Med; Soc Nuclear Med (pres, 76-77); Am Phys Soc. *Res:* Techniques of radionuclide and functional scanning; application of radionuclide techniques to organ dynamic measurements; applications of computers to imaging and dynamic studies; measurement and analysis of electrical parameters of the brain. *Mailing Add:* 3108 Huntington Rd Shaker Heights OH 44120

MACIOLEK, JOHN A, b Milwaukee, Wis, Nov 2, 28; m 56; c 5. LIMNOLOGY, TROPICAL STREAM ECOLOGY. *Educ:* Ore State Univ, BS, 50; Univ Calif, Berkeley, MA, 54; Cornell Univ, PhD(limnol), 61. *Prof Exp:* Fishery biologist, East Fish Nutrit Lab, NY, 56-61 & Sierra Nevada Aquatic Res Lab, Calif, 61-65, leader, Hawaii Coop Fishery Res Unit, 66-77, sr adv, Hawaii Coop Fishery Res Unit, 77-79, CHIEF AQUATIC ECOL RES, SEATTLE NAT FISHERY RES CTR, US FISH & WILDLIFE SERV, 79- *Concurrent Pos:* NSF-Am Soc Limnol & Oceanog travel grant, XIV Cong, Int Soc Limnol, Austria, 59 & XVI Cong, Poland, 65; assoc prof, Univ Hawaii, 67-77; assoc zoologist, Hawaii Inst Marine Biol, 69-79; actg chmn, Hawaii State Natural Area Reserves Syst Comn, 73-76; affil grad fac, Univ Wash, 75-79; affil fac, Univ Guam, 80- *Mem:* Am Soc Limnol & Oceanog; Int Soc Limnol; Sigma Xi; Explorers Club. *Res:* Insular estuary and stream ecology; diadromous fauna of Oceania; insular aquatic ecosystem classification and inventory; anchialine pool crustaceans; aquatic zoogeography. *Mailing Add:* Nat Fisheries Res Ctr Bldg 204 Naval Support Activity Seattle WA 98115

MACIOLEK, RALPH BARTHOLOMEW, b Milwaukee, Wis, July 30, 39; m 74; c 2. METALLURGICAL ENGINEERING, PHYSICS. *Educ:* Univ Wis, BS, 61, MS, 62, PhD(metall eng), 66. *Prof Exp:* Res scientist mat sci, Corp Mat Sci Ctr, Honeywell Inc, 65-78; RES SPECIALIST MAT SCI, 3M CO, 78- *Mem:* Am Soc Metals; Am Asn Crystal Growth; Metall Soc Am; Inst Mining Metall & Petrol Engrs. *Res:* Crystal growth; solidification; hybrid microelectronics; metallurgy; thin films; soft and hard ferrites. *Mailing Add:* 10031 James Circle Bloomington MN 55431

MACIOR, LAZARUS WALTER, b Yonkers, NY, Aug 26, 26. BOTANY. *Educ:* Columbia Univ, AB, 48, MA, 50; Univ Wis, PhD(bot, zool), 59. *Prof Exp:* Asst bot, Columbia Univ, 48-50; head dept biol, St Francis Col, Wis, 60-62; instr, Marquette Univ, 62-64; asst prof biol, Loras Col, 65-67; from asst prof to assoc prof, 67-72, PROF BIOL, UNIV AKRON, 72- *Concurrent Pos:* Res assoc, Inst Arctic & Alpine Res, Univ Colo, 66-67 & Inst Polar Studies, Ohio State Univ, 71-73. *Mem:* Arctic Inst N Am; Soc Study Evolution; Int Asn Plant Taxon; Am Inst Biol Sci; Am Bryological & Lichenological Soc. *Res:* insect-flower pollination relationships; evolution^^ry systematics. *Mailing Add:* Dept Biol Univ Akron Akron OH 44325

MCIRVINE, EDWARD CHARLES, b Winnipeg, Man, Dec 19, 33; nat US; m 54; c 2. THEORETICAL PHYSICS, INFORMATION SCIENCE. *Educ:* Univ Minn, BS, 54; Cornell Univ, PhD(theoret physics), 59. *Prof Exp:* Asst physics, Cornell Univ, 54-58; mem res staff, Theoret Physics, Gen Atomic Div, Gen Dynamics Corp, 58-60; res scientist, Sci Lab, Ford Motor Co, 60-66; mgr mfg systs planning, Gen Parts Div, 66-68, mgr comput applns proj new bus develop off, 68-69, mgr tech anal, Xerox Corp, 69-71, mgr physics res lab, Xerox Webster Res Ctr, 71-73, dir forward tech planning, 74-76, mgr tech anal, 77-78, mgr prod concepts, reprographic technol, 79-81, ENG CONCEPTS MGR, CENTRALIZED BUS UNIT, XEROX CORP, 81- *Concurrent Pos:* Dir Detection Systs, Inc, Fairport, NY, 73- *Mem:* Am Phys Soc; Asn Comput Mach; Sigma Xi. *Res:* Product development; systems engineering; quantum theory of transport phenomena; real-time computer applications; research management; theory of solids. *Mailing Add:* Xerox Corp Rochester NY 14644

MCISAAC, PAUL R(OWLEY), b Brooklyn, NY, Apr 20, 26; m 49; c 4. ELECTRICAL ENGINEERING. *Educ:* Cornell Univ, BEE, 49; Univ Mich, MSE, 50, PhD(elec eng), 54. *Prof Exp:* Engr, Sperry Gyroscope Co, 54-59; assoc prof elec eng, 59-65, PROF ELEC ENG, CORNELL UNIV, 65-, ASSOC DEAN ENG, 75- *Concurrent Pos:* Vis prof, Chalmers Univ Technol, Sweden, 65-66. *Mem:* Inst Elec & Electronics Engrs. *Res:* Electromagnetic theory; microwave theory; symmetry analysis. *Mailing Add:* Col of Eng Cornell Univ Ithaca NY 14853

MCISAAC, ROBERT JAMES, b Brooklyn, NY, Jan 9, 23; m 48; c 2. PHARMACOLOGY. *Educ:* Univ Buffalo, BS, 49, PhD, 54. *Prof Exp:* Assoc pharmacol, Sch Med, Univ Buffalo, 54-55; from asst prof to assoc prof, 58-66, PROF PHARMACOL, SCH MED, STATE UNIV NY BUFFALO, 66- *Concurrent Pos:* Res fel, Grad Sch Med, Univ Pa, 56-58. *Mem:* AAAS; Am Soc Pharmacol & Exp Therapeut; NY Acad Sci; Soc Neurosci. *Res:* Synaptic transmission; neuroeffector release; distribution and transport of drugs. *Mailing Add:* Dept of Pharmacol State Univ of NY Sch of Med Buffalo NY 14214

MACIVER, DONALD STUART, b Cambridge, Mass, Oct 3, 27; m 47; c 2. INDUSTRIAL CHEMISTRY. *Educ:* Univ Boston, AB, 52; Univ Pittsburgh, PhD(phys chem), 57. *Prof Exp:* Sect head catalysis, Gulf Res & Develop Co, 57-64; mgr chem res, Eastern Res Ctr, NY, 64-67, dir, Western Res Ctr, Richmond, Calif, 67-74, dir, St Gabriel Plant, La, 72-74, vpres & gen mgr, Wyo, 74-76, vpres, Agr Chem Div, 76-81, VPRES & GEN MGR, AGR & DRUG INTERMEDIATES DIV, STAUFFER CHEM CO, 81- *Mem:* Am Chem Soc. *Res:* Adsorption; catalysis; resonance spectroscopy; fuel cell technology; petroleum processing; petrochemicals; chemical processes; agricultural chemicals; caustic-chlorine manufacture. *Mailing Add:* 68 Branch Brook Rd Wilton CT 06897

MCIVER, JAMES W, JR, quantum chemistry, see previous edition

MCIVER, NORMAN L, b Abbey, Sask, Sept 7, 31; m 58; c 3. GEOLOGY. *Educ:* Univ Sask, BA, 56; Johns Hopkins Univ, PhD(geol), 61. *Prof Exp:* Res geologist, Shell Develop Co, Tex, 60-68, staff geologist, Shell Oil Co, La, 68-71, staff geologist, Shell Can Ltd, 71, sr staff geologist, 71-77, dist mgr, 77-81, MGR GEOL, SHELL OIL CO, 81- *Mem:* Soc Econ Paleontologists & Mineralogists; Am Asn Petrol Geologists. *Res:* Stratigraphy and sedimentation of clastic sediments. *Mailing Add:* Shell Oil Co Box 991 Houston TX 77001

MCIVER, ROBERT THOMAS, JR, b Macon, Ga, June 19, 45; m 69; c 4. SPECTROMETRY, PHYSICAL CHEMISTRY. *Educ:* Univ Kans, BS, 67; Stanford Univ, PhD(chem), 71. *Prof Exp:* Asst prof, 71-75, assoc prof, 75-77, PROF CHEM, UNIV CALIF, IRVINE, 77- *Concurrent Pos:* Prin investr, NSF & Petrol Res Fund, 72-, NIH, 75-; Alfred P Sloan fel, Sloan Found, 73; vis fel, Joint Inst Lab Astrophysics, Univ Colo, 79. *Mem:* Am Chem Soc; Am Soc Mass Spectrometry; Am Phys Soc; Sigma Xi. *Res:* Ion-molecule reactions in the gas phase; effects of solvation on chemical reactions; development of analytical applications of Fourier transform mass spectrometry. *Mailing Add:* Dept Chem Univ Calif Irvine CA 92717

MCIVER, SUSAN BERTHA, b Hutchinson, Kans, Nov 6, 40. ENTOMOLOGY. *Educ:* Univ Calif, Riverside, BA, 62; Wash State Univ, MS, 64, PhD(entom), 67. *Prof Exp:* Asst prof, 67-71, assoc prof, 71-80, PROF PARASITOL, UNIV TORONTO, 80- *Honors & Awards:* C Gordon Hewitt Award, Entom Soc Can, 78. *Mem:* Entom Soc Am; Can Soc Zoologists; fel Entom Soc Can. *Res:* Medical entomology; behavior and sensory physiology and morphology of blood feeding arthropods. *Mailing Add:* Dept Zool Univ of Toronto Toronto ON M5S 1A1 Can

MACK, ALEXANDER ROSS, b Oberon, Man, May 6, 27; c 4. SOIL FERTILITY, PLANT PHYSIOLOGY. *Educ:* Univ Man, BSA, 49; Iowa State Univ, MS, 52; Purdue Univ, PhD(soil), 59. *Prof Exp:* Agronomist plant & soil, 49-54, res scientist soil environ, 55-70, RES SCIENTIST REMOTE SENSING, CAN DEPT AGR, 71- *Concurrent Pos:* Consult, Food & Agr Orgn, 66; chmn, Ont Soil Fertil Comt, 67-69; chmn, Climate & Soil Classifaction, Nat Soil Survey comt, 70-71; secy, Agr & Geog Working Group Prog Planning for Resource Satellites, 71-; chmn, Agr Working Group Remote Sensing, 72-79; reg Agr Can, Can Adv Comt Remote Sensing, 72- *Mem:* Soil Sci Soc Am; Can Soc Soil Sci (secy, 66-69); Int Soc Soil Sci; Am Soc Photogram; Can Soc Remote Sensing (secy, 72-75). *Res:* Effect of soil environment on fertilizer requirement for crop production in various soil climatic zones. *Mailing Add:* Agrometerol Sect LRR1 Res Br Agr Can Ottawa ON K1A 0C6 Can

MACK, CHARLES EDWARD, JR, b Freeport, NY, July 31, 12; m 43; c 2. AERODYNAMICS. *Educ:* Mass Inst Technol, BS, 34; Stevens Inst Technol, MS, 44; NY Univ, ScD(aerodyn), 48. *Prof Exp:* Instr math, Stanton Prep Acad, 40-41; asst, Iowa State Univ, 41-42; res engr appl math & head theoret sect, Res Dept, Grumman Aircraft Eng Corp, 42-48, dir res, Res Dept, 48-78, CONSULT, GRUMMAN AEROSPACE CORP, 78- *Concurrent Pos:* Lectr, NY Univ, 48- & Adelphi Col, 52- *Mem:* Sigma Xi; Inst Aeronaut & Space. *Res:* Flutter and vibration of aircraft; transonic and supersonic aerodynamics; dynamic analysis; linearized treatment of supersonic flow through and around ducted bodies of narrow cross section. *Mailing Add:* Midline South Soyoset NY 11791

MACK, CHARLES LAWRENCE, JR, b Cleveland, Ohio, July 20, 26; m 50; c 4. APPLIED PHYSICS. *Educ:* Harvard Univ, BSc, 48; Univ Pa, MSc, 53. *Prof Exp:* Instr physics, Univ Pa, 49-50, instr med, Sch Med, 52-53; mem staff physics, Lincoln Lab, Mass Inst Technol, 53-57; tech consult, Supreme Hq, Allied Powers Europe, Paris, 57-59; mem staff, Mitre Corp, Bedford, Mass, 59; MEM STAFF PHYSICS, LINCOLN LAB, MASS INST TECHNOL, 59- *Res:* Conversion of solar to electrical energy by low temperature fluids in gravity-driven engines. *Mailing Add:* 7 Parker St Lexington MA 02173

MACK, DAVID J(OSEF), b Madison, Wis, Dec 25, 09; m 34; c 2. METALLURGY. *Educ:* Univ Wis, BSChE, 31, MSChE, 32; Purdue Univ, PhD(metall), 44. *Prof Exp:* Jr engr, C F Burgess Labs, Inc, Wis, 32-33 & Globe-Union Mfg Co, 33-35; asst chem eng, Purdue Univ, 35-37, instr metall, 37-39; asst prof chem eng, Univ Tenn, 39-45; engr, Forest Prods Lab, US Forest Serv, 45; instr drawing, 45-46, asst prof metall & admin asst col eng, 46-47, asst prof metall, 47-52, assoc prof mining & metall eng, 52-57, prof, 57-77, EMER PROF MINING & METALL ENG, UNIV WIS-MADISON, 77- *Concurrent Pos:* Assoc metall engr, Fertilizer Div, Tenn Valley Auth, 39-44; vis scientist, Univ Ariz, 61-62; gen consult, Tenn, 42-45 & Wis, 47- *Mem:* Am Soc Metals; Nat Asn Corrosion Engrs; Am Inst Mining, Metall & Petrol Engrs; Metals Soc; Int Metallog Soc. *Res:* Heat treatment of copper-base alloys; phase transformations; archeological metallurgy. *Mailing Add:* Dept of Metall & Mineral Eng Univ of Wis Madison WI 53706

MACK, DICK A, b Santa Cruz, Calif, Nov 22, 21; m 45; c 2. ELECTRONICS ENGINEERING. *Educ:* Univ Calif, Berkeley, BS, 43. *Prof Exp:* Radio engr, Naval Res Lab, DC, 43-46; electronics engr, Lawrence Radiation Lab, Univ Calif, 46-51; res engr, Stanford Res Inst, 51-52; electronics engr bevatron elec eng, 52-55, electronics engr nuclear instrumentation, 55-69, head, Dept Electronics Eng, 69-77, DEPT HEAD EMER, DEPT ELECTRONICS ENG, LAWRENCE BERKELEY LAB, 77- *Concurrent Pos:* chmn, US Camac Mech & Power Supply working group, 71-76 & Fast Syst Design Group, Dept Energy, 78-; prin investr, Surv Instrumentation for Environ Qual Monitoring, NSF, 71-77; consult control systs & nuclear instrumentation, 77-; assoc ed, Inst Elec & Electronic Engrs Transactions on Nuclear Sci, 78- *Mem:* sr mem Inst Elec & Electronics Engrs. *Mailing Add:* 600 Lockewood Ln Santa Cruz CA 95066

MACK, DONALD R(OY), b Seattle, Wash, Mar 14, 25; m 54; c 2. ELECTRICAL ENGINEERING. *Educ:* Univ Wash, BSEE, 48; Polytech Inst Brooklyn, MS, 67, PhD(syst sci), 69. *Prof Exp:* Engr, 48-56, supvr proj eng, Mat Lab, Large Steam Turbine Generator Dept, 56-61, consult eng educ, 61-70, prog mgr advan course eng, 70-78, MGR TECH EDUC, GEN ELEC CO, 78- *Concurrent Pos:* Adj prof, Rensselaer Polytech Inst, 69- *Mem:* Inst Elec & Electronics Engrs; Am Soc Eng Educ. *Res:* Industrially oriented graduate education in electrical and mechanical engineering; system engineering. *Mailing Add:* Gen Elec Co Fairfield CT 06431

MACK, HARRY JOHN, b Gatesville, Tex, Mar 18, 26; m 55; c 4. HORTICULTURE. *Educ:* Tex A&M Univ, BS, 50, MS, 52; Ore State Univ, PhD(hort), 55. *Prof Exp:* Instr hort, Tex A&M Univ, 50-51; from instr to assoc prof, 55-69, PROF HORT, ORE STATE UNIV, 69- *Mem:* Am Soc Hort Sci; Am Sci Affil. *Res:* Vegetable crops physiology; population density; mineral nutrition; irrigation and water relations. *Mailing Add:* Dept of Hort Ore State Univ Corvallis OR 97331

MACK, HARRY PATTERSON, anatomy, see previous edition

MACK, IRVING, internal medicine, deceased

MACK, JAMES PATRICK, b Newark, NJ, Dec 9, 39; m 68; c 1. CELL BIOLOGY. *Educ:* Monmouth Col, NJ, BS, 62; William Paterson Col NJ, MA, 66; Columbia Univ, EdD(cell biol), 71. *Prof Exp:* Teacher biol, Shore Regional High Sch, NJ, 62-66; asst prof cell physiol, Monmouth Col, NJ, 68-69; teacher biol chem, Lakewood High Sch, NJ, 71-74; res scientist cell biol, Lamont Doherty Geol Observ, Columbia Univ, 69-71; ASSOC PROF BIOL & CHMN DEPT, MONMOUTH COL, NJ, 74- *Concurrent Pos:* Teacher biol, Jersey City State Col, 70-73 & biol & chem, Ocean County Col, NJ, 71-; res scientist cell biol, Creedmore Inst, Queens Village, NY, 74-75; NSF grant. *Mem:* Sigma Xi; Am Chem Soc; Am Inst Biol Sci. *Res:* Determining the role of vitamin A, outside the visual cycle, in cellular membranes; antimicrobial activity in lichens; effect of vitamin E and hydrocortisone on aging cells. *Mailing Add:* 58 Cold Indian Springs Rd Wayside NJ 07712

MACK, JULIUS L, b Gadsden, SC, June 14, 30; m 58; c 3. CHEMICAL PHYSICS. *Educ:* SC State Col, BS, 52; Howard Univ, MS, 57, PhD(phys chem), 65. *Prof Exp:* Res chemist, Naval Ord Sta, 56-71; chmn div natural sci, 71-73, dean sch natural, appl & health sci, 72-78, PROF CHEM, UNIV DC, 71- *Mem:* AAAS; Am Chem Soc; Am Phys Soc; NY Acad Sci. *Res:* Study of structural and thermodynamic properties of high temperature molecules; infrared spectroscopy of matrix isolated species and mass and infrared spectra of hot vapors; vibrational spectra of unstable species; laser studies of molecular dynamics; gas-surface interactions; kinetics of decompostions. *Mailing Add:* Col Phys Sci Eng & Technol Univ DC Washington DC 20005

MACK, LAWRENCE LLOYD, b Springfield, Mo, Dec 10, 42; m 66; c 2. PHYSICAL CHEMISTRY, BIOCHEMISTRY. *Educ:* Middlebury Col, AB, 65; Northwestern Univ, PhD(phys chem), 69. *Prof Exp:* Fel, Univ Calif, Berkeley, 69-70, instr chem & NIH fel, 70; asst prof chem, St Lawrence Univ, 70-72; ASSOC PROF CHEM, BLOOMSBURG STATE COL, 72- *Mem:* Am Chem Soc; Sigma Xi. *Res:* Development and employment of physical methods to study solution behavior of biopolymers; biophysical chemistry and biophysics; computer assisted instruction. *Mailing Add:* Dept of Chem Bloomsburg State Col Bloomsburg PA 17815

MACK, LAWRENCE R(IEDLING), b Detroit, Mich, Oct 9, 32; m 54; c 4. FLUID MECHANICS. *Educ:* Univ Mich, BSE(eng mech) & BSE(math), 54, MSE, 55, PhD(eng mech), 58. *Prof Exp:* Asst prof mech & hydraulics & res engr, Inst Hydraulic Res, Univ Iowa, 58-60; res engr, 60-62, asst prof eng mech, 60-65, head, Dept Eng Mech, 60-68, head, Dept Civil Eng, 60-73, ASSOC PROF ENG MECH, UNIV TEX, AUSTIN, 65-, HEAD, DEPT AEROSPACE ENG & ENG MECH, 68- *Concurrent Pos:* NSF sci fac fel, Case Western Reserve Univ, 68. *Mem:* Am Geophys Union; Am Soc Eng Educ; Soc Natural Philos; Am Acad Mech. *Res:* Nonlinear oscillations; gravity waves; flow through porous media; slow viscous flow; convective heat transfer. *Mailing Add:* 5824 Trailridge Dr Austin TX 78731

MACK, MARK PHILIP, b Buffalo, NY, Jan 14, 50. ORGANIC CHEMISTRY, POLYMER CHEMISTRY. *Educ:* State Univ NY, Col Buffalo, BA, 71; State Univ NY Buffalo, PhD(chem), 76. *Prof Exp:* Res assoc, Duke Univ, 75-77; res scientist chem, Continental Oil Co, Okla, 77-80, GROUP LEADER, CONOCO, INC, 80- *Concurrent Pos:* Samuel B Silbert fel, State Univ NY, Buffalo, 74-75. *Mem:* Am Chem Soc; Sigma Xi; Soc Plastic Engrs. *Res:* Synthesis and processing of alpha-olefin polymers; drag reducers; flow improvers; high density polyethylene; linear, low density polyethylene. *Mailing Add:* Conoco Res & Develop Bldg PO Box 1267 Ponca City OK 74603

MACK, REX CHARLES, physics, see previous edition

MACK, RICHARD BRUCE, b South Paris, Maine, Sept 18, 28; m 54. ELECTROMAGNETIC MEASUREMENT TECHNIQUES, ANTENNAS. *Educ:* Colby Col, BA, 51; Harvard Univ, MS, 57, PhD, 64. *Prof Exp:* Physicist electromagnetic, Air Force Cambridge Res Labs, 51-77; CONSULT ELECTROMAGNETIC MEASUREMENT TECH, 80- *Concurrent Pos:* consult, appl electromagnetics, 77-80. *Mem:* Inst Elec & Electronics Engrs; Antenna & Propagation Soc; Microwave Theory & Tech Soc; Antenna Measurement Tech Asn. *Res:* Experimental techniques for measurement of electromagnetic scattered fields; radar scattering control; measurment techniques for evaluating microwave properties of materials. *Mailing Add:* 35 Kenwin Rd Winchester MA 01890

MACK, RICHARD NORTON, b Providence, RI, July 31, 45; m 72; c 1. PLANT ECOLOGY. *Educ:* Western State Col Colo, BA, 67; Wash State Univ, PhD(bot), 71. *Prof Exp:* Instr bot, Wash State Univ, 70; asst prof biol sci, Kent State Univ, 71-75; asst prof, 75-79, ASSOC PROF BOT/BIOL, WASH STATE UNIV, 79- *Concurrent Pos:* Res assoc, Univ Col N Wales, Bangor, 73-74. *Mem:* Ecol Soc Am; Brit Ecol Soc; Am Quaternary Asn. *Res:* Plant population biology; community ecology; Holocene vegetation history of Pacific Northwest. *Mailing Add:* Dept of Bot Wash State Univ Pullman WA 99164

MACK, ROBERT EMMET, b Morris, Ill, Mar 26, 24; m 51; c 5. INTERNAL MEDICINE. *Educ:* Univ Notre Dame, BS, 46; St Louis Univ, MD, 48. *Prof Exp:* From intern to resident internal med, St Louis Univ, 48-52, from instr to asst prof, 53-61; chief med serv, Hutzel Hosp, 61-66, med dir, 65-66, dir, 66-70; asst prof, 61-67, PROF INTERNAL MED, SCH MED, WAYNE STATE UNIV, 67-; PRES, HUTZEL HOSP, 70- *Concurrent Pos:* Chief, Med Serv, Vet Admin Hosp, 56-61; consult, St Louis City Hosp. *Mem:* Am Thyroid Asn; Am Physiol Soc; Endocrine Soc; Am Col Physicians; Am Fedn Clin Res. *Res:* Thyroid gland; cardiac output and coronary blood flow; radioisotopes. *Mailing Add:* Detroit Med Ctr Corp 4201 St Antoine Detroit MI 48201

MACK, TIMOTHY PATRICK, b Poughkeepsie, NY, Mar 17, 53; m 76; c 2. INTEGRATED PEST MANAGEMENT. *Educ:* Colgate Univ, BA, 75; Pa State Univ, MS, 79, PhD(entom), 81. *Prof Exp:* Res technologist statist, Pa State Univ, 81; ASST PROF ENTOM, INTEGRATED PEST MANAGEMENT & ZOOL, AUBURN UNIV, 81- *Concurrent Pos:* Res award, Sigma Xi, 81. *Honors & Awards:* Elco Award, Entom Soc Pa, 80; Award, Potato Asn Am, 80. *Mem:* Entom Soc Am; Am Peanut Res & Educ Soc. *Res:* Integrated pest management systems for soybean and peanut insects; population dynamics, modelling and statistical analysis of insect populations; predator-prey theory. *Mailing Add:* Zool & Entom Dept Auburn Univ 331 Funchess Hall Auburn Univ AL 36849

MCKAGUE, ALLAN BRUCE, b Weston, Ont, Oct 21, 40; m 63; c 2. ORGANIC CHEMISTRY. *Educ:* McMaster Univ, BSc, 62; Univ BC, PhD(chem), 67. *Prof Exp:* Chemist I, Toronto Food & Drug Directorate, 62-63; Nat Res Coun fel, Australian Nat Univ, 67-69; res chemist & res dir indust org chem, Orchem Res Co, 69-71; RES OFF ORGANIC CHEMISTRY, BC RES COUN, 71- *Mem:* Chem Inst Can; Entom Soc Am; Entom Soc Can. *Res:* Applied organic synthesis; organic chemical aspects of pollution; non-poisonous insect control through insect hormones and attractants. *Mailing Add:* Div of Appl Biol 3650 Wesbrook Crescent Vancouver BC V6S 2L2 Can

MCKAGUE, HERBERT LAWRENCE, b Altoona, Pa, June 24, 35; m 63; c 2. GEOLOGY, GEOCHEMISTRY. *Educ:* Franklin & Marshall Col, BS, 57; Wash State Univ, MS, 60; Pa State Univ, PhD(mineral, petrol), 64. *Prof Exp:* Fel gem minerals, Gemol Inst Am, 64-66; asst prof geol, Rutgers Univ, New Brunswick, 66-72; physicist, 72-80, CONTAINMENT PROG LEADER, LAWRENCE LIVERMORE NAT LAB, UNIV CALIF, 72- *Res:* Genesis, mineralogy, petrology and geochemistry of alpine ultramafic rocks; mineralogy of gem minerals; genesis of stratiform type ore deposits; geochemistry of chromite; geologic and geophysical criteria for containment of explosions, geologic interpretation of borehole gravimetry; zeolite mineralogy. *Mailing Add:* Lawrence Livermore Lab Univ of Calif Livermore CA 94550

MACKAL, ROY PAUL, b Milwaukee, Wis, Aug 1, 25; div; c 1. ZOOLOGY, BIOCHEMISTRY. *Educ:* Univ Chicago, BS, 49, PhD(biochem), 53. *Prof Exp:* From instr to asst prof, 53-64, ASSOC PROF BIOCHEM, UNIV CHICAGO, 64-, RES ASSOC BIOL, 53-, UNIV SAFETY & ENERGY COORDR, 74- *Mem:* Am Soc Biol Chemists; Int Soc Cryptozool. *Res:* Virus; bacteriophage; chemical physical anthropology; synthesis of DNA; energy conservation; vertebrate zoology; safety and environmental health. *Mailing Add:* 9027 S Oakley Ave Chicago IL 60620

MACKANESS, GEORGE BELLAMY, b Sydney, Australia, Aug 20, 22; m 45; c 1. IMMUNOLOGY. *Educ:* Univ Sydney, MB & BS, 45; Univ London, dipl clin path, 48; Oxford Univ, MA, 49, DPhil(path), 53. *Prof Exp:* Resident med, Sydney Hosp, 45-46; resident path, Kanematsu Inst, Univ Sydney, 46-47; demonstr, Oxford Univ, 48-53; asst prof, Australian Nat Univ, 54-62; prof microbiol, Univ Adelaide, 62-65; DIR, TRUDEAU INST, 65-; PRES, SQUIBB INST MED RES, 76- *Concurrent Pos:* USPHS traveling fel, Rockefeller Univ, 59-60; USPHS res grant, Trudeau Inst, 65-; consult, USPHS, 66-; adj prof, Sch Med, NY Univ, 68-; consult, Nat Acad Med, 69-71 & US Armed Force Epidemiol Br, 69-; Mem, Bd Sci Consult, Mem Sloan-Kettering Cancer Ctr, 81-, Assembly Life Sci, Nat Res Coun, 81-, Bd Trustees, Josiah Macy Found, 81- *Mem:* AAAS; Am Soc Microbiol; Am Thoracic Soc; Am Asn Immunol. *Res:* Cellular aspects of immunology; resistance to infectious disease; antitumor immunity. *Mailing Add:* Squibb Inst for Med Res PO Box 4000 Princeton NJ 08540

MACKAUER, MANFRED, b Wiesbaden, Ger, June 3, 32; m 59; c 1. ENTOMOLOGY, BIOLOGICAL CONTROL. *Educ:* Univ Frankfurt, Drphilnat, 59. *Prof Exp:* Res asst parasitol, Univ Frankfurt, 59-61; res scientist, Res Inst Belleville, Can Dept Agr, 61-67; chmn dept, 76-81, PROF BIOL SCI, SIMON FRASER UNIV, 67- *Concurrent Pos:* Chmn, Biol Control of Myzus Persicae Proj, Int Biol Prog, 68-74, 68-74. *Mem:* Entom Soc Am; Soc Syst Zool; fel Entom Soc Can; Biol Coun Can. *Res:* Bionomics, phylogeny and taxonomy of parasitic Hymenoptera; host specificity of hymenopterous parasites of aphids; biological controls of pest insects, especially aphids; insect parasitology. *Mailing Add:* Dept of Biol Sci Simon Fraser Univ Burnaby BC V5A 1S6 Can

MCKAVENEY, JAMES P, b Pittsburgh, Pa, Sept 26, 25; m 52; c 2. ANALYTICAL CHEMISTRY. *Educ:* Univ Pittsburgh, BS, 49, MS, 51, PhD(anal chem), 57. *Prof Exp:* Asst technologist chem, Res Div, US Steel Corp, 51-56; assoc chemist, Res Div, Crucible Steel Co Am, 56-58, res engr, 58-59, supvr anal chem, 59-64, mgr, 64-67, assoc dir chem & melting, 67-69; mgr anal serv, 69-76, sr scientist, 76-80, TECHNOL REVIEW SCIENTIST, OCCIDENTAL RES CORP, 80- *Concurrent Pos:* Pres, Pittsburgh Conf Anal Chem & Appl Spectros, 65-66. *Mem:* Am Chem Soc; Am Inst Chemists; Am Soc Testing & Mat; NY Acad Sci; Electrochem Soc. *Res:* Spectroscopy of steel and refractory metals; analysis of industrial acids; semiconductor electrodes as analytical sensors; separation of mercury and other heavy metals from water; protective coatings for metals; analysis of coal and non-ferrous minerals; electrically conductive coatings and articles. *Mailing Add:* 940 Fenn Ct Claremont CA 91711

MACKAY, ALEXANDER LLOYD, b Pictou, Novia Scotia, Sept 20, 47. MOLECULAR BIOLOGY. *Educ:* Dalhousie Univ, BSc, 69; Univ BC, MSc, 71; Univ Oxford, DPhil, 75. *Prof Exp:* RES FEL PHYSICS, UNIV BC, 75- *Res:* Applicaton of nuclear magnetic resonance techniques to the structure and motion of molecules in biological membranes and other systems of biological interest. *Mailing Add:* Dept Physics Univ BC Vancouver BC V6T 1W5 Can

MACKAY, COLIN FRANCIS, b Waterbury, Conn, Sept 21, 26. PHYSICAL CHEMISTRY. *Educ:* Univ Notre Dame, BS, 50; Univ Chicago, PhD(chem), 56. *Prof Exp:* From asst prof to assoc prof, 56-68, PROF CHEM, HAVERFORD COL, 68- *Mem:* AAAS; Am Chem Soc. *Res:* Atomic reactions; chemistry of highly reactive species. *Mailing Add:* Dept of Chem Haverford Col Haverford PA 19041

MCKAY, DALE ROBERT, b Oakland, Calif, Oct 26, 46; m 77; c 1. NUCLEAR MAGNETIC RESONANCE. *Educ:* Calif State Univ, Hayward, BA, 68; Univ Wyo, PhD(physics), 80. *Prof Exp:* RES ASSOC, COLO STATE UNIV, 79- *Mem:* AAAS. *Res:* Solid state nuclear magnetic resonance, applied especially to surfaces studies and semi-conductors. *Mailing Add:* Chem Dept Colo State Univ Fort Collins CO 80523

MACKAY, DONALD ALEXANDER MORGAN, b Gt Brit, Feb 8, 26; nat US; m 52; c 4. FOOD CHEMISTRY. *Educ:* Oxford Univ, BA, 48; Yale Univ, PhD(chem), 54. *Prof Exp:* Proj leader, Evans Res & Develop Corp, NY, 53-56, from assoc dir res to dir res, 56-61; mgr corp res, Gen Foods Corp, 61-64; asst to vpres technol, Coca-Cola Co, 64-66; vpres res & develop, Evans Res & Develop Corp, 66-69; dir spec projs, Snell Div, Booz Allen & Hamilton Inc, 69-73; VPRES RES & DEVELOP, LIFE SAVERS, INC, SQUIBB CORP, 73- *Mem:* Am Chem Soc; Int Asn Dent Res; NY Acad Sci. *Res:* Chromatography; trace analysis; odor measurement; flavor, sulfur and keratin; reaction mechanisms; biogenesis of natural products; product development; consumer studies; new product planning; research organization; dental research; nutrition. *Mailing Add:* 135 Deerfield Lane Pleasantville NY 10570

MACKAY, DONALD CYRIL, b St Stephen, NB, Can, Aug 10, 23; m 51; c 2. SOIL CHEMISTRY, PLANT NUTRITION. *Educ:* McGill Univ, BSc, PhD(agr chem), 54; Cornell Univ, MS, 49. *Prof Exp:* Soil surveyor & lectr chem, Nova Scotia Agr Col, 45-48, soil specialist, 49-51; plant nutritionist, 54-61, HEAD SOIL SCI SECT, RES STA, AGR CAN, 61- *Mem:* Soil Sci Soc Am; Am Soc Agron; Can Soc Soil Sci; Agr Inst Can; Int Soc Soil Sci. *Res:* Diagnosis of plant nutrient status; determination of optimum soil management and fertilizer practices for crop production. *Mailing Add:* Soil Sci Sect Can Agr Res Sta Lethbridge AB T1K 4B1 Can

MACKAY, DONALD DOUGLAS, b Lorne, NS, Apr 29, 08; m 36; c 2. CHEMISTRY. *Educ:* Acadia Univ, BSc, 29. *Prof Exp:* Chemist, Aluminum Co Can, Ltd, 29-31; chemist, McColl-Frontenac Oil Co, 31-35; chemist, Aluminum Co Can, Ltd, 35-36, head tech control, Alumina Plant, 36-37, chief chemist, Demerara Bauxite Co, Ltd Div, 38, from supvr to asst supt, Chem Div, Aluminum Co, 39-42, chem engr, 42-45, chief alumina div, Raw Mat Dept, Aluminium Labs, Ltd Div, 45-49, head, 49-66, vpres div, 59-66, dir, 65-66; managing dir, Indian Aluminium Co, Ltd, Calcutta, 66-69; exec vpres raw mat, Alcan Aluminium Ltd & pres, Alcan Ore Ltd, Montreal, Que, 69-73; ALUMINUM INDUST ADV & CONSULT, 73- *Concurrent Pos:* Dir & vpres, Fluoresqueda, SA, Mex, 57-66; dir, Nfld Fluorspar, Ltd, Nfld & Southeast Asia Bauxites, Ltd, Singapore, 58-66; dir, Alcan Queensland Pty, Ltd, 64-66. *Mem:* Am Chem Soc; Chem Inst Can. *Res:* Investigation and acquisition of raw material deposits throughout the world for the aluminum industry, especially bauxite and fluorspar; appraisal of economics of producing alumina and fluoride materials from these deposits. *Mailing Add:* 200 Clearview Ave Apt 2630 Ottawa ON K1Z 8M2 Can

MCKAY, DONALD EDWARD, b Washington, DC, Aug 21, 38; m 63; c 4. ORGANIC CHEMISTRY. *Educ:* Univ Calif, BS, 60; Univ Ill, PhD(org chem), 66. *Prof Exp:* Asst, Univ Ill, 60-66; res chemist, 66-74, SR RES CHEMIST, ORG CHEM DIV, AM CYANAMID CO, 74- *Mem:* Am Chem Soc. *Res:* Synthetic organic chemistry; small ring compounds; dyestuffs; chemiluminescent reactions; process development. *Mailing Add:* Org Chem Div Am Cyanamid Co Bound Brook NJ 08805

MCKAY, DONALD GEORGE, b Sacramento, Calif, July 24, 21; m 45; c 2. PATHOLOGY. *Educ:* Univ Calif, BS, 43, MD, 45. *Prof Exp:* Instr, Sch Med, Boston Univ, 47-49; asst prof path, Harvard Med Sch, 57-60; Delafield prof & chmn dept, Col Physicians & Surgeons, Columbia Univ, 60-67; PROF PATH, SCH MED, UNIV CALIF, SAN FRANCISCO, 67-, VCHMN DEPT, 69- *Concurrent Pos:* Instr, Sch Med, Tufts Univ, 47-48; mem staff, Dept Path, San Francisco Gen Hosp, 67- *Mem:* AMA; Am Col Path; Am Gynec Soc; Am Col Obstet & Gynec; Am Soc Exp Path. *Res:* Maternal pathology; disseminated intravascular coagulation; toxemia of pregnancy. *Mailing Add:* Dept of Path San Francisco Gen Hosp San Francisco CA 94110

MCKAY, DOUGLAS WILLIAM, b Howland, Maine, Mar 10, 27; c 3. ORTHOPEDIC SURGERY. *Educ:* Univ Maine, BA, 51; Tufts Univ, MD, 55. *Prof Exp:* Intern, Maine Gen Hosp, Bangor, 55-56; resident adult orthop surg & trauma, Vet Admin Prog, McKinney & Dallas, Tex, 56-57; children's orthop surg, Newington Hosp Crippled Children, Conn, 59-60; pvt pract orthop surg, Covington, Ky, 60-61; chief surgeon, Carrie Tingley Hosp Crippled Children Truth or Consequences, NMex, 61-67; chief surgeon, Shriner's Hosp Crippled Children, 67-72; PROF ORTHOP SURG & CHILD HEALTH & DEVELOP, MED SCH, GEORGE WASHINGTON UNIV, 72-; CHIEF PEDIAT ORTHOP SURG, CHILDREN'S HOSP NAT MED CTR, 72-, CHMN DEPT, 78- *Concurrent Pos:* Clin instr, Univ Colo, 61-67; consult, William Beaumont Gen Hosp, US Army, El Paso, Tex, 64-67; adj prof, Univ NMex, 66-67; consult, US Air Force Hosp, Lackland AFB, 67- & Vet Admin Hosp, Shreveport; dir orthop residency prog, Confederate Mem Med Ctr, 68-74; prof orthop & head dept, Sch Med, La State Univ, Shreveport, 69-74. *Mem:* Pediat Orthop Soc (secy, 71-72). *Res:* Orthopedic pathology. *Mailing Add:* Childrens Hosp Nat Med Ctr 111 Michigan Ave NW Washington DC 20010

MCKAY, EDWARD DONALD, III, b Robinson, Ill, June 30, 49; m 69; c 3. QUATERNARY GEOLOGY, ENGINEERING GEOLOGY. *Educ:* Hanover Col, BA, 71; Univ Ill, Urbana, MS, 75, PhD(geol), 77. *Prof Exp:* Geologist, Ill State Geol Surv, 76-80; GEOLOGIST, CONSOL OIL & GAS INC, 80- *Mem:* Am Quaternary Asn. *Res:* Pleistocene glacial history; computer modeling of groundwater flow; geologic disposal of radioactive wastes; geologic site characterization; instrumentation to measure rock mass displacements around excavations; rock and soil mechanics. *Mailing Add:* Consol Oil & Gas Inc 104 W University Ave Urbana IL 61801

MACKAY, FRANCIS PATRICK, b Waterbury, Conn, July 12, 29. ORGANIC CHEMISTRY. *Educ:* Univ Notre Dame, BS, 51; Col Holy Cross, MS, 52; Pa State Univ, PhD(chem). *Prof Exp:* Res chemist, E I Du Pont de Nemours & Co, Inc, 56-58; asst prof, 58-70, ASSOC PROF CHEM, PROVIDENCE COL, 70-, CHMN DEPT, 73- *Mem:* Am Chem Soc; Sigma Xi. *Mailing Add:* 75 Smith Ave Centerdale RI 02911

MCKAY, GORDON B(USH), b Bangor, Maine, Apr 4, 19; m 66; c 9. MECHANICAL ENGINEERING. *Educ:* Univ Maine, BS, 41; Columbia Univ, MS, 46, PhD(mech eng), 51. *Prof Exp:* Trainee, Wright Aeronaut Div, Curtiss-Wright Corp, 41-42, from test engr to sr test engr, 42-46, asst proj engr, 46-48; assoc mech eng, Columbia Univ, 48-51, from asst prof to assoc prof, 51-59; assoc prof & head dept, Univ Wichita, 59-60, prof & head dept, 60-64; prof eng, 64-69, coordr grad study mech eng & aerospace eng depts, 64-69, PROF MECH ENG, UNIV ALA, TUSCALOOSA, 69- *Concurrent Pos:* Consult, Wright Aeronaut Div, Curtiss-Wright Corp, 48-54, Res Div, 57-59, Kennecott Copper Corp, 53-55 & Bergen Res Eng Corp, 55-59; lectr, Sch Med, NY Univ, 57-59; consult, Beech Aircraft Corp, Kans, 63-64, Hayes Int Corp, Ala, 64-70, Que Metal Powders Ltd, Can, 67-71 & Remtech Corp, 71- *Mem:* Am Soc Mech Engrs; Am Helicpoter Soc; Am Inst Aeronaut & Astronaut; Nat Soc Prof Engrs. *Res:* Heat transfer and transport phenomena; thermal problems at hypersonic gas speeds; thermal radiation of gases and particles. *Mailing Add:* 2728 Claymont Cir Tuscaloosa AL 35404

MCKAY, JACK ALEXANDER, b Alhambra, Calif, Apr 3, 42; m 65. PHYSICS. *Educ:* Stanford Univ, BS, 63, MS, 67; Carnegie-Mellon Univ, PhD(physics), 74. *Prof Exp:* RES PHYSICIST, NAVAL RES LAB, 74- *Mem:* Am Phys Soc; Inst Elec & Electronics Engrs; AAAS; Sigma Xi. *Res:* Interaction of high-energy pulsed laser radiation with metals. *Mailing Add:* Code 6630 Naval Res Lab Washington DC 20375

MCKAY, JAMES BRIAN, b Uniontown, Pa, Sept 2, 40; m 65; c 3. ANALYTICAL CHEMISTRY. *Educ:* Phila Col Pharm, BSc, 62; Wayne State Univ, MS, 64, PhD(anal chem), 66. *Prof Exp:* Asst prof chem, Univ Conn, 66-72; CHMN DEPT CHEM, EDINBORO STATE COL, 72-, ASSOC PROF CHEM, 76- *Mem:* Am Chem Soc. *Res:* Solvent extraction; column chromatography; organic reagents; radiochemistry; ion exchange. *Mailing Add:* Dept of Chem Edinboro State Col Edinboro PA 16444

MCKAY, JAMES HAROLD, b Seattle, Wash, July 23, 28; m 47; c 4. MATHEMATICS. *Educ:* Univ Seattle, BS, 48; Univ Wash, MS, 50, PhD(math), 53. *Prof Exp:* Assoc math, Univ Wash, 51-53, instr, 53-54; instr, Mich State Univ, 54-56, asst prof, 56-57; asst prof, Univ Seattle, 57-59; assoc prof, 59-63, PROF MATH, OAKLAND UNIV, 63- *Concurrent Pos:* Assoc dean sci & eng, Oakland Univ, 61-65, chmn dept math, 63-65; NSF fac fel, Univ Calif, Berkeley, 66-67; mem, Nat Coun, Am Asn Univ Profs, 75-78. *Mem:* Am Math Soc; Math Asn Am. *Res:* Algebra. *Mailing Add:* Dept of Math Oakland Univ Rochester MI 48063

MCKAY, JERRY BRUCE, b Wyandotte, Mich, Dec 20, 35; m 58; c 2. ORGANIC CHEMISTRY, POLYMER CHEMISTRY. *Educ:* Mich State Univ, BS, 58; Stanford Univ, MS, 60; Univ Ohio, PhD(org chem), 66. *Prof Exp:* Chemist, Stanford Res Inst, 59-62; res chemist, Dacron Res Lab, 65-68, res supvr, Textile Fibers Dept, 68-71, res & develop supvr, Kinston Plant, 71-73, process supvr, 73-78, DEVELOP ASSOC DACRON RES & DEVELOP, KINSTON PLANT, E I DU PONT DE NEMOURS & CO, INC, 78- *Mem:* Am Chem Soc; Sigma Xi. *Res:* Structure of synthetic fibers, polymer structure and property analysis; monomer and polymer synthesis; organic synthesis; structural analysis of alkaloids; mechanism of organic reactions; polymer process development; resource management; recovery of polymer wastes. *Mailing Add:* E I du Pont de Nemours & Co Box 800 Kinston NC 28501

MACKAY, JOHN KELVIN, surface chemistry, see previous edition

MACKAY, JOHN WARWICK, b Can, June 1, 23; m 48; c 4. SOLID STATE PHYSICS. *Educ:* Univ Sask, BSc, 45; Purdue Univ, MS, 49, PhD(physics), 53. *Prof Exp:* Asst physics, Nat Res Coun Can, 45-46; asst, 46-53, from asst prof to assoc prof, 53-66, PROF PHYSICS, PURDUE UNIV, 66- *Concurrent Pos:* Consult, NASA, 63- *Mem:* Am Phys Soc. *Res:* Microwave electron accelerators; radiation damage in semiconductors. *Mailing Add:* Dept of Physics Purdue Univ West Lafayette IN 47907

MACKAY, JOHNSTONE SINNOTT, chemistry, deceased

MACKAY, KENNETH DONALD, b Detroit, Mich, July 18, 42; m 64; c 2. ORGANIC CHEMISTRY. *Educ:* Univ Mich, BS, 64; Univ Minn, PhD(chem), 69. *Prof Exp:* Sr res chemist, Gen Mills, Inc, 68-74, group leader, Gen Mills Chem, Inc, 74-75, res assoc, 75-77, tech mgr, 77-80, ASSOC DIR RES & DEVELOP, HENKEL CORP, 80- *Mem:* Am Chem Soc; Am Inst Mining, Metall & Petrol Engrs. *Res:* Conformational analysis; physical organic chemistry; organic synthesis; solvent extraction. *Mailing Add:* Henkel Corp 2010 E Hennepin Ave Minneapolis MN 55413

MCKAY, KENNETH GARDINER, b Montreal, Que, Apr 8, 17; m 42; c 2. SOLID STATE ELECTRONICS, TELECOMMUNICATIONS. *Educ:* McGill Univ, BSc, 38, MSc, 39; Mass Inst Technol, ScD(physics), 41. *Prof Exp:* Demonstr physics, McGill Univ, 38-39; jr radio res engr, Nat Res Coun Can, 41-46; res physicist, Bell Tel Labs, 46-52, head phys electronics res, 52-54, physics of solids res, 54-57, dir solid state device develop, 57-59, vpres systs eng, 59-62, exec vpres, 62-66, vpres eng, Am Tel & Tel Co, 66-73; EXEC VPRES, BEL TEL LABS, INC, 73- *Concurrent Pos:* Mem tech adv bd, Dept Com, 70-72; counr, Nat Acad Eng, 71- *Mem:* Nat Acad Sci; Nat Acad Eng; fel Am Phys Soc; fel Inst Elec & Electronics Engrs. *Res:* Secondary electron emission; electron bombardment conductivity; electrical breakdown; light emitting diodes; semiconducting nuclear detectors. *Mailing Add:* Bell Labs 600 Mountain Ave Murray Hill NJ 07974

MACKAY, KENNETH PIERCE, JR, b Detroit, Mich, Feb 7, 39; m 63; c 1. METEOROLOGY, AIR POLLUTION. *Educ:* Univ Mich, BSE, 61, MS, 65; Univ Wis, PhD(meteorol), 70. *Prof Exp:* Asst res meteorologist, Univ Mich, 61-65; res asst meteorol, Univ Wis, 65-69; asst prof, 69-75, assoc prof, 75-80, PROF METEOROL, SAN JOSE STATE UNIV, 80- *Concurrent Pos:* Vis scientist, Univ Autonoma Metropolitana, Mex, 78, Environ Protection Agency, 80. *Mem:* Am Meteorol Soc; Air Pollution Control Asn. *Res:* Statistical analysis applied to wind power potential; performance evaluation of air quality models; boundary layer wind dynamics and turbulence. *Mailing Add:* Dept of Meteorol San Jose State Univ San Jose CA 95192

MCKAY, LARRY LEE, b Oregon City, Ore, June 3, 43; m 64; c 2. MICROBIOLOGY. *Educ:* Univ Mont, BA, 65; Ore State Univ, PhD(microbiol), 69. *Prof Exp:* Res assoc, Mich State Univ, 69-70; from asst prof to assoc prof, 70-78, PROF MICROBIOL, UNIV MINN, ST PAUL, 78- *Honors & Awards:* Pfizer Award, Am Dairy Sci Asn, 76. *Mem:* Am Dairy Sci Asn; Am Soc Microbiol; Inst Food Technol; Int Asn Milk, Food & Environ Sanit. *Res:* Improvement of production strains of microorganisms useful to the dairy and food industry; bacteriophages in food fermentations; physiological and genetic control of acid and flavor production by lactic streptococci; plasmids in food fermenting microorganisms. *Mailing Add:* Dept of Food Sci & Nutrit 1334 Eckles Ave St Paul MN 55108

MACKAY, LOTTIE ELIZABETH BOHM, b Vienna, Austria, June 7, 27; US citizen; m 52; c 4. SCIENCE WRITING, SCIENCE EDUCATION. *Educ:* Vassar Col, AB, 47; Yale Univ, PhD(org chem), 52. *Prof Exp:* Sr res chemist, Standard Oil Develop Corp, 52-53 & Burroughs-Wellcome Co, 53-55; sci consult, Hudson Inst, 67; sci & math ed AV educ mat, Educ AV Corp, 68-70; ed, 70-77, EXEC ED SCI & MATH, AV EDUC MAT, PRENTICE-HALL MEDIA, INC, 77- *Mem:* Nat Sci Teachers Asn; Nat Coun Teachers Math; Am Chem Soc; Am Asn Physics Teachers; Am Nat Metric Coun. *Mailing Add:* 135 Deerfield Lane Pleasantville NY 10570

MCKAY, MICHAEL DARRELL, b Temple, Tex, Jan 5, 44; m 66; c 3. STATISTICS. *Educ:* Univ Tex, BA, 66; Tex A&M Univ, PhD(statist), 72. *Prof Exp:* Res mathematician, Southwest Res Inst, 66-68; asst prof statist, Tex A&M Univ, 71-73; STAFF MEM, LOS ALAMOS NAT LAB, 73- *Mem:* Am Statist Asn; Inst Mgt Sci. *Res:* Model validation; mathematical modeling; computer applications in statistics. *Mailing Add:* Los Alamos Nat Lab MS600 Los Alamos NM 87545

MACKAY, RALPH STUART, b San Francisco, Calif, Jan 3, 24; m 60. BIOPHYSICS, ELECTRONICS. *Educ:* Univ Calif, Berkeley, AB, 44, PhD(physics), 49. *Prof Exp:* Asst physics, Univ Calif, Berkeley, 44-48, elec eng, 47-49, lectr, 49-52, electron microscopist, 46-51, asst prof elec eng, 52-57, dir res & develop lab, Med Ctr, San Francisco, 54-58, assoc res biophysicist, 54-57, lectr, 55-60, assoc clin prof exp radiol & assoc res physicist, 58-60, res biophysicist, Berkeley, 60-67, assoc clin prof optom, 60-62, clin prof, 62-64, biophysicist, Space Sci Lab, 63, lectr med physics, 63-67; PROF BIOL, BOSTON UNIV & PROF SURG, MED CTR, 67- *Concurrent Pos:* Guggenheim fel, Karolinska Inst, Sweden, 56 & 57; vchmn, Inst Elec & Electronics Engrs, 56-58, mem comt eng med & biol, 72-74; vis prof med physics, Alcohol Res Inst, Karolinska Inst, Sweden, 59; Fulbright fel, Cairo Univ, Egypt, 60, vis prof, 60-61; sr scientist, Galapagos Int Sci Proj, 64; US ed, Ultrasonics, 65-; mem res comt, Franklin Park & Stoneham Zoos, Boston, 67-70; Erskine fel, Univ Canterbury, NZ, 69; consult, Dep Proj Off, US Naval Radiol Defense Lab, 56; chronic uremia consult, Nat Inst Arthritis & Metab Dis, 66-69; mem bd dir, Biotronics, Inc, 60-67, mine adv comt, Nat Acad Sci-Nat Res Coun, 61-74, bio-instrumentation adv coun, Am Inst Biol Sci, 65-71 & comt emergency med serv, Nat Res Coun, 68-70; distinguished visitor, US Antarctic Prog, 70; mem bd gov, Int Inst Med Electronics & Biol Eng, Paris, 70-73; vis prof elec eng & comput sci, Univ Calif, Berkeley, 73-74; vis prof radiol, Univ Calif, Davis, 78. *Honors & Awards:* Apollo Award, Am Optom Asn, 62. *Mem:* Sigma Xi; Fel Inst Elec & Electronics Eng; Am Inst Biol Sci; Undersea Med Soc; Biomed Eng Soc. *Res:* Medical engineering; biology. *Mailing Add:* Dept of Biol Boston Univ Boston MA 02215

MACKAY, RAYMOND ARTHUR, b New York, NY, Oct 30, 39; m 66; c 1. PHYSICAL CHEMISTRY. *Educ:* Rensselaer Polytech Inst, BS, 61; State Univ NY Stony Brook, PhD(phys chem), 66. *Prof Exp:* Guest res assoc nuclear eng dept, Brookhaven Nat Lab, 63-64, res assoc chem, 66; res chemist phys res lab, US Army Edgewood Arsenal, Md, 67-69; asst prof, 69-74, assoc prof, 74-80, PROF CHEM, DREXEL UNIV, 80- *Concurrent Pos:* Asst prof exten div, Univ Del, 67-68; consult, Edgewood Arsenal, Md, 70-80; assoc ed, J Am Oil Chemists Soc, 81- *Mem:* AAAS; Am Chem Soc; Sigma Xi; NY Acad Sci; fel Am Inst Chemists. *Res:* Gas-aerosol reactions; photochemistry; liquid crystals; reactions in microemulsions. *Mailing Add:* Dept of Chem Drexel Univ Philadelphia PA 19104

MCKAY, RICHARD A(LAN), b Salt Lake City, Utah, May 19, 27. CHEMICAL & ELECTRICAL ENGINEERING. *Educ:* Calif Inst Technol, BS, 49, MS, 50, PhD(chem eng), 59. *Prof Exp:* Res engr, Dow Chem Co, 50-52; mgr, Nevin H McKay & Co, 52-54; MEM TECH STAFF, JET PROPULSION LAB, CALIF INST TECHNOL, 59- *Mem:* Am Chem Soc. *Res:* Solid propellant engineering; chemical thermodynamics; geothermal process engineering. *Mailing Add:* 3108 Lincoln Ave Altadena CA 91001

MCKAY, ROBERT HARVEY, b Cordova, Alaska, June 12, 27; m 58; c 3. BIOCHEMISTRY. *Educ:* Univ Wash, BS, 53; Univ Calif, PhD(biochem), 59. *Prof Exp:* Asst biochem, Univ Calif, 53-58; fel, Brandeis Univ, 58-61; Am Cancer Soc fel, Harvard Med Sch, 61-63; asst prof, 63-68, ASSOC PROF BIOCHEM, UNIV HAWAII, 68- *Concurrent Pos:* NIH fel, Univ Hawaii, 64-73. *Mem:* AAAS; Am Chem Soc; Am Soc Biol Chem. *Res:* Enzymology; protein chemistry; optical and fluorescent properties of proteins; enzyme-coenzyme interactions; iron metabolism; iron storage proteins. *Mailing Add:* Dept of Biochem & Biophys Univ of Hawaii Honolulu HI 96822

MCKAY, ROBERT JAMES, JR, b New York, NY, Oct 8, 17; m 43; c 4. PEDIATRICS. *Educ:* Princeton Univ, AB, 39; Harvard Univ, MD, 43. *Prof Exp:* From asst prof to assoc prof, 50-55, PROF PEDIAT, UNIV VT, 55-, CHMN DEPT, 50- *Concurrent Pos:* Markle scholar med sci, 50-55; Fulbright lectr, State Univ Groningen, 60. *Mem:* Soc Pediat Res; Am Pediat Soc; Am Soc Human Genetics; Can Pediat Soc; fel Am Acad Pediat. *Res:* Rheumatoid arthritis; chromosomes; genetics. *Mailing Add:* Dept of Pediat Univ of Vt Burlington VT 05401

MACKAY, ROSEMARY JOAN, b Eng, July 18, 36; m 62. FRESH WATER ECOLOGY. *Educ:* Univ London, BSc, 57, Dipl, 58; McGill Univ, MSc, 68, PhD(biol), 72. *Prof Exp:* High sch teacher biol, Govt Kenya, 58-61; high sch teacher biol, St Mary's Acad, Winnipeg, 61-62; engr water anal, Winnipeg Water Works, 62-63; technician med, Montreal Gen Hosp, 63-65; res fel entom, Royal Ont Mus, 73-74; asst prof, 74-79, ASSOC PROF ZOOL, UNIV TORONTO, 79- *Concurrent Pos:* Fel, McGill Univ, 72-73; Nat Res Coun Can fel, 73. *Mem:* NAm Benthol Soc (pres, 81-82); Ecol Soc Am; British Ecol Soc; Freshwater Biol Asn. *Res:* Ecology of aquatic insects, especially trichoptera, with emphasis on resource-partitioning among closely related species; investigating ecology of sympatric Hydropsychidae in streams and rivers; effects of acid precipitation on stream-living invertebrates. *Mailing Add:* Dept of Zool Univ of Toronto Toronto ON M5S 1A1 Can

MCKAY, SANDRA J, b Philadelphia, Pa, Sept 6, 47. SYNTHETIC ORGANIC CHEMISTRY. *Educ:* Dickinson Col, BS, 69; Princeton Univ, MA, 71, PhD(chem), 73. *Prof Exp:* Res chemist, Jackson Lab, 73-78, res chemist, Elastomer Chem Dept, 78-81, SR LAB SUPVR, POLYMER PROD DEPT, E I DU PONT DE NEMOURS & CO, INC, 81- *Mem:* Am Chem Soc. *Res:* Management of laboratory. *Mailing Add:* Polymer Prod Dept Chambers Works E I Du Pont de Nemours & Co Inc Deepwater NJ 08023

MACKAY, THERON L, metallurgy, see previous edition

MACKAY, VIVIAN LOUISE, b Columbus, Ohio, Jan 8, 47. MOLECULAR BIOLOGY, BIOCHEMICAL GENETICS. *Educ:* Capital Univ, BS, 68; Case Western Reserve Univ, PhD(microbiol), 72. *Prof Exp:* Fel biochem, Univ Calif, Berkeley, 72-74; asst res prof, 74-79, ASSOC PROF MICROBIOL, WAKSMAN INST MICROBIOL, RUTGERS UNIV, 79- *Mem:* Am Soc Microbiol; AAAS; Genetics Soc Am. *Res:* Biochemical and genetic investigations of cellular regulatory system in yeast that controls sexual conjugation, meiosis, genetic recombination, and DNA repair. *Mailing Add:* Waksman Inst Microbiol Rutgers Univ PO Box 759 Piscataway NJ 08854

MACKAY, W(ILLIAM) B(RYDON) F(RASER), b Winnipeg, Man, May 21, 14; m 41; c 3. PHYSICAL METALLURGY. *Educ:* Univ Man, BSc, 38; Univ Minn, BMetE, 40, MS, 47, PhD(phys metall), 53. *Prof Exp:* Instr metall eng, Univ Minn, 46-53, asst prof, 53-56; prod develop engr, Atlas Steels Ltd, 56-57, res & develop engr, 58, chief metall engr, 59, actg mgr metall, 60, mgr res & develop, 60-61, dir res & technol, Atlas Titanium Ltd, 62-63, mgr appl res, Atlas Steels Co, 63-66; head dept, 66-77, actg dean, Fac Appl Sci, 76-77, assoc dean, 78-81, PROF METALL ENG, QUEEN'S UNIV, ONT, 66-; PROF MECH ENG, ROYAL MILITARY COL, CAN, 80- *Mem:* Fel Am Soc Metals; fel Eng Inst Can; Metals Soc Brit; Can Soc Mech Engrs; Can Inst Mining & Metall. *Res:* Alloy development; tool, stainless and high strength steels; metal failures; metal processing. *Mailing Add:* Box 95 Ravensview RR 1 Kingston ON K7L 4V1 Can

MACKAY, WILLIAM CHARLES, b Innisfail, Alta, Nov 29, 39; m 63; c 3. ENVIRONMENTAL PHYSIOLOGY, COMPARATIVE PHYSIOLOGY. *Educ:* Univ Alta, BSc, 61, BEd, 65, MSc, 67; Case Western Reserve Univ, PhD(biol), 71. *Prof Exp:* Res assoc physiol, Yale Univ, 70-71; asst prof zool, 71-75, ASSOC PROF ZOOL, UNIV ALTA, 75- *Mem:* AAAS; Freshwater Biol Asn, UK; Am Soc Zool; Can Soc Zool. *Res:* Comparative and environmental physiology of aquatic animals. *Mailing Add:* Dept of Zool Univ of Alta Edmonton AB T6G 2G7 Can

MCKAYE, KENNETH ROBERT, b Camp Lejeune, NC, July 12, 47. ECOLOGY, BEHAVIORAL BIOLOGY. *Educ:* Univ Calif, Berkeley, AB, 70, MA, 72, PhD(zool), 75. *Prof Exp:* Asst prof biol, Yale Univ, 75-81; RES ASSOC PROF, DUKE UNIV, 81- *Mem:* Ecol Soc Am; Soc Study Evolution; Animal Behav Soc; Am Soc Ichthyologists & Herpetologists. *Res:* Evolution of social behavior and the role behavior plays in determining the community structure of animals; study of the behavioral ecology of cichlid fishes. *Mailing Add:* Duke Marine Lab Duke Univ Beaufort NC 28516

MACKE, H(ARRY) JERRY, b Newport, Ky, Aug 26, 22; m 48; c 2. MECHANICAL ENGINEERING. *Educ:* Univ Ky, BS, 47; Harvard Univ, SM, 48, ScD(appl mech), 51. *Prof Exp:* Mech anal specialist, Flight Propulsion Div, Gen Elec Co, 51-63, sr engr, 63-68, mgr appl mech, Aircraft Engine Group, 68-71, consult engr appl mech, Group Eng Div, 71-76, MGR APPL EXP STRESS, AIRCRAFT ENGINE GROUP, AIRCRAFT ENGINE ENG DIV, GEN ELEC CO, 77- *Concurrent Pos:* Adj assoc prof aerospace eng, Univ Cincinnati, 61-67. *Mem:* Am Soc Mech Engrs; Soc Exp Stress Anal. *Res:* Experimental stress analysis; mechanical vibrations; mechanical analysis of aircraft gas turbines. *Mailing Add:* 7305 Drake Rd Indian Hill Cincinnati OH 45243

MCKEAGUE, JUSTIN ALEXANDER, b Sibbald, Alta, Nov 7, 24; m 52; c 5. SOIL GENESIS, SOIL CLASSIFICATION. *Educ:* Univ BC, BA, 47, BSA, 55; Univ Alta, MSc, 58; Cornell Univ, PhD(soils), 61. *Prof Exp:* Res officer, Alta Soil Surv, Can Agr, Edmonton, 55-59, res scientist soil genesis, Soil Res Inst, Can Agr, Ottawa, 62-71, 72-78; RES SCIENTIST, LAND RESOURCE RES INST, 78- *Concurrent Pos:* Res scientist, Res Sta, Ste Foy, Que, 71-72; mem, Can Soil Surv Comt, 65-75; actg dir, Soil Res Inst, Can Agr, Ottawa, 74-75. *Mem:* Soil Sci Soc Am; Int Soc Soil Sci. *Res:* Diagnostic criteria of soil classification; genesis of soils; soil micromorphology. *Mailing Add:* Land Res Inst Agr Can Ottawa ON K1A 0C6 Can

MCKEAN, HARLLEY ELLSWORTH, mathematics, statistics, see previous edition

MCKEAN, JOSEPH WALTER, JR, b Sewickly, Pa, June 11, 44; m 64; c 2. STATISTICS. *Educ:* Geneva Col, Pa, BS, 66; Univ Ariz, MS, 68; Pa State Univ, PhD(statist), 75. *Prof Exp:* Instr math, Waynesburg Col, Pa, 68-72; asst prof math, Univ Tex, Dallas, 75-78; ASST PROF MATH, WESTERN MICH UNIV, KALAMAZOO, 78- *Mem:* Inst Math Statist; Am Statist Asn; Biometric Soc; Math Asn Am. *Res:* Non-parametric statistics; particularly robust statistical methods for linear models based on ranks. *Mailing Add:* Western Mich Univ Kalamazoo MI 49008

MCKEAN, THOMAS ARTHUR, b Boise, Idaho, Jan 27, 41. PHYSIOLOGY. *Educ:* Whitman Col, AB, 63; Univ Ore, PhD(physiol), 68. *Prof Exp:* Fel physiol, Sch Med, Univ Minn, 68-69; asst dir sci mkt, Hoechst Pharmaceut Co, 69-70; asst prof zool & physiol, Univ Wyo, 70-74; ASSOC PROF ZOOL, UNIV IDAHO, 74- *Mem:* AAAS; Am Physiol Soc. *Res:* Oxygen transport to tissues; physiology of diving mammals. *Mailing Add:* Dept of Biol Sci Univ of Idaho Moscow ID 83843

MCKEAN, WILLIAM THOMAS, JR, b Littleton, Colo, Jan 23, 38; m 67; c 1. CHEMICAL ENGINEERING. *Educ:* Univ Colo, BS, 60; Univ Wash, PhD(chem eng), 68. *Prof Exp:* Sr develop engr, Battelle-Northwest, 67-70; assoc prof wood & paper sci & chem eng, NC State Univ, 70-76; MEM STAFF, WEYERHAEUSER CO, WASH, 76- *Concurrent Pos:* Consult, Battelle-Northwest, 71-72. *Mem:* Am Chem Soc; Tech Asn Pulp & Paper Indust; Am Inst Chem Eng. *Res:* Oxidative pulping and odor reduction; slow release agents from pulping waste; kinetics of formation and destruction of malodorous sulfur compounds from pulping systems; recovery of heavy metal from industrial waste water. *Mailing Add:* Weyerhaeuser Co PO Box 1228 Everett WA 98206

MCKEARNEY, JAMES WILLIAM, b Bayshore, NY, Apr 4, 38; div; c 2. PSYCHOPHARMACOLOGY. *Educ:* C W Post Col, LI Univ, BA, 62; Univ Pittsburgh, MS, 65, PhD(psychol, 66. *Prof Exp:* Res fel pharmacol, Harvard Med Sch, 66-68, instr psychobiol, 68-69; staff scientist, 70-72, SR SCIENTIST, WORCESTER FOUND FOR EXP BIOL, 72- *Concurrent Pos:* Prin investr, Nat Inst Mental Health & Nat Inst on Drug Abuse res grants, 70-; adj prof psychol, Boston Univ, 77- *Mem:* Am Soc Pharmacol & Exp Therapeut; Am Psychol Asn; Behav Pharmacol Soc. *Res:* Control of human and animal behavior by external environmental events; the determinants of the effects of drugs on behavior. *Mailing Add:* Worcester Found for Exp Biol 222 Maple Ave Shrewsbury MA 01545

MCKECHNIE, JOHN CLIFF, b Detroit, Mich, Dec 16, 29; m 56; c 5. ELECTRICAL ENGINEERING. *Educ:* Wayne State Univ, BS, 63; Rollins Col, MCS, 70. *Prof Exp:* Lab engr, Redstone Missile, Chrysler Corp, 54-56; elec engr, Dart Missile, Curtiss Wright Corp, 56-58; elec engr, Vickers Hydraulics, 58-62; elec res engr, Martin Marietta Corp, 62-68; ELEC RES ENGR, ADVAN SIMULATION CONCEPTS LABS, NAVAL TRAINING EQUIP CTR, DEPT NAVY, 68- *Res:* Electrooptics; information theory applied to spatial scenes; electrodydraulic and mechanical design; human brainwaves; wheeled vehicle simulation cost studies; electromagnetic interference. *Mailing Add:* Naval Training Equip Ctr Orlando FL 32813

MCKEE, BATES, b Mt Kisco, NY, Jan 10, 34; m 54, 67; c 6. REGIONAL GEOLOGY. *Educ:* Yale Univ, BS, 55; Stanford Univ, PhD(geol), 59. *Prof Exp:* Eng geologist, Calif State Dept Water Resources, 57; from asst prof to assoc prof geol, Univ Wash, 58-72; PRES, MCKEE & MOONEY, INC, 72- *Concurrent Pos:* Affil prof, Dept Geol Sci, Univ Wash, 72- *Mem:* Geol Soc Am; Asn Eng Geologists. *Res:* Engineering geology consulting; petrology and structure; regional tectonics. *Mailing Add:* McKee & Mooney Inc 301 W Kinnear Place Seattle WA 98119

MCKEE, CHRISTOPHER FULTON, b Washington, DC, Sept 6, 42; m 65; c 3. ASTROPHYSICS. *Educ:* Harvard Univ, AB, 63; Univ Calif, Berkeley, PhD(physics), 70. *Prof Exp:* Physicist, Lawrence Livermore Lab, Univ Calif, 69-70; res fel astrophys, Calif Inst Technol, 70-71; asst prof astron, Harvard Univ, 71-74; asst prof, 74-77, assoc prof physics, 77-78, PROF PHYSICS & ASTRON, UNIV CALIF, BERKELEY, 78- *Mem:* Am Astron Soc; Am Phys Soc; Int Astron Union. *Res:* Theoretical astrophysics. *Mailing Add:* Dept Physics Univ Calif Berkeley CA 94720

MCKEE, CLAUDE GIBBONS, b Md, June 30, 30; m 58; c 2. AGRONOMY. *Educ:* Univ Md, BS, 51, MS, 55, PhD(agron), 59. *Prof Exp:* Asst, Univ Md, 51-54, exten instr, 54-56; exec secy, Md Tobacco Improv Found, Inc, 57-62; EXTEN TOBACCO SPECIALIST, UNIV MD, 62- *Res:* Production of Maryland tobacco, especially quality constituents. *Mailing Add:* Box 2005 Largo Rd Upper Marlboro MD 20870

MCKEE, DAVID EDWARD, b Pittsburgh, Pa, July 18, 38; m 61; c 2. MECHANICAL ENGINEERING. *Educ:* Lehigh Univ, BSME, 60; WVa Univ, MSE, 63, PhD(mech eng), 67. *Prof Exp:* Mech design engr, Rust Eng, Pa, 60-62; from instr to asst prof mech eng, WVa Univ, 63-73; eng consult, 77-79, CONSULT SUPVR ENG, E I DU PONT DE NEMOURS & CO INC, 79- *Concurrent Pos:* Consult, Morgantown Energy Res Ctr, US Bur

Mines, 71-73. *Mem:* Am Soc Mech Eng; Am Soc Eng Educ; Sigma Xi. *Res:* Fluid mechanics; two phase flow; irreversible thermodynamics; heat transfer. *Mailing Add:* E I du Pont de Nemours & Co Inc 1007 Market St Wilmington DE 19898

MCKEE, DAVID JOHN, b Detroit, Mich, Jan 11, 47; m 65; c 2. BIOCHEMISTRY. *Educ:* Univ S Fla, BA, 68; Fla State Univ, MS, 71, PhD(sci & human affairs), 76; Duke Univ, MBA, 80. *Prof Exp:* Chemist, Oak Ridge Nat Lab, 65-67; biochem trainee res, Fla State Univ, 68-72; chem lectr gen med chem, Univ S Pac, Suva, Fiji, 73-74; lab dir & environ chemist environ regulation, Tallahassee, Fla, 75-77; chemist & proj mgr criteria doc & health assessments, Environ Criteria & Assessment Off, 77-80, PHYSICAL SCIENTIST & NAT PROG MGR, OFF AIR QUAL PLANNING & STANDARDS, US ENVIRON PROTECTION AGENCY, RES TRIANGLE PARK, NC, 80- *Concurrent Pos:* Mem environ comt, Fla Elec Power Coord Group, 75-77; chmn carbon monoxide criteria doc task force, Environ Criteria & Assessment Off, US Environ Protection Agency, 77-80, co-chmn sulfur oxides/particulate matter criteria doc task force, 78-; prog mgr, Nat Ambient Air Qual Standards, hydrocarbons & ozone, Off Air Qual Planning & Standards/US Environ Protection Agency, 80- *Mem:* Am Chem Soc; NY Acad Sci; AAAS. *Res:* Biochemistry of blood proteins; science and human affairs; organic synthesis; health effects of air and water pollution. *Mailing Add:* Mail Drop 12 Off Air Qual Planning & Standards US Environ Protection Agency Research Triangle Park NC 27711

MCKEE, DOUGLAS WILLIAM, b Toronto, Ont, Can, Oct 6, 30; m 59; c 4. PHYSICAL CHEMISTRY. *Educ:* Univ London, BSc, 51, PhD(chem), 54. *Prof Exp:* Res fel, Nat Res Coun Can, 54-55; Welch fel, Rice Univ, 55-56; res chemist, Linde Co div, Union Carbide Corp, 56-60; RES CHEMIST, RES LABS, GEN ELEC CO, 60- *Concurrent Pos:* Lectr, Canisius Col, 58-60. *Mem:* Am Carbon Soc; Royal Soc Chem; Catalysis Soc. *Res:* Surface chemistry; adsorption; diffusion; ion exchange; catalysis; surface chemistry of carbon; carbon fibers; colloid chemistry and surface activity; fuel cells; corrosion; high temperature materials; coal reactivity. *Mailing Add:* Gen Elec Co PO Box 1088 Schenectady NY 12305

MCKEE, EDWIN DINWIDDIE, b Washington, DC, Sept 24, 06; m 29; c 3. GEOLOGY. *Educ:* Cornell Univ, AB, 28. *Hon Degrees:* ScD, Northern Ariz Univ, 57. *Prof Exp:* Park naturalist, Grand Canyon Nat Park, Nat Park Serv, 29-40; asst dir, Mus Northern Ariz, 41-53; from asst prof to prof geol & head dept, Univ Ariz, 42-53; head, Paleotectonic Mapping Proj, US Geol Surv, 53-63, RES GEOLOGIST, US GEOL SURV, 63- *Concurrent Pos:* Res assoc, Carnegie Inst; collabr, Nat Park Serv, 41-; trustee, Mus Northern Ariz, 54-; prin investr, ERTS-A proj, NASA, 72-74, discipline expert deserts, Sci Support Team, SKYLAB IV, NASA, 73-74; mem, Team Earth Observs, Apollo-Soyuz Test Proj, 74-75. *Honors & Awards:* Twenhofel Medal, Soc Econ Paleont & Mineral, 74. *Mem:* Geol Soc Am; Soc Econ Paleont & Mineral; Paleont Soc; Am Asn Petrol Geologists; AAAS. *Res:* Sedimentation; stratigraphy; paleogeography; global sand seas; the Supai of Grand Canyon. *Mailing Add:* US Geol Surv Fed Ctr Denver CO 80225

MCKEE, EDWIN H, b Phoenix, Ariz, Nov 30, 35; m 65; c 2. GEOLOGY. *Educ:* Yale Univ, BS, 57; Univ Calif, Berkeley, PhD(geol), 62. *Prof Exp:* GEOLOGIST, REGIONAL GEOL BR, US GEOL SURV, 64- *Mem:* Geol Soc Am. *Res:* General geology state of Nevada; potassium-argon radiometric dating. *Mailing Add:* US Geol Surv 345 Middlefield Rd Menlo Park CA 94025

MCKEE, EMBRY ARNOLD, b Columbia, Tenn, July 6, 38; m 81; c 3. PSYCHIATRY. *Educ:* Vanderbilt Univ, BA, 60; Univ Tenn, Memphis, MD, 71. *Prof Exp:* Asst dir, Vanderbilt Univ Hosp, 74-75, dir, Adult Psychiat Outpatient Clin, 75-79. *Concurrent Pos:* Asst prof psychiat, Vanderbilt Univ, 74-78, assoc prof, 78-79, assoc clin prof, 79- *Mem:* Am Psychiat Asn; Soc for Sci Study Sex; Am Asn Sex Educr & Counr. *Res:* Gender identity disorders; sexual dysfunction, heterosexual and homosexual; marital and relationship difficulties. *Mailing Add:* 2012 W End Nashville TN 37203

MCKEE, GUY WILLIAM, b Renovo, Pa, Apr 14, 19; m 45; c 5. AGRONOMY. *Educ:* Pa State Univ, BS, 52, MS, 54, PhD(agron), 59. *Prof Exp:* Soil conservationist, Soil Conserv Serv, USDA, 49-51 & 54; from instr to assoc prof, 54-70, PROF AGRON, PA STATE UNIV, 70- *Honors & Awards:* Pugh Medal, 52. *Mem:* Fel AAAS; Soil Conservation Soc Am; Am Soc Plant Physiol; Am Meteorol Soc; Ecol Soc Am; Am Soc Agron. *Res:* Crop ecology and physiology; microclimatology; seed technology and physiology; improvement of quality of the environment; intra-specific taxonomy of crop species; revegetation of disturbed sites. *Mailing Add:* 219 Tyson Bldg Pa State Univ University Park PA 16802

MCKEE, HERBERT C(HARLES), b San Antonio, Tex, Feb 26, 20; m 48; c 2. RESEARCH ADMINISTRATION. *Educ:* Muskingum Col, BSc, 42; Ohio State Univ, MSc, 47, PhD(chem eng), 49. *Prof Exp:* Res assoc chem eng, Res Found, Ohio State Univ, 48-50; chem engr, Jefferson Chem Co, 50-53; from engr to dir, Southwest Res Inst, 53-76; ASST HEALTH DIR ENVIRON CONTROL, CITY OF HOUSTON HEALTH DEPT, 76- *Concurrent Pos:* Chmn, Tex Air Control Bd, 66-73; mem, Tex Energy Adv Comt, 73-79; mem, Tex Nuclear Adv Comt, 77-80. *Mem:* Am Inst Chem Engrs; Air Pollution Control Asn; Am Acad Environ Engrs; Am Chem Soc; Am Soc Testing & Mat. *Res:* Environmental control; occupational health, noise and radiation; air and water pollution; corrosion; pilot plant design and operation; instrumentation; catalysis. *Mailing Add:* City of Houston Health Dept 1115 N MacGregor Houston TX 77030

MCKEE, J(EWEL) CHESTER, JR, b Madison, Wis, Nov 4, 23; m 69; c 5. ELECTRICAL ENGINEERING. *Educ:* Miss State Univ, BS, 44; Univ Wis, MS, 49, PhD(elec eng), 52. *Prof Exp:* Instr math & elec eng, Miss State Univ, 46-47; part-time instr elec eng, Univ Wis, 47-48; from asst prof to prof, 49-71, head dept elec eng, 57-61, asst dean grad sch, 61-62, coordr res, 62-71, DEAN, GRAD SCH, MISS STATE UNIV, 62-, VPRES RES, 69- *Concurrent Pos:* Exec dir, Gov Emergency Coun for Recovery & Redevelop Planning Following Hurricane Camille, Miss, 69-70; pres, Conf Southern Grad Schs, 73-74; chmn, Coun Grad Schs US, 77-78. *Mem:* AAAS; Sigma Xi; Inst Elec & Electronic Engrs; Nat Soc Prof Engrs; Am Soc Eng Educ. *Res:* Application of analog computers to system analysis; application of digital computers to network synthesis using linear programming techniques. *Mailing Add:* Drawer G Mississippi State MS 39762

MCKEE, JAMES JOSEPH, microbiology, see previous edition

MCKEE, JAMES ROBERT, organic chemistry, see previous edition

MCKEE, JAMES STANLEY COLTON, b Belfast, Northern Ireland, June 6, 30; m 62; c 2. PHYSICS. *Educ:* Queens Univ Belfast, BSc, 52, PhD(theoret physics), 56; Univ Birmingham, DSc, 68. *Prof Exp:* Asst lectr physics, Queens Univ Belfast, 54-56; lectr, Univ Birmingham, 56-64, sr lectr, 64-74; vis prof, Lawrence Radiation Lab, 66-67 & 72; PROF PHYSICS & DIR CYCLOTRON LAB, UNIV MAN, 74- *Mem:* Fel Inst Physics London; Can Asn Physicists. *Res:* Few body problems, nuclear reaction mechanisms, environmental physics, polarisation phenomena and solar physics. *Mailing Add:* Cyclotron Lab Dept Physics Univ Man Winnipeg MB R3T 2N2 Can

MCKEE, JAMES W, b Lawrenceburg, Ky, Sept 25, 32; m 50; c 3. PALEONTOLOGY, SEDIMENTOLOGY. *Educ:* La State Univ, BS, 60, MS, 64, PhD(geol), 67. *Prof Exp:* From instr to prof geol, Univ Wis-Oshkosh, 65. *Res:* Sediment-fossil relationships; paleolimnology; stratigraphy and tectonics, northern Mexico. *Mailing Add:* Geol Dept Univ Wis Oshkosh WI 54901

MCKEE, PATRICK ALLEN, b Tulsa, Okla, Apr 30, 37; m 63; c 5. MEDICAL RESEARCH, HEMATOLOGY. *Educ:* Univ Okla, MD, 62. *Prof Exp:* From intern to resident internal med, Med Ctr, Duke Univ, 62-65; clin assoc epidemiol heart dis, Nat Heart Inst, 65-67; chief resident & fel internal med & hemat, Med Ctr, Univ Okla, 67-69; from assoc med to assoc prof internal med & hemat, 69-75, ASST PROF BIOCHEM, MED CTR, DUKE UNIV, 71-, PROF INTERNAL MED, 75-, CHIEF DIV GEN MED, 76- *Concurrent Pos:* Assoc ed, Circulation, 73-; mem hemat study sect, NIH, 73-; fel coun thrombosis, Am Heart Asn. *Mem:* Am Fedn Clin Res; Am Heart Asn; Am Soc Hemat; Am Soc Biol Chemists; Am Soc Clin Invest. *Res:* Biochemistry of structure-function relationships of human blood coagulation proteins, particularly with respect to mechanisms of thromboses in human disease. *Mailing Add:* Box 3705 Duke Univ Med Ctr Durham NC 27710

MCKEE, RALPH WENDELL, b Boynton, Okla, Nov 13, 12; m 38; c 3. BIOLOGICAL CHEMISTRY. *Educ:* Kalamazoo Col, AB, 34, MS, 35; St Louis Univ, PhD(biochem), 40. *Prof Exp:* Asst, St Louis Univ, 35-39, sr asst, 39-40; instr indust hyg, Sch Pub Health, Harvard Univ, 40-45, assoc biochem, Harvard Med Sch, 45-47, asst prof, 47-52; prof, 53-81, EMER PROF BIOL CHEM & EMER ASST DEAN, UNIV CALIF, LOS ANGELES, 81- *Concurrent Pos:* Head biochem, Cancer Res Inst, New Eng Deaconess Hosp, 50-52. *Mem:* Fel AAAS; Am Chem Soc; Am Soc Biol Chemists; Soc Exp Biol & Med. *Res:* Isolation and chemistry of vitamin K; physiology and toxicology of carbon disulfide; biochemical studies of lewisite and mustard gas; growth, metabolism and nutrition of malarial parasites; interrelationship of ascorbic acid and cortical hormones; cytochemistry; chemistry and metabolism of cancer cells; methycation of niacinamide. *Mailing Add:* Dept Biol Chem Univ Calif Sch Pub Health Los Angeles CA 90024

MCKEE, ROBERT B(RUCE), JR, b Kalispell, Mont, Jan 15, 24; m 49; c 3. MECHANICAL ENGINEERING. *Educ:* Mont State Col, BSc, 48; Univ Wash, MSc, 52; Univ Calif, Los Angeles, PhD(eng), 67. *Prof Exp:* Test engr, Pratt & Whitney Aircraft Div, United Aircraft Corp, 48-50; mech engr, Dow Chem Co, 52-56; from asst prof to assoc prof mech eng, 57-72, PROF MECH ENG, UNIV NEV, RENO, 72- *Mem:* Am Soc Mech Engrs; Nat Soc Prof Engrs; Am Soc Heating, Ventilating & Refrig Engrs; Int Solar Energy Soc. *Res:* Plastics fabrication and physical testing; energy conservation; solar energy. *Mailing Add:* Dept of Mech Eng Univ of Nev Reno NV 89557

MCKEE, ROBERT LAMBERT, b Wilkes-Barre, Pa, June 8, 16; m 44. CHEMISTRY. *Educ:* Rice Inst, AB, 38; Univ Tex, MA, 40, PhD(org chem), 43. *Prof Exp:* Instr anal chem, Univ Tex, 38-42 & Naval Flight Prep Sch, 43; Merrell fel, 43-45, from asst prof to assoc prof, 46-55, prof, 55-81, EMER PROF CHEM, UNIV NC, CHAPEL HILL, 81- *Mem:* Am Chem Soc. *Res:* Synthesis of heterocyclic organic compounds to be tested for possible therapeutic use; preparation of N-substituted hydantoins; synthesis of fused pyrimidine systems. *Mailing Add:* Dept of Chem Univ of NC Chapel Hill NC 27514

MCKEE, RODNEY ALLEN, b Freeport, Tex, Oct 1, 47; m 69; c 1. SOLID STATE KINETICS. *Educ:* Lamar Univ, BS, 70; Univ Tex, PhD(mat sci), 75. *Prof Exp:* Metallurgist, Nat Bur Standards, 74-75; MEM STAFF, METALS & CERAMICS DIV, OAK RIDGE NAT LAB, 75- *Concurrent Pos:* Nat Acad Sci-Nat Res Coun assoc, Nat Bur Standards, 74-75. *Mem:* Am Phys Soc; Am Crystallog Asn. *Res:* Kinetics of diffusion processes in solids; thermomigration; oxidation of metals and alloys. *Mailing Add:* Metals & Ceramics Div Oak Ridge Nat Lab PO Box X Oak Ridge TN 37830

MCKEE, RUTH STAUFFER, b Harrisburg, Pa, July 16, 10; m 37; c 2. ALGEBRA. *Educ:* Swarthmore Col, AB, 31; Bryn Mawr Col, MA, 33, PhD(math), 35. *Prof Exp:* Teacher pvt sch, Md, 35-36 & NJ, 36-37; instr algebra, Bryn Mawr Col, 38-39; ANALYST MATH STATIST, JOINT STATE GOVT COMN, 53- *Mem:* Am Math Soc. *Res:* Abstract algebra and statistics. *Mailing Add:* Joint State Govt Comn Main Capital Bldg Harrisburg PA 17120

MCKEE, THOMAS BENJAMIN, b New Castle, Pa, Dec 14, 35; m 59; c 2. ATMOSPHERIC SCIENCE. *Educ:* Univ NC, BS, 58; Col William & Mary, MA, 63; Colo State Univ, PhD(atmospheric sci), 72. *Prof Exp:* Res engr physics, NASA Langley Res Ctr, 58-72; fel atmospheric sci, Colo State Univ, 72, asst prof, 72-73; asst prof environ sci, Univ Va, 73-74; asst prof, 74-77, assoc prof, 77-81, PROF ATMOSPHERIC SCI, COLO STATE UNIV, 81- *Concurrent Pos:* Colo State climatologist, Colo State Univ, 74- *Mem:* Am Meteorol Soc; Am Asn State Climatologists. *Res:* Remote sensing in the atmosphere; transfer of solar radiation in clouds; temperature inversions in mountain valleys; climate. *Mailing Add:* Dept of Atmospheric Sci Colo State Univ Ft Collins CO 80523

MCKEE, W(ILLIAM) DEAN, JR, b Sigourney, Iowa, May 23, 20; m 42; c 3. CERAMICS ENGINEERING. *Educ:* Tarkio Col, AB, 41; Univ Mo-Rolla, BSc, 51, MSc, 52, PhD(ceramic eng), 55. *Prof Exp:* Develop engr, Receiving Tube Sub-Dept, Gen Elec Co, Ky, 53-56; prin ceramist, Ceramic Div, Battelle Mem Inst, 56-57; sr ceramist, Res & Develop Div, Carborundum Co, NY, 57-60, sr res assoc, 60-62; res specialist, Autonetics Div, NAm Aviation, Inc, 62-69, supvr thin film process eng, Rockwell Int, 69-73; HEAD, HYBRID MICROCIRCUIT BR, NAVAL OCEAN SYSTS CTR, 73- *Mem:* Am Ceramic Soc; Inst Elec & Electronics Engrs; Int Soc Hybrid Microelectronics. *Res:* Materials and processes for microelectronics; electronic ceramics; high temperature chemistry and crystal growth; refractory materials. *Mailing Add:* 1279 Bangor St San Diego CA 92106

MCKEE, WILLIAM HENRY, JR, agronomy, see previous edition

MCKEEHAN, CHARLES WAYNE, b Greencastle, Ind, Nov 16, 29; m 53; c 4. PHARMACEUTICAL CHEMISTRY, RESEARCH ADMINISTRATION. *Educ:* Purdue Univ, BS, 51, MS, 53, PhD(pharmaceut chem), 57. *Prof Exp:* Sr pharmaceut chemist, Eli Lilly & Co, 57-62, corp trainee, 62-64, proj coordr new prod, 64-68, head liquid-ointment parenteral prod pilot plants, 68-69, head pharmaceut res, 69-71, head liquid-ointment prod develop, 72-78, HEAD PARENTERAL LIQUID-OINTMENT PROD DEVELOP, ELI LILLY & CO, 79- *Mem:* Am Chem Soc; Am Pharmaceut Asn. *Res:* Planning and coordination of new product development; physical pharmacy; medical and health sciences; research and development administration in the area of new drug dosage forms. *Mailing Add:* 304 Daffon Dr Indianapolis IN 46227

MCKEEHAN, WALLACE LEE, b Texarkana, Tex, Jan 22, 44. CELL BIOLOGY, BIOCHEMISTRY. *Educ:* Univ Fla, BS, 65; Univ Tex, Austin, PhD, 69. *Prof Exp:* Res scientist assoc III, Univ Tex, Austin, 69-70; res scientist, Basel Inst Immunol, Switzerland, 71-73; res assoc molecular, cellular & develop biol, Univ Colo, Boulder, 74-78; asst scientist, 78-79, ASSOC SCIENTIST, W ALTON JONES CELL SCI CTR, 81- *Mem:* Tissue Cult Asn; AAAS; Am Chem Soc. *Res:* Control regulation of cell growth and function. *Mailing Add:* W Alton Jones Cell Sci Ctr Old Barn Rd Lake Placid NY 12946

MCKEEMAN, WILLIAM MARSHALL, b Pasadena, Calif, Aug 20, 34; c 5. SOFTWARE SYSTEMS. *Educ:* Univ Calif, BA, 56; George Washington Univ, MS, 61; Stanford Univ, PhD(comput sci), 66. *Prof Exp:* Instr physics, US Naval Acad, 59-61; asst prof comput sci, Stanford Univ, 66-68; prof info sci, Univ Calif, Santa Cruz, 68-78; staff scientist, Palo Alto Res Ctr, Xerox Corp, 79-80; CHAIR FAC, WANG INST GRAD STUDIES, MASS, 80- *Concurrent Pos:* Indust consult, 61- *Mem:* Asn Comput Mach; Sigma Xi; Inst Elec & Electronics Engrs; Am Asn Univ Professors. *Res:* N-dimensional geometry; design of algorithms; mechanical translators and computing machines; software engineering. *Mailing Add:* Sch Info Technol Inst Grad Studies Tyngsboro MA 01879

MCKEEN, COLIN DOUGLAS, b Strathroy, Ont, June 23, 16; m 42; c 3. PLANT PATHOLOGY. *Educ:* Univ Western Ont, BA, 38; Univ Toronto, MA, 40, PhD(plant path), 42. *Prof Exp:* Class asst bot, Univ Toronto, 38-42; mem, Harrow Res Sta, Can Dept Agr, 46-62, head plant & vegetable path, 62-73, nat res coordr plant path, 73-77, nat leader crop protection coord, 75-78; ed-in-chief, Can J Plant Path, 78-81. *Mem:* AAAS; Am Phytopath Soc; fel Can Phytopath Soc; Can Microbiol Soc; Australian Phytopathol Soc. *Res:* Crop protection in greenhouse and field crops; soil-borne fungal pathogens. *Mailing Add:* 3 Keppler Cresant Ottawa ON K2H 5Y1 Can

MCKEEN, WILBERT EZEKIEL, b Strathroy, Ont, Can, Feb 20, 22; m 50; c 6. PLANT PATHOLOGY. *Educ:* Univ Western Ont, BSc, 45, MSc, 46; Univ Toronto, PhD, 49. *Prof Exp:* Plant pathologist, Sci Serv Ont, 49-51, BC, 51-57; assoc prof, 57-60, PROF PLANT SCI, UNIV WESTERN ONT, 60- *Honors & Awards:* Gold Medal, Univ Western Ont, 45; Wintercorbyn Award, Univ Toronto. *Mem:* AAAS; Am Phytopath Soc; Can Soc Phytopath; Can Soc Microbiol. *Mailing Add:* Dept of Plant Sci Univ of Western Ont London ON N6A 3S5 Can

MCKEEVER, CHARLES H, b Gibson City, Ill, June 6, 12. ORGANIC CHEMISTRY. *Educ:* Ill Wesleyan Univ, BS, 36; Univ Ill, PhD(chem), 40. *Prof Exp:* Org res chemist, Rohm & Haas Co, 40-60, res supvr, 60-72, process & employee health adv, 72-78; RETIRED. *Mem:* Am Chem Soc. *Res:* Process research. *Mailing Add:* 1406 Holcomb Rd Meadowbrook PA 19046

MCKEEVER, L DENNIS, b Pittsburgh, Pa, Jan 23, 41; m 63; c 3. POLYMER CHEMISTRY, PHYSICAL CHEMISTRY. *Educ:* Univ Pittsburgh, BS, 62; Univ Calif, Irvine, PhD(phys chem), 66. *Prof Exp:* Lab dir, Dow Chem Co, 66-73, dir, Cent Res Plastics Lab, Mich, 73-77, MGR CHEM PROD DEPT, DOW CHEM LATIN AM, 77- *Mem:* Am Chem Soc. *Res:* Organo-electrochemistry; organo-alkali metal chemistry; anionic and free radical polymerization; thermoplastics; styrene based polymers; plastic foams. *Mailing Add:* Dow Chem Co Box 340400 Coral Gables FL 33134

MCKEEVER, PAUL EDWARD, b Pasadena, Calif, Dec 3, 46; m 71; c 3. NEUROPATHOLOGY, IMMUNOLOGY. *Educ:* Brown Univ, BS, 68; Univ Calif, Davis, MD, 72; Med Univ SC, PhD(path), 76. *Prof Exp:* Intern anat path, Univ Calif, San Diego, 72-73; resident neuropath, Med Univ SC, 73-76; res assoc immunol, Nat Inst Allergy & Infectious Dis, 76-79, DIR NEUROPATH, SURG NEUROL BR, NAT INST NEUROL DISORDERS & STROKE, NIH, 79- *Concurrent Pos:* USPHS trainee cardiopulmonary med, Univ Calif, San Diego, 72-73; Southern Med Asn guest scientist, Path Inst, Med Univ SC, 75-76; consult neuropath, Lab Path, Nat Cancer Inst, 76-; clin assoc prof, Uniformed Serv Univ Health Sci, 78- *Mem:* Int Acad Path; Am Asn Neuropathologists; Reticuloendothelial Soc; Am Col Physicians; AAAS. *Res:* Membrane and protein receptor cell biology; neoplasms as models of normal neural and immune cell structure. *Mailing Add:* Lab Microbial Immunity NIH Bethesda MD 20014

MCKEEVER, STURGIS, b Renick, WVa, Sept 6, 21; m 46. ECOLOGY, MAMMALOGY. *Educ:* NC State Univ, BS, 48, MS, 49, PhD(animal ecol), 55. *Prof Exp:* Proj leader biol res, WVa Conserv Comn, 49-51; biologist, Commun Dis Ctr, USPHS, 55-57; asst zoologist, Agr Exp Sta, Univ Calif, Davis, 57-63; from asst prof to assoc prof, 63-67, PROF BIOL, GA SOUTHERN COL, 67- *Mem:* Sigma Xi. *Res:* Animal ecology; mammalian reproduction; wildlife diseases and pathology; parasitology of mammals. *Mailing Add:* Dept of Biol Ga Southern Col Statesboro GA 30458

MCKEITH, FLOYD KENNETH, b Billings, Mont, July 3, 55; m 81. MEAT SCIENCE, MUSCLE BIOLOGY. *Educ:* Wash State Univ, BS, 77; Tex A&M Univ, MS, 79, PhD(animal sci), 82. *Prof Exp:* Teaching asst animal sci, Tex A&M Univ, 77-79, res asst, 79-81; ASST PROF ANIMAL SCI, UNIV ILL, URBANA, 81- *Mem:* Am Meat Sci Asn; Am Soc Animal Scientist; Inst Food Technologists. *Res:* Palatability and cutability characteristics of beef, pork, and lamb. *Mailing Add:* 1712 Valley Rd Champaign IL 61820

MACKEL, DONALD CHARLES, b Madison, SDak, Nov 29, 27; m 52; c 3. MEDICAL MICROBIOLOGY. *Educ:* Univ Fla, BS, 50, MS, 51; Tulane Univ, MPH, 65. *Prof Exp:* Bacteriologist, Fla State Bd Health, 50-52 & Armed Forces Epidemiol Bd, Korea, 51; comn officer, 52, lab officer airborne & enteric dis, Centers Dis Control, La, 52-53, asst, Enteric Dis Invest Unit, 53-57, bacteriologist, Phoenix Field Sta, 57-64, asst chief, Biophys Sect, 65-68, asst chief, Microbiol Control Sect, 68-73, dep chief, Epidemiol Invests Lab Br, 73-81, DEP CHIEF, HOSP INFECTIONS LAB BR, USPHS, 81- *Mem:* Fel Am Acad Microbiol; Am Pub Health Asn; Am Soc Microbiol; Sigma Xi; Royal Soc Health. *Res:* Infectious diseases of man and animals; epidemiology of enteric infections; hospital infections. *Mailing Add:* 1742 Timothy Dr NE Atlanta GA 30329

MCKELL, CYRUS MILO, b Payson, Utah, Mar 19, 26; m 47; c 3. RANGE MANAGEMENT, ENVIRONMENTAL SCIENCES. *Educ:* Univ Utah, BS, 49, MS, 50; Ore State Univ, PhD(bot), 56. *Prof Exp:* Asst plant ecol, Univ Utah, 49-50; prin high sch, Utah, 52-53; asst bot, Ore State Univ, 53-55, instr, 55-56; agr res scientist plant physiol, Agr Res Serv, USDA, Univ Calif, Davis, 56-61, assoc prof agron & vchmn dept, Univ Calif, Davis & Univ Calif, Riverside, 61-66, chmn dept, Univ Calif, Riverside, 66-69; head range dept, Utah State Univ, 69-71, dir environ & man prog, 71-76, prof range sci, 69-81, dir inst land rehab, 76-81; VPRES RES, NATIVE PLANTS INC, SALT LAKE CITY, UTAH, 81- *Concurrent Pos:* Consult, Ford Found Mex, 65 & US AID, Bolivia & Ford Found, Agr, 71; Fulbright res fel, Spain, 67-68; panelist, Nat Acad Sci, Brazil, 74 & 76; consult, Food & Agr Orgn, UN, 75 & 78; technol innovation, Nat Acad Sci Comt, 79- *Mem:* Am Soc Agron; Soc Range Mgt; Soil Conserv Soc Am; Sigma Xi. *Res:* Environmental physiology of range plants; rehabilitation of disturbed arid lands; land use planning; range improvement. *Mailing Add:* UMC 52 Utah State Univ Logan UT 84322

MACKELLAR, ALAN DOUGLAS, b Detroit, Mich, Sept 3, 36; m 60; c 2. PHYSICS. *Educ:* Univ Mich, BSE(physics) & BSE(math), 58; Tex A&M Univ, PhD(physics), 66. *Prof Exp:* Nuclear engr, Oak Ridge Nat Lab, 60-61; instr physics, Tex A&M Univ, 61-63; fel, Oak Ridge Nat Lab, 63-65; instr, Mass Inst Technol, 65-67; mem fac, Dept Physics, Rice Univ, 67-68; from asst prof to assoc prof, 68-78, PROF PHYSICS, UNIV KY, 78- *Res:* Theoretical nuclear physics, especially scattering theory; nuclear many body problems and relativistic heavy-ion collisions; theoretical atomic physics, including ion-atom collisions. *Mailing Add:* Dept of Physics & Astron Univ of Ky Lexington KY 40506

MCKELLAR, ARCHIE, electrical engineering, see previous edition

MCKELLAR, HENRY NORTHINGTON, JR, b Lumberton, NC, Feb 4, 47; m 71; c 2. ENVIRONMENTAL SCIENCES, AQUATIC ECOLOGY. *Educ:* Univ NC, BS, 69, MS, 71; Univ Fla, PhD(environ eng sci), 75. *Prof Exp:* Guest researcher plankton ecol, Asko Lab, Univ Stockholm, 75-76; fel ecol models, Baruch Inst, 76-77, ASST PROF ENVIRON HEALTH SCI & MARINE SCI, UNIV SC, 77- *Concurrent Pos:* Baruch res assoc, Belle Baruch Inst Marine Biol & Coastal Res, 77-; co-prin investr, NSF res grant, 77-81, Sci Educ Admin grant, 80-81. *Mem:* Am Soc Limnol & Oceanog; Estuarine Res Fedn. *Res:* Systems ecology; ecological modeling; productivity and nutrient cycling in aquatic envirnoments; eutrophication; environmental impact analysis; environmental planning. *Mailing Add:* Dept of Environ Health Sci Univ of SC Columbia SC 29208

MACKELLAR, WILLIAM JOHN, b Detroit, Mich, July 14, 35; m 62; c 4. ANALYTICAL CHEMISTRY. *Educ:* Concordia Col, Moorhead, Minn, BA, 65; Wayne State Univ, PhD(chem), 70. *Prof Exp:* Asst prof, 69-74, PROF CHEM, CONCORDIA COL, MOORHEAD, MINN, 74- *Concurrent Pos:* Chem analyst, Ctr Environ Studies, Tri Col Univ, 74 & Lower Sheyenne River Basin Study, NDak Water Resources Res Inst, 75-78; res assoc, NDak State Univ, 76-78; chem analyst, Fish & Wildlife Serv, 78-79; res assoc, USDA, 79-80; mem staff, microprocessor controlled instrumentation develop, 79- *Mem:* Am Chem Soc. *Res:* Coordination complex formation reactions and mechanisms; chemical instrumentation; microprocessor based systems; electroanalytical determination of chemical pollutants. *Mailing Add:* 2207 19 1/2 St S Moorhead MN 56560

MCKELLIPS, TERRAL LANE, b Terlton, Okla, Dec 2, 38; m 58; c 2. MATHEMATICS. *Educ:* Southwestern State Col, BSEd, 61; Okla State Univ, MS, 63, EdD(math), 68. *Prof Exp:* Asst prof math, Southwestern State Col, 62-66; instr math & educ, Okla State Univ, 67-68; PROF MATH & CHMN DEPT, CAMERON UNIV, 68- *Concurrent Pos:* Vis assoc prof, Okla State Univ, 72-; consult, Consult Bur, Math Asn Am, 73- *Mem:* Math Asn Am. *Res:* Point set topology. *Mailing Add:* Dept Math Cameron Univ Lawton OK 73501

MCKELVEY, DONALD RICHARD, b Indiana, Pa, June 19, 38; m 60. PHYSICAL ORGANIC CHEMISTRY. *Educ:* NMex Inst Mining & Technol, BS, 60; Carnegie Inst Technol, PhD(chem), 64. *Prof Exp:* Res assoc & instr chem, Univ Pittsburgh, 64-66; asst prof, Cornell Univ, 66-69; assoc prof, 69-73, PROF CHEM, INDIANA UNIV PA, 73- *Concurrent Pos:* Mem staff, Mellon Inst, 64-66. *Mem:* Am Chem Soc; Royal Soc Chem. *Res:* Reaction mechanisms and solvent effects. *Mailing Add:* Dept of Chem Indiana Univ of Pa Indiana PA 15701

MCKELVEY, EUGENE MOWRY, b Greensburg, Pa, June 13, 34; m 60; c 2. INTERNAL MEDICINE, HEMATOLOGY. *Educ:* Yale Univ, BS, 56; Johns Hopkins Univ, MD, 60. *Prof Exp:* From Intern to resident, Boston City Hosp, 60-62; clin assoc, Med Br, Nat Cancer Inst, 62-64; assoc staff physician, Cleveland Clin, 66-67; asst prof med, Northwestern Univ, Chicago, 67-73; assoc prof & assoc internist, 73-80, PROF MED & INTERNIST, M D ANDERSON HOSP & TUMOR INST, 80- *Concurrent Pos:* Fel med, Cleveland Clin, 64-66; hematologist, Vet Admin Res Hosp, Chicago, 67-73. *Mem:* Am Hemat Soc; Am Soc Clin Oncol; Am Asn Cancer Res; AMA; AAAS. *Res:* Oncology; investigational chemotherapy; combined modality treatment; antibody and antigen detection in malignancy. *Mailing Add:* Dept of Develop Therapeut M D Anderson Hosp & Tumor Inst Houston TX 77030

MCKELVEY, JAMES M(ORGAN), b St Louis, Mo, Aug 22, 25; m 52; c 2. CHEMICAL ENGINEERING. *Educ:* Mo Sch Mines, BS, 45; Wash Univ, MS, 47, PhD(chem eng), 50. *Prof Exp:* Instr chem eng, Wash Univ, 46-50; res engr, Exp Sta, E I du Pont de Nemours & Co, 50-54; asst prof chem eng, Johns Hopkins Univ, 54-57; from assoc prof to prof, 57-64, DEAN SCH ENG, WASH UNIV, 64- *Mem:* Am Chem Soc; Am Inst Chem Engrs; Soc Rheol; Soc Plastics Engrs; Am Soc Eng Educ. *Res:* Flow of non-Newtonian fluids; plastics extrusion; polymer processing. *Mailing Add:* Sch of Eng Wash Univ St Louis MO 63130

MCKELVEY, JOHN MURRAY, b Stanley, NC, Nov 1, 37; m 73; c 1. THEORETICAL CHEMISTRY, PHOTOCHEMISTRY. *Educ:* Mercer Univ, AB, 61; Univ of Ga, MS, 65; Ga Inst Technol, PhD(phys org chem), 71. *Prof Exp:* Fel theoret chem, Chem Lab, Advan Normal Sch for Women, Paris, France, 71-73 & Dept of Chem, Univ Calif, Berkeley, 73-75; RES SCIENTIST, EASTMAN KODAK CO, 75- *Mem:* Am Chem Soc. *Res:* Applied quantum mechanics in photochemistry and mechanistic and synthetic organic chemistry. *Mailing Add:* Res Lab Eastman Kodak Co Rochester NY 14650

MCKELVEY, JOHN PHILIP, b Ellwood City, Pa, Nov 9, 26; m 50; c 2. SOLID STATE PHYSICS. *Educ:* Pa State Univ, BS, 49, MS, 50; Univ Pittsburgh, PhD(physics), 57. *Prof Exp:* Asst physics, Pa State Univ, 49-50, instr math, 50-51; res physicist, Res Labs, Westinghouse Elec Corp, 51-59, supvry physicist, 59-62; from assoc prof to prof physics, Pa State Univ, 62-74; PROF PHYSICS & HEAD DEPT PHYSICS & ASTRON, CLEMSON UNIV, 74- *Concurrent Pos:* Asst dean col sci, Pa State Univ, 69-73. *Mem:* Am Asn Physics Teachers; fel Am Phys Soc. *Res:* Semiconductor physics; solid state theory; statistical physics. *Mailing Add:* Dept of Physics & Astron Clemson Univ Clemson SC 29631

MCKELVEY, ROBERT WILLIAM, b Ligonier, Pa, Apr 27, 29; m 52; c 2. MATHEMATICS. *Educ:* Carnegie Inst Technol, BS, 50; Univ Wis, MS, 52, PhD(math), 54. *Prof Exp:* Instr math, Purdue Univ, 54; res fel, Inst Fluid Dynamics & Appl Math, Univ Md, 54-56; from asst prof to prof, Univ Colo, 56-70; PROF MATH, UNIV MONT, 70- *Concurrent Pos:* Fac fel, Univ Colo, 60, chmn dept math, 65-66; mem, Math Res Ctr, Madison, Wis, 64-65; vis prof, Univ Utah, 66-67; exec dir, Rocky Mountain Math Consortium, 67-75. *Mem:* Am Math Soc; Math Asn Am; Soc Indust & Appl Math. *Res:* Asymptotic theory of differential equations; differential boundary value problems; linear operations in Hilbert space; functional analysis; mathematical models. *Mailing Add:* Dept of Math Univ of Mont Missoula MT 59812

MCKELVEY, RONALD DEANE, b Battle Creek, Mich, June 24, 44; div; c 1. PHYSICAL ORGANIC CHEMISTRY, PHOTOCHEMISTRY. *Educ:* Western Mich Univ, BS, 66; Univ Wis-Madison, PhD(org chem), 71. *Prof Exp:* Fel org chem, Univ Calif, Berkeley, 72; assoc prof org chem, Inst Paper Chem, 72-78; LECTR DEPT CHEM, UNIV WIS-LA CROSSE, 78- *Mem:* Am Chem Soc. *Res:* Free radical reactions of carbohydrates; nuclear magnetic resonance. *Mailing Add:* Dept Chem Univ Wis La Crosse WI 54601

MCKELVEY, VINCENT ELLIS, b Huntington, Pa, Apr 6, 16; m 37; c 1. GEOLOGY. *Educ:* Syracuse Univ, BA, 37; Univ Wis, MA, 39, PhD(geol), 47. *Hon Degrees:* DSc, Syracuse Univ, 75 & SDak Sch Mines & Technol, 76. *Prof Exp:* Asst geol, Univ Wis, 37-40; geologist, US Geol Surv, 41-60, asst chief geologist, 60-65, res geologist, 65-71, chief geologist & dir, 71-78, sr res geologist, 78-81; CONSULT, 81- *Honors & Awards:* Distinguished Serv Award, US Dept Interior, 63; Career Serv Award, Nat Civil Serv League, 72; Rockefeller Pub Serv Award, 73; Spec Award Meritorious Serv, Am Asn Petrol Geologists, 77, Human Needs Award, 78; Named Mount McKelvey, Antarctica, US Bd Geog Names, 78. *Mem:* Hon mem Soc Explor Geophysicists; Sigma Xi; Am Inst Mining Engrs; Am Asn Petrol Geologists; Marine Technol Soc. *Res:* Economic geology; physical stratigraphy; mineral economics; seabed resources. *Mailing Add:* 510 Runnymeade Rd St Cloud FL 32769

MCKELVIE, DOUGLAS H, b Collbran, Colo, Mar 15, 27; m 50; c 3. VETERINARY PATHOLOGY. *Educ:* Colo Agr & Mech Col, BS, 50, DVM, 52; Univ Calif, Davis, PhD(comp path), 68; Am Col Lab Animal Med, dipl. *Prof Exp:* Pvt pract, 52-60; res vet, Radiobiol Lab, Univ Calif, 60-68; prof clin sci & dir lab animal med, Col Vet Med & Biomed Sci, Colo State Univ, 68-74; DIR DIV ANIMAL RESOURCES & ASSOC PROF PATH, COL MED, UNIV ARIZ, 74- *Concurrent Pos:* Consult, Hill Found dog breeding grant, Med Sch, Univ Ore, 66-; consult, Am Asn Accreditation Lab Animal Care; assoc ed, Lab Animal Sci, 69-76. *Mem:* Am Vet Med Asn; Am Asn Lab Animal Sci; Am Soc Lab Animal Practr (pres-elect, 77-78, pres, 78). *Res:* Production and care of laboratory dogs; serum chemistry of the dog; effects of internal and external irradiation on maturing and adult bone; laboratory animal medicine and biology. *Mailing Add:* Div Animal Resources Col Med Univ of Ariz Tucson AZ 85724

MCKELVIE, NEIL, b Welwyn Garden City, Eng, Dec 9, 30; US citizen; m 59; c 1. ORGANIC CHEMISTRY. *Educ:* Cambridge Univ, BA, 53; Columbia Univ, PhD(chem), 61. *Prof Exp:* Chemist, Fairey Aviation Co, Eng, 53-54; res chemist, Am Cyanamid Co, Conn, 59-61; res asst, Yale Univ, 61-62; asst prof, 62-76, ASSOC PROF CHEM, CITY COL NEW YORK, 70- *Mem:* Am Chem Soc; Royal Soc Chem; Sigma Xi; NY Acad Sci. *Res:* Organophosphorus chemistry; chemistry of other elements in groups IV, V and VI. *Mailing Add:* Dept Chem City Col New York New York NY 10031

MACKELVIE, ROBIN MAXWELL, bacteriology, see previous edition

MCKELVY, JEFFREY FORRESTER, b Akron, Ohio, Aug 25, 38; m 63; c 2. NEUROBIOLOGY. *Educ:* Univ Akron, BSc, 63; Johns Hopkins Univ, PhD(biochem), 68. *Prof Exp:* Asst prof anat, Health Ctr, Univ Conn, 71-76; ASSOC PROF BIOCHEM, HEALTH SCI CTR, UNIV TEX, DALLAS, 76-, ASSOC PROF PSYCHIAT, 78- *Concurrent Pos:* Jane Coffin Childs Found fel, Weizman Inst Sci, Rehovot, Israel, 68-69 & Roche Inst Molecular Biol, 69-71; panel mem adv panel neurobiol, NSF, 74-77; mem neurol B study sect, NIH, 78-82. *Mem:* Am Soc Neurochem; Am Soc Biol Chemists; Soc Neurosci; Int Soc Neuroendocrinol. *Res:* Biochemical aspects of neuroendocrinology; biosynthesis of hypothalmic releasing hormones; regulation of hypothalamic hormone metabolism; structure and role of central nervous system peptides. *Mailing Add:* Dept of Biochem Univ of Tex Health Sci Ctr Dallas TX 75235

MCKENNA, ARTHUR LEO, III, organic chemistry, see previous edition

MCKENNA, CHARLES EDWARD, b Long Beach, Calif, May 9, 44; m 74. BIO-ORGANIC CHEMISTRY. *Educ:* Oakland Univ, BA, 66; Univ Calif, San Diego, PhD(chem), 71. *Prof Exp:* Res assoc chem, Univ Calif, San Diego, 71-72; NIH fel, Harvard Univ, 72-73; Nat Acad Sci exchange scholar, Bakh Inst, Moscow, 73; asst prof, 73-79, ASSOC PROF CHEM, UNIV SOUTHERN CALIF, 80- *Mem:* Am Chem Soc; Am Soc Biol Chemists. *Res:* Mechanism of biological dinitrogen fixation; molybdoenzymes; biologically important organophosphorous compounds. *Mailing Add:* Dept of Chem Univ of Southern Calif Los Angeles CA 90007

MCKENNA, FRANCIS EUGENE, information science, deceased

MCKENNA, JAMES, mathematics, physics, see previous edition

MCKENNA, JOHN MORGAN, b Providence, RI, Oct 11, 27; m 54; c 6. IMMUNOLOGY. *Educ:* Providence Col, BS, 50, MS, 52; Lehigh Univ, PhD(biol), 59; Am Bd Microbiol, dipl. *Prof Exp:* Res assoc, Sharp & Dohme Res Labs div, Merck & Co, Inc, 55-59; assoc, Harrison Dept Surg Res, Sch Med, Univ Pa, 59-66; from assoc prof to prof microbiol, Sch Med, Univ Mo, 66-72, res assoc, Space Sci Res Ctr, 66-72; chmn dept, 72-78, PROF MICROBIOL, SCH MED, TEX TECH UNIV, 72- *Mem:* AAAS; fel Am Acad Microbiol; Am Soc Microbiol; NY Acad Sci; Reticuloendothelial Soc. *Res:* Antibody formation; virology; tumor immunity. *Mailing Add:* Dept of Microbiol Tex Tech Univ Sch of Med Lubbock TX 79430

MCKENNA, MALCOLM CARNEGIE, b Pomona, Calif, July 21, 30; m 52; c 4. VERTEBRATE PALEONTOLOGY. *Educ:* Univ Calif, AB, 54, PhD(paleont), 58. *Prof Exp:* Instr paleont, Univ Calif, 58-59; asst prof, 60-64, ASSOC PROF GEOL, COLUMBIA UNIV, 64-; FRICK CUR, DEPT VERT PALEONT, AM MUS NATURAL HIST, 68- *Concurrent Pos:* From asst cur to assoc cur, Dept Vert Paleont, Am Mus Natural Hist, 60-65, Frick assoc cur, 65-68. *Mem:* AAAS; Soc Vert Paleont; Am Soc Mammalogists; Soc Study Evolution; Geol Soc Am. *Res:* Evolution of the Mammalia during the late Mesozoic and Cenozoic eras; stratigraphic paleontology of Mesozoic and Cenozoic continental sediments; mammalian order Insectivora and its close allies; plate tectonics; biogeography. *Mailing Add:* Dept Geol Columbia Univ New York NY 10027

MCKENNA, MICHAEL JOSEPH, b Buffalo, NY, Oct 9, 46; m 69; c 2. TOXICOLOGY, PHARMACOLOGY. *Educ:* St John Fisher Col, BA, 68; Univ Rochester, PhD(toxicol), 75. *Prof Exp:* RES SPECIALIST INHALATION TOXICOL, TOXICOL RES LAB, HEALTH & ENVIRON RES, DOW CHEM USA, 75- *Mem:* AAAS; Am Indust Hyg Asn; Sigma Xi; Soc Toxicol. *Res:* Inhalation toxicology, especially assessment of the toxicity, metabolism and pharmacokinetics of inhaled materials as applied to evaluation of their safety. *Mailing Add:* Toxicol Res Lab Dow Chem USA Midland MI 48640

MCKENNA, OLIVIA CLEVELAND, b Pittsburgh, Pa, Mar 6, 39; m 74. NEUROBIOLOGY, NEUROCYTOLOGY. *Educ:* Mt Holyoke Col, AB, 61; Boston Univ, PhD(physiol), 68. *Prof Exp:* From asst res scientist to assoc res scientist neurocytol, Med Ctr, NY Univ, 68-72, asst prof physiol, 72-74; lectr biol & res assoc, Columbia Univ, 74-75; asst prof biol, 75-79, ASSOC PROF BIOL, CITY COL NEW YORK, 80- *Concurrent Pos:* NIH fel, 68-70; adj asst prof physiol, Hunter Col, 74-75. *Mem:* Am Soc Cell Biol; Soc Neurosci; Am Asn Anatomists; NY Acad Sci; Am Soc Zoologists. *Res:* Identification and cytological characterization of brain areas involved in processing of visual information necessary for stabilizing eye movements. *Mailing Add:* Dept of Biol 138th St & Convent Ave New York NY 10031

MCKENNA, ROBERT WILSON, b Graceville, Minn, Oct 30, 40; m 64; c 4. PATHOLOGY. *Educ:* Col St Thomas, Minn, BS, 62; Univ Minn, MD, 66. *Prof Exp:* Med intern, Univ Calif, San Diego, 66-67; fel, 69-73, from instr to asst prof path, 73-77, ASSOC PROF PATH, UNIV MINN, MINNEAPOLIS, 77- *Mem:* Am Soc Hemat; Am Asn Cancer Res; Acad Clin Lab Physicians & Scientists; Am Soc Clin Path. *Res:* Morphology, cytochemistry immunology and ultrastructure of hematologic malignancies. *Mailing Add:* 6939 Morgan Ave S Minneapolis MN 55423

MCKENNA, WILLIAM GILLIES, b Kilmarnock, Scotland, Sept 18, 49; c 74. MEDICAL SCIENCES. *Educ:* Univ Edinburgh, BSc, 72; Albert Einstein Col Med, MD & PhD(cell biol), 81. *Prof Exp:* Intern med, 81-82, ASST RADIATION ONCOL, JOHNS HOPKINS HOSP, 82-, RES ASSOC, DEPT PHARMACOL & EXP THERAPEUTS, SCH MED, 82- *Res:* Use of monoclonal antibodies in cancer therapy. *Mailing Add:* Dept Radiation Oncol Johns Hopkins Hosp Baltimore MD 21218

MCKENNEY, DEAN BRINTON, b Newton, Mass, Mar 1, 40; m 62; c 1. OPTICS. *Educ:* Bowdoin Col, AB, 62; Univ Rochester, MS, 65; Univ Ariz, PhD(optics), 69. *Prof Exp:* Res assoc optics, Univ Ariz, 67-69, asst prof, 69-71; pres, Helio Assocs, Inc, 71-80; MEM STAFF, HUGHES AIRCRAFT CO, 80- *Mem:* Optical Soc Am. *Res:* Physical and thin film optics; optical properties of solids. *Mailing Add:* 440 N Madris Tucson AZ 85710

MCKENNEY, DONALD JOSEPH, b Eganville, Ont, May 3, 33; m 59; c 3. PHYSICAL CHEMISTRY. *Educ:* Univ Western Ont, BSc, 57, MSc, 58; Univ Ottawa, PhD(phys chem), 63. *Prof Exp:* Lectr gen chem, Royal Mil Col Can, 58-60 & Exten Div, Univ Ottawa, 62-63; Nat Res Coun Can fel, Cambridge Univ, 63-64; asst prof, 64-70, ASSOC PROF GEN & PHYS CHEM, UNIV WINDSOR, 70- *Mem:* Chem Inst Can. *Res:* Chemical kinetics; sources and sinks of atmospheric trace gases. *Mailing Add:* Dept Chem Univ Windsor Windsor ON N9B 3P4 Can

MCKENNEY, HENRY F(IELDS), electrical engineering, see previous edition

MCKENNEY, THOMAS WILLIAM, ichthyology, marine biology, see previous edition

MCKENZIE, ALLISTER ROY, b Moose Jaw, Sask. PHYTOPATHOLOGY. *Educ:* Alberta Univ, BSc, 59, MSc, 62; Univ Adelaide, PhD(fungal genetics), 67. *Prof Exp:* RES SCIENTIST, RES BR, AGR CAN, 66- *Mem:* Agr Inst Can; Can Phytopath Soc; Potato Asn Am. *Res:* Tuber-borne potato diseases; disease-indexed stem cuttings. *Mailing Add:* Res Br Agr Can PO Box 20280 Fredericton NB E3B 4Z7 Can

MACKENZIE, ANGUS FINLEY, b Elrose, Sask, Can, Oct 2, 32; m 55; c 3. SOIL CHEMISTRY. *Educ:* Univ Sask, BSA, 54, MSc, 57; Cornell Univ, PhD(soil chem), 59. *Prof Exp:* Asst prof soil chem, Ont Agr Col, 59-62; from asst prof to assoc prof, 62-72, head dept, 66-77, PROF SOIL SCI, MACDONALD COL, MCGILL UNIV, 72-, ASSOC DEAN RES, 80- *Mem:* Am Soc Agron; Can Soc Soil Sci; Int Soc Soil Sci. *Res:* Chemistry of the major forms of nutrients in the soil; soil pollution; organic matter transformations. *Mailing Add:* Dept of Renewable Resources 21111 Lake Shore Rd Ste Anne de Bellevue PQ H9X 1C0 Can

MCKENZIE, BASIL EVERARD, b Jamaica, WI, Sept 14, 35; m 66; c 2. VETERINARY PATHOLOGY. *Educ:* Jamaica Sch Agr, dipl agr, 56; Tuskegee Inst, DVM, 66; Cornell Univ, MSc, 69; Univ Wis, PhD(vet path), 71. *Prof Exp:* Artificial insemination officer, Ministry of Agr & Lands, Jamaica, 56-60; res asst reprod path, Cornell Univ, 66-68; exp pathologist, Lederle Labs, Pearl River, NY, 71-73; from asst prof to assoc prof path, Tuskegee Inst, 73-76; head path, Drug Safety Eval Div, 76-77, DIR DRUG SAFETY EVAL DIV, ORTHO PHARMACEUT CORP, 77- *Concurrent Pos:* Adj prof toxicol, Philadelphia Col Pharm, 81-; expert toxicol & pharmacol, French Ministry Health. *Mem:* Am Vet Med Asn; Sigma Xi; Soc Environ & Pharmacol Pathologists; Am Col Vet Pathologists; Int Acad Path. *Res:* Viral myocarditis; comparative cardiovascular pathology; pathology of the male and female reproductive system. *Mailing Add:* Drug Safety Eval Div Ortho Pharmaceut Corp Raritan NJ 08869

MACKENZIE, CHARLES WESTLAKE, III, b New York, NY, Jan 25, 46; m 69; c 2. BIOCHEMISTRY. *Educ:* Univ Pac, BS, 68; Univ Southern Calif, PhD(biochem), 74. *Prof Exp:* Res chemist, Curtis Nuclear Corp, Los Angeles, 69-70; from teaching asst to res asst biochem, Univ Southern Calif, 71-74; fel pharmacol, Univ Minn, 74-76, res specialist med, 76-78; res assoc pharmacol, 78-79, instr, 79-81, ASST PROF PHARMACOL, UNIV NEBR MED CTR, 81- *Concurrent Pos:* Fel, USPHS, NIH, 75-77. *Res:* Mechanism of action and roles of cyclic nucleotides; biochemical control mechanisms in animal cells; mechanism of action of hormones. *Mailing Add:* Dept Pharmacol Univ Nebr Med Ctr 42nd & Dewey Ave Omaha NE 68105

MACKENZIE, CLYDE LEONARD, JR, b Oak Bluffs, Mass, June 4, 31; m 65; c 1. MARINE BIOLOGY, MARINE ECOLOGY. *Educ:* Univ Mass, BS, 55; Col William & Mary, MA, 58. *Prof Exp:* Res asst marine biol, Va Fisheries Lab, 55-58; asst biologist, Biol Lab, US Bur Com Fisheries, Conn, 58-61, fishery biologist, Lab Exp Biol, Nat Marine Fisheries Serv, US Dept Com, 61-72; oyster consult, Prov Dept Fisheries, PEI, Can, 72-73; FISHERY BIOLOGIST, NAT MARINE FISHERIES SERV, US DEPT COM, 73- *Concurrent Pos:* Oyster consult, Miss Marine Conserv Comn, 75. *Mem:* AAAS; Nat Shellfisheries Asn. *Res:* Predator-prey relationships and food chain systems in benthic communities; biology of predacious gastropods, echinoderms and crustaceans; development of oyster culture. *Mailing Add:* Nat Marine Fisheries Serv Vanderburg Rd Marlboro NJ 07746

MACKENZIE, CORTLANDT JOHN GORDON, b Toronto, Ont, Sept 6, 20; m 45; c 3. PUBLIC HEALTH, EPIDEMIOLOGY. *Educ:* Queens Univ, Ont, MD, CM, 51; Univ Toronto, DPH, 56; Royal Col Physicians Can, cert, 61. *Prof Exp:* Dir health units, Peace River, 54-55, West Kootenay & Selkirk, 56-59 & Cent Vancouver Island, 59-63; from asst prof to assoc prof prev med, 63-71, PROF & DEPT HEAD, HEALTH CARE & EPIDEMIOL, UNIV BC, 71- *Concurrent Pos:* Res fel, Univ BC, 61-62; mem main bd exam, Med Coun Can, 66, chmn prev med exam comt, 72-; vpres, Family Planning Fedn Can, 71-72; consult family planning & birth control, Dept Nat Health & Welfare, 71-72, mem med adv group health of immigrants, 72-; Can deleg, Int Planned Parenthood Western Hemisphere, 72; chmn adv comt pub health option, Brit Col Inst Technol; mem, Pollution Control Bd BC & Traffic Injury Res Found Can; chmn, Royal Comn Herbicides & Pesticides; mem test comt, Med Coun Can. *Mem:* Fel Royal Soc Health; Can Med Asn; Can Pub Health Asn; Can Asn Teachers Social & Prev Med (secy); Asn Teachers Prev Med. *Mailing Add:* Dept of Health Care & Epidemiol Univ of BC Vancouver BC V6T 1W5 Can

MACKENZIE, COSMO GLENN, b Baltimore, Md, May 22, 07; m 36; c 2. BIOCHEMISTRY. *Educ:* Johns Hopkins Univ, AB, 32, ScD(biochem), 36. *Prof Exp:* Asst prof biochem, Sch Hyg & Pub Health, Johns Hopkins Univ, 38-42; from asst prof to assoc prof, Med Col, Cornell Univ, 46-50; chmn dept, 50-73, prof, 50-75, EMER PROF BIOCHEM, SCH MED, UNIV COLO, 75-; ASSOC INVESTR, WEBB-WARING LUNG INST, 75- *Concurrent Pos:* USPHS fel, Johns Hopkins Univ, 36-38. *Mem:* Am Soc Biol Chem; Soc Exp Biol & Med; fel NY Acad Sci; Am Inst Nutrit; fel AAAS. *Res:* Vitamin E; antioxidants; antithyroid action of thioureas and sulfonamides; thyroid-pituitary axis; biochemistry of one-carbon compounds; s-amino acids and enzymes; regulation of lipid metabolism, lipid accumulation and lipid-rich particles in cultured mammalian cells. *Mailing Add:* Webb-Waring Lung Inst 4200 E Ninth Ave Denver CO 80262

MACKENZIE, DAVID BRINDLEY, b Victoria, BC, May 1, 27; nat US; m 54; c 4. GEOLOGY. *Educ:* Calif Inst Technol, BS, 50; Princeton Univ, PhD(geol), 54. *Prof Exp:* Geologist, Am Overseas Petrol Ltd, 53-57; res geologist, 57-63, mgr geol res, 63-77, mgr regional explor, 77-80, MGR MINERALS EXPLOR, DENVER RES CTR, MARATHON OIL CO, 80- *Mem:* Geol Soc Am; Am Asn Petrol Geol; Am Inst Prof Geologists; Geol Asn Can. *Res:* Sedimentology; economic geology; petroleum geology. *Mailing Add:* Marathon Oil Co 1515 Arapahoe St Suite 1300 Denver CO 80120

MACKENZIE, DAVID ROBERT, b Beverly, Mass, Oct 19, 41; m 63; c 3. PLANT PATHOLOGY, PLANT BREEDING. *Educ:* Univ NH, BS, 64; Pa State Univ, MS, 67, PhD(plant path), 70. *Prof Exp:* Res asst plant path, Pa State Univ, 64-70; mem field staff, Rockefeller Found, 70-73; plant breeder, Asian Veg Res & Develop Ctr, 73-74; ASST PROF PLANT PATH, PA STATE UNIV, UNIVERSITY PARK, 74- *Mem:* Am Phytopath Soc. *Res:* Potato breeding and pathology for the development of improved potato cultivars; basic epidemiological investigations through genetic modeling. *Mailing Add:* Dept of Plant Path Buckhout Lab Pa State Univ University Park PA 16802

MCKENZIE, DONALD EDWARD, b Rivers, Man, Aug 9, 24; nat US; m 50; c 3. PHYSICAL CHEMISTRY, ENVIRONMENTAL CHEMISTRY. *Educ:* Univ Man, BSc, 45, MSc, 47; Univ Southern Calif, PhD, 50. *Prof Exp:* Res officer, Atomic Energy Can, Ltd, Chalk River, Ont, 50-57; MGR CHEM TECHNOL, ENERGY SYSTS GROUP, ROCKWELL INT CORP, 57- *Mem:* Am Chem Soc; Sigma Xi; Air Pollution Control Asn. *Res:* High temperature chemistry; fused salts; electrochemistry; air and water pollution; management of research and development for coal gasification and liquefaction; chemical reactions in fused salts; high temperature batteries; disposal of combustible waste; gas scrubbing. *Mailing Add:* Chem Technol Rockwell Int PO Box 309 Canoga Park CA 91304

MACKENZIE, DONALD ROBERTSON, b Man, Can, Dec 9, 21; m 49; c 3. PHYSICAL CHEMISTRY. *Educ:* Queen's Univ, Ont, MA, 44; Univ Toronto, PhD, 50. *Prof Exp:* Asst res officer, Atomic Energy Can, Ltd, 50-58; chemist, Dept Appl Sci, 58-78, CHEMIST, DEPT NUCLEAR ENERGY, BROOKHAVEN NAT LAB, 78- *Mem:* Am Chem Soc; NY Acad Sci; Fedn Am Sci; AAAS; Royal Soc Chem. *Res:* Radiation, fluorine and nuclear chemistry; chemical kinetics of high temperature reactions in coal hydrogenation. *Mailing Add:* Dept of Nuclear Energy Brookhaven Nat Lab Upton NY 11973

MACKENZIE, FREDERICK THEODORE, b Garwood, NJ, Mar 17, 34; m 60; c 2. GEOCHEMISTRY, SEDIMENTOLOGY. *Educ:* Upsala Col, BS, 55; Lehigh Univ, MS, 59, PhD(geol), 62. *Prof Exp:* Geologist, Shell Oil Co, 62-63; staff geochemist & mem corp, Bermuda Biol Sta Res, 63-65; res fel geol, Harvard Univ, 65; vis scholar, 65-66, asst prof geol, 67-69, assoc prof geol sci, 70-72, chmn dept, 70-77, PROF GEOL SCI, NORTHWESTERN UNIV, EVANSTON, 72- *Concurrent Pos:* Vis lectr, Lehigh Univ, 63-65; comt mem, Nat Acad Sci, 72-74; res fel, Univ Brussels, 74; assoc ed, J Sedimentry Petrol, 77-80, Geochem, 79-; prof ocean, Univ Hawaii, 81- *Mem:* Int Asn Cosmochem & Geochem; Am Asn Petrol Geologists; AAAS; Soc Econ Paleont & Mineral; Geol Soc Am. *Res:* Control of the chemical composition of seawater; history of the oceans from a chemical and sedimentologic approach; chemical cycles of the elements and man's contributions. *Mailing Add:* Dept Geol Sci Northwestern Univ Evanston IL 60201

MCKENZIE, GARRY DONALD, b Niagara Falls, Ont, June 8, 41; m 65; c 1. GEOLOGY. *Educ:* Univ Western Ont, BSc, 63, MSc, 64; Ohio State Univ, PhD(geol), 68. *Prof Exp:* Asst to dir, Inst Polar Studies, 68-69, exec officer dept, 69-72, asst prof, 69-75, ASSOC PROF GEOL, OHIO STATE UNIV, 72- *Concurrent Pos:* NSF grant glacial geol, Adams Inlet, Alaska, 66-69; prog assoc, Polar Prog Div, NSF, 80-82. *Mem:* Geol Soc Am; Sigma Xi; Geol Asn Can. *Res:* Quaternary stratigraphy and geomorphology; environmental geology. *Mailing Add:* Dept Geol & Mineral Ohio State Univ Columbus OH 43210

MACKENZIE, GEORGE HENRY, b Bishop Auckland, Eng, Feb 11, 40; m 70; c 2. APPLIED PHYSICS. *Educ:* Univ Birmingham, BSc, 61, PhD(physics), 65. *Prof Exp:* Res assoc physics, Cyclotron Lab, Mich State Univ, 65-68; res assoc physics, 68-75, RES PHYSICIST, TRI-UNIV MESON FACIL PROJ, UNIV BC, 75- *Mem:* Can Asn Physicists. *Res:* Cyclotron beam dynamics and diagnostics; linear and nonlinear optics calculations for beam transport systems; design and commissioning of beam lines; accelerator physics. *Mailing Add:* TRIUMF Proj Univ of BC Vancouver BC V6T 1W5 Can

MACKENZIE, GLENN S, geophysics, see previous edition

MCKENZIE, HUGH, b Indian Head, Sask, Nov 24, 19; m 43; c 3. PLANT BREEDING, PLANT GENETICS. *Educ:* Univ Sask, BSA, 49, MSc, 50; Univ Minn, PhD(plant genetics), 63. *Prof Exp:* Tech officer, Exp Farm, Agr Can, Sask, 50-51, res officer, Res Sta, 51-66, RES SCIENTIST, RES STA, AGR CAN, ALTA, 66- *Mem:* Agr Inst Can; Can Soc Agron; Prof Inst Pub Serv Can. *Res:* Inheritance studies of disease and insect reactions in wheat; breeding improved hard red spring wheat varieties which are resistant to the wheat stem sawfly. *Mailing Add:* Agr Can Res Sta Lethbridge AB T1K 3W1 Can

MACKENZIE, INNES KEITH, b Stornoway, Scotland, Nov 16, 22; Can citizen; m 46; c 5. PHYSICS. *Educ:* Univ Western Ont, BSc, 48, MSc, 49; Univ BC, PhD(physics), 53. *Prof Exp:* Sci officer physics, Can Defence Res Bd, 53-60; from assoc prof to prof, Dalhousie Univ, 60-67; chmn dept, 67-70, PROF PHYSICS, UNIV GUELPH, 67- *Concurrent Pos:* Res grants, 61-; mem, Can Assoc Comt Space Res, 61- *Res:* Positron annihilation; metal defects; physics in archaeology. *Mailing Add:* Dept of Physics Univ of Guelph Guelph Can

MCKENZIE, JAMES MONTGOMERY, b Ashburton, NZ, Nov 10, 25; US citizen; m 51; c 4. RADIATION PHYSICS, ELECTRONICS. *Educ:* Univ Canterbury, BSc, 49, MSc, 51; Univ Otago, PhD(physics), 57. *Prof Exp:* Res physicist, Atomic Energy Can, 56-60; mgr, Amperex Electronic Corp, 60-63; tech dir, Harshaw Chem Co, 63-65; MEM TECH STAFF, BELL LABS, 65- *Mem:* Brit Inst Elec Engrs. *Res:* Use of unfolding codes with quantitative measurements to determine dependent parameters; differential neutron spectra by foil activation; location and source strength of spent-fuel from time-variant radiation measurements; surveillance and containment safeguards for nuclear fuel; radiation detraction. *Mailing Add:* Sandia Labs PO Box 5800 Albuquerque NM 87185

MACKENZIE, JAMES W, b Cleveland, Ohio, Oct 17, 25; m 50; c 1. THORACIC SURGERY. *Educ:* Univ Mich, BS, 48, MD, 51. *Prof Exp:* Resident surg, Univ Mich, 52-53, 55-58, resident thoracic surg, 58-60, instr surg, 60-62; from asst prof to prof, Univ Mo, 62-69; dean, 71-75, PROF SURG & CHMN DEPT, RUTGERS MED SCH, COL MED & DENT NJ, 69- *Concurrent Pos:* Chief sect thoracic & cardiovasc surg, Sch Med, Univ Mo, 62-69; consult, Ellis Fischel State Cancer Hosp, 64-69. *Mem:* Am Col Surg. *Res:* Cardiac surgery. *Mailing Add:* Rutgers Med Sch Col of Med & Dent of NJ Piscataway NJ 08854

MCKENZIE, JESS MACK, b Woodsboro, Tex, Sept 2, 32; m 55; c 2. PHYSIOLOGY. *Educ:* NTex State Col, BA, 54, MA, 56; Univ Tex, PhD(physiol), 59. *Prof Exp:* Physiologist, Dept Space Med, US Air Force Sch Aerospace Med, 58-59; chief hemat sect, 59-67, CHIEF STRESS ANAL RES, PHYSIOL LABS, CIVIL AEROMED INST, 67- *Concurrent Pos:* Adj asst prof zool, Univ Okla, 59-67, adj assoc prof, 67-73, asst prof, Sch Med, 59-74; adj prof zool, Univ Okla, 73- *Mem:* Am Physiol Soc; Soc Exp Biol & Med; Sigma Xi. *Res:* Blood physiology; automated and computer-aided measurement of stress in large populations; effects of stress on health. *Mailing Add:* AAC-115 Civil Aeromed Inst PO Box 25082 Oklahoma City OK 73125

MACKENZIE, JOHN D(OUGLAS), b Hong Kong, Feb 18, 26; nat US; m 54; c 3. MATERIALS SCIENCE, PHYSICAL CHEMISTRY. *Educ:* Univ London, BSc, 52, PhD(phys chem), 54; Royal Inst Chem, FRIC. *Prof Exp:* Asst chem, Princeton Univ, 54-56; Imperial Chem Industs fel, Cambridge Univ, 56-57; phys chemist, Res Labs, Gen Elec Co, 57-63; prof mat sci, Rensselaer Polytech Inst, 63-69; PROF MAT SCI, UNIV CALIF, LOS ANGELES, 69- *Concurrent Pos:* Lectr, Princeton Univ, 55-56; guest lectr, Nat Bur Standards, 59; ed, Physiochem Measurements at High Temperatures, 59; ed, Modern Aspects of the Vitreous State, 60, 62 & 64; ed-in-chief, J Non-Crystalline Solids. *Honors & Awards:* Lebeau Medal, High Temperature Soc France; Meyer Award, Am Ceramic Soc, 64, Toledo Award, 69. *Mem:* Nat Acad Eng; Am Chem Soc; Electrochem Soc; Am Phys Soc; Am Soc Testing & Mat. *Res:* Structure of glasses and liquids; high pressure and high temperature physical chemistry; electronic ceramics; solid waste recycling; biomaterials; glass technology. *Mailing Add:* Mat Div Sch Eng & Appl Sci Univ Calif Los Angeles CA 90024

MCKENZIE, JOHN MAXWELL, b Glasgow, Scotland, Nov 13, 27; m; c 4. INTERNAL MEDICINE, ENDOCRINOLOGY. *Educ:* Univ St Andrews, MB, ChB, 50, MD, 58. *Prof Exp:* House surgeon, Dundee Royal Infirmary, Scotland, 50-51; house physician therapeut unit, Maryfield Hosp, 51; asst, Dept Pharmacol & Therapeut, Univ St Andrews, 53-55; registr, Maryfield Hosp, 55-56; asst med, Sch Med, Tufts Univ, 56-57; registr, Maryfield Hosp, 57-58; instr med, Sch Med, Tufts Univ, 58-59; lect med, McGill Univ, 60-61, from asst prof to prof med & clin med, 61-81; PROF MED & CHMN DEPT, SCH MED, UNIV MIAMI, 81- *Concurrent Pos:* Res fel endocrinol, New Eng Ctr Hosp, 56-57; res assoc endocrinol, New Eng Ctr Hosp, 58-59; clin asst, Royal Victoria Hosp, Montreal, Que, 59-63, assoc physician, 64-67, physician, 67-81; physician-in-chief, Jackson Mem Hosp, Miami, Fla, 81- *Honors & Awards:* Ayerst Award, Endocrine Soc, 61; Killam Award, Can Coun, 80; Park Davis distinguished lectr, Am Thyroid Asn, 81. *Mem:* AAAS; Endocrine Soc; Am Fedn Clin Res; Am Soc Clin Invest; Am Thyroid Asn. *Res:* Pathogenesis of Graves' disease, particularly the role of the thyroid stimulating antibody in that syndrome; investigations of mode of action of thyrotropin in the thyroid gland. *Mailing Add:* Dept Med Med Sch Univ Miami Coral Gables FL 33124

MCKENZIE, JOHN WARD, b Dillon, SC, Sept 11, 18; m 49; c 1. HISTOLOGY, EMBRYOLOGY. *Educ:* The Citadel, BS, 40; Univ SC, MS, 50; Univ NC, PhD(zool), 54. *Prof Exp:* Asst gen biol, Univ SC, 49-50; asst gen zool, Univ NC, 51-54; from asst prof to assoc prof micros anat, 54-74, PROF ANAT, MED COL GA, 74- *Concurrent Pos:* Wilson scholar, Marine Biol Lab, Woods Hole, 52; mem staff, Eugene Talmadge Mem Hosp. *Mem:* AAAS; Electron Micros Soc Am. *Res:* Neurophysiology in primates. *Mailing Add:* Dept of Anat Med Col of Ga Augusta GA 30902

MCKENZIE, JOSEPH ADDISON, b Trinidad, WI, Nov 6, 30; Can citizen; m 57; c 2. ETHOLOGY, BIOCHEMICAL SYSTEMATICS. *Educ:* McMaster Univ, BA, 57; Univ Toronto, MA, 60; Univ Western Ont, PhD(ethology), 64. *Prof Exp:* Fisheries officer, Govt Trinidad & Tobago, 60-61; asst prof zool, Laurentian Univ, 64-67; asst prof zool, 67-69, assoc prof animal behav, 69-76, PROF ANIMAL BEHAV, UNIV NB, 76- *Concurrent Pos:* Nat Res Coun Can operating grants, 64- *Mem:* Can Soc Zoologists. *Res:* Comparative behavior of stickleback family; biochemical systematics of fish. *Mailing Add:* Dept Biol Univ NB Fredericton NB E3B 5A3 Can

MACKENZIE, KENNETH VICTOR, b Brandon, Man, Aug 29, 11; nat US; m 33, 68; c 4. PHYSICS, ACOUSTICS. *Educ:* Univ Wash, Seattle, BS, 34, MS, 36. *Prof Exp:* Physicist, Ore State Hwy Dept, 36-41; head physicist, Puget Sound Magnetic Degaussing Range, US Navy, 41-44; assoc physicist, Appl Physics Lab, Univ Wash, Seattle, 44-46; physics group leader deep & shallow water propagation, US Navy Electronics Lab, San Diego, 46-51, sect head, Oceanog Br, 51-55, head shallow water acoust processes sect, 55-61; exchange scientist from US Off Naval Res to HM Underwater Weapons Estab, Eng, 61-62; head dep submergence group, 62-67, supvry physicist, Acoust Propagation Div, Ocean Sci Dept, Naval Undersea Ctr, 67-73; sr staff physicist & primary adv sci & eng directorate, US Naval Oceanog Off, Washington, DC, 73-76; sr staff physicist, Naval Ocean Res & Develop Activ, 76-79; PRES, MACKENZIE MARINE SCI CONSULT, 80- *Concurrent Pos:* Consult allied govts & defense indust; hon comt mem, Int Ocean Develop Confs, Tokyo, 71-; consult, Japanese & Chinese Oceanog Inst. *Mem:* Fel Acoust Soc Am; Am Geophys Union; fel Marine Technol Soc (co-founder). *Mailing Add:* Marine Sci Consults Midway Sta PO Box 80715 San Diego CA 92138

MCKENZIE, MALCOLM ARTHUR, b Providence, RI, Apr 21, 03. FOREST PATHOLOGY. *Educ:* Brown Univ, PhB & MA, 26, PhD(forest path), 35. *Prof Exp:* Field asst forest path, Forest Prod Lab, US Forest Serv, 26-27; instr biol, Univ NC, 27-29; agent forest path, Bur Plant Indust, USDA, 29-35; pathologist shade tree dis, 35-36, from asst res prof to res prof bot, 36-50, prof plant path & dir shade tree labs, 50-73, EMER PROF PLANT PATH, UNIV MASS, AMHERST, 73-; CONSULT SHADE TREE MGT, 73- *Concurrent Pos:* Lectr, Brown Univ, 29-35; actg head dept entom & plant path, Univ Mass, Amherst, 65-68. *Honors & Awards:* Hon life award, Int Shade Tree Conf, 75. *Mem:* Am Phytopath Soc; Mycol Soc Am; Soc Indust Microbiol; Int Soc Arboriculture. *Res:* Tree pests; Dutch Elm disease; wood decay; tree hazards in public utility work; municipal tree maintenance; continuing education programs in tree workshops and environmental pollution control. *Mailing Add:* PO Box 651 North Amherst MA 01059

MACKENZIE, MALCOLM R, b Oakland, Calif, Jan 15, 35; m 59; c 3. INTERNAL MEDICINE, IMMUNOLOGY. *Educ:* Univ Calif, Berkeley, AB, 56; Univ Calif, San Francisco, MD, 59. *Prof Exp:* Intern & resident, Univ Calif Hosps, San Francisco, 59-62; asst res physician, Div Hemat, Univ Calif, 66-67; asst prof med, Univ Calif, San Francisco, 67-68; asst prof, Univ Cincinnati, 68-70; assoc prof, 70-76, PROF MED, SCH MED, UNIV CALIF, DAVIS, 76- *Concurrent Pos:* USPHS fel physiol chem, Univ Wis, 62-64; Am Cancer Soc fel, Div Hemat, Univ Calif, 65-66; Am Cancer Soc scholar, 66-68. *Mem:* Am Fedn Clin Res; Am Rheumatism Asn; Am Soc Hemat; Am Asn Immunol. *Res:* Structure and function of human IgM antibodies; origin of human lymphocyte malignancies; human multiple myeloma. *Mailing Add:* Dept of Internal Med Univ of Calif Sch of Med Davis CA 95616

MCKENZIE, RALPH NELSON, b Cisco, Tex, Oct 20, 41. MATHEMATICS. *Educ:* Univ Colo, Boulder, BA, 63, PhD(math), 66. *Prof Exp:* From asst prof to assoc prof, 67-77, PROF MATH, UNIV CALIF, BERKELEY, 77- *Concurrent Pos:* NSF fel, Inst Advan Study, 71-72. *Mem:* Am Math Soc; Asn Symbolic Logic. *Res:* Direct products of relational systems; equational varieties of algebras; algorithmicity in algebra. *Mailing Add:* 301 Campbell Hall Univ of Calif Berkeley CA 94720

MACKENZIE, RICHARD STANLEY, b Detroit, Mich, Dec 28, 33; m 57; c 2. DENTISTRY. *Educ:* Univ Mich, DDS, 58, MS, 60; Univ Pittsburgh, PhD(psychol), 65. *Prof Exp:* Assoc prof dent behav sci & head dept, Univ Pittsburgh, 65-68, dir educ res, Sch Dent, 66-69, prof higher educ, Sch Dent Med, 68-69; dir, Off Dent Educ, 69-74, PROF DENT EDUC, COL DENT & COL EDUC, UNIV FLA, 69-, CHMN DEPT, 75- *Concurrent Pos:* Mem USPHS adv comt, Dent Health Res & Educ, 68-72; mem oral biol training comt, Vet Admin Hosps, Washington, DC, 69-72, mem res serv merit rev bd, 72-75; USPHS career develop award, 70-75; consult, WHO-Pan Am Health Orgn, 71-76 & Am Dent Asn, 72-; chmn adv comt, Educ Testing Serv, 73- *Mem:* AAAS; Am Dent Asn; Am Educ Res Asn. *Res:* Analysis and evaluation of clinical judgment. *Mailing Add:* 3715 SE 37th St Gainesville FL 32601

MACKENZIE, ROBERT DOUGLAS, b Chicago, Ill, Aug 18, 28; m 52; c 4. BIOCHEMISTRY. *Educ:* Univ Cincinnati, BS, 52; Mich State Univ, MS, 54, PhD(biochem), 57. *Prof Exp:* Asst, Mich State Univ, 53-57, res assoc, 57; res biochemist, 57-63, head hemat sect, Pharmacol Dept,63-76, sect head, Drug Metab Dept, Merrell-Nat Labs Div, Richards-Merrell, Inc, 76-81, MGR, OPER SAFETY PROCEDURES, MERRELL DOW PHARMACEUT INC, DOW CHEM CO, 81- *Concurrent Pos:* Adj assoc prof, Univ Cincinnati, 67-69; mem coun thrombosis, Am Heart Asn. *Mem:* AAAS; Am Chem Soc; Soc Exp Biol & Med; Am Soc Pharmacol & Exp Therapeut; Sigma Xi. *Res:* Animal and lipid metabolism; blood coagulation; radiobiochemistry; toxicology; nutrition. *Mailing Add:* Merrell Dow Pharmaceut Inc 2110 Galbraith Rd Cincinnati OH 45215

MACKENZIE, ROBERT EARL, b Calif, Mar 17, 20; m 50; c 4. MATHEMATICS. *Educ:* Calif Inst Technol, BS, 42; Princeton Univ, MA, 48, PhD(math), 50. *Prof Exp:* Physicist, US Naval Ord Lab, 42-45; from instr to asst prof math, 50-61, asst chmn dept, 62-67, ASSOC PROF MATH, IND UNIV, BLOOMINGTON, 61- *Concurrent Pos:* Ed, J Math & Mech, 56-62 & 71-76. *Mem:* Am Math Soc. *Res:* Modern algebra and algebraic number theory. *Mailing Add:* 6695 E State Rd 46 Bloomington IN 47401

MCKENZIE, ROBERT LAWRENCE, US citizen. LASER SPECTROSCOPY. *Educ:* Univ Cincinnati, BS, 59; Stanford Univ, MS, 67; York Univ, PhD(physics), 76. *Prof Exp:* RES SCIENTIST, AMES RES CTR, NASA, 59- *Concurrent Pos:* Consult laser applications. *Honors & Awards:* H J Allen Award, NASA, 74. *Mem:* Am Phys Soc. *Res:* Diagnostic applications to turbulent flows. *Mailing Add:* N230-3 Ames Res Lab NASA Moffett Field CA 94035

MCKENZIE, RONALD IAN HECTOR, b Saskatoon, Sask, Oct 8, 30; m 51; c 4. PLANT BREEDING, PLANT GENETICS. *Educ:* Univ Sask, BSA, 51, MSc, 54; Univ Minn, PhD(plant genetics), 57. *Prof Exp:* RES SCIENTIST PLANT BREEDING, AGR CAN RES BR, 56- *Concurrent Pos:* Hon prof plant sci, Univ Man, 65- *Mem:* Agr Inst Can; Genetics Soc Can; Am Soc Agron. *Res:* Development of high yielding strong-strawed rust resistant oats for western Canada and the study of the genetics of rust resistance in oats. *Mailing Add:* Res Sta Agr Can 195 Dafoe Rd Winnipeg MB R3T 3E3 Can

MACKENZIE, SCOTT, JR, b Sedalia, Mo, Mar 10, 20; m 47; c 3. CHEMISTRY. *Educ:* Univ Pa, BS, 42; Univ Ill, MS, 44, PhD(org chem), 47. *Prof Exp:* Res chemist, E I du Pont de Nemours & Co, Va, 44-46; fel, Gen Mills Co, Univ Minn, 47-48; instr chem, Columbia Univ, 48-51; from asst prof to assoc prof, 51-66, PROF CHEM, UNIV RI, 66- *Mem:* Am Chem Soc. *Res:* Organic chemistry; carbanions; ultraviolet spectroscopy. *Mailing Add:* Dept of Chem Univ of RI Kingston RI 02881

MCKENZIE, THOMAS CHARLES, b Auburn, Wash, Aug 20, 45; m 69; c 2. ORGANIC CHEMISTRY. *Educ:* Calif Inst Technol, BS, 67; Columbia Univ, PhD(org chem), 71. *Prof Exp:* Res fel x-ray crystallog, Calif Inst Technol, 72-74; res assoc org synthesis & photochem, Univ SC, 74-75; SR RES CHEMIST, LEDERLE LABS, AM CYANAMID CO, 75- *Mem:* Am Chem Soc; The Chem Soc; Sigma Xi. *Res:* Organic synthesis; x-ray diffraction; discovery of new drugs which act on the central nervous system. *Mailing Add:* Cyanamid Med Res Div Lederle Labs Pearl River NY 10965

MCKENZIE, WALTER LAWRENCE, industrial pharmacy, research administration, see previous edition

MCKENZIE, WENDELL HERBERT, b Wykoff, Minn, Nov 23, 42; m 64; c 2. HUMAN GENETICS. *Educ:* Westmar Col, BA, 64; NC State Univ, MS, 69, PhD(genetics), 73. *Prof Exp:* Teacher, Pub Schs, Iowa, 64-67; res asst genetics, NC State Univ, 68-69, univ instr human genetics, 69-71; res cytogeneticist, Univ Colo Med Ctr, Denver, 72; univ instr human genetics, 73, asst prof, 73-77, ASSOC PROF HUMAN GENETICS, NC STATE UNIV, 77- *Concurrent Pos:* travel grant, Genetics Soc Am, 78. *Mem:* Genetics Soc Am; Am Soc Human Genetics; Am Inst Biol Sci; AAAS; Inst Soc, Ethics & Life Sci. *Res:* Human cytogenetics, including chromosome structure and variation, methodologies of chromosome banding techniques and mutagenic effects of environmental agents as pollutants. *Mailing Add:* Dept of Genetics NC State Univ Raleigh NC 27650

MCKEON, CATHERINE, b Babylon, NY, March 23, 53. GENE REGULATION. *Educ:* Souther Univ NY, Buffalo, BA, 75; Med Col Va, PhD(human genetics), 80. *Prof Exp:* FEL, LAB MOLECULAR BIOL, NAT CANCER INST, NIH, 80- *Concurrent Pos:* Fel, NIH, 80- *Mem:* Am Soc Human Genetics; Sigma Xi. *Res:* Mechanisms controlling the chick and 2(I) collagen gene; methylation status of the gene and the sensitivity of the gene to DNase I in active and inactive chromatin; study of the promoter region to determine which sequences are important for regulation of transcription. *Mailing Add:* Lab Molecular Biol NIH Bldg 37 Room 2D27 Bethesda MD 20205

MCKEON, JAMES EDWARD, b Derby, Conn, June 25, 30; m 52; c 4. ORGANIC CHEMISTRY. *Educ:* Wesleyan Univ, BA, 51, MA, 53; Yale Univ, PhD(org chem), 60. *Prof Exp:* Res chemist, Chem Div, 59-63, res scientist & group leader, 63-69, sr res scientist, 69-73, assoc dir res, 73-77, DIR RES, CHEM & PLASTICS DIV, UNION CARBIDE CORP, 77- *Mem:* Am Chem Soc; Sigma Xi. *Res:* Reactions of molecules coordinated with metals; homogeneous catalysis; oxidation processes. *Mailing Add:* 1103 Washington Common Somerville NJ 08876

MCKEON, MARY GERTRUDE, b New Haven, Conn, June 8, 26. ELECTROCHEMISTRY. *Educ:* Albertus Magnus Col, BA, 47; Yale Univ, MS, 52, PhD(chem), 53. *Prof Exp:* Lab asst, Yale Univ, 49-52; from instr to assoc prof chem, 52-71, dean sophomores, 63-69, Margaret W Kelly prof, 74-77, PROF CHEM, CONN COL, 71-, CHMN DEPT, 77- *Concurrent Pos:* NSF sci fac fel, Harvard Univ, 59-60; vis assoc prof, Wesleyan Univ, 70-71. *Mem:* Am Chem Soc. *Res:* Synthetic organic; organic polarography; electroanalytical chemistry. *Mailing Add:* Dept of Chem Conn Col New London CT 06320

MCKEON, WARREN HOWARD, wildlife management, economic botany, see previous edition

MCKEOWN, JAMES JOHN, b Albert Lea, Minn, Oct 29, 30; m 58; c 3. PHYSICAL CHEMISTRY. *Educ:* St John's Univ, Minn, BS, 53; Iowa State Univ, PhD(chem), 58. *Prof Exp:* Asst chem, Iowa State Univ, 58; res chemist, Procter & Gamble Co, 58-60; sr chemist, 60-64, supvr, 64-66, mgr appl res, 66-69, tech dir dielec mat & systs lab, 69-73, TECH DIR ELECTRONIC PRODS LAB, MINN MINING & MFG CO, 73- *Res:* Ceramics; electronics; engineering management; materials science; microelectronics; polymers. *Mailing Add:* 10055 Ideal Ave N White Bear Lake MN 55115

MCKEOWN, JAMES PRESTON, b Vicksburg, Miss, Mar 2, 37; m 62; c 1. ETHOLOGY. *Educ:* Univ of the South, BS, 59; Univ Miss, MS, 62; Miss State Univ, PhD, 68. *Prof Exp:* From instr to assoc prof, 62-75, PROF BIOL & CHMN DEPT, MILLSAPS 75- *Mem:* AAAS; Am Soc Ichthyol & Herpet. *Res:* Celestial navigation by amphibians; experimental embryology. *Mailing Add:* Dept of Biol Millsaps Col Jackson MS 39210

MCKEOWN, JOSEPH, physics, see previous edition

MCKERNS, KENNETH (WILSHIRE), b Hong Kong, Mar 5, 19; nat US; m 43; c 2. BIOCHEMISTRY. *Educ:* Univ Alta, BSc, 42, MSc, 46; McGill Univ, PhD(biochem), 51. *Prof Exp:* Demonstr, Univ Alta, 40-42; sr demonstr & lectr, McGill Univ, 46-51; chief biochemist, Can Packers, Ltd, Toronto, 51-55; lectr, Univ St Andrews, 55-56; sr res scientist & group leader, Lederle Labs Div, Am Cyanamid Co, NY, 56-60; from assoc prof to prof obstet & gynec, Col Med, Univ Fla, 60-78; PRES, INT FOUND BIOCHEM ENDOCRINOL, 78-; PRES & CHIEF EXEC OFFICER, BIOMOL, INC, 81- *Concurrent Pos:* Fel, McGill-Montreal Gen Hosp Res Inst, 50-51; NIH spec res fel, 69-70; vis lectr, Harvard Med Sch, 69-70; consult, AID, 81- *Mem:* AAAS; Am Soc Biol Chem. *Res:* Endocrine regulation of intermediate metabolism; protein hormone action and purification; effect of hormones on growth, metabolism and disease states; biologically active peptides, synthesis and mechanism action. *Mailing Add:* Roselea House Blue Hill Falls ME 04615

MCKETTA, JOHN J, JR, b Wyano, Pa, Oct 17, 15; m; c 4. CHEMICAL ENGINEERING. *Educ:* Tri-State Col, BS, 37; Univ Mich, BSE, 43, MS, 44, PhD(chem eng), 46. *Hon Degrees:* DrEng, Tri-State Col, 67, Drexel Univ, 77; DrSc, Univ Toledo, 73. *Prof Exp:* Group leader, Tech Dept, Wyandotte Chems Corp, Mich, 37-40, asst supt, Caustic Soda Div, 40-41; chem dir, C B Schneible Co, 41-42; instr chem eng, Univ Mich, 44-45; from asst prof to prof, Univ Tex, 46-52; ed dir, Gulf Pub Co, 52-54; grad prof chem eng, 54-63, chmn dept chem eng, 50-52, 55-63, dean col eng, 63-69, E P SCHOCH PROF CHEM ENG, UNIV TEX, AUSTIN, 70- *Concurrent Pos:* Asst dir, Tex Petrol Res Comt, 51-52, 54-55 & 58-60; mem bd dirs, Vulcan Mat Co, 66- & Eng Joint Coun, 67-; exec vchancellor acad affairs, Univ Tex Syst, 69-70; mem bd dirs, Houston Oil & Mineral Corp, 72-, Marley Corp, 77-, Big Three Corp, 77 & Howell Corp, 78- *Mem:* Nat Acad Eng; Am Chem Soc; Am Gas Asn; Am Inst Mining, Metall & Petrol Engrs; Am Inst Chem Engrs (pres, 62). *Res:* Solubility of hydrocarbon systems at high pressure; vapor-liquid-liquid equilibrium in hydrocarbon-water systems. *Mailing Add:* 310A E P Schoch Labs Univ of Tex Austin TX 78712

MACKEY, BRUCE ERNEST, b Akron, Ohio, Feb 9, 39; m 61; c 2. BIOMETRICS, PLANT BREEDING. *Educ:* Univ Akron, BS, 61; Cornell Univ, MS, 64, PhD(plant breeding), 66. *Prof Exp:* Statistician, Biomet Serv, Md, 66-69, biometrician, Biomet Serv, Calif, 69-71, BIOMETRICIAN, WESTERN REGIONAL RES LAB, SCI & EDUC ADMIN-AGR RES, USDA, 71- *Mem:* Am Stat Asn. *Res:* Applications of quantitative genetics to plant breeding research; design and analysis of agricultural research data. *Mailing Add:* Western Regional Res Lab 800 Buchanan St Berkeley CA 94710

MACKEY, GEORGE WHITELAW, b St Louis, Mo, Feb 1, 16; m 60; c 1. MATHEMATICS. *Educ:* Rice Inst, BA, 38; Harvard Univ, AM, 39, PhD(math), 42; Oxford Univ, MA, 66. *Prof Exp:* Instr math, Ill Inst Technol, 42-43 & Harvard Univ, 43-44; oper analyst, Off Field Servs, Off Sci Res & Develop, 44; assoc res mathematician, Appl Math Group, Columbia Univ, 44-45; from fac instr to prof math, 45-69, LANDON T CLAY PROF MATH & THEORETICAL SCI, HARVARD UNIV, 69- *Concurrent Pos:* Guggenheim fels, 49-50, 61-62, 70-71; George Eastman vis prof, Oxford Univ, 66-67; vis prof, Tata Inst Fundamental Res, India, 70-71. *Mem:* Nat Acad Sci; Am Math Soc (vpres, 64-65); Am Acad Arts & Sci; Am Philos Soc. *Res:* Abstract analysis; infinite dimensional representations of locally compact groups and applications to quantum mechanics and other branches of mathematics. *Mailing Add:* Dept of Math Harvard Univ Cambridge MA 02138

MACKEY, HENRY JAMES, b Vicksburg, Miss, Nov 25, 35; m 59; c 4. SOLID STATE PHYSICS. *Educ:* La State Univ, BS, 57, MS, 59, PhD(physics), 63. *Prof Exp:* Res assoc physics, La State Univ, 63-64; from asst prof to assoc prof, 64-69, PROF PHYSICS, NTEX STATE UNIV, 69- *Mem:* Am Phys Soc. *Res:* Electron, phonon transport phenomena in metals; Fermi surface mappings; surface scattering contribution to electrical resistivity. *Mailing Add:* Dept of Physics NTex State Univ Denton TX 76203

MACKEY, JAMES E, b Tupelo, Miss, Feb 4, 40; m 65; c 4. ENERGY CONSERVATION. *Educ:* Tulane Univ, BS, 62; Univ Miss, MS, 65, PhD(physics), 69. *Prof Exp:* From asst prof to assoc prof, 68-78, PROF PHYSICS, HARDING UNIV, 78- *Concurrent Pos:* Physicist, Westinghouse-Hanford Co, Richland, Wash, 81. *Mem:* Am Asn Physics Teachers. *Res:* Residential energy conservation; ultrasonic second-harmonic generation in solids. *Mailing Add:* Dept Physics Harding Univ Box 582 Searcy AR 72143

MACKEY, JAMES P, b Akron, Ohio, Feb 28, 30; m 50; c 1. BIOLOGY. *Educ:* Univ Akron, BS, 51; Ohio State Univ, MS, 54; Univ Ore, PhD(biol), 57. *Prof Exp:* From asst prof to assoc prof, 57-74, PROF BIOL, SAN FRANCISCO STATE UNIV, 74- *Mem:* Ecol Soc Am; Soc Study Evolution; Am Soc Ichthyol & Herpet. *Res:* Vertebrate ecology; herpetology; intraspecific variation of tree frogs. *Mailing Add:* Div of Natural Sci San Francisco State Univ San Francisco CA 94132

MACKEY, KAREN ETHEL, b Philadelphia, Pa, Jan 13, 45. COMPUTER SCIENCE. *Educ:* Pa State Univ, BS, 65, MS, 68, PhD(comput sci), 73. *Prof Exp:* Instr, Pa State Univ, 71 & 73; asst prof comput sci, State Univ NY Binghamton, 73-76; ASST PROF COMPUT SCI, NORTHERN ILL UNIV, 76- *Mem:* Asn Comput Mach; Am Math Soc; Asn Women in Math. *Res:* Adaptive operating systems; telecommunication networks; data Barr systems; systems programming. *Mailing Add:* 561 Psychol-Math Bldg Northern Ill Univ De Kalb IL 60115

MACKEY, MICHAEL CHARLES, b Kansas City, Kans, Nov 16, 42; m 77; c 5. CYTOLOGY. *Educ:* Univ Kans, BA, 63; Univ Wash, PhD(physiol), 68. *Prof Exp:* Res assoc electrocardiol, Sch Med, Univ Okla, 63-64; biophysicist, Phys Sci Lab, Div Comput Res & Technol, NIH, 69-71; asst prof physiol, 71-75, ASSOC PROF PHYSIOL, MCGILL UNIV, 75- *Mem:* Int Soc Exp Hemat; Am Math Soc; Cell Kinetic Soc; Soc Indust & Appl Math; Soc Math Biol. *Res:* Mathematical modeling of the kinetic aspects of transmembrane ion movement; modeling of the generation of oscillatory behaviour in neural networks; theoretical considerations of normal and neoplastic growth in mammalian breast tissue; oretical studies on biochemistry and control of cell cycle. *Mailing Add:* Rm 1124 Dept Physiol McGill Univ 3655 Drummond Montreal PQ H3G 1Y6 Can

MCKHANN, CHARLES FREMONT, b Boston, Mass, Jan 29, 30; m 54; c 3. SURGERY, MICROBIOLOGY. *Educ:* Harvard Univ, BA, 51; Univ Pa, MD, 55. *Prof Exp:* From instr to asst prof surg, Harvard Med Sch, 64-67; PROF SURG & MICROBIOL, MED CTR, UNIV MINN, MINNEAPOLIS, 68- *Concurrent Pos:* Nat Cancer Inst spec res fel tumor biol, Karolinska Inst, Sweden, 61-62; Am Cancer Soc clin fel, Mass Gen Hosp, Boston, 63-64; Andres Soriano investr oncol, Mass Gen Hosp, 64-67. *Mem:* Am Asn Cancer Res; Transplantation Soc; Am Surg Soc; Am Asn Immunol; Am Col Surg. *Res:* Tumor immunology. *Mailing Add:* Univ of Minn Hosp Box 85 Minneapolis MN 55455

MCKHANN, GUY MEAD, b Boston, Mass, Mar 20, 32; m 57; c 4. NEUROLOGY, NEUROCHEMISTRY. *Educ:* Yale Univ, MD, 55. *Prof Exp:* Intern med, NY Hosp, 55-56; resident pediatrics, Johns Hopkins Hosp, 56-57; res assoc neurochem, Nat Inst Neurol Dis & Blindness, 57-60; resident neurol, Mass Gen Hosp, 60-63; from asst prof to assoc prof pediat & neurol, Sch Med, Stanford Univ, 63-69; PROF NEUROL & EXEC HEAD DEPT, SCH MED, JOHNS HOPKINS UNIV, 69- *Concurrent Pos:* Joseph P Kennedy, Jr scholar, 63-66; John & Mary R Markle scholar acad med, 64-69. *Mem:* Am Acad Neurol; Am Neurol Asn; Am Neurochem Soc; Soc Neurosci. *Res:* Lipid metabolism in the developing nervous system; metabolism of myelin; cellular neurophathology; neuroimmunology. *Mailing Add:* Dept of Neurol Johns Hopkins Univ Sch of Med Baltimore MD 21205

MACKI, JACK W, b Mullan, Idaho, June 16, 39; m 62; c 3. MATHEMATICS. *Educ:* Univ Idaho, BS, 60; Calif Inst Technol, PhD(math), 64. *Prof Exp:* Staff mem, Los Alamos Sci Lab, 64-65; from asst prof to assoc prof, 66-75, PROF MATH, UNIV ALTA, 75-, CHMN, MATH DEPT, 81- *Concurrent Pos:* VChmn, Rocky Mountain Math Consortrum. *Mem:* Soc Indust & Appl Math; Math Asn Am; Am Math Soc. *Res:* Ordinary differential equations; control theory. *Mailing Add:* Dept of Math Univ of Alta Edmonton AB T6G 2G7 Can

MCKIBBEN, GERALD HOPKINS, b Baldwyn, Miss, Aug 23, 39; m 61; c 2. ENTOMOLOGY. *Educ:* Miss State Univ, BSc, 62. *Prof Exp:* RES ENTOMOLOGIST, USDA, 62- *Mem:* Am Chem Soc; Entom Soc Am. *Res:* Insect pheromones; controlled release formulations; computer simulation modeling. *Mailing Add:* PO Box 5367 Mississippi State MS 39762

MCKIBBEN, JOHN SCOTT, b Toledo, Ohio, Jan 25, 37; m 55; c 3. VETERINARY ANATOMY. *Educ:* Purdue Univ, BS, 59, DVM, 63; Iowa State Univ, MS, 66, PhD(vet anat), 69. *Prof Exp:* Clinician vet med, Rowley Mem Animal Hosp, Soc Prev Cruelty Animals, Mass, 63-64; from instr to asst prof vet anat, Iowa State Univ, 64-69; assoc prof, 69-75, PROF ANAT & HISTOL, AUBURN UNIV, 75- *Mem:* Am Vet Med Asn; Am Asn Vet Anat; World Asn Vet Anat; Am Asn Anatomists; Am Asn Vet Neurol. *Res:* Neurology, cardiology, arthrology and teaching methods, primarily in cardiac autonomic innervation and denervation, fetlock injuries in horses and multimedia programming of teaching materials. *Mailing Add:* Sylvan Vet Hosp Rd 9 S Rome City IN 46784

MCKIBBEN, ROBERT BRUCE, b Cincinnati, Ohio, Sept 1, 43. COSMIC RAY PHYSICS. *Educ:* Harvard Col, BA, 65; Univ Chicago, MS, 67, PhD(physics), 72. *Prof Exp:* Res assoc physics, 72-74, SR RES ASSOC PHYSICS, ENRICO FERMI INST, UNIV CHICAGO, 75- *Mem:* Am Geophys Union; Sigma Xi; Am Physical Soc. *Res:* Distribution of solar and galactic cosmic rays within the solar system and studies of energetic charged particles in planetary magnetospheres. *Mailing Add:* Enrico Fermi Inst 933 E 56th St Chicago IL 60637

MCKIBBIN, JOHN MEAD, b Tucson, Ariz, Nov 15, 15; m 44; c 4. BIOCHEMISTRY. *Educ:* Mich State Univ, BS, 38; Univ Wis, MS, 40, PhD(biochem), 42. *Prof Exp:* Instr nutrit, Harvard Med Sch & Sch Pub Health, Harvard Univ, 42-45; from asst prof to prof biochem, Col Med, Syracuse Univ & State Univ NY Med Ctr, 45-61; PROF BIOCHEM & CHMN DEPT, MED CTR, UNIV ALA, BIRMINGHAM, 61- *Mem:* Am Chem Soc; Soc Exp Biol & Med; Am Soc Biol Chem; Soc Complex Carbohydrates. *Res:* Nutrition, chemistry and metabolism of phospholipids and glycolipids. *Mailing Add:* Dept Biochem Univ Ala Birmingham AL 35294

MCKIBBINS, SAMUEL WAYNE, b West Allis, Wis, Nov 27, 31; m 53; c 3. CHEMICAL ENGINEERING. *Educ:* Univ Wis-Madison, BS, 53, MS, 55, PhD(chem eng), 58. *Prof Exp:* Chem engr, Kimberly-Clark Corp, 57-62; group leader process res, Union-Camp Corp, 62-64; assoc dir paper res, res planning & environ control, Continental Can Co, 64-70; dir res & develop, Am Can Co, Greenwich, 70-76; dir, Chem, Energy & Effluent Technol, 76-80, DIR, PROCESS ENG & DEV, ST REGIS PAPER CO, 80- *Concurrent Pos:* Mem pulp indust liaison comt, US Dept Health Educ & Welfare, 69. *Mem:* Am Inst Chem Engrs; Tech Asn Pulp & Paper Indust. *Res:* Environmental control; chemical kinetics; mass transfer; pulp and paper; process and systems analysis. *Mailing Add:* 42 Meadow View Rd Westport CT 06880

MACKICHAN, BARRY BRUCE, b Danville, Pa, May 15, 44; m 69; c 4. MATHEMATICS. *Educ:* Harvard Col, AB, 65; Stanford Univ, MS, 67, PhD(math), 68. *Prof Exp:* C L E Moore instr math, Mass Inst Technol, 69-70; asst prof, Duke Univ, 70-75; ASSOC PROF MATH, NMEX STATE UNIV, 76- *Concurrent Pos:* Mem, Inst Advan Study, Princeton, NJ, 68-69 & 75-76; pres, Triad Comput, Inc, 81- *Res:* Overdetermined systems of partial differential equations; theory of functions of several complex variables; computer systems for technical text processing; computer aided instruction in mathematics. *Mailing Add:* Box MB NMEx State Univ Las Cruces NM 88003

MACKICHAN, JANIS JEAN, b Detroit, Mich, Aug 23, 51. PHARMACOKINETICS. *Educ:* Univ Mich, BS, 75, PharmD, 77. *Prof Exp:* Fel pharmacokinetics, Sch Pharm, State Univ NY Buffalo, 77-78, res instr neurol, Sch Med, 78-79; ASST PROF PHARM, DIV PHARM PRACTICE, SCH PHARM, OHIO STATE UNIV, 79- *Concurrent Pos:* Clin asst prof, Dept Pediat, Col Med, Ohio State Univ, 79-81; Young Investr Award, Am Heart Asn, 81. *Honors & Awards:* William H Rorer Award, Am Col Gastroenterol, 80. *Mem:* Am Pharmaceut Asn; Am Soc Clin Pharmacol & Therapeut; Am Col Clin Pharmacol; AAAS. *Res:* Quantitation of the time-course of drugs in the human body and correlation of pharmacokinetics with physiologic processes to predict and avoid drug-drug interactions and to design improved drug dosage regimens in patients. *Mailing Add:* Col Pharm 217 Lloyd M Parks Hall Ohio State Univ 500 W 12th Ave Columbus OH 43210

MACKIE, GEORGE ALEXANDER, b Winnipeg, Man, Nov 11, 45; m 78. MOLECULAR BIOLOGY, BIOCHEMISTRY. *Educ:* Univ Toronto, BSc, 67; Cornell Univ, PhD(biochem & molecular biol), 71. *Prof Exp:* Med Res Coun fel, Dept Molecular Biol, Univ Geneva, Switz, 71-73, researcher, 73-74; asst prof, 74-79, ASSOC PROF BIOCHEM, UNIV WESTERN ONT, 74- *Res:* Regulation of gene expression; structure of the ribosome. *Mailing Add:* Dept of Biochem Univ of Western Ont London ON N6A 5B8 Can

MACKIE, GEORGE OWEN, b Louth, Eng, Oct 20, 29; m 56; c 5. ZOOLOGY. *Educ:* Oxford Univ, BA, 53, MA & DPhil, 56. *Prof Exp:* Lectr zool, Univ Alta, 56-58, from asst prof to prof, 58-68; chmn dept biol, 71-74, PROF BIOL, UNIV VICTORIA, BC, 68- *Concurrent Pos:* Nat Res Coun Can overseas fel, 63-64; assoc ed, Can J Zool, 71-77, ed, 81-; assoc ed, Biol Bull, Woods Hole, 74-77 & 79- & Acta Zool, 81-; vis prof biol, Univ Calif, Los Angeles, 78. *Mem:* Am Soc Cell Biol; Am Soc Zool; Soc Exp Biol & Med; Can Soc Zool; Brit Soc Exp Biol. *Res:* Neurobiology, especially coelenterata; Tunicata. *Mailing Add:* Dept of Biol Univ of Victoria Victoria BC V8W 2Y4 Can

MACKIE, RICHARD JOHN, b Foster City, Mich, July 6, 33; m 57; c 4. WILDLIFE MANAGEMENT, ECOLOGY. *Educ:* Mich State Univ, BS, 58; Wash State Univ, MS, 60; Mont State Univ, PhD(wildlife mgt), 65. *Prof Exp:* Res biologist, Mont Fish & Game Dept, 60-65, res coordr, 65-66; from asst prof to assoc prof entom, fisheries & wildlife, Univ Minn, St Paul, 66-70; assoc prof, 70-76, PROF WILDLIFE MGT, MONT STATE UNIV, 76- *Concurrent Pos:* Coordr statewide deer & habitat res, Mont Dept Fish, Wildlife & Parks, 70- *Mem:* Wildlife Soc; Ecol Soc Am; Soc Range Mgt. *Res:* Reproductive cycle of chukar; range ecology and relations of mule deer, elk and cattle; big game habitat relationships; big game range survey techniques; mule deer population ecology; browse plant ecology; interspecific relations. *Mailing Add:* Dept of Biol Mont State Univ Bozeman MT 59717

MCKIERNAN, MICHEL AMEDEE, b Chicago, Ill, Feb 17, 30; m 58. MATHEMATICS. *Educ:* Loyola Univ, Ill, BS, 51, MA, 52; Ill Inst Technol, PhD(math), 56. *Prof Exp:* Mathematician, Armour Res Found, 55-56; from instr to asst prof math, Ill Inst Technol, 56-61; mathematician, Inst Air Weapons Res, Univ Chicago, 61-62; assoc prof, 62-68, PROF MATH, UNIV WATERLOO, 68- *Mem:* Am Math Soc; Math Asn Am. *Res:* Functional equations. *Mailing Add:* Dept of Math Univ of Waterloo Waterloo ON N2L 3G1 Can

MACKIEWICZ, JOHN STANLEY, b Waterbury, Conn, July 12, 30; m 57; c 1. PARASITOLOGY. *Educ:* Cornell Univ, BS, 53, MS, 54, PhD(parasitol), 60. *Prof Exp:* Asst med entom & parasitol, Cornell Univ, 54-57, 59-60, instr, 57-59; NIH fel parasitol, Switz, 60-61; from asst prof to assoc prof biol, 61-68, prof biol sci, 68-73, DISTINGUISHED TEACHING PROF BIOL SCI, STATE UNIV NY ALBANY, 73- *Concurrent Pos:* Vis assoc prof, Univ Tenn, 67-68; vis scientist, India, 79. *Mem:* AAAS; Am Soc Parasitol; Am Soc Trop Med & Hyg; Soc Syst Zool; Am Micros Soc. *Res:* Parasites of freshwater fish; Cestoidea; Caryophylidea; conservation. *Mailing Add:* Dept of Biol Sci State Univ of NY Albany NY 12222

MCKIGNEY, JOHN IGNATIUS, b Marshall, Minn, Nov 14, 24; m 53; c 4. NUTRITION, BIOCHEMISTRY. *Educ:* Univ Fla, BS, 51, PhD(nutrit), 56. *Prof Exp:* Res adv animal nutrit, AID, 56-64; nutrit adv, Off Int Res, NIH, 64-67; dep dir, Food & Agr Orgn, UN, 67-71; sci adminr, Nat Inst Child Health & Human Develop, 71-76; NUTRIT ADV, AID, WASHINGTON, DC, 76- *Mem:* Am Inst Nutrit. *Res:* Human nutrition; food economics; human development. *Mailing Add:* TA/N-AID Dept of State Washington DC 20523

MCKILLOP, ALLAN A, b Calif, July 24, 25; m 54. MECHANICAL ENGINEERING. *Educ:* Univ Calif, BS, 50, PhD, 62; Mass Inst Technol, ME, 59. *Prof Exp:* Lectr agr eng, 51-53, from instr to assoc prof, 53-70, PROF AGR ENG, UNIV CALIF, DAVIS, 70- *Mem:* Am Soc Eng Educ; Am Soc Mech Engrs. *Res:* Experimental and numerical analysis in fluid mechanics and heat transfer. *Mailing Add:* Dept of Mech Eng Univ of Calif Davis CA 95616

MCKILLOP, J H, b Detroit, Mich, Sept 21, 27; Can citizen; m 54; c 2. GEOLOGY. *Educ:* St Francis Xavier Univ, BSc, 51; Mem Univ Nfld, MSc, 61. *Prof Exp:* Geologist, Geol Surv Can, 51; asst govt geologist, Govt Nfld, 51-61, chief geologist, 61-62, dir mineral resources, Nlfd Dept Mines, Agr & Resources, 62-72, DEP MINISTER, DEPT MINES & ENERGY, GOVT NFLD & LABRADOR, 72- *Mem:* Can Inst Mining & Metall (vpres, 73-74); Geol Asn Can. *Mailing Add:* 17 Dublin Rd St John's NF A1B 2E7 Can

MCKILLOP, LUCILLE MARY, b Chicago, Ill, Sept 28, 24. MATHEMATICS. *Educ:* St Xavier Col, Ill, BS, 51; Univ Notre Dame, MS, 59; Univ Wis, PhD(math educ), 65. *Prof Exp:* Elem teacher, St Patrick Acad, Ill, 47-51, St Xavier Acad, 51-52, Siena High Sch, 52-57 & Marquette High Sch, 57-58; from instr to prof math, St Xavier Col, Ill, 58-73; PRES, SALVE REGINA-NEWPORT COL, 73- *Concurrent Pos:* Consult, Archdioceasan Sch Bd Prog Math, 65-66; chmn div liberal arts & humanities, St Xavier Col, 66-73; secy, Comt Math Prep Teachers Elem Sch Math, 67-72. *Res:* Evolution of concepts in mathematics, particularly the evolution of concepts in finite geometries; investigations of collineations in projective planes with coordinates in a Galois field; self-generative quality of historical studies of mathematical creativity. *Mailing Add:* Ochre Point Ave Newport RI 02840

MCKILLOP, WILLIAM L M, b Aberdeen, Scotland, June 3, 33; m 58; c 4. FOREST ECONOMICS. *Educ:* Univ Aberdeen, BSc, 54; Univ NB, MSc, 59; Univ Calif, Berkeley, MA & PhD(agr econ), 65. *Prof Exp:* Res officer forestry, Can Dept Forestry, 58-59, forest economist, 59-61; asst prof forestry & forest economist, 64-69, assoc prof, 69-75, PROF FORESTRY, UNIV CALIF, BERKELEY, 75- *Mem:* Am Econ Asn; Am Agr Econ Asn; Soc Am Foresters. *Res:* Econometrics; economic theory; forest economics and statistics. *Mailing Add:* Dept of Forestry Univ of Calif Berkeley CA 94720

MCKIM, HARLAN L, b Gothenburg, Nebr, Sept 28, 37; m 61; c 1. GEOLOGY, SOIL SCIENCE. *Educ:* Univ Nebr, BS, 62, MS, 67; Iowa State Univ, PhD(soil sci), 72. *Prof Exp:* Soil scientist, US Army Cold Regions Res & Eng Lab, 62-64, Soil Conserv Serv, 64-66 & Soil Surv Lab, 66-68; phys scientist, Water Resources Support Ctr, 79-81, SOIL SCIENTIST, COLD REGIONS RES & ENG LAB, US ARMY, 81- *Concurrent Pos:* Res assoc soil sci, Iowa State Univ, 68-72. *Mem:* Soil Conserv Soc Am; Soil Sci Soc Am; Am Quaternary Asn; Am Soc Agron; Am Soc Photogram. *Res:* Influence of soil moisture on runoff and utilization of remote sensing on water resources; field experiments and performance and management requirements on new data acquisition systems; use of remote sensing in Corps of Engineers programs; satellite sensor projects. *Mailing Add:* US Army Col Regions Res & Eng Lab 72 Lyme Rd Hanover NH 03755

MCKIMMY, MILFORD D, b Beaverton, Mich, Dec 22, 23; m 54; c 3. WOOD TECHNOLOGY. *Educ:* Mich State Univ, BS, 49; Ore State Col, MS, 51; State Univ NY, PhD(wood technol), 55. *Prof Exp:* From instr to assoc prof, 53-72, PROF FOREST PROD, ORE STATE UNIV, 72- *Concurrent Pos:* Charles Bullard forest res fel, Harvard Univ, 66-67. *Mem:* Soc Am Foresters; Soc Wood Sci & Technol; Forest Prod Res Soc; Tech Asn Pulp & Paper Indust. *Res:* Growth quality relationships of wood; application of genetics to wood quality. *Mailing Add:* Sch of Forestry Ore State Univ Corvallis OR 97331

MACKIN, ROBERT JAMES, JR, b Little Rock, Ark, Dec 4, 25; c 6. PHYSICS. *Educ:* Yale Univ, BE, 49; Calif Inst Technol, MS, 51, PhD(physics), 53. *Prof Exp:* Res assoc, Calif Inst Technol, 53-54 & Nuclear Physics Br, Off Naval Res, 54-56; res assoc, Thermonuclear Exp Div, Oak Ridge Nat Lab, 56-59, group leader, 59-62; mgr physics sect, Space Sci Div, 62-67, mgr, Lunar & Planetary Sci Sect, 67-69, mgr, Space Sci Div, 69-78, MGR ENERGY TECHNOL DEVELOP, JET PROPULSION LAB, CALIF INST TECHNOL, 79- *Concurrent Pos:* Traveling lectr, Oak Ridge Inst Nuclear Studies, 58-60; mem staff, Off Energy Res, Dept Energy, 78-79. *Mem:* AAAS; Am Phys Soc. *Res:* Plasma and interplanetary physics; controlled fusion; planetary science. *Mailing Add:* 2626 N Holliston Ave Altadena CA 91001

MCKINLEY, CAROLYN MAY, b Lima, Ohio, May 13, 45. GENETICS, CYTOGENETICS. *Educ:* Ohio Northern Univ, BA, 72; Univ Toledo, PhD(biol), 77. *Prof Exp:* investr, Oak Ridge Nat Lab-Univ Tenn Grad Sch Biomed Sci, 77-79, res assoc comp mutagenesis, 79-81; ASST PROF, WIDENER UNIV, 81- *Mem:* Genetics Soc Am; Environ Mutagen Soc. *Res:* Genetics of recombination; mutagenesis and sister chromatid exchange. *Mailing Add:* Widener Univ Chester PA 19013

MCKINLEY, CLYDE, b Mongo, Ind, Apr 19, 17; m 74; c 4. CHEMICAL ENGINEERING. *Educ:* Tri-State Col, BS, 37; Univ Mich, MS, 41, ScD(chem eng), 43. *Prof Exp:* Chem engr, Gas Corp Mich, 38 & Ohio Gas Light & Coke Co, 39; consult, Eng Div, Dow Chem Co, 40-42; chem engr, sect leader & supt, Spec Prod Dept, Gen Aniline & Film Corp, 43-53; dir res & develop, 53-69, dir, Cryogenic Systs Div Res, 69-77, DIR, CORP RES SERV, AIR PROD & CHEM INC, 77- *Mem:* AAAS; Am Chem Soc; Am Inst Chem Engrs. *Res:* Cryogenic processes and new product research and development. *Mailing Add:* Allentown Labs Air Prod & Chem Inc Box 538 Allentown PA 18105

MCKINLEY, JOHN MCKEEN, b Wichita, Kans, Feb 1, 30; m 53; c 3. THEORETICAL PHYSICS. *Educ:* Univ Kans, BS, 51; Univ Ill, PhD(physics), 62. *Prof Exp:* Asst prof physics, Kans State Univ, 60-66; assoc prof, 66-71, PROF PHYSICS, OAKLAND UNIV, 71- *Concurrent Pos:* Assoc ed, Am J Physics, 79-82; res assoc, Goddard Space Flight Ctr, NASA, 80-81. *Mem:* Am Phys Soc; AAAS; Am Asn Physics Teachers. *Res:* Theoretical nuclear physics. *Mailing Add:* Dept Physics Oakland Univ Rochester MI 48063

MCKINLEY, KELTON RAY, b Mansfield, Ohio, Apr 11, 48; m 67; c 1. AQUATIC ECOLOGY, MICROBIOLOGICAL ECOLOGY. *Educ:* Case Western Reserve Univ, BA, 70; Mich State Univ, MS, 72, PhD(aquatic ecol), 75. *Prof Exp:* Res asst limnol, Mich State Univ, 72-75, res assoc & asst prof freshwater ecol, 75-76; assoc res scientist, Johns Hopkins Univ, 76-78; TUTOR & RES SCIENTIST, ST JOHN'S COL, 78- *Concurrent Pos:* NSF res grants, 73-76 & 78-81. *Mem:* Am Soc Limnol & Oceanog; Ecol Soc Am; Int Asn Theoret & Appl Limnol; Brit Ecol Sci; Phycol Soc Am. *Res:* Aquatic Ecology; physiological mechanisms in freshwater, estuarine and marine systems; photosynthesis, heterotrophy, microbial interactions, succession, ecosystem structure and function in space and time. *Mailing Add:* Dept Biol St John's Col Annapolis MD 21404

MCKINLEY, MARVIN DYAL, b Ocala, Fla, Mar 3, 37; m 58; c 3. CHEMICAL ENGINEERING. *Educ:* Univ Fla, BChE, 59, MSE, 60, PhD(chem eng), 63. *Prof Exp:* Engr, E I du Pont de Nemours & Co, Tex, 63-65; from asst prof to assoc prof, 65-76, PROF CHEM ENG, UNIV ALA, 76-, ACTG HEAD, DEPT CHEM & METALL ENG, 81- *Concurrent Pos:* Vis assoc prof, Busan Nat Univ, Korea, 72-73. *Mem:* Am Inst Chem Engrs. *Res:* Phase equilibria and physical properties; coal gasification, separation process, oil shale processing. *Mailing Add:* Dept of Chem & Metall Eng Univ of Ala Box G University AL 35486

MCKINLEY, RAYMOND EARL, veterinary medicine, animal nutrition, see previous edition

MCKINLEY, WILLIAM ALBERT, b Dallas, Tex, Aug 23, 17; m 40; c 2. PHYSICS. *Educ:* Univ Tex, BA, 39; Mass Inst Technol, PhD(physics), 47. *Prof Exp:* Mem staff, Radiation Lab, Mass Inst Technol, 44-46, res assoc, Instrumentation Lab, 46-47; from asst prof to assoc prof, 47-54, PROF PHYSICS, RENSSELAER POLYTECH INST, 54- *Mem:* AAAS; Am Phys Soc; Am Asn Physics Teachers. *Res:* Quantum field theory; theory of atomic and nuclear collissions. *Mailing Add:* Dept of Physics Rensselaer Polytech Inst Troy NY 12181

MCKINNELL, ROBERT GILMORE, b Springfield, Mo, Aug 9, 26; m 64; c 3. DEVELOPMENTAL BIOLOGY. *Educ:* Univ Mo, AB, 48; Drury Col, BS, 49; Univ Minn, PhD(zool), 59. *Prof Exp:* Res assoc embryol, Inst Cancer Res, 58-61; asst prof zool, Tulane Univ, 61-65, assoc prof biol, 65-69, prof, 69-70; prof zool, Univ Minn, Minneapolis, 70-76; PROF GENETICS & CELL BIOL, UNIV MINN, ST PAUL, 76- *Concurrent Pos:* Instr, Univ Minn, 58; sr sci fel, NATO, St Andrews Univ, Scotland, 74; mem, Adv Coun, Inst Lab Animal Resources, 74-77; vis scientist biomed res, Dow Chem USA, Tex Div, Freeport, 76; royal soc guest res fel, Nuffield Dept Path, Oxford Univ, 81-82. *Mem:* AAAS; fel Linnean Soc London; Am Asn Lab Animal Sci; Environ Mutagen Soc; Sigma Xi. *Res:* Transplantation of nuclei from normal neoplastic and aging anuran cells; use of mutant genes as nuclear markers; viral oncogenesis and epidemiology of Lucke renal adenocarcinoma; mutagenesis screening with anurans. *Mailing Add:* Dept Genetics & Cell Biol Univ Minn St Paul MN 55108

MCKINNELL, W(ILLIAM) P(ARKS), JR, b Springfield, Mo, Dec 24, 24; m 50; c 4. METALLURGY. *Educ:* Univ Minn, BChE, 45; Univ Mo, BS, 47; Ohio State Univ, MS, 54, PhD(metall), 56. *Prof Exp:* Metallurgist, Chrysler Corp, 47-50; asst prof metall, Va Polytech Inst, 50-51; advan res engr, Denver Res Ctr, 56-60, mgr, Anal Dept, 60-62, Chem Eng Dept, 62-63, Eng & Chem Dept, 63-67 & Commercial Develop Div, 67-72, RES DIR, DENVER RES CTR, MARATHON OIL CO, 73- *Concurrent Pos:* Adj assoc prof, Univ Denver, 63-67. *Mem:* Am Soc Metals; Nat Asn Corrosion Engrs; Am Inst Chem Engrs; Am Inst Mining, Metall & Petrol Engrs. *Res:* Corrosion of and brittle failure of metals. *Mailing Add:* Marathon Oil Co 7400 S Broadway Littleton CO 80160

MCKINNEY, ALFRED LEE, b Houston, Tex, Aug 19, 37; m 60; c 1. MATHEMATICAL ANALYSIS, NUMERICAL ANALYSIS. *Educ:* La Tech Univ, BS, 59, MS, 61; Univ Okla, PhD(math), 72. *Prof Exp:* Res mathematician, United Gas Res Lab, 61-65; chmn math dept, Okla Col Lib Arts, 68-72, chmn math & sci div, 72-74; assoc prof, 74-81, PROF MATH, LA STATE UNIV, SHREVEPORT, 81- *Mem:* Asn Comput Mach; Data Processing Mgt Asn; Math Asn Am. *Res:* Numerical approximations, particularly computer-oriented approaches to solutions of calculus of variations or control problems. *Mailing Add:* Dept of Math La State Univ Shreveport LA 71115

MACKINNEY, ARCHIE ALLEN, JR, b St Paul, Minn, Aug 16, 29; m 55; c 3. HEMATOLOGY. *Educ:* Wheaton Col, Ill, BA, 51; Univ Rochester, MD, 55; Am Bd Internal Med, dipl, 62. *Prof Exp:* Resident med, Univ Wis Hosps, 55-59; clin assoc hemat, Nat Inst Arthritis & Metab Dis, 59-61; clin investr, 61-64, from asst prof to assoc prof med, 64-74, PROF MED, SCH MED, UNIV WIS-MADISON, 74-; CHIEF HEMAT, VET ADMIN HOSP, 64- *Concurrent Pos:* Vet admin res grants, 61-; NIH res grants, 64-67 & 70-75; chief nuclear med, Vet Admin Hosp, 64-74. *Mem:* Am Fedn Clin Res; Cent Soc Clin Res; Am Soc Hemat; Sigma Xi. *Res:* Cell proliferation in vitro; lymphomagenesis. *Mailing Add:* Dept Med Sch Med Univ Wis Madison WI 53706

MACKINNEY, ARLAND LEE, b Hendersonville, NC, Nov 29, 31; m 55; c 3. NUCLEAR PHYSICS, RESEARCH ADMINISTRATION. *Educ:* NC State Col, BS, 53; Ind Univ, MS, 55; Mass Inst Technol, SM, 67. *Prof Exp:* Physicist, Knolls Atomic Power Lab, AEC, 55-58; physicist, 58-60, supvr, 60-64, sect chief, 64-67, tech adv to mgr physics lab, 67-68, from asst mgr to mgr, Qual Control Dept, 68-71, spec asst nuclear opers to div vpres, Mount Vernon Plant, Ind, 71-72, plant mgr, 73-75, qual assurance mgr, 76-79, MGR GEN SERV, NUCLEAR POWER GENERATION DIV, BABCOCK & WILCOX CO, 79- *Mem:* Am Nuclear Soc; Am Soc Qual Control. *Mailing Add:* Babcock & Wilcox Co PO Box 1260 Lynchburg VA 24505

MCKINNEY, CHARLES DANA, JR, b Chattanooga, Tenn, Mar, 30, 20; m 47; c 1. PHYSICAL CHEMISTRY. *Educ:* Univ Chattanooga, BS, 41; Ill Inst Technol, PhD(phys chem), 50. *Prof Exp:* Lab shift supvr anal chem, Vol Ord Works, 44-45; asst instr, Univ Pa, 45-47; asst instr phys chem, Ill Inst Technol, 47-50; res chemist, Hercules Powder Co, 50-52, res supvr, 52-55, dir res, Allegany Ballistics Lab, Md, 55-58; proj dir, Aeroprojs, Inc & Technidyne, Inc, 58-70; SR RES CHEMIST, HERCULES, INC, 70- *Mem:* Am Chem Soc; Sigma Xi; Soc Plastics Engrs. *Res:* Polymer chemistry; explosives; reaction kinetics; rapid reactions; solid and liquid rocket propellants. *Mailing Add:* 705 Halstead Rd Wilmington DE 19803

MCKINNEY, CHESTER MEEK, b Cooper, Tex, Jan 29, 20; m 48; c 2. PHYSICS. *Educ:* ETex State Teachers Col, BS, 41; Univ Tex, MA, 47, PhD(physics), 50. *Prof Exp:* Res physicist, Univ Tex, 45-65, dir, Appl Res Lab, 65-80; RETIRED. *Concurrent Pos:* Assoc prof, Tex Tech Col, 50-53; mem, Lab Adv Bd Naval Ships, Naval Res Adv Comt, 75-77; mem, US Navy Underwater Sound Adv Group, 62-64 & 75-77, chmn, 71-73; mem, Nat Res Coun Mine Adv Comt, 59-72 & Naval Studies Bd, 79-82. *Mem:* Fel Acoust Soc Am; Am Inst Elec & Electronics Engrs; Brit Inst Acoust. *Res:* Underwater acoustics; electronics; microwaves; dielectric waveguides and antennae. *Mailing Add:* 4305 Farhills Dr Austin TX 78731

MCKINNEY, DAVID SCROGGS, b Atwood, Pa, Aug 16, 02. PHYSICAL CHEMISTRY. *Educ:* Carnegie Inst Technol, BS, 23, DSc(phys chem), 38. *Prof Exp:* Analyst, NJ Zinc Co, 23; from analyst to chief chemist, Duquesne Light Co, Pa, 24-34; asst, 34-35, instr, 36-38, from asst prof to prof, 39-71, EMER PROF CHEM, CARNEGIE-MELLON UNIV, 71- *Concurrent Pos:* Sect chief, Anal Sect, Chem Div, Metall Lab, Univ Chicago, 44; assoc head dept chem, Carnegie-Mellon Univ, 63-68. *Mem:* Am Chem Soc; NY Acad Sci; Sigma Xi. *Res:* Infrared absorption spectra; thermodynamics; equilibria in water solution; conductance; corrosion, industrial water treatment. *Mailing Add:* 114 Ridge Rd Pittsburgh PA 15237

MCKINNEY, EARL H, b Wilkinsburgh, Pa, May 24, 29; m 52; c 3. NUMERICAL ANALYSIS. *Educ:* Washington & Jefferson Col, AB, 51; Univ Pittsburgh, MS, 56, PhD(math), 61. *Prof Exp:* Instr math, Univ Pittsburgh, 55-59; asst prof, Northern Ill Univ, 59-62; prof math & head dept, 62-70, PROF, BALL STATE UNIV, 70- *Concurrent Pos:* NSF res grant appl math, Argonne Nat Lab, 68-69. *Mem:* Am Math Soc; Math Asn Am; Soc Indust & Appl Math. *Res:* Analysis; applied mathematics; numerical analysis--interpolation and numerical integration. *Mailing Add:* Dept of Math Ball State Univ Muncie IN 47306

MCKINNEY, FRANK KENNETH, b Birmingham, Ala, Apr 13, 43; m 64; c 4. INVERTEBRATE PALEONTOLOGY, BIOSTRATIGRAPHY. *Educ:* Old Dom Col, BS, 64; Univ NC, Chapel Hill, MS, 67, PhD(paleont), 70. *Prof Exp:* Asst prof, 68-76, PROF GEOL, APPALACHIAN STATE UNIV, 76- *Concurrent Pos:* Fel, Smithsonian Inst, 72-73; vis prof, Univ Durham, 78; exchange scientist, USSR, 78 & Czechoslavakia, 81. *Mem:* Paleont Soc; Int Palaeont Asn; Soc Econ Paleont & Mineral; Int Bryozool Asn; Am Soc Zoologists. *Res:* Paleozoic bryozoans, particularly Fenestrata. *Mailing Add:* Dept Geol Appalachian State Univ Boone NC 28608

MCKINNEY, GORDON R, b Indianapolis, Ind, Oct 14, 23; m 47; c 1. PHARMACOLOGY, MEDICAL INFORMATION. *Educ:* DePauw Univ, AB, 46; Univ Notre Dame, MS, 48; Duke Univ, PhD, 51. *Prof Exp:* Lectr pharmacol, Duke Univ, 52-53; from asst prof to assoc prof, Sch Med, WVa Univ, 53-59; res pharmacologist, 59-61, sr res fel, 61-68, dir pharmacol, 68-75, dir biol res, 75-78, assoc dir med serv, 78-80, DIR MED COMMUN, PHARMACEUT DIV, MEAD JOHNSON & CO, 80- *Concurrent Pos:* Am Cancer Soc res fel med, Duke Univ, 51-53; Lederle med fac award, WVa Univ, 55-57. *Mem:* Drug Info Asn; Am Soc Pharmacol & Exp Therapeut; Am Med Writers Asn; Soc Exp Biol & Med; Endocrine Soc. *Res:* Adrenergic, biochemical and endocrine pharmacology; medical/drug information service. *Mailing Add:* Pharmaceut Med Serv Mead Johnson & Co Evansville IN 47721

MACKINNEY, HERBERT WILLIAM, b London, Eng, Feb 22, 07; nat US; m 44; c 1. POLYMER CHEMISTRY, ENVIRONMENTAL CHEMISTRY. *Educ:* Swiss Fed Inst Technol, dipl, 28; McGill Univ, MSc, 33, PhD(cellulose chem), 35. *Prof Exp:* Chemist, Lever Bros Ltd, Eng, 28-31; res chemist, Can Int Paper Co, Ont, 31-32; res assoc, Macdonald Col, McGill Univ, 36; res chemist, Kendall Co, 36-39, Sylvania Indust Corp, 39-40 & Bakelite Corp Div, Union Carbide Corp, 41-58; staff chemist, Int Bus Mach Corp, 58-61, adv chemist, 61-66, sr chemist, IBM Corp, 66-72; CONSULT, 72- *Honors & Awards:* Honor Scroll, Am Inst Chemists, 57. *Mem:* Am Chem Soc; fel Am Inst Chemists. *Res:* Polymers and plastics; adhesives; environmental deterioration of materials; plastic laminates. *Mailing Add:* 740 S Alton Way Denver CO 80231

MCKINNEY, JAMES DAVID, b Gainesville, Ga, Dec 28, 41; m 70; c 3. ENVIRONMENTAL CHEMISTRY. *Educ:* Univ Ga, BS, 63, PhD(org chem), 68. *Prof Exp:* Pub health scientist, Pesticide Toxicol Lab, Food & Drug Admin, Ga, 67-69; res scientist environ chem, 69-74, head chem sect, 74-78, chief, Environ Chem Br, 78-79, CHIEF, LAB ENVIRON CHEM, NAT INST ENVIRON HEALTH, 80- *Mem:* Am Chem Soc. *Res:* Environmental health chemistry; structure-activity relationships as predictive tools in chemical toxicology; analytical chemistry and residue analysis of environmental/biological samples; bioorganic chemistry and biomechanism elucidation; synthetic organic chemistry. *Mailing Add:* Lab Environ Chem Nat Inst Environ Health Sci Research Triangle Park NC 27709

MCKINNEY, JAMES T, b Detroit, Mich, May 28, 38; m 61; c 2. SURFACE PHYSICS. *Educ:* Univ Detroit, BS, 60; Univ Wis, MS, 62, PhD(physics), 66. *Prof Exp:* Scientist, Fundamental Res Lab, US Steel Res Ctr, 66-71; sr physicist, 72-76, RES SCIENTIST, 3M CO, 77- *Mem:* Am Phys Soc. *Res:* Ion scattering; secondary ion mass spectroscopy; interaction of charged particles with solid surfaces; surface analytical instrumentation. *Mailing Add:* Bldg 53-5 3M Co 3M Ctr St Paul MN 55101

MCKINNEY, JOHN EDWARD, b Altoona, Pa, Apr 6, 25; m 58. THERMODYNAMICS, RHEOLOGY. *Educ:* Pa State Univ, BS, 50. *Prof Exp:* PHYSICIST, POLYMERS DIV, NAT BUR STANDARDS, 50- *Concurrent Pos:* Guest worker, Nat Physics Lab, Teddington, Eng, 64. *Mem:* Rheology Soc; Int Asn Dent Res. *Res:* Experimental rheology, acoustics, thermodynamics, dynamic mechanical, dielectric, piezoelectric and pyroelectric properties of polymers and glasses; physical properties including wear and fatigue of dental restorative materials; related theoretical development of liquid and glassy states; development of related instrumentation. *Mailing Add:* Polymer Sci & Standards Div Nat Bur Standards Washington DC 20234

MCKINNEY, MAX TERRAL, b Esto, Fla, Sept 25, 35; m 53; c 2. MATHEMATICS. *Educ:* Troy State Univ, BS, 56; Auburn Univ, MEd, 62, DEd, 64. *Prof Exp:* Proj mathematician, Vitro Corp Am, 56-57; high sch teacher, Ga, 57-61; asst prof, 64-66, assoc prof, 66-81, PROF MATH, GA SOUTHWESTERN COL, 81-, CHMN DEPT, 66- *Res:* Statistics and algebraic fields. *Mailing Add:* Dept of Math Ga Southwestern Col Americus GA 31709

MCKINNEY, PAUL CAYLOR, b Otterbein, Ind, Aug 21, 30. PHYSICAL CHEMISTRY. *Educ:* Wabash Col, AB, 52; Northwestern Univ, PhD, 58. *Prof Exp:* from asst prof to assoc prof, 58-76, chmn dept, 78-81, PROF CHEM, WABASH COL, 77-, DEAN COL, 82- *Res:* Molecular mechanics. *Mailing Add:* Dept of Chem Wabash Col Crawfordsville IN 47933

MCKINNEY, PETER, b Baltimore, Md, Nov 2, 34; m 73; c 2. PLASTIC SURGERY. *Educ:* Harvard Univ, AB, 56; McGill Univ, MD, CM, 60. *Prof Exp:* Intern, Montreal Gen Hosp & resident, New York City Hosp, 60-61; asst, Bellevue-Jacobi Hosp & teacher gen surg, Albert Einstein Col Med, 61-64; resident plastic surg, New York Hosp, Med Ctr, Cornell Univ, 64-67, chief resident, 66-67; instr & assoc surg, 67-70, asst prof, 70-74, ASSOC PROF CLIN SURG, SCH MED, NORTHWESTERN UNIV, CHICAGO, 74- *Concurrent Pos:* Instr surg, Sch Med, Cornell Univ, 64-67. *Mem:* Am Soc Aesthet Plastic Surg; Plastic Surg Res Coun; Am Soc Plastic & Reconstruct Surgeons; Am Asn Plastic Surgeons; Am Col Surgeons. *Res:* Experimental closure of perforation in dog septums. *Mailing Add:* Northwestern Univ 707 N Fairbanks Chicago IL 60611

MCKINNEY, RALPH VINCENT, JR, b Columbus, Ohio, Jan 9, 33; m 55; c 4. PATHOLOGY, CELL BIOLOGY. *Educ:* Bowling Green State Univ, BS, 54; Ohio State Univ, DDS, 61; Univ Rochester, PhD(path), 71. *Prof Exp:* Asst instr dent hyg, Ohio State Univ, 60-61; clin asst prof oper dent, Case Western Reserve Univ, 61-65; PROF ORAL PATH & ORAL BIOL, GRAD FAC, MED COL GA, 70-, CHMN, 79- *Concurrent Pos:* NIH fel path, Univ Rochester, 65-70; NIH grants, 72-74 & 72-78; Nat Inst Dent Res contract, 73-77; pvt dent pract, Ohio, 61-65; mem dent staff, Talmadge Mem Hosp, Augusta, 70-; oral path diag serv, Med Col Ga, 73-; pres dent found, 74-76; chmn, Med Col Ga Fac, 79; consult, Vet Admin Hosps, Augusta, 79- *Mem:* AAAS; Int Acad Path; Am Acad Oral Path; Am Soc Cell Biol; Int Asn Dent Res. *Res:* Wound healing; microcirculation, emphasis of the biochemical, histochemical and morphological fine structure of capillary basement membrane; dental implants; peripheral interests, inflammation, connective tissue. *Mailing Add:* Dept of Oral Path Med Col of Ga Augusta GA 30902

MCKINNEY, RICHARD LEROY, b Altoona, Pa, May 23, 28; m 56; c 3. MATHEMATICS. *Educ:* Syracuse Univ, AB, 51, MA, 52; Univ Wash, PhD(math), 58. *Prof Exp:* Asst, Univ Wash, 53-58; from instr to asst prof math, Univ Calif, Riverside, 58-62; asst prof, 62-67, ASSOC PROF MATH, UNIV ALTA, 67- *Concurrent Pos:* Hon res assoc, Univ Col, Univ London, 68-69. *Mem:* Am Math Soc; Can Math Soc; Math Asn Am. *Res:* Linear spaces; convex sets; functional analysis; topology. *Mailing Add:* Dept Math Univ Alta Edmonton AB T6G 2G7 Can

MCKINNEY, ROBERT WESLEY, b East St Louis, Ill, Dec 11, 31; m 61; c 2. ANALYTICAL CHEMISTRY. *Educ:* Southern Ill Univ, BA, 53; Univ Kans, PhD(anal chem), 57. *Prof Exp:* Anal chemist, Celanese Corp Am, 57-60; anal chemist, 60-64, group leader anal chem, 64-72, MGR ANAL CHEM, W R GRACE & CO, 72- *Mem:* Am Chem Soc. *Res:* Instrumental and wet analytical chemistry; gas and liquid chromatography. *Mailing Add:* Washington Res Ctr W R Grace & Co 7379 Rte 32 Columbia MD 21044

MCKINNEY, ROGER MINOR, b Deerbrook, Wis, May 31, 26; m 52; c 3. ORGANIC CHEMISTRY, IMMUNOCHEMISTRY. *Educ:* Wis State Col, River Falls, BS, 50; St Louis Univ, MS, 56, PhD(chem), 58. *Prof Exp:* Chemist, Lambert Pharmacal Co, Mo, 50-52; chemist, Universal Match Corp, 52-55; res chemist, USPHS, Ga, 58-66, Aedes Aegypti Eradication Prog, 66-68, Tech Develop Labs, 68-71, res chemist, Tech Develop Labs, 71-72, RES CHEMIST, CTR INFECTIOUS DIS, CTR DIS CONTROL, DEPT HEALTH & HUMAN SERVS, USPHS, 72- *Mem:* AAAS; Am Chem Soc. *Res:* Synthesis of radioactive isotope labeled insecticides; technical aspects of immunofluorescent staining; basic immunochemistry studies; diagnostic reagents through hybridoma technology. *Mailing Add:* 4872 Cambridge Dr Dunwoody GA 30338

MCKINNEY, ROSS E(RWIN), b San Antonio, Tex, Aug 2, 26; m 52; c 4. SANITARY ENGINEERING. *Educ:* Southern Methodist Univ, BS & BA, 48; Mass Inst Technol, SM, 49, ScD(sanit eng), 51. *Prof Exp:* Asst sanit chem, Mass Inst Technol, 49-51; actg head, Div Sanit Sci, Southwest Found Res & Educ, 51-53; asst prof sanit eng, Mass Inst Technol, 53-59, assoc prof, 59-60; prof civil eng, 60-66, chmn dept, 63-66, PARKER PROF CIVIL ENG, UNIV KANS, 66- *Honors & Awards:* Harrison Prescott Eddy Award, Water Pollution Control Fedn, 62; Rudolph Hering Award, Am Soc Civil Engrs, 62; Presidential Commendation, 71. *Mem:* Am Chem Soc; Am Soc Microbiol; Am Soc Civil Engrs; Am Pub Health Asn; Am Water Works Asn. *Res:* Application of fundamental microbiology to design of liquid waste treatment systems. *Mailing Add:* Dept of Civil Eng Univ of Kans Lawrence KS 66044

MCKINNEY, TED MEREDITH, b Huntsville, Ala, Apr 18, 38. ANALYTICAL CHEMISTRY. *Educ:* Harvard Univ, AB, 60; Cornell Univ, PhD(chem), 65. *Prof Exp:* Res assoc chem, Cornell Univ, 64-66; asst prof, Univ Calif, Riverside, 66-71; WRITER & ED, 71-; CONSULT, ROCKWELL INT SCI CTR, THOUSAND OAKS, CALIF, 81- *Concurrent Pos:* Consult, Beckman Instruments, Inc, Calif, 69. *Mem:* Am Chem Soc. *Res:* Magnetic resonance; electroanalytical chemistry; optical spectroscopy. *Mailing Add:* 5156 Colina Way Riverside CA 92507

MCKINNEY, THURMAN DWIGHT, b Bowling Green, Ky, June 23, 47; m 69; c 2. NEPHROLOGY. *Educ:* Western Ky Univ, BS, 70; Vanderbilt Univ, MD, 73. *Prof Exp:* Med intern & resident, Univ Calif, San Francisco, 73-75; res assoc renal physiol, NIH, 75-77; ASST PROF MED, VANDERBILT UNIV, 77-; STAFF NEPHROLOGIST, NASHVILLE VET ADMIN MED CTR, 77- *Mem:* Am Soc Nephrology; Am Fedn Clin Res; Am Col Physicians. *Res:* Renal physiology with emphasis on renal acidification and organic base transport by renal tubules in vitro. *Mailing Add:* Vet Admin Med Ctr Nashville TN 37203

MCKINNEY, WILLIAM ALAN, b Omaha, Nebr, Dec 18, 27; m 52; c 2. METALLURGICAL ENGINEERING. *Educ:* Univ Ariz, BS, 51. *Prof Exp:* Process engr, Grand Cent Aircraft Co, 51-52; metallurgist, 52-68, supvry metallurgist, 68-75, RES DIR, US BUR MINES, 75- *Concurrent Pos:* Adj prof metall eng, Univ Utah, 76- *Mem:* Am Inst Mining, Metall & Petrol Engrs. *Res:* Minerals beneficiation, hydrometallurgy and pyrometallurgy of copper; chemical processing of copper and byproduct molybdenite concentrates; flue gas desulfurization. *Mailing Add:* 3936 Sunny Dale Dr Salt Lake City UT 84117

MCKINNEY, WILLIAM JAN, analytical chemistry, see previous edition

MCKINNEY, WILLIAM MARK, b Spring Valley, NY, Dec 26, 23; m 51; c 1. PLANETARY SCIENCES, PHYSICAL GEOGRAPHY. *Educ:* New Sch Social Res, BA, 48; Univ Fla, PhD(geog), 58. *Prof Exp:* Consult pub health, Ga Dept Pub Health, 53-58; from instr to asst prof geog, Southern Ore Col, 58-63; from asst prof to assoc prof, 63-68, PROF GEOG & GEOL, UNIV WIS-STEVENS POINT, 68- *Concurrent Pos:* Guest investr, Lowell Observ, 73-78; fel physics, Northern Ariz Univ, 79-80. *Mem:* Asn Am Geogrs; Nat Coun Geog Educ. *Res:* Analysis and mapping of atmospheric phenomena of Mars as photographed in various wavelengths of light; study and development of instrumentation for demonstrating principles of astronomical geography. *Mailing Add:* Dept of Geog & Geol Univ of Wis Stevens Point WI 54481

MCKINNEY, WILLIAM MARKLEY, b Roanoke, Va, June 6, 30; m 52; c 3. NEUROLOGY. *Educ:* Univ NC, Chapel Hill, BA, 51; Univ Va, MD, 59. *Prof Exp:* From instr to assoc prof neurol, 63-76, PROF NEUROL, BOWMAN GRAY SCH MED, 76-, RES ASSOC RADIOL, 67-, FAC CHMN, POSTGRAD COURSE MED SONICS, 75- *Concurrent Pos:* Dir sonic lab, Bowman Gray Sch Med, 63-76, mem subcomt on stroke, Regional Med Prog, 67-; consult, Vet Admin Hosp, Salisbury, NC; chairperson, Adv Comt, Ultrasonic Tissue Signature Characterization, Nat Bur Standards, NIH, NSF, Gaithersburg, 77- *Mem:* Am Acad Neurol; Am Fedn Clin Res; Asn Res Nerv & Ment Dis; fel Am Inst Ultrasound in Med (secy, 67, pres, 74-76). *Res:* Diagnostic ultrasound in medicine; the application of ultrasound to medicine; cerebrovascular disease; crystallography; urinary lithiasis. *Mailing Add:* Dept of Neurol Bowman Gray Sch of Med Winston-Salem NC 27103

MCKINNIS, CHARLES LESLIE, b Cape Girardeau, Mo, July 10, 23; m 44; c 1. CHEMISTRY. *Educ:* Southeast Mo State Col, BS, 46; Univ Mo, BS, 47, MS, 48; Ohio State Univ, PhD(glass chem), 54. *Prof Exp:* Res engr, Res Lab, Pittsburgh Plate Glass Co, 48-50; res assoc, Res Found, Ohio State Univ, 50-54; res chemist, Midwest Res Inst, 54-55; sr res scientist, Owens Corning Fiberglas Corp, 55-75, RES ASSOC SUPPORT SCI & TECHNOL, GLASS RES & DEVELOP, TECH CTR, OWENS CORNING FIBERGLAS CORP, 75- *Concurrent Pos:* Chmn glass div, Am Ceramic Soc, 74. *Mem:* Am Ceramic Soc; Nat Inst Ceramic Engrs; Sigma Xi. *Res:* Glass chemistry; glass structure and physical properties; heat transfer. *Mailing Add:* Owens-Corning Fiberglas Corp Tech Ctr Box 415 Granville OH 43023

MCKINNON, DAVID M, b Scotland, Aug 11, 38; m 63; c 2. ORGANIC CHEMISTRY. *Educ:* Univ Edinburgh, BSc, 60, PhD(chem), 63. *Prof Exp:* Fel chem, Dalhousie Univ, 63-65; from asst prof to assoc prof, 65-76, PROF CHEM, UNIV MAN, 76- *Mem:* Royal Soc Chem; Chem Inst Can. *Res:* Chemistry of heterocyclic sulphur and nitrogen compounds. *Mailing Add:* Dept of Chem Univ of Man Winnipeg MB R3T 2N2 Can

MACKINNON, JUAN ENRIQUE, b Montevideo, Uruguay, June 24, 04; m 34; c 5. MEDICAL MYCOLOGY, INSECT TOXICOLOGY. *Educ:* Univ of the Repub, Uruguay, MD, 33. *Prof Exp:* Microbiologist, 69-74, EMER PROF, FAC MED, UNIV OF THE REPUB, URUGUAY, 74- *Honors & Awards:* Rhoda Benham Award, Med Mycol Soc of the Americas, 70. *Mem:* Am Acad Microbiol; Uruguay Nat Acad Med; Royal Soc Trop Med & Hyg; Int Soc Human & Animal Mycol (pres, 58-62); Soc Dermat & Syphil Uruguay. *Res:* Pathogenic yeasts; causal organisms of mycetoma; morphology of pathogenic fungi in the tissues; poisonous spiders; necrotic arachnidism; pathogenesis of South American Blastomycosis; effect of ambient temperature and of climate on the mycoses; ecology of pathogenic fungi. *Mailing Add:* Achilles (M Uriarte) 6208 Montevideo Uruguay

MCKINNON, WILLIAM BEALL, b Montreal, Que, Aug 14, 54; US citizen. PLANETARY SCIENCE. *Educ:* Mass Inst Technol, SB, 76; Calif Inst Technol, MS, 79, PhD(planetary sci & geophysics), 80. *Prof Exp:* RES ASSOC, LUNAR & PLANETARY LAB, UNIV ARIZ, 80- *Concurrent Pos:* Vis res assoc, Dept Earth & Space Sci, State Univ NY, Stony Brook, 81. *Mem:* Am Geophys Union; Am Astron Soc; AAAS. *Res:* Cratering and tectonics, including physical gemorphology, planetary interiors and radio astronomy. *Mailing Add:* Lunar & Planetary Lab Univ Ariz Tucson AZ 85721

MCKINNON, WILLIAM MITCHELL PATRICK, b Houston, Tex, Mar 17, 24; m 53; c 6. SURGERY. *Educ:* St Edward's Univ, BS, 49; Baylor Univ, MD, 52. *Prof Exp:* From asst prof to assoc prof surg, NY Med Col, 61-67; STAFF SURGEON, OCHSNER CLIN, 68-, ASSOC CHMN, DEPT SURG, 79- *Concurrent Pos:* Nat Heart Inst fel surg res, Maimonides Hosp Brooklyn, NY, 58-59; consult, Vet Admin Hosp, Lyons, NJ, 62- & E A Conway Mem Hosp, Monroeka, 68- clin assoc prof, Tulane Univ & vis surgeon, Tulane Surg Div, Charity Hosp, 68- *Mem:* Fel Am Col Surg; Am Gastroenterol Asn; Soc Int Chirurgie; Soc Surg Alimentary Tract; AMA. *Res:* Clinical abdominal surgery and breast surgery. *Mailing Add:* Dept of Surg Ochsner Clin 1514 Jefferson Highway New Orleans LA 70121

MCKINSEY, RICHARD DAVIS, b New York, NY, May 20, 21; m 44; c 3. BOTANY. *Educ:* Ill Inst Technol, BS, 48; Stanford Univ, MA, 53, PhD(biol), 58. *Prof Exp:* From instr to asst prof, 57-65, ASSOC PROF BIOL, FAC ARTS & SCI, UNIV VA, 65- *Res:* Intermediate metabolism of fungi. *Mailing Add:* Dept of Biol Fac of Arts & Sci Univ of Va Charlottesville VA 22904

MCKINSTRY, DONALD MICHAEL, b Lancaster, Pa, June 10, 39; m 66; c 2. ANIMAL PHYSIOLOGY, HERPETOLOGY. *Educ:* Univ Md, BS, 64, MS, 65, PhD(dairy sci), 71. *Prof Exp:* Lab technician dairy sci, Univ Md, 67-70; asst prof biol, 70-75, ASSOC PROF BIOL, BEHREND COL, PA STATE UNIV, 75- *Res:* Toxinology. *Mailing Add:* Behrend Col Pa State Univ Station Rd Erie PA 16563

MCKINSTRY, DORIS NAOMI, b McVeytown, Pa, Sept 8, 36. CLINICAL PHARMACOLOGY. *Educ:* Pa State Univ, BS, 58; Univ Pa, PhD(pharmacol), 65. *Prof Exp:* Res assoc pharmacol, Merck Sharp & Dohme Res Labs, 58-61; sr scientist, McNeil Labs, Inc, 66-69; sr res toxicologist, Merck Sharp & Dohme Res Labs, 69-70; sr res investr, 71-75, assoc clin pharmacol dir, 75-79, DIR CLIN PHARMACOL, SQUIBB INST MED RES, 79- *Concurrent Pos:* Fel pharmacol, Univ Pa, 65-66. *Mem:* Am Soc Pharmacol & Exp Therapeut; Am Soc Clin Pharmacol & Therapeut; Am Col Clin Pharmacol; NY Acad Sci; AAAS. *Res:* Cardiovascular pharmacology and physiology; radiocontrast agents; anti-inflammatory agents; ancitiotics. *Mailing Add:* Squibb Inst for Med Res PO Box 4000 Princeton NJ 08540

MCKINSTRY, HERBERT ALDEN, b Rochester, NY, Apr 22, 25; m 45; c 4. SOLID STATE PHYSICS. *Educ:* Alfred Univ, BS, 47; Pa State Univ, MS, 50, PhD, 60. *Prof Exp:* Res asst, 47-60, res assoc, 60-64, asst prof, 64-69, ASSOC PROF SOLID STATE SCI, PA STATE UNIV, UNIVERSITY PARK, 69- *Res:* X-ray diffraction; x-ray fluorescence; computer modeling of material properties; computer generated movies for instruction; ceramics. *Mailing Add:* 144 Mat Res Lab Pa State Univ University Park PA 16802

MCKINSTRY, KARL ALEXANDER, b Phoenix, Ariz, Oct 10, 43; m 68; c 3. CHEMICAL ENGINEERING. *Educ:* Univ Mich, Ann Arbor, BSE, 66; Col Sch Mines, MS, 69, PhD(chem eng), 70. *Prof Exp:* Group leader res & develop, 70-80, MGR PROCESS ENG & RES ASSOC PHARMACEUT & PROCESS DESIGN, DOW CHEM CO, 80- *Mem:* Am Chem Soc; Am Inst Chem Eng. *Res:* Process engineering; process development; reaction engineering; heat transfer; evaporation; pharmaceuticals. *Mailing Add:* Res & Develop Sect 566 Bldg Dow Chem Co Midland MI 48640

MACKINTOSH, WILLIAM DOUGLAS, physical chemistry, see previous edition

MCKISSON, R(ALEIGH) L(EWELLYN), b Stockton, Calif, Feb 10, 22; m 44; c 2. CHEMICAL ENGINEERING. *Educ:* Univ Calif, BS, 47, MS, 48, PhD(chem eng), 50. *Prof Exp:* Chemist, Radiation Lab, Univ Calif, 50; chem engr, Calif Res & Develop Co, 50-53; proj leader, Food Mach & Chem Corp, 53-55; sect leader, NAm Aviation, Inc, Calif, 55-71, MGR, ENERGY SYSTS GROUP, ROCKWELL INT, 71- *Mem:* Am Chem Soc; Sigma Xi. *Res:* High temperature chemistry; liquid metal chemistry; flue gas desulfurization. *Mailing Add:* 23315 Calvert St Woodland Hills CA 91367

MACKIW, VLADIMIR NICOLAUS, b Stanislawiw, Western Ukraine, Sept 4, 23; nat Can; m 51; c 3. INORGANIC CHEMISTRY, PHYSICAL CHEMISTRY. *Educ:* Univ Breslau, dipl, 44; Univ Erlangen, dipl, 46. *Hon Degrees:* DSc, Univ Alta, 76. *Prof Exp:* Chemist, Lingman Lake Mines, 48 & Prov Bur Mines, Man, 49; chemist, Ont, 49-50, chief res chemist, 50-51, dir res, Alta, 52-55, dir res & develop div, 55-68, vpres, 67-72, dir & mem bd, 64-72, vpres, 67-72, vpres technol & corp develop, 68-72, EXEC VPRES, SHERRITT GORDON MINES, LTD, 72- *Concurrent Pos:* Mem, Nat Res Coun Can. *Honors & Awards:* Jules Garnier Prize, Fr Metall Soc, 66; Int Nickel Co Medal, Can Inst Mining & Metall, 66; R S Jane Mem Lect Award, Chem Inst Can, 67; Gold Medal, Inst Mining & Metall Engrs, UK, 77. *Mem:* Fel Chem Inst Can; Can Inst Mining & Metall; Am Inst Mining, Metall & Petrol Eng; Am Powder Metall Inst; Soc Chem Indust Can. *Res:* Extraction from ores by chemical methods; powder metallurgy; inorganic chemicals; kinetics and thermodynamics of inorganic reactions. *Mailing Add:* 9 Blairathol Cres Islington ON M9A 1X6 Can

MACKLEM, PETER TIFFANY, b Kingston, Ont, Oct 4, 31; m 54; c 5. PULMONARY PHYSIOLOGY, EXPERIMENTAL MEDICINE. *Educ:* Queen's Univ, Ont, BA, 52; McGill Univ, MD, CM, 56; FRCPS(C), 62. *Prof Exp:* Fel, Royal Victoria Hosp, Montreal, Que, 60-61, res fel, 61-63; Meakins Mem fel, 63-64; McLaughlin traveling res fel, Sch Pub Health, Harvard Univ, 64-65; from asst prof to assoc prof, 65-71, PROF EXP MED, McGILL UNIV, 71-, CHMN, DEPT MED, 80-; PHYSICIAN-IN-CHIEF, ROYAL VICTORIA HOSP, 79- *Concurrent Pos:* Watson scholar, McGill Univ, 61-63; asst physician, Royal Victoria Hosp, 67-71, sr physician, 71-, dir, Meakins-Christie Labs, 71-79. *Mem:* Am Physiol Soc; Am Soc Clin Invest; Am Thoracic Soc; Can Soc Clin Invest; Asn Am Physicians. *Res:* Mechanical properties of lungs; relationship between lung structure and function; airway dynamics. *Mailing Add:* Dept of Med 687 Pine Ave W Montreal PQ H3A 1A1 Can

MACKLER, BRUCE, b Philadelphia, Pa, May 23, 20; m 49; c 2. PEDIATRICS. *Educ:* Temple Univ, MD, 43. *Prof Exp:* Intern, Temple Univ Hosp, 43-44; resident physician pediat, Willard Parker Hosp, New York, 44; resident physician, Univ Iowa, 46-47; resident physician, Children's Hosp, Univ Cincinnati, 47-48, res assoc, 50-53, asst prof pediat, Univ, 53-54; asst prof enzyme chem, Univ Wis, 55-57; assoc prof, 57-61, PROF PEDIAT, SCH MED, UNIV WASH, 61- *Concurrent Pos:* USPHS fel res found, Children's Hosp, Univ Cincinnati, 48-50; fel, Inst Enzyme Res, Univ Wis, 53-55; estab investr, Am Heart Asn, 55-60. *Mem:* Am Soc Biol Chem; Am Soc Pediat Res. *Res:* Carbohydrate metabolism; metalloflavoproteins; electron transport systems. *Mailing Add:* Dept of Pediat Univ of Wash Seattle WA 98195

MACKLER, SAUL ALLEN, b New York, NY, Dec 9, 13; m 40; c 3. SURGERY. *Educ:* Columbia Univ, BS, 33; Univ Chicago, MD, 37. *Prof Exp:* Intern, Michael Reese Hosp, 38-39, resident surg, 40; ASSOC PROF THORACIC SURG, MED SCH, UNIV CHICAGO, 47-; PROF THORACIC SURG, COOK COUNTY GRAD SCH MED, 46- *Concurrent Pos:* Fel thoracic surg, Barnes Hosp, St Louis, 41 & 42; attend, assoc & consult thoracic surgeon var hosps, 46-; chmn dept surg, Michael Reese Hosp, 62-64. *Mem:* Fel AMA; Soc Thoracic Surg; fel Am Col Surg; fel Int Col Surg; fel Am Col Chest Physicians. *Res:* Physiology and disease of the esophagus and mediastinum; cancer of the esophagus; disease of the heart and great vessels; injuries of the chest. *Mailing Add:* 111 Woodley Rd Winnetka IL 60093

MACKLES, LEONARD, b New York, NY, Jan 17, 29; m 54; c 2. COSMETIC CHEMISTRY, PHARMACEUTICAL CHEMISTRY. *Educ:* Long Island Univ, BS, 51. *Prof Exp:* Org chemist, Colloids Inc, 53-56, head org chemist, Arlen Chem Corp, 56-58; tech dir, Chemclean Corp, 58-61; head chemist, Schenley Res Inst, 61-63, asst dir res, 63-65; sr res scientist prod develop, 65-73, PRIN RES INVESTR CONCEPT DEVELOP, PROD DIV, BRISTOL MYERS CO, 73- *Mem:* Fel AAAS; Am Chem Soc; fel Am Inst Chemists; NY Acad Sci; Soc Cosmetic Chemists. *Res:* Development of consumer products in the fields of pharmaceuticals, toiletries and household specialties. *Mailing Add:* 311 E 23rd St New York NY 10010

MACKLIN, JOHN WELTON, b Ft Worth, Tex, Dec 11, 39. INORGANIC CHEMISTRY, SPECTROSCOPY. *Educ:* Linfield Col, BA, 62; Cornell Univ, PhD(inorg chem), 68. *Prof Exp:* ASST PROF CHEM, UNIV WASH, 68- *Mem:* Am Chem Soc. *Res:* Spectroscopic measurements, particularly Raman, applied to elucidation of structural characteristics of inorganic solids, liquids and solutions. *Mailing Add:* Dept of Chem Univ of Wash Seattle WA 98195

MACKLIN, MARTIN, b Raleigh, NC, Aug 27, 34; m 79; c 2. BIOMEDICAL ENGINEERING, ALCOHOLISM. *Educ:* Cornell Univ, BME, 57, MIE, 58; Case Western Reserve Univ, PhD(biomed eng), 67, MD, 77. *Prof Exp:* Instr mech eng, Cornell Univ, 56-58; sr engr, Hamilton Standard Div, United Aircraft Corp, 58-61; prod planning specialist, Moog Servocontrols, Inc, 61-62; staff specialist, Thompson-Ramo-Wooldridge, Inc, 62-65; asst prof, 67-72, ASSOC PROF BIOMED ENG, CASE WESTERN RESERVE UNIV, 72-, ASST PROF PSYCHIAT, 81- *Concurrent Pos:* Established investr, Am Heart Asn, 69-74; resident psychiat, Case Western Reserve Univ Hosps. *Mem:* Am Psychiat Asn; Soc Gen Physiologists. *Res:* Nature and causes of alcoholism; transport of ions and electrogenesis in coelenterate epithelia and intestinal villi; fetal electrocardiography. *Mailing Add:* Dept Psychiat Case Western Reserve Univ Cleveland OH 44106

MACKLIN, PHILIP ALAN, b Richmond Hill, NY, Apr 13, 25; m 53; c 3. QUANTUM MECHANICS, MATHEMATICAL PHYSICS. *Educ:* Yale Univ, BS, 44; Columbia Univ, MA, 49, PhD(physics), 56. *Prof Exp:* Physicist, Carbide & Carbon Chem Corp, Tenn, 46-47; res scientist, AEC, Columbia Univ, 49-51; instr physics, Middlebury Col, 51-54, actg chmn dept, 53-54; from asst prof to assoc prof, 54-61, PROF PHYSICS, MIAMI UNIV, 61-, CHMN DEPT, 72- *Concurrent Pos:* Vis prof, Univ NMex, 57-68; physicist, Los Alamos Sci Labs, 60-62. *Mem:* AAAS; Am Phys Soc; Am Asn Physics Teachers; Sigma Xi. *Res:* Beta and gamma spectroscopy; interpretation of quantum mechanics. *Mailing Add:* 211 Oakhill Dr Oxford OH 45056

MACKLIN, RICHARD LAWRENCE, b Jamaica, NY, Dec 24, 20; m 45; c 4. NUCLEAR PHYSICS. *Educ:* Yale Univ, BS, 41, PhD(org chem), 44. *Prof Exp:* Lab asst, Yale Univ, 41-44; chemist, Indust Labs, Carbide & Carbon Chem Co, 44-48, sr physicist, 48-52; SR PHYSICIST, OAK RIDGE NAT LAB, 52- *Mem:* Fel AAAS; fel Am Phys Soc; Int Asn Geochem & Cosmochem. *Res:* Radioactivity; nuclear data; neutron capture experiments; nuclear physics instrumentation; astrophysics and cosmology experiments; nuclear safety. *Mailing Add:* Physics Div Oak Ridge Nat Lab PO Box X Oak Ridge TN 37831

MCKLVEEN, JOHN R(OBERT), b Trafford, Pa, Apr 29, 19; m 52; c 3. CHEMICAL ENGINEERING. *Educ:* Univ Pittsburgh, BS, 41. *Prof Exp:* Res engr, Gypsum Calcination, Mellon Inst, 41-43, jr fel navy aircraft instrument lubricants, 43-46; asst prof chem eng, Ala Polytech Inst, 46-50; spec projs engr, Petrol Res & Develop Dept, Celanese Corp Am, 51-56, staff asst to mgr res, Chem Div, 56-59, asst to vpres res, Celanese Chem Co, 59-63; staff planner, Fibers Div, Allied Chem Corp, 63-70; CONSULT, BUS SERV OF RICHMOND, 71-; MEM STAFF, MGT INFO SYSTS, ARMY LOGISTICS CTR, DEPT ARMY, FT LEE, 81. *Res:* Synthetic fiber processes and utilization; economics of synthetic fiber utilization, long-range planning; polymers, fibers and ceramics. *Mailing Add:* PO Box 10251 Richmond VA 23240

MCKLVEEN, JOHN WILLIAM, b Washington, DC, May 31, 43; m 66; c 2. NUCLEAR ENGINEERING, ENVIRONMENTAL ENGINEERING. *Educ:* US Naval Acad, BS, 65; Univ Va, ME, 71, PhD(nuclear environ eng), 74. *Prof Exp:* RADIATION SAFETY OFFICER & MEM FAC NUCLEAR ENG, ARIZ STATE UNIV, 74- *Concurrent Pos:* Consult, low-level radiation measurements, environ monitoring, radioactive waste disposal, fast neutorn activation analysis & energy educ, several nat labs, utilities, indust & mining orgns, 74-; pres, Radiation & Environ Monitoring, Inc, 81-; radiation safety officer, Ariz State Univ, 74-80; adv radiation & hazardous mat, Ariz Senate, 79- *Mem:* Am Nuclear Soc; Health Physics Soc; Sigma Xi. *Res:* Uranium exploration; mining and milling; assay of natural radioactivity; uranium and thorium by liquid scintillation techniques; fast neutron activation analysis applications; energy education. *Mailing Add:* Col Eng & Appl Sci Ariz State Univ Tempe AZ 85287

MACKNIGHT, FRANKLIN COLLESTER, b Louisville, Ky, June 30, 09; m 32; c 1. PALEONTOLOGY, SCIENCE EDUCATION. *Educ:* Univ Chicago, PhB, 32, PhD, 38. *Prof Exp:* Asst geologist, Pure Oil Co, 37 & Ill State Geol Surv, 39-40; asst exam phys sci, Bd Exams, Chicago, 40-41; asst prof geol, Mt Union Col, 41-43; asst prof geog, Fenn Col, 43-44; geologist, Tex Co, 44-47; prof geol & geog, Evansville Col, 47-51; chief geologist, S C Yingling Oil Opers, 51-52; asst prof geol, Univ Pittsburgh, 53-61; assoc prof gen studies, 61-63, assoc prof sci, 63-66, prof gen sci, 66-77, prof geosci, 72-77, EMER PROF GEOSCI & INTERDISCIPLINARY SCI, STATE UNIV NY COL BUFFALO, 77- *Concurrent Pos:* Consult, 52- *Res:* Carboniferous paleobotany; history and philosophy of science; evolution; phylogeny; aesthetics; paranormal phenomena. *Mailing Add:* 2235 Terrell Pl Rock Hill SC 29730

MCKNIGHT, JAMES DAWSON, JR, mathematics, see previous edition

MCKNIGHT, JAMES POPE, b Arlington, Tenn, Sept 19, 21; m 49; c 4. DENTISTRY. *Educ:* Memphis State Univ, BS, 48; Univ Tenn, DDS, 51, cert, 52; Ind Univ, MSD, 64. *Prof Exp:* Pvt pract, 52-56; from instr to assoc prof, 56-69, PROF PEDODONT & CHMN DEPT, COL DENT, UNIV TENN, MEMPHIS, 69- *Mem:* Am Dent Asn; Am Soc Dent for Children. *Res:* Treatment of the dental pulp; dental care of handicapped children. *Mailing Add:* Dept of Pedodontics Univ of Tenn Col of Dent Memphis TN 38103

MCKNIGHT, JOHN LACY, b Monroe, Mich, Sept 13, 31; m 64; c 1. THEORETICAL PHYSICS, HISTORY OF SCIENCE. *Educ:* Univ Mich, AB, 53; Yale Univ, MS, 54, PhD(physics), 57. *Prof Exp:* Asst prof, 57-59, assoc prof, 59-68, PROF PHYSICS, COL WILLIAM & MARY, 68- *Mem:* Am Phys Soc; Soc Hist Technol; Philos Sci Asn; Hist Sci Soc. *Res:* Logical foundations of quantum mechanics; 18th century physics and scientific apparatus; history of scientific ideas. *Mailing Add:* Dept Physics Col William & Mary Williamsburg VA 23185

MCKNIGHT, LEE GRAVES, b Washington, DC, Sept 7, 33; m 55; c 2. CHEMICAL PHYSICS. *Educ:* Va Mil Inst, BS, 55; Univ Mich, MS & PhD(chem), 61. *Prof Exp:* NATO fel, Univ Col, Univ London, 61-62; lectr chem, Univ Mich, 63; mem tech staff physics, Bell Labs, Whippany, NJ, 63-73, MEM TECH STAFF, BELL LABS, MURRAY HILL, NJ, 73- *Mem:* Am Chem Soc; Am Phys Soc. *Res:* Ion-molecule interactions; carbon arcs; computer-process monitor-control. *Mailing Add:* Bell Labs 2b 214 Murray Hill NJ 07974

MACKNIGHT, MARTHA LEE, protein chemistry, photobiology, see previous edition

MCKNIGHT, MELVIN EDWARD, entomology, see previous edition

MCKNIGHT, RANDY SHERWOOD, b Los Angeles, Calif, June 18, 43. APPLIED MATHEMATICS. *Educ:* Univ Calif, BS, 66; Rice Univ, MS, 69, PhD(math sci), 72. *Prof Exp:* Sci programmer, IBM Corp, 66; res scientist geophys & reservoir modeling, 71-78, MGR GEOPHYS RES, DENVER RES CTR, MARATHON OIL CO, 78- *Mem:* Soc Indust & Appl Math; Inst Elec & Electronics Engrs. *Res:* Application of optimization theory and numerical analysis to direct and inverse problems in exploration geophysics and petroleum engineering; system theory to processing and interpretation of seismic data. *Mailing Add:* Denver Res Ctr Marathon Oil Co PO Box 269 Littleton CO 80160

MCKNIGHT, RICHARD D, b Cincinnati, Ohio, June 30, 44. REACTOR PHYSICS. *Educ:* Univ Cincinnati, BS, 67, MS, 69, PhD(nuclear eng), 73. *Prof Exp:* NUCLEAR ENGR, APPL PHYSICS DIV, ARGONNE NAT LAB, 73- *Mem:* Am Nuclear Soc. *Res:* Zero power reactor critical assembly theory and analysis; measurement and calculation of integral reactor parameters; reactor analysis methods development and validation; nuclear data testing. *Mailing Add:* Appl Physics Div Argonne Nat Lab 9700 S Cass Ave Argonne IL 60439

MCKNIGHT, THOMAS JOHN, b Marietta, Ohio, Nov 5, 06; m; c 3. PARASITOLOGY. *Educ:* Okla Agr & Mech Col, BS, 25; Univ Okla, MS, 47, PhD, 59. *Prof Exp:* Instr high sch, 29-30; supt schs, 31-41; instr zool, Univ Okla, 46; prof biol, 47-76, chmn dept, 58-76, EMER PROF BIOL & CONSULT, EAST CENT STATE COL, 76- *Concurrent Pos:* Consult, Environ Survs, Kerr Magee Corp, Okla, 74-75 & US Corps Engrs, 73-74. *Mem:* AAAS; Am Soc Parasitologists; Nat Sci Teachers Asn; fel Royal Soc Health. *Res:* Bacteriology; animal parasitology and microbiology; taxonomy and physiology of parasites; taxonomy of parasites of reptiles, soil bacteria and Actinomycetes. *Mailing Add:* 1020 S Stockton Ada OK 74821

MCKNIGHT, WILLIAM BALDWIN, b Macon, Ga, July 4, 23; m 55; c 2. LASERS. *Educ:* Purdue Univ, BS, 50; Oxford Univ, PhD(physics), 68. *Prof Exp:* Physicist, Navy Underwater Sound Reference Lab, 52-53; test engr, Ord Missile Labs, Redstone Arsenal, 53-56, chief, Infrared Br, 56-58, Electro-Optical Br, 58-62, chief appl physics br, Res & Develop Directorate, US Missile Command, 62-74; RES PROF, UNIV ALA, HUNTSVILLE, 74- *Mem:* Am Phys Soc; Optical Soc Am; Inst Elec & Electronics Engrs. *Res:* Infrared radiation and detection; rocketry; missile guidance systems; solid state, molecular and x-ray lasers. *Mailing Add:* 7702 Treeline Dr Hunstville AL 35802

MAC KNIGHT, WILLIAM JOHN, b New York, NY, May 5, 36; m 67. PHYSICAL CHEMISTRY. *Educ:* Univ Rochester, BS, 58; Princeton Univ, MA, 63, PhD(phys chem), 64. *Prof Exp:* Res assoc, Princeton Univ, 64-65; from asst prof to assoc prof, 65-74, PROF CHEM, UNIV MASS, AMHERST, 74-, HEAD DEPT POLYMER SCI & ENG, 76- *Mem:* Am Chem Soc; fel Am Phys Soc; AAAS. *Res:* Physical chemistry of high polymers; sulfur chemistry. *Mailing Add:* Polymer Sci & Eng Univ of Mass Amherst MA 01003

MACKO, DOUGLAS JOHN, b Tarrytown, NY, Jan 27, 43; m 69; c 2. DENTISTRY, PEDIATRICS. *Educ:* Bates Col, BS, 65; Univ Pa, DMD, 69; Univ Conn, Pediat Dent, 75. *Prof Exp:* ASST PROF PEDIAT DENT, UNIV CONN HEALTH CTR, 75-, ASST PROF PEDIAT, 76- *Concurrent Pos:* Prin investr, Nat Inst Dent Res, 78- *Mem:* Int Soc Dent Res; Am Acad Pediat Dent. *Res:* Basic and applied research in dental caries and its prevention; salivary research related to glucose metabolism; histochemical studies of materials on the dental pulp. *Mailing Add:* Dept of Pediat Dent Univ of Conn Health Ctr Farmington CT 06032

MACKOWIAK, ELAINE DECUSATIS, b Hazleton, Pa, Apr 28, 40; m 64; c 2. PHARMACOLOGY, PHARMACEUTICAL CHEMISTRY. *Educ:* Temple Univ, BS, 62, MS, 65; Thomas Jefferson Univ, PhD(pharmacol), 74. *Prof Exp:* Asst chief pharmacist, Holy Redeemer Hosp, Meadowbrook, Pa, 62-63; lectr radiol health, Sch Dist Philadelphia, 64-68; from instr to asst prof, 64-77, actg chmn, 74-75, PROF PHARMACEUT CHEM, TEMPLE UNIV, 77- *Mem:* Am Pharmaceut Asn; Health Physics Soc. *Res:* Melanin formation; human autopsied samples for research; enzyme purification; pharmacy manpower, especially women and pharmaceutical education; trace metal analysis. *Mailing Add:* Temple Univ Sch of Pharm 3307 N Broad St Philadelphia PA 19140

MACKOWIAK, ROBERT CARL, b Hazleton, Pa, May 13, 38; m 64; c 2. INTERNAL MEDICINE, CARDIOLOGY. *Educ:* Univ Pa, AB, 60; Thomas Jefferson Univ, MD, 64; Am Bd Internal Med, dipl & dipl cardiovascular dis. *Prof Exp:* Intern med, Methodist Hosp, Philadelphia, 64-65; instr physiol, 65-66, asst prof, 67-70, assoc prof med, 71-81, ASSOC PROF PHYSIOL, THOMAS JEFFERSON UNIV, 71-, ASSOC DEAN, 73-, PROF MED, 82- *Concurrent Pos:* Resident med & cardiol, Mercy Cath Med Ctr, Philadelphia, 68-70, consult cardiol, 71- *Mem:* Am Physiol Soc; fel Am Col Physicians; fel Am Col Cardiol; Aerospace Med Asn; Am Educ Res Asn. *Mailing Add:* Dept Physiol Thomas Jefferson Univ Philadelphia PA 19107

MCKOY, BASIL VINCENT, b Trinidad, BWI, Mar 25, 38. THEORETICAL CHEMISTRY. *Educ:* NS Tech Col, BE, 60; Yale Univ, PhD(chem), 64. *Prof Exp:* From instr to assoc prof chem, 64-73, PROF THEORET CHEM, CALIF INST TECHNOL, 73- *Concurrent Pos:* Sloan Found fel, 69-71; Guggenheim fel, 73; consult, Lawrence Livermore Lab, Univ Calif, 75- *Mem:* Am Phys Soc. *Res:* Electron scattering and photoionization processes in molecules. *Mailing Add:* Dept of Chem Calif Inst of Technol Pasadena CA 91109

MCKOY, JAMES BENJAMIN, JR, b Americus, Ga, Oct 31, 27; m 47; c 5. POLYMER SCIENCE & TECHNOLOGY. *Educ:* Ga Inst Technol, BS, 48. *Prof Exp:* Engr chem synthesis, Union Carbide Corp, 48-52; tech supvr tire yarn, Chemstrand, 52-57, tech supvr textile yarns, 57-61, sect head nylon develop, 61-65, mgr acrilan develop, Monsanto Co, 65-66, prod tech dir, Monsanto Textiles, Europe, 67-70, SR RES SPECIALIST, MONSANTO TEXTILES, US, 70- *Mem:* Am Inst Chem Engrs; Am Chem Soc; Instrument Soc Am. *Res:* Polymer and fiber science, with particular interest in melt spinning dynamics and properties of fibers; fluid-bed catalysis, synthesis of organic chemicals. *Mailing Add:* Monsanto Textiles Co Box 12830 Pensacola FL 32575

MACKSEY, HARRY MICHAEL, b Detroit, Mich, Feb 20, 47; m 68. SEMICONDUCTORS. *Educ:* Univ Mich, Ann Arbor, BS, 68; Univ Ill, Urbana, MS, 70, PhD(physics), 72. *Prof Exp:* Fel physics, Univ Ill, Urbana, 72-73; MEM TECH STAFF, TEX INSTRUMENTS, INC, 73- *Mem:* Am Phys Soc; Inst Elec & Electronics Engrs. *Res:* Development of high power gallium arsenide field-effect transistors for microwave amplification. *Mailing Add:* Tex Instruments Inc 13500 N Cent Expressway MS 118 Dallas TX 75222

MACKSON, CHESTER JOHN, b Crystal Falls, Mich, July 14, 19; m 46; c 5. AGRICULTURAL ENGINEERING, PACKAGING. *Educ:* Mich State Univ, BS, 43, MA, 49, MS, 55; Cornell Univ, PhD(agr eng), 62. *Prof Exp:* High sch teacher, Mich, 49-51; from asst prof to assoc prof agr eng, 54-68, PROF AGR ENG, MICH STATE UNIV, 68-, DIR SCH PACKAGING, 77- *Mem:* Am Soc Agr Engrs; Am Soc Eng Educ. *Res:* Farm power and machinery; technical training. *Mailing Add:* Dept of Agr Eng Mich State Univ East Lansing MI 48823

MACKULAK, GERALD THOMAS, b Gary, Ind, Mar 19, 52; m 80. SIMULATION. *Educ:* Purdue Univ, BS, 74, MS, 75, PhD(indust eng), 79. *Prof Exp:* Systs analyst info systs, Burroughs Corp, 75-76; systs engr simulation, Pritsker & Assoc, 79-80; ASST PROF INDUST ENG, ARIZ STATE UNIV, 80- *Mem:* Sr mem Inst Int Educ. *Res:* Application of simulation techniques to areas of production control, computer graphics and computer aided manufacturing. *Mailing Add:* Dept Indust-Mgt Systs Eng Ariz State Univ Tempe AZ 85281

MCKUNE, WILLIAM J(AMES), electrical engineering, see previous edition

MCKUSICK, VICTOR ALMON, b Parkman, Maine, Oct 21, 21; m 49; c 3. MEDICINE. *Educ:* Johns Hopkins Univ, MD, 46; Am Bd Internal Med, dipl, 54. *Prof Exp:* Intern med, Johns Hopkins Hosp, 46-47, asst resident, 47-48; researcher, USPHS, 48-50; intern, Johns Hopkins Hosp, 50-51, resident, 51-52; from instr to assoc prof, Sch Med, 52-60, assoc epidemiol, Sch Hyg & Pub Health, 66-70, PROF MED, SCH MED, JOHNS HOPKINS UNIV, 60-, PROF EPIDEMIOL, SCH HYG & PUB HEALTH, 70-, CHMN DEPT MED, 73- *Concurrent Pos:* Exec chief cardiovasc unit, Baltimore Marine Hosp, 48-50; resident, Osler Med Clin, 51-52, physician, 53-; physician, Johns Hopkins Hosp, 53-73, chief div med genetics, 57-73, physician-in-chief. *Mem:* Nat Acad Sci; hon fel Am Acad Orthop Surg; Am Soc Clin Invest; Am Soc Human Genetics; fel Am Col Physicians. *Res:* Medical genetics; cardiology. *Mailing Add:* Dept of Med Johns Hopkins Hosp Baltimore MD 21205

MCLACHLAN, DAN, JR, b Arcola, Sask, Can, Dec 5, 05; nat US; m 34; c 3. CHEMICAL PHYSICS. *Educ:* Kans State Col, BS, 30; Pa State Col, MS, 33, PhD(phys chem), 36. *Prof Exp:* Asst, Sinclair Refining Co, 30-32 & Pa State Col, 33-36; phys chemist, Corning Glass Works, 36-41; physicist, Am Cyanamid Co, 41-47; prof metall, mineral & physics, Univ Utah, 47-53; asst chmn, Poulter Labs, Stanford Res Inst, 53-54, fundamental res scientist, 54-61; coordr dept physics, Univ Denver, 61-62, prof metall, 62-63; Battelle prof, 63-64, prof, 64-76, EMER PROF MINERAL, OHIO STATE UNIV, 76- *Concurrent Pos:* Del, Int Cong Crystallog, Univ London, 46, Harvard Univ, 49, Univ Stockholm, 51 & Univ Toronto, 57; mem, Nat Comt Crystallog, 54, Arctic Exped, Off Naval Res, 58 & Nat Res Coun, 65-68. *Mem:* AAAS; fel Am Phys Soc; fel Mineral Soc Am; Am Crystallog Asn (pres, 58); fel NY Acad Sci. *Res:* Information theory; crystallography; mechanics of metals. *Mailing Add:* 1934 Langham Rd Columbus OH 43221

MACLACHLAN, DONALD STUART, b Kenmore, Ont, Can, Sept 1, 23; m 48; c 3. PLANT PATHOLOGY. *Educ:* McGill Univ, BSc, 48, MSc, 49; Univ Wis, PhD, 52. *Prof Exp:* Chief seed potato cert, 46-66, DIR PLANT PROTECTION DIV, AGR CAN, 66- *Mem:* Potato Asn Am; Can Phytopath Soc (secy-treas, 54); Agr Inst Can. *Res:* Seed potato certification; plant quarantine. *Mailing Add:* Plant Protection Div Agr Can Sir John Carling Bldg Ottawa ON K2G 2C8 Can

MCLACHLAN, EUGENE KAY, mathematics, see previous edition

MACLACHLAN, GORDON ALISTAIR, b Saskatoon, Sask, June 30, 30; m 59; c 2. PLANT BIOCHEMISTRY. *Educ:* Univ Sask, MA, 54; Univ Man, PhD(biochem), 56. *Prof Exp:* Nat Res Coun res fel plant physiol, Imp Col, Univ London, 56-58, sci officer, Res Inst Plant Physiol, 58-59; asst prof bot, Univ Alta, 59-62; assoc prof, 62-69, chmn dept, 70-75, PROF BIOL, MCGILL UNIV, 70-, DEAN GRAD STUDIES & VPRIN RES, 80- *Concurrent Pos:* Assoc ed, Can J Biochem, 72-75, Can J Botany, 79- & Plant Physiol, 80-; vis commonwealth prof, Australia, 75-76. *Mem:* Can Soc Plant Physiol (pres, 74); Am Soc Phytochem; Am Soc Plant Physiol; Am Soc Cell Biol; Can Soc Cell Biol (pres, 81). *Res:* Metabolism of growing plants; biosynthesis and hydrolysis of cellulose. *Mailing Add:* Dept Biol McGill Univ 1205 Penfield Ave Montreal PQ H3A 1B1 Can

MCLACHLAN, JACK (LAMONT), b Huron, SDak, Apr 1, 30; m 51; c 2. PHYCOLOGY. *Educ:* Ore State Univ, BSc, 53, MA, 54, PhD, 57. *Prof Exp:* Asst, Ore State Univ, 55-57; NIH res fel, Woods Hole Oceanog Inst, 57-59; NIH res fel appl biol, 60-61, from asst res officer to assoc res officer, 61-74, SR RES OFFICER, DEPT MARINE PLANTS, ATLANTIC REGIONAL LAB, NAT RES COUN CAN, 74- *Mem:* Phycol Soc Am; Am Soc Limnol & Oceanog; Brit Phycol Soc; Int Phycol Soc. *Res:* Marine algae. *Mailing Add:* Dept of Marine Plants Atlantic Regional Lab Nat Res Coun Halifax NS B3H 3Z1 Can

MACLACHLAN, JAMES ANGELL, b Cambridge, Mass, May 18, 38; m 60; c 2. HIGH ENERGY PHYSICS, ACCELERATOR PHYSICS. *Educ:* Univ Mich, AB, 59; Yale Univ, MS, 62, PhD(physics), 68. *Prof Exp:* Consult programmer, Yale Comput Ctr, 69; PHYSICIST, FERMI NAT ACCELERATOR LAB, 69- *Mem:* Am Phys Soc. *Res:* Hadron physics, especially small angle elastic and inelastic scattering of mesons, nucleons, and hyperons; meson form factors; hyperon decays; accelerator and storage ring design-proton/anti proton-proton. *Mailing Add:* Fermi Nat Accelerator Lab PO Box 500 Batavia IL 60510

MACLACHLAN, JAMES CRAWFORD, b Detroit, Mich, Jan 13, 23; m 50. GEOLOGY. *Educ:* Wayne State Univ, AB, 48; Princeton Univ, MA, 51, PhD(geol), 52. *Prof Exp:* Consult geologist, Ministerio de Minas e Hidrocarburos, Caracas, Venezuela, 49-51; geologist, Mineral Deposits Br, US Geol Surv, 52-53 & Fuels Br, 53-56; mem explor projs group, Phillips Petrol Co, 57-62; consult, Shallow Well Explor Co, 62-67, secy-treas, 65-67; asst prof, 67-68, chmn dept earth sci, 70-74, assoc prof, 68-80, PROF GEOL, METROP STATE COL, 81- *Concurrent Pos:* Consult geologist, 62- *Mem:* Geol Soc Am; Am Asn Petrol Geol. *Res:* Stratigraphy and sedimentation of Paleozoic rocks of Eastern Colorado and Wyoming; Precambrian basement; mineralogy and petrology. *Mailing Add:* Dept Earth Sci Metrop State Col 1006 11th St Box 22 Denver CO 80204

MCLAEN, DONALD FRANCIS, b Butte, Mont, Sept 22, 42; m 64; c 3. ORGANIC CHEMISTRY, PHOTOGRAPHIC CHEMISTRY. *Educ:* Carroll Col, Mont, BA, 64; Univ Nebr, Lincoln, PhD(org chem), 68. *Prof Exp:* NIH fel org chem, Univ Ill, Urbana, 68-69; RES ASSOC, EASTMAN KODAK CO, 69- *Mem:* Am Chem Soc; Soc Photog Sci & Eng. *Res:* Organic chemical research related to photographic chemistry and processing. *Mailing Add:* Res Labs Eastman Kodak Co 343 State St Rochester NY 14650

MCLAFFERTY, FRED WARREN, b Evanston, Ill, May 11, 23; m 48; c 5. ANALYTICAL CHEMISTRY. *Educ:* Univ Nebr, BS, 43, MS, 47; Cornell Univ, PhD(org chem), 50. *Prof Exp:* Fel, Univ Iowa, 50; chemist, Dow Chem Co, 50-52, div leader, Mass Spectrometry Sect, Spectros Lab, 52-56, dir, Eastern Res Lab, Framingham, Mass, 56-64; prof chem, Purdue Univ, 64-68; PROF CHEM, CORNELL UNIV, 68- *Honors & Awards:* Am Chem Soc Award, 71; Spectros Soc Pittsburgh Award, 75; Anal Chem Award, Am Chem Soc, 81. *Mem:* AAAS; Am Chem Soc; The Chem Soc. *Res:* Mass spectrometry; molecular structure determination; on-line computers. *Mailing Add:* Dept of Chem Cornell Univ Ithaca NY 14850

MCLAFFERTY, GEORGE H(OAGLAND), JR, b Newport, RI, June 11, 26; m 50; c 2. AERONAUTICAL ENGINEERING. *Educ:* Mass Inst Technol, BS, 47, MS, 48. *Prof Exp:* Res engr, Res Labs, United Aircraft Corp, 48-55, supvr inlet group, 55-59, asst to chief res engr, 59-62, sr prog mgr, 62-76; mgr chem, 76-80, MGR NOZZLE PROG, LASER DEVELOP, PRATT & WHITNEY AIRCRAFT, 80- *Mem:* Am Inst Aeronaut & Astronaut; AAAS. *Res:* Fluid dynamics, particularly supersonic and hypersonic inlets; all phases of advanced nuclear rockets; high power lasers; jet engine nozzles. *Mailing Add:* Pratt & Whitney Aircraft PO Box 2691 West Palm Beach FL 33402

MCLAFFERTY, JOHN J, b Carbondale, Ill, July 6, 29; m 60; c 1. ANALYTICAL CHEMISTRY. *Educ:* Southern Ill Univ, BA, 51; Loyola Univ, Ill, MS, 64, PhD(anal chem), 66. *Prof Exp:* Lab supvr, Fansteel Metall Corp, 51-62; staff chemist, Union Carbide Corp, 66-70; CHIEF CHEMIST, STELLITE DIV, CABOT CORP, 70- *Mem:* Am Soc Testing & Mat; Soc Appl Spectros (pres, 75-); Am Chem Soc. *Res:* X-ray spectroscopy; emission spectroscopy. *Mailing Add:* 5423 West 80th South Kokomo IN 46901

MCLAIN, DAVID KENNETH, b Marietta, Ga, Aug 23, 37; m 64; c 2. MATHEMATICAL ANALYSIS. *Educ:* Ga Inst Technol, BS, 59, MS, 61; Carnegie Inst Technol, MS, 64, PhD(math), 67. *Prof Exp:* Assoc scientist, Bettis Atomic Power Lab, 60-62, sr mathematician, 66-73, FEL MATHEMATICIAN, RES LABS, WESTINGHOUSE ELEC CORP, 73- *Mem:* AAAS; Am Math Soc; Soc Indust & Appl Math. *Res:* Calculus of variations; differential and integral equations; linear algebra; electromagnetic fields. *Mailing Add:* Dept of Math Westinghouse Res Labs Pittsburgh PA 15235

MCLAIN, DONALD DAVIS, JR, mycology, morphology, see previous edition

MCLAIN, DOUGLAS ROBERT, oceanography, fisheries, see previous edition

MCLAIN, STEPHAN JAMES, b Tacoma, Wash, Sept 5, 53; m 75. CATALYSIS, TRANSITION METAL ORGANOMETALLICS. *Educ:* Iowa State Univ, BS, 75; Mass Inst Technol, PhD(inorg chem), 79. *Prof Exp:* Miller fel, Univ Calif, Berkeley, 79-80; RES CHEMIST, E I DUPONT DE NEMOURS & CO, INC, 80- *Mem:* Am Chem Soc; Sigma Xi. *Res:* Synthetic organometallic chemistry directed toward the development of new catalysts for organic reactions. *Mailing Add:* E328/321 E I DuPont de Nemours & Co Inc Wilmington DE 19898

MCLAIN, WILLIAM HARVEY, b Chicago, Ill; c 6. CHEMICAL ENGINEERING. *Educ:* Univ Chicago, BA, 50; Univ Denver, BSCh, 52, PhD(chem eng), 69; Univ Wash, MS, 60. *Prof Exp:* Mem staff combustion, Aeronaut Res Lab, Wright-Patterson AFB, 52-56; mem staff chem kinetics, Dept Chem, Univ Wash, 56-58; res chemist systs eng, Boeing Sci Res Labs, 58-61; scientist propulsion technol, Denver Div, Martin Marietta Corp, 61-63; chemist, Denver Res Inst, 63-73; asst mgr & mgr, Fire Res & Technol Sect, Div Struct Res & Ocean Eng, Southwest Res Inst, 74-76, inst scientist fire sci & prin investr, 76-79; TECH DIR, STAN CHEM INC, 79- *Concurrent Pos:* Sr physicist high temperature processes, Ger Res Inst Aeronaut & Rocket Propulsion, 71-72; mem life safety comt & fire test comt, Nat Fire Protection Asn; mem code admin comt, Nat Conf States Bldg Codes & Standards. *Mem:* Am Inst Astronaut & Aeronaut; Am Chem Soc; Nat Fire Protection Asn; Sigma Xi; Soc Fire Protection Engrs. *Res:* Combustion; fire science and technology; chemical kinetics; thermodynamics. *Mailing Add:* 178 Savage Hill Rd Berlin CT 06037

MCLAMORE, WILLIAM MERRILL, b Shreveport, La, Mar 15, 21; m 49; c 2. DRUG RESEARCH. *Educ:* Rice Inst, BA, 41, MA, 43; Harvard Univ, PhD(org chem), 49. *Prof Exp:* Jr chemist, Shell Develop Co, 43-45; res chemist, 50-58, res assoc, 58-61, sect mgr, 61-68, res adminr, 68-76, SCI LIAISON DIR, PFIZER INC, 76- *Mem:* Am Chem Soc. *Res:* Constituents of bone oil; polymers and resins; synthesis of substituted benzoquinones; synthesis of alkaloids; total synthesis of steroids; structure and synthesis of antibiotics; synthesis of organic medicinals. *Mailing Add:* Cent Res Pfizer Inc Eastern Point Rd Groton CT 06340

MCLANE, GEORGE FRANCIS, b Philadelphia, Pa, Nov 19, 38. SOLID STATE ELECTRONICS. *Educ:* Villanova Univ, Pa, BA, 60; Univ Pa, Philadelphia, PhD(elec eng), 71. *Prof Exp:* Elec engr, Sperry Univac, 60-62 & RCA Serv Co, 62-64; NASA fel, Univ Pa, 65-68, res asst, 68-71; ELECTRONICS ENGR, NAVAL RES LAB, 71- *Mem:* Inst Elec & Electronics Engrs; Am Phys Soc. *Res:* Solid state electronics, including fabrication and characterization of lead salt hetero junction diode lasers and determination of the laser volunerability of satellite solar cell arrays. *Mailing Add:* Naval Res Lab Washington DC 20375

MCLANE, PETER JOHN, b Vancouver, BC, July 6, 41; m 67; c 2. COMMUNICATION SYSTEMS. *Educ:* Univ BC, BASc, 65; Univ Pa, MSEE, 66; Univ Toronto, PhD(elec eng). *Prof Exp:* Jr res officer, Dept Mech Eng, Nat Res Coun, 66-67; asst prof, 69-73, assoc prof, 73-78, PROF, DEPT ELEC ENG, QUEEN'S UNIV, 78-, CHMN GRAD STUDIES, 78- *Concurrent Pos:* Vis assoc prof, Dept Elec Eng, Univ BC, 77-78; consult, Can Fed Dept Commun, 72-; mem, Scholarship Comt, Nat Sci & Eng Res Coun, 79-82, chmn, 81-82; assoc ed, Inst Elec & Electronics Engrs Commun Mag, 80- *Mem:* Inst Elec & Electronics Engrs; Can Asn Univ Teachers. *Res:* Digital signal processing in communication and radar systems; application of microprocessors and very large scale integration technologies to communications receivers; author of over 70 publications. *Mailing Add:* Dept Elec Eng Queen's Univ Kingston ON K7L 3N6 Can

MCLANE, ROBERT CLAYTON, b Hinsdale, Ill, May 12, 24; m 50; c 3. ELECTRICAL ENGINEERING. *Educ:* Univ Ill, BSEE, 49; Univ Wis, MSEE, 50. *Prof Exp:* Engr, Eng Labs, Firestone Tire & Rubber Co, 50-51; res assoc air defense systs, Eng Res Inst-Willow Run Res Ctr, Univ Mich, 51-53; res engr, Aeronaut Div, Minneapolis-Honeywell Regulator Co, 53-58, sr develop engr, 58-62, sect head eng dept, 67-68, staff engr res dept & prin systs engr, Systs & Res Ctr, 69-73, automatic test equip engr, 73-76, reliability & automatic test engr, Defense Syst Div, 76-79, SR TRAINING ENGR, AVIONICS DIV, HONEYWELL INC, 79- *Mem:* Inst Elec & Electronics Engrs; Nat Soc Prof Engrs; Am Inst Aeronaut & Astronaut. *Res:* Study of control and display relationships for manned systems; analysis and synthesis of control and display systems; hybrid computer simulation techniques for man-in-the-loop system experiments. *Mailing Add:* 4527 Arden Ave Edina MN 55424

MACLANE, SAUNDERS, b Norwich, Conn, Aug 4, 09; m 33; c 2. MATHEMATICS. *Educ:* Yale Univ, PhB,30; Univ Chicago, MA, 31; Univ Gottingen, PhD(math), 34. *Hon Degrees:* MA, Harvard Univ, 42; DSc, Purdue Univ, 65, Yale Univ, 69, Coe Col, 74 & Univ Pa, 77; LLD, Glasgow Univ, 71. *Prof Exp:* Pierce instr math, Harvard Univ, 34-36; instr, Cornell Univ, 36-37; instr, Univ Chicago, 37-38; from asst prof to prof, Harvard Univ, 38-47; prof, 47-63, MAX MASON DISTINGUISHED SERV PROF MATH, UNIV CHICAGO, 63- *Concurrent Pos:* Dir, Appl Math Group, Columbia Univ, 44-45; Guggenheim fel, Swiss Fed Inst Technol & Columbia Univ, 47-48; mem exec comt, Int Math Union, 54-58; vis prof, Univ Heidelberg, 58, 65 & 76, Univ Frankfurt, 60 & Tulane Univ, 69; mem coun, Nat Acad Sci, 59-62 & 69-72; Fulbright fel, Australian Nat Univ, 69; mem, Nat Sci Bd, 74-80; US Sr Scientist Alexander von Humboldt prize, Ger, 82-83; Guggenheim fel, 47-48 & 72-73. *Honors & Awards:* Chauvenet Prize, Math Asn Am, 41; Distinguished Serv Award, Math Asn Am, 75. *Mem:* Nat Acad Sci (vpres, 73-77, 77-81); Am Math Soc (vpres, 46-48, pres, 73-74); Am Philos Soc (vpres, 68-71); Math Asn Am (vpres, 48, pres, 50); Am Acad Arts & Sci. *Res:* Algebra; topology; algebraic topology; logic; category theory; philosophy of mathematics. *Mailing Add:* Dept of Math 5734 University Ave Chicago IL 60637

MCLANE, STANLEY REX, JR, b Kansas City, Mo, Aug 11, 22; m 45; c 3. HORTICULTURE, PLANT PHYSIOLOGY. *Educ:* Univ Mo, BS, 46, PhD(hort), 51. *Prof Exp:* Plant physiologist, Physicochem Corps Div, US Civil Serv, Ft Detrick, Md, 51-57; PLANT PHYSIOLOGIST & WEED CONTROL SPECIALIST, AGR CHEM DIV, AMCHEM PROD DIV, UNION CARBIDE CORP, 57- *Mem:* Am Soc Hort Sci; Weed Sci Soc Am. *Res:* Supervising development of new herbicides and growth regulators on agronomic and horticultural crops. *Mailing Add:* Union Carbide Agr Prod Co PO Box 12014 TW Alexander Dr Res Triangle Park NC 27709

MCLAREN, ARTHUR DOUGLAS, biophysics, biology, deceased

MCLAREN, DIGBY JOHNS, b Carrickfergus, Northern Ireland, Dec 11, 19; m 42; c 3. SCIENCE ADVISOR. *Educ:* Univ Cambridge, BA, 41, MA, 47; Univ Mich, PhD(geol), 51. *Hon Degrees:* DSc, Univ Ottawa, 80. *Prof Exp:* Mem staff, 48-59, chief paleontologist, 59-67, dir, Inst Sedimentary & Petrol Geol, 67-73, dir, 73-80, asst dep minister sci & technol, 81, SR SCI AVD, DEPT ENERGY, MINES & RESOURCES, GEOL SURV CAN, 81- *Concurrent Pos:* Chmn, Comn on Stratig, Int Union Geol Sci, 68-72; chmn, Bd Int Geol Correlation Prog, UNESCO-Int Union Geol Sci, 76-78; vis prof, Univ Ottawa, 81- *Mem:* Foreign assoc Nat Acad Sci; fel Am Geol Soc; fel Royal Soc Can; Geol Soc France; Am Paleont Soc (pres, 69). *Res:* Devonian paleontology and stratigraphy of Western Canada. *Mailing Add:* Dept Geol Univ Ottawa Ottawa ON K1N 6N5 Can

MCLAREN, EUGENE HERBERT, b Troy, NY, Aug 3, 24; m 57; c 3. ATMOSPHERIC CHEMISTRY. *Educ:* NY State Col Teachers Albany, BA, 48, MA, 49; Washington Univ, PhD(phys chem), 55. *Prof Exp:* Instr chem, State Univ NY Col Teachers Albany, 50-52, assoc prof, 55-57; sr res chemist, Pan-Am Petrol Corp, 57-60; prof sci & math, 60-69, PROF CHEM & SR RES ASSOC ATMOSPHERIC SCI RES CTR, STATE UNIV NY ALBANY, 69- *Concurrent Pos:* Assoc dean, State Univ NY Albany, 68-69, chmn div sci & math, 61-68; univ fel & res scientist, Max Planck Inst Chem, 69-70. *Mem:* AAAS; Am Chem Soc; Am Meteorol Soc; Air Pollution Control Asn. *Res:* Physical chemistry of atmospheric particulates and gases; geochemistry of carbonates; x-ray diffraction and spectroscopy. *Mailing Add:* Dept Chem State Univ NY Albany NY 12222

MCLAREN, IAN ALEXANDER, b Montreal, Que, Jan 11, 31; m 56; c 3. BIOLOGY. *Educ:* McGill Univ, BSc, 52, MSc, 55; Yale Univ, PhD(zool), 61. *Prof Exp:* Asst scientist, Fisheries Res Bd Can, 55-63; asst prof biol, Marine Sci Ctr, McGill Univ, 63-66; assoc prof, 66-69, PROF BIOL, DALHOUSIE UNIV, 69- *Concurrent Pos:* Can Coun fel, McGill Univ, 64-66. *Mem:* Can Soc Zoologists; Am Soc Naturalists; Ecol Soc Am. *Res:* Population; evolutionary ecology; birds; sea mammals; zooplankton. *Mailing Add:* Dept of Biol Dalhousie Univ Halifax NS B3H 4J1 Can

MCLAREN, LEROY CLARENCE, b Bishop, Calif, Jan 18, 24; m 45; c 3. MICROBIOLOGY, VIROLOGY. *Educ:* San Jose State Col, AB, 49; Univ Calif, Los Angeles, MA, 51, PhD(microbiol), 53; Am Bd Med Microbiol, dipl. *Prof Exp:* Asst microbiol, Univ Calif, Los Angeles, 49-50, asst bact, 50-52, instr infectious dis, Sch Med, 53-55; from instr to assoc prof bact, Sch Med, Univ Minn, 55-64; PROF MICROBIOL & CHMN DEPT, SCH MED, UNIV NMEX, 64- *Concurrent Pos:* USPHS career res award, 62-64; mem microbiol fel rev panel, NIH, 64-68; consult, Lilly Res Labs, 64-68; mem comt personnel for res, Am Cancer Soc, 73-77; mem bd educ & training, Am Soc Microbiol, 72-76. *Mem:* Fel AAAS; fel Am Acad Microbiol; Am Soc Microbiol; Am Asn Immunol; Tissue Cult Asn. *Res:* Tissue culture of animal viruses; stability of viruses; animal virus multiplication; mechanisms of viral susceptibility and resistance; infectious agents in inflammatory bowel disease. *Mailing Add:* Dept of Microbiol Univ of NMex Sch of Med Albuquerque NM 87131

MACLAREN, MALCOLM DONALD, b Tarrytown, NY, Aug 5, 36. PROGRAMMING LANGUAGES, COMPILERS. *Educ:* Harvard Univ, AB, 58, MA, 60, PhD(math), 62. *Prof Exp:* Mem staff math, Boeing Sci Res Labs, Wash, 60-64; from asst mathematician to assoc mathematician, Argonne Nat Lab, 64-72; mgr advan lang systs develop, Cambridge Info Systs Lab, Honeywell, Inc, 74-76; CONSULT ENGR, DIGITAL EQUIP CORP, 76- *Concurrent Pos:* Vchmn comt X3J1, Am Nat Standards Inst, 71-72. *Mem:* Am Math Soc; Asn Comput Mach; Soc Indust & Appl Math. *Res:* Computation and programming, especially design, definition and implementation of languages, operating systems and similar software; formal theory of languages and programming. *Mailing Add:* Digital Equip Corp 2265 116th Ave NE Bellevue WA 98004

MCLAREN, MALCOLM G(RANT), b Denver, Colo, July 22, 28; m 50; c 3. CERAMICS. *Educ:* Rutgers Univ, BS, 50, MS, 51, PhD, 62. *Prof Exp:* Res asst, Rutgers Univ, 50-54; res scientist, Wright Air Develop Ctr, Ohio, 55-57; assoc prof ceramics, 62-69, PROF CERAMICS & CHMN DEPT, RUTGERS UNIV, NEW BRUNSWICK, 69- *Concurrent Pos:* Chief ceramist, Paper Makers Importing Co, Inc, 54-55, vpres, 57-62; indust consult ceramics; govt appt, US Dept Energy Technol Panel, 78. *Mem:* Am Ceramic Soc (pres-elect, 78); Ceramic Educ Coun (pres, 71-72); Can Ceramic Asn; Sigma Xi; Am Soc Eng Educ. *Res:* Whitewares; refractories; electronic ceramics. *Mailing Add:* Dept of Ceramics Rutgers Univ New Brunswick NJ 08903

MACLAREN, RICHARD OLIVER, b Missoula, Mont, Sept 4, 24; m 48; c 5. PHYSICAL CHEMISTRY. *Educ:* Univ Ore, BA, 49, MA, 50; Univ Wash, PhD(chem), 54. *Prof Exp:* Res chemist, Olin Mathieson Chem Corp, 54-55, pilot plant supvr, 55-56, group leader, 56-57, head thermodyn sect, 57-60; chief chem sect, United Tech Ctr, United Aircraft Corp, 60-63, MGR COMBUSTION RES & DEVELOP BR, CHEM SYSTS DIV, UNITED TECHNOL CORP, 63- *Mem:* Am Chem Soc. *Res:* Physical and inorganic chemistry involving high temperature processes; electrochemistry; solid propellant combustion, ignition and propellant chemistry; chemistry of fluorine compounds; chemical propulsion concepts. *Mailing Add:* 1031 Pinenut Ct Sunnyvale CA 94087

MCLAREN, ROBERT ALEXANDER, b Hamilton, Ont, Mar 29, 46; m 69; c 3. INFRARED ASTRONOMY, ASTRONOMICAL INSTRUMENTATION. *Educ:* Univ Toronto, BSc, 68, MSc, 69, PhD(physics), 73. *Prof Exp:* NATO fel astron, Univ Calif, Berkeley, 73-75; asst prof, 75-80, ASSOC PROF ASTRON, DEPT ASTRON & DEPT PHYSICS, UNIV TORONTO, 80- *Mem:* Can Asn Physicists; Am Astron Soc; Can Astron Soc. *Res:* Infrared photometry, spectrophotometry, and heterodyne spectroscopy of astronomical objects. *Mailing Add:* Dept Astron Univ Toronto Toronto ON M5S 1A7 Can

MCLAREN, ROBERT WAYNE, b Chicago, Ill, Aug 31, 36; m 69; c 1. ELECTRICAL ENGINEERING. *Educ:* Univ Ill, Urbana, BScEE, 59, MScEE, 60; Purdue Univ, PhD(elec eng), 66. *Prof Exp:* Res engr, Autonetics Div, N Am Aviation, Inc, 61-62; instr elec eng, Purdue Univ, 62-66; asst prof, 66-69, eng exp sta res grant, 67-68, ASSOC PROF ELEC ENG, UNIV MO-COLUMBIA, 69- *Mem:* Inst Elec & Electronics Engrs; Optical Soc Am; Asn Comput Mach; Am Soc Cybernet. *Res:* Artificial intelligence; pattern recognition; learning and control systems; automata theory; image analysis. *Mailing Add:* Dept of Elec Eng Univ of Mo Columbia MO 65201

MACLATCHY, CYRUS SHANTZ, b Galt, Ont, May 24, 41; m 63; c 3. PLASMA PHYSICS, COMBUSTION. *Educ:* Acadia Univ, BS, 64; Univ BC, MS, 66, PhD(physics), 70. *Prof Exp:* Asst prof, 70-76, assoc prof, 76-81, PROF PHYSICS, ACADIA UNIV, 81- *Res:* Use of Langmuir probes in diagnostics of diffusion plasmas. *Mailing Add:* Dept Physics Acadia Univ Wolfville NS B0P 1X0 Can

MACLAUCHLAN, DONALD WELLS, b Bedegue, PEI, June 8, 05; m 38. PHYSICAL CHEMISTRY. *Educ:* Mt Allison Univ, BSc, 29; McGill Univ, PhD(chem), 37. *Prof Exp:* Lab technician, Atlantic Sugar Refining Co, NB, 23-24; instr chem, McGill Univ, 35-37; lectr physics, Univ NB, 40-42; prof chem, 42-74, dean men, 43-60, assoc dean arts & sci, 66-69, exec dir alumni, 69-73, EMER PROF CHEM, MT ALLISON UNIV, 74- *Res:* Properties of hydrogen peroxide. *Mailing Add:* Box 91 Sackville NB E0A 3C0 Can

MCLAUGHLIN, ALAN CHARLES, b Vancouver, BC, Aug 17, 45. BIOPHYSICS. *Educ:* Univ BC, BSc, 68; Univ Pa, PhD(biophysics), 73. *Prof Exp:* Fel biochem, Oxford Univ, 73-76; ASSOC BIOPHYSICIST BIOL, BROOKHAVEN NAT LAB, 77- *Mem:* Biophys Soc. *Res:* Application of nuclear magnetic resonance to the structure of model and biological membranes. *Mailing Add:* Dept of Biol Brookhaven Nat Lab Upton NY 11793

MCLAUGHLIN, BARBARA JEAN, b Miami, Fla, Nov 3, 41. NEUROBIOLOGY. *Educ:* Univ Fla, BS, 63; Stanford Univ, PhD(anat), 71. *Prof Exp:* Asst prof, 74-76, ASSOC PROF ANAT, CTR HEALTH SCI, UNIV TENN, MEMPHIS, 76- *Concurrent Pos:* Agr Res Coun, Eng Underwood Fund grant zool, Univ Cambridge, 71-73; fel neurosci, City of Hope Med Ctr, Duarte, Calif, 73-74; mem comt to study status of women in anat, Am Asn Anatomists, 78-80; mem proj rev A comt, NIH Neurol Disorders Prog, 78-82. *Mem:* Soc Neurosci; Am Asn Anat; Am Soc Cell Biol. *Res:* Developmental neurobiology; cytochemical and immunocytochemical localization of various molecular components in adult and developing nervous tissue; anatomy of developing photoreceptors; pigment epithelial-photoreceptor interactions; retinal degeneration; cytochemistry of developing synapses. *Mailing Add:* Dept of Anat Univ of Tenn Ctr Health Sci Memphis TN 38163

MCLAUGHLIN, CALVIN STURGIS, b St Joseph, Mo, May 29, 36; m 60; c 3. BIOCHEMISTRY, GENETICS. *Educ:* King Col, BS, 58; Mass Inst Technol, PhD(biochem), 64. *Prof Exp:* From asst prof to assoc prof, 66-72, PROF BIOCHEM, UNIV CALIF, IRVINE, 72-, VCHAIR, DEPT BIOL CHEM, 79-; DIR, CANCER RES INST, 81- *Concurrent Pos:* Am Cancer Soc fel, Inst Phys Chem Biol, Paris, 64-66. *Mem:* Genetics Soc Am; Am Soc Microbiol; Am Soc Biol Chem. *Res:* Biochemistry and biochemical genetics of protein and RNA synthesis; mechanism of action of antibiotics; regulation of protein and RNA synthesis; mycology. *Mailing Add:* Dept of Biol Chem Univ of Calif-Calif Col of Med Irvine CA 92717

MCLAUGHLIN, CHARLES ALBERT, b Chatham, Ill, Nov 12, 26; m 49; c 2. ZOOLOGY. *Educ:* Univ Ill, BS, 49, MS, 51, PhD(zool), 58. *Prof Exp:* Asst, Mus Natural Hist, Univ Ill, 50-51, exhibit preparator, 56, sci artist zool, Univ 51-55, asst, 55-56; assoc curator ornith & mammal, Los Angeles County Mus Natural Hist, 57-62, curator, 62-65, sr curator mammal, 65-67; assoc prof zool & curator mammal, Univ Wyo, 67-71; dir educ & gen cur, San Diego Zoo, 71-80; EXEC DIR, NATURAL HIST MUS, SAN DIEGO, 80- *Mem:* Am Soc Mammal; Am Asn Zool Parks & Aquariums; Soc Syst Zool; Am Asn Mus; Am Soc Zool. *Res:* Mammalogy, especially taxonomy, ecology and distribution, particularly of rodents and bats. *Mailing Add:* San Diego Natural Hist Mus Balboa Park San Diego CA 92112

MCLAUGHLIN, CHARLES WILLIAM, JR, b Washington, Iowa, Feb 3, 06; m 39; c 2. SURGERY. *Educ:* Univ Iowa, BS, 27; Wash Univ, MD, 29; Am Bd Surg, dipl, 40. *Prof Exp:* From instr to assoc prof, 35-55, prof surg, Col Med, 55-77, MEM FAC, SCH MED & SR CONSULT SURGEON, UNIV NEBR, OMAHA, 77- *Concurrent Pos:* Res fel surg, Univ Pa, 31-34; nat consult, Gen Surgeon, US Air Force. *Mem:* Fel Am Col Surg; AMA; Asn Mil Surg US. *Res:* Abdominal and pediatric surgery. *Mailing Add:* 10085 Fieldcrest Dr Omaha NE 68114

MCLAUGHLIN, DAVID, b Sumter, SC, Nov 1, 34; div. ZOOLOGY. *Educ:* Clark Col, BS, 56; Howard Univ, MS, 62, PhD(zool), 65. *Prof Exp:* Res asst biochem & physiol protozoa, 57-62, res assoc, 62-65, asst prof zool, 65-69, assoc prof, 69-74, chmn div nat sci, 70-71, PROF ZOOL, HOWARD UNIV, 74- *Concurrent Pos:* Partic, Biospace Training Prog, NASA, Va, 65 & Gemini Summary Conf, Manned Spacecraft Ctr, 67. *Mem:* AAAS; Am Soc Protozool; Am Inst Biol Sci; Am Micros Soc; Sigma Xi. *Res:* Biochemistry and physiology of cells. *Mailing Add:* Dept Zool Howard Univ Washington DC 20001

MCLAUGHLIN, DONALD REED, b Los Angeles, Calif, Oct 6, 38; m 64; c 6. CHEMICAL PHYSICS. *Educ:* Univ Calif, Los Angeles, BS, 60; Univ Utah, PhD(chem), 65. *Prof Exp:* Asst prof, 65-72, ASSOC PROF CHEM, UNIV N MEX, 72- *Concurrent Pos:* Assoc, Rocky Mt Univs, Inc, Fac Orientation & Training Summers Fels, 65-69. *Res:* Theoretical chemistry, especially quantum mechanics, statistical mechanics, chemical kinetics and thermodynamics. *Mailing Add:* Dept of Chem Univ of NMex Albuquerque NM 87131

MACLAUGHLIN, DOUGLAS EARL, b Indiana, Pa, Nov 18, 38; m 67. SOLID STATE PHYSICS. *Educ:* Amherst Col, BA, 60; Univ Calif, Berkeley, PhD(physics), 66. *Prof Exp:* NATO fel physics, Atomic Energy Res Estab, Harwell, Eng, 66-67; res assoc, Lab Physique Solides, Fac Sci, Orsay, France, 67-69; from asst prof to assoc prof, 69-78, PROF PHYSICS, UNIV CALIF, RIVERSIDE, 78- *Concurrent Pos:* Vchmn Physics Dept, Univ Calif, Riverside, 76-81; chmn, Muon Spin Relaxation working group, Los Alamos Meson Physics Facil, 80-81; vis fac mem, Univ Amsterdam, 80; vis staff mem, Los Alamos Nat Lab, 80- *Mem:* Am Phys Soc; AAAS; Sigma Xi. *Res:* Use of magnetic resonance and relaxation to investigate electronic structure of metals, superconductors, spin glasses, and rare earth compounds. *Mailing Add:* Dept of Physics Univ of Calif Riverside CA 92502

MCLAUGHLIN, EDWARD, b Ballymena, Ireland, Oct 16, 28; m 56; c 4. CHEMICAL ENGINEERING, PHYSICAL CHEMISTRY. *Educ:* Queen's Univ, Belfast, BSc, 53, MSc, 54; Univ London, PhD(phys chem), 56, DSc, 74, Imp Col, dipl, 57. *Prof Exp:* Asst lectr phys chem, Imp Col, Univ London, 56-58, from lectr to sr lectr chem physics, 58-66, reader, 66-70; asst dir dept chem eng, 61-70; PROF CHEM ENG, LA STATE UNIV, BATON ROUGE, 70- *Concurrent Pos:* Sr foreign scientist, NSF, 67-68. *Mem:* Faraday Soc; Am Chem Soc; Am Inst Chem Engrs. *Res:* Transport properties of fluids and the thermodynamic properties of solutions; influence of high pressure and strong electric fields on the properties of liquids; statistical theories of transport phenomena. *Mailing Add:* Dept of Chem Eng La State Univ Baton Rouge LA 70803

MCLAUGHLIN, ELLEN WINNIE, b Roosevelt, NY, Aug 17, 37. EXPERIMENTAL EMBRYOLOGY. *Educ:* State Univ NY Albany, BS, 58; Univ NC, Chapel Hill, MA, 62; Emory Univ, PhD(biol), 67. *Prof Exp:* Instr biol, Converse Col, 60-63; from asst prof to assoc prof, 67-75, PROF BIOL, SAMFORD UNIV, 75- *Concurrent Pos:* Res grants, Samford Univ, 68-69. *Mem:* AAAS; Am Soc Zool; Am Sci Affiliation. *Res:* Effects of heavy metals and pesticides on aquatic vertebrate and invertebrate embryos, including amphibians, fish and snails. *Mailing Add:* Dept of Biol Samford Univ Birmingham AL 35229

MCLAUGHLIN, FOIL WILLIAM, b NC, Dec 9, 23; m 48; c 4. AGRONOMY. *Educ:* NC State Univ, BS, 49, MS, 53. *Prof Exp:* Res asst prof field crops, 53-63, exten assoc prof, 63-68, DIR, NC CROP IMPROV ASN, NC STATE UNIV, 48-, EXTEN PROF CROP SCI, 63- *Concurrent Pos:* Exec vpres, Asn Off Seed Certifying Agencies in US & Can, 81- *Honors & Awards:* Hon Seedsman Award, Am Seed Trade Asn, 81. *Res:* Crop and seed improvement, especially breeding and quality control in seed development and production; seed certification. *Mailing Add:* Dept Crop Sci 3709 Hillsborough St Raleigh NC 27607

MCLAUGHLIN, FRANCIS X(AVIER), b Philadelphia, Pa, Sept 2, 30. DATA PROCESSING, STATISTICS. *Educ:* Villanova Univ, BS, 52, MS, 59. *Prof Exp:* Jr chemist, Waste Control Lab, Atlantic Refining Co, 52-54, asst chemist, 54-55, asst chemist, Res & Develop Dept, 55-56; res engr, Franklin Inst, Pa, 56-58, methods analyst, 58, sr methods analyst, 58-60; specialist mgt sci, Missile & Space Div, Gen Elec Co, 60-64, mgr, 65-69; vpres mgt & comput sci, Sci Resources Corp, 69-70; consult data processing, 70-71; vpres mgt & comput sci, Mauchly Mgt Serv, Inc, 71-73; mgr statist, Union Fidelity Ins Corp, 73-76; CONSULT, 76- *Mem:* Am Soc Qual Control; Sigma Xi; Biomet Soc; The Inst Mgt Sci; Am Statist Asn. *Res:* Operations research; systems analysis and design; computer applications and programming; time-shared and remote computer processing systems. *Mailing Add:* 911 Lindale Ave Drexel Hill PA 19026

MCLAUGHLIN, GERALD WAYNE, b Nashville, Tenn, Aug 16, 42; m 65; c 2. RESEARCH MANAGEMENT, APPLIED STATISTICS. *Educ:* Univ Tenn, BS, 64, MS, 65, PhD(orgn psychol), 69. *Prof Exp:* Res asst indust mgt, Univ Tenn, 64-65, res asst econ, 65-66; asst dir instnl res, US Mil Acad, 69-71; asst prof, 71-81, ASSOC PROF OFF INSTNL RES, VA POLYTECH INST & STATE UNIV, 81- *Mem:* Asn Instnl Res; Psychomet Soc. *Res:* Administration and conducting applied research; testing and measurement; role analysis in education, industry and other fields. *Mailing Add:* Va Polytech Inst & State Univ Blacksburg VA 24061

MCLAUGHLIN, HARRY WRIGHT, b Highland Park, Mich, June 28, 37; m 61; c 2. MATHEMATICS, COMPUTER GRAPHICS. *Educ:* DePauw Univ, BS, 59; Kans State Univ, MS, 61; Univ Md, PhD(math), 66. *Prof Exp:* Assoc mathmatician, Applied Physics Lab, Johns Hopkins Univ, 61-63; asst prof math, Univ Calif, Riverside, 66-67; asst prof, 67-72, assoc prof, 72-77, PROF MATH, RENSSELAER POLYTECH INST, 77- *Mem:* Math Asn Am; Am Math Soc; Soc Indust & Applied Math. *Res:* Mathematical models for computer aided design; algorithms for optimal knot location in spline theory; approximation techniques. *Mailing Add:* Dept Math Sci Rensselaer Polytech Inst Troy NY 12181

MCLAUGHLIN, J(OHN) F(RANCIS), b New York, NY, Sept 21, 27; m 50; c 4. CIVIL ENGINEERING. *Educ:* Syracuse Univ, BCE, 50; Purdue Univ, MSCE, 53, PhD(civil eng), 57. *Prof Exp:* From instr to prof civil eng, 50-68, head, Sch Civil Eng, 68-78, asst dean eng, 78-80, ASSOC DEAN ENG, PURDUE UNIV, 80- *Mem:* Am Soc Civil Engrs; Nat Soc Prof Engrs; Am Concrete Inst (vpres, 77-79, pres, 79-80). *Res:* Mineral aggregates for construction purposes; properties of portland cement concrete. *Mailing Add:* Sch of Civil Eng Purdue Univ Lafayette IN 47907

MCLAUGHLIN, JACK ENLOE, b St Maries, Idaho, Aug 17, 23; m 49. MATHEMATICS. *Educ:* Univ Idaho, BS, 44; Calif Inst Technol, PhD(math), 50. *Prof Exp:* From instr to assoc prof, 50-62, PROF MATH, UNIV MICH, ANN ARBOR, 62- *Concurrent Pos:* Res fel, Harvard Univ, 60. *Mem:* Am Math Soc; Math Asn Am. *Res:* Group theory. *Mailing Add:* Dept Math Univ Mich Ann Arbor MI 48109

MCLAUGHLIN, JAMES L, b Detroit, Mich, July 16, 42; m 64; c 1. PLANT PATHOLOGY. *Educ:* Eastern Mich Univ, BA, 64; Univ Ill, MS, 66, PhD(plant path), 69. *Prof Exp:* Asst prof biol, Univ Wis-Superior, 69-72; asst prof, 72-73, chmn dept, 73-77, ASSOC PROF BIOL, COL ST SCHOLASTICA, 73- *Mem:* Am Inst Biol Sci; Am Phytopath Soc. *Res:* Mycology; plant physiology; bacteriology. *Mailing Add:* Dept of Biol Col of St Scholastica Duluth MN 55811

MCLAUGHLIN, JERRY LOREN, b Coldwater, Mich, Oct 14, 39; m 60, 81; c 2. PHARMACOGNOSY. *Educ:* Univ Mich, BS, 61, MS, 63, PhD(pharmacog), 65. *Prof Exp:* Asst prof pharmacog, Univ Mich, 65-66 & Univ Mo-Kansas City, 66-67; mem fac, Col Pharm, Univ Wash, 67, from asst prof to assoc prof pharmacog, 67-71; assoc prof, 71-75, exec asst to dean, 75-80, PROF PHARMACOG, SCH PHARM & PHARMACAL SCI, PURDUE UNIV, 75- *Concurrent Pos:* Nat Inst Ment Health res grants, 66-67, 69-72; NIH res grants, 74-77 & 81-82; Nat Sci Found res grants, 74, 75 & 79. *Mem:* AAAS; Am Pharmaceut Asn; Am Soc Pharmacog (vpres, 81-82, pres, 82-83); Soc Econ Bot; Acad Pharmaceut Sci. *Res:* Cactus alkaloids, their isolation and biosynthesis; active constituents of psychotropic and poisonous plants. *Mailing Add:* 2940 St Rd 26W West Lafayette IN 47906

MCLAUGHLIN, JOHN J (ANTHONY), b Long Island, NY, Aug 26, 24; m 51; c 5. MICROBIOLOGY. *Educ:* St Francis Col, NY, BS, 50; St John's Univ, NY, MS, 52; NY Univ, PhD, 56. *Prof Exp:* Asst microbiol, Haskins Labs, 52-56, mem staff, 56-69; assoc prof biol, St Francis Col, NY, 56-69; chmn dept, 69-74, PROF BIOL SCI, FORDHAM UNIV, BRONX, 69- *Res:* Anexic culturing of microscopic and macroscopic organisms; phytoplanktonic and symbiotic organisms from the marine environment. *Mailing Add:* Dept of Biol Sci Fordham Univ Bronx NY 10458

MCLAUGHLIN, JOHN ROSS, b Clayton, NMex, June 4, 39; m 64; c 2. ENTOMOLOGY. *Educ:* Colo State Univ, BS, 66, MS, 67; Univ Calif, Riverside, PhD(entom), 72. *Prof Exp:* Res assoc insect behav, Dept Entom, Univ Calif, Riverside, 71-72, res assoc insect ecol, Dept Plant Sci, 72-73; asst prof insect behavior, Dept Entom & Nematol, Univ Fla, 73-74; RES ENTOMOLOGIST INSECT ATTRACTANTS, BEHAV & BASIC BIOL RES LAB, AGR RES SERV, USDA, 74- *Concurrent Pos:* Assoc ed, Fla Entomologist, 78- *Mem:* Entom Soc Am; AAAS. *Res:* Insect behavior and ecology, particularly the study of pheromones and related semiochemicals. *Mailing Add:* Insect Attractants PO Box 14565 Gainesville FL 32604

MCLAUGHLIN, JOYCE ROGERS, b Milwaukee, Wis; c 2. DIFFERENTIAL EQUATIONS. *Educ:* Kans State Univ, BS, 61; Univ Md, MA, 63; Univ Calif, Riverside, PhD(math), 68. *Prof Exp:* Mathematician, Electromagnetic Res Corp, 63-65; mathematician, Naval Res Lab, 65-66; res assoc, 69-78, ASST PROF, RENSSELAER POLYTECH INST, 78- *Mem:* Am Math Soc; Soc Indust & Appl Math; Math Asn Am; Asn Am Univ Prof. *Res:* Inverse eigenvalue problems; algorithms for constructing solutions as well as existence, uniqueness and continuous dependence questions; determining the construction of the earth's crust, the structure of vibrating bars and the study of nonlinear partial differential equations, such as the Korteweg-de Uries Equation. *Mailing Add:* Dept Math Sci Rensselaer Polytech Inst Troy NY 12181

MCLAUGHLIN, KENNETH PHELPS, b Blackfoot, Idaho, Apr 16, 17; m 41; c 3. GEOLOGY. *Educ:* Univ Mo, AB, 39, MA, 41; La State Univ, PhD(geol), 47. *Prof Exp:* Instr geol, Centenary Col, 42-43; geologist, Stanolind Oil & Gas Co, Tex, 43-45; instr geol, La State Univ, 45-47; asst prof, State Col Wash, 47-50; prof & chmn dept, Univ Mont, 50-55; staff geologist, Tex Industs Inc, 55-62, consult, 62-65; chmn dept, 65-81, PROF GEOL & GEOL ENG, UNIV MISS, 65- *Concurrent Pos:* Geologist, US Geol Surv, 48-50 & Shell Oil Co, 51-53. *Mem:* Am Asn Petrol Geologists; Asn Eng Geologists. *Res:* Industrial minerals. *Mailing Add:* Dept of Geol & Geol Eng Univ of Miss Sch of Eng University MS 38677

MCLAUGHLIN, MICHAEL RAY, b Carroll, Iowa, June 20, 49; m 70; c 2. PLANT VIROLOGY. *Educ:* Iowa State Univ Sci & Technol, BS, 71, MS, 74; Univ Ill, PhD(plant path), 78. *Prof Exp:* Vis asst prof plant path, Clemson Univ, 78-79; ASST PROF PLANT PATH, UNIV TENN, 79- *Mem:* Am Phytopath Soc; AAAS; Int Working Group Legume Virologists; Sigma Xi. *Res:* Plant virology, especially legume viruses; serology. *Mailing Add:* Dept Entom & Plant Path Univ Tenn Knoxville TN 37996

MCLAUGHLIN, PATSY ANN, b Seattle, Wash, May 27, 32; m 70. SYSTEMATIC ZOOLOGY, ENVIRONMENTAL BIOLOGY. *Educ:* Univ Wash, BA, 57; George Washington Univ, MPh, 69, PhD(zool), 72. *Prof Exp:* Fishery biologist res, US Bur Com Fisheries, 57-60; zoologist, Dept Oceanog, Univ Wash, 60-65; supvr, Smithsonian Oceanog Sorting Ctr, 65-68; from res asst to asst prof, Rosenstiel Sch Marine & Atmospheric Sci, Univ Miami, 69-75; courtesy assoc prof res teaching, 75-77, PROF RES TEACHING, DEPT BIOL SCI, FLA INT UNIV, 75- *Concurrent Pos:* Res assoc, Nat Mus Natural Hist, 73-76 & 80-83; prin investr, NSF, 73-75 & 76-78; prin investr, Fla State Univ Syst Sea Grant Prog, 77-78; contrib specialist, Norwegian Res Coun Sci & Humanities, 73-; dir, Appl Marine Ecol Serv, Inc, 75-76. *Mem:* Am Soc Zoologists; Soc Syst Zool; Crustacean Soc. *Res:* Systematics and comparative morphology of crustaceans, with particular emphasis on pagurids, cirripeds and cephalocarids; marine environmental assessment, with emphasis on benthic communities. *Mailing Add:* Dept of Biol Sci Tamiami Campus Miami FL 33199

MCLAUGHLIN, PHILIP V(AN DOREN), JR, b Elizabeth, NJ, Nov 10, 39; m 61; c 3. SOLID MECHANICS, COMPOSITE MATERIAL. *Educ:* Univ Pa, BS, 61, MS, 64, PhD(eng mech), 69. *Prof Exp:* Assoc engr, Vertol Div, Boeing Co, 62-63, engr, 63; res engr, Tech Ctr, Scott Paper Co, 63-65, res proj engr, 65-69, sr res proj engr, 69; asst prof theoret & appl mech, Univ Ill, Urbana, 69-73, asst dean, Col Eng, 71-72; proj mgr, Mat Sci Corp, Pa, 73-76; assoc prof, 76-81, PROF MECH ENG, VILLANOVA UNIV, 81- *Concurrent Pos:* NSF grant, Univ Ill, Urbana, 70-72, Nat Asn Eng Co grants, 78- & Lawrence Livermore Nat Lab grants, 79-81; fac res grant, Villanova Univ, 78; consult, US Naval Air Eng, 77-79 & US Steel Corp, 80-81. *Mem:* Am Acad Mechanics; Am Soc Eng Educ; Sigma Xi; Am Soc Civil Engrs; Am Soc Mech Engrs. *Res:* Plasticity; composite materials; materials, flow and fracture. *Mailing Add:* Dept Mech Eng Villanova Univ Villanova PA 19085

MCLAUGHLIN, ROBERT EVERETT, b Aurora, Ind, Nov 30, 19; m 45; c 3. PALEONTOLOGY. *Educ:* Tulane Univ, BS, 51, MS, 52; Univ Tenn, Knoxville, PhD(paleont), 57. *Prof Exp:* Asst bot, Tulane Univ, 50-51, asst geol, 52; from asst to instr bot, 52-54, from instr to assoc prof geol, 54-71, PROF GEOL, UNIV TENN, KNOXVILLE, 71- *Concurrent Pos:* Southern Fels Fund award, 55-56. *Mem:* Bot Soc Am; Paleont Soc; Geol Soc Am; Am Asn Stratig Palynologists. *Res:* Palynology of tertiary and older deposits; Paleozoic paleontology. *Mailing Add:* Dept of Geol Univ of Tenn Knoxville TN 37916

MCLAUGHLIN, ROBERT H(UGH) B(ENSON), b Ft Fairfield, Maine, July 19, 22; m 49; c 2. CIVIL ENGINEERING. *Educ:* Univ New Brunswick, BSc, 43, MSc, 59; Mass Inst Technol, BldgE, 60. *Prof Exp:* From asst prof to assoc prof, 46-66, PROF CIVIL ENG, UNIV NB, 66- *Concurrent Pos:* Mem, Masonry & Forest Prod Steering Comts, Can Standards Asn. *Mem:* Am Soc Eng Educ; Asn Prof Engrs; Masonry Soc. *Res:* Building materials and construction. *Mailing Add:* Dept Civil Eng Univ NB Fredericton NB E3B 5A3 Can

MCLAUGHLIN, ROBERT LAWRENCE, b Beaver, Pa, Sept 17, 23; m 46; c 2. RESEARCH ADMINISTRATION, ORGANIC CHEMISTRY. *Educ:* Pa State Univ, BS, 44, MS, 46, PhD(org chem), 49. *Prof Exp:* Mem, Am Petrol Inst Proj, Pa State Univ, 44-46, asst, 44-49; res scientist, NASA, Ohio, 49-50, group leader, 50-51; fel, Mellon Inst, 51-55, sr fel, 55-57; sr res chemist, Res & Develop Lab, Socony-Mobil Oil Co, 57-60, group leader, 60-62, sect leader, 62-64; coordr res, Velsicol Chem Co, 64-65, dir res, Resin Prod Div, 65-69; res mgr, Armour Dial Inc, 69-73; TECH DIR, DESOTO, INC, 73- *Mem:* Am Chem Soc; Am Oil Chemists Soc. *Res:* Hydrocarbon analysis, synthesis, purifications, separations, adducts, processing and properties; organic and petroleum chemicals; monomers and polymeric materials, synthesis, processing and evaluations; soaps and detergents; personal care products; cleaning products. *Mailing Add:* 2333 Schiller Ave Wilmette IL 60091

MCLAUGHLIN, ROY EARL, entomology, protozoology, see previous edition

MCLAUGHLIN, STUART GRAYDON ARTHUR, b NVancouver, BC, Dec 15, 42; m 80. MEMBRANE BIOPHYSICS. *Educ:* Univ BC, BSc, 64; PhD(biophysics), 68. *Prof Exp:* Fel biophysics, Univ Dundee, Scotland, 68, Univ Calif, Los Angeles & Univ Chicago, 69; res physiologist, Univ Calif, Los Angeles, 70; res fel, Calif Inst Technol, 71; from asst prof to assoc prof, 72-81,

PROF PHYSIOL & BIOPHYSICS, STATE UNIV NY, STONY BROOK, 81- *Concurrent Pos:* Mem, Physiol Study Sect, NIH, 79-82; prin investr, NIH & NSF grants . *Mem:* Biophys Soc; Soc Gen Physiologists; AAAS. *Res:* Electrostatic potentials at membrane-solution interfaces; molecular mechanisms of action of proton ionophores; interaction of calcium with biological membranes. *Mailing Add:* Physiol & Biophys Health Sci Ctr State Univ NY Stony Brook NY 11794

MCLAUGHLIN, THOMAS G, b McIntosh, SDak, Nov 26, 33; m 69; c 1. MATHEMATICS. *Educ:* Univ Calif, Los Angeles, BA, 59, MA, 62, PhD(math), 63. *Prof Exp:* From instr to asst prof math, Univ Ill, Urbana, 63-66; vis asst prof, Cornell Univ, 66-67; assoc prof math, Univ Ill, Urbana, 67-74; vis assoc prof, 73-74, assoc prof, 74-75, PROF MATH, TEX TECH UNIV, 75- *Concurrent Pos:* Vis lectr math, Rutgers Univ, 79. *Mem:* Am Math Soc. *Res:* Recursive function theory. *Mailing Add:* Dept of Math Tex Tech Univ Lubbock TX 79409

MCLAUGHLIN, WALLACE ALVIN, b Calgary, Alta, May 5, 27; m 51; c 5. CIVIL ENGINEERING. *Educ:* Univ Sask, BSc, 51; Purdue Univ, MSCE, 58, PhD(civil eng), 65. *Prof Exp:* Proj engr, Sask Dept Hwy, 51-54, div engr, 54-57, asst planning engr, 58-61; from asst prof to assoc prof civil eng, 61-66, assoc chmn dept, 65-66, PROF CIVIL ENG & CHMN DEPT, UNIV WATERLOO, 66- *Concurrent Pos:* Dept Trans fel, Inst Transp & Traffic Eng, Univ Calif, Berkeley, 59-70; mem hwy res bd, Nat Acad Sci. *Res:* Transportation planning; construction engineering and planning. *Mailing Add:* Dept Civil Eng Univ Waterloo Waterloo ON N2L 3G1 Can

MCLAUGHLIN, WILLIAM IRVING, b Oak Park, Ill, Mar 6, 35; m 60; c 4. MONTE CARLO METHODS. *Educ:* Univ Calif, Berkeley, BS, 63, MA, 66, PhD(math), 68. *Prof Exp:* Mem tech staff celestial mech, Bellcomm, Inc, 68-71; mem tech staff celestial mech, 71-81, SUPVR, INNER PLANETS TRAJECTORY & MISSION DESIGN GROUP, JET PROPULSION LAB, CALIF INST TECHNOL, 81- *Honors & Awards:* Apollo Achievement Award, Nat Aeronautics & Space Admin, 69, Pioneer 10 Mission Anal Award, 74, Viking Flight Award, 77. *Mem:* Fel Brit Interplanetary Soc; Am Math Soc. *Res:* Statistical mechanics; interstellar communication. *Mailing Add:* Jet Propulsion Lab 4800 Oak Grove Dr Pasadena CA 91109

MCLAUGHLIN, WILLIAM LOWNDES, b Stony Point, Tenn, Mar 30, 28; m 51; c 2. RADIATION PHYSICS. *Educ:* Hampden-Sydney Col, BS, 49; George Washington Univ, MS, 63. *Prof Exp:* Physicist, Radiation Phys Div, 51-54, 56-64, proj leader, 64-69, PROJ LEADER, CTR RADIATION RES, NAT BUR STANDARDS, 69- *Concurrent Pos:* Ed, Int J Appl Radiation & Isotopes, 73-, Radiation Physics & Chem, 81- *Honors & Awards:* Silver Medal, Dept Commerce, 69; Gold Medal, Dept Com, 79. *Mem:* AAAS; Am Phys Soc; Optical Soc Am; Health Physics Soc; Radiation Res Soc. *Res:* Measurement of ionizing radiation; x-ray, gamma-ray and electron spectrometry, absorption and scattering measurement and computation; radiation chemistry; photographic prosesses; industrial radiation processing. *Mailing Add:* Ctr for Radiation Res Nat Bur Standards Washington DC 20234

MCLAURIN, JAMES WALTER, b Natchez, Miss, July 1, 10; m 35. MEDICINE, SURGERY. *Educ:* Univ Ark, MD, 34. *Prof Exp:* Instr, Eye, Ear, Nose & Throat Clins, Univ Ark, 34; intern, Mary's Help Hosp, San Francisco, Calif, 34-35; resident, Los Angeles Children's Hosp, 35-36; instr otolaryngol, Sch Med, La State Univ, 46-49; chmn dept otolaryngol, 49-58, med dir, Speech & Hearing Ctr, 52-63, Otto Joachiem Prof otolaryngol, 49-69, CLIN PROF OTOL, SCH MED, TULANE UNIV, 69- *Concurrent Pos:* Mem, Nat Comt Deafness Res Found; pvt pract otolaryngology, Baton Rouge, 36- *Mem:* Am Laryngol, Rhinol & Otol Soc; Am Otol Soc; AMA; fel Am Col Surg; Am Acad Opthal & Otolaryngol. *Res:* Otitis externa and otitis media; speech and hearing problems. *Mailing Add:* 3888 Government St Baton Rouge LA 70806

MCLAURIN, ROBERT L, b Dallas, Tex, Jan 5, 22; m 46; c 5. NEUROSURGERY. *Educ:* Rice Inst, BA, 44; Harvard Med Sch, MD, 44. *Prof Exp:* Asst surg, Harvard Med Sch, 51-53; from instr to assoc prof surg, 53-60, actg dir div neurosurg, 54-55, PROF SURG, COL MED, UNIV CINCINNATI, 53-, DIR DIV NEUROSURG, 55- *Concurrent Pos:* Res fel neurosurg, Children's Hosp & Peter Bent Brigham Hosp, Boston, Mass, 51-53. *Mem:* Cong Neurol Surg; Am Asn Neurol Surg; Am Acad Neurol Surg (secy-treas, 58-63, pres, 71-72); Soc Brit Neurol Surg; Soc Neurol Surg (treas, 70-). *Res:* Clinical and experimental aspects of intracranial trauma and hemorrhage. *Mailing Add:* Neurosurg Dept 231 Bethesda Ave Cincinnati OH 45267

MCLAURIN, WAYNE JEFFERSON, b Hattiesburg, Miss, July 1, 42; m 66; c 2. HORTICULTURE. *Educ:* Southeastern La Univ, BS, 71; La State Univ, MS, 74, PhD(hort), 79. *Prof Exp:* County agent, Ark Coop Extension Serv, 74-75; ASST PROF VEGETABLE RES, UNIV TENN INST AGR, 79- *Mem:* Am Soc Hort Sci. *Res:* Environmental manipulation of vegetable crops; breeding of sweet potatoes; breeding and adaptability of heat tolerance in tomatoes; nitrogen fixiation in legume crops; plant stress due to soil fertility levels. *Mailing Add:* Plant & Soil Sci 342 Univ Tenn PO Box 1071 Knoxville TN 37996

MACLAURY, MICHAEL RISLEY, b Hays, Kans, Dec 28, 43; m 66. ORGANOMETALLIC CHEMISTRY. *Educ:* Antioch Col, BS, 67; Stanford Univ, PhD(inorg chem), 74. *Prof Exp:* Res asst nuclear med, Stanford Med Ctr, 70-72; staff chemist, 74-81, TECH COORDR CHEM REACTIONS & SYSTS, POLYMER PHYSICS & ENG BR, GEN ELEC RES & DEVELOP CTR-, 81- *Concurrent Pos:* Fel chem catalysis, NSF US/USSR Exchange Prog, 74. *Mem:* Am Chem Soc. *Res:* Mechanisms of organometallic reactions as they relate to possible catalytic reactions; the role of inorganic materials in flame retarding polymers. *Mailing Add:* Gen Elec Res & Develop Ctr PO Box 8 Bldg K-1 Rm 5A54 Schenectady NY 12301

MACLAY, CHARLES WYLIE, b Fannettsburg, Pa, Oct 17, 29; m 50; c 2. MATHEMATICS. *Educ:* Shippensburg State Col, BS, 56; Univ Va, MEd, 59, EdD(math educ), 68. *Prof Exp:* Teacher math, Seaford Spec Schs, Del, 56-58; instr, Shippensburg State Col, 60-62; teacher, Abington Schs, 62-69; PROF MATH, EAST STROUDSBURG STATE COL, 69- *Mem:* Math Asn Am; Nat Coun Teachers Math. *Res:* Learning sequences and sequencing in math; curriculum constructing and testing. *Mailing Add:* East Stroudsburg State Col 1006 Lindberg Ave East Stroudsburg PA 18301

MCLAY, DAVID BOYD, b Toronto, Ont, Feb 29, 28; m 53. MOLECULAR PHYSICS. *Educ:* McMaster Univ, BSc, 50, MSc, 51; Univ BC, PhD(physics), 56. *Prof Exp:* Lectr physics, Victoria Col, 54-56; asst prof, Univ New Brunswick, 56-62; from asst prof to assoc prof, 62-77, ASSOC DEAN STUDIES & PROF PHYSICS, QUEEN'S UNIV, ONT, 77- *Mem:* Can Asn Physicist; Am Asn Physics Teachers; Can Astron Soc. *Res:* Microwave spectroscopy and paramagnetic spectroscopy of gases; dielectric and nuclear paramagnetic relaxation; paramagnetic resonance. *Mailing Add:* Dept Physics Queen's Univ Kingston ON K7L 3N6 Can

MACLAY, G JORDAN, b Washington, DC, May 17, 42; c 1. SOLID STATE ELECTRONICS. *Educ:* Queens Col, City Univ New York, MA, 65; Yale Univ, MPh, 68, PhD(physics), 72. *Prof Exp:* Fel res asst physics, High Energy Physics Div, Argonne Nat Lab, 72; lectr, Roosevelt Univ, 74-77; consult eng, Innovator Assocs, 77-81; ASST PROF ELEC ENG, DEPT INFO ENG, UNIV ILL, CHICAGO, 81- *Concurrent Pos:* Physicist, Control Instrument Div, Warner & Swasey Co, Flushing, Long Island, 61-65; vis asst prof elec eng, Univ Ill, Chicago, 79-81. *Mem:* Am Phys Soc; Am Vacuum Soc. *Res:* Solid state devices and materials; laser diodes, metal semiconductor and metal insulator semiconductor devices. *Mailing Add:* Dept Info Eng Univ Ill Box 4348 Chicago IL 60680

MACLAY, WILLIAM NEVIN, b Belleville, Pa, Dec 30, 24; m 49; c 5. PHYSICAL CHEMISTRY, RESEARCH ADMINISTRATION. *Educ:* Juniata Col, BS, 47; Yale Univ, PhD(phys chem), 50. *Prof Exp:* Assoc prof chem, Davis & Elkins Col, 50-51; res chemist, B F Goodrich Co, 51-59; mgr latices res, 59-65, mgr polystyrene res, 62-65, asst mgr plastics res, 65-67, mgr com develop, 67-68, asst mgr res, 68, VPRES & DIR RES, KOPPERS CO INC, 68- *Mem:* Am Chem Soc. *Res:* Surface and colloid chemistry; high polymer latices; polystyrene molding resins; copolymerization; graft polymers. *Mailing Add:* 539 Greenleaf Dr Monroeville PA 15146

MCLEAN, ALASTAIR, range ecology, see previous edition

MACLEAN, BONNIE KUSESKE, b St Cloud, Minn, Jan 23, 42; m 64; c 2. ENTOMOLOGY. *Educ:* Gustavus Adolphus Col, BA, 63; Purdue Univ, MS, 65, PhD(entom), 72. *Prof Exp:* Instr biol, Youngstown State Univ, 68-69; RES & WRITING, 69-; instr, 77-80, ASST PROF BIOL, THIEL COL, 80- *Mem:* Sigma Xi; Entom Soc Am; AAAS; Am Inst Biol Sci; Ecol Soc Am. *Res:* Trichoptera of Ohio. *Mailing Add:* 280 E Western Reserve Rd Poland OH 44514

MACLEAN, DAVID ANDREW, b Fredericton, NB, Feb 27, 52; div. FOREST ECOLOGY. *Educ:* Univ NB, BSc Hons, 73, PhD(ecol), 78. *Prof Exp:* RES SCIENTIST FOREST ECOL, MARITIMES FOREST RES CTR, CAN FORESTRY SERV, 78- *Concurrent Pos:* Postgrad scholar, Nat Res Coun Can, 75-78; postdoctoral fel, Nat Res Coun Can, 78. *Mem:* Ecol Soc Am; Can Inst Forestry. *Res:* Impact of spruce budworm defoliation on tree growth and productivity, mortality and stand deterioration; modelling of forest growth and effects of defoliation on growth. *Mailing Add:* Maritimes Forest Res Ctr Box 4000 Fredericton NB E3B 5P7 Can

MACLEAN, DAVID BAILEY, b Summerside, PEI, July 15, 23; m 45; c 7. ORGANIC CHEMISTRY. *Educ:* Acadia Univ, BSc, 42; McGill Univ, PhD(chem), 46. *Prof Exp:* Res chemist, Dom Rubber Co, 46-49; assoc prof indust chem, NS Tech Col, 49-54; assoc prof chem, 54-60, PROF CHEM, MCMASTER UNIV, 60- *Mem:* Am Chem Soc; Chem Inst Can. *Res:* Isolation and structure of alkaloids; mass spectrometry of organic compounds. *Mailing Add:* Dept Chem McMaster Univ Hamilton ON L85 4M1 Can

MACLEAN, DAVID BELMONT, b Cleveland, Ohio, Sept 15, 41; m 64; c 1. INSECT ECOLOGY, INSECT TAXONOMY. *Educ:* Heidelberg Col, BS, 63; Purdue Univ, MS, PhD(entom, biometry), 69. *Prof Exp:* Asst prof, 68-76, ASSOC PROF BIOL, YOUNGSTOWN STATE UNIV, 76- *Mem:* Sigma Xi; Entom Soc Am; Entom Soc Can. *Res:* Interrelationships of insect and plant communities; symbiotic relationship of ambrosia beetles and associated fungi; systematics of Polistes; cytotaxonomic techniques. *Mailing Add:* Dept of Biol Youngstown State Univ Youngstown OH 44503

MACLEAN, DAVID CAMERON, b New Rochelle, NY, Dec 8, 33; m 56; c 3. PLANT PHYSIOLOGY. *Educ:* Univ Conn, BS, 60; Mich State Univ, MS, 62, PhD(plant physiol), 65. *Prof Exp:* Res assoc plant physiol, Mich State Univ, 61-65; PLANT PHYSIOLOGIST, BOYCE THOMPSON INST PLANT RES, 65- *Concurrent Pos:* Consult air pollution, 65-; mem panel on med & biol effects of environ pollutants, Nat Res Coun-Nat Acad Sci, 73-; pres, Environ Strategies Inc, 77- *Honors & Awards:* Dow Award, Am Soc Hort Sci, 70. *Mem:* AAAS; Am Soc Plant Physiol; Am Soc Hort Sci; NY Acad Sci; Sigma Xi. *Res:* Physiology of senescence in plant tissues; effects of air pollutants on vegetation; plant growth and development. *Mailing Add:* Boyce Thompson Inst Plant Res Tower Rd Ithaca NY 14853

MACLEAN, DONALD ISADORE, b Norwalk, Conn, Nov 25, 29. PHYSICAL CHEMISTRY. *Educ:* Boston Col, AB, 53; LicPhil, Weston Col, 54; Catholic Univ, PhD(phys chem), 58. *Prof Exp:* Humboldt res fel, Univ Gottingen, 62-65; from asst prof to assoc prof phys chem, Boston Col, 66-73; vpres acad affairs, Creighton Univ, 73-76; PRES, ST JOSEPH'S UNIV, 76- *Concurrent Pos:* Adj prof, Boston Col, 73-75; mem bd trustees, St Louis Univ, 75-81, bd dirs, Am Coun Educ, 78-, Philadelphia Urban Coalition, 76- *Mem:* AAAS. *Res:* Fast reaction kinetics; combustion chemistry; mass, electron spin resonance and optical spectroscopy. *Mailing Add:* Off of Pres St Joseph's Univ Philadelphia PA 19131

MCLEAN, DONALD LEWIS, b Norwood, Mass, Oct 2, 28; m 52; c 3. ENTOMOLOGY. *Educ:* Tufts Univ, BS, 53; Univ Mass, MS, 55; Univ Calif, PhD(entom), 58. *Prof Exp:* chmn dept, 74-79 PROF ENTOM, UNIV CALIF, DAVIS, 58-, DEAN BIOL SCI, 79- *Mem:* Entom Soc Am; AAAS. *Res:* Insect transmission of plant viruses, especially aphid vectors; biological studies dealing with aphid feeding; culturing and chemical studies with aphid cells and symbiotes. *Mailing Add:* Div Biol Sci Univ of Calif Davis CA 95616

MCLEAN, DONALD MILLIS, b Melbourne, Australia, July 26, 26; Can citizen; m 76. VIROLOGY, MEDICAL MICROBIOLOGY. *Educ:* Univ Melbourne, BSc, 47, MD, 50; FRCP(C), 67. *Prof Exp:* Dir virol, Hosp Sick Children, Toronto, 58-67; head div med microbiol, 67-80, PROF MED MICROBIOL, UNIV BC, 67- *Concurrent Pos:* Consult microbiol, Health Sci Ctr Hosp, Children's Hosp, Vancouver Gen Hosp, Shaughnessy Hosp & St Paul's Hosp, Vancouver, 68- *Mem:* Am Soc Trop Med & Hyg; Am Soc Microbiol; Am Epidemiol Soc; Can Med Asn. *Res:* Arbovirus vectors and reservoirs; same-day virus diagnostic tests. *Mailing Add:* Div of Med Microbiol Univ of BC 2075 Wesbrook Pl Vancouver BC V6T 1W5 Can

MCLEAN, EDGAR ALEXANDER, b Gastonia, NC, July 25, 27; m 51; c 5. PLASMA PHYSICS. *Educ:* Univ NC, Chapel Hill, BS, 49; Univ Del, MS, 51. *Prof Exp:* RES PHYSICIST, NAVAL RES LAB, 51- *Concurrent Pos:* Res consult, Space Sci Dept, Cath Univ Am, 64-69 & Univ Western Ont, 73- *Honors & Awards:* Res Publ Award, Naval Res Lab, 71, 74 & 77. *Mem:* Inst Elec & Electronics Engrs; AAAS; Am Phys Soc; Sigma Xi. *Res:* Optical diagnostics in the field of plasma physics, including spectroscopic, interferometric, laser-scattering, and high-speed photographic measurements on shock tubes, laser-produced plasmas, and various controlled fusion devices. *Mailing Add:* Naval Res Lab Washington DC 20375

MCLEAN, EDWARD BRUCE, b Washington Court House, Ohio, Jan 10, 37; m 68; c 3. ORNITHOLOGY, MAMMALOGY. *Educ:* Ohio State Univ, BSc, 58, MSc, 63, PhD(zool), 68. *Prof Exp:* Asst prof biol, Southern Univ, Baton Rouge, 68-70; from asst prof to assoc prof, 70-78, PROF BIOL, JOHN CARROLL UNIV, 78-, CHMN DEPT, 81- *Concurrent Pos:* Ecol consult, 72- *Mem:* Am Ornith Union; Wilson Ornith Soc. *Res:* Bioacoustics; vertebrate ecology; ethology. *Mailing Add:* Dept of Biol John Carroll Univ Cleveland OH 44118

MCLEAN, EUGENE OTIS, b Nixa, Mo; m 43; c 2. SOIL CHEMISTRY. *Educ:* Univ Mo, BS, 42, MA, 43, PhD(soil chem), 48. *Prof Exp:* Instr math, Univ Mo, 42-43, soils, 43-48, asst prof, 48-50; from asst prof to assoc prof agron, Univ Ark, 50-56; assoc prof, 56-58, PROF AGRON, OHIO STATE UNIV, 58- *Mem:* AAAS; Am Chem Soc; Am Soc Agron; Soil Sci Soc Am; Int Soil Sci Soc. *Res:* Activities and bonding energies of cations in relation to plant availability from colloidal systems; chemistry of phosphate and potassium in soils with reference to forms available to plants; strontium-calcium relationships in soils; exchangeable aluminum as a factor in soil acidity and lime requirement of acid soils; improved soil testing methodology and interpretations. *Mailing Add:* 202 ANRPP Bldg 2021 Coffey Rd Ohio State Univ Columbus OH 43210

MCLEAN, FLYNN BREVARD, b Ft Bragg, NC, Nov 15, 41; m 66; c 2. SOLID STATE PHYSICS, SOLID STATE ELECTRONICS. *Educ:* Rensselaer Polytech Inst, ScB, 63; Brown Univ, ScM, 66, PhD(physics), 68. *Prof Exp:* Physicist, Harry Diamond Labs, 68-69; res assoc solid state physics, Brookhaven Nat Lab, 70-71; PHYSICIST, HARRY DIAMOND LABS, 71- *Mem:* Am Phys Soc; Inst Elec & Electronics Engrs. *Res:* Radiation effects in solids; electrical transport in amorphous insulators; physics of metal-oxide-semiconductor systems. *Mailing Add:* Radiation Effects Physics Br Harry Diamond Labs 2800 Powder Mill Rd Adelphi MD 20783

MACLEAN, GEORGE RUNDELL, b Syracuse, NY, Nov 5, 19; m 46; c 1. MECHANICAL ENGINEERING. *Educ:* Clarkson Col Technol, BME, 42; Univ Del, MME, 51. *Prof Exp:* Test engr, Foster Wheeler Corp, 42-43; instr mech eng, Smith Tech High Sch, 46; from instr to assoc prof, 46-58, chmn dept, 58-68, PROF MECH ENG, CLARKSON COL TECHNOL, 58-, DIR CORP & FOUND RELS, 68- *Mem:* Am Soc Mech Eng; Am Soc Eng Educ. *Res:* Thermodynamics; control systems; manufacturing. *Mailing Add:* Clarkson Col of Technol Potsdam NY 13676

MACLEAN, GRAEME STANLEY, b Melbourne, Australia, Feb 11, 50. PHYSIOLOGY, PHYSIOLOGICAL ECOLOGY. *Educ:* Monash Univ, Australia, BSc, 72; Univ Mich, Ann Arbor, MS, 74, PhD(biol sci), 77. *Prof Exp:* Lectr, Univ Mich, 77; ASST PROF PHYSIOL, UNIV TEX, ARLINGTON, 77- *Mem:* Am Soc Zoologists; Am Soc Mammalogists; Am Physiol Soc. *Res:* Environmental physiology of vertebrates; respiratory and cardiovascular physiology of reptiles, hibernating mammals, and fossorial mammals. *Mailing Add:* Dept of Biol Univ of Tex Arlington TX 76019

MCLEAN, HUGH, b El Centro, Calif, Nov 8, 39; div; c 1. GEOLOGY, SEDIMENTARY PETROLOGY. *Educ:* San Diego State Col, BA, 66; Univ Wash, MS, 68, PhD(geol), 70. *Prof Exp:* Geologist petrol explor, Texaco, Inc, 70-74; GEOLOGIST, US GEOL SURV, 74- *Mem:* Geol Soc Am; Am Asn Petrol Geologists. *Res:* Reservoir properties of clastic rocks; depositional environments and sedimentary processes as a reflection of tectonic setting; geologic mapping in Alaska and California. *Mailing Add:* US Geol Surv MS 99 345 Middlefield Rd Menlo Park CA 94025

MCLEAN, IAN WILLIAM, b Durham, NC, Sept 21, 43; m 66; c 2. PATHOLOGY, OPHTHALMOLOGY. *Educ:* Univ Mich, BS, 65, MD, 69; Univ Colo Med Ctr, cert path, 73; Am Bd Path, cert anat path, 74. *Prof Exp:* Fel ophthal path, Armed Forces Inst Path, 71-72; vis scientist, Inst Biol Sci, Oakland Univ, 72; STAFF PATHOLOGIST, OPHTHAL DIV, ARMED FORCES INST PATH, 73- *Mem:* Asn Res Vision & Ophthalmol. *Res:* Evaluation of factors relating to mortality in patients with intraocular malignant melanomas and development of a mathematical model describing the transport of ions in the ocular lens. *Mailing Add:* Ophthal Div Armed Forces Inst of Path Washington DC 20305

MACLEAN, JAMES ALEXANDER, b Toronto, Ont, Sept 24, 45. FISHERIES SCIENCE, ECOLOGY. *Educ:* Univ Man, BSc, 66, MSc, 69; Univ BC, PhD(zool), 74. *Prof Exp:* RES SCIENTIST FISHERIES, ONT MINISTRY NATURAL RESOURCES, 74- *Mem:* Am Fisheries Soc; Ecol Soc Am; Can Soc Zoologists. *Res:* Fisheries science and ecology. *Mailing Add:* Res Sect Fisheries Br Box 50 Maple ON L0J 1E0 Can

MCLEAN, JAMES AMOS, b Flint, Mich, Dec 2, 21; m 54; c 2. INTERNAL MEDICINE, ALLERGY. *Educ:* Univ Mich, BS & MD, 46; Baylor Univ, MS, 52. *Prof Exp:* From asst prof to assoc prof, 56-67, asst allergy, Health Serv, 65-77, PROF INTERNAL MED, MED CTR, UNIV MICH, ANN ARBOR, 67- *Mem:* AMA; Am Acad Allergy; Am Fedn Clin Res; Am Thoracic Soc. *Res:* Clinical allergy. *Mailing Add:* Univ of Mich Hosp Box 027 Ann Arbor MI 48109

MCLEAN, JAMES DENNIS, b Bay City, Mich, Nov 23, 40; m 68. ANALYTICAL CHEMISTRY, POLAROGRAPHY. *Educ:* Univ Mich, Ann Arbor, BS, 62; Mich State Univ, PhD(anal chem), 67. *Prof Exp:* Anal specialist, 67-79, RES ASSOC, DOW CHEM CO, 80- *Honors & Awards:* A O Beckmann Award, Instrument Soc Am, 75. *Mem:* Am Chem Soc; Instrument Soc Am; NY Acad Sci; Sigma Xi; AAAS. *Res:* Polarographic analysis; anodic stripping voltammetry; electrochemical flo-thru detectors and liquid chromatography detectors. *Mailing Add:* Dow Chemical Co 1602 Bldg Midland MI 48640

MCLEAN, JAMES DOUGLAS, b Regina, Sask, Feb 12, 20; m 50; c 4. DENTISTRY. *Educ:* Univ Toronto, DDS, 42. *Hon Degrees:* FRCD(C). *Prof Exp:* From lectr to asst prof dent, Univ Alta, 47-53; dean, Fac Dent, 54-75, PROF DENT, DALHOUSIE UNIV, 53- *Mem:* Fel Int Col Dent; fel Am Col Dent. *Mailing Add:* Fac of Dent Dalhousie Univ Halifax NS B3H 3J5 Can

MCLEAN, JAMES H, b Detroit, Mich, June 17, 36. INVERTEBRATE ZOOLOGY. *Educ:* Wesleyan Univ, BA, 58; Stanford Univ, PhD(biol), 66. *Prof Exp:* CURATOR INVERT ZOOL, LOS ANGELES COUNTY MUS NATURAL HIST, 64- *Mem:* Am Malac Union; Soc Syst Zool. *Res:* Systematics of marine mollusks, especially prosobranch gastropods and chitons of the eastern Pacific. *Mailing Add:* Invert Zool 900 Exposition Blvd Los Angeles CA 90007

MCLEAN, JEFFERY THOMAS, b Memphis, Tenn, July 5, 44; m 74. MATHEMATICS. *Educ:* Hendrix Col, BA, 66; Ohio State Univ, MS, 67, PhD(math), 73. *Prof Exp:* Asst prof math, Ohio Northern Univ, 73-74 & Ohio State Univ, Lima, 74-75; assoc prof & chmn dept math, Ohio Northern Univ, 75-78; ASSOC PROF MATH & CHMN DEPT, COL ST TERESA, MINN, 78- *Mem:* Am Math Soc; Math Asn Am. *Res:* Finite projective planes; mathematical perspective in art; mathematical limitations of technology. *Mailing Add:* Dept of Math Sci Col of St Teresa Winona MN 55987

MCLEAN, JOHN A, JR, b Chapel Hill, Tenn, Nov 8, 26; m 58; c 3. INORGANIC CHEMISTRY. *Educ:* Tenn State Univ, BS, 48; Univ Ill, MS, 56, PhD(chem), 59. *Prof Exp:* High sch teacher, Ill, 48-53; PROF CHEM, UNIV DETROIT, 59-, ASST CHMN UNDERGRAD PROGS, 74- *Mem:* Am Chem Soc. *Res:* Synthesis, structure and reaction kinetics and mechanisms of transition metal coordination compounds. *Mailing Add:* 9260 W Outer Dr Detroit MI 48219

MCLEAN, JOHN ROBERT, b St Thomas, Ont, Apr 15, 26; m 51; c 2. BIOCHEMISTRY. *Educ:* Queen's Univ, Ont, BSc, 50, PhD(biochem), 54. *Prof Exp:* Instr biochem, Yale Univ, 54-56; assoc res chemist, 56-60, sr res biochemist, 60-72, sect dir neuropharmacol, 72-77, ASSOC DIR NEUROCHEM SEC, PARKE DAVIS & CO, 77- *Mem:* Am Soc Pharmacol & Exp Therapeut. *Res:* Drugs acting on the central nervous system. *Mailing Add:* Res Div Parke Davis & Co Ann Arbor MI 48106

MCLEAN, KATHARINE WEIDMAN, b Camden, NJ, Oct 18, 27; m 51; c 3. BIOCHEMISTRY. *Educ:* Cornell Univ, AB, 48; Univ Ill, MS, 49, PhD(biochem), 51. *Prof Exp:* Org res chemist, Rohm and Haas Co, 51-52; anal chemist, Ariz Testing Labs, 52-57; TEACHER CHEM, PHOENIX COL, 57- *Mem:* Am Chem Soc; Am Inst Chemists. *Res:* Vitamin BT; explosives. *Mailing Add:* Dept of Chem Phoenix Col Phoenix AZ 85013

MCLEAN, LEE VANCE, b Laurel, Miss, Mar 26, 13. ELECTRICAL ENGINEERING, ACOUSTICS. *Educ:* La State Univ, BS, 34, MS, 36. *Prof Exp:* Instr elec eng, La State Univ, 36-37; engr & party chief, Schlumberger Well Surv Corp, 37-41; instr elec eng, 41-42, from asst prof to prof, 46-76, EMER PROF ELEC ENG, LA STATE UNIV, 76- *Concurrent Pos:* Consult, US Naval Reserve Training Publ Proj, Naval Gun Factory, DC, 48-49, AEC-NSF-Am Soc Eng Educ grant, Int Sch, Argonne Nat Lab, 56, res assoc, Lab, 57; dir, Surv Manpower in Educ, Nuclear Activities, AEC-Am Soc Eng Educ, 57-58; consult to chief eng div, Coast & Geodetic Surv, Environ Sci Serv Admin, 63-68; pres & chmn bd, Nocon Corp. *Mem:* AAAS; Inst Elec & Electronics Engrs. *Res:* Systems engineering; electronic computing machines; nuclear, noise control and ocean engineering. *Mailing Add:* Nocon Corp 4840 Newcomb Dr Baton Rouge LA 70808

MACLEAN, LLOYD DOUGLAS, b Calgary, Alta, June 15, 24; m 54; c 5. SURGERY. *Educ:* Univ Alta, BSc, 43, MD, 59; Univ Minn, PhD(surg), 57; FRCPS(C). *Prof Exp:* From instr to assoc prof, Univ Minn, 56-65; PROF SURG, McGILL UNIV, 65-, CHMN DEPT, 68- *Concurrent Pos:* Chief surg serv, Ancker Hosp, St Paul, 57-65; surgeon-in-chief, Royal Victoria Hosp, Montreal, 65- *Mem:* Am Physiol Soc; Soc Exp Biol & Med; Soc Univ Surgeons; AMA; Am Surg Asn. *Res:* Blood flow to heart; intestinal blood flow in shock due to hemorrhage and endotoxin and cardiac excitability; shock and transplantation. *Mailing Add:* Dept of Surg 687 Pine Ave W Montreal PQ H3A 1A1 Can

MCLEAN, NORMAN, JR, b San Diego, Calif, May 8, 26; m 63; c 1. INVERTEBRATE ZOOLOGY. *Educ:* Univ Calif, Berkeley, BS, 51, PhD(zool), 65. *Prof Exp:* Asst prof to assoc prof, 65-74, PROF ZOOL, SAN DIEGO STATE UNIV, 74- *Res:* Functional morphology of the molluscan digestive tract. *Mailing Add:* Dept of Zool San Diego State Univ San Diego CA 92115

MACLEAN, PAUL DONALD, b Phelps, NY, May 1, 13; m 42; c 5. NEUROPHYSIOLOGY. *Educ:* Yale Univ, BA, 35, MD, 40. *Prof Exp:* Intern, Johns Hopkins Hosp, 40-41; asst resident med, New Haven Hosp, Conn, 41-42; res asst path, Sch Med, Yale Univ, 42; clin instr med, Med Sch, Washington Univ, 46-47; USPHS res fel psychiat, Harvard Med Sch & Mass Gen Hosp, 47-49; asst prof physiol, Sch Med, Yale Univ, 49-51, from asst prof to assoc prof psychiat, 51-56, assoc prof physiol, 56; chief limbic integration & behav sect, NIH, 57-71, CHIEF LAB BRAIN EVOLUTION & BEHAV, NIMH, 71- *Concurrent Pos:* Dir EEG lab, New Haven Hosp, Conn, 51-52; attend physician, Grace-New Haven Hosp, 53-56; NSF sr res fel, Switz, 56-57; Salmon lectr award, NY Acad Med, 66; Hincks lectr award, Ont Ment Health Found, 69; Mider lectr award, NIH, 72. *Honors & Awards:* Distinguished Res Award, Asn Res Nerv & Ment Dis, 64; Salmon Medal Distinguished Res in Psychiat, 66; Superior Serv Award, US Dept Health, Educ & Welfare, 67; Spec Award, Am Psychopath Asn, 71; Karl Spencer Lashley Award, Am Philos Soc, 72. *Mem:* Am Electroencephalog Soc; Am Neurol Asn; Am Asn Hist Med; Soc Neurosci; Am Physiol Soc. *Res:* Forebrain mechanisms of species-typical and emotional behavior. *Mailing Add:* Lab Brain Evolution & Behav NIMH Bldg 110-NIHAC Bethesda MD 20014

MCLEAN, R T, b Westerville, Ohio, July 18, 22; m 53. ALGEBRA. *Educ:* Otterbein Col, BS, 46; Bowling Green State Univ, MA, 50; Univ Pittsburgh, PhD(group theory), 61. *Prof Exp:* High sch teacher math, Ohio, 45-49, 50-51; asst chem, Bowling Green State Univ, 49-50; from asst prof to prof math, Col Steubenville, 52-67, head dept, 53-67, chmn div natural sci, 63-67; chmn dept math sci, 67-73, dir, NSF Math Teacher Develop Prog, 77-80, PROF MATH, LOYOLA UNIV, LA, 67-, CHMN DEPT, 79- *Concurrent Pos:* Nat Defense Act Workshops Elem & Secondary Math Teacher Improvement, 59-67; NSF In-Serv Insts, 62-67; HEW Experienced Teacher Fel Prog strengthening elem sch sci teaching, 68-70; Loyola Univ fac res grants, 73-77 & 78-81; innovation & expansion grant for Radio for Blind & Print Handicapped, 77-80; nat chmn, Affil Leadership League of & for the Blind, vpres, Am Coun of the Blind & Light House for the Blind; mem bd dirs, Nat Accredidation Coun & Nat Industs for the Blind. *Mem:* Am Math Soc; Nat Coun Teachers Math; Sigma Xi; Math Asn Am. *Res:* Theory of groups; higher education program design; careers through mathematics; group generators; braille large print and voice output for computers and all other digital information devices; institutional research. *Mailing Add:* Dept of Math Sci Loyola Univ St Charles Ave New Orleans LA 70118

MCLEAN, RICHARD BEA, b Raleigh, NC, Aug 27, 46; m 68; c 1. MARINE BIOLOGY. *Educ:* Fla State Univ, BA, 68, PhD(marine biol), 75. *Prof Exp:* Res asst spiny lobsters, Fla State Univ, 69-70, instr biol, 70-73; res assoc marine environ impact, 74-76, RES STAFF FISH POP DYNAMICS-RESERVOIRS, CASUE & EFFECTS INPINGEMENT, OAK RIDGE NAT LAB, 76- *Concurrent Pos:* NASA fel, 72. *Mem:* Am Inst Biol Sci; Am Soc Zool; Animal Behav Soc; Sigma Xi. *Res:* Behavioral ecology of marine benthic communities, emphasizing interactions such as predation, symbiosis and competition; population dynamics and bioenergetics of reservoir fishes. *Mailing Add:* Equatic Ecol Sect Bldg 1505 Oak Ridge Nat Lab Oak Ridge TN 37830

MCLEAN, ROBERT GEORGE, b Warren, Ohio, Jan 10, 38; m 60; c 2. EPIZOOTIOLOGY, VERTEBRATE ECOLOGY. *Educ:* Bowling Green State Univ, BSE & BS, 61, MA, 63; Pa State Univ, PhD(zool), 66. *Prof Exp:* Chief parasitol br, Third US Army Med Lab, Ft McPherson, Ga, 66-68; chief rabies ecol subunit, 68-69, mem rabies control unit, Viral Zoonoses Sect, Viral Dis Br, Epidemiol Prog, 69-73, mem, Vert Ecol Br & Vector-Borne Dis Br, 73-79, ASST CHIEF, ARBOVIRUS ECOL BR, CTR DIS CONTROL, 79- *Concurrent Pos:* Part-time instr biol, Ga State Univ, 67-68; fac affil zool, Colo State Univ, 73- *Mem:* Wildlife Dis Asn; Am Soc Trop Med & Hygiene; Ecol Soc Am. *Res:* Homing ability and courtship behavior of pigeons; population control of vertebrate pest animals with chemosterilants; ecological studies of zoonotic diseases in birds and mammals; ecology of Colorado tick fever in northern Colorado and St Louis encephalitis in western Tennessee. *Mailing Add:* Arbovirus Ecol Br Ctr Dis Control PO Box 2087 Ft Collins CO 80522

MCLEAN, ROBERT J, b New Haven, Conn, Aug 15, 40; m 63; c 4. CELL BIOLOGY. *Educ:* Univ Conn, BA, 62, MS, 64, PhD(phycol), 67. *Prof Exp:* NIH fel bot, Univ Tex, 67-68; from asst prof to assoc prof, 68-75, PROF BIOL SCI, STATE UNIV NY COL BROCKPORT, 75- *Mem:* AAAS; Am Inst Biol Sci; Phycol Soc Am; Am Soc Cell Biol; Int Phycol Soc. *Res:* Cell recognition and membrane biology. *Mailing Add:* Dept of Biol Sci State Univ of NY Brockport NY 14420

MACLEAN, STEPHEN FREDERICK, JR, b Los Angeles, Calif, Jan 18, 43; m 67; c 1. ECOLOGY. *Educ:* Univ Calif, Santa Barbara, BA, 64; Univ Calif, Berkeley, PhD(ecol), 69. *Prof Exp:* Actg asst prof zool, Univ Mont, 69-70; asst prof, Univ Ill, 70-71; NSF res grant Arctic Alaska, 71-72, asst prof, 71-74, assoc prof biol sci, 74-76, ASSOC PROF BIOL SCI, ZOOL, UNIV ALASKA, 77- *Concurrent Pos:* NSF res grant Arctic Alaska, Univ Mon, 70-71; prog integrator, US Int Biol Prog Tundra Biome, 71- *Mem:* Ecol Soc Am; Brit Ecol Soc; Arctic Inst NAm; Am Ornithologists Union; Cooper Ornith Soc. *Res:* Population ecology and energetics of arctic birds, mammals and insects; systems analysis of tundra ecosystem. *Mailing Add:* Dept of Zool Univ of Alaska Fairbanks AK 99701

MCLEAN, STEWART, b Moascar, Egypt, Nov 19, 31; m 57; c 3. ORGANIC CHEMISTRY. *Educ:* Glasgow Univ, BSc, 54; Cornell Univ, PhD(org chem), 58. *Prof Exp:* Fel org chem, Univ Wis, 57-58; fel, Nat Res Coun Can, 58-60; from asst prof to assoc prof, PROF ORG CHEM, UNIV TORONTO, 70- *Mem:* Am Chem Soc; fel Chem Inst Can; Royal Soc Chem. *Res:* Structural and synthetic organic chemistry; mechanistic studies. *Mailing Add:* Dept of Chem Univ of Toronto 80 St George St Toronto ON M5S 1A1 Can

MACLEAN, WALLACE H, b PEI, Jan 10, 31; m 60; c 2. GEOLOGY, GEOCHEMISTRY. *Educ:* Colo Sch Mines, GeolE, 55; McGill Univ, MSc, 64, PhD(geol), 68. *Prof Exp:* Mine geologist, United Keno Hill Mines, Can, 55-57; econ geologist, Ministry Petrol & Mineral Resources, Saudi Arabia, 57-62; prof assoc, 67-70, asst prof, 70-74, ASSOC PROF GEOL SCI, MCGILL UNIV, 74- *Honors & Awards:* Waldemar Lindgren Citation Award, 69; Barlow Mem Medal, Can Inst Mining & Metall, 82. *Mem:* Geol Asn Can; Mineral Asn Can; Can Inst Mineral Metall; Soc Econ Geologists. *Res:* Genesis of mineral deposits; phase equilibria of sulfide-silicate liquid systems pertaining to magmatic ores; field studies on Archean massive sulfides. *Mailing Add:* 195 Macaulay St Lambert PQ G0S 2W0 Can

MACLEAN, WALTER M, b Modesto, Calif, Mar 15, 24; m 54; c 2. MECHANICAL ENGINEERING. *Educ:* Merchant Marine Acad, grad, 45; Univ Calif, Berkeley, BS, 56, ME, 57, DEng(naval archit), 67. *Prof Exp:* Asst engr, US Lines, Inc, 45-46 & Am Pres Lines, Inc, 46-52; from draftsman to naval architect, Morris Guralnick, Naval Architect, 55-59; jr engr, Univ Calif, Berkeley, 59-65; prof eng, Webb Inst Naval Archit, 65-72; head eng, US Merchant Marine Acad, 72-75; mgr, 75-80, ACTG DIR, REQUIREMENTS DEVELOP LAB, NAT MARITIME RES CTR, 80- *Concurrent Pos:* Mem comt 8, slamming & impact, Int Ship Struct Cong, 70 & 73. *Mem:* Am Soc Mech Engrs; Am Soc Naval Engrs; Soc Naval Archit & Marine Engrs; NY Acad Sci. *Res:* Naval architecture; structural design; structural seaworthiness of ships, particularly ship slamming and the resulting structural damage and means of obviating such damages. *Mailing Add:* 24 Harbor Way Sea Cliff NY 11579

MCLEAN, WILLIAM L, b Dunedin, NZ, May 22, 33. PHYSICS. *Educ:* Univ Otago, NZ, BSc, 54, MSc, 56; Cambridge Univ, PhD(physics), 60. *Prof Exp:* Asst lectr physics, Univ Otago, NZ, 56-57; instr, Univ BC, 60-61; asst prof, 61-66, ASSOC PROF PHYSICS, RUTGERS UNIV, NEW BRUNSWICK, 66- *Mem:* Am Phys Soc. *Res:* Radio-frequency techniques on superconductors; propagation of helicon waves through metals and the relation to the band structure; superconductivity; low temperature, solid state and statistical physics. *Mailing Add:* Dept of Physics Rutgers Univ New Brunswick NJ 08903

MACLEAN, WILLIAM PLANNETTE, III, b Bainbridge, Md, Sept 20, 43; m 66. BIOLOGY. *Educ:* Princeton Univ, BA, 65; Univ Chicago, PhD(evolutionary biol), 69. *Prof Exp:* Asst prof, 69-75, assoc prof, 75-81, PROF BIOL, COL VIRGIN ISLANDS, 81-, CHMN DIV SCI & MATH, 78-, DIR MARINE SCI CTR, 81- *Mem:* Ecol Soc Am; Am Soc Ichthyologists & Herpetologists; Soc Study Evolution. *Res:* Island biogeography; co-evolution; environmental impacts. *Mailing Add:* Col Virgin Islands St Thomas VI 00801

MACLEAY, RONALD E, b Buffalo, NY, Dec 3, 35; m 60; c 4. SYNTHETIC ORGANIC CHEMISTRY. *Educ:* St Bonaventure Univ, BS, 57, MS, 59; Univ Buffalo, PhD(org chem), 65. *Prof Exp:* Res & develop chemist, 59-61, sr res chemist, 64-66, res group leader nitrogen chem, 66-75, sr group leader res, 75-79, res fel, 79-80, mgr process develop, Lucidol Div, 80-82, RES FEL, PENNWALT CORP, 82- *Mem:* Am Chem Soc. *Res:* Reduction of carbonyl compounds with lithium tetrakis-aluminate; synthesis of azo compounds for free radical initiation of polymerization. *Mailing Add:* 10 Mahogany Dr Buffalo NY 14221

MCLELLAN, ALDEN, IV, b Meridian, Miss, Mar 7, 36; m 72. ENVIRONMENTAL MANAGEMENT, RESOURCE MANAGEMENT. *Educ:* Univ Calif, Berkeley, BA, 60, MA, 64; Univ Nev, PhD(physics), 67. *Prof Exp:* Theoret Naval Air Missile Test Ctr, 57; res physicist, Lawrence Radiation Lab, Univ Calif, 59; res physicist, Univ Calif, Berkeley, 64; fel physics, Univ Nev, 64-65; res assoc, Desert Res Inst, 67-69, dep dir lab space res, 69; res scientist, Atmospheric Pollution Prog, Space Sci & Eng Ctr, Univ Wis-Madison, 69-72, sr scientist, Environ Res Group, Inst Environ Studies, 73-75; pres, Impact Environ Res, 73-77; PHYSICIST, W M GRENGG & ASSOC, 78- *Concurrent Pos:* Europ Space Res Orgn res asst, Europ Space Res Inst, Italy, 67; vis res prof, Int Ctr Theoret Physics, Int Atomic Energy Agency, 67-68; res lectr, Nat Ctr Atmospheric Res, Colo, 68. *Mem:* AAAS; Am Phys Soc; Am Inst Aeronaut & Astronaut; Am Geophys Union; Am Nuclear Soc. *Res:* Theoretical optics; radar analysis; global atmospheric pollution; neutron-proton nuclear evaporation theory; theoretical plasms and space physics; astrophysics; solar and atmospheric physics; computational mathematics; air and water pollution; environmental impact from land use; telecommunications. *Mailing Add:* W M Grengg & Assoc 4669 Beltline Hwy Madison WI 53711

MACLELLAN, CHARLES ROGER, b New Glasgow, NS, May 8, 23; m 45; c 2. ENTOMOLOGY. *Educ:* McGill Univ, BSc, 50; Queen's Univ Ont, MA, 54. *Prof Exp:* Res scientist & ecologist, Res Br, Can Dept Agr, 50-78; CONSULT INSECT & MITE MONITORING SERV, 78- *Concurrent Pos:* Res fel entom, Commonwealth Sci & Indust Res Orgn, Australia, 62-64. *Mem:* Entom Soc Can. *Mailing Add:* P O Box 775 Kentville NS B4N 3X9 Can

MCLELLAN, JAMES C(HARLES), environmental engineering, see previous edition

MCLELLAN, REX B, b Leeds, Eng, Nov 21, 35; m 58; c 1. METALLURGY. *Educ:* Univ Sheffield, BMet, 57; Univ Leeds, PhD(metall), 62. *Prof Exp:* Sci officer metall, UK Atomic Energy Comn, 57-59; sr res fel, Univ Leeds, 62-63; res assoc, Univ Ill, Urbana, 63-64; from asst prof to assoc prof mat sci, 64-69, PROF MAT SCI, RICE UNIV, 77- *Honors & Awards:* Mappin Medal, 57. *Mem:* Metall Soc; Am Inst Mining, Metall & Petrol Engrs; Am Soc Metals. *Res:* Thermodynamics and statistical mechanics of solid solutions; diffusion and relaxation phenomena in solid solutions. *Mailing Add:* Dept Mech Eng Rice Univ Houston TX 77001

MCLELLAN, WILLIAM L, JR, biochemistry, microbiology, see previous edition

MCLELLON, WALDRON MURRILL, b Washington, DC, Apr 21, 18; m 41; c 1. CIVIL & ENVIRONMENTAL ENGINEERING. *Educ:* US Naval Acad, BS, 41; Ohio State Univ, MS, 52; Rensselaer Polytech Inst, BCE, 44, MCE, 45, MS, 64, PhD(environ eng), 67. *Prof Exp:* Engr, US Navy, 41-54, prof dir, Weapons Effects Test, Sandia Base, NMex, 54-55, asst for design, Dist Pub Works Off, 11th Naval Dist, Calif, 55-58, mgr atomic energy br, Bur Yards & Docks, Navy Dept, Washington, DC, 58, dir eng div, 58-60, dir pub works off, US Naval Shipyard & Sta, SC, 60-61, chief opers & training br, Joint Civil Defense Support Group, Off Chief Engrs, US Army, DC, 61-63; assoc prof environ systs eng, Univ Clemson, 66-69; prof civil eng & environ sci & chmn dept, 69-73, PROF ENG, FLA TECHNOL UNIV, 73- *Concurrent Pos:* Mem & chmn, SC Bd Cert for Pub Water Treatment Plant Operators, 67-69; res grant, Water Resources Res Inst, SC, 68-70; consult, Eng Sci, Inc, Calif, 69; partner & secy, ECO Systs, Inc, 70-71; res grant, Orange County, Fla, 70-73; Dept Labor, Manpower Develop & Training Act training grant, 71. *Mem:* Water Works Asn; Water Pollution Control Fedn; Am Soc Civil Engrs; Asn Environ Eng Prof. *Res:* Water quality control; water and wastewater treatment by chemical and physical processes; radiological health; nuclear weapons effects; removal of radionuclides from water; civil defense; health physics practices. *Mailing Add:* Dept of Civil Eng & Environ Sci Fla Technol Univ Box 25000 Orlando FL 32816

MCLEMORE, BENJAMIN HENRY, JR, b Memphis, Tenn, Oct 4, 24; m; c 2. MATHEMATICAL STATISTICS. *Educ:* Dillard Univ, AB, 44; Univ Ill, MS, 52, AM, 55, PhD(statist), 59. *Prof Exp:* High sch instr, Tex, 44-45; instr math, Dillard Univ, 45-47; instr, Jackson State Col, 47-53, head dept, 56-64; ASSOC PROF MATH, CLEVELAND STATE UNIV, 64- *Mem:* Am Statist Asn; Math Asn Am; Inst Math Statist. *Mailing Add:* Dept of Math Cleveland State Univ Cleveland OH 44115

MCLEMORE, BOBBIE FRANK, b Jasper, Tex, May 22, 32; m 50; c 2. PLANT PHYSIOLOGY. *Educ:* Tex A&M Univ, BS, 53; La State Univ, MS, 57, PhD(forestry), 67. *Prof Exp:* Lab asst bot, Tex A&M Univ, 50-53; res asst agron, Tex Agr Exp Sta, 55; SILVICULTURIST, SOUTHERN FOREST EXP STA, US FOREST SERV, 57- *Mem:* Soc Am Foresters. *Res:* Storage, processing, testing and dormancy of southern pine seed; pine seed, cone and conelet physiology; herbicides, uneven-aged management of loblolly-shortleaf pines. *Mailing Add:* Southern Forest Exp Sta US Forest Serv Monticello AR 71655

MCLENDON, DAVID MARK, b Lufkin, Tex, Feb 18, 47; m 78. PSYCHOPHARMACOLOGY. *Educ:* NTex State Univ, MS, 70; Univ Houston, BS, 69, PhD(psychol), 74. *Prof Exp:* Res asst behav pharmacol, Tex Res Inst Ment Sci, 70-72; res asst, 72-74, Nat Inst Drug Abuse fel psychophysiol, Baylor Col Med, 74-77; dir psychol serv, Fabre Clin & Res Testing Inc, 77-80; PRES, BIO-PSYCH DATA CORP, 77-; ASST PROF PHYSIOL, BAYLOR COL MED, 79- *Mem:* Am Soc Clin Pharmacol & Therapeut; Am Group Psychother Asn; Am Psychol Asn; Soc Neurosci; Soc Behav Med. *Res:* Abuse liability of marihuana studied in rhesus monkeys; aggression and marihuana in rats; behavioral effects and toxicology of new drugs in animals; self administration of drugs in monkeys; safety and efficacy of anxiolytics, anti-depressants and neuroleptics in humans; efficacy of benzodiazepines in humans. *Mailing Add:* Dept Physiol Baylor Col Med Tex Med Ctr Houston TX 77030

MCLENDON, GEORGE L, b Fortworth, Tex, June 6, 52; m 72; c 2. BIOINORGANIC CHEMISTRY. *Educ:* Univ Tex, El Paso, BS, 72; Tex A&M Univ, PhD(chem), 76. *Prof Exp:* Asst prof, 76-81, ASSOC PROF CHEM, UNIV ROCHESTER, 81- *Concurrent Pos:* Henry & Camille Dreyfuss teacher scholar award, 79-85; A P Sloan fel, 80-84. *Mem:* Am Chem Soc. *Res:* Inorganic chemistry and protein chemistry; electron transfer reactions; structure and function of heme proteins; photocatalysis. *Mailing Add:* Dept Chem Univ Rochester Rochester NY 14627

MCLENDON, WILLIAM WOODARD, b Durham, NC, Oct 29, 30; m 52; c 3. PATHOLOGY, LABORATORY MEDICINE. *Educ:* Univ NC, BA, 53, MD, 56. *Prof Exp:* Intern & resident path, Columbia-Presby Med Ctr, New York, 56-58; resident, Univ NC, Chapel Hill, 58-61; asst chief path serv, US Army Hosp, Landstuhl, Ger, 61-63; assoc pathologist, Moses Cone Hosp, Greensboro, NC, 63-69, dir labs, 69-73; PROF PATH, SCH MED, UNIV NC, CHAPEL HILL, 73-, CHMN DEPT HOSP LABS, NC MEM HOSP, 73- *Concurrent Pos:* Asst chief ed, Arch Path, 74-; assoc ed, Yearbook Pathol, 81- *Mem:* AAAS; Soc Comput Med; Acad Clin Lab Physicians & Sci (pres, 81-82); Col Am Path; Am Soc Clin Path. *Res:* Endocrine pathology; automation and computerization of the clinical laboratory. *Mailing Add:* Dept of Hosp Labs NC Mem Hosp Chapel Hill NC 27514

MCLENNAN, BARRY DEAN, b Bracken, Sask, Apr 15, 40; m 63; c 3. BIOCHEMISTRY. *Educ:* Brandon Univ, BSc, 60; Univ Sask, MSc, 63; Univ Alta, PhD(biochem), 66. *Prof Exp:* Instr chem, Brandon Univ, 60-61; asst prof biochem, 69-73, assoc prof, 73-78, PROF BIOCHEM, UNIV SASK, 78- *Concurrent Pos:* Inst fel biochem, Roswell Park Mem Inst, 66-67, Nat Cancer Inst Can fel, 66-68; fel McMaster Univ, 67-69; Med Res Coun Can grant, Univ Sask, 69-, vis scientist award, 79-80. *Mem:* AAAS; Can Biochem Soc (secy, 80-). *Res:* Structure and chemistry of nucleic acids; function of modified nucleosides in transfer RNA and bacterial pathogenicity. *Mailing Add:* Dept Biochem Univ Sask Col Med Saskatoon SK S7N 0W0 Can

MCLENNAN, CHARLES EWART, b Duluth, Minn, Dec 26, 09; m 37; c 4. OBSTETRICS & GYNECOLOGY. *Educ:* Univ Minn, BA, 30, MA, 32, MD, 34, PhD(obstet & gynec), 42; Am Bd Obstet & Gynec, dipl, 42. *Prof Exp:* From instr to assoc prof obstet & gynec, Univ Minn, 38-44; prof & head dept, Univ Utah, 44-47; prof & head dept, 47-75, EMER PROF GYNEC & OBSTET, SCH MED, STANFORD UNIV, 75- *Concurrent Pos:* Dir, Am Bd Obstet & Gynec, 66-72; consult gynec, Menlo Med Clin, Menlo Park, Calif, 75-78. *Mem:* AAAS; Am Gynec Soc (pres, 73); Soc Gynec Invest (pres, 62); AMA; Am Fedn Clin Res. *Res:* Gynecological histopathology and cancer; exfoliative cytology. *Mailing Add:* 39 Pearce Mitchell Stanford CA 94305

MACLENNAN, DONALD ALLAN, b San Turse, PR, Mar 27, 36; m 67; c 1. ATOMIC PHYSICS. *Educ:* Univ Calif, Berkeley, BS, 59, PhD(physics), 66; Case Western Reserve Univ, MBA, 72. *Prof Exp:* Engr, Atomic Power & Equip Div, 59, 60, res scientist, Res & Develop Ctr, 66-68, group leader discharge eng, 68-70, mgr fluorescent lamp eng, Lamp Div, Gen Elec Co, 70-75; mgr flash tube eng, 75-78, MGR FLASH SOURCES & LAMP SYSTS BUS, ELECTRO-OPTICS DIV, EG&G, INC, 79- *Mem:* Am Phys Soc. *Res:* Experimental atomic and molecular physics; gaseous electronics; surface physics. *Mailing Add:* Electro-Optics Div 35 Congress St Salem MA 01970

MCLENNAN, DONALD ELMORE, b London, Ont, Dec 5, 19; m 43, 66; c 5. ELECTRODYNAMICS, CLASSICAL. *Educ:* Univ Western Ont, BA, 41; Univ Toronto, PhD(physics), 50. *Prof Exp:* Res scientist ballistics, Can Armament Res & Develop Estab, 50-59; prof physics, Col William & Mary, 59-67; PROF PHYSICS & ASTRON, YOUNGSTOWN STATE UNIV, 67- *Mem:* Am Phys Soc; AAAS. *Res:* Unified field theory. *Mailing Add:* Dept of Physics & Astron Youngstown State Univ Youngstown OH 44555

MCLENNAN, HUGH, b Montreal, Que, Oct 22, 27; m 49; c 2. PHYSIOLOGY. *Educ:* McGill Univ, BSc, 47, MSc, 49, PhD(biochem), 51. *Prof Exp:* Asst lectr biophys, Univ Col, Univ London, 52-53; res fel, Montreal Neurol Inst, 53-55; asst prof physiol, Dalhousie Univ, 55-57; from asst prof to assoc prof, 57-65, PROF PHYSIOL, UNIV BC, 65- *Mem:* Am Physiol Soc; Can Physiol Soc (secy, 65-); Brit Biochem Soc; Brit Physiol Soc. *Res:* Neurophysiology. *Mailing Add:* Dept of Physiol Univ of BC Vancouver BC V6T 1W5 Can

MCLENNAN, JAMES ALAN, JR, b Atlanta, Ga, Nov 24, 24; m 52; c 2. STATISTICAL MECHANICS. *Educ:* Harvard Univ, AB, 48; Lehigh Univ, MS, 50, PhD(physics), 52. *Prof Exp:* Tech engr, Gen Elec Co, 52-53; from instr to assoc prof, 53-62, chmn dept, 68-78, PROF PHYSICS, LEHIGH UNIV, 62- *Concurrent Pos:* Nat Sci Found fel, Lehigh Univ, 60-61; consult, Los Alamos Sci Lab. *Mem:* Fel Am Phys Soc; Sigma Xi. *Res:* Quantum theory of elementary particles; nonequilibrium statistical mechanics and kinetic theory. *Mailing Add:* Dept of Physics Lehigh Univ Bethlehem PA 18015

MACLEOD, ALASTAIR WILLIAM, b Vancouver, BC, Aug 26, 16; m 54. PSYCHIATRY. *Educ:* Glasgow Univ, BSc, 38, MB, ChB, 41, DPH, 42. *Prof Exp:* Asst dir dept psychol med, York Clin, Guy's Hosp, London, Eng, 45-50; from asst prof to assoc prof, 52-72, PROF PSYCHIAT, MCGILL UNIV, 72-; EXEC DIR, MENT HYG INST, 69- *Concurrent Pos:* Mem attend staff, Royal Victoria Hosp, 52-, sr psychiatrist attend staff, 71-; from asst dir to assoc dir, Ment Hyg Inst, 57-69, exec dir, 69-81; consult ment health, Protestant Sch Bd Gtr Montreal, 59-; training analyst, Can Inst Psychoanal; psychiat consult, Montreal Gen, Jewish Gen & Queen Elizabeth Hosps, Montreal, 66-; spec lectr, Dept Health & Social Med & Sch Social Work, McGill Univ; from asst dir to assoc dir, Ment Hyg Inst, 57-69. *Mem:* Fel Am Psychiat Asn; Am Psychoanal Asn; Can Psychoanal Soc (pres, 53-55). *Res:* Aftereffects of early maternal deprivation, their recognition and response to treatment. *Mailing Add:* Ment Hyg Inst 3647 Peel St Montreal PQ H3A 1X1 Can

MACLEOD, CHARLES FRANKLYN, b Halifax, NS, Jan 15, 24; m 51; c 3. ECOLOGY. *Educ:* McGill Univ, BSc, 48; Univ BC, MA, 50; Univ Minn, PhD(ecol, statist), 59. *Prof Exp:* Teaching asst zool, NC State Col, 51-53; res officer small mammal ecol, Can Dept Forestry, 56-62; asst prof, 62-66, actg chmn dept, 65-66, chmn dept, 66-69, ASSOC PROF BIOL, SIR GEORGE WILLIAMS CAMPUS, CONCORDIA UNIV, 66- *Mem:* Ecol Soc Am; Am Inst Biol Sci; Am Soc Mammal; Can Soc Zoologists. *Res:* Small mammal population studies. *Mailing Add:* Dept Biol Sci Sir Geo Wms Campus Concordia Univ Montreal PQ H3G 1M8 Can

MACLEOD, DONALD IAIN ARCHIBALD, b Glasgow, Scotland, Oct 2, 45; m 74. VISION. *Educ:* Univ Glasgow, MA, 67; Cambridge Univ, PhD(exp psychol), 74. *Prof Exp:* Res assoc vision, Inst Perception, Soesterberg, 67-68; res assoc zool, Cambridge Univ, 72; vis asst prof psychobiol, Fla State Univ, 72-74; asst prof, 74-78, ASSOC PROF PSYCHOL, UNIV CALIF, SAN DIEGO, 78- *Honors & Awards:* WAH Rushton Mem Lectr, 81. *Mem:* Psychonomic Soc; Asn Res Vision & Ophthal; fel Optical Soc Am. *Res:* Retinal mechanisms in human vision; human color vision. *Mailing Add:* Dept of Psychol Univ of Calif San Diego La Jolla CA 92093

MCLEOD, DONALD WINGROVE, b Rochester, NY, Feb 15, 35; m 58; c 3. HIGH ENERGY PHYSICS. *Educ:* Univ Rochester, BS, 56; Cornell Univ, PhD(exp physics), 62. *Prof Exp:* Res assoc, Argonne Nat Lab, 62-64, asst scientist, 64-66; from asst prof to assoc prof, 66-77, PROF EXP HIGH ENERGY PHYSICS, UNIV ILL, CHICAGO CIRCLE, 77- *Concurrent Pos:* Part-time instr, Univ Ill, Chicago, 64-66. *Mem:* Am Phys Soc. *Res:* Experimental high energy physics, using counter and wire chamber techniques, emphasis on strong interactions. *Mailing Add:* Dept of Physics Univ of Ill Box 4348 Chicago IL 60680

MCLEOD, DOUGALD GLENN ROSS, b Winnipeg, Man, Apr 10, 34; m 62; c 6. ENTOMOLOGY, BIOCHEMISTRY. *Educ:* Univ Man, BSA, 58; Univ Wis, MS, 60, PhD(entom), 62. *Prof Exp:* RES SCIENTIST ENTOM, CAN AGR RES INST, 62- *Mem:* Entom Soc Can; Entom Soc Am. *Res:* Improvement in insect control by prediction of the temporal and spatial distribution of pest insects. *Mailing Add:* Can Agr Res Inst Univ Sub PO London ON N6A 5B7 Can

MCLEOD, EDWARD BLAKE, b Los Angeles, Calif, July 25, 24. MATHEMATICS. *Educ:* Occidental Col, BA, 47, MS, 49; Stanford Univ, PhD(math), 54. *Prof Exp:* Mathematician, NAm Aviation, Inc, 47-48; asst, Stanford Univ, 51-53; instr math, Univ Colo, 53-55; asst prof, Ore State Col, 55-63; sr mathematician, Dynamics Sci Corp, 63-64; assoc prof, 64-72, PROF MATH, CALIF STATE UNIV, LONG BEACH, 72- *Mem:* Am Math Soc; Math Asn Am; Soc Indust & Appl Math; Am Inst Aeronaut & Astronaut. *Res:* Complex variables; fluid dynamics; time series forecasting and applications of mathematics to biology. *Mailing Add:* Dept of Math Calif State Univ Long Beach CA 90804

MACLEOD, ELLIS GILMORE, b Washington, DC, Sept 3, 28. EVOLUTIONARY BIOLOGY, ENTOMOLOGY. *Educ:* Univ Md, BS, 55, MS, 60; Harvard Univ, PhD(biol), 64. *Prof Exp:* Fel evolutionary biol, Harvard Univ, 64-66; asst prof, 66-69, assoc prof entom, 69-77, ASSOC PROF GENETICS & DEVELOP, UNIV ILL, URBANA, 78- *Concurrent Pos:* NSF grant syst biol, 69- *Mem:* Royal Entom Soc London; AAAS. *Res:* Speciation and higher levels of evolution of insects, including studies of phylogeny deduced from the fossil record, and such comparative studies of contemporary species as behavior, ecology and chromosome cytology. *Mailing Add:* Dept of Genetics & Develop Univ of Ill Urbana IL 61801

MCLEOD, GUY COLLINGWOOD, b Brockton, Mass, Feb 18, 28; m 50; c 3. PLANT PHYSIOLOGY. *Educ:* Harvard Univ, BA, 51; Trinity Col, MS, 54. *Prof Exp:* Asst geochem, Boston Univ, 51-52; sr fel, Sias Inst Res, Brooks Hosp, Brookline, Mass, 58-59, mem, 61-63; res fel, Dept Plant Biol, Carnegie Inst, 59-61; group leader photobiol, Air Force Cambridge Res Labs, Mass, 63-64; sr scientist, Tyco Labs, 64-66, asst dept head phys-chem, 66-69; DIR RES, NEW ENG AQUARIUM, 69- *Concurrent Pos:* Res assoc, Med Sch, Tufts Univ, 64-; lectr, Dept Environ Sci, Univ Mass, 67-; adj prof, Boston Univ, 69- *Mem:* Am Soc Plant Physiol; Biophys Soc; NY Acad Sci; Scandinavian Soc Plant Physiol. *Res:* Photosynthesis; cellular physiology. *Mailing Add:* New Eng Aquarium Central Wharf Boston MA 02110

MCLEOD, HARRY O'NEAL, JR, b Shreveport, La, Feb 26, 32; m 59; c 2. PETROLEUM ENGINEERING, INFORMATION SCIENCE. *Educ:* Colo Sch Mines, BPeEng, 53; Univ Okla, MPeEng, 63, PhD(eng sci), 65. *Prof Exp:* Petrol engr, Phillips Petrol Co, 53-54 & 56-58; res engr, Jersey Prod Res Co, 63-64; sr res engr, Dowell Div, Dow Chem Co, 65-69; asst prof petrol eng & dir info serv, Univ Tulsa, 69-75; STAFF ENGR, CONTINENTAL OIL CO, 75- *Mem:* Soc Petrol Engrs; Am Inst Chem Engrs; Sigma Xi. *Res:* Fluid flow through porous media; oil and gas well stimulation; pressure transient testing of oil and gas wells; information retrieval. *Mailing Add:* 2006 Southwick Houston TX 77080

MCLEOD, HENRY GEORGE, electrochemistry, see previous edition

MACLEOD, HUGH ANGUS, b Glasgow, UK, June 20, 33; m 57; c 5. THIN FILM OPTICS. *Educ:* Univ Glasgow, BSc, 54; Inst Physics, UK, FInstP, 69; Coun Nat Acad, DTech, 79. *Prof Exp:* Engr, Sperry Gyroscope Co, Ltd, 54-60; chief develop engr, Williamson Mfg Co, Ltd, 60-62; sr physicist, Mervyn Instruments Ltd, 62-63; thin films mgr, Sir Howard Grubb Parsons & Co, Ltd, 63-71; reader thin film physics, Newcastle Upon Tyne Polytech, 71-79; PROF OPTICAL SCI, UNIV ARIZ, 79- *Mem:* Inst Physics; Optical Soc Am; Am Vacuum Soc. *Res:* Optical thin films, coatings and filters, properties, processes, design, manufacture and measurement. *Mailing Add:* Optical Sci Ctr Univ Ariz Tucson AZ 85721

MACLEOD, JOHN ALEXANDER, b Brantford, Can, Mar 15, 45; m 67; c 2. SOIL SCIENCE, AGRONOMY. *Educ:* Macdonald Col, BSc, 66; McGill Univ, MSc, 68; Cornell Univ, PhD(soil fertil), 71. *Prof Exp:* RES SCIENTIST SOIL FERTIL, AGR CAN, RES STA, 71- *Mem:* Am Soc Agron; Soil Sci Soc Am; Agr Inst Can; Can Soc Soil Sci; Can Soc Agron. *Res:* Nutrient sources and methods of application for forages and cereals; nitrogen nutrition, disease and lodging interaction of cereals; ammonia losses from fertilizer. *Mailing Add:* Res Sta Agr Can Charlottetown PE C1A 7M8 Can

MCLEOD, JOHN HUGH, JR, b Hattiesburg, Miss, Feb 27, 11; m 51; c 2. MECHANICAL & ELECTRICAL ENGINEERING. *Educ:* Tulane Univ, BS, 33. *Prof Exp:* Engr var indust orgns, 33-39; field engr, Taylor Instrument Co, NY, 40-42; res & develop engr, Leeds & Northrup Co, Pa, 43-47; sect head guid systs & guided missiles, US Naval Air Missile Test Ctr, Calif, 47-56; design specialist, Gen Dynamics/Astronaut, 56-63, consult, 63-64; INDEPENDENT CONSULT, 64- *Concurrent Pos:* Ed & publ, Simulation Coun Newsletter, 52-55, ed, 55-, ed, Simulation, 63-, chmn Simulation Coun, 52; mem exec comt, Fall Joint Comput Conf, Am Fedn Info Processing Socs, 65; ed & publ, Simulation in the Serv of Soc, 71- *Honors & Awards:* Sr Sci Simulation Award, Electronic Assocs, Inc, 65. *Mem:* Inst Elec & Electronics Engrs; Simulation Coun. *Res:* Application of computer modeling and simulation technology, especially for study, analysis and prediction of response of physiological, societal and global systems to therapy or corrective measures. *Mailing Add:* Simulation in Serv of Soc 8484 La Jolla Shores Dr La Jolla CA 92037

MCLEOD, JOHN MALCOLM, b Montreal, Que, Oct 8, 28; m 54; c 3. ENTOMOLOGY. *Educ:* Univ NB, BSc, 53; State Univ NY Col Forestry, Syracuse Univ, MSc, 55, PhD(insect ecol), 61. *Prof Exp:* Res officer pop ecol forest insects, Can Dept Forestry, Can Dept Environ, 55-78; RES ASSOC, UNIV BC, 78- *Mem:* Entom Soc Can; Entom Soc Am; AAAS. *Res:* Taxonomy and bionomics of microlepidoptera; population ecology; Swaine jack pine sawfly; ecological modeling; policy analysis; mammalian and avian predators of Neodiprion swainei. *Mailing Add:* Inst of Resource Ecol 2204 Main Mall Vancouver BC Can

MACLEOD, JOHN MUNROE, b Vermilion, Alta, Sept 3, 37; m 59; c 3. RADIO ASTRONOMY. *Educ:* Univ Alta, BSc, 59; Univ Ill, MS, 60, PhD(elec eng), 64. *Prof Exp:* RES OFFICER, ASTRON SECT, HERZBERG INST ASTROPHYS, NAT RES COUN CAN, 64- *Mem:* Can Astron Soc; Am Astron Soc. *Res:* Interstellar molecules; extragalactic variable sources; recombination lines. *Mailing Add:* Astron Sect Nat Res Coun of Can Ottawa ON K1B 3G6 Can

MCLEOD, KENNETH WILLIAM, b Miami, Okla, Oct 14, 47. PLANT ECOLOGY. *Educ:* Okla State Univ, BS, 69, MS, 71; Mich State Univ, PhD(plant ecol), 74. *Prof Exp:* res assoc plant ecol, 74-80, ASSOC RES ECOL, SAVANNAH RIVER ECOL LAB, UNIV GA, 80- *Mem:* Ecol Soc Am; Am Inst Biol Sci; AAAS. *Res:* Factors that govern the establishment and distribution of plant populations, especially seed germination and subsequent seedling growth; elemental cyling in forests; radioecology. *Mailing Add:* Savannah River Ecol Lab Drawer E Aiken SC 29801

MCLEOD, LIONEL EVERETT, b Wainwright, Alta, Aug 9, 27; m 52; c 4. MEDICAL EDUCATION, MEDICAL ADMINISTRATION. *Educ:* Univ Alta, BSc, 49, MD, 51; McGill Univ, MSc, 56; FRCP, 57; FRCPS(C). *Prof Exp:* Attend physician, Univ Alta Hosp, 58-69, assoc prof med, Univ Alta, 59-69; head dept, 69-77, PROF DEPT MED, UNIV CALGARY, 69-, DEAN FAC MED, 73- *Mem:* Am Soc Artificial Internal Organs; Can Soc Clin Invest; Can Fedn Biol Soc. *Res:* Endocrinology and metabolism; application of intermittent hemodialysis in chronic renal failure. *Mailing Add:* Fac of Med Univ of Calgary Calgary AB T2N 1N4 Can

MACLEOD, LLOYD BECK, b Apr 27, 30; Can citizen; m 55; c 3. AGRONOMY. *Educ:* McGill Univ, BSc, 52, MSc, 53; Cornell Univ, PhD(soil sci), 62. *Prof Exp:* Res officer agron, Res Br, Can Dept Agr, 53-59, head soils & plant nutrit sect, 62-65, res scientist, PEI, 65-67, head soils & plant nutrit sect, 67-70, DIR RES STA, AGR CAN, 70-, CHIEF LIAISON OFFICER, PEI, 78- *Mem:* Am Soc Agron; Soil Sci Soc Am; fel Can Soc Soil Sci; Can Soc Agron; Int Soc Soil Sci. *Res:* Soil fertility and plant nutrition of forage species; nutrient competition; aluminum tolerance; effect of potassium on utilization of ammonium and nitrate sources of nitrogen by forage and cereal crops; research management and administration. *Mailing Add:* Can Agr Res Sta PO Box 1210 Charlottetown PE C1A 7M8 Can

MACLEOD, MICHAEL CHRISTOPHER, b Allentown, Pa, Feb 7, 47; m 69; c 2. CHEMICAL CARCINOGENESIS. *Educ:* Calif Inst Technol, BS, 69; Univ Ore, PhD(molecular biol), 74. *Prof Exp:* Fel biol, Univ Ore, 74-75; fel gene regulation, 75-77, RES ASSOC CHEM CARCINOGENESIS, BIOL DIV, OAK RIDGE NAT LAB, 77- *Mem:* Am Soc Biol Chem; Am Asn Cancer Res; AAAS. *Res:* Metabolism of polycyclic aromatic hydrocarbons by cultured cells and their interactions with cellular macromolecules; analysis of components of nuclei which bind hydrocarbons; identification of those interactions which lead to neoplasia. *Mailing Add:* Biol Div Oak Ridge Nat Lab Oak Ridge TN 37830

MCLEOD, NORMAN BARRIE, b Regina, Sask, Apr 7, 32; m 57; c 3. NUCLEAR ENGINEERING, PHYSICS. *Educ:* Univ Toronto, BASc, 55; Univ Mich, MSE, 57; Mass Inst Technol, PhD(nuclear eng), 62. *Prof Exp:* Instrumentation engr jet engines, Orenda Engines, Malton, Ont, 55-57; teaching asst nuclear reactor, Mass Inst Technol, 57-61; staff consult nuclear fuel, 61-72, vpres, South East Opers, 73-77, vpres & gen mgr energy syst div, 77-80, VPRES NUCLEAR WASTE PROJ, NUS CORP, 80- *Mem:* Sigma Xi; Am Nuclear Soc. *Res:* Resources, production capability, costs and prices of major fuels, with emphasis on uranium and coal. *Mailing Add:* NUS Corp 4 Research Pl Rockville MD 20850

MCLEOD, NORMAN WILLIAM, b Nichol Township, Ont, Nov 26, 04; m 31; c 5. CIVIL ENGINEERING, CHEMICAL ENGINEERING. *Educ:* Univ Alta, BSc, 30; Univ Sask, MSc, 36; Univ Mich, ScD(civil eng), 38. *Hon Degrees:* DEng, Univ Waterloo, Ont, 80. *Prof Exp:* Head asphalt construct & maintenance, Sask Dept Hwys & Transp, 30-38; asphalt consult, Imperial Oil Ltd, 38-69; V PRES ASPHALT, McASPHALT ENG SERV, 70- *Concurrent Pos:* Adj prof, Univ Waterloo, 70-; consult, Can Dept Transp, 45-59, LaMarre Valois Int, Montreal, 72-74, Dejardins et Sauriol et Assoc, Montreal, 73-74, Kampsax, Bangkok, 73, Can Dept Nat Defence, 77 & 78, Techint, Argentina, 79, US Corps Engrs, Alaska, 80 & Aldluhairy Gen Contract Co, Abu Dhabi, 81. *Honors & Awards:* USA Hwy Res Bd Award, 46; Charles B Dudley Medal, Am Soc Testing & Mat, 52, Prevost Hubbard Award, 78; Asn Asphalt Paving Technologists Ann Award, 52; R F Legget Award, Can Geotech Soc, 72. *Mem:* Fel Royal Soc Can; fel Am Soc Testing & Mat; fel AAAS; Asn Asphalt Paving Technologists (past pres). *Res:* Asphalt as a material and its applications for pavements, roofings and other uses. *Mailing Add:* McAsphalt Eng Serv PO Box 247 West Hill Toronto ON M1E 4R5 Can

MCLEOD, RICHARD KENNETH, physical organic chemistry, deceased

MACLEOD, ROBERT ANGUS, b Athabasca, Alta, July 13, 21; m 48; c 6. MICROBIOLOGY. *Educ:* Univ BC, BA, 43, MA, 45; Univ Wis, PhD(biochem), 49. *Prof Exp:* Instr chem, Univ BC, 45-46; asst prof biochem, Queen's Univ, Ont, 49-52; biochemist, Fisheries Res Bd, Can, 52-60; assoc prof agr bact, 60-64, chmn dept, 68-70 & 74-79, PROF MICROBIOL, MCGILL UNIV, MACDONALD CAMPUS, 64- *Concurrent Pos:* Mem marine sci ctr, McGill Univ. *Honors & Awards:* Harrison Prize, Royal Soc Can, 60; Award, Can Soc Microbiol, 73. *Mem:* Fel Royal Soc Can; Am Soc Biol Chem; Am Soc Microbiol; Can Soc Microbiol. *Res:* Nutrition and metabolism of marine bacteria; function of inorganic ions in bacterial metabolism; microbial biochemistry. *Mailing Add:* Dept of Microbiol MacDonald Col McGill Univ Ste Anne de Bellevue PQ H9X 1C0 Can

MCLEOD, ROBERT MELVIN, b Newco, Miss, June 19, 29; m 65; c 2. MATHEMATICAL ANALYSIS. *Educ:* Miss State Univ, BS, 50; Rice Univ, MA, 53, PhD(math), 55. *Prof Exp:* Instr math, Duke Univ, 55-58, asst prof, 58-61; assoc prof, Am Univ Beirut, 61-65; assoc prof, Univ Tenn, 65-66; ASSOC PROF MATH, KENYON COL, 66- *Mem:* Am Math Soc; Math Asn Am. *Res:* Function theory. *Mailing Add:* Box 187 Gambier OH 43022

MACLEOD, ROBERT MEREDITH, b Newark, NJ, May 14, 29; m 51; c 4. BIOCHEMISTRY. *Educ:* Seton Hall Univ, BS, 52; NY Univ, MS, 56; Duke Univ, PhD(biochem), 59. *Prof Exp:* Res biochemist, Schering Corp, NJ, 48-56; instr biochem, Sch Med, Duke Univ, 59-60; asst prof biochem in internal med, 60-66, chmn div biomed eng, 64-65, dir div cancer studies, 69-72, assoc prof, 66-73, PROF INTERNAL MED, SCH MED, UNIV VA, 73-, DIR, ENDOCRINOL LAB, 78- *Concurrent Pos:* Am Heart Asn res fel, 59-60; USPHS res grant, 64-, career develop award, 65-71; cancer travel fel, WHO, 68. *Mem:* AAAS; Am Physiol Soc; Am Fedn Clin Res; Am Asn Cancer Res; Int Soc Neuroendocrinol. *Res:* Hormonal control of biochemical mechanisms which regulate normal and neoplastic growth. *Mailing Add:* Dept of Internal Med Univ of Va Sch of Med Charlottesville VA 22901

MCLEOD, ROBIN JAMES YOUNG, b Arbroath, Scotland. NUMERICAL ANALYSIS. *Educ:* St Andrews Univ, BSc, 66; Dundee Univ, PhD(math), 73. *Prof Exp:* Res fel math, Dundee Univ, 73-74; lectr, Univ Man, 74-75; asst prof, Univ Calgary, 75-76; scientist, Inst Comput Appln Sci & Eng, 76-77; asst prof, Rensselaer Polytech Inst, 77-78; ASSOC PROF MATH, NMEX STATE UNIV, 78- *Mem:* Inst Math; Int Asn Math & Comput Simulation. *Res:* Numerical analysis; curved finite elements; parametric curve and surface inter-polation; techniques in computer aided design and difference methods for trajectomy problems in ordinary differential equations; application of geometry in numerical analysis. *Mailing Add:* Dept Math Sci NMex State Univ Las Cruces NM 88003

MCLEOD, SAMUEL ALBERT, b Tampa, Fla, Nov 13, 52. ADAPTIVE FUNCTIONAL MORPHOLOGY. *Educ:* Univ Calif, Berkeley, AB, 74, PhC, 77, PhD(paleont), 81. *Prof Exp:* Curatorial asst, 81, ASST CUR, LOS ANGELES CO MUS NATURAL HIST, 81- *Mem:* Soc Vert Paleont; Am Soc Mammalogists; Am Soc Zoologists. *Res:* Evolutionary biology, paleobiology, including functional morphology, systematics and paleocology of selected marine vertebrates (primarily cetaceans and chelonions and elasmobranchs). *Mailing Add:* Sect Vert Paleontol Mus Natural Hist 900 Exposition Blvd Los Angeles CA 90007

MCLEOD, WILLIAM D, b Toronto, Ont, Nov 16, 30; m 56; c 1. BIOMEDICAL ENGINEERING. *Educ:* Univ Toronto, BASc, 58, MAS, 61; Case Western Reserve Univ, PhD(mech eng), 65. *Prof Exp:* Asst dir cybernetic systs group, Case Western Reserve Univ, 64-66; asst prof mech eng & res assoc bioeng inst, Univ NB, 66-68; dir bioeng res, Insts Achievement Human Potential, Pa, 68-69; asst prof phys med, Emory Univ, 69-77, clin asst prof rehab med, 77-80; MEM STAFF, HUSHOTON ARTHOPEDIC CLIN, COLUMBUS, GA, 80- *Mem:* Inst Elec & Electronics Eng; Int Soc Electromyographic Kinesiology. *Res:* Information processing from bio-electric signals, primarily myo-electric signals; electroencephalographic signals; human operator modelling with handicapped people using electromyographic and electroencephalographic signals. *Mailing Add:* c/o Hushoton Arthop Clinic 105 Physicians Bldg Columbus GA 31901

MCLERAN, JAMES HERBERT, b Audubon, Iowa, Apr 9, 31; m 57; c 1. DENTISTRY, ORAL SURGERY. *Educ:* Simpson Col, BS & BA, 53; Univ Iowa, DDS, 57, MS, 62; Am Bd Oral Surg, dipl, 64. *Prof Exp:* Instr oral surg, Univ Iowa, 59-60; resident, Univ Hosps, Iowa City, Iowa, 60-62; pvt pract, Calif, 62-63; from asst prof to assoc prof oral surg, Univ Iowa, 63-69; prof & chmn dept, Sch Dent, Univ NC, Chapel Hill, 69-72; assoc dean, 72-74, PROF ORAL SURG, COL DENT, UNIV IOWA, 72-, DEAN COL, 74- *Mem:* Am Asn Dent Schs (pres, 78-79; Int Asn Dent Res; Am Soc Oral & Maxillofacial Surg; Am Dent Asn. *Res:* Pain control in dentistry; temporomandibular joint disfunction; bacteremia following oral surgical procedures. *Mailing Add:* Off of the Dean Univ Iowa City IA 52242

MCLEROY, EDWARD GLENN, b Atlanta, Ga, June 23, 26; c 2. PHYSICS. *Educ:* Emory Univ, BA, 49, MS, 51. *Prof Exp:* Asst math, Ga Inst Technol, 49; physicist, US Navy Mine Defense Lab, 51-53, 54-56; asst physics, Brown Univ, 53-54; asst prof, Marine Lab, Univ Miami, 57; head acoustics sect, US Navy Mine Defense Lab, 57-72; physicist, Naval Coastal Systs Lab, 72-81; CONSULT, TECH MARINE SERV INC, 81- *Mem:* AAAS; Acoust Soc Am; Am Asn Physics Teachers; Am Geophys Union; Soc Explor Geophys. *Res:* Marine physics, particularly marine acoustics. *Mailing Add:* Box 4647 Panama City FL 32401

MCLIMANS, WILLIAM FLETCHER, b Duluth, Minn, Aug 22, 16; m 40; c 3. VIROLOGY, MICROBIOLOGY. *Educ:* Univ Minn, BA, 38, PhD(bact, immunol), 46. *Prof Exp:* Res virologist, Minn Dept Health, 41-42; from instr to asst prof bact & immunol, Sch Med, Univ Minn, 46-49; res virologist, Rocky Mt Lab, USPHS, 49-50; head bact dept, Upjohn Co, 50-54; res & assoc prof microbiol, Vet Sch, asst prof, Med Sch & assoc mem, Wistar Inst, Univ Pa, 54-59; supvry microbiologist & chief tissue cult unit, Commun Dis Ctr, USPHS, 59-61; CAREER SCIENTIST, ROSWELL PARK MEM INST, 61- *Concurrent Pos:* Consult, US Air Force Proj Big Ben, 54-58; mem cell cult comt, Nat Res Coun, 57-58. *Honors & Awards:* Presidential Award, Int Cong Poliomyelitis, 58. *Mem:* AAAS; Am Soc Microbiol; Sci Res Soc Am; Am Asn Immunol; fel NY Acad Sci. *Res:* Cell culture; host cell-virus interaction; culture of mammalian cells; chemotherapy; cell physiology. *Mailing Add:* Roswell Park Mem Inst 666 Elm St Buffalo NY 14203

MCLINDEN, LYNN, b 43; US citizen. CONVEX ANALYSIS, OPTIMIZATION THEORY. *Educ:* Princeton Univ, AB, 65; Univ Wash, PhD(math), 71. *Prof Exp:* Vis asst prof math, Math Res Ctr, Univ Wis-Madison, 71-73; asst prof, 73-78, ASSOC PROF MATH, UNIV ILL, URBANA, 78- *Concurrent Pos:* NSF res grant, 75- *Mem:* Math Prog Soc; Opers Res Soc Am; Am Math Soc; Soc Indust & Appl Math. *Res:* Convex analysis and optimization theory, including conjugate duality, nonlinear programming, minimax problems and complementarity problems. *Mailing Add:* Dept Math 273 Atlgeld Hall Univ Ill at Urbana-Champaign Urbana IL 61801

MCLOUGHLIN, DONALD KEITH, b Fairbury, Ill, July 5, 23; m 46; c 2. PROTOZOOLOGY, PARASITOLOGY. *Educ:* George Washington Univ, BS, 48, MS, 49; Univ Ill, PhD, 55. *Prof Exp:* Fishery biologist, US Fish & Wildlife Serv, 55; parasitologist, Animal Parasitol Inst, Agr Res Serv, USDA, 55-81; RETIRED. *Mem:* AAAS; Am Soc Parasitol; Soc Protozool. *Res:* Chemotherapy of protozoan diseases; control and prevention of parasitic diseases; parasite physiology. *Mailing Add:* 900 Elm Ave Takoma Park MD 20012

MCLUCAS, JOHN L(UTHER), b Fayetteville, NC, Aug 22, 20; m 46; c 4. ELECTRONICS, PHYSICS. *Educ:* Davidson Col, BS, 41; Tulane Univ, MS, 43; Pa State Univ, PhD(physics), 50. *Hon Degrees:* DSc, Davidson Col, 76. *Prof Exp:* Physicist servomechanism design, Air Force Cambridge Res Ctr, 46-47; proj engr, Radio Countermeasures, HRB-Singer Co, Pa, 48-50, vpres & tech dir, 50-57, pres, 57-62; dep dir defense res & eng, Off Secy of Defense, Pentagon, 62-64, asst secy gen for sci affairs, NATO, France, 64-66; pres, Mitre Corp, Mass, 66-69; secy, from undersecy to secy of Air Force, 69-75; adminr, Fed Aviation Admin, 75-77; pres, Comsat Gen Corp, 77-80, PRES, COMSAT WORLD SYSTS, 80- *Concurrent Pos:* Mem, US Air Force Sci Adv Bd, 67-69, 77- *Honors & Awards:* Distinguished Civilian Serv Award, Dept Defense, 64, First Bronze Palm, 73, Silver Palm, 75; Exceptional Civilian Serv Award, Dept of Air Force, 73; Distinguished Serv Medal, NASA, Washington, DC, 75; Secy's Award Outstanding Achievement, Dept of Transp, 77. *Mem:* Nat Acad Eng; Opers Res Soc Am; fel Am Inst Aeronaut & Astronaut; fel Inst Elec & Electronics Engrs; Am Phys Soc. *Res:* Management. *Mailing Add:* 309 N Lee St Alexandria VA 22314

MCMACKEN, ROGER L, JR, b Spokane, Wash, July 24, 43; m 68; c 3. BIOCHEMISTRY, GENETICS. *Educ:* Univ Wash, BS, 65; Univ Wis, Madison, PhD(biochem), 70. *Prof Exp:* Res assoc biochem, Sch Med, Yale Univ, 70-71; fel, Univ Fla, 72-74, Stanford Univ, 74-76; ASST PROF BIOCHEM, JOHNS HOPKINS UNIV, 77- *Mem:* Am Soc Microbiol; Am Soc Biol Chemists. *Res:* Enzymology and genetics of DNA replication of bacterial and bacteriophage chromosomes; regulation of prokaryotic gene expression. *Mailing Add:* Dept Biochem Johns Hopkins Univ 615 N Wolfe St Baltimore MD 21205

MCMAHAN, ELIZABETH ANNE, b Davie Co, NC, May 5, 24. ZOOLOGY. *Educ:* Duke Univ, AB, 46, MA, 48; Univ Hawaii, PhD(entom), 60. *Prof Exp:* Res asst, Parapsychol Lab, Duke Univ, 43-54; Am Asn Univ Women fel, Univ Chicago, 60-61; from asst prof to assoc prof, 61-72, PROF ZOOL, UNIV NC, CHAPEL HILL, 72- *Mem:* AAAS; Animal Behav Soc; Am Inst Biol Sci; Am Soc Zool; Entom Soc Am. *Res:* Termite colony development; termite feeding behavior and temporal polyethism; biology of dragonflies. *Mailing Add:* Dept Zool Univ NC Chapel Hill NC 27514

MACMAHAN, HORACE ARTHUR, JR, b Freeport, Maine, Aug 13, 28; div; c 1. EARTH SCIENCE. *Educ:* Univ Maine, BA, 54; Univ Utah, MSEd, 63; Univ Colo, EdD(sci educ), 67. *Prof Exp:* Staff asst, Earth Sci Curric Proj, Univ Colo, 63-64; assoc prof earth sci, State Univ NY Col Oneonta, 67-68; assoc prof sci educ, Weber State Col, 68-69; PROF GEOG & GEOL, EASTERN MICH UNIV, 69- *Mem:* AAAS; Nat Asn Geol Teachers; Nat Sci Teachers Asn; Am Educ Res Asn. *Res:* Developed composite paleogeographic maps of North America for each geologic time period; determination of the most effective mode of presenting map concepts in geology. *Mailing Add:* Dept of Geog & Geol Eastern Mich Univ Ypsilanti MI 48197

MCMAHAN, UEL JACKSON, II, b Kansas City, Mo, July 22, 38; m 60; c 4. ANATOMY. *Educ:* Westminster Col, BA, 60; Univ Tenn, PhD(anat), 64. *Prof Exp:* Instr anat, Sch Med, Yale Univ, 65-67; instr, 67-72, asst prof, 72-75, assoc prof neurobiol, Harvard Med Sch, 72-77; PROF NEUROBIOL, SCH MED, STANFORD UNIV, 77- *Res:* Structure and function of synapses. *Mailing Add:* Dept of Neurobiol Stanford Univ Sch Med Stanford CA 94305

MCMAHAN, WILLIAM H, b Sylacauga, Ala, Apr 19, 37; m 61. INORGANIC CHEMISTRY. *Educ:* Auburn Univ, BS, 59, MS, 61; Univ Kans, PhD(chem), 65. *Prof Exp:* Assoc prof chem, 65-77, PROF CHEM, MISS STATE UNIV, 77-, COORDR GEN CHEM, 65- *Mem:* Am Chem Soc. *Res:* Solution chemistry of low dielectric nonaqueous solvents; coordination chemistry of hydroxamic acids; chemical education. *Mailing Add:* Dept of Chem Miss State Univ Box CH State College MS 39762

MACMAHON, BRIAN, b Eng, Aug 12, 23; m 48; c 4. EPIDEMIOLOGY. *Educ:* Univ Birmingham, MB, ChB & DPH, 49, PhD, 52, MD, 55; Harvard Univ, SM, 53. *Prof Exp:* Lectr social med, Univ Birmingham, 53-54; from assoc prof to prof environ med & community health, State Univ NY Downstate Med Ctr, 55-58; prof epidemiol, 58-80, HENRY PICKERING WALCOTT PROF EPIDEMIOL, SCH PUB HEALTH, HARVARD UNIV, 80, HEAD DEPT, 58- *Mem:* Am Pub Health Asn; Am Epidemiol Soc. *Res:* Epidemiology of noninfectious diseases. *Mailing Add:* Dept of Epidemiol Harvard Univ Sch of Pub Health Boston MA 02115

MCMAHON, BRIAN ROBERT, b Harrow, Eng, May 27, 36. ANIMAL PHYSIOLOGY. *Educ:* Univ Southampton, BSc, 64; Bristol Univ, PhD(zool), 68. *Prof Exp:* ASSOC PROF BIOL, UNIV CALGARY, 68- *Mem:* Brit Soc Exp Biol; Can Soc Zool; Am Physiol Soc; Sigma Xi; Div Comp Physiol & Biochem. *Res:* physiological compensation to environmental stress; neural control of respiration in invertebrates; evolution of respiratory mechanisms; gas exchange dynamics across gill surfaces; toxicology. *Mailing Add:* Dept Biol 2500 Univ Dr Univ of Calgary Calgary AB T2N 1N4 Can

MCMAHON, CHARLES J, JR, b Philadelphia, Pa, July 10, 33; m 59; c 5. METALLURGY, MATERIALS SCIENCE. *Educ:* Univ Pa, BS, 55; Mass Inst Technol, ScD(metall), 63. *Prof Exp:* Instr phys metall, Mass Inst Thchnol, 59-63; fel, 63-64, asst prof, 64-68, assoc prof, 68-73, PROF METALL ENG, UNIV PA, 73- *Concurrent Pos:* Overseas fel, Churchill Col, Cambridge Univ, 73-74. *Honors & Awards:* Howe Medal, Am Soc Metall, 75; Mathewson Gold Medal, Am Inst Mech Engrs, 75; Sauver Award, Am Soc Metals, 81. *Mem:* Nat Acad Eng; fel Am Soc Metals; Fel Inst of Metallurgists, Eng; AAAS; Am Inst Mining, Metall & Petrol Engrs. *Res:* Deformation and fracture of solids; segregation to interfaces. *Mailing Add:* Dept Mat Sci & Eng K1 Univ of Pa 3231 Walnut St Philadelphia PA 19104

MCMAHON, DANIEL STANTON, b Cleveland, Ohio, Aug 2, 39. BIOCHEMISTRY, THEORETICAL BIOLOGY. *Educ:* Case Western Reserve Univ, AB, 61; Univ Chicago, MS, 62, PhD, 66. *Prof Exp:* NIH fel, 66-67; lectr math biol, Univ Chicago, 67-68; asst prof biol, Calif Inst Technol,

68-77; ASSOC PROF GENETICS & ZOOL, WASH STATE UNIV, 78-, ASSOC BIOCHEM & BACT, 78- *Mem:* AAAS; Am Chem Soc; Am Soc Plant Physiol; Am Soc Biol Chemists; Am Soc Cell Biol. *Res:* Development and differentiation of cellular slime molds; development and function of nervous systems; cell membranes; theoretical biology; development of the chloroplast. *Mailing Add:* Dept of Genetics Wash State Univ Pullman WA 99163

MCMAHON, DAVID HAROLD, b Troy, NY, Apr 27, 42. ANALYTICAL CHEMISTRY. *Educ:* Col of the Holy Cross, BS, 63; Univ NH, PhD(chem), 68. *Prof Exp:* Res chemist, Esso Res & Eng Co, NJ, 67-70; res chemist, 70-74, group leader, 74-78, RES ASSOC, RES & DEVELOP DIV, UNION CAMP CORP, 78- *Mem:* Am Chem Soc. *Res:* Chromatographic analysis of natural products; polynuclear aromatic hydrocarbon pollution analyses; characterization of natural products and polymers. *Mailing Add:* Res & Develop Div Union Camp Corp PO Box 412 Princeton NJ 08540

MCMAHON, DONALD HOWLAND, b Buffalo, NY, Apr 18, 34; m 54. OPTICAL PHYSICS. *Educ:* Univ Buffalo, BA, 57; Cornell Univ, PhD(exp physics), 64. *Prof Exp:* Staff scientist, 63-73, DEPT MGR OPTICS, SPERRY RAND RES CTR, 73- *Mem:* Am Phys Soc; Inst Elec & Electronics Engrs; Optical Soc Am. *Res:* Fiber Optics; optical pattern recognition; modern optics; optical information processing; holography; quantum electronics; nonlinear optics; paramagnetic resonance. *Mailing Add:* Sperry Rand Res Ctr 100 North Rd Sudbury MA 01776

MCMAHON, DOUGLAS CHARLES, b Rockville Center, NY, Nov 13, 47. MATHEMATICS. *Educ:* Case Western Reserve Univ, BS & MS, 70, PhD(math), 72. *Prof Exp:* Vis asst prof math, Univ Cincinnati, 72-74, Univ Ore, 74-75, NMex State Univ, 75-76 & Oakland Univ, 76-77; vis asst prof, 77-78, asst prof, 78-80, ASSOC PROF MATH, ARIZ STATE UNIV, 80- *Mem:* Am Math Soc. *Res:* Topological dynamics. *Mailing Add:* Dept of Math Ariz State Univ Tempe AZ 85287

MCMAHON, E(DWARD) LAWRENCE, b Peoria, Ill, Nov 19, 31; m 54; c 4. ELECTRICAL ENGINEERING. *Educ:* Fournier Inst Technol, BS, 52; Univ Ill, MS, 53, PhD(elec eng), 55. *Prof Exp:* Res engr, Hughes Aircraft Co, 55-56; asst prof elec eng, Mich State Univ, 56-59; assoc prof elec eng, 59-77, fac consult, Radiation Lab, 65-71, consult, electronic defense group, Res Inst, ASSOC PROF ELEC ENG & COMPUT SCI, UNIV MICH, ANN ARBOR, 77- *Mem:* Inst Elec & Electronics Engrs. *Res:* Network theory and synthesis. *Mailing Add:* Dept of Elec Eng Univ of Mich Ann Arbor MI 48109

MCMAHON, FRANCIS GILBERT, b Kalamazoo, Mich Sept 10, 23; m 54; c 4. INTERNAL MEDICINE. *Educ:* Univ Notre Dame, BS, 45; Univ Mich, MS, 51, MD, 53; Am Bd Internal Med, dipl, 59. *Prof Exp:* Intern, Univ Wis Hosps, 56-58; vis physician, Charity Hosp & Med Sch, La State Univ, 58-60, clin asst prof med, 59-60; dir med res, Upjohn Co, Mich, 60-64; vpres-in-charge med res, Ciba Pharmaceut Co, 64-67; exec dir, Merck Sharp & Dohme, 67-68; prof med & head therapeut & dir clin pharmacol, 68-77, CLIN PROF MED, MED SCH, TULANE UNIV, 77- *Honors & Awards:* Univ Notre Dame Sci Award, 64. *Mem:* Int Soc Clin Pharmacol (vpres); Am Soc Clin Pharmacol & Therapeut; fel Am Col Physicians; Endocrine Soc; AMA. *Res:* Hypertension; diabetes; clinical pharmacology; endocrinology; bioavailability of drugs and drug metabolism. *Mailing Add:* Dept of Med Tulane Univ Med Ctr New Orleans LA 70118

MCMAHON, GARFIELD WALTER, b Man, Feb 25, 32. ACOUSTICS. *Educ:* Univ Man, BSc, 52; Univ BC, MSc, 55. *Prof Exp:* Sci officer, 55-70, TRANSDUCER GROUP LEADER, DEFENSE RES ESTAB ATLANTIC, 70- *Mem:* Fel Acoust Soc Am. *Res:* Underwater acoustics; transducer calibration and design; properties of piezo-electric ceramics; vibrations of solid cylinders. *Mailing Add:* Defence Res Estab Atlantic Box 1012 Dartmouth NS B3A 2H6 Can

MACMAHON, HAROLD EDWARD, b Aylmer, Ont, Mar 30, 01; US citizen; m 34; c 4. PATHOLOGY, BACTERIOLOGY. *Educ:* Univ Western Ont, MD, 25; Am Bd Path, dipl & cert path anat. *Hon Degrees:* BA, Univ Western Ont, 22, ScD, 48. *Prof Exp:* Intern, Montreal Gen Hosp, 25-26; asst, Boston City Hosp, 26-29; asst path, Univ Hamburg, 29-30; prof path & chmn dept, 30-71, EMER PROF PATH, SCH MED & SCH DENT MED, TUFTS UNIV, 71- *Concurrent Pos:* Instr, Harvard Med Sch, 28-29; asst, Univ Berlin, 31-32; pathologist-in-chief, Tufts-New Eng Med Ctr Hosps; consult pathologist, Mt Auburn Hosp, New Eng Med Ctr Hosps, Carney Hosp, Lynn Hosp, Leonard Morse Hosp, Malden Hosp & Cape Cod Hosp; consult, Armed Forces Inst Path, Boston Vet Hosp & USPHS Hosp, Boston; vis prof, Med Sch, Univ Mass, 71-; vis prof pathol, Med Sch, Univ Mass, Worcester, 80- *Mem:* Hon fel Royal Coı Physicians; Am Asn Path & Bact; Am Med Asn; Int Acad Path; Ger Path Soc. *Res:* Pathology of the heart, lungs, liver, kidneys and blood vessels. *Mailing Add:* 19 Hubbard Park Cambridge MA 02138

MACMAHON, JAMES A, b Dayton, Ohio, Apr 7, 39; m 63. ECOLOGY, VERTEBRATE ZOOLOGY. *Educ:* Mich State Univ, BS, 60; Univ Notre Dame, PhD(biol), 64. *Prof Exp:* Asst dir biol, Dayton Mus Natural Hist, 63-64; from asst prof to assoc prof, Univ Dayton, 64-71; assoc prof zool, 71-74, PROF BIOL, UTAH STATE UNIV, 74-, ASST DIR US INT BIOL PROG-DESERT BIOME, 71- *Mem:* Soc Study Evolution; Soc Syst Zool; Ecol Soc Am; Am Soc Zoologists; Am Soc Ichthyologists & Herpetologists. *Res:* Theory of community organization; community ecology of deserts; biology of desert perennials; energy exchange in plant and animal populations; biology of reptiles and amphibians; biology of arachnids. *Mailing Add:* Dept of Biol Utah State Univ Logan UT 84321

MCMAHON, JOHN MARTIN, b Buffalo, NY, Dec 24, 15; m 42; c 6. MEDICINE. *Educ:* Georgetown Univ, BS, 36, MD, 40; Univ Minn, MS, 50. *Prof Exp:* Instr psychosom med, Sch Med, Tulane Univ, 50-52; CLIN PROF MED, SCH MED, UNIV ALA, BIRMINGHAM, 52-, DIR ARTHRITIS CLIN, MED CTR, 66-; CHIEF MED & ASSOC DIR MED EDUC, BIRMINGHAM BAPTIST HOSP, 54- *Concurrent Pos:* Attend consult, Vet Admin Hosp, Birmingham. *Honors & Awards:* Benemerenti Medal by Pope Paul VI, 67. *Mem:* AMA; Am Rheumatism Asn; Am Heart Asn; fel Am Col Physicians; Am Col Gastroenterol (past pres). *Res:* Internal medicine; gastroenterology; arthritis. *Mailing Add:* 800 Clinic Lane Bessemer AL 35020

MCMAHON, JOHN MICHAEL, b St Paul, Minn, May 13, 41; m 65; c 2. ATOMIC PHYSICS, QUANTUM ELECTRONICS. *Educ:* Boston Col, BS, 63; Dartmouth Col, MA, 65. *Prof Exp:* Physicist, 65-74, supvry res physicist, Laser Res, 74-81, ASSOC SUPT, OPTICAL SCI DIV, NAVAL RES LAB, 81- *Concurrent Pos:* Consult, Div Laser Fusion, Dept of Energy, 76- & var US Navy commands, 68- *Mem:* Am Phys Soc; Sigma Xi. *Res:* Solid state lasers; non-linear optics; laser produced plasma; laser fusion; optical diagnostics of plasmas; laser applications. *Mailing Add:* Optical Sci Div Code 6501 Naval Res Lab Washington DC 20375

MCMAHON, KENNETH JAMES, b Flandreau, SDak, July 9, 22; m 47; c 2. BACTERIOLOGY. *Educ:* SDak State Univ, BS, 47; Okla State Univ, MS, 49; Kans State Univ, PhD(bact), 54. *Prof Exp:* Asst bact, Okla State Univ, 47-48, instr, 48-49; from instr to prof, Kans State Univ, 49-70, actg head dept, 61-62, 63-64; actg chmn, Dept Vet Sci, 80-81, PROF BACT & CHMN DEPT, NDAK STATE UNIV, 70- *Mem:* Am Soc Microbiol; fel Am Acad Microbiol. *Res:* Bacteriology of animal diseases and insect pathogens; serology of brucellosis. *Mailing Add:* Dept of Bacteriol NDak State Univ Fargo ND 58105

MCMAHON, PAUL E, b Burlington, Vt, July 2, 31; m 54; c 1. PHYSICAL CHEMISTRY. *Educ:* St Michael's Col, Vt, BS, 54; Univ Vt, MS, 56; Univ Ill, PhD(phys chem), 61. *Prof Exp:* Spectroscopist, Ill State Geol Surv, 56-5756-57 & Univ Ill, 57-61; res chemist, Chemstrand Div, Monsanto Co, NC, 61-68; SR RES ASSOC, CELANESEPLASTICS & SPECIALTIES CO, 68. *Res:* Molecular structure and motion in small molecules and polymers; structure-property relations of polymers and composites; characterization and evaluation of fiber reinforced composites. *Mailing Add:* Celanese Plastics & Specialties Co 86 Morris Ave Summit NJ 07901

MCMAHON, RITA MARY, b New York, NY, Mar 5, 22. CYTOLOGY. *Educ:* Fordham Univ, BS, 49, MS, 51, PhD(biol), 53. *Prof Exp:* From instr to assoc prof sci, Sch Educ, Fordham Univ, 54-67, chmn dept, 57-67; assoc prof, 67-77, prof, 77-81, EMER PROF BIOL, WESTERN CONN STATE UNIV, 81- *Concurrent Pos:* Adj prof, Grad Sch, New Eng Inst, 69- *Mem:* AAAS; Bot Soc Am; Am Inst Biol Sci; Environ Mutagen Soc; Genetics Soc Am. *Res:* Plant tissue and cell culture; polyploidy in development. *Mailing Add:* Dept of Biol Western Conn State Univ Danbury CT 06810

MCMAHON, ROBERT FRANCIS, III, b Syracuse, NY, June 17, 44; m 80. INVERTEBRATE PHYSIOLOGICALECOLOGY, AQUATIC BIOLOGY. *Educ:* Cornell Univ Sch Arts & Sci, BA, 66; Syracuse Univ, PhD(zool), 72. *Prof Exp:* From teaching asst biol to res asst, Syracuse Univ, 67-72; asst prof, 72-77, ASSOC PROF BIOL, UNIV TEX, ARLINGTON, 77- *Concurrent Pos:* Fulbright-Hayes res fel, Trinity Col, Dublin, Ireland, 78-79. *Mem:* Marine Biol Lab; Malacol Soc London; Marine Biol Asn UK; Sigma Xi; Am Soc Limnol & Oceanog. *Res:* Physiological ecology of aquatic invertebrate organisms; study of growth and reproduction, bioenergetic and physiological variation in freshwater animals and the physiological basis for intertidal zonation in marine animals. *Mailing Add:* Dept of Biol Univ of Tex Arlington TX 76019

MCMAHON, THOMAS ARTHUR, b Dayton, Ohio, Apr 21, 43; m 65; c 2. BIOMECHANICS, BIOENGINEERING. *Educ:* Cornell Univ, BS, 65; Mass Inst Technol, SM, 67, PhD(fluid mech), 70. *Prof Exp:* Res fel, 69-71, lectr, 70-71, from asst prof to assoc prof, 71-77, PROF BIOMECH, DIV ENG & APPL PHYSICS, HARVARD UNIV, 77- *Mem:* Am Physiol Soc; Biomed Eng Soc. *Res:* The theory of models applied to living systems; non-invasive biomedical instrumentation; mechanics of locomotion; cardiac mechanics; theory of models applied to living systems. *Mailing Add:* Div of Eng & Appl Physics Pierce Hall Harvard Univ Cambridge MA 02138

MCMAHON, THOMAS JOSEPH, b Rahway, NJ, 1943; m 66; c 2. SEMICONDUCTORS, ELECTROOPTICS. *Educ:* Univ Ill, Urbana, BS, 65, MS, 66; Univ Mo-Rolla, PhD(physics), 69. *Prof Exp:* Res physicist, Naval Weapons Ctr, China Lake, 69-80; SR SCIENTIST, SOLAR ENERGY RES INST, GOLDEN, COLO, 80- *Mem:* Am Phys Soc. *Res:* Glow discharge amorphous silicon and vapor phase epitaxial semiconductors are grown for application in the areas of infrared and visible photo detection, photo thermal and photovoltaic solar energy conversion and electrooptic devices. *Mailing Add:* Solar Energy Res Inst 1617 Cole Blvd Golden CO 80401

MCMAHON, VERN AUGUST, plant biochemistry, see previous edition

MCMANAMON, PETER MICHAEL, b Chicago, Ill, June 15, 37; m 68; c 2. ENGINEERING SCIENCE. *Educ:* Ill Inst Technol, BS, 59, MS, 62, PhD(elec eng), 70. *Prof Exp:* Staff engr, IIT Res Inst, 59-66, sect mgr commun, 66-71; group chief, Off Telecommun, 71-77, group chief telecommun, Nat Telecommun & Info Admin, 77-78, ASSOC DIR, INST FOR TELECOMMUN SCI, US DEPT COM, 79- *Honors & Awards:* Gold Medal Award, US Dept Com, 78. *Mem:* Inst Elec & Electronics Engrs. *Res:* Statistical communication theory; information theory; telecommunications. *Mailing Add:* Inst for Telecommun Sci 325 Broadway Boulder CO 80303

MCMANIGAL, PAUL GABRIEL MOULIN, b Los Angeles, Calif, Apr 15, 36; m 59; c 2. PHYSICS, ENGINEERING. *Educ:* Pomona Col, BA, 58; Univ Calif, Berkeley, PhD(physics), 63. *Prof Exp:* Mgr, Missile Systs Eng, Aeronutronic Div, Philco Ford Corp, 63-71; dir advan sensors, Defense Advan Res Proj Agency, Dept of Defense, 71-73; dir develop planning, Aeronutronic Div, 73-81, VPRES TECH AFFAIRS, FORD AEROSPACE & COMMUN CORP, 81- *Res:* Applied research in optics, photography and atmospheric physics; development in tactical missiles; advanced sensors; elementary particles. *Mailing Add:* 16 Inverness Lane Newport Beach CA 92660

MCMANUS, DEAN ALVIS, b Dallas, Tex, July 8, 34; m 72. GEOLOGY, OCEANOGRAPHY. *Educ:* Southern Methodist Univ, BS, 54; Univ Kans, MS, 56, PhD(geol), 59. *Prof Exp:* From res assoc to res asst prof, 59-65, from asst prof to assoc prof, 65-71, PROF OCEANOG, UNIV WASH, 71-, ADJ PROF MARINE STUDIES, 73-, ADJ PROF, QUATERNARY RES CTR, 76- *Concurrent Pos:* Mem, Joint Oceanog Inst for Deep Earth Sampling & Pac Ocean Adv Panel, 65-71, asst chmn planning comt, 76-78. *Honors & Awards:* McManus Seamount. *Mem:* AAAS; Am Asn Petrol Geologists; Soc Econ Paleontologists & Mineralogists; Geol Soc Am; Am Geophys Union. *Res:* continental shelf topography and sediments; Arctic shelf sedimentation; holocene stratigraphy on continental shelf of Chukchi and Bering Sea; shelf sediments in archaeology. *Mailing Add:* Sch Oceanog Univ of Wash Seattle WA 98195

MCMANUS, EDWARD CLAYTON, b McIntosh, Minn, Aug 19, 18; m 66. PARASITOLOGY, PHARMACOLOGY. *Educ:* Univ Minn, BS, 40, PhD(pharmacol), 50; Iowa State Univ, DVM, 44. *Prof Exp:* Asst pharmacol, Univ Minn, 44-48; res assoc, Sharp & Dohme, Inc, 48-53, res assoc, Merck Sharp & Dohme Res Labs, 53-55, pathologist, 55-58, RES ASSOC & RES FEL BASIC ANIMAL SCI RES, MERCK SHARP & DOHME RES LABS, 58- *Mem:* Am Vet Med Asn; Am Soc Pharmacol & Exp Therapeut; Am Soc Vet Physiol & Pharmacol; Am Asn Vet Parasitol; World's Poultry Sci Asn. *Res:* Gastrointestinal pharmacology; pathology; toxicology; parasitologic chemotherapy. *Mailing Add:* Merck Inst Rahway NJ 07065

MCMANUS, ELIZABETH CATHERINE, b Albany, NY, Sept 10, 12. PHYSICS, MATHEMATICS. *Educ:* Col St Rose, BA, 32; Catholic Univ, MS, 43. *Prof Exp:* High sch teacher parochial schs, NY, 35-43; from asst prof to assoc prof, 43-70, chmn dept, 43-68, prof physics & comput sci, 71-78, PROF COMPUT SCI & METEOROL, COL ST ROSE, 78- *Concurrent Pos:* Mem conf vibrations & waves, Reed Col, 66, Pa State Univ, 69, comput undergrad physics educ, Ill Inst Technol, 71. *Mem:* Am Asn Physics Teachers; Am Meteorol Soc. *Res:* Teacher training in meteorology. *Mailing Add:* Dept of Phys Sci Col of St Rose 432 Western Ave Albany NY 12203

MCMANUS, HUGH, b West Bromwich, Eng, May 10, 18; m 53; c 3. THEORETICAL PHYSICS. *Educ:* Univ Birmingham, BSc, 39, PhD(math, physics), 47. *Prof Exp:* Res officer ionosphere & commun, Brit Admiralty, London, 40-42, res officer opers res, 42-43, res officer tech intel, 43-44; res fel theoret physics, Univ Birmingham, 47-49, lectr, 49-51; assoc res officer, Theoret Physics Div, Atomic Energy Can, Ltd, 51-60; PROF PHYSICS & ASTRON, MICH STATE UNIV, 60- *Concurrent Pos:* Res assoc, Mass Inst Technol, 57-58, 70 & 79; Guggenheim fel, Nordic Inst Theoret Atomic Physics, 63-64; Sci Res Coun fel, Oxford Univ, 69-70; staff mem, Ctr Nuclear Studies, Saclay, France, 77; consult, Trionf, BC, 80. *Mem:* Fel Am Phys Soc. *Res:* Nuclear theory; scattering of elementary particles. *Mailing Add:* Dept of Physics Mich State Univ East Lansing MI 48823

MCMANUS, IVY ROSABELLE, b Erie, Pa, Oct 29, 23. BIOCHEMISTRY. *Educ:* Villa Maria Col, BS, 45; Western Reserve Univ, MS, 47, PhD(biochem), 51. *Prof Exp:* USPHS res fel, Univ Chicago, 51-52; instr biochem, Yale Univ, 52-54, asst prof, 54-57; from asst res prof to assoc res prof, Grad Sch Pub Health, 57-65, assoc prof, 65-73, PROF FAC ARTS & SCI, UNIV PITTSBURGH, 73- *Mem:* Am Chem Soc; Am Soc Biol Chem; Brit Biochem Soc. *Res:* Amino acid and protein metabolism; developmental biochemistry of skeletal muscle. *Mailing Add:* Biol Sci Dept Fac Arts & Sci Univ of Pittsburgh Pittsburgh PA 15260

MCMANUS, JAMES MICHAEL, b Brooklyn, NY, May 22, 30; m 55; c 3. ORGANIC CHEMISTRY. *Educ:* Col Holy Cross, BS, 52; Niagara Univ, MS, 54; Mich State Univ, PhD(chem), 58. *Prof Exp:* Res chemist, 58-69, PATENT CHEMIST, PFIZER, INC, 69- *Concurrent Pos:* US patent agent, 77- *Mem:* Am Chem Soc. *Res:* Chemistry of tetrazoles, indoles and benzimidazoles; preparation and pharmacology of diuretics and sulfonylureas. *Mailing Add:* Pfizer Inc 235 E 42nd St New York NY 10017

MACMANUS, JOHN PATRICK, b Dublin, Ireland, July 15, 43; Can citizen. BIOCHEMISTRY. *Educ:* Nat Univ Ireland, BSc, 65; Univ Lancaster, Eng, PhD(biochem), 68. *Prof Exp:* Fel biochem, 68-69, RES OFFICER BIOCHEM, NAT RES COUN CAN, 69- *Mem:* Biochem Soc; NY Acad Sci. *Res:* Mechanism of control of the initiation of DNA synthesis, and the role of calmadulin, cyclic-nucleotides and ions therein. *Mailing Add:* Div of Biol Sci Nat Res Coun of Can Ottawa ON K1A 0R6 Can

MCMANUS, LAWRENCE ROBERT, b North Bergen, NJ, Mar 21, 21; m 53; c 2. ECOLOGY. *Educ:* Cornell Univ, BS, 49, MEd, 51, PhD(animal ecol), 60. *Prof Exp:* Instr biol, Orange County Community Col, 54-57; asst zool, Cornell Univ, 57-60; from asst prof to assoc prof, 60-73, PROF BIOL, HAMILTON COL, 73- *Mem:* AAAS; Ecol Soc Am; Am Micros Soc; Am Inst Biol Sci. *Res:* Ecology of crayfish, branchiobdellid annelids and entocytherid ostracods. *Mailing Add:* Dept of Biol Hamilton Col Clinton NY 13323

MCMANUS, MYRA JEAN, b St Micheldes Saints, Que, Sept 7, 25; m 54; c 3. ENDOCRINOLOGY, HISTOLOGY. *Educ:* McGill Univ, MS, 48; Univ Western Ont, PhD(endocrinol), 52. *Prof Exp:* Res officer, Atomic Energy Can, Ltd, 52-56; res asst, Zool Dept, 70-75, RES ASSOC, ANAT DEPT, MICH STATE UNIV, 75- *Mem:* Am Asn Cancer Res; AAAS. *Res:* Distribution and function of zinc in the male reproductive system (rats) and the effects of zinc deficiency (dietary) on this system; hormones, steroid and polypeptide involved in development, differentitation and carcinogenesis of human breast epithelium, using organ culture and xenografts to athymic nude mice. *Mailing Add:* 526 Kedzie Dr East Lansing MI 48823

MCMANUS, SAMUEL PLYLER, b Edgemoor, SC, Oct 29, 38; m 59; c 2. ORGANIC CHEMISTRY. *Educ:* The Citadel, BS, 60; Clemson Univ, MS, 62, PhD(chem), 64. *Prof Exp:* Res chemist, Marshall Lab, E I du Pont de Nemours & Co, 64; from asst prof to assoc prof, 66-73, chmn dept, 70-72 & 77-78, PROF CHEM, UNIV ALA, HUNTSVILLE, 73- *Concurrent Pos:* Consult, US Army Res Off, Durham, 68-73; indust consult; vis prof, Univ SC, 74-75; fel Am Soc Environ Educ, NASA, 81. *Honors & Awards:* Army Commendation Medal; Nat Defense Serv Medal. *Mem:* AAAS; Am Chem Soc; fel Am Inst Chem; Sigma Xi (secy, 67-69, pres, 70-71). *Res:* Acid catalyzed rearrangements; structure of heteronuclear substituted carbonium ions; neighboring group participation; polymer chemistry. *Mailing Add:* Dept of Chem Univ of Ala Huntsville AL 35807

MCMANUS, THOMAS (JOSEPH), b Omaha, Nebr, Feb 5, 25; m 51; c 5. CELL PHYSIOLOGY, HEMATOLOGY. *Educ:* Antioch Col, BS, 51; Boston Univ, MD, 55. *Prof Exp:* Asst hemat, Sloan-Kettering Inst, NY, 49-51; res fel med, Harvard Med Sch, 55-58, asst med, 58-59, res assoc, 59-61; asst prof, 61-67, dir grad studies, 72-75, ASSOC PROF PHYSIOL & PHARMACOL, SCH MED, DUKE UNIV, 67-, DIR, LAB MEMBRANE PHYSIOL, 68- *Concurrent Pos:* Asst physician, Peter Bent Brigham Hosp, Boston, Mass, 55-58; vis prof, NC Col, 63; mem sci staff, Res Vessel Alpha Helix Amazon Exped, Brazil, 67; vis prof, Univ Melbourne, 81. *Mem:* Fel AAAS; Am Physiol Soc; Biophys Soc; Soc Gen Physiol. *Res:* Membrane transport and metabolism. *Mailing Add:* Dept Physiol Pharmacol Duke Univ Med Ctr Box 3709 Durham NC 27710

MCMASTER, MARVIN CLAYTON, JR, b Gering, Nebr, June 27, 38; m 62; c 1. BIOCHEMISTRY. *Educ:* SDak Sch Mines & Technol, BS, 60; Univ Nebr, PhD(org chem), 66. *Prof Exp:* Fel polypeptides, Inst Molecular Biophys, Fla State Univ, 70-71; Nat Heart & Lung Inst spec fel biochem, Webb-Waring Lung Inat, Univ Colo Med Ctr, Denver, 71-73; scholar biochem lipid storage dis, Ment Health Res Inst, Univ Mich, Ann Arbor, 73-75; sr develop chemist pesticide prod, Ciba-Geigy Corp, 75-78; TECH SPECIALIST, WATERS ASSOCS, ST LOUIS OFF, 78- *Concurrent Pos:* Res chemist, Indust & Biochem Dept, E I du Pont de Nemours & Co, Inc, 65-68; sr scientist I, Indust Chem Div, Kraftco Corp, 68-70. *Mem:* Am Chem Soc. *Res:* Small ring heterocyclic compounds; polypeptide synthesis; biochemistry of lung metabolism; high pressure liquid chromatography; pesticides. *Mailing Add:* Waters Assocs 2070 Cordoba Dr Florissant MO 48104

MCMASTER, PAUL D, b Norwich, Conn, Feb 24, 32; m 63; c 3. BIOCHEMISTRY, ORGANIC CHEMISTRY. *Educ:* Col Holy Cross, BS, 54; Clark Univ, PhD(chem), 61. *Prof Exp:* From asst prof to assoc prof, 61-80, chmn dept, 72-79, PROF CHEM, COL HOLY CROSS, 80- *Concurrent Pos:* Consult drug design, Astra Pharmaceut Prod, Inc, Worcester, Mass, 73-80. *Mem:* Am Chem Soc. *Res:* Conformational analysis; drug design. *Mailing Add:* Dept of Chem Col of the Holy Cross Worcester MA 01610

MCMASTER, PHILIP ROBERT BACHE, immunology, experimental pathology, see previous edition

MCMASTER, ROBERT CHARLES, b Wilkinsburg, Pa, May 13, 13; m 37; c 3. ELECTRICAL ENGINEERING. *Educ:* Carnegie Inst Technol, BS, 36; Calif Inst Technol, MS, 38, PhD(elec eng), 44. *Prof Exp:* Student engr, Gen Elec Co, 36-37; asst elec eng, Calif Inst Technol, 37-38; instr, Case Inst Technol, 38-40 & Calif Inst Technol, 42-45; res engr, Battelle Mem Inst, 45, asst res supvr, 45-48, res supvr, Elec Eng Div, 48-52, asst coord dir, 52-55; prof welding eng, 55-67, res supvr, Eng Exp Sta, 55-67, Regents prof elec & welding eng, 67-77, EMER PROF, DEPT ELEC ENG & WELDING ENG, OHIO STATE UNIV, 77- *Concurrent Pos:* Res engr, Naval Ord Lab, 41; res supvr, Calif Inst Technol, 42-45; mem panel aerospace mfg techniques, Mat Adv Bd, Nat Acad Sci, 58-60; supvr, Ultrasonic Power Res Labs & Nondestructive Test Res Labs; indust consult; ed, handbk, Am Soc Nondestructive Testing, 59 & 77-81. *Mem:* Nat Acad Eng; Am Soc Metals; Am Welding Soc; Am Soc Nondestructive Testing (treas, 50, vpres, 51, pres, 52); Inst Elec & Electronics Engrs. *Res:* Welding processes and control systems; sonic and ultrasonic power systems for highway engineering; television x-ray image systems; ultrasonic and magnetic reaction analyzer nondestructive tests; high energy density welding processes; analysis of analogous engineering systems. *Mailing Add:* 6435 Dublin Rd Delaware OH 43015

MCMASTER, ROBERT H, b Flint, Mich, Feb 26, 16; m 39; c 2. MEDICINE. *Educ:* Ohio Univ, AB, 38; Univ Cincinnati, MD, 50. *Prof Exp:* Physician, Gallipolis Clin, Ohio, 51-56; physician, Chas Pfizer & Co, 56; assoc dir med res, Wm S Merrell Co, 56-67, dir sci training, 67-74, DIR, EMPLOYEE HEALTH SERV, MERRELL DOW PHARMACEUT, INC, 74- *Concurrent Pos:* Asst, Col Med, Univ Cincinnati, 57-66, instr, 66-70, asst clin prof med, 70-77, assoc prof, 77-; clinician, Cincinnati Gen Hosp, 64- *Mem:* Am Soc Clin Pharm & Therapeut; AMA; Am Heart Asn; fel Royal Soc Health. *Res:* Employee health and safety; training of nonprofessionals in medical subjects. *Mailing Add:* Merrell-Dow Pharmaceut Inc 2110 E Galbraith Rd Cincinnati OH 45215

MCMASTER, WILLIAM H, b Ft Lewis, Wash, Apr 16, 26; m 51; c 1. HYDRODYNAMICS, FLUID STRUCTURE INTERACTIONS. *Educ:* US Mil Acad, BS, 46; Univ Va, MS, 52, PhD(physics), 54. *Prof Exp:* Sr physicist, 55-62, group leader, 62-74, STAFF PHYSICIST, LAWRENCE LIVERMORE NAT LAB, UNIV CALIF, 74- *Mem:* Am Phys Soc; NY Acad Sci. *Res:* Polarization of radiation; nuclear test diagnostics; computational methods; x-ray physics; equation of state-solids; calculational methods in hydrodynamics. *Mailing Add:* Lawrence Livermore Nat Lab PO Box 808 Livermore CA 94550

MCMASTERS, ALAN WAYNE, b Ottawa, Kans, Dec 19, 34; m 57; c 4. OPERATIONS RESEARCH. *Educ:* Univ Calif, Berkeley, BS, 57, MS, 62, PhD(indust eng, opers res), 66. *Prof Exp:* Res engr, Pac Southwest Forest & Range Exp Sta, US Forest Serv, 55-61, opers analyst, 61-65; ASSOC PROF OPERS RES, NAVAL POSTGRAD SCH, 65- *Concurrent Pos:* Consult, Mellonics Systs Div, Litton Indust, 69-70. *Mem:* Opers Res Soc Am. *Res:* Flows in networks; locational problems on networks; inventory models; forest fire spread modeling. *Mailing Add:* Dept of Oper Res & Admin Sci Naval Postgrad Sch Monterey CA 93940

MCMASTERS, DENNIS WAYNE, b Chickasha, Okla, July 9, 40; m 68; c 1. PLANT PHYSIOLOGY. *Educ:* Okla Christian Col, BSE, 62; Univ Okla, MNS, 68; Univ Ark, PhD(bot), 73. *Prof Exp:* Teacher biol & chem, McAlester Pub Schs, 62-68; teacher, Tulsa Pub Schs, 68-69; instr bot, 72-80, ASSOC PROF BIOL, HENDERSON STATE UNIV, 80- *Mem:* Scand Soc Plant Physiologists. *Res:* Gibberellins; algal physiology. *Mailing Add:* Box H-1052 Henderson State Univ Arkadelphia AR 71923

MCMASTERS, DONALD L, b Crawfordsville, Ind, July 14, 31. ANALYTICAL CHEMISTRY. *Educ:* Wabash Col, AB, 53; Univ NDak, MS, 55; Ind Univ, PhD(anal chem), 59. *Prof Exp:* Asst prof chem, Beloit Col, 59-63; lectr, Univ Ill, 63-64; lectr chem, 64-75, CHEMIST & SAFETY CONSULT, DEPT ENVIRON HEALTH & SAFETY, IND UNIV, BLOOMINGTON, 75- *Mem:* Am Chem Soc; Sigma Xi. *Res:* Polarography in aqueous and non-aqueous solvents. *Mailing Add:* Dept Environ Health & Safety Ind Univ Bloomington IN 47405

MCMEEKIN, DOROTHY, b Boston, Mass, Feb 24, 32. PLANT PATHOLOGY. *Educ:* Wilson Col, AB, 53; Wellesley Col, MA, 55; Cornell Univ, PhD(plant path), 59. *Prof Exp:* Prof natural sci, Upsala Col, 59-64 & Bowling Green State Univ, 64-66; PROF NATURAL SCI, MICH STATE UNIV, 66- *Mem:* Am Phytopath Soc; Bot Soc Am; Mycol Soc Am. *Res:* Physiology of plant disease. *Mailing Add:* Dept of Natural Sci Kedzie Lab Mich State Univ East Lansing MI 48824

MCMENAMIN, JOHN WILLIAM, b Tacoma, Wash, Apr 1, 17; m 42; c 2. DEVELOPMENTAL BIOLOGY. *Educ:* Occidental Col, AB, 40; Univ Calif, Los Angeles, MA, 46, PhD(zool), 49. *Prof Exp:* High sch & jr col teacher, Calif, 42-45; spec appt, 46-47, from instr to assoc prof, 47-57, PROF BIOL, OCCIDENTAL COL, 57- *Mem:* AAAS; Am Soc Zoologists; Am Micros Soc. *Res:* Role of the thyroid gland in the development of the chick embryo; lipid and porphyrin metabolism in the chick embryo as influenced by hormones; histology and reproduction of fishes. *Mailing Add:* Dept of Biol Occidental Col 1600 Campus Rd Los Angeles CA 90041

MCMENAMY, RAPIER HAYDEN, b O'Fallon, Mo, Jan 12, 17; m 43; c 1. BIOCHEMISTRY, PHYSICAL CHEMISTRY. *Educ:* Univ Southern Calif, AB, 47, MS, 48; Harvard Univ, PhD, 58. *Prof Exp:* Res chemist, Turco Prod, Inc, 47-50; biol chemist, Protein Found, 53-58; res assoc, Harvard Univ, 58-60; from asst prof to assoc prof, 60-69, PROF BIOCHEM, STATE UNIV NY BUFFALO, 69- *Mem:* Am Soc Biol Chem; Am Chem Soc; Biophys Soc. *Res:* Properties of protein and protein solutions; protein-small molecule interactions; distribution and transport into cells; metabolism and amino acid utilization in critical illness. *Mailing Add:* Dept of Biochem State Univ NY Buffalo NY 14214

MCMICHAEL, FRANCIS CLAY, b Philadelphia, Pa, Aug 8, 37; m 69; c 2. HYDRAULIC & ENVIRONMENTAL ENGINEERING. *Educ:* Lehigh Univ, BS, 58; Calif Inst Technol, MS, 59, PhD(civil eng), 63. *Prof Exp:* Res fel civil eng, Calif Inst Technol, 63-65; asst prof, Princeton Univ, 65-67; Am Iron & Steel Inst fel, 67-69, sr fel, 69-73, PROF CIVIL ENG, ENGR & PUB POLICY & HEAD DEPT CIVIL ENG, MELLON INST, CARNEGIE-MELLON UNIV, 67- *Mem:* Am Soc Civil Engrs; Am Geophys Union; Water Pollution Control Fedn; Int Asn Hydraul Res; Am Inst Chem Engrs. *Res:* Sedimentation; filtration; applied statistics; aerosol science. *Mailing Add:* Dept of Eng & Pub Policy Carnegie-Mellon Univ Pittsburgh PA 15213

MCMICHAEL, JOHN CALHOUN, b Imperial, Pa, Feb 12, 41. BIOPHYSICS. *Educ:* Univ Pittsburgh, BS, 62, PhD(biophys), 73. *Prof Exp:* Res assoc, Dept Biophys & Microbiol, Univ Pittsburgh, 74-77; asst prof, 77-81, ASSOC PROF BIOL, EDINBORO STATE COL, 81- *Mem:* Sigma Xi; Am Soc Microbiol. *Res:* Studies of bacterial pili as virulence factors for pathogenic bacteria. *Mailing Add:* Dept of Biol Edinboro State Col Edinboro PA 16444

MCMICHAEL, KIRK DUGALD, b Schenectady, NY, July 13, 35; m 58; c 2. ORGANIC CHEMISTRY. *Educ:* Shimer Col, AB, 53; Univ Chicago, MS, 56, PhD(chem), 60. *Prof Exp:* Res assoc chem, Univ Wis, 60-62; asst prof, 62-68, asst to chmn dept, 68-71, ASSOC PROF CHEM, WASH STATE UNIV, 68- *Concurrent Pos:* Petrol Res Fund grant, 64-66. *Mem:* AAAS; Am Chem Soc; Sigma Xi. *Res:* Characterization of allylic rearrangement pathways using deuterium isotope effects; long range allylic rearrangements in steroidal systems; thermodynamic isotope effects and their relationship to theory. *Mailing Add:* Dept of Chem Wash State Univ Pullman WA 99164

MCMICKING, JAMES H(ARVEY), b Detroit, Mich, Aug 5, 29; m 55; c 4. CHEMICAL ENGINEERING. *Educ:* Wayne State Univ, BS, 53, MS, 55; Ohio State Univ, PhD, 61. *Prof Exp:* ASSOC PROF CHEM ENG, WAYNE STATE UNIV, 58-, ASSOC CHMN, DEPT CHEM & METALL ENG, 69- *Mem:* Am Inst Chem Engrs. *Res:* Thermodynamic properties; process dynamics. *Mailing Add:* Dept of Chem Eng & Metall Eng Wayne State Univ Detroit MI 48202

MCMICKLE, ROBERT HAWLEY, b Paterson, NJ, July 30, 24; m 49; c 5. PHYSICS. *Educ:* Oberlin Col, BA, 47; Univ Ill, MS, 48; Pa State Univ, PhD(physics), 52. *Prof Exp:* Physicist, Res Ctr, B F Goodrich Co, 52-59; assoc prof, Robert Col, Istanbul, 59-63, prof & head dept, 63-71; prof & head dept physics, Bogazici Univ, Turkey, 71-76, vis prof, 76-79; prof physics, Schreiner Col, Kerrville, Tex, 79-80; prof physics, Luther Col, Decorah, Iowa, 80-81; SR LECTR, CTR NUCLEAR STUDIES, MEMPHIS STATE UNIV, 81- *Mem:* Am Phys Soc; Am Asn Physics Teachers. Res; High pressure and polymer physics; solid state phenomena. *Mailing Add:* Ctr Nuclear Studies Memphis State Univ Memphis TN 38152

MCMILLAN, ALAN F, b Ont, Can, Feb 11, 25; m 59; c 2. PHYSICAL CHEMISTRY, CHEMICAL ENGINEERING. *Educ:* Queen's Univ, Ont, BSc, 48, MSc, 49; Mass Inst Technol, PhD(phys chem), 53. *Prof Exp:* Res chemist, Naval Res Estab, NS, 53-64; assoc prof chem eng, 64-76, PROF CHEM ENG, TECH UNIV NS, 76, HEAD DEPT, 79- *Mem:* Chem Inst Can; Can Soc Chem Eng. *Res:* Liquid-vapor equilibrium; corrosion; modelling of dispersion of pollutants in estuaries. *Mailing Add:* Dept Chem Eng Tech Univ NS Halifax NS B3S 2X4 Can

MCMILLAN, BROCKWAY, b Minneapolis, Minn, Mar 30, 15; m 42; c 3. RANDOM PROCESSES. *Educ:* Mass Inst Technol, BS, 36, PhD(math), 39. *Prof Exp:* H B Fine instr math, Princeton Univ, 40-41, res assoc fire control, 41-43; res mathematician, Bell Labs, 46-55, exec officer, 55-61; asst secy res & develop, Dept Air Force, 61-63, under secy, 63-65; exec dir mil res, Bell Labs, 65-69, vpres mil syst, 69-80; RETIRED. *Concurrent Pos:* Mem staff, Pres Sci Adv Off, 58-59; chmn, Conf Bd Math Sci, 81-82. *Mem:* Nat Acad Eng; Inst Math Statist; Math Asn Am; Soc Indust & Appl Math (pres, 60-61); fel Inst Elec & Electronics Engrs. *Res:* Applications of random processes to communications and to statistical mechanics; physical realizability of electrical networks. *Mailing Add:* PO Box 27 Sedgwick ME 04676

MACMILLAN, BRUCE GREGG, b Cincinnati, Ohio, Apr 19, 20; m 45; c 2. SURGERY. *Educ:* Col Wooster, BA, 42; Univ Cincinnati, MD, 45; Am Bd Surg, dipl, 54. *Prof Exp:* From instr to assoc prof, 52-64, SHRINE PROF SURG, COL MED, UNIV CINCINNATI, 64-; CHIEF STAFF, SHRINERS BURNS INST, 67- *Concurrent Pos:* Mem active staff, C R Holmes & Children's Hosps, 52-; attend surgeon, clinician & dir dept surg photog, Cincinnati Gen Hosp, 52-; consult surg res unit, Brooke Army Med Ctr, Ft Sam Houston, Tex. *Mem:* AMA; Am Col Surgeons; Am Asn Surg of Trauma; Int Soc Burn Injuries; Am Surg Asn. *Res:* Thermal trauma; surgical infections; audio-visual education. *Mailing Add:* 202 Goodman St Cincinnati OH 45219

MCMILLAN, CALVIN, b Murray, Utah, Feb 20, 22; m 50; c 4. PLANT ECOLOGY. *Educ:* Univ Utah, BS, 47, MS, 48; Univ Calif, Berkeley, PhD(bot), 52. *Prof Exp:* From asst prof to assoc prof bot, Univ Nebr, 52-58; assoc prof, 58-65, PROF BOT, UNIV TEX, AUSTIN, 65- *Concurrent Pos:* Vis assoc prof & actg dir, Bot Garden, Univ Calif, Berkeley, 64-65. *Mem:* AAAS; Bot Soc Am; Ecol Soc Am. *Res:* Ecotypes and ecosystem functions; ecology of colonizing species. *Mailing Add:* Plant Ecol Res Lab Univ of Tex Austin TX 78712

MCMILLAN, CAMPBELL WHITE, b Soochow, China, Jan 10, 27; US citizen; m 55; c 6. PEDIATRICS, HEMATOLOGY. *Educ:* Wake Forest Col, BS, 48, Bowman-Gray Sch Med, MD, 52. *Prof Exp:* Intern, Boston City Hosp, 52-53; asst resident pediat, Children's Hosp Med Ctr, 53-55; pediat registr, St Mary's Hosp Med Sch, London, Eng, 55-56; asst med, Nemazee Hosp, Shiraz, Iran, 56-58; fel pediat hemat, Harvard Med Sch, 58-61; from asst prof to assoc prof, 63-72, assoc dir clin res unit, 66-79, PROF PEDIAT, MED SCH, UNIV NC, CHAPEL HILL, 72- *Mem:* Soc Pediat Res; Am Pediat Soc. *Res:* Coagulation. *Mailing Add:* Dept of Pediat Univ of NC Sch of Med Chapel Hill NC 27514

MCMILLAN, DANIEL RUSSELL, JR, b Atlanta, Ga, Feb 26; 35; m 65; c 1. TOPOLOGY. *Educ:* Emory Univ, BA, 56; Univ Wis, MA, 57, PhD(math), 60. *Prof Exp:* Res instr math, La State Univ, 60-61; asst prof, Fla State Univ, 61-62; vis mem, Inst Advan Study, 62-64; actg assoc prof, Univ Va, 64-65, assoc prof, 65-66; assoc prof, 66-69, PROF MATH, UNIV WIS-MADISON, 69- *Concurrent Pos:* Nat Sci Found fel, 62-63; Inst Adv Study fel, 63-64, 69-70; Sloan fel, 65-67. *Mem:* Math Asn Am; Am Math Asn. *Res:* Topology of combinatorial manifolds; local homotopy properties of topological embeddings; cellular sets in combinatorial manifolds; geometric topology of mappings, three-manifolds. *Mailing Add:* Dept of Math Univ of Wis Madison WI 53706

MCMILLAN, DONALD BURLEY, b Toronto, Ont, Apr 25, 29. ZOOLOGY, COMPARATIVE HISTOLOGY. *Educ:* Univ Western Ont, BSc, 51, MSc, 53; Univ Toronto, PhD(zool), 58. *Prof Exp:* Demonstr zool, Univ Toronto, 53-56; instr, 56-59, lectr, 59-60, from asst prof to assoc prof, 60-78, PROF ZOOL, UNIV WESTERN ONT, 78- *Mem:* Am Soc Zoologists; Can Asn Anat; Can Soc Zool; Can Soc Cell Biol; Am Soc Anat. *Res:* Haemopoietic organs of vertebrates; comparative histology of the vertebrate kidney and gonad; ultrastructure. *Mailing Add:* Dept of Zool Univ of Western Ont London ON N6A 5B7 Can

MCMILLAN, DONALD EDGAR, b Butler, Pa, Sept 23, 37; m 61; c 2. PHARMACOLOGY, TOXICOLOGY. *Educ:* Grove City Col, BS, 59; Univ Pittsburgh, MS, 62, PhD(psychol), 65. *Prof Exp:* From instr to asst prof pharmacol, State Univ NY Downstate Med Ctr, 67-69; from asst prof to prof pharmacol, Univ NC, Chapel Hill, 69-78, asst prof psychol, 70-72, from clin assoc prof to clin prof psychol, 72-78; PROF PHARMACOL & CHMN DEPT, UNIV ARK FOR MED SCI CAMPUS, LITTLE ROCK, 78- *Concurrent Pos:* NIH training grant, Harvard Med Sch, 65-66; mem, NSF Neurobiol Rev Bd & Vet Admin Rev Bd; mem, Nat Res Coun Comt. *Mem:* AAAS; NY Acad Sci; Int Narcotics Res Club; Behav Pharmacol Soc; Am Soc Pharmacol & Exp Therapeut. *Res:* Behavioral pharmacology; mechanisms of drug tolerance and drug dependence; operant conditioning. *Mailing Add:* Dept of Pharmacol 4301 W Markham Little Rock AR 72201

MACMILLAN, DOUGLAS CLARK, b Dedham, Mass, July 15, 12; m 39; c 2. NAVAL ARCHITECTURE. *Educ:* Mass Inst Technol, BS, 34. *Prof Exp:* Engr, Fed Shipbuilding & Dry Dock Co, Kearny, NJ, 34-41; from chief marine engr to tech mgr, George G Sharp, 41-51, pres, 51-69, chmn bd, 69-70; CONSULT NAVAL ARCHIT, 70- *Concurrent Pos:* Mem bd dirs, Atomic Indust Forum, 65-67; asst to gen mgr & consult, Quincy Shipbuilding Div, Gen Dynamics Corp, 72-77; mem comts, Nat Acad Sci-Nat Res Coun. *Honors & Awards:* Elmer A Sperry Medal, Am Soc Mech Engrs & David W Taylor Gold Medal, Soc Naval Architects & Marine Engrs, 69. *Mem:* Nat Acad Eng; fel Soc Naval Architects & Marine Engrs (hon vpres, vpres, 57-72); Am Soc Naval Engrs. *Mailing Add:* Box 834 Colony Dr East Orleans MA 02643

MCMILLAN, EDWIN MATTISON, b Redondo Beach, Calif, Sept 18, 07; m 41; c 3. PHYSICS. *Educ:* Calif Inst Technol, BS, 28, MS, 29; Princeton Univ, PhD(physics), 32. *Hon Degrees:* DSc, Rensselaer Polytech Inst, 61 & Gustavus Adolphus Col, 63. *Prof Exp:* Nat Res Coun fel, Berkeley, 32-34, res assoc, 34-35, from instr to prof physics, 35-73, mem staff, Lawrence Radiation Lab, 34-54, assoc dir, 54-58, dir, 58-71, dir, Lawrence Berkeley Lab, 71-73, EMER PROF PHYSICS, UNIV CALIF, 73- *Concurrent Pos:* Researcher, Radiation Lab, Mass Inst Technol, 40-41, Radio & Sound Lab, US Navy, 41-42 & Los Alamos Sci Lab, 42-45; mem gen adv comt, USAEC, 54-58; trustee, Rand Corp, 59-69; mem comn high energy physics, Int Union Pure & Appl Physics, 60-66; sci policy comt mem, Stanford Linear Accelerator Ctr, 62-66; physics adv comt, Nat Accelerator Lab, 67-69; chmn class I, Nat Acad Sci, 68-71; trustee, Univs Res Asn, Washington, DC, 69-74. *Honors & Awards:* Co-recipient, Nobel Prize in Chem, 51; Sci Award, Res Corp, 51; Atoms for Peace Award, 63. *Mem:* Nat Acad Sci; fel Am Phys Soc; fel Am Acad Arts & Sci; Am Philos Soc. *Res:* Nuclear physics; design and construction of particle accelerators. *Mailing Add:* Lawrence Berkeley Lab Univ of Calif Berkeley CA 94720

MCMILLAN, GARNETT RAMSAY, b Madison, SC, June 11, 32; m 58. PHOTOCHEMISTRY. *Educ:* Univ Ga, BS, 53; Univ Rochester, PhD(chem), 58. *Prof Exp:* Res chemist, Celanese Corp Am, 57-62; res assoc, Ohio State Univ, 62-64; from asst prof to assoc prof, 64-73, prof chem, 73-77, PROF PHOTOCHEM, CASE WESTERN RESERVE UNIV, 77- *Res:* Reaction kinetics. *Mailing Add:* Dept of Chem Case Western Reserve Univ Cleveland OH 44106

MCMILLAN, HARLAN L, b Cabot, Ark, Sept 28, 26; m 48; c 4. BIOLOGY. *Educ:* Col Ozarks, BS, 50; Univ Ark, MS, 55; Purdue Univ, PhD(entom), 60. *Prof Exp:* Biol aide, Ark State Bd Health, 50-52, malaria control supvr, 52-53; med entomologist, Tech Develop Labs, Commun Dis Ctr, USPHS, Ga, 60-61; assoc prof biol, Col Ozarks, 61-64, prof & dean of men, 64-68, head dept biol, 61-69, chmn div natural sci & math, 68-69; assoc prof biol, 69-72, chmn dept, 72-73, dean sch arts & sci, 72-78, PROF BIOL, ARK TECH UNIV, 78- *Mem:* AAAS; Am Soc Allied Health Prof. *Res:* Culture of insect cells in artificial media; electrophoresis studies of proteins in aquatic organisms. *Mailing Add:* Dept of Biol Sci Ark Tech Univ Russellville AR 72801

MCMILLAN, HARRY KING, b Columbia, SC, Jan 27, 30; m 51; c 3. MECHANICAL ENGINEERING. *Educ:* Univ SC, BS, 51; NC State Col, MS, 58; Purdue Univ, PhD(two phase flow), 63. *Prof Exp:* Instr mech eng, NC State Col, 54-59; asst, Purdue Univ, 59-62; assoc prof, 62-77, PROF MECH ENG, UNIV SC, 77- *Res:* Radiant and convective heat transfer. *Mailing Add:* Dept of Mech Eng Univ of SC Columbia SC 29208

MACMILLAN, J(OHN) H(ENRY), b Providence, RI, Dec 9, 28; m 51; c 3. NUCLEAR ENGINEERING. *Educ:* Mass Inst Technol, BS, 50; Univ London, DIC, 51. *Prof Exp:* Res engr, Boeing Airplane Co, 51-57; asst sect chief reactor eng, Atomic Energy Div, 57-60, chief preliminary design sect, 60-61, asst mgr Savannah Nuclear Power, 61-62, asst mgr appl develop dept, 62-65, mgr reactor eng, 65-66, eng mgr nuclear power generation dept, 66-71, gen mgr reactor dept, 71-73, vpres, Nuclear Power Generation Dept, 75-80, SR VPRES & GROUP EXEC, NUCLEAR POWER GROUP, BABCOCK & WILCOX CO, 80- *Mem:* Am Nuclear Soc; Atomic Indust Forum; Am Nuclear Energy Coun. *Res:* Nuclear reactor technology, especially fluid flow, heat transfer, nuclear physics and transient reactor characteristics. *Mailing Add:* Babcock & Wilcox Co Nuclear Power Group PO Box 1260 Lynchburg VA 24505

MCMILLAN, JAMES ALEXANDER, b Atascadero, Calif, Dec 18, 41; m 65. NEUROPHYSIOLOGY. *Educ:* Univ Calif, Davis, BS(vet sci), 63, BS(animal husb), 65, MS, 70, PhD(physiol), 72. *Prof Exp:* Asst prof, 73-80, ASSOC PROF PHYSIOL, MONT STATE UNIV, 80- *Concurrent Pos:* NIH training grant, Sch Med, Univ Wash, 72-73; hon fel, Univ Edinburgh, 80-81. *Mem:* AAAS; Sigma Xi; Soc Neurosci; Am Physiol Soc. *Res:* Spinal cord and brain stem integration of motor and sensory functions; pain perception in humans. *Mailing Add:* Dept Biol Mont State Univ Bozeman MT 59717

MACMILLAN, JAMES G, b Bellingham, Wash, Feb 16, 42; m 64; c 2. ORGANIC CHEMISTRY. *Educ:* Western Wash State Col, BA, 64; Ohio State Univ, PhD(org chem), 69. *Prof Exp:* Fel org chem, Univ Calif, Berkeley, 69-70; lectr chem, Western Wash State Col, 70-71; lectr org chem, Ohio State Univ, 71-72; asst prof, 72-77, ASSOC PROF ORG CHEM, UNIV NORTHERN IOWA, 77- *Concurrent Pos:* Grants, Univ Northern Iowa, 73-78 & Res Corp, 77- *Mem:* Am Chem Soc; AAAS. *Res:* The synthesis of natural products of medicinal interest; the total synthesis of fungal metabolites. *Mailing Add:* Dept of Chem Univ of Northern Iowa Cedar Falls IA 50613

MCMILLAN, JAMES MALCOLM, b Victoria, BC, Aug 10, 36; m 57; c 3. THEORETICAL PHYSICS. *Educ:* Univ BC, BSc, 58, MSc, 59; McGill Univ, PhD(theoret nuclear physics), 61. *Prof Exp:* Nat Res Coun Can fel physics, Univ Turin, 61-62 & Cambridge Univ, 62-63; from asst prof to assoc prof, 63-74, asst dean sci, 71, PROF PHYSICS, UNIV BC, 74- *Mem:* Am Phys Soc; Can Asn Physicists. *Res:* Direct-interaction theories of relativistic particles; construction of Hamiltonians for systems of pions and nucleons at intermediate energies pion scattering, production and absorption by nuclei at intermediate energies; unification of the classifications of triton state components; construction and application of approximate triton wave functions; Regge poles in potential scattering. *Mailing Add:* Dept of Physics Univ of BC Vancouver BC V6T 1W5 Can

MACMILLAN, JOHN RANDOLPH, b Amittyville, NY, Aug 15, 52; m 77. EXPERIMENTAL HEMATOLOGY, CELL BIOLOGY. *Educ:* Univ Md, BSc, 74; Mich State Univ, MS, 76; Univ Wash, PhD(path), 80. *Prof Exp:* MICROBIOLOGIST PATH & VIROL, NAT FISHERIES RES CTR, 77-; SR RES FEL, DEPT PATH, UNIV WASH, 80- *Mem:* NY Acad Sci; AAAS; Wildlife Dis Asn; Am Fisheries Soc; Am Soc Zoologists. *Res:* Experimental hematology immundregulation, cellualar and developmental biology aging; kinetics and regulation of pluripotent hemopoietic stem cell; comparative oncology and oncogenesis. *Mailing Add:* Dept Path SM-30 Univ Washington Seattle WA 98195

MACMILLAN, JOSEPH EDWARD, b Richmond, VA, Mar 3, 30; m 58; c 3. PHYSICAL CHEMISTRY, BIOCHEMISTRY. *Educ:* The Citadel, BS, 51; Univ SC, MS, 54; Cornell Univ, PhD(phys chem), 69. *Prof Exp:* Chemist, E I du Pont de Nemours, Inc, 53-54 & Allied Chem Corp, 54-56; LAB DIR CHEM, MacMILLAN RES, 56- *Mem:* Am Chem Soc; Am Oil Chemists' Soc; Nat Asn Corrosion Engrs; Cereal Chemists Asn; Am Soc Testing & Mat. *Res:* Oil chemistry; chemical corrosion research; spectrographic studies (emission, AA, IR, & UV). *Mailing Add:* 657 Old Mountain Rd Marietta GA 30064

MCMILLAN, JOSEPH PATRICK, b San Diego, Calif, Jan 17, 45. ECOLOGY, TOXICOLOGY. *Educ:* St Norbert Col, BSc, 67; Univ Ga, PhD(zool), 71. *Prof Exp:* NIH fel zool, Univ Tex, Austin, 71-72, asst prof, 73-75; asst prof, 75-80, ASSOC PROF, COL OF VIRGIN ISLANDS, 80- *Concurrent Pos:* Dir, Ciguatera Res Proj, 77- *Mem:* AAAS; Am Soc Zool; Am Inst Biol Sci. *Res:* Ecological physiology; ecology, toxicology and epidemiology of ciguatera fish poisoning, a circumtropical public health problem. *Mailing Add:* Div Sci & Math Col of the Virgin Islands St Thomas VI 00801

MCMILLAN, JUAN ALEJANDRO, b Buenos Aires, Arg, July 15, 18; m 46; c 2. PHYSICAL CHEMISTRY. *Educ:* Univ Buenos Aires, PhD(chem), 46. *Prof Exp:* Asst physics, Univ Buenos Aires, 46-53; scientist, Arg AEC, 53-55; prof chem & chmn dept, Cuyo, 55-59; assoc chemist, 59-74, CHEMIST, ARGONNE NAT LAB, 74- *Concurrent Pos:* Guggenheim fel, 58. *Mem:* AAAS; Am Chem Soc. *Res:* Crystallography; electron paramagnetic resonance; irreversible phase transformations; radiation of solids, solar materials. *Mailing Add:* 1440 N Lake Shore Dr Chicago IL 60610

MCMILLAN, MICHAEL LATHROP, b Detroit, Mich, Feb 1, 42; m 64; c 3. CHEMICAL ENGINEERING. *Educ:* Univ Mich, Ann Arbor, BSChE, 64, MSChE, 65; Ohio State Univ, PhD(chem eng), 70. *Prof Exp:* Res engr, 65-67, sr res engr, 70-77, STAFF RES ENGR, FUELS & LUBRICANTS DEPT, GEN MOTORS RES LABS, 78- *Mem:* Am Inst Chem Engrs; Am Chem Soc; Am Soc Testing & Mat; Soc Automotive Engrs; Sigma Xi. *Res:* Lubrication; rheology; non-Newtonian fluid flow; mass transfer; viscoelasticity; viscosity behavior of fluids; drag reduction; diessel fuels; wax formation. *Mailing Add:* Fuels & Lubricants Dept 12 Mile & Mound Rd Warren MI 48090

MCMILLAN, NEIL JOHN, b Souris, Man, Nov 11, 25; m 52; c 3. GEOLOGY, SOIL SCIENCE. *Educ:* Univ Man, BSc, 48; Univ Sask, MSc, 51; Univ Kans, PhD(geol), 55. *Prof Exp:* Geologist, Int Nickel Co, Can, summers, 48-50 & Chevron Standard, 51-52; field geologist, Gulf Oil Co, 53, Geol Surv Kans, 54 & Geol Surv Can, 55-56; sr geologist, Bur Mining Resource, Australia, 56-58; res geologist, Tenneco Oil Co, Houston, 59-71; SR GEOLOGIST, AQUITANE CO CAN LTD, 71- *Concurrent Pos:* World Petrol Cong invited deleg, 79. *Mem:* Geol Soc Australia; Geol Soc Am; Geol Soc Can; Can Soc Petrol Geologists (pres, 77). *Res:* Contintental break-up as it relates to basin development and oil exploration; comparison of sediments on each side of the North Atlantic; provenance of clastics in the Labrador Sea. *Mailing Add:* 211 Scarboro Ave SW Calgary AB T3C 2H4 Can

MACMILLAN, NORMAN HILLAS, b Montrose, Scotland, June 20, 41. MATERIALS SCIENCE. *Educ:* Cambridge Univ, BA, 63, MA, 67, PhD(metall), 69; Harvard Univ, MA, 64. *Prof Exp:* Res scientist, Res Inst Advan Studies, Martin-Marietta Corp, 69-74; asst prof metall, 75-78, assoc prof metall & mat res, 78-80, SR RES ASSOC, PA STATE UNIV, 80- *Concurrent Pos:* Lectr physics, Univ Aberdeen, Scotland, 74-75. *Res:* Structure and properties of defects in crystals; mechanical properties; crystallography; interatomic bonding; erosion and wear. *Mailing Add:* Mat Res Lab Pa State Univ University Park PA 16802

MCMILLAN, ODEN J, b Atlantic City, NJ, Mar 8, 44; m 66; c 3. MECHANICAL ENGINEERING. *Educ:* Ga Inst Technol, BME, 65; Stanford Univ, MS, 66, PhD(mech eng), 70. *Prof Exp:* Assoc sr res engr, Gas Turbine Res Dept, Gen Motors Res Labs, 70-75; res engr, 75-80, PROG MGR, NIELSEN ENG & RES, INC, 80- *Mem:* Am Soc Mech Engrs; Am Inst Aeronaut & Astronaut. *Res:* Turbulence; internal flow; aerodynamics. *Mailing Add:* Nielson Eng & Res Inc 510 Clyde Ave Mountain View CA 94043

MCMILLAN, PAUL JUNIOR, b Atlanta, Ga, Sept 13, 30; m 55; c 4. BIOCHEMISTRY, HISTOCHEMISTRY. *Educ:* Southern Missionary Col, BA, 51; Loma Linda Univ, MS, 57, PhD(biochem), 60. *Prof Exp:* Instr, 60-61, from asst prof to assoc prof, 63-79, PROF ANAT, LOMA LINDA UNIV, 79- *Concurrent Pos:* USPHS fel histochem, NIH, 61-63; res assoc, Univ Mainz, 80-81. *Mem:* AAAS; Am Asn Anat; Int Soc Stereology; Histochem Soc. *Res:* Interactions of form and function; metabolic and endocrine interrelations at the cellular level, with reference to the morphological design of tissues. *Mailing Add:* Dept of Anat Sch of Med Loma Linda Univ Loma Linda CA 92350

MCMILLAN, R BRUCE, b Springfield, Mo, Dec 3, 37; m 61; c 3. ARCHAEOLOGY, BIOGEOGRAPHY. *Educ:* Southwest Mo State Col, BS, 60; Univ Mo-Columbia, MA, 63; Univ Colo, PhD(anthrop), 71. *Prof Exp:* Res assoc archaeol, Univ Mo, 64-66; from assoc cur to cur anthrop, 69-73, asst mus dir, 73-77, MUS DIR, ILL STATE MUS, 77- *Concurrent Pos:* NSF fels, Ozark Pleistocene Springs, Ill State Mus, 71-72 & 72-73; lectr, Northwestern Univ, 72-73; consult, Midwest Res Inst, 72- *Mem:* Fel AAAS; fel Am Anthrop Asn; Soc Am Archaeol. *Res:* Late Pleistocene and post-Pleistocene environments, especially eastern North America; man's adaptation to environmental change during the early Holocene in the eastern North American Praire Peninsula. *Mailing Add:* Ill State Mus Spring & Edwards Springfield IL 65201

MCMILLAN, ROBERT, b Pittsburgh, Pa, Nov 19, 34; m 66; c 2. IMMUNOHEMATOLOGY. *Educ:* Pa State Univ, BS, 56; Univ Pa, MD, 60. *Prof Exp:* Assoc hemat, 68-74, ASSOC MEM HEMAT & ONCOL, SCRIPPS CLIN RES FOUND, 74-, DIR, WEINGART BONE MARROW TRANSPLANTATION CTR, 80- *Concurrent Pos:* Adj asst prof hemat, Univ Calif, San Diego, 68-75, assoc adj prof, 75-; consult, Vet Admin Hosp, San Diego, 74- *Mem:* Am Soc Clin Invest; Am Soc Hemat; Soc Exp Biol & Med. *Res:* Evaluation of antiplatelet antibodies in human disease, their synthesis, site of origin and antigens; study of platelet surface proteins; synthesis of human immunoglobulins. *Mailing Add:* Scripps Clin Res Found 10666 N Torrey Pines Rd La Jolla CA 92037

MCMILLAN, ROBERT MCKEE, b Morris, Ill, Dec 18, 24; m 51; c 5. MICROSCOPY, RUBBER CHEMISTRY. *Educ:* NDak State Normal & Indust Col, BS, 48; Univ Colo, MS, 57. *Prof Exp:* Instr chem, NDak State Sch Sci, 48-53; assoc prof, Northern State Teachers Col, SDak, 53-55 & Wis State Col, Superior, 55-57; res chemist micros, 57-59, staff microscopist, 59-64, sr microscopist, 64-80, SECT HEAD, GOODYEAR TIRE & RUBBER CO, 80- *Mem:* AAAS. *Res:* The microscopy of rubber, rubber chemicals, rubber products, plastics and fibers. *Mailing Add:* Dept 455B 1144 E Market St Akron OH 44316

MACMILLAN, ROBERT S(MITH), b Los Angeles, Calif, Aug 28, 24; m 62; c 1. ELECTRICAL ENGINEERING. *Educ:* Calif Inst Technol, BS, 48, MS, 49, PhD(elec eng, physics), 54. *Prof Exp:* Res engr, Jet Propulsion Lab, Calif Inst Technol, 53-55, asst prof elec eng, 55-58; assoc prof, Univ Southern Calif, 58-70; mem staff, Litton Systs, Inc, 69-79, MGR, SYSTS ENG, LITTON DATA COMMAND SYSTS, 79- *Concurrent Pos:* Consult, Space Technol Labs, Thompson Ramo Wooldridge, Inc, 56-59 & US Air Force, 57-76. *Mem:* Am Phys Soc; Sigma Xi; Inst Elec & Electronics Engrs. *Res:* Ionosphere and the earth's upper atmosphere; ionospheric radio-wave propagation of very-low-frequency radio waves; quantum electronics; communications antennas; electromagnetic wave propagation. *Mailing Add:* 350 Starlight Crest Dr La Canada CA 91011

MCMILLAN, ROBERT THOMAS, JR, b Miami, Fla, June 1, 34; m 54; c 2. PLANT PATHOLOGY. *Educ:* Univ Miami, BS, 61, MS, 64; Wash State Univ, PhD(plant path), 68. *Prof Exp:* Asst plant pathologist, 67-74, ASSOC PROF PLANT PATH & ASSOC PLANT PATHOLOGIST, AGR RES & EDUC CTR, UNIV FLA, 67- *Mem:* Am Phytopath Soc; Am Soc Agron; Crop Sci Soc Am. *Res:* Tissue culture, physiology, etiology and control of fruit and vegetable diseases. *Mailing Add:* Agr Res & Educ Ctr Univ Fla 18905 SW 280th St Homestead FL 33031

MCMILLAN, WILLIAM GEORGE, b Montebello, Calif, Oct 19, 19; m 46; c 3. CHEMICAL PHYSICS. *Educ:* Univ Calif, Los Angeles, BA, 41; Columbia Univ, MA, 43, PhD(chem), 45. *Prof Exp:* Teaching asst chem, Columbia Univ, 41-44; Guggenheim fel, Inst Nuclear Studies, Chicago, 46-47; from asst prof to assoc prof, 47-58, chmn dept, 59-65, PROF CHEM, UNIV CALIF, LOS ANGELES, 58- *Concurrent Pos:* Chmn ad hoc group radiation effects, US Air Force, US Navy & Dir, Defense Res & Eng, 63-66, mem, 66-; chmn advan res projs agency defense sci sem, Univ Calif, Los Angeles, 64-66; chmn, Joint Chiefs-of-Staff Panel on Nuclear Test Ban, 65-66; vchmn sci adv comt, Defense Intel Agency, 65-71, mem, 71-; sci adv to Comdr, US Mil Assistance Command, Vietnam, 66-68; mem, Army Sci Adv Panel, 69- & Oak Ridge Nat Lab Adv Group on Civil Defense, 71-; chmn, Nat Acad Army Countermine Study Group, 71-72. *Honors & Awards:* Distinguished Civilian Serv Award, Dept of Army, 68; Distinguished Pub Serv Award, Dept of Defense, 69; Knight, Nat Order of Vietnam, 69. *Mem:* AAAS; Am Phys Soc; Am Chem Soc. *Res:* Statistical and quantum mechanics of small molecules; adsorption; equation of state; spectroscopy at high pressure; electrolytes. *Mailing Add:* Dept of Chem Univ of Calif Los Angeles CA 90024

MACMILLAN, WILLIAM HOOPER, b Boston, Mass, Oct 21, 23; m 48; c 3. PHARMACOLOGY. *Educ:* McGill Univ, BA, 48; Yale Univ, PhD, 54. *Prof Exp:* From instr to prof pharmacol, Col Med, Univ Vt, 54-76, chmn dept, 62-63, dean grad col, 63-69 & 71-76; PROF BIOL & DEAN GRAD SCH, UNIV ALA, 76- *Concurrent Pos:* USPHS fel, Oxford Univ, 58-59; Ford Found sci adv, Haile Selassie I Univ, Addis Ababa, Ethiopia, 69-71; consult, African Am Inst, 71-; educ consult, World Bank, 72-74; consult, New Eng Asn Schs & Cols, 72-76. *Mem:* Sigma Xi; AAAS; Am Soc Pharmacol & Exp Therapeut; NY Acad Sci. *Res:* Autonomic pharmacology; mechanism of drug action; graduate studies in biomedical sciences. *Mailing Add:* Grad Sch Univ of Ala Tuscaloosa AL 35486

MCMILLEN, JANIS KAY, b El Dorado, Kans, Oct 21, 37. VIROLOGY. *Educ:* Trinity Univ, Tex, BS, 59; Univ Kans, PhD(microbiol), 71. *Prof Exp:* Res technician virol, Pitman-Moore Div, Dow Chem Co, 59-60 & Dept Pediat, Univ Kans Med Ctr, 60-66; Nat Inst Allergy & Infectious Dis fel, Div Biol, Kans State Univ, 71-74, res assoc, 74-76; sr res virologist, Jensen-Salsbery Labs Div, Richardson-Merrell, Inc, 76-80; HEAD, VIROL RES, WELLCOME RES LABS, BURROUGHS-WELLCOME CO, 80- *Mem:* Am Soc Microbiol; Sigma Xi; NY Acad Sci; Tissue Cult Asn. *Res:* Viral pathogenesis; molecular mechanisms of viral infections. *Mailing Add:* Virus Res Div 2000 S 11th St Kansas City KS 66103

MCMILLEN, LARRY BYRON, b Defiance, Ohio, Apr 18, 42; m 64; c 2. PROSTHODONTICS. *Educ:* Ohio State Univ, DDS, 66, MS, 70. *Prof Exp:* Instr prosthodont, Col Dent, Ohio State Univ, 69-70; asst prof, Sch Dent, La State Univ Med Ctr, New Orleans, 70-75; CONSULT PVT PRACT, 75- *Mem:* Int Asn Dent Res. *Res:* Border movements of human mandible; dental crown contours in relation to periodontal health. *Mailing Add:* 4300 Houma Blvd Metairie LA 70002

MACMILLEN, RICHARD EDWARD, b Upland, Calif, Apr 19, 32; div; c 2. PHYSIOLOGICAL ECOLOGY, VERTEBRATE BIOLOGY. *Educ:* Pomona Col, BA, 54; Univ Mich, MS, 56; Univ Calif, Los Angeles, PhD(zool), 61. *Prof Exp:* Res zoologist, Univ Calif, Los Angeles, 59-60; from instr to assoc prof zool, Pomona Col, 60-68; assoc prof, 68-77, PROF BIOL, UNIV CALIF, IRVINE, 77- *Concurrent Pos:* NSF res grants, 61-79; Fulbright advan res grant zool & comp physiol, Monash Univ, Australia, 66-67; partic island ecosysts, Int Ref Prog, US/Int Biol Prog, 71-74; mem, Panel Pop Biol & Physiol Ecol, NSF, 76-79; ed, J Mammal, 78-80. *Mem:* Fel AAAS; Am Soc Zool; Ecol Soc Am; Am Soc Mammal; Australian Soc Mammal. *Res:* Physiological ecology of energy and water regulation in terrestrial vertebrates. *Mailing Add:* Dept of Ecol & Evolutionary Biol Univ of Calif Irvine CA 92717

MCMILLIAN, FRANK LEBARRON, organic chemistry, see previous edition

MCMILLIN, CARL RICHARD, b Warren, Ohio, Aug 4, 46; m 70; c 3. MEDICAL RESEARCH, METHODS DEVELOPMENT. *Educ:* Gen Motors Inst, BME, 69; Case Western Reserve Univ, MS, 71, PhD(macromolecular sci), 74. *Prof Exp:* Prod engr, Packard Elec Div, Gen Motors Corp, 68-69; res assoc polymer stress cracking,Queen Mary Col, Univ London, 71-72; NIH res fel, Case Western Reserve Univ & vis scientist, Artificial Organs Div, Cleveland Clin, 74-75; sr res chemist, 75-78, CONTRACT MGR, MONSANTO RES CORP, 78- *Mem:* Biophys Soc; Am Inst Biol Sci; Am Chem Soc. *Res:* Development and application of novel biomedical, biophysical and analytical techniques and instrumentation. *Mailing Add:* Monsanto Res Corp 1515 Nicholas Rd Dayton OH 45407

MCMILLIN, CHARLES W, b Indianapolis, Ind, Aug 22, 32. WOOD SCIENCE & TECHNOL. *Educ:* Purdue Univ, BS, 54; Univ Mich, MWT, 57, PhD(wood sci), 69. *Prof Exp:* Assoc mech engr, Am Mach & Foundry Co, 57-64; res coordr, Southern Pine Asn, 64-65; PRIN WOOD SCIENTIST, SOUTHERN FOREST EXP STA, FOREST SERV, USDA, 65- *Concurrent Pos:* Chmn, Pulp & Paper Tech Comt, Forest Prod Res Soc, 71, 72, chmn-elect, Div C Processes, 71, chmn, 72, chmn-elect, Mid-South Sect, 73, chmn, 73. *Honors & Awards:* Wood Award, Wood & Wood Prod Mag, 57. *Mem:* Forest Prod Res Soc; Sigma Xi; Soc Wood Sci & Technol; Int Asn Wood Anatomists; Tech Asn Pulp & Paper Indust. *Res:* Wood machining; mechanical pulping; modification of properties; characterization; applications of scanning electron microscopy to wood science. *Mailing Add:* 531 Highpoint Dr Alexandria LA 71301

MCMILLIN, DAVID ROBERT, b East St Louis, Ill, Jan 1, 48; m 78; c 2. INORGANIC CHEMISTRY. *Educ:* Knox Col, BA, 69; Univ Ill, PhD(inorg chem), 73. *Prof Exp:* Fel, Calif Inst Technol, 73-74; asst prof, 75-80, ASSOC PROF INORG CHEM, PURDUE UNIV, 80- *Concurrent Pos:* NIH fel, Calif Inst Technol, 74. *Mem:* Am Chem Soc. *Res:* Chemical and physical studies of copper proteins and related model systems; transition metal chemistry; photochemistry; photoluminescence spectroscopy; electron paramagnetic resonance spectroscopy. *Mailing Add:* Dept of Chem Purdue Univ West Lafayette IN 47907

MCMILLIN, KENNETH M, b Britt, Iowa, Jan 7, 19; m 47; c 1. MATHEMATICS. *Educ:* Cent Col, Iowa, BA, 44; Univ Minn, MS, 47; Univ Cincinnati, PhD(math), 53. *Prof Exp:* Instr math & mech, Univ Minn, 48-51; asst prof math, US Air Force Inst Technol, Wright Field, Ohio, 51-53 & Col of St Thomas, 53-55; assoc prof, 55-63, PROF MATH & DIR SIMULATION LAB, MICH TECHNOL UNIV, 63- *Res:* Computers; control devices; Fourier series; hybrid computation. *Mailing Add:* Dept of Math Mich Technol Univ Houghton MI 49931

MCMILLIN-WOOD, JEANIE, b Spartanburg, SC, Sept 26, 39; c 2. BIOCHEMISTRY, CHEMISTRY. *Educ:* Converse Col, BA, 61; Univ NC, Chapel Hill, PhD(biochem), 67. *Prof Exp:* Instr biochem, Univ NC, Chapel Hill, 67-68; res assoc, Dept Med, Cornell Univ & Inst Muscle Dis, Inc, 68-69; res assoc, 69-70, res instr, 70-71, instr, 71-72, res asst prof myocardial biol, 72-73, asst prof cell biophys, 73-77, asst prof med & biochem, 77-80, ASSOC PROF MED & BIOCHEM, BAYLOR COL MED, 80- *Concurrent Pos:* USPHS grant, Univ NC, Chapel Hill, 67-68; Musclar Dystrophy Asn Am grant, Cornell Univ & Inst Muscle Dis, Inc, 68-69, 80-; Tex Med Ctr grant myocardial biol, Baylor Col Med, 69-70; Tex Heart Asn grant, 70-72; NIH grants, 75-79, 78-81 & 81-86; mem, Int Study Group Res Cardiac Metab; consult, NIH, 79-82; mem, Cardiovasc Pulmonary Study Sect, NIH86. *Mem:* Am Soc Biol Chemists; NY Acad Sci; Sigma Xi; Biophys Soc; Am Physiol Soc. *Res:* Effect of myocardial ischemia on the mitochondrial functions of energy production and fatty acid transport and oxidation; carnitine palmityltransferase system; coenzyme A turnover in liver and muscle. *Mailing Add:* Dept Med Sect Cardiovasc Sci Baylor Col Med Houston TX 77030

MCMILLION, C ROBERT, b Avon, WVa, Aug 5, 27; m 49; c 2. PHARMACEUTICAL CHEMISTRY, ORGANIC CHEMISTRY. *Educ:* Glenville State Col, AB, 51; Johns Hopkins Univ, MA, 59; Univ Md, PhD(pharmaceut chem), 64. *Prof Exp:* Res chemist, 51-64, CHEM PROD MGR, HYNSON WESTCOTT & DUNNING, INC, 64- *Mem:* Am Chem Soc. *Res:* Chromatography of triphenylmethane dyes; fluorescent isothiocyanates for antibody labeling; synthesis of catechol amines; spiroindolenines; micron and submicron sized particles and crystals associated with seriological reactions. *Mailing Add:* Hynson Westcott & Dunning Inc Charles & Chase St Baltimore MD 21201

MCMILLION, LESLIE GLEN, b Nallen, WVa, June 24, 30; m 54; c 2. HYDROLOGY. *Educ:* Marshall Univ, BA, 52; Mich State Univ, MS, 57. *Prof Exp:* Geologist, US Geol Surv, 54-56; geologist, Tex Water Comn, 56-59, div dir, Tex Water Develop Bd, 59-65; RES HYDROLOGIST, US ENVIRON PROTECTION AGENCY, 66- *Concurrent Pos:* Prin partic, Tex-US Study Comn, 59-60; mem, Tex Govr's Water Pollution Adv Coun, 60-61, Working Group Preparation Regulations Safe Drinking Water Act, 75-76 & chmn, Nat Aquifer Protection Comn, 67-70. *Mem:* Nat Water Well Asn; Am Water Resources Asn; Geol Soc Am; Am Water Works Asn. *Mailing Add:* US Environ Protection Agency PO Box 15027 Las Vegas NV 89114

MCMILLION, THEODORE MILLER, b Friars Hill, WVa, Oct 5, 03; m 29, 49; c 2. ZOOLOGY. *Educ:* WVa Univ, BA, 27, MA, 29; Univ Pittsburgh, PhD(zool), 41. *Prof Exp:* From instr to prof, 26-74, EMER PROF BIOL, GENEVA COL, 74- *Concurrent Pos:* Instr, Beaver Valley Gen Hosp, Pa. *Mem:* AAAS; Am Inst Biol Sci. *Res:* Mammalian chromosomes; stain technology; spermatogenesis and chromosome complexes in the rabbit. *Mailing Add:* 3208 Sixth Ave Beaver Falls PA 15010

MCMINN, CURTIS J, b Lexington, Tenn, Oct 25, 29; m 54; c 3. CHEMICAL ENGINEERING. *Educ:* Middle Tenn State Univ, BS, 51; Vanderbilt Univ, MS, 55. *Prof Exp:* Design engr, Redstone Arsenal, 51-52; proj engr, 55-60, proj dir, 60-75, RES DIR, REDUCTION RES DIV, REYNOLDS METALS CO, 75- *Mem:* Am Inst Chem Engrs; Am Inst Mining, Metall & Petrol Engrs; Sigma Xi. *Res:* Oxidation of P-Xylene to terephthalic acid; reduction of alumina electrochemically; design of reduction cells; use of new materials in reduction cells; new processes for production of primary aluminum. *Mailing Add:* Reduction Res Div Reynolds Metals Co Box 1200 Sheffield AL 35660

MCMINN, T(ALMAGE) D(EWITT), JR, b Clovis, NMex, Oct 13, 20; m 47; c 3. CHEMICAL ENGINEERING. *Educ:* Univ Tex, BS, 43, MS, 47, PhD(chem, mech eng), 52. *Prof Exp:* Res engr, Process & Prod Develop, Southwest Res Inst, 47-50; from res engr to sr res engr, 50-60, fel, 60-78, SR FEL, MONSANTO CO, 78- *Concurrent Pos:* Instr, Trinity Univ, 48-50. *Mem:* Am Inst Chem Engrs; AAAS. *Res:* Adsorption of hydrocarbons on alumina; vibration analysis; low temperature natural gasoline plant design; petrochemical processes; hydrocarbon cracking processes. *Mailing Add:* Monsanto Co 800 N Lindbergh Blvd St Louis MO 63166

MCMINN, TREVOR JAMES, b Salt Lake City, Utah, Jan 23, 21. MATHEMATICS. *Educ:* Univ Utah, BA, 42; Univ Calif, Berkeley, PhD(math), 55. *Prof Exp:* Instr math, Univ Rochester, 50, Univ Calif, Riverside, 54-55 & Univ Calif, Berkeley, 55-56; asst prof, Univ Wash, 56-63; assoc prof, 63-69, PROF MATH, UNIV NEV, RENO, 69- *Mem:* Am Math Soc. *Res:* Measure theory; real analysis. *Mailing Add:* Dept of Math Univ of Nev Reno NV 89557

MACMORINE, HILDA MILDRED GRACE, b Kars, Ont, June 26, 16. ORGANIC CHEMISTRY. *Educ:* Univ Toronto, BA, 38, MA, 43, PhD(chem), 55. *Prof Exp:* From res asst to res assoc, Connaught Med Res Labs, Univ Toronto, 40-61, res mem, Univ, 61-71, dir, 71-73, div dir human biol, Connaught Labs, Ltd, 73-74, res dir, 74-77, asst prof microbiol, Sch Med, Univ Toronto, 71-81, sr sci consult, Connaught Labs, Ltd, 77-81; SCI CONSULT, DEXTRAN PRODS LTD, 81- *Concurrent Pos:* Can Pub Health grant improved methods viral vaccine prod, 71- *Mem:* Can Pub Health Asn; fel Chem Inst Can; Am Soc Microbiol; Tissue Cult Asn; NY Acad Sci. *Res:* Animal cell nutrition and improved methods for cell culture; recomb DNA. *Mailing Add:* Dextran Prods Ltd 415 Comstock Rd Scuborough ON M1L 2H5 Can

MCMORRIS, F ARTHUR, b Lawton, Okla, Sept 17, 44. NEUROCHEMISTRY, GENETICS. *Educ:* Brown Univ, BA, 66; Yale Univ, PhD(biol), 72. *Prof Exp:* Teaching asst, Brown Univ, 66 & Yale Univ, 67-70; res assoc biol, Mass Inst Technol, 72-74; ASST PROF, WISTAR INST, 74- *Concurrent Pos:* asst prof human genetics, 75-79, asst prof, Grad Groups Molecular Biol & Genetics, Sch Med, Univ Pa, 75- *Mem:* Am Soc Cell Biol; Am Soc Neurochem; Soc Develop Biol; Am Soc Human Genetics; Soc Neurosci. *Res:* Control mechanisms of cell diffferentiation in the nervous system; somatic cell and molecular genetics; neurobiology; somatic cell genetics. *Mailing Add:* The Wistar Inst 36th St at Spruce Philadelphia PA 19104

MCMORRIS, FRED RAYMOND, b Gary, Ind, Aug 28, 43; m 65; c 2. MATHEMATICS, BIOMATHEMATICS. *Educ:* Beloit Col, BS, 65; Univ Calif, Riverside, MA, 66; Univ Wis-Milwaukee, PhD(math), 69. *Prof Exp:* Asst prof, 69-74, assoc prof, 74-79, PROF MATH, BOWLING GREEN STATE UNIV, 79- *Concurrent Pos:* Nat Inst Gen Med Sci fel, Biomath Prog, NC State Univ, 71-73; vis assoc prof, Dept Math Sci, Clemson Univ, 78; vis prof dept math, Univ SC, 81. *Mem:* Am Math Soc; Math Asn Am; Soc Indust & Appl Math; Soc Math Biol. *Res:* Discrete mathematics; mathematical biology; numerical taxonomy. *Mailing Add:* Dept of Math Bowling Green State Univ Bowling Green OH 43403

MCMULLEN, BRYCE H, b Tarkio, Mo, Apr 18, 21; m 44; c 2. CHEMICAL ENGINEERING. *Educ:* Centre Col, AB, 43; Ohio State Univ, MSc, 46, PhD(chem eng), 49. *Prof Exp:* Res chemist, Titanium Div, Nat Lead Co, 50-52, from develop engr to sr develop engr, 52-57, staff asst, 57-62, supvr develop & eng dept, 62-69, chief engr feed mat dept, 70, mgr, 71-77; SR DEVELOP ENGR, GLIDDEN PIGMENTS, 77- *Mem:* Sigma Xi; Am Chem Soc. *Res:* Catalyst for olefin polymerization; process for recovery of waste sulfuric acid; chloride process for manufacture of titanium dioxide. *Mailing Add:* 3901 Greenway Baltimore MD 21218

MACMULLEN, CLINTON WILLIAM, b St Cloud, Minn, May 16, 09; m 33; c 1. ORGANIC CHEMISTRY. *Educ:* Univ Minn, BChE, 30, PhD(org chem), 35. *Prof Exp:* Group leader, Rohm & Haas Co, Pa, 35-43; tech dir, Cowles Chem Co, 43-52; sect chief, Olin Industs, Inc, 52-53, mgr res, Org Chem Div, Olin Mathieson Chem Corp, 53-60, dir applns res, Chem Div, 60-62, tech adv to corp vpres res & develop, 62-65, tech dir chem div, 65-69, tech dir new venture identification, Olin Corp, 69-72; CONSULT, 72- *Mem:* Am Chem Soc; Am Oil Chem Soc; Sigma Xi; Soc Plastics Eng; fel Am Inst Chemists. *Res:* Petrochemicals; polymers; lubricants; plastics; sodium metasilicate; organosilicon compounds; surface active agents; bactericides; fungicides. *Mailing Add:* 73 Jesswig Dr Hamden CT 06517

MCMULLEN, JAMES CLINTON, b Alton, Ill, July 6, 42; m 63; c 3. CHEMISTRY. *Educ:* Wis State Univ-Superior, BS, 65; Univ SDak, PhD(chem), 69. *Prof Exp:* Asst prof, 69-76, assoc prof, 76-81, PROF CHEM, ST CLOUD STATE UNIV, 81- *Mem:* Am Chem Soc. *Res:* Analytical instrumentation; computer applications to chemistry. *Mailing Add:* Dept of Chem St Cloud State Univ St Cloud MN 56301

MCMULLEN, JAMES ROBERT, b Clinton, Ind, May 22, 42; m 64; c 1. MICROBIOLOGY, BIOCHEMISTRY. *Educ:* Ind State Univ, BS, 64; Univ Wis-Madison, MS, 66. *Prof Exp:* Res microbiologist, Com Solvents Corp, 66-75; RES MICROBIOLOGIST, INT MINERALS & CHEM CORP, 75- *Mem:* Am Soc Microbiol. *Res:* Industrial fermentations; fungal metabolism; enzymes; cellulose utilization; rumen microbiology, microbiology of silage. *Mailing Add:* 236 Van Buren Blvd Terre Haute IN 47803

MCMULLEN, ROBERT DAVID, b Medicine Hat, Alta, Feb 25, 30; m 53; c 2. ENTOMOLOGY, ECOLOGY. *Educ:* Univ Alta, BSc, 53; Wash State Univ, MSc, 60; Univ Calif, Berkeley, PhD(entom), 64. *Prof Exp:* Tech officer entom, Defence Res Bd Can, Suffield Exp Sta, Ralston, Alta, 53-56; res scientist entom, Res Sta, Agr Can, Harrow, Ont, 56-64; RES SCIENTIST ENTOM, RES STA, AGR CAN, SUMMERLAND, BC, 64- *Concurrent Pos:* Adj prof, Simon Fraser Univ, 74-; assoc ed, Can Entomologist, Entom Soc Can, 78- *Mem:* Entom Soc Can; Entom Soc Am. *Res:* Integrated pest management of insects and mites on deciduous fruits; vectors of diseases of deciduous fruit crops. *Mailing Add:* Agr Can Res Sta Summerland BC V0H 1Z0 Can

MCMULLEN, ROBERT MICHAEL, b Toronto, Ont, Nov 20, 35; m 62; c 1. MARINE GEOLOGY, OCEAN SCIENCE. *Educ:* Univ Alta, BSc, 57, MSc, 59; Univ Reading, PhD(sedimentology), 65. *Prof Exp:* Info specialist in-chg explor, Imp Oil Ltd, Alta, 59-61; explor geologist & trainee, Imp Oil Explor, 64-65; explor geologist, Hudson's Bay Oil & Gas Co, 65; res sci, Bedford Inst Oceanog, NS, 66-68, head sci info serv & libr, Atlantic Oceanog Lab, 68-70; chief, Commun Data & Libr Serv, Dept Commun, 70-71, dir info retrieval serv, 71-73, DIR POLICY & PROG COORD, OCEAN & SCI & SURVS, DEPT FISHERIES & OCEANS, 73- *Concurrent Pos:* Managing ed, Maritime Sediments, 67-71. *Mem:* Am Asn Petrol Geol; fel Geol Asn Can; fel Geol Soc London; Brit Inst Info Sci. *Res:* Sedimentary petrology and structures; sediment transport; marine geology; scientific information and data storage and retrieval; intertidal sedimentation; information technology; on-line systems; information networks; science policy. *Mailing Add:* Ocean Sci & Survs 240 Sparks St Ottawa ON K1A 0E6 Can

MCMULLEN, WARREN ANTHONY, b Faulkton, SDak, Oct 22, 07; m 29; c 3. ORGANIC CHEMISTRY. *Educ:* Greenville Col, BS, 28; Univ Nebr, MA, 36; NY Univ, PhD(sci ed), 60. *Prof Exp:* Teacher high sch, Nebr, 28-43; teacher chem & physics, Cent Col, Kans, 43-45; from asst prof to prof, 45-73, EMER PROF CHEM, GREENVILLE COL, 73-; prin, Oakdale Christian High Sch, 75-77; EMER PROF CHEM, GREENVILLE COL, 73- *Concurrent Pos:* Sci teacher, Oakdale Christian High Sch, Jackson, Ky, 75-80. *Mem:* Am Chem Soc. *Mailing Add:* 320 N First St Greenville IL 62246

MCMULLEN, WILLIAM D(ALE), metallurgy, deceased

MCMURCHY, ROBERT CONNELL, b Arden, Man, Sept 15, 02; m 36; c 3. GEOLOGY. *Educ:* Univ Man, BSc, 30; Univ Minn, PhD(geol), 34. *Prof Exp:* Lectr geol, Univ Man, 34-35; asst geologist, Geol Surv Can, 35-39; geologist, Powell-Rouyn Gold Mines, Ltd, 39-51; explor engr, Chesterville Mines, Ltd, 51-53; CONSULT GEOLOGIST, 53- *Mem:* Geol Asn Can; Can Inst Mining & Metall; Asn Prof Engrs. *Res:* Mining exploration and development. *Mailing Add:* 95 Southvale Dr Toronto ON M4G 1G4 Can

MCMURDIE, HOWARD FRANCIS, b Detroit, Mich, Feb 5, 05; m 28; c 3. CHEMISTRY. *Educ:* Northwestern Univ, BS, 28. *Prof Exp:* Jr chemist, Joint Comt Powder Diffraction Standards, Washington, DC, 28-33, Calif, 33-35, jr petrographer, DC, 35-44, gen phys scientist, 44-48, chief sect crystallog, 48-65, RES FEL, INT CTR DIFFRACTION DATA, NAT BUR STANDARDS, 66- *Mem:* Fel Am Ceramic Soc; Mineral Soc Am; Am Crystallog Asn. *Res:* Crystal chemistry; phase equilibrium of refractory oxides; high temperature x-ray diffraction; chemical analysis by x-ray diffraction; effect of heat on crystals; data compilation. *Mailing Add:* Nat Bur Standards Washington DC 20234

MCMURPHY, WILFRED E, b Lamont, Okla, Aug 3, 34; m 59; c 1. AGRONOMY. *Educ:* Okla State Univ, BS, 56, MS, 59; Univ Kans, PhD(agron), 63. *Prof Exp:* Res asst agron, Kans State Univ, 59-62; asst prof, SDak State Univ, 62-64; asst prof, 64-70, assoc prof, 70-76, PROF AGRON, OKLA STATE UNIV, 76- *Mem:* Am Soc Agron; Crop Sci Soc Am; Soc Range Mgt; Am Forage & Grassland Coun. *Res:* Range and pasture management; pasture production and ecology. *Mailing Add:* Dept of Agron Okla State Univ Stillwater OK 74078

MCMURRAY, BIRCH LEE, b Polk Co, NC, Oct 18, 31; m 56; c 3. VETERINARY MEDICINE, AGRICULTURE. *Educ:* NC State Univ, BS, 54; Univ Ga, DVM, 57. *Prof Exp:* Dir lab, Fla Dept Agr, 58-60; vet, Dr Robert E Lee Vet Hosp, 60-62; res vet, 62-64, mgr vet res, 64-72, dir int feed res, 72-78, PRIN VETERINARIAN POULTRY FIELD RES & TECH SERV, CENT SOYA CO, INC, 78- *Mem:* Am Vet Med Asn; Am Asn Avian Pathologists. *Res:* Programmed preventive veterinary medicine; preventive programs for coccidiosis, fowl cholera, Marek's disease, respiratory diseases of cattle, enteridides or swine, mastitis-metritis complex; interrelations of disease, nutrition and management. *Mailing Add:* PO Box 1668 Athens GA 30601

MCMURRAY, DAVID CLAUDE, b Greenville, Tex, May 3, 27; m 52; c 1. MECHANICAL ENGINEERING. *Educ:* Tex Tech Col, BSME, 50; Univ Wis, PhD(mech eng), 66. *Prof Exp:* Installation engr, Nordberg Mfg Co, 50-52, prod designer, 52-55; designer, W C Heath Assocs Inc, 55-57; mech engr, 57-60, head eng anal, 60-62, consult engr, Res Div, 62-82, MGR, CONSULT SERV, DATA SYSTS DIV, A O SMITH CORP, 82- *Concurrent Pos:* Lectr, Marquette Univ, 66. *Res:* Industrial research and development in the areas of heat transfer, fluid flow, machinery and processes. *Mailing Add:* A O Smith Corp 8901 N Kildeer Ct Brown Deer WI 53209

MCMURRAY, LOREN ROBERT, b Topeka, Kans, June 15, 31; m 58; c 2. MATHEMATICS, COMPUTER SIMULATION. *Educ:* Washburn Univ, BS, 53; Iowa State Univ, MS, 55; Univ Ill, MS, 57, PhD(math), 58. *Prof Exp:* Mem tech staff inertial guidance, 58-61, supvr, 61-62, MEM TECH STAFF ELECTRONIC DESIGN ANAL AUTONETICS, ROCKWELL INT, 62- *Mem:* Inst Elec & Electronics Engrs. *Res:* Adaptive digital filters; modeling electronic components; algorithms for computers. *Mailing Add:* Rockwell Int 3370 Miraloma Ave Anaheim CA 92803

MCMURRAY, WALTER JOSEPH, b Montague, Mass, Aug 22, 35; m 60; c 4. BIOCHEMISTRY. *Educ:* Amherst Col, AB, 58; Univ Ill, PhD, 62; Univ New Haven, MBA, Sch Law, Univ Conn, MBA, 76. *Prof Exp:* Res assoc chem, Mass Inst Technol, 63-64; instr med, 65-66, asst prof pharmacol, 66-67, from asst prof to assoc prof health sci resources, 67-75, res assoc, 75-81, SR RES ASSOC LAB MED, SCH MED, YALE UNIV, 81- *Mem:* Am Soc Mass Spectrometry; Am Chem Soc. *Res:* Organic biochemistry; application of mass spectrometry to problems in organic chemistry; use of computers in chemistry. *Mailing Add:* Lab Med Sch Med Yale Univ New Haven CT 06520

MCMURRAY, WILLIAM COLIN CAMPBELL, b Bangor, Northern Ireland, Mar 16, 31; nat Can; m 53; c 2. BIOCHEMISTRY. *Educ:* Univ Western Ont, BSc, 53, PhD(biochem), 56. *Prof Exp:* Proj assoc, Inst Enzyme Res, Univ Wis, 56-58; asst prof cancer res & lectr biochem, Univ Sask, 58-59; asst prof biochem & Jr Red Cross Res Prof ment retardation, 59-65, assoc prof biochem, 65-70, PROF BIOCHEM, UNIV WESTERN ONT, 70- *Concurrent Pos:* Vis scientist, Inst Animal Physiol, Agr Res Coun, Cambridge, Eng, 67-68. *Mem:* Am Soc Biol Chem; Can Biochem Soc; Nutrit Soc. *Res:* Biochemistry of the brain; inborn errors of metabolism; metabolism of differentiation; lipid metabolism; mitochondrial enzymes and oxidative phosphorylation; membrane synthesis; mitochonrdial biogenesis; hormone interactions in cultured cells. *Mailing Add:* Dept Biochem Univ Western Ont Fac Med London ON N6A 5C1 Can

MCMURRY, EARL WILLIAM, physics, geophysics, see previous edition

MCMURRY, JOHN EDWARD, b New York, NY, July 27, 42; m 64; c 2. SYNTHETIC ORGANIC CHEMISTRY. *Educ:* Harvard Univ, BA, 64; Columbia Univ, MA & PhD(chem), 67. *Prof Exp:* From asst prof to assoc prof chem, Univ Calif, Santa Cruz, 67-75, prof, 75-80; PROF CHEM, BAKER LAB, CORNELL UNIV, 80- *Concurrent Pos:* Alfred P Sloan fel, 69-71; NIH career develop award, 75-80. *Mem:* AAAS; Am Chem Soc; Royal Soc Chem. *Res:* Natural product synthesis; new synthetic reactions. *Mailing Add:* Dept Chem Baker Lab Cornell Univ Ithaca NY 14853

MCMURTRY, CARL HEWES, b Wellsville, NY, Dec 6, 31; m 55; c 3. CERAMICS, INORGANIC CHEMISTRY. *Educ:* Alfred Univ, BS, 53, MS, 58. *Prof Exp:* Res assoc ceramics, Alfred Univ, 53-57, instr mineral, 57-58; MGR ENG, RES & DEVELOP DIV, CARBORUNDUM CO, 58- *Mem:* Am Ceramic Soc; Nat Inst Ceramic Engrs. *Res:* Refractories; semiconductors; nuclear ceramics; carbides, nitrides, borides and silicides; carbon and graphite. *Mailing Add:* Res & Develop Div Lab Carborundum Co PO Box 1054 Niagara Falls NY 14302

MCMURTRY, GEORGE JAMES, b Crawfordsville, Ind, July 19, 32; m 61; c 6. ELECTRICAL ENGINEERING. *Educ:* US Naval Acad, BS, 55; Univ Notre Dame, MS, 61; Purdue Univ, Lafayette, PhD(elec eng), 65. *Prof Exp:* Instr elec eng, Purdue Univ, 61-65; engr, Gen Elec Co, 65-67; from asst prof to assoc prof elec, 67-76, engr, Ord Res Lab, 67-69, co-dir off remote sensing earth resources, 70-80, PROF ELEC ENG, PA STATE UNIV, UNIVERSITY PARK, 76-, ASSOC DEAN INSTR, COL ENG, 80- *Mem:* Inst Elec & Electronics Engrs; Am Soc Eng Educ. *Res:* Adaptive and learning control systems; remote sensing of earth resources by aircraft and spacecraft; pattern recognition; optimization procedures. *Mailing Add:* Dept of Elec Eng Pa State Univ University Park PA 16802

MCMURTRY, JAMES A, b Lodi, Calif, Sept 21, 32; m 54; c 2. ENTOMOLOGY. *Educ:* San Jose State Col, AB, 54; Univ Calif, Davis, PhD(entom), 60. *Prof Exp:* Res assoc entom, Univ Calif, Davis, 56-60; asst entomologist, 60-66, ASSOC ENTOMOLOGIST & LECTR BIOL CONTROL, UNIV CALIF, RIVERSIDE, 66-, PROF ENTOM, 81- *Concurrent Pos:* Guggenheim fel, 68. *Mem:* Entom Soc Am; Entom Soc Can. *Res:* Biological control and population ecology of phytophagous mites. *Mailing Add:* Div of Biol Control Univ of Calif Riverside CA 92502

MACNAB, ROBERT MARSHALL, b Barnsley, Eng, Feb 3, 40. BIOPHYSICS. *Educ:* Univ St Andrews, Scotland, BSc, 62; Univ Calif, Berkeley, PhD(chem), 69. *Prof Exp:* Technologist petrochem, Brit Petrol Co, 62-65; res assoc biochem, Univ Calif, Berkeley, 70-73; asst prof, 73-78, ASSOC PROF BIOPHYS, YALE UNIV, 78- *Res:* Bacterial chemotaxis as a model for chemo-mechanical and sensory transduction. *Mailing Add:* Molecular Biophys & Biochem Yale Univ Box 1937 Yale Sta New Haven CT 06520

MCNABB, CLARENCE DUNCAN, JR, b Beloit, Wis, July 7, 28; m 53; c 7. LIMNOLOGY. *Educ:* Loras Col, BA, 51; Univ Wis, MS, 57, PhD(algal ecol), 60. *Prof Exp:* Pub health biologist, Wis State Bd Health, 57-59; from asst prof to assoc prof biol, Wis State Univ, Whitewater, 59-63; assoc prof biol & assoc dir hydrobiol sta, St Mary's Col, Minn, 63-68; assoc prof, 68-72, PROF LIMNOL, MICH STATE UNIV, 72- *Concurrent Pos:* Dir field ecol progs, Wis State Univ Pigeon Lake Field Sta, 62-63. *Mem:* Int Asn Aquatic Vascular Plant Biologists; Am Soc Limnol & Oceanog; Ecol Soc Am; Am Inst Biol Sci; Aquatic Weed Mgt Soc. *Res:* Ecology of aquatic macrophytes; mineral cycles in lakes; ecological implications of aquatic weed control. *Mailing Add:* Dept of Fisheries & Wildlife Mich State Univ East Lansing MI 48823

MCNABB, DAVID HOWARD, b Pleasanton, Kans, June 4, 47. FOREST SOIL SCIENCE, SOIL PHYSICS. *Educ:* Univ Mo, BSF, 70, MS, 72. *Prof Exp:* Res asst, Dept Soil Sci, 72-74 & Dept Forest Sci, 77-78, EXTEN WATERSHED SPECIALIST, DEPT FOREST ENG, ORE STATE UNIV, 78- *Concurrent Pos:* Instr, Sch Forestry, Univ Mont, 78. *Mem:* Am Soc Agron; Soil Sci Soc Am; Soc Am Foresters. *Res:* Soil compaction; slope stability; road construction; forest soil/site productivity; mechanical site preparation; prescribed burning. *Mailing Add:* 1301 Maple Grove Dr Medford OR 97501

MCNABB, F M ANNE, b Edmonton, Alta, Jan 17, 39; m 63; c 1. COMPARATIVE PHYSIOLOGY. *Educ:* Univ Alta, BEd, 60, BSc, 61; Univ Calif, Los Angeles, MA, 65, PhD(zool), 68. *Prof Exp:* Asst prof biol & allied health, Quinnipiac Col, 68-69; adj asst prof, 69-72, asst prof, 72-80, ASSOC PROF ZOOL, VA POLYTECH INST & STATE UNIV, 80- *Concurrent Pos:* Fel zool, Yale Univ, 68-69. *Mem:* Fel AAAS; Am Soc Zoologists; Sigma Xi. *Res:* Avian kidney function, particularly nitrogen excretion, including urate solubility problems, electrolyte excretion, water balance in different environments; role of the thyroid gland in development of temperature regulation in precocial and altricial birds. *Mailing Add:* Dept of Biol Va Polytech Inst & State Univ Blacksburg VA 24061

MCNABB, HAROLD SANDERSON, JR, b Lincoln, Nebr, Nov 20, 27; m 49; c 2. FOREST PATHOLOGY. *Educ:* Univ Nebr, BSc, 49; Yale Univ, MS, 51, PhD(plant sci), 54. *Prof Exp:* Asst bot, Univ Nebr, 46-49; asst plant sci, Yale Univ, 49-52; asst prof bot, 53-54, asst prof bot & forestry, 54-56, assoc prof, 56-64, assoc inst atomic res, 54-76, PROF FORESTRY & PLANT PATH, IOWA STATE UNIV, 64- *Concurrent Pos:* Sci adv, Tree Res Inst; coordr forestry res, Iowa State Conserv Comn, 53-59; mem, Int Bot Cong, France, 54, Can, 59 & Gt Brit, 64; ed, Iowa Acad Sci, 64- *Mem:* AAAS; Soc Am Foresters; Am Phytopath Soc; Mycol Soc Am. *Res:* Diseases of forest and shade trees; deterioration of wood. *Mailing Add:* 223 B Charles E Bessey Hall Iowa State Univ Ames IA 50010

MCNABB, ROGER ALLEN, b Moose Jaw, Sask, May 21, 38; m 63; c 1. COMPARATIVE PHYSIOLOGY. *Educ:* Univ Alta, BSc, 61, MSc, 63; Univ Calif, Los Angeles, PhD(zool), 68. *Prof Exp:* Res staff biologist, Yale Univ, 68-69; asst prof, 69-75, ASSOC PROF BIOL, VA POLYTECH INST & STATE UNIV, 75- *Concurrent Pos:* Assoc ed, Am Zoologist, 78-82. *Mem:* Am Soc Zool; Am Physiol Soc; Am Inst Biol Sci. *Res:* Physiology of environmental adaptations in lower vertebrate animals. *Mailing Add:* Dept of Biol Va Polytech Inst & State Univ Blacksburg VA 24061

MCNAIR, DOUGLAS MCINTOSH, b Rockingham, NC, July 19, 27; m 51; c 1. PSYCHOPHARMACOLOGY, PSYCHOLOGY. *Educ:* Univ NC, Chapel Hill, AB, 48, PhD(clin psychol), 54. *Prof Exp:* Sr clin psychologist, Guildford County Ment Health Clin, 52-55; psychologist, Col Infirmary & asst prof psychol, Univ NC, Greensboro, 55-56; res psychologist & asst chief outpatient psychiat res lab, Vet Admin, Washington, DC, 56-64; asst prof, 64-65, assoc prof psychiat, 65-70, PROF PSYCHIAT, SCH MED, BOSTON UNIV, 70-, PROF PSYCHOL & DIR, CLIN PSYCHOPHARM LAB & CLIN PSYCHOL TRAINING, 80- *Concurrent Pos:* Consult, 72-; mem psychopharmacol agents adv comt, Food & Drug Admin, 77- *Mem:* Psychomet Soc; Am Col Neuropsychopharmacol; Am Psychol Asn. *Res:* Drugs and behavior; psychotherapy; experimental design. *Mailing Add:* Psychol Dept 64 Cummington St Boston MA 02215

MCNAIR, HAROLD MONROE, b Miami, Ariz, May 31, 33; m 60; c 3. ANALYTICAL CHEMISTRY. *Educ:* Univ Ariz, BS, 55; Purdue Univ, MS, 57, PhD(anal chem), 59. *Prof Exp:* Fulbright & univ fels, Eindhoven Technol Univ, 59-60, Perkin Elmer res fel, 60; res chemist, Esso Res & Eng, NJ, 60-61; tech dir, Europe Div, F&M Sci Corp, Amsterdam, 61-63, gen mgr, 63-64; dir int opers, Varian Aerograph, Switz, 64-66, dir mkt, Calif, 66-68; assoc prof, 68-71, PROF ANAL CHEM, VA POLYTECH INST & STATE UNIV, 71- *Concurrent Pos:* Consult, Instrument Group, Varian Assocs, 68-; adj prof, Nat Univ Mex; Air Pollution Control Off, Res Triangle, NC; vis prof, Eindhoven Tech Univ, Holland, 81. *Mem:* Am Chem Soc; Am Soc Test & Mat; NY Acad Sci; Sigma Xi. *Res:* Gas chromatography; quantitative analysis of ionization detectors and temperature programming; trace gas analysis by ionization detectors; selection of selective liquid phases; theory of chromatography; liquid chromatography; quantitative analysis by capillary column gas chromatography; influence of injection systems; multidimensional chromatography. *Mailing Add:* Dept Chem Va Polytech Inst & State Univ Blacksburg VA 24061

MCNAIR, IRVING M, JR, b Herndon, Va, Dec 18, 32; m 59; c 2. ELECTRICAL ENGINEERING. *Educ:* Pa State Univ, BS, 54; Stevens Inst Technol, MS, 61. *Prof Exp:* Mem tech staff, 54-61, supvr test sets & methods, 61-64, supvr outside plant & signaling group, 64-71, subscriber loop multiplexer group, 71-74, supvr test access automated distributing, 74-76, SUPVR SPEC SERV, BELL LABS, 76- *Mem:* Inst Elec & Electronics Engrs. *Res:* Low power logic circuits; low power transistor circuits for use in portable test equipment; system design for switching and carrier systems for telephone loop application; circuit design for special services. *Mailing Add:* Bell Tel Labs Rm 1F-214 Whippany NJ 07981

MACNAIR, RICHARD NELSON, b Newton, Mass, Oct 19, 29; m 60; c 1. ORGANIC CHEMISTRY. *Educ:* Middlebury Col, AB, 52; Univ Del, PhD(org chem), 60. *Prof Exp:* Chemist, Arthur D Little, Inc, 60-63; sr chemist, Tracerlab Div, Lab for Electronics, Inc, 64; res chemist, 64-69, SUPVRY RES CHEMIST, US ARMY NATICK RES & DEVELOP

COMMAND, 69- *Concurrent Pos:* Mem, Int Oceanog Found; comt chmn 52nd nat meeting printing & advertising, Am Inst Chemists, 75. *Mem:* Am Chem Soc; Am Carbon Soc; Am Asn Textile Chemists & Colorists; Sigma Xi; Am Inst Chemists. *Res:* Heterocyclic chemistry; graft polymerization; chemical protective clothing; activated carbon sorption-desorption; carbon fibers and fabrics. *Mailing Add:* Individual Protection Lab US Army Res & Develop Lab Natick MA 01760

MCNAIR, ROBERT J(OHN), JR, b Owego, NY, Mar 24, 18; m 51; c 2. ELECTRICAL ENGINEERING. *Educ:* Univ Mich, BS, 50; Univ Wis, MS, 55, PhD(elec eng), 58. *Prof Exp:* Electronics engr, Bell Aircraft Corp, NY, 51-53, staff engr, 56-58; prin staff engr, Electronics Div, 58-73, SCI CONSULT, AVCO CORP, 74- *Concurrent Pos:* Patent agent, US Patent & Trademark Off. *Mem:* Inst Elec & Electronics Engrs. *Res:* Radio communications theory and practice; subatomic particle sensing instruments; solid state circuitry and devices. *Mailing Add:* 2920 Blue Haven Terr Cincinnati OH 45238

MCNAIR, RUTH DAVIS, b Flint, Mich, Mar 18, 21; m 50; c 2. CLINICAL CHEMISTRY. *Educ:* Univ Mich, BS, 41; Univ Cincinnati, BS, 42; Wayne State Univ, PhD(biochem), 48; Am Bd Clin Chem, dipl. *Prof Exp:* DIR BIOCHEM, PROVIDENCE HOSP, 48- *Mem:* AAAS; Sigma Xi; fel Am Inst Chemists; Am Chem Soc; fel Am Asn Clin Chemists. *Res:* Protein, nutrition and metabolism. *Mailing Add:* Lab Providence Hosp 16001 W Nine Mile Rd Southfield MI 48037

MCNAIRN, ROBERT BLACKWOOD, b San Francisco, Calif, Mar 13, 40; m 62; c 2. PLANT PHYSIOLOGY. *Educ:* Univ Calif, Berkeley, BS, 62; Univ Calif, Davis, MS, 64, PhD(plant physiol), 67. *Prof Exp:* From asst prof to assoc prof, 67-76, PROF BOT, CALIF STATE UNIV, CHICO, 76- *Concurrent Pos:* Plant physiologist, Thornton Wholesale Florist & Flower Grower, 74-75. *Mem:* Am Soc Plant Physiol. *Res:* Phloem translocation; flowering; stress physiology. *Mailing Add:* Dept of Biol Calif State Univ Chico CA 95929

MCNALL, EARL GEORGE, b Guernsey, Wyo, Sept 18, 24; m 48; c 2. BIOCHEMISTRY. *Educ:* Univ Southern Calif, AB, 52; Univ Calif, Los Angeles, PhD(chem), 57. *Prof Exp:* Asst res biochemist, Sch Med, Univ Calif, Los Angeles, 58-61; asst prof biochem, Sch Med, Univ Southern Calif, 61-68; assoc dir artificial heart prog, Nat Inst Sci Res, Calif, 68-70; vpres res & develop, Consyne Corp, 70-75; PRES, ALLIED SCI, INC, 75- *Mem:* AAAS; Am Chem Soc. *Res:* Protein and polymer chemistry; intermediary metabolism; enzymology; immunochemistry. *Mailing Add:* 9701 Wilshire Blvd 700 Beverly Hills CA 90212

MCNALL, LESTER R, b Gaylord, Kans, Oct 28, 27. PLANT NUTRITION. *Educ:* Univ Wis, BS, 50; Univ Calif, Los Angeles, PhD(org chem), 55. *Prof Exp:* Res chemist, Esso Res & Eng Co, 55-56; res chemist, Paper Mate Mfg Co, Gillette Co, 56-58, head chem res, 58-62, res div, 62-64; tech dir, Leffingwell Chem Co, 66-77, GEN MGR LEFFINGWELL DIV, THOMPSON-HAYWARD CHEM CO, 77- *Mem:* AAAS; Am Chem Soc; Am Soc Hort Sci. *Res:* Chemistry of natural products; agricultural chemistry; minor elements in plant nutrition; foliar feeding. *Mailing Add:* Leffingwell Div 111 Berry St Brea CA 92621

MCNALL, PRESTON E(SSEX), JR, b Madison, Wis, June 8, 23; m 47; c 3. MECHANICAL ENGINEERING. *Educ:* Univ Wis, BS, 47; Purdue Univ, MS, 49, PhD(mech eng), 51. *Prof Exp:* Res engr, Minneapolis-Honeywell Regulator Co, 51-53, supvr res, 53-55, sect head, 55-57, chief engr appl res, Temperature Controls Group, 57-65; prof mech eng & assoc dir, Inst Environ Res, Kans State Univ, 65-71; sr group mgr eng div, Johnson Serv Co, 71-72, dir eng, 72-77; CHIEF, BLDG THERMAL & SERV SYSTS DIV, NAT BUR STANDARDS, DEPT COMMERCE, 77- *Mem:* Am Soc Mech Engrs; Am Soc Heating, Refrig & Air-Conditioning Engrs. *Res:* Environmental controls; human response to physical environment. *Mailing Add:* 15000 Good Meadow Ct Gaithersburg MD 20760

MCNALLY, JAMES GREEN, JR, organic chemistry, see previous edition

MCNALLY, JAMES HENRY, b Orange, NJ, Dec 18, 36; m 76. NUCLEAR PHYSICS, INERTIAL FUSION. *Educ:* Cornell Univ, BEng Phys, 59; Calif Inst Technol, PhD(physics), 66. *Prof Exp:* Physicist & prog mgr, Los Alamos Sci Lab, 65-74; asst dir lasers & isotope separation, Energy Res & Develop Admin, 74-75; assoc div leader, Laser Fusion & Dep, Inertial Fusion, 76-81, ASST NAT SECURITY ISSUES PROG MGR, LOS ALAMOS NAT LAB, 81- *Concurrent Pos:* Mem subpanel impact on nat security of nuclear physics, Nat Acad Sci-Nat Res Coun, 70; mem US delegation, Conf on Disarmament, Geneva, 69, 73, 74 & threshold test ban treaty talks, Moscow, 74; consult, Elec Power Res Inst, 75 & 79. *Mem:* Int Inst Strategic Study; AAAS; Am Phys Soc. *Res:* Low energy nuclear spectroscopy; neutron time-of-flight; nuclear weapons design; inertial fusion; laser isotope separation; national security issues. *Mailing Add:* Los Alamos Nat Lab Los Alamos NM 87545

MCNALLY, JAMES RAND, JR, b Boston, Mass, Nov 10, 17; m 42; c 7. PLASMA PHYSICS. *Educ:* Boston Col, BS, 39; Mass Inst Technol, SM, 41; PhD(physics), 43. *Prof Exp:* Asst spectros, Mass Inst Technol, 39-41, spectros & physics, 41-44, instr physics, 44-48; physicist, Stable Isotopes Div, Oak Ridge Nat Lab, 48-55, assoc dir div, 55-57, sr physicist, Physics Div, 57-60, sr staff physicist, Fusion Energy Div, 60-81; CONSULTANT, 82- *Concurrent Pos:* Mem advan fuels adv comt, Elec Power Res Inst. *Mem:* Fel AAAS; Am Phys Soc; fel Optical Soc Am; Soc Appl Spectros; Am Asn Physics Teachers. *Res:* Atomic physics; atomic spectroscopy; fusion physics; ion-layer; advanced fusion fuels; fusion chain reactions. *Mailing Add:* 103 Norman Lane Oak Ridge TN 37830

MCNALLY, JOHN G, b Brooklyn, NY, Mar 5, 32; m 64. ANALYTICAL CHEMISTRY. *Educ:* Polytech Inst Brooklyn, BS, 55, MS, 63. *Prof Exp:* Technician, Chas Pfizer & Co, 49-55, chemist, 55-57; chemist, Escambia Chem Corp, 57-61, head anal dept, 61-68; proj leader, 68-70, head chromatography group, 70-80, GROUP LEADER CHROMATOGRAPHY & SEPARATIONS, AM CYANAMID CO, STAMFORD, 80- *Mem:* Am Chem Soc. *Res:* high performance liquid chromatography; size exclusion chromatography; polymer characterization; computerization; gas chromatography. *Mailing Add:* Am Cyanamid Co 1937 W Main St Stamford CT 06904

MCNALLY, KAREN COOK, b Clovis, Calif. GEOPHYSICS. *Educ:* Univ Calif, Berkeley, AB, 71, MA, 73, PhD(geophysics), 76. *Prof Exp:* Seismologist res asst geophysics, uUniv Calif, Berkeley, 71-75; seismologist, Woodward-Clyde Consults, San Francisco, 75-76; fel, 76-78, SR RES FEL GEOPHYSICS, CALIF INST TECHNOL, 78- *Concurrent Pos:* Consult Seismologist, Woodward-Clyde Consults, 76-; res assoc, Sierra Geophysics, Inc, 77- *Mem:* Seismol Soc Am; Am Geophys Union; AAAS. *Res:* Regional tectonics; earthquake statistics; fracture mechanics; earthquake source mechanism; crust and upper mantle structure. *Mailing Add:* Dept of Geophysics 252-21 1201 E California Blvd Pasadena CA 91125

MCNAMARA, ALLEN GARNET, b Regina, Sask, Feb 28, 26; m 52; c 1. AERONOMY. *Educ:* Univ Sask, BE, 47, MSc, 49, PhD(physics), 54; Univ Mich, MA, 51. *Prof Exp:* From res officer to assoc res officer, 51-63, SR RES OFFICER, NAT RES COUN CAN, 63-, HEAD PLANETARY SCI SECT, HERZBERG INST ASTROPHYS, 75- *Concurrent Pos:* Mem, Can Nat Comt Radio Sci, Int Sci Radio Union. *Mem:* Can Asn Physicists; Inst Elec & Electronics Eng; Am Geophys Union. *Res:* Physics of upper atmosphere; scattering of radio waves by meteor ionization and aurora; rocket investigators of the aurora and upper atmosphere. *Mailing Add:* Nat Res Coun Ottawa ON K1A 0R6 Can

MCNAMARA, DAN GOODRICH, b Waco, Tex, Oct 19, 22; m 49; c 5. PEDIATRICS. *Educ:* Baylor Univ, BS, 43, MD, 46. *Prof Exp:* Resident, Hermann Hosp, Houston, Tex, 49-50; from asst prof to assoc prof, 53-69, PROF PEDIAT, BAYLOR COL MED, 69- *Concurrent Pos:* Fel pediat cardiol, Cardiac Clin, Harriet Lane Home, Johns Hopkins Hosp, 51-53; dir cardiac clin, Tex Children's Hosp, Houston, Tex, 53- *Mem:* Am Acad Pediat. *Res:* Pediatric cardiology, especially secondary pulmonary hypertension and malfunctions of heart in infancy. *Mailing Add:* 6621 Fannin St Houston TX 77030

MCNAMARA, DELBERT HAROLD, b Salt Lake City, Utah, June 28, 23; m 45; c 3. ASTROPHYSICS, ASTRONOMY. *Educ:* Univ Calif, BA, 47, PhD(astron), 50. *Prof Exp:* Asst astronomer, Univ Calif, Berkeley, 50-52, assoc res astronomer, 52-55; asst prof astron, 55-57, assoc prof, 57-62, PROF PHYSICS & ASTRON, BRIGHAM YOUNG UNIV, 62- *Concurrent Pos:* Prin scientist space sci lab, NAm Aviation, Inc. *Mem:* Am Astron Soc; Int Astron Union. *Res:* Stellar spectroscopy and photometry; variable stars; eclipsing binaries. *Mailing Add:* Dept of Physics & Astron Brigham Young Univ Provo UT 84601

MCNAMARA, EDWARD P(AUL), b Troy, NY, Sept 27, 10; m 33; c 3. CERAMICS, PHYSICAL CHEMISTRY. *Educ:* Alfred Univ, BS, 35; Pa State Col, MS, 36. *Prof Exp:* Asst, Pa State Col, 35-36, head ceramic exten dept, 36-42; dir ceramics dept & NJ ceramic res sta, Rutgers Univ, 42-45; pres & gen mgr, Pfaltzgraff Pottery Co, 45-46; dir ceramics, Shenango Pottery Co, 46-53; tech dir, Cambridge Tile Mfg Co, 53-63, vpres res & develop, Ohio, 63-69; vpres res & develop, Marshall Tiles Inc, 69-71; pres, Monarch Tile Mfg Inc, 72-77, sr consult, 77-80. *Concurrent Pos:* Vol exec, Int Exec Serv Corps, Mex, 80-81. *Mem:* Fel Am Ceramic Soc; Am Soc Testing & Mat; Am Soc Qual Control; Nat Inst Ceramic Engrs (pres, 71-72). *Res:* Elastico-viscous properties of glasses; properties of borate glasses; reaction rates of limestone calcination; high temperature solution of limestones in slags; glassy and crystalline states of ceramic dielectrics; rheology of clays. *Mailing Add:* 2644 W Twohig San Angelo TX 76901

MCNAMARA, JAMES ALYN, JR, b San Francisco, Calif, June 11, 43; m 70. ORTHODONTICS, ANATOMY. *Educ:* Univ Calif, Berkeley, AB, 64; Univ Calif, San Francisco, BS, DDS & cert orthod spec, 68; Univ Mich, Ann Arbor, MS, 69, PhD(anat), 72. *Prof Exp:* Res assoc, Ctr Human Growth & Develop, 70-72, assoc res scientist and prog dir exp craniofacial res, 72-77, asst prof anat, 72-77, ASSOC PROF ANAT, UNIV MICH, ANN ARBOR, 77-, RES SCIENTIST, CTR HUMAN GROWTH & DEVELOP, 79- *Honors & Awards:* Milo Hellman Res Award, Am Asn Orthodontists, 73; E Sheldon Friel Mem Award, Europ Orthod Soc, 79; Chalmers J Lyons Mem lectr, Am Asn Oral & Maxillofacial Surgeons, 81. *Mem:* Am Asn Orthod; Int Asn Dent Res; Am Asn Anat; Am Dent Asn; Europ Orthod Soc. *Res:* Experimental studies of musculoskeletal interaction; craniofacial growth in man and non-human primates; cephalometric studies of treatment response; relationship of upper respiratory obstruction to craniofacial growth. *Mailing Add:* Dept Anat Univ Mich Ann Arbor MI 48109

MCNAMARA, JOHN EDWARD, b Galesburg, Ill, June 14, 26; m 47; c 2. PHYSICAL INORGANIC CHEMISTRY. *Educ:* Knox Col, Ill, AB, 47; Univ Ill, MA, 49, PhD(chem), 52. *Prof Exp:* Asst chem, Univ Ill, 47-52; res chemist, Calif Res Corp, Stand Oil Co Calif, 52-54, Bell Tel Labs, Inc, 54-55, Semiconductor Prod Div, Motorola, Inc, 55-67 & Integrated Circuits Eng Corp, 67-71; CONSULT, SOLAR ENERGY ASSOCS, 71- *Mem:* Am Chem Soc. *Res:* Semiconductor materials and processes. *Mailing Add:* 4508 E Earll Dr Phoenix AZ 85018

MCNAMARA, JOSEPH JUDSON, b Oakland, Calif, Sept 12, 36; m 58; c 4. SURGERY. *Educ:* Wash Univ, MD, 61; cert, Am Bd Surg, 67, cert thoracic surg, 68. *Prof Exp:* Surgeon, Peter Bent Brigham & Mass Gen Hosps, 61-67; thoracic & cardiovasc surgeon, Baylor Univ Hosp, Dallas, 67-68; actg dir div surg, Walter Reed Army Inst Res, 69-70; PROF SURG, SCH MED, UNIV

HAWAII, MANOA, 70- *Concurrent Pos:* Dir surg educ & cardiovasc res lab, Queen's Med Ctr, 70- *Honors & Awards:* Sheard-Sanford Award, Am Soc Clin Path, 61. *Mem:* Fel Am Col Surg; fel Am Col Cardiol; Am Asn Thoracic Surg; Pan-Pac Surg Asn; Am Heart Asn. *Res:* Myocardial viability after coronary occulsion; defective function of blood elements with storage; platelet function. *Mailing Add:* Dept of Surg Univ of Hawaii Manoa Honolulu HI 96822

MCNAMARA, MARY COLLEEN, b Albuquerque, NMex, Apr 5, 47. NEUROBIOLOGY, NEUROCHEMISTRY. *Educ:* Univ NMex, BS, 71, MS, 72; Univ NC, Chapel Hill, PhD(neurobiol), 75. *Prof Exp:* Teaching asst, Univ NMex, 71-72; instr introd psychol, Sch Med, Univ NC, 74-76, fel physiol, 75-77; asst prof physiol & psychol, Miami Univ, Oxford, 77-78; fel, Duke Univ Med Ctr, 78-80; RES ANALYST, DEPT PEDIAT, SCH MED, UNIV NC, CHAPEL HILL, 80- *Concurrent Pos:* Adj asst prof, Dept Psychol, Univ NC, 78-80. *Mem:* Sigma Xi; Soc Neurosci; Geront Soc; Am Physiol Soc. *Res:* Delineating age related changes in central neurotransmitters in response to stress. *Mailing Add:* Dept Pediat Clin Sci Bldg Rm 362 Chapel Hill NC 27514

MCNAMARA, MICHAEL JOSEPH, b New York, NY, May 16, 29; m 57; c 3. COMMUNITY HEALTH, PREVENTIVE MEDICINE. *Educ:* Fordham Univ, AB, 51; NY Univ, MD, 55; Am Bd Prev Med, dipl. *Prof Exp:* Intern med, Bellevue Hosp, NY Univ, 55-56, asst resident internal med, 56-58; from asst prof to assoc prof community med, Col Med, Univ Ky, 61-70; prof & chmn dept, 70-78, PROF MED & CHIEF, DIV COMMUNITY MED, MED COL OHIO, 78-, ASSOC DEAN, STUDENT AFFAIRS, 79- *Concurrent Pos:* Nat Found fel virus res, Col Med, Cornell Univ, 58-59. *Mem:* Soc epidemiol Res; Asn Teachers Prev Med; Am Pub Health Asn; fel Am Col Prev Med. *Res:* Epidemiology of viral agents in human diseases; epidemiology of hospital acquired infection; development and evaluation of measurement of quality of medical care and programs for risk management in hospitals; teaching of community medicine to medical students and residents in general preventive medicine. *Mailing Add:* Dept of Med Med Col of Ohio CS No 10008 Toledo OH 43699

MACNAMARA, THOMAS E, b Airdrie, Scotland, May 23, 29; US citizen; m; c 5. ANESTHESIOLOGY. *Educ:* Glasgow Univ, MB, ChB, 52. *Prof Exp:* Instr anesthesia, Med Ctr, Georgetown Univ, 57-60; asst, Mass Gen Hosp & Harvard Med Sch, 60-62; PROF ANESTHESIA & CHMN DEPT, MED CTR, GEORGETOWN UNIV, 63- *Concurrent Pos:* Lectr, Bethesda Naval Med Ctr, 63-75, consult, 63-; vpres fac senate, Georgetown Univ, 67-71, pres, 73-75; chief anesthesia dept, NIH Clin Ctr, Bethesda, Md, 75-; consult, DC Gen & Vet Admin Hosps & Charles Town Gen Hosp, Ranson, WVa. *Mem:* Am Soc Anesthesiol; Brit Med Asn; Royal Soc Med; Int Anesthesia Res Soc. *Mailing Add:* Dept of Anesthesia Georgetown Univ Med Ctr Washington DC 20007

MCNAMEE, BERNARD M, b Philadelphia, Pa, Sept 13, 30; m 57; c 5. CIVIL ENGINEERING. *Educ:* Drexel Inst, BS, 53, MBA, 60; Univ Pa, MS, 63; Lehigh Univ, PhD(civil eng), 67. *Prof Exp:* Civil engr, Pa RR, 53; from instr to assoc prof, 55-73, PROF CIVIL ENG, DREXEL UNIV, 74-, CHMN DEPT, 76- *Mem:* Am Soc Civil Engrs; Am Soc Eng Educ; Am Concrete Inst. *Res:* Inelastic frame buckling; fatigue study; composite materials. *Mailing Add:* Dept of Civil Eng Drexel Univ Philadelphia PA 19104

MCNAMEE, JAMES EMERSON, b Englewood, NJ, Sept 17, 46; m 69; c 2. PHYSIOLOGY, BIOMEDICAL ENGINEERING. *Educ:* Rutgers Univ, BS, 69; Univ Southern Calif, MS, 71, PhD(biomed eng), 74. *Prof Exp:* Fel physiol, Cardiovascular Res Inst, Univ Calif, San Francisco, 74-76; ASST PROF PHYSIOL, UNIV SC, 76- *Concurrent Pos:* NIH prin investr, Cardiovascular Res Inst, Univ Calif, San Francisco, 74-76. *Mem:* Microcirculatory Soc; Inst Elec & Electronics Engrs; Am Physiol Soc. *Res:* Pulmonary edema; microvascular transport phenomena. *Mailing Add:* Dept of Physiol Univ of SC Sch of Med Columbia SC 29208

MACNAMEE, JAMES K, b Philadelphia, Pa, May 15, 16; m 50. COMPARATIVE PATHOLOGY, MICROBIOLOGY. *Educ:* Auburn Univ, BS, 36, DVM, 37, MS, 42. *Prof Exp:* Prof & chmn dept path & parasitol, Col Vet Med, Auburn Univ, 42-47; prof path, Col Vet Med, Univ Ga, 47-49; comp pathologist, Med Res Labs, Edgewood Arsenal, Md, 49-55 & Biol Res Labs, Ft Detrick, Md, 55-58; dir diag lab, Hawaiian Med Lab, Hawaii, 58-62; dir vet sect, Sixth Army Med Lab, Ft Baker, Calif, 62-65; health scientist adminr, NIH, 65-76; CONSULT & LECTR DIS EXOTIC BIRDS, 76- *Mem:* Sci Res Soc Am; Am Asn Zool Parks; Avicult Soc Am; Am Asn Vet Toxicologists; Am Vet Med Asn. *Res:* Diseases of exotic birds. *Mailing Add:* 133 Caribe Isle Bel Marin Keys Ignacio CA 94947

MCNAMEE, LAWRENCE PAUL, b Pittsburgh, Pa, Sept 12, 34; m 57; c 7. ELECTRICAL ENGINEERING, COMPUTER SCIENCE. *Educ:* Univ Pittsburgh, BSEE, 56, MSEE, 58, PhD(elec eng), 64. *Prof Exp:* Teaching asst elec eng, Univ Pittsburgh, 56-57, from instr to asst prof, 58-66; from asst to assoc prof comput sci, 66-76, ASSOC PROF ENG & APPL SCI, UNIV CALIF, LOS ANGELES, 76- *Concurrent Pos:* Consult, Knowledge Availability Ctr, NASA, Pa, 65-66, TRW Systs, Inc, Calif, 68- & Hughes Aircraft Co, Calif, 71- *Mem:* Inst Elec & Electronics Engrs; Asn Comput Mach; Simulation Coun; Opers Res Soc Am; Am Math Soc. *Res:* Computer aided design; simulation; digital filtering. *Mailing Add:* Dept of Comput Sci Univ of Calif Los Angeles CA 90024

MCNANEY, JOHN A, inorganic chemistry, see previous edition

MCNARY, ROBERT REED, b Dayton, Ohio, Oct 9, 03; m 48. BIOCHEMISTRY. *Educ:* Univ Cincinnati, Chem E, 26, PhD(biochem), 36; Antioch Col, AM, 33. *Prof Exp:* Res chemist, Thomas & Hochwalt Labs, Ohio, 26-28, Frigidaire Corp, 28-32, Kettering Lab, Col Med, Univ Cincinnati, 36-43 & Citrus Exp Sta, Fla Citrus Comn, 46-59; consult chemist, 59-74; RETIRED. *Res:* By-product development of citrus fruits; methods of treating citrus cannery waste water; industrial hygiene chemistry; chlorophyll decompositions; freon refrigerants. *Mailing Add:* 31 Cunningham Dr New Smyrna Beach FL 32069

MCNAUGHT, DONALD CURTIS, limnology, see previous edition

MACNAUGHTAN, DONALD, JR, b Keene, NH, Apr 13, 39; m 68; c 3. ANALYTICAL CHEMISTRY. *Educ:* Univ NH, BS, 67; Purdue Univ, PhD(anal chem), 72. *Prof Exp:* Asst prof, Univ Ill, 71-74 & Loras Col, 74-75; res specialist, 75-80, GROUP LEADER, MOBAY CHEM CORP, 80- *Mem:* Am Chem Soc. *Res:* The application and development of analytical methodology for the solution of industrial problems in production and applications, especially utilizing mass spectrometry. *Mailing Add:* Mobay Chem Corp New Martinsville WV 26155

MACNAUGHTON, EARL BRUCE, b Maple, Ont, Aug 29, 19; m 43; c 2. PHYSICS. *Educ:* Univ Toronto, BA, 41, MA, 46, PhD(physics), 48. *Prof Exp:* Instr physics, Univ Toronto, 41-44; prof, Ont Agr Col, 48-56, head dept, 56-65; prof & head dept, Wellington Col, 65-70, assoc dean sci, 66-70, dean col phys sci, 70-81, PROF PHYSICS, UNIV GUELPH, 82- *Mem:* Am Phys Soc; Am Asn Physics Teachers; Can Asn Physicists. *Res:* Molecular spectroscopy; electronics and instrumentation. *Mailing Add:* Dept Physics Univ of Guelph Guelph ON N1G 2W1 Can

MCNAUGHTON, JAMES LARRY, b Morton, Miss, Sept 22, 48; m 77. NUTRITION. *Educ:* Miss State Univ, BS, 70, MS, 72, PhD(nutrit), 75. *Prof Exp:* Nutritionist, Miss State Univ, 70-75; NUTRITIONIST, POULTRY RES LAB, AGR RES STA, USDA, 75- *Mem:* Am Inst Nutrit; US Poultry Sci Asn; World Poultry Sci Asn; Sigma Xi. *Res:* Increase poultry productivity; improve quality of feeds and feed components of farm animals; develop processing techniques for feeds. *Mailing Add:* S Cent Poultry Res Lab PO Box 5367 Mississippi State MS 39762

MCNAUGHTON, MICHAEL WALFORD, b Durban, SAfrica, Mar 2, 43; Eng citizen; m 69; c 2. EXPERIMENTAL NUCLEAR PHYSICS, ELEMENTARY PARTICLE PHYSICS. *Educ:* Univ London, BSc, 62, PhD(physics), 72; Oxford Univ, MA, 66. *Prof Exp:* Physicist, Crocker Nuclear Lab, Univ Calif, Davis, 72-75; sr res assoc nuclear physics, Case Western Reserve Univ, 75-78; STAFF MEM, LOS ALAMOS SCI LAB, 78- *Res:* Polarized few nucleon nuclear physics, neutron physics, polarised proton beams and targets; proton polarimeters. *Mailing Add:* MP13 MS 838 Los Alamos Sci Lab Los Alamos NM 87545

MCNAUGHTON, ROBERT, b Brooklyn, NY, Mar 13, 24; m 74; c 2. MATHEMATICS, COMPUTER SCIENCES. *Educ:* Columbia Univ, BA, 48; Harvard Univ, PhD(philos), 51. *Prof Exp:* Asst prof philos, Stanford Univ, 54-57; from asst prof to assoc prof elec eng, Univ Pa, 57-64; vis assoc prof elec eng & mem staff, Proj MAC, Mass Inst Technol, 64-66; PROF MATH, RENSSELAER POLYTECH INST, 66- *Honors & Awards:* Levy Medal, 56. *Mem:* Asn Comput Mach; Asn Symbolic Logic. *Res:* Theory of automata and applications of symbolic logic. *Mailing Add:* Dept of Math Sci Rensselaer Polytech Inst Troy NY 12181

MCNAUGHTON, SAMUEL J, b Takoma Park, Md, Aug 10, 39; m 59; c 2. PLANT ECOLOGY. *Educ:* Northwest Mo State Col, BS, 61; Univ Tex, PhD(bot), 64. *Prof Exp:* Asst prof biol, Portland State Col, 64-65; USPHS trainee, Stanford Univ, 65-66; from asst prof to assoc prof bot, 66-73, PROF BOT, SYRACUSE UNIV, 73- *Concurrent Pos:* Res scientist, Serengeti Res Inst, Tanzania, 74-; adj prof, Univ Dar es Salaam, 74-75. *Mem:* AAAS; Bot Soc Am; Ecol Soc Am; Brit Ecol Soc. *Res:* Ecotype physiology, community organization, and grazing ecology. *Mailing Add:* Biol Res Labs Syracuse Univ Syracuse NY 13210

MCNEAL, BRIAN LESTER, b Cascade, Idaho, Jan 27, 38; m 58; c 4. SOIL CHEMISTRY. *Educ:* Ore State Univ, BS, 60, MS, 62; Univ Calif, Riverside, PhD(soil chem), 65. *Prof Exp:* Lab asst soil chem, Ore State Univ, 58-59; student trainee, Agr Res Serv, USDA, 59-60, soil scientist, 60-61, res soil scientist, US Salinity Lab, Calif, 61-70; assoc prof, 70-76, PROF SOILS, WASH STATE UNIV, 76- *Concurrent Pos:* Vis prof, Colo State Univ, 80. *Mem:* Soil Sci Soc Am; Am Soc Agron. *Res:* Pollution chemistry; chemistry of salt-affected soils; soil physical chemistry; modeling of soil chemical processes. *Mailing Add:* Dept Agron & Soils Wash State Univ Pullman WA 99164

MCNEAL, DALE WILLIAM, JR, b Kansas City, Kans, Nov 23, 39; m 66. BOTANY. *Educ:* Colo Col, AB, 62; State Univ NY Col Forestry, Syracuse Univ, MS, 65; Wash State Univ, PhD(bot), 69. *Prof Exp:* Asst prof, 69-74, assoc prof, 74-79, PROF BIOL, UNIV OF THE PAC, 79-, CHMN, DEPT BIOL SCI, 78- *Mem:* Am Bot Soc; Am Soc Plant Taxon; Int Soc Plant Taxon. *Res:* Biosystematics of Allium; floristics of unusual environments. *Mailing Add:* Dept of Biol Sci Univ of the Pac Stockton CA 95211

MCNEAL, FRANCIS H, b Bartlett, Ore, Dec 9, 20; m 47; c 2. PLANT BREEDING, PLANT GENETICS. *Educ:* Ore State Col, BS, 43, MS, 48; Univ Minn, PhD(genetics), 53. *Prof Exp:* RES AGRONOMIST, AGR RES SERV, USDA, 47- *Concurrent Pos:* Mem, Hard Red Spring Wheat Regional Comt, 49-; secy & tech adv, Western Wheat Improv Comt, 56-; mem, Nat Wheat Improv Comt, 59- *Mem:* Fel Am Soc Agron. *Res:* Development of improved wheat varieties for western states; genetic and related studies of the wheat plant. *Mailing Add:* Dept of Plant & Soil Sci Mont State Univ Bozeman MT 59715

MCNEAL, ROBERT JOSEPH, b Knoxville, Tenn, Dec 23, 37; m 62; c 2. CHEMICAL PHYSICS, SPACE PHYSICS. *Educ:* Univ Calif, Berkeley, BS, 59; Columbia Univ, MA, 61, PhD(chem), 63. *Prof Exp:* NSF fel, Harvard Univ, 63-64; head lab aeronomy dept, Space Physics Lab, Los Angeles, 64-70, asst dir, Chem & Physics Lab, Aerospace Corp, 72-78; mgr policy analysis div, Environ Res & Tech, 79-80; MGR AIR QUALITY PROF, NASA HQ, WASHINGTON, DC, 80- *Concurrent Pos:* Prog dir atmospheric chem, NSF, 78-79. *Mem:* Fel Am Phys Soc; Am Geophys Union. *Res:* Atomic and molecular physics; chemical kinetics; aeronomy; atmospheric chemistry and physics. *Mailing Add:* 342 Chesapeake Dr Great Falls VA 22066

MACNEE, ALAN B(RECK), b New York, NY, Sept 19, 20; m 46; c 4. ELECTRICAL ENGINEERING. *Educ:* Mass Inst Technol, SB & SM, 43, ScD(elec eng), 48. *Prof Exp:* Asst engr, Western Elec Co, NY, 41; asst, Bell Tel Labs, Inc, 41; mem staff, Radiation Lab, Mass Inst Technol, 43-45; group leader, Continental TV Co, Mass, 46; asst elec commun, Mass Inst Technol, 46-48, res assoc, 48-49 & Chalmers Tech Sweden, 49-50; from asst prof to assoc prof elec eng, 50-56, PROF ELEC ENG, UNIV MICH, ANN ARBOR, 56- *Concurrent Pos:* Vis prof, Chalmers Tech Sweden, 61-62; NASA sr assoc, Goddard Space Flight Ctr, 71-72; mem tech staff, Sandia Labs, 80-81. *Mem:* Fel Inst Elec & Electronics Engrs; for mem Swedish Royal Soc Lit & Sci; fel AAAS. *Res:* Design of wideband amplifiers and receivers; electronic computing devices; semiconductor modeling; semiconductor and distributed circuit design; computer aided circuit analysis and optimization; network synthesis. *Mailing Add:* Dept Elec & Computer Eng Univ Mich Ann Arbor MI 48104

MCNEELY, ROBERT LEWIS, b Morganton, NC, June 5, 38. ANALYTICAL CHEMISTRY. *Educ:* Duke Univ, BS, 60; Univ NC, Chapel Hill, PhD(chem), 69. *Prof Exp:* Teaching asst chem, Calif Inst Technol, 60-62; Peace Corps teacher chem, Govt Col Nigeria, 63-65; res asst, Univ NC, Chapel Hill, 65-69; asst prof, 69-73, assoc prof, 73-78, PROF CHEM, UNIV TENN, CHATTANOOGA, 78- *Mem:* AAAS; Am Chem Soc; Am Inst Chem; Am Asn Univ Professors. *Res:* Instrumental analysis, particularly in elecro- chemistry and absorption spectroscopy; analysis of air and water pollutants. *Mailing Add:* Dept of Chem Univ of Tenn Chattanooga TN 37402

MCNEES, ROGER WAYNE, b San Antonio, Tex, May 26, 44; m 70. HUMAN FACTORS ENGINEERING. *Educ:* St Mary's Univ, Tex, BBA, 66, MA, 68; Tex A&M Univ, MBA, 71, PhD(indust eng), 76. *Prof Exp:* Acct, Southwest Res Inst, 67-68; res asst, 71-76, res assoc human factors, 77-79, ENG RES ASSOC, TEX TRANSP INST, 79- *Concurrent Pos:* Lectr, Civil Eng Dept, Tex A&M Univ, 81-82. *Mem:* Human Factors Soc; Am Inst Indust Engrs. *Res:* Simulation development for traffic systems; static and real-time information systems; perception-decision-reaction time systems; safety and human factors engineering; accident investigation analysis. *Mailing Add:* 3113 Hummingbird Circle Bryan TX 77801

MCNEESE, LEONARD EUGENE, b Round Rock, Tex, May 11, 35; m 54; c 3. CHEMICAL ENGINEERING. *Educ:* Tex Technol Univ, BS, 57; Univ Tenn, MS, 63. *Prof Exp:* Develop engr chem eng, 57-68, proj mgr molten salt reactor processing, 68-73, sect chief unit opers, Chem Technol Div, 73, dir molten salt reactor prog, 74-76, sect head eng coord & anal, Chem Technol Div, 76, assoc dir, Chem Technol Div, 76, DIR FOSSIL ENERGY PROG, OAK RIDGE NAT LAB, 77- *Concurrent Pos:* Consult to commissioners, Generic Environ Statement on Mixed Oxides, Nuclear Regulatory Agency, 76. *Honors & Awards:* Engr of the Yr, Am Inst Chem Engrs, 76. *Mem:* Am Inst Chem Engrs; Am Nuclear Soc; Am Soc Mech Engrs; Sigma Xi. *Res:* Fossil energy research and development; coal liquefaction, gasification, and combustion; nuclear fuel reprocessing; nonaqueous high temperature molten salt systems; uranium hexafluoride-sodium fluoride sorption reactions. *Mailing Add:* Fossil Energy Prog Oak Ridge Nat Lab Oak Ridge TN 37830

MCNEICE, GREGORY MALCOLM, b Bracebridge, Ont, Aug 11, 39; m 64; c 4. BIOENGINEERING, CIVIL ENGINEERING. *Educ:* Univ Waterloo, BASc, 64; Univ London, PhD(struct eng), 68. *Prof Exp:* Res asst prof, 68-69, from asst prof to assoc prof, 69-76, PROF CIVIL ENG, UNIV WATERLOO, 76- *Concurrent Pos:* Univ Waterloo fel & vis asst prof, Brown Univ, 71-72; vis assoc prof, Univ Calif, Los Angeles. *Mem:* Am Acad Mech; Int Soc Biomech; Am Soc Biomech. *Res:* Finite element research and ortaopadeic bioengineering; applications of engineering mechanics and materials science to areas of orthopaedic bioengineering; design and implementation of spinal implants for non-fusion paediatrics; theoretical and experimental design of adult total joint replacement implants; full scale testing and analysis of spinal stability, hip joints, knee joints and various musculo/skeletal joints; stress analysis, including finite element techniques of various engineering structures including total joint replacements; analytical modelling and full scale testing of various engineering structures, including automotive parts, truck frames and tractor-trailer experimentation; mathematical modelling and experimental testing of impact dynamics on the human body; test facilities include the Hybrid III anthropomorphic dummy and supporting electronics; studies of head/neck injury in sports and the work place. *Mailing Add:* Dept of Civil Eng Univ of Waterloo Waterloo ON N2L 3G1 Can

MCNEIL, BARBARA JOYCE, b Cambridge, Mass, Feb 11, 41. RADIOLOGY, NUCLEAR MEDICINE. *Educ:* Harvard Med Sch, MD, 66; Harvard Univ, PhD(biol chem), 72. *Prof Exp:* Intern pediat, Mass Gen Hosp, 66-67; instr radiol, Harvard Med Sch, 74-75, asst prof, 75-78, STAFF RADIOLOGIST NUCLEAR MED, JOINT PROG NUCLEAR MED, HARVARD MED SCH, 74-, ASSOC PROF RADIOL, 78- *Concurrent Pos:* Consult, Mass Radiol Soc Comt Nuclear Med, 74-; mem, Spec Comt Pub Health & Efficacy, Soc Nuclear Med, 75-; mem, Radiopharmaceut Adv Comt, Food & Drug Admin, HEW, 76-80; res career develop award, NIH, 76-81; Kieckhefer lectr, Harvard-Mass Inst Technol Div Health Sci & Technol, 78-79. *Mem:* Inst Med-Nat Acad Sci; Am Chem Soc; Soc Nuclear Med; Asn Univ Radiologists; AAAS. *Res:* Cost effectiveness of diagnostic medicine, particularly radiology; value of diagnostic tests in oncology. *Mailing Add:* Dept of Radiol 25 Shattuck St Boston MA 02115

MCNEIL, JEREMY NICHOL, b Tonbridge, Eng, Nov 20, 44; Can citizen. ENTOMOLOGY, ECOLOGY. *Educ:* Univ Western Ont, BSc, 69; NC State Univ, PhD(entom, ecol), 72. *Prof Exp:* Asst prof, 72-78, ASSOC PROF ENTOM, LAVAL UNIV, 78- *Concurrent Pos:* Assoc ed, Can Entomologist, 76- *Honors & Awards:* C Gordon Hewitt Award, Entom Soc Can, 79. *Mem:* Entom Soc Am; fel Entom Soc Can; Sigma Xi. *Res:* Development of management programmes for agricultural pests; pheromone ecology; control of forest pests by an imported predaceous ant. *Mailing Add:* Dept of Biol Laval Univ Quebec PQ G1K 7P4 Can

MACNEIL, JOSEPH H, b Sydney, NS, Apr 13, 31; m 57; c 5. FOOD SCIENCE. *Educ:* McGill Univ, BSA, 55; Mich State Univ, MS, 58, PhD(food sci), 61. *Prof Exp:* Asst agr rep, NS Dept Agr, 52-53; field serv rep, Maritime Coop Serv, 55-57; res asst poultry mkt, Mich State Univ, 57-61; asst prof poultry sci, Univ Conn, 61-62; sr res assoc food res, Lever Bros Co, NJ, 62-64; asst prof poultry sci, 64-71, assoc prof food sci, 71-73, PROF FOOD SCI, PA STATE UNIV, UNIVERSITY PARK, 73- *Concurrent Pos:* Fulbright scholar, 74-75. *Mem:* Inst Food Technol; Poultry Sci Asn; Sigma Xi. *Res:* Processing technology of poultry meat, quality maintenance, sensory evaluation techniques, flavor changes and nutritional status of food. *Mailing Add:* Dept of Food Sci Pa State Univ University Park PA 16802

MCNEIL, KENNETH MARTIN, b Edinburgh, Scotland, Oct 20, 41. CHEMICAL ENGINEERING. *Educ:* Univ Edinburgh, BSc, 62; Cambridge Univ, PhD(chem eng), 65. *Prof Exp:* Proj chem engr, Amoco Chem Corp, 65-67, sr proj chem engr, 67-70; asst prof chem eng, Drexel Univ, 70-76; CONSULT CHEM ENG, KENNETH M McNEIL ASSOCS, 77-; ASSOC PROF ENG, WIDENER UNIV, 82- *Concurrent Pos:* Adj prof continuing educ, Drexel Univ, 72-78. *Mem:* Am Inst Chem Engrs; Brit Inst Chem Engrs; Am Chem Soc. *Res:* Fluid-fluid reactions; catalytic fluid-solid reactions; gas absorption; pollution control systems; coal conversion. *Mailing Add:* 1620 Rolling Glen Dr Boothwyn PA 19061

MCNEIL, MICHAEL BREWER, b Houston, Tex, July 26, 38; m 60; c 1. METALLURGY. *Educ:* Rice Univ, BA, 59, MA, 62; Univ Mo, Rolla, PhD(metall eng), 66. *Prof Exp:* Mem tech staff, Tex Instruments Inc, 62-64; lectr metall, Univ Mo, Rolla, 66; res asst physics, Univ Bristol, 66; assoc physicist, Midwest Res Inst, Mo, 66-68; assoc prof ceramic & metall eng, Miss State Univ, 68-72; metallurgist, Nat Bur Standards, 72-77, DIV INDUST ENERGY CONSERV, US DEPT ENERGY, 77- *Concurrent Pos:* Nat Acad Sci vis lectr, Univs Bucuresti & Cluj, Romania, 71. *Mem:* Fel Brit Inst Metallurgists. *Res:* Electrometallurgy; electron theory of metals; metals extraction. *Mailing Add:* Div Indust Energy Conserv US Dept of Energy Washington DC 20585

MCNEIL, PHILLIP EUGENE, b Cincinnati, Ohio, May 13, 41; m 66; c 3. ALGEBRA. *Educ:* Ohio Univ, BS, 63; Pa State Univ, MA, 65, PhD(math), 68. *Prof Exp:* Asst prof math, Xavier Univ, 68- 70 & Univ Cincinnati, 70-73; prog assoc math, Inst Serv Educ, 71-73; assoc prof, 73-77, PROF MATH, NORFOLK STATE COL, 77-, HEAD DEPT, 80- *Concurrent Pos:* Consult, Educ Develop Prog, Univ Cincinnati, 70-71, Minorities Comt, Nat Res Coun, 72, Norfolk Pub Schs, Va, 73 & Inst Serv Educ, 73-; consult & lectr, SEEK Proj, Hunter Col, 72-73 & Racine Pub Schs, Wis, 73; dir, Minority Inst Sci Improv Prog, 74-; nat pres, Men's & Women's Develop Asn, 75. *Honors & Awards:* Inst Serv Educ Plaque, 73. *Mem:* Am Math Soc; Math Asn Am; Nat Asn Mathematicians; Asn Educ Data Systs. *Res:* Development of structure theorems in the area of algebraic semigroups; curriculum development in undergraduate mathematics. *Mailing Add:* Dept of Math Norfolk State Col 2401 Corprew Ave Norfolk VA 23504

MCNEIL, RAYMOND, b St Fabien de Panet, Que, Nov 30, 36; m 63; c 1. ORNITHOLOGY. *Educ:* Laval Univ, BA, 59; Univ Montreal, BSc, 62, MSc, 64, PhD(ornith), 68. *Prof Exp:* Teacher ecol & ornith, Oriente, Venezuela, 65-67; asst prof, 67-81, PROF BIOL SCI, ECOL RES CTR MONTREAL, UNIV MONTREAL, 81- *Mem:* Am Ornith Union; Cooper Ornith Soc; Wilson Ornith Soc; Brit Ornith Union. *Res:* Population ecology of birds; natural history of birds; fat deposition in migratory birds and its relationships with flyways and the phenomenon of summering in southern latitudes. *Mailing Add:* Dept of Biol Sci Ecol Res Ctr Univ of Montreal Montreal PQ H3C 3J7 Can

MCNEIL, RICHARD JEROME, b Marquette, Mich, Dec 22, 32; m 60; c 3. ECOLOGY. *Educ:* Mich State Univ, BS, 54, MS, 57; Univ Mich, PhD(wildlife mgt), 63. *Prof Exp:* Biologist, Mich Dept Conserv, 57-59, res biologist deer, 60-64; asst prof, 64-69, assoc prof conserv, 70-81, ASSOC PROF NATURAL RESOURSES, CORNELL UNIV, 81- *Concurrent Pos:* Fulbright scholar, NZ, 62-63. *Mem:* Ecol Soc Am; Wildlife Soc. *Res:* International natural resource problems; ecology of ungulates; man and environment; conservation education; social surveys in environmental affairs. *Mailing Add:* Fernow Hall Col of Agr Cornell Univ Ithaca NY 14853

MACNEILL, IAN B, b Regina, Sask, Dec 12, 31; m 52; c 3. MATHEMATICS, STATISTICS. *Educ:* Univ Sask, BA, 62; Queen's Univ, Ont, MA, 65; Stanford Univ, PhD(statist), 69. *Prof Exp:* Asst prof math, Univ Toronto, 66-71; assoc prof appl math, 71-80, PROF & CHMN STATIST & ADVAN SCI, UNIV WESTERN ONT, 80-, DIR STATIST LAB, 77- *Res:* Time series analysis; statistical ecology. *Mailing Add:* Dept of Appl Math Univ of Western Ont London ON N6A 5B8 Can

MCNEILL, JOHN, b Edinburgh, Scotland, Sept 15, 33; m 61; c 2. BOTANY. *Educ:* Univ Edinburgh, BSc, 55, PhD(plant taxon), 60. *Prof Exp:* From asst lectr to lectr agr bot, Univ Reading, 57-61; lectr bot, Univ Liverpool, 61-69; actg assoc prof pop & environ biol, Univ Calif, Irvine, 69; sect chief taxon & econ bot, Plant Res Inst, Can Dept Agr, 69-73, res scientist, Agr Can, 73-77, sr res scientist, Biosyst Res Inst, 77-81; PROF & CHMN, DEPT BIOL, UNIV OTTAWA, 81- *Concurrent Pos:* Vis assoc prof, Univ Wash, 69; adj prof, Carleton Univ, Ottawa, 74-80. *Mem:* Am Soc Naturalists; Am Soc Plant Taxonomists; Can Bot Asn; Int Asn Plant Taxon; Soc Syst Zool. *Res:* Taxonomy and biosystematics of vascular plants, especially weeds; applications of numerical taxonomy to plant classification. *Mailing Add:* Dept Biol Univ Ottawa Ottawa ON K1N 6N5 Can

MCNEILL, JOHN HUGH, b Chicago, Ill, Dec 5, 38; Can citizen; m 63; c 2. PHARMACOLOGY. *Educ:* Univ Alta, BSc, 60, MSc, 62; Univ Mich, PhD(pharmacol), 67. *Prof Exp:* Lab asst pharm, Univ Alta, 59-62, lectr, 63; lectr, Dalhousie Univ, 62-63; asst instr pharmacol, Mich State Univ, 66-65, asst prof, 67-71; assoc prof pharmacol, 71-75, PROF & CHMN, DIV PHARMACOL & TOXICOL, UNIV BC, 75-, ASST DEAN, RES & GRAD

STUDIES, 78- *Concurrent Pos:* Teaching fel pharmacol, Univ Mich, 63-66; res prof, Med Res Coun, 81-82. *Mem:* AAAS; Am Fedn Clin Res; Pharmacol Soc Can; Am Soc Pharmacol & Exp Therapeut; NY Acad Sci. *Res:* Drug interactions with the adrenergic amines on cardiac cyclic AMP; role of cyclic AMP in the cardiac actions of drugs; diabetes; induced cardiac changes. *Mailing Add:* Fac of Pharmaceut Sci Univ of BC Vancouver BC V6T 1W5 Can

MCNEILL, JOHN J, b Washington, DC, Dec 4, 22; m 65; c 2. MICROBIOLOGY. *Educ:* Univ Md, BS, 51, MS, 53, PhD(bact), 57. *Prof Exp:* Asst bact, Univ Md, 51-55; asst prof animal sci & microbiol, 56-66, ASSOC PROF ANIMAL SCI & MICROBIOL, NC STATE UNIV, 66- *Mem:* AAAS; Am Soc Microbiol; fel Am Acad Microbiol; Brit Soc Gen Microbiol. *Res:* Bacterial lipid metabolism; rumen microbiology. *Mailing Add:* 310 Polk Hall NC State Univ Raleigh NC 27607

MCNEILL, KENNETH GORDON, b Appleton, Eng, Dec 21, 26; m 59; c 1. NUCLEAR PHYSICS, NUCLEAR MEDICINE. *Educ:* Oxford Univ, BA, 47, MA & DPhil(physics), 50. *Prof Exp:* Fel nuclear physics, Yale Univ, 50-51; fel, Glasgow Univ, 51-52, lectr physics, 52-57; assoc prof, 57-63, PROF PHYSICS, UNIV TORONTO, 63-, PROF MED, 69- *Concurrent Pos:* Spec staff mem, Toronto Gen Hosp, 74- *Mem:* Am Phys Soc; Can Asn Physicists; fel Inst Nuclear Eng; Can Soc Clin Invest; Soc Nuclear Med. *Res:* Low energy nuclear physics; photodisintegration; applications of nuclear physics to medicine. *Mailing Add:* Dept of Physics Univ of Toronto Toronto ON M5S 1A7 Can

MCNEILL, MICHAEL JOHN, b Algona, Iowa, Sept 12, 42; m 67; c 3. GENETICS, PLANT BREEDING. *Educ:* Iowa State Univ, BS, 64, MS, 67, PhD(plant breeding), 69. *Prof Exp:* Res plant pathologist plant path div, US Biol Res Lab, 69-71; RES GENETICIST, FUNK SEEDS INT, INC, 71- *Mem:* Am Phytopath Soc; Am Soc Agron; Crop Sci Soc Am. *Res:* Plant breeding and pathology dealing mainly with cereal crops. *Mailing Add:* Funk Seeds Int Inc Box 477 Algona IA 50511

MCNEILL, ROBERT BRADLEY, b Martinsburg, WVa, June 20, 41; m; c 2. MATHEMATICS. *Educ:* Univ WVa, AB, 63; Pa State Univ, MA, 65, PhD(math), 68. *Prof Exp:* Asst prof, 68-72, assoc prof, 72-79, PROF MATH, NORTHERN MICH UNIV, 79- *Mem:* AAAS; Am Math Soc; Math Asn Am; Soc Indust & Appl Math. *Res:* Qualitative behavior of solutions of differential equations and differential systems. *Mailing Add:* Dept of Math Northern Mich Univ Marquette MI 49855

MACNEILL, RUPERT HEATH, b PEI, Can, July 13, 14; m 39; c 1. PHYSICS, GEOLOGY. *Educ:* Acadia Univ, BSc, 50, MSc, 51. *Prof Exp:* Lectr geol, 51-52, from asst prof to assoc prof, 52-68, Edwin David King assoc prof geol, 68-76, dir exten, Summer Sch & Student Assistance, 68-78, prof, 76-79, EMER PROF GEOL, ACADIA UNIV, NS, 80- *Concurrent Pos:* Geologist, NS Res Found, summers 49-75, consult, 75-; mem meteorite comt, Nat Res Coun, 67-; chmn, Curric Comt Geol, NS Dept of Educ, 70-75; dir, Navaco, 79- *Honors & Awards:* Hunt Prize, 49; Mining Soc NS Prize, 51. *Mem:* Nat Asn Geol Teachers; hon mem Geol Asn Can; Mineral Asn Can; Geol Soc Am; Soc Explor Geophys. *Res:* Pleistocene of Nova Scotia; supervision of student research. *Mailing Add:* PO Box 340 Wolfville NS B0P 1X0 Can

MCNELIS, EDWARD JOSEPH, b Philadelphia, Pa, Aug 17, 30; m 56; c 2. ORGANIC CHEMISTRY. *Educ:* Villanova Univ, BS, 53; Columbia Univ, PhD(chem), 60. *Prof Exp:* Res chemist, Sun Oil Co, Pa, 60-67; chmn dept chem, 70-73, assoc prof, 67-76, PROF & CHMN DEPT CHEM, WASH SQ COL NY UNIV, 77- *Concurrent Pos:* Vis assoc prof, Haverford Col, 66-67. *Mem:* Am Chem Soc. *Res:* Phenolic oxidation; olefin metathesis. *Mailing Add:* Dept of Chem Wash Univ New York NY 10003

MCNERNEY, JAMES MURTHA, b Pittsburgh, Pa, Apr 3, 27; m 56; c 3. TOXICOLOGY, ENVIRONMENTAL HEALTH. *Educ:* Univ Pittsburgh, BS, 51, ML, 56, MPH, 57. *Prof Exp:* Res asst, Indust Hyg Found, Mellon Inst, 51-53, res assoc, 53-55, res toxicologist, 55-57, chief toxicologist, 57-64; assoc dir toxic hazard res unit, Aerojet-Gen Corp, 64-66; chief animal toxicol, Environ Health Lab, Am Cyanamid Co, 66-68, toxicol group leader, 68-69; dir inhalation toxicol dpet, TRW Hazleton Labs, 69-70; staff toxicologist, Am Petrol Inst, 70-77; dir toxicol, 77-81, VPRES TOXICOL, COSMETIC, TOILETRY & FRAGRANCE ASN INC, 81- *Mem:* Am Indust Hyg Asn; Soc Toxicol. *Res:* Occupational and environmental toxicology; industrial hygiene. *Mailing Add:* Cosmetic Toiletry & Fragrance Asn Inc 1110 Vermont Ave NW Washington DC 20005

MACNERNEY, JOHN SHERIDAN, mathematical analysis, see previous edition

MCNESBY, JAMES ROBERT, b Bayonne, NJ, Apr 16, 22; m 49; c 3. PHYSICAL CHEMISTRY. *Educ:* Univ Ohio, Athens, BS, 43; NY Univ, PhD(chem), 52. *Prof Exp:* Res chemist, Interchem Corp, 45-49; phys chemist, US Naval Ord Test Sta, Calif, 51-56; phys chemist, Nat Bur Standards, 57-62, chief photochem sect, 62-67, chief phys chem div, 67-74, chief off air & water measurement, 74-76; PROF & CHMN CHEM DEPT, UNIV MD, 76- *Concurrent Pos:* Rockefeller pub serv fel, Univ Leeds, 58-59. *Mem:* Am Chem Soc; The Chem Soc. *Res:* Kinetics of free radical reactions; photochemistry. *Mailing Add:* Dept of Chem Univ of Md Col Park MD 20742

MACNICHOL, EDWARD FORD, JR, b Toledo, Ohio, Oct 24, 18; m 40; c 2. BIOPHYSICS. *Educ:* Princeton Univ, AB, 41; Johns Hopkins Univ, PhD, 52. *Prof Exp:* Mem staff, Radiation Lab, Mass Inst Technol, 41-43, assoc group leader, 43-44, group leader, 45-46; asst, Johnson Found, Univ Pa, 46-48; asst biophys, Johns Hopkins Univ, 49-51, from instr to prof, 52-68; dir, Nat Inst Neurol Dis & Stroke, 68-73; asst dir, Marine Biol Lab, 73-76, DIR, LAB SENSORY PHYSIOL MARINE BIOL LAB, WOODS HOLE, 73- *Concurrent Pos:* Vis prof, Venezuelan Inst Sci Res, 57; guest scientist, US Naval Res Inst, 57-60; actg dir, Nat Eye Inst, 68-69; mem bd dirs, Deafness Res Found, 73-; prof physiol, Sch Med, Boston Univ, 73-; mem exec coun, Comt Vision, Nat Res Coun, 75-79, chmn, 78; co-ed, Sensory Processes, 78-81. *Mem:* Am Phys Soc; Biophys Soc; Am Physiol Soc; fel Inst Elec & Electronics Engrs; NY Acad Sci. *Res:* Neurophysiology of retina and other sensory systems; instrumentation for biological research. *Mailing Add:* Lab Sensory Physiol Marine Biol Lab Woods Hole MA 02543

MCNICHOLAS, JOHN VINCENT, b Youngstown, Ohio, Sept 18, 36; m 63; c 3. ACOUSTICS. *Educ:* John Carroll Univ, BS, 58, MS, 59; Cath Univ Am, PhD(physics), 68. *Prof Exp:* Physicist, Naval Ship Res & Develop Ctr, 61-68, Hydrospace Res Corp, 68-71; PHYSICIST, APPL HYDRO ACOUST RES, INC, 71- *Mem:* Acoust Soc Am. *Res:* Truck noise measurements; quiet truck development. *Mailing Add:* 9700 Delaware Ct Rockville MD 20850

MCNICHOLS, GERALD ROBERT, b Cleveland, Ohio, Nov 21, 43; m 64; c 3. ENGINEERING, OPERATIONS RESEARCH. *Educ:* Case Inst Technol, BS, 65; Univ Pa, MS, 66; George Washington Univ, ScD(eng), 76. *Prof Exp:* Sr analyst, Off Secy Defense, 70-76; vpres, J Watson Noah Assocs Inc, 76-78; PRES, MGT CONSULT & RES INC, 78- *Concurrent Pos:* Adj prof, Am Univ, 67-72, Southeastern Univ, 74-75, George Washington Univ, 69- *Mem:* Opers Res Soc Am; Inst Mgt Sci; Int Soc Parametric Analysts; Soc Logistics Engrs. *Res:* Operations research, resource analysis, risk assessment, statistical methods useful to solve military and government analytical and economic problems. *Mailing Add:* 8133 Rondelay Lane Fairfax Station VA 22039

MCNICHOLS, ROGER JEFFERY, b Columbus, Ohio, Sept 25, 38; m 67; c 2. ENGINEERING. *Educ:* Ohio State Univ, BIE, 62, MS, 64, PhD(indust eng), 66. *Prof Exp:* Asst mgr, Summit Hardware Co, 50-63; instr math, Ohio State Univ, 62-66; from asst prof to prof indust eng, Tex A&M Univ, 66-76; assoc dean eng, 77-80, PROF INDUST ENG, UNIV TOLEDO, 76- *Concurrent Pos:* Mem staff, Ohio Malleable Div, Dayton Malleable Iron Co, 56-60; steering comt, Annual Reliability & Maintainability Conf, 69-71; consult, Frankford Arsenal, 71-; mem bd dirs, Annual Reliability & Maintainability Symposium, 71-77; pres, McNichols, Street & Assocs, Consult Engrs, 69-76; head grad eng exten progs, Red River Army Depot, Tex A&M Univ, 74-76. *Honors & Awards:* Reliability & Maintainability Award, Soc Logistics Engrs, 77. *Mem:* Am Inst Indust Engrs; Math Asn Am; Am Soc Qual Control; Am Soc Eng Educ. *Res:* Operations research; reliablity; maintainability; automatic control systems; applied mathematics; engineering economics. *Mailing Add:* Col of Eng Univ of Toledo Toledo OH 43606

MCNICOL, LORE ANNE, b La Jolla, Calif; m 67. MICROBIOLOGY, MOLECULAR BIOLOGY. *Educ:* Univ Mont, BA, 65; Boston Univ, PhD(med sci), 68. *Prof Exp:* NIH fel microbiol & molecular biol, Sch Med, Tufts Univ, 68-70, res fel, 70-71; assoc microbiol, Sch Med, Univ Pa, 71-75, asst prof, 75-76; sr res assoc biol, Calif Inst Technol, 76-77; fel, 77-78, ASST PROF MICROBIOL, UNIV MD, 78- *Concurrent Pos:* Guest lectr infectious dis, Med Sch, Univ Mass, 71-72; Pa plan scholar human genetics, Sch Med, Univ Pa, 72-74; assoc, Inst Cancer Res, 74-75, NIH fel, 75-76. *Mem:* AAAS; Am Soc Microbiol. *Res:* Restriction and modification of T-even phage DNA; plasmids in estuarine bacteria. *Mailing Add:* Dept of Microbiol Univ of Md College Park MD 20742

MCNIEL, JAMES S(AMUEL), JR, b Dallas, Tex, July 4, 21; m 45; c 3. CHEMICAL ENGINEERING. *Educ:* Univ Tex, BS, 43, MS, 46, PhD(chem eng), 50. *Prof Exp:* Sr res technologist, Field Res Lab, Magnolia Petrol Co Div, Socony Mobil Oil Co, Inc, 49-57, res assoc, 57-58, res sect supvr, 58-64, mgr explor & prod res div, Mobil Res & Develop Corp, 64-74, pres, Mobil Tyco Solar Energy Corp, 74-80, sr res adv, Mobil Res & Develop Corp, 80-81; VPRES, RES & DEVELOP, CORE LABS, INC, 82- *Mem:* Am Inst Chem Engrs; Am Inst Mining, Metall & Petrol Engrs; Sigma Xi; Int Solar Energy Soc. *Res:* Secondary recovery of petroleum. *Mailing Add:* 28 Hampshire Rd Wayland MA 01778

MCNIFF, EDWARD J, JR, b Danvers, Mass, Sept 26, 35; m 58; c 4. EXPERIMENTAL SOLID STATE PHYSICS. *Educ:* Boston Col, BS, 57; Northeastern Univ, MS, 61. *Prof Exp:* Electronics engr missile systs div, Sylvania Elec Prods, Inc, 57-61; staff physicist, Arthur D Little Co, 61-64; STAFF PHYSICIST, NAT MAGNET LAB, MASS INST TECHNOL, 64- *Mem:* Am Phys Soc; AAAS. *Res:* Magnetic effects in metals and dilute alloys; high temperature, high field superconductors. *Mailing Add:* Nat Magnet Lab Bldg NW 14 Mass Inst of Technol Cambridge MA 02139

MACNINTCH, JOHN EDWIN, b Moncton, NB, Nov 7, 35; m 58; c 2. BIOCHEMISTRY. *Educ:* McGill Univ, BScAgr, 58; Purdue Univ, MS, 63, PhD(biochem), 65. *Prof Exp:* Nat Heart Asn fel cardiovasc training prog, Bowman Gray Sch Med, 65-66; sr res biochemist, Biochem Dept, 66-72, sr res biochemist, Pharmacol Dept, Fibrinolytic Res & Develop, 72-74, asst dir res planning, 74-79, DIR SCI INFO SERV, BRISTOL LABS INC, 79- *Res:* Atherosclerosis and general cardiovascular disease biochemistry; lipid biochemistry; biochemistry of drug addiction; administration and scientific information services; drug evaluations; research planning. *Mailing Add:* Bristol Labs Inc PO Box 657 Syracuse NY 13201

MCNITT, JAMES R, b Chicago, Ill, May 10, 32; m 63; c 4. GEOTHERMAL RESOURCES EXPLORATION. *Educ:* Univ Notre Dame, BS, 53; Univ Ill, MS, 54; Univ Calif, PhD(geol), 61. *Prof Exp:* Geologist, Calif Div Mines & Geol, 58-65; tech adv geothermal energy, UN, 65-70, proj mgr, Geothermal Explor Proj, Kenya, 70-74, sr tech adv geothermal energy, 74-80; VPRES, GEOTHERMAL, INC, 80- *Mem:* Geol Soc Am; Soc Petrol Eng; Am Geophys Union. *Res:* Exploration and development of geothermal energy. *Mailing Add:* 1860 San Juan Ave Berkeley CA 94707

MCNITT, RICHARD PAUL, b Reedsville, Pa, Aug 1, 35; m 57; c 4. ENGINEERING SCIENCE & MECHANICS. *Educ:* Pa State Univ, BS, 57, MS, 60; Purdue Univ, PhD(eng sci), 65. *Prof Exp:* Instr eng mech, Pa State Univ, 57-59; instr eng sci, Purdue Univ, 59-65; from asst prof to assoc prof eng mech, Va Polytech Inst & State Univ, 65-74, prof eng sci & mech, 74-81; PROF & HEAD ENG SCI & MECH, PA STATE UNIV, 81- *Mem:* Soc Eng Sci (secy, 74-80); Am Soc Eng Educ; Soc Exp Stress Anal; Am Acad Mech (treas, 77-). *Res:* Fatigue; hydrogen embrittlement; continuum mechanics; fracture; environmental degradation of materials. *Mailing Add:* Dept Eng Sci & Mech Pa State Univ University Park PA 16802

MCNIVEN, HUGH D(ONALD), b Toronto, Ont, Aug 6, 22; nat US; m 59; c 1. MECHANICS. *Educ:* Univ Toronto, BASc, 44; Cornell Univ, MCE, 47; Columbia Univ, PhD(pure sci), 58. *Prof Exp:* Assoc prof, 57-64, PROF ENG SCI, UNIV CALIF, BERKELEY, 64- *Concurrent Pos:* NSF fel, 63-64. *Mem:* Am Soc Civil Engrs; Am Soc Mech Engrs; fel Acoust Soc Am; Am Math Soc. *Res:* Applied mechanics; high frequency vibrations of elastic solids; wave propagation in deformable media; earthquake engineering; mathematical modeling of earthquake structure. *Mailing Add:* 707 Davis Hall Univ of Calif Berkeley CA 94720

MCNULTY, CHARLES LEE, JR, b Dallas, Tex, Feb 4, 18; m 42; c 3. PALEONTOLOGY. *Educ:* Southern Methodist Univ, BS, 40; Syracuse Univ, MS, 48; Univ Okla, PhD, 55. *Prof Exp:* Asst geol, Syracuse Univ, 40-42; asst prof Arlington State Col, 46-48; instr, Univ Okla, 48-49; assoc prof, Arlington State Col, 50-51; geologist, Concho Petrol Co, 51-53 & Continental Oil Co, 53-57; PROF GEOL, UNIV TEX, ARLINGTON, 57- *Mem:* Geol Soc Am; Soc Vert Paleont: Soc Econ Paleont & Mineral; Am Asn Petrol Geol; Swiss Geol Soc. *Res:* Micropaleontology, mainly small foraminifera; stratigraphy of Texas. *Mailing Add:* Dept of Geol Univ of Tex Arlington TX 76019

MCNULTY, GEORGE FRANK, b Palo Alto, Calif, June 18, 45; m 81. EQUATIONAL LOGIC, UNIVERSAL ALGEBRA. *Educ:* Harvey Mudd Col, BS, 67; Univ Calif, Berkeley, Cand Phil, 69, PhD(math), 72. *Prof Exp:* Nat Res Coun fel, Univ Man, 72-73; res instr, Dartmouth Col, 73-75; asst prof, 75-81, ASSOC PROF MATH, UNIV SC, 81- *Concurrent Pos:* vis asst prof, Univ Calif, San Diego, 79 & Univ Hawaii, 82. *Mem:* Am Math Soc; Asn Symbolic Logic. *Res:* Foundations of mathematics and general theory of algebraic structures, especially on the connections between model theory, set theory and the theory of equational classes. *Mailing Add:* Dept Math & Statist Univ of SC Columbia SC 29208

MCNULTY, IRVING BAZIL, b Salt Lake City, Utah, Jan 6, 18; m 43; c 3. PLANT PHYSIOLOGY. *Educ:* Univ Utah, BS, 42, MS, 47; Ohio State Univ, PhD(plant physiol), 52. *Prof Exp:* Instr biol, bot & plant physiol, 47-53, from asst prof to assoc prof, 53-65, PROF BIOL, UNIV UTAH, 65- *Concurrent Pos:* Head dept biol, Univ Utah, 60-69. *Mem:* AAAS; Bot Soc Am; Am Soc Plant Physiol. *Res:* Physiology of sodium-potassium nutrition of plants; fluoride effects on plant metabolism. *Mailing Add:* Dept of Biol Univ of Utah Salt Lake City UT 84112

MCNULTY, JOHN ALEXANDER, b Bogota, Colombia, July 14, 46; US citizen. COMPARATIVE MORPHOLOGY, CELL BIOLOGY. *Educ:* Univ of the Pac, BA, 68; Univ Southern Calif, PhD(biol), 76. *Prof Exp:* Res asst biol, Univ Southern Calif, 70; asst prof, 76-81, ASSOC PROF ANAT, LOYOLA UNIV, CHICAGO, 81- *Mem:* Am Asn Anatomists; Am Inst Biol Sci; Am Soc Ichthyologists & Herpetologists; Am Soc Zoologists; Int Soc Chronobiol. *Res:* Comparative morphology and function of the pineal gland. *Mailing Add:* Dept of Anat Loyola Univ 2160 S First Ave Maywood IL 60153

MCNULTY, PETER J, b New York, NY, Aug 2, 41; m 66. BIOPHYSICS, RADIATION PHYSICS. *Educ:* Fordham Univ, BS, 62; State Univ NY Buffalo, PhD(physics), 65. *Prof Exp:* Asst physics, State Univ NY Buffalo, 62-65, fel, 65-66; from asst prof to assoc prof, 66-75, PROF PHYSICS, CLARKSON COL TECHNOL, 75- *Concurrent Pos:* Nat Acad Sci-Nat Res Coun sr resident res assoc, 70-71 & 79-80; vis assoc scientist, Brookhaven Nat Lab, 72-73, res collabr, Med Dept, 71- *Mem:* AAAS; Am Phys Soc; Inst Elec & Electronics Engrs; Radiation Res Soc. *Res:* Biological effects of radiation; radiation dosimetry; soft errors in microelectronics; fluorescent and Raman scattering by microstructures. *Mailing Add:* PO Box 292 Canton NY 13617

MCNULTY, RICHARD PAUL, b Scranton, Pa, Apr 23, 46. METEOROLOGY. *Educ:* New York Univ, BS, 68, MS, 72, PhD(meteorol), 74. *Prof Exp:* Weather officer, US Navy, 69-72; acad assoc meteorol, Polytech Inst NY, 74-76; res meteorologist, Nat Severe Storms Forecast Ctr, Kansas City, Mo, 76-80; DEP METEOROLOGIST IN CHARGE, NAT WEATHER SERV FORECAST OFFICE, KANS, 80- *Concurrent Pos:* Adj instr, Washburn Univ, 82- *Mem:* Am Meteorol Soc; Am Geophys Union; Nat Weather Asn. *Res:* Techniques for forecasting severe thunderstorms and tornadoes, specifically the use of the jet stream, differential advection and statistical techniques. *Mailing Add:* Nat Weather Serv Forecast Office 1116 NE Strait St Topeka KS 66616

MCNULTY, WILBUR PALMER, b Iowa City, Iowa, Sept 23, 25; m 59; c 5. TOXICOLOGY. *Educ:* Yale Univ, BS, 47, MD, 52. *Prof Exp:* Asst prof path, Yale Med Sch, 59-63; ASSOC PROF PATH, ORE HEALTH SCI UNIV, 63-, CHMN PATH, ORE REGIONAL PRIMATE RES CTR, 63- *Res:* Pathogenesis of poisoning of primates by halogenated aromatic compounds. *Mailing Add:* Ore Regional Primate Res Ctr 505 NW 185th Ave Beaverton OR 97006

MCNUTT, CLARENCE WALLACE, b Ozan, Ark, Aug 5, 13; m 39; c 4. GENETICS. *Educ:* Henderson State Col, AB, 35; La State Univ, MS, 38; Brown Univ, PhD(biol, genetics), 41. *Prof Exp:* Instr gross anat, Univ Wis, 46-50; assoc prof anat, Univ Tex Med Br Galveston, 50-67; PROF ANAT, UNIV TEX HEALTH SCI CTR, SAN ANTONIO, 67- *Concurrent Pos:* Muellhaupt fel, Ohio State Univ, 41-42; vis staff dept surg, Brooke Gen Hosp, Ft Sam Houston, Tex. *Mem:* Fel AAAS; Soc Exp Biol & Med; Genetics Soc Am; Am Soc Human Genetics; Am Asn Anat. *Res:* Mammalian developmental genetics; human genetics; neurological conditions in mice and man. *Mailing Add:* Dept of Anat Univ of Tex Health Sci Ctr San Antonio TX 78284

MCNUTT, DOUGLAS P, b Rome, Ga, Apr 24, 35; m 59; c 4. PHYSICS. *Educ:* Wesleyan Univ, BA, 56; Univ Wis, MS, 57, PhD(physics), 62. *Prof Exp:* Proj assoc interference spectros, Univ Wis, 62-63; RES PHYSICIST, US NAVAL RES LAB, 63- *Mem:* AAAS; Optical Soc Am; Am Geophys Union; Am Astron Soc. *Res:* Spectroscopic determination of atmospheric sodium; x-ray infrared and microwave rocket astronomy and aeronomy. *Mailing Add:* Code 4122 US Naval Res Lab Washington DC 20375

MCNUTT, JOHN DEWIGHT, atomic physics, molecular physics, see previous edition

MCNUTT, MARCIA KEMPER, b Minneapolis, Minn, Feb 19, 52; m 78; c 1. TECTONOPHYSICS. *Educ:* Colo Col, BA, 73; Scripps Inst Oceanog, PhD(earth sci), 78. *Prof Exp:* Vis asst prof, Univ Minn, 78-79; geophysicist, US Geol Surv, 79-82; ASST PROF GEOPHYSICS, MASS INST TECHNOL, 82- *Concurrent Pos:* Assoc ed, J Geophysical Res, 80-83; mem, Dedicated Gravity Satellite Comt, NASA, 78. *Mem:* Am Geophys Union; John Muir Geophys Soc (secy, 79-). *Res:* Studies of long-term rheology of the earth's crust and upper mantle using gravity and topography data, paleomagnetism of seamounts, tidal triggering of earthquakes, lithospheric reheating. *Mailing Add:* Dept Earth & Planetary Sci Mass Inst Technol Cambridge MA 02139

MCNUTT, MICHAEL JOHN, b Rochester, NY, April 22, 47. SILICON INTEGRATED CIRCUITS. *Educ:* Mass Inst Technol, SB, 69; Univ Ill, MS, 70, PhD(elec eng), 74. *Prof Exp:* Res assoc, Univ Ill, 74-75, asst prof elec eng, 75-77; mem tech staff, Charge Transfer Devices, 77-81, MGR, PROCESS RELIABILITY & CHARACTERIZATION, ROCKWELL INT, 81- *Mem:* Am Phys Soc; Electrochem Soc; Inst Elec & Electronics Engrs. *Res:* Process reliability and parameter characterization for complementary metal-oxide semiconductor silicon-on-sapphire; characterization for complementary metal-oxide semiconductor bulk silicone; gallium arsenide technologies used in manufacturing very large scale integrated circuits; high frequency integrated circuit design and functional test. *Mailing Add:* Defense Electronics Oper Rockwell Int 3370 Miraloma Ave PO Box 4761 Anaheim CA 92803

MCNUTT, RALPH LEROY, JR, b Fort Worth, Tex, Oct 29, 53. SPACE PHYSICS, PLANETARY SCIENCE. *Educ:* Tex A&M Univ, BS, 75; Mass Inst Technol, PhD(physics), 80. *Prof Exp:* Mem tech staff, Sandia Nat Lab, Albuquerque, NMex, 80-81; RES SCIENTIST, CTR SPACE RES, MASS INST TECHNOL, 81- *Mem:* Am Geophys Union; British Interplanetary Soc; Sigma Xi. *Res:* Analysis and interpretation of plasma data taken inside of the Jovian and Saturnian magnetospheres. *Mailing Add:* Rm 37-635 Mass Inst Technol 77 Mass Ave Cambridge MA 02139

MCNUTT, ROBERT HAROLD, b Moncton, NB, July 4, 37; m 64; c 3. GEOCHEMISTRY, PETROLOGY. *Educ:* Univ NB, BSc, 59; Mass Inst Technol, PhD(geol), 65. *Prof Exp:* From asst prof to assoc prof, 65-81, PROF GEOL, MCMASTER UNIV, 81- *Concurrent Pos:* Ed, Geosci Can, 78-82. *Mem:* Am Geophys Union; Geol Asn Can; Asn Earth Sci Ed. *Res:* Petrology and geochemistry of Archean greenstone belts; geochemistry and rubidium-strontium isotopic studies of Archean and Grenville gneissic terrains; rubidium-stronium isotopic studies in the Andes of South America. *Mailing Add:* Dept of Geol McMaster Univ Hamilton ON L8S 4L8 Can

MCNUTT, RONALD CLAY, b Birmingham, Ala, Oct 29, 29; m 54; c 1. ANALYTICAL CHEMISTRY, INORGANIC CHEMISTRY. *Educ:* Athens Col, BS, 59; Vanderbilt Univ, MS, 61, PhD(chem), 66. *Prof Exp:* Res technician chem, Chemstrand Corp, Ala, 53-59, res chemist, Chemstrand Res Ctr, NC, 61-62; assoc prof, 66-68, PROF CHEM & CHMN DEPT, ATHENS COL, 68- *Mem:* Am Chem Soc. *Res:* Analysis of polymers related to textile and tire industry; reactivity of coordinated ligands; analysis of liquid rocket fuels; analysis of contaminants on spacecraft surfaces. *Mailing Add:* Dept of Chem Athens State Col Athens AL 35611

MCNUTT, WALTER SCOTT, b Ozan, Ark, July 21, 18; m 54; c 2. BIOCHEMISTRY, PHARMACOLOGY. *Educ:* Henderson State Teachers Col, AB, 40; Brown Univ, MSc, 43; Univ Wis, PhD(biochem), 49. *Prof Exp:* Asst prof biochem, Vanderbilt Univ, 51-53; res fel & sr res fel plant biochem, Calif Inst Technol, 53-58; assoc scientist, Conn Exp Sta, 58-59; assoc prof, 59-65, PROF PHARMACOL, SCH MED, TUFTS UNIV, 65-, PROF BIOCHEM, 68- *Concurrent Pos:* Jane Coffin Childs res fel biochem, Inst Cytophysiol, Copenhagen Univ, 49-50; Jane Coffin Childs res fel chem, Cambridge Univ, 50-51. *Mem:* Am Soc Biol Chem. *Res:* Metabolism of nucleosides; biogenesis of riboflavin and other pteridines. *Mailing Add:* Dept of Pharmacol Tufts Univ Sch of Med Boston MA 02111

MACOMBER, JAMES DALE, chemical physics, see previous edition

MACOMBER, RICHARD WILTZ, b Chicago, Ill, June 6, 32; m 57. PALEONTOLOGY, STRATIGRAPHY. *Educ:* Northwestern Univ, BS, 54, MS, 59; Harvard Univ, AM, 63; Univ Iowa, PhD(paleont), 68. *Prof Exp:* Geologist, Bear Creek Mining Co, 57-58; geologist, US Geol Surv, 62-63; cur geol, Northwestern Univ, 65-66; from instr to assoc prof, 66-76, PROF EARTH SCI, LONG ISLAND UNIV, 76-, PROF PHYSICS, 80- *Res:* Ordovician brachiopod paleontology; Ordovician stratigraphy of North America and Europe. *Mailing Add:* Dept of Physics Long Island Univ Brooklyn NY 11201

MACOMBER, THOMAS WESSON, b Bakersfield, Calif, Nov 1, 12; m 46; c 4. MECHANICAL ENGINEERING. *Educ:* Stanford Univ, AB, 34, ME, 38. *Prof Exp:* Res engr, Ray Oil Burner Co, Calif, 34-35; design engr, F Jaden Mfg Co, Nebr, 38; designer, Cent Nebr Pub Power & Irrig Dist, 38; asst proj engr, Soil Conserv Serv, USDA, Nebr, 39; stress anal engr, N Am Aviation, Inc, Calif, 39-40; asst engr, Ames Aeronaut Lab, Nat Adv Comt Aeronaut, Calif, 40-43; mech res engr, Radiation Lab, Univ Calif, 43-45; design engr, Westinghouse Elec Corp, Calif, 45-55 & Ampex Corp, Calif, 55; test facility design engr, Atomic Power Equip Dept, Gen Elec Co, Calif, 55-57; design specialist, Lockheed Missile & Space Co, 57-70; consult, 71-72; SR ENGR, WESTERN CONSULT ENGRS, GEN ELEC CO, SAN JOSE, 73- *Mem:* Am Soc Mech Engrs; Audio Eng Soc. *Res:* Heat transfer; patent, hydraulic control device for aircraft; analysis of systems; analytical design of mechanism and structure; design to resist severe environments; computerized analysis and design of piping systems and of fuel storage units for nuclear power plants. *Mailing Add:* 216 Marich Way Los Altos CA 94022

MACON, NATHANIEL, numerical analysis, systems science, see previous edition

MACOSKO, CHRISTOPHER WARD, b Bridgeport, Conn, June 14, 44; m 67; c 4. POLYMER SCIENCE, RHEOLOGY. *Educ:* Carnegie-Mellon Univ, BS, 66; Univ London, MSc, 67, Imp Col, dipl, 67; Princeton Univ, PhD(chem eng), 70. *Prof Exp:* Mem res staff, Western Elec Eng Res Ctr, 68-70; asst prof, 70-74, assoc prof, 74-79, PROF CHEM ENG & MAT SCI, UNIV MINN, MINNEAPOLIS, 79- *Concurrent Pos:* Consult, Rheometrics, Inc, 70- *Mem:* Am Inst Chem Engrs; Am Chem Soc; Soc Plastics Engrs; Soc Rheology; Brit Soc Rheology. *Res:* Polymer rheology; polymer processing; model networks, thermosets and polymer reaction molding; dynamic mechanical properties; suspension and biorheology. *Mailing Add:* Dept of Chem Eng & Mat Sci Univ of Minn Minneapolis MN 55455

MACOVSKI, ALBERT, b New York, NY, May 2, 29; m 50; c 2. ELECTRICAL ENGINEERING, MEDICAL INSTRUMENTS. *Educ:* City Col New York, BEE, 50; Polytech Inst Brooklyn, MEE, 53; Stanford Univ, PhD, 68. *Prof Exp:* Engr, RCA Labs, Inc, 50-57; asst prof elec eng, Polytech Inst Brooklyn, 57-60, assoc prof, 60; res engr, SRI Inst, 60-61, sr res engr, 61-68, staff scientist, 68-72; PROF, STANFORD UNIV, 72- *Concurrent Pos:* Consult, RCA Labs, Inc, NJ, 57-60; NIH spec res fel diag radiol, Univ Calif, San Francisco, 71-72. *Honors & Awards:* Award, Inst Elec & Electronics Engrs, 57, Zworykin Award, 73. *Mem:* Fel Inst Elec & Electronics Engrs; fel Optical Soc Am. *Res:* Optical devices and systems; medical imaging systems. *Mailing Add:* Dept of Elec Eng Stanford Univ Stanford CA 94305

MACPEEK, DONALD LESTER, b Andover, NJ, Apr 4, 28; m 50; c 3. INDUSTRIAL ORGANIC CHEMISTRY. *Educ:* Rensselaer Polytech Inst, BS, 49, MS, 51, PhD(chem), 52. *Prof Exp:* Asst, Rensselaer Polytech Inst, 49-52; res chemist, Union Carbide Chem Co, 52-67, tech mgr oxidation prod opers group, Chem & Plastics Develop Div, 67-69, technol mgr aldehydes, alcohols & plasticizer intermediates opers group, 69-71 & acrolein, acrylic acid & acrylate esters opers group, 72-74, ASSOC DIR RES & DEVELOP DEPT, CHEM & PLASTICS DIV, UNION CARBIDE CORP, 74- *Mem:* Am Chem Soc. *Res:* Oxidation of organic compounds, especially hydrocarbons and aldehydes; hydroformylation; specialty organic chemicals; process development; management of research and development. *Mailing Add:* 1518 Village Dr South Charleston WV 25309

MCPETERS, ARNOLD LAWRENCE, b Sept 13, 25; m 51; c 4. POLYMER SCIENCE. *Educ:* Univ NC, BS, 50, PhD(chem), 54. *Prof Exp:* Res chemist, Am Enka Corp, 53-58, head develop sect, Rayon Res Dept, 58-60; chemist, Chemstrand Corp, 60-61, group leader, 62-67, SR GROUP LEADER, MONSANTO TEXTILES CO, MONSANTO CO, 68- *Mem:* Am Chem Soc; Fiber Soc. *Res:* Improved acrylic and modacrylic fibers polymer structure; fiber morphology; fiber production processes; textile performance. *Mailing Add:* 3111 Village Creek Trail SE Decatur AL 35603

MCPETERS, RICHARD DOUGLAS, b Florence, Ala, July 3, 47. ATMOSPHERIC PHYSICS, OZONE MEASUREMENTS. *Educ:* Mass Inst Technol, BS, 69; Univ Fla, PhD(physics), 75. *Prof Exp:* assoc physics, Univ Fla, 75-76; staff scientist, Systs & Appl Sci Corp, 76-78, SPACE SCIENTIST, NASA GODDARD SPACE FLIGHT CTR, 78- *Mem:* Sigma Xi; Optical Soc Am; Am Meteorol Soc; Am Geophys Union. *Res:* Atmospheric optics of the solar aureole; total ozone and ozone profile determination from satellite measurements of backscattered ultraviolet. *Mailing Add:* Goddard Space Flight Ctr-9640 Greenbelt MD 20771

MCPHAIL, ANDREW TENNENT, b Glasgow, Scotland, Sept 23, 37; m 61; c 2. CHEMISTRY. *Educ:* Glasgow Univ, BSc, 59, PhD(chem), 63. *Prof Exp:* Asst lectr chem, Glasgow Univ, 61-64; res assoc, Univ Ill, Urbana, 64-66; lectr, Univ Sussex, 66-68; assoc prof, 68-73, PROF CHEM, DUKE UNIV, 73- *Mem:* Royal Soc Chem; Am Crystallog Asn. *Res:* X-ray crystal structure analysis of organic molecules, particularly biologically active compounds; molecular conformations; studies of structure and bonding in transition metal complexes and in organometallic compounds. *Mailing Add:* Paul M Gross Chem Lab Duke Univ Durham NC 27706

MACPHAIL, MORAY ST JOHN, b Kingston, Ont, May 27, 12; m 39; c 1. MATHEMATICS. *Educ:* Queen's Univ Ont, BA, 33; McGill Univ, MA, 34; Oxford Univ, DPhil, 36; Univ Carleton, DSc, 78. *Prof Exp:* From instr to prof math, Acadia Univ, 37-47; vis lectr, Queen's Univ Ont, 47-48; from assoc prof to prof, 48-77, dir sch grad studies, 60-63, dean fac grad studies, 63-69, EMER PROF MATH, CARLETON UNIV, 77- *Concurrent Pos:* Instr, Princeton Univ, 41-42; vis prof, Univ Toronto, 47-48. *Mem:* Am Math Soc; Math Asn Am; fel Royal Soc Can; Can Math Cong. *Res:* Analysis; theory of series. *Mailing Add:* Dept of Math Carleton Univ Ottawa ON K1S 5B6 Can

MACPHEE, CRAIG, b San Francisco, Calif, Nov 3, 18; m 42; c 3. ZOOLOGY. *Educ:* Univ BC, BA, 47, MA, 49; Univ Wash, PhD(zool), 54. *Prof Exp:* Asst prof biol, Eastern Wash Col Educ, 54-57; from asst prof to assoc prof, 57-66, prof fishery mgt, 66-77, PROF FISHERY RESOURCES & CHMN DEPT, UNIV IDAHO, 78- *Mem:* Am Soc Limnol & Oceanog; Am Soc Ichthyologists & Herpetologists; Am Fisheries Soc; Am Inst Fishery Res Biol. *Res:* Limnology; ecology. *Mailing Add:* Col of Forestry Univ of Idaho Moscow ID 83843

MACPHEE, KENNETH ERSKINE, b Toronto, Ont, Sept 17, 26; m 49; c 3. ORGANIC CHEMISTRY, POLYMER CHEMISTRY. *Educ:* Acadia Univ, BSc, 47; Univ Oxford, BSc, 51, DPhil(org chem), 53. *Prof Exp:* Res scientist polymer chem, Res Lab, Dom Rubber Co, 53-64, group leader, 64-74; MEM STAFF, UNIROYAL LTD RES LABS, 74- *Mem:* Chem Inst Can. *Res:* Organic synthesis; pharmacological action of chemicals; elastomers and plastics. *Mailing Add:* Uniroyal Ltd Res Labs Guelph ON N1H 6N5 Can

MCPHEE, WILLIAM JOHN, plant pathology, see previous edition

MCPHERRON, ROBERT LLOYD, b Chelan, Wash, Jan 14, 37; m 58; c 2. GEOPHYSICS, SPACE PHYSICS. *Educ:* Univ Wash, BS, 59; Univ Southern Calif, MS, 61; Univ Calif, Berkeley, PhD(physics), 68. *Prof Exp:* Res physicist space sci lab, Univ Calif, Berkeley, 66-68; res geophysicist, Inst Geophys & Planetary Physics, 68-69, asst prof space physics, 69-73, asst prof, 73-77, PROF PLANETARY PHYSICS & GEOPHYS, UNIV CALIF, LOS ANGELES, 77- *Mem:* AAAS; Am Geophys Union. *Res:* Magnetic field variations within the magnetosphere, including both macroscopic currents and wave phenomena and the part they play in magnetic storms and substorms; particles and fields; auroral phenomena. *Mailing Add:* Dept of Geophys & Space Sci Univ of Calif Los Angeles CA 90024

MCPHERSON, ALEXANDER, biological structure, see previous edition

MACPHERSON, ALISTAIR KENNETH, b Sydney, Australia, Jan 29, 36; m 59; c 4. MECHANICAL ENGINEERING. *Educ:* Univ Sydney, BE, 57, MEngSc, 66, PhD(mech eng), 68. *Prof Exp:* Res asst fire res, Commonwealth Exp Bldg Sta, 59-60; asst proj engr, Qantas Airways, 60-66; fel, Inst Aerospace Studies, Univ Toronto, 68-69; asst prof mech eng, Univ Man, 69-71; assoc prof, 71-74, PROF MECH ENG, LEHIGH UNIV, 74- *Concurrent Pos:* Adj prof, Univ Man, 71-72. *Mem:* Am Phys Soc; Am Meteorol Soc; Royal Meteorol Soc; Combustion Inst; Am Geophys Union. *Res:* Atmospheric flows; fluid flow at the molecular level; plasma flows; shock and detonation waves. *Mailing Add:* Dept of Mech Eng & Mech Lehigh Univ Bethlehem PA 18015

MCPHERSON, ALVADUS BRADLEY, b West Frankfort, Ill, July 10, 37; m 59; c 3. BIOLOGY. *Educ:* Southeastern La Col, BS, 60; La State Univ, MS, 67; Southern Ill Univ, PhD(biol), 71. *Prof Exp:* ASSOC PROF BIOL & CHMN DEPT, CENTENARY COL LA, 71- *Concurrent Pos:* Fel trop med, La State Univ Med Sch, 66, 69-70; NSF fel marine ecol, Duke Univ, 68; alumni grant, Centenary Col La, 75. *Mem:* Am Soc Mammalogists; Sigma Xi. *Res:* Mammalian ecology, taxonomy, distribution, and parasitology. *Mailing Add:* 153 E Wilkinson Shreveport LA 71104

MACPHERSON, ANDREW HALL, b London, Eng, June 2, 32; Can citizen; m 57; c 3. ECOLOGY, ZOOGEOGRAPHY. *Educ:* Carleton Univ, BS, 54; McGill Univ, MSc, 57, PhD, 67. *Prof Exp:* Asst cur zool, Nat Mus Can, 57-58; res wildlife biologist, Can Wildlife Serv, 58-64, regional supvr wildlife biol, 64-67; sci adv, Sci Secretariat, Privy Coun Off, 67-68 & Sci Coun Can, 68-69; res supvr mammal, 69-70, dir western region, 70-74, dir-gen environ mgt serv, 74-79, REGIONAL DIR-GEN, WESTERN & NORTHERN REGION, ENVIRON CAN, 79- *Concurrent Pos:* Mem, Tech Comt for Caribou Preservation, 64-69; chmn, Polar Bear Group and mem, Survival Serv Comn, Int Union Conserv of Nature & Natural Resources, 70-72; mem, Mackenzie R Basin Comt, 74-, Grants Comt & Wildlife Fund, Can, 78- *Honors & Awards:* Centennial Medal, 67. *Mem:* Fel Arctic Inst NAm (gov, 72-76). *Res:* Taxonomy of Laridae; ecology and population dynamics of Alopex; zoogeography of Arctic mammals; ecology and population processes of Rangifer; management of arctic wildlife resources. *Mailing Add:* Environ Can 9942 108 St Edmonton AB T5K 2J5 Can

MCPHERSON, CHARLES ALLEN, organic chemistry, see previous edition

MCPHERSON, CHARLES WILLIAM, b Rugby, NDak, Feb 24, 32; m 56; c 2. LABORATORY ANIMAL MEDICINE. *Educ:* Univ Minn, BS, 54, DVM, 56; Univ Calif, Berkeley, MPH, 64; Am Col Lab Animal Med, dipl. *Prof Exp:* Vet, Animal Hosp Sect, NIH, 56-57, head, Primate Unit, 57-58, vet microbiologist, Comp Path Sect, 58-69, chief, Animal Prod Sect, Lab Aids Br, 60-64, head, Pathogen Free Unit & asst to chief, 64-66, chief, Lab Animal Med & Vivarium Sci Sect, Animal Resources Br, Div Res Resources, 66-70, chief br, 71-80; DIR ANIMAL RES, SCH VET MED, NC STATE UNIV, 80- *Honors & Awards:* Co-recipient Res Award, Am Asn Lab Animal Sci, 63; Griffin Award, Am Asn Lab Animal Sci, 80. *Mem:* Am Vet Med Asn; Am Asn Lab Animal Sci; Am Soc Lab Animal Practitioners (pres, 82-83). *Res:* Diseases of laboratory animals; production of microbiologically defined laboratory animals. *Mailing Add:* Sch Vet Med NC State Univ Raleigh NC 27606

MCPHERSON, CLARA, b Roscoe, Tex, Mar 10, 22; m 43; c 3. NUTRITION, FOODS. *Educ:* Tex Tech Col, BS, 43, MS, 47. *Prof Exp:* Instr food & nutrit, 47-48 & 55-60, asst prof, 61-68, ASSOC PROF FOOD & NUTRIT, TEX TECH UNIV, 68- *Mem:* Am Dietetic Asn; Am Home Econ Asn; Inst Food Technol; Soc Nutrit Educ. *Res:* Dietary studies of college students; frozen foods; development of high protein foods using cottonseed and soy protein; determination of quality of pork fed various rations. *Mailing Add:* Dept of Food & Nutrit Tex Tech Univ Lubbock TX 79409

MCPHERSON, CLINTON MARSUD, b Gainesville, Tex, Oct 6, 18; m 43; c 3. CHEMISTRY. *Educ:* Tex Tech Col, BS, 47, MEd, 52, DEd(psychol), 59. *Prof Exp:* Teacher pub schs, Tex, 50-56; instr chem, 56-59, asst prof, 60-74, assoc prof food & nutrit, 74-77, asst prof chem, 77-81, ASSOC PROF CHEM, TEX TECH UNIV, 81- *Res:* Inorganic chemistry; use of audio-visual materials. *Mailing Add:* Dept of Chem Tex Tech Univ Lubbock TX 79409

MACPHERSON, COLIN ROBERTSON, b Aberdeen, Scotland, Sept 2, 25; m 49; c 4. PATHOLOGY. *Educ:* Univ Cape Town, MB, ChB, 46, MMed & MD, 54. *Prof Exp:* Asst lectr path, Univ Cape Town, 48-50, lectr, 50-55; asst renal physiol, Post-Grad Sch Med, Univ London, 55-56; from asst prof to prof bact & path, Ohio State Univ, 56-75, vchmn dept path, 60-72, actg chmn dept, 72-75; DIR, DIV LAB MED, UNIV CINCINNATI, 75-, VCHMN, DEPT LAB MED, 79- *Concurrent Pos:* Consult, Vet Admin Hosp, Cincinnati, Ohio, 65- *Res:* Immuno-hematology; laboratory screening procedures. *Mailing Add:* Cincinnati Hosp 234 Goodman St Cincinnati OH 45267

MACPHERSON, CULLEN H, b San Mateo, Calif, Dec 6, 27; m 51; c 3. BIOPHYSICS. *Educ:* San Jose State Col, AB, 49; Stanford Univ, MA, 51. *Prof Exp:* Mgr reproducing components div, Electro-Voice Inc, 54-56; biophysicist, Tektronix, Inc, 56-61; pres & chmn bd, Argonaut Assocs, Inc, 59- 78; chief res engr, Advan Develop Group, Temperature Controls Div, Cutler-Hammer, Inc, Beaverton, 78-80, Eaton Corp, 80-81; TECH DIR NAM, AUTOMATION DIV, KOCKUMS INDUST, 81- *Concurrent Pos:* Scientist, Dept Neurophysiol, Ore Regional Primate Res Ctr, 64-78, chmn, Dept Biophys, 70-78. *Mem:* AAAS; Am Asn Physics Teachers; Acoust Soc Am; Audio Eng Soc; Inst Elec & Electronics Eng. *Res:* Limited energy measurements in biological systems; constant current neuronal stimulation; stereo vector electrocardiography. *Mailing Add:* 2677 NW Westover Rd Portland OR 97210

MCPHERSON, DONALD ATTRIDGE, b Cleveland, Ohio, Jan 1, 34; m 57; c 3. SPACE PHYSICS. *Educ:* Ohio State Univ, BA, 57; Univ Calif, Berkeley, MA, 58, PhD(physics), 62. *Prof Exp:* Engr, Battelle Mem Inst, 56-57; staff mem high energy nuclear physics, Lawrence Radiation Lab, 61-62; mem tech staff, Aerospace Corp, 62-73, dir survivability, 73-75; MGR SPACE SYSTS DIV, SCI APPLN, INC, 75- *Mem:* Am Phys Soc; Am Geophys Union. *Res:* Nuclear reactor technology; high energy, plasma and magnetospheric physics; atmospheric reentry. *Mailing Add:* Sci Appln Inc 101 Continental Blvd Suite 310 El Segundo CA 90245

MCPHERSON, DONALD FRANK, b Kittanning, Pa, Dec 7, 31; m 75; c 4. AUDIOLOGY, SPEECH PATHOLOGY. *Educ:* Indiana Univ, Pa, BS, 61; Univ Hawaii, MA, 63; Purdue Univ, West Lafayette, PhD(audiol, speech sci), 66. *Prof Exp:* Asst prof audiol & speech sci, Ohio Univ, 66-68; assoc prof audiol, Univ Northern Colo, 68-70; ASSOC PROF SPEECH PATH & AUDIOL, UNIV HAWAII, 70- *Mem:* Am Speech & Hearing Asn; Acoust Soc Am. *Res:* Psychoacoustics; speech science; language development. *Mailing Add:* Div Speech Path & Audiol Univ Hawaii Honolulu HI 96822

MCPHERSON, DONALD J(AMES), b Columbus, Ohio, Nov 18, 21; m 45; c 2. PHYSICAL METALLURGY. *Educ:* Ohio State Univ, BMetE, 43, MSc, 47, PhD(metall), 49. *Hon Degrees:* DSc, Ohio State Univ, 75. *Prof Exp:* Metall inspector, Carnegie-Ill Steel Corp, 43-44; res engr, Battelle Mem Inst, 46; assoc, Res Found, Ohio State Univ, 47-49; assoc metallurgist, Argonne Nat Lab, 49-50; from supvr phys metall & alloy develop to dir metals res, Ill Inst Technol Res Inst, 50-63, vpres, 63-69; vpres & dir technol, 69-81, PRES KAISER ALUMINUM & CHEM CORP & VPRES, KAISER ALUMINUM TECH SERV, INC, 81-; VPRES, KAISER ALUMINUM TECH SERV, INC, 81- *Concurrent Pos:* Chmn, Nat Mat Adv Bd, 82- *Honors & Awards:* Citation, Bur Aeronaut, 55; Campbell Mem Lectr, Am Soc Metals, 74. *Mem:* AAAS; hon mem Am Soc Metals; Am Inst Mining, Metall & Petrol Engrs; Am Ceramic Soc; Brit Inst Metals. *Res:* Phase diagrams; alloy development; research management. *Mailing Add:* Kaiser Aluminum & Chem Corp 300 Lakeside Dr Oakland CA 94643

MCPHERSON, GEORGE, JR, b Westfield, NY, July 16, 21. ELECTRICAL ENGINEERING. *Educ:* Ohio State Univ, BEE, 43, BSc, 48, MSc, 49. *Prof Exp:* Proj engr, Sound Div, Naval Res Lab, 43-44, 45-47; instr elec eng, Ohio State Univ, 48-49; teacher pub schs, Ohio, 49-50; prin elec engr, Battelle Mem Inst, 50-54; asst prof elec eng, Univ Ky, 54-56; PROF ELEC ENG, UNIV MO-ROLLA, 56- *Concurrent Pos:* Consult, elec motors and power lab design. *Mem:* Inst Elec & Electronics Engrs; Am Asn Univ Professors; Sigma Xi. *Res:* Electromagnetic machines. *Mailing Add:* Dept of Elec Eng Univ Mo-Rolla Rolla MO 65401

MCPHERSON, HAROLD JAMES, b Newry, NIreland, May 28, 39; Can citizen. PHYSICAL GEOGRAPHY, ENVIRONMENTAL HAZARDS. *Educ:* Queen's Univ, Ont, BA, 61; Univ Alta, MSc, 63; McGill Univ, PhD(geog), 67. *Prof Exp:* Asst prof geog, Queen's Univ, Ont, 66-70; from asst prof to assoc prof, 70-78, PROF GEOG, UNIV ALTA, 78- *Concurrent Pos:* Vis scholar, Univ Ariz, 74-75; Can Coun leave fel, Can Coun, 74. *Mem:* Asn Am Geog. *Res:* Water resources in developing countries; natural hazards; environmental quality; perception of environment; mountain geomorphology. *Mailing Add:* Dept of Geog Univ of Alta Edmonton AB T6G 2G7 Can

MACPHERSON, HERBERT GRENFELL, b Victorville, Calif, Nov 2, 11; m 37; c 2. NUCLEAR SCIENCE, NUCLEAR ENGINEERING. *Educ:* Univ Calif, AB, 32, PhD(physics), 37. *Prof Exp:* Jr meteorologist, USDA, 36-37; res physicist, Nat Carbon Co, 37-50, asst dir res, 50-56; with Oak Ridge Nat Lab, 56-60, assoc dir reactor prog, 60-63, asst lab dir, 63-64, dep dir, 64-70; prof nuclear eng, Univ Tenn, 70-76; RETIRED. *Concurrent Pos:* Consult, Oak Ridge Nat Lab, 70- & US AEC, 72-74; actg dir, Inst Energy Anal, 74-75, consult, 75- *Mem:* Nat Acad Eng; Am Nuclear Soc; Am Phys Soc; Am Soc Metals. *Res:* Fundamentals of the carbon arc; high temperature properties of carbon and graphite; heavy particles in cosmic radiation; nuclear reactor technology; safety of nuclear reactors; energy policy. *Mailing Add:* 102 Orchard Circle Oak Ridge TN 37830

MCPHERSON, JAMES BEVERLEY, JR, organic chemistry, see previous edition

MCPHERSON, JAMES C, JR, b Hamilton, Tex, Dec 27, 26; m 45; c 4. BIOCHEMISTRY, MEDICINE. *Educ:* NTex State Col, BS, 46; Univ Tex, MA, 55, MD, 60. *Prof Exp:* Res scientist, Univ Tex Southwestern Med Sch Dallas, 60-61, from instr to asst prof biochem, 61-63; asst res prof biochem, 63-70, ASSOC PROF SURG, CELL & MOLECULAR BIOL, MED COL GA, 70- *Mem:* AAAS; Am Chem Soc; Am Oil Chem Soc; Am Asn Clin Chem; Soc Exp Biol & Med. *Res:* Lipid absorption and metabolism. *Mailing Add:* Dept of Biochem Med Col of Ga Augusta GA 30902

MCPHERSON, JAMES KING, b Tucson, Ariz, Nov 11, 37; m 62. PLANT ECOLOGY. *Educ:* Univ Idaho, BS, 59; Univ Calif, Santa Barbara, MA, 66, PhD(bot), 68. *Prof Exp:* Asst prof bot, 68-74, ASSOC PROF BOT, OKLA STATE UNIV, 74- *Mem:* AAAS; Bot Soc Am; Ecol Soc Am. *Res:* Ecological aspects of forest tree water relations; allelopathy and competition among plants. *Mailing Add:* Dept Bot Okla State Univ Stillwater OK 74074

MCPHERSON, JAMES LOUIS, b Chattanooga, Tenn, June 25, 22; m 48; c 3. POLYMER CHEMISTRY. *Educ:* Ga Inst Technol, BS, 44; Univ Tex, MA, 49; Ohio State Univ, PhD(org chem), 53. *Prof Exp:* Asst lab, Univ Tex, 47-48; res chemist explor sect, Plastics Dept, Exp Sta, E I du Pont de Nemours & Co, 53-58; proj leader, Cent Res Lab, Gen Aniline & Film Corp, 59-61; lab dir basic polymer res, Cent Res & Eng Div, Continental Can Co, 61-64; sr fel, Mellon Inst, 64-67; mgr chem activ div, DeBell & Richardson, Inc, Mass, 67-69; ASSOC PROF CHEM, LEE COL, TENN, 69- *Mem:* Am Chem Soc; The Royal Soc Chem. *Res:* Synthesis, properties and applications of polymers. *Mailing Add:* 7231 Short Tail Springs Rd Harrison TN 37341

MCPHERSON, JOHN EDWIN, b San Diego, Calif, June 8, 41; m 66; c 2. ENTOMOLOGY. *Educ:* San Diego State Univ, BS, 63, MS, 64; Mich State Univ, PhD(entom), 68. *Prof Exp:* Asst prof, 69-74, assoc prof, 74-78, PROF ZOOL, SOUTHERN ILL UNIV, CARBONDALE, 78- *Mem:* Entom Soc Am; Entom Soc Can; Sigma Xi. *Res:* Bionomics and taxonomy of North American Pentatomoidea of the group Insecta; effects of photoperiod on morphology and pigmentation of Pentatomidae of the order Hemiptera. *Mailing Add:* Dept of Zool Southern Ill Univ Carbondale IL 62901

MCPHERSON, JOHN GORDON, b Nelson, NZ, Nov 18, 47. GEOLOGY. *Educ:* Victoria Univ, Wellington, BSc, 70, BSc hons, 71, PhD(geol), 75. *Prof Exp:* Lectr geol, Univ Cape Town, 76-80; ASSOC PROF GEOL, UNIV TEX, ARLINGTON, 81- *Mem:* Int Asn Sedimentologists; Geol Soc SAfrica; Geol Soc Am; Soc Econ Paleontologists & Mineralogists. *Res:* Alluvial plain sedimentation both modern and ancient specializing in the depositional environment and diagenesis of red beds; pedogenic and geochemical aspects of red bed genesis. *Mailing Add:* Dept Geol Univ Tex Arlington TX 76019

MACPHERSON, L W, b Glasgow, Scotland, June 1, 20; Can citizen; m 45; c 4. MICROBIOLOGY, PUBLIC HEALTH. *Educ:* Univ Edinburgh, dipl vet state med, 49, PhD(virol), 55. *Prof Exp:* Vet officer, Ministry Agr, 49-52; fel microbiol, Can Dept Nat Defence, 52-55; res officer virol & head virus sect, Animal Dis Res Inst, Can Dept Agr, 55-57; actg head dept microbiol, 57-68, PROF MICROBIOL & VET PUB HEALTH, SCH HYG, UNIV TORONTO, 57- *Concurrent Pos:* Consult, Res Inst, Hosp Sick Children, Toronto, 59-; mem adv comt bact warfare, Can Dept Nat Defence, 62-64. *Mem:* Fel Royal Soc Health; Royal Col Vet Surg. *Res:* Zoonotic diseases, particularly myxoviruses and enteroviruses. *Mailing Add:* Dept of Microbiol Sch of Hyg Univ of Toronto Toronto ON M5S 1A1 Can

MACPHERSON, LLOYD BERTRAM, b Annapolis Royal, NS, July 6, 13; m 45; c 3. BIOCHEMISTRY. *Educ:* Acadia Univ, BSc, 34; Univ Toronto, PhD(path chem), 49. *Hon Degrees:* DSc, Acadia Univ, 73; LID, Dalhousie Univ, 81. *Prof Exp:* Asst, Banting Inst, Univ Toronto, 46-49, asst prof, 49-52; from asst prof to assoc prof biochem, Dalhousie Univ, 52-63, from asst dean fac med to assoc dean fac med, 58-71, prof biochem, 63-78, dean fac med, 71-75. *Honors & Awards:* Mem, Order of Brit Empire, 44. *Res:* Chemistry of phospholipids and inositol; lipid metabolism. *Mailing Add:* Howe House Maitland Hants Maitland NS B0N 1T0 Can

MCPHERSON, M(URRAY) B(URNS), water resources, deceased

MACPHERSON, ROBERT DUNCAN, b Lakewood, Ohio, May 25, 44; m 69. TOPOLOGY. *Educ:* Swarthmore Col, BA, 66; Harvard Univ, MA, 69, PhD(math), 70. *Prof Exp:* Instr, Brown Univ, 70-72, from asst prof to assoc prof, 72-76; vis prof, Univ Paris, 76-77; PROF MATH, BROWN UNIV, 77- *Concurrent Pos:* Res fel fel, Oak Ridge Nat Lab, 64-65; mathematician, US Brazil exchange prog, 73; vis mem, Inst Advan Sci Studies, 74-75; fel, Nat Sci Res Ctr, France, 75. *Mem:* Am Math Soc. *Res:* Differential topology; topology of algebraic varieties; singularities. *Mailing Add:* Dept of Math Brown Univ Providence RI 02912

MACPHERSON, RODERICK IAN, b St Thomas, Ont, Feb 22, 35; m 57; c 5. RADIOLOGY, PEDIATRICS. *Educ:* Univ Man, BSc & MD, 58; Royal Col Physicians Can, cert radiol, 63; FRCP(C), 64. *Prof Exp:* Asst radiologist, Montreal Children's Hosp, Que, 64-65; asst radiologist, Royal Victoria Hosp, Montreal, 65; asst radiologist, Shaughnessy Hosp, Vancouver, BC, 65-67; assoc radiologist, Children's Hosp Winnipeg, 67-69; asst prof, 67-69, ASSOC PROF RADIOL, UNIV MAN, 69-, ASSOC PROF PEDIAT, 71-; DIR DEPT RADIOL, CHILDREN'S HOSP WINNIPEG, 69- *Concurrent Pos:* Instr, McGill Univ, 65 & Univ BC, 65-67. *Mem:* Can Asn Radiol; Am Roentgen Ray Soc; Soc Pediat Radiol. *Res:* Diagnostic radiology; clinical, pathologic and radiologic aspects of pediatric chest diseases, renal diseases and skeletal diseases. *Mailing Add:* Dept of Radiol Univ of Manitoba Winnipeg MB R3T 2N2 Can

MCPHERSON, ROSS, b Buffalo, NY, May 30, 34; m 57; c 3. PHYSICS. *Educ:* Queen's Univ, Ont, BSc, 59, MSc, 61; McGill Univ, PhD(physics), 64. *Prof Exp:* Res assoc, Brookhaven Nat Lab, 64-66; asst prof physics, Cornell Univ, 66-72; assoc prof physics, Univ Guelph, 72-79, MEM STAFF, BELL LABS, 79- *Mem:* AAAS; Am Phys Soc; Can Asn Physicists. *Res:* Nuclear physics; nuclear and digital instrumentation; nuclear engineering. *Mailing Add:* 4E-320A Bell Labs Whippany NJ 07981

MCPHERSON, THOMAS ALEXANDER, b Calgary, Alta, Mar 1, 39; m 67; c 4. IMMUNOLOGY. *Educ:* Univ Alta, MD, 62; Univ Melbourne, PhD(med, immunol), 69. *Prof Exp:* Sr resident med officer, Royal Adelaide Hosps, SAustralia, 63-64, med registr, 64-65, sr med registr, Renal Unit, 65; asst physician, Clin Res Univ, Walter & Eliza Hall Inst Med Res, Melbourne, 66-68; asst prof, 69-70, assoc prof, 70-77, PROF MED, UNIV ALTA, 77-DIR DEPT MED, CROSS INST, 73-, ASST DEAN MED, 81- *Concurrent Pos:* R S McLaughlin Res Found traveling fel, Southeast Asia & Europe, 68-69. *Mem:* Australasian Soc Med Res; Can Soc Immunol; Can Soc Clin Invest. *Res:* Induction and inhibition of experimental allergic encephalomyelitis using human encephalitogenic basic protein and synthetic polypeptides; the carcinoembryonic antigen in the human colon; trial of anti-thymocyte globulin in acute relapses of multiple sclerosis. *Mailing Add:* Dept of Med Cross Inst 11560 Univ Ave Edmonton AB T6G 1Z2 Can

MCPHERSON, THOMAS C(OATSWORTH), b Atlanta, Ga, May 12, 22; m 78; c 4. ALLERGY, IMMUNOLOGY. *Educ:* Emory Univ, AB, 43; Univ Md, Sch Med, MD, 46. *Prof Exp:* Admin asst to the dir of res, The Children's Cancer Res Found, 69-71; assoc med dir, Fisons Corp, Bedford, Mass, 72-77; clin res consult serv, Nashua, NH, 78; assoc dir, Domestic Clin Res, 3M Ctr, Minn, 78-80, ASSOC DIR MED SERV, RIKER LABS, INC, CA, 80-; assoc dir, Domestic Clin Res, 3M Ctr, Minn, 78-80, ASSOC DIR, MED SERV, RIKER LABS, INC, 3M CO, CALIF, 80- *Concurrent Pos:* Consult pediat, Martin Army Hosp, Ft Benning, Ga, 57-61; sr fel, Dept Biochem, Brandeis Univ, 66-67; consult, The Children's Cancer Res Found, Boston, Mass, 72-77. *Mem:* Am Acad Pediat; Drug Info Asn; Am Soc Clin Pharmacol & Therapeut; Am Acad Allergy. *Res:* Clinical research in allergy and hematology. *Mailing Add:* Riker Labs Inc Box one Northridge CA 91324

MCPHERSON, WILLIAM HAKES, b Poplar Bluff, Mo, Oct 10, 20; m 48. PAPER CHEMISTRY. *Educ:* Syracuse Univ, BS, 42; Inst Paper Chem, MS, 44, PhD, 48. *Prof Exp:* Chemist, Tenn Eastman Corp, 44-46; res chem engr, Int Paper Co, 48-50; res chem engr, Mead Corp, 50-52; res mgr, Minn & Ont Paper Co Div, Boise Cascade Corp, 52-65, dir pulp & paper res lab, 65-73; PVT CONSULT, WILLIAM H McPHERSON, CONSULT, 73- *Concurrent Pos:* Consult, Forest Prod Dept, Univ Minn, 74. *Mem:* Am Chem Soc; Tech Asn Pulp & Paper Indust; Can Pulp & Paper Asn. *Res:* Pulping and bleaching of wood fibers; development of paper specialties; paper coatings; mechanism of softening paper; insulation board research; waste water treatment; papermaking; properties of Tropical Hardwoods. *Mailing Add:* Island View Route PO Box 218 International Falls MN 56649

MCPHIE, PETER, b Leeds, Eng, Oct 3, 42; US citizen; m 66; c 3. BIOPHYSICAL CHEMISTRY, ENZYMOLOGY. *Educ:* Univ Durham, BSc, 63; Univ London, PhD(biophys), 66. *Prof Exp:* Fel, Stanford Univ, 66-68; vis scientist, 68-74, RES CHEMIST BIOCHEM, NIH, 74- *Res:* Structure and function of proteins and nucleic acids. *Mailing Add:* Lab Biochem NIH 9000 Rockville Pike Bethesda MD 20014

MCPHILLIPS, JOSEPH JOHN, pharmacology, see previous edition

MCQUADE, HENRY ALONZO, b St Louis, Mo, Nov 1, 15. CYTOLOGY, CYTOGENETICS. *Educ:* Wash Univ, AB, 38, PhD, 49; Univ Mo, MA, 40. *Prof Exp:* Asst prof biol, Harris Teachers Col, 49-54; res assoc, Mallinckrodt Inst Radiol, Sch Med, Wash Univ, 54-56; res assoc, Radiation Res Lab, Col Med, Univ Iowa, 56-57; assoc prof radiobiol, Sch Med, 57-64, dir radioisotope lab, Med Ctr, 57-70, PROF RADIOBIOL, SCH MED, UNIV MO-COLUMBIA, 64-, CHIEF RADIOL SCI SECT, MED CTR, 70- *Mem:* Genetics Soc Can; Genetics Soc Am; Bot Soc Am. *Res:* Electron microscopy of cells including neiocytes of wheat. *Mailing Add:* Dept Radiol Univ Mo Med Ctr Columbia MO 65201

MCQUAID, RICHARD WILLIAM, b Woodland, Calif, Jan 6, 23; m 44; c 3. FUEL SCIENCE & TECHNOLOGY. *Educ:* Univ Calif, AB, 43; Johns Hopkins Univ, AM, 50, PhD(chem), 51. *Prof Exp:* Jr instr phys chem, Johns Hopkins Univ, 50-51; res chemist, Mutual Chem Co, 51-55; res chemist, Catalyst Res Corp, 55-57, mgr res & develop, 57-61; prin staff scientist, Aircraft Armaments Inc, 61-65; sr proj eng, 65-74, LUBRICANTS & HYDRAUL FLUIDS SPECIALIST, ANNAPOLIS LAB, DAVID TAYLOR NAVAL SHIP RES & DEVELOP CTR, 74- *Concurrent Pos:* Dept Defense Liason Rep, Comt Indust Hazards, Nat Acad Sci/Nat Market Adv Bd, 79- *Mem:* AAAS; Am Chem Soc; Sigma Xi; Am Soc Testing & Mat. *Res:* Thermodynamics and structural inorganic chemistry; properties of highly desiccated silica and alumina gels; chemistry of chromium compounds; crystal optics; electrochemistry; corrosion; pyrotechnics; fuels and lubricants chemistry and technology. *Mailing Add:* Lubrication Friction & Wear Br Naval Ship Res & Develop Ctr Annapolis MD 21402

MCQUARRIE, BRUCE CALE, b Easton, Pa, Jan 6, 29; m 48; c 3. ALGEBRA. *Educ:* Lafayette Col, AB, 51; Univ NH, MA, 56; Boston Univ, PhD(math), 71. *Prof Exp:* From instr to assoc prof, 60-79, PROF MATH, WORCESTER POLYTECH INST, 79- *Concurrent Pos:* Vis instr, Tex A&M Univ, 69-70 & Trent Polytech, Nottingham, Eng, 79-80. *Mem:* Am Math Soc; Math Asn Am. *Res:* Near rings; endomorphisms of nonabelian groups. *Mailing Add:* 125 Hampton St Auburn MA 01501

MCQUARRIE, DONALD ALLAN, b Lowell, Mass, May 20, 37; m 59; c 2. THEORETICAL CHEMISTRY. *Educ:* Lowell Technol Inst, BS, 58; Johns Hopkins Univ, MA, 60; Univ Ore, PhD(chem), 62. *Prof Exp:* Asst prof chem, Mich State Univ, 62-64; mem tech staff, NAm Aviation Sci Ctr, Calif, 64-68; prof chem, Ind Univ, Bloomington, 68-78; PROF CHEM, UNIV CALIF, DAVIS, 78- *Concurrent Pos:* Guggenheim fel, 75-76; vis prof, Univ Andes, Colombia, 76. *Mem:* Am Chem Soc; Biophys Soc. *Res:* Statistical thermodynamics; stochastic processes; biophysics. *Mailing Add:* Dept of Chem Univ of Calif Davis CA 95616

MCQUARRIE, DONALD G, b Richfield, Utah, Apr 17, 31; m 56; c 2. SURGERY, COMPUTER SCIENCES. *Educ:* Univ Utah, BS, 53, MD, 56; Univ Minn, Minneapolis, PhD(surg), 65. *Prof Exp:* From instr to assoc prof, 65-72, PROF SURG, MED SCH, UNIV MINN, MINNEAPOLIS, 72-; STAFF SURGEON & DIR SURG RES LAB, MINNEAPOLIS VET ADMIN HOSP, 64- *Concurrent Pos:* USPHS fel, Univ Minn, Minneapolis, 62-65; Navy liaison mem, Div Med Sci, Nat Res Coun, 59-61; chmn surg partic comt, Vet Admin Ctr Off; dir, Biophys Comput Proj. *Mem:* AAAS; Asn Acad Surg; Soc Exp Biol & Med; Soc Univ Surg; Am Surg Asn. *Res:* Tissue immunology; respiratory physiology; computer sciences. *Mailing Add:* Minneapolis Vet Admin Hosp 54th & 48th Ave S Minneapolis MN 55417

MACQUARRIE, IAN GREGOR, b Hampton, PEI, July 6, 33; m 57; c 4. BOTANY, PLANT PHYSIOLOGY. *Educ:* Dalhousie Univ, BSc, 57, MSc, 58; Univ London, PhD(plant physiol), 61. *Prof Exp:* Asst prof biol, Dalhousie Univ, 61-65 & St Dunstan's Univ, 65-67; asst prof, 67-74, ASSOC PROF BIOL, UNIV PEI, 74- *Mem:* Can Biol Asn; Can Soc Wildlife & Fishery Biol. *Res:* Upland game; fragile habitats; sand dune systems; hedgerows. *Mailing Add:* Dept of Biol Univ of PEI Charlottetown PE C1K 4P3 Can

MCQUARRIE, IRVINE GRAY, b Ogden, Utah, June 27, 39; m 80; c 2. EXPERIMENTAL NEUROLOGY, NEUROSURGERY. *Educ:* Univ Utah, BS, 61; Cornell Univ, MD, 65, PhD, 77; Am Bd Neurol Surg, cert, 79. *Prof Exp:* Chief neurosurg, Naval Hosp, Boston, 73-74; intern & asst surgeon gen surg, Cornell-New York Hosp Med Ctr, 65-68, asst surgeon neurosurg, 68-69, surgeon, 69-73; res fel physiol, Col Med, Cornell Univ, 70-72, res assoc, 74, res fel, 74-76, asst prof physiol, 76-81, asst prof neurosurg, 77-80; ASST PROF NEUROSURG & ADJ ASST PROF ANAT, CASE WESTERN RESERVE UNIV, 81- *Concurrent Pos:* Extramural res fel, Nat Inst Neurol & Commun Disorders & Strokes, 74-76; Andrew W Mellon teacher-scientist, 77-79; asst attend surgeon neurosurg, Cornell-New York Hosp Med Ctr, 77-; asst attend neurosurg, NY Hosp, 77-79; vis asst prof anat, Case Western Reserve Univ, 79-81; consult, Dept Physiol, Med Col, Cornell Univ, 81-; asst attend neurosurg, Univ Hosp Cleveland, 81-; clin investr, Vet Admin Med Ctr, Cleveland, Ohio, 81- *Mem:* AAAS; Cong Neurol Surgeons; Soc Neurosci; Am Soc Cell Biol; Am Asn Neurol Surg. *Res:* Nerve regeneration in rat peripheral nerves and goldfish optic nerves, studied by means of histochemistry, axonal transport of radioactive proteins, axolemmal uptake of radioactive neurotransmitters, and electron microscopy. *Mailing Add:* 2119 Abington Rd Cleveland OH 44106

MCQUATE, JOHN TRUMAN, b Upper Sandusky, Ohio, Aug 28, 21; m 46; c 3. GENETICS. *Educ:* Heidelberg Col, BS, 43; Ind Univ, PhD(zool), 51. *Prof Exp:* From asst prof to assoc prof, 51-70, PROF ZOOL, OHIO UNIV, 70- *Concurrent Pos:* Am Cancer Soc res fel, Case Western Reserve Univ, 56-57, USPHS res fel, 57-59. *Mem:* AAAS; Am Soc Human Genetics. *Res:* Radiation and chemical mutagenesis in Drosophila; human genetics and cytogenetics. *Mailing Add:* Dept Zool & Microbiol Ohio Univ Athens OH 45701

MCQUATE, ROBERT SAMUEL, b Lebanon, Pa, Sept 4, 47; m 70; c 2. BIOINORGANIC CHEMISTRY. *Educ:* Lebanon Valley Col, BS, 69; Ohio State Univ, PhD(chem), 73. *Prof Exp:* Res fel, NMex State Univ, 73-74; asst prof chem, Willamette Univ, 74-77; consumer safety officer, Regulatory Affairs, Bur Foods, Food & Drug Admin, 77-80; GROUP LEADER, REGULATORY AFFAIRS & NUTRIT, ARMOUR-DIAL, INC, 80- *Concurrent Pos:* Sigma Xi grant-in-aid, 75; Petrol Res Fund grant-in-aid, 75. *Mem:* Am Chem Soc; AAAS; Inst Food Technologists; Soc Risk analysis; Soc Environ Toxicol & Chem. *Res:* Study of metal ions in metalloenzyme systems and metal ion catalysis of interligand reactions; regulatory affairs pertaining to foods, drugs, cosmetics and household products. *Mailing Add:* Armour Res Ctr 1510 N Scottsdale Rd Scottsdale AZ 85260

MCQUAY, RUSSELL MICHAEL, JR, medical parasitology, see previous edition

MCQUEEN, DONALD JAMES, b Vancouver, BC, Sept 8, 43; m 65; c 1. LIMNOLOGY. *Educ:* Univ BC, BSc, 66, MSc, 68, PhD(ecol), 70. *Prof Exp:* Asst prof biol, 70-74, ASSOC PROF BIOL, YORK UNIV, 74- *Concurrent Pos:* Nat Res Coun Can fel & res fund, Nat Sci & Eng Res Coun, 70-79. *Mem:* Can Soc Zool; Int Asn Theoret & Appl Limnol; Am Soc Naturalists; Brit Ecol Asn; Ecol Soc Am. *Res:* Lake restoration using hypolimnetic aevahon and manipulation of fish, zooplankton and phytoplankton populations. *Mailing Add:* Dept of Biol York Univ 4700 Keele St Toronto ON M3J 1P3 Can

MCQUEEN, HUGH J, b Alloa, Scotland, Sept 29, 33; Can citizen; m 59; c 6. MECHANICAL METALLURGY, SCIENCE POLICY. *Educ:* Loyola Col Montreal, BSc, 54; McGill Univ, BEng, 56; Univ Notre Dame, MS, 58, PhD, 61. *Prof Exp:* Assoc prof metall, Ecole Polytech, Montreal, 61-66; res scientist, Phys Metall Div, Dept Energy, Mines & Resources, Can, 66-68; assoc prof mech eng, Sir George Williams Univ, 68-72, chmn dept, 71-72, PROF MECH ENG, CONCORDIA UNIV, 73- *Honors & Awards:* Western Elec Fund Award, Am Soc Eng Educ, 76. *Mem:* Am Soc Metals; Am Inst Mining, Metall & Petrol Engrs; Metals Soc, Eng; Am Soc Testing & Mat; Can Inst Mining & Metall. *Res:* Mechanical properties of metals, especially dislocation, substructures, strengthening mechanisms, hot working, transmission electron microscopy. *Mailing Add:* Dept of Mech Eng Concordia Univ Montreal PQ H3G 1M8 Can

MCQUEEN, JOHN DONALD, b Bently, Alta, Oct 17, 23; m 55; c 3. MEDICINE. *Educ:* Univ Toronto, MD, 46, MA, 50. *Prof Exp:* Neurosurgeon, Johns Hopkins Hosp, 56; from instr to asst prof neurol surg, Johns Hopkins Univ, 56-65, assoc prof neurosurg, 65-77; PROF CLIN NEUROL SCI & DIR NEUROSURG, UNIV SASK, 78- *Concurrent Pos:* Asst chief surg in chg neurosurg, Baltimore City Hosps, 56-61, assoc chief, 61-; consult, Perry Point Vet Hosp, 62; consult, Loch Raven Vet Admin Hosp, 66, chief neurosurg, 70- *Mem:* AAAS; Am Soc Cell Biol; fel Royal Col Surgeons; Am Asn Neurol Surg; fel Am Col Surg. *Res:* Experimental head injury; intracranial hypertension; acute ethanolism. *Mailing Add:* Dept Clin Neurol Sci Univ Sask Univ Hosp Saskatoon SK S7N 0W0 Can

MCQUEEN, RALPH EDWARD, Can citizen. RUMINANT NUTRITION, BIOCHEMISTRY. *Educ:* Univ BC, BSA, 66, MSc, 69; Cornell Univ, PhD(nutrit), 73. *Prof Exp:* RES SCIENTIST RUMINANT NUTRIT, AGR CAN, 74- *Mem:* Am Soc Animal Sci; Am Dairy Sci Asn; Nutrit Soc Can; Can Soc Animal Sci; Agr Inst Can. *Res:* Fermentation of fiber by ruminal microorganisms; chemical and biochemical methods for evaluating nutritive quality of feedstuffs. *Mailing Add:* Res Sta Agr Can PO Box 20280 Fredericton NB E3B 4Z7 Can

MACQUEEN, ROBERT MOFFAT, b Memphis, Tenn, Mar 28, 38; m 60; c 2. SOLAR PHYSICS. *Educ:* Southwestern at Memphis, BS, 60; Johns Hopkins Univ, PhD(atmospheric sci), 68. *Prof Exp:* Actg asst prof physics, Southwestern at Memphis, 61-63; instr astron, Goucher Col, 64-66; consult, Appl Physics Lab, Johns Hopkins Univ, 66; SR STAFF SCIENTIST, HIGH ALTITUDE OBSERV, NAT CTR ATMOSPHERIC RES, 67-, DIR, 79- *Concurrent Pos:* Lectr, Dept Astrogeophys, Univ Colo, Boulder, 69-79, adj prof, 79- *Honors & Awards:* Exceptional Sci Achievement Medal, NASA, 74. *Mem:* Am Asn Physics Teachers; Am Geophys Union; Optical Soc Am; Am Astron Soc; Int Astron Union. *Res:* Structure and evolution of the solar electron corona; infrared thermal emission of the interplanetary medium; temperature structure of solar photosphere and corona. *Mailing Add:* Nat Ctr for Atmospheric Res High Altitude Observ Box 3000 Boulder CO 80307

MACQUEEN, ROGER WEBB, b Toronto, Ont, Nov 5, 35; m 59; c 4. GEOLOGY. *Educ:* Univ Toronto, BA, 58, MA, 60; Princeton Univ, MA & PhD(geol), 65. *Prof Exp:* Geologist, V C Illing & Partners, Eng, 60-62; res scientist, Inst Sedimentary & Petrol Geol, Geol Surv Can, 65-76; assoc prof, 76-79, PROF EARTH SCI, UNIV WATERLOO, 79- *Concurrent Pos:* Spec lectr, Dept Geol, Univ Calgary, 67-68; vis assoc prof, Erindale Col, Univ Toronto, 71-72; chmn, Am Comn Stratig Nomenclature, 74-75. *Mem:* AAAS; Geol Soc Am; Soc Econ Paleontologists & Mineralogists; fel Geol Asn Can (pres, 77-78); Can Soc Petrol Geologists. *Res:* Regional geology; sedimentology; base metals in sedimentary rocks. *Mailing Add:* Dept Earth Sci Univ Waterloo Waterloo ON N2L 3G1 Can

MCQUIGG, ROBERT DUNCAN, b Wooster, Ohio, Apr 7, 36; m 59; c 4. PHYSICAL CHEMISTRY, ENVIRONMENTAL CHEMISTRY. *Educ:* Muskingum Col, BS, 58; Ohio State Univ, PhD(phys chem), 64. *Prof Exp:* Asst prof chem, Univ Toledo, 64-65; from asst prof to assoc prof, 65-75, chmn dept, 72-75, PROF CHEM, OHIO WESLEYAN UNIV, 75-, CHMN DEPT, 78- *Concurrent Pos:* Vis scientist, Nat Ctr Atmospheric Res, Colo, 69-70; dir & res supvr, Undergrad Res Participation, NSF, Ohio Wesleyan Univ, 68, 80 & 81. *Mem:* Am Chem Soc. *Res:* Atmospheric chemistry, including photochemical kinetics, computer modelling, sampling and analysis; photochemistry of inorganic coordination compounds. *Mailing Add:* Dept Chem Ohio Wesleyan Univ Delaware OH 43015

MACQUILLAN, ANTHONY M, b London, Eng, Feb 3, 28; Can citizen; m 53; c 4. MICROBIAL PHYSIOLOGY, BIOCHEMISTRY. *Educ:* Univ BC, BSA, 56, MSc, 58; Univ Wis, PhD(bact), 62. *Prof Exp:* Nat Res Coun Can fel, 61-63; asst prof, 63-72, ASSOC PROF MICROBIOL, UNIV MD, COLLEGE PARK, 72- *Mem:* AAAS; Am Soc Microbiol; Am Soc Photobiol. *Res:* Ultraviolet photobiology; DNA repair mechanisms in yeast; genetics of photoreactivation activity and physiology of photokilling in yeast; metabolic control; physiological and genetic control of fermentative and respiratory metabolism in yeast; yeast genetics. *Mailing Add:* Dept Microbiol Univ Md College Park MD 20742

MCQUILLEN, HOWARD RAYMOND, b Dubuque, Iowa, May 6, 24; m 56; c 3. ELECTRONIC & OPTICAL ENGINEERING. *Educ:* Iowa State Col, BSEE, 50; Univ Ariz, MSEE, 60; Ariz State Univ, PhD(elec eng), 67. *Prof Exp:* Res engr, Radio Corp Am, 50-55 & Admiral Corp, 55-56; sr eng specialist, Goodyear Aerospace Corp, 56-67; mgr systs res & develop dept, GTE-Sylvania, 67-71; STAFF ENGR, ELECTROMAGELECTROMAGNETIC SYSTS DIV, RAYTHEON CORP, 71- *Concurrent Pos:* Designer & conductor training courses practicing electronic engrs, 81- *Mem:* Sr mem Inst Elec & Electronics Engrs. *Res:* Electronic systems research and development using microwave, analog and digital circuits and optical processing; applications to electronic warfare, television, radar, communications, telemetry, navigation and other sensors and radiators. *Mailing Add:* Electromagnetic Systs Div Raytheon Corp Dept 9280 Goleta CA 93017

MCQUISTAN, RICHMOND BECKETT, b West New York, NJ, June 12, 27; m 51; c 2. PHYSICS, STATISTICAL MECHANICS. *Educ:* Purdue Univ, BS, 50, MS, 52, PhD(physics, heat transfer), 54. *Prof Exp:* Instr, Purdue Univ, 52-54; head solid state sect, Farnsworth Electronics Co, 54-56; res supvr phys electronics, Honeywell Res Ctr, 56-61; assoc prof elec eng, Univ Minn, Minneapolis, 61-63; staff physicist, Honeywell Res Ctr, 63-66; chmn dept physics, 68-69, assoc dean col lett & sci, 69-71, asst to vchancellor, 65-66; dean grad sch, 72-75, PROF PHYSICS, UNIV WIS-MILWAUKEE, 66-, DIR LAB SURFACE STUDIES, 78- *Concurrent Pos:* Vis assoc prof, Univ Minn, Minneapolis, 63-64; vis prof, Univ Liverpool, 73-76; sr res fel, Brit Sci Res Coun, 75-76. *Mem:* Am Optical Soc; Am Phys Soc; Am Vacuum Soc; Orthop Res Soc. *Res:* Infrared detectors and detection theory; electrical and optical properties of vacuum deposited thin films; radiative heat transfer and thermodynamics; infrared gonimetric reflectance measurements; resistance-temperature characteristics of semiconductors; infrared modulation by free carrier absorption; statistical mechanics of lattice spaces. *Mailing Add:* Dept of Physics Univ of Wis 1900 E Kenwood Ave Milwaukee WI 53201

MCQUISTON, FAYE C(LEM), b Perry, Okla, Jan 23, 28; m 55; c 3. MECHANICAL ENGINEERING, THERMAL SCIENCES. *Educ:* Okla State Univ, BS, 58, MS, 59; Purdue Univ, Lafayette, PhD(mech eng), 70. *Prof Exp:* Aerothermodyn engr, Gen Dynamics Corp, 59-61; res scientist gas dynamics, Ling-Temco-Vought Res Ctr, 61-62; from asst prof to assoc prof thermal environ eng, 62-75, PROF THERMAL ENVIRON ENG, OKLA STATE UNIV, 75- *Concurrent Pos:* Consult, Peerless Boiler Co, Oklahoma City, 63, C A Mathey Mach Works, Tulsa, 64, Evans & Throup, Ponca City, 66, Brewer Corp, Ft Worth, 70, Lapco, Inc, Tulsa, 71-, Collins-Soter Eng, Oklahoma City, 71-, Russell Coil Co, Los Angeles, 77- & Thermal Corp, Houston, 78-; NSF sci fac fel, 67-69. *Mem:* Am Soc Mech Engrs; Am Soc Heating, Refrig & Air-Conditioning Engrs. *Res:* Compact heat exchanger design and optimization; condensation from binary gas mixtures; general heat transfer and fluid dynamics problems of air-conditioning industry; building thermal systems simulation. *Mailing Add:* Sch of Mech & Aerospace Eng Okla State Univ Stillwater OK 74074

MACQUOWN, WILLIAM CHARLES, JR, b Pittsburgh, Pa, Sept 8, 15; m 39; c 2. GEOLOGY. *Educ:* Univ Rochester, BS, 38, MS, 40; Cornell Univ, PhD(struct geol), 43. *Prof Exp:* Asst geol, Univ Rochester, 38-40 & Cornell Univ, 40-43; petrol geologist, Magnolia Petrol Co, 43-46; asst prof geol, Univ Ky, 47-48; dist geologist, Coop Ref Asn, 48-50; geologist, Denver Area, Deep Rock Oil Corp, 50-54; chief geologist, Sohio Petrol Co, Okla, 54-57, mgr, Calgary, 57-60; PROF GEOL, UNIV KY, 61-; PETROL CONSULT, 60- *Mem:* AAAS; fel Geol Soc Am; Am Inst Prof Geologists; Am Asn Petrol Geol; Soc Econ Paleont & Mineral. *Res:* Stratigraphy and carbonate petrology. *Mailing Add:* Dept of Geol Univ of Ky Lexington KY 40506

MAC RAE, ALFRED URQUHART, b New York, NY, Apr 14, 32; m 67; c 2. PHYSICS. *Educ:* Syracuse Univ, BS, 54, PhD(physics), 60. *Prof Exp:* Head, Explor Semiconductor Technol Dept, 60-80, DIR, INTEGRATED CIRCUITS LAB, BELL LABS, 80- *Mem:* Fel Am Phys Soc; sci mem Bohmische Phys Soc; fel Inst Elec & Electronics Engrs. *Res:* Low energy electron diffraction; surfaces; infrared photoconductivity; fluctuations in solids; ion implantation; silicon integrated circuits. *Mailing Add:* Bell Labs Murray Hill NJ 07974

MCRAE, DANIEL GEORGE, b Jordan, Mont, Nov 25, 38; m 63; c 2. MATHEMATICS, OPERATIONS RESEARCH. *Educ:* Univ Mont, BA, 60, MA, 61; Univ Wash, PhD(math), 67. *Prof Exp:* Instr math, Univ Mont, 61-62; asst prof, Univ Ill, Urbana, 67-70; from asst prof to assoc prof, 70-79, PROF MATH, UNIV MONT, 79- *Concurrent Pos:* Vis lectr, Math Asn Am, 72- *Mem:* Am Math Soc; Math Asn Am; Opers Res Soc Am; Am Inst Decision Sci. *Res:* Ring theory; operations research; homological algebra; microcomputers in education. *Mailing Add:* Dept Math Sci Univ of Mont Missoula MT 59812

MACRAE, DONALD ALEXANDER, b Halifax, NS, Feb 19, 16; m 39; c 3. ASTRONOMY. *Educ:* Univ Toronto, BA, 37; Harvard Univ, PhD(astron), 43. *Prof Exp:* Asst, Univ Toronto, 37-38; res astronr, Univ Pa, 41-42; instr, Cornell Univ, 42-44; res physicist, Manhattan Proj, Tenn, 45-46; asst prof astron, Case Inst Technol, 46-53; assoc prof, 53-55, chmn dept astron & dir, David Dunlap Observ, 65-78, PROF ASTRON, UNIV TORONTO, 56- *Concurrent Pos:* Mem bd trustees, Univs Space Res Asn, 69-76; mem bd dirs, Can-France-Hawaii Telescope Corp, 73-79. *Mem:* Fel Royal Soc Can; Royal Astron Soc Can; fel Royal Astron Soc; Can Astron Soc; Am Astron Soc. *Res:* Galactic and radio astronomy; stellar spectroscopy. *Mailing Add:* David Dunlap Observ Univ of Toronto Richmond Hill ON L4C 4Y6 Can

MACRAE, DONALD RICHARD, b Poughkeepsie, NY, July 14, 34; c 1. PROCESS DEVELOPMENT, PLASMA PROCESSING. *Educ:* Syracuse Univ, BSCHE, 56; Princeton Univ, 58; Royal Inst Technol, Stockholm, Sweden, PhD(chem eng), 61. *Prof Exp:* Res assoc, Dept Ferrous Metall, Royal Inst Technol, Sweden, 62-67; res engr, 67-69, RES SUPVR, BETHLEHEM STEEL CORP, 69- *Mem:* Am Inst Metall Engrs; Iron & Steel Inst Japan; World Future Soc. *Res:* Fundamental phenomena of high temperature extractive metallurgical processes including development of plasma reactors for reduction of iron ore directly to steel and for ferroalloy production. *Mailing Add:* Dept Res Bethlehem Steel Corp Bethlehem PA 18016

MACRAE, EDITH KRUGELIS, b Waterbury, Conn, Jan 24, 19; m 50; c 1. ANATOMY. *Educ:* Bates Col, BS, 40; Columbia Univ, MA, 41, PhD(zool), 46. *Prof Exp:* Instr, Vassar Col, 45-47; Donner Found fel, Carlsberg Lab, Denmark, 47-48, Am Cancer Soc fel, 48-49; res assoc, Yale Univ, 49-51; instr biol, Mass Inst Technol, 51-53; asst res zoologist, Univ Calif, Berkeley, 54-56; from asst prof to prof anat, Univ Ill Med Ctr, 57-72, actg head dept, 69-70; PROF ANAT, MED SCH, UNIV NC, CHAPEL HILL, 72- *Concurrent Pos:* Guggenheim fel, 64-65. *Mem:* AAAS; Am Soc Anatomists; Am Soc Cell Biol; Electron Micros Soc Am. *Res:* Histology; cytochemistry; fine structure. *Mailing Add:* Dept Anat 207H Univ NC Med Sch Chapel Hill NC 27514

MCRAE, EION GRANT, b Tambellup, Australia, Dec 25, 30; m 54; c 2. PHYSICS. *Educ:* Univ Western Australia, BSc, 52, MSc, 54; Fla State Univ, PhD(phys chem), 57. *Prof Exp:* Fel chem, Ind Univ, 57-58; sr res officer, Commonwealth Sci & Indust Res Orgn, Australia, 58-63; MEM TECH STAFF, BELL LABS, 63- *Mem:* Fel Am Phys Soc. *Res:* Theoretical and experimental work on the development of low-energy electron scattering techniques for studying the surface structures of crystals. *Mailing Add:* Room 1C320 Bell Labs Murray Hill NJ 07974

MACRAE, HERBERT F, b Middle River, NS, Mar 30, 26; m 55; c 4. BIOCHEMISTRY, ANIMAL SCIENCE. *Educ:* McGill Univ, BSc, 54, MSc, 56, PhD(biochem), 60. *Prof Exp:* Chemist, Can Dept Nat Health & Welfare, 60-61; asst prof biochem, MacDonald Col, McGill Univ, 61-67, assoc prof, 67-70, prof animal sci, 70-72, chmn dept, 67-72; PRIN, NS AGR COL, 72- *Mem:* Agr Inst Can; Can Soc Animal Sci. *Res:* Estrogens of avian species; milk proteins; organophosphorus insecticides; skeletal muscle enzymes and proteins. *Mailing Add:* NS Agr Col Truro NS B2N 5E3 Can

MCRAE, LORIN POST, b Tucson, Ariz, Feb 20, 36. BIOMEDICAL ENGINEERING, ELECTRONICS. *Educ:* Univ Ariz, BS, 61, PhD(elec eng), 68; NY Univ, MEE, 63. *Prof Exp:* Mem tech staff, Bell Tel Labs, 61-63; instr elec eng, Univ Ariz, 63-68; asst prof, Univ Wyo, 68-70; DIR MED ELECTRONICS, TUCSON MED CTR, 70- *Concurrent Pos:* Chmn elec safety comt, Southern Ariz Hosp Coun, 71-72. *Mem:* Asn Advan Med Instrumentation; Inst Elec & Electronics Engrs. *Mailing Add:* 3540 N Bonanza Ave Tucson AZ 85715

MACRAE, NEIL D, b Scotstown, Que, Oct 9, 35. GEOLOGY. *Educ:* Queen's Univ, Ont, BSc, 61; McMaster Univ, MSc, 63, PhD(geol), 66. *Prof Exp:* Res assoc petrol, Univ Minn, 65-66; fel, 66-68, asst prof, 68-72, ASSOC PROF GEOL, UNIV WESTERN ONT, 72- *Res:* Geochemistry and petrology of silicate-oxide-sulfide relations in mafic and ultramafic intrusions and skarns. *Mailing Add:* Dept of Geol Univ of Western Ont London ON N6A 5B8 Can

MACRAE, PATRICK DANIEL, b Calgary, Alta, Apr 26, 28; m 58. DENTISTRY. *Educ:* Univ Alta, DDS, 60, cert pediat dent, 67. *Prof Exp:* Assoc prof, 60-73, PROF PEDIAT DENT, UNIV ALTA, 73-, CHMN, DIV PEDIAT DENT, 78- *Concurrent Pos:* Dir dent serv, Glenrose Hosp, Edmonton, Alta, 66- *Mem:* Can Dent Asn. *Res:* Sociology of health care. *Mailing Add:* Dept of Pediat Dent Univ of Alta Fac of Dent Edmonton AB T6E 2N8 Can

MACRAE, ROBERT ALEXANDER, b Charlotte, NC, Dec 8, 35; m 71; c 1. PHYSICS. *Educ:* Davidson Col, BS, 58; Vanderbilt Univ, MS, 60. *Prof Exp:* Instr physics, Davidson Col, 60-62; asst prof, Univ NC, Charlotte, 62-65; prof, Cent Piedmont Community Col, 65-67; ASST PROF PHYSICS, JACKSONVILLE STATE UNIV, 67- *Concurrent Pos:* Consult physics, Oak Ridge Nat Lab, 61- & Aircraft Performance & Air Traffic Control, 75-; pres, Air Brake Consult, 75- *Mem:* Am Phys Soc; Optical Soc Am; Air Brake Asn; Am Asn Physics Teachers; Sigma Xi. *Res:* Optical properties of materials; vacuum ultraviolet spectroscopy; railroad train stopping performance. *Mailing Add:* Dept of Physics Jacksonville State Univ Jacksonville AL 36265

MACRAE, ROBERT E, b Detroit, Mich, May 1, 34; m 57; c 1. MATHEMATICS. *Educ:* Univ Chicago, AB, 53, SM, 56, PhD(math), 61. *Prof Exp:* Staff mem, Los Alamos Sci Lab, 57-59; NSF fel, 61-62; Ritt instr math, Columbia Univ, 62-65; asst prof, Univ Mich, 65-67; assoc prof, 67-72, PROF MATH, UNIV COLO, BOULDER, 72- *Concurrent Pos:* Consult, Inst Defense Anal, 65 & Math Rev, 65- *Res:* Commutative ring theory; homological algebra; algebraic curves. *Mailing Add:* Dept of Math Univ of Colo Boulder CO 80309

MCRAE, ROBERT JAMES, b Jordan, Mont, Aug 16, 31; m 56; c 7. SCIENCE EDUCATION. *Educ:* Univ Mont, BA, 54, MA, 57; Univ Wis, Madison, PhD(hist sci), 69. *Prof Exp:* Asst prof, 58-60, assoc prof, 60-62 & 66-69, PROF PHYSICS, EASTERN MONT COL, 69-, DEAN SCH LIBERAL ARTS, 81- *Mem:* Hist Sci Soc; Am Asn Physics Teachers; Nat Sci Teachers Asn. *Res:* History of nineteenth and early twentieth century physics. *Mailing Add:* Dept of Phys Sci Eastern Mont Col Billings MT 59101

MCRAE, VINCENT VERNON, b Columbia, SC, Sept 2, 18; m 41; c 1. SCIENCE POLICY, INFORMATION SCIENCE. *Educ:* Miner Teachers Col, BS, 40; Cath Univ, MS, 44, PhD(math), 55. *Prof Exp:* Teacher high sch, Washington, DC, 41-52; analyst opers res off, Johns Hopkins Univ, 52-60, chmn Stratspiel group & chief strategic div, 60-61; mem sr staff, Res Anal Corp, 61-64; tech asst, Off Sci & Technol, White House, 64-74; DIR STRATEGIC PLANNING, FED SYSTS DIV, IBM CORP, 74- *Concurrent Pos:* Mem tech staff, Gaither Comt, 57; adv to del & mem US del, Surprise Attack Conf, Geneva, 58; res assoc, Coolidge Comt, 59; consult, Nat Security Coun, Dept of Defense, 73-78 & Off Sci & Technol Policy, White House; mem Defense Sci Bd, 73-80 & Naval Studies Bd. *Mem:* Fel AAAS; NY Acad Sci; Am Math Soc; Opers Res Soc Am. *Res:* Operations research; military operations research. *Mailing Add:* 1501 Emerson St NW Washington DC 20011

MCRAE, WAYNE ALAN, b Chicago, Ill, Aug 8, 25; c 2. PHYSICAL CHEMISTRY. *Educ:* Harvard Univ, AB, 47, AM, 48. *Prof Exp:* Chemist, 49-50, patents supvr, 50-52, asst tech dir, 52-57, dir org div, 57-59, VPRES & DIR, IONICS, INC, 59- *Res:* Membrane transport processes; ultra-filtration; reversed osmosis; electrodialysis; electrochemistry; fuel cells; membrane chlor-alkali cells; saline water conversion. *Mailing Add:* Ionics Inc 65 Grove St Watertown MA 02172

MACRANDER, ALBERT TIEMEN, b Hilversum, Holland, Apr 23, 50; US citizen; m 79. POINT DEFECTS. *Educ:* Univ Ill, Urbana, BS, 72, MS, 73, PhD(physics), 77. *Prof Exp:* Assoc fel, Dept Mat Sci & Eng, Cornell Univ, 77-80; MEM TECH STAFF, BELL LABS, 80- *Mem:* Am Phys Soc. *Res:* Point defects in noble gas solids, defects in III-IV semiconductors; hydrogen in tungsten; Monte Carlo simulations of ion implantation; ultra-precise x-ray lattice parameter determinations; x-ray double crystal diffractometry; atom-probe field-ion microscopy; capacitance transient spectroscopy. *Mailing Add:* 7C-312 Bell Telephone Labs Murray Hill NJ 07974

MCREE, G(RIFFITH) J(OHN), JR, b Blackstone, Va, Sept 21, 34; m 56; c 3. ELECTRICAL ENGINEERING. *Educ:* US Mil Acad, BS, 56; Univ Ariz, MS, 62; Univ Va, PhD(elec eng), 70. *Prof Exp:* Instr math, US Mil Acad, 65-67; teaching asst elec eng, Univ Va, 67-68, res asst control systs, 68-70; asst prof, 70-73, ASSOC PROF, DEPT ELEC ENG, OLD DOMINION UNIV, 73- *Concurrent Pos:* Prin investr, NASA contracts, 70- *Mem:* Inst Elec & Electronics Eng. *Res:* Automatic control of systems; simulation and modeling of systems to include large, complex socio-economic systems; studies in the improvement of engineering curricula. *Mailing Add:* Dept of Elec Eng Sch of Eng Old Dominion Univ Norfolk VA 23508

MCREYNOLDS, LARRY AUSTIN, b Eugene, Ore, May 27, 46; m 77. BIOCHEMISTRY, MOLECULAR BIOLOGY. *Educ:* Ore State Univ, BSc, 68; Mass Inst Technol, PhD(biol), 74. *Prof Exp:* Teaching asst cell biol, Mass Inst Technol, 68-70; NIH fel, Baylor Col Med, 74-77; vis scientist DNA sequencing, Med Res Coun Lab Molecular Biol, Eng, 77-78; ASST PROF BIOCHEM, COL MED, UNIV ARIZ, 78- *Concurrent Pos:* Am Cancer Soc Inst res grant, 78-79; biomed res grant, Univ Ariz, 78-79; NIH grant, 79-82. *Mem:* Am Soc Cell Biol. *Res:* Structure of eukaryotic genes by using bacterial cloning and DNA sequencing; function and structure of the genes studied by their transfer to cells in culture. *Mailing Add:* Dept Biochem Univ Ariz Col Med Tucson AZ 85724

MACRI, FRANK JOHN, b Portland, Maine, Jan 12, 23; m 48; c 4. PHARMACOLOGY. *Educ:* Univ Maine, BA, 43; George Washington Univ, BS, 50; Georgetown Univ, PhD(pharmacol), 53. *Prof Exp:* Anal chemist, Naval Powder Factory, 43-45, org chemist, 46-48; biochemist, NIH, 48-50; pharmacologist, Irwin, Neisler & Co, 51-53; chief pharmacologist, Eaton Labs, Inc, 53-55; head, Sect Pharmacol, Nat Eye Inst, Bethesda, 55-79; PROF OPHTHAL & PHARMACOL & DIR OCULAR PHARMACOL, MED CTR, GEORGETOWN UNIV, 79- *Mem:* Am Soc Pharmacol & Exp Therapeut; Asn Res Vision & Ophthal; NY Acad Sci. *Res:* Pharmacodynamics of autonomic nervous system agents; effect of hormones on vascular physiology and pharmacology; structure-activity relationships in biological processes; pharmacology of the eye. *Mailing Add:* 3602 Janet Rd Silver Spring MD 20906

MCRIPLEY, RONALD JAMES, b Detroit, Mich, Nov 17, 32; m 55; c 3. MEDICAL MICROBIOLOGY. *Educ:* Mich State Univ, BS, 54; Univ Mich, MS, 61, PhD(microbiol), 64. *Prof Exp:* Bacteriologist, Mich State Dept Health, 58-59; res asst microbiol, St Margaret's Hosp, 64-67; sr res scientist, Norwich Pharmacal Co, 67-69; sr res bacteriologist, 69-74, RES FEL, SQUIBB INST MED RES, 74- *Concurrent Pos:* Fel sch med, Tufts Univ, 64- *Mem:* AAAS; Am Burn Asn; NY Acad Sci; Am Soc Microbiol. *Res:* Host defense mechanisms against bacterial infection; chemotherapy in infectious diseases; host-parasite interactions. *Mailing Add:* Squibb Inst for Med Res Box 4000 Princeton NJ 08540

MACRISS, ROBERT A, b Athens, Greece, Nov 8, 30; US citizen; m 60; c 2. CHEMICAL ENGINEERING, ENERGY CONSERVATION RESEARCH. *Educ:* Nat Tech Univ Athens, Ing Dipl, 55; Univ Alta, MSc, 59. *Prof Exp:* Pilot plant engr, Can Chem Co, Edmonton, 59-60; asst chem engr, 60-62, assoc chem engr, 62-64, chem engr air conditioning res & develop, 64-67, res supvr, 67-72, res supvr environ res & develop, 72-73, res mgr, 73-75, asst res dir, 75-77, ASSOC RES DIR ENERGY CONSERV, INST GAS TECHNOL, 77- *Mem:* Am Soc Heating, Air Conditioning & Refrig Engrs. *Res:* Indoor pollution; environmental control; air conditioning; absorption cooling; thermodynamics; properties of fluid mixtures, gases and chemicals; gas appliances; solar heating/cooling; energy modeling; solar applications; energy conservation; air infiltration; energy management. *Mailing Add:* Inst Gas Technol 3424 S State St Chicago IL 60616

MCROBBIE, HENRY WILLIAM, chemical engineering, deceased

MCROBERTS, J WILLIAM, b Rochester, Minn, Dec 6, 32; m 59; c 2. UROLOGY. *Educ:* Princeton Univ, BA, 55; Cornell Univ, MD, 59. *Prof Exp:* Intern surg, New York Hosp & Cornell Univ Med Col, 59-60; resident surg, Mayo Clin, 60-61, resident urol, 61-64; from instr to assoc prof urol, Sch Med, Univ Wash, 67-72; assoc prof, 72-74, PROF SURG, COL MED, UNIV KY, 74-, CHIEF DIV UROL, 72- *Mem:* Am Col Surg; Am Urol Asn; Am Acad Pediat; Soc Pediat Urol; Soc Univ Urol. *Res:* Renal transplantation; pediatric urology, intersex. *Mailing Add:* Div of Urol Univ of Ky Col of Med Lexington KY 40506

MCROBERTS, KEITH L, b Clinton, Iowa, July 16, 31; m 52; c 4. INDUSTRIAL ENGINEERING, OPERATIONS RESEARCH. *Educ:* Iowa State Univ, BS, 53, MS, 59, PhD(eng valuation, opers res), 66. *Prof Exp:* Methods analyst, E I du Pont de Nemours & Co, 53-57; from instr to asst prof indust eng, Iowa State Univ, 57-61, asst prof indust eng & opers res, 62-67; opers analyst, Off Opers Analysis, US Air Force, 61-62; vis lectr mgt sci, Univ Bradford, 67-68; assoc prof, 68-72, PROF INDUST ENG & OPERS RES, IOWA STATE UNIV, 72-, CHMN DEPT INDUST ENG, 74- *Concurrent Pos:* Analyst consult, US Air Force, 58-, dir, Opers Anal Standby Unit, 66-70; consult to indust, 60- *Mem:* Fel Am Inst Indust Engrs; Opers Res Soc Am; Am Soc Eng Educ; Brit Oper Res Soc; Sigma Xi. *Res:* Search theory; simulation; material control. *Mailing Add:* Dept of Indust Eng 212 Marston Hall Ames IA 50010

MCROBERTS, MILTON R, b Hazleton, Ind, Dec 11, 24. BIOCHEMISTRY. *Educ:* Purdue Univ, BS, 49, MS, 58; Aberdeen Col, PhD(biochem, nutrit), 61. *Prof Exp:* Teacher high schs, Ind, 49-51; res chemist, Purdue Univ, 55-58; res chemist, Rowett Res Inst, 58-61, Univ Reading, 61 & Hy-Line Poultry Farms & Pioneer Hi-Bred Corn Co, 62-65; asst dir res life sci, Res Div, W R Grace & Co, 65-67; nutrit officer, Food & Agr Orgn, UN, 67-75; asst prof, Dept Human Nutrit, Syracuse Univ, 75-80; MEM STAFF, SAUDI ARABIAN NAT CTR, RIYADH, SAUDI ARABIA, 80- *Mem:* AAAS; Am Inst Nutrit; Am Soc Animal Sci; Poultry Sci Asn; Brit Nutrit Soc. *Res:* Genetic-nutrition interactions; mineral and vitamin metabolism in tooth and bone formation; influence of specific nutrients to lipid components of blood and influence upon atherosclerosis development; thyroid activity; nutrient biological availability. *Mailing Add:* c/o Saudi Arabian Nat Ctr PO Box 6086 Riyadh Saudi Arabia

MCRORIE, ROBERT ANDERSON, b Statesville, NC, May 7, 24; m 46; c 3. BIOCHEMISTRY. *Educ:* NC State Col, BS, 49, MS, 51; Univ Tex, PhD(biochem), 54. *Prof Exp:* From asst prof to assoc prof, 53-63, PROF BIOCHEM, UNIV GA, 63- *Concurrent Pos:* Res partic, Oak Ridge Inst Nuclear Study, 57 & 58; assoc dean grad sch & dir gen res, Univ Ga, 59-71, asst vpres res, 68-71. *Mem:* AAAS; Am Chem Soc; Am Soc Microbiol; Am Soc Biol Chem. *Res:* Microbial nutrition; intermediary metabolism; enzymology; sperm enzymes; reproduction. *Mailing Add:* Dept of Biochem Univ of Ga Athens GA 30601

MCROWE, ARTHUR WATKINS, b San Francisco, Calif, Aug 16, 37; m 65; c 3. ORGANIC CHEMISTRY. *Educ:* Univ Calif, Berkeley, BS, 60; Univ Wis-Madison, PhD(org chem), 66. *Prof Exp:* Res chemist, 66-71, SR RES CHEMIST, B F GOODRICH RES CTR, 71- *Mem:* Am Chem Soc. *Res:* Physical organic chemistry; carbonium ion rearrangements; monomer processes; metallo-organic chemistry; polymer flammability. *Mailing Add:* B F Goodrich Res Ctr Brecksville OH 44141

MCROY, C PETER, b East Chicago, Ind, Jan 17, 41. BIOLOGICAL OCEANOGRAPHY. *Educ:* Mich State Univ, BS, 63; Univ Wash, MS, 66; Univ Alaska, College, PhD(marine sci), 70. *Prof Exp:* Asst prof, 69-74, assoc prof, 74-79, PROF MARINE SCI, INST MARINE SCI, UNIV ALASKA, FAIRBANKS, 79- *Concurrent Pos:* Fel, Univ Ga, 71-72. *Mem:* AAAS; Am Soc Limnol & Oceanog; Ecol Soc Am; Arctic Inst NAm; Int Asn Aquatic Vascular Plant Biologists. *Res:* Ecology of seagrass communities; productivity and ecology of northern seas. *Mailing Add:* Inst of Marine Sci Univ of Alaska Fairbanks AK 99701

MCSHAN, WILLIAM HARTFORD, b Lonoke, Ark, May 4, 03; m 54; c 1. ENDOCRINOLOGY, BIOCHEMISTRY. *Educ:* Ark State Teachers Col, BS, 28; Univ Mo, AM, 33, PhD(org chem), 36. *Prof Exp:* Asst, Univ Mo, 33-36; res assoc, 36-41, asst prof, 41-46 assoc prof, 46-51, prof, 51-73, EMER PROF ENDOCRINOL, DEPT ZOOL, UNIV WIS-MADISON, 73- *Mem:* AAAS; Am Chem Soc; Am Soc Biol Chem; Am Soc Zool; Endocrine Soc. *Res:* Preparation and biochemistry of gonadotropic hormones; isolation and study of pituitary cytoplasmic organelles. *Mailing Add:* 2714 Harvard Dr Madison WI 53705

MCSHANE, EDWARD JAMES, b New Orleans, La, May 10, 04; m; c 3. MATHEMATICS. *Educ:* Tulane Univ, BE & BS, 25, MS, 27; Univ Chicago, PhD(math), 30. *Hon Degrees:* ScD, Tulane Univ, 47. *Prof Exp:* Instr math, Tulane Univ, 25-27; asst prof, Univ Wichita, 28-29; Nat Res Coun fel, Univ Chicago, Princeton Univ, Ohio State Univ & Harvard Univ, 30-32; instr math, Princeton Univ, 33-34, asst prof, 34-35; prof, 35-57, alumni prof, 57-74, ALUMNI EMER PROF MATH, UNIV VA, 74- *Concurrent Pos:* Head mathematician, Ballistic Res Labs, Aberdeen Proving Grounds, 42-45; ed, Trans Am Math Soc, 44-46. *Mem:* Nat Acad Sci; Am Math Soc (pres, 58-59); Am Philos Soc; Math Asn Am (pres, 53-54). *Res:* Existence theorems in calculus of variations; integration; exterior ballistics; problems of Bolza in calculus of variations; stochastic processes. *Mailing Add:* Dept Math Univ Va Charlottesville VA 22903

MCSHARRY, JAMES JOHN, b Newark, NJ, May 28, 42; m 67; c 2. MICROBIOLOGY, VIROLOGY. *Educ:* Manhattan Col, BS, 65; Univ Va, MS, 67, PhD(microbiol), 70. *Prof Exp:* Asst prof, 73-76, ASSOC PROF MICROBIOL & IMMUNOL, ALBANY MED COL, 76- *Concurrent Pos:* Nat Inst Allergy & Infectious Dis fel, Rockefeller Univ, 70-73. *Mem:* AAAS; Am Soc Microbiol; Harvey Soc; Sigma Xi. *Res:* Studies on the structure and function of the membrane proteins and surface glycoproteins of enveloped RNA viruses; mode of action of antiviral agents. *Mailing Add:* Dept of Microbiol Albany Med Col Albany NY 12208

MCSHARRY, WILLIAM OWEN, b Hammels, NY, Oct 14, 39; m 70; c 1. ANALYTICAL CHEMISTRY. *Educ:* Fordham Univ, BS, 61, MS, 67, PhD(chem), 69. *Prof Exp:* Sr scientist anal chem, 69-75, group leader, 75-79, MGR ANAL CHEM, HOFFMANN-LA ROCHE INC, 79- *Mem:* Am Pharm Asn; Sigma Xi. *Res:* Determination of vitamin D and vitamin A in pharmaceutical and food preparations by liquid chromatography; measurement of color in the pharmaceutical industry. *Mailing Add:* Hoffmann-LaRoche Inc Nutley NJ 07110

MCSHEFFERTY, JOHN, b Akron, Ohio, Mar 14, 29; m 59; c 2. PHARMACEUTICAL CHEMISTRY. *Educ:* Univ Glasgow, BSc, 53, PhD(medicinal chem), 57. *Prof Exp:* Asst lectr pharm, Univ Strathclyde, 53-54; res assoc, Sterling-Winthrop Res Inst, NY, 57-62; sr scientist, Ortho Pharmaceut Corp, Raritan, 62-63, dir pharmaceut develop, 63-80; PRES, GILLETTE RES INST, 80- *Mem:* AAAS; Am Chem Soc; Am Pharmaceut Asn; NY Acad Sci; Am Acad Pharmaceut Sci. *Res:* Pharmaceutical research and development. *Mailing Add:* Gillette Res Inst 1413 Res Blvd Rockville MD 20850

MCSHERRY, CHARLES K, b New York, NY, Nov 22, 31; m 57; c 1. SURGERY. *Educ:* Fordham Univ, BS, 53; Cornell Univ, MD, 57; Am Bd Surg, dipl, 65; Bd Thoracic Surg, dipl, 66. *Prof Exp:* Asst surg, Med Col, Cornell Univ, 58-63, instr, 63-64, from clin instr to clin asst prof, 65-71, assoc prof, 71-77; PROF SURG, MT SINAI SCH MED, 77-; DIR SURG, BETH ISRAEL MED CTR, 77- *Concurrent Pos:* Asst attend surgeon, New York Hosp, 65-72, assoc attend surgeon, 72-77. *Mem:* Am Col Surg; Am Gastroenterol Asn; Asn Study Liver Dis; Soc Univ Surg; Am Surg Asn. *Res:* Gastrointestinal malignancy; gallstone formation. *Mailing Add:* Beth Israel Med Ctr 10 Nathan D Perlman Pl New York NY 10003

MCSHERRY, DIANA HARTRIDGE, b Long Branch, NJ; m 77; c 1. MEDICAL PHYSICS, COMPUTER SCIENCE. *Educ:* Harvard Univ, BA, 65; Rice Univ, MA, 67, PhD(nuclear physics), 69. *Prof Exp:* Fel nuclear physics, Rice Univ, 69; res physicist ultrasonics, Digicon, Inc, 69-74,, exec vpres med ultrasound, 74-77, pres cardiol anal systs, Digisonics, Inc, 77-82; CHMN BD, INFO PROD SYSTS, HOUSTON, 82- *Mem:* Inst Elec & Electronics Engrs; Am Inst Ultrasound in Med; Am Phys Soc; Am Heart Asn. *Res:* Development of computer based cardiology analysis systems in the specific areas of echocardiology, ventriculography and hemodynamics. *Mailing Add:* 3034 Underwood Houston TX 77025

MCSORLEY, ROBERT, b Cincinnati, Ohio, July 23, 49; m 76. NEMATOLOGY. *Educ:* Univ Cincinnati, BS, 71, MS, 74; Purdue Univ, PhD(entom), 78. *Prof Exp:* ASST PROF NEMATOL, UNIV FLA, 78- *Mem:* Soc Nematologists; Entom Soc Am; Org Trop Am Nematologists. *Res:* Pest management; population dynamics; ecology of plant-parasitic and free-living nematodes associated with subtropical crops. *Mailing Add:* 18905 SW 280th St Homestead FL 33031

MCSPADDEN, WILLIAM ROBERT, b Cedar City, Utah, May 9, 31; m 52; c 2. ELECTRICAL ENGINEERING, APPLIED MATHEMATICS. *Educ:* Univ Ariz, BS, 56, MS, 59; Univ Wash, PhD(elec eng, math), 65. *Prof Exp:* Engr, Motorola, Inc, 56-58 & Radio Corp Am, 58-59; asst prof elec eng, NMex State Univ, 59-62; instr, Univ Wash, 62-65; assoc prof, NMex State Univ, 65-68; sr res scientist, Pac Northwest Labs, Battelle Mem Inst, 68-79; MGR, ADVAN STUDIES, UNC NUCLEAR INDUST, 79- *Concurrent Pos:* Consult, CTS-Knights Co, Ill, 59-68, White Sands Missile Range, 61-66, Navy Proj Transit, 62 & Boeing Co, 62-63. *Mem:* AAAS; Inst Elec & Electronics Engrs; Soc Indust & Appl Math; Am Soc Eng Educ. *Res:* Development of algorithms for solution of differential equations; analysis of random signals; math models of precision oscillators; geothermal and solar energy systems and exploration; electric energy systems and energy storage; nuclear engineering and nuclear materials production. *Mailing Add:* UNC Nuclear Indust PO Box 490 Richland WA 99352

MCSPADEN, JAY BYRON, audiology, see previous edition

MCSWAIN, BERAH DAVIS, biophysics, see previous edition

MACSWAN, IAIN CHRISTIE, b Ocean Falls, BC, Apr 15, 21; US citizen; m 43; c 3. PLANT PATHOLOGY. *Educ:* Univ BC, BSA, 42, MSA, 62. *Prof Exp:* Prin res asst, Dom Lab Plant Path, Univ BC, 46-47; asst prof & plant pathologist, BC Dept Agr, 47-55; from asst prof to assoc prof, 55-67, PROF PLANT PATH, ORE STATE UNIV, 67-, EXTEN PLANT PATHOLOGIST, 55- *Mem:* Am Phytopath Soc; Can Phytopath Soc. *Res:* Extension pathology; diseases of horticultural crops. *Mailing Add:* Dept of Plant Path Ore State Univ Corvallis OR 97331

MACSWEEN, JOSEPH MICHAEL, b Antigonish, NS, Mar 1, 33; m 57; c 4. IMMUNOLOGY. *Educ:* St Francis Xavier Univ, BSc, 52; Dalhousie Univ, MD, 57, MSc, 69; FRCP(C), 70. *Prof Exp:* Resident med, Dalhousie Univ, 66-69; fel clin immunol, Montreal Gen Hosp, 69-70; Med Res Coun res fel immunol, Walter & Eliza Hall Inst Med Res, Australia, 71-72; lectr med, 72-74, asst prof, 74-75, ASSOC PROF MED, DALHOUSIE UNIV, 75- *Concurrent Pos:* Regional coordr myeloma chemother nat trial, Nat Cancer Inst Can, 74- *Mem:* Can Soc Clin Invest; Can Soc Immunol; AAAS; Am Fedn Clin Res. *Res:* Identification and characterization of human tumor antigens; age related changes in lymphocyte-macrophage interactions; functional changes in mononuclear cell subpopulations in chronic lymphocytic leukemia. *Mailing Add:* Camphill Hosp 1763 Robie Halifax NS B3H 3G2 Can

MCSWEENY, EDWARD SHEARMAN, b Tucson, Ariz, Oct 5, 34; m 68; c 2. AQUACULTURE, INVERTEBRATE SYSTEMATICS. *Educ:* Univ Ariz, BS, 64; Univ Miami, MS, 68, PhD(biol oceanog), 71. *Prof Exp:* Assoc res dir aquacult, Ocean Protein Corp, Dania, Fla, 70-75; mgr aquacult sci div, Syntex Corp, Palo Alto, Calif, 75-77; PRAWN RES DIR CORP RES & DEVELOP AQUACULT, WEYERHAEUSER CO, 77- *Mem:* AAAS; Am Fisheries Soc; World Maricult Soc. *Res:* Crustacean aquaculture; systematics of peracarid crustaceans and cephalopods. *Mailing Add:* Weyerhaeuser Co PO Box 1584 Homestead FL 33030

MCTAGGART, KENNETH C, b Vancouver, BC, Can, Aug 10, 19; m 51; c 2. PETROLOGY. *Educ:* Univ BC, BASc, 43; Queen's Univ, Ont, MSc, 46; Yale Univ, PhD(geol), 48. *Prof Exp:* Geologist, Geol Surv Can, 48-50; PROF GEOL, UNIV BC, 50- *Mem:* Geol Asn Can; fel Geol Soc. *Res:* Petrology and structure. *Mailing Add:* Dept of Geol Univ of BC Vancouver BC V6T 1W5 Can

MCTAGGART-COWAN, PATRICK DUNCAN, b Edinburgh, Scotland, May 31, 12; m 39; c 2. METEOROLOGY, SCIENCE POLICY. *Educ:* Univ BC, BA, 33; Oxford Univ, BA, 36. *Hon Degrees:* DSc, Univ BC, 60, McGill Univ, 74, Lakehead Univ, 74 & Univ NB, 76, Univ Guelph, 81; LLD, St Francis Xavier Univ, 70 & Simon Fraser Univ, 72. *Prof Exp:* Instr physics, Univ BC, 33-34; meteorologist in training, British Meteorol Off, 36; officer in charge, Meteorol Off, Botwood & Nfld, 37-42; chief meteorol officer, Royal Air Force Ferry Command, Que, 42-45; secy air navig, Provisional Int Civil Aviation Orgn, 45; asst dir & chief forecast div, Meteorol Br, Can Dept Transport, 46-57, from assoc dir to dir, 58-64; pres, Simon Fraser Univ, 63-68; exec dir, Sci Coun Can, 68-75; RETIRED. Educ: Mem exec comt, World Meteorol Orgn, UN, 60-63; head task force, Oper Oil, 70-72; DIR, JOHN WILEY & SONS CO, LTD, 76- *Honors & Awards:* Mem, Order of Brit Empire, 44; Losey Award, Inst Aeronaut Sci, 59; Paterson Medal, Meteorol Serv Can, 65; Charles F Brookes Award, Am Meteorol Soc, 65, Cleveland Abbe Award, 76; Can Centennial Medal, 67. *Mem:* Am Meteorol Soc (vpres, 60); Can Meteorol & Oceanog Soc; AAAS; Am Acad Arts & Sci; Royal Meteorol Soc (pres, Can Br, 52). *Res:* Environment; climatic change. *Mailing Add:* High Falls Rd RR2 Bracebridge ON P0B 1C0 Can

MCTAGUE, JOHN PAUL, b Jersey City, NJ, Nov 28, 38; m 61; c 4. CHEMICAL PHYSICS. *Educ:* Georgetown Univ, BS, 60; Brown Univ, PhD(phys chem), 65. *Prof Exp:* Mem tech staff sci ctr, NAm Aviation Inc, 64-70; from asst prof to assoc prof chem, Univ Calif, Los Angeles, 70-74, prof, 74-82; DIR, NAT SYNCHROTRON LIGHT SOURCE, BROOKHAVEN NAT LAB, 82- *Concurrent Pos:* Alfred P Sloan res fel, 71-74; John Simon Guggenheim Mem fel, 75-76. *Mem:* Am Phys Soc; Am Chem Soc. *Res:* Spectroscopic studies of molecular interactions; x-ray and neutron scattering; dynamics of condensed phases; surface physics; quantum solids and liquids. *Mailing Add:* Nat Synchrotron Light Source Brookhaven Nat Lab Los Angeles CA 90024

MACTAVISH, JOHN N, b Detroit, Mich, May 23, 39; m; c 1. ENVIRONMENTAL SCIENCES, GEOLOGY. *Educ:* Bowling Green Univ, BS, 61, MA, 63; Case Western Reserve Univ, PhD(geol), 71. *Prof Exp:* Asst prof geol, Col Arts & Sci, 68-71, ASST PROF ENVIRON STUDIES, ASST TO THE DEAN & DIR ENVIRON STUDIES PROG, WILLIAM JAMES COL, GRAND VALLEY STATE COLS, 71- *Mem:* Geol Soc Am; Paleont Soc; Nat Asn Geol Teachers. *Res:* Invertebrate paleontology. *Mailing Add:* William James Col Grand Valley State Cols Allendale MI 49401

MCTERNAN, EDMUND J, b Hollis, NY, June 15, 30; m 52; c 6. PUBLIC HEALTH ADMINISTRATION. *Educ:* New Eng Col, BS, 56; Columbia Univ, MS, 58; Univ NC, Chapel Hill, MPH, 63; Boston Univ, EdD, 74. *Prof Exp:* Asst adminr, Emerson Hosp, Concord, Mass, 58-60; adminr, Mem Hosp, North Conway, NH, 60-62; adminr, Boston Dispensary & Rehab Inst, Mass, 63-65; assoc prof & dean div health sci, Northeastern Univ, 65-69; PROF HEALTH SCI & DEAN, SCH ALLIED HEALTH PROFESSIONS, HEALTH SCI CTR, STATE UNIV NY, STONY BROOK, 69- *Concurrent Pos:* USPHS fel core curric allied health educ, Northeastern Univ, 65-67; Bruner Found fel physician assoc educ, State Univ NY Stony Brook, 70-; mem nat adv allied health professions coun, NIH, 67-70; consult col proficiency exam prof health educ, State Dept Educ, NY, 71- *Mem:* Asn Schs Allied Health Professions. *Res:* Education patterns and role relationships of allied health profession; continuing education needs in allied health professions. *Mailing Add:* Sch Allied Health Professions State Univ of NY Health Sci Ctr Stony Brook NY 11790

MCTIGUE, DAVID FRANCIS, b Wilmington, Del, June 4, 52. EARTH SCIENCES. *Educ:* Williams Col, BA, 74; Stanford Univ, MS, 77, PhD(geol), 79. *Prof Exp:* Assoc, Mass Inst Technol, 79-81; MEM TECH STAFF, SANDIA NAT LABS, 81- *Mem:* Am Geophys Union. *Res:* Mechanics of geological materials; porous media; multiphase flow; crustal deformation. *Mailing Add:* Div 5511 Sandia Nat Labs Albuquerque NM 87185

MCTIGUE, FRANK HENRY, b Holyoke, Mass, Dec 19, 19; m 43; c 2. PLASTICS CHEMISTRY. *Educ:* Williams Col, BA, 41; Yale Univ, PhD(org chem), 49. *Prof Exp:* Res chemist, 49-69, res supvr, 69-75, mgr prod technol, 75-78, RES SCIENTIST, POLYMERS TECH CTR, HERCULES INC, 78- *Mem:* Am Chem Soc; Soc Plastics Eng; Am Soc Testing & Mat. *Res:* Polymers, plastics and fibers; plastics formulation, stabilization, degradation. *Mailing Add:* 2551 Deepwood Dr Wilmington DE 19810

MACUR, GEORGE J, b Chicago, Ill, Feb 22, 33; m 60; c 2. PHYSICAL CHEMISTRY. *Educ:* DePaul Univ, BS, 54, MS, 57; Ill Inst Technol, PhD(chem), 65. *Prof Exp:* Chemist, IIT Res Inst, 60-65 & Argonne Nat Lab, 65-68; CHEMIST, IBM CORP, 68- *Res:* Surface chemistry and technology; ozone technology. *Mailing Add:* IBM Corp 1701 North St Endicott NY 13760

MACURDA, DONALD BRADFORD, JR, b Boston, Mass, Aug 8, 36. PALEONTOLOGY, MARINE BIOLOGY. *Educ:* Univ Wis, BS, 56, PhD(geol), 63. *Prof Exp:* From instr to prof geol & mineral, Univ Mich, Ann Arbor, 63-78, assoc cur invert paleont, Mus Paleont, 63-77, cur, 77-78; res specialist, Exxon Prod Res Co, 78-81; CONSULT, ENERGISTS, 81- *Concurrent Pos:* NSF grants, Univ Mich. *Mem:* Am Asn Petrol Geologists; Geol Soc Am; Int Paleont Asn; Paleont Soc; Soc Econ Paleontologists & Mineralogists. *Res:* The study of the functional morphology and ecology of modern and ancient crinoids, invertebrate. *Mailing Add:* Energists 10260 Westheimer Suite 110 Houston TX 77042

MCVAUGH, ROGERS, b Brooklyn, NY, May 30, 09; m 37; c 2. BOTANY. *Educ:* Swarthmore Col, AB, 31; Univ Pa, PhD(bot), 35. *Prof Exp:* Asst inst bot, Univ Pa, 33-35; from instr to asst prof, Univ Ga, 35-38; assoc botanist, Div Plant Explor & Introd, Bur Plant Indust, USDA, 38-43, Div Soils & Agr Eng, 43-46; from assoc prof to prof bot, Univ Mich, Ann Arbor, 46-74, dir, Univ Herbarium, 72-75, Harley Harris Bartlett Prof Bot, 74-79, Cur Phanerogams, Herbarium, 46-79, vascular plants, 56-79; RES PROF BOT, UNIV NC, CHAPEL HILL, 80- *Concurrent Pos:* Prog dir syst biol, NSF, 55-56; adj res scientist, Hunt Inst Bot Doc, Carnegie Mellon Univ, 81- *Mem:* Am Soc Plant Taxon (pres, 56); Int Asn Plant Taxon (vpres, 69-72, pres, 72-75); hon mem Soc Bot Mex; Bot Soc Am. *Res:* Taxonomy of flowering plants; history of botany; flora of Mexico. *Mailing Add:* Dept Bot Coker Hall Univ NC Chapel Hill NC 27514

MCVAY, FRANCIS EDWARD, b Peace Dale, RI, Sept 27, 17; m 49. APPLIED STATISTICS. *Educ:* Univ RI, BS, 42; NC State Univ, MS, 44; Univ NC, Chapel Hill, PhD(econ), 46. *Prof Exp:* Agr statistician, USDA, 45-47; asst prof econ & statist, NC State Univ, 47-52; statist consult, US Naval Ord Test Sta, Calif, 52-54, head test design & eval br, 54-57; assoc prof statist, NC State Univ, 57-62, PROF STATIST, NC STATE UNIV, 62- *Mem:* AAAS; Am Statist Asn; Biomet Soc. *Mailing Add:* Dept of Statist 612 Cox Hall NC State Univ Raleigh NC 27607

MCVEAN, DUNCAN EDWARD, b Pontiac, Mich, June 8, 36; m 60; c 2. PHARMACEUTICAL CHEMISTRY. *Educ:* Univ Mich, BS, 58, MS, 60, PhD(pharmaceut chem), 63; Xavier Univ, MBA, 78. *Prof Exp:* Pharmaceut res chemist, William S Merrell Co, 65-71, head methods develop sect, Qual Control Dept, 71-74, proj asst to vpres qual opers, 74-75, head chem control sect, 75-78, dir qual control, Merrel-Nat Labs, 78-79; vpres Gentek Corp, 79-81; MGR PHARMACEUT DEVELOP, ADRIA LABS INC, 81- *Mem:* AAAS; Sigma Xi; Am Acad Pharmaceut Sci; affiliate Am Med Asn. *Res:* Analytical chemistry; physical pharmacy; biopharmaceutics; pharmaceutical product development. *Mailing Add:* Mgr Pharmaceut Develop Adria Labs Inc PO Box 16529 Cincinnati OH 45215

MCVEY, EUGENE STEVEN, b Wayne, WVa, Dec 6, 27; m 49; c 5. ELECTRICAL ENGINEERING. *Educ:* Univ Louisville, BS, 50; Purdue Univ, MS, 55, PhD(elec eng), 60. *Prof Exp:* Mem staff, Naval Ord, Ind, 50-56; group leader elec eng, Fransworth Electronics, 56-57; from instr to asst prof elec eng, Purdue Univ, 57-61; assoc prof, 61-66, PROF ELEC ENG, UNIV VA, 66- *Concurrent Pos:* Co-chmn control & info systs group, Univ Va, 67- *Mem:* Fel Inst Elec & Electronics Engrs. *Res:* Automatic control systems; electronics; instrumentation; discrete signal processing; advanced automation. *Mailing Add:* Thornton Hall Univ of Va Charlottesville VA 22901

MCVEY, JEFFREY KING, b Chicago, Ill, May 15, 50. CHEMICAL PHYSICS. *Educ:* Northwestern Univ, BS & MS, 72; Univ Chicago, PhD(chem), 77. *Prof Exp:* Fel chem, Columbia Univ, 77-78; ASST PROF CHEM, PRINCETON UNIV, 78- *Concurrent Pos:* Vis researcher, Exxon, 78; consult, Union Camp, 81; vis res, Dow Chem, 81, consult, 80- *Mem:* Am Chem Soc; Am Inst Physics. *Res:* Chemical physics, specifically exploring detailed mechanisms of unimolecular and biomolecular elementary processes in the gas phase; developing new techniques in molecular synthesis employing lasers to prepare reactants or facilitate the chemical reaction. *Mailing Add:* Dept Chem Frick Lab Princeton Univ Princeton NJ 08544

MCVEY, WILLIAM HENRY, chemistry, see previous edition

MCVICAR, JOHN WEST, b Rochester, NY, Oct 15, 28; m 56; c 4. VETERINARY MEDICINE, VIROLOGY. *Educ:* State Univ NY Vet Col, Cornell Univ, DVM, 52. *Prof Exp:* Partner, Loudoun Animal Hosp, 56-66; RES VET, SCI & EDUC ADMIN-AGR RES, USDA, 66- *Mem:* US Animal Health Asn; Infectious Dis Soc; NY Acad Sci; Am Vet Med Asn. *Res:* Transmission, early growth and pathogenesis of foot-and-mouth disease virus in cattle, sheep and goats and African swine fever virus in pigs; methods of virus detection and detection of infection. *Mailing Add:* Plum Island Animal Dis Ctr USDA PO Box 848 Greenport NY 11944

MCVICAR, KENNETH E(ARL), b Detroit, Mich, Nov 30, 20; m 45; c 3. ELECTRICAL ENGINEERING. *Educ:* Antioch Col, BS, 44; Mass Inst Technol, SM, 50. *Prof Exp:* Engr, Naval Res Lab, 44-46; owner, McVicar Radio Lab, 46-48; engr, Servomechanisms Lab, Mass Inst Technol, 48-51, staff mem, Digital Comput Lab, 51-54, sect leader, Lincoln Lab, 54-56, assoc group leader comput prog, 56-58, group leader syst design, 58-59; assoc tech dir syst res & planning, 59-62, tech dir syst planning, 62-67, tech dir strategic & range systs, 67-70, asst vpres, 70-72, VPRES, BEDFORD OPERS, MITRE CORP, 72-, GEN MGR, 75- *Mem:* Inst Elec & Electronics Engrs. *Res:* Military systems research, planning, engineering and test; Air Defense, Command and Control data processing systems design. *Mailing Add:* Mitre Corp PO Box 208 Bedford MA 01730

MACVICAR, MARGARET LOVE AGNES, b Hamilton, Ont, Nov 20, 43; US citizen. SOLID STATE PHYSICS, MATERIALS SCIENCE. *Educ:* Mass Inst Technol, SB, 64, ScD(metall, mat sci), 67. *Prof Exp:* NATO fel, Univ Cambridge, 67-68, Am Asn Univ Women Marie Curie fel, 68-69; from instr to asst prof physics, 69-74, ASSOC PROF PHYSICS, MASS INST TECHNOL, 74- *Concurrent Pos:* Mem bd dirs, Oral Educ Ctr of Southern Calif, Los Angeles; assoc, Danforth Found, 72-; Chancellor's distinguished prof, Univ Calif, Berkeley, 79; Cecil & Ida Green prof educ, Mass Inst Technol, 80-, mem, Corp Draper Lab, 81-; consult, W H Brady Co; mem adv coun, Sch Sci & Math, Univ NC & Tex Instruments, Inc; young fac res award, Gen Elec Found, 76-79. *Mem:* Am Inst Mining, Metall & Petrol Engrs; Am Soc Metals; Am Phys Soc; Sigma Xi; Am Vacuum Soc. *Res:* Superconductivity, especially of thin films, refractory metals, single crystals, tunnelling and barrier fabrication; deaf education. *Mailing Add:* PO Box 304 Mass Inst of Technol Br Cambridge MA 02139

MACVICAR, ROBERT WILLIAM, b Princeton, Minn, Sept 28, 18; m 48; c 2. CHEMISTRY. *Educ:* Univ Wyo, BA, 39; Okla State Univ, MS, 40; Univ Wis, PhD(biochem), 46. *Hon Degrees:* LLD, Univ Wyo, 77; DrSci, Dankook Univ, Korea, 80. *Prof Exp:* Assoc prof biochem, Okla State Univ, 46-49, prof & head dept, 49-57, dean grad sch, 53-64, vpres, 57-64; vpres acad affairs, Southern Ill Univ Syst, 64-68; chancellor, Southern Ill Univ, Carbondale, 68-70; PRES, ORE STATE UNIV, 70- *Mem:* Am Chem Soc; Am Soc Biol Chemists; Am Inst Nutrit. *Res:* Nitrogen metabolism of plants and animals; nutrition and metabolism of large animals. *Mailing Add:* Off of th Pres Ore State Univ Corvallis OR 97331

MACVICAR-WHELAN, PATRICK JAMES, b St John's, Nfld, Oct 19, 38; m 65; c 1. ATOMIC PHYSICS, PLASMA PHYSICS. *Educ:* St Francis Xavier Univ, BSc, 59; Dalhousie Univ, MSc, 61; Univ BC, PhD(physics), 65. *Prof Exp:* Asst prof physics, St Francis Xavier Univ, 64-65; asst prof math, St Mary's Univ NS, 65-66; Off Naval Res grant, Univ Calif, Berkeley, 66-70; assoc prof physics, Grand Valley State Col, 70-80; PRIN ENGR, BOEING AEROSPACE CO, 81- *Concurrent Pos:* Res assoc, Nat Ctr Sci Res, France, 75-76 & 77-78; vis, Artificial Intel Lab, Stanford Univ, 79-81. *Mem:* Am Phys Soc; Math Asn Am; Am Geophys Union; Am Asn Physics Teachers. *Res:* Fuzzy logic and applications; pattern representation by tesselations atomic collisions; electrical breakdown; acoustics; low temperature physics; applied mathematics; physical systems in relation to those in (robotics). *Mailing Add:* Boeing Aerospace Co POB 3949 M/S 82-26 Seattle WA 98124

MACVITTIE, THOMAS JOSEPH, b Buffalo, NY, Aug 21, 41; m 64; c 3. EXPERIMENTAL HEMATOLOGY, INFECTIOUS DISEASE. *Educ:* Alfred Univ, BA, 64; Southern Univ NY, Buffalo, MS, 66, PhD(radiation biol), 70. *Prof Exp:* US Army, radiobiologist, Med Res Lab, Ft Knox, 70-72, RES PHYSIOLOGIST, ARMED FORCES RADIOBIOL RES INST, 72- *Mem:* Int Sci Exp Hematol. *Res:* Hematoporetic stem cell physiology in response to radiation and infectious disease; methods for enhancing recovery of stem cells and white blood cell production as well as increased non-specific resistance to gram segative bacteria. *Mailing Add:* Armed Forces Radiobiol Res Lab Nat Naval Med Ctr Bethesda MD 20814

MCVOY, KIRK WARREN, b Minneapolis, Minn, Feb 22, 28; m 53; c 3. THEORETICAL NUCLEAR PHYSICS. *Educ:* Carleton Col, BA, 50; Oxford Univ, BA, 52; Univ Gottingen, dipl, 53; Cornell Univ, PhD(physics), 56. *Prof Exp:* Res assoc physics, Brookhaven Nat Lab, 56-58; asst prof, Brandeis Univ, 58-62; from asst prof to assoc prof, 62-67, PROF PHYSICS, UNIV WIS-MADISON, 67- *Concurrent Pos:* Fulbright res grant, Univ Utrecht, 60-61; vis distinguished prof, Brooklyn Col, 70-71; vis prof, Ind Univ, 71-72 & Univ Groningen, Holland, 81; Alexander von Humboldt sr scientist award, Hedelberg, Ger, 80-81. *Honors & Awards:* Alexaner von Humboldt Sr Scientist Award, Hedelberg, Ger, 80-81. *Mem:* Fel Am Phys Soc. *Res:* Nuclear structure; scattering theory; nuclear reaction theory. *Mailing Add:* Dept of Physics Univ of Wis Madison WI 53706

MCWHAN, DENIS B, b New York, NY, Dec 10, 35; m 59; c 3. SOLID STATE PHYSICS. *Educ:* Yale Univ, BS, 57; Univ Calif, Berkeley, PhD(phys chem), 61. *Prof Exp:* Am-Scand Found Berquist fel, Royal Inst Technol, Sweden, 61-62; MEM TECH STAFF, PHYS RES LAB, BELL LABS, 62- *Mem:* AAAS; Am Phys Soc. *Res:* X-ray and neutron scattering studies at high pressure and low temperature. *Mailing Add:* Phys Res Lab Bell Labs Murray Hill NJ 07974

MCWHINNEY, IAN RENWICK, b Burnley, Eng, Oct 11, 26; m 55; c 2. MEDICINE. *Educ:* Cambridge Univ, BA, 46, MB, ChB, 49, MD, 59. *Prof Exp:* Pvt pract, Eng, 55-68; PROF & CHMN DEPT FAMILY MED, UNIV WESTERN ONT, 68- *Concurrent Pos:* Nuffield travelling fel, US, 64-65. *Mem:* Fel Royal Col Gen Practitioners; Col Family Physicians Can; Soc Teachers Family Med. *Res:* Diagnostic process; social and behavioral aspects of medical practice. *Mailing Add:* Dept of Family Med Univ of Western Ont London ON N6A 5C1 Can

MCWHINNIE, DOLORES J, b Elmhurst, Ill, Sept 13, 33. DEVELOPMENTAL BIOLOGY, COMPARATIVE ENDOCRINOLOGY. *Educ:* DePaul Univ, BS, 55, MS, 58; Marquette Univ, PhD(develop biol), 65. *Prof Exp:* Res assoc radiation biol, Argonne Nat Lab, 59-60; ASSOC PROF DEVELOP BIOL & ENDOCRINOL, DePAUL UNIV, 65- *Mem:* AAAS; Am Soc Zool; Am Inst Biol Sci. *Res:* Metabolic aspects of bone growth and differentiation; metabolism of amphibian bone; effects of hormones on mineral metabolism. *Mailing Add:* Dept of Biol Sci DePaul Univ 1036 W Belden Ave Chicago IL 60614

MCWHINNIE, MARY ALICE, polar biology, comparative animal physiology, deceased

MCWHORTER, CHESTER GRAY, b Brandon, Miss, May 3, 27; m 52; c 2. PLANT PHYSIOLOGY, WEED SCIENCE. *Educ:* Miss State Univ, BS, 50, MS, 52; La State Univ, PhD(bot), 58. *Prof Exp:* Agronomist, Agr Exp Sta, Miss State Univ, 52-56; plant physiologist, 58-75, LAB CHIEF, SOUTHERN WEED SCI LAB, SCI & EDUC ADMIN-AGR RES, USDA, 75- *Concurrent Pos:* Plant physiologist, Agr Exp Sta, Miss State Univ, 58-, adj assoc prof weed control, 73-; mem, Nat Herbicide Assessment Team, 77-80; mem bd dirs, Coun Agr Sci & Technol, 78-80. *Honors & Awards:* Superior Serv Award, USDA, 78. *Mem:* AAAS; Am Soc Plant Physiologists; Am Soybean Asn; fel Weed Sci Soc Am; NY Acad Sci. *Res:* General weed control; Johnson grass control; weed control in soybeans. *Mailing Add:* Southern Weed Sci Lab PO Box 225 Stoneville MS 38776

MCWHORTER, CLARENCE AUSTIN, b Wheatland, Wyo, July 19, 18; m 47; c 3. MEDICINE. *Educ:* Univ Nebr, BS & MD, 44. *Prof Exp:* From instr to asst prof, 49-59, PROF PATH, UNIV NEBR MED CTR, OMAHA, 59-, CHMN DEPT, 64- *Mem:* Col Am Path (pres, 69-71); Am Soc Clin Path; Int Acad Path. *Res:* Neoplasms. *Mailing Add:* Dept of Path Sch of Med Univ Nebr Med Ctr Omaha NE 68105

MCWHORTER, EARL JAMES, b Argyle, NY, Sept 12, 29. ORGANIC CHEMISTRY. *Educ:* Rensselaer Polytech, BS, 50; Cornell Univ, PhD(org chem), 55. *Prof Exp:* Instr chem, 54-56, asst prof, 56-69, ASSOC PROF CHEM, UNIV MASS, AMHERST, 69- *Concurrent Pos:* Res assoc, New York Bot Garden, 63-64. *Mem:* Am Chem Soc. *Res:* Polynuclear aromatic hydrocarbons; fungal polyacetylenes. *Mailing Add:* Dept of Chem Univ of Mass Amherst MA 01003

MCWHORTER, MALCOLM M(YERS), b Norfolk, Va, Jan 8, 26; m 51; c 1. ELECTRONICS. *Educ:* Ore State Col, BS, 49; Stanford Univ, MS, 50, PhD, 52. *Prof Exp:* Radio engr, KOAC, Ore State Col, 46-49; asst electronics, 51-52, res assoc nuclear induction, 52-53, wide band amplifiers, 53-54, from asst prof to assoc prof electronics, 54-69, PROF ELECTRONICS, STANFORD UNIV, 69- *Concurrent Pos:* Vpres, Vidar Corp, 58-69. *Res:* Transistor circuits; electronic measurement techniques. *Mailing Add:* Dept Elec Eng ERL 102 Stanford Univ Stanford CA 94305

MACWILLIAM, EDGAR ALEXANDER, b McAdam, NB, Nov 6, 20; m 44; c 3. PHYSICAL CHEMISTRY. *Educ:* Mt Allison Univ, BSc, 41; Univ Toronto, MA, 42, PhD(phys chem), 44. *Prof Exp:* RES CHEMIST, EASTMAN KODAK CO, 46- *Mem:* Am Chem Soc; Soc Photog Sci & Eng. *Res:* Electrochemistry of silver halides; improved photographic emulsions. *Mailing Add:* 527 Peck Rd Rochester NY 14609

MACWILLIAMS, DALTON CARSON, b Winnipeg, Man, Mar 22, 28; US citizen; m 54; c 4. POLYMER CHEMISTRY. *Educ:* Univ Alta, BSc, 50; Univ Minn, PhD(anal phys chem), 55. *Prof Exp:* From chemist to sr res chemist, 55-75, SR RES SPECIALIST, DOW CHEM, USA, WESTERN DIV RES, 72-, PROJ MGR, 75- *Res:* Synthesis, rheology, interfacial properties and applications of water soluble polymers; physical organic chemistry; crystal growth; secondary oil recovery; wet end paper chemistry. *Mailing Add:* Dow Chem USA 2800 Mitchell Dr Walnut Creek CA 94598

MACWILLIAMS, DONALD GRIBBLE, chemistry, see previous edition

MCWILLIAMS, EDWARD LACAZE, b Shreveport, La, May 22, 41; m 65; c 2. ORNAMENTAL HORTICULTURE. *Educ:* Univ Southwestern La, BS, 63; Iowa State Univ, MS, 65, PhD(hort plant ecol), 66. *Prof Exp:* Hort botanist, Bot Gardens & asst prof bot, Univ Mich, Ann Arbor, 67-72; assoc prof, 72-78, PROF HORT, TEX A&M UNIV, 78- *Mem:* AAAS; Am Soc Plant Taxon; Ecol Soc Am; Am Asn Bot Gardens & Arboretums; Am Soc Hort Sci. *Res:* Horticultural taxonomy; introduction and propagation of ornamental plants; ecology and evolution of Amaranthus and Billbergia. *Mailing Add:* Dept of Hort Sci Tex A&M Univ College Station TX 77843

MACWILLIAMS, FLORENCE JESSIE, b Stoke-on-Trent, Eng, Jan 4, 17; US citizen; m 41; c 3. MATHEMATICS. *Educ:* Cambridge Univ, BA, 39, MA, 40; Harvard Univ, PhD, 62. *Prof Exp:* Tech asst comput prog, Bell Tel Labs, Inc, 56-58, assoc mem tech staff, 58-61, res mathematician, 61-64; Dept Sci & Indust Res vis fel, Cambridge Univ, 64-65; MEM TECH STAFF, BELL LABS, 65- *Mem:* Am Math Soc; Math Asn Am. *Res:* Algebraic theory of error correcting codes; group theory; use of computer in above fields. *Mailing Add:* Bell Labs 2C377 Murray Hill NJ 07971

MCWILLIAMS, JAMES CYRUS, b Oklahoma City, Okla, Aug 22, 46; c 1. PHYSICAL OCEANOGRAPHY, ATMOSPHERIC PHYSICS. *Educ:* Calif Inst Technol, BS, 68; Harvard Univ, MS, 69, PhD(appl math), 71. *Prof Exp:* Fel, Harvard Univ, 71-74; RES SCIENTIST OCEANOG, NAT CTR ATMOSPHERIC RES, 74- *Concurrent Pos:* Vis prof, Dept Oceanog, Univ Wash, 79; mem, Comt Atmospheric Sci, Nat Acad Sci, 80- *Mem:* Am Geophys Union. *Res:* General circulations of atmospheres and oceans; geostrophic turbulence; statistical estimation. *Mailing Add:* Oceanog Sect PO Box 3000 Boulder CO 80307

MCWILLIAMS, MARGARET ANN, b Osage, Iowa, May 26, 29; c 2. NUTRITION, FOOD. *Educ:* Iowa State Univ, BS, 51, MS, 53; Ore State Univ, PhD(food, nutrit), 68. *Prof Exp:* From asst prof to assoc prof food & nutrit, 61-68, chmn dept, 68-76, PROF HOME ECON, CALIF STATE UNIV, LOS ANGELES, 68- *Concurrent Pos:* Mem, Nat Coun Home Econ Adminr, 68-; mem nat coord comt, Col Teachers Food & Nutrit, 69-; mem nat steering comt plan local prof involvement, White House Conf Food, Nutrit & Health, 69- *Mem:* Inst Food Technol; Am Dietetic Asn; Am Home Econ Asn; Soc Nutrit Educ; Nutrit Today Soc. *Res:* Experimental foods; nutrition education; organic chemistry; psychology; consumerism and relation to food and nutrition. *Mailing Add:* Dept Home Econ Calif State Univ 5151 State University Dr Los Angeles CA 90032

MCWILLIAMS, RALPH DAVID, b Ft Myers, Fla, Nov 5, 30; m 59; c 2. MATHEMATICAL ANALYSIS. *Educ:* Fla State Univ, BS, 51, MS, 53; Univ Tenn, PhD(math), 57. *Prof Exp:* Instr math, Univ Tenn, 56-57; instr, Princeton Univ, 57-59; from asst prof to assoc prof, 59-69, PROF MATH & ASSOC CHMN DEPT, FLA STATE UNIV, 69- *Mem:* AAAS; Am Math Soc; Math Asn Am. *Res:* Functional analysis; weak topologies in Banach spaces. *Mailing Add:* Dept of Math & Comput Sci Fla State Univ Tallahassee FL 32306

MCWILLIAMS, ROBERT GENE, b Junction City, Ore, Dec 26, 39; m 66; c 2. STRATIGRAPHY. *Educ:* Stanford Univ, BS, 62; Univ Wash, MS, 65, PhD(geol), 68. *Prof Exp:* Consult micropaleontologist, Phillips Petrol Co, 66; asst prof geol, 68-73, ASSOC PROF GEOL, MIAMI UNIV, 73- *Concurrent Pos:* Penrose grant, Geol Soc Am, 72; coordr sci & math, Miami Univ-Hamilton, 74-78; exchange prof, Mt Union Col, 75-76; vis scholar, Miami Univ Europ Ctr, Luxembourg, 78. *Mem:* AAAS; Geol Soc Am. *Res:* Biostratigraphy and paleoecology of West Coast Tertiary Foraminifera and Mollusca; plate tectonics of Pacific Northwest United States. *Mailing Add:* Dept of Geol Miami Univ Oxford OH 45056

MCWRIGHT, CORNELIUS GLEN, b Sebree, Ky, Aug 3, 29; m 57; c 3. IMMUNOLOGY, MICROBIOLOGY. *Educ:* Univ Evansville, BA, 52; George Washington Univ, MS, 65, PhD(microbiol), 70. *Prof Exp:* Supvry spec agent forensic biol, 56-73, chief biol sci res, 73-78; chief res, Fed Bur Invest Lab, 78-79; CONSULT FORENSIC MED, NAT INST JUSTICE, 79- *Concurrent Pos:* Assoc prof biol sci, George Washington Univ, 70-75, res consult immunochem & forensic biol, Grad Sch, 72-73, immunochemist, Lab Virus & Cancer Res, Sch Med, 72-73, adj prof biol sci & forensic sci, 75-; res consult physiol fluids, Law Enforcement Assistance Admin, 75-79; asst prof forensic sci, Univ Va, 76-79. *Mem:* Fel Am Acad Forensic Sci; AAAS; Am Soc Microbiol; Sigma Xi. *Res:* Molecular biology and genetics of cell membranes and plasma proteins; immunochemistry; immunohematology; immunogenetics. *Mailing Add:* 7409 Estaban Pl Springfield VA 22151

MACY, JOSIAH, JR, mathematical biophysics, see previous edition

MACY, RALPH WILLIAM, b McMinnville, Ore, July 6, 05; m 31; c 1. PARASITOLOGY. *Educ:* Linfield Col, BA, 29; Univ Minn, MA, 31, PhD(zool), 34. *Prof Exp:* Asst zool, Univ Minn, 29-33; from instr to prof biol, Col St Thomas, 34-42; prof biol, Reed Col, 42-55, head dept, 43-55; prof, 55-72, exec off dept, 58-65, EMER PROF BIOL, PORTLAND STATE UNIV, 72- *Concurrent Pos:* Lectr, Med Sch, Univ Ore, 43-45, prof exten div, 44-45; USPHS grants, 49-50 & 64-67; chief investr res proj, Off Naval Res, 50-59; trustee, Ore Mus Sci & Indust, 53-59 & Northwestern Sci Asn, 56-59; NSF grants, 60-64 & 66-72; del, Int Cong Trop Med & Malaria, Lisbon, 58, Int Cong Parasitol, Rome, 64 & DC, 70; guest investr, Univ Helsinki, 61, US Naval Med Res Unit, Cairo, 61-62 & Inst Trop Med, Lisbon, 62 & 69. *Mem:* Fel AAAS; charter fel Am Acad Microbiol; Am Micros Soc; Am Soc Parasitol; Wildlife Dis Asn. *Res:* Biology of helminths and trematodes; entomology. *Mailing Add:* Dept Biol Portland State Univ Portland OR 97207

MACY, WILLIAM WRAY, JR, b Urbana, Ill, Nov 10, 44; m 71; c 2. PLANETARY SCIENCES, ASTRONOMY. *Educ:* Pomona Col, BA, 67; Univ Ill, Urbana, MS, 68; Princeton Univ, PhD(astrophys), 73. *Prof Exp:* Physicist, Corona Naval Weapons Lab, 68-70; res assoc astron, Univ Tex, 73-76; astronomer, Univ Hawaii, 76-80; RES SCIENTIST, LOCKHEED RES LAB, 80- *Concurrent Pos:* Peyton fel, Princeton Univ, 70-72. *Mem:* Am Astron Soc; Sigma Xi; Int Astron Union. *Res:* Planetary atmospheres; optics. *Mailing Add:* Lockheed Res Lab Bldg 202-org 52-13 3251 Hanover St Palo Alto CA 94304

MACZURA, GEORGE, b Granite City, Ill, Jan 8, 30; m 52; c 10. CERAMICS ENGINEERING. *Educ:* Univ Mo-Rolla, BS, 52. *Hon Degrees:* CerEngr, Univ Mo-Rolla, 72. *Prof Exp:* Res engr, 52-64, sr res engr, 64-67, leader ceramic group, 67-71, SCI ASSOC, ALCOA LABS, ALUMINUM CO AM, 71- *Mem:* Fel Am Ceramic Soc; Nat Inst Ceramic Engrs; Sigma Xi; Am Soc

Testing & Mat; Am Concrete Inst. *Res:* Manufacture of alumina for abrasives, ceramics, glass and refractory uses; refractory cements and castables; alumina fusion processes; high temperature measurement and processing; microscopy and particle size analysis. *Mailing Add:* Alcoa Labs Seventh St Rd-Rte 780 Alcoa Center PA 15069

MADACSI, DAVID PETER, experimental solid state physics, magnetic resonance, see previous edition

MADAN, RABINDER NATH, b New Delhi, India, Mar 11, 35; m 69. SYSTEMS DESIGN & ANALYSIS. *Educ:* Univ Delhi, BSc, 54, MSc, 56; Princeton Univ, MA, 64, PhD(physics), 67. *Prof Exp:* Lectr physics & math, Ramjas Col, Univ Delhi, 56-57; sr sci asst, Nat Phys Lab, Univ New Delhi, 57-62; res assoc theoret physics, Univ Calif, Santa Barbara, 67-68; res assoc & lectr, Univ Mass, Amherst, 68-69; assoc prof physics, NC A&T State Univ, 69-77; mgr systs anal, Electronic Systs Div, Bunker-Ramo Corp, 77-79; SR STAFF ENGR, HUGHES AIRCRAFT CO, 79- *Concurrent Pos:* Fulbright travel award, Inst Int Educ, 62; prin investr, NASA res grant, 70-74; NSF res grant theoret physics, 73-75. *Mem:* Am Phys Soc; Inst Elec & Electronics Engrs. *Res:* Systems analysis of airborne radars; detection and estimation of signals in noise; digital signal processing and variational and optimization principles; spectral line satellites in alkalis; Eikonal-Glauber exchange amplitudes. *Mailing Add:* 20025-49 Community St Canoga Park CA 91306

MADAN, STANLEY KRISHEN, b Lahore, Pakistan, May 1, 22; US citizen; m 58; c 1. INORGANIC CHEMISTRY. *Educ:* Forman Christian Col, Lahore, Pakistan, BSc, 45; Punjab Univ, Pakistan, MA, 50, MSc, 54; Univ Ill, Urbana, MS, 57, PhD(inorg chem), 60. *Prof Exp:* Res assoc irrig, Punjab Irrig Res Inst, Lahore, Pakistan, 45-48; demonstr physics, Forman Christian Col, 48-55; asst chem, Univ Ill, Urbana, 57-60; from asst prof to assoc prof, 60-67, PROF CHEM, STATE UNIV NY BINGHAMTON, 67- *Mem:* Am Chem Soc. *Res:* Synthesis and structure determination of new coordination compounds; kinetics and substitution reactions of triaminotriethylamine metallic complexes. *Mailing Add:* Dept of Chem State Univ of NY Binghamton NY 13901

MADAN, VED P, b Karachi, June 28, 42; Can citizen; m 68; c 2. ENGINEERING MECHANICS, GOEMETRY. *Educ:* Delhi Univ, BSc, 61, MSc, 63; Univ Toronto, PhD(appl math), 68. *Prof Exp:* Sr res asst math, Indian Inst Technol, 63-65; fel, Univ Alberta, Edmonton, 68-70; COORDR MATH, RED DEER COL, ALBERTA, 70- *Concurrent Pos:* Vis prof, Univ Western Ont, 75-76; bd dir, Red Deer Col Press, 78-82. *Mem:* Indian Math Soc; Am Math Soc; Can Math Cong. *Res:* Viscoelasticity; fluid-mechanics; biomathematics; applied mathematics. *Mailing Add:* Dept Appl Sci PO Box 5005 Red Deer College AB T4N 5H5 Can

MADANSKY, ALBERT, b Chicago, Ill, May 16, 34; m 56; c 4. STATISTICS. *Educ:* Univ Chicago, AB, 52, MS, 55, PhD(statist), 58. *Prof Exp:* Mathematician, Rand Corp, Calif, 57-65; vpres, Interpub Group of Co, Inc, NY, 65-68; pres, Dataplan, Inc, NY, 68-71; prof comput sci & chmn dept, City Col New York, 71-74; PROF BUS ADMIN, GRAD SCH BUS, UNIV CHICAGO & DIR, CTR FOR MGT PUB & NONPROFIT ENTERPRISE, 74- *Concurrent Pos:* Fel, Ctr Advan Study Behav Sci, 61-62; Fulbright-Hayes lectr, 81. *Mem:* Fel Am Statist Asn; fel Inst Math Statist; fel Economet Soc. *Res:* Multivariate analysis; mathematical models in the social sciences. *Mailing Add:* Grad Sch of Bus Univ of Chicago Chicago IL 60637

MADANSKY, LEON, b Brooklyn, NY, Jan 11, 23; m 47; c 2. NUCLEAR PHYSICS. *Educ:* Univ Mich, BS, 42, MS, 44, PhD(physics), 48. *Prof Exp:* From asst prof to assoc prof, 48-58, chmn dept, 65-68, prof physics, 58-77, DECKER PROF IN SCI & ENG, JOHNS HOPKINS UNIV, 78- *Concurrent Pos:* Res physicist, Brookhaven Nat Lab, 52-53; NSF sr fel, 61, 69. *Mem:* Fel Am Phys Soc. *Res:* Atomic properties of elementary particles; radiative effects in elementary particles; particle counters; nuclear spectroscopy; radiative effects in beta-decay; meson-nuclear scattering. *Mailing Add:* Dept of Physics Johns Hopkins Univ Baltimore MD 21218

MADAPPALLY, MATHEW MATHAI, nutritional biochemistry, see previous edition

MADARAS, RONALD JOHN, b Summit, NJ, Dec 18, 42; m 65; c 2. EXPERIMENTAL HIGH ENERGY PHYSICS. *Educ:* Cornell Univ, BEP, 65, MS, 65; Harvard Univ, PhD(physics), 73. *Prof Exp:* Res physicist, Lab Accelerateur Lineaire, Orsay, France, 72-75; RES PHYSICIST, LAWRENCE BERKELEY LAB, UNIV CALIF, 75- *Mem:* Am Phys Soc. *Res:* Electron-positron colliding beam physics. *Mailing Add:* Lawrence Berkeley Lab Univ Calif Berkeley CA 94720

MADAY, CLARENCE J, b Chicago, Ill, Sept 18, 29; m 60; c 1. ENGINEERING MECHANICS. *Educ:* Ill Inst Technol, BS, 51, MS, 54; Northwestern Univ, PhD(lubrication), 60. *Prof Exp:* Jr engr, Hotpoint Co, 51-52, res engr, IIT Res Inst, 52-54 & Borg-Warner Res Ctr, 56-59; res scientist, Martin Co, 60-62; staff engr, Cook Elec Co, 62-64; asst prof, 64-65, ASSOC PROF ENG MECH, NC STATE UNIV, 65- *Concurrent Pos:* Consult, Hayes Int Corp, 65- *Mem:* Am Inst Aeronaut & Astronaut; Am Astronaut Soc. *Res:* Approximation methods in astrodynamics; variational principles in lubrication; dynamics; acoustics. *Mailing Add:* Dept of Eng Mech NC State Univ Raleigh NC 27607

MADDAIAH, VADDANAHALLY THIMMAIAH, b Mysore, India, Nov 10, 29; m 53; c 2. BIOCHEMISTRY. *Educ:* Univ Mysore, BSc, 53, MSc, 54; Univ Ariz, PhD(biochem), 63. *Prof Exp:* Lectr chem, Univ Mysore, 54-60; NIH fel biol, Univ Calif, San Diego, 63-64; NIH fel biochem, Univ Alta, 64-66; sr res biochemist, Res & Develop Labs, Can Packers Ltd, 66-67; res assoc physiol & biophys, Sch Med, Univ Louisville, 67-69; RES BIOCHEMIST, NASSAU COUNTY MED CTR, 69-; ASSOC PROF PEDIAT, HEALTH SCI CTR, STATE UNIV NY STONY BROOK, 72- *Mem:* Am Physiol Soc. *Res:* Enzymology; mitochondrial metabolism; polypeptide hormones; membrane composition-function. *Mailing Add:* Dept of Pediat Nassau County Med Ctr East Meadow NY 11554

MADDEN, DAVID LARRY, b Willow Hill, Ill, Aug 10, 32; m 53; c 3. VETERINARY MICROBIOLOGY. *Educ:* Kans State Univ, BS, 56, DVM & MS, 58; Purdue Univ, PhD(vet microbiol), 63. *Prof Exp:* Instr vet microbiol, Sch Vet Sci & Med, Purdue Univ, 58-63; resident microbiol, Lab Bact Dis, Nat Inst Allergy & Infectious Dis, 63-68, off assoc dir, Nat Inst Child Health & Human Develop, 68-77, res microbiologist, Infectious Dis Br, Nat Inst Neurol Dis & Stroke, 70-77, HEAD SECT IMMUNOCHEM & CLIN INVEST, NAT INST NEUROL & COMMUN DIS & STROKE, 77- *Concurrent Pos:* Instr NIH Grad Sch Prog, 67- *Mem:* AAAS; Am Vet Med Asn; Am Asn Avian Path; Poultry Sci Asn. *Res:* Etiology of neurological diseases; concerned with isolation of etiological agent and immunological response of the host. *Mailing Add:* Nat Inst Neurol & Commun Dis & Stroke NIH Infectious Dis Br Bldg 36 Rm 5D-04 Bethesda MD 20014

MADDEN, GEORGE D, horticulture, plant physiology, see previous edition

MADDEN, HANNIBAL HAMLIN, JR, b New York, NY, Oct 5, 31; m 64; c 2. PHYSICS. *Educ:* Williams Col, Mass, BA, 52, MA, 54; Brown Univ, PhD(physics), 59. *Prof Exp:* Asst physics, Williams Col, 52-54; asst, Brown Univ, 54-57, assoc, 58-59, instr, 59-60; asst prof, 60-67, assoc prof physics, Wayne State Univ, 67-75; MEM TECH STAFF, SANDIA LABS, 74- *Concurrent Pos:* Fulbright travel grant, Hannover Tech Univ, 71-72. *Mem:* Am Phys Soc; Am Vacuum Soc. *Res:* Solid state and low temperature physics; solid state surface phenomena; auger electron spectroscopy; low energy electron diffraction; transport properties of liquid helium II. *Mailing Add:* Surface Physics Div 5114 Sandia Labs Albuquerque NM 87115

MADDEN, JAMES H(OWARD), b Flint, Mich, Sept 2, 24; m 47; c 6. SYSTEMS ENGINEERING, HUMAN ENGINEERING. *Educ:* Univ Notre Dame, BS, 49, MS, 52. *Prof Exp:* Instr eng mech, Univ Notre Dame, 50-51; engr, Missile Div, Bendix Aviation Corp, 51-52; head reliability sect, Aviation Ord Dept, US Naval Ord Test Sta, 52-55, head, Weapon Support Br, 55-58; mgr, reliability dept, Aerojet-Gen Corp, 58-59, Reliability Div, 59-63, Reliability & Qual Assurance Div, 63-64, advan tactical weapons, 64-65, Apollo reliability, 65-66 & Apollo tech prog control, 66-70, mgr systs eval, Surface Effects Ships Div, 70-74; RETIRED. *Mem:* Assoc fel Am Inst Aeronaut & Astronaut. *Res:* Systems optimization engineering and analysis; reliability, maintainability and safety engineering, analysis and evaluation; physiological and psychological noise, vibration and acceleration habitability design and limit analysis. *Mailing Add:* 9725 Harborview Pl Gig Harbor WA 98335

MADDEN, JOHN JOSEPH, b New York, NY, Oct 4, 43. BIOCHEMISTRY, X-RAY CRYSTALLOGRAPHY. *Educ:* Manhattan Col, BS, 64; Emory Univ, PhD(biochem), 68. *Prof Exp:* Fel crystalog, Univ Pittsburgh, 68-70 & Princeton Univ, 70-72; res assoc biophys, Univ Tex, Dallas, 72-76; ASST PROF PSYCHIAT, EMORY UNIV, 79- *Concurrent Pos:* Robert A Welch Found res fel, 72-76. *Mem:* AAAS; Sigma Xi; Am Soc Photobiol; Am Crystallog Soc; Biophys Soc. *Res:* Relationship between DNA repair and mutagenesis in humans; structure-function relationships in protein-nucleic acid interactions; mechanisms of light-activation of proteins. *Mailing Add:* Dept of Psychiat Sch of Med Atlanta GA 30322

MADDEN, KEITH PATRICK, b Buffalo, NY, Jan 7, 53. RADIATION CHEMISTRY, FREE RADICAL CHEMISTRY. *Educ:* Cornell Univ, BA, 74; Univ Rochester, MS, 77, PhD(biophys), 79. *Prof Exp:* Res assoc chem, Univ Ill, Chicago Circle, 79-80; RES ASSOC CHEM, RADIATION LAB, UNIV NOTRE DAME, 80- *Concurrent Pos:* Vis res assoc, Wayne State Univ, 79-80. *Mem:* Am Phys Soc; Am Chem Soc; Sigma Xi. *Res:* Characterization of transient intermediates produced in chemical and biological systems by radiolysis and photolysis; free radical molecular dynamics and reactions using time domain magnetic resonance spectroscopy. *Mailing Add:* Radiation Lab Univ Notre Dame Notre Dame IN 46556

MADDEN, RICHARD M, b Waubay, SDak, Apr 1, 28; m 54; c 1. DENTISTRY. *Educ:* Northern State Col, BS, 53; Univ Minn, DDS, 57; Univ Iowa, MS, 62; Am Bd Endodont, dipl, 65. *Prof Exp:* Pvt pract, Minn, 57-60; assoc prof dent, Univ Iowa, 62-70; assoc prof, 70-74, PROF ENDODONT & CHMN DEPT, UNIV TEX DENT BR, HOUSTON, 74- *Concurrent Pos:* Consult, M D Anderson Tumor Hosp, Tex Childrens Hosp, Vet Admin Hosp & USPHS. *Mem:* Am Asn Endodont; Int Asn Dent Res; Am Dent Asn; Am Asn Dent Schs; Sigma Xi. *Res:* Endodontics; aerosols. *Mailing Add:* Dept of Endodont Univ of Tex Dent Br Houston TX 77025

MADDEN, ROBERT E, b Oak Park, Ill, Sept 16, 25; c 4. THORACIC SURGERY, CARDIOVASCULAR SURGERY. *Educ:* Univ Ill, BS, 50, MS & MD, 52. *Prof Exp:* Am Cancer Soc fel, Hammersmith Hosp, London, 58-59; PROF SURG, NEW YORK MED COL, 71- *Concurrent Pos:* Ed-in-chief, NY Med Quartery, 79- *Honors & Awards:* Borden Res Award, Univ Ill, 52. *Mem:* Am Col Surgeons; Am Soc Clin Oncol; Am Asn Cancer Educ (pres, 79-80); Am Asn Cancer Res; Soc Surg Oncol. *Res:* Surgical oncology; dissemination of cancer via lymphatics and blood stream; clinical chemotherapy studies; cellular immunology in clinical cancer; non invasive vascular testing. *Mailing Add:* New York Med Col Munger Pavilion Valhalla NY 10595

MADDEN, ROBERT PHYFE, b Schenectady, NY, Dec 20, 28; m 50; c 3. PHYSICS. *Educ:* Univ Rochester, BS, 50; Johns Hopkins Univ, PhD(physics), 56. *Prof Exp:* Physicist, Lab Astrophys & Phys Meteorol, Johns Hopkins Univ, 53-58; physicist & sect chief, US Army Eng Res & Develop Labs, Ft Belvoir, Va, 58-61; CHIEF FAR ULTRAVIOLET PHYSICS SECT, OPTICAL PHYSICS DIV, NAT BUR STANDARDS, 61- *Mem:* Fel Am Phys Soc; fel Optical Soc Am. *Res:* Atomic and molecular spectroscopy; optical instrumentation; surface physics; thin films. *Mailing Add:* Div Phys A257 Nat Bur of Standards Washington DC 20234

MADDEN, ROLAND ALOYSIUS, b Chicago, Ill, May 8, 38; m 61; c 4. METEOROLOGY. *Educ:* Loyola Univ, BS, 61; Univ Chicago, MS, 67; Colo State Univ, PhD(atmospheric sci), 78. *Prof Exp:* Weather forecaster, US Air Force, 62-65; METEOROLOGIST, NAT CTR ATMOSPHERIC RES, 67- *Concurrent Pos:* NASA fel, 65-70. *Mem:* Am Meteorol Soc. *Res:* Climate statistics and large-scale atmospheric waves. *Mailing Add:* Nat Ctr for Atmospheric Res PO Box 3000 Boulder CO 80307

MADDEN, SIDNEY CLARENCE, b Fresno, Calif, Oct 27, 07; m 33; c 4. PATHOLOGY. *Educ:* Stanford Univ, AB, 30, MD, 34. *Prof Exp:* Intern, Johns Hopkins Hosp, 33-34; asst resident path, Strong Mem Hosp, Univ Rochester, 34-40; asst path, Sch Med & Dent, Univ Rochester, 34-37, from instr to assoc prof, 37-45; prof & chmn dept, Sch Med, Emory Univ, 45-48; head div, Brookhaven Nat Lab, 48-51, sr physician, Lab Hosp, 49-51; chmn dept, 51-70, prof path, 51-75, EMER PROF PATH, SCH MED, UNIV CALIF, LOS ANGELES, 75- *Concurrent Pos:* Dir labs, Park Ave Hosp, 40-45; pathologist, Emory Hosp, 45-48 & Eggleston Hosp for Children, 45-48; consult, Vet Admin Ctr, Los Angeles, 51-70, Los Angeles County Harbor Gen Hosp, 52-70 & Armed Forces Inst Path, 55-65; sr adv, Atomic Bomb Casualty Comn, 58-66. *Honors & Awards:* Smith Award, AAAS, 43. *Mem:* AAAS; Am Soc Exp Path (pres, 52); Soc Exp Biol & Med; fel AMA; Am Asn Path & Bact (pres, 63). *Res:* Nucleic acid and protein metabolism after tissue injury; chemical carcinogenesis; immunology of neoplasia. *Mailing Add:* Dept of Path Univ of Calif Sch of Med Los Angeles CA 90024

MADDEN, STEPHEN JAMES, JR, b Newton, Mass, June 8, 36; m 58; c 2. COMPUTER SCIENCE, GEODESY. *Educ:* Mass Inst Technol, BS, 59, MS, 62, PhD(appl math), 66. *Prof Exp:* Staff mathematician, Instrumentation Lab, 59-61, instr math, 65-66, assoc dir, Measurement Systs Lab, 66-74, SECT CHIEF, C S DRAPER LAB, MASS INST TECHNOL, 74- LECTR, DEPT AERONAUT & ASTRONAUT, 68- *Mem:* Am Math Soc; Soc Indust & Appl Math; Inst Elec & Electronics Engrs; Am Geophys Union. *Res:* Geometricmodeling; numerical control; gradiometry. *Mailing Add:* 5 Constitution Rd Lexington MA 02173

MADDEN, THEODORE RICHARD, b Boston, Mass, Mar 14, 25; m 74; c 1. GEOPHYSICS. *Educ:* Mass Inst Technol, BS, 49, PhD(geophys), 61. *Prof Exp:* From lectr to assoc prof, 52-64, PROF GEOPHYS, MASS INST TECHNOL, 64- *Res:* Geoelectricity and geomagnetism, inversion theory, atmospheric gravity waves. *Mailing Add:* Dept of Earth & Planetary Sci Rm 54-614 Mass Inst of Technol Cambridge MA 02139

MADDEN, THOMAS LEE, b Bellefontaine, Ohio, May 21, 42; m 65; c 4. ELECTRONIC ENGINEERING, ELECTROMAGNETIC THEORY. *Educ:* Ohio Univ, BS, 65; Ohio State Univ, MS, 73. *Prof Exp:* Proj engr electronic countermeasures, Systs Eng Group, 65-68; proj engr, 68-78, TASK MGR ELECTRONIC COUNTERMEASURES, AIR FORCE AVIONICS LAB, 78- *Honors & Awards:* Lett Commendation, Electronic Countermeasures Advan Develop Br, Air Force Avionics Lab, 78. *Mem:* Inst Elec & Electronics Engrs. *Res:* Development of passive and active countermeasures to devices utilizing electromagnetic energy for the control of weapon systems to prevent them from destroying United States Air Force aircraft. *Mailing Add:* Air Force Avionics Lab (WRD) Wright-Patterson Air Force Base Dayton OH 45433

MADDEX, PHILLIP J(OSEPH), b Mechanicsburg, Ohio, Oct 24, 17; m 41; c 2. CHEMICAL ENGINEERING. *Educ:* Ohio State Univ, BChE, 41. *Prof Exp:* Design engr, Ken-Rad Tube & Lamp Co, Ky, 41-43 & Gen Elec Co, 43-47; res engr, Battelle Mem Inst, 47-50 & Nat Lead Co, 50-52; plant mgr, Titanium Metals Corp Am, 52-59; chief engr, US Borax & Chem Corp, 59-65, consult transp eng & mgt, 65-73; VPRES, MET-L-CHEK CO, 73- *Res:* Shipping world wide; ores, metals and forest products. *Mailing Add:* 1639 Euclid St Santa Monica CA 90404

MADDIN, CHARLES MILFORD, b Vernon, Tex, Sept 7, 27; m 48; c 1. ANALYTICAL CHEMISTRY. *Educ:* Univ Tex, BA, 50, PhD(chem), 53. *Prof Exp:* Res scientist, Univ Tex, 51-53; lab group leader, 53-64, sect supvr, 64-73, RES MGR, DOWELL DIV, DOW CHEM USA, 73- *Concurrent Pos:* Lectr, Univ Tulsa, 64-65. *Mem:* Am Chem Soc; Am Inst Chemists. *Res:* Instrumental analysis; chemical separations. *Mailing Add:* 7705 E 25th Pl Tulsa OK 74129

MADDIN, ROBERT, b Hartford, Conn, Oct 20, 18; m 45; c 2. METALLURGY, MATERIALS SCIENCE. *Educ:* Purdue Univ, BS, 42; Yale Univ, DrEng(metall), 48. *Hon Degrees:* MA, Univ Pa, 71. *Prof Exp:* Instr, New Haven Jr Col, 46-48; res assoc & fel, Yale Univ, 48-49; asst prof phys metall, Johns Hopkins Univ, 49-52, assoc prof, 52-55; prof metall, 55-72, from actg dir to dir sch metall & mat sci, 55-72, UNIV PROF METALL, UNIV PA, 72- *Concurrent Pos:* Vis prof, Univ Birmingham, 54 & Oxford Univ, 70; ed-in-chief, Mat Sci & Eng. *Mem:* Fel Am Soc Metals; Am Inst Mining, Metall & Petrol Engrs; Brit Inst Metals; fel Metall Soc. *Res:* Deformation of materials; high temperature metals; diffusion; x-ray diffraction; structure and properties of amorphous alloys; history of metallurgy. *Mailing Add:* Sch of Metall & Mat Sci Univ of Pa Philadelphia PA 19104

MADDISON, SHIRLEY EUNICE, b SAfrica, Apr 12, 25; US citizen; m 50. IMMUNOLOGY, PARASITOLOGY. *Educ:* Univ Capetown, SAfrica, BSc, 44, PhD(microbiol), 62. *Prof Exp:* Lab technician microbiol, Prov Health Serv, Natal, SAfrica, 45-54; asst instr bact, Med Sch, Univ Natal, 54-56; sr tech officer parasitol, Amoebiasis Res Inst, Coun Sci & Indust Res, Natal, 56-64; USPHS int fel, Ctr Dis Control, Atlanta, Ga, 64-66; guest researcher, Biochem Inst, Uppsala, Sweden, 66; vis scientist & fel parasitol, 67-71, actg chief parasitic immunochem unit, 72-73, CHIEF PARASITIC IMMUNOCHEM BR, CTR DIS CONTROL, USPHS, 73- *Concurrent Pos:* Adv ad hoc study group parasitic dis, US Army Med Res & Develop Command, 74-; consult to Surgeon Gen, US Army, 74- *Mem:* Fel Am Acad Microbiol; Am Soc Trop Med & Hyg; AAAS; Reticuloendothelial Soc; Am Asn Immunologists. *Res:* Immunology of parasitic diseases with emphasis on the immune mechanisms and antigens related to protective immunity in schistosomiasis; immunologic response to parasitic infections in terms of immunoglobulin subclasses. *Mailing Add:* Bldg 5 Rm SB-15 Ctr Dis Control 1600 Clifton Rd NE Atlanta GA 30333

MADDOCK, MARSHALL, b Glendale, Calif, Sept 2, 28; m; c 3. GEOLOGY. *Educ:* Univ Calif, AB, 49, PhD, 55. *Prof Exp:* PROF GEOL, SAN JOSE STATE UNIV, 55- *Mem:* Geol Soc Am; Nat Asn Geol Teachers. *Res:* Mineralogy; petrology; field geology. *Mailing Add:* Dept of Geol San Jose State Univ San Jose CA 95192

MADDOCK, THOMAS, JR, b Williams, Ariz, Apr 6, 07; m 35; c 1. CIVIL ENGINEERING. *Educ:* Univ Ariz, BS, 28. *Hon Degrees:* DSc, Univ Ariz, 71. *Prof Exp:* Dir mission, Food Supply Div, Inst Inter-Am Affairs, 43-46; head sedimentation sect, Bur Reclamation, 46-49, head flood sect, 49-50, asst chief hydrol br, 50-52, chief irrig opers br, 52-54; chief irrig analyst, Hoover Comn, 54-55; hydraul engr, 56-57; staff scientist, US Geol Surv, 57-59, chief gen hydrol br, 60-62, sr scientist, 63-71, sr scientist, Water Resources Div, 71-74; CONSULT, 76- *Concurrent Pos:* Consult, Orgn Am States, 74-, US Geol Surv, 75- & UNESCO, 76-80; vis scientist, Univ Ariz, 78-; mem, Indian Conferences on Ganges Flood Control & Village Water Supplies, Nat Acad Sci, 71 & 81. *Honors & Awards:* Bryan Award, Geol Soc Am, 58; Stevens Award, Am Soc Civil Engrs, 63. *Mem:* Fel Am Soc Civil Engrs; Am Geophys Union; hon mem Am Water Resources Asn. *Res:* Hydrology; fluvial morphology; effect of discharge and sediment load on channel characteristics; analysis of effectiveness of different types of flood control projects. *Mailing Add:* 2453 Avenida de Posada Tucson AZ 85718

MADDOCKS, ROSALIE FRANCES, b Lewiston, Maine, Aug 27, 38. GEOLOGY, MICROPALEONTOLOGY. *Educ:* Univ Maine, Orono, BA, 59; Univ Kans, MA, 62, PhD(geol), 65. *Prof Exp:* Res assoc, Smithsonian Inst, 65-67; PROF GEOL, UNIV HOUSTON, 67- *Mem:* Fel AAAS; Paleont Soc; Soc Syst Zool; Int Paleont Union; NAm Micropaleont Soc. *Res:* Systematics, ecology and evolution of living and fossil Ostracoda. *Mailing Add:* Dept of Geol Univ of Houston Houston TX 77004

MADDOX, BILLY HOYTE, b Pahokee, Fla, July 2, 32; m 53; c 4. MATHEMATICS. *Educ:* Troy State Univ, BS, 53; Univ Fla, MEd, 57; Univ SC, PhD(math), 65. *Prof Exp:* Instr math, Troy State Univ, 57-60; prof & chmn dept, Presby Col SC, 64-66; assoc prof, 66-71, PROF MATH, ECKERD COL, 71- *Concurrent Pos:* Reviewer, Zentralblatt fur Mathematics, 66-; partic, NSF Summer Inst Comput-Oriented Calculus, Fla State Univ, 70. *Honors & Awards:* Nat Defense Serv Medal; Europ Occup Medal. *Mem:* Am Math Soc; Math Asn Am. *Res:* Algebra; ring and module theory, specifically absolutely pure modules; application of mathematics to evaluation in higher education. *Mailing Add:* Dept of Math Eckerd Col St Petersburg FL 33733

MADDOX, JOSEPH VERNARD, b Montgomery, Ala, Apr 14, 38; m 71. INSECT PATHOLOGY. *Educ:* Auburn Univ, BS, 59, MS, 61; Univ Ill, PhD(entom), 66. *Prof Exp:* ASST PROF AGR ENTOM & ASSOC ENTOMOLOGIST, ILL NATURAL HIST SURV, UNIV ILL, URBANA, 66- *Mem:* AAAS; Entom Soc Am; Soc Invert Path. *Res:* Insect pathology, especially microsporidian diseases of insects. *Mailing Add:* Sect of Econ Entom Ill Nat Hist Surv Univ of Ill Urbana IL 61801

MADDOX, LARRY A(LLEN), b Bryan, Tex, July 2, 43; m 65; c 1. CHEMICAL ENGINEERING. *Educ:* Tex A&M Univ, BS, 65; Univ Tex, Austin, PhD(chem eng), 70. *Prof Exp:* Chem engr, Res & Tech Lab, Mobil Chem Co, 65; res engr, Tech Ctr, 69-75, unit supvr, 75-76, process eng group leader, 76-78, PLANNING ASSOC, CELANESE CHEM CO, 78- *Mem:* AAAS; Am Inst Chem Engrs. *Res:* Heterogeneous and homogeneous catalysis; industrial crystallization; process design and development. *Mailing Add:* Celanese Chem Co Box 47320 Dallas TX 75247

MADDOX, R(OBERT) N(OTT), b Winslow, Ark, Sept 29, 25; m 51; c 2. CHEMICAL ENGINEERING. *Educ:* Univ Ark, BS, 48; Univ Okla, MChE, 50; Okla State Univ, PhD(chem eng), 55. *Prof Exp:* Instr, Sch Chem Eng, Okla State Univ, 50-51; design engr, Process Div, Black, Sivalls & Bryson, Inc, 51-52; asst & instr, 52-53, from asst prof to prof, 53-76, head, Sch Chem Eng, 58-77, LEONARD F SHEERAR PROF CHEM ENG, OKLA STATE UNIV, 76-, DIR, PHYS PROPERTIES LAB, 77- *Concurrent Pos:* Consult, Cities Serv Oil Co, Black, Sivalls & Bryson, Inc, Humble Oil & Refining Co, Pace Co & Iraq Petrol Corp; vis prof, Univ Cincinnati, 67; tech dir, Fluid Properties Res, Inc, 73- *Honors & Awards:* Joseph Stewart Award, Am Chem Soc, 71. *Mem:* Fel Am Inst Chem Engrs; Am Chem Soc; Am Soc Eng Educ; Am Inst Mining, Metall & Petrol Engrs; fel Am Inst Chemists. *Res:* Computer applications; stagewise operations; physical properties; transport properties. *Mailing Add:* Sch of Chem Eng Okla State Univ Stillwater OK 74074

MADDOX, V HAROLD, JR, b New York, NY, Sept 25, 23; m 49; c 3. ORGANIC CHEMISTRY. *Educ:* Carnegie Inst Technol, BS, 49; Rutgers Univ, MS, 52, PhD(chem), 53. *Prof Exp:* Lab technician, Reichhold Chem, 41-43; asst chem, Rutgers Univ, 49-53; from assoc res chemist to res chemist, Parke, Davis & Co, 53-60, res leader org chem, 60-62, dir lab, 62-70, sect dir org chem, 70-80; MEM STAFF, PHARM RES DIV, WARNER-LAMBERT CO, 80- *Mem:* Am Chem Soc; NY Acad Sci; The Chem Soc. *Res:* Synthesis in the chrysene series; synthesis of sernyl; synthetic organic medicinals; process research. *Mailing Add:* Parke Davis & Co Bldg 48 Joseph Campau Ave Detroit MI 48232

MADDOX, WILLIAM EUGENE, b Owensboro, Ky, Aug 3, 37; m 63. NUCLEAR PHYSICS. *Educ:* Murray State Univ, BS, 62; Ind Univ, MS, 64, PhD(physics), 68. *Prof Exp:* Asst prof, 67-69, assoc prof, 69-80, PROF PHYSICS, MURRAY STATE UNIV, 80- *Mem:* Am Phys Soc. *Res:* Experimental nuclear reaction physics. *Mailing Add:* Dept of Physics Murray State Univ Murray KY 42071

MADDY, KEITH THOMAS, b Knoxville, Iowa, Oct 28, 23; m 46; c 6. VETERINARY MEDICINE, PUBLIC HEALTH. *Educ:* Iowa State Col, DVM, 45; Univ Calif, MPH, 54; Am Col Vet Preventive Med, Am Col Vet Microbiol, Am Col Vet Toxicol & Am Col Toxicol, dipl. *Prof Exp:* Asst prof, Univ Nev, 45-47; vet pathologist, USDA, 48-51; epidemiologist, Nat Commun Dis Ctr, 54-60, scientist, Lab Med & Biol Sci, Div Air Pollution, 60-62; scientist adminstr, Nat Inst Allergy & Infectious Dis, 62-64 & Nat Heart Inst, 64-69, chief pulmonary dis br, Nat Heart & Lung Inst, 69-71; STAFF TOXICOLOGIST PESTICIDE HEALTH & SAFETY UNIT, CALIF DEPT FOOD & AGR, 71-, UNIT CHIEF, 80- *Mem:* AAAS; Am Vet Med Asn; Am Pub Health Asn; Soc Occup & Environ Health; Soc Epidemiol Res. *Res:* Fungal infections occurring in man and animals; coccidioidomycosis; toxicology of pesticides. *Mailing Add:* 1413 Notre Dame Davis CA 95616

MADDY, KENNETH HILTON, b Cleveland, Ohio, May 31, 23; m 46; c 3. BIOCHEMISTRY. *Educ:* Pa State Univ, BS, 44; Univ Wis, MS, 48; Pa State Univ, PhD(biochem), 52. *Prof Exp:* Res biochemist, Monsanto Co, Mo, 52-54, develop biochemist, 54-58, proj mgr, 58-60, mgr feed chem develop, 60-66, mgr new proj develop, 66-68, mgr life sci, New Enterprise Div, 68-69, Dir, Computerized Tech Dept, 69-71; pres, Maddy Assocs Inc, 71-75; mgr prod develop, Lonza Inc, 75-76; mgr tech serv, BASF Wyandotte Corp, 76-80; MEM FAC AGR, ARIZ STATE UNIV, 80- *Mem:* Am Chem Soc; Am Soc Animal Sci; Inst Food Technologists; Am Feed Mfrs Asn; fel Am Inst Chemists. *Res:* Animal and human nutrition, specifically amino acids; dietary energy and vitamins; computer program design and development for animal production and human nutrition. *Mailing Add:* Div Agr Ariz State Univ Tempe AZ 85287

MADER, CHARLES LAVERN, b Dewey, Okla, Aug 8, 30; m 60; c 1. PHYSICAL CHEMISTRY. *Educ:* Okla State Univ, BS, 52, MS, 54; Pacific Western Univ, PhD, 80. *Prof Exp:* Mem staff, 55-74, asst group leader, 74-76, GROUP LEADER, LOS ALAMOS NAT LAB, 76- *Concurrent Pos:* Consult, Defense Standard Labs, Melbourne, Australia, 69 & Swedish Detonic Res Found, 75 & 78; mem fac, Hawaii Inst Geophys, Univ Hawaii, 72-73; adj prof chem, Univ NMex, 80- *Mem:* Am Chem Soc; fel Am Inst Chemists; Am Phys Soc; Combustion Inst. *Res:* Explosives; thermodynamics; hydrodynamics; equation of state; the study of detonation chemistry and physics; chemically reactive fluid dynamics; water waves and tsunamis; oceanography. *Mailing Add:* Los Alamos Nat Lab Mail Stop 214 PO Box 1663 Los Alamos NM 87545

MADER, DONALD LEWIS, b Baltimore, Md, Nov 7, 26; m 50; c 3. FOREST SOILS, FOREST HYDROLOGY. *Educ:* NY State Univ of Forestry, BS, 50; Univ Wis, MS, 54, PhD(soils), 56. *Prof Exp:* From asst prof to assoc prof forestry, 56-70, PROF FORESTRY, UNIV MASS, AMHERST, 70- *Mem:* AAAS; Soc Am Foresters; Soil Sci Soc Am; Ecol Soc Am; Am Inst Biol Sci. *Res:* Forest soils and ecology; watershed management. *Mailing Add:* Dept of Forestry & Wildlife Mgt Univ of Mass Amherst MA 01003

MADER, GEORGE EDWARD, b Waverly, Ill, Aug 7, 28; m 54; c 4. ELECTRONIC ENGINEERING, PHYSICS. *Educ:* Univ Ill, BS, 50. *Prof Exp:* Res asst, Univ Ill, 50-52 & 55-57; prog mgr, Syracuse Univ Res Corp, 57-67, lab dir, NY, 67-71, engr, 71-73; ELECTRONIC ENGR, WHITE SANDS MISSILE RANGE, NMEX, 73- *Mem:* Inst Elec & Electronics Engrs. *Res:* Military electronic systems, especially ground and airborne radars, electronic countermeasures and reconnaissance devices; laser countermeasures. *Mailing Add:* 8704 Catalpa Lane El Paso TX 79925

MADER, IVAN JOHN, b Iowa, Dec 29, 23; m 46; c 4. MEDICINE. *Educ:* Cornell Col, 41-43; Wayne State Univ, MS, 49, MD, 51; Am Bd Internal Med, dipl, 61. *Prof Exp:* Chief med & dir med educ, 62-68, chief of staff, 68-76, EXEC V PRES & MED DIR, WILLIAM BEAUMONT HOSP, 76- *Concurrent Pos:* Jr assoc, Detroit Gen Hosp, Mich, 56-; consult, Vet Admin, 57-; adj asst prof, Col Med, Wayne State Univ, 58- *Mem:* AMA; fel Am Col Physicians; Am Fedn Clin Res. *Res:* Renal disease. *Mailing Add:* William Beaumont Hosp 3535 W 13 Mile Rd Royal Oak MI 48072

MADERA-ORSINI, FRANK, b Mayaguez, PR, Sept 29, 16; m 45; 5. BIOCHEMISTRY. *Educ:* Ohio Univ, BS, 39; Univ Mo, MS, 56, PhD(biochem), 59. *Prof Exp:* Biochemist clin chem, St Joseph Mercy Hosp, 58-64; DIR CLIN BIOCHEM & RES, WEST SUBURBAN HOSP, 64- *Concurrent Pos:* Consult, Ment Health State Hosp, Ill; consult, Peoples Community Hosps, Wayne, Mich, 58-64. *Mem:* Am Chem Soc; Am Asn Clin Chem; Am Soc Cell Biol; NY Acad Sci; Am Acad Clin Biochem. *Res:* Clinical and cell chemistry; aldosterone, antagonists and immunology; iron metabolism. *Mailing Add:* Biochem Dept West Suburban Hosp 518 N Austin Blvd Oak Park IL 60302

MADERSON, PAUL F A, b Kent, Eng, Dec 19, 38; m 61; c 1. DEVELOPMENTAL ANATOMY. *Educ:* Univ London, BSc, 60, PhD(zool), 62, DSc(zool), 72. *Prof Exp:* Asst lectr zool, Univ Hong Kong, 62-65; lectr, Univ Calif, Riverside, 65-66; NIH res assoc dermat, Mass Gen Hosp, Harvard Med Sch, 66-68; from asst prof to assoc prof, 68-73, PROF BIOL, BROOKLYN COL, 73- *Concurrent Pos:* Asst Prof, Boston Univ, 67-68; prof path, Univ Ark Med Ctr, 75- *Mem:* Fel AAAS; Zool Soc London; Anat Soc Gt Brit & Ireland; Am Soc Zoologists; Am Soc Naturalists. *Res:* Anatomy and cell dynamics squamate epidermis; evolutionary morphology; evolution and development. *Mailing Add:* Dept Biol Brooklyn Col Brooklyn NY 11210

MADERSPACH, VICTOR, b Alsobarbatyen, Hungary, Oct 6, 18; m 44, 60; c 3. ENGINEERING MECHANICS. *Educ:* Hungarian Tech Mil Acad, BS, 39; Va Polytech Inst, MS, 62; Vienna Tech Univ, Dr Tech(solid mech), 64. *Prof Exp:* Asst prof, 57-64, ASSOC PROF ENG MECH, VA POLYTECH INST & STATE UNIV, 64- *Mem:* Am Soc Eng Educ. *Res:* Plates; shells; thermal stresses; plasticity. *Mailing Add:* Dept of Eng Mech Norris Hall Va Polytech Inst & State Univ Blacksburg VA 24061

MADEY, RICHARD, b Brooklyn, NY, Feb 23, 22; m 51; c 6. NUCLEAR PHYSICS. *Educ:* Rensselaer Polytech Inst, BEE, 42; Univ Calif, Berkeley, PhD(physics), 52. *Prof Exp:* Elec engr, Allen B DuMont Labs, 43-44; physicist, Lawrence Radiation Lab, Univ Calif, 47-53; assoc physicist, Brookhaven Nat Lab, 53-56; from scientist to sr scientist, Repub Aviation Corp, 56-61, chief staff scientist mod physics, 61-62, chief appl physics res, 63-64; prof physics, Clarkson Col Technol, 65-71, chmn dept, 65; PROF PHYSICS & CHMN DEPT, KENT STATE UNIV, 71- *Concurrent Pos:* Guest scientist, Nevis Cyclotron Lab, Columbia Univ, 55, 76 & 77, Brookhaven Nat Lab, 61 & 74, Foster Radiation Lab, McGill Univ, 67 & 68, Nat Res Coun Can, 68-70, Nuclear Struct Lab, Univ Rochester, 70 & Lawrence Berkeley Lab, Univ Calif, 71, 72, 77, 78, 79 & 81; consult, Ross Radio Corp, 52-53, Wcoast Electronics Lab, Willys Motors Co, 53-55, Kaiser Aircraft & Electronics Corp, 55-56, US AEC, 65-75, US Energy Res & Develop Admin, 75-77, US Dept Energy, 78-, Lawrence Berkeley Lab, 78, Ecol Energy Systs, 79-80 & Life Systs, Inc, 81-; prin investr contracts & grants, US Air Force, US AEC, NSF, Energy Res & Develop Admin, Dept of Energy, NASA & NIH; guest scientist, Univ Md Cyclotron Lab, 73-75 & 78, Ohio Univ Accelerator Lab, 75 & Ind Univ Cyclotron Facil, 76-78; mem, Am Inst Biol Sci Radiation Adv Panel, NASA Off Life Sci, 79 & Site Visit Team & Rev Panel, Nat Cancer Inst, 79. *Honors & Awards:* Army-Navy E Award, 43; Letter of Commendation, British Admiralty, 46; Naval Ordn Develop Award, Naval Ordn Lab, 46. *Mem:* Fel AAAS; Am Nuclear Soc; Am Phys Soc; sr mem Inst Elec & Electronics Eng; fel NY Acad Sci. *Res:* Nuclear, space and environmental sciences; interaction of radiation with matter and with biological systems; transport of gases through porous media; nuclear instrumentation. *Mailing Add:* Kent State Univ Kent OH 44242

MADEY, ROBERT W, b Norwalk, Conn, May 2, 33; m 60; c 3. NUCLEAR PHYSICS, ENGINEERING. *Educ:* Mass Inst Technol, BS, 55; Univ Md, PhD(nuclear eng), 63. *Prof Exp:* Consult, West Coast Electronics Lab, Willys Motors Co, 54 & Kaiser Aircraft & Electronics Corp, 55; instr nuclear eng, Univ Md, 57-60; nuclear engr, Nat Bur Standards, 60-62, sci & eng asst to chief of reactor group, 62-63; head nuclear physics & eng group, 63-69, HEAD SPACE SCI, GRUMMAN AEROSPACE CORP, 69- *Concurrent Pos:* Adj prof, NY Inst Technol, 69. *Mem:* AAAS; Am Nuclear Soc; Am Inst Aeronaut & Astronaut; NY Acad Sci. *Res:* High energy physics and astronomy; space radiation; radiation detection and measurement techniques; radiation effects; nuclear reactor design; reactor instrumentation; shielding; Cerenkov radiation; high vacuum technology, thermionic emission; electrostatic deflection systems. *Mailing Add:* 7 Milford Lane Huntington Sta NY 11746

MADEY, THEODORE EUGENE, b Wilmington, Del, Oct 24, 37; m 60; c 4. SURFACE PHYSICS, SURFACE CHEMISTRY. *Educ:* Loyola Col Md, BS, 59; Univ Notre Dame, PhD(physics), 63. *Prof Exp:* Nat Res Coun res assoc, 63-65, PHYSICIST, NAT BUR STANDARDS, 65- *Concurrent Pos:* Vis scientist, Tech Univ Munich, 73 & Sandia Labs, 77; Chevron vis prof, Calif Inst Technol, 81. *Mem:* Fel Am Phys Soc; Am Vacuum Soc (pres, 81). *Res:* Physics and chemistry of solid surfaces; kinetics of adsorption on single crystal surfaces; interaction of slow electrons with adsorbed species; reactions at surfaces; spectroscopy of surfaces; surface standards; catalysis. *Mailing Add:* Nat Bur of Standards Washington DC 20234

MADHAV, R, b Bangalore, India, Jan 14, 38; m 67; c 1. ORGANIC CHEMISTRY. *Educ:* Univ Madras, BS, 57; Univ Delhi, MS, 60, PhD(chem), 65. *Prof Exp:* Res asst agr chem, Agr Res Inst, India, 57-58; res assoc chem, Univ Delhi, 65-68; res chemist, Carnegie-Mellon Univ, 68-71, res chemist, Mellon Inst, 71-75; RES BIOCHEMIST MICROBIOL, SCH MED, UNIV PITTSBURGH, 75- *Concurrent Pos:* USDA fel, Univ Delhi, 65-68; NIH fel, Carnegie-Mellon Univ, 68-71, Walter Reed Army Hosp fel, Mellon Inst, 71-75. *Mem:* Am Chem Soc; Sigma Xi; Nat Geog Soc. *Res:* Natural products chemistry; oxygen heterocycles; synthesis of nitrogen heterocycles; synthesis of fatty acids; synthesis of spin labeled compounds, analogs of coenzymes; preparation of substrates on polymer supports for studying enzyme properties; kidney cell inhibitor on nucleoside kinases; serum factor with growth promoting property. *Mailing Add:* Dept of Microbiol Sch of Med Univ of Pittsburgh Pittsburgh PA 15213

MADHAVAN, KUNCHITHAPATHAM, b Mayuram, India, Feb 9, 45; m 71; c 1. CIVIL ENGINEERING, FOUNDATION ENGINEERING. *Educ:* Annamalai Univ, Madras, India, BS, 67; Indian Inst Technol, Kanpur, MS, 69; Univ Miss, PhD(civil eng), 75. *Prof Exp:* Sci teacher, Calhoun County Sch Syst, 72-74; design engr civil eng, Brice, Petrides & Assoc, Inc, Iowa, 75-76; asst prof, 76-80, ASSOC PROF CIVIL ENG, CHRISTIAN BROS COL, MEMPHIS, TENN, 80- *Concurrent Pos:* Found analyst, Test Inc, Consult Engrs, Memphis, 77; res grant & proj mgr water quality control, Off Planning & Develop, Memphis & Shelby County Govt, Tenn, 78. *Mem:* Am Soc Civil Engrs. *Res:* Structural mechanics; foundation engineering and wastewater treatment and water quality control. *Mailing Add:* Christian Bros Col 650 E Parkway S Memphis TN 38104

MADHOSINGH, CLARENCE, b Trinidad, WI, Sept 19, 31; m 59; c 1. MYCOLOGY, BIOCHEMISTRY. *Educ:* Univ BC, BSA, 54, MA, 58; Univ Western Ont, PhD(adv mycol), 59. *Prof Exp:* Res scientist, Plant Res Inst, Can Dept Agr, 60-67; HEAD PLANT PATH SECT & RES SCIENTIST, AGR RES BR, CHEM & BIOL RES INST, AGR CAN, 67- *Concurrent Pos:* Fel, Biochem Inst, Univ Uppsala, 71-72. *Mem:* Asn Trop Biol; Can Bot Soc; Can Soc Microbiol; Can Phytopath Soc. *Res:* Comparative biochemistry of the fungi, involving a study of genetic and cytoplasmic factors affecting sexuality, pathogenicity, toxin production and chemical resistance in plant pathogenic fungi. *Mailing Add:* Chem & Biol Res Inst Res Br Agr Can Carling Ave Ottawa ON K1A 0C6 Can

MADHU, SWAMINATHAN, b Madras, India, Jan 29, 31; US citizen; m 59; c 3. ELECTRICAL ENGINEERING. *Educ:* Madras Univ, MA, 51; Indian Inst Sci, Bangalore, dipl, 54; Univ Tenn, MS, 57; Univ Wash, PhD(elec eng), 64. *Prof Exp:* Instr elec eng, Univ Wash, 57-63; sr engr, Gen Dynamics/

Electronics, 63-65; asst prof elec eng, Rutgers Univ, 65-68; assoc prof, 68-72, PROF ELEC ENG, ROCHESTER INST TECHNOL, 72-, ASSOC DEAN GRAD STUDIES, 80- *Concurrent Pos:* Consult, Naval Res Lab, Washington, DC, 70- & Eastman Kodak Co, 73-75; educ consult, Nigerian Army Signal Corps, 76-79. *Mem:* Inst Elec & Electronics Engrs. *Res:* Automatic language translation; target classification and pattern recognition studies; application of lasers to communications; switching circuits. *Mailing Add:* Dept of Elec Eng 1 Lomb Mem Dr Rochester NY 14623

MADIGOSKY, WALTER MYRON, b Derby, Conn, Dec 15, 33; m 62. PHYSICS. *Educ:* Fairfield Univ, BS, 55; Univ Del, MS, 57; Catholic Univ, PhD(physics), 63. *Prof Exp:* RES PHYSICIST, US NAVAL SURFACE WEAPONS CTR, 57- *Concurrent Pos:* Sci officer phys acoust, Off Naval Res, 75-76. *Mem:* Fel Acoust Soc Am. *Res:* Physical acoustics; liquid state; ultrasonics; underwater acoustics; author of over 70 publications. *Mailing Add:* US Naval Surface Weapons Ctr White Oak Silver Spring MD 20910

MADIN, STEWART HARVEY, b Sheffield, Eng, Apr 3, 18; nat US; m 43; c 3. ANIMAL PATHOLOGY, VIROLOGY. *Educ:* Univ Calif, AB, 40, PhD, 60; Agr & Mech Col Tex, DVM, 43. *Prof Exp:* Asst histopath, Agr & Mech Col Tex, 42-43; assoc, Exp Sta, Off Naval Res, 43-44, assoc vet sci, 46-49, prin pathologist, 49-51, res pathologist, Naval Biol Lab, 51-57, asst sci dir, 57-60, from actg sci dir to dir, 60-68; PROF PUB HEALTH, EXP PATH & MED MICROBIOL, UNIV CALIF, BERKELEY, 61-; PROF EPIDEMIOL & PREV MED, SCH VET MED, UNIV CALIF, DAVIS, 67- *Concurrent Pos:* Lectr, Univ Calif, Berkeley, 50-61; mem res comt foot-and-mouth dis & chmn adv comt, Nat Acad Sci-Nat Res Coun, 67-; consult, Pan-Am Health Orgn, 67-; mem cell cult comt & consult-at-large, Nat Cancer Inst; chmn consults, Agr Res Serv; mem, Navy Sr Scientist's Coun; mem, US Foot-and-Mouth Dis Comn II; mem, Comt Vesicular Dis & Animal Virus Classification. *Mem:* Am Vet Med Asn; US Animal Health Asn; NY Acad Sci. *Res:* Pathology of infectious diseases; vesicular viruses of domestic animals; pathogenesis of viral diseases; experimental pathology; tissue culture; comparative medicine of terrestrial and marine animals and oncology. *Mailing Add:* 3510 Life Sci Bldg Sch Pub Health Univ Calif Berkeley CA 94720

MADISON, BERNARD L, b Rocky Hill, Ky, Aug 1, 41. MATHEMATICS. *Educ:* Western Ky Univ, BS, 62; Univ Ky, MS, 64, PhD(math), 66. *Prof Exp:* Asst prof, La State Univ, Baton Rouge, 66-71, assoc prof math, 71-80; PROF & CHMN MATH, UNIV ARK, FAYETTEVILLE, 80- *Mem:* Am Math Soc; Math Asn Am. *Res:* Topology and algebraic semigroups. *Mailing Add:* Univ Ark La State Univ Fayetteville AR 72701

MADISON, CAROLINE RABB, b Charleston, SC, Mar 25, 21; m 44; c 1. ZOOLOGY, GENETICS. *Educ:* Univ Ga, BS, 42; Ohio State Univ, MS, 49, PhD(genetics), 52. *Prof Exp:* Asst radiotracers, Am Cyanamid Co, 42-46; from asst prof to assoc prof, 62-69, PROF BIOL, KEAN COL NJ, 69- *Mem:* AAAS; Genetics Soc Am; Am Inst Biol Sci. *Res:* Embryology. *Mailing Add:* Dept of Biol Kean Col of NJ Union NJ 07083

MADISON, DALE MARTIN, b Urbana, Ill, Oct 20, 42; m 66; c 2. RODENT SOCIOBIOLOGY. *Educ:* Univ Md, BSc, 65, MSc, 68, PhD(ethology), 71. *Prof Exp:* Res specialist, Univ Wis, 70-71, res assoc, 71-73; asst prof, McGill Univ, 73-77; asst prof, 77-81, ASSOC PROF BIOL, STATE UNIV NY BINGHAMTON, 82- *Honors & Awards:* Stoye Herpetol Award, Sigma Xi. *Mem:* AAAS; Animal Behav Soc; Am Soc Mammalogists; Am Soc Ichthyologists & Herpetologists. *Res:* Space utilization and social organization in vertebrates, especially small mammals; chemical communication and scent marking in vertebrates. *Mailing Add:* Dept Biol State Univ NY Binghamton NY 13901

MADISON, DON HARVEY, b Pierre, SDak, Jan 4, 45; m 66; c 2. ATOMIC PHYSICS. *Educ:* Sioux Falls Col, BA, 67; Fla State Univ, MS, 70, PhD(physics), 72. *Prof Exp:* Instr physics, Fla State Univ, 72; res assoc, Univ NC, 72-74; from asst prof to assoc prof, 74-81, PROF PHYSICS, DRAKE UNIV, 81- *Mem:* Am Phys Soc; Am Asn Physics Teachers. *Res:* Theoretical aspects of collisions between charged particles and atoms. *Mailing Add:* Dept of Physics Drake Univ Des Moines IA 50311

MADISON, JAMES ALLEN, b Woodstock, Ill, Jan 12, 28; m 54; c 4. GEOLOGY. *Educ:* Univ NC, BS, 51, MS, 55; Wash Univ, PhD(earth sci), 68. *Prof Exp:* assoc prof, 54-76, PROF EARTH SCI & CHMN DEPT, DePAUW UNIV, 78- *Concurrent Pos:* Lectr, Jr Engrs & Scientists Summer Prog & NSF Summer Inst Jr High Sch Teachers, 59-70, 72 & 78; vis lectr high schs, Ind. *Mem:* Nat Asn Geol Teachers; Sigma Xi; Asn Eng Geologists; Am Inst Prof Geologists. *Res:* Mineralogy; geophysics; engineering geology; alpine ultramafics. *Mailing Add:* Dept of Earth Sci DePauw Univ Greencastle IN 46135

MADISON, JAMES THOMAS, b Adrian, Minn, Oct 23, 33; m 58; c 1. BIOLOGICAL CHEMISTRY. *Educ:* Colo State Univ, BS, 55; Univ Utah, PhD(biol chem), 62. *Prof Exp:* Res assoc biochem, Cornell Univ, 62-64; RES CHEMIST, PLANT, SOIL & NUTRIT LAB, AGR RES SERV, USDA, 64- *Concurrent Pos:* NIH fel, 62-64. *Mem:* AAAS; Am Chem Soc; Am Soc Biol Chemists; Am Soc Plant Physiol. *Res:* Regulation of amino acid and protein synthesis in plants. *Mailing Add:* Plant Soil & Nutrit Lab Tower Rd Ithaca NY 14853

MADISON, JOHN HERBERT, JR, b Burlington, Iowa, Jan 16, 18; m 42; c 4. HORTICULTURE. *Educ:* Oberlin Col, BA, 42; Cornell Univ, PhD(plant physiol), 53. *Prof Exp:* Instr, Cornell Univ, 52-53; from asst prof landscape hort & asst horticulturist to assoc prof & assoc horticulturist, 53-71, prof landscape hort & horticulturist, 71-80, EMER PROF ENVIRON HORT, UNIV CALIF, DAVIS, 80- *Concurrent Pos:* Fel, Univ Edinburgh, 69-70; res assoc, Univ BC, 75. *Mem:* Bot Soc Am; Am Soc Plant Physiologists; Am Soc Agron; Soil Sci Soc Am. *Res:* Monocotyledon biology, soil-water-plant relations of amended soils. *Mailing Add:* Dept of Environ Hort Univ of Calif Davis CA 95616

MADISON, LEONARD LINCOLN, b New York, NY, Feb 11, 20; div; c 2. ENDOCRINOLOGY, METABOLISM. *Educ:* Ohio State Univ, BA, 41; Long Island Col Med, MD, 44. *Prof Exp:* From asst prof to assoc prof, 52-64, PROF INTERNAL MED, UNIV TEX HEALTH SCI CTR, DALLAS, 64- *Concurrent Pos:* Mem gen med study sect, NIH, 62-66. *Mem:* Am Soc Clin Invest; Asn Am Physicians; Endocrine Soc; Am Diabetes Asn. *Res:* Cerebral, carbohydrate and hepatic metabolism; diabetes mellitus. *Mailing Add:* Dept of Internal Med Univ of Tex Health Sci Ctr Dallas TX 75235

MADISON, ROBERTA SOLOMON, b Brooklyn, NY, Feb 10, 32; div; c 2. PUBLIC HEALTH, EPIDEMIOLOGY. *Educ:* Univ Calif, Los Angeles, AB, 66, MA, 69, MSPH, 72, DrPH(environ health, behav sci), 74. *Prof Exp:* Chief epidemiol analyst, County Los Angeles Occup Health Serv Scheduling Supvr, 72-75; asst prof, 75-79, PROF BIOSTATIST & EPIDEMIOL, CALIF STATE UNIV NORTHRIDGE, 79-; EPIDEMIOLOGIST, DEPT OCCUP HEALTH, CITY HOPE NAT MED CTR, 77- *Mem:* AAAS; Soc Occup & Environ Health; Am Pub Health Asn; assoc mem Am Col Epidemiol. *Res:* Effect of occupational and environmental exposure on coke oven workers; alpha-1 antitrypsin deficiency as a risk factor in development of chronic obstructive lung disease. *Mailing Add:* Dept of Health Sci 18111 Nordhoff Northridge CA 91330

MADISON, VINCENT STEWART, b Adrian, Minn, Feb 10, 43; m 70; c 2. BIOPHYSICAL CHEMISTRY. *Educ:* Univ Minn, Minneapolis, BChem, 65; Univ Ore, PhD(chem), 69. *Prof Exp:* Instr chem, Nat Univ Trujillo, Peru, 70; fel biochem, Univ Calif Med Ctr, 70-71, Sch Med, Harvard, 71-74; asst prof, 75-78, ASSOC PROF MED CHEM, UNIV ILL MED CTR, 78- *Concurrent Pos:* NIH fel, 71-73; vis scholar, Univ Calif, San Diego, 81-82. *Res:* Molecular forces which determine peptide conformation and function; determination of conformation by circular dichroism and nuclear magnetic resonance spectroscopy. *Mailing Add:* Dept of Chem Col of Pharm Univ of Ill 833 S Wood St Chicago IL 60680

MADISON, WILLIAM LEON, b Westerly, RI, Dec 28, 19; m 47; c 3. PHARMACEUTICAL CHEMISTRY. *Educ:* RI Col Pharm, BS, 42; Purdue Univ, MS, 48, PhD(pharmaceut chem), 49. *Prof Exp:* Anal chemist, Burroughs Wellcome & Co, 42-43; sr res scientist, Bristol Labs, Inc, 49-53; mgr, Pharmaceut Develop Dept, McNeil Labs, Inc, 53-60, asst dir res & dir pharm res, 60-71, assoc dir clin res & serv, 71-77, assoc dir regulatory & med affairs, 77-81; RETIRED. *Mem:* Am Chem Soc; Am Pharmaceut Asn. *Res:* Biological research with radioactive isotopes; pharmaceutical development. *Mailing Add:* McNeil Consumer Prod Co Camp Hill Rd Ft Washington PA 19034

MADISSOO, HARRY, b Paide, Estonia, July 4, 24; US citizen; m 64; c 2. VETERINARY TOXICOLOGY. *Educ:* Hannover Vet Col, DVM, 60. *Prof Exp:* Res asst physiol, Med Col, Cornell Univ, 52-57; from res scientist to sr res scientist toxicol, Squibb Inst Med Res, 60-64; res scientist, 64-65, DIR TOXICOL, BRISTOL LABS, 65- *Mem:* AAAS; Am Vet Med Asn; NY Acad Sci; Soc Toxicol. *Res:* Kidney physiology; veterinary pharmacology; toxicology of drugs, natural products and cosmetics. *Mailing Add:* Dept of Toxicol Bristol Labs Po Box 657 Syracuse NY 13201

MADIX, ROBERT JAMES, b Beech Grove, Ind, June 22, 38; c 2. CHEMISTRY, CHEMICAL ENGINEERING. *Educ:* Univ Ill, BS, 61; Univ Calif, PhD(chem eng), 63. *Prof Exp:* From asst prof to assoc prof, 65-77, fel, 69-72, PROF CHEM ENG, STANFORD UNIV, 77- *Concurrent Pos:* NSF fel, Max Planck Inst Phys Chem, 64-65; von Humboldt sr scientist, 78; consult, Monsanto Chem Intermediates Co, 78-, Shell Develop Co, 80- *Mem:* AAAS; Am Inst Chem Engrs; Am Chem Soc; Faraday Soc. *Res:* Reactive gas-solid collisions on clean surfaces, molecular beam techniques employed to elucidate the reaction dynamics. *Mailing Add:* Dept Chem Eng Stanford Univ Stanford CA 94305

MADL, RONALD, b Lawrence, Kans, Nov 23, 44; m 69; c 1. BIOCHEMISTRY. *Educ:* Baker Univ, BS, 66; Kans State Univ, MS, 69, PhD(biochem), 73. *Prof Exp:* Food chemist protein chem, 73-76, mgr proj develop, 76-78, dir prod qual, 78-81, DIR TECH PLANNING & PROD QUAL, PROTEIN DIV, RALSTON PURINA CO, 81- *Mem:* Am Chem Soc; Am Asn Cereal Chemists; Inst Food Technologists. *Res:* Characterization of soy protein; study effects of processing parameters on functional characteristics; define tests to insure consistent processing. *Mailing Add:* Ralston Purina Co 900 Checkerboard Sq St Louis MO 63188

MADOC-JONES, HYWEL, b Cardiff, Wales, Nov 7, 38; m 67; c 2. RADIOTHERAPY. *Educ:* Oxford Univ, BA, 60, MA, 66; Univ London, PhD(biochem), 65; Univ Chicago, MD, 73. *Prof Exp:* Fel cell biol, Ont Cancer Inst & Dept Med Biophys, Univ Toronto, 65-67; res asst prof radiation & cell biol, Mallinckrodt Inst Radiol, Sch Med, Wash Univ, 67-68, asst prof, 68-69; res assoc radiol, Univ Chicago, 69-73, intern, Univ Chicago Hosps, 73-74; fel, M D Anderson Hosp & Tumor Inst, 74-77; assoc prof radiol, Mallinckrodt Inst Radiol, Sch Med, Washington Univ, 77-80; PROF & CHMN, SCH MED TUFTS UNIV, BOSTON, 80. *Mem:* Am Col Radiol. *Res:* Radiosensitivity of tumor cells in tissue culture; mechanisms of action of cytotoxic drugs; control of cell division. *Mailing Add:* Div Radiation Oncol New England Med Ctr 171 Harrison Ave St Louis MO 63110

MADOFF, MORTON A, b Clinton, Mass, Oct 20, 27; m 53; c 3. INFECTIOUS DISEASES, IMMUNOLOGY. *Educ:* Tulane Univ, BA, 51, MD, 55; Harvard Sch Pub Health, MPH, 73. *Prof Exp:* Asst med, New Eng Ctr Hosp, 58-60, asst physician, 60-64; chief infectious dis serv, Lemuel Shattuck Hosp, 64-69; dir biol lab, Mass Dept Pub Health, 67-70, dir, Bur Adult & Maternal Health Servs, 70-72, supt, State Lab Inst, 72-77; PROF COMMUNITY HEALTH, SCH MED, TUFTS UNIV, 77- *Concurrent Pos:* Nat Found res fel, 58-60; Nat Inst Allergy & Infectious Dis res career develop award, 62-67; prof, Sch Med, Tufts Univ. *Mem:* AAAS; Am Asn Immunologists; Infectious Dis Soc Am; Am Fedn Clin Res; Soc Exp Biol & Med. *Res:* Cell membranes; staphylococcal toxins; microbial exotoxins; public health and epidemiology. *Mailing Add:* Dept Community Health Tufts Med Sch 136 Harrison Ave Boston MA 02111

MADONNA, LOUIS A, b Pittsburgh, Pa, May 11, 24; m 48; c 4. CHEMICAL ENGINEERING. *Educ:* Carnegie Inst Technol, BS, 47, MS, 54. *Prof Exp:* Develop engr, Westinghouse Elec Corp, 47-48; design engr, Blaw-Knox Construct Co, 48-49; prod engr, Schenley Industs, 49-50; asst metals res lab, Carnegie Inst Technol, 50-52, res assoc chem eng, 53-54; chem engr, US Bur Mines, 52-53; prof chem eng & chmn dept, Univ Ottawa, 54-60; dir mech & processing labs, Continental Can Co, Ill, 60-62; PROF ENG & ASST DEAN SCH, WIDENER COL, 62- *Concurrent Pos:* Partic year in indust prog, Eng Dept, E I du Pont de Nemours & Co, Inc, Del, 71-72. *Mem:* Am Chem Soc; Am Inst Chem Eng; Tensor Soc; fel Am Inst Chem. *Res:* Fluid dynamics; heat transfer; phase transition kinetics; process simulation; solids flow systems; air pollution. *Mailing Add:* Sch of Eng Widener Col Chester PA 19013

MADOR, IRVING LESTER, b Chicago, Ill, July 4, 21; m 43; c 2. CATALYSIS. *Educ:* Univ Md, BS, 41, PhD(phys chem), 49; Univ Chicago, MS, 48. *Prof Exp:* Res chemist, Nat Bur Standards, 42-45; sr chemist, Applied Physics Lab, Johns Hopkins Univ, 49-54; chemist, Res Div, Nat Distillers & Chem Corp, 54-58, asst mgr, 58-61, mgr, Explor Res, 61-74; assoc dir corp res, 74-80, SR STAFF SCIENTIST, ALLIED CHEM CORP, 81- *Concurrent Pos:* Consult, Free Radicals, Nat Bur Standards, 55-57. *Mem:* Am Chem Soc; AAAS; Sigma Xi. *Res:* Free radicals; organometallics; transition metal complexes; catalysis. *Mailing Add:* Allied Chem Corp Res Ctr PO Box 1021-R Morristown NJ 07960

MADORE, BERNADETTE, b Barnston, Que, Jan 24, 18; US citizen. BOTANY, BACTERIOLOGY. *Educ:* Univ Montreal, AB, 42, BEd, 43; Catholic Univ, MS, 49, PhD(ecol, bot), 51. *Prof Exp:* Instr math, Marie Anne Col, Can, 43-44, dean, 52-75, vpres, 75-78, PROF BIOL, ANNA MARIA COL, 49-, PRES, 78- *Mem:* AAAS; Am Soc Microbiol; Nat Asn Biol Teachers. *Res:* Ecology. *Mailing Add:* Anna Maria Col Paxton MA 01612

MADOW, LEO, b Cleveland, Ohio, Oct 18, 15; m 42; c 2. PSYCHIATRY, NEUROLOGY. *Educ:* Western Reserve Univ, BA, 37, MD, 42; Ohio State Univ, MA, 38. *Prof Exp:* Prof neurol, 56-64, PROF PSYCHIAT & CHMN DEPT, MED COL PA, 64- *Concurrent Pos:* Training analyst, Philadelphia Psychoanal Inst. *Mem:* Am Psychoanal Asn; Am Neurol Asn; Am Col Physicians; Am Col Phychiatrists. *Mailing Add:* Med Col Pa Dept Psychiat 3300 Henry Ave Philadelphia PA 19129

MADOW, WILLIAM GREGORY, b New York, NY, Feb 22, 11; m 42. MATHEMATICAL STATISTICS. *Educ:* Columbia Univ, AB, 32, MA, 33, PhD(math), 38. *Prof Exp:* Asst math adv, Pop Div, US Bur Census, 40-41; actg chief, Statist Sect, Div Health & Disability Studies, Social Security Bd, 42; statist adv, Rationing Dept, Off Price Admin, 43-44; sampling specialist, US Bur Census, 44-46; vis prof statist, Univ Sao Paulo, 46-48; prof math statist, Univ NC, 48-49; prof, Univ Ill, 49-57; consult prof statist, Stanford Univ & staff scientist statist, Stanford Res Inst, 57-75. *Concurrent Pos:* Fel, Fund Advan Educ, Inst Advan Study, NJ, 53-54; assoc ed, Ann Math Statist, Inst Math Statist, 53-55; chmn, Comt Math Training Social Scientists, Soc Sci Res Coun, 53-61; assoc ed, J Am Statist Asn, 51-53 & 57-63; mem res adv comt, Calif Dept Ment Hyg, 61-66; mem census adv comt, Am Statist Asn, 73-75, chmn, 75; consult, Comt Nat Statist, Nat Res Coun, 76-; mem adv coun educ statist, HEW, 77-80. *Mem:* fel AAAS; fel Am Statist Asn; fel Inst Math Statist; Biomet Soc; Economet Soc. *Res:* Sample survey design and analysis; analysis of quasi-experiments; mathematical models in social science. *Mailing Add:* 700 New Hampshire Ave NW Washington DC 20037

MADRAZO, ALFONSO A, b Tabasco, Mex, Mar 6, 31; US citizen; m 60; c 2. PATHOLOGY. *Educ:* Nat Univ Mex, MD, 54; Am Bd Path, dipl, 65. *Prof Exp:* From instr to asst prof path, Col Med, Seton Hall Univ, 63-67; attend pathologist, St Vincents Hosp & Med Ctr, New York, 67-73; dir labs, Christ Hosp, Jersey City, NJ, 73-76; ASSOC DIR LABS, ST VINCENT'S HOSP & MED CTR, 76-; CHIEF ELECTRON-MICROS LAB, ST VINCENT'S HOSP, 76- *Concurrent Pos:* Res assoc path, Mt Sinai Sch Med, New York, 69-, assoc clin prof path, 77-; clin assoc prof path, NJ Col Med, 73-76; consult & attend pathologist, St Vincents Hosp & Med Ctr, 75- *Mem:* Fel Int Acad Path; fel NY Acad Med; fel Am Soc Cell Biol; fel Am Soc Clin Path; fel Col Am Pathologists. *Res:* Effects of radiation on human tissues, especially the kidney parenchyma and blood vessels. *Mailing Add:* St Vincent's Hosp 153 W 11th St New York NY 10011

MADSEN, DAVID CHRISTY, b Chelsea, Mass, May 3, 43; m 67; c 2. PHYSIOLOGY, BIOCHEMISTRY. *Educ:* Merrimack Col, BA, 64; Univ Mass, Amherst, MA, 67, PhD(zool), 72. *Prof Exp:* Fel microbiol, Univ Notre Dame, 72-73, asst fac fel, Lobund Lab, 73-79; SR TECH DEVELOP MGR, CLINICAL NUTRIT, TRAVENOL LABS, INC, DEERFIELD, IL, 79- *Mem:* AAAS; NY Acad Sci; Asn Gnotobiotics; Am Soc Pareneral & External Nutrit. *Res:* Bile acid and cholesterol metabolism; role of dietary factors and of microflora of the intestine. *Mailing Add:* Travenol Labs Inc Parenteral Prod LCII02 Deerfield IL 60015

MADSEN, DONALD H(OWARD), b Council Bluffs, Iowa, Oct 7, 22; m 49; c 2. MECHANICAL ENGINEERING. *Educ:* Iowa State Univ, BS, 44; Purdue Univ, MS, 48, PhD(mech eng), 53. *Prof Exp:* Asst engr, Eastman Kodak Co, 44-45; asst instr, Purdue Univ, 45-48; instr, Univ Kans, 49-51; res engr, Armour Res Found, Ill Inst Technol, 53; asst prof mech eng, SDak State Col, 53-54; from asst prof to prof, Univ Iowa, 54-74, assoc dean, Col Eng, 67-74; CONSULT ENGR, 74- *Honors & Awards:* Naval Ord Develop Award, 46. *Mem:* Am Soc Mech Engrs; Am Soc Eng Educ. *Res:* Heat transfer and thermodynamics. *Mailing Add:* 1315 Whiting Ave Court Iowa City IA 52240

MADSEN, FRED CHRISTIAN, b Rocksprings, Wyo, Dec 9, 45; m 73; c 1. ANIMAL NUTRITION. *Educ:* Austin Peay State Univ, BS, 68; Univ Tenn, Knoxville, MS, 72, PhD(animal nutrit), 74. *Prof Exp:* Res assoc nutrit & physiol, Comp Animal Res Lab, 74-76; tech serv coordr, Syntex Agribus, Inc, 76-78; ruminant nutritionist & consult, 78-81, DIR NUTRIT & RES, CONAGRA, INC, 81- *Mem:* Am Inst Nutrit; Am Soc Animal Sci. *Res:* Factors affecting insulin secretion and metabolism in the ruminant animal; energy supplementation and the relationship to mineral utilization and physical characteristics in the gastrointestinal tract. *Mailing Add:* Conagra Inc 938 Van St Knoxville TN 37901

MADSEN, HAROLD F, b San Jose, Calif, Mar 31, 21; m 45; c 3. ENTOMOLOGY. *Educ:* San Jose Col, AB, 43; Univ Calif, PhD, 49. *Prof Exp:* Exten entomologist, Univ Calif, 49-52, from asst entomologist to assoc entomologist, 52-64; RES SCIENTIST, AGR CAN, 64- *Mem:* AAAS; Entom Soc Am; Entom Soc Can. *Res:* Pest management of insect pests of deciduous fruits. *Mailing Add:* Res Sta Agr Can Summerland BC V0H 1Z0 Can

MADSEN, JAMES HENRY, JR, b Salt Lake City, Utah, July 28, 32; m 56; c 2. GEOLOGY, VERTEBRATE PALEONTOLOGY. *Educ:* Univ Utah, BS, 57, MS, 59. *Prof Exp:* cur dinosaur lab, 59-77, asst res prof geol & geophys sci, 69-77, MEM STAFF, UTAH MUS NAT HIST, UNIV UTAH, 71-, STATE PALEONTOLOGIST 77- *Mem:* Paleont Soc; Soc Vert Paleont. *Res:* Stratigraphic and field geology; vertebrate paleontology, especially Late Jurassic Carnosaurs. *Mailing Add:* Antiquities Sect 307 W Second S Salt Lake City UT 84101

MADSEN, KENNETH OLAF, b Lavoye, Wyo, May 30, 26; m 50; c 3. NUTRITIONAL BIOCHEMISTRY. *Educ:* Univ Wyo, BS, 50; Univ Wis, MS, 53, PhD(biochem), 58. *Prof Exp:* From instr to assoc prof, 58-70, PROF BIOCHEM, DENT BR, UNIV TEX, HOUSTON, 70- *Mem:* AAAS; Soc Exp Biol & Med; Int Asn Dent Res. *Res:* Bull semen metabolism; fluorine metabolism and toxicity; trace mineral nutrition; oral biology and dental research, especially dental caries in rats; redox substances in nutrition; biology of the cotton rat. *Mailing Add:* 4908 Florence Houston TX 77009

MADSEN, N(IELS), b Aarup, Denmark, June 8, 05; nat US; m 43. CHEMICAL ENGINEERING. *Educ:* Cooper Union, BChE, 44, Stevens Inst Technol, MS, 50; Columbia Univ, PhD, 60. *Prof Exp:* Res chem engr, Foster Wheeler Corp, 44-48; teacher high sch, NJ, 48-54; asst, Columbia Univ, 54-57; from assoc prof to prof chem eng, 57-77, EMER PROF CHEM ENG, UNIV RI, 77- *Concurrent Pos:* Vis prof, Eindhoven Technol Univ, 63-64 & 70-71. *Mem:* AAAS; Am Inst Chem Engrs. *Res:* Heat transfer to liquid metals and boiling liquids; heat and momentum transfer; two-phase flow. *Mailing Add:* Oxenbjergvej 20 Dk5700 Svendborg Denmark

MADSEN, NEIL BERNARD, b Grande Prairie, Alta, Feb 8, 28; m 52; c 2. BIOCHEMISTRY. *Educ:* Univ Alta, BSc, 50, MSc, 52; Wash Univ, PhD, 55. *Prof Exp:* Instr biol chem, Wash Univ, 55-56; fel biochem, Oxford Univ, 56-57; res off, Microbiol Res Inst, Can Dept Agr, 57-62; assoc prof, 62-69, PROF BIOCHEM, UNIV ALTA, 69- *Concurrent Pos:* Med Res Coun Can vis scientist, Oxford Univ, Eng, 72-73; chmn sci policy comt, 73-75, chmn bd, Can Fedn Biol Soc, 77-78. *Mem:* Am Soc Biol Chemists; Biophys Soc; Can Biochem Soc (past pres); fel Royal Soc Can. *Res:* Enzyme chemistry; structure-function relationships in glycogen phosphorylase as determined by protein chemistry, kinetics and x-ray crystallography; biological control of glycogen metabolism. *Mailing Add:* Dept of Biochem Univ of Alta Edmonton AB T6G 2H7 Can

MADSEN, OLE SECHER, b Aarhus, Denmark, Feb 24, 41; m 69; c 1. HYDRODYNAMICS, CIVIL ENGINEERING. *Educ:* Tech Univ Denmark, MSc, 64; Mass Inst Technol, ScD(hydrodynamics), 70. *Prof Exp:* Oceanogr, US Army Coastal Eng Res Ctr, Washington, DC, 69-72; ASSOC PROF CIVIL ENG, MASS INST TECHNOL, 72- *Res:* Transformation of water waves; the interaction between water waves and the coastal environment. *Mailing Add:* Ralph M Parsons Lab Mass Inst of Technol Cambridge MA 02139

MADSEN, PAUL O, b Denmark, July 25, 27; US citizen; m 55; c 3. UROLOGY. *Educ:* Copenhagen Univ, MD, 52, DrMed, 76; Univ Heidelberg, DrMed, 58. *Prof Exp:* Intern surg, Genesee Hosp, Rochester, NY, 53-54; resident surg & urol, Gen Hosp, Buffalo, 55-57; resident, Buffalo Gen Hosp & Roswell Park Mem Inst, 59-61; vis urologist, Univ Homburg, 61-62; assoc prof, 68-71, PROF UROL, UNIV WIS-MADISON, 71-; CHIEF UROL, VET ADMIN HOSP, 62- *Mem:* Int Soc Urol; Int Soc Surg; Am Urol Asn; Soc Univ Urologists. *Res:* Treatment of urinary tract infections; experimental pyelonephritis and hydronephrosis; prostatic tissue cultures; prostatilis. *Mailing Add:* Vet Admin Hosp Dept of Urol 2500 Overlook Terr Madison WI 53705

MADSEN, RICHARD ALFRED, b Sheffield, Ill, Feb 15, 33; m 57; c 4. MECHANICAL ENGINEERING, HEAT TRANSFER. *Educ:* Iowa State Univ, BS, 55; Purdue Univ, MS, 62, PhD(mech eng), 65. *Prof Exp:* Trainee, Caterpillar Tractor Co, 55-56, res design engr, 58-59; res asst, Jet Propulsion Ctr, Purdue Univ, 59-62, res asst, Heat Transfer Lab, 62-65; eng specialist, AiRes Mfg Co, Ariz, 65-66; sr eng scientist, McDonnell Douglas Corp, 66-78; ENG SPECIALIST, AIRES MFG CO, 78- *Mem:* Am Soc Mech Engrs. *Res:* Fluid mechanics; thermodynamics. *Mailing Add:* AiRes Mfg Co 2525 W 190th St Torrance CA 90509

MADSEN, VICTOR ARVIEL, b Idaho Falls, Idaho, Feb 14, 31; m 55; c 2. THEORETICAL NUCLEAR PHYSICS. *Educ:* Wash Univ, BS, 53, PhD(physics), 61. *Prof Exp:* Res assoc physics, Case Inst Technol, 61-63; asst prof, 63-66, assoc prof, 66-71, PROF PHYSICS, ORE STATE UNIV, 71- *Concurrent Pos:* Physicist, Niels Bohr Inst, Copenhagen & Atomic Energy Res Estab, Eng, 69-70; consult, Los Alamos Sci Lab, Group P9, 75-76, Lawrence Livermore Lab, 64-; guest scientist, KFA Julich, W Ger, 76-77. *Mem:* Am Phys Soc. *Res:* Theory of nuclear inelastic scattering; core-polarization effects; charge-exchange reactions, isospin effects; theory of imaginary optical potential and inelastic form factor. *Mailing Add:* Dept of Physics Ore State Univ Corvallis OR 97331

MAECK, JOHN VAN SICKLEN, b Shelburne, Vt, Mar 10, 14; m 39; c 2. OBSTETRICS & GYNECOLOGY. *Educ:* Univ Vt, BS, 36, MD, 39; Am Bd Obstet & Gynec, dipl, 49. *Prof Exp:* Asst clin instr path, Yale Univ, 39; intern, Lenox Hill Hosp, 40-41; resident obstet & gynec, Woman's Hosp, New York, 47-48; from instr to assoc prof, 48-56, chmn dept, 50-75, chief serv, med ctr hosp, 67-75, prof, 56-79, EMER PROF OBSTET & GYNEC, COL MED, UNIV VT, 79- *Concurrent Pos:* Chief serv, Mary Fletcher Hosp, 50-66 & DeGoesbriand Mem Hosp, 64-66; dir, examr & first vpres, Am Bd Obstet & Gynec, 69-76. *Mem:* Fel Am Col Surgeons; fel Am Col Obstet & Gynec; Am Fertil Soc; Am Gynec Soc (pres-elect, 81); Asn Profs Gynec & Obstet. *Res:* Carcinoma of the cervix and endometrium; toxemia of pregnancy; early detection of carcinoma; rubella and pregnancy; urinary bladder dynamics; computerized problem-oriented medical records. *Mailing Add:* Given Bldg Rm C-250 Univ of Vt Col of Med Burlington VT 05401

MAEDER, P(AUL) F(RITZ), b Basel, Switz, June 29, 23; nat US; m 46; c 2. ENGINEERING. *Educ:* Swiss Fed Inst Technol, Dipl Ing, 46; Brown Univ, PhD, 51. *Prof Exp:* Res assoc, Swiss Fed Inst Technol, 46-47; res assoc 47-51, assoc prof eng, 51-54, chmn exec comt div eng, 62-68, assoc provost, 68-77, vpres finance & opers, 72-77, PROF ENG, BROWN UNIV, 54- *Concurrent Pos:* Consult, Aro, Inc, Tenn, Res Dept, United Aircraft Corp, Conn, Indust Div, Speidel Corp, RI, 56-63 & Agard, France, 58; mem transonic subcomt, Arnold Eng Develop Ctr, Tenn, 52-55; vis prof, Swiss Fed Inst Technol, 58; vis prof, Stanford Univ, Calif, 78-79; mem energy comt, Brown Univ, 79-; mem Gov Task Force Energy, 81-; consult, Elmwood Sensors, Inc, Fed Prod Corp, State Univ NY, Binghampton, RI Sch Design. *Mem:* Am Soc Mech Engrs; Am Inst Aeronaut & Astronaut; Am Soc Eng Educ; Nat Soc Prof Engrs; AAAS. *Res:* Engineering sciences, especially fluid mechanics, aerodynamics, magnetohydrodynamics and instrumentation. *Mailing Add:* University Hall Brown Univ Box 1940 Providence RI 02912

MAEHL, RONALD CHARLES, space physics, see previous edition

MAEHR, HUBERT, b Schlins, Austria, Feb 25, 35. NATURAL PRODUCTS CHEMISTRY. *Educ:* State Univ Agr & Forestry, Austria, Dipl Ing, 60; Rutgers Univ, PhD(chem microbial prod), 64; Vienna, Techn Dr, 77. *Prof Exp:* Res assoc chem antibiotics, Inst Microbiol, Rutgers Univ, 64-65; RES CHEMIST DIV CHEM RES, HOFFMANN-LA ROCHE INC, 66- *Concurrent Pos:* Univ lectr, Dept Org & Phamaceut Chem, Univ Innsbruck, 79- *Mem:* Am Chem Soc. *Res:* Separations, structure structure, elucidations and syntheses of natural products. *Mailing Add:* Chem Res Div Hoffmann-La Roche Inc Nutley NJ 07110

MAEKS, JOEL, b Jamaica, NY, Apr 27, 34; m 71. COMMUNICATIONS, COMPUTER SCIENCE. *Educ:* Cornell Univ, BEP, 57; Mass Inst Technol, SM, 59, PhD(commun), 67; Imp Col, Univ London, dipl, 60. *Prof Exp:* Staff assoc, Lincoln Lab, Mass Inst Technol, 57-58, staff mem, 58-64, staff assoc, 64-67, staff mem, 67-69; mem tech staff, GTE Labs, Waltham, 69-73; MEM TECH STAFF, MITRE CORP, BEDFORD, 73- *Mem:* Inst Elec & Electronics Engrs. *Res:* Information theory; communication theory and systems; switching system control. *Mailing Add:* 9 Tyler Rd Lexington MA 02173

MAENCHEN, GEORGE, b Moscow, Russia, Apr 27, 28; nat US; m 47; c 3. PHYSICS. *Educ:* Univ Calif, AB, 50, PhD(physics), 57. *Prof Exp:* PHYSICIST, LAWRENCE LIVERMORE LAB, 57- *Mem:* Am Phys Soc. *Res:* Nuclear and general physics. *Mailing Add:* Lawrence Livermore Lab Univ of Calif PO Box 808 Livermore CA 94550

MAENDER, OTTO WILLIAM, b Brooklyn, NY, Jan 18, 40; m 63; c 2. ORGANIC CHEMISTRY. *Educ:* Rochester Inst Technol, BS, 63; Iowa State Univ, MS, 65; Univ Ga, PhD(org chem), 69. *Prof Exp:* Sr res chemist, 69-79, RES SPECIALIST, MONSANTO CO, 79- *Mem:* Am Chem Soc. *Res:* Electron spin resonance study of oxidative processes; antidegradants; vulcanization. *Mailing Add:* Monsanto Co 260 Springside Dr Akron OH 44313

MAENGWYN-DAVIES, GERTRUDE DIANE, b Paris, France, Dec 28, 10; nat US; m 46. PHARMACOLOGY. *Educ:* Univ Vienna, MPharm, 37; Johns Hopkins Univ, PhD(biochem), 52. *Prof Exp:* Asst pharmacog, Univ Vienna, 37-38; res chemist, Warwick Chem Co, 42-43; head analyst fermentation, Overly Biochem Res Found, 43-44; asst, NY Univ, 44-45; res chemist, Quaker Oats Co, 46; from instr to asst prof ophthal, Med Sch, Johns Hopkins Univ, 52-55; assoc res prof pharmacol, Sch Med, George Washington Univ, 55-56; assoc prof, 56-63, prof pharmacol, 63-76, prof physiol & biophys, 75-76, EMER PROF PHARMACOL, PHYSIOL & BIOPHYS, SCHS MED & DENT, GEORGETOWN UNIV, 76-; CONSULT, 76- *Concurrent Pos:* Guest worker, Lab Clin Sci, NIMH, 70- *Mem:* Fel AAAS; Am Soc Biol Chemists; Am Soc Pharmacol & Exp Therapeut; Soc Exp Biol & Med; Brit Pharmacol Soc. *Res:* Enzyme and pharmacological kinetics; biochemistry; autonomics; catecholamines biosynthesis and release; stress. *Mailing Add:* 15205 Tottenham Terr Silver Spring MD 20906

MAENZA, RONALD MORTON, b New York, NY, May 8, 36; m 60; c 3. PATHOLOGY. *Educ:* Columbia Univ, BA, 57, MD, 61; Am Bd Path, dipl, 66. *Prof Exp:* Intern med, Bronx Munic Hosp, 61-62; resident path, Columbia Presby Hosp, NY, 62-65; resident, Englewood Hosp, NJ, 65-66; asst prof, 68-73, ASSOC PROF PATH, SCHS MED & DENT MED, UNIV CONN, 73- *Concurrent Pos:* Consult, Vet Admin Hosp, Newington, Conn, 68-; teaching affil, Hartford Hosp, 68-; pathologist, New Britain Gen Hosp, 78- *Mem:* Int Acad Path; Am Asn Path & Bact. *Res:* Chemical carcinogenesis. *Mailing Add:* Dept of Path New Britain Gen Hosp New Britain CT 06050

MAERKER, GERHARD, b Bernburg, Ger, Nov, 4, 23; nat US; m 51; c 2. ORGANIC CHEMISTRY, LIPID CHEMISTRY. *Educ:* Philadelphia Col Pharm, BS, 51; Temple Univ, MA, 52, PhD(chem), 57. *Prof Exp:* Res chemist, Allied Chem Corp, 52-58; res chemist, 58-71, chief animal fat lab, 71-80, RES LEADER FOOD ADDITIVES, EASTERN REGIONAL RES CTR, USDA, 80- *Mem:* AAAS; Am Chem Soc; Am Oil Chem Soc; Inst Food Technologists; Sigma Xi. *Res:* Synthesis, properties and reactions of chemical derivatives of fats and fatty acids, particularly small ring heterocyclic derivatives such as epoxides and aziridines. *Mailing Add:* Eastern Regional Res Ctr USDA Philadelphia PA 19118

MAERKER, JOHN B(ELMONT), b Jackson, Mich, Nov 11, 20; m 42; c 3. CHEMICAL ENGINEERING. *Educ:* Univ Tenn, BS, 43. *Prof Exp:* Engr & dir develop, Houdry Process & Chem Co, 43-69, dir res admin, Houdry Labs of Air Prod & Chem, Inc, 69-78; RETIRED. *Res:* Research administration. *Mailing Add:* Denise Dr RD 5 West Chester PA 19380

MAERKER, JOHN MALCOLM, b Philadelphia, Pa, July 20, 45; div; c 1. ENHANCED OIL RECOVERY, RHEOLOGY. *Educ:* Univ Del, BChE, 67; Princeton Univ, MA, 69, PhD(chem eng), 71. *Prof Exp:* Sr res engr, chem oil recovery, 71-76, res specialist, 76-78, sr res specialist, 78-81, RES ASSOC, COMPLEX FLUIDS, LONG RANGE RES, EXXON PROD RES CO, 81- *Mem:* Soc Rheology; Soc Petrol Engrs. *Res:* Flow of polymer solutions and microemulsions through porous media; mechanics of oil displacement and recovery from porous media through interfacial tension reduction. *Mailing Add:* Exxon Prod Res Co Box 2189 Houston TX 77001

MAERKER, RICHARD ERWIN, b Jackson, Mich, July 9, 28; m 59; c 1. PHYSICS. *Educ:* Univ Tenn, BS, 49, MS, 51, PhD(physics), 53. *Prof Exp:* Res physicist solid state, Kodak, Rochester, NY, 53-54; res assoc rocketry, Univ Tenn, 54-55; res assoc, Tulane Univ, 55-59; PHYSICIST REACTOR SHIELDING, UNION CARBIDE CORP, 59- *Concurrent Pos:* Mem, Cross Sect Eval Working Group, 69- *Mem:* Am Nuclear Soc; NY Acad Sci; Sigma Xi; Am Soc Testing & Mat. *Res:* Shielding of neutrons and photons from reactors; analysis of integral experiments on shielding; reactor dosimetry. *Mailing Add:* Oak Ridge Nat Lab PO Box X Oak Ridge TN 37830

MAEROV, SIDNEY BENJAMIN, b Calgary, Alta, Feb 25, 27; US citizen; m 53; c 3. ORGANIC CHEMISTRY. *Educ:* Univ Alta, BSc, 49; Univ Wash, PhD(org chem), 54. *Prof Exp:* From res chemist to sr res chemist, 54-59, res assoc dacron res lab, 62-77, RES ASSOC CENT RES & DEVELOP DEPT, E I DU PONT DE NEMOURS & CO, INC, 77- *Mem:* Am Chem Soc. *Res:* Polymer morphology especially polyesters; photochemistry of dyes and polymers; basic fiber studies; organic coatings and photopolymers. *Mailing Add:* Du Pont Exp Sta E I Du Pont de Nemours Wilmington DE 19898

MAESTRE, MARCOS FRANCISCO, b San Juan, PR, June 20, 32; US citizen; m 58; c 2. BIOPHYSICS. *Educ:* Univ Mich, BS, 54; Wayne State Univ, MS, 58; Yale Univ, PhD(biophysics), 63. *Prof Exp:* Res assoc, 63-65, ASSOC RES CHEMIST, SPACE SCI LABS, UNIV CALIF, BERKELEY, 65-, LECTR MED PHYSICS, 73- *Concurrent Pos:* USPHS fel, 63-65. *Mem:* Biophys Soc. *Res:* X-ray studies on virus structure; theory of the birefringence of nucleic adids; electric birefringence of bacteriophage; optical rotatory dispersion of viruses; viral nucleic acids and protein components. *Mailing Add:* 1222 Josephine Berkeley CA 94703

MAESTRELLO, LUCIO, b Legnago, Italy, Mar 4, 28; US citizen; m 58; c 4. ACOUSTICS. *Educ:* Galileo-Ferraris Inst, Dipl eng, 50; Univ Southampton, DPhil(acoustics), 76. *Prof Exp:* Res asst aerodynamics, Imp Col, Univ London, 53-54; res assoc acoustics, Inst Aerophys, Univ Toronto, 56-57; res engr, Boeing Co, 58-70; HEAD AEROACOUSTICS SECT, NASA-LANGLEY RES CTR, 70- *Res:* Jet and boundary layer noise. *Mailing Add:* Aeroacoustics Sect NASA-Langley Res Ctr Hampton VA 23665

MAESTRONE, GIANPAOLO, b Urgnano, Italy, Jan 31, 30; US citizen; m 56; c 3. VETERINARY MEDICINE, MICROBIOLOGY. *Educ:* Univ Milan, DVM, 51; Am Col Vet Microbiol, dipl, 67. *Prof Exp:* Asst prof infectious dis, Vet Sch, Univ Milan, 51-56; res assoc microbiol, Animal Med Ctr, NY, 57-61; sr res microbiologist, Squibb Inst Med Res, NJ, 61-66; sr res microbiologist, 66-75, asst group chief res, 76-78, CLIN VET, HOFFMANN-LA ROCHE, INC, 79- *Mem:* AAAS; Am Col Lab Animal Med; Am Vet Med Asn; Am Asn Indust Vets; assoc felNY Acad Med. *Res:* Diagnosis of infectious diseases; chemotherapy of infectious diseases and parasites; immunofluorescence applied to diagnosis of leptospiral and viral diseases; antibiotic sensitivity of clinical isolates; epidemiology of leptospirosis; experimental infections; fish and wildlife sciences. *Mailing Add:* Hoffmann-La Roche Inc Nutley NJ 07100

MAEWAL, AKHILESH, b July 1, 49; Indian citizen. ENGINEERING MECHANICS, STRUCTURAL DYNAMICS. *Educ:* Indian Inst Technol, BS, 70; Univ Calif, San Diego, PhD(eng sci), 76. *Prof Exp:* Res engr, Univ Calif, San Diego, 76-77; staff scientist, Systs, Sci & Software, La Jolla, Calif, 77-79; ASST PROF APPL MECH, YALE UNIV, 79- *Mem:* Am Soc Mech Engrs. *Res:* Mechanical behavior of composite materials; nonlinear structural mechanics; computational mechanics. *Mailing Add:* Becton Ctr Yale Univ Box 2157 Yale Sta New Haven CT 06520

MAFFETT, ANDREW L, b Port Royal, Pa, Oct 23, 21; m 43. MATHEMATICS. *Educ:* Gettysburg Col, AB, 43; Univ Mich, MA, 48. *Prof Exp:* From instr to asst prof math, Gettysburg Col, 47-54; res assoc, Univ Mich, 51-52, res engr, Radiation Lab, 54-56, asst head lab, 56-57; sr mathematician, Bendix Aviation Corp, 58-59; res mathematician, Inst Sci & Technol, Univ Mich, 60-61; assoc head sr anal staff, Conductron Corp, 61-67; sr scientist, KMS Indust, Inc, 67-69; INDEPENDENT CONSULT, 69-; ADJ PROF MATH, UNIV MICH-DEARBORN, 70- *Concurrent Pos:* US mem comn VI, Int Sci Radio Union. *Res:* Electromagnetic boundary value problems arising from both the radiation and scattering of enrgy from various geometric shapes and configurations. *Mailing Add:* 2250 N Zeeb Rd R D 1 Dexter MI 48130

MAFFLY, LEROY HERRICK, b Berkeley, Calif, Nov 26, 27; m 52; c 3. INTERNAL MEDICINE, NEPHROLOGY. *Educ:* Univ Calif, AB, 49, MD, 52. *Prof Exp:* Intern med, Univ Calif Hosp, 52-53, asst resident, 53-54; resident, Herrick Mem Hosp, 54-55; res fel, Harvard Med Sch & Mass Gen Hosp, 57-59; res fel, Sch Med, Univ Calif, San Francisco, 59-61; from asst prof to assoc prof, 61-70, PROF MED, SCH MED, STANFORD UNIV, 70-, CHIEF RENAL SERV, VET ADMIN HOSP, PALO ALTO, CALIF, 68- *Concurrent Pos:* NSF fel, 57-58; USPHS fel, 58-60; Am Heart Asn fel, 60-61; estab investr, Am Heart Asn, 61-66, mem exec comt, Coun Kidney in Cardiovasc Dis, 68-, chmn comt, 71-73, mem cardiovasc A res study comt, res study comt, 76-, mem comt teaching scholars, 76-; mem adv comt renal dialysis ctrs, State of Calif, 66-70; mem gen med B study sect, NIH, 67-71; mem sci adv bd, Nat Kidney Found, 70-77. *Mem:* Am Soc Nephrology; Asn Develop Comput-based Instructional Systs; Am Physiol Soc; Am Soc Clin Invest. *Res:* Transport processes and permeability of biological membranes; nephrology; computer-assisted education. *Mailing Add:* Dept Med Stanford Univ Sch Med Stanford CA 94305

MAGA, JOSEPH ANDREW, b New Kensington, Pa, Dec 25, 40; m 64; c 2. FOOD SCIENCE, BIOCHEMISTRY. *Educ:* Pa State Univ, BS, 62, MS, 64; Kans State Univ, PhD(food sci), 70. *Prof Exp:* Proj leader dairy prod, Borden Foods Co, 64-66; group leader simulated dairy prod, Cent Soya Co, 66-68; from asst prof to assoc prof, 70-74, PROF FOOD SCI, COLO STATE UNIV, 78- *Mem:* Am Dairy Sci Asn; Am Asn Cereal Chemists; Am Chem Soc. *Res:* Flavor aspects of foods, especially high protein foods, including composition, chemistry and preferences. *Mailing Add:* Dept of Food Sci & Nutrit Colo State Univ Ft Collins CO 80523

MAGAARD, LORENZ CARL, b Wallsbuell, Ger, May 21, 34; m 61; c 1. PHYSICAL OCEANOGRAPHY. *Educ:* Univ Kiel, Ger, BS, 58, MS, 61, PhD(math & phys oceanog), 63. *Prof Exp:* Asst scientist, Univ Kiel, Ger, 61-64, asst prof, 64-68, assoc prof, 69-75; PROF OCEANOG, UNIV HAWAII, HONOLULU, 75- *Concurrent Pos:* Vis investr, Woods Hole Oceanog Inst, Mass, 71; vis assoc prof, Univ Hawaii, Honolulu, 74-75. *Mem:* Am Geophys Union; Am Meteorol Soc. *Res:* Physical oceanography, especially internal waves and oceanic turbulence. *Mailing Add:* Dept of Oceanog 2525 Correa Rd Honolulu HI 96822

MAGARIAN, CHARLES ARAM, b Boston, Mass, Dec 18, 27; m 51; c 3. CHEMICAL ENGINEERING. *Educ:* Mass Inst Technol, BS, 50. *Prof Exp:* Sect leader, Prod Control Lab, Monsanto Co, 50-52, prod supvr, 52-53, res engr, Plastics Res & Develop Div, 53-57, res group leader, 57-62, res mgr, 62-65, mgr res, 65-76, MGR COM DEVELOP, RESIN PROD DIV, MONSANTO CO, 76- *Mem:* Am Inst Chem Engrs; Forest Prod Res Soc. *Res:* Organic and polymer chemistry; polymer synthesis and process development; thermosetting polymers; coating technology; wood products; synthetic adhesives; industrial polymer applications; research and development management. *Mailing Add:* Monsanto Co 190 Grochmal Ave Indian Orchard MA 01151

MAGARIAN, EDWARD O, b East St Louis, Ill, Oct 3, 35; m 59; c 2. PHARMACEUTICAL CHEMISTRY. *Educ:* Univ Miss, BA, 58, PhD(pharmaceut chem), 64. *Prof Exp:* Asst prof, Univ RI, 64-67; assoc prof, Col Pharm, Univ Ky, 67-73; ASSOC PROF PHARMACEUT SCI & CHMN DEPT, COL PHARM, NDAK STATE UNIV, 73- *Mem:* Am Chem Soc; Am Pharmaceut Asn; NY Acad Sci. *Res:* Anticonvulsants; enzyme inhibitors. *Mailing Add:* Dept Pharmaceut Sci NDak State Univ Fargo ND 58105

MAGARIAN, ELIZABETH ANN, b Orlando, Fla, July 13, 40. ALGEBRA. *Educ:* Asbury Col, AB, 60; Fla State Univ, MS, 61, PhD(math), 68. *Prof Exp:* Instr math, La State Univ, New Orleans, 61-64; asst prof, 68-73, ASSOC PROF MATH, STETSON UNIV, 73- *Mem:* Am Math Soc; Asn Women in Math; Math Asn Am. *Res:* Commutative ring theory. *Mailing Add:* Dept of Math Stetson Univ De Land FL 32720

MAGARIAN, ROBERT ARMEN, b East St Louis, Ill, July 27, 30; m 50; c 4. MEDICINAL CHEMISTRY, ORGANIC CHEMISTRY. *Educ:* Univ Miss, BS, 56, BSPh, 60, PhD, 66. *Prof Exp:* NIH fel, Col Pharm, Univ Kans, 66-67; asst prof med chem, St Louis Col Pharm, 67-70; assoc prof, 70-78, PROF MED CHEM, COL PHARM, UNIV OKLA, 78- *Concurrent Pos:* NSF grant, St Louis Col Pharm, 69-70. *Honors & Awards:* Baldwin award, 78. *Mem:* Sigma Xi; Am Chem Soc; The Chem Soc; Am Pharmaceut Asn; Acad Pharmaceut Sci. *Res:* Synthetic medicinal chemistry; relation of molecular structure to biological activity; synthetic anti-estrogens in breast cancer and radiopharmaceuticals. *Mailing Add:* Col of Pharm Univ of Okla Oklahoma City OK 73190

MAGASANIK, BORIS, b Kharkoff, Russia, Dec 19, 19; nat US; m 49. MICROBIOLOGY. *Educ:* City Col NY, BS, 41; Columbia Univ, PhD(biochem), 48. *Hon Degrees:* MA, Harvard Univ, 58. *Prof Exp:* Res asst biochem, Columbia Univ, 48-49; Ernst fel bact & immunol, Harvard Univ, 49-51, assoc, 51-53, from asst prof to assoc prof, 53-60; prof microbiol, 60-77, head dept biol, 67-77, JACQUES MONOD PROF MICROBIOL, MASS INST TECHNOL, 77- *Concurrent Pos:* Markle scholar, Harvard Univ, 51-56; Guggenheim fel, Pasteur Inst, Paris, 59; ed, Biochem & Biophys Res Commun, 64-, bd tutors, biochem sci, 51- *Mem:* Am Chem Soc; Am Soc Biol Chem; Am Soc Microbiol; Am Acad Arts & Sci. *Res:* Microbial physiology and biochemistry. *Mailing Add:* Dept of Biol Mass Inst of Technol Cambridge MA 02139

MAGASI, LASZLO P, b Szekesfehervar, Hungary, June 30, 35; Can citizen; m 62; c 2. MYCOLOGY, FORESTRY. *Educ:* Univ BC, BScF, 59, MSc, 63; State Univ NY Col Environ Sci & Forestry, PhD(mycol), 72. *Prof Exp:* Res officer mycol, 63-73, identification officer, 73-75, SURV HEAD INSECTS & DIS, CAN FORESTRY SERV, 75- *Concurrent Pos:* Lectr, Univ NB, Fredericton, 78. *Mem:* Mycol Soc Am; Can Bot Asn; Can Inst Forestry. *Res:* Forest insect and disease surveys; scleroderris canker. *Mailing Add:* Maritimes Forest Res Ctr PO Box 4000 Frederiction NB E3P 5P7 Can

MAGAT, EUGENE EDWARD, b Kharkov, Russia, July 8, 19; nat US; m 45; c 3. CHEMISTRY. *Educ:* Mass Inst Technol, BS, 43, PhD(org chem), 45. *Prof Exp:* Res chemist, Carothers Res Lab, Exp Sta, E I Du Pont de Nemours & Co, Inc, 45-50, res assoc, 50-52, res supvr, 52-62, res fel, 62-64, res mgr, Textile Fibers Dept, 64-79; VIS PROF & PROG DIR, CTR INDUST RES POLYMERS, UNIV MASS, 79- *Mem:* Am Chem Soc. *Res:* Condensation polymers; textile chemistry; radiation chemistry; fiber technology; university-industry interaction. *Mailing Add:* Polymer Sci & Eng Dept Univ Mass Amherst MA 01003

MAGAZINE, MICHAEL JAY, b New York, NY, Apr 29, 43; m 65; c 2. OPERATIONS RESEARCH, MANAGEMENT SCIENCE. *Educ:* City Col New York, BS, 64; NY Univ, MS, 66; Univ Fla, MEng & PhD(opers res), 69. *Prof Exp:* Res assoc opers res, Univ Fla, 67-69; asst prof indust eng, NC State Univ, 69-75; ASSOC PROF MGT SCI, UNIV WATERLOO, 75- *Concurrent Pos:* NSF res grant, 70-71; vis Orgn Am State Prof opers res, Cath Univ Rio de Janeiro, 72; grant, Nat Res Coun, Can, 76-; consult; assoc ed three journals; vis scientist, Inst Nat Rech Info & Automatique, 82. *Mem:* Opers Res Soc Am; Sigma Xi; Can Oper Res Soc; Inst Mgt Sci; Math Prog Soc. *Res:* Development of efficient approximation algorithms for production, scheduling, routing and other combinatorial problems; development of problem solving studio, an innovative teaching workshop for technical students. *Mailing Add:* Dept Mgt Sci Univ Waterloo Waterloo ON W2L 3G1 Can

MAGDE, DOUGLAS, b Rochester, NY, Feb 12, 42. CHEMICAL PHYSICS, LASER TECHNOLOGY. *Educ:* Boston Col, BS, 63; Cornell Univ, MS, 68, PhD(physics), 70. *Prof Exp:* Res assoc biophys, Cornell Univ, 70-72; res assoc chem physics, Wash State Univ, 72-74; asst prof, 74-80, ASSOC PROF CHEM, UNIV CALIF, SAN DIEGO, 80- *Mem:* Am Asn Physics Teachers. *Res:* Concentration correlation analysis, a new kinetic probe of biophysical processes; picosecond flash photolysis and spectroscopy in the study of fast molecular dynamics; photosynthesis. *Mailing Add:* Dept of Chem B-014 Univ of Calif at San Diego La Jolla CA 92093

MAGDER, JULES, b Toronto, July 17, 34; m 63; c 2. PHYSICAL CHEMISTRY, INORGANIC CHEMISTRY. *Educ:* Univ Toronto, BA, 58, PhD(inorg chem), 61. *Prof Exp:* Proj supvr, Horizons, Inc, 61-64; proj mgr pigments & chem div, Glidden Co, 64-65; dir res, Princeton Chem Res, Inc, 65-71; vpres, 72-73, PRES, PRINCETON ORGANICS, INC, 73- *Mem:* Am Chem Soc; Am Ceramic Soc. *Res:* Heterogeneous catalysis; inorganic polymers; polymer technology; composites; inorganic foams; refractory and structural clay materials; cement and concrete materials. *Mailing Add:* Princeton Organics Inc PO Box 420 Princeton NJ 08540

MAGDOFF, FREDERICK ROBIN, b Washington, DC, Apr 5, 42; c 1. SOIL CHEMISTRY, ENVIRONMENTAL SCIENCE. *Educ:* Oberlin Col, BA, 63; Cornell Univ, MS, 65, PhD(soil sci), 69. *Prof Exp:* Res scientist soils, Soil Conserv Div, Israeli Ministry Agr, 69-71; fel, Univ Wis, 72-73; asst prof, 73-79, PROF SOILS, UNIV VT, 79- *Mem:* Am Soc Agron; Soil Sci Soc Am. *Res:* Land disposal of human and agricultural wastes; soil fertility. *Mailing Add:* Dept of Plant & Soil Sci Univ of Vt Burlington VT 05401

MAGE, MICHAEL GORDON, b New York, Aug 17, 34; m 55; c 3. IMMUNOLOGY. *Educ:* Cornell Univ, AB, 55; Columbia Univ, DDS, 60. *Prof Exp:* USPHS fel microbiol, Columbia Univ, 60-62; res immunochemist, Nat Inst Dent Res, 62-66, RES IMMUNOCHEMIST, NAT CANCER INST, 66- *Mem:* AAAS; Am Chem Soc; Am Asn Immunologists; Am Pub Health Asn. *Res:* Protein chemistry; antibody structure and specificity; immunoglobulin structure; mammalian cell separation; lymphocyte differentiation. *Mailing Add:* 7008 Wilson Lane Bethesda MD 20034

MAGEAU, RICHARD PAUL, b Flushing, NY, Oct 24, 41; m 64; c 3. MICROBIOLOGY, IMMUNOLOGY. *Educ:* Univ Conn, BA, 63; Univ Md, MS, 66, PhD(microbiol), 68. *Prof Exp:* Res fel & asst microbiol, Univ Md, 63-68; from asst prof to assoc prof, Kans State Col Pittsburgh, 68-74; res microbiologist, Sci Microbiol Div, Med Microbiol Group, Animal, Plant & Health Inspection Serv, 74-77, MICROBIOLOGIST-IN-CHG, IMMUNOL LAB, SCI MICROBIOL DIV, FOOD, SAFETY & QUALITY SERV, USDA, 77- *Mem:* Am Soc Microbiol; NY Acad Sci; AAAS. *Res:* Radioimmunoassay and other immunological methods of staphylococcal enterotoxin quantitation and detection; laboratory methods development. *Mailing Add:* 4500 Oaklyn Lane Bowie MD 20715

MAGEE, ADEN COMBS, III, b Dimmitt, Tex, Dec 8, 30; m 56; c 2. NUTRITION. *Educ:* Tex A&M Univ, BS, 53; NC State Univ, MS, 57, PhD(animal nutrit), 60. *Prof Exp:* Asst animal nutrit, NC State Univ, 55-60; from asst prof to assoc prof, 60-68, PROF NUTRIT, UNIV N C, GREENSBORO, 68- *Mem:* AAAS; Am Chem Soc; Biomet Soc; Am Inst Nutrit; Am Dietetic Asn. *Res:* Mineral metabolism and toxicities; mineral interrelationships. *Mailing Add:* Sch of Home Econ Univ of N C Greensboro NC 27412

MAGEE, CHARLES BRIAN, b Detroit, Mich, Sept 26, 26; m 55; c 7. PHYSICAL CHEMISTRY, INORGANIC CHEMISTRY. *Educ:* Univ Detroit, BS, 50; Purdue Univ, PhD(phys chem), 54. *Prof Exp:* Sr engr, Aircraft Nuclear Propulsion Dept, Gen Elec Co, Ohio, 55-59; proj scientist, Booz Allen Appl Res, Inc, Ill, 59-61; from asst prof to prof metall, Univ Denver, 61-75, actg chmn dept, 65-66, RES METALLURGIST, DENVER RES INST, UNIV DENVER, 61- *Mem:* Am Chem Soc; Am Nuclear Soc. *Res:* Molecular structure; compounds of saline hydrides and transition-metals; thermodynamic properties of metal hydrides; structure-stability relationships in intermetallic compound hydrides; thermionic and photoelectric emission of metals and inorganic compounds; nuclear reactor materials. *Mailing Add:* Div Metall & Mat Sci Denver Res Inst Univ Denver Denver CO 80208

MAGEE, CHRISTOPHER LYMAN, materials science, metallurgy, see previous edition

MAGEE, DONAL FRANCIS, b Aberdeen, Scotland, June 4, 24; nat US; m 50; c 5. PHYSIOLOGY, PHARMACOLOGY. *Educ:* Oxford Univ, BA, 44, MA, BM & BCh, 48, DM, 72; Univ Ill, PhD(physiol), 52. *Prof Exp:* Instr & res assoc clin sci, Univ Ill, 48-51; from asst prof to prof pharmacol, Sch Med, Univ Wash, 51-65; prof physiol & chmn dept physiol & pharmacol, 65-76, PROF & CHMN DEPT PHYSIOL, CREIGHTON UNIV, 76- *Concurrent Pos:* Guggenheim Mem Found fel, Rowett Inst, Scotland, 59-60; Fogarty Inst fel, Inst Nat Sante Rech Medicale, Marseille, France, 78-79. *Mem:* Soc Exp Biol & Med; Am Physiol Soc; Am Soc Pharmacol & Exp Therapeut; Am Gastroenterol Asn; Brit Med Asn. *Res:* Gastrointestinal tract, especially physiology and pharmacology of pancreas and biliary canal and stomach. *Mailing Add:* Dept of Physiol Creighton Univ Omaha NE 68178

MAGEE, ELLINGTON MCFALL, physical chemistry, see previous edition

MAGEE, JOHN FRANCIS, b Bangor, Maine, Dec 3, 26; m 49; c 3. MATHEMATICS. *Educ:* Bowdoin Col, AB, 46; Harvard Univ, MBA, 48; Univ Maine, AM, 53. *Prof Exp:* Mem staff financial anal, Johns-Manville Co, 49-50; dir res, Opers Res Group, 50-59, head, 59-62, vpres mgt serv div, 63-68, mem corp tech staff, 68-69, exec vpres & dir, 69, chief operating officer, 71, CHIEF EXEC OFFICER, ARTHUR D LITTLE INC, 74-, PRES, 72- *Concurrent Pos:* Pres, Inst Mgt Sci, 71-72. *Honors & Awards:* Kimball Medal, Opers Res Soc Am. *Mem:* Opers Res Soc Am (pres, 66-67); distinguished life mem Am Soc Math. *Res:* Operations research; marketing; financial planning and policy; managerial controls. *Mailing Add:* Arthur D Little Inc 25 Acorn Park Cambridge MA 02140

MAGEE, JOHN LAFAYETTE, b Franklinton, La, Oct 28, 14; m 48; c 3. PHYSICAL CHEMISTRY. *Educ:* Miss Col, AB, 35; Vanderbilt Univ, MS, 36; Univ Wis, PhD(chem), 39. *Prof Exp:* Nat Res Coun fel, Princeton Univ, 39-40, res assoc, 40-41; res physicist, B F Goodrich Co, 41-43; group leader, Los Alamos Sci Lab, 43-45 & Naval Ord Testing Sta, Calif, 45-46; sr scientist, Argonne Nat Lab, 46-48; from asst prof to assoc prof chem, Univ Notre Dame, 48-53, prof, 53-77, head, Dept Chem, 67-71, assoc dir, Radiation Lab, 54-71, dir, 71-75; vis sr staff mem, 76-77, STAFF SR SCIENTIST, BIOL & MED DIV, LAWRENCE BERKELEY LAB, 77- *Concurrent Pos:* Observer, Proj Bikini, 46; mem weapons systs eval group, US Dept Defense, 55-57. *Mem:* AAAS; Am Chem Soc; Am Phys Soc; Radiation Res Soc; The Chem Soc. *Res:* Photochemistry; chemical reaction rate theory; radiation chemistry; application of statistical mechanics and quantum mechanics to chemistry. *Mailing Add:* Biol & Med Div Lawrence Berkeley Lab Berkeley CA 94720

MAGEE, JOHN ROBERT, b Bristol, RI, Aug 27, 16; m 49; c 5. TEXTILE CHEMISTRY. *Educ:* Brown Univ, AB, 39. *Prof Exp:* Chem supt, Nat Dairy Prod Corp, 39-48; gen supt, Va-Carolina Chem Corp, 48-58; asst mgr spec prod, Charles Pfizer & Co, Inc, 58; staff assoc res & develop, 58-60, sect head nylon develop, 60-61, MGR DEVELOP OPERS & TECH SERV, MONSANTO TEXTILES CO, 62- *Concurrent Pos:* Consult, Charles Pfizer & Co, Inc & Textile Res Inst, NJ, 58. *Mem:* Am Chem Soc; Am Asn Textile Technol. *Res:* Melt and wet spun man-made fibers, especially nylon, polyester, acrylics, protein and copolymer blends. *Mailing Add:* 3844 Dunwoody Dr Pensacola FL 32503

MAGEE, JOHN STOREY, JR, b Baltimore, Md, Mar 23, 31; m 53; c 3. INORGANIC CHEMISTRY, PHYSICAL CHEMISTRY. *Educ:* Loyola Col, Md, BS, 53; Univ Del, PhD(inorg chem), 61. *Prof Exp:* Chemist, Davison Chem Corp Div, W R Grace & Co, 53-55, res chemist, Res Div, 61-63, res chemist, Davison Chem Corp Div, 63-71, res dir, 71-78, tech adminr, Petrol Catalyst Dept, 79-81; DIR RES & DEVELOP, KATALISTIKS, INC, 82- *Mem:* Am Chem Soc. *Res:* Preparation of catalysts for heterogeneous reactions; study of compounds containing metals in unusual oxidation states; preparation and evaluation of petroleum catalysts. *Mailing Add:* 242 W Quadrangle Village Cross Key Balitmore MD 21210

MAGEE, KENNETH RAYMOND, neurology, see previous edition

MAGEE, LYMAN ABBOTT, b Bogalusa, La, Apr 10, 26; m 57; c 2. MICROBIOLOGY. *Educ:* La Col, BS, 46; La State Univ, MS, 54, PhD(bact), 58. *Prof Exp:* Sr analyst, Cities Serv Refining Corp, La, 47-48; asst prof chem, La Col, 48-51, dean men, 51; Hite fel cancer res, M D Anderson Hosp & Tumor Inst, Univ Tex, 58-59; Nat Inst Allergy & Infectious Diseases fel & instr microbiol, Sch Med, 60-61, assoc prof biol, Univ, 61-65, assoc prof microbiol, Sch Med, 63-77, chmn dept, 71-77, PROF BIOL, UNIV MISS, 65-, ASST DEAN, 78- *Concurrent Pos:* Am Soc Microbiol Pres fel virol, Commun Dis Ctr, USPHS & Southern Res Inst, Ga, 65. *Mem:* Am Soc Microbiol; fel Am Acad Microbiol. *Res:* Cancer viruses; metabolism of exanthem viruses; microbial decomposition of pesticides. *Mailing Add:* Dept of Biol Univ of Miss University MS 38677

MAGEE, MICHAEL JACK, b Coleman, Tex, Feb 16, 46; m 69; c 1. COMPUTER SCIENCES. *Educ:* Univ Tex, BA, 68, MA, 72, PhD(comput sci), 75. *Prof Exp:* Assoc programmer, Int Bus Mach Corp, 68-71; ASSOC PROF COMPUT SCI, UNIV WYO, 75- *Res:* Artificial intelligence; pattern recognition; computational linguistics. *Mailing Add:* Dept of Comput Sci Univ of Wyo Laramie WY 82070

MAGEE, PATRICK MASON, heat transfer, nuclear engineering, see previous edition

MAGEE, PAUL TERRY, b Los Angeles, Calif, Oct 26, 37; m 64; c 2. GENETICS, MOLECULAR BIOLOGY. *Educ:* Yale Univ, BS, 59; Univ Calif, Berkeley, PhD(biochem), 64. *Prof Exp:* Am Cancer Soc fel, Lab Enzymol, Nat Ctr Sci Res, Gif-sur-Yvette, France, 64-66; from asst prof to assoc prof microbiol, 66-74, assoc prof human genetics, Sch Med, Yale Univ, 74-77; PROF & CHMN DEPT MICROBIOL & PUB HEALTH, MICH STATE UNIV, 77- *Concurrent Pos:* Mem adv bd, Genetic Biol Prog, NSF, 78-81. *Mem:* AAAS; Am Soc Microbiol; Genetic Soc Am; Am Soc Biol Chem. *Res:* Regulation of gene expression; developmental biology. *Mailing Add:* Dept of Microbiol & Pub Health Mich State Univ East Lansing MI 48824

MAGEE, PHILIP STEWART, physical organic chemistry, see previous edition

MAGEE, RICHARD JOSEPH, organic chemistry, deceased

MAGEE, RICHARD STEPHEN, b East Orange, NJ, Mar 26, 41; m 69; c 1. MECHANICAL ENGINEERING. *Educ:* Stevens Inst Technol, BEng, 63, MS, 64, DSc(appl mech), 68. *Prof Exp:* Res engr, Combustion Lab, 66-68, from asst prof to assoc prof mech eng, 68-77, NSF & NASA grants, 69-70, PROF MECH ENG, STEVENS INST TECHNOL, 77- *Concurrent Pos:* Consult, Photochem, Inc, 70- *Mem:* Am Soc Mech Engrs; Am Soc Eng Educ; Combustion Inst. *Res:* Flammability characteristics of combustible materials, including ignition, flame spread and burning characteristics; pyrolysis characteristics of polymeric materials; basic incinerator design parameters. *Mailing Add:* Dept of Mech Eng Castle Point Sta Hoboken NJ 07030

MAGEE, STEVE CARL, biochemistry, see previous edition

MAGEE, THOMAS ALEXANDER, b Brookhaven, Miss, Apr 19, 30; m 61; c 1. ORGANIC CHEMISTRY. *Educ:* Tulane Univ, BS, 52, MS, 55; Univ Tenn, PhD(chem), 57. *Prof Exp:* Chemist, 57-76, res assoc 76-78, SR RES ASSOC, T R EVANS RES CTR, DIAMOND SHAMROCK CORP, 78-, GROUP LEADER, 80- *Mem:* Am Chem Soc. *Res:* Organometallic chemistry of the transition elements; pesticide chemistry. *Mailing Add:* 7301 Case Ave Mentor OH 44060

MAGEE, WAYNE EDWARD, b Big Rapids, Mich, Apr 11, 29; m 51; c 3. VIROLOGY, BIOCHEMISTRY. *Educ:* Kalamazoo Col, BA, 51; Univ Wis, MS, 53, PhD(biochem), 55. *Prof Exp:* Res scientist microbiol, Upjohn Co, 55-60, proj leader biochem, 60-63, proj leader virol res, 63-66, sr res scientist, 67-71, sr scientist exp biol, 71; prof life sci, Ind State Univ, Terre Haute, 71-74; prof biol, Div Allied Health & Life Sci, Univ Tex, San Antonio, 75-81, dir, 75-80, prof biochem, Univ Tex Health Sci Ctr, 75-81; PROF BIOCHEM, HEAD, DEPT BACTERIOL & BIOCHEM, UNIV IDAHO, 81- *Concurrent Pos:* Mem adj staff, Dept Biol, Western Mich Univ, 68-70, adj prof, 71; adj prof microbiol, Terre Haute Ctr Med Educ, Sch Med, Ind Univ, 72-74; adj found scientist, Southwest Found Res Educ, San Antonio, Tex, 78- *Mem:* AAAS; Am Chem Soc; Am Soc Biol Chem; Am Soc Microbiol; NY Acad Sci. *Res:* Nitrogen fixation; nucleic acid biochemistry; biochemistry of virus infection; mechanism of action of therapeutic agents and interferon; phospholipid vesicles as carriers for drugs and nucleic acids. *Mailing Add:* Dept Bacteriol & Biochem Univ Idaho Moscow ID 83843

MAGEE, WILLIAM LOVEL, b Ft William, Ont, Mar 24, 29; m 55; c 2. BIOCHEMISTRY. *Educ:* Univ Western Ont, BSc, 52, MSc, 54, PhD(biochem), 57. *Prof Exp:* Nat Multiple Sclerosis Soc overseas fel biochem, Guy's Hosp Med Sch, London, Eng, 58-61; res asst, 61-62, lectr, 62-63, asst prof, 63-68, ASSOC PROF BIOCHEM, HEALTH SCI CTR, UNIV WESTERN ONT, 68- *Mem:* AAAS; Can Biochem Soc. *Res:* Biochemistry of brain and peripheral nerve; biochemistry of demyelination; phospholipid chemistry and metabolism. *Mailing Add:* Dept of Biochem Health Sci Ctr Univ of Western Ont London ON N6A 5B8 Can

MAGEE, WILLIAM THOMAS, b San Antonio, Tex, Apr 22, 23; m 48; c 3. ANIMAL BREEDING. *Educ:* Tex A&M Univ, BS, 47; Iowa State Univ, MS, 48, PhD(animal husb), 51. *Prof Exp:* Asst animal husbandman, Tex A&M Univ, 53-55; from asst prof to assoc prof, 55-65, PROF ANIMAL BREEDING, MICH STATE UNIV, 65- *Mem:* Am Soc Animal Sci; Am Genetic Asn. *Res:* Evaluation of the effects of selection and mating systems on performance traits in beef cattle and swine. *Mailing Add:* Dept of Animal Husb Mich State Univ East Lansing MI 48823

MAGER, ARTUR, b Nieglowice, Poland, Sept 21, 19; nat US; m 42; c 1. AERONAUTICS. *Educ:* Univ Mich, BS, 43; Case Inst Technol, MS, 51; Calif Inst Technol, PhD(aeronaut, physics) 53. *Prof Exp:* Test engr, Continental Aviation & Eng Co, 43-44; aeronaut res scientist, Nat Adv Comt Aeronaut, 46-53; res engr & consult, Naval Ord Test Sta, 53-54; res consult, Astro-Marquardt Corp, 54-60; dir, Nat Eng Sci Co, 60-61; dir spacecraft sci, 61-64, gen mgr, Appl Mech Div, 64-68, vpres & gen mgr eng sci opers, 68-78, GROUP VPRES ENG, AEROSPACE CORP, 78- *Concurrent Pos:* Res fel, Calif Inst Technol, 53-54; mem ballistic syst div reentry panel, Air Force Systs Command, 61-62; mem res adv comt space vehicle aerodyn, NASA, 63-65; mem bd counr, Sch Eng, Univ Southern Calif. *Mem:* Nat Acad Eng; AAAS; fel Am Inst Aeronaut & Astronaut (pres, 80-81); Am Phys Soc; Am Soc Mech Engrs. *Res:* Boundary layers; heat transfer; gas dynamics; cycle analysis; chemical and electrical propulsion; magnetohydrodynamics. *Mailing Add:* Aerospace Corp PO Box 92957 Los Angeles CA 90009

MAGER, MILTON, b New York, NY, Dec 13, 20; m 47; c 3. BIOCHEMISTRY. *Educ:* NY Univ, BA, 43; Rensselaer Polytech Univ, MS, 49; Boston Univ, PhD(biochem), 54. *Prof Exp:* Instr chem, Albany Col Pharm, 46-49; biochemist, Qm Res & Eng Ctr, 53-56, chief biochem sect physiol br, 56-61; chief biochem lab, 61-67, dir biochem & pharmacol lab, 67-75, DIR HEAT RES DIV, US ARMY RES INST ENVIRON MED, 75- *Concurrent Pos:* Asst, Sch Med, Boston Univ, 52-55, instr, 55-59, asst res prof, 59-65, assoc res prof, 65- *Mem:* AAAS; Am Chem Soc; Am Asn Clin Chemists; Am Physiol Soc. *Res:* Biochemical and physiological responses of man and animals to environmental stress, primarily heat; temperature regulation; blood and tissue enzymes; methodology. *Mailing Add:* 19 Fenno Rd Newton Ctr Boston MA 02159

MAGERLEIN, BARNEY JOHN, b Columbus, Ohio, Nov 11, 19; m 44; c 4. MEDICINAL CHEMISTRY. *Educ:* Capital Univ, BS, 41; Ohio State Univ, PhD(org chem), 46. *Hon Degrees:* DSci Capital Univ, 78. *Prof Exp:* Asst org chem, Ohio State Univ, 41-44, Off Sci Res & Develop contract, Univ Res Found, 44-45; chemist, 46-71, DISTINGUISHED RES SCIENTIST, UPJOHN CO, 71- *Concurrent Pos:* Vis scholar, Univ Calif, Los Angeles, 60-61. *Mem:* Am Chem Soc; Sigma Xi. *Res:* Organic synthesis; synthetic studies of morphine series; steroids and pteridines; antibiotics. *Mailing Add:* Infectious Dis Res Upjohn Co Kalamazoo MI 49007

MAGERLEIN, JAMES MICHAEL, b Kalamazoo, Mich, Aug 25, 50. OPERATIONS RESEARCH, INDUSTRIAL ENGINEERING. *Educ:* Kalamazoo Col, BA, 72; Univ Mich, AM, 73, PhD(indust & opers eng), 78. *Prof Exp:* Res asst, Univ Mich, 74-78; mathematician oper res, 78-81, SR MATHEMATICIAN, UPJOHN CO, 81- *Mem:* Inst Mgt Sci. *Res:* Hospital systems; methodology for scheduling elective surgery; modelling, design and simulation of production systems. *Mailing Add:* 9960 242 51 Upjohn Co Kalamazoo MI 49008

MAGGARD, SAMUEL P, b Whitesburg, Ky, June 19, 33; m 54; c 4. CIVIL ENGINEERING, STRUCTURAL ENGINEERING. *Educ:* Univ Ky, BS, 56, MS, 57; Purdue Univ, PhD(struct eng), 63. *Prof Exp:* Design engr, Ky Dept Hwy, 55-57; instr struct design, Univ Ky, 57-58, asst prof, 58-59; res assoc, Purdue Univ, 59-63; from asst prof to assoc prof, 63-67, PROF STRUCT DESIGN, N MEX STATE UNIV, 67-, HEAD DEPT CIVIL ENG, 66- *Concurrent Pos:* Consult nuclear effects br, Army Missile Test & Eval Directorate, White Sands Missile Range, 64- *Mem:* Am Soc Civil Engrs; Am Soc Eng Educ; Nat Soc Prof Engrs. *Res:* Structural analysis and design; economy and adequacy of structural materials and structures. *Mailing Add:* Dept of Civil Eng NMex State Univ Las Cruces NM 88003

MAGGENTI, ARMAND RICHARD, b San Jose, Calif, Feb 15, 33; m 63; c 2. PLANT NEMATOLOGY. *Educ:* Univ Calif, Berkeley, BS, 54, PhD, 59. *Prof Exp:* From asst nematologist to nematologist, Univ Calif, Davis, 58-74, lectr nematol & chmn dept, 74-79. *Concurrent Pos:* Fulbright fels, Pakistan, 65, Iraq, 65-66. *Honors & Awards:* ASO distinguished lectr, 80. *Mem:* Soc Nematol; Soc Syst Zool. *Res:* Taxonomy and morphology of soil and freshwater nematodes; nematode parasites of fish; nematode parasites of birds. *Mailing Add:* Dept Nematol Univ Calif Davis CA 95616

MAGGIO, EDWARD THOMAS, b Brooklyn, NY, Mar 28, 47. PROTEIN CHEMISTRY, NON-ISOTOPIC IMMUNOASSAYS. *Educ:* Polytech Inst Brooklyn, BS, 68; Univ Mich, MS, 69, PhD(biol chem), 73. *Prof Exp:* Fel biochem dept pharmaceut chem, Univ Calif, San Francisco, 73-74, NIH fel pharmaceut chem, 74-75; group leader enzym, Int Diag Technol, Syva Res Inst, 75, mgr, Biochem Sect, 75-77, dir res & develop, 77-79; vpres res & develop, Scripps-Miles Inc, 80-82; PRES, SYNBIOTEX, INC, 82- *Mem:* Am Chem Soc; Am Soc Microbiol; Am Asn Clin Chem; NY Acad Sci. *Res:* Enzymology in clinical and pharmaceutical chemistry; enzyme kinetics; chemical modification of proteins; physical biochemistry; non-isotopic immunoassay methodology. *Mailing Add:* Synbiotex 12588 Chetenham Lane San Diego CA 92128

MAGGIO, FRANCIS XAVIER, b Brooklyn, NY, Jan 5, 25; m 56; c 4. CHEMISTRY. *Educ:* LI Univ, BS, 48. *Prof Exp:* Res chemist, Am Alkyd Industs, 49-51, Crown Oil Chem Co, 51-54 & Interchem Corp, 52-57; chief chemist, Mitchell-Rand Corp, 57-60; sr proj scientist, Aerovox Corp, 60; sr res chemist, Am Potash & Chem, 60-65; MGR POLYMER RES, SWEDLOW, INC, GARDEN GROVE, 65- *Mem:* Am Inst Chem. *Res:* Phosphorus-boron polymers; epoxy chemistry; free radical polymerization of methylmethacrylates. *Mailing Add:* Swedlow Inc 12122 Western Ave Garden Grove CA 92645

MAGGIO-CAVALIERE, MARY, b White Castle, La, Aug 15, 40; m 71; c 2. CLINICAL PHARMACOLOGY. *Educ:* Loyola Univ, La, BS, 63; Tulane Univ, MS, 65, PhD(pharmacol), 68. *Prof Exp:* Asst prof pharmacol, Northeast La State Col, 68-69; asst dir med div, Ciba-Geigy Corp, 69-77, assoc dir res dept, 77-80; ASSOC DIR CLIN RES, AM HOME PROD CORP, 80- *Concurrent Pos:* Adj asst prof, Col Med & Dent of NJ, Newark, 75-; bd regents & exec comt, Am Col Clin Pharmacol, 78-, registered pharmacist. *Mem:* fel Am Col Clin Pharmacol; Am Soc Clin Pharmacol & Therapeut; Am Rheumatism Asn. *Res:* Anti-inflammatory agents; endocrine drugs; drug metabolism; analgesic drugs. *Mailing Add:* 25 Seven Oaks Dr Summit NJ 07901

MAGGIORA, GERALD M, b Oakland, Calif, Aug 11, 38; m 63; c 2. MOLECULAR BIOPHYSICS. *Educ:* Univ Calif, Davis, BS, 64, PhD(biophys), 68. *Prof Exp:* Res assoc, 68-69, USPHS fel, 69-70, asst prof, 70-74, ASSOC PROF BIOCHEM, UNIV KANS, 74- *Mem:* Am Chem Soc; Am Phys Soc; Int Soc Quantum Biol. *Res:* Molecular quantum mechanics; quantum biochemistry; photosynthesis; vision; electromagnetic properties of large molecules; interaction of light with matter. *Mailing Add:* Dept of Biochem Univ of Kans Lawrence KS 66044

MAGGIORE, CARL JEROME, b Grand Island, Nebr, June 28, 43; m 77; c 2. NUCLEAR PHYSICS, SOLID STATE PHYSICS. *Educ:* Creighton Univ, BS, 65; Mich State Univ, PhD(physics), 72. *Prof Exp:* Res assoc environ sci, Mt Sinai Med Sch, 70-74; mgr x-ray, Princeton Gamma Technol, 74-76; asst group leader solid state electronics, 76-81, STAFF MEM ELECTRONICS RES & DEVELOP, LOS ALAMOS NAT LAB, UNIV CALIF, 81- *Mem:* Am Phys Soc; AAAS; NY Acad Sci. *Res:* Ion beam analysis of the near surfaces of materials using backscattering, channeling, and ion-induced x-rays; compound semiconductor interfaces and device physics; electrochemistry and catalysis. *Mailing Add:* MS 429 Los Alamos Nat Lab Los Alamos NM 87545

MAGID, ANDY ROY, b St Paul, Minn, May 4, 44; m 66. MATHEMATICS. *Educ:* Univ Calif, Berkeley, BA, 66; Northwestern Univ, PhD(math), 69. *Prof Exp:* J F Ritt asst prof math, Columbia Univ, 69-72; assoc prof, 72-77, PROF MATH, UNIV OKLA, 77- *Concurrent Pos:* Vis assoc prof math, Univ Ill, 75-76, Univ Calif, Berkeley, 80. *Mem:* Am Math Soc; Math Asn Am. *Res:* Commutative algebra; Galois theory; algebraic geometry. *Mailing Add:* Dept of Math Univ of Okla Norman OK 73069

MAGID, LEONARD MORTON, electrical engineering, see previous edition

MAGID, LINDA JENNY, b Omaha, Nebr, Dec 13, 46; m 69. PHYSICAL ORGANIC CHEMISTRY. *Educ:* Rice Univ, BA, 69; Univ Tenn, Knoxville, PhD(chem), 73. *Prof Exp:* Instr chem, 73-74, ASST PROF CHEM, UNIV TENN, KNOXVILLE, 74- *Mem:* Sigma Xi. *Res:* Thermodynamics of micellization and micellar solubilization in aqueous and nonaqueous solvents; micellar catalysis. *Mailing Add:* Dept of Chem Univ of Tenn Knoxville TN 37916

MAGID, RONALD, b Brooklyn, NY, Dec 19, 38; m 60, 69; c 2. ORGANIC CHEMISTRY. *Educ:* Yale Univ, BS, 59, MS, 60, PhD(chem), 64. *Prof Exp:* Asst prof, Rice Univ, 64-70; asst prof, 70-72, assoc prof, 72-81, PROF CHEM, UNIV TENN, KNOXVILLE, 81- *Mem:* Am Chem Soc; Royal Soc Chem. *Res:* Orbital symmetry rules; mechanisms of organolithium reactions; mechanisms of reactions of allylic compounds; synthesis of strained compounds. *Mailing Add:* Dept of Chem Univ of Tenn Knoxville TN 37916

MAGIE, ALLAN RUPERT, b Umatilla, Fla, July 21, 36; m 61; c 3. PUBLIC HEALTH. *Educ:* Univ Calif, BA, 58, PhD(physiol), 63; Loma Linda Univ, MPH, 71. *Prof Exp:* Assoc prof biol, Pac Union Col 63-65; prof & dean sci & technol, Mountain View Col, Philippines, 65-70; asst prof environ health, 71-73, coordr, Doctor Health Sci Prog, 72-78, assoc prof, 73-77, PROF & CHMN ENVIRON & TROP HEALTH, SCH HEALTH, LOMA LINDA UNIV, 77- *Concurrent Pos:* Dir external MPH prog, Western Consortium Schs Pub Health, 73- *Mem:* Am Pub Health Asn; Sigma Xi. *Res:* Human health effects of ambient air pollutants, including fetal development, birth anomalies, respiratory disease and hospitalization; animal diseases transferrable to humans. *Mailing Add:* Dept Environ & Trop Health Loma Linda Sch Health Loma Linda CA 92354

MAGIE, ROBERT OGDEN, b Madison, NJ, July 30, 06; m 33; c 2. PLANT PATHOLOGY. *Educ:* Rutgers Univ, BS, 29; Univ Wis, MS, 30, PhD(plant path), 34. *Prof Exp:* Agt, Dutch elm dis invest, Bur Plant Indust, USDA, 35; Crop Protection Inst fel, NY Agr Exp Sta, Geneva, 35-36, res assoc, 36-40; asst prof plant path, Cornell Univ, 40-45; prof, 45-77, EMER PROF PLANT PATH, INST FOOD & AGR SCI, AGR RES & EDUC CTR, UNIV FLA, 77- *Concurrent Pos:* Consult, Israel, SAfrica, Brazil, NZ, Australia & France. *Mem:* Am Phytopath Soc; Int Soc Plant Path. *Res:* Diseases of cut flowers crops; gladiolus flower and corm production; control of Botrytis and Fusarium diseases; caladium tuber production. *Mailing Add:* Agr Res & Educ Ctr Inst of Food & Agr Sci Univ Fla Bradenton FL 33508

MAGILL, CLINT WILLIAM, b Washington, DC, Sept 15, 41; m 65. GENETICS. *Educ:* Univ Ill, BS, 63; Cornell Univ, PhD(genetics), 69. *Prof Exp:* NIH fel biochem genetics, Univ Minn, 67-69; asst prof, 69-75, ASSOC PROF GENETICS, TEX A&M UNIV, 75- *Mem:* Genetics Soc Am. *Res:* Mutation; reverse mutation; genetic complementation; rice tissue culture. *Mailing Add:* Genetics Sect Tex A&M Univ College Station TX 77843

MAGILL, DAVID THOMAS, b Evanston, Ill, May 14, 35; m 57; c 4. COMMUNICATIONS ENGINEERING. *Educ:* Princeton Univ, BSE, 57; Stanford Univ, MS, 60, PhD(elec eng), 64. *Prof Exp:* Engr, RS Electronics Corp, 57-58; asst ionospheric res, Stanford Univ, 58-60; res scientist commun & control syst theory, Lockheed Missiles & Space Co, 60-64; staff scientist commun theory & design & dept mgr, Philco-Ford Corp, 64-70; SR RES ENGR, SRI INT, 70- *Concurrent Pos:* Lectr, Exten Prog, Univ Calif, Berkeley, 64-65 & Santa Barbara, 70- *Mem:* Inst Elec & Electronics Engrs. *Res:* Satellite communication; modulation-demodulation and estimation-detection theories. *Mailing Add:* 2521 Webster St Palo Alto CA 94301

MAGILL, JANE MARY (OAKES), b Hamilton, Ont, Sept 30, 40; m 65. BIOCHEMISTRY, GENETICS. *Educ:* Univ Western Ont, BSc, 63; Cornell Univ, PhD(genetics), 68. *Prof Exp:* Asst scientist genetics, Univ Minn, 68-69; instr, 70-71, ASST PROF BIOCHEM, TEX A&M UNIV, 71-, ASST PROF BIOPHYSICS, 77- *Mem:* Genetics Soc Am; Am Chem Soc. *Res:* Utilization of exogenous purines and pyrimidines. *Mailing Add:* Dept of Biochem Tex A&M Univ College Station TX 77843

MAGILL, JOSEPH HENRY, b Drumnabreeze, Northern Ireland, Dec 16, 28; US citizen; m 56; c 2. MATERIALS ENGINEERING, PHYSICAL ORGANIC CHEMISTRY. *Educ:* Queen's Univ, Belfast, BSc, 52, PhD(chem), 56; Univ London, DIC, 57; FRSC, 62 & 65. *Prof Exp:* Chem technologist polymer mfg, Chemstrand Ltd, Northern Ireland, 57-58; sr tech officer polymers, Brit Nylon Spinners Ltd, UK, 59-65; res fel polymer sci, Mellon Inst, 65-68; assoc prof mat eng, 68-75, PROF MAT ENG, UNIV PITTSBURGH, 75-, PROF CHEM-PETROL ENG, 80- *Concurrent Pos:* Asst tech officer, Imperial Chem Indust, UK, 54; fel, Nat Coal Bd, Imperial Col, 56-57; asst lectr, Northampton Polytech, London, 57-58; eve lectr, Newport Col Technol, UK, 61-62; vis fel, Mellon Inst, 62-64; sr res fel, Sci Res Coun, Univ Bristol, 75-76. *Mem:* Fel Am Inst Physics; Am Chem Soc; Sigma Xi. *Res:* Physical properties and structural aspects of polymers and small molecules; flammability, thermal stability and toxicity of polymers. *Mailing Add:* Dept of Metall & Mat Eng Univ of Pittsburgh Pittsburgh PA 15261

MAGILL, KENNETH DERWOOD, JR, b Duncansville, Pa, Oct 21, 33; m 52; c 2. MATHEMATICS. *Educ:* Shippensburg State Col, BS, 56; Pa State Univ, MA, 60, PhD(math), 63. *Prof Exp:* Teacher, Central Cove Schs, 56-57; instr math, Pa State Univ, 58-63; from asst prof to assoc prof, 63-67, chmn dept, 67-70, PROF MATH, STATE UNIV NY BUFFALO, 67- *Concurrent Pos:* Vis prof, Univ Leeds, 68; vis mem, Inst Advan Studies, Australian Nat Univ, 70; vis prof, Univ Fla. *Mem:* Math Asn Am; Am Math Soc; London Math Soc. *Res:* Topology; rings of continuous functions; semigroups. *Mailing Add:* Dept of Math State Univ of NY Buffalo NY 14214

MAGILL, ROBERT EARLE, b Ft Worth, Tex, May 8, 47; m 68; c 3. BRYOLOGY, TAXONOMY. *Educ:* Sul Ross State Univ, BS, 69, MS, 71; Tex A&M Univ, PhD(bot), 75. *Prof Exp:* curatorial trainee, Mo Bot Garden, 75-76, cur cryptogams, Bot Res Inst, Pretoria, 76-81, ASST CUR, MO BOT

GARDEN, 82- *Mem:* Am Bryol & Lichenological Soc; Brit Bryol Soc; Int Asn Plant Taxon; Am Fern Soc. *Res:* Taxonomy and phytogeography of bryophytes; use of scanning electron microscope in systematic studies of mosses. *Mailing Add:* PO Box 299 Mo Bot Garden St Louis MO 63166

MAGILL, THOMAS PLEINES, b Philadelphia, Pa, May 24, 03; m 43. MICROBIOLOGY, IMMUNOLOGY. *Educ:* Johns Hopkins Univ, AB, 25, MD, 30. *Prof Exp:* Instr med, Sch Med, Johns Hopkins Univ, 33-35; asst, Rockefeller Inst, NY, 35-36; mem staff, Rockefeller Found, 36-38; from asst prof to assoc prof bact & immunol, Med Col, Cornell Univ, 38-48; prof microbiol & immunol & chmn dept, Long Island Col Med, 48-50; chmn dept, 50-70, prof, 50-73, EMER PROF MICROBIOL & IMMUNOL, COL MED, STATE UNIV NY DOWNSTATE MED CTR, 73- *Mem:* Am Soc Immunologists (pres, 53); Soc Exp Biol & Med; Am Soc Microbiol; Harvey Soc. *Res:* Infectious diseases; filterable viruses and rickettsia; variation of influenza virus. *Mailing Add:* 140 Main St East Hampton NY 11937

MAGIN, RALPH WALTER, b Belleville, Ill, Oct 22, 37; m 61; c 2. ORGANIC CHEMISTRY, POLYMER CHEMISTRY. *Educ:* Univ Ill, BS, 59; Mass Inst Technol, PhD(org chem), 63. *Prof Exp:* Assignment, Univ Ariz, 63-65; sr res chemist, Org Chem Div, Monsanto Co, 66-68 & Monsanto Indust Chem Co, Mo, 68-75, res specialist, Monsanto Polymers & Petrochem, 75-78, SR RES SPECIALIST, MONSANTO AGR PROD CO, 78- *Mem:* AAAS; Am Chem Soc. *Res:* Polyelectrolytes, both bioactive and watersoluble, and their effect on environment; polyester condensation polymers; encapsulation of agricultural products. *Mailing Add:* Monsanto Agr Prod Co 800 N Lindbergh Blvd St Louis MO 63166

MAGINNES, EDWARD ALEXANDER, b Ottawa, Ont, Can, Apr 19, 33; m 64; c 1. HORTICULTURE. *Educ:* McGill Univ, BS, 56; Cornell Univ, MS, 60, PhD(floricult), 64. *Prof Exp:* Res officer horticult, Can Dept Agr, 56-60; from asst prof to assoc prof, 64-77, EXTEN SPECIALIST & PROF HORT SCI, UNIV SASK, 77- *Mem:* Am Soc Hort Sci. *Res:* Culture of horticultural crops; influence of photoperiod and temperature on flowering, light quality and plant growth; nutrition of floriculture crops; growth retardants; moisture stress and plant growth. *Mailing Add:* Dept of Hort Univ of Sask Saskatoon SK S7N 0W0 Can

MAGISON, ERNEST CARROLL, b Ft Lauderdale, Fla, Oct 15, 26; m 50; c 6. ELECTRICAL ENGINEERING, STANDARDS MANAGEMENT. *Educ:* Tufts Univ, BS, 48. *Prof Exp:* Prod engr, 48-52, supvr prod develop, 52-74, MGR STANDARDS & REGULATORY AFFAIRS, PROCESS CONTROL DIV, HONEYWELL INC, 74- *Concurrent Pos:* Adj prof dept elec eng, Eve Col, Drexel Univ, 52-; comt hazardous mat, Nat Res Coun, 68-74, comt eval indust hazards, 75-; secy, Int Electrotech Comn Sub-committee. *Honors & Awards:* Standards & Practices Award, Instrument Soc Am, 74. *Mem:* Fel Instrument Soc Am (vpres); Am Soc Testing & Mat; Nat Fire Protection Asn. *Mailing Add:* Honeywell Inc 1100 Virginia Dr Ft Washington PA 19034

MAGLEBY, KARL LEGRANDE, b Provo, Utah. NEUROPHYSIOLOGY, BIOPHYSICS. *Educ:* Univ Utah, BS, 66; Univ Wash, PhD(physiol, biophys), 70. *Prof Exp:* NIH neurophys training grant, Univ Wash, 70-71; from asst prof to assoc prof, 71-80, PROF PHYSIOL & BIOPHYS, SCH MED, UNIV MIAMI, 80- *Concurrent Pos:* NIH res grants, Univ Miami, 72- *Mem:* Biophysical Soc; Soc Neurosci; Soc Gen Physiologists; Fedn Am Soc Exp Biol. *Res:* Synaptic transmission; mechanism of transmitter release; transmitter-receptor interaction. *Mailing Add:* Dept of Physiol & Biophys Univ of Miami Sch of Med Miami FL 33101

MAGLIARO, ANTONIO ALESSANDRO, Avellino, Italy, July 4, 49; US citizen; m 73; c 1. MATHEMATICS. *Educ:* Yale Univ, BS, 71; Mich State Univ, MS, 73; Boston Univ, PhD(math), 82. *Prof Exp:* ASST PROF MATH, RI COL, 73- *Mem:* Am Math Soc. *Res:* Optimal control theory, specifically the application of perturbation methods to nonlinear control systems. *Mailing Add:* 104 Walnut St Johnston RI 02919

MAGLICH, BOGDAN, b Sombor, Yugoslavia, Aug 5, 28; c 2. EXPERIMENTAL NUCLEAR PHYSICS, PARTICLE PHYSICS. *Educ:* Univ Belgrade, dipl physics, 50; Univ Liverpool, MSc, 55; Mass Inst Technol, PhD(physics), 59. *Prof Exp:* UNESCO fel, Mass Inst Technol, 55-56; res assoc, Lawrence Radiation Lab, Univ Calif, Berkeley, 59-62; sr staff mem, European Orgn Nuclear Res, Geneva, 63-67; prof physics, Univ Pa, 67-68; prof & prin investr high energy physics, Rutgers Univ, 69-74; PRES & CHIEF SCIENTIST, FUNSION ENERGY CORP, 74-; CHMN, MIGMA INST HIGH ENERGY FUSION, FUSION ENERGY CORP, 74-, CHMN & PRES, 72- *Concurrent Pos:* Dir, Nat Comput Analysts, 72-; vis prof, dept elec eng, Polytech Inst NY, 81-; proj mgr, Univ Res Ctr, Jeddah, Saudi Arabia, 81- *Mem:* Fel Am Phys Soc. *Res:* Non-proliferating nuclear process for production of electrical energy; author or coauthor of over 100 publications; pi-meson scattering and polarization at 3 bev cosmotron; antiproton experiments and short lived mesons Bevatron 6 Bev; missing-mass spectrometry and heavy bosons, at 30 Bev motor synchrotron; self-colliding beams and migma cell, high energy (Mev) fusion. *Mailing Add:* Fusion Energy Corp 3684 US Rte 1 PO Box 2005 Princeton NJ 08540

MAGLIULO, ANTHONY RUDOLPH, b Brooklyn, NY, July 23, 31; m 67; c 6. NUTRITION, BIOCHEMISTRY. *Educ:* Brooklyn Col, BS, 55; Long Island Univ, MS, 61; St John's Univ, PhD(microbiol), 68. *Prof Exp:* Lab technician, Maimonides Hosp, Brooklyn, 55-56; res microbiol, Armed Forces Inst Path, 56-58; res asst, New York Hosp, 58-60; microbiologist chg clin microbiol, Misericordia Hosp, 60-61 & 62-63; lectr microbiol, Queens Col, NY, 61-62; teaching asst biol, St John's Univ, 63-65; lectr & instr, 65-68, asst prof, 68-73, ASSOC PROF BIOCHEM, JOHN JAY COL CRIMINAL JUSTICE, 73- *Concurrent Pos:* Instr nursing sci, Roosevelt Hosp, 68-69; coordr nursing chem & lectr nursing sci, Hunter Col, 68-69; consult nutrit, 79- *Mem:* AAAS; fel Am Inst Chemists; Am Chem Soc; Nat Sci Teachers Asn. *Res:* Isolation of new and unique microbial lipids; nutrition and behavior, forensic applications. *Mailing Add:* Dept Sci John Jay Col 445 W 59th St New York NY 10019

MAGLIVERAS, SPYROS SIMOS, b Athens, Greece, Sept 6, 38; US citizen; m 62; c 2. MATHEMATICS. *Educ:* Univ Fla, BEE, 61, MA, 63; Univ Birmingham, PhD(math), 70. *Prof Exp:* Teaching asst math, Univ Fla, 61-62, interim instr, 62-63; instr, Fla Presby Col, 63-64; systs analyst, Inst Social Res, Univ Mich, Ann Arbor, 65-68; res fel math, Univ Birmingham, 68-70; from asst prof to prof math, State Univ NY Col Oswego, 70-78; ASSOC PROF MATH & COMPUT SCI, UNIV NEBR-LINCOLN, 78- *Concurrent Pos:* Consult, Nat Broadcasting Co, 67-68; consult, Ctr Human Growth & Develop, Univ Mich, Ann Arbor, 68, res assoc, 71; vis scholar, Univ Mich, 72; vis assoc prof math, State Univ NY, Binghamton, 76. *Mem:* Am Math Soc; Math Asn Am; Edinburgh Math Soc; London Math Soc. *Res:* Combinatorial designs, permutation groups, finite geometrics; data encryption, data security systems in computers and communications. *Mailing Add:* Dept Math Univ Nebraska Lincoln NE 68588

MAGNANI, NICHOLAS J, b Mason City, Iowa, Apr 11, 42; m 63; c 2. METALLURGY. *Educ:* Iowa State Univ, BS, 64, PhD(metall), 68. *Prof Exp:* Mem tech staff, 68-73, supvr, Chem Metall Div, 73-79, MGR CHEM & CERAMICS, SANDIA NAT LABS, 79- *Mem:* Nat Asn Corrosion Engrs; Am Soc Metals; Am Ceramics Soc; Mat Res Soc. *Res:* Corrosion and stress corrosion cracking emphasizing uranium and uranium alloys; corrosion resistant materials. *Mailing Add:* Orgn 5831 Sandia Labs Albuquerque NM 87185

MAGNARELLI, LOUIS ANTHONY, b Syracuse, NY, Mar 27, 45; m 69. ENTOMOLOGY. *Educ:* State Univ NY Col Oswego, BS, 67; Univ Mich, MS, 68; Cornell Univ, PhD(med entom), 75. *Prof Exp:* Teacher biol, WGenesee Cent Sch Dist, NY, 68-71; res asst, Cornell Univ, 71-75, experimentalist, 75; asst scientist, 75-78, assoc scientist entom, 78-81, AGR SCIENTIST, CONN AGR EXP STA, 81- *Mem:* Entom Soc Am; Am Mosquito Control Asn; Am Soc Trop Med & Hyg; Am Soc Rickettsiologists; Am Inst Biol Sci. *Res:* Blood feeding, sugar feeding, and ovarian studies of mosquitoes, deer flies and horse flies; Rocky Mountain Spotted Fever; rickettsiae in ticks and antibodies in mammals. *Mailing Add:* Dept of Entom Conn Agr Exp Sta PO Box 1106 New Haven CT 06504

MAGNELL, KENNETH ROBERT, b Detroit, Mich, July 27, 38; m 63; c 2. INORGANIC CHEMISTRY. *Educ:* Wayne State Univ, BS, 62, MS, 66; Univ Minn, Minneapolis, PhD(inorg chem), 70. *Prof Exp:* ASST PROF CHEM, CENT MICH UNIV, 70- *Mem:* AAAS; Am Chem Soc. *Res:* Non-aqueous solvent equilibrium studies. *Mailing Add:* Dept of Chem Cent Mich Univ Mt Pleasant MI 48858

MAGNESS, T(OM) A(LAN), b San Diego, Calif, Oct 22, 27; m 61, 67; c 5. ASTRONAUTICAL ENGINEERING, SYSTEMS DESIGN. *Educ:* Univ Calif, Los Angeles, AB, 49, MA, 51, PhD(math), 56. *Prof Exp:* Asst math, Exten Div, Univ Calif, Los Angeles, 49-51; asst physics, Scripps Inst, Univ Calif, 51-53; mem tech staff, Appl Physics Dept, Ramo-Wooldridge Corp, 56-60, head sect guid anal, Space Tech Labs, 60-63, assoc mgr, Space Guid Dept, 63-64, mgr, Space Guid Dept, TRW Systs Group, Tex, 64-66, asst mgr, Systs Anal Lab, TRW Systs, 66-69, sr staff engr, Operational Software Opers, 69-73, PROJ MGR, DEFENSE SYSTS, TRW SYSTS, 73- *Mem:* Inst Elec & Electronics Engrs. *Res:* Stochastic processes and noise theory applied to underwater sound; statistical analysis of geophysical observations; guidance and navigation of spacecraft in presence of noise; computer sciences and software systems. *Mailing Add:* 30471 Camino Porvenir Rancho Palos Verdes CA 90274

MAGNIEN, ERNEST, b Ger, Mar 28, 25; nat US; m 49; c 2. ORGANIC CHEMISTRY. *Educ:* City Col New York, BS, 49; Polytech Inst Brooklyn, MS, 58. *Prof Exp:* Org chemist, Gane & Ingram, 49-53; res chemist, Burroughs-Wellcome, Inc, 53-60; sr res chemist, USV Pharmaceut Corp, 60-80, ASST RES FEL, REVLON HEALTH CARE GROUP, REVLON INC, 80- *Mem:* Am Chem Soc. *Res:* Isolation of alkaloids and natural products; pharmaceutical compounds; organic synthesis; heterocyclic chemistry; nuclear chemistry. *Mailing Add:* 67-37 166th St Flushing NY 11365

MAGNIN, ETIENNE NICOLAS, b Valloire, France, Feb 8, 22; Can citizen; m 68. ICHTHYOLOGY. *Educ:* Univ Grenoble, Lic es Sc, 52; Univ Nancy, DES, 57; Univ Paris, Doct Etat Ichthyol, 62. *Prof Exp:* Prof zool, Univ Lyon, 55-64; PROF ICHTHYOL, UNIV MONTREAL, 64- *Concurrent Pos:* Consult, Nat Coun Fisheries, France, 57-64, Dept Fisheries, Que, Can, 62-64 & Conserv Dept, Wis, 63. *Mem:* Can Soc Zoologists; Am Fisheries Soc; Int Acad Fishery Scientists. *Res:* Freshwater benthos. *Mailing Add:* Dept of Biol Univ of Montreal PO Box 6128 Montreal PQ H3C 3J7 Can

MAGNO, MICHAEL GREGORY, b Newark, NJ, Aug 9, 42; m 65; c 3. PHYSIOLOGY. *Educ:* Rutgers Univ, New Brunswick, BS, 64, PhD(physiol), 69. *Prof Exp:* Instr physiol, Albany Med Col, 68-73; res fel, 73-75, RES ASSOC, CARDIOVASC-PULMONARY DIV, HOSP UNIV PA, 75- *Mem:* Am Physiol Soc. *Res:* Capillary exchange in the lung; cardio-pulmonary adjustments to hypoxic in birds and mammals; bronchial circulation. *Mailing Add:* Cardiovasc-Pulmonary Div Hosp of the Univ of Pa Philadelphia PA 19104

MAGNO, RICHARD, b Newark, NJ, May 5, 44; m 68; c 1. SOLID STATE PHYSICS. *Educ:* Stevens Inst Technol, BS, 66; Rutgers Univ, PhD(physics), 74. *Prof Exp:* fel physics, Univ Alta, 74-79; RES PHYSICIST, NAVAL RES LABS, 79- *Mem:* Sigma Xi; Am Phys Soc. *Res:* Inelastic electron tunneling is being used to study metal-insulator-metal junctions whose barriers contain organic molecules or were formed in an organic vapor glow discharge. *Mailing Add:* Code 6871 Naval Res Labs Washington DC 20375

MAGNUS, ARNE, b Oslo, Norway, Aug 17, 22; nat US; m 50; c 3. MATHEMATICS. *Educ:* Univ Oslo, Cand Real, 52; Washington Univ, PhD(math), 53. *Prof Exp:* Instr math, Univ Kans, 52-54; asst prof, Univ Nebr, 54-56; asst prof, Univ Colo, 56-65, prof, 65-66; PROF MATH, COLO STATE UNIV, 66- *Mem:* Math Asn Am; Am Math Soc. *Res:* Analytic function of one and several variables; analytic theory of continued fractions; iteration. *Mailing Add:* Dept Math Colo State Univ Ft Collins CO 80523

MAGNUS, DANIEL E, b Chicago, Ill, Feb 14, 29; m 54; c 3. MECHANICAL ENGINEERING, APPLIED MATHEMATICS. *Educ:* Mass Inst Technol, BS, 51, MS & MechE, 53. *Prof Exp:* Res asst, Mass Inst Technol, 52; team leader mech design pract, Small Aircraft Engine Dept, Gen Elec Co, 55-56; mem staff, 56-70, V PRES, GEN APPL SCI LABS, INC, WESTBURY, 70-; PRES & FOUNDER, KLD ASSOCS, INC, 71- *Mem:* Asn Comput Mach; Am Soc Mech Engrs; Am Inst Aeronaut & Astronaut. *Res:* Vibration and stress analysis; heat transfer; computer sciences and numerical analysis; advanced transportation technology. *Mailing Add:* KLD Assocs Inc 300 Broadway Huntington Station NY 11743

MAGNUS, GEORGE, b Ganister, Pa, Jan 16, 30; m 54; c 4. PLASTICS CHEMISTRY. *Educ:* Franklin & Marshall Col, BS, 52; Univ Pittsburgh, PhD(org chem), 56. *Prof Exp:* Chemist, Union Carbide Chem Co, 56-71; chemist, 71-74, technol mgr urethanes, 74-81, SR RES CHEMIST, STEPAN CHEM CO, 81- *Mem:* Am Chem Soc. *Res:* Applied research and product development in rigid urethane foams; solid and microcellular urethane elastomers; applied research in spandex fibers; development of new poly-e-caprolactone and polyadipate polyols for solid and microcellular urethane elastomers; development of class I and class II rated rigid urethane foams; development of new polyols for class I and class II rated rigid urethane foams. *Mailing Add:* Edens & Winnetka Stepan Chem Co Northfield IL 60093

MAGNUSON, EUGENE ROBERT, b Emerson, Nebr, Dec 5, 33; m 60. ORGANIC CHEMISTRY. *Educ:* Univ Nebr, BS, 55, MS, 58; Kans State Univ, PhD(org chem), 66. *Prof Exp:* Res chemist, Standard Oil Co Div, Am Oil Co, Ind, 60 & Allis-Chalmers Mfg Co, Wis, 63-69; PROF CHEM, MILWAUKEE SCH ENG, 69- *Mem:* Am Chem Soc; Soc Plastics Eng. *Res:* Insulation of electrical components as applied to motors, generators and transformers by encapsulation using various thermal and electrical resin systems. *Mailing Add:* 4725 N 147th St Brookfield WI 53005

MAGNUSON, GUSTAV DONALD, b Chicago, Ill, Aug 22, 26; m 50; c 4. SOLID STATE PHYSICS, ATOMIC PHYSICS. *Educ:* Univ Chicago, PhB, 49, BS, 50; Univ Ill, MS, 52, PhD(physics), 57. *Prof Exp:* Asst, Univ Ill, 53-57; sr staff scientist, Gen Dynamics-Convair, Calif, 57-66; res assoc prof aerospace eng & eng physics, Univ Va, 66-69; res scientist, Atomic Physics Lab, Gulf Energy & Environ Systs, 69-73; res physicist, IRT Corp, 73-76; STAFF SCIENTIST, GEN DYNAMICS-CONVAIR, 77- *Concurrent Pos:* Asst, Anderson Phys Lab, Ill, 53-55. *Mem:* AAAS; Am Phys Soc; Am Asn Physics Teachers. *Res:* Molecular physics; radiation damage; surface-particle interactions; atomic collisions; large superconducting magnet systems for fusion research. *Mailing Add:* 1755 Catalina Blvd San Diego CA 92107

MAGNUSON, HAROLD JOSEPH, b Halstead, Kans, Mar 31, 13; m 35; c 2. OCCUPATIONAL MEDICINE. *Educ:* Univ Southern Calif, AB, 34, MD, 38; Johns Hopkins Univ, MPH, 42; Am Bd Prev Med, dipl. *Prof Exp:* Intern med & surg, Los Angeles County Hosp, 37-39; instr internal med, Sch Med, Univ Southern Calif, 39-41; asst surgeon, USPHS, 41-44, sr asst surgeon, 44-46, surgeon, 47-49, sr surgeon, 49-53, med dir, 53-62, chief oper res sect venereal dis prog, 55-56, chief div occup health, 56-62; dir inst indust health & chmn dept, Sch Pub Health, 62-69, prof indust health, Sch Pub Health & Prof Internal Med, Med Sch, 62-76, assoc dean sch pub health, 69-76, EMER PROF ENVIRON & INDUST HEALTH, SCH PUB HEALTH, UNIV MICH, 76- *Concurrent Pos:* Spec consult, USPHS, 40-41; instr, Johns Hopkins Univ, 43-45; res prof, Univ NC, 45-55; spec lectr, George Washington Univ, 59-62; vpres, Permanent Comn & Int Asn Occup Health; vchmn occup med, Am Bd Prev Med. *Honors & Awards:* Bronze Hektoen Medal, AMA, 55; William S Knudsen Award, Indust Med Asn, 70. *Mem:* Fel AAAS; fel Am Col Physicians; fel Am Pub Health Asn; fel AMA. *Res:* Public health; internal medicine. *Mailing Add:* 12305 Fernando Dr San Diego CA 92128

MAGNUSON, JAMES ANDREW, b Oak Park, Ill, Oct 21, 42; m 64. BIOCHEMISTRY, BIOPHYSICS. *Educ:* Stanford Univ, BS, 64; Calif Inst Technol, PhD(chem), 68. *Prof Exp:* Res fel org chem, Mellon Inst, 67-68; asst prof chem & molecular biophys, 68-75, assoc prof, 75-78, PROF CHEM & BIOPHYS, WASH STATE UNIV, 78- *Mem:* Am Chem Soc; Am Soc Biol Chemists. *Res:* Application of nuclear magnetic resonance spectroscopy to the study of ion binding and small molecular binding to bio-organic molecules; use of both wide-line and high resolution techniques. *Mailing Add:* Dept of Chem 531 Fulmer Hall Wash State Univ Pullman WA 99163

MAGNUSON, JOHN JOSEPH, b Evanston, Ill, Mar 8, 34; m 59; c 2. HYDROBIOLOGY, MARINE SCIENCES. *Educ:* Univ Minn, BS, 56, MS, 58; Univ BC, PhD(zool), 61. *Prof Exp:* Chief tuna behav prog, Biol Lab, Bur Commercial Fisheries, US Fish & Wildlife Serv, 61-67; from asst prof to assoc prof, 68-74, PROF ZOOL & DIR TROUT LAKE BIOL STA, UNIV WIS-MADISON, 74-, CHMN OCEANOG & LIMNOL GRAD PROG, 77- *Concurrent Pos:* Mem affil grad fac, Univ Hawaii, 63-67; prog dir ecol, NSF, 75-76; mem, Adv Comt on Marine Resources Res, Fleet Admin Off, 81-, Ocean Policy Comt, Nat Acad Sci, 79, Fisheries Task Group, Chmn, 81-, Sci Adv Comt to Great Lakes Fishery Comn, 76-81, bd tech exports chmn, 81. *Mem:* Am Fisheries Soc (pres, 80-81); Am Soc Ichthyol & Herpet; Animal Behav Soc; Ecol Soc Am; Am Inst Biol Sci. *Res:* Behavioral ecology of fishes; locomotion of scombrids; distributional ecology of fishes and macroinvertebrates in thermal fronts or gradients; comparative studies of factors determining community structure in lakes; ecology of Great Lakes; long term ecological research on northern lake ecosystems; ecology; fish and wildlife sciences. *Mailing Add:* Dept of Zool Lab of Limnol Univ of Wis Madison WI 53706

MAGNUSON, VINCENT RICHARD, b Laurel, Nebr, May 5, 42; m 62. INORGANIC CHEMISTRY, CRYSTALLOGRAPHY. *Educ:* Univ Nebr, BS, 63; Univ Wis, MS, 65; Univ Ill, PhD(chem), 68. *Prof Exp:* ASSOC PROF CHEM, UNIV MINN, DULUTH, 68- *Mem:* Am Chem Soc; Am Crystallog Asn; Sigma Xi. *Res:* Structural properties of organometallic complexes of Group II and III metals; x-ray crystallography; computer modeling; chemical information storage and retrieval. *Mailing Add:* Dept Chem Univ Minn Duluth MN 55812

MAGNUSON, WINIFRED LANE, b Brady, Tex, Oct 12, 35; m 58. INORGANIC CHEMISTRY. *Educ:* McMurry Col, AB, 59; Univ Kans, PhD(chem), 63. *Prof Exp:* Asst prof chem, McMurry Col, 63-69; CHMN DEPT CHEM, KY WESLEYAN COL, 69-, PROF CHEM, 80- *Concurrent Pos:* Petrol Res Fund grant, 63-64; Res Corp grant, 65-66; Robert A Welch Found grant, 66-69. *Mem:* Am Chem Soc. *Res:* Inorganic reactions in molten salts; reaction of metal carbonyls. *Mailing Add:* Dept of Chem Ky Wesleyan Col Owensboro KY 42301

MAGNUSSON, LAWRENCE BERSELL, b Moline, Ill, Jan 3, 19; m 42; c 4. PHYSICAL INORGANIC CHEMISTRY. *Educ:* Augustana Col, AB, 41; Univ Calif, PhD(phys chem), 49. *Prof Exp:* Chemist, Chem Warfare Serv, US Dept Army, 42-43, metall lab, Univ Chicago, 43-46, Radiation Lab, Univ Calif, Berkeley, 46-49 & Argonne Nat Lab, 49-71; chemist, Betz Labs, 71-79; CONSULT, 79- *Concurrent Pos:* Res fel, City Univ, London, 64-65. *Mem:* Am Chem Soc. *Res:* Complex ions; electrolytes; water treatment. *Mailing Add:* 10279 Smugglers Cove Aurora OH 44202

MAGNUSSON, PHILIP C(OOPER), b Seattle, Wash, Jan 18, 17; m 45; c 3. ELECTRICAL ENGINEERING. *Educ:* Univ Wash, BS, 37, EE, 47; Univ Calif, MS, 38; Mass Inst Technol, ScD(elec eng), 41. *Prof Exp:* Asst elec eng, Univ Calif, 37-38; asst elec engr, US Naval Ord Lab, Wash, 41-43 & Bonneville Power Admin, Ore, 46; from asst prof to assoc prof elec eng, 46-59, PROF ELEC ENG, ORE STATE UNIV, 59- *Concurrent Pos:* Elec engr, Bonneville Power Admin, 65- *Mem:* Inst Elec & Electronics Engrs; Am Soc Eng Educ; Sigma Xi. *Res:* Transient stability of electric power systems; numerical solution of differential equations and field problems; traveling waves on transmission systems. *Mailing Add:* Dept of Elec Eng Ore State Univ Corvallis OR 97331

MAGO, GYULA ANTAL, b Budapest, Hungary, Aug 16, 38. COMPUTER SCIENCE. *Educ:* Budapest Tech Univ, dipl elec eng, 62; Cambridge Univ, PhD(comput sci), 70. *Prof Exp:* Asst prof control eng, Budapest Tech Univ, 62-68; asst prof, 70-80, PROF COMPUT SCI, UNIV NC, CHAPEL HILL, 80- *Mem:* Asn Comput Mach. *Res:* Computer architecture; parallel computation. *Mailing Add:* Dept Comput Sci Univ NC Chapel Hill NC 27514

MAGOON, LESLIE BLAKE, III, b San Jose, Calif, Aug 15, 41; m 64; c 1. GEOLOGY, ORGANIC GEOCHEMISTRY. *Educ:* Univ Ore, BS, 64, MS, 66. *Prof Exp:* Geologist explor, Shell Oil Co, 66-74; GEOLOGIST, US GEOL SURV, 74- *Mem:* Sigma Xi; Am Asn Petrol Geologists. *Res:* Origin, migration, and accumulation of oil and gas; research stresses geology and organic geochemistry of petroleum. *Mailing Add:* US Geol Surv 345 Middlefield Rd MS 99 Menlo Park CA 94025

MAGORIAN, THOMAS R, b Charleston, WVa, Nov 26, 28; m 50; c 3. GEOPHYSICS. *Educ:* Univ Chicago, PhD(geol), 52. *Prof Exp:* Res geologist, Ohio River Div Labs, US Corps Engrs, 50-52, Pure Oil Co, 52-53 & Shell Develop Co, 56-62; consult petrol explor, Tex, 62-63; prin geophysicist, Cornell Aeronaut Lab, 63-73; CHIEF GEOPHYSICIST, ECOL & ENVIRON, INC, 73- *Concurrent Pos:* Mem joint environ effects prog, Environ Characterization Comt, US Dept Defense, 65-; consult, Ltd War Lab & Ballistics Res Lab, US Army, 65-; mem air staff, US Air Force, 66-; dir earth sci prog, Rosary Hill Col, 70-, prof earth sci, 71-74. *Mem:* Fel AAAS; Am Asn Petrol Geol; Am Geophys Union; Geol Soc Am; Ecol Soc Am. *Res:* Geomorphology; biophysics; stratigraphic seismology; hydrology; plant ecology and paleocology; operations research; origin of oil; geotechnical analysis of energy systems. *Mailing Add:* Box D Ecol & Environ Inc Buffalo NY 14225

MAGOSS, IMRE V, b Nagykata, Hungary, July 19, 19; US citizen; m 44; c 2. UROLOGY. *Educ:* Pazmany Peter Univ, Hungary, MD, 43; Am Bd Urol, dipl, 60. *Prof Exp:* Assoc cancer res urologist, Roswell Park Mem Inst, 55-60; from asst prof to assoc prof urol surg, 60-71, prof surg, 71-76, PROF UROL, STATE UNIV NY BUFFALO, 76- *Mem:* AMA; Am Urol Asn; fel Am Col Surg. *Res:* Histochemical changes of prostatic carcinoma during progression. *Mailing Add:* Dept of Surg State Univ of NY Sch of Med Buffalo NY 14214

MAGOUN, HORACE WINCHELL, b Philadelphia, Pa, June 23, 07; m 31; c 3. NEUROANATOMY. *Educ:* Univ RI, BS, 29; Syracuse Univ, MS, 31; Northwestern Univ, PhD(anat), 34. *Hon Degrees:* DSc, Northwestern Univ, 59 & Univ RI, 60; LHD, Wayne State Univ, 65. *Prof Exp:* Instr neurol, Inst Neurol, Northwestern Univ, 34-37, asst prof, Inst & Sch Med, 37-40, assoc prof, Sch Med, 40-43, prof microanat, 43-50; prof anat, Sch Med, 50-62, chmn dept, 50-55, Salmon mem lectr, 56, dean grad div, 62-72, EMER DEAN GRAD DIV, UNIV CALIF, LOS ANGELES, 72-, EMER PROF PSYCHIAT, SCH MED, 74- *Concurrent Pos:* Rockefeller fel, Sch Med, Johns Hopkins Univ, 39-40; staff mem, Nat Res Coun, 72-74. *Honors & Awards:* Jacoby Award, Am Neurol Asn, 56; Borden Award, 61; Passano Award, 63; Lashley Prize, Am Philos Soc, 70; Order Sacred Treasure, Japan, 71. *Mem:* Nat Acad Sci; Am Asn Anat (pres, 64); Am Neurol Asn. *Res:* Neurophysiology; history of neurosciences. *Mailing Add:* 427 25th St Santa Monica CA 90402

MAGOVERN, GEORGE JEROME, b Brooklyn, NY, Nov 17, 23; m; 6. THORACIC SURGERY, CARDIOVASCULAR SURGERY. *Educ:* Marquette Univ, MD, 47; Am Bd Surg, dipl, 55; Am Bd Thoracic Surg, dipl, 60. *Prof Exp:* Intern, Kings County Hosp, 49; resident gen surg, St Vincent's Hosp, NY, 50; resident, Brooklyn Vet Admin Hosp & Kings County Hosps, 50-53; instr surg, Col Med, State Univ NY, 53-54; resident thoracic & cardiovasc surg, George Washington Univ Hosp, 56-58; clin asst prof, 58-64, CLIN ASSOC PROF SURG & DIR SURG RES LAB, SCH MED, UNIV PITTSBURGH, 64- *Concurrent Pos:* Staff physician, Presby-Univ Hosp, 58-; staff physician, Allegheny Gen Hosp, 58-59, dir dept surg, 69-; consult staff physician, St Margaret's, Mercy & Columbia Hosps, 58-; Health Res & Serv Found grant, NIH grant & Am Heart Asn grant. *Mem:* AMA; Asn Thoracic Surg; Am Surg Asn; Am Col Chest Physicians; fel Am Col Surgeons. *Res:* Lung transplantation; sutureless prosthetic heart valve; total heart replacement; reverse coronary perfusion. *Mailing Add:* Dept Surg Allegheny Gen Hosp Pittsburgh PA 15212

MAGRUDER, WILLIS JACKSON, b Lentner, Mo, Aug 7, 35; m 54; c 3. CHEMISTRY, SCIENCE EDUCATION. *Educ:* Northeast Mo State Col, BS, 57; State Col Iowa, MA, 61; Colo State Col, EdD(chem, sci educ), 66. *Prof Exp:* High sch teacher, Mo, 58-60; instr gen & org chem, Fullerton Jr Col, 61-64; from asst prof to assoc prof sci educ, 64-67, PROF SCI & SCI EDUC, NORTHEAST MO STATE COL, 67- *Concurrent Pos:* Mem sci curric comt, Sec Sch Chem & Phys, State Dept Educ, 65-67; Danforth Assoc, 68-; dir, Northeast Mo Regional Sci Fair, 69; mem, Adv Comt Kirksville R-III Bd Educ, 77-78; pres, Sci Teachers Mo, 78-80. *Mem:* Am Chem Soc; Nat Sci Teachers Asn. *Res:* Organolithium chemistry. *Mailing Add:* Dept of Sci Northeast Mo State Univ Kirksville MO 63501

MAGUDER, THEODORE LEO, JR, b Meriden, Conn, Oct 14, 39; m 64; c 3. WILDLIFE BIOLOGY, ECOLOGY. *Educ:* Fairfield Univ, BS, 61; St John's Univ, MS, 63; State Univ NY Col Forestry, Syracuse Univ, PhD(forest zool), 68. *Prof Exp:* ASST PROF BIOL, UNIV HARTFORD, 68-, EDUC DIR ENVIRON CTR, GREAT MT FOREST, 73- *Concurrent Pos:* NSF Col Sci Improv Prog grant prin investr, Woodcock Study, Conn, 70 & US Fish & Wildlife Serv, 71-73. *Mem:* Wildlife Soc; Sigma Xi. *Res:* Wildlife biology including the study of woodchuck, woodcock, crow and seagull population dynamics; development of environmental education programs in ecology and field biology. *Mailing Add:* Dept of Biol 200 Bloomfield Ave West Hartford CT 06117

MAGUE, JOEL TABOR, b New Haven, Conn, Nov 23, 40; m 64; c 2. INORGANIC CHEMISTRY, ORGANOMETALLIC CHEMISTRY. *Educ:* Amherst Col, BA, 61; Mass Inst Technol, PhD(chem), 65. *Prof Exp:* NIH fel, Imp Col, Univ London, 65-66; asst prof, 66-71, ASSOC PROF CHEM, TULANE UNIV, 71- *Mem:* AAAS; Am Chem Soc; NY Acad Sci; Royal Soc Chem. *Res:* Organometallic complexes of the platinum metals; synthetic and structural studies. *Mailing Add:* Dept of Chem Tulane Univ New Orleans LA 70118

MAGUIRE, BASSETT, b Alabama City, Ala, Aug 4, 04. SYSTEMATIC BOTANY. *Educ:* Univ Ga, BS, 26; Cornell Univ, PhD, 38. *Prof Exp:* Instr bot, Univ Ga, 27-29; asst, Cornell Univ, 29-31; from asst prof to assoc prof, Utah State Univ, 31-43; from cur to head cur, 43-68, coordr trop res, 53-68, asst dir, 68-69, dir bot, 69-71 & 73-75, NATHANIEL LORD BRITTON DISTINGUISHED SR CUR, NY BOT GARDEN, 61-, SR SCIENTIST & EMER DIR, 75- *Concurrent Pos:* Botanist, NY Conserv Dept, 30-31; aquatic biologist, US Bur Fish, 32 & 34; cur, Intermountain Herbarium, 32-43; field agt, USDA, 34-35, range examr, Soil Conserv Serv, 35; instr, Cornell Univ, 37-38; non-resident prof, Utah State Univ, 43-; dir expeds SAm, 44-; adj prof, Columbia Univ, 64 & Herbert H Lehman Col, 69-; mem adv comt, Cary Arboretum; consult, Nat Bulk Carriers, Inc, 55-, Eli Lilly & Co, 55-, Tex Instruments, Inc, 64- & US Army Edgewood Arsenal, 64-; consult, Cent Insts Sci & rector, Univ Brasilia, 65; consult, Nat Bot Garden, Dominican Repub, 74- *Honors & Awards:* Sarah Gildersleeve Fife Mem Award, 52; David Livingstone Centenary Medal, Am Geog Soc, 65. *Mem:* AAAS; hon fel Asn Trop Biol (pres, 64-65); hon mem Dom Bot Soc; Orgn Flora Neotropica; NY Acad Sci. *Res:* Phytogeography, South America; flora of Guayana; taxonomy of the Clusiaceae, Theaceae, Rapateaceae, Abolbodaceae, Gentianaceae. *Mailing Add:* New York Bot Garden Bronx NY 10458

MAGUIRE, BASSETT, JR, b Birmingham, Ala, Aug 30, 27; m 50; c 2. ECOLOGY. *Educ:* Cornell Univ, AB, 53, PhD(zool), 57. *Prof Exp:* From instr to assoc prof, 57-78, PROF ZOOL, UNIV TEX, AUSTIN, 78- *Concurrent Pos:* Ed, Ecol Modeling & Eng, 74- *Mem:* AAAS; Ecol Soc Am; Am Soc Limnol & Oceanog; Am Micros Soc; Am Soc Naturalists. *Res:* Mechanisms of community structure determination; internal niche structure; ecological and ecosystem analysis; physiological ecology; ecology of closed systems. *Mailing Add:* Dept of Zool Univ of Tex Austin TX 78712

MAGUIRE, HENRY C, JR, b New York, NY, May 4, 28; m 53; c 3. IMMUNOLOGY, DERMATOLOGY. *Educ:* Princeton Univ, BA, 49; Columbia Univ, 49-50; Univ Chicago, MD, 54; Univ Pa, dipl, 61. *Prof Exp:* Asst instr dermat, Sch Med, Univ Pa, 58-61, instr, 61, assoc, 61-64, asst prof, 64-67, asst instr, Div Grad Med, 58-61, instr, 61-63, assoc, 63-65, asst prof, 65-67; assoc prof med, 67-75, assoc prof microbiol, 69-75, PROF MICROBIOL, IMMUNOL & MED, HAHNEMANN MED COL, 75- *Concurrent Pos:* Guest investr, Rockefeller Univ, 66-67; chief investr, NIH res grant, 68-; investr, Inst Cancer Res, 72-75. *Mem:* AAAS; Am Fedn Clin Res; fel Am Col Physicians; Am Asn Immunologists; Am Acad Dermat. *Res:* Delayed hypersensitivity; tumor immunology; immunological adjuvants; hair growth. *Mailing Add:* Dept Dermatol Hahnemann Med Col 230 N Broad St Philadelphia PA 19102

MAGUIRE, JAMES DALE, b Chelan, Wash, Sept 16, 30; m 55; c 4. AGRONOMY. *Educ:* Wash State Univ, 52; Iowa State Univ, MS, 57; Ore State Univ, PhD(crops), 68. *Prof Exp:* Settler assistance agt irrig eng, US Bur Reclamation, 54-56; instr seed technol, Wash State Univ, 57-66; res assoc seed physiol, Ore State Univ, 66-67; assoc prof, 67-77, PROF AGRON, WASH STATE UNIV, 77- *Concurrent Pos:* Wash Crop Improv Asn fel, Wash State Univ, 68-70; vis prof, Univ Nottingham, 71-, Lisbon & Nat Ctr Sci Res, Paris,79- & Warsaw, 81; consult, Indian Agr Res Conf, 79- *Mem:* Sigma Xi; Am Soc Agron; Asn Off Seed Analysts. *Res:* Seed physiology studies dealing with seed vigor evaluation and determination of metabolic processes involved in dormancy, germination and seedling growth. *Mailing Add:* 291 Johnson Hall Dept of Agron Wash State Univ Pullman WA 99164

MAGUIRE, KEITH DEAN, inorganic chemistry, see previous edition

MAGUIRE, MARJORIE PAQUETTE, b Pearl River, NY, Sept 2, 25; m 50; c 2. CYTOGENETICS. *Educ:* Cornell Univ, BS, 47, PhD(cytol), 52. *Prof Exp:* Instr bot, Cornell Univ, 52-53; res assoc, Genetics Found, 57-60, res scientist, 60-75, assoc prof, 75-81, PROF ZOOL, UNIV TEX, AUSTIN, 81- *Concurrent Pos:* NIH career develop award, 65. *Mem:* Genetics Soc Am; Am Genetic Asn; Bot Soc Am; Am Soc Cell Biol. *Res:* Chromosome mechanisms of synapsis; crossing over and disjunction. *Mailing Add:* Dept Zool Univ Tex Austin TX 78712

MAGUIRE, MILDRED MAY, b Leetsdale, Pa, May 7, 33. PHYSICAL CHEMISTRY. *Educ:* Carnegie-Mellon Univ, BS, 55; Univ Wis, MS, 60; Pa State Univ, PhD(chem), 67. *Prof Exp:* Chemist, Koppers Co, 55-58 & Am Cyanamid Co, 60-63; PROF CHEM, WAYNESBURG COL, 67- *Concurrent Pos:* Leverhulme vis res fel, Univ Leicester, Eng, 80-81; Oak Ridge fac res partic, US Dept Energy, Pittsburgh, 79-80. *Mem:* Am Chem Soc; Am Phys Soc. *Res:* Gas phase electron spin resonance; electron spin resonance of transition metal complexes. *Mailing Add:* Dept Chem Waynesburg Col Waynesburg PA 15370

MAGUIRE, ROBERT JAMES, b Saskatoon, Sask, Sept 13, 46; m 71; c 1. PHYSICAL CHEMISTRY, BIOCHEMISTRY. *Educ:* Univ Ottawa, BSc, 68; Univ Alta, PhD(chem), 72. *Prof Exp:* Fel, Univ Ottawa, 72-73; RES SCIENTIST CHEM, NAT WATER RES INST, CAN DEPT ENVIRON, 73- *Mem:* Chem Inst Can. *Res:* Environmental modeling of toxic substance distribution and transformation in aquatic systems; macromolecule and small molecule interactions. *Mailing Add:* 3274 Northgate Dr Burlington ON L7N 2N5 Can

MAGWIRE, CRAIG A, b Meadow Grove, Nebr, July 9, 22; m 56; c 4. MATHEMATICAL STATISTICS. *Educ:* Nebr State Col, BA, 43; Univ Mich, MS, 47; Stanford Univ, PhD(math statist), 53. *Prof Exp:* Appl sci rep, Int Bus Mach, 53-55; assoc prof math, US Naval Postgrad Sch, 55-59; res mathematician, Aerojet Gen Corp, 59-65; dir comput ctr, Desert Res Inst, Univ Nev, 65-69; dir comput ctr, 69-73, PROF MATH, PORTLAND STATE UNIV, 73- *Mem:* Inst Math Statist; Am Statist Asn. *Res:* Sequential decision theory. *Mailing Add:* 1560 Cherry Crest Ave Lake Oswego OR 97034

MAGYAR, ELAINE STEDMAN, b York, Maine, Feb 21, 46; m 72; c 2. ORGANIC CHEMISTRY. *Educ:* Mt Holyoke Col, AB, 68; Northwestern Univ, PhD(chem), 72. *Prof Exp:* Instr chem, Northwestern Univ, 72-73; lectr, Univ Mass, Amherst, 73-75; adj asst prof, Brandeis Univ, 77-78; ASST PROF CHEM, RI COL, 78- *Concurrent Pos:* Fel, Univ Mass, 73-75. *Mem:* Am Chem Soc; AAAS. *Res:* Organic reaction mechanisms; nuclear magnetic resonance spectroscopy. *Mailing Add:* Dept of Phys Sci RI Col Providence RI 02908

MAGYAR, JAMES GEORGE, b New Milford, Conn, Aug 29, 47; m 72; c 2. ORGANIC CHEMISTRY, PHOTOCHEMISTRY. *Educ:* Dartmouth Col, AB, 69; Northwestern Univ, PhD(chem), 73. *Prof Exp:* Res & teaching fel chem, Mt Holyoke Col, 73-75; asst prof, Hamilton Col, 75-77; adj asst prof, Brandeis Univ, 77-78; lectr, 78-80, ASST PROF CHEM, RI COL, 80- *Mem:* Am Chem Soc. *Res:* Mechanistic organic photochemistry; nuclear magnetic resonance spectroscopy. *Mailing Add:* Dept of Phys Sci RI Col Providence RI 02908

MAH, ALLA DORA, b Stockton, Calif; m 45; c 1. THERMODYNAMICS, PHYSICAL CHEMISTRY. *Educ:* Univ Calif, Berkeley, BS, 42. *Prof Exp:* Chemist analytical chem, Gen Serv Admin, San Francisco, 50-53; phys chemist, Berkeley Thermodyn Lab, Berkeley, 53-67, RES CHEMIST THERMODYN, ALBANY METALL RES CTR, US BUR MINES, 67- *Concurrent Pos:* Grants, Int Copper Res Asn, 68-71. *Honors & Awards:* Meritorious Serv Award Sci Achievement, US Dept Interior, 76. *Mem:* Sigma Xi. *Res:* Combustion calorimetry; critical compilations thermochemical data. *Mailing Add:* PO Box 894 Albany OR 97321

MAH, RICHARD S(ZE) H(AO), b Shanghai, China, Dec 16, 34; m 62; c 1. CHEMICAL ENGINEERING. *Educ:* Univ Birmingham, BSc, 57; Univ London, PhD(chem eng), 61, Imp Col, dipl, 61. *Prof Exp:* Jr chem engr, APV Co Ltd, Eng, 57-58; res fel chem eng, Univ Minn, 61-63; res engr, Tech Ctr, Union Carbide Corp, 63-67; group head & sr proj analyst, Esso Math & Systs, Inc, 67-72; assoc prof chem eng, 72-77, PROF CHEM ENG, NORTHWESTERN UNIV, EVANSTON, 77- *Concurrent Pos:* Consult, Argonne Nat Lab, 75-78 & E I Du Pont de Nemours & Co, Inc, 81-; secy, CACHE Corp, 77- *Honors & Awards:* Comput in Chem Eng Award, Am Inst Chem Engrs, 81. *Mem:* Am Inst Chem Engrs; Am Chem Soc; Asn Comput Mach; Am Soc Eng Educ. *Res:* Computer-aided process planning, design and analysis. *Mailing Add:* Dept of Chem Eng Northwestern Univ Evanston IL 60201

MAH, ROBERT A, b Fresno, Calif, Oct 28, 32. MICROBIOLOGY. *Educ:* Univ Calif, Davis, AB, 57, MA, 58, PhD(microbiol), 63. *Prof Exp:* Asst prof biol, San Fernando Valley State Col, 62-64; from asst prof to assoc prof microbiol, Univ NC, Chapel Hill, 64-71; PROF PUB HEALTH, UNIV CALIF, LOS ANGELES, 71- *Mem:* AAAS; Am Soc Microbiol; Soc Protozoologists. *Res:* Physiology and metabolism of anaerobic bacteria and protozoa; microbial physiology and ecology of anaerobic habitats, especially methane producing bacteria; cycling of matter by microbes. *Mailing Add:* Div of Environ & Nutrit Sci Univ of Calif Sch of Pub Health Los Angeles CA 90024

MAHA, GEORGE EDWARD, b Elgin, Ill, Feb 15, 24; m 53; c 5. MEDICINE, PHARMACOLOGY. *Educ:* Univ Notre Dame, BS, 50; St Louis Univ, MD, 53. *Prof Exp:* Rotating intern, Mt Carmel Mercy Hosp, Detroit, 54; resident med, Cochrane Vet Admin Hosp, St Louis, 55; fel, St Louis Univ Hosp, 56; Nat Heart Inst fel cardiol, Med Ctr, Duke Univ, 56-58; internist & cardiologist, pvt pract, 58-59; asst dir clin res, Lilly Labs Clin Res, 59-61; internist & cardiologist, Hosp Pract, 61-64; rev officer, Div New Drugs, US Food & Drug Admin, 64-66; EXEC DIR CLIN RES, MERCK SHARP & DOHME RES LABS, 66- *Concurrent Pos:* Clin asst prof med, Jefferson Med Col, 66- *Mem:* AAAS; Am Heart Asn; Am Col Cardiologists; Am Diabetes Asn; Am Soc Clin Pharmacol & Therapeut. *Res:* Internal medicine; clinical pharmacology. *Mailing Add:* Merck Sharp & Dohme Res Labs West Point PA 19486

MAHADEVA, MADHU NARAYAN, b Kallidaikurichi, India, Apr 27, 30; US citizen; m 57; c 2. ZOOLOGY. *Educ:* Univ Madras, MA, 51, MS, 52; Univ Calif, Los Angeles, PhD(zool), 56. *Prof Exp:* Lectr biol & head dept, Harward Col, Ceylon, 50-51; lect & head dept, Dharmaraja, Kandy & Zahira Cols, Ceylon, 52-53; res officer, Fisheries Res Sta, Govt of Ceylon, 53-61; head dept biol, Jamshedpur Coop Col, India, 61-67, Govt of India Univ Grants Comn fac res grant, 66-67; actg assoc prof zool & Acad Senate res grant, Univ Calif, Los Angeles, 67-68; assoc prof, 68-76, PROF BIOL, UNIV WIS-OSHKOSH, 76- *Concurrent Pos:* Teaching asst, Univ Calif, Los Angeles, 54-55; hon head dept biol, Navalar Hall, Tamil Univ Movement, Ceylon, 56-61; NSF instnl grant, Univ Wis, 70-71, fac res grants from Pres/chancellor, 72-73 & 74-75. *Mem:* AAAS; Sigma Xi; Nat Asn Biol Teachers; Am Inst Biol Sci; Am Fisheries Soc. *Mailing Add:* Dept of Biol Univ of Wis Oshkosh WI 54901

MAHADEVAN, PARAMESWAR, b India, Apr 23, 26; m 58; c 2. ATOMIC PHYSICS, MOLECULAR PHYSICS. *Educ:* Univ Kerala, BSc, 44, MSc, 46; Univ London, PhD(physics), 58. *Prof Exp:* Lectr physics, Univ Kerala, 47-54; fel elec eng, Univ Fla, 59-60; consult physics, Gen Dynamics/Convair, 60-66; res scientist, Douglas Advan Res Labs, 67-74; STAFF SCIENTIST, AEROSPACE CORP, EL SEGUNDO, 74- *Mem:* AAAS; Am Phys Soc; fel Brit Inst Physics. *Res:* Atomic and molecular collision processes; measurement of interaction crossections; phenomena accompanying the impact of ions and atoms on clean metallic surfaces, such as sputtering, secondary electron emission and ion reflection; chemistry and physics of the earth's ionosphere; space science. *Mailing Add:* Areospace Corp 2350 El Segundo Bl El Segundo CA 90245

MAHADEVAN, SELVAKUMARAN, b Madras, India, Sept 29, 48. BIOLOGICAL OCEANOGRAPHY, BENTHIC ECOLOGY. *Educ:* Univ Madras, BSc, 67; Annamalai Univ, MSc, 71; Fla State Univ, PhD(oceanog), 77. *Prof Exp:* Environ scientist, Conserv Consult Inc, Palmetto, Fla, 75-78; staff scientist marine biol, 78-80, DIR ENVIRON ASSESSMENT, MOTE MARINE LAB, SARASOTA, FLA, 80- *Mem:* Int Asn Meiobenthologists; NAm Benthological Soc; Estuarine Res Fedn; Marine Biol Asn, India; Deep-Sea Biol Soc. *Res:* Marine benthic ecology; thermal pollution; environmental assessment and prediction; biological data analysis; ecological theories and applications to benthic communities; deep-sea ecology; recolonization patterns of benthos. *Mailing Add:* Mote Marine Lab 1600 City Island Park Sarasota FL 33577

MAHADEVIAH, INALLY, b Hoovinamoda, India, May 25, 28; m 60; c 3. NUCLEAR CHEMISTRY, INORGANIC CHEMISTY. *Educ:* Univ Mysore, BSc, 50, MSc, 54; Univ Cincinnati, PhD(chem), 63. *Prof Exp:* Lectr chem, Univ Mysore, 50-56; asst prof, Ft Hays Kans State Col, 60-61; from asst prof to assoc prof, 61-74, PROF CHEM, YOUNGSTOWN STATE UNIV, 74- *Concurrent Pos:* Res assoc, Univ Col, Univ London, 69-70. *Mem:* Am Chem Soc. *Mailing Add:* Dept of Chem Youngstown State Univ Youngstown OH 44555

MAHAFFEY, KATHRYN ROSE, b Johnstown, Pa, Dec 24, 43. NUTRITION, EXPERIMENTAL PATHOLOGY. *Educ:* Pa State Univ, BS, 64; Rutgers Univ, MS, 66, PhD(nutrit), 68. *Prof Exp:* NIH fel endocrine pharmacol, Sch Med, Univ NC, Chapel Hill, 67-69, res assoc, 69-70, asst prof path, 70-72; proj mgr lead contamination of foods, 72-78, asst to dir, Div Nutrit, 75-78, RES BIOCHEMIST, FOOD & DRUG ADMIN, 78- *Concurrent Pos:* Lectr, Sch Home Econ, Univ NC, Greensboro, 68-71; prog coordr, Univs Assoc Res & Educ in Path, Inc, Bethesda, Md, 71-72; adj asst prof community med, Sch Med, Georgetown Univ, 72-74. *Mem:* Am Inst Nutrit; Am Soc Exp Path; Am Pub Health Asn. *Mailing Add:* Div Nutrit Bur of Foods 1090 Tusculum Ave Cincinnati OH 45226

MAHAFFY, JOHN HARLAN, b Kansas City, Mo. COMPUTATIONAL PHYSICS, PHYSICS. *Educ:* Univ Nebr, BS, 70; Univ Colo, PhD(astrophys), 74. *Prof Exp:* staff mem nuclear reactor safety, 76-81, ASSOC GROUP LEADER, SAFETY CODE DEVELOP GROUP, ENERGY DIV, LOS ALAMOS NAT LAB, 81- *Res:* Numerical modeling of multi-phase fluid flow and application of these models on multiprocessor computers. *Mailing Add:* Q-9 MS553 Los Alamos Nat Lab Los Alamos NM 87545

MAHAJAN, DAMODAR K, b Pilode, Maharastra; m 54; c 2. BIOCHEMISTRY, ENDOCRINOLOGY. *Educ:* Univ Poona, BSc(Hons), 51, MSc, 53, PhD(biochem), 64; Univ Utah, dipl steroid biochem, 61. *Prof Exp:* Pop Coun New York fel, Inst Steroid Biochem, Univ Utah, 60-62, Am Cancer Soc fel, Dept Biochem, 62-63; sr res asst steroid biochem, Cancer Res Inst, Bombay, India, 63-65, res officer, 65-69; instr steroid hormones, Dept Med & dir, Intermountain Regional Lab, Univ Utah, 69-72; asst prof hormones, Dept Obstet & Gynec, Pa State Univ, 72-75; ASST PROF HORMONES, DEPT REPRODUCTIVE BIOL, CASE WESTERN RESERVE UNIV, 75- *Concurrent Pos:* Teacher biochem, Univ Bombay, 68; vis prof, Univ del Salvador, Inst Latino Am de Fisiologia de la Reproduction, Buenos Aires, Argentina, 72. *Mem:* AAAS; Endocrine Soc; Soc Study Reproduction. *Res:* Metabolism of steroid hormones in health and endocrine disorders; inhibitory effect of progesterone, steroidogenic ability of different cells of the ovary; bioconversion of steroids by reproductive organs; radioimmunoassay of steroids; steroid binding proteins; isolation and physiological effects of ovarian peptides. *Mailing Add:* Dept of Reproductive Biol Case Western Reserve Univ Cleveland OH 44106

MAHAJAN, OM PRAKASH, b Sujanpurtira, India, July 13, 36; m 66; c 2. FUEL CHEMISTRY. *Educ:* Panjab Univ, BSc Hons, 57, MS, 59, PhD(chem), 65. *Prof Exp:* Lectr chem, Panjab Univ, 61-66; res assoc, Pa State Univ, 66-69; lectr, Panjab Univ, 69-73; sr res assoc, Pa State Univ, 73-79; SR RES CHEMIST, AMOCO RES CTR, 79- *Mem:* Am Chem Soc. *Res:* Coal: characterization and reactivity, liquifaction, gasification, and catalysis; activated carbons: adsorption characteristics, nature of surface and surface complexes; adsorption: physical adsorption, pore structure, surface area, and molecular sieves; author or coauthor of over 70 publications. *Mailing Add:* Amoco Res Ctr PO Box 400 Naperville IL 60566

MAHAJAN, SATISH CHANDER, b Chandigarh, India, Dec 6, 35; m 62; c 2. REPRODUCTIVE PHYSIOLOGY, ENDOCRINOLOGY. *Educ:* Punjab Univ, India, BVSc, 57; Agra Univ, MVSc, 60; Rutgers Univ, PhD(animal sci), 65. *Prof Exp:* Exten officer vet sci, Block Develop Area, 57-58; res asst animal sci, Indian Vet Res Inst Izatnagar, 60-61; PROF BIOL, LANE COL, 65- *Concurrent Pos:* Ford Found fel, Univ Wis-Madison, 65-66. *Mem:* AAAS; Am Soc Animal Sci. *Res:* Study of factors which affect fertilization and survival of embryo in various animals. *Mailing Add:* Dept of Biol Lane Col Jackson TN 38301

MAHAJAN, SUBHASH, b Gurdaspur, India, Oct 4, 39; m 65; c 3. STRUCTURE-PROPERTY RELATIONS, PHYSICAL MET. *Educ:* Panjab Univ, Chandigarh, BSc, 59; Indian Inst Sci, BE, 61; Univ Calif, Berkeley, PhD(mat sci), 65. *Prof Exp:* Res asst mat sci, Univ Calif, Berkeley, 61-65; res metallurgist res, Univ Denver, 65-68; Harwell fel mat sci, Ukaea, Harwell, Eng, 68-71; MEM TECH STAFF PHYS METALL, BELL LABS, MURRAY HILL, 71-, GROUP SUPVR, 81- *Concurrent Pos:* Daad fel, Univ Gottingen, WGer, 76. *Mem:* Sigma Xi; AAAS; NY Acad Sci; Am Inst Mining Metall & Petroleum Engrs; Electrochem Soc. *Res:* Correlations between structure and properties of materials encompassing magnetic mats, metals, ceramics and semiconductors. *Mailing Add:* Bell Labs 600 Mountain Ave Murray Hill NJ 07974

MAHALINGAM, LALGUDI MUTHUSWAMY, b Madras, India, May 19, 46. SOLID STATE PHYSICS, SOLAR ENERGY. *Educ:* Univ Madras, BSc, 66; Carnegie-Mellon Univ, MS, 72, PhD(solid state physics), 76. *Prof Exp:* Sci officer nuclear reactor physics, Bhabha Atomic Res Ctr, India, 67-70; FEL & RES PHYSICIST SOLAR ENERGY, CARNEGIE-MELLON UNIV, 76- *Mem:* Assoc Sigma Xi. *Res:* Solar energy, both thermal and direct conversion processes; materials research particularly optical, thermal, electric, magnetic and surface-applied properties; applied magnetism. *Mailing Add:* Dept of Physics Carnegie-Mellon Univ Pittsburgh PA 15213

MAHALL, BRUCE ELLIOTT, b Springfield, Mass, Apr 21, 46. PLANT ECOLOGY. *Educ:* Dartmouth Col, AB, 68; Univ Calif, Berkeley, PhD(bot), 74. *Prof Exp:* Fel physiol plant ecol, Carnegie Inst Washington, 74-75; asst prof physiol plant ecol, 75-80, PROF DEPT BIOL SCI, UNIV CALIF, SANTA BARBARA, 80- *Mem:* Ecol Soc Am; Brit Ecol Soc; Am Soc Plant Physiologists; AAAS. *Res:* Environmental and physiological restrictions of plant distributions and dimensions of plant niches. *Mailing Add:* Dept of Biol Sci Univ of Calif Santa Barbara CA 93106

MAHAN, ARCHIE IRVIN, b Portland, Maine, Sept 1, 09; m 41; c 1. PHYSICS. *Educ:* Friends Univ, AB, 31; Johns Hopkins Univ, PhD(physics), 40. *Prof Exp:* Jr instr physics, Univ Kans, 31-32; jr instr optics, Johns Hopkins Univ, 34-38; instr physics, Georgetown Univ, 38-41; physicist, US Naval Ord Lab, 41-42, sr physicist, 45-53, div chief & optics dir, 53-55; assoc physicist, US Naval Gun Factory, 42-45; sr res physicist, 55-62, PRIN PHYSICIST, APPL PHYSICS LAB, JOHNS HOPKINS UNIV, 62- *Concurrent Pos:* Lectr, Grad Sch, Georgetown Univ, 52-54 & Am Inst Physics, 61-; mem, Nat Acad Sci Postdoctoral Eval Panel, 69- *Mem:* Fel AAAS; fel Am Phys Soc; fel Optical Soc Am (treas, 60-). *Res:* Infrared; optical design; interferometry; roof prisms; diffraction by telescopes, plane-parallel plates, cones and circularly symmetric apertures; radiation fields; radome boresight error; astronomical refraction; spontaneous and stimulated emission in cylinders; optical properties of cylinders; boundary value problems. *Mailing Add:* Appl Physics Lab Johns Hopkins Rd Laurel MD 20810

MAHAN, BRUCE HERBERT, b New Britain, Conn, Aug 17, 30. PHYSICAL CHEMISTRY. *Educ:* Harvard Univ, AB, 52, PhD(chem), 56. *Prof Exp:* From instr to assoc prof, 56-66, chmn dept, 68-71, PROF CHEM, UNIV CALIF, BERKELEY, 66-, PRIN INVESTR MAT RES, 73- *Concurrent Pos:* Vis fel, Joint Inst Lab Astrophys, Univ Colo, Boulder, 72. *Honors & Awards:* Calif Sect Award, Am Chem Soc, 68. *Mem:* Nat Acad Sci; Am Chem Soc. *Res:* Gas phase reaction kinetics, particularly ionic and electronic collision phenomena. *Mailing Add:* Dept of Chem Univ of Calif Berkeley CA 94720

MAHAN, DONALD CLARENCE, b East Chicago, Ind, May 28, 38; m 62; c 2. ANIMAL NUTRITION. *Educ:* Purdue Univ, West Lafayette, BS, 60, MS, 65; Univ Ill, Urbana, PhD(nutrit), 69. *Prof Exp:* Asst prof, Univ, 69-75, assoc prof, 75-81, PROF ANIMAL SCI, OHIO STATE UNIV & OHIO AGR RES DEVELOP CTR, 81- *Mem:* Am Soc Animal Sci; Am Inst Nutrit; Sigma Xi. *Res:* Protein nutrition in reproducing swine; selenium and vitamin E nutrition in swine; calcium and phosphorus nutrition in swine; management and nutrition interrelationship with weanling swine. *Mailing Add:* Dept of Animal Sci Ohio Agr Res Develop Ctr Wooster OH 44691

MAHAN, GERALD DENNIS, b Portland, Ore, Nov 24, 37; m 65; c 3. THEORETICAL SOLID STATE PHYSICS. *Educ:* Harvard Univ, AB, 59; Univ Calif, Berkeley, PhD(physics), 64. *Prof Exp:* Physicist, Gen Elec Res & Develop Ctr, 64-67; assoc prof physics, Univ Ore, 67-73; PROF PHYSICS, IND UNIV, BLOOMINGTON, 73- *Concurrent Pos:* Alfred P Sloan res fel, 68-70. *Mem:* Fel Am Phys Soc. *Res:* Theory of optical and transport phenomena in solids. *Mailing Add:* Dept of Physics Ind Univ Bloomington IN 47401

MAHAN, HAROLD DEAN, b Ferndale, Mich, June 11, 31; m 54; c 5. ORNITHOLOGY, ECOLOGY. *Educ:* Wayne State Univ, BA, 54; Univ Mich, MS, 57; Mich State Univ, PhD(zool), 64. *Prof Exp:* From instr to prof biol, Cent Mich Univ, 57-72, dir environ interpretation ctr, 71-72; DIR, CLEVELAND MUS NATURAL HIST, 72- *Mem:* Am Ornithologists Union; Wilson Ornith Soc; Animal Behav Soc. *Res:* Growth and temperature regulation in birds; animal behavior. *Mailing Add:* Cleveland Mus Natural Hist Wade Oval University Circle Cleveland OH 44106

MAHAN, KENT IRA, b Springfield, Mo, June 7, 42; m 65; c 1. ANALYTICAL CHEMISTRY, PHYSICAL CHEMISTRY. *Educ:* Southwest Mo State Col, BS, 64; Columbia Univ, PhD(chem), 69. *Prof Exp:* From asst prof to assoc prof, 69-77, PROF CHEM, UNIV SOUTHERN COLO, 77- *Concurrent Pos:* Fel, Univ Denver, 81. *Mem:* Sigma Xi; Am Chem Soc. *Res:* Environmental chemistry; applied atomic spectroscopy; trace metal. *Mailing Add:* Dept Chem Univ Southern Colo Pueblo CO 81005

MAHANEY, WILLIAM C, b Utica, NY, May 17, 41. PHYSICAL GEOGRAPHY, GEOMORPHOLOGY. *Educ:* Syracuse Univ, BA, 65; Ind Univ, MA, 67; Univ Colo, PhD(geog), 70. *Prof Exp:* Asst prof geog, Univ NDak, 70-71; asst prof, Brock Univ, summer 71; asst prof, 71-74, ASSOC PROF GEOG, YORK UNIV, 74- *Mem:* AAAS; Brit Soc Soil Sci; Glaciol Soc; Clay Minerals Soc; Am Quaternary Asn. *Res:* Pedology; Quaternary geology; glacial geomorphology. *Mailing Add:* 1 Bathgate Dr West Hill ON M1C 1X4 Can

MAHANTHAPPA, KALYANA T, b Hirehalli, India, Oct 29, 34; m 61; c 3. ELEMENTARY PARTICLE PHYSICS. *Educ:* Univ Mysore, BSc, 54; Univ Delhi, MSc, 56; Harvard Univ, PhD(physics), 61. *Prof Exp:* Res assoc physics, Univ Calif, Los Angeles, 61-63; asst prof, Univ Pa, 63-66; assoc prof, 66-69, fac res fel, 70-71, 76-77, PROF PHYSICS, UNIV COLO, BOULDER, 69- *Concurrent Pos:* Mem, Inst Advan Study, 64-65; dir, Boulder Summer Inst Theoret Physics, 68-69; vis scientist, Int Ctr Theoret Physics, Trieste, 70-71; dir, NATO Advanced Study Inst, 79. *Mem:* AAAS; fel Am Phys Soc. *Res:* Quantum field theory; elementary particle physics; quantum electro-dynamics; gauge theories and symmetries as applied to weak, electromagnetic and strong interactions. *Mailing Add:* Dept of Physics Univ of Colo Boulder CO 80309

MAHANTI, SUBHENDRA DEB, b Cuttack, India, Sept 24, 45; m 72; c 2. THEORETICAL SOLID STATE PHYSICS, BIOPHYSICS. *Educ:* Utkal Univ, India, BSc, 61; Univ Allahabad, MSc, 63; Univ Calif, Riverside, PhD(physics), 68. *Prof Exp:* Res asst physics, Univ Allahabad, 63-64 & Univ Calif, Riverside, 64-68; mem tech staff physics, Bell Tel Lab, Murray Hill, NJ, 68-70; asst prof, 70-76, ASSOC PROF PHYSICS, MICH STATE UNIV, 76- *Mem:* Am Phys Soc. *Res:* Structural, electronic and magnetic phase transitions; electron nuclear interactions in solids; energy and charge transport in biological systems. *Mailing Add:* Dept of Physics Mich State Univ East Lansing MI 48823

MAHAR, THOMAS J, b Albany, NY, July 29, 49; m 76; c 1. DIFFERENTIAL EQUATIONS, BIFURCATION THEORY. *Educ:* Rensselaer Polytech Inst, BSc, 71, PhD(math), 75. *Prof Exp:* Vis mem res, Courant Inst Math Sci, NY Univ, 75-77; asst prof, Math Dept, Utah State Univ, 77-78; ASST PROF APPL MATH, DEPT ENG SCI & APPL MATH, NORTHWESTERN UNIV, 78- *Concurrent Pos:* Vis prof, Rensselaer Polytech Inst, 75 & 79. *Mem:* Soc Indust & Appl Math; Am Math Soc. *Res:* Bifurcation phenomena in nonlinear problems; analysis of discontinuous boundary value problems; numerical models in mechanics and population biology. *Mailing Add:* Dept Eng Sci & Appl Math Technol Inst Northwestern Univ Evanston IL 60201

MAHARRY, DAVID EDWIN, theoretical physics, see previous edition

MAHAVIER, WILLIAM S, b Houston, Tex, July 30, 30; m; c 2. MATHEMATICS. *Educ:* Univ Tex, BS, 51, PhD(math), 57. *Prof Exp:* Physicist, US Air Missile Test Ctr, Calif, 51-52; mathematician, Defense Res Lab, Univ Tex, 54-57; instr math, Ill Inst Technol, 57-59; asst prof, Univ Tenn, 59-64; from asst prof to assoc prof, 64-70, PROF MATH, EMORY UNIV, 70- *Mem:* Am Math Soc; Math Asn Am. *Mailing Add:* Dept of Math Emory Univ Atlanta GA 30322

MAHDY, MOHAMED SABET, b Heliopolis, Egypt, Oct 29, 30; Can citizen; m 51; c 2. VIROLOGY, IMMUNOLOGY. *Educ:* Cairo Univ, BSc, 50; Univ Pittsburgh, MPH, 60, DScHyg(virol, microbiol), 63. *Prof Exp:* Res asst tissue cult & virol, US Naval Med Res Unit 3, 52-59; investr virol & head sect, Microbiol Unit, Med Res Inst, Egypt, 63-65; head lab virus res, 65-71, res scientist, 65-68, asst to chief virologist, 71-75, HEAD ARBOVIRUSES & SPEC PATHOGENS, LAB SERV BR, ONT MINISTRY HEALTH, 76- *Concurrent Pos:* Guest investr, US Naval Med Res Unit 3, 63-64; lectr, Sch Hyg, Univ Toronto, 68-71, asst prof, 71-72; consult microbiol labs, Can Ctr Inland Waters, 72-77; asst prof, Univ Toronto & Erindale Col, 78-, chmn comt surveillance of anthropod-borne dis, 78-; consult contingency planning comt, Dangerous Exotic Dis, 78- *Mem:* Am Soc Microbiol; Can Soc Microbiol; Brit Soc Gen Microbiol; Can Pub Health Asn; Am Soc Trop Med Hyg. *Res:* Immune and non-specific responses to viral infections; assay of immunoglobulins to identify viral infections; health hazards of environmental pollution with viruses; arboviruses; high-hazard viruses and containment. *Mailing Add:* Arboviruses & Spec Pathogens Labs Ont Ministry Health Box 9000 Term A Toronto ON M5W 1R5 Can

MAHENDRAPPA, MUKKATIRA KARIAPPA, b Coorg, India, Sept 20, 41; Can citizen; m 61; c 3. FOREST SOILS. *Educ:* Karnatak Univ, India, BSc, 61; Utah State Univ, MS, 63, PhD(soil chem), 66. *Prof Exp:* Res soil scientist, Univ Calif, Riverside, 66; RES SCIENTIST, CAN FOREST SERV, CAN DEPT ENVIRON, 66- *Mem:* Am Soc Agron; Soil Sci Soc Am; Can Soc Soil Sci; Int Soc Soil Sci. *Res:* Forest fertilization; nitrogen transformations; nutrition of forest nurseries and trees; organic matter decomposition; acid precipitation and nutrient cycling. *Mailing Add:* Can Forest Serv Can Dept of Environ PO Box 4000 Fredericton NB E3B 5P7 Can

MAHENDROO, PREM P, b Indore, India, July 4, 30; m 62; c 2. SOLID STATE PHYSICS, CHEMICAL PHYSICS. *Educ:* Agra Univ, BSc, 50; Panjab Univ, MA, 55; Univ Tex, Austin, PhD(physics), 60. *Prof Exp:* Physicist, Div Acoust, Nat Phys Lab, India, 51-56; from asst prof to assoc prof physics, Tex Christian Univ, 60-74, prof, 73-80; DIR SPECTROS RES & DEVELOP, ALCON LABS, INC, FORT WORTH, TEX, 81- *Concurrent Pos:* Consult, Gen Dynamics Corp, Tex, 61- & Alcon Labs, 65-66; vis prof, Univ Nottingham, 73-74; cancer sci fel, Nat Cancer Inst, 76-78. *Mem:* Fel AAAS; Am Phys Soc; Am Chem Soc. *Res:* Acoustics and ultrasonics; nuclear magnetic and electron spin resonance; biophysics. *Mailing Add:* Alcon Labs Inc PO Box 1959 Ft Worth TX 76101

MAHER, F(RANCIS) J(OSEPH), b Brooklyn, NY, June 11, 15; m 39; c 2. ENGINEERING MECHANICS. *Educ:* Manhattan Col, BS, 36; Va Polytech Inst, MS, 37. *Prof Exp:* Instr appl mech, Va Polytech Inst, 37-41, asst prof, 41-44; contract employee, Ballistics Sect, Naval Res Lab, 44-45; assoc prof eng mech, 45-52, prof, 52-79, EMER PROF ENG SCI & MECH, VA POLYTECH INST & STATE UNIV, 79- *Concurrent Pos:* Instr, Mass Inst Technol, 50; res grants, Res Corp, 52-55, US Army Res Off, 63-65, NSF, 73-78 & NASA, 65-66; consult, Thompson Ramo Wooldridge, Inc, Bethlehem Steel Co, Greiner Eng Sci, Inc & Steinman, Boynton, Gronquist & Birdsall. *Mem:* Am Soc Eng Educ; fel Am Inst Aeronaut & Astronaut; Nat Soc Prof Engrs; Sigma Xi. *Res:* Aerodynamic properties of suspension bridges and other structures; structural vibrations, dynamics and properties of materials; aerodynamic interference of adjacent structures. *Mailing Add:* Box 817 Blacksburg VA 24060

MAHER, GALEB HAMID, b Lebanon, Dec 2, 37; US citizen; m 65; c 3. MATERIALS SCIENCE, PHYSICAL CHEMISTRY. *Educ:* North Adams State Col, BS, 62; Williams Col, MS, 68; Rensselaer Polytech Inst, PhD(mat sci), 72. *Prof Exp:* Ceramic engr, 62-68, ceramic sr engr res & develop, 68-72, SR SCIENTIST MAT RES & DEVELOP, SPRAGUE ELEC CO, 72- *Mem:* Am Ceramic Soc. *Res:* Electrical properties of ceramic dielectrics; physical and electrical properties of thin film dielectrics. *Mailing Add:* Sprague Elec Co 87 Marshell St North Adams MA 01247

MAHER, GEORGE GARRISON, b Washington, DC, Apr 17, 19; m 43; c 5. BIO-ORGANIC CHEMISTRY. *Educ:* NDak Agr Col, BSc, 41, MSc, 49; Ohio State Univ, PhD(org chem), 54. *Prof Exp:* Chemist, Weldon Springs Ord Works, 41-42; chief chemist, Ky Ord Works, 43-44; chemist, Tenn Eastman Corp, 44-45; asst agr chemist, NDak Agr Col, 45-49; res assoc, Res Found, Ohio State Univ, 49-54; sr res chemist, Clinton Corn Processing Co, 54-64; PRIN RES CHEMIST, NORTHERN REGIONAL RES LAB, USDA, 64- *Mem:* AAAS; Am Chem Soc; NY Acad Sci; Sigma Xi. *Res:* Carbohydrate chemistry; starch derivatives; sugars and syrups; physical characterization; enzymology; propellant and explosive chemistry; chemical research and development of agriculturally derived commodities. *Mailing Add:* Northern Regional Res Lab 1815 N University St Peoria IL 61604

MAHER, JAMES VINCENT, b New York, NY, Aug 25, 42; m 66; c 2. PHYSICS. *Educ:* Univ Notre Dame, BS, 64; Yale Univ, MS, 65, PhD(physics), 69. *Prof Exp:* Appointee, Argonne Nat Lab, 68-70; asst prof physics, 70-74, assoc prof, 74-80, PROF PHYSICS, UNIV PITTSBURGH, 80- *Mem:* Am Phys Soc; Sigma Xi. *Res:* Nuclear reactions and spectroscopy; nuclear reactions induced by heavy projectiles; fluctuation phenomena in fluids. *Mailing Add:* Dept of Physics Univ of Pittsburgh Pittsburgh PA 15213

MAHER, JOHN FRANCIS, b Hempstead, NY, Aug 3, 29; m 53; c 5. MEDICINE, NEPHROLOGY. *Educ:* Georgetown Univ, BS, 49, MD, 53. *Prof Exp:* Intern med, Boston City Hosp, 53-54; resident, Georgetown Univ Hosp, 56-58, Nat Inst Arthritis & Metab Dis fel nephrol, Univ & Hosp, 58-60, from instr to assoc prof med, Sch Med, 60-69; prof med & dir div nephrol & clin res ctr, Univ Mo-Columbia, 69-74; prof med & dir, Div Nephrol, Univ Conn, Farmington, 74-79; PROF MED & DIR, DIV NEPHROL, UNIFORMED SERV UNIV HEALTH SCI, 79- *Concurrent Pos:* Ed, J Am Fedn Clin Res, 67-69. *Mem:* Am Fedn Clin Res; Am Soc Artificial Internal Organs; Am Col Physicians; Am Soc Nephrol; Am Heart Asn. *Res:* Hemodialysis, kinetics; toxic nephropathy; dialysis of poisons; fluid and electrolyte homeostasis; transplantation immunology; uremia; renal pathology. *Mailing Add:* Dept Med Uniformed Serv Univ Health Sci Bethesda MD 20814

MAHER, JOHN PHILIP, b Pittsfield, Mass, Oct 2, 42; m 65; c 2. PHYSICS, ELECTRICAL ENGINEERING. *Educ:* Northeastern Univ, BS, 65; Williams Col, MS, 69. *Prof Exp:* Engr, Sprague Elec Co, 65-69, sr engr, 69-73; SR SCIENTIST MAT SCI, SPRAGUE ELEC DIV OF GEN CABLE CORP, 73- *Honors & Awards:* IR 100, Indust Res Mag, 71. *Mem:* Inst Elec & Electronic Engrs; Int Soc Hybrid Microcircuits. *Res:* Electronic properties of materials; high frequency measurements; thin and thick films; ceramics; electronic and electromechanical devices. *Mailing Add:* 21 Alger St North Adams MA 01220

MAHER, JOHN THOMAS, b Milford, Mass, Sept 17, 32; m 56; c 4. PHYSIOLOGY. *Educ:* Boston Col, BS, 53; Boston Univ, PhD(physiol), 71. *Prof Exp:* Instr anat, physiol & chem, Milford Hosp Sch Nursing, 54-55 & 58-59; res physiologist, 59-76; DIR, ALTITUDE RES DIV, US ARMY RES INST ENVIRON MED, 76- *Concurrent Pos:* Adj prof health sci, Boston Univ, 81- *Mem:* Am Col Sports Med; Am Physiol Soc; Asn Mil Surgeons US; Sigma Xi. *Res:* Cardiovascular physiology; environmental physiology and exercise; altitude acclimatization; electrophysiology of the heart; cardiac dynamics. *Mailing Add:* US Army Res Inst of Environ Med Natick MA 01760

MAHER, LOUIS JAMES, JR, b Iowa City, Iowa, Dec 18, 33; m 56; c 3. PALYNOLOGY, QUATERNARY GEOLOGY. *Educ:* Univ Iowa, BA, 55, MS, 59; Univ Minn, Minneapolis, PhD(geol), 61. *Prof Exp:* NATO fel, Cambridge Univ, 61-62; from asst prof to assoc prof, 62-70, PROF GEOL, UNIV WIS-MADISON, 70-, CHMN DEPT, 80- *Mem:* AAAS; Geol Soc Am; Ecol Soc Am. *Res:* Quaternary palynology in central and western United States. *Mailing Add:* Dept of Geol & Geophys Univ of Wis Madison WI 53706

MAHER, MICHAEL JOHN, b Napa, Calif, Oct 28, 28; m 54; c 2. COMPARATIVE ENDOCRINOLOGY. *Educ:* Univ Calif, Los Angeles, AB, 52, PhD(zool), 58. *Prof Exp:* Asst, Univ Calif, Los Angeles, 53-57; res scientist zool, Barnard Col, Columbia Univ, 58-59; res fel anat, Albert Einstein Col Med, 59-60, instr, 60-62; from asst prof to assoc prof zool, 62-69, ASSOC PROF PHYSIOL & CELL BIOL, UNIV KANS, 69- *Mem:* AAAS; Am Soc Zool. *Res:* Reptilian physiology; vertebrates; role of the thyroid gland in metabolism, especially cold blooded vertebrates; role of pancreatic and adrenal hormones in carbohydrate metabolism of reptiles. *Mailing Add:* Dept of Physiol & Cell Biol Univ of Kans Lawrence KS 66044

MAHER, PHILIP KENERICK, b Catonsville, Md, Dec 13, 30; m 56; c 4. PHYSICAL CHEMISTRY. *Educ:* Randolph-Macon Col, BS, 52; Cath Univ Am, MS, 55, PhD(phys chem), 56. *Prof Exp:* Sr res chemist, W R Grace & Co, Md, 56-60, res supvr, 60-62, mgr, 62-68, dir, 68-75; PRES, CATALYST RECOVERY INC, 75-, PRES, KATALISTIKS INST, 81- *Mem:* Am Chem Soc; Am Inst Chem Eng; Am Inst Chemists; Am Mgt Asn; Catalysis Soc. *Res:* Physical and surface chemistry of inorganic materials, including catalysis, adsorption and desorption phenomena; thermal and hydrothermal reactions of inorganic materials such as silicates, aluminate and phosphates; catalyst preparation, regeneration and rejuvenation. *Mailing Add:* Catalyst Recovery Inc 2 Village Square Baltimore MD 21210

MAHER, STUART WILDER, b Knoxville, Tenn, Aug 11, 18; m 43; c 2. GEOLOGY. *Educ:* Univ Tenn, AB, 46, MS, 48. *Prof Exp:* Asst geol, Univ Tenn, 45-46, instr, 46-48; geologist, US Geol Surv, 48-51; res assoc, Univ Tenn, 51-54; sr geologist, Tenn State Div Geol, 54-57, prin geologist, 57-66, chief geologist, 66-81; PRIN GEOLOGIST, KENWILL INC, 81- *Concurrent Pos:* Asst prof, Univ Tenn, Knoxville, 71. *Mem:* AAAS; Am Inst Prof Geologists; Int Asn Genesis Ore Deposits; Soc Econ Geol. *Res:* Economic geology. *Mailing Add:* Kenwill Inc 505 E Broadway Maryville TN 37801

MAHER, VERONICA MARY, b Detroit, Mich, Feb 20, 31. CANCER, MOLECULAR BIOLOGY. *Educ:* Marygrove Col, BS, 51; Univ Mich, MS, 58; Univ Wis, PhD(molecular biol), 68. *Prof Exp:* Res assoc radiol, Sch Med, Yale Univ, 68-69; asst prof biol, Marygrove Col, 69-70; res scientist & chief carcinogenesis lab, Mich Cancer Found, 70-76; assoc prof, 76-80, PROF MICROBIOL, PUB HEALTH & BIOCHEM, MICH STATE UNIV, 80-, CO-DIR CARCINOGENESIS LAB, 76- *Concurrent Pos:* Mem carcinogenesis contract comt, Nat Cancer Inst, NIH, 75-77, sci adv, Carcinogenesis Prog, Div Cancer Cause & Prev, 75-76; sci adv, Nat Ctr Toxicol Res, Food & Drug Admin & Midland Macromolecular Inst, 78-80; mem, Special Cancer Proj Adv Bd, Nat Cancer Inst, 81- *Mem:* Am Asn Cancer Res; Am Soc Microbiol; Environ Mutagen Soc; Tissue Cult Asn; Genetics Soc Am. *Res:* Mutagenic and carcinogenic action of physical and of chemical carcinogenic agents in human cells in culture and the effect of DNA repair on this interaction. *Mailing Add:* Carcinogenesis Lab Fee Hall Mich State Univ East Lansing MI 48824

MAHER, WILLIAM J, b Brooklyn, NY, Mar 10, 27. VERTEBRATE ECOLOGY. *Educ:* Purdue Univ, BS, 51; Univ Mich, MS, 53; Univ Calif, Berkeley, PhD(zool), 61. *Prof Exp:* Lectr biol, San Francisco State Col, 61-62; actg asst prof, Univ Calif, Santa Barbara, 62-63; from asst prof to assoc prof, 63-74, PROF BIOL, UNIV SASK, 74- *Mem:* AAAS; Ecol Soc Am; Am Ornith Union; Arctic Inst NAm. *Res:* Predator-prey relationships; competition between closely related predators; adaptability of developmental rates to arctic environments. *Mailing Add:* Dept of Biol Univ of Sask Saskatoon SK S7H 0W0 Can

MAHESH, VIRENDRA B, b Khanki Punjab, India, Apr 25, 32; m 55; c 3. ORGANIC CHEMISTRY, ENDOCRINOLOGY. *Educ:* Patna Univ, BSc, 51; Univ Delhi, MSc, 53, PhD(org chem), 55; Oxford Univ, DPhil(biol sci), 58. *Prof Exp:* J H Brown Mem fel physiol, Sch Med, Yale Univ, 58-59; from asst res prof to assoc res prof, 59-66, prof, 66-70, REGENTS PROF ENDOCRINOL, MED COL GA, 70-, DIR, CTR POP STUDIES, 71-, CHMN DEPT ENDOCRINOL, 72- *Honors & Awards:* Rubin Award, Am Soc Study Sterility, 63; Billings Silver Medal, 65. *Mem:* Am Fertil Soc; Sigma Xi; Endocrine Soc; Int Soc Neuroendocrinol; Int Asn Clin Res Human Reproduction. *Res:* Isolation, secretion, biosynthesis and metabolism of various steroid hormones; mechanism of hormone action; control of gonadotropin secretion; ovulation; reproductive physiology. *Mailing Add:* Dept of Endocrinol Med Col of Ga Augusta GA 30901

MAHGOUB, AHMED, b Alexandria, Egypt, Aug 20, 41; US citizen. PHARMACOLOGY. *Educ:* Univ Alexandria, BS, 64, MS, 67; Univ NC, PhD(pharmacol), 71. *Prof Exp:* Fel pharmacol, Med Sch, Northwestern Univ, 71-73; sr biologist cell biol, Hoffmann-La Roche Inc, NJ, 73-76; ASST PROF PHARMACOL, SCH MED, UNIV PR, SAN JUAN, 76- *Res:* Studies of the mechanism of actions of parathyroid hormone, thyrocalcitonin, and cholecalciferol derivatives on bone culture and bone cells. *Mailing Add:* Dept of Pharmacol Univ of PR Sch of Med San Juan PR 00936

MAHIG, JOSEPH, b New York, NY, Aug 25, 30; m 56; c 2. ACOUSTICS, AUTOMATIC CONTROL SYSTEMS. *Educ:* City Col New York, BME, 51; Ohio State Univ, MS, 59, PhD(mech eng), 62. *Prof Exp:* Engr, Gen Elec Co, Ohio, 56-57; instr mech, Ohio State Univ, 57-62, asst prof, 62-66; assoc prof, 66-73, PROF MECH ENG, UNIV FLA, 73- *Concurrent Pos:* NSF fel. *Mem:* Am Soc Eng Educ; Am Soc Mech Engrs; Am Inst Aeronaut & Astronaut; Acoust Soc Am. *Res:* Noise and vibration transmission; nonlinear multivariable stability analyses; experimental impedance of human brain; hydrofoil flutter theory and development. *Mailing Add:* Dept of Mech Eng Univ of Fla Gainesville FL 32601

MAHILUM, BENJAMIN COMAWAS, b Calatrava, Philippines, Sept 9, 31; m 56; c 6. SOIL SCIENCE, CROP SCIENCE. *Educ:* Cent Mindanao Univ, Bukidnon, Philippines, BS, 57; Univ Hawaii, MS, 66; Okla State Univ, PhD(soil sci), 71. *Prof Exp:* Asst prof soil sci, Mindanao Inst Technol, Kabacan, Philippines, 71-73; assoc prof & res coordr, Univ Eastern Philippines, 73-74; assoc prof agron & soils & chmn dept, Visayas State Col Agr, Philippines, 74-77; vis asst prof agron, Okla State Univ, 77-79; ASST PROF SOIL SCI, UNIV HAWAII, 79- *Concurrent Pos:* Dir, Regional Coconut Res Ctr, VISCA, Baybay, Philippines, 74-77; mem nat res comts, Philippine Coun Agr & Resources Res, Los Banos Col, Philippines, 74-75 & 75-77. *Mem:* Int Soil Sci Soc; AAAS; Soil Sci Soc Am; Am Soc Agron; Sigma Xi. *Res:* Sewage and industrial waste utilization for crop production and nutrient recycling; utilization of hilly lands for crop and animal production and reforestation; revegetation of eroded lands, mine spoils and roadsides; fertilizer efficiency studies and cropping systems. *Mailing Add:* Dept Agr Univ Hawaii Hilo HI 96720

MAHL, MEARL CARL, b Pipestone, Minn, Sept 13, 38; m; c 3. MICROBIOLOGY, BIOCHEMISTRY. *Educ:* SDak State Univ, BS, 60, MS, 62; Univ Wis-Madison, PhD(microbiol), 66. *Prof Exp:* Res microbiologist, 66-75, SR RES MICROBIOLOGIST, S C JOHNSON & SON, INC, 75- *Concurrent Pos:* Chmn, Bd Wastewater Standards, Racine, Wis, 68-; test collabr, Am Soc Testing Mat, 76- *Mem:* Am Soc Microbiol; Am Soc Testing Mat. *Res:* Virucidal effects of disinfectant chemicals; epidemiology of viruses and their control in the environment; disinfectants and antiseptics. *Mailing Add:* S C Johnson & Son Inc 1525 Howe St Racine WI 53403

MAHLBERG, PAUL GORDON, b Milwaukee, Wis, Aug 1, 28; m 54; c 2. PLANT ANATOMY, CELL BIOLOGY. *Educ:* Univ Wis, BS, 50, MS, 51; Univ Calif, Berkeley, PhD, 58. *Prof Exp:* Drug salesman, Pitman-Moore Co, Wis, 53-54; asst, Univ Calif, 55-58; instr bot, Univ Pittsburgh, 58-65; ASSOC PROF BOT, IND UNIV, BLOOMINGTON, 77- *Mem:* AAAS; Bot Soc Am. *Res:* Lacticifer ontogeny and physiology in normal and abnormal tissues; localization and biosynthesis of alkaloids, terpenoids and hydrocarbons in plant cells. *Mailing Add:* Dept of Biol Ind Univ Bloomington IN 47401

MAHLE, NELS H, b Highland Park, Mich, June 23, 43. ANALYTICAL CHEMISTRY. *Educ:* Eastern Mich Univ, BS, 66; Northern Ill Univ, PhD(anal chem), 74. *Prof Exp:* Res assoc anal chem, Purdue Univ, 72-74; sr anal chemist, 74-77, res specialist, 77-79, PROJ LEADER, ANAL LABS, DOW CHEM CO, 79- *Mem:* Sigma Xi; AAAS; Am Soc Mass Spectrometry; Am Chem Soc. *Res:* Mass spectrometry; polymer characterization; gas science; computer analysis of spectrometry data; environmental analysis. *Mailing Add:* Anal Labs Dow Chem Co Midland MI 48640

MAHLER, HENRY RALPH, b Vienna, Austria, Nov 12, 21; nat US; m 48; c 3. BIOCHEMISTRY. *Educ:* Swarthmore Col, AB, 43; Univ Calif, PhD(org chem), 48. *Prof Exp:* Sr chemist, Tex Res Found, 48-49; res assoc, Univ Wis, 49-50; asst prof enzyme res, 50-55; from assoc prof to prof, 55-66, RES PROF CHEM, IND UNIV, BLOOMINGTON, 66- *Concurrent Pos:* Travel award, NSF, 55 & Rockefeller Found, 57; vis prof, Univ Sao Paulo, 57; vis investr & mem corp, Marine Biol Lab, Woods Hole, 60-; vis prof, Lab Biol Genetics, Nat Ctr Sci Res, France & Univ Paris, 62-63 & 69-70; NIH res career award, 62-, res career investr, 66-, mem biochem study sect, 67-71; vis fel, Univ Col, London, 76- & Univ Vienna, 77; mem, Phys Biochem Study Sect, NIH, 81-83 & Sci Adv Bd, Max Planck Inst, Gottingen, 80-84; dep chief ed, J Neurochem, 81- *Mem:* Am Chem Soc; Am Soc Biol Chemists; Am Soc Cell Biologists; Am & Int Soc Neurochem; Brit Biochem Soc. *Res:* Function, structure, genetics and biosynthesis of cell organelles and their constituents, especially of mitochondria and nerve cell synaptic membranes. *Mailing Add:* Dept of Chem Ind Univ Bloomington IN 47405

MAHLER, RICHARD JOSEPH, b New York, NY, Mar 4, 34; m 60; c 2. INTERNAL MEDICINE, ENDOCRINOLOGY. *Educ:* NY Univ, BA, 55; New York Med Col, MD, 59. *Prof Exp:* Am Diabetes Asn metabolic res fel, New York Med Col, 62-63; NY Acad Med Glorney-Raisbeck traveling fel, Univ Durham, 63-64; from instr to assoc prof med, New York Med Col, 64-71; assoc dir dept metab & endocrinol, City of Hope Med Ctr, Duarte, Calif, 71-72; DIR METAB & ENDOCRINOL, EISENHOWER MED CTR, 72- *Concurrent Pos:* Am Diabetes Asn res & develop award, 66-68; NSF res grant, 66-69; New York City Health Res Coun res grants, 66-70, career scientist award, 68-71. *Mem:* Am Fedn Clin Res; Am Diabetes Asn; Asn Am Med Cols; Endocrine Soc; Am Physiol Soc. *Res:* Hormonal and non-hormonal influences on insulin action, the influence of these factors on its mechanism and its relationship to diabetes mellitus. *Mailing Add:* Eisenhower Med Ctr 39000 Bob Hope Dr Rancho Mirage CA 92270

MAHLER, ROBERT JOHN, b Los Angeles, Calif, Mar 17, 32; m 59; c 2. SOLID STATE PHYSICS. *Educ:* Univ Calif, Los Angeles, BA, 55; Univ Colo, PhD(physics), 63, MBA, 81. *Prof Exp:* Oceanogr, US Navy Hydrographic Off, 57-58; asst nuclear magnetic resonance, Univ Colo, 58-63; physicist, Nat Bur Standards, 63-68, chief solid state electronics sect, 68-71, res physicist, 71-74, chief off prog develop, 74-80; DIR OFF PROG, ENVIRON RES LABS, NAT OCEANIC & ATMOSPHERIC ADMIN, 80- *Concurrent Pos:* Res assoc, Univ Colo, Boulder, 63-64, lectr, 64- *Mem:* Am Phys Soc. *Res:* Investigations of phonon-nuclear spin system interactions using pulsed nuclear magnetic resonance techniques; infrared detectors; measurement techniques. *Mailing Add:* Div 524 Nat Bur of Standards Boulder CO 80302

MAHLER, WALTER, inorganic chemistry, organic chemistry, see previous edition

MAHLER, WILLIAM FRED, b Iowa Park, Tex, Aug 30, 30; m 55; c 2. PLANT TAXONOMY. *Educ:* Midwestern Univ, BS, 55; Okla State Univ, MS, 60; Univ Tenn, Knoxville, PhD(bot), 68. *Prof Exp:* From instr to asst prof bot, Hardin-Simmons Univ, 60-66; asst prof, 68-74, ASSOC PROF BOT, SOUTHERN METHODIST UNIV, 74-, CUR HERBARIUM, 71- *Concurrent Pos:* Ed & publ, Sida, Contrib to Bot, 71- *Mem:* Int Asn Plant Taxon; Am Soc Plant Taxon; Am Bryol & Lichenological Soc. *Res:* Floristic studies and pollen morphology in relation to taxonomic concepts. *Mailing Add:* Herbarium Southern Methodist Univ Dallas TX 75275

MAHLMAN, BERT H, b Bismarck, NDak, Nov 2, 22; m 48; c 3. POLYMER CHEMISTRY, MATERIALS SCIENCE. *Educ:* Univ Minn, BChE, 49. *Prof Exp:* Chemist, Hercules Powder Co, 49-61; res chemist, 61-72, RES SCIENTIST, HERCULES, INC, 77- *Mem:* Am Chem Soc. *Res:* Polymer and coatings research and development; radiation chemistry. *Mailing Add:* 576 W Lafayette Dr W Chester PA 19380

MAHLMAN, GEORGE WILLIAM, b Buffalo, NY, Sept 21, 19; m 43; c 2. PHYSICS. *Educ:* Univ Mich, BSE, 41; Mass Inst Technol, ScD(physics), 48. *Prof Exp:* Assoc physicist, Res Lab, Linde Co Div, Union Carbide Corp, 48-52; sr physicist, Photoswitch Div, Electronics Corp Am, 52-55; adv develop engr, Semiconductor Div, Sylvania Elec Prod, Inc, 55-56; physicist, Res Lab, Hughes Aircraft Co, 57-61; adv engr, Westinghouse Astroelectronics Lab, 62-63; res scientist, Northrop Nortronics, 63-67; sr tech specialist, Autonetics Div, NAm Rockwell Corp, 67-71; design specialist, 71-73, CONSULT PHYSICIST, POMONA DIV, GEN DYNAMICS CORP, 73- *Res:* Physical electronics; highcurrent arcs; infrared; photoconductors; semiconductor physics. *Mailing Add:* 2000 Port Albans Circle Newport Beach CA 92660

MAHLMAN, HARVEY ARTHUR, b La Crosse, Wis, Aug 8, 23; m 45; c 2. ANALYTICAL CHEMISTRY, INORGANIC CHEMISTRY. *Educ:* Univ Minn, BChem & BBA, 49; Univ Tenn, PhD, 56. *Prof Exp:* Chemist, Clinton Lab, Tenn, 44-46; asst, Gen Elec Co, 49-52; chemist, Oak Ridge Nat Lab, 52-73; nuclear staff power resources specialist, Fla Power & Light, Miami, 73-74; RADIATION WASTE & RADIATION CHEM STAFF, TENN VALLEY AUTH, 74- *Concurrent Pos:* NIH spec fel, Inst Radium, Paris, 63-64. *Mem:* Am Soc; Chem. *Res:* Radiochemical and neutron activation analysis; radiation chemistry. *Mailing Add:* 5605 Kingston Park Knoxville TN 37919

MAHLMAN, JERRY DAVID, b Crawford, Nebr, Feb 21, 40; m 62; c 2. NUMERICAL MODELING, STRATOSPHERE. *Educ:* Chadron State Col, AB, 62; Colo State Univ, MS, 64, PhD(atmospheric sci), 67. *Prof Exp:* Instr atmospheric sci, Colo State Univ, 64-67; from asst prof to assoc prof, US Naval Postgrad Sch, 67-70; RES METEOROLOGIST, METEOROL, GEOPHYS FLUID DYNAMICS LAB, NAT OCEANIC & ATMOSPHERIC ADMIN, 70- *Concurrent Pos:* Vis lectr & assoc prof, Princeton Univ, 77-80, prof, 80-; sci adv comt, High Altitude Pollution Prog, Fed Aviation Agency, 78-; mem panel, Middle Atmosphere Prog, Nat Acad Sci, 78-, chmn, 81-, mem comt solar terrestrial res, 81-; assoc ed, J Atmospheric Sci, 79-; mem, Int Comn Meteorol Upper Atmosphere, 80- *Mem:* Sigma Xi; fel Am Meteorol Soc. *Res:* Modeling and diagnosis of the general circulation of the atmosphere, including the transport and chemistry of atmospheric trace constituents. *Mailing Add:* Geophys Fluid Dynamics Lab NOAA Princeton Univ Princeton NJ 08540

MAHLO, EDWIN K(URT), b Berlin, Ger, Dec 24, 23; US citizen; m 48; c 2. CHEMICAL ENGINEERING, ORGANIC CHEMISTRY. *Educ:* Chemotechnicum, Berlin, BS, 48. *Prof Exp:* Indust chemist, Dr S Goetze & Co, Ger, 48-50, prod mgr, 50-53; mfg supt petrochem, Thiochem, Inc, Tex, 53-55; chem engr, Monsanto Co, 55-59, sr engr, 59-61, group leader, Plastics Div, 61-65, SR RES GROUP LEADER, MONSANTO PLASTICS & RESINS CO, 65- *Mem:* Am Chem Soc. *Res:* Chemical process research and development in plastics and organic chemicals. *Mailing Add:* Monsanto Plastics & Resins Co 190 Grochmal Ave Indian Orchard MA 01151

MAHLSTEDE, JOHN PETER, b Cleveland, Ohio, June 5, 24; m 48; c 4. ORNAMENTAL HORTICULTURE. *Educ:* Miami Univ, Ohio, BS, 47; Mich State Univ, MS, 48, PhD(ornamental hort), 51. *Prof Exp:* From asst prof to assoc prof, 51-57, asst dir, 65-66, actg assoc dir, 66-67, head dept hort, 61-65, PROF HORT, IOWA STATE UNIV, 57-, ASSOC DIR, AGR & HOME ECON EXP STA, 67-, ASSOC DEAN, COL AGR, 75- *Concurrent Pos:* Vpres, Agr Res Inst, 74-75; chmn, Exp Sta Comt Policy, Nat Asn State Univ & Land Grant Col, 75-76, mem, Environ Quality Comt, Div Agr, 77; mem, Joint Coun & Exec Comt, Food & Agr Sci, Sci & Educ Admin, US Dept Agr, 77-79. *Honors & Awards:* Colman Award, Am Asn Nueserymen, 58. *Mem:* Fel AAAS(chmn agr sect, 77); Sigma Xi; fel Am Soc Hort Sci (pres, 71-72); Int Plant Propagators Soc (pres, 65). *Res:* Nursery management; plant propagation; morphological subjects; packaging and propagation. *Mailing Add:* 104 Curtiss Hall Iowa State Univ Ames IA 50011

MAHLUM, DANIEL DENNIS, b Wolf Point, Mont, May 5, 33; m 56; c 2. BIOCHEMISTRY. *Educ:* Whitworth Col, Wash, BS, 55; Univ Idaho, MS, 58; Univ Wis, PhD(biochem), 62. *Prof Exp:* Res technician agr chem, Univ Idaho, 55-57, asst agr chemist, 57-58; biol scientist, Hanford Labs, Gen Elec Co, 61-63, sr scientist, 63-65; sr scientist, 65-75, radiobiologist, Energy Res & Develop Admin, 75-76; STAFF SCIENTIST, BATTELLE-NORTHWEST, 76- *Concurrent Pos:* Co-chmn, Conf Early Nutrit & Environ Influences upon Behav Develop, 71; co-chmn, Develop Toxicol Energy Related Pollutants, 77, Coal Conversion & Environ, 80 & chmn, Nat Coun Radiation Protection & Measurements Comt, Biol Effects Magnetic Fields. *Mem:* Radiation Res Soc; Sigma Xi; Am Inst Nutrit; Soc Toxicol. *Res:* Radionuclide metabolism and toxicity; lipid metabolism; nutrition; toxicology of fossil fuel materials. *Mailing Add:* Harrington Rd Richland WA 99352

MAHMOODI, PARVIZ, b Tehran, Iran, Sept 1, 31; m 58; c 2. ENGINEERING, PHYSICS. *Educ:* Abadan Inst Technol, Iran, BSc, 55; Univ Minn, MS, 56, PhD(mech eng), 59. *Prof Exp:* Asst, Univ Minn, 56-58, instr mech eng, 58-59; sr res engr, Minn Mining & Mfg Co, 59-60; res fel, Harvard Univ, 60-61; prof physics & head dept, Abadan Inst Technol, 61-62; res specialist, 62-74, CORP SCIENTIST, 3M CO, 74- *Concurrent Pos:* Lectr, Boston Univ, 60-61; dean Sch Allied Health Sci, Univ Med Sci Iran, 78-79. *Mem:* AAAS; Am Soc Testing & Mat; Acoust Soc Am. *Res:* Heat transfer; elasticity; viscoelasticity; vibration and acoustics. *Mailing Add:* Cent Res Labs 3M Ctr 3M Co 201-BE PO Box 33221 St Paul MN 55133

MAHMOUD, ALY AHMED, b Cairo, Egypt, Jan 25, 35; m 62; c 2. ELECTRICAL ENGINEERING, POWER SYSTEMS. *Educ:* Ain Shams Univ, Cairo, BSc, 58; Purdue Univ, MS, 61, PhD, 64. *Prof Exp:* Instr elec eng, Ain Shams Univ, 58-60; asst prof, Univ NB, 64 & Univ Assiut, 64-66; from asst prof to prof, Univ Mo-Columbia, 66-76; PROF ELEC ENG & DIR POWER AFFIL PROG, IOWA STATE UNIV, 76-, DIR IOWA TEST & EVAL FACIL, 80- *Concurrent Pos:* Vis prof, Ain Shams Univ, Cairo, 64-66; consult, Nat Res Ctr, Cairo, 64-66; sr res elec engr, Naval Civil Eng Lab, 68-69; prog mgr, NSF, 74-76. *Mem:* Inst Elec & Electronics Engrs; Am Phys Soc; Am Soc Eng Educ. *Res:* Power system analysis, transmission and distribution systems; load modeling and management; power system operation and control. *Mailing Add:* 111A Coover Hall Iowa State Univ Ames IA 50011

MAHMOUD, HORMOZ MASSOUD, b Teheran, Iran, May 2, 18; nat US; m 54. THEORETICAL PHYSICS. *Educ:* Univ Tehran, EE, 40; Ind Univ, MS, 49, PhD(physics), 53. *Prof Exp:* Res assoc theoret physics, Ind Univ, 53-54 & Cornell Univ, 54-56; asst prof physics & assoc physicist, Ames Lab, Iowa State Univ, 56-60; assoc prof, 60-70, PROF PHYSICS, UNIV ARIZ, 70- *Mem:* Am Phys Soc. *Res:* Field theory; elementary particles. *Mailing Add:* Dept of Physics Univ of Ariz Tucson AZ 85721

MAHMOUD, IBRAHIM YOUNIS, b Baghdad, Iraq, Sept 9, 33; m 65; c 4. HERPETOLOGY. *Educ:* Ark Agr & Mech Col, BS, 53; Univ Ark, MA, 55; Univ Okla, PhD(zool), 60. *Prof Exp:* Prof biol, Northland Col, 60-63; assoc prof, 63-68, PROF BIOL, UNIV WIS-OSHKOSH, 68- *Concurrent Pos:* Bd regents res grants, Univ Wis, 63-65, 67-69 & 70-71; CAS grant, 75-81. *Mem:* AAAS; Am Soc Zool; Am Soc Ichthyol & Herpet; NY Acad Sci. *Res:* Reptilian physiology with special emphasis on steroid metabolism in reptiles. *Mailing Add:* Dept of Biol Univ of Wis Oshkosh WI 54901

MAHON, RITA, b Eng, Sept 23, 49; m 75. PHYSICS. *Educ:* Univ London, BSc, 70, PhD(physics), 73. *Prof Exp:* Nat Res Coun Can fel, Ctr Res Exp Space Sci, York Univ, 73-75; res assoc physics, Inst Phys Sci & Technol, 75-80, RES ASSOC PHYSICS, DEPT PHYSICS & ASTRON, UNIV MD, 80- *Mem:* Am Phys Soc; Optical Soc Am. *Res:* Quantum optics; laser spectroscopy; atomic and plasma physics. *Mailing Add:* Lab Plasma & Fusion Energy Studies Univ Md College Park MD 20742

MAHON, WILLIAM A, b Airdrie, Scotland, Aug 20, 29; m 56; c 4. CLINICAL PHARMACOLOGY. *Educ:* Harvard Univ, SM, 62; FRCP(C), 60. *Prof Exp:* Sr resident med, St Joseph's Hosp, London, Ont, 56-57; teaching fel path, Univ Western Ont, 57-58; asst resident, Lemuel Shattuck Hosp, 58-59, chief resident, 59-60; assoc, Sch Med, Tufts Univ, 60-62; from asst prof to assoc prof pharmacol & med, Univ Alta, 62-66; asst prof therapeut & assoc med, 66-68, ASSOC PROF PHARMACOL, UNIV TORONTO, 66-, ASSOC PROF MED, 68- *Mem:* Am Fedn Clin Res; Can Soc Pharmacol. *Res:* Cardiovascular pharmacology in man and animals; distribution of antibiotics in normal man and in man with renal failure; methods for studying drug action in man. *Mailing Add:* Toronto Gen Hosp Toronto ON M5G 1L7 Can

MAHONEY, BERNARD LAUNCELOT, JR, b Boston, Mass, Nov 1, 36; m 65; c 2. ANALYTICAL CHEMISTRY, PHYSICAL CHEMISTRY. *Educ:* Boston Col, BS, 58, MS, 60; Univ NH, PhD(phys chem), 67. *Prof Exp:* From asst prof to assoc prof, 65-74, CHMN DEPT, MARY WASHINGTON COL, 71-, PROF CHEM, 74- *Mem:* Am Chem Soc; Soc Appl Spectros; fel Am Inst Chem. *Res:* Spectroscopy; photochemistry; chemical kinetics. *Mailing Add:* Dept of Chem Mary Washington Col Fredericksburg VA 22401

MAHONEY, CHARLES LINDBERGH, b Geneva, NY, Mar 18, 28; m 57; c 2. ENVIRONMENTAL SCIENCES. *Educ:* Colo State Univ, BS, 53; State Univ NY Col Environ Sci & Forestry, MS, 55, PhD(ecol, forest zool), 65. *Prof Exp:* From asst prof to prof biol, State Univ NY Col Geneseo, 55-68; dir, Pingree Park Campus, 68-74, PROF RESOURCE CONSERV, COL FORESTRY & NATURAL RESOURCES, COLO STATE UNIV, 68- *Concurrent Pos:* Mem Yellowstone field res exped, Atmospheric Sci Res Ctr, State Univ NY Albany, 63-64; res scientist, Bahamas Marine Surv, Off Naval Res, 67; staff mem, Coop Sci Prog, Univ Sopron, Hungary, 74; consult atmospheric monitoring, Stillwater Platinum Mines, Mont, 76; res scientist, Nowcast Weather Satellite Prog, NASA-Colo State Univ, 76; fel explor San Francisco, Fund Improv Secondary Educ, HEW, 80; consult ed, J Environ Educ, 81- *Mem:* AAAS; Explorers Club; Nat Wildlife Fedn; Sigma Xi; Conserv Educ Asn. *Res:* Soil insects as indicators of use patterns in recreation areas. *Mailing Add:* Col Forestry & Natural Resources Colo State Univ Ft Collins CO 80523

MAHONEY, FRANCIS JOSEPH, b Boston, Mass, Mar 18, 36; m 70; c 2. PHYSICS, BIOLOGY. *Educ:* Col Holy Cross, BS, 57; Univ Rochester, MS, 58; Harvard Univ, MS, 60; Mass Inst Technol, PhD(nuclear eng), 68. *Prof Exp:* Asst radiation physics, Harvard Univ, 58-60, asst radiation physics & biol, 60-61; physicist, Cambridge Nuclear Corp, 61-64; res asst nuclear eng, Mass Inst Technol, 64-67; res physicist, US Army Natick Labs, 67-71; grants assoc, NIH, 71-72; PROG DIR FOR RADIATION, NAT CANCER INST, 72- *Concurrent Pos:* Radiation physicist, Avco Corp, 66-67. *Mem:* AAAS; Am Phys Soc; Am Nuclear Soc; Radiation Res Soc. *Res:* Radiation physics and biology; nuclear physics and engineering. *Mailing Add:* Nat Cancer Inst NIH Bethesda MD 20014

MAHONEY, JOAN MUNROE, b Providence, RI, May 13, 38; m 71; c 2. BIOCHEMISTRY. *Educ:* Chatham Col, BS, 60; St Lawrence Univ, MS, 62; State Univ NY Upstate Med Ctr, PhD(biochem), 69. *Prof Exp:* Instr chem labs, St Lawrence Univ, 60-62; USPHS training grant, Inst Enzyme Res, Univ Wis, 68-69; res assoc mitochondrial metab, Sch Med, Ind Univ, Indianapolis, 69-71; instr, 71-74, asst prof biochem, Terre Haute Ctr Med Educ, Ind State Univ, 74-78; asst prof biochem, 78-80, ASSOC PROF, UNIV OSTEOP MED & HEALTH SCI, 80- *Mem:* AAAS; Am Chem Soc; Biophys Soc. *Res:* Mitochondrial metabolism; drugs and liposomes; membranes and their control of processes; enzyme regulation. *Mailing Add:* Univ Osteopo Med & Health Sci 3200 Grand Ave Des Moines IA 50312

MAHONEY, JOSEPH JAMES, ecology, biology, see previous edition

MAHONEY, LEE ROBERT, organic chemistry, physical chemistry, deceased

MAHONEY, RICHARD THEODORE, b Mishawaka, Ind, July 21, 43; m 63; c 2. REPRODUCTIVE BIOLOGY, CONTRACEPTIVE DEVELOPMENT. *Educ:* Purdue Univ, West Lafayette, BS, 65; Univ Calif, San Diego, PhD(chem), 70. *Prof Exp:* Proj specialist, Ford Found, 70, asst prog officer, 70-72, prog officer pop, 72-79. *Concurrent Pos:* Assoc dir, Prog Intro & Adoption Contraceptive Technol, Jakarta, Indonesia, 79- *Mem:* Int Soc Study Reproduction; Soc Study Fertil; Am Fertil Soc. *Res:* Monitoring of grants supporting research on new methods of human fertility control and products for health. *Mailing Add:* Pop Off Ford Found 320 E 43rd St New York NY 10017

MAHONEY, ROBERT PATRICK, b Poughkeepsie, NY, Dec 27, 34; m 61; c 5. MICROBIAL PHYSIOLOGY, ELECTRON MICROSCOPY. *Educ:* State Univ NY Co, New Paltz, BS, 58; Syracuse Univ, MS, 61, PhD(microbiol), 64. *Prof Exp:* Asst prof, 64-68, chmn dept, 77-80, ASSOC PROF BIOL, SKIDMORE COL, 68- *Concurrent Pos:* NSF fac fel & guest investr, Biol Dept, Woods Hole Oceanog Inst, 70-71. *Mem:* AAAS; Am Soc Microbiol; Electron Micros Soc Am; NY Acad Sci. *Res:* Physiology and electron microscopy of autotrophic bacteria; iron and sulfur oxidizing species. *Mailing Add:* Dept of Biol Skidmore Col Saratoga Springs NY 12866

MAHONEY, WILLIAM C, b New York, NY, Jan 6, 27; m 53; c 4. GEODESY, PHOTOGRAMMETRY. *Educ:* Syracuse Univ, BS, 51; Ohio State Univ, MS, 55, PhD(photogrammetry), 61. *Prof Exp:* Proj engr, Engineer Res & Develop Lab, Ohio State Univ, 51-53, res asst photogram, Univ Res Found, 53-55, res assoc, 55-59; supvry cartographer, Missile Support Div, Aeronaut Chart & Info Ctr, US Air Force, 59-64, phys scientist & chief tech develop, 64-69, chief, Missile Support Div, 69-71, tech adv to chief P&D plant, Sci & Tech Off, 71-72; chief, Advan Technol Div, 72-78, DEP DIR SYSTS & TECH, AEROSPACE CTR, DEFENSE MAPPING AGENCY, 78- *Mem:* Am Soc Photogram; Am Geophys Union; Am Cong Surv & Mapping. *Res:* Analytical photogrammetry; block adjustment; map compilation, celestial mechanics; computer technology. *Mailing Add:* Defense Mapping Agency Aerospace Ctr Second & Arsenal St St Louis MO 63118

MAHONY, DAVID EDWARD, b St John, NB. MICROBIOLOGY. *Educ:* Acadia Univ, BSc, 62; Dalhousie Univ, MSc, 64; McGill Univ, PhD(bact), 67. *Prof Exp:* Lectr, 67-69, asst prof, 69-76, assoc prof, 76-81, PROF MICROBIOL, FAC MED, DALHOUSIE UNIV, 81- *Mem:* Can Soc Microbiol; Am Soc Microbiol; Can Col Microbiologists. *Res:* Bacteriophages and bacteriocins of Clostridium perfringens. *Mailing Add:* Dept of Microbiol Dalhousie Univ Fac of Med Halifax NS B3H 4H7 Can

MAHONY, JOHN DANIEL, b New York, NY, Jan 15, 31. NUCLEAR CHEMISTRY. *Educ:* St John's Univ, NY, 51; Univ Conn, MS, 53; Univ Calif, Berkeley, PhD(nuclear chem), 65. *Prof Exp:* Asst prof chem, Marquette Univ, 65-67; asst prof, 67-71, assoc prof, 71-81, PROF CHEM, MANHATTAN COL, 81- *Concurrent Pos:* Vis res collabr, State Univ NY Stony Brook, 67-72. *Mem:* Am Chem Soc; Am Microchem Soc; Sigma Xi. *Res:* Environmental applications of chemisorption; radiochemical tracers; activation analysis; nuclear reactions and nuclear fission. *Mailing Add:* Dept of Chem Manhattan Col Bronx NY 10471

MAHOWALD, ANTHONY P, b Albany, Minn, Nov 24, 32; m 71. DEVELOPMENTAL BIOLOGY. *Educ:* Spring Hill Col, BS, 58; Johns Hopkins Univ, PhD(biol), 62. *Prof Exp:* Res fel biol, Johns Hopkins Univ, 62-66; asst prof, Marquette Univ, 66-70; asst mem & vis scientist, Inst Cancer Res, 70-72; assoc prof, 72-76, PROF BIOL, IND UNIV, BLOOMINGTON, 76- *Mem:* Genetics Soc Am; AAAS; Am Soc Zoologists; Am Soc Cell Biologists; Soc Develop Biol. *Res:* Developmental and molecular genetics of drosophila; oogenesis-chorion formation and vitellogenesis; molecular analysis of maternal effect mutations affecting both germ cell formation and gastrulation. *Mailing Add:* Dept of Biol Ind Univ Bloomington IN 47401

MAHOWALD, MARK EDWARD, b Albany, Minn, Dec 1, 31; m 54; c 5. MATHEMATICS. *Educ:* Univ Minn, BA, 53, MA, 54, PhD(math), 55. *Prof Exp:* Sr engr, Gen Elec Co, 56-57; asst prof math, Xavier Univ, Ohio, 57-59 & Syracuse Univ, 59-63; chmn dept, 72-75, PROF MATH, NORTHWESTERN UNIV, EVANSTON, 63- *Concurrent Pos:* Sloan fel, 65-67. *Mem:* Am Math Soc; Math Asn Am. *Res:* Homotopy theory; algebraic topology; topological groups. *Mailing Add:* 2109B Sherman Ave Evanston IL 60201

MAHOWALD, THEODORE AUGUSTUS, b St Cloud, Minn, June 22, 30; m 54; c 7. BIOCHEMISTRY. *Educ:* St John's Univ, Minn, BA, 52; St Louis Univ, PhD(biochem), 57. *Prof Exp:* USPHS fel, Enzyme Inst, Univ Wis, 57-60; mem staff, Scripps Clin & Res Found, Univ Calif, 60-62; asst prof biochem, Med Col, Cornell Univ, 62-69; ASSOC PROF BIOCHEM, MED COL, UNIV NEBR AT OMAHA, 69- *Mem:* AAAS; Am Soc Biol Chemists; Am Chem Soc. *Res:* Metabolism of bile acids; mechanism and sites of enzyme action; metabolism of methionine. *Mailing Add:* 3347 S 114th Ave Omaha NE 68144

MAHR, DANIEL LOUIS, entomology, acarology, see previous edition

MAHROUS, HAROUN, b Fayum, Egypt, Apr 15, 21; m 51; c 1. ELECTRICAL ENGINEERING. *Educ:* Cairo Univ, BSEE, 43; Swiss Fed Inst Technol, DSc(elec eng), 51. *Prof Exp:* Asst physics, Cairo Univ, 43-45; sr lectr elec eng, Ibrahim Univ, Egypt, 51-54; assoc prof, Pratt Inst, 54-56; assoc prof, Univ Ill, 56-58; PROF ELEC ENG & CHMN DEPT, PRATT INST, 58- *Concurrent Pos:* Consult, Solid State Memory Div, Int Bus Mach Corp, 63 & Bell Tel Labs, 66-; prog dir, Eng Div, NSF, 68. *Mem:* Sr mem Inst Elec & Electronics Engrs; NY Acad Sci. *Res:* Computer systems; memory; microwaves and electromagnetic theory; electrical power field. *Mailing Add:* Dept of Elec Eng Pratt Inst Brooklyn NY 11205

MAHRT, JEROME L, b Colon, Nebr, Dec 20, 37; m 60; c 3. PARASITOLOGY, ZOOLOGY. *Educ:* Utah State Univ, BS, 60, MS, 63; Univ Ill, PhD(vet parasitol), 66. *Prof Exp:* Asst prof, 66-71, assoc dean sci, 80-81, ASSOC PROF ZOOL, UNIV ALTA, 71- *Mem:* Can Soc Zoologists; Am Soc Parasitologists; Soc Protozoologists. *Res:* Protozoan parasitology with specialization in the avian and mammalian Coccidia and sarcocystis blood parasites of birds and malaria of reptiles. *Mailing Add:* Dept of Zool Univ of Alta Edmonton AB T6G 2G7 Can

MAHTAB, M ASHRAF, b Ambala, India, Oct 15, 35; Can citizen; c 2. ROCK MECHANICS, NUMERICL ANALYSIS. *Educ:* Mont Univ, Butte, BS, 59; McGill Univ, MEng, 65; Univ Calif, Berkeley, PhD(civil eng), 70. *Prof Exp:* Lectr mining eng, Eng Univ, Pakistan, 59-63; res asst mining eng, McGill Univ, 63-65; teaching fel geol eng, Univ Calif, Berkeley, 65-69; mining engr, US Bur Mines, Colo, 70-75; rock mech engr, Acres Consult Serv Ltd, Can, 75-79; ASSOC PROF MINING, COLUMBIA UNIV, 80- *Concurrent Pos:* Sr mining engr, Iron Ore Co, Can, 64-65; consult, Consult Engrs, GeoMech Inc & Engrs Int, 82- *Mem:* Am Inst Mining Engrs Soc Mining Eng; Asn Eng Geologists; Int Soc Rock Mech. *Res:* Characterization of jointed rock mass; support of tunnels in loosening rock; rock bursts and gas outbursts; progressive failure and directional strength of pillars; thermal-mechanical analysis of radioactive waste repositories. *Mailing Add:* Henry Krumb Sch Mines 814 Mudd Columbia Univ New York NY 10027

MAI, KLAUS L(UDWIG), b Changsha, China, Mar 7, 30; US citizen; m 57; c 4. CHEMICAL ENGINEERING. *Educ:* Gonzaga Univ, BS, 51; Univ Wash, MS, 52, PhD(chem eng), 54. *Prof Exp:* Develop engr, Procter & Gamble Co, 55-57; technologist process develop, Shell Chem Co, 57-59, asst mgr opers, 59-60, chief technologist, 60-61, mgr lab tech, 61-63, res dir tech serv & appln, 64, div mgr opers, 65-66, plant mgr, 66-68, mgr mfg, 68-69, gen mgr, Indust Chem Div, 69-72, gen mgr, Polymers Div, 72-74, overseas assignment, 74-76, vpres transp & supplies, Shell Oil Co, 76-77, vpres, 77-81, PRES, SHELL DEVELOP CO, 81- *Mem:* Am Inst Chem Engrs; Am Chem Soc; Soc Chem Indust; Indust Res Inst; Coun Chem Res. *Res:* Business, manufacturing, marketing and research administration. *Mailing Add:* Shell Develop Co PO Box 2463 Houston TX 77001

MAI, WILLIAM FREDERICK, b Greenwood, Del, July 23, 16; m 41; c 3. PLANT PATHOLOGY. *Educ:* Univ Del, BS, 39; Cornell Univ, PhD(plant path), 45. *Prof Exp:* Asst prof, 46-52, PROF PLANT PATH, CORNELL UNIV, 52- *Mem:* Fel Am Phytopath Soc; Soc Nematol (vpres, 68, pres, 69); Am Inst Biol Sci; Potato Asn Am; Soc Europ Nematol. *Res:* Plant pathogenic and soil inhabiting nematodes; diseases of plants caused by nematodes. *Mailing Add:* Dept of Plant Path Cornell Univ Ithaca NY 14850

MAIBACH, HOWARD I, b New York, NY, July 18, 29. DERMATOLOGY. *Educ:* Tulane Univ, AB, 50, MD, 55; Am Bd Dermat, dipl, 61. *Prof Exp:* Asst instr, Sch Med, Univ Pa, 58-61; from asst prof to assoc prof, 61-71, PROF DERMAT, SCH MED, UNIV CALIF, SAN FRANCISCO, 71-, VCHMN DIV DERMAT, 62- *Concurrent Pos:* USPHS fel, Pa Hosp, 59-61; lectr, Grad Sch Med, Univ Pa, 60-61; pvt pract, 61-; mem staff, Herbert C Moffitt Hosps, Univ Calif, 61-; consult, Sonoma State Hosp, Eldridge, 62-64, Calif State Pub Health Serv, Stanford Res Inst, Calif Med Facil, Vacaville, Letterman & San Francisco Gen Hosps, 62- & Vet Admin Hosp, San Francisco, 63- *Mem:* AAAS; Soc Invest Dermat; Am Acad Dermat; fel Am Col Physicians; Am Fedn Clin Res. *Mailing Add:* Dept Dermat Univ Calif Sch Med San Francisco CA 94143

MAIBENCO, HELEN CRAIG, b Scotland, June 9, 17; nat US; m 57; c 2. ANATOMY. *Educ:* Wheaton Col, Ill, BS, 48; De Paul Univ, MS, 50; Univ Ill, PhD, 56. *Prof Exp:* Instr pharmacol, Presby Hosp Sch Nursing, 50-54; asst, Univ Ill Col Med, 54-56, from instr to prof anat, 56-73; PROF ANAT, RUSH MED COL, 73- *Mem:* AAAS; Am Soc Zoologists; Endocrine Soc; Am Asn Anatomists. *Res:* Physiology of connective tissues; endocrine relationships; morphological changes associated with aging; connective tissues of the female reproductive system. *Mailing Add:* Dept of Anat Rush Med Col 1725 W Harrison St Chicago IL 60612

MAICKEL, ROGER PHILIP, b Floral Park, NY, Sept 8, 33; m 56; c 2. PHARMACOLOGY, SCIENCE ADMINISTRATION. *Educ:* Manhattan Col, BS, 54; Georgetown Univ, MS, 57, PhD(chem), 60. *Prof Exp:* Chemist, Lab Chem Pharmacol, Nat Heart Inst, 55-60, biochemist, 60-63, sect head biochem function, 63-65; assoc prof, 65-69, prof pharmacol, Ind Univ, Bloomington, 69-77, chief med sci sect, Inst Res Pub Safety, 70-75, dir pharmacol, Univ, 71-77; PROF PHARMACOL & TOXICOL & HEAD DEPT, SCH PHARM & PHARMACAL SCI, PURDUE UNIV, WEST LAFAYETTE, 77- *Concurrent Pos:* Exec ed, Life Sci, 65-69; Am Chem Soc tour lectr, 65- *Mem:* Fel AAAS; Am Chem Soc; Am Soc Pharmacol & Exp Therapeut; fel Am Inst Chemists; NY Acad Sci. *Mailing Add:* Dept of Pharmacol & Toxicol Purdue Univ West Lafayette IN 47907

MAIDANIK, GIDEON, b Safad, Israel, July 3, 25; US citizen. PHYSICS. *Educ:* Univ Manchester, BSc, 54, MSc, 55; Brown Univ, PhD(physics), 59. *Prof Exp:* Asst physics, Brown Univ, 56-58; sr scientist, Brit Oxygen Res & Develop Ltd, 58-60; Sr scientist, Bolt Beranek & Newman, Inc, Mass, 60-66; SR RES SCIENTIST TECH ADV, NAVAL SHIP RES & DEVELOP CTR, 66- *Mem:* Fel Acoust Soc Am; Brit Inst Physics & Phys Soc. *Res:* Nuclear physics, especially nucleon scattering; acoustics, especially structural vibration and radiation; sonar systems; hydroacoustics. *Mailing Add:* Code 1902 Ship Acoust Dept Naval Ship Res & Develop Ctr Bethesda MD 20034

MAIDMENT, BERTRAM WALTER, JR, b Newark, NJ, Jan 25, 47; m 73; c 1. BIOTECHNOLOGY. *Educ:* Dickinson Col, BS, 69; State Univ NY, Buffalo, MS, 75, PhD(exp path), 80. *Prof Exp:* Jr scientist, Ethicon Inc, 69-70; sr develop engr, Baxter/Travenol Labs Inc, 70-72; res scientist, Johnson & Johnson, 73-76; SR ANALYST BIOMED & BIOTECHNOL SCI ASSESSMENT, US GOVT, 80- *Mem:* AAAS. *Res:* Application of biochemistry and immunology to the development and isolation of specific markers useful for the diagnosis, treatment, monitoring and imaging of neoplastic diseases and disease processes. *Mailing Add:* 4401 Manor Hall Lane Fairfax VA 22023

MAIELLO, JOHN MICHAEL, b New York, NY, Oct 5, 42. MYCOLOGY, ENVIRONMENTAL BIOLOGY. *Educ:* Hunter Col, BA, 65; Rutgers Univ, PhD(mycol), 72. *Prof Exp:* Asst prof, 72-80, ASSOC PROF MYCOL, RUTGERS UNIV, NEWARK, 80- *Concurrent Pos:* Dir & cur mycol cult collection, Rutgers Univ, 72- *Mem:* Sigma Xi; Mycol Soc Am; Am Phytopath Soc; AAAS. *Res:* Morphology and physiology of pycnidial development in the sphaeropsidales; pathology of economically important plants; air pollutants injurious to vegetation in New Jersey. *Mailing Add:* Dept of Bot Rutgers Univ Newark NJ 07102

MAIENSCHEIN, FRED (CONRAD), b Belleville, Ill, Oct 28, 25; m 48; c 2. REACTOR PHYSICS & SHIELDING. *Educ:* Rose Polytech Inst, BS, 45; Ind Univ, MS, 48, PhD(physics), 49. *Prof Exp:* Sr physicist, Nuclear Energy Propulsion for aircraft div, Fairchild Engine & Airplane Corp, 49-51; sr physicist, 51-66, DIR NEUTRON PHYSICS DIV, OAK RIDGE NAT LAB, 66- *Mem:* Am Phys Soc; Sigma Xi; fel Am Nuclear Soc. *Res:* Neutron and reactor physics; shielding. *Mailing Add:* 838 W Outer Dr Oak Ridge TN 37830

MAIENTHAL, E JUNE, b Paris, Mo, Oct 4, 28; m 49. CHEMISTRY. *Educ:* Millikin Univ, BS, 50. *Prof Exp:* Control chemist, Beatrice Food Co, Decatur, Ill, 50-51; chemist, Lincoln Lab, Decatur, Ill, 51-52; chemist, 52-62, RES CHEMIST, NAT BUR STANDARDS, 62- *Mem:* Am Chem Soc; Royal Soc Chem; Am Soc Testing & Mat. *Res:* Development of voltammetric methods of analysis of metals, ores, lunar rocks, biological materials, standard reference materials and environmental samples, particularly for trace elements. *Mailing Add:* A227 Chem Bldg Div Anal Chem Nat Bur of Standards Washington DC 20234

MAIER, CHARLES ROBERT, b Leoti, Kans, Oct 9, 28; m 56; c 3. BOTANY. *Educ:* Kans State Teachers Col, Emporia, BS, 53, MS, 55; Ore State Col, PhD(plant path), 59. *Prof Exp:* Asst, Kans State Col, 54-55; from asst prof to assoc prof plant path, NMex State Univ, 58-68; PROF BIOL, WAYNE STATE COL, 68-, CUR ARBORETUM, 77- *Mem:* Nat Asn Biol Teachers; Nat Sci Teachers Asn. *Res:* Soil microbiology; control of diseases of cotton; antibiotic chemotherapy of hop downy mildew; organismal pollution of irrigation water. *Mailing Add:* Dept of Biol Wayne State Col Wayne NE 68787

MAIER, CHRIS THOMAS, b Pontiac, Mich, Jan 14, 49; m 81. INSECT ECOLOGY. *Educ:* Univ Mich, Ann Arbor, BS, 71; Univ Ill, Urbana, MS, 73, PhD(entom), 77. *Prof Exp:* ASST SCIENTIST & ENTOMOLOGIST, CONN AGR EXP STA, 77- *Mem:* AAAS; Ecol Soc Am; Entom Soc Am; Entom Soc Can. *Res:* Host-specificity of leafminers; behavioral ecology of insect parasitoids attacking leafminers; insect reproductive potential on different host plants; ecology of cicadas; mating behavior of flower flies. *Mailing Add:* Dept Entom Conn Agr Exp Sta 123 Huntington Ave New Haven CT 06504

MAIER, EUGENE ALFRED, b Tillamook, Ore, May 7, 29; m 52; c 4. MATHEMATICS. *Educ:* Univ Ore, BA, 50, MA, 51, PhD(math), 54. *Prof Exp:* From asst prof to assoc prof & chmn dept, 55-61; assoc prof, 61-70, PROF MATH, UNIV ORE, 70- *Mem:* Am Math Soc; Math Asn Am. *Res:* Number theory; mathematics education. *Mailing Add:* Dept of Math Univ of Ore Eugene OR 97403

MAIER, EUGENE JACOB RUDOLPH, b Washington, DC, Sept 1, 31; m 59; c 3. GEOPHYSICS. *Educ:* Mass Inst Technol, BS, 53; Carnegie Inst Technol, MS, 59, PhD(meson physics), 62. *Prof Exp:* Physicist, Appl Physics Lab, Johns Hopkins Univ, 56; PHYSICIST, GODDARD SPACE FLIGHT CTR, NASA, GREENBELT, 62- *Mem:* AAAS; Am Phys Soc; Am Geophys Union. *Res:* Structure and direct measurements of ionosphere and atmosphere; measurements of interplanetary medium; spacecraft experiment instrumentation; high energy meson physics; energetic particle experiments. *Mailing Add:* 1173 River Bay Rd Annapolis MD 21401

MAIER, GEORGE D, b Chicago, Ill, July 24, 30. BIOCHEMISTRY. *Educ:* Cornell Col, BA, 53; Iowa State Univ, MS, 56, PhD(biochem), 62. *Prof Exp:* Asst biochemist, Am Meat Inst Found, Chicago, 57-59; fel, Mass Gen Hosp, Boston, 62-63; fel, Sch Med, Western Reserve Univ, 63-65; asst prof chem, 65-74, ASSOC PROF CHEM, COLBY COL, 74- *Res:* Protein primordial synthesis; thiamine and renin chemistry. *Mailing Add:* Dept of Chem Colby Col Waterville ME 04910

MAIER, HERBERT NATHANIEL, b Baltimore, Md, Oct 15, 43; m 76. PHYSICAL CHEMISTRY, ANALYTICAL CHEMISTRY. *Educ:* Wilkes Col, BS, 65, MS, 67; Pa State Univ, PhD(phys chem), 71. *Prof Exp:* Dir labs, Precision Gas Prods Inc & Burdox Inc, 75-77; dir labs, 78-80, PLANT MGR, IDEAL GAS PRODS INC, 80- *Mem:* Am Chem Soc; Instrument Soc Am. *Res:* Obtaining response factors; obtaining difficult separations; increasing sensitivity on gas chromatographic analysis of gas mixtures. *Mailing Add:* 95 Oakey Dr Kendall Park NJ 08824

MAIER, JOHN G, medicine, radiobiology, see previous edition

MAIER, MARY LOUISE, inorganic chemistry, physical chemistry, see previous edition

MAIER, ROBERT HAWTHORNE, b New York, NY, Oct 26, 27; m 52; c 3. PLANT PHYSIOLOGY, ENVIRONMENTAL MANAGEMENT. *Educ:* Univ Miami, BS, 51; Univ Ill, MS, 52, PhD(soil & plant chem), 54. *Prof Exp:* Asst agron, Univ Ill, 51-54; from asst prof to prof agr chem & soils, Univ Ariz, 56-67, asst dean grad col, 66-67; asst chancellor & prof chem, Univ Wis-Green Bay, 67-70, vchancellor & prof environ sci, 70-75, prof sci, Environ Change & Pub & Environ Admin, 75-79; PROF BIOL & POLIT SCI & VCHANCELLOR ACAD AFFAIRS, EAST CAROLINA UNIV, 79- *Concurrent Pos:* Am Coun Educ fel acad admin, Univ NC, 65-66. *Mem:* Fel AAAS; fel Am Inst Chemists; fel Am Soc Agron; fel Soil Sci Soc Am; Am Chem Soc. *Res:* Cellular physiology and biochemistry of metals, metal chelates and chelating agents; analytical chemistry of biological material; chemistry of soil-plant-human relationships. *Mailing Add:* VChancellor Acad Affairs East Carolina Univ Greenville NC 27834

MAIER, SIEGFRIED, b Stuttgart, Ger, Apr 22, 30; US citizen; m 54; c 3. MICROBIOLOGY. *Educ:* Capital Univ, BS, 58; Ohio State Univ, MSc, 60, PhD(microbiol), 63. *Prof Exp:* Asst prof bact, 63-68, assoc prof microbiol, 68-77, PROF MICROBIOL, OHIO UNIV, 77- *Concurrent Pos:* AEC res partic, Argonne Nat Lab, 69-70; vis prof, Univ Kiel, Ger, 76; taxonomist, Comt Approved Bact Names, Int Comt Syst Bact, 75-80. *Mem:* Am Soc Microbiol; Can Soc Microbiol. *Res:* Bacteriophages; physiology and structure of Beggiatoaceae; anaerobic sporulation in bacillus. *Mailing Add:* Dept of Zool & Microbiol Ohio Univ Athens OH 45701

MAIER, THOMAS O, b Rochester, NY, June 28, 45; m 69; c 2. INORGANIC CHEMISTRY. *Educ:* Mass Inst Technol, BS, 67; Univ Ill, Urbana, PhD(chem), 71. *Prof Exp:* SR RES CHEMIST, EASTMAN KODAK CO, 71- *Res:* Use of transition metal elements in photographic processes. *Mailing Add:* Eastman Kodak Co Kodak Park Rochester NY 14650

MAIER, V(INCENT) P(AUL), b Carteret, NJ, Dec 11, 30; m 53; c 2. BIOCHEMISTRY, PHYTOHORMONES. *Educ:* Univ Calif, Los Angeles, BS, 52; Univ Calif, MS, 54, PhD(agr chem), 57. *Prof Exp:* Chemist, 57-58, prin chemist, 59-61, invest head, 62-69, lab chief, 70-77, DIR, FRUIT & VEG CHEM LAB, SCI & EDUC ADMIN, AGR RES, USDA, 77- *Mem:* AAAS; Phytochem Soc NAm; Am Chem Soc; Inst Food Technol. *Res:* Sub-zero enzyme kinetics; heme compound catalyzed lipid oxidation; chemistry of dates; biochemistry and enzymes of citrus fruits; biosynthesis and regulation of flavonoid and limonoid bitter principles; bioregulation of plant hormones. *Mailing Add:* Fruit & Veg Chem Lab USDA Pasadena CA 91106

MAIER, WILLIAM BRYAN, II, b Oklahoma City, Okla, Jan 30, 37; m 58; c 4. ATOMIC & MOLECULAR COLLISIONS, OPTICAL SPECTROSCOPY. *Educ:* Univ Chicago, BS, 59, MS, 60, PhD(physics), 65. *Prof Exp:* STAFF MEM, LOS ALAMOS NAT LAB, 64- *Concurrent Pos:* Fel, NSF, 61-64; sci res coun vis fel, Gt Brit, 79-80. *Mem:* Am Phys Soc. *Res:* Ion-molecule reactions; electron-impact excitation of molecules; upper atmospheric chemistry; long-lived ionic states of small molecules; optical spectroscopy; photochemistry; synthesis of unstable compounds in cold solutions; isotope separation; spectra of solid solutions; properties of UF_6; classical field theory. *Mailing Add:* Los Alamos Nat Lab Los Alamos NM 87545

MAIERHOFER, CHARLES RICHARD, b Seguin, Tex, Dec 8, 11; m 36; c 3. CIVIL ENGINEERING. *Prof Exp:* Field engr, US Bur Reclamation, 36-37, construct engr, 37-40, off engr, 40-42, res physicist, 42-44, planning engr, 44-48, chief drainage & groundwater engr, 48-72; CONSULT, WORLD BANK, 72- *Concurrent Pos:* Consult, US Dept State, Pakistan, 52 & Afghanistan, 53 & 60; consult, Can, 55, UN, Israel, 56, Govt, PR, 56-61 & Govt Dom Repub, 71; mem exec comt, US Nat Comt, Int Comn Irrig & Drainage, 55-61, chmn, 59-61, permanent ex-officio mem, 61- *Honors & Awards:* Royce J Tipton Award, Am Soc Civil Engrs, 75. *Mem:* Fel Am Soc Civil Engrs. *Res:* Design and construction of facilities for control, conservation and use of groundwater for agriculture, industry and municipality; soil physics and chemistry; groundwater phenomena, movement and quality; salinity control irrigated lands; hydraulic engineering. *Mailing Add:* 666 Marion St Denver CO 80218

MAILEN, JAMES CLIFFORD, b Colorado Springs, Colo, Aug 19, 37; m 63; c 1. CHEMICAL ENGINEERING. *Educ:* Kans State Univ, BS, 59; Univ Fla, PhD(chem eng), 64. *Prof Exp:* Develop engr, Oak Ridge Nat Lab, Union Carbide Nuclear Co, 63-73; GROUP LEADER, OAK RIDGE NAT LAB, 73- *Mem:* AAAS; Am Chem Soc; Am Inst Chem Engrs; Am Nuclear Soc; Sigma Xi. *Res:* Nuclear fuel reprocessing. *Mailing Add:* 134 Cumberland View Dr Oak Ridge TN 37830

MAILLIE, HUGH DAVID, b Chester, Pa, Nov 2, 32; m 58; c 3. RADIOBIOLOGY, HEALTH PHYSICS. *Educ:* La Salle Col, BA, 54; Univ Rochester, MS, 56, PhD(radiation biol), 63. *Prof Exp:* From instr to asst prof, 62-70, ASSOC PROF RADIATION BIOL, UNIV ROCHESTER, 70-, DIR HEALTH PHYSICS DIV, 72- *Mem:* AAAS; Health Physics Soc. *Res:* Radiation dosimetry and its application to the understanding of biological effects in man and laboratory animals. *Mailing Add:* Health Physics Div Univ of Rochester Rochester NY 14642

MAILLOUX, GERARD, b Montreal, Que, Jan 17, 45. BIOLOGY, ENTOMOLOGY. *Educ:* Univ Sherbrooke, BS, 68; Univ Montreal, MSc, 71; Rutgers Univ, PhD(entom), 76. *Prof Exp:* Researcher entom, St Jean Res Sta, 76-79, RESEARCHER ENTOM, AGR QUEBEC, L'ASSOMPTION RES STA, CAN DEPT AGR, 79- *Mem:* Entom Soc Can; Japanese Soc Pop Ecol. *Res:* Economic entomology; population pest management; sampling and forecasting insect pests populations. *Mailing Add:* Sta de Res en Def Des Cult Quebec 867 bowl L'Ange-Gardien CP 10 L'Assomption PQ J0K 1G0 Can

MAILLOUX, ROBERT JOSEPH, b Lynn, Mass, June 20, 38; m 67; c 3. ELECTROMAGNETISM, APPLIED PHYSICS. *Educ:* Northeastern Univ, BS, 61; Harvard Univ, SM, 62, PhD(appl physics), 65. *Prof Exp:* Res engr microwave technol, NASA Electronics Res Ctr, 65-70; res physicist, Air Force Cambridge Res Lab, 70-76; RES PHYSICIST ANTENNAS, ELECTROMAGNETIC SCI DIV, ROME AIR DEVELOP CTR, 76- *Concurrent Pos:* Res fel, Harvard Univ, 68; tech coop prog deleg, US, Brit, Can & Australian Exchange Agreement, 77-82; Inst Elec & Electronics Engrs fel, 78. *Honors & Awards:* Marcus O'Day Award, Air Force Cambridge Res Lab, 71. *Mem:* Inst Elec & Electronics Engrs; Sigma Xi; Antenna & Propagation Soc (vpres, 82). *Res:* Antennas; periodic structures; electromagnetic scattering; diffraction. *Mailing Add:* 98 Concord Rd Wayland MA 01778

MAILMAN, DAVID SHERWIN, b Chicago, Ill, June 29, 38; m 61; c 4. PHYSIOLOGY. *Educ:* Univ Chicago, BS, 58; Univ Ill, PhD(physiol), 64. *Prof Exp:* Fel biophys, Univ Md, 62-64; asst prof, 64-70, assoc prof, 70-75, PROF BIOL, UNIV HOUSTON, 75- *Concurrent Pos:* Adj assoc prof physiol, Univ Tex Med Sch Houston, 73- *Mem:* Am Physiol Soc; Am Soc Zoologists; Soc Exp Biol & Med; Sigma Xi. *Res:* Salt and water transport regulation by physical forces and hormones; membrane physiology. *Mailing Add:* Dept of Biol Univ of Houston Houston TX 77004

MAILMAN, RICHARD BERNARD, b New York, NY, Feb 6, 45. NEUROPHARMACOLOGY, TOXICOLOGY. *Educ:* Rutgers Univ, New Brunswick, BS, 68; NC State Univ, MS, 72, PhD(physiol, toxicol), 74. *Prof Exp:* Res assoc toxicol, NC State Univ, 74-75; fel neurobiol, 76-77, res asst prof psychiat, 78-80, RES ASSOC PROF PSYCHIAT & PHARMACOL & CHIEF NEUROTOXICOL SECT, BIOL SCI RES CTR, UNIV NC, CHAPEL HILL, 80- *Mem:* Am Soc Pharmacol & Exp Therapeut; Int Soc Neurochem; Am Soc Neurochem; Sigma Xi; AAAS. *Res:* Pharmacological and toxicological actions of drugs on the central nervous system, especially during development. agents. *Mailing Add:* Rte 3 Box 190 Chapel Hill NC 27514

MAIMAN, THEODORE HAROLD, b Los Angeles, Calif, July 11, 27. PHYSICS, ADVANCED TECHNOLOGY. *Educ:* Univ Colo, BS, 49; Stanford Univ, MS, 51, PhD(physics), 55. *Prof Exp:* Sect head, Hughes Res Labs, 55-61; pres & founder, Korad Corp, Santa Monica, Calif, 61-68, Maiman Assoc, Los Angeles, 68-76; vpres & founder, Laser Video Corp, Los Angeles, 72-75; VPRES TECHNOL, TRW ELECTRONICS CO, LOS ANGELES, 75- *Honors & Awards:* Fannie & John Hertz Found Award, 66; Ballantine Award, Franklin Inst, 62. *Mem:* Nat Acad Engrs; fel Am Phys Soc; Optical Soc Am; Inst Elec & Electronic Engrs; Soc Motion Picture & TV Engrs. *Res:* Lasers. *Mailing Add:* TRW Electronics Co 10880 Wilshire Blvd Suite 1700 Los Angeles CA 90024

MAIMONI, ARTURO, b Bogota, Colombia, Jan 24, 27; nat US; m 52; c 3. CHEMICAL ENGINEERING, NUCLEAR ENGINEERING. *Educ:* Calif Inst Technol, MSChE, 49; Univ Calif, PhD(chem eng), 56. *Prof Exp:* Asst to chief chemist, Cementos Diamante, Colombia, 45-46; jr res engr, Fluor Corp, 49; chemist, 52-55, chem engr, 55-64, dep div leader process & mat develop, 64-68, asst div leader, Gen Chem Div, 68-70, div leader, Inorg Mat Div, 70-76, proj leader nuclear mat safeguards, 76-79, proj leader, Int Energy Technol Assessment, 79-80, MEM STAFF LONG RANGE PLANNING, LAWRENCE LIVERMORE NAT LAB, 81- *Concurrent Pos:* Fulbright prof, Univ Seville, 63-64. *Mem:* Am Chem Soc; Am Inst Chem Engrs. *Res:* Heat transfer; diffusion; high temperature materials; cryogenics; nuclear safeguards and technology; coal gasification; materials selection for complex engineering systems. *Mailing Add:* Chem Eng Div PO Box 808 Livermore CA 94550

MAIN, ALEXANDER RUSSELL, b Pincher Creek, Alta, Oct 28, 25; m 51; c 2. BIOCHEMISTRY, ENZYMOLOGY. *Educ:* Queen's Univ, Ont, BA, 50, MA, 52; Cambridge Univ, PhD(biochem), 59. *Prof Exp:* Chemist, Can Fed Mines Br, 52-54 & Can Dept Health & Welfare, 54-63; assoc prof, 63-67, prof enzyme kinetics, 67-76, PROF BIOCHEM, N C STATE UNIV, 76- *Concurrent Pos:* NIH grant. *Mem:* Am Soc Biol Chemists; AAAS. *Res:* Pesticide toxicology; carboxyl esterases; irreversible inhibition kinetics of organophosphate and carbamate inhibitors; purification of horse and human serum cholinesterases. *Mailing Add:* Dept of Biochem N C State Univ PO Box 5050 Raleigh NC 27650

MAIN, ANDREW JAMES, b Taunton, Mass, May 13, 42; m 64; c 2. MEDICAL ENTOMOLOGY, EPIDEMIOLOGY. *Educ:* Univ Mass, BS, 64, MS, 70; Yale Univ, MPH, 72, DrPh, 76. *Prof Exp:* Biologist, Encephalitis Field Sta, Mass Dept Pub Health, 60-70; instr med entom, 76-78, ASST PROF MED ENTOM, DEPT EPIDEMIOL & PUB HEALTH, YALE UNIV, 78- *Mem:* Am Entom Soc; Can Entom Soc; Am Soc Trop Med & Hyg; Wildlife Dis Asn; Am Mosquito Control Asn. *Res:* Arbovirology; disease ecology; diseases of wildlife; arthropods of medical and veterinary importance. *Mailing Add:* Yale Univ Sch Med PO Box 3333 New Haven CT 06510

MAIN, CHARLES EDWARD, b Triadelphia, WVa, July 25, 33; m 54; c 2. PLANT PATHOLOGY, PLANT PHYSIOLOGY. *Educ:* WVa Univ, BS, 59, MS, 61; Univ Wis, PhD(plant path), 64. *Prof Exp:* Fel plant path, Univ Wis, 64; asst prof plant path, NC State Univ, 64-76; RES PLANT PATHOLOGIST, AGR RES SERV, USDA, 64-; ASSOC PROF PLANT PATH, NC STATE UNIV, 76- *Mem:* AAAS; Am Phytopath Soc; Am Soc Plant Physiol. *Res:* Biochemical and physiological effects of bacterial and fungal phytopathogens on plants; chemical nature of disease resistance. *Mailing Add:* Dept of Plant Path N C State Univ PO Box 5126 Raleigh NC 27607

MAIN, FREDERIC HALL, b Webster, Mass, Aug 1, 20; m 48; c 5. ECONOMIC GEOLOGY. *Educ:* Dartmouth Col, AB, 42; Columbia Univ, MA, 48, PhD(geol), 55. *Prof Exp:* Miner, Callahan Mining Co, 42; asst to supt, Vt Copper Co, 42-44; geologist, US Geol Surv, 44-46 & Eagle-Picher Co, 47-48; geologist, NJ Zinc Co, 49-60, planning engr, 60-65, asst to pres, 65-70, vpres explor, 71-74; pres, NJ Zinc Explor Co, 74-78, vpres mining, Jersey Miniera Zinc Co, 78-80; VPRES MINING, GULF & WESTERN NAT RESOURCES GROUP, 80- *Mem:* Soc Econ Geologists; Soc Mining Eng; Am Inst Mining, Metall & Petrol Engrs. *Mailing Add:* G&W Nat Resources Group One Commerce Pl Nashville TN 37239

MAIN, JAMES HAMILTON PRENTICE, b Biggar, Scotland, June 7, 33; m 61; c 2. ORAL PATHOLOGY. *Educ:* Univ Edinburgh, BDS, 55, PhD(path), 64. *Prof Exp:* Lectr oral path, Univ Edinburgh, 61-66, sr lectr & consult, 66-69; PROF ORAL PATH, UNIV TORONTO, 69- *Concurrent Pos:* USPHS int res fel, NIH, 64-65; USPHS res grant, Univ Edinburgh, 66-69; Nat Cancer Inst Can res grant, Univ Toronto, 70-; mem nat educ comt, Nat Cancer Inst Can, 70-; head dent, Sunnybrook Hosp, 71- *Honors & Awards:* Colgate Prize, Int Asn Dent Res, 66; Clarke Prize Cancer Res, 68. *Mem:* AAAS; Am Acad Oral Path; Royal Col Path; Int Asn Dent Res; Royal Col Dentists Can. *Res:* Induction of neoplasia; epithelio-mesenchymal interactions; developmental aspects of oncogenesis; biological testing of dental materials; salivary gland tumors. *Mailing Add:* Dept of Oral Path Univ of Toronto Fac of Dent Toronto ON M5S 2R8 Can

MAIN, ROBERT ANDREW, b Billings, Mont, Sept 23, 23; div. ZOOLOGY, LIMNOLOGY. *Educ:* Univ Calif, Santa Barbara, AB, 48; Univ Wash, MS, 53; Univ Mich, PhD(zool), 61. *Prof Exp:* Asst zool, Univ Mich, 53-57, instr, 61; instr, Univ NH, 58-61; asst prof biol, Va Polytech, 61-62, Western Ill Univ, 62-64 & Tex Woman's Univ, 64-66; assoc prof, 66-70, PROF BIOL, CALIF STATE UNIV, HAYWARD, 70- *Mem:* Am Soc Limnol & Oceanog; Int Asn Theoret & Applied Limnol; Western Soc Naturalists. *Res:* Freshwater zooplankton and bottom fauna; life histories of planktonic copepods; biological illustration. *Mailing Add:* Dept of Biol Sci Calif State Univ Hayward CA 94542

MAIN, STEPHEN PAUL, b Iowa City, Iowa, Aug 26, 40; m 63. BOTANY, AQUATIC ECOLOGY. *Educ:* Valparaiso Univ, BS, 62, MALS, 65; Ore State Univ, PhD(bot), 72. *Prof Exp:* Teacher biol, Crescent-Iroquois Community High Sch, Ill, 62-63; lab instr, Valparaiso Univ, 63-65; teacher, Santiam High Sch, Ore, 65-69; asst prof, 71-79, ASSOC PROF BIOL, WARTBURG COL, 79- *Mem:* Sigma Xi; Am Inst Biol Sci; Phycol Soc Am; Ecol Soc Am; Bot Soc Am. *Res:* Ecology and taxonomy of diatoms in rivers, marshlands, and marine shoreline systems. *Mailing Add:* Dept Biol Wartburg Col Waverly IA 50677

MAIN, WILLIAM FRANCIS, b Fresno, Calif, July 2, 21; m 43; c 3. PHYSICS. *Educ:* Fresno State Col, AB, 43. *Prof Exp:* Electronic scientist, US Naval Res Lab, 43-55; mgr radar & data link dept, Missile & Space Div, Lockheed Aircraft Corp, 55-56, mgr electronic res, 56-65; dir electronics, Lockheed Missiles & Space Co, Calif, 65-66, asst gen mgr electronics, 66-69, asst chief engr space systs, 69-72, asst prog mgr, 72-74; pres, Pan Data Corp, 74-76; pres, 76-79, TECH DIR, WACKENHUT CORP, 79- *Mem:* AAAS; Am Phys Soc; Sigma Xi; Inst Elec & Electronics Engrs. *Res:* Radar; communications and data processing systems. *Mailing Add:* 2042 NE 121 Rd N Miami FL 33181

MAINBERGER, WALTER A(UGUST), b Wurzburg, Ger, June 28, 22; nat US; m 45; c 4. ELECTRICAL ENGINEERING. *Educ:* City Col New York, BEE, 43; NY Univ, MEE, 51. *Prof Exp:* Sr engr, Fed Telecommun Labs, 46-51; proj mgr, W L Maxson Corp, NY, 51-55; sect head, Nat Co, Inc, 55-58, mgr electronic systs dept, 58-61; mem tech staff, Dunn Eng Corp, 61-62; sect head avionics ground systs lab, 62-68, eng mgr surface tacan systs, 68-80, SR MEM TECH STAFF, ITT AVIONICS DIV, ITT FED LABS, 80- *Mem:* Sr mem Inst Elec & Electronics Engrs. *Res:* Atomic beam frequency standards; precision radar displays; navigational aids; tactical air navigation test, monitor and control equipment. *Mailing Add:* CNI Systs Eng Dept 62111 ITT Avionics Div 500 Washington Ave Nutley NJ 07110

MAINEN, EUGENE LOUIS, b Baltimore, Md, May 9, 40; m 66; c 1. ORGANIC CHEMISTRY. *Educ:* Univ Md, BS, 63; Univ Iowa, MS, 65, PhD(org chem), 68. *Prof Exp:* Sr res chemist, Cent Res Labs, 67-69 & Photog Prod Div, 69-71, tech serv specialist, 71-74, customer serv supvr, Photog Prod Div, 74-76, mkt develop mgr, 76-79, MKT MGR, MINN MINING & MFG CO, 79- *Mem:* Fel Bush Found, 77. Am Chem Soc; Soc Photog Scientists & Engrs; Sigma Xi. *Res:* High performance polymers; emulsion technology in photographic sciences; product development. *Mailing Add:* Chem Resources Div Bldg 223-6-04 3M Ctr St Paul MN 55144

MAINES, MAHIN D, b Arak, Iran, July 31, 41; m 62; c 2. PHARMACOLOGY. *Educ:* Ball State Univ, BS, 64, MA, 67; Univ Mo, PhD(pharmacol), 70. *Prof Exp:* Res assoc pharmacol, Univ Mo, 70-71; NIH fel, Univ Minn, 71-73; res assoc, 73-75, from asst prof to assoc prof pharmacol, Rockefeller Univ, 75-78; ASSOC PROF PHARMACOL, MED CTR, UNIV ILL, 78- *Concurrent Pos:* Irma T Hirschl Trust career scientist award, 76-80; mem, Toxicol Study Sect, NIH, 81-84. *Mem:* Am Soc Pharmacol & Exp Therapeut; Soc Toxicol; Am Soc Biol Chemists; Sigma Xi; NY Acad Sci. *Res:* Biosynthesis and degradation of cellular heme and hemoproteins, with emphasis on the elucidation of the mechanisms of regulatory activities of metal ions. *Mailing Add:* Dept Pharmacol 901 S Wolcott St PO Box 6998 Chicago IL 60680

MAINIER, ROBERT, b Pittsburgh, Pa, Oct 27, 25; m 50; c 6. ANALYTICAL CHEMISTRY. *Educ:* Univ Pittsburgh, BS, 49. *Prof Exp:* Chemist, Barrett Co, Allied Chem & Dye, 49-50; fel anal chem, Mellon Inst, 50-53; LAB GROUP MGR ABSORPTION SPECTROS, RES DEPT, KOPPERS CO INC, 53- *Mem:* Am Chem Soc; Soc Appl Spectros; Coblentz Soc. *Res:* Utilization of infrared, ultraviolet and nuclear magnetic resonance spectroscopy for characterization and analyses of commercial products. *Mailing Add:* 143 Cresent Garden Dr Pittsburgh PA 15235

MAINLAND, GORDON BRUCE, b Elmhurst, Ill, May 22, 45; m 67; c 2. THEORETICAL HIGH ENERGY PHYSICS. *Educ:* Cornell Univ, BS, 67; Univ Tex, PhD(theoret high energy physics), 71. *Prof Exp:* Fel theoret high energy physics, Univ Tex, 72; scholar, Sch Theoret Physics, Dublin Inst Advan Studies, 72-74; fel, fel theoret high energy physics, 74-75, asst prof, 75-80, ASSOC PROF THEORET HIGH ENERGY PHYSICS, OHIO STATE UNIV, 80- *Res:* Field theory, gauge theory, weak interactions, symmetries. *Mailing Add:* Dept of Physics Ohio State Univ 174 W 18th Ave Columbus OH 43210

MAINS, GILBERT JOSEPH, b Clairton, Pa, Apr 20, 29; m 51; c 2. PHYSICAL CHEMISTRY. *Educ:* Duquesne Univ, BS, 51; Univ Calif, PhD(chem), 54. *Prof Exp:* Fulbright fel, Cambridge Univ, 54-55; from asst prof to assoc prof chem, Carnegie Inst Technol, 55-65; prof, Univ Detroit, 65-68, Poetker prof physics & chem, 68-71, chmn dept chem, 65-68; prof chem

& head dept chem, 71-77, PROF CHEM, OKLA STATE UNIV, 77- *Concurrent Pos:* Fel, Lawrence Radiation Lab, Univ Calif, 59-60. *Mem:* AAAS; Am Chem Soc; Am Phys Soc; Radiation Res Soc. *Res:* Photochemistry; solar energy; fossil fuel chemistry; chemical kinetics; elementary reactions in photolysis, radiolysis and pyrolysis; reactions of free radicals; excited molecules and ions. *Mailing Add:* 301 E Redbud Dr Stillwater OK 74074

MAINS, ROBERT M(ARVIN), b Denver, Colo, Jan 18, 18; m 40; c 2. ENGINEERING MECHANICS. *Educ:* Univ Colo, BS, 38; Univ Ill, MS, 40; Lehigh Univ, PhD(civil eng), 46. *Prof Exp:* Asst, Univ Ill, 38-40; instr mech, Mo Sch Mines, 40-41; engr tests, Eng Lab, Lehigh Univ, 41-42, asst dir, 42-44; engr & proj supvr, Appl Physics Lab, Johns Hopkins Univ, 44-46, engr & asst group supvr, 50-55; from asst prof to assoc prof civil eng, Cornell Univ, 46-50; specialist shock & vibration anal, Submarine Adv Reactor Eng, Knolls Atomic Power Lab, Gen Elec Co, 55-57, consult engr, Proj D1G, 57-60, sr mech engr, Gen Eng Lab, 60-65; chmn dept civil eng, 65-69, PROF CIVIL ENG, WASHINGTON UNIV, 65- *Honors & Awards:* Irwin Vigness Award, Inst Environ Sci. *Mem:* Fel Am Soc Civil Engrs; Am Soc Mech Engrs; Am Soc Eng Educ; Soc Exp Stress Anal; fel Inst Environ Sci. *Res:* Properties of materials; static and dynamic behavior of structures; bi-axial stress effects; bond stresses in concrete; applications of models; vibration testing machine for heavy equipment; strain gage wind tunnel balance; process for steptapering aircraft tubing; galvanized sheet bend tester; methods of controlling vibration response by increased structural damping. *Mailing Add:* Dept of Civil Eng Washington Univ St Louis MO 63130

MAINSTER, MARTIN ARON, b Toronto, Ont, June 30, 42; US citizen; m 65, 76; c 5. OPHTHALMOLOGY, OPTICS. *Educ:* NC State Univ, BS, 63, PhD(physics), 69; Univ Tex Med Br Galveston, MD, 75. *Prof Exp:* Sr res scientist, Life Sci Div, Technol Inc, 68-70, mgr biomath anal, 70-71; resident ophthal, Scott & White Mem Inst, 76-79; ASSOC SCIENTIST, RETINA FOUND, 79-, DIR CLIN RES CTR, 81-; ASSOC SCIENTIST, INST OPHTHAL, HARVARD UNIV, 80-; ASSOC, RETINA ASSOCS, BOSTON, 81- *Concurrent Pos:* Ford Found fel; Nat Sci Found fel; fel retinal dis, Retina Found & Mass Eye & Ear Infirmary, 81. *Mem:* AAAS; Am Phys Soc; Asn Res Vision & Ophthal; Optical Soc Am; AMA. *Res:* Molecular disease; ophthalmic psychophysics; ophthalmic computer systems; radiational eye hazards; clinical optics and lasers. *Mailing Add:* Retina Assocs 100 Charles River Plaza Boston MA 02114

MAIO, DOMENIC ANTHONY, b Washington, DC, June 22, 35; m 58; c 3. PHYSIOLOGY, AEROSPACE MEDICINE. *Educ:* Georgetown Univ, BS, 56; George Washington Univ, MS, 57; Tex A&M Univ, PhD(physiol), 68. *Prof Exp:* US Air Force, 58-, res scientist, US Air Force Sch Aerospace Med, 63-71, staff officer, Aerospace Biotechnol, Off Dep Chief Staff Res & Develop, Hq US Air Force, 71-74, spec asst int res & develop, off asst secy Air Force for res & develop, Pentagon, Washington, DC, 74-76; prog mgr, med & biosci, Air Force Off of Sci Res, 76-78; DIR BIOTECHNOL, AIRFORCE SYSTS COMMAND, WASHINGTON, DC, 78- *Concurrent Pos:* Liaison rep to appl physiol study group, NIH. *Mem:* Assoc fel Aerospace Med Asn. *Res:* Altitude and hyperbaric physiology; Biotechnology. *Mailing Add:* 5306 Stonington Dr Fairfax VA 22030

MAIO, JOSEPH JAMES, b Priest River, Idaho, July 29, 29. MOLECULAR BIOLOGY, MICROBIOLOGY. *Educ:* Univ Wash, BS, 55, MS, 57, PhD(microbiol), 61. *Prof Exp:* NIH fel tissue cult, Univ Pavia, 61-63; NIH trainee, 64-66, fel cell biol, 66-67, asst prof, 67-72, assoc prof, 72-78, PROF CELL BIOL, ALBERT EINSTEIN COL MED, 78- *Concurrent Pos:* NIH career develop award, Albert Einstein Col Med, 69-74. *Mem:* AAAS; Am Soc Cell Biol; NY Acad Sci; Fedn Am Soc Exp Biol. *Res:* Host-induced modification in bacteriophage; predatory fungi; enzymology and active transport processes of tissue culture cells; mammalian cytogenetics; nucleic acids of mammalian cells. *Mailing Add:* Dept of Cell Biol Albert Einstein Col of Med Bronx NY 10461

MAIORANA, VIRGINIA CATHERINE, b Hagerstown, Md, Aug 16, 47; m 74. EVOLUTIONARY BIOLOGY. *Educ:* Univ Md, BS, 69; Univ Calif, Berkeley, MA, 71, PhD(zool), 74. *Prof Exp:* Actg asst prof biol, Univ Calif, Berkeley, 74; RES ASSOC BIOL, 74- & ASST PROF BIOL, UNIV CHICAGO, 78- *Concurrent Pos:* Asst prof biol, Mundelein Col, 75-76; postdoc fel, NIMH, 76-78. *Mem:* Soc Study Evolution; Am Soc Zoologists; Animal Behav Soc; Am Soc Naturalists; Fel, Linnean Soc of London. *Res:* Empirical and theoretical investigations on the evolution of life history and behavior within and among phylogenetic groups and their relations to community structure and function; herbivore-plant interactions. *Mailing Add:* Univ of Chicago Dept of Biol 1103 E 57th St Chicago IL 60637

MAIR, ROBERT DIXON, b Tide Head, NB, Feb 11, 21; nat US; m 43; c 4. OLEFIN POLYMERIZATION CATALYSTS. *Educ:* Univ NB, BSc, 41; Brown Univ, ScM, 43, PhD(chem), 49. *Prof Exp:* Chemist, Polymer Corp, 43-46; res chemist anal methods develop, 48-58, sr res chemist, 58-71, res scientist, 71-78, RES ASSOC POLYMER CHARACTERIZATION & CATALYST DEVELOP, HERCULES INC, 78- *Mem:* Am Chem Soc; Sigma Xi. *Res:* Infrared spectroscopy; molecular structure of benzene; catalysis; organic peroxide analysis; polymer fractionation; thermal analysis; molecular characterization of polyolefins. *Mailing Add:* Hercules Res Ctr Hercules Inc Wilmington DE 19899

MAIRHUBER, JOHN CARL, b Rochester, NY, Dec 14, 22; m 46; c 2. MATHEMATICS. *Educ:* Univ Rochester, BS, 42, MS, 50; Univ Pa, PhD(math), 59. *Prof Exp:* Instr math, Univ Rochester, 56-58; from asst prof to assoc prof, Univ NH, 58-64; prof, Univ Richmond, 64-68; head dept, 68-77, PROF MATH, UNIV MAINE, ORONO, 68- *Mem:* Am Math Soc; Math Asn Am. *Res:* Complex variables; theory of numbers and approximations. *Mailing Add:* Dept of Math 304 Shibles Hall Univ of Maine Orono ME 04473

MAISCH, WELDON FREDERICK, b Pana, Ill, Jan 19, 35; m 60; c 2. FOOD MICROBIOLOGY, INDUSTRIAL MICROBIOLOGY. *Educ:* Ill Wesleyan Univ, BS, 57; Univ Ill, MS, 60, PhD(microbiol), 67. *Prof Exp:* Asst plant bacteriologist, A E Staley Mfg Co, 59-61; sr scientist, Mead Johnson & Co Div, Bristol-Meyers Co, 66-68; assoc res scientist, Hiram Walker & Sons, Inc, 68-71, sr res scientist, 71-74, dir res, 74-80; MGR MICROBIOL GROUP, ARCHER DANIELS MIDLAND CO, 80- *Mem:* Am Soc Microbiol; Am Chem Soc; Am Cereal Chem; Inst Food Technologists. *Res:* Microbial metabolism and fermentation; product development; animal feedstuffs. *Mailing Add:* Archers Daniels Midland Co Box 1470 Decatur IL 62525

MAISCH, WILLIAM GEORGE, b Philadelphia, Pa, Feb 15, 29. PHYSICAL CHEMISTRY. *Educ:* Univ Pa, BS, 51; Brown Univ, PhD(chem), 56. *Prof Exp:* Res assoc phys chem, Eng Exp Sta, Univ Ill, 55-57; asst prof, Inst Molecular Physics, Univ Md, 57-63; RES CHEMIST, US NAVAL RES LAB, 63- *Mem:* Am Chem Soc; Am Phys Soc. *Res:* Optical properties of magnetic materials; molecular and crystal structure; high pressure spectroscopy. *Mailing Add:* Code 6452M US Naval Res Lab Washington DC 20375

MAISEL, DANIEL S(CHWARZ), chemical engineering, see previous edition

MAISEL, HERBERT, b Brooklyn, NY, Sept 22, 30; m 57; c 2. COMPUTER SCIENCE, STATISTICS. *Educ:* City Col New York, BS, 51; NY Univ, MS, 52; Cath Univ Am, PhD(math), 64. *Prof Exp:* Anal statistician, Develop & Proof Serv, Aberdeen Proving Ground, 52-56, chief statist sect, 56-58; chief methodology & reliability div, Off Naval Inspector Ord, Washington, DC, 58-59; mathematician, Oper Math Br, Off Qm Gen, 59-62; tech chief modeling div, US Army Strategy & Tactics Group, 62-63; from asst prof to assoc prof, 63-76, PROF COMPUT SCI & DIR, COMPUT CTR, GEORGETOWN UNIV, 76-; SYSTS ADV, SOCIAL SECURITY ADMIN, 76- *Concurrent Pos:* Consult, Social Security Admin, 66-73, Nat Bur Standards, 68-72 & Baltimore Housing Authority, 72-73; app to spec study group for suppl security income prog, Dept Health, Educ & Welfare, 75-76. *Mem:* AAAS; Am Statist Asn; Asn Comput Mach; Fedn Am Scientists. *Res:* Simulation and other stochastic applications of computers; application of numerical and statistical methods to problems in physical and life sciences; teaching of computer science. *Mailing Add:* 9432 Curran Rd Silver Spring MD 20901

MAISSEL, LEON I, b Cape Town, SAfrica, May 31, 30; US citizen; m 56; c 2. PHYSICS, COMPUTER SCIENCES. *Educ:* Cape Town Univ, BSc, 49, MSc, 51; Univ London, PhD(physics), 55. *Prof Exp:* Res physicist, Philco Corp, Pa, 56-60; SR PHYSICIST, IBM CORP, 60- *Mem:* Inst Elec & Electronics Engrs. *Res:* Thin films, particularly cathodic sputtering, and their application; computer aided design, particularly array logic. *Mailing Add:* Dept Ci4 Bldg 704 Data Syst Div IBM Corp Poughkeepsie NY 12602

MAITLAND, ROBERT (HUGH), chemical engineering, deceased

MAITRA, KARUNA K, b Dinajpur, India, Jan 2, 23; US citizen; m 60; c 2. MATHEMATICS, ELECTRICAL ENGINEERING. *Educ:* Jadavpur Univ, India, BEE, 46; Univ Wash, MS, 54; Columbia Univ, EE, 57; Polytech Inst Brooklyn, DEE(elec eng, math, physics), 60. *Prof Exp:* Asst elec eng, Columbia Univ, 54-55, instr, 55-57; mem tech staff, RCA Res Lab, NJ, 57-60; prin engr, Gen Dynamics/Electronics, NY, 60-61; mem tech staff, Mitre Corp, 62-65, subdept head, 65-69; mem tech staff, Gen Res Corp, 69-76; staff engr, TRW Systs & Energy Group, 76-80, PROG MGR, TRW DEFENSE & SPACE SYSTS GROUP, TRW INC, 80- *Mem:* Inst Elec & Electronics Engrs; Am Inst Aeronaut & Astronaut. *Res:* Computer sciences; switching theory and logical design; optimal control theory; trajectory estimation and tracking system analysis. *Mailing Add:* TRW Systs & Energy Group One Space Park Dr Redondo Beach CA 90278

MAITRA, UMADAS, b Jalpaiguri, India. BIOCHEMISTRY, MOLECULAR BIOLOGY. *Educ:* Univ Calcutta, BSc, 56, MSc, 58; Univ Mich, Ann Arbor, PhD(biol chem), 63. *Prof Exp:* Jane Coffin Childs Found Med Res fel, 63-65, from instr to asst prof, 65-72, assoc prof, 72-77, PROF DEVELOP BIOL & CANCER, ALBERT EINSTEIN COL MED, 77- *Concurrent Pos:* Am Heart Asn estab investr, Albert Einstein Col Med, 67-72, Am Cancer Soc fac res award, 72-77. *Mem:* Am Soc Biol Chemists. *Res:* Enzymatic synthesis of biologically active macromolecules. *Mailing Add:* Dept of Develop Biol Albert Einstein Col of Med Bronx NY 10461

MAIZELL, ROBERT EDWARD, b Baltimore, Md, Aug 3, 24; m 54; c 2. INDUSTRIAL CHEMISTRY. *Educ:* Loyola Col, BS, 45; Columbia Univ, BS, 47, MS, 49, DLS, 57. *Prof Exp:* Chemist, Manhattan Proj, 45-46; reference asst, Sci & Technol Div, New York Pub Library, 47-48; teaching asst sci lit, Columbia Univ, 50; chg tech info serv, Olin Mathieson Chem Corp, NY, 50-58; NSF doc res proj dir, Am Inst Physics, NY, 58-60; supvr tech info serv, 60-65, mgr, 65-72, tech mgr, 72-74, MGR BUS & SCI INFO SERV, OLIN CORP, 74- *Concurrent Pos:* Chmn continuing educ comt, Olin Corp, 69-75; mem adv coun, Smithsonian Sci Info Exchange, 74-; chmn, Subcomt On-line Serv, Mfg Chemists Asn, 75-78; mem, Data Comt & Public Liaison Subcomt, US Interagency Toxic Substances Info Network, 81- *Mem:* Am Chem Soc; Sigma Xi. *Res:* New uses, processes, and products; industrial processes for chemicals; technical and marketing intelligence; technological forecasting; new methods for disseminating chemical information. *Mailing Add:* Olin Corp Res Ctr 275 Winchester Ave New Haven CT 06511

MAJAK, WALTER, b Montreal, Que, Mar 7, 42; m 68; c 2. PLANT BIOCHEMISTRY, ORGANIC CHEMISTRY. *Educ:* McGill Univ, BSc, 63; Dalhousie Univ, MSc, 65; Univ BC, PhD(plant biochem), 72. *Prof Exp:* RES SCIENTIST TOXIC PLANTS, AGR CAN, 72- *Mem:* NAm Phytochem Soc. *Res:* Isolation, identification and quantitative determination of toxic constituents in cultivated and native forages and the effect of environmental parameters on toxin levels in poisonous plants; insoluble phenolic esters in plants (thesis); animal and microbiol metabolism of toxic compounds. *Mailing Add:* Agr Can 3015 Ord Rd Kamloops BC V2B 8A9 Can

MAJARAKIS, JAMES DEMETRIOS, b Chicago, Ill, Oct 11, 15. SURGERY. *Educ:* Univ Chicago, BS, 36, MD, 40; Univ Ill, MS, 46; Am Bd Surg, dipl, 48. *Prof Exp:* From asst prof to assoc prof, 46-72, PROF SURG, COL MED, UNIV ILL, 72- *Concurrent Pos:* Surg assoc attend, Cook County Hosp, 45-55; from sr surgeon to pres med staff, mem bd gov & mem exec comt, Henrotin Hosp, 52-; consult, Cancer Prev Ctr, Chicago, 52- & Univ Ill Res Hosp, 53-; sr surg consult, Westside Vet Admin Hosp, 55- *Mem:* Am Geriat Soc; Soc Nuclear Med; Asn Mil Surgeons US; Am Thyroid Asn; fel Am Col Surgeons. *Res:* Cancer, especially of the thyroid, breast and rectum. *Mailing Add:* Suite 808 30 N Michigan Ave Chicago IL 60602

MAJCHROWICZ, EDWARD, b Stryj, Poland, Mar 18, 20; m 56; c 2. BIOCHEMISTRY, BIOCHEMICAL PHARMACOLOGY. *Educ:* Univ Birmingham, BSc, 48; McGill Univ, PhD(biochem), 59. *Prof Exp:* Asst chemist, A Guinness, Son & Co, Eng, 49-56; res assoc biochem, McGill Univ & McGill Montreal Gen Hosp Res Inst, 56-59, fel neurochem, 59-60; res assoc biochem, Med Sch, Univ Va, Charlottesville, 61-62, asst prof, 62-63; asst prof, Sch Med, Univ NC, Chapel Hill, 63-67; sr res scientist, Squibb Inst Med Res, 67-68; res scientist, Nat Ctr Prev & Control Alcoholism, NIMH, 68-71, head biochem prog, Nat Inst Alcohol Abuse & Alcoholism, 71-76, DIR, NAT INST ALCOHOL ABUSE, ALCOHOL, DRUG ABUSE & MENT HEALTH ADMIN, 76- *Mem:* AAAS; Am Chem Soc; NY Acad Sci; Am Soc Pharmacol & Exp Therapeut; Am Soc Neurochem. *Res:* Neurochemistry, metabolism and metabolic effects of aliphatic alcohols, aldehydes and fatty acids; biogenic amine metabolism; biological aspects of mental diseases; biochemistry and microbiology of fermentation processes. *Mailing Add:* Nat Inst Alcohol Abuse 12501 Washington Ave Rockville MD 20857

MAJDE, JEANNINE ADKINS, b Chicago, Ill, Feb 17, 40; m 65. INFECTIOUS DISEASES, IMMUNOPATHOLOGY. *Educ:* Univ Chicago, BS, 64; Univ Notre Dame, PhD(microbiol), 70. *Prof Exp:* USPHS fel immunol, La Rabida Res Inst, Univ Chicago, 70-72; MICROBIOLOGIST, OFF NAVAL RES, 72- *Concurrent Pos:* Adj asst prof microbiol, Stritch Sch Med, Loyola Univ Chicago, 75- *Mem:* Am Soc Microbiol. *Res:* Immunopathology of chronic viral diseases; role of occult viruses in autoimmune diseases; cellular immunity; chemotherapy of viral infections; immunopharmacology. *Mailing Add:* Off Naval Res 1030 E Green St Pasadena CA 91106

MAJERUS, PHILIP W, b Chicago, Ill, July 10, 36; m; c 4. HEMATOLOGY, MEDICINE. *Educ:* Washington Univ, MD, 61. *Prof Exp:* Intern & asst resident med, Mass Gen Hosp, 61-63; res assoc, Lab Biochem, Nat Heart Inst, Bethesda, Md, 63-65; asst prof biochem, 66-75, asst prof med, 66-69, assoc prof, 69-71, PROF MED, SCH MED, WASHINGTON UNIV, ST LOUIS, 71-, PROF BIOCHEM, 76-, DIR, DIV HEMAT, 73- *Concurrent Pos:* Mem, Biochem Fel Rev Comt, NIH, 69-70, Hemat Study Sect, 74-78; prin investr & dir, Spec Ctr Res Thrombosis, Washington Univ, 74-; ed, J Clin Invest, 77- *Honors & Awards:* Am Cancer Soc Awards, 66 & 75; Dameshek Medal & Prize, Am Soc Hematol, 81. *Mem:* Sigma Xi; Am Soc Hemat; Am Soc Biol Chemists; Am Soc Clin Invest (pres, 81); Am Fedn Clin Res. *Res:* Structure and function of human blood platelets. *Mailing Add:* Dept Biochem & Med Sch Med Washington Univ St Louis MO 63110

MAJERUS, THOMAS CHARLES, b Red Wing, Minn, Aug 6, 46; m 68; c 2. CLINICAL PHARMACY, PHARMACOKINETICS. *Educ:* SDak State Univ, BSc, 69; Univ Minn, DPh, 76. *Prof Exp:* Teaching asst, Col Pharmacol, Univ Minn, 74-76; instr, 76-77, asst prof clin pharmacol, Univ Md, 77-81, CLINICAL PHARMACOLOGIST PHARMACOL, MD INST EMERGENCY MED SERV, 77- *Mem:* Am Soc Hosp Pharmacists; Soc Critical Care Med; Shock Soc. *Res:* Pharmacokinetic studies in humans of drugs; nutritional status of trauma patients including total parenteral nutrition; drug effects on fluid and electrolyte balance of trauma patients. *Mailing Add:* Md Inst for Emergency Med Serv 22 S Greene St Baltimore MD 21201

MAJESKI, STANLEY JOHN, design engineering, see previous edition

MAJEWSKI, ROBERT FRANCIS, b Chicago, Ill, Oct 1, 27; m 61; c 3. ORGANIC CHEMISTRY. *Educ:* Univ Ill, BS, 51; Univ Notre Dame, PhD(org chem), 55. *Prof Exp:* Chemist, Armour & Co labs, 51; sr chemist res & develop, 54-60, group leader, 60-68, sect leader chem res, 68-72, SR PRIN INVESTR, MEAD JOHNSON RES CTR, 72- *Mem:* AAAS; Am Chem Soc; Sigma Xi. *Res:* Unsaturated lactones; medicinal chemistry in endocrine, central nervous and cardiovascular systems; development of organic chemical processes. *Mailing Add:* 401 Kings Valley Rd Evansville IN 47711

MAJEWSKI, THEODORE E, b Boonton, NJ, July 5, 25; m 53; c 6. ORGANIC CHEMISTRY. *Educ:* Syracuse Univ, BA, 51; Univ Del, MS, 53, PhD(org chem), 60. *Prof Exp:* Res chemist, Dow Chem Co, 57-64, proj leader benzene chem, 64-66, org process titled specialist, 66-69; RES SCIENTIST, PHILIP MORRIS, INC, 69- *Mem:* Am Chem Soc. *Res:* Brominated salicylanilides; salicylanilides; aniline; biphenyl; nonyl phenol; chloromethylation of aromatics; bromination of aromatic compounds; flavor technology on cigaret; taste research on cigaret; menthol research; tobacco pyrolysis research; cellulose pyrolysis research; filter research. *Mailing Add:* JRC Bldg 36 PO Box 26583 Richmond VA 23261

MAJKOWSKI, RICHARD FRANCIS, plasma physics, spectroscopy, see previous edition

MAJMUDAR, HARIT, b Baroda, India, Dec 19, 29; m 60. ELECTRICAL ENGINEERING. *Educ:* Benares Hindu Univ, BSc, 52; Indian Inst Sci, dipl, 54; Lehigh Univ, MSEE, 56; Syracuse Univ, PhD(elec eng), 61. *Prof Exp:* Instr elec eng, Syracuse Univ, 56-61; from asst prof to assoc prof, Carleton Univ, Can, 61-64; assoc prof, 64-70, PROF ELEC ENG & DIR ELEC POWER ENG PROG, WORCESTER POLYTECH INST, 70-, HEAD DEPT ELEC ENG, 73- *Mem:* Am Soc Eng Educ; Inst Elec & Electronics Engrs. *Res:* Power system engineering; electrical machine theory; Kron's generalized theory of machines. *Mailing Add:* Dept of Elec Eng Worcester Polytechnic Inst Worcester MA 01609

MAJMUNDAR, HASMUKHRAI HIRALAL, b Baroda, India, Nov 18, 32; m 62; c 2. GEOCHEMISTRY, GEOLOGY. *Educ:* Univ Baroda, India, BSc, 55; Banaras Hindu Univ, MSc, 57; Univ Nancy, PhD(geochem, mineral), 61. *Prof Exp:* Assoc prof geol, Univ Baroda, India, 57-64; Nat Acad Sci-Nat Res Coun resident res assoc geochem, Goddard Space Flight Ctr, NASA, 64-66; Nat Res Coun Can fel, spec lectr & head geochem labs, Dalhousie Univ, 66-68; prof geol, Appalachian State Univ, 68-70; MGR GEOCHEM SECT, DIV MINES & GEOL, STATE OF CALIF, 70- *Concurrent Pos:* Consult geologist agate mines & limestone & dolomite opers, Gujarat State, India, 57-64. *Mem:* Geochem Soc; Mineral Asn Can. *Res:* Development of procedures for major, minor and trace element determination in geological samples; computer data collection; mineralogical, geochemical and geothermal exploration. *Mailing Add:* Geochem Sect Calif Div of Mines & Geol San Francisco CA 94111

MAJOR, CHARLES WALTER, b Framingham, Mass, Jan 31, 26; m 51; c 3. PHYSIOLOGY. *Educ:* Dartmouth Col, AB, 48; Univ Tenn, MS, 54, PhD(zool), 57. *Prof Exp:* Res fel, Nat Cancer Inst, 57; instr physiol, Sch Med, Univ Rochester, 57-59; from asst prof to assoc prof, 59-71, PROF ZOOL, UNIV MAINE, 71- *Mem:* Soc Environ Toxicol & Chem; Am Zool Soc. *Res:* Comparative physiology and toxicology in marine ecosystems. *Mailing Add:* 5 Charles Pl Orone ME 04473

MAJOR, DAVID JOHN, b Paisley, Scotland, Sept 6, 47; Can citizen; m 77; c 2. CROP PHYSIOLOGY, CLIMATOLOGY. *Educ:* Univ Guelph, BSc, 70, MSc, 71; Univ Mo, PhD(soybean physiol), 74. *Prof Exp:* RES SCIENTIST, AGR CAN RES BR, 74- *Mem:* Am Soc Agron; Can Soc Agron; Crop Sci Soc Am; Int Soc Biometeorology. *Res:* Adaptation of crop species; response to photoperiod and temperature; genetic control of photoperiod and temperature response and breeding strategies to improve crop adaptation; developmental control of partitioning of photosynthates. *Mailing Add:* Agr Can Res Sta Res Br Lethbridge AB T1J 4B1 Can

MAJOR, FOUAD GEORGE, b Lebanon, Feb 7, 29; US citizen. ATOMIC PHYSICS, SPECTROSCOPY. *Educ:* Victoria Univ, Wellington, NZ, BSc, 49, MSc, 52; Univ Wash, PhD(physics), 62. *Prof Exp:* Guest prof physics, Univ Bonn, 65-67; physicist, NASA Goddard Space Flight Ctr, 67-73; vis scientist, Univ Paris, 73-74; prof math, Univ DC, 74-77; PROF PHYSICS, KUWAIT UNIV-SUD, 77- *Concurrent Pos:* Consult, Litton Guid & Control Div, 76-77; vis prof, Cath Univ Am, 77-78. *Mem:* Am Phys Soc. *Mailing Add:* Kuwait Univ PO Box 5969 University Park Kuwait

MAJOR, JACK, b Salt Lake City, Utah, Mar 15, 17; m 47; c 3. PLANT ECOLOGY. *Educ:* Utah State Agr Col, BS, 42; Univ Calif, PhD(soil sci), 53. *Prof Exp:* Range researcher, US Forest Serv, Utah, 42-49; range weed control researcher, 53-60, from asst prof to assoc prof bot, 55-71, PROF BOT, UNIV CALIF, DAVIS, 71- *Mem:* Ecol Soc Am; Am Bryol & Lichenol Soc; Brit Ecol Soc; Brit Soc Soil Sci. *Res:* Plant community and soil relationships; California vegetation; vegetation near Atlin Lake, British Columbia; vegetation of Teton and Gros Ventre Ranges, Wyoming. *Mailing Add:* Dept of Bot Univ of Calif Davis CA 95616

MAJOR, ROBERT WAYNE, b Newark, Ohio, Sept 5, 37; m 63; c 2. PHYSICS. *Educ:* Denison Univ, BS, 58; Iowa State Univ, MS, 60; Va Polytech Inst, PhD(physics), 66. *Prof Exp:* Instr physics, Denison Univ, 60-61; asst prof, The Citadel, 61-62; from asst prof to assoc prof, 66-74, prof physics, 74-80, chmn dept, 79, R E LOVING PROF PHYSICS, UNIV RICHMOND, 80- *Concurrent Pos:* Oak Ridge Assoc Univs fac res fel, 74. *Mem:* AAAS; Am Asn Physics Teachers; Sigma Xi. *Res:* Laser-modulated optical absorption in II-VI crystals; photoacoustic kinetics in solids. *Mailing Add:* Dept of Physics Univ of Richmond Richmond VA 23173

MAJOR, SCHWAB SAMUEL, JR, b Windsor, Mo, July 2, 24; m 51; c 3. PHYSICS. *Educ:* Wichita State Univ, BA, 49; Kans State Univ, MS, 53, PhD(physics), 67. *Prof Exp:* Elec engr, Derby Oil Refinery, Kans, 51; staff engr, Boeing Airplane Co, 51-53; instr physics, Southwestern Col, Kans, 53-55; asst prof, Midland Col, 55-59; assoc prof physics, Univ Mo-Kansas City, 59-81; ADMINR ENG STAFF DEVELOP, BENDIX CORP, KANSAS CITY, 81- *Concurrent Pos:* Res assoc, Midwest Res Inst, Mo, 62-64. *Mem:* Am Phys Soc; Am Asn Physics Teachers; Optical Soc Am; Am Inst Aeronaut & Astronaut. *Res:* Applied quantum statistical mechanics; development of physics science techniques to model building for socio-economic interactions in political milieu. *Mailing Add:* Kansas City Div Bendix Corp PO Box 1159 Kansas City MO 64141

MAJORS, RIAS HILTON, b Montgomery, Ala, Mar 8, 24; m 43; c 2. ANIMAL SCIENCE. *Educ:* Ala Polytech Univ, BS, 48, MS, 50; Univ Ga, PhD(animal sci), 65. *Prof Exp:* Chief, Animal Husb Sub-unit, Commun Dis Ctr, 50, Animal Husb Unit, Virus & Rickettsia Sect, 50-59, actg chief, Sci Serv Sect, Ctr Dis Control, 59-60, chief, 60-72, dep chief, Off Res Grants, 72-73, CHIEF, REAL PROPERTY & COMMUN MGT BR, CTR DIS CONTROL, USPHS, 73- *Mem:* AAAS; Sigma Xi. *Res:* Physiology of reproduction of farm and laboratory animals; gnotobiotic and axenic laboratory animal production. *Mailing Add:* 1600 Clifton Rd NE Atlanta GA 30333

MAJORS, RONALD E, b Ellwood City, Pa, Apr 10, 41; m 71. ANALYTICAL CHEMISTRY. *Educ:* Fresno State Col, BS, 63; Purdue Univ, PhD(anal chem), 68. *Prof Exp:* Res asst, Purdue Univ, 63-68; res chemist, Celanese Res Co, NJ, 68-71; res chemist, Varian Aerograph, 71-73, prod mgr, Varian European opers, 73-75, applns mgr, 75-77, MGR, LC APPLN & COLUMN DEVELOP, VARIAN ASSOCS, 77- *Mem:* Am Chem Soc; Royal Soc Chem; Soc Anal Chem. *Res:* Liquid and gas chromatography applications; column technology. *Mailing Add:* Varian Instrument Div 2700 Mitchell Dr Walnut Creek CA 94303

MAJUMDAR, DALIM K, b Feni, East Bengal, Feb 1, 34; m 66; c 1. CIVIL ENGINEERING. *Educ:* Indian Inst Technol, Kharagpur, BTech, 57; Univ Iowa, MS, 60; Utah State Univ, PhD(soil mech & found eng), 64. *Prof Exp:* Asst engr, Durgapur Steel Proj, India, 57-59; trainee earth lab & earth dam design, US Bur Reclamation, Colo, 60-61; teaching asst civil eng, Utah State Univ, 62-63; asst prof, NDak State Univ, 63-65; soil mech & found engr, Gannett-Fleming-Corddry & Carpenter, Inc, 65-67; partner & soils eng consult, 67-75, PRES, SAFE INT, INC, 75- *Concurrent Pos:* Lectr, Grad Ctr, Pa State Univ, 66-; adj prof, PMC Cols, 70-, Temple Univ, 74- & Villanova Univ, 79- *Mem:* Fel Am Soc Civil Engrs; Int Soc Geotech Engrs. *Res:* Seepage under dams and the use of blanket; stability of soil slopes and soil-cement stabilization. *Mailing Add:* Safe Int Inc 1704 Walnut St Philadelphia PA 19103

MAJUMDAR, DEBAPRASAD, b Calcutta, India, Dec 10, 41; m 71. NUCLEAR ENGINEERING, PHYSICS. *Educ:* Univ Calcutta, BS, 61, MS, 63; Univ Pa, MS, 66; Univ Mich, Ann Arbor, MS, 73; State Univ NY Stony Brook, PhD(physics), 69. *Prof Exp:* Res assoc physics, Syracuse Univ, 69-71; res assoc & lectr, Univ Mich, Ann Arbor, 71-73, assoc res scientist nuclear eng, Phoenix Mem Lab, 73-74; nuclear engr reactor safety, Brookhaven Nat Lab, 74-80; NUCLEAR ENGR, IDAHO OPERS OFF, US DEPT ENERGY, 80- *Mem:* Am Phys Soc; Am Nuclear Soc. *Res:* Water reactor safety; liquid metal fast breeder reactor safety analysis; nuclear waste management; production of hydrogen, solar and nuclear, and its use as energy; thermal hydraulic and core disruptive computer code developments and applications. *Mailing Add:* 1749 Delmar Dr Idaho Falls ID 83401

MAJUMDAR, SAMIR RANJAN, b Chittagong, Pakistan, Nov 26, 36; m 62; c 2. APPLIED MATHEMATICS. *Educ:* Univ Calcutta, BA, 56, MA, 58; Jadavpur Univ, India, PhD(fluid mech), 63; Univ London, PhD(mech of continuous medium), 65. *Prof Exp:* Lectr math, Jadavpur Univ, 59-62; asst prof, Univ Ariz, 65-69; assoc prof, 69-76, PROF MATH & CHMN DEPT, UNIV CALGARY, 76- *Concurrent Pos:* Assoc fel, Inst Math & Appln, UK, 65. *Mem:* Am Math Soc; Soc Natural Philos; Calcutta Math Soc. *Res:* Hydrodynamics, especially slow motion of viscous liquids. *Mailing Add:* Dept of Math Statist & Comput Sci Univ of Calgary Calgary AB T2N 1N4 Can

MAK, LINDA LOUISE, b Oakland, Calif, Sept 16, 47; m 77. CELL BIOLOGY, EMBRYOLOGY. *Educ:* Univ Calif, Berkeley, AB, 69, PhD(zool), 75; Ariz State Univ, MS, 71. *Prof Exp:* res biologist path, Vet Admin Hosp, San Francisco, 75-81. *Concurrent Pos:* Scholar anat, Univ Calif, San Francisco, 76-79. *Mem:* Am Soc Cell Biol; Soc Develop Biol; Sigma Xi; AAAS. *Res:* Cell adhesion and movement; morphology and function of cardiac tissue; vertebrate neurulation. *Mailing Add:* 2041 Greenwood San Carlos CA 94070

MAK, SIOE THO, b Medan, Indonesia, Sept 3, 32; US citizen; m 59; c 2. ELECTRICAL ENGINEERING, ENGINEERING PHYSICS. *Educ:* Univ Indonesia, Engr, 58; Ill Inst Technol, MSc, 63, PhD(elec eng), 70. *Prof Exp:* Sr lectr, Bandung Inst Technol, 61-67; sr scientist, Res Div, Joslyn Mfg & Supply Co, 70-76, res proj mgr, 76-78; SR STAFF ENGR, ELECTRONICS & SPACE DIV, EMERSON ELEC, 78- *Concurrent Pos:* Mem tech working group, Am Nat Standards Inst, 76-78; instr, Ill Inst Technol, 70-78. *Mem:* Inst Elec & Electronic Engrs. *Res:* Applications of dielectrics to extra and ultra high voltage power transmission; two-way communication on power lines for load management and automated distribution systems. *Mailing Add:* Emerson Elec Co 8100 W Florissant Ave St Louis MO 63136

MAK, STANLEY, b Canton, China, Sept 20, 33; Can citizen; m; c 1. VIROLOGY. *Educ:* Univ Sask, BSc, 58, MSc, 59; Univ Toronto, PhD(biophys), 62. *Prof Exp:* Asst prof biol, Queen's Univ, Ont, 62-68; assoc prof, 68-74, PROF BIOL, MCMASTER UNIV, 74- *Concurrent Pos:* Mem, Cancer Res Unit, Nat Cancer Inst Can, 76- *Mem:* Can Asn Physicists; Can Soc Cell Biol; Am Soc Microbiol. *Res:* Molecular biology of animal virus infection; transcription cellular transformation of oncogenic viruses. *Mailing Add:* Dept of Biol McMaster Univ Hamilton ON L8S 4K1 Can

MAKANSI, MUNZER, chemical engineering, chemistry, see previous edition

MAKAR, BOSHRA HALIM, b Sohag, Egypt, Sept 23, 28; m 60; c 2. PURE MATHEMATICS, MATHEMATICAL ANALYSIS. *Educ:* Univ Cairo, BSc, 47, MSc, 52, PhD(math anal), 55. *Prof Exp:* Lectr math, Univ Cairo, 48-55, from asst prof to assoc prof, 55-65; vis assoc prof, Am Univ, Beirut, 66; assoc prof, Mich Tech Univ, 66-67; PROF MATH, ST PETER'S COL, NJ, 67- *Concurrent Pos:* Egyptian Govt sci exchange mission, Moscow State Univ, 63-64. *Mem:* AAAS; Math Asn Am; Am Math Soc. *Res:* Functions of a complex variable; functional analysis. *Mailing Add:* 410 Fairmount Ave Jersey City NJ 07306

MAKAREM, ANIS H, b Rasel-Metn, Lebanon, Dec 21, 33; US citizen; m 66; c 2. BIOCHEMISTRY. *Educ:* Concord Col, BS, 57; Univ Calif, San Francisco, MS, 64, PhD(biochem), 65. *Prof Exp:* Fel nutrit, Univ Calif, Berkeley, 65-66; res training fel clin chem, Med Sch, Yale Univ, 66-67, instr, 67-68; asst dir endocrinol, 68-69, ASST DIR CHEM, BIOSCI LABS, VAN NUYS, 69- *Mem:* Am Asn Clin Chem. *Res:* Radio immunoassays for quantitation of hormones and vitamins; disc and agarose gel electrophoresis for serum proteins; lipoproteins and hemoglobins. *Mailing Add:* 18250 Rosco Blvd Suite 120 Northridge CA 91324

MAKAREWICZ, JOSEPH CHESTER, b Attleboro, Mass, Aug 5, 47; m 71. LIMNOLOGY. *Educ:* Southeastern Mass Univ, BS, 69; Cornell Univ, PhD(aquatic ecol), 75. *Prof Exp:* Res asst ecol, Cornell Univ, 69-71; instr pop biol, Southeastern Mass Univ, 71-72; instr biol, Bristol Community Col, 72; res asst ecol, Hubbard Brook Ecosyst Study, 72-74; ASSOC PROF BIOL, STATE UNIV NY COL BROCKPORT, 74- *Mem:* AAAS; Am Soc Limnol & Oceanog; Int Asn Theoret & Appl Limnol; Sigma Xi. *Res:* Zooplankton and phytoplankton dynamics; production biology of zooplankton; pesticide dynamics especially mirex. *Mailing Add:* State Univ of NY 113 Lennon Hall Brockport NY 14420

MAKAREWICZ, PETER JAMES, b Buffalo, NY, Feb 15, 52; m 75. CHEMICAL ENGINEERING. *Educ:* Univ Notre Dame, BS, 73; Princeton Univ, MA, 75, PhD(chem eng), 77. *Prof Exp:* res chemist, 77-80, SR RES SCIENTIST CHEM ENG, RES LABS, EASTMAN KODAK CO, 80- *Concurrent Pos:* NSF grad fel, 73-76; fel, Textile Res Inst, 75-77. *Mem:* Assoc mem Am Inst Chem Engrs; Am Chem Soc. *Res:* Polymer structure-property relationships; separation phenomena and membrane fabrication; bioengineering; gelatin and gelation phenomena. *Mailing Add:* Res Labs Eastman Kodak Co Rochester NY 14650

MAKEMSON, JOHN CHRISTOPHER, b San Francisco, Calif, Sept 20, 42. MARINE MICROBIOLOGY. *Educ:* San Francisco State Col, BA, 64, MA, 66; Wash State Univ, PhD(bacteriol), 70. *Prof Exp:* Asst prof biol, Am Univ Beirut, 70-75; special fel, Harvard Univ, 75-77; ASSOC PROF BIOL, FLA INT UNIV, 78- *Concurrent Pos:* Vis lectr biol, San Francisco State Univ, 77-78; vis lectr biochem, Univ Ill, 78. *Mem:* AAAS; Am Soc Microbiol. *Res:* Bioluminescence and cellular regulation; coral tumor associated algae. *Mailing Add:* Dept Biol Sci Fla Int Univ Miami FL 33199

MAKEPEACE, GERSHOM REYNOLDS, b Ludlow, Mass, Oct 8, 19; m 40; c 2. AEROSPACE ENGINEERING, WEAPONS TECHNOLOGY. *Educ:* Calif Inst Technol, BS, 42. *Prof Exp:* Mat lab supvr, Menasco Mfg Co, Calif, 42-47; mgr propulsion dept, Naval Ord Test Sta, 47-55; pres, Sandshell Corp, 55-58; propulsion prog mgr, Lockheed Aircraft Corp, 58-59, vpres & tech dir, 59-69; DIR ENG TECH & RES, US DEPT DEFENSE, OFF UNDER SECY, 69- *Mem:* Am Inst Aeronaut & Astronaut; Am Defense Preparedness Asn; Sci Res Soc Am. *Res:* Rocket propulsion engineering. *Mailing Add:* Off Under Secy Defense Res & Eng Washington DC 20301

MAKER, PAUL DONNE, b Detroit, Mich, Dec 7, 34; m 56; c 2. SPECTROSCOPY. *Educ:* Univ Mich, BSE, 56, MS, 57, PhD(physics), 61. *Prof Exp:* Assoc res scientist, Univ Mich Willow Run Lab, 60-61; PRIN RES SCIENTIST, PHYSICS DEPT, ENG & RES STAFF, FORD MOTOR CO, 61- *Concurrent Pos:* Assoc ed, Optics Letters, 81-84. *Mem:* Am Phys Soc. *Res:* Fourier transform infrared spectroscopy; hyper-raman scattering; nonlinear optics. *Mailing Add:* 2078 Chaucer Dr Ann Arbor MI 48103

MAKHIJA, SURAJ PARKASH, b Campbellpur, Pakistan, Apr 8, 36; India citizen; m 64; c 3. INORGANIC CHEMISTRY, ANALYTICAL CHEMISTRY. *Educ:* Agra Univ, BSc, 57; Sagar Univ, MSc, 59; Ind Univ, Bloomington, PhD(chem), 67. *Prof Exp:* Instr chem, DAV Col, Jullundur, India, 59-60; asst prof, JV Col, India, 60-61; grad res asst, Ind Univ, 61-66; assoc prof, 66-69, PROF CHEM, ALA STATE UNIV, 69- *Mem:* Am Chem Soc. *Res:* Electrochemistry in non-aqueous solvents, coordination compounds. *Mailing Add:* Ala State Univ Montgomery AL 36101

MAKHLOUF, GABRIEL MICHEL, b Haifa, Israel, June 11, 29; m 60; c 3. MEDICINE, PHYSIOLOGY. *Educ:* Univ Liverpool, MB, ChB, 53; Univ Edinburgh, PhD(med), 65; FRCP, 72. *Prof Exp:* Sr res asst gastroenterol, Univ Edinburgh, 62-65; asst prof med, Tufts Univ, 66-68; assoc prof, Med Col, Univ Ala, Birmingham, 68-70; assoc prof, 70-72, PROF MED, MED COL VA, 72-, DIR GASTROENTEROL RES, 70- *Concurrent Pos:* Consult, Lemuel Shattuck Hosp, Boston, 66-68 & Med Ctr, Univ Ala, 68- *Mem:* AAAS; Am Gastroenterol Asn; Am Fedn Clin Res; Am Physiol Soc; Biophys Soc. *Res:* Exocrine physiology, particularly gastric physiology; membrane transport; gut peptides. *Mailing Add:* Div of Gastroenterol Med Col of Va Richmond VA 23298

MAKHOUL, JOHN IBRAHIM, b Lebanon, Sept 19, 42; US citizen. ELECTRICAL ENGINEERING, COMPUTER SCIENCE. *Educ:* Am Univ Beirut, BE, 64; Ohio State Univ, MSc, 65; Mass Inst Technol, PhD(elec eng), 70. *Prof Exp:* sr scientist, Speech Commun, 70-80, PRIN SCIENTIST & MGR, SPEECH SIGNAL PROCESSING DEPT, SPEECH COMMUN, BOLT BERANEK & NEWMAN INC, 80- *Concurrent Pos:* Res affil, Res Lab Electronics, Mass Inst Technol, 70- *Mem:* Fel Inst Elec & Electronics Engrs; Fel Acoust Soc Am; Asn Comput Mach; Am Asn Phonetic Sci. *Res:* Speech communication (speech analysis, synthesis, compression, recognition, enhancement); digital signal processing (spectral analysis and modeling, linear prediction, lattice methods, adaptive filtering). *Mailing Add:* Bolt Beranek & Newman Inc 10 Moulton St Cambridge MA 02238

MAKI, ARTHUR GEORGE, JR, b Portland, Ore, Nov 24, 30; m 66, 80; c 1. SPECTROSCOPY, MOLECULAR STRUCTURE. *Educ:* Univ Wash, Seattle, BS, 53; Ore State Col, PhD(phys chem), 60. *Prof Exp:* PHYSICIST, NAT BUR STANDARDS, 58- *Concurrent Pos:* Lectr, Louvain Univ, Belgium, 82. *Mem:* AAAS; Am Phys Soc; Optical Soc Am. *Res:* Molecular spectroscopy studies relating to frequency standards and calibration, the measurement of atmospheric pollutants, and molecular structure determination; infrared studies of unstable molecules and high temperature species; studies related to molecular lasers. *Mailing Add:* Molecular Spectros Div Nat Bur of Standards Washington DC 20234

MAKI, AUGUST HAROLD, b Brooklyn, NY, Mar 18, 30; m 52; c 4. BIOPHYSICAL CHEMISTRY. *Educ:* Columbia Univ, AB, 52; Univ Calif, PhD(chem), 57. *Prof Exp:* Instr chem, Harvard Univ, 57-60, asst prof, 60-64; from assoc prof to prof, Univ Calif, Riverside, 64-74, PROF CHEM, UNIV CALIF, DAVIS, 74- *Concurrent Pos:* Guggenheim fel, 70-71; assoc ed, Photochem & Photobiol, 75- *Mem:* AAAS; Am Phys Soc; Am Chem Soc. *Res:* Studies of molecular paramagnetism, principally by electron paramagnetic resonance and electron-nuclear double resonance; applications to free radicals, transition metal complexes and phosphorescent and ground state triplets. *Mailing Add:* Dept of Chem Univ of Calif Davis CA 95616

MAKI, KAZUMI, b Takamatsu, Japan, Jan 27, 36; m 69. THEORETICAL PHYSICS. *Educ:* Kyoto Univ, BS, 59, MS, 61, PhD(physics), 64. *Prof Exp:* Res assoc physics, Res Inst Math Sci, Kyoto Univ, 64 & Enrico Fermi Inst, Univ Chicago, 64-65; from asst prof to assoc prof, Univ Calif, San Diego, 65-67; prof, Tohoku Univ, 67-74; PROF PHYSICS, UNIV SOUTHERN

CALIF, 74- *Concurrent Pos:* Fulbright travel grants, 64-66; vis scientist, Laue-Langevin Inst, France, 79, vis prof, Univ Paris-Sud, 80-; sabbatical leave, vis scientist, Laue-Langevin Inst, France, 79 & vis prof, Univ Paris-Sud, 80- *Honors & Awards:* Nishina Found Prize, 72. *Mem:* AAAS; Am Phys Soc; Phys Soc Japan. *Res:* Theory of condensed matter physics; theory of superconductivity and charge density wave condensate. *Mailing Add:* Dept of Physics Univ of Southern Calif Los Angeles CA 90007

MAKI, LEROY ROBERT, b Astoria, Ore, May 27, 27; m 51; c 5. BACTERIOLOGY. *Educ:* State Col Wash, BS, 51; Univ Wis, PhD(bact), 55. *Prof Exp:* From asst prof to assoc prof, 55-65, PROF MICROBIOL, UNIV WYO, 65- *Mem:* Fel Am Acad Microbiol; AAAS; Am Soc Microbiol. *Res:* Pulmonary emphysema of cattle; taxonomy of fresh-water bacteria; bacterially induced ice nucleation. *Mailing Add:* Div of Microbiol & Vet Med Univ of Wyo Laramie WY 82070

MAKIELSKI, SALLY KIMBALL, b Ft Defiance, Ariz, Nov 23, 38; m 63. POPULATION BIOLOGY, ENVIRONMENTAL HEALTH. *Educ:* Columbia Univ, BA, 60, MA, 61, PhD(zool), 65; Univ Va, MUP, 68. *Prof Exp:* Asst prof biol, Loyola Univ, La, 70-72; health planner, New Orleans Area Health Planning Coun, 72-75; SPEC ASST TO DIR URBAN ENERGY STUDIES, INST HUMAN RELS, LOYOLA UNIV, LA, 75- *Concurrent Pos:* Fac res grant, Loyola Univ, La, 71-72. *Mem:* AAAS; Am Soc Cell Biol; Lepidop Soc; Pop Asn Am; Am Soc Planning Offs. *Res:* Biological approach to the study of urban systems. *Mailing Add:* Inst of Human Rels Loyola Univ New Orleans LA 70118

MAKIN, EARLE CLEMENT, JR, b Maple Shade, NJ, Nov 13, 17; m 43; c 2. CHEMISTRY. *Prof Exp:* Lab technician, United Gas Improv Co, Pa, 37-39, asst chemist, 39-40, chemist, 40-41, group leader, 41-44, asst off mgr, 44-45; asst lab mgr, Co-polymer Corp, 45-46, lab mgr, 46-48; group leader, Lion Oil Co Div, Monsanto Co, 48-65, sr group leader, Hydrocarbons & Polymers Div, 65-74, SR PROCESS SPECIALIST, MONSANTO POLYMERS & PETROCHEMS CO, 74- *Mem:* Am Chem Soc; Am Inst Chem Engrs. *Res:* Synthesis and separation processes using clathrates and complexes; membrane processes for gas separations; supercritical gas extraction systems. *Mailing Add:* 1208 Deats Rd Dickinson TX 77539

MAKINEN, MARVIN WILLIAM, b Chassell, Mich, Aug 19, 39; m 66; c 2. BIOPHYSICS. *Educ:* Univ Pa, AB, 61, MD, 68; Univ Oxford, DPhil, 76. *Prof Exp:* Intern, Columbia-Presbyterian Med Ctr NY, 68-69; res assoc, USPHS, Nat Inst Health, 69-71; NIH fel, Lab Molecular Biophys, Univ Oxford, 71-74; asst prof, 74-80, ASSOC PROF BIOPHYS & THEORET BIOL, UNIV CHICAGO, 80- *Concurrent Pos:* Estab investr, Am Heart Asn, 75-80. *Mem:* Am Chem Soc; Biophys Soc; Am Soc Biol Chemists. *Res:* Electronic structure and molecular spectroscopy of heme complexes in enzymes; structural basis of enzyme function; stereochemical and electronic basis of catalytic action of enzymes. *Mailing Add:* Dept Biophys & Theoret Biol Cummings Life Sci Ctr Univ Chicago 920 E 58th St Chicago IL 60637

MAKINODAN, TAKASHI, b Hilo, Hawaii, Jan 19, 25; m 54. IMMUNOLOGY. *Educ:* Univ Hawaii, BS, 48; Univ Wis, MS, 50, PhD(zool, biochem), 53. *Prof Exp:* Asst serol, Univ Wis, 50-53; res assoc immunohemat, Mt Sinai Med Res Found, Ill, 53-54; NIH fel, 54-55; assoc biologist, Biol Div, Oak Ridge Nat Lab, 55-56, biologist, 56-57, head immunol group, 57-72; chief cellular & comp physiol br, Geront Res Ctr, Baltimore City Hosps, 72-76; DIR, GERIAT RES, EDUC & CLIN CTR, VET ADMIN, WADSWORTH MED CTR, 76- *Concurrent Pos:* NSF sr fel, 61-62; mem microbiol fel rev comt, NIH, 67-70; prof, Grad Sch Biomed Sci, Univ Tenn, 68-72; dir training prog, Nat Inst Child Health & Human Develop, 68-72; mem adv panel regulatory biol prog, NSF, 71-73; mem adv panel, Lobund Inst, Notre Dame, 71-73; mem pub info comt, Fedn Am Socs Exp Biol, 74- *Mem:* AAAS; Int Soc Hemat; Geront Soc (vpres, 74-75); Am Soc Microbiol; Am Asn Immunologists. *Res:* Radiation immunology; mechanism of antibody formation; aging of the immune system. *Mailing Add:* Geriat Res Educ Clin Ctr 691/11G Wilshire & Sawtelle Blvds Los Angeles CA 21224

MAKMAN, MAYNARD HARLAN, b Cleveland, Ohio, Oct 6, 33; m 59; c 2. PHARMACOLOGY, BIOCHEMISTRY. *Educ:* Cornell Univ, BA, 55; Case Western Reserve Univ, MD & PhD(pharmacol), 62. *Prof Exp:* Asst prof, 64-70, assoc prof, 70-79, PROF BIOCHEM & MOLECULAR PHARMACOL, ALBERT EINSTEIN COL MED, 79- *Concurrent Pos:* NIH spec fel, 65-66, career develop award, 66-71. *Mem:* AAAS; Am Soc Biol Chemists; Am Soc Pharmacol & Exp Therapeut. *Res:* Hormone action; neurotransmitter action; control of hormone receptors in normal and malignant cells; biochemical influence of hormones, neurotransmitters, cyclic adenosine monophosphate and related drugs on cultured cells, brain and retina. *Mailing Add:* Dept of Biochem Albert Einstein Col of Med Bronx NY 10461

MAKOFSKI, ROBERT ANTHONY, b Newport Township, Pa, Dec 27, 30; m 53; c 4. TRANSPORTATION ENGINEERING. *Educ:* Pa State Univ, BS, 52; Univ Va, MS, 56. *Prof Exp:* Aeronaut res scientist, Nat Adv Comt Aeronaut, 52-56; sr engr, 57-68, PROG MGR URBAN TRANSP SYSTS, APPL PHYSICS LAB, JOHNS HOPKINS UNIV, 68- *Res:* Internal and unsteady flow; helicopters; hypersonic fluid mechanics; boundary layers; research facility development; transportation system design and evaluation; transportation system operation and control; system costs and economics. *Mailing Add:* 9438 N Penfield Rd Ellicott City MD 21043

MAKOMASKI, ANDRZEJ HENRYK, b Chojnice, Poland, July 15, 32; Can citizen; m 62; c 3. MECHANICAL ENGINEERING. *Educ:* Univ London, BSc, 54, PhD(mech eng), 57. *Prof Exp:* Tech asst, De Havilland Engine Co Ltd, 57-58; lectr, Dept Mech Eng, Univ Col, London, 58-62; Nat Res Coun Can res assoc, Inst Aerospace Studies, Univ Toronto, 62-64; assoc res officer, 64-72, SR RES OFFICER, NAT RES COUN CAN, 73- *Mem:* The Am Phys Soc; Brit Inst Mech Engrs. *Res:* Fluid mechanics; plasma physics. *Mailing Add:* 2257 Prospect Ave Ottawa ON K1H 7G2 Can

MAKOOI, MINA, microbiology, immunology, see previous edition

MAKOW, DAVID, physics, electronics, see previous edition

MAKOWSKI, EDGAR LEONARD, b Milwaukee, Wis, Oct 27, 27; m 52; c 6. OBSTETRICS & GYNECOLOGY. *Educ:* Marquette Univ, BS, 51, MD, 54. *Prof Exp:* Intern, Evangelical Deaconess Hosp, Milwaukee, Wis, 54-55; resident obstet & gynec, Univ Minn, 55-59, from instr to assoc prof, 59-66; assoc prof, 66-69, prof obstet & gynec, 69-76, PROF & CHMN DEPT OBSTET & GYNEC, MED CTR, UNIV COLO, DENVER, 76- *Concurrent Pos:* Fel physiol, Sch Med, Yale Univ, 63-64. *Res:* Reproductive and fetal physiology. *Mailing Add:* Dept of Obstet & Gynec Univ of Colo Med Ctr Denver CO 80262

MAKOWSKI, GARY GEORGE, mathematics, statistics, see previous edition

MAKOWSKI, LEE, b Providence, RI, Nov 4, 49. STRUCTURAL BIOLOGY, X-RAY DIFFRACTION. *Educ:* Brown Univ, BS, 71; Mass Inst Technol, MS, 73, PhD(elec eng), 76. *Prof Exp:* Fel, Structural Biol Lab, Brandeis Univ, 76-78, res assoc, 78-80; ASST PROF BIOCHEM, DEPT BIOCHEM, COLUMBIA UNIV, 80- *Mem:* Biophys Soc; Optical Soc Am; AAAS; Inst Elec & Electron Engrs. *Res:* X-ray diffraction and electron microscopy to determine the structure of macromolecular assemblies; image and data processing strategies are being developed for extracting information from data collected using non-crystalline specimens. *Mailing Add:* Dept Biochem Col Physicians & Surgeons Columbia Univ 630 W 168th St New York NY 10032

MAKOWSKI, MIECZYSLAW PAUL, b Warsaw, Poland, Jan 15, 22; US citizen; m 45; c 2. ELECTROCHEMISTRY, PHYSICAL CHEMISTRY. *Educ:* Western Reserve Univ, BA, 57, MS, 61, PhD(electrochem), 64. *Prof Exp:* Asst mgr plastics technol, Smith-Phoenix Mfg Co, Ohio, 50-55; res chemist, Clevite Corp, 55-61; res asst electrochem, Western Reserve Univ, 61-62; sr res chemist, 62-64, mgr chem & polymers sect, 64-74, assoc dir explor develop, 74-76, dir, Gould Labs, 76-80, vpres tech admin, 80-81, VPRES SCI AFFAIRS, GOULD, INC, 81- *Concurrent Pos:* Mem, Frontiers in Chem Lecture Series Comt, Case Western Reserve Univ, 72- *Mem:* Am Chem Soc; Electrochem Soc; AAAS; Inst Elec & Electronics Engrs. *Res:* Electrode kinetics; hydrogen electrode; fuel cell electrode structure; electrodeposition; electroless deposition of metals; surface area studies; applied polymer research; supervision of electron microprobe; x-ray diffraction; electron microscope; spectrograph. *Mailing Add:* Gould Inc 40 Gould Ctr Rolling Meadows IL 60008

MAKRIYANNIS, ALEXANDROS, b Cairo, Egypt, Sept 3, 39; US citizen. MEDICINAL CHEMISTRY, MOLECULAR PHARMACOLOGY. *Educ:* Univ Cairo, BPharmChem, 60; Univ Kans, PhD(med chem), 67. *Prof Exp:* Fel org chem, Univ Calif, Berkeley, 67-69; sr res chemist drug synthesis, Smith Kline & French Labs, Pa, 69-70; res assoc biochem & pharmacol, Tufts Med Sch, Mass, 71-72, asst prof, 72-74; asst prof, 74-80, ASSOC PROF MED CHEM, UNIV CONN, 80- *Concurrent Pos:* Mem, Inst Mat Sci, Univ Conn, 74-, polymer sci prog, 80- *Mem:* Am Chem Soc; Sigma Xi. *Res:* Drug and neurotransmitter conformations; drug design and synthesis; drug-membrane interactions; nuclear magnetic resonance spectroscopy. *Mailing Add:* Univ of Conn U-92 Storrs CT 06268

MAKSOUDIAN, Y LEON, b Beirut, Lebanon, Oct 30, 33; US citizen; m; c 3. MATHEMATICS. *Educ:* Calif State Polytech Col, BS, 57; Univ Minn, Minneapolis, MS, 61, PhD, 70. *Prof Exp:* Instr math, Westmont Col, 57-58, Northwestern Col, Minn, 58-62 & Univ Minn, Minneapolis, 62-63; from asst prof to assoc prof, 63-72, PROF STATIST, CALIF STATE POLYTECH UNIV, SAN LUIS OBISPO, 72- *Mem:* Am Statist Asn; Math Asn Am. *Res:* Probability and statistics. *Mailing Add:* Dept of Comput Sci & Statist Calif State Polytech Univ San Luis Obispo CA 93407

MAKSUD, MICHAEL GEORGE, b Chicago, Ill, Mar 26, 32; m 59; c 2. EXERCISE PHYSIOLOGY. *Educ:* Univ Ill, Urbana, BS, 55; Syracuse Univ, MA, 57; Mich State Univ, PhD(phys educ, physiol), 65. *Prof Exp:* Instr phys educ, Univ Ill, Chicago, 59-63; from asst prof to assoc prof phys educ, Univ Wis-Milwaukee, 65-72, prof, 72-80, dir exercise physiol lab, 65-80, assoc dean, Grad Sch, 76-80; DEAN, SCH HEALTH & PHYS EDUC, ORE STATE UNIV, 80- *Concurrent Pos:* Clin assoc, Med Col Wis, 66-; consult physiol, Res Serv, Wood Vet Admin Ctr, 67- *Mem:* Am Physiol Soc; Am Col Sports Med; Am Asn Health, Phys Educ & Recreation. *Res:* Physiological basis of performance; nutritional effects of biochemical adaptation. *Mailing Add:* Sch Health & Phys Educ Ore State Univ Corvallis OR 97331

MAKSYMIUK, BOHDAN, b Stanyslaviv, Ukraine, Sept 17, 26; US citizen; m 58; c 2. ENTOMOLOGY, FORESTRY. *Educ:* Univ Mich, BSF, 53, MF, 55; Univ Md, PhD(entom), 65. *Prof Exp:* Res entomologist, US Forest Serv, Washington, DC, 55-65, Forestry Sci Lab, Ore, 65-70, PRIN ENTOMOLOGIST & RES LEADER, FORESTRY SCI LAB, US FOREST SERV, ORE, 70- *Mem:* Entom Soc Am; Soc Am Foresters; Soc Invert Path. *Res:* Aerial application of pesticides, environmental contamination, spray formulations, aircraft dispersal equipment, kinetics and physics of sprays; spray behavior, deposition and assessment; biological and chemical insecticides; ecological principles; insect pathology; antimicrobial substances in plants; biological insect control. *Mailing Add:* Forestry Sci Lab Pac NW Forest & Range Exp Sta Corvallis OR 97331

MAKSYMOWYCH, ROMAN, b Kaminka, Ukraine, Oct 15, 24; nat US; m 51; c 4. BOTANY. *Educ:* Univ Pa, MS, 56, PhD, 59. *Prof Exp:* Asst bot, Univ Pa, 52-54 & 55-57, lab instr, 54-55, asst instr biol, 57-58; from instr to assoc prof, 59-65, chmn dept, 76-80, PROF BIOL, VILLANOVA UNIV, 66- *Concurrent Pos:* NSF res grants, 59-67. *Mem:* Bot Soc Am; Am Soc Plant Physiol. *Res:* Plant growth and development; cell division and DNA biosynthesis during leaf development in Xanthium; regulation of Xanthium shoot development with gibberellic acid. *Mailing Add:* Dept of Biol Villanova Univ Villanova PA 19085

MAL, AJIT KUMAR, b West Bengal, India, Oct 2, 37. MECHANICS, GEOPHYSICS. *Educ:* Univ Calcutta, MSc, 59, DPhil(appl math), 64. *Prof Exp:* Lectr math, Bengal Eng Col, India, 61-63; geophysicist, Univ Calif, Los Angeles, 64-66; asst res engr & lectr appl mech, Univ Calif, Berkeley, 66-67; from asst prof to assoc prof mech, 67-74, PROF MECH, UNIV CALIF, LOS ANGELES, 74- *Concurrent Pos:* NSF grants earthquake eng & mech; consult, 80- *Mem:* Seismol Soc Am; Earthquake Eng Res Inst. *Res:* Wave propagation in solids; earthquake engineering; applied mathematics. *Mailing Add:* Dept of Mech & Struct Univ of Calif Sch Eng & Appl Sci Los Angeles CA 90024

MALACARA, DANIEL, optics, see previous edition

MALACINKSI, GEORGE M, b Norwood, Mass, Nov 25, 40; m 65; c 2. DEVELOPMENTAL BIOLOGY, BIOCHEMISTRY. *Educ:* Boston Univ, AB, 62; Univ Ind, MA, 64, PhD(microbiol), 66. *Prof Exp:* USPHS fel biochem & develop biol, Univ Wash, 66-68; asst prof, 68-74, assoc prof zool, 74-80, PROF BIOL DEPT, IND UNIV, BLOOMINGTON, 80- *Concurrent Pos:* Res assoc, Univ Zurich, Switz, 74-75. *Mem:* AAAS; Soc Develop Biol. *Res:* Biochemical and molecular basis of the regulatory mechanisms which control the ordered sequence of events which characterize the various stages in the developmental cycle of various animals. *Mailing Add:* Dept of Biol Ind Univ Bloomington IN 47401

MALAHOFF, ALEXANDER, b Moscow, USSR, Feb 7, 39; m 62. GEOLOGY, GEOPHYSICS. *Educ:* Univ NZ, BS, 60; Victoria Univ, NZ, MSc, 62; Univ Hawaii, PhD(geophys), 65. *Prof Exp:* Sci officer, Dept Sci & Indust Res, NZ, 59-60; asst geophys, Univ Wis, 63-64; asst geophys, Univ Hawaii, 64-65, asst geophysicist & asst prof geosci, 65-69, asst prof oceanog, 66-69, assoc prof geosci & oceanog, 69-71; prog dir marine geol & geophys prog, Off Naval Res, 71-75; CHIEF SCIENTIST, NAT OCEAN SURV, DEPT COM, NAT OCEANIC & ATMOSPHERIC ADMIN, 76- *Concurrent Pos:* prof geosci & oceanog, Off Naval Res, 74. *Mem:* Am Geophys Union; Soc Explor Geophys; Royal Soc NZ; Geol Soc NZ; Geol Soc Am. *Res:* Solid earth geophysics; marine geophysical studies of the Pacific Ocean crust; tectonics of the ocean ridge system; minerals of the ocean floor. *Mailing Add:* 722 Calvert Lane Ft Washington MD 20022

MALAIYA, YASHWANT KUMAR, b Sagour, India, May 19, 51; m 79. RELIABILITY & FAULT TOLERANCE. *Educ:* Univ Saugor, India, MS, 71; Birla Inst Technol & Sci, MS, 74; Utah State Univ, PhD(elec eng), 79. *Prof Exp:* Asst prof comput sci, State Univ NY, 78-82; ASSOC PROF COMPUT SCI, COLO STATE UNIV, 82- *Concurrent Pos:* Co-prin investr, Proj Intermittent Faults, NSF, 79-83, Proj Testability Very Large Scale Integration, Rome Air Develop Ctr, 81-82 & Proj Functional Testing, US Army, 82-84. *Mem:* Inst Elec & Electronics Engrs. *Res:* Modeling, testing and reliability analysis of systems with intermittent faults; testing and testability of complementary metal-oxide semiconductor very large scale integration; design automation; multiple processor systems. *Mailing Add:* Dept Comput Sci Colo State Univ Ft Collins CO 80521

MALAIYANDI, MURUGAN, organic chemistry, analytical chemistry, see previous edition

MALAMED, SASHA, b New York, NY, May 6, 28; m 56; c 1. CELL BIOLOGY. *Educ:* Univ Pa, BA, 48, MS, 50; Columbia Univ, PhD(zool), 55. *Prof Exp:* Asst zool, Univ Pa, 49-50; asst, Columbia Univ, 50-54; res assoc, Univ Iowa, 54-55 & Columbia Univ, 55-56; USPHS res fel physiol, Western Reserve Univ, 56-58; instr anat, Albert Einstein Col Med, 58-59, asst prof, 59-67; assoc prof, 67-74, PROF ANAT, RUTGERS MED SCH, UNIV MED & DENT NJ, 74- *Concurrent Pos:* Vis lectr, Cornell Col, 55; instr, Hunter Col, 55; Lederle med fac award, 61-64. *Mem:* Am Soc Cell Biol; Am Asn Anatomists; Biophys Soc; Am Soc Zoologists; Am Physiol Soc. *Res:* Ultrastructural and steroidogenic relationships of adrenocortical cells. *Mailing Add:* Univ Med & Dent NJ Rutgers Med Sch Piscataway NJ 08854

MALAMUD, DANIEL F, b Detroit, Mich, June 5, 39; m 61; c 2. CELL BIOLOGY, BIOCHEMISTRY. *Educ:* Univ Mich, BS, 61; Western Mich Univ, MA, 62; Univ Cincinnati, PhD(zool), 65. *Prof Exp:* Instr biol, Univ Cincinnati, 65-66; asst prof path, Temple Univ, 68-69; asst prof path, Harvard Med Sch, 70-77; ASSOC PROF BIOCHEM, SCH DENT MED, UNIV PA, 77- *Concurrent Pos:* USPHS res fel, Fels Res Inst, Sch Med, Temple Univ, 66-68; asst biologist, Mass Gen Hosp, 69-77; res career develop award, 72-77; Fulbright Scholar, Univ Philippines, 75. *Mem:* Am Soc Biol Chemists; Am Soc Cell Biol; Soc Develop Biol; Sigma Xi; Soc Exp Biol & Med. *Res:* Autoradiography; control of desoxyribonucleic acid synthesis and cell proliferation; salivary gland growth and secretion; human salivary proteins. *Mailing Add:* Dept of Biochem Univ of Pa Sch of Dent Med Philadelphia PA 19104

MALAMUD, ERNEST ILYA, b New York, NY, May 8, 32. PHYSICS. *Educ:* Univ Calif, Berkeley, AB, 54; Cornell Univ, PhD(physics), 59. *Prof Exp:* Res assoc, Cornell Univ, 59-60; privat docent, Univ Lausanne, 61-62; Ford fel, Europ Orgn Nuclear Res, 63; guest prof, Univ Heidelberg, 64; from asst prof to assoc prof physics, Univ Ariz, 64-66; vis assoc prof, Univ Calif, Los Angeles, 66-67, assoc prof in residence, 67-68; head, Main Ring Accelerator Sect, 70-71, head internal target sect, 72-73, ombudsman, 76, head, Meson Dept, 78-81, PHYSICIST, FERMI NAT ACCELERATOR LAB, 68- *Mem:* Inst Elec & Electronics Engrs; Am Phys Soc; Sigma Xi. *Res:* High energy physics; designing, constructing and commissioning of Fermilab 400 GEV main accelerator; initiating Soviet-American joint experiment on pp scattering; investigations of hadron jets. *Mailing Add:* Fermi Nat Accelerator Lab PO Box 500 Batavia IL 60510

MALAMUD, HERBERT, b New York, NY, June 28, 25; m 51; c 3. MEDICAL PHYSICS. *Educ:* City Col, New York, BS, 49; Univ Md, MS, 52; NY Univ, PhD(physics), 57; Long Island Univ, MS, 76; Am Bd Sci Nuclear Med, dipl, 79. *Prof Exp:* Sr engr, Physics Labs, Sylvania Elec Prod Co, 57-59; specialist res engr, Repub Aviation Corp, 59-64; res sect head, Sperry Gyroscope Co, 64-65; dir physics res, Radiation Res Corp, 65-67; vpres, Plasma Physics Corp, 67-70; sr physicist, Dept Nuclear Med, Queen's Hosp Ctr, 70-79; CONSULT PHYSICS, 76-; TECH DIR & NUCLEAR ASSOC, VICTOREEN, 79- *Mem:* AAAS; Am Phys Soc; Soc Nuclear Med; Am Asn Physicists in Med; Health Phys Soc. *Res:* Nuclear medicine; plasma and atomic physics. *Mailing Add:* 30 Wedgewood Dr Westbury NY 11590

MALAMUD, NATHAN, b Kishinev, Russia, Jan 28, 03; nat US; m 30; c 2. NEUROPATHOLOGY. *Educ:* McGill Univ, MD, 30. *Prof Exp:* Asst neuropathologist & instr psychiat, Med Sch, Univ Mich, 34-45; prof, 46-71, neuropathologist, Langley Porter Neuropsychiat Inst, 46-75, EMER PROF NEUROPATH IN RESIDENCE, SCH MED, UNIV CALIF, SAN FRANCISCO, 71-, NEUROPATHOLOGIST, DEPT PATH, SCH MED, 75- *Concurrent Pos:* Consult, Armed Forces Inst Path, 44-, Letterman Army Med Ctr, 46-, Oakland Naval Hosp, 51-, Nat Inst Neurol Dis & Stroke, 55- & Vet Admin Hosps, Martinez & San Francisco, 60-75. *Mem:* Am Asn Neuropath (vpres, 58-59); Am Psychiat Asn; Am Acad Neurol. *Res:* Cerebral palsy; mental retardation; geriatric disorders; chronic alcoholism; encephalitis; radiation; epilepsy; heredodegenerative disorders. *Mailing Add:* 240 Dept of Path Univ of Calif Med Sch San Francisco CA 94143

MALAMY, MICHAEL HOWARD, b Brooklyn, NY, Apr 20, 38; m 58; c 2. MOLECULAR BIOLOGY, BACTERIAL GENETICS. *Educ:* NY Univ, BA, 58, PhD(microbiol), 63. *Prof Exp:* From asst prof to assoc prof, 66-76, PROF MOLECULAR BIOL, TUFTS UNIV, 76- *Mem:* Am Soc Biol Chemists; Am Soc Microbiol. *Res:* Regulation of gene expression in bacteria, bacterial viruses and plasmids. *Mailing Add:* Dept Molecular Biol 136 Harrison Ave Boston MA 02111

MALAN, RODWICK LAPUR, b Du Quoin, Ill, Sept 7, 16; m 43; c 6. ORGANIC CHEMISTRY. *Educ:* Univ Ariz, BS & MS, 41; Univ Colo, PhD(org chem), 46. *Prof Exp:* Lab asst, Univ Ariz, 40-41; asst, Univ Colo, 41-44; chemist, Res Labs, 44-49, Film Emulsion Div, 50-56, TECH ASSOC, FILM EMULSION DIV, EASTMAN KODAK CO, 57- *Concurrent Pos:* Lectr eve div, Rochester Inst Technol, 48-68. *Mem:* Am Chem Soc. *Res:* Hemicelluloses and pectic materials in corn leaves; pyridine chemistry; photographic chemicals for the color processes; chemical emulsions. *Mailing Add:* Eastman Kodak Co Kodak Park Bldg 30 Rochester NY 14650

MALANGA, CARL JOSEPH, b New York, NY, Aug 26, 39; m 66; c 1. CELL PHYSIOLOGY, PHARMACOLOGY. *Educ:* Fordham Univ, BS, 61, MS, 67, PhD(biol sci), 70. *Prof Exp:* Instr biol sci labs, Col Pharm, Fordham Univ, 64-67, instr anat, physiol & pharmaceut, 67-70; from asst prof to assoc prof therapeut, 70-76, PROF BIOPHARM, SCH PHARM, WVA UNIV, 78-, CHMN BASIC PHARM SCI, 80- *Concurrent Pos:* Chmn curriculum comt, Sch Pharm Exec Comn & Grad Sch Exec Comn, WVa Univ. *Mem:* AAAS; Am Pharmaceut Asn; Am Inst Biol Sci; Am Soc Zoologists; Am Soc Pharmacol & Exp Therapeut. *Res:* Effects of serotonin, catecholamines and drugs on ciliary activity and energy metabolism. *Mailing Add:* WVa Univ Sch of Pharm Morgantown WV 26506

MALANIFY, JOHN JOSEPH, b Troy, NY, Apr 26, 34; m 56; c 2. NUCLEAR PHYSICS. *Educ:* Rensselaer Polytech Inst, BS, 55, PhD(physics), 64. *Prof Exp:* Staff mem nuclear physics, Los Alamos Sci Lab, Univ Calif, 64-66 & Oak Ridge Nat Lab, 66-69; ALTERNATE GROUP LEADER Q-3, LOS ALAMOS NAT LAB, 69- *Mem:* Am Nuclear Soc; Inst Nuclear Mat Mgt; Am Phys Soc. *Res:* Direct nuclear reaction mechanism and the nucleon-nucleon problem, especially polarization; delayed neutrons and gamma rays from fission; nuclear accountability; x-ray fluorescence; muonic atoms; neutron time of flight. *Mailing Add:* 346 Kimberly Lane White Rock NM 87544

MALARKEY, EDWARD CORNELIUS, b Girardville, Pa, Dec 7, 36; m 65; c 1. OPTICAL PHYSICS, LASERS. *Educ:* La Salle Col, AB, 58; Mass Inst Technol, PhD(phys chem), 63. *Prof Exp:* FEL PHYSICIST, APPL SCI GROUP, ADVANCED TECHNOL DIV, WESTINGHOUSE ELEC CORP, 63- *Concurrent Pos:* Assoc prof, Anne Arundel Community Col, Md, 67. *Mem:* NY Acad Sci; Optical Soc Am; Soc Photo-Optical Instrumentation Engrs. *Res:* Integrated optics system design, component analysis and device development; laser development and imaging; laser resonator design and development; gas discharge analysis and computer modeling. *Mailing Add:* Westinghouse Advan Technol Lab MS 3714 Box 1521 Baltimore MD 21203

MALASANOS, LOIS JULANNE, physiology, nursing, see previous edition

MALASHOCK, EDWARD MARVIN, b Omaha, Nebr, Mar 27, 23; m 44; c 3. UROLOGY. *Educ:* Univ Nebr, BA, 43, MD, 46; Am Bd Urol, dipl, 56. *Prof Exp:* Resident urol surg, Beth Israel Hosp, New York, 50-53; clin asst, 53-55, assoc, 55-57, from asst prof to assoc prof, 57-76, CLIN PROF UROL, COL MED, UNIV NEBR, OMAHA, 76-, ASSOC, PHYS MED & REHAB, 58- *Concurrent Pos:* Chief urol sect, Tenth Gen Hosp, Manila, 48-49; pres med staff, Bishop Clarkson Mem Hosp, 76-78. *Mem:* AMA; Am Urol Asn; Am Col Surgeons. *Res:* Urological surgery; neurogenic bladder dysfunction; new drugs as related to urological problems. *Mailing Add:* 447 Doctors Bldg N 4242 Farnam St Omaha NE 68131

MALASPINA, ALEX, b Athens, Greece, Jan 4, 31; nat US; m 54; c 4. NUTRITION, FOOD REGULATION. *Educ:* Mass Inst Technol, BS, 52, SM, 53, PhD(food tech), 55. *Prof Exp:* Asst, Mass Inst Technol, 53-55; coordr, New Prod Dept, Chas Pfizer & Co, 55-61; mgr qual control dept, 61-69, vpres qual control & develop dept, Coca-Cola Export Corp, 69-77, VPRES EXTERNAL TECH AFFAIRS DEPT, COCA-COLA CO, 78- *Concurrent Pos:* Pres, Int Life Sci Inst & Int Tech Caramel Asn, 78-; vpres, Toxicol Forum, 78- *Mem:* AAAS; Am Chem Soc; Am Inst Chemists; Int Food Technologists; NY Acad Sci. *Res:* Quality control and new product development on carbonated beverages and protein drinks; ingredient safety, food regulations, nutrition and health. *Mailing Add:* Coca-Cola Co PO Drawer 1734 Atlanta GA 30301

MALAVIYA, BIMAL K, b Allahabad, India, Oct 28, 35. ENERGY TECHNOLOGY. *Educ:* Banaras Univ, BSc, 54, MSc, 56; Harvard Univ, AM, 59, PhD, 64. *Prof Exp:* Lectr, Banaras Univ, 56-58; DSR res fel, Mass Inst Technol, 61-65; from asst prof to assoc prof nuclear eng & sci, 65-76, PROF NUCLEAR ENG & DIR SPEC PROGS IN NUCLEAR TECHNOL, RENSSELAER POLYTECH INST, 76- *Mem:* AAAS; Am Nuclear Soc; NY Acad Sci; Am Soc Eng Educ. *Res:* Energy technology; energy planning and policy; nuclear power; reactor physics and engineering. *Mailing Add:* Nuclear Eng & Sci Bldg Rensselaer Polytech Inst Troy NY 12181

MALAWISTA, STEPHEN E, b New York, NY, Apr 4, 34; m 69. INTERNAL MEDICINE. *Educ:* Harvard Univ, AB, 54; Columbia Univ, MD, 58; Am Bd Internal Med, dipl, 65; Am Bd Dermat, dipl, 66. *Prof Exp:* Intern internal med, Yale-New Haven Med Ctr, 58-59, asst resident, 59-60; clin assoc, Nat Inst Arthritis & Metab Dis, 60-62; asst resident, Yale-New Haven Med Ctr, 62-63, NIH spec fel, 63-66; from asst prof to assoc prof, 66-75, PROF MED, SCH MED, YALE UNIV, 75-, CHIEF RHEUMATOL, 67- *Concurrent Pos:* Asst attend physician, Yale-New Haven Med Ctr, 66-69, attend physician, 69-; attend physician, Vet Admin Hosp, West Haven, 66-69, consult rheumatology, 69-; sr investr, Arthritis Found, 66-70; consult, Gaylord Hosp, 68-; Nat Inst Arthritis & Metab Dis career res develop award, 70-75; vis scientist, Inst Cell Path, Nat Inst Health & Med Res, Le Kremlin-Bicetre, France, 79-80. *Mem:* AAAS; fel Am Col Physicians; Am Fedn Clin Res; Am Rheumatism Asn; Am Soc Cell Biol. *Res:* Rheumatic diseases; gout; inflammation; phagocytosis. *Mailing Add:* Dept of Internal Med Yale Univ Sch of Med New Haven CT 06510

MALBICA, JOSEPH ORAZIO, b Brooklyn, NY, Apr 6, 25; m 47; c 4. BIOCHEMISTRY. *Educ:* Brooklyn Col, BS, 49; Fordham Univ, MS, 54; Rutgers Univ, PhD(biochem), 67. *Prof Exp:* Chemist, Hoffman-La Roche Inc, NJ, 54-65; instr physiol & biochem Rutgers Univ, 66-67; res biochemist, Hess & Clark Div, Richardson-Merrell, Inc, 67-69; supvr biochem-pharmacol, 69-80, SECTION MANAGER, DRUG METAB, ICI AMERICAS, INC, 80- *Mem:* Am Chem Soc; Am Soc Pharmacol & Exp Therapeut; NY Acad Sci; Sigma Xi; Am Soc Mass Spectrom. *Res:* Biosynthesis of natural and unnatural products of pharmacology; fermentation; isolation and purification of natural products; drug metabolism; anti-inflammatories; muscle relaxants; drug-related studies with cellular organelles; ion-transport; drug kinetics; bioanalytical methods development. *Mailing Add:* Biomed Dept ICI Americas Inc Wilmington DE 19897

MALBON, CRAIG CURTIS, b Providence, RI, June 1, 50; m 72. BIOCHEMISTRY, PHARMACOLOGY. *Educ:* Worcester State Col, BA, 72; Case Western Reserve Univ, PhD(biochem), 76. *Prof Exp:* NIH fel, Div Biol & Med, Brown Univ, 76-78; ASST PROF PHARMACOL SCI, SCH BASIC HEALTH SCI, STATE UNIV NY, STONY BROOK, 78- *Concurrent Pos:* Res career develop award, NIH, 81. *Honors & Awards:* Samuel A Talbot Award, Biophys Soc, 75. *Mem:* Biophys Soc; NY Acad Sci; Sigma Xi; Am Soc Biol Chemists. *Res:* Hormone action and regulation of metabolism; regulation of catecholamine and insulin action by thyroid hormones; biochemistry of cell surface hormone receptors; membrane biochemistry. *Mailing Add:* Dept Pharmacol Sci State Univ NY Stony Brook NY 11794

MALBON, WENDELL ENDICOTT, b Norfolk, Va, July 18, 18; m 42; c 1. MATHEMATICS. *Educ:* Univ Va, BCh, 41, MA, 52, PhD(math), 55. *Prof Exp:* Asst math, Univ Va, 50-54, from instr to assoc prof, 54-69; PROF MATH, OLD DOM UNIV, 69- *Mem:* Am Math Soc; Math Asn Am. *Res:* Point set topology; quasi-compact mappings; application of topology to theory of functions of a complex variable. *Mailing Add:* Dept of Math Old Dominion Univ Norfolk VA 23508

MALBROCK, JANE C, b NJ. MATHEMATICAL ANALYSIS. *Educ:* Montclair State Col, BA, 64; Pa State Univ, MA, 66, PhD(math anal), 71. *Prof Exp:* Asst prof, 71-78, ASSOC PROF MATH & COMPUT SCI, KEAN COL NJ, 78- *Mem:* Am Math Soc; Math Asn Am; Asn Comput Mach; Inst Elec & Electronics Engrs; Comput Soc. *Res:* Approximation theory. *Mailing Add:* Dept of Math & Comput Sci Kean Col of NJ Union NJ 07083

MALCHICK, SHERWIN PAUL, b St Paul, Minn, Aug 13, 29; m 51; c 3. ORGANIC CHEMISTRY. *Educ:* Univ Minn, BA, 49; Univ Rochester, PhD(chem), 52. *Prof Exp:* Lab asst, Univ Rochester, 49-51, asst, 51-52; chemist, Stand Oil Co, Ind, 52-59, group leader explor res, 59-60; group leader, Nalco Chem Co, 60-66, sect head corp res, 66-67, tech mgr corp res, 67-69, tech dir com develop, 69-71, mgr textile chem, 71-73; dir res, Pigments Div, Chemetron Corp, 73-77, dir technol, 77-79; gen mgr, Pigments Div, 80-81, VPRES, PIGMENTS & ORG SPECIALTIES GROUP, BASF WYANDOTTE CORP, 81- *Mem:* Federated Socs Coating Technol; Am Chem Soc. *Res:* Organic synthesis; polymerization; polymer application; additives; coordination complexes; paper chemicals; colloid chemistry; textile chemistry; surface chemistry; organic pigments and dispersions. *Mailing Add:* Pigments & Org Specialties Group BASF Wyandotte Corp 100 Cherry Hill Rd Parsippany NJ 07054

MALCOLM, ALEXANDER RUSSELL, b Providence, RI, June 28, 36; m 64. BIOCHEMICAL GENETICS, GENETIC TOXICOLOGY. *Educ:* Univ RI, BS, 64, MS, 70, PhD(biophys), 76. *Prof Exp:* Chemist, Elec Boat Div, Gen Dynamics Corp, 64-67 & USPHS, 67-69; chemist, 69-72, RES CHEMIST, ENVIRON RES LAB, US ENVIRON PROTECTION AGENCY, 72- *Concurrent Pos:* Panel mem subcomt environ mutagenesis, Comt Coord Toxicol & Related Progs, Dept Health, Educ & Welfare, 74-; adj asst prof, Dept Pharmacol & Toxicol, Col Pharm, Univ RI, Kingston, 79- *Mem:* Am Chem Soc; Genetic Toxicol Asn; Environ Mutagen Soc; Sigma Xi; Tissue Cult Asn. *Res:* Development and application of in vitro mammalian cell methods in relation to investigations of the genetic toxicity of chemicals. *Mailing Add:* US Environ Protection Agency South Ferry Rd Narragansett RI 02882

MALCOLM, DAVID ROBERT, b Green Lake, Wis, Jan 11, 26; m 49. ENTOMOLOGY. *Educ:* Minn State Teachers Col, Winona, BS, 49; State Col Wash, MS, 51, PhD(zool), 54. *Prof Exp:* Asst zool, State Col Wash, 49-53, res assoc entom, 50-51; instr, Iowa State Col, 54; from instr to prof, Portland State Col, 54-69; prof biol & chmn div sci, 69-76, DEAN COL ARTS & SCI, PAC UNIV, 76- *Concurrent Pos:* Asst dean grad studies, Portland State Col, 67-69. *Mem:* Sigma Xi; Soc Syst Zool; Am Inst Biol Sci. *Res:* Biology and taxonomy of Chelonethida. *Mailing Add:* Off of the Dean Pac Univ Forest Grove OR 97116

MALCOLM, EARL WALTER, b Menominee, Mich, July 17, 37; m 59; c 2. PULP & PAPER CHEMISTRY. *Educ:* Western Mich, BS, 59; Lawrence Inst Paper Chem, MS, 61, PhD(chem), 64. *Prof Exp:* Chemist, Dow Chem, 63-65; res mgr, Dexter Corp, 65-76; DIV DIR, INST PAPER CHEM, 76- *Mem:* Tech Asn Pulp & Paper Indust; Am Chem Soc. *Res:* Pulp and paper technology with emphasis on reactor kinetics. *Mailing Add:* Inst of Paper Chem PO Box 1039 Appleton WI 54912

MALCOLM, JANET MAY, b Bronx, NY, Mar 25, 25; m 46; c 3. OPERATIONS RESEARCH, RESOURCE MANAGEMENT. *Educ:* Rutgers Univ, New Brunswick, BS, 45; Northwestern Univ, MS, 46; Columbia Univ, PhD(phys chem), 51. *Prof Exp:* Lectr, Hunter Col, 48-49; res instr phys chem, Univ Miami, 51-53, Sch Med, 57-59; prof chem, Univ El Salvador, 62; asst prof opers res & info sci & dir opers res prog, Am Univ, 70-75; PVT CONSULT, 75- *Mem:* Fel AAAS; Asn Comput Mach; Opers Res Soc Am; Inst Mgt Sci; Am Chem Soc. *Res:* Rank sum statistics; physical chemistry of blood serum; refrigerant desiccants; kinetics; fluid dynamics analogs to linear, quadratic and separable convex programming; indigenous marketing system in Ghana and Nigeria; socioeconomic system modelling. *Mailing Add:* 1607 Kirby Rd McLean VA 22101

MALCOLM, JOHN LOWRIE, b Westfield, NJ, July 30, 20; m 46; c 3. SOILS. *Educ:* Rutgers Univ, BSc, 43, MSc, 45, PhD(soils), 48. *Prof Exp:* Assoc soil chemist, Subtrop Exp Sta, Univ Fla, 48-59; soils adv, US Opers Mission, Int Coop Admin, El Salvador, 59-63, USAID, India, 63-69; soils specialist, Tech Off, East Asia Bur, AID, Washington, DC, 70, proj mgr fertilizer specialist, Off Agr, Develop & Support Bur, 70-81, SOIL & FERTILIZER SPECIALIST, BUR SCI & TECHNOL, AID, 81- *Concurrent Pos:* Proj mgr, Food & Agr Orgn, UN, Ghana, 69. *Mem:* AAAS; Am Chem Soc; Soil Sci Soc Am. *Res:* Soil and analytical chemistry; agronomy; vegetable and sub-tropical fruit production. *Mailing Add:* 1607 Kirby Rd McLean VA 22101

MALCOLM, MICHAEL ALEXANDER, b Denver, Colo, Feb 7, 45; m 73. COMPUTER SCIENCES, NUMERICAL ANALYSIS. *Educ:* Univ Denver, BSME, 66, MS, 68; Stanford Univ, MS, 70, PhD(comput sci), 73. *Prof Exp:* Asst prof, 73-77, ASSOC PROF COMPUT SCI, UNIV WATERLOO, 77- *Mem:* Asn Comput Mach; Soc Indust & Appl Math. *Res:* Portable programming techniques; portable operating systems; mathematical software. *Mailing Add:* Dept Comput Sci Univ Waterloo Waterloo ON N2C 3G1 Can

MALCOLM, RICHARD EVELYN REGINALD, physiology, see previous edition

MALCUIT, ROBERT JOSEPH, b Fredericksburg, Ohio, Feb 11, 36. PETROLOGY, ASTROGEOLOGY. *Educ:* Kent State Univ, BS, 68, MS, 70; Mich State Univ, PhD(geol), 73. *Prof Exp:* asst prof, 72-78, ASSOC PROF GEOL, DENISON UNIV, 78- *Mem:* Geol Soc Am; Am Geophys Union; AAAS; Sigma Xi. *Res:* Igneous and metamorphic petrology; zircons as petrogenetic indicators; geologic evidence relating to origin and evolution of Earth-Moon system; origin of massif-type anorthosite; origin of continents. *Mailing Add:* Dept of Geol & Geog Denison Univ Granville OH 43023

MALDACKER, THOMAS ANTON, b New York, NY, Apr 3, 46. ANALYTICAL CHEMISTRY. *Educ:* Fordham Univ, BS, 67; Purdue Univ, MS, 69, PhD(anal chem), 73. *Prof Exp:* SR SCIENTIST RES & DEVELOP, SANDOZ INC, 73- *Mem:* Am Chem Soc. *Res:* Development of liquid and gas chromatographic techniques for the analysis of drug substance and dosage, degradation and by-products. *Mailing Add:* 30 Countrywood Dr Morris Plains NJ 07950

MALDAGUE, PIERRE FRANCOIS, b Louvain, Belg, May 19, 49; m 71; c 2. COMPUTER-AIDED DESIGN. *Educ:* Louvain Univ, Belg, BS, 71; Mass Inst Technol, PhD(physics), 75. *Prof Exp:* Fel asst, Physics Dept, Purdue Univ, 75-76; fel, T J Watson Res Ctr, IBM, 76-78; asst prof, Brandeis Univ, 78-79; SR RES SCIENTIST PHYSICS, FORD MOTOR CO, 79- *Mem:* Am Phys Soc. *Res:* Advanced computer-based techniques for the design of high-efficiency internal combustion engines. *Mailing Add:* Res Staff Ford Motor Co PO Box 2053 Dearborn MI 48121

MALDE, HAROLD EDWIN, b Reedsport, Ore, July 9, 23; m 54; c 2. GEOLOGY, ARCHAEOLOGY. *Educ:* Willamette Univ, AB, 47. *Prof Exp:* GEOLOGIST, US GEOL SURV, 51- *Concurrent Pos:* Affil prof, Univ Idaho, 68-77; mem Colo consult comt, Nat Register Hist Places, 72-80; mem Nat Acad Sci comts, Potential Rehab Lands Surface Mined for Coal Western US, 73, Surface Mining & Reclamation, 78-79 & Aloha Surface Coal Mining, 80, mem, Oil Shale Environ Panel, 76-80; mem, Nat Acad Sci Deleg Paleoanthrop, People's Repub China, 75. *Honors & Awards:* Kirk Bryan Award, Geol Soc Am, 70. *Mem:* Fel Geol Soc Am; Soc Am Archaeol; fel AAAS; Am Quaternary Asn; Am Soc Conserv Archaeol. *Res:* Cenozoic and Quaternary geology; geomorphology; environmental geology; stratigraphy and paleo-geomorphology applied to early man; technical photography. *Mailing Add:* US Geol Surv Mail Stop 913 Box 25046 Denver Fed Ctr Denver CO 80225

MALDONADO, C(LIFFORD) DANIEL, b Honolulu, Hawaii, Apr 21, 28; m 51; c 3. ELECTRICAL ENGINEERING, PHYSICS. *Educ:* Univ Wis, BS, 53, MS, 55, PhD(elec eng), 58. *Prof Exp:* Asst elec eng, Univ Wis, 54-58, fel, 58-59; res engr, Gen Tel & Electronics Corp, 59-62; sr scientist, Northrop Space Labs, 62-63, mem res staff, 63-67, sr mem res staff, Northrop Corp Labs, 67-69; SR MEM TECH STAFF, AUTONETICS DIV, ROCKWELL INT CORP, 69- *Mem:* AAAS; Inst Elec & Electronics Engrs; Am Phys Soc. *Res:* Mathematical and theoretical physics; electromagnetic theory; transport phenomena in semiconductors; collective behavior studies in gaseous and solid state plasmas. *Mailing Add:* Rockwell Int 1700 E Imperial Hwy El Segundo CA 90245

MALDONADO, JUAN RAMON, b Holguin, Cuba, May 6, 38; US citizen; m 62; c 3. APPLIED PHYSICS. *Educ:* Univ Havana, MSc, 61; Univ Md, College Park, PhD(exp solid state physics), 68. *Prof Exp:* Elec engr, CMQ TV, Havana, 57-61; instr physics-math, Univ Havana, 60-61; supvr electronics, Univ Md, College Park, 62-65, res asst solid state physics, 65-68; mem tech staff physics, Bell Tel Labs, 68-80; MGR X-RAY LITHOGRAPHY PROCESSES, T J WATSON RES CTR, IBM CORP, 80- *Mem:* Am Inst Physics; Inst Elec & Electronic Engrs; AAAS; Sigma Xi. *Res:* X-ray fluorescence systems for special applications; x-ray lithography and integrated circuit technology. *Mailing Add:* Thomas J Watson Res Lab IBM Corp PO Box 218 Rt 134 Yorktown Heights NY 10598

MALE, CAROLYN JOAN, microbiology, see previous edition

MALE, JAMES WILLIAM, b Schenectady, NY, Dec 8, 45. SYSTEMS ANALYSIS. *Educ:* Union Col, BS, 68; Johns Hopkins Univ, PhD(environ eng), 73. *Prof Exp:* Asst prof enivron eng, Ill Inst Technol, 73-77; ASSOC PROF CIVIL ENG, UNIV MASS, 77-, PROG COORDR, ENVIRON ENG, 81- *Mem:* Asn Environ Eng Professionals; Opers Res Soc Am; Am Water Resources Asn; Am Soc Civil Eng; Am Geophys Union. *Res:* Water resource systems analysis; solid waste management; transportation systems; environmental engineering. *Mailing Add:* Dept Civil Eng Univ Mass Amherst MA 01003

MALEADY, N(OEL) R(ICHARD), b Pittsfield, Mass, Dec 25, 16; m 46; c 5. CHEMICAL ENGINEERING. *Educ:* Worcester Polytech Inst, BS, 40. *Prof Exp:* Group leader, Gen Elec Co, Mass, 41-52, mgr eng lab, Ga, 53-61, mat design lab, oper, Ind, 62-68, advan mfg eng, Neutron Devices Dept, 68-71; CONSULT INDUST PROCESSES, MAT RES & DEVELOP & MGT ORGN, 71- *Honors & Awards:* Coffin Award, Gen Elec Co, 50. *Mem:* Am Chem Soc; Am Inst Chem Engrs. *Res:* Vacuum processing; drying; laboratory administration. *Mailing Add:* 1436 Stewart Blvd Clearwater FL 33516

MALECHA, SPENCER R, b Chicago, Ill, Nov 13, 43; m 71. GENETICS. *Educ:* Loyola Univ, Ill, BS, 65; Univ Hawaii, MS, 68, PhD(genetics), 71. *Prof Exp:* Asst zool, 66-68, asst genetics, 68-69, asst prof genetics, 71-80, ASSOC PROF ANIMAL SCI, SCH MED, UNIV HAWAII, MANOA, 80- *Concurrent Pos:* Ford Found fel, Univ Chicago, 72-73. *Mem:* AAAS; Soc Study Evolution; Am Soc Nat; Nat Asn Biol Teachers. *Res:* Ecological genetics; genetic variation in natural populations. *Mailing Add:* Dept of Genetics Univ of Hawaii Sch of Med Honolulu HI 96822

MALECHEK, JOHN CHARLES, b San Angelo, Tex, Aug 6, 42. RANGE SCIENCE, ECOLOGY. *Educ:* Tex Tech Univ, BS, 64; Colo State Univ, MS, 66; Tex A&M Univ, PhD(range sci), 70. *Prof Exp:* Asst prof, 70-76, ASSOC PROF RANGE SCI, UTAH STATE UNIV, 76- *Mem:* Am Soc Animal Sci; Soc Range Mgt; Wildlife Soc. *Res:* Nutrition and behavior of wild and domestic herbivores on rangelands. *Mailing Add:* Dept of Range Sci Utah State Univ Logan UT 84321

MALECKA-GRIGGS, BLANCHE, b Flushing, NY, Dec 31, 22; m 52; c 2. MICROBIOLOGY, HEALTH SCIENCE. *Educ:* Catholic Univ Am, BSNE, 48, MSNE, 50; Ga State Univ, PhD(sci educ), 74. *Prof Exp:* Teacher biol sci, Gordon Keller Sch Nursing, 47-48; instr & sci coordr nursing, 49-52, asst prof & sci coordr nursing, 52-54, instr, 61-67, ASST PROF BIOL & MICROBIOL, GA STATE UNIV, 68- *Concurrent Pos:* Asst prof microbiol, Ga State Univ, 74-; grants, Olympic Corp, Seattle, 77, Col Urban Life, Ga State Univ, 77-78 & 78-79. *Mem:* Nat League Nursing; Am Pub Health Asn; Am Soc Microbiol; Asn Practitioners Infection Control; Int Union Health Educ. *Res:* Infection control; monitoring and surveillance of respiratory therapy equipment; microbial quality control of contact lens solution and lens containers; nosocomial infection in cancer patients. *Mailing Add:* Dept Biol Ga State Univ University Plaza Atlanta GA 30303

MALECKI, GEORGE JERZY, b Sevastopol, Russia, July 4, 07; US citizen; m 37; c 2. LIFE SCIENCES, METALLURGY. *Educ:* Warsaw Polytech, dipl chem eng, 31; Univ London, DIC, 48; Mass Inst Technol, MS, 54. *Prof Exp:* Res asst metall, Warsaw Polytech, 33-44; lectr metall & inorg chem technol, Polish Univ Col, London, 46-48; res assoc combustion technol, Brown Univ, 48-49; consult food technol, H C Baxter & Bro, Brunswick, Maine, 50; res asst, Mass Inst Technol, 51-53; consult, Green Giant Co, Le Suer, Minn, 54-47; dir res life sci, Malecki Labs, Inc, 57-72; RES FEL LIFE SCI, WELLESLEY COL, 77- *Concurrent Pos:* Secy gasification comn, Polish Br World Power Conf, 33-35; prof abstractor, Am Chem Abstracts, 60-; res leader, Life Sci Res, Labs, 63- *Mem:* Am Chem Soc; Inst Food Technologists. *Res:* Food technology; chemical engineering; new products; processes development. *Mailing Add:* Dept of Biol Sci Wellesley Col Wellesley MA 02181

MALECKI, RICHARD A, wildlife ecology, see previous edition

MALEENY, ROBERT TIMOTHY, b Staten Island, NY, Jan 1, 31; m 54; c 2. CHEMISTRY. *Educ:* Wagner Col, BS, 52; St John's Univ, MS, 54. *Prof Exp:* NSF res asst chem, St John's Univ, 52-53; asst tech dir, Dodge & Olcott, 53-66; tech dir, Globe Extracts, 66-68; vpres tech dir, Major Prod, 68-70 & Aromatics, Int, 70-74; dir res, Monsanto Flavor/Essence, Monsanto Co, 74-79; GEN MGR, SYNFLEUR, DIV NESTLE ENTERPRISES, 79- *Mem:* Am Chem Soc; AAAS; Soc Flavor Chemists; Soc Cosmetic Chemists. *Res:* Development of flavors, fragrances and unique aromatic chemicals, including malodor counteractants. *Mailing Add:* 16 Mohawk Dr Ramsey NJ 07446

MALEK, EMILE ABDEL, b El Mansura, Egypt, Aug 22, 22; US citizen; m 54; c 3. MEDICAL PARASITOLOGY. *Educ:* Cairo Univ, BSc, 43, MSc, 47; Univ Mich, Ann Arbor, PhD(parasitol), 52. *Prof Exp:* Teaching asst zool, Cairo Univ, 43-47; scientist schistosomiasis control, Ministry of Health, Egypt, 52-53; from lectr to reader parasitol, Univ Khartoum, 53-59; from asst prof to assoc prof, 59-73, PROF PARASITOL, MED SCH & SCH PUB HEALTH, TULANE UNIV, 74- *Concurrent Pos:* NIH res career award, 62-; consult, WHO & Pan Am Health Orgn, 56, 61-64, 66 & 74, Peace Corps, 67 & USPHS, 74-; mem expert adv panel, WHO, 64-, scientist parasitic dis, 67-69. *Mem:* Am Soc Parasitol; Am Malacol Soc; Am Soc Trop Med & Hyg; Royal Soc Trop Med & Hyg. *Res:* Epidemiology and control of schistosomiasis; medical malacology; snail-transmitted helminthiases. *Mailing Add:* Dept of Parasitol Tulane Univ Med Ctr New Orleans LA 70112

MALEK, RICHARD BARRY, b Westfield, NJ, July 6, 36; m 63; c 3. PLANT NEMATOLOGY. *Educ:* Univ Maine, BS, 58; Rutgers Univ, MS, 60, PhD(plant nematol), 64. *Prof Exp:* Res asst entom, Rutgers Univ, 58-64; asst prof plant path, SDak State Univ, 64-68; asst prof, 68-75, ASSOC PROF NEMATOL, UNIV ILL, URBANA, 75- *Mem:* Soc Nematol; Helminthol Soc Wash; Europ Soc Nematologists; Orgn Trop Am Nematologists. *Res:* Nematode diseases of plants and their control. *Mailing Add:* Dept Plant Path Univ Ill N-519 Turner Hall 1102 S Goodwin Urbana IL 61801

MALENFANT, ARTHUR LEWIS, b Wakefield, RI, May 17, 37; m 57; c 3. ANALYTICAL CHEMISTRY. *Educ:* Univ RI, BS, 60; Mass Inst Technol, PhD(anal chem), 67. *Prof Exp:* Chemist, Corning Glass Works, NY, 60-63; res asst anal chem, Mass Inst Technol, 63-67; dir tech serv, 67-74, vpres res & develop, 74-79, VPRES INT DIV, INSTRUMENTATION LAB, INC, 79- *Mem:* Am Chem Soc; Soc Appl Spectros; Asn Advan Med Instrumentation; Am Asn Clin Chemists. *Res:* Analytical techniques and methods to promote new approaches in biomedical instrumentation. *Mailing Add:* Instrumentation Lab Inc 113 Hartwell Ave Lexington MA 02173

MALENKA, BERTRAM JULIAN, b New York, NY, June 8, 23; m 48; c 2. THEORETICAL HIGH ENERGY PHYSICS. *Educ:* Columbia Univ, AB, 47; Harvard Univ, AM, 49, PhD(physics), 51. *Prof Exp:* Res fel, Harvard Univ, 51-54; asst prof physics, Washington Univ, 54-56; assoc prof, Tufts Univ, 56-60; assoc prof, 60-62, PROF PHYSICS, NORTHEASTERN UNIV, 62- *Concurrent Pos:* Adv, Harvard Univ & Mass Inst Technol, 54-; consult, Arthur D Little Inc, 59- & Am Sci & Eng, 59- *Mem:* Am Phys Soc; NY Acad Sci; Ital Phys Soc. *Res:* Theoretical nuclear physics; scattering theory at high energies; elementary particles; accelerator theory and design. *Mailing Add:* Dept of Physics Northeastern Univ Boston MA 02115

MALER, GEORGE J(OSEPH), b Denver, Colo, Aug 12, 24; m 45; c 2. ELECTRICAL ENGINEERING. *Educ:* Univ Colo, BS, 45, MS, 57. *Prof Exp:* Instr eng, Univ Colo, 46-51; engr, Mountain States Tel & Tel Co, 54-56; actg asst prof eng, 56-57, from asst prof to assoc prof, 57-66, PROF ENG & ASSOC DEAN, UNIV COLO, BOULDER, 66- *Mem:* Inst Elec & Electronics Engrs; Am Soc Eng Educ; Nat Soc Prof Engrs. *Res:* Circuit theory. *Mailing Add:* Dept of Elec Eng Univ of Colo Boulder CO 80309

MALERICH, CHARLES, b Rochester, Minn, Sept 25, 44; m 73; c 1. PHYSICAL CHEMISTRY. *Educ:* St John's Univ, BS, 66; Yale Univ, PhD(phys chem), 71. *Prof Exp:* Res assoc, Univ Calif, Irvine, 70-71; instr chem, Univ Utah, 71-73; PROF CHEM, BARACH COL, 73- *Concurrent Pos:* NSF indust res fel, Grumman Aerospace Corp, 81. *Mem:* Am Chem Soc; Am Asn Univ Professors. *Res:* Dependence of the physical chemistry of metal parphyrins on molecular structures; develop model systems for heme proteins. *Mailing Add:* Dept Natural Sci Chem Barach Col New York NY 10010

MALES, JAMES ROBERT, animal science, see previous edition

MALETSKY, EVAN M, b Pompton Lakes, NJ, June 9, 32; m 54; c 4. MATHEMATICS. *Educ:* Montclair State Col, BA, 53, MA, 54; NY Univ, PhD(math educ), 61. *Prof Exp:* PROF MATH, MONTCLAIR STATE COL, 57- *Mem:* Math Asn Am; Nat Coun Teachers Math. *Res:* Training of mathematics teachers and mathematics curriculum changes in the junior and senior high school. *Mailing Add:* 34 Pequannock Ave Pompton Lakes NJ 07442

MALETTE, WILLIAM GRAHAM, b Springfield, Mo, Mar 27, 22; m 45; c 2. SURGERY. *Educ:* Drury Col, 40-42; Washington Univ, MD, 53. *Prof Exp:* Physician, US Air Force, 53-58, chief exp surg, US Air Force Sch Aviation Med, 58-61, chief unit II surg & chief vascular surg serv, Air Force Hosp, Tex, 61-63; from asst prof to assoc prof surg, Med Ctr, Univ Ky, 63-75, assoc dean Vet Admin affairs, 71-75; dir emergency med serv, Kern Med Ctr, Bakersfield, Calif, 75-77; PROF SURG, COL MED, UNIV NEBR & SCH MED, CREIGHTON UNIV, 77- *Concurrent Pos:* Chief surg serv, Vet Admin Hosp, Lexington, Ky, 63-75, chief staff, Univ Div, 71-75; participating nat surg consult & mem surg res comt, Vet Admin, Washington, DC; consult, USPHS Hosp, Lexington; chief surg serv, Vet Admin Med Ctr, Omaha, Nebr, 77- *Mem:* Fel Am Col Chest Physicians; fel Am Col Cardiol; Aerospace Med Asn; Am Soc Artificial Internal Organs; fel Am Col Surgeons. *Res:* Cardiovascular surgery; tissue transplantation; aerospace physiology. *Mailing Add:* 4101 Woolworth Ave Omaha NE 68105

MALEWITZ, THOMAS DONALD, b Holland, Mich, Apr 13, 29; m 57; c 3. ANATOMY. *Educ:* Hope Col, AB, 51; Univ Kans, MA, 53; Mich State Univ, PhD(anat, histol), 56. *Prof Exp:* Asst instr biol, Univ Kans, 52-53; instr anat, Mich State Univ, 56-57; asst prof anat & physiol, Col Pharm, Univ Fla, 57-61 & anat, Woman's Med Col Pa, 61-66; asst prof, 66-67, ASSOC PROF BIOL, VILLANOVA UNIV, 67-, HEALTH RELATED SCI ADV, 77- *Mem:* Am Asn Anat; Am Soc Cell Biol. *Res:* Human and animal histology; animal pathology; parasitology. *Mailing Add:* Dept Biol Villanova Univ Villanova PA 19085

MALEY, FRANK, b Brooklyn, NY, July 26, 29; m 53; c 3. BIOCHEMISTRY. *Educ:* Brooklyn Col, BS, 52; Univ Wis, MS, 53, PhD, 56. *Prof Exp:* USPHS res fel, Sch Med, NY Univ, 56-58; from asst prof to assoc prof, Albany Med Col, 58-61, prof, 70-81; sr res scientist, 58-61, assoc res scientist, 61-69, DIR DEVELOP BIOCHEM, DIV LAB & RES, NY STATE DEPT HEALTH, 69- *Concurrent Pos:* Mem exp therapeut study sect, NY State Dept Health, 80- *Mem:* Am Soc Biol Chem; Am Chem Soc. *Res:* Nucleotide interconversions and nucleic acid metabolism; one carbon and hexosamine metabolism; chemical synthesis of hexosamine derivatives; glycoprotein structure and biosynthesis; regulation of enzyme activity and synthesis; isolation of phage induced enzymes. *Mailing Add:* Div of Lab & Res NY State Dept of Health Albany NY 12201

MALEY, GLADYS FELDOTT, b Aurora, Ill, June 7, 26; m 53; c 3. BIOCHEMISTRY. *Educ:* NCent Col, Ill, BA, 48; Univ Wis, MS, 50, PhD, 53. *Prof Exp:* Am Heart Asn res fel, Sch Med, NY Univ, 56-58; adv res fel, 58-60, Am Heart Asn estab investr, 60-65, USPHS res career develop award, 65-70, ASSOC RES SCIENTIST, NY STATE DEPT HEALTH, 70- *Concurrent Pos:* Asst prof, Albany Med Col, Union Univ, NY, 59-65; adj prof, Rensselaer Polytech Inst, 81- *Mem:* AAAS; Am Soc Biol Chem. *Res:* Nucleotide interconversions; nucleic acid metabolism; structure and function of regulatory proteins. *Mailing Add:* Div of Labs & Res NY State Dept of Health Albany NY 12201

MALEY, MARTIN PAUL, b Seattle, Wash, Aug 27, 36; m 66. PHYSICS. *Educ:* Yale Univ, BS, 56; Rice Univ, MA, 63, PhD(physics), 65. *Prof Exp:* Fel, Los Alamos Sci Lab, 65-68; asst prof physics, Rensselaer Polytech Inst, 68-77; STAFF MEM, LOS ALAMOS NAT LAB, 77- *Res:* Low temperature physics; magnetism; ferromagnetic resonance; microwave ultrasonics. *Mailing Add:* Los Alamos Nat Lab PO Box 1663 Los Alamos NM 87542

MALEY, S(AMUEL) W(AYNE), b Sidney, Nebr, Mar 1, 28; m 63; c 2. ELECTRICAL ENGINEERING, APPLIED MATHEMATICS. *Educ:* Univ Colo, BS, 52, MS, 57, PhD(elec eng), 59. *Prof Exp:* Elec engr, Beech Aircraft Corp, 52-53 & Land-Air Div, Dynalectron Corp, 53-56; res assoc elec eng, 58-60, vis lectr, 60-61, from asst prof to assoc prof, 61-67, PROF ELEC ENG, UNIV COLO, BOULDER, 67- *Concurrent Pos:* Consult, Automation Industs, Inc, 58-68, Nat Ctr Atmospheric Res, 63-66 & IBM Corp. *Mem:* AAAS; Inst Elec & Electronics Engrs; Soc Indust & Appl Math; Int Union Radio Sci. *Res:* Electromagnetic propagation in the trophosphere, ionosphere and space; electromagnetic waves in plasmas; communication theory, including information theory, stochastic processes and coding theory; theory of automata; computer logic. *Mailing Add:* Dept of Elec Eng Univ of Colo Boulder CO 80309

MALFAIT, BRUCE TERRY, b Tacoma, Wash, Mar 4, 47. GEOLOGICAL OCEANOGRAPHY. *Educ:* Stanford Univ, BS, 69; Ore State Univ, PhD(oceanog), 74. *Prof Exp:* ASSOC PROF MGR, INT DECADE OCEAN EXPLOR, NSF, 74- *Mem:* Am Geophys Union; AAAS; Geol Soc Am. *Mailing Add:* 5711 Eliot Ct #373 Alexandria VA 22311

MALHERBE, ROGER F, b Lausanne, Switz, Jan 5, 46; m 77. ORGANIC CHEMISTRY. *Educ:* Univ Lausanne, Switz, Dipl, 68, PhD(org chem), 72. *Prof Exp:* Res asst org chem, Yale Univ, 73-75; sr scientist, 75-81, STAFF SCIENTIST ORG CHEM, CHEM INDUST CIBA-GEIGY CORP, 81- *Honors & Awards:* Brenner Award, Univ Lausanne, Switz, 74. *Mem:* Swiss Chemists Soc; Am Chem Soc. *Res:* Synthesis of additives for polymers, in particular antioxidants and light stabilizers for plastics and coatings; new synthetic methods; reactive intermediates. *Mailing Add:* 425 Atlantic St East Northport NY 11731

MALHIOT, ROBERT, b Chicago, Ill, Nov 21, 26; m 53; c 3. PHYSICS. *Educ:* Denver Univ, BS, 49; Ill Inst Technol, MS, 54, PhD(physics), 57. *Prof Exp:* From asst prof to assoc prof, 57-70, PROF PHYSICS, ILL INST TECHNOL, 70- *Concurrent Pos:* Actg chmn dept physics, Ill Inst Technol, 62-68, chmn dept, 68-70. *Mem:* AAAS; Am Phys Soc; Fedn Am Scientists; Am Asn Physics Teachers; Sigma Xi. *Res:* Gravitation and general relativity. *Mailing Add:* Dept of Physics Ill Inst of Technol Chicago IL 60616

MALHOTRA, ASHWANI, b Lahore, WPakistan, July 6, 43; m 71; c 1. ENZYMOLOGY, CARDIOVASCULAR PHYSIOLOGY. *Educ:* Univ Delhi, BS, 62, MS, 64, PhD(org chem), 69. *Prof Exp:* Res asst chem, Univ Conn, 69-70; Fogarty Int vis fel cancer res, Nat Cancer Inst, 70-72; fel, New Eng Inst, 72-73; RES ASSOC CARDIOL, MONTEFIORE HOSP & MED CTR, ALBERT EINSTEIN COL MED, 73- *Mem:* Am Chem Soc. *Res:* Cardiovascular physiology and biochemistry with special emphasis on excitation-contraction coupling of contractile proteins and protein synthesis. *Mailing Add:* Div of Cardiol Dept of Med Montefiore Hosp & Med Ctr Bronx NY 10467

MALHOTRA, SUDARSHAN KUMAR, b Bhera, India, June 20, 33; m 63; c 2. CELL BIOLOGY. *Educ:* Oxford Univ, DrPhil(biol sci), 60. *Prof Exp:* Sr studentship, Royal Comn for Exhib of 1851, 60-62; res fel biol, Calif Inst Technol, 63-65, sr res fel, 66-67; prof zool, Univ Alta, 67-71; dean life sci, Jawaharlal Nehru Univ, New Delhi, 71-72; PROF CYTOL & DIR BIOL SCI ELECTRON MICROS & PROF, DEPT ZOOL, UNIV ALTA, 67- *Concurrent Pos:* Res fel, New Col, Oxford Univ, 61-63; Del E Webb vis assoc, Calif Inst Technol, 80-81. *Mem:* AAAS; Am Soc Cell Biol; Soc Exp Biol & Med; Can Soc Cell Biol; NY Acad Sci. *Res:* Cytology of nerve cells; nerve-muscle interaction; structure, function and biogenesis of cellular membranes and membranous organelle. *Mailing Add:* 12916-63rd Ave Edmonton AB TGH 1S1 Can

MALICH, CHARLES WILSON, b Somerville, Tex, Feb 4, 19; m 51; c 2. BIOPHYSICS. *Educ:* Rice Inst, BA, 40, PhD(physics), 47; Univ Minn, MA, 42. *Prof Exp:* Assoc prof physics, Univ Alaska, 42-44; sr observer & physicist, Carnegie Inst, 44-46; instr physics, Univ Pa, 47-48; physicist, Naval Res Lab, 48-58; assoc prof physics, Southern Ill Univ, 58-59; physicist, Nat Inst Arthritis & Metab Dis, 59-62; res scientist, Ames Res Ctr, NASA, 62-79; RETIRED. *Mem:* Am Phys Soc; Biophys Soc. *Res:* Ionospheric and nuclear physics; radiation biology. *Mailing Add:* 2124 Rock St Mountain View CA 94043

MALICK, JEFFREY BEVAN, b Brooklyn, NY, Nov 14, 42; m 62; c 5. NEUROPHARMACOLOGY. *Educ:* Rutgers Univ, BA, 65, MS, 68; NY Univ, PhD(psychobiol & pharmacol), 73. *Prof Exp:* Res asst neuropharmacol & biochem, Lederle Labs, Div Am Cyanamid, 62-67; supvr neurophysiol, Union Carbide Corp, 67-69; sr res scientist neuropharmacol, Schering Corp, 69-74; sr res pharmacologist, 74-76, MGR CENT NERVOUS SYST PHARMACOL, ICI AMERICAS, INC, 76- *Concurrent Pos:* Adj assoc prof neurophysiol, Fairleigh Dickinson Univ, 74-75; adj assoc prof neurochem, Univ Del, 80- *Mem:* Am Soc Pharmacol & Exp Therapeut; Soc Neurosci; Col Int Neuro-psychopharmacologium; Soc Exp Biol & Med; Am Psychol Asn. *Res:* Psychopharmacology; neurochemical and neuroanatomical substrates of behavior and drug action; aggressive behavior; depression; alcoholism and drug abuse; neuropharmacology; neurophysiology; anxiety and antipsychotic research. *Mailing Add:* Stuart Pharmaceut Div ICI Americas Inc Biomed Res Dept Pharmacol Sect Wilmington DE 19897

MALIK, ASRAR B, b Lahore, Pakistan, Dec 1, 45; Can citizen. CARDIOVASCULAR PHYSIOLOGY. *Educ:* Univ Western Ont, BSc(Hons), 68; Univ Toronto, MSc, 69, PhD(physiol), 71. *Prof Exp:* Demonstr physiol, Univ Toronto, 68-71, demonstr histol, 69-70; instr physiol, Wash Univ, 71-73; asst prof, 73-77, assoc prof, 77-80, PROF PHYSIOL, ALBANY MED COL, 80- *Concurrent Pos:* Assoc staff surg, Jewish Hosp St Louis, 72-73; res career develop award, 77-82. *Mem:* Am Physiol Soc; Biophys Soc. *Res:* Regional circulation; lung fluid exchange; regulation of pulmonary circulation; cardiac hypertrophy. *Mailing Add:* Dept of Physiol Albany Med Col Albany NY 12208

MALIK, FAZLEY BARY, b Bankura, India, Aug 16, 34. ATOMIC PHYSICS, NUCLEAR PHYSICS. *Educ:* Univ Calcutta, BS, 53; Univ Dacca, MS, 55; Univ Gottingen, Dr rer nat(physics), 58. *Prof Exp:* Res assoc physics, Max Planck Inst Physics, 59-60; asst prof, Yale Univ, 64-68; assoc prof physics, Ind Univ, Bloomington, 68-76, prof, 76-82; PROF PHYSICS & CHMN DEPT, SOUTHERN ILL UNIV, 82- *Concurrent Pos:* AID res fel, Princeton Univ, 60-63; vis assoc prof, Fordham Univ, 61-62; sr sci officer, Pakistan AEC, 60-68; consult, US AEC, 66-72; vis prof, Comn Physics, Switz, 71-72; adv, Bangladesh Planning Comn, 72. *Mem:* Am Phys Soc. *Res:* Theory of atomic, molecular and nuclear structure; reactions and many body aspects; fission. *Mailing Add:* Dept Physics Southern Ill Univ Carbondale IL 62901

MALIK, JIM GORDEN, b Elyria, Ohio, Oct 5, 28; m 53; c 3. PHYSICAL CHEMISTRY, INORGANIC CHEMISTRY. *Educ:* Wabash Col, AB, 50; Mich State Univ, PhD, 54. *Prof Exp:* Instr, Univ Minn, Duluth, 54-55, asst prof, 55-56; asst prof chem, Knox Col, 56-57; from asst prof to assoc prof, San Diego State Col, 57-64; prof, Sonoma State Col, 64-65; PROF CHEM, SAN DIEGO STATE UNIV, 65- *Res:* Preparation of inorganic coordination compounds; atomic and molecular structure; interferometric measurements; chemical education. *Mailing Add:* Dept of Chem San Diego State Univ San Diego CA 92182

MALIK, JOHN S, b Geddes, SDak, Sept 3, 20; m 54; c 1. EXPERIMENTAL PHYSICS. *Educ:* Kans State Teachers Col, AB, 42; Univ Mich, MS, 47, PhD, 50. *Prof Exp:* PHYSICIST, LOS ALAMOS NAT LAB, 50- *Concurrent Pos:* Staff mem & sci adv, Opers Off, Dept Energy, Nev, 69- *Mem:* Fel AAAS; Am Phys Soc. *Res:* Nuclear weapon testing and phenomenology; diagnostics; gamma rays; electro-magnetic pulse; nuclear weapons test hazards evaluation. *Mailing Add:* Los Alamos Nat Lab Los Alamos NM 87545

MALIK, JOSEPH MARTIN, b Monroe, Mich, Dec 2, 44; m 71; c 2. PESTICIDE METABOLISM, MASS SPECTROMETRY. *Educ:* Mich State Univ, BS, 66; Univ Wis, Madison, PhD(org chem), 72. *Prof Exp:* Res assoc, Univ Ill, Urbana, 72-73; sr res chemist, 73-77, sr group leader, 77-81, RES MGR METAB, MONSANTO AGR PROD CO, 81- *Mem:* Am Chem Soc; Am Soc Mass Spectrometry; Am Soc Testing & Mat. *Res:* Pesticide metabolism in soil, plants and animals; high pressure liquid chromatography; environmental fate determination; enzyme kinetics. *Mailing Add:* Monsanto Agr Prod Co U2E 800 N Lindbergh Blvd St Louis MO 63167

MALIK, MAZHAR ALI KHAN, b Jullunder, India, Feb 5, 34; m 78; c 3. INDUSTRIAL ENGINEERING, STATISTICS. *Educ:* Eng Univ, Lahore, Pakistan, BS, 57; NY Univ, MS, 70, PhD(indust eng), 75. *Prof Exp:* Instr mech eng, Eng Univ, Lahore, 57-58; trainee engr, St Gobain Chem Co, Paris, 58-59; mech engr, PIDC Fertilizer Factory, Multan, Pakistan, 59-60; works engr, Carstairs & Cumming Shipyard, Karachi, Pakistan, 60-62; mech engr, Adamjee Cotton Textile Mills, Dacca, Bangladesh, 62-63; Regie Autonomme Des Petrole, Paris, 63-64; power engr, Libyan Broadcasting Corp, 64-68; eval engr, Port Authority NY & NJ, 69-76; adv econ planning, Arab Develop Inst, Libya, 76-78, chmn, Indust Eng Dept, 78-81; MEM RES, NAT ACAD SCI RES, LIBYA, 81- *Concurrent Pos:* Adj prof, New York City Univ, 71, Adelphi Univ, 73-74, Polytech Inst NY, 75 & NY Inst Technol, 75-76; adv curriculum, Eng Fac, Benghazi Univ, 77; prof, Al-Fateh Univ, Tripoli, 78-79; vis prof, Mehran Univ Eng & Technol, Pakistan, 80. *Mem:* Fel Am Inst Indust Engrs; Am Econ Asn; Am Soc Opers Res; Am Soc Mech Engrs; Inst Elec & Electronic Engrs. *Res:* Industrial engineering applications in factories; statistical evaluations; industrial and economic planning in developing countries; strategy of industrialization, technology transfer, food forecasting, agro-industrial integration, manpower planning and engineering education. *Mailing Add:* Nat Acad Sci Res PO Box 8004 Tripoli Libya

MALIK, NORBERT RICHARD, b Cedar Rapids, Iowa, June 6, 36; m 65; c 3. ELECTRICAL ENGINEERING. *Educ:* Univ Iowa, BS, 59, MS, 60; Iowa State Univ, PhD(elec eng), 64. *Prof Exp:* Instr elec eng, Univ Iowa, 59-60; asst prof, Kans State Univ, 64-67; asst prof, 67-69, assoc prof, 69-80, PROF ELEC & COMPUT ENG, UNIV IOWA, 80- *Concurrent Pos:* Consult, Autonetics

Div, NAm Aviation, Teleglobe, Booze-Hamilton-Jordan, Rockwell Collins, Intext Inc & Phillips Oil Co. *Mem:* Am Soc Eng Educ; Inst Elec & Electronics Engrs. *Res:* Digital signal processing; microprocessor applications; speech processing. *Mailing Add:* Info Eng Div Univ of Iowa Iowa City IA 52242

MALIK, OM PARKASH, b Sargodha, WPakistan, Apr 20, 32; m 68; c 3. ELECTRICAL MACHINES, DIGITAL CONTROL. *Educ:* Delhi Polytech Inst, NDEE, 52; Roorkee Univ, ME, 62; Univ London, PhD(elec eng) & dipl, Imp Col, 65. *Prof Exp:* Asst engr, Punjab State Elec Bd, India, 53-61; elec engr, English Elec Co, Eng, 65-66; asst prof elec eng, Univ Windsor, 66-68; assoc prof, 68-74, PROF ELEC ENG, UNIV CALGARY, 74-, ASSOC DEAN, ACAD FAC ENG, 79- *Mem:* Am Soc Eng Educ; Brit Inst Elec Engrs; Inst Elec & Electronics Engrs; Can Elec Asn. *Res:* Mathematical models for simulation and analysis of electrical machines and power systems; optimal control of synchronous machines; on-line digital control of generating units; digital protection of power systems. *Mailing Add:* Dept of Elec Eng Univ of Calgary Calgary AB T2N 1N4 Can

MALIK, VEDPAL SINGH, b Sunna, India, Jan 1, 42; Can citizen; m 72; c 1. MEDICAL RESEARCH. *Educ:* Indian Agr Res Inst, New Delhi, MSc, 64; Dalhousie Univ, PhD(biol), 70. *Prof Exp:* Teaching asst biol, Dalhousie Univ, 65-68; res assoc microbiol, Sherbrooke Med Ctr, Can, 70, Tex Med Ctr, Houston, 70-71 & Mass Inst Technol, 71-72; RES SCIENTIST MICROBIOL, UPJOHN CO, 72- *Concurrent Pos:* Res assoc, Nat Cancer Inst, 72. *Mem:* Am Soc Microbiol. *Res:* Physiology and genetics of industrial organisms; novel microbial metabolites. *Mailing Add:* Infectious Dis Res Uphohn Co Kalamazoo MI 49001

MALIN, DAVID HERBERT, b Washington DC, June 9, 44; m 70. BIOPSYCHOLOGY, PSYCHOPHARMACOLOGY. *Educ:* Harvard Univ, BA, 66; Univ Mich, PhD(psychobiol), 72. *Prof Exp:* Res assoc neuropharmacol, Baylor Col Med, 72-74; asst prof, 74-77, ASSOC PROF PSYCHOL, UNIV HOUSTON, CLEAR LAKE CITY, 77- *Concurrent Pos:* Adj asst prof, Baylor Col Med, 74-76. *Mem:* Soc Neurosci; Am Psychol Asn; AAAS; Psychonomic Soc. *Res:* Neurochemical factors in learning, memory and drug dependence. *Mailing Add:* Univ of Houston Clear Lake City 2700 Bay Area Blvd Houston TX 77058

MALIN, EDYTH THERESA LASKY, b Fitchburg, Mass, May 21, 26; m 47; c 3. BIOCHEMISTRY, BIOPHYSICAL CHEMISTRY. *Educ:* Vanderbilt Univ, BA, 47; Am Univ, MS, 69; Bryn Mawr Col, PhD(chem), 75. *Prof Exp:* Chemist, Nat Bur Standards, 50-51; ed asst, Chem & Eng News, 51-53; fel dept biochem, Sch Med, Univ Pa, 75-77; Nat Res Coun assoc, 77-79, RES CHEMIST BIOCHEM, EASTERN REGIONAL RES CTR, USDA, 77- *Concurrent Pos:* NIH trainee dept biochem, Sch Med, Univ Pa, 75-76; lectr biochem, Chem Dept, St Joseph's Univ, 80 & Spring Garden Col, 82. *Mem:* Am Chem Soc; Sigma Xi; NY Acad Sci; AAAS; Int Asn Women Biochemists. *Res:* Chemical modification, and hydrogen-tritium exchange studies of protein structure; protein dynamics in solution; lipid-protein interactions; anti-oxidant mechanisms. *Mailing Add:* Eastern Regional Res Ctr USDA 600 E Mermaid Lane Philadelphia PA 19118

MALIN, HOWARD GERALD, b Providence, RI, Dec 2, 41. PODIATRIC MEDICINE, PODIATRIC DERMATOLOGY. *Educ:* Univ RI, Kingston, AB, 64; Brigham Young Univ, MA, 69; Calif Col Podiatric Med, BSc, 69, PhD(podiatric med), 72; Am Bd Podiatric Orthopedisc, dipl, 82. *Prof Exp:* Asst instr basic sci, Calif Col Podiatric Med, 69-72, res asst, 70-72; instr, NY Col Podiatric Med, 73-74; staff podiatrist, Prospect Hosp, NY, 74-77; staff podiatrist & chief, Podiatry Serv, David Grant US Air Force Med Ctr, Travis AFB, Calif, 77-80; CHIEF, PODIATRIC SECT, VET ADMIN MED CTR, WVA, 80-, STAFF PODIATRIST, 80- *Concurrent Pos:* Practitioner, 74-77; ed, Futura Publ Co & David Grant US Air Force Med Ctr, 79-80; staff reserve podiatrist, Malcolm Grow US Air Force Med Ctr, 80-; consult podiatric sports med, Travis AFB, 77-80. *Honors & Awards:* Basic Sci Award, Calif Col Podiatric Med, 72. *Mem:* Am Podiatry Asn; NY Acad Sci; AAAS; Asn Military Surgeons US; fel Am Col Foot Orthopedics. *Res:* Specialties of podiatric medicine and podiatric dermatology. *Mailing Add:* Podiatry Dept Vets Admin Med Ctr Martinsburg WV 25401

MALIN, JOHN MICHAEL, b Cleveland, Ohio, July 9, 42; m 67; c 2. INORGANIC CHEMISTRY, PHOTOCHEMISTRY. *Educ:* Univ Calif, Berkeley, BS, 63; Univ Calif, Davis, PhD(chem), 68. *Prof Exp:* NIH fel inorg chem, Stanford Univ, 68-70; Nat Acad Sci fel, Inst Chem, Univ Sao Paulo, Brazil, 70-73; vis asst prof inorg chem, Univ Mo, Columbia, 73-74, asst prof, 74-77, assoc prof, 77-81; prog officer, Chem Dynamics, NSF, 79-81; ASST PROG ADMINR, PETROL RES FUND-AM CHEM SOC, WASHINGTON, DC, 81- *Mem:* Sigma Xi; Am Chem Soc; AAAS. *Res:* Studies of the synthesis, spectra, structures and reactivity, both thermal and photoinduced, of transition metal complexes. *Mailing Add:* ASC-PRF Rm 406 1155 16th St NW Washington DC 20036

MALIN, MICHAEL CHARLES, b Burbank, Calif, May 10, 50. PLANETARY GEOLOGY, GEOMORPHOLOGY. *Educ:* Univ Calif, Berkeley, AB, 71; Calif Inst Technol, PhD(planetary sci), 76. *Prof Exp:* Sr scientist, Jet Propulsion Lab, Calif Inst Technol, 75-78, mem tech staff planetary geol, 78-79; ASST PROF GEOL, ARIZ STATE UNIV, 79- *Mem:* Am Geophys Union; Am Astron Soc. *Res:* Evolution of landforms; volcanology; remote sensing; specific areas; Mars, heavily cratered terrains, channels and other erosional landforms; polar regions; Venus, tectonic and volcanic features. *Mailing Add:* Dept Geol Ariz State Univ Tempe AZ 85287

MALIN, MURRAY EDWARD, b New York, NY, June 25, 27; m 52; c 2. PHYSICAL CHEMISTRY. *Educ:* City Col New York, BS, 48; Harvard Univ, AM & PhD(phys chem), 51. *Prof Exp:* Mem staff, Los Alamos Sci Lab, 51-56; vpres res & technol, Res & Develop Div, Avco Corp, 56-57, tech opers, Avco Space Systs Div, 57-68; mgr spec systs, 68-71, prog mgr, 71-75, DIV VPRES, POLAROID CORP, 75- *Concurrent Pos:* Mem, Adv Comt Fluid Mech, NASA, 65- *Mem:* Am Phys Soc; Am Chem Soc; fel Am Inst Aeronaut & Astronaut. *Res:* High temperature; thermodynamics; theory and structure of detonation waves; instant color transparencies; space and missile physics. *Mailing Add:* Polaroid Corp 1 Upland Rd Norwood MA 02062

MALIN, SHIMON, b Ramat-Gan, Israel, July 7, 37; m 60; c 3. THEORETICAL PHYSICS. *Educ:* Hebrew Univ, Jerusalem, MSc, 61; Univ Colo, Boulder, PhD(physics), 68. *Prof Exp:* Asst prof, 68-77, ASSOC PROF PHYSICS, COLGATE UNIV, 77- *Mem:* Am Phys Soc; Am Asn Physics Teachers. *Res:* Group theory and its applications to general relativity; foundations of quantum mechanics; cosmology. *Mailing Add:* Dept Physics & Astron Colgate Univ Hamilton NY 13346

MALINA, FRANK J(OSEPH), astronautics, deceased

MALINA, JOSEPH F(RANCIS), JR, b Brooklyn, NY, Aug 24, 35; m 65; c 3. ENVIRONMENTAL & CIVIL ENGINEERING. *Educ:* Manhattan Col, BCE, 57; Univ Wis, MSSE, 59, PhD(sanit eng), 61; Environ Eng Intersoc, dipl. *Prof Exp:* Instr civil eng, Univ Wis, 57-58, asst sanit eng, 58-61; from asst prof to assoc prof environ health eng, 61-70, dir environ health eng res lab, 70-76, PROF CIVIL ENG, UNIV TEX, AUSTIN, 70-, CHMN DEPT, 76- *Concurrent Pos:* Res grant, 62-65; Eng Found award, Univ Tex, Austin, 62. *Mem:* Am Soc Civil Engrs; Am Water Works Asn; Water Pollution Control Fedn; Am Soc Eng Educ; Inter-Am Asn Sanit Engrs. *Res:* Water and wastewater treatment; water pollution control; water renovation and reuse; solid wastes disposal. *Mailing Add:* Dept of Civil Eng ECJ 4-2 Univ of Texas Austin TX 78712

MALINA, MARSHALL ALBERT, b Chicago, Ill, July 11, 28; m 55; c 2. RESOURCE MANAGEMENT. *Educ:* Ill Inst Technol, BS, 49; Northwestern Univ, MBA, 69. *Prof Exp:* Qual control chemist, Capitol Chem Co, 49-50; prod mgr, Hamilton Industs, 50-52; mgr, Gen Anal Sect, 52-68, mgr qual control, 68-69, dir qual control & tech serv, 69-70, dir res, 71-74, mgr corp develop, 74-76, dir corp develop, 76-79, DIR CAPITAL EXPENDITURES, VELSICOL CHEM CORP, 80- *Mem:* Am Chem Soc; Am Soc Testing & Mat; fel Asn Off Anal Chem; Com Develop Asn; Soc Plastics Eng. *Res:* Agricultural pesticides; polymers; polymer additives; plasticizers; benzoic acid and derivatives; pollution control; statistics; licensing, acquisitions, capital budgeting and planning, corporate planning. *Mailing Add:* Velsicol Chem Corp 341 E Ohio Chicago IL 60611

MALINA, ROBERT MARION, b Brooklyn, NY, Sept 19, 37. PHYSICAL ANTHROPOLOGY. *Educ:* Manhattan Col, BS, 59; Univ Wis, MS, 60, PhD(phys educ), 63; Univ Pa, PhD(anthrop), 68. *Prof Exp:* Asst prof, 67-71, assoc prof, 71-77, PROF ANTHROP, UNIV TEX, AUSTIN, 77- *Concurrent Pos:* Vis prof, Cath Univ Leuven, Belgium, 81. *Mem:* Am Asn Health, Phys Educ & Recreation; Am Asn Phys Anthrop; Soc Study Human Biol; Human Biol Coun; Soc Res Child Develop. *Res:* Human growth and development; motor development; growth and nutrition in Mexico and Central America; growth and athletic performance. *Mailing Add:* Dept of Anthrop Univ of Tex Austin TX 78712

MALINAUSKAS, ANTHONY PETER, b Ashley, Pa, Mar 24, 35; m 57; c 6. PHYSICAL CHEMISTRY. *Educ:* Kings Col, Pa, BS, 56; Boston Col, MS, 58; Mass Inst Technol, PhD(phys chem), 62. *Prof Exp:* Mem res staff, 62-73, CHIEF, CHEM DEVELOP SECT, OAK RIDGE NAT LAB, 73- *Honors & Awards:* Am Nuclear Soc Award, 81. *Mem:* Sigma Xi; Am Chem Soc; Am Phys Soc; Am Nuclear Soc. *Res:* Thermal transpiration; transport properties of gases; nuclear safety; fission product chemistry and transport; nuclear fuel reprocessing. *Mailing Add:* Oak Ridge Nat Lab Oak Ridge TN 37830

MALINDZAK, GEORGE STEVE, JR, b Cleveland, Ohio, Jan 3, 33; m 59; c 4. MEDICAL CARDIOVASCULAR PHYSIOLOGY, ENVIRONMENTAL PHYSIOLOGY. *Educ:* Western Reserve Univ, AB, 56; Ohio State Univ, MSc, 58, PhD(physiol, biophys), 61. *Prof Exp:* Consult comput, NIH, 61-62; res assoc physiol, Ohio State Univ; from instr to assoc prof, Bowman Gray Sch Med, 62-73, dir comput ctr, 64-65; res physiologist, Clin Studies Div, Environ Protection Agency, Univ NC, Chapel Hill, 73-76; PROF PHYSIOL & CHMN DEPT, COL MED, NORTHEASTERN OHIO UNIV, 77-; PROF BIOL SCI, KENT STATE UNIV, 77- *Concurrent Pos:* Partic, LINC eval prog, Bowman Gray Sch Med-Mass Inst Technol, 63-65; sr res investr, NC Heart Asn, 65-75, res comt, 68-69 & 71-; consult NASA, 67-73; adj assoc prof biomath & bioeng, Dept Physiol & Surg, Univ NC, Chapel Hill, 73-76; adj prof elec eng, Univ Akron, 77- *Mem:* Am Heart Asn; Am Physiol Soc; Biomed Eng Soc; Am Soc Pharmacol & Exp Therapeut; Asn Comput Mach (secy-treas, 73-77). *Res:* experimental echocardiography; pathophysiology of coronary and peripheral atherosclerosis; cardiovascular modeling; cardiopulmonary function and environmental toxicology; control of coronary blood flow in health and disease; indicator-dilution techniques and analyses; transmission-line characteristics of the arterial tree; environmental toxicology. *Mailing Add:* Dept Physiol Col Med Northeastern Ohio Univ Rootstown OH 44272

MALING, GEORGE CROSWELL, JR, b Boston, Mass, Feb 24, 31; m 60; c 2. PHYSICS. *Educ:* Bowdoin Col, AB, 54; Mass Inst Technol, SB & SM, 54, EE, 58, PhD(physics), 63. *Prof Exp:* Mem res staff, Mass Inst Technol, 63-65; SR PHYSICIST, IBM CORP, 65- *Concurrent Pos:* Consult, pvt pract, 59-65 & Indust Acoustics Co, 63-65. *Mem:* Fel Inst Elec & Electronics Engrs; fel Acoust Soc Am; Inst Noise Control Eng (secy, 71-74, pres, 75). *Res:* Physical acoustics; large amplitude wave propagation; instabilities in inhomogeneous media; radiation phenomena; noise control. *Mailing Add:* Dept C18 Bldg 704 IBM Corp PO Box 390 Poughkeepsie NY 12602

MALING, HARRIET MYLANDER, b Baltimore, Md, Oct 2, 19; m 43; c 4. PHARMACOLOGY. *Educ:* Goucher Col, AB, 40; Radcliffe Col, AM, 41, PhD(med sci physiol), 44. *Prof Exp:* Asst pharmacol, Harvard Med Sch, 44-45, instr, 45-46; asst prof, Sch Med, George Washington Univ, 51-52, asst res prof, 52-54; PHARMACOLOGIST, NAT HEART & LUNG INST, BETHESDA, 54- *Mem:* AAAS; Soc Exp Biol & Med; Am Soc Pharmacol; NY Acad Sci. *Res:* Autonomic and cardiovascular drugs. *Mailing Add:* Nat Heart Lung & Blood Inst Bldg 10 Rm 8N118 Bethesda MD 20205

MALING, HENRY FORBES, JR, b Arlington, Mass, Dec 6, 16; m 43; c 2. ELECTRONICS. *Educ:* Northeastern Univ, SB, 39; Harvard Univ, SM, 40, ScD(elec eng), 47. *Prof Exp:* Inspector mach shop, Gen Radio Co, Mass, 35-37, technician, Elec Lab, 37-40; instr electronics, Harvard Univ, 43-45; asst prof, US Naval Postgrad Sch, 46-49; from asst prof to assoc prof electronics, US Naval Acad, 49-58, prof, 58-80; RETIRED. *Mem:* Inst Elec & Electronics Engrs. *Res:* Tuned power amplifiers and oscillators. *Mailing Add:* 406 Taylor Ave Annapolis MD 21401

MALININ, GEORGE I, b Krasnodar, USSR, Sept 9, 29; US citizen; m 64. ANALYTICAL HISTOCHEMISTRY, CRYOBIOLOGY. *Educ:* Concord Col, BS, 58; George Washington Univ, MS, 60; Catholic Univ Am, PhD(cell biol), 72. *Prof Exp:* Res scientist, Am Found Biol Res, 68-70; guest scientist, Naval Med Res Inst, 71-72; res assoc, Dept Biol, Georgetown Univ, 72-74; res assoc, 74-76, chief, Biochem Res Lab, Children's Hosp, 76-77; assoc res prof, 77-79, RES PROF BIOPHYSICS, GEORGETOWN UNIV, 79- *Concurrent Pos:* Consult, Washington Hosp Ctr, 77- *Mem:* AAAS; Soc Cryobiol; Histochem Soc; Tissue Culture Asn. *Res:* Cell differentiation induction by membrane active compounds; effects of trace elements on defferentiation and on cell membranes; interaction of external electric and magnetic fields on cells and their components at ambient and ultra low temperatures. *Mailing Add:* Dept Physics Georgetown Univ Washington DC 20057

MALININ, THEODORE I, b Krasnodar, USSR, Sept 13, 33; US citizen; m 60; c 4. PATHOLOGY, EXPERIMENTAL SURGERY. *Educ:* Concord Col, BS, 55; Univ Va, MS, 58, MD, 60. *Prof Exp:* Fel path, Johns Hopkins Univ, 60-61; pathologist, Nat Cancer Inst, 61-64; asst prof path, Sch Med, Georgetown Univ, 64-69; clin assoc prof, 69-70, PROF SURG & PATH, SCH MED, UNIV MIAMI, 70- *Concurrent Pos:* Guest scientist, Tissue Bank, Naval Med Res Inst, 64-70; ed, Cryobiol, 64-70; consult, Bur Health Manpower, USPHS, 66-67; mem staff, Vet Admin Hosp, Miami, 70- *Mem:* AAAS; Am Asn Path & Bact; Soc Cryobiol; Am Soc Exp Path; Path Soc Gt Brit & Ireland. *Res:* Organ perfusion and preservation; experimental myocardial infarction; hemorrhagic shock; tissue banking; bone marrow preservation and transplantation; biological behavior of neoplastic tissue. *Mailing Add:* Dept of Surg Univ of Miami Sch of Med Miami FL 33101

MALINOW, MANUEL R, b Buenos Aires, Arg, Feb 27, 20; m 52; c 3. CARDIOLOGY. *Educ:* Univ Buenos Aires, MD, 45. *Prof Exp:* Res fel cardiovasc med, Michael Reese Hosp, Chicago, 45-46; dir res dept & electrocardiologist, Hosp Ramos Mejia, Buenos Aires, 47-57; chief res physiol, Buenos Aires Med Sch, 56-63; PROF MED, MED SCH, UNIV ORE, 64-; SECT HEAD CARDIOVASC DIS, ORE REGIONAL PRIMATE RES CTR, 64- *Concurrent Pos:* Chief cardiol serv, Munic Inst Radiol & Physiother, Arg, 50-53; chief sect atherosclerosis, Nat Acad Med, Buenos Aires, 60-63, physician, Hosp, 62-63. *Honors & Awards:* Paul D White Prize, Arg Soc Cardiol, 54 & Gold Medal, 60; Ciba Found Award, 59; Rafael M Bullrich Prize, Nat Acad Med, Buenos Aires, 59; Gold Medal, Inter-Am Cong Cardiol, Brazil, 60; Sesquicentenary Prize, Arg Med Asn; Gold Medal & Malenky Prize, Arg Comt for Weizmann Inst, 60. *Mem:* AAAS; Royal Soc Med; NY Acad Sci; Am Heart Asn. *Res:* Experimental cardiology; atherosclerosis; blood cholesterol; cardiovascular diseases; exercise and electrocardiography. *Mailing Add:* Ore Regional Primate Res Ctr 505 NW 185th Beaverton OR 97005

MALINOWSKI, EDMUND R, b Mahanoy City, Pa, Oct 16, 32; m 58; c 2. PHYSICAL CHEMISTRY. *Educ:* Pa State Univ, BS, 54; Stevens Inst Technol, MS, 56, PhD(phys chem), 61. *Prof Exp:* Res assoc, Nuclear Magnetic Resonance Lab, 60-63, from asst prof to assoc prof, 63-70, PROF CHEM, STEVENS INST TECHNOL, 70- *Mem:* Am Chem Soc. *Res:* Nuclear magnetic resonance; dipole moments; conformation of organic molecules; structure of water and electrolyte solutions; applications of factor analysis to chemistry. *Mailing Add:* Dept of Chem Stevens Inst of Technol Hoboken NJ 07030

MALINS, DONALD CLIVE, b Lima, Peru, May 19, 31; US citizen; m 62; c 3. BIOCHEMISTRY. *Educ:* Univ Wash, BA, 53; Univ Seattle, BS, 56; Univ Aberdeen, PhD(biochem), 67. *Hon Degrees:* DSc, Univ Aberdeen, 76. *Prof Exp:* Org chemist, Tech Lab, US Bur Com Fisheries, 56-62, res chemist, 62-66, Food Sci Pioneer Res Lab, 66-71, prog dir, Pioneer Res Unit, Northwest Fisheries Ctr, 71-74, DIR, ENVIRON CONSERV DIV, NORTHWEST FISHERIES CTR, NAT MARINE FISHERIES SERV, 74- *Concurrent Pos:* Lectr, Univ Wash, 68-74, affil assoc prof, 74-78, affil prof, 78-; res prof, Seattle Univ, 71-; ed, Biochem & Biophys Perspectives in Marine Biol, 74-79, Effects Petrol on Arctic & Subarctic Marine Environ, 77; ed-in-chief, Aquatic Toxicol, 80-; consult pollution marine environ, UN Environ Prog, 80- *Honors & Awards:* US Dept Interior Achievement Awards, 56-, Dept Com Spec Achievement Award, 74. *Mem:* Am Chem Soc; Am Soc Biol Chem. *Res:* Synthesis and metabolism of lipids; chemistry of bioacoustics; chemistry of nitrogen compounds; biochemistry of and pathology arising from toxic metals, hydrocarbons, and other xenobiotics in marine biological systems. *Mailing Add:* Environ Conserv Div NW & Alaska Fisheries Ctr NMFS Seattle WA 98102

MALIS, LEONARD I, b Philadelphia, Pa, Nov 23, 19; m; c 2. NEUROSURGERY. *Educ:* Univ Va, MD, 43. *Prof Exp:* Attend neurosurgeon, 51-70, NEUROSURGEON IN CHIEF & DIR DEPT, MT SINAI HOSP, 70-; PROF NEUROSURG & CHMN DEPT, MT SINAI SCH MED, 70- *Concurrent Pos:* Res collabr, Med Dept, Brookhaven Nat Lab, 56-70; consult neurosurgeon, Beth Israel Med Ctr, NY. *Mem:* Am Acad Neurol Surg; Soc Neurol Surg; Am Asn Neurol Surg; Am Physiol Soc; Cong Neurol Surg. *Res:* Neurophysiology. *Mailing Add:* Dept of Neurosurg Mt Sinai Sch of Med New York NY 10029

MALISCH, WARD ROYCE, b Farmington, Ill, May 13, 39; m 63; c 2. CIVIL ENGINEERING. *Educ:* Univ Ill, BS, 61, MS, 63, PhD(civil eng), 66. *Prof Exp:* Asst prof, 66-70, ASSOC PROF CIVIL ENG, UNIV MO-ROLLA, 70- *Concurrent Pos:* Grants, Environ Protection Agency Off Res & Monitoring, Univ Mo-Rolla, 69-72 & Glass Container Mfrs Inst, 71-72. *Mem:* Am Concrete Inst; Asn Asphalt Paving Technol. *Res:* Use of solid wastes as construction materials. *Mailing Add:* Dept of Civil Eng Univ of Mo Rolla MO 65401

MALITSON, HARRIET HUTZLER, b Richmond, Va, June 30, 26; m 51; c 2. ASTRONOMY. *Educ:* Goucher Col, AB, 47; Univ Mich, MS, 51. *Prof Exp:* Jr physicist, Nat Bur Standards, 47-49 & 51-52 & US Naval Res Lab, 52-57; ASTRONOMER, GODDARD SPACE FLIGHT CTR, NASA, 60- *Concurrent Pos:* Mem, Comn J, Int Union Radio Sci & Comn 10, Int Astron Union. *Mem:* Am Astron Soc. *Res:* Solar physics; solar-terrestial relationships; radio and space astronomy. *Mailing Add:* Code 684 Goddard Space Flight Ctr NASA Greenbelt MD 20771

MALITZ, SIDNEY, b Brooklyn, NY, Apr 20, 23; m 45; c 2. PSYCHIATRY, PSYCHOPHARMACOLOGY. *Educ:* Univ Chicago, MD, 46; Columbia Univ, cert psychoanal med, 59; Am Bd Psychiat & Neurol, dipl, 53. *Prof Exp:* Resident psychiatrist, NY State Psychiat Inst, 48-51, sr resident psychiatrist, 51-52; asst, 55-57, assoc, 57-59, asst clin prof, 60-65, assoc prof, 65-69, vchmn dept psychiat, 72-75 & 76-78, actg chmn dept, 75-76, PROF CLIN PSYCHIAT, COL PHYSICIANS & SURGEONS, COLUMBIA UNIV, 70-, ACTG CHMN DEPT, 81- *Concurrent Pos:* Sr res psychiatrist, NY State Psychiat Inst, 54-56, actg chief psychiat res, 56-65, chief dept biol psychiat, 65-72, dep dir, Inst, 72-75; asst vis psychiatrist, Francis Delafield Hosp, 54-; asst attend psychiatrist, Vanderbilt Clin & Presby Hosp, 56-58, assoc attend psychiatrist, 58-71, attend psychiatrist, Presby Hosp, 71-, actg dir psychiat serv, 75-76 & 81-; actg dir, NY State Psychiat Inst, 75-76 & 81-, dep dir & asst dir, Psychiat Serv, 76-78; asst examr, Am Bd Psychiat & Neurol, 57- *Mem:* fel Am Col Psychoanalysts; fel Am Psychiat Asn; fel Am Col Psychiatrists; Am Psychopath Asn; fel Royal Col Psychiatrists. *Res:* Psychopharmacology and psychoanalysis. *Mailing Add:* NY State Psychiat Inst 722 W 168th St New York NY 10032

MALKANI, MOHAN J, b Hyderabad, Pakistan, Sept 17, 33; m 66; c. COMMUNICATIONS, CONTROL ENGINEERING. *Educ:* Univ Baroda, BS, 53, MS, 55; Miss State Univ, MS, 64; Vanderbilt Univ, PhD, 80. *Prof Exp:* Instr elec eng, Tuskegee Inst, 63, asst prof, 64-67; prof elec eng & head dept, 67-79, ASSOC DEAN, SCH ENG & TECHNOL, TENN STATE UNIV, 79- *Mem:* Sr mem Inst Elec & Electronics Engrs; Am Soc Energy Engrs. *Res:* Optics; control systems; electronics; energy; microprocessors. *Mailing Add:* Sch Eng & Technol Tenn State Univ Nashville TN 37203

MALKEVITCH, JOSEPH, b Brooklyn, NY, May 24, 42. MATHEMATICS. *Educ:* Queens Col, NY, BS, 63; Univ Wis-Madison, MS, 65, PhD(math), 69. *Prof Exp:* Teaching asst, Univ Wis-Madison, 63-68; from asst prof to assoc prof, 68-80, PROF MATH, YORK COL, NY, 81- *Mem:* AAAS; Am Math Soc; Math Asn Am; AAAS; NY Acad Sci. *Res:* Convex polytopes; graph theory; arrangements of curves; euclidean geometry. *Mailing Add:* Dept of Math York Col Jamaica NY 11451

MALKIEL, SAUL, b Boston, Mass, Dec 28, 12; m 45; c 3. IMMUNOCHEMISTRY, ALLERGY. *Educ:* Clark Univ, AB, 34; Boston Univ, MA, 36, PhD(chem), 42, MD, 44. *Prof Exp:* Asst med sci, Sch Med, Boston Univ, 35-37, asst chem, 37-44; asst path, Yale Univ, 44-45; vis investr, Rockefeller Inst, 45-48; asst prof med, Med Sch, Northwestern Univ, 48-54; ASSOC PATH, HARVARD MED SCH, 54-, RES ASSOC, SIDNEY FARBER CANCER INST INC, 63-; ASSOC PROF MED, MED SCH, UNIV MASS, 71- *Concurrent Pos:* Fel, Sch Med, Boston Univ, 45; Nat Res Coun fel med sci, Rockefeller Inst, 45-46, Am Cancer Soc sr fel, 46-48; lectr, Univ Pa, 48; assoc, Peter Bent Brigham Hosp, 54-63; res assoc, Children's Hosp, 63-; mem corp, Marine Biol Lab, Woods Hole. *Mem:* AAAS; Am Asn Immunologists; Soc Exp Biol & Med; Am Acad Allergy (pres, 70-71); Reticuloendothelial Soc. *Res:* Immunochemistry of hemocyanins, hemoglobin, viruses and allergic reactions; effects of stress on experimental asthma; clinical and experimental studies with the antihistamines; effect of cortisone on antibody production; fractionation and adjuvant studies on Bordetella pertussis; allergens from ragweed pollen; immuno-competence of the leukemic cell; tumor viruses; immune response to malarial infection. *Mailing Add:* Sidney Farber Cancer Inst Inc 35 Binney St Boston MA 02115

MALKIN, HAROLD MARSHALL, b San Francisco, Calif, Oct 9, 23; m 49; c 4. BIOCHEMISTRY. *Educ:* Univ Calif, AB, 47, MA, 49; Univ Chicago, MD, 51. *Prof Exp:* Nat Found Infantile Paralysis res fel, Univ Calif, 51-53; Am Cancer Soc fel, Univ Brussels, 53-54; dir, Malkin Med Lab, Malkin Med Lab/Solano Labs, 54-72, pres & med dir, 72-78; MED DIR, OSLERWELCH LABS, 78- *Concurrent Pos:* Asst, Univ Calif, 51-; clin instr histol, Sch Med, Stanford Univ, 56-62; intern path, Sch Med, Stanford Univ, 61-62. *Mem:* AAAS; Am Chem Soc; Am Asn Clin Chemists; Nat Sci Teachers Asn. *Res:* Cellular physiology as related to structure; nucleic acid and protein metabolism; cancer; clinical chemistry. *Mailing Add:* 488 McCormick St San Leandro CA 94577

MALKIN, IRVING, b Cleveland, Ohio, Dec 28, 25; m 47; c 3. INORGANIC CHEMISTRY, ELECTROCHEMISTRY. *Educ:* Western Reserve Univ, BS, 54; Case Inst Technol, MS, 60. *Prof Exp:* Chief chemist, I Schumann & Co, 50-56; res & process control inorg chem, Precision Metalsmiths Inc, 56-59; MGR ELECTRODE TECHNOL, ELECTROLYTIC SYSTS DIV, DIAMOND SHAMROCK CORP, 59- *Mem:* Am Chem Soc; Electrochem Soc. *Res:* Catalytically active electrode surfaces; electrochemical processes; heterogeneous catalysis; corrosion inhibiting metal coatings; controlled release technology. *Mailing Add:* T R Evans Res Ctr PO Box 348 Diamond Shamrock Corp Painesville OH 44077

MALKIN, LEONARD ISADORE, b New York, NY, Dec 17, 36; m 59; c 2. BIOCHEMISTRY. *Educ:* NY Univ, AB, 57; Univ Calif, San Francisco, PhD(biochem), 62. *Prof Exp:* Resident res assoc biochem, Western Regional Res Lab, USDA, Calif, 62-63; NIH fel, Brown Univ, 63-65 & Mass Inst Technol, 65-68; asst prof biochem, Dartmouth Med Sch, 68-73; ASSOC PROF BIOCHEM, SCH MED, WAYNE STATE UNIV, 73- *Mem:* AAAS; Am Soc Biol Chemists. *Res:* Protein synthesis in animal cells; production and utilization of messenger RNA, both endogenous and viral, in animal systems. *Mailing Add:* Dept of Biochem Wayne State Univ Sch of Med Detroit MI 48201

MALKIN, MARTIN F, b Newark, NJ, June 28, 37; m 60; c 1. RESEARCH ADMINISTRATION. *Educ:* Univ Mich, BS, 59; Brooklyn Col, MA, 65; NY Univ, PhD(biol), 68. *Prof Exp:* Res assoc biochem, Rockefeller Univ, 67-69; sr res scientist, Merck Inst Therapeut Res, 69-72, res fel, Dept Basic Animal Sci Res, Merck & Co, 72-74, proj coordr, Dept Proj Planning & Mgt, 74-76, dir, Dept Proj Planning & Mgt, Nippon Merk Banyu, 76-78, dir, Proj Planning & Mgt, 78-81, DIR, PROJ PLANNING & MGT, MERCK & CO, 81- *Mem:* AAAS; Proj Mgt Inst. *Res:* Management of development research projects in animal and human health areas; drug development in Japan. *Mailing Add:* Merck & Co Inc PO Box 2000 Rahway NJ 07065

MALKIN, RICHARD, b Chicago, Ill, Mar 25, 40; m 60; c 3. BIOCHEMISTRY. *Educ:* Antioch Col, BS, 62; Univ Calif, Berkeley, PhD(biochem), 67. *Prof Exp:* Fel biochem, Univ Gothenburg, 67-69; res biochemist, LECTR CELL PHYSIOL, UNIV CALIF, BERKELEY, 71-, ASSOC BIOCHEMIST, 75- *Concurrent Pos:* NATO fel, 67-68; Am Cancer Soc fel. *Mem:* Am Chem Soc; Am Soc Photobiol; Am Soc Plant Physiol; Am Soc Biol Chemists; Biophys Soc. *Res:* Photosynthesis; investigations of electron transport; biological applications of electron paramagnetic resonance spectroscopy. *Mailing Add:* Dept of Cell Physiol Univ of Calif Berkeley CA 94720

MALKIN, STEPHEN, b Boston, Mass, June 20, 41; m 64. MECHANICAL ENGINEERING. *Educ:* Mass Inst Technol, SB, 63, SM, 65, ScD(mech eng), 68. *Prof Exp:* Asst prof mech eng, Univ Tex, Austin, 68-74; assoc prof, State Univ NY, Buffalo, 74-76; ASSOC PROF MECH ENG, TECHNION, ISRAEL INST TECHNOL, 76- *Mem:* Am Soc Mech Engrs. *Res:* Materials processing; metal cutting; friction and wear of materials; mechanical behavior of materials. *Mailing Add:* Fac Mech Eng Technion Haifa Israel

MALKIN, WILLIAM, b New York, NY, Aug 19, 08; m 47; c 4. METEOROLOGY. *Educ:* Univ Minn, Minneapolis, BS, 31 & 41; NY Univ, MS, 65. *Prof Exp:* Meteorologist, US Weather Bur, 37-67; DIR RES & DEVELOP, ABBOTT SCI CO, 70- *Concurrent Pos:* Vis prof, Univ NDak, 61 & 71 & Univ Notre Dame, 70; lectr, Northern Ill Univ, 67-69; meteorologist, Joule Tech Corp, Wallops Island, Va, 80-81. *Mem:* Fel AAAS; Am Meteorol Soc; Am Geophys Union. *Res:* Chemical and medical meteorology; air pollution; hydro-meteorology; water and air quality and pollution; environmental quality; aviation meteorology; environmental impact studies and statements for such industries as chemical plants and power generating plants. *Mailing Add:* Abbott Sci Co Box 35 Rte 4 Leesburg VA 22075

MALKINSON, ALVIN MAYNARD, b Buffalo, NY, Jan 5, 41; m 67; c 2. BIOCHEMISTRY, PHARMACOLOGY. *Educ:* Univ Buffalo, BA, 62; Johns Hopkins Univ, PhD(biol), 68. *Prof Exp:* Lectr biochem, Univ Nairobi, 69-71; fel, Leicester Univ, 71-72; fel pharmacol, Yale Med Sch, 72-74; asst prof psychiat, Sch Med, Univ Minn, 74-78; ASST PROF PHARMACOL, UNIV COLO, 78- *Concurrent Pos:* NIH fel, 72-74; asst prof, Nat Found Basil O'Connor starter grant, 75-78, Nat Inst Gen Med Sci grant, 76-78, Am Cancer Soc Instnl grant, 78, Colo Heart Asn Grant, 79 & Nat Inst Environ Health grant, 81-83. *Mem:* Am Asn Cancer Res; Am Soc Pharmacol & Exp Therapeut. *Res:* Role of cyclic adenosine monophosphate dependent protein kinases in the control of normal and neoplastic lung growth; pulmonary effects of butylated hydroxytoluene. *Mailing Add:* Sch of Pharmacol Univ of Colo Boulder CO 80309

MALKINSON, FREDERICK DAVID, b Hartford, Conn, Feb 26, 24; m 79; c 3. MEDICINE. *Educ:* Harvard Univ, DMD, 47, MD, 49. *Prof Exp:* From instr to assoc prof dermat, Sch Med, Univ Chicago, 54-68; CHMN DEPT DERMAT, RUSH-PRESBY-ST LUKE'S MED CTR, 68-, PROF DERMAT, RUSH MED SCH, 71-, CLARK W FINNERUD PROF DERMAT, 81- *Concurrent Pos:* Assoc prof oral med, Zoller Dent Clin, Univ Chicago, 67-68, res assoc, Sect Dermat, Dept Med, 68-70; prof med & dermat, Univ Ill, 68-70; ed, Yearbk of Dermat, 70-78; chief ed, AMA Archives Dermat, 79- *Mem:* AAAS; Soc Invest Dermat; Am Acad Dermat; Am Dermat Asn; Radiation Res Soc. *Res:* Percutaneous absorption; adrenal steroid effects on skin; radiation effects on skin. *Mailing Add:* Presby-St Luke's Hosp 1753 W Congress Pkwy Chicago IL 60612

MALKUS, DAVID STARR, b Chicago, Ill, June 30, 45; m 77; c 1. NUMERICAL MATHEMATICS, COMPUTATIONAL ENGINEERING. *Educ:* Yale Univ, BA, 68; Boston Univ, MA, 75, PhD(math), 76. *Prof Exp:* Nat Res Coun fel & mathematician, US Nat Bur Standards, 75-77; ASST PROF MATH, ILL INST TECHNOL, 77- *Concurrent Pos:* Ill Inst Technol fac res fel, 78-79. *Mem:* Soc Indust & Appl Math; Soc Rheology; Am Acad Mech. *Res:* Finite element analysis; computational methods in fluid dynamics; computational methods in nonlinear elasticity; numerical methods in approximation and interpolation; nonlinear functional analysis. *Mailing Add:* Dept of Math Ill Inst of Technol Chicago IL 60616

MALKUS, WILLEM VAN RENSSELAER, b Brooklyn, NY, Nov 19, 23; m 48; c 4. PHYSICS. *Educ:* Univ Chicago, PhD(physics), 50. *Prof Exp:* Asst prof natural sci, Univ Chicago, 50-51; phys oceanogr, Woods Hole Oceanog Inst, 51-60; prof geophys, Univ Calif, Los Angeles, 60-67, prof geophys & math, 67-69; PROF APPL MATH, MASS INST TECHNOL, 69- *Concurrent Pos:* Prof appl math, Mass Inst Technol, 59-60; Guggenheim fel, Cambridge Univ & Univ Stockholm, 71-72. *Mem:* Nat Acad Sci; Am Phys Soc; fel Am Acad Arts & Sci. *Res:* Fluid dynamics. *Mailing Add:* Dept of Math Mass Inst of Technol Cambridge MA 02139

MALL, SHANKAR, b Varanasi, India, June 10, 43; m 65; c 1. FRACTURE MECHANICS, STRESS ANALYSIS. *Educ:* Banaras Hindu Univ, India, BS, 64, MS, 66; Univ Wash, PhD(mech eng), 77. *Prof Exp:* Lectr mech eng, Banaras Hindu Univ, India, 67-74; res asst, Univ Wash, 74-77, res assoc, 77-78; asst prof, 78-81, ASSOC PROF MECH ENG, UNIV MAINE, ORONO, 81- *Mem:* Am Soc Mech Engrs; Am Soc Eng Educ. *Res:* Finite element method; fracture dynamics; wood fracture fatigue failure of adhesive bonds; author of 24 technical papers. *Mailing Add:* 209 Boardman Hall Univ Maine Orono ME 04469

MALLAMS, ALAN KEITH, b Johannesburg, SAfrica, June 11, 40. NATURAL PRODUCTS CHEMISTRY. *Educ:* Univ Witwatersrand, BSc, 62, PhD(chem), 64; Univ London, PhD(chem), 67. *Prof Exp:* Res off org chem, African Exlosives & Chem Industs, SAfrica, 64; Exhibit 1851 fel, Queen Mary Col, Univ London, 64-66, res asst, 66-67; sr scientist, Med Res Div, 67-70, prin scientist, 70-72, SECT HEAD, ANTIBIOTICS & ANTIINFECTIVES CHEM RES, SCHERING CORP, 72- *Mem:* Am Chem Soc; Royal Soc Chem. *Res:* Synthesis and structural elucidation of carotenoids, antibiotics, carbohydrates and natural products of medicinal interest; antibiotics research. *Mailing Add:* Res Div Schering Corp Bloomfield NJ 07003

MALLAMS, JOHN THOMAS, b Ashland, Pa, Aug 29, 23; m 45; c 3. MEDICINE, RADIOLOGY. *Educ:* Temple Univ, MD, 46; Am Bd Radiol, dipl. *Prof Exp:* Intern, US Naval Hosp, Philadelphia, 46-47, resident radiol, 47-48, radiologist, Parris Island, SC, 48-49, chief radiol, Beaufort, 49-50; asst prof radiol, Baylor Col Med, 52-54, mem attend staff & dir irradiation ther & tumor clins & dir, Sammons Res Div, Med Ctr, 54-68, prof radiother, Col Dent, 66-68; prof clin radiol, Med Sch, Yale Univ, 68-70; assoc dean patient serv, 71-72, PROF RADIOL & CHMN DEPT, MARTLAND HOSP UNIT, COL MED & DENT NJ, 70- *Concurrent Pos:* Fel, Robert Packer Hosp & Guthrie Clin, Sayre, Pa, 50-51; Am Cancer Soc fel clin radiation ther, Frances Delafield Hosp, New York, 51-52; assoc radiologist, Jefferson Davis Hosp, Houston & attend radiologist, Vet Admin Hosp, 52-54; prof, Univ Tex Southwest Med Sch, 66-68; vis prof, Med Sch, Yale Univ, 67-68; Am Col Radiol consult, State of NJ, 70; consult, Conn Hosp Planning Comn, Branford, 71. *Mem:* Fel Am Col Radiol; AMA; Am Radium Soc; Am Roentgen Ray Soc; Radiol Soc NAm. *Res:* Radiotherapy. *Mailing Add:* Martland Hosp Col of Med & Dent of NJ Newark NJ 07107

MALLAY, JAMES FRANCIS, nuclear physics, see previous edition

MALLER, OWEN, b Brooklyn, NY, Jan 27, 30; m 52; c 5. PSYCHOPHYSIOLOGY, HEALTH PSYCHOLOGY. *Educ:* Univ Ill, BS, 52, PhD(psychol), 64. *Prof Exp:* USPHS fel, 63-65; res assoc, Duke Univ, 65-66; res psychologist, Vet Admin Hosp, Coatesville, Pa, 66-68; mem, Monell Chem Senses Ctr, Univ Pa, 68-76; GROUP HEAD BEHAV SCI DIV, SCI & ADVAN TECHNOL LAB, US ARMY RES & DEVELOP LABS, NATICK, MASS, 76- *Concurrent Pos:* Res assoc physiol, Med Sch, Univ Pa, 68-76; mem staff, Vet Admin Hosp, Philadelphia, 68-76. *Mem:* Am Pub Health Asn; Am Psychol Asn; Psychonomics Soc; Sigma Xi. *Res:* Chemoreception, food preferences, habits and attitudes in humans. *Mailing Add:* Behav Sci Div/Sci & Advan Technol Lab US Army Res & Develop Labs Natick MA 01760

MALLERY, CHARLES HENRY, b Southampton, NY, June 3, 43; m 66; c 2. DEVELOPMENTAL PHYSIOLOGY, BIOCHEMISTRY. *Educ:* Univ Ga, BS, 65, PhD(bot, biochem), 70. *Prof Exp:* Res fel, Lab Quant Biol, 70-72, asst prof, 72-78, ASSOC PROF BIOL, UNIV MIAMI, 78-, ASSOC CHMN BIOL DEPT, 80- *Concurrent Pos:* NSF grants, 74, 77-79 & 81-83; consult, Dade County Dept Educ & State Atty Off, 74- *Mem:* Am Soc Plant Physiologists; Am Soc Zoologists; Bot Soc Am. *Res:* Biochemical development in the establishment of a mature eucaryotic plant cell; ion regulating mechanisms in plants and animals; sodium-potassium-AtPase and bicarbonate AtPases in teleosts. *Mailing Add:* Dept of Biol Univ of Miami Coral Gables FL 33124

MALLET, VICTORIN NOEL, b Shippegan, NB, Dec 12, 44; m 66; c 2. ANALYTICAL CHEMISTRY, PESTICIDE CHEMISTRY. *Educ:* Univ Moncton, BSc, 66, MSc, 70; Dalhousie Univ, PhD(anal chem), 71. *Prof Exp:* Lab supvr chem, Can Celanese Co, 66-67; chmn chem dept, 72-78, PROF CHEM, UNIV MONCTON, 71- *Mem:* Chem Inst Can; Asn Can Fr Advan Sci. *Res:* Analytical chemistry of pesticides and derivatives thereof; gas chromatography; thin-layer chromatography; high performance liquid chromatography; fluorescence spectroscopy. *Mailing Add:* Dept of Chem Univ of Moncton Moncton NB E1A 3E9 Can

MALLETT, GORDON EDWARD, b Lafayette, Ind, Nov 30, 27; m 50; c 4. MICROBIOLOGY. *Educ:* Purdue Univ, BS, 49, MS, 52, PhD(bact), 56. *Prof Exp:* Bacteriologist, US Army Res & Develop Labs, Md, 56-57; sr microbiologist, Eli Lilly & Co, 57-69, head fermentation prod res dept, 66-69, dir res, Lilly Res Ctr, Ltd, Eng, 69-75, DIR CORP QUAL ASSURANCE, ELI LILLY & CO, IND, 75- *Mem:* Sigma Xi; Am Chem Soc; Am Soc MIcrobiol; NY Acad Sci. *Res:* Bacterial cell structure; microbiological conversions of steroids, alkaloids, antibiotics; microbiological conversion mechanisms. *Mailing Add:* Eli Lilly & Co PO Box 618 Indianapolis IN 46206

MALLETT, RUSSELL LLOYD, b Seattle, Wash, Nov 2, 35; m 61; c 2. APPLIED MECHANICS, DYNAMICS. *Educ:* Mass Inst Technol, BS, 58, PhD(appl math), 70; Stanford Univ, MS, 66. *Prof Exp:* Res engr, Boeing Co, 58-65; asst prof, 70-75, sr res assoc appl mech, 75-81, ASSOC PROF MECH, STANFORD UNIV, 81- *Mem:* Am Acad Mech; Am Soc Mech Engrs; Soc Indust & Appl Math; Sigma Xi. *Res:* Rigid body, structural and continuum dynamics, shell theory and nonlinear continuum mechanics; efficient modeling, computational techniques and finite element analysis; cable dynamics and metal forming analysis. *Mailing Add:* Dept Mech Eng Aero Eng & Mech Stanford Univ Stanford CA 94305

MALLETT, WILLIAM ROBERT, b Painesville, Ohio, Sept 12, 32; m 57; c 2. ANALYTICAL CHEMISTRY, PETROLEUM CHEMISTRY. *Educ:* Miami Univ, BA, 61, MS, 63; Rensselaer Polytech Inst, PhD(energy transfer), 66. *Prof Exp:* Res chemist, 66-68, sr res chemist, 68-81, RES ASSOC, UNION OIL CO CALIF, 81- *Concurrent Pos:* Vis res chemist, Maruzen Oil Co, Japan, 73-75. *Mem:* Am Chem Soc; Soc Automotive Engrs; Am Soc Testing & Mat. *Res:* Fuels research. *Mailing Add:* 1273 Genoa Pl Placentia CA 92670

MALLETTE, JOHN M, b Houston, Tex, Aug 6, 32; m 59; c 3. ENDOCRINOLOGY, EXPERIMENTAL EMBRYOLOGY. *Educ:* Xavier Univ, BS, 54; Tex Southern Univ, MS, 58; Pa State Univ, PhD(zool), 62. *Prof Exp:* Res technician anat, Dent Br, Univ Tex, 57-58; instr biol, Tex Southern Univ, 58-59; asst zool, Pa State Univ, 59-62; assoc prof biol, Tenn State Univ, 62-64, prof biol sci & chmn grad curric, 64-74; vchancellor acad affairs, Univ Tenn, Nashville, 74-79; ASSOC VPRES RES & DEVELOP, TENN STATE UNIV, NASHVILLE, 79- *Concurrent Pos:* Dir undergrad res participation prog, NSF, 64-66; grants assoc, NIH, 67; dir allied health, Meharry Med Col & Tenn State Univ. *Honors & Awards:* Knight of St Gregory, 71. *Mem:* AAAS; Am Soc Zool; Nat Inst Sci. *Res:* Growth of trypsin; dissociated glands in vitro and vivo; teratogenic effects of drugs in avian embryos. *Mailing Add:* Res & Develop Tenn State Univ Nashville TN 37203

MALLEY, ARTHUR, b Chicago, Ill, Jan 7, 31; m 61. IMMUNOLOGY. *Educ:* San Francisco State Col, BA, 53, BS, 57; Ore State Univ, PhD(biochem), 61. *Prof Exp:* Fel immunochem, Calif Inst Technol, 61-63; from asst prof to assoc prof, 63-71, PROF BACT, ORE REGIONAL PRIMATE RES CTR, 71- *Mem:* AAAS; Am Chem Soc; Transplantation Soc; Am Asn Immunologists. *Res:* Isolation of antigens and antibodies involved in various allergic diseases, and the regulation of antibody formation. *Mailing Add:* Ore Regional Primate Res Ctr 505 NW 185th Ave Beaverton OR 97005

MALLI, GULZARI LAL, b Lehlian, India, Feb 12, 38. QUANTUM CHEMISTRY, CHEMICAL PHYSICS. *Educ:* Univ Delhi, BSc, 58; McMaster Univ, MSc, 60; Univ Chicago, MS, 63, PhD(chem physics), 64. *Prof Exp:* Mem res staff physics, Yale Univ, 64-65; asst prof theoret chem, Univ Alta, 65-66; asst prof, 66-69, assoc prof, 69-75, PROF CHEM, SIMON FRASER UNIV, 75- *Concurrent Pos:* Vis fel, Mellon Inst, 67-68; vis assoc prof, Univ Houston, 72; Alexander von Humboldt fel, 78, 82. *Mem:* Sigma Xi; Am Phys Soc. *Res:* Quantum mechanics of atoms and molecules; quantum mechanics of atoms and molecules; relativistic quantum chemistry; tensor operators in atomic and molecular spectroscopy; relativistic many-electron atomic and molecular self-consistent field theory; electron correlation in many-electron systems. *Mailing Add:* Dept of Chem Simon Fraser Univ Burnaby BC V5A 1S6 Can

MALLIA, ANANTHA KRISHNA, b Kerala, India, May 22, 41; m 71; c 1. PROTEIN CHEMISTRY, AFFINITY CHROMATOGRAPHY. *Educ:* Kerala Univ, India, BSc, 62; Banaras Hindu Univ, MSc, 64; Indian Inst Sci, PhD(biochem), 70. *Prof Exp:* Res assoc biochem, Columbia Univ, 71-74, neurochem, Univ Mich, Ann Arbor, 74-77; MGR RES BIOCHEM, PIERCE CHEM CO, ROCKFORD, 77- *Mem:* Am Chem Soc; AAAS. *Res:* Isolation, purification and characterization of enzymes and proteins; application of affinity chromatography for the purification of enzymes, lectins and other proteins; use of affinity chromatography to develop new procedures for clinical tests. *Mailing Add:* Pierce Chem Co PO Box 117 Rockford IL 61105

MALLIN, MORTON LEWIS, b Feb 13, 26; m 60; c 2. MICROBIOLOGY, BIOCHEMISTRY. *Educ:* Phila Col Pharm, BS, 50; Hahnemann Med Col, MS, 52; Cornell Univ, PhD(bact), 56. *Prof Exp:* Res fel biochem, McCollum-Pratt Inst, Johns Hopkins Univ, 56-57; NIH res fel, Brandeis Univ, 57-59; res assoc, May Inst Med Res, Jewish Hosp, Cincinnati, 59-65; assoc prof, 65-71, PROF MICROBIOL & CHMN DEPT, OHIO NORTHERN UNIV, 71- *Mem:* Am Soc Microbiol. *Res:* Biochemical problems related to hypertension; oxidative phosphorylation in animal mitochondria and bacterial particles; phosphorous metabolism in anaerobic bacteria. *Mailing Add:* Dept of Microbiol Ohio Northern Univ Ada OH 45810

MALLING, GERALD F, b Evanston, Ill, Apr 27, 38; m 65; c 2. CHEMICAL ENGINEERING, APPLIED MATHEMATICS. *Educ:* Northwestern Univ, BS, 61, PhD(chem eng), 66; Univ Ill, Urbana, MS, 63. *Prof Exp:* DEVELOP SPECIALIST, OAK RIDGE GASEOUS DIFFUSION PLANT, NUCLEAR DIV, UNION CARBIDE CORP, 66- *Mem:* AAAS; Am Phys Soc; Am Chem Soc; Am Inst Chem Engrs. *Res:* Rarefied and continuum gas flow and diffusion phenomena. *Mailing Add:* 902 W Outer Dr Oak Ridge TN 37830

MALLING, HEINRICH VALDEMAR, b Copenhagen, Denmark, Apr 21, 31; m 55, 68; c 7. GENETICS, MICROBIOLOGY. *Educ:* Univ Copenhagen, BSc, 51, MSc, 53, PhD(genetics), 57. *Prof Exp:* Lectr genetics, Univ Copenhagen, 57; res staff mem, Leo Pharmaceut Prod, Denmark, 53-58; fel genetics, Univ Copenhagen, 58-61, lectr, 61-63; mem res staff, Biol Div, Oak Ridge Nat Lab, 63-72; MEM MUTAGENESIS BR, NAT INST ENVIRON HEALTH SCI, 72- *Mem:* Genetics Soc Am; Danish Microbiol Soc; Danish Biol Soc; Danish Biochem Soc; Scand Soc Cell Biol. *Res:* Botany; cytology; mutation induction; mutugenesis in mammals; induction of cancer; antineoplastic activity of chemicals. *Mailing Add:* Lab Biochem Genetics Nat Inst of Environ Health Sci Research Triangle Park NC 27709

MALLINSON, GEORGE GREISEN, b Troy, NY, July 4, 18; m 43, 54; c 4. SCIENCE ADMINISTRATION, SCIENCE EDUCATION. *Educ:* NY State Col Teachers Albany, BA, 38, MA, 41; Univ Mich, PhD(sci educ, statist), 47. *Prof Exp:* Teacher high schs, NY, 37-42; dir sci educ, Iowa State Teachers Col, 47-48; from assoc prof to prof exp psychol & statist, 48-53, prof sci educ & res methodology, 54-77, dean grad studies, 56-77, DISTINGUISHED PROF SCI EDUC, WESTERN MICH UNIV, 77- *Concurrent Pos:* Burke Aaron Hinsdale scholar, Univ Mich, 47-48; actg dir, Grad Div, Western Mich Univ, 54-55, dir grad studies, 55-56; dir, NSF summer insts, 58-, in-serv insts, 59-, sec sci training progs, 59-; Nat Defense Educ Act grant, 63-66; ed, Sch Sci & Math, 57-; mem, Coun & Coop Comt, Teaching Sci & Math, AAAS, 49-; chmn coun, Cent States Univs, Inc, 65-66, pres, Bd Dirs, 70-73. *Mem:* AAAS; Nat Asn Res Sci Teaching (pres, 53-54); Nat Sci Teachers Asn; Am Asn Workers Blind. *Res:* Scientific manpower; factors related to achievement in science; basic hydrothermal methods for amelioration of taconite ore. *Mailing Add:* Sangren Hall Rm 3409 Western Mich Univ Kalamazoo MI 49008

MALLIS, ARNOLD, b New York, NY, Oct 15, 10; m 43; c 2. ENTOMOLOGY. *Educ:* Univ Calif, BS, 34, MS, 39. *Prof Exp:* Field aide entom, Bur Entom & Plant Quarantine, USDA, 38; entomologist, Univ Calif, Los Angeles, 39-42; asst entomologist malaria control, USPHS, 43; res fel, Hercules Powder Co, Del, 44; entomologist, Gulf Res & Develop Co, 45-68; exten entomologist, Pa State Univ, 68-75; RETIRED. *Mem:* AAAS; Entom Soc Am. *Res:* Household and livestock insects and insecticides; history of entomology. *Mailing Add:* 15301 Wallbrook Ct 48-3B Silver Spring MD 20906

MALLISON, GEORGE FRANKLIN, b Suffolk Co, NY, May 31, 28; m 53, 69; c 3. ENVIRONMENTAL HEALTH, PUBLIC HEALTH. *Educ:* Cornell Univ, BCE, 51; Univ Calif, MPH, 57. *Prof Exp:* Asst sanit engr, Cornell Univ, 51; from jr asst to asst sanit engr & asst to chief tech develop labs, Tech Br, USPHS, 51-53, sr asst sanit engr, Phoenix Field Sta, 54-57, sanit engr & asst to chief, Tech Br, 57-59, asst chief & sr sanit engr, 59-63, chief microbiol control sect, Ctr Dis Control, 63-74, asst dir bact dis div, 74-81, SANIT ENGR DIR, CTR DIS CONTROL, USPHS, 66- *Concurrent Pos:* Mem, Conf Fed Environ Engrs; consult environ epidemiol, US Environ Protection Agency, 71-, consult environ & infection control, 81- *Mem:* Water Pollution Control Fedn; Am Water Works Asn; Am Pub Health Asn; Am Soc Microbiol; Asn Practr Infection Control. *Res:* Control of nosocomial infections; hospital and environmental sanitation; water supply; epidemiologic aspects and control of environmental contamination; sanitary engineering; microbiology; solid and other waste disposal; vector control. *Mailing Add:* 88 Kenmore Place Glen Rock NJ 07452

MALLMANN, VIRGINIA H, b Letts, Iowa, Feb 2, 18; m 45, 57. MICROBIOLOGY. *Educ:* Mich State Univ, BS, 54, MS, 55, PhD(microbiol), 60. *Prof Exp:* Instr, 60-64, asst prof, 64-69, ASSOC PROF VETERINARY IMMUNOL, MICH STATE UNIV, 69- *Mem:* Am Soc Microbiol; fel Am Pub Health Asn; Am Thoracic Soc; NY Acad Sci. *Res:* Immunobiology; cellular immunity; allergenicity and pathogenicity of mycobacteria. *Mailing Add:* Dept of Microbiol Mich State Univ East Lansing MI 48823

MALLON, ARTHUR H(ENRY), b Worcester, Mass, Apr 27, 12; m 40; c 6. CIVIL & SANITARY ENGINEERING. *Educ:* Worcester Polytech Inst, BS, 40; Northeastern Univ, MS, 59. *Prof Exp:* Asst prof eng drawing, Univ Mo-Rolla, 46-48; instr appl mech, Wentworth Inst, Boston, 49-51, 52-53, sr instr, 53-55; from asst prof to assoc prof civil eng, Merrimack Col, 55-63; assoc prof, Tufts Univ, 63-66; civil engr, Dept of Defense, 66-69; CIVIL ENGR MUNIC CONSTRUCT DIV, OFF WATER PROGS, ENVIRON PROTECTION AGENCY, 70- *Mem:* Am Soc Civil Engrs; Nat Soc Prof Engrs; Am Soc Eng Educ; Am Concrete Inst; Water Pollution Control Fedn. *Res:* Program management for research, development and demonstration grants and contracts for industrial pollution control technology. *Mailing Add:* Munic Construct Div Off Water Progs EPA Washington DC 20460

MALLONEE, JAMES EDGAR, b Frederick, Md, June 20, 15; m 43; c 2. INDUSTRIAL ORGANIC CHEMISTRY. *Educ:* Col William & Mary, BS, 35; Univ Va, PhD(org chem), 40. *Prof Exp:* Control chemist, Solvay Process Co, Va, 36-37; res chemist, Jackson Lab, E I du Pont de Nemours & Co, 40-43, chemist, Louisville Works, 43-47, res chemist, Fine Chem Div, 47-52, sr process supvr, Chambers Works, 52-79; RETIRED. *Mem:* Am Chem Soc. *Res:* Morphine chemistry; neoprene intermediates; industrial organic chemical research and development. *Mailing Add:* 45 Shellburne Dr Wilmington DE 19803

MALLORY, BOB FRANKLIN, b Blackwell, Okla, June 11, 32; m 61; c 4. GEOLOGY, PALEONTOLOGY. *Educ:* Wichita State Univ, BA, 61; Univ Mo-Columbia, PhD(geol), 68. *Prof Exp:* Asst prof geol, Northwest MO State Univ, 68-70, assoc prof, 70-78. prof, 78-81; CONSULT GEOLOGIST, 81- *Res:* Environmental geology; paleoecology. *Mailing Add:* 611 W 3rd St Maryville MO 64468

MALLORY, CHARLES WILLIAM, b Brewster, Kans, Sept 17, 25; m 50; c 1. NUCLEAR & CIVIL ENGINEERING. *Educ:* Univ Colo, BSME, 46; Rensselaer Polytech Inst, BCE, 50. *Prof Exp:* Proj officer, Bur Yards & Docks Proving Ground, US Navy, Calif, 46-47, staff construct officer, Opers Highjump & Windmill, Antarctica, 46-47, 47-48, div dir automatic tel commun syst, Island Pub Works Dept, Guam, 49, supt pub works dept, Portsmouth Naval Shipyard, NH, 50-52; spec asst, Schenectady Opers Off, Atomic Energy Comn, 52-54, proj officer, 54-58, chief water syst proj br, Div Reactor Develop, 58-62; dir nuclear power div, Bur Yards & Docks, US Navy, DC, 62-64; mgr eng dept, 65-71, vpres & dir environ sci, 71-77, VPRES ENG, HITTMAN ASSOCS, INC, 77- *Mem:* Am Soc Metall Engrs; Am Nuclear Soc; Am Water Resources Asn; Water Pollution Control Fedn. *Res:* Urban hydrology; wastewater treatment; energy utilization; power systems; water resources, reuse and desalination; nuclear and hazardous waste disposal. *Mailing Add:* 536 Heavitree Hill Severna Park MD 21146

MALLORY, CLELIA WOOD, b Brooklyn, NY, Feb 9, 38; m 65. ORGANIC CHEMISTRY. *Educ:* Bryn Mawr Col, BA, 59, MA, 60, PhD(chem), 63. *Prof Exp:* Res assoc chem, Bryn Mawr Col, 63-77; LECTR CHEM, UNIV PA, 80- *Concurrent Pos:* Lectr chem, Yale Univ, 77-80. *Mem:* Am Chem Soc; AAAS. *Res:* Photochemistry; nuclear magnetic resonance spectroscopy. *Mailing Add:* Dept Chem D5 Univ Pa Philadelphia PA 19104

MALLORY, FRANK BRYANT, b Omaha, Nebr, Mar 17, 33; m 51, 65; c 3. ORGANIC CHEMISTRY. *Educ:* Yale Univ, BS, 54; Calif Inst Technol, PhD(chem), 58. *Prof Exp:* From asst prof to assoc prof, 57-69, acad dep to pres, 78-81, PROF CHEM, BRYN MAWR COL, 69- *Concurrent Pos:* Guggenheim fel, 63-64; Sloan res fel, 64-68; NSF sr fel, 70-71; vis assoc, Calif Inst Technol, 63-64; vis prof, State Univ NY, Albany, 67 & Yale Univ, 68; vis fel, Cornell Univ, 70-71; vis prof, Yale Univ, 77-79. *Honors & Awards:* Bond Award, Am Oil Chemists Asn. *Mem:* Am Chem Soc. *Res:* Preparative and mechanistic aspects of organic photochemistry; nuclear magnetic resonance spectroscopy. *Mailing Add:* Dept of Chem Bryn Mawr Col Bryn Mawr PA 19010

MALLORY, HERBERT DEAN, b Wayland, Iowa, Oct 3, 23; div; c 3. PHYSICAL CHEMISTRY. *Educ:* Univ Iowa, BS, 46, PhD(phys chem, Raman spectra), 50. *Prof Exp:* Res chemist, US Naval Ord Lab, Md, 49-56; mem staff, Sandia Corp, NMex, 56-59; head, Explosives Detonation Br, 59-69, HEAD, DETONATION MECHANISMS BR, NAVAL WEAPONS CTR, CHINA LAKE, 69- *Mem:* Sigma Xi; Am Chem Soc; Combustion Inst; Am Inst Chemists. *Res:* Shock and detonation phenomena; explosive devices. *Mailing Add:* Code 6034 Chine Lake CA 93555

MALLORY, KENNETH BRANDT, applied physics, see previous edition

MALLORY, MERRIT LEE, b Lansing, Mich, May 21, 38; m 63; c 3. ACCELERATOR PHYSICS. *Educ:* Mich State Univ, BS, 60, MS, 61, PhD(physics), 66. *Prof Exp:* Fel accelerators, Oak Ridge Nat Lab, 66-68, staff physicist, 68-76; PHYSICIST ACCELERATORS, MICH STATE UNIV, 76- *Mem:* Am Phys Soc; AAAS; Inst Elec & Electronics Engrs. *Res:* Cyclotron design and operation with main interest in ion sources; cryogenics and vacuums. *Mailing Add:* Cyclotron Lab Mich State Univ East Lansing MI 48824

MALLORY, THOMAS E, b Alhambra, Calif, July 2, 40. PLANT MORPHOLOGY, PLANT CYTOLOGY. *Educ:* Univ Redlands, BS, 62; Univ Calif, Davis, MS, 65, PhD, 68. *Prof Exp:* Asst prof, 68-72, assoc prof, 72-76, PROF BIOL, CALIF STATE UNIV, FRESNO, 76- *Mem:* Bot Soc Am. *Res:* Plant morphogenesis; morphogenesis of lateral roots; mechanisms of action of herbicides. *Mailing Add:* Dept of Biol Calif State Univ Fresno CA 93740

MALLORY, VIRGIL STANDISH, b Englewood, NJ, July 14, 19; m 46; c 4. GEOLOGY. *Educ:* Oberlin Col, AB, 46; Univ Calif, MA, 48, PhD(paleont), 52. *Prof Exp:* Lectr paleont, Univ Calif, 50-51, consult, Mus Paleont, 52; from asst prof to assoc prof, 53-61, PROF GEOL, UNIV WASH, 61-, CUR INVERT PALEONT, THOMAS BURKE WASH STATE MUS, 62- *Concurrent Pos:* Consult, 54-; mem, Gov Comn Petrol Laws, Wash, 56-57; chmn, Geol & Paleont Div, Thomas Burke Wash State Mus, 61-; geologist, US Geol Surv, 63-; ed invert paleont, Quaternary Res, 70-77; mem, Abstr Rev Comt, Geol Soc Am, 75-76 & Minerals Mus Adv Comt, 75- *Mem:* Fel AAAS; fel Geol Soc Am; Int Paleont Union; Soc Econ Paleont & Mineral; Am Asn Petrol Geol. *Res:* Biostratigraphy of west coast ranges, especially Lower Tertiary; west coast Lower Tertiary foraminifera; Lower Tertiary and Cretaceous molluscan paleontology; Pacific coast structural geology. *Mailing Add:* Paleont Div Burke Wash State Mus Univ of Wash Seattle WA 98105

MALLORY, WILLAM R, b Dudley, Mo. THEORETICAL PHYSICS, OPTICS. *Educ:* Univ Ill, Urbana-Champaign, BS, 59; Syracue Univ, PhD(physics), 70. *Prof Exp:* Physicist, Gen Elec Co, 59-67; asst prof physics & astron, Univ Mont, 70-75; SR SCIENTIST, SYSTS RES LABS, INC, 75- *Mem:* Optical Soc Am; Soc Photo Instrumentation Engrs; Soc Photog Scientists Engrs. *Res:* Theoretical optics; quantum and statistical optics; design of optical instrumentation. *Mailing Add:* Systs Res Labs Inc 2800 Indian Ripple Rd Dayton OH 45440

MALLORY, WILLIAM WYMAN, b New Rochelle, NY, Apr 19, 17; m 42; c 2. GEOLOGY. *Educ:* Columbia Univ, BA, 39, MA, 46, PhD(geol), 48. *Prof Exp:* Asst geol, Columbia Univ, 40-41; asst geologist, Phillips Petrol Co, Okla, 43-45, explor geologist, 46-55, supvr explor projs, 55-57; petrol consult, Ball Assocs, 58; mem, Paleotectonic Map Proj, US Geol Surv, 59-75, tech supv officer, Oil & Gas Br, 75-79; PRES, DIGITAL DATA FOR OIL INDEPENDENTS, 79- *Concurrent Pos:* Ed-in-chief, Geol Atlas Rocky Mountains Region, Rocky Mountain Asn Geologist, 72. *Mem:* Fel Geol Soc Am; Am Asn Petrol Geologists; Sigma Xi. *Res:* Stratigraphy and tectonics of Colorado and western United States; continental framework and petroleum exploration in western United States. *Mailing Add:* Digital Data Oil Independents 11350 W 25th Pl Denver CO 80215

MALLOTT, I FLOYD, b Chicago, Ill, Oct 20, 22; m 50; c 4. PSYCHIATRY. *Educ:* Manchester Col, AB, 44; Loyola Univ, Ill, MD, 51. *Prof Exp:* Fel psychiat, 52-55, from asst instr to asst prof, 55-65, CLIN ASSOC PROF PSYCHIAT, SCH MED, UNIV PITTSBURGH, 65-; SR PSYCHIATRIST, OFF REGIONAL PROGRAMMING, WESTERN PSYCHIAT INST & CLIN, 73- *Concurrent Pos:* Asst chief outpatient serv, Western Psychiat Inst & Clin, 55-57, chief outpatient serv, 57-72, coordr educ, 72-73; consult, Magee-Woman's Hosp, Pittsburgh, 63- & Presby-Univ Hosp, 63- *Mem:* AAAS; assoc mem Am Psychoanal Asn; AMA; Asn Am Med Cols; Am Psychiat Asn. *Res:* Clinical psychiatry and psychiatric education. *Mailing Add:* 3700 Fifth Ave Pittsburgh PA 15213

MALLOV, SAMUEL, b New York, NY, Apr 19, 19; m 43; c 2. PHARMACOLOGY. *Educ:* City Col New York, BS, 39; NY Univ, MS, 41; Syracuse Univ, PhD(biochem), 52. *Prof Exp:* Chemist, Labs, Westinghouse Elec Co, 43-44; org chemist, US Bur Mines, 44-45; res chemist, Coal Lab, Carnegie Inst Technol, 45-48; asst, 48-52, from instr to assoc prof, 53-70, PROF PHARMACOL, COL MED, STATE UNIV NY UPSTATE MED CTR, 71- *Concurrent Pos:* Am Heart Asn fel, State Univ NY Upstate Med Ctr, 52-53. *Mem:* AAAS; Am Soc Pharmacol & Exp Therapeut. *Res:* Cardiovascular, alcohol. *Mailing Add:* 210 DeForest Rd Syracuse NY 13214

MALLOW, GARY KEITH, b Frostburg, Md; m 71; c 2. ANIMAL PHYSIOLOGY, ECOLOGY. *Educ:* Frostburg State Col, BS, 71; Univ Ga, PhD(zool), 78. *Prof Exp:* Asst prof physiol, Univ NDak, 77-78; ASST PROF PHYSIOL, KEAN COL, NJ, 78- *Concurrent Pos:* Coauth NSF approved grant instrnl equip, 78. *Mem:* Am Soc Zoologists; Sigma Xi. *Res:* Hormonal influences on behavior and population regulation; sensory physiology. *Mailing Add:* Dept of Biol Kean Col NJ Union NJ 07083

MALLOW, JEFFRY VICTOR, b New York, NY, June 28, 38; m 70. ATOMIC PHYSICS, SCIENCE ANXIETY. *Educ:* Columbia Univ, AB, 64; Northwestern Univ, MS, 66, PhD(physics astron), 70. *Prof Exp:* Fel physics, Hebrew Univ, Jerusalem, 70-71; res assoc, Northwestern Univ, 71-74; asst prof physics, Oakland Univ, 74-76; asst prof, 76-78, ASSOC PROF PHYSICS, LOYOLA UNIV CHICAGO, 78- *Concurrent Pos:* Res consult, Northwestern Univ, 74- *Mem:* AAAS; Am Phys Soc; Sigma Xi. *Res:* Atomic Hartee-Fock and Dirac-Fock theory; laser radar investigation of atmospheric constituents; theory of muonic atoms. *Mailing Add:* Dept Physics Loyola Univ Chicago Chicago IL 60626

MALLOWS, COLIN LINGWOOD, b Great Sampford, Eng, Sept 10, 30; m 56; c 3. MATHEMATICAL STATISTICS. *Educ:* Univ London, BSc, 51, PhD(statist), 53. *Prof Exp:* Asst lectr statist, Univ Col London, 55-57, lectr, 58-60; res assoc statist tech res group, Princeton Univ, 57-58; mem tech staff, 60-69, DEPT HEAD, BELL LABS, 69- *Concurrent Pos:* Adj assoc prof, Columbia Univ, 60-64. *Mem:* Fel Inst Math Statist; fel Am Statist Asn; Math Asn Am; Int Statist Inst; Royal Statist Soc. *Res:* Data analysis, especially informal and graphical methods; algebraic coding theory. *Mailing Add:* Bell Labs Inc Murray Hill NJ 07974

MALLOY, ALFRED MARCUS, b Pittsburgh, Pa, Oct 6, 03; m 43; c 1. PHYSICAL CHEMISTRY, ELECTROCHEMISTRY. *Educ:* Carnegie Inst Technol, BS, 25; Mich State Univ, MS, 27. *Prof Exp:* Asst electrochem, Mich State Univ, 25-27; foundry chemist, Cadillac Motorcar Co, Mich, 27-29; res chemist, Behr-Manning Corp, NY, 30-35; metall observer, Carnegie-Ill Steel Corp, Pa, 36-37; chemist, Bur Tests, Allegheny County, 37-40; chem engr, Bur Aeronaut, DC, 40-59; head mat protection sect, Bur Naval Weapons, 59-72, PROJ OFFICER, NAVAL AIR SYSTS COMMAND, 65-, MAT BR ENGR, 72- *Concurrent Pos:* Mem, Working Group Aircraft Camouflage, NATO, France, 52. *Mem:* Nat Asn Corrosion Engrs; fel Am Inst Chemists. *Res:* Environmental behavior of aircraft and missile material on land, sea and air; corrosion; thin free films; organic coatings; camouflage and visibility; adhesion; surface effects; biomedical techniques; air and water pollution control. *Mailing Add:* Jefferson Plaza One 1411 Jefferson Davis Hwy Arlington VA 20361

MALLOY, DONALD JON, b Rochester, NY, Dec 21, 50; m 72; c 1. NUCLEAR ENGINEERING, PROBABILITY. *Educ:* Purdue Univ, BS, 72, MSNE, 74, nuclear eng), 76. *Prof Exp:* ENGR NUCLEAR REACTOR ANAL SYSTS DESIGN, ARGONNE NAT LAB, 76- *Res:* Reactor analysis; fuel cycle analysis; reactor physics and safety; reactor thermal-hydraulics analysis, advanced concepts. *Mailing Add:* Argonne Nat Lab 9700 S Cass Ave Argonne IL 60439

MALLOY, JOHN B, b Chicago Ill, May 6, 28; m 53; c 2. CHEMICAL ENGINEERING. *Educ:* Mass Inst Technol, BS, 50, MS, 51; Univ Chicago, MBA, 61. *Prof Exp:* Chem engr, Am Oil Co, 51-54, group leader, 54-64; specialist mgt sci, Amoco Chem Corp, 64-70, mgr planning & environ anal, 70-76; DIR CHEM INDUST ANAL, STANDARD OIL IND, 76- *Mem:* Am Inst Chem Engrs; Am Chem Soc. *Res:* Application of scientific methods to business problems; analysis of economic environment for chemicals. *Mailing Add:* 1524 Melbrook Dr Munster IN 46321

MALLOY, THOMAS BERNARD, JR, b El Campo, Tex, Aug 20, 41; m 68; c 2. MOLECULAR SPECTROSCOPY. *Educ:* Univ St Thomas, Tex, BA, 64; Tex A&M Univ, PhD(chem), 70. *Prof Exp:* Res assoc chem, Mass Inst Technol, 70-71; from asst prof to prof physics & chem, Miss State Univ, 71-79; SR RES CHEMIST, SHELL DEVELOP CO, 79- *Concurrent Pos:* Sabbatical, Univ Ga, 76-77. *Mem:* Am Phys Soc; Am Chem Soc; Coblenty Soc; Sigma Xi. *Res:* Analytical applications of infrared, ultraviolet-visible spectroscopy, Raman spectroscopy, and coherent Raman spectroscopy. *Mailing Add:* Shell Develop Co PO Box 1380 Houston TX 77001

MALLOY, THOMAS PATRICK, b Chicago, Ill, July 28, 41; m 64; c 2. ORGANIC CHEMISTRY. *Educ:* Ill Inst Technol, BS, 65; Loyola Univ, PhD(org chem), 70. *Prof Exp:* Sr res scientist, De Soto, Inc, 70-71; consult org chem, Bernard Wolnak & Assocs, 71-74; group leader, 74-80, MGR, UNIVERSAL OIL PROD, INC, 80- *Mem:* Am Chem Soc; Inst Food Technologists. *Res:* Physical organic, mainly molecular, rearrangements; mechanisms of reaction and organic synthesis. *Mailing Add:* 730 Red Bridge Lake Zurich IL 60047

MALLOZZI, PHILIP JAMES, b Norwalk, Conn, Feb 12, 37; m 61; c 4. PHYSICS. *Educ:* Harvard Univ, BA, 60; Yale Univ, MS, 61, PhD(physics), 64. *Prof Exp:* Instr physics, Yale Univ, 64-66; mem tech staff, Columbus Labs, Battelle Mem Inst, 66-70, dir, Laser Applications Ctr, 70-81; CONSULT LASER APPLICATIONS, 81- *Honors & Awards:* Indust Res 100 Award, 80. *Mem:* Am Phys Soc; AAAS; Sigma Xi. *Res:* Plasma physics; laser produced plasmas; laser physics; astrophysics; use of laser-generated plasmas for x-ray production; applications of laser-produced x-rays, especially to x-ray microscopy, exafs, and x-ray lithography. *Mailing Add:* 1783 Home Rd Delaware OH 43015

MALM, DONALD E G, b Tallant, Okla, June 3, 30; m 57; c 1. NUMBER THEORY. *Educ:* Northwestern Univ, BS, 52; Brown Univ, AM, 54, PhD(math), 59. *Prof Exp:* Instr math, Rutgers Univ, 57-59; vis lectr, Royal Holloway Col, Univ London, 59-60; asst prof, State Univ NY Stony Brook, 60-62; asst prof, 62-65, assoc prof, 65-76, PROF MATH, OAKLAND UNIV, 76- *Mem:* AsnComput Mach; Am Asn Univ Prof; Am Math Soc; Math Asn Am. *Res:* Algebraic topology; number theory. *Mailing Add:* Dept of Math Oakland Univ Rochester MI 48063

MALM, NORMAN R, b Boulder, Colo, June 9, 31; m 55; c 3. PLANT BREEDING, AGRONOMY. *Educ:* Colo State Univ, BS, 54; Univ Ill, MS, 56, PhD(agron), 60. *Prof Exp:* Agronomist, NMex State Univ, 61-68 & Univ Nebr, Lincoln, 68-69; agronomist, 69-72, assoc prof, 72-77, PROF AGRON & COTTON BREEDER, NMEX STATE UNIV, 77- *Mem:* Am Soc Agron; Crop Sci Soc Am. *Res:* Cotton breeding research for high quality fiber, disease resistance and insect resistance. *Mailing Add:* Dept of Agron NMex State Univ Las Cruces NM 88003

MALMBERG, EARL WINTON, b Bernadotte Twp, Minn, Oct 18, 19; m 49; c 5. CHEMISTRY. *Educ:* Gustavus Adolphus Col, BA, 40; Univ Nebr, MA, 42, PhD(org chem), 47. *Prof Exp:* Res chemist, Nat Defense Res Comt, Calif Inst Technol, 43-46 & Am Cyanamid Co, 47-48; Du Pont fel, Univ Minn, 48-49; from asst prof to assoc prof chem, Ohio State Univ, 49-59; res chemist, 59-69, sr res scientist, 69-74, CHIEF SCIENTIST CHEM, SUN OIL CO, 74- *Mem:* Am Chem Soc; Soc Petrol Engrs. *Res:* Electrochemistry; mechanism of oxidation of organic compounds; chromatography; cis-trans isomerizations; chemical reactions in shock tubes; Athabasca tar sands; petroleum recovery; petroleum source bed geochemistry. *Mailing Add:* Sun Oil Co 503 N Central Expressway Richardson TX 75080

MALMBERG, JOHN HOLMES, b Gettysburg, Pa, July 5, 27; m 52; c 2. PLASMA PHYSICS. *Educ:* Ill State Univ, BS, 49; Univ Ill, MS, 51, PhD(physics), 57. *Prof Exp:* Mem staff plasma physics, Gen Atomic Div, Gen Dynamics Corp, 57-69; PROF PHYSICS, UNIV CALIF, SAN DIEGO, 67- *Mem:* AAAS; Am Phys Soc. *Res:* Experimental plasma physics; fundamental properties of waves; controlled thermonuclear research; development of seismic prospecting systems; physics of elementary particles. *Mailing Add:* Dept of Physics Univ of Calif at San Diego La Jolla CA 92037

MALMBERG, MARJORIE SCHOOLEY, b Estherville, Iowa, Aug 20, 21; m 45; c 5. PHYSICAL CHEMISTRY. *Educ:* Wellesley Col, AB, 42; Univ Md, College Park, PhD(phys chem), 67. *Prof Exp:* Jr chemist, Nat Bur Standards, 42-45, chemist, 48-55; US Army grant & res assoc, Univ Md, College Park, 67-70; Nat Inst Gen Med Sci-Nat Inst Arthritis & Metab Dis spec res fel nuclear magnetic resonance, Nat Bur Standards, 70-72, guest worker, 72-74; eng analyst, 74-75, sect leader, 75-78, CONSULT, NUS CORP, 78- *Mem:* Am Chem Soc; Health Phys Soc. *Res:* Molecular microdynamics in fluids; structure of liquids; relaxation phenomena in biological molecules and polymers; infrared, raman and nuclear magnetic resonance spectroscopy; light scattering; radiological environmental monitoring. *Mailing Add:* 3300 Gregg Rd Brookeville MD 20833

MALMBERG, PAUL ROVELSTAD, b New Haven, Conn, Apr 15, 23; m 44; c 5. SOLID STATE ELECTRONICS. *Educ:* Thiel Col, BS, 44. *Prof Exp:* Fel life preservers, Mellon Inst, 46-48; instr physics, Univ Pittsburgh, 50-51; physicist, Westinghouse Res Labs, 51-60; Int Atomic Energy Agency UN vis prof, Tsing Hua Univ, Taiwan, 60-61; mgr sci instrumentation, 61-66, fel engr, 66-68, mgr advan circuit fabrication technol, 68-70, mgr electron beam fabrication technol, 70-72, mgr electron imaging technol, Elec Sci Div, 72-75, fel engr, 75-77, MGR THIN FILM TECHNOL, WESTINGHOUSE RES & DEVELOP LABS, 77- *Mem:* Am Phys Soc; Inst Elec & Electronic Engrs; Electrochem Soc; Soc Info Display; Fedn Am Scientists. *Res:* Advanced integrated circuits and solid state devices made by electron and ion beam techniques; thin film devices and systems for information processing and display and for signal transduction. *Mailing Add:* Thin Film Technol Westinghouse Res & Develop Labs Pittsburgh PA 15235

MALMBERG, PHILIP RAY, b Norwood, Mass, Oct 13, 20; m 56; c 3. NUCLEAR PHYSICS, SOLID STATE PHYSICS. *Educ:* Ill State Norm Univ, BEd, 40; Univ Iowa, MS, 44, PhD(physics), 55. *Prof Exp:* Jr engr, Res Lab, Sylvania Elec Prod, Inc, 44-46; res assoc nuclear physics, Univ Iowa, 50-53; PHYSICIST, NAVAL RES LAB, 55- *Mem:* Sigma Xi; Am Phys Soc. *Res:* Radiation damage by charged particles; ion implantation; materials analysis; development of specialized equipment. *Mailing Add:* Naval Res Lab 4555 Overlook Ave SW Washington DC 20375

MALME, CHARLES I(RVING), b Crookston, Minn, Aug 13, 31; m 61; c 2. ELECTRICAL ENGINEERING, ACOUSTICS. *Educ:* Univ Minn, BEE & BS, 54; Mass Inst Technol, SM, 58, EE, 59. *Prof Exp:* Res asst acoustics, Mass Inst Technol, 56-59; consult appl physics, 60-69, mgr phys sci lab, 69-75, SR SCIENTIST, BOLT BERANEK & NEWMAN, INC, 76- *Mem:* Acoust Soc Am; Marine Technol Soc. *Res:* High intensity sound instrumentation; speech research; sound propagation measurements; explosive effects research; underwater sound propagation. *Mailing Add:* Bolt Beranek & Newman Inc 50 Moulton St Cambridge MA 02138

MALMGREN, RICHARD AXEL, b St Paul, Minn, Dec 31, 21; m 46; c 2. PATHOLOGY. *Educ:* Wagner Col, BS, 42; Cornell Univ, MD, 45; Am Bd Path, dipl, 57. *Prof Exp:* Intern, Grasslands Hosp, 45-46; head serol unit, Biol Sect, Nat Cancer Inst, 48-53, med officer chg cancer invest unit, Tenn, 53-56, head cytopath serv, 56-72; head cytopath serv, Dept Path, Med Ctr, George Washington Univ, 74-76; RETIRED. *Mem:* Am Soc Cytol. *Res:* Cancer immunology; cytology; pathologic physiology of cancer. *Mailing Add:* 1686 N Harbor Ct Annapolis MD 21401

MALMQUIST, CARL PHILLIP, b St Paul, Minn, Mar 10, 31; m 56; c 2. PSYCHIATRY. *Educ:* Univ Minn, BA, 52, MD, 58, MS, 61. *Prof Exp:* Resident psychiat & child psychiat, Univ Minn & Columbia Med Ctr, 58-63; training dir, Hennepin County Gen Hosp, Minneapolis, 63-65; assoc prof psychiat, Med Sch, Univ Mich, 65-66; assoc prof, Inst Child Develop, Univ Minn, Minneapolis, 66-70, prof child psychiat & dir dept, Univ, 70-71, prof, Law & Criminal Justice, 71-80, PROF SOCIOL & SOCIAL PSYCHIAT, UNIV MINN, MINNEAPOLIS, 80- *Concurrent Pos:* Psychiat consult, Minneapolis Dist Ct, 66-; mem task force on right to treatment, Am Psychiat Asn, 72-73; chmn comt on psychiat & law, Group for the advan of Pschiat, 74- *Mem:* Am Psychiat Asn; Am Orthopsychiat Asn; Acad Child Psychiat; Am Col Psychiat. *Res:* Depression; childhood psychopathology; psychiatry and law; depression and acting out behaviors. *Mailing Add:* 5010 Bruce Ave Minneapolis MN 55424

MALMSTADT, HOWARD VINCENT, b Marinette, Wis, Feb 17, 22; m 47; c 3. CHEMISTRY. *Educ:* Univ Wis, BS, 43, MS, 48, PhD(chem), 50. *Prof Exp:* Res assoc chem, Univ Wis, 50-51; from instr to asst prof chem, 51-57, assoc prof anal chem, 57-61, prof, 61-78, EMER PROF CHEM, UNIV ILL, URBANA, 78-; VPRES ACAD AFFAIRS, PAC & ASIA CHRISTIAN UNIV, HAWAII, 79- *Concurrent Pos:* Guggenheim fel, 60; mem adv bd, NIH, 72-76, res grants, 75- *Honors & Awards:* Chem Instrumentation Award, Am Chem Soc, 63; Educ Award, Instrument Soc Am, 70; Analytical Chemistry Fisher Award, Am Chem Soc, 76; ISCO Award Biochem Instrumentation, 80. *Mem:* Am Chem Soc; Am Asn Clin Chemists; Soc Appl Spectros. *Res:* Clinical/analytical methodology; short-time phenomena in sparks, laser plumes and flames; applied spectroscopy; spectrochemical methods; automatic titrations; atomic and molecular absorption spectrometry; time-resolved spectroscopy; automation; reaction-rate methods. *Mailing Add:* 75-5786 Niau Place Kailua-Kona HI 96740

MALMUTH, NORMAN DAVID, fluid mechanics, applied mathematics, see previous edition

MALO, SALVADOR ALEJANDRO, surface physics, experimental atomic spectroscopy, see previous edition

MALO, SIMON E, horticulture, nematology, see previous edition

MALOFF, BRUCE LARRIE, b Syracuse, NY, Aug 26, 53; m 76. DIABETES, ENDOCRINOLOGY. *Educ:* Syracuse Univ, BS, 73; State Univ NY, Albany, PhD(cell physiol), 78. *Prof Exp:* Res assoc physiol, Sch Med, Upstate Med Ctr, State Univ NY, 77-78; instr & fel med & endocrinol, Sch Med, Univ Rochester, 78-81, sr instr, 81; RES PHARMACOLOGIST, PHARMACEUT DIV, E I DU PONT DE NEMOURS & CO, INC, GLENOLDEN, PA, 81- *Mem:* Biophys Soc; AAAS; Endocrine Soc; Am Diabetes Asn. *Res:* Develop diabetes research program with emphasis on cellular mechanism of antidiabetic agents, and basic research on the biochemical aspects of insulin action at the cellular and molecular levels of response; mitochondria, oxidative phosphorylation, energy transduction, biophysics, electrophysiology, cellular metabolism, biochemistry, physiology, and microscopy. *Mailing Add:* Dept Metabolic Dis Sect E I du Pont de Nemours & Co Inc Glenolden PA 19036

MALOFSKY, BERNARD MILES, b New York, NY, Oct 7, 37; m 64; c 2. ORGANIC POLYMER CHEMISTRY. *Educ:* Calif Inst Technol, BS, 59; Univ Wash, PhD(org chem), 64. *Prof Exp:* Res chemist, Textile Fibers Dept, E I du Pont de Nemours & Co, Inc, 64-70; from res & develop chemist to technol mgr, 72-74, mgr prod develop, 74-77, ASSOC DIR CHEM TECHNOL, LOCTITE CORP, 77- *Mem:* Am Chem Soc. *Res:* Anaerobic adhesives and sealants, particularly thermal resistance, cure systems, structural adhesives of high peel and impact strength, primers, ultraviolet curing adhesives, powdered metal and casting impregnation; cyanoacrycate manufacture and products. *Mailing Add:* Loctite Corp 705 N Mountain Rd Newington CT 06111

MALONE, CHARLES R, b Sweetwater, Tex, May 9, 38; m 64; c 1. ECOLOGY. *Educ:* Tex Tech Col, BS, 63, MS, 65; Rutgers Univ, PhD(zool), 68. *Prof Exp:* AEC fel ecol, Oak Ridge Nat Lab, 68-70, res scientist, 70-71; prof assoc, environ studies bd, Nat Acad Sci-Nat Acad Eng, 71-75; exec secy, Water Supply Rev Comt, 76-80, EXEC DIR, WATER RESOURCES ENG BD, NAT RES COUN, 80- *Concurrent Pos:* Chmn, Prog Comt, Ecol Soc Am, 72-74; mem Pub Responsibilities Comt, Am Inst Biol Sci, 74-76. *Mem:* AAAS; Ecol Soc Am: Am Inst Biol Sci; Water Pollution Control Fedn; Sigma Xi; Am Soc Chem Engrs. *Res:* Environmental impacts of pollutants; water resources engineering and management; science advisory process; environmental planning. *Mailing Add:* Bd Water Resources Eng Nat Res Coun Washington DC 20418

MALONE, CREIGHTON PAUL, b Beaver City, Nebr, May 3, 33; m 57; c 2. PHYSICAL CHEMISTRY. *Educ:* Univ Colo, BA, 58, PhD(phys chem), 62. *Prof Exp:* Asst phys chem, Univ Colo, 58-62; res chemist, Eng Dept, 62-65, sr res chemist, 65-69, sr res chemist, 69-78, RES ASSOC, TEXTILE FIBERS DEPT, E I DU PONT DE NEMOURS & CO, INC, 78- *Mem:* Am Chem Soc. *Res:* Magnetic susceptibility of small particles; infrared adsorption and reflection spectroscopy; liquid chromatography; polymer physical chemistry; textile physical chemistry. *Mailing Add:* Textile Res Lab Chestnut Run E I du Pont de Nemours & Co Inc Wilmington DE 19898

MALONE, DENNIS P(HILIP), b Buffalo, NY, Sept 3, 32; m 54; c 2. PHYSICS, ELECTRICAL ENGINEERING. *Educ:* Univ Buffalo, BA, 54; Yale Univ, MSc, 55, PhD(physics), 60. *Prof Exp:* Res physicist, Cornell Aeronaut Lab, 59-60, head mod physics br, 60-65; assoc prof eng, 65-70, PROF ELEC ENG & CHMN DEPT, STATE UNIV NY BUFFALO, 70- *Mem:* Am Phys Soc; Am Nuclear Soc; Inst Elec & Electronics Engrs. *Res:* Quantum electronics; frequency multiplication techniques; coherent optics; electron polarization studies; ion molecule reactions. *Mailing Add:* Dept of Elec Eng State Univ NY Buffalo NY 14214

MALONE, DIANA, b Chicago, Ill, May 6, 35. ANALYTICAL CHEMISTRY, CHEMICAL EDUCATION. *Educ:* Mundelein Col, BS, 56; Univ Notre Dame, MS, 65; Univ Iowa, PhD(sci educ, chem), 77. *Prof Exp:* Instr chem & math, Assumption High Sch, Davenport, Iowa, 59-69; ASSOC PROF CHEM, CLARKE COL, 69- *Mem:* Am Chem Soc. *Res:* Analytical and inorganic chemistry; coordination compounds preparation and characterization. *Mailing Add:* Dept of Chem Clarke Col Dubuque IA 52001

MALONE, JAMES MICHAEL, b Berkeley, Calif, Sept 13, 46; m 74; c 2. VASCULAR SURGERY. *Educ:* Univ Calif, San Francisco, BMS, 68, MD, 71. *Prof Exp:* Intern surg, Univ Calif, San Francisco, 71-72, asst resident, 72-76, chief resident, 76-77; ASST PROF SURG & ASST CHIEF VASCULAR SURG, UNIV ARIZ HEALTH SCI CTR, 77- *Concurrent Pos:* Vet Admin career develop award, 77-80. *Mem:* Asn Acad Surg; Am Col Emergency Physicians; Am Fedn Clin Res. *Res:* Mechanisms of tumor metastasis; prosthetic vascular graft healing. *Mailing Add:* Dept of Surg 1501 N Campbell Tucson AZ 85724

MALONE, JAMES W(ILLIAM), b Arizona, La, Apr 11, 25; m 52; c 3. CHEMICAL ENGINEERING. *Educ:* La Polytech Inst, BS, 47; La State Univ, MS, 55. *Prof Exp:* Asst prof chem, 47-54, 55-56, assoc prof chem eng, 56-67, PROF CHEM ENG, LA TECH UNIV, 67- *Mem:* Am Inst Chem Engrs. *Res:* Heat transfer; concentration of native iron ore; liquid-liquid solubility. *Mailing Add:* Dept of Chem Eng La Tech Univ Ruston LA 71270

MALONE, JOHN IRVIN, b Altoona, Pa, Oct 10, 41; m; c 4. PEDIATRICS. *Educ:* Pa State Univ, BS, 63; Univ Pa, MD, 67. *Prof Exp:* Intern pediat, Children's Hosp, Philadelphia, 67-68, resident, 68-69; instr, Sch Med, Univ Pa, 69-72; asst prof, 72-76, assoc prof, 76-80, PROF PEDIAT, UNIV SOUTH FLA, 80-, CO-DIR, DIABETES CENTER, 79- *Concurrent Pos:* Res fel, Div Biochem Develop & Molecular Dis, Children's Hosp, Philadelphia, 69-71; chief resident pediat hosp, Univ Pa, 71-72; mem staff, Philadelphia Gen Hosp, 71, Tampa Gen Hosp, 72 & All Children's Hosp, St Petersburg, Fla, 73; co-dir, Fla's Camp Children & Youth Diabetes, 73-; dir, SunCoast Regional Diabetes Prog, Tampa, 76- *Mem:* AAAS; Am Diabetes Asn; Soc Pediat Res; Am Fedn Clin Res. *Res:* Diabetic control in children. *Mailing Add:* Dept Pediat Box 15 Univ South Fla Tampa FL 33612

MALONE, JOSEPH JAMES, b St Louis, Mo, Sept 9, 32; m 60; c 4. ALGEBRA. *Educ:* St Louis Univ, BS, 54, MS, 58, PhD(math), 62. *Prof Exp:* Instr math, Rockhurst Col, 60-62; asst prof, Univ Houston, 62-67; from assoc prof to prof, Tex A&M Univ, 67-71; head dept, 71-78, PROF MATH, WORCESTER POLYTECH INST, 71- *Mem:* Am Math Soc; Math Asn Am. *Res:* Abstract algebra; groups; near rings. *Mailing Add:* 45 Adams St Westboro MA 01581

MALONE, LEO JACKSON, JR, b Wichita, Kans, July 24, 38; m 64; c 4. INORGANIC CHEMISTRY. *Educ:* Univ Wichita, BS, 60, MS, 62; Univ Mich, PhD(inorg chem), 64. *Prof Exp:* From asst prof to assoc prof, 64-73, PROF CHEM, ST LOUIS UNIV, 73- *Mem:* AAAS; Am Chem Soc; Sigma Xi. *Res:* Chemistry of carbon-monoxide-borane. *Mailing Add:* Dept Chem St Louis Univ St Louis MO 63103

MALONE, LINDA CATRON, statistics, see previous edition

MALONE, MARVIN HERBERT, b Fairbury, Nebr, Apr 2, 30; m 52; c 2. PHARMACOLOGY. *Educ:* Univ Nebr, BS, 51, MS, 53, PhD(pharmacol, pharmaceut sci), 58. *Prof Exp:* Asst pharmacol, Univ Nebr, 51-53; asst pharmacodyn, Squibb Inst Med Res, 53-56; asst pharmacol, Univ Nebr, 56-58; asst prof pharmacol, Col Pharm, Univ NMex, 58-60; assoc prof, Sch Pharm, Univ Conn, 60-69; PROF PHYSIOL & PHARMACOL, UNIV OF THE PAC, 69- *Concurrent Pos:* Consult, Drug Plant Lab, Univ Wash, 60-64, Res Path Assocs, Md, 67-70, Amazon Natural Drug Co, NJ, 67-70 & Imp Chem Indust US Inc, Del, 68-78; ed, Wormwood Rev, 61- & Am J Pharm Educ, 75-79. *Honors & Awards:* Mead Johnson Labs Award, 64. *Mem:* fel AAAS; Am Pharmaceut Asn; Am Soc Pharmacol & Exp Therapeut; Am Soc Pharmacog; sr mem Acad Pharmaceut Sci. *Res:* Screening and assay of natural products; pharmacodynamics of psychotropic and autonomic agents; biometrics; pharmacology of inflammation and antiinflammation. *Mailing Add:* Physiol-Pharmacol Unit Univ Pac Sch Pharm Stockton CA 95207

MALONE, MICHAEL JOSEPH, b Portland, Maine, Apr 28, 30; m 57; c 1. NEUROLOGY, NEUROCHEMISTRY. *Educ:* Boston Col, AB, 51; Georgetown Univ, MD, 56. *Prof Exp:* Resident neurol, Boston Vet Admin Hosp, Boston Univ, 60-63; Nat Inst Neurol Dis & Stroke spec fel neurochem, Harvard Med Sch, 63-65; res assoc, Mass Gen Hosp, 65-69; lectr, Boston City Hosp, 69-70; prof, Med Sch, George Washington Univ, 70-75; prof neurol & pediat & dir neurol res, Boston City Hosp, 75-76; DIR, GRECC BEDFORD VET ADMIN MED CTR, 76-; PROF NEUROL & PSYCHIAT, BOSTON UNIV, 76- *Concurrent Pos:* Vet Admin clin investr, Harvard Med Sch, 65-68; asst prof, Sch Med, Boston Univ, 67-70; Nat Inst Neurol Dis & Stroke res grant, Boston Univ, 68-71, career develop award, 69; chief neurol, Children's Hosp, Washington, DC, 70-75; consult, Walter Reed Army Med Ctr, Washington, DC, 71-, US Naval Hosp, Bethesda, Md, 71- & NIH, 71- *Mem:* Am Acad Neurol; Am Soc Neurochem; Int Soc Neurochem; Soc Neurosci; NY Acad Sci. *Res:* Biochemistry of maturation; biochemical pathology of nervous tissue; gerontology. *Mailing Add:* 45 Greenhill Rd Sudbury MA 01776

MALONE, PHILIP GARCIN, b Louisville, Ky, Jan 12, 41; m 75; c 2. GEOCHEMISTRY. *Educ:* Univ Louisville, BA, 62; Ind Univ, Bloomington, MA, 64; Case Western Reserve Univ, PhD(geol), 69. *Prof Exp:* Nat Acad Sci-Nat Res Coun res assoc, Smithsonian Inst, 69-70; from asst prof to assoc prof geol, Wright State Univ, 70-78; GEOLOGIST, US ARMY ENG, WATERWAYS EXP STA, 78- *Mem:* AAAS; Sigma Xi; Am Asn Prof Geologists. *Res:* Containment, treatment and disposal of toxic and hazardous wastes. *Mailing Add:* US Army Eng PO Box 631 Vicksburg MS 39180

MALONE, ROBERT CHARLES, b Wichita, Kans, Mar 14, 45; m 68. THEORETICAL PHYSICS. *Educ:* Washington Univ, BA, 67; Cornell Univ, MS, 70, PhD(theoret physics), 73. *Prof Exp:* STAFF PHYSICIST THEORET PHYSICS, LOS ALAMOS NAT LAB, 72- *Mem:* Am Phys Soc; Am Meteorol Soc. *Res:* Hydrodynamics, plasma physics and magnetohydrodynamics, atmospheric dynamics. *Mailing Add:* T-1 MS 269 Los Alamos Nat Lab Los Alamos NM 87545

MALONE, THOMAS FRANCIS, b Sioux City, Iowa, May 3, 17; m 42; c 6. ENVIRONMENT. *Educ:* SDak Sch Mines & Technol, BS, 40; Mass Inst Technol, ScD, 46. *Hon Degrees:* DEng, SDak Sch Mines & Technol, 62; DHL, St Joseph Col, 65. *Prof Exp:* Asst, Mass Inst Technol, 41-42, from asst prof to assoc prof meteorol, 43-55; dir weather res ctr, Travelers Ins Co, Conn, 55-57, dir res, 57-64, second vpres, 64-66, vpres & dir res, 66-67, sr vpres, 68-70; dean grad sch, Univ Conn, 70-73; DIR, HOLCOMB RES INST, BUTLER UNIV, 73- *Concurrent Pos:* With Off Naval Res, 50-53; ed, Compendium Meteorol; mem adv panel sci & technol, Comt Sci & Astronaut, US House of Rep; mem geophys res bd & comt water, Nat Acad Sci, chmn comt atmospheric sci, 62-68, dep foreign secy, 68-73, chmn geophys res bd, 69-75, chmn bd int orgn & progs, 69-76, mem space applns bd, 72-77, foreign secy, 78-; secy-gen comt atmospheric sci, Int Union Geod & Geophys, 65-68; chmn, Nat Motor Vehicle Safety Adv Coun, 67-69; secy-gen sci comt probs of environ, Int Coun Sci Unions, 64-68; mem, Nat Adv Comt Oceans & Atmosphere, 71-75; chmn bd trustees, Univ Corp Atmospheric Res, 73-74; mem, Weather Modification Adv Bd, Dept Commerce, 77-80; pres, Inst Ecol, 78-81; trustee, Int Found Sci. *Honors & Awards:* Losey Award, Int Aerospace Sci, 60; Brooks Award, Am Meteorol Soc, 64; Abbe Award, 68. *Mem:* Nat Acad Sci; fel AAAS; fel Am Meteorol Soc (secy, 57-60, pres, 60-62); fel Am Geophys Union (vpres, 60-61, pres, 61-64, secy int partic, 64-72); Int Coun Sci Unions (vpres, 70-72, treas, 78-). *Res:* Applied meteorology; synoptic climatology; environment. *Mailing Add:* Holcomb Res Inst Butler Univ Indianapolis IN 46208

MALONE, WILLIAM MAXTON, organic chemistry, see previous edition

MALONE, WINFRED FRANCIS, b Revere, Mass, Feb 10, 35; m 75. ENVIRONMENTAL HEALTH. *Educ:* Univ Mass, Amherst, BS, 57, MS, 61; Rutgers Univ, New Brunswick, MS, 64; Univ Mich, Ann Arbor, PhD(environ health sci), 70. *Prof Exp:* Asst prof environ health, Lowell Technol Inst, 64-66; res & develop officer environ health, NIH, 69-72; sci adv, Hazardous Mat Adv Comt, Environ Protection Agency, 72-73, staff dir, Sci Adv Bd, 73-74; PROG DIR, PREV CANCER CONTROL PROG, NAT CANCER INST, 74- *Mem:* Health Physics Soc; Am Indust Hyg Asn; Royal Soc Health; NY Acad Sci; Am Pub Health Asn. *Mailing Add:* Nat Cancer Inst Blair Rm 614 Bethesda MD 20014

MALONEY, CLIFFORD JOSEPH, b Wheelock, NDak, Mar 25, 10; m 42; c 1. STATISTICS. *Educ:* NDak Agr Col, BS, 34; Univ Minn, MA, 37; Iowa State Col, PhD(statist), 48. *Prof Exp:* Instr math, NDak Agr Col, 35-41; instr math, Iowa State Col, 41-42; statistician, Bur Agr Econ, USDA, 42-46; instr math, Iowa State Col, 46, res assoc statist method, 46-47; chief statist br, Chem Corps, Ft Detrick, Md, 47-58, Biol Labs, Biomath Div, 58-62; chief biomet sect, div biol stand, 61-78, CONSULT STATIST, NIH, 78- *Mem:* AAAS; Biomet Soc; Math Asn Am; Am Statist Asn; Inst Math Statist. *Res:* Biometrics; computing; retrieval. *Mailing Add:* 6021 Landon Ln Bethesda MD 20817

MALONEY, DANIEL EDWIN, b Jericho, Vt, Feb 9, 26; m 53; c 8. POLYMER CHEMISTRY. *Educ:* St Michael's Col, BS, 47; Univ Notre Dame, MS, 49, PhD(org chem), 51. *Prof Exp:* Res chemist, 51-61, sr res chemist, 61-67, RES ASSOC, PLASTICS DEPT, E I DU PONT DE NEMOURS & CO, 67- *Mem:* Am Chem Soc; Electrochem Soc. *Res:* Plastics; polyolefins; ion exchange membranes. *Mailing Add:* Highland Meadows RD 2 Box 304 Hockessin DE 19707

MALONEY, J(AMES) O(HARA), b St Joseph, Mo, Apr 29, 15; m 40; c 3. CHEMICAL ENGINEERING. *Educ:* Univ Ill, BS, 36; Pa State Col, MS, 39, PhD(chem eng), 41. *Prof Exp:* Chem engr, Exp Sta, E I du Pont de Nemours & Co, 41-43, 45; sect chief, Plutonium Proj, Univ Chicago, 43-45; exec dir, Res Found, 45-59, chmn chem eng dept, Univ, 45-65, PROF CHEM ENG, UNIV KANS, 45- *Concurrent Pos:* Fulbright lectr, Univ Naples, 56-57; Smith-Mundt lectr, UAR, 60; Ford Found consult, Univ Alexandria, 66; Fulbright lectr, Nat Tech Univ Athens, 69; lectr, Chonnam Univ, Korea, 79. *Mem:* Am Chem Soc; Am Inst Chem Engrs; Am Asn Univ Prof; AAAS. *Res:* Absorption of gases in liquids; scale up of centrifugal equipment; development of laboratory experiments; structuring of technical information. *Mailing Add:* Dept of Chem Eng Univ of Kans Lawrence KS 66045

MALONEY, JAMES EUGENE, b Rollette, NDak, July 11, 35. OPERATIONS RESEARCH, FOREST ECONOMICS. *Educ:* Univ Calif, Berkeley, BSc, 62, MF, 63, PhD(quant methods), 72. *Prof Exp:* Researcher opers res, Univ Calif, Berkeley, 63-72; res scientist & proj leader opers res, Forest Fire Res Inst, Ottawa, Ont, 72-76; mgr, econ & statist div, 76-77, DIR, OPERS RES, CAN POST OFF, 77-, DIR, ENERGY MGT & INFO SYSTS, 80- *Concurrent Pos:* Consult & prof, Univ Toronto, 72-74 & Can Comt on Forest Fire Control, 72-76. *Mem:* AAAS; Soc Am Foresters; Can Inst Forestry. *Res:* Development and application of complex postal systems using advanced operations research models, economic principles, statistical techniques; planning and implementing major information systems. *Mailing Add:* Post Off Opers Res Br Campbell Bldg Ottawa ON K1A 0C1 Can

MALONEY, JAMES VINCENT, JR, b Rochester, NY, June 30, 25; m 57; c 4. SURGERY. *Educ:* Univ Rochester, MD, 47; Am Bd Surg, dipl, 55; Am Bd Thoracic Surg, dipl, 57. *Prof Exp:* Lectr biol, Sampson Col, 47; surg house officer, Johns Hopkins Univ Hosp, 47-48, from asst res to res surgeon, 50-55, instr, Sch Med, 54-55; res fel physiol, Sch Pub Health, Harvard Univ, 48-50; from asst prof to assoc prof, 55-65, chief div thoracic surg, 59-76, PROF SURG, SCH MED, UNIV CALIF, LOS ANGELES, CHMN DEPT, 76-

Concurrent Pos: Consult, Vet Admin Hosp, Los Angeles & Harbor County Gen Hosp, Torrance, 57-; Markle scholar, 58- *Mem:* Soc Univ Surgeons; Soc Clin Surgeons; Am Physiol Soc; AMA; Am Col Surg. *Res:* Surgery and physiology, especially the cardiorespiratory system. *Mailing Add:* Dept Surg Sch Med Univ Calif Los Angeles CA 90024

MALONEY, JOHN F, b Waltham, Mass, Feb 14, 36; m 64; c 3. FOOD SCIENCE & TECHNOLOGY. *Educ:* Northeastern Univ, BS, 59; Mass Inst Technol, PhD(food sci & technol), 65. *Prof Exp:* Sr res food scientist, Gen Mills, Inc, Minneapolis, 65-69, develop leader, 69-71, head prod develop, 71-72; mgr & dir res, 72-76, VPRES RES & DEVELOP & TECH SERV, H P HOOD INC, 76- *Mem:* Inst Food Technologists; Am Dairy Sci Asn; Nat Restaurant Asn; Sigma Xi. *Res:* Technical management including research and development, quality assurance and engineering for food and dairy products; development of new food products. *Mailing Add:* H P Hood Inc 56 Roland St Boston MA 02129

MALONEY, JOHN P, b Omaha, Nebr, Dec 9, 29. FUNCTIONAL ANALYSIS. *Educ:* Iowa State Univ, BS, 58; Georgetown Univ, MA, 62, PhD(math), 65. *Prof Exp:* Prod engr, Western Elec Co, 58-59; elec engr, US Govt, 58-63; instr math, Georgetown Univ, 63-65; asst prof, Univ Nebr, Lincoln, 65-67; from asst prof to assoc prof, 67-76, PROF MATH, UNIV NEBR, OMAHA, 76- *Mem:* Math Asn Am; Soc Indust & Appl Math. *Res:* Integral equations; solar energy. *Mailing Add:* Dept of Math & Comput Sci Univ of Nebr Omaha NE 68132

MALONEY, KENNETH LONG, b Wilkes-Barre, Pa, Oct 1, 45. FUEL SCIENCE, PHYSICAL CHEMISTRY. *Educ:* Wilkes Col, BS, 67; Pa State Univ, PhD(fuel sci), 71. *Prof Exp:* Res assoc, Drexel Univ, 71-72 & Princeton Univ, 72-73; sr scientist, Ultrasysts, Inc, 73-74; MGR, FOSSIL FUEL SYSTS STUDIES, KVB, INC, 74- *Concurrent Pos:* Instr, Drexel Univ, 71-73; adj prof, Univ Calif, Irvine, 74-76; vpres, Calpenn Assocs, 77- *Mem:* Am Chem Soc; Combustion Inst; Soc Photo-optical Engrs; Sigma Xi. *Res:* Combustion generated-pollutants; fossil fuel flame processes; chemistry of post flame reactions. *Mailing Add:* KVB Inc PO Box 19518 Irvine CA 92714

MALONEY, KENNETH MORGAN, b New Orleans, La, Oct 11, 41. MATERIALS SCIENCE, PROCESS DESIGN. *Educ:* Southern Univ, BS, 63, Univ Wash, PhD(phys chem), 68. *Prof Exp:* Res asst phys chem, Univ Wash, 63-68; sr res scientist reaction dynamics, Pac Northwest Labs, Battelle Mem Inst, 68-70; sr scientist & tech leader, Lamp Div, Gen Elec Co, 70-74, mgr advan eng mat sci, 74-76; mgr mat tech & mat eng, Xerox Corp, 76-81; ASSOC DIR FORWARD & CONTRACT RES, ALLIED CORP, 81- *Concurrent Pos:* Mem, Nat Res Coun Adv Comt to US Army Res Off, 74-; fel, Am Inst Chemists, 75. *Mem:* Am Chem Soc; Am Inst Chemists; Sigma Xi. *Res:* Reaction dynamics of metal-oxygen combustion systems; properties of liquid and solid state photoconductive materials; process dynamics of controlling high temperature processes. *Mailing Add:* Allied Corp PO Box 1087R Morristown NJ 07960

MALONEY, MARY ADELAIDE, b Quincy, Mass, Apr 30, 18. BIOLOGY. *Educ:* Col St Elizabeth, AB, 40. *Prof Exp:* Lab technician, Quincy City Hosp, Mass, 40-43; lab asst, Thorndike Mem Lab, Harvard Med Sch, 43-47; hematologist, Med Nutrit Lab, Univ Chicago, 47-51; chief lab asst hepatitis surv group from Harvard Univ, Off Sci Res & Develop, Japan, 51-52; asst biologist, Argonne Nat Lab, 52-64; res assoc biologist, 64-71, RES BIOLOGIST, LAB RADIOBIOL, SCH MED, UNIV CALIF, SAN FRANCISCO, 71- *Mem:* AAAS; Sigma Xi. *Res:* Radiobiology; hematologic problems. *Mailing Add:* Lab of Radiobiol Univ of Calif Sch of Med San Francisco CA 94143

MALONEY, PETER CHARLES, b Boston, Mass, Nov 5, 41. MEMBRANE BIOCHEMISTRY, PHYSIOLOGY. *Educ:* Swarthmore Col, BA, 63; Brown Univ, PhD(biol sci), 70. *Prof Exp:* Res fel physiol, Harvard Med Sch, 72-74, res assoc, 74-76; asst prof, 76-82, ASSOC PROF PHYSIOL, JOHNS HOPKINS MED SCH, 82- *Res:* Physiology of ionic movements across cell membranes. *Mailing Add:* Dept Physiol Sch Med Johns Hopkins Univ Baltimore MD 21205

MALONEY, THOMAS EDWARD, b Niagara Falls, NY, Sept 7, 23; m 46; c 3. ENVIRONMENTAL SCIENCES. *Educ:* Univ Buffalo, BA, 49, MA, 53. *Prof Exp:* Res biologist, Robert A Taft Sanit Eng Ctr, USPHS, 51-65; chief plankton res sect, Nat Marine Water Qual Lab, Fed Water Pollution Control Admin, 65-68, chief, Physiol Control Br, Nat Eutrophication res prog, 68-71, dep chief prog & chief, Physiol Control Br, Environ Protection Agency, 71-72, chief, Eutrophication & Lake Restoration Br, 72-78, ACTING DIR, ASSESSMENT & CRITERIA DEVELOP DIV, CORVALLIS ENVIRON RES LAB, US ENVIRON RES LAB, US ENVIRON PROTECTION AGENCY, 78- *Concurrent Pos:* Chmn, Plankton Subcomt, Biol Methods Comt, Environ Protection Agency, Biostimulation Joint Task Group & Phytoplankton Subcomt, Standard Methods for Examination Water & Wastewater, 73- *Honors & Awards:* Superior Serv Award, Dept Health, Educ & Welfare, 65. *Mem:* AAAS; Am Soc Limnol & Oceanog; Water Pollution Control Fedn; Am Phycol Soc; Am Inst Biol Sci. *Res:* Culturing of algae; algal physiology; chemical control of algal growth; environmental requirements of planktonic organisms; coordination and review of research and development programs to provide for control of accelerated eutrophication and development of lake restoration technology. *Mailing Add:* Environ Protection Agency 200 SW 35th St Corvallis OR 97330

MALONEY, WILLIAM THOMAS, b Warren, Ohio, Dec 12, 35; m 58; c 2. MAGNETISM, MAGNETIC RECORDING. *Educ:* Case Western Reserve Univ, BS, 57, MS, 58; Harvard Univ, AM, 61, PhD(appl physics), 64. *Prof Exp:* Asst appl physics, Harvard Univ, 60-63, lectr & res fel, 63-65; RES STAFF MEM, SPERRY RAND RES CTR, 65- *Mem:* Inst Elec & Electronics Engrs; Am Phys Soc; Magnetics Soc. *Res:* Plasma physics; optical signal processing; optical memories; magnetic materials; magnetic recording. *Mailing Add:* 119 Willis Rd Sudbury MA 01776

MALOOF, FARAHE, b Boston, Mass, Jan 24, 21; m 47; c 2. INTERNAL MEDICINE, ENDOCRINOLOGY. *Educ:* Harvard Univ, BA, 42; Tufts Univ, MD, 45. *Prof Exp:* Asst, 54-60, instr, 60-64, clin assoc, 64-66, asst prof, 66-72, assoc prof, 72-81, PROF MED, HARVARD MED SCH, 81-; PHYSICIAN, MASS GEN HOSP, 73- *Concurrent Pos:* USPHS fel, Mass Gen Hosp, 49-51; asst res med, 51-52, teaching fel med, 52-54; asst med, Mass Gen Hosp, 54-60, assoc physician, 65-73; sr res assoc, Grad Dept Biochem, Brandeis Univ, 58-64, adj assoc prof, 64-; chief thyroid unit, Mass Gen Hosp, 66-80. *Mem:* Am Thyroid Asn; Am Fedn Clin Res; Endocrine Soc; Am Soc Clin Invest; Am Col Physicians. *Res:* Biochemistry and pharmacology of the thyroid. *Mailing Add:* Thyroid Unit Mass Gen Hosp Boston MA 02114

MALOOF, GILES WILSON, b San Bernardino, Calif, Jan 4, 32; m 58; c 2. MATHEMATICS, GEOPHYSICS. *Educ:* Univ Calif, Berkeley, BA, 53; Univ Ore, MA, 58; Ore State Univ, PhD(math), 62. *Prof Exp:* Engr, Creole Petrol Corp, 53-54; engr, US Navy Ord Res Labs, 58-59; instr math, Ore State Univ, 61-62, asst prof, 62-68, res assoc geophys oceanog, 63-68; head dept, 68-75, dean grad sch, 70-75, PROF MATH, BOISE STATE COL, 68- *Concurrent Pos:* Dir, Northwest Col & Univ Asn Sci, 73-; dir, Northwest Sci Asn, 77-; vis prof, Ore State Univ, 77-78. *Mem:* Soc Indust & Appl Math; Am Math Soc; Math Asn Am. *Res:* Numerical filtering as applied in the interpretation of geophysical data; nonlinear functional analysis applied to integral equations. *Mailing Add:* Dept of Math Boise State Col 1907 Campus Dr Boise ID 83707

MALOTKY, LYLE OSCAR, b New London, Wis, Apr 14, 46; m 68; c 2. POLYMER CHEMISTRY. *Educ:* Augsburg Col, BA, 68; Univ Akron, PhD(polymer sci), 73; George Wash Univ, MEA, 80. *Prof Exp:* chemist, Naval Explosive Ord Disposal Facil, 73-81, HEAD, CHEM ENG DIV, NAVAL EXPLOSIVE ORD DISPOSAL TECHNOL CTR, 81- *Mem:* Am Chem Soc. *Res:* Applications of polymeric materials; explosive analysis and detection. *Mailing Add:* Naval Explosive Ord Disposal Technol Ctr Code 503 Indian Head MD 20640

MALOUF, EMIL EDWARD, b Ogden, Utah, Mar 23, 16; m 42; c 4. HYDROMETALLURGY, INORGANIC CHEMISTRY. *Educ:* Univ Utah, BS, 39. *Prof Exp:* Chief exp mfg, Ogden Arsenal, US Army, 40-44; res chemist, Kennecott Copper Corp, 47-52, proj, develop engr, 52-65, chief sect hydrometall develop, 65-77; CONSULT, 77- *Concurrent Pos:* Adj prof, Univ Utah. *Honors & Awards:* Robert Earll McConnell Award, Am Inst Mech Engrs, 72. *Mem:* Am Inst Mech Engrs; Am Inst Mining, Metall & Petrol Engrs; Am Soc Metals; Sigma Xi. *Res:* Analytical procedures and processes for recovery of rhenium; copper leaching processes from mine waste; copper precipitation units for efficient high volume recovery of copper from solutions. *Mailing Add:* 132 Dorchester Dr Salt Lake City UT 84103

MALOUF, GEORGE M, b San Diego, Calif, Mar 21, 50; m 76; c 1. PROCESS CHEMISTRY, SURFACE CHEMISTRY. *Educ:* Univ Calif, San Diego, BA, 72; Santa Barbara, PhD(inorg chem), 77. *Prof Exp:* Fel surface chem, Aerospace Corp, Univ Southern Calif, 77-78; RES CHEMIST INORG CHEM, US BORAX RES CORP, 78- *Mem:* Am Chem Soc. *Res:* Photochemistry of transition metal complexes; surface chemistry of aluminum with emphasis on developing corrosion resistant coatings; solubility kinetics and thermodynamics of borate solutions; scale prediction in process equipment; fine particle analysis; corrosion of process equipment. *Mailing Add:* 11330 Delphinium Ave Fountain Valley CA 92708

MALOUF, ROBERT EDWARD, b Dallas, Tex, Aug 21, 46; m 66; c 2. MARINE BIOLOGY, FISH BIOLOGY. *Educ:* Univ Mont, BA, 68; Ore State Univ, MS, 70, PhD(fisheries), 77. *Prof Exp:* Res biologist aquacult, Col Marine Studies, Univ Del, 70-72; res asst fisheries, Ore State Univ, 72-77; ASST PROF MARINE BIOL, STATE UNIV NY, STONY BROOK, 77- *Concurrent Pos:* Sea Grant prof, NY Sea Grant Inst, 77-80. *Mem:* Nat Shellfisheries Asn; World Mariculture Soc. *Res:* Biology of commercially important bivalve molluscs, particularly reproductive processes and growth energetics; application of findings to resource management and aquaculture. *Mailing Add:* Marine Sci Res Ctr State Univ of NY Stony Brook NY 11794

MALOWANY, ALFRED STEPHEN, b Joliette, Que, Aug 16, 39; m 64; c 2. ELECTRICAL ENGINEERING. *Educ:* McGill Univ, BEng, 59, MEng, 62, PhD(control), 67. *Prof Exp:* Lectr, 60-65, asst prof, 67-77, ASSOC PROF ELEC ENG, MCGILL UNIV, 77- *Mem:* Can Pulp & Paper Asn; Inst Elec & Electronics Engrs. *Res:* Biological and industrial modelling; control and optimization; computer graphics. *Mailing Add:* Dept of Elec Eng McGill Univ Montreal PQ Can

MALOY, JOHN OWEN, b Orange, NJ, Feb 7, 32; div; c 1. HIGH ENERGY PHYSICS, SPACE PHYSICS. *Educ:* Univ Ariz, BS, 54; Calif Inst Technol, PhD(physics), 61. *Prof Exp:* Group leader systs anal, Jet Propulsion Lab, Calif Inst Technol, 60-61, res fel physics, Syncrotron Lab, 61-63, sr res fel, 63-67; mgr advan develop div, Analog Technol Corp, 67-71; chief scientist, Beckman Instruments Inc, 71-74; staff scientist, Ball Bros Res Corp, 74-77; res staff physicist, Univ Southern Calif, 74-77; PRES, MOUNTAIN INSTRUMENTS CORP, 77- *Concurrent Pos:* Consult, Electro-Optical Systs, Inc, Calif, 63-66, Beckman Instruments, Inc, 74-, Jet Propulsion Lab, Calif Inst Technol, 76- & Melcon, 76- *Mem:* AAAS; Am Phys Soc; Am Geophys Union. *Res:* Photoproduction of pi mesons; accelerator physics and technology; development of radio frequency acceleration system; solar and planetary science; space science instrumentation systems design; instrument program management. *Mailing Add:* 4591 Green Tree Lane Irvine CA 92715

MALOY, JOSEPH T, b Mt Pleasant, Pa, Apr 19, 39; m 70; c 1. ANALYTICAL CHEMISTRY, ELECTROCHEMISTRY. *Educ:* St Vincent Col, BA, 61; Univ Tex, Austin, MA, 67, PhD(chem), 70. *Prof Exp:* Teacher, Mt Pleasant area schs, Pa, 61-65; asst prof, WVa Univ, 70-75, assoc prof, 75-79; ASSOC PROF CHEM, SETON HALL UNIV, 79- *Concurrent Pos:* Sr investr, Air Force Aero-Propulsion Lab, Wright-Patterson AFB, 78-81; sr investr, Res Inst, Univ Dayton, 81-; prin, Electro-Anal Consult Assocs, 81-

Mem: Am Chem Soc; Electrochem Soc; Sigma Xi. *Res:* Electrochemistry; electroanalytical techniques; computer applications; digital simulation of problems involving mass transport and chemical reactions; high energy density batteries; chromatography. *Mailing Add:* Dept of Chem Seton Hall Univ South Orange NJ 07079

MALOY, OTIS CLEO, JR, b Coeur d'Alene, Idaho, Jan 19, 30; m 53. PLANT PATHOLOGY. *Educ:* Univ Idaho, BS, 51, MS, 55; Cornell Univ, PhD, 58. *Prof Exp:* Asst plant path, Cornell Univ, 55-58; forest pathologist, US Forest Serv, 58-59; res forester, Potlatch Forests, Inc, 59-63; exten plant pathologist, 63-76, PROF PLANT PATH, WASH STATE UNIV, 76- *Mem:* Am Phytopath Soc. *Res:* Ecology and physiology of soil microorganisms; root rots; diseases of forest trees. *Mailing Add:* Dept of Plant Path Wash State Univ Pullman WA 99164

MALOZEMOFF, PLATO, b Russia, 1909. MINING ENGINEERING. *Prof Exp:* Chmn & chief exec officer, Newmont Mining Corp. *Concurrent Pos:* Pres & dir, Resurrection Mining Co, Newmont Exploration Ltd & Carlin Gold Mining Co; chmn, Newmont Mines Ltd & Newmont Proprietary Ltd; chmn & dir, Idarado Mining Co; vpres & dir, Newmont Mining Corp Can, Ltd; vchmn & dir, Magma Copper Co; dir, O'Okiep Copper Co, Cassiar Asbestos Corp, Ltd, SPeru Copper Corp, Sherritt Gordon Mines, Ltd, Atlantic Cement Co Inc, Peabody Coal Co, Bankers Trust Co, Palabora Mining Co, Ltd, Tsumeb Corp, Ltd, Foote Mineral Co, Bethlehem Copper Corp, Browning-Ferris Industs & Highveld Steel & Vanadium Corp; trustee, Am Mus Natural Hist; chmn, Tolstoy Found. *Mem:* Nat Acad Eng. *Mailing Add:* Newmont Mining Corp 300 Park Ave New York NY 10022

MALSBERGER, RICHARD GRIFFITH, b Philadelphia, Pa, Jan 12, 23; m 44; c 1. BIOLOGY. *Educ:* Lehigh Univ, BA, 48, MS, 49, PhD(bact), 58. *Prof Exp:* Mem staff, Biol Prod Dept, Merck Sharp & Dohme, 50-53, res assoc virol, 53-57, mgr control, 57-59; from asst prof to assoc prof, 59-66, PROF BIOL, LEHIGH UNIV, 66- *Mem:* AAAS; Am Inst Biol Sci; Tissue Cult Asn; Am Soc Microbiol. *Res:* Viral vaccines, immunology and multiplication; viral diseases of freshwater fishes; immunology. *Mailing Add:* Dept Biol Lehigh Univ Bethlehem PA 18015

MALSKY, STANLEY JOSEPH, b New York, NY, July 15, 25; m 65; c 2. RADIOLOGICAL PHYSICS, MEDICAL PHYSICS. *Educ:* NY Univ, BSc, 46, MA, 50, MSc, 53, PhD, 63. *Prof Exp:* Nuclear physicist, US Navy, 50-54; asst chief radiother, Vet Admin Hosp, Bronx, 54-73; PRES, RADIOL PHYSICS ASSOCS, INC, 73- *Concurrent Pos:* Asst prof, NY Univ, 59-63; res collab, Med Div, Brookhaven Nat Lab, 60-67; co-dir & prof radiol sci, Manhattan Col, 63-74; chief physicist, Fordham Hosp, 71-; res prof radiol, Sch Med, NY Univ, 74-76. *Honors & Awards:* James Picker Award Res Dosimetry. *Mem:* Fel AAAS; fel Am Pub Health Asn; Royal Soc Health; Am Asn Physicists Med; Health Physics Soc. *Res:* Solid state dosimetry; medical and radiological physics. *Mailing Add:* Radiol Physics Assocs Inc 809 Hartsdale Rd White Plains NY 10607

MALT, RONALD A, b Pittsburgh, Pa, Nov 12, 31; m 51; c 3. SURGERY, MOLECULAR BIOLOGY. *Educ:* Wash Univ, AB, 51; Harvard Univ, MD, 55; Am Bd Surg, dipl, 62; Bd Thoracic Surg, dipl, 63. *Prof Exp:* Intern surg, Mass Gen Hosp, 55-56, resident, 58-62; asst, 62-64, instr, 64-67, assoc, 67-68, from asst prof to assoc prof, 68-75, PROF SURG, HARVARD MED SCH, 75-; CHIEF GASTROENTEROL SURG, MASS GEN HOSP, 70- *Concurrent Pos:* USPHS spec res fel biol, Mass Inst Technol, 62-63, fel, Sch Advan Study, 63-64; Am Heart Asn estab investr, 63-68; res assoc, Mass Inst Technol, 62-64, from asst surgeon to surgeon, Mass Gen Hosp, 62-; assoc surgeon, Shriners Burns Inst, 67- *Mem:* Am Surg Asn; Am Soc Clin Invest; Soc Develop Biol; Am Soc Cell Biol; Am Physiol Soc. *Res:* Regeneration; molecular events in renal, hepatic, and enteric growth and neoplasia; liver, biliary and portal-system surgery; replantation of limbs. *Mailing Add:* Mass Gen Hosp Boston MA 02114

MALTBY, FREDERICK L(ATHROP), b Bradford, Pa, Dec 14, 17. ELECTRICAL ENGINEERING. *Educ:* Grove City Col, BS, 40; Univ Buffalo, MA, 43. *Prof Exp:* Fel, Radium Lab, State Inst Malignant Dis, NY, 40-42; instr physics, Univ Buffalo, 42-44; elec eng, Rudloph Wurlitzer Co, 44; from sr engr to tech dir measurement & control, Bristol Co, 44-52, tech dir, Fielden Instrument Div, 52-57; PRES, DREXELBROOK ENG CO, 57- *Mem:* Am Phys Soc; Instrument Soc Am; Inst Elec & Electronics Engrs. *Mailing Add:* Drexelbrook Controls Inc 205 Keith Valley Rd Horsham PA 19044

MALTENFORT, GEORGE GUNTHER, b Landsberg, Ger, Aug 13, 13; US citizen; m 46; c 1. CHEMISTRY. *Educ:* Northwestern Univ, BS, 34. *Prof Exp:* Chemist, Transparent Package Co, 34-42 & 45-46; chemist, Container Div Lab, Container Corp Am, 46-58, tech dir, 58-78; CONSULT, 78- *Concurrent Pos:* Dir, Res & Develop Assocs, 65-68 & 74-76; mem packaging comt, Nat Acad Sci-Nat Res Coun, 74-77. *Honors & Awards:* Container Div Medal, Tech Asn Pulp & Paper Indust, 67, Tappi Gold Medal, 79. *Mem:* Am Chem Soc; Am Soc Qual Control; Tech Asn Pulp & Paper Indust; Am Soc Test & Mat. *Res:* Packaging, sampling, statistics and development of test methods and instruments. *Mailing Add:* 3355 Capitol St Skokie IL 60076

MALTER, MARGARET QUINN, b Philadelphia, Pa, May 12, 26; m 51; c 2. ORGANIC CHEMISTRY. *Educ:* Bryn Mawr Col, BA, 47, MA, 48, PhD, 52. *Prof Exp:* From instr to asst prof, Drexel Inst, 52-57; from asst prof to assoc prof, 57-69, PROF CHEM, IMMACULATA COL, PA, 69- *Mem:* AAAS; Am Chem Soc. *Res:* Reaction mechanisms. *Mailing Add:* Dept of Chem Immaculata Col Immaculata PA 19345

MALTESE, GEORGE J, b Middletown, Conn, June 24, 31; m 56; c 2. MATHEMATICS. *Educ:* Wesleyan Univ, BA, 53; Yale Univ, PhD(math), 60. *Prof Exp:* NATO fel, Univ Gottingen, 60-61; instr math, Mass Inst Technol, 61-63; from asst prof to prof, Univ Md, College Park, 63-74; PROF MATH, UNIV MUNSTER, GER, 74- *Concurrent Pos:* Vis prof, Univ Frankfurt, 66-67 & 70-71, Univ Palermo, 70-71, Univ Kuwait, 77 & Univ Bari, 79. *Mem:* Am Math Soc; Austrian Math Soc; Ital Math Soc; Ger Math Soc. *Res:* Functional analysis with emphasis on Banach algebra theory and the spectral theory of linear operators. *Mailing Add:* Math Inst Univ Munster Roxeler Str 64 44 Munster West Germany

MALTHANER, W(ILLIAM) A(MOND), b Columbus, Ohio, July 9, 15; m 50; c 2. ELECTRICAL ENGINEERING, SYSTEMS RESEARCH & ADMINISTRATION. *Educ:* Rensselaer Polytech Inst, BEE, 37. *Prof Exp:* Mem tech staff, Bell Tel Labs, 37-58, systs res engr, 58-63, systs develop engr, 63-75; CONSULT COMMUN SYSTS, 75- *Concurrent Pos:* Consult, Consult Commun Engrs, Inc, Villanova, Pa, 75- *Mem:* AAAS; fel Inst Elec & Electronics Engrs. *Res:* Transmission, handling and storage of information; complex communication switching systems; electronic computing and control systems. *Mailing Add:* 3001 Seventh Ave W Bradenton FL 33505

MALTZ, MARTIN SIDNEY, b Bronx, NY, Jan 6, 41; m 69; c 2. MODEL IMAGING SYSTEMS. *Educ:* Rensselaer Polytech Inst, BSEE, 62; Mass Inst Technol, MS, 63, PhD(solid state physics), 68. *Prof Exp:* SR SCIENTIST ELEC ENG & SOLID STATE PHYSICS, XEROX RES, 68- *Mem:* Inst Elec & Electronics Engrs. *Res:* Xerography; image science. *Mailing Add:* Wilson Technol Ctr 800 Phillips Rd Webster NY 14580

MALTZ, MICHAEL D, b Brooklyn, NY, Dec 18, 38; m 66; c 3. OPERATIONS RESEARCH. *Educ:* Rensselaer Polytech Inst, BEE, 59; Stanford Univ, MSEE, 61, PhD(elec eng), 63. *Prof Exp:* Res assoc control systs, Tech Univ, Denmark, 63-64; staff assoc systs eng, Arthur D Little, Inc,, 64-69; opers res analyst, Nat Inst Law Enforcement & Criminal Justice, 69-72; dir grad studies, Dept Criminal Justice, 73-74 & 77-78, assoc prof criminal justice & syts eng, 72-80, ASSOC PROF CRIMINAL JUSTICE & QUANT METHODS, UNIV ILL, CHICAGO CIRCLE, 80- *Concurrent Pos:* Lectr, Grad Sch Eng, Northeastern Univ, 65; vis lectr, Opers Res Soc Am & Inst Mgt Sci, 73-75; eval consult to numerous agencies & industs, 73-; mem bd dirs, Int Pub Prog Anal, St Louis, 74-80; consult, Task Force on Criminal Justice Res & Develop, Nat Adv Comn on Criminal Justice Standards & Goals, 75-76, Task Force on Bid-Rigging, Nat Dist Attys Asn, Econ Crime Proj, 77-78, Rand Corp, 75-, Police Exec Res Forum, 76-; mem acad adv coun, 10th Cong Dist Ill, 75-80; mem bd dirs, Bus & Prof People for Pub Interest, Chicago, 76-; consult ed, J Res Crime & Delinquency, 76-; mem working group on FBI Comput Criminal Hist Prog, Off Technol Assessment, Cong US, 77-78; adv, Deadly Force Proj, Chicago Law Enforcement Study Group & MINS Proj, 77-78. *Mem:* Fel AAAS; Opers Res Soc Am; Int Asn Chiefs Police; Sigma Xi; Acad Criminal Justice Sci. *Res:* Criminal justice system research. *Mailing Add:* Dept Criminal Justice Box 4348 Univ Ill Chicago Cir Chicago IL 60680

MALTZEFF, EUGENE M, b Khabarovsk, Russia, Oct 31, 12; US citizen; m 46; c 2. FISHERIES. *Educ:* U Wash, BS, 39. *Prof Exp:* Aquatic biologist, Fish & Wildlife Serv, US Bur Com Fisheries, 44-48, fishery res biologist, 42-57, fishery biologist, 58-68, foreign fisheries analyst, Pac Northwest Region I, 68-70, foreign fisheries analyst, Nat Marine Fisheries Serv, 70-74; CONSULT MARINE AFFAIRS, 75- *Mem:* Am Fisheries Soc; Am Inst Fishery Res Biol. *Res:* Pacific salmon; stream improvement; Indian fisheries; foreign fishing. *Mailing Add:* 4501 Stanford Ave NE Seattle WA 98105

MALUEG, KENNETH WILBUR, b Appleton, Wis, Apr 19, 38; m 64; c 2. LIMNOLOGY. *Educ:* Univ Wis, BS, 60, MS, 63, PhD(zool), 66. *Prof Exp:* RES AQUATIC BIOLOGIST, CORVALLIS ENVIRON RES LAB, ENVIRON PROTECTION AGENCY, 66- *Mem:* Am Soc Limnol & Oceanog; Sigma Xi; Amer Inst Biol Sci; Int Asn Theoret & Appl Limnol; NAm Lake Mgt Soc. *Res:* Lake restoration; eutrophication control; nonpoint source pollution control; sediment; sediment-water exchange; sediment bioassays. *Mailing Add:* Corvallis Environ Res Lab 200 SW 35th St Corvallis OR 97330

MALVEAUX, FLOYD J, b Opelousas, La, Jan 11, 40; m 65; c 4. MICROBIOLOGY, MICROBIAL PHYSIOLOGY. *Educ:* Creighton Univ, BS, 61; Loyola Univ, La, MS, 64; Mich State Univ, PhD(microbiol), 68. *Prof Exp:* Instr soil microbiol, Mich State Univ, 68; ASST PROF MICROBIOL, COL MED, HOWARD UNIV, 68- *Mem:* AAAS; Am Soc Microbiol. *Res:* Characterization of enzymes and extracellular proteins of pathogenic bacteria as these products relate to virulence; physiology of microorganisms associated with plaque formation and periodontal disease. *Mailing Add:* 2041 Georgia Ave NW Washington DC 20001

MALVEN, PAUL VERNON, b Annapolis, Md, Oct 24, 38; m 63; c 2. NEUROENDOCRINOLOGY, REPRODUCTIVE PHYSIOLOGY. *Educ:* Univ Ill, Urbana, BS, 60; Cornell Univ, PhD(animal physiol), 64. *Prof Exp:* NIH fel, Univ Calif, Los Angeles, 64-65; from asst to assoc prof animal sci, 66-72, PROF ANIMAL SCI, PURDUE UNIV, 72- *Mem:* Am Physiol Soc; Endocrine Soc; Soc Neurosci; Am Soc Animal Sci; Soc Study Reproduction. *Res:* Neuroendocrinology of reproduction. *Mailing Add:* Dept of Animal Sci Purdue Univ West Lafayette IN 47906

MALVICK, ALLAN J(AMES), b Chicago, Ill, Oct 15, 35; m 63; c 3. ENGINEERING MECHANICS. *Educ:* Univ Notre Dame, BS, 57, MS, 59, ScD(eng sci), 61. *Prof Exp:* Asst prof eng sci, Univ Notre Dame, 61-65; assoc prof civil eng, 65-71, assoc prof optical sci, 67-71, PROF CIVIL ENG, UNIV ARIZ, 71- *Mem:* Am Soc Civil Engrs; Optical Soc Am. *Res:* Deformation of optical mirrors. *Mailing Add:* Dept of Civil Eng Univ of Ariz Tucson AZ 85721

MALVILLE, JOHN MCKIM, b San Francisco, Calif, Apr 24, 34; m 60; c 2. ASTROPHYSICS. *Educ:* Calif Inst Technol, BS, 56; Univ Colo, PhD(astrophys), 61. *Prof Exp:* Res assoc astron, Univ Mich, 62-63, asst prof, 63-65; mem sr staff solar physics, High Altitude Observ, 65-70; asst dean col arts & sci, 69-70, assoc prof, 70-73, PROF ASTRO GEOPHYS, UNIV COLO, BOULDER, 73-, CHMN DEPT, 77- *Concurrent Pos:* Am Astron

Soc vis prof, 64- *Mem:* AAAS; Am Astron Soc; Int Astron Union. *Res:* Solar physics; radio astronomy; auroral, atomic and molecular physics; interstellar medium; philosophy of science; science education. *Mailing Add:* Dept of Astro Geophys Univ of Colo Boulder CO 80302

MALVIN, RICHARD L, b Aug 19, 27; US citizen; m; c 2. PHYSIOLOGY. *Educ:* McGill Univ, BSc, 50; NY Univ, MS, 54; Univ Cincinnati, PhD(physiol), 56. *Prof Exp:* Res assoc, 56-57, from instr to assoc prof, 57-67, PROF PHYSIOL, MED SCH, UNIV MICH, 67- *Concurrent Pos:* Lederle med fac award, 59-62; USPHS career develop award, 62-72. *Mem:* AAAS; Am Physiol Soc; Am Soc Nephrology. *Res:* Renal physiology; salt and water balance; control of secretion of renin and antidiuretic hormone. *Mailing Add:* Dept of Physiol 7730 Med Sci II Univ of Mich Ann Arbor MI 48104

MALY, EDWARD J, b Troy, NY, Nov 10, 42; m 67. ECOLOGY, EVOLUTION. *Educ:* Univ Rochester, BS, 64; Princeton Univ, PhD(biol), 68. *Prof Exp:* Asst prof biol, Tufts Univ, 68-75; asst prof, 75-77, ASSOC PROF BIOL, CONCORDIA UNIV, 77- *Mem:* AAAS; Ecol Soc Am; Am Soc Limnol & Oceanog. *Res:* Population dynamics; predator-prey interactions and population growth rates; life histories and diversity of fresh-water animals. *Mailing Add:* Dept of Biol Sci Concordia Univ 1455 De Maisonneuve Blvd W Montreal PQ H3G 1M8 Can

MALZAHN, DON EDWIN, b Perry, Okla, June 8, 45; m 78. INDUSTRIAL ENGINEERING, REHABILITATION ENGINEERING. *Educ:* Okla State Univ, BS, 68, MS, 69, PhD(indust eng), 75. *Prof Exp:* Industr engr, Charles Mach Works, 70-73; asst prof, 73-81, ASSOC PROF INDUST ENG, WICHITA STATE UNIV, 81- *Concurrent Pos:* Dir proj 1, Rehab Eng Ctr, Wichita State Univ, 76- *Mem:* Am Inst Indust Engrs; Am Soc Eng Educ; Human Factors Soc. *Res:* Development of job modification and adaptive device strategies for the employment of the severely handicapped in mainstream industry. *Mailing Add:* Dept of Indust Eng Wichita State Univ Wichita KS 67208

MALZAHN, RAY ANDREW, b Ft Madison, Iowa, July 8, 29; m 53; c 2. ORGANIC CHEMISTRY, ACADEMIC ADMINISTRATION. *Educ:* Gustavus Adolphus Col, BA, 51; Univ NDak, MS, 53; Univ Md, PhD(org chem), 62. *Prof Exp:* Assoc prof chem, WTex State Univ, 63-67, dean col arts & sci, 67-71, vpres acad affairs, 71-77, prof chem, 67-80; PROF CHEM & DEAN, SCH ARTS & SCI, MO SOUTHERN STATE COL, 80- *Concurrent Pos:* Fel, Univ Ariz, 61-63. *Mem:* Am Chem Soc; Sigma Xi; AAAS. *Res:* Pyrolysis of allyl and propargyl ethers; polymerization of monomers derived from natural products; synthesis of arylsilanes containing carboxyl groups. *Mailing Add:* Dean Sch Arts & Sci Mo Southern State Col Joplin MO 64801

MALZER, GARY LEE, b Nebraska City, Nebr, Nov 8, 45; m 68; c 1. SOIL FERTILITY, CHEMISTRY. *Educ:* Univ Nebr, BS, 67, MS, 70; Purdue Univ, PhD(agron soil fertil), 73. *Prof Exp:* Soil conservationist, Soil Conservation Serv, USDA, 67-68; res assoc agron, Purdue Univ, 73-74; asst prof, 74-79, ASSOC PROF SOIL SCI, UNIV MINN, ST PAUL, 79- *Mem:* Am Soc Agron; Soil Sci Soc Am; Soil Conserv Soc Am. *Res:* Soil fertility and plant nutrition, particularly methodology to characterize and improve fertilizer use efficiency for agricultural production. *Mailing Add:* Dept of Soil Sci Univ of Minn St Paul MN 55108

MAMANTOV, GLEB, b Karsava, Latvia, Apr 10, 31; US citizen; m 56; c 3. ANALYTICAL & INORGANIC CHEMISTRY. *Educ:* La State Univ, BS, 53, MS, 54, PhD(chem), 57. *Prof Exp:* Res chemist electrochem dept, E I du Pont de Nemours & Co, 57-58; instr & res assoc chem, Univ Wis, 60-61; from asst to assoc prof, 61-71, PROF CHEM, UNIV TENN, KNOXVILLE, 71-, HEAD DEPT, 79- *Concurrent Pos:* Consult, Oak Ridge Nat Lab, 62-; NATO sr fel, Ger, 71. *Mem:* Fel AAAS; Am Chem Soc; Electrochem Soc; fel Am Inst Chemists. *Res:* Electrochemistry and chemistry in molten salts; fluorine chemistry; electroanalytical chemistry; matrix isolation spectroscopy. *Mailing Add:* Dept Chem Univ Tenn Knoxville TN 37916

MAMAY, SERGIUS HARRY, b Akron, Ohio, May 20, 20; m 53; c 2. PALEOBOTANY. *Educ:* Univ Akron, BS, 44; Washington Univ, MA, 48, PhD(bot), 50. *Prof Exp:* Asst bot, Washington Univ, 49-50; Guggenheim fel, Cambridge Univ, 50-51; PALEOZOIC PALEOBOTANIST, US GEOL SURV, 51- *Mem:* Paleont Soc; Bot Soc Am. *Res:* Permian floras of southwestern United States; American coal ball floras. *Mailing Add:* US Geol Surv US Nat Mus Washington DC 20560

MAMELAK, JOSEPH SIMON, b Lodz, Poland, Dec 14, 23; US citizen; m 59; c 2. COMPUTER SCIENCE, APPLIED MATHEMATICS. *Educ:* McGill Univ, BS, 45, MS, 46; Univ Pittsburgh, PhD(math), 49. *Prof Exp:* Asst prof math, Univ WVa, 53-56; sr analyst opers res, Univac, Sperry Rand Corp, 56-59; mgr sci appln, RCA, 59-62, proj mgr automated design, 62-65; head dept, 65-71, PROF MATH, COMMUNITY COL PHILADELPHIA, 66- *Concurrent Pos:* Consult, City Philadelphia, 65-; mem, var med & educ insts, 66-; mem, Am Stand Inst, 64- *Mem:* Am Math Soc; Am Statist Asn; Asn Comput Mach; Math Asn Am; Can Math Cong. *Res:* Water pollution models using computer simulation; automated circuit design and integrated circuit layout using computers; computer utilization in schools. *Mailing Add:* 70 Knollwood Dr Cherry Hill NJ 08034

MAMER, ORVAL ALBERT, chemistry, see previous edition

MAMET, BERNARD LEON, b Brussels, Belg, Feb 7, 37; m 63; c 1. GEOLOGY. *Educ:* Free Univ Brussels, LSc, 57, PhD(stratig), 62; French Petrol Inst, cert eng geol, 59; Univ Calif, Berkeley, MA, 60. *Prof Exp:* Researcher, Royal Inst Natural Sci, Belg, Brussels, 56-61; asst researcher, Nat Found Sci Res, Belg, 63-65; from asst prof to assoc prof, 65-76, PROF GEOL, UNIV MONTREAL, 76- *Mem:* Geol Soc Belg; Geol Soc France; Belg Soc Geol, Paleont & Hydrol; Am Asn Petrol Geologists; Soc Econ Paleontologists & Mineralogists. *Res:* Carboniferous microfacies. *Mailing Add:* Univ of Montreal PO Box 6128 Montreal PQ Can

MAMIYA, RICHARD T, b Honolulu, Hawaii, Mar 8, 25; m 50; c 8. THORACIC SURGERY, CARDIOVASCULAR SURGERY. *Educ:* Univ Hawaii, BSc, 50; St Louis Univ, MD, 54. *Prof Exp:* From instr to sr instr surg, Sch Med, St Louis Univ, 59-61, dir sect surg, Cochran Vet Admin Hosp, 59-61; from assoc prof to prof surg, Sch Med, Univ Hawaii, Manoa, 67-74, chmn dept, 67-74. *Concurrent Pos:* Consult, US Army Tripler Gen Hosp, 68- *Mem:* AMA; Am Col Surg. *Mailing Add:* 1380 Lusitana St Suite 710 Honolulu HI 96813

MAMOLA, KARL CHARLES, b Greenport, NY, May 23, 42; m 63; c 1. SOLID STATE PHYSICS. *Educ:* State Univ NY, Stony Brook, BS, 63; Fla State Univ, MS, 65; Dartmouth Col, PhD(physics), 73. *Prof Exp:* From instr to asst prof physics, 65-69, asst prof, 72, ASSOC PROF PHYSICS, APPALACHIAN STATE UNIV, 72-, CHAIRPERSON DEPT, 76- *Mem:* Am Phys Soc; Am Asn Physics Teachers; Nat Sci Teachers Asn; Sigma Xi. *Res:* Point deflects in crystals at high pressures using optical absorption and magnetic resonance spectroscopy. *Mailing Add:* Dept of Physics Appalachian State Univ Boone NC 28608

MAMRAK, SANDRA ANN, b Cleveland, Ohio, Sept 8, 44. COMPUTER SCIENCES. *Educ:* Notre Dame Col, BS, 67; Univ Ill, Urbana-Champaign, MS, 73, PhD(comput sci), 75. *Prof Exp:* Comput scientist, Nat Bur Standards, 75-79; asst prof, 75-80, ASSOC PROF COMPUT SCI, OHIO STATE UNIV, 80-; MEM TECH STAFF, BELL LABS, 80- *Concurrent Pos:* Invited lectr, Urbino Italy, Sarajevo, Yugoslavia & Bogata, Columbia, 80 & Lisbon, Portugal, 81; fac appointee, Lawrence Livermore Nat Lab, 81. *Mem:* Asn Comput Mach. *Res:* Software support for distributed processing systems with heterogeneous computer sites having functional and administrative autonomy. *Mailing Add:* Dept of Comput & Info Sci Ohio State Univ Columbus OH 43210

MAN, EUGENE H, b Scranton, Pa, Dec 14, 23; m 45; c 4. MARINE GEOCHEMISTRY. *Educ:* Oberlin Col, AB, 48; Duke Univ, PhD(chem), 52. *Prof Exp:* Res chemist chem dept, E I du Pont de Nemours & Co, 51-58, textile fibers dept, 58-60, supvr nylon tech div, 60-61, sr supvr, 61-62; coordr res, 62-66, dean res & sponsored progs, 66-79, PROF CHEM & MARINE & ATMOSPHERIC CHEM, UNIV MIAMI, 68- *Concurrent Pos:* Vis investr, Scripps Inst Oceanog, Univ Calif, San Diego, 71-72. *Mem:* AAAS; Am Chem Soc; Sigma Xi; fel Am Inst Chem. *Res:* Characterization of reactions in deep ocean sediments involving racemization and diagenesis of amino acids; organic chemistry of ocean sediments; geochemistry of amino acids and porphyrins in deep-sea drilling cores; reactions involving conversion of chlorophyll to petroporphyrins to develop thermal models of oceanic basins. *Mailing Add:* Dept Chem Univ Miami Coral Gables FL 33124

MAN, EVELYN BROWER, b Lawrence, NY, Oct 7, 04. CLINICAL CHEMISTRY. *Educ:* Wellesley Col, AB, 25; Yale Univ, PhD(physiol chem), 32. *Prof Exp:* Instr chem, Conn Col, 25-27; technician sch med, Yale Univ, 28-29, asst, 29-30, Am Asn Univ Women fel, 33-34, from instr to asst prof psychiat, 34-50, res assoc med, 50-61; assoc mem, 61-71, EMER ASSOC MEM, INST HEALTH SCI, BROWN UNIV, 71- *Honors & Awards:* Cert Distinguished Serv, Am Thyroid Asn, 76. *Mem:* AAAS; Endocrine Soc; Am Thyroid Asn; Am Chem Soc; Am Soc Biol Chem. *Res:* Lipemia and iodemia in thyroid diseases; pregnancy and infancy; screening for neonatal hypothyroidism. *Mailing Add:* 540 Norwich-Westerly Rd North Stonington CT 06359

MANABE, SYUKURO, b Japan, Sept 9, 31; US citizen; m 61; c 2. CLIMATE DYNAMICS, CLIMATE MODELING. *Educ:* Tokyo Univ, BA, 53, MA, 55, DSc, 58. *Prof Exp:* RES METEROLOGIST CLIMATE MODELING, GEOPHYS FLUID DYNAMICS LAB, NAT OCEANIC & ATMOSPHERIC ADMIN, 58- *Concurrent Pos:* Vis prof, Dept Geol & Geophysics, Princeton Univ, 68- *Honors & Awards:* Meisinger Award, Am Meteorol Soc, 67 & Second Half Century Award, 77; Fujiwara Award, Japan Meteorol Soc, 66; Gold Medal Award, Dept Com, 70. *Mem:* Fel Am Meterol Soc; fel Am Geophys Union; Japan Meteorol Soc. *Res:* Physical mechanisms for climate variation by use of mathematical models of climate; climate change resulting from the future increase of atmospheric carbon dioxide. *Mailing Add:* Geophys Fluid Dynamics Lab/NOAA Princeton Univ PO Box 308 Princeton NJ 08540

MANAKER, ROBERT ANTHONY, b Avenel, NJ, Feb 28, 18; m 53; c 1. MICROBIOLOGY. *Educ:* Rutgers Univ, BS, 50, PhD(microbiol), 53. *Prof Exp:* Merck-Waksman res fel, Rutgers Univ, 53-54, instr microbiol, Inst Microbiol, 54-55, asst prof virol, 55-56; res microbiologist, 56-72, chief viral biol br, 72-76, CHIEF, LAB OF DNA TUMOR VIRUSES, NAT CANCER INST, 76- *Mem:* AAAS; Am Asn Cancer Res; Am Soc Microbiol. *Res:* Virus-tumor relationships. *Mailing Add:* Lab of DNA Tumor Viruses 9000 Rockville Pike Bethesda MD 20205

MANAKKIL, THOMAS JOSEPH, b Gothuruthy, India, Dec 31, 33. PHYSICS. *Educ:* Univ Kerala, BSc, 53; Univ Saugar, MSc, 58; NMex State Univ, MS, 65, PhD(physics), 67. *Prof Exp:* Instr physics, Sacred Heart Col, India, 53-55 & 57-58; from asst prof to assoc prof, 67-77, PROF PHYSICS, MARSHALL UNIV, 77- *Concurrent Pos:* NSF. *Mem:* Am Phys Soc; Am Asn Physics Teachers; Inst Fundamental Studies Asn. *Res:* Magnetic resonance; crystal field studies; nuclear physics; interactions of gamma photons with fibers. *Mailing Add:* Dept of Physics Marshall Univ Huntington WV 25701

MANASEK, FRANCIS JOHN, b New York, NY, July 22, 40. CELL BIOLOGY, DEVELOPMENTAL BIOLOGY. *Educ:* NY Univ, AB, 61; Harvard Univ, DMD, 66. *Prof Exp:* Fel anat, Harvard Med Sch, 66-68; vis investr develop biol, Carnegie Inst Washington, 68-69; from instr to asst prof anat, Harvard Med Sch, 69-74; ASSOC PROF ANAT, UNIV CHICAGO, 74-, ASSOC PROF PEDIAT & COMT DEVELOP BIOL, 80- *Concurrent Pos:* Res assoc path & cardiol, Children's Hosp, 69-74; NIH res career develop award, 71. *Honors & Awards:* Fel, Med Found, Inc, 69. *Mem:* Am

Asn Anatomists; Am Soc Cell Biol; Biophys Soc; Int Soc Heart Res; Soc Develop Biol. *Res:* Cell biology of developing cardiac muscle particularly synthesis of structural macromolecules and their role in myocardial morphogenesis. *Mailing Add:* 1025 E 57th St Chicago IL 60637

MANASEVIT, HAROLD MURRAY, b Bridgeport, Conn, Nov 1, 27; m 53; c 3. PHYSICAL INORGANIC CHEMISTRY, ORGANOMETALLIC CHEMISTRY. *Educ:* Univ Ohio, BS, 50; Pa State Univ, MS, 51; Ill Inst Technol, PhD(phys inorg chem), 59. *Prof Exp:* Chemist, Armour Res Found, 51-55; inorg chemist, US Borax Res Corp, 59-60; sr res engr, Autonetics Div, NAm Aviation, Inc, 60-61, res specialist, 61-63, sr tech specialist, 63-67, mem tech staff, NAM Rockwell, Inc, 67-70, MEM TECH STAFF, ROCKWELL INT, 70- *Honors & Awards:* 1975 Electronics Div Award, Electrochem Soc. *Mem:* Am Asn Crystal Growth; Am Chem Soc; Electrochem Soc; Sigma Xi. *Res:* Thin film growth of metals and semiconductors on semiconductors and insulating substrates; epitaxy; gas phase acid-base reactions; metalorganics; diboron compounds. *Mailing Add:* 1855 Janette Lane Anaheim CA 92802

MANASSE, FRED KURT, b Frankfurt, Ger, July 27, 35; m 56; c 5. ELECTRICAL ENGINEERING, PHYSICS. *Educ:* City Col New York, BEE, 56, MEE, 58; Princeton Univ, AM, 59, PhD(physics), 62. *Prof Exp:* Mem tech staff, Bell Tel Labs, 56-63; asst prof elec eng, City Col New York, 63-65 & Princeton Univ, 65-68; assoc prof, Dartmouth Col, 68-72; prof, chmn dept elec eng, asst dean continuing educ & dir, Ctr Teaching Innovations, Drexel Univ, 72-75; vis prof & Nat Acad Sci fel, Bucharest Inst Physics, 73; vis prof elec eng, State Univ NY, Stony Brook, 76; prof elec eng, Univ NH, 76-80; VPRES & CHIEF SCIENTIST, AETA CORP, 80- *Concurrent Pos:* Consult, Int Bus Mach Corp, NY, 59-60, Pitt Precision Prod, 60-61, Opinion Res Corp, 67-68 & US Energy Res & Develop Admin, 76-77; mem, Comt Gravitation & Relativity, 60-; mem adv comt nonionizing radiation, NJ Dept Health, 67-68; elec eng ed, Addison-Wesley Publ Corp, 67-78; ed-in-chief, T H E J; vpres, AETA Corp, 75- *Mem:* AAAS; Inst Elec & Electronics Engrs; Am Phys Soc; Am Soc Eng Educ. *Res:* Semiconductor device physics; switching circuits; memory devices; computer language and system design; general relativity; field interactions in solids; solid state devices; educational innovation; minority education; solar energy; small scale hydro; magnetics. *Mailing Add:* Aeta Corp 117 Silver St Dover NH 03820

MANASSE, ROBERT JAMES, microbiology, see previous edition

MANASSE, ROGER, b New York, NY, Apr 9, 30; m 52; c 2. PHYSICS. *Educ:* Mass Inst Technol, BS, 50, PhD(physics), 55. *Prof Exp:* Mem staff instrumentation lab, Mass Inst Technol, 50-52, Lincoln Lab, 54-59; subdept head radar dept, Mitre Corp, 59-60, assoc dept head, 60-64, dept head, 64-67; staff mem, Gen Res Corp, 67-70; independent consult, 70-71; vpres & chief scientist, Spectra Res Systs, 72-73; INDEPENDENT CONSULT, 74- *Concurrent Pos:* Mem, Air Force Sci Adv Bd, 69-78. *Mem:* Inst Elec & Electronics Eng; Sigma Xi. *Res:* Radar systems analysis and measurement theory. *Mailing Add:* 234 Canon Dr Santa Barbara CA 93105

MANASTER, ALFRED B, b Chicago, Ill, May 25, 38; m 60; c 3. MATHEMATICAL LOGIC. *Educ:* Univ Chicago, BS, 60; Cornell Univ, PhD(math), 65. *Prof Exp:* Res assoc math, Cornell Univ, 65; instr, Mass Inst Technol, 65-67; asst prof, 67-71, ASSOC PROF MATH, UNIV CALIF, SAN DIEGO, 71- *Mem:* Am Math Soc; Math Asn Am; Asn Symbolic Logic. *Res:* Recursive function theory. *Mailing Add:* Dept of Math Univ of Calif San Diego La Jolla CA 92093

MANATT, STANLEY L, b Glendale, Calif, July 13, 33; m 58; c 4. ORGANIC CHEMISTRY. *Educ:* Calif Inst Technol, BS, 55, PhD(chem, physics), 59. *Prof Exp:* Wis Alumni Res Found fel, Univ Wis, 58-59; sr scientist, Jet Propulsion Lab, Calif Inst Technol, 59-64, res specialist, 65-66, mem tech staff, 66-70, asst mgr biosci & planetology sect, 70-73, staff scientist, Sci Data Anal Sect, 73-78, STAFF SCIENTIST, INFO SYSTS RES SECT, JET PROPULSION LAB, CALIF INST TECHNOL, 78- *Concurrent Pos:* Vis prof, Inst Org Chem, Univ Cologne, 74-75 & Univ Siegen, Ger, 81; Am ed, Org Magnetic Resonance, 68-; Alexander von Humboldt Award, 74-75; Int Cancer Res Technol Transfer travel grant, Univ Siegen, 81. *Mem:* AAAS; Am Chem Soc. *Res:* Nuclear magnetic resonance; polymers; propellant and fluorocarbon chemistry; gas chromatography techniques; spacecraft material problems; extraterrestrial life detection; analytical chemistry; small-ring compounds; theoretical calculations on aromatic molecules; polypeptide synthesis; steric effects in organic molecules. *Mailing Add:* Jet Propulsion Lab 1201 E California Blvd Pasadena CA 91109

MANCALL, ELLIOTT L, b Hartford, Conn, July 31, 27; m; c 2. NEUROPATHOLOGY, NEUROLOGY. *Educ:* Trinity Col, BS, 48; Univ Pa, MD, 52; Am Bd Psychiat & Neurol, dipl & cert neurol, 59. *Prof Exp:* Asst prof neurol, Jefferson Med Col, 53-64, assoc prof, 64-65; prof med & neurol, 65-75, CHMN DEPT NUEROLOGY, HAHNEMANN MED COL, 75- *Concurrent Pos:* Fulbright fel, Nat Hosp Neurol Dis, London, 54-55; teaching gel neuropath, Harvard Med Sch, 56-57; mem vis fac, Sch Med, Emory Univ, 64; vis lectr, US Naval Hosp, 64-; consult, Valley Forge Gen Army Hosp, 67-74 & Pennhurst State Sch & Hosp, 68-73; chief neurol serv, Philadelphia Gen Hosp, 69-74. Mem. *Mem:* fel Am Acad Neurol; Am Asn Neuropath; Am Neurological Asn; Soc Neurosci; Asn Univ Prof Neurol. *Res:* Neurology and neuropathology of metabolic diseases of the nervous system. *Mailing Add:* 230 N Broad St Philadelphia PA 19107

MANCERA, OCTAVIO, b Oaxaca, Mex, Mar 28, 19; m 50; c 4. ORGANIC CHEMISTRY. *Educ:* Nat Univ Mex, MS, 43; Oxford Univ, DPhil(chem), 46. *Prof Exp:* Lectr org chem, Nat Univ Mex, 47-50; res asst steroid chem, SA group leader, 53-56, asst res dir, 57-59, process res dir, 60-61, prod dir, 62-63, dir opers, 64-68, GEN MGR CHEM DIV, SYNTEX, 68- *Res:* Chemistry of penicillin and natural products; steroid chemistry. *Mailing Add:* Apartado Postal 517 Cuernavaca Mexico

MANCHE, EMANUEL PETER, b New York, NY, Apr 30, 31; m 61; c 3. CHEMISTRY. *Educ:* City Col New York, BS, 56; Brooklyn Col, MA, 59; Rutgers Univ, NB, PhD(chem), 65. *Prof Exp:* Res chemist, Am Chicle Co, 56-57; lectr chem, Brooklyn Col, 58-62, sch gen studies, 58-59; teaching asst, Rutgers Univ, 62-64, instr, 65; advan res engr, Gen Tel & Electronics Res Labs, 65-68; asst prof chem, 68-72, assoc prof, 73-80, PROF CHEM, YORK COL, CITY UNIV NEW YORK, 81- *Concurrent Pos:* Instr univ col, Rutgers Univ, 64-73, prof, 73-74; invited lectr, United Hosps, Newark, 72-73. *Mem:* Am Chem Soc; Electron Micros Soc Am; Sigma Xi. *Res:* Chemical instrumentation; thermal methods of analysis including thermogravimetry and differential thermal analysis; thermoluminescent dating. *Mailing Add:* Dept of Natural Sci York Col City Univ of New York Jamaica NY 11451

MANCHEE, ERIC BEST, b Toronto, Oct 16, 18; m 45; c 3. GEOPHYSICS, SCIENCE ADMINISTRATION. *Educ:* Univ Toronto, BASc, 49, MA, 51. *Prof Exp:* Geophysicist, Calif Standard Co, Alta, 51-59, dist geophysicist, 59-62; head array seismol sect, 62-74, head spec proj, 74-75, BR PROG OFFICER, EARTH PHYSICS BR, DEPT ENERGY, MINES & RESOURCES, 75- *Mem:* Can Asn Physicists; Can Geophys Union. *Res:* Exploration and array seismology; earthquake-explosion differentiation, administration science programs. *Mailing Add:* Earth Physics Br Dept Energy Mines & Resources Ottawa ON K1A 0Y3 Can

MANCHESTER, DONALD FRASER, b Fairville, NB, Apr 18, 20; m 45; c 7. ORGANIC CHEMISTRY. *Educ:* Queen's Univ, Ont, BSc, 43, MSc, 49; McGill Univ, PhD(chem), 52. *Prof Exp:* MGR PROCESS RES, RES CTR, ABITIBI PAPER CO, LTD, 51- *Mem:* Tech Asn Pulp & Paper Indust; Can Pulp & Paper Asn; Chem Inst Can. *Res:* Polymerization of hydrogen cyanide; nitration of unsubstituted diazocycloalkines; oxidation and methylation of cellulose; recovery of pulping reagents from sulphite spent liquors; brightening of high yield chemical and mechanical pulps; pulping processes; environmental research and waste treatment. *Mailing Add:* Abitibi Paper Co Ltd Res Ctr Sheridan Park Mississauga ON L5K 1A9 Can

MANCHESTER, KENNETH EDWARD, b Winona, Minn, Mar 22, 25; m 46; c 2. SURFACE CHEMISTRY. *Educ:* San Jose State Col, AB, 49; Stanford Univ, MS, 50, PhD(thermochem), 55. *Prof Exp:* Fel chem, Stanford Univ, 52-55; chemist surface chem, Shell Develop Co, 55-62; sect head semiconductor chem, 62-63, dept head, 63-69, dir semiconductor res & develop, 69-76, chief scientist, 76-79, DIR SEMICONDUCTUR QUALITY ASSURANCE & RELIABILITY, SPRAGUE ELEC CO, 79- *Mem:* Am Chem Soc; Am Asn Contamination Control; Am Inst Mining, Metal & Petrol Eng; Sigma Xi. *Res:* Energetics of liquid-liquid and liquid-solid interfaces; interaction of energetic ions or electrons with solid substrates. *Mailing Add:* Sprague Elec Co 115 NE Cutoff Worcester MA 01606

MANCINELLI, ALBERTO L, b Rome, Italy, Nov 22, 31; m 62. PLANT PHYSIOLOGY. *Educ:* Univ Rome, Dr rer nat(bot), 54. *Prof Exp:* Vol asst prof bot, Univ Rome, 54-64; from asst prof to assoc prof plant physiol, 64-81, PROF BIOL SCI, COLUMBIA UNIV, 81- *Concurrent Pos:* Ital Nat Res Coun fel, 56-59; Ital Nat Comt Nuclear Energy fel, 59-62; NATO fel, 62-63; NSF res grant, 65-82. *Mem:* AAAS; Am Soc Plant Physiol; Am Inst Biol Sci; Japanese Soc Plant Physiol; Am Soc Photobiol. *Res:* Metabolism during seed germination; reactions controlling light responses in plant growth and development, particularly phytochrome controlled and high energy reaction controlled responses. *Mailing Add:* Dept of Biol Sci Columbia Univ New York NY 10027

MANCINI, ERNEST ANTHONY, b Reading, Pa, Feb 27, 47; m 69; c 2. GEOLOGY, PALEONTOLOGY. *Educ:* Albright Col, BS, 69; Southern Ill Univ, MS, 72; Tex A&M Univ, PhD(geol), 74. *Prof Exp:* Explor geologist, Cities Serv Co, 74-76; asst prof, 76-79, ASSOC PROF GEOL, UNIV ALA, 79- *Concurrent Pos:* Petrol geologist, Mineral Resources Inst, Univ Ala, 76-78; consult, State Oil & Gas Bd Ala, 77-78. *Honors & Awards:* A I Levorsen Petrol Geol Award. *Mem:* Am Asn Petrol Geologists; Soc Econ Paleontologists & Mineralogists; Int Micropaleont Soc; Sigma Xi; NAm Micropaleont Soc. *Res:* Cretaceous and paleogene biostratigraphy and paleoecology. *Mailing Add:* Dept Geol Univ of Ala University AL 35486

MANCLARK, CHARLES ROBERT, b Rochester, NY, June 22, 28; m 53; c 2. MICROBIOLOGY, IMMUNOLOGY. *Educ:* Calif Polytech State Univ, BS, 53; Univ Calif, Los Angeles, PhD(bact), 63. *Prof Exp:* Asst prof microbiol, Calif State Univ, Long Beach, 61-64; asst res bacteriologist, Univ Calif, Los Angeles, 63-65, asst prof microbiol, Col Med, Univ Calif, Irvine, 65-67; res microbiologist, Lab Bact Prod, Div Biologics Stand, NIH, 67-72; RES MICROBIOLOGIST, DIV BACT PROD, BUR BIOLOGICS, FOOD & DRUG ADMIN, 72- *Mem:* AAAS; Am Soc Microbiol; Mycol Soc Am; Am Soc Indust Microbiol; Int Asn Biol Stand. *Res:* Immunity and the immune response; diagnostic bacteriology; delayed hypersensitivity; the immune basis of infertility and sterility; host-parasite relationships in pertussis. *Mailing Add:* Div of Bact Prod Bur Biologics Food & Drug Admin Bethesda MD 20205

MANCUSI, MICHAEL D, b New York, NY, Aug 31, 40; m 61; c 3. COMPUTER SCIENCE. *Educ:* Univ Notre Dame, BS, 62; Univ Iowa, PhD(nuclear physics), 66. *Prof Exp:* Res asst nuclear physics, Univ Iowa, 63-66; US AEC fel, Oak Ridge Nat Lab, 66-68; mem tech staff, 68-76, supvr, 76-78, DEPT HEAD, BELL LABS, 78- *Mem:* Am Phys Soc; Inst Elec & Electronics Eng. *Res:* Data networks, high level computer languages; systems architecture. *Mailing Add:* Room 2E-532 Bell Labs Holmdel NJ 07733

MANCUSO, ANTHONY JOHN, organic chemistry, see previous edition

MANCUSO, JAMES FRANK, b Farmingdale, NY, Jan 25, 50; m 69; c 2. MATERIALS ENGINEERING. *Educ:* State Univ NY, Stony Brook, BS, 72, MS, 73; Cornell Univ, Phd(nuclear mat eng), 77. *Prof Exp:* Prin engr core mat, Combustion Eng, 77-79; SR ENGR, POWER GENERATOR MAT, RES & DEVELOP, WESTINGHOUSE ELEC, 79- *Mem:* Am Soc Testing

& Mat; Am Soc Metalls; Am Inst Metal Engrs. *Res:* Radiation damage to structural materials; fracture toughness; mechanical metallurgy; computer aided methods of microstructural analysis. *Mailing Add:* Westinghouse Elec Corp 1310 Beulah Rd Pittsburgh PA 15235

MANCUSO, JOSEPH J, b Hibbing, Minn, Dec 9, 33; m 57; c 4. ECONOMIC GEOLOGY. *Educ:* Carleton Col, BA, 55; Univ Wis, MS, 57; Mich State Univ, PhD(geol), 60. *Prof Exp:* Instr geol, Mich State Univ, 58-60; asst prof, 60-71, chmn dept, 75-78, PROF GEOL, BOWLING GREEN STATE UNIV, 71- *Concurrent Pos:* Consult geologist. *Mem:* Am Inst Prof Geologists; Soc Econ Geol. *Res:* Economic geology, mineralogy and stratigraphy of the Lake Superior iron formations; Precambrian geology of Wisconsin, Michigan and Minnesota. *Mailing Add:* Dept of Geol Bowling Green State Univ Bowling Green OH 43402

MANCUSO, RICHARD VINCENT, b Rochester, NY, Nov 4, 38; m 64; c 2. NUCLEAR PHYSICS. *Educ:* St Bonaventure Univ, BS, 60; State Univ NY Buffalo, PhD(physics), 65. *Prof Exp:* Teaching asst physics, State Univ NY Buffalo, 61-65; Nat Acad Sci-Nat Res Coun res assoc nuclear physics, Van De Graaff Br, Naval Res Lab, Washington, DC, 67-69; asst prof, 69-74, ASSOC PROF PHYSICS, STATE UNIV NY COL BROCKPORT, 74- *Mem:* Am Phys Soc. *Res:* Gamma ray spectroscopy; level structures of medium weight nuclei; charged particle reactions and reaction mechanisms; application of nuclear techniques to non-nuclear problems. *Mailing Add:* Dept of Physics State Univ of NY Col Brockport NY 14420

MANCUSO, VINCENT J, mathematics, see previous edition

MANDAL, ANIL KUMAR, b West Bengal, India, Nov 12, 35; m 64; c 2. CARDIOVASCULAR DISEASES. *Educ:* Univ Calcutta, MB, BS, 59; Am Bd Internal Med, dipl, 72. *Prof Exp:* Med officer, Inst Postgrad Med Educ & Res, Calcutta, 63-66; registr, R G Kar Med Col, Calcutta, 66-67; lectr path, Univ Edinburgh, 68-69; instr med, Univ Ill, Chicago Circle, 71-72; asst prof, 72-75, ASSOC PROF MED, COL MED, UNIV OKLA, 75- *Concurrent Pos:* Consult physician, Vet Admin Hosp, Muskogee, Okla, 72-; asst physician, Okla Med Res Found, 72-; attend nephrologist, Vet Admin Hosp & Univ Hosp, Oklahoma City, 75- *Honors & Awards:* Recognition Award, AMA, 69, 70, 71 & 72. *Mem:* Fel Am Col Physicians; Am Fedn Clin Res; Am Soc Nephrol; Electron Micros Soc Am; Sigma Xi. *Res:* Pathological study by light, electron and fluorescence microscopy of kidney in experimental renal disease and hypertension. *Mailing Add:* 921 NE 13th St Oklahoma City OK 73104

MANDARINO, JOSEPH ANTHONY, b Chicago, Ill, Apr 20, 29; m 56; c 4. MINERALOGY. *Educ:* Mich Col Mining & Technol, BS, 50, MS, 51; Univ Mich, PhD(mineral), 58. *Prof Exp:* Asst prof mineral, Mich Col Mining & Technol, 57-59; assoc cur, 59-65, CUR DEPT MINERAL, ROYAL ONT MUS, 65- *Concurrent Pos:* Mem, Joint Comt Powder Diffraction Standards; Nat Res Coun Can sr res fel, Fr Bur Geol Mines Res, 68-69. *Mem:* Mineral Soc Am; Mineral Asn Can; Mineral Soc Gt Brit & Ireland. *Res:* Crystal optics; crystallography; descriptive mineralogy. *Mailing Add:* Dept of Mineral & Geol Royal Ont Mus 100 Queen's Park Toronto ON M5S 2C6 Can

MANDAVA, NAGA BHUSHAN, b Bhushanagulla, India, Oct 14, 34; m 57; c 3. BIO-ORGANIC CHEMISTRY. *Educ:* Univ Andhra, India, BSc, 55; Banaras Hindu Univ, MSc, 57; Indian Inst Sci, Bangalore, PhD(chem), 62. *Prof Exp:* Res assoc, Okla State Univ, 63-65, State Univ NY Stony Brook, 65-66 & Laval Univ, 66-68; chemist, Plant Sci Res Div, 68, RES CHEMIST, PLANT PHYSIOL INST, SCI & EDUC AGR RES SERV, USDA, 68- *Concurrent Pos:* Nat Res Coun Can fel, 66-68. *Mem:* Fel Am Inst Chem; Am Chem Soc; Int Plant Growth Substances Asn. *Res:* Organophosphorus compounds; plant hormones, lipids, steroids, carbohydrates, alkaloids, pesticides and heterocyclic compounds; application of specroscopy and computers to structural and stereochemical problems; bioassays and tracer techniques. *Mailing Add:* Plant Physiol Inst USDA Bldg 050 Beltsville MD 20705

MANDEL, BENJAMIN, b New York, NY, Aug 17, 13; m 46; c 2. VIROLOGY. *Educ:* City Col New York, BS, 40; NY Univ, MS, 48, PhD(microbiol), 51. *Prof Exp:* Assoc mem div infectious dis, Pub Health Res Inst New York, Inc, 52-67; res assoc prof, 66-71, Col Med, NY Univ, 66-71, res prof microbiol, 71-80; mem div infectious dis, Pub Health Res Inst New York, Inc, 67-80; RETIRED. *Mem:* AAAS; Am Soc Microbiol; fel NY Acad Sci. *Res:* Fundamentals of virus-cell relationship. *Mailing Add:* Pub Health Res Inst New York Inc 455 First Ave New York NY 10016

MANDEL, BENJAMIN J, b Poland, Sept 1, 12; US citizen; m 37; c 2. APPLIED STATISTICS. *Educ:* City Col New York, BS, 34; George Washington Univ, MA, 38; Goteborg Sch Econ & Bus Admin, Sweden, Ekonomie Licentiate, 67. *Prof Exp:* Jr & asst statistician, Social Security Admin, 38-44, chief statist div, 44-60; asst dir statist standards & opers, US Off Educ, 60-61; dir off statist prog, US Post Off Dept, 61-70; STATIST SCI CONSULT, 70- *Concurrent Pos:* Prof statist, Univ Baltimore, 46-70, chmn dept, 48-70, Emer prof, 70-; vis prof mgt & statist, Dept Agr Grad Sch, 62-; lectr statist for mgt, Bur Training, US Civil Serv Comn, 65-; vis lectr statist, Am Statist Asn, NSF, 71-72; consult var agencies. *Honors & Awards:* Dir Citation Outstanding Contrib Mgt, Dept Health, Educ & Welfare, 59; Superior Accomplishment Award, US Post Off Dept, 67, Meritorious Serv Award, 68 & Superior Accomplishment Award, 70. *Mem:* Am Statist Asn; fel Am Soc Qual Control; Am Asn Retired Teachers; Smithsonian Assocs. *Res:* Extension of application of statistical theory and techniques to new areas of management, administration, accounting, auditing, inspection and quality assurance. *Mailing Add:* 6101 16th St NW Washington DC 20011

MANDEL, HAROLD GEORGE, b Berlin, Ger, June 6, 24; nat US; m 53; c 2. PHARMACOLOGY. *Educ:* Yale Univ, BS, 44, PhD(org chem), 49. *Prof Exp:* Asst & lab instr chem, Yale Univ, 42-44, lab instr org chem, 47-49; res assoc, 49-50, asst res prof, 50-52, assoc prof, 52-58, PROF PHARMACOL, SCH MED, GEORGE WASHINGTON UNIV, 58-, CHMN DEPT, 60- *Concurrent Pos:* Advan Commonwealth Fund fel, Molteno Inst, Eng, 56 & Pasteur Inst, France, 57; travel award, Int Pharmacol Cong, Prague, 63, Helsinki, 75 & Paris, 78; Commonwealth Fund sabbatical leave, Univ Auckland & Univ Med Sci, Thailand, 64; Am Cancer Soc Eleanor Roosevelt Int fel, Chester Beatty Res Inst, London, 70-71; Am Cancer Soc scholar cancer res clin pharmacol, Univ Calif, San Francisco, 78-79; lectr, US Naval Dent Sch, 59-61, 71-75, Washington Hosp Ctr, 60-66, US Army Dent Sch, 72-75, Holy Cross Hosp, 72-74 & Food & Drug Admin, 67, 78, 79 & 81; consult, Fed Aviation Agency, 61-62; mem biochem comt, Cancer Chemother Nat Serv Ctr, 58-61, med adv comt, Therapeut Res Found, Inc, 62-, pharmacol & exp therapeut B study sect, USPHS, 63-68, comt probs drug safety, Nat Acad Sci-Nat Res Coun, 65-71 & 72-76, mem drug metab workshop progs, NY Univ, 66, George Washington Univ, 67 & Univ Calif, 68; mem cancer chemother comt, Int Union Against Cancer, 66, res comt, Children's Hosp, Washington, DC, 69- & sci adv comt, Registry Tissue Reactions to Drugs, 70-76; mem cancer chemother training progs, Poland, 68, Curacao, 71, Ger, 73, Belg, 73 & Arg, 73; mem chemother comt, Am Cancer Soc, 69-73; mem cancer res training comt, Nat Cancer Inst, 71-73, mem cancer spec prog adv comt, 74-78, chmn, 76-78; consult, Roswell Park Inst, Buffalo, 72-74; consult toxicol & mem toxicol adv comt, Food & Drug Admin, 75-78; mem merit rev bd, Vet Admin, 75-78; mem comt Toxicol, Nat Acad Sci, Nat Res Coun, 78-; vis prof pharmacol, Sch Med, Stanford Univ, 78; working cadre, Nat Large Bowel Cancer Proj, 80-; vis prof, Mahidol Univ, Thailand, 81. *Honors & Awards:* Abel Award, Am Soc Pharmacol & Exp Therapeut, 58. *Mem:* AAAS; Am Soc Pharmacol & Exp Therapeut (secy, 61-63, pres, 73-74); Am Chem Soc; Asn Med Sch Pharmacol (treas, 71-73, pres, 76-78); Am Asn Cancer Res. *Res:* Drug metabolism; mechanism of action of antimetabolites and other anti-cancer drugs; action of growth inhibitory drugs. *Mailing Add:* Dept Pharmacol Sch Med George Washington Univ Washington DC 20037

MANDEL, IRWIN D, b New York, NY, Apr 9, 22; m 44; c 3. PREVENTIVE DENTISTRY, ORAL BIOLOGY. *Educ:* City Col New York, BS, 42; Columbia Univ, DDS, 45. *Hon Degrees:* DSc, Col Med & Dent NJ, 81. *Prof Exp:* Res asst dent & oral surg, 46-50, instr, 50-57, from asst clin prof to clin prof, 57-69, dir, Lab Clin Res, 60-69, PROF DENT & ORAL SURG, COLUMBIA UNIV, 69-, DIR DIV PREV DENT, 69- *Concurrent Pos:* USPHS grant, 64-; Health Res Coun City of New York career scientist award, 69-72; consult & chmn, Oral Biol & Med Study Sect, Coun Dent Therapeut, 68- *Mem:* Fel AAAS; Coun Dent Res; Am Asn Dent Res (pres); Am Dent Asn; Int Asn Dent Res. *Res:* Plaque, calculus and periodontal disease; salivary composition and relation to oral and systemic disease; host factors in caries resistance. *Mailing Add:* Sch of Dent & Oral Surg Columbia Univ New York NY 10032

MANDEL, JAMES A, b Pittsburgh, Pa, Dec 25, 34; m 59; c 2. CIVIL ENGINEERING. *Educ:* Carnegie-Mellon Univ, BS, 56, MS, 62; Syracuse Univ, PhD(civil eng), 67. *Prof Exp:* Design engr, Richardson, Gordon & Assocs, Pa, 56-61; sr stress engr, Goodyear Aerospace Corp, Ohio, 62-64; from asst prof to assoc prof civil eng, 67-78, PROF CIVIL ENG, SYRACUSE UNIV, 78- *Mem:* Am Soc Civil Engrs. *Res:* Structural analysis; materials; shell structures; mechanics. *Mailing Add:* Dept Civil Eng Syracuse Univ Syracuse NY 13210

MANDEL, JOHN, b Antwerp, Belgium, July 12, 14; nat US; m 38; c 2. MATHEMATICAL STATISTICS. *Educ:* Univ Brussels, BS, 35, MS, 37; Eindhoven Technol Univ, PhD(appl statist), 65. *Prof Exp:* Res chemist, Soc Belge De Recherches, Belgium, 38-40; anal & develop chemist, Foster D Snell, Inc, 41-43; res chemist, B G Corp, 44-47; gen phys scientist, 47-48, anal statistician, 48-57, MATH STATISTICIAN, NAT BUR STANDARDS, 58- *Honors & Awards:* Silver Medal for Meritorious Serv, US Dept Commerce, 57, Gold Medal Award, 73; Shewhart Medal, Am Soc Qual Control, 80, Deming Medal, 81. *Mem:* Fel Am Statist Asn; Inst Math Statist; fel Am Qual Control; fel Royal Statist Soc. *Res:* Statistical design of experiments; statistical analysis of data obtained in physical and chemical experimentation; development of statistical techniques for the physical sciences; interlaboratory testing; statistical evaluation of measuring processes. *Mailing Add:* 10710 Lombardy Rd Silver Spring MD 20901

MANDEL, JOHN HERBERT, b New York, NY, Mar 11, 25; m 50; c 3. MEDICAL MICROBIOLOGY. *Educ:* City Col New York, BS, 47; Univ Calif, Berkeley, MA, 49. *Prof Exp:* Chief diag serol sect & res bacteriologist, US Army Grad Sch, Walter Reed Army Med Ctr, 50-51; chief serol & hemat sect, FDR Vet Admin Hosp, Montrose, NY, 51-55; DIR, LEHIGH VALLEY LABS, INC, 55- *Concurrent Pos:* Bioanalyst dir, Am Bd Bioanalysts; specialist-microbiologist, Nat Registry Microbiologists; instr microbiol, Pa State Univ, 69-74; pres, Allentown Bd Health, 80- *Mem:* Am Soc Microbiol; Am Asn Bioanalysts; Am Pub Health Asn; Int Soc Human & Animal Mycol. *Res:* Rapid isolation and identification of pathogenic microoorganisms from biological materials, food and water; identification and significance of yeasts isolated from clinical specimens. *Mailing Add:* Lehigh Valley Labs Inc Microbiol Dept 1740 Allen St Allentown PA 18104

MANDEL, LAZARO J, b Lima, Peru, Oct 13, 40; US citizen; m 63. PHYSIOLOGY, BIOPHYSICS. *Educ:* Mass Inst Technol, BS, 61, MS, 62; Univ Pa, PhD(biomed eng), 69. *Prof Exp:* USPHS fel, Yale Univ Med Sch, 69-72; asst prof, 72-78, ASSOC PROF PHYSIOL, MED CTR, DUKE UNIV, 78- *Mem:* AAAS; Biophys Soc; Am Physiol Soc. *Res:* Active and passive transport; biological energy conversion; properties of biological membranes. *Mailing Add:* Dept of Physiol Duke Univ Med Ctr Durham NC 27710

MANDEL, LEONARD, b May 9, 27; US citizen; m 53; c 2. QUANTUM OPTICS, LASERS. *Educ:* Univ London, BSc, 47, BSc, 48, PhD(physics), 51. *Prof Exp:* Tech officer, Imp Chem Indust Res Labs, 51-54; lectr & sr lectr physics, Imp Col, London, 54-64; PROF PHYSICS, UNIV ROCHESTER, 64- *Concurrent Pos:* Prof optics, Univ Rochester, 77-80. *Mem:* Fel Am Phys

Soc; fel Optical Soc Am. *Res:* Optical coherence; quantum interactions of light; lasers; phase transitions in quantum optics; author or coauthor of over 160 publications. *Mailing Add:* Dept Physics & Astron Univ Rochester Rochester NY 14627

MANDEL, LEWIS RICHARD, b Brooklyn, NY, Nov 13, 36; m 60; c 3. BIOCHEMISTRY, RESEARCH ADMINISTRATION. *Educ:* Columbia Univ, BS, 58, PhD(biochem), 62. *Prof Exp:* Asst prof pharmacol, Col Pharm, Columbia Univ, 62-64; sr res biochemist, 64-67, sect head, 67-71, asst dir, 71-74, dir biochem, 74-76, dir univ rel, 76-79, SR DIR UNIV & INDUST REL, MERCK SHARP & DOHME RES LABS, 79- *Concurrent Pos:* NIH Res Grant, 63-64. *Mem:* Soc Neurosci; Int Soc Neurochem; NY Acad Sci; Am Soc Biol Chem; Am Soc Pharmacol & Exp Therapeut. *Res:* Lipid metabolism; prostaglandins; transmethylation reactions. *Mailing Add:* Merck Sharp & Dohme Res Labs PO Box 2000 Rahway NJ 07065

MANDEL, MANLEY, b Philadelphia, Pa, July 10, 23; m 52; c 3. MICROBIOLOGY, MOLECULAR BIOLOGY. *Educ:* Brooklyn Col, BA, 43; Mich State Univ, MS, 47, PhD(bact), 52. *Prof Exp:* Asst biol, Brooklyn Col, 46; guest investr microbiol, Haskins Labs, 46 & 52; asst bact, Univ Calif, 48-50; instr, Univ Mass, 52-53, asst prof, 53-63; res assoc, Brandeis Univ, 63; assoc prof biol, Grad Sch Biomed Sci, Univ Tex, Houston, 63-66, assoc biologist, 63-66, prof, 66-81, chief, Sect Molecular Biol, Univ Tex M D Anderson Hosp & Tumor Inst, 63-79, biologist, 66-81; DIR RES, IMMUNOPATH LABS INT, 81- *Concurrent Pos:* Mem molecular biol study sect, NIH, 66-70, sci review comt health related facil, 70-74; mem bd trustees, Am Type Cult Collection, 73-79, Nucleic Acid & Protein Biosynthesis Adv Comt, Am Cancer Soc, 70-75, Res Comt, 79-80. *Mem:* Am Soc Microbiol; Biophys Soc; Genetics Soc Am; Brit Soc Gen Microbiol; fel Am Acad Microbiol. *Res:* Molecular and genetic relations of protists; role of modification in viral DNA-host interactions. *Mailing Add:* Immunopath Labs Int 7000 Fannin M-110 Houston TX 77030

MANDEL, MORTON, b Brooklyn, NY, July 6, 24; m 52; c 2. MOLECULAR BIOLOGY. *Educ:* City Col New York, BCE, 44; Columbia Univ, MS, 49, PhD(physics), 57. *Prof Exp:* Instr civil eng, Stevens Inst Technol, 48; asst microwave components, Columbia Univ, 52-56; mem tech staff solid state devices, Bell Tel Labs, 56-57; res assoc paramagnetic resonance, Stanford Univ, 57-61, asst prof physics, 59-61; eng specialist, Gen Tel & Electronics Lab, 61-63; res assoc genetics, Sch Med, Stanford Univ, 63-64; USPHS fel microbial genetics, Karolinska Inst, Sweden, 64-66; assoc prof biophys, 66-69, chmn dept biochem & biophys, 71-72, PROF BIOPHYS, SCH MED, UNIV HAWAII, 69- *Concurrent Pos:* Consult, Fairchild Semiconductor Corp, 57-58, Hewlett-Packard Co, 58 & Rheem Semiconductor Corp, 59; vis prof, Worcester Found Exp Biol, 72-73, vis prof human genetics, Sch Med, Yale Univ, 79-80; prin investr, Am Cancer Soc, 79- *Mem:* Fel Am Phys Soc; Genetics Soc Am; Biophys Soc; Sigma Xi. *Res:* Phage genetics; bacterial transformation and transfection; carcinogenesis in colon cancer; cloning of sea urchin genes and study of their regulation. *Mailing Add:* Dept Biochem & Biophys Univ Hawaii Sch Med Honolulu HI 96822

MANDEL, ZOLTAN, b Czech, July 18, 24; US citizen; m 57; c 1. TEXTILE CHEMISTRY. *Educ:* Western Reserve Univ, BS, 51, MS, 52, PhD(org chem), 55. *Prof Exp:* Res chemist, Diamond Alkali Co, 54-55; res chemist, 55-63, sr res chemist, 63-65, res assoc, 65-72, SR RES CHEMIST, E I DU PONT DE NEMOURS & CO, INC, 72- *Mem:* Am Chem Soc. *Res:* Synthetic fibers. *Mailing Add:* E I du Pont de Nemours & Co Inc 1007 Market St Wilmington DE 19898

MANDELBAUM, HUGO, b Sommerhausen, Bavaria, Oct 18, 01; nat US; m 31; c 5. PHYSICAL OCEANOGRAPHY. *Educ:* Univ Hamburg, Dr rer nat(geophys), 34. *Prof Exp:* Teacher high sch, Hamburg, 30-38; prin, Jewish Day Sch, Mich, 40-48; prof geol, 48-71, EMER PROF GEOL, WAYNE STATE UNIV, 71- *Mem:* AAAS; Soc Explor Geophys; Seismol Soc Am; Am Geophys Union. *Res:* Tides and tidal currents; air-sea boundary problems; sedimentation; the astronomical foundation of the Jewish calendar. *Mailing Add:* Givath Beth Hakerem Block 1 Number 37 96268 Jerusalem Israel

MANDELBAUM, ISIDORE, b New York, NY. SURGERY. *Educ:* NY Univ, AB, 48; State Univ NY Downstate Med Ctr, MD, 52. *Prof Exp:* From instr to assoc prof, 61-72, PROF SURG, SCH MED, IND UNIV, INDIANAPOLIS, 72- *Concurrent Pos:* Dazian fel path, Mt Sinai Hosp, New York, 54-55; Nat Heart Inst fel, Ind Univ, Indianapolis, 61-62; consult, Vet Admin Hosp, Indianapolis, 61- *Mem:* Am Asn Thoracic Surg; Soc Vascular Surg; Int Cardiovasc Soc; Am Soc Clin Invest; Am Col Surg. *Res:* Cardiothoracic surgery; cardiovascular and pulmonary research. *Mailing Add:* Dept of Surg Ind Univ Sch of Med Indianapolis IN 46202

MANDELBERG, HIRSCH I, b Baltimore, Md, Apr 16, 34; m 58; c 2. PHYSICS. *Educ:* Johns Hopkins Univ, BE, 54, PhD(physics), 60. *Prof Exp:* Res physicist res inst adv study div, Martin Co, 56-60; RES PHYSICIST, US DEPT DEFENSE, 60- *Concurrent Pos:* Visitor, Univ Col, Univ London, 67-68; assoc prof, Univ Col, Univ Md, 61-66. *Mem:* Am Phys Soc. *Res:* Atomic collisions; optics; optical propagation; non-linear optics; lasers; electron collisions; optical spectroscopy; laser applications. *Mailing Add:* 6800 Pimlico Dr Baltimore MD 21209

MANDELBROT, BENOIT, b Warsaw, Poland, Nov 20, 24; m 55; c 2. APPLIED MATHEMATICS. *Educ:* Polytech Sch, Paris, Engr, 47; Calif Inst Technol, MS, 48, Prof Eng, 49; Univ Paris, PhD(math), 52. *Prof Exp:* Mathematician, Philips Electronics, Paris, 50-53; mem staff sch math, Inst Adv Study, NJ, 53-54; assoc, Inst Henri Poincare, Paris, 54-55; asst prof math, Univ Geneva, 55-57; jr prof, Lille Univ & Polytech Sch, Paris, 57-58; res staff mem, 58-72, SCI ADV TO DIR RES, IBM CORP, 72-, IBM FEL, 74- *Concurrent Pos:* Vis prof, Harvard Univ, 62-64 & 79-80; inst lectr, Mass Inst Technol, 64-68 & 74-76; Guggenheim fel, 69; staff mem, Nat Bur Econ Res, 69-78; Trumbull lectr & vis prof, Yale Univ, 70; vis prof, Albert Einstein Col Med, 71; lectr, Col France, 73, 74 & 77; vis prof, Downstate Med Ctr, State Univ NY, 74. *Honors & Awards:* S S Wilks Lectr, Princeton Univ; A Wald lectr, Columbia Univ, 74; Goodspeed-Richards lectr, Univ Pa, 78. *Mem:* Fel Inst Math Statist; fel Economet Soc; fel Am Statist Asn; fel Inst Elec & Electronics Eng; Am Math Soc. *Res:* Theory of stochastic processes, especially its applications; thermodynamics, noise and turbulence; natural languages; astronomy; geomorphology; commodity and security prices; self-similar or sporadic chance phenomena; computer art and graphics; fractals and fractal geometry of nature. *Mailing Add:* Thomas J Watson Res Ctr PO Box 218 Yorktown Heights NY 10598

MANDELCORN, LYON, b Montreal, Que, June 27, 26; nat US; m 55; c 3. PHYSICAL CHEMISTRY. *Educ:* NY Univ, BA, 47; McGill Univ, PhD(phys chem), 51. *Prof Exp:* Res fel photochem, Nat Res Coun Can, 51-53; res assoc microcalorimetry, Univ Montreal, 53-54; SECT MGR, WESTINGHOUSE ELEC CORP RES & DEVELOP CTR, 54- *Mem:* Am Chem Soc; Electrochem Soc; Inst Elec & Electronics Eng. *Res:* Electrochemistry; free radicals; clathrates; dielectrics and insulation; research on development and behavior and properties of dielectrics for high voltage power equipment. *Mailing Add:* Westinghouse Res & Develop Ctr Beulah Rd Churchill Borough Pittsburgh PA 15235

MANDELES, STANLEY, b Brooklyn, NY, Dec 8, 24; m 47; c 2. BIOCHEMISTRY. *Educ:* NY Univ, BA, 47; Univ Chicago, PhD, 53. *Prof Exp:* Res assoc & instr biochem, Univ Chicago, 53-56; assoc chemist, Western Util Res Lab, USDA, 56-61; assoc res biochemist, Univ Calif, Berkeley, 61-71; chmn dept chem, 71-75, PROF CHEM, DOUGLASS COL, RUTGERS UNIV, NEW BRUNSWICK, 71- *Mem:* Am Soc Biol Chemists; Am Chem Soc; Brit Biochem Soc. *Res:* Biochemistry of growth; differentiation, especially role of proteins and nucleic acids. *Mailing Add:* Dept of Chem Douglass Col Rutgers Univ New Brunswick NJ 08903

MANDELKERN, LEO, b New York, NY, Feb 23, 22; m 46; c 3. POLYMER CHEMISTRY, BIOPHYSICS. *Educ:* Cornell Univ, AB, 42, PhD(chem), 49. *Prof Exp:* Res assoc chem, Cornell Univ, 49-52; phys chemist, Nat Bur Standards, 52-62; PROF CHEM & BIOPHYS, FLA STATE UNIV, 62- *Concurrent Pos:* Vis prof, Med Sch, Univ Miami, 63, Med Sch, Univ Calif, San Francisco, 64 & Cornell Univ, 67; consult, NIH, 70- *Honors & Awards:* Fleming Award, 59; Polymer Award, Am Chem Soc, 75. *Mem:* Fel NY Acad Sci; AAAS; Am Chem Soc; fel Am Phys Soc; Biophys Soc. *Res:* Physical chemistry of high polymers; biophysics and macromolecules. *Mailing Add:* 1503 Old Fort Dr Tallahassee FL 32301

MANDELKERN, MARK, b Milwaukee, Wis, July 18, 33. MATHEMATICS. *Educ:* Marquette Univ, BS, 55; Univ Rochester, PhD(math), 66. *Prof Exp:* Instr math, State Univ NY Stony Brook, 62-65; asst prof, Univ Kans, 66-69; asst prof, 69-70, ASSOC PROF MATH, NMEX STATE UNIV, 70- *Mem:* Am Math Soc. *Res:* Constructive mathematics. *Mailing Add:* Dept Math NMex State Univ Las Cruces NM 88003

MANDELKERN, MARK ALAN, b New York, NY, Jan 28, 43; m 69. ELEMENTARY PARTICLE PHYSICS, MEDICAL PHYSICS. *Educ:* Columbia Univ, AB, 63; Univ Calif, Berkeley, PhD(physics), 67; Univ Miami, MD, 75. *Prof Exp:* Asst prof physics, 68-73, ASSOC PROF PHYSICS, UNIV CALIF, IRVINE, 73- *Concurrent Pos:* Researcher, Saclay Nuclear Res Ctr, France, 70-71, CERN, Switzerland, 77-78 & Brookhaven Nat Lab, 78-79; vis prof, Univ Brasilia, 75. *Res:* Strong interactions; physiology. *Mailing Add:* Dept of Physics Univ of Calif Irvine CA 92664

MANDELL, ALAN, b New Bedford, Mass, Feb 26, 26; m 46; c 2. SCIENCE EDUCATION, BIOLOGY. *Educ:* Holy Cross Col, BS, 46; Univ Va, MEd, 56; Univ NC, DEd, 66. *Prof Exp:* Prof biol, Frederick Col, 61-65, chmn dept, 65-67; PROF SCI EDUC, OLD DOMINION UNIV, 67- *Concurrent Pos:* Consult surplus property div, US Off Educ, 56. *Mem:* Sci Teachers Asn. *Mailing Add:* Sch of Educ Old Dominion Univ Norfolk VA 23508

MANDELL, ARNOLD J, b Chicago, Ill, July 21, 34; c 2. PSYCHIATRY, NEUROCHEMISTRY. *Educ:* Stanford Univ, BA, 54; Tulane Univ, MD, 58. *Prof Exp:* Resident psychiat, Sch Med, Univ Calif, Los Angeles, 59-62, chief resident, 62-63, from asst prof to assoc prof, 63-68; assoc prof psychiat, human behav & psychobiol, Univ Calif, Irvine, 68-69; chmn dept, 69-74, co-chmn, 75-77, PROF PSYCHIAT, UNIV CALIF, SAN DIEGO, 69- *Concurrent Pos:* NIMH career teacher award, Univ Calif, Los Angeles, 62-67; referee, Science, Psychopharmacologica, Community Behav Sci & Am J Psychiat, 64-; mem res comt, Calif Interagency Coun Drug Abuse, 69-; ctr study narcotic addiction & drug abuse, NIMH, 69-, ad hoc sci adv bd biol res, 71-, consult, Lab Clin Sci; mem adv bd, Jerusalem Ment Health Ctr, Israel, 71-; ad hoc sci adv bd, President's Spec Actg Off Drug Abuse Prev, 71-; staff psychiatrist, Vet Admin Hosp, San Diego, Calif, 72-; consult, Ill State Psychiat Res Inst. *Honors & Awards:* A E Bennett Award Res Biol Psychiat, 62. *Mem:* AAAS; Am Inst Chem; Am Psychiat Asn; Soc Biol Psychiat; Am Col Psychiat. *Res:* Neurochemical and biochemical correlates of behavior in animals and man. *Mailing Add:* Dept of Psychiat Sch of Med Univ of Calif San Diego La Jolla CA 92093

MANDELL, LEON, b Bronx, NY, Nov 19, 27; m 59, 71; c 2. ORGANIC CHEMISTRY. *Educ:* Polytech Inst Brooklyn, BS, 48; Harvard Univ, MA, 49, PhD(chem), 51. *Prof Exp:* Sr chemist, Merck & Co, Inc, 51-53; from asst to assoc prof org chem, 55-64, PROF ORG CHEM, EMORY UNIV, 64-, CHMN, 68- *Concurrent Pos:* Consult, Schering Corp, 58- . *Mem:* Am Chem Soc. *Res:* Synthetic methods in organic chemistry; nuclear magnetic resonance spectroscopy; mechanisms of organic reactions; natural product chemistry. *Mailing Add:* Dept of Chem Emory Univ Atlanta GA 30322

MANDELL, ROBERT BURTON, b Alhambra, Calif, Nov 13, 33; m 59; c 2. OPTOMETRY, VISUAL PHYSIOLOGY. *Educ:* Los Angeles Col Optom, OD, 56; Ind Univ, MS, 58, PhD(physiol optics), 62. *Prof Exp:* From asst prof to assoc prof, 62-73, PROF OPTOM, UNIV CALIF, BERKELEY, 73- *Concurrent Pos:* USPHS grant, 64-66. *Mem:* AAAS; Optical Soc Am; Am Acad Optom; Am Optom Asn. *Res:* Corneal contour; contact lenses. *Mailing Add:* Dept of Optom Univ of Calif Berkeley CA 94720

MANDELS, GABRIEL RAPHAEL, microbial physiology, plant physiology, deceased

MANDELS, MARY HICKOX, b Rutland, Vt, Sept 12, 17; m 42; c 2. MICROBIAL PHYSIOLOGY. *Educ:* Cornell Univ, BS, 39, PhD(plant physiol), 47. *Prof Exp:* Microbiologist Pioneering Res Div, Qm Res & Eng Ctr, 55-62, microbiologist, Food Lab, Natick Develop Ctr, 62-71, MICROBIOLOGIST ENVIRON SCI DIV, US ARMY RES & DEVELOP COMMAND, 71- *Mem:* Bot Soc Am; Am Soc Microbiol. *Res:* Fungal enzymes; cellulose saccharification; fermentation technology. *Mailing Add:* US Army Res & Develop Command Kansas St Natick MA 01760

MANDELSTAM, PAUL, b Boston, Mass, Apr 18, 25; m. BIOCHEMISTRY, INTERNAL MEDICINE. *Educ:* Harvard Univ, AB, 44, AM, 46, MD, 50, PhD, 53; Am Bd Internal Med, dipl, 57. *Prof Exp:* Intern, Med Serv, Beth Israel Hosp, Boston, 50-51, asst resident, 52-53; from asst prof to assoc prof, 60-73, PROF MED, COL MED, UNIV KY, 73- *Concurrent Pos:* Res fel, Sch Med, Yale Univ, 55-57; Nat Found res fel, Sch Med, Wash Univ, 57-59; Nat Inst Neurol Dis & Blindness spec trainee, 59-60; asst physician, New Haven Hosp, 55-57. *Mem:* Fel Am Col Physicians; Am Soc Gastrointestinal Endoscopy; Cent Soc Clin Res; Am Gastroenterol Asn; Am Physiol Soc. *Res:* Active transport; gastroenterology. *Mailing Add:* Univ of K Col of Med Lexington KY 40536

MANDELSTAM, STANLEY, b Johannesburg, SAfrica, Dec 12, 28. THEORETICAL PHYSICS. *Educ:* Univ Witwatersrand, BSc, 51; Cambridge Univ, BA, 54; Univ Birmingham, PhD(math physics), 56. *Prof Exp:* Asst math physics, Univ Birmingham, 56-57; Boese fel physics, Columbia Univ, 57-58; asst res physics, Univ Calif, Berkeley, 58-60; prof math physics, Univ Birmingham, 60-63; PROF PHYSICS, UNIV CALIF, BERKELEY, 63- *Mem:* Fel Royal Soc Chem. *Res:* Theoretical physics of elementary particles. *Mailing Add:* Dept Physics Univ Calif Berkeley CA 94720

MANDERS, PETER WILLIAM, b London, UK, Apr 1, 53; Brit citizen. MATERIALS ENGINEERING. *Educ:* Univ Cambridge, BA, 74, MA, 76; Univ Surrey, PhD(composites), 79. *Prof Exp:* Res fel, Univ Surrey, 76-81; RES ASSOC, UNIV DEL, 81- *Mem:* Inst Metallurgists. *Res:* Strength and fracture of fiber reinforced composite materials; statistical aspects of failure, and the experimental and theoretical study of the micromechanisms of failure in composite materials; mechanics of composite materials. *Mailing Add:* Dept Mech & Aerospace Eng Univ Del Newark DE 19711

MANDEVILLE, CHARLES EARLE, b Dallas, Tex, Sept 3, 19; m 43; c 2. PHYSICS. *Educ:* Rice Univ, BA, 40, MA, 41, PhD(physics), 43. *Prof Exp:* Mem staff radiation lab, Mass Inst Technol, 43-45; instr physics, Rice Univ, 45-46; physicist, Bartol Res Found, 46-53, asst dir, 53-59; prof physics & head dept, Univ Ala, 59-61, res physicist, 61; prof physics, Kans State Univ, 61-67; head dept, 67-75, PROF PHYSICS, MICH TECHNOL UNIV, 67-, DIR SPEC PROJ, COMT ENERGY RES, 75- *Concurrent Pos:* Vis lectr, Philadelphia Col Osteop Med, 50-68; consult, US Naval Ord Test Sta, 54-60, Curtiss-Wright Corp, 56-60, res ctr, Babock & Wilcox Co, 58-60, US Army Rocket & Guided Missile Agency, Redstone Arsenal, 59-61, US Naval Radiol Defense Lab, 62-64, Kaman Nuclear Corp, 64-67 & Commonwealth-Edison Co, 73-74. *Mem:* Fel AAAS; fel Am Phys Soc. *Res:* Nuclear, experimental and solid state physics; primary disintegrations; energies of gamma rays; coincidence experiments; neutron scattering; luminescence; biophysics; theory of magnetism. *Mailing Add:* Dept Physics Mich Technol Univ Houghton MI 49931

MANDICS, PETER ALEXANDER, b Budapest, Hungary, May 29, 37; US citizen; m 68; c 2. WEATHER SERVICE SYSTEMS, ATMOSPHERIC PHYSICS. *Educ:* Univ Colo, Boulder, BS, 62; Mass Inst Technol, SM, 63; Stanford Univ, PhD(elec eng), 71. *Prof Exp:* Instr & res asst elec eng, Univ Colo, Boulder, 63-65; physicist, Wave Propagation Lab, 71-79, SUPERVRY PHYSICIST, ENVIRON RES LAB, NAT OCEANIC & ATMOSPHERIC ADMIN, US DEPT COM, 79- *Concurrent Pos:* Nat Res Coun res assoc atmospheric physics, Wave Propagation Lab, Nat Oceanic & Atmospheric Admin, US Dept Com, 71-73. *Mem:* Inst Elec & Electronic Engrs; Int Union of Radio Sci. *Res:* Development of improved short-term, local weather forecasting systems by invorporating latest research and technological advances; remote atmospheric sensing using coherent lidar techniques; atmospheric wave propagation. *Mailing Add:* Environ Res Lab NOAA Rm 6 325 Broadway Boulder CO 80303

MANDIL, I HARRY, b Istanbul, Turkey, Dec 11, 19; US citizen; m 46; c 2. ELECTRICAL ENGINEERING. *Educ:* Univ London, BSc, 39; Mass Inst Technol, MS, 41; dipl, Oak Ridge Sch Reactor Technol, 50. *Hon Degrees:* DSc, Thiel Col, 60. *Prof Exp:* Field engr, Norcross Corp, 41-42, asst to pres, 46-49; chief reactor eng br, Naval Reactors, AEC, proj mgr, Shippingport Atomic Power Sta & dir reactor eng div, Naval Nuclear Propulsion Hq, Bur Ships, 50-64; PRIN OFFICER & DIR, MPR ASSOCS, INC, 64- *Honors & Awards:* Meritorious Civilian Serv Award, US Navy, 52, Distinguished Civilian Serv Award, 59; Prime Movers Award, Am Soc Mech Engrs, 56. *Mem:* Am Soc Mech Engrs; Am Nuclear Soc; NY Acad Sci. *Res:* Development of nuclear power for generation of electricity and for application to merchant ships and oceanographic vehicles. *Mailing Add:* 6900 Forest Hill Dr University Park MD 20782

MANDL, ALEXANDER ERNST, b Vienna, Austria, May 18, 38; US citizen; m 60; c 2. CHEMICAL KINETICS, LASER PHYSICS. *Educ:* City Col New York, BS, 60; New York Univ, MS, 63, PhD(physics), 67. *Prof Exp:* Instr physics, New York Univ, 66-67; fel physics, Nat Bur Standards, 67-69; STAFF SCIENTIST PHYSICS, AVCO EVERETT RES LAB, 69- *Mem:* Am Phys Soc. *Res:* Basic shock tube studies on alkali halides; mercury halides; halide negative ions; rare gas halides; author of 40 major journal publications. *Mailing Add:* Avco Everett Res Lab Everett MA 02149

MANDL, INES, b Vienna, Austria, Apr 19, 17; nat US; m 36. BIOCHEMISTRY. *Educ:* Nat Univ Ireland, dipl, 44; Polytech Inst Brooklyn, MS, 47, PhD(chem), 49. *Prof Exp:* Res chemist, Res Labs, Interchem Corp, 45-49; res assoc, 49-55, assoc, 55-56, asst prof biochem, 56-72, assoc prof reprod biochem, 72-76, PROF REPROD BIOCHEM, COL PHYSICIANS & SURGEONS, COLUMBIA UNIV, 76- *Concurrent Pos:* Dir gynec labs, Delafield Hosp, 59-76; ed-in-chief, Connective Tissue Res-An Int Jour. *Honors & Awards:* Neuberg Medal, 77. *Mem:* AAAS; Am Soc Biol Chem; Am Chem Soc; Am Asn Cancer Res; NY Acad Sci. *Res:* Enzymes; proteins; amino acids; carbohydrates; proteolytic enzyme inhibitors; alpha-antitrypsin; emphysema; respiratory distress syndrome; enzymes of bacterial origin and their medical applications; microstructure of collagen and elastin. *Mailing Add:* 166 W 72nd St New York NY 10023

MANDL, PAUL, b Vienna, Austria, Feb 9, 17; nat US; m 50. APPLIED MATHEMATICS. *Educ:* Univ Toronto, BA, 45, MA, 48, PhD(math), 51. *Prof Exp:* Jr res officer aerodyn, Nat Res Coun Can, 45-48, from asst to assoc res officer, 48-60, sr res officer, 60-66; PROF MATH, CARLETON UNIV, 66- *Concurrent Pos:* Lectr univ exten dept, McGill Univ, 58-61 & Carleton Univ, 60-61, vis assoc prof math, 64-65, part-time lectr wing theory, Grad Div, 65-; consult lab unsteady aerodynamics, Nat Aeronaut Estab; vis prof mechanics of fluids, Univ Manchester, Eng, 74; vis prof, Inst Gasdynamics & Thermodynamics, Tech Univ Vienna, Austria, 81. *Mem:* Can Aeronaut Inst; Can Math Cong; Can Soc Mech Eng. *Res:* Theoretical fluid mechanics; aerodynamics; rheology; diffraction of shockwaves by solid obstacles. *Mailing Add:* Dept Math Carleton Univ Ottawa ON K1S 5B6 Can

MANDL, RICHARD H, b New York, NY, Oct 20, 34; m 56; c 4. BIOLOGY. *Educ:* NY Univ, BA, 66. *Prof Exp:* Res assoc environ biol, 52-69, asst plant physiologist, 69-77, ASSOC ENVIRON BIOLOGIST, BOYCE THOMPSON INST PLANT RES, 77- *Mem:* AAAS. *Res:* Environmental biology; development of new food products; methods for protein, amino acid, iodo-amino acid, organic phosphate and fluoride analysis; effects of air pollutants on plants. *Mailing Add:* Boyce Thompson Inst for Plant Res Tower Rd Ithaca NY 14853

MANDLE, ROBERT JOSEPH, b New York, NY, May 18, 19; m 43; c 4. MICROBIOLOGY. *Educ:* Lebanon Valley Col, BS, 42; Univ Pa, PhD, 51. *Prof Exp:* Asst microbiol, Rockefeller Inst, NJ, 45-50; instr, Univ Del, 50-51; asst prof, 51-65, PROF MICROBIOL, JEFFERSON MED COL, 65- *Concurrent Pos:* Fulbright-Hays grant, Sch Med Technol, Catholic Univ, Quito, Ecuador, 80-81. *Honors & Awards:* William H Rorer Award, Am Col Gastroenterol, 74. *Mem:* Am Soc Microbiol; Sigma Xi; Reticuloendothelial Soc; Mycol Soc Am; Mycol Soc NAm. *Res:* Physiology of micro-organisms; infections and resistance. *Mailing Add:* Dept of Microbiol Jefferson Med Col 1020 Locus St Philadelphia PA 19107

MANDLE, ROBERT JOSEPH, JR, immunology, see previous edition

MANDLIK, JAYANT V, b Dapoli, India, Aug 6, 30; m 71; c 1. ORGANIC CHEMISTRY, PHARMACOLOGY. *Educ:* Karnatak Univ, India, BS, 53, MS, 55; Univ Poona, PhD(org chem), 64. *Prof Exp:* Instr chem, NWadia Col, India, 55-63, asst prof, 63-69; res assoc pharmacol, Univ Ill Med Ctr, 69-73; CHEMIST, CHICAGO BD HEALTH, 73- *Concurrent Pos:* Univ Grants Comn India grants, NWadia Col, 63-64 & 68-69. *Mem:* Am Chem Soc; Am Asn Clin Chemists. *Res:* Synthesis of organic compounds of biological importance; toxicology; drug metabolism; toxicology. *Mailing Add:* 5652 W Sunnyside Chicago IL 60630

MANDRA, YORK T, b New York, NY, Nov 24, 22; m 46. GEOLOGY. *Educ:* Univ Calif, AB, 47, MA, 49; Stanford Univ, PhD(geol), 58. *Prof Exp:* Asst paleont, Univ Calif, 49-50; instr geol, 50-58, from asst to assoc prof, 58-65, head geol sect & chmn dept, 60-67, PROF GEOL, SAN FRANCISCO STATE UNIV, 65- *Concurrent Pos:* NSF fac fel & vis prof, Univ Glasgow & Univ Aix Marseille, 60; res assoc, Calif Acad Sci, 66-; NSF res grants, 67- *Mem:* Fel AAAS; fel Geol Soc Am; Paleont Soc; Nat Asn Geol Teachers; Soc Econ Paleont & Mineral. *Res:* Micropaleontology, especially stratigraphic and paleoecologic aspects of Mesozoic and Cenozoic silicoflagellates. *Mailing Add:* 8 Bucareli Dr San Francisco CA 94132

MANDULA, BARBARA BLUMENSTEIN, biochemistry, see previous edition

MANDULA, JEFFREY ELLIS, b New York, NY, July 23, 41; m 63. PHYSICS. *Educ:* Columbia Col, NY, AB, 62; Harvard Univ, AM, 64, PhD(physics), 66. *Prof Exp:* NSF fel, Harvard Univ, 66-67; res fel physics, Calif Inst Technol, 67-69; mem natural sci, Inst Advan Study, 69-70; asst prof theoret physics, Calif Inst Technol, 70-74; assoc prof appl math, Mass Inst Technol, 74-79; PROF MATH & PHYSICS, WASHINGTON UNIV, 79- *Concurrent Pos:* Dir theoret physics prog, NSF, 80-81. *Mem:* AAAS; Am Phys Soc. *Res:* Theoretical elementary particle physics; quantum field theory. *Mailing Add:* Dept Physics Washington Univ St Louis MO 63130

MANDULEY, ILMA MORELL, b Holquin, Cuba, Sept 19, 29. MATHEMATICS. *Educ:* Univ Havan, PhD(math), 53. *Prof Exp:* From asst prof to prof math, Polytech Inst Holquin, Cuba, 55-61; instr, 61-64, ASST PROF MATH, GUILFORD COL, 64- *Concurrent Pos:* Instr, Friends Sch, Cuba, 52-61. *Mem:* AAAS; Math Asn Am; Am Asn Univ Professors. *Res:* Euclidean and projective geometry; differential analysis; ordinary and partial differentiation equations. *Mailing Add:* Dept of Math Guilford Col Greensboro NC 27410

MANDY, WILLIAM JOHN, b Lackawanna, NY, Mar 12, 33; m 59; c 3. IMMUNOBIOLOGY, IMMUNOGENETICS. *Educ:* Elmhurst Col, 58; Univ Ill, Urbana, PhD(microbiol), 63; Univ Houston, MS, 62. *Prof Exp:* From asst prof to assoc prof, 65-73, PROF IMMUNOL, UNIV TEX, AUSTIN, 73- *Concurrent Pos:* NIH fel immunochem, Sch Med, Univ Calif, 63-65; USPHS career develop award, 66- *Mem:* AAAS; Am Soc Microbiol; Am Soc Immunol. *Res:* Structure of the gamma globulin molecule and nature of naturally occurring antiglobulin factors. *Mailing Add:* Dept of Microbiol Univ of Tex Austin TX 78712

MANEN, CAROL-ANN, b Newark, NJ, Feb 4, 43. DEVELOPMENTAL BIOLOGY, BIOCHEMICAL PHARMACOLOGY. *Educ:* Gettysburg Col, AB, 64; Univ Ill, MSc, 66; Univ Maine, PhD(zool), 73. *Prof Exp:* Fel pharmacol, Med Sch, Univ Ariz, 73-77; res asst biochem, Roche Inst Molecular Biol, 77-78; asst prof biol, Univ Ala, 78-80; MEM STAFF, NAT OCEANIC & ATMOSPHERIC ADMIN, 80- *Concurrent Pos:* NIH fel, Nat Inst Child Health Develop, 75-77. *Mem:* Am Soc Zoologists; Soc Develop Biol. *Res:* Role of the polyamines in growth and differentiation, specifically the regulation of hypertrophy by ornithine decarboxylase. *Mailing Add:* Nat Oceanic & Atmospheric Admin PO Box 1808 Juneau AK 99802

MANERA, PAUL ALLEN, b Clovis, Calif, Nov 11, 30; m 59; c 2. HYDROGEOLOGY. *Educ:* Fresno State Col, BA, 55; Ariz State Univ, MA, 63 & 71, PhD(geog), 78. *Prof Exp:* Mining geologist, Holly Minerals Corp, 55-56; geohydrologist, Samuel F Turner & Assocs, 57-62; CONSULT GEOHYDROLOGIST, MANERA & ASSOCS, INC, 62- *Mem:* Geol Soc Am; Am Geophys Union; Am Water Resources Asn; Soc Explor Geophysicists; Europ Soc Explor Geophysicists. *Res:* Availability of groundwater resources and its impact on the population of the Cave Creek-Carefree Basin, Maricopa County, Arizona. *Mailing Add:* 5251 N 16th St Suite 302 Phoenix AZ 85016

MANERI, CARL C, b Cleveland, Ohio, Jan 25, 33; m 53; c 3. MATHEMATICS. *Educ:* Case Western Reserve Univ, BS, 54; Ohio State Univ, PhD(math), 59. *Prof Exp:* Res fel & instr math, Univ Chicago, 60-62; asst prof, Syracuse Univ, 62-65; chmn dept, 68-71, ASSOC PROF MATH, WRIGHT STATE UNIV, 65- *Mem:* Am Math Soc; Math Asn Am. *Res:* Algebra; combinatorics and finite mathematics; geometry. *Mailing Add:* Dept Math Wright State Univ Dayton OH 45435

MANES, COLE, developmental biology, see previous edition

MANES, ERNEST GENE, b New York, NY, 1943; m 63; c 2. MATHEMATICS. *Educ:* Harvey Mudd Col, BSc, 63; Wesleyan Univ, PhD(math), 67. *Prof Exp:* Asst prof math, Harvey Mudd Col, 67-68 & Univ Hawaii, 68-69; Killam fel, Dalhousie Univ, 69-71; asst prof, 71-75, ASSOC PROF MATH, UNIV MASS, AMHERST, 75- *Concurrent Pos:* NSF grants, 72-74, 75-77 & 77-79. *Mem:* Math Asn Am; Am Math Soc; Asn Comput Mach. *Res:* Applied category theory, semantics of computation, universal algebra. *Mailing Add:* Dept of Math & Statist Univ of Mass Amherst MA 10003

MANES, KENNNETH RENE, b Brooklyn, NY, Oct, 9, 42; m 69; c 3. INERTIAL CONFINEMENT FUSION, LASER PHYSICS. *Educ:* Purdue Univ, BS, 65; Stanford Univ, MS, 67, PhD(elec eng),70. *Prof Exp:* Killam fel teaching & res, Elec Eng Dept, Univ Alberta, Can, 70-72; PROJ MGR & PROJ SCIENTIST, LASER FUSION RES Y-PROG, NOVETTE PROJ, LAWRENCE LIVERMORE NAT LAB, 72- *Mem:* Am Physical Soc. *Res:* Green laser for fusion studies. *Mailing Add:* Lawrence Livermore Nat Lab Box 5508 Livermore CA 94550

MANES, MILTON, b New York, NY, Oct 14, 18; m 45; c 2. PHYSICAL CHEMISTRY. *Educ:* City Col New York, BS, 37; Duke Univ, PhD(phys chem), 47. *Prof Exp:* From lab asst to jr chemist, US Food & Drug Admin, 37-41; phys chemist, US Bur Mines, 47-52; sr chemist & mgr statist design group, Koppers Co, Inc, 52-58; supvr phys chem res, Pittsburgh Chem Co, 59-64; sr fel & head adsorption fel, Mellon Inst, 64-67; PROF CHEM, KENT STATE UNIV, 67- *Concurrent Pos:* Vis prof, Cornell Univ, 64. *Mem:* AAAS; Am Chem Soc. *Res:* Adsorption; near equilibrium thermodynamics and kinetics. *Mailing Add:* Dept of Chem Kent State Univ Kent OH 44242

MANEY, CHARLES THOMAS, systems analysis & engineering, see previous edition

MANGAN, GEORGE FRANCIS, JR, b Lowell, Mass, Feb 4, 25; m 48. BIOCHEMISTRY. *Educ:* St Anselm's Col, BA, 50; Georgetown Univ, MS, 54, PhD, 56. *Prof Exp:* Res chemist, US Fish & Wildlife Serv, 50-51; res chemist, USDA, 51-53; res biochemist, Walter Reed Army Inst Res, 53-57; proj leader, US Fish & Wildlife Serv, 57-58; sr chemist, Ionics, Inc, 58-61; chief br org & biol chem, Off Saline Water, 61-65, water resources scientist, Off Water Resources Res, 65-74, CHIEF PHYS CHEM DIV, OFF WATER RES & TECHNOL, US DEPT INTERIOR, 74- *Mem:* AAAS; Am Chem Soc; Am Geophys Union. *Res:* Water resources planning and management; urban water resources research; contract and grant research program administration. *Mailing Add:* Off of Water Res & Technol US Dept Interior 19th & C St NW Washington DC 20240

MANGAN, JERROME, b Columbus, Ohio, Nov 18, 34; div; c 2. DEVELOPMENTAL BIOLOGY, GENETICS. *Educ:* Univ Cincinnati, BA, 60, MS, 63; Brown Univ, PhD(biol), 66. *Prof Exp:* NSF fel, Albert Einstein Col Med, 66-67; asst prof biol, Univ Chicago, 67-70; asst prof, 70-72, assoc prof, 72-76, PROF BIOL, CALIF STATE UNIV, FRESNO, 76-, CHMN DEPT, 78- *Concurrent Pos:* Am Cancer Soc & NIH grants, Univ Chicago, 67-68; NSF grant, Univ Chicago & Fresno State Col, 68-72. *Mem:* Genetics Soc Am; Am Soc Microbiol. *Res:* The nature of control of biochemical processes in bacteria and lower eukaryotic organisms. *Mailing Add:* Dept of Biol Calif State Univ Fresno CA 93740

MANGAN, ROBERT LAWRENCE, b Washington, DC, Aug 6, 45; m 78. ECOLOGY, ENTOMOLOGY. *Educ:* Kent State Univ, BA, 67; Univ Ariz, PhD(ecol), 78. *Prof Exp:* Res asst ecol, US Int Biol Prog, Desert Biome Validation Prog, 74-77; res assoc ecol, US Pasture Res Lab, Pa State Univ, 78-81; RES ENTOMOLOGIST, SCREWWORM PROJ, TEX A&M UNIV, 82- *Mem:* Entom Soc Am; Ecol Soc Am; Pan Pac Entom Soc; AAAS. *Res:* Theoretical and experimental studies of insect community ecology; reproductive behavior and population genetics; systematics of acalypterate diptera; agricultural applications of insect population and community ecology. *Mailing Add:* Tex A&M Univ College Station TX 77843

MANGANARO, JAMES LAWRENCE, b Brooklyn, NY, Aug 27, 39; m 74; c 2. PROCESS DEVELOPMENT, ECONOMIC EVALUATION. *Educ:* Mass Inst Technol, SB, 61, SM, 62; Rensselaer Polytech Inst, PhD(chem eng), 65. *Prof Exp:* Res engr electrochem, Res & Develop Ctr, Gen Elec Co, 65-67; asst prof, Manhattan Col, 67-70; SR PRIN ENGR CHEM ENG, FMC CORP, 70- *Concurrent Pos:* Consult, Charles A Manganaro Engrs, 67- *Mem:* Am Inst Chem Engrs; Sigma Xi. *Res:* Process development for production of chlorinated isocyanurates, sodium tripolyphosphate, barium and strontium salts and organic phophate esters; heat, mass and momentum transfer; math modeling and economic evaluation. *Mailing Add:* FMC Corp PO Box 8 Princeton NJ 08540

MANGANELLI, RAYMOND M(ICHAEL), b Elizabeth, NJ. ENVIRONMENTAL SCIENCES, CHEMISTRY. *Educ:* Rutgers Univ, PhD(environ sci), 53. *Prof Exp:* PROF ENVIRON SCI, RUTGERS UNIV, 60- *Mem:* Am Indust Hyg Asn; Water Pollution Control Fedn; Air Pollution Control Asn; Am Chem Soc. *Res:* Chemistry, physics and biology of air and water pollution. *Mailing Add:* 60 Bauer Terr Hillside NJ 07205

MANGANELLO, S(AMUEL) J(OHN), b Johnstown, Pa, Jan 2, 30; m 57; c 4. PHYSICAL METALLURGY, PROCESS. *Educ:* Univ Pittsburgh, BS, 51, MS, 57. *Prof Exp:* Technologist, Res Lab, 53-56, head forgings sect, 56-62, sr res engr ord prod, 63-66, group leader heavy prod, 68-80, ASSOC RES CONSULT, RES LAB, US STEEL CORP, 66- *Mem:* Am Soc Metals; Am Inst Mining, Metall & Petrol Engrs; Am Defense Preparedness Asn. *Res:* Steel products; patents; heavy forgings; alloy steels; ordnance products; armor; rolls; railroad products; steel processing. *Mailing Add:* Res Lab US Steel Corp Monroeville PA 15146

MANGANIELLO, EUGENE J(OSEPH), b New York, NY, June 8, 14; m 45; c 4. MECHANICAL ENGINEERING. *Educ:* City Col New York, BSE, 34, EE, 35. *Prof Exp:* Mech engr, Nat Adv Comt Aeronaut, Langley Field, Va, 36-42, head heat transfer sect, 42-45, chief thermodyn br, 45-49, asst chief res, Lewis Res Ctr, NASA, 49-52, from asst dir to dep dir, 61-73; RETIRED. *Mem:* AAAS; Soc Automotive Engrs; Am Inst Aeronaut & Astronaut. *Res:* Aircraft; missiles; spacecraft propulsion; power generation. *Mailing Add:* 329 Hillcrest Dr Leucadia CA 92024

MANGANIELLO, LOUIS O J, b Waterbury, Conn, June 6, 15; m 50; c 1. NEUROSURGERY. *Educ:* Harvard Univ, AB, 37; Univ Md, MD, 42; Augusta Law Sch, JD, 67; Am Bd Neurol Surg, dipl. *Prof Exp:* Fel neurosurg, Sch Med, Univ Md, 46-47; asst resident, Univ Md Hosp, 47-48, chief resident, 49-50; asst resident, Baltimore City Hosp, 48-49; instr neuroanat & neurosurg, Sch Med, Univ Md, 50-51; ASSOC PROF NEUROSURG, MED COL GA, 51- *Concurrent Pos:* Consult, Hosps, Ga. *Mem:* Am Asn Neurol Surg; Am Asn Cancer Res; AMA; Am Psychiat Asn; fel Am Col Surg. *Res:* Cancer detection and therapy; porphyrin metabolism. *Mailing Add:* 656 Milledge Rd Augusta GA 30904

MANGANO, RICHARD MICHAEL, b Mt Vernon, NY, Mar 2, 50. NEUROCHEMISTRY, NEUROPHARMACOLOGY. *Educ:* Iona Col, BS, 72; Fordham Univ, PhD(biochem), 80. *Prof Exp:* Instr gen chem, Manhattan Col, 77-79; fac res assoc, Md Psychiat Res Ctr, Sch Med, Univ Md, 79-81; FEL, DEPT PHARMACOL, HOFFMANN-LA ROCHE INC, 81- *Concurrent Pos:* Teaching asst, Dept Chem, Fordham Univ, 73-77. *Mem:* Am Chem Soc; Soc Neurosci; Sigma Xi. *Res:* Biochemistry and biochemical pharmacology involving investigations in the area of cellular metabolism; model systems development toxicity and cellular degeneration and regulation of receptor liquid interaction. *Mailing Add:* Dept Pharmacol Sect Biochem Pharmacol Hoffmann-La Roche Inc Nutley NJ 07110

MANGASARIAN, OLVI LEON, b Baghdad, Iraq, Jan 12, 34; US citizen; m 59; c 3. APPLIED MATHEMATICS. *Educ:* Princeton Univ, BSE, 54, MSE, 55; Harvard Univ, PhD(appl math), 59. *Prof Exp:* Mathematician, Shell Develop Co, 59-67; lectr math programming, Univ Calif, Berkeley, 65-67; assoc prof comput sci, 67-69, chmn dept, 70-73, PROF COMPUT SCI, UNIV WIS-MADISON, 69- *Mem:* Math Prog Soc; Opers Res Soc; Soc Indust & Appl Math; Asn Comput Mach. *Res:* Development and use of theory and computational methods of mathematical programming in various fields of applied mathematics such as operations research, optimal control theory and numerical analysis. *Mailing Add:* Dept of Comput Sci Univ of Wis 1210 W Dayton St Madison WI 53706

MANGAT, BALDEV SINGH, b Ludhiana, India, May 7, 35; m 60; c 2. ENTOMOLOGY, ZOOLOGY. *Educ:* Univ Punjab, India, MSc, 58; Univ Wis, PhD(entom), 65. *Prof Exp:* Instr entom, Punjab Agr Col & Res Inst, 58-60; assoc prof biol, Alcorn Agr & Mech Col, 65-66; assoc prof, 66-69, PROF BIOL, ALA A&M UNIV, 69- *Mem:* AAAS; Entom Soc Am. *Res:* Biology and physiology of corn earworm, Heliothis zea. *Mailing Add:* Dept of Biol Ala A&M Univ Normal AL 35762

MANGE, ARTHUR P, b St Louis, Mo, Jan 28, 31; m 60; c 3. GENETICS. *Educ:* Cornell Univ, BEngPhys, 54; Univ Wis, MS, 58, PhD(genetics), 63. *Prof Exp:* Instr biol, Case Western Reserve Univ, 62-64; asst prof zool, 64-70, ASSOC PROF ZOOL, UNIV MASS, AMHERST, 70- *Concurrent Pos:* Sr res assoc, Univ Wash, 71-72. *Mem:* AAAS; Am Soc Human Genetics; Genetics Soc Am. *Mailing Add:* Dept of Zool Univ of Mass Amherst MA 01003

MANGE, FRANKLIN EDWIN, b St Louis, Mo, Feb 12, 28; m 54; c 4. ORGANIC CHEMISTRY. *Educ:* Mass Inst Technol, SB, 48; Univ Ill, PhD(org chem), 51. *Prof Exp:* Res chemist, 51-57, group leader, 57-63, sect mgr, 63-67, res dir, Tretolite Div, 67-80, SR VPRES, RES & DEVELOP, PETROLITE CORP, 80- *Mem:* Am Chem Soc; Sigma Xi. *Res:* Polymer synthesis; surfactants; waxes; demulsification; flocculation; petroleum chemistry; water treatment. *Mailing Add:* 18 Granada Way St Louis MO 63124

MANGE, PHILLIP WARREN, b Kalamazoo, Mich, June 5, 25; m 51; c 2. PLANETARY ATMOSPHERES, SPACE PHYSICS. *Educ:* Kalamazoo Col, AB, 49; Pa State Univ, MS, 52, PhD(physics), 54. *Prof Exp:* Asst prof eng res, Ionosphere Res Lab, Pa State Univ, 54-55; admin asst to gen secy, Spec Comt, Int Geophys Year, Belgium, 55-57, prog officer, US Nat Comt, Nat Acad Sci, DC, 57-59; physicist, 59-70, ASSOC SUPVR, SPACE SCI DIV, US NAVAL RES LAB, 70- *Mem:* AAAS; Am Phys Soc; Am Geophys Union; Am Astron Soc. *Res:* Structure of high atmosphere; ultraviolet environment in the solar system. *Mailing Add:* Code 4101 US Naval Res Lab Washington DC 20375

MANGELSDORF, CLARK P, b Bryan, Tex, Oct 28, 28; m 51; c 3. CIVIL ENGINEERING. *Educ:* Swarthmore Col, BS, 53; Mass Inst Technol, MS, 54, ScD, 64. *Prof Exp:* Instr civil eng, Swarthmore Col, 54-56 & Univ Ill, 56-59; from asst prof to assoc prof, Swarthmore Col, 59-68; ASSOC PROF CIVIL ENG, UNIV PITTSBURGH, 68-, DIR MINING ENG, 79- *Concurrent Pos:* Res assoc, Scott Paper Co, 62-69; sr sci officer, Tech Inst Delft, Netherlands, 66-67. *Mem:* Am Soc Civil Engrs; Am Soc Eng Educ; Soc Mining Engrs. *Res:* Structural mechanics; stability of structures; mine roof support systems. *Mailing Add:* Dept Civil Eng Univ Pittsburgh Pittsburgh PA 15261

MANGELSDORF, PAUL CHRISTOPH, b Atchison, Kans, July 20, 99; m 23; c 2. ECONOMIC BOTANY, GENETICS. *Educ:* Kans State Univ, BSc, 21, LLD, 61; Harvard Univ, MS, 23, ScD(genetics), 25. *Hon Degrees:* DSc, Park Col, 60, St Benedict's Col, 65, Univ NC, 75, Harvard Univ, 77. *Prof Exp:* Asst geneticist, State Agr Exp Sta, Conn, 21-27; agronomist exp sta, Agr & Mech Col Tex, 27-36, agronomist & asst dir, 36-40, vdir, 40; prof bot, 40-62, asst dir bot mus, 40-45, dir bot mus, 45-68, chmn inst exp & appl bot, 46-68, Fisher prof natural hist, 62-68, EMER FISHER PROF NATURAL HIST, HARVARD UNIV, 68-; LECTR BOT, UNIV NC, CHAPEL HILL, 68- *Concurrent Pos:* Hon prof, San Carlos Univ, Guatemala, 56, Nat Sch Agr, Peru, 59 & Univ Buenos Aires, 80; with USDA, 44; mem, Rockefeller Agr Comn, Mex, 41, bd consults for agr, Rockefeller Found, 43-45 & 56-58; mem Nat Res Coun, 43-; mem basic res group, US Dept Defense, 53. *Mem:* Nat Acad Sci; AAAS; Am Soc Nat (pres, 51); Am Genetics Soc Am (vpres, pres, 55); Soc Econ Bot (pres, 62-63). *Res:* Genetics of maize; origin of cultivated plants. *Mailing Add:* Apt 1200 Carol Woods Chapel Hill NC 27514

MANGELSDORF, PAUL CHRISTOPH, JR, b New Haven, Conn, Jan 31, 25; m 49; c 4. MARINE GEOCHEMISTRY. *Educ:* Swarthmore Col, BA, 49; Harvard Univ, PhD(chem physics), 55. *Prof Exp:* Instr, Univ Chicago, 55-57, asst prof chem, 57-60; RES ASSOC PHYS CHEM, WOODS HOLE OCEANOG INST, 60-; assoc prof, 61-69, PROF PHYSICS, SWARTHMORE COL, 69-, CHMN DEPT, 78- *Mem:* Geochem Soc; Am Phys Soc; Am Soc Limnol & Oceanog; Am Geophys Union; Am Asn Physics Teachers. *Res:* Fluid dynamics; transport properties in liquids; thermodynamics of electrolyte solutions; chemistry of sea water. *Mailing Add:* Dept of Physics Swarthmore Col Swarthmore PA 19081

MANGELSON, FARRIN LEON, b Levan, Utah, May 12, 12; m 36; c 9. BIOCHEMISTRY, NUTRITION. *Educ:* Univ Wash, BS, 38; Utah State Univ, MS, 50, PhD, 63. *Prof Exp:* Teacher high schs, Utah, 36-41; chemist, Remington Arms Co, Inc Div, E I du Pont de Nemours & Co, 42-43; asst state chemist, Utah, 44-47; asst chem, Exp Sta, Utah State Univ, 47-49, res instr, 49-51; from instr to assoc prof, 51-67, prof chem, 67-80, CHMN DIV PHYS SCI & MATH, 69-, EMER PROF CHEM, 80- *Concurrent Pos:* Mem res staff, Univ Calif, Berkeley, 64. *Mem:* AAAS; Am Chem Soc. *Res:* Kidney function in cattle as affected by ingestion of inorganic fluorides; effect of animal fats and proteins on blood serum cholesterol level in humans; molecular size of myosin; human nutrition. *Mailing Add:* 490 E College Ave Ephraim UT 84627

MANGELSON, NOLAN FARRIN, b Nephi, Utah, Jan 17, 36; m 61; c 7. PHYSICAL CHEMISTRY, NUCLEAR PHYSICS. *Educ:* Utah State Univ, BS, 61; Brigham Young Univ, MS, 63; Univ Calif, Berkeley, PhD(chem), 68. *Prof Exp:* Res fel, Nuclear Physics Lab, AEC, Univ Wash, 67-69; asst prof, 69-78, PROF CHEM, BRIGHAM YOUNG UNIV, 78- *Mem:* Am Chem Soc; Am Phys Soc; Sigma Xi. *Res:* Particle induced x-ray emission methods are developed and used for element analysis of air particulates, plant and animal samples, water, etc; Nuclear reactions and spectroscopy. *Mailing Add:* Dept of Chem Brigham Young Univ Provo UT 84601

MANGEN, LAWRENCE RAYMOND, b Minneapolis, Minn, Sept 12, 27; m 50; c 3. GEOLOGY, PETROLEUM ENGINEERING. *Educ:* Univ Minn, BS, 55, MS, 57. *Prof Exp:* Jr engr, Shell Oil Co, 57, field engr, 57-59, work over engr, 59-61, prod geologist, 61-62; engr, US Fed Power Comn, 62-68, supvr eng, 68, asst sect head eng, 68-77; br chief, Fed Energy Admin, 77-78; sr staff engr, Energy Info Admin, 78-79, sr tech advr, 79-81, SR STAFF ENGR, OIL & GAS RESERVES & PROD EVAL, US DEPT ENERGY, 81- *Mem:* Fel AAAS; Soc Petrol Eng. *Mailing Add:* 2724 Keystone Lane Bowie MD 20715

MANGER, MARTIN C, b Bethlehem, Pa, Sept 20, 37; m 63. ORGANIC CHEMISTRY, ENVIRONMENTAL SCIENCES. *Educ:* Muhlenberg Col, BS, 59; St Lawrence Univ, MS, 61; Rutgers Univ, MS, 65; Sheffield Univ, PhD(chem), 68. *Prof Exp:* Res chemist, E R Squibb & Sons, Inc, 64-65; assoc prof, 68-73, PROF CHEM, ALA A&M UNIV, 73- *Concurrent Pos:* Sci consult, Asn Educ & Prof Opportunities Found prog for gifted children, 68- *Mem:* Am Chem Soc; Royal Soc Chem; Am Inst Chem. *Res:* Natural products; conformational inversion of bridged biphenyls; pollution technology; biological pigments. *Mailing Add:* Dept of Chem Ala A&M Univ Normal AL 35762

MANGER, WALTER LEROY, b Baltimore, Md, Sept 24, 44; m 67; c 1. BIOSTRATIGRAPHY, PALEONTOLOGY. *Educ:* Col Wooster, BA, 66; Univ Iowa, MS, 69, PhD(geol), 71. *Prof Exp:* Asst prof geol, Northeastern Univ, 71-72; from asst prof to assoc prof, 72-81, PROF GEOL, UNIV ARK, FAYETTEVILLE, 81- *Concurrent Pos:* Cur geol, Univ Ark, Fayetteville, 72-; NSF grants Carboniferous ammonoids, 75-77, 77-79 & 80-73; subcontractor, Dames & Moore, Houston, 76; consult, Northwest Minerals, Inc, Fayetteville, 79-; expert witness, Ark Oil & Gas Comn, 80- *Mem:* Soc Econ Paleontologists & Mineralogists; Paleont Soc; Brit Palaeont Asn; Paleont Res Inst; Res Soc NAm. *Res:* Ammonoid biostratigraphy of the Carboniferous Period, particularly the Mississippian-Pennsylvanian boundary, on a worldwide basis; ammonoid phylogeny and taxonomy, and carboniferous lithostratigraphy of North American midcontinent. *Mailing Add:* Dept of Geol Univ of Ark Fayetteville AR 72701

MANGER, WILLIAM MUIR, b Greenwich, Conn, Aug 13, 20; m 64; c 4. MEDICINE. *Educ:* Yale Univ, BS, 44; Columbia Univ, MD, 46; Univ Minn, PhD(med), 58; Am Bd Internal Med, dipl, 57. *Prof Exp:* Intern med, Columbia Presby Med Ctr, 46-47, resident, 49-50; instr, Col Physicians & Surgeons, Columbia Univ, 57-66; asst clin prof, Med Ctr, NY Univ, 68-75; assoc, 66-69, LECTR, COL PHYSICIANS & SURGEONS, COLUMBIA UNIV, 80-; ASSOC CLIN PROF, MED CTR, NY UNIV, 75- *Concurrent Pos:* Dir, Manger Res Found, 58-77; chmn, Nat Hypertension Asn, 77-; asst physician, Presby Hosp, 57-66, asst attend, 66-70; clin asst vis physician, Columbia Div, Bellevue Hosp, 64-68; asst attend, Dept Med, Bellevue Hosp, 69-77, assoc attend, 77-; trustee, Found Res in Med & Biol, 70-77; consult, Southampton Hosp, 71-; trustee, Found For Advan Int Res in Microbiol, 75-; mem cent adv comt sect circulation, Am Heart Asn, fel coun circulation, mem coun high blood pressure res; ed, Am Lect in Endocrinol, 62-75. *Honors & Awards:* Meritorious Res Award, Mayo Found, 55. *Mem:* Am Physiol Soc; Soc Pharmacol & Exp Therapeut; fel Am Col Clin Pharmacol; fel Acad Psychosom Med; Soc Exp Biol & Med. *Res:* Chemical quantitation of epinephrine and norepinephrine in plasma and relationship of these pressor amines to hypertension, circulatory shock and mental disease; phiochromocytoma; endocrine aspects of tumor development. *Mailing Add:* 8 E 81st St New York NY 10028

MANGHAM, JESSE ROGER, b Plains, Ga, Nov 18, 22; m 43; c 5. ORGANIC CHEMISTRY. *Educ:* Univ Ga, BS, 43; Ohio State Univ, MS, 46, PhD(org chem), 48. *Prof Exp:* Asst, Ohio State Univ, 43-44 & 46-48; res chemist, Va-Carolina Chem Corp, 49-51, group leader org chem, 51-53, sect leader, 53-54; proj leader, 54-67, sr appln chemist, 67-71, appln res assoc, 70-77, SR ENVIRON HEALTH ASSOC, ETHYL CORP, 77- *Mem:* Am Chem Soc; Sigma Xi. *Res:* Organometallics of aluminum, magnesium and boron; organophosphorus chemistry; brominated chemicals; chlorinated solvents. *Mailing Add:* Ethyl Corp 451 Florida Blvd Baton Rouge LA 70801

MANGHNANI, MURLI HUKUMAL, b Karachi, Pakistan, Apr 4, 36; m 62; c 4. GEOPHYSICS, GEOCHEMISTRY. *Educ:* Jaswant Col, India, BS, 54; Indian Sch Mines & Appl Geol, Dhanbad, BS, 57; Bihar Univ, MS, 58; Mont State Univ, PhD(geochem, geol, geophys), 62. *Prof Exp:* Fel geophys & NSF res grant, Univ Wis, 62-63; from asst prof to assoc prof geophys & geochem, 64-76, PROF GEOPHYS, UNIV HAWAII, 76-; GEOPHYSICIST, HAWAII INST GEOPHYS, 74- *Concurrent Pos:* Asst geophysicist, Hawaii Inst Geophys, 63-74; prog dir, Exp & Theoret Geophys, Div Earth Sci, NSF, Washington, DC, 81-82. *Mem:* Am Geophys Union; Am Ceramic Soc; AAAS; Geol, Mining & Metall Soc India. *Res:* High pressure and temperature laboratory experimentation of rock materials believed to form the lower crust and upper mantle of the earth; gravity; seismology. *Mailing Add:* Hawaii Inst of Geophys Univ of Hawaii 2525 Correa Rd Honolulu HI 96822

MANGLITZ, GEORGE RUDOLPH, b Washington, DC, Aug 26, 26; m 53; c 5. ENTOMOLOGY. *Educ:* Univ Md, BS, 51, MS, 52; Univ Nebr, PhD(entom), 62. *Prof Exp:* Asst entomologist, United Fruit Co, Guatemala, 51; assoc prof entom, 65-73, RES ENTOMOLOGIST, USDA, UNIV NEBR, LINCOLN, 52-, PROF ENTOM, UNIV, 73- *Mem:* Entom Soc Am; Am Inst Biol Sci. *Res:* Field crop insects, particularly plant resistance to insects. *Mailing Add:* Forage Insect Lab USDA Univ of Nebr Lincoln NE 68583

MANGO, FRANK DONALD, b San Francisco, Calif, Dec 31, 32; m 59; c 2. ORGANIC CHEMISTRY, INORGANIC CHEMISTRY. *Educ:* San Jose State Col, BS, 59; Stanford Univ, PhD(chem), 63. *Prof Exp:* ORG CHEMIST, SHELL DEVELOP CO, 63- *Mem:* Am Chem Soc. *Res:* Geochemistry, catalysis. *Mailing Add:* 806 Soboda Ct Houston TX 77079

MANGOLD, DONALD J, b Lacoste, Tex, July 1, 29; m 61; c 3. ORGANIC CHEMISTRY, POLYMER CHEMISTRY. *Educ:* St Edward's Univ, BS, 50; Univ Tex, Austin, PhD(chem), 54. *Prof Exp:* Group leader, Olin Corp, 54-60, sect chief, 60-63, tech field rep, 63-66, proj mgr, 66-69; dir res & develop, Flecto Co, 69-72; mgr floor prod div, West Chem Prod, Inc, 72-77; MGR ORG & POLYMER SECT, DEPT APPL CHEM & CHEM ENG, SOUTHWEST RES INST, 77- *Mem:* Am Chem Soc; Am Inst Chemists; Am Inst Astronaut & Aeronaut; Sigma Xi. *Mailing Add:* Dept Appl Chem & Chem Eng PO Drawer 28510 San Antonio TX 78284

MANGULIS, VISVALDIS, b Tukums, Latvia, Nov 25, 30; US citizen; m 53; c 2. APPLIED MATHEMATICS, SYSTEMS ENGINEERING. *Educ:* Brooklyn Col, BS, 56; NY Univ, MS, 58. *Prof Exp:* Scientist, TRG, Inc, Control Data Corp, 56-62, sect head, 62-68; mem tech staff, Gen Tel & Electronics Labs, 68; sr staff consult, Comput Applns, Inc, 68-70; vpres & treas, Questek, Inc, 70-75; prin mem eng staff, Missile & Surface Radar Div, 75-78, MEM TECH STAFF, RCA LABS, 78- *Mem:* Am Phys Soc; Acoust Soc Am; Inst Elec & Electronics Engrs. *Res:* Design of radar systems, satellite communications; aircraft collision avoidance; operations research; sonar, phased arrays; acoustics; wave radiation and propagation; hydrodynamics; nuclear reactor shielding. *Mailing Add:* 127 Ainsworth Ave East Brunswick NJ 08816

MANGUM, BILLY WILSON, b Mize, Miss, Dec 8, 31; m 63; c 1. LOW TEMPERATURE PHYSICS, SOLID STATE PHYSICS. *Educ:* Univ Southern Miss, BA, 53; Tulane Univ, MS, 55; Univ Chicago, PhD(phys chem), 60. *Prof Exp:* NSF fel physics, Clarendon Lab, Oxford, 60-61; actg sect chief low temperature physics, 67-68, PHYSICIST, NAT BUR STANDARDS, 61- *Mem:* Am Phys Soc. *Res:* Magnetism at very low temperatures; cooperative phenomena; electron-lattice interactions. *Mailing Add:* Nat Bur Standards Phys B128 Washington DC 20234

MANGUM, CHARLOTTE P, b Richmond, Va, May 19, 38. INVERTEBRATE ZOOLOGY, COMPARATIVE PHYSIOLOGY. *Educ:* Vassar Col, AB, 59; Yale Univ, MS, 61, PhD(biol), 63. *Prof Exp:* Res assoc biol, Yale Univ, 63; NIH res fel zool, Bedford Col, London, 63-64; from asst prof to assoc prof biol, 64-74, PROF BIOL, COL WILLIAM & MARY, 74- *Concurrent Pos:* Assoc, Va Inst Marine Sci, 64-; vis investr, Marine Biol Lab, Mass, 66, instr, 69-73; NSF res grants, 66-75; Col William & Mary fac res fel, 73; mem, Corp Marine Biol Lab, Woods Hole; lectr, Univ Aarhus, Denmark, 74. *Mem:* Fel AAAS; fel Am Soc Zool; Marine Biol Asn UK; Am Physiol Soc; Brit Soc Exp Biol. *Res:* Comparative physiology of respiratory pigments; temperature adaptation. *Mailing Add:* Dept of Biol Col of William & Mary Williamsburg VA 23185

MANGUM, JOHN HARVEY, b Rexburg, Idaho, Apr 16, 33; m 57; c 3. BIOCHEMISTRY. *Educ:* Brigham Young Univ, BS, 57, MS, 59; Univ Wash, PhD(biochem), 63. *Prof Exp:* Res assoc biochem, Scripps Clin & Res Found, 62-63; from asst prof to assoc prof, 63-74, PROF CHEM, BRIGHAM YOUNG UNIV, 74- *Mem:* Am Chem Soc. *Res:* Enzymology; one-carbon metabolism; methionine biosynthesis; virus-induced acquisition of metabolic function; folate mediated reactions in brain metabolism. *Mailing Add:* Dept of Chem Brigham Young Univ Provo UT 84601

MANGUS, MARVIN D, b Altoona, Pa, Sept 13, 24; m 50; c 2. GEOLOGY. *Educ:* Pa State Univ, BS, 45, MS, 46. *Prof Exp:* Geologist, US Geol Surv, 47-58; sr geologist, Guatemalan Atlantic Corp, 58-60; surface geologist, Atlantic Refining Co, Pa, 60-65, sr surface geologist, Alaska, 65-69; consult geologist, Calderwood & Mangus, 69-76; INDEPENDENT CONSULT GEOLOGIST, 76- *Mem:* Explorer's Club; Am Asn Petrol Geol; Can Soc Petrol Geol; fel Geol Soc Am; Am Inst Prof Geol. *Res:* Surface geologic mapping and regional geologic studies in Alaska, Central America, Canada and Bolivia; geological mapping in arctic Alaska, the British Mountains of northern Yukon Territory, the arctic islands of Canada and the Northwest Territories of Canada; geological well site; environmental studies of Alaska. *Mailing Add:* 1045 E 27th Ave Anchorage AK 99504

MANHART, JOSEPH HERITAGE, b Greencastle, Ind, Mar 26, 30; m 57; c 2. ORGANIC CHEMISTRY. *Educ:* DePauw Univ, AB, 52; Ohio State Univ, PhD(org chem), 60. *Prof Exp:* SR SCIENTIST, ALCOA TECH CTR, ALUMINUM CO AM, 60- *Mem:* Am Chem Soc; Sci Res Soc Am. *Res:* Anodizing electrolytes; fire retardant fillers; lithographic printing plates; ultraviolet curable coatings. *Mailing Add:* Alcoa Center PA 15069

MANHART, ROBERT (AUDLEY), b Charleston, Ill, Oct 5, 25; m 49; c 2. ELECTRICAL ENGINEERING. *Educ:* Rose Polytech Inst, BS, 45; Univ Ill, MS, 47; Stanford Univ, PhD(elec eng), 61. *Prof Exp:* Design engr, Radio Corp Am, 45-46; develop engr, NAm Aviation, Inc, 47-48; head electronics dept, Res & Develop Div, NMex Sch Mines, 48-50; develop engr, Bell Aircraft Corp, 50-51; supvr electronic instruments group, Calif Res & Develop Co, Standard Oil Co Calif, 51-54, res engr, Calif Res Corp, 54-55; from asst to assoc prof elec eng, Univ Ariz, 55-58 & Ariz State Univ, 59-61; chmn dept, 61-77, PROF ELEC ENG, UNIV NEV, RENO, 61- *Concurrent Pos:* Consult, Wesix Elec Heater Co, 56-57, US Army Electronic Proving Ground, 57-58, Sperry Phoenix Co, 59, Motorola, Inc, 60, Edgerton, Germeshausen & Grier, Inc, Nev, 61-65, Lawrence Livermore Lab, 71- & Los Alamos Nat Lab, 72- *Mem:* Sr mem Inst Elec & Electronics Engrs; Am Soc Eng Educ; Nat Soc Prof Engrs; Sigma Xi. *Res:* Theoretical and experimental semiconductor device research; circuit theory and network synthesis; nanosecond pulse systems including superconductors; fiber optic communication systems. *Mailing Add:* Dept Elec Eng Univ Nev Reno NV 89557

MANHAS, MAGHAR SINGH, b Kothe Manhasan, India, Aug 17, 22; m 53; c 5. ORGANIC CHEMISTRY. *Educ:* Punjab Univ, India, BSc, 43; Allahabad Univ, MSc, 45, DPhil, 50. *Hon Degrees:* MEng, Stevens Inst Technol, 74. *Prof Exp:* Asst prof chem, BR Col, Agra, India, 50-52 & Univ Saugar, 52-60; from asst prof to assoc prof, 61-70, PROF CHEM, STEVENS INST TECHNOL, 70- *Concurrent Pos:* Res assoc, Stevens Inst Technol, 60-61; Ottens res award, 68. *Honors & Awards:* Davis Award, 81. *Mem:* Am Chem Soc; fel Royal Soc Chem; Sigma Xi. *Res:* Heterocyclic chemistry; medicinal chemistry; stereochemistry. *Mailing Add:* Dept of Chem & Chem Eng Stevens Inst of Technol Hoboken NJ 07030

MANHEIM, FRANK T, b Leipzig, Ger, Oct 14, 30; US citizen; m 61; c 3. GEOCHEMISTRY. *Educ:* Harvard Univ, AB, 51; Univ Minn, MSc, 53; Univ Stockholm, Fil Lic, 61, DSc(geochem), 74. *Prof Exp:* Geochemist, Geol Surv, Sweden, 61-62; fel & res asst strontium isotopes, Yale Univ, 63; res geologist, US Geol Surv, 64-73; chmn dept marine sci, Univ S Fla, 74-76; OFFICER MARINE GEOL, US GEOL SURV, 76- *Concurrent Pos:* Mem, Nat Acad Sci Comt on USSR & Eastern Europe, 75-78; Deep Sea Drilling Proj; Adv Panel Inorg Geochem. *Mem:* AAAS; Am Geophys Union; Geochem Soc; Swedish Geol Soc. *Res:* Geochemistry of recent and fossil sediments; marine resources; chemistry of ground and natural waters; suspended matter in ocean waters; aquaculture marine policy and scientific communications. *Mailing Add:* US Geol Surv Off Marine Geol Woods Hole MA 02543

MANHEIM, JEROME HENRY, mathematics, see previous edition

MANHEIM, MARVIN LEE, b Elizabeth, NJ, May 14, 37. CIVIL ENGINEERING. *Educ:* Mass Inst Technol, BS, 59, PhD(transp, urban planning), 64. *Prof Exp:* Asst transp & urban planning, Joint Ctr Urban Studies, Mass Inst Technol & Harvard Univ, 59-60; asst civil eng systs lab, 60-62, from instr to assoc prof civil eng, 62-72, PROF CIVIL ENG, MASS INST TECHNOL, 72-, DIR TRANSP & COMMUNITY VALUES PROJ, URBAN SYSTS LAB, 68- *Concurrent Pos:* Mem, Hwy Res Bd, Nat Acad Sci-Nat Res Coun & Transp Res Forum. *Res:* Transportation systems analysis; urban and regional planning; social and environmental aspects of engineering projects; decision theories. *Mailing Add:* Dept of Civil Eng Mass Inst of Technol 1-138 Cambridge MA 02139

MANHEIMER, WALLACE MILTON, b New York, NY, Feb 10, 42; m 65; c 3. PLASMA PHYSICS. *Educ:* Mass Inst Technol, BS, 63, PhD(physics), 67. *Prof Exp:* Prof physics, Mass Inst Technol, 68-70; PHYSICIST, NAVAL RES LABS, 70- *Mem:* Am Phys Soc. *Res:* Turbulence theory; laser plasma interaction; relativistic beams; controlled thermonuclear fusion. *Mailing Add:* Code 4790 Naval Res Labs Washington DC 20390

MANHOLD, JOHN HENRY, JR, b Rochester, NY, Aug 20, 19; m 71; c 1. PATHOLOGY. *Educ:* Univ Rochester, BA, 40; Harvard Univ, DMD, 44; Wash Univ, MA, 56. *Prof Exp:* Instr oral path, Med & Dent Schs, Tufts Univ, 47-48, dir cancer teaching prog, 48-50; asst prof gen & oral path, Sch Dent, Wash Univ, 55-56; assoc prof path, 56-57, PROF GEN & ORAL PATH & DIR DEPT, UNIV MED & DENT NJ, 57- *Concurrent Pos:* Ed, Clin Prev Dent. *Mem:* AAAS; Acad Psychosom Med (pres); Am Psychol Asn; AMA; fel Am Col Dent. *Res:* Psychosomatics; oral diagnosis; tissue metabolism. *Mailing Add:* Univ Med & Dent NJ Newark NJ 07103

MANI, INDER, b India, Feb 15, 28; m 55; c 2. POLYMER CHEMISTRY. *Educ:* Agra Univ, BS, 46, MS, 48, LLB, 51; Univ Fla, PhD(chem), 66. *Prof Exp:* Asst prof chem, Meerut Col, Agra Univ, 48-63; res assoc Argonne Nat Lab, 66-68; res chemist, 68-73, res specialist, 73-79, RES LEADER, DOW CHEM CO, 79- *Res:* Gamma-radiolysis and pulsed-radiolysis of organic compounds in the vapor and liquid state; radiation curing of organic coatings; preparation, characterization and applications of polymer latexes; polyelectrolyte complexes and new membranes for separation. *Mailing Add:* Dow Chem Co Bldg 1712 Midland MI 48640

MANI, RAMA I, b Madras, India, Apr 10, 27. ORGANIC CHEMISTRY, BIOLOGICAL CHEMISTRY. *Educ:* Univ Bombay, BSc, 47, MSc, 51, PhD(chem), 61. *Prof Exp:* Res scientist chem, Indian Coun Med Res, India, 51-53; res scientist chem, Coun Sci & Indust Res, 57-60; res assoc, Stanford Univ, 60-62 & Univ Southern Calif, 62-63; res assoc biol chem, Vanderbilt Univ & Meharry Med Col, 63-65; ASSOC PROF CHEM, TENN STATE UNIV, 65- *Mem:* Am Chem Soc; Sigma Xi. *Res:* Organic and medicinal chemistry; radiation research; chemical and biological studies of proteins and chemical allergenic materials inducing hypersensitivity in human and animal tissues. *Mailing Add:* Dept of Chem Tenn State Univ Nashville TN 37203

MANIAR, ATISH CHANDRA, b Unjha, India, Jan 21, 26; Can citizen; m 51; c 4. MICROBIOLOGY, PUBLIC HEALTH. *Educ:* Univ Bombay, BSc, 48, MSc, 52, PhD(microbiol), 56, DSc(microbiol), 69. *Prof Exp:* Bacteriologist, Caius Res Lab, Bombay, India, 48-55; res bacteriologist, Alembic Chem, India, 55; bacteriologist, Glaxo Labs, Bombay, 55-59; bacteriologist, Hindustan Antibiotics Ltd, India, 61-63; bacteriologist, Winnipeg Gen Hosp, 64-67; BACTERIOLOGIST, PROVENCHER MED DIAG LABS, MAN, 67- *Concurrent Pos:* Nat Res Coun Can fel antibiotics, Can Commun Dis Ctr, Ottawa, 59-61; Royal Soc Health fel, Med Col, Winnipeg, 71; lectr, St Xavier's Col, India, 48-52; mem bd studies & fac sci, Univ Bombay, 57-59; lectr, Univ Man, 64- *Mem:* Am Soc Microbiol; Can Pub Health Asn; Indian Asn Microbiol; Royal Soc Health. *Res:* Mode of action of antibiotics; aminoacidopathy in newborn babies; staphylococcal toxins. *Mailing Add:* Provencher Med Diagnostic Labs 139 Goulet St Winnipeg MB R2H 0R9 Can

MANIATIS, THOMAS PETER, molecular biology, see previous edition

MANILOFF, JACK, b Baltimore, Md, Nov 6, 38; m 60; c 2. BIOPHYSICS, MICROBIOLOGY. *Educ:* Johns Hopkins Univ, BA, 60; Yale Univ, MS, 64, PhD(biophys), 65. *Prof Exp:* Res assoc chem, Brown Univ, 64-66; asst prof, 66-71, assoc prof, 71-79, PROF MICROBIOL, UNIV ROCHESTER, 79- *Concurrent Pos:* NIH res career develop award, 70-75. *Mem:* AAAS; Biophys Soc; Am Soc Microbiol; Sigma Xi. *Res:* Molecular and cellular biology of mycoplasma cells and their viruses; theoretical aspects of biological processes. *Mailing Add:* Dept of Microbiol Univ of Rochester Rochester NY 14642

MANINGER, RALPH CARROLL, b Harper, Kans, Dec 24, 18; m 42; c 3. PHYSICS. *Educ:* Calif Inst Technol, BS, 41. *Prof Exp:* Res engr & group leader, Off Sci Res & Develop Proj, Columbia, 41-45; contract physicist, Taylor Model Basin, US Dept Navy, DC, 45, sect head, US Navy Electron Lab, Calif, 45-48; physicist, Vitro Corp Am, 48-51, from asst dir to dir phys res & develop, 51-53; tech dir, Precision Tech, Inc, 53-57, br mgr librascope div, Gen Precision, Inc, 57-62; head, Eng Res Div, Electronics Dept, 62-68, dept head electronics, Eng Dept, 68-71, head environ studies, 71-74, head, Technol Appln Group, 75-78, SR STAFF CONSULT, LAWRENCE LIVERMORE NAT LAB, UNIV CALIF, 79- *Concurrent Pos:* Mem adv comt, Statewide Air Pollution Res Ctr, Univ Calif, 71-73. *Mem:* AAAS; Acoust Soc Am; Am Defense Prep Asn; fel Inst Elec & Electronics Engrs; Nuclear & Plasma Sci Soc (pres, 81-82). *Res:* Under-water acoustics and electronics; non-linear vibrations; solid state radiation detectors and electron devices; high speed pulse circuity; microwave generation and propagation; initiation of explosives; fast reactions in solids; quantum electronics; environmental systems research; radioactve waste management. *Mailing Add:* 146 Roan Dr Danville CA 94526

MANION, JAMES J, b Butte, Mont, May 17, 22; m 46; c 3. ECOLOGY. *Educ:* Univ Portland, BS, 48; Univ Notre Dame, MS, 50, PhD(zool), 52. *Prof Exp:* Asst prof biol & head dept, St Mary's Col, 52-58; assoc prof biol sci, 58-71, chmn div natural sci & math, 58-77, PROF BIOL, CARROLL COL, 71- *Concurrent Pos:* Dean fac, Carroll Col, 54-71, acad vpres, 66-71. *Mem:* AAAS. *Res:* Ecology of amphibians. *Mailing Add:* Div of Natural Sci & Math Carroll Col Helena MT 59601

MANION, JERALD MONROE, b Beebe, Ark, Sept 24, 40; m 59; c 2. ORGANIC CHEMISTRY. *Educ:* Harding Col, BS, 62; Univ Miss, PhD(chem), 65. *Prof Exp:* PROF CHEM & CHMN DEPT, UNIV CENT ARK, 65- *Mem:* Am Chem Soc. *Res:* Gas phase kinetics of reverse Diels-Alder reactions. *Mailing Add:* Dept of Chem Univ of Cent Ark Conway AR 72032

MANIOTIS, JAMES, b Detroit, Mich, Aug 17, 29; m 55; c 1. MYCOLOGY. *Educ:* Wayne State Univ, AB, 52, MS, 57; Univ Iowa, PhD(bot), 60. *Prof Exp:* Res assoc virol, Child's Res Ctr, Mich, 56-57; asst bot, Univ Iowa, 57-60; instr bot, Univ Tex, 60-61; asst prof biol, Wayne State Univ, 61-65; assoc prof bot, 65-69, ASSOC PROF BIOL, WASH UNIV, 69- *Mem:* AAAS; Mycol Soc Am; Bot Soc Am; Am Inst Biol Sci. *Res:* Biochemical-genetical bases for pathogenicity in ringworm fungi; biology of membrane fusion in slime molds. *Mailing Add:* Dept of Biol Wash Univ St Louis MO 63130

MANIRE, GEORGE PHILIP, b Roanoke, Tex, Mar 25, 19; m 43; c 2. MICROBIOLOGY. *Educ:* NTex State Col, BS, 40, MS, 41; Univ Calif, Berkeley, PhD(bact), 49. *Prof Exp:* Instr bact, Univ Tex Southwestern Med Sch, 49-50; from asst prof to assoc prof, 50-59, asst vchancellor health sci, 65-66, chmn dept, 66-79, PROF BACT, SCH MED, UNIV NC, CHAPEL HILL, 59-, KENAN PROF, 71-, VCHANCELLOR & GRAD DEAN, 79- *Concurrent Pos:* Fulbright scholar, Serum Inst, Copenhagen, 56; China Med Bd Alan Gregg fel, Virus Inst, Kyoto, Japan, 63-64; USPHS spec fel, Lister Inst, London, 71-72; mem health sci advan award comt, NIH, 67-71 & chmn, 69-71; vis scientist, Japan Soc Promotion Sci, 79. *Mem:* Am Asn Immunol; Am Acad Microbiol; Infectious Dis Soc Am; Am Soc Microbiol; fel AAAS. *Res:* Mechanisms of pathogenesis of microorganisms, especially diseases of Chlamydia. *Mailing Add:* Dept of Bact & Immunol Univ of NC Sch of Med Chapel Hill NC 27514

MANIS, ARCHIE L, b Oklahoma City, Okla, Nov 1, 39; m 71; c 2. PLANT PATHOLOGY, MYCOLOGY. *Educ:* Abilene Christian Univ, BS, 61; Sam Houston State Univ, MEd, 66; Tex A&M Univ, PhD(plant path), 71. *Prof Exp:* Asst prof biol, David Lipscomb Col, 71-73; asst prof & chmn div math & sci, Jackson State Community Col, 73-76; ASSOC PROF BIOL, ABILENE CHRISTIAN UNIV, 76- *Mem:* Int Soc Plant Pathologists; Am Phytopathological Soc. *Res:* Fungal physiology; antibiotics, fungicides and fungistats. *Mailing Add:* Dept of Biol Box 8035 ACU Sta Abilene TX 79601

MANIS, MERLE E, b St Ignatius, Mont, Aug 20, 34; m 61; c 4. MATHEMATICS. *Educ:* Univ Mont, BA, 60, MA, 61; Univ Ore, PhD(math), 66. *Prof Exp:* From instr to asst prof, 62-73, assoc prof, 73-78, PROF MATH, UNIV MONT, 78- *Concurrent Pos:* NSF res contract, 67-68. *Mem:* Am Math Soc. *Res:* Ring theory; valuation theory; D K Harrison's theory of primes; pruffer rings; rings with several objects. *Mailing Add:* Dept Math Univ Mont Missoula MT 59812

MANISCALCO, IGNATIUS ANTHONY, b New York, NY, June 25, 44; m 67; c 2. ORGANIC CHEMISTRY, BIOCHEMISTRY. *Educ:* Manhattan Col, BS, 65; Fordham Univ, PhD(org chem), 71. *Prof Exp:* Instr chem, Univ Va, 70-71; asst prof, 71-78, ASSOC PROF CHEM, SPRINGFIELD COL, 78- *Concurrent Pos:* Res fel, Univ Va, 70-71. *Mem:* Am Chem Soc. *Res:* Heterocyclic organic chemistry. *Mailing Add:* Dept of Chem Springfield Col Box 1656 Springfield MA 01109

MANISCALCO, JAMES ANDREW, nuclear engineering, fusion engineering, see previous edition

MANITIUS, ANDRZEJ ZDZISLAW, control theory, applied mathematics, see previous edition

MANJARREZ, VICTOR M, b Los Angeles, Calif, June 13, 33; m 66. MATHEMATICS. *Educ:* Spring Hill Col, BS, 57; Harvard Univ, MA, 58, PhD(math), 63. *Prof Exp:* Instr math, Cath Univ Am, 65-67; asst prof, Univ Houston, 67-71; assoc prof, 71-75, PROF MATH, CALIF STATE UNIV, HAYWARD, 75- *Mem:* Am Math Soc; Math Asn Am. *Res:* Interpolation and approximation in the complex domain; topological vector spaces. *Mailing Add:* Dept of Math Calif State Univ Hayward CA 94542

MANJOINE, MICHAEL J(OSEPH), b Muscatine, Iowa, Apr 29, 14; m 38; c 2. MECHANICAL METALLURGY. *Educ:* Iowa State Univ, BSME, 36, BSEE, 37; Univ Pittsburgh, MS, 39. *Prof Exp:* Res engr, Res Labs, 40-61, mgr eng mech, 61-63, consult reactor eng, Astronuclear Lab, 63-69, CONSULT ENGR, MECH DEPT, WESTINGHOUSE ELEC CORP, 69- *Concurrent Pos:* Am chmn, Int Conf on Creep, 63. *Honors & Awards:* Dudley Medal, Am Soc Testing & Mat, 53. *Mem:* Fel Am Soc Mech Engrs; fel Am Soc Metals. *Res:* Mechanics of materials; elevated temperature properties of materials; high speed tensile testing; effect of notches; testing machine design. *Mailing Add:* 25 Lewin Lane Pittsburgh PA 15235

MANKA, CHARLES K, b Flemington, Mo, Sept 28, 38; m 61; c 1. PLASMA PHYSICS, SPECTROSCOPY. *Educ:* William Jewell Col, AB, 60; Univ Ark, MS, 64, PhD(plasma physics), 65. *Prof Exp:* Asst prof, 65-68, dir dept, 68-75, PROF PHYSICS, SAM HOUSTON STATE UNIV, 75- *Res:* Temperatures of exploding wires and other transient plasma formed in vacuum; applications to criminology and police science; forensic physics. *Mailing Add:* Dept of Physics Sam Houston State Univ Huntsville TX 77341

MANKAU, REINHOLD, b Chicago, Ill, July 22, 28; m 54; c 2. NEMATOLOGY, SOIL BIOLOGY. *Educ:* Univ Ill, BS, 51, MS, 53, PhD(plant path), 56. *Prof Exp:* Res asst, Univ Ill, 54-56; Fulbright res fel, India, 56-57; asst nematologist, 58-63, assoc nematologist & assoc prof, 63-75, PROF NEMATOL, UNIV CALIF, RIVERSIDE, 75- *Concurrent Pos:* Fulbright res fel, India, 64-65. *Mem:* Am Phytopath Soc; Mycol Soc Am; Soc Nematol; Indian Phytopath Soc; Soc Europ Nematologists. *Res:* Biological control of plant-parasitic nematodes; soil biology and biochemistry; nematode-soil microbial relationships. *Mailing Add:* Dept of Nematol Univ of Calif Riverside CA 92502

MANKAU, SAROJAM KURUDAMANNIL, b Kottayam, India, June 5, 30; nat US; m 54; c 1. PARASITOLOGY, NEMATOLOGY. *Educ:* Univ Madras, BS, 49; Univ Ill, PhD(zool), 56. *Prof Exp:* Asst, Univ Ill, 53-56; instr biol, Univ Redlands, 58-59; res assoc plant nematol, Citrus Exp Sta, Univ Calif, Riverside, 59-60, asst prof zool, Univ, 60-63, res assoc nematol, 59-68; asst prof biol, 68-72, assoc prof, 72-81, PROF BIOL, CALIF STATE UNIV, SAN BERNADINO, 81- *Mem:* Am Soc Parasitol. *Res:* Helminthology; biology of soil nematodes and invertebrates. *Mailing Add:* Div Natural Sci Calif State Univ 5500 State College Pkwy San Bernadino CA 92407

MANKE, PHILLIP GORDON, b Pawhuska, Okla, Aug 27, 29; m 51; c 4. CIVIL ENGINEERING. *Educ:* Okla State Univ, BS, 56, MS, 57; Tex A&M Univ, PhD(civil eng), 65. *Prof Exp:* Civil engr, Humble Oil & Refining Co, 57-59; instr civil eng, Okla State Univ, 59-60, asst prof, 60-63; res asst pavement design, Tex A&M Univ, 64-65; from asst prof to assoc prof civil eng, 65-72, PROF CIVIL ENG, OKLA STATE UNIV, 72- *Concurrent Pos:* NSF res initiation grant, 66-67, sci res grant, 68-70; mem, Hwy Res Bd, Nat Acad Sci-Nat Res Coun; prin investr sponsored highway mat res projs, Okla Dept Transp, 72- *Mem:* Asn Asphalt Paving Technologists. *Res:* Soil-asphalt stabilization; asphaltic materials; asphalt paving mixtures; nondestructive testing of soils and highway materials. *Mailing Add:* Sch of Civil Eng Okla State Univ Stillwater OK 74078

MANKIN, CHARLES JOHN, b Dallas, Tex, Jan 15, 32; m 53; c 3. GEOLOGY. *Educ:* Univ Tex, BS, 54, MA, 55, PhD(geol), 58. *Prof Exp:* Instr geol, Univ Tex, 56-57; asst prof, Calif Inst Technol, 58-59; asst prof, 59-63, dir Sch Geol & Geophys, 64-77, PROF GEOL, UNIV OKLA, 66-, DIR ENERGY RESOURCES CTR, 78-; DIR OKLA GEOL SURV, 67- *Concurrent Pos:* Assoc prof, Univ Okla, 63-66, actg dir sch geol & geophys, 63-64; mem, Gulf Univ Res Consortium-Energy Coun, 74- & Nat Petrol Coun-Exec Adv Coun Nat Gas Surv, 75; mem, Comn Nat Resources, Nat Acad Sci-Nat Res Coun, 77- & Bd on Mineral & Energy Resources, 76- (vchmn, 77-); mem, US Nat Comt Geol, 77- *Mem:* Asn Am State Geol (pres, 75-76); Am Asn Petrol Geologists; Am Inst Prof Geologists; Geol Soc Am; Soc Econ Paleont & Mineral. *Res:* Sedimentary petrology and geochemistry; clay mineralogy. *Mailing Add:* Okla Geol Surv 830 Van Vleet Oval Norman OK 73019

MAN-KIN, MAK, b Hong Kong, China, Oct 17, 39; Brit citizen; m 66; c 2. ATMOSPHERIC SCIENCE. *Educ:* Univ Toronto, BASc, 63; Mass Inst Technol, MS, 66, PhD(meteorol), 68. *Prof Exp:* Res fel meteorol, Nat Res Coun Can, 68-69; vis assoc prof, Nat Taiwan Univ, China, 69-70; assoc prof, 70-80, PROF METEOROL, UNIV ILL, URBANA-CHAMPAIGN, 80- *Concurrent Pos:* Res grants, NSF, 72- *Mem:* Am Meteorol Soc. *Res:* Dynamics of global atmospheric waves; tropical meteorology; monsoonal circulation; general circulation of the atmosphere. *Mailing Add:* Lab Atmospheric Res Univ of Ill Urbana IL 61801

MANKIN, WILLIAM GRAY, b Memphis, Tenn, Sept 2, 40. ATMOSPHERIC SCIENCE. *Educ:* Southwestern, Memphis, BS, 62; Johns Hopkins Univ, PhD(physics), 69. *Prof Exp:* Res asst astron, Univ Mass, 67-69; sci visitor, 69-71, staff scientist, High Altitude Observ, 71-73, SCIENTIST, ATMOSPHERIC CHEM & AERONOMY DIV, NAT CTR ATMOSPHERIC RES, 73- *Concurrent Pos:* Lectr, Univ Mass, Amherst & Smith & Mt Holyoke Cols, 68-69. *Mem:* Optical Soc Am; Am Asn Physics Teachers. *Res:* Infrared spectroscopy and radiometry for geophysical and astrophysical applications; stratospheric composition; solar atmosphere; development of optical techniques for geophysics. *Mailing Add:* 545 S 44 Boulder CO 80303

MANKOVITZ, RALPH, b New York, NY, Dec 25, 33; m 56; c 2. CELL BIOLOGY. *Educ:* City Col New York, BS, 56; Univ Calif, MS, 60; Wash Univ, PhD(molecular biol), 67. *Prof Exp:* Fel, Dept Med Biophys, Univ Toronto, 68-71 & Med Res Coun, 69-71; RES SCHOLAR, NAT CANCER INST CAN & ASST PROF, DEPT PATH, QUEEN'S UNIV, 71- *Res:* Genetics of somatic mammalian cells with the long range goal of developing tools for the study of the molecular biology of growth, differentiation and cancer. *Mailing Add:* Dept of Path Richardson Lab Queen's Univ Kingston ON K7L 1M6 Can

MANLEY, CHARLES HOWLAND, b Acushnet, Mass, Feb 27, 43; m 65; c 1. FOOD CHEMISTRY. *Educ:* Southeastern Mass Univ, BS, 64; Univ Mass, Amherst, MS, 68, PhD(food sci), 69. *Prof Exp:* Sr food technologist, Nestle Co, 69-71; sr res chemist, Givaudan Corp, 71-74; group leader tea res, 74-76, mgr beverage prods develop, 76-77; mgr indust prods, Thomas J Lipton Inc, 77-81; MKT MGR, NAT FLAVORS & SEASONINGS DIV, NAT STARCH & CHEM CORP, 81- *Mem:* Am Chem Soc; Inst Food Technologists; Sigma Xi; Am Inst Chemists. *Res:* Chemistry of flavor components in natural foods; isolation and characterization of volatile and non-volatile constitutents of tea by the use of chromatographic and chemical techniques. *Mailing Add:* Nat Flavors & Seasonings Div Nat Starch/Chem Co Four Pearl Ct Allendale NJ 07401

MANLEY, EMMETT S, b Jackson, Tenn, Nov 6, 36; m 58; c 2. PHARMACOLOGY, PHYSIOLOGY. *Educ:* Univ Tenn, BS, 59, PhD(pharmacol, physiol), 63. *Prof Exp:* Asst physiol, Bowman Gray Sch Med, 64-65; from instr to asst prof, 65-72, assoc prof pharmacol, Med Units, Univ Tenn, Memphis, 72-75; PROF & CHMN, DEPT OF PHARMACOL, KIRKSVILLE COL OSTEOPATH MED, 75- *Concurrent Pos:* USPHS trainee, 64. *Mem:* Am Soc Pharmacol & Exp Therapeut. *Res:* Cardiovascular pharmacology; catecholamines; hypercapnia; acid-base balance and drug response; blood flow determination; hemorrhagic shock; myocardial function. *Mailing Add:* Dept of Pharmacol Kirksville Col Osteop Med Kirksville MO 63501

MANLEY, HAROLD J(AMES), b Brooklyn, NY, July 7, 30; m 52; c 3. COMMUNICATIONS ENGINEERING, ENGINEERING MANAGEMENT. *Educ:* Worcester Polytech Inst, BS, 52, MS, 54; Stanford Univ, Eng, 68. *Prof Exp:* Physicist, Eng Labs, Signal Corps, 52; consult, David Clark Co, Mass, 53-54; electronic engr, Appl Res Lab, Sylvania Elec Prod, Inc Div, 54-56, sr engr, 56-58, adv res engr, 58-59, eng specialist, 59-64, sr eng specialist, 64-68, mgr speech systs res dept, 68-70, mgr advan signal processing, 70-73, mgr systs eng, 73-77, ASST DIR ENG, GTE SYLVANIA ELECTRONIC SYSTS, EASTERN DIV, GEN TEL & ELECTRONICS CORP, 77- *Honors & Awards:* Leslie H Warner Tech Achievement Award, Gen Tel & Electronics Inc, 76. *Mem:* Assoc mem Inst Elec & Electronics Engrs; Acoust Soc Am. *Res:* Digital signal processing; digital communications; modulation and demodulation systems; speech processing; speech analysis-synthesis. *Mailing Add:* 33 Clark Rd Sudbury MA 01776

MANLEY, JOHN HENRY, b Harvard, Ill, July 21, 07; m 35; c 2. NUCLEAR PHYSICS. *Educ:* Univ Ill, BS, 29; Univ Mich, PhD(physics), 34. *Prof Exp:* Instr physics, Univ Mich, 31-33; lectr, Columbia Univ, 34-37; assoc, Univ Ill, 37-41, asst prof, 41-45; assoc prof, Wash Univ, 46-47; assoc dir, Los Alamos Sci Lab, 47-51; prof physics & exec officer, Univ Wash, 51-57; res adv, 57-72, CONSULT, LOS ALAMOS NAT LAB, 72- *Concurrent Pos:* Res assoc, Univ Chicago, 42-43; scientist, Los Alamos Sci Lab, 43-46; asst dir res, AEC, Washington, DC, 47; Guggenheim fel, 54; US State Dept fel, 58. *Mem:* Fel AAAS; fel Am Phys Soc. *Res:* Biophysics; nuclear physics; electron microscopy. *Mailing Add:* 1469 46th St Los Alamos NM 87544

MANLEY, ROCKLIFFE ST JOHN, b Kingston, Jamaica, Mar 26, 25; Can citizen; m 58; c 1. POLYMER CHEMISTRY. *Educ:* McGill Univ, BSc, 50, PhD(phys chem), 53; Uppsala Univ, DSc, 56. *Prof Exp:* Nat Res Coun Can fel, 53-55; RES ASSOC CHEM, McGILL UNIV, 58-; SR SCIENTIST, PULP & PAPER RES INST CAN, 58-, PRIN SCIENTIST, 78- *Concurrent Pos:* Secy-treas, Can High Polymer Forum, 67-69, prog chmn, 69-71, chmn forum, 71-73. *Mem:* AAAS; Fiber Soc; Am Phys Soc; Chem Inst Can; Tech Asn Pulp & Paper Indust. *Res:* Macromolecular science; flow properties of model disperse systems; polymer solution properties; morphology of crystalline polymers; polymer crystallization; molecular morphology and biosynthesis of cellulose. *Mailing Add:* Dept Chem McGill Univ 3420 University St Montreal PQ H3A 2A7 Can

MANLEY, RONALD PAUL, b Columbia, La, Sept 1, 54; m 81. PHOTOGRAPHIC SCIENCE, DYE CHEMISTRY. *Educ:* Northeast La Univ, BS, 74; Duke Univ, AM, 76; Pa State Univ, PhD(chem), 81. *Prof Exp:* RES SCIENTIST, ROCHESTER FILM CO, DIV OF RHONE-POULENC SYSTS CO, 81- *Mem:* Am Chem Soc; AAAS; Soc Photog Scientists & Engrs. *Res:* Investigated selective oxidations of saturated steroid side chains and carbonium ion rearrangements; photographic hardeners and dyes. *Mailing Add:* 230 Kendrick Rd Rochester NY 14620

MANLEY, STEPHEN ALEXANDER, forest genetics, see previous edition

MANLEY, THOMAS CLINTON, b Ithaca, NY, Feb 15, 11; m 40; c 2. ELECTROCHEMISTRY. *Educ:* Cornell Univ, BChem, 32, MChem, 33; Rutgers Univ, PhD(phys chem), 38. *Prof Exp:* Pilot plant engr, Welsbach Corp, 40, res engr, 41-47, asst dir res, 48-49, dir res, 49-76; CONSULT, 76- *Mem:* Am Chem Soc. *Res:* Electric discharges in gases; chemical reactions in electric discharges; ozone production properties; reactions of ozone; absorption of gases. *Mailing Add:* 3141 Maple Rd Huntingdon Valley PA 19006

MANLEY, THOMAS ROY, b McKeesport, Pa, June 15, 18; m 43; c 2. ENTOMOLOGY. *Educ:* Fairmont State Col, AB, 40; WVa Univ, MS, 46. *Prof Exp:* Horticulturist, Oglebay Inst, 46-48 & Case Western Reserve Univ, 49-52; mgr, Champlain View Gardens, 52-55; teacher, Selinsgrove Area High Sch, 56-64; prof, 64-81, EMER PROF, BLOOMSBURG STATE COL, 81- *Concurrent Pos:* John Hay fel, Yale Univ, 61-62, curatorial affil, Peabody Mus, 64-; NSF res grants, 64-65. *Honors & Awards:* NAm Gladiolus Coun Gold Medal, 48; Dean Herbert Medal, Plant Life Soc, 54; New Eng Gladiolus Soc Gold Medal, 54. *Mem:* Soc Study Evolution; Lepidopterist Soc; Entom Soc Am; Sigma Xi. *Res:* Evolution of Lepidopterous insects in suture zones of North America; genetics of genus Automeris and taxonomic status of subspecies in sympatry. *Mailing Add:* Rte 1 Box 159A Port Trevorton PA 17864

MANLY, DONALD G, b Cleveland, Ohio, Oct 7, 30; m 52; c 3. ORGANIC CHEMISTRY. *Educ:* Brown Univ, ScB, 52; Lehigh Univ, MS, 54, PhD(org chem), 56. *Prof Exp:* Proj leader chem, Quaker Oats Co, 56-57, group leader, 57-63, sect leader chem res, 63-65; res mgr chem, Glyco Chem Inc, 65-67, dir res, 67-69; assoc dir appln res, 69-71, Air Prod & Chem, Inc, dir corp res, 71-76, group dir res, 76-77; vpres res & develop, Abex Corp, 77-80; VPRES TECHNOL, ANACONDA INDUST, 80- *Mem:* Am Chem Soc; Am Oil Chem Soc; Indust Res Inst. *Res:* Heterogeneous catalysis; heterocyclic compounds; fluorine chemistry; enzyme technology; pollution control. *Mailing Add:* Anaconda Indust Two Continental Towers Rolling Meadows IL 60008

MANLY, JETHRO OATES, b NC, Jan 21, 14; m 41; c 3. PHYCOLOGY. *Educ:* Col William & Mary, BS, 37; Duke Univ, PhD, 53. *Prof Exp:* Instr biol, Col William & Mary, 46-49; instr zool, Duke Univ, 49-50, bot, 52-55; PROF BIOL, PFEIFFER COL, 55- *Mem:* Fel AAAS. *Res:* Taxonomy and distribution of marine diatoms. *Mailing Add:* Dept of Biol Pfeiffer Col Misenheimer NC 28109

MANLY, KENNETH FRED, b Cincinnati, Ohio, July 12, 41; m 62; c 2. VIROLOGY. *Educ:* Calif Inst Technol, BS, 64; Mass Inst Technol, PhD(microbiol), 69. *Prof Exp:* Sr cancer res scientist, 71-74, assoc cancer res scientist, 74-78, actg head, viral oncol dept, 78-79, CANCER RES SCIENTIST V, ROSWELL PARK MEM INST, 78- *Concurrent Pos:* Am Cancer Soc fel, Mass Inst Technol, 69-71; Nat Cancer Inst grant, 72-75, 78-81. *Mem:* AAAS; Am Soc Microbiol. *Res:* Biochemistry of tumor viruses; etiology of cancer. *Mailing Add:* Cell & Tumor Biol Dept Roswell Park Mem Inst Buffalo NY 14263

MANLY, PHILIP JAMES, b Cincinnati, Ohio, Apr 12, 44; m 67; c 4. HEALTH PHYSICS. *Educ:* Mass Inst Technol, BS, 67; Rensselaer Polytech Inst, MS, 71. *Prof Exp:* Shift radcon dir, 71-72, head tech div, 72-74, sr health physicist, 74, head training div, Pearl Harbor Naval Shipyard, 74-78, PRES, GAMMA CORP, HEALTH PHYSICS CONSULTING, 78- *Mem:* Health Physics Soc; assoc mem Sigma Xi. *Res:* Measurement of radiation and radionuclides in the environment; diagnostic radiology and nuclear medicine; practical application of radiation protection principles. *Mailing Add:* PO Box 430 Wahiawa HI 96786

MANLY, RICHARD SAMUEL, biochemistry, deceased

MANN, ALAN EUGENE, b New York, NY, Sept 19, 39; c 2. PHYSICAL ANTHROPOLOGY, PRIMATOLOGY. *Educ:* Univ Pittsburgh, BA, 61; Univ Calif, Berkeley, MA & PhD(anthrop), 68. *Prof Exp:* Teaching asst phys anthrop, Columbia Univ, 63-64; asst, Univ Calif, Berkeley, 66-68, actg asst prof, 68-69; asst prof & asst cur mus, 69-75, ASSOC PROF ANTHROP & ASSOC CUR PHYS ANTHROP, MUS, UNIV PA, 75- *Mem:* Am Asn Phys Anthrop; Am Anthrop Asn; Royal Anthrop Inst Gt Brit & Ireland. *Res:* Analysis of hominid evolution, with emphasis on the reconstruction of behavior. *Mailing Add:* Dept Anthrop Univ Pa Philadelphia PA 19174

MANN, ALFRED KENNETH, b New York, NY, Sept 4, 20; m 46; c 4. PHYSICS. *Educ:* Univ Va, AB, 42, MS, 46, PhD(physics), 47. *Prof Exp:* Instr physics, Columbia Univ, 47-49; from asst prof to assoc prof, 49-57, PROF PHYSICS, UNIV PA, PHILADELPHIA, 57- *Concurrent Pos:* Fulbright fel, 55-56; NSF sr fel, 62-63, bd trustees, Assoc Univ, Inc, 70-; assoc dir, Princeton-Pa Acceleration, 66-67; phys prog eval comt, Regents of NY State, 74-75; subpanel on new facil, High Energy Physics Adv Panel, ERDA, 75; Guggenheim fel, 81-82; bd trustees, Univ Res Asn, Inc, 79- *Mem:* Sigma Xi; fel Am Phys Soc. *Res:* Mass spectroscopy; molecular beams; photonuclear reactions; electrodynamics; elementary particle physics; structure of weak interactions through studies of K-meson decays and high energy neutrino interactions. *Mailing Add:* Dept of Physics Univ of Pa Philadelphia PA 19104

MANN, BENJAMIN MICHAEL, b Philadelphia, Pa, Apr 17, 48; m 80; c 1. TOPOLOGY. *Educ:* Univ Calif, Los Angeles, BA, 70; Stanford Univ, MS, 71, PhD(math), 75. *Prof Exp:* lectr math, Rutgers Univ, 75-76; asst prof, Harvard Univ, 76-80; ASST PROF MATH, BOWDOIN COL, 80- *Mem:* Am Math Soc. *Res:* Corbordism; infinite loop space theory; surgery; homotopy theory. *Mailing Add:* Dept Math Bowdoin Col Brunswick ME 04011

MANN, CHARLES KENNETH, b Fairmont, WVa, Jan 2, 28; m 57; c 2. ANALYTICAL CHEMISTRY. *Educ:* George Washington Univ, BS, 50, MS, 52; Univ Va, PhD(chem), 55. *Prof Exp:* Anal chemist, Nat Bur Standards, 50-52; instr chem, Univ Tex, 55-58; from asst prof to assoc prof, 58-68, PROF CHEM, FLA STATE UNIV, 68- *Mem:* Am Chem Soc; Soc Appl Spectros. *Res:* Organic electrochemistry; electroanalytical chemistry. *Mailing Add:* Dept of Chem Fla State Univ Tallahassee FL 32306

MANN, CHARLES ROY, b New York, NY, Mar 27, 41. MATHEMATICAL STATISTICS, APPLIED STATISTICS. *Educ:* Polytech Inst Brooklyn, BS, 61; Mich State Univ, MS, 63; Univ Mo, PhD(statist), 69. *Prof Exp:* Instr math, Univ Maine, 63-64; asst prof statist, George Washington Univ, 69-73; head statist div, Group Opers Inc, 73-77; PRES, CHARLES R MANN ASSOCS, INC, 77- *Concurrent Pos:* Consult, US Info Agency, 71-, Equal Employment Opportunity Comn & Dept Justice, 75- *Mem:* Inst Math Statist; Am Statist Asn; Math Asn Am. *Res:* Bayesian statistics; density estimation; data analysis; legal applications of statistics. *Mailing Add:* Charles R Mann Assocs Inc Suite 820 818 18th St NW Washington DC 20006

MANN, CHRISTIAN JOHN, b Junction City, Kans, Oct 16, 31; m 61; c 4. MATHEMATICAL GEOLOGY, PETROLEUM GEOLOGY. *Educ:* Univ Kans, BS, 53, MS, 57; Univ Wis, PhD(geol), 61. *Prof Exp:* Geologist, Gulf Oil Corp, 53 & Calif Oil Co, 57-64; sr earth scientist, Hazleton Nuclear Sci Corp, 64-65; asst prof geol, 65-69, assoc prof, 69-78, PROF GEOL, UNIV ILL, URBANA, 81- *Concurrent Pos:* Dept ed, Math Geol, 80-; mem, Nat Comt Math Geol, 81-82. *Mem:* AAAS; fel Geol Soc Am; Int Asn Math Geol; Math Geologists of US (pres, 76-78); Am Asn Petrol Geologists. *Res:* Mesozoic and Paleozoic stratigraphy; quantitative lithostratigraphic correlation; quantitative analysis of cycles in geology; nature of geologic data; data enhancement; regional stratigraphic synthesis; archaeological geology. *Mailing Add:* Dept of Geol Univ of Ill Urbana IL 61801

MANN, DAVID EDWIN, JR, b Johnson City, Tenn, Feb 13, 22; m 50; c PHARMACOLOGY. *Educ:* Harvard Univ, BS, 44; Purdue Univ, MS, 48, PhD(physiol), 51. *Prof Exp:* Asst prof physiol & pharmacol, Sch Pharm, 50-54, assoc prof pharmacol & chmn dept, 54-60, PROF PHARMACOL, SCH PHARM & SCH DENT, TEMPLE UNIV, 60- *Honors & Awards:* Lindback Award, 66. *Mem:* AAAS; Am Pharmaceut Asn. *Res:* Teratology; toxicology; carcinogenesis. *Mailing Add:* Dept of Pharmacol Temple Univ Philadelphia PA 19140

MANN, DENNIS KEITH, medical microbiology, see previous edition

MANN, DIANA WITHERSPOON, neurophysiology, see previous edition

MANN, ERNEST LEIGH, geology, see previous edition

MANN, FREDERICK MICHAEL, b San Francisco, Calif, May 8, 48. NUCLEAR PHYSICS. *Educ:* Stanford Univ, BS, 70; Calif Inst Technol, PhD(physics), 75. *Prof Exp:* Res fel physics, Calif Inst Technol, 75; advan engr, 75-78, SR ENGR PHYSICS, WESTINGHOUSE HANFORD CO, 78- *Concurrent Pos:* Sub-comt chmn, Cross Sect Eval Working Group, 80. *Mem:* Am Phys Soc; Am Nuclear Soc. *Res:* Nuclear data evaluation, nuclear computer code development, nuclear cross section measurement. *Mailing Add:* 240 Saint Court Richland WA 99352

MANN, GEORGE VERNON, b Lehigh, Iowa, Sept 15, 17; m 47. BIOCHEMISTRY, HUMAN NUTRITION. *Educ:* Cornell Col, BA, 39; Johns Hopkins Univ, DSc(biochem), 42, MD, 45. *Prof Exp:* Asst chemist, State Health Dept, Md, 40-41; intern med, Johns Hopkins Hosp, 44-45; intern, Peter Bent Brigham Hosp, 46; asst prof nutrit, Harvard Univ, 49-55, asst med, 50-58; asst prof med, 58-68, ASSOC PROF BIOCHEM, SCH MED, VANDERBILT UNIV, 58-, ASSOC PROF MED, 68- *Concurrent Pos:* Nutrit Found res fel, Sch Pub Health, Harvard Univ, 47-49; asst resident, New Eng Deaconess Hosp, 46; asst, Peter Bent Brigham Hosp, 47-48; estab investr, Am Heart Asn, 54-62; asst dir Framingham Heart Study, USPHS, 55-58, consult, 58-; career investr, Nat Heart Inst, 62- *Mem:* AAAS; Am Heart Asn; Am Inst Nutrit; NY Acad Sci. *Res:* Atherosclerosis-cardiovascular diseases; epidemiology; cardiovascular disease. *Mailing Add:* Sch Med Vanderbilt Univ Nashville TN 37232

MANN, JACINTA, b Pinckneyville, Ill, May 13, 25. APPLIED STATISTICS. *Educ:* Southern Ill Univ, BS, 46; Univ Wis, MS, 47, PhD(educ measurement & statist), 58. *Prof Exp:* Statistician, Univ Wis, 48-50; sec sch teacher math, Pa, 52-56; res asst, Univ Wis, 56-57; asst prof educ, Seton Hill Col, 58-61, from asst dir admis to dir admis, 59-67; asst to pres, Scripps Col, 67-68; acad dean, 68-71, assoc prof-at-large, 71-72, PROF-AT-LARGE, SETON HILL COL, 72- *Concurrent Pos:* Am Coun Educ acad admin internship prog fel, Scripps Col, 67-68; NSF comput grant, Holland Col, 72. *Mem:* Nat Coun Measurement Educ; Am Statist Asn. *Mailing Add:* Seton Hill Col Greensburg PA 15601

MANN, JAMES, b Paterson, NJ, Nov 29, 13; m 42; c 4. MEDICINE. *Educ:* Univ Ill, AB, 35; Wash Univ, MD, 40; Am Bd Psychiat & Neurol, dipl. *Prof Exp:* From asst prof to assoc prof, 54-63, PROF PSYCHIAT, SCH MED, BOSTON UNIV, 63- *Concurrent Pos:* Dir psychiat, Briggs Clin, Boston State Hosp, 49-52, dir psychiat, Hosp, 52-59; mem fac, Sch Social Work, Smith Col, 51-58; mem, Boston Psychoanal Inst, 53-, training analyst, 62-, dean, 71-73; vis prof, Hadassah Med Sch, Hebrew Univ Jerusalem, 55-56, Inst Living, Hartford, Conn, 58 & Grad Sch, Brandeis Univ, 59. *Mem:* AAAS; fel Am Psychiat Asn; Am Psychoanal Asn. *Res:* Psychotherapy of schizophrenia; time limited psychotherapy; group psychotherapy; dynamics of teaching. *Mailing Add:* 20 Locke Rd Waban MA 02168

MANN, JAMES EDWARD, JR, b Bluefield, WVa, Nov 17, 36; m 62; c 3. APPLIED MATHEMATICS, APPLIED MECHANICS. *Educ:* Va Polytech Inst, BS, 59; Harvard Univ, SM, 60, PhD(eng), 64. *Prof Exp:* Res engr, Esso Prod Res Co, 63-65; asst prof appl math, 65-68, ASSOC PROF APPL MATH, UNIV VA, 68- *Mem:* Soc Indust & Appl Math; Math Asn Am. *Res:* Wave propagation phenomena; problems that arise in electrodynamics, acoustics and water waves. *Mailing Add:* 2224 Greenbrier Dr Charlottesville VA 22901

MANN, JOHN ALLEN, b NJ, Sept 28, 21; m 43; c 3. GEOLOGY. *Educ:* Princeton Univ, BA, 43, MA, 49, PhD(geol), 50. *Prof Exp:* Geologist, Stand Oil Co, Calif, 50-54, dist geologist, 54-64; geol res supvr, Chevron Res Co, 64-68, sr staff geologist, Chevron Oil Field Res Co, 68, div geologist, Sotex Div, Chevron Oil Co, 68-71, SR STAFF GEOLOGIST-SCHS COORDR, CHEVRON OIL FIELD RES CO, 71- *Mem:* Geol Soc Am; Sigma Xi; Am Asn Petrol Geologists; Nat Asn Geol Teachers. *Res:* Petroleum exploration; education. *Mailing Add:* Chevron Oil Field Res Co PO Box 446 La Habra CA 90631

MANN, JOHN FRANCIS, JR, b Brooklyn, NY, Mar 21, 21; m 49. GEOLOGY. *Educ:* Univ Southern Calif, MS, 47, PhD(geol), 51. *Prof Exp:* Field geologist, Frontier Refining Co, 43-44; res geologist, US Geol Surv, 46-47; asst, Univ Southern Calif, 47-49, from asst prof to assoc prof geol, 51-58; ground water geologist, State Geol Surv, Ill, 49-51; CONSULT GEOLOGIST & HYDROLOGIST, 51- *Concurrent Pos:* Vis assoc prof, Univ Southern Calif, 58-77. *Mem:* Fel Geol Soc Am; Am Asn Petrol Geol; Am Water Works Asn; Am Geophys Union; hon mem Nat Water Well Asn (vpres, 58-60). *Res:* Ground water geology. *Mailing Add:* 945 Reposado Dr La Habra CA 90631

MANN, JOSEPH BIRD, (JR), b Kearny, NJ, Dec 1, 23; m 45; c 3. CHEMICAL PHYSICS. *Educ:* Union Univ, NY, BS, 44; Mass Inst Technol, PhD(phys chem), 50. *Prof Exp:* Asst photochem, Cabot Solar Energy Fund, Mass Inst Technol, 48-50; MEM STAFF, LOS ALAMOS SCI LAB, 50- *Mem:* Fel AAAS; Am Inst Chem. *Res:* Atomic structure studies; ion excitation cross sections; relativistic Hartree-Fock calculations. *Mailing Add:* 2551 35th St Los Alamos NM 87544

MANN, KENNETH GERARD, b Floral Park, NY, Jan 1, 41; m 64; c 3. BIOCHEMISTRY. *Educ:* Manhattan Col, BS, 63; Univ Iowa, PhD(biochem), 67. *Prof Exp:* Fel, Univ Iowa, 67-68; NIH fel, Duke Univ, 68-70; asst prof biochem, 70-75, ASSOC PROF BIOCHEM, UNIV MINN, 75-; ASSOC PROF HEMATOL, MAYO MED SCH, MAYO FOUND, 74- *Concurrent Pos:* NIH res grant, Univ Minn, St Paul, 71-74, Dreyfus teacher grant, 71-76; estab investr, Am Heart Asn, 74-79. *Mem:* Am Soc Biol Chemists; Am Chem Soc; Sigma Xi; Am Soc Hematol; Am Heat Asn. *Res:* Protein chemistry; blood clotting. *Mailing Add:* Hematol Res Mayo Clin Rochester MN 55901

MANN, KENNETH H, b Dovercourt, Eng, Aug 15, 23; m 46; c 3. ECOLOGY. *Educ:* Univ London, BSc, 49, DSc(zool), 66; Univ Reading, PhD(zool), 53. *Prof Exp:* Asst lectr zool, Univ Reading, 49-51, lectr, 51-64, reader, 64-67; sr biologist, Marine Ecol Lab, Bedford Inst, Fisheries Res Bd Can, 67-72; chmn dept, Dalhousie Univ, Halifax, NS, 72-77, prof biol, 72-80; DIR, MARINE ECOL LAB, DEPT FISHERIES & OCEANS, BEDFORD INST CAN, 80- *Concurrent Pos:* Mem productivity freshwater subcomt, Brit Nat Comt Int Biol Prog, 64-67; consult, London Anglers Asn, 58-64; ed, J Animal Ecol, 66-67; mem, Can Comt Man & Biosphere, 73-80; Can rep, Sci Comt Oceanic Res & chmn, Working Group Math Models & Biol Oceanogog, 77- *Mem:* Am Soc Limnol & Oceanog; Brit Ecol Soc; Brit Freshwater Biol Asn; Ecol Soc Am. *Res:* Functioning of aquatic ecosystems; primary and secondary productivity in coastal, estuarine and fresh waters; dynamics of marine food chains. *Mailing Add:* Marine Ecol Lab Bedford Inst Oceanog Box 1006 Dartmouth NS B2Y 4A2 Can

MANN, KINGSLEY M, b Prince Albert, Sask, Nov 12, 19; nat US; m 48; c 3. SCIENCE WRITING. *Educ:* Univ Alta, BSc, 44; Univ Sask, MSc, 46; Univ Wis, PhD(biochem), 49. *Prof Exp:* Lectr, radio-carbon lab, Univ Ill, 49-50; biochemist, 50-75, consult, science writer & ed, 75-80, MEDICAL EDITOR, UPJOHN CO, 80- *Concurrent Pos:* Vis scientist, NIH, 58-59. *Mailing Add:* 5240 Maple Ridge Dr Kalamazoo MI 49008

MANN, LARRY N, b Philadelphia, Pa, Aug 21, 34; m 59; c 3. TOPOLOGY. *Educ:* Univ Pa, BS, 55, MA, 56, PhD(math), 59. *Prof Exp:* Mathematician, Radio Corp Am, 58-60; lectr math, Univ Va, 60-61, asst prof, 61-63; mem, Inst Defense Anal, 63-64; asst, Inst Advan Study, 64-65; assoc prof, 65-70, PROF MATH, UNIV MASS, AMHERST, 70- *Concurrent Pos:* Assoc, Off Naval Res, 60-61. *Mem:* Am Math Soc. *Res:* Applications of algebraic and differential topology to topological transformation groups. *Mailing Add:* Dept of Math Univ of Mass Amherst MA 01002

MANN, LAWRENCE, JR, b Baton Rouge, La, Feb 12, 26; m 52; c 2. INDUSTRIAL ENGINEERING. *Educ:* La State Univ, BS, 49; Purdue Univ, MS, 50, PhD(indust eng), 65. *Prof Exp:* Engr, Esso Standard Oil Co, 50-57; sr design engr, Lummus Co, 57-59; assoc prof indust eng, 59-68, PROF INDUST ENG, LA STATE UNIV, 68- *Concurrent Pos:* Bur Pub Rds res grants, 61-62, 65-66; mem res rev panel, Nat Acad Sci, 65-66. *Mem:* Am Inst Indust Engrs; Am Soc Mech Engrs; Am Soc Eng Educ; Nat Soc Prof Engrs. *Res:* Highway maintenance costs; highway accident causes; general industrial maintenance. *Mailing Add:* Dept of Indust Eng La State Univ Baton Rouge LA 70803

MANN, LEONARD ANDREW, b Cleveland, Ohio, June 30, 15. PHYSICS. *Educ:* Univ Dayton, BS, 37; Ohio State Univ, MSc, 45; Carnegie Mellon Univ, PhD(physics), 54. *Prof Exp:* Teacher high sch, Ohio, 37-48; assoc prof physics, 54-62, assoc dean, 56-61, chmn dept, 55, dean Col Arts & Sci, 61-81, PROF PHYSICS, UNIV DAYTON, 62- *Mem:* AAAS; Am Phys Soc; Am Soc Eng Educ; Am Asn Physics Teachers. *Res:* Meson scattering; beta spectrometry. *Mailing Add:* Univ of Dayton Col of Arts & Sci Dayton OH 45469

MANN, LESLIE BERNARD, b Granger, Wash, Oct 19, 19; m 44; c 3. NEUROLOGY. *Educ:* La Sierra Col, BS, 44; Loma Linda Univ, MD, 45. *Prof Exp:* Intern, Los Angeles County Hosp, 44-45; intern, 50, DIR ELECTROENCEPHALOG LAB, WHITE MEM MED CTR, 50-; ASSOC PROF NEUROL, COL MED, LOMA LINDA UNIV, 58- *Concurrent Pos:* Chief neuromed serv, White Mem Med Ctr, 52-62; assoc prof, Univ Calif, Irvine-Calif Col Med, 66-69; consult, Los Angeles County Gen Hosp, 52-62, Glendale Adventist Hosp, Rancho Los Amigos Hosp, 62-77 & Alhambra Community Hosp. *Mem:* Am Acad Neurol; Am Electroencephalog Soc; Am Epilepsy Soc. *Res:* Pediatric neurology; electroencephalography; epilepsy. *Mailing Add:* Neurosci Med Group 1710 Brooklyn Ave Suite 121 Los Angeles CA 90033

MANN, LEWIS THEODORE, JR, b New York, NY, Aug 5, 25; m 57; c 3. CLINICAL BIOCHEMISTRY, IMMUNOCHEMISTRY. *Educ:* Mass Inst Technol, SB, 46; Columbia Univ, AM & PhD(org chem), 51; Am Bd Clin Chem, dipl. *Prof Exp:* Lectr biochem, Harvard Med Sch, 58-66; asst prof immunol, 68-72, Sch Med, Univ Conn, 68-72, assoc prof radiol, 72-75; clin chemist, Fresno Community Hosp, 75-79; CLIN CHEMIST, VET ADMIN MED CTR, FRESNO, 79-; ASST PROF LAB MED, UNIV CALIF, SAN FRANCISCO, 79- *Concurrent Pos:* Res fel path, Harvard Med Sch, 56-58; Nat Inst Gen Med Sci spec fel, McIndoe Mem Res Inst, East Grinstead, Eng, 66-67 & Inst for Exp Immunol, Copenhagen, 67-68; vis scientist, Hartford Hosp, Conn, 74-75; adj assoc prof chem, Calif State Univ, Fresno, 75-, adj prof chem, 81- *Mem:* AAAS; Am Chem Soc; Am Asn Clin Chem. *Res:* Radioimmunoassay and non-radio immune assay techniques; chromatographic methods in clinical analyses. *Mailing Add:* Lab Serv-113 Vet Admin Med Ctr Fresno CA 93703

MANN, LLOYD GODFREY, b Sterling, Mass, July 2, 22; m 59; c 3. EXPERIMENTAL NUCLEAR PHYSICS. *Educ:* Worcester Polytech, BS, 44; Univ Ill, MS, 47, PhD(physics), 50. *Prof Exp:* Mem staff radiation lab, Mass Inst Technol, 44-46; instr physics, Stanford Univ, 50-53; MEM STAFF, LAWRENCE LIVERMORE LAB, UNIV CALIF, 53- *Mem:* Am Phys Soc; AAAS. *Res:* Properties of nuclear energy levels. *Mailing Add:* Lawrence Livermore Lab Univ of Calif Box 808 Livermore CA 94550

MANN, MARION, b Atlanta, Ga, Mar 29, 20; m 43; c 2. PATHOLOGY. *Educ:* Tuskegee Inst, BS, 40; Howard Univ, MD, 54; Georgetown Univ, PhD, 61; Nat Bd Med Examiners, dipl; Am Bd Path, dipl. *Hon Degrees:* DSc, Georgetown Univ, 79. *Prof Exp:* Intern, USPHS Hosp, Staten Island, NY, 54-55; resident, Univ Hosp, Georgetown Univ, 56-60, instr path, 60-61; from asst prof to prof, 61-70, dean, Col Med, 70-79, PROF, HOWARD UNIV, 79- *Concurrent Pos:* Pvt pract med, Washington, DC, 61-; prof lectr, Sch Med, Georgetown Univ, 70-73; mem bd dirs, Nat Med Fel, Inc. *Mem:* Inst Med-Nat Acad Sci; Nat Med Asn; AMA; Int Acad Path; Asn Mil Surgeons US. *Mailing Add:* Howard Univ Col of Med 520 W St NW Washington DC 20059

MANN, MICHAEL DAVID, b Gold Beach, Ore, May 20, 44; m 66; c 2. NEUROPHYSIOLOGY. *Educ:* Univ Southern Calif, BA, 66; Cornell Univ, PhD(neurobiol & behav), 71. *Prof Exp:* Ford Found fel, Cornell Univ, 71; USPHS fel, Univ Wash, 71-73; asst prof 73-77, ASSOC PROF PHYSIOL & BIOPHYSICS, UNIV NEBR MED CTR, OMAHA, 77- *Mem:* Am Physiol Soc; Soc Neurosci; Cajal Club. *Res:* Somatosensory system, especially in the cerebral cortex, with a view to understanding the role of the system in controlling and modulating behavior; evolution and development of the central nervous system. *Mailing Add:* Dept of Physiol & Biophysics Univ of Nebr Med Ctr Omaha NE 68105

MANN, NANCY ROBBINS, b Chillicothe, Ohio, May 6, 25; m 49; c 2. STATISTICAL ANALYSIS. *Educ:* Univ Calif, Los Angeles, BA, 48, MA, 49, PhD(biostatist), 65. *Prof Exp:* Mathematician, Inst Numerical Anal, Nat Bur Standards, 49-50; sr physicist, NAm Rockwell Corp, 62-70, mem tech staff & proj develop engr, 70-74, sr scientist, 74-75, proj mgr reliability & statist, Rockwell Sci Ctr, Rockwell Int Corp, 75-78; vis res statistician, 78-80, RES BIOMATHEMATICIAN, DEPT BIOMATH & PSYCHIAT, UNIV CALIF, LOS ANGELES, 80- *Concurrent Pos:* Consult, US Army Mat Command & Missile Command; mem adv comt, US Census Bur, 72-74; mem, Comt Nat Statist, Nat Acad Sci, 78-80 & Bd Adv, US Naval Postgrad Sch, Monterey, Calif, 78-82. *Honors & Awards:* Reliability Soc Annual Award, Inst Elec & Electronics Engrs, 82. *Mem:* Fel Am Statist Asn (vpres, 82-84); Inst Math Statist; Int Statist Inst; Sigma Xi. *Res:* Point and interval estimation theory; order statistics; statistical methods in reliability. *Mailing Add:* Dept of Biomath Univ Calif Med Sch Los Angeles CA 90024

MANN, NIRMAL SINGH, b India, Aug 10, 36; US citizen; m 70; c 2. GASTROENTEROLOGY, GASTROINTESTINAL ENDOSCOPY. *Educ:* Delhi Univ, BSc, 56; Christian Med Col, Panjab Univ, MD, 62; Northwestern Univ, Evanston, MS, 69; FRCP(C), 71. *Prof Exp:* Resident & clin asst, Northwestern Univ Med Ctr, Chicago, Ill, 65-67, fel gastroenterology, 67-69; fel internal med, Univ Alberta, Edmonton, Can, 69-71; staff physician internal med & gastroentestinal, Vet Admin Med Ctr, Topeka, Kans, 71-173; asst prof, 73-78, ASSOC PROF MED, SCH MED, UNIV LOUISVILLE, KY, 78- *Concurrent Pos:* Clin asst, Univ Alberta Hosp, Edmonton, Can, 69-71; clin tutor, Vet Admin Med Ctr, Topeka, Kans, 71-73, chief gastroenterol & dir, Gastroentestinal Lab, Louisville, Ky, 73-; ed-in-chief gastroentestinal, Am J Proctol, Gastroentol, 80- *Mem:* Am Col Physicians; Am Col Gastroenterol; Am Gastroenterol Asn; Am Soc Gastrointestinal Endscopy; Int Acad Proctol (vpres, 79). *Res:* Experimental pancreatitis and experimental colitis; fiberoptic endoscopy in small animals and experimental gastric ulcers. *Mailing Add:* 800 Zorn Ave Louisville KY 40202

MANN, PAUL, b Lewiston, Idaho, Sept 3, 17; m 44; c 5. ELECTRICAL ENGINEERING. *Educ:* Univ Idaho, BS, 38, MS, 51. *Prof Exp:* Power sta operator, Pac Power & Light Co, 38-39; elec tester & field serv engr, Westinghouse Elec Corp, 39-46; asst prof elec eng, Va Polytech Inst, 47-48; from asst prof to assoc prof, 48-65, PROF ELEC ENG, UNIV IDAHO, 65- *Mem:* Nat Soc Prof Engrs; Inst Elec & Electronics Engrs. *Res:* Electric power systems; energy sources. *Mailing Add:* Dept of Elec Eng Univ of Idaho Moscow ID 83843

MANN, RALPH WILLARD, b Robinson, Ill, July 12, 16; m 44; c 2. PHYSICS. *Educ:* DePauw Univ, AB, 38; Wash Univ, St Louis, MS, 40. *Prof Exp:* Asst physics, Wash Univ, St Louis, 39-41; physicist, Naval Ord Lab, 41-45; sr res geophysicist, Humble Oil & Refining Co, 46-54, res specialist, 54-63, sr res specialist geophys, Esso Prod Res Co, Tex, 64-71; environ health specialist, Tex Air Pollution Control Serv, 71-73, MEM STAFF, TEX AIR CONTROL BD, 73- *Mem:* Comput Soc; Air Pollution Control Asn; Inst Elec & Electronics Eng. *Res:* Conductivity of liquid dielectrics; underwater ordnance; geophysical research and instrumentation; underwater gravity meter; seismic prospecting methods and apparatus; digital computer applications. *Mailing Add:* 5013 Westview Dr Austin TX 78731

MANN, RANVEER S, b Mirzapur, India, Mar 31, 24; Can citizen; m 44; c 2. CHEMICAL ENGINEERING. *Educ:* Univ Allahabad, BSc, 42, MSc, 44; Polytech Inst Brooklyn, MChE, 48; Univ Hull, PhD(eng chem), 58. *Prof Exp:* Res chemist, Dept Sci & Indust Res, Govt India, 44-46; asst dir indust, Govt Punjab, 48-53; res scientist, Univ Tex, 53-54; instr chem eng, Univ BC, 54-56; res scientist, Nat Res Coun Can, 56; sci officer, Bur Mines, Can, 58-60; asst prof, 60-64, ASSOC PROF CHEM ENG, UNIV OTTAWA, 64- *Mem:* Fel Royal Inst Chem; Am Inst Chem Engrs; Am Chem Soc; fel Brit Inst Petrol. *Res:* Kinetics and mechanism of vapor phase catalytic reactions and heat transfer in fluidized beds and two phase flow of fluids; reactions, including dehydrogenation of cyclohexane, hydrogenation of methylacetylene and allene; oxidation of hydrocarbons. *Mailing Add:* Dept of Chem Eng Univ of Ottawa Ottawa ON K1N 6N5 Can

MANN, RICHARD A(RNOLD), b Lake Geneva, Wis, Dec 15, 21; m 66; c 1. ENGINEERING MECHANICS, COMPUTER SCIENCE. *Educ:* Univ Wis, BS, 44, PhD(eng mech), 66; Northwestern Univ, MS, 48. *Prof Exp:* Engr, Douglas Aircraft Co, Inc, 44, 48-49 & Nat Adv Comt Aeronaut, 44-47; instr mech eng, Univ Wis, 49-51, instr eng mech, 51-65; asst prof eng, Wright State Campus, Miami-Ohio State Univ, 65-70; assoc prof civil eng, 70-77, prof civil eng, 77-79, PROF INDUST ENG & COMPUT SCI, UNIV NEW HAVEN, 79- *Concurrent Pos:* Consult, Forest Prod Lab, USDA, 57-65. *Mem:* Am Soc Eng Educ. *Res:* Elastic stability. *Mailing Add:* Univ New Haven West Haven CT 06516

MANN, ROBERT LESLIE, b Decatur, Ind, Oct 2, 22; m 45; c 1. AGRICULTURAL CHEMISTRY. *Educ:* Ind Univ, BS, 45; Univ Minn, PhD(biochem), 49. *Prof Exp:* From sr scientist biochem to head dept, Eli Lilly & Co, 49-63, dir chem res, 63-66 & plant sci res, 66-67, EXEC DIR AGR CHEM & PLANT SCI RES, ELI LILLY & CO, 67- *Mem:* Am Soc Biol Chemists; Am Chem Soc; AAAS. *Res:* Synthesizing, evaluating and developing agricultural chemicals for use in plants and animals. *Mailing Add:* Lilly Res Labs Eli Lilly & Co Greenfield IN 46140

MANN, ROBERT W(ELLESLEY), b Brooklyn, NY, Oct 6, 24; m 50; c 2. REHABILITATION ENGINEERING, ENGINEERING DESIGN. *Educ:* Mass Inst Technol, SB, 50, SM, 51, ScD(mech eng), 57. *Prof Exp:* Draftsman, Bell Tel Labs, Inc, NY, 42-43, 46-47; res supvr dynamic anal & control lab, 51-57, from asst prof to prof mech eng, 53-70, head eng design div, 57-66, Germeshausen prof, 70-72, prof eng, 72-74, WHITAKER PROF BIOMED ENG, MASS INST TECHNOL, 74- *Concurrent Pos:* Engr, Bell Tel Labs, Inc, NY, 50; mem comt prosthetic res & develop, Nat Acad Sci-Nat Res Coun, 63-69; founding chmn steering comt, Ctr Sensory Aids Eval & Develop, Mass Inst Technol, 64-; mem bd dirs, Carroll Ctr for the Blind, 67-74, pres, 68-74; consult eng sci, Mass Gen Hosp, 69-; mem comt interplay eng with biol & med, Nat Acad Eng, 69-73; chmn sensory aids subcomt, 68-73; mem comt skeletal syst, Nat Res Coun, 69-71 ; eng lectr, Fac Med, Harvard Univ, 73-; res assoc orthop surg, Children's Hosp Med Ctr, 73-; Sigma Xi nat lectr, 79-81; consult. *Honors & Awards:* Talbert Abrams Photogram Award, 62; citation, Asn Blind of Mass, 69; IR-100 Innovation Award, 72; Goldenson Award for Outstanding Res Phys Handicapped, 76; Am Soc Mech Engrs Gold Medal, 77; H R Lissner Award for Outstanding Bioeng, 77. *Mem:* Inst Med-Nat Acad Sci; Nat Acad Eng; fel Am Acad Arts & Sci; AAAS; fel Inst Elec & Electronics Engrs. *Res:* Engineering design; technology and human rehabilitation; human musculo-skeletal biomechanics; pathogenesis of osteoarthritis. *Mailing Add:* Mass Inst Technol Rm 3-144 77 Massachusetts Ave Cambridge MA 02139

MANN, RONALD FRANCIS, b Winnipeg, Man, Aug 18, 31; m 55; c 3. CHEMICAL ENGINEERING, NUCLEAR ENGINEERING. *Educ:* Queen's Univ, Ont, BSc, 56, MSc, 60, PhD(chem eng), 66. *Prof Exp:* Lectr chem, Royal Mil Col, Ont, 58-60; develop engr, Atomic Power Dept, Can Gen Elec Co, 60-62; from asst prof to assoc prof chem eng, 62-75, PROF CHEM ENG, ROYAL MIL COL CAN, 75- *Concurrent Pos:* Res grant, Defence Res Bd, 65- & Dept Nat Defence, 77-78; consult, Dept Nat Defence, 75- *Mem:* Fel Chem Inst Can; Can Soc Chem Eng; Am Soc Eng Educ; Can Nuclear Asn. *Res:* Chemical reaction engineering; catalysis; heat transfer. *Mailing Add:* Dept of Chem & Chem Eng Royal Mil Col Kingston ON K7L 2W3 Can

MANN, STANLEY JOSEPH, b Worcester, Mass, Sept 18, 32; m 69; c 2. GENETICS, BIOLOGY. *Educ:* Clark Univ, AB, 53, MA, 58; Brown Univ, PhD(biol), 61. *Prof Exp:* Cancer res scientist, Springville Labs, Roswell Park Mem Inst, 61-63, sr cancer res scientist, 63-66; asst prof anat in dermat, 66-69, ASSOC PROF ANIMAL GENETICS DERMAT, TEMPLE UNIV, 69-, DIR LAB ANIMAL RESOURCES, 77-, EXEC DIR, FEDERATED MED RESOURCES, 79- *Concurrent Pos:* Asst res prof biol, State Univ NY Buffalo, 64-66. *Mem:* Genetics Soc Am; Am Genetic Asn. *Res:* Mammalian genetics; biology of the skin; phenogenetics of hair mutants in the house mouse; morphology and development of normal and abnormal mammalian hair follicles. *Mailing Add:* Skin & Cancer Hosp Philadelphia Temple Univ Health Sci Ctr Philadelphia PA 19140

MANN, THURSTON (JEFFERSON), b Lake Landing, NC, June 22, 20; m 45; c 3. GENETICS. *Educ:* NC State Univ, BS, 41, MS, 47; Cornell Univ, PhD(genetics, plant breeding), 50. *Prof Exp:* From asst prof to assoc prof agron, 49-53, in charge agron teaching, 53-55, prof crop sci, 55-64, prof genetics & head dept, 64-73, prof genetics & crop sci, 73-76, ASST DIR RES, SCH OF AGR & LIFE SCI, NC STATE UNIV, 76- *Concurrent Pos:* Vis agronomist, Coop State Res Serv, USDA, 74. *Mem:* Am Soc Agron; Am Genetic Asn; Genetics Soc Am. *Res:* Tobacco genetics; interspecific hybridization and breeding procedures; inheritance of alkaloids in Nicotiana. *Mailing Add:* NC Agr Res Serv NC State Univ Box 5847 Raleigh NC 27650

MANN, WALLACE VERNON, JR, b Pembroke, Mass, Mar 17, 30; m 52; c 4. DENTISTRY. *Educ:* Williams Col, BA, 51; Tufts Univ, DMD, 55; Univ Ala, MS, 62. *Prof Exp:* From instr to prof dent, Sch Dent, Univ Ala, Birmingham, 62-74, chmn dept periodont, 65-74, asst dean sch, 66-74; DEAN DENT, UNIV MISS MED CTR, 74-, PROF ENDODONTICS & PERIODONTICS, 77-, DENTIST-IN-CHIEF, UNIV HOSP, 77- *Concurrent Pos:* Sr res trainee, Sch Dent, Univ Ala, Birmingham, 62-63; NIH career develop award, 63-66; dir clin res training grant for DMD|PhD prog, Sch Dent Univ Ala, Birmingham, 67-74. *Mem:* Am Dent Asn; Am Asn Dent Schs; fel Am Col Dentists; Int Asn Dent Res. *Res:* Physiology and biochemistry of periodontal tissues. *Mailing Add:* Sch of Dent Univ of Miss Med Ctr Jackson MS 39216

MANN, WILFRID BASIL, b London, Eng, Aug 4, 08; m 38; c 3. PHYSICS. *Educ:* Univ London, BSc, 30, PhD(physics), 34, DSc, 51. *Prof Exp:* Lectr physics, Imp Col, Univ London, 33-46; Nat Res Coun Can atomic energy proj, 46-48; attache, Brit Embassy, DC, 48-51; chief, Radioactivity Sect, Nat Bur Standards, 51-80. *Concurrent Pos:* Sci liaison officer, Brit Commonwealth Sci Off, DC, 43-45; sci adv, UK Del, UN AEC, 46-51; adj prof, Am Univ, 61-68; NAm ed-in-chief, Int J Appl Radiation & Isotopes, 65-; mem, Fed Radiation Coun, 69-70; dep chief, Appl Radiation Div, Ctr Radiation Res, 74-78; chmn sci 18A, Nat Coun Radiation Protection & Measurements, 72-; ed, Int J Nuclear Med & Biol, 73-, Environ Int, 77-; pres, Int Comt Radionuclide Metrology, 78-80. *Honors & Awards:* Medal of Freedom, 48; Gold Medal, US Dept Com, 58; Edward Bennett Rosa Award, 77. *Mem:* Am Phys Soc; Brit Inst Physics & Phys Soc (ed, Reports Progress Physics, 41-46); hon mem Nat Coun Radiation Protection & Measurements. *Res:* Radioactivity standardization; microcalorimetry. *Mailing Add:* Nuclear Radiation Div Nat Bur of Standards Washington DC 20234

MANN, WILLIAM ANTHONY, b Trenton, NJ, Oct 12, 43. EXPERIMENTAL HIGH ENERGY PHYSICS. *Educ:* Yale Univ, BS, 65; Univ Mass, MS, 67, PhD(physics), 70. *Prof Exp:* Res assoc, Argonne Nat Lab, 70-72; res assoc, 72-74, asst prof, 74-79, ASSOC PROF PHYSICS, TUFTS UNIV, 79- *Concurrent Pos:* Vis prof physics, State Univ NY, Stonybrook, 80-81. *Mem:* Am Phys Soc; Sigma Xi; Fedn Am Scientists. *Res:* Experimental fundamental particle interactions; neutrino interactions, structure of nucleons; exotic mesons, baryonium, high-mass resonances; dynamics of multiparticle production; neutral current reactions. *Mailing Add:* Dept Physics Tufts Univ Medford MA 02155

MANN, WILLIAM ROBERT, b Honea Path, SC, Sept 21, 20; m 47; c 3. APPLIED MATHEMATICS. *Educ:* Univ Rochester, AB, 41; Univ Calif, PhD(math), 49. *Prof Exp:* Instr, 49-50, from asst prof to assoc prof, 50-60, PROF MATH, UNIV NC, CHAPEL HILL, 60- *Mem:* Am Math Soc. *Res:* Nonlinear boundary value problems; iterative techniques. *Mailing Add:* Dept of Math Univ of NC Chapel Hill NC 27514

MANNA, ZOHAR, b Haifa, Israel, Jan 17, 39; c 3. COMPUTER SCIENCE. *Educ:* Israel Inst Technion, BS, 61, MS, 65; Carnegie-Mellon Univ, PhD(comput sci), 68. *Prof Exp:* PROF COMPUT SCI, STANFORD UNIV, 68- *Concurrent Pos:* prof appl math, Weizmann Inst, Israel, 72-; Guggenheim fel. *Res:* Mathematical theory of computation. *Mailing Add:* Dept Comput Sci Stanford Univ Stanford CA 94305

MANNELL, WILLIAM ARNOLD, b Belmont, Ont, June 30, 21; m 46; c 2. TOXICOLOGY. *Educ:* Univ Western Ont, BSc, 49, PhD(biochem), 52. *Prof Exp:* Sr res assoc biochem, Univ Western Ont, 52-54; chemist food & drug labs, Dept Nat Health & Welfare, 54-65, head food additives & pesticides sect, Pharmacol Eval Div, Food & Drug Directorate, 65-67, chief div toxicol, Food Adv Bur, 67-74, chief toxicol eval div, Bur Chem Safety, Food Directorate, Health Protection Br, 74-80; CONSULT TOXICOL, 80- *Concurrent Pos:* Mem, Expert Adv Panel Food Additives, WHO, 68-83. *Mem:* Soc Toxicol Can. *Res:* Biochemical studies of Wallerian degeneration; nucleic acids; toxicological evaluation of food additives, food contaminants and pesticides. *Mailing Add:* 28 Okanagan Dr Nepean ON K2H 7G1 Can

MANNER, HAROLD WALLACE, b Brooklyn, NY, July 31, 25; m 45; c 2. BIOLOGY. *Educ:* John Carroll Univ, BS, 49; Northwestern Univ, MS, 50, PhD, 52. *Prof Exp:* Nat Arthritis & Rheumatism Found fel, 52-53; asst prof biol, Utica Col, 53-57, assoc prof, 57-62, prof & chmn div sci & math, 62-69; prof biol & chmn dept, St Louis Univ, 69-72; prof chem, 72-78, PROF BIOL, LOYOLA UNIV CHICAGO, 72- *Concurrent Pos:* Vis asst prof, Kenyon Col, 52-53; res assoc, NSF, 53-55 & NIH, 60-62; pres, Metabolic Res Found, Glenview, Ill, 79- *Mem:* AAAS; Am Soc Zool. *Res:* Regeneration of Salamander limbs; influence of steroids on morphogenesis; effect of aquatic pollutants on teleost embryogenesis; development of metabolic therapies for cancer and arthritis. *Mailing Add:* Dept Biol Loyola Univ Chicago 6525 N Sheridan Rd Chicago IL 60626

MANNER, RICHARD JOHN, b Buffalo, NY, Mar 22, 20; m 43; c 4. MEDICAL RESEARCH. *Educ:* Rensselaer Polytech Inst, BS, 41; Univ Rochester, MD, 51. *Prof Exp:* Physicist, Eastman Kodak Co, 41-42, electronics develop engr, 46-47; intern med, Rochester Gen Hosp, 51-52, preceptorship internal med, 52-55; pvt pract, NY, 55-60; assoc dir clin res, Mead Johnson Res Ctr, 60-65; staff physician, Wyeth Labs, 65-67; dir med affairs, Warren-Teed Pharmaceut Inc, Columbus, 67-75; dir pharmaceut res, Ross Labs, Columbus, 75-76; vpres res & develop, Dome Div, 76-81, VPRES MED SERV, MILES PHARMACEUT DIV, MILES LABS, 81- *Concurrent Pos:* Consult, Rochester Inst Technol, 53-54 & Stecher-Traung Lithograph Corp, 54-60. *Mem:* AMA; Inst Elec & Electronics Eng; Am Soc Clin Pharmacol & Therapeut; Sigma Xi; Am Col Gastroenterol. *Res:*Allergy and immunology; gastrointestinal pharmacology and instrumentation. *Mailing Add:* 12 Cassway Rd Woodbridge CT 06525

MANNERING, GILBERT JAMES, b Racine, Wis, Mar 9, 17; m 39, 69; c 3. PHARMACOLOGY, BIOCHEMISTRY. *Educ:* Univ Wis, BS, 40, MS, 43, PhD(biochem), 44. *Prof Exp:* Sr biochemist, Parke, Davis & Co, 44-50; consult, Chem Dept, 406th Med Gen Lab, Tokyo, Japan, 50-54; from asst prof to assoc prof pharmacol & toxicol, Univ Wis, 54-62; PROF PHARMACOL, MED SCH, UNIV MINN, MINNEAPOLIS, 62- *Concurrent Pos:* Consult, Wis State Crime Lab, 54-62; spec consult, Interdept Comt Nutrit Nat Defense, NIH, Ethiopia, 58; mem toxicol study sect, USPHS, 62-65, mem pharmacol-toxicol rev comt, 65-67 & pharmacol study sect, 68-69; mem comt probs drug safety, Nat Acad Sci-Nat Res Coun, 65-71. *Mem:* Am Soc Pharmacol & Exp Therapeut. *Res:* Biochemical pharmacology; drug metabolism; toxicology. *Mailing Add:* 1865 N Fairview Ave St Paul MN 55113

MANNERING, JERRY VINCENT, b Custer City, Okla, June 14, 29; m 53; c 3. AGRONOMY. *Educ:* Okla State Univ, BS, 51; Purdue Univ, MS, 56, PhD, 67. *Prof Exp:* Asst agronomist, Univ Idaho, 56-58; soil scientist, Agr Res Serv, USDA, 58-67; EXTEN AGRONOMIST, PURDUE UNIV, 67- *Mem:* Am Soc Agron; Soil Sci Soc Am; Int Soil Sci Soc; fel Soil Conserv Soc Am; Int Soil Tillage Res Orgn. *Res:* Soil erosion; waste management; efficient water use; soil management for crop production. *Mailing Add:* Dept of Agron Purdue Univ West Lafayette IN 47907

MANNEY, THOMAS RICHARD, b El Paso, Tex, Dec 20, 33; m 56; c 3. BIOPHYSICS. *Educ:* Western Wash State Col, BA, 57; Univ Calif, Berkeley, PhD(biophys), 64. *Prof Exp:* Teaching asst, Western Wash State Col, 56-58; res asst, Univ Calif, Berkeley, 58-59, biophysicist, Donner Lab, 59-60; staff biologist, Oak Ridge Nat Lab, 64-65; asst prof microbiol, Case Western Reserve Univ, 65-71; assoc prof biol, 71-77, PROF PHYSICS, KANS STATE UNIV, 71- *Concurrent Pos:* USPHS res career develop award, 67-70; vis assoc prof, Univ Calif, 70-71. *Honors & Awards:* Chem Achievement Award, Western Wash State Col, 55, Physics Achievement Award, 56. *Mem:* AAAS; Genetics Soc Am; Am Soc Microbiol. *Mailing Add:* Dept of Physics Kans State Univ Manhattan KS 66502

MANNING, BRENDA DALE, b Spartanburg, SC, Oct 6, 45. BIOLOGICAL CHEMISTRY. *Educ:* Antioch Col, BS, 67; Univ Mich, MS, 69, PhD(biol chem), 73. *Prof Exp:* Res assoc genetics, Univ Mich, 73-76; ASST PROF CHEM, EASTERN MICH UNIV, 76- *Concurrent Pos:* Fac res grant, Eastern Mich Univ, 77-78. *Mem:* Sigma Xi. *Res:* Steroid hormone control in the eukaryotic systems of mammals. *Mailing Add:* Dept of Chem Eastern Mich Univ Ypsilanti MI 48197

MANNING, CHARLES RICHARD, JR, b Erie, Pa, Mar 12, 30; m 55; c 3. CERAMICS ENGINEERING. *Educ:* Fla State Univ, BS, 58; Va Polytech Inst, MS, 62; NC State Univ, PhD(ceramic eng), 67. *Prof Exp:* Mat res engr & group leader, NASA Langley Res Ctr, Va, 58-67; assoc prof ceramic eng, 67-72, PROF CERAMIC ENG, SCH ENG, NC STATE UNIV, 72- *Honors & Awards:* Outstanding Achievement Award, NASA, 66. *Mem:* Am Ceramic Soc; Am Soc Metals. *Res:* Metal-ceramic bonding; high-temperature behavior of materials and stress corrosion. *Mailing Add:* Sch of Eng 100 Page Hall Raleigh NC 27607

MANNING, CLEO WILLARD, b Woodhull, Ill, Oct 10, 15; m 38; c 5. PLANT BREEDING. *Educ:* Ill Wesleyan Univ, BS, 40; Agr & Mech Col, Univ Tex, MS, 42; Iowa State Univ, PhD, 54. *Prof Exp:* Agent, Bur Plant Indust, Soils & Agr Eng, USDA, 41-45; asst agronomist, Agr & Mech Col, Univ Tex, 41-45, agronomist, 45-48, botanist, 48, agronomist & assoc prof, 48-51; PLANT BREEDER IN CHARGE, STONEVILLE PEDIGREED SEED CO, 51- *Mem:* AAAS; Am Inst Biol Sci; Am Genetic Asn; Crop Sci Soc Am; Cotton Improv Conf. *Res:* Genetics and breeding of cotton; soybeans; plant exploration; interspecific relationships in Gossypium. *Mailing Add:* PO Box 213 Stoneville MS 38776

MANNING, DAVID TREADWAY, b Santa Monica, Calif, Sept 19, 28; m 56; c 2. BIO-ORGANIC CHEMISTRY, AGRICULTURAL CHEMISTRY. *Educ:* Calif Inst Technol, BS, 51, PhD(chem), 55. *Prof Exp:* Res proj chemist, 54-62, res scientist, 62-75, SR RES SCIENTIST, UNION CARBIDE CORP, 75- *Mem:* AAAS; Am Chem Soc; NY Acad Sci; Plant Growth Regulator Working Group; Am Soc Plant Physiologists. *Res:* Nitrosation reactions; organic reactions of nitrosyl chloride; chemistry of oximes; nitrogen-containing heterocyclic compounds; pesticide chemistry and formulants; plant growth regulators. *Mailing Add:* PO Box 12014 T W Alexander Dr Union Carbide Agr Prod Co Inc Research Triangle Park NC 27709

MANNING, DEAN DAVID, b Grand Junction, Colo, Oct 11, 40; m 66. IMMUNOLOGY. *Educ:* Colo State Univ, BS, 62, MS, 64; Mont State Univ, PhD(microbiol), 72. *Prof Exp:* Fel microbiol, Mont State Univ, 72-74; asst prof, 75-77, ASSOC PROF MED MICROBIOL, MED SCH, UNIV WIS-MAD'SON, 77- *Concurrent Pos:* NIH fel, 73-74. *Mem:* Am Asn Immunol. *Res:* Control of the immune reponse with particular reference to heavy chain isotype suppression. *Mailing Add:* Dept of Med Microbiol Univ of Wis Med Sch Madison WI 53706

MANNING, ERIC G(EORGE), b Windsor, Ont, Aug 4, 40; m 61. COMPUTER SCIENCE. *Educ:* Univ Waterloo, BSc, 61, MSc, 62; Univ Ill, PhD(elec eng), 65. *Prof Exp:* Asst elec eng, Univ Ill, 62-63, asst, Coord Sci Lab, 63-65; asst prof elec eng & Ford fel, Proj Mac, Mass Inst Technol, 65-66; mem tech staff, Bell Tel Labs, 66-68; assoc prof comput sci, 68-76, PROF COMPUT SCI, UNIV WATERLOO, 76-, DIR, COMPUT COMMUN NETWORKS GROUP, 73- *Concurrent Pos:* Sci adv, Sci Coun Can, 70-71. *Mem:* Inst Elec & Electronics Engrs; Can Info Processing Soc; Natural Sci & Org Res Coun Can. *Res:* Computer maintenance problems; computer networks. *Mailing Add:* Dept Comput Sci Univ Waterloo Waterloo ON N2L 3G1 Can

MANNING, FRANCIS S(COTT), b Barbados, WI, Sept 16, 33; nat US; m 60, 78; c 2. CHEMICAL ENGINEERING. *Educ:* McGill Univ, BEng, 55; Princeton Univ, MSE & AM, 57, PhD, 59. *Prof Exp:* From instr to assoc prof chem eng, Carnegie Inst Technol, 59-68; head dept, 68-76, PROF CHEM ENG, UNIV TULSA, 68-, DIR, PETROL & ENERGY RES INST, 76-, HEAD DEPT, 79- *Honors & Awards:* Robert W Hunt Award, Am Inst Mining, Metall & Petrol Engrs, 69. *Mem:* Am Inst Chem Engrs; Am Inst Mining, Metall & Petrol Engrs; Am Soc Eng Educ. *Res:* Mixing; thermodynamics; kinetics; water pollution control. *Mailing Add:* Dept of Chem Eng Univ of Tulsa Tulsa OK 74104

MANNING, GERALD STUART, b New York, NY, Dec 9, 40; m 64. BIOPHYSICAL CHEMISTRY. *Educ:* Rice Univ, BA, 62; Univ Calif, San Diego, PhD(phys chem), 65. *Prof Exp:* NATO fel, Univ Brussels, 65-66; Nat Sci Found fel, Rockefeller Univ, 66-67, asst prof chem, 67-69; assoc prof, 69-75, PROF CHEM, RUTGERS UNIV, 75- *Honors & Awards:* Alfred P Sloan fel, 70-72. *Res:* Polyelectrolytes; biopolymer conformation; transport across membranes. *Mailing Add:* Dept of Chem Rutgers Univ New Brunswick NJ 08903

MANNING, HAROLD EDWIN, b Huntsville, Ala, Mar 18, 35; m 66; c 4. HETEROGENEOUS CATALYSIS. *Educ:* Auburn Univ, BS, 58; Trinity Univ, MS, 62. *Prof Exp:* Chemist, 62-66, res chemist, 66-67, HEAD RES GROUP, PETRO-TEX CHEM CORP, 67- *Mem:* Am Chem Soc; Catalysis Soc. *Res:* Heterogeneous catalysis; reaction mechanisms and surface chemistry. *Mailing Add:* Petro-Tex Chem Corp 8600 Park Place Blvd Houston TX 77017

MANNING, HERBERT LEE, microbiology, water pollution, see previous edition

MANNING, HERBERT LYBRAND, industrial engineering, deceased

MANNING, IRWIN, b Brooklyn, NY, Mar 7, 29; m 64; c 2. THEORETICAL PHYSICS. *Educ:* Mass Inst Technol, BS, 51, PhD(physics), 55. *Prof Exp:* Res assoc & asst prof, Syracuse Univ, 55-57; res assoc, Univ Wis, 57-59; res physicist, 59-73, SUPVRY RES PHYSICIST, US NAVAL RES LAB, 73- *Concurrent Pos:* Mem ad hoc panel on the use of accelerators to study irradiation effects, Nat Acad Sci, 74. *Mem:* Am Phys Soc. *Res:* Atomic scattering at high energies; phenomena associated with the penetration of matter by energetic particles such as ion implantation, sputtering, neutron radiation damage; scattering theory; quantum mechanics; thermodynamic and statistical mechanics of irreversible processes; defect processes in ionic crystals; polymer physics. *Mailing Add:* US Naval Res Lab Washington DC 20375

MANNING, JAMES HARVEY, b Hancock, Mich, Aug 13, 40; m 66; c 4. PAPER CHEMISTRY. *Educ:* Mich Technol Univ, BS, 62; Lawrence Univ, MS, 64, PhD(paper technol), 67. *Prof Exp:* Prod engr paper, Kimberly-Clark Corp, 61, res chem tissue, 62; qual control engr bd, Westvaco, 63; proj engr pulping, Int Paper Co, 64, res scientist cellulose, 67-72, group dir nonwovens, 73-77, tech dir, 77-79; ASSOC DIR, AM CAN CO, 79- *Concurrent Pos:* Secy, Dissolving Pulp Comt, Tech Asn Pulp & Paper Indust, 72-74. *Mem:* Tech Asn Pulp & Paper Indust; NY Acad Sci. *Res:* Direction of a group responsible for the development of new nonwoven products, with emphasis on wet-laid nonwoven products and processes. *Mailing Add:* American Can Co PO Box 899 Neenah WI 54956

MANNING, JAMES MATTHEW, biochemistry, see previous edition

MANNING, JARUE STANLEY, b Indiana, Pa, Sept 25, 34; m 60; c 1. VIROLOGY, BIOPHYSICS. *Educ:* San Francisco State Col, BA, 62; Univ Calif, Berkeley, PhD(biophys), 69. *Prof Exp:* Nat Cancer Inst fel, Univ Calif, Berkeley, 69-70; asst prof microbiol, sch vet med, 71-73, asst res virologist, comp oncol lab, 71-73, asst prof 73-75, ASSOC PROF BACTERIOL, UNIV CALIF, DAVIS, 75- *Honors & Awards:* Hektoen Gold Medal, Am Med Asn, 68. *Mem:* AAAS; Am Soc Microbiol; Biophys Soc. *Res:* Animal virology, including oncogenic viruses; cell-virus interaction, including virus-induced cytopathology and transformation; mechanisms of viral replication; characterization of viral components; viral immunity, including host defense mechanisms. *Mailing Add:* Dept of Bacteriol 155 Hutchison Univ of Calif Davis CA 95616

MANNING, JEROME EDWARD, b Minneapolis, Minn, Dec 31, 40; m 62; c 2. ACOUSTICS. *Educ:* Mass Inst Technol, SB, 62, SM, 63, ScD(mech eng), 65. *Prof Exp:* Sr scientist, Bolt Beranek & Newman, Inc, Mass, 65-68; MEM STAFF, CAMBRIDGE COLLABORATIVE, INC, 68- *Concurrent Pos:* Lectr, Mass Inst Technol, 67-69. *Mem:* Acoust Soc Am. *Res:* Sound induced vibration; noise; random vibrations. *Mailing Add:* Cambridge Collaborative Inc 169 Bent st Cambridge MA 02141

MANNING, JERRY EDSEL, b Redland, Calif, Oct 19, 44; m 67; c 2. BIOCHEMISTRY. *Educ:* Univ Utah, BS, 66, PhD(biochem), 71. *Prof Exp:* Res fel biol, Univ Utah, 71-72 & chem, Calif Inst Technol, 73-74; ASST PROF MOLECULAR BIOL, UNIV CALIF, IRVINE, 75- *Concurrent Pos:* Jane Coffin Childs fel, 73; Petrol Res Fund res grant, 74; NIH & Res Corp res grants, 75. *Mem:* Am Soc Cell Biol. *Res:* Molecular mechanisms that govern the regulation of genetic activity in the eukaryotic genome. *Mailing Add:* Dept of Molecular Biol & Biochem Univ of Calif Irvine CA 92664

MANNING, JOHN CRAIGE, geology, see previous edition

MANNING, JOHN RANDOLPH, b Norristown, Pa, Aug 24, 32; m 60; c 2. SOLID STATE PHYSICS, METALLURGY. *Educ:* Ursinus Col, BS, 53; Univ Ill, MS, 54, PhD(physics), 58. *Prof Exp:* Asst physics, Univ Ill, 57, res assoc, 58; physicist, 58-67, chief metal physics sect, 67-75, chief transformations & kinetics group, 75-79, CHIEF METALL PROCESSING GROUP, NAT BUR STANDARDS, 79- *Mem:* Am Phys Soc; Am Inst Mining, Metall & Petrol Engrs; Am Soc Metals. *Res:* Diffusion in solids; kinetic processes and defects in metals. *Mailing Add:* Metall Div Nat Bur of Stand Washington DC 20234

MANNING, JOHN W, b New Orleans, La, Nov 14, 30; m 54; c 6. PHYSIOLOGY. *Educ:* Loyola Univ, La, BS, 51; Tulane Univ, MS, 55; Loyola Univ Chicago, PhD(physiol), 58. *Prof Exp:* Vis scientist, Karolinska Inst, Sweden, 63-64; from asst prof to assoc prof physiol, 64-70, assoc prof anat, 67-71, dir grad studies physiol, 70-74, actg chmn, 79-81, PROF PHYSIOL, EMORY UNIV, 70- *Concurrent Pos:* USPHS fel, Emory Univ, 58-61, Am Heart Asn Advan res fel, 61-65; guest referee, Am J Physiol, 70-; vis prof, Shinshu Univ, Matsumoto, Japan, 72. *Mem:* AAAS; Am Physiol Soc; Am Asn Anat; Soc Neurosci; Can Physiol Soc. *Res:* Central nervous system regulation of cardiovascular activity; central response and transmission small cutaneous afferents; energetics of cardiac muscle. *Mailing Add:* Dept of Physiol Emory Univ Atlanta GA 30322

MANNING, LAURENCE A(LBERT), b Palo Alto, Calif, Apr 28, 23; m 54; c 3. ELECTRICAL ENGINEERING. *Educ:* Stanford Univ, AB, 44, MSc, 48, PhD, 49. *Prof Exp:* Asst elec eng, Stanford Univ, 43-44; res assoc, Radio Res Lab, Harvard Univ, 44-45; asst physics, 45-46, res assoc elec eng, 46-47, actg asst prof, 47-50, from asst prof to assoc prof, 51-59, PROF ELEC ENG, STANFORD UNIV, 60- *Mem:* Int Union Radio Sci; fel Inst Elec & Electronics Engrs; Am Geophys Union. *Res:* Ionospheric physics; radio communications; radar astronomy; electrical circuits; computer organization. *Mailing Add:* Dept of Elec Eng Stanford Univ Stanford CA 94305

MANNING, M(ELVIN) L(ANE), b Miller, SDak, Nov 26, 00; m 41; c 2. POWER ENGINEERING. *Educ:* SDak State Col, BS, 27; Univ Pittsburgh, MS & cert, 36. *Hon Degrees:* DrEng, SDak State Univ, 78. *Prof Exp:* Motor design engr, Westinghouse Elec Corp, 28-32, res engr, High Voltage Lab, 36-42; instr math, Univ Pittsburgh, 32-36; assoc prof elec eng, Ill Inst Technol, 42-43 & Cornell Univ, 43-45; chief engr, Kuhlman Elec Co, 45-49; res engr, McGraw Edison Co, 49-59; dean eng, 59-66, prof elec eng, 59-72, EMER PROF ELEC ENG, S DAK STATE UNIV, 72-; CONSULT, CHASE-FOSTER DIV, KEENE CORP, RI, 71- *Concurrent Pos:* mem transformer comt, Inst Elec & Electronics Engrs, 73- *Mem:* Am Soc Eng Educ; Am Soc Testing & Mat; fel Inst Elec & Electronics Engrs; Sigma Xi. *Res:* Transformer insulation; electrical insulation, silicones; application to dry-type transformers; power engineering, transformers. *Mailing Add:* 405 State Ave Brookings SD 57006

MANNING, MAURICE, b Loughrea, Ireland, Apr 10, 37; m 65; c 3. BIOCHEMISTRY, CHEMISTRY. *Educ:* Nat Univ Ireland, BSc, 57, MSc, 58, DSc, 74; Univ London, PhD(chem), 61. *Prof Exp:* Res assoc biochem, Med Col, Cornell Univ, 61-64; res assoc, Rockefeller Univ, 64-65; asst prof, McGill Univ, 65-69; assoc prof, 69-73, PROF BIOCHEM, MED COL OHIO, 73- *Concurrent Pos:* Fulbright travel grant, 61-64. *Mem:* Am Soc Biol Chem; AAAS; The Chem Soc; Am Chem Soc; NY Acad Sci. *Res:* Solid phase peptide synthesis; study of structure-function relationships of oxytocin and vasopressin; investigation of the toles and mechanism of action of oxytocin and vasopressin with selective agonists and antagonists. *Mailing Add:* Dept of Biochem Med Col of Ohio CS 10008 Toledo OH 43699

MANNING, MONIS JOSEPH, b Allentown, Pa, Mar 7, 31; m 57; c 3. PHOTOGRAPHIC CHEMISTRY, ANALYTICAL CHEMISTRY. *Educ:* Pa State Univ, BS, 53; Univ Cincinnati, MS, 58, PhD(org chem, molecular spectros), 60. *Prof Exp:* Chemist, Arthur D Little, Inc, 60-66; CHEMIST, POLAROID CORP, 66- *Mem:* AAAS; Am Chem Soc. *Res:* Application of chemical and physical science to photographic problem-solving; thermal analysis; analytical spectrophotometry; chromatographic analysis; spectral color-matching in plastic; plastics molding; spectral properties of optical plastics; photographic film sensitometry. *Mailing Add:* Polaroid Corp 784 Memorial Dr Cambridge MA 02139

MANNING, PHIL RICHARD, b Kans City, Mo, May 14, 21; m 48; c 2. INTERNAL MEDICINE. *Educ:* Univ Southern Calif, AB, 45, MD, 48. *Prof Exp:* Intern, Los Angeles County Hosp, 47-48; resident internal med, Vet Admin Hosp, Van Nuys & Long Beach, Calif, 48-50; from instr to assoc prof, 54-64, dir postgrad div, 53-59, PROF MED, SCH MED, UNIV SOUTHERN CALIF, 64-, ASSOC DEAN POSTGRAD DIV, 59-, ASSOC VPRES HEALTH AFFAIRS, 79-, PAUL INGALLS HONGLAND PROF CONTINUING MED EDUC & DIR, CONTINUING EDUC HEALTH PROF DEVELOP DEMONSTRATION CTR, 80- *Concurrent Pos:* Fel, Mayo Clin, 50-52. *Res:* evaluation of teaching techniques in continuing in health sciences education; development of the community hospital and physician's office as an intramural teaching center. *Mailing Add:* Postgrad Div Univ of South Calif Sch of Med Los Angeles CA 90033

MANNING, R(OBERT) E(DWARD), b Williamstown, Mass, May 23, 27; m 47; c 4. CHEMICAL ENGINEERING. *Educ:* Pa State Univ, BS, 48, MS, 49, PhD(chem eng), 54. *Prof Exp:* TECH DIR, CANNON INSTRUMENT CO, 54- *Mem:* Am Chem Soc; Am Soc Testing & Mat; Soc Rheology. *Res:* Distillation and viscosity measurement. *Mailing Add:* PO Box 16 State College PA 16801

MANNING, RAYMOND B, b Brooklyn, NY, Oct 11, 34; m 57; c 3. INVERTEBRATE ZOOLOGY, MARINE BIOLOGY. *Educ:* Univ Miami, BS, 56, MS, 59, PhD(marine sci), 63. *Prof Exp:* Res instr, Inst Marine Sci, Univ Miami, 59-63; assoc curator Crustacea, Div Marine Invert, 63-65, curator in charge div Crustacea, 65-67, chmn dept invert zool, 67-71, CURATOR DIV CRUSTACEA, SMITHSONIAN INST, 71- *Res:* Systematics and biology of decapod and stomatopod Crustacea. *Mailing Add:* IZ NHB W323 Smithsonian Inst Washington DC 20560

MANNING, ROBERT JOSEPH, b Kansas City, Kans, Jan 12, 20; m 49; c 4. PHYSICAL CHEMISTRY, ORGANIC CHEMISTRY. *Educ:* St Benedict's Col, Kans, BS, 43; Univ Kansas City, MS, 48. *Prof Exp:* Phys chemist, US Naval Ord Test Sta, 48-53; sr chemist, 53-63, prod line mgr, 63-73, PRIN CHEMIST, BECKMAN INSTRUMENTS, INC, 73- *Mem:* Am Chem Soc; Optical Soc Am; Soc Appl Spectros (pres-elect, 76, pres, 77). *Res:* Ultraviolet and infrared absorption spectroscopy, especially the near infrared; reflectance spectroscopy. *Mailing Add:* Beckman Instruments Inc 2500 Harbor Blvd Fullerton CA 92634

MANNING, ROBERT THOMAS, b Wichita, Kans, Oct 16, 27; m 49; c 3. MEDICINE, BIOCHEMISTRY. *Educ:* Univ Wichita, AB, 50; Univ Kans, MD, 54; Am Bd Internal Med, dipl, 62, recertified, 74. *Prof Exp:* Intern, Kans City Gen Hosp, 54-55; resident, Med Ctr, Univ Kans, 55-58, instr internal med, 58-59, assoc, 59-62, asst prof, 62-64, assoc prof internal med & biochem, 64-69, prof med & assoc dean, 69-71; assoc prof internal med, Eastern Va Med Sch, 71-77, dean, 71-74, chmn dept, 74-77; PROF MED, SCH MED, UNIV KANS & DIR INTERNAL MED, WESLEY MED CTR, WICHITA, KANS, 77- *Concurrent Pos:* Nat Inst Arthritis & Metab Dis fel, 56-58; chief first med serv, Univ Kans Med Ctr, 62-71; physician Wichita Vet Admin Hosp, 77- nat consult, US Air Force, 73-78. *Mem:* Fel Am Col Physicians; Am Fedn Clin Res; Cent Soc Clin Res; Am Asn Study Liver Dis; AMA. *Res:* Liver disease; biometrics. *Mailing Add:* 1001 Minneapolis Dr Wichita KS 67214

MANNING, SHERRELL DANE, US citizen. STRUCTURAL ENGINEERING. *Educ:* Tex Tech Univ, BS, 57, PhD(eng mech), 69; Southern Methodist Univ, MS, 62. *Prof Exp:* Assoc engr, Gen Dynamics Corp, 57-58; struct engr, 58-62; lead struct engr, Vought Corp, 62-63; sr struct engr, Gen Dynamics Corp, 63-66; instr civil eng, Tex Tech Univ, 67-68; res engr, Struct Res Dept, Southwest Res Inst, 68-69; eng specialist, 69-80, SR ENG SPECIALIST, GEN DYNAMICS CORP, 80- *Mem:* Am Soc Civil Engrs; Am Soc Testing & Mat. *Res:* Fatigue and fracture, structural reliability, advanced composites, computer applications, stress analysis. *Mailing Add:* Gen Dynamics Corp MZ 5984 PO Box 748 Ft Worth TX 76101

MANNING, T(HOMAS) A(RTHUR), JR, b Beaumont, Tex, Nov 20, 31; m 53; c 2. ENGINEERING SCIENCE, CIVIL ENGINEERING. *Educ:* Lamar State Col Technol, BS, 57; La State Univ, MS, 60; Stanford Univ, PhD(civil eng), 70. *Prof Exp:* ASSOC PROF ENG SCI, LA STATE UNIV, BATON ROUGE, 57- *Concurrent Pos:* Eng consult var indust firms, 60-; secy-treas, Stress Anal, Inc, 68- *Mem:* Am Soc Civil Engrs; Am Soc Eng Educ. *Res:* Solid mechanics; stress analysis; structural vibrations; computer applications; experimental stress and vibration analysis. *Mailing Add:* Dept of Civil Eng La State Univ Baton Rouge LA 70803

MANNING, WILLIAM JOSEPH, b Grand Rapids, Mich, June 13, 41; m 69; c 2. PHYTOPATHOLOGY BOTANY & MICROBIOLOGY. *Educ:* Mich State Univ, BS, 63; Univ Del, MS, 65, PhD, 68. *Prof Exp:* From asst to assoc prof plant path, Suburban Exp Sta, Univ Mass, Waltham, 68-77; assoc prof, 77-81, PROF PLANT PATH, UNIV MASS, AMHERST, 81- *Mem:* AAAS; Am Phytopath Soc; Sigma Xi; Am Air Pollution Control Asn. *Res:* Ecology of soil-borne fungi that cause root diseases of plants; interactions between air pollutants and biological incitants of plant diseases; air pollution effects on economic plants. *Mailing Add:* 51 Middle St Amherst MA 01002

MANNING, WILLIAM P, chemical engineering, see previous edition

MANNING, WILMER RAY, b McComb, Miss, Sept 5, 18; m 48; c 3. CHEMICAL ENGINEERING. *Educ:* Tulane Univ, BE, 39; Univ Ill, PhD(chem eng), 44. *Prof Exp:* Instr chem eng, Univ Ill, 43-44; process design engr, 44-56, proj leader, Eng Dept, 56-65, eng mgr vinyl monomers & resins, styrene & polystyrene, 65-77, SR STAFF ENGR, UNION CARBIDE

CORP, 77- *Mem:* Fel Am Inst Chem; Am Inst Chem Engrs. *Res:* Influence of diffusion and fluid properties yields in contact catalysis; chemical plant design; chemical engineering economics; process evaluation. *Mailing Add:* Coatings Mat Eng Union Carbide Box 8361 Charleston WV 25304

MANNINO, JOSEPH ROBERT, b Altoona, Pa, May 6, 41; m 78; c 1. ENDOCRINOLOGY, MEDICINE. *Educ:* Juniata Col, BS, 63; ECarolina Univ, MA, 65; Kansas City Col Osteop Med, DO, 71; Colo State Univ, PhD(endocrinol), 74. *Prof Exp:* Pvt pract, Denver, Colo, 72-77; prof family osteop med & dir med educ, Kans City Col Osteop Med, 77-80; DIR GEN PRACTICE RESIDENCY, DOCTORS HOSPITAL, COLUMBUS, OHIO, 80- *Concurrent Pos:* Lectr, Searle & Co, 74-; dir med educ, Rocky Mt Hosp, Denver, 75-77; lectr, Sandoz Pharmaceut, 78-; prof family med, Col Osteopathic Med, Ohio Univ, 80- *Mem:* Sigma Xi; fel Am Col Gen Pract; NY Acad Sci. *Res:* Applied endocrinology, especially as it pertains to hypertension; metabolic disease models. *Mailing Add:* Doctors Hospital 1087 Dennison Ave Columbus OH 43201

MANNIS, FRED, physical chemistry, see previous edition

MANNO, BARBARA REYNOLDS, b Columbus, Ohio, Mar 16, 36; m 68; c 2. TOXICOLOGY, PHARMACOLOGY. *Educ:* Otterbein Col, BS, 57; Ind Univ, Indianapolis, MS, 68, PhD(pharmacol), 70; dipl, Am Bd Forensic Toxicol, 77. *Prof Exp:* Asst prof pharmacol, Sch Pharm, Auburn Univ, 70-71; asst prof, 71-74, pharmacologist, Vet Admin Hosp, 71-78, assoc prof, 74-80, PROF PHARMACOL, MED SCH, LA STATE UNIV, SHREVEPORT, 80-, ASSOC MEM GRAD FAC, 71-, DIR, CLIN TOXICOL LAB, 76- *Concurrent Pos:* Assoc prof clin med technol, La Tech Univ, 74-79; consult, Schumpert Mem Hosp, 79-; reviewer, J Anal, Toxicol, 79- *Mem:* AAAS; Soc Toxicol; Am Acad Forensic Sci; Am Asn Clin Chem; Am Acad Clin Toxicol. *Res:* Cardiovascular actions of marihuana; analytical and experimental toxicology; environmental toxicology. *Mailing Add:* Dept Pharmacol & Therapeut La State Univ Med Sch Shreveport LA 71130

MANNO, JOSEPH EUGENE, b Warren, Pa, May 5, 42; m 68; c 2. TOXICOLOGY, PHARMACOLOGY. *Educ:* Duquesne Univ, BS, 65, MS, 67; Ind Univ, Indianapolis, PhD(toxicol), 70; dipl, Am Bd Forensic Toxicol, 77. *Prof Exp:* Asst prof pharmacol & toxicol, Sch Pharm, Auburn Univ, 70-71; asst prof, 71-74, assoc prof, 74-78, PROF PHARMACOL & TOXICOL & CHIEF, SECT TOXICOL, SCH MED, LA STATE UNIV, SHREVEPORT, 78- *Mem:* Soc Toxicol; Am Acad Forensic Sci; Am Chem Soc; Am Acad Clin Toxicol; Am Soc Pharmacol & Exp Therapeut. *Res:* Cardiovascular actions of marihuana and its chemical components; analytical toxicology. *Mailing Add:* Dept Pharmacol & Therapeut La State Univ Med Sch Shreveport LA 71101

MANNWEILER, GORDON B(ANNATYNE), b Naugatuck, Conn, Dec 1, 16; m 50; c 1. METALLURGICAL ENGINEERING. *Educ:* Yale Univ, BS, 41. *Prof Exp:* Eng trainee, 41-43, res engr, 47-53, dir res, 53-60 & 69-70, CHIEF MATALLURGIST, EASTERN CO, 60- *Concurrent Pos:* consult cast metals, 70- *Honors & Awards:* Silver Award, Am Soc Metals. *Mem:* Am Soc Metals; Am Foundrymen's Soc; Am Ord Asn; Inst Brit Foundrymen; fel Am Soc Testing & Mat. *Res:* Production, development and control of cast aluminum, carbon and alloy steels, gray, malleable and pearlitic malleable irons; casting alloys and their processing. *Mailing Add:* 435 Hillside Ave Naugatuck CT 06770

MANNY, BRUCE ANDREW, b Dayton, Ohio, May 24, 44. LIMNOLOGY, AQUATIC ECOLOGY. *Educ:* Oberlin Col, AB, 66; Rutgers Univ, MS, 68; Mich State Univ, PhD(bot), 71. *Prof Exp:* Nat Sci Found res assoc limnol, W K Kellogg Biol Sta, Mich State Univ, 71-73; PROJ LEADER, GREAT LAKES FISHERY LAB, US FISH & WILDLIFE SERV, 73- *Honors & Awards:* Nat Sci Found travel Award, Int Cong Limnol, Leningrad, 71. *Mem:* Ecol Soc Am; Am Soc Limnol & Oceanog; Int Asn Great Lakes Res; Int Asn Theoret & Appl Limnol; Am Fisheries Soc. *Res:* Ecological interactions of organic and inorganic nitrogen compounds in lake and stream metabolism; nitrogen cycle; ecosystem eutrophication. *Mailing Add:* Great Lakes Fishery Lab 1451 Green Rd Ann Arbor MI 48105

MANO, KOICHI, b Numazu, Japan, Nov 12, 20; m 45; c 2. THEORETICAL PHYSICS. *Educ:* Tokyo Univ Lit & Sci, BS, 45; Calif Inst Technol, PhD(physics), 55. *Prof Exp:* Lectr, Kyoto Univ, 50-55, asst prof, 55-58; scientist, Comstock & Wescott, Inc, Cambridge, Mass, 58-59; scientist, Wentworth Inst, Boston, 59-64; physicist, Air Force Cambridge Res Labs, 64-75; PHYSICIST, ELECTROMAGNETIC SCI DIV, ROME AIR DEVELOP CTR, HANSCOM AFB, 76- *Mem:* Am Phys Soc; Sigma Xi. *Res:* Quantum mechanics; mathematical physics; electromagnetic wave propagation. *Mailing Add:* 334 Gray St Arlington MA 02174

MANO, M(OSHE) MORRIS, b Salonika, Greece, Apr 3, 27; US citizen; m 58; c 2. COMPUTER & ELECTRICAL ENGINEERING. *Educ:* NY Univ, BEE, 52; Northwestern Univ, MS, 58; Worcester Polytech Inst, PhD(elec eng), 68. *Prof Exp:* Develop engr, Electronics Div, Israel Air Force, 53-56; design engr, Beckman Instruments, Calif, 57-58; sr engr, Ampex Comput Prod, 59-60; PROF ENG, CALIF STATE UNIV, LOS ANGELES, 60- *Concurrent Pos:* Sr engr, Space & Info Systs Div, NAm Aviation, Inc, 62-66; consult engr, Burroughs Corp, 69-72. *Mem:* Sr mem Inst Elec & Electronics Engrs. *Res:* Digital computer logic and systems. *Mailing Add:* Sch of Eng Calif State Univ Los Angeles CA 90032

MANOCHA, AMARJIT SINGH, physical chemistry, see previous edition

MANOCHA, MANMOHAN SINGH, b Sheikhupura, India, Feb 25, 35; Can citizen; m 63; c 2. MYCOLOGY, PLANT PATHOLOGY. *Educ:* Punjab Univ, India, BSc, 55, MSc, 57; Indian Agr Res Inst, New Delhi, PhD(mycol, plant path), 61. *Prof Exp:* Coun Sci & Indust Res fel, Indian Agr Res Inst, New Delhi, 61-63; Can Dept Agr grant, Univ Sask, 63-65; fel, Nat Res Coun Can, 65-66; from asst prof to assoc prof, 66-75, chmn biol, 80-83, PROF BIOL, BROCK UNIV, 75- *Concurrent Pos:* Alexander von Humboldt-Stiftung fel, Inst Plant Path, Univ Gottingen, WGer, 71-72. *Mem:* Can Phytopath Soc; Can Soc Cell Biol; Indian Phytopath Soc; Mycol Soc Am. *Res:* Fine structure and physiology of microorganisms; study of host-parasite interaction at cellular and molecular level; high resolution autoradiography associated with biochemical studies of diseased tissue. *Mailing Add:* Dept Biol Sci Brock Univ St Catharines ON L2S 3A1 Can

MANOCHA, SOHAN LALL, b Sultan Pur Lodhi, India, Aug 12, 36; m 64; c 2. HISTOCHEMISTRY, NEUROANATOMY. *Educ:* Punjab Univ, India, BSc, 56, MSc, 57, PhD(biol), 61. *Prof Exp:* Lectr zool, Govt Col, Rupar, India, 61-62; Ont Cancer Res Found fel, Queen's Univ, Ont, 62-64; res assoc histochem, 64-67, from asst prof to assoc prof neurohistochem, 67-75, CHMN DIV NEUROHISTOCHEM, YERKES PRIMATE RES CTR, EMORY UNIV, 75- *Mem:* Histochem Soc; Am Asn Anat; Soc Neurosci; Int Primatol Soc. *Res:* Fields of cytology, cytogenetics, histology, histochemistry, neuroanatomy and experimental nutrition using biological material related to reproductive system, skin, nervous system and biology of malnutrition; alteration of the nervous system under the impact of experimental dietary deficiency of protein in the diets of pregnant female and multigenerational study of its impact. *Mailing Add:* Yerkes Primate Res Ctr Emory Univ Atlanta GA 30322

MANOFF, GUS PETER, organic chemistry, analytical chemistry, see previous edition

MANOGUE, WILLIAM H(ENRY), b Queens, NY, Nov 27, 26; m 51; c 5. CHEMICAL ENGINEERING. *Educ:* Cornell Univ, BChE, 49; Univ Del, PhD(chem eng), 57. *Prof Exp:* Chem engr, Chem Warfare Labs, US Army Chem Ctr, Md, 50-56; sr res chem engr, Eastern Lab, 57-69, SR RES CHEM ENGR, CENT RES DEPT, EXP STA, E I DU PONT DE NEMOURS & CO, INC, 69- *Concurrent Pos:* Lectr, Univ Del, 57-; vis lectr, Univ Colo, 67-68. *Mem:* Am Chem Soc; Am Inst Chem Engrs. *Res:* Process development; thermodynamics; kinetics; catalysis. *Mailing Add:* 224 Beverly Rd Wilmington DE 19898

MANOHAR, MURLI, b Amritsar, India, Oct 3, 47. PHYSIOLOGY, CARDIOVASCULAR SURGERY. *Educ:* Panjab Agr Univ, BVSc, 68; Haryana Agr Univ, MVSc, 70; Univ Wis, PhD(physiol), 78. *Prof Exp:* Res assoc, Univ Wis, 78; asst prof, 79-80, ASSOC PROF CARDIOPULMONARY PHYSIOL, COL VET MED, UNIV ILL, 81- *Concurrent Pos:* Sr res fel, Indian Coun Agr Res, 70-73. *Honors & Awards:* Animal Health Book Prize, Commonwealth Animal Health Bur, Eng, 69. *Mem:* Am Soc Vet Physiologists & Pharmacologists; Am Physiol Soc; Am Heart Asn; Sigma Xi. *Res:* Coronary physiology and pharmacology in large domestic animals; cardiopulmonary aspects of high altitude physiology; coronary circulation. *Mailing Add:* 411 S Dodson St Urbana IL 61801

MANOLEV, LAZAR D, b Kara-Kioi, Greece, Dec 28, 24; US citizen; m 70; c 1. CHEMICAL ENGINEERING. *Educ:* Slovak Tech Univ, Bratislava, ChemEng, 52. *Prof Exp:* Anal chemist, Iron Works, Czech, 52-56, Gas Factory, 56-57, Drew Chem Co, NJ, 59-60 & Onyx Chem Co, 60-61; AGR RES CHEMIST, S B PENICK CHEM CO, 61- *Mem:* Am Chem Soc. *Res:* Analyses of iron ores; production of synthetic gas; agricultural chemicals and pesticides. *Mailing Add:* 58 Hoover St North Arlington NJ 07032

MANOOCH, CHARLES SAMUEL, III, b Big Springs, Tex, Aug 18, 43; m 65; c 3. VERTEBRATE ZOOLOGY, FISH ECOLOGY. *Educ:* Campbell Col, BS, 66; NC State Univ, MS, 72, PhD(zool), 75. *Prof Exp:* Biologist, Fla Game & Fresh Water Fish Comn, 68-70; res asst fisheries, NC State Univ, 70-72; BIOLOGIST, NAT MARINE FISHERIES SERV, 72- *Concurrent Pos:* Adj asst prof zool, NC State Univ, 78- *Mem:* AAAS; Am Fisheries Soc; Am Soc Ichthyologists & Herpetologists. *Res:* Population physiology of fish: growth, mortality, reproduction, population dynamics; reproductive histology. *Mailing Add:* Beaufort Lab Nat Marine Fisheries Serv Beaufort NC 28516

MANOOGIAN, ARMEN, b Galt, Ont, June 16, 34; m 64; c 2. PHYSICS. *Educ:* McMaster Univ, BA, 59; Fresno State Col, MSc, 61; McGill Univ, MS, 63; Univ Windsor, PhD(physics), 66. *Prof Exp:* Asst prof, 66-70, assoc prof, 70-79, PROF PHYSICS, UNIV OTTAWA, 79- *Mem:* Can Asn Physicists. *Res:* Paramagnetic resonance of transition metal impurities in crystals. *Mailing Add:* Dept of Physics Univ of Ottawa Ottawa ON K1N 9B4 Can

MANOS, CONSTANTINE T, b White Plains, NY, Jan 2, 33; m 71; c 2. GEOLOGY, SEDIMENTOLOGY. *Educ:* City Col New York, BS, 58; Univ Ill, MS, 60, PhD(geol), 63. *Prof Exp:* Res asst, State Geol Surv, Ill, 58-63; asst prof, Plattsburgh, 63-64, New Paltz, 64-66, assoc prof, 66-70, chmn dept geol sci, 69-72, PROF GEOL, STATE UNIV NY COL, NEW PALTZ, 70- *Concurrent Pos:* Grants-in-aid, State Univ NY Res Found, 65 & 68; NSF fels, Am Univ, 66, Hofstra Univ, N Ill Univ & Fairleigh Dickinson Univ, 73. *Mem:* Fel Geol Soc Am; Sigma Xi; Soc Econ Paleontologists & Mineralogists; Electron Micros Soc Am; Nat Asn Geol Teachers. *Res:* Heavy mineral analysis; sedimentation; stratigraphy; heavy mineral, thin section analysis of Tertiary flysch sediments of northwest Greece. *Mailing Add:* Dept Geol Sci State Univ NY Col New Paltz NY 12561

MANOS, NICHOLAS EMMANUEL, b Modesto, Calif, Dec 19, 16; m 49; c 5. MATHEMATICS. *Educ:* Univ Calif, BA, 39, MA, 40. *Prof Exp:* Meteorologist, US Weather Bur, 46-49; statistician, USPHS, 50-73; assoc dir, Asn State & Territorial Health Officers Health Progs Reporting Syst, 74-75; PVT CONSULT STATIST, PUB HEALTH, AIR POLLUTION, OCCUP HEALTH AND METEOROLOGY, 75-; CONSULT, DEPT STATE, 80- *Concurrent Pos:* Asst prof epidemiol & environ health, Med Sch, George Washington Univ, 68-75. *Mem:* Am Statist Asn; Am Pub Health Asn. *Res:* Statistics; public health; air pollution; occupational health; mathematics; meteorology. *Mailing Add:* 9847 Singleton Dr Washington DC 20034

MANOS, PHILIP, b Thessaloniki, Greece, May 8, 28; US citizen; m 57; c 2. ORGANIC POLYMER CHEMISTRY. *Educ:* Univ Thessaloniki, BS, 51; Boston Univ, PhD(chem), 61. *Prof Exp:* USPHS fel, Boston Univ, 59-60; res chemist, 60-68, to sr res chemist, 60-75, RES ASSOC PETROCHEM DEPT, E I DU PONT DE NEMOURS & CO, INC, 75- *Mem:* Am Chem Soc; AAAS. *Res:* Synthetic and mechanistic studies in organic chemistry; polymer and membrane chemistry; petroleum additives. *Mailing Add:* E I du Pont de Nemours & Co Inc Petrochem Dept Petrol Lab Deepwater NJ 08023

MANOS, THOMAS, b Detroit, Mich, Apr 21, 26; m 56; c 3. AERONAUTICAL & MECHANICAL ENGINEERING. *Educ:* Univ Mich, BS(aeronaut) & BS(math), 48, MS, 55, PhD(mech eng), 56; Wayne State Univ, MS, 50. *Prof Exp:* Design engr, Detroit Arsenal, 48-51; aeronaut engr, Continental Aviation, 52-53; sr stress engr, Am Motor Corp, 54-55; prin engr, Ford Motor Co, 55-59; assoc prof mech eng, 59-69, PROF MECH ENG, UNIV DETROIT, 69- *Concurrent Pos:* Spec lectr, Detroit Col Appl Sci, 50-51; mem grad fac, Wayne State Univ, 55-60; spec lectr, Henry Ford Community Col, 55-62; consult, Freuhauf Trailer Co, 59; lectr, Gen Motors Tech Ctr, 63-64. *Mem:* Soc Automotive Engrs. *Res:* Automotive safety; controlled collision; vehicle controllibility. *Mailing Add:* Dept of Mech Eng Univ of Detroit Detroit MI 48021

MANOS, WILLIAM P, b Milwaukee, Wis, May 2, 19; m 49; c 3. MECHANICAL ENGINEERING. *Educ:* Ill Inst Technol, BS, 50, MS, 54, PhD(mech eng), 62. *Prof Exp:* Res engr, Mech Eng, Pullman-Standard, Pullman, Inc, 50-52; res engr, Armour Res Found, Ill Inst Technol, 52-55; sr staff mem, Labs Appl Sci, Univ Chicago, 55-62; sr staff mem supv anal, Pullman-Standard, Pullman, Inc, 62-63, assoc dir res & develop, 63-65, eng mgr, 65-66, vpres res & develop, 68-78; CONSULT ENG. *Honors & Awards:* Railroad Award, Am Soc Mech Engrs, 65. *Mem:* Am Soc Mech Engrs. *Res:* Dynamic analysis of machines and ordnance weapons; guidance systems; missiles; rail vehicles. *Mailing Add:* 10350 S Longwood Dr Chicago IL 60643

MANOUGIAN, EDWARD, b Highland Park, Mich, Apr 11, 29; m 62; c 2. THEORETICAL BIOLOGY. *Educ:* Wayne State Univ, BS, 51; Univ Mich, MD, 55. *Prof Exp:* NIH fel math, Univ Calif, Berkeley, 60-62; res assoc biomed, Donner Lab, Univ Calif, Berkeley, 62-77; PVT RESEARCHER, 77- *Mem:* AAAS; Am Math Soc. *Res:* Biological rhythms. *Mailing Add:* 1517 Summit Rd Berkeley CA 94708

MANOUGIAN, MANOUG N, b Jerusalem, Palestine, Apr 29, 35; m 60; c 1. MATHEMATICS. *Educ:* Univ Tex, Austin, BA, 60, MA, 64, PhD(math), 68. *Prof Exp:* Instr math, Haigazian Col, Lebanon, 60-62, asst prof, 64-66; PROF MATH, UNIV SOUTH FLA, 68-, CHMN DEPT, 74- *Concurrent Pos:* Nat Sci Found grant, Univ S Fla, 71 & 77. *Mem:* Am Math Soc; Math Asn Am. *Res:* Analysis; differential and integral equations. *Mailing Add:* Dept of Math Univ of SFla Tampa FL 33620

MANOWITZ, BERNARD, b Jersey City, NJ, Mar 6, 22; m 51; c 2. CHEMICAL ENGINEERING. *Educ:* Newark Col Eng, BS, 43; Columbia Univ, MS, 47. *Prof Exp:* Assoc chem engr reactor eng, Clinton Lab, Monsanto Chem Co, 44-46; chem engr waste processing & radiation chem, 47-60, assoc head chem eng div, Nuclear Eng Dept, 60-62, head radiation div, Dept Appl Sci, 62-74, assoc chmn, 74-79, CHMN ENERGY & ENVIRON DEPT, BROOKHAVEN NAT LAB, 79- *Concurrent Pos:* Ed, J Appl Radiation & Isotopes, 57-75. *Honors & Awards:* Radiation Indust Award, Am Nuclear Soc, 71. *Mem:* Fel Am Nuclear Soc; Am Inst Chem Engrs; Am Geophys Union. *Res:* Applied radiation; atmospheric chemistry; atmospheric physics; oceanography. *Mailing Add:* 216 Lakeview Ave E Brightwaters NY 11718

MANRING, EDWARD RAYMOND, b Springfield, Ohio, Mar 21, 21; m 40; c 3. PHYSICS. *Educ:* Ohio Univ, BS, 44, MS, 48, PhD(physics), 52. *Prof Exp:* Res physicist, Monsanto Chem Co, 48-51; physicist, Geophys Res Directorate, Upper Air Observ, NMex, 52-60; head, Observational Physics Group, Geophys Corp Am, 60-66; PROF PHYSICS, NC STATE UNIV, 66- *Mem:* Am Phys Soc. *Res:* Nuclear physics; radio frequency spectroscopy; night sky intensity. *Mailing Add:* 1601 Dixie Trail Raleigh NC 27607

MANRIQUEZ, ROLANDO PAREDES, b Quezon City, Philippines, Apr 19, 51; US citizen. ELECTRICAL ENGINEERING. *Educ:* Am Univ, BS, 76; Cath Univ, MS, 78. *Prof Exp:* PHYSICIST ELECTROMAGNETIC EFFECTS, HARRY DIAMOND LABS, 74- *Mem:* Am Phys Soc; Inst Elec & Electronics Engrs. *Res:* Electromagnetic effects on equipment. *Mailing Add:* 3705 S George Mason Dr 901S Falls Church VA 22041

MANS, RUSTY JAY, b Newark, NJ, Sept 30, 30; m 52; c 5. BIOCHEMISTRY, ENZYMOLOGY. *Educ:* Univ Fla, BS, 52, MS, 54, PhD(biochem), 59. *Prof Exp:* Res assoc, Enzyme Group, Biol Div, Oak Ridge Nat Lab, 59-61, biochemist, 61-64; assoc prof biochem genetics, Univ Md, 64-69; prof immunol, med microbiol & radiol, Radiation Biol Lab, 69-72, PROF BIOCHEM, UNIV FLA, 72- *Concurrent Pos:* AEC res contract, 65- *Mem:* Am Soc Biol Chem; NY Acad Sci; Am Soc Plant Physiol. *Res:* Biosynthesis of proteins and nucleic acids; mechanism of eukaryotic transcription; mechanism of control of light induced nucleic acid synthesis in higher plants; mode of regulatin of cytoplasmic male sterility im maize; molecular genetics. *Mailing Add:* Dept Biochem & Molecular Biol J245 JHMHC Univ Fla Gainesville FL 32610

MANSBERGER, ARLIE ROLAND, JR, b Turtle Creek, Pa, Oct 13, 22; m 46; c 3. SURGERY. *Educ:* Univ Md, MD, 47. *Prof Exp:* Res fel surg, Univ Md, Baltimore City, 49-50, asst, Sch Med, 53-56, instr, 56-59, from asst prof to prof surg, 59-74, dir clin res, Shock-Trauma Unit, 62-66, chief clin adv, 66-71, head div gen surg, Univ Md Hosp, 71-74; PROF SURG & CHMN DEPT, MED COL GA, 73- *Concurrent Pos:* Consult surgeon, Montebello State Hosp, Baltimore, 56-73; consult surgeon, Div Voc Rehab, State of Md, 58-73; actg chmn dept surg, Univ Md Hosp, 70-71; examr, Am Bd Surg, 73-; chief consult, Vet Admin Hosp, Augusta, Ga, 73- *Mem:* AMA; fel Am Col Surg. *Res:* Ammonia metabolism in surgical diseases; biochemical and metabolic factors in shock. *Mailing Add:* Dept of Surg Med Col of Ga Augusta GA 30902

MANSELL, ROBERT SHIRLEY, b Roswell, GA, Apr 28, 38; m 65; c 3. SOIL PHYSICS. *Educ:* Univ Ga, BSA, 60, MS, 63; Iowa State Univ, PhD(agron), 68. *Prof Exp:* Fertilizer sales rep, Int Mineral & Chem Corp, Ga, 61; res asst soil fertility, Dept Agron, Univ Ga, 61-63; res asst soil physics, Iowa State Univ, 63, res assoc, 63-68; asst prof, 68-73, assoc prof, 73-79, PROF SOIL PHYSICS, UNIV FLA, 79- *Mem:* AAAS; Soil Sci Soc Am; Am Soc Agron; Am Geophys Union. *Res:* Movement of chemicals and water through saturated-unsaturated soil; water movement in layered soils; soil and water pollution. *Mailing Add:* G149 McCarty Hall Dept of Soil Sci Univ of Fla Gainesville FL 32611

MANSFELD, FLORIAN BERTHOLD, b Leipzig, Ger, Mar 6, 38; m 63; c 2. ELECTROCHEMISTRY, CORROSION. *Educ:* Univ Munich, BS, 60, MS, 64, PhD(phys chem), 67. *Prof Exp:* Fel, Mass Inst Technol, 67-68; Nat Acad Sci fel, NASA, 68-69; group leader, 69-80, GROUP MGR, ROCKWELL INT SCI CTR, 80- *Concurrent Pos:* US Sr Scientist Award, Humboldt Found, WGer. *Mem:* Electrochem Soc; Nat Asn Corrosion Engrs; Am Soc Testing & Mat. *Res:* Theoretical and practical problems of electrochemistry and corrosion. *Mailing Add:* Rockwell Int Sci Ctr 1049 Camino Dos Rios Thousand Oaks CA 91360

MANSFIELD, ARTHUR WALTER, b London, Eng, Mar 29, 26; m 57; c 3. MARINE BIOLOGY. *Educ:* Cambridge Univ, BA, 47, MA, 51; McGill Univ, PhD, 58. *Prof Exp:* Meteorologist, Falkland Islands Dependencies Surv, South Georgia Island, 51, base leader & biologist, S Orkneys, 52-53; demonstr zool, McGill Univ, 54-56; scientist & dir, Arctic Biol Sta, Fisheries & Marine Serv, Environment Can, 56-80, SCIENTIST & DIR, ARCTIC BIOL STA, FISHERIES & OCEANS CAN, 80- *Concurrent Pos:* Lectr, McGill Univ, 64-65. *Mem:* Fel Arctic Inst NAm. *Res:* Arctic marine biology, principally marine mammals. *Mailing Add:* Arctic Biol Sta Fisheries & Oceans Can 555 St Pierre Blvd St Anne de Bellevue PQ H9X 3R4 Can

MANSFIELD, CHARLES ROBERT, b Lewiston, Idaho, July 27, 38; m 65; c 1. PHYSICS, OPTICS. *Educ:* Ore State Univ, BS, 62; Univ Idaho, MS, 65, PhD(physics), 70. *Prof Exp:* Sr scientist, EG&G, Los Alamos Div, 73-76; STAFF MEM, LOS ALAMOS SCI LABS, UNIV CALIF, 76- *Concurrent Pos:* Fel, NASA-Nat Res Coun, Johnson Space Ctr, 69-71; res assoc, William Marsh Rice Univ, 71-73. *Mem:* Optical Soc Am. *Res:* Applications of modern optics to problems in science and engineering; specializing in atomic and molecular physics; interferometry and metrology. *Mailing Add:* Los Alamos Sci Lab MS 532 Los Alamos NM 87545

MANSFIELD, CLIFTON TYLER, b Sept 12, 36; US citizen; m 77; c 2. ANALYTICAL CHEMISTRY, ENVIRONMENTAL SCIENCE. *Educ:* Miss Col, BS, 59; Univ Fla, PhD(anal chem), 63. *Prof Exp:* Asst prof chem, Millsaps Col, 63-67; sr chemist, 67-73, group leader, 73-77, sect head, 77-81, PROG MGR FILTERS & MAT, RES DEPT, R J REYNOLDS TOBACCO CO, 81- *Mem:* Am Soc Testing & Mat. *Res:* Analytical chemistry of sugars, high pressure liquid chromatography of natural products, environmental monitoring. *Mailing Add:* Res Dept R J Reynolds Tobacco Co Winston-Salem NC 27102

MANSFIELD, JOHN E, b Cleveland, Ohio, July 2, 38; m 68; c 2. TECHNICAL INTELLIGENCE, THEORETICAL PHYSICS. *Educ:* Univ Detroit, AB, 60; St Louis Univ, MS & PhL, 63; Harvard Univ, AM, 66, PhD(physics), 70. *Prof Exp:* Res fel physics, Univ Notre Dame, 68-71; res physicist, Sci Applns, Inc, 71-74; sr scientist, 75-76, CHIEF NUCLEAR ENERGY & APPL SCI DIV, DEFENSE INTELLIGENCE AGENCY, 76- *Mem:* Am Phys Soc. *Res:* Internal symmetries; bootstraps; S-matrix theory; hydrodynamics; statistical physics, thermodynamics. *Mailing Add:* Defense Intelligence Agency Washington DC 20301

MANSFIELD, JOHN MICHAEL, b Louisville, Ky, Nov 5, 45; m 66; c 1. IMMUNOLOGY, MICROBIOLOGY. *Educ:* Miami Univ, BA, 67, MA, 69; Ohio State Univ, PhD(microbiol), 71. *Prof Exp:* NSF trainee, 71; fel microbiol & immunol, 71-73, ASST PROF MICROBIOL & IMMUNOL, SCH MED, UNIV LOUISVILLE, 73- *Mem:* AAAS; Am Soc Microbiol; Am Soc Trop Med & Hyg. *Res:* Tumor immunobiology; immunopathology of experimental African trypanosomiasis; cellular immunology; cytogenetics. *Mailing Add:* Dept of Microbiol & Immunol Univ of Louisville Sch of Med Louisville KY 40232

MANSFIELD, JOSEPH VICTOR, b Chicago, Ill, Mar 9, 07; m 35; c 1. ORGANIC CHEMISTRY. *Educ:* Iowa State Col, BS, 31; Univ Chicago, PhD(org chem), 42. *Prof Exp:* Chemist, Chicago Steel Co, 28-29; instr physiol chem, Chicago Med Sch, 31-36; pres & res dir, Mansfield Photo Res Labs, 35-42; chief specialist photog, Air Ctr, Photog Sch, US Navy, Fla, 42-43, chief photog mate, Photo Sci Lab, Va, 43-45; dir educ, Chicago Sch Photog, 45-46; from asst prof to prof, 46-75, EMER PROF CHEM, UNIV ILL, CHICAGO CIRCLE, 75- *Mem:* AAAS; Am Chem Soc; Photog Soc Am; Am Inst Chem; Royal Photog Soc. *Res:* Photographic chemical products; analytical chemistry. *Mailing Add:* 6455 La Jolla Blvd Apt 339 La Jolla CA 92037

MANSFIELD, KEVIN THOMAS, b Yonkers, NY, Mar 26, 40; m 62; c 3. ORGANIC POLYMER CHEM. *Educ:* Fordham Univ, BS, 62; Ohio State Univ, MS, 65, PhD(org chem), 67. *Prof Exp:* Res chemist, Silicones Res Ctr, Union Carbide Corp, NY, 67-69; prod develop chemist, 69-71, process develop chemist, 71-74, develop chemist, Basel, Switzerland, 74-75, group leader plastics develop, 75-78, SR GROUP LEADER PROCESS DEVELOP, PLASTICS & ADDITIVES DIV, CIBA-GEIGY CORP, 78- *Mem:* Am Chem Soc. *Res:* Process development; epoxies and other polymers of commercial interest; polymer antioxidants. *Mailing Add:* CIBA-GEIGY Corp PO Box 2055 Providence RI 02095

MANSFIELD, LARRY EVERETT, b Seattle, Wash, Sept 8, 39; m 62. MATHEMATICS. *Educ:* Whitman Col, AB, 61; Univ Wash, PhD(math), 65. *Prof Exp:* Asst prof, 65-74, ASSOC PROF MATH, QUEENS COL, NY, 74- *Mem:* Am Math Soc; Math Asn Am. *Res:* Differential geometry. *Mailing Add:* Dept of Math Queens Col Flushing NY 11367

MANSFIELD, LOIS E, b Portland, Maine, Jan 2, 41. NUMERICAL ANALYSIS. *Educ:* Univ Mich, BS, 62; Univ Utah, MS, 66, PhD(math), 69. *Prof Exp:* Vis asst prof comput sci, Purdue Univ, 69-70; from asst prof to assoc prof, Univ Kans, 70-78; assoc prof math, NC State Univ, 78-79; ASSOC PROF APPL MATH, UNIV VA, 79- *Concurrent Pos:* Vis asst prof math, Univ Utah, 73-74; mem, Adv Panel, Comput Sci Sect, NSF, 75-78; vis scientist, Inst Comput Appln Sci & Eng, NASA Langley Res Ctr, Hampton, Va, 77, consult, 78- *Mem:* Am Math Soc; Soc Indust & Appl Math; Asn Comput Mech. *Res:* Numerical solution of partial differential equations, approximation theory. *Mailing Add:* Dept Appl Math & Comput Sci Univ Va Charlottesville VA 22901

MANSFIELD, MAYNARD JOSEPH, b Marietta, Ohio, Jan 28, 30; m 53; c 2. TOPOLOGY. *Educ:* Marietta Col, BA, 52; Purdue Univ, MS, 54, PhD(math), 56. *Prof Exp:* Asst math, Purdue Univ, 52-54, statist, Statist Lab, 54-55, instr math, 56-57; asst prof, Washington & Jefferson Col, 57-60, assoc prof, 60-63; assoc prof, 63-65, asst dean, Grad Sch, 77-81, PROF MATH, INDIANA-PURDUE UNIVS, FT WAYNE, 65-, CHMN DEPT MATH SCI, 63- *Mem:* Am Math Soc; Math Asn Am; Asn Comput Mach. *Res:* Abstract topological spaces. *Mailing Add:* Dept of Math Sci Indiana-Purdue Univs Ft Wayne IN 46805

MANSFIELD, RALPH, b Chicago, Ill, Aug 21, 12; m 40; c 4. ELECTRICAL ENGINEERING, MATHEMATICS. *Educ:* Univ Chicago, BS, 35, SM, 37. *Prof Exp:* Instr math, Lewis Inst Technol, 36; statistician, Cost of Living Surv, US Dept Commerce, 36; teacher, Chicago Teachers Col, 37-43; res engr, Joseph Weidennoff, Inc, 43-45, asst chief engr, 45-46, actg chief engr, 46-47; chief engr & vpres, Auto-Test, Inc, 47-77; RETIRED. *Concurrent Pos:* Mem, Chicago Eclipse Exped, 32; instr, Armour Inst Technol, 37-40 & Ill Inst Technol, 40-; chmn dept math, Wright Jr Col, 62-65; chmn dept math, Loop Col, 66-77. *Mem:* AAAS; Am Math Soc; Math Asn Am; Am Statist Asn; Inst Elec & Electronics Engrs. *Res:* Differential equations; population problems; internal combustion engine ignition; testing circuits; electrical measurements. *Mailing Add:* Calle Zaragoza 58 Esporlas Mallorca Spain

MANSFIELD, ROBERT F, b Brackenridge, Pa, Oct 13, 28; m 54; c 4. CHEMICAL ENGINEERING. *Educ:* Carnegie Inst Technol, BS, 50. *Prof Exp:* Chem engr, Gen Elec Co, 50; chem engr, Gulf Res & Develop Co, 53-69, group leader petrol refining res, 57-61, sr proj engr, 63-65, sect supvr petrol econ, 66-69, mgr proj eval, Gulf Oil Corp, 69-73, dir spec studies, 73-74, vpres develop, Asia, 75-76, Asia coordr, Gulf Refining & Mkt Co, 76-79, pres, Korea Gulf Oil Co, 79-80, gen mgr admin control, Gulf Refining & Mkt Co, 81, PRES EASTERN HEMISPHERE, GULF OIL CO, 81- *Mem:* Am Inst Chem Engrs; Am Petrol Inst; Am Chem Soc. *Res:* Petroleum process development, design and evaluation; capital project analysis; petroleum refining and marketing operations and development; corporate long range planning. *Mailing Add:* Gulf Refining & Mkt Co PO Box 2001 Houston TX 77001

MANSFIELD, VICTOR NEIL, b Norwalk, Conn, Mar 7, 41; m 68; c 2. ASTROPHYSICS, COMPUTER SCIENCE. *Educ:* Dartmouth Col, BA, 63, MS, 64; Cornell Univ, PhD(astrophys), 72. *Prof Exp:* Res assoc astron, Cornell Univ, 71-73; asst prof, 73-81, ASSOC PROF PHYSICS & ASTRON, COLGATE UNIV, 81- *Concurrent Pos:* Vis asst prof astron, Cornell Univ & vis scientist, Nat Astron & Ionosphere Ctr, 75-76; sr systs analyst, comput sci, Digicomp Res, Ithaca, NY, 81. *Mem:* Int Astron Union; Am Astron Soc. *Res:* Theoretical astrophysics, general relativity and cosmology, physics and philosophy, computer science. *Mailing Add:* Picnic Area Rd Burdelt NY 14818

MANSINHA, LALATENDU, b Orissa, India, July 2, 37; m 63. GEOPHYSICS, APPLIED MECHANICS. *Educ:* Indian Inst Technol, Kharagpur, BSc, 57, MTech, 59; Univ BC, PhD(geophys, physics), 63. *Prof Exp:* Fel geophys, Rice Univ, 62-65; vis lect, 65-66, from asst prof to assoc prof, 66-79, PROF GEOPHYS, UNIV WESTERN ONT, 79- *Concurrent Pos:* NASA-Nat Res Coun sr res assoc, Goddard Space Flight Ctr, Md, 70-71. *Mem:* Am Geophys Union; Seismol Soc Am; Soc Explor Geophys. *Res:* Time series analysis; electical, seismic and gravity methods of exploration; Chandler wobble. *Mailing Add:* Dept Geophys Univ Western Ont London ON N6A 5B8 Can

MANSKE, WENDELL J(AMES), b Minneapolis, Minn, Apr 6, 24; m 47; c 3. CHEMICAL ENGINEERING. *Educ:* Univ Minn, BChemEng, 49; US Merchant Marine Acad, BS, 50. *Prof Exp:* Proj engr solvent extraction, Swift & Co, Tenn, 49-51; proj engr process develop, 51-54, group supvr tape develop, 54-57, group supvr chem eng res, 57-60, supvr prod develop, 60-64, proj supvr, 64-66, mgr new prod develop, Paper Prod Div, 66-73, sr new bus developer, New Bus Ventures Div, 73-78, sr prod develop specialist, Med Prod Div, Minn Mining & Mfg Co, 78-81, SR PROD DEVELOP SPECIALIST, PACKAGING SYSTS DIV, 3M CO, 81- *Res:* Oxidation catalysis; combustion of lean gas mixtures; microencapsulation; paper based feedback systems for programmed education; temperature, time and humidity indicators. *Mailing Add:* Packaging Systs Div 3M Res Ctr Minn Mining & Mfg Co St Paul MN 55119

MANSKI, WLADYSLAW J, b Lwow, Poland, May 15, 15; US citizen; m 41; c 2. MICROBIOLOGY, IMMUNOCHEMISTRY. *Educ:* Univ Warsaw, PhM, 39; Univ Wroclaw, DSc, 51. *Prof Exp:* Instr anal chem, Inst Inorg & Phys Chem, Univ Warsaw, 36-39; instr, Inst Chem, Univ Lublin, 44-45; head chem lab, Inst Microbiol, Univ Wroclaw, 45-49; Rockefeller fel, US, Denmark & Sweden, 49-50; head immunochem, Inst Immunol & Exp Ther, Polish Acad Sci, 51-55, head macromolecular biochem, Inst Biochem & Biophys & head biochem lab, State Inst Hyg, 55-57; from asst prof to assoc prof, 58-75, PROF MICROBIOL, ASSIGNED TO OPHTHALMOL, COL PHYSICIANS & SURGEONS, COLUMBIA UNIV, 75- *Mem:* AAAS; Am Asn Immunol; Am Chem Soc; Harvey Soc; Brit Biochem Soc. *Mailing Add:* Columbia Univ 630 W 168th St New York NY 10032

MANSMANN, HERBERT CHARLES, JR, b Pittsburgh, Pa, Apr 11, 24; m 47; c 6. ALLERGY IMMUNOLOGY. *Educ:* Univ Pittsburgh, BS, 49; Jefferson Med Col, MD, 51; Am Bd Pediat, cert, 59, Bd Pediat Allergy, cert, 60, Am Bd Allergy & Immunol, cert, 71. *Prof Exp:* Rotating intern, St Francis Hosp, 51-52; resident pediat, Children's Hosp, Pittsburgh, 52-54; fel allergy immunol, Mass Gen Hosp, 54-55; fel microbiol, Col Med, NY Univ, 55-56; fel path, Sch Med, Univ Pittsburgh, 56-69, asst prof pediat, 62-68; ASSOC PROF MED, DIR ALLERGY & CLIN IMMUNOL & PROF PEDIAT, JEFFERSON MED COL, 68- *Concurrent Pos:* Dir, Pulmonary Prog, Children's Heart Hosp, 70-; vis prof, Clin Pharmacol, Children's Hosp Philadelphia, 75-76; mem & consult, Adv Comt, Pulmonary-Allergy & Clin Immunol, Food & Drug Admin, 75- *Mem:* Am Acad Pediat; Am Acad Allergy; Care Asn Am; Asn Care Asthma; Am Pediat Soc. *Res:* Management of the child with chronic and acute asthma; management of asthma with the use of therapeutic theopohylline dosing. *Mailing Add:* Dept Pediat Jefferson Med Col 1025 Walnut St Philadelphia PA 19107

MANSON, ALLISON RAY, b Boonville, Mo, Jan 24, 39; m 61. CHEMICAL ENGINEERING. *Educ:* Va Polytech Inst, BS, 62, PhD(statist), 65. *Prof Exp:* Coop engr, Oak Ridge Gaseous Diffusion Plant, Tenn, 59-61; from asst prof to assoc prof statist, 65-78, PROF STATIST, NC STATE UNIV, 78- *Concurrent Pos:* VPres, Assessment Anal Assocs, Inc, 79-; treas, Kilkelly Environ Assocs, Inc, 81- *Mem:* Am Inst Chem Engrs; Am Chem Soc; Am Statist Asn; Inst Math Statist; Biomet Soc. *Res:* Design and analysis of experiments; engineering applications of statistics; response surface methodology and its application to engineering problems. *Mailing Add:* Dept of Exp Statist NC State Univ PO Box 5457 Raleigh NC 27650

MANSON, DONALD JOSEPH, b Chewelah, Wash, Dec 10, 30; m 67; c 3. PHYSICS, ELECTRONICS. *Educ:* St Louis Univ, BA, 59, PhL, 60, MS, 63, PhD(physics), 67. *Prof Exp:* Fel physics, St Louis Univ, 66-67, asst prof, 67-69; asst prof radiol, Med Ctr, Univ Mo-Columbia, 69-71, assoc prof radiol sci & elec eng, 71-75; vpres res, 76-78, PRES, ALPHA ELECTRONIC LABS, 76- *Concurrent Pos:* Res asst biomed comput labs, Washington Univ, 67-69; assoc investr, Space Sci Res Ctr, 70-; res coordr, Nat Inst Gen Med Sci grant, 70-; tech proj dir, USPHS grant, 71- *Mem:* Am Phys Soc; Am Asn Physics Teachers; Asn Comput Mach; Inst Elec & Electronics Engrs; Am Asn Physicists in Med. *Res:* Computer diagnosis in radiology; computer applications in medicine; image analysis; ecological systems analysis; computer modeling of biological systems; energy conservation; consumer electronics. *Mailing Add:* Alpha Electronic Labs 2302 Oakland Columbia MO 65201

MANSON, EARLE LOWRY, JR, molecular physics, see previous edition

MANSON, JEANNE MARIE, b Boston, Mass, Dec 14, 47. REPRODUCTIVE TOXICOLOGY, TERATOLOGY. *Educ:* Emmanuel Col, BA, 69; Ohio State Univ, PhD(develop biol), 74. *Prof Exp:* Fel, 74-76, asst prof, 76-81, ASSOC PROF REPRODUCTIVE TOXICOL, COL MED, UNIV CINCINNATI, 81- *Concurrent Pos:* Mem, Sci Adv Bd, Environ Protection Agency, 78-80, Nat Adv Environ Health Sci Coun, NIH, 79-; assoc ed, Teratogenesis, Carcinogenesis & Mutagenesis, 79-; study sect, Health Effects Panel & Environ Protection Agency grants rev, 81- *Mem:* Develop Biol; Teratol Soc; Soc Toxicol; Environ Mutagen Soc. *Res:* Environmental compounds for effects on the reproductive system and on the offspring; study of solvents, pesticides, heavy metals and other agents encountered in the environment for their effects on fertility and on embryonic, fetal and neonatal development. *Mailing Add:* Environ Health Kettering Lab Univ Cincinnati 32323 Eden Ave Cincinnati OH 45267

MANSON, JOHN ALEXANDER, b Dundas, Ont, Can, Aug 4, 28; m 51; c 4. POLYMER SCIENCE, PHYSICAL CHEMISTRY. *Educ:* McMaster Univ, BSc, 49, MSc, 51, PhD(chem), 56. *Prof Exp:* Asst, McMaster Univ, 47-50, 51-55; instr chem, Royal Mil Col Can, 50-51; assoc res engr, Eng Res Inst, Univ Mich, 56-57; sr res chemist, Cent Res Labs, Air Reduction Co, Inc, 57-59, sect head chem res, 59-61, supvr, 61-66; assoc prof, 66-70, PROF CHEM, LEHIGH UNIV, 70-, DIR POLYMER LAB, MAT RES CTR, 66- *Concurrent Pos:* Res assoc, Phoenix Proj, Univ Mich, 56-57; Airco sr staff award, Macromolecular Res Ctr, Strasbourg, France, 64-65; consult, Indust & Govt Labs. *Mem:* Am Chem Soc; Chem Inst Can. *Res:* Physical and engineering properties of high polymers and composite systems; fracture phenomena. *Mailing Add:* Coxe Lab Bldg 32 Lehigh Univ Bethlehem PA 18015

MANSON, JOSEPH RICHARD, b Petersburg, Va, Nov 6, 42; m 67; c 2. SURFACE PHYSICS. *Educ:* Univ Richmond, BS, 65; Univ Va, PhD(physics), 69. *Prof Exp:* PROF PHYSICS, CLEMSON UNIV, 81- *Res:* Theoretical work in the field of scattering of low energy atoms by solid surfaces. *Mailing Add:* Dept Physics & Astron Clemson Univ Clemson SC 29631

MANSON, LIONEL ARNOLD, b Toronto, Ont, Dec 24, 23; nat US; m 45; c 3. IMMUNOBIOLOGY, MOLECULAR BIOLOGY. *Educ:* Univ Toronto, BA, 45, MA, 47; Wash Univ, PhD(biol chem), 49. *Prof Exp:* Nat Res Coun fel med sci, Western Reserve Univ, 49-50, from instr to sr instr microbiol, 50-54; res asst prof, Sch Med, Univ Pa, 54-66, assoc prof, 66-73; res assoc, 54-57, assoc mem, 58-65, mem, 65-77, PROF, WISTAR INST ANAT & BIOL, 77-; PROF MICROBIOL, SCH MED, UNIV PA, 74- *Concurrent Pos:* Mem grad group microbiol, Grad Fac, Univ Pa, 55-, molecular biol, 65-, immunology, 71-, chmn immunology, 74-81; sr Fulbright scholar, France, 63-64; fel, Nat Cancer Inst Israel, 71-72. *Mem:* Sigma Xi; Am Soc Microbiol; Am Asn Biol Chemists; Am Asn Immunol; Am Chem Soc. *Res:* Transplantation immunobiology; molecular biology and biochemical genetics of humoral and cell-mediated immunity; structure, function and biosynthesis of cellular membranes; cell membrane differentiation; interaction of sub-cellular organelles in macromolecular biosynthesis; molecular biology of the immune response induced by tumor-specific and transplantation antigens; biochemical analysis of subcellular organelles. *Mailing Add:* Wistar Inst Anat & Biol 36th & Spruce St Philadelphia PA 19104

MANSON, S(AMUEL) S(TANFORD), b Jerusalem, July 4, 19; nat US; m 46; c 5. ENGINEERING. *Educ:* Cooper Union Inst Technol, BS, 41; Univ Mich, MS, 42. *Prof Exp:* Head, Stress & Vibration Sect, NASA, 45-49, chief, Strength of Mat Br, 49-55, asst chief, Mat & Thermodyn Div, 55-56, chief, Mat & Struct Div, Lewis Res Ctr, 74; PROF MECH & AEROSPACE ENG, CASE WESTERN RESERVE UNIV, 74- *Concurrent Pos:* Lectr, Univ Mich, 52, Mass Inst Technol, 57, Pa State Univ, 58-, Univ Calif, 59, Wayne State Univ, 63-64, Ga Inst Technol, 63 & Carnegie Inst Technol, 64-65; mem comt vibration & flutter, NASA, 48-49, res adv comt mat, 56-65, res adv fatigue, 62-72, Nat Acad Sci fracture guid comt res prog ship steel fracture, Univ Ill, 63-64. *Honors & Awards:* NASA Medal for Sci Achievement, 67; Von Karmon 2nd Prize, 74; Austen Lilligren Award, Am Die Casting Inst, 74. *Mem:* Soc Exp Anal(pres, 56); Am Soc Mech Engrs; Am Soc Test & Mat; hon mem Japan Soc Mat Sci; fel Royal Aeronaut Soc. *Mailing Add:* Dept of Mech & Aerospace Eng Case Western Reserve Univ Cleveland OH 44106

MANSON, SIMON V(ERRIL), b Jerusalem, Palestine, Mar 9, 21; US citizen; m 54. MECHANICAL ENGINEERING, MATHEMATICS. *Educ:* Columbia Univ, BA, 41, BS, 43. *Prof Exp:* Aeronaut res scientist, Aircraft Powerplants, Lewis Lab, Nat Adv Comt Aeronaut, 43-53; head heat transfer & asst chief anal, Nuclear Powerplants, Res Div, Curtiss-Wright Corp, 53-59, head heat transfer & cooling, Aerospace Powerplants, Wood-Ridge Div, 59-60; chief engr, Rocket Res & Develop, Dynetics, Inc, 60-61; pres, S V Manson & Co, Inc, 61-66; head advan component technol, Space Nuclear Power, Off Advan Res & Technol, Hq, NASA, 66-70, head space nuclear systs off, Atomic Energy Comn, 70-73, chief solar energy Appln, Off of Appln, 73-74, PROG MGR SATELLITE POWER SYSTS, OFF ENERGY PROGS & OFF AERONAUT & SPACE TECHNOL, NASA, 74- *Concurrent Pos:* Nat Adv Comt Aeronaut consult, Aircraft Reactor Exp, Oak Ridge Nat Lab, 50-51; mem, NASA-AEC Adv Rankine Ad Hoc Comt, 67-68; chmn, NASA-AEC-Dept Defense Organic Rankine Coord Comt, 67-68; mem, Proj Independence Energy Conserv Comt, 74; mem solar & mech group, Interagency Power Group, 75- *Mem:* AAAS; Am Nuclear Soc; Am Inst Aeronaut & Astronaut; Nat Soc Prof Engrs; NY Acad Sci. *Res:* Heat transfer; fluid flow; conceptual design in aircraft, rocket and aerospace powerplants; technology of advanced components of aerospace nuclear power systems; technology of satellite power systems. *Mailing Add:* 12608 Lincolnshire Dr Potomac MD 20854

MANSON, STEVEN TRENT, b Brooklyn, NY, Dec 12, 40; m 68; c 2. ATOMIC PHYSICS, CHEMICAL PHYSICS. *Educ:* Rensselaer Polytech Inst, 61; Columbia Univ, MA, 63, PhD(physics), 66. *Prof Exp:* Nat Acad Sci-Nat Res Coun res assoc, Nat Bur Standards, 66-68; from asst prof to assoc prof, 68-75, PROF PHYSICS, GA STATE UNIV, 75- *Concurrent Pos:* Consult, Oak Ridge Nat Lab, 68-69 & 75-; consult, Argonne Nat Lab & Pac Northwest Labs, Battelle Mem Inst, 73- *Mem:* Fel Am Phys Soc; Brit Inst Physics. *Res:* Theoretical atomic collisions; photoionization; generalized oscillator strengths; angular distribution of ionized electrons; penetration of charged particles into matter. *Mailing Add:* Dept Physics Astron Ga State Univ Atlanta GA 30303

MANSON-HING, LINCOLN ROY, b Georgetown, Guyana, May 20, 27; US citizen; m 51; c 3. DENTISTRY. *Educ:* Tufts Univ, DMD, 48; Univ Ala, MS, 61. *Prof Exp:* From asst prof to assoc prof, 56-58, PROF DENT, SCH DENT, UNIV ALA, BIRMINGHAM, 68-, CHMN DEPT DENT RADIOL, 62- *Concurrent Pos:* USPHS grants, 58-72; consult, State Ala Cleft Palate Clins, 57-65, Vet Admin Hosp & US Air Force; Fulbright-Hays lectr, UAR, 64-65. *Mem:* AAAS; Int Asn Dent Res; Am Dent Asn; Am Acad Dent Radiol; Am Bd Oral Maxillofacial Radiol. *Res:* Dental radiology. *Mailing Add:* Dept of Dent Radiol Univ of Ala Med Ctr Birmingham AL 35233

MANSOORI, G ALI, b Naragh, Iran, Oct 8, 40; m 73. CHEMICAL ENGINEERING. *Educ:* Univ Tehran, BS, 63; Univ Minn, Minneapolis, MS, 67; Univ Okla, PhD(chem eng), 69. *Prof Exp:* NSF fel, Rice Univ, 69-70; asst prof chem eng, 70-73, assoc prof, 73-77, PROF CHEM ENG, UNIV ILL, CHICAGO CIRCLE, 77- *Concurrent Pos:* Consult, Argonne Nat Lab, 75- & Int Inst Technol, 80- *Mem:* Am Inst Chem Eng; Am Chem Soc; Am Asn Univ Professors; Soc Petrol Engrs. *Res:* Thermodynamics and statistical mechanics of solutions, liquids and phase transitions; heterogenous chemical reactions. *Mailing Add:* Box 4348 Univ Ill Chicago Circle Chicago IL 60680

MANSOUR, A MAHER, b Kallin, Egypt, July 20, 28; m 66; c 2. MOLECULAR BIOLOGY, ENDOCRINOLOGY. *Educ:* Cairo Univ, BSc, 50; Cambridge Univ, PhD(endocrinol), 57. *Prof Exp:* Lectr physiol & endocrinol, Ain Shams Univ, Cairo, 58-63; res assoc molecular biol, Temple Univ, 63-65; MED RES SCIENTIST BIOCHEM RES, EASTERN PA PSYCHIAT INST, 65- *Concurrent Pos:* Pop Coun fel, Rutgers Univ, 62-64; res assoc, Bur Biol Res, Rutgers Univ, 62-63. *Mem:* AAAS; Endocrine Soc; Am Chem Soc; Am Soc Cell Biol. *Res:* Intracellular mechanism of hormone action and the relationship between mitochondrial and nuclear RNA synthesis. *Mailing Add:* Eastern Pa Psychiat Inst Henry & Abbotsville Rds Philadelphia PA 19129

MANSOUR, TAG ELDIN, b Belkas, Egypt, Nov 6, 24; nat US; m 55; c 3. PHARMACOLOGY, BIOCHEMISTRY. *Educ:* Cairo Univ, BVSc, 46; Univ Birmingham, PhD(pharmacol), 49, DSc(biochem), 74. *Prof Exp:* Lectr, Cairo Univ, 50-51; Fulbright instr physiol, Sch Med, Howard Univ, 51-52; sr instr & res assoc pharmacol, Med Sch, Western Reserve Univ, 52-54; res assoc, Sch Med, La State Univ, 54-56, from asst prof to assoc prof, 56-61; from assoc prof to prof, 61-78, DONALD E BAXTER PROF PHARMACOL & CHMN DEPT, SCH MED, STANFORD UNIV, 78- *Concurrent Pos:* Res fel pharmacol, Univ Birmingham, 49-50; Commonwealth Fund fel, 65; vis prof, Univ Wis, 69-70; consult, WHO, 70; mem study sect pharmacol, USPHS, 72-75. *Honors & Awards:* Josiah Macy, Jr, Award, 81; Heath Clark lectr, London Sch Hygiene & Trop Med, 81. *Mem:* AAAS; Am Soc Pharmacol & Exp Therapeut; Am Soc Biol Chemists. *Res:* Molecular and biochemical pharmacology; enzyme regulation; action of drugs on enzyme systems; regulation of cellular metabolism; chemotherapy of helminthiasis; physiology and biochemistry of parasitic helminths. *Mailing Add:* Dept of Pharmacol Stanford Univ Sch of Med Stanford CA 94305

MANSPEIZER, WARREN, b New York, NY, July 16, 33; m 62; c 4. GEOLOGY. *Educ:* City Col New York, BS, 56; WVa Univ, MS, 58; Rutgers Univ, PhD(geol), 63. *Prof Exp:* Assoc dean acad affairs, 70-71, chmn dept geol, 71-77, ASSOC PROF GEOL, RUTGERS UNIV, NEWARK, 69- *Concurrent Pos:* Scientist, Nat Sci Found-Moroccan Study Group, 72-75; vis scientist, Israel Geol Surv, Jerusalem. *Mem:* Geol Soc Am; Am Asn Petrol Geol; Nat Asn Geol Teachers; Soc Econ Paleontol & Mineral. *Res:* Paleoflow structures in Triassic lava flows, Eastern North America; stratigraphy of the Triassic basalts in Morocco and Eastern North America; Dead Sea; tectonism and sedimentation. *Mailing Add:* Dept of Geol Rutgers Univ 195 University Ave Newark NJ 07102

MANSUR, CHARLES I(SAIAH), b Kansas City, Mo, Dec 22, 18; m 60; c 2. CIVIL ENGINEERING. *Educ:* Univ Mo, BS, 39; Harvard Univ, MS, 41. *Prof Exp:* Jr sanit engr, W K Kellogg Health Found, 39; asst sanit eng, Grad Sch Eng, Harvard Univ, 39-41; chief, Embankment Found & Seepage Sect, Waterways Exp Sta, 41-43, chief, Design & Anal Sect, 46-54, asst chief, Embankment & Found Br, 54-57; chief, Geol, Soils & Mat Br, Miss River Comn, 57; chief engr, Luhr Bros, Inc, 58-59; supv engr, Fruin-Colnon Contracting Co, 59-61; vpres, Fruco & Assocs, 61-66, pres, 66-69; vpres, 69-80, PRES, MCCLELLAND ENGRS, INC, 80- *Concurrent Pos:* In charge, Meramec stream pollution surv, State Dept Health, Mo, 40; vpres & chief engr, Independent Wellpoint Corp, 57-58. *Mem:* Am Soc Civil Engrs. *Res:* Soil mechanics and foundation engineering; dewatering. *Mailing Add:* 1715 N Geyer Rd Frontenac St Louis MO 63131

MANTAI, KENNETH EDWARD, b Jamaica, NY, Oct 19, 42; m 62; c 2. PLANT PHYSIOLOGY. *Educ:* Univ Maine, BS, 64; Ore State Univ, PhD(plant physiol), 68. *Prof Exp:* Res fel plant physiol, Carnegie Inst, Washington, 68-69; res assoc, Brookhaven Nat Lab, 69-71; asst prof biol, 71-76, ASSOC PROF BIOL, STATE UNIV NY COL FREDONIA, 76-, CHMN BIOL DEPT, 80- *Concurrent Pos:* NSF res grant, 76. *Mem:* Am Soc Plant Physiologists; Int Asn Great Lakes Res; Sigma Xi; Am Soc Limnol & Oceanog; AAAS. *Res:* Physiology of the green alga Cladophora glomerata in response to environmental conditions found in Lake Erie; control of root growth in aquatic and terrestrial angiosperms. *Mailing Add:* Dept of Biol State Univ NY Col Fredonia NY 14063

MANTEI, ERWIN JOSEPH, b Benton Harbor, Mich, Nov 1, 38. GEOCHEMISTRY. *Educ:* St Joseph's Col, Ind, BS, 60; Univ Mo, MS, 62, PhD(geochem), 65. *Prof Exp:* Asst prof earth sci, 65-68, assoc prof geochem, 68-70, assoc prof geol, 70-72, PROF GEOL, SOUTHWEST MO STATE UNIV, 72- *Concurrent Pos:* Dr Carl Hasselman stipend, Mineral Inst, Univ Heidelberg, 71-72. *Mem:* AAAS; Geochem Soc; Mineral Soc Am. *Res:* Trace element distribution in minerals and rocks associated with ore deposits. *Mailing Add:* Dept of Geol Southwest Mo State Univ Springfield MO 65802

MANTEI, KENNETH ALAN, b Los Angeles, Calif, Nov 22, 40; m 67; c 2. PHYSICAL CHEMISTRY. *Educ:* Pomona Col, BA, 62; Ind Univ, Bloomington, PhD(chem), 67. *Prof Exp:* Res scientist, Univ Calif, Los Angeles, 67-68; assoc prof, 68-80, PROF CHEM, CALIF STATE COL, SAN BERNARDINO, 80-, CHMN DEPT, 75- *Mem:* Am Chem Soc. *Res:* Kinetics and mechanism of gas-phase reactions; flash photolysis. *Mailing Add:* Dept Chem Calif State Col San Bernardino CA 92407

MANTEL, LINDA HABAS, b New York, NY, May 12, 39; m 66. COMPARATIVE PHYSIOLOGY. *Educ:* Swarthmore Col, BA, 60; Univ Ill, Urbana, MS, 62, PhD(physiol), 65. *Prof Exp:* Res fel living invert, Am Mus Natural Hist, 65-68; asst prof, 68-76, ASSOC PROF BIOL, CITY COL NEW YORK, 76- *Concurrent Pos:* Nat Inst Child Health & Human Develop fel, 65-66; res assoc, Am Mus Natural Hist, 68-; mem, Extra-Mural Assoc, NIH, 82. *Mem:* AAAS; Am Inst Biol Sci; Am Soc Zool; Asn Women Sci; Am Soc Zoologists. *Res:* Adaptations of animals to their environment, particularly invertebrates; comparative physiology of salt and water balance, particularly in crustaceans; neuroendocrine control of adaptive mechanisms; effect of pollutants on physiology of crustaceans. *Mailing Add:* Dept of Biol City Col of New York New York NY 10031

MANTELL, CHARLES L(ETNAM), b Brooklyn, NY, Dec 9, 97; m 26; c 2. CHEMICAL ENGINEERING. *Educ:* City Col New York, BA & BS, 18; Columbia Univ, MA, 24, PhD(chem eng), 27. *Prof Exp:* Chem engr, Aluminum Co Am, 18-21; indust engr, Celluloid Corp, 21-22; prof chem eng, Pratt Inst, 22-37; tech dir, Wilbur B Driver Co, NJ, 34-39 & United Merchants & Mfrs, Inc, 40-47; PROF CHEM ENG, NEWARK COL ENG, 48- *Concurrent Pos:* Consult, 24-; dir res, Am Gum Importers Asn, 34-40; dir res, Netherlands Indies Labs, 36-50. *Mem:* Am Chem Soc; Electrochem Soc (vpres); fel Am Inst Chem Engrs; Am Inst Mining, Metall & Petrol Engrs. *Res:* Nonferrous metallurgy; electrochemical engineering. *Mailing Add:* 447 Ryder Rd Manhasset NY 11030

MANTELL, GERALD JEROME, b US, May 11, 23; m 48; c 4. ORGANIC POLYMER CHEMISTRY. *Educ:* Queen's Univ, Ont, BSc, 45; NY Univ, PhD(chem), 49. *Prof Exp:* Res chemist, E I du Pont de Nemours & Co, 50-58; mgr applns res, Spencer Chem Co, 58-63; mgr, Gulf Oil Corp, 63-66; dir polymer res, 66-69, dir polymer & applns res & develop, 69-71, dir res & appln develop, Plastics Div, 71-77, CHEM GROUP MGR PLANNING & COORD, AIR PROD & CHEM, INC, 77- *Mem:* Am Chem Soc; Tech Asn Pulp & Paper Indust; Am Asn Textile Chemists & Colorists; Soc Plastics Engrs. *Res:* Elastomers; free radical reactions; textile chemicals; polymers; adhesive and paper applications; polyvinyl chloride polymers and uses. *Mailing Add:* Air Prods & Chem Inc PO Box 538 Allentown PA 18105

MANTELL, M(URRAY) I(RWIN), b New York, NY, Sept 6, 17; m 44; c 4. CIVIL ENGINEERING. *Educ:* Univ Fla, BME, 40, ME, 48; Univ Southern Calif, MS, 45; Univ Tex, PhD, 52. *Prof Exp:* Pres & supt construct, Mantell Construct Co, 40-41, 46; struct engr, R A Belsham, 41; supvr sci sect, Charleston Navy Yard, 41-43; supvr alignment sect, Terminal Island Naval Shipyard, 43-45; chmn civil eng dept, 48-76 & 82-83, PROF CIVIL ENG,

UNIV MIAMI, 46- *Concurrent Pos:* Vis prof, Univ Sheffield, 65-66. *Mem:* Am Soc Civil Engrs; Nat Soc Prof Engrs; Am Soc Eng Educ. *Res:* Structures; construction; naval architecture; engineering economics and administration; planning and zoning. *Mailing Add:* Dept of Civil Eng Univ of Miami Coral Gables FL 33124

MANTEUFFEL, THOMAS ALBERT, b Woodstock, Ill, Nov 15, 48; m 72. NUMERICAL ANALYSIS. *Educ:* Univ Wis-Madison, BS, 70; Univ Ill, Urbana, MS, 72, PhD(math), 75. *Prof Exp:* Asst prof math, Emory Univ, 75-76; MEM TECH STAFF, SANDIA LABS, 76- *Mem:* Am Math Soc; Soc Indust & Appl Math. *Res:* Numerical linear algebra. *Mailing Add:* Appl Math Div 8332 Sandia Labs Livermore CA 94550

MANTEY, PATRICK E(DWARD), b Ft Morgan, Colo, Dec 15, 38; div; c 2. COMPUTER SCIENCE, ELECTRICAL ENGINEERING. *Educ:* Univ Notre Dame, BS, 60; Univ Wis-Madison, MS, 61; Stanford Univ, PhD(elec eng), 65. *Prof Exp:* Res assoc elec eng, Stanford Univ, 65-67; mem res staff systs, 67-72, MGR EXP SYSTS DEPT, COMPUTER SCI, IBM RES, 72- *Concurrent Pos:* Lectr, Stanford Univ, 65-, res assoc dept anesthesia, Med Sch, 65-67; consult, Philco-Ford Corp, 66-67. *Mem:* Inst Elec & Electronics Engrs. *Res:* Mathematical system theory; computer systems and applications; digital signal processing; computer graphics; image processing; text and document processing; computer aided engineering design; decision suport systems; pictorial information systems. *Mailing Add:* IBM Res K54/282 San Jose CA 95193

MANTHEY, ARTHUR ADOLPH, b New York, NY, June 7, 35; m 62. PHYSIOLOGY. *Educ:* Dartmouth Col, BA, 57; Columbia Univ, PhD(physiol), 65. *Prof Exp:* Fel physiol, Col Physicians & Surgeons, Columbia Univ, 65; instr med, 66-70, asst prof, 70-74, ASSOC PROF PHYSIOL & BIOPHYS, CTR HEALTH SCI, UNIV TENN, MEMPHIS, 74- *Res:* Electrophysiology of muscle and nerve. *Mailing Add:* Dept of Physiol & Biophys Univ of Tenn Ctr Health Sci Memphis TN 38163

MANTHEY, JOHN AUGUST, b Akron, Ohio, Mar 22, 25; m 49; c 5. PLANT PHYSIOLOGY. *Educ:* Kent State Univ, BS, 49; Univ Wyo, MS, 52. *Prof Exp:* Bacteriologist, Cleveland City Hosp, Ohio, 50-51; anal res chemist, Strong, Cobb & Co, Inc, 51-54; biochemist, Res Labs, 54-63, ANAL BIOCHEMIST, ELI LILLY & CO, INC, 63- *Concurrent Pos:* Lectr, Butler Univ, 58- *Mem:* Am Soc Plant Physiol. *Res:* Subcellular fractionation techniques in plant and animal tissues; mechanisms of metabolism of agrichemicals and therapeutic drug agents. *Mailing Add:* 1016 N Cumberland Rd Indianapolis IN 46229

MANTHY, ROBERT SIGMUND, b Chicago, Ill, Apr 4, 39. FOREST ECONOMICS. *Educ:* Mich State Univ, BS, 60, MS, 63, PhD(forest econ), 64. *Prof Exp:* Proj leader, Govt Asst Progs, Northeastern Forest Exp Sta, US Forest Serv, 63-66; PROF FOREST ECON & POLICY, MICH STATE UNIV, 66- *Concurrent Pos:* Pres, Greentree Consults, Inc, 73- *Mem:* AAAS; Soc Am Foresters. *Res:* Economics and scarcity of natural resources. *Mailing Add:* Dept of Forestry Mich State Univ East Lansing MI 48824

MANTLE, J(OHN) B(ERTRAM), b London, Eng, June 17, 19; m 42; c 2. MECHANICAL ENGINEERING. *Educ:* Univ Sask, BE, 41; Univ Ill, MSc, 47. *Prof Exp:* Instr mech eng, 45-47, from asst prof to prof, 47-66, head dept, 58-66, dean fac eng, 66-79, EMER PROF, UNIV REGINA, 79- *Mem:* Am Soc Eng Educ; Soc Exp Stress Anal; fel Eng Inst Can (vpres, 63-65); Can Soc Mech Engrs (vpres, 71-73). *Res:* Photoelastic and experimental stress analysis. *Mailing Add:* PO Box 2892 Creston BC V0B 1G0 Can

MANTSCH, HENRY H, b Mediasch, Transylvania, July 30, 35; Can citizen; m 59; c 2. BIOPHYSICAL CHEMISTRY, MOLECULAR SPECTROSCOPY. *Educ:* Univ Cluj, BSc, 58, PhD(phys chem), 64. *Prof Exp:* Res scientist phys chem, Romanian Acad Sci, 58-65; res fel phys chem, Univ Munich, 66-68; res assoc molecular spectros, Nat Res Coun Can, 68-72; prof phys biochem, Babes Univ, Cluj, 73-74; Humboldt prof biophys chem, Justus Liebig Univ, Giessen, 75-77; SR RES OFFICER & HEAD MOLECULAR SPECTROS SECT, NAT RES COUN CAN, 77- *Concurrent Pos:* Adj prof biophy chem, Carleton Univ, Ottawa, 78- *Mem:* Am Biophys Soc; fel Chem Inst Can; Can Spectros Soc; fel Royal Soc Can. *Res:* Physical biochemistry; fourier transform infrared spectroscopy; raman spectroscopy; multinuclear magnetic resonance; use of molecular spectroscopic techniques for the study of complex biological systems. *Mailing Add:* Div Chem Nat Res Coun Can 100 Sussex Dr Ottawa ON K1A 0R6 Can

MANTSCH, PAUL MATTHEW, b Ravenna, Ohio, Apr 10, 41; m 70; c 3. CRYOGENICS, SUPERCONDUCTING MAGNETS. *Educ:* Case Inst Technol, BS, 63; Univ Ill, MS, 65, PhD(physics), 70. *Prof Exp:* Res fel, physics, Deutsches Elektronen Synchtronen, Hamburg, 70-73; assoc head, Res Serv Dept, 75-78, head physics 78-80, PHYSICIST, FERMI NAT ACCELERATOR LAB, 73-, DEP HEAD, ENERGY SAVER MAGNETIC FACIL, 80- *Res:* High energy physics; hadron jets and photon interactions at 400 GeV. *Mailing Add:* Fermi Nat Accelerator Lab Box 500 Batavia IL 60150

MANTZ, ARLAN WARREN, chemical physics, spectroscopy, see previous edition

MANUCK, BARBARA ANN, physical biochemistry, see previous edition

MANUDHANE, KRISHNA SHANKAR, b Bombay, India, Aug 20, 27; m 54; c 2. INDUSTRIAL PHARMACY. *Educ:* Univ Poona, BSc, 49; Univ Bombay, BS, 51, MS, 54; Univ Md, PhD(pharm), 67. *Prof Exp:* Res chemist, Unichem Labs, Bombay, 54-55; pharmaceut chemist, Bd Experts, Drugs Control Admin, 55-59, tech officer, 59-64; head prod develop, Smith, Miller & Patch, Inc, 67-69; scientist, Parke Davis & Co, 69-71; dir tech serv-qual control, Cord Labs, 71-75; DIR PROD DEVELOP, ICN PHARMACEUT, INC, 75- *Mem:* Acad Pharmaceut Sci; Am Pharmaceut Asn. *Res:* Research associated with development of new pharmaceutical products, improvement of marketed products, scale up, trouble shooting, improving yields and reducing costs; quality control, quality assurance, and regulatory affairs; new drug application, stability, expiration dating, labeling and good manufacturing practices compliance. *Mailing Add:* 7839 Stonehill Dr Cincinnati OH 45230

MANUEL, OLIVER K, b Wichita, Kans, Oct 13, 36; m 60; c 9. NUCLEAR CHEMISTRY, GEOCHEMISTRY. *Educ:* Kans State Col, Pittsburg, BS, 59; Univ Ark, MS, 62, PhD(chem), 64. *Prof Exp:* Nat Sci Found fel, Univ Calif, Berkeley, 64; from asst prof to assoc prof, 64-73, PROF CHEM, UNIV MO-ROLLA, 73- *Concurrent Pos:* Res chemist, US Geol Surv, Denver, 79-80. *Mem:* AAAS; Am Chem Soc; Meteoritical Soc. *Res:* Cosmochemistry; noble gas mass spectrometry to study chronology of solar system; geochemistry of tellurium and the halogens; formation of the earth's atmosphere; element synthesis. *Mailing Add:* Dept Chem Univ Mo Rolla MO 65401

MANUEL, THOMAS ASBURY, b Austin, Tex, Jan 3, 36; m 58; c 2. RUBBER CHEMISTRY. *Educ:* Ohio Wesleyan Univ, BA, 57; Harvard Univ, AM, 58, PhD(chem), 61. *Prof Exp:* Res chemist, Cent Basic Res Lab, Esso Res & Eng Co, 60-63, sr chemist, 63-66, proj leader, Enjay Polymer Labs, 66-67, res assoc & sect head, 67-73, mgr, European Elastomers Tech Serv, Esso Chem Europe, Inc, 74-75, mgr new elastomers, Elastomers Technol Div, Exxon Chem Co, 75-77; DIR RES & DEVELOP, DEPT POLYMER CHEM, AIR PRODS & CHEM, INC, 77- *Mem:* Am Chem Soc. *Res:* Metal carbonyls; organometallic compounds; coordination compounds; polymers; elastomer emulsions. *Mailing Add:* Air Prod & Chem Inc PO Box 538 Allentown PA 18105

MANUELIDIS, ELIAS EMMANUEL, b Constantinople, Turkey, Aug 15, 18; US citizen; m 66; c 2. PATHOLOGY, NEUROPATHOLOGY. *Educ:* Univ Munich, MD, 42. *Hon Degrees:* MA, Yale Univ, 64. *Prof Exp:* Sci asst path, Univ Munich, 43-46; lab dir, Ger Res Inst Psychiat, Max Planck Inst, 46-49; lab dir, Hosp Int Refugee Orgn, 49-50; neuropathologist, US Army Europ Command, 98th Gen Hosp, 50-51; from instr to assoc prof neuropath, 51-64, PROF PATH, SCH MED, YALE UNIV, 64-, PROF NEUROL, 72-, CUR BRAIN TUMOR REGISTRY, 58- *Concurrent Pos:* USPHS spec fel, 66-67; vis lectr, Harvard Med Sch, 66-67; consult, Fairfield, Norwich & Norwalk Hosps & NIH. *Mem:* AAAS; Am Acad Neurol; Am Asn Path & Bact; Am Asn Neuropath; NY Acad Sci. *Res:* Encephalitides and tumors; tissue cultures and transplantation of brain tumors; electron microscope utilizing transplanted tumors. *Mailing Add:* Dept of Path Yale Univ Sch of Med New Haven CT 06510

MANULA, CHARLES BASIL, mining engineering, computer science, deceased

MANUWAL, DAVID ALLEN, b South Bend, Ind, Oct 13, 42; m 68. WILDLIFE ECOLOGY. *Educ:* Purdue Univ, BS, 66; Univ Mont, MS, 68; Univ Calif, Los Angeles, PhD(zool), 72. *Prof Exp:* Biologist, Pt Reyes Bird Observ, Bolinas, Calif, 71; asst prof, 72-78, ASSOC PROF WILDLIFE SCI, COL FOREST RESOURCES, UNIV WASH, 78- *Concurrent Pos:* Consult, Ctr Northern Studies, Wolcott, Vt, 73; Nat Wildlife Fedn fel, 73 & 75. *Mem:* Ecol Soc Am; Am Ornithologists Union; Wildlife Soc. *Res:* Timing and synchrony of reproduction and the social structure of seabird populations; impact of timber management on forest bird communities. *Mailing Add:* Col of Forest Resources Wildlife Sci Group Univ of Wash Seattle WA 98195

MANVEL, BENNET, b Springfield, Ill, Jan 23, 43; m 64; c 3. GRAPH THEORY, ALGORITHMS. *Educ:* Oberlin Col, BS, 64; Univ Mich, MS, 66, PhD(math), 70. *Prof Exp:* PROF MATH, COLO STATE UNIV, 70- *Concurrent Pos:* Vis scholar, Cambridge Univ, 76-77. *Mem:* Am Math Soc; Soc Indust & Appl Math; Math Asn Am. *Res:* Graph theory and computer applications, including graph reconstruction, connectivity and coloring algorithms. *Mailing Add:* Dept Math Colo State Univ Ft Collins CO 80523

MANVILLE, JOHN FIEVE, b Victoria, BC, Mar 18, 41; m 65; c 3. WOOD CHEMISTRY. *Educ:* Univ BC, BSc, 64, PhD(chem), 68. *Prof Exp:* Res scientist, Forest Prod Lab, 68-79, RES SCIENTIST, PAC FOREST RES CTR, CAN FORESTRY SERV, 79- *Mem:* Chem Inst Can; Weed Sci Soc Am. *Res:* Extractives. *Mailing Add:* Pac Forest Res Ctr Can Forestry Serv 506 W Burnside Rd Victoria BC V8Z 1M5 Can

MANWILLER, FLOYD GEORGE, b Bailey, Iowa, May 8, 34; m 59; c 2. FOREST PRODUCTS. *Educ:* Iowa State Univ, BS, 61, PhD(wood tech, plant cytol), 66. *Prof Exp:* Res assoc wood anat, Iowa State Univ, 64-65; wood scientist, Southern Forest Exp Sta, US Forest Serv, 66-78; PROF FORESTRY, IOWA STATE UNIV, 78- *Concurrent Pos:* Affil mem grad fac, La State Univ, 74- *Honors & Awards:* Wood Award, Forest Prod Res Soc & Wood & Wood Prod Mag, 66. *Mem:* Forest Prod Res Soc; Int Asn Wood Anatomists; Soc Wood Sci & Technol. *Res:* Wood anatomy; physical, mechanical and chemical properties of wood. *Mailing Add:* Dept of Forestry Iowa State Univ Ames IA 50011

MANYAN, DAVID RICHARD, b Providence, RI, Nov 9, 36; m 65; c 2. BIOCHEMISTRY. *Educ:* Bowdoin Col, AB, 58; Univ RI, MS, 65, PhD(biochem), 67. *Prof Exp:* Asst chemist, Metals & Controls Div, Tex Instruments, Inc, 59-60; NIH fel dermat, Sch Med, Univ Miami, 67-69, res scientist, 69-71, instr med, 71-72; dir, Am Heart Asn, 72-73; vis investr, Howard Hughes Med Inst, Univ Miami, 73-75; asst prof, St Frances Col, 75-78, assoc prof chem, 78-80; asst prof biochem & nutrit, Univ New England, New Eng Col Osteop Med, 80- *Mem:* AAAS; Am Chem Soc; fel Am Inst Chem; Am Soc Clin Invest; NY Acad Sci. *Res:* Enzymology, protein synthesis and drug effects in mitochondria; biochemistry of certain blood dyscrasias. *Mailing Add:* Dept Biochem Univ New England Biddeford ME 04005

MANYIK, ROBERT MICHAEL, b San Francisco, Calif, June 11, 28; m 52; c 2. PETROLEUM CHEMISTRY. *Educ:* Univ Calif, BS, 49; Duke Univ, PhD(org chem), 54. *Prof Exp:* RES CHEMIST, UNION CARBIDE CORP, 53- *Mem:* Am Chem Soc. *Res:* Organo-metallic reagents; olefins polymerization; homogeneous catalysis. *Mailing Add:* 1146 Summit Dr St Albans WV 25177

MANZ, BRUNO JULIUS, b Dortmund, Ger, June 26, 21; US citizen; m 53; c 4. THEORETICAL PHYSICS, MATHEMATICS. *Educ:* Univ Mainz, Dipl, 53; Aachen Tech Univ, Dr rer Nat(physics), 57. *Prof Exp:* Asst, Inst Theoret Physics, Aachen Tech Univ, 53-55; phys adv, Div Gas Turbines, Siemens Schuckert Werke, Ger, 55-57; specialist, Aeroballistics Lab, Army Ballistic Missile Agency, Redstone Arsenal, Ala, 57-59; res physicist, Air Force Missile Develop Ctr, 59-65, chief opers res div, Off Res Anal, Air Force Off Aerospace Res, 65-71, asst for study support, Kirtland AFB, 71-74, CHIEF OPERS RES DIV, DIRECTORATE AEROSPACE STUDIES, US AIR FORCE, 74- *Concurrent Pos:* Adj prof, Univ NMex. *Res:* Thermodynamics of irreversible processes; absorption and dispersion of sound in crystals and fluids; theory of shock waves; relativity; electromatic wave propagation; geometrical probability; military operations. *Mailing Add:* 1004 Casa Grande Ct Albuquerque NM 87112

MANZELLI, MANLIO ARTHUR, b New Market, NJ, Mar 19, 17; m 47; c 1. ENTOMOLOGY. *Educ:* Rutgers Univ, BS, 39, MS, 41, PhD, 48. *Prof Exp:* Res entomologist, Va-Carolina Chem Corp, 47-54, sect leader, 55-57, sr specialist plant chem, Merck & Co, Inc, 57-60; self-employed, 60-64; res scientist & leader tech info facility, 64-67, sr scientist, 67-73, ENTOMOLOGIST, PHILIP MORRIS RES CTR, 73-, ASSOC PRIN SCIENTIST, 79- *Mem:* AAAS; Entom Soc Am; Am Inst Biol Sci. *Res:* Biological control of insects; plant growth regulators; medical entomology; insect growth regulators; stored products entomology; information retrieval and storage. *Mailing Add:* Philip Morris Res Ctr PO Box 26583 Richmond VA 23621

MANZER, FRANKLIN EDWARD, b Maine, Feb 28, 32; m 54; c 4. PLANT PATHOLOGY. *Educ:* Univ Maine, BS, 55; Iowa State Col, PhD(plant path), 58. *Prof Exp:* From asst prof to assoc prof, 58-66, PROF PLANT PATH, UNIV MAINE, ORONO, 66- *Mem:* Am Phytopath Soc; Potato Asn Am; Europ Asn Potato Res. *Res:* All phases of potato disease; remote sensing. *Mailing Add:* Dept of Plant Path Univ of Maine Orono ME 04469

MANZER, JAMES IVAN, b Regina, Sask, Nov 6, 21; m 49; c 3. MARINE BIOLOGY, FISH ECOLOGY. *Educ:* Univ Man, BS, 44; Univ BC, MA, 49. *Prof Exp:* From sci asst to sr scientist, 45-63, SCIENTIST, PAC BIOL STA, 63- *Concurrent Pos:* Scientist, Int Fur Seal Invest, Can, 52-54; sci adv to Can, Int NPac Fisheries Comn, 56-65. *Res:* Marine life, population biology of Pacific salmon; migration and distribution of northern fur seal; production of aquatic resources through fertilization; ecological systems. *Mailing Add:* Dept Fisheries & Oceans Pac Biol Sta Nanaimo BC V9R 5K6 Can

MANZER, LEO ERNEST, organometallic chemistry, see previous edition

MAO, CHENG-HOW (ANDREW), chemical engineering, see previous edition

MAO, CHUNG-LING, b Nanking, China, Apr 21, 36; m 66; c 2. ORGANIC CHEMISTRY, POLYMER CHEMISTRY. *Educ:* Cheng Kung Univ, Taiwan, BSc, 59; Tex Tech Univ, MS, 64; Va Polytech Inst, PhD(chem), 67. *Prof Exp:* NSF & NIH fels & res assoc org chem, Duke Univ, 67-69; res chemist org chem & polymerizations, Res Ctr, World Hq, Uniroyal Inc, 69-73, res scientist, Oxford Mgt & Res Ctr, 73-77, sr res scientist, 77-80; SR RES ASSOC, AVERY INT RES & DEVELOP CTR, 80- *Mem:* Am Chem Soc; Sci Res Soc Am. *Res:* Organic syntheses; carbanion chemistry; molecular rearrangements; high temperature resistant polymers; elastomers and polyurethane chemistry. *Mailing Add:* Avery Int Res & Develop Ctr 325 N Altadena Dr Pasadena CA 91107

MAO, GEORGE W(ENJUNG), metallurgy, chemistry, see previous edition

MAO, HO-KWANG, b Shanghai, China, June 18, 41; m 68. HIGH PRESSURE GEOPHYSICS, GEOCHEMISTRY. *Educ:* Taiwan Nat Univ, BS, 63; Univ Rochester, MS, 66, PhD(geol sci), 68. *Prof Exp:* Res assoc geochem, Univ Rochester, 67-68; res fel, 68-80, GEOPHYSICIST, GEOPHYS LAB, CARNEGIE INST, 80- *Mem:* AAAS; Am Geophys Union; Mineral Soc Am. *Res:* High-pressure geochemistry. *Mailing Add:* Carnegie Inst Geophys Lab 2801 Upton St NW Washington DC 20008

MAO, IVAN LING, b Shanghai, China, Sept 16, 40; US citizen; m 67; c 2. BIOMETRICAL GENETICS, LIVESTOCK BREEDING. *Educ:* Nat Taiwan Univ, BSc, 64; Univ Guelph, MSc, 67; Cornell Univ, PhD(animal breeding), 70. *Prof Exp:* Res assoc, Cornell Univ, 70-71 & Univ Guelph, 71-72; asst prof, 72-78, ASSOC PROF DAIRY SCI, MICH STATE UNIV, 78- *Mem:* Am Dairy Sci Asn; Biomet Soc. *Res:* Application of biometrical procedures in livestock breeding and genetics. *Mailing Add:* Dept of Dairy Sci Mich State Univ East Lansing MI 48824

MAO, JAMES CHIEH HSIA, b China, Apr 3, 28; m 58; c 1. BIOCHEMISTRY. *Educ:* Taiwan Nat Univ, BS, 52; Univ Wis, MS, 59, PhD(biochem), 63. *Prof Exp:* Sr biochemist, 63-66, ASSOC RES FEL, ABBOTT LABS, 66- *Mem:* AAAS; Am Chem Soc; Am Soc Biol Chemists; NY Acad Sci; Am Soc Microbiol. *Res:* Metabolism of erythromycin; mode of action of antibiotics; antiviral research; nucleic acid histochemistry; enzymology. *Mailing Add:* Abbott Labs Abbott Park North Chicago IL 60064

MAO, SHING, b Kiangsi, China, May 21, 35; m 60; c 5. SOLID STATE ELECTRONICS. *Educ:* Nat Taiwan Univ, BS, 57; Carnegie Inst Technol, MS, 59; Stanford Univ, PhD(microwave electronics), 63. *Prof Exp:* Asst instrumentation, inst fluid dynamics & appl math, Univ Md, 58; engr, Semiconductor Div, Westinghouse Elec Corp, 59; res asst microwave electronics, Electron Devices Res Labs, Stanford Univ, 59-62, instr physics, 61-62; sr res scientist, Raytheon Co, 62-66; sect mgr, Semiconductor Res & Develop Labs, Tex Instruments, Inc, 66-68, eng mgr, Tex Instruments Singapore (PTE) Ltd, 68-71, prog mgr, Tex Instruments Taiwan Ltd, 71-76, progs mgr, Semi Conductor Group, 76-77; VPRES, UTL CORP, 77- *Mem:* Inst Elec & Electronics Engrs. *Res:* Transversewaves interaction in electron beam; field effect transistors; solid-state physics, particularly III-V compounds; bulk semiconductor effect; microwave solid-state devices and applications. *Mailing Add:* UTL Corp 4500 Mockingbird Ln Dallas TX 75209

MAO, SIMON JEN-TAN, b Taipei, Taiwan, Oct 10, 46; m 73; c 2. BIOCHEMISTRY. *Educ:* Fu Jen Univ, BS, 69; Univ Southwestern La, MS, 72; Baylor Col Med, PhD(biochem), 78. *Prof Exp:* Res assoc, Baylor Col Med, 78-79; ASST PROF BIOCHEM, MAYO MED CLIN & GRAD SCH, 80- *Concurrent Pos:* NIH career develop award, 80- *Res:* Structural and functional studies on human plasma lipoproteins; cause of atheriosclerosis. *Mailing Add:* Mayo Clin Rochester MD 55905

MAPES, GENE KATHLEEN, b Oakland, Calif, Feb 21, 46; m 65; c 1. BOTANY, PHYTOPATHOLOGY. *Educ:* Univ Ark, BS, 68; Univ Iowa, MS, 75, PhD(bot), 78. *Prof Exp:* ASST PROF, DEPT BOT, OHIO UNIV, ATHENS, 78- *Mailing Add:* Dept Bot Ohio Univ Athens OH 45701

MAPES, ROYAL HERBERT, b Manhattan, Kans, Nov 16, 42. PALEONTOLOGY, PETROLEUM GEOLOGY. *Educ:* Univ Ark, BS, 66, MS, 68; Univ Iowa, PhD(geol), 77. *Prof Exp:* Geologist, Phillips Petrol Co, 72-74, explor geologist, 77-78; ASST PROF PALEONT, OHIO UNIV, 78- *Mem:* Soc Econ Paleontologists & Mineralogists; Paleont Res Inst. *Res:* Paleobiology, taxonomy and biostratigraphy of Devonian, Mississippian, Pennsylvanian and Permian coiled nautiloids, ammonoids, orthoconic nautiloids, bactritoids, and coleoids; recent Nautilus. *Mailing Add:* Dept of Geol Ohio Univ Athens OH 45701

MAPES, WILLIAM HENRY, b Jonesboro, Ark, Dec 30, 39; m 64; c 2. THERMODYNAMICS. *Educ:* Carnegie Inst Technol, BS, 61; Univ Wash, PhD(chem), 66. *Prof Exp:* Chemist, 69-76, sr chemist, Major Appliance Lab, 76-80, SR CHEMIST, APPL SCI & TECHNOL LAB, GEN ELEC CO, 80- *Mem:* Int Inst Refrigeration; Royal Soc Chem. *Res:* Halocarbon thermodynamics; solution thermodynamics; absorption refrigeration systems. *Mailing Add:* Appl Sci & Technol Lab GE Co Appliance Park Louisville KY 40225

MAPLE, CLAIR GEORGE, b Glenwood, Ind, Mar 17, 16; m 42. APPLIED MATHEMATICS. *Educ:* Earlham Col, AB, 39; Univ Cincinnati, MA, 40; Carnegie Inst Technol, DSc(math), 48. *Prof Exp:* Instr math, WVa Inst Technol, 40-41; instr, Ohio State Univ, 41-44; res scientist & instr, Carnegie Inst Technol, 46-48; assoc prof, NTex State Col, 48-49; assoc prof, 49-55, PROF MATH, IOWA STATE UNIV, 55-, DIR COMPUT CTR, 63- *Concurrent Pos:* Asst prog dir, Math & Comput Sci Div, Ames Lab, Atomic Energy Comn, 67-78. *Mem:* AAAS; Am Math Soc; Math Asn Am. *Res:* Partial differential equations; computer science. *Mailing Add:* Computation Ctr Iowa State Univ Ames IA 50011

MAPLE, M BRIAN, b Chula Vista, Calif, Nov 20, 39; m 62. PHYSICS, PHYSICAL CHEMISTRY. *Educ:* San Diego State Col, BS & AB, 63; Univ Calif, San Diego, MS PhD(physics), 69. *Prof Exp:* Asst res physicist, 69-75, actg assoc prof, 75-77, assoc prof, 77-81, PROF PHYSICS, UNIV CALIF, SAN DIEGO, 81- *Concurrent Pos:* Vis scientist, Univ Chile, Santiago, 71 & 73; asst adj prof physics, Univ Calif, San Diego, 73-75; vis prof, Inst de Fisica Jose Balseiro, Argentina, 74; assoc res physicist, Univ Calif, San Diego, 75-79, Inst Theoret Physics, Univ Calif, Santa Barbara, 80. *Mem:* Am Phys Soc; AAAS; Am Vacuum Soc. *Res:* Superconductivity; magnetism; properties of alloys; high pressure physics; surface physics; catalysis. *Mailing Add:* B-019 Univ Calif La Jolla CA 92093

MAPLE, WILLIAM THOMAS, b Salem, Ohio, Aug 14, 42; m 66; c 1. VERTEBRATE ZOOLOGY, ECOLOGY. *Educ:* Miami Univ, AB, 64; Kent State Univ, MA, 68, PhD(ecol), 74. *Prof Exp:* Instr biol, Kent State Univ, 65-68; asst prof, 73-79, ASSOC PROF BIOL & DIR ECOL FIELD STA, BARD COL, 79- *Mem:* Am Soc Ichthyologists & Herpetologists; Soc Study Amphibians & Reptiles; Sigma Xi; Herpetologists League. *Res:* Vertebrate ecology and natural history; evolutionary ecology of amphibians and reptiles. *Mailing Add:* Dept of Biol Bard Col Annandale-on-Hudson NY 12504

MAPLES, GLENNON, b Perkinston, Miss, Aug 24, 32; m 68. MECHANICAL ENGINEERING. *Educ:* Miss State Univ, BS, 55, MS, 61; Okla State Univ, PhD(mech eng), 67. *Prof Exp:* Mech engr, Shell Oil Co, 55-58; instr eng graphics, Miss State Univ, 58-61, asst prof mech eng, 61-62; res assoc, Univ Fla, 62-63; asst, Okla State Univ, 63-66; asst prof, 66-77, ASSOC PROF MECH ENG, AUBURN UNIV, 77- *Concurrent Pos:* NSF grant, 68-69. *Mem:* AAAS; Am Soc Mech Engrs; Am Inst Aeronaut & Astronaut. *Res:* Convection and radiation heat transfer; cavitation; water resources. *Mailing Add:* Dept of Mech Eng Auburn Univ Auburn AL 36830

MAPLES, WILLIAM PAUL, b Jefferson City, Mo, Sept 1, 29; m 49; c 2. PARASITOLOGY. *Educ:* George Peabody Col Teachers, BS, 53, MA, 56; Univ Ga, PhD(parasitol), 66. *Prof Exp:* Soil engr, State Tenn Hwy Dept, 53-54; teacher, Davidson County Bd Educ, Tenn, 54-56; asst prof physics & zool, WGa Col, 56-59; res asst parasitol, Univ Ga, 59-63, res scholar, Southeastern Coop Wildlife Dis Study, 63-64, res assoc, 64-66, asst dir lab serv, 66-67; assoc prof, 67-70, PROF BIOL, W GA COL, 70- *Mem:* Am Soc Parasitol; Am Micros Soc. *Res:* Physiology, life history, embryology and taxonomy of helminths; pathobiology. *Mailing Add:* 128 Belva St Carrollton GA 30117

MAPLES, WILLIAM ROSS, b Dallas, Tex, Aug 7, 37; m 58; c 2. PHYSICAL ANTHROPOLOGY, FORENSIC ANTHROPOLOGY. *Educ:* Univ Tex, Austin, BA, 59, MA, 62, PhD(anthrop), 67; Am Bd Forensic Anthrop, dipl, 78. *Prof Exp:* Mgr, Darajani Primate Res Sta, Kenya, 62-63; mgr, Southwest Primate Res Ctr, Nairobi, Kenya, 64-65; asst prof anthrop, Western Mich Univ, 66-68; asst prof, 68-72, assoc prof, 72-78, chmn, Dept Soc Sci & assoc cur mus, 73-78, PROF ANTHROP & CUR PHYS ANTHROP, FLA STATE MUS, UNIV FLA, 78- *Concurrent Pos:* Western Mich Univ Fac Res Fund grant path of the Kenya baboon, 67-68, Univ Fla biomed sci grant, Kenya, 69-70, NSF grant, Kenya, 69-71, Univ Fla biomed sci grant, Kenya, 72-73. *Mem:* Am Asn Phys Anthrop; fel Am Anthrop Asn; fel Am Acad Forensic Sci. *Res:* Primate taxonomy and primate behavior, particularly as related to adaptation; forensic identification and trauma analysis of human skeletal remains. *Mailing Add:* Dept of Soc Sci Fla State Mus Gainesville FL 32611

MAPOTHER, DILLON EDWARD, b Louisville, Ky, Aug 22, 21; m 46; c 3. ACADEMIC ADMINISTRATION, PHYSICS. *Educ:* Univ Louisville, BS, 43; Carnegie-Mellon Univ, DSc(physics), 49. *Prof Exp:* Engr, Res Lab, Westinghouse Elec Co, 43-46; from instr to assoc prof, 49-59, dir off comput serv, 71-76, PROF PHYSICS, UNIV ILL, URBANA-CHAMPAIGN, 59-, ASSOC VCHANCELLOR RES, 76-, ASSOC DEAN, GRAD COL, 79- *Concurrent Pos:* Consult, govt labs, indust & univs, 54-, Sloan fel, 57-61; Guggenheim fel, 60-61; vis prof, Cornell Univ, 60-61. *Mem:* Fel Am Phys Soc; Am Asn Physics Teachers; AAAS; Sigma Xi. *Res:* Experimental physics of solids; low temperature physics; superconductivity; calorimetry; magnetic phase transitions; thermodynamics. *Mailing Add:* Grad Col 330 Admin Bldg Univ Ill 506 S Wright St Urbana IL 61801

MAPP, FREDERICK EVERETT, b Atlanta, Ga, Oct 12, 10; m 63; c 2. ZOOLOGY. *Educ:* Morehouse Col, BS, 32; Atlanta Univ, MS, 34; Harvard Univ, MA, 42; Univ Chicago, PhD(zool), 50. *Prof Exp:* Instr high sch, Ga, 33-40; prof biol & head dept, Knoxville Col, 44-46; lectr, Roosevelt Col, 48-50; prof & head dept, Tenn Agr & Indust State Col, 51-52; prof, 52-73, DAVID PACKARD PROF BIOL, MOREHOUSE COL, 73-, CHMN DEPT, 62- *Mem:* AAAS; Am Soc Zool; Am Micros Soc; NY Acad Sci. *Res:* Regeneration; experimental morphology; transplantation; tissue culture. *Mailing Add:* 703 Waterford Rd NW Atlanta GA 30318

MAR, BRIAN W(AYNE), b Seattle, Wash, Aug 5, 33; m 55; c 4. ENVIRONMENTAL SYSTEMS ENGINEERING. *Educ:* Univ Wash, BS, 55, MS, 56, PhD(chem eng), 58, MS, 67. *Prof Exp:* Asst chem eng, Univ Wash, 55-58, asst prof chem & nuclear eng, 58-59; res specialist, Boeing Co, 59-67; res assoc prof civil eng, 67-71, res prof, 71-73, assoc dean, Col Eng, 75-81, PROF CIVIL ENG, UNIV WASH, 73- *Mem:* Water Pollution Control Fedn; Sigma Xi; Am Soc Civil Engrs. *Res:* Water management; nuclear power; environmental systems engineering and management; simulation gaming. *Mailing Add:* Dept of Civil Eng Univ of Wash Seattle WA 98105

MAR, HENRY Y B, b Seattle, Wash, Oct 29, 39; m 67. CERAMICS ENGINEERING. *Educ:* Univ Wash, BS, 62, MS, 64, PhD(ceramic eng), 68. *Prof Exp:* Prin res scientist, 68-71, sr prin res engr, 71-73, staff engr, 73-75, sect chief, 75-79, RES MGR, SYSTS & RES CTR, HONEYWELL, INC, 79- *Mem:* Am Ceramic Soc; Nat Inst Ceramic Engrs. *Res:* Electrooptical materials and components for application to satellite survivability and solar energy systems; electrooptical sensor design and analysis. *Mailing Add:* Honeywell Systs & Res Ctr 2600 Ridgway Pkwy Minneapolis MN 55413

MAR, JAMES WAH, b Oakland, Calif, Mar 10, 20; m 42; c 4. AERONAUTICS. *Educ:* Mass Inst Technol, SB, 41, SM, 47, ScD(civil eng), 49. *Prof Exp:* Head struct test sect, Curtiss-Wright Corp, 41-44; engr, Struct Res Group, 49-50, from asst prof to assoc prof, 50-64, PROF AERONAUT & ASTRONAUT, MASS INST TECHNOL, 64-, DEPT HEAD, 81- *Concurrent Pos:* Mem panel thermal protection syst, Mat Adv Bd, Nat Acad Sci-Nat Res Coun, 57-69; mem comt thermal protection aerospace vehicles, Mat Adv Bd, Nat Acad Sci, 63-65; consult, Comt Space Vehicle Struct, NASA, 63- & Res & Technol Adv Comt Mat & Struct; mem adv bd, Mat Comt Struct Design with Fibrous Composites, Nat Acad Sci-Nat Res Coun-Nat Acad Eng, 67-; chief scientist, US Air Force, 71-72, mem sci adv bd vehicles panel. *Mem:* Am Inst Aeronaut & Astronaut. *Res:* Structural design of flight vehicles; aerothermoelastic problems; use of new materials. *Mailing Add:* Dept of Aeronaut & Astronaut Rm 33-207 Mass Inst of Technol Cambridge MA 02139

MAR, RAYMOND W, b Seattle, Wash, Oct 22, 42; m 64; c 3. MATERIALS SCIENCE, CHEMISTRY. *Educ:* Univ Wash, BS, 64; Univ Calif, Berkeley, MS, 66, PhD(mat sci), 68. *Prof Exp:* Ministry of Defense res fel, Univ Leeds, 68-69; STAFF MEM, MAT DIV, SANDIA LABS, 70- *Mem:* Am Ceramic Soc. *Res:* Synthesis and thermochemical characterization of materials and compounds; equilibrium and kinetic studies of sublimation reactions; calorimetric studies; high temperature phase relationships. *Mailing Add:* Mat Div Sandia Labs Livermore CA 94550

MARA, MICHAEL KELLY, b Westport, NZ, July 17, 52; m 80; c 1. APPLIED STATISTICS. *Educ:* Univ Canterbury, BSc, 74, MSc, 76, PhD(math statist), 79. *Prof Exp:* Teaching fel math, Univ Canterbury, 77-78, scientist, Appl Math Div, Dept Sci & Indust Res, 79-80; ASST PROF STATIST, UNIV MINN, 80- *Mem:* NZ Math Soc; NZ Statist Asn; Am Statist Asn. *Res:* Empirical Bayesian decision theory; nonparametric density estimation; biometrics, specifically capture-recapture methods. *Mailing Add:* Dept Appl Statist Univ Minn 1994 Buford Ave St Paul MN 55108

MARA, RICHARD THOMAS, b New York, NY, Mar 18, 23; m 46; c 1. PHYSICS. *Educ:* Gettysburg Col, AB, 48; Univ Mich, MS, 50, PhD(physics), 53. *Prof Exp:* From asst prof to prof, 53-70, SAHM PROF PHYSICS, GETTYSBURG COL, 70-, CHMN DEPT, 58- *Mem:* Am Phys Soc. *Res:* Molecular structure; classical field theory. *Mailing Add:* Dept of Physics Gettysburg Col Gettysburg PA 17325

MARABLE, JAMES HOLLEY, mathematical physics, engineering physics, see previous edition

MARABLE, NINA LOUISE, b Wilmington, NC, July 26, 39. PROTEIN & ENERGY METABOLISM, FOOD CHEMISTRY. *Educ:* Agnes Scott Col, BA, 61; Emory Univ, MS, 63; Mt Holyoke Col, PhD(chem), 67. *Prof Exp:* Instr chem, Mary Baldwin Col, 66-67; asst prof, Sweet Briar Col, 67-69; asst prof chem, Va Polytech Inst & State Univ, 69-72, asst prof human nutrit, 73-80; RES CHEMIST, PROTEIN NUTRIT LAB, USDA, 80- *Mem:* Am Chem Soc; Inst Food Technologists; Am Col Sports Med; Sigma Xi; Am Inst Nutrit. *Res:* Protein nutritive quality; processing effects on food quality; methods of protein quality evaluation; protein and energy metabolism in humans. *Mailing Add:* Protein Nutrit Lab Bldg 308 Rm 313 Human Nutrit Res Ctr USDA Beltsville MD 20705

MARADUDIN, ALEXEI, b San Francisco, Calif, Dec 14, 31; m 54; c 2. THEORETICAL SOILD STATE PHYSICS. *Educ:* Stanford Univ, BS, 53, MS, 54; Bristol Univ, PhD(physics), 56. *Prof Exp:* Res assoc physics, Univ Md, 56-57, res asst prof, 57-58, asst res prof, Inst Fluid Dynamics & Appl Math, 58-60; physicist, Westinghouse Res Labs, 60-65; chmn dept, 68-71, PROF PHYSICS, UNIV CALIF, IRVINE, 65- *Concurrent Pos:* Consult, Semiconductor Br, US Naval Res Lab, 58-60, Los Alamos Sci Lab, 65-67 & Gen Atomic Div, Gen Dynamics Corp, 65-71; Alexander von Humboldt US sr scientist award, 80-81. *Mem:* Am Phys Soc. *Res:* Lattice dynamics; electronic properties of solids; statistical mechanics; surface physics. *Mailing Add:* Dept of Physics Univ of Calif Irvine CA 92664

MARAGOUDAKIS, MICHAEL E, b Myrthios, Greece, Aug 4, 32; m 68; c 1. BIOCHEMICAL PHARMACOLOGY. *Educ:* Nat Univ Athens, BS, 56; Ore State Univ, MS, 61, PhD(biochem), 64. *Prof Exp:* Res asst biochem, Ore State Univ, 61-63, instr, 64; res assoc, Albert Einstein Med Ctr, 64-66; Ciba fel, Ciba Pharmaceut Co, 66-67, sr biochemist, Ciba-Geigy Corp, 67-69, head biochem pharmacol, 69-72, mgr basic biochem, 72-78; CHMN DEPT PHARMACOL, MED SCH UNIV PATRAS, GREECE, 78- *Mem:* Am Chem Soc; Am Soc Biol Chem; Am Soc Pharmacol & Exp Therapeut. *Res:* Intermediary metabolism and enzymology; mode of action of drugs at the molecular level; diabetic microanolopathy; basement membrane biosynthesis. *Mailing Add:* Med Sch Univ Patras Patras Greece

MARAMAN, GRADY VANCIL, biomathematics, physiology, see previous edition

MARAMOROSCH, KARL, b Vienna, Austria, Jan 16, 15; nat US; m 38; c 1. VIROLOGY, ENTOMOLOGY. *Educ:* Warsaw Tech Univ, MA, 38; Columbia Univ, PhD(bot, plant path), 49. *Prof Exp:* Lectr biol & animal breeding, Agr Sch Rumania, 45-46; from asst to assoc, Rockefeller Inst, 49-60; entomologist, Boyce Thompson Inst Plant Res, 60-63, prog dir, 63-74; PROF MICROBIOL, RUTGERS UNIV, NEW BRUNSWICK, 74- *Concurrent Pos:* Vis prof, State Agr Univ, Wageningen, 53; del, Int Cong Microbiol, Italy, 53, Sweden, 58, Can, 62, USSR, 66, Mex, 70; vis prof, Cornell Univ, 57; Lalor sr fel, 57; del, Int Cong Plant Protection, Ger, 57; virologist, Food & Agr Orgn, UN, Philipine Islands, 60, world-wide coconut dis surv, 63; del, Int Cong Entom, Austria, 60, Eng, 64, USSR, 68; coordr, US-Japan Virus-Vector Conf, Japan, 65; coordr, Invertebrate Tissue Culture, Tokyo, 74; mem exec comt, Int Comn Virus Nomenclature, 65-78; mem, Leopoldina Acad, 71-; food & fiber panel, Nat Acad Sci, 66; consult, US State Dept, Agency Int Develop, India, 67 & Int Rice Res Inst, Philippines, 67; vis prof, Rutgers Univ, 67-68; consult, All India Cent Rice Improv Proj, Hyderabad, & Ford Found, Nigeria, 71; del, II Int Conf Virol, Hungary, 71, Madrid, 75 & The Hague, 78; Fulbright distinguished prof, Yugoslavia, 72 & 78; vis prof, Fordham Univ, 73; pres, Int Conf Comp Virol, 69, 73, 77 & 82; mem trop med panel, NIH, 72-76; ed-in-chief, J NY Entom Soc, 72-; 4th Int Conf Invert Tissue Culture, Can, 75 & Switz, 79; mem, Int Conf in Vitro Techniques, Nairobi, Kenya, 78; fel, Nat Acad Sci, India, 78-; consult, Food & Agr Orgn, Sri Lanka, 81. *Honors & Awards:* Morrison Prize, NY Acad Sci, 51; Campbell Award, AAAS, 58; Ciba-Geigy Nat Award, Entomological Soc Am, 76; Waksman Award, Theobald Smith Soc, 78; Jurzykowski Award, 80; Wolf Prize, 80. *Mem:* AAAS; Harvey Soc; Soc Develop Biol; Am Phytopath Soc; NY Acad Sci (recording secy, 60-62, vpres, 62-63). *Res:* Plant pathology; insect transmission of viruses and mycoplasma-like agents; comparative virology; parasitology. *Mailing Add:* Waksman Inst of Microbiol Rutgers Univ New Brunswick NJ 08903

MARAN, JANICE WENGERD, b Baltimore, Md, June 30, 42. ELECTROPHYSIOLOGY, NEUROPHARMACOLOGY. *Educ:* Juniata Col, BS, 64; Stanford Univ, PhD(physiol), 74. *Prof Exp:* Res asst, Stanford Univ, 64-66, res assoc, 66-69; NATO fel, Univ Bristol, 74-75; NIH fel, Med Sch, Johns Hopkins Univ, 76-77; res scientist, McNeil Labs, 77-78, SR SCIENTIST, NCNEIL PHARMACEUT, 78- *Mem:* Am Physiol Soc; Soc Neurosci; Biomed Eng Soc; Sigma Xi; NY Acad Sci. *Res:* Discovery of novel psychotrophic drugs; elucidation of the mechanism of action of novel and existing central nervous system active drugs through electrophysiological techniques; techniques used include recording of single and multiple neurons, electroencephalogram, and evoked potentials. *Mailing Add:* PO Box 14 Ft Washington PA 19034

MARAN, STEPHEN PAUL, b Brooklyn, NY, Dec 25, 38; m 71; c 3. ASTROPHYSICS. *Educ:* Brooklyn Col, BS, 59; Univ Mich, MA, 61, PhD(astron), 64. *Prof Exp:* Astronomer-in-charge remotely controlled telescope, Kitt Peak Nat Observ, Ariz, 64-69; proj scientist for orbiting solar observs, 69, mgr, Oper Kohovtek, 73-74, head advan systs & ground observations br, 70-77, SR STAFF SCIENTIST, GODDARD SPACE FLIGHT CTR, NASA, 77- *Concurrent Pos:* Assoc ed, Earth & Extraterrestrial Sci, 69-79; ed, Astrophys Letters, 75-77, assoc ed, 77-; sr lectr, Dept Astron, Univ Calif, Los Angeles, 76; co-investr, Space Telescope High Resolution Spectrograph, 77-; consult, Nat Geographic Soc, 79-81. *Mem:* Am Astron Soc; Am Phys Soc; Royal Astron Soc; Int Astron Union; Am Geophys Union. *Res:* Comets; radio astronomy; infrared astronomy; space instrumentation; nebulae; ultraviolet astronomy. *Mailing Add:* NASA Goddard Space Flight Ctr Code 680 Greenbelt MD 20771

MARANO, GERALD ALFRED, b Philadelphia, Pa, Feb 15, 44; m 79; c 1. TECHNICAL MANAGEMENT, TRACER STUDIES. *Educ:* LaSalle Col, BA, 66; Univ Pa, PhD(inorg anal), 71. *Prof Exp:* Asst prof chem, Ky State Univ, 71-75; res & teaching fel, Ga Inst Technol, 75-76; sr develop chemist res & develop, Ciba-Geigy Corp, 76-80; SR RES ASSOC RES & DEVELOP, INT PAPER CO, 80- *Concurrent Pos:* Prin investr res projs, NASA, 73-75 & NSF, 74-75. *Mem:* Am Chem Soc. *Res:* Hydrolic flow mechanisms of waste water lagoons and their efficiencies; heat flow calorimetry as related to process development and safety; synthesis of novel and interesting inorganic and organo metallic compounds. *Mailing Add:* Erling Riis Res Lab Int Paper Co PO Box 2787 Mobile AL 36652

MARANS, NELSON SAMUEL, b Washington, DC, June 5, 24; m 54; c 3. CHEMISTRY. *Educ:* George Washington Univ, BS, 44; Pa State Univ, MS, 47, PhD, 49. *Prof Exp:* Asst anal develop, Allegany Ballistics Lab, George Washington Univ, 44-45; fel & lectr, De Paul Univ, 49-50; res assoc chem invest, Allegany Ballistics Lab, Hercules Powder Co, 50-54; group leader, Org Group, Mineral Benefication Lab, Columbia Univ, 54-55; sr scientist, Westinghouse Elec Corp, 55-57; res supvr, 57-62, RES ASSOC, RES DIV, W R GRACE & CO, 62- *Honors & Awards:* IR 100 Award. *Mem:* AAAS; Am Chem Soc; Sigma Xi. *Res:* Radiation chemistry; polymers; amino acids; organosilicon chemistry. *Mailing Add:* 12120 Kerwood Rd Silver Spring MD 20904

MARANTZ, LAURENCE BOYD, b Los Angeles, Calif, July 8, 35; m 62; c 3. ANALYTICAL CHEMISTRY. *Educ:* Calif Inst Technol, BS, 57; Univ Calif, Los Angeles, PhD(org chem), 62. *Prof Exp:* Res chemist, Rocket Power Res Lab, Maremont Corp, 62-64, head org sect, 64-66; mat res & develop engr, Douglas Aircraft Missile & Space Systs Div, McDonnell Douglas Corp, 66-67; spec mem staff, Marquardt Corp, Calif, 67, spec mem advan tech staff, CCI-Marquardt Corp, 67-71, chief chemist, Med Systs Div, CCI Corp, Van Nuys, 71-73, dir chem, CCI Life Systs, 73-75, dir sci serv, 75-76, dir chem, Redy labs, 76-78; dir chem, Organon Teknika Corp, 78-81; MEM STAFF, MARANTZ CONSULTING, 81- *Mem:* AAAS; Am Chem Soc; Sigma Xi. *Res:* Organo fluorine compounds; phosphorous polymers; high temperature thermodynamics; explosives and rocket propellants; ion exchange systems; polymers; instrumental design and operation; zirconium compounds; electrochemistry; medical equipment; analytical chemistry. *Mailing Add:* 3447 Alana Dr Sherman Oaks CA 91403

MARANVILLE, JERRY WESLEY, b Hutchinson, Kans, Sept 21, 40; m 67; c 1. AGRONOMY. *Educ:* Colo State Univ, BS, 62, MS, 64; Kans State Univ, PhD(agron), 67. *Prof Exp:* Asst prof, 67-73, assoc prof, 73-80, PROF AGRON, UNIV NEBR, LINCOLN, 80- *Mem:* Crop Sci Soc Am; Am Soc Agron. *Res:* Crop physiology and protein biochemistry; development of grain sorghum strains which are high in mineral uptake and utilization efficiency. *Mailing Add:* 102 Kiesselbach Lab Dept Agron Univ of Nebr Lincoln NE 68503

MARANVILLE, LAWRENCE FRANK, b Utica, Kans, Jan 6, 19; m 45; c 3. PULP CHEMISTRY. *Educ:* Phillips Univ, BA, 40; State Col Wash, MS, 42; Univ Chicago, PhD(phys chem), 49. *Prof Exp:* Anal chemist, Aluminum Co Am, 42-45, res chemist, 49-51; res chemist, Olympic Res Div, Rayonier Inc, 51-59, group leader, ITT Rayonier Inc, 60-72, asst to res supvr, 72-76, technol assessment specialist, 77-81; RETIRED. *Mem:* AAAS; Am Chem Soc; Tech Asn Pulp & Paper Indust. *Res:* Raman spectroscopy; medium strong electrolytes; electrical conductivity of molten salts; lignin and tannin chemistry; ultraviolet and infrared spectrophotometry; chemical cellulose; pulp chemistry. *Mailing Add:* 1128 Harvard Ave Shelton WA 98584

MARASCIA, FRANK JOSEPH, b New York, NY, Aug 6, 28; m 51; c 3. ORGANIC CHEMISTRY. *Educ:* Bucknell Univ, BS, 52; Univ Maine, MS, 54; Univ Del, PhD(chem), 58. *Prof Exp:* Control chemist, M W Kellogg Co, Pullman, Inc, 52; asst to sales & tech supvr, Southern Dist, Bound Brook Labs, Am Cyanamid Co, 54, res chemist, 54-55; res supvr org chem dept, Jackson Labs, NJ, 55-57, res chemist, 57-63, asst to sales, 64, tech supvr southern dist, 64-65, res supvr, Jackson Labs, 65-66, sales supvr southern district, NC, 66-67, asst mgr chem, Org Chem Div, 67-70, asst dir tech lab, 70-73, RES MGR, CHEM, DYES & PIGMENTS DEPT, SPEC CHEM & PRODS DIV, E I DU PONT DE NEMOURS & CO, INC, 73- *Mem:* AAAS; Am Asn Textile Chem & Colorists; Am Chem Soc; Tech Asn Pulp & Paper Indust. *Res:* Synthetic organic chemistry; sulfur and nitrogen compounds; textile chemicals in intermediates; paper chemicals. *Mailing Add:* E I Du Pont de Nemours Spec Chem & Prod Div Wilmington DE 19898

MARASPIN, LYNO EVELINO, human anatomy, endocrinology, see previous edition

MARATHAY, ARWIND SHANKAR, b Bombay, India, Dec 11, 33; m 63; c 1. OPTICAL PHYSICS. *Educ:* Univ Bombay, BSc, 54; Imp Col, Univ London, dipl, 56; Univ London, MSc, 57; Boston Univ, PhD(physics), 63. *Prof Exp:* Fel physics, Boston Univ, 63-64; sr scientist optical physics, Tech Opers, Mass, 64-69; ASSOC PROF OPTICAL SCI, UNIV ARIZ, 69- *Concurrent Pos:* Fel mech eng, Univ Pa, 66-67; consult, McCown Labs, Ariz & Tech Opers, Mass, 69-; vis prof, Indian Inst Sci, Bangalore, 75-76 & Sch Optom, Univ Ala, Birmingham, 78. *Mem:* Optical Soc Am; Am Asn Physics Teachers. *Res:* Physical optics; coherence theory; partial polarization; quantum coherence theory; electro-optic light modulators and scanners; optical bistability. *Mailing Add:* Dept Optical Sci Univ Ariz Tucson AZ 85721

MARAVETZ, LESTER L, b Cresco, Iowa, May 6, 37; m 62; c 4. AGRICULTURAL CHEMISTRY. *Educ:* Loras Col, BS, 59; Creighton Univ, MS, 61; Loyola Univ, PhD(org chem), 65. *Prof Exp:* Res chemist, Esso Res & Eng Co, 65-70; sr res chemist, Mobil Chem Co, 70-79, assoc chemist, 80, agr chem res, 70-81; RES ASSOC, HERBICIDE RES, FMC CORP, 81- *Mem:* Am Chem Soc. *Mailing Add:* 843 Carleton Rd Westfield NJ 07090

MARAVOLO, NICHOLAS CHARLES, b Chicago, Ill, Dec 4, 40. PLANT MORPHOGENESIS. *Educ:* Univ Chicago, BS, 62, MS, 64, PhD(bot), 66. *Prof Exp:* Asst prof, 66-75, ASSOC PROF BOT, LAWRENCE UNIV, 75- *Concurrent Pos:* Consult, State of Wis, 72-73 & East-Cent Wis Regional Planning Comt, 73- *Mem:* Bot Soc Am; Am Asn Plant Physiol; Am Bryol & Lichenological Soc. *Res:* Plant growth and development; biochemical changes associated with differentiation in lower green plants; hormonal physiology of development in bryophytes. *Mailing Add:* Dept of Biol Lawrence Univ Appleton WI 54911

MARBERRY, JAMES E(DWARD), b Carbondale, Ill, Jan 11, 31; m 62; c 2. CHEMICAL ENGINEERING. *Educ:* Purdue Univ, BSChE, 52, MSChE, 54; Univ Mich, PhD(chem eng), 60. *Prof Exp:* Res asst, Lilly Varnish Co, Ind, 53-54; sr res technologist, Mobil Oil Corp, 60-68, staff reservoir engr, Mobil Oil Can, Ltd, 68-71, sr res engr, Field Res Lab, Mobil Res & Develop Corp, 71-74, staff engr, Mobil Oil AG in Deutschland, 74-77, ASSOC ENGR, MOBIL RES & DEVELOP CORP, 77- *Mem:* Soc Petrol Engrs; Sigma Xi. *Res:* Chemical recovery of oil; simulation of laboratory and field experiments. *Mailing Add:* Field Res Lab PO Box 900 Dallas TX 75221

MARBLE, ALEXANDER, b Troy, Kans, Feb 2, 02; m 30; c 1. MEDICINE. *Educ:* Univ Kans, AB, 22, AM, 24; Harvard Univ, MD, 27. *Prof Exp:* Moseley traveling fel, Austria, Ger & Eng, 31-32; pres, Joslin Diabetes Found, 68-77, STAFF PHYSICIAN, JOSLIN CLIN, 32-, EMER PRES, JOSLIN DIABETES CTR, INC, 77- *Concurrent Pos:* Staff physician, New Eng Deaconess Hosp, 32-; from asst clin prof to clin prof med, Harvard Med Sch, 55-68, emer prof, 68- *Honors & Awards:* Banting Medal, Am Diabetes Asn, 59. *Mem:* AAAS; Am Soc Clin Invest; Endocrine Soc; Am Diabetes Asn (pres, 58-59). *Res:* Diabetes mellitus and carbohydrate metabolism. *Mailing Add:* Joslin Diabetes Ctr Inc One Joslin Pl Boston MA 02215

MARBLE, EARL R(OBERT), JR, b Hayden, Ariz, Sept 25, 20; m 56; c 2. METALLURGY. *Educ:* Tufts Univ, BS, 41; Mass Inst Technol, MS, 42. *Prof Exp:* Metallurgist, copper smelter, Am Smelting & Ref Co, 42-44, cent metall dept, Federated Metals Div, 46-57, res investr, Cent Res Lab, 57-59, asst to dir res, 59-70; CONSULT NON-FERROUS EXTRACTIVE METALL INDUST, 71- *Mem:* Sci Res Soc Am; Am Inst Mining, Metall & Petrol Eng. *Res:* Extractive metallurgy of copper, lead and zinc, especially pyrometallurgical treatment of ores and concentrates in extraction. *Mailing Add:* 2 Golf Rd Edison NJ 08817

MARBLE, FRANK E(ARL), b Cleveland, Ohio, July 21, 18; m 43; c 2. AERONAUTICS, MATHEMATICS. *Educ:* Case Inst Technol, BS, 40, MS, 42; Calif Inst Technol, AE, 47, PhD(aeronaut, math), 48. *Prof Exp:* Proj engr, Flight Propulsion Lab, Nat Adv Comt Aeronaut, Ohio, 42-44, head anal sect, 44-45, chief, Fundamental Compressor & Turbine Res Br, 45-46; instr aeronaut, 48-49, asst prof aeronaut & mech eng, 49-53, assoc prof 53-57, PROF JET PROPULSION & MECH ENG, CALIF INST TECHNOL, 57- *Concurrent Pos:* Consult. *Mem:* Am Phys Soc; fel Am Inst Aeronaut & Astronaut. *Res:* Fluid mechanics; gas dynamics; magnetohydrodynamics; propulsion. *Mailing Add:* Grad Aeronaut Lab Calif Inst Technol Pasadena CA 91125

MARBLE, HOWARD BENNETT, JR, b Shelburne Falls, Mass, June 14, 23; m 48; c 5. DENTISTRY, ORAL SURGERY. *Educ:* Tufts Univ, DMD, 47; Am Bd Oral & Maxillofacial Surg, dipl, 62. *Prof Exp:* Assoc prof, 69-78, PROF ORAL SURG, SCH DENT, MED COL GA, 78- *Concurrent Pos:* Chief dent serv, Vet Admin Hosp, Augusta, Ga, 69- *Mem:* Am Soc Oral Surg; Int Asn Oral Surg; Int Asn Dent Res. *Res:* Bone graft substitutes; bone healing. *Mailing Add:* Sch of Dent Med Col of Ga Augusta GA 30902

MARBLE, VERN L, agronomy, field crops, see previous edition

MARBURG, STEPHEN, b Frankfurt, Ger, July 16, 33; US citizen; m 56; c 2. ORGANIC CHEMISTRY. *Educ:* City Col New York, BS, 55; Harvard Univ, MA, 57, PhD(org chem), 60. *Prof Exp:* Chemist, Hoffman-La Roche, Inc, 55; NIH fel biochem, Brandeis Univ, 59-61; NIH fel phys org chem, Mass Inst Technol, 61-62; asst prof chem, Boston Univ, 62-65; sr res chemist, 65-74, res fel, 74-80, SR RES FEL, MERCK SHARP & DOHME INC, 80- *Mem:* Am Chem Soc. *Res:* Synthetic organic and physical organic chemistry; organic fluorine chemistry. *Mailing Add:* Merck Sharp & Dohme Inc Rahway NJ 07065

MARBURGER, RICHARD EUGENE, b Detroit, Mich, May 26, 28; m 50; c 2. PHYSICS. *Educ:* Wayne State Univ, BS, 50, MS, 52, PhD, 62. *Prof Exp:* Physicist, Res Labs, Gen Motors Corp, 52-53, res physicist, 55-58, sr res physicist, 58-69; mem staff, 69-70, dir, Sch Arts & Sci, 70-72, dean acad affairs, 72-75, PROF PHYSICS, LAWRENCE INST TECHNOL, 75-, VPRES ACAD AFFAIRS, 75-, PRES & CHIEF ADMIN OFFICER, 77- *Mem:* Am Phys Soc; Am Asn Physics Teachers. *Res:* Phase transformations in solids; residual stress analysis by x-ray diffraction; metal physics; x-ray diffraction techniques; Mossbauer effect. *Mailing Add:* Lawrence Inst of Technol 21000 W 10 Mile Rd Southfield MI 48075

MARCATILI, ENRIQUE A J, b Arg, 1925. ELECTRICAL ENGINEERING. *Prof Exp:* Elec & aeronaut engr, Cordoba Univ, Arg, 47-48, aircraft design engr & univ prov, 48-53; HEAD TRANSMISSION & CIRCUIT RES DEPT, BELL LABS, 53- *Honors & Awards:* Co-recipient W R G Baker Prize Award, 75. *Mem:* Nat Acad Eng; fel Inst Elec & Electronics Engrs. *Res:* Millimeter waveguide; optical communications. *Mailing Add:* Crawford Hill Lab Bell Labs Box 400 Holmdel NJ 07733

MARC-AURELE, JULIEN, b June 20, 29; Can citizen; m 55; c 3. PHYSIOLOGY. *Educ:* Univ Montreal, AB, 50, MD, 55. *Prof Exp:* Resident res collab, Brookhaven Nat Lab, 60-62; assoc dir clin res dept, Hotel-Dieu Hosp, 62-66; assoc prof med, 70-77, PROF MED, UNIV MONTREAL, 77-; CHIEF, DIV NEPHROLOGY, DEPT MED, SACRE-COEUR HOSP, 75-, DIR, DEPT MED, 80- *Concurrent Pos:* Res fel nephrology, Georgetown

Univ Hosp, 58-60; Can Heart Found fel, 58-62; Med Res Coun Can & Que Heart Found grants, 62-; lectr, Univ Montreal, 63-69; hon lectr, McGill Univ, 65- *Mem:* Am Fedn Clin Res; Am Soc Artificial Internal Organs; Can Med Asn; Can Soc Clin Invest; Am Soc Nephrology. *Res:* Nephrology; renal physiology in relation to human and experimental arterial hypertension; mechanisms of action of hormones in the kidney. *Mailing Add:* Dept of Med Univ of Montreal Montreal PQ H3C 3J7 Can

MARC DE CHAZAL, L E, b St Denis, Reunion, Nov 23, 21; US citizen; m 51; c 2. CHEMICAL & NUCLEAR ENGINEERING. *Educ:* La State Univ, BS, 49, MS, 51; Okla State Univ, PhD(chem eng), 53. *Prof Exp:* Asst prof chem eng, 53-57, assoc prof chem & nuclear eng, 57-66, PROF CHEM & NUCLEAR ENG, UNIV MO-COLUMBIA, 66- *Concurrent Pos:* Vis res assoc, Atomic Energy Res Estab, Eng, 59-60; res assoc, United Kingdom Atomic Energy Authority, 66-67. *Mem:* AAAS; Am Inst Chem Engrs; Am Chem Soc; Am Soc Eng Educ. *Res:* Mass transfer; drop formation and interfacial tension of liquid-liquid systems; statistics of solid mixtures; fluid mechanics. *Mailing Add:* Dept of Chem Eng Univ of Mo Columbia MO 65201

MARCEAU, NORMAND LUC, b Lambton, Que, Nov 11, 42; m 65; c 3. BIOPHYSICS, BIOCHEMISTRY. *Educ:* Laval Univ, BASc, 66; Univ Toronto, MSc, 68, PhD(biophys), 71. *Prof Exp:* Asst prof, 71-74, ASSOC PROF MED, LAVAL UNIV, 77-, SCIENTIST BIOPHYS, CTR HOSP, UNIV LAVAL, 71- *Concurrent Pos:* Main investr, Coun Res Health, Que grant, 72-73, Defense Res Bd grant, 73-76, Med Res Coun grant, 73-, Dept Educ, Que, grant 76- & Nat Cancer Inst Can, 78- *Mem:* Biophys Soc; Tissue Culture Asn; Can Soc Biochem. *Res:* Role(s) of plasma membrane glycoproteins and cytoskeletal elements in cell adhesion; maturation of hepatocytes during normal development and their transformation during chemical carcinogenesis. *Mailing Add:* Ctr Rech L'Hotel-Dieu de Quebec 11 Cote de Palais Quebec PQ G1R 2J6 Can

MARCELLI, G(LADYS) MARIE AGNEW, b Albany, NY, Mar 20, 27. BIOMEDICAL SCIENCES, EPIDEMIOLOGY. *Educ:* Rensselaer Polytech Inst, BSCh, 48, MS, 52; Univ Sussex, PhD(biol sci & pub admin), 74. *Prof Exp:* Tech asst, Pharm Div, Sterling-Winthrop Res Inst, 48-51, res asst, Chem-Biol Coord Sect, 51-53, res assoc new drug develop, Off Dir Res, 54-57, sci liaison officer, Europ-Australian Tech Opers, Sterling Drug, Inc, 58-67, assoc mem new drug develop, Sterling-Winthrop Res Inst, 61-65, res chemist, 65-71, mem new prod develop comt, 70-71, dir spec projs, Prod Develop & Regulatory Affairs, 71-72; CONSULT SCI & MED INFO, 72- *Concurrent Pos:* Curric adv comt, State Univ NY, Hudson Valley Community Col, 56-71; spec proj asst mild analgesics, Sterling Drug Res Bd, 67-70; sci consult, Ritual Object Sources & Authentication, Yeshiva Univ, Mus, 80 & mem, Mus Adv comt, 81- *Mem:* Am Chem Soc; Am Soc Metals; Sigma Xi; Am Pub Health Asn; Biomet Soc. *Res:* Mild analgesics; barbiturates; toxicity of chemicals, occupational and environmental pollutants; epidemiology of chronic diseases; development of pharmaceuticals, toiletries and household products; scientific, medical and regulatory aspects of consumer product liability. *Mailing Add:* 61 Maple Ave Hastings-on-Hudson NY 10706

MARCELLI, JOSEPH F, b Schenectady, NY, Nov 22, 26; m 52. ORGANIC CHEMISTRY. *Educ:* Rensselaer Polytech Inst, BS, 48, MS, 50, PhD, 57. *Prof Exp:* Asst, Rensselaer Polytech Inst, 49-51, res assoc, 53-56; from instr to assoc prof, 56-59, PROF CHEM, HUDSON VALLEY COMMUNITY COL, 59-, CHMN DEPT, 58-, DEAN HEALTH & PHYS SCI, 71- *Concurrent Pos:* Actg chmn, Dept Chem, Hudson Valley Community Col, 57-58, dir phys sci div, 67-70, dean sci & actg dean arts, 70-71. *Mem:* AAAS; fel Am Inst Chem; Am Pub Health Asn; Am Chem Soc; Health Physics Soc. *Mailing Add:* Hudson Valley Community Col 80 Vandenburgh Ave Troy NY 12180

MARCELLINI, DALE LEROY, b Oakland, Calif, Mar 19, 37; m 58; c 3. HERPETOLOGY, ANIMAL BEHAVIOR. *Educ:* San Francisco State Univ, BA, 64, MA, 66; Univ Okla, PhD(zool), 70. *Prof Exp:* Instr biol, Calif State Univ, Hayward, 71-74; RES CUR AMPHIBIANS & REPTILES, NAT ZOOL PARK, SMITHSONIAN INST, 74-, CUR HERPOTOL, 78- *Mem:* Soc Study Amphibians & Reptiles; Animal Behav Soc; Am Soc Ichthyologists & Herpetologists; Am Asn Zool Parks & Aquariums. *Res:* Behavior and ecology of Gekkonid lizards, expecially acoustic behavior; breeding and captive maintenance of vertebrates. *Mailing Add:* Nat Zool Park Off of Animal Mgt Smithsonian Inst Washington DC 20560

MARCELLINO, GEORGE RAYMOND, b Brooklyn, NY, Apr 28, 49; m 69; c 2. AUDIOLOGY, PSYCHOACOUSTICS. *Educ:* City Univ New York, BA, 70, MSc, 72, PhD(hearing sci), 77. *Prof Exp:* Res assoc psychoacoust, NY Univ Med Ctr, 71-72; audiologist, Bellevue Hosp, New York, 71-72; clin res audiologist, Mt Sinai Hosp, New York, 72-73; asst prof audiol & hearing sci, Brooklyn Col, City Univ New York, 73-78; AUDITORY PROD MGR, TELESENSORY SYSTS, INC, 78- *Mem:* Acoust Soc Am; Am Speech & Hearing Asn; Soc Med Audiol. *Res:* Auditory time and frequency analysis; synthetic speech perception in sensorineural hearing-impairment; neonatal hearing detection. *Mailing Add:* Telesensory Systs Inc 3408 Hillview Ave Palo Alto CA 93404

MARCH, BERYL ELIZABETH, b Port Hammond, BC, Aug 30, 20; m 46; c 1. POULTRY NUTRITION. *Educ:* Univ BC, BA, 42, MSA, 62. *Prof Exp:* Res asst, Can Fishing Co, 44-47; instr, 47-59, res assoc, 59-62, from asst prof to assoc prof, 62-70, PROF POULTRY SCI, UNIV BC, 70- *Honors & Awards:* Nutrit Res Award, Am Feed Mfg Asn. *Mem:* AAAS; fel Poultry Sci Asn; Can Soc Nutrit Sci; fel Agr Inst Can; fel Royal Soc Can. *Res:* Physiology and nutrition. *Mailing Add:* Dept of Poultry Sci Univ of BC Vancouver BC V6T 2A2 Can

MARCH, JERRY, b Brooklyn, NY, Aug 1, 29; m 54; c 3. ORGANIC CHEMISTRY. *Educ:* City Col NY, BS, 51; Brooklyn Col, MA, 53; Pa State Univ, PhD(chem), 57. *Prof Exp:* From asst prof to assoc prof, 56-68, PROF CHEM, ADELPHI UNIV, 68- *Concurrent Pos:* Vis prof, Univ Strasbourg, 67-68 & Imp Col, Univ London, 78. *Mem:* Am Chem Soc; Royal Soc Chem. *Res:* Organic synthesis; organometallic compounds; aromaticity. *Mailing Add:* Dept of Chem Adelphi Univ Garden City NY 11530

MARCH, JOSEPH WOLF, JR, b Scranton, Pa, June 26, 25; m 45; c 2. ELECTRICAL ENGINEERING, ELECTRONICS. *Educ:* George Washington Univ, BEE, 54. *Prof Exp:* Asst electronics res, Combined Res Group, Naval Res Lab, 44-46; electronics engr, Bur Ships, Dept Navy, 51-57, head, Electronic Countermeasures Passive Unit, 57-59, electronic reconnaissance syst coordr, Off Chief Naval Opers, 59-61, tech adv reconnaissance & intel, 61-64, asst dir anti-war warfare, Phys Sci Admin, 64-73, dep dir, Res & Develop Plans Div, Off Chief Naval Opers, 73-80; RETIRED. *Mem:* Inst Elec & Electronics Engrs. *Res:* Microwave antennas; research, test and development of electronic reconnaissance and intelligence systems; system appraisal, coordination and planning. *Mailing Add:* 6514 King Palm Way Apollo Beach FL 33570

MARCH, LOUIS CHARBONNIER, organic chemistry, see previous edition

MARCH, RALPH BURTON, b Oshkosh, Wis, Aug 5, 19; m 42; c 3. ENTOMOLOGY. *Educ:* Univ Ill, AB, 41, MA, 46, PhD(entom, chem), 48. *Prof Exp:* From jr entomologist to assoc entomologist, Citrus Exp Sta, 48-57, dean grad div, Univ, 61-69, head div toxicol & physiol, Dept Entom, 69-72, PROF ENTOM, UNIV CALIF, RIVERSIDE, 61-, CHMN DEPT ENTOM, 78- ENTOMOLOGIST, CITRUS EXP STA, 57- *Mem:* AAAS; Entom Soc Am; Am Chem Soc. *Res:* Physiological, biochemical and toxicological studies on the mode of action of insecticides; relation of chemical structure to insecticidal activity; resistance of insects to insecticides. *Mailing Add:* Div of Toxicol & Physiol Dept of Entom Univ of Calif Riverside CA 92521

MARCH, RAYMOND EVANS, b Newcastle upon Tyne, Eng, Mar 13, 34; m 58; c 3. PHYSICAL CHEMISTRY. *Educ:* Leeds Univ, BSc, 57; Univ Toronto, PhD(phys chem), 61. *Prof Exp:* Res chemist, Johnson & Johnson Ltd, Can, 61-62; res assoc & res fel, McGill Univ, 62-65; from asst prof to prof chem, 65-76, MEM STAFF DEPT CHEM, TRENT UNIV, 76-, CHMN DEPT, 79- *Mem:* Fel Chem Inst Can; Am Soc Mass Spectrometry; Can Inst Phys; Spectrometry Soc Can. *Res:* Gas phase reaction kinetics and ion storage mass spectrometry; multiphoton absorption by gaseous ions. *Mailing Add:* Dept Chem Trent Univ Peterborough ON K9J 7B8 Can

MARCH, RICHARD PELL, b Medford, Mass, May 1, 22; m 46; c 3. FOOD SCIENCE. *Educ:* Univ Mass, BS, 44; Cornell Univ, MS, 48. *Prof Exp:* From instr to assoc prof, 48-65, prof, 65-77, EMER PROF DAIRY INDUST, CORNELL UNIV, 77- *Mem:* Am Dairy Sci Asn; Int Asn Milk, Food & Environ Sanit (secy-treas, 70-). *Res:* Dairy industry extension in the field of milk and milk handling on farms; processing in fluid milk plants. *Mailing Add:* Dept of Food Sci Cornell Univ Col of Agr Ithaca NY 14853

MARCH, ROBERT EUGENE, b Jefferson, Ohio, Feb 14, 20; m 46; c 2. ORGANIC CHEMISTRY, PULP & PAPER SCIENCE & TECHNOLOGY. *Educ:* DePauw Univ, BA, 41; Lawrence Col, MS, 44, PhD(chem, chem eng), 47. *Prof Exp:* Process engr, Gaylord Container Corp, La, 44-45; process control engr, Pa, 46-47, tech dir, NY, 47-53, tech control dir, Pa, 53-56, asst plant mgr, 56-57, plant mgr, Ore, 57-60, paper mill mgr, Wash, 60-62, asst plant mgr, 62-63, gen mgr w coast div, 63-66, vpres res & eng, 66-73, vpres opers serv, 73-75, DIV VPRES OPERS, MIDWEST REGION, SCOTT PAPER CO, 75- *Concurrent Pos:* Co rep, Indust Res Inst; bd dir, exec comt, NC State Pulp & Paper Found, 76. *Mem:* Tech Asn Pulp & Paper Indust. *Res:* Product and process research, development and engineering for pulp and paper industry. *Mailing Add:* Scott Paper Co Scott Plaza One Philadelphia PA 19113

MARCH, ROBERT HENRY, b Yarmouth, NS, Can, July 30, 37; m 63; c 2. PHYSICS. *Educ:* Dalhousie Univ, MSc, 60; Oxford Univ, DPhil(physics), 65. *Prof Exp:* From asst prof to assoc prof, 65-77, PROF PHYSICS, DALHOUSIE UNIV, 77-, CHMN DEPT, 69- *Mem:* Can Asn Physicists. *Res:* Low temperature physics. *Mailing Add:* Dept of Physics Dalhousie Univ Halifax NS B3H 3J5 Can

MARCH, ROBERT HERBERT, b Chicago, Ill, Feb 28, 34; m 53, 79; c 1. PHYSICS. *Educ:* Univ Chicago, AB, 52, SM, 55, PhD(physics), 60. *Prof Exp:* Lectr physics, Midwest Univ Res Asn, 60-61; from instr to assoc prof, 61-71, PROF PHYSICS, UNIV WIS-MADISON, 71- *Concurrent Pos:* Vis scientist, Europ Orgn Nuclear Res, 65 & 67, Fermi Nat Accelerator Lab, 71- & Stanford Linear Accelerator Ctr, 75-77; vis prof, Univ Athens, Greece, 81- *Honors & Awards:* Sci Writing Award, Am Inst Physics-US Steel Found, 71 & 75. *Mem:* Am Phys Soc. *Res:* Experimental high-energy physics and astrophysics; science writing. *Mailing Add:* Dept of Physics Univ of Wis Madison WI 53706

MARCHALONIS, JOHN JACOB, b Scranton, Pa, July 22, 40; m 78; c 2. BIOCHEMISTRY, IMMUNOLOGY. *Educ:* Lafayette Col, AB, 62; Rockefeller Univ, PhD(biochem), 67. *Prof Exp:* Am Cancer Soc fel, Walter & Eliza Hall Inst Med Res, Melbourne, 67-68; asst prof med sci, Brown Univ, 69-70; sr lectr, Walter & Eliza Hall Inst Med Res, Melbourne, 70-73, assoc prof molecular immunol & head lab, 73-76; head, Cell Biol & Biochem Sect, Cancer Biol, Frederick Cancer Res Ctr, Nat Cancer Inst, 77-79; PROF & CHMN DEPT BIOCHEM, MED UNIV SC, CHARLESTON, 80- *Concurrent Pos:* Consult, Miriam Hosp, Providence, RI, 69-70; assoc, dept microbiol, Monash Univ Med Sch, Melbourne, 75-76; adj prof pathol, Med Sch, Univ Penn, 77-; F R Lillie fel, Marine Biol Lab; mem, Allergy & Immunol Study Sect, NIH, 79-; ed, Cancer Biol Rev, J Immunogenetics, Develop Comp Immunol, Quart Rev Biol, Continued Topics Immunobiol, Immunochem,

Exp Parasitol. *Mem:* AAAS; Am Asn Immunol; Am Soc Biol Chemists; NY Acad Sci; Sigma Xi. *Res:* Molecular and cellular basis of immunological specificity. *Mailing Add:* Dept Biochem Med Univ SC 171 Ashley Ave Charleston SC 29425

MARCHAND, ALAN PHILIP, b Cleveland, Ohio, May 23, 40. PHYSICAL ORGANIC CHEMISTRY. *Educ:* Case Western Reserve Univ, BS, 61; Univ Chicago, PhD(org chem), 65. *Prof Exp:* Instr phys chem, Huston-Tillotson Col, 63-65; NIH fel phys org chem, Univ Calif, Berkeley, 65-66; from asst prof to assoc prof, 66-75, PROF ORG CHEM, UNIV OKLA, 76-, ADJ PROF PHARM, 79- *Concurrent Pos:* Sr res fel, Fulbright-Hays grant, Inst Chem, Univ Liege, Belg, 72-73. *Mem:* Am Chem Soc; Royal Soc Chem; Sigma Xi. *Res:* Reactions of carbethoxycarbene with carbon-halogen bonds; nuclear magnetic resonance of rigid bicyclic systems; synthesis of new high energy polycyclic hydrocarbon fuels; organometallic chemistry; enzyme-substrate interactions. *Mailing Add:* Dept of Chem Univ of Okla 620 Parrington Oval Norman OK 73019

MARCHAND, E ROGER, b Palo Alto, Calif, June 17, 36; m 59; c 2. ANATOMY. *Educ:* San Diego State Col, BS, 63; Univ Calif, Los Angeles, PhD(anat), 68. *Prof Exp:* ADJ ASSOC PROF NEUROSCI & ACAD ADMINR, OFF LEARNING RESOURCES, SCH MED, UNIV CALIF, SAN DIEGO, 68- *Mem:* AAAS; Soc Neurosci; Am Asn Anatomists; Am Soc Zoologists. *Mailing Add:* Dept of Neurosci Univ Calif Sch of Med San Diego La Jolla CA 92038

MARCHAND, ERICH WATKINSON, b Hartford, Conn, July 7, 14; m 41; c 3. OPTICS. *Educ:* Harvard Univ, AB, 36; Univ Wash, MS, 41; Univ Rochester, PhD(math), 52. *Prof Exp:* Instr math, Univ Rochester, 43-49; physicist optics, Res Labs, Eastman Kodak Co, 49-79; CONSULT, 79- *Mem:* Optical Soc Am; Math Asn Am. *Res:* Mathematics. *Mailing Add:* 192 Seville Dr Rochester NY 14617

MARCHAND, JEAN-PAUL, b Murten, Switz, Mar 25, 33. MATHEMATICAL PHYSICS. *Educ:* Univ Bern, Dipl math, 58; Univ Geneva, DrSc(physics), 63. *Prof Exp:* Asst physics, Univ Bern, 58-60; asst, Univ Geneva, 60-63, res assoc, 63-67; asst prof physics & math, Univ Denver, 67-68, math, 68-69, assoc prof, 69-79, prof, 79-81. *Concurrent Pos:* Lectr, Univ Bern, 65-66; invited prof, Swiss Fed Inst Technol, Lausanne, 81. *Res:* Mathematical foundations of quantum mechanics and statistical mechanics. *Mailing Add:* Dept of Math Univ of Denver Denver CO 80208

MARCHAND, MARGARET O, b Shorncliffe, Man, Can, Oct 17, 25; US citizen; m 57; c 3. MATHEMATICS, STATISTICS. *Educ:* Univ Man, BA, 45; Univ Minn, MA, 48, PhD(math), 50. *Prof Exp:* Assoc prof math, Southwest Mo State Col, 50-52; statistician, Man Cancer Res Inst, Can, 52-56; asst prof math, Bemidji State Col, 56-57, 58-59, 65-66; asst prof, Univ Denver, 57-58; instr corresp dept, Univ Minn, 59-66; asst prof math, Lakehead Univ, 66-68; prof, Wis State Univ-Superior, 68-71; assoc prof, 71-79, PROF MATH, ADRIAN COL, 79- *Mem:* AAAS; Am Math Soc; Math Asn Am; Sigma Xi. *Mailing Add:* Dept of Math Adrian Col Adrian MI 49221

MARCHAND, NATHAN, b Shawinigan Falls, Que, June 20, 16; US citizen; m 37; c 4. ELECTRICAL ENGINEERING, ELECTRONICS. *Educ:* City Col New York, BS, 37; Columbia Univ, MS, 41. *Prof Exp:* Sr engr, Int Tel & Tel Corp Labs, 41-45; consult engr, 45-49; head sect electronic circuits, Sylvania Elec Prods, Inc, 49-51; ELECTRONIC CONSULT & PRES, MARCHAND ELECTRONIC LABS, INC, 51- *Concurrent Pos:* Lectr, Grad Sch Elec Eng, Columbia Univ, 45-47; consult & staff mem, NY Univ-Bellevue Med Ctr, 47-60; expert consult, US Air Force Atlantic Missile Range, 51-54; mem bd dirs, Panoramic Radio Prod Inc, 54-63; consult, Air Navig Develop Bd, Spec Asst to the President on Aviation Facilities, Airways Modernization Bd & Fed Aviation Agency, 55-64; consult, US Army Aviation Res & Develop Command, 76-; mgr, Special Electronics Mission Aircraft Proj, US Army Troop Readiness and Support Command, 80- *Mem:* Fel AAAS; fel Inst Elec & Electronics Engrs. *Res:* Communications, navigation, data acquisition, transmission, radiation, electronic counter measures, electronic counter counter measures, data links and system analysis as accomplished by electronics. *Mailing Add:* 311 Riversville Rd Greenwich CT 06830

MARCHANT, DAVID DENNIS, b Murray, Utah, May 1, 43; m 66; c 5. CERAMICS, METALLURGY. *Educ:* Univ Utah, BS, 68; Mass Inst Technol, ScD(ceramics), 74. *Prof Exp:* Systs analyst comput, Food & Drug Admin, 68-70; scientist mat, Argonne Nat Lab, 74-77; SR RES SCIENTIST MAT, PAC NORTHWEST LAB, BATTELLE MEM INST, 77- *Mem:* Am Ceramic Soc. *Res:* High temperature thermophysical properties of ceramics and metals; high temperature electrochemical interactions between ceramics, metal and coal slag; electro-optical materials. *Mailing Add:* 1825 Norwood Ct Richland WA 99352

MARCHANT, DOUGLAS J, b Malden, Mass, Dec 31, 25; m 55; c 5. OBSTETRICS & GYNECOLOGY. *Educ:* Tufts Univ, BS, 47, MD, 51; Am Bd Obstet & Gynec, dipl, cert gynec oncol, 74. *Prof Exp:* Assoc prof, 65-75, dir gynec oncol, Tufts New Eng Med Ctr, 74-77, PROF OBSTET & GYNEC, SCH MED, TUFTS UNIV, 75-, DIR, OFF CANCER CONTROL, 76-, DIR, CANCER CTR, TUFTS NEW ENG MED CTR, 77-, DIR GYNEC ONCOL, 81- *Concurrent Pos:* Consult, St Margaret's Hosp, Dorchester, Mass, 57- & Boston City Hosp, 58-; sr gynecologist, New Eng Med Ctr Hosp, 67-; consult, Sturdy Mem Hosp, Attleboro, Mass, Choate Hosp, Wouborn & Lemuel Shattuck Hosp, Boston. *Mem:* AMA; Am Col Obstet & Gynec; Am Col Surg; Soc Gynec Oncol; Am Asn Obstet & Gynec. *Res:* Transport of urine; ureteral activity; breast cancer--epidemiology and receptor studies; immunology of pregnancy; gynecologic oncology. *Mailing Add:* Dept of Obstet & Gynec Tufts Univ Boston MA 02111

MARCHANT, GUILLAUME HENRI (WIM), JR, b Brisbane, Australia, Mar 8, 46; m 72; c 4. ENVIRONMENTAL SCIENCES. *Educ:* Univ Southern Miss, BS, 71. *Prof Exp:* Asst geologist, Southern Res Inst, 72-73; start up & testing engr, Pollution Control Div, Carborundum Co, 73-74; assoc engr, 74-76, supvr, Control Device Sect, 76-77, SECT HEAD, CONTROL DEVICE EVAL SECT, CONTROL DEVICE RES DIV, SOUTHERN RES INST, 77- *Res:* Prepartaion of proposals, plans and manage field test programs for evaluation of environmental control devices; data analysis; reporting; evaluation. *Mailing Add:* Southern Res Inst PO Box 3307-A Birmingham AL 35255

MARCHANT, LELAND CONDO, b Columbus, NDak, May 17, 31; m 54; c 4. ENGINEERING MANAGEMENT, PETROLEUM ENGINEERING. *Educ:* Univ Okla, BS, 60. *Prof Exp:* Petrol res engr, Petrol Res Lab, US Bur Mines, WVa, 60-62 & Laramie Energy Technol Ctr, 62-76; PROJ MGR, LARAMIE ENERGY TECHNOL CTR, US DEPT ENERGY, 76- *Honors & Awards:* Sustained Superior Performance Award, US Bur Mines, 64. *Mem:* Am Inst Mining, Metall & Petrol Engrs. *Res:* Thermal methods of oil recovery; general petroleum reservoir evaluation; well log analysis; petroleum reservoir engineering; tar sand research. *Mailing Add:* 1215 Reynolds Laramie WY 82070

MARCHELLO, JOSEPH M(AURICE), b East Moline, Ill, Oct 6, 33. CHEMICAL ENGINEERING. *Educ:* Univ Ill, BS, 55; Carnegie Inst Technol, PhD(chem eng), 59. *Prof Exp:* Asst prof chem eng, Okla State Univ, 59-61; from assoc prof to prof, Univ Md, College Park, 62-78, head dept, 67-73, provost, Div Math & Phys Sci & Eng, 73-78; CHANCELLOR, UNIV MO-ROLLA, 78- *Mem:* Am Chem Soc; Am Inst Chem Engrs; AAAS; Nat Soc Prof Engrs. *Res:* Transport phenomena; fluid mechanics; mass and heat transfer; reaction kinetics; applied mathematics and models. *Mailing Add:* 210 Parker Hall Univ of Mo Rolla MO 65401

MARCHESE, FRANCIS THOMAS, b Brooklyn, NY, May 12, 49. THEORETICAL CHEMISTRY. *Educ:* Niagara Univ, BS, 71; Youngstown State Univ, MS, 73; Univ Cincinnati, PhD(chem), 79. *Prof Exp:* FEL RES FOUND, CITY UNIV NEW YORK, 78- *Mem:* Am Chem Soc. *Res:* Statistical mechanical treatments of liquids and solutions; solvent effects on ground and excited state properties and structure; quantum theory of molecules; theoretical spectroscopy. *Mailing Add:* Dept of Chem 695 Park Ave New York NY 10021

MARCHESI, VINCENT T, b New York, NY, Sept 4, 35; m 59; c 3. BIOCHEMISTRY, PATHOLOGY. *Educ:* Yale Univ, BA, 57, MD, 63; Oxford Univ, PhD(exp path), 61. *Prof Exp:* From intern to resident path, Wash Univ, 63-65; res assoc cell biol, Rockefeller Univ, 65-66; staff assoc, Nat Cancer Inst, 66-68; chief sect chem path, Nat Inst Arthritis, Metab & Digestive Dis, 68-77; ANTHONY N BRADY PROF PATH, SCH MED, YALE UNIV, 77- *Mem:* Am Soc Cell Biol; Histochem Soc; NY Acad Sci. *Res:* Inflammation, blood vessel permeability and the biochemical properties of cell surfaces; physical and chemical properties of cell membranes. *Mailing Add:* Dept of Path Yale Univ Sch of Med New Haven CT 06520

MARCHESSAULT, J H VICTOR HENRI, b West Shefford, Que, Nov 16, 29; c 4. PEDIATRICS, MICROBIOLOGY. *Educ:* Univ Montreal, BA, 50, MD, 55; FRCP(C), 59. *Prof Exp:* Lectr pediat, McGill Univ, 62-66; prof & head dept, Univ, 66-71, head, Div Clin Sci, 71-74, PROF PEDIAT & INFECTIONS DIS, HOSP CTR, UNIV SHERBROOKE, 64- *Concurrent Pos:* Asst physician, Montreal Children's Hosp, 59-66. *Mem:* Can Pediat Soc (exec vpres, 64-); Am Pediat Soc; Can Soc Clin Invest. *Res:* Infectious disease in virology associated with measles; mumps; rubella vaccines. *Mailing Add:* Titular Prof Pediat Univ Sherbrooke Sherbrooke PQ J1H 5N4 Can

MARCHESSAULT, ROBERT HENRI, b Montreal, Que, Sept 16, 28; m 52; c 6. PHYSICAL CHEMISTRY, POLYMER CHEMISTRY. *Educ:* Univ Montreal, BSc, 50; McGill Univ, PhD(phys chem), 54. *Prof Exp:* Res chemist, Am Viscose Corp, 56-59, res assoc, 59-61; assoc prof polymer & phys chem, State Univ NY Col Forestry, Syracuse Univ, 61-65, prof, 65-69; prof chem & dir dept, Univ Montreal, 69-78; MGR, XEROX RES CTR CAN, 78- *Concurrent Pos:* Fel, Univ Uppsala, 55; distinguished res fel, State Univ NY & vis prof, Univ Strasbourg, 67-68. *Mem:* AAAS; Am Chem Soc; Am Phys Soc; Tech Asn Pulp & Paper Indust. *Res:* Physical chemical studies on natural and synthetic polymers, especially solid state characterization by electromagnetic scattering techniques. *Mailing Add:* Xerox Res Ctr of Can 2480 Dunwin Dr Mississauga ON L5L 1J9 Can

MARCHETTA, FRANK CARMELO, b Utica, NY, Apr 28, 20; m 49; c 3. MEDICINE. *Educ:* Univ Buffalo, MD, 44; Am Bd Surg, dipl, 54. *Prof Exp:* Resident gen surg, Deaconess Hosp, Buffalo, 47-50; resident, 50-51, assoc surgeon, 51-54, ASSOC CHIEF CANCER RES HEAD & NECK SURG, ROSWELL PARK MEM INST, 54-; CLIN ASSOC PROF ORAL PATH, DENT SCH & RES ASSOC PROF SURG, MED SCH, STATE UNIV NY BUFFALO, 59- *Concurrent Pos:* Consult, head & neck onc, Roswell Park Mem Inst, 76- & Buffalo Vet Admin Hosp, 77. *Mem:* Fel Am Col Surg; Soc Head & Neck Surgeons. *Res:* Cancer. *Mailing Add:* 192 High Park Blvd Eggertsville NY 14226

MARCHETTE, NYVEN JOHN, b Murphys, Calif, June 26, 28; m 50; c 1. VIROLOGY, RICKETTSIAL DISEASES. *Educ:* Univ Calif, BA, 50, MA, 53; Univ Utah, PhD, 60. *Prof Exp:* Bacteriologist, Ecol Res Lab, Univ Utah, 55-61, res microbiologist, 60-61; asst res microbiologist, Hooper Found, Univ Calif, San Francisco, 61-69, from asst res prof rickettsiology to assoc res prof virol, Univ, 63-70, assoc res microbiologist, Med Ctr, 69-70; assoc prof, 70-74, PROF TROP MED, SCH MED, UNIV HAWAII, MANOA, 74- *Concurrent Pos:* Fel, Inst Ctr Med Res & Training, Med Ctr, Univ Calif, San Francisco, 61-63; fel, Inst Med Res, Kuala Lumpur, 61-69; chief arbovirus res lab, Fac Med, Univ Malaya, 61-69; Fogarty sr int fel, John Curtin Sch Med Res, Australian Nat Univ, Canberra, 77-78. *Mem:* AAAS; Am Soc Microbiol; Am Soc Trop Med. *Res:* Ecology infectious diseases, such as virology, rickettsiology; immunology; immunopathology; pathogenesis of virus infections. *Mailing Add:* Univ of Hawaii Sch of Med Leahi Hosp Honolulu HI 96816

MARCHETTI, ALFRED PAUL, b Bakersfield, Calif, Feb 16, 40; m 63; c 3. PHYSICAL CHEMISTRY. *Educ:* Univ Calif, Riverside, BA, 61, PhD(phys chem, spectros), 66; Univ Calif, Berkeley, MS, 63. *Prof Exp:* NIH fel, Univ Pa, 66-69; sr res chemist, 69-75, RES ASSOC, EASTMAN KODAK CO, 75- *Mem:* Am Chem Soc; Sigma Xi. *Res:* Electronic spectroscopy of organic molecules and crystals; Stark and Zeeman effect in molecules; exciton theory and energy transfer processes in organic and inorganic crystals; latent image formation in silver halides. *Mailing Add:* Res Labs Eastman Kodak Co Kodak Park Bldg 59 Rochester NY 14650

MARCHETTI, MARCO ANTHONY, b New York, NY, Feb 15, 36; m 58; c 4. PLANT PATHOLOGY. *Educ:* Pa State Univ, BS, 57; Iowa State Univ, MS, 59, PhD(plant path), 62. *Prof Exp:* Res plant pathologist, US Army Biol Ctr, Ft Detrick, 62-71; res plant pathologist, Epiphytology Res Lab, 71-73, res plant pathologist, Plant Dis Res Lab, 73-74, RES PLANT PATHOLOGIST, RICE RES, TEX A&M UNIV AGR RES & EXTEN CTR, USDA, 74- *Mem:* Am Phytopath Soc; Mycol Soc Am; Sigma Xi. *Res:* Rice diseases. *Mailing Add:* Tex A&M Univ Agr Res & Exten Ctr Rte 7 Box 999 Beaumont TX 77706

MARCHIN, GEORGE LEONARD, b Kansas City, Kans, July 12, 40; m 74; c 2. MOLECULAR BIOLOGY, PARASITOLOGY. *Educ:* Rockhurst Col, AB, 62; Univ Kans, PhD(microbiol), 67. *Prof Exp:* Res assoc microbiol, Purdue Univ, 67-68, NIH fel, 68-70; asst prof, 70-75, ASSOC PROF BIOL, KANS STATE UNIV, 75- *Concurrent Pos:* Comnr, Adv Lab Comn, Kans State Bd Health, 70-75; dir allied health prog, Div Biol, Kans State Univ, 70-75; NIH res grant, 72-75, 75-78; vis scientist, Microbiol Inst, Umea Univ, Umea, Sweden, 77-78. *Mem:* AAAS; Am Soc Microbiol. *Res:* Enzymology; bacterial physiology. *Mailing Add:* Div of Biol Kans State Univ Manhattan KS 66502

MARCHINTON, ROBERT LARRY, b New Smyrna Beach, Fla, Mar 3, 39; m 64; c 1. WILDLIFE ECOLOGY, ETHOLOGY. *Educ:* Univ Fla, BSF, 62, MS, 64; Auburn Univ, PhD(zool), 68. *Prof Exp:* Mgr, Loxahatchee Refuge, US Fish & Wildlife Serv, Fla, 62; wildlife biologist, Fla Game & Fresh Water Fish Comn, 64; asst prof, 67-73, ASSOC PROF WILDLIFE ECOL, SCH FOREST RESOURCES, UNIV GA, 73- *Concurrent Pos:* Ga Forest Res Coun & McIntire-Stennis grant, Univ Ga, 68-75, Southeastern Coop Wildlife Dis Study Group Contract, 71-72. *Mem:* Soc Am Foresters; Am Soc Mammal; Wildlife Soc; Animal Behav Soc; Wildlife Dis Asn. *Res:* Radiotelemetric studies of the behavioral ecology of large vertebrates. *Mailing Add:* Sch of Forest Resources Univ of Ga Athens GA 30602

MARCHIORO, THOMAS LOUIS, b Spokane, Wash, Aug 1, 28; c 7. SURGERY. *Educ:* Gonzaga Univ, BS, 51; St Louis Univ, MD, 55. *Prof Exp:* Intern, St Mary's Group of Hosps, Mo, 55-56; asst in surg, Sch Med, Univ Colo, 59-60, from instr to assoc prof, 60-67; assoc prof, 67-69, PROF SURG, SCH MED, UNIV WASH, 69- *Concurrent Pos:* Clin investr, Denver Vet Admin Hosp, Colo, 62-65; consult, Children's Orthop, Vet Admin, USPHS & Harborview Hosps, Seattle, Wash, 67-; chmn, End Stage Renal Disease Network Coord Coun #2, 81-82. *Mem:* Soc Univ Surg; Asn Acad Surg (secy, 67-70, pres, 74); Soc Vasc Surg; Am Heart Asn; Am Soc Transplant Surgeons (pres-elect, 76, pres, 77). *Res:* Transplantation. *Mailing Add:* Dept Surg Univ Wash Seattle WA 98195

MARCHMAN, JAMES F(RANKLIN), III, b Lexington, Ky, May 15, 43; m 66. AEROSPACE ENGINEERING. *Educ:* NC State Univ, BS, 64, PhD(mech eng), 68. *Prof Exp:* Aerospace engr, US Army Aviation Test Activity, Edwards AFB, 66; asst mech eng, NC State Univ, 67-68; asst prof aerospace eng, 68-72, ASSOC PROF AEROSPACE & OCEAN ENG, VA POLYTECH INST & STATE UNIV, 72- *Mem:* Assoc fel Am Inst Aeronaut & Astronaut; Am Soc Eng Educ. *Res:* Subsonic aerodynamics; leading edge vortices; natural wind effects; wind tunnel aerodynamics. *Mailing Add:* Dept of Aerospace & Ocean Eng Va Polytech Inst & State Univ Blacksburg VA 24061

MARCIAL-ROJAS, RAUL ARMANDO, pathology, see previous edition

MARCIANI, DANTE JUAN, b Lima, Peru, Feb 23, 43; m 81; c 3. PROTEIN CHEMISTRY, PHYSICAL CHEMISTRY. *Educ:* San Marcos Univ, BS, 62, ScD(biol), 63; Univ Colo, Boulder, PhD(biochem), 70. *Prof Exp:* Asst prof, San Marcos Univ, 62-65; res asst, Univ Colo, Boulder, 65-70; vis fel, Nat Cancer Inst, 71-73, vis assoc, 73-76, res chemist, Lab Biochem & Expert, Lab Virus Genetics, 76-79; dir, Lab Biochem, 80-81, RES DIR, BETHESDA RES LAB, 81- *Concurrent Pos:* Vis lectr, San Marcos Univ, 78. *Res:* Chromatographic methods; protein structure and purification. *Mailing Add:* 13520 Walnutwood Lane Germantown MD 20874

MARCIANO, WILLIAM JOSEPH, b New York, NY, Oct 11, 47; m 74; c 2. ELEMENTARY PARTICLE PHYSICS. *Educ:* New York Univ, BS, 69, MS, 71, PhD(physics), 74. *Prof Exp:* Res assoc physics, Rockefeller Univ, 74-78, asst prof, 78-80; assoc prof physics, Northwestern Univ, 80-81; PHYSICIST, BROOKHAVEN NAT LAB, 81- *Mem:* Am Phys Soc. *Res:* Gauge theories of weak electromagnetic and strong interactions. *Mailing Add:* Dept Physics York Ave & 66th St New York NY 10021

MARCIANO-CABRAL, FRANCINE, virology, electron microscopy, see previous edition

MARCINKOWSKI, M(ARION) J(OHN), b Baltimore, Md, Feb 27, 31; div; c 2. MATERIALS SCIENCE, PHYSICS. *Educ:* Univ Md, BS, 53; Univ Pa, MS, 55, PhD(metall eng), 59. *Prof Exp:* Supv scientist, Edgar C Bain Lab Fundamental Res, US Steel Corp, 56-63; assoc prof metall, univ assoc & metallurgist, Inst Atomic Res, Iowa State Univ, 63-68; PROF MAT SCI, DEPT MECH ENG, UNIV MD, COLLEGE PARK, 68- *Concurrent Pos:* Alexander von Humboldt sr US scientist award. *Res:* Theory of the mechanical behavior of matter. *Mailing Add:* Dept of Mech Eng Univ of Md College Park MD 20742

MARCINKOWSKY, ARTHUR ERNEST, b Moosehorn, Man, Nov 8, 31; m 59; c 4. PHYSICAL CHEMISTRY. *Educ:* Univ Man, BSc, 55, MSc, 58; Rensselaer Polytech Inst, PhD(phys chem), 61. *Prof Exp:* Sci teacher, Foxwarren Collegiate, Man, 52-53; lectr phys chem, Royal Mil Col, Ont, 57-58; res assoc & fel, Rensselaer Polytech Inst, 58-61; develop chemist, Chem & Plastics Div, Union Carbide Can, Ltd, 61-63; res assoc, Chem Div, Oak Ridge Nat Lab, 64-67; RES SCIENTIST, TECH CTR, UNION CARBIDE CORP, 67- *Honors & Awards:* Sci Award, Am Chem Soc, 72. *Mem:* Am Chem Soc; Catalysis Soc; ?Royal Soc Chem. *Res:* Physical chemistry of electrolyte solutions in aqueous, non-aqueous and mixed solvent media; polymerization of olefins via stereospecific catalysis; water purification and desalination; heterogeneous catalysis; chromatography; industrial separations; process development. *Mailing Add:* Tech Ctr Union Carbide Corp PO Box 8361 South Charleston WV 25303

MARCO, GINO JOSEPH, b Leechburg, Pa, Dec 19, 24; m 51; c 5. BIOCHEMISTRY, ORGANIC CHEMISTRY. *Educ:* Carnegie Inst Technol, BS, 50; Univ Pittsburgh, MS, 52, PhD(biochem), 56. *Prof Exp:* Res biochemist agr chem, Monsanto Chem Co, 56-60, proj leader animal nutrit & biochem, 60, group leader chem biol & animal feed res, Agr Chem Div, Res Dept, Monsanto Co, 60-66, group leader biochem of pesticide metab & resudues, 66-69; MGR METAB INVESTS, AGR BIOCHEM DEPT, GEIGY AGR CHEM DIV, CIBA-GEIGY CORP, 69- *Mem:* Fel AAAS; Am Chem Soc; Sigma Xi; fel Am Inst Chemists. *Res:* Animal biochemistry; especially in ruminant metabolism, physiology and biochemistry; organic synthesis of agricultural and radioactive chemicals; process development; development of analytical methods and metabolic information in plants, animals, fish and environment systems for use in submitting pesticide petitions. *Mailing Add:* Agr Dept Ciba Geigy Corp PO Box 11422 Greensboro NC 27409

MARCONI, GARY G, b Columbus, Ohio, Aug 31, 44; c 1. NATURAL PRODUCTS CHEMISTRY, LABORATORY AUTOMATION. *Educ:* Univ Dayton, BS, 66; Case Western Reserve Univ, PhD(chem), 70. *Prof Exp:* sr biochemist, 70-81, RES SCIENTIST, ELI LILLY & CO, 81- *Mem:* Am Chem Soc; Am Soc Pharmacog. *Res:* Isolation and purification of natural products produced in fermentations; automated chromatography; computer systems. *Mailing Add:* 307 McCarty St Indianapolis IN 46285

MARCOTTE, DAVID BACON, psychiatry, see previous edition

MARCOTTE, FRANK BASIL, b Derry, NH, June 6, 23; m 47. INDUSTRIAL CHEMISTRY. *Educ:* Univ NH, BS, 46, MS, 48; Univ Rochester, PhD(chem), 51. *Prof Exp:* Instr chem, Univ NH, 47-48; res chemist, Celanese Corp Am, 51-53, group leader, 53-54, sect head, 54-55, dir chem res, 55-60, vpres & tech dir, 60-63, res fel, 63-69; dir res, M W Kellogg Co, 69-71; DIR RES CHEM, SONNEBORN DIV WITCO CHEM CORP, 72- *Mem:* AAAS; Soc Petrol Engrs. *Res:* Photochemistry; hydrocarbon oxidation; industrial organic chemistry. *Mailing Add:* 100 Bauer Dr Oakland NJ 07438

MARCOTTE, RONALD EDWARD, b Taunton, Mass, Aug 27, 39; m 64; c 1. CHEMICAL KINETICS, MASS SPECTROMETRY. *Educ:* Univ Fla, BS, 62, PhD(phys chem), 68. *Prof Exp:* Ohio State Univ Res Found, vis res assoc, Aerospace Res Labs, Wright-Patterson AFB, 68-70; from asst prof to assoc prof, 70-80, PROF CHEM, TEX A&I UNIV, 80- *Mem:* Am Chem Soc; Am Soc Mass Spectrometry. *Res:* Formation and decay of reactive intermediates; design and construction of double mass spectrometer system for study of ion-molecule reaction energetics; special interest in halocarbons and atmospheric gases. *Mailing Add:* Dept of Chem Tex A&I Univ Kingsville TX 78363

MARCOUX, JULES E, b Charny, Que, Jan 26, 24; m 55; c 6. PHYSICS. *Educ:* Laval Univ, BA, 47, BASc, 52; Univ Toronto, MA, 54, PhD(physics), 56. *Prof Exp:* Nat Res Coun Can fel, 56-57; prof physics, Royal Mil Col, Que, 57-62; prof, Laval Univ, 62-64; PROF PHYSICS, ROYAL MIL COL, QUE, 64- *Mem:* Can Asn Physicists; Am Asn Physics Teachers; NY Acad Sci. *Res:* Physical constants of rare gases in the liquid and solid states. *Mailing Add:* Dept of Physics Royal Mil Col St Jean PQ J2X 2K8 Can

MARCOVITZ, ALAN BERNARD, b Boston, Mass, July 4, 36; m 60; c 2. ELECTRICAL & COMPUTER ENGINEERING. *Educ:* Mass Inst Technol, SBEE & SMEE, 59; Columbia Univ, PhD(elec eng), 63. *Prof Exp:* Instr elec eng, Columbia Univ, 59-63; from asst prof to assoc prof, Univ Md, 63-70; chmn dept, 70-76, PROF ELEC ENG, FLA ATLANTIC UNIV, 70- *Concurrent Pos:* Reviewer, Acad Press, 67-; consult, US Army Logistics Mgt Ctr, 68- *Mem:* Inst Elec & Electronics Engrs; Am Asn Eng Educ. *Res:* Computer systems; time-sharing system design; computer-aided design; computer education. *Mailing Add:* Dept of Elec Eng Fla Atlantic Univ Bldg T-9 Boca Raton FL 33432

MARCUM, BEVERLY ANNA, developmental biology, see previous edition

MARCUM, JAMES BENTON, b Cedar Co, Mo, June 25, 38; m 64; c 3. ANIMAL GENETICS, CYTOGENETICS. *Educ:* Univ Mo-Columbia, BSAgr, 60, PhD(animal genetics), 69; Cornell Univ, MS, 61; Midwestern Baptist Theol Sem, MDiv, 65. *Prof Exp:* Lectr animal breeding, Univ Libya, 69-71; asst prof, 71-77, ASSOC PROF ANIMAL GENETICS, UNIV MASS, AMHERST, 77-, CHMN DEPT VET & ANIMAL SCI, 78- *Mem:* Am Soc Animal Sci; Am Genetic Asn; Genetics Soc Can; Am Dairy Sci Asn; Sigma Xi. *Res:* Chromosomal identification and mapping in domestic animals; relationships between cytogenetics and reproductive biology; freemartin syndrome. *Mailing Add:* Dept of Vet & Animal Sci Univ of Mass Amherst MA 01003

MARCUS, AARON JACOB, b Brooklyn, NY, Nov 6, 25; m 55; c 3. INTERNAL MEDICINE, HEMATOLOGY. *Educ:* Univ Va, BA, 48; New York Med Col, MD, 53. *Prof Exp:* CHIEF HEMAT SECT, NEW YORK VET ADMIN HOSP, 58-; PROF MED, MED COL, CORNELL UNIV, 74-

Concurrent Pos: NIH res fel, Montefiore Hosp, 56-58; attend physician, New York Hosp, 74- *Mem:* Am Soc Clin Invest; Asn Am Physicians; Am Physiol Soc; Am Soc Hemat. *Res:* Hemostasis, coagulation and thrombosis; biochemistry and physiology of blood platelets. *Mailing Add:* Hemat Sect Vet Admin Hosp 408 First Ave New York NY 10010

MARCUS, ABRAHAM, b New York, NY, Oct 26, 30; m 55; c 4. BIOCHEMISTRY. *Educ:* Yeshiva Univ, BA, 50; Univ Buffalo, AM, 54, PhD, 56. *Prof Exp:* Asst, Univ Buffalo, 52-54; biochemist, Agr Mkt Serv, Plant Indust Sta, USDA, 58-67; mem staff biol div, 67, assoc mem, 67-71, SR MEM, INST CANCER RES, 71- *Concurrent Pos:* USPHS res fel, Univ Chicago, 56-58; mem staff biophys, Weizmann Inst Sci, 64-65; vis prof, Bar-Ilan Univ, Israel, 70-71. *Mem:* Am Chem Soc; Am Soc Biol Chem; Am Soc Plant Physiol. *Res:* Metabolic pathways as ascertained by enzymatic studies; metabolic control of growth and development. *Mailing Add:* Inst for Cancer Res 7701 Burholme Ave Philadelphia PA 19111

MARCUS, ALLAN H, b New York, NY, July 14, 39. STATISTICS, ENVIRONMENTAL SCIENCES. *Educ:* Case Western Reserve Univ, BS, 61; Univ Calif, Berkeley, MA, 63, PhD(statist), 65. *Prof Exp:* Asst prof math, Case Western Reserve Univ, 64-67; mem staff, Bellcomm, Inc, DC, 67-68; assoc prof statist & earth & planetary sci, Johns Hopkins Univ, 68-73; assoc prof math, Univ Md, Baltimore County, 73-77; assoc prof math, 77-79, PROF MATH, WASH STATE UNIV, 79-, STATIST CONSULT, WASH STATE UNIV COMPUT CTR, 79- *Concurrent Pos:* Consult, Rand Corp, 63-65; fel, Statist Lab, Cambridge Univ, 65-66; exec secy, Power Plant Siting Adv Comt, State of Md, 73-77. *Mem:* Am Statist Asn; Biometrics Soc; Soc Comput Simulation. *Res:* Applied statistics; urban transportation and environmental sciences; environmental health; biomathematics; air pollution; traffic noise. *Mailing Add:* Dept of Math Wash State Univ Pullman WA 99164

MARCUS, ANTHONY MARTIN, b London, Eng, June 21, 29; Can citizen; div; c 1. PSYCHIATRY. *Educ:* Cambridge Univ, BA, 52, MA, 56; Univ London, LMS, 56; McGill Univ, dipl psychiat, 62; Royal Col Physicians & Surgeons Can, spec cert, 62; Am Bd Psychiat & Neurol, dipl, 63. *Prof Exp:* From instr to asst prof, 62-70, actg head dept, 70-72, ASSOC PROF PSYCHIAT, UNIV BC, 70-, DIR DIV FORENSIC PSYCHIAT, 67- *Concurrent Pos:* Res fel psychiat, Montreal Gen Hosp, Que, 61-62; Can Penitentiary Serv res grant study dangerous sexual offenders; assoc attend staff, Vancouver Gen Hosp. *Honors & Awards:* Bronze Medal for Bravery, Royal Can Humane Asn, 77. *Mem:* Am Psychiat Asn; Nat Coun Crime & Delinq; Can Psychiat Asn; Brit Med Asn; fel Royal Soc Med. *Res:* Forensic psychiatry; clinical psychiatry and psychopathology; teaching. *Mailing Add:* Dept Psychiat Univ BC Vancouver BC V6T 1W5 Can

MARCUS, ARNOLD DAVID, b Brooklyn, NY, Feb 25, 28; m 56; c 3. PHARMACY. *Educ:* Brooklyn Col Pharm, BS, 46; Purdue Univ, MS, 49; Univ Wis, PhD(pharm), 54. *Prof Exp:* From asst prof to assoc prof pharmaceut chem, 49-54; asst prof pharm, Rutgers Univ, 54-57; res assoc, Merck Sharp & Dohme Res Labs, Pa, 57-64, mgr pharmaceut res, 64-66; asst dir res, 66-67, dir res coord, 67-69, ASSOC DIR RES & DEVELOP, BRISTOL MYERS CO, 69- *Mem:* AAAS; Am Chem Soc; Am Pharmaceut Asn. *Res:* Kinetics; biopharmaceutics; pharmaceutical research and development. *Mailing Add:* Bristol Myers Co Hillside NJ 07205

MARCUS, BRUCE DAVID, thermal sciences, fluid mechanics, see previous edition

MARCUS, BRYAN HARRY, b Los Angeles, Calif, Aug 29, 49. MATHEMATICS. *Educ:* Pomona Col, BA, 71; Univ Calif, Berkeley, MA, 72, PhD(math), 75. *Prof Exp:* Asst prof, 75-81, ASSOC PROF MATH, UNIV NC, 81- *Concurrent Pos:* IBM Corp fel, 76-77; NSF res grants, 76- *Res:* Erogodic theory; dynamical systems. *Mailing Add:* Dept of Math Univ of NC Chapel Hill NC 27514

MARCUS, CAROL JOYCE, b New York, NY, Aug 13, 43; c 1. BIOCHEMISTRY. *Educ:* Cornell Univ, BS, 65; Duke Univ, PhD(biochem), 72. *Prof Exp:* From instr to asst prof biochem, Univ Tenn Ctr Health Sci, Memphis, 72-78; SR STAFF FEL, EXP PATH LAB, NIH, 78- *Concurrent Pos:* Vis scientist, Biochem & Metab Lab, NIH, 76-78. Acad Sci. *Res:* Adeno associated virus; viral proteins; viral replication; Xenopus oocyte microinjection. *Mailing Add:* Exp Path Lab NIH Bldg 4 Rm 318 Bethesda MD 20014

MARCUS, CAROL SILBER, b New York, NY, July 2, 39; m 58; c 2. RADIATION BIOLOGY, BIOPHYSICS. *Educ:* Cornell Univ, BS, 60, MS, 61, PhD(biochem, genetics), 63; Univ Southern Calif, MD, 77. *Prof Exp:* Vis res scientist, Lab Biol Med, Netherlands, 63-64; asst res chemist, Lab Nuclear Med & Radiation Biol, Univ Calif, Los Angeles, 65-67; ASSOC PROF RADIATION BIOL, RADIOPHARM PROG SCH PHARM, UNIV SOUTHERN CALIF, 69- *Concurrent Pos:* Instr, Santa Monica City Col Exten, 66-69; Pfeiffer Found fel, Sch Pharm, Univ Southern Calif, 69-70; consult, Gen Elec Co, 70-72, Innotek, Inc, 70-73 & XMI Assocs, Inc, 71-73; vis asst prof, Univ Calif, Los Angeles, 73; adv & consult, Radiobiol for Nuclear Med Technol Training Prog, Los Angeles City Col, 71-73; consult radiopharmaceut, Food & Drug Admin, 71-76 & 81-86. *Mem:* AAAS; Soc Nuclear Med; Am Col Physicians. *Res:* Use of semiconductor microprobe radiation detectors and short lived radionuclides for biomedical applications. *Mailing Add:* Radiopharm Prog Sch of Pharm Univ of Southern Calif Los Angeles CA 90033

MARCUS, DAVID, b New York, NY, Feb 17, 32; m 60. PHARMACY. *Educ:* Columbia Univ, BS, 53, MS, 55; Univ Fla, PhD(pharm), 59. *Prof Exp:* Asst pharm, Univ Fla, 57-58; sr res pharmacist, 59-64, labeling mgr, 64-74, regulatory proj dir, Drug Regulatory Affairs, E R Squibb & Sons, Inc, 74-77; dir regulatory affairs, Barnes-Hind Pharmaceut, Inc, 77-81; DIV DIR, DRUG REGULATORY AFFAIRS & INFO SERV, REVLON HEALTH CARE GROUP, 81- *Concurrent Pos:* Fel, Am Found Pharmaceut Educ. *Mem:* Am Pharmaceut Asn; NY Acad Sci; Sigma Xi. *Res:* Effects of medicinal agents on the blood; rheology and suspension; food, drug and cosmetic law. *Mailing Add:* 59 Richmondville Ave Westport CT 06880

MARCUS, DONALD M, b New York, NY, Dec 10, 30; m 58; c 3. INTERNAL MEDICINE, IMMUNOCHEMISTRY. *Educ:* Princeton Univ, BA, 51; Columbia Univ, MD, 55. *Prof Exp:* Intern internal med, Presby Hosp, New York, 55-56, asst resident, 56-57; assoc resident, Strong Mem Hosp, Rochester, 59-60; assoc med, Albert Einstein Col Med, 63-64, asst prof, 64-70, assoc prof med & microbiol, 70-75, prof med, microbiol & immunol, 75-80, dir, Div Rheumatology & Immunol, 73-80; PROF, DEPTS MICROBIOL & IMMUNOL & MED, BAYLOR COL MED, 80- *Concurrent Pos:* Helen Hay Whitney Found fel, 60-63; career scientist, Health Res Coun, New York, 63- *Mem:* Am Asn Immunol; Am Soc Biol Chem; Am Chem Soc; Am Rheumatism Asn; Am Soc Clin Invest. *Res:* Immunochemistry of human blood group antigens; blood group and cell membrane antigens; glycosphingolipids; tumor antigens; mechanism of hapten-antibody interactions. *Mailing Add:* Depts Microbiol, Immunol & Med Baylor Col Med 1200 Moursund Ave Houston TX 77030

MARCUS, ERICH, synthetic organic chemistry, textile chemistry, see previous edition

MARCUS, FRANK I, b Haverstraw, NY, Mar 23, 28; m 57; c 3. CARDIOLOGY, INTERNAL MEDICINE. *Educ:* Columbia Univ, BA, 48; Tufts Univ, MS, 51; Boston Univ, MD, 53. *Prof Exp:* Intern med, Peter Bent Brigham Hosp, Boston, 53-54, asst resident, 56-57; clin fel, Georgetown Univ Hosp, 58-59, chief med resident, 59-60; from instr to assoc prof med, Georgetown Univ, 60-68; PROF MED & CHIEF CARDIOL, ARIZ MED CTR, UNIV ARIZ, 69- *Concurrent Pos:* Mass Heart Asn res fel cardiol, Peter Bent Brigham Hosp, 57-58; Markle scholar, Georgetown Univ, 60-65, NIH career develop award, 65-68; chief cardiol, Georgetown Univ Med Serv Div, DC Gen Hosp, 60-68; fel coun clin cardiol, Am Heart Asn, 65-; consult, Vet Admin & Davis-Monthan AFB Hosps, Tucson, 69-; ed, Modern Concepts Cardiovas Dis, 82- *Mem:* Am Fedn Clin Res; Am Heart Asn; fel Am Col Physicians; Asn Univ Cardiol; Am Soc Pharmacol & Exp Therapeut. *Res:* Cardiovascular research; pharmacology; digitalis; metabolism; clinical electrophysiology. *Mailing Add:* Ariz Med Ctr Cardiol Sect Univ of Ariz Tucson AZ 85724

MARCUS, GAIL HALPERN, nuclear engineering, physics, see previous edition

MARCUS, GEORGE JACOB, b Toronto, Ont, Mar 17, 33; m 56; c 2. REPRODUCTIVE BIOLOGY. *Educ:* Univ Toronto, BA, 56, PhD(biochem), 61. *Prof Exp:* Res assoc biodynamics, Weizmann Inst, 63-68; asst prof pop dynamics, Sch Hyg, Johns Hopkins Univ, 68-72; asst prof reproductive biol, Dept Anat & Lab Human Reproduction & Reproductive Biol, Harvard Med Sch, 72-74; RES SCIENTIST, ANIMAL RES INST, RES BR, CAN DEPT AGR, 75- *Concurrent Pos:* Pop Coun med fel, Weizmann Inst, 61-63; asst ed, Biol Reproduction, 70-74. *Res:* Biochemical aspects of nidation; decidual induction; preimplantation embryonic development; maternal recognition of pregnancy. *Mailing Add:* 43 Higgins Rd Ottawa ON K2G 0R3 Can

MARCUS, HARRIS L, b Ellenville, NY, July 5, 31. METALLURGY, MATERIALS SCIENCE. *Educ:* Purdue Univ, BS, 63; Northwestern Univ, PhD(mat sci), 66. *Prof Exp:* Shift supvr, Channel Master Corp, NY, 56-60; mem tech staff, metals & controls div, Tex Instruments, Inc, Mass, 66-68; group leader fracture & metal physics, Sci Ctr, N Am Rockwell Corp, 68-75; HARRY L KENT JR PROF MECH ENG & MAT SCI & ENG, UNIV TEX, AUSTIN, 75- *Mem:* Am Inst Mining, Metall & Petrol Engrs; Am Soc Metals; Am Phys Soc; Am Soc Testing & Mat; Metall Soc. *Res:* Application of Auger and Mossbauer spectroscopy to metallurgy; fracture and fatigue of structural alloys;effect of metallurgical variables and environment; precipitation studies in aluminum, titanium, nickel, copper and iron based alloys. *Mailing Add:* Dept of Metall Eng & Mat Sci & Eng Univ of Tex Austin TX 78712

MARCUS, JOSEPH, b Cleveland, Ohio, Feb 27, 28; c 2. CHILD PSYCHIATRY. *Educ:* Hadassah Med Sch, Hebrew Univ, MD, 58; Western Reserve Univ, BSc, 63. *Prof Exp:* Resident psychiat, Ministry of Health, Israel, 58-61; actg head child psychiat, Ness Ziona Rehab Ctr; sr psychiatrist, Lasker Dept Child Psychiat, Hadassah Hosp, 62-64, consult, Tel Hashomer Govt Hosp, 65-66; res assoc, Israel Inst Appl Social Res, 66-69; assoc dir, Jerusalem Infant & Child Develop Ctr, 69-70; head dept child psychiat, Eytanim Hosp, 70-72; dir child psychiat & develop, Jerusalem Ment Health Ctr, 72-75; PROF PSYCHIAT, UNIV CHICAGO & DIR UNIT RES CHILD PSYCHIAT & DEVELOP, 75- *Mem:* Am Acad Child Psychiat; Soc Res Child Develop. *Res:* Development of infants of parents with serious mental diseases, especially behavioral, neurological, physiological and biochemical aspects. *Mailing Add:* Dept of Psychiat Box 411 950 E 59th St Chicago IL 60637

MARCUS, JULES ALEXANDER, b Coytesville, NJ, May 10, 19; div; c 4. PHYSICS. *Educ:* Yale Univ, BS, 40, MS, 44, PhD(physics), 47. *Prof Exp:* Instr physics, Yale Univ, 42-44; res physicist, Appl Physics Lab, Johns Hopkins Univ, 44-46; asst physics, Yale Univ, 46-47; fel, Inst Study Metals, Univ Chicago, 47-49; from asst prof to assoc prof, 49-61, PROF PHYSICS, NORTHWESTERN UNIV, 61- *Mem:* Fel Am Phys Soc; Am Asn Physics Teachers. *Res:* Low temperature solid state physics; de Haas-van Alphen effect; experimental determination of Fermi surfaces; Overhauser spin-density-waves in chromium; galvanomagnetic effects in metals. *Mailing Add:* Dept of Physics Northwestern Univ Evanston IL 60201

MARCUS, LESLIE F, b Los Angeles, Calif, Oct 22, 30; m 58; c 1. BIOMETRY, PALEONTOLOGY. *Educ:* Univ Calif, Berkeley, BA, 51, MA, 59, PhD(paleont), 62. *Prof Exp:* From asst prof to assoc prof statist, Kans State Univ, 60-67; assoc prof, 67-70, PROF BIOL, QUEENS COL, NY, 70-; RES ASSOC, DEPT INVERT, AM MUS NATURAL HIST, 76- *Concurrent Pos:* Vis asst prof, Univ Kans, 63-64; NSF sci fac fel, Columbia Univ, 66-67. *Mem:* AAAS; Soc Study Evolution; Soc Syst Zool; Am Statist Asn; Biomet Soc. *Res:* Vertebrate paleontology; statistical methods application to study of natural selection in fossils; geographic variation; morphology; numerical classification; data base management of museum collections; multivariate statistics. *Mailing Add:* Dept of Biol Queens Col Flushing NY 11367

MARCUS, MARVIN, b Albuquerque, NMex, July 31, 27; m 65; c 2. ALGEBRA. *Educ:* Univ Calif, Berkeley, BA, 50, PhD(math), 54. *Prof Exp:* Res assoc, Univ Calif, Berkeley, 53-54; assoc prof math, Univ BC, 54-60, 61-62; res mathematician, Numerical Anal Sect, Nat Bur Standards, 60-61; chmn dept, 63-68, PROF MATH, UNIV CALIF, SANTA BARBARA, 62-, DEAN RES DEVELOP, 78-, ASSOC VCHANCELLOR, RES & ACADEMIC DEVELOP, 78- *Concurrent Pos:* Fulbright grant, 54; consult, US Naval Test Sta, 55; Nat Res Coun fel, 56-57; NSF grant, 58-59, 63-66, 81-83; vis distinguished prof, Univ Islamabad, W Pakistan, 70; dir, Inst Interdisciplinary Applns of Algebra and Combinatorics, 73-79; Air Force grant, 79-80; Fund Improv Postsecondary Educ grant, 79-81. *Mem:* Am Math Soc; Math Asn Am; Soc Indust & Appl Math; Soc Tech Commun. *Res:* Linear and multilinear algebra. *Mailing Add:* Dept of Math Univ of Calif Santa Barbara CA 93106

MARCUS, MELVIN GERALD, b Seattle, Wash, Apr 13, 29; m 53; c 4. PHYSICAL GEOGRAPHY. *Educ:* Univ Miami, BA, 56; Univ Colo, MS, 57; Univ Chicago, PhD(geog), 63. *Prof Exp:* Res asst climat, Lab Climat, 58-59; from instr to asst prof geog, Rutgers Univ, 60-64; from asst prof to prof, Univ Mich, Ann Arbor, 64-73, chmn dept, 67-71; dir, Ctr Environ Studies, 74-81, PROF GEOG, ARIZ STATE UNIV, 74- *Concurrent Pos:* Res asst, Am Geog Soc, 57-58; sr scientist, Icefield Ranges Res Proj, Arctic Inst NAm, 64-71; vis lectr, Univ Colo, 67; consult, High Sch Geog Proj, Boulder, 67; chmn, Comn Col Geog, 68-71; vis prof, Univ Canterbury, 72. *Mem:* Asn Am Geog; Am Geog Soc; Glaciol Soc; Arctic Inst NAm. *Res:* Glaciological and climatological work, particularly in Alpine regions; physical geography to include geographic education and urban environments; environmental education. *Mailing Add:* Ctr Environ Studies Ariz State Univ Tempe AZ 85281

MARCUS, MELVIN L, b Milwaukee, Wis, July 22, 40; m 62; c 4. CARDIOLOGY. *Educ:* Univ Wis, Milwaukee, BS, 62, MD, 66. *Prof Exp:* From intern to resident internal med, Bronx Munic Hosp Ctr, Albert Einstein Col Med, 66-69; fel cardiol, NIH, 69-71; cardiologist, US Army Med Corps, Walson Army Hosp, 71-73; assoc prof, 74-77, PROF MED, UNIV IOWA, 77- *Concurrent Pos:* Fel coun circulation, Am Heart Asn, 75; res career develop award, Nat Heart & Lung Inst, 76-81. *Honors & Awards:* Irving S Wright Award, Stroke Coun, Am Heart Asn, 75. *Mem:* Fel Am Col Cardiol; fel Am Heart Asn; Am Fedn Clin Res; Am Phys Soc. *Res:* Regional coronary blood flow; segmental ventricular function in the presence of ischemia; neural control of regional cerebral blood flow; progression and regression of ventricular hypertrophy; clinical applications of nuclear cardiology. *Mailing Add:* Cardiovasc Div Dept of Internal Med Univ of Iowa Hosp Iowa City IA 52242

MARCUS, MICHAEL ALAN, b New York City, NY, Nov 13, 52; m 72; c 3. POLYMER PHYSICS. *Educ:* Rensselaer Polytech Inst, BS, 73; Cornell Univ, PhD(appl physics), 78. *Prof Exp:* NIH fel appl physics, Cornell Univ, 75-78; SR RES SCIENTIST, KODAK RES LABS, 78- *Concurrent Pos:* Lectr, Brockport State Univ, 79-, Univ Rochester, 80-81. *Mem:* Am Phys Soc; Optical Soc Am; Am Vacuum Soc. *Res:* Electrical, thermal and mechanical properties of ferroelectric materials; polymeric ferroelectrics and device applications of these materials. *Mailing Add:* 52 Boxwood Lane Fairport NY 14450

MARCUS, MICHAEL BARRY, b Brooklyn, NY, Mar 5, 36; m 64; c 3. MATHEMATICS. *Educ:* Princeton Univ, BSE, 57; Mass Inst Technol, MS, 58, PhD(math), 65. *Prof Exp:* Staff mem math & electronics, Rand Corp, 58-67; asst prof, 67-73, assoc prof, 73-77, PROF MATH, NORTHWESTERN UNIV, 77- *Concurrent Pos:* Asst, Mass Inst Technol, 62-65; NSF vis prof, Westfield Col, Univ London, 70-71; vis mem, Courant Inst, NY Univ, 73-74; guest prof, Arhus Univ Denmark, 77-78. *Mem:* Fel Inst Math Statist; Am Math Soc. *Res:* Probability theory; analysis. *Mailing Add:* Dept of Math Northwestern Univ Evanston IL 60201

MARCUS, NANCY HELEN, b New York, NY, May 17, 50. DEVELOPMENTAL GENETICS. *Educ:* Goucher Col, BA, 72; Yale Univ, MPhil, 75, PhD(biol), 76. *Prof Exp:* Scholar, 76-77, investr, 77-78, ASST SCIENTIST BIOL OCEANOG, WOODS HOLE OCEANOG INST, 78- *Concurrent Pos:* Woods Hole Oceanog Inst fel, 76-77; instr develop biol, Marine Biol Lab, 78- *Mem:* Am Soc Zoologists; Soc Develop Biol; Soc Study Evolution; Am Soc Limnol & Oceanog; AAAS. *Res:* Developmental and population genetics of marine invertebrates; phenotypic plasticity; dormancy of marine invertebrates. *Mailing Add:* Woods Hole Oceanog Inst Woods Hole MA 02543

MARCUS, PAUL MALCOLM, b New York, NY, Feb 4, 21. MATHEMATICAL PHYSICS. *Educ:* Columbia Univ, BA, 40; Harvard Univ, MA, 42, PhD(chem physics), 43. *Prof Exp:* Mem staff, Radiation Lab, Mass Inst Technol, 43-46; fel, Nat Res Coun, 46-47, res assoc physics, 47-48; sci liaison officer, Off Naval Res, US Govt, Eng, 49-50; res asst prof physics, Univ Ill, 50-52; lectr, Carnegie Inst Technol, 52-53, res physicist, 53-58, asst prof physics, 58-59; PHYSICIST, T J WATSON RES CTR, IBM CORP, 59- *Mem:* Fel Am Phys Soc. *Res:* Low temperature and solid state physics; radiation theory. *Mailing Add:* IBM Res Ctr Yorktown Heights NY 10598

MARCUS, PHILIP IRVING, b Springfield, Mass, June 3, 27; m 54; c 3. VIROLOGY. *Educ:* Univ Southern Calif, BS, 50; Univ Chicago, MS, 53; Univ Colo, PhD(microbiol, biophys), 57. *Prof Exp:* Lab asst infrared studies bacteria, Univ Chicago, 51-52, lab asst med & gen microbiol & microbiologist, 52-53, asst steroid enzyme induction, 53-54; asst biophys, Med Ctr, Univ Colo, 54-57, instr, 57-59, asst prof, 59-60; asst prof microbiol & immunol, Albert Einstein Col Med, 60-62, assoc prof, 62-66, prof, 66-69; head microbiol sect, 69-74, PROF BIOL, MICROBIOL SECT, UNIV CONN, 69- *Concurrent Pos:* USPHS sr res fel, 60-65, res career develop awardee, 65-69; on leave from Albert Einstein Col Med to Salk Inst, 67-68; mem sci bd, Damon Runyon Mem Fund Cancer Res, 69-73; ed, J Cellular Physiol, 69-, J Interferon Res, 80- *Mem:* AAAS; British Soc Microbiol; Am Soc Microbiol; Am Soc Cell Biol; NY Acad Sci. *Res:* Single-cell cloning techniques for mammalian cells; host-cell animal virus interactions; mechanism of cell-killing by viruses; interferon induction and viral inhibition; cell surfaces; viral hemadsorption; viral interference; interferon action; persistent infection. *Mailing Add:* Microbiol Sect U-44 Univ of Conn Storrs CT 06268

MARCUS, PHILIP SELMAR, b New York, NY, Jan 30, 36; m 66; c 1. MATHEMATICS. *Educ:* Univ Chicago, AB, 56, BS, 58, MS, 59; Ill Inst Technol, PhD(math), 68. *Prof Exp:* Instr math, De Paul Univ, 62-66; mem fac, Shimer Col, 66-70, dir Shimer-in-Oxford prog, 68-69, chmn dept nat sci, 67-70; asst prof math, Ind Univ, South Bend, 70-76; assoc prof math, Christian Bros Col, Memphis, 76-79; ASSOC PROF MATH, EUREKA COL, 79- *Mem:* Math Asn Am; Am Math Soc. *Res:* Probability; geometry; mathematics education. *Mailing Add:* 701 S Henry Eureka IL 61530

MARCUS, ROBERT BORIS, b Chicago, Ill, Nov 26, 34; m 57; c 2. PHYSICAL CHEMISTRY. *Educ:* Univ Chicago, BS, 56, SM, 58; Univ Mich, PhD(phys chem), 62. *Prof Exp:* Fel phys chem, Univ Mich, 61-62, instr, 62-63, mem tech staff, 63-67, SUPVR STRUCT ANAL GROUP, BELL LABS, 67- *Mem:* Electron Micros Soc; Am Vacuum Soc. *Res:* Microstructure and electrical properties of materials; microelectronics. *Mailing Add:* 2C-174 Bell Labs Murray Hill NJ 07974

MARCUS, ROBERT BROWN, b Phila, Pa, Dec 1, 18; m 42; c 2. PHYSICAL GEOGRAPHY. *Educ:* Pa State Teachers Col, W Chester, BS, 40; Univ Fla, MA, 53, EdD(geog), 56. *Prof Exp:* Teacher high sch, NC, 41-42; head sci dept & master chem & physics, Pennington Sch, NJ, 46-51; from instr to prof phys sci & geog, 54-76, PROF GEOG, UNIV FLA, 76-, CHMN DEPT, 79- *Mem:* Asn Am Geog; Nat Coun Geog Educ; Int Geog Union. *Res:* Utilization of water and natural resources. *Mailing Add:* 3141 GPA Univ of Fla Gainesville FL 32611

MARCUS, ROBERT TOBY, b Brookline, Mass, Dec 18, 46; m 74; c 3. COLOR SCIENCE. *Educ:* Rensselaer Polytech Inst, BS, 68, PhD(chem), 74. *Prof Exp:* Asst systs eng, Int Bus Mach Corp, Providence, RI, 68-69; res asst color sci, Rensselaer Polytech Inst, 69-74; sr res physicist, 74-78, RES ASSOC, COATINGS & RESINS DIV, PPG INDUSTS, INC, 78- *Mem:* Inter-Soc Color Coun; Fedn Socs Coatings Technol; Optical Soc Am. *Res:* Computer color control systems; instrumental color difference evaluation; standardization and comparison of color-measuring instrumentation. *Mailing Add:* 5172 Carterton Dr Gibsonia PA 15044

MARCUS, RUDOLPH ARTHUR, b Montreal, Que, July 21, 23; nat US; m 49; c 3. PHYSICAL CHEMISTRY. *Educ:* McGill Univ, BSc, 43, PhD(phys chem), 46. *Prof Exp:* Jr res officer photochem, Nat Res Coun Can, 46-49; res assoc theoret chem, Univ NC, 49-51; asst prof phys chem, Polytech Inst Brooklyn, 51-54, assoc prof, 54-58, prof, 58-64; prof phys chem, Univ Ill, Urbana, 64-78; A A NOYES PROF CHEM, CALIF INST TECHNOL, PASADENA, 78- *Concurrent Pos:* Temp mem, Courant Inst Math Sci, 60-61; NSF sr fel, 60-61; Sloan fel, 60-63; vis sr scientist, Brookhaven Nat Lab, 62-64; coun mem, Gordon Res Conf, 65-68, chmn bd trustees, 68-69; mem adv coun chem dept, Princeton Univ, 72-78, Calif Inst Technol, 77-78 & Polytech Inst NY, 77-80; Fulbright-Hays sr scholar, 72 & 73; Alexander von Humboldt sr US scientist award, 76; mem, Nat Res Coun-Nat Acad Sci Climatic Impact Comt, Panel Atmospheric Chem, 75-78; chmn, Nat Res Coun-Nat Acad Sci Comt, Kinetics of Chem Reactions, 75-77 & Sci Comt, Chem Sci, 77-78; mem, Review Comt, Radiation Lab, Univ Notre Dame, 75-80; vis prof theoret chem, Oxford Univ, 75-76; prof fel, Univ Col, Oxford, UK, 75-76; distinguished vis prof, Univ Tex, Austin, 77; distinguished lectr, Univ Rochester, 77; lectr, Northwestern Univ, Electrochem Soc, Los Angeles, 79. *Honors & Awards:* Henry Werner lectr, Univ Kans; Venable lectr, Univ NC; Seydel-Wooley lectr, Ga Inst Technol; Foster lectr, State Univ NY Buffalo; Kelly lectr, Purdue Univ; William Draper Harkins lectr, Univ Chicago; Kolthoff lectr, Univ Minn; Raymond & Beverly Sackler distinguished lectr chem, Tel Aviv Univ, 80; Irving Langmuir Award, Am Chem Soc, 78. *Mem:* Nat Acad Sci; Am Chem Soc; Am Phys Soc; Am Acad Arts & Sci. *Res:* Theoretical chemical kinetics; electron transfer, electrode and unimolecular reactions; semiclassical theory of reactive and nonreactive collisions of bound states and of spectra. *Mailing Add:* Div of Chem & Chem Eng Calif Inst of Technol Pasadena CA 91125

MARCUS, RUDOLPH JULIUS, b Frankfurt, Ger, Mar 30, 26; nat US; m 78. PHYSICAL CHEMISTRY. *Educ:* Wayne State Univ, BS, 48; Univ Utah, PhD, 54. *Prof Exp:* Chemist, Sun Oil Co, 48-49; phys chemist, Stanford Res Inst, 54-64; CHEMIST, OFF NAVAL RES, PASADENA, CALIF, 64- *Concurrent Pos:* Sci dir, Off Naval Res, Tokyo, 79-80. *Mem:* Fel AAAS; fel Am Inst Chem; Am Chem Soc (secy, Div Comput Chem, 74-79); Solar Energy Soc; NY Acad Sci. *Res:* Statistical thermodynamics; photosynthesis; solar energy; fluorescence and phosphorescence measurements; experimental design; interactive computer applications; structure-activity relationships. *Mailing Add:* Off Naval Res 1030 E Green St Pasadena CA 91106

MARCUS, S PHILIP, b Pittsburgh, Pa, Sept 9, 15; m 40; c 1. CHEMICAL ENGINEERING. *Educ:* Carnegie Inst Technol, BS, 37, MS, 38. *Prof Exp:* Anal chemist, Kendall Refining Co, 37; anal chemist, Food Mach & Chem Corp, 38, prod supvr, 39, process develop & control engr, 40-45, supvr process develop & control, 45-48, asst to resident mgr, 51, asst div prod mgr, 51-54, asst to div mgr, 54-55, bus mgr, Chem Res & Develop Ctr, 55-62, MGR TECH SERV, FMC CORP, 62- *Res:* Applied mathematics to chemical engineering; analytical chemistry; technical information; process development and control; chemical research administration. *Mailing Add:* 865 Lower Ferry Rd Trenton NJ 08628

MARCUS, SANFORD M, b New York, NY, Mar 18, 32; m 59; c 2. PHYSICS. *Educ:* Brooklyn Col, BS, 54; Columbia Univ, MS, 57; Univ Pa, PhD(physics), 64. *Prof Exp:* Engr, Radio Corp Am, 57-59; PHYSICIST, E I DU PONT DE NEMOURS & CO, 64- *Mem:* Am Phys Soc. *Res:* Superconductivity, especially experimental work by means of tunneling; thick film materials for display, microcircuit and hybrid applications; solid state devices; transport properties of metals; printing technology. *Mailing Add:* Photo Prod 352/N3 E I du Pont de Nemours & Co Wilmington DE 19898

MARCUS, SHELDON H, research administration, see previous edition

MARCUS, STANLEY, b New York, NY, Jan 20, 16; m 39; c 2. MICROBIOLOGY, IMMUNOLOGY. *Educ:* City Col New York, BA, 37; Univ Mich, MS, 39, PhD(microbiol), 42. *Prof Exp:* PROF MICROBIOL, COL MED, UNIV UTAH, 49- *Concurrent Pos:* Nat Inst Allergy & Infectious Dis res career award, 61. *Mem:* AAAS; Am Soc Microbiol; Am Asn Immunol; Soc Exp Biol & Med; Reticuloendothelial Soc. *Res:* Mechanisms of specific and nonspecific resistance to infectious and neoplastic disease; theory of testing; pyrogen tests; nontoxic enteric vaccines; standardization of mycotic sensitins; proficiency testing as basis of evaluation surveys. *Mailing Add:* Dept of Microbiol Univ of Utah Col of Med Salt Lake City UT 84132

MARCUS, STANLEY RAYMOND, b Providence, RI, Feb 29, 16; m 42; c 1. ENGINEERING ADMINISTRATION, RESEARCH MANAGEMENT. *Educ:* Univ RI, BS, 38; George Washington Univ, MS, 58. *Prof Exp:* Mech engr, Naval Torpedo Sta, Newport, 40-45; chief engr, Div War Res, Columbia Univ, 45-46; self employed, 46-51; proj engr, Bur Ord, US Navy, 51-56; coordr underwater ord, Off Naval Res, 56-59; coordr antisubmarine warfare weapons systs, Dep Chief Naval Opers, 59-60; asst tech dir systs planning, Dept Chief Naval Opers, 60-63; dir res div, Bur Naval Weapons, 63-66; dep commander & chief scientist res & technol, Naval Ord Systs Command, 66-74; asst dep commander & tech dir res & technol, 74-77, dir, Off Res & Technol, 77-80, CONSULT, NAVAL SEA SYSTS COMMAND, 80- *Honors & Awards:* Cindy Award, Int Film Producers Am, 72; Distinguished Civilian Serv Award, US Navy, 73; Naval Ord Systs Command Achievement Recognition Medallion, 74; Recognition of Achievement for Sr Execs, Dept Navy, 75. *Mem:* Am Mgt Asn; AAAS; Nat Soc Prof Engrs; Acoust Soc Am; Opers Res Soc Am. *Res:* Management, planning, appraisal and development of research and development efforts for a broad area of technology applications for ordnance and ship systems. *Mailing Add:* 2111 Jeff Davis Hwy Apt 809N Arlington VA 22202

MARCUS, STEPHEN, b New York, NY, Dec 27, 39; m 70; c 2. LASERS. *Educ:* Rensselaer Polytech Inst, BS, 61; Columbia Univ, MA, 63, PhD(physics), 68. *Prof Exp:* Res assoc elec eng, Cornell Univ, 67-69; staff scientist laser physics, United Aircraft Res Labs, 69-70; MEM STAFF, LINCOLN LAB, MASS INST TECHNOL, 70- *Mem:* Am Phys Soc. *Res:* Gas lasers, primarily pulsed and continuous wave carbon dioxide lasers and their applications to laser radar systems. *Mailing Add:* Mass Inst Technol Lincoln Lab 244 Wood St Lexington MA 02173

MARCUSE, DIETRICH, b Koenigsberg, Ger, Feb 27, 29; m 59; c 2. PHYSICS. *Educ:* Free Univ Berlin, Dipl phys, 54; Karlsruhe Tech Univ, DrIng, 62. *Prof Exp:* Mem tech staff, Siemens & Halske, Ger, 54-57; MEM TECH STAFF, BELL LABS, 57- *Honors & Awards:* Quantum Electronics Award, Inst Elec & Electronics Engrs, 81. *Mem:* Fel Inst Elec & Electronics Eng; fel Optical Soc Am. *Res:* Circular electric waveguide; microwave masers; light communications. *Mailing Add:* Crawford Hill Lab Bell Labs Box 400 Holmdel NJ 07733

MARCUVITZ, NATHAN, b Brooklyn, NY, Dec 29, 13; m 46; c 2. MATHEMATICAL PHYSICS. *Educ:* Polytech Inst Brooklyn, BEE, 35, MEE, 41, DEE, 47. *Prof Exp:* Develop engr, Radio Corp Am, 35-40; mem staff, Radiation Lab, Mass Inst Tech, 42-46; asst prof elec eng, Polytech Inst Brooklyn, 46-49, assoc prof, 49-51, prof, 51-65, dir microwave res inst, 57-61, vpres res & actg dean, Grad Ctr, 61-63, prof electrophys, 61-65, dean res & grad ctr, 64-65, inst prof, 65-66; prof appl physics, NY Univ, 66-73; prof, 73-78, INST PROF APPL PHYSICS, POLYTECH INST NEW YORK, 78- *Concurrent Pos:* Asst dir res, Defense Res & Eng, Dept Defense, DC, 63-64; Gordon MacKay vis prof, Harvard Univ, 71. *Mem:* Nat Acad Eng; Am Phys Soc; fel Inst Elec & Electronics Eng. *Res:* Electromagnetics; plasma dynamics; nonlinear and turbulent wave phenomena. *Mailing Add:* Dept of Elect Eng & Electrophys Polytech Inst of New York Rte 110 Farmingdale NY 11735

MARCY, JOSEPH EDWIN, b Bristol, Va; m 73; c 1. FOOD SCIENCE. *Educ:* Univ Tenn, Knoxville, BS, 74, MS, 76; NC State Univ, PhD(food sci), 80. *Prof Exp:* Res asst, Univ Tenn, 74-76; res asst, NC State Univ, 76-80; ASST PROF FOOD SCI, UNIV FLA, 80- *Mem:* Am Chem Soc; Inst Food Technologists. *Res:* Citrus juice processing including analysis of chemical constituents and evaluation of processing procedures. *Mailing Add:* Agr Res & Educ Ctr 700 Exp St Rd Lake Alfred FL 33850

MARCY, WILLARD, b Newton, Mass, Sept 27, 16; m 38; c 2. ORGANIC CHEMISTRY, CHEMICAL ENGINEERING. *Educ:* Mass Inst Technol, SB, 37, PhD(org chem), 49. *Prof Exp:* Asst supt, Am Sugar Ref Co, 37-42; res assoc org chem, Mass Inst Technol, 46-49; chem engr, Res & Develop Div, Am Sugar Ref Co, 49-58, head process develop, 58-64; dir patent progs, 64-67, vpres patents, 67-80, VPRES, INVENTION ADMIN RES CORP, 80- *Mem:* AAAS; Am Chem Soc; fel Am Inst Chem; NY Acad Sci. *Res:* Carbohydrates; war gases; sugar refining; sugar by-products; invention administration. *Mailing Add:* Res Corp 405 Lexington Ave New York NY 10017

MARCZYNSKA, BARBARA MARY, b Cracow, Poland; US citizen; m 56; c 1. IMMUNOLOGY, GENETICS. *Educ:* Acad Med Cracow, MS, 56, PhD(immunol, genetics), 62. *Prof Exp:* From instr to assoc prof genetics & embryol, Med Sch, Cracow, 56-64; res asst, 65-72, ASST PROF VIROL, RUSH-PRESBY-ST LUKE'S MED CTR, 72- *Mem:* Am Soc Microbiol. *Res:* Virological and immunological aspects of virus-induced oncogenic transformation in non-human primates. *Mailing Add:* Dept of Microbiol Rush-Presby-St Luke's Med Ctr Chicago IL 60612

MARCZYNSKI, THADDEUS JOHN, b Poznan, Poland, Nov 30, 20; m 56; c 2. PHARMACOLOGY, NEUROPHYSIOLOGY. *Educ:* Cracow Acad Med, MD, 51, DMSc, 59. *Prof Exp:* Res asst pharmacol, Cracow Acad Med, 54-59, asst prof, 62-64; asst prof, 64-68, assoc prof, 68-73, PROF PHARMACOL, UNIV ILL COL MED, 73-, STAFF MEM, INTERCAMPUS BIOENG DEPT, 78-, PROF, DEPT PSYCHIAT, 78- *Concurrent Pos:* Rockefeller Found & Brain Res Inst fel, Univ Calif, Los Angeles, 61-62; NIH res grant, Univ Ill Col Med, 66-72. *Mem:* AAAS; Soc Neurosci; Am Soc Pharmacol & Exp Therapeut. *Res:* Pharmacology and electrophysiology of the central nervous system; analysis of information and its transmission coding in neuronal pathways; positive reinforcement and sensory input. *Mailing Add:* Dept of Pharmacol Univ of Ill Col of Med Chicago IL 60680

MARDELLIS, ANTHONY, b Neuville-sur-Saone, France, July 17, 20; wid. MATHEMATICS. *Educ:* Univ Calif, Berkeley, BA, 50, MA, 52. *Prof Exp:* Asst math, Univ Calif, Berkeley, 51-55; instr, Loyola, Calif, 55-56; from asst prof to assoc prof, 56-70, chmn dept, 63-67, PROF MATH, CALIF STATE UNIV, LONG BEACH, 70- *Mem:* Am Math Soc; Math Asn Am; Math Soc France; Sigma Xi. *Res:* Picard-Vessiot theory; differential algebra. *Mailing Add:* Dept of Math Calif State Univ Long Beach CA 90840

MARDEN, JOHN IGLEHART, b Chicago, Ill, Sept 24, 51. STATISTICS. *Educ:* Univ Chicago, AB, 73, PhD(statist), 78. *Prof Exp:* Vis lectr, 77-78, ASST PROF MATH, UNIV ILL, URBANA-CHAMPAIGN, 78- *Mem:* Am Statist Asn; Inst Math Statist. *Res:* Hypothesis testing in multivariate analysis, combining independent tests of significance. *Mailing Add:* Dept of Math Altgeld Hall Urbana IL 61801

MARDEN, MORRIS, b Boston, Mass, Feb 12, 05; m 32; c 2. MATHEMATICS. *Educ:* Harvard Univ, AB, 25, AM, 27, PhD(math), 28. *Prof Exp:* Instr math, Harvard Univ, 25-27; Nat Res Coun fel, Uni- Wis, Princeton Univ, Univ Zurich & Univ Paris, 28-30; from asst prof to prof, 30-64, distinguished prof, 64-75, chmn dept, 57-61, 63-64, EMER DISTINGUISHED PROF MATH, UNIV WIS-MILWAUKEE, 75- *Concurrent Pos:* Invited lectr, Math Inst, Polish Acad Sci, 58-62, Math Insts, Univs Jerusalem, Haifa & Tel Aviv, 62, 68 & 73, Greece, 62, Japan, India, Spain & Eng, 64, Mex, Peru, Chile, Argentina Uruguay & Brazil, 65, Budapest, Belgrade, Goteburg, 67, Montreal, 67 & 70, Finland & NZ, 70 & Australia, 71; consult, Allis-Chalmers Co, 48-60; asst ed, Bull, Am Math Soc, 42-45; vis distinguished prof math, Calif Poly State Univ, San Luis Obispo, 75-77. *Mem:* Fel AAAS; Am Math Soc; Math Asn Am. *Res:* Zeros of polynomials; entire and potential function; functions of a complex variable. *Mailing Add:* Dept of Math Univ of Wis Milwaukee WI 53201

MARDER, HERMAN LOWELL, b New York, NY, Mar 3, 31; m 55; c 4. ORGANIC POLYMER CHEMISTRY, RESEARCH ADMINISTRATION. *Educ:* State Univ NY, BS, 54, MS, 57, PhD(chem), 59. *Prof Exp:* Res chemist, E I du Pont de Nemours & Co, Inc, 58-61; sect head, Colgate Palmolive Co, 61-66; dir res & develop, Boyle Midway Div, Am Home Prod Corp, 66-69; vpres res & develop, Int Playtex Co, 69-78; vpres res & develop, 78-81, VPRES OPERS & TECHNOL, CHURCH & DWIGHT CO, INC, 81- *Mem:* Am Chem Soc. *Mailing Add:* Church & Dwight Co Inc PO Box 369 Piscataway NJ 08854

MARDER, STANLEY, b Philadelphia, Pa, Aug 21, 26; m 53; c 3. INFORMATION SCIENCE, SYSTEMS ANALYSIS. *Educ:* Univ Pa, BA, 50; Columbia Univ, PhD(physics), 58. *Prof Exp:* Res physicist, Carnegie Inst Technol, 56-60; staff mem, Inst Defense Anal, 60-73; res physicist, 73-74, DIR, WASHINGTON OFF, ENVIRON RES INST MICH, ARLINGTON, VA, 74- *Mem:* Inst Elec & Electronic Engrs; Am Econ Asn; Am Phys Soc. *Res:* Signal processing; image evaluation; radar system analysis. *Mailing Add:* 9608 McAlpine Rd Silver Spring MD 20901

MARDIAN, JAMES K W, b Pasadena, Calif, July 1, 46; m 72; c 2. BIOCHEMISTRY. *Educ:* Cornell Univ, BS, 68; Calif Inst Technol, MS, 70; Pac Sch Relig, MA, 73; Ore State Univ, PhD(biophys), 78. *Prof Exp:* res assoc biochem, Grad Sch Biomed Sci, Univ Tenn-Oak Ridge, 78-80; ENGR AERODYN, GARRETT TURBINE ENGINE, CO, PHOENIX, 80- *Mem:* Am Soc Cell Biol. *Res:* Compressor aerodynamics; yeast chromatin; structure of active chromatin; chromosomal proteins. *Mailing Add:* 5826 N 70th Pl Paradise Valley AZ 85253

MARDINEY, MICHAEL RALPH, JR, b Brooklyn, NY, Dec 16, 34; m 60; c 4. IMMUNOLOGY, INTERNAL MEDICINE. *Educ:* Hamilton Col, AB, 56; Seton Hall Col Med & Dent, MD, 60; Am Bd Allergy & Immunol, dipl, 74. *Prof Exp:* Intern med, Kings County Hosp Ctr, Brooklyn, 60-61; resident med, Col Med, Baylor Univ, 61-62; clin assoc, Immunol Br, Nat Cancer Inst, 65-67, head immunol & cell biol sect, Baltimore Cancer Res Ctr, Nat Cancer Inst, 67-77; PRES, IMMUNODIAG & IMMUNOTHERAPEUT, INC, 78- *Concurrent Pos:* Res fel, Exp Path Div, Scripps Clin & Res Found, Univ Calif, 62-65; instr, Sch Med, Johns Hopkins Univ & physician, Allergy & Infectious Dis Clin, Johns Hopkins Hosp; physician to med staff, Good Samaritan Hosp; staff physician, Howard County Gen Hosp, South Baltimore Gen Hosp, 70-; consult med, Greater Baltimore Med Ctr. *Mem:* Transplantation Soc; Am Soc Exp Path; Am Asn Immunol; Am Asn Cancer Res; Am Acad Allergy. *Res:* Immunopathology; tumor immunology; allergy. *Mailing Add:* Immundiag & Immunotherapeut Inc 9380 Baltimore Nat Pike Ellicott City MD 21043

MARDIX, SHMUEL, b Lodz, Poland, May 22, 31; Israel & US citizen; m 57. SOLID STATE PHYSICS. *Educ:* Hebrew Univ Jerusalem, MSc, 66, PhD(physics), 69. *Prof Exp:* Res assoc x-ray topog, Bristol Univ, 69-70; res assoc x-ray imaging, 71-72, assoc prof solid state physics, 73-77, PROF SOLID STATE PHYSICS, UNIV RI, 78- *Res:* Photoelectronic effects in materials, x-ray imaging and recording, x-ray crystallography, and photographic processes. *Mailing Add:* Dept of Physics Univ of RI Kingston RI 02881

MARE, CORNELIUS JOHN, b Middleburg, SAfrica, Aug 27, 34; m 60; c 4. VETERINARY MICROBIOLOGY, TROPICAL DISEASES. *Educ:* Pretoria Univ, BVSc, 57; Iowa State Univ, PhD(vet microbiol), 65. *Prof Exp:* Private practice, 57-58; vet diagnostician, Allerton Diag Lab, SAfrica, 58-59;

res virologist, Onderstepoort Vet Res Inst, 59-62, sr res virologist, 65-67; res assoc microbiol, Vet Med Res Inst Iowa, 62-65; assoc prof virol, Iowa State Univ, 67-72, prof vet microbiol, 72-76; PROF VET SCI & HEAD DEPT, UNIV ARIZ, 76-, HEAD, VET DIAG LAB, 76- *Concurrent Pos:* Vis prof, Plum Island Animal Dis Ctr, NY, 73 & EAfrican Vet Res Inst, Nairobi, Kenya, 74; vis scientist, Upper Volta, 79, Egypt, 81. *Mem:* Conf Res Workers Animal Dis; US Animal Health Asn; Am Vet Med Asn. *Res:* Viruses, mycoplasma and chlamydia of domestic animals and man, expecially viruses of the herpes virus group; bovine malignant Catawhol fever; disease ecology in arid lands. *Mailing Add:* Dept Vet Sci Univ of Ariz Tucson AZ 85721

MARECKI, NELDA MAY, b Richmond, Va, Apr 29, 47; m 68. MICROBIOLOGY, BIOCHEMISTRY. *Educ:* Bridgewater Col, BA, 69; Med Col Va, Va Commonwealth Univ, MS, 72, PhD(microbiol), 74. *Prof Exp:* Res fel microbiol, Univ Kans, 74-75, asst prof, 75-76; asst prof biol & chem, Lake Erie Col, 77-79; res chemist, 79-80, GROUP LEADER, RES & DEVELOP, AVERY INT, 80- *Mem:* Am Soc Microbiol; AAAS; Sigma Xi. *Res:* Heavy metal-lipopolysaccharide interactions; mechanisms of pathogenicity of gram-negative organisms; lipopolysaccharide-cell membrane interactions. *Mailing Add:* 250 Chester St Avery Int/Fasson Indust Div Painesville OH 44077

MAREK, CECIL JOHN, b Chicago, Ill, Mar 12, 40; m 61; c 4. CHEMICAL ENGINEERING. *Educ:* Ill Inst Technol, BS, 61, PhD(chem eng), 67. *Prof Exp:* Instr chem eng, Ill Inst Technol, 64-67; asst prof, Drexel Inst, 67-70; AEROSPACE ENGR, NASA LEWIS RES CTR, 70- *Mem:* Am Inst Chem Engrs; Combustion Inst. *Res:* Combustion modeling; radiant heat transfer; film cooling; turbulent mixing; solid-gas interaction; photochemical reactions. *Mailing Add:* NASA Lewis Res Ctr 21000 Brookpark Rd Cleveland OH 44135

MAREK, CHARLES R(OBERT), b Chicago, Ill, May 8, 40; m 62; c 3. ENGINEERING, MATERIALS SCIENCE. *Educ:* Univ Ill, Urbana, BS, 63, MS, 64, PhD(civil eng), 67. *Prof Exp:* Asst civil eng, Univ Ill, Urbana, 62-66, from instr to asst prof, 66-72; construct mat engr, 72-80, SR MAT ENGR, VULCAN MAT CO, BIRMINGHAM, 80- *Concurrent Pos:* Mem comt, Transp Res Bd, Nat Acad Sci-Nat Res Coun. *Mem:* Am Soc Civil Engrs; Asn Asphalt Paving Technol; Am Soc Testing & Mat; Nat Slag Asn. *Res:* Highway and airfield pavement constituent material properties and behavior and pavement design; quality control of aggregate production. *Mailing Add:* 1404 Cosmos Circle Vestavia Hills AL 35216

MAREN, THOMAS HARTLEY, b New York, NY, May 26, 18; m 41; c 3. PHARMACOLOGY. *Educ:* Princeton Univ, AB, 38; Johns Hopkins Univ, MD, 51. *Prof Exp:* Res chemist, Wallace Labs, Carter Prods, Inc, NJ, 38-40, group leader, 41-44; chemist, Sch Hyg & Pub Health, Johns Hopkins Univ, 44-46, instr pharmacol, Med Sch, 46-51; pharmacologist, Chemother Dept, Res Div, Am Cyanamid Co, 51-54, group leader, 54-55; prof pharmacol & therapeut & chmn dept, Col Med, 55-78, GRAD RES PROF, UNIV FLA, 78- *Concurrent Pos:* Investr, Mt Desert Island Biol Lab, 53- *Mem:* Am Soc Pharmacol & Exp Therapeut. *Res:* Renal ocular, cerebrospinal and electrolyte pharmacology and physiology; carbonic anhydrase and its inhibitors; chemotherapy of infectious diseases; comparative pharmacology. *Mailing Add:* Univ of Fla Col of Med Gainesville FL 32610

MARENGO, NORMAN PAYSON, b New York, NY, Feb 21, 13; m 39; c 2. BOTANY. *Educ:* NY Univ, BS, 36, MA, 39, MS, 42, PhD(biol), 49. *Prof Exp:* Asst ed, NY Univ, 36-39, instr, 39-43, biol, 46-48; instr biol, Lafayette Col, 48-49, asst prof, 49-50; asst prof biol, Hofstra Col, 50-54; teacher sci, Cent High Sch, Merrick, 54-55; asst prof biol & gen sci, 55-57, assoc prof, 57-60, dir div sci, 61-67, chmn dept biol, 63-67, prof, 61-81, EMER PROF BIOL, C W POST COL, LONG ISLAND UNIV, 81-; RETIRED. *Mem:* Bot Soc Am; Am Fern Soc. *Res:* Developmental genetics; botanical cytology; microscopical technique. *Mailing Add:* Dept of Biol C W Post Col Long Island Univ Greenvale NY 11548

MARES, FRANK, b Czech, Nov 1, 32; US citizen; m 58; c 2. ORGANOMETALLIC CHEMISTRY, PHYSICAL ORGANIC CHEMISTRY. *Educ:* Prague Tech Univ, MS, 57; Czech Acad Sci, PhD(org chem), 60. *Prof Exp:* Staff mem, Czech Acad Sci, 60-65; fel org chem, Univ Calif, Berkeley, 65-67; res group leader, Czech Acad Sci, 67; res assoc, Univ Tubingen, 68; res assoc, Univ Calif, Berkeley, 69, lectr, 69-70; sr res chemist, 70-74, res group leader organometallic chem, 76-77, tech res supvr organometallic chem, 77-80, SCIENTIST, ALLIED CHEM CORP, 80- *Concurrent Pos:* Assoc ed, Collection Czech Chem Commun, 61-68. *Mem:* Am Chem Soc. *Res:* Transition metals in organic reactions, catalytic and stoichiometric reactions; kinetics and mechanism of organic reactions; organic systhesis. *Mailing Add:* Allied Chem Corp PO Box 1021R Columbia Rd Morristown NJ 07960

MARES, MICHAEL ALLEN, b Albuquerque, NMex, Mar 11, 45; m 66; c 2. MAMMALIAN BIOGEOGRAPHY. *Educ:* Univ NMex, BS, 68; Ft Hays Kans State Univ, MS, 69; Univ Tex, Austin, PhD(zool), 73. *Prof Exp:* From asst prof to assoc prof ecol, Univ Pittsburgh, 73-81; ASSOC PROF ZOOL & CUR MAMMALS, STOVALL MUS, UNIV OKLA, 81- *Concurrent Pos:* Adj prof ecol, Univ Nac de Cordoba, Argentina, 71-72 & Univ Nac de Tucuman, 72; Fulbright res fel, ecol, Salta, Argentina, 74; Nat Chicano Coun fel, Mus Northern Ariz, Flagstaff, 78; Ford Found res fel, Univ Ariz, Tucson, 80-81; vis prof, Univ Nac de Tucuman, 74; scientist fel, Univ Ariz, Tucson, 80-81; ecol consult, NUS Corp, 80-81. *Mem:* Ecol Soc Am; Am Soc Mammalogists; AAAS; Soc Study Evolution; Interam Asn Adv Sci. *Res:* Examination of convergent evolution, adaptation and community organization of desert rodents of the world; ecology, conservation, evolution and systematics of South American mammals; spatial organization in vertebrates; island biogeographic patterns of birds; tropical ecology. *Mailing Add:* Stovall Mus Univ Okla Norman OK 73019

MARETZKI, ANDREW, b Berlin, Ger, Feb 23, 26; nat US; m 57; c 2. BIOCHEMISTRY. *Educ:* Univ Cincinnati, BS, 52; Pa State Univ, MS, 58, PhD, 60. *Prof Exp:* Asst res biochemist, Parke, Davis & Co, 52-53, res asst biochem, Pa State Univ, 55-60; res biochemist, Kitchwan Res Labs, 60-61; assoc scientist, Nuclear Ctr & Sch Med, Univ Puerto Rico, 61-65; assoc biochemist, 66-69, BIOCHEMIST, EXP STA, HAWAIIAN SUGAR PLANTERS ASN, 69- *Mem:* Am Soc Plant Physiol; Sigma Xi. *Res:* Structure of antibiotics; toxins; plant enzyme systems; membrane transport. *Mailing Add:* 99-193 Aiea Heights Dr Aiea HI 96701

MAREZIO, MASSIMO, b Rome, Italy, Aug 25, 31; US citizen. CRYSTALLOGRAPHY. *Educ:* Univ Rome, Dr(chem), 54, Lib Doc, 65. *Prof Exp:* Ital Atomic Energy Comn fel physics, Univ Chicago, 59-60, res assoc, 60-63; mem tech staff, Bell Tel Labs, Inc, 63-73; res dir, 73-81, DIR, LAB DE CRISTALLOG, NAT CTR SCI RES, GRENOBLE, FRANCE, 81- *Mem:* Am Crystallog Asn. *Res:* Inorganic crystal chemistry, solid state physical and high pressure chemistry. *Mailing Add:* Lab de Cristallographie Centre Nat de la Recherche Sci 38 Grenoble France

MARFEY, SVIATOPOLK PETER, b Kobaki, Poland, June 1, 25; nat US; m 64; c 1. ORGANIC CHEMISTRY, BIOCHEMISTRY. *Educ:* Wayne State Univ, BS, 49, MS, 53, PhD(chem), 55. *Prof Exp:* Res asst chem, Princeton Univ, 55-56; res assoc, Rockefeller Inst, 56-59; res assoc, Harvard Univ, 59-67; ASSOC PROF BIOL SCI, STATE UNIV NY ALBANY, 67- *Concurrent Pos:* Dir biochem res lab, Mass Eye & Ear Infirmary, 59-67. *Mem:* AAAS; Am Chem Soc; Biophys Soc. *Res:* Chemistry of proteins and nucleic acids; structure and function of cellular membranes. *Mailing Add:* Dept of Biol Sci 1400 Washington Ave Albany NY 12222

MARFURT, KURT JOHN, b Buffalo, NY, Mar 23, 51; m 74. APPLIED GEOPHYSICS. *Educ:* Hamilton Col, AB, 73; Columbia Univ, MS, 75, MPhil, 77, PhD(appl geophys), 78. *Prof Exp:* Instr, 77-78, ASST PROF APPL GEOPHYS, COLUMBIA UNIV, 78- *Mem:* Soc Explor Geophysicists; Am Inst Mining Engrs; Am Geophys Union; Geol Soc Am; Europ Asn Explor Geophysicists. *Res:* Elastic wave inversion, especially migration and acoustic emission problems; physical rock properties, seismic data processing. *Mailing Add:* 828A SW Mudd Bldg Columbia Univ New York NY 10027

MARG, ELWIN, b San Francisco, Calif, Mar 23, 18; m 42; c 1. VISION, NEUROSCIENCES. *Educ:* Univ Calif, AB, 40, PhD(physiol optics), 50. *Prof Exp:* Instr optom, 50-51, asst prof, 51-56, assoc prof, 56-62, Miller res prof, 67-68, PROF OPTOM & PHYSIOL OPTICS, UNIV CALIF, BERKELEY, 62- *Concurrent Pos:* NSF sr fel, Nobel Inst Neurophysiol, Karolinska Inst, Sweden, 57; Guggenheim fel, Madrid, 64; res assoc neurosci, Mt Zion Hosp & Med Ctr, San Francisco, 69- *Honors & Awards:* Apollo Award, Am Optom Asn, 62; Chas F Prentice Award, Am Acad Optom, 81. *Mem:* Am Physiol Soc; Optical Soc Am; Asn Res Vision & Ophthal; Am Acad Optom; Soc Neurosci. *Res:* Neurophysiology of visual system and brain; automated eye examination; phosphene visual prosthesis; diagnosis and prognosis by single neuron responses from the brain in neurosurgery; visual acuity and development in infants; visual evoked potentials. *Mailing Add:* Sch of Optom Univ of Calif Berkeley CA 94720

MARGACH, CHARLES BOYD, b Utica, NY, Aug 11, 12; m 37, 73; c 2. OPTOMETRY. *Educ:* Northern Ill Col Optom, OD, 48; Pac Univ, BS, 50, MS, 51. *Prof Exp:* Prof optom, Col Optom, Pac Univ, 60-72; pvt pract optom, 72-74; PROF OPTOM, SOUTHERN CALIF COL OPTOM, 74- *Concurrent Pos:* ed, J Am Optom Asn, 65-66; contrib ed, Rev Optom, 75- *Mem:* Fel Am Acad Optom; clin assoc Optom Exten Prog Found. *Res:* Ophthalmic optics; holistic aspects of visual care. *Mailing Add:* Southern Calif Col of Optom 2001 Associated Rd Fullerton CA 92631

MARGALIT, NEHEMIAH, chemistry, see previous edition

MARGANIAN, VAHE MARDIROS, b Jlala, Lebanon, May 28, 38; US citizen; m 62; c 3. INORGANIC CHEMISTRY. *Educ:* San Francisco State Col, BS, 60; Clemson Univ, MS, 64, PhD(inorg chem), 66. *Prof Exp:* Teaching & res fel chem, Clemson Univ, 62-66; NSF res fel inorg chem, Univ Mass, Amherst, 66-67, from asst prof to assoc prof, 67-74, PROF CHEM, BRIDGEWATER STATE COL, 74- *Mem:* Am Chem Soc; Sigma Xi. *Res:* Synthesis and structural studies of oxo-compounds with tellurium IV halides; characterization of the products of cadmium II halides with N-bases; P-NMR of platinum II hydride systems. *Mailing Add:* Dept of Chem Bridgewater State Col Bridgewater MA 02324

MARGARETTEN, WILLIAM, b Brooklyn, NY, Sept 19, 29. PATHOLOGY. *Educ:* NY Univ, AB, 50; Northwestern Univ, MS, 51; State Univ NY, MD, 55; Am Bd Path, dipl, 67. *Prof Exp:* Asst prof path, Columbia Univ, 66-67; from asst prof to assoc prof, 67-75, PROF PATH, UNIV CALIF, SAN FRANCISCO, 75- *Concurrent Pos:* Mem coun thrombosis, Am Heart Asn. *Mem:* AAAS; Am Asn Path & Bact; Am Soc Exp Path. *Res:* Coagulation; endotoxin; inflammation. *Mailing Add:* Dept of Path Univ of Calif San Francisco CA 94110

MARGARIS, ANGELO, b Worcester, Mass, Dec 3, 21. MATHEMATICS. *Educ:* Cornell Univ, BEE, 43, PhD(math), 56; Syracuse Univ, MA, 51. *Prof Exp:* Elec engr, Fed Tel & Radio Corp, 46-50; instr math, Oberlin Col, 54-57; from asst prof to assoc prof, Ohio State Univ, 57-68; PROF MATH & CHMN DEPT, SOUTHWESTERN AT MEMPHIS, 68- *Mem:* Am Math Soc; Asn Symbolic Logic. *Res:* Mathematical logic and foundations. *Mailing Add:* Dept of Math 2000 N Pkwy Memphis TN 38112

MARGARITONDO, GIORGIO, b Rome, Italy, Aug 24, 46; m 71; c 2. SOLID STATE PHYSICS, SURFACE SCIENCE. *Educ:* Univ Rome, PhD(physics), 69. *Prof Exp:* Fel physics, Ital Nat Res Coun, 69-71, mem res staff, 71-78; asst prof, 78-80, ASSOC PROF PHYSICS, UNIV WIS-MADISON, 80- *Concurrent Pos:* Elected mem scientific coun, Nat Group Struct Matter, Ital

Nat Res Coun, 74-75; consult, Bell Labs, Murray Hill, NJ, 75-77. *Mem:* Am Phys Soc; Am Vacuum Soc; Ital Phys Soc; Europ Phys Soc. *Res:* Photoemission spectroscopy with synchrotron radiation and electron spectroscopy in general on clean surfaces, interfaces, and bulk states. *Mailing Add:* Dept of Physics Univ of Wis Madison WI 53706

MARGAZIOTIS, DEMETRIUS JOHN, b Athens, Greece, Oct 14, 38; m 67. NUCLEAR PHYSICS. *Educ:* Univ Calif, Los Angeles, BA, 59, MA, 61, PhD(physics), 66. *Prof Exp:* From instr to assoc prof, 64-73, PROF PHYSICS, CALIF STATE UNIV, LOS ANGELES, 73- *Mem:* Am Phys Soc. *Res:* Few nucleon problem; nuclear structure. *Mailing Add:* Dept of Physics Calif State Univ Los Angeles CA 90032

MARGEN, SHELDON, b Chicago, Ill, May 9, 19; m 44; c 4. HUMAN NUTRITION. *Educ:* Univ Calif, AB, 38, MA, 39, MD, 43. *Prof Exp:* USPHS sr res fel, 47-48; res assoc, US Metab Unit, 47-50, clin instr med, Sch Med, 48-56, lectr soc res, Sch Soc Welfare, 56-62, assoc res biochemist, 52-60, res biochemist, 60-62, nutritionist, Agr Exp Sta, 62-70, chmn dept nutrit sci, 70-74, PROF HUMAN NUTRIT, UNIV CALIF, BERKELEY, 62- *Concurrent Pos:* Schering fel, 48-49; Damon Runyon fel, Nat Res Coun, 49-51; res assoc, Inst Metab Res, Alameda, 50-52. *Mem:* Endocrine Soc; Am Fedn Clin Res; Am Med Asn; Am Inst Nutrit; Am Soc Clin Nutrit. *Res:* Energy and general protein metabolism; protein turnover; human nutrition, experimental and programatic; hormone effects on intermediate metabolism; water and electrolyte regulation. *Mailing Add:* Dept of Nutrit Sci Univ of Calif Berkeley CA 94720

MARGERISON, RICHARD BENNETT, b Phila, Pa, Feb 24, 32; m 53; c 4. ORGANIC CHEMISTRY. *Educ:* Lehigh Univ, BS, 53, MS, 55; Univ Va, PhD(chem), 57. *Prof Exp:* Asst, Lehigh Univ, 53-55; res chemist med chem, Wallace & Tiernan, Inc, 57-58; sr chemist develop res, Ciba Pharmaceut Prods, Inc, 58-67, mgr process res & develop, Ciba Agrochem Co, 67-70, mgr chem mfg, 70-74, DIR CHEM MFG, PHARMACEUT DIV, CIBA GEIGY CORP, 74- *Concurrent Pos:* Chmn, bulk pharmaceut chem comt, Pharmaceut Mfrs Asn. *Mem:* AAAS; NY Acad Sci. *Res:* Preparation of nitrogen and sulfur aliphatic, aromatic and heterocyclic compounds as medicinal agents; substituted piperazines, diphenyl sulfides, gem-diphenyl compounds; medium size heterocyclic rings; sulfonamides; ureas. *Mailing Add:* 556 Morris Ave Summit NJ 07901

MARGERUM, DALE WILLIAM, b St Louis, Mo, Oct 20, 29; m 53; c 3. INORGANIC CHEMISTRY, ANALYTICAL CHEMISTRY. *Educ:* Southeast Mo State Col, BA, 50; Iowa State Univ, PhD, 55. *Prof Exp:* Chemist, Ames Lab, Iowa State Univ, 52-53; from instr to assoc prof, 54-65, PROF CHEM, PURDUE UNIV, 65- *Concurrent Pos:* NSF sr fel, Max Planck Inst Phys Chem, Gottingen, 63-64; vis prof, Univ Kent, Canterbury, 70; adv bd, Res Corp, 73- *Mem:* AAAS; Am Chem Soc. *Res:* Coordination chemistry; bio-inorganic; kinetics; fast reactions in solution; analytical applications of kinetics; inorganic-analytical studies of environmental solution chemistry. *Mailing Add:* Dept of Chem Purdue Univ West Lafayette IN 47907

MARGERUM, DONALD L(EE), b St Louis, Mo, Mar 29, 26; m 49; c 3. ELECTRONICS ENGINEERING. *Educ:* Univ Mo, BSEE, 49; Northwestern Univ, MSEE, 50. *Prof Exp:* Res engr antennas, Aerophys Lab, N Am Aviation, Inc, 50-52; proj engr, Microwave Eng Co, 52-53; sr engr, Stanford Res Inst, 53-56; dir electronics, Systs Labs Corp, 56-59; asst gen mgr electronic warfare systs, Electronic Specialty Co, 59-66; vpres, Raven Electronics, Inc, 66-70; sr staff engr, Aerospace Corp, 70-71; chief engr, Rantec Div, Emerson Elec, 71-73; mem tech mgt, Ventura Div, Northrop Corp, 73-78; PRIN ENGR, ELECTROMAGNETICS SYSTS DIV, RAYTHEON, 78- *Mem:* Inst Elec & Electronics Engrs; Sigma Xi. *Res:* Design, development and analysis of electronic warfare systems. *Mailing Add:* 1897 San Leandro Lane Santa Barbara CA 93108

MARGERUM, JOHN DAVID, b St Louis, Mo, Oct 20, 29; m 54; c 3. PHYSICAL CHEMISTRY. *Educ:* Southeast Mo State Col, AB, 50; Northwestern Univ, PhD(phys chem), 56. *Prof Exp:* Res chemist spectros, Wood River Res Lab, Shell Oil Co, 54-55; mem staff, Qm Res Eng Ctr, US Army, 55-57, sect chief, 57-59; res specialist photochem, Turbo Div, Sunstrand Corp, 59-62; mem tech staff chem, 62-67, SECT HEAD CHEM, RES LABS, HUGHES AIRCRAFT CO, 67-, SR SCIENTIST, 78- *Honors & Awards:* Holley Medal, Am Soc Mech Engrs, 77. *Mem:* Fel AAAS; Sigma Xi, Am Chem Soc; Inter-Am Photochem Soc; Electrochem Soc. *Res:* Photochemistry on polymers, dyes, lasers, photochromic materials, photogalvanic and fuel cells; liquid crystal materials and electrooptical devices; electrochemical studies on secondary batteries and displays. *Mailing Add:* Hughes Res Labs 3011 Malibu Canyon Rd Malibu CA 90265

MARGETTS, EDWARD LAMBERT, b Vancouver, BC, Mar 8, 20; m 41; c 2. MEDICINE, PSYCHIATRY. *Educ:* Univ BC, BA, 41; McGill Univ, MD, CM, 44; FRCP(C); FRCPsychiat. *Prof Exp:* Psychiatrist, Royal Victoria Hosp, Montreal, 49-55; specialist psychiatrist, Kenya Govt & med supt, Mathari Hosp, Nairobi, 55-59; PROF PSYCHIAT & LECTR HIST MED, UNIV BC, 60-; HEAD, DEPT PSYCHIAT, VANCOUVER GEN HOSP, 72- *Concurrent Pos:* Asst to dir, Allan Mem Inst Psychiat, 49-51; chief serv, Shaughnessy Vet Hosp, Vancouver, BC, 64-70; Ment Health Unit, WHO, Switz, 70-72. *Mem:* Am Psychiat Asn; Am Asn Hist Med; Am Anthrop Asn; Can Psychiat Asn; Royal Micros Soc. *Res:* Ethnic, cultural and international psychiatry; history of medicine; archaeology and anthropology applied to medicine. *Mailing Add:* Dept Psychiat Univ BC Vancouver BC V6T 1W5 Can

MARGOLIASH, EMANUEL, b Cairo, Egypt, Feb 10, 20; m 44; c 2. MOLECULAR BIOLOGY, PROTEIN CHEMISTRY. *Educ:* American Univ, Beirut, BA, 40, MA, 42, MD, 45. *Prof Exp:* Res fel exp path, Hebrew Univ, Israel, 45-48, sr asst, 49-51, lectr & actg head, Cancer Res Labs, Hadassah Med Sch, 54-58; res assoc biochem, Molteno Inst, Cambridge Univ, 51-53; res assoc, Nobel Inst, Sweden, 58, Univ Utah, 58-60 & Montreal Res Inst, McGill Univ, 60-62; head protein sect, Abbott Labs, 62-71; PROF BIOCHEM & MOLECULAR BIOL, NORTHWESTERN UNIV, 71- *Concurrent Pos:* Prof lectr, Univ Chicago, 64-71. *Mem:* Nat Acad Sci; AAAS; Am Soc Biol Chem; Am Chem Soc; Brit Biochem Soc. *Res:* Structure-function relations of heme proteins; molecular evolution and immunology; energy conservation mechanisms. *Mailing Add:* Dept Biochem & Molecular Biol Northwestern Univ Evanston IL 60201

MARGOLIN, BARRY HERBERT, b New York, NY, Jan 8, 43; m 69; c 1. MATHEMATICAL STATISTICS, APPLIED STATISTICS. *Educ:* City Col New York, BS, 63; Harvard Univ, MA, 64, PhD(statist), 67. *Prof Exp:* Instr educ statist, Harvard Univ, 66-67; asst prof statist, Yale Univ, 67-72, assoc prof statist, 72-77; MATH STATISTICIAN, NAT INST ENVIRON HEALTH SCI, 77- *Concurrent Pos:* Consult, Consumers Union, 67-77 & IBM Co, 69-70. *Honors & Awards:* Shewall Award, Chem Div, Am Soc Quality Control, 77. *Mem:* Fel Am Statist Asn; Int Statist Inst; fel Inst Math Statist; Environ Mutagen Soc. *Res:* Data analysis; design and analysis of experiments; categorical data; contingency tables; statistical evaluation of computer system performance. *Mailing Add:* Nat Inst Environ Health Sci PO Box 12233 Research Triangle Park NC 27709

MARGOLIN, ESAR GORDON, b Omaha, Nebr, Mar 17, 24; m 56; c 2. INTERNAL MEDICINE. *Educ:* Univ Nebr, BA, 45, MD, 47. *Prof Exp:* From asst prof to assoc prof, 58-69, clin prof, 69-72, PROF MED, COL MED, UNIV CINCINNATI, 72-; DIR DEPT INTERNAL MED, JEWISH HOSP, 59- *Concurrent Pos:* Fel med, Harvard Univ, 53-55. *Mem:* Am Col Physicians; Am Soc Nephrology; Int Soc Nephrology; Am Heart Asn; Am Soc Artificial Internal Organs. *Res:* Kidney and electrolytes. *Mailing Add:* 7258 Laurel Oak Lane Cincinnati OH 45237

MARGOLIN, HAROLD, b Hartford, Conn, July 12, 22; m 46; c 3. PHYSICAL & MECHANICAL METALLURGY. *Educ:* Yale Univ, BE, 43, MEng, 47, DEng(metall), 50. *Prof Exp:* Res assoc, Res Div, NY Univ, 49-55, eng scientist, 55-56, assoc prof metall, 56-63, prof metall eng, 63-73; PROF PHYS & ENG METALL, POLYTECH INST NEW YORK, 73- *Concurrent Pos:* Consult various industs, 56- *Mem:* Fel Am Soc Metals; Am Inst Mining, Metall & Petrol Engrs; Brit Inst Metals; Sigma Xi; AAAS. *Res:* Titanium metallurgy; plastic flow and fracture; grain boundary strengthening; Bauschinger behavior fatigue. *Mailing Add:* Polytech Inst New York 333 Jay St Brooklyn NY 11201

MARGOLIN, JEROME, b Brooklyn, NY, Nov 13, 27; m 65; c 3. ELECTRICAL ENGINEERING. *Educ:* Univ Mich, BSE(math) & BSE(elec eng), 51, MSE, 52. *Prof Exp:* Staff mem radar, Lincoln Lab, Mass Inst Technol, 52-59 & Shape Air Defense Tech Ctr, 59; sub dept head, Mitre Corp, 59-61; SR STAFF MEM, LINCOLN LAB, MASS INST TECHNOL, 61- *Concurrent Pos:* Consult, Weapons Systs Eval Group, Inst Defense Anal, 59-61. *Mem:* Inst Elec & Electronics Engrs. *Res:* Radar system synthesis and signal processing. *Mailing Add:* Mass Inst Technol Lincoln Lab 244 Wood St PO Box 73 Lexington MA 02173

MARGOLIN, LEONARD GERALD, b NJ, Jan 17, 47; m 76. PHYSICS. *Educ:* The Cooper Union, BS, 67; Univ Mich, MS, 68, PhD(physics), 77. *Prof Exp:* STAFF MEM PHYSICS, LOS ALAMOS SCI LAB, 69- *Res:* Mechanics of continuous media; statistical mechanics; hydrodynamics; computer modelling. *Mailing Add:* Los Alamos Nat Lab MS665 Los Alamos NM 87545

MARGOLIN, PAUL, b New York, NY, Aug 31, 23; m 46. GENETICS, MICROBIOLOGY. *Educ:* NY Univ, BS, 47; Ind Univ, PhD(genetics), 55. *Prof Exp:* Asst zool, Ind Univ, 50-52; res fel, Calif Inst Technol, 55-56; USPHS fel, Univ Edinburgh, 57-58 & Brookhaven Nat Lab, 58; geneticist, Biol Lab, Long Island Biol Asn, 58-62; sr staff investr, Cold Spring Harbor Lab Quant Biol, NY, 62-66; MEM & CHIEF DEPT GENETICS, PUB HEALTH RES INST OF CITY OF NEW YORK, INC, 66- *Concurrent Pos:* Res prof, Dept Microbiol, Sch Med, NY Univ; mem sci adv comt virol & cell biol, Am Cancer Soc, 69-73. *Mem:* AAAS; Genetics Soc Am; Am Soc Microbiol; Am Inst Biol Sci. *Res:* Bacterial genetics; molecular biology. *Mailing Add:* Dept of Genetics 455 First Ave Pub Health Res Inst of New York New York NY 10016

MARGOLIN, SOLOMON, b Philadelphia, Pa, May 16, 20; m 47; c 4. PHARMACOLOGY, ENDOCRINOLOGY. *Educ:* Rutgers Univ, BSc, 41, MSc, 43, PhD(physiol, biochem), 45. *Prof Exp:* Asst, Rutgers Univ, 43-45; consult, 46-47; res biologist, Silmo Chem Co, 47-48; res biologist, Schering Corp, 48-52, dir pharmacol res, 52-54; chief pharmacologist, Maltbie Labs Div, Wallace & Tiernan, Inc, 54-56; chief pharmacologist, Wallace Labs, Carter-Wallace, Inc, 56-60, dir biol res, 60-64, vpres, 64-68; pres, AMR Biol Med Res, Inc, 68-78; PROF & CHMN, DEPT PHARMACOL, SCH MED, ST GEORGE'S UNIV, GRENADA, WEST INDIES, 78- *Mem:* AAAS; Am Soc Animal Sci; Endocrine Soc; Am Chem Soc; Soc Exp Biol & Med. *Res:* Antihistamines; anticholinergics; cholecystographic media; sedative-hypnotics; tranquilizers; muscle relaxants; adrenal hormones; cardiovascular agents. *Mailing Add:* Dept Pharmacol Sch Med St George's Univ St George's Grenada West Indies

MARGOLIN, SYDNEY GERALD, b New York, NY, Apr 25, 09; m 41; c 2. PSYCHIATRY. *Educ:* Columbia Univ, BS, 30, MA, 31; State Univ NY Downstate Med Ctr, MD, 36; Am Bd Psychiat & Neurol, dipl, 43. *Prof Exp:* Mem fac, Columbia Univ, 30-32; assoc attend psychiatrist, Mt Sinai Hosp, 46-55; chief div psychosom med, Med Ctr, 55-58, PROF PSYCHIAT, SCH MED, UNIV COLO, DENVER, 55-, DIR HUMAN BEHAV LAB & UTE INDIAN PROJ, 56- *Concurrent Pos:* Abrahamson fel neurol, Mt Sinai Hosp, NY, 39-40; Josiah Macy Jr Found grant, Columbia Univ, 41-42; psychiatrist in chg, Male Med Serv, Worcester State Hosp, Mass, 41; mem fac, NY Psychoanal Inst, 46-55. *Mem:* Fel AAAS; fel Am Col Physicians; fel Am Psychiat Asn; Am Psychoanal Asn; Am Psychosom Soc (pres, 52-53). *Res:* Psychoanalysis; psychophysiology; neuropsychology of consciousness; psychosomatic medicine; ethno-psychiatry; behavioral science. *Mailing Add:* 4375 S Lafayette Englewood CO 80110

MARGOLIS, ASHER J(ACOB), b New York, NY, Nov 22, 14; m 39; c 2. CHEMICAL ENGINEERING. *Educ:* Columbia Univ, AB, 35, BS, 36, ChE, 37. *Prof Exp:* Chemist, Am Smelting & Ref Co, Utah, 37-38; chief chemist & chem engr, Sweets Co Am, NJ, 38-41; chief chemist, Nutrine Candy Co, 41-43; chem engr, Emulsol Corp, 43; assoc chem engr, metall lab, Univ Chicago, 43-45; sr chem engr, Sherwin-Williams Co, 45-51; mgr, pilot plant, Simoniz Co, 51-66; group leader process develop, Armour-Dial, 66-70; dir test & rentals, Eimco Process Mach Div, Envirotech Corp, 70-72; civil engr, Metrop Sanit Dist Greater Chicago, 72-79; RETIRED. *Mem:* AAAS; Am Chem Soc; Am Inst Chem Engrs. *Res:* Emulsion technology; polishes and waxes; polyurethane foams; aerosol technology; soap and detergents; filtration and other liquid-solids separations. *Mailing Add:* 1338 E Madison Park Chicago IL 60615

MARGOLIS, BERNARD, b Montreal, Que, Aug 15, 26; m 54. PHYSICS. *Educ:* McGill Univ, BSc, 47, MSc, 49; Mass Inst Technol, PhD, 52. *Prof Exp:* Instr physics, Mass Inst Technol, 53-54; instr, Columbia Univ, 54-57, res physicist, 57-59; assoc prof physics, Ohio State Univ, 59-61; assoc prof math physics, 61-63, PROF PHYSICS, MCGILL UNIV, 63- *Mem:* Am Phys Soc. *Res:* Theoretical physics. *Mailing Add:* Dept of Physics McGill Univ Montreal PQ H3A 2T5 Can

MARGOLIS, FRANK L, b Brooklyn, NY, Jan 21, 38; m 61; c 3. NEUROCHEMISTRY. *Educ:* Antioch Col, BS, 59; Columbia Univ, PhD(biochem), 64. *Prof Exp:* USPHS trainee biochem, Columbia Univ, 64-65; fel, Lab Comp Physiol, Univ Paris, 65-66; asst res microbiologist, Sch Med, Univ Calif, Los Angeles, 66-69; res assoc, 69-71, asst mem, 71-74, assoc mem, 74-81, FULL MEM, ROCHE INST MOLECULAR BIOL, 81- *Concurrent Pos:* Adj prof, City Univ New York, 71-; mem, Panel Sensory Physiol & Perception, NSF, 79-81. *Mem:* Am Soc Pharmacol Exp Therapeut; Am Soc Neurochem; Int Soc Neurochem; Am Soc Biol Chemists; Soc Neurosci. *Res:* Regulation of mammalian gene expression; biochemistry of brain regions associated with specific sensory function, especially olfaction. *Mailing Add:* Roche Inst Molecular Biol Nutley NJ 07110

MARGOLIS, JACK SELIG, b Los Angeles, Calif, Mar 9, 32. CHEMICAL PHYSICS, SPECTROSCOPY. *Educ:* Univ Calif, Los Angeles, AB, 54, PhD(physics), 60. *Prof Exp:* Engr, Collins Radio Co, 54-55; asst physics, Univ Calif, Los Angeles, 55-60; mem tech staff, Sci Ctr, NAm Aviation, Inc, 60-64; lectr physics, Univ Calif, Santa Barbara, 64-65, asst prof, 65-66; MEM TECH STAFF, JET PROPULSION LAB, CALIF INST TECHNOL, 66- *Concurrent Pos:* Asst, Scripps Inst, Univ Calif, 55-56; prof dept earth & planetary sci, Washington Univ, 78-79. *Mem:* Am Phys Soc; Am Astron Soc. *Res:* Spectroscopy of the earth's atmosphere; theoretical rare earth and molecular spectroscopy; induced Raman effect; charge transfer complexes; atmospheric radiation. *Mailing Add:* 1842 Rose Villa Pasadena CA 91107

MARGOLIS, LEO, b Montreal, Que, Dec 18, 27. PARASITOLOGY, FISH PATHOLOGY. *Educ:* McGill Univ, BSc, 48, MSc, 50, PhD(parasitol), 52. *Prof Exp:* Asst parasitol, McGill Univ, 49-52; asst zool, Macdonald Col, 50-51; from assoc scientist to prin scientist, Fisheries Res Bd Can, 52-67, head var res div & sect, 67-81, HEAD FISH HEALTH & PARASITOL SECT, PAC BIOL STA, 81- *Concurrent Pos:* Co-chmn, Can Comt Fish Dis, 70-73; assoc ed, Can J Zool, 71-; mem comt Biol & Res, Int North Pac Fisheries Comn, 71-; chmn Parasitol Sect, Can Soc Zool, 77-78; mem, Sci Subvention Comt, Dept Fisheries & Oceans, Can, 78-81, Adv Bd Sci Info, 79- *Mem:* Am Soc Parasitol; Wildlife Dis Asn; Can Soc Zool; fel Royal Soc Can; Am Fisheries Soc. *Res:* Parasites of fish and marine mammals; diseases of fish. *Mailing Add:* Pac Biol Sta Dept Fisheries & Marine Serv Nanaimo BC V9R 5K6 Can

MARGOLIS, PHILIP MARCUS, b Lima, Ohio, July 7, 25; m 59. PSYCHIATRY. *Educ:* Univ Minn, BA, 46, BS, 47, BM, 48, MD, 49; Am Bd Psychiat & Neurol, dipl. *Prof Exp:* Harvard fel psychiat, Univ Minn, 49-53, instr, Med Sch, Univ Minn, 53-56; from asst prof to assoc prof, Sch Med, Univ Chicago, 56-66; dir med educ, 78-81, PROF PSYCHIAT, MED SCH, UNIV MICH, ANN ARBOR, 66-, PROF COMMUNITY MENT HEALTH, SCH PUB HEALTH, 71-, ASSOC CHIEF, CLIN AFFAIRS, UNIV MICH HOSP, 81- *Concurrent Pos:* Clin fel, Mass Gen Hosp, Boston, 52-53; consult, Vet Admin Hosp, Minneapolis, Minn, 53-54 & Family Serv Agency, St Paul, 54-56; chief psychiat in-patient serv, Billings Hosp, Univ Chicago Clins, 56-66; consult, Child & Family Serv, Chicago, 57-60 & State Psychiat Inst, 60-66; sr psychiat consult, Peace Corps, 61-66; dir, Washtenaw County Ment Health Clin, 66-72; consult, Geriatric Clin, 77- *Mem:* Fel Am Psychiat Asn; AMA; fel Am Orthopsychiat Asn; World Fedn Ment Health; Int Asn Social Psychiat. *Res:* Social and community psychiatry; preventive psychiatry; crisis and brief therapy; suicide studies; consultation process; inpatient psychosocial issues. *Mailing Add:* 228 Riverview Dr Ann Arbor MI 48104

MARGOLIS, RENEE KLEIMANN, b Paris, France, Oct 31, 38; US citizen; m 59. PHARMACOLOGY, NEUROCHEMISTRY. *Educ:* Univ Chicago, BS, 60, PhD(pharmacol), 66. *Prof Exp:* Res scientist, NY State Res Inst Neurochem, 66-68; instr pharmacol, Mt Sinai Sch Med, 68-70; asst prof, 70-75, assoc prof pharmacol, 75-81, PROF PHARMACOL, STATE UNIV NY DOWNSTATE MED CTR, 81- *Concurrent Pos:* mem, Behav & Neurosci Study Sect, NIH, 80- *Mem:* Am Soc Pharmacol & Exp Therapeut; Am Soc Neurochem; Int Soc Neurochem; Soc Complex Carbohydrates; Soc Neurosci. *Res:* Glycoproteins and proteoglycans of nervous tissue. *Mailing Add:* Dept of Pharmacol State Univ NY Downstate Med Ctr Brooklyn NY 11203

MARGOLIS, RICHARD URDANGEN, b Pittsburgh, Pa, Sept 7, 37; m 59. PHARMACOLOGY, BIOCHEMISTRY. *Educ:* Univ Chicago, BS, 59, PhD(pharmacol), 63, MD, 66. *Prof Exp:* Res assoc pharmacol, Univ Chicago, 63-66; from instr to assoc prof, 66-77, PROF PHARMACOL, SCH MED, NY UNIV, 77- *Concurrent Pos:* mem neurol study sect, Div Res Grants, NIH, 80- *Mem:* Soc Neurosci; Brit Biochem Soc; Int Soc Neurochem; Am Soc Pharmacol & Exp Therapeut; Am Soc Neurochem. *Res:* Complex carbohydrates of nervous tissue. *Mailing Add:* Dept of Pharmacol NY Univ Sch of Med New York NY 10016

MARGOLIS, RONALD NEIL, b Brooklyn, NY, Oct 12, 50; m 76; c 1. METABOLISM, CELLULAR ENDOCRINOLOGY. *Educ:* State Univ NY, Albany, BS, 71; Upstate Med Ctr, Syracuse Univ, NY, PhD(anat), 76. *Prof Exp:* Fel cell biol, Univ Va, Charlottesville, 76-79, fel metab, Diabetes Res Training Ctr, 79-80; ASST PROF CELL BIOL & HIST, COL MED & ASST PROF, DEPT ONCOL, CANCER RES CTR, HOWARD UNIV, 80- *Mem:* Am Asn Anatomists; Am Soc Cell Biol; AAAS; Endocrine Soc. *Res:* Hormonal and metabolic regulation of hepatic glycogen metabolism and the effects of diabetes mellitus on the regulation. *Mailing Add:* Dept Anat Col Med Howard Univ 520 West St NW Washington DC 20059

MARGOLIS, SAM AARON, b Cambridge, Mass, Nov 17, 33; m 60; c 2. BIOCHEMISTRY, MOLECULAR BIOLOGY. *Educ:* Boston Univ, AB, 55, PhD(biochem), 63; Univ RI, MS, 57. *Prof Exp:* Staff scientist, Worcester Found Exp Biol, 63-64; pharmacologist, Food & Drug Admin, 66-68; staff fel biochem, Nat Inst Allergy & Infectious Dis, 68-69, sr staff fel, 69-70; sr staff fel biochem, Nat Cancer Inst, 70-72; RES CHEMIST, NAT BUR STANDARDS, 72- *Concurrent Pos:* Fel, Inst Enzyme Res, Univ Wis, 64-66; instr, Sch Med, Boston Univ, 63-64. *Mem:* AAAS; Am Chem Soc; NY Acad Sci. *Res:* Protein hormones and antihormones, characterization and isolation; association of metabolic pathways with biological membranes; modification of viral growth and reproduction by natural and synthetic substances. *Mailing Add:* 5902 Roosevelt St Bethesda MD 20034

MARGOLIS, SIMEON, b Johnstown, Pa, Mar 29, 31; m 54; c 3. BIOCHEMISTRY. *Educ:* Johns Hopkins Univ, BA, 53, MD, 57, PhD(lipoprotein struct), 64. *Prof Exp:* From intern to asst resident, Johns Hopkins Hosp, 57-59; res assoc biochem, Nat Heart Inst, 59-61; resident med, Johns Hopkins Hosp, 64-65; asst prof med & physiol chem, 65-68, assoc prof med, 68-77, assoc prof, 75-81, PROF PHYSIOL CHEM, SCH MED, JOHNS HOPKINS UNIV, 81-, PROF MED, 77- *Concurrent Pos:* Fel biochem, Sch Med, Johns Hopkins Univ, 61-64; Nat Heart Inst res grant, 65-; mem metab study sect, USPHS, mem gen clin res ctr study sect; mem coun on arteriosclerosis, Am Heart Asn; investr, Howard Hughes Med Inst, 76-81; assoc ed, Am J Clin Nutrit, 81- *Mem:* Am Diabetes Asn; Endocrine Soc; Am Soc Clin Invest; Am Soc Biol Chem; Am Chem Soc. *Res:* Lipid biochemistry; regulation of lipid biosynthesis; metabolism of isolated hepatocytes; structure of human serum lipoproteins; role of serum lipoproteins in atherosclerosis; regulation of bile acid synthesis. *Mailing Add:* Dept of Med Johns Hopkins Univ Sch of Med Baltimore MD 21205

MARGOLIS, STEPHEN G(OODFRIEND), b Philadelphia, Pa, Dec 15, 31; m 55; c 2. ELECTRICAL & NUCLEAR ENGINEERING. *Educ:* Univ Pa, BS, 53; Mass Inst Technol, SM, 55; Univ Pittsburgh, PhD(elec eng), 62. *Prof Exp:* Res engr, Jet Propulsion Lab, Univ Calif, 55-56; engr, Bettis Atomic Power Lab, Westinghouse Elec Corp, 56-60, sr engr, 60-63, fel engr, 63-66; assoc prof, Div Interdisciplinary Studies & Res, 66-71, PROF ELEC ENG & ENG SCI, SCH ENG, STATE UNIV NY BUFFALO, 71- *Mem:* Inst Elec & Electronics Engrs. *Res:* Dynamics, stability and control of nuclear reactors and power plants. *Mailing Add:* Fac of Eng Sci & Elec Eng State Univ of NY Buffalo NY 14214

MARGOLIUS, HARRY STEPHEN, b Albany, NY, Jan 29, 38; m 64; c 2. CLINICAL PHARMACOLOGY. *Educ:* Union Univ, BS, 59; Albany Med Col, PhD(pharmacol), 63; Univ Cincinnati, MD, 68. *Prof Exp:* From intern to resident med, Harvard Med Serv II & IV, Boston City Hosp, 68-70; res assoc pharmacol, Exp Therapeut Br, Nat Heart & Lung Inst, 70-72, sr clin investr hypertension res, Hypertension-Endocrine Br, 72-74; asst prof med, 74-77, assoc prof, 77-80, assoc prof pharmacol, 74-77, PROF PHARMACOL, MED UNIV SC, 77-, PROF MED, 80-, PROG DIR, GEN CLIN RES CTR, 74- *Concurrent Pos:* Attend physician, Clin Ctr, NIH, 70-74; attend physician, Med Univ SC Hosp, Charleston County Hosp & Vet Admin Hosp, 74-; mem, Hypertension Task Force, Nat Heart & Lung Inst, 75-77; Nat Heart, Lung & Blood Inst res grant, 75-; mem, Cardiovasc & Renal Study Sect, Nat Heart & Lung Inst, 76-80; Burroughs-Wellcome scholar clin pharmacol, 76; mem med adv bd, Coun High Blood Pressure Res, Am Heart Asn; vis scholar, Univ Cambridge, 80-81. *Mem:* Am Soc Clin Invest; Am Fedn Clin Res; Am Soc Pharmacol & Exp Therapeut; Am Heart Asn; Am Soc Clin Pharmacol & Therapeut. *Res:* Studies of the glandular kallikrein-kinin system and its role in organ function and in cardiovascular and renal diseases using isolated cells tissues, whole animals and clinical investigation. *Mailing Add:* Dept Pharmacol Med Univ SC 171 Ashley Ave Charleston SC 29403

MARGON, BRUCE HENRY, b New York, NY, Jan 7, 48; m 76. ASTROPHYSICS. *Educ:* Columbia Univ, AB, 68; Univ Calif, Berkeley, MA, 71, PhD(astron), 73. *Prof Exp:* NATO fel astron, Univ Col, Univ London, 73-74; asst res astronomer, Univ Calif, Berkeley, 74-76; asst prof astron, Univ Calif, 76-78, assoc prof, 78-80; PROF & CHMN ASTRON, UNIV WASH, 80- *Concurrent Pos:* Alfred P Sloan Fel, 79-83. *Honors & Awards:* Pierce Prize, Am Astron Soc, 81. *Mem:* Am Astron Soc; Royal Astron Soc; Int Astron Union; Astron Soc Pac. *Res:* Extrasolar x-ray and ultraviolet astronomy; optical observations of x-ray sources. *Mailing Add:* Dept Astron FM-20 Univ Wash Seattle WA 98195

MARGOSHES, MARVIN, b New York, NY, May 23, 25; m 55; c 4. ANALYTICAL CHEMISTRY. *Educ:* Polytech Inst Brooklyn, BS, 51; Iowa State Col, PhD(phys chem), 53. *Prof Exp:* Asst, Inst Atomic Res, Iowa State Col, 50-53; res fel med, Harvard Med Sch, 54-56, res assoc, 56-57; res assoc spectrochem anal sect, Nat Bur Standards, 57-69; proj dir, Digilab Div, Block Eng, Inc, 69-70; TECH DIR, TECHNICON INSTRUMENT CORP, 71- *Concurrent Pos:* Ed, Atomic Spectra Sect, Spectrochimica Acta, 66-73. *Mem:* Am Chem Soc; Soc Appl Spectros (pres, 74); NY Acad Sci; Sigma Xi; Licensing Exec Soc. *Res:* Analytical spectroscopy; clinical chemistry. *Mailing Add:* Technicon Instrument Corp Tarrytown NY 10591

MARGRAVE, JOHN LEE, b Kansas City, Kans, Apr 13, 24; m 50; c 2. PHYSICAL INORGANIC CHEMISTRY, FLUORINE CHEMISTRY. *Educ:* Univ Kans, BS, 48, PhD(chem), 50. *Prof Exp:* Atomic Energy Comn fel, Univ Calif, 51-52; from instr to prof chem, Univ Wis, 52-63; chmn dept chem, 67-72, dean advan studies & res, 72-80, PROF CHEM, RICE UNIV, 63-, VPRES, 80- *Concurrent Pos:* Sloan res fel, 57-58; Guggenheim fel, 61; pres, Marchem, Inc, 70-; mem bd trustees, Ctr Res, Inc, Univ Kans, 71-75; consult, Nat Bur Standards, Argonne Nat Lab, Lawrence Radiation Lab, Oak Ridge Nat Lab, NASA & private indust; vpres bd dir, Rice Ctr for Community Design & Res, 72-; dir bd of dirs, Gulf Universities Res Consortium, 74-; ed, High Temp Sci, 69- *Honors & Awards:* IR 100 award, 70; Southwest Regional Award, Am Chem Soc, 73. *Mem:* Nat Acad Sci; AAAS; Am Phys Soc; Am Ceramic Soc; Am Chem Soc. *Res:* High temperature chemistry and thermodynamics; fluorine chemistry; optical and mass spectroscopy; synthetic inorganic, plasma and high pressure chemistry; ESCA. *Mailing Add:* Dept of Chem Rice Univ Houston TX 77001

MARGRAVE, THOMAS EWING, JR, b Langley Field, Va, Nov 15, 38; div; c 4. ASTRONOMY. *Educ:* Univ Notre Dame, BS, 61; Rensselaer Polytech Inst, MS, 63; Univ Ariz, PhD(astron), 67. *Prof Exp:* Physicist, US Naval Avionics Facil, 61; aerospace technologist, NASA Manned Spacecraft Ctr, 63; asst prof astron, Georgetown Univ, 67-69; asst prof, 69-73, assoc prof, 73-80, PROF ASTRON, UNIV MONT, 80- *Concurrent Pos:* NSF sci equip grants, Univ Mont, 70-72 & 75-77; Univ Mont Found res grants, 71-72, 73-75 & 78-81. *Mem:* Am Astron Soc; Astron Soc Pacific. *Res:* Photoelectric photometry of variable stars, ephemerides of eclipsing binary stars; frequency analysis of Delta Scuti variable stars. *Mailing Add:* Dept of Physics & Astron Univ of Mont Missoula MT 59812

MARGULIES, GABRIEL, b Bucharest, Rumania, Jan 4, 31; nat US; m 53; c 2. MATHEMATICS. *Educ:* Univ Paris, BA, 49, Sorbonne, CES, 50; Univ Wash, Seattle, BS, 53; Ind Univ, MA, 54, PhD(math, mech), 58. *Prof Exp:* Assoc math, Grad Inst Math & Mech, Ind Univ, 53-58; assoc prof, Fla State Univ, 58-59, res dir, Grad Ctr, Eglin AFB, 59-61; sr math specialist, Space Div, West Develop Labs, Philco Corp, 61-66; CONSULT SCIENTIST & SR MEM STAFF, LOCKHEED PALO ALTO RES LAB, LOCKHEED MISSILES & SPACE CO, 66- *Res:* Differential geometry; tensor analysis; analytical mechanics and dynamics; applied mathematics; gyrodynamics and rigid body mechanics; flexible spacecraft dynamics ; modern optimal control. *Mailing Add:* 1143 Maraschino Dr Sunnyvale CA 94087

MARGULIES, MAURICE, b Brooklyn, NY, Feb 9, 31; m 67; c 3. BIOCHEMISTRY, PLANT PHYSIOLOGY. *Educ:* Brooklyn Col, BA, 52; Yale Univ, MS, 53, PhD(microbiol), 57. *Prof Exp:* Res assoc biol, Haverford Col, 57; McCollum Pratt fel, Johns Hopkins Univ, 57-59; BIOCHEMIST, RADIATION BIOL LAB, SMITHSONIAN INST, 59- *Concurrent Pos:* Lectr, George Washington Univ, 64-67; res fel, Harvard Univ, 69-70. *Mem:* AAAS; Am Soc Plant Physiol; Am Soc Biol Chem; Am Soc Cell Biol; Am Chem Soc. *Res:* Chloroplast biochemistry-protein synthesis, synthesis of chloroplast membranes, photosynthesis, electron transport. *Mailing Add:* Radiation Biol Lab Smithsonian Inst 12441 Parklawn Rockville MD 20852

MARGULIES, SEYMOUR, b Jaslo, Poland, Oct 3, 33; US citizen; m 59; c 2. EXPERIMENTAL HIGH-ENERGY PHYSICS. *Educ:* Cooper Union, BEE, 55; Univ Ill, MS, 56, PhD(physics), 62. *Prof Exp:* Nat Acad Sci-Nat Res Coun res fel, Max Planck Inst Nuclear Physics, Ger, 61-63; res assoc nuclear & high energy physics, Nevis Labs, Columbia Univ, 63-65; asst prof, 65-69, ASSOC PROF HIGH-ENERGY PHYSICS, UNIV ILL, CHICAGO CIRCLE, 69- *Concurrent Pos:* Res grant, co-prin investr, NSF, 73- *Mem:* Am Phys Soc; Sigma Xi. *Res:* Mossbauer effect; nuclear spectroscopy; nuclear disintegrations following capture of negative pi-mesons; strong interactions of elementary particles, particularly multiparticle production; hadron jets and particle constituents; high transverse-momemtum reactions. *Mailing Add:* Dept of Physics Univ of Ill Chicago Circle Chicago IL 60680

MARGULIES, WILLIAM GEORGE, b New York, NY, Oct 31, 40; m 64; c 2. MATHEMATICS. *Educ:* State Univ NY Col Long Island, BS, 62; Brandeis Univ, MS, 64, PhD(math), 67. *Prof Exp:* Asst prof math, Wash Univ, 66-69; asst prof, 69-76, PROF MATH, CALIF STATE UNIV, LONG BEACH, 76- *Concurrent Pos:* NSF grant, 70-72. *Mem:* Math Asn Am; Am Math Soc; Soc Indust & Appl Math. *Res:* Analysis, partial differential equations; least action principle. *Mailing Add:* Dept of Math Calif State Univ Long Beach CA 90840

MARGULIS, ALEXANDER RAFAILO, b Belgrade, Yugoslavia, Mar 31, 21; nat US; m 46. RADIOLOGY. *Educ:* Harvard Med Sch, MD, 50. *Prof Exp:* Intern, Henry Ford Hosp, Detroit, 50-51; resident radiol, Univ Mich Hosps, 51-53; jr clin instr, Univ Mich, 53-54; from instr to asst prof radiol, Univ Minn, 54-57; vis assoc, Duke Univ, 58-59; from asst prof to prof, Mallinckrodt Inst Radiol, Sch Med, Wash Univ, 59-63; PROF RADIOL & CHMN DEPT, UNIV CALIF, SAN FRANCISCO, 63- *Concurrent Pos:* Mem comt radiol, Nat Acad Sci-Nat Res Coun, 64-; consult, Off Surgeon Gen, 67-71, Vet Admin Hosp, Ft Miley & Letterman Gen Hosp, San Francisco & Oak Knoll Naval Hosp, Oakland. *Honors & Awards:* Medaille Antoine Beclere, France, 78. *Mem:* AMA; fel Am Col Radiol; Am Roentgen Ray Soc; Asn Univ Radiol (past pres); Soc Gastrointestinal Radiol (pres, 72). *Res:* Gastroenterology and arteriography. *Mailing Add:* Dept of Radiol Univ of Calif San Francisco CA 94143

MARGULIS, LYNN, b Chicago, Ill, Mar 5, 38; m 57, 67; c 4. CELL BIOLOGY, MICROBIAL EVOLUTION. *Educ:* Univ Chicago, AB, 57; Univ Wis, MS, 60; Univ Calif, Berkeley, PhD(genetics), 65. *Prof Exp:* Lectr & res assoc biol, Brandeis Univ, 63-64; from asst prof to assoc prof, 66-77, PROF BIOL, BOSTON UNIV, 77- *Concurrent Pos:* Sherman Fairchild Distinguished fel, Calif Inst Technol, 77; Guggenheim fel, 79. *Honors & Awards:* Dimond Award, Bot Soc Am, 75. *Mem:* Soc Protozool; Am Inst Biol Sci; Am Soc Cell Biol; Am Soc Microbiol; fel AAAS. *Res:* Origin and evolution of cells; cytoplasmic genetics; microtubules and kinetosomes; evolution of biochemical pathways; morphogenesis in protists; spirochetes of termites. *Mailing Add:* Dept Biol Boston Univ Boston MA 02215

MARGULIS, THOMAS N, b New York, NY, Sept 7, 37. STRUCTURAL CHEMISTRY. *Educ:* Mass Inst Technol, BS, 59; Univ Calif, Berkeley, PhD(chem), 62. *Prof Exp:* Asst prof chem, Brandeis Univ, 62-67; assoc prof, 67-75, PROF CHEM, UNIV MASS, BOSTON, 75- *Mem:* Am Crystallog Asn; Am Chem Soc. *Res:* Crystal and molecular structure by x-ray diffraction; small ring compounds; structural chemistry of drugs. *Mailing Add:* Dept of Chem Univ of Mass Boston MA 02125

MARIA, NARENDRA LAL, b Chamba, India, Apr 22, 28; m 57; c 1. APPLIED MATHEMATICS. *Educ:* Panjab Univ, India, BA, 48, MA, 49; Univ Calif, Berkeley, PhD(appl Math), 68. *Prof Exp:* Lectr math, Panjab Univ, India, 50-51, sr lectr, 51-59, asst prof, 59-65; teaching assoc, Univ Calif, Berkeley, 65-67; vis lectr, 67-68, assoc prof, 68-70, PROF MATH, STANISLAUS STATE COL, 70-, CHMN DEPT, 70- *Mem:* Am Math Soc. *Res:* Partial differential equations; analysis. *Mailing Add:* Dept of Math Stanislaus State Col Turlock CA 95350

MARIAN, JOSEF ERIC, chemical & microbiological engineering, deceased

MARIANELLI, ROBERT SILVIO, b Wilmington, Del, Dec 17, 41; m 61; c 2. INORGANIC CHEMISTRY. *Educ:* Univ Del, BA, 63; Univ Calif, Berkeley, PhD(chem), 66. *Prof Exp:* Asst prof chem, Univ Nebr, Lincoln, 66-71, assoc prof, 71-80; MEM STAFF, DIV CHEM SCI, OFF BASIC ENERGY, DEPT ENERGY, 80- *Concurrent Pos:* Staff mem, Div Chem Sci, Dept Energy, 77-79. *Mem:* AAAS; Am Chem Soc; Royal Soc Chem. *Res:* The chemistry of metalloporphyrins and related compounds. *Mailing Add:* Div Chem Sci Off Basic Energy Dept Energy Washington DC 20545

MARIANI, HENRY A, b Medford, Mass, Sept 13, 24. BIOCHEMISTRY, PHYSICAL CHEMISTRY. *Educ:* Boston Col, AB, 47, Tufts Univ, MS, 49; Boston Col, PhD, 81. *Prof Exp:* Instr chem, St Anselm's Col, 49-50; asst prof org chem & biochem, Merrimack Col, 52-60; chmn dept sci, Medford Pub Schs, Mass, 60-62; ASSOC PROF BIOCHEM & PHYS CHEM, BOSTON STATE COL, 62- *Mem:* AAAS; Am Chem Soc. *Res:* Cell membranes and transport-photosynthesis; electro-organic fluorination of aromatic polycyclics, application to chemical carcinogenesis. *Mailing Add:* Dept of Chem Boston State Col Boston MA 02115

MARIANO, PATRICK S, b Passaic, NJ, Aug 31, 42. CHEMISTRY. *Educ:* Fairleigh Dickinson Univ, BSc, 64; Univ Wis, PhD(chem), 69. *Prof Exp:* NIH fel, Yale Univ, 68-70; asst prof, 70-77, ASSOC PROF CHEM, TEX A&M UNIV, 77- *Mem:* Am Chem Soc; The Chem Soc. *Res:* Organic chemistry; photochemistry; synthetic chemistry. *Mailing Add:* Dept of Chem Tex A&M Univ College Station TX 77843

MARIANOWSKI, LEONARD GEORGE, b Hammond, Ind, Oct 31, 35; m 59; c 4. CHEMICAL ENGINEERING, ELECTROCHEMISTRY. *Educ:* Purdue Univ, BS, 57, MS, 59. *Prof Exp:* Process engr, Commercial Solvents Corp, 59-60, chem engr, 60-65, supvr, 65-70, mgr, 70-76, asst dir, 76-78; ASSOC DIR ENERGY CONVERSION, & STORAGE RES, INST GAS TECHNOL, 78- *Mem:* Am Chem Soc; Am Inst Chem Engrs; Electrochem Soc. *Res:* Direct energy conversion processes for electricity production; fuel cells, using molten carbonate electrolytes. *Mailing Add:* 3424 S State St Chicago IL 60616

MARICICH, TOM JOHN, b Anacortes, Wash, Dec 20, 38; m 64; c 3. ORGANIC CHEMISTRY. *Educ:* Univ Wash, BS, 61; Yale Univ, MS, 63, PhD(chem), 65. *Prof Exp:* Chemist, Shell Develop Co, Calif, 65-67; asst prof org chem, N Dak State Univ, 67-70, assoc prof, 70-75; asst prof, 75-79, ASSOC PROF CHEM, CALIF STATE UNIV, LONG BEACH, 79- *Mem:* Am Chem Soc. *Res:* Reactive organic intermediates, nitrenes; sulfur-nitrogen functional groups and heterocycles; synthesis of antitumor agents. *Mailing Add:* Dept Chem Calif State Univ Long Beach CA 90840

MARICONDI, CHRIS, b Oct 13, 41; US citizen; m 70. INORGANIC CHEMISTRY. *Educ:* WVa Univ, AB, 64; Univ Pittsburgh, PhD(chem), 69. *Prof Exp:* Asst prof, 69-75, ASSOC PROF CHEM, PA STATE UNIV, McKEESPORT, 75- *Mem:* Am Chem Soc. *Res:* Molecular structure. *Mailing Add:* Dept of Chem Pa State Univ McKeesport PA 15132

MARICQ, HILDEGARD RAND, b Rakvere, Estonia, Apr 23, 25; US citizen; m 48; c 3. MEDICINE, HEALTH SCIENCES. *Educ:* Free Univ Brussels, Cand, 49, MD, 53. *Prof Exp:* Intern, Jersey City Med Ctr, 55-56; resident psychiat, Essex County Overbrook Hosp, Cedar Grove, NJ, 57-61; resident, Vet Admin Hosp, Lyons, NJ, 61-62, res assoc, 62-63, clin investr, 63-65, dir microcirc lab, 67-69, sr psychiatrist, 67-73, dir schizophrenia res sect, 69-73; res assoc dept med, Col Physicians & Surgeons, Columbia Univ, 73-75; assoc prof, 75-81, PROF RES MED, MED UNIV SC, 81- *Concurrent Pos:* Res fel psychiat, Col Physicians & Surgeons, Columbia Univ, 65-67; res assoc, Dept Psychiat, Rutgers Med Sch, 67-71, res asst prof, 71-73. *Mem:* AAAS; Am Soc Human Genetics; Am Physiol Soc; Microcirc Soc; Soc Psychophysiol Res. *Res:* Somatic research in schizophrenia; microcirculation; human genetics; psychophysiology; microcirculation in connective tissue diseases; peripheral circulation. *Mailing Add:* Dept of Med Med Univ of SC Charleston SC 29403

MARICQ, JOHN, b Anderlecht, Belg, Sept 14, 22; US citizen; m 48; c 3. ORGANIC CHEMISTRY, MEDICAL ELECTRONICS. *Educ:* Free Univ Brussels, Lic en Sc, 48, Dr en Sc, 51. *Prof Exp:* Res chemist, Pharmaceut Div, Belgian Union Chem, 50-54; sr chemist, Hoffmann-La Roche, Inc, 54-74, tech fel, Tech Develop Dept, 74-77; RETIRED. *Concurrent Pos:* Adj asst prof med, Med Univ SC, 80- *Mem:* Am Chem Soc. *Res:* Synthetic organic chemistry; research and development of new drugs, vitamins, carotenoids and aromatics; medical electronics. *Mailing Add:* 728 Jim Isle Dr Battery Point Charleston SC 29412

MARIEB, ELAINE NICPON, b Northhampton, Mass, Apr 5, 36; m 58; c 2. ANATOMY, PHYSIOLOGY. *Educ:* Westfield State Col, BSEd, 64; Mt Holyoke Col, MA, 66; Univ Mass, Amherst, PhD(cell biol), 69. *Prof Exp:* Instr zool, anat, physiol & embryol, Springfield Col, 66-67; from asst prof to assoc prof, 69-78, PROF BOT, ANAT & PHYSIOL, HOLYOKE COMMUNITY COL, 78-, PROF BIOL, 81- *Mem:* AAAS; Am Soc Zool; Sigma Xi. *Res:* Kinetic studies on the synthesis of sRNA in yeast; species and tissue variations in transfer RNA populations. *Mailing Add:* Dept of Biol Holyoke Community Col Holyoke MA 01040

MARIELLA, RAYMOND PEEL, b Philadelphia, Pa, Sept 5, 19; m 43; c 4. ORGANIC CHEMISTRY. *Educ:* Univ Pa, BS, 41; Carnegie Inst Technol, MS, 42, DSc(org chem), 45. *Prof Exp:* Asst, Carnegie Inst Technol, 41-44, instr, 44, res chemist, 44-45; Eli Lilly & Co fel, Univ Wis, 45-46; from instr to asst prof chem, Northwestern Univ, 46-51; from assoc prof to prof chem, Loyola Univ Chicago, 51-77, chmn dept, 51-70, dean grad sch, 69-77; EXEC DIR, AM CHEM SOC, 77- *Concurrent Pos:* Mem, Gov Sci Adv Coun, Ill; exec comt, Coun Grad Schs, 71-74; exec comt mem, Midwestern Asn Grad Schs, 72-77; ed, annual Proc, Midwestern Asn Grad Schs, 72-77; assoc vpres res, Loyola Univ, Chicago, 74-77. *Mem:* AAAS; Am Chem Soc. *Res:* Synthesis of new pyridine compounds; hyperconjugations; ultraviolet absorption spectra; small ring synthesis; synthesis of carcinolytic substances. *Mailing Add:* Am Chem Soc 1155 16th St NW Washington DC 20036

MARIELLA, RAYMOND PEEL, JR, b Evanston, Ill, July 12, 47. SEMICONDUCTOR SURFACE CHEMISTRY. *Educ:* Rice Univ, BA, 69; Harvard Univ, AM, 70, PhD(phys chem), 73. *Prof Exp:* Vis scientist, Dept Physics, Mass Inst Technol, 73-75; lectr, Dept Chem, Harvard Univ, 75-76; domestic fel, IBM Res Labs, 76-77; staff chem physicist, 77-79, SR RES CHEMIST, MAT RES CTR, ALLIED CORP, 79- *Mem:* Am Chem Soc; AAAS. *Res:* Laser induced chemistry; gas-surface reactions with particular interest in chemical modification of semiconductor surfaces. *Mailing Add:* Allied Corp Mat Res Ctr PO Box 1021R Morristown NJ 07960

MARIEN, DANIEL, b New York, NY, Aug 19, 25; m 59; c 3. GENETICS, ZOOLOGY. *Educ:* Cornell Univ, BS, 49; Columbia Univ, MA, 51, PhD, 56. *Prof Exp:* From instr to assoc prof, 53-70, PROF BIOL, QUEENS COL, NY, 70- *Res:* Population genetics and evolution. *Mailing Add:* Dept of Biol Queens Col Flushing NY 11367

MARIENFELD, CARL J, b Chicago, Ill, July 11, 17; m 43; c 4. PEDIATRICS, PREVENTIVE MEDICINE. *Educ:* Lake Forest Col, BA, 38; Univ Ill, MD, 43; Johns Hopkins Univ, MPH, 60; Am Bd Pediat, dipl, 50. *Prof Exp:* Resident pediat, Cook County Hosp, Chicago, Ill, 43-45; from instr to assoc prof pediat, Col Med, Univ Ill, 47-57; dir, Maternal & Child Health & Crippled Children's Serv, Mo Div Health, 75-76; dir interdiv health related res, 65-68, PROF COMMUNITY HEALTH & MED PRACT, SCH MED, UNIV MO-COLUMBIA, 61-, PROF PEDIAT, 74-, DIR, ENVIRON HEALTH SURVEILLANCE CTR, 68- *Concurrent Pos:* USPHS fel cardiol, Univ Ill, 48-49; assoc dir, Children's Heart Sta, Cook County Hosp, 52-57; consult, USPHS, 62-, mem, Dis Control Study Sect, 64-68; chmn subcomt young cardiac, Am Heart Asn, 64-; partic, White House Conf Health, 65; mem ment retardation res & training comt, Nat Inst Child Health & Human Develop, 67-71; mem subcomt geochem & health, Nat Acad Sci, 70-72. *Mem:* AAAS; Sigma Xi; Am Fedn Clin Res; Am Orthop Asn; Soc Geochem & Health. *Res:* Chronic disease epidemiology; rheumatic fever etiology and clinical management; carcinogenesis; environmental health and comparative medicine; trace substances in health research. *Mailing Add:* Rt 1 Ashland MO 65010

MARIER, GUY, b Que, Sept 6, 20; m 49; c 3. PHARMACOLOGY. *Educ:* Sem of Que, Can, BA, 40; Laval Univ, BSc, 44, PhD(pharmacol), 47. *Prof Exp:* Res scientist & supt, Northern Labs, Defence Res Bd, Can, 47-56; dir sci dept, Poulenc, Ltd, 56-67; VPRES, BIO-RES LABS LTD, 67- *Concurrent Pos:* Consult, Life Sci. *Mem:* Can Pharmacol Soc; Can Fedn Biol Soc; Can Soc Chemother; Can Asn Res Toxicol (pres). *Res:* Pharmaceuticals and biologicals; toxicology; pharmacokinetics; liaison with government agencies. *Mailing Add:* 2380 Charles-Gill Montreal PQ H3M 1V7 Can

MARIK, JAN, b Ungvar, USSR, Nov 12, 20; m 48; c 1. MATHEMATICAL ANALYSIS. *Educ:* Univ Prague, RNDr(math), 49. *Prof Exp:* Asst math, Prague Tech Univ, 48-50; grant, Czech Acad Sci, 50-52, sci worker, 52-53; asst, Prague Univ, 53-56, docent, 56-60, prof, 60-69; vis prof, 69-70, PROF MATH, MICH STATE UNIV, 70- *Res:* Surface integral and non-absolute convergent integrals in Euclidean spaces; representation of functionals by integrals; oscillatory properties of differential equations of second order. *Mailing Add:* Dept of Math Mich State Univ East Lansing MI 48824

MARIMONT, ROSALIND BROWNSTONE, b New York, NY, Feb 3, 21; m 51; c 2. APPLIED MATHEMATICS. *Educ:* Hunter Col, BA, 42. *Prof Exp:* Physicist electronics, Nat Bur Stand, 42-51, electronic scientist digital comput design, 51-60; mathematician, NIH, 60-79. *Mem:* AAAS; Am Women Math; Classification Soc. *Res:* Applications of linear algebra to biological problems including compartmental analysis and classification schemes; mathematical modeling of biological systems, particularly human visual and auditory systems; applications of high level computer language to development of mathematical models of biological systems; statistical analysis of employment with regard to sex or race discrimination. *Mailing Add:* 11512 Yates St Wheaton MD 20902

MARIN, MIGUEL ANGEL, b Seville, Spain, Dec 26, 38; m 79; c 5. COMPUTER ENGINEERING, DATA PROCESSING. *Educ:* Univ Madrid, Licenciado, 63, DSc(phys sci), 69; Univ Calif, Los Angeles, PhD(eng), 68. *Prof Exp:* Asst prof elec eng, McGill Univ, 68-72; vpres, Assyst Assocs Ltd, 69-71; MGR, HARDWARE & SOFTWARE, EDP PLANNING, HYDRO-QUEBEC, 77- *Concurrent Pos:* Nat Res Coun Can fel, McGill Univ, 68-71; design engr, Cent Dynamics, Que, 69; comput scientist, Philips Data Systs, Holland, 71-72; mgr sci appln, Hydro-Quebec, 72-77; auxiliary prof, McGill Univ, 72-; adj prof, Concordia Univ, 78- *Mem:* Inst Elec & Electronics Engrs; Asn Comput Mach. *Res:* Computer systems engineering; logic design of digital systems; computer applications to power utilities, instruction and to computer design. *Mailing Add:* PO Box 631 Succ Desjardins Montreal PQ H5B 1B7 Can

MARINACCIO, PAUL J, b Bridgeport, Conn, May 30, 37; m 59; c 3. POLYMER CHEMISTRY, PHYSICAL CHEMISTRY. *Educ:* Fairfield Univ, BS, 59; Purdue Univ, MS, 61. *Prof Exp:* Res chemist, Rexall Chem Co, 61-64, supvr additives, 64-67; sr chemist, 67-70, mgr plastics eng, 70-78, DIR PLASTICS ENG, AMF INC, 78- *Mem:* Am Chem Soc; Am Mgt Asn; Indust Res Inst; Soc Plastics Engrs; Soc Advan Mat & Process Eng. *Res:* Membranes; stereospecific polymer catalysts; polymer additives; composites. *Mailing Add:* AMF Inc 689 Hope St Stamford CT 06907

MARINE, IRA WENDELL, b Washington, DC, Apr 15, 27; m 53; c 4. GEOLOGY, HYDROLOGY. *Educ:* St John's Col, Md, BA, 49; Univ Utah, PhD(geol), 60. *Prof Exp:* Geologist, US Geol Surv, 51-71; RES ASSOC, E I DU PONT DE NEMOURS & CO, INC, 71- *Concurrent Pos:* Teaching assoc, Univ SC. *Mem:* Geol Soc Am; Am Asn Petrol Geol; Am Geophys Union; Am Water Well Asn; Seismol Soc Am. *Res:* Ground water geology and hydrology. *Mailing Add:* 1002 Hitchcock Dr Aiken SC 29801

MARINE, WILLIAM MURPHY, b Cleveland, Ohio, Oct 21, 32; c 4. PREVENTIVE MEDICINE, INTERNAL MEDICINE. *Educ:* Emory Univ, BA, 53, MD, 57; Univ Mich, MPH, 63; Am Bd Internal Med, dipl, 65. *Prof Exp:* From intern to resident med, NY Hosp-Cornell Med Ctr, 57-59; mem staff, Epidemic Intel Serv Kansas City Field Sta, 59-61; resident med, Grady Mem Hosp, Atlanta, Ga, 61-62; trainee epidemiol, Univ Mich, 62-64; from asst prof to assoc prof prev med, Sch Med, Emory Univ, 64-70, prof prev med & community health, 70-75; PROF & CHMN DEPT PREV MED & COMPREHENSIVE HEALTH CARE, UNIV COLO MED CTR, 75- *Concurrent Pos:* Milbank Mem Fund fac fel, 65; med consult, Southeastern Region, Job Corps, 73- *Mem:* Am Epidemiol Soc; AMA; Am Fedn Clin Res; Am Pub Health Asn; Asn Teachers Prev Med (secy-treas, 74). *Res:* Epidemiology and immunology of respiratory virus infections, especially influenza; evaluation of health care delivery. *Mailing Add:* Dept Prev Med Univ Colo Med Ctr 4200 E Ninth Ave C245 Denver CO 80262

MARINELARENA, RAFAEL, bacteriology, see previous edition

MARINETTI, GUIDO V, b Rochester, NY, June 26, 18; m 42; c 2. BIOCHEMISTRY. *Educ:* Univ Rochester, BS, 50, PhD(biochem), 53. *Prof Exp:* Res biochemist, West Regional Res Lab, USDA, 53-54; from instr to assoc prof, 54-66, PROF BIOCHEM, SCH MED & DENT, UNIV ROCHESTER, 66- *Concurrent Pos:* Lederle med fac award, 55-56; Nat Heart Inst & Nat Sci Found grants, 55- *Mem:* AAAS; Am Chem Soc; Sigma Xi; Am Soc Biol Chem. *Res:* biosynthesis of phosphatides and neutral glycerides and regulatory or control mechanisms in this process; the topology and function of phospholinids in cellular membranes; catecholamine receptors on cell membranes. *Mailing Add:* Dept of Biochem Univ of Rochester Med Ctr Rochester NY 14642

MARINO, ANDREW ANTHONY, biophysics, see previous edition

MARINO, JOSEPH PAUL, b Hazleton, Pa, Apr 20, 42; m 67; c 3. ORGANIC CHEMISTRY. *Educ:* Pa State Univ, BS, 63; Harvard Univ, AM, 65, PhD(chem), 67. *Prof Exp:* NIH fel, Harvard Univ, 67-69; asst prof, 69-75, ASSOC PROF CHEM, UNIV MICH, ANN ARBOR, 75- *Mem:* Am Chem Soc. *Res:* Sulfur chemistry; ylides; synthesis of natural products; organometallic chemistry. *Mailing Add:* Dept of Chem Univ of Mich Ann Arbor MI 48109

MARINO, LAWRENCE LOUIS, b Belleville, Ill, Nov 1, 30; m 53; c 3. HYDRODYNAMICS, NUCLEAR PHYSICS. *Educ:* Purdue Univ, BS, 52; Univ Calif, MA, 58, PhD, 59. *Prof Exp:* Systs analyst, NAm Aviation, Inc, 55; asst, Univ Calif, 57-59; staff scientist, Gen Dynamics/Convair, 59-66; physicist, Lawrence Livermore Lab, Univ Calif, 66-82; PHYSICIST, LOS ALAMOS NAT LAB, 82- *Mem:* AAAS; Am Phys Soc. *Res:* Atomic and molecular beams; nuclear moments; atomic collisions; hydrodynamics; nuclear and plasma physics. *Mailing Add:* Los Alamos Nat Lab Los Alamos NM 87545

MARINO, MARYANN SANDRA ENGSTER, cell biology, electron microscopy, see previous edition

MARINO, PASQUALE, chemical & mechanical engineering, see previous edition

MARINO, ROBERT ANTHONY, b Positano, Italy, Feb 19, 43; US citizen; m 67; c 1. PHYSICS. *Educ:* City Col York, BS, 64; Brown Univ, PhD(physics), 69. *Prof Exp:* Res assoc physics, Brown Univ, 69-70; asst prof, 70-76, ASSOC PROF, PHYSICS, HUNTER COL, CITY UNIV NEW YORK, 76- *Concurrent Pos:* Consult, US Army Res Off, 70- *Mem:* Am Phys Soc; Am Asn Physics Teachers. *Res:* Nitrogen-14 nuclear quadrupole resonance; hydrogen bond studies. *Mailing Add:* Dept of Physics Hunter Col 695 Park Ave New York NY 10021

MARINOS, PETE NICK, b Sparta, Greece, July 9, 35; US citizen; m 68. COMPUTER SCIENCE, SYSTEMS ENGINEERING. *Educ:* Clemson Univ, BSEE, 59, MSEE, 61; NC State Univ, PhD(elec eng), 64. *Prof Exp:* Electronic engr, Lockheed-Georgia Co, 59; instr elec eng, Clemson Univ, 59-61, asst prof, 64-66; instr, NC State Univ, 61-64; assoc prof, Univ Ala, Huntsville, 66-68; assoc prof, 68-72, PROF ELEC ENG, DUKE UNIV, 72- *Concurrent Pos:* Consult, Southern Bell Tel Co, 64-66, US Army Missile Command, 67-68, Chrysler Corp, 68 & US Naval Res Lab, 71- *Mem:* Inst Elec & Electronics Engrs; Simulation Coun. *Res:* Switching, automata and systems theory. *Mailing Add:* Dept of Elec Eng Duke Univ Durham NC 27706

MARIN-PADILLA, MIGUEL, b Jumilla, Spain, July 9, 30; nat US; m 58; c 2. PATHOLOGY. *Educ:* Univ Granada, BS, 49, MD, 55; Educ Coun Foreign Med Grads, cert, 60; Am Bd Path, dipl & cert anat path, 65. *Prof Exp:* Teaching fel path, Sch Med, Boston Univ, 60-62 & Harvard Med Sch, 61-62; from instr to assoc prof, 62-75, PROF PATH, DARTMOUTH MED SCH, 75- *Concurrent Pos:* Consult, Vet Admin Hosp, White River Junction, Vt, 64- *Mem:* Teratol Soc; Am Asn Anat; Soc Neurosci. *Res:* Development pathology; neurohistology; human and experimental teratology. *Mailing Add:* Dept of Path Dartmouth Med Sch Hanover NH 03755

MARINUS, MARTIN GERARD, b Amsterdam, Neth, June 22, 44; m 70; c 3. MICROBIAL GENETICS. *Educ:* Univ Otago, NZ, BSc, 65, PhD(microbiol), 68. *Prof Exp:* Fel microbiol, Yale Univ, 68-70; vis fel microbiol, Free Univ, Amsterdam, Neth, 70-71; instr pharmacol, Col Med & Dent NJ, Rutgers Med Sch, 71-74; asst prof, 74-77, ASSOC PROF PHARMACOL, MED SCH, UNIV MASS, 77- *Concurrent Pos:* Fac res award, Am Cancer Soc, 76-81. *Mem:* Am Soc Microbiol. *Res:* Function of methylated bases in nucleic acids. *Mailing Add:* Dept Pharmacol Med Sch Univ Mass 55 Lake Ave N Worcester MA 01605

MARION, ALEXANDER PETER, b New York, NY, Apr 24, 15; m 43. PHYSICAL CHEMISTRY. *Educ:* City Col New York, BS, 36, MS, 39; NY Univ, PhD(chem), 44. *Prof Exp:* Lectr asst, 37-41, tutor, 41-43, from instr to prof, 43-76, EMER PROF CHEM, QUEENS COL, NY, 76- *Concurrent Pos:* Designer, Microchem Serv, 42-48. *Mem:* AAAS; Am Chem Soc. *Res:* Chemical kinetics; teaching aids; electronic laboratory apparatus. *Mailing Add:* 19 Highland Pl Great Neck NY 11020

MARION, C(HARLES) P(ARKER), b Montclair, NJ, Jan 22, 20; m 43; c 2. CHEMICAL ENGINEERING. *Educ:* Univ Calif, Los Angeles, BS, 47; Mass Inst Technol, ScD(chem eng), 52. *Prof Exp:* Chem engr, Montebello Res Lab, Texaco, Inc, 52-58, res chem engr, 59-61, sr res chem engr, 61-62, process rep, 62-67, sr process rep, 67-79, asst mgr process licensing, 79-80, MGR PROCESS LICENSING, TEXACO DEVELOP CORP, 80- *Mem:* Fel Am Inst Chem; Am Inst Chem Engrs; AAAS. *Res:* Process development and design, particularly combustion and heat transfer; synthesis-gas-generation process; coal gasification. *Mailing Add:* 655 Shore Acres Dr Mamaroneck NY 10543

MARION, JAMES EDSEL, b Cana, Va, May 30, 35; m 57; c 2. FOOD SCIENCE, NUTRITION. *Educ:* Berea Col, BS, 57; Univ Ky, MS, 59; Univ Ga, PhD(nutrit), 62. *Prof Exp:* Res asst poultry nutrit, Univ Ky, 57-59; res asst poultry nutrit, Univ Ga, 59-62, asst food technologist, Ga Exp Sta, 62-67, assoc food scientist & head food sci dept, 67-69; asst dir res, 69-72, DIR RES, GOLD KIST RES CTR, 72- *Mem:* AAAS; Am Inst Nutrit; Inst Food Technol; Oil Chem Soc; Poultry Sci Asn. *Res:* Feed and nutrition; plant breeding; product development. *Mailing Add:* Gold Kist Res Ctr 2230 Industrial Blvd Lithonia GA 30058

MARION, JERRY BASKERVILLE, b Mobile, Ala, Dec 19, 29; m 52; c 2. NUCLEAR PHYSICS. *Educ:* Reed Col, BA, 52; Rice Univ, MA, 53, PhD(physics), 55. *Prof Exp:* NSF fel, Calif Inst Technol, 55-56; instr physics, Univ Rochester, 56-57; physicist, Los Alamos Sci Lab, Univ Calif, 57; PROF PHYSICS, UNIV MD, COLLEGE PARK, 57- *Concurrent Pos:* Sr staff scientist, Convair Div, Gen Dynamics Corp, Calif, 60-61; Guggenheim fel, Calif Inst Technol, 65-66; consult, Oak Ridge Nat Lab, 58-70; Grumman Aircraft Eng Co, 62-67; mem nuclear data group, Nat Acad Sci, 57-61; subcomt nuclear struct, Nat Acad Sci-Nat Res Coun, 59-69. *Mem:* Fel Am Phys Soc; AAAS. *Res:* Experimental low-energy nuclear physics; physical education; theory of nuclear structure and reactions. *Mailing Add:* Dept of Physics & Astron Univ of Md College Park MD 20472

MARION, ROBERT HOWARD, b Paterson, NJ, Dec 10, 45; m 71; c 2. MATERIALS SCIENCE, CERAMICS. *Educ:* Stevens Inst Technol, BEng, 67; Northwestern Univ, Evanston, PhD(mat sci), 72. *Prof Exp:* mem tech staff mat sci, Sandia Labs, Albuquerque, NMex, 72-80; MGR PROCESS TECHNOL, CORP RES LAB, AVX CERAMICS CORP, 80- *Mem:* Am Soc Metals; Am Ceramic Soc. *Res:* Structure-property relationships in ceramics and glasses; mechanical properties, fracture, high temperature mechanical testing, nuclear fuels for pulsed reactors, thermal stress resistance, residual stress measurement. *Mailing Add:* AVX Ceramics Corp Corp Res Lab Box 867 Myrtle Beach SC 29577

MARION, WILLIAM W, b Hillsville, Va, Feb 3, 30; m 54; c 4. FOOD SCIENCE. *Educ:* Berea Col, BS, 53; Purdue Univ, MS, 55, PhD(food technol), 58. *Prof Exp:* Instr poultry husb, Purdue Univ, 55-58; from asst prof to prof animal sci, 58-74, chmn dept poultry sci, 68-71, PROF FOOD TECHNOL & HEAD DEPT, IOWA STATE UNIV, 74- *Mem:* Inst Food Technol; Am Oil Chem Soc; Poultry Sci Asn; Am Inst Nutrit. *Res:* Structure and composition of muscle lipids; post-mortem biochemical changes in muscle. *Mailing Add:* Dept Food Technol Iowa State Univ Ames IA 50011

MARIS, HUMPHREY JOHN, b Ipswich, Eng, Apr 25, 39. SOLID STATE PHYSICS. *Educ:* Imp Col, Univ London, BSc, 60, PhD(physics), 63. *Prof Exp:* Fel physics, Case Inst Cleveland, 63-65; from asst prof to assoc prof, 65-76, PROF PHYSICS, BROWN UNIV, 76- *Concurrent Pos:* Vis fel, Univ EAnglia, 72-73, Chalmers Inst, 73, & Nat Ctr Sci Res, Grenoble, France, 73. *Mem:* Am Phys Soc. *Res:* Low temperature physics; ultrasonics; lattice dynamics. *Mailing Add:* Dept of Physics Brown Univ Providence RI 02912

MARISCAL, RICHARD NORTH, b Los Angeles, Calif, Oct 4, 35; m 74; c 3. MARINE BIOLOGY, INVERTEBRATE ZOOLOGY. *Educ:* Stanford Univ, AB, 57, MA, 61; Univ Calif, Berkeley, PhD(zool), 66. *Prof Exp:* Asst entom, Univ Calif, Berkeley, 60-61, asst zool, 61-64, lectr, 66; fac asst, Te Vega & Int Indian Ocean Expeds, Hopkins Marine Sta, Stanford Univ, 64-65; NIH fel, Lab Quant Biol, Univ Miami, 67-68; asst prof, 68-72, assoc prof, 72-78, PROF BIOL SCI, FLA STATE UNIV, 78- *Mem:* AAAS; Am Soc Zool; Ecol Soc Am; Asn Trop Biol; Am Inst Biol Sci; NY Acad Sci. *Res:* Morphology and ecology of the entoprocta; coelenterate nematocyst physiology, biochemistry and morphology; symbiosis between sea anemones, fishes and crustaceans; chemical control of feeding in corals and other coelenterates; invertebrate behavior, ecology and electron microscopy. *Mailing Add:* Dept of Biol Sci Fla State Univ Tallahassee FL 32306

MARISKA, JOHN THOMAS, b Fairbanks, Alaska, Feb 25, 50; m 72; c 1. ASTROPHYSICS, ASTRONOMY. *Educ:* Univ Colo, BA, 72; Harvard Univ, AM, 73, PhD(astron), 77. *Prof Exp:* resident res assoc space sci, 77-79, res physicist, 79-81, ASTROPHYSICIST, E O HULBURT CTR SPACE RES, NAVAL RES LAB, 81- *Mem:* AAAS; Am Astron Soc; Am Geophys Union. *Res:* Solar and stellar physics; structure of the solar corona; extreme ultraviolet spectroscopy. *Mailing Add:* Code 4175M Naval Res Lab Washington DC 20375

MARK, A(LEXANDER) H(ING), b Toronto, Ont, Sept 11, 24; nat US; m 47; c 3. MECHANICS. *Educ:* Univ Toronto, BASc, 46; Purdue Univ, MSME, 47, PhD(fluid mech), 51. *Prof Exp:* Res & develop engr, Massey-Harris Co, Ltd, 51-53, proj engr, 53-55, chief engr adv design, Massey-Ferguson, Inc, Mich, 55-60, chief engr res & adv eng, 60-67; mgr eng farm equip div, Allis-Chalmers Mfg Corp, Wis, 67-69; asst to vpres eng, Rockwell-Standards Co, 69-71, dir eng oper, Rockwell-Standard Div, N Am Rockwell Corp, 71-73, dir bus develop, Automotive Opers, Rockwell Int Corp, 73-77; DIR DEVELOP TRUCK COMPONENTS GROUP, EATON CORP, 77- *Honors & Awards:* Award, Am Soc Agr Engrs, 71 & 72. *Mem:* Soc Automotive Engrs; Am Soc Agr Engrs; Am Mgt Asn. *Res:* Development of transmissions and axles for mobile equipment and heavy duty trucks. *Mailing Add:* 100 Erieview Plaza Cleveland OH 44114

MARK, DANIEL LEE, parasitology, nematology, see previous edition

MARK, EARL LARRY, b Ogden, Utah, Dec 13, 40; m 62; c 4. PHYSICAL CHEMISTRY. *Educ:* Weber State Col, BS, 65; Univ Idaho, PhD(phys chem), 70. *Prof Exp:* Res chemist, Amalgamated Sugar Co, 70-73; dir res, Water Refining Co, 73-74; PROD MGR, BLACK CLAWSON CO, 74- *Mem:* Am Chem Soc; Filtration Soc; Am Soc Testing & Mats. *Res:* Ion exchange; surface adsorption; use of radiotracers in adsorption studies; activated carbon adsorption; liquid-solid separation; liquid filtration. *Mailing Add:* 8716 Meadowlark Franklin OH 45005

MARK, HANS MICHAEL, b Mannheim, Ger, June 17, 29; nat US; m 51; c 2. PHYSICS. *Educ:* Univ Calif, AB, 51; Mass Inst Technol, PhD(physics), 54. *Hon Degrees:* ScD, Fla Inst Technol, 77. *Prof Exp:* Asst, Mass Inst Technol, 52-54, res assoc, 54-55; jr res physicist, Univ Calif, 55-56, physicist, Lawrence Radiation Lab, 56-58; asst prof physics, Mass Inst Technol, 58-60; assoc prof nuclear eng, Univ Calif, Berkeley, 60-66, prof, 66-69, chmn dept, 64-69, physicist, Lawrence Radiation Lab, 60-69; leader exp physics div, 60-64, dir, Ames Res Ctr, NASA, 69-77; undersecy, Air Force, 77-79, secy, 79-81, DEP ADMINR, NASA, 81- *Concurrent Pos:* Lectr, Dept Appl Sci, Univ Calif, Davis, 69-73; consult, Inst Defense Anal, US Army, DC; consult prof sch eng, Stanford Univ, 73-; consult, US Air Force, US Army & Inst Defense Anal. *Mem:* Nat Acad Eng; Am Geophys Union; fel Am Phys Soc; Am Nuclear Soc; fel Am Inst Aeronaut & Astronaut. *Res:* Nuclear and atomic physics; nuclear instrumentation; astrophysics. *Mailing Add:* Dept of Air Force Washington DC 20330

MARK, HAROLD WAYNE, b Chanute, Kans, May 2, 49. PHYSICAL ORGANIC CHEMISTRY, SULFUR CHEMISTRY. *Educ:* Univ Kans, BS, 71; Northwestern Univ, PhD(chem), 75. *Prof Exp:* res chemist, 75-80, SR RES CHEMIST, PHILLIPS PETROL CO, 80- *Mem:* AAAS; Am Chem Soc; Sigma Xi. *Res:* Sulfur chemistry, catalysis, carbonium ion chemistry and nucleophilic substitution reactions. *Mailing Add:* Phillips Petrol Co Phillips Res Ctr Bartlesville OK 74004

MARK, HARRY BERST, JR, b Camden, NJ, Feb 28, 34; m 60; c 3. ELECTROCHEMISTRY, ANALYTICAL CHEMISTRY. *Educ:* Univ Va, BA, 56; Duke Univ, PhD(electrochem), 60. *Prof Exp:* Assoc, Univ NC, 60-62; fel, Calif Inst Technol, 62-63; from asst prof to assoc prof chem, Univ Mich, Ann Arbor, 63-70; PROF CHEM, UNIV CINCINNATI, 70- *Concurrent Pos:* Vis prof, Free Univ Brussels, 70; cong legis Counr, Am Chem Soc, 74- *Mem:* AAAS; Am Chem Soc; Electrochem Soc; NY Acad Sci; Am Inst Chem. *Res:* Heterogeneous electron transfer kinetics; electrical double layer phenomena; electroanalytical techniques; neutron activation analysis; kinetic methods for the analysis of closely related mixtures; bioelectrochemistry; environmental analysis methods. *Mailing Add:* Dept of Chem Univ of Cincinnati Cincinnati OH 45221

MARK, HERBERT, b Jersey City, NJ, June 10, 21; m 45; c 3. MEDICINE, CARDIOLOGY. *Educ:* Columbia Univ, AB, 42; Long Island Col Med, MD, 45; Am Bd Internal Med, dipl, 53. *Prof Exp:* Resident med, Montefiore Hosp, New York, 48-49; resident, Vet Admin Hosp, Bronx, 49-50; pvt pract, 51-64; assoc prof med, NY Med Col, 64-67; asst prof prev med & med, Albert Einstein Col Med, 67-69; clin assoc prof med, NJ Col Med, 69-72, prof med, 72-75; CHIEF, MED SERV, VET ADMIN MED CTR, BRONX, NY & PROF, MT SINAI SCH MED, 75- *Concurrent Pos:* Fel cardiol, Montefiore Hosp, New York, 48-49, mem staff, Montefiore Hosp, assoc attend physician, 61-67, attend physician, 67-75; attend physician, Vet Admin Hosp, Bronx; assoc chief med, chief cardiol & assoc attend physician, Bird S Coler Hosp, 64-67; assoc attend physician, Flower & Metrop Hosps, 64-67; dir ambulatory serv, Montefiore-Morrisania Affiliation, 67-69; chief med, Jersey City Med Ctr, 69-75; adj attend physician, Med Serv, Mt Sinai Hosp, New York, 75- *Mem:* Am Fedn Clin Res; fel Am Col Physicians; fel Am Col Cardiol; Am Heart Asn. *Res:* Vectorcardiography; electrophysiology; congenital heart disease. *Mailing Add:* Bronx Vet Admin Med Ctr 130 W Kingsbridge Rd Bronx NY 10468

MARK, HERMAN FRANCIS, b Vienna, Austria, May 3, 95; nat US; m 22; c 2. PHYSICAL CHEMISTRY. *Educ:* Univ Vienna, PhD, 21, Dr rer nat, 56. *Hon Degrees:* EngD, Univ Leige, 49; PhD, Uppsala Univ, 42, Lowell Technol Inst, 57 & Munich Tech Univ, 60. *Prof Exp:* Instr physics & phys chem, Univ Vienna, 19-21; instr org chem, Univ Berlin, 21-22; from res fel to group leader, Kaiser Wilhelm Inst, Dahlem, 22-26; res chemist, I G Farben-Indust, 27-28, group leader, 28-30, asst res dir, 30-32; prof chem, Univ Vienna, 32-38; adj prof org chem, 40-42, prof, 42-46, dir polymer res inst, 46-70, EMER DEAN, POLYTECH INST NEW YORK, 70- *Concurrent Pos:* Assoc prof, Karlsruhe Tech Inst, 27-32; tech consult, US Navy, Qm Corps, US Army; NSF ed, J Polymer Sci, J Appl Polymer Sci; Series on Highpolymer, Rev in Polymer Sci, Resins, Rubbers, Plastics & Natural & Synthetic Fibers; chmn tech comt wood chem, Food & Agr Orgn, UN; chmn comn macromolecules, Int Union Pure & Appl Chem; chmn comt macromolecules, Nat Res Coun; vpres in-chg proj res, Am Comt, Weizmann Inst, Israel & Gov Inst; chmn, Gordon Res Conf Macromolecules & Textiles. *Mem:* Nat Acad Sci; AAAS; Am Chem Soc; fel Am Phys Soc; Soc Rheol. *Res:* Use of x-rays and electrons in the synthesis, characterization, reactions and properties of natural and synthetic macromolecules. *Mailing Add:* Polytech Inst New York 333 Jay St Brooklyn NY 11201

MARK, J CARSON, b Lindsay, Ont, July 6, 13; US citizen; m 35; c 6. MATHEMATICS, MATHEMATICAL PHYSICS. *Educ:* Univ Western Ont, BA, 35; Univ Toronto, PhD(math), 38. *Prof Exp:* Instr math, Univ Man, 38-43; scientist, Montreal Lab, Nat Res Coun Can, 43-45; scientist, Los Alamos Sci Lab, 45-46, mem staff, theoret physics div, Los Alamos Sci Lab, Univ Calif, 46-73, div leader, 47-73; MEM ADV COMT, REACTOR SAFEGUARDS OF US NUCLEAR REGULATORY COMN, 76- *Concurrent Pos:* Mem, Sci Adv Bd, US Air Force; sci adv, US Deleg, Conf Experts Means of Detection Nuclear Explosions, Geneva, 58. *Mem:* Am Math Soc; Am Phys Soc. *Res:* Finite group theory; transport theory; hydrodynamics; neutron physics. *Mailing Add:* 4900 Sandia Dr Los Alamos NM 87544

MARK, JAMES EDWARD, b Wilkes-Barre, Pa, Dec 14, 34; m 64; c 2. POLYMER CHEMISTRY. *Educ:* Wilkes Col, BS, 57; Univ Pa, PhD(phys chem), 62. *Prof Exp:* Res chemist, Rohm & Haas Co, 55-56; res asst, Stanford Univ, 62-64; asst prof chem, Polytech Inst Brooklyn, 64-67; from asst prof to prof chem, Univ Mich, Ann Arbor, 67-77; PROF CHEM, CHMN PHYS CHEM DIV & DIR POLYMER RES CTR, UNIV CINCINNATI, 77- *Concurrent Pos:* Consult var industs, 63-; vis prof, Stanford Univ, 73-74; spec res fel, NIH, 75-76; lectr short course prog, Am Chem Soc, 73- *Mem:* AAAS; Am Chem Soc; Am Phys Soc; NY Acad Sci. *Res:* Statistical properties of chain molecules; elastic properties of polymer networks. *Mailing Add:* Dept of Chem Univ of Cincinnati Cincinnati OH 45221

MARK, LESTER CHARLES, b Boston, Mass, July 16, 18; m 46; c 2. MEDICINE. *Educ:* Univ Toronto, MD, 41; Am Bd Anesthesiol, dipl, 52. *Prof Exp:* Intern, Jewish Mem Hosp, 41-43; asst resident surg, Grace Hosp, New Haven, Conn, 43; resident anesthesiol, Hosp Spec Surg, New York, 47-48; clin instr, Col Med, State Univ NY, 52-53; assoc, 53-54, from asst prof to assoc prof, 54-65, PROF ANESTHESIOL, COL PHYSICIANS & SURGEONS, COLUMBIA UNIV, 65- *Concurrent Pos:* Res fel, Res Serv, NY Univ-Bellevue Med Ctr & Goldwater Mem Hosp, 48-51; Am Heart Asn res fel, 49-51; travel award, Int Cardiol Cong, Paris, 50; Guggenheim fel, 60-61; Macy fac scholar, Switz, 74-75; asst adj anesthesiologist, Jewish Mem Hosp, New York, 47-52; asst clin vis anesthesiologist, Jewish Mem Hosp, New York, 47-52; asst clin vis anesthesiologist, Goldwater Mem Hosp, 48-50; dir anesthesiol, Brunswick Gen Hosp, Amityville, & anesthesiologist, SNassau Communities Hosp, Oceanside, 51-53; dir anesthesiol, Freeport Hosp, assoc vis anesthesiologist, Kings County Hosp, Brooklyn & anesthesiologist, Vet Admin Hosp, Northport, 52-53; from asst attend anesthesiologist to assoc attend anesthesiologist, Presby Hosp, New York, 53-65, attend anesthesiologist, 65-, collab med & exp pharmacol, 59-67; Fulbright res prof, Denmark, 60-61; actg consult, WHO Anaesthesia Ctr, Copenhagen, 60-61; consult, Coun Drugs, AMA, 62-; mem, adv comt respiratory & anesthetic drugs, Food & Drug Admin, 66-70, over-the-counter hypnotics, tranquillizers & sleep-aids rev panel, 72-78; mem pharmacol-toxicol rev comt, Nat Inst Gen Med Sci, 68-70, prog comt, 70-72, chmn, 71-72; mem prof adv bd, Found Thanatology, 68-, exec comt, 74-; China Med Bd vis prof, Sapporo Med Col, Japan, 67; guest scientist, Med Dept & vis attend physician, Med Res Ctr, Brookhaven Nat Lab, 68-71; Fulbright sr scholar, Sch Pharmaceut Sci, Victorian Col Pharm, Melborne, Australia, 81. *Honors & Awards:* Hiroshima Univ Medal, 67; Distinguished Serv Award, NY State Jour Med, 67. *Mem:* AAAS; Am Soc Anesthesiol; Am Soc Pharmacol & Exp Therapeut; sr mem Asn Univ Anesthet; fel Am Col Anesthesiol. *Res:* Barbiturates; drug metabolism and distribution; mechanisms of drug action in man; thanatology; hypnosis; acupuncture. *Mailing Add:* Col of Physicians & Surgeons Columbia Univ New York NY 10032

MARK, MELVIN, b St Paul, Minn, Nov 15, 22; m 51; c 3. MECHANICAL ENGINEERING. *Educ:* Univ Minn, BME, 43, MS, 46; Harvard Univ, ScD(mech eng), 50. *Prof Exp:* Instr physics & mech eng, NDak Agr Col, 43-44; instr mech eng, Univ Minn, 45-47; proj engr, Aircraft Gas Turbine Div, Gen Elec Co, 50-52; sr mech engr, Raytheon Co, 52-54, sect head, appl mech group, 54-56; prof mech eng, Lowell Technol Inst, 57-59, dean fac, 59-62; dean col eng, 68-79, PROF MECH ENG, NORTHEASTERN UNIV, 63-, PROVOST & SR VPRES, 79- *Concurrent Pos:* Consult engr to various industs, 56-; pres, Cambridge Develop & Eng Corp, 56-59; vis lectr, Brandeis Univ, 58. *Mem:* Fel Am Soc Mech Engrs; Am Soc Eng Educ; Sigma Xi. *Res:* Photoelasticity; residual stresses in welding; viscosity of lubricants; aircraft gas turbine cooling; aerodynamic loads on radar antennas; heat transfer in electronic equipment; thermodynamics; author or co-author of numerous publications. *Mailing Add:* 17 Larch Rd Waban MA 02168

MARK, PETER HERMAN, surface physics, materials science, deceased

MARK, ROBERT, b New York, NY, July 3, 30; m 55; c 3. EXPERIMENTAL MECHANICS, ARCHITECTURAL HISTORY. *Educ:* City Col NY, BCE, 52; State Univ NY, PE, 58. *Prof Exp:* Stress analyst, Combustion Eng Nuclear Power Div, 52-57, res staff engr, 57-64, PROF CIVIL ENG, PRINCETON UNIV, 64- *Mem:* Sigma Xi; Soc Exp Stress Anal. *Res:* Application of modern engineering analysis to historic structures and construction. *Mailing Add:* Sch Archit Princeton Univ Princeton NJ 08540

MARK, ROBERT VINCENT, b Jamaica, NY, Dec 22, 42. ORGANIC CHEMISTRY. *Educ:* St John's Univ, NY, BS, 64, MS, 66, PhD(org chem), 71. *Prof Exp:* Instr, 70-73, asst prof gen & org chem, 73-77, spec asst actg pres, 76-77, chmn dept chem, 77-81, ASSOC PROF CHEM, STATE UNIV NY AGR & TECH COL FARMINGDALE, 77-, DEAN, SCH ARTS & SCI, 81- *Concurrent Pos:* NSF traineeship, 70; res assoc, Long Island Jewish-Hillside Med Ctr, 73-74; consult, Pall Corp, 75-77. *Mem:* Am Chem Soc. *Res:* Preparation and mass spectral characteristics of small ring heterocyclic compounds. *Mailing Add:* Dept Chem State Univ NY Agr & Tech Col Farmingdale NY 11735

MARK, ROGER G, b Boston, Mass, June 4, 39; m 66; c 4. BIO-ELECTRICAL ENGINEERING, INTERNAL MEDICINE. *Educ:* Mass Inst Technol, BS, 60, PhD(elec eng), 66; Harvard Med Sch, MD, 65. *Prof Exp:* Intern & resident internal med, Harvard Med Serv-Boston City Hosp, 65-67; med officer, Spec Weapons Defense, US Air Force, 67-69; instr med, Harvard Med Sch, 69-72; asst prof, 69-72, ASSOC PROF ELEC ENG, MASS INST TECHNOL, 72-; ASST PROF MED, HARVARD MED SCH, 72- *Res:* Biomedical instrumentation; medical care delivery systems; cardiovascular physiology. *Mailing Add:* Rm 36-789 Mass Inst Technol Cambridge MA 02139

MARK, SHEW-KUEY, b China, Aug 8, 36; Can citizen. EXPERIMENTAL NUCLEAR PHYSICS. *Educ:* McGill Univ, BSc, 60, MSc, 62, PhD(nuclear physics), 65. *Prof Exp:* Nat Res Coun Can fel, Univ Man, 65-66; from asst prof to assoc prof, 66-75, dir, Foster Radiation Lab, 71-79, PROF PHYSICS, MCGILL UNIV, 75- *Concurrent Pos:* Sr vis scientist, Nat Ctr Sci Res, France, 79-80. *Mem:* Can Asn Physicists. *Res:* Nuclear reactions; spectroscopy; structural studies. *Mailing Add:* Foster Radiation Lab McGill Univ Montreal PQ H3A 2T5 Can

MARK, STANLEY D(AVID), JR, b Washington Court House, Ohio, June 27, 25; m 47; c 6. CERAMICS ENGINEERING. *Educ:* Ohio State Univ, BCerE & MSc, 51. *Prof Exp:* Res assoc, Res Found, Ohio State Univ, 49-51; res engr, Carborundum Co, 51-59, mgr tech br, Bonded Abrasives Div, 59-65, mgr new prod, 65-68, pres, Torrax Systs, Inc, 68-70, gen mgr, Pollution Control Div, 70-73; VPRES, ANDCO INC, 73- *Mem:* Am Ceramic Soc. *Res:* Special refractories; cermets; abrasives; electrical ceramics; high temperature fibers; incineration processes; air and water pollution control equipment. *Mailing Add:* 52 Crown Point Lane Williamsville NY 14221

MARK, VICTOR, b Marosvasarhely, Hungary, Feb 9, 21; nat US; m 55; c 6. ORGANIC CHEMISTRY. *Educ:* Polytech Budapest, Hungary, Dipl, 44; Northwestern Univ, PhD(chem), 55. *Prof Exp:* Res chemist insecticides, Arzola, Hungary, 44-46, Atox, 46-48; consult, Montecatini, Italy, 49-50, Bombrini, 50-51; res chemist, Universal Oil Prod Co, 51-53, Union Oil Co Calif, 55-56 & Monsanto Chem Co, Mo, 57-62; res scientist, Pennsalt Co, 63; sr res assoc, Hooker Chem Corp, 64-71; specialist, 71-80, SR SCIENTIST, GEN ELEC CO, 80- *Mem:* Am Chem Soc; NY Acad Sci. *Res:* Chlorocarbons; phosphorus chemistry; reaction mechanisms; phosphorus and proton nuclear magnetic resonance spectroscopy; organic polymer chemistry; flame retardants; author of over 40 publications. *Mailing Add:* Plastics Dept Gen Elec Co Mt Vernon IN 47620

MARKAKIS, PERICLES, b Cassaba, Turkey, Mar 3, 20; nat US; m 53; c 3. FOOD SCIENCE. *Educ:* Univ Salonika, Greece, BS, 42 & 49; Univ Mass, MS, 52, PhD(food technol), 56. *Prof Exp:* Instr food sci, Univ Salonika, Greece, 42-50; asst res prof food technol, Univ Mass, 55-56; sr food technologist, DCA Food Industs, Inc, 56-57; res food technologist, Univ Calif, 57-59; from asst prof to assoc prof, 59-69, PROF FOOD SCI, MICH STATE UNIV, 70- *Concurrent Pos:* Tech assignments, Latin Am, Asia & Africa. *Honors & Awards:* Fulbright Study Award. *Mem:* Am Chem Soc; Inst Food Technologists; NY Acad Sci; Sigma Xi. *Res:* chemistry and technology of foods; irradiation preservation of foods. *Mailing Add:* Dept of Food Sci Mich State Univ East Lansing MI 48823

MARKEES, DIETHER GAUDENZ, b Basel, Switz, Oct 16, 19; nat US; div; c 1. ORGANIC CHEMISTRY. *Educ:* Univ Basel, Dr phil, 46. *Prof Exp:* Res fel med chem, Univ Va, 47-48; res assoc E R Squibb & Sons, 49-53 & Amherst Col, 53-58; from asst prof to assoc prof, 58-68, PROF CHEM, WELLS COL, 68- *Mem:* Am Chem Soc; Swiss Chem Soc. *Res:* Medicinal chemistry; chemistry of heterocycles; synthetic organic chemistry. *Mailing Add:* Dept of Chem Wells Col Aurora NY 13026

MARKELL, EDWARD KINGSMILL, b Brooklyn, NY, Apr 14, 18; m 53; c 2. PARASITOLOGY, TROPICAL MEDICINE. *Educ:* Pomona Col, BA, 38; Univ Calif, PhD(zool), 42; Stanford Univ, MD, 51. *Prof Exp:* Asst zool, Univ Calif, 38-41; intern, Stanford Univ Hosps, 50-51; asst prof infectious dis, Sch Med, Univ Calif, Los Angeles, 51-58; MEM DEPT INTERNAL MED, KAISER FOUND MED CTR, 58- *Concurrent Pos:* Markle scholar, 52-57; clin assoc prof prev med, Sch Med, Stanford Univ, 61-70, clin prof, 70- *Mem:* Royal Soc Trop Med & Hyg; Am Soc Parasitol; Am Soc Trop Med & Hyg. *Res:* Parasitic diseases of man; filariasis. *Mailing Add:* Kaiser Found Med Ctr Oakland CA 94611

MARKELS, MICHAEL, JR, b New York, NY, Feb 4, 26; div; c 3. CHEMICAL ENGINEERING. *Educ:* Columbia Univ, BS, 48, MS, 49, DES, 57. *Prof Exp:* Technologist, Wood River Refinery, Shell Oil Co, 49-52; engr heat transfer opers & res assoc, Columbia Univ, 52-57; dir advan technol dept, Atlantic Res Corp, Va, 57-68, asst gen mgr res div, 68-69; PRES, VERSAR

INC, 69- *Concurrent Pos:* Dep dir corp res lab, Susquehanna Corp, Va, 68-69. *Mem:* AAAS; Nat Soc Prof Engrs; Am Nuclear Soc; Am Inst Aeronaut & Astronaut; Am Inst Chem Engrs. *Res:* Mass transfer operations; fluid mechanics; small particle dynamics; rheology; research administration; general management. *Mailing Add:* VERSAR Inc 6621 Electronic Dr Springfield VA 22151

MARKENSCOFF, PAULINE, b Serres, Greece, Apr 30, 52. COMPUTER ARCHITECTURE. *Educ:* Nat Tech Univ, Greece, dipl, 75; Univ Minn, MS, 77, PhD(elec eng), 80. *Prof Exp:* ASST PROF COMPUT ENG, UNIV HOUSTON, 80- *Mem:* Inst Elec & Electronics Engrs; Asn Comput Mach; Greek Chamber Engrs. *Res:* Modeling of comuter systems; computer architecture; performance evaluaion and distributed processing. *Mailing Add:* Dept Elec Eng Univ Houston Houston TX 77004

MARKER, DAVID, b Atlantic, Iowa, Mar 20, 37; m 66; c 2. THEORETICAL PHYSICS. *Educ:* Grinnell Col, BA, 59; Pa State Univ, MS, 62, PhD(physics), 66. *Prof Exp:* From asst prof to assoc prof, 65-72, assoc dean nat sci, 73-74, PROF PHYSICS, HOPE COL, 72-, PROVOST, 74- *Mem:* Am Phys Soc; Sigma Xi. *Res:* Theoretical high energy physics; calculation of nucleon-nucleon bremsstrahlung cross sections; analytic approximation theory. *Mailing Add:* Off of Provost Hope College Holland MI 49423

MARKER, LEON, b Lancaster, Pa, Jan 6, 22; m 53; c 3. PHYSICAL CHEMISTRY. *Educ:* Temple Univ, AB, 47; Univ Utah, PhD(phys chem), 51. *Prof Exp:* Res chemist, Gen Res Labs, Olin Industs, 52-57, res chemist, Film Res Dept, Olin Mathieson Chem Co, Conn, 57-63; head polymer physics sect, Res & Develop Div, 63-73, SR RES ASSOC, GEN, TIRE & RUBBER CO, 73- *Mem:* AAAS; Am Chem Soc; Soc Rheol; Sigma Xi. *Res:* Polymer physics; rheology; polymer processing; physical chemistry of polymers; chemical kinetics; kinetics of electrode reactions. *Mailing Add:* Res Div Gen Tire & Rubber Co 2990 Gizohrist Rd Akron OH 44305

MARKER, THOMAS F(RANKLIN), b Denver, Colo, June 25, 19; m 44; c 2. ELECTRICAL ENGINEERING. *Educ:* Yatesbury Sch Eng, cert elec eng, 42; Malvern Col, Eng, cert elec eng, 43. *Prof Exp:* Mil observer, Am Embassy, London, Eng, 41-43; sr engr, Fed Telecommun Labs, 46-48; staff mem, 48-52, mgr electronic develop, 52-56, mgr advan data systs, 56-68, mgr nuclear test dept, 68-70, MGR PATENT DEPT, SANDIA CORP, 70- *Mem:* Sr mem Inst Elec & Electronics Engrs. *Res:* Radar systems; management of advanced data systems development; patent management; new systems for oil and gas geophysical exploration. *Mailing Add:* 7613 Pickard Ave NE Albuquerque NM 87110

MARKERT, CLEMENT LAWRENCE, b Las Animas, Colo, Apr 11, 17; m 40; c 3. DEVELOPMENTAL GENETICS, ENZYMOLOGY. *Educ:* Univ Colo, BA, 40; Univ Calif, Los Angeles, MS, 42; Johns Hopkins Univ, PhD(biol), 48. *Prof Exp:* Merck-Nat Res Coun fel, Calif Inst Technol, 48-50; from asst prof to assoc prof zool, Univ Mich, 50-57; prof biol, John Hopkins Univ, 57-65; chmn dept, 65-71, PROF BIOL, YALE UNIV, 65-, DIR CTR REPRODUCTIVE BIOL, 74- *Concurrent Pos:* Managing ed, J Exp Zool, 63-; trustee, Bermuda Biol Sta, 59-; panelist, NSF, 59-63; co-chmn, Develop Biol Cluster, President's Biomed Res Panel, 75; council mem, Am Cancer Soc, 76-78. *Mem:* Nat Acad Sci; Am Soc Naturalists (vpres, 67); Am Soc Zoologists (pres, 67); Soc Develop Biol (pres, 63-64); Am Inst Biol Sci (pres, 66). *Res:* Mammalian reproductive physiology; cellular differentiation; developmental genetics; enzymology. *Mailing Add:* Dept of Biol Yale Univ New Haven CT 06520

MARKESBERY, WILLIAM RAY, b Florence, Ky, Sept 30, 32; m 58; c 3. NEUROLOGY, NEUROPATHOLOGY. *Educ:* Univ Ky, BA, 60, MD, 64. *Prof Exp:* Resident neurol, Col Physicians & Surgeons, Columbia Univ, 65-67, instr, 68-69, asst neurologist, Vanderbilt Clin, Columbia Presby Med Ctr, 68-69; asst prof path & neurol, Sch Med & Dent, Univ Rochester, 69-72; assoc prof, 72-77, PROF NEUROL & PATH, UNIV KY, 77- *Concurrent Pos:* USPHS-NIH-Nat Inst Neurol Dis & Blindness spec fel, Col Physicians & Surgeons, Columbia Univ, 67-69; USPHS res grant, Univ Rochester Med Ctr, 69-70; assoc neurologist, Strong Mem Hosp, 69-, asst pathologist, 70-; assoc neurologist, Univ Hosp, Univ Ky, 72; USPHS-NIH res grant, Univ Ky, 77-79. *Mem:* Am Acad Neurol; Am Asn Neuropath; Am Neurol Asn. *Res:* Aging of the central nervous system; dementia; ultrastructure of central nervous system tumors, neurological degenerative disorders and muscle diseases. *Mailing Add:* Dept of Neurol & Path Univ of Ky Med Ctr Lexington KY 40506

MARKEVICH, DARLENE JULIA, b Elizabeth, NJ, Aug 31, 49. ATOMIC PHYSICS. *Educ:* New York Univ, BA, 71, MS, 73, PhD(physics), 81. *Prof Exp:* STAFF SCIENTIST, LAWRENCE BERKELEY LAB, 81- *Mem:* Am Phys Soc. *Res:* Cross section for inner-shell x-ray production in atomic collision processes; atomic inner-shell fluorescence yields. *Mailing Add:* Bldg 4 Lawrence Berkeley Lab Berkeley CA 94720

MARKEY, SANFORD PHILIP, b Cleveland, Ohio, June 15, 42; m 66; c 2. ORGANIC CHEMISTRY, PHARMACOLOGY. *Educ:* Bowdoin Col, AB, 64; Mass Inst Technol, PhD(chem), 68. *Prof Exp:* Instr pediat, Med Sch, Univ Colo, 69, asst prof, 69-74, asst prof pharmacol, 71-74; RES SCIENTIST PHARMACOL, NIMH, 74- *Concurrent Pos:* NIH grant mass spectrometry, Med Sch, Univ Colo, 70-74; assoc ed, Org Mass Spectrometry, 72-74. *Mem:* Am Chem Soc; Am Soc Mass Spectrometry. *Res:* Mass spectrometry applied to clinical research. *Mailing Add:* Lab Clin Sci Nat Inst Ment Health Bethesda MD 20205

MARKEY, WINSTON ROSCOE, b Buffalo, NY, Sept 20, 29; m 55; c 3. ENGINEERING. *Educ:* Mass Inst Technol, SB, 51, ScD(instrumentation), 56. *Prof Exp:* Instr aeronaut eng, 54-56, mem res staff, Instrumentation Lab, 56-57, from asst prof to assoc prof aeronaut & astronaut, 57-66, PROF AERONAUT & ASTRONAUT, MASS INST TECHNOL, 66-, DIR EXP ASTRON LAB, 61- *Concurrent Pos:* Consult, United Aircraft Corp, 62-; chief scientist, US Dept Air Force, 64-65, mem sci adv bd, 66-69. *Mem:* Assoc fel Am Inst Aeronaut & Astronaut. *Res:* Navigation system design; instrumentation for physical measurements. *Mailing Add:* 11 Edgewood Rd Lexington MA 02173

MARKGRAF, JOHN HODGE, b Cincinnati, Ohio, Mar 16, 30; m 57; c 2. ORGANIC CHEMISTRY. *Educ:* Williams Col, BA, 52; Yale Univ, MS, 54, PhD, 57. *Prof Exp:* Fel, Univ Munich, 56-57; chemist, Procter & Gamble Co, 58-59; from asst prof to assoc prof, 59-69, PROF CHEM, WILLIAMS COL, 69- *Concurrent Pos:* Provvost, Williams Col, 80-83. *Mem:* Am Chem Soc; Sigma Xi. *Res:* Physical organic studies of heterocyclic systems. *Mailing Add:* Dept of Chem Williams Col Williamstown MA 01267

MARKHAM, CHARLES HENRY, b Pasadena, Calif, Dec 24, 23; m 45, 71; c 6. NEUROLOGY, NEUROPHYSIOLOGY. *Educ:* Stanford Univ, BS, 47, MD, 51; Am Bd Psychiat & Neurol, dipl, 59. *Prof Exp:* Teaching fel neurol, Harvard Med Sch, 54-55; from instr to assoc prof, 56-71, PROF NEUROL, SCH MED, UNIV CALIF, LOS ANGELES, 71- *Concurrent Pos:* Consult, Wadsworth Vet Admin Hosp, Los Angeles, 56- *Mem:* Am Epilepsy Soc; Am Neurol Asn; Am Acad Neurol. *Res:* Vestibular, brain-stem and basal ganglia physiology; Parkinson's disease and other movement disorders. *Mailing Add:* Dept of Neurol Univ of Calif Sch of Med Los Angeles CA 90024

MARKHAM, ELIZABETH MARY, b New Haven, Conn, Oct 12, 29. MATHEMATICS. *Educ:* St Joseph Col, Conn, BA, 51; Univ Notre Dame, MS, 60, PhD(math), 64. *Prof Exp:* Teacher high sch, Conn, 54-59; instr math, St Joseph Col, Conn, 64-65; teacher, Our Lady of Mercy Acad, 65-66; asst prof, 66-68, ASSOC PROF MATH & CHMN DEPT, ST JOSEPH COL, CONN, 68-, CHMN NATURAL SCI DIV, 78- *Concurrent Pos:* Dir & instr, NSF in serv inst high sch math teachers, 66-69; instr, Cent Conn State Col, 68; NSF consult, US Agency Int Develop Inst High Sch Math Teachers, Ramjas Col, Delhi Univ, 68; mem, Conn State Adv Comt Math, 69-74. *Mem:* Math Asn Am; Am Math Soc; Am Women Math; Nat Coun Teachers Math; Am Asn Univ Prof. *Res:* Mathematical modeling and applications. *Mailing Add:* Dept of Math St Joseph Col West Hartford CT 06117

MARKHAM, JAMES J, b Oreland, Pa, Aug 23, 28; m 52; c 8. ANALYTICAL CHEMISTRY, OCEANOGRAPHY. *Educ:* Villanova Univ, BS, 50; Univ Minn, PhD(chem), 58. *Prof Exp:* Res chemist, Whitemarsh Res Lab, Pa Salt Mfg Co, 50-51; from asst prof to assoc prof, 56-67, PROF CHEM & ASSOC DEAN SCI, VILLANOVA UNIV, 68- *Concurrent Pos:* USPHS vis res fel, Dept Inorg & Struct Chem, Univ Leeds, 65-66. *Mem:* Franklin Inst; Am Chem Soc; Royal Soc Chem. *Res:* Instrumentation; marine chemistry; water supply and pollution control. *Mailing Add:* Dept of Chem Villanova Univ Villanova PA 19085

MARKHAM, JORDAN JEPTHA, b Samokov, Bulgaria, Dec 25, 16; US citizen; m 43; c 2. PHYSICS. *Educ:* Beloit Col, BS, 38; Syracuse Univ, MS, 40; Brown Univ, PhD(physics), 46. *Prof Exp:* Res physicist, Div War Res, Columbia Univ, Conn, 42-45, NY, 45; fel, Clinton Labs, Tenn, 46-47; instr physics, Univ Pa, 47-48; asst prof, Brown Univ, 48-50; physicist, Appl Physics Lab, Johns Hopkins Univ, 50-53; physicist, Zenith Radio Corp, 53-60; sci adv physics res, IIT Res Inst, 60-62, PROF PHYSICS, ILL INST TECHNOL, 62- *Mem:* Fel Am Phys Soc. *Res:* Oceanographic effect on underwater sound; theory of imperfections in ionic crystals; absorption of sound; second order acoustic fields; spectroscopy of solids; color centers. *Mailing Add:* Dept of Physics Ill Inst of Technol Chicago IL 60616

MARKHAM, M CLARE, b New Haven, Conn, Aug 12, 19. PHYSICAL CHEMISTRY. *Educ:* St Joseph Col, Conn, AB, 40; Cath Univ Am, PhD(chem), 52. *Prof Exp:* Lab instr chem, St Joseph Col, Conn, 42-45; teacher, Sacred Heart High Sch, 45-49; chmn nat sci div, 75-77, prof chem, St Joseph Col, Conn, 52-77; undersecy for energy, Conn State Off Policy & Mgt, 77-79; DEAN GRAD DIV, CHEM DEPT, ST JOSEPH COL, CONN, 80- *Concurrent Pos:* Res grants, Res Corp & Sigma Xi; consult, US Air Force contracts solar energy conversion, 60-64; sci fac fel with M Calvin, Univ Calif, Berkeley, 67-68; counr, Am Chem Soc, 68-71 & 74-76; coop US scientist, Indian Inst Technol, Madras, 74-76. *Mem:* AAAS; Am Chem Soc. *Res:* Photochemical reactions; surface reactions; factors influencing energy transfer between chlorophylls and carotenoids, or oxidant-reductant pairs. *Mailing Add:* Chem Dept St Joseph Col W Hartford CT 06117

MARKHAM, THOMAS LOWELL, b Apex, NC, Jan 2, 39. ALGEBRA. *Educ:* Univ NC, Chapel Hill, BS, 61, MA, 64; Auburn Univ, PhD(math), 67. *Prof Exp:* Asst prof math, Univ NC, Charlotte, 67-68; asst prof math, 68-73, ASSOC PROF MATH, UNIV SC, 73- *Mem:* Am Math Soc; Math Asn Am; Sigma Xi. *Res:* Linear algebra. *Mailing Add:* Dept of Math & Statist Univ of SC Columbia SC 29208

MARKHART, ALBERT H, JR, b Elizabeth, NJ, June 17, 19; m 46; c 2. ORGANIC CHEMISTRY, POLYMER CHEMISTRY. *Educ:* Univ of Ala, BS, 42; Univ Calif, Berkeley, PhD(org chem), 49. *Prof Exp:* Chemist, org chem, 42-44, 50-56, group leader, 56-65, res sect mgr, 65-65, sr group leader, 72-76, FEL, POLYMER CHEM, MONSANTO CO, 76- *Concurrent Pos:* Fel Univ Ill, 49-50. *Mem:* Am Chem Soc. *Res:* Polymer synthesis and structure determination; photocon- ductivity; electrical insulation; high temperature resins; coating resins; nuclear magnetic resonance; liquid chromatography. *Mailing Add:* Monsanto Co 190 Grochmal Ave Indian Orchard MA 01151

MARKHART, ALBERT HENRY, III, b Maldon, Mass, Nov 15, 51; m 78. BOTANY, PLANT PHYSIOLOGY. *Educ:* Gettysburg Col, BA, 73; Duke Univ, MA, 76, PhD(botany), 78. *Prof Exp:* Res assoc plant physiol, Duke Univ, 78-80; ASST PROF, DEPT HORT, UNIV MINN, 80- *Concurrent Pos:* Alexander von Humboldt fel, 79. *Mem:* Am Asn Plant Physiol; Soc Exp Biol; Am Soc Hort Sci. *Res:* Biochemical and physiological response of plants to a fluctuating environment; primarily the role of membrane and hormone changes as related to photosynthesis, water permeability and ion transport. *Mailing Add:* Dept Hort Univ Minn St Paul MN 55108

MARKIEWICZ, ROBERT STEPHEN, b Worcester, Mass, Apr 18, 47; m 70. SOLID STATE PHYSICS. *Educ:* Mass Inst Technol, SB, 69; Univ Calif, Berkeley, PhD(physics), 75. *Prof Exp:* Res assoc physics, Univ Calif, Berkeley, 75-77; res physicist, Gen Elec Res & Develop Ctr, 77-80; ASSOC PROF PHYSICS, NORTHEASTERN UNIV, 80- *Concurrent Pos:* Fel, Int Bus Mach, 75-76. *Mem:* Am Phys Soc. *Res:* Electron-hole droplets; electron-phonon interaction; intercalated graphite; localization in metals. *Mailing Add:* Dept Physics Northeastern Univ 360 Huntington Ave Boston MA 02115

MARKIEWITZ, KENNETH HELMUT, b Breslau, Ger, May 18, 27; nat US; m 57; c 3. POLYMER CHEMISTRY. *Educ:* City Col New York, BS, 51; Columbia Univ, MA, 54, PhD(chem), 57. *Prof Exp:* Chemist, Schwarz Labs, Inc, NY, 51-52; sr chemist, Atlas Powder Co, 57-63; res chemist, 63-67, SR RES CHEMIST, ICI AMERICA INC, 68- *Mem:* Am Chem Soc. *Res:* Isolation of natural products; poison ivy; synthesis of alkenyl phenols; carbohydrates; amines; conformational analysis and structural determinations; polymer synthesis. *Mailing Add:* ICI America Inc Wilmington DE 19899

MARKING, RALPH H, b Holmen, Wis, Jan 24, 35; m 63. INORGANIC CHEMISTRY. *Educ:* Wis State Univ, La Crosse, BS, 57; Univ Minn, PhD(inorg chem), 65. *Prof Exp:* Assoc prof, 63-74, PROF CHEM, UNIV WIS-EAU CLAIRE, 74- *Mem:* Am Chem Soc; Am Asn Physics Teachers. *Res:* Thermochemistry and thermodynamics; molecular structure. *Mailing Add:* Dept of Chem Univ of Wis Eau Claire WI 54701

MARKIW, ROMAN TEODOR, b Tarnopol, Ukraine, June 25, 23; US citizen; m 50. BIOCHEMISTRY, ORGANIC CHEMISTRY. *Educ:* Univ Conn, BA, 54, PhD(biochem), 66; Rensselaer Polytech, MS, 55. *Prof Exp:* Biochemist, Vet Admin Hosp, 57-62; USPHS grants, Yale Univ, 65-68; res chemist, 68-72, chief biochem res lab, Vet Admin Ctr, 72-77; BIOCHEMIST, VET ADMIN MED CTR, CANANDAIGUA, NY, 78- *Mem:* Am Chem Soc; NY Acad Sci. *Res:* Isolation and identification of peptides in biological fluids; chemical reactions of polynucleotides and derivatives; clinical chemistry. *Mailing Add:* Vet Admin Med Ctr Canandaigua NY 14424

MARKLAND, ALAN COLIN, b Bolton, Eng, Aug 26, 29; US citizen; m 54; c 3. SURGERY, UROLOGY. *Educ:* Cambridge Univ, MB, ChB, 53, MA, 54. *Prof Exp:* Researcher, Mass Gen Hosp, Boston, 60-64; asst prof urol, Univ Iowa Hosp, 64; from assoc prof to prof urol, Univ Minn Hosp, Minneapolis, 64-79; PROF & HEAD DEPT UROL, LA STATE UNIV MED CTR, SHREVEPORT, 79- *Concurrent Pos:* USPHS fel, Univ Leeds, 62-63; consult surgeon, Minneapolis Vet Admin Hosp, 65; sr Fullbright prof to gov Burma, 78; vis prof & scientist, Worcester Found, Univ Melbourne, Australia & Christ Church, NZ, 78. *Mem:* Am Fertil Soc; fel Am Col Surg; fel Am Acad Pediat; Soc Univ Urol; Soc Pediat Urol. *Res:* Urological surgery; pediatric urology; gender identity; neurologic vesical dysfunction. *Mailing Add:* Sch Med La State Univ PO Box 33932 Shreveport LA 71130

MARKLAND, FRANCIS SWABY, JR, b Philadelphia, Pa, Jan 15, 36. BIOCHEMISTRY. *Educ:* Pa State Univ, BS, 57; Johns Hopkins Univ, PhD(biochem), 64. *Prof Exp:* Asst prof biochem, Sch Med, Univ Calif, Los Angeles, 66-73; ASSOC PROF BIOCHEM, SCH MED, UNIV SOUTHERN CALIF, 74- *Concurrent Pos:* NIH fel, Sch Med, Univ Calif, Los Angeles, 64-66 & career develop award, 68-73. *Mem:* Am Soc Hemat; Am Soc Biol Chem; Am Chem Soc; Sigma Xi; Endocrine Soc. *Res:* Structure of proteins and relation of structure to function in enzymes; biochemistry of blood coagulation; receptor proteins for steroid hormones. *Mailing Add:* Cancer Res Inst Univ Southern Calif Sch of Med Los Angeles CA 90033

MARKLAND, WILLIAM R, b Brooklyn, NY, Jan 3, 19; m 42; c 3. COSMETIC CHEMISTRY. *Educ:* Middlebury Col, AB, 41. *Prof Exp:* Lab supvr, Hercules Powder Co, 42-45; chief chemist, John H Breck Inc, 45-57; res group leader hair prep, Revlon, Inc, 57-58; res mgr hair & makeup prods, Chesebrough-Pond's Inc, 58-71; CONSULT COSMETICS & TOILETRIES, 71- *Concurrent Pos:* Ed, Norda Briefs. *Mem:* Am Chem Soc; fel Am Inst Chem; Soc Cosmetic Chem. *Res:* Surfactant and shampoo chemistry; physical and chemical behavior of the hair; transparent microemulsions of mineral oil and water; cosmetic colors and pigments. *Mailing Add:* Box 124 Whately MA 01093

MARKLE, DOUGLAS FRANK, b Terre Haute, Ind, Aug 29, 47; m 71, 81. ICHTHYOLOGY. *Educ:* Cornell Univ, BS, 69; Col William & Mary, MA, 72, PhD(ichthyol), 76. *Prof Exp:* ICHTHYOLOGIST & SUPVR, LARVAL FISH IDENTIFICATION, HUNTSMAN MARINE LAB, 77- *Mem:* Am Soc Ichthyol & Herpetol; Soc Syst Zool; Am Soc Naturalists. *Res:* Systematics of deep-sea fishes; deep-sea ecology; larval fish taxonomy and ecology. *Mailing Add:* Huntsman Marine Lab St Andrews NB E0G 2X0 Can

MARKLE, H CHESTER, JR, physical chemistry, see previous edition

MARKLEY, FRANCIS LANDIS, b Philadelphia, Pa, July 20, 39; m 65, 78; c 1. ATTITUDE DYNAMICS, ORBIT DYNAMICS. *Educ:* Cornell Univ, BEP, 62; Univ Calif, Berkeley, PhD(high energy physics), 67. *Prof Exp:* Physicist, Lawrence Radiation Lab, Univ Calif, 67; NSF res fel theoret physics, Univ Md, 67-68; asst prof physics, Williams Col, 68-74; mem tech staff, Computer Sci Corp, 74-78; PHYSICIST, NAVAL RES LAB, 78- *Mem:* AAAS; Am Asn Physics Teachers; Am Inst Aeronaut & Astronaut. *Res:* Spacecraft attitude and orbit dynamics, estimation, and control. *Mailing Add:* Naval Res Lab Main Site 4555 Overlook Ave SW Columbia MD 20032

MARKLEY, JOHN LUTE, b Denver, Colo, Mar 6, 41; m 75; c 1. PHYSICAL BIOCHEMISTRY, PROTEIN CHEMISTRY. *Educ:* Carleton Col, BA, 63; Harvard Univ, PhD(biophys), 69. *Prof Exp:* Res chemist, Merck Inst Therapeut Res, 67-68, sr res chemist, 68-69; USPHS sr fel biophys, Chem Biodynamics Lab, Univ Calif, Berkeley, 70-71; asst prof, 72-76, assoc prof, 76-81, PROF CHEM, PURDUE UNIV, WEST LAFAYETTE, 81- *Concurrent Pos:* USPHS res career develop award, Nat Heart & Lung Inst, 75-80; dir, Purdue Biochem NMR Lab, 77-; Fogarty sr int fel, 80-81. *Mem:* AAAS; Am Chem Soc; Am Soc Biol Chem; Int Soc Magnetic Resonance; Sigma Xi. *Res:* Structure-function relationships in biological macromolecules; applications of nuclear magnetic resonance spectroscopy to the study of local environments of groups; proteinases and their inhibitors; electron transport proteins; protein-nucleic acid interactions; nuclear magnetic resonance of living cells. *Mailing Add:* Dept Chem Purdue Univ West Lafayette IN 47907

MARKLEY, KEHL, III, physiology, see previous edition

MARKLEY, LOWELL DEAN, b Mishawaka, Ind, Aug 27, 42; m 62; c 2. ORGANIC CHEMISTRY. *Educ:* Manchester Col, BA, 64; Purdue Univ, PhD(org chem), 69. *Prof Exp:* Res chemist, 68-72, res specialist, 72-79, RES ASSOC AGR PRODS DEPT, DOW CHEM CO, 79- *Mem:* Am Chem Soc. *Res:* Synthesis of biologically active organic compounds including pharmaceuticals and agricultural products; synthesis of agricultural products. *Mailing Add:* 1307 Wildwood Midland MI 48640

MARKLEY, WILLIAM A, JR, b Sinking Springs, Pa, Aug 24, 25; m 54; c 4. MATHEMATICS. *Educ:* Bucknell Univ, BS, 49; Univ Pittsburgh, MLitt, 56, PhD(math), 68. *Prof Exp:* From asst prof to assoc prof, 56-70, PROF MATH, MT UNION COL, 70- *Mem:* NY Acad Sci. *Res:* Analysis; summability of infinite series. *Mailing Add:* Dept of Math Mt Union Col Alliance OH 44601

MARKO, ARTHUR MYROSLAW, medicine, biochemistry, see previous edition

MARKO, JOHN ROBERT, b Bayonne, NJ, Jan 28, 38; m 65; c 1. SOLID STATE PHYSICS, OCEANOGRAPHY. *Educ:* Mass Inst Technol, BS, 59; Syracuse Univ, MS, 63, PhD(physics), 67. *Prof Exp:* Instr physics, Univ BC, 67-68, asst prof, 68-72; res assoc physics, Queen's Univ, 72-73; contract scientist, Pac Region, Marine Sci Directoriate, 74-76; PRES & MEM STAFF, ARCTIC SCI LTD, 77- *Mem:* Am Phys Soc. *Res:* Magnetic resonance; spin-lattice relaxation and electron spin resonance in semiconductors; transport properties of heavily doped semiconductors; arctic oceanography; remote sensing. *Mailing Add:* Arctic Sci Ltd 1986 Mills Rd Sidney BC V8L 3S1 Can

MARKO, KENNETH ANDREW, b Bayonne, NJ, Aug 29, 46; m 69; c 2. NONLINEAR OPTICS, SPECTROSCOPY. *Educ:* Mass Inst Technol, BS, 68; Univ Mich, MS, 69, PhD(physics), 74. *Prof Exp:* Fel, Physics Dept, Univ Mich, 74-76; RES SCIENTIST, PHYSICS DEPT, ENG & RES STAFF, FORD MOTOR CO, 76- *Mem:* Am Phys Soc. *Res:* Laser spectroscopic techniques for application to combustion research; nonlinear Raman spectroscopy; laser induced fluorescence; laser velocimetry. *Mailing Add:* Physics Dept Rm S-1021 Eng & Res Staff Ford Motor Co PO Box 2053 Dearborn MI 48121

MARKOFF, ELLIOTT LEE, b Baltimore, Md, Nov 27, 32; m 55; c 4. PSYCHIATRY, PSYCHOANALYSIS. *Educ:* Harvard Univ, AB, 54; Univ Pa, MD, 58; Univ Calif, Los Angeles, MS, 64; Southern Calif Psychoanal Inst, PhD, 76. *Prof Exp:* Intern, USPHS Hosp, Staten Island, NY, 58-59; resident psychiat, Lexington, Ky, 59-60; staff psychiatrist, Ft Worth, Tex, 60-61; resident psychiat, Neuropsychiat Inst, Univ Calif, Los Angeles, 61-64; pvt pract, 64-; sr consult drug abuse, Los Angeles County Dept Ment Health, 69-70; ASSOC CLIN PROF PSYCHIAT & ASSOC DIR GRAD EDUC IN PSYCHIAT, SCH MED, UNIV SOUTHERN CALIF, 70- *Concurrent Pos:* USPHS fel social & community psychiat, Univ Calif, Los Angeles, 64-65, lectr psychiat, Sch Med, 64-69; consult, Calif Rehab Ctr, 64 & Los Angeles County Ment Health Dept, 65-70; pvt pract, 69-; consult, White House Drug Abuse Task Force, 70 & Spec Action Off for Drug Abuse Prev, 71-73; mem tech adv comt drug abuse, Los Angeles County Bd Supvr, 73-76; chmn res, eval & adv panel, Los Angeles County Drug Abuse Task Force, 74-76; mem, Methadone Med Adv Bd, Los Angeles County Dept Health Serv, 74-; counr, Southern Calif Psychiat Soc, 77-78. *Mem:* AAAS; fel Am Psychiat Asn; Am Acad Psychoanal; assoc mem Am Psychoanal Asn. *Res:* Psychiatric education; drug dependency, development of models for local school and local community response to drug dependence and drug abuse; organization and delivery of psychiatric program services and consultations. *Mailing Add:* Univ of Southern Calif 1934 Hospital Pl Los Angeles CA 90033

MARKOVETZ, ALLEN JOHN, b Aberdeen, SDak, Apr 17, 33. MICROBIOLOGY, BIOCHEMISTRY. *Educ:* Univ SDak, BA, 57, MA, 58; PhD(bact), 61. *Prof Exp:* NIH fel microbial metab, 61-62, from instr to assoc prof, 62-73, PROF MICROBIOL, UNIV IOWA, 73- *Concurrent Pos:* Spec res fel, NIH, Dept Biochem, Univ Calif, Davis, 69-70; Career develop award, NIH, 72-76. *Mem:* Am Soc Microbiol; Am Chem Soc. *Res:* Microbial physiology and metabolism; microbial hydrocarbon and ketone metabolism; microbial-insect interactions. *Mailing Add:* Dept of Microbiol Univ of Iowa Iowa City IA 52241

MARKOVITZ, ALVIN, b Chicago, Ill, May 30, 29; m 52; c 4. MICROBIOLOGY. *Educ:* Univ Ill, BS, 50, MS, 52; Univ Wash, PhD, 55. *Prof Exp:* Fel, Nat Heart Inst, 55-57; instr, La Rabida Inst, 57-59, from asst prof to assoc prof, 59-74, PROF MICROBIOL, UNIV CHICAGO, 74- *Concurrent Pos:* Assoc prof, La Rabida Inst, 64-67. *Mem:* AAAS; Am Soc Biol Chem; Am Soc Microbiol; Genetics Soc Am. *Res:* Regulation of cell division, radiation sensitivity and capsular polysaccharide synthesis in bacteria and their relation to proteolytic enzymes. *Mailing Add:* Dept of Microbiol Univ Chicago 920 E 58th St Chicago IL 60637

MARKOVITZ, HERSHEL, b McKeesport, Pa, Oct 11, 21; m 49; c 3. POLYMER PHYSICS, RHEOLOGY. *Educ:* Univ Pittsburgh, BS, 42; Columbia Univ, AM, 43, PhD(phys chem), 49. *Prof Exp:* Mathematician, Kellex Corp, 43-45; asst, Columbia Univ, 45-49; fel, 49-51, sr fel, 51-56, sr fel fundamental res group synthetic rubber properties, Mellon Inst, 56-69, PROF MECH & POLYMER SCI, CARNEGIE-MELLON UNIV, 67- *Concurrent Pos:* Lectr, Univ Pittsburgh, 56-58; vis lectr, Johns Hopkins Univ, 58-59;

Fulbright lectr, Weizmann Inst, 64-65; asst ed, J Polymer Sci, 65-68, assoc ed, 69-; mem gov bd, Am Inst Physics, 70-72; adj prof, Univ Pittsburgh, 72-; mem US Nat Comt Theoret & Appl Mech; mem nat bd dirs, Comt Concerned Scientists. *Honors & Awards:* Bingham Medal, Soc Rheol, 67. *Mem:* Am Chem Soc; Am Phys Soc; Soc Rheol (vpres, 67-69, pres, 69-71); Soc Natural Philos (treas, 65-66). *Res:* Physics of polymers; continuum mechanics; rheology. *Mailing Add:* Carnegie-Mellon Univ Mellon Inst 4400 Fifth Ave Pittsburgh PA 15213

MARKOVITZ, MARK, b Rosario, Argentina, June 3, 38; US citizen. ORGANIC CHEMISTRY, POLYMER CHEMISTRY. *Educ:* City Col New York, 58; NY Univ, PhD(thiophene chem), 63. *Prof Exp:* Res fel, Thiophene Chem, NY Univ, 58-62; CHEMIST, MAT & PROCESSES LAB, GEN ELEC CO, 62- *Mem:* Am Chem Soc. *Res:* Electrical insulating materials; organo-metallic polymers; thermosetting resins; epoxy and silicone resins. *Mailing Add:* Mat & Processes Lab Gen Elec Co Lge Steam Turbine-Generator Div Schenectady NY 12345

MARKOWITZ, ABRAHAM SAM, immunology, see previous edition

MARKOWITZ, ALLAN HENRY, b Jersey City, NJ, Oct 22, 41; m 66. ASTRONOMY, ASTROPHYSICS. *Educ:* Univ Calif, Los Angeles, AB, 63; Ohio State Univ, MSc, 66, PhD(astron), 69. *Prof Exp:* Analyst sci appln, Comput Sci Corp, 69-71; mgr adv systs studies, Aerojet Electrosysts Co, 71-75; eng specialist, Pomona Div, Gen Dynamics Corp, 75-76; PRES ME ENTERPRISES, 76-; INSTR ASTRON, CITRUS COL, 73- *Mem:* Astron Soc Pac; Am Astron Soc. *Res:* Spectroscopy of close binary stars; stellar statistics; peculiar A-type stars; early phases stellar evolution; teaching of undergraduate astronomy. *Mailing Add:* 2650 Country Club Dr Glendora CA 91740

MARKOWITZ, DAVID, b Paterson, NJ, Mar 24, 35; m 61; c 3. SOLID STATE PHYSICS, BIOLOGICAL PHYSICS. *Educ:* Mass Inst Technol, BS, 56; Univ Ill, PhD(physics), 63. *Prof Exp:* Res assoc physics, Rutgers Univ, 63-65; asst prof, 65-73, ASSOC PROF PHYSICS, Univ Conn, 73- *Concurrent Pos:* Adj prof, New Eng Inst, 70-; vis res scientist, Univ Sussex, 71-72. *Mem:* Am Phys Soc. *Mailing Add:* Dept of Physics Univ of Conn Storrs CT 06268

MARKOWITZ, HAROLD, b New York, NY, Sept 1, 25; m 53; c 4. IMMUNOCHEMISTRY. *Educ:* City Col New York, BS, 47; Columbia Univ, MA, 52, PhD(biochem), 53; Univ Utah, MD, 58. *Prof Exp:* Res assoc immunochem, Columbia Univ, 52-53; res fel med, Univ Utah, 53-59, intern, 58-59, instr, 59-61; asst prof microbiol, 62-68, ASSOC PROF MICROBIOL, MAYO GRAD SCH MED, UNIV MINN, 68-, CONSULT, MAYO CLIN, 61- *Concurrent Pos:* NIH fel, 59-60; assoc attend physician, Salt Lake County Gen Hosp, Utah, 59-61. *Mem:* Am Asn Immunol; Am Soc Microbiol; Soc Exp Biol & Med; NY Acad Sci; Cent Soc Clin Res. *Res:* Carbohydrate chemistry; trace metal and copper metabolism; antigens of erythrocytes and pathogenic fungi; immunohematology; phytohemagglutinins. *Mailing Add:* Dept of Lab Med Mayo Clinic 200 First St SW Rochester MN 55902

MARKOWITZ, JOSEPH MORRIS, physical chemistry, see previous edition

MARKOWITZ, MELVIN MYRON, b New York, NY, Sept 17, 46. PHYCOLOGY. *Educ:* City Col New York, BS, 68; Univ Ill, Urbana, MS, 70, PhD(bot), 75. *Prof Exp:* Lectr bot, Univ Ill, Urbana, 75-77, ASST PROF BIOL, STATE UNIV NY, OSWEGO, 77- *Mem:* Am Phycol Soc; Brit Phycol Soc. *Res:* Ultrastructure and histochemical investigations of the reproductive cells of algae. *Mailing Add:* Dept of Biol State Univ of NY Oswego NY 13126

MARKOWITZ, MILTON, b New York, NY, June 6, 18; c 4. PEDIATRICS. *Educ:* Syracuse Univ, AB, 39, MD, 43. *Prof Exp:* Asst pediat, Sch Med, Johns Hopkins Hosp, 48-49, instr, 50-55, asst prof, Sch Med, Univ, 55-62, dir pediat rheumatic clins, Children's Med & Surg Ctr, 61-69; assoc pediatrician-in-chief, Sinai Hosp, Baltimore, 63-69; PROF PEDIAT & HEAD DEPT, SCH MED, UNIV CONN HEALTH CTR, 69- *Concurrent Pos:* Pvt pract, 49-52; dir streptococcal dis res lab, Sinai Hosp, Baltimore, 60-69; assoc prof pediat, Sch Med, Johns Hopkins Univ, 62-69. *Mem:* Fel Am Acad Pediat; Am Pediat Soc. *Res:* Rheumatic heart disease. *Mailing Add:* Dept of Pediat Univ of Conn Health Ctr Farmington CT 06032

MARKOWITZ, SAMUEL SOLOMON, b Brooklyn, NY, Oct 31, 31; m 58; c 3. NUCLEAR CHEMISTRY. *Educ:* Rensselaer Polytech, BS, 53; Princeton Univ, MA, 55, PhD, 57. *Prof Exp:* Jr res assoc nuclear chem, Brookhaven Nat Lab, 55-57; NSF fel, Univ Birmingham, 57-58; from asst prof to assoc prof chem, Univ Calif, Berkeley, 58-72, mem staff, Lawrence Berkeley Lab, 58-64, sr scientist, 64-80, PROF CHEM, UNIV CALIF, BERKELEY, 72-, SR SR SCIENTIST, LAWRENCE BERKELEY LAB, 80- *Concurrent Pos:* Imp Chem Industs hon fel, Univ Birmingham, 57-58; NSF sr fel, fac sci, Univ Paris, 64-65; vis prof, Weizmann Inst Sci, Israel, 73-74. *Mem:* AAAS; Am Chem Soc; Am Phys Soc; Sigma Xi. *Res:* Nuclear reactions for analysis of atmospheric aerosols; chemistry of atmospheric aerosols; nucler reactions at billion-electron-volt energies; fission and spallation; meson-induced reactions; nuclear activation analysis by He-3-induced reactions; radiochemistry; chemical fate of atoms produced via nuclear transformations. *Mailing Add:* Dept of Chem & Lawrence Lab Univ of Calif Berkeley CA 94720

MARKOWITZ, WILLIAM, b Poland, Feb 8, 07; nat US; m 43; c 1. ASTRONOMY. *Educ:* Univ Chicago, BS, 27, MS, 29, PhD(astron), 31. *Prof Exp:* Instr math, Pa State Col, 31-32; astronr, US Naval Observ, 36-66, dir time serv, 53-66; prof physics, Marquette Univ, 66-68, Wehr prof, 68-72; ADJ PROF, NOVA UNIV, FLA, 72- *Concurrent Pos:* Ed, Geophys Surv, 72-79. *Mem:* Int Astron Union; Int Union Geod & Geophys; Am Astron Soc; Am Geophys Union. *Res:* Time and frequency; variations in earth rotation; motion of pole; SI Units. *Mailing Add:* 2800 East Sunrise Blvd Apt 15-B Ft Lauderdale FL 33304

MARKOWSKI, GREGORY RAY, b Milwaukee, Wis, June 23, 47. AEROSOL SCIENCE. *Educ:* Calif Inst Technol BS, 69; Univ Calif, Berkeley, MS, 72. *Prof Exp:* SR SCIENTIST, METEOROL RES INC, 73- *Mem:* AAAS. *Res:* Measuring the particle mass and elemental concentrations as a function of size of the fine particles generated in coal combustion and the secondary aerosol formed in the plume from coal fired power plants. *Mailing Add:* Meteorol Res Inc Box 637 Altadena CA 91001

MARKOWSKI, HENRY JOSEPH, b Worcester, Mass, July 1, 29; m 54; c 6. ORGANIC POLYMER CHEMISTRY. *Educ:* Providence Col, BS, 52. *Prof Exp:* Anal chemist, Nitrogen Div, Allied Chem Corp, 52-56; mgr, Markowski's Bakery, RI, 56-57; develop chemist, Lowe Brothers Paint Co, 57-60 & Hysol Corp, 60-64; develop chemist, Insulation Mat Dept, Gen Elec Corp, 64-68; mgr resin develop, P D George Paint & Varnish Co, 68-70; tech dir, Windecker Res, Tex, 70-71; SR RES CHEMIST, CARBOLINE CO, 71- *Mem:* Am Chem Soc. *Res:* Polymer synthesis and research; urethane elastomers; epoxy coatings, organo-metallic polymers; resins, coatings, and adhesives used for electrical insulation and corrosion resistance. *Mailing Add:* Carboline Co 350 Hanley Industrial Ct St Louis MO 63144

MARKS, ALFRED FINLAY, b Yorktown Heights, NY, Sept 13, 32; c 4. AGRICULTURAL CHEMISTRY. *Educ:* Iowa State Univ, BS, 55. *Prof Exp:* Res chemist, Am Cyanamid Corp, 55-67; sr res chemist, Esso Res & Eng Corp, 67-70; group leader biochem formulations, 70-81, MGR ENVIRON SCI, DIAMOND SHAMROCK CORP, 81- *Mem:* Am Chem Soc; fel Am Inst Chemists. *Res:* Development of residue and environmental fate data on new and existing products, particulary pesticides and animal health drugs, for support of registrations. *Mailing Add:* Diamond Shamrock Corp T R Evans Res Ctr PO Box 348 Painesville OH 44077

MARKS, ASHER, b Atlanta, Ga, Sept 5, 26; m 49; c 2. MEDICINE. *Educ:* Emory Univ, MD, 50; Am Bd Internal Med, dipl, 59; Am Bd Pulmonary Dis, dipl, 69. *Prof Exp:* From intern to jr asst resident med, Boston City Hosp, 50-52; from instr to asst prof, 57-63, ASSOC PROF MED, MED SCH, UNIV MIAMI, 63- *Concurrent Pos:* Fel chest dis, Boston City Hosp, 54-56; res fel, Med Sch, Univ Miami, 56-58; consult, Vet Admin Hosp, Coral Gables, Fla, 57-, Southeast Fla Tuberc Hosp, Lantana, 58- & Miami Vet Admin Hosp, 78-; attend, Jackson Mem Hosp, 78-, Cedars Lebanon Hosp, 68-, med dir, 76- *Mem:* Am Thoracic Soc; Am Col Physicians; Am Col Chest Physicians. *Res:* Disease of chest; cardio-pulmonary physiology. *Mailing Add:* 1150 NW 14th St Miami FL 33136

MARKS, BERNARD HERMAN, b Cleveland, Ohio, Apr 21, 21; m 43; c 1. PHARMACOLOGY, BIOCHEMISTRY. *Educ:* Ohio State Univ, BA, 42, MD, 45, MA, 50. *Prof Exp:* Instr pharm & biochem, Ohio State Univ, 48-53, asst prof pharmacol, 54-56, from assoc prof to prof pharm, 57-73, chmn dept, 63-73; PROF PHARMACOL & CHMN DEPT, WAYNE STATE UNIV, 74- *Mem:* AAAS; Am Soc Pharmacol & Exp Therapeut. *Res:* Cellular, cardiovascular and endocrine pharmacology; digitalis; radio-labeled drugs. *Mailing Add:* Dept of Pharmacol Wayne State Univ Sch of Med Detroit MI 48201

MARKS, BURTON STEWART, b New York, NY, Oct 23, 24; m 48; c 3. POLYMER CHEMISTRY. *Educ:* Univ Miami, Fla, BS, 48, MS, 50; Polytech Inst Brooklyn, PhD(chem), 55. *Prof Exp:* Sr res chemist, Hooker Chem Co, 55-58; adv scientist, Continental Can Co, Inc, Ill, 58-62; STAFF SCIENTIST, LOCKHEED-PALO ALTO RES LABS, 62- *Concurrent Pos:* Adj prof, Niagara Univ, 57-58 & Roosevelt Univ, 60-62. *Mem:* Am Chem Soc; Royal Soc Chem. *Res:* Organic and polymer synthesis and chemistry; monomers; polymerization; resins; coatings; adhesives; foams; composite structures; ceramics; carbides. *Mailing Add:* 3415 Louis Rd Palo Alto CA 94303

MARKS, CHARLES, b Kremenchug, Russia, Jan 28, 22; US citizen; m 49; c 4. MEDICINE. *Educ:* Univ Cape Town, BA, 42, MD, 45; Marquette Univ, MS, 65; FRCS; FRCP; Tulane Univ, PhD, 73. *Prof Exp:* Hunterian prof surg, Royal Col Surgeons, Eng, 56; assoc prof, Sch Med, Marquette Univ, 63-67; clin prof, Sch Med, Case Western Reserve Univ, 67-71; PROF SURG, SCH MED, UNIV NEW ORLEANS, 71- *Concurrent Pos:* Consult surg, Salisbury, Rhodesia, 53-65, Vet Admin Hosp & Milwaukee County Gen Hosp, 63-, St Francis Hosp & Mt Sinai Hosp, Milwaukee, Wis, 64-; dir div surg, Mt Sinai Hosp, Cleveland, Ohio, 67-71; attend surgeon, Charity Hosp, Touro Infirmary & Hotel Dieu Hosp, 71-; consult cardiovasc surg, E Jefferson Gen Hosp, New Orleans, La, 71- *Mem:* AMA; Am Col Chest Physicians; fel Am Col Surg; fel Am Col Cardiol; fel Royal Soc Med. *Res:* Hepatocyte synthesis measured with tritiated thymidine autoradiography in response to variable hepatic blood flow; haemodynamic effects of protal hypertension. *Mailing Add:* 1680 State St New Orleans LA 70118

MARKS, CHARLES FRANCIS, nematology, plant pathology, see previous edition

MARKS, COLIN H, b Cardiff, Wales, Oct 8, 33; US citizen. MECHANICAL ENGINEERING. *Educ:* Carnegie Inst Technol, BSME, 56, MS, 57; Univ Md, PhD(mech eng), 65. *Prof Exp:* From instr to assoc prof, 59-78, PROF MECH ENG, UNIV MD, COLLEGE PARK, 78- *Concurrent Pos:* Vis scientist, Woods Hole Oceanog Inst, 67. *Mem:* Am Soc Mech Engrs. *Res:* Ground vehicle aerodynamics; bubble induced flows. *Mailing Add:* Dept of Mech Eng Univ of Md College Park MD 20740

MARKS, DARRELL L, b Mountain Home, Idaho, July 23, 36; m 55; c 4. PHYSICS. *Educ:* Northwest Nazarene Col, AB, 58; Mass Inst Technol, MS, 59; Ore State Univ, PhD(biophys), 66. *Prof Exp:* Mem fac, 59-75, CHMN DIV MATH & NATURAL SCI, NORTHWEST NAZARENE COL, 75- *Concurrent Pos:* Mem curric comn, Idaho State, 75-81. *Mem:* AAAS; Am Asn Physics Teachers. *Res:* science education; microprocessors used in teaching large lab classes. *Mailing Add:* Dept of Physics Northwest Nazarene Col Nampa ID 83651

MARKS, DAVID HUNTER, b White Plains, NY, Feb 22, 39; m 65. CIVIL & ENVIRONMENTAL ENGINEERING. *Educ:* Cornell Univ, BCE, 62, MS, 64; Johns Hopkins Univ, PhD(environ eng), 69. *Prof Exp:* From asst prof to assoc prof, 69-75, PROF CIVIL ENG, MASS INST TECHNOL, 75-, ASSOC DIR, RALPH M PARSONS LAB FOR WATER RESOURCES & HYDRODYN, 77- *Honors & Awards:* Huber Res Prize, Am Soc Civil Engrs, 77. *Mem:* Am Soc Civil Engrs; Am Geophys Union; Am Water Resources Asn; Water Pollution Control Fedn; Opers Res Soc Am. *Res:* Water resource systems; water quality management. *Mailing Add:* Dept Civil Eng 77 Massachusetts Ave Cambridge MA 02139

MARKS, DAWN BEATTY, b West Reading, Pa, July 16, 37; m 59; c 3. BIOCHEMISTRY. *Educ:* Bucknell Univ, BA, 59; Univ Pa, MS, 63, PhD(biochem), 65. *Prof Exp:* Asst prof, 70-76, ASSOC PROF BIOCHEM, TEMPLE UNIV SCH MED, 76- *Mem:* Am Soc Biol Chemists. *Res:* Chromatin structure and function; regulation of protein synthesis. *Mailing Add:* Dept of Biochem Temple Univ Sch Med Philadelphia PA 19140

MARKS, DENNIS WILLIAM, b Madison, Wis, Nov 5, 44; m 68. ASTROPHYSICS, RELATIVITY. *Educ:* Fordham Univ, BS, 66; Univ Mich, Ann Arbor, PhD(astron), 70. *Prof Exp:* Fel & asst prof, David Dunlap Observ, Univ Toronto, 70-71; asst prof, 71-74, dir planetarium & observ, 73-80, assoc prof, 74-78, PROF PHYSICS & ASTRON, VALDOSTA STATE COL, 78- *Mem:* Int Soc Gen Relativity & Gravitation; Am Asn Univ Prof; Am Astron Soc. *Res:* Internal differential rotation of stars; viscosity of gases and radiation; relativistic stellar structure and evolution. *Mailing Add:* Dept Phys Astron & Geol Valdosta State Col Valdosta GA 31698

MARKS, GERALD A, b New York, NY, May 17, 49; m 76. NEUROSCIENCE, NEUROPHYSIOLOGY. *Educ:* City Col New York, BS, 72; City Univ New York, PhD(physiol psychol), 78. *Prof Exp:* Res asst neurosci, Montefiore Hosp & Med Ctr, 75-77; fac assoc, 77-81, res instr, neurosci, 81-83, ASST PROF PSYCHIAT, UNIV TEX HEALTH SCI CTR, SOUTHWESTERN MED SCH, DALLAS, 83- *Concurrent Pos:* Adj lectr psychol, City Col New York, 74-76; NIH fel neurosci, 79-81; NIH grant prin investr, 81-82. *Mem:* AAAS; Asn Psychophysiol Study Sleep; NY Acad Sci; Soc Neurosci. *Res:* Basic mechanisms of the central nervous system with an emphasis on those mechanisms relating to sleep behavior. *Mailing Add:* Dept Psychiat Univ Tex Health Sci Ctr Dallas TX 75235

MARKS, GERALD SAMUEL, b Cape Town, SAfrica, Feb 13, 30; m 55; c 2. ORGANIC CHEMISTRY, PHARMACOLOGY. *Educ:* Univ Cape Town, BSc, 50, MSc, 51; Oxford Univ, DPhil(org chem), 54. *Prof Exp:* Res chemist, SAfrican Inst Med Res, 55-56; res assoc porphyrin biosynthesis, Univ Chicago, 57-59; assoc prof pharmacol, Univ Alta, 62-69; HEAD DEPT PHARMACOL, QUEEN'S UNIV, ONT, 69- *Concurrent Pos:* Nat Res Coun Can fel, 56-57; Brit Empire Cancer Campaign fel, Dept Chem Path, St Mary's Hosp, London, 60-62. *Mem:* Pharmacol Soc Can; The Chem Soc; Am Soc Pharmacol & Exp Therapeut. *Res:* Porphyrin biosynthesis; organic nitrates; mechanism of action and pharmacokinetics. *Mailing Add:* Dept of Pharmacol Queen's Univ Kingston ON K7L 3N6 Can

MARKS, HENRY L, b Waynesboro, Va, Sept 6, 35; m 59; c 1. ANIMAL GENETICS. *Educ:* Va Polytech Inst, BS, 58, MS, 60; Univ Md, PhD, 67. *Prof Exp:* Res geneticist, 60-67, RES GENETICIST, SOUTH REGIONAL POULTRY BREEDING PROJ, AGR RES SERV, USDA, 67- *Mem:* Poultry Sci Asn; World Poultry Sci Asn. *Res:* Design and test animal breeding systems for increasing production by genetic selection. *Mailing Add:* Room 107 Livestock-Poultry Bldg Univ Ga Athens GA 30601

MARKS, JAY STEWART, b Ottawa, Ill, Apr 10, 37; m 61; c 3. FOOD ENGINEERING, CHEMICAL ENGINEERING. *Educ:* Univ Kans, BS, 59, PhD(chem eng), 65. *Prof Exp:* Chem engr, Mallinckrodt, Inc, 63-66, prod supt, 66-69, asst to mfg dir, 69-70, mgr mkt res, 70-73; plant mgr protein, Ralston Purina, 73-78; ASSOC PROF FOOD ENG, PURDUE UNIV, WEST LAFAYETTE, 78- *Mem:* Am Inst Chem Engrs; Inst Food Technologists; Am Soc Agr Engrs. *Res:* Energy conservation in food processing; solar utilization in food processing; physical properties of food. *Mailing Add:* Dept of Agr Eng Purdue Univ West Lafayette IN 47907

MARKS, LAWRENCE EDWARD, b New York, NY, Dec 28, 41; m 63; c 2. EXPERIMENTAL PSYCHOLOGY. *Educ:* Hunter Col, AB, 62; Harvard Univ, PhD(psychol), 65. *Prof Exp:* Res fel lectr, Harvard Univ, 65-66; res psychologist, 66-69, asst prof epidemiol, 70-76, ASSOC PROF EPIDEM & PSYCHOL, YALE UNIV, 76- *Concurrent Pos:* Asst fel psychol, John B Pierce Found 66-69, assoc fel, 69- *Mem:* Fel Am Psychol Asn; Soc Neurosci; Optical Soc Am; Acoust Soc Am; Int Asn Artificial Organs. *Res:* Sensory processes, especially hearing and temperature senses; interrelations among the senses; psychophysical measurement; psychology of language, particularly metaphor. *Mailing Add:* John B Pierce Found Lab 290 Congress Ave New Haven CT 06519

MARKS, LEON JOSEPH, b Providence, RI, Nov 30, 25; m 56; c 2. INTERNAL MEDICINE, ENDOCRINOLOGY. *Educ:* Brown Univ, AB, 44; Johns Hopkins Univ, MD, 48; Am Bd Internal Med, dipl, 56. *Prof Exp:* Intern med, Jewish Hosp, Brooklyn, NY, 48-49; jr resident, Kings County Hosp, 49-50; sr resident, Montefiore Hosp, 50-51; staff physician & dir steroid res lab, 52-73, chief outpatient serv & ambulatory health care, 52-75, assoc chief staff, Ambulatory Health Care, 75-78, CHIEF STAFF, BOSTON VET ADMIN HOSP, 79-; ASSOC PROF MED, SCH MED, BOSTON UNIV, 77-, ASST DEAN, 79- *Concurrent Pos:* Milton res fel, Harvard Univ, 51-52; res fel pediat, Mass Gen Hosp, 51-52; clin instr, Sch Med, Tufts Univ, 61-66, sr clin instr, 66-68, asst prof, 68-, asst dean, 79- *Mem:* Endocrine Soc; Am Geriat Soc; AMA; fel Am Col Physicians; Am Fedn Clin. *Res:* Res: Metabolism and endocrinology, especially adrenal steroid biochemistry and physiology as applied clinically to medicine, surgery and psychiatry; cancer of the prostate. *Mailing Add:* Vet Admin Hosp Boston MA 02130

MARKS, LOUIS SHEPPARD, b New York, NY, Dec 13, 17; m 44; c 4. ENTOMOLOGY, MATHEMATICAL BIOLOGY. *Educ:* City Col New York, BS, 39; Fordham Univ, MS, 51, PhD(entom), 54. *Prof Exp:* Statist analyst, US Dept Com, 40-42; prof chem & sanit sci, Am Acad, 46-51; instr biol, Fordham Univ, 51-54, from asst prof to assoc prof, 54-65; prof & head dept, Pace Col, 65-66; chmn dept, 66-78, PROF BIOL ST JOSEPH'S COL, PA, 66- *Concurrent Pos:* Smith Mundt vis prof, Nat Univ Mex, 56; vis prof, Hunter Col, 57; fel, Harvard Univ, 62-64; fel, NC State Univ, 63 & Williams Col, 65; Lilly fel, Barnes Arboretum, 70-, Univ Pa, 80- *Mem:* Fel Linnean Soc; Soc Syst Zool; fel Royal Entom Soc; Soc Bibliog Natural Hist; Soc Study Evolution. *Res:* Human pedigree analysis; systematic entomology; taxonomy; morphology and zoogeography of the Lepidoptera; vertebrate coronary circulation; mathematical and evolutionary biology; zoological bibliography; chordate morphology. *Mailing Add:* Dept of Biol St Joseph's Univ Philadelphia PA 19131

MARKS, LUTHER WHITFIELD, III, b Fairfax, Okla, Nov 2, 26; m 48; c 4. PHYSICS. *Educ:* Cent State Univ, Okla, BS, 49; Univ Okla, MS, 51, PhD(physics), 55. *Prof Exp:* Asst physics, Univ Okla, 49-55; instr, 55, from asst prof to assoc prof, 55-58, chmn dept, 58-78, PROF PHYSICS, CENT STATE UNIV, OKLA, 58- *Mem:* Sigma Xi; Am Asn Physics Teachers. *Res:* Electrode process energetics, particularly analysis of decay of activation overpotential for cathodic hydrogen. *Mailing Add:* Dept Physics Cent State Univ Edmond OK 73034

MARKS, MEYER BENJAMIN, b Chicago, Ill, Feb 16, 07; m 32; c 2. PEDIATRIC ALLERGY. *Educ:* Univ Ill, BS, 31, MD, 33. *Prof Exp:* Assoc clin prof & dir pediat allergy, 54-70, CLIN PROF PEDIAT & CHIEF DIV PEDIAT ALLERGY, SCH MED, UNIV MIAMI, 70- *Concurrent Pos:* Dir pediat, Mt Sinai Hosp, Miami Beach, 50-59; dir pediat allergy clin, Jackson Mem Hosp, Miami, 55-; consult pediat allergy, Mt Sinai Med Ctr, Miami Beach, 60- *Honors & Awards:* William Beaumont Prize, Univ Ill Col Med, 35; Cert of Merit, AMA, 66; Silver Award, Am Acad Pediat, 75; Award Merit, Am Col Allergists, 77. *Mem:* Am Acad Allergy; Am Col Allergists; Am Acad Pediat. *Res:* Clinical research in all phases of pediatric allergy; identification of the allergic child; prophylaxis of childhood asthma; bruxism in allergic children; prevalence of allergy in school children in subtropical climates; inhalational medications in treatment of asthmatic children; ultrasonic nebulized cromolyn mist in childhood asthma. *Mailing Add:* 333 Arthur Godfrey Rd Miami Beach FL 33140

MARKS, MORTON, b Vineland, NJ, Oct 26, 18; m 74; c 6. NEUROLOGY, PSYCHIATRY. *Educ:* Temple Univ, AB, 39, MD, 43; Am Bd Psychiat & Neurol, dipl & cert neurol, 51, cert psychiat, 52. *Prof Exp:* Clin asst neurol, 49-51, instr, 51-52, dir neurol res, Inst Phys Med & Rehab, Med Ctr, 50-62, ASST PROF CLIN NEUROL, COL MED, NY UNIV, 52- *Concurrent Pos:* Asst attend physician, Univ Hosp, New York, 50-; mem med adv bd, Nat Multiple Sclerosis Soc, 58. *Mem:* AMA; Am Psychiat Asn; Am Fedn Clin Res; Am Acad Neurol. *Res:* Research in rehabilitation of chronic neurological patients and degenerative neurological diseases. *Mailing Add:* 566 First Ave New York NY 10016

MARKS, NEVILLE, b Dublin, Ireland, Apr 10, 30. NEUROBIOLOGY. *Educ:* Univ London, MSc, 55, PhD(neurochem), 59. *Prof Exp:* Lectr neurochem, Inst Psychiat, Univ London, 57-59; fel biochem, Northwestern Univ, 59-60; neurochem, Ment Health Res Inst, Univ Mich, 60-61; sr res scientist, 61-68, assoc res scientist, 68-70, PRIN RES SCIENTIST, NY STATE RES INST NEUROCHEM & DRUG ADDICTION, 70-; ASSOC PROF, DEPT PSYCHIAT, NY UNIV, 79- *Concurrent Pos:* Ed, Res Methods Neurochem, Vols I-V, assoc ed, Neurochem Res, 75; consult, Vet Admin Hosp, East Orange, 71-78; assoc ed, Neurochem Int, 80- *Mem:* Am Acad Neurol; Am Soc Neurochem; Int Soc Neurochem; Biochem Soc UK; Am Soc Biol Chemists. *Res:* Protein breakdown and turnover in brain; purification of catabolic enzymes; myelin turnover in experimental demyelination; formation and breakdown of hormonal peptides; neurochemistry of senile disorders and neuropathies. *Mailing Add:* NY State Inst of Neurochem Ward's Island New York NY 10035

MARKS, PAUL A, b New York, NY, Aug 16, 26; m 53; c 3. INTERNAL MEDICINE, BIOCHEMISTRY. *Educ:* Columbia Univ, AB, 45, MD, 49. *Prof Exp:* Res fel med, Med Col, Cornell Univ, 49; intern med, Presby Hosp, New York, 50, asst resident, 51; fel, Col Physicians & Surgeons, Columbia Univ, 52-53; assoc investr, Nat Inst Arthritis & Metab Dis, 53-55; instr med, Sch Med, George Washington Univ, 54-55; instr, 55-56, assoc, 56-57, from asst prof to assoc prof, 57-67, dir hemat training, 61-74, chmn dept human genetics & develop, 69-70, dean fac med & vpres in chg med affairs, 70-73, vpres health sci & dir cancer res ctr, 73-80, Frode Jensen prof med, 74-80, PROF MED, COL PHYSICIANS & SURGEONS, COLUMBIA UNIV, 67-, PROF HUMAN GENETICS & DEVELOP, 69-; PRES, MEM SLOAN-KETTERING CANCER CTR, 80-, MEM, SLOAN-KETTERING INST CANCER RES, 80- *Concurrent Pos:* Commonwealth Fund fel, 61-62; vis scientist, Lab Cellular Biochem, Pasteur Inst, 61-62; consult, Vet Admin Hosp, 62-69; mem adv panel develop biol, NSF, 64-67; Swiss-Am Found lectr & award in med res, 65; ed-in-chief, J Clin Invest, Am Soc Clin Invest, 67-71; mem adv panel hemat training grants prog, NIH, 69-73, chmn hemat training grants comn, 71-73; trustee, Roosevelt Hosp & St Luke's Hosp, 70-80; mem div med sci, Nat Res Coun, 72-, chmn exec comt, 73-76; Carl R Moore lectr, Sch Med, Wash Univ, 73; honors prog lectr, Sch Med, NY Univ, 73; mem jury, Albert Lasker Awards, 74-76 & 80-81; mem adv comt, XV Int Cong Hemat, Israel, 74; mem rev comt blood dis & blood resources panel, Nat Res & Demonstration Ctr, Nat Heart & Lung Inst, 74; mem, Dartmouth Med Sch Conf on Health Systs, 75; President's Biomed Res Panel, 75-76; Frontiers in Biol Sci lectr, Case Western Reserve Univ Sch Med, 75; Sci Coun adv to bd dirs, Radiation Effects Res Found, Japan, 75-77; mem President's Cancer Panel, 76-79; mem bd gov, Weizmann Inst Sci, 76-; dir, Charles H. Revson Found, Inc, 76-; ed-in-chief, Blood, J Am Soc Hemat, 78-; adj prof, Rockefeller Univ, 80-; vis physician, Rockefeller Univ Hosp, 80-; mem hon staff med, NY Hosp, 81-; attend physician, Mem Hosp Cancer & Allied Dis,

80-; chmn, Sect Med Genetics, Hemat & Oncol, Nat Acad Sci, 80-; mem comt planning study for ongoing study of costs of environ related health effects, 80; chmn acad forum adv comt, Nat Acad Sci, 80-81; mem, President's comn on accident at Three Mile Island, 79; ad hoc adv, 1981 White House Conf Aging, 80-81; mem bd sci counrs, Div Cancer Treatment, Nat Cancer Inst, 80-, tech bd, Milbank Mem Fund, 78-; adv, Leopold Schepp Found, 80-; mem sci adv comt, Mass Gen Hosp, 81- *Honors & Awards:* Charles Janeway Prize, 49; Joseph Mather Smith Prize, 59; Stevens Triennial Prize, Columbia Univ, 60. *Mem:* Nat Acad Sci; Nat Inst Med; fel Am Acad Arts & Sci, Am Soc Clin Invest (pres, 71-72); Harvey Soc (treas, 67-70, vpres, 72-73, pres, 73-74). *Res:* Cellular development; protein synthesis; human genetics; hematology. *Mailing Add:* Mem Sloan-Kettering Cancer Ctr 1275 York Ave New York NY 10021

MARKS, PETER J, US citizen. ENVIRONMENTAL ENGINEERING. *Educ:* Franklin & Marshall Col, BS, 63; Drexel Univ, MS, 65. *Prof Exp:* Mem staff res lab anal methods develop, Lancaster County Gen Hosp, 63-64; VPRES, WESTON, 65- *Mem:* Am Soc Testing & Mat; Water Pollution Control Fedn. *Res:* Environmental analytical laboratory analysis; source emmissions and ambient air sampling; wastewater treatment; biological monitoring methods. *Mailing Add:* Weston Weston Way West Chester PA 19380

MARKS, PETER LAWRENCE, plant ecology, see previous edition

MARKS, RICHARD HENRY LEE, b Richmond, Va, Nov 23, 43; m 66; c 2. BIOCHEMISTRY. *Educ:* Univ Richmond, BS, 65; Ind Univ, Bloomington, PhD(biol chem), 69. *Prof Exp:* USPHS fel, Univ Calif, Santa Barbara, 69-70, univ fel, 71-72; asst prof biochem, Col Med & Dent NJ, 72-76; asst prof, 76-77, ASSOC PROF BIOCHEM, SCH MED, E CAROLINA UNIV, 77- *Mem:* NY Acad Sci; Am Chem Soc. *Res:* Structure-function relationships in proteins, especially metalloproteins; oxidation-reduction of metalloproteins. *Mailing Add:* Dept of Biochem East Carolina Univ Sch of Med Greenville NC 27834

MARKS, RONALD LEE, b Jersey Shore, Pa, May 23, 34; m 71; c 3. INORGANIC CHEMISTRY. *Educ:* Lock Haven State Col, BS, 56; Pa State Univ, MEd, 59, EdD(chem educ), 66. *Prof Exp:* PROF CHEM, INDIANA UNIV, PA, 59- *Mem:* Am Chem Soc. *Res:* Hydroboration of aromatic heterocycles. *Mailing Add:* Dept of Chem Indiana Univ of Pa Indiana PA 15705

MARKS, SANDY COLE, JR, b Wilmington, NC, Nov 16, 37; m 62; c 2. ANATOMY. *Educ:* Washington & Lee Univ, BS, 60; Univ NC, DDS, 64; Johns Hopkins Univ, PhD(anat), 68. *Prof Exp:* Res officer, Dent Res Dept, Naval Med Res Inst, Bethesda, Md, 68-70; asst prof, 70-73, assoc prof 73-77, PROF ANAT, MED SCH, UNIV MASS, 77-, COORDR ANAT DONATIONS 76- *Mem:* AAAS; Int Asn Dent Res; Am Asn Anatomists; Am Soc Bone Mineral Res. *Res:* Bone metabolism; calcium homeostasis; tooth eruption. *Mailing Add:* Dept Anat Univ Mass Med Sch Worcester MA 01605

MARKS, SIDNEY, b Chicago, Ill, June 28, 18; m 46; c 2. PATHOLOGY, BIOSTATISTICS. *Educ:* Univ Ill, BS, 38, MD, 42; Univ Idaho, MS, 61; Univ Calif, Los Angeles, PhD, 70. *Prof Exp:* Pathologist, Vet Admin Hosp, Albuquerque, NMex, 47-48, Kadlec Hosp & Biol Lab, Gen Elec Co, Wash, 50-53 & Kadlec Methodist Hosp, Richland, 53-65; assoc prof surg & internal med, Sch Med, Univ Md, 70-71; coordr human studies & biostatist, Div Biomed & Environ Res, Energy Res & Develop Admin, 71-76; ASSOC MGR, ENVIRON, HEALTH & SAFETY RES PROG, BATTELLE PAC NORTHWEST LAB, 76- *Concurrent Pos:* Consult, Biol Lab & Occup Health Oper, Gen Elec Co, Wash, 53-65, Hanford Environ Health Found, Richland, 65-68 & Radiobiol Lab, Univ Calif, Davis, 66-70. *Mem:* Col Am Pathologists; Biomet Soc; Air Pollution Control Asn; Am Statist Asn; Soc Epidemiol Res. *Res:* Occupational air pollution and radiation epidemiology; radiation health risk assessment. *Mailing Add:* Battelle Northwest PO Box 999 Richland WA 99352

MARKS, THOMAS, JR, b Rock Hill, SC, May 17, 51. NUCLEAR PHYSICS. *Educ:* Univ SC, BS, 72, PhD(nuclear phys), 77. *Prof Exp:* Res asst, Los Alamos Meson Physics Facil, 75-77; fel nuclear physics, TRIUMF Lab Vancouver, 77-78; STAFF MEM NUCLEAR PHYSICS INSTRUMENTATION, DOE'S LOS ALAMOS SCI LAB, 78- *Concurrent Pos:* Vis staff mem, ERDA's Los Alamos Sci Lab, 77. *Mem:* Am Asn Physics Teachers. *Mailing Add:* Mail Stop 540 Los Alamos Sci Lab Los Alamos NM 87545

MARKS, TOBIN JAY, b Washington, DC, Nov 25, 44. CHEMISTRY. *Educ:* Univ Md, College Park, BS, 66; Mass Inst Technol, PhD(chem), 70. *Prof Exp:* Asst prof, 70-74, ASSOC PROF CHEM, NORTHWESTERN UNIV, ILL, 74- *Mem:* Am Chem Soc. *Res:* Inorganic and organometallic chemistry; structural chemistry in solution; catalysis. *Mailing Add:* Dept of Chem Northwestern Univ Evanston IL 60201

MARKSON, RALPH JOSEPH, b Feb 25, 31; US citizen; m 67; c 1. ATMOSPHERIC PHYSICS. *Educ:* Reed Col, BA, 56; Pa State Univ, MA, 67; State Univ NY Albany, PhD(atmospheric sci), 74. *Prof Exp:* Res engr, Convair Astronauts, 56-58; physicist, self employed, 58-65; res assoc atmospheric elec, State Univ NY Albany, 67-74; RES ASSOC ATMOSPHERIC PHYSICS, MASS INST TECHNOL, 74- *Concurrent Pos:* Pres, Airborne Res Assocs Inc; res pilot high altitude atmospheric aircraft. *Mem:* Am Geophys Union; Am Meteorol Soc; AAAS. *Res:* Atmospheric electrical global circuit; thundercloud electrification; extra-terrestrial modulation of atmospheric electricity and weather; use of atmospheric space charge as an air tracer; remote thermal detection for soaring; maritime convection and fog. *Mailing Add:* 46 Kendal Common Rd Weston MA 02193

MARKSTEIN, GEORGE HENRY, b Vienna, Austria, June 22, 11; nat US; m 37; c 1. APPLIED PHYSICS. *Educ:* Vienna Tech Univ, Ing, 35, PhD(appl physics), 37. *Prof Exp:* Res physicist, Allgem Gluhlampenfabrics AG, Austria, 37-38; asst seismologist, Shell Petrol Co, Colombia, 39-40, prod supt, Plastic Molding Plant, 42-43; prod supt, Globe Soc Ltd, 44-46; res physicist, Cornell Aeronaut Lab, Inc, 46-50, head combustion sect, 50-56, prin physicist, 56-71; prin res scientist, 71-81, CONSULT, FACTORY MUTUAL RES CORP, 81- *Mem:* AAAS; Am Phys Soc; Am Inst Aeronaut & Astronaut; Combustion Inst. *Res:* Combustion; fluid dynamics; reaction kinetics; fire research; radiative energy transfer. *Mailing Add:* Factory Mutual Res Corp 1151 Boston-Providence Turnpike Norwood MA 02062

MARKUNAS, PETER CHARLES, b Chicago, Ill, Nov 5, 11; m 41; c 3. ANALYTICAL CHEMISTRY. *Educ:* Shurtleff Col, BS, 34; Univ Ill, MS, 37, PhD(anal chem), 40. *Prof Exp:* Asst, Univ Ill, 37-40; res chemist, Nat Distillers & Chem Corp, 40-41 & Com Solvents Corp, 41-51; dir anal res, R J Reynolds Industs, Inc, 51-72; RETIRED. *Mem:* AAAS; Am Chem Soc. *Res:* Instrumentation methods of analysis; chromatography; development of methods for analysis of nitroparaffins and derivatives; penicillin; bacitracin; hexachlorocyclohexanes; complex cations in microanalysis; titrimetry in nonaqueous solvents; functional group analysis. *Mailing Add:* 2425 Westchester Blvd Springfield IL 62704

MARKUS, GABOR, b Budapest, Hungary, June 8, 22; nat US; m 64; c 3. BIOCHEMISTRY. *Educ:* Univ Budapest, MD, 47; Stanford Univ, PhD, 50. *Prof Exp:* Estab investr, Am Heart Asn, 60-63; assoc res prof, State Univ NY Buffalo, 63-67, chmn dept biochem, Roswell Park Div, 67-71; assoc cancer res scientist, 63-67, prin cancer res scientist, 67-79, ASSOC CHIEF CANCER RES SCIENTIST, ROSWELL PARK MEM INST, 79-; RES PROF BIOCHEM, STATE UNIV NY BUFFALO, 67- *Mem:* AAAS; Am Soc Biol Chemists; Soc Exp Biol & Med. *Res:* Protein structure and conformations; enzyme regulation; biochemistry of fibrinolysis; proleolytic enzymes in cancer. *Mailing Add:* 430 Starin Ave Buffalo NY 14216

MARKUS, HELENE BABAD, biochemistry, see previous edition

MARKUS, LAWRENCE, b Hibbing, Minn, Oct 13, 22; m 50; c 2. MATHEMATICS. *Educ:* Univ Chicago, BS, 42, MS(meteorol) & MS(math), 47; Harvard Univ, PhD(math), 51. *Prof Exp:* Instr meteorol, Univ Chicago, 42-44, res meteorologist, Atomic Energy Proj, 44; instr math, Harvard Univ, 51-52 & Yale Univ, 52-55; lectr, Princeton Univ, 55-57; from asst prof to assoc prof, 57-60, assoc head dept math, 61-63, PROF MATH, UNIV MINN, MINNEAPOLIS, 60-, DIR, CONTROL & DYNAMICAL SYSTS CTR, 65- *Concurrent Pos:* Fulbright fel, Paris, France, 50-51; Guggenheim fel, Univ Lausanne, 63-64; Nuffield prof, Univ Warwick, 68-69, dir control theory ctr, 70-; course dir, Int Ctr Theoret Physics, 74; lectr, Int Math Cong; prin lectr, Iranian Math Soc, 75; mem panel, Int Math Cong, 78; Sci Res Coun sr vis fel, Imp Col, Eng, 78; mem sci adv comt, US Educ Sci & Cult Orgn, Univ Strasbourg, France, 80. *Mem:* Am Math Soc; Math Asn Am; Sigma Xi. *Res:* Ordinary differential equations; control theory; differential geometry; cosmology. *Mailing Add:* Dept of Math Univ of Minn Minneapolis MN 55455

MARKUSZEWSKI, RICHARD, b Pinsk, Poland, July 18, 41; US citizen. COAL ANALYSIS, DESULFURIZATION OF COAL. *Educ:* Loyola Univ, BS, 63; Univ Wis, MS, 66; Iowa State Univ, PhD(anal chem), 76. *Prof Exp:* Assoc ed anal chem, Chem Abstracts Serv, 73-75; instr gen & anal chem, Dept Chem, Iowa State Univ, 76-77; res assoc, 77-79, assoc chemist, 79-81, PRIN INVESTR FOSSIL ENERGY, AMES LAB, 81-, ASST PROG DIR, 81- *Concurrent Pos:* Vis scientist, Warsaw Tech Univ, Poland, 77; asst prof, Dept Chem, Iowa State Univ, 78-81, lectr, 81; actg sci adminr, Fossil Energy, Ames Lab, 80-81. *Mem:* Am Chem Soc; Am Inst Chem Engrs; Am Soc Testing & Mat; Sigma Xi. *Res:* To characterize coal, especially for various sulfur components; develop chemical and physical methods for the removal of sulfur from coal. *Mailing Add:* 319 Spedding Hall Fossil Energy Off Iowa State Univ Ames IA 50011

MARKWALD, ROGER R, b Benton Harbor, Mich, Aug 21, 43; m; c 3. CELLULAR & DEVELOPMENTAL BIOLOGY. *Educ:* Calif State Univ, BS, 65; Colo State Univ, MS, 68, PhD(anat), 69. *Prof Exp:* Fel, Sch Med, Med Univ SC, 69-70, asst prof, Dept Anat, 70-75, grad fac mem, 71-75, res affil, Cardiol Sect, 73-75, assoc prof, Dept Anat, 75; assoc chmn, 77-81, ASSOC PROF, DEPT ANAT, HEALTH SCI CTR, TEX TECH UNIV, 75-, ACTG CHMN, 81- *Concurrent Pos:* Univ res award, 65, NIH Res Career Develop Award, Med Univ SC, 75 & Tex Tech Univ, 76; prin investr grants, Am Heart Asn, 70-72, SC Heart Asn, 73, NIH, 73-75, 76-79, 76-81, 78-81, 79-84 & 81. *Honors & Awards:* Lyndon Baines Johnson Res Award, Am Heart Asn, 77. *Mem:* Sigma Xi; Am Asn Antomists; Int Soc Develop Biol; Int Soc Cell Biol. *Res:* Capacity for and mechanisms (structural and biochemical) by which extracellular macromolecules mediate genetic expression in cardiac morphogenesis, neural crest development and limb regeneration; cell biological basis of in situ cell movement; cardiac and neural crest related malformations (teratology); author or coauthor of over 50 publications. *Mailing Add:* Dept Anat Tex Tech Univ Health Sci Ctr Lubbock TX 79430

MARKWELL, DICK ROBERT, b Muskogee, Okla, Feb 20, 25; m 49; c 4. ANALYTICAL CHEMISTRY. *Educ:* Univ Wichita, BS, 48, MS, 50; Univ Wis, PhD(chem), 56. *Prof Exp:* Res & develop coordr, Off Chief Res & Develop, Hq, US Army, 65-67; assoc prof chem, San Antonio Col, 67-74; chemist, Corpus Christi Dept of Health, 75-77; SUPVR CHEM SECT, SAN ANTONIO METROP HEALTH DIST, 77- *Mem:* Am Chem Soc. *Mailing Add:* 1406 Haskin Dr San Antonio TX 78209

MARKWORTH, ALAN JOHN, b Cleveland, Ohio, July 13, 37; c 3. PHYSICS. *Educ:* Case Inst Technol, BSc, 59; Ohio State Univ, MSc, 61, PhD(physics), 69. *Prof Exp:* prin res physicist, 66-80, SR RES SCIENTIST, BATTELLE COLUMBUS LABS, 80- *Mem:* Am Asn Physics Teachers; Am Inst Mining, Metall & Petrol Engrs; Sigma Xi. *Res:* Computer-simulation studies of macroscopic kinetic processes in solids and liquids; computer-simulation studies of macroscopic kinetic processes in solids and liquids; atmostic computer simulation; theory of phase transformation kinetics. *Mailing Add:* Phys Metall Sect Battelle Columbus Labs 505 King Ave Columbus OH 43201

MARLAND, GREGG (HINTON), b Oak Park, Ill, Sept 16, 42; m 63; c 3. GEOCHEMISTRY. *Educ:* Va Polytech Inst & State Univ, BS, 64; Univ Minn, PhD(geol), 72. *Prof Exp:* Asst prof geochem, Ind State Univ, Terre Haute, 70-75; ASSOC SCIENTIST, INST FOR ENERGY ANAL, 75- *Mem:* AAAS; Geochem Soc; Am Geophys Union; Soc Environ Geochem & Health. *Res:* Aqueous geochemistry; phase equilibria; environmental geochemistry, energy options and environmental implications. *Mailing Add:* Inst for Energy Anal Oak Ridge Assoc Univs Oak Ridge TN 37830

MARLATT, ABBY LINDSEY, b Manhattan, Kans, Dec 5, 16. NUTRITION. *Educ:* Kans State Univ, BS, 38; Univ Calif, cert, 40, PhD(animal nutrit), 47. *Prof Exp:* Asst home econ, Univ Calif, 40-45; from assoc prof to prof foods & nutrit, Kans State Univ, 45-56; vis prof home econ, Beirut Col Women, 53-54; dir col, 56-63, PROF NUTRIT & FOOD SCI, COL HOME ECON, UNIV KY, 63- *Concurrent Pos:* Consult, Ky State Col, 68-70 & Bd Int Food & Agr Develop, AID, 78- *Mem:* AAAS; Am Home Econ Asn; Am Dietetic Asn; Soc Nutrit Educ; Gerontol Soc. *Res:* Human nutrition; nutrient interrelationships; nutritional status and dietary surveys; pyridoxine requirements. *Mailing Add:* Dept Nutrit & Food Sci Col Home Econ Univ Ky Lexington KY 40506

MARLATT, ROBERT BRUCE, b Cleveland, Ohio, July 18, 20; m 46; c 3. PLANT PATHOLOGY. *Educ:* Univ Ariz, PhD(plant path), 52. *Prof Exp:* Asst plant pathologist, State Dept Agr, Calif, 52; assoc plant pathologist, Univ Ariz, 52; assoc plant pathologist, Subtrop Exp Sta, 64-70, PROF PLANT PATH & PLANT PATHOLOGIST, AGR RES & EDUC CTR, UNIV FLA, 70- *Mem:* Am Phytopath Soc. *Res:* Diseases of tropical ornamentals; tropical fruits. *Mailing Add:* Agr Res & Educ Ctr Univ of Fla Homestead FL 33030

MARLATT, WILLIAM EDGAR, b Kearney, Nebr, June 5, 31; m 56; c 2. ATMOSPHERIC SCIENCE. *Educ:* Nebr State Col Kearney, BA, 56; Rutgers Univ, MS, 58, PhD(soil physics), 61. *Prof Exp:* Res asst forestry, US Forest Serv, 54-55; res asst meteorol, Rutgers Univ, 56-58, asst prof, 58-61; prof atmospheric sci, 61-69, chmn dept earth resources, 70-74, assoc dean, Grad Sch, 67-68, PROF EARTH RESOURCES, COLO STATE UNIV, 75- *Concurrent Pos:* Consult, Nat Bur Stand, 64-67; mem, Colo Natural Resource Ctr Coun, 66-71; consult, Martin Marietta Co, 67-73; mem, Int Biol Prog Biometeorol Panel, Nat Res Coun-Nat Acad Sci, 68-70; sr scientist, Environ Resources Assocs, Inc, 69-70; consult, Manned Spaceflight Ctr, NASA, 70 & Colspan Environ Systs, Inc, 70-71; Int Biol Prog mem, Nat Adv Comt Aerobiol, 70-; consult, Thorne Ecol Found, 71-, mem bd dirs, 78- chmn educ comt, Colo Environ Res Ctr, 71- *Mem:* AAAS; Am Meteorol Soc; Am Astronaut Soc; Am Geophys Union; Coun Agr Sci & Technol; Agr Res Inst. *Res:* Remote sensing of atmosphere and earth surface, environment quality, interaction of climate and environment. *Mailing Add:* 3611 Richmond Dr Ft Collins CO 80526

MARLBOROUGH, JOHN MICHAEL, b Toronto, Ont, Aug 1, 40. ASTRONOMY. *Educ:* Univ Toronto, BSc, 62, MA, 63; Univ Chicago, PhD(astron), 67. *Prof Exp:* Lectr, 67, asst prof, 67-70, assoc prof, 70-76, PROF ASTRON, UNIV WESTERN ONT, 76- *Concurrent Pos:* Vis scientist, Dominion Astrophys Observ, Victoria, BC, 73-74. *Mem:* Am Astron Soc; Can Astron Soc; Royal Astron Soc. *Res:* Stellar interiors and evolution; early-type stars with extended atmospheres; radiative transfer; gas dynamics. *Mailing Add:* Dept of Astron Univ of Western Ont London ON N6A 5B8 Can

MARLER, PETER, b London, Eng, Feb 24, 28; US citizen; m 54; c 3. ZOOLOGY. *Educ:* Univ London, BSc, 48, PhD(bot), 52; Cambridge Univ, PhD(zool), 54. *Prof Exp:* Res fel, Jesus Col, Cambridge Univ, 54-56; from asst prof to prof zool, Univ Calif, Berkeley, 57-66; dir, Field Res Ctr Ethol & Ecol, 72-81; PROF, ROCKEFELLER UNIV, 66- *Concurrent Pos:* Guggenheim fel, 64-65; mem, Study Sect Exp Psychol, NIH, 64-69; sr res zoologist, NY Zool Soc, 66-72; mem & chmn comt, Walker Prize Biol, 67-68; dir, Inst Res Animal Behav, 69-72; mem health primate ctr rev comt, NIH, 74-78; external adv, Res Dept, Cent Inst Deaf, 78; mem external adv comt, Duke Primate Ctr, 78-79, Calif Reg Primate Ctr, 78- & Caribbean Primate Res Ctr, 79-; mem bd sci counsrs, Naat Inst Child Health & Human Develop, 78 & Smithsonian Coun, 79- *Honors & Awards:* Elliott Coyes Award, Am Ornithologist Union, 76. *Mem:* Nat Acad Sci; fel AAAS; fel Am Acad Arts & Sci; Animal Behav Soc (pres, 69-70); Am Soc Zoologists. *Res:* Behavior of animals, with special reference to the development of vocalizations in birds and primates; processes of communication in animals; field studies of social behavior. *Mailing Add:* Dept of Zool Rockefeller Univ New York NY 10021

MARLETT, JUDITH ANN, b Toledo, Ohio, June 20, 43. NUTRITION. *Educ:* Miami Univ, BS, 65; Univ Minn, PhD(nutrit), 72. *Prof Exp:* Therapeut dietician, Minneapolis Vet Admin Hosp, 66-67; res fel nutrit, Sch Pub Health, Harvard Univ, 73-74; asst prof, 75-80, ASSOC PROF NUTRIT, UNIV WIS-MADISON, 80- *Mem:* Sigma Xi; Am Inst Nutrit; Am Dietics Asn; Soc Nutrit Educ. *Res:* Role of dietary fiber in human nutrition and in the human gastrointestinal tract; role of the gastrointestinal tract in lipid metabolism. *Mailing Add:* Dept of Nutrit Sci Univ of Wis 1300 Linden Dr Madison WI 53706

MARLETTE, RALPH R(OY), b Bowdle, SDak, Oct 16, 20; m 43; c 3. CIVIL ENGINEERING. *Educ:* Univ Nebr, BS, 43, MS, 52. *Hon Degrees:* DHE, Delft Univ, 61. *Prof Exp:* Res engr, Black & Veatch, Consults, 47-50; PROF CIVIL ENG, UNIV NEBR, LINCOLN, 50- *Concurrent Pos:* Off engr, Garrison Dam, US Corps Engrs, 46-47; consult, President's Mo Basin Surv Comn, 52 & Sanit Dist 1, Lancaster County, Nebr, 57-60; NSF fac fel, Delft Univ, 60-61; mem, Int Water Supply Cong. *Mem:* Fel Am Soc Civil Engrs. *Res:* Hydraulic engineering; problems of alluvial channels and sediment transport and ground water yield. *Mailing Add:* Dept of Civil Eng Univ of Nebr Lincoln NE 68588

MARLEY, GERALD C, b Lovington, NMex, Nov 11, 38; m 59. MATHEMATICS. *Educ:* Eastern NMex Univ, BSc, 59; Tex Tech Col, MSc, 61; Univ Ariz, PhD(math), 67. *Prof Exp:* Res engr, Gen Dynamics/ Astronaut, 61; lectr math, Univ Ariz, 67; from asst prof to assoc prof, 67-74, PROF MATH, CALIF STATE UNIV, FULLERTON, 74- *Mem:* Am Math Soc; Math Asn Am; Am Sci Affil; Sigma Xi. *Res:* Subdivisions of Euclidean space by convex bodies. *Mailing Add:* Dept of Math Calif State Univ Fullerton CA 92634

MARLEY, JAMES ALOYSIUS, b Philadelphia, Pa, July 16, 33; m 59; c 3. INORGANIC CHEMISTRY, ENGINEERING MANAGEMENT. *Educ:* St Joseph's Col, BS, 55; Univ Pa, PhD(inorg chem), 60. *Prof Exp:* Res chemist, Corning Glass Works, 59-64, mgr solid state chem dept, 64-68, mgr solid state res, 68-72, DEPT MGR, RES & DEVELOP LAB, SIGNETICS CORP, 72- *Mem:* Am Phys Soc; Am Ceramic Soc; Electrochem Soc. *Res:* Crystal growth; materials characterization; ion implantation studies in semiconductors; silicon processins and characterization; lithography. *Mailing Add:* Res & Develop Lab Signetics Corp 811 E Arques Ave Sunnyvale CA 94086

MARLEY, STEPHEN J, b Blencoe, Iowa, Mar 5, 30; m 53; c 4. AGRICULTURAL ENGINEERING. *Educ:* Iowa State Univ, BS, 59, MS, 60, PhD(agr eng), 65. *Prof Exp:* From instr to assoc prof, 60-74, PROF AGR ENG, IOWA STATE UNIV, 74- *Concurrent Pos:* Vis lectr & Fulbright grant, Univ Col, Dublin, 70-71. *Mem:* Am Soc Agr Engrs. *Mailing Add:* Dept of Agr Eng Iowa State Univ Ames IA 50011

MARLIAVE, JEFFREY BURTON, b Oroville, Calif, Feb 28, 49; m 72; c 1. ICHTHYOLOGY, MARINE ECOLOGY. *Educ:* Univ Wash, BSc, 70; Univ BC, PhD(zool), 76. *Prof Exp:* Res assoc, 76-77, RESIDENT SCIENTIST, VANCOUVER PUB AQUARIUM, 77- *Concurrent Pos:* Marine biologist, EVS Consults, Ltd, 76- *Honors & Awards:* Edward H Bean Award, Am Asn Zool Parks & Aquariums, 79 & 81. *Mem:* Am Asn Zool Parks & Aquariums. *Res:* Ichthyoplankton; laboratory culture of planktonic larvae; behavioral ecology of marine fish larvae; developmental marine bioassays; reproductive ecology of intertidal fishes; ecological genetics of marine life. *Mailing Add:* Vancouver Pub Aquarium PO Box 3232 Vancouver BC V6B 3X8 Can

MARLIN, JOE ALTON, b Naylor, Mo, July 3, 35; m 60; c 2. APPLIED MATHEMATICS. *Educ:* Southeast Mo State Col, BS, 58; Univ Mo-Columbia, MA, 60; NC State Univ, PhD(math), 65. *Prof Exp:* Mem tech staff, Bell Tel Labs, 60-63; instr, 64-66, asst prof, 66-68, assoc prof, 68-78, PROF MATH, NC STATE UNIV, 78- *Mem:* Am Math Soc; Math Asn Am. *Res:* Oscillatory and asymptotic behavior of systems of ordinary differential equations which represent equations of motion for mechanical systems; Hamiltonians systems and foliations. *Mailing Add:* Dept of Math NC State Univ Raleigh NC 27607

MARLIN, ROBERT LEWIS, b Bronx, NY, June 28, 37; m 59; c 2. INFORMATION SCIENCE, RESEARCH ADMINISTRATION. *Educ:* Syracuse Univ, AB, 58, MPA, 62; Rutgers Univ, PhD, 78. *Prof Exp:* Asst psychologist, NY State Dept Ment Hyg, 57-59; asst scientist exp psychol, Sterling-Winthrop Res Inst, 59-60, asst scientist statist, 60-62; asst to dir new prod develop, Winthrop Labs, Sterling Drug, Inc, 62-65; coordr med affairs, Knoll Pharm Co, 65-68; coordr prod develop, Schering Corp, 68-69; clin res assoc, Sandoz Pharm Co, 69-71; sr clin res assoc med, Sandoz Pharm Co, 71-75; BIOMED CONSULT, 75- *Concurrent Pos:* Ed newslett, NJ Acad Sci, 70-74; mem staff, Ctr Prof Advan, 78-; adj asst prof biomed sci, Mass Col Pharm & Allied Health Sci, 81- *Mem:* AAAS; Drug Info Asn (secy, 68-69, vpres, 70-71); Biomet Soc; NY Acad Sci; Am Statist Asn. *Mailing Add:* 8 Biscay Dr Parsippany NJ 07054

MARLOW, KEITH WINTON, b Madison, Kans, Nov 14, 28; m 51; c 3. NUCLEAR PHYSICS. *Educ:* Kans State Univ, BS, 51; Univ Md, PhD, 66. *Prof Exp:* Physicist, 51-67, head reactors br, 67-70, consult, Radiation Technol Div, 71-80, HEAD RADIATION SURVIVABILITY & DETECTION BR, NAVAL RES LAB, 80- *Concurrent Pos:* Physicist, Inst Nuclear Physics Res, Amsterdam, 67-68. *Mem:* AAAS; Am Phys Soc; Sigma Xi. *Res:* Experimental study of nuclear structure, principally by investigating decay of radioactive nuclides; development of instrumentation for detecting low levels of radioactivity. *Mailing Add:* Naval Res Lab Code 6610 Washington DC 20375

MARLOW, RONALD WILLIAM, b San Diego, Calif, Feb 9, 49. PHYSIOLOGICAL ECOLOGY, FUNCTIONAL MORPHOLOGY. *Educ:* Univ Calif, Berkeley, BA, 73, PhD(zool), 79. *Prof Exp:* Fel animal behav, Univ Chicago, 79-80; scholar functional morphol, Univ Mich, 80-81; vis asst prof ecol, Univ Santa Clara, Calif, 81; RES ASSOC, MUS VERT ZOOL, UNIV CALIF, BERKELEY, 82- *Mem:* AAAS; Am Soc Ichthyologists & Herpetologists; Ecol Soc Am. *Res:* Ecology and physiological ecology of lower vertebrates; evolutionary relationships of the family Testudinidae; functional morphology of feeding and locomotion in lower vertebrates. *Mailing Add:* Mus Vert Zool Univ Calif Berkeley CA 94720

MARLOW, WILLIAM HENRY, b Beaumont, Tex, Mar 1, 44; m 72. PHYSICS. *Educ:* Mass Inst Technol, BS, 66; Univ Tex Austin, PhD(physics), 74. *Prof Exp:* Res assoc environ sci, Univ NC, Chapel Hill, 73-74; asst physicist, 75-76, assoc physicist, 76-79, PHYSICIST, ATMOSPHERIC SCI, BROOKHAVEN NAT LAB, 79- *Concurrent Pos:* Prin investr, US Dept Energy, Bookhaven Nat Lab, 75-; adj asst prof environ med, Med Sch, NY Univ, 81-; organizer-ed, Aerosol Microphysics I: Particle Interactions & Aerosol Microphysics II: Chem Physics of Microparticles; invited lectr, 13th Int Symp Rarefied Gas Dynamics, Novosibiask, USSR, 82. *Mem:* Am Phys Soc. *Res:* Aerosol microphysics; measurement methodology for sub- micron particulate matter; particle van der Waals forces. *Mailing Add:* Brookhaven Nat Lab Upton NY 11973

MARLOW, WILLIAM HENRY, b Waterloo, Iowa, Nov 26, 24; m 48; c 5. OPERATIONS RESEARCH, MATHEMATICS. *Educ:* St Ambrose Col, BS, 47; Univ Iowa, MS, 48, PhD(math), 51. *Prof Exp:* Instr math, Univ Iowa, 48-51; res assoc, Logistics Res Proj, 51-56, prin investr, 56-69, chmn dept opers res, 71-77, PROF OPERS RES & DIR INST MGR SCI & ENG, GEORGE WASHINGTON UNIV, 69- *Concurrent Pos:* Assoc res mathematician, Univ Calif, Los Angeles, 54-55. *Mem:* Opers Res Soc Am; Am Math Soc; Math Asn Am; Soc Indust & Appl Math; Inst Mgt Sci. *Res:* Mathematical methods and numerical procedures in operations research and management science; logistics; systems effectiveness. *Mailing Add:* Sch of Eng & Appl Sci George Washington Univ Washington DC 20052

MARLOWE, DONALD E(DWARD), b Worcester, Mass, Mar 27, 16; m 39; c 2. MECHANICAL ENGINEERING, PHYSICS. *Educ:* Univ Detroit, BCE, 38; Univ Mich, MSE, 39; DEng, Milwaukee Sch Eng 81, Stevens Inst Technol, 81, Villanova Univ, 81. *Hon Degrees:* ScD, Merrimack Col, 62. *Prof Exp:* Asst physics, Univ Detroit, 37-38, instr, 40-41; asst res engr, Univ Mich, 39-41; res engr, US Naval Ord Lab, Md, 41-46, chief eval engr, 46-50, asst tech dir, 50-51, assoc dir, 52-55; dean, Sch Eng & Archit, Cath Univ Am, 55-70, vpres for admin, 70-75; exec dir, Am Soc Eng Educ, 75-81; RETIRED. *Concurrent Pos:* Consult, US Res & Develop Bd, Weapon Systs Eval Group, Nat Res Coun & US Navy Bur Ord; dir & mem exec comt, Eng Joint Coun, 60-65; pres, Nat Coun Eng Exam, 66-67; secy, Educ Affairs Coun, Am Asn Eng Socs, 80- *Honors & Awards:* Ord Develop Award, US Navy, 44, Distinguished Civilian Serv Award, 46; Award of Merit, Am Inst Consult Engrs, 70; Marlowe Award, Am Soc Engr Educ, 81. *Mem:* Fel AAAS (secy, Eng Sect, 77-81); fel & hon mem Am Soc Mech Engrs (vpres, 59-63 & 67-69, pres, 69-70); Am Soc Eng Educ; Nat Soc Prof Engrs; Inst Elec & Electronics Engrs. *Res:* Engineering mechanics; mechanical engineering; research administration; engineering education; educational administration. *Mailing Add:* 15402 Short Ridge Ct Silver Spring MD 20906

MARLOWE, EDWARD, b New York, NY, May 5, 35; m 59; c 2. PHARMACEUTICAL CHEMISTRY. *Educ:* Columbia Univ, BS, 56, MS, 58; Univ Md, PhD(pharm chem), 62. *Prof Exp:* Res assoc pharm res & develop, Merck Sharp & Dohme Res Lab, 62-64; sr scientist, Ortho Pharmaceut Corp, 64-67; dir res & develop, Whitehall Labs Div, Am Home Prod, NJ, 67-72; vpres res & develop, Res & Tech Div, Shering-Plough Inc, 72-81; VPRES RES & DEVELOP, CONSUMER PROD GROUP, WARNER LAMBERT CO, 81- *Concurrent Pos:* Vis prof pharmaceut, Univ Tenn, 73- *Mem:* Acad Pharmaceut Sci; Soc Cosmetic Chemists; Am Pharmaceut Asn; Cosmetic Toiletry & Fragrance Asn; Sigma Xi. *Res:* Product development, pharmacology, toxicology and photobiology; analytical development; exploratory product design research; drug delivery systems; oral cavity research. *Mailing Add:* 56 Dean Rd Short Hills NJ 07078

MARLOWE, ELBERT W(INFIELD), b Lawrenceburg, Ind, Aug 26, 12. ENGINEERING. *Educ:* Univ Chicago, BS, 34. *Prof Exp:* Jr chemist, Universal Oil Prod Co, Ill, 37-42; asst physicist, Naval Ord Lab, Washington, DC, 44; assoc scientist, Univ Calif, Los Angeles, 44-45; sect engr, Union Switch & Signal Co, 45-51 & Union Switch & Signal Div, Westinghouse Air Brake Co, 51-58; mgr indust control systs eng, Crosley Div, Avco Corp, 58-62; prin scientist, Opers Res, Inc, 62-80; RETIRED. *Mem:* Inst Elec & Electronics Engrs. *Res:* Absorption of gases in solids; electronic measuring equipment for underwater ordnance; electronic measuring instruments for physical research; remote control systems; industrial computers; railway simulations; transportation research; information systems. *Mailing Add:* 9505 Curran Rd Silver Spring MD 20901

MARLOWE, GEORGE ALBERT, JR, b Detroit, Mich, May 25, 25; m 53; c 1. HORTICULTURE. *Educ:* George Washington Univ, BS, 49, MS, 50; Univ Md, PhD(hort), 55. *Prof Exp:* Exten specialist hort, Univ Ky, 56-62; assoc prof hort, Ohio State Univ, 62-65; exten specialist veg crops, Univ Calif, Davis, 65-69; PROF HORT & HORTICULTURIST, INST FOOD & AGR SCI, UNIV FLA, 69- *Concurrent Pos:* Chmn, Dept Veg Crops, Univ Fla, 69-72. *Mem:* Am Soc Hort Sci; Am Phys Soc. *Res:* Precision production technology; crop nutrition. *Mailing Add:* Dept of Veg Crops Univ of Fla Gainesville FL 32611

MARLOWE, THOMAS JOHNSON, b Fairview, NC, Sept 15, 17; m 45; c 4. ANIMAL GENETICS, ANIMAL PHYSIOLOGY. *Educ:* NC State Univ, BS, 40, MS, 49; Okla State Univ, PhD(animal genetics & physiol), 54. *Prof Exp:* High sch teacher, 40-42; training specialist & asst supvr, Vet Admin, NC, 46-48; asst county agt & livestock specialist, Va Agr Exten Serv, 49-50; instr animal husb, Miss State Univ, 51-52; res asst, Okla State Univ, 52-54; assoc prof, 54-64, PROF ANIMAL SCI, VA POLYTECH INST & STATE UNIV, 64- *Honors & Awards:* Distinguished Serv Award, Am Soc Animal Sci, 78. *Mem:* Am Inst Biol Sci; Am Genetic Asn; hon fel Am Soc Animal Sci (secy-treas, 71-74, pres, 75-76); Am Registry Cert Animal Scientists. *Res:* Beef cattle performance testing; heritability of economic traits; genetics and pathology of hereditary dwarfism cattle; effectiveness of selection in beef cattle; cytogenetics; evaluation of sire and dam breed for crossbreeding. *Mailing Add:* Dept of Animal Sci Va Polytech Inst & State Univ Blacksburg VA 24061

MARMAR, EARL SHELDON, b St Boniface, Man, July 3, 50. PLASMA PHYSICS. *Educ:* Univ Man, BSc, 72; Princeton Univ, MS, 75, PhD(physics), 76. *Prof Exp:* Res asst, Physics Dept, Princeton Univ, 72-73, Plasma Physics Lab, 73-76; sponsored res staff, Francis Bitter Nat Magnet Lab, 76-80, PRIN RES SCIENTIST, PLASMA FUSION CTR, MASS INST TECHNOL, 80- *Mem:* Am Phys Soc. *Res:* Impurity problems in magnetic confinement fusion devices; plasma wall interactions; impurity radiation and power balance; atomic physics of highly stripped materials; particle diffusion and recycling in tokamaks. *Mailing Add:* NW16-280 167 Albany St Cambridge MA 02139

MARMARELIS, VASILIS Z, b Mytilini, Greece, Nov 16, 49. NONLINEAR SYSTEMS, DATA ANALYSIS. *Educ:* Nat Tech Univ Athens, Dipl, 72; Calif Inst Technol, MS, 73, PhD(eng sci), 76. *Prof Exp:* Lectr & res fel syst sci, Calif Inst Technol, 76-78; ASST PROF BIOMED & ELEC ENG, UNIV SOUTHERN CALIF, 78- *Concurrent Pos:* Vis assoc, Calif Inst Technol, 78-79. *Mem:* Inst Elec & Electronics Engrs. *Res:* Analysis of signals and systems; spectral and correlation analysis; system identification and modeling; random processes and estimation methods; analysis and modeling of physiological systems with emphasis on nonlinear/nonstationary systems. *Mailing Add:* OHE 500 Univ Southern Calif Los Angeles CA 90007

MARMER, GARY JAMES, b Cincinnati, Ohio, Nov 28, 38; m 60; c 3. ENVIRONMENTAL SCIENCE. *Educ:* Case Inst Technol, BS, 60; Auburn Univ, MS, 62; Ohio State Univ, PhD(physics), 68. *Prof Exp:* Physicist high energy physics, Accelerator Res, 68-72, PHYSICIST ENVIRON STUDIES, ARGONNE NAT LAB, 72- *Mem:* Am Water Resources Asn; Air Pollution Control Asn. *Res:* Assess environmental effects of construction and operation of energy facilities. *Mailing Add:* Argonne Nat Lab Bldg 214 9700 S Cass Ave Argonne IL 60439

MARMER, WILLIAM NELSON, b Philadelphia, Pa, July 19, 43; m 73; c 2. ORGANIC CHEMISTRY, LIPID CHEMISTRY. *Educ:* Univ Pa, AB, 65; Temple Univ, PhD(chem), 71. *Prof Exp:* Nat Res Coun-Agr Res Serv res assoc org chem, 70-72, res scientist, Fats & Proteins Res Found, Inc, 72-75, RES CHEMIST, EASTERN REGIONAL RES CTR, USDA, 75- *Concurrent Pos:* Lectr chem, Pa State Univ. *Mem:* Am Chem Soc; Am Oil Chemists' Soc; Sigma Xi. *Res:* Amine oxides; epoxides; O-acylhydroxylamines; fatty acid derivatives; acylations; fabric treatment; mixed anhydrides; lime soap dispersing agents; lipid extraction, analysis and synthesis. *Mailing Add:* Eastern Regional Res Ctr USDA 600 E Mermaid Lane Philadelphia PA 19118

MARMET, PAUL, b Levis, Que, May 20, 32; m 59; c 4. ATOMIC PHYSICS, MOLECULAR PHYSICS. *Educ:* Laval Univ, BSc, 56, DSc(physics), 60. *Prof Exp:* Asst molecular physics, Commonwealth Sci & Indust Res Orgn, Australia, 60-61; from asst prof to assoc prof, 61-67, PROF PHYSICS, LAVAL UNIV, 67- *Concurrent Pos:* Nat Res Coun Can fel, 60-61, grant, 61-, mem adv comt physics, 70-73; Defence Res Bd Can grants, 63-64 & 66-75. *Honors & Awards:* Herzberg Medal, Can Asn Physicists, 71; Order of Canada, 81; Pariseau Medal, Asn Can-French pour l'Avancement des Sci, 76; Rutherford Prize, 60. *Mem:* Can Asn Physicists; Royal Astron Soc Can; Fr-Can Asn Advan Sci; fel Royal Soc Can; Chem Inst Can. *Mailing Add:* Dept of Physics Laval Univ Ste-Foy PQ G1K 7P4 Can

MARMO, FREDERICK FRANCIS, b Boston, Mass, Oct 25, 20; m 43; c 3. AERONOMY, ENVIRONMENTAL CHEMISTRY. *Educ:* Boston Univ, AB, 49; Harvard Univ, MS, 51, PhD(chem physics), 53. *Prof Exp:* Chief chem physics br, US Air Force Cambridge Res Ctr, 53-58; mgr chem physics dept, GCA Corp, Mass, 58-61, dir space sci lab, 61-66, dir space sci opers, 66-67, tech dir & vpres tech div, 67, vpres & dir res, 67-72; PRIN SCIENTIST, DEPT OF TRANSP, 72- *Honors & Awards:* Fermi Outstanding Scientist Award, 60 & Superior Performance & Outstanding Achievement Award, Air Force Cambridge Res Ctr, 58. *Mem:* Am Geophys Union; Am Meteorol Soc; Am Inst Aeronaut & Astronaut. *Res:* Planetary physics; environmental sciences; photochemistry; design of satellite probes for global monitoring; transportation planning-air quality. *Mailing Add:* 138 Main St Wakefield MA 01880

MARMOR, ROBERT SAMUEL, b Los Angeles, Calif, Nov 8, 43; m 68; c 3. ORGANIC CHEMISTRY. *Educ:* Univ Calif, Los Angeles, BS, 65; Mass Inst Technol, PhD(org chem), 70. *Prof Exp:* Res nat prod, 70-71, res organometallic chem, Mass Inst Technol, 71-72; sr res chemist, 72-75, supvr, 75-80, MGR ORG CHEM SECT, LORILLARD CORP, DIV LOEWS THEATERS, 80- *Mem:* Am Chem Soc. *Res:* Organic synthesis; flavor chemistry; chemistry of tobacco. *Mailing Add:* 2712 Twin Lakes Dr Greensboro NC 27407

MARMOR, SOLOMON, b New York, NY, Feb 25, 26; m 54; c 2. ORGANIC CHEMISTRY. *Educ:* City Col New York, BS, 48; Syracuse Univ, PhD(org chem), 52. *Prof Exp:* Res chemist, Becco Chem Div, FMC Corp, 52-56; asst prof chem, Utica Col, Syracuse Univ, 56-62; assoc prof, NMex Highlands Univ, 62-66, head dept, 64-66; assoc prof, 66-70, coordr interdept progs, 68-70, chmn dept, 68-71, actg dean sch natural sci & math, 73-74, PROF CHEM, CALIF STATE UNIV, DOMINGUEZ HILLS, 70- *Mem:* AAAS; Am Chem Soc. *Res:* Epoxides; hypochlorous acid reactions; hydrogen peroxide oxidations of organic compounds. *Mailing Add:* Dept of Chem Calif State Univ Carson CA 90747

MARMUR, JULIUS, b Byelostok, Poland, Mar 22, 26; Can citizen; m 58; c 2. MOLECULAR BIOLOGY, BIOCHEMISTRY. *Educ:* McGill Univ, BS, 46, MS, 47; Iowa State Col, PhD(bact physiol), 51. *Prof Exp:* Mem staff, NIH, 51-52, Rockefeller Inst, 52-54, Pasteur Inst, Paris, 54-55 & Inst Microbiol, Rutgers Univ, 55-56; res assoc chem, Harvard Univ, 56-60; asst prof biochem, Brandeis Univ, 60-61, assoc prof, 61-63; actg chmn dept biochem, 74-76, PROF BIOCHEM, ALBERT EINSTEIN COL MED, 63-, PROF GENETICS, 74- *Mem:* Am Soc Biol Chemists; Am Soc Microbiol. *Res:* Biological and physical-chemical properties of yeast nucleic acids. *Mailing Add:* Dept of Biochem Albert Einstein Col of Med New York NY 10461

MARNER, WILBUR JOSEPH, b Greentown, Ind, Jan 15, 37; m 57; c 2. MECHANICAL ENGINEERING. *Educ:* Purdue Univ, Lafayette, BS, 62, MS, 65; Univ SC, PhD(mech eng), 69. *Prof Exp:* Foreman qual control, Sarkes Tarzian, Inc, 62-63; asst prof mech eng, SDak Sch Mines & Technol, 69-73; res engr, Heat Transfer Res, Inc, 73-80; MEM TECH STAFF, JET PROPULSION LAB, CALIF INST TECHNOL, 80- *Concurrent Pos:* Consult, Hanford Eng Develop Lab, Westinghouse Hanford Co, 76-77; lectr, Calif State Univ, Los Angeles, 80- *Mem:* Am Soc Mech Engrs; Am Soc Eng Educ; Am Inst Aeronaut & Astronaut; Sigma Xi. *Res:* Single-phase convective heat transfer; extended surfaces heat transfer; augmentation of convective heat transfer. *Mailing Add:* 1654 Oakwood Ave Arcadia CA 91006

MARNETT, LAWRENCE JOSEPH, b Kansas City, Kans, Nov 22, 47; m 71; c 2. BIOCHEMISTRY. *Educ:* Rockhurst Col, BS, 69; Duke Univ, PhD(chem), 73. *Prof Exp:* Assoc biochem, Karolinska Inst, 73-74; assoc biochem, 74-75, asst prof, 75-80, ASSOC PROF CHEM, WAYNE STATE UNIV, 80- *Mem:* Am Chem Soc; Sigma Xi. *Res:* Prostaglandin biochemistry; chemical carcinogenesis. *Mailing Add:* 435 Chemistry Wayne State Univ Detroit MI 48202

MAROIS, ROBERT LEO, b Troy, NY, Apr 27, 35; m 61; c 4. PHARMACOLOGY. *Educ:* Siena Col, NY, BS, 64; Albany Med Col, PhD(pharmacol), 69. *Prof Exp:* Res assoc, State Univ NY Albany, 68-69; ASSOC PROF PHARMACOL, ALBANY COL PHARM, 69- *Concurrent Pos:* USPHS fel, State Univ NY Albany, 68-69. *Res:* Cardiovascular and neuromuscular pharmacology. *Mailing Add:* Dept of Biol Sci Albany Col of Pharm Albany NY 12208

MARON, MELVIN EARL, b Bloomfield, NJ, Jan 23, 24; m 48; c 2. INFORMATION SCIENCE. *Educ:* Univ Nebr, BS, 45, BA, 47; Univ Calif, Los Angeles, PhD(philos), 51. *Prof Exp:* Instr, Univ Calif, Los Angeles, 51-52; tech engr, Int Bus Mach Corp, 52-55; mem tech staff, Ramo-Wooldridge Corp, 55-59; mem sr res staff, Rand Corp, 59-66; prof librarianship, 66-80, PROF, LIBRARY & INFORMATION STUDIES, UNIV CALIF, BERKELEY, 80- *Mem:* AAAS; Asn Comput Mach; Philos Sci Asn. *Res:* Philosophy; computer sciences; cybernetics; theory and foundations of automatic information searching and data retrieval. *Mailing Add:* 63 Ardilla Rd Orinda CA 94563

MARONDE, ROBERT FRANCIS, b Calif, Jan 13, 20; m 70; c 4. INTERNAL MEDICINE, CLINICAL PHARMACOLOGY. *Educ:* Univ Southern Calif, BA, 41, MD, 44; Am Bd Internal Med, dipl, 51. *Prof Exp:* Resident med, Los Angeles County Gen Hosp, 46-48; asst prof physiol, 48-49, from asst clin prof to assoc clin prof med, 49-63, assoc prof med & pharmacol, 63-68, PROF MED & PHARMACOL, SCH MED, UNIV SOUTHERN CALIF, 68-, CHIEF CLIN PHARMACOL SECT, 70- *Concurrent Pos:* Consult, Food & Drug Admin, Dept Health & Human Serv, Presidential Task Force Prescription Drugs & Calif State Dept Health. *Mem:* Am Soc Clin Pharmacol & Therapeut. *Res:* Medical computer applications for drug utilization review. *Mailing Add:* Dept of Med Univ Southern Calif Sch of Med Los Angeles CA 90033

MARONEY, SAMUEL PATTERSON, JR, b Wilmington, Del, Feb 3, 26; m 51; c 3. ZOOLOGY. *Educ:* Wesleyan Univ, BA, 50; Univ Del, MA, 53; Duke Univ, PhD(zool), 57. *Prof Exp:* Asst prof, 56-62, ASSOC PROF BIOL, UNIV VA, 62- *Mem:* Fel AAAS; Am Soc Zoologists; Sigma Xi. *Res:* Cell physiology; permeability and hemolysis of amphibian erythrocytes. *Mailing Add:* Dept Biol Univ Va Charlottesville VA 22903

MARONI, GUSTAVO PRIMO, b Merlo, Arg, Nov 20, 41; m 74. DEVELOPMENTAL GENETICS, BIOCHEMICAL GENETICS. *Educ:* Univ Buenos Aires, Lic, 67; Univ Wis, PhD(zool), 72. *Prof Exp:* Res assoc genetics, Dept Zool, Univ NC, 73-74 & Inst Genetics, Univ Cologne, 74-75; asst prof, 75-80, ASSOC PROF, DEPT ZOOL, UNIV NC, CHAPEL HILL, 80- *Mem:* Genetics Soc Am; AAAS. *Res:* Regulation of sex-linked gene activity in Drosophila; control of alcohol dehydrogenase and other gene-enzyme systems; genetic and molecular analyses of metal-binding proteins. *Mailing Add:* Dept Zool Wilson Hall Univ NC Chapel Hill NC 27514

MARONI, VICTOR AUGUST, b Athol, Mass, Sept 8, 42; m 69; c 2. STRUCTURE CHEMISTRY. *Educ:* Worcester Polytech Inst, BS, 64; Princeton Univ, PhD(chem), 67. *Prof Exp:* SR CHEMIST & GROUP LEADER, ARGONNE NAT LAB, 67- *Res:* Chemical and structure properties of ionic liquids including ligand field theory and spectroscopic studies (Raman, nuclear magnetic resonance, electronic absorption); controlled nuclear fusion. *Mailing Add:* Argonne Nat Lab 9700 S Cass Ave Argonne IL 60439

MAROTTA, CHARLES ANTHONY, b New York, NY, Apr 12, 45. MOLECULAR BIOLOGY, PSYCHIATRY. *Educ:* City Col New York, BS, 65; Duke Univ, MD, 69; Yale Univ, MPhil, 72, PhD(molecular biophys & biochem), 75. *Prof Exp:* NIH fel molecular biophys & internal med, Med Sch, Yale Univ, 69-73, fel molecular biophys & internal med, fel internal med, 71-72, fel med res, Clin Res Training Prog, 71-73, res fel human genetics, 72-73; clin fel psychiat, 73-76, res fel, 75-76, instr, 76-77, ASST PROF PSYCHIAT BIOCHEM, HARVARD MED SCH, 77- *Concurrent Pos:* Fel med, Yale-New Haven Hosp, 70-73; resident psychiat, Mass Gen Hosp, 73-76, asst neurochem, 76-77, clin assoc, 77-78, asst neurochem, psychiat, 78-; asst neurochem, McLean Hosp, 77, asst biochem, 77-; Mellon fac award, Harvard Med Sch, 76-77; McKnight Found Scholars award, 77-80. *Honors & Awards:* Physician Recognition Award, AMA, 72; Ethel B Dupont-Warren Award & William F Milton Fund Award, Harvard Med Sch, 75. *Mem:* AAAS; Soc Neurosci; Am Soc Neurochem. *Res:* Molecular genetics; molecular psychobiology; neurochemistry; neurobiology. *Mailing Add:* Neurochem Lab Mailman Res Ctr McLean Hosp Belmont MA 02178

MAROTTA, SABATH FRED, b Chicago, Ill, Aug 26, 29. PHYSIOLOGY. *Educ:* Univ Ill, MS, 53, PhD(physiol), 57. *Prof Exp:* Res assoc animal sci, 57-58, from instr to assoc prof physiol, Col Med, 58-70, res assoc, Aeromed Lab, Med Ctr, 58-60, asst dir, 60-64, assoc dean grad col, 75, assoc dir, Res Resources Ctr, 75-80, PROF PHYSIOL, MED CTR, UNIV ILL, 70-, DIR, RES RESOURCES CTR, 80- *Concurrent Pos:* Univ Ill adv, Chiengmai Proj, Thailand, 64-66. *Mem:* Aerospace Med Asn; Am Physiol Soc; Soc Exp Biol & Med. *Res:* Neuroendocrinology; biologic rhythms; role of the adrenal cortex in the adaption to environmental stresses. *Mailing Add:* Res Resources Ctr Bldg 933 Univ Ill Med Ctr PO 6998 Chicago IL 60680

MAROULIS, PETER JAMES, b Norfolk, Va, Apr 27, 51. CHROMATOGRAPHY, MASS SPECTROMETRY. *Educ:* Old Dominion Univ, BS, 73; Drexel Univ, MS, 77, PhD(anal chem), 80. *Prof Exp:* RES ASSOC ANAL CHEM & GEN CHEM, DREXEL UNIV, 80- *Mem:* Sigma Xi; Am Chem Soc; Am Geophys Union; AAAS. *Res:* Design and construct instrumentation to measure background levels of sulfur, nitrogen and hydrocarbon gases in the atmosphere, and to interpret the data from a global atmospheric sciences standpoint. *Mailing Add:* Chem Dept Drexel Univ Philadelphia PA 19104

MAROUSKY, FRANCIS JOHN, b Shenandoah, Pa, Oct 28, 35; m 59; c 5. HORTICULTURE. *Educ:* Pa State Univ, BS, 57; Univ Md, MS, 64; Va Polytech Inst, PhD(hort), 67. *Prof Exp:* Res asst, Univ Md, 62-64; instr, Va Polytech Inst, 64-67; res horticulturist, Agr Res & Educ Ctr, Sci & Educ Admin-Agr Res, USDA, Univ Fla, 67-79, RES HORTICULTURIST & DIR, EUROP MKT RES LAB, AGR RES SERV, USDA, ROTTERDAM, NETHERLANDS, 80- *Mem:* Am Soc Hort Sci; Int Soc Hort Sci. *Res:* Market quality and post harvest aspects and senescence of horticultural crops. *Mailing Add:* Agr Res & Educ Ctr Univ Fla Bradenton FL 33508

MAROV, GASPAR J, b Unije, Yugoslavia, Jan 3, 20; US citizen; m 46. SUGAR CHEMISTRY. *Educ:* City Col New York, BS, 42; Columbia Univ, MA, 50. *Prof Exp:* Asst food chem, Columbia Univ, 49-50; anal chemist, Thomas J Lipton, Inc, NJ, 50-51; res chemist, 51-57, chief control chemist, Pepsi-Cola Co, 57-76; mgr qual assurance, 76-81, PRIN SCIENTIST, INT PEPSI CO INC, 81- *Mem:* Am Chem Soc; Sugar Indust Technologists; Soc Soft Drink Technologists; Am Water Works Asn. *Res:* Determination of solids in sugar solutions, syrups and carbonated beverages; measurement of sugar color. *Mailing Add:* Res & Tech Serv Pepsi Co Inc 100 Stevens Ave Valhalla NY 10595

MAROVITZ, WILLIAM F, b Salt Lake City, Utah, Dec 10, 41; m 64. ANATOMY, OTOLARYNGOLOGY. *Educ:* Univ Calif, BA, 62, PhD(human anat), 66. *Prof Exp:* From asst prof to assoc prof anat in otolaryngol, Sch Med, Wash Univ, 66-73; DIR RES, DEPT OTOLARYNGOL, ASSOC PROF OTOLARYNGOL & ASSOC PROF ANAT, MT SINAI SCH MED, 73- *Concurrent Pos:* Res grant deafness, Mt Sinai Sch Med, 73-; prin investr, Nat Inst Neurol Dis & Blindness grant, 66-73; consult, Nat Inst Neurol Dis & Blindness report on human commun & its disorders, 68; actg prof anat & chmn dept, Israel Inst Technol, 72. *Mem:* AAAS; Am Asn Anat; NY Acad Sci. *Res:* Male reproductive endocrinology; developmental anatomy and biochemistry of temporal bone and its contents. *Mailing Add:* Dept Otolaryngol Mt Sinai Sch Med New York NY 10029

MARPLE, DENNIS NEIL, b Storm Lake, Iowa, Oct 31, 45; m 66; c 2. ANIMAL PHYSIOLOGY, ANIMAL SCIENCE. *Educ:* Iowa State Univ, BS, 67, MS, 68; Purdue Univ, PhD(physiol), 71. *Prof Exp:* NIH fel swine physiol, Meat & Animal Sci Dept, Univ Wis, 71-73; asst prof, 73-77, ASSOC PROF ANIMAL & DAIRY SCI, AUBURN UNIV, 77- *Mem:* Am Soc Animal Sci; Am Meat Sci Asn; Sigma Xi. *Res:* Endocrinological interactions and their regulation of growth in meat animals; study of animal physiology and meat quality. *Mailing Add:* Dept Animal & Dairy Sci Auburn Univ Auburn AL 36830

MARPLE, DUDLEY TYNG FISHER, b Portland, Ore, Sept 18, 27. PHYSICS. *Educ:* Kenyon Col, AB, 48; Syracuse Univ, MS, 50, PhD(physics), 54. *Prof Exp:* PHYSICIST, GEN ELEC RES & DEVELOP CTR, 54- *Mem:* Optical Soc Am; Am Phys Soc. *Res:* Optical properties of solids; energy transmission in optical fibers. *Mailing Add:* 1135 Earl Ave Schenectady NY 12309

MARPLE, LELAND WARREN, analytical chemistry, see previous edition

MARPLE, STANLEY, JR, b Camden, NJ, Feb 4, 20; m 44; c 2. CHEMICAL ENGINEERING, PHYSICAL CHEMISTRY. *Educ:* Mass Inst Technol, SB, 41, PhD(phys chem), 43. *Prof Exp:* Sr res chemist, refining processes, Houston Res Lab, 43-47, sr technologist, res admin, Head Office, NY, 47-48, group leader Houston Res Lab, 48-56, asst chief res chem, 56-57, vis scientist, Royal Dutch-Shell Lab, Amsterdam, 57-58, asst chief res chem, Houston, 58-64, engr Head Office, 64-74, TECH MGR REFINING & CHEM PROCESSES HEAD OFFICE ENG DEPT, SHELL OIL CO, 74- *Concurrent Pos:* Mem tech comt Fractionation Res Inc, 73-; chmn tech comts, Fraction Res, Inc, 79- *Mem:* Am Chem Soc; Am Inst Chem Eng. *Res:* Separation processes; distillation tower equipment performance; lubricating oil manufacture; wax products; vapor pressure and PVT of hydrocarbons; energy recovery in separation processes. *Mailing Add:* 810 Soboda Ct Houston TX 77079

MARPLE, VIRGIL ALAN, b Wendall, Minn, Aug 16, 39; m 62; c 3. MECHANICAL ENGINEERING. *Educ:* Univ Minn, Minneapolis, BME, 62, PhD(mech eng), 70; Univ Southern Calif, MSME, 65. *Prof Exp:* Engr, Aeronutronic Div, Ford Motor Co, 62-65; sr engr, Fluidyne Eng Corp, 65-67; res asst mech eng, 67-70, res assoc, 70-71, asst prof, 71-77, ASSOC PROF MECH ENG, UNIV MINN, MINNEAPOLIS, 78- *Mem:* AAAS; Am Soc Mech Engrs; Am Indust Hyg Asn. *Res:* Particle technology and aerosol physics; application to particulate air pollution and to dust problems in the coal mining industry. *Mailing Add:* Dept of Mech Eng Univ of Minn Minneapolis MN 55455

MARQUARDT, CHARLES LAWRENCE, b Chicago, Ill, Dec 12, 36; m 63; c 3. EXPERIMENTAL SOLID STATE PHYSICS. *Educ:* DePaul Univ, BS, 60, MS, 63; Cath Univ Am, PhD, 72. *Prof Exp:* Gen physicist, 63-65, SOLID STATE RES PHYSICIST, US NAVAL RES LAB, 65- *Mem:* AAAS; Am Phys Soc; Sigma Xi. *Res:* Electromagnetic theory; ionic transport phenomena; radiation defects in solids; lunar sample analysis; laser damage in semiconductors; photochromic glasses. *Mailing Add:* Code 5550 US Naval Res Lab Washington DC 20375

MARQUARDT, DONALD WESLEY, b New York, NY, Mar 13, 29; m 52; c 1. STATISTICS, MATHEMATICS. *Educ:* Columbia Univ, AB, 50; Univ Del, MA, 56. *Prof Exp:* Res engr & mathematician, Exp Sta, 53-57, res proj engr & sr mathematician, 57-64, consult supvr, 64-72, field mgr, 70-73, CONSULT MGR, E I DU PONT DE NEMOURS & CO, INC, 72- *Concurrent Pos:* Assoc ed, Technometrics, 74-80; mem, Comt Qual Assurance, Am Nat Standards Inst, 78-; Am Nat Standards Inst rep to Tech Comt Appln Statist Methods, Int Orgn Standards, 79, 80 & 81, Tech Comt Qual Assurance, 80 & 81, chmn subcomt statist qual control, 81; mem eval panel appl math for Nat Bur Standards, Nat Res Coun, 81- *Honors & Awards:* Youden Prize, Am Soc Qual Control, 74. *Mem:* Fel Am Statist Asn; Am Soc Qual Control; Soc Indust & Appl Math; Sigma Xi; Asn Comput Mach. *Res:* Statistics of nonlinear models; biased estimation; strategy of experimentation; smooth regression; mixture models and experiments; computer algorithms; applications in engineering, physical and biological sciences; time series analysis of unequally spaced data. *Mailing Add:* Eng Dept E I du Pont de Nemours & Co Inc Wilmington DE 19898

MARQUARDT, HANS WILHELM JOE, b Berlin, Ger, Aug 28, 38; m 74. PHARMACOLOGY, CANCER. *Educ:* Univ Cologne, MD, 64. *Prof Exp:* Instr pharmacol, Univ Cologne, 64-68; vis investr, Div Pharmacol, Sloan-Kettering Inst Cancer Res, 68-70; vis investr cancer res, McArdle Lab Cancer Res, Univ Wis-Madison, 70-71; assoc, 71-74, ASSOC MEM, SLOAN-KETTERING INST CANCER RES, 74- *Concurrent Pos:* Asst prof pharmacol, Grad Sch Med Sci, Cornell Univ, 71-74, assoc prof, 75-; NIH-USPHS res career develop award, 75. *Mem:* Cell Kinetics Soc; Soc Toxicol; Europ Asn Cancer Res; Am Soc Pharmacol & Exp Therapeut; Am Asn Cancer Res. *Res:* Pharmacology and toxicology of antitumor agents and chemical carcinogens; chemical carcinogenesis and mutagenesis in tissue culture. *Mailing Add:* Sloan-Kettering Inst Cancer Res 410 E 68th St New York NY 10021

MARQUARDT, ROLAND PAUL, b Tulare, SDak, Sept 2, 13. ANALYTICAL CHEMISTRY, ORGANIC CHEMISTRY. *Educ:* Huron Col, SDak, AB, 35; Univ SDak, AM, 36. *Prof Exp:* Chemist, 39-58, ANAL RES SPECIALIST CHEM, DOW CHEM CO, 58- *Mem:* Fel Am Inst Chemists; Am Chem Soc; Sigma Xi. *Res:* Industrial analytical research; analytical method development, including fundamental methods for unsaturation in organic compounds and for residue analysis of pesticides, especially phenoxy acid herbicides. *Mailing Add:* 1212 Baldwin St Midland MI 48640

MARQUARDT, RONALD RALPH, b Bassano, Alta, May 24, 35; m 59; c 2. BIOCHEMISTRY, AVIAN PHYSIOLOGY. *Educ:* Univ Sask, BSA, 58; Univ Alta, MSc, 61; Wash State Univ, PhD(animal sci), 65. *Prof Exp:* Asst dist agriculturist, Alta Dept Agr, 58-59; asst animal sci, Univ Alta, 59-61; asst, Wash State Univ, 61-65, res assoc biochem, 65-67; assoc prof, 67-77, PROF ANIMAL SCI, UNIV MAN, 77- *Mem:* Am Chem Soc; Can Biochem Soc; Can Nutrit Soc; Can Soc Animal Sci. *Res:* Purification and characterization of avian glycolytic enzymes; sex hormones control mechanisms; influence of diet on synthesis and degradation of hepatic enzymes. *Mailing Add:* Dept of Animal Sci Univ of Man Winnipeg MB R3T 2N2 Can

MARQUARDT, WILLIAM CHARLES, b Ft Wayne, Ind, Oct 9, 24; m 48; c 3. PROTOZOOLOGY, PARASITOLOGY. *Educ:* Northwestern Univ, BS, 48; Univ Ill, MS, 50, PhD(zool), 54. *Prof Exp:* Asst, Col Vet Med, Univ Ill, 52-54; from asst prof to assoc prof parasitol, Mont State Col, 54-61; assoc prof biol, DePaul Univ, 61-62; assoc prof parasitol, Univ Ill, 62-66; PROF ZOOL, COLO STATE UNIV, 66- *Concurrent Pos:* Consult, Thorne Ecol Inst, Colo, 72-76. *Mem:* Am Soc Parasitologists; Soc Protozoologists (asst treas, 67-70, pres, 74); Am Soc Zoologists; Am Soc Trop Med & Hyg. *Res:* Transmission and host-parasite relationships in parasitic protozoa and helminths. *Mailing Add:* Dept of Zool & Entom Colo State Univ Ft Collins CO 80523

MARQUART, JOHN R, b Benton Harbor, Mich, Feb 3, 33. PHYSICAL CHEMISTRY. *Educ:* Univ Ariz, BS, 55; Univ Ill, MS, 61, PhD(phys chem), 63. *Prof Exp:* Chem test officer, Dugway Proving Ground, US Army Chem Corps, Utah, 57-58; res assoc physics, Argonne Nat Lab, 62; chemist, Shell Develop Co, 63-68; assoc prof chem, Mercer Univ, 68-74, prof, 74-80; MEM FAC, CHEM DEPT, EASTERN ILL UNIV, 80- *Concurrent Pos:* Vis lectr & res assoc, Univ Ill, Champaign-Urbana, 72, 74, 75, 76, 77 & 78, vis prof, 78-79. *Mem:* Am Chem Soc; Sigma Xi. *Res:* Mass spectroscopy; thermodynamics; solution behavior; high temperature gas phase kinetics. *Mailing Add:* Chem Dept Eastern Ill Univ Charleston IL 61920

MARQUART, RONALD GARY, b Winnipeg, Man, Apr 22, 38; m 76. COMMUNICATIONS SCIENCE, CHEMICAL INFORMATION SYSTEMS. *Educ:* Univ Man, BSc, 59; Purdue Univ, MS, 62, PhD(eng), 64. *Prof Exp:* Systs engr, Can Aviation Electronics, Ltd, Man, 59-61; res asst digital coding, Sch Elec Eng, Purdue Univ, 63-64; sr engr surface div, Westinghouse Defense & Space Ctr, 64-68; VPRES, FEIN-MARQUART ASSOCS, INC, 68- *Mem:* Asn Comput Mach; Inst Elec & Electronics Engrs; Sigma Xi. *Res:* Computer software systems analysis and design; data management techniques; interactive methods and systems; real-time data collection and analysis systems; chemical information storage and retrieval systems; pattern recognition applications. *Mailing Add:* Fein-Marquart Assocs Inc 7215 York Rd Baltimore MD 21212

MARQUET, LOUIS C, b Philadelphia, Pa, May 9, 36; m 58; c 4. ATOMIC PHYSICS, SPECTROSCOPY. *Educ:* Carnegie Inst Technol, BS, 58; Univ Calif, Berkeley, MA, 60, PhD(physics), 64. *Prof Exp:* Asst prof physics, Univ Ariz, 65-67; staff scientist, 67-75, leader appl radiation group, 74-79, ASSOC HEAD, OPTICS DIV, LINCOLN LAB, MASS INST TECHNOL, 80- *Mem:* Optical Soc Am. *Res:* High power/laser technology and applications, especially propagation in the atmosphere. *Mailing Add:* Appl Radiation Group Lincoln Lab Mass Inst of Technol PO Box 73 Lexington MA 02173

MARQUEZ, ERNEST DOMINGO, b Tranquillity, Calif, Nov 13, 38; m 74. BIOLOGICAL CHEMISTRY. *Educ:* Calif State Univ, Fresno, BA, 62, MA, 68; Univ Southern Calif, PhD(microbiol), 72. *Prof Exp:* USPHS fel, Scripps Inst Oceanog, 71-73; ASST PROF MICROBIOL, COL MED, HERSHEY MED CTR, PA STATE UNIV, 73- *Mem:* Am Soc Microbiol; Soc Exp Biol Med; AAAS. *Res:* Analyses of malignant cell surfaces transformed by herpesviruses using biochemical, immunological and biological methods. *Mailing Add:* Dept of Microbiol Col Med Pa State Univ Hershey PA 17033

MARQUEZ, JOSEPH A, b New York, NY, Nov 5, 30; m 53; c 4. BIOCHEMISTRY. *Educ:* City Col New York, BS, 57; Fairleigh Dickinson Univ, MAS, 70. *Prof Exp:* Lab asst steroid identification & isolation, Columbia Univ, 54-56; lab asst natural prod isolation, 56-58, res asst antibiotic isolation, 58-61, res assoc, 62-67, res scientist, 67-68, sr scientist, 68-75, MGR ANTIBIOTIC DEPT, SCHERING CORP, 75- *Mem:* AAAS; Am Chem Soc; Am Soc Microbiol; NY Acad Sci; Am Inst Biol Sci. *Mailing Add:* Schering Corp 60 Orange St Bloomfield NJ 07003

MARQUEZ, VICTOR ESTEBAN, b Caracas, Venezuela, Aug 7, 43; m 66; c 3. NUCLEOSIDES, NUCLEOTIDES. *Educ:* Cent Univ Venezuela, BS, 66; Univ Mich, MS, 68, PhD(chem), 70. *Prof Exp:* Fel chem, Nat Cancer Inst, NIH, 70-71; res dir chem, Labs Cosmos, Caracas, 72-77; VIS SCIENTIST CHEM, NAT CANCER INST, NIH, 77- *Mem:* Am Chem Soc; AAAS; Am Asn Cancer Res. *Res:* Design and synthesis of neucleosides as anticancer agents with a specific site of action such as enzyme inhibitors of cytidine deaminase, or cytidine trophosphate synthase. *Mailing Add:* Nat Cancer Inst Bldg 37 Rm 6D-24 NIH Bethesda MD 20205

MARQUIS, DAVID ALAN, b Pittsburgh, Pa, Jan 16, 34; m 73; c 3. FOREST ECOLOGY. *Educ:* Pa State Univ, BS, 55; Yale Univ, MF, 63, PhD(forest ecol), 73. *Prof Exp:* Res forester forest ecol, Laconia, NH, 57-65, staff asst forest mgt, Upper Darby, Pa, 65-69, RES PROJ LEADER FOREST ECOL, NORTHEASTERN FOREST EXP STA, WARREN, PA, 69- *Concurrent Pos:* Vis prof, State Univ NY Col Environ Sci & Forestry, Syracuse, 80. *Mem:* Soc Am Foresters. *Res:* Conduct research on ecological factors affecting regeneration and growth of hardwood forests. *Mailing Add:* Forestry Sci Lab PO Box 928 Warren PA 16365

MARQUIS, DAVID MALEY, b Yonkers, NY, Apr 14, 29; m 55. INDUSTRIAL ORGANIC CHEMISTRY. *Educ:* Stanford Univ, BS, 50; Harvard Univ, MA, 54, PhD(org chem), 55. *Prof Exp:* Res chemist, Jackson Lab, E I du Pont de Nemours & Co, 56-58; vpres, Minerals Refining Co, 58-61; SR RES ASSOC, CHEVRON RES CO, STANDARD OIL CO CALIF, 61- *Mem:* Am Chem Soc. *Res:* Organic and inorganic fluorine chemistry; high temperature reactions; reaction mechanisms; petrochemicals; synthetic detergents; process development. *Mailing Add:* Chevron Res Co 576 Standard Ave Richmond CA 94802

MARQUIS, EDWARD THOMAS, b South Bend, Ind, July 10, 39; m 61; c 6. ORGANIC CHEMISTRY. *Educ:* Ind Univ, AB, 61; Univ Tex, PhD(org chem), 67. *Prof Exp:* Res chemist, 66-68, sr res chemist, Jefferson Chem Co, 68-77, SR PROJ CHEMIST, TEXACO CHEM CO, TEXACO, INC, 77- *Mem:* Am Chem Soc; Sigma Xi. *Res:* Hydrocarbon oxidations and reductions; aromatic and aliphatic isocyanates and their amine precursors; reactions and synthetic use of phosgene. *Mailing Add:* Texaco Chem Co PO Box 4128 Austin TX 78751

MARQUIS, NORMAN RONALD, b Laconia, NH, Jan 3, 36; m 57; c 3. PHYSIOLOGY, BIOCHEMISTRY. *Educ:* Univ NH, BA, 59, MS, 60; Univ Mich, PhD(physiol), 65. *Prof Exp:* Res fel, Harvard Med Sch, 65-67, teaching fel, 66-67; group leader biochem, 67-70, prin investr, 70-77, PRIN RES ASSOC, MEAD JOHNSON RES CTR, 77- *Concurrent Pos:* Adj prof, Univ Evansville, 74- *Mem:* Am Soc Biol Chemists; Soc Exp Biol & Med; Am Physiol Soc; Am Heart Asn; NY Acad Sci. *Res:* Functions of carnitine in lipid metabolism; interrelationships of thrombosis, fibrinolysis and atherosclerosis; role of prostaglandins and cyclic adenosine monophosphate in platelet aggregation and thrombosis. *Mailing Add:* Dept of Biol Res Mead Johnson Res Ctr Evansville IN 47721

MARQUIS, ROBERT E, b Sarnia, Ont, Jan 21, 34; US citizen; m 57; c 3. MICROBIAL PHYSIOLOGY. *Educ:* Wayne State Univ, BS, 56; Univ Mich, MS, 58, PhD(bact), 61. *Prof Exp:* NATO fel, Univ Edinburgh, 61-62, NSF fel, 62-63; from sr instr to asst prof, 63-70, assoc prof, 63-78, PROF MICROBIOL, SCH MED, UNIV ROCHESTER, 78- *Concurrent Pos:* NIH fel, Scripps Inst Oceanog, Univ Calif, San Diego, 70-71. *Mem:* AAAS; Am Soc Microbiol; Undersea Med Soc; Brit Soc Gen Microbiol. *Res:* Bacterial physiology; physical structure of bacterial plasma membranes; basic studies of microbial barophysiology; investigation of the physiology of bacteria in dental plaque. *Mailing Add:* Dept of Microbiol Univ of Rochester Rochester NY 14642

MARQUISS, ROBERT W, range science, see previous edition

MARQUIT, ERWIN, b New York, NY, Aug 21, 26. PHYSICS, PHILOSOPHY OF SCIENCE. *Educ:* City Univ New York, BEE, 48; Univ Warsaw, MA, 57, DSc(math & phys sci), 63. *Prof Exp:* Res assoc high energy physics, Univ Mich, 63-65; asst prof physics, Univ Colo, 65-66; ASSOC PROF PHYSICS, UNIV MINN, 66- *Concurrent Pos:* Dir & treas, Marxist Educ Press, Minneapolis, 77-; Alexander von Humboldt res fel, Berlin, 78-79. *Mem:* Am Physics Soc; Philos Sci Asn. *Res:* Conceptual foundations of physics; philosophical and methodological problems of science; problems of dialectical materialism. *Mailing Add:* Univ of Minn 116 Church St SE Minneapolis MN 55455

MARR, ALLEN GERALD, b Tulsa, Okla, Apr 24, 29; m 48, 70; c 6. MICROBIOLOGY. *Educ:* Univ Okla, BS, 48, MA, 49; Univ Wis, PhD(bact), 52. *Prof Exp:* Proj assoc bact, Univ Wis, 52; instr, 52-54, from asst prof to assoc prof, 54-63, PROF BACT, UNIV CALIF, DAVIS, 63-, DEAN GRAD STUDIES & RES, 69- *Mem:* Am Soc Microbiol. *Res:* Growth and division of bacteria; microbial physiology. *Mailing Add:* Grad Div Univ of Calif Davis CA 95616

MARR, DAVID HENRY, b Tillsonburg, Ont, Nov 14, 38; m 58; c 2. SPECTROSCOPY. *Educ:* Univ Western Ont, BSc, 62, PhD(chem), 66. *Prof Exp:* Res fel, Ill Inst Technol, 66-67; res engr, Fairchild Camera & Instrument Corp, 67-68; res chemist, Hooker Chem Corp, 68-70, sr leader spectros, 70-72; sr res chemist, 72-74, res assoc, 74-78, MGR ANAL RES, STAUFFER CHEM CO, 78- *Mem:* Am Chem Soc. *Res:* Analytical chemistry; application of spectroscopic techniques to problem solving. *Mailing Add:* Stauffer Chem Co Eastern Res Ctr Dobbs Ferry NY 10522

MARR, HAROLD EVERETT, III, physical chemistry, see previous edition

MARR, JAMES JOSEPH, b Hamilton, Ohio, Oct 21, 38; m 63; c 5. INFECTIOUS DISEASES, INTERNAL MEDICINE. *Educ:* Xavier Univ, Ohio, BS, 59; Johns Hopkins Univ, MD, 64; St Louis Univ, MS, 68; Am Bd Internal Med, dipl, 72, cert infectious dis, 74. *Prof Exp:* Am Cancer Soc fel & instr microbiol, Sch Med, St Louis Univ, 67-69; asst prof internal med, 70-75, asst prof path, 73-75, asst prof microbiol, 71-75, assoc prof internal med & path sch med, Wash Univ, 75-76; PROF INTERNAL MED & MICROBIOL & DIR DIV INFECTIOUS DIS, SCH MED, ST LOUIS UNIV, 76- *Concurrent Pos:* Fel trop med, USPHS-La State Univ Int Ctr Med Res & Training, Costa Rica, 72; med dir, Microbiol Labs, Barnes Hosp, St Louis, 73-76; consult, Vet Admin Hosp, St Louis, 72-, St Louis Childrens Hosp, 74-76 & Jewish Hosp, St Louis, 75-76. *Mem:* Am Fedn Clin Res; fel Am Col Physicians; Infectious Dis Soc Am; Am Soc Clin Invest. *Res:* Metabolic regulation in microorganisms and its relationship to the pathogenesis of intracellular infections in man. *Mailing Add:* Sect Infectious Dis Dept Med 1325 S Grand Blvd St Louis MO 63104

MARR, JOHN DOUGLAS, b Denver, Colo, Dec 3, 00; m 29. EXPLORATION GEOPHYSICS, EXPLORATION GEOLOGY. *Educ:* Univ Colo, BS, 26; Colo Sch Mines, MSc, 31, DSc(geophys eng), 32. *Prof Exp:* Party chief seismic, Independent Explor Co, Houston, 33-36; supvr opers interpretation, Seismic Explor Inc, Houston, 37-49, vpres, 49-63, asst mgt, Ray Geophys Div, Mandrel Indust Inc, 63, vpres & mgr data processing & interpretation, 64-65, vpres, 66; PETROL EXPLOR CONSULT, 67- *Mem:* Am Asn Petrol Geologists; Am Inst Mining, Metall & Petrol Engrs; Soc Explor Geophysicists; fel Geol Soc Am. *Res:* Application of advanced concepts in geological and geophysical exploration for hydrocarbon deposits; specializing in stratigraphic exploration and direct hydrocarbon detection. *Mailing Add:* 803 Old Lake Rd Houston TX 77057

MARR, JOHN MAURICE, b Jefferson City, Mo, June 15, 20; m 49. MATHEMATICS. *Educ:* Cent Mo State Col, BS, 41; Univ Mo, MA, 48; Univ Tenn, PhD, 53. *Prof Exp:* Instr math, Mo Sch Mines, 46-47; from asst instr to instr, Univ Mo, 47-49; asst, Univ Tenn, 49-53; from asst prof to assoc prof, 53-62, PROF MATH, KANS STATE UNIV, 62- *Mem:* Am Math Soc; Math Asn Am. *Res:* Topology; convexity. *Mailing Add:* Dept of Math Kans State Univ Manhattan KS 66504

MARR, ROBERT B, b Quincy, Mass, Mar 25, 32; m 54; c 3. PHYSICS. *Educ:* Mass Inst Technol, SB, 53; Harvard Univ, MA, 55, PhD(physics), 59. *Prof Exp:* Res assoc theoret physics, 59-61, assoc physicist, 61-64, physicist, 64-69, chmn, Appl Math Dept, 75-78, SR PHYSICIST, BROOKHAVEN NAT LAB, ASSOC UNIVS, INC, 69- *Mem:* Asn Comput Mach; Am Phys Soc. *Res:* Applied mathematics; computers; applications in physical and biological sciences; theoretical physics. *Mailing Add:* Dept of Appl Math Brookhaven Nat Lab Assoc Univs Inc Upton NY 11973

MARRA, DOROTHEA CATHERINE, b Brooklyn, NY, Jan 23, 22; m 47; c 1. SURFACE CHEMISTRY, COLLOID CHEMISTRY. *Educ:* Brooklyn Col, BA, 43. *Prof Exp:* Anal chemist, Matam Corp, 43-44; res chemist, Foster D Snell Inc, 44-69; vpres, Omar Res, Inc, New York, 69-80; VPRES, AEROSOL PROD TECHNOL, INC, 81- *Mem:* AAAS; Sigma Xi; Soc Cosmetic Chemists; fel Am Inst Chemists. *Res:* Creation and development of new products, specifically in cosmetics, toiletries and pharmaceuticals. *Mailing Add:* 107 Fernwood Rd Summit NJ 07901

MARRA, EDWARD FRANCIS, b Poughkeepsie, NY, May 25, 16. PREVENTIVE MEDICINE. *Educ:* Trinity Col, Conn, BS, 45; Boston Univ, MD, 50; Harvard Univ, MPH, 55. *Prof Exp:* From instr to assoc prof prev med, Sch Med, Boston Univ, 53-60; prof, 60-76, EMER PROF SOCIAL & PREV MED & HEAD DEPT & ASSOC PROF MED, SCH MED, STATE UNIV NY BUFFALO, 76- *Concurrent Pos:* Asst, Mass Mem Hosps, 52-53, from asst vis physician to vis physician, 53-59, chief serv, 59-60. *Mem:* Fel Am Pub Health Asn; Asn Teachers Prev Med; AMA; Int Epidemiol Asn. *Res:* Evaluation of medical care; control of infectious disease; development of teaching programs in social and preventive medicine in medical schools. *Mailing Add:* Dept of Social & Prev Med 2211 Main St Buffalo NY 14214

MARRA, MICHAEL DOMINICK, b Brooklyn, NY, Dec 4, 22; m 47; c 1. BIOCHEMISTRY, BIOANALYSIS. *Educ:* Brooklyn Col, BA, 44; Rutgers Univ, MS, 56; Am Bd Bioanalysts, dipl, 69; Jackson State Univ, PhD(biochem), 74. *Prof Exp:* DIR CLIN LAB, SUMMIT MED GROUP, 46- *Concurrent Pos:* Res consult, Summit Testing Lab, 50-; Warner-Lambert res grant, 71- *Mem:* Am Asn Clin Chemists; fel Am Inst Chemists; Am Asn Bioanalysts. *Res:* Microbiology; immunology. *Mailing Add:* 107 Fernwood Rd Summit NJ 07901

MARRACK, PHILIPPA CHARLOTTE, b Ewell, Surrey, Eng, June 28, 45; US citizen; m 74; c 2. IMMUNOLOGY. *Educ:* Univ of Cambridge, Eng, BA, 67, MA, 70, PhD(biol sci), 70. *Prof Exp:* Fel immunol, Univ Calif, San Diego, 71-73; fel immunol, Univ Rochester, 71-74, assoc, 74-75, asst prof immunol, 75-79; ASSOC PROF, DEPT MED, NAT JEWISH HOSP, 79- *Mem:* Am Asn Immunol; Brit Soc Immunol. *Res:* Study of functional and maturational heterogeneity of mouse T-cells; mode of antigen recognition and action of helper T-cells. *Mailing Add:* Dept Med Nat Jewish Hosp 3800 E Colfax Ave Denver CO 80206

MARRANZINO, ALBERT PASQUALE, b Denver, Colo, Oct 5, 27; m 50; c 5. GEOCHEMISTRY. *Educ:* Regis Col, BS, 49. *Prof Exp:* Phys sci aide, Geol & Petrol Br, 51-55, chemist, Geochem Explor Sect, 55-57, chemist, Mineral Deposits Br, 58-60, chemist, Geochem Explor & Minor Elements Br, 60-65, chief field serv sect mobile & anal chem, 65-71, adv, Geochem Labs, Off Int Geol, 71-73, dep regional geologist, 74-78, NUCLEAR REACTOR ADMIN, CENT REGION, US GEOL SURV, 78- *Honors & Awards:* Meritorious Serv Award, US Dept Interior, 66. *Mem:* Am Chem Soc; Soc Appl Spectros; Asn Explor Geochem. *Res:* Geochemical prospecting basin and range province; mobile spectrographic techniques as applied to geochemical exploration. *Mailing Add:* US Geol Surv Box 25046 MS424 Federal Ctr Denver CO 80225

MARRARO, ROBERT V, b Brooklyn, NY, May 24, 30; c 5. CLINICAL MICROBIOLOGY. *Educ:* Colby Col, Maine, BA, 51; Columbia Univ, BS, 55; Ariz State Univ, MS, 64; Ohio State Univ, PhD(microbiol), 71. *Prof Exp:* Chief microbiol br, US Air Force Hosp, Wiesbaden, Ger, 65-67, US Air Force Med Ctr, Wright-Patterson AFB, Ohio, 67-68, US Air Force Sch Aerospace Med, Brooks AFB, Tex, 71-74 & Wilford Hall US Air Force Med Ctr, Lackland AFB, Tex, 74-77; vpres & mem bd dirs, Home Tutorial Systs, Inc, 78-81. *Concurrent Pos:* Consult microbiol, Surg Gen, US Air Force, Europe, 65-67; clin instr path, Univ Tex Health Sci Ctr, San Antonio, 72-76; exam proctor, Registry Am Med Technologists, 72-, contrib ed, J, 73-; consult microbiol, Bac-Data, Med Info Systs Inc, 75-77; adj prof, Div Natural Sci Dept Biol, Incarnate Word Col, 79-; lectr microbiol, Div Allied Health & Life Sci, Univ Tex, 80. *Honors & Awards:* Fisher Award Med Technol, Fisher Sci Co, 72 & 76. *Mem:* Am Soc Microbiol; Am Pub Health Asn; Electron Micros Soc Am; Am Med Technologists; NY Acad Sci. *Res:* Investigation of the etiology of chronic, recurrent diseases of the human genitourinary tract, especially the role of cell wall-deficient forms of bacteria. *Mailing Add:* 12511 Domingo San Antonio TX 78233

MARRAZZI, AMEDEO S, neuropharmacology, neurophysiology, deceased

MARRAZZI, MARY ANN, b Ann Arbor, Mich, Dec 22, 45. NEUROPHARMACOLOGY, NEUROCHEMISTRY. *Educ:* Univ Minn, BA, 66; Wash Univ, PhD(pharmacol), 72. *Prof Exp:* NIH fel pharmacol, Sch Med, Wash Univ, 72-74; vis investr neuropharmacol, Inst Psychiat, Univ Mo, 74; asst prof, 74-78, ASSOC PROF PHARMACOL, SCH MED, WAYNE STATE UNIV, 78- *Concurrent Pos:* Assoc, Dept Psychiat, Harper Grace Hosp, 81- *Mem:* Soc Neurosci; Am Soc Pharmacol & Exp Therapeut. *Res:* Hypothalamic glucoreceptors in central nervous system regulation of metabolic homeostasis and appetite; anorexia nervosa; neurophysiology; neuropharmacology; relation to possible insulin central nervous system actions; energy metabolism in brain; metabolic encephalopathics; Reye's Syndrome; prostaglandin assay, metabolism and role in nervous system; microchemical methodology. *Mailing Add:* Dept of Pharmacol Sch of Med Wayne State Univ Detroit MI 48201

MARRELLO, VINCENT, b Belsito, Italy, Apr 20, 47; Can citizen; m 72; c 1. SOLID STATE PHYSICS. *Educ:* Univ Toronto, BASc, 70; Calif Inst Technol, MS, 71, PhD(elec eng), 74. *Prof Exp:* Fel appl physics, Calif Inst Technol, 74-75; MEM RES STAFF APPL PHYSICS, IBM RES LAB, 75- *Mem:* Am Phys Soc; Sigma Xi. *Res:* Device physics; material physics; optical and electrical properties of amorphous materials. *Mailing Add:* IBM Res Lab 5600 Cottle Rd San Jose CA 95193

MARRERO, THOMAS RAPHAEL, b New York, NY, May 21, 36. CHEMICAL ENGINEERING. *Educ:* Polytech Inst Brooklyn, BS, 58; Villanova Univ, MS, 59; Univ Md, College Park, PhD(chem eng), 70. *Prof Exp:* Engr, Nuclear Div, Martin-Marietta Corp, 59-64 & Res Div, WR Grace & Co, 64-65; res assoc gases, Univ Mo-Columbia, 70-71; res specialist, Res & Develop Div, Babcock & Wilcox Co, 71-73; sr engr, Gen Elec Co, 73-78; ASSOC PROF, UNIV MO-COLUMBIA, 79- *Concurrent Pos:* Vis prof, Texas A&M Univ, 78-79. *Mem:* Am Inst Chem Eng; Am Chem Soc. *Res:* Transport properties of gases; corresponding states correlations. *Mailing Add:* Univ Mo 2406 Spruce Dr Columbia MO 65202

MARRESE, RICHARD JOHN, b New York, NY, Sept 1, 31; m 53; c 4. AGRONOMY, PLANT PHYSIOLOGY. *Educ:* Cornell Univ, BS, 53, MS, 55; Rutgers Univ, PhD(agron), 59. *Prof Exp:* Asst prof agron, Iowa State Univ, 59-60; mem staff tech serv agr, Diamond-Shamrock Corp, 60-64; biol coordr plant protection, Tenneco, 64-66; mgr field develop, Esso Agr Res Labs, 66-70; DIR FIELD DEVELOP PLANT PROTECTION, AM HOECHST CORP, 70- *Mem:* Weed Sci Soc Am; Entomol Soc Am; Am Phytopath Soc. *Res:* Discovery and development of candidate compounds in plant protection, especially herbicides. *Mailing Add:* Am Hoechst Corp Rte 202/206 N Somerville NJ 08876

MARRIAGE, LOWELL DEAN, b New Rockford, NDak, June 28, 23; m 49; c 3. WILDLIFE CONSERVATION. *Educ:* Ore State Univ, BS, 48. *Prof Exp:* Aquatic biologist, Fish Comn Ore, 48-56, water resources analyst, 56-60, asst dir, 60-62, regional fisheries biologist, Soil Conserv Serv, 62-71, REGIONAL BIOLOGIST, SOIL CONSERV SERV, USDA, 71- *Mem:* Am Fisheries Soc; Wildlife Soc; Am Inst Fishery Res Biol; Soil Conserv Soc Am. *Res:* Shellfish management and research; water projects effects on fisheries and wildlife populations; anadromous fisheries biology and management; water quality and wildlife habitat management in land and water development projects. *Mailing Add:* Soil Conserv Serv 510 Fed Off Bldg 511 NW Broadway Portland OR 97209

MARRIAGE, PAUL BERNARD, b London, Ont, Dec 15, 42; m 65; c 3. PLANT BIOCHEMISTRY, PLANT PHYSIOLOGY. *Educ:* Univ Western Ont, BSc, 64, PhD(bot), 69. *Prof Exp:* RES SCIENTIST, RES STA, AGR CAN, 68- *Mem:* Weed Sci Soc Am. *Res:* Effect of herbicides on plant physiology and biochemical processes as related to agricultural problems. *Mailing Add:* Res Sta Agr Can Harrow ON N0R 1G0 Can

MARRINER, JOHN P, b Dover-Foxcroft, Maine, Nov 15, 48; m 70; c 1. ELEMENTARY PARTICLE PHYSICS. *Educ:* Univ Calif, PhD(physics), 77. *Prof Exp:* Physicist, Lawrence Berkeley Lab, 77-78; PHYSICIST, FERMI NAT ACCELERATOR LAB, 78- *Res:* High energy physics and accelerators. *Mailing Add:* Fermilab PO Box 500 Batavia IL 60510

MARRIOTT, HENRY JOSEPH LLEWELLYN, b Hamilton, Bermuda, June 10, 17; nat US; m 51; c 3. CARDIOLOGY. *Educ:* Oxford Univ, BA, 41, MA, 43, BM, BCh, 44. *Prof Exp:* House physician, St Mary's Hosp London, 44, resident med officer, Sir Alexander Fleming's Penicillin Res Unit, 45; resident, King Edward Hosp, Bermuda, 45-46; from asst to asst prof med, Med Sch, Univ Md, 48-53, assoc prof med & head div phys diag, 53-62, head div arthritis, 56-59; dir med educ & cardiol ctr, Tampa Gen Hosp, Fla, 62-65; dir coronary care, St Anthony's Hosp, 68-78; CLIN PROF PEDIAT, COL MED, UNIV FLA, 70-, CLIN PROF MED, 72-; DIR CLIN RES, ROGERS HEART FOUND, 65- *Concurrent Pos:* Fel med, Johns Hopkins Hosp, 46-47; chief EKG dept, Mercy Hosp, Baltimore, Md, 54-62; consult, Vet Admin Hosp, Bay Pines, Fla, 63-; clin prof med, Sch Med, Emory Univ, 66- *Mem:* AMA; Am Heart Asn; fel Am Col Cardiol; fel Am Col Physicians; Brit Med Asn. *Res:* Electrocardiography and clinical cardiology. *Mailing Add:* Rogers Heart Found St Anthony's Hosp St Petersburg FL 33705

MARRIOTT, LAWRENCE FREDERICK, b Browns, Ill, Dec 18, 13; m 38; c 1. AGRONOMY, SOILS. *Educ:* Univ Ill, BS, 35; Univ Wis, MS, 53, PhD(soils), 55. *Prof Exp:* Asst soil exp fields, Univ Ill, 35-42; self employed, 46-51; asst soils, Univ Wis, 51-55; asst prof, Pa State Univ, 55-59, assoc prof soil technol, 59-77; RETIRED. *Mailing Add:* PO Box 233 State Col PA 16801

MARRIOTT, RICHARD, b London, Eng, Nov 17, 29; US citizen; m 52; c 2. MATHEMATICAL PHYSICS, COMPUTER SCIENCE. *Educ:* Univ London, BSc, 54, PhD(atomic physics), 56. *Prof Exp:* Res asst, Univ Col, Univ London, 56; design engr, Atomic Energy Div, Can Westinghouse, Atomic Energy Can Ltd, 56-59; staff mem res div, Radiation Inc, 59-61; consult, Space Sci Lab, Gen Dynamics/Convair, 61-65; res fel, Inst Pure & Appl Physics, Univ Calif, San Diego, 65-67; sr res fel atomic physics, Royal Holloway Col, Univ London, 67-68; PROF CHEM ENG, WAYNE STATE UNIV, 68- *Concurrent Pos:* Consult, Space Sci Lab, Gen Dynamics/Convair, 61-66, Inst Pure & Appl Physics, Univ Calif, San Diego, 68-69, Atomic Energy Res Estab, Harwell, Eng, 68- & Phys Dynamics, Inc, 77-; sr vis fel, Dept Theoret Physics, Queen's Univ, Belfast, 69-70. *Mem:* Fel Brit Phys Soc. *Res:* Computer applications; theoretical studies of atomic structure and collision processes. *Mailing Add:* Res Inst for Eng Sci Col of Eng Wayne State Univ Detroit MI 48202

MARROCCO, RICHARD THOMAS, b Rochester, NY, July 27, 43; m 70. SENSORY PHYSIOLOGY, NEUROSCIENCES. *Educ:* Univ Calif, Los Angeles, BA, 65; Ind Univ, PhD(psychol), 71. *Prof Exp:* Res assoc, Ind Univ, 65-68; fel, 68-71, fel neurophysiol, Univ Calif, Berkeley, 72-73; asst prof, 73-79, ASSOC PROF SENSORY PHYSIOL, UNIV ORE, 79- *Mem:* Soc Neurosci; AAAS. *Res:* Physiology of color, form and binocular vision in primates. *Mailing Add:* Dept of Psychol Univ Ore Eugene OR 97403

MARRON, MICHAEL THOMAS, b Jan 31, 43; US citizen; m 66; c 2. THEORETICAL CHEMISTRY, PHYSICAL CHEMISTRY. *Educ:* Univ Portland, BS, 64; Johns Hopkins Univ, MA, 65, PhD(theoret chem), 69. *Prof Exp:* Res assoc, Theoret Chem Inst, Univ Wis, 69-70; from asst prof to assoc prof chem, 70-80, chmn chem dept, 76-78, PROF CHEM, UNIV WIS-PARKSIDE, 80-, CHMN DIV SCI, 78- *Mem:* AAAS; Am Chem Soc; Bioelectromagnetics Soc. *Res:* Molecular quantum mechanics; biological effects of extremely low frequency electromagnetic fields; application of computer technology to chemical problems. *Mailing Add:* Box 2000 Univ of Wis-Parkside Kenosha WI 53141

MARRONE, MICHAEL JOSEPH, b Lewistown, Pa, July 19, 37; m 61; c 4. SOLID STATE PHYSICS. *Educ:* Univ Notre Dame, BS, 59; Univ Pittsburgh, MS, 61; Cath Univ Am, PhD(physics), 71. *Prof Exp:* RES PHYSICIST, US NAVAL RES LAB, 61- *Mem:* Am Phys Soc; Sigma Xi. *Res:* Optical properties of solids; optical absorption and emission; radiation effects in solids; magneto-optics. *Mailing Add:* Code 6570 US Naval Res Lab Washington DC 20375

MARRONE, PAUL VINCENT, b Niagara Falls, NY, Mar 14, 32; m 55; c 5. GAS DYNAMICS, FLUID PHYSICS. *Educ:* Univ Notre Dame, BS, 54; Princeton Univ, MS, 56; Univ Toronto, PhD(aero physics), 66. *Prof Exp:* Res scientist gas dynamics, 56-63, prin res scientist, fluid physics, Cornell Aeronaut Lab, 66-76; prog mgr fluid physics, 76-78, asst dept head, 78-80, DEPT HEAD, AERODYN RES DEPT, CALSPAN CORP, 80- *Mem:* Am Inst Aeronaut & Astronaut; Sigma Xi. *Res:* High temperature gas dynamics; molecular radiation; chemical kinetics; thermodynamics; computational modeling; experiment methods in gas dynamics. *Mailing Add:* Calspan-Adv Technol Ctr PO Box 400 Buffalo NY 14225

MARRS, BARRY LEE, b Newark, NJ, Sept 23, 42; m 66; c 2. MICROBIOL GENETICS, PHOTOSYNTHESIS. *Educ:* Williams Col, BA, 63; Western Reserve Univ, PhD(biol), 68. *Prof Exp:* NSF fel, Univ Ill, Urbana, 67-69; Am Cancer Soc fel, Stanford Univ, 69-71; res assoc microbiol, Ind Univ, Bloomington, 71-72; asst prof, 72-75, assoc prof, 75-78, PROF BIOCHEM, SCH MED, ST LOUIS UNIV, 78- *Mem:* Am Soc Microbiol; Am Soc Biol Chemists. *Res:* Regulation of membrane formation and genetics of photosynthetic bacteria; structure and function of photosynthetic bacterial membranes. *Mailing Add:* Dept of Biochem St Louis Univ Sch of Med St Louis MO 63104

MARRS, ROSCOE EARL, b Schenectady, NY, Oct 21, 46; m 74. NUCLEAR PHYSICS. *Educ:* Cornell Univ, AB, 68; Univ Wash, MS, 69, PhD(physics), 75. *Prof Exp:* Res fel physics, Calif Inst Technol, 75-76; sr res assoc, Ind Univ Cyclotron Facil, 76-78; res assoc, Triumf, Univ BC, 78-80; MEM STAFF, LAWRENCE LIVERMORE NAT LAB, 80- *Mem:* Am Phys Soc. *Res:* Experimental low and intermediate energy nuclear physics. *Mailing Add:* Lawrence Livermore Nat Lab PO Box 808 L-401 Livermore CA 94550

MARRUS, RICHARD, b Brooklyn, NY, Sept 14, 32. ATOMIC PHYSICS, NUCLEAR PHYSICS. *Educ:* NY Univ, BS, 54; Univ Calif, Berkeley, MA, 56, PhD(physics), 59. *Prof Exp:* Asst, Univ, 54-56, res physicist, Lawrence Radiation Lab, 56-66, assoc prof, Univ, 66-71, PROF PHYSICS, UNIV CALIF, BERKELEY, 71- *Concurrent Pos:* Guggenheim fel, 70-71. *Mem:* Am Phys Soc. *Res:* Atomic beam magnetic resonance spectroscopy; optical pumping. *Mailing Add:* Dept of Physics Univ of Calif Berkeley CA 94720

MARSAGLIA, GEORGE, b Denver, Colo, Mar 12, 25; m 54; c 1. MATHEMATICS, COMPUTER SCIENCE. *Educ:* Colo Agr & Mech Col, BSc, 47; Ohio State Univ, MA, 48, PhD(math), 50. *Prof Exp:* Instr math, Ohio Univ, 48; asst prof, Univ Mont, 51-53, dir statist lab, 52-53; res assoc math statist, Univ NC, 53-54; vis lectr, Okla State Univ, 54-55; Fulbright vis prof, Univ Rangoon, 55-56; mem staff, Sci Res Labs, Boeing Co, Wash, 56-70; prof comput sci & dir sch comput sci, McGill Univ, 70-76; PROF COMPUT SCI & CHMN DEPT, WASH STATE UNIV, 76- *Concurrent Pos:* Vis lectr, Univ NC, 53-54; consult, Westinghouse Elec Corp, 56; from lectr to vis prof, Univ Wash, 59-70. *Res:* Probability and measure theory; stochastic processes; mathematical statistics; biomathematics; computer sciences. *Mailing Add:* Comput Sci Dept Wash State Univ Pullman WA 99163

MARSCHALL, CHARLES W(ALTER), b Rosendale, Wis, Sept 25, 30; m 52; c 5. METALLURGY. *Educ:* Univ Wis, BS, 53, MS, 57; Case Inst Technol, PhD(metall), 60. *Prof Exp:* Res engr, Gen Motors Corp, 53; instr metall, Univ Wis, 55-57; asst, Case Inst Technol, 57-59; sr metallurgist, Battelle Mem Inst, 59-65, assoc chief mech metall, 65-66; asst prof mat, Univ Wis, Milwaukee, 66-67; assoc chief mech metall div, 67-71, assoc chief deformation & fracture res div, 71-74, PRIN SCIENTIST, BATTELLE COLUMBUS LABS, 74- *Concurrent Pos:* Battelle Seattle Res Ctr fel, 73-74. *Mem:* Am Inst Mining, Metall & Petrol Engrs; Am Soc Metals; Am Soc Testing & Mat. *Res:* Physical metallurgy of steels; controlled-modulus alloy development; stress-corrosion cracking; distortion and residual stress; mechanical behavior of materials; dimensional stability and micromechanical properties of materials for precision applications; fracture resistance of nuclear reactor components. *Mailing Add:* Battelle Columbus Labs Metal Sci Sect 505 King Ave Columbus OH 43201

MARSCHKE, CHARLES KEITH, biochemistry, microbiology, see previous edition

MARSCHNER, BERNARD W, b New Ulm, Minn, Apr 8, 21; m 46; c 6. AERONAUTICS. *Educ:* Univ Minn, BS, 42; Calif Inst Technol, MS, 47, PhD(aeronaut), 54. *Prof Exp:* Dir res & Develop, A Model Eng Develop Ctr, US Air Force, 52-57, dir ballistic missile test, Missile Develop Ctr, 57-61, prof aeronaut & head dept, US Air Force Acad, 61-63, dir sci & tech, Air Force Syst Command, 63-65; vpres univ affairs, 68-70, PROF MECH ENG & HEAD DEPT, COLO STATE UNIV, 65-, DIR COMPUT CTR, 69-, SPEC ASST TO PRES, 70- *Mem:* Assoc fel Am Inst Aeronaut & Astronaut. *Res:* Aerodynamic and propulsion test facilities. *Mailing Add:* Univ Comput Ctr Colo State Univ Ft Collins CO 80523

MARSDEN, BRIAN GEOFFREY, b Cambridge, Eng, Aug 5, 37; m 64; c 2. CELESTIAL MECHANICS, PLANETARY SCIENCES. *Educ:* Oxford Univ, BA, 59, MA, 63; Yale Univ, PhD(astron), 66. *Prof Exp:* Res asst astron, Yale Univ Observ, 59-65; ASTRONR, SMITHSONIAN ASTROPHYS OBSERV, 65- *Concurrent Pos:* Lectr, Harvard Univ, 66-; dir cent bur astron telegrams, Int Astron Union, 68-; dir minor planet ctr, Int Astron Union, 78- *Honors & Awards:* Merlin Medal, Brit Astron Asn, 65. *Mem:* Am Astron Soc; Royal Astron Soc; Sigma Xi; Brit Astron Asn; Int Astron Union. *Res:* Orbits of comets, minor planets and natural satellites; celestial mechanics; astrometry; physics of comets. *Mailing Add:* Smithsonian Astrophys Observ 60 Garden St Cambridge MA 02138

MARSDEN, D(AVID) J(OHN), b Provost, Alta, Sept 23, 33; m 59; c 4. AERONAUTICAL ENGINEERING, AERODYNAMICS. *Educ:* Univ Alta, BSc, 55; Col Aeronaut Eng, dipl, 57; Univ Toronto, PhD(rarefied gas dynamics), 65. *Prof Exp:* Asst res officer aerodyn, Nat Res Coun Can, 57-60; res engr, DeHavilland Aircraft of Can Ltd, 64-65; assoc prof mech eng, 65-75, PROF MECH ENG, UNIV ALTA, 75- *Mem:* Can Aeronaut & Space Inst. *Res:* Experimental low speed aerodynamics; aerodynamics of sailplanes; aerofoil theory and development. *Mailing Add:* Dept of Mech Eng Univ of Alta Edmonton AB T6G 2G7 Can

MARSDEN, DAVID HENRY, b Dighton, Mass, Jan 31, 21; m 43; c 5. AGRICULTURAL MICROBIOLOGY. *Educ:* Univ Mass, BS, 43, MS, 48; Harvard Univ, PhD(biol), 52. *Prof Exp:* Asst prof res, Univ Mass, 47-54; plant pathologist, Eastern States Farmers' Exchange, 54-64; PROF MGR CHEM, AGWAY, INC, 64- *Mem:* Am Phytopath Soc (treas, 64-67); Am Inst Biol Sci; Weed Sci Soc Am. *Res:* Pesticides; farm chemicals. *Mailing Add:* Agway Inc Syracuse NY 13201

MARSDEN, HALSEY M, b July 25, 33; US citizen; m 62; c 2. ZOOLOGY, RESEARCH ADMINISTRATION. *Educ:* Univ Conn, BS, 55; Univ Mo, MA, 57, PhD(zool), 63. *Prof Exp:* NIH fel animal behav reproduction, Jackson Lab, 63-65; res biologist, Primate Ecol Sect, Nat Inst Neurol Dis & Stroke, 65-69 & Behav Systs Sect, Lab Brain Evolution & Behav, NIMH, 69-72; res biologist, 72-77, HEALTH SCI ADMINR, DEVELOP NEUROL BR, NAT INST NEUROL & COMMUNICATIVE DIS & STROKE, 77- *Mem:* AAAS; Int Soc Res Aggression. *Res:* Ecology; animal behavior; mammalian reproduction; behavioral-environmental systems; child and human development; primatology. *Mailing Add:* 9804 Inglemere Dr Bethesda MD 20014

MARSDEN, JAMES G, b St Louis, Mo, Dec 12, 25; m 48; c 6. CHEMISTRY. *Educ:* St Louis Univ, BS, 48. *Prof Exp:* Chemist, Linde Co, 48-56 & Silicones Div, 56-67, group leader, 67-76, develop scientist, Res & Develop, Chem & Plastics Div, Union Carbide Corp, 76-81. *Res:* Synthesis and properties of organo-functional silanes; reinforced and filled composites. *Mailing Add:* Union Carbide Corp Tarrytown Tech Ctr PO Box 65 Tarrytown NY 10591

MARSDEN, JERROLD ELDON, b Ocean Falls, BC, Aug 17, 42; m 65; c 1. MATHEMATICS. *Educ:* Univ Toronto, BSc, 65; Princeton Univ, PhD(math), 68. *Prof Exp:* Instr math, Princeton Univ, 68; lectr, 68-69, asst prof, 69-72, assoc prof, 72-77, PROF MATH, UNIV CALIF, BERKELEY, 77- *Concurrent Pos:* Asst prof, Univ Toronto, 70-71. *Res:* Mathematical physics; global analysis; hydrodynamics; quantum mechanics; nonlinear Hamiltonian systems. *Mailing Add:* Dept Math Evans Hall Univ of Calif Berkeley CA 94720

MARSDEN, RALPH WALTER, b Sumner, Wis, Apr 11, 11; m 57; c 2. GEOLOGY. *Educ:* Univ Wis, PhB, 32, PhM, 33, PhD(geol), 39. *Prof Exp:* Asst instr geol, Univ Wis, 36-39; geologist, Philippine Geol Surv, 39-40, chief geol surv div, 40-45; assoc prof geol, Univ Okla, 46-47; geologist, Jones & Laughlin Steel Corp, Pa, 45-46 & 47-51; mgr geol invest, Oliver Iron Mining Div, US Steel Corp, Minn, 51-64, mgr geol invest iron ore Pa, 64-67; chmn dept, 67-74, prof, 67-80, EMER PROF GEOL, UNIV MINN, DULUTH, 80- *Concurrent Pos:* Intern, Cebu, Santo Tomas & Los Banos Camps, Philippines, 42-45. *Mem:* AAAS; fel Geol Soc Am; Soc Econ Geologists; Mining & Metall Soc Am; distinguished mem Am Inst Mining, Metall & Petrol Engrs Soc Mining Engrs (vpres, 69). *Res:* Mineral deposits; economic and mining geology; geology of iron ores including their origin, extent of reserves and resources. *Mailing Add:* Dept of Geol Univ of Minn Duluth MN 55812

MARSDEN, SULLIVAN S(AMUEL), JR, b St Louis, Mo, June 3, 22; m 48, 63, 71; c 4. PETROLEUM ENGINEERING, PHYSICAL CHEMISTRY. *Educ:* Stanford Univ, BA, 44, PhD(phys chem), 48. *Prof Exp:* Asst, Off Sci Res & Develop, Stanford Univ, 44; res chemist, Manhattan Proj, Tenn Eastman Co, 45; assoc chemist, Stanford Res Inst, 47-50; asst dir, Nat Chem Lab, India, 50-53; assoc prof petrol & natural gas eng, Pa State Univ, 53-57; assoc prof petrol eng, 57-62, PROF PETROL ENG, STANFORD UNIV, 62- *Concurrent Pos:* Fulbright vis prof, Univ Tokyo, 63-64. *Mem:* Soc Petrol Engrs. *Res:* Flow of non-Newtonian fluids in tubes and porous media; transportation of oil and gas in the arctic; pipeline engineering; petroleum, natural gas and geothermal reservoir engineering; rheology of non-Newtonian fluids; development of offshore and remote natural gas fields. *Mailing Add:* Mitchell Bldg Rm 357 Stanford Univ Stanford CA 94305

MARSH, ALICE GARRETT, b Berrien Center, Mich, Feb 20, 08; m 27; c 2. NUTRITION, FOODS. *Educ:* Emmanuel Missionary Col, BS, 29; Univ Nebr, MS, 38. *Hon Degrees:* ScD, Andrews Univ, 73. *Prof Exp:* Instr, Hinsdale Acad, Ill, 28-30; dietitian, Hindsdale Sanitarium & Hosp, 30-36; instr foods & nutrit, Union Col, 37-39; asst, Human Nutrit Lab, Univ Nebr, 39-44; instr, Pub Sch, 45-47; instr, Union Col, 47, asst prof foods & nutrit, 47-48, assoc prof home econ, 48-50; assoc prof, 59-59, PROF HOME ECON, ANDREWS UNIV, 59- *Concurrent Pos:* Instr, Univ Nebr, 40-44, mem staff, State & Fed Res Exp Sta. *Mem:* Am Dietetic Asn; Am Home Econ Asn. *Res:* Human nutrition, especially response of blood serum lipids to a controlled diet; animal nutrition; effect of food supplementary proteins upon successive generations of animals; dietary relationships to bone mineral density of human subjects. *Mailing Add:* Dept of Home Econ Andrews Univ Berrien Springs MI 49104

MARSH, BENJAMIN BRUCE, b Petone, NZ, Nov 15, 26; m 52; c 2. MEAT SCIENCE, MUSCULAR PHYSIOLOGY. *Educ:* Univ NZ, BSc, 46, MSc, 47; Cambridge Univ, PhD(biochem), 51. *Prof Exp:* Chemist, Fats Res Lab, Wellington, NZ, 47; biochemist, Low Temperature Res Sta, Cambridge, Eng, 47-51 & Dominion Lab, Wellington, NZ, 51-57; biochemist & dep dir, Meat Indust Res Inst, Hamilton, NZ, 57-71; PROF MUSCLE BIOL & MEAT SCI & DIR LAB, UNIV WIS-MADISON, 71- *Honors & Awards:* Distinguished Meats Res Award, Am Meat Sci Asn, 70; Meat Res Award, Am Soc Animal Sci, 78. *Mem:* Am Meat Sci Asn; Am Soc Animal Sci; Inst Food Technologists. *Res:* Early postmortem muscle metabolism; rigor mortis; meat quality; muscular contraction and relaxation; effects of muscle shortening on meat tenderness. *Mailing Add:* Muscle Biol & Meat Sci Lab Univ of Wis Madison WI 53706

MARSH, BERTRAND DUANE, b Bellingham, Wash, June 22, 38; m 60; c 2. CHEMICAL ENGINEERING, RHEOLOGY. *Educ:* Univ Wash, BS, 61, MS, 63, PhD(chem eng), 65. *Prof Exp:* Fel, Univ Wis, 66-67; res engr, 67-69, proj scientist, 69-71, group leader process res, 71-74, assoc dir process res, 74-77, GEN MGR RES & DEVELOP, PARMA TECH CTR, CARBON PRODS DIV, UNION CARBIDE CORP, 77- *Concurrent Pos:* Mem bd dirs, Cuyahoga Community Col Found. *Mem:* Am Inst Chem Engrs; Soc Rheol. *Res:* Rheological characterization of viscoelastic and elasticoviscous materials; flow description of rheologically complex fluids in processing equipment. *Mailing Add:* 17207 Gold Rush Dr Strongsville OH 44136

MARSH, BRUCE BURTON, b Dickinson Center, NY, Aug 8, 34; m 60; c 3. PARTICLE-SOLID INTERACTIONS. *Educ:* State Univ NY Albany, BS, 56; Univ Rochester, PhD(physics), 62. *Prof Exp:* Assoc prof, 62-64, PROF PHYSICS, STATE UNIV NY ALBANY, 64- *Concurrent Pos:* Vis scientist, Univ Aarhns, Denmark, 80-81. *Mem:* Am Phys Soc; Am Asn Physics Teachers. *Res:* Electron channeling; corrosion inhibition by ion implantation. *Mailing Add:* Dept of Physics State Univ of NY Albany NY 12222

MARSH, BRUCE DAVID, b Munising, Mich, Jan 4, 47; m 70. GEOLOGY. *Educ:* Mich State Univ, BS, 69; Univ Ariz, MS, 71; Univ Calif, Berkeley, PhD(geol), 74. *Prof Exp:* Geophysicist, Anaconda Co, 69-70, geologist, 70-71; asst prof, 74-78, assoc prof, 78-81, PROF EARTH & PLANETARY SCI, JOHNS HOPKINS UNIV, 81- *Concurrent Pos:* Geophysicist, US Geol Surv, 75- *Mem:* Am Geophys Union; Geol Soc Am; Soc Explor Geophysicists. *Res:* Physical geology and the physics and chemistry of the generation ascension and general evolution of magma within the earth, as well as the earth's internal global dynamics. *Mailing Add:* Dept of Earth & Planetary Sci Johns Hopkins Univ Baltimore MD 21218

MARSH, CEDRIC, b Wigan, Eng, March 2, 24; Can citizen; m 48; c 3. STRUCTURAL ENGINEERING. *Educ:* Cambridge Univ, BA, 44, MA, 66. *Prof Exp:* Tech asst, Royal Aircraft Estab, 44-46; asst chief designer, Struct & Mech, Develop Eng, Ltd, 46-52; chief design, Aluminum Lab, Ltd, 52-56; sr designer, Aluminum Co, Can, 56-67; PROF, CONCORDIA UNIV, MONTREAL, 69- *Concurrent Pos:* Consult engr, Ceoric Marsh, Montreal, 67-, Cardona, Trol, Marsh, Hioalgo, Colombia, 80- & Polygenie Inc, Montreal, 79- *Mem:* Can Soc Civil Engrs; Instr Struct Engrs. *Res:* Aluminum as a structural and engineering material; large span aluminum roofs; ultimate limit state analysis of components and structures; elastic instability and post-buckling behavior. *Mailing Add:* 443 Mt Pleasant Westmount PQ H3Y 3G9 Can

MARSH, CONNELL LEROY, b Pagosa Springs, Colo, June 9, 18; m 42; c 2. BIOCHEMISTRY. *Educ:* Univ Nebr, BS, 49, MS, 51, PhD(chem), 53. *Prof Exp:* Asst, USPHS Proj, 49-53, from asst biochemist to assoc biochemist, Dept Animal Path & Hyg, 53-71, from assoc prof to prof vet sci, 58-71, PROF ORAL BIOL, COL DENT, UNIV NEBR, LINCOLN, 71- *Concurrent Pos:* Mem bd adv, Lincoln Med Res Found, 64-70, pres, 70-; consult, Beckman Instrument Co, Inc. *Mem:* Conf Res Workers Animal Dis; Am Asn Clin Chem. *Res:* Enzymology of metazoan parasites; colostrum absorption in young animals; leukemia in man and cattle; biochemical aspects of diseases in domestic animals; oral biology; immunology; research on human antiproteases. *Mailing Add:* Dept of Oral Biol Univ of Nebr Col of Dent Lincoln NE 68503

MARSH, DAVID GEORGE, b London, Eng, Mar 29, 40. IMMUNOGENETICS, BIOCHEMISTRY. *Educ:* Univ Birmingham, BSc, 61; Cambridge Univ, PhD(biochem), 64. *Prof Exp:* asst prof med, 69-76, asst prof microbiol, 72-77, ASSOC PROF MED, SCH MED, JOHNS HOPKINS UNIV, 76-, VCHMN, IMMUNOL COUN, 81- *Concurrent Pos:* USPHS fel, Calif Inst Technol, 66-69; USPHS res grant, Johns Hopkins Univ, 70- & res career develop award, 71-76; investr, Howard Hughes Med Inst, 76-81; mem asthma & allergic dis task force, Nat Inst Allergy & Infectious Dis, 78-79, ad hoc grant rev comt, NIH, 77- *Mem:* Fel Am Acad Allergy; Am Asn Immunol; NY Acad Sci; Am Soc Human Genetics; Col Int Allergol. *Res:* Immunochemistry and genetics of immediate hypersensitivity. *Mailing Add:* Sch Med Johns Hopkins Univ Good Samaritan Hosp Baltimore MD 21239

MARSH, DAVID PAUL, b Seattle, Wash, Dec 10, 34; m 58; c 3. COMPUTER APPLICATIONS IN PHYSICS. *Educ:* DePauw Univ, BA, 57; Univ Calif, Berkeley, PhD(physics), 62. *Prof Exp:* Asst prof physics, Univ Hawaii, 62-63; asst prof, 63-69, ASSOC PROF PHYSICS, UNIV NEV, RENO, 69- *Mem:* AAAS; Am Asn Physics Teachers. *Mailing Add:* Dept of Physics Univ of Nev Reno NV 89557

MARSH, DEAN MITCHELL, b Greenwich, Ohio, May 23, 25; m 48; c 6. CHEMICAL ENGINEERING, ORGANIC CHEMISTRY. *Educ:* Case Inst Technol, BS, 48; Western Reserve Univ, PhD(org chem), 55. *Prof Exp:* Chemist, Sherwin-Williams Co, 48-52; res chemist, 54-57, group leader, 58, develop supvr, 58-59, tech supt, 59-63, res mgr, 63-64, lab dir, Tenn, 64-71, LAB DIR, E I DU PONT DE NEMOURS & CO, INC, DEL, 71- *Res:* Exploratory research; new ventures and products. *Mailing Add:* Chambers Rock Rd Newark DE 19711

MARSH, DONALD CHARLES BURR, b Jackson, Mich, July 20, 26; m 80. NUMBER THEORY. *Educ:* Univ Ariz, BS, 47, MS, 48; Univ Colo, PhD(math), 54. *Prof Exp:* Instr math, Univ Ariz, 48-50; asst prof, Tex Tech Col, 54-55; from instr to assoc prof, 55-66, PROF MATH, COLO SCH MINES, 66- *Concurrent Pos:* Asst to dir, Nat Number Theory Inst, Univ Colo, 59; ed, Aristocrat Dept, The Cryptogram. *Honors & Awards:* C B Warner Award, 78; Damon Award, 80. *Mem:* Sigma Xi; Am Cryptogram Asn (pres, 68-70). *Res:* Heuristics; cryptanalysis; number theory. *Mailing Add:* Dept of Math Colo Sch of Mines Golden CO 80401

MARSH, DONALD JAY, b New York, NY, Aug 5, 34; div; c 2. PHYSIOLOGY, BIOMEDICAL ENGINEERING. *Educ:* Univ Calif, Berkeley, AB, 55; Univ Calif, San Francisco, MD, 58. *Prof Exp:* NIH fel, 59-63; from asst prof to assoc prof physiol, Sch Med, NY Univ, 63-71; prof biomed eng, Sch Eng, 71-78, PROF & CHMN DEPT PHYSIOL, SCH MED, UNIV SOUTHERN CALIF, 78- *Concurrent Pos:* NIH spec fel, 70-71. *Mem:* Am Physiol Soc; Am Soc Nephrol; Biophys Soc; Soc Gen Physiologists. *Res:* Renal physiology, mechanism of hypertonic urine formation; regulation of glomerular filtration and proximal tubule reabsorption; dynamics of organ level regulation of glucose metabolism. *Mailing Add:* Mudd Hall 110 Sch Med Univ of Southern Calif Los Angeles CA 90033

MARSH, FRANK LEWIS, b Aledo, Ill, Oct 18, 99; m 27; c 2. ECOLOGY. *Educ:* Emmanuel Missionary Col, Andrews Univ, AB, 27, BS, 29; Northwestern Univ, MS, 35; Univ Nebr, PhD(bot), 40. *Prof Exp:* Instr sci & math, Hinsdale Acad, Ill, 29-34; asst zool, Northwestern Univ, 34-35; from instr to prof biol, Union Col, Nebr, 35-50; prof & head dept, Emmanuel Missionary Col, Andrews Univ, 50-58; researcher, Geo-Sci Res Inst, 58-64; prof 64-71, EMER PROF BIOL, ANDREWS UNIV, 71- *Res:* Ecological entomology and botany; hyperparasitism; origin of species; variation; hybridization. *Mailing Add:* 216 Hillcrest Dr Berrien Springs MI 49103

MARSH, FREDERICK LEON, b Richmond, Va, Dec 20, 35; m 64. ANALYTICAL CHEMISTRY, PHYSICAL CHEMISTRY. *Educ:* Blackburn Univ, AB, 58; Univ Minn, PhD(anal chem), 65. *Prof Exp:* Trainee microchem, Northern Util Res & Develop Br, Agr Res Serv, USDA, 57, microchemist, 58; instr chem, Univ Toledo, 64-65; sr res electrochemist, Gould Labs, 65-76, SUPVR ADVAN DEVELOP, AUTOMOTIVE BATTERY DIV, GOULD INC, 76- *Mem:* AAAS; Am Chem Soc;

Electrochem Soc. *Res:* Microanalytical chemistry; electrochemistry; electroanalytical chemistry. *Mailing Add:* Gould Inc Auto Battery Div 1110 Hwy 110 Mendota Heights MN 55118

MARSH, GLENN ANTHONY, b Chicago, Ill, Dec 20, 24; m 46; c 4. PHYSICAL CHEMISTRY, CORROSION. *Educ:* Ill Inst Technol, BS, 45; Northwestern Univ, MS, 46. *Prof Exp:* Res fel corrosion, Ill Inst Technol, 46-48; sr res chemist, Pure Oil Co, Ill, 48-56, proj technologist, 56-60, res assoc & head corrosion res sect, 60-65; SUPVR CORROSION SECT, UNION OIL CO CALIF, 66- *Concurrent Pos:* Ed, Corrosion Div, Electrochem Soc, 62-65. *Honors & Awards:* Willis Rodney Whitney Award, Nat Asn Corrosion Engrs, 71. *Mem:* Nat Asn Corrosion Engrs; Electrochem Soc. *Res:* Corrosion mechanisms, measurements and preventive methods. *Mailing Add:* Res Ctr Union Oil Co of Calif Box 76 Brea CA 92621

MARSH, HOWARD STEPHEN, b New York, NY, Feb 4, 42; m 68; c 2. SYSTEMS ENGINEERING, COMMUNICATIONS ENGINEERING. *Educ:* Rensselaer Polytech Inst, BS, 63; Cornell Univ, PhD(physics), 69. *Prof Exp:* Asst physics, Cornell Univ, 63-65, asst, Lab Atomic & Solid State Physics, 64-69; group leader, 79-81, ASSOC DEPT HEAD, MITRE CORP, 81- *Res:* Signal transmission and detection; command, control and communications systems. *Mailing Add:* Mitre Corp 1820 Dolley Madison Blvd McLean VA 22102

MARSH, JAMES ALEXANDER, JR, b Wilson, NC, Dec 8, 40. MARINE ECOLOGY. *Educ:* Duke Univ, BS, 63; Univ Ga, PhD(zool), 68. *Prof Exp:* Fel environ sci, Univ NC, Chapel Hill, 68-70; asst prof marine sci, 70-74, dir, 76-79, ASSOC PROF MARINE SCI, MARINE LAB, UNIV GUAM, 74- *Mem:* Ecol Soc Am; Am Soc Limnol & Oceanog; Am Inst Biol Sci; AAAS; Int Soc Reef Studies. *Res:* Coral reef ecology; primary productivity; nutrient and energy cycling in tropical marine ecosystems. *Mailing Add:* Univ of Guam Marine Lab Univ Guam Sta Mangilao GU 96913

MARSH, JAMES LAWRENCE, b San Francisco, Calif, Oct 24, 45; m 70; c 2. BIOCHEMISTRY, GENETICS. *Educ:* Univ Calif, Santa Barbara, BA, 68; Univ Wash, PhD(biochem), 74. *Prof Exp:* Fel develop genetics, Bio Ctr, Univ Basel, Switz, 74-76; res assoc, Dept Biol, Univ Va, 77-80; ASST PROF GENETICS, UNIV CALIF, IRVINE, 80- *Mem:* Am Chem Soc; Genetics Soc Am. *Res:* Recombinant DNA techniques and genetic chromosomal analysis of the control of gene extension during embryonic development; inonoclonal antibodies to probe developmentally important cell surface molecules. *Mailing Add:* Develop Biol Ctr Univ Calif Irvine CA 92717

MARSH, JOHN LEE, b Washington, DC, Feb 25, 16; m 43, 72; c 6. INFORMATION SCIENCE. *Educ:* Univ Ill, PhD(org chem), 41. *Prof Exp:* Res chemist, Hooker Electrochem Co, NY, 41-43; res chemist, 43-57, SR INFO SCIENTIST, CIBA-GEIGY PHARMACEUT CO, 57- *Mem:* Am Chem Soc; NY Acad Sci; Chem Notation Asn. *Res:* Processing of scientific data and drug information by classical and computer techniques; communication of research knowledge; chemical nomenclature; molecular notations; published and proprietary scientific information. *Mailing Add:* 108 Beekman Rd Summit NJ 07901

MARSH, JOHN MACCLENAHAN, biochemistry, deceased

MARSH, JULIAN BUNSICK, b New York, NY, Jan 21, 26; m 48; c 1. BIOCHEMISTRY. *Educ:* Univ Pa, MD, 47. *Prof Exp:* Intern, Episcopal Hosp, Philadelphia, 47-48; NIH fel biochem, Dept Res Med, Univ Pa, 48-50, instr res med, 50-51, assoc biochem, Grad Sch Med, 52-53, asst prof, 53-59, assoc prof, Sch Med & Grad Sch Med, 59-63, prof, Grad Sch med, 63-65, prof biochem & chmn dept, Sch Dent Med, 65-75; PROF PHYSIOL & PROF BIOCHEM & CHMN DEPT, MED COL PA, 75- *Concurrent Pos:* Guggenheim Mem fel, Nat Inst Med Res, Eng, 60-61. *Mem:* AAAS; Am Soc Biol Chemists; Am Physiol Soc; Soc Exp Biol & Med. *Res:* Action of insulin and other hormones; carbohydrate, chromoprotein and lipoprotein metabolism; experimental nephrosis. *Mailing Add:* Dept of Physiol & Biochem Med Col of Pa Philadelphia PA 19129

MARSH, LELAND C, b Lyons, NY, Nov 19, 28; m 53; c 4. BOTANY. *Educ:* Syracuse Univ, BS, 51, PhD(bot), 62. *Prof Exp:* Asst prof bot & biol, Marshall Univ, 57-60; assoc prof, State Univ NY Col Buffalo, 60-65; PROF BIOL, STATE UNIV NY COL OSWEGO, 65-, CHMN DEPT BOT & PHYSIOL, 71- *Mem:* Bot Soc Am; Soc Study Evolution. *Res:* Botanical research of Typha species, including ecological, genetic and systematic studies; industrial uses of Typha. *Mailing Add:* Dept of Biol State Univ of NY Oswego NY 13126

MARSH, MAX MARTIN, b Indianapolis, Ind, Feb 25, 23; m 41; c 4. PHYSICAL CHEMISTRY, ANALYTICAL CHEMISTRY. *Educ:* Ind Univ, BS, 47. *Prof Exp:* Anal chemist, 47-56, head anal, Res Dept, 56-61, RES ADV, RES LABS, ELI LILLY & CO, 66- *Concurrent Pos:* Dir phys chem res div, Eli Lilly & Co, 67-69; indust prof chem, Ind Univ, 71-76. *Mem:* AAAS; Am Chem Soc; Sigma Xi; NY Acad Sci. *Res:* Optical analytical techniques; molecular structure-activity relationships. *Mailing Add:* Lilly Res Labs Eli Lilly & Co Indianapolis IN 46285

MARSH, NAT HUYLER, b Ft Worth, Tex, Aug 1, 14; m 42; c 3. ORGANIC CHEMISTRY. *Educ:* Rice Inst, BA, 38, MA, 40, PhD(org chem), 42. *Prof Exp:* Res chemist, Humble Oil & Ref Co, Tex, 42-45; res chemist, Am Cyanamid Co, 45-54, mgr synthetic fibers dept, 54-56, mgr synthetic fibers dept, Santa Rosa Plant, Fla, 56-60, dir res & develop, Fibers Div, 60-65, sr managing dir, Cyanamid, Japan, Ltd, 67-68; pres, 68-80, CHMN, NIHON MILLIPORE LTD, 80- *Mem:* Am Chem Soc. *Res:* Petroleum and nitrogen chemistry; guanidines and triazines; cracked gasoline and reaction of bromine with alcohols. *Mailing Add:* Nihon Millipore Ltd 4-15 1 Chome Shiroganedai Minato-Ku Tokyo 108 Japan

MARSH, PAUL MALCOLM, b Fresno, Calif, Nov 7, 36; m 65; c 2. ENTOMOLOGY. *Educ:* Univ Calif, Davis, BS, 58, MS, 60, PhD(entom), 64. *Prof Exp:* Lab technician, Univ Calif, Davis, 61-63; RES ENTOMOLOGIST, SYST ENTOM LAB, SCI EDUC ADMIN-AGR RES, USDA, 64- *Mem:* Entom Soc Am; Am Entom Soc. *Res:* Systematic entomology; taxonomy and biology of parasitic wasps of the family Braconidae. *Mailing Add:* Syst Entom Lab USDA US Nat Mus Washington DC 20560

MARSH, RICHARD EDWARD, b Jackson, Mich, Mar 6, 22; m 47; c 4. PHYSICAL CHEMISTRY. *Educ:* Calif Inst Technol, BS, 43; Univ Calif, Los Angeles, PhD(phys chem), 50. *Prof Exp:* Fel struct of metals, 50-51, fel struct of proteins, 51-55, sr fel, 55-74, res assoc structure of proteins, 74-77, res assoc, 77-81, SR RES ASSOC CHEMIST, CALIF INST TECHNOL, 81- *Concurrent Pos:* Instr, Univ Calif, Los Angeles, 53. *Mem:* Am Crystallog Asn. *Res:* Crystal structure analysis; molecular structure; structure of biologic molecules. *Mailing Add:* Dept of Chem Calif Inst of Technol Pasadena CA 91125

MARSH, RICHARD FLOYD, b Portland, Ore, Mar 3, 39; m 59; c 5. VETERINARY VIROLOGY, VETERINARY PATHOLOGY. *Educ:* Wash State Univ, BS, 61, DVM, 63; Univ Wis-Madison, MS, 66, PhD(vet sci), 68. *Prof Exp:* Res veterinarian, Kellogg Co, Battle Creek, Mich, 63-64; NIH trainee vet sci, Univ Wis-Madison, 64-66, NIH spec fel, 66-68; vet officer, Nat Inst Neurol Dis & Stroke, NIH, USPHS, 68-70; res assoc, 70-78, ASSOC PROF VET SCI, UNIV WIS-MADISON, 78- *Concurrent Pos:* Romnes Fac Fel, 80. *Mem:* AAAS; Am Soc Microbiol. *Res:* Development and study of animal models of human disease, especially persistent virus infections of the central nervous system. *Mailing Add:* Dept of Vet Sci Univ of Wis Madison WI 53706

MARSH, RICHARD HAYWARD, b Detroit, Mich, Jan 6, 40; m 61; c 4. ANALYTICAL CHEMISTRY. *Educ:* Univ Mich, BS, 61; Wayne State Univ, MS, 64, PhD(anal chem), 67. *Prof Exp:* Sanit chemist, Detroit Water Dept, 61-63; teaching asst, Wayne State Univ, 64-67; SR RES SCIENTIST, FORD MOTOR CO, 67- *Mem:* Asn Comput Mach; Sigma Xi. *Res:* Neutron activation analysis; radiochemistry; environmental chemistry; computer science. *Mailing Add:* 7442 Churchill Dearborn MI 48206

MARSH, ROBERT CECIL, b Lexington, Ky, Feb 27, 44; m 65; c 2. MOLECULAR BIOLOGY. *Educ:* Western Ky Univ, BS, 65; Vanderbilt Univ, PhD(molecular biol), 71. *Prof Exp:* Res assoc biochem, Soc Molecular Biol Res, Stoeckheim, Ger, 71-75; res assoc, Princeton Univ, 75-76; ASST PROF BIOCHEM, UNIV TEX, DALLAS, 76- *Mem:* Am Chem Soc. *Res:* Mechanism of action of elongation factors in protein biosynthesis; DNA replication and gene expression by bacteriophage T4; structure of E coli origin of replication. *Mailing Add:* 1700 Westridge Plano TX 75075

MARSH, TERRENCE GEORGE, b Winnipeg, Man, Jan 12, 41; US citizen; m 65; c 2. ENVIRONMENTAL BIOLOGY. *Educ:* Earlham Col, AB, 63; Ore State Univ, MS, 65; Univ Ky, PhD(zool), 69. *Prof Exp:* Instr biol, Asbury Col, 68-69; asst prof, 69-76, ASSOC PROF BIOL, N CENT COL, ILL, 76- *Mem:* AAAS; Nat Speleol Soc. *Res:* urban biology; insect ecology. *Mailing Add:* Dept of Biol N Cent Col Naperville IL 60566

MARSH, WALTON HOWARD, b Bay City, Mich, Mar 26, 19; m 44; c 2. BIOCHEMISTRY. *Educ:* Columbia Col, AB, 40; Polytech Inst New York, MS, 43; Case Western Reserve Univ, PhD(biochem), 51. *Prof Exp:* Asst polymer res, Am Cyanamid Co, 40-43, asst pharm, 45-46; med res biochemist and clin biochemist, Vet Admin Hosp, 51-54; PROF PATH, STATE UNIV NY DOWNSTATE MED CTR, 54-; CHIEF BIOCHEMIST, KINGS COUNTY HOSP, BROOKLYN, 54- *Concurrent Pos:* Instr, Case Western Reserve Univ, 51-54. *Res:* Differentiation and regeneration metabolism. *Mailing Add:* Dept of Path State Univ NY Downstate Med Ctr Brooklyn NY 11203

MARSH, WILLIAM ERNEST, b New Brunswick, NJ, Nov 22, 39; m 62; c 2. MATHEMATICAL LOGIC. *Educ:* Dartmouth Col, AB, 62, MA, 65, PhD(math), 66. *Prof Exp:* Asst prof math & chmn dept, Talledega Col, 66-69; asst prof, 69-74, ASSOC PROF MATH, HAMPSHIRE COL, 74- *Mem:* Asn Symbolic Logic; Am Math Soc. *Res:* Model theory; foundations of mathematics; mathematical linguistics; automata theory. *Mailing Add:* Dept of Math Hampshire Col Amherst MA 01002

MARSHAK, HARVEY, b Brooklyn, NY, Nov 9, 27; m 58, 78; c 2. NUCLEAR PHYSICS. *Educ:* Univ Buffalo, BA, 50; Univ Conn, MA, 52; Duke Univ, PhD(physics), 55. *Prof Exp:* Res assoc, Duke Univ, 54-55; assoc physicist, Brookhaven Nat Lab, 55-62; PHYSICIST, NAT BUR STANDARDS, 62- *Concurrent Pos:* Vis prof, Katholieke Univ, Leuven, Belg, 80- *Mem:* Fel Am Phys Soc. *Res:* Nuclear orientation and spectroscopy; neutron physics; low temperature physics. *Mailing Add:* Physics Bldg B 128 Nat Bur of Standards Washington DC 20234

MARSHAK, MARVIN LLOYD, b Buffalo, NY, Mar 11, 46; m 72; c 2. PHYSICS. *Educ:* Cornell Univ, AB, 67; Univ Mich, MS, 69, PhD(physics), 70. *Prof Exp:* Res assoc physics, Univ Mich, 70; res assoc, 70-74, asst prof, 74-78, ASSOC PROF PHYSICS, UNIV MINN, 78- *Concurrent Pos:* NSF grant, 77-79 & 81. *Mem:* Am Phys Soc. *Res:* Experimental elementary particle physics. *Mailing Add:* 116 Church St SE Univ Minn Physics Dept Minneapolis MN 55455

MARSHAK, ROBERT EUGENE, b New York, NY, Oct 11, 16; m 43; c 2. THEORETICAL PHYSICS, ASTROPHYSICS. *Educ:* Columbia Col, AB, 36; Cornell Univ, PhD(physics), 39. *Prof Exp:* From instr to prof physics, Univ Rochester, 39-50, Harris prof & chmn dept, 50-64, distinguished univ prof, 64-70; pres, City Col NY, 70-79; UNIV DISTINGUISHED PROF, VA POLYTECHNIC INST, 79- *Concurrent Pos:* Physicist, Radiation Lab, Mass Inst Technol, 42-43 & Dept Sci & Indust Res Gt Brit, 43-44; dep group leader, Los Alamos Sci Lab, 44-46; mem, Inst Advan Study, 48; Guggenheim fel & prof, Sorbonne, 53-54; Guggenheim fel & guest prof, Ford Found, Europ Orgn Nuclear Res, Switz, 60-61, Yugoslavia, Israel & Japan, 67-68; vis prof, Columbia Univ, Univ Mich, Harvard Univ, Cornell Univ & Tata Inst Fundamental Res, India; Niels Bohr vis prof, Madras Univ, 63, Yalta Int Sch, Carnegie-Mellon Univ & Univ Tex; Nobel lectr, Sweden; Solvay Cong, 67; trustee, Atoms for Peace Awards. Secy, High Energy Physics Comn, Int Union Pure & Appl Physics, 57-63; chmn, Int Conf High Energy Physics, 60; mem, Nat Acad Sci Adv Comt Soviet Union & Eastern Europe, 63-66, head deleg to Poland, 64 & Yugoslavia, 65; mem, US Mission to Soviet Labs, 60; chmn vis physics comn, Brookhaven Nat Lab, 65; vis physics comn, Carnegie Inst, 66-70; mem, Sloan Fel Comt, 67-73, chmn, 72-73; mem sci coun, Int Ctr Theoret Physics, Trieste, 67-75; mem, US-Japan Sci Comt, 68-72; mem exec comt, Nat Comn, UNESCO, 71-73; mem coun, Nat Acad Sci, 71-74. *Honors & Awards:* Morrison Prize, NY Acad Sci, 40. *Mem:* Nat Acad Sci; fel AAAS; Am Acad Arts & Sci; Am Phys Soc (pres-elect, 82, pres, 83); Fedn Am Scientists (chmn, 47-48). *Res:* Energy sources of stars; atomic nuclei; neutron diffusion; elementary particles. *Mailing Add:* VA Polytech Inst & State Univ 202 Fincastle Dr Blacksburg VA 24060

MARSHAK, ROBERT REUBEN, b New York, NY, Feb 23, 23; m 48; c 3. VETERINARY MEDICINE. *Educ:* Cornell Univ, DVM, 45. *Hon Degrees:* Dr Vet Med, Univ Bern, 68. *Prof Exp:* Pvt pract & clin invest, 45-56; chmn dept clin studies, 61-73, dir, Bovine Leukemia Res Ctr, 66-75, PROF MED, SCH VET MED, UNIV PA, 56-, DEAN SCH VET MED, 73- *Concurrent Pos:* Mem comt vet med sci, Nat Acad Sci, 74-76; mem, Adv Coun, James A Baker Inst, Cornell Univ, 77- *Mem:* AAAS; Am Asn Cancer Res; fel NY Acad Sci; Am Col Vet Internal Med (pres, 75-76); Am Vet Med Asn. *Res:* Bovine leukemia; metabolic diseases of cattle. *Mailing Add:* Sch of Vet Med Univ of Pa Philadelphia PA 19104

MARSHALEK, EUGENE RICHARD, b New York, NY, Jan 17, 36; m 62; c 2. NUCLEAR PHYSICS. *Educ:* Queen's Col, NY, BS, 57; Univ Calif, Berkeley, PhD(nuclear struct), 62. *Prof Exp:* NSF fel nuclear physics, Niels Bohr Inst, Copenhagen, Denmark, 62-63; res assoc physics theory group, Brookhaven Nat Lab, 63-65; asst prof, 65-69, assoc prof, 69-78, PROF PHYSICS, UNIV NOTRE DAME, 78- *Res:* Nuclear structure theory; nuclear theory, particularly collective effects in atomic nuclei. *Mailing Add:* Dept of Physics Univ of Notre Dame Notre Dame IN 46556

MARSHALL, ALBERT WALDRON, b Portland, Ore, Aug 3, 28; m 51; c 2. MATHEMATICS. *Educ:* Univ Ore, BS, 51; Univ Wash, PhD(math), 58. *Prof Exp:* Actg asst prof statist, Stanford Univ, 58-60; staff mem, Inst Defense Anal, 60-61 & Boeing Sci Res Labs, 61-70; vis prof math, Univ Wash, 70-71; prof statist & math, Univ Rochester, 71-75; PROF MATH, UNIV BC, 75- *Mem:* Am Math Soc; Math Asn Am; fel Inst Math Statist. *Res:* Probability theory; inequalities; reliability theory. *Mailing Add:* Dept of Math Univ of BC Vancouver BC V6T 1W5 Can

MARSHALL, ANNE (CORINNE), b Zanesville, Ohio, Oct 8, 04. BIOLOGICAL SCIENCE. *Educ:* Denison Univ, BS, 25; Ohio State Univ, AM, 28, PhD(entom), 39. *Prof Exp:* Instr zool, McCook Jr Col, 29-32, La State Univ, 32-35 & Ohio State Univ, 35-39; from assoc prof to prof biol & head dept sci, 39-69, EMER PROF BIOL, UNIV WIS-STOUT, 69- *Mem:* AAAS; Sigma Xi. *Res:* Trichoptera. *Mailing Add:* 2950 Fairway Lane Zanesville OH 43701

MARSHALL, ARVLE EDWARD, b Canyon, Tex, Dec 24, 37; m 60; c 2. VETERINARY MEDICINE, VETERINARY NEUROLOGY. *Educ:* Tex Tech Col, BS, 60; Tex A&M Univ, DVM, 64; Univ Mo-Columbia, PhD(vet neurol), 71. *Prof Exp:* Asst vet pract, Tex, 64; vet meat inspector, Meat Inspection Div, USDA, Tex, 64-65; instr vet med & surg, Okla State Univ, 65-67; Nat Inst Child Health & Human Develop fel vet anat, Univ Mo-Columbia, 67-71; asst prof vet med, Univ Ill, Urbana, 71-75; ASST PROF VET MED, ANAT & RADIOLOGY, UNIV GA, 75- *Mem:* Am Vet Med Asn; Am Asn Vet Neurol. *Res:* Auditory evoked response in diagnosis of hearing and vestibular disease in domestic mammals. *Mailing Add:* Col of Vet Med Univ of Ga Athens GA 30602

MARSHALL, BILLY JACK, solid state physics, low temperature physics, see previous edition

MARSHALL, CARTER LEE, b New Haven, Conn, Mar 31, 36; c 2. PREVENTIVE MEDICINE. *Educ:* Harvard Univ, BA, 58; Yale Univ, MD, 62, MPH, 64; Am Bd Prev Med, dipl, 70. *Prof Exp:* Proj dir, Conn Dept Health, New Haven, 64-65; asst prof prev med, Sch Med, Univ Kans Med Ctr, Kansas City, 67-69; from assoc prof community med to prof community med & med educ, Mt Sinai Sch Med, 69-77, assoc dean, 73-77; PROF MED & PREV MED, COL MED & DENT NJ, NJ MED SCH, DIR, OFF PRIMARY HEALTH CARE EDUC & DIR AMBULATORY CARE, COL HOSP, 77- *Concurrent Pos:* Fel epidemiol & pub health, Yale Univ, 64-65; consult, New York Health Serv Admin, 70-71; univ dean health affairs, City Univ New York, 72-74. *Mem:* AAAS; fel Am Pub Health Asn; Asn Teachers Prev Med; AMA; Am Col Prev Med. *Res:* Health services delivery. *Mailing Add:* Off Primary Care NJ Med Sch Newark NJ 07103

MARSHALL, CHARLES EDMUND, b Bredbury, Eng, Jan 9, 03; nat US; m 32; c 1. COLLOID CHEMISTRY, SOIL SCIENCE. *Educ:* Univ Manchester, BSc, 24, MS, 25; Univ London, PhD(agr chem), 27. *Prof Exp:* Asst lectr agr chem, Leeds Univ, 28-36; vis assoc prof, 35-36, from assoc prof to prof, 36-73, assoc dean grad sch, 65-66, actg dean, 66-67, EMER PROF SOILS, UNIV MO-COLUMBIA, 73- *Concurrent Pos:* NSF sr res fel, Imp Col, Univ London, 60-61. *Honors & Awards:* Hoblizelle Award, 51. *Mem:* AAAS; Am Chem Soc; Soil Sci Soc Am (vpres, 45, pres, 46); fel Am Soc Agron; fel Mineral Soc Am. *Res:* Colloid chemistry and mineralogy of clays; electrochemistry of membranes; mineral nutrition of plants; soil formation processes. *Mailing Add:* Dept of Agron Univ of Mo Columbia MO 65201

MARSHALL, CHARLES WHEELER, b Syracuse, NY, Oct 20, 06; m 39; c 2. ORGANIC CHEMISTRY. *Educ:* Univ Chicago, BS, 31, MS, 33, PhD(biochem), 49. *Prof Exp:* Chemist, Edwal Labs, 38-39; chief control chemist, Lakeside Labs, 39-43; res chemist, Off Sci Res & Develop, Chicago, 43-45 & G D Searle & Co, 49-67; SCI WRITER, 67- *Mem:* Am Chem Soc. *Res:* Synthesis of steroids related to adrenal cortical hormones and steroids with new pharmacological properties. *Mailing Add:* 729 N Shore Dr South Haven MI 49090

MARSHALL, CLAIR ADDISON, b Bluffton, Ohio, Jan 20, 11; m 35; c 1. CHEMICAL ENGINEERING. *Educ:* Univ Mich, BS, 34. *Prof Exp:* Chem engr, Tenn Eastman Co, 34-39, asst supt, Acetic Acid Dept, 39-43; consult, Clinton Eng Works, 43-44, supt, Acid Div Process Improvement, 44-50, sr chem engr, Div Staff, 50-59, supvr acid maintenance eng, 59-63, tech asst to div supt, Tenn Eastman Co, 63-75; RETIRED. *Mem:* Am Inst Chem Eng. *Res:* Organic acids and anhydrides; equipment and process for making anhydrides by direct oxidation of aldehydes. *Mailing Add:* 1525 Fairige Dr Kings Port TN 37664

MARSHALL, CLIFFORD WALLACE, b New York, NY, Mar 11, 28; m 55. APPLIED MATHEMATICS, APPLIED STATISTICS. *Educ:* Hofstra Col, BA, 49; Syracuse Univ, MA, 50; Polytech Inst Brooklyn, MS, 55; Columbia Univ, PhD, 61. *Prof Exp:* Instr math, Polytech Inst Brooklyn, 50-57; mem staff, Inst Defense Anal, 58-59; prin dynamics engr, Repub Aviation Corp, 59-60; from instr to assoc prof, 60-68, PROF MATH, POLYTECH INST NEW YORK, 68- *Concurrent Pos:* Consult, Urban Inst, 72-76. *Mem:* Soc Indust & Appl Math; assoc Opers Res Soc Am; Math Asn Am; Am Statist Asn. *Res:* Combinatorial theory; finite graph theory; probability; time series analysis and forecasting. *Mailing Add:* Polytech Inst NY Dept Math Rte 110 Farmingdale NY 11735

MARSHALL, DAVID JONATHAN, b Montreal, PQ, June 26, 28; m 60; c 3. MEDICINAL CHEMISTRY, RESEARCH ADMINISTRATION. *Educ:* McGill Univ, BSc, 49; Mass Inst Technol, PhD(chem), 53. *Prof Exp:* Res fel chem, Harvard Univ, 53-54; res chemist, 54-65, group leader steroids, 65-69, asst dir admin, 69-71, DIR ADMIN SERV, AYERST LABS DIV, AM HOME PROD CORP, 72- *Mem:* Chem Inst Can; Soc Res Admin. *Mailing Add:* Ayerst Labs 1025 Laurentien Blvd Montreal PQ H4R 1J6 Can

MARSHALL, DELBERT ALLAN, b Topeka, Kans, July 22, 37; m 64. ANALYTICAL CHEMISTRY. *Educ:* Kans State Teachers Col, BS, 59; Kans State Univ, MS, 65, PhD(anal chem), 68. *Prof Exp:* High sch teacher, Kans, 61-63; instr chem, Mo Valley Col, 63-64; from asst prof to assoc prof, 67-77, PROF CHEM, FT HAYS STATE UNIV, 77- *Mem:* Am Chem Soc; Soc Appl Spectros; Coblentz Soc; Royal Soc Chem; Sigma Xi. *Res:* Chemistry of metal chelates; atomic absorption spectroscopy. *Mailing Add:* Dept of Chem Ft Hays State Univ 600 Park St Hays KS 67601

MARSHALL, DONALD D, b Woodland, Calif, Aug 8, 34; m 64; c 2. ANALYTICAL CHEMISTRY, INORGANIC CHEMISTRY. *Prof Exp:* Anal chemist, US Bur Mines, Nev, 58-60; asst prof chem, Southern Ore Col, 65-66; from asst prof to assoc prof, 66-73, PROF CHEM, SONOMA STATE UNIV, 73-, CHMN, 79- *Mem:* Am Chem Soc. *Res:* Determination of stability constants of inorganic compounds in aqueous solutions; water and air pollution; computer applications in chemistry. *Mailing Add:* Dept of Chem Sonoma State Univ Rohnert Park CA 94928

MARSHALL, DONALD IRVING, b Houston, Tex, Jan 22, 24; div; c 3. CHEMICAL ENGINEERING. *Educ:* Sam Houston Col, BS, 44; Univ Tex, MA, 46, PhD(chem), 48. *Prof Exp:* Develop assoc, Plastics Div, Union Carbide Corp, 48-58; sr res engr, 58-65, res leader, 65-71, SR STAFF ENGR, WESTERN ELEC CO, 71- *Mem:* Am Chem Soc; Soc Rheol; Soc Plastics Engrs. *Res:* Rheology; material characterization; extrusion, molding and calendering processes. *Mailing Add:* Western Elec Co 2000 Northeast Expwy Norcross GA 30071

MARSHALL, DONALD JAMES, b Marlboro, Mass, Apr 14, 33; m 54; c 1. PHYSICS. *Educ:* Mass Inst Technol, BS, 54, PhD(geophys), 59; Calif Inst Technol, MS, 55. *Prof Exp:* Dir res, Nuclide Corp, 58-74, GEN MGR & PUB RELS OFFICER, ALLOYD GEN VACUUM CORP, NUCLIDE CORP, 74- *Mem:* Am Soc Testing & Mat; NY Acad Sci. *Res:* Mass spectrometry; ion physics; electron beam technology. *Mailing Add:* Alloyd Gen Vacuum Corp 916 Main St North Acton MA 01720

MARSHALL, FRANCIS J, b New York, NY, Sept 5, 23; m 52; c 4. AERODYNAMICS, COMPUTER SCIENCES. *Educ:* City Col New York, BME, 48; Rensselaer Polytech Inst, MS, 50; NY Univ, DrEngSci, 55. *Prof Exp:* Engr, Gen Elec Co, 50-51 & Wright Aeronaut Corp, 51-52; group leader, Lab Appl Sci, Univ Chicago, 55-60; PROF AERONAUT & ASTRONAUT, PURDUE UNIV, 60- *Concurrent Pos:* Res mech engr, US Naval Underseas Warfare Ctr, Calif, 66-67. *Mem:* Assoc fel Am Inst Aeronaut & Astronaut; Am Asn Univ Professors; Am Soc Eng Educ. *Res:* Synthesis of computational aerodynamics with computer aided design of aircraft. *Mailing Add:* Sch Aeronaut & Astronaut Purdue Univ West Lafayette IN 47907

MARSHALL, FRANKLIN NICK, b Chicago, Ill, July 5, 33; m 55. PHARMACOLOGY. *Educ:* Univ Iowa, BS, 57, MS, 59, PhD(pharmacol), 61. *Prof Exp:* From pharmacologist to sr pharmacologist, Pitman-Moore Div, Dow Chem USA, 61-65, proj leader, 65-67, group leader, Dow Human Health Res Labs, 67-68, asst head dept pharmacol, Dow Human Health Res Labs, Ind, 68-72, HEAD DEPT PHARMACOL, DOW PHARMACEUT, 72-,

ASSOC SCIENTIST, 73- *Mem:* AAAS; Am Soc Pharmacol & Exp Therapeut. *Res:* Autonomic neuromuscular and renal pharmacology; pharmacology of antibiotics and anesthetic agents; lipid metabolism in neoplasms; blood coagulation and fibrinolysis. *Mailing Add:* Dow Chem Co PO Box 68511 Indianapolis IN 46268

MARSHALL, FREDERICK J, b Detroit, Mich, Aug 14, 20; m 46; c 7. ORGANIC CHEMISTRY. *Educ:* Univ Detroit, BS, 41, MS, 43; Iowa State Col, PhD(org chem), 48. *Prof Exp:* Res chemist, 48-76, RES SCIENTIST, ELI LILLY & CO, 76- *Mem:* Am Chem Soc; NY Acad Sci. *Res:* Pharmaceuticals; antibiotic structure; radioactive carbon synthesis. *Mailing Add:* Drug Metab Res Group Eli Lilly & Co Res Labs Indianapolis IN 46285

MARSHALL, FREDERICK JAMES, b Vancouver, BC, Feb 11, 25; m 48; c 4. HISTOLOGY. *Educ:* Univ Ore, DMD, 49; Univ Ill, MS, 59; Am Bd Endodont, dipl. *Prof Exp:* Assoc prof histol & endodont, Fac Dent, Univ Man, 59-65; assoc prof oper dent, Sch Dent, Univ Pittsburgh, 65-67; prof endodont & head dept, Col Dent, Ohio State Univ, 67-72; PROF ENDODONT & CHMN DEPT, SCH DENT, ORE HEALTH SCI UNIV, 72- *Concurrent Pos:* Consult, Vet Admin Hosp, Portland, Ore; vpres, Am Asn Dent Schs. *Mem:* Fel Am Col Dentists; Am Dent Asn; Am Asn Endodont; Int Asn Dent Res; assoc Can Dent Asn. *Res:* Endodontic culturing techniques; root canal medications; computer-assisted instruction for the diagnosis of toothache; electron microscopy of dentin. *Mailing Add:* Dept Endodont Sch Dent Ore Health Sci Univ Portland OR 97201

MARSHALL, GARLAND ROSS, b San Angelo, Tex, Apr 16, 40; m 59; c 4. BIOCHEMISTRY. *Educ:* Calif Inst Technol, BS, 62; Rockefeller Univ, PhD(biochem), 66. *Prof Exp:* From instr to assoc prof, 66-76, PROF PHYSIOL & BIOPHYS, SCH MED, WASH UNIV, 76- *Concurrent Pos:* Fel, Oxford Univ, 66; res assoc, Comput Systs Lab, 68-; estab investr, Am Heart Asn, 70-75, mem coun high blood pressure res; guest investr, Massey Univ, NZ, 75- *Mem:* Biophys Soc; Am Physiol Soc; Am Soc Biol Chemists; Am Chem Soc; Am Heart Asn. *Res:* Solid phase peptide synthesis; conformation of peptides; computer-aided drug design; endocrinology. *Mailing Add:* Dept of Physiol & Biophys Wash Univ Sch of Med St Louis MO 63110

MARSHALL, GRAYSON WILLIAM, JR, b Baltimore, Md, Feb 12, 43; m 70. BIOMATERIALS, DENTAL RESEARCH. *Educ:* Va Polytech Inst & State Univ, BS, 65; Northwestern Univ, PhD(materials sci), 72. *Prof Exp:* Res assoc materials sci, Design & Develop Ctr, Northwestern Univ, 72-73; instr, 73-74, asst prof, 74-78, ASSOC PROF BIOMAT, DENT SCH, NORTHWESTERN UNIV, CHICAGO, 78- *Concurrent Pos:* Nat Inst Dent Res fel, Dent Sch, Northwestern Univ, 72-73, spec dent res award, 75; vis fel dent prosthetics, Univ Melbourne, 81. *Honors & Awards:* Res Prize, Am Asn Dent Res, 74. *Mem:* Fel AAAS; Int Asn Dent Res; Electron Micros Soc Am; Am Inst Mining, Metall & Petroleum Eng; Am Col Sport Med. *Res:* Use of metals, polymers and ceramics in dentistry and surgery; scanning electron microscopy of enamel, dentin and bone; corrosion resistance of new alloys, amalgams. *Mailing Add:* Dept of Biomaterials Northwestern Univ Dent Sch Chicago IL 60611

MARSHALL, HAROLD GENE, b Evansville, Ind, May 7, 28; m 53; c 2. PLANT BREEDING, PLANT GENETICS. *Educ:* Purdue Univ, BS, 52; Kans State Col, MS, 53; Univ Minn, PhD(plant genetics), 59. *Prof Exp:* Asst agron, Kans State Col, 52-53; asst, Univ Minn, 56-58; RES AGRONOMIST, OAT SECT, USDA, PA STATE UNIV, UNIVERSITY PARK, 59-, ADJ PROF PLANT BREEDING, 74- *Mem:* Am Soc Agron. *Res:* Nature of winter hardiness of winter oats and the development of winter-hardy varieties; genetics and breeding of spring oats. *Mailing Add:* Dept of Agron Pa State Univ Col of Agr University Park PA 16802

MARSHALL, HAROLD GEORGE, b Bedford, Ohio, May 17, 29; m 51; c 3. MARINE BIOLOGY. *Educ:* Baldwin-Wallace Col, BS, 51; Western Reserve Univ, MS, 53, PhD(biol), 62. *Prof Exp:* Biologist, Nat Dairy Labs, 51-52; instr, Cleveland City Schs, Ohio, 52-58, chmn sci dept, Bedford, 58-62; instr, Western Reserve Univ, 62-63; from asst prof to assoc prof, 63-69, PROF BIOL & CHMN DEPT, OLD DOMINICH UNIV, 69- *Concurrent Pos:* NSF res grants, 64-78; environ consult, 72-82; NASA, NSF & Nat Oceanic & Atmospheric Admin res grants, 65-82. *Mem:* AAAS; Am Soc Limnol & Oceanog; Phycol Soc Am; Int Phycol Soc; NY Acad Sci. *Res:* Spatial distribution and ecology of phytoplankton off the eastern coast of the United States, Chesapeake Bay and Caribbean Sea. *Mailing Add:* Dept Biol Old Dom Univ Norfolk VA 23508

MARSHALL, HARRY BORDEN, b Listowel, Ont, July 15, 09; m 36; c 3. CHEMISTRY. *Educ:* Univ BC, BA, 29, MA, 31; McGill Univ, PhD(chem), 34. *Prof Exp:* Demonstr chem, Univ BC, 29-31; res chemist, Dow Chem Co, Mich, 35-37; res fel, Ont Res Found, 37-46; asst dir dept chem, 46-57, dir, 58-62; assoc res dir, 62-70, res dir, Domtar Ltd, 70-75; consult, 75-80; RETIRED. *Concurrent Pos:* Howard Smith Paper Mills fel, 35-36; mem res comt, Can Chem Producers Asn & Nat House Builders Asn, 65. *Honors & Awards:* Montreal Medal, Chem Inst Can, 61. *Mem:* Tech Asn Pulp & Paper Indust; Can Pulp & Paper Asn; Chem Inst Can. *Res:* Research administration in pulp and paper, construction materials and chemicals. *Mailing Add:* RR 2 Portland ON K0G 1V0 Can

MARSHALL, HEATHER, b Montreal, Can, Apr 28, 49. RADIOANALYSIS. *Educ:* McGill Univ, BSc, 69, MSc, 72; Queen's Univ, Ont, PhD(anal chem), 76. *Prof Exp:* Instr chem, Loyola Col, Montreal, 70-71; fel nuclear chem, McGill Univ, 76-79; res assoc anal chem, Nat Res Coun Can, 79-80; asst prof, Univ Sask, 80-82; CHEMIST ANAL CHEM, SASK RES COUN, 82- *Mem:* Chem Inst Can; Can Asn Physicists; Spectros Soc Can; Sigma Xi. *Res:* Radioanalytical chemistry, activation analysis, and radioanalysis of natural radionuclides. *Mailing Add:* Anal Chem Lab Sask Res Coun 30 Campus Dr Saskatoon SK S7N 0W0 Can

MARSHALL, HENRY PETER, b Altoona, Pa, May 12, 24; m 51; c 3. PHYSICAL ORGANIC CHEMISTRY. *Educ:* Pa State Univ, BS, 47; Univ Calif, Los Angeles, PhD(chem), 52. *Prof Exp:* Fel chem, Fla State Univ, 52-53; res chemist, Celanese Corp, 53-56 & Stanford Res Inst, 56-58; SR STAFF SCIENTIST MAT, LOCKHEED MISSILES & SPACE CO, INC, 58- *Mem:* Am Chem Soc; Am Inst Physics; Sigma Xi. *Res:* Study of chemical structural aging effects of non-metallics; identification and kinetic measurements of chemical processes occurring in non-metallics, principally polymers, in all types of environments. *Mailing Add:* 1082 Yorkshire Dr Los Altos CA 94022

MARSHALL, J HOWARD, III, b San Francisco, Calif, Feb 6, 36. PHYSICS, ELECTRONICS. *Educ:* Calif Inst Technol, BS, 57, PhD(high energy physics), 65. *Prof Exp:* Sr res engr, Jet Propulsion Lab, Calif Inst Technol, 62-65; vpres prod, 65-66, chmn bd & vpres advan planning, 66-71, chmn bd & vpres technol, Analog Technol Corp, 71-73, pres, 73; CHMN BD & PRES, MDH INDUSTS, INC, 73- *Mem:* AAAS; sr mem Inst Elec & Electronics Engrs; Am Inst Aeronaut & Astronaut. *Res:* Electronic and system design of instrumentation for spaceborne and earthbound applications involving nuclear physics, high-energy physics, mass spectroscopy, gas chromatography and infrared and ultraviolet radiation; corporate management. *Mailing Add:* MDH Industs Inc 426 W Duarte Rd Monrovia CA 91016

MARSHALL, JACK STANTON, b Topeka, Kans, Apr 28, 29; m 53; c 7. LIMNOLOGY. *Educ:* Univ Colo, BA, 54, MA, 56; Univ Mich, PhD(zool), 61. *Prof Exp:* Asst res limnologist, Great Lakes Res Div, Inst Sci & Technol, Univ Mich, 61-62, assoc res limnologist, 62-63; res biologist, Savannah River Lab, E I du Pont de Nemours & Co, SC, 63-69; aquatic ecologist, AEC, Md, 69-71; ecologist, Argonne Nat Lab, 71-81. *Mem:* Am Soc Limnol & Oceanog; Ecol Soc Am. *Res:* Limnology; zooplankton ecology; aquatic toxicology; aquatic ecology. *Mailing Add:* Apt A 462 E 700 S St George UT 84770

MARSHALL, JAMES ARTHUR, b Oshkosh, Wis, Aug 7, 35; m 57. ORGANIC CHEMISTRY. *Educ:* Univ Wis, BS, 57; Univ Mich, PhD(chem), 60. *Prof Exp:* USPHS fel org chem, Stanford Univ, 60-62; from asst prof to assoc prof chem, Northwestern Univ, 62-68, prof, 68-80; PROF CHEM, UNIV SC, 80- *Concurrent Pos:* Sloan Found fel, 66-70; Seidel Wooley lectr, Ga Inst Technol, 70, Am-Swiss Found lectr, 71-72; vis prof, Univ Calif, Los Angeles, 68; mem, Nat Acad Sci Panel for Grad Educ in Brazil, 73-77; mem, Med Chem Study Sect, USPHS, 77-80; exec ed, Synthetic Commun, 72-; consult, Ortho Res Corp & Givaudan; mem adv comn, NSF, 80- *Honors & Awards:* Guenther Award, Am Chem Soc, 79. *Mem:* Am Chem Soc; Chem Soc Japan; Royal Soc Chem; fel AAAS. *Res:* Synthetic organic chemistry related to natural products; stereochemistry and organic reaction mechanisms. *Mailing Add:* Dept Chem Univ SC Columbia SC 29208

MARSHALL, JAMES JOHN, b Edinburgh, Scotland, July 7, 43; m 66; c 2. BIOCHEMISTRY, MEDICAL RESEARCH. *Educ:* Univ Edinburgh, BSc, 65; Heriot-Watt Univ, PhD(appl biochem), 69. *Prof Exp:* Res assoc biochem, Sch Med, Univ Miami, 69-71; fel, Royal Holloway Col, Univ London, 71-72; asst prof biochem, Sch Med, Univ Miami, 73-75, assoc prof & asst prof med, 75-80; dir lab biochem res, Howard Hughes Med Inst, 73-80; MEM STAFF, MILES LAB INC, 80- *Concurrent Pos:* Ed-in-chief, J Appl Biochem. *Mem:* Biochem Soc; Am Soc Microbiol; Am Chem Soc; Am Soc Biol Chemists; Am Asn Cereal Chemists. *Res:* Structure and mechanism of action of glycoside hydrolases; structure, function and metabolism of polysaccharides; glycoproteins, especially structure, function and synthesis; naturally occurring enzyme inhibitors. *Mailing Add:* Miles Labs Inc PO Box 932 Elkart IN 46515

MARSHALL, JAMES LAWRENCE, b Denton, Tex, May 19, 40; m 63, 81; c 2. ORGANIC CHEMISTRY. *Educ:* Ind Univ, Bloomington, BS, 62; Ohio State Univ, PhD(org chem), 66. *Prof Exp:* NIH fel org chem, Univ Colo, 66-67; asst prof chem, NTex State Univ, 67-71, assoc prof, 71-75, prof chem, 75-; MEM STAFF, CELANESE CHEMICAL CO, 81- *Mem:* Am Chem Soc. *Res:* Proton and carbon magnetic resonance studies of carbon-13 labeled compounds; conformational analysis; small polycyclic compounds; ammonia-metal reductions of aromatic compounds; nuclear magnetic resonance studies of small polycyclic compounds. *Mailing Add:* Celanese Chem Co PO Box 9077 Corpus Christi TX 78408

MARSHALL, JAMES R, pharmaceutics, health sciences, see previous edition

MARSHALL, JAMES TILDEN, JR, b Canadian, Tex, July 30, 45; m 68; c 2. FOOD SCIENCE, DAIRY SCIENCE. *Educ:* Tex Tech Univ, BS, 68, MS, 69; Mich State Univ, PhD(food sci), 74. *Prof Exp:* Res asst dairy sci, Tex Tech Univ, 68-69 & food sci, Mich State Univ, 69-73; asst prof dairy & food sci, Miss State Univ, 74-77; asst prof dairy & food sci, Kans State Univ, 77-80; DIR RES & QUAL ASSURANCE, FRIGO CHEESE CORP, 80- *Mem:* Am Dairy Sci Asn; Inst Food Technologists; Int Asn Milk, Food & Environ Sanitarians. *Res:* Chemical and physical properties of dairy and food products; formulation and processing of marketable products from dairy and other food by-products. *Mailing Add:* Frigo Cheese Corp PO Box 158 Lena WI 54139

MARSHALL, JEAN MCELROY, b Chambersburg, Pa, Dec 31, 22. PHYSIOLOGY. *Educ:* Wilson Col, AB, 44; Mt Holyoke Col, MA, 46; Univ Rochester, PhD, 51. *Prof Exp:* Instr physiol, Mt Holyoke Col, 46-47; from instr to asst prof, Sch Med, Johns Hopkins Univ, 51-60; asst prof, Harvard Med Sch, 60-66; assoc prof, 66-69, PROF BIOL & MED SCI, BROWN UNIV, 69- *Concurrent Pos:* Res fel pharmacol, Oxford Univ, 54-55; mem physiol study sect, NIH, 67-71 & eng in biol & med training comt, 71-73; mem physiol testing comt, Nat Bd Med Examrs, 71-76, Neurobiol Comt, 78-82. *Mem:* Am Physiol Soc; Soc Gen Physiol; Am Soc Pharmacol & Exp Therapeut; Soc Reprod Biol. *Res:* Electrical and mechanical properties of smooth muscle. *Mailing Add:* Div of Biol & Med Sci Brown Univ Providence RI 02912

MARSHALL, JOHN CLIFFORD, b Whitewater, Wis, Jan 23, 35; m 57; c 2. ANALYTICAL CHEMISTRY. *Educ:* Luther Col, Iowa, BA, 56; State Univ Iowa, MS, 58, PhD(chem), 60. *Prof Exp:* Instr chem, State Univ Iowa, 60; fel, Univ Minn, 60-61; from asst prof to assoc prof, 61-74, PROF CHEM, ST OLAF COL, 74- *Concurrent Pos:* NSF res grant, St Olaf Col, 62-64, Petrol Res Fund grant, 64-67; res assoc, Argonne Nat Lab, 68-69; NSF fac res fel sci, Univ NC, 69-70. *Mem:* Am Chem Soc. *Res:* Flame spectroscopy and computer applications in chemistry. *Mailing Add:* Dept of Chem St Olaf Col Northfield MN 55057

MARSHALL, JOHN DEAN, JR, b Pittsburgh, Pa, Sept 22, 24; m 50; c 5. MICROBIOLOGY. *Educ:* Univ Pittsburgh, BS, 49, MS, 50; Univ Md, College Park, PhD(microbiol), 62. *Prof Exp:* Med Serv Corps, US Army, 50-, med bacteriologist, McGee Hosp, Pittsburgh, Pa, 50, chief bact, Serol & Blood Bank Sect, Madigan Army Hosp, Tacoma, Wash, 50-53, chief anaerobic bact, 406th Med Gen Lab, Tokyo, Japan, 53-56, asst chief, Dept Bact & Immunol, Armed Forces Inst Path, Washington, DC, 56-59, chief, Microbiol Div, Army Med Unit, Ft Detrick, Md, 62-65, chief, Infectious Dis Lab, Army Med Res Team, Walter Reed Army Inst Res, Washington, DC, 65-66, chief, Microbiol Div, Army Med Res Inst Infectious Dis, 66-72, comndr, US Army Res & Develop Gen Purpose (Far E), 72-75, chief cutaneous infection div, 75-78, COMDR/DIR, LETTERMAN ARMY INST RES, 78- *Concurrent Pos:* Lectr, Howard Univ, 63-71; assoc mem comn on immunization, Armed Forces Epidemiol Bd, Washington, DC, 66-71. *Mem:* Soc Exp Biol & Med. *Res:* Immunology and epidemiology of infectious diseases. *Mailing Add:* Letterman Army Inst of Res Presidio of San Francisco CA 94129

MARSHALL, JOHN FOSTER, b Boston, Mass, Sept 5, 48; m 77. NEUROSCIENCE, NEUROPHARMACOLOGY. *Educ:* Williams Col, Mass, BA, 70; Univ Pa, Philadelphia, PhD(psychobiol), 73. *Prof Exp:* Vis scientist histochem, Karolinska Inst, Stockholm, 74-75; asst prof psychobiol, Univ Pittsburgh, 73-77; asst prof, 77-81, ASSOC PROF PSYCHOBIOL, UNIV CALIF, IRVINE, 81- *Concurrent Pos:* Mem, Task Force Obesity & Am Pub, Fogarty Ctr, 77; consult, Neurobiol Panel, Nat Sci Found, 80-82; fel, Found Fund Res Psychiat, 74-75 & Alfred P Sloan Found, 80-82. *Mem:* Sigma Xi; AAAS; Soc Neurosci. *Res:* Neural changes occurring within motor regions of the brain during pathology and senescence; nervous system comensation for cell death and how this compensation is affected in advanced age. *Mailing Add:* Dept Psychobiol Univ Calif Irvine CA 92717

MARSHALL, JOHN HART, physics, see previous edition

MARSHALL, JOHN ROMNEY, b Los Angeles, Calif, Apr 27, 33; m 56; c 5. OBSTETRICS & GYNECOLOGY. *Educ:* Univ Pa, MD, 58; Am Bd Obstet & Gynec, cert, 67. *Prof Exp:* Intern, Los Angeles Gen Hosp, 58-59; instr pharmacol, Sch Med, Univ Pa, 59-60; resident obstet & gynec, George Washington Univ Hosp, 60-63, asst clin prof, 63-69; PROF OBSTET & GYNEC & VCHMN DEPT, SCH MED, UNIV CALIF, LOS ANGELES, 70-; CHMN DEPT, HARBOR GEN HOSP, 70- *Concurrent Pos:* Resident, DC Gen Hosp, 60-63; sr investr, Nat Cancer Inst, 63-69; consult, Long Beach Naval Hosp, Calif, 71-; mem hon fac staff, Mem Hosp Med Ctr, Long Beach, Calif, 71- *Mem:* Fel Am Col Obstet & Gynec; Soc Study Reprod; Endocrine Soc; Soc Gynec Invest; Am Fertility Soc. *Res:* Clinical pharmacology of reproductive biology. *Mailing Add:* Harbor Gen Hosp 1000 W Carson Torrance CA 90509

MARSHALL, JOSEPH ANDREW, b New Brunswick, NJ, Mar 25, 37; m 58; c 2. ANIMAL BEHAVIOR. *Educ:* Univ Md, BS, 60, PhD(zool), 66. *Prof Exp:* USPHS fel, 66-68; asst prof, 68-73, ASSOC PROF BIOL, WVA UNIV, 73- *Mem:* Animal Behav Soc; Am Soc Ichthyol & Herpet; AAAS; Sigma Xi; assoc mem Ecol Soc Am. *Res:* Acoustical behavior of fishes. *Mailing Add:* Dept Biol WVa Univ Morgantown WV 26506

MARSHALL, KNEALE THOMAS, b Filey, Eng, Feb 13, 36; US citizen; m 64. OPERATIONS RESEARCH. *Educ:* Univ London, BSc, 58; Univ Calif, Berkeley, MS, 64, PhD(opers res), 66. *Prof Exp:* Metallurgist, Beaverlodge Oper, Eldorado Mining & Refining Ltd, 58-60, chief metallurgist, 60-62; mem tech staff, Bell Tel Labs, NJ, 66-68; from asst prof to assoc prof, 68-75, adv dep chief naval opers, 78-80, PROF OPERS RES, NAVAL POSTGRAD SCH, 74-, CHMN, DEPT OPER RES, 80- *Concurrent Pos:* Consult, Res Proj in Higher Educ, Univ Calif, 68-70; assoc ed, Opers Res, 70-78 & Soc Indust & Appl Math J Appl Math, 71-78; vis prof, London Sch Econ, 78. *Mem:* Opers Res Soc Am; Inst Mgt Sci; Oper Res Soc UK; sr mem Am Inst Indust Engrs. *Res:* Stochastic models of congested systems; theory of manpower and budget planning. *Mailing Add:* Dept Oper Res Code 55 Naval Postgrad Sch Monterey CA 93940

MARSHALL, LAURISTON CALVERT, physics, deceased

MARSHALL, LOUISE HANSON, b Perrysburg, Ohio, Oct 2, 08; wid; c 2. NEUROSCIENCES, MAMMALIAN PHYSIOLOGY. *Educ:* Vassar Col, MA, 32; Univ Chicago, PhD(physiol), 35. *Prof Exp:* Asst physiol, Vassar Col, 30-32, instr, 36-37; asst, Univ Chicago, 34-35; physiologist, NIH, 43-65; prof assoc, Div Med Sci, Nat Acad Sci-Nat Res Coun, 65-75; ADMIN ANALYST, BRAIN RES INST, UNIV CALIF, 75- *Concurrent Pos:* Ed, Neurosci Newsletter, 70-75; managing ed, Exp Neurol, 75- *Mem:* Am Physiol Soc; Soc Neurosci (secy-treas, 69-70). *Res:* Circulatory and renal response to plasma expanders; peripheral circulation; neuroscience administration; neuroscience history and archives. *Mailing Add:* Brain Res Inst Univ of Calif Los Angeles CA 90024

MARSHALL, LYNNOR BEVERLY, b Melbourne, Australia, Mar 11, 43; m 65; c 2. BIOCHEMISTRY. *Educ:* Univ Melbourne, BSc, 63, BEd, 67; Monash Univ, Australia, PhD(biochem), 72. *Prof Exp:* Sr sci teacher chem, Victorian Educ Dept, 65; res asst biochem, Monash Univ, 66, sr teaching fel, 67-70; fel biochem, Sch Med, Stanford Univ, 71; sr res chemist, 72-74, PROD MGR PEPTIDES, BECKMAN INSTRUMENTS, INC, 75- *Mem:* Am Chem Soc; AAAS; Australian Biochem Soc. *Res:* Chemistry and biology of biologically active peptides. *Mailing Add:* Beckman Instruments Inc 1117 California Ave Palo Alto CA 94304

MARSHALL, MARYAN LORRAINE, b New Haven, Conn, Jan 18, 40. PHYSICAL CHEMISTRY. *Educ:* Conn Col, BA, 60; Yale Univ, PhD(phys chem), 65. *Prof Exp:* Instr chem, Randolph-Macon Woman's Col, 64-66, asst prof, 66-72; assoc prof, 72-75, PROF CHEM, CENT VA COMMUNITY COL, 75- *Mem:* AAAS; Am Chem Soc; Nat Sci Teachers' Asn. *Mailing Add:* Cent Va Community Col PO Box 4098 Lynchburg VA 24502

MARSHALL, MAURICE K(EITH), b Monroe, Iowa, May 15, 21; m 47; c 3. MECHANICAL ENGINEERING. *Educ:* Purdue Univ, BS(mech eng) & BS(aeronaut eng), 46; Univ Ky, MS, 56. *Prof Exp:* Engr, Otis Elevator Co, 47-49, sales engr, 49-52; from instr to assoc prof, 53-63, PROF MECH ENG, UNIV KY, 63- *Concurrent Pos:* NSF fel, 60-61. *Mem:* Am Soc Mech Engrs; Am Soc Eng Educ. *Res:* Mechanical engineering, particularly fluid flow, heat transfer and propulsion. *Mailing Add:* Dept of Mech Eng Univ of Ky Lexington KY 40506

MARSHALL, NELSON, b Yonkers, NY, Dec 16, 14; m 40; c 4. BIOLOGICAL OCEANOGRAPHY, MARINE SCIENCES. *Educ:* Rollins Col, BS, 37; Ohio State Univ, MS, 38; Univ Fla, PhD(biol), 41. *Prof Exp:* Asst, Univ Fla, 39-41; from instr to asst prof zool, Univ Conn, 41-45; asst prof & fisheries biologist, Marine Lab, Univ Miami, 45-46; assoc prof, Univ NC, 46-47; prof biol, Col William & Mary, 47-51, dean, 49-51, dir, Va Fisheries Lab, 47-51; assoc dir oceanog inst, Fla State Univ, 52-54; vis investr, Bingham Oceanog Lab, Yale Univ, 54-55; dean col lib arts, Alfred Univ, 55-59; dir int ctr marine resource develop, 72-75, PROF OCEANOG, GRAD SCH OCEANOG, UNIV RI, 59-, PROF MARINE AFFAIRS, 75- *Concurrent Pos:* Hon mem bd trustees, Rollins Col. *Mem:* Fel AAAS; Am Soc Limnol & Oceanog; Ecol Soc Am; hon mem Atlantic Estuarine Res Soc; Nat Shellfisheries Asn. *Res:* Estuarine and coral reef ecology; higher education for marine resource development in developing countries. *Mailing Add:* Grad Sch Oceanog Univ of RI Narragansett RI 02882

MARSHALL, NORMAN BARRY, b Brooklyn, NY, Oct 3, 26; m 52; c 3. PHYSIOLOGY. *Educ:* Long Island Univ, BS, 49; Clark Univ, MA, 52; Harvard Univ, PhD(med sci), 56. *Prof Exp:* Instr physiol, Med Ctr, Duke Univ, 56-58, assoc, 58-59; res assoc nutrit, 59-61, head, Lipid Metab Sect, 61-67, mgr, Dept Biochem, 67-68, mgr, Hypersensitivity Dis Res, 68-79, group mgr, Therapeut Res, 79-81, RES DIR, UPJOHN C0, 81- *Mem:* Am Physiol Soc; NY Acad Sci; AAAS. *Res:* Regulation of food intake; endocrine control of metabolism. *Mailing Add:* Upjohn Co 301 Henrietta St Kalamazoo MI 49001

MARSHALL, NORTON LITTLE, b Washington, DC, Dec 30, 27. BOTANY. *Educ:* Pa State Univ, BS, 49; Univ Md, MS, 52, PhD(bot), 55. *Prof Exp:* Asst pathologist, Trop Res Dept, United Fruit Co, Honduras, 49-50; asst, Univ Md, 50-54, instr bot, 55-56; pathologist, Res Dept, Firestone Plantations Co, Liberia, 56-58; from asst prof to assoc prof, 58-66, PROF BOT, AUBURN UNIV, 66- *Mem:* Bot Soc Am; Am Phytopath Soc. *Res:* Plant pathology; microbiology. *Mailing Add:* Dept of Bot Auburn Univ Auburn AL 36849

MARSHALL, PHILIP RICHARD, physical chemistry, see previous edition

MARSHALL, RICHARD, b Monett, Mo, Aug 9, 22; m 51; c 2. BIOCHEMISTRY. *Educ:* Okla State Univ, BS, 48, MS, 50; Univ Wis, PhD, 55; Am Bd Clin Chem, dipl. *Prof Exp:* Biochemist, Biol Div, Hanford Works Res Dept, Gen Elec Co, 50-51; assoc chemist, Res Dept, Corn Prod Co, Ill, 55-57; sr biochemist, Grain Processing Corp, Iowa, 57-59 & Cent Res Dept, Minn Mining & Mfg Co, 59-60; res dir, Producers Creamery Co, 60-68; CLIN BIOCHEMIST, ST JOHN'S HOSP, 68- *Mem:* Fel Am Inst Chemists; Am Asn Clin Chemists; Am Chem Soc; fel Nat Acad Clin Biochem. *Res:* Reduction of nitrates, oxidation of molecular tritium, and fumaric acid production by microorganisms; biosynthesis of citrulline; production and application of mold amylases; enzymatic isomerization of glucose; insect metabolism; submerged mushroom fermentation; removal of radionuclides from milk; clinical enzymology. *Mailing Add:* St John's Hosp Lab 1235 E Cherokee St Springfield MO 65804

MARSHALL, RICHARD ALLEN, b Madisonville, Tex, Aug 25, 35; m 59; c 2. POLYMER CHEMISTRY. *Educ:* Rice Univ, BA, 57; Ohio State Univ, PhD(org chem), 62. *Prof Exp:* Res chemist, Baytown Res & Develop Div, Esso Res & Eng Co, 62-64, sr res chemist, 64-68; mem staff, Chem Div, Vulcan Mat Co, Kans, 68-74; SR RES CHEMIST, GOODYEAR RES, 74- *Mem:* Am Chem Soc. *Res:* Charge transfer complexes; exploratory polymers and polymerization processes; process and exploratory research in chlorinated organics; polyvinyl chloride polymerization. *Mailing Add:* Goodyear Res 142 Goodyear Blvd Akron OH 44316

MARSHALL, RICHARD BLAIR, b Melrose, Mass, July 25, 28; m 53; c 5. PATHOLOGY. *Educ:* Boston Univ, BA, 49, MD, 55. *Prof Exp:* Intern, Detroit Receiving Hosp, 55-56; resident path, Henry Ford Hosp, Detroit, 56-60; from asst prof to prof path, Univ Tex Med Br Galveston, 64-75; prof path, Bowman Gray Sch Med, 75-77, dir anat path, 75-77; MEM STAFF DEPT PATH, UNIV TEX MED BR, 77- *Mem:* Am Soc Clin Path; Int Acad Path. *Res:* Cytochemical and ultrastructural studies of human endocrine pathology. *Mailing Add:* Dept of Path Univ of Tex Med Br Galveston TX 77550

MARSHALL, ROBERT HERMAN, b Decatur, Ill, June 26, 25. INORGANIC CHEMISTRY. *Educ:* Ill State Normal Univ, 47, MS, 50; Univ Ill, PhD(inorg chem), 54. *Prof Exp:* Res chemist, Ethyl Corp, 54-58; assoc prof chem, La Polytech Inst, 58-60; assoc prof, 60-67, actg chmn dept, 70-71, PROF CHEM, MEMPHIS STATE UNIV, 67- *Mem:* Am Chem Soc. *Res:* Organometallic compounds. *Mailing Add:* Dept of Chem Memphis State Univ Memphis TN 38152

MARSHALL, ROBERT P(AUL), b Detroit, Mich, Dec 26, 30; m 57; c 2. METALLURGY. *Educ:* Univ Detroit, BS, 54. *Prof Exp:* Engr, Res Lab, Chrysler Corp, 53-54; proj mgr, Savannah River Lab, E I du Pont de Nemours & Co, Inc, 54-67; proj mgr, 67-69, assoc mgr metall & ceramics dept, 69-70, mgr metall, 70-74, mgr fuels & mat dept, 74-76, mgr mat dept, 76-79, DIR PROG, PAC NORTHWEST DIV, BATTELLE MEM INST, 79- *Mem:* Am Inst Metall Engrs; Am Soc Metal. *Res:* Physical metallurgy; solid state diffusion; mechanisms of deformation of metals; irradiation effects; mechanical metallurgy; biomaterials; bioengineering. *Mailing Add:* 306 Saint Richland WA 99352

MARSHALL, ROBERT STEWART, mechanical engineering, fluid dynamics, see previous edition

MARSHALL, ROBERT T, b Halltown, Mo, July 27, 32; m 53; c 4. MICROBIOLOGY, FOOD SCIENCE. *Educ:* Univ Mo, BS, 54, MS, 58, PhD(food microbiol), 60. *Prof Exp:* From instr to asst prof dairy microbiol, 60-65, assoc prof dairy microbiol & mfrs, 65-70, PROF FOOD SCI & NUTRIT, UNIV MO-COLUMBIA, 70- *Mem:* Int Asn Milk, Food & Environ Sanit (pres elect); Am Dairy Sci Asn; Inst Food Technol. *Res:* Biology of psychrotrophic bacteria and their enzymes. *Mailing Add:* 203 Eckles Hall Univ Mo Columbia MO 65211

MARSHALL, ROSEMARIE, b Medford, Ore, Jan 28, 43. BACTERIOLOGY, BIOSTATISTICS. *Educ:* Univ Wash, BS, 64; Iowa State Univ, MS, 66, PhD(bact), 68. *Prof Exp:* NIH fel, Retina Found, Harvard Med Sch, 68-70; head dept bact, Grays Harbor Hosp, 70-71; from asst prof to assoc prof, Ga Southern Col, 71-78; ASST PROF MICROBIOL, CALIF STATE UNIV, LOS ANGELES, 78-; MEM INST ANTHROPODOLOGY & PARISTOL, 74- *Mem:* AAAS; Am Soc Microbiol. *Res:* Clinical bacteriology; turnover of macromolecules in vivo in differentiating systems; systems analysis of differentiating systems. *Mailing Add:* Dept of Microbiol Calif State Univ Los Angeles CA 90032

MARSHALL, SALLY JEAN, b Racine, Wis, Jan 8, 49; m 70. BIOMATERIALS, DENTAL RESEARCH. *Educ:* Northwestern Univ, BS, 70; PhD(mat sci & eng), 75. *Prof Exp:* Instr, 74-75, asst prof, 75-80, ASSOC PROF BIOMAT, NORTHWESTERN UNIV, 80- *Concurrent Pos:* Dent res award, Nat Inst Dent Res, 77-; mem, NIH Oral Biol & Med Study Sect, 80- *Mem:* Am Soc Metals; Am Inst Mining, Metall & Petrol Eng; Int Asn Dent Res; Am Col Sports Med; Soc Biomat. *Res:* X-ray diffraction of biomaterials; identification of corrosion products and mechanisms; materials for use in restorative dentistry and maxillofacial prosthetics, amalgams, biomechanics. *Mailing Add:* Dept of Bio Mat 311 E Chicago Ave Chicago IL 60611

MARSHALL, SAMSON A, b Chicago, Ill, Oct 25, 24. SOLID STATE PHYSICS. *Educ:* Ill Inst Technol, BS, 50; Univ Mich, MS, 51; Cath Univ, PhD(physics), 56. *Prof Exp:* Physicist, Nat Bur Standards, 51-53, Naval Ord Lab, 53-56 & Armour Res Found, 56-65; physicist, Argonne Nat Lab, 65-80; MEM FAC, MICH TECHNOL UNIV, 80- *Mem:* AAAS; Am Phys Soc. *Res:* Microwave and radiofrequency spectroscopy of solids and gases. *Mailing Add:* Dept Physics Fisher Hall Michigan Technol Univ Houghton MI 49931

MARSHALL, SAMUEL WILSON, b Dallas, Tex, Sept 8, 34; m 56; c 3. PHYSICS. *Educ:* Va Mil Inst, BS, 55; Tulane Univ, MS, 63, PhD(physics), 65. *Prof Exp:* Jr res engr, Prod Res Div, Humble Oil & Refining Co, 55-56, 59-60; from asst prof to assoc prof physics, Colo State Univ, 65-70; mem staff, Naval Res Lab, 70-77; DIV DIR, OCEAN SCI & TECHNOL LAB, NAVAL OCEAN RES & DEVELOP ACTIVITY, 77- *Mem:* Am Phys Soc; Acoust Soc Am. *Res:* Mossbauer effect; acoustic propagation and scattering. *Mailing Add:* NORDA Code 340 NSTL Station MS 39529

MARSHALL, STANLEY V(ERNON), b Long Lane, Mo, Oct 3, 27; m 50; c 3. ELECTRICAL ENGINEERING, ELECTROMAGNETICS. *Educ:* Ore State Univ, BSEE, 54; Univ Mo-Columbia, MS, 65, PhD(elec eng), 67. *Prof Exp:* Mem tech staff radar systs, Bell Tel Labs, 54-63; res physicist, Naval Ord Labs, 67; ASSOC PROF ELEC ENG, UNIV MO-ROLLA, 67- *Mem:* Inst Elec & Electronics Engrs; Nat Soc Prof Engrs. *Res:* Magnetic field sensors; lightning detection. *Mailing Add:* Dept of Elec Eng Univ of Mo Rolla MO 65401

MARSHALL, THEODORE, b Chicago, Ill, Dec 31, 27; m 54; c 3. PLASMA PHYSICS. *Educ:* Ill Inst Technol, BS, 51; Cath Univ Am, PhD(physics), 62. *Prof Exp:* Scientist, US Naval Ord Lab, 55-62; sr consult scientist, Res & Develop Div, Avco Corp, 62-64; mgr exp physics, Parametrics Inc, Mass, 65; assoc prof elec eng, Univ RI, 65-68; chmn dept, 68-80, PROF PHYSICS, SUFFOLK UNIV, 68- *Concurrent Pos:* vis scientist, Argonne Nat Lab, 79. *Mem:* Am Phys Soc; Sigma Xi; AAAS. *Res:* Propagation of electromagnetic waves in ionized gas; physics of fluids; high temperature properties of gases; electron spin resonance in crystalline solids. *Mailing Add:* Dept Physics Suffolk Univ Boston MA 02114

MARSHALL, THOMAS BALL, polymer chemistry, see previous edition

MARSHALL, THOMAS C, b Cleveland, Ohio, Jan 29, 35; m 64; c 1. PHYSICS. *Educ:* Case Inst Technol, BS, 57; Univ Ill, MS, 58, PhD(physics), 60. *Prof Exp:* Asst prof elec eng, Univ Ill, 61-62; from asst prof to assoc prof, 62-70, PROF APPL PHYSICS, COLUMBIA UNIV, 70- *Mem:* Fel Am Phys Soc. *Res:* Plasma and atomic physics; microwave scattering and radiation from plasmas; lasers; shock waves; plasma stability; relativistic beams; toroidal containment experiments; free electron lasers. *Mailing Add:* Plasma Lab Columbia Univ New York NY 10027

MARSHALL, VINCENT DEPAUL, b Washington, DC, Apr 5, 43; div; c 2. MICROBIAL PHYSIOLOGY. *Educ:* Northeastern State Col, BS, 65; Univ Okla, MS, 67, PhD(microbiol), 70. *Prof Exp:* From res asst to res assoc microbiol, Univ Okla, 65-70; res assoc biochem, Univ Ill, 70-73; res scientist fermentation microbiol, Fine Chem Div, 73-74, res head microbial control, Prod Control Div, 75, res scientist cancer res, 75-78, res scientist, 78-80, SR RES SCIENTIST, INFECTIOUS DIS DIV, UPJOHN CO, 80- *Concurrent Pos:* NIH fel, Univ Okla, 68-70, Univ Ill, 71-73. *Mem:* Am Soc Microbiol; Am Soc Biol Chemists; Sigma Xi. *Res:* Microbial metabolism and transformation of antibiotics, amino acids and terpenes; fermentation microbiology; phagocyte-antibiotic interactions. *Mailing Add:* Upjohn Co 301 Henrietta St Kalamazoo MI 49001

MARSHALL, WALTER LINCOLN, b Princeton, NJ, May 6, 25; m 53; c 3. PHYSICAL CHEMISTRY. *Educ:* Princeton Univ, AB, 46; Harvard Univ, PhD(chem), 50. *Prof Exp:* Chemist, Mat & Processes Lab, 50-53, supvr appl res & insulation mat, 53-58, mgr chem & elec insulation, 58-67, MGR MAT & PROCESSES LAB, LARGE STEAM TURBINE & GENERATOR DIV, GEN ELEC CO, SCHENECTADY, 67- *Concurrent Pos:* Mem, Nat Res Coun, 53. *Mem:* Inst Elec & Electronics Engrs; Am Chem Soc. *Res:* Electrical insulation of large rotating electrical apparatus. *Mailing Add:* Box 292 Garnsey Rd Delanson NY 12053

MARSHALL, WAYNE EDWARD, b Washington, DC, Dec 20, 44; m 68; c 1. BIOLOGICAL CHEMISTRY, FOOD CHEMISTRY. *Educ:* Univ Md, BS, 66; Univ Ill, PhD(biol chem), 71. *Prof Exp:* Res assoc physiol, Univ Ill Med Ctr, 71-77; GROUP LEADER PROTEIN PROD, KRAFT, INC, 77- *Mem:* Am Chem Soc; Sigma Xi. *Res:* Food proteins; microbiological fermentations; enzymology. *Mailing Add:* Kraft Inc Res & Develop 801 Waukegan Rd Glenview IL 60025

MARSHALL, WILLIAM DEFORREST, pesticide chemistry, see previous edition

MARSHALL, WILLIAM HAMPTON, b Montreal, Que, Apr 20, 12; nat US; m 37; c 1. WILDLIFE MANAGEMENT. *Educ:* Univ Calif, BS, 33; Univ Mich, MF, 35, PhD(wildlife mgt), 42. *Prof Exp:* Foreman, US Forest Serv, Calif, 33 & Ark, 34, asst conservationist, Mass, 35; asst, Univ Mich, 34-35; instr wildlife mgt, Utah State Col, 36; jr biologist, US Fish & Wildlife Serv, Idaho, 36-43; area supvr, War Food Admin, 43-44, wage control off, 44-45; from assoc prof to prof econ zool, 45-70, from assoc dir to dir, Lake Itasca Forestry & Biol Sta, 55-70, prof, 70-78, EMER PROF WILDLIFE MGT, UNIV MINN, ST PAUL, 78- *Mem:* Hon mem Wildlife Soc. *Res:* Ecology and management of woodcock and grouse. *Mailing Add:* 7248 Oakmont Dr Santa Rosa CA 95405

MARSHALL, WILLIAM JOSEPH, b Pittsburgh, Pa, Apr 10, 29; m 56; c 3. PHYSICAL CHEMISTRY. *Educ:* Univ Pittsburgh, BS, 51; Carnegie Inst Technol, MS, 55, PhD, 56. *Prof Exp:* Res supvr, E I du Pont de Nemours & Co, Inc, 56-68, res mgr pigments dept, 68-69, asst lab dir, 69-74, TECH SUPT, EDGE MOOR LAB, E I DU PONT DE NEMOURS & CO, INC, 74- *Mem:* Am Chem Soc. *Res:* Pigment technology; solid state chemistry. *Mailing Add:* Edge Moor Lab E I du Pont de Nemours & Co Inc Edge Moor DE 19809

MARSHALL, WILLIAM LEITCH, b Columbia, SC, Dec 3, 25; m 49; c 2. PHYSICAL CHEMISTRY. *Educ:* Clemson Univ, BS, 45; Ohio State Univ, PhD(phys org chem), 49. *Prof Exp:* Asst chem, Clemson Univ, 44-45; asst chem, Ohio State Univ, 45-46; Naval res fel, Ohio State Univ, 47-49; from chemist to sr chemist, 49-57, group leader, 57-74, SR STAFF SCIENTIST, OAK RIDGE NAT LAB, 75- *Concurrent Pos:* Guggenheim fel, Van der Waals Lab, Univ Amsterdam, 56-57; mem, Org Comt, First Int Cong High Temperature Aqueous Electrolytes, Eng, 73 & Int Asn Properties of Steam Working Groups, 75- *Honors & Awards:* Charles Holmes Herty Gold Medal Award, Am Chem Soc, 77. *Mem:* AAAS; Geochem Soc; Sigma Xi; Am Chem. *Res:* High temperature high presssure thermodynamics of aqueous systems; geothermal energy solubilities; electrical conductance of aqueous electrolytes to 800 degrees centigrade and 4000 atmospheres; chemistry of aqueous homogeneous reactors; aqueous uranium and thorium salt systems; effect of pressure on elastic constants of quartz; constitution of Grignard-type reagents. *Mailing Add:* Chem Div Oak Ridge Nat Lab Oak Ridge TN 37830

MARSHALL, WILLIAM ROBERT, JR, b Calgary, Alta, May 19, 16; nat US; m 43; c 3. CHEMICAL ENGINEERING. *Educ:* Armour Inst Technol, BS, 38; Univ Wis, PhD, 41. *Hon Degrees:* Dr, Ill Inst Technol, 81. *Prof Exp:* Chem engr, Exp Sta, E I du Pont de Nemours & Co, 41-47; assoc prof chem eng, 48-53, assoc dir eng exp sta, 53-71, dean, Col Eng, 71-81, PROF CHEM ENG, UNIV WIS-MADISON, 53-, DIR, UNIV-INDUST RES PROG, 81- *Concurrent Pos:* Mem eng sci adv panel, NSF, 57-59, chmn adv comt eng div, 66-67, chmn sci appln task force, 77; mem chem eng rev comt, Argonne Nat Lab, 58-66, chmn, 59 & 66; mem bd dirs, Comn Eng Educ, 65-68; mem comt interplay eng with biol & med, Nat Acad Eng, 67-, vchmn, 69-70, chmn, 70-, mem comn educ, 68-70, chmn, 70-73; mem adv comt, Dept Appl Sci, Brookhaven Nat Lab, 73-75. *Honors & Awards:* William H Walker Award, 53; Gold Medal, Verein Deutsches Inqineurs, WGer, 75. *Mem:* Nat Acad Eng; fel Am Acad Arts & Sci; fel Am Inst Chem Engrs (vpres, 62, pres, 63, treas, 75-80); Am Soc Eng Educ. *Res:* Atomization and spray processes; basic design principle for atomizers and spray dryers. *Mailing Add:* Univ-Indust Res Prog Univ Wis-Madison 610 Walnut St Madison WI 53706

MARSHALL, WINSTON STANLEY, b Nashville, Tenn, Jan 16, 37; m 61; c 3. MEDICINAL CHEMISTRY. *Educ:* Vanderbilt Univ, AB, 59; Wayne State Univ, PhD(org chem), 63. *Prof Exp:* Sr org chemist, 63-69, res scientist med chem, 69-72, res assoc, 72-73, head org chem, 73-77, RES ASSOC, LILLY RES LABS, ELI LILLY & CO, 77- *Mem:* AAAS; Am Chem Soc. *Res:* Drug design in the areas of arthritis, especially relating non-steroidal anti-inflammatory agents, and of antipsychotic agents. *Mailing Add:* Chem Res Div Lilly Res Labs Indianapolis IN 46206

MARSHECK, WILLIAM JOHN, b Baltimore, Md, Mar 26, 42; m 63; c 3. MICROBIOLOGY. *Educ:* Univ Pittsburgh, BS, 64; Rutgers Univ, PhD(microbiol), 69. *Prof Exp:* Res investr microbiol, G D Searle & Co, Chicago, 68-74, tech dir, Harbor Beach Fermentation Facil, Searle Labs,

74-80; GROUP LEADER FERMENTATION BIOTECHNOL, T R EVANS RES CTR, DIAMOND SHAMROCK, 80- *Mem:* Am Soc Microbiol; Am Soc Indust Microbiol. *Res:* Microbiological fermentations; general bacteriology. *Mailing Add:* Diamond Shamrock Corp PO Box 348 Painesville OH 44077

MARSHEK, KURT M, b Clintonville, Wis, Oct 13, 43; m 71; c 2. MECHANICAL ENGINEERING DESIGN. *Educ:* Univ Wis-Madison, BS, 66, MS, 68; Ohio State Univ, PhD(mech eng), 71. *Prof Exp:* Engr, Falk Corp, 64-65 & Perfex Corp, 66; instr eng, State Univ NY, 67-68; spec tech asst, Western Elec Co, 68; instr mech eng, Ohio State Univ, 69-71; prof, Univ Conn, 71-75; prof, Univ Houston, 75-81; PROF MECH ENG, UNIV TEX, AUSTIN, 81- *Concurrent Pos:* Fel, Ames Res Ctr & Stanford Univ, 72; Lectr, Rogers Corp, 74, Pullman-Kellogg Co, 75 & Brown & Root, 77. *Honors & Awards:* Ralph R Teetor Award, Soc Automotive Engrs, 73. *Mem:* Soc Automotive Engrs; Soc Mfg Engrs; Am Soc Metals; Am Gear Mfg Asn. *Res:* Implementation of finite difference method for determining load distributions in engaged machine elements: chains, sprockets, bearings, timing belts, pulleys, and threaded connectors; tribology and stress analysis. *Mailing Add:* Dept Mech Eng Univ Tex Austin TX 78712

MARSHO, THOMAS V, b Cleveland, Ohio, Mar 15, 40; m 63; c 3. PLANT BIOCHEMISTRY. *Educ:* Case Western Reserve Univ, BA, 61; Miami Univ, MA, 63; Univ NC, PhD(plant physiol), 68. *Prof Exp:* NIH fel photosynthesis, Res Inst Advan Studies, 68-70; asst prof, 70-76, ASSOC PROF BIOL, UNIV MD, BALTIMORE COUNTY, 76- *Honors & Awards:* William Chambers Coker Res Award. *Mem:* AAAS; Am Soc Plant Physiol. *Res:* Photosynthetic electron transport; photosynthetic regulation. *Mailing Add:* Dept of Biol Sci Univ Md Baltimore Co 5401 Wilkins Ave Baltimore MD 21228

MARSI, KENNETH LARUE, b Los Banos, Calif, Dec 13, 28; m 55; c 4. PHYSICAL ORGANIC CHEMISTRY. *Educ:* San Jose State Col, AB, 51; Univ Kans, PhD(org chem), 55. *Prof Exp:* Instr chem, Univ Kans, 54; sr res chemist, Sherwin-Williams Co, 55-57; from asst prof to assoc prof chem, Ft Hays Kans State Col, 57-61; from asst prof to assoc prof, 61-70, PROF CHEM, CALIF STATE UNIV, LONG BEACH, 70-, CHMN DEPT, 75- *Concurrent Pos:* Petrol Res Fund grant, 59-61; NIH spec fel, Rutgers Univ, 67-68; NSF grants, 68-79; Danforth assoc, 77-82. *Mem:* Am Chem Soc; Sigma Xi. *Res:* Synthesis and stereochemistry of reactions of organophosphorus compounds; ring closure reactions of compounds leading to phosphorus and nitrogen heterocycles. *Mailing Add:* Dept of Chem Calif State Univ Long Beach CA 90840

MARSLAND, DAVID B(OYD), b Ft Meade, Fla, Dec 27, 26; m 51; c 4. CHEMICAL ENGINEERING. *Educ:* Cornell Univ, BChE, 51, PhD(chem eng), 58. *Prof Exp:* Jr res assoc, Brookhaven Nat Lab, 55-58; res engr, Eng Res Lab, E I du Pont de Nemours & Co, 58-61; asst prof chem eng, 61-63, assoc prof, 63-81, PROF CHEM ENG, NC STATE UNIV, 81- *Concurrent Pos:* Consult, Corning Glass Works, 63-66 & 73, Monsanto, 76 & Res Triangle Inst, 77-80; Ford Found resident in eng pract, Esso Res & Eng Co, NJ, 66-67; staff engr, Cost Anal, US Environ Protection Agency, 73-74. *Mem:* Am Inst Chem Engrs; Am Asn Cost Engrs; Air Pollution Control Asn; Am Soc Eng Educ; Am Asn Univ Professors. *Res:* Heat and mass transfer; air pollution control; engineering economics; numerical methods. *Mailing Add:* Dept Chem Eng NC State Univ Box 5035 Raleigh NC 27650

MARSLAND, T(HOMAS) ANTHONY, b Dundee, Scotland, Apr 24, 37; m 60; c 3. COMPUTER SCIENCE. *Educ:* Univ Nottingham, BSc, 58; Univ Wash, PhD(elec eng), 67. *Prof Exp:* Engr, Eng Elec Co, Luton, Eng, 58-62; res engr, Boeing Co, 62-65; res asst elec eng, Univ Wash, 65-67, asst prof, 67-68; mem tech staff, Bell Tel Labs, 68-70; assoc prof, 70-80, PROF COMPUT SCI, UNIV ALTA, 80- *Mem:* Asn Comput Mach; Inst Elec & Electronics Engrs; Sigma Xi. *Res:* Chess playing computer programs; distributed computing applications; control of multiple concurrent emulation processes; deadlock avoidance in distributed systems. *Mailing Add:* Dept of Comput Sci Univ of Alta Edmonton AB T6G 2H1 Can

MARSOCCI, VELIO ARTHUR, b Corona, NY, June 7, 28; m 55; c 1. ELECTRICAL ENGINEERING. *Educ:* NY Univ, BEE, 53, MEE, 55, EngScD, 64. *Prof Exp:* Instr elec eng, NY Univ, 54-56; from asst prof to assoc prof, Stevens Inst Technol, 56-65; assoc prof, 65-67, acting chmn dept, 69-71, chmn dept, 71-74, acting assoc dean, Col Eng & Appl Sci, 74-76, PROF ELEC ENG, STATE UNIV NY, STONY BROOK, 67-, CLIN PROF HEALTH SCI, 75- *Mem:* AAAS; Inst Elec & Electronics Engrs; Am Soc Eng Educ; Am Phys Soc; Asn Advan Med Instrumentation. *Res:* Solid state theory; physical electronics; electronic devices; biomedical electronics. *Mailing Add:* Dept Elec Eng State Univ NY Stony Brook NY 11794

MARSTEN, RICHARD B(ARRY), b New York, NY, Oct 28, 25; m 49; c 2. ELECTRONICS ENGINEERING, COMMUNICATIONS ENGINEERING. *Educ:* Mass Inst Technol, SB & SM, 46; Univ Pa, PhD(elec eng), 51. *Prof Exp:* Asst commun & electronics, Mass Inst Technol, 46-49; instr & asst electronics, Moore Sch Elec Eng, Univ Pa, 49-51; engr, Lab Electronics, 51-52; head res & develop sect, Allen B DuMont Labs, 52-55; chief microwave engr, Polarad Electronics Corp, 55; staff engr, Res & Develop Div, Air Assocs, 55-56; proj leader tactical radar systs, Missile & Surface Radar Div, Radio Corp Am, 56-59, mgr radar systs proj, 59-61, adv radar systs, 61, mgr commun systs, Astro-Electronics Div, 61-64, mgr spacecraft electronics, 64-66, mgr reliability & sr tech staff, 66-67, chief engr, 67-69; dir commun progs, Off Space Sci & Appln, NASA, 69-75; dean, Sch Eng, City Col, City Univ New York, 75-79; mgr, Space Policy & Applns Prog, Off Technol Assessment, US Cong, 80; EXEC DIR, BD TELECOMMUN & COMPUT APPLN, NAT ACAD SCI/NAT ACAD ENG, 81- *Concurrent Pos:* Mem space appl study, Panel Space Broadcasting, Nat Acad Sci, 67, chmn panel, Points-to-Point Commun, Space Appln Study, 67-68; consult, Arthur D Little, Inc, 75-, Western Union Space Commun, Inc, 78- & Secy of Space, Govt India, 78- *Honors & Awards:* White House Citation for Sustained Superior Performance, 72; NASA Except Serv Medal, 74, Group Achievement Award, ATS-6 Proj, 74. *Mem:* Fel Inst Elec & Electronics Engrs; NY Acad Sci; AAAS; Nat Energy Found. *Res:* Network synthesis; computer logical synthesis; microwave devices and circuits; signal processing; radar systems and equipment; spacecraft systems; electronics and equipment; space exploration and communications. *Mailing Add:* Bd Telecommun Comput Appln Nat Res Coun 2100 Pennsylvania Ave NW Suite 617 Washington DC 20418

MARSTERS, GERALD F, b Summerville, NS, Dec 18, 32; m 54; c 1. MECHANICAL ENGINEERING, AEROSPACE ENGINEERING. *Educ:* Queen's Univ, Ont, BSc, 62; Cornell Univ, PhD(aerospace eng), 67. *Prof Exp:* From asst prof to assoc prof, 67-76, PROF MECH ENG, QUEEN'S UNIV, ONT, 76- *Concurrent Pos:* Consult, Defence Res Bd Can, 67- *Mem:* Am Inst Aeronaut & Astronaut; Am Soc Eng Educ; Nat Soc Prof Engrs; Can Soc Mech Engrs; Am Soc Mech Engrs. *Res:* General fields of heat transfer and low velocity fluid mechanics; vistol aerodynamics. *Mailing Add:* Dept of Mech Eng Queen's Univ Kingston ON K7L 3N6 Can

MARSTON, CHARLES H, b Lynbrook, NY, Jan 3, 32; m 56; c 4. MECHANICAL ENGINEERING. *Educ:* Stevens Inst Technol, ME, 53; Mass Inst Technol, MS, 59, MechE, 61, ScD(mech eng), 62. *Prof Exp:* Trainee, Allis-Chalmers Mfg Co, 53-54; res engr, 62-71, sr res engr, Power Generation Group, Space Sci Lab, Space Div, 72-76, mgr, Magnetohydrodynamic Systs Anal, 76-82, MGR ANAL SERV, GEN ELEC CO, 82- *Concurrent Pos:* Lectr, grad sch, Pa State Univ, Radnor Ctr, 65- *Mem:* Am Soc Mech Engrs; Am Inst Aeronaut & Astronaut; Sigma Xi. *Res:* Power plant systems analysis; magnetohydrodynamic power generation; electric arc radiation at high pressure; magnetohydrodynamic acceleration; hypersonic flow in shock tunnels. *Mailing Add:* 301 Greene Rd Berwyn PA 19312

MARSTON, GEORGE ANDREWS, b Montague City, Mass, Oct 5, 08; m 34; c 2. HYDRAULIC ENGINEERING. *Educ:* Worcester Polytech Inst, BS, 30, CE, 40; Univ Iowa, MS, 33. *Hon Degrees:* DEng, Worcester Polytech Inst, 58. *Prof Exp:* Field engr, Turners Falls Power Co, Mass, 30-31; instr math & civil eng, Mass State Col, 33-37; jr engr, Bur Reclamation, US Dept Interior, Colo, 34 & US Geol Surv, Mass, 36-37; asst prof civil eng, 37-43, prof, 46-63, head dept, 46-48, acting dean, sch eng, 46-47, dean, 48-63, EMER PROF CIVIL ENG & EMER DEAN SCH ENG, UNIV MASS, AMHERST, 63- *Concurrent Pos:* Jr engr, US Eng Dept, RI, 38-39, asst engr, 39; asst engr, US Geol Surv, Mass, 41; prof eng & dean sch eng, Western New Eng Col, 63-68, prof mech eng, 68-73. *Mem:* Am Soc Civil Engrs; Am Soc Eng Educ; Am Geophys Union. *Res:* Rainfall intensity-frequency relations; New England climatology; runoff-frequency. *Mailing Add:* 323 E Pleasant St Amherst MA 01002

MARSTON, NORMAN LEE, b Hartman, Colo, Jan 8, 37; m 74; c 2. ENTOMOLOGY. *Educ:* Colo State Univ, BS, 58; Kans State Univ, MS, 62, PhD(entom), 65. *Prof Exp:* Instr entom, Kans State Univ, 65-66; asst prof, Univ Wyo, 66-67; RES ENTOMOLOGIST, BIOL CONTROL INSECTS RES LAB, USDA, 67- *Mem:* Entom Soc Am. *Res:* Population ecology. *Mailing Add:* Biol Control of Insects Res Lab USDA PO Box A Columbia MO 65201

MARSTON, PHILIP LESLIE, b Seattle, Wash, Feb 1, 48; m 76; c 1. OPTICS, NONLINEAR ACOUSTICS. *Educ:* Seattle Pac Col, BS, 70; Stanford Univ, MS, 72 & 74, PhD(physics), 76. *Prof Exp:* Res asst, Stanford Univ, 71-76; fel, Yale Univ, 76-78; ASST PROF PHYSICS, WASH STATE UNIV, 78- *Concurrent Pos:* Teaching asst, Stanford Univ, 74; res fel, Alfred P Sloan Found, 80-; consult, Jet Propulsion Lab, 81. *Mem:* Sigma Xi; Am Phys Soc; Acoustical Soc Am; Am Asn Physics Teachers; Optical Soc Am. *Res:* Scattering of acoustical and optical waves: scattering of light and sound by bubbles, radiation pressure of ultrasound, and cavitation of liquids induced by shock wave reflection; quantum liquids. *Mailing Add:* Dept Physics Wash State Univ Pullman WA 99164

MARSTON, ROBERT QUARLES, b Toano, Va, Feb 12, 23; m 46; c 3. MEDICINE. *Educ:* Va Mil Inst, BS, 43; Med Col Va, MD, 47; Oxford Univ, BSc, 49. *Prof Exp:* House officer med, Johns Hopkins Hosp, 49-50; asst resident, Vanderbilt Univ, 50-51; asst resident, Med Col Va, 53-54, from asst prof to assoc prof, 54-61, asst dean, 59-61; vchancellor & dean sch med, Univ Miss, 61-66; assoc dir, Regional Med Prog, NIH, 66-68, adminstr, Health Serv & Ment Health Admin, 68, dir, NIH, 68-73; scholar-in-residence, Univ Va, Charlottesville, 73-74; PRES, UNIV FLA, 74- *Concurrent Pos:* Markle scholar, Med Col Va, 54-59; mem staff, Armed Forces Spec Weapons Proj, NIH, 51-53, chmn int fels rev panel, 64-66; asst prof, Univ Minn, 58-59; consult rev comt, Div Hosp & Med Facil, Dept Health, Educ & Welfare, 61-66; distinguished fel, Inst Med, Nat Acad Sci; mem bd vis, Charles R Drew Postgrad Sch; chmn bd vis, Air Univ; mem, Fla Coun 100; mem, Vet Admin Scholars Bd; mem bd dirs, Johnson & Johnson; mem coun, Inst Med, Nat Acad Sci; mem, Inst Med Comt Aging; chmn, Nat Asn State Univs & Land Grant Col Comt on Health Policy; mem, Macy Found Comn on Present Conditon & Future of Acad Psychiat in US; chmn, Sloan Found Cognitive Sci Adv Comt. *Mem:* Am Cancer Soc; Am Heart Asn; fel Am Pub Health Asn; hon mem Nat Med Asn; hon mem Am Hosp Asn. *Res:* Infectious diseases; medical administration. *Mailing Add:* Off of the Pres Univ of Fla Gainesville FL 32601

MARSTRANDER, JAN H, electrical engineering, see previous edition

MARTEL, HARDY C(ROSS), b Pasadena, Calif, Jan 4, 27; m 54; c 5. ELECTRICAL ENGINEERING. *Educ:* Calif Inst Technol, BS, 49, PhD(elec eng), 56; Mass Inst Technol, MS, 50. *Prof Exp:* Res engr elec eng, Jet Propulsion Lab, 50-51, from instr to asst prof, 53-58, ASSOC PROF ELEC ENG, CALIF INST TECHNOL, 58-, EXEC ASST TO PRES, 69-, SECY BD TRUSTEES, 73- *Concurrent Pos:* Mem tech staff, Bell Tel Labs, Inc, 59-60. *Mem:* Inst Elec & Electronics Engrs. *Res:* Communication theory; stochastic processes; decision and information theory. *Mailing Add:* Dept of Elec Eng 1201 E California Blvd Pasadena CA 91125

MARTEL, RENE R, b Montreal, Que, May 20, 30; m 57; c 3. PHARMACOLOGY. *Educ:* Univ Montreal, DVM, 56; McGill Univ, PhD, 60. *Prof Exp:* Mem staff pharmacol, Charles E Frosst & Co, Can, 61-63 & Bristol Labs, Can, 63-69; MEM STAFF PHARMACOL, AYERST LAB, 69- *Mem:* Pharmacol Soc Can. *Res:* Inflammation. *Mailing Add:* Ayerst Lab 1025 Laurentien Blvd St Laurent PQ H4R 1J5 Can

MARTEL, WILLIAM, b New York, NY, Oct 1, 27; m 55; c 4. RADIOLOGY. *Educ:* NY Univ, BS, 50, MD, 53. *Prof Exp:* PROF RADIOL, UNIV MICH, ANN ARBOR, 66- *Mem:* AMA; Radiol Soc NAm. *Mailing Add:* Dept of Radiol Univ of Mich Ann Arbor MI 48104

MARTELL, ARTHUR EARL, b Natick, Mass, Oct 18, 16; m 44, 65; c 8. CHEMISTRY. *Educ:* Worcester Polytech Inst, BS, 38; NY Univ, PhD(chem), 41. *Hon Degrees:* DSc, Worcester Polytech Inst, 62. *Prof Exp:* Asst, NY Univ, 38-40; instr chem, Worcester Polytech Inst, 41-42; from asst prof to prof, Clark Univ, 42-61, chmn dept, 59-61; prof & chmn dept, Ill Inst Technol, 61-66; head dept chem, 66-80, DISTINGUISHED PROF CHEM, TEX A&M UNIV, 66-, ADV TO PRES FOR RES, 80- *Concurrent Pos:* Res fel, Univ Calif, 49-50; Guggenheim fel, Univ Zurich, 54-55; NSF sr fel, 59-60; fel, Sch Advan Studies, Mass Inst Technol, 59-60; NIH fel, Univ Calif, Berkeley, 64-65; ed, J Coord Chem. *Honors & Awards:* Inorg Chem Award, Am Chem Soc, 80. *Mem:* AAAS; Am Chem Soc; fel Am Acad Arts & Sci; hon mem NY Acad Sci; Am Soc Biol Chemists. *Res:* Synthesis; potentiometry; spectroscopy; physical and chemical properties, stabilities and catalytic effects of metal chelate compounds. *Mailing Add:* Dept of Chem Tex A&M Univ College Station TX 77843

MARTELL, EDWARD A, b Spencer, Mass, Feb 23, 18; m 42; c 4. RADIOCHEMISTRY, NUCLEAR GEOCHEMISTRY. *Educ:* US Mil Acad, BS, 42; Univ Chicago, PhD(nuclear chem), 50. *Prof Exp:* Prog dir, Armed Forces Spec Weapons Proj, Washington, DC, 50-54; res assoc, Enrico Fermi Inst Nuclear Studies, Univ Chicago, 54-56; group leader atmospheric radioactivity & fallout, Geophys Res Div, Air Force Cambridge Res Lab, Mass, 56-62; RES SCIENTIST, NAT CTR ATMOSPHERIC RES, 62- *Concurrent Pos:* Secy, Int Comn Atmospheric Chem & Global Pollution, Int Asn Meteorol & Atmospheric Physics, 63-71, pres, 75-79. *Mem:* Fel AAAS; Am Geophys Union; Health Phys Soc; Sigma Xi. *Res:* Natural radioactivity; discovery of indium-115 beta negative activity; radiation and fallout effects of nuclear explosions; nuclear meteorology; upper atmosphere composition with rocket samplers; radioactive aerosols; environmental and biomedical distribution and effects of alpha emitting radioisotopes. *Mailing Add:* Nat Ctr for Atmospheric Res PO Box 3000 Boulder CO 80307

MARTELL, MICHAEL JOSEPH, JR, b Minneapolis, Minn, May 20, 32. INDUSTRIAL CHEMISTRY, PHARMACY. *Educ:* Univ Minn, BS, 54, PhD(pharmaceut chem), 58; Fairleigh Dickinson Univ, MBA, 75. *Prof Exp:* NIH fel, Univ Ill, 59-60; res chemist, Lederle Labs Div, 60-70, mgr prod develop, 70-75, DIR, OVERSEAS PROD DEVELOP, MED RES DIV, AM CYNAMID CO, 75- *Mem:* Am Chem Soc. *Res:* Tetracycline antibiotics; alkaloids; biopharmaceutics as pertains to product development. *Mailing Add:* Dept 990 Am Cyanamid Co Pearl River NY 10965

MARTELLOCK, ARTHUR CARL, b Detroit, Mich, Jan 7, 28; m 49; c 3. POLYMER CHEMISTRY, ORGANIC CHEMISTRY. *Educ:* Wayne State Univ, AB, 51; Rutgers Univ, PhD(org chem), 57. *Prof Exp:* Chemist, Silicone Prod Dept, Gen Elec Co, 56-68, specialist silicone rubber develop, 68-70; tech specialist & proj mgr, Spec Mat Eng Area, 70-80, SR TECH SPECIALIST MAT, XEROX CORP, 70- *Mem:* Fel Am Inst Chemists; Am Chem Soc. *Res:* Materials development; polymer molecular structure and rheology; silicone polymer synthesis; characterization and degradation kinetics. *Mailing Add:* Xerox Corp Bldg 129 Joseph C Wilson Ctr Technol Webster NY 14580

MARTEN, DAVID FRANKLIN, b Springfield, Ill, Feb 1, 48; m 67; c 2. ORGANIC CHEMISTRY, ORGANOMETALLIC CHEMISTRY. *Educ:* Western Ill Univ, BS, 70; Univ Wis, Madison, PhD (chem), 74. *Prof Exp:* Res assoc organometallic chem, Brandeis Univ, 74-76; asst prof, Univ Iowa, 76-77; ASST PROF ORG CHEM, UNIV OKLA, 77- *Mem:* Am Chem Soc; Royal Soc Chem. *Res:* Organic synthesis and reaction mechanisms. *Mailing Add:* Dept of Chem Univ Okla Norman OK 73019

MARTEN, ELAINE HOFFMEISTER, b Niagara Falls, NY, Sept 1, 40. ORGANIC CHEMISTRY, PHOTOCHEMISTRY. *Educ:* Univ Rochester, BS, 62, PhD(org chem), 65. *Prof Exp:* Res chemist, E I du Pont de Nemours & Co, 65-67; sr res chemist, 67-80, chem prod supvr, 80-81, COORDR MAJOR PROD CHEM, EASTMAN KODAK CO, 80- *Mem:* Am Chem Soc. *Res:* Organic reaction mechanisms, organic photochemistry; polymer synthesis and development; organic research; improvements in production methods. *Mailing Add:* Synthetic Chem Div Bldg 151 Kodak Park Rochester NY 14650

MARTEN, GORDON C, b Wittenberg, Wis, Sept 14, 35; m 61; c 1. AGRONOMY. *Educ:* Univ Wis, BS, 57; Univ Minn, MS, 59, PhD(agron), 61. *Prof Exp:* Res agronomist, Sci & Educ Admin-Agr Res, 61-80, SUPVR RES AGRONOMIST & RES LEADER, AGR RES SERV, USDA, 80- *Concurrent Pos:* From asst prof to assoc prof agron & plant genetics, Univ Minn, St Paul, 61-71, prof, 71-; prog chmn, XIV Int Grassland Cong, 81. *Mem:* Crop Sci Soc Am; fel Am Soc Agron; Am Forage & Grassland Coun. *Res:* Lab techniques for evaluating forage crops; nutritive value of forage crops as influenced by genetics and agronomic practices; cattle and sheep grazing management; effects of ecological factors on forage quality. *Mailing Add:* 404 Agron & Plant Genetics Bldg Univ of Minn St Paul MN 55108

MARTEN, JAMES FREDERICK, b Liverpool, Eng, Sept 11, 31; m 53; c 2. BIOCHEMISTRY. *Educ:* Royal Inst Chem, ARIC, 52; Univ Leeds, PhD, 56. *Prof Exp:* Sr sci off, UK Atomic Energy Auth, 55-57; mgr, Borax Consol Res Labs, 57-58; tech mgr, Technicon Instruments Co Ltd, 59-64, gen mgr, Technicon Controls Inc, NY, 64-67, tech coordr, Technicon Corp, 67-69; vpres med develop, Damon Corp, Boston, 69-73; FOUNDER & DIR, DELMED INC, MASS 73- *Concurrent Pos:* Dir & secy, Dakton Ltd, BWI, 74-; dir, Armendaris Corp, Mo, 75- *Mem:* Assoc Royal Soc Chem. *Res:* Conception and design of automated medical diagnostic instrumentation. *Mailing Add:* 78 Nichols Rd Cohasset MA 02025

MARTENS, ALEXANDER E(UGENE), b Schemnitz, Czech, June 27, 23; m 48; c 2. ELECTRONICS, ENGINEERING MANAGEMENT. *Educ:* Breslau Tech Univ, BSEE, 42; Univ Rochester, MS, 64. *Prof Exp:* Dept head electronics, US Army Spec Serv, 46-52; engr, Motorola Ltd, Can, 53-54; vpres eng, Tele-Tech Electronics Ltd, 55-60; engr, 60-64, dept head electronics res & develop, 64-68, vpres res & develop, Anal Systs Div, 68-76, VPRES IMAGE ANAL, BAUSCH & LOMB, 76- *Concurrent Pos:* Adj prof, Rochester Inst Technol, 78- *Honors & Awards:* IR 100 Award, Indust Res Mag, 66 & 68. *Mem:* Inst Elec & Electronics Engrs; Brit Inst Electronics & Radio Engrs. *Res:* Research and development of biomedical, analytical and metrological instruments and systems. *Mailing Add:* 104 Nettlecreek Rd Fairport NY 14450

MARTENS, CHRISTOPHER SARGENT, b Akron, Ohio, Jan 11, 46; m 68; c 2. MARINE CHEMISTRY. *Educ:* Fla State Univ, BS, 68, MS, 69, PhD(chem oceanog), 72. *Prof Exp:* Res technician Antarctic sediment chem, Fla State Univ, 68-69; res chemist & partic guest scientist, Lawrence Livermore Radiation Lab, 71-72; res staff marine chem, Dept Geol & Geophys, Yale Univ, 72-74; asst prof geol & asst prof marine sci, 74-78, ASSOC PROF MARINE SCI & ASSOC PROF GEOL, MARINE SCI PROG, UNIV NC, CHAPEL HILL, 78- *Concurrent Pos:* Guest investr, Woods Hole Oceanog Inst, 81-82. *Mem:* AAAS; Am Soc Limnol & Oceanog; Am Geophys Union; Geochem Soc. *Res:* Chemical processes in organic-rich marine environments, particularly, microbially-mediated gas production and consumption; nutrient regeneration; organic matter remineralization; volatile fatty acid cycling; chemical exchanges between sediments; water and atmosphere; tracer studies utilizing radon-222 and lead-210, in situ flux measurements; kinetic modeling. *Mailing Add:* Marine Sci Prog 045A 12-5 Venable Hall Univ of NC Chapel Hill NC 27514

MARTENS, DAVID CHARLES, b Shawano, Wis, Apr 17, 33; m 57; c 2. SOIL SCIENCE. *Educ:* Univ Wis, BS, 60, MS, 62, PhD(soil sci), 64. *Prof Exp:* Asst prof, 64-68, assoc prof soil sci, 68-81, PROF AGRON, VA POLYTECH INST & STATE UNIV, 81- *Mem:* Am Soc Agron; Soil Sci Soc Am; Soil Conserv Soc. *Res:* Micronutrient chemistry of soil; diagnosis of chemical factors of soil responsible for abnormal plant growth; by-product disposal. *Mailing Add:* Dept of Agron Va Polytech Inst & State Univ Blacksburg VA 24061

MARTENS, EDWARD JOHN, b Evergreen Park, Ill, July 31, 38; m 59; c 2. NUCLEAR PHYSICS. *Educ:* Mass Inst Technol, BS, 61, MS, 65, PhD(physics), 67. *Prof Exp:* Instr physics, Northeastern Univ, 67-69; sr scientist, Am Sci & Eng, Inc, 69-71; instr, 71-74, ASST PROF INDUST ARTS, FITCHBURG STATE COL, 74- *Mem:* Am Phys Soc. *Res:* X-ray astronomy. *Mailing Add:* Dept of Indust Arts Fitchburg State Col Fitchburg MA 01420

MARTENS, HINRICH R, b Luebeck, Ger, Apr 21, 34; US citizen; m 57; c 4. MECHANICAL & ELECTRICAL ENGINEERING. *Educ:* Univ Rochester, BSME, 57, MS, 59; Mich State Univ, PhD(elec & mech eng), 62. *Prof Exp:* Instr mech eng, Mich State Univ, 58-60, instr mech & elec eng, 60-62; from asst prof to assoc prof, 62-70, PROF MECH & ELEC ENG, STATE UNIV NY BUFFALO, 70- *Concurrent Pos:* Res engr, Cornell Aeronaut Lab, 62-67. *Mem:* Inst Elec & Electronics Engrs; Am Soc Eng Educ. *Res:* Systems modeling; computer applications. *Mailing Add:* Dept of Elec Eng State Univ NY Buffalo NY 14214

MARTENS, JOHN WILLIAM, b Desalaberry, Man, July 31, 34; m 59; c 4. PLANT PATHOLOGY. *Educ:* Univ Man, BSc, 62; Univ Wis-Madison, PhD(plant path, mycol), 65. *Prof Exp:* RES SCIENTIST CEREAL RUSTS, RES BR, AGR CAN, 65- *Concurrent Pos:* Head plant path sect, Plant Breeding Sta, Njoro, Kenya, under Can Int Develop Agency, 71-72; vis res scientist, Dept Sci & Indust Res, Christchurch, NZ, 75-76; adj prof, Univ Man, 77- *Mem:* Can Phytopath Soc; Am Phytopath Soc; Sigma Xi. *Res:* Physiologic specialization in cereal rusts; host resistance; collection, preservation and utilization of wild avena species. *Mailing Add:* Can Agr Res Sta 195 Dafoe Rd Winnipeg MB R3T 2M9 Can

MARTENS, LESLIE VERNON, b Peoria Heights, Ill, Oct 15, 38; m 61; c 4. DENTISTRY. *Educ:* Loyola Univ Chicago, DDS, 63; Univ Minn, Minneapolis, MPH, 69. *Prof Exp:* Pvt pract, Ill, 63; lectr prev dent, Sch Dent, 68-69, asst prof maternal & child health, Sch Pub Health, 69-70, asst prof prev med, Sch Dent, 69-71, assoc prof health ecol & assoc chmn div, Sch Dent, 71-80, prof, Sch Pub Health & dir, Gen Pract Residency, 77-81, PROF & CHMN, DEPT HEALTH ECOL, UNIV MINN, MINNEAPOLIS, 81- *Concurrent Pos:* Consult, Cambridge State Hosp & Sch for Ment Retarded, 68-77; pvt pract, 69-; lectr, Schs Nursing & Pharm, Univ Minn, Minneapolis, 70- & Normandale State Jr Col, 71-77; consult, Minneapolis Pub Schs, 72- & USPHS, 73- *Mem:* Am Dent Asn; Int Asn Dent Res; Am Pub Health Asn; Behav Sci in Dent Res. *Res:* Preventive dentistry; health manpower; team dentistry; practice management; dental epidemiology; health education; health behavior. *Mailing Add:* Dept Health Ecol Univ of Minn Sch of Dent Minneapolis MN 55455

MARTENS, VERNON EDWARD, b St Louis, Mo, Aug 15, 12; m; c 7. PATHOLOGY. *Educ:* St Louis Univ, BS, 35, MD, 37; Am Bd Path, dipl, 48. *Prof Exp:* Intern, St Louis City Hosp, Mo, 37-38; resident med, US Naval Hosps, Chelsea, Mass, 38-39, pathologist, Norman, Okla, 44-45, asst pathologist, Philadelphia, Pa, 45-47, pathologist, 50-51; dir labs, US Navy Med Sch, 51-58; DIR LABS, WASHINGTON HOSP CTR, 58- *Concurrent Pos:* Fel path, Hosp Univ Pa, 47-50, instr, 50-51; assoc clin prof, Sch Med, George Washington Univ, 63, 65 & 66. *Mem:* AMA; Am Soc Clin Path; Asn Clin Sci (pres, 57-58); Col Am Path; Int Acad Path. *Res:* Clinical and anatomical pathology. *Mailing Add:* Washington Hosp Ctr 110 Irving St NW Washington DC 20010

MARTENS, WILLIAM STEPHEN, b Pittsburgh, Pa, June 14, 35. ENVIRONMENTAL CHEMISTRY. *Educ:* Rutgers Univ, BS, 56, PhD(anal & inorg chem), 60. *Prof Exp:* Sr res chemist, Int Minerals & Chem Corp, 60-62 & Agr Div, Allied Chem Corp, 62-69; consult, State of Va Health Dept, 69-70; SECT LEADER ENVIRON ENHANCEMENT, US NAVAL SURFACE WEAPONS CTR, 70- *Mem:* Am Chem Soc. *Res:* Sodium polyphosphate analyses; ion exchange; phosphate rock and wet-process phosphoric acid; inorganic polymers; air pollution detector development; environmental assessment, enhancement and control; air, water and solid waste pollution abatement; incineration technology. *Mailing Add:* US Naval Weapons Ctr Code DG-30 Dahlgren VA 22448

MARTH, ELMER HERMAN, b Jackson, Wis, Sept 11, 27; m 57. FOOD MICROBIOLOGY, DAIRY MICROBIOLOGY. *Educ:* Univ Wis, BS, 50, MS, 52, PhD(bact), 54. *Prof Exp:* Asst bact, Univ Wis, 49-54, proj assoc, 54-55, instr, 55-57; bacteriologist, Kraftco Corp, 57-59, from res bacteriologist to sr res bacteriologist, 59-63, group leader bact, 63-66, assoc mgr microbiol, 66; assoc prof, 66-71, PROF FOOD SCI & BACT, UNIV WIS-MADISON, 71- *Concurrent Pos:* Ed, J Food Protection, Int Asn Milk, Food & Environ Sanit, 67-; chmn, Intersoc Coun Stand Methods Exam Dairy Prods, 72-78; WHO travel fel, 75; vis prof, Swiss Fed Inst Technol, 81; Dairy Res Found Award, Am Dairy Sci Asn, 80. *Honors & Awards:* Pfizer Award, Am Dairy Sci Asn, 75; Educator Award, Int Asn Milk, Food & Environ Sanitarians, 77; Nordica Award, Am Cultural Dairy Prod Inst, 79. *Mem:* Am Soc Microbiol; Am Dairy Sci Asn; Inst Food Technol; Int Asn Milk, Food & Environ Sanit; Coun Biol Ed. *Res:* Microbiology of dairy and food products; psychrotrophic bacteria; mycotoxins; dairy starter cultures; fermentations; manufacturing of buttermilk and cottage cheese; fate of pathogenic bacteria in foods. *Mailing Add:* Dept of Food Sci Univ of Wis-Madison Madison WI 53706

MARTI, KURT, b Berne, Switz, Aug 18, 36; m 63; c 3. COSMOCHEMISTRY. *Educ:* Univ Berne, MSc, 63, PhD(geophys), 65. *Prof Exp:* Res chemist, 65-67, asst res chemist, 67-68, asst prof, 69-74, assoc prof, 74-80, PROF COSMOCHEM, UNIV CALIF, SAN DIEGO, 80- *Concurrent Pos:* NASA grant, Univ Calif, San Diego, 71-; prin investr, Lunar Sample Anal, 72- *Mem:* AAAS; Am Geophys Union; Meteoritical Soc. *Res:* Isotopic and nuclear cosmochemistry; origin and history of the moon and the solar system; products of extinct elements; origin of elements. *Mailing Add:* Dept of Chem Univ of Calif San Diego La Jolla CA 92037

MARTIGNOLE, JACQUES, b Carcassonne, France, Oct 11, 39; m 62. GEOLOGY. *Educ:* Univ Toulouse, Lic es Sci, 61, Dr 3rd Cycle, 64, Dr Univ, 68, DSc, 75. *Prof Exp:* Nat Coun Arts Can fel, 64-66, lectr geol, 66-68, asst prof, 68-72, assoc prof, 72-79, PROF GEOL, UNIV MONTREAL, 79- *Mem:* Geol Asn Can; Asn Study Deep Zones Earth's Crust. *Res:* Precambrian geology; igneous and metamorphic petrology; structural geology. *Mailing Add:* Dept Geol Univ Montreal Montreal PQ H3C 3J7 Can

MARTIGNONI, MAURO EMILIO, b Lugano, Switz, Oct 30, 26; nat US; m 53; c 2. VIROLOGY, INVERTEBRATE PATHOLOGY. *Educ:* Swiss Fed Inst Technol, dipl ing agr, 50, PhD(microbiol, entom), 56. *Prof Exp:* Asst entom, Swiss Fed Inst Technol, 50 & 52, entomologist, Swiss Forest Res Inst, 53-56; from asst insect pathologist to assoc insect pathologist & lectr invert path, Univ Calif, Berkeley, 56-63, assoc prof, 63-65; prin microbiologist, 65-68, CHIEF MICROBIOLOGIST RES, US FOREST SERV, 69-; PROF ENTOM, ORE STATE UNIV, 65- *Concurrent Pos:* Consult entomologist, Food & Agr Orgn, UN, Rome, Italy, 52-53; USPHS grants, 58-64; mem trop med & parasitol study sect, NIH, 64-65; consult med zool dept, US Naval Med Res Unit 3, 66-69; mem, Int Comt Nomenclature Viruses, 66-78; consult, NASA, 66-67; vis scientist insect virol, Agr Res Coun, Littlehampton, Gt Brit, 72-73; proj coordr, Microbiol Working Group, NSF & Am Soc Microbiol, 77- *Honors & Awards:* Kern Award & Silver Medal, Swiss Fed Inst Technol, 57; Superior Serv Group Honor Award, USDA, 77. *Mem:* AAAS; Entom Soc Am; Sigma Xi; Am Soc Microbiol; Soc Invert Path. *Res:* Insect pathology, especially viral diseases of insects; pathologic physiology; insect tissue culture; bioassay; safety evaluation of viral preparations. *Mailing Add:* Forestry Sci Lab US Forest Ser 3200 Jefferson Way Corvallis OR 97331

MARTIN, AARON JAY, b Lancaster, Pa, June 2, 28; m 52; c 1. ANALYTICAL CHEMISTRY. *Educ:* Franklin & Marshall Col, BS, 50; Pa State Col, MS, 52, PhD(anal chem), 53. *Prof Exp:* AEC res asst, Pa State Univ, 51-53; res chemist, E I du Pont de Nemours & Co, Inc, 53-58, res supvr, 58-59; dir res, F&M Sci Corp, 59-65, mgr res & eng, F&M Sci Div, Hewlett Packard Co, 65-69; PRES, MARLABS, INC, 69- *Concurrent Pos:* trustee, Franklin & Mardell Col. *Mem:* AAAS; Instrument Soc Am; Am Chem Soc. *Res:* Polarographic behavior of organic compounds; analytical instrumentation. *Mailing Add:* 102 Redwood Lane Kennett Square PA 19348

MARTIN, ALBERT EDWIN, b Mifflintown, Pa, Nov 25, 31; m 53; c 2. ANALYTICAL CHEMISTRY, PHARMACEUTICAL CHEMISTRY. *Educ:* Franklin & Marshall Col, BS, 53; Univ Calif, Los Angeles, MS, 56; Univ NC, Chapel Hill, PhD(chem), 59. *Prof Exp:* Sr res chemist, Chas Pfizer & Co, Inc, Conn, 59-62; mgr, 62-74, dir anal res, 74-75, DIR & ASST VPRES GOOD MFG PRACT, A H ROBINS CO, INC, 75- *Concurrent Pos:* Spec lectr, Va Commonwealth Univ, 67-70; mem revision comt, US Pharmacopeia XIX; consult, Gov Mgt Study Comn, Va; vchmn, Lab Serv Adv Bd, Commonwealth Va, 78- *Mem:* Am Chem Soc. *Res:* Complex solution analysis; instrumental and electrochemical techniques; analytical chemistry of organic compounds; pharmaceutical dosage formulations. *Mailing Add:* 1407 Cummings Dr Richmond VA 23220

MARTIN, ALBERT ERSKINE, JR, b Rome, Ga, Jan 22, 19; m; c 1. APPLIED PHYSICS. *Educ:* Tulane Univ, BS, 45, MS, 46. *Prof Exp:* Instr physics, Tulane Univ, 45-47 & 53-57; instr, Brown Univ, 47-50; res physicist, Southern Regional Res Lab, USDA, 50-57; sr physicist, Courtaulds, Inc, 57-58, textile physics sect head, 59-62; MGR APPL RES & SERV, FIRESTONE SYNTHETIC FIBERS CO, 62- *Concurrent Pos:* Lectr, Spring Hill Col, 57-59. *Mem:* Am Soc Testing & Mat; Fiber Soc; Am Asn Textile Technol; Soc Plastics Engrs. *Res:* Fiber physics; x-ray diffractometry; ultrasonics; electronics. *Mailing Add:* Firestone Fibers & Textiles PO Box 450 Hopewell VA 23860

MARTIN, ALEXANDER ROBERT, b Can, Oct 12, 28; m 51; c 3. NEUROPHYSIOLOGY. *Educ:* Univ Man, BSc, 51, MSc, 53; Univ London, PhD(biophys), 55; Yale Univ, MA, 68. *Prof Exp:* Asst biophys, Univ Col, Univ London, 53-55; from instr to assoc prof physiol, Col Med, Univ Utah, 57-66; prof, Yale Univ, 66-70; PROF PHYSIOL & CHMN DEPT, SCH MED, UNIV COLO, DENVER, 70- *Concurrent Pos:* Bronfmann fel neurophysiol, Montreal Neurol Inst, 55-57. *Mem:* Am Physiol Soc; Brit Physiol Soc. *Res:* Synaptic transmission. *Mailing Add:* Dept of Physiol Univ of Colo Sch of Med Denver CO 80262

MARTIN, ALFRED, b Pittsburgh, Pa, May 1, 19; m 46; c 2. PHYSICAL MEDICINAL CHEMISTRY. *Educ:* Philadelphia Col Pharm, BS, 42; Purdue Univ, MS, 48, PhD, 50. *Prof Exp:* From asst prof to assoc prof pharm, Temple Univ, 50-55; from assoc prof to prof, Sch Pharm, Purdue Univ, 55-66; prof, Sch Pharm, Med Col Va, 66-68; prof phys med chem & dean, Sch Pharm, Temple Univ, 68-72; prof & dir, 73-78, COULTER R SUBLETT PROF, DRUG DYNAMICS INST, COL PHARM, UNIV TEX AUSTIN, 77- *Concurrent Pos:* Pfeiffer mem res fel, Ctr Appl Wave Mech, France, 62-63; indust consult, 62- *Honors & Awards:* Ebert Medal, Am Pharmaceut Asn, 66, Achievement Award, 67. *Mem:* AAAS; Am Chem Soc; Am Pharmaceut Asn; fel Acad Pharmaceut Sci. *Res:* Application of physical chemistry to pharmaceutical and medicinal sciences. *Mailing Add:* Drug Dynamics Inst Col Pharm Univ Tex Austin TX 78712

MARTIN, ARLENE PATRICIA, b Binghamton, NY, June 30, 26. BIOCHEMISTRY. *Educ:* Cornell Univ, BA, 48, MNutritS, 52; Univ Rochester, PhD(biochem), 57. *Prof Exp:* Fel, Sch Med & Dent, Univ Rochester, 57-58, instr biochem, 58-65; asst prof radiol, Jefferson Med Col, 65-67, asst prof biochem, 67-68; assoc prof, 68-74, PROF PATH & BIOCHEM, SCH MED, UNIV MO-COLUMBIA, 74- *Mem:* Fel AAAS; Am Chem Soc; NY Acad Sci. *Res:* Isolation, characterization and function of enzymes concerned with biological oxidation, especially respiratory enzymes, including components of the peroxidase, succinoxidase and pyridine nucleotide oxidase systems; structure-function relationships of mitochondria. *Mailing Add:* Dept of Path Univ Mo Sch of Med Columbia MO 65201

MARTIN, ARNOLD R, b Missoula, Mont, Mar 6, 36; m 59; c 4. MEDICINAL CHEMISTRY. *Educ:* Wash State Univ, BS, 59, MS, 61; Univ Calif, San Francisco, PhD(pharm chem), 64. *Prof Exp:* From actg asst prof to assoc prof pharm, Wash State Univ, 64-74, prof pharm chem, 74-77; PROF MED CHEM, UNIV ARIZ, 77- *Concurrent Pos:* Mem, Am Found Pharmaceut Educ. *Mem:* AAAS; Am Chem Soc; Am Pharmaceut Asn; Acad Pharmaceut Sci. *Res:* Medicinal chemistry; phenothiazine tranquilizers; tricyclic antidepressants; stereochemical and conformational studies; aminotetralin as analgesics; adrenergic blocking agents. *Mailing Add:* Col of Pharm Univ of Ariz Tucson AZ 85721

MARTIN, ARTHUR FRANCIS, b Elkins, WVa, Feb 5, 18; m 53; c 3. CHEMISTRY. *Educ:* Ursinus Col, AB, 38; Mass Inst Technol, PhD(org chem), 42. *Hon Degrees:* ScD, Ursinus Col, 63. *Prof Exp:* Res chemist, Exp Sta, Hercules, Inc, 41-42, sr chemist, Va, 43, asst leader, Cellulose Prod Group, Del, 44, chief chemist & head lab, Cellulose Plant, Va, 45-49, mgr, Va Cellulose Res Div, Exp Sta, 49-53, spec assignment, Argonne Nat Lab, 54-55, actg mgr, Phys Chem Res Div, Res Ctr, 56, sr res chemist, Phys Chem Res Div, 57-58 & Appl Math Div, 59-63, mgr, 63-67, mgr, Opers Res Div, 67-71, sr financial analyst, 71-76; APPL MATH CONSULT, 77- *Mem:* Am Chem Soc. *Res:* Cellulose and cellulose products; research administration; applied mathematics; operations research. *Mailing Add:* RD3 Box 223 Hockessin DE 19707

MARTIN, ARTHUR WESLEY, JR, b Nanking, China, Dec 13, 10; US citizen; m 31, 58; c 2. PHYSIOLOGY. *Educ:* Col Puget Sound, BS, 31; Stanford Univ, PhD(physiol), 36. *Prof Exp:* Asst physiol, Stanford Univ, 34-35; asst microbiol, Marine Sta, Johns Hopkins Univ, 35-36, instr physiol, 36-37; from instr to assoc prof, Univ Wash, 37-50, exec off dept, 48-63, prof zool, 50-81; RETIRED. *Concurrent Pos:* Dir prog regulatory biol, Div Biol & Med Sci, NSF, 58-59. *Mem:* AAAS; Am Physiol Soc; Am Soc Zool. *Res:* Comparative circulatory physiology; cellular metabolism; muscle atrophy; anesthetics; excretory processes in molluscs. *Mailing Add:* Dept of Zool Univ of Wash Seattle WA 98105

MARTIN, ARTHUR WESLEY, III, b Palo Alto, Calif, July 5, 35; m 58; c 3. THEORETICAL PHYSICS. *Educ:* Harvard Univ, AB, 57; Stanford Univ, MS, 59, PhD(particle physics), 62. *Prof Exp:* Res assoc physics, Argonne Nat Lab, 62-64; asst prof, Stanford Univ, 64-67; assoc prof, Rutgers Univ, 67-69; ASSOC PROF PHYSICS, UNIV MASS, BOSTON, 69- *Mem:* Am Phys Soc. *Res:* Elementary particle physics; dispersion theory; general relativity. *Mailing Add:* Dept of Physics Univ of Mass Harbor Campus Boston MA 02125

MARTIN, ASHLEY MARVIN, III, nuclear physics, optical physics, see previous edition

MARTIN, BARBARA BURSA, b Oak Park, Ill, Aug 2, 34; m 56; c 6. INORGANIC CHEMISTRY, ANALYTICAL CHEMISTRY. *Educ:* Grinnell Col, AB, 56, Pa State Univ, MSc, 59. *Prof Exp:* ASST PROF CHEM, UNIV S FLA, 75- *Mem:* Am Chem Soc; Sigma Xi. *Res:* Chelating tendencies; certain aspects of environmental and marine chemistry. *Mailing Add:* Dept of Chem Univ S Fla Tampa FL 33620

MARTIN, BERNARD LOYAL, b Whittier, Calif, Jan 1, 28; m 55; c 3. MATHEMATICS. *Educ:* Cent Wash State Col, BA, 55, MEd, 57; Ore State Univ, MS, 64, PhD(math), 66. *Prof Exp:* Instr high schs, Wash, 55-59, chmn dept math, 56-59; from instr to asst prof, 59-66, assoc prof & asst dean arts & sci, 66-69, dean arts & sci, 69-72, dean sch natural sci & math, 72-80, PROF MATH, CENT WASH STATE UNIV, 69- *Mem:* Math Asn Am. *Res:* Statistics; computer science. *Mailing Add:* Dept of Math Cent Wash State Univ Ellensburg WA 98926

MARTIN, BILLY JOE, b Talpa, Tex, May 24, 33; m 55; c 2. CELL BIOLOGY, CYTOCHEMISTRY. *Educ:* Univ Southern Miss, BS, 62, MS, 63; Rice Univ, PhD(biol), 70. *Prof Exp:* Asst prof biol, William Carey Col, 63-66; fel, Inst Pathobiol, Med Univ SC, 70-71, asst prof path, 71-73, asst prof, Sch Dent, 72-73; assoc prof, 73-79, PROF BIOL & RES COORDR, COL SCI & TECHNOL, UNIV SOUTHERN MISS, 79- *Concurrent Pos:* Mem, Grad Fac, Med Univ SC, 72-73. *Mem:* AAAS; Sigma Xi; Electron Micros Soc Am; Am Soc Cell Biol. *Res:* Ultrastructure of cells specialized for electrolyte transport; dynamics of cell transport; cytochemistry of cell surface; use of lectins as cytochemical tools; experimental oncology of lower vertebrates (teleosts). *Mailing Add:* Univ Southern Miss Box 5165 Southern Sta Hattiesburg MS 39401

MARTIN, BILLY RAY, b Winston-Salem, NC, Apr 25, 43; m 71. PHARMACOLOGY. *Educ:* Univ NC, AB, 65, PhD(pharmacol), 74. *Prof Exp:* Jr chemist, Res Triangle Inst, 65-69, res analyst, Univ NC, 69-73; fel pharmacol, Uppsala Univ, Sweden, 75-76, Univ Oxford, 76-77; ASST PROF PHARMACOL, MED COL VA, 76- *Concurrent Pos:* Fel, Swedish Med Res Coun, 75-76, Wellcome Trust Found, 76-77; asst prof, Pharmaceut Mfrs Asn, 78- *Mem:* Sigma Xi; Am Soc Pharmacol & Exp Therapeut. *Res:* Pharmacology of drugs of abuse such as the pharmacokinetics of marijuana constituents, nicotine and phencyclidine; agents that alter neurotransmission in the brain. *Mailing Add:* Dept Pharmacol Box 726 Med Col Va Richmond VA 23298

MARTIN, BOSTON FAUST, b Tampa, Fla, June 1, 27; m 67; c 4. NEUROSURGERY. *Educ:* Howard Univ, BS, 49; Univ Fribourg, Switzerland, BMS, 54; Univ Geneva, MD, 58. *Prof Exp:* Resident to chief, 62-66, fel neurosurgery, NY Univ Med Ctr, 66-67; insular neurosurgeon, US Govt VI, 67-69; asst prof, Univ PR Sch Med, 69-75, interim chief, neurosurgery, 69-70; CHIEF SPINAL CORD INJURY SERV, VET ADMIN MED CTR, 75- *Concurrent Pos:* Sr clin res fel neurosurgery, NY Univ Med Ctr, 66-67; co- investr brain tumor chemotherapy, Nat Cancer Inst, 66-67. *Mem:* Am Col Surg; Am Acad Neurol & Orthop Surgeons; Cong Neurol Surg; Soc Neurosci; Int Col Surg. *Res:* Effects of Urecholine on the external urethral sphincter; use of Dantrium in Detrusor Sphincter Dyssynergia; use of Septra in intermittent catheterization; effects of transcutaneous nerve stimulation on vesico- urethral function; etiology, neuropathophysiology and altered responses of spinal cord injury patients. *Mailing Add:* 111 Northfield Ave West Orange NJ 07052

MARTIN, BRUCE DOUGLAS, b Rochester, NY, Apr 8, 34; m 57; c 2. PHARMACEUTICAL CHEMISTRY. *Educ:* Albany Col Pharm, BS, 55; Univ Ill, MS, 59, PhD(pharmaceut chem), 62. *Prof Exp:* From asst prof to assoc prof, 61-68, dean sch pharm, 71-78, actg vpres acad affairs, 81, PROF PHARMACEUT CHEM, DUQUESNE UNIV, 68- *Concurrent Pos:* Fulbright lectr, Univ Sci & Technol, Ghana, 68-69; mem, Coun Pharm in Pa, 72-, chmn, 79. *Mem:* Am Chem Soc; Am Pharmaceut Asn; The Chem Soc. *Res:* Organic synthesis of potential antiradiation compounds; sulfonamides; large ring compounds. *Mailing Add:* 511 Admin Bldg Duquesne Univ Pittsburgh PA 15282

MARTIN, CHARLES EVERETT, b Cape Girardeau, Mo, Nov 21, 44; m 67. MEMBRANE BIOLOGY, BIOCHEMICAL GENETICS. *Educ:* Univ Ill, BS, 66; Fla State Univ, PhD(biol), 72. *Prof Exp:* Fel biochem genetics, Univ Tex, Austin, 72-75, membrane biol, 75-78; ASST PROF MEMBRANE BIOL, RUTGERS UNIV, 78- *Concurrent Pos:* Fel, NIH, 72-74. *Mem:* Genetics Soc Am; Am Soc Cell Biol; Sigma Xi; Am Soc Biol Chemists. *Res:* Biology and chemistry of cell membranes; lipid-protein interactions; genetic aspects of membrane assembly and function. *Mailing Add:* Dept of Biol Sci Rutgers Univ New Brunswick NJ 08903

MARTIN, CHARLES EVERETT, b Moscow Mills, Mo, Nov 7, 29; m 52; c 3. VETERINARY PHYSIOLOGY. *Educ:* Univ Mo, BS & DVM, 58; Purdue Univ, Lafayette, MS, 67. *Prof Exp:* Practitioner, Green Hills Animal Hosp, 58-65; from instr to asst prof vet med & surg, Purdue Univ, Lafayette, 65-67; from asst prof to prof vet med & surg, Univ Mo-Columbia, 67-80, chmn dept, 74-80; TECH SERV VET, UPJOHN CO, MICH, 80- *Concurrent Pos:* Mem, NCent Res Comt, 64 & 68- & Nat Pork Producers Res Coord Comt, 70-74; Mo Pork Producers, Agr Exp Sta & USDA grants, Univ Mo-Columbia, 70-76. *Mem:* Am Vet Med Asn; Am Asn Equine Practitioners; Am Col Theriogenologists; Soc Theriogenology; Am Asn Swine Practrs. *Res:* Bovine, equine and swine reproduction; physiology, endocrinology and pathology of lactation failure in swine. *Mailing Add:* RR 1 Box 206 Rocheport MO 65279

MARTIN, CHARLES J, b New Castle, Pa, Dec 5, 21; m 45; c 4. BIOCHEMISTRY. *Educ:* Univ Pittsburgh, BS, 44, PhD(chem), 51. *Prof Exp:* Asst, Western Pa Hosp, 49-51; instr path, Western Reserve Univ, 51-53, sr instr biochem, 53-54; res assoc, Sch Med, Univ Pittsburgh, 54-57, asst res prof, 57-63; res assoc prof enzymol & hypersensitivity, 63-67, asst dean acad affairs, 68-72, asst to the pres acad affairs, Univ Health Sci-Chicago Med Sch, 72-75, PROF BIOCHEM, UNIV HEALTH SCI-CHICAGO MED SCH, 67-, V PRES, 77- *Mem:* AAAS; Am Chem Soc; Am Soc Biol Chemists; Am Calorimetry Conf; NY Acad Sci. *Res:* Mechanism of enzyme action; protein modifications, calorimetry of biological systems. *Mailing Add:* Univ Hlth Sci-Chicago Med Sch 2020 W Ogden Ave Chicago IL 60612

MARTIN, CHARLES JOHN, b Sloatsburg, NY, Apr 3, 35; m 59; c 2. APPLIED MATHEMATICS. *Educ:* Union Col, NY, BS, 56; Mich State Univ, MS, 57; Rensselaer Polytech Inst, PhD(math), 61. *Prof Exp:* Instr math, Union Col, NY, 58-59; res asst, Rensselaer Polytech Inst, 59-61; sr staff scientist, Res & Advan Develop Div, Avco Corp, 61-66; from assoc prof to prof math, Mich State Univ, 66-75; PROF MATH & HEAD DEPT, WESTERN CAROLINA UNIV, 75- *Concurrent Pos:* NASA res grant, Mich State Univ, 67-71; NSF grants, Western Carolina Univ, 79-80 & 81-83. *Mem:* Am Soc Mech Eng; Asn Comput Mach. *Res:* Mechanics. *Mailing Add:* Dept Math Western Carolina Univ Cullowhee NC 28723

MARTIN, CHARLES SAMUEL, b Staunton, Va, May 22, 36. FLUID MECHANICS, HYDRAULICS. *Educ:* Va Polytech Inst, BS, 58; Ga Inst Technol, MS, 61, PhD(civil eng), 64. *Prof Exp:* Hydraul designer, Newport News Shipbldg & Dry Dock Co, 59-60; res asst fluid mech, 60-63, from asst prof to assoc prof, 63-76, PROF CIVIL ENG, GA INST TECHNOL, 76- *Concurrent Pos:* Ford Found fac resident, Harza Eng Co, Chicago, 66-67; Fulbright travel grant, 70-71; Am Soc Mech Engrs John R Freeman fel, 70-71; guest prof, Univ Karlsruhe, 70-71. *Mem:* Am Soc Civil Engrs; Am Soc Mech Engrs; Inst Asn Hydraul Res; Am Soc Eng Educ. *Res:* Pressure and hydraulic transients; two-phase flow; free streamline hydrodynamics. *Mailing Add:* Sch of Civil Eng Ga Inst of Technol Atlanta GA 30332

MARTIN, CHARLES WAYNE, b Shenandoah, Iowa, June 9, 32; m 55; c 2. ENGINEERING MECHANICS. *Educ:* Iowa State Univ, BS, 54, MS, 59, PhD(theoret & appl mech), 62. *Prof Exp:* Asst theoret & appl mech, Iowa State Univ, 57-58, instr, 58-59, res assoc, eng exp sta, 60-62, asst prof eng sci, univ, 62-63; sr mech engr, Melpar Inc, Westinghouse Air Brake Co, 63-65; assoc prof eng mech, 65-75, PROF ENG MECH, UNIV NEBR, LINCOLN, 75- *Mem:* Am Concrete Inst; Am Soc Eng Educ; Am Soc Civil Engrs; Soc Exp Stress Anal. *Res:* Structures; finite element analysis; similitude; explosive and impact loading; automatic structural design; wind energy systems. *Mailing Add:* Dept of Eng Mech Bancroft Bldg Univ of Nebr Lincoln NE 68588

MARTIN, CHARLES WELLINGTON, JR, b Omaha, Nebr, Apr 28, 33; m 59; c 3. PETROLOGY, GEOLOGY. *Educ:* Dartmouth Col, AB, 54; Univ Wis, MS, 59, PhD(geol), 62. *Prof Exp:* From asst prof to assoc prof, 60-71, PROF GEOL, EARLHAM COL, 71-, ASSOC ACADEMIC DEAN, 81- *Mem:* Geol Soc Am; Nat Asn Geol Teachers. *Res:* Petrology; structural and regional geology of western Connecticut Highlands; geology of Northern Honsho, Japan. *Mailing Add:* Dept of Geol Earlham Col Richmond IN 47374

MARTIN, CHARLES WILLIAM, b Kansas City, Mo, July 16, 43; m 68; c 2. FLUOROCARBON CHEMISTRY, GAS PROCESSING. *Educ:* Univ Pa, BS, 65; Univ Kans, PhD(chem), 73. *Prof Exp:* Res chemist process res, 71-72, sr res chemist amine chem, 72-75, res specialist amine chem, 75-79, GAS PROCESSING SPECIALIST, FLUOROCARBON CHEM, DOW CHEM CO, 79- *Concurrent Pos:* Instr, Saganaw Valley Col, 75. *Mem:* Am Chem Soc. *Res:* Development of new amine products and applications with emphasis on the gas processing industry. *Mailing Add:* 110 Flag Dr W Lake Jackson TX 77566

MARTIN, CHRISTOPHER MICHAEL, b New York, NY, Sept 25, 28; m 54; c 3. MEDICINE. *Educ:* Harvard Univ, AB, 49, MD, 53. *Prof Exp:* Intern med, Boston City Hosp, 53-54, asst resident, 56-57; res fel, Thorndike Mem Lab, Boston City Hosp & Harvard Med Sch, 57-59; res fel, Med Found Metrop Boston, Inc, 58-59; from asst prof to assoc prof, Seton Hall Col Med & Dent, 59-65; prof med & pharmacol, Sch Med, Georgetown Univ, 65-70; sr dir med affairs, Merck, Sharp & Dohme Res Labs, 70-77; PROF MED, JEFFERSON MED COL, 70-; EXEC DIR INFECTIOUS DIS, MERCK, SHARP & DOHME RES LABS, 77- *Concurrent Pos:* Dir, Georgetown Med Div, DC Gen Hosp. *Mem:* Am Soc Pharmacol & Exp Therapeut; Am Soc Clin Pharmacol & Therapeut; Am Asn Immunol; Infectious Dis Soc Am; Am Soc Microbiol. *Res:* Infectious diseases; immunology; virology; chemotherapy; virus synthesis; clinical pharmacology; carcinogens. *Mailing Add:* Med Affairs Merck Sharp & Dohme Res Labs West Point PA 19486

MARTIN, CONSTANCE RIGLER, b Brooklyn, NY, Dec 31, 23; m 43, 71; c 2. ENDOCRINOLOGY. *Educ:* Long Island Univ, BS, 44; Univ Iowa, PhD(physiol), 51. *Prof Exp:* Res assoc physiol & pharmacol, NY Med Col, 50-51; sr physiologist, Creedmoor Inst Psychobiol Studies, 51-53; from instr physiol & pharmacol to asst prof physiol & pharmacol, NY Med Col, 53-57; from asst prof to assoc prof biol, Long Island Univ, 59-63; asst prof physiol, 63-66, assoc prof biol sci, 66-76, PROF BIOL SCI, HUNTER COL, 76- *Concurrent Pos:* Am Cancer Soc Res grant, 65-68. *Mem:* AAAS; Am Physiol Soc; Endocrine Soc; Soc Study Reproduction; Am Soc Zoologists. *Res:* Thymus gland function; reproduction physiology; biological rhythms; electrolyte metabolism. *Mailing Add:* Dept of Biol Sci Hunter Col 695 Park Ave New York NY 10021

MARTIN, DANIEL WILLIAM, b Georgetown, Ky, Nov 18, 18; m 41; c 4. PHYSICS. *Educ:* Georgetown Col, AB, 37; Univ Ill, MS, 39, PhD(physics), 41. *Hon Degrees:* ScD, Georgetown Univ, 81. *Prof Exp:* Asst instr, Univ Ill, 37-41; acoust develop engr, Radio Corp Am, 41-49; supvr engr, Acoust Res, Baldwin Piano Co, 49-57, res dir, 57-70, res & eng dir, D H Baldwin Co, 70-74, RES & PATENT DIR, BALDWIN PIANO & ORGAN CO, 74- *Concurrent Pos:* Instr, Purdue Univ, 41-46; ed, Audio Trans, 54-56; asst prof, Univ Cincinnati, 65-74. *Mem:* Fel Acoust Soc Am; fel Audio Eng Soc (exec vpres, 63-64, pres, 64-65); fel Inst Elec & Electronics Engrs. *Res:* Acoustics of piano, organ, brass wind instruments, auditoriums; sound powered telephones; aircraft intercommunication; microphones; loudspeaker enclosures; reverberation simulation; analog-to-digital encoders; optoelectronics; audio systems. *Mailing Add:* Baldwin Piano & Organ Co 1801 Gilbert Ave Cincinnati OH 45202

MARTIN, DAVID E(DWIN), b Elmhurst, Ill, Sept 11, 29; div; c 2. MECHANICAL ENGINEERING. *Educ:* Univ Ill, BS, 53, MS, 56. *Prof Exp:* Instr theoret & appl mech, Univ Ill, 54-56; res engr, 56-57, sr res engr, 57-66, supvr dynamics & stress, 66-67, asst dept head automotive safety res, vehicle res dept, 67-72, asst dir, 72-74, DIR, AUTOMOTIVE SAFETY ENG, ENVIRON ACTIVITIES STAFF, GEN MOTORS RES LABS, 74- *Mem:* Soc Exp Stress Anal; Am Soc Testing & Mat; Soc Automotive Engrs. *Res:* Biomechanics; structural research; fatigue of metals. *Mailing Add:* Environ Activities Staff 12 Mile & Mound Rds Warren MI 48090

MARTIN, DAVID EDWARD, b Green Bay, Wis, Oct 1, 39. REPRODUCTIVE PHYSIOLOGY, EXERCISE PHYSIOLOGY. *Educ:* Univ Wis, Madison, BS, 61, MS, 63, PhD(physiol), 70. *Prof Exp:* Ford found trainee, Univ Wis Regional Primate Res Ctr, 66-70; asst prof health sci, Ga State Univ, 70-74; collaborating scientist reproductive biol, Yerkes Primate Res Ctr, Atlanta, 70-74; assoc prof health sci, Ga State Univ, 74-80; collaborating scientist, 74-79, AFFIL SCIENTIST REPRODUCTIVE BIOL, VERKES PRIMATE RES CTR, ATLANTA, 79-; PROF HEALTH SCI, GA STATE UNIV, 80- *Concurrent Pos:* Prin investr, Nat Sci Found Res Grant, 71-74, NIH Res grant, 75-78 & NIMH Res Grant, 76-79. *Mem:* Am Physiol Soc; Soc Study Reproduction; Am Col Sports Med; Am Soc Primatologists; Int Primatol Soc. *Res:* Male and female great ape reproductive physiology; fertility dysfunction in male spinal cord injured patients; performance physiology of elite distance runners. *Mailing Add:* Col of Allied Health Sci Ga State Univ Atlanta GA 30303

MARTIN, DAVID LEE, b St Louis, Mo, May 30, 41; m 66; c 2. BIOCHEMISTRY. *Educ:* Univ Minn, St Paul, BS, 63; Univ Wis-Madison, MS, 65, PhD(biochem), 68. *Prof Exp:* From asst prof to assoc prof chem, Univ Md, College Park, 72-80; RES SCIENTIST, DIV LABS & RES, NEW YORK STATE DEPT HEALTH, 80- *Concurrent Pos:* Vis scientist, Armed Forces Radiobiol Res Inst, Md, 75-77, 78-80, chemist, 77-78. *Mem:* AAAS; Am Chem Soc; Biochem Soc; Soc Neurosci; Am Soc Biol Chemists. *Res:* Membrane transport of small molecules; neurotransmitter metabolism. *Mailing Add:* Div Labs & Res New York State Dept Health Albany NY 12201

MARTIN, DAVID P, b New Holland, Pa, Jan 12, 42; m 75; c 2. AGRONOMY. *Educ:* Goshen Col, BA, 66; Mich State Univ, MS, 70, PhD(crop sci), 72. *Prof Exp:* Res assoc agron, Mich State Univ, 72-73; asst prof, 73-78, ASSOC PROF AGRON, OHIO STATE UNIV, 78- *Mem:* Am Soc Agron; Crop Sci Soc Am; Int Turfgrass Soc. *Res:* Turfgrass management; ecology; pest control. *Mailing Add:* Dept of Agron Ohio State Univ Columbus OH 43210

MARTIN, DAVID WILLIAM, b Chicago, Ill, Mar 7, 42; m 64; c 2. METEOROLOGY. *Educ:* Univ Wis, BS, 64, MS, 66, PhD(meteorol), 68. *Prof Exp:* Meteorologist, Aerophys Br, Phys Sci Lab, Redstone Arsenal, 68-69; asst scientist, 70-75, assoc scientist, 75-79, SR SCIENTIST, SPACE SCI & ENG CTR, UNIV WIS, 79- *Concurrent Pos:* Satellite meteorologist, Global Atmospheric Res Prog Atlantic Trop Exp, Dakar, Senegal, 74. *Mem:* Am Meteorol Soc; Nat Oceanic & Atmospheric Admin. *Res:* Understanding the structure and behavior of tropical convective systems and their relationship to larger disturbances; applications of meteorological satellites, including measurements of cloud properties, dust and wind; estimates of rainfall from visible, infrared and microwave image data; description of the monsoon; history of meteorological satellites. *Mailing Add:* Space Sci & Eng Ctr Univ of Wis 1225 W Dayton St Madison WI 53706

MARTIN, DAVID WILLIS, b Philadelphia, Pa, Sept 19, 27; m 50; c 6. PHYSICS. *Educ:* Univ Mich, BS, 50, MS, 51; PhD(physics), 57. *Prof Exp:* Res assoc, Univ Mich, 53-54; resident student assoc nuclear spectros, Argonne Nat Lab, 54-56, res assoc, 56-57; from asst prof to assoc prof physics, 57-65, PROF PHYSICS, GA INST TECHNOL, 65- *Concurrent Pos:* Consult, Oak Ridge Nat Lab, 65-71. *Mem:* Am Phys Soc. *Res:* Ion-molecule reactions in gases at thermal energies; ionization and charge-transfer cross sections in gases at high energies; nuclear spectroscopy. *Mailing Add:* Sch of Physics Ga Inst of Technol Atlanta GA 30332

MARTIN, DEAN FREDERICK, b Woodburn, Iowa, Apr 6, 33; m 56; c 6. INORGANIC CHEMISTRY. *Educ:* Grinnell Col, AB, 55; Pa State Univ, PhD(chem), 58. *Prof Exp:* NSF fel chem, Univ Col, London, 58-59; from instr to asst prof inorg chem, Univ Ill, 59-64; assoc prof, 64-69, affil prof biol, 74-80, PROF CHEM, UNIV SOUTH FLA, 69-, AFFIL PROF BIOL, 74- *Concurrent Pos:* USPHS career develop award, Nat Inst Gen Med Sci, 69-74. *Mem:* AAAS; Am Chem Soc; The Chem Soc. *Res:* Coordination chemistry; environmental chemistry. *Mailing Add:* Dept Chem Univ South Fla Tampa FL 33620

MARTIN, DENNIS JOHN, b Berwyn, Ill, Jan 24, 47. BEHAVIORAL ECOLOGY, ORNITHOLOGY. *Educ:* Ill State Univ, BS, 70; Univ NMex, MS, 71; Utah State Univ, PhD(zool), 76. *Prof Exp:* Asst prof, 75-81, ASSOC PROF BIOL, PAC LUTHERAN UNIV, 81- *Concurrent Pos:* Frank M Chapman Mem grant, Am Mus Nat Hist, 73-75; 77-78; NSF grant, 76-79. *Mem:* Sigma Xi; Am Ornith Union; Cooper Ornith Soc. *Res:* Structure and function of communication systems, primarily in vertebrates as they relate to the ecology of the organism. *Mailing Add:* Dept of Biol Pac Lutheran Univ Tacoma WA 94447

MARTIN, DEWAYNE, b Wausau, Wis, July 17, 35; m 57; c 2. PETROLOGY, PLANETARY GEOLOGY. *Educ:* Univ Wis, BS, 57, MS, 60. *Prof Exp:* Asst prof, 61-65, ASSOC PROF GEOL, MINOT STATE COL, 65-, HEAD DEPT PHYS SCI, 69- *Concurrent Pos:* Co-dir, NASA Regional Space Sci Prog, 73-74. *Mem:* Nat Asn Geol Teachers; Nat Asn Sci Teachers; Sigma Xi; Geol Soc Am. *Res:* Development of geology program for enery exploration; petrography and petrology of meteorites. *Mailing Add:* Dept of Phys Sci Minot State Col Minot ND 58701

MARTIN, DON STANLEY, JR, b Indianapolis, Ind, Feb 19, 19; m 49; c 3. PHYSICAL INORGANIC CHEMISTRY. *Educ:* Purdue Univ, BS, 39; Calif Inst Technol, PhD(chem), 44. *Prof Exp:* Asst, Nat Defense Res Comt, Calif Inst Technol, 41-42; res assoc, Northwestern Univ, 42-44; assoc scientist, Manhattan Dist, 44-46; from asst prof to assoc prof, 46-55, chemist, AEC, 46-66, sect chief, Ames Lab, Energy Res & Develop Admin, 66-76, PROF CHEM, IOWA STATE UNIV, 55- *Mem:* Am Chem Soc; Am Phys Soc. *Res:* Chemistry of the platinum elements; chemical kinetics; optical absorption spectra of single crystals of coordination compounds; radiochemistry; applications of radioactive materials; inorganic chemistry. *Mailing Add:* Dept of Chem Iowa State Univ Ames IA 50011

MARTIN, DONALD BECKWITH, b Philadelphia, Pa, July 24, 27; m 56; c 4. MEDICINE. *Educ:* Haverford Col, AB, 50; Harvard Univ, MD, 54. *Prof Exp:* From intern to asst resident med, Mass Gen Hosp, 54-56, resident, 58, chief resident, 59; Med Found Boston fel, Nat Heart Inst, 60-61; Fulbright res scholar, Nat Ctr Sci Res, France, 62; from instr to asst prof med, Harvard Med Sch, 63-71; asst in med, Mass Gen Hosp, 63-71; assoc prof med, Harvard Med Sch, 71-80; PROF MED, UNIV PA, 80- *Concurrent Pos:* Res fel, Harvard Med Sch & Peter B Brigham Hosp, 56-58, USPHS fel, 57-58; assoc ed, Metabolism, 68 & Diabetes; Guggenheim fel, Univ Geneva, 74-75; assoc physician, Mass Gen Hosp, 71-73, physician, Diabetes Unit, 73-80. *Mem:* Endocrine Soc; fel Am Col Physicians; Am Diabetes Asn; NY Acad Sci; Royal Col Med. *Res:* Academic medicine; diabetes mellitus; intermediate metabolism; glucose transport in mammalian systems. *Mailing Add:* Hosp Univ Pa 36th & Spruce St Philadelphia PA 19104

MARTIN, DONALD CROWELL, b Floral Park, NY, June 16, 29; m 51; c 2. CHEMICAL ENGINEERING. *Educ:* Univ SC, BS, 51, MS, 60; NC State Univ, PhD(chem eng), 65. *Prof Exp:* From instr to assoc prof chem eng, 60-77, PROF CHEM ENG & COMPUT SCI & HEAD DEPT COMPUT SCI, NC STATE UNIV, 77- *Mem:* Am Inst Chem Engrs; Instrument Soc Am. *Res:* Digital, analog and hybrid simulation of physical systems, process control applications in particular; adaptive process modeling and control. *Mailing Add:* Dept of Comput Sci NC State Univ Raleigh NC 27607

MARTIN, DONALD RAY, b Marion, Ohio, Oct 21, 15; m 39; c 2. INORGANIC CHEMISTRY. *Educ:* Otterbein Col, AB, 37; Western Reserve Univ, MS, 40, PhD(inorg chem), 41. *Prof Exp:* Lectr chem, Cleveland Col, Western Reserve Univ, 40-42, lab mgr, Naval Res Proj, 41-43; from instr to asst prof chem, Univ Ill, 43-51; head chem metall br, Metall Div, US Naval Res Lab, 51-52; lab mgr, Govt Res, Mathieson Chem Corp, 52-56, mgr chem res, Aviation Div, Olin Mathieson Chem Corp, 56-57, assoc dir fuels res, Energy Div, 57-60; dir res, Libbey-Owens-Ford Glass Co, 60-61; dir tech develop, Harshaw Chem Co, 61-63, dir chem res, 63-67, vpres res & develop div, Kewanee Oil Co, 67-68; chmn dept, 69-75, PROF CHEM, UNIV TEX, ARLINGTON, 69- *Concurrent Pos:* Res chemist, E I du Pont de Nemours & Co, Inc, 41; mem chem adv comt, Air Force Off Sci Res, 55-60; trustee, Otterbein Col, 62-72. *Honors & Awards:* Distinguished Sci Achievement Award, Otterbein Col, 70. *Mem:* AAAS; Am Chem Soc; Electrochem Soc; The Chem Soc. *Res:* Coordination compounds of boron halides; boron and silicon hydrides; reactions with hydrogen fluoride; fluoroborates; gaseous halides; corrosion; hafnium; inorganic nomenclature; glass; electroplating; color in compounds; gold compounds. *Mailing Add:* 3311 Cambridge Dr Arlington TX 76013

MARTIN, DOUGLAS LEONARD, b London, Eng, Nov 11, 30. METAL PHYSICS, THERMAL PHYSICS. *Educ:* Univ London, BSc, 51, PhD(physics), 54, DSc, 70. *Prof Exp:* Nat Res Coun Can fel, 54-55; sci officer physics, Royal Aircraft Estab, Eng, 55-56; from asst res officer to assoc res officer, 57-64, SR RES OFFICER PHYSICS, NAT RES COUN CAN, 64- *Mem:* Brit Inst Physics; Can Asn Physicists. *Res:* Solid state physics; calorimetry; cryogenics. *Mailing Add:* Div of Physics Nat Res Coun Can Ottawa ON K1A 0R6 Can

MARTIN, DUNCAN WILLIS, b Durango, Colo, Mar 26, 31; m 64; c 2. PHYSIOLOGY, BIOPHYSICS. *Educ:* Univ NMex, BS, 55, MS, 56; Univ Ill, Urbana, PhD(physiol), 62. *Prof Exp:* Asst biol, Univ NMex, 55-56; asst physiol, Univ Ill, 56-60, res asst, 60-62, USPHS trainee, 62; fel, Marine Biol Lab, Woods Hole, 62; fel biophys, Harvard Univ, 62-65; from asst prof to assoc prof, 65-75, PROF ZOOL, UNIV ARK, 75- *Concurrent Pos:* Vis assoc prof physiol, Yale Univ Sch Med, 74-75; chmn, Ark Game & Fish Comn, 80- *Mem:* Am Soc Zool; Am Physiol Soc. *Res:* Membrane physiology; active transport of ions; energy requirements of active transport systems. *Mailing Add:* Dept of Zool Univ of Ark Fayetteville AR 72701

MARTIN, EDGAR J, b Brno, Czech, Nov 10, 08; US citizen; m 52. TROPICAL MEDICINE, PHARMACOLOGY. *Educ:* Ger Univ, Prague, MD, 33; Inst Trop Med, Antwerp, Belg, cert, 38. *Prof Exp:* Res asst biochem, Ger Univ, Prague, 33-35; med officer, Mining Co & Health Serv, Belg Congo, 38-46; res assoc malaria parasites, Inst Microbiol, Univ Montreal, 47-48; res assoc & lectr pharmacol & radiation biol, Univ Toronto, 49-53; med officer, Health Serv, Govt of Am Samoa, 55-57; consult, Environ Health Br, 62-66, MED OFFICER, FOOD & DRUG ADMIN, US DEPT HEALTH, EDUC & WELFARE, 68- *Concurrent Pos:* NIH grant, Lab Comp Biol, Kaiser Found Res Inst, Calif, 60-64; mem, Galapagos Int Res Proj, Univ Calif & Darwin Found, 64; assoc res physiologist, Univ Calif, Berkeley, 64-67; free lance consult, 64-68. *Mem:* Am Soc Trop Med & Hyg. *Res:* Parasitology; drug antigenicity; tropical diseases; kinetics of dialysis; erythrocyte development; radon and radium metabolism; pulmonary gas exchange; coelenterate toxins. *Mailing Add:* Food & Drug Admin Bur of Drugs 5600 Fishers Lane Rockville MD 20857

MARTIN, EDWARD EUGENE, b Roodhouse, Ill, July 28, 26; m 47; c 3. AGRICULTURAL CHEMISTRY. *Educ:* Northeast Mo State Teachers Col, AB & BS, 49; Univ Mo, MS, 52. *Prof Exp:* Analyst, Univ Mo, 49-52; feed chemist, Moorman Mfg Co, 52-53; nutrit res chemist, Com Solvents Corp, 53-56; chief chemist, Cent Soya Co, 56-58, prod supvr, 58-60; lab mgr, 60-77, DIR LAB OPERS, RALTECH SCI SERV, RALSTON PURINA CO, 78- *Mem:* Am Chem Soc; Animal Nutrit Res Coun. *Res:* Feed research. *Mailing Add:* Ralston Purina Co 835 S Eighth St St Louis MO 63188

MARTIN, EDWARD G(EORGE), b New York, NY, May 22, 29; m 52; c 5. CHEMICAL ENGINEERING, ORGANIC CHEMISTRY. *Educ:* Brooklyn Polytech Inst, BChE, 51. *Prof Exp:* Chem engr, Chas Pfizer & Co, 51-61, group leader process develop, 61-62, mgr process develop, Med Pilot Plant, 62-69, ASST DIR PROCESS RES, PFIZER, INC, 69- *Mem:* Am Inst Chem Engrs. *Res:* Isolation and characterization of fermentation and natural products; organic synthesis of medicinal products and process development work required for their large scale manufacture; separation techniques; ion exchange; dialysis; diffusion. *Mailing Add:* Pfizer Inc Groton CT 06340

MARTIN, EDWARD SHAFFER, b Terre Haute, Ind, Jan 14, 39. PHYSICAL CHEMISTRY. *Educ:* DePauw Univ, BA, 60; Northwestern Univ, PhD(chem), 67. *Prof Exp:* Lectr chem, Ind Univ, South Bend, 65-66, asst prof, 66-72; scientist, 72-74, sr scientist, 74-78, staff scientist, 78-81, TECH SPECIALIST, ALCOA LABS, ALUMINUM CO AM, 81- *Mem:* Am Chem Soc; AAAS; Sigma Xi. *Res:* Kinetics and thermodynamics applied to the production of high purity alumina and anhydrous aluminum choride. *Mailing Add:* Alcoa Labs Aluminum Co Am Alcoa Ctr PA 15069

MARTIN, EDWARD WILLIFORD, b Sumter, SC, Nov 29, 29; m 57; c 3. EMBRYOLOGY. *Educ:* Fisk Univ, AB, 50; Ind Univ, MA, 52; Univ Iowa, PhD, 62. *Prof Exp:* Actg head dept biol, Fayetteville State Teachers Col, 52; asst prof zool, 52-65, assoc prof, 65-73, PROF BIOL, HEAD DEPT & CHMN, DIV NATURAL SCI, PRAIRIE VIEW A&M UNIV, 73- *Mem:* AAAS; Nat Inst Sci; Am Soc Zoologists; Am Inst Biol Sci; Sigma Xi. *Res:* Synergic action and individual actions of streptomycin and aureomycin on Brucella abortus and Brucella melentensis. *Mailing Add:* Dept Biol Prairie View A&M Univ Prairie View TX 77445

MARTIN, EDWIN J, JR, b Kansas City, Mo, Dec 1, 25; m 46; c 3. ELECTRICAL ENGINEERING. *Educ:* Mass Inst Technol, SB, 50; Univ Kans, MS, 56, PhD(elec eng), 64. *Prof Exp:* Res engr, Midwest Res Inst, 50-55; sr res engr, Vendo Co, 55-56; res asst, Univ Kans Res Found, 56-59; sr engr, Midwest Res Inst, 59-65; STAFF ENGR, ELEC ENG, WILCOX ELEC, INC, SUBSID NORTHROP CORP, 65- *Mem:* Sigma Xi. *Res:* Ante..nas and antenna arrays; radio aids to navigation. *Mailing Add:* Wilcox Elec Inc 1400 Chestnut Kansas City MO 64127

MARTIN, ELDEN WILLIAM, b Frankfort, Kans, Feb 2, 32; m 55; c 4. ANIMAL PHYSIOLOGY, ECOLOGY. *Educ:* Kans State Univ, BS, 54, MS, 59; Univ Ill, PhD(zool, ecol), 65. *Prof Exp:* Res grant & instr physiol, 63-65, asst prof, 65-69, asst chmn dept, 76-77, ASSOC PROF PHYSIOL, BOWLING GREEN STATE UNIV, 69- *Concurrent Pos:* Frank M Chapman Fund & Marcia Brady Tucker travel awards, 62; Peavey Co res grant, 65-68; var fac res grants, Bowling Green State Univ, 65-80; Frank M Chapman Mem Fund grant, 68-69; NSF int travel grant, 70; mem working group granivorous birds, Int Biol Prog; mem Int Ornith Cong; Ohio Biol Survey grant, 74-76; vis assoc prof, Dept Poultry Sci, Univ Wis, 79-80. *Mem:* AAAS; Am Ornith Union; Wilson Ornith Soc; Am Soc Zool; Int Union Physiol Sci. *Res:* Physiology and physiological ecology of vertebrate animals; temperature regulation, nutrition and bioenergetics of birds and other animals; effects of gaseous pollutants on the physiology of birds. *Mailing Add:* Dept of Biol Sci Bowling Green State Univ Bowling Green OH 43403

MARTIN, ELMER DALE, b Lancaster Co, Pa, Apr 22, 34; m 55; c 2. FLUID DYNAMICS. *Educ:* Franklin & Marshall Co, BA, 57; Rensselaer Polytech Inst, BAeroE, 57, MAeroE, 58; Stanford Univ, PhD(aeronaut, astronaut), 68. *Prof Exp:* Aeronaut res engr, US Air Force, 58-61, RES SCIENTIST, AMES RES CTR, NASA, 61- *Mem:* Assoc fel Am Inst Aeronaut & Astronaut; Am Phys Soc. *Res:* Viscous and compressible flows; gas-kinetic theory; singular-perturbation techniques; computational and mathematical methods. *Mailing Add:* Ames Res Ctr Moffett Field CA 94035

MARTIN, ETHELBERT COWLEY, b Liverpool, Eng, Nov 1, 10; nat US; m 41; c 3. ENTOMOLOGY. *Educ:* Univ Guelph, BS, 33; Cornell Univ, MS, 38, PhD(entom), 57. *Prof Exp:* Lectr apicult, Ont Agr Col, 33-38; lectr entom, Univ Man, 39-42; prov apiarist, Man Dept Agr, 45-50; from asst prof to prof entom, Mich State Univ, 50-75; mem staff, Nat Prog Crop Pollination Bees & Honey, Agr Res Serv, USDA, 75-79; RETIRED. *Concurrent Pos:* Tech adv, Man Coop Honey Producers, 45-50; sci adv, Univ Nigeria, 61-63; entom develop consult, Gadjah Mada Univ, Jogjakarta & Agr Inst, Bogor, Indonesia, 71. *Mem:* Entom Soc Am; Bee Res Asn; Sigma Xi. *Res:* Physical properties and fermentation of honey; nectar and pollen collecting by bees; pollination of fruit and seed crops. *Mailing Add:* 1387 Desert Meadows Circle Green Valley AZ 85614

MARTIN, EUGENE CHRISTOPHER, b Evansville, Ind, Dec 17, 25. ORGANIC POLYMER CHEMISTRY. *Educ:* Evansville Col, BA, 49; De Paul Univ, MS, 51; Univ Ky, PhD(chem), 54. *Prof Exp:* From assoc chemist to chemist, Am Oil Co, 54-60; sr res chemist, Southwest Res Inst, 60-71; res chemist, 71-79, HEAD, POLYMER SCI BR, NAVAL WEAPONS CTR, 79- *Mem:* Am Chem Soc. *Res:* Polymer synthesis and modification of polyethylene and polybutadiene, cellulose derivatives, polyurethanes, polyureas and polypeptides for commerical use and biomedical applications; polymer synthesis and modification for membrane separation processes; gelation of liquids; microencapsulation of liquids and solids; organic synthesis. *Mailing Add:* Michelson Labs Naval Weapons Ctr Code 3858 China Lake CA 93555

MARTIN, FLOYD DOUGLAS, b Idabel, Okla, Aug 14, 42; m 70; c 2. ICHTHYOLOGY, AQUATIC ECOLOGY. *Educ:* La State Univ, BS, 64; Univ Tex, Austin, MA, 67, PhD(zool), 68. *Prof Exp:* Asst prof zool, Ind Univ, Bloomington, 68-71; sr scientist marine biol, Univ PR, PR Nuclear Ctr, 71-74; res assoc ichthyol, 75-77, ASST PROF ICHTHYOL, CHESAPEAKE BIOL LAB, UNIV MD, 77- *Mem:* Am Soc Ichthyologists & Herpetologists; Soc Study Evolution; AAAS; Ecol Soc Am; Sigma Xi. *Res:* Systematics and general ecology of larval and juvenile fishes; nearshore tropical marine fish communities; resource partitioning in closely related fish species; zoogeography of nearshore tropical western Atlantic species. *Mailing Add:* Chesapeake Biol Lab PO Box 38 Solomons MD 20688

MARTIN, FRANCIS W, b Minneapolis, Minn, Mar 7, 11; m 44; c 3. PHYSICAL CHEMISTRY. *Educ:* Univ Minn, BChem, 33, PhD(phys chem), 38. *Prof Exp:* Instr inorg chem, Univ Mont, 38-39; res assoc, Battelle Mem Inst, 39-40; res chemist, Corning Glass Works, 40-42; res assoc, Radiation Lab, Mass Inst Technol, 42-46; res assoc, Corning Glass Works, 46-74, sr res assoc, 74-76; CONSULT, 76- *Mem:* AAAS; Am Chem Soc; Am Ceramic Soc; Brit Soc Glass Technol. *Res:* Glass; glass ceramics. *Mailing Add:* 101 Hornby Dr Painted Post NY 14870

MARTIN, FRANK BURKE, mathematics, see previous edition

MARTIN, FRANK ELBERT, b Warrensburg, Mo, Nov 21, 13. SOLID STATE PHYSICS. *Educ:* Univ Mo, AB, 34, PhD(physics), 63; Univ Ill, MS, 56. *Prof Exp:* Instr sr high sch, Mo, 38-42; instr physics, Little Rock Jr Col, 42-43; from instr to asst prof, Cent Mo State Col, 43-58; physicist, Metall Div, US Naval Res Lab, DC, 45-54; asst instr math, Univ Ill, 55-56; instr physics, Univ Mo, 58-59; 60-62; from asst prof to assoc prof, Cent Mo State Col, 62-67, prof, 67-79, EMER PROF PHYSICS, CENT MO STATE UNIV, 79-; INSTR PHYSICS & ENG, PENN VALLEY COMMUNITY COL, KANSAS CITY, 79- *Concurrent Pos:* NSF equip grant, Cent Mo State Col. *Mem:* AAAS; Am Phys Soc; Sigma Xi; Inst Elec & Electronics Eng; Am Asn Physics Teachers. *Res:* Elastic constants; electric contact transients; low-carbon steel dilatometry; photoelectric emission; electronic structure of semiconductors; cryogenics; charge carriers in crystalline solids. *Mailing Add:* 123 W South St Warrensburg MO 64903

MARTIN, FRANK GARLAND, b New Orleans, La, Oct 9, 32; m 55; c 3. EXPERIMENTAL STATISTICS. *Educ:* Okla State Univ, BS, 54, MS, 55; NC State Univ, PhD(exp statist), 59. *Prof Exp:* Sr scientist, Bettis Atomic Power Lab, Westinghouse Elec Corp, Pa, 58-62; res statistician, Stamford Res Lab, Am Cyanamid Co, Conn, 62-64; ASSOC PROF STATIST, UNIV FLA, 64- *Concurrent Pos:* Consult, Fla Agr Exp Sta. *Mem:* Am Statist Asn; Biomet Soc. *Mailing Add:* Dept of Statist Univ of Fla Gainesville FL 32601

MARTIN, FRANK GENE, b Clarksville, Tenn, Mar 15, 38; m 59; c 2. PHARMACOLOGY. *Educ:* Univ Tenn, BSPh, 59, MS, 65, PhD(pharmacol), 69. *Prof Exp:* Teaching fel pharmacol, Univ Tenn, 63-68; from asst prof to assoc prof, 68-77, PROF, SCH PHARM, UNIV KANS, 77- CHMN DEPT PHARM PRACT, 73- *Mem:* AAAS; Sigma Xi. *Res:* Autonomic pharmacology, especially release and degradation of transmitters. *Mailing Add:* Dept of Pharm Pract Univ of Kans Sch Pharm Lawrence KS 66045

MARTIN, FRANK WINSTEAD, b St Louis, Mo, Sept 19, 22; m 51; c 2. BOTANY. *Educ:* St Louis Col Pharm, BS, 49; Wash Univ, AM, 53, PhD(bot), 58. *Prof Exp:* Instr biol & pharmacog, St Louis Col Pharm, 50-56; from assoc prof to prof pharmacog, Northeast La State Col, 56-68; dir bur financial aid & res, 68-72, vpres res & planning, 72-77, V PRES RES DEVELOP, PLANNING & FED PROGS, NORTHWESTERN STATE UNIV, 77- *Concurrent Pos:* Comnr, La Higher Educ Asst Comn Bd, 74-; mem, Nat Coun Univ Res Adminr. *Mem:* AAAS; Asn Inst Res. *Mailing Add:* Res & Planning Northwestern State Univ Natchitoches LA 71457

MARTIN, FRANKLIN WAYNE, b Salt Lake City, Utah, Apr 14, 28; m 56; c 4. GENETICS. *Educ:* Okla Baptist Univ, BS, 48; Univ Calif, PhD(genetics), 60. *Prof Exp:* Sr lab technician, Univ Calif, 54-60; asst horticulturist, Western Wash Exp Sta, 60-61; mem staff, Fed Exp Sta, Agr Res Serv, 61-71, dir, Mayaguez Inst Trop Agr, PR, 71-79; consult Cent Am, 79-80; BREEDER, MAYAGUEZ INST TROP AGR, AGR RES SERV, 81- *Mem:* Bot Soc Am; Am Soc Hort Sci; Soc Econ Bot. *Res:* Genetics, breeding and development of tropical root and tuber crops; development of small scale food production systems for the tropics; introduction and development of little known tropical fruits and vegetables; breeding of sweet potatoes for the tropics; prebreeding of tropical tomatoes. *Mailing Add:* Mayaguez Inst of Trop Agr PO Box 70 Mayaguez PR 00708

MARTIN, FREDDIE ANTHONY, b Raceland, La, Nov 17, 45; m 69; c 3. PLANT PHYSIOLOGY, PLANT BREEDING. *Educ:* Nicholls State Col, BS, 66; Cornell Univ, MS, 68, PhD(veg crops), 70. *Prof Exp:* Asst prof, 71-76, assoc prof, 76-80, PROF PLANT PHYSIOL, LA STATE UNIV, BATON ROUGE, 80- *Concurrent Pos:* Ed agr sect, J Am Soc Sugarcane Technologists. *Mem:* Am Soc Plant Physiologists; Crop Sci Soc Am; Am Soc Sugarcane Technologists; Am Soc Agronomists; Plant Growth Regulation Soc. *Res:* Improving the system of breeding sugarcane and developing improved sugarcane varieties for Louisiana. *Mailing Add:* Dept Agron La State Univ Baton Rouge LA 70803

MARTIN, FREDERICK JOHNSON, b York, Maine, Sept 6, 15; m 43; c 3. PHYSICAL CHEMISTRY. *Educ:* Bates Col, BS, 37; Mass Inst Technol, PhD(phys chem), 41. *Prof Exp:* Chemist, S D Warren Pulp & Paper Co, Maine, 40-41; phys chemist, Nat Defense Res Comt Explosives Res Lab, Pa, 42-45; sect leader, Manhattan Dist, Los Alamos Sci Lab, 45; phys chemist, Res Found, Ohio State Univ, 45-46 & M W Kellogg Co, NJ, 46-54; phys chemist, Res Lab, Gen Elec Co, 54-82. *Mem:* AAAS; Am Chem Soc; Combustion Inst. *Res:* Explosives; propellants; flames and detonations; flame retardant polymers; gas turbine combustion and emissions; combustion of coal-derived fuels. *Mailing Add:* 2504 Peters Lane Schenectady NY 12309

MARTIN, FREDERICK N, b Brooklyn, NY, July 24, 31; m 54; c 2. AUDIOLOGY. *Educ:* Brooklyn Col, BA, 57, MA, 58; City Univ New York, PhD(speech), 68. *Prof Exp:* Speech therapist, Lenox Hill Hosp, 57-58; audiologist, Ark Rehab Serv, 58-60 & Bailey Ear clin, 60-66; lectr, Speech & Hearing Ctr, Brooklyn Col, 66-68, asst prof audiol, 68; from asst prof to assoc prof, 68-74, PROF AUDIOL, UNIV TEX, AUSTIN, 74- *Mem:* Am Speech & Hearing Asn. *Res:* Clinical audiology and normal audition. *Mailing Add:* Speech & Hearing Clin Univ of Tex Austin TX 78712

MARTIN, FREDERICK WIGHT, b Boston, Mass, Feb 16, 36; m 65; c 2. EXPERIMENTAL PHYSICS. *Educ:* Princeton Univ, AB, 57; Yale Univ, MS, 58, PhD(physics), 64. *Prof Exp:* From physicist to sr physicist, Ion Physics Corp, High Voltage Eng Corp, 63-66; asst prof atomic & solid state physics, Aarhus Univ, Denmark, 66-68; res assoc atomic physics, Univ Ky, 68-69, asst prof, 69-70; asst prof physics & astron, Univ Md, College Park, 70-78; PRES, MICROSCOPE ASSOCS, INC, 78- *Mem:* Am Phys Soc; Inst Elec & Electronics Engrs. *Res:* Penetration of high energy particles in matter; single atomic collisions involving electron capture or loss or x-ray production by heavy ions; channeling, ion implantation and radiation damage in solids; microscopy, electron and ion optics. *Mailing Add:* 50 Village Ave Dedham MA 02026

MARTIN, G(ODFREY) Q(UENTIN), b Bombay, India, Nov 8, 28; nat US; m 57; c 3. CHEMICAL ENGINEERING. *Educ:* Univ Bombay, BSc, 48; Univ Idaho, BS, 53; Columbia Univ, MS, 56; Univ Wash, Seattle, PhD, 63. *Prof Exp:* Asst, Columbia Univ, 53-55; chemist, Bunker Hill & Sullivan Co, 55-56; assoc prof chem eng, Univ Idaho, 56-64; vis Fulbright prof, Univ Cairo, 64-65; engr, Calif, 65-72, ENGR, SHELL DEVELOP CO, TEX, 72- *Mem:* Am Chem Soc; Am Inst Chem Engrs. *Res:* Mixing mass, heat and momentum. *Mailing Add:* Shell Develop Co One Shell Plaza Houston TX 77001

MARTIN, G(UY) WILLIAM, JR, b Abbeville, SC, Mar 12, 46; div; c 1. ANALYTICAL CHEMISTRY, ELECTROCHEMISTRY. *Educ:* Erskine Col, BA, 68; Univ NC, Chapel Hill, PhD(anal chem), 77. *Prof Exp:* DEVELOP SCIENTIST, BURROUGHS WELLCOME CO, 78- *Concurrent Pos:* Asst, Univ Ga, Athens, 77-78. *Mem:* Am Chem Soc. *Res:* Non-aqueous electrochemistry. *Mailing Add:* Burroughs Wellcome Co 3030 Cornwallis Rd Research Triangle Park NC 27709

MARTIN, GAIL ROBERTA, b New York, NY, Apr 12, 44; m 69. BIOLOGY, EMBRYOLOGY. *Educ:* Univ Wis, Madison, BA, 64; Univ Calif, Berkeley, PhD(molecular biol), 71. *Prof Exp:* Fel embryol, Univ Col London, Eng, 73-75; fel pediatrics, 75-76, asst prof, 76-81, ASSOC PROF ANATOMY, UNIV CALIF, SAN FRANCISCO, 81- *Concurrent Pos:* Mem, Am Cancer Soc Comt, cell & develop biol, 82-86. *Honors & Awards:* Fac Res Award, Am Cancer Soc, 79-84. *Mem:* Soc Develop Biol; Brit Soc Develop Biol. *Res:* Teratocarcinoma cell biology and early mouse embryogenesis. *Mailing Add:* Dept of Anat Univ Calif San Francisco CA 94143

MARTIN, GARY EDWIN, b Wilkensburg, Pa, Oct 14, 49; m 80. HETERONUCLEAR NUCLEAR MAGNETIC RESONANCE SPECTROSCOPY. *Educ:* Univ Pittsburgh, BS, 72; Col Pharm, Univ Ky, PhD(med chem), 76. *Prof Exp:* Asst prof, 75-81, ASSOC PROF MED CHEM, COL PHARM, UNIV HOUSTON, 81- *Concurrent Pos:* Adj assoc prof chem, Dept Chem, Univ Tex, Arlington, 81- *Mem:* Int Soc Heterocyclic Chem; Am Chem Soc. *Res:* Synthesis of new heterocyclic ring systems; the correlation of molecular geometry with structural features; spectroscopic parameters and the potential role of these features in the central nervous systems activity of related drugs; two-dimensional nuclear magnetic resonance spectroscopy. *Mailing Add:* Dept Med Chem & Pharmacog Col Pharm Univ Houston Houston TX 77004

MARTIN, GEORGE, US citizen. MECHANICAL & METALLURGICAL ENGINEERING. *Educ:* Univ Birmingham, BSc, 50, PhD, 52. *Prof Exp:* Sr develop engr, John Gardom & Co, Eng, 52-56; tech mgr, Chromizing Co, Calif, 56-57; chief metallurgist, Honolulu Oil Co, 57-61; prog mgr metals sci, Los Angeles Div, N Am Aviation, Inc, 61-70; chief advan fabrication dept, McDonnell-Douglas Astronaut Co, 70-72; CONSULT, 72-; PRES, CREATIVE METAL CRAFTS INC, 72- *Concurrent Pos:* Lectr, Dept Eng, Univ Calif, Los Angeles, 58-, adj prof eng, 72-80; Nat Endowments Arts res fel, 78. *Mem:* Am Soc Metals; Opers Res Soc Am; Am Soc Testing & Mat; Brit Inst Mech Engrs. *Res:* Materials and production research and development management; manufacturing engineering; material properties, corrosion and fracture; nondestructive testing; blacksmithing. *Mailing Add:* 1708 Berkeley St Santa Monica CA 90404

MARTIN, GEORGE C(OLEMAN), b Everett, Wash, May 16, 10; m 35; c 2. AERONAUTICS. *Educ:* Univ Wash, Seattle, BS, 31. *Prof Exp:* Engr struct res, Boeing Co, 31-35, eng supvr, 35-39, chief struct design, 39-41, staff engr, 41-45, proj engr, 45-47, chief preliminary design, 47-48, proj engr bomber prod design, 48-52, chief engr, 53-58, vpres & gen mgr, Seattle Div, 58-59, vpres & asst gen mgr, Aerospace Div, 59-61, vpres & gen mgr, Seattle Br, Mil Aircraft Systs Div, 61-63, vpres & prog mgt dir, Airplane Div, 63-64, vpres eng, 64-71, vpres design & develop, 71-72, CONSULT, BOEING CO, 72- *Mem:* Fel Am Inst Aeronaut & Astronaut; Aerospace Indust Asn Am. *Res:* Airplane and missile design, development and production. *Mailing Add:* 425 SE Shoreland Dr Bellevue WA 98004

MARTIN, GEORGE C, b San Francisco, Calif, Sept 15, 33; m 53; c 2. POMOLOGY. *Educ:* Calif State Polytech Col, BS, 55; Purdue Univ, MS, 60, PhD(plant physiol), 62. *Prof Exp:* Res asst plant physiol & hort, Purdue Univ, 58-62; res plant physiologist, Crops Res Div, Agr Res Serv, USDA, Wash, 62-67; assoc pomologist, 67-73, POMOLOGIST, UNIV CALIF, DAVIS, 73- *Honors & Awards:* J H Gourley Award in Pomol, Am Soc Hort Sci, 71, Stark Award, 80 & Miller Award, 81. *Mem:* Am Philos Soc; Am Soc Hort Sci; Am Soc Plant Physiol. *Res:* Chemical thinning; mechanism of fruit set, dormancy and rest; use of chemicals to aid mechanical harvest of fruit; measurement of hormones. *Mailing Add:* Dept of Pomol Univ of Calif Davis CA 95616

MARTIN, GEORGE EDWARD, b Batavia, NY, July 3, 32; m 69. GEOMETRY COMBINATORICS. *Educ:* State Univ NY Albany, AB, 54, MA, 55; Univ Mich, PhD(math), 64. *Prof Exp:* Asst prof math, Univ RI, 64-66; asst prof, 66-70, ASSOC PROF MATH, STATE UNIV NY ALBANY, 70- *Mem:* Am Math Soc; Math Asn Am. *Res:* Geometry, specializing in tessellations and the foundations of geometry. *Mailing Add:* Dept of Math State Univ NY Albany NY 12222

MARTIN, GEORGE FRANKLIN, JR, b Englewood, NJ, Feb 20, 37; m 60; c 2. NEUROANATOMY. *Educ:* Bob Jones Univ, BS, 60; Univ Ala, MS, 63, PhD(anat), 65. *Prof Exp:* From instr to assoc prof, 65-73, PROF ANAT, COL MED, OHIO STATE UNIV, 73- *Concurrent Pos:* NIH res grants, 65-75. *Mem:* AAAS; Soc Neurosci; Am Asn Anat; Pan-Am Asn Anat. *Res:* Determining the various connections, functions and development of motor systems. *Mailing Add:* Dept Anat Col Med Ohio State Univ Columbus OH 43210

MARTIN, GEORGE H(ENRY), b Chicago, Ill, June 8, 17. MECHANICAL ENGINEERING. *Educ:* Ill Inst Technol, BS, 41, MS, 44; Northwestern Univ, PhD(mech eng), 55. *Prof Exp:* Jr design engr, Teletype Corp, 41-42; from instr to asst prof, Ill Inst Technol, 43-50; lectr, Northwestern Univ, 50-55; assoc prof, 55-79, EMER ASSOC PROF MECH ENG, MICH STATE UNIV, 79- *Mem:* Am Soc Eng Educ; Am Soc Mech Engrs. *Res:* Kinematics and dynamics of machines. *Mailing Add:* 1320 Westview East Lansing MI 48823

MARTIN, GEORGE MONROE, b New York, NY, June 30, 27; m 52; c 4. EXPERIMENTAL PATHOLOGY. *Educ:* Univ Wash, BS, 49, MD, 53. *Prof Exp:* Intern med, surg & gynec, Montreal Gen Hosp, 53-54; asst resident path, Univ Chicago, 54-55, asst, 55-56, instr, 56-57; from asst prof to assoc prof path, 60-68, dir cytogenetics lab, Hosp, 64-68, dir med scientist training prog, 70-73, PROF PATH, UNIV WASH, 68-, ATTEND PATHOLOGIST, 59-, ADJ PROF GENETICS, 75-, ACTG CHMN, DEPT PATH, 80- *Concurrent Pos:* Consult, Firlands Sanitarium, Seattle, Wash, 57-59 & Northern State Hosp, Sedro Woolley, 59-63; mem path B Study sect, NIH, 66-70, mem adult develop & aging res comn, 73-, chmn aging res rev comt, 75-77; Josiah Macy Jr Found fac scholar, Dunn Sch Path, Oxford, 78-79; chmn nat res plan aging, Nat Inst Aging, 80-82; mem geriat & geront adv comt, Vet Admin, 81- *Honors & Awards:* Brookdale Award, 81. *Mem:* Am Asn Path; Am Soc Human Genetics; Tissue Cult Asn; Genetics Soc Am; Gerontol Soc Am. *Res:* Mammalian cell culture; somatic cell and human biochemical genetics; cell senescence; genetic aspects of aging. *Mailing Add:* Dept of Path SM-30 Univ of Wash Seattle WA 98195

MARTIN, GEORGE REILLY, b Boston, Mass, Jan 20, 33. PHARMACOLOGY. *Educ:* Colgate Univ, AB, 55; Univ Rochester, PhD, 59. *Prof Exp:* Asst, Atomic Energy Proj, Univ Rochester, 55-58; guest worker, Nat Heart Inst, 58-59, res assoc, Nat Inst Dent Res, 59-67, CHIEF CONNECTIVE TISSUE SECT, NAT INST DENT RES, 67-, CHIEF LAB DEVELOP BIOL & ANOMALIES, 80- *Mem:* Am Chem Soc; Biophys Soc; Am Soc Biol Chemists. *Res:* Structure and metabolism of collagen and elastin; chemistry of connective tissue. *Mailing Add:* Connective Tissue Sect Nat Inst of Dent Res Bethesda MD 20205

MARTIN, GEORGE STEVEN, b Oxford, Eng, Sept 19, 43; m 69; c 1. VIROLOGY, TUMOR BIOLOGY. *Educ:* Cambridge Univ, BA, 64, PhD(molecular biol), 68. *Prof Exp:* Fel viral oncol, Dept Molecular Biol, Univ Calif, Berkeley, 68-71; staff mem, Imp Cancer Res Fund, London, 71-75; asst prof, 75-79, ASSOC PROF VIRAL ONCOL, DEPT ZOOL, UNIV CALIF, BERKELY, 79- *Mem:* Am Soc Microbiol; AAAS; Am Soc Cell Biol; Am Soc Virol. *Res:* Transformation by RNA tumor viruses; transformation of differentiating cells. *Mailing Add:* Dept of Zool Univ of Calif Berkeley CA 94720

MARTIN, GERALD CHARLES, JR, b Berrien Center, Mich, Feb 21, 37; m 65. NUCLEAR CHEMISTRY. *Educ:* Western Mich Univ, BS, 59; Univ Notre Dame, MS, 62, PhD(nuclear chem), 64. *Prof Exp:* NUCLEAR CHEMIST, BOILING WATER REACTOR SYSTS DEPT, VALLECITOS NUCLEAR CTR, GEN ELEC CO, 64- *Mem:* Am Nuclear Soc; Am Soc Testing & Mat; Am Nat Stand Inst. *Res:* Absolute measurements of radioactivities and neutron flux. *Mailing Add:* 821 Sundial Circle Livermore CA 94550

MARTIN, GLEN L, soil mechanics, foundation engineering, see previous edition

MARTIN, GLENN ELLIS, b Eureka, Mont, May 22, 47; m 70. PHYSICAL CHEMISTRY. *Educ:* NDak State Univ, BS, 69, PhD(phys chem), 74. *Prof Exp:* SR CHEMIST, INMONT CORP, 74- *Mem:* Am Chem Soc. *Res:* Synthesizing polymers to be used for industrial coatings with emphasis in automobile coatings. *Mailing Add:* 905 Liberty Dr Waterville OH 43519

MARTIN, GORDON EUGENE, physics, engineering, see previous edition

MARTIN, GORDON MATHER, b Brookline, Mass, Mar 2, 15; m 40; c 3. PHYSICAL MEDICINE. *Educ:* Nebr Wesleyan Univ, AB, 36; Univ Nebr, MD, 40; Univ Minn, MS, 44. *Prof Exp:* Asst prof phys med, Sch Med, Univ Kans, 44-47; from asst prof to assoc prof, Mayo Grad Sch Med, 47-73, prof phys med, 73-81, EMER PROF & CONSULT MED & REHAB, MAYO MED SCH, UNIV MINN, 81- *Concurrent Pos:* Consult, Mayo Clin, 47-73, sr consult phys med & rehab, 73-; exec secy, Am Bd Phys Med & Rehab, 81- *Mem:* Am Cong Rehab Med; Am Acad Phys Med & Rehab; AMA. *Res:* Clinical research. *Mailing Add:* Mayo Clin 200 First St SW Rochester MN 55901

MARTIN, HANS CARL, b Winnipeg, Man, Nov 20, 37. MICROMETEOROLOGY. *Educ:* Univ Man, BSc, 58; Univ Western Ont, MSc, 61, PhD(physics), 66. *Prof Exp:* Res scientist meteorol physics, Commonwealth Sci & Indust Res Orgn, Australia, 66-68; res scientist meteorol physics, Can Meteorol Serv, Dept Environ, 69-77; RES MGR, LONG-RANGE TRANSPORT AIR POLLUTION PROG (ACID RAIN), DEPT ENVIRON, 77- *Concurrent Pos:* Lectr, Mgt Training Prog, Fed Govt; Lectr, various Univ. *Mem:* Am Meteorol Soc; Royal Meteorol Soc. *Res:* Air-sea interactions; energy exchange processes near the surface of the earth over land, water and ice; air pollution transport, transformation and deposition and impact on material and man-made receptors. *Mailing Add:* 4905 Dufferin St Downsview ON M3H 5T4 Can

MARTIN, HAROLD ROLAND, b White Co, Ind, Nov 11, 19; m 52; c 3. MEDICINE. *Educ:* Purdue Univ, BS, 42; Ind Univ, MD, 44. *Prof Exp:* First asst & spec asst psychiat, Mayo Clin, 50-52; from asst to clin dir, Inst Living, 52-54; from asst prof to assoc prof neurol & psychiat, Col Med, Univ Nebr, 54-60; CONSULT PSYCHIATRIST, MAYO CLIN, 60-, ASSOC PROF PSYCHIAT, MAYO MED SCH, UNIV MINN, 70- *Concurrent Pos:* Clin dir, Adult Inpatient Serv, Nebr Psychiat Inst, 54-; consult, Vet Admin Hosp, Omaha, Nebr, 55 & State Div Rehabil Servs, Nebr, 59. *Mem:* AAAS; AMA; fel Am Psychiat Asn. *Res:* Psychiatry; rehabilitation. *Mailing Add:* Dept of Psychiat Mayo Clin 200 First St SW Rochester MN 55901

MARTIN, HERBERT LLOYD, b Somerville, Mass, Dec 7, 21; m 51; c 6. NEUROLOGY. *Educ:* Boston Univ, BS, 47, MD, 50. *Prof Exp:* Teaching fel neurol, Montreal Neurol Inst, McGill, 57-58; assoc prof clin neurol, 58-69, PROF NEUROL, UNIV VT, 69-, ASSOC CHMN DEPT, 71- *Mem:* AMA; Am Acad Neurol; Am Epilepsy Soc; Am Asn Res Nerv & Ment Dis; Asn Am Med Cols. *Mailing Add:* Dept of Neurol Univ of Vt Burlington VT 05401

MARTIN, HORACE F, b Azores, Jan 11, 31; US citizen; m 54; c 7. CLINICAL CHEMISTRY, CLININCAL PATHOLOGY. *Educ:* Providence Col, BS, 53; Univ RI, MS, 55; Boston Univ, PhD(biochem), 61; Brown Univ, MA(ad eundum), 67, MD, 75. *Prof Exp:* Sr res chemist, Monsanto chem Co, 57-59, group leader life sci, Monsanto Res Corp, 61-63; assoc prof med sci, 66-78, prof, 78-81, PROF PATH, BROWN UNIV, 81- *Concurrent Pos:* Consult, Monsanto Chem Co, 63-64 & indust toxicol; biochemist, RI Hosp, Providence, 63-78, dir clin chem, 79- *Mem:* Am Chem Soc; Asn Comput Mach; Am Soc Clin Pathologists; Am Asn Clin Chemists; AMA. *Res:* Automation and analytical procedures; clinical pathology; normal values; instrumental methods of analysis. *Mailing Add:* Dept Med Brown Univ Providence RI 02912

MARTIN, HUGH JACK, JR, b San Diego, Calif, Sept 1, 26; m 50; c 6. HIGH ENERGY PHYSICS. *Educ:* Calif Inst Technol, BS, 51, PhD(physics), 56. *Prof Exp:* Res assoc, 55-57, from asst prof to assoc prof, 57-61, PROF PHYSICS, IND UNIV, BLOOMINGTON, 65- *Mem:* Am Phys Soc; Asn Comput Mach; An Asn Univ Professors. *Res:* Experimental high energy, bubble chamber and spark chamber physics; pattern recognition and computer applications. *Mailing Add:* Dept Physics Col Arts & Sci Ind Univ Bloomington IN 47401

MARTIN, J(AMES) W(ILLIAM), b Lenox, Iowa. ENGINEERING. *Educ:* Kans State Col, BS, 33 & 38; Iowa State Col, MS, 39. *Prof Exp:* Asst, Kans State Col, 33-35, lab asst, 37-38, from instr to assoc prof eng, 40-46; prof eng, Univ Idaho, 46-81; RETIRED. *Concurrent Pos:* Field engr, John Deere Plow Co, 35-37; instr eng, Iowa State Col, 38-39 & Univ Ill, 39-40. *Mem:* Am Soc Eng Educ; Am Soc Agr Engrs. *Res:* Agricultural machinery. *Mailing Add:* Dept of Eng Univ of Idaho Moscow ID 83843

MARTIN, JACK, b Tuscaloosa, Ala, Aug 11, 27; m 57; c 4. PSYCHIATRY. *Educ:* Univ Ala, BS, 49; Vanderbilt Univ, MD, 53. *Prof Exp:* Intern, Charity Hosp, New Orleans, La, 53-54; resident physician gen psychiat, Cincinnati Gen Hosp, 54-56, res fel child psychiat, Cincinnati Gen Hosp & Child Guid Home, 56-58; from instr to asst prof, 58-63, CLIN PROF PSYCHIAT, UNIV TEX HEALTH SCI CTR DALLAS, 63- *Concurrent Pos:* Med dir & pres, Shady Brook Schs. *Res:* Child development; clinical child psychiatry. *Mailing Add:* 3636 Dickason St Dallas TX 75219

MARTIN, JACK E, b Bogard, Mo, June 4, 31; m 55; c 3. NUTRITION, BIOCHEMISTRY. *Educ:* Univ Mo, BS, 53, MS, 60; Univ Fla, PhD(nutrit), 63. *Prof Exp:* Prod supvr biochem, Monsanto Co, Mo, 63-67; asst res nutritionist, Ralston Purina Co, 67-69; nutritionist, Ceres Land Co, 69-71; NUTRITIONIST, STERLING NUTRIT SERV, INC, 71- *Mem:* Am Soc Animal Sci. *Res:* Effect of mineral nutrition on cellulose digestion in ruminants. *Mailing Add:* Rte 4 407 Highland Dr Sterling CO 80751

MARTIN, JAMES CULLEN, b Dover, Tenn, Jan 14, 28; m 51; c 5. ORGANIC CHEMISTRY. *Educ:* Vanderbilt Univ, BA, 51, MS, 52; Harvard Univ, PhD(chem), 56. *Prof Exp:* From instr to assoc prof, 56-65, PROF ORG CHEM, UNIV ILL, URBANA, 65- *Concurrent Pos:* Sloan Found fel, 62-66; Guggenheim Mem Found fel, 65-66; assoc mem, Ctr Advan Study, Univ Ill, Urbana, 71-72; Humboldt Found Sr US Scientist Award, 78-79. *Honors & Awards:* Buck-Whitney Medal, Am Chem Soc, 79. *Mem:* Am Chem Soc; fel AAAS; fel Japan Soc Prom Sci. *Res:* Mechanisms of organic reactions; free-radical reactions; synthesis of compounds expected to show unusual physical properties or reactivity; compounds of hypervalent non-metals; sulfuranes. *Mailing Add:* Dept of Chem Univ of Ill Urbana IL 61801

MARTIN, JAMES CUTHBERT, b Wilson, NC, May 8, 27; m 66. INDUSTRIAL ORGANIC CHEMISTRY. *Educ:* Univ NC, BS, 47. *Prof Exp:* From res chemist to sr res chemist, 48-67, res assoc, 67-72, sr res assoc, 72-78, RES FEL, TENN EASTMAN CO, 78- *Mem:* Am Chem Soc; AAAS; Sigma Xi. *Res:* Chemistry of ketenes; small ring compounds; new polymer systems; applied organic chemistry; exploratory research in catalysis; new product development. *Mailing Add:* 601 N Mountain View Circle Johnson City TN 37601

MARTIN, JAMES D, b Michigan City, Ind, Nov 24, 34; m 55; c 4. ORGANIC CHEMISTRY. *Educ:* Purdue Univ, BS, 56, MS, 58. *Prof Exp:* Chief propellant chem, Thiokol Chem Corp, 64-66; head propellant chem, 66-67, chief solid propellant chem, 67, MGR, SOLID PROPELLANT DEPT & DIR TECHNOL, ATLANTIC RES CORP, 67- *Mem:* Am Chem Soc; Am Inst Aeronaut & Astronaut. *Res:* Solid propellant research and development; binder chemistry; high energy and fuel rich propellants; controllable and slurry propellants. *Mailing Add:* Atlantic Res Corp Alexandria VA 22314

MARTIN, JAMES EDWARD, b Rock Springs, Wyo, Oct 8, 49. TERTIARY BIOSTRATIGRAPHY, TAXONOMY. *Educ:* SDak Sch Mines & Technol, BS, 71, MS, 73; Univ Washington, PhD(geol), 79. *Prof Exp:* Res assoc paleont, Mus Geol, SDak Sch Mines, 67-74; asst instr, Dept Geol, Univ Washington, 74-77; cur paleont, Thomas Burke Mus, Univ Washington, 77-79; ASST PROF, DEPT GEOL & GEOL ENG, SDAK SCH MINES & TECHNOL, 79-, DIR, BLACK HILLS NATURAL SCI FIELD STA, 79-, CUR, MUS GEOL, 79- *Concurrent Pos:* Consult, Wash Pub Power Supply Systs, 75, Shannon & Wilson Geotech Consult, 77 & Bur Land Mgt, 77. *Mem:* Geol Soc Am; Soc Vertebrate Paleont; Sigma Xi. *Res:* Vertebrate paleontology, stratigraphy and biostratigraphy; biostratigraphy of Hemphillian deposits in Oregon and Washington, of marine vertebrates in the Pierre Shale of South Dakota, of Miocene sediments in South Dakota; taxonomic studies of Cretaceous, Miocene, and Pleistocene vertebrates; survey of Pleistocene taxa associated with a clovis kill site in South Dakota. *Mailing Add:* Mus Geol SDak Sch Mines & Technol Rapid City SD 57701

MARTIN, JAMES ELLIS, b Cleveland, Ohio, Dec 25, 52. POLYMER PHYSICS, SCATTERING MEASUREMENTS. *Educ:* Univ Wash, BS, 76, PhD(phys chem), 81. *Prof Exp:* STAFF SCIENTIST, DEPT SOLID STATE RES, SANDIA NAT LAB, 81- *Mem:* Am Chem Soc. *Res:* Theory of the statistical and dynamical properties of polymers in solution and in the bulk state; photon correlation spectroscopy measurement of the dynamical properties of polymers. *Mailing Add:* Div 5152 Sandia Nat Lab Albuquerque NM 87185

MARTIN, JAMES FRANKLIN, b Harrison Co, WVa, Nov 24, 24; m 46. MICROBIOLOGY. *Educ:* WVa Univ, AB, 52, MS, 56; Nat Registry Microbiologists, registered. *Prof Exp:* Res microbiologist, Ralph M Parsons Co, Ft Detrick, Md, 54-55 & Lambert Pharmacal Co, St Louis, Mo, 55-56; scientist microbiol, 56-72, SR SCIENTIST MICROBIOL, WARNER-LAMBERT RES INST, 72- *Mem:* Am Soc Microbiol; Soc Indust Microbiol. *Res:* Pharmaceutical research and development of synthetic and natural antimicrobial agents; general diagnostics; research and development of disinfection agents and systems. *Mailing Add:* Warner-Lambert Gen Diagnostics Mt Tabor Rd Morris Plains NJ 07950

MARTIN, JAMES FRANKLIN, b St Mary's, WVa, Mar 20, 17; m 42; c 2. MEDICINE, RADIOLOGY. *Educ:* Marietta Col, AB, 38; Western Reserve Univ, MD, 42. *Prof Exp:* Teaching fel radiol, Western Reserve Univ Hosp, 47-48, demonstr radiol, Western Reserve Univ, 48, from instr to sr instr, 48-50; from asst prof to assoc prof, 50-61, prof radiol, 61-75, PROF MED SONICS, ASST RADIOL, BOWMAN GRAY SCH MED, 75-, DIR POSTGRAD MED SONICS, 81- *Concurrent Pos:* Physician, NC Baptist Hosp. *Mem:* Radiol Soc NAm; Am Roentgen Ray Soc (pres, 81-82); AMA; fel Am Col Radiol; Am Inst Ultrasound Med. *Res:* Clinical radiology. *Mailing Add:* Bowman Gray Sch Med Box 229 Winston-Salem NC 27103

MARTIN, JAMES HAROLD, b Collinwood, Tenn, Oct 12, 31; m 54; c 2. DAIRY MICROBIOLOGY. *Educ:* Univ Tenn, BSc, 57; Ohio State Univ, MSc, 58, PhD(microbiol), 63. *Prof Exp:* Res asst dairy tech, Ohio State Univ, 57-58, res assoc, 60-63, asst prof, 63-65; instr dairy mfg, Miss State Univ, 58-60; from asst prof to assoc prof dairy microbiol, Univ Ga, 65-72; prof dairy sci & head dept, SDak State Univ, 72-78; PROF DAIRY SCI & HEAD DEPT, CLEMSON UNIV, 78- *Mem:* Am Soc Microbiol; Am Dairy Sci Asn; Inst Food Technol. *Res:* Physiology and metabolism of microorganisms common to milk, especially as related to bacterial spores, starter and spoilage organisms. *Mailing Add:* Dept of Dairy Sci Clemson Univ Clemson SC 29631

MARTIN, JAMES HENRY, III, b New Orleans, La, Mar 31, 43; m 66; c 4. VERTEBRATE PHYSIOLOGY. *Educ:* Univ Va, BA, 65; Univ Richmond, MS, 67; Univ Tenn, PhD(zool), 70. *Prof Exp:* Instr anat & physiol, Univ Tenn, Knoxville, 68; NIH fel & instr physiol, Med Col Va, Va Commonwealth Univ, 71-73; asst prof natural sci, 73-76, assoc prof biol, 76-78, PROF BIOL, J S REYNOLDS COMMUNITY COL, 79- *Concurrent Pos:* Vis lectr, Math & Sci Ctr, Richmond, Va, 72-; vis scientist, Va Acad Sci. *Mem:* AAAS; Am Soc Ichthyologists & Herpetologists; Am Inst Biol Sci; Soc Vert Paleont; Am Soc Zoologists. *Res:* Physiology and biophysics of muscle contraction; transport across epithelial membranes. *Mailing Add:* Dept Biol Parham Campus J S Reynolds Community Col Richmond VA 23241

MARTIN, JAMES MILTON, b Waxahachie, Tex, May 15, 14; m 41; c 3. GEOPHYSICS. *Educ:* Univ Okla, BS, 38; Rensselaer Polytech Inst, MS, 46. *Prof Exp:* Seismic explor, Geophys Serv, Inc, 34-35 & 37-39; seismol & seismic prospecting, Magnolia Petrol Co, 40-41 & 47; tech eval, 42 & 47-57, chief underwater eval dept, 57-73, PROJ MGR TORPEDOES, US NAVAL ORD LAB, MD, 73- *Honors & Awards:* Superior Civil Serv Award, Dept Navy, 72. *Mem:* Soc Explor Geophys; Am Geophys Union. *Res:* Technical evaluation of naval ordnance; geophysics. *Mailing Add:* 314 Williamsburg Dr Silver Spring MD 20901

MARTIN, JAMES PAXMAN, b Cowley, Wyo, Sept 22, 14; m 37; c 2. SOIL MICROBIOLOGY. *Educ:* Brigham Young Univ, BS, 38; Rutgers Univ, PhD(soil microbiol), 41. *Prof Exp:* Asst soil microbiol, NJ Exp Sta, 38-41; coop agent, Soil Conserv Serv, USDA & NJ Exp Sta, 41-43; asst prof bact & asst soil microbiologist exp sta, Univ Idaho, 43-45; from asst chemist to asssoc chemist, 45-57, prof, 61-80, EMER PROF SOIL SCI, UNIV CALIF, RIVERSIDE, 81-, CHEMIST, CITRUS RES CTR, 57- *Concurrent Pos:* Soil Sci Res Award, Soil Sci Soc Am, 79; vis prof, Univ Rio, Jameire, Brazil, 80. *Mem:* Fel AAAS; Am Soc Microbiol; Soil Sci Soc Am; fel Am Soc Agron. *Res:* Decomposition and stabilization of 14-C-labelled phenolic substances; model and plant lignins; fungal melanins; model humic polymers in relation to soil humus formation; citrus replant problem; influence of pesticides on soil properties. *Mailing Add:* Dept of Soil & Environ Sci Univ of Calif Riverside CA 92521

MARTIN, JAMES RICHARD, b Schenectady, NY, July 13, 49. PHYSIOLOGICAL PSYCHOLOGY. *Educ:* Allegheny Col, BS, 71; Univ Minn, PhD(physiol psychol), 75; Univ Calif, Los Angeles, cert physiol psychol, 77. *Prof Exp:* Asst res psychologist physiol psychol, Univ Calif, Los Angeles, 75-77; RES SCIENTIST BEHAV SCI, SWISS FED INST TECHNOL, 77- *Concurrent Pos:* NIMH fel, Univ Calif, Los Angeles, 75-77. *Mem:* Soc Neurosci; Psychonomic Soc; Am Psychol Asn; Europ Brain & Behav Soc; Europ Neurosci Asn. *Res:* Neuropsychology of hunger and thirst; behavioral pharmacology; neuroscience; behavioral science; animal learning. *Mailing Add:* Inst für Verhaltenswissenschaft Eidg Tech Hochschule CH-8092 Zurich Switzerland

MARTIN, JAMES TILLISON, b Bluefield, WVa, Aug 10, 46. BEHAVIORAL PHYSIOLOGY. *Educ:* WVa Univ, AB, 67; Univ Conn, MS, 71; Univ Munich, PhD(zool), 74. *Prof Exp:* Asst pharmacologist, RMI Inst Pharmacol, State Univ Utrecht, 73-74; assoc animal sci, Univ Minn, St Paul, 74-76; ASST PROF BIOL, STOCKTON STATE COL, 76- *Concurrent Pos:* Translr Ger to English, French Nat Mus Natural Hist, 73-75; Nat Inst Child Health & Human Develop fel, 74-76. *Mem:* Soc Neurosci; Am Soc Zoologists; Int Soc Psychoneuroendocrinol; Animal Behav Soc. *Res:* Behavioral and endocrine factors involved in the domestication process; neuroendocrine basis of emotional behavior and adrenosteroid influences on reproductive function. *Mailing Add:* Fac of Natural Sci & Math Stockton State Col Pomona NJ 08240

MARTIN, JAY RONALD, b Sanford, Maine, Jan 27, 44; m 67; c 2. CHEMICAL ENGINEERING, POLYMER SCIENCE. *Educ:* LaFayette Col, BS, 66; Princeton Univ, PhD(chem eng), 72. *Prof Exp:* Staff scientist, 71-75, sr scientist, Textile Res Inst, 75-76; asst prof, 76-80, ASSOC PROF, LAFAYETTE COL, 80- *Concurrent Pos:* Res assoc, Textile Res Inst, 77-80. *Mem:* Am Inst Chem Eng. *Res:* Dynamic mechanical properties of polymers; polymer flammability; polymer degradation; thermal analysis. *Mailing Add:* Dept of Chem Eng Lafayette Col Easton PA 18042

MARTIN, JEROME, b Bisbee, Ariz, Jan 12, 02; m 28; c 2. CHEMISTRY. *Educ:* Univ Colo, BS, 24; Univ Calif, PhD(phys chem), 28. *Prof Exp:* Res chemist, Com Solvents Corp, 27-39, res dir, 39-57, sci dir, 57-67; consult, 67-77; CHEM CONSULT, IMC CHEM GROUP INC, 77- *Mem:* AAAS; Am Chem Soc; Math Asn Am. *Res:* Catalysis; organic chemistry; antibiotics. *Mailing Add:* IMC Chem Group Inc PO Box 207 Terre Haute IN 47808

MARTIN, JERRY JUNIOR, b Darwin, Okla, Oct 28, 30; m 53; c 4. ANIMAL NUTRITION, ANIMAL PHYSIOLOGY. *Educ:* Okla State Univ, BS, 57, MS, 59, PhD(animal nutrit & physiol), 61. *Prof Exp:* Instr animal sci, Murray State Agr Col, 61-67; ASSOC PROF BIOL & ANIMAL SCI, PANHANDLE STATE UNIV, 67-, CHMN DIV AGR, 73- *Mem:* Am Inst Biol Sci; Am Soc Animal Sci. *Res:* Grain processing; additives in feedlot rations. *Mailing Add:* Div of Agr Panhandle State Univ Goodwell OK 73939

MARTIN, JIM FRANK, b Millersburg, Iowa, Nov 24, 44; m 76; c 2. NONDESTRUCTIVE EVALUATION, AUTOMATION. *Educ:* Iowa State Univ, BS, 65; Mass Inst Technol, PhD(physics), 71. *Prof Exp:* Engr, Chevron Res Lab, Standard Oil Calif, 65; res asst, Lab Nuclear Sci, Mass Inst Technol, 71-75; res assoc, Stanford Linear Accelerator Ctr, Stanford Univ, 75-78; MEM TECH STAFF, SCI CTR, ROCKWELL INT, 78- *Mem:* Am Phys Soc; Inst Elec & Electronics Engrs; Am Soc Nondestructive Testing; Sigma Xi. *Res:* Research and development of advanced techniques for ultrasonic nondestructive evaluation: including transducer development, digital data acquisition signal and image processing, and device control (robotics). *Mailing Add:* Rockwell Int 1049 Camino Dos Rios Thousand Oaks CA 91360

MARTIN, JOEL JEROME, b Jamestown, NDak, Mar 27, 39. SOLID STATE PHYSICS. *Educ:* SDak Sch Mines & Technol, BS, 61, MS, 63; Iowa State Univ, PhD(physics), 67. *Prof Exp:* AEC fel, Ames Lab, Iowa State Univ, 67-69; asst prof physics, 69-74, ASSOC PROF PHYSICS, OKLA STATE UNIV, 74- *Mem:* Am Phys Soc. *Res:* Radiation damage in insulators; thermal conductivity. *Mailing Add:* Dept of Physics Okla State Univ Stillwater OK 74074

MARTIN, JOHN B(RUCE), b Auburn, Ala, Feb 2, 22; m 43, 63; c 3. CHEMICAL ENGINEERING. *Educ:* Ala Polytech Inst, BS, 43; Ohio State Univ, MSc, 47, PhD(chem eng), 49. *Prof Exp:* Asst chem eng, Ohio State Univ, 46-49; chem engr, res & develop dept, 49-77, CHEM ENGR, MKT RES DEPT, PROCTER & GAMBLE CO, 77- *Mem:* Am Chem Soc; Am Inst Chem Engrs; Am Soc Eng Educ; Chem Mkt Res Asn. *Res:* Detergents; spray drying; organization development; chemical market research. *Mailing Add:* 644 Doepke Lane Cincinnati OH 45231

MARTIN, JOHN CAMPBELL, b Orangeburg, SC, Dec 6, 26; m 50; c 3. ELECTRICAL & SYSTEMS ENGINEERING. *Educ:* Clemson Univ, BS, 48; Mass Inst Technol, MS, 53; NC State Univ, PhD(elec eng), 62. *Prof Exp:* Instr elec eng, Clemson Univ, 48-50; asst, Mass Inst Technol, 50-52; proj engr, Gen Electronic Lab, Mass, 52; design engr, Spencer-Kennedy Lab, 52-53; asst prof physics, 53-55, from asst prof to assoc prof elec eng, 55-66, PROF ELEC ENG, CLEMSON UNIV, 66- *Concurrent Pos:* Consult, Sangamo Elec Co, Ill, 63; NASA res grant, 65-70. *Mem:* Inst Elec & Electronics Engrs. *Res:* Modern control theory; automatic controls; very high frequency filters; frequency multipliers using varactors; minimum phase shift band-pass filters; social system engineering. *Mailing Add:* Dept of Elec & Computer Eng Clemson Univ Clemson SC 29631

MARTIN, JOHN DAVID, b Chicago, Ill, Nov 8, 39; m 62; c 2. NUCLEAR PHYSICS, ATMOSPHERIC PHYSICS. *Educ:* Va Mil Inst, BS, 61; Col William & Mary, MA, 63; Univ Fla, PhD(physics), 67. *Prof Exp:* Nuclear res officer physics, McClellan Cent Labs, McClellan Air Force Base, 67-70; physicist, 70-76; VPRES TECH, TELEDYNE ISOTOPES, 77- *Mem:* Am Phys Soc. *Res:* Research in measurement of stable and radioactive trace gases in the atmosphere; development of nuclear counting techniques for measurement of environmental-level fission and activation radioisotopes. *Mailing Add:* 23 Twin Oak Dr Montvale NJ 07645

MARTIN, JOHN ELMSLIE, inorganic chemistry, see previous edition

MARTIN, JOHN F, analytical chemistry, see previous edition

MARTIN, JOHN HARVEY, b Chambersburg, Pa, Jan 20, 32; m 58; c 3. INTERNAL MEDICINE, RHEUMATOLOGY. *Educ:* Gettysburg Col, BA, 54; Temple Univ, MD, 58; Mayo Grad Sch Med, Univ Minn, MS, 62; Am Bd Internal Med, dipl, 65, cert med, 74. *Prof Exp:* From asst to staff med, Mayo Clin, 64-65; from instr to prof med, Temple Univ, 66-78; PROF MED & DIR DIV GEN MED, THOMAS JEFFERSON UNIV, 78-, INTERIM CHMN, DEPT MED, 81- *Concurrent Pos:* Fel rheumatol, Temple Univ, 65-66; P S Hench scholar, Mayo Grad Sch Med, Univ Minn, 66. *Mem:* Fel Am Col Physicians; Am Rheumatism Asn; Am Asn Clin Res. *Res:* Clinical research. *Mailing Add:* Thomas Jefferson Univ Hosp 111 S 11th St Suite 4138 Philadelphia PA 19107

MARTIN, JOHN HOLLAND, b Old Lyme, Conn, Feb 27, 35; m 69; c 2. OCEANOGRAPHY, MARINE POLLUTION. *Educ:* Colby Col, BA, 59; Univ RI, MS, 64, PhD(oceanog), 66. *Prof Exp:* Assoc scientist oceanog, PR Nuclear Ctr, Univ PR, Mayagüez, 66-69; sr scientist, Hopkins Marine Sta, Stanford Univ, 69-72; from asst prof to assoc prof oceanog, 72-77, PROF OCEANOG, CALIF STATE UNIV, SAN FRANCISCO, 77-, DIR, MOSS LANDING MARINE LABS, 76- *Concurrent Pos:* Dir, Vertex Prog, 79-; vchmn, Univ Nat Oceanog Lab Syst, Nat Sci Found, 80 & 81. *Mem:* Am Soc Limnol & Oceanog. *Res:* Trace elements in sea water and marine organisms; marine pollution problems. *Mailing Add:* Moss Landing Marine Labs Moss Landing CA 95039

MARTIN, JOHN J(OSEPH), b Detroit, Mich, Oct 19, 22; m 48; c 3. ENGINEERING SCIENCE. *Educ:* Notre Dame, BSME, 43, MSME, 50; Purdue Univ, PhD(mech eng), 51. *Prof Exp:* Instr, Mech Eng Lab, Notre Dame, 46-47, calculus, 47; engr, Clark Equip Co, 47-49; res engr, NAm Aviation, Inc, 51-53; chief eng res, Bendix Prods Div, Bendix Aviation Corp, 53-60; mem tech staff, Inst Defense Anal, 60-63 & 64-66, spec asst to vpres res, 66-67, asst to pres, 67-68, dir, Systs Eval Div, 68-69; tech asst for nat scurity affairs, Off Sci & Technol, Exec Off of the President, 69-73; asst secy res & develop, US Air Force, 74-79; VPRES & GEN MGR, ADVAN TECHNOL CTR, BENDIX CORP, 79- *Concurrent Pos:* Consult, US Army Asst Chief Staff Intel, 59; resident consult, UK Royal Aircraft Estab, 63-64. *Mem:* Am Inst Aeronaut & Astronaut; Acoust Soc Am. *Res:* Heat transfer and thermodynamics; high altitude and reentry aerophysics, aerodynamics and aeromechanics; physical oceanography. *Mailing Add:* Bendix Advan Tech Ctr 9140 Old Annapolis Rd Columbus MD 21045

MARTIN, JOHN LEE, b Houston, Tex, Nov 19, 23; m 48; c 4. NUTRITION. *Educ:* Southern Methodist Univ, BS, 49; Univ Ark, MS, 53; Tex A&M Univ, PhD(biochem, nutrit), 56. *Prof Exp:* From instr to asst prof chem, Colo State Univ, 55-59; prof & head dept, Baker Univ, 59-60; assoc prof, Colo State Univ, 60-67; prof chem, Metrop State Col, 67-77; PROF FOOD & NUTRIT, TEX TECH UNIV, 78- *Mem:* Sigma Xi; Am Inst Nutrit. *Res:* Selenium-sulfur interrelationships; selenium enhancement of the immune response. *Mailing Add:* Dept of Food & Nutrit Tex Tech Univ Lubbock TX 79419

MARTIN, JOHN MUNSON, b Eldora, Iowa, Nov 8, 48. AGRONOMY, PLANT BREEDING. *Educ:* Iowa State Univ, BS, 71, MS, 74, PhD(agron), 78. *Prof Exp:* ASST PROF AGRON, MONT STATE UNIV, 78- *Mem:* Am Soc Agron; Crop Sci Soc Am. *Mailing Add:* Dept of Plant & Soil Sci Mont State Univ Bozeman MT 59717

MARTIN, JOHN PERRY, JR, b Dunbar, Pa; m 81; c 2. PHYSICAL CHEMISTRY, ANALYTICAL CHEMISTRY. *Educ:* Carnegie Inst Technol, BS, 47, MS, 55, PhD(chem), 62. *Hon Degrees:* MHL, Davis & Elkins Col. *Prof Exp:* Asst chem, Metals Res Lab, Carnegie Inst Technol, 47-50; chemist, Dunbar Corp, 50-52; chief chemist, Duraloy Co, 52-59; from asst prof to assoc prof, 62-75, from actg chmn to chmn dept, 62-68, PROF CHEM, DAVIS & ELKINS COL, 75- *Concurrent Pos:* Consult, Pa Wire Glass Co, 50-52. *Mem:* Am Chem Soc; Am Inst Chemists; Sigma Xi. *Res:* X-ray, ultraviolet visible and infra-red spectroscopy; hydrogen bonding of secondary amines with polar organic compounds and of amine complexes; educationally valuable demonstrations and student performable laboratory investigations, both introductory and advanced. *Mailing Add:* Dept of Chem Davis & Elkins Col Elkins WV 26241

MARTIN, JOHN ROBERT, b Lancaster, Pa, Dec 6, 23; m 45; c 3. ANALYTICAL CHEMISTRY. *Educ:* Goshen Col, AB, 44; Pa State Col, MS, 49, PhD(chem), 50. *Prof Exp:* Res chemist, 50-51, supvr, 51-64, div head, 64-75, CONSULT SUPVR OCCUP HEALTH, E I DU PONT DE NEMOURS & CO, INC, 77- *Mem:* Am Chem Soc. *Res:* Application of ion exchange to analytical chemistry; analysis of fluoro compounds; functional group analysis; microanalysis. *Mailing Add:* 213 Hullihen Dr Newark DE 19711

MARTIN, JOHN SAMUEL, b Philadelphia, Pa, Oct 5, 43. PHYSIOLOGY, BIOPHYSICS. *Educ:* Temple Univ, AB, 65; Woman's Med Col, MS, 68; Thomas Jefferson Univ, PhD, 73. *Prof Exp:* Instr biol, Holy Family Col, 71-72; instr, 72-74, asst prof physiol, 74-80, ASSOC PROF ORAL BIOL & PHYSIOL, SCH DENT, TEMPLE UNIV, 80- *Concurrent Pos:* Smith Kline & French Labs fel, Dept Physiol & Biophys, Sch Dent, Temple Univ, 72-74. *Mem:* Am Fedn Clin Res. *Res:* Gastrointestinal and autonomic physiology; upper airway physiology; membrane phenomena. *Mailing Add:* Dept of Physiol & Biophys Temple Univ Sch of Dent Philadelphia PA 19140

MARTIN, JOHN SCOTT, b Toronto, Ont, Sept 1, 34; m 57; c 2. SCIENCE EDUCATION, PHYSICAL CHEMISTRY. *Educ:* Univ Toronto, BA, 56; Columbia Univ, PhD(chem), 62. *Prof Exp:* Fel chem, Nat Res Coun Can, 61-63; asst prof, 63-69, ASSOC PROF CHEM, UNIV ALTA, 69- *Mem:* Chem Inst Can; Sigma Xi; AAAS; Asn Develop Comput Instr Systs. *Res:* Computer assisted instruction in chemistry; hydrogen bonding and ionic solvation processes by nuclear magnetic resonance; structure and spectra of bihalide ions; computer analysis of nuclear magnetic resonance spectra of symmetric molecules. *Mailing Add:* Dept of Chem Univ of Alta Edmonton AB T6G 2G7

MARTIN, JOHN WALTER, JR, b Hagerstown, Md, Oct 31, 22; m 43; c 4. PHARMACEUTICAL CHEMISTRY. *Educ:* Bridgewater Col, BA, 47; Med Col Va, BS, 49; Univ NC, PhD(pharmaceut chem), 52. *Prof Exp:* From asst prof to assoc prof pharmaceut chem, Col Pharm, Butler Univ, 52-61; PROF CHEM, BRIDGEWATER COL, 61- *Concurrent Pos:* Fulbright lectr, Cairo Univ, 65-66; fel, Univ London, 70-71. *Mem:* Am Chem Soc; AAAS. *Res:* Derivatives of amino acids and nitrogen heterocycles. *Mailing Add:* Dept of Chem Bridgewater Col Bridgewater VA 22812

MARTIN, JOSEPH B, b Bassano, Alta, Oct 20, 38; US citizen; c 4. NEUROLOGY, NEUROENDOCRINOLOGY. *Educ:* Eastern Mennonite Col, BSc, 59; Univ Alta, MD, 62; Univ Rochester, PhD(anat), 70, FRCP(c). *Prof Exp:* From asst prof to prof neurol, McGill Univ, 70-78; BULLARD PROF NEUROL, HARVARD MED SCH, 78-; CHIEF NEUROL SERV, MASS GEN HOSP, 78- *Concurrent Pos:* Res scholar, Med Res Coun Can, 70-75, res assoc, 75-78, mem centennial fel comt, 76-78; mem study sect endocrinol, NIH, 76-80. *Honors & Awards:* MA, Harvard Univ, 78. *Mem:* Am Soc Clin Invest; Endocrine Soc; Am Neurol Asn; Am Physiol Soc; Asn Am Physicians. *Res:* Neurobiology; mechanisms of hypothalamic regulation of anterior pituitary function; actions of peptides in brain. *Mailing Add:* Neurol Serv Mass Gen Hosp Boston MA 02114

MARTIN, JOSEPH J, b Anita, Iowa, Dec 23, 16; m 41; c 4. CHEMICAL ENGINEERING. *Educ:* Iowa State Univ, BS, 39; Univ Rochester, MS, 44; Carnegie Inst Technol, DSc(chem eng), 48. *Hon Degrees:* DSc, Univ Nebr, 71. *Prof Exp:* Chem engr, Eastman Kodak Co, NY, 39-41; from instr to asst prof unit opers & thermodyn, Univ Rochester, 40-45; instr, Carnegie Inst Technol, 45-47; from asst prof to assoc prof chem eng, 47-56, assoc dir, Inst Sci & Technol, 65-81, actg dir, Inst Sci & Technol, 78-81, PROF CHEM ENG, UNIV MICH, ANN ARBOR, 56- *Concurrent Pos:* Vis prof, Univ Calif, Los Angeles, 59-60; consult various industs; mem, Nat Res Coun, 67-73; pres, Eng Joint Coun, Am Inst Chem Engrs, 73-75. *Mem:* Am Chem Soc; Am Nuclear Soc; Am Soc Eng Educ (vpres, 68-70, pres, 78-79); fel Am Inst Chem Engrs (pres, 71); Asn Coop Eng. *Res:* Thermodynamics; distillation; agitation; fluid flow and measurement; nuclear engineering; radiation chemical processing; published 110 articles and books. *Mailing Add:* Dept of Chem Eng Univ of Mich Ann Arbor MI 48109

MARTIN, JULIA MAE, b Snow Hill, Md, Nov 9, 24. BIOCHEMISTRY. *Educ:* Tuskegee Inst, BS, 46, MS, 48; Pa State Univ, PhD(biochem), 63. *Prof Exp:* Instr chem, Tuskegee Inst, 48-49; from instr to asst prof, Fla Agr & Mech Univ, 49-59; assoc prof, Tuskegee Inst & res assoc, Carver Res Found, 63-66; actg dean, Grad Sch & A&M Col, 74-76, PROF CHEM, SOUTHERN UNIV, BATON ROUGE, 66-, DEAN COL SCI, 78- *Mem:* Am Chem Soc; AAAS; fel Am Inst Chemists; NY Acad Sci; Nat Inst Sci. *Res:* Biochemical abnormalities of red blood cells of patients with hemolytic disorders. *Mailing Add:* Dept of Chem Southern Univ Box 9608 Baton Rouge LA 70813

MARTIN, JULIO MARIO, b Salta, Arg, Sept 16, 22; m 53; c 3. PHYSIOLOGY. *Educ:* Nat Univ La Plata, MD, 50. *Prof Exp:* Res asst, Inst Biol & Exp Med, Univ Arg, 51-55; assoc prof physiol, Nat Univ La Plata, 56-60; res fel exp path, Wash Univ, 61-63; asst prof, Univ Toronto, 63-71; asst scientist, 63-70, assoc scientist, 70-75, SR SCIENTIST, RES INST, HOSP SICK CHILDREN, 75-; assoc prof, 71-79, PROF PHYSIOL & PEDIAT, UNIV TORONTO, 79- *Concurrent Pos:* Squibb res fel, 51-53. *Mem:* Am Diabetes Asn; Can Physiol Soc; Arg Med Asn; Arg Physiol Soc; Endocrine Soc. *Res:* Experimental diabetes; pancreatic islets transplantation; insulin synthesis and release; neuroendocrine control of insulin secretion; relationship between growth hormone and beta-cells activity. *Mailing Add:* Hosp for Sick Children Res Inst 555 University Ave Toronto ON M5G 1X8 Can

MARTIN, KATHRYN HELEN, b Hartford, Conn, Oct 5, 40. HISTOPHYSIOLOGY. *Educ:* Cath Univ Am, AB, 62; Cornell Univ, PhD(zool), 73. *Prof Exp:* Asst prof, 72-77, ASSOC PROF ZOOL, STATE UNIV NY COL OSWEGO, 77- *Mem:* Sigma Xi; Am Soc Mammalogists; AAAS. *Res:* Histophysiological analysis of reproductive and stress phenomena in small mammals. *Mailing Add:* Dept of Zool State Univ NY Col Piez Hall Oswego NY 13126

MARTIN, KENNETH EDWARD, b Cheney, Kans, Apr 5, 44; m 65; c 1. MATHEMATICS. *Educ:* St Benedict's Col, Kans, BA, 64; Ind Univ, Bloomington, MA, 66; Univ Notre Dame, PhD(math), 70. *Prof Exp:* From asst prof to assoc prof math, Gonzaga Univ, 70-77; ASSOC PROF MATH & HEAD DEPT, VALDOSTA STATE COL, 77- *Mem:* Math Asn Am. *Res:* Group theory and its generalizations; algebraic number theory. *Mailing Add:* Dept of Math & Comput Sci Valdosta State Col Valdosta GA 21629

MARTIN, KENNETH JOHN, b New York, NY, July 16, 31; m 74; c 5. CLINICAL CHEMISTRY, ANALYTICAL CHEMISTRY. *Educ:* Univ St Louis, BS, 53; Univ Wis, PhD(electrochem), 60. *Prof Exp:* Res chemist, Redstone Res Labs, Ala, 60-69, tech liaison, Micromedic Systs, 70-71 & Res Div, 72-74, DIR INT OPERS, MICROMEDIC SYSTS, INC, ROHM AND HAAS CO, 74- *Mem:* Am Chem Soc; Am Asn Clin Chem. *Res:* Clinical chemistry; electroanalytical chemistry. *Mailing Add:* 102 Witmer Rd Horsham PA 19044

MARTIN, KUMIKO OIZUMI, b Chiba, Japan, Jan 17, 41; m 73. BIOCHEMISTRY, NUTRITION. *Educ:* Univ Tokyo, BA, 63, PhD(biochem), 70; Ochanomizu Univ, MS, 65. *Prof Exp:* Lectr biochem, Bunka Women's Col, 66-67; fac assoc nutrit, Univ Tokyo, 71-73; fel, 70-71, RES ASSOC, RES INST SKELETOMUSCULAR DIS, HOSP JOINT DIS, 73- *Mem:* AAAS. *Res:* Metabolism of corticosteroids; enzymology. *Mailing Add:* Res Inst Hosp Joint Dis 1919 Madison Ave New York NY 10035

MARTIN, L(AURENCE) ROBBIN, b Annapolis, Md, Sept 21, 39. PHYSICAL CHEMISTRY. *Educ:* Pomona Col, BA, 61; Mass Inst Technol, PhD(phys chem), 66. *Prof Exp:* Noyes fel, Calif Inst Technol, 66-68; asst prof chem, Univ Calif, Riverside, 68-73; MEM TECH STAFF, AEROSPACE CORP, 73- *Mem:* AAAS; Am Phys Soc; Sigma Xi. *Res:* Aqueous and gas phase chemical kinetics of interest in atmospheric chemistry; gas-aerosol interactions; photoacoustic spectroscopy; thermodynamics; molecular beam kinetics. *Mailing Add:* Chem & Physics Lab Aerospace Corp Box 92957 Los Angeles CA 90009

MARTIN, LARRY DEAN, b Bartlett, Nebr, Dec 8, 43; m 67; c 2. VERTEBRATE PALEONTOLOGY. *Educ:* Univ Nebr, BS, 66, MS, 69; Univ Kans, PhD(biol), 73. *Prof Exp:* Asst prof systs & ecol, 72-81, ASSOC PROF SYSTS & ECOL, UNIV KANS, 81-, ASST CUR VERT PALEONT, MUS NATURAL HIST, 72- *Concurrent Pos:* Res affil, Univ Nebr State Mus, 72-; mem, US Nat Working Group Neogene Quaternary Boundry, 74- *Mem:* Soc Vert Paleont; Am Soc Mammalogists; Am Quaternary Asn. *Res:* Fossil history of certain birds, rodents and Saber-toothed cats with emphasis on functional morphology; relationship between climatic history and vertebrate extinctions. *Mailing Add:* Mus of Natural Hist Univ of Kans Lawrence KS 66045

MARTIN, LEROY BROWN, JR, b Elkin, NC, June 6, 26; m 61; c 3. MATHEMATICS, OPERATIONS RESEARCH. *Educ:* Wake Forest Col, BS, 49; NC State Univ, MS, 52; Harvard Univ, MS, 53, PhD(appl math), 58. *Prof Exp:* Appl sci rep, Int Bus Mach Corp, 55-56, spec rep, Serv Bur Corp, 56-59, asst mgr planning & develop, 59-61; from asst prof to assoc prof math, 61-68, PROF COMPUT SCI, DIR COMPUT CTR & ASST PROVOST, NC STATE UNIV 68- *Mem:* AAAS; Am Asn Comput Mach; Inst Mgt Sci. *Res:* Mathematical optimization; numerical analysis; management science. *Mailing Add:* Comput Ctr Box 5445 NC State Univ Raleigh NC 27650

MARTIN, LESTER W, b Edwards, Mo, Aug 15, 23; m 49; c 5. PEDIATRIC SURGERY. *Educ:* Univ Mo, BS, 44, BSc, 47; Harvard Med Sch, MD, 49; Am Bd Surg, dipl, 57. *Prof Exp:* From asst prof to assoc prof, 57-72, PROF SURG, COL MED, UNIV CINCINNATI, 72-; DIR PEDIAT SURG, CHILDREN'S HOSP, 57- *Mem:* Affil fel Am Acad Pediat; fel Am Col Surg; AMA; Brit Asn Paediat Surg. *Res:* Various aspects of surgery of infancy and childhood; esophageal anomalies and Hirschsprung's disease. *Mailing Add:* Children's Hosp 240 Bethesda Ave Cincinnati OH 45229

MARTIN, LOREN GENE, b Danville, Ill, Oct 31, 42; m 67; c 1. CARDIOVASCULAR PHYSIOLOGY, ENDOCRINE PHYSIOLOGY. *Educ:* Ind Univ, AB, 65, PhD(physiol), 69. *Prof Exp:* Res assoc environ physiol, Ind Univ, 69-70; asst prof physiol, Sch Med, Temple Univ, 70-73; asst prof & assoc prof, Col Med, Univ Ill, Chicago & Peoria, 73-78; assoc prof, Va Commonowelth Univ, 78-81; ASSOC PROF PHYSIOL, OKLA COL OSTEOP MED & SURG, 81- *Concurrent Pos:* Adj prof physiol, Gwyned-Mercy Col, 71-73, Philadelphia Community Col, 72-73, Eureka Col, 74-78; adj prof biol, Bradley Univ, 74-78; adj assoc prof optom, Northeastern Okla State Univ, 81- *Mem:* Sigma Xi (nat chmn, 84); Am Physiol Soc; Endocrine Soc; Soc Exp Biol & Med; Int Soc Heart Res. *Res:* Environmental effects upon thyroid and heart metabolism; effects of sex steroids upon coronary flow and myocardial anoxic resistance. *Mailing Add:* Okla Col Ostep Med & Surg 1111 W 17th St PO Box 2280 Tulsa OK 74101

MARTIN, LOUIS NORBERT, b Baton Rouge, La, July 29, 42; m 68; c 1. IMMUNOLOGY. *Educ:* Tulane Univ, BS, 66, PhD(microbiol), 72. *Prof Exp:* ASSOC SCIENTIST IMMUNOL, DELTA REGIONAL PRIMATE CTR, TULANE UNIV, 73-, ADJ ASST PROF MICROBIOL & IMMUNOL, 81- *Res:* Ontogeny of immune function in chickens; oncogenic herpes viruses in non-human primates; function of immunoglobulin D. *Mailing Add:* Delta Regional Primate Res Ctr Tulane Univ Covington LA 70433

MARTIN, M CELINE, b Huntington, Ind, Oct 14, 09. ECOLOGY, BIOLOGY. *Educ:* Ind Univ, BS, 40; Loyola Univ, Ill, MEd, 47; Univ Notre Dame, MS, 48, PhD(biol), 63. *Prof Exp:* Assoc prof, 48-60, chmn dept, 48-81, PROF BIOL, ST FRANCIS COL, IND, 63- *Mem:* Nat Asn Biol Teachers; Ecol Soc Am; Am Inst Biol Sci. *Res:* Life history and ecology of the American wild geranium; effect of anesthesia on the protein levels of blood plasma. *Mailing Add:* Dept of Biol St Francis Col 2701 Spring St Ft Wayne IN 46808

MARTIN, MALCOLM MENCER, b Vienna, Austria, Dec 10, 20; US citizen; m 62; c 3. PEDIATRIC ENDOCRINOLOGY. *Educ:* Univ Durham, MB, BS, 45, MD, 52; Am Bd Internal Med, dipl & cert, 66; FRCP, 72. *Prof Exp:* Resident, Postgrad Sch Med, Univ London, 48-50, first asst, Diabetic & Metab Unit, King's Col Hosp, 50-53, registr, Med Unit, 53-56; physician, Out-Patient Dept, Harriet Lane Home, Johns Hopkins Hosp, 57; asst med, Peter Bent Brigham Hosp, Boston, 57-59; from asst prof to assoc prof pediat, 59-67, PROF PEDIAT & MED, SCH MED, GEORGETOWN UNIV, 67- *Concurrent Pos:* Ministry Educ fel, Eng, 48-49; Lund res fel, Brit Diabetes Asn, 50-51; King's Col res grant, 52-55; Leverhulme res fel, Inst Clin Res, Middlesex Hosp Med Sch, 56; NIH spec res fel, 57-59; Lederle fac award, 62-65; consult endocrinol & metab dis, Childrens' Convalescent Hosp, DC, 63; mem acad staff, Childrens' Hosp, DC, 63; mem Worcester Found, 66. *Mem:* AAAS; Endocrine Soc; Am Pediat Soc; Am Soc Human Genetics; Am Diabetes Asn. *Res:* Endocrinology and metabolism, particularly as related to growth and development. *Mailing Add:* Dept Pediat Georgetown Univ Med Ctr Washington DC 20007

MARTIN, MARGARET EILEEN, b Albright, WVa, Oct 17, 15. BIOCHEMISTRY. *Educ:* WVa Wesleyan Col, BS, 40; Georgetown Univ, MS, 54, PhD(chem), 58. *Prof Exp:* Teacher pub schs, WVa, 35-43; med technician, Emergency Hosp, Wash, DC, 47-49 & St Elizabeth's Hosp, 49-52; chemist, US Food & Drug Admin, 52-54, Phys Biol Lab, Nat Inst Arthritis & Metab Dis, 54, Nat Heart Inst, 54-57 & Food Qual Lab, Agr Res Ctr, USDA, 57-62; chemist, Lab Br, St Elizabeth's Hosp, Dept Health, Educ & Welfare, Wash, DC, 62-78; RETIRED. *Concurrent Pos:* Mem spec ment health res neurochem sect, Nat Inst Ment Health, 70. *Mem:* Am Chem Soc; Am Inst Chemists; Am Soc Microbiol; AAAS. *Res:* Basic biochemistry; mental illness; toxicology; clinical chemistry. *Mailing Add:* 4006 Rickover Rd Silver Spring MD 20902

MARTIN, MARGARET ELIZABETH, b New York, NY, May 6, 12. STATISTICS. *Educ:* Barnard Col, AB, 33; Columbia Univ, MA, 34, PhD(econ), 42. *Prof Exp:* Economist, Div Placement & Unemployment Ins, NY State Dept Labor, 38-42; anal statistician, Statist Stand Div, US Bur Budget, 43-67; asst chief, Statist Policy Div, Off Mgt & Budget, 67-72; exec dir, Nat Acad Sci-Nat Res Coun, 73-78, sr res assoc, Comt Nat Statist, 78-81; CONSULT, 81. *Concurrent Pos:* Exec secy, President's Comt Appraise Employment & Unemployment Statist, 61-62; Nat Acad Sci rep, Int Statist Inst Biennial Meeting, Warsaw, 75. *Honors & Awards:* Dir Except Serv Award, US Bur Budget, 68. *Mem:* AAAS; fel Am Statist Asn (pres, 80); Am Econ Asn; Int Statist Inst; Pop Asn Am. *Res:* Statistical planning and coordination with application especially in demographic and economic statistics; confidentiality of statistical records. *Mailing Add:* Comt Nat Statist Nat Acad Sci-Nat Res Coun Washington DC 20418

MARTIN, MARGARET PEARL, b Duluth, Minn, Apr 22, 15. FOREST BIOMETRY. *Educ:* Univ Minn, BA, 37, MA, 39, PhD(math), 44. *Prof Exp:* Instr biostatist, Univ Minn, 40-41 & Columbia Univ, 42-45; statist consult, Health Dept, NY, 45; asst prof biostatist, Univ Minn, 45-46; from asst prof to assoc prof prev med, Vanderbilt Univ, 47-58; assoc prof biostatist, Sch Hyg & Health, Johns Hopkins Univ, 59-64; asst prof biomet, Univ Minn, St Paul, 67-68; PRIN BIOMETRICIAN, NCENT FOREST EXP STA, USDA, 68- *Mem:* Fel Am Statist Asn; Biomet Soc; Inst Math Statist. *Res:* Applied statistics; biological fields. *Mailing Add:* 1366 Selby Ave St Paul MN 55104

MARTIN, MARK WAYNE, b Twin Falls, Idaho, June 17, 30; m 52; c 5. GENETICS. *Educ:* Univ Idaho, BS, 52; Cornell Univ, MS, 54, PhD(plant breeding), 59. *Prof Exp:* Geneticist, Agr Res Serv, USDA, Utah State Univ, 59-67, GENETICIST, RES & EXTEN CTR, AGR RES SERV, USDA, Wash, 67- *Mem:* Am Soc Hort Sci; Am Phytopath Soc. *Res:* Breeding vegetables; disease resistance, especially resistance to virus diseases. *Mailing Add:* USDA Res & Exten Ctr Prosser WA 99350

MARTIN, MARTIN CLAUDE, b Mulgrave, NS, May 27, 21; m 49; c 4. EXPERIMENTAL SOLID STATE PHYSICS. *Educ:* St Francis Xavier Univ, Can, BSc, 45; Univ Western Ont, MSc, 51; Univ Alta, PhD, 56. *Prof Exp:* Lectr physics, Univ Man, 46-49; lectr, Univ Alta, 51-53, asst prof, 53-56; sci officer, Defense Res Bd, 56-57; asst prof, 57-62, ASSOC PROF PHYSICS, CLARKSON COL TECHNOL, 62- *Mem:* Am Asn Physics Teachers. *Res:* Solid state physics. *Mailing Add:* Dept of Physics Clarkson Col of Technol Potsdam NY 13676

MARTIN, MARVIN D(EWITT), b Lincoln, Nebr, Dec 7, 14; m; c 2. MECHANICAL ENGINEERING. *Educ:* Univ Calif, BS, 37. *Prof Exp:* Mech engr, Marchant Calculating Mach Co, 37-42; staff engr, Tenn Eastman Corp, 43-45; mech engr, Radiation Lab, Univ Calif, 42-43, 45-55, leader weapons eng div, Lawrence Radiation Lab, 55-68; prof mech eng, 68-76, PROF AEROSPACE & MECH ENG, UNIV ARIZ, 76- *Mem:* Fel Am Soc Mech Engrs; Am Phys Soc; Soc Exp Stress Anal. *Res:* Design, especially multidisciplinary aspects; engineering behavior of materials. *Mailing Add:* Dept of Aerospace & Mech Eng Univ of Ariz Tucson AZ 85721

MARTIN, MICHAEL, b Vallejo, Calif, Jan 16, 43; m 67; c 1. POLLUTION BIOLOGY. *Educ:* Univ Calif, Davis, BS, 65; Sacramento State Col, MA, 67; Univ Southern Calif, PhD(biol), 72. *Prof Exp:* Instr physiol & biol, Glendale Community Col, 71; head instr ichthyol & freshwater ecol, NAm Sch Conserv & Ecol, 71, dean, 71-73; assoc water qual biologist, 73-79, SR WATER QUAL BIOLOGIST, CALIF DEPT FISH & GAME, 80- *Mem:* AAAS; Am Soc Ichthyol & Herpet; Am Fisheries Soc; Am Inst Fish Res Biol; Sigma Xi. *Res:* Vertebrate biology, morphology, systematics and ecology of fishes; marine pollution; heavy metal toxicity. *Mailing Add:* 2201 Garden Rd Monterey CA 93940

MARTIN, MICHAEL MCCULLOCH, b Junction City, Kans, Mar 21, 35; m 65; c 2. BIOLOGICAL CHEMISTRY. *Educ:* Cornell Univ, AB, 55; Univ Ill, PhD(org chem), 58. *Prof Exp:* NSF res fel, Mass Inst Technol, 58-59; from instr to assoc prof chem, 59-70, assoc prof zool, 68-70, PROF CHEM & BIOL, UNIV MICH, ANN ARBOR, 70- *Concurrent Pos:* Res chemist, Entom Div, USDA, 64; Sloan Found fel, 66-68; NSF fac fel, 76-77. *Mem:* AAAS; Am Soc Zoologists; Am Inst Biol Sci; Soc Study Evolution. *Res:* Molecular aspects of ecological interactions and physiological adaptations; insect biochemistry. *Mailing Add:* Div Biol Sci Univ Mich Ann Arbor MI 48104

MARTIN, MONROE HARNISH, b Lancaster, Pa, Feb 7, 07; m 32; c 1. APPLIED MATHEMATICS. *Educ:* Lebanon Valley Col, BS, 28; Johns Hopkins Univ, PhD(math), 32. *Hon Degrees:* DSc, Lebanon Valley Col, 58. *Prof Exp:* Nat res fel, Harvard Univ, 32-33; instr math, Trinity Col, 33-36; from asst prof to prof, 36-68, from actg head dept to head dept, 42-53, from actg dir to dir, Inst Fluid Dynamics & Appl Math, 53-68, res prof, 68-71, EMER RES PROF MATH, UNIV MD, COLLEGE PARK, 71- *Concurrent Pos:* Mem, US Nat Comt Theoret & Appl Math, 53-56; exec secy, Div Math, Nat Acad Sci-Nat Res Coun, 55-57 & 58-59, chmn comt appl math, 58-59, mem, 60-61; Guggenheim fel, 60; hon lectr, Univ St Andrews, 60; consult, Naval Ord Lab. *Mem:* Am Math Soc; Math Asn Am. *Res:* Matrices; dynamics; ergodic theory; mathematical theory of the flow of a compressible fluid; partial differential equations; the flow of a viscous fluid mathematical biology; chemical transport through cells. *Mailing Add:* RR 2 Box 64 Denton MD 21629

MARTIN, MURRAY JOHN, nuclear physics, see previous edition

MARTIN, NANCY CAROLINE, b Chicago, Ill, Feb 5, 48. MOLECULAR BIOLOGY, GENETICS. *Educ:* Pitzer Col, AB, 70; Harvard Univ, AM, 72, PhD(biol), 74. *Prof Exp:* Fel biochem, Univ Chicago, 74-77; asst prof biochem, Univ Minn, 77-79; ASST PROF BIOCHEM, UNIV TEX HEALTH SCI CTR, DALLAS, 79- *Concurrent Pos:* Fel, Am Cancer Soc, 75-77. *Mem:* Am Soc Cell Biol; Am Soc Biol Chemists. *Res:* Organelle biogenesis, control of eukaryotic gene expression; ribonucleic acid, transfer structure and function. *Mailing Add:* Univ Tex Health Sci Ctr 5323 Harry Hines Blvd Dallas TX 75235

MARTIN, NATHANIEL FRIZZEL GRAFTON, b Wichita Falls, Tex, Oct 10, 28; m 54; c 2. ERGODIC THEORY, REAL VARIABLES. *Educ:* NTex State Col, BS, 49, MS, 50; Iowa State Col, PhD(math), 59. *Prof Exp:* Asst math, NTex State Col, 49-50; instr, Midwestern Univ, 50-52; asst, Iowa State Col, 55-58, instr, 58-59; from instr to asst prof, 59-64, asst chmn dept, 74-75, assoc dean grad sch arts & sci, 75-81, ASSOC PROF MATH, UNIV VA, 64- . *Concurrent Pos:* NSF fac fel & res assoc, Univ Calif, Berkeley, 65-66; vis lectr, Copenhagen Univ, 69-7O; consult ed, McGraw-Hill Book Co, 72-79; vis fel, Univ Warwick, 82. *Mem:* Am Math Soc; Math Asn Am. *Res:* Analysis; real function theory and measure theory, particularly differentiation of set functions; ergodic theory; entropy; isomorphisms of dynamical systems. *Mailing Add:* Dept of Math Univ of Va Charlottesville VA 22903

MARTIN, NED HAROLD, b New Brunswick, NJ, May 18, 45. BIO-ORGANIC CHEMISTRY. *Educ:* Denison Univ, AB, 67; Duke Univ, PhD(org chem), 72. *Prof Exp:* Chemist, Res Triangle Inst, 69-70; asst prof, 72-80, PROF ORG CHEM, UNIV NC, WILMINGTON, 80- *Mem:* Am Chem Soc; AAAS. *Res:* Singlet oxygen chemistry of enamines; alkaloid biosynthesis; novel photochemical syntheses of natural products. *Mailing Add:* Dept Chem PO Box 3725 Univ of NC Wilmington NC 28406

MARTIN, NORMAN MARSHALL, b Chicago, Ill, Jan 16, 24; m 50; c 3. SYSTEMS OF LOGIC. *Educ:* Univ Chicago, MA, 47; Univ Calif, Los Angeles, PhD(philos), 52. *Prof Exp:* Instr philos, Univ Ill, 50-51 & Univ Calif, Los Angeles, 52-53; res assoc, Willow Run Res Ctr, Mich, 53-55; mem tech staff, Space Tech Labs, Thompson-Ramo-Wooldridge, Inc, 55-59, head logic tech group, 59-61; mem tech staff & bd dirs, Logicon, Inc, 61-65, treas, 62-65; assoc prof, 66-68, res scientist, Comput Ctr, 66-71, PROF PHILOS & COMPUT SCI, UNIV TEX, AUSTIN, 68-, PROF ELEC ENG, 74- *Concurrent Pos:* Lectr, Univ Calif, Los Angeles, 57-65; consult, Logicon, Inc, 65-74; chmn dept comput sci, Univ Tex, 75-78. *Mem:* Am Math Soc; Math Asn Am; Asn Symbolic Logic; Asn Comput Mach; Am Philos Asn. *Res:* Systems, organization and logical design of digital computing equipment; missile guidance system engineering; applications of digital equipment; mathematical logic, especially many-valued logic; philosophy of language; switching theory. *Mailing Add:* 4423 Crestway Dr Austin TX 78731

MARTIN, PAUL BAIN, b Nixon, Tex, Nov 24, 46; m 71; c 3. ENTOMOLOGY. *Educ:* Tex A&M Univ, BS, 69, MS, 71; Univ Fla, PhD(entom), 76. *Prof Exp:* Assoc entom, Agr Res & Educ Ctr, Quincy, Univ Fla, 71-73; entomologist & fieldman, Peggie Martin & Assocs, Pearsall, Tex, 75-76; asst prof entom, Univ Ga, 77-81; SPECIALIST IN ENTOM, INST INTERAM DE COOPERACAO PARA AGR, OFF AGR SERV, CAMPO GRANDE, BRAZIL, 81- *Concurrent Pos:* Consult, cotton, grain sorghum pest mgt; res grant award, Univ Ga, 80. *Mem:* Entom Soc Am; AAAS; Int Org Biol Control Noxious Animals & Plants. *Res:* Spittlebug-pasture management in Brazil; host plant resistance habitat management, biological control (fungus) and integrated pest systems management; dynamics of populations of three noctuids; biological control of cotton pests. *Mailing Add:* EMBRAPA-CNPGC Cx Postal 15Y 79100 Campo Grande MS Brazil

MARTIN, PAUL CECIL, b Brooklyn, NY, Jan 31, 31; m 57; c 3. STATISTICAL & CONDENSED MATTER THEORY. *Educ:* Harvard Univ, AB, 51, AM, 52, PhD(physics), 54. *Prof Exp:* NSF res fel, Univ Birmingham, UK, 55 & Inst Theoret Physics, Denmark, 56; from asst prof to prof physics, 56-82, chmn dept, 72-75, JOHN HASBROUCK VAN VLECK PROF PURE & APPL PHYSICS, HARVARD UNIV, 82-, DEAN, DEPT APPL SCI, 77-, ASSOC DEAN, FAC ARTS & SCI, 81- *Concurrent Pos:* Res fel, Sloan Found, 59-62; vis prof, Ecole Normale Superieure, 63 & 66; ed, J Math Physics, 63-66, Ann Physics, 68-, Transp Theory & Statist Physics, 71- & J Statist Physics, 75-79; Guggenheim Found fel, 65 & 71; vis prof, Univ Paris, 71; consult, Brookhaven Nat Lab; mem adv bd, Nat Inst Theoret Physics, Santa Barbara, 80-82, chmn, 78-80; mem bd dirs, Asn Univ Res Astron, 78-, bd trustees, Assoc Univ Inc, 81- *Mem:* Fel Nat Acad Sci; Am Acad Arts & Sci; Am Phys Soc; AAAS; NY Acad Arts & Sci. *Res:* Quantum theory of fields; physics of solids and fluids; statistical physics. *Mailing Add:* Dept of Physics Harvard Univ Cambridge MA 02138

MARTIN, PAUL JOSEPH, b Hammond, Ind, May 22, 36; m 60; c 4. PHYSIOLOGY, BIOMEDICAL ENGINEERING. *Educ:* Univ Tex, Austin, BS, 61; Drexel Univ, MS, 62; Case Western Res Univ, PhD(biomed eng), 67. *Prof Exp:* Res fel cardiovasc physiol, Latter Day Saints Hosp, Salt Lake City, 62-63; biomed res engr, Technol Inc, Dayton, 63-64; res assoc, 67-73, HEAD BIOENG SECT, CARDIOVASC PHYSIOL, MT SINAI HOSP, 73- *Concurrent Pos:* Consult, Cleveland Clin Found, 70-72; mem chmn, Res Study Sect, Am Heart Asn, 73; asst assoc prof, Case Western Reserve Univ, Dept Physiol & Biomed Eng, 67-, assoc ed, Am J Physiol, 75-, ed bd, Circulation Res, 76-, teaching consult, Ohio Col Podiatric Med, 73- *Mem:* Am Heart Asn; Am Physiol Soc; Biomed Eng Soc; Inst Elec & Electronics Engrs; Sigma Xi. *Res:* Cardiovascular physiology; nervous control of the heart; applied pharmacokinetics; computers in medicine. *Mailing Add:* Mt Sinai Hosp University Circle Cleveland OH 44106

MARTIN, PAUL SCHULTZ, b Allentown, Pa, Aug 22, 28; m 50; c 3. ECOLOGY. *Educ:* Cornell Univ, BA, 51; Univ Mich, MA, 53, PhD, 56. *Prof Exp:* Rackham fel, Univ Mich & Yale Univ, 55-56; Nat Res Coun Can res fel, Univ Montreal, 56-57; res assoc palynol, 57-62, assoc prof, 62-68, PROF PALYNOL & CHIEF SCIENTIST, PALEOENVIRON STUDIES,

GEOCHRONOL LABS, UNIV ARIZ, 68- *Concurrent Pos:* Guggenheim fel, 65-66. *Mem:* AAAS; Soc Study Evolution; Am Soc Nat; Ecol Soc Am. *Res:* Pleistocene biogeography; pollen stratigraphy; faunal extinction and its causes. *Mailing Add:* Dept of Geosci Univ of Ariz Tucson AZ 85721

MARTIN, PETER GORDON, b Owen Sound, Ont, Sept 19, 47; m 80; c 1. ASTROPHYSICS. *Educ:* Univ Toronto, BSc, 68, MSc, 69; Univ Cambridge, PhD(astron), 72. *Prof Exp:* From asst prof to assoc prof, 72-80, PROF ASTRON, UNIV TORONTO, 80- *Mem:* Int Astron Union; Can Astron Soc. *Res:* Interstellar dust; optical polarization; galactic nuclei; late-type stars. *Mailing Add:* Dept of Astron 60 St George St Toronto ON M5S 1A1 Can

MARTIN, PETER WILSON, b Glasgow, Scotland, Jan 7, 38; m 65. NUCLEAR PHYSICS. *Educ:* Glasgow Univ, BSc, 60, PhD(nuclear physics), 64. *Prof Exp:* Asst lectr physics, Univ Glasgow, 64-65; from asst prof to assoc prof, 65-80, PROF PHYSICS, UNIV BC, 81- *Res:* Nuclear orientation; solid state physics; biophysics. *Mailing Add:* Dept of Physics Univ of BC Vancouver BC V6T 2A6 Can

MARTIN, RALPH H(ARDING), b Youngstown, Ohio, Dec 22, 23; m 45; c 2. CHEMICAL ENGINEERING. *Educ:* Carnegie Inst Technol, BS, 44, MS, 49. *Prof Exp:* Asst proj engr res & develop, Consol Coal Co, 48-53, supvr, Pittsburgh Coke & Chem Co, 53-55, gen mgr, Pitt-Consol Chem Co, 55-58; vpres, Dixon Chem & Res Corp & Dixon Chem Industs, Inc, 58-59; asst to pres, Standard Packaging Corp, 59-60, vpres res & develop, 60-64; exec vpres, gen mgr & dir, C H Dexter & Sons, Inc, 64-66, vchmn, Dexter Int SA, Belg, 65-66, pres, C H Dexter & Sons Co & vpres & dir, Dexter Corp, 66-76, PRES, C H DEXTER DIV, DEXTER CORP, 76- *Mem:* Am Chem Soc; Am Inst Chem Engrs. *Res:* Pulp and paper; packaging materials; graphic arts; hydrocarbon vapors; coal gasification; low temperature carbonization of coal; tar chemicals and refined tar products; spectroscopic analysis; smokeless rocket propellants. *Mailing Add:* C H Dexter Div One Elm St Windsor Locks CT 06096

MARTIN, RANDOLPH J, b Waltham, Mass, July 20, 42; m 66; c 4. ROCK MECHANICS. *Educ:* Boston Col, BS, 64; Mass Inst Technol, MS, 68, PhD(geol), 71. *Prof Exp:* Res assoc, Univ Colo, Boulder, 73-78; ASSOC PROF GEOPHYSICS, PA STATE UNIV, 78- *Concurrent Pos:* Res award, US Nat Comt Rock Mech, 72. *Mem:* Am Geophys Union. *Res:* Chemical effect (stress corrosion) of pore water pressure on the deformation and failure of brittle rocks at temperatures to 500 degrees celcius and effective confining pressures to 1500 bars; stress and volumetric strain on magnetic susceptibility of rocks during cyclic loading and fracture tests at confining pressures to 2000 bars. *Mailing Add:* Dept Geosci Pa State Univ University Park PA 16802

MARTIN, RICHARD ALAN, fluid mechanics, heat transfer, see previous edition

MARTIN, RICHARD BLAZO, b Winchendon, Mass, July 1, 17; m 41; c 4. CHEMISTRY, SCIENCE ADMINISTRATION. *Educ:* Clark Univ, AB, 39, AM, 40, PhD(chem), 49. *Prof Exp:* From instr to asst prof chem, Clark Univ, 46-53; chemist, Res Br, Oak Ridge Opers, AEC, 53-57, chief, 57-59, dep dir lab & univ div, 59-72, asst br chief, Waste Mgt Br, Res & Tech Support Div, 72-73, phys scientist, Classification & Tech Support Br, Oak Ridge Opers, 73-77; RETIRED. *Concurrent Pos:* Consult, US Dept Energy, 78-, Los Alamos Tech Assoc Inc, 81- *Mem:* Am Chem Soc; Am Nuclear Soc; Sigma Xi; AAAS; NY Acad Sci. *Res:* Radiochemical processing; isotopic separations; reactions of aliphatic diazo compounds with alicyclic ketones; synthesis of alicyclic ketones; spectrophotometric analysis. *Mailing Add:* 117 Meadow Rd Oak Ridge TN 37830

MARTIN, RICHARD HADLEY, JR, b Worcester, Mass, May 15, 24; m 46; c 3. POLYMER CHEMISTRY. *Educ:* Worcester Polytech Univ, BS, 45; Princeton Univ, MS, 47. *Prof Exp:* Res chemist, Plastics Div, 47-58, RES SPECIALIST, HYDROCARBONS & POLYMERS DIV, MONSANTO CO, 58- *Mem:* Am Chem Soc; AAAS. *Res:* Polymerization, processing and analytical characterization of high polymers. *Mailing Add:* 57 Brewster St Springfield MA 01119

MARTIN, RICHARD HARVEY, b LaPorte, Ind, Aug 27, 32; m 54; c 2. MEDICINE, PHYSIOLOGY. *Educ:* Johns Hopkins Univ, 50-53; Univ Rochester, MD, 57. *Prof Exp:* Intern, Strong Mem Hosp, 57-58; resident, Univ Wash, 58-59 & 61-62, asst med, Div Cardiol, 62-65; asst prof med, 65-68, assoc prof med & physiol, 68-73, dir coronary care unit, 69-75, PROF MED, SCH MED, UNIV MO-COLUMBIA, 73-, DIR DIV CARDIOL, 70- *Concurrent Pos:* Fel, Coun Clin Cardiol, Am Heart Asn; res fel med, Div Cardiol, Univ Wash, 62-64; res fel physiol & biophys, 64-65. *Mem:* Sigma Xi; fel Am Col Cardiol; Am Fedn Clin Res; fel Am Col Physicians. *Res:* Hemodynamic and clinical observations in acute myocardial infarction; ventricular aneurysm; left ventricular function; effect of atrial systole in man. *Mailing Add:* Div of Cardiol C7A Univ of Mo Med Ctr Columbia MO 65201

MARTIN, RICHARD HUGO, b Hanover, Pa, Aug 16, 36; m 59; c 2. PHYSICAL CHEMISTRY. *Educ:* Gettysburg Col, AB, 58; Pa State Univ, PhD(chem), 65. *Prof Exp:* Res assoc fel ion molecule res, Pa State Univ, 66-67; sr res chemist, Chem Div, 67-69, sr res chemist, Ecusta Paper Div, 69-74, res assoc, Fine Paper & Film Group, 74-75, sr res assoc, Ecusta Paper & Film Group, 75-78, RES MGR, OLIN CORP, 78- *Mem:* Am Chem Soc; Sigma Xi. *Res:* Energetics and kinetics of organic reactions; homogeneous and heterogeneous catalysis; reaction mechanisms and substituent effects; vapor phase synthesis; photochemical synthesis; instrumental measurements of dynamic systems; analysis of cigarette smoke; cigarette papers. *Mailing Add:* 168 Glen Cannon Dr Pisgah Forest NC 28768

MARTIN, RICHARD LEE, b Garden City, Kans, Oct 13, 50. PHYSICAL CHEMISTRY, QUANTUM CHEMISTRY. *Educ:* Kans State Univ, BS, 72; Univ Calif, Berkeley, PhD(chem), 76. *Prof Exp:* Res & teaching asst chem, Univ Calif, Berkeley, 72-76; res assoc, Univ Wash, 76-78; MEM STAFF CHEM, LOS ALAMOS SCI LAB, UNIV CALIF, 78- *Concurrent Pos:* Chaim Weizmann fel, Univ Wash, 77-78. *Mem:* Am Chem Soc; Am Phys Soc; Sigma Xi. *Res:* Electronic structure of molecules; interaction of light with matter, especially photoabsorption and photoionization processes. *Mailing Add:* Theoret Div MS 569 Los Alamos Sci Lab Los Alamos NM 87545

MARTIN, RICHARD MCFADDEN, b Somerville, Tenn, Aug 19, 42; m 64; c 2. PHYSICS. *Educ:* Univ Tenn, Knoxville, SB, 64; Univ Chicago, MS, 66, PhD(physics), 69. *Prof Exp:* Mem tech staff, Bell Tel Labs, 69-71; SCIENTIST, XEROX PALO ALTO RES CTR, 71- *Mem:* Am Phys Soc. *Res:* Solid state physics, mainly lattice dynamics of insulators, interaction of light with insulators and semiconductors. *Mailing Add:* Xerox Palo Alto Res Ctr 3333 Coyote Hill Rd Palo Alto CA 94304

MARTIN, RICHARD MCKELVY, b Los Angeles, Calif, Jan 26, 36; m 54, 74; c 3. PHYSICAL CHEMISTRY. *Educ:* Univ Calif, Riverside, BA, 59; Univ Wis, PhD(phys chem), 63. *Prof Exp:* NIH fel, Harvard Univ, 63-65; from asst prof to assoc prof, 65-79, PROF CHEM, UNIV CALIF, SANTA BARBARA, 79- *Mem:* AAAS; Am Chem Soc; Am Phys Soc. *Res:* Photochemistry; molecular beams; electronic energy transfer; surface chemistry; reactions of electronically excited atoms and molecules with crossed molecular beams and with surfaces. *Mailing Add:* Dept of Chem Univ of Calif Santa Barbara CA 93106

MARTIN, ROBERT ALLEN, b New York, NY, Feb 19, 44; m 69. VERTEBRATE PALEOBIOLOGY, VERTEBRATE PHYSIOLOGICAL ECOLOGY. *Educ:* Hofstra Univ, BA, 65; Tulane Univ, La, MS, 67; Univ Fla, PhD(zool), 69. *Prof Exp:* Asst prof biol, SDak Sch Mines & Technol, 69-72; from asst prof to assoc prof, 72-81, PROF BIOL, FAIRLEIGH DICKINISON UNIV, 81- *Concurrent Pos:* Sigma Xi grant, SDak Sch Mines & Technol, 70-71; NSF grants, 70-72. *Mem:* Soc Study Evolution; AAAS; Soc Vert Paleont; Am Soc Mammal; Am Quaternary Asn. *Res:* Mammalian evolution, ecology, physiology. *Mailing Add:* Dept of Biol Fairleigh Dickinson Univ Madison NJ 07940

MARTIN, ROBERT BRUCE, b Chicago, Ill, Apr 29, 29; m 53. BIOPHYSICAL CHEMISTRY, BIOINORGANIC CHEMISTRY. *Educ:* Northwestern Univ, BS, 50; Univ Rochester, PhD(phys chem), 53. *Prof Exp:* Asst prof chem, Am Univ Beirut, 53-56; res fel, Calif Inst Technol, 56-57 & Harvard Univ. 57-59; from asst prof to assoc prof chem, 59-65, chmn dept, 68-71, PROF CHEM, UNIV VA, 65- *Concurrent Pos:* NIH spec fel. Oxford Univ, 61-62; prog dir molecular biol sect, NSF, 65-66. *Mem:* AAAS; Am Chem Soc. *Res:* Structure, equilibrium and mechanism investigations of systems with biological interest; metal ion interactions with proteins and nucleic acids; nuclear magnetic resonance studies; optical activity of transition metal ion complexes and disulphides. *Mailing Add:* Dept of Chem Univ of Va Charlottesville VA 22901

MARTIN, ROBERT EDWARD, JR, b Flint, Mich, Jan 9, 31; m 53; c 3. FORESTRY. *Educ:* Marquette Univ, BS, 53; Univ Mich, BS, 58, MF, 59, PhD(forestry), 63. *Prof Exp:* Res forester, Southern Forest Fire Lab, US Forest Serv, Ga, 60-63; from asst prof to prof wood technol & forest fires, Va Polytech Inst & State Univ, 63-71; prof forest resources, Col Forest Resources, Univ Wash, 71-75, res physicist, 71-75, PROJ LEADER & SUPVR RES FORESTER, US FOREST SERV, 75- *Concurrent Pos:* NSF-Soc Wood Sci & Technol vis scientist wood sci, Univ Minn, 71, Univ Idaho & Washington Univ, 72. *Mem:* AAAS; Forest Prod Res Soc; Sigma Xi; Soc Am Foresters. *Res:* Forest fire physics, effects and behavior; forest fire and fuel management; bark structure, properties and utilization. *Mailing Add:* Silviculture Lab 1027 NW Trenton Ave Bend OR 97701

MARTIN, ROBERT EUGENE, b Monterey, Tenn, July 19, 30; m 56; c 2. ANIMAL ECOLOGY. *Educ:* Tenn Tech Univ, BS, 52; Univ Tenn, MS, 59, PhD(zool), 63. *Prof Exp:* From asst prof to assoc prof, 63-72, PROF BIOL, TENN TECHNOL UNIV, 72- *Mem:* Ecol Soc Am; Am Fisheries Soc. *Res:* Fish and insect population dynamics; biometrics; fish scale structure and development. *Mailing Add:* Dept of Biol Box 52A Tenn Technol Univ Cookeville TN 38501

MARTIN, ROBERT FRANCOIS CHURCHILL, b Ottawa, Ont, Nov 3, 41; m 63; c 3. GEOLOGY. *Educ:* Univ Ottawa, Ont, BSc, 63; Pa State Univ, MS, 66; Stanford Univ, PhD(geol), 69. *Prof Exp:* Res assoc geol, Stanford Univ, 68-70; asst prof, 70-74, ASSOC PROF GEOL, MCGILL UNIV, 74- *Concurrent Pos:* Ed, Can Mineralogist, 78- *Mem:* Mineral Soc Am; Mineral Asn Can; Swiss Soc Mineral & Petrog. *Res:* Igneous and metamorphic mineralogy and petrology. *Mailing Add:* Dept Geol Sci McGill Univ Montreal PQ H3A 2T5 Can

MARTIN, ROBERT FREDERICK, b Weehawken, NJ, Nov 10, 38; m 60; c 3. VERTEBRATE ZOOLOGY, ECOLOGY. *Educ:* Fairleigh Dickinson Univ, BS, 60; Univ Tex, Austin, MA, 64, PhD(zool), 69. *Prof Exp:* Res sci asst zool, Univ, 64-65, CUR VERT, TEX MEM MUS, UNIV TEX, AUSTIN, 69-, DIR, TEXAS NAT HIST LAB, 80- *Concurrent Pos:* Lectr zool, Univ Tex, Austin, 75- *Mem:* Soc Study Evolution; AAAS; Am Soc Ichthyologists & Herpetologists; Am Ornithologists Union. *Res:* Reproductive ecology of reptiles and birds; anuran morphology and evolution; human impact on vertebrate populations; ecology of endangered species; Yucatan avifauna. *Mailing Add:* Cur Vert Tex Mem Mus 24th & Trinity Austin TX 78705

MARTIN, ROBERT G, b New York, NY, May 21, 35; m 60; c 2. VIROLOGY, CELL BIOLOGY. *Educ:* Harvard Univ, AB, 56, Med Sch, MD, 60. *Prof Exp:* SCIENTIST, NAT INST HEALTH, 60- *Mem:* Am Soc Biol Chemists; Am Soc Microbiol; Genetics Soc; Am Soc Virologists; AAAS. *Res:* Molecular biology of cellular and viral DNA replication; mechanisms of the control of cellular proliferation. *Mailing Add:* Molecular Biol Lab NIH 9000 Rockville Pike Bethesda MD 20014

MARTIN, ROBERT LAWRENCE, b Washington, DC, Nov 18, 33; m 55. MAMMALOGY, ZOOLOGY. *Educ:* Univ Maine, BS, 56; Kans State Univ, MS, 59; Univ Conn, PhD, 71. *Prof Exp:* Teacher high sch, Maine, 56-57; from instr to asst prof anat & biol, State Univ NY Col Plattsburgh, 61-64; collabr, Great Smoky Mountain Nat Park, Nat Park Serv, Tenn, 64-65; assoc prof, 66-71, PROF MAMMAL & BIOL, UNIV MAINE, FARMINGTON, 71- *Concurrent Pos:* Res assoc, Mt Washington Observ, NH, 68-74; ed, Bat Res News, 70-75; res assoc, Univ Conn Paraguayan Exped, 73; mem, Univ Conn Chaco Exped, 74 & 75; mem, Ind Bat Recovery Team, US Fish & Wildlife Serv, 75-; hon consult, Chiropiera Specialist Group, Int Union for the Conserv of Nature and Natural Resources, 76- *Mem:* Fel AAAS; Am Soc Mammal; NY Acad Sci; Mammal Soc Brit Isles; fel Zool Soc London. *Res:* Comparative vertebrate anatomy; bat studies; mammalian natural history. *Mailing Add:* Cape Cod Hill New Sharon ME 04955

MARTIN, ROBERT LEONARD, b Seattle, Wash, July 14, 19; m 46; c 4. PHYSICS. *Educ:* Reed Col, BA, 41; Univ Mich, MS, 47, PhD(physics), 56. *Prof Exp:* Res systs analyst, Willow Run Res Lab, Univ Mich, 50-52; asst prof physics, Reed Col, 56-62; assoc prof, 62-74, PROF PHYSICS, LEWIS & CLARK COL, 74-, CHMN DEPT, 63- *Mem:* Am Asn Physics Teachers; Am Phys Soc. *Res:* Solid state; logic of physics; optical and electrical properties of ionic solids, especially in silver and alkali halides. *Mailing Add:* Dept of Physics Lewis & Clark Col Portland OR 97219

MARTIN, ROBERT O, b Honolulu, Hawaii, Jan 8, 31; m 56; c 3. BIOCHEMISTRY, ORGANIC CHEMISTRY. *Educ:* Univ San Francisco, BS, 56; Univ Calif, Berkeley, PhD(biochem), 59. *Prof Exp:* USPHS fel chem, Kings Col, Newcastle-on-Tyne, 59-61; chemist, Lawrence Radiation Lab, Univ Calif, 61-65; from asst prof to assoc prof biochem, 65-74, PROF BIOCHEM, UNIV SASK, 74- *Concurrent Pos:* Can Med Res Coun vis scientist, Neurol Inst, London, 72-73. *Mem:* fel Chem Inst Can; Can Fedn Biol Sci. *Res:* Alkaloid structures and biosynthesis; neurochemistry; diabetes and other disorders of carbohydrate metabolism. *Mailing Add:* Dept of Biochem Univ of Sask Saskatoon SK S1H 0W0 Can

MARTIN, ROBERT PAUL, b Hartford, Conn, Mar 10, 43; m 67; c 3. MATHEMATICAL ANALYSIS. *Educ:* Cent Conn State Col, BS, 65, MS, 68; Univ Md, MA, 72, PhD(math), 73. *Prof Exp:* Teacher math, Washington Jr High Sch, New Britain, Conn, 65-66; instr, Northwestern Community Col, 66-69; instr, Univ Pa, 73-76; ASST PROF MATH, MIDDLEBURY COL, 76- *Mem:* Am Math Soc; Math Asn Am. *Res:* Non-abelian harmonic analysis and representation theory of lie groups. *Mailing Add:* Dept of Math Middlebury Col Middlebury VT 05753

MARTIN, ROGER CHARLES, b Janesville, Wis, June 12, 31; m 64. GEOLOGY. *Educ:* Univ Calif, Los Angeles, AB, 53; Univ Idaho, MS, 57; Victoria Univ Wellington, PhD(geol), 63. *Prof Exp:* Geologist, NZ Geol Surv, 59-60 & 63-64; geologist, Calif Dept Water Resources, 64-68; geologist, Earth Resources Opers, NAm Rockwell Corp, 68-73; geologist, Calif State Lands Div, 73-77, GEOLOGIST, CALIF DIV MINES & GEOL, 77-, SR SCIENTIST VOLCANOLOGY & VOLCANO HAZARDS ASSESSMENT COORDR, 80- *Concurrent Pos:* Geol consult, NZ Forest Prod, Ltd, 61-64. *Mem:* Geol Soc Am; Am Geophys Union; Asn Eng Geologists. *Res:* Application of remote sensing to geoscience problems; discrimination of mineral desposits and lithologic bodies by thermal infrared and other multispectral sensors; geothermal research and exploration also environmental problems; program management of statewide assessment of low-moderate temperature geothermal resources. *Mailing Add:* Calif Div Mines and Geol 2815 O St Sacramento CA 95816

MARTIN, RONALD LAVERN, b Devereaux, Mich, Sept 13, 22; m 49; c 6. NUCLEAR PHYSICS. *Educ:* US Naval Acad, BS, 44; Mich State Univ, MS, 48, Univ Chicago, PhD(physics), 52. *Prof Exp:* Res assoc physics, Univ Chicago, 52-53 & Cornell Univ, 53-56; mem staff, Bell Tel Labs, 56-59; sr scientist, TRG, Inc, 59-62; assoc dir particle accelerator div, 62-67, DIR ACCELERATOR DIV, ARGONNE NAT LAB, 67- *Mem:* Fel Am Phys Soc. *Res:* High energy nuclear physics; accelerators; laser development; nonlinear properties of ferrites at microwave frequencies. *Mailing Add:* Accelerator Div Argonne Nat Lab Argonne IL 60439

MARTIN, RONALD LEROY, b Beloit, Wis, Sept 14, 32; m 53; c 3. ANALYTICAL CHEMISTRY. *Educ:* Beloit Col, BS, 53; Univ Wis, MS, 55, PhD, 57. *Prof Exp:* Res chemist, Standard Oil Co (Ind), 57-75; dir additives eval & formulation div, 75-78, DIR, PETROL ADDITIVES & OIL PROD CHEM RES DIV, AMOCO CHEM CO, 78- *Mem:* Am Chem Soc. *Res:* Gas chromatography; spectrochemical analysis; lubricant development. *Mailing Add:* 1013 Summit Hills Lane Naperville IL 60540

MARTIN, ROSS J, b Bay City, Mich, Dec 27, 16; m 41; c 2. MECHANICAL ENGINEERING. *Educ:* Mich State Univ, BS, 40; Univ Ill, MS, 46. *Prof Exp:* Asst mech eng, 41-42, 45-46, from asst prof to assoc prof, 46-53, assoc dir, Eng Exp Sta, 51-58, chmn nuclear eng prog, 58-76, PROF MECH ENG, UNIV ILL, URBANA, 53-, DIR, ENG EXP STA, 58-, ASSOC DEAN, 76- *Concurrent Pos:* Educ consult, AEC, Argonne Nat Lab, Ill; eng consult, UNESCO, Brazil, Chili & Ecuador & USAID, Afghanistan & India. *Mem:* Am Soc Eng Educ; Am Soc Heating, Refrig & Air-Conditioning Engrs; Sigma Xi; Nat Coun Univ Adminrs. *Res:* Applied thermodynamics, including heating, ventilating and air conditioning; heat transfer; fluid flow; systems analysis. *Mailing Add:* 106 Eng Hall Univ Ill 1308 W Green St Urbana IL 61801

MARTIN, ROY A, b Coffee Co, Tenn, Mar 8, 20; m 42; c 2. ELECTRICAL ENGINEERING. *Educ:* Ga Inst Technol, BS, 42, MS, 51. *Prof Exp:* Builder, Fla, 36-37; jr engr, Ga Power Co, 37-42; engr, Western Union Tel Co, NY, 46; res asst, Eng Exp Sta, Ga Inst Technol, 46-47, res engr, asst prof & proj dir indust res, 47-53, spec res eng, 53-65, prin res engr, 65-68, lectr elec eng, 61-68; pres, Packer Eng Assocs, Inc, Ga, 68-71; PRES, ROY A MARTIN ASSOCS, INC, GA, 71- *Concurrent Pos:* Consult, Nat Res Coun, 48 & US Air Force, 57; pvt consult, 52-; asst secy, Res Inst, Ga Inst Technol, 60-68; pres, Hydrol Loader Acceptance Corp, 67- *Mem:* Nat Fire Protection Asn. *Res:* Electro-mechanical devices; instrumentation; patent technology; research administration; principal failure analysis; fire and industrial accident reconstruction and technical investigation; forensic science; materials technology and engineering. *Mailing Add:* 1001 Monroe Dr NE Atlanta GA 30306

MARTIN, ROY JOSEPH, JR, b Lutcher, La, Jan 3, 43; m 67; c 2. NUTRITION, BIOCHEMISTRY. *Educ:* Univ Southwestern La, BS, 64; Univ Fla, MS, 65; Univ Calif, Davis, PhD(nutrit), 70. *Prof Exp:* Asst prof nutrit, 70-74, ASSOC PROF ANIMAL NUTRIT, PA STATE UNIV, UNIVERSITY PARK, 74- *Mem:* Am Dairy Sci Asn; Am Soc Animal Sci. *Res:* Metabolic regulation of growth and development; effects of early nutritional experiences. *Mailing Add:* Dept of Nutrit Pa State Univ University Park PA 16802

MARTIN, RUFUS RUSSELL, b Decatur, Ga, Mar 3, 36; m 61; c 3. INTERNAL MEDICINE, INFECTIOUS DISEASES. *Educ:* Yale Univ, AB, 56; Med Col Ga, MD, 60. *Prof Exp:* NIH fel infectious dis, 65-67; from asst prof to assoc prof med, Sch Med, Ind Univ, Indianapolis, 67-71; assoc prof, 71-75, PROF MED & MICROBIOL, BAYLOR COL MED, 75- *Concurrent Pos:* Attend physician, Vet Admin Hosp, Houston, 71-; NIH career develop award, 75-79. *Mem:* Fel Am Col Physicians; Am Fedn Clin Res; NY Acad Sci; Infectious Dis Soc Am; Am Thoracic Soc. *Res:* Staphylococcal immunology; histamine; lysosomes; leukocytes and inflammation; pulmonary macrophages and smoking. *Mailing Add:* Dept of Med Baylor Col of Med Houston TX 77030

MARTIN, RUSSELL JAMES, b Beaumont, Tex, May 15, 39; m 64; c 2. EPIDEMIOLOGY. *Educ:* Tex A&M Univ, BS, 61, DVM, 63; Univ Mich, MPH, 66. *Prof Exp:* Epidemiol intel serv officer, Ctr Dis Control, USPHS, 63-65, regional pub health vet, 66-72, chief pub health vet, 72-75, COMMUN DIS EPIDEMIOLOGIST, ILL DEPT PUB HEALTH, 75- *Concurrent Pos:* Asst prof vet pub health, Col Vet Med, Univ Ill, 68-72, assoc prof, 72-; clin assoc prof prev med, Peoria Sch Med, Univ Ill, 75- *Mem:* Am Pub Health Asn; Conf Pub Health Vets (pres, 76-77); Am Bd Vet Pub Health; Am Vet Med Asn. *Res:* Zoonotic diseases that occur naturally in the United States, particularly delineating the epidemiology of this group. *Mailing Add:* 219 Wild Rose Lane Rochester IL 62563

MARTIN, SAMUEL CLARK, b McNeal, Ariz, Apr 16, 16; m 44; c 2. RANGE CONSERVATION. *Educ:* Univ Ariz, BS, 42, MS, 47, PhD, 64. *Prof Exp:* Range conservationist, Southwestern Forest & Range Exp Sta, US Forest Serv, 42-49, range conservationist, Cent States Forest Exp Sta, 49-55, prin range scientist, Rocky Mountain Forest & Range Exp Sta, 55-79; PROF RANGE MGT, UNIV ARIZ, 79- *Mem:* Soc Range Mgt. *Res:* Grazing management; noxious plant control; range revegetation. *Mailing Add:* 4402 E Sixth St Tucson AZ 85711

MARTIN, SAMUEL PRESTON, III, b East Prairie, Mo, May 2, 16; m 70; c 3. INTERNAL MEDICINE, COMMUNITY HEALTH. *Educ:* Wash Univ, MD, 41. *Hon Degrees:* MA, Univ Pa, 71. *Prof Exp:* Am Col Physicians fel, Rockefeller Inst, 48-49; Markle Found fel, Duke Univ, 50-55; prof internal med & chmn dept, Univ Fla, 56-62, provost health affairs, 62-69; vis prof health econ, Harvard Univ, 69-71; exec dir, Leonard Davis Inst, 74-77, PROF MED COL MED & PROF HEALTH CARE SYSTS, WHARTON SCH, UNIV PA, 71-; DIR, ROBERT W JOHNSON CLIN SCHOLARS PROG, 74- *Concurrent Pos:* Dir, Fla Regional Med Prog, 67-68; mem comt accreditation, US Off Educ, 68-70; Commonwealth & USPHS fels, Harvard Univ & London Sch Hyg, 69-71; dir, Smith Kline Corp, Philadelphia, 72- *Honors & Awards:* Order of Leopold, Belg. *Mem:* Asn Am Physicians; Am Asn Immunol; Am Col Physicians; Am Fedn Clin Res (vpres, 54); Am Pub Health Asn. *Res:* Immunology microbiology; medical economics. *Mailing Add:* Dept of Community Med Univ of Pa Philadelphia PA 19104

MARTIN, SCOTT ELMORE, b Wilmington, Del, Sept 17, 46; m 71; c 2. FOOD MICROBIOLOGY. *Educ:* Tarkio Col, BA, 68; Wichita State Univ, MS, 70; Kans State Univ, PhD(microbiol), 73. *Prof Exp:* Res asst gen microbiol, Kans State Univ, 70-73; res assoc, Univ Calif, Irvine, 73-75; res assoc, 75-77, asst prof, 77-81, ASSOC PROF FOOD MICROBIOL, UNIV ILL, URBANA, 81- *Mem:* Am Soc Microbiol; Inst Food Technologists; Sigma Xi. *Res:* Examination of sublethally-stressed bacteria; determination of the effects of oxygen toxicity on microbial enumeration; ribosome assembly mechanisms; analysis of the antimutagenic and anticarcinogenic properties of the element selenium. *Mailing Add:* 580 Bevier Hall Univ Ill 905 S Goodwin Ave Urbana IL 61801

MARTIN, SEELYE, b Northampton, Mass, Sept 22, 40. OCEANOGRAPHY. *Educ:* Harvard Univ, BA, 62; Johns Hopkins Univ, PhD(mech), 67. *Prof Exp:* Res assoc oceanog, Mass Inst Technol, 67-69; res asst prof, 69-77, res assoc, 77-79, RES PROF OCEANOG, UNIV WASH, 79- *Mem:* Am Geophys Union; AAAS. *Res:* desalination of sea ice, marginal ice zone processes, Bering Sea ice. *Mailing Add:* Dept of Oceanog MSB-108 Univ of Wash Seattle WA 98195

MARTIN, STANLEY BUEL, b Tulsa, Okla, Oct 21, 27; m 51; c 4. PHYSICAL CHEMISTRY. *Educ:* San Jose State Col, AB, 50. *Prof Exp:* Chemist, US Naval Radiol Defense Lab, 50-61, supvry chemist, 61-66; prin res chemist, URS Corp, 66-69; mgr fire res prog, 69-76, DIR, FIRE RES DEPT, STANFORD RES INST INT, 76- *Mem:* Am Chem Soc; Combustion Inst; Soc Fire Protection Engrs. *Res:* Thermal radiation transport and effects; nuclear weapons effects; fire phenomenology; transient heat conduction in solids; thermal decomposition of organic solids; ignition processes; kinetics of pyrolysis; reactions in unsteady-state systems; combustion and fire protection research. *Mailing Add:* Stanford Res Inst Int 333 Ravenswood Ave Menlo Park CA 94025

MARTIN, STANLEY MORRIS, b Ottawa, Ont, Oct 26, 20; m 44; c 3. BIOCHEMISTRY, MICROBIOLOGY. *Educ:* Univ Toronto, BSA, 44; Univ Wis, MS, 48, PhD(bact), 50. *Prof Exp:* Asst res officer, 50-55, assoc res officer, 55-62, SR RES OFFICER, NAT RES COUN CAN, 62- *Mem:* Can Soc Microbiol; Int Asn Plant Tissue Cult; Am Chem Soc. *Res:* Fermentation biochemistry; production of metabolites by plant cell cultures; enzymes of plant cell cultures; large-scale cultivation of bacteria. *Mailing Add:* 1-169 Holmwood Ottawa ON Can

MARTIN, STEPHEN FREDERICK, b Albuquerque, NM, Feb 8, 46. SYNTHETIC ORGANIC CHEMISTRY. *Educ:* Univ NMex, BS, 68; Princeton Univ, MA, 70, PhD(org chem), 72. *Prof Exp:* Alexander von Humboldt Found fel org chem, Univ Munich, 72-73; NIH fel, Mass Inst Technol, 73-74; ASST PROF ORG CHEM, UNIV TEX, AUSTIN, 74- *Concurrent Pos:* NIH career develop award, 80- *Mem:* The Chem Soc; Am Chem Soc; Sigma Xi. *Res:* Design and development of new synthetic methods; chemistry and total synthesis of natural products, particularly alkaloids and terpenes; heterocyclic chemistry. *Mailing Add:* Dept of Chem Univ of Tex Austin TX 78712

MARTIN, STEPHEN GEORGE, b Eagle Grove, Iowa, Sept 20, 41; m 65; c 2. ENVIRONMENTAL CONSULTING ADMINISTRATION. *Educ:* Univ Wis-Madison, BS, 64; MS, 67; Ore State Univ, PhD(zool), 70. *Prof Exp:* Asst prof zool, Colo State Univ, 70-73; vpres, Ecol Consult, Inc, 73-80; VPRES, ENVIRON RES & TECH INC, 80- *Concurrent Pos:* Affil fac mem, Colo State Univ. *Honors & Awards:* A Brazier Howell Award, Cooper Ornith Soc, 70. *Mem:* AAAS; Ecol Soc Am; Am Ornith Union; Cooper Ornith Soc; The Wildlife Soc. *Res:* Administration of the technical activities of environmental scientists and engineers in applied ecological and environmental research, nationally and internationally; adaptations for niche diversification in vertebrates; analysis of environmental impact; applied ecology; structural analysis of vertebrate communication systems. *Mailing Add:* 7121 County Rd 9 Wellington CO 80549

MARTIN, SUSAN SCOTT, b Paducah, Ky, May 18, 38. PLANT CHEMISTRY. *Educ:* Univ Colo, BA, 60; Utah State Univ, MS, 68; Univ Calif, Santa Cruz, PhD(biol), 73. *Prof Exp:* Res chemist, Dept Wildlife Resources, Utah State Univ, 60-68; PLANT PHYSIOLOGIST, CROPS RES LAB, SCI & EDUC-AGR RES SERV, USDA, 74- *Mem:* Phytochem Soc NAm; Bot Soc Am; AAAS. *Res:* Biochemical aspects of plant-pathogen interaction, including pathogen-produced toxins and phytoalexins; physiological factors affecting sugarbeet quality and sucrose production; resin and glucosinolate chemistry and chemical ecology. *Mailing Add:* Sci & Educ-Agr Res Serv USDA Colo State Univ Ft Collins CO 80523

MARTIN, TELLIS ALEXANDER, b Hickory, NC, May 20, 19; m 49; c 4. ORGANIC CHEMISTRY. *Educ:* Berea Col, BA, 42; Univ Va, MS, 45, PhD(org chem), 48. *Prof Exp:* Asst chem, Berea Col, 40-42, Univ Va, 42-44 & Off Sci Res & Develop, 44-48; res chemist, Gen Aniline & Film Corp, 48-53; sr chemist, 53-63, res assoc, 63-70, sr investr, 70-73, prin investr, 73-76, prin res assoc, 76-80, PRIN RES SCIENTIST, MEAD JOHNSON & CO, 80- *Mem:* AAAS; Am Chem Soc. *Res:* Synthesis of benzalacetophenones; aminoketones and amino alcohols of phenyl, quinoline and phenylquinoline series for possible use as antimalarials, cancer agents and antitubercular drugs; phthalocyanines; phenanthridines; biphenylsulfones; carbohydrates; steric hindrance; ring-chain tautomerism; cysteines; sulfa drugs; hypnotics; betalactams and aspartic acids; anti-inflammatory, fibrinolytic and mucolytic agents; cardiovascular agents. *Mailing Add:* 602 SE 1st St Evansville IN 47713

MARTIN, TERENCE EDWIN, b Adelaide, Australia, Apr 28, 41; m 63; c 2. MOLECULAR BIOLOGY, CELL BIOLOGY. *Educ:* Univ Adelaide, BSc, 62; Cambridge Univ, PhD(biochem), 66. *Prof Exp:* Univ fel, Univ Chicago, 66-68, Am Cancer Soc fel, Univ Wash, 69-70, asst prof, 71-77, ASSOC PROF BIOL, UNIV CHICAGO, 77- *Concurrent Pos:* USPHS res grant, Univ Chicago, 71- *Mem:* Brit Biochem Soc; Am Soc Cell Biol. *Res:* Control of gene expression in eukaryotic cells; nucleic acid synthesis and metabolism; control of protein synthesis; molecular basis of cancer; structure of the cell nucleus and nuclear antigens. *Mailing Add:* Dept of Biol Univ of Chicago Chicago IL 60637

MARTIN, TERRY JOE, b Baxter Springs, Kans, Dec 28, 47; m 66; c 3. PLANT PATHOLOGY. *Educ:* Kans State Col, Pittsburg, BS, 70; Kans State Univ, MS, 71; Mich State Univ, PhD(plant path), 74. *Prof Exp:* asst prof plant path, 74-79, ASST PROF, WHEAT BREEDER, FT HAYS BR EXP STA, KANS STATE UNIV, 79- *Mem:* Am Phytopath Soc; Am Soc Agron; Crop Sci Soc Am. *Res:* Development of improved hard red winter wheat cultivars for Kansas with emphasis on pest resistance. *Mailing Add:* Hays Exp Sta Hays KS 67601

MARTIN, TERRY ZACHRY, b New York, NY, Aug 7, 46. PLANETARY ASTRONOMY. *Educ:* Univ Calif, Berkeley, AB, 67; Univ Hawaii, MS, 69, PhD (astron), 75. *Prof Exp:* Res assoc, Inst Astron, Univ Hawaii, 68-74; res geophysicist planetary astron, Dept Earth & Space Sci, Univ Calif, Los Angeles, 75-79; MEM TECH STAFF, INFRARED INSTRUMENTS SECT, JET PROPULSION LAB, CALIF INST TECHNOL, 79- *Mem:* Am Astron Soc. *Res:* Planetary astronomy, especially atmospheric composition and thermal behavior; design of infrared instruments; testing of infrared detector systems; planetary spectroscopy; pressure induced deuterium absorption, Jupiter and Saturn; Mars atmosphere thermal behavior and opacity. *Mailing Add:* 2031 Ahlin Dr La Canada CA 91011

MARTIN, THEODORE A, electrical engineering, physics, see previous edition

MARTIN, THOMAS A(DDENBROOK), b Cleveland, Ohio, July 7, 24; m 50; c 2. ELECTRONICS. *Educ:* Cleveland State Univ, BEE, 50; Rensselaer Polytech Inst, MEE, 54, PhD(commun), 62. *Prof Exp:* Engr, electro-motive div, Gen Motors Corp, 50; instr electronics, Rensselaer Polytech Inst, 50-55, res assoc, 53-56, asst prof, 55-59; eng specialist, Goodyear Aerospace Corp, 59-63, sr specialist systs eng, 63-68, asst dept mgr weapon syst anal, 68-70; leader strategic progs systs eng, Missile & Surface Radar Div, 70-74, tech dir, Tradex Radar Site, 74-77, STAFF TECH ADV, GOVT SYSTS DEV, RCA CORP, 78- *Concurrent Pos:* Consult, Empire Res Corp, 58-59; lectr, Univ Akron, 65-69. *Mem:* Sr mem Inst Elec & Electronics Engrs; Sigma Xi. *Res:* Navigation; guidance control; missile systems; weapon systems; radar systems; automatic data processing systems. *Mailing Add:* 179 Conawaga Trail Medford Lakes NJ 08055

MARTIN, THOMAS FABIAN JOHN, b Rahway, NJ, June 10, 46; c 2. MOLECULAR ENDOCRINOLOGY, CELL BIOLOGY. *Educ:* Cornell Univ, AB, 68; Harvard Univ, PhD(biophysics), 74. *Prof Exp:* Fel endocrinol, Pharmacol Dept, Harvard Med Sch, 74-78; ASST PROF ZOOL, ZOOL DEPT, UNIV WIS, 78- *Mem:* Endocrine Soc; AAAS. *Res:* Molecular mechanisms by which peptide hormones alter cellular function, including intracellular mediators different from cyclic AMP. *Mailing Add:* Zool Res Bldg Univ Wis 1117 W Johnson St Madison WI 53706

MARTIN, THOMAS GEORGE, III, b Boston, Mass, Jan 14, 31; m 51; c 2. HEALTH PHYSICS. *Educ:* Northeastern Univ, BS, 58; Am Bd Health Physics, dipl, 65. *Prof Exp:* Head radiol safety dept, Controls for Radiation Inc, 58-61, head labs, 61-62; radiation chemist, Mass Inst Technol, 62-63; DIR SAFETY & RADIATION PROTECTION, NATICK LAB, US ARMY, 63- *Concurrent Pos:* Consult tech points of contact, Interdept Comt on Radiation Preservation of Food, 64- *Mem:* Health Physics Soc; Sigma Xi; Conf Radiol Health; NY Acad Sci. *Res:* Induced radioactivity in food sterilized by ionizing radiation; health physics problems associated with particle accelerators; trace metals in foods; activation analysis. *Mailing Add:* 588 Winter St Framingham MA 01701

MARTIN, THOMAS L(YLE), JR, b Memphis, Tenn, Sept 26, 21; m 43; c 2. ELECTRICAL ENGINEERING. *Educ:* Rensselaer Polytech Inst, BEE, 42, MEE, 48; Stanford Univ, PhD(elec eng), 51. *Hon Degrees:* DEng, Rensselaer Polytech Inst, 68. *Prof Exp:* Instr elec eng, Rensselaer Polytech Inst, 46-48; asst prof, Univ NMex, 48-51, assoc prof, 51-53; prof & head dept, Univ Ariz, 53-58, dean, col eng, 58-63; dean, Col Eng, Univ Fla, 63-66; dean, Inst Technol, Southern Methodist Univ, 66-74; PRES, ILL INST TECHNOL, 74- *Concurrent Pos:* Dir, Stewart-Warner, 74-, Inland Steel, 75-, Amsted Industs, 78-, Hyatt Int, 78, Sundstrand Corp, 79, Cherry Elec Prods, 79, Commonwealth Edison, 80 & Kemper Mutual Funds, 81. *Mem:* Nat Acad Engrs; Am Soc Eng Educ; Inst Elec & Electronics Engrs. *Mailing Add:* Off of Pres Ill Inst of Technol Chicago IL 60616

MARTIN, THOMAS WARING, b Cumberland, Md, July 24, 25; m 47; c 4. PHYSICAL CHEMISTRY. *Educ:* Franklin & Marshall Col, BS, 50; Northwestern Univ, PhD(chem), 54. *Prof Exp:* Res fel photochem, Nat Res Coun Can, 54-55; instr chem, Williams Col, Mass, 55-57; from asst prof to assoc prof, 57-66, chmn dept, 67-73, PROF CHEM, VANDERBILT UNIV, 66- *Mem:* AAAS; Am Chem Soc; The Chem Soc; Royal Inst Chem. *Res:* Photochemistry; electron spin resonance and magneto-chemical effects; biochemical oxidoreduction and model systems; chemical kinetics and catalysis; mass spectrometry. *Mailing Add:* Dept of Chem Box 1506/B Vanderbilt Univ Nashville TN 37240

MARTIN, TREVOR IAN, b Southall, Eng, Apr 3, 43; m 68; c 2. ANALYTICAL CHEMISTRY, INDUSTRIAL ORGANIC CHEMISTRY. *Educ:* Royal Inst Chem, grad, 69, ARIC, 74, Cert chem, 76; McMaster Univ, PhD(chem), 74. *Prof Exp:* Anal chemist, Laporte Titanium Ltd, Eng, 64-68; org analyst, 74-79, AREA MGR, ORG CHEM & SPEC CHEM, XEROX RES CTR CAN, LTD, 79- *Mem:* Am Chem Soc; Royal Inst Chem. *Res:* Organic synthesis of electrophotographic dyes and pigments; elucidation of molecular structure and analysis of trace levels of organic and elemental impurities using high performance liquid chromatography and plasma emission spectroscopy; on line liquid chromatography, mass spectrometry. *Mailing Add:* Xerox Res Centre of Can Ltd 2480 Dunwin Dr Mississauga ON L5L 1J9 Can

MARTIN, TRUMAN GLEN, b Wortham, Tex, May 24, 28; m 50; c 3. ANIMAL GENETICS. *Educ:* Tex A&M Univ, BS, 49; Iowa State Univ, MS, 51, PhD(animal breeding & nutrit), 54. *Prof Exp:* Asst dairy husb, Iowa State Univ, 49-51, asst animal breeding, 53-55; from asst prof to assoc prof, 55-63, PROF ANIMAL BREEDING, PURDUE UNIV, 63- *Mem:* Am Dairy Sci Asn; Am Soc Animal Sci; Brit Soc Animal Prod; Sigma Xi. *Res:* Crossbreeding and selection of dairy and beef cattle; factors affecting body composition of swine, sheep and cattle. *Mailing Add:* Dept of Animal Sci Purdue Univ West Lafayette IN 47907

MARTIN, VIRGINIA LORELLE, b Mount Olive, NC, Nov 29, 39. BIOLOGY, PARASITOLOGY. *Educ:* Wake Forest Col, BS, 61; Emory Univ, MS, 63, PhD(biol), 67. *Prof Exp:* Asst prof, 66-72, assoc prof, 77-81, PROF BIOL, QUEENS COL, NC, 81- *Concurrent Pos:* Sr lectr, Univ Calabar, Nigeria, 75-77. *Mem:* AAAS; Am Soc Parasitol; Am Inst Biol Sci. *Res:* fluorescent antibody immunodiagnosis of parasitic diseases; taxonomy and life cycle of Spirorchiidae. *Mailing Add:* Dept of Biol Queens Col Charlotte NC 28274

MARTIN, WAYNE DUDLEY, b Watertown, Ohio, Nov 22, 20; m 53; c 2. GEOLOGY. *Educ:* Marietta Col, BS, 48; Univ WVa, MS, 50; Univ Cincinnati, PhD(geol), 55. *Prof Exp:* Instr geol, Bowling Green State Univ, 51-52; from instr to assoc prof, 52-69, PROF GEOL, MIAMI UNIV, 69- *Mem:* Geol Soc Am; Soc Econ Paleontologists & Mineralogists; Nat Asn Geol Teachers; Am Asn Petrol Geologists; Int Asn Sedimentologists. *Res:* Petrology of the Cincinnatian Series limestone; sedimentary facies of the Dunkard Basin; petrology of the Cambrian System, NW Wind River Basin, Wyo. *Mailing Add:* Dept of Geol Miami Univ Oxford OH 45056

MARTIN, WAYNE HOLDERNESS, b Manchester, Ohio, Mar 15, 31; m 54; c 7. POLYMER CHEMISTRY. *Educ:* Ohio State Univ, BS, 52, PhD(chem), 58. *Prof Exp:* Instr chem, Ohio State Univ, 57-58; from chemist to sr chemist, Plastics Dept, Washington Works, WVa, 58-78, SR RES CHEMIST, PLASTIC PROD & RESINS DEPT, EXP STA, E I DU PONT DE NEMOURS & CO, INC, 78- *Mem:* Am Chem Soc. *Res:* Plastics research and development; industrial hygiene; air pollution. *Mailing Add:* Plastic Prod & Resins Dept Exp Sta B-323 E I du Pont de Nemours & Co Inc Wilmington DE 19898

MARTIN, WILFRED SAMUEL, b Adamsville, Pa, June 11, 10; m 38; c 4. CHEMICAL ENGINEERING. *Educ:* Iowa State Univ, BS, 30; Univ Cincinnati, MS, 38. *Prof Exp:* Analyst, res dept, Procter & Gamble Co, 30, res chemist, 31, develop chem engr, develop dept, 32-36, lab head, 37-42, sect head, 42-47, assoc dir chem div, 48-53, chem dir, 53-54, dir prod develop, Res & Develop Div, 54-57, dir, Soap Prod Div, 57-63, mgr mfg & prod develop, Food Prod Div, 64-71, sr dir res & develop, 71-75; RETIRED. *Mem:* AAAS; Am Chem Soc; Am Inst Chem Engrs; Soc Chem Indust; NY Acad Sci. *Res:* Soap, synthetic detergent, food products; toilet goods and paper manufacture. *Mailing Add:* 504 Hickory Hill Lane Wyoming OH 45215

MARTIN, WILLARD JOHN, b Minneapolis, Minn, May 29, 15; m 42; c 5. PHYSICAL CHEMISTRY. *Educ:* Univ Minn, BS, 37; Cornell Univ, PhD(phys chem), 41. *Prof Exp:* Lab asst, Cornell Univ, 37-41; asst prof in-chg chem dept, Univ Maine, Brunswick Campus, 46-49; prof chem, SDak Sch Mines & Technol, 49-78; RETIRED. *Mem:* Am Chem Soc. *Res:* X-ray diffraction; atomic and molecular structure; general chemistry; computer science. *Mailing Add:* 3902 Ponderosa Trail Rapid City SD 57701

MARTIN, WILLIAM BUTLER, JR, b Winchendon, Mass, Aug 31, 23; m 50; c 3. PHYSICAL ORGANIC CHEMISTRY, SPECTROSCOPY. *Educ:* Clark Univ, AB, 48, AM, 49; Yale Univ, PhD(org chem), 53. *Prof Exp:* Lab instr chem, Clark Univ, 47-49 & Yale Univ, 49-50; fel, Hickrill Res Fedn, NY, 52-53; from asst prof to assoc prof, 53-63, PROF CHEM, UNION COL (NY), 63- *Concurrent Pos:* NIH spec res fel, Sch Advan Studies, Mass Inst Technol, 59-61; res assoc, Swiss Fed Inst Technol, 67-68 & Univ Basel, 74-75 & 81-82. *Mem:* AAAS; Am Chem Soc; Fedn Am Sci; NY Acad Sci. *Res:* Photochemistry; biochemistry; synthetic organic chemistry; electron spin resonance in pi-electron systems. *Mailing Add:* Dept Chem Union Col Schenectady NY 12308

MARTIN, WILLIAM C, agronomy, see previous edition

MARTIN, WILLIAM CLARENCE, b Dayton, Ky, Nov 27, 23; m 47; c 3. PLANT TAXONOMY, FLORISTICS. *Educ:* Purdue Univ, BS, 50; Ind Univ, MA, 56, PhD(bot), 58. *Prof Exp:* From asst prof to assoc prof, 58-71, PROF BIOL, UNIV NMEX, 71- *Res:* Floristics; genetics; plant geography; analysis of taxa; distribution of species; studies of threatened and endangered species. *Mailing Add:* Dept of Biol Univ of NMex Albuquerque NM 87131

MARTIN, WILLIAM CLYDE, b Cullman, Ala, Nov 27, 29; m 59; c 2. ATOMIC SPECTROSCOPY, ATOMIC PHYSICS. *Educ:* Univ Richmond, BS, 51; Princeton Univ, MA, 53, PhD(physics), 56. *Prof Exp:* Instr physics, Princeton Univ, 55-57; physicist, 57-62, CHIEF SPECTROS SECT, NAT BUR STANDARDS, 62- *Mem:* Am Phys Soc; Optical Soc Am; Am Astron Soc; Int Astron Union. *Res:* Optical atomic spectroscopy; atomic structure. *Mailing Add:* A167 Physics Bldg Nat Bur of Standards Washington DC 20234

MARTIN, WILLIAM DAVID, b Anaconda, Mont, June 24, 42; m 64; c 4. ANATOMY. *Educ:* Carroll Col, Mont, AB, 64; Creighton Univ, MS, 66; Univ Minn, Minneapolis, PhD(vet anat), 72. *Prof Exp:* Instr vet anat, Univ Minn, 66-72; instr, 72-74, ASST PROF ANAT, UNIV KY, 75- *Mem:* Am Asn Anatomists; Am Soc Zoologists. *Res:* Muscle histochemistry and ultrastructure. *Mailing Add:* Dept of Anat Univ of Ky Med Ctr Lexington KY 40506

MARTIN, WILLIAM EUGENE, b St Joseph, Mo, Dec 19, 41; m 64; c 2. PHYSICS, PHYSICAL OPTICS. *Educ:* San Diego State Univ, BS, 69, MS, 70; Univ Calif, San Diego, PhD(appl physics), 74. *Prof Exp:* Physicist solid state res, US Naval Electronics Lab Ctr, 70-75; PHYSICIST & GROUP LEADER, LASER FUSION PROJ, LAWRENCE LIVERMORE LAB, 75- *Mem:* Optical Soc Am; AAAS. *Res:* Laser amplifier and oscillator physics; optical pulse shaping; physics of II-VI and III-V materials; integrated and fiber optics device research; non linear optics. *Mailing Add:* Lawrence Livermore Lab PO Box 5508 Livermore CA 94550

MARTIN, WILLIAM GERALD, b Ottawa, Ont, Mar 18, 19; m 47; c 3. PHYSICAL CHEMISTRY, BIOCHEMISTRY. *Educ:* Carleton Univ, BSc, 52; McGill Univ, MSc, 55, PhD(chem), 58. *Prof Exp:* Examr, Inspection Bd UK & Can, 40-47; res officer, 55-69, SR RES OFFICER, NAT RES COUN CAN, 69- *Mem:* Can Biochem Soc. *Res:* Biological production of hydrogen and structure and function of biological membranes. *Mailing Add:* Div of Biol Sci Nat Res Coun Can Sussex Dr Ottawa ON K1A 0R6 Can

MARTIN, WILLIAM GILBERT, b Shreveport, La, June 15, 31; m 53; c 3. NUTRITION, BIOCHEMISTRY. *Educ:* La Polytech Inst, BS, 56; NC State Univ, MS, 58, WVa Univ, PhD(biochem), 63. *Prof Exp:* Res asst animal nutrit, NC State Univ, 56-58; res asst agr biochem, 58-60, from instr to assoc prof, 60-74, AGR BIOCHEMIST & PROF AGR BIOCHEM, WVA UNIV, 74- *Mem:* Am Inst Nutrit; Am Chem Soc; Soc Exp Biol & Med; Poultry Sci Asn; Am Soc Animal Sci. *Res:* Amino acid and mineral metabolism; sulfur metabolism. *Mailing Add:* Comt of Agr Biochem WVa Univ Morgantown WV 26505

MARTIN, WILLIAM HARRY, organic chemistry, textiles, deceased

MARTIN, WILLIAM HAYWOOD, III, b Bath Springs, Tenn, Nov 29, 38; div; c 2. PLANT ECOLOGY, FOREST ECOLOGY. *Educ:* Tenn Polytech Inst, BS, 60; Univ Tenn, Knoxville, MS, 66, PhD(bot), 71. *Prof Exp:* PROF BIOL SCI, EASTERN KY UNIV, 69-, DIR, DIV NATURAL AREAS, 77- *Concurrent Pos:* Inst grants, Eastern Ky Univ, 71, 73, 78 & 79; consult, Nat Natural Landmark Theme Studies, Dept Interior; prin investr, Natural Plant Comt Study, Dept Energy. *Mem:* AAAS; Ecol Soc Am; Sigma Xi. *Res:* Relationships among plant components of forests and soil and geologic, topographic parameters; relationship of plant communities and populations to climatic, soil, geologic, topographic and biotic factors; major areas of interest and expertise in forest, natural and cultivated grassland ecosystems. *Mailing Add:* Div of Natural Areas Eastern Ky Univ Richmond KY 40475

MARTIN, WILLIAM J, b Somerville, Tenn, July 24, 38; m 60; c 2. CHEMICAL ENGINEERING. *Educ:* Ga Inst Technol, BChE, 61, MSChE, 63, PhD(chem eng), 65. *Prof Exp:* RES ENGR, DEERING-MILLIKEN RES CORP, 64- *Mem:* Am Chem Soc; Am Inst Chem Engrs. *Res:* Radiation and textile finishing chemistry. *Mailing Add:* 308 Arrowhead Circle Spartanburg SC 29301

MARTIN, WILLIAM L, JR, b St Louis, Mo, Feb 21, 36; m; c 3. MATHEMATICS, ELECTRONICS. *Educ:* Washington Univ, St Louis, BS, 65. *Prof Exp:* Engr, Gen Cable Corp, 62-66 & Conrow Co, 66; engr, 66-69, dir elec insulation & conductors, 69-78, ENGR MKT & SALES, MAGNET WIRE PRODUCTS, P D GEORGE CO, 78- *Mem:* Inst Elec & Electronics Engrs. *Res:* Commercial evaluation and application of organic electrical insulating systems for magnet wire. *Mailing Add:* P D George Co 5200 N Second St St Louis MO 63147

MARTIN, WILLIAM MACPHAIL, b Heatherdale, PEI, Aug 16, 19; m 45; c 4. NUCLEAR PHYSICS. *Educ:* Queen's Univ, Ont, BSc, 41; McGill Univ, PhD(physics), 51. *Prof Exp:* Jr res assoc physics, Chalk River Labs, 45-46; from asst prof to assoc prof, Queen's Univ, Ont, 51-55; assoc prof, 55-63, PROF PHYSICS, McGILL UNIV, 63-, ASST CHMN DEPT, 70- *Mem:* Can Asn Physicists; Am Phys Soc. *Res:* Radioactivity; nuclear reactions and isomerism. *Mailing Add:* Dept of Physics McGill Univ Montreal PQ H3A 2T8 Can

MARTIN, WILLIAM PAXMAN, b American Fork, Utah, July 15, 12; m 37; c 3. SOIL MICROBIOLOGY. *Educ:* Brigham Young Univ, AB, 34; Iowa State Col, MS, 36, PhD(soil bact), 37. *Prof Exp:* Instr soil microbiol, Univ Ariz, 37-40, asst prof, 40-45; forest ecologist, Southwestern Forest & Range Exp Sta, US Forest Serv, 45-48; prof agron & bact, Ohio State Univ, 48-54; PROF SOILS & HEAD DEPT, COL AGR, UNIV MINN, ST PAUL, 54- *Concurrent Pos:* Asst soil microbiologist exp sta, Univ Ariz, 37-45; asst res chemist, Soil Conserv Serv, USDA, 41-44, soil chemist, 44-45, microbiologist, Regional Salinity Lab, Calif, 45; mem comn zero tolerance & residue regulation pesticides, Nat Acad Sci-Nat Res Coun, 64-65; mem agr libr network comt, Inter-Univ Commun Coun Educ Commun, 68-69; bd mem, Agron Sci Found, 71-74; mem, Nat Soybean Crop Improv Coun. *Mem:* Fel AAAS; hon mem Am Soc Agron (pres, 75); fel Soil Sci Soc Am (pres, 66); fel Soil Conserv Soc Am; Coun Agr Sci Technol. *Res:* Soil fertility; soil and water conservation; soil microbiology. *Mailing Add:* Dept of Soil Sci Univ of Minn St Paul MN 55101

MARTIN, WILLIAM RANDOLPH, b Knoxville, Tenn, Apr 19, 22; m 49; c 2. MICROBIOLOGY. *Educ:* Univ Tenn, BA, 47, MS, 50; Univ Tex, PhD(bact), 55. *Prof Exp:* Res asst biophys, Oak Ridge Nat Lab, 47-48; res asst bact, Univ Tex, 51-52, res scientist, 52-55; assoc bacteriologist, Am Meat Inst Found, 55-57; from instr to assoc prof microbiol, Univ Chicago, 57-80, sr adv biol sci, 76-80; PROF BASIC MED SCI, SCH MED, MERCER UNIV, MACON, GA, 80- *Concurrent Pos:* USPHS career develop award, 60-; Guggenheim fel, 65-66; vis investr, Inst Microbiol, Gottingen, Ger, 65-66. *Mem:* Am Soc Microbiol; NY Acad Sci; Brit Soc Gen Microbiol. *Res:* Microbial metabolism; filamentous fungi and mechanisms of cellular resistance to anti-tumor drugs. *Mailing Add:* Sch Med Mercer Univ Macon GA 31207

MARTIN, WILLIAM ROBERT, b Aberdeen, SDak, Jan 30, 21; m 49; c 3. PHARMACOLOGY. *Educ:* Univ Chicago, BS, 48; Univ Ill, MS & MD, 53. *Prof Exp:* Intern, Cook County Hosp, Chicago, Ill, 53-54; from instr to asst prof pharmacol, Univ Ill, 54-57; neuropharmacologist, Nat Inst Drug Abuse, 57-63, dir, Addiction Res Ctr, 63-77; PROF PHARMACOL & CHMN DEPT, UNIV KY, 77- *Concurrent Pos:* Adj assoc prof, Univ Ky, 62, adj prof, Sch Med, 71; mem expert adv panel drug dependence, WHO, 65; prof pharmacol, Univ Ill Col Med, 67. *Honors & Awards:* Nathan B Eddy Mem Award, Nat Acad Sci-Nat Res Coun. *Mem:* AAAS; Am Soc Pharmacol & Exp Therapeut; Am Soc Clin Pharmacol & Therapeut; Am Col Neuropsychopharmacol; Soc Neurosci. *Res:* Neuropharmacology; clinical pharmacology; drug addiction. *Mailing Add:* Dept Pharmacol Col Med Univ Ky Lexington KY 40506

MARTIN, WILLIAM ROYALL, JR, b Raleigh, NC, Sept 3, 26; m 52; c 2. ORGANIC CHEMISTRY, BUSINESS ADMINISTRATION. *Educ:* Univ NC, AB, 48, MBA, 63; NC State Univ, BS, 52. *Prof Exp:* Chemist, Am Cyanamid Co, 52-54; plant chemist, Dan River Mills, Inc, 54-56; group leader, Union Carbide Corp, 56-59; res assoc & head appl chem res, NC State Univ, 59-63; tech dir, 63-73, EXEC DIR, AM ASN TEXTILE CHEMISTS & COLORISTS, 74- *Concurrent Pos:* US deleg & secy meeting subcomt color-fastness tests, Int Orgn Standardization, NC, 64, Würzburg, Ger, 68, US deleg tech comt textiles, London, 65, 70, 75 & 80, secy meetings subcomt color fastness & color measurement & subcomt dimensional stability, Newton, Mass, 71, Paris, 74, Ottawa, 77 & Copenhagen, 81; mem comt textiles, Pan Am Standards Comn, Montevideo, 66; spec lectr & adj asst prof, NC State Univ, 66- *Mem:* Textile Inst; Am Chem Soc; Fiber Soc; fel Soc Dyers & Colourists. *Res:* Business and technical administration. *Mailing Add:* Am Asn Textile Chemists & Colorists PO Box 12215 Research Triangle Park NC 27709

MARTIN, WILLIAM TED, b Springdale, Ark, June 4, 11; m 38; c 4. MATHEMATICS. *Educ:* Univ Ark, AB, 30; Univ Ill, MA, 31, PhD(math), 34. *Hon Degrees:* ScD, Oklahoma City Univ, 75. *Prof Exp:* Asst math, Univ Ill, 32-33; Nat Res Coun fel math, Princeton Univ & sch math, Inst Advan Study, 34-36; from instr to asst prof, Mass Inst Technol, 36-43; prof & chmn dept, Syracuse Univ, 43-46; prof math, 46-73, exec officer dept, 46-47, head, 47-68, chmn fac, 69-71, dir div study & res in educ, 73-75, prof, 73-76, sr lectr, 76-80, EMER PROF EDUC & MATH, MASS INST TECHNOL, 76- *Concurrent Pos:* Res assoc, Princeton Univ, 40-41; mem exec comt, Div Math & Phys Sci, Nat Res Coun, 47-48; ed, Math Surv, Am Math Soc, 50-52, Bulletin, 51-56; mem, Inst Advan Study, 51-52; trustee, Oklahoma City Univ, 66-80. *Mem:* AAAS (vpres, 51, chmn sect A, 51); Am Math Soc (vpres, 49-50, treas, 65-73); Math Asn Am; Am Acad Arts & Sci. *Res:* Several complex variables; integration in function space. *Mailing Add:* Box 327 Cambridge RI 02807

MARTIN, YVONNE CONNOLLY, b St Paul, Minn, Sept 13, 36; m 63; c 2. RECEPTOR MAPPING. *Educ:* Carleton Col, BA, 58; Northwestern Univ, PhD(chem), 64. *Prof Exp:* Res asst, 58-60, sr pharmacologist, 64-70, assoc res fel, 70-74, RES FEL, ABBOTT LABS, 74- *Concurrent Pos:* Mem, Carcinogenesis Prog Sci Review Comt, Nat Cancer Inst, 78-81. *Mem:* AAAS; Am Chem Soc. *Res:* Quantitative structure-activity relationships of drugs; conformational and quantum chemical calculations; application of computer graphics to drug design. *Mailing Add:* Dept 466 RINC Abbott Labs Abbott Park North Chicago IL 60064

MARTINDALE, WILLIAM EARL, b Nashville, Ark, Sept, 4, 23; m 50; c 3. BIOCHEMISTRY. *Educ:* Henderson State Teachers Col, BA, 47; Univ Ark, MS, 49; Univ Ala, MS, 57, PhD(biochem), 62. *Prof Exp:* Biochemist, Thayer Vet Admin Hosp, Nashville, Tenn, 50-54; asst chief radioisotope serv, Birmingham Vet Admin Hosp, 54-62; asst prof chem, Miss State Univ, 62-64; PROF CHEM & CHMN DEPT, BELMONT COL, 64- *Concurrent Pos:* Vis prof org chem, Trevecca Col, 69- *Res:* Carbohydrate metabolism in thyroid tissues; synovial permeability in arthritis; chronic vitamin B-6 deficiency in rat; folic acid deficiency in chicks. *Mailing Add:* Dept of Chem Belmont Col Nashville TN 37203

MARTIN-DELEON, PATRICIA ANASTASIA, b Port Maria, Jamaica, WI; Can citizen; c 2. HUMAN GENETICS. *Educ:* Univ WI, BSc, 67, MSc, 69; Univ Western Ont, PhD(genetics), 72. *Prof Exp:* Res asst human cytogenetics, Univ WI, 67-69; sessional lectr genetics, McGill Univ, 75-76; asst prof, 76-81, ASSOC PROF HUMAN GENETICS, UNIV DEL, 81- *Concurrent Pos:* Fel, McGill Univ, 72-75; UDRF res grant, Univ Del, 77-78. *Mem:* AAAS; Genetic Soc Can; Am Soc Human Genetics; Sigma Xi. *Res:* The role of the aging sperm in the induction of chromosome anomalies in resulting embryos; regulation of the activity of nucleolar organizer regions. *Mailing Add:* Sch of Life & Health Sci Univ Del Newark DE 19711

MARTINEAU, BERNARD, b Chateauguay, Que, Dec 6, 21; m 51; c 2. MEDICAL BACTERIOLOGY. *Educ:* Bourget Col, BA, 43; Univ Montreal, MD, 49. *Prof Exp:* From lectr to assoc prof med bact, 40-70, PROF MICROBIOL & IMMUNOL, UNIV MONTREAL, 70- *Concurrent Pos:* Bacteriologist, Clin Lab, Hospital Ste-Justine, 54-, dir microbiol lab, 72- *Mem:* Can Med Asn; Asn Fr Speaking Physicians Can. *Res:* Clinical bacteriology; virology; mycology; neonatal virus infection, especially cytomegalovirus. *Mailing Add:* Dept of Med Univ of Montreal Montreal PQ H3C 3J7 Can

MARTINEAU, PERRY CYRUS, b Boise, Idaho, Jan 25, 18; m 41; c 4. PATHOLOGY, PHARMACOLOGY. *Educ:* Idaho State Univ, BS, 39; Univ Mich, MD, 43, MS, 48; Am Bd Path, dipl & cert clin path, 49, cert anat path, 50. *Prof Exp:* Intern, Henry Ford Hosp, Detroit, 43-44, asst resident surg, 44-45, resident path, 45-48; from asst prof to assoc prof, Col Med, Wayne State Univ, 50-65; assoc prof path, 66-72, CLIN PROF PHARMACOL, UNIV PITTSBURGH, 70-, CLIN PROF PATH, 72- *Concurrent Pos:* Dir labs & pathologist, City Health Dept, Detroit, 50-65; assoc, Detroit Receiving Hosp, 51-65; consult pathologist, Northville State Hosp, 59-; pathologist, McKeesport Hosp, Pa, 66- *Mem:* Fel AAAS; Am Soc Clin Path; fel Am Pub Health Asn; fel Col Am Path; Int Acad Path. *Res:* Anatomical, oral and surgical pathology. *Mailing Add:* Dept Pathology McKeesport Hosp McKeesport PA 15132

MARTINEAU, ROBERT JEAN, b Woonsocket, RI, Mar 29, 40. THEORETICAL PHYSICS, ELECTRONICS. *Educ:* Providence Col, BS, 62; Rensselaer Polytech Inst, PhD(physics), 66; Stanford Univ, MS, 75. *Prof Exp:* From asst prof to assoc prof physics, Providence Col, 66-73; res engr, Honeywell Radiation Ctr, Mass, 75-77; MEM STAFF, NEW ENG RES CTR, 77- *Mem:* Am Phys Soc. *Res:* Physics of infrared detectors; general relativity; quantum field theory. *Mailing Add:* 64 Wayside Inn Rd Marlboro MA 01752

MARTINEC, EMIL LOUIS, b Chicago, Ill, July 28, 27; m 54; c 3. EDUCATIONAL ADMINISTRATION, TECHNICAL MANAGEMENT. *Educ:* Ill Inst Technol, BS, 50; Univ Idaho, MS, 57; Northwestern Univ, MBA, 65. *Hon Degrees:* Dr Engr Mgt, Midwest Col Eng, 73. *Prof Exp:* Design engr brake systs, Am Steel Foundries, 50-51; design engr exp equip, Taylor Forge and Pipe Works, 51-52; proj engr furnaces, Standard Oil Co, Ind, 52-55; asst engr exp loop design, 55-62, engr reacctor standards, 62-73, asst div dir admin, Reactor Anal & Safety Div, 73-79, DIR PROG ADMIN, ENERGY & ENVIRON TECHNOL PROG, ARGONNE NAT LAB, 79- *Concurrent Pos:* Prof, Midwest Col Eng, 69-, chmn, engr mgt dept, 69-, acad dean, 72-75; consult, C E Miller Assocs, 78- *Mem:* Fel Am Soc Mech Engrs; Am Soc Qual Control; Am Soc Eng Educ; Am Soc Eng Mgt. *Res:* Management of energy and environmental research and development; heat transfer and fluid dynamics. *Mailing Add:* Reactor Anal & Safety Div 9700 S Cass Ave Argonne IL 60439

MARTINEK, GEORGE WILLIAM, b Chicago, Ill, Apr 23, 32. GENETICS. *Educ:* Concordia Teachers Col, Ill, BS, 53; Los Angeles State Col, MA, 60; Univ Calif, Los Angeles, PhD(bot), 68. *Prof Exp:* Teacher, Trinity Lutheran Sch, 53-58; instr biol, Concordia Teachers Col, Ill, 58-62; from asst prof to assoc prof biol, 67-75, PROF BIOL, CALIF STATE POLYTECH UNIV, POMONA, 75- *Mem:* AAAS; Genetics Soc Am. *Res:* Genetics of Chlamydomonas reinhardi; recombination. *Mailing Add:* Dept of Biol Sci Calif State Polytech Univ Pomona CA 91768

MARTINEK, JOHN JOEL, b Milwaukee, Wis, Jan 20, 42; m 65; c 2. ANATOMY. *Educ:* Wis State Univ-Whitewater, BEd, 65; Tulane Univ, PhD(anat), 69. *Prof Exp:* Asst prof anat, Col Med, Ohio State Univ, 69-74; MEM FAC, ANAT-HISTOL DEPT, GRINNELL COL, 74-, ASSOC PROF BIOL, 81- *Concurrent Pos:* NIH grants, Col Med, Ohio State Univ, 69-70 & 71-72. *Mem:* Am Asn Anat. *Res:* Electron microscopy of normal and abnormal human placentas. *Mailing Add:* Anat-Histol Dept Grinnell Col Grinnell IA 50112

MARTINEK, ROBERT GEORGE, b Chicago, Ill, Nov 25, 19; m 52. CLINICAL CHEMISTRY. *Educ:* Univ Ill, BS, 41 & 45, MS, 43; Univ Southern Calif, PharmD, 54; Am Bd Bioanal, cert. *Prof Exp:* Pharmacist & pharmaceut chemist, Bates Labs, Inc, 45-47; chemist res lab, Diversey Corp, Victor Chem Works, 47-50; assoc chemist, AMA, 50-55; sr chemist, Mead Johnson & Co, 55-56; clin chemist, Butterworth Hosp, Grand Rapids, Mich, 56-58, Iowa Methodist Hosp, 58-62 & Chicago Dept Health, 62-65; CLIN BIOCHEMIST & CHIEF LAB IMPROV SECT, DEPT PUB HEALTH, ILL, 65-, DIR, 78- *Concurrent Pos:* Assoc ed, J Am Med Technologists, 64-; consult, Abel Labs & Thornburg Labs, 65; consult, Lab-Line Instruments, 71-, bd dirs, 73-; lectr dept prev med & community health, Col Med, Univ Ill Med Ctr; ed consult, Med Electronics; mem clin chem adv bd, Ctr Dis Control, USPHS, Atlanta, Ga, 74-; mem subcomt temperature measurement, Nat Comt Clin Lab Standards 76-; scientist & dir, US Pub Health Serv Reserve Corps, 52- *Mem:* AAAS; AMA; Am Pharmaceut Asn; Am Inst Econ; fel Am Inst Chemists. *Res:* Pharmaceutical and detergent chemistry; vitamin assay; sympathomimetic amines; clinical chemistry methodology. *Mailing Add:* 4736 N Tripp Ave Chicago IL 60630

MARTINELLI, ERNEST A, b Lucca, Italy, Dec 15, 19; nat US; m 46; c 3. NUCLEAR PHYSICS. *Educ:* Univ Calif, BS, 41, PhD(physics), 50. *Prof Exp:* Mem staff radiation lab, Mass Inst Technol, 42-45; instr physics, Stanford Univ, 50-51; physicist radiation lab, Univ Calif, Berkeley, 51-52, Livermore, 52-56; physicist, Aeronutronics Systs, Inc, 56-57 & Rand Corp, 57-71; HEAD DEPT PHYSICS, RES & DEVELOP ASSOCS, 71- *Mem:* Am Phys Soc. *Res:* Nuclear weapon effects; weapon systems. *Mailing Add:* R&D Assocs PO Box 9695 Marina del Rey CA 90291

MARTINELLI, LOUIS CARL, b Oroville, Calif, Sept 2, 37; m 59; c 3. PHARMACEUTICAL CHEMISTRY. *Educ:* Univ Calif, San Francisco, PharmD, 63, PhD(pharmaceut chem), 68. *Prof Exp:* Asst prof med chem, Sch Pharm, Univ Ga, 68-74; assoc prof clin pharm & coordr, Sch Pharm, WVa Univ, 74-80; MEM FAC, SCH PHARM, UNIV PAC, 80- *Mem:* Am Pharmaceut Asn. *Res:* Synthesis and study of physical-chemical properties of organic molecules potentially useful as drugs in humans. *Mailing Add:* Sch Pharm Univ Pac 751 Brookside Rd Stockton CA 95207

MARTINELLI, MARIO, JR, b Covington, Va, May 7, 22; m 53; c 1. METEOROLOGY, FORESTRY. *Educ:* Univ Chicago, BS, 44; Duke Univ, MF, 48; State Univ NY, PhD, 56. *Prof Exp:* Forester, Southern Pine Lumber Co, Tex, 48-49; instr & asst, Purdue Univ, 49-54; RES METEOROLOGIST, ROCKY MOUNTAIN FOREST & RANGE EXP STA, US FOREST SERV, 54- *Mem:* Am Meteorol Soc; Glaciol Soc. *Res:* Watershed management of alpine areas, especially late-lying snow-beds and avalanche research. *Mailing Add:* Rocky Mtn Forest & Range Exp Sta 240 W Prospect St Ft Collins CO 80521

MARTINELLI, RAMON U, b Pittsburgh, Pa, Dec 28, 38; m 61. SOLID STATE ELECTRONICS. *Educ:* Dartmouth Col, AB, 60, MS, 62; Princeton Univ, PhD(lasers), 66. *Prof Exp:* MEM TECH STAFF, RCA LABS, 65- *Mem:* Am Phys Soc; Inst Elec & Electronics Engrs. *Res:* Laser and surface physics; electronic photoemission from solids; physical electronics; secondary emission. *Mailing Add:* RCA Labs Princeton NJ 08540

MARTINEZ, ALBERTO MAGIN, b Matanzas, Cuba, Oct 12, 43; US citizen. ORGANIC CHEMISTRY, PHOTOGRAPHY. *Educ:* Univ Ill, Chicago Circle, BS, 67, MS, 69, PhD(org chem), 72. *Prof Exp:* SR RES CHEMIST CHEM & PHOTOG, EASTMAN KODAK CO RES LABS, 72- *Mem:* Am Chem Soc. *Res:* Study of properties of light sensitive photographic materials, synthetic aspects of compounds used in such materials; properties of small ring alicyclic organic compounds. *Mailing Add:* 93 Alderwood Ln Rochester NY 14615

MARTINEZ, JOE L, JR, b Albuquerque, NMex, Aug 1, 44. NEUROBIOLOGY, PSYCHOPHARMACOLOGY. *Educ:* Univ San Diego, BA, 66; NMex Highlands Univ, MS, 68; Univ Del, PhD(physiol psychol), 71. *Prof Exp:* Vis scientist, NEng Regional Primate Res Ctr, 71-72; from asst prof to assoc prof, Dept Psychol, Calif State Col, 72-77; ASSOC RES PSYCHOBIOLOGIST & LECTR, UNIV CALIF, IRVINE, 77- *Concurrent Pos:* Res fel, Univ Del, 67-68; NIMH fel, 75-77; fel, Neth, 79; affil prof, Span Speaking Ment Health Res Ctr, 77-; managing ed, Behav & Neural Biol, 78-; consult ed, J Hisp Behav Sci, 79-81. *Mem:* Am Psychol Asn; Soc Neurosci. *Res:* Neurobiological basis of learning and memory; psychopharmacology; cross cultural psychology. *Mailing Add:* Dept of Psychobiol Univ of Calif Irvine CA 92717

MARTINEZ, JOHN L(UIS), b New Orleans, La, June 19, 22; m 55. MECHANICAL ENGINEERING. *Educ:* Tulane Univ, BE, 43; La State Univ, MS, 50. *Prof Exp:* From instr to assoc prof mech eng, 46-66, asst dean, Sch Eng, 58-76, PROF MECH ENG, TULANE UNIV, 66-, DEAN ADMIS, 76- *Concurrent Pos:* Ford Found lectr, 58-59. *Mem:* Am Soc Eng Educ; Nat Soc Prof Engrs. *Res:* Design, biomechanics. *Mailing Add:* Off of Admis Tulane Univ Sch of Eng New Orleans LA 70118

MARTINEZ, JOHN STANLEY, nuclear & chemical engineering, see previous edition

MARTINEZ, JOSE E(DWARDO), b Laredo, Tex, Feb 28, 43; m 64; c 3. MECHANICAL ENGINEERING. *Educ:* Tex A&M Univ, BS, 63, ME, 65, PhD(mech eng), 67. *Prof Exp:* Struct engr, Gen Dynamics Corp, 63-64; from instr to assoc prof, 67-75, PROF CIVIL ENG, TEX A&M UNIV, 75- *Concurrent Pos:* Consult, Trans-Alaska Pipeline Serv Co, 68-70; grad faculty assoc mem, Tex A&M Univ, 68-; consult Alyeska Pipeline Serv Co, 70- & Continental Oil Co, 71- *Mem:* Am Soc Civil Engrs; Am Soc Eng Educ; Am Inst Aeronaut & Astronaut. *Res:* Analysis and design of safer highway structures; computer methods in structural mechanics. *Mailing Add:* Dept of Civil Eng Tex A&M Univ College Station TX 77840

MARTINEZ, JOSE E(LEAZAR), b Questa, NMex, Jan 13, 22; m 64; c 4. CIVIL ENGINEERING. *Educ:* Univ NMex, BS, 43; Iowa State Univ, MS, 50. *Prof Exp:* Instr sanit eng, 47-51, asst prof fluid mech, 51-57, assoc prof hwy mat, 57-64, prof hwy mat, 64-80, PROF CIVIL ENG, UNIV NMEX, 80- *Mem:* Am Soc Civil Engrs; Am Soc Eng Educ; Nat Soc Prof Engrs. *Res:* Hydrology; applied hydraulics; highway materials; pavement design. *Mailing Add:* 9715 Admiral Nimitz NE Albuquerque NM 87111

MARTINEZ, LUIS OSVALDO, b Havana, Cuba, Dec 27, 27; US citizen; m 55; c 3. RADIOLOGY. *Educ:* Inst Sec Educ, BS, 47; Univ Havana, MD, 54. *Prof Exp:* From instr to prof, 65-76, clin asst prof, 68-70, PROF RADIOL, SCH MED, UNIV MIAMI, 76- *Concurrent Pos:* Counr, Interam Col Radiol, 70-79; chief, Div Diag Radiol, Mt Sinai Med Ctr, 70-, prog dir, Diag Radiol Residency Prog, 70- & assoc dir radiol, 70-; ed, J InterAm Col Radiol. *Honors & Awards:* Recognition Awards, AMA, 71-74; Gold Medal, Interam Col Radiol, 75. *Mem:* Fel Am Col Radiol; Am Roentgen Ray Soc; Radiol Soc NAm; Am Asn Univ Radiologists; Soc Gastrointestinal Radiologists. *Res:* Clinical evaluation of contrast media for intravenous cholangiography. *Mailing Add:* Mt Sinai Med Ctr 4300 Alton Rd Miami Beach FL 33140

MARTINEZ, MARGARET YARNALL, b West Grove, Pa, Dec 26, 20; m 46; c 3. HUMAN ANATOMY, PHYSIOLOGY. *Educ:* Univ Pa, AB, 43; Columbia Univ, MA, 44. *Prof Exp:* Teacher, Tatnall Sch, 62-67; ASSOC PROF BIOL, WEST CHESTER STATE COL, 67- *Mem:* AAAS. *Res:* Cetaceans; whaling. *Mailing Add:* Dept of Biol West Chester State Col West Chester PA 19380

MARTINEZ, MARIO GUILLERMO, JR, b Havana, Cuba, Mar 6, 24; US citizen; m 49; c 3. ORAL PATHOLOGY. *Educ:* Univ Havana, DDS, 47; Univ Ala, Birmingham, DMD, 64, MS, 68; Am Bd Oral Path, dipl. *Prof Exp:* From instr to asst prof oral path, Sch Dent, Univ Havana, 49-59, prof, 59-60; from asst prof to assoc prof, 67-75, PROF PATH, MED CTR, UNIV ALA, BIRMINGHAM, 71-, DIR CLIN CANCER TRAINING PROG, SCH DENT, 70-, DIR DIV ORAL PATH, MED CTR, 71-, SR SCIENTIST COMPREHENSIVE CANCER CTR, 75- *Concurrent Pos:* Consult, Vet Admin Hosp, Birmingham, Ala. *Mem:* Int Asn Dent Res; Fel Am Acad Oral Path; fel Am Col Dent; Am Dent Asn; Am Asn Cancer Educ. *Res:* Ultrastructure of giant cell lesion of the jaws; oral oncology. *Mailing Add:* Div of Oral Path Univ of Ala Med Ctr Birmingham AL 35294

MARTINEZ, OCTAVIO VINCENT, b Jacksonville, Fla, Nov 14, 47. BACTERIOLOGY, CLINICAL MICROBIOLOGY. *Educ:* Univ Miami, BS, 69, PhD(microbiol), 76. *Prof Exp:* Res asst, 77-78, RES INSTR SURG MICROBIOL & RES ASST PROF SURG, SCH MED, UNIV MIAMI, 78- *Mem:* Am Soc Microbiol; Am Soc Clin Path. *Res:* Surgical bacteriology. *Mailing Add:* Dept Surg (R-12) Sch Med Univ Miami PO Box 016960 Miami FL 33101

MARTINEZ, RAFAEL JUAN, b Santurce, PR, Feb 28, 27; div; c 3. BACTERIAL PHYSIOLOGY. *Educ:* Univ Southern Calif, AB, 52, PhD, 56. *Prof Exp:* From asst prof to assoc prof bact, 61-69, chmn dept, 71-73, PROF BACT, UNIV CALIF, LOS ANGELES, 69- *Concurrent Pos:* Fulbright fel, 70-71; NIH res grants bact & mycol, 73-77. *Mem:* Am Soc Microbiol; Brit Soc Gen Microbiol. *Res:* Biochemistry of pathogenesis; host-parasite interactions. *Mailing Add:* Dept of Bact Univ of Calif Los Angeles CA 90024

MARTINEZ, RICHARD ISAAC, b Havana, Cuba, Aug 16, 44; US citizen; m 78. PHYSICAL CHEMISTRY. *Educ:* McGill Univ, BSc, 64; Univ Calif, Los Angeles, PhD(chem), 76. *Prof Exp:* Lab asst chem, DuPont of Can, Ltd, 62; chemist, Shell Chem Co, 67-70; res chemist, Univ Calif, Los Angeles, 71-76; RES CHEMIST, NAT BUR STANDARDS, DEPT COM, 76- *Concurrent Pos:* Res assoc, Nat Res Coun/Nat Acad Sci, 76-78. *Mem:* Am Chem Soc; Am Phys Soc; AAAS. *Res:* Kinetics and mechanisms of the oxidation chemistry of sulfur compounds; free-radical reactions; ozone-olefin reactions; established existence of dioxiranes, of metastable excited sulfur dioxide, and of vicinal hydroxy-substituted alkyl and oxoalkyl nitrates and peroxynitrates. *Mailing Add:* A147 Chem Nat Bur Standards Washington DC 20234

MARTINEZ-CARRION, MARINO, b Felix, Spain, Dec 2, 36; US citizen; m 57; c 2. BIOCHEMISTRY. *Educ:* Univ Calif, Berkeley, BA, 59, MA, 61, PhD(comp biochem), 64. *Prof Exp:* NIH fel biochem, Rome, 64-65; from asst prof to prof chem, Univ Notre Dame, 65-77; PROF BIOCHEM & CHEM DEPT, MED COL VA, VA COMMONWEALTH UNIV, 77- *Concurrent Pos:* NIH career develop award, 72-77; chmn biophysics & biophys chem B study sect, NIH, 77-82; assoc ed, J Protein Chem, 81- *Mem:* Spanish Biochem Soc; fel NY Acad Sci; Am Soc Biol Chemists; Am Chem Soc. *Res:* Mechanisms of enzyme action; active center of pyridoxal dependent enzymes; isoenzymes; nuclear magnetic resonance of enzyme-substrate interaction; acetylcholine neuroreptors; neurochemistry; membrane research. *Mailing Add:* Dept of Biochem Va Commonwealth Univ Richmond VA 23298

MARTINEZ DE PINILLOS, JOAQUIN VICTOR, b Havana, Cuba, Mar 10, 41; US citizen; m 67; c 2. CHEMICAL PHYSICS, CATALYSIS. *Educ:* Univ Miami, BS, 66; Bowling Green State Univ, MA, 68; Univ Fla, PhD(chem physics), 74. *Prof Exp:* Teacher sci & math, Fla City Shelter for Unaccompanied Cuban Children, 62-63; plant chemist anal develop, Cyclo-Chem Corp, 68-70; chmn sci dept, Christopher Columbus High Sch, 64-70; asst physics & chem, Univ Fla, 70-74; develop engr polymer catalysis, Am Cyanamid Co, 74-75; res chemist, 75-80, SR PRIN RES CHEMIST-IN-CHARGE SURFACE CHARACTERIZATION LAB, AIR PROD & CHEM, INC, 80- *Mem:* Am Chem Soc; Am Soc Testing & Mat. *Res:* Electron spin resonance of trapped radicals; electron spectroscopy for chemical analysis and auger; catalytic reactions, electron microscopy and surface phenomena; catalysis and process development. *Mailing Add:* 170 Pine Grove Circle Wescosville PA 18106

MARTINEZ-HERNANDEZ, ANTONIO, b Calahorra, Spain, Apr 20, 44; m 68; c 2. EXPERIMENTAL PATHOLOGY, CARDIOVASCULAR PATHOLOGY. *Educ:* Univ Madrid, MD, 68. *Prof Exp:* Instr path, Med Sch, Univ Colo, 73-74, asst prof, 74-77, assoc prof, 77-78; assoc prof, 78-80, PROF PATH, HAHNEMANN MED COL, 80- *Concurrent Pos:* Mem, NIH Pathobiol Study Sect, 78- *Mem:* Am Asn Path; Int Acad Path; Histochem Soc. *Res:* Biology and pathology of connective tissues; basement membrane, elastic fibers, collagen. *Mailing Add:* 209 Drakes Drum Dr Bryn Mawr PA 19010

MARTINEZ-LOPEZ, JORGE IGNACIO, b Santurce, PR, Oct 5, 26; m 50; c 4. INTERNAL MEDICINE, CARDIOLOGY. *Educ:* La State Univ, MD, 50. *Prof Exp:* Intern, Arecibo Dist Hosp, PR, 50-51; physician, Elizabeth, La, 53-54; resident internal med, Charity Hosp, New Orleans, La, 54-57; from instr to assoc prof, 57-69, PROF MED, LA STATE UNIV MED CTR, NEW ORLEANS, 69- *Concurrent Pos:* Vis physician, Charity Hosp, New Orleans, 57-64, sr vis physician, 64-, dir, Cardiol Dept, 60-; cardiologist, Heart Sta, Hotel Dieu Hosp, 63-71, head, 71-74, mem consult staff, 75- *Mem:* Fel Am Heart Asn; fel Am Col Chest Physicians; fel Am Col Physicians; fel Am Col Cardiol. *Res:* Clinical cardiology; cardiac catheterization and other special diagnostic procedures; electrocardiography. *Mailing Add:* Dept of Med La State Univ Med Ctr New Orleans LA 70112

MARTINEZ-LOPEZ, NORMAN PETRONIO, b Managua, Nicaragua, Mar 31, 43; c 4. DENTISTRY. *Educ:* Univ Costa Rica, DDS, 64; Marquette Univ, MS, 68, MEd, 75, PhD(curric instr), 77; Am Bd Pedodont, dipl. *Prof Exp:* Asst prof dent, Nat Univ Nicaragua, 68-73; asst prof, Marquette Univ, 73-76; assoc prof, 76-81, PROF DENT, SOUTHERN ILL UNIV, EDWARDSVILLE, 81-, HEAD, SECT PEDIAT DENT, 76- *Mem:* Am Dent Asn; Int Asn Dent Res; Am Acad Pedodontics; Am Asn Educ Res; Fedn Dentaire Int. *Res:* Caries; educational development in higher education; role of behavioral science in dentistry. *Mailing Add:* Sch Dent Med Southern Ill Univ Edwardsville IL 62025

MARTINEZ-MALDONADO, MANUEL, b Yauco, PR, Aug 25, 37; m 59; c 4. INTERNAL MEDICINE, NEPHROLOGY. *Educ:* Univ PR, San Juan, BS, 57; Temple Univ, MD, 61. *Prof Exp:* Intern, St Charles Hosp, Toledo, Ohio, 61-62; resident internal med, Vet Admin Hosp & Sch Med, Univ PR, San Juan, 62-65; USPHS fel, Univ Tex Southwestern Med Sch Dallas, 65-67; Lederle Labs int fel, 66-67; instr, Univ Tex Southwestern Med Sch Dallas, 67-68; from asst prof to prof, Baylor Col Med, 68-73; PROF MED & PHYSIOL, SCH MED, UNIV PR, 72-, ACTG CHMN DEPT PHYSIOL, 74- *Concurrent Pos:* Dir chronic dialysis unit, Parkland Mem Hosp, Dallas, Tex, 67-68; attend physician, Ben Taub Gen Hosp, Houston, 68-73 & Methodist Hosp, Houston, 69-73; assoc chief staff for res, Vet Admin Hosp, San Juan, 73, chief med serv, 74-; mem nat adv bd, Nat Inst Arthritis, Metabolism, Digestive Dis & Kidneys, 79-82; vis prof med, Harvard Univ, 79-80; mem sci adv bd, Nat Kidney Found, 81-84. *Mem:* Am Soc Clin Invest; Cent Soc Clin Res; Am Fedn Clin Res; Am Soc Nephrology; Am Physiol Soc. *Res:* Renal physiology; electrolyte metabolism; biochemistry of transport. *Mailing Add:* Med Serv Vet Admin Hosp GPO Box 4867 San Juan PR 00936

MARTINEZ-PICO, JOSE LUIS, b Coamo, PR, July 16, 18; m 48; c 6. PHYSICAL CHEMISTRY. *Educ:* Univ PR, BS, 39; Univ Mich, MS, 47; Carnegie Inst Technol, MS, 61, PhD(chem), 62. *Prof Exp:* From instr to assoc prof chem, 40-62, dean sch arts & sci, 67-71, prof, 61-80, DEAN STUDIES, UNIV PR, MAYAGUEZ, 71-, EMER PROF CHEM, 80- *Concurrent Pos:* Consult, Univ Nicaragua, 65- *Res:* Use of nuclear magnetic resonance and mass spectra in analysis of petroleum. *Mailing Add:* Res del Coligio Mayaguez PR 00708

MARTINEZ-RIVERA, NILDA, organometallic chemistry, see previous edition

MARTINI, CATHERINE MARIE, b New York, NY, July 7, 24. PHYSICAL CHEMISTRY. *Educ:* Hunter Col, BA, 46; Univ Pa, MS, 48. *Prof Exp:* Tutor chem, Hunter Col, 47-49; asst, 49-53, res assoc, 53-60, res chemist, 61-66, SR RES CHEMIST, STERLING-WINTHROP RES INST DIV, STERLING DRUG, INC, 66- *Mem:* Am Chem Soc; Coblentz Soc. *Res:* Infrared, ultraviolet and nuclear magnetic resonance spectroscopy of organic molecules. *Mailing Add:* Sterling-Winthrop Res Inst Rensselaer NY 12144

MARTINI, IRENEO PETER, b Dec 14, 35; Can citizen; m 62; c 2. SEDIMENTOLOGY. *Educ:* Univ Florence, DrGeolSci, 61; McMaster Univ, PhD(geol), 66. *Prof Exp:* From geologist to sr geologist, Shell Can Ltd, 66-69; PROF SEDIMENTOLOGY, UNIV GUELPH, 69- *Mem:* Soc Econ Paleontologists & Mineralogists; Int Asn Sedimentol. *Res:* Sedimentary geology; sedimentology of Recent and Pleistocene clastic sediments and ancient sedimentary rocks; fabric of soils and sediments; analysis of hydrocarbon potentials of selected regions. *Mailing Add:* Dept Land Resource Sci Univ Guelph Guelph ON N1G 2W1 Can

MARTINI, MARIO, b Florence, Italy, Mar 24, 39; m 66; c 3. PHYSICS, RESEARCH MANAGEMENT. *Educ:* Univ Bologna, Italy, Dr(physics), 62. *Prof Exp:* Asst prof physics, Univ Bologna, 62-68; assoc prof, Univ Modena, 69-70; tech dir, Simtec Indust, Montreal, 71-73, NRD Div Electron Assoc Can Ltd, 73-74; TECH DIR, NUCLEAR TECHNOL DIV, EG&G ORTEC, OAK RIDGE, TENN, 75- *Concurrent Pos:* Fel physics, Chalk River Nuclear Labs, Ont, 68-69. *Mem:* Sr mem Inst Elec & Electronics Engrs; Can Asn Physicists. *Res:* Semiconductor physics (transport properties), interaction of ionizing radiation with semiconductors. *Mailing Add:* 942 W Outer Dr Oak Ridge TN 37830

MARTINI, WILLIAM ROGERS, b Glendale, Calif, Apr 27, 26; m 52; c 5. CHEMICAL & MECHANICAL ENGINEERING. *Educ:* Univ Colo, BS, 47; Univ Southern Calif, MS, 52; Univ Mich, PhD(chem eng), 56. *Prof Exp:* Res engr, Atomics Int, N Am-Rockwell Corp, 52-54, group leader org reactor tech, 59-60, prin investr, 61-65; staff mem, Los Alamos Sci Lab, 56-59; br chief dynamic conv, Donald W Douglas Labs, McDonnell Douglas Corp, 66-75; res prof, Joint Ctr Grad Study, Univ Wash, 76-79; OWNER, MARTINI ENG, 80- *Mem:* Am Inst Chem Engrs; Am Soc Mech Engrs. *Res:* Heat transfer, particularly natural convection; energy conversion, particularly thermionics, thermoelectrics thermophotovoltaics and Stirling engine; artificial heart development. *Mailing Add:* 100 Sprout Rd Richland WA 99352

MARTINO, JOSEPH PAUL, b Warren, Ohio, July 16, 31; m 57; c 3. OPERATIONS RESEARCH, SCIENCE ADMINISTRATION. *Educ:* Miami Univ, AB, 53; Purdue Univ, MS, 55; Ohio State Univ, PhD(math), 61. *Prof Exp:* With US Air Force, 53-75, proj engr, Wright Air Develop Ctr, 55-58, mathematician, Air Force Off Sci Res, 60-62, staff scientist, 63-67, opers analyst, Res & Develop Field Univ, Bangkok, Thailand, 62-63, chief tech anal div, Air Force Off Res Anal, 68-71, staff scientist, Avionics Lab, Wright-Patterson AFB, 72-73, dir eng standardization, Defense Electronics Supply Ctr, 73-75; res scientist, 75-80, SR RES SCIENTIST, RES INST, UNIV DAYTON, 80- *Mem:* AAAS; Opers Res Soc Am; fel Inst Elec & Electronics Eng; Am Inst Aeronaut & Astronaut; Inst Mgt Sci. *Res:* Application of operations research to problems of technological change, with emphasis on technological forecasting. *Mailing Add:* 819 N Maple Ave Fairborn OH 45324

MARTINS, DONALD HENRY, b Poplar Bluff, Mo, July 31, 45; m 69; c 1. ASTROPHYSICS, PHYSICS. *Educ:* Univ Mo, Columbia, BS, 67, MS, 69; Univ Fla, PhD(astron), 74. *Prof Exp:* Res assoc astron, Nat Res Coun, Johnson Space Ctr, 74-76; res assoc, Houston Baptist Univ, 76; adj fac mem, Univ Houston, 76-77; ASST PROF ASTRON & PHYSICS, UNIV GA, 77- *Mem:* Am Astron Soc; Am Inst Physics; Astron Soc Pac. *Res:* Active in photoelectric photometry of variable stars; photographic and photoelectric surface photometry of galaxies and globular clusters, with emphasis on nuclear structure. *Mailing Add:* Dept of Physics & Astron Univ of Ga Athens GA 30602

MARTINSON, CANDACE, b Cleveland, Ohio, Jan 12, 49. ENTOMOLOGY. *Educ:* Ohio State Univ, BS, 71, MS, 74, PhD(entom), 77. *Prof Exp:* Technician, Dept Entom, 72-73, ASST CUR ENTOM, COL INSECTS & SPIDERS, OHIO STATE UNIV, 77- *Concurrent Pos:* Illusr entom, NSF grant, 71-72. *Mem:* Entom Soc Am. *Res:* Systematics of leafhoppers. *Mailing Add:* Dept of Entom 1735 Neil Ave Columbus OH 43210

MARTINSON, CHARLIE ANTON, b Orchard, Colo, Sept 15, 34; m 57; c 4. PLANT PATHOLOGY. *Educ:* Colo State Univ, BS, 57, MS, 59; Ore State Univ, PhD(plant path), 64. *Prof Exp:* Asst prof plant path, Cornell Univ, 63-68; ASSOC PROF, IOWA STATE UNIV, 68- *Concurrent Pos:* Consult, Corn Prod Syst, Inc, 72- *Mem:* Fel AAAS; Am Phytopath Soc. *Res:* Root diseases of economically important crops; physiology of plant disease; corn diseases; role of toxins in pathogenesis; aflatoxins; disease resistance breeding; international programs in corn production and plant disease control. *Mailing Add:* Dept Plant Path Iowa State Univ Ames IA 50011

MARTINSON, EDWIN O(SCAR), b Seattle, Wash, Mar 10, 10; m 41; c 2. ELECTRICAL ENGINEERING. *Educ:* Univ Wash, BS, 32. *Prof Exp:* Mech engr, Mason Walsh Atkinson Kier Co, Wash, 34-36 & Tenn Valley Authority, 36-37; chief engr, DeBothezat Ventilating Equip Div, Am Mach & Metals, Inc, Ill, 37-41; pres & gen mgr, C S Johnson Co Div, Koehring Co, 41-48, vpres & chief engr, 48-53, pres & gen mgr, Koehring-Waterous, Ltd Div, 53-57, vpres res, Develop & Mfg Cent Off, 57-68; OWNER, MARTINSON ENG, 68- *Mem:* Soc Automotive Engrs; Nat Soc Prof Engrs. *Res:* Construction machinery; hydrostatic hydraulic devices; machines for concrete and asphalt industries; new type power operated indoor swim pools and propellers. *Mailing Add:* 6615 N River Rd Milwaukee WI 53217

MARTINSON, HAROLD GERHARD, b Hartford, Conn, Sept 9, 43; m 68; c 2. MOLECULAR BIOLOGY. *Educ:* Augsburg Col, BA, 65; Univ Calif, Berkeley, PhD(molecular biol), 71. *Prof Exp:* Fel biol, Univ Lethbridge, 71-73 & biochem, Univ Calif, San Francisco, 73-75; ASST PROF CHEM, UNIV CALIF, LOS ANGELES, 75- *Res:* Chromosome structure and chemistry; control of gene expression in eucaryotes. *Mailing Add:* Dept of Chem Univ of Calif 405 Hilgard Ave Los Angeles CA 90024

MARTINSON, IDA MARIE, b Mentor, Minn, Nov 8, 36; m 62; c 2. PHYSIOLOGY. *Educ:* Univ Minn, BS, 60, MNA, 62; Univ Ill, PhD(physiol), 72. *Prof Exp:* Instr nursing, Thorton Jr Col, 67-69; asst prof nursing, 72-74, assoc prof & dir res, 75-77, PROF & DIR RES NURSING, SCH NURSING, UNIV MINN, 77-, LECTR, DEPT OF PHYSIOL, MED SCH, 72- *Concurrent Pos:* Res consult, Clin Ctr, Bethesda, 77-78; proj dir, HEW, 75-77 & 77-79; prin investr, Nat Cancer Inst, 76-79 & Am Cancer Soc, 78-; mem, Adv Coun, Nat Inst Aging, 80-83; mem, Geriat & Geront Adv Comt, Vet Admin, 81-85. *Mem:* Inst Med-Nat Acad Sci; Am Nurses Asn; Sigma Xi. *Res:* Home care for the child with cancer; psychosocial impact of childhood cancer on child-family. *Mailing Add:* Sch Nursing Univ Minn B-140 Unit F 308 Harvard St Minneapolis MN 55455

MARTINSONS, ALEKSANDRS, b Russia, Nov 30, 12; US citizen; m 39; c 2. ELECTROCHEMISTRY. *Educ:* Univ Mich, MS, 55. *Prof Exp:* Sr res chemist, Am Potash & Chem Corp, 57-60; sr res chemist, Chem Div, PPG Industs, Inc, 60-77; RETIRED. *Mem:* Electrochem Soc. *Res:* Overvoltage; electro-winning and metal deposition; thin film coatings. *Mailing Add:* 135 Westview Ave Wadsworth OH 44281

MARTIRE, DANIEL EDWARD, b New York, NY, June 3, 37; m 61. PHYSICAL CHEMISTRY, ANALYTICAL CHEMISTRY. *Educ:* Stevens Inst Technol, BE, 59, MS, 60, PhD(chem), 63. *Prof Exp:* Instr chem, Stevens Inst Technol, 62-63; NSF fel, Cambridge Univ, 63-64; from asst prof to assoc prof, 64-74, PROF CHEM, GEORGETOWN UNIV, 74- *Concurrent Pos:* Vis prof, Col France, 72, Univ Col Swansea, UK, 76 & Ecole Polytechique Federale de Lausanne, Switz, 80. *Mem:* Am Asn Univ Profs; Am Chem Soc. *Res:* Thermodynamics and statistical mechanics of liquid crystals and liquid mixtures; theory of retention and selectivity in gas and liquid chromatography; weak organic complexes. *Mailing Add:* Dept Chem Georgetown Univ Washington DC 20057

MARTLAND, CARL DOUGLAS, b Providence, RI, Sept 22, 46; m 69; c 1. OPERATIONS RESEARCH. *Educ:* Mass Inst Technol, SB, 68, SM & CE, 72. *Prof Exp:* Res engr, 72-77, res assoc, 77-81, PRIN RES ASSOC & LECTR, MASS INST TECHNOL 81- *Concurrent Pos:* Sr consult, Multisyst, Inc, 78-; mem, Transportation Res Bd, Comt Railroad Operations Mgt, 79-; dir, Rail Group, Ctr Transportation Studies, Mass Inst Technol, 80- *Mem:* Am Railroad Eng Asn; AAAS. *Res:* Rail freight transportation, with a special emphasis on the use of the techniques of systems analysis in operations management, especially service reliability and equipment utilization. *Mailing Add:* Rm 1-142 Mass Inst Technol Cambridge MA 02139

MARTNER, SAMUEL (THEODORE), b Prairie du Chien, Wis, Apr 20, 18; m 42; c 2. GEOPHYSICS. *Educ:* Univ Calif, BA, 40, Calif Inst Technol, MS, 46, PhD(geophys), 49. *Prof Exp:* From prod engr to prod control mgr, Los Angeles Shipbldg & Drydock Co, 41-43; ship supvr & asst to repair gen mgr, Todd Shipyards Corp, 43-45; geologist, Standard Oil Co Calif, 46; geologist, Stanolind Oil & Gas Co Div, Standard Oil Co, Ind, 47-48, seismic interpreter, 48, asst party chief, 48-49, party chief, 49-50, tech group supvr, 51-52, res group supvr, 52-58, res sect supvr, Pan Am Petrol Corp, 58-64, div geophysicist, 65-67, asst chief geophysicist, 67-68, geophys res dir, 68-71, RES CONSULT, AMOCO PROD CO, 71- *Mem:* Seismol Soc Am; Soc Explor Geophys; Geol Soc Am; Am Geophys Union; Inst Elec & Electronics Eng. *Res:* Petroleum; earth sciences. *Mailing Add:* 2520 S Woodward Bl PO Box 591 Tulsa OK 74114

MARTO, PAUL JAMES, b Flushing, NY, Aug 15, 38; m 61; c 4. MECHANICAL & NUCLEAR ENGINEERING. *Educ:* Univ Notre Dame, BS, 60; Mass Inst Technol, SM, 62, ScD(nuclear eng), 65. *Prof Exp:* From asst prof to assoc prof, 65-76, PROF MECH ENG, NAVAL POSTGRAD SCH, 76-, CHMN MECH ENG, 78- *Concurrent Pos:* Consult, Lawrence Radiation Lab, 67-68 & SKF Industs, 71-73. *Mem:* Am Soc Mech Engrs; Am Soc Eng Educ. *Res:* Heat transfer; boiling, condensation; heat pipe operation; energy conversion. *Mailing Add:* Naval Postgrad Sch Monterey CA 93940

MARTOF, BERNARD STEPHEN, zoology, see previous edition

MARTON, JOHN PETER, b Budapest, Hungary, May 13, 33; Can citizen. SOLID STATE ELECTRONICS. *Educ:* Sci Univ, Budapest, BSc, 54; Univ Western Ont, PhD(solid state), 69. *Prof Exp:* DIR RES & DEVELOP, WELWYN CAN LTD, 63-; ASSOC PROF ENG PHYSICS, MCMASTER UNIV, 71- *Mem:* AAAS; Asn Prof Engrs Ont; Inst Elec & Electronics Engrs. *Res:* Solid state plasmas in thin films; electroless Ni-P deposition and properties; optical communication; cooperative physical phenomena in biological cells. *Mailing Add:* Dept of Eng Physics McMaster Univ Hamilton ON L8S 4K1 Can

MARTON, JOSEPH, b Budapest, Hungary, Mar 5, 19; US citizen; m 49; c 1. WOOD & FIBER CHEMISTRY. *Educ:* Pazmany Peter Univ, Hungary, BS & MS, 42, PhD(org chem), 43. *Prof Exp:* Asst prof org chem, Budapest Tech Univ, 45-47, lectr, 49-56; chemist, Arzola Chem Co, 47-49; res supvr, Res Inst Indust Org Chem, 49-56; res fel wood chem, Chalmers Univ Technol, Sweden, 56-60; res assoc wood & phys org chem, Charleston Res Lab, Westvaco Corp, SC, 60-66, res assoc, Phys Org & Surface Chem, 66-72, SR RES ASSOC, LAUREL RES CTR, WESTVACO CORP, 72- *Mem:* AAAS; Am Chem Soc; fel Tech Asn Pulp & Paper Indust; Swedish Chem Soc. *Res:* Chemistry and reaction of polymeric compounds; analysis and chemistry of fiber surfaces; colloid and surface chemistry of pulp and papermaking; printability of paper; forest improvement, lignin chemistry, enzyme reactions. *Mailing Add:* Laurel Res Ctr 11101 Johns Hopkins Rd Laurel MD 20810

MARTON, LAURENCE JAY, b Brooklyn, NY, Jan 14, 44; m 67; c 1. LABORATORY MEDICINE, CANCER. *Educ:* Yeshiva Univ, BA, 65; Albert Einstein Col Med, MD, 69. *Prof Exp:* Clin assoc cancer med, Baltimore Cancer Res Ctr, Nat Cancer Inst, 71-73; asst res biochemist neurosurg, Brain Tumor Res Ctr, 73-74, asst clin prof & asst dir clin chem, Dept Lab Med & Neurosurg, 74-75, asst prof & dir div clin chem, 75-78, assoc prof & actg chmn, 78-79, PROF LAB MED & NEUROSURG & CHMN, DEPT LAB MED, UNIV CALIF, SAN FRANCISCO, 79- *Concurrent Pos:* Nat Cancer Inst res career develop award, 75 & res grant, 75- *Mem:* Am Asn Cancer Res; Am Asn Clin Chem; AAAS; Asn Clin Sci; Acad Clin Lab Physicians & Scientists. *Res:* Biochemical markers for brain tumors; molecular and cellular biology of the polyamines; polyamine biosynthesis inhibitors as cancer chemotherapeutic agents; application of liquid chromatography to the clinical laboratory. *Mailing Add:* Dept of Lab Med Univ of Calif San Francisco CA 94143

MARTON, RENATA, b Krakow, Poland, July 27, 10; US citizen; m 38; c 2. CHEMISTRY. *Educ:* Univ Jagello, Poland, MS, 34, PhD, 36. *Prof Exp:* Asst chem, Univ Jagello, Poland, 34-38; res asst cellulose derivatives, Inst Chem, Sorbonne, 38-43; from researcher to tech mgr, Chem Indust, Hungary, 45-50; head dept, Pulp & Paper Res Inst, 50-56; Rockefeller Found fel, Austrian Wood Res Inst, 56-57; from asst prof to assoc prof pulp & paper res, 57-68, prof pulp & paper res, State Univ NY Col Forestry, 68-77, PROF & SR RES ASSOC, EMPIRE STATE PAPER RES INST, STATE UNIV NY COL ENVIRON SCI & FORESTRY, 77- *Honors & Awards:* Silver Medal, Pulp & Paper Indust, 77 & 80. *Mem:* Tech Asn Pulp & Paper Indust. *Res:* Fundamentals of pulp and papermaking fibers; morphology and nature of coloring materials in wood. *Mailing Add:* Empire State Paper Res Inst State Univ NY Col Environ Sci & Forestry Syracuse NY 13210

MARTONOSI, ANTHONY, b Szeged, Hungary, Nov 7, 28; US citizen; m 59; c 4. BIOCHEMISTRY. *Educ:* Univ Szeged, MD, 53. *Prof Exp:* Asst prof physiol, Univ Szeged, 54-57; Nat Acad Sci res fel biochem, Mass Gen Hosp, Boston, 57-59; assoc, Retina Found, 59-63, asst dir, 64-65; prof biochem, Sch Med, St Louis Univ, 65-79; PROF BIOCHEM, STATE UNIV NY, UPSTATE MED CTR, 79- *Concurrent Pos:* USPHS grant, 59-; estab investr, Am Heart Asn, 61-66; NSF grant, 63- *Mem:* Am Soc Biol Chem; Biophys Soc. *Res:* Biochemistry of muscle contraction; contractile proteins; structure and function of membranes. *Mailing Add:* Upstate Med Ctr State Univ NY Syracuse NY 13210

MARTSOLF, J DAVID, b Beaver Falls, Pa, Nov 26, 32; m 55; c 2. AGRICULTURAL METEOROLOGY. *Educ:* Univ Fla, BSA, 54, MSA, 62; Univ Mo-Columbia, PhD(atmospheric sci), 66. *Prof Exp:* Asst county agr agt, Agr Exten Serv, Univ Fla, 58-62, asst prof hort, 62-64; res asst surface energy balance study, Univ Mo-Columbia, 64-66; assoc prof agr climat, Pa State Univ, University Park, 66-77, prof microclimat, 77-79; PROF CLIMAT, INST FOOD & AGR SCI, UNIV FLA, GAINESVILLE, 79- *Mem:* Am Meteorol Soc; Agron Soc Am; Am Soc Hort Sci. *Res:* Frost protection of citrus and other tree crops; modification of plant microclimate; general energy balance of vegetative canopies. *Mailing Add:* Inst Food & Agr Sci 2121 HS-PP Univ Fla Gainesville FL 32605

MARTT, JACK M, b Ashland, Ky, Nov 9, 22; m 48; c 2. INTERNAL MEDICINE, CARDIOLOGY. *Educ:* Univ Mo, BS, 43; Wash Univ, MD, 46. *Prof Exp:* Asst prof internal med, Col Med, Univ Iowa, 55-56; from asst prof to prof, Sch Med, Univ Mo-Columbia, 56-69, dir cardiopulmonary lab, Med Ctr, 65-69; CARDIOLOGIST, SCOTT & WHITE CLIN, 69- *Concurrent Pos:* Fel coun clin cardiol, Am Heart Asn, 63. *Mem:* Fel Am Col Physicians; fel Am Col Cardiol. *Res:* Cardiology research primarily in atherosclerosis. *Mailing Add:* Dept of Med Scott & White Clin 2401 S 31st Temple TX 76501

MARTUCCI, JOHN A, b Charleroi, Pa, Sept 21, 32. NUCLEAR POWER CHEMISTRY, WATER CHEMISTRY. *Educ:* Univ Pittsburgh, BS, 54; Carnegie Inst Technol, BSIM, 65. *Prof Exp:* Chemist, Duquesne Light Co, Shippingport Atomic Power Sta, Pa, 56-57, actg radiochemist, 57-58, radiochemist, 58-60, reactor control chemist, 60-66; res engr, Kreisinger Develop Lab, Combustion Eng Inc, 66-67, sr proj engr, 67-68, mgr chem group, Nuclear Power Lab, 68-72, asst to dir, Nuclear Labs, 72-73; dir, Manor Mining & Minerals Co, 66-72, pres & dir, 73-80; CONSULT, 80- *Concurrent Pos:* Secy & treas, Laurel Ridge Coal Inc, 75-80. *Mem:* Fel Am Inst Chem; Am Soc Test & Mat; Am Nuclear Soc; Nat Asn Corrosion Engrs; United Surface Mine Operators. *Res:* Chemistry and corrosion problems for nuclear power plant technology, specifically stress corrosion, fission product release studies, neutron activation product problems and high temperature behavior of inorganic materials in aqueous solutions; radioactive waste preparation and management; coal technology. *Mailing Add:* 518 McKean Ave Charleroi PA 15022

MARTY, ROBERT JOSEPH, b Evanston, Ill, July 6, 31; m 62; c 2. FOREST ECONOMICS. *Educ:* Mich State Univ, BS, 54; Duke Univ, MF, 55; Harvard Univ, MPA, 59; Yale Univ, PhD(forestry), 62. *Prof Exp:* Res forester economics, Forest Serv, USDA, 55-65, chief forest econ br, 65-67; assoc prof forestry, 67-71, PROF FORESTRY, MICH STATE UNIV, 71-, PROF RESOURCE DEVELOP, 77- *Mem:* Soc Am Foresters; Econ Asn. *Res:* Timber production economics; economics of public, natural resource programs and policies. *Mailing Add:* Dept of Forestry Mich State Univ East Lansing MI 48824

MARTY, ROGER HENRY, b Sterling, Ohio, Oct 16, 42; m 64; c 2. TOPOLOGY. *Educ:* Kent State Univ, BS, 64; Pa State Univ, MS, 66, PhD(math), 69. *Prof Exp:* Asst prof math, 69-73, ASSOC PROF MATH, CLEVELAND STATE UNIV, 73- *Mem:* Am Math Soc. *Res:* Set-theoretic topology; general topology; set-theory. *Mailing Add:* Dept of Math Cleveland State Univ Cleveland OH 44115

MARTY, WAYNE GEORGE, b LuVerne, Iowa, Feb 14, 32; m 54; c 3. PARASITOLOGY. *Educ:* Westmar Col, BA, 53; Univ Iowa, MS, 59, PhD(zool), 62. *Prof Exp:* Teacher high sch, Iowa, 55-57; PROF BIOL, WESTMAR COL, 59- *Concurrent Pos:* NIH fel malariology, 69-70; instr & researcher, Silliman Univ, Philippines, 78-79. *Mem:* Am Soc Parasitol; Nat Asn Biol Teachers. *Res:* Experimental infections of parasites in abnormal hosts, specifically Trichinella Spiralis in chickens. *Mailing Add:* RR 2 LeMars IA 51031

MARTZ, BILL L, b Anderson, Ind, Jan 17, 22; m 48; c 3. MEDICINE. *Educ:* DePauw Univ, AB, 44; Ind Univ, MD, 45; Am Bd Internal Med, dipl. *Prof Exp:* Asst med serv, 53-55, from asst prof to assoc prof, 55-67, PROF MED, SCH MED, IND UNIV, INDIANAPOLIS, 67-; DIR CLIN INVEST, DOW CHEM CO, 74- *Concurrent Pos:* Assoc med serv, Indianapolis Gen Hosp, 53-55, mem vis staff, Med Serv, 56-; mem coun high blood pressure res, Am Heart Asn; res physician, Marion County Gen Hosp, 51-60, dir, Lilly Lab Clin Res, 60-72; chief med, Kansas City Gen Hosp, 72-74. *Mem:* AMA; Am Col Physicians; Am Fedn Clin Res; Am Col Cardiol; Am Soc Clin Pharmacol & Therapeut. *Res:* Cardiovascular renal disease and clinical pharmacology. *Mailing Add:* Dow Chem Co PO Box 68511 Indianapolis IN 46268

MARTZ, DOWELL EDWARD, b Livonia, Mo, Sept 29, 23; m 50; c 4. PHYSICS. *Educ:* Union Col, Nebr, BA, 50; Vanderbilt Univ, MS, 53; Colo State Univ, PhD, 68. *Prof Exp:* Physicist, US Naval Ord Lab, 53-61; assoc prof physics, Pac Union Col, 61-62; sr res physicist, Calif Inst Technol, 62-64; assoc prof physics, 64-74, PROF PHYSICS, PAC UNION COL, 74- *Concurrent Pos:* Consult, Calif Inst Technol, 61- & Ames Res Lab, NASA, 64-65. *Mem:* Optical Soc Am; Sigma Xi; Am Inst Physics. *Res:* Infrared optics, detectors, astronomy and space research; application to long wavelength. *Mailing Add:* Dept of Physics Pac Union Col Angwin CA 94508

MARTZ, ERIC, b Columbus, Ind, Apr 30, 40; m 71; c 2. CELLULAR IMMUNOLOGY. *Educ:* Oberlin Col, AB, 63; Johns Hopkins Univ, PhD(biol), 69. *Prof Exp:* Fel, Dept Biol, Princeton Univ, 69-70; fel, Dept Pathol, Harvard Med Sch, 70, assoc prof immunol, 77-81; ASSOC PROF IMMUNOL, DEPT MICROBIOL, UNIV MASS, AMHERST, 81- *Concurrent Pos:* Assoc ed, J Immunol, 77-79. *Mem:* Am Asn Immunologists. *Res:* Mechanism of T lymphocyte mediated killing; cell adhesion; role of calcium in lymphocyte function. *Mailing Add:* Dept Microbiol Univ Mass Amherst MA 01003

MARTZ, FREDRIC A, b Columbia City, Ind, May 24, 35; m 59; c 5. ANIMAL NUTRITION, DAIRY SCIENCE. *Educ:* Purdue Univ, BS, 57, MS, 59, PhD(dairy sci), 61. *Prof Exp:* Instr dairy sci, Purdue Univ, 60-61; from asst prof to assoc prof, 61-73, forage livestock res coord-agr, 73-78, PROF DAIRY SCI, UNIV MO-COLUMBIA, 73-, CHMN DEPT, 78- *Concurrent Pos:* NIH grant, 69; vis assoc prof, Cornell Univ, 71-72; USDA grants, 80 & 81. *Honors & Awards:* Award of Merit, Gamma Sigma Delta, 73; Res Award, NSF, 75; Award of Merit, Am Forage & Grassland Soc, 78. *Mem:* Am Inst Nutrit; Am Dairy Sci Asn; Am Soc Animal Sci. *Res:* Digestibility of feedstuffs for ruminant; regulation of food intake in ruminant; recycling of fibrous wastes through ruminant feeds; forage utilization. *Mailing Add:* Dept Dairy Sci 104 Eckles Hall Univ of Mo Columbia MO 65201

MARTZ, HARRY FRANKLIN, JR, b Cumberland, Md, June 16, 42; m 64; c 2. STATISTICS, OPERATIONS RESEARCH. *Educ:* Frostburg State Col, BS, 64; Va Polytech Inst, PhD(statist), 68. *Prof Exp:* From asst prof to assoc prof indust eng & statist, Tex Tech Univ, 67-77; MEM STAFF, ENERGY SYSTS & STATIST, LOS ALAMOS SCI LAB, 77- *Concurrent Pos:* NASA grants, 69-71. *Mem:* AAAS; Inst Math Statist; Am Inst Indust Eng; Am Statist Asn. *Res:* Empirical Bayes decision theory; reliability theory; trajectory estimation and filter theory; stochastic processes. *Mailing Add:* Group S-1/MS 600 Los Alamos Sci Lab PO Box 1663 Los Alamos NM 87544

MARTZ, LYLE E(RWIN), b Grand Rapids, Mich, Feb 15, 22; m 52; c 2. CHEMICAL ENGINEERING. *Educ:* Univ Mich, BSE, 43. *Prof Exp:* Chem engr, 43-44 & 46-64, proj leader, 64-67, sr process engr, 67-71, res engr, 71-72, RES SPECIALIST, DOW CHEM USA, 72- *Mem:* Am Chem Soc; Am Inst Chem Engrs. *Res:* Pilot plant operation in research and development of industrial organic chemicals; design of organic chemical processes. *Mailing Add:* 2008 Airfield Lane Midland MI 48640

MARUCA, ROBERT EUGENE, b Buckhannon, WVa, Nov 25, 41; m 62; c 2. INORGANIC CHEMISTRY. *Educ:* WVa Wesleyan Col, BS, 63; Cornell Univ, PhD(chem), 66. *Prof Exp:* NIH fel chem, Ind Univ, 66-68; asst prof, Miami Univ, 68-72; assoc prof, 72-80, CHMN DIV NATURAL SCI, ALDERSON-BROADDUS COL, 75-, PROF CHEM, 80-, CHARLES MCCLUNG SWITZER CHMN CHEM, 80- *Res:* Chemistry of the mixed compounds of boron, silicon and nitrogen. *Mailing Add:* Dept of Natural Sci Alderson-Broaddus Col Philippi WV 24616

MARUCCI, AMERICO ALVIN, b Orange, NJ, July 19, 23; m; c 2. IMMUNOCHEMISTRY. *Educ:* Rutgers Univ, BS, 44; Johns Hopkins Univ, ScM, 51, ScD, 54. *Prof Exp:* Res biochemist immunochem, USDA, Denmark, 54-56; from asst prof to assoc prof microbiol, 56-74, PROF MICROBIOL, COL MED, STATE UNIV NY UPSTATE MED CTR, 74- *Concurrent Pos:* Consult, Syracuse Bur Labs, 60- *Mem:* Am Asn Immunol; Am Soc Microbiol. *Res:* Immunochemistry of staphylococcal hemolysins; mechanism and measurement of antigen-antibody reactions; enzyme-antienzyme studies; immunohistochemical techniques. *Mailing Add:* Dept of Microbiol 766 Irving Ave State Univ of NY Upstate Med Ctr Syracuse NY 13210

MARULLO, NICASIO PHILIP, b Apr 13, 30; US citizen; m 54; c 2. ORGANIC CHEMISTRY. *Educ:* Queen's Col, NY, BS, 52; Polytech Inst Brooklyn, PhD(chem), 61. *Prof Exp:* NIH fel & res assoc chem, Calif Inst Technol, 60-61; from asst prof to assoc prof, 61-74, PROF CHEM, CLEMSON UNIV, 74- *Mem:* Am Chem Soc. *Res:* Organic reaction mechanisms; rate processes by nuclear magnetic resonance; coordination compounds of alkali metal salts. *Mailing Add:* Dept of Chem Clemson Univ Clemson SC 29631

MARUM, JAMES PATRICK, biological oceanography, see previous edition

MARUSYK, RAYMOND GEORGE, b Yellowknife, NT, Mar 19, 42; m 66. VIROLOGY. *Educ:* Univ Alta, BSc, 65, MSc, 67; Karolinska Inst, Sweden, Fil dr(virol), 72. *Prof Exp:* Asst prof biochem, 72-73, asst prof med bact, 73-77, ASSOC PROF MED MICROBIOL, UNIV ALTA, 77- *Concurrent Pos:* vis prof & exchange scientist molecular virol, Nat Inst Health & Med Res, Lille, France, 78-79; Can deleg, Fifth Int Cong Virol, 81, chmn, Seventh Int Cong Virol, 87; chmn, Sixth Int Conf Comp Virol, 82. *Mem:* Can Soc Microbiologists; Am Microbiol Soc; NY Acad Sci; Tissue Cult Asn; Can Col Microbiologists (pres, 80-810. *Res:* Structural and functional relationships of viral capsid components. *Mailing Add:* Dept Med Microbiol Fac Med Univ Alta Edmonton AB T6G 2G7 Can

MARUYAMA, GEORGE MASAO, b Las Animas, Colo, June 15, 18; m 46; c 2. CHEMISTRY. *Educ:* Western State Col Colo, BA, 41; Univ Wis, MS, 48; Am Bd Bioanal, dipl, 67. *Prof Exp:* BIOCHEMIST & ASST DIR LAB, MED ASSOCS CLIN, 48- *Mem:* AAAS; Am Asn Bioanalysts (pres-elect, 65-66, pres, 66-67); Am Chem Soc; Am Asn Clin Chem; fel Am Inst Chemists. *Res:* Clinical chemistry. *Mailing Add:* 1650 Atlantic St Dubuque IA 52001

MARUYAMA, YOSH, b Pasadena, Calif, Apr 30, 30; m 54; c 4. RADIOTHERAPY, RADIOBIOLOGY. *Educ:* Univ Calif, Berkeley, AB, 51; Univ Calif, San Francisco, MD, 55. *Prof Exp:* Intern, San Francisco Hosp, Calif, 55-56; residency, Mass Gen Hosp, Boston, 58-61; James Picker advan acad fel, Stanford Univ, 62-64, traveling fel, Eng, France, Scand, 64; from asst prof to assoc prof radiol, Col Med Sci, Univ Minn, 64-70, admin dir div radiother, 68-70; PROF RADIATION MED, CHMN DEPT & DIR, RADIATION CANCER CTR, COL MED, UNIV KY, 70- *Concurrent Pos:* Consult, Vet Admin Hosp; assoc ed, Appl Radiol. *Mem:* AAAS; Radiation Res Soc; Am Asn Cancer Res; Radiol Soc NAm; Am Soc Therapeut Radiol. *Res:* Radiation medicine, tumor cell biology; mouse leukemia; cell kinetics; neutron therapy. *Mailing Add:* Dept of Radiation Med Univ of Ky Med Ctr Lexington KY 40506

MARVEL, CARL SHIPP, b Waynesville, Ill, Sept 11, 94; m 33; c 2. ORGANIC POLYMER CHEMISTRY. *Educ:* Ill Wesleyan Univ, AB & MS, 15; Univ Ill, MA, 16, PhD(org chem), 20. *Hon Degrees:* DSc, Ill Wesleyan Univ, 46 & Univ Ill, 63; hon Dr, Cath Univ Louvain, 70. *Prof Exp:* Instr chem, 20-21, assoc, 21-23, from asst prof to prof, 23-53, res prof, 53-61, EMER RES PROF, UNIV ILL, 61-; prof chem, Univ Ariz, 61-78; RETIRED. *Concurrent Pos:* Mem Bd Coord Malaria Studies, 44-46; chmn panel synthesis antimalarial drugs, Nat Res Coun, 44-46, mem mat adv bd, 54-64, chmn, 62-64; mem, Nat Adv Health Coun, 45-47; chmn, Int Union Chem Comn Encyclop Compendia, 47-50; chmn adv panel, NSF, 52-54; collabr southern utilization res br, Agr Res Serv, USDA, 54-56; mem sci adv bd, Robert A Welch Found, Tex, 71- *Honors & Awards:* Nichols Medal, 44, Gibbs Medal, 50, Priestley Medal, 56, Witco Award, 64, Madison Marshall Award, 66 & Borden Found Award, 73, Am Chem Soc; Gold Medal, Am Inst Chem, 55; Int Award, Soc Plastics Eng, 64; Perkin Medal, Soc Chem Indust, 65; Distinguished Serv Award, Air Force Mat Lab, 66; Air Force Systs Command Award, 66; Chem Pioneer Award, 67; John R Kuebler Award, Alpha Chi Sigma Fraternity, 70. *Mem:* Nat Acad Sci; AAAS; Am Chem Soc (pres, 45); Am Acad Arts & Sci; fel NY Acad Sci. *Res:* Synthetic organic chemistry; chemistry of high polymers; polynes; organometallic compounds; free radicals; rearrangements; natural products; hydrogen bonding; synthesis of polymers, especially those with high thermal stability; heat stable organic polymers. *Mailing Add:* Dept of Chem Univ of Ariz Bldg 37 Rm 618 Tucson AZ 85721

MARVEL, JOHN THOMAS, b Champaign, Ill, Sept 14, 38; div; c 3. ORGANIC CHEMISTRY, BIOCHEMISTRY. *Educ:* Univ Ill, AB, 59; Mass Inst Technol, PhD(chem), 64. *Prof Exp:* Res assoc agr biochem, Univ Ariz, 64-65, asst agr biochemist, 65-68; sr res chemist, 68-72, sr res group leader, Monsanto Agr Prod Co, 72-75, mgr res, 75-78, assoc dir res, 78-79, DIR RES, MONSANTO AGR PROD CO, MONSANTO CO, 81-, PRES & GEN MGR, RES DIV, 81- *Mem:* AAAS; Am Chem Soc; Royal Chem Soc; NY Acad Sci; Weed Sci Soc Am. *Res:* Synthesis of carbohydrates and nucleic acids; nuclear magnetic resonance spectroscopy; mass spectrometry; photochemistry; pesticide metabolism; synthesis and plant growth regulators, plant biochemisty, cell biology. *Mailing Add:* 800 N Lindbergh Blvd St Louis MO 63166

MARVEL, MASON E, b Brewton, Ala, Dec 11, 21; m 45; c 3. HORTICULTURE, PLANT PATHOLOGY. *Educ:* Univ Mass, BS, 50; Va Polytech Inst, MS, 52; WVa Univ, PhD, 70. *Prof Exp:* Instr hort, WVa Univ, 51-56; tech rep, Calif Chem Corp, 56-57; from asst prof to assoc prof, Univ Fla, 57-70, prof veg crops, 70-80; RETIRED. *Concurrent Pos:* Chief party, Contract Team to Nat Agr Ctr, Saigon, SVietnam, 70-72, asst dir tech assistance, Int Progs Ctr Trop Agr Inst, 72-75, team leader, Pulse Prod Prog, Near East Found, Ethiopia, 75-77; consult, Hanover Brands Inc, 73-75, AID & World Bank, 78-; veg crops scientist, Int Agr Develop Serv, Bandung, Indonesia, 79. *Mem:* Am Soc Hort Sci; Asn Univ Dirs Int Agr Progs. *Res:* Tropical vegetable crops production and marketing. *Mailing Add:* 3026 McCarty IFAS Univ of Fla Gainesville FL 32611

MARVELL, ELLIOT NELSON, b New Bedford, Mass, Sept 10, 22; m 44; c 2. ORGANIC CHEMISTRY. *Educ:* Brown Univ, BS, 43; Univ Ill, PhD(org chem), 48. *Prof Exp:* From instr to assoc prof org chem, 48-63, PROF ORG CHEM, ORE STATE UNIV, 63- *Concurrent Pos:* NSF fel, 56-57; Petrol Res Fund int award, 65-66. *Mem:* Am Chem Soc; Royal Soc Chem; Swiss Chem Soc. *Res:* Molecular rearrangements; synthesis of alicyclic molecules; pericyclic reactions; sesquiterpene synthesis. *Mailing Add:* Dept of Chem Ore State Univ Corvallis OR 97330

MARVIN, DONALD ARTHUR, b New York, NY, June 25, 34; m 61. STRUCTURAL BIOLOGY. *Educ:* Yale Univ, BS, 56; Univ London, PhD(physics), 60. *Prof Exp:* Fel molecular biol, Max Planck Inst Virus Res, Tubingen, Ger, 60-65; from asst prof to assoc prof, Yale Univ, 66-75; vis scholar, Stanford Univ, 76; HEAD GROUP, EUROP MOLECULAR BIOL LAB, 76- *Mem:* Biophys Soc. *Res:* Structure and function of biologic systems on molecular level. *Mailing Add:* Europ Molecular Biol Lab Postfach 10.2209 Heidelberg Germany, Federal Republic of

MARVIN, HENRY HOWARD, JR, b Lincoln, Nebr, Mar 9, 23; m 44; c 2. PHYSICAL CHEMISTRY. *Educ:* Univ Nebr, BA, 47; Univ Wis, PhD(chem), 50. *Prof Exp:* Res assoc phys chem, Res Lab, Gen Elec Co, 50-53, liaison scientist chem, 53-55, personnel adminr, 56-58, mgr solid state chem, 59-61, mgr eng capacitor dept, 62-64, mgr lighting res lab, Ohio, 64-69, gen mgr, High Intensity Quartz Lamp Dept, 69-75; dir div solar energy, Dept Energy, 75-79; VPRES TECHNOL, BRUNSWICK CORP, 79- *Mem:* Am Chem Soc. *Mailing Add:* Brunswick Corp One Brunswick Plaza Skokie IL 60077

MARVIN, HORACE NEWELL, b Camden, Del, Apr 20, 15; m 40; c 5. ANATOMY, ENDOCRINOLOGY. *Educ:* Morningside Col, BA, 36; Univ Wis, MA, 38, PhD(zool), 41. *Hon Degrees:* DSc, Morningside Col, 69. *Prof Exp:* Asst, Morningside Col, 32-36; asst zool, Univ Wis, 36-41; spec investr, Dept Genetics, Carnegie Inst, 41-42; from instr to asst prof anat, Med Sch, Univ Ark, 42-48, head dept biol res, Univ Tex M D Anderson Hosp Cancer Res, 48-49; assoc prof anat, 49-58, head dept, 58-67, assoc dean, 65-77, PROF ANAT, COL MED, UNIV ARK MED SCI CAMPUS, LITTLE ROCK, 58- *Concurrent Pos:* Vis prof, Univ Lagos, 63. *Mem:* Am Asn Anat; Asn Am Med Cols. *Res:* Reproductive endocrinology; curriculum. *Mailing Add:* Dept of Anat Slot 510 Univ Ark Med Sci Campus Little Rock AR 72201

MARVIN, PHILIP ROGER, b Troy, NY, May 1, 16; m 42. SOLID STATE SCIENCE. *Educ:* Rensselaer Polytech Inst, BS, 37; Ind Univ, DCS, 51; La Salle Col, LLB, 54. *Prof Exp:* Engr, Gen Elec Co, 37-42; dir chem & metall eng, Bendix Aviation Corp, NY, 43-44; dir res & develop, Milwaukee Gas Specialty Co, 45-52; vpres & dir, Commonwealth Eng Co, Ohio, 52-54 & Am Viscose Corp, 54-56; mgr res & develop div, Am Mgt Asn, 56-64; pres, Clark, Cooper, Field & Wohl, 64-65; dean prof develop, 65-73, PROF DEVELOP & ADMIN, UNIV CINCINNATI, 73- *Concurrent Pos:* Lectr, Bridgeport Eng Inst, 37-43, Jr Col Conn, 40-41 & war training prog, Yale Univ, 41-44; lectr, US Air Force Inst Technol, 53-; consult, NASA, 66- & Am Tel & Tel, 76- *Mem:* AAAS; Am Inst Aeronaut & Astronaut; Am Defense Preparedness Asn; Inst Elec & Electronics Eng. *Res:* Bio-mechanics; physics of the solid state; metallurgy of electrical steel and beryllium copper; x-ray diffraction; design of electronic controls; thermoelectric phenomena; rectification phenomena. *Mailing Add:* Mail Code 115 Univ of Cincinnati Cincinnati OH 45221

MARVIN, RICHARD F(REDERICK), b Bozeman, Mont, May 1, 26; m 55; c 2. GEOLOGICAL ENGINEERING, GEOLOGY. *Educ:* Mont Sch Mines, BS, 50, MS, 52. *Prof Exp:* Geologist, Petrol & Geochem Br, 52-57, geologist, Ground Water Br, 57-61, GEOLOGIST, ISOTOPE GEOL BR, US GEOL SURV, 61- *Mem:* AAAS; Am Geophys Union; Geol Soc Am. *Res:* Determination and evaluation of potassium-argon ages pertaining to geologic investigations. *Mailing Add:* 2470 Miller St Lakewood CO 80215

MARVIN, URSULA BAILEY, b Bradford, Vt, Aug 20, 21; m 52. MINERALOGY, METEORITICS. *Educ:* Tufts Univ, BA, 43; Harvard Univ, MS, 46, PhD, 69. *Prof Exp:* Asst silicate chem, Univ Chicago. 47-50; mineralogist, Union Carbide Ore Co, NY, 53-58; instr mineral, Tufts Univ, 58-61; coordr, Fed Women's Prog, 73-76, GEOLOGIST, SMITHSONIAN ASTROPHYS OBSERV, 61- *Concurrent Pos:* Assoc. Harvard Col Observ, 65-; lectr, Tufts Univ, 68-69, mem bd of trustees, 75-; lectr, Harvard Univ, 74-; mem, Lunar Sample Anal Planning Team, NASA, 76-78; vis prof, Dept Chem, Ariz State Univ, 78; mem, Antarctic Search Meteorites Team, Univ Pittsburgh, NSF, 78-79 & 81-82; mem exec comt, Hist Geol, Nat Res Coun, Nat Acad Sci, 79- *Mem:* AAAS; fel Geol Soc Am; Meteoritical Soc (vpres, 73-74, pres, 75-76); Am Geophys Union; Sigma Xi. *Res:* Mineralogy and petrology of meteorites and lunar samples; history of geology. *Mailing Add:* Smithsonian Astrophys Observ 60 Garden St Cambridge MA 02138

MARWICK, IAN J, electrical engineering, see previous edition

MARWIL, S(TANLEY) J(ACKSON), b Henderson, Tex, Aug 13, 21; m; c 2. CHEMICAL ENGINEERING. *Educ:* Agr & Mech Col, Tex, BS, 43, MS, 47. *Prof Exp:* Staff asst data correlation, 47-49, group leader adsorption develop, 49-50, staff asst surv & correlation, 50-51, staff engr, 51-55, staff engr oil prod develop, 55-56, group leader crystallization develop, 56-57, group leader exp plastics, 57-60, sect mgr, Chem Processes Sect, 60-66, Explor Chem Sect, 66-69 & Chem Develop Sect, Org Chem Br, Res & Develop Div, 69-75, sect leader, Chem Develop Sect, Chem Br, 75-80, SUPVR, CHEM DEVELOP SECT, CHEM DEVELOP BR, RES & DEVELOP DIV, PHILLIPS PETROL CO, 80- *Mem:* Am Inst Chem Engrs. *Res:* High temperature and high pressure thermal and catalytic reactions; high vacuum distillation; high density particle-form polyethylene; hydrocarbon separations, including crystallization, extraction and adsorption; semi-works production of high productivity catalysts, specialty olefins, alkylaromatics and other petrochemicals. *Mailing Add:* Phillips Petrol Co Phillips Res Ctr Bartlesville OK 74004

MARWIN, RICHARD MARTIN, b Minneapolis, Minn, Dec 10, 18; m 42; c 1. MEDICAL MICROBIOLOGY, MEDICAL MYCOLOGY. *Educ:* Univ Minn, BA, 41, MS, 43, PhD(bact), 47; Am Bd Med Microbiol, dipl, 62. *Prof Exp:* Teaching asst med bact, Med Sch, Univ Minn, 41-44, instr, 45-48; assoc prof, 48-51, chmn dept, 48-62, prof bact, 51-80, PROF MICROBIOL, MED SCH, UNIV NDAK, 80- *Concurrent Pos:* Chief lab bact & blood bank, Univ Minn Hosps, 45-47. *Mem:* Am Soc Microbiol; Mycol Soc Am. *Res:* Culture media modification for growth of pathogenic bacteria; effects of chemicals on pathogenic fungi of man. *Mailing Add:* Dept of Microbiol Univ NDak Sch of Med Grand Forks ND 58201

MARWITZ, JOHN D, b Brownwood, Tex, March 6, 37; m 59; c 5. ATMOSPHERIC SCIENCE. *Educ:* Colo State Univ, BS, 59, MS, 65; McGill Univ, PhD(meteorol), 71. *Prof Exp:* Res asst meteorol, Colo State Univ, 62-65, instr, 65-67; assoc prof, 67-78, PROF ATMOSPHERIC SCI, UNIV WYO, 78- *Mem:* Am Meteorol Soc; Sigma Xi; Royal Meteorol Soc; AAAS. *Res:* Severe thunderstorms; hailstorm modification; the dynamics, kinematics, precipitation processes and modification of orographic winter storms; wind energy and characteristics. *Mailing Add:* Dept Atmospheric Sci PO Box 3038 Univ Sta Laramie WY 82071

MARX, DONALD HENRY, b Ocean Falls, BC, Oct 3. 36; US citizen; m 57; c 5. PLANT PATHOLOGY, SOIL MICROBIOLOGY. *Educ:* Univ Ga, BSA, 61, MS, 62; NC State Univ, PhD(plant path), 66. *Prof Exp:* PLANT PATHOLOGIST, FORESTRY SCI LAB, SOUTHEASTERN FOREST EXP STA, 62- *Concurrent Pos:* Adv, Int Union Forest Res Orgn, 63. *Honors & Awards:* Arthur Fleming Award, 75; Barrington Moore Award, 77; Ruth Allen Award, 77. *Mem:* AAAS; Am Phytopath Soc; Am Inst Biol Scientists. *Res:* Mycorrhizae of conifers and hardwoods; ecology and parasitism of soil-borne organisms; reforestation of adverse sites by use of specific mycorrhizae. *Mailing Add:* Forestry Sci Lab Carlton St Southeastern Forest Exp Sta Athens GA 30602

MARX, EGON, b Cologne, Ger, Apr 4, 37; m 65; c 2. WAVE OPTICS, RELATIVISTIC QUANTUM MECHANICS. *Educ:* Univ Chile, EE, 59; Calif Inst Technol, PhD(physics), 63. *Prof Exp:* Assoc investr physics, Univ Chile, 63-65, independent investr, 65; asst prof, Clarkson Col Technol, 65-67; asst prof, Drexel Univ, 67-72; physicist, Harry Diamond Labs, 72-80; PHYSICIST, NAT BUR STANDARDS, 80- *Res:* Theory and computation of electromagnetic wave propagation and scattering; classical and quantized fields, including probability amplitudes in relativistic quantum mechanics; discrete computer simulation of communications systems. *Mailing Add:* Nat Bur Standards Washington DC 20234

MARX, GEORGE DONALD, b Antigo, Wis, Apr 30, 36; m 64; c 2. AGRICULTURE, ANIMAL PHYSIOLOGY. *Educ:* Univ Wis-River Falls, BS, 58; SDak State Univ, MS, 60; Univ Minn, Minneapolis, PhD(animal sci), 64. *Prof Exp:* Farm planner, Soil Conserv Serv, USDA, 57-58; asst dairy sci, SDak State Univ, 58-60; asst animal sci, Univ Minn, Minneapolis & St Paul, 60-64; from instr to assoc prof, 64-77, PROF AGR, AGR EXP STA, UNIV MINN, CROOKSTON, 77- *Mem:* Am Dairy Sci Asn; Am Soc Animal Sci; Int Asn Immunity. *Res:* Animal management. *Mailing Add:* Agr Exp Sta Univ of Minn Crookston MN 56716

MARX, GERALD ALVIN, b Milwaukee, Wis, Mar 7, 30; m 65. AGRONOMY, PLANT PATHOLOGY. *Educ:* Univ Wis, BS, 53, MS, 56, PhD(agron), 59. *Prof Exp:* PLANT BREEDER, DEPT SEED & VEG SCI, AGR EXP STA, CORNELL UNIV, 59- *Mem:* AAAS; Am Soc Agron; Am Genetic Asn; Crop Sci Soc Am; Am Phytopath Soc. *Res:* Vegetable crop breeding and genetics; specialty genetics of pisum. *Mailing Add:* Dept of Seed & Veg Sci Cornell Univ Agr Exp Sta Geneva NY 14456

MARX, GERTIE F, b Frankfurt am Main, Ger, Feb 13, 12; US Citizen; m 40. ANESTHESIOLOGY. *Educ:* Univ Bern, MD, 37. *Prof Exp:* From asst attend to assoc atten anesthesiologist, Beth Israel Hosp, New York, 43-55; from asst prof to assoc prof, 55-70, PROF ANESTHESIOL, ALBERT EINSTEIN COL MED, 70-; ATTEND ANESTHESIOLOGIST, BRONX MUNIC HOSP CTR, 55- *Concurrent Pos:* Attend anesthesiologist, Bronx Vet Admin Hosp, 66-72, consult, 72- *Honors & Awards:* Gold Medal, Obstet Anaesthetist Asn, Eng, 80. *Mem:* Fel Am Soc Anesthesiol; AMA; fel NY Acad Med; NY Acad Sci; assoc fel, Am Col Obstetricians & Gynecologists. *Res:* Obstetric anesthesia. *Mailing Add:* Dept of Anesthesiol Albert Einstein Col of Med Bronx NY 10461

MARX, HYMEN, b Chicago, Ill, June 27, 25; m 50; c 2. HERPETOLOGY. *Educ:* Roosevelt Univ, BS, 49. *Prof Exp:* Asst cur, Div Amphibians & Reptiles, 50-64, assoc cur, 65-73, head div, 70-79, CUR, FIELD MUS NATURAL HIST, 73- *Concurrent Pos:* Consult, US Naval Med Res Unit, Egypt, 53; vis scientist, NSF Field Mus, 67-71; lectr, Univ Chicago, 73- *Mem:* Am Soc Ichthyol & Herpet; Soc Study Amphibians & Reptiles. *Res:* Reptiles; systematics; North Africa and Southwestern Asia herpetology; zoogeography of Old World reptiles; phyletic character analysis; phylogeny of vipers; phylogenetic theory. *Mailing Add:* Field Mus Natural Hist Roosevelt Rd & Lakeshore Dr Chicago IL 60605

MARX, JAMES JOHN, JR, b Paris, Tex, Dec 17, 44; m 73; c 1. IMMUNOPATHOLOGY. *Educ:* St Vincent Col, BA, 66; WVa Univ, MS, 70, PhD(microbiol), 73. *Prof Exp:* RES SCIENTIST IMMUNOL, MARSHFIELD MED FOUND, 73- *Concurrent Pos:* Investr grants, Am Lung Asn, 74 & Nat Heart & Lung Inst, 75; lectr, Sch Med Technol, St Joseph's Hosp, 74-79; co investr, Nat Inst Occup Safety & Health, 76 & Muscular Dystrophy Asn, 79. *Mem:* Am Acad Allergy; Am Asn Immunologists; Am Lung Asn; Am Soc Microbiol; Am Sco Clin Immunol. *Res:* Immunologic mechanisms involved in occupational diseases; drug sensitivity of human tumor cells; clinical immunology. *Mailing Add:* Marshfield Med Found 510 NSt Joseph Ave Marshfield WI 54449

MARX, JOHN NORBERT, b Columbus, Ohio, Oct 31, 37. ORGANIC CHEMISTRY. *Educ:* St Benedict's Col, Kans, BS, 62; Univ Kans, PhD(org chem), 65. *Prof Exp:* Fel org chem, Cambridge Univ, 65-66 & Johns Hopkins Univ, 66-67; asst prof, 67-73, ASSOC PROF ORG CHEM, TEX TECH UNIV, 73- *Mem:* Am Chem Soc; Am Inst Chemists; The Chem Soc. *Res:* Structural determination and synthesis of natural products, especially terpenes and steroids; new synthetic methods; stereochemistry; cyclohexadienone rearrangements; migrations of electronegative groups. *Mailing Add:* Dept of Chem Tex Tech Univ Lubbock TX 79409

MARX, JOSEPH VINCENT, b Joplin, Mo, Mar 19, 43; m 67. CLINICAL BIOCHEMISTRY. *Educ:* Johns Hopkins Univ, AB, 65; State Univ NY Upstate Med Ctr, PhD(biochem), 69. *Prof Exp:* From assoc scientist to sr scientist biochem, 69-73, PRIN SCIENTIST APPL SCI, ORTHO DIAGNOSTICS, INC, 74- *Mem:* Am Asn Clin Chemists; Am Chem Soc; Soc Cryobiol; NY Acad Sci. *Res:* Applied research and development including techniques in protein separation and purification, clinical enzymology, blood coagulation and clinical hematology. *Mailing Add:* RD 1 Sidney Rd Pittstown NJ 08867

MARX, KENNETH ALLAN, b US. BIOPHYSICAL CHEMISTRY. *Educ:* Univ San Diego, BS, 68; Univ Calif, Berkeley, PhD(chem), 73. *Prof Exp:* Res assoc chem, Univ Calif, Berkeley, 73-74; fel epigenetics, Muscular Dystrophy Asn Am, Univ Edinburgh, 74-76 & cell biol, Worcester Found, 76-77; ASST PROF CHEM, DARTMOUTH COL, 77- *Concurrent Pos:* Prin investr, NIH grants. *Mem:* Am Chem Soc; Biophys Soc; Am Soc Cell Biol. *Res:* Structure and function of chromosomes; organization of nucleic acids in bacteriophage and viruses; unusual nuclease-resistancy; conserved DNA sequences in eukaryotic chromosomes. *Mailing Add:* Dept Chem Dartmouth Col Hanover NH 03755

MARX, KENNETH DONALD, b Amity, Ore, Mar 13, 40; m 63; c 2. PHYSICS, ELECTRICAL ENGINEERING. *Educ:* Ore State Univ, BS, 61; Univ Calif, Davis, MS, 65, PhD(appl sci), 68. *Prof Exp:* Staff mem, Sandia Labs, 61-65 & 68-74; physicist, Lawrence Livermore Lab, 74-79; MEM STAFF, SANDIA NAT LABS, 79- *Concurrent Pos:* Lectr, Univ Calif, Davis/Livermore, 69-79. *Mem:* Am Phys Soc. *Res:* Plasma physics; collisional effects; computational physics; electromagnetic theory. *Mailing Add:* Div 8153 Sandia Nat Lab Livermore CA 94550

MARX, MICHAEL, b Stuttgart, Ger, Nov 10, 33; US citizen; m 63; c 3. ORGANIC CHEMISTRY. *Educ:* Dartmouth Col, BA, 54; Columbia Univ, MA, 64, PhD(chem), 66. *Prof Exp:* Chemist, Lederle Labs Div, Am Cyanamid Co, 54-63; fel, Stanford Univ, 66-67; chemist, 67-69, dept head, Synthetic Org Chem, 69-74, asst dir, Inst Org Chem, 74-80, SR SCIENTIST, BASIC CHEM RES, SYNTEX RES CTR, 80- *Mem:* Am Chem Soc; Royal Soc Chem. *Res:* Synthetic methods; synthesis and transformations of steroids and terpenoid natural products; synthesis of medicinal agents. *Mailing Add:* Inst Org Chem Syntex Res Ctr Hillview Ave Palo Alto CA 94304

MARX, MICHAEL DAVID, b Durban, SAfrica, July 14, 46; US citizen. EXPERIMENTAL PARTICLE PHYSICS. *Educ:* City Col New York, BS, 67; Mass Inst Technol, PhD(physics), 74. *Prof Exp:* Res assoc physics, Mass Inst Technol, 74-75; asst physicist, Brookhaven Nat Lab, 75-77, assoc physicist, 77-80; ASST PROF, STATE UNIV NY, STONY BROOK, 80- *Mem:* Am Phys Soc. *Res:* Measurement of neutrino elastic scattering off electrons and protons; search for exotic dibaiyon states; hadronic total cross sections at high energies; low energy proton-antiproton resonances. *Mailing Add:* State Univ NY Stony Brook NY 11794

MARX, PAUL CHRISTIAN, b Los Angeles, Calif, Jan 21, 29; m 66; c 1. PHYSICAL CHEMISTRY. *Educ:* Univ Calif, Los Angeles, BS, 51; Northwestern Univ, PhD(chem), 55. *Prof Exp:* Res chemist, Stand Oil Co Calif, 54-57; sr res chemist, Gillette Co, 57-61; mem tech staff high temperature chem, Aerospace Corp, 61-71; consult, 71-73; MGR ADVAN DEVELOP, FORTIN LAMINATING CORP, 73- *Mem:* Am Chem Soc; Sigma Xi; Am Electrolaters Soc. *Res:* Catalytic chemical plating of metals and alloys, electroplating, electroforming of thin metallic foils, electrogeochemistry. *Mailing Add:* Fortin Laminating Corp 12840 Bradley Ave Sylmar CA 91342

MARX, PRESTON AUGUST, JR, b New Orleans, La, Dec 1, 43; m 67; c 1. VIROLOGY. *Educ:* Univ New Orleans, BS, 66; La State Univ Med Ctr, MS, 67, PhD(microbiol), 69. *Prof Exp:* Instr microbiol, Med Ctr, Univ New Orleans, 69-72; fel, St Jude Children's Res Hosp, 72-74; asst prof microbiol, Thomas Jefferson Univ, 74-81; ASST PROF, XAVIER UNIV, LA, 81- *Mem:* AAAS; Am Soc Microbiol. *Res:* Combined bacterial and viral infections; biosynthesis of viruses; biochemistry of RNA viruses. *Mailing Add:* Xavier Univ New Orleans LA 70125

MARX, STEPHEN JOHN, b New York, NY, Nov 23, 42; m 74. ENDOCRINOLOGY. *Educ:* Yale Univ, BA, 64; Johns Hopkins Univ, MD, 68; Am Bd Internal Med, cert, 74; Am Bd Endocrinol, cert, 76. *Prof Exp:* Med intern, Mass Gen Hosp, 68-69, med resident, 69-70 & 72-73; clin assoc, 70-72, SR INVESTR METAB DIS, NAT INST ARTHRITIS & DIGESTIVE DIS, NIH, 73- *Mem:* Endocrine Soc; Am Fedn Clin Res; AAAS; Am Soc Bone & Mineral Res. *Res:* Mechanism of action of hormones, hormone-receptor interaction, adenylate cyclase regulation, disorders of calcium metabolism, diagnosis and treatment of disorders of parathyroid gland. *Mailing Add:* Bldg 10 Rm 90-20 NIH Bethesda MD 20014

MARX, WALTER, b Karlsruhe, Ger, June 26, 07; nat US; m 54; c 1. BIOCHEMISTRY. *Educ:* Karlsruhe Tech Univ, Dipl Ing, 31, DIng, 33. *Prof Exp:* Instr, Inst Phys Chem, Karlsruhe Tech Univ, 30-33; Justus Liebig res fel, Kaiser Wilhelm Inst Med Res, Heidelberg, 33-34; Isadore Hernsheim fel, 34-36; fel, Mt Sinai Hosp, 34-37; res assoc, Sch Med, Duke Univ, 37-39; res assoc, Univ Calif, 39-44; res fel, Calif Inst Technol, 45-46; from asst prof to prof, 46-76, EMER PROF BIOCHEM, SCH MED, UNIV SOUTHERN CALIF, 76- *Concurrent Pos:* USPHS spec fel, 61-62. *Mem:* Fel AAAS; Am Soc Biol Chemists. *Res:* Glycosaminoglycans; proteoglycans; heparin biosynthesis; sulfate metabolism; cholesterol metabolism; pituitary hormones. *Mailing Add:* Dept Pharmacol Univ Southern Calif Sch of Med Los Angeles CA 90033

MARXHEIMER, RENE B, b Cologne, Ger, Mar 14, 23; US citizen; m 58; c 2. ELECTRICAL ENGINEERING. *Educ:* Univ Lausanne, Ing Elec, 47; Univ Calif, Berkeley, MS, 52. *Prof Exp:* Elec engr, Soc Electroradiol, Paris, France, 47; elec draftsman, Pac Gas & Elec Co, Calif, 48; instructional asst elec eng, Univ Calif, Berkeley, 48-50; elec designer, Bechtel Corp, 50-51; jr res engr, Inst Eng Res, Richmond Field Sta, Univ Calif, 51-52; elec engr, Henry Kaiser Ctr, Kaiser Engrs, 52-53; elec engr & lighting specialist, Div Hwy & San Francisco Bay Toll Crossings, Calif Dept Pub Works, 53-57; illum engr & in chg indust lab, Globe Illum Co, 57-59; from asst prof to assoc prof eng, San Francisco State Col, 59-69, PROF ENG, SAN FRANCISCO STATE UNIV, 69-, COORDR, ENERGY INFO CTR, 79- *Concurrent Pos:* Asst elec engr, Westinghouse Elec Corp, Calif, 48-50; elec designer, Brown & Caldwell, 50-51; mem, Nat Roadway Lighting Comt, 56-62; NSF stipends, Numerical Anal Inst, 60-61, Appl Probability & Statist Inst, 64; consult, McGraw Hill Co, 61-64; eng consult, Holden-Day Pub Co, Calif, 67-69. *Mem:* Sr mem Inst Elec & Electronics Engrs; Am Soc Eng Educ; Nat Soc Prof Engrs. *Mailing Add:* Dept Eng 1600 Holloway Ave San Francisco CA 94132

MARY, NOURI Y, b Baghdad, Iraq, June 25, 29; m 58; c 2. PHARMACOGNOSY. *Educ:* Univ Baghdad, PhC, 51; Ohio State Univ, MSc, 53, PhD(pharm, pharmacog), 55. *Prof Exp:* Asst prof pharmacog, Col Pharm, Univ Baghdad, 56-60, assoc prof & actg dean, 60-61; vis res scientist, Sch Pharm, Univ Calif, San Francisco, 61-63; fel, Univ Conn, 63-65; assoc prof pharmacog, 65-72, PROF PHARMACOG, ARNOLD & MARIE SCHWARTZ COL PHARM & HEALTH SCI, LONG ISLAND UNIV, 72-

Mem: Am Pharmaceut Asn; Am Soc Pharmacog; Acad Pharmaceut Sci; Am Asn Col Pharm; Am Asn Clin Chem. *Res:* Chemical and biochemical studies of natural products. *Mailing Add:* Div of Pharmacotherapeut 75 DeKalb Ave at Univ Plaza Brooklyn NY 11201

MARYANOFF, BRUCE ELIOT, b Philadelphia, Pa, Feb 26, 47; m 71. SYNTHETIC ORGANIC CHEMISTRY, MEDICINAL CHEMISTRY. *Educ:* Drexel Univ, BS, 69, PhD(org chem), 72. *Prof Exp:* Fel phys org chem, Princeton Univ, 72-74; prin scientist, McNeil Labs, 74-80, RES FEL ORG CHEM, MCNEIL PHARMACEUT, JOHNSON & JOHNSON, 80- *Mem:* Am Chem Soc; Royal Soc Chem; Sigma Xi. *Res:* Synthesis of biologically active compounds; new synthetic reactions and processes; isoquinoline and indole alkaloids; sterochemistry and asymmetric synthesis. *Mailing Add:* McNeil Pharmaceut Spring House PA 19477

MARYANOFF, CYNTHIA ANNE MILEWSKI, b Ringtown, Pa, Nov 27, 49; m 71. ORGANIC CHEMISTRY, MEDICINAL CHEMISTRY. *Educ:* Drexel Univ, BS, 72; Princeton Univ, MA, 74, PhD(org chem), 76. *Prof Exp:* Fel heterocyclic chem, Princeton Univ, 76-77; assoc sr investr, Smith Kline & French Labs, 77-81; GROUP LEADER CHEM DEVELOP, MCNEIL PHARMACEUT, 81- *Mem:* Am Chem Soc; Sigma Xi. *Res:* Synthesis of biologically active molecules; bioinorganic and organometallic chemistry; development of synthetic reactions; stereochemistry and asymmetric synthesis. *Mailing Add:* McNeil Pharmaceut Spring House PA 19477

MARYNOWSKI, CHESTER WALDEMAR, b Amsterdam, NY, June 5, 25; m 56; c 4. CHEMICAL ENGINEERING. *Educ:* Univ Southern Calif, BE, 49. *Prof Exp:* SR CHEM ENGR, SRI INT, 59- *Mem:* Am Inst Chem Engrs; Sigma Xi. *Res:* Chemical process development; pollution abatement research; waste recovery and utilization; high temperature chemistry. *Mailing Add:* 2351 Adele Ave Mountain View CA 94043

MARZETTI, LAWRENCE ARTHUR, b Mt Vernon, Ohio, Apr 17, 17; m 42; c 5. APPLIED STATISTICS. *Educ:* Morehead State Col, AB, 39. *Prof Exp:* Opers head 1940 census, Pop Div, Bur Census, 40-42, surv statistician, 46-51, asst budget officer, Budget Off, 52-56, chief overseas consult foreign census & statist, Int Statist Progs, 56-70, tech adv statist legis, Subcomt Census & Statist, Post Off & Civil Serv Comt, US House Rep 92nd Cong, 71-73; spec asst, Econ Census Staff, Bur Census, 73-74; STATIST CONSULT, 75- *Concurrent Pos:* Census consult, Tech Coop Admin, Amman, Jordan, 52; consult, US Bur of Census, 78; head, statist adv team, Qatar, 78, researcher for develop of cent statist off, 79, consult, 80. *Honors & Awards:* Meritorious Award, Dept Com, 52. *Mem:* Am Statist Asn; Soc Int Develop. *Res:* Foreign census methodology; mid-decade census; census confidentiality; national vote registration and election practice; international statistical consultation. *Mailing Add:* 2587 Golfers Ridge Rd Annapolis MD 21401

MARZKE, ROBERT FRANKLIN, b Worcester, Mass, Oct 19, 38; m 62; c 3. MAGNETIC RESONANCE, SURFACES. *Educ:* Princeton Univ, BA, 59; Columbia Univ, PhD(physics), 66. *Prof Exp:* Res assoc, Univ NC, 66-70; asst prof, 70-79, ASSOC PROF PHYSICS, ARIZ STATE UNIV, 79- *Concurrent Pos:* Co-prin investr, Nat Sci Found, 76- & Petrol Res Fund, 77-79. *Mem:* Am Phys Soc; Calif Catalysis Soc. *Res:* Physical and chemical properties of condensed matter by magnetism and magnetic resonance; metal ammonia compounds; small metallic particles; catalysis. *Mailing Add:* Dept Physics Ariz State Univ Tempe AZ 85287

MARZLUF, GEORGE A, b Columbus, Ohio, Sept 29, 35; m 60; c 4. GENETICS, BIOCHEMISTRY. *Educ:* Ohio State Univ, BSc, 57, MS, 60; Johns Hopkins Univ, PhD(genetics), 64. *Prof Exp:* NSF fel biochem genetics, Sch Med, Univ Wis, 64-66; asst prof biol, Marquette Univ, 68-69; assoc prof biochem, 70-75, PROF BIOCHEM, OHIO STATE UNIV, 75-, DIR, PROG MOLECULAR, CELLULAR & DEVELOP BIOL, 80- *Concurrent Pos:* NIH grants biochem genetics, 67-71, 71-76 & career develop award, 75-80; NSF grants molecular genetics, 78-82. *Mem:* AAAS; Genetics Soc Am; Am Soc Microbiol; Am Asn Biol Chemists. *Res:* Developmental and biochemical genetics; synthesis, allosteric control and turnover of enzymes and permeases in higher organisms; control of differential gene action and morphogenesis; molecular genetics. *Mailing Add:* Dept of Biochem Ohio State Univ Columbus OH 43210

MARZLUFF, WILLIAM FRANK, JR, b Washington, DC, May 7, 45; m 66; c 2. BIOCHEMISTRY. *Educ:* Harvard Univ, AB, 67; Duke Univ, PhD(biochem), 71. *Prof Exp:* NIH fel biol, Johns Hopkins Univ, 71-74; asst prof, 74-78, ASSOC PROF CHEM, FLA STATE UNIV, 78- *Res:* Organization and expression of histone genes and genes coding for small nuclear RNAs; RNA synthesis in sea urchin development; RNA transcription and processing. *Mailing Add:* Dept of Chem Fla State Univ Tallahassee FL 32306

MARZOLF, GEORGE RICHARD, b Columbus, Ohio, Dec 13, 35; m 58; c 2. LIMNOLOGY. *Educ:* Wittenberg Col, AB, 57; Univ Mich, MS, 61, PhD(zool), 62. *Prof Exp:* From asst prof zool to assoc prof biol, 62-75, assoc dir div biol, 73-75, PROF BIOL, KANS STATE UNIV, 75-, LIMNOLOGIST, AGR EXP STA, 80- *Concurrent Pos:* Vis prof zool, Univs Wis, Okla & Ore, 66, 67 & 75. *Mem:* Int Asn Theoret & Appl Limnol; Am Soc Limnol & Oceanog; Ecol Soc Am; Am Micros Soc. *Res:* Reservoir limnology; plankton; benthos; trophic structure. *Mailing Add:* Div of Biol Kans State Univ Manhattan KS 66506

MARZULLI, FRANCIS NICHOLAS, b New York, NY, Feb 2, 17; m 45; c 2. PHARMACOLOGY, TOXICOLOGY. *Educ:* St Peters Col, BS, 37; Johns Hopkins Univ, MA, 40, PhD(physiol), 41. *Prof Exp:* Aquatic biologist, US Fish & Wildlife Serv, 41-43; toxicologist, Dugway Proving Ground, Utah, 46-47; toxicologist & physiologist, Army Chem Res & Develop Labs, 47-63; chief dermal toxicity br, Pharmacol Div, 63-73, spec assignment, Med Ctr, Univ Calif, San Francisco, 73-75; sr scientist, Food & Drug Admin, 75-80; SR TOXICOLOGIST, NAT ACAD SCI, 80- *Concurrent Pos:* Exchange scientist, Chem Defense Exp Estab, Eng, 60-61. *Mem:* Soc Invest Dermat; Soc Exp Biol & Med; Soc Cosmetic Chem; Soc Toxicol; Asn Res Vision & Ophthal. *Res:* Environmental, skin and eye physiology. *Mailing Add:* 8044 Park Overlook Dr Bethesda MD 20817

MARZZACCO, CHARLES JOSEPH, b Philadelphia, Pa, May 1, 42; m 64; c 1. PHYSICAL CHEMISTRY. *Educ:* Temple Univ, AB, 64; Univ Pa, PhD(chem), 68. *Prof Exp:* Grant, Princeton Univ, 68-69, instr chem, 69-70; asst prof, NY Univ, 70-73; asst prof, 73-76, PROF CHEM, RI COL, 76- *Mem:* Am Chem Soc; Int-Am Photochem Soc. *Res:* Photophysical and photochemical properties of organic molecules. *Mailing Add:* Dept of Phys Sci RI Col Providence RI 02908

MASAITIS, CESLOVAS, b Kaunas, Lithuania, Mar 2, 12; nat US; m 40; c 1. MATHEMATICS. *Educ:* Vytauto Didziojo Univ, Lithuania, MA, 37; Univ Tenn, Knoxville, PhD(math), 56. *Prof Exp:* Asst astron, Vytauto Didziojo Univ, 37-40; instr, Univ Vilnius, 40-44; instr math, Nazareth Col, Ky, 50-52, Univ Ky, 52-53 & Univ Tenn, Knoxville, 53-56; mathematician, Ballistic Res Labs, Aberdeen Proving Ground, 56-63, res mathematician, 63-80; RETIRED. *Concurrent Pos:* Lectr, Univ Del, 57-64; res assoc surg, Univ Md, Baltimore, 64-71, res asst prof, 70-71, asst prof, 71-72; consult, Shock-Trauma Ctr, Univ Md Hosp, 72- *Honors & Awards:* Sustained Superior Performance Award, US Army, 62, Army Materiel Command Res & Develop Achievement Awards, 69 & 73, Army Ord Kent Award, 70. *Mem:* Math Asn Am. *Res:* Numerical analysis; approximations; application of system theory; optimization. *Mailing Add:* Ballistic Res Labs Aberdeen Proving Ground MD 21005

MASAKI, BEVERLY WONG, b Denver, Colo, June 20, 38; div. PHARMACEUTICAL CHEMISTRY, CLINICAL PHARMACOLOGY. *Educ:* Univ Southern Calif, PharmD, 62, PhD(pharmaceut chem), 67. *Prof Exp:* Res assoc health care delivery & respiratory dis, Univ Southern Calif, 67-68, asst prof pharm, Los Angeles County Med Ctr, 68-69, asst prof, 69-78, ASSOC PROF CLIN PHARMACOL, SCH PHARM, LOS ANGELES COUNTY/UNIV SOUTHERN CALIF MED CTR, 78- *Mem:* Am Asn Cols Pharm; Am Soc Hosp Pharmacists; Am Pharmaceut Asn; NY Acad Sci. *Res:* Accidental ingestions of the pediatric age group; anticoagulant and antiplatelet drug activity on heart valve prothesis; adverse drug reactions. *Mailing Add:* Sch Pharm Los Angeles County Univ Southern Calif Med Ctr 1985 Zonal Ave Los Angeles CA 90033

MASAMUNE, SATORU, b Fukuoka, Japan, July 24, 28; m 56; c 2. ORGANIC CHEMISTRY. *Educ:* Tohuku Univ, Japan, AB, 52; Univ Calif, PhD(chem), 57. *Prof Exp:* Proj assoc chem, Univ Wis, 56-59, lectr, 59-61; fel, Mellon Inst, 61-64; from assoc prof to prof chem, Univ Alta, 64-79; PROF CHEM, MASS INST TECHNOL, 78- *Concurrent Pos:* Ed, Organic Syntheses Inc, 71- *Honors & Awards:* Am Chem Soc Award, 78; Centenary lectr, Royal Soc Chem, 80. *Mem:* Am Chem Soc; The Chem Soc; fel Royal Soc Can; Japan Chem Soc. *Res:* Organic synthesis of biologically important compounds, chemistry of cyclic pi-electron and strained systems. *Mailing Add:* Dept of Chem Mass Inst Technol Cambridge MA 02139

MASANI, PESI RUSTOM, b Bombay, India, Aug 1, 19. MATHEMATICS. *Educ:* Univ Bombay, BSc, 40; Harvard Univ, MA, 42, PhD(math), 46. *Prof Exp:* Teaching fel math, Harvard Univ, 43-45; mem, Inst Advan Study, Princeton, NJ, 46-48; sr res fel, Tata Inst Fundamental Res, Bombay, 48-49; prof math & head dept, Inst Sci, Bombay, 49-59; vis lectr, Brown Univ, 59-60; prof math, Ind Univ, Bloomington, 60-72; prof, 72-73, UNIV PROF MATH, UNIV PITTSBURGH, 73- *Concurrent Pos:* Vis lectr, Harvard Univ & Mass Inst Technol, 57-58; vis prof, Math Res Ctr, Univ Wis, 65-66 & Statist Lab, Cath Univ Am, 66-67; vis researcher, Battelle Seattle Res Ctr, 69-70; vis prof, Fed Polytech Sch, Lausanne, 75; Alexander von Humboldt vis sr scientist, Fed Repub Ger, 79-80. *Mem:* Am Math Soc; Soc Indust & Appl Math; Math Asn Am. *Res:* Noncommutative analysis, specifically the factorization of operator-valued functions; prediction and filter theory of stationary stochastic processes; Hilbert spaces, specifically isometric flows, spectral integrals and vector-valued measures; ordinary linear differential systems. *Mailing Add:* Dept of Math Univ of Pittsburgh Pittsburgh PA 15260

MASAT, ROBERT JAMES, b Greeley, Colo, Sept 6, 28; m 64; c 2. COMPARATIVE PHYSIOLOGY, BIOCHEMISTRY. *Educ:* Univ Portland, BSc, 54; Wash State Univ, MSc, 58; St Louis Univ, PhD(biol), 64. *Prof Exp:* Instr biol, Rockhurst Col, 58-61, head dept, 59-61; res assoc cryobiol, Am Found Biol Res, 62; res assoc biochem, Med Ctr, La State Univ, 64, Nat Heart Inst fel, 64-66; Am Found Biol Res, 66-68; assoc prof biol, 68-73, prof biol, St Ambrose Col, 73-78, chmn div natural & math sci, 75-78; ASSOC PROF BIOCHEM & PHYSIOL, PALMER COL OF CHIROPRACTIC, 78- *Mem:* AAAS; Am Soc Zool; Am Chem Soc; Am Physiol Soc. *Res:* Comparative biochemistry and physiology of plasma proteins; physiology of biological cyclic phenomena of hibernation and migration; active transport of substances across living membranes; physiology of hypothermia. *Mailing Add:* Palmer Col of Chiropractic 1000 Brady St Davenport IA 52803

MASCARENHAS, JOSEPH PETER, b Nairobi, Kenya, Nov 19, 29; m 60; c 2. DEVELOPMENTAL BIOLOGY. *Educ:* Univ Poona, BSc, 52, MSc, 54; Univ Calif, Berkeley, PhD(plant physiol), 62. *Prof Exp:* Res officer, Parry & Co, India, 53-56; instr biol, Amherst Col, 62-63; Res Corp Brown-Hazen Fund grant & instr bot, Wellesley Col, 63-64, asst prof, 64-67; res assoc biol, Mass Inst Technol, 67-68; assoc prof, 69-74, PROF BIOL, STATE UNIV NY ALBANY, 74- *Concurrent Pos:* NSF grants, Wellesley Col, Mass Inst Technol & State Univ NY Albany, 65-; vis asst prof, Mass Inst Technol, 66-67; res found fel & grant, State Univ NY Albany, 69-74. *Mem:* AAAS; Int Soc Develop Biol; Soc Develop Biol; Bot Soc Am; Am Soc Plant Physiol. *Res:* Molecular control of plant development. *Mailing Add:* Dept of Biol Sci State Univ NY 1400 Washington Ave Albany NY 12222

MASCHERONI, P LEONARDO, b Tucuman, Arg, July 20, 35; US citizen; m 67; c 2. THEORETICAL PHYSICS. *Educ:* Univ Cuyo, Arg, BS, 62; Univ Calif, Berkeley, PhD(physics), 68. *Prof Exp:* Res assoc & lectr physics, Temple Univ, 68-70, vis asst prof chem & physics, 70-71; res scientist assoc physics, Ctr Statist Mechanics & Thermodynamics, 71-74; res scientist assoc physics, Fusion Res Ctr, Univ Tex, Austin, 74-77; sr res scientist, Sci Appln, Inc, La Jolla, 77-79; STAFF SCIENTIST, LOS ALAMOS NAT LAB, 79- *Mem:* Am Phys Soc; AAAS. *Res:* Current research in plasma physics; laser interaction with matter and laser fusion; turbulent heating of a plasma, anomalous transport; fusion research in Tokomak systems; inertial confinement fusion. *Mailing Add:* Los Alamos Nat Lab Los Alamos NM 87545

MASCIA, PETER NICHOLAS, b Port Chester, NY, Dec 24, 50; m 77. PLANT GENETICS. *Educ:* St Anselm's Col, BA, 72; Iowa State Univ, PhD(genetics), 78. *Prof Exp:* RES SPECIALIST GENETICS, UNIV MINN, 78- *Mem:* Genetics Soc Am. *Res:* Maize genetics; chlorophyll biosynthesis; chloroplast development; genome organization; molecular cytogenetics. *Mailing Add:* Dept Genetics & Cell Biol Univ Minn St Paul MN 55108

MASCIANTONIO, PHILIP (X), b Monongehela City, Pa, Mar 14, 29; m 50; c 5. PHYSICAL CHEMISTRY, ORGANIC CHEMISTRY. *Educ:* St Vincent Col, BS, 50; Carnegie Inst Technol, MS, 57, PhD(chem), 60. *Prof Exp:* Asst chemist, Robertshaw-Fulton Div, Nat Roll & Foundry Co, 50, chief chemist, 51; prod supvr dyestuffs, Pittsburgh Chem Co, 51-55; sr res chemist, Appl Res Lab, 55-67, sect supvr, 67-69, div chief chem, 69-74, asst dir environ control, 74-75, dir environ control, 75-80, VPRES ENVIRON ENERGY, US STEEL CORP, 80- *Concurrent Pos:* Instr, Carnegie Inst Technol, 62-64; abstractor, Chem Abstr, 63-70. *Mem:* Am Chem Soc; Water Pollution Control Fedn; Air Pollution Control Asn. *Res:* Chemistry, properties and structure of coal; process research of chemicals polymer properties and development of air and water pollution abatement systems. *Mailing Add:* US Steel Corp 600 Grant St Rm 1876 Pittsburgh PA 15230

MASCIOLI, ROCCO LAWRENCE, b Mt Carmel, Pa, May 7, 28; m 54; c 7. ORGANIC CHEMISTRY. *Educ:* Bucknell Univ, BS, 52; Univ Pa, MS, 54, PhD(chem), 57. *Prof Exp:* Res chemist, 56-57, proj dir, 67-69, sect head appln res & develop, 69-71, asst dir res & develop, Chem Additives Div, 71-79, DIR RES & PERFORMANCE, HOUDRY PROCESS CORP LABS, AIR PROD & CHEM, INC, 79- *Mem:* Am Chem Soc. *Res:* Nitrogen chemistry; catalysis; urethane polymers. *Mailing Add:* Pennell Manor 205 Kevin Lane Media PA 19063

MASCOLI, CARMINE CHARLES, b Waterbury, Conn, Jan 28, 28; m 53; c 5. VIROLOGY. *Educ:* Col Holy Cross, BS, 49; Univ Conn, MS, 53; Ohio State Univ, PhD(bact), 56. *Prof Exp:* Clin bacteriologist, Meriden Hosp, Conn, 52-53; asst bact, Ohio State Univ, 53-55; virologist & immunologist, Eli Lilly & Co, 56-60; from asst prof to assoc prof microbiol, Sch Med, WVa Univ, 60-64; from res fel to sr res fel, Merck Inst Therapeut Res, Pa, 64-70; dir qual control, Nat Drug Co, 70-71; dir qual control & dir res, Merrell Nat Labs, 71-75; CORP DIR MICROBIOL, RES & DEVELOP DEPT, BAXTER-TRAVENOL LABS, 76- *Concurrent Pos:* Instr, Butler Univ, 58-60. *Mem:* AAAS; Am Soc Microbiol; Am Asn Immunol. *Res:* Epidemiology; viral immunology. *Mailing Add:* Baxter-Travenol Labs Morton Grove IL 60053

MASDEN, GLENN W(ILLIAM), b Denver, Colo, Jan 17, 33; m 58; c 2. ENERGY CONVERSION, COMPUTER SCIENCE. *Educ:* Univ Colo, BS, 55, MS, 58. *Prof Exp:* Elec engr, Univac Div, Remington Rand Corp, 55-56; instr elec eng, Univ Colo, 56-57; from instr to assoc prof, 57-72, PROF ENG, WALLA WALLA COL, 72- *Mem:* Inst Elec & Electronics Engrs. *Res:* Photovoltaics. *Mailing Add:* Sch of Eng Walla Walla Col College Place WA 99324

MASE, DARREL JAY, b Delphos, Kans, Nov 13, 05; m 35; c 2. SPEECH PATHOLOGY. *Educ:* Emporia Teachers Col, BS, 28; Univ Mich, MA, 32; Columbia Univ, PhD(speech path & clin psychol), 41. *Hon Degrees:* DSc, Col Med & Dent NJ, 81. *Prof Exp:* Teacher speech & math, Mankato High Sch, Kans, 28-29; prof speech correction, Calif State Teachers Col, 33-40; prof spec educ, NJ State Teachers Col, 40-46, prof speech & educ, 50-71, coordr, Fla Ctr Clin Serv, 50-58, dean, Col Health Related Professions, 58-71, EMER PROF SPEECH & EDUC & EMER DEAN, COL HEALTH RELATED PROFESSIONS, UNIV FLA, GAINESVILLE, 71- *Concurrent Pos:* Consult, J Hillis Miller Health Ctr, Univ Fla, 50-; vis prof, Los Angeles State Col, 53 & Ark Polytech Col, 58; adj prof, Dept Community Health & Family Med, Univ Fla, 76- *Honors & Awards:* Hon Award, Asn Schs Allied Health Professions, 72; W F Faulkes Award, Nat Rehab Asn, 72. *Mem:* Fel Am Asn Mental Deficiency; Am Asn Social Psychiat; fel Am Speech & Hearing Asn; Am Soc Allied Health Professions; Int Soc Rehab Disabled. *Res:* Social and behavioral sciences; rehabilitation; physical disabilities; speech pathology; education of exceptional children; manpower in allied health professions. *Mailing Add:* Dept of Community Health & Family Med Col of Med Univ of Fla Gainesville FL 32605

MASEK, GEORGE EDWARD, b Norfolk, Va, Feb 10, 27; m 55; c 2. PHYSICS. *Educ:* Stanford Univ, PhD(physics), 56. *Prof Exp:* Res assoc physics, Hansen Lab, Stanford Univ, 55-56; instr, Princeton Univ, 56-57; from asst prof to prof, Univ Wash, 57-65; assoc prof, 65-67, PROF PHYSICS, UNIV CALIF, SAN DIEGO, 67- *Concurrent Pos:* Dir, Inst Res Particle Acceleration, Univ Calif, 77-; mem, Sci & Educ Adv Comt, Livermore Res Lab, 79- *Res:* Elementary particle and high energy physics. *Mailing Add:* Dept of Physics Univ of Calif at San Diego La Jolla CA 92037

MASELLI, JAMES MICHAEL, b Pottsville, Pa, Mar 29, 35; m 61; c 2. INORGANIC CHEMISTRY. *Educ:* Lafayette Col, AB, 57; Univ Pa, PhD(inorg chem), 61. *Prof Exp:* Univ fel, Harvard Univ, 61-62; sr res chemist, 63-66, res supvr, 66-68, mgr, 68-75, dir, Clarksville, 75-76; vpres res & develop, Emission Control Dept, 76-78, VPRES RES, DAVISON CHEM DIV, W R GRACE & CO, 78- *Mem:* Am Chem Soc. *Res:* Inorganic synthesis and catalysis. *Mailing Add:* 6413 Amherst Ave Columbia MD 21046

MASELLI, JOHN ANTHONY, food chemistry, see previous edition

MASER, CHRIS, b Bronxville, NY, Oct 13, 38; m 81. ECOSYSTEM FUNCTIONING, LAND MANAGEMENT. *Educ:* Ore State Univ, BS, 62, MS, 66. *Prof Exp:* Vert zoologist, Yale Univ Prehist Exped, Nubia, Egypt, 63-64; mammalogist, US Naval Med Res, Cairo & Nepal, Egypt, 66-67; mem staff, 67-81, RES WILDLIFE BIOLOGIST, BUR LAND MGT, US DEPT INTERIOR, 81-; ASST PROF FORESTRY, ORE STATE UNIV, 80- *Concurrent Pos:* Prin investr, Ore Coast Ecol Surv, Puget Sound Mus Nat Hist, Univ Puget Sound, Tacoma, Wash, 70-72; mem, Nat Adv Comt, H J Andrews Exp Forest Exp Ecol Res, 77-79. *Mem:* Am Soc Mammalogists; Wildlife Soc; Soc Am Foresters; Soc Range Mgt; Sigma Xi. *Res:* Conduct ecological research in forest lands and range lands and apply (through synthesis) such research to management of public lands. *Mailing Add:* Forestry Sci Lab USDA Forest Serv 3200 Jefferson Way Corvallis OR 97331

MASER, MORTON D, b Hagerstown, Md, Nov 24, 34; m 55; c 2. CELL BIOLOGY. *Educ:* Univ Pa, AB, 55; Univ Pittsburgh, PhD(biophys), 62. *Prof Exp:* Res asst, Mellon Inst, 56-58, res assoc, 58-60, jr fel, 60-62, fel, 63; res assoc, Marine Biol Lab, Woods Hole, 62; res assoc, Biol Labs, Harvard Univ, 62-64, lectr, 64-66; dir cell biol lab, Millard Fillmore Hosp, Buffalo, 66-70; asst prof biol, Erie County Community Col, 70; assoc prof continuing educ, Northeastern Univ, 70-73; assoc prof path, Creighton Univ, 73-77; coordr continuing educ, 77-79, ASST DIR EDUC & RES SERV, MARINE BIOL LAB, 79- *Mem:* AAAS; Electron Micros Soc Am; Am Soc Cell Biol. *Res:* Electron microscopical techniques; pathogenetic mechanisms. *Mailing Add:* Marine Biol Lab Woods Hole MA 02543

MASERICK, PETER H, b Washington, DC, Feb 8, 33; m 56; c 4. MATHEMATICS. *Educ:* Univ Md, BS, 55, MA, 57, PhD(math), 60. *Prof Exp:* NSF fel math, Univ Wis, 63-64; asst prof, 64-71, ASSOC PROF MATH, PA STATE UNIV, UNIVERSITY PARK, 71- *Res:* Functional analysis; convexity. *Mailing Add:* Dept of Math Pa State Univ University Park PA 16802

MASERJIAN, JOSEPH, b Albany, NY, Feb 10, 29; m 53; c 4. SEMICONDUCTORS, MICROELECTRONICS. *Educ:* Rensselaer Polytech Inst, BS, 52; Univ Southern Calif, MS, 55; Calif Inst Technol, PhD(mat sci), 66. *Prof Exp:* Mem tech staff, Semiconductor Div, Hughes Aircraft Co, 52-60; res specialist, 60-66, SUPVR, SEMICONDUCTOR TECHNOL GROUP, JET PROPULSION LAB, CALIF INST TECHNOL, 66- *Concurrent Pos:* Vis prof, Chalmers Inst Technol, 72-73, Jubilee prof, 82. *Mem:* Am Phys Soc; Am Vacuum Soc; Inst Elec & Electronics Engrs; Sigma Xi. *Res:* Physics and chemistry of semiconductor interfaces with emphasis on si/siO2 and III-V heterojunctions; thin films; interface physics; reliability of semiconductor devices; solar energy conversion. *Mailing Add:* 5668 Pine Cone Rd La Crescenta CA 91214

MASHALY, MAGDI MOHAMED, b Alexandria, Egypt, Feb 5, 44; US citizen; m 76; c 1. ENDOCRINOLOGY. *Educ:* Cairo Univ, BS, 64, MS, 70; Univ Wis, MS, 73, PhD(physiol), 76. *Prof Exp:* Res assoc, Miss State Univ, 76-78; ASST PROF PHYSIOL, PA STATE UNIV, 78- *Mem:* Poultry Sci Asn; AAAS; Soc Study Fertility. *Res:* Role of endocrine system in affecting Avian reproduction; relationships between endocrine and immune systems in chickens. *Mailing Add:* 202 Animal Indust Bldg University Park PA 16802

MASHBURN, LOUISE TULL, b Wayne, Pa, Aug 27, 30; m 58. BIOCHEMISTRY. *Educ:* Westhampton Col, BA, 52; Duke Univ, PhD(biochem), 61. *Prof Exp:* Fel biochem, Univ Del, 61-63, res assoc biochem, 63-64; res assoc biochem, Res Inst, Hosp Joint Dis, 64-76; ASSOC PROF BIOCHEM, CTR HEALTH SCI, UNIV TENN, 76- *Concurrent Pos:* Asst prof, Mt Sinai Sch Med, 71-76; USPHS spec res fel, 65-67, grant, 66-75; Am Cancer Soc grant, 68-74; Leukemia Soc Am scholar, 71-76. *Mem:* Am Chem Soc; Am Soc Biol Chemists; NY Acad sci; Am Asn Cancer Res. *Res:* Biochemistry of malignant diseases; amino acid metabolism; enzymology in therapy; tissue culture. *Mailing Add:* 2221 Washington Ave Memphis TN 38104

MASHBURN, THOMPSON ARTHUR, JR, b Morganton, NC, Oct 9, 36; m 58. BIOCHEMISTRY. *Educ:* Univ NC, AB, 56; Duke Univ, PhD(org chem), 61. *Prof Exp:* Res chemist, Plastics Dept, E I du Pont de Nemours & Co, Inc, 60-62, res chemist, Org Chem Dept, 62-64; res assoc biochem, Res Inst Skeletomuscular Dis, Hosp Joint Dis, New York, 64-76; ASSOC PROF BIOCHEM, UNIV TENN CTR HEALTH SCI, MEMPHIS, 76- *Concurrent Pos:* Advan res fel, Am Heart Asn, Inc, 65-69, estab investr, 69-74; res asst prof biochem, Mt Sinai Sch Med, 73-76. *Mem:* AAAS; Am Soc Biol Chemists; Am Chem Soc. *Res:* Structure, chemistry and biochemistry of connective tissue and mucopolysaccharides; structure and chemistry of natural highpolymers; sugar chemistry. *Mailing Add:* Dept of Biochem 894 Union Ave Memphis TN 38163

MASHEY, JOHN RUSSELL, b Dayton, Ohio, May 22, 46. COMPUTER SCIENCE, SOFTWARE ENGINEERING. *Educ:* Pa State Univ, BS, 68, MS, 69, PhD(comput sci), 74. *Prof Exp:* Mem tech staff, 73-78, SUPERVR, SOFTWARE ENG, BELL LAB, 78- *Concurrent Pos:* Nat lectr, Asn Comput Mach, 79- *Mem:* Asn Comput Mach; Inst Elec & Electronics Engrs. *Res:* Programming methodology; command languages; programming environment systems. *Mailing Add:* Bell Lab Whippany Rd Whippany NJ 07981

MASHIMO, PAUL AKIRA, b Osaka, Japan, Oct 25, 26; m 55; c 2. ORAL MICROBIOLOGY. *Educ:* Osaka Dent Univ, Japan, DDS, 48; Kyoto Med Univ, Japan, PhD(microbiol), 55. *Prof Exp:* Instr oral surg, Osaka Dent Univ, 48-50, lectr microbiol, 50-53, from asst prof microbiol to assoc prof pub health, 53-65; prof res assoc oral biol, 66, asst res prof, 66-67, asst prof oral biol, 68-69, ASSOC PROF ORAL BIOL, SCH DENT, STATE UNIV NY BUFFALO, 70-, MEM FAC GRAD SCH, 69- *Concurrent Pos:* Louise C Ball fel, Sch Dent & Oral Surg, Columbia Univ, 56-58; Japan Soc fel, 56-67; fac honor, Osaka Dent Univ, 72-; vis prof, Gifu Col Dent, 78-; hon consult, Sunstar Co, Osaka, 79- *Mem:* Am Soc Microbiol; Int Asn Dent Res; NY Acad Sci. *Res:* Oral microbiology; immunology; dentistry. *Mailing Add:* Dept of Oral Biol State Univ of NY Sch of Dent Buffalo NY 14214

MASI, ALFONSE THOMAS, b New York, NY, Oct 29, 30; m 60; c 4. EPIDEMIOLOGY, INTERNAL MEDICINE. *Educ:* City Col New York, BS, 51; Columbia Univ, MD, 55; Johns Hopkins Univ, MPH, 61, DrPH(epidemiol), 63. *Prof Exp:* Intern med, Osler Serv, Johns Hopkins Hosp, 55-56; sr asst surgeon, Commun Dis Ctr, USPHS, 56-58; asst resident, Johns Hopkins Hosp, 58-59; assoc resident, Med Ctr, Univ Calif, Los Angeles, 59-60; res fel epidemiol, Sch Hyg & Pub Health, Johns Hopkins Univ, 60-63, asst prof epidemiol, 63-65; instr med, Sch Med, 63-67, assoc prof epidemiol, Sch Hyg & Pub Health, 65-67; prof med & prev med & chief sect rheumatol, Dept Med, Univ Tenn Ctr Health Sci, Memphis, 67-72, dir div connective tissue dis, 72-78; PROF MED & HEAD DEPT, SCH MED, UNIV ILL, PEORIA, 78-, PROF EPIDEMIOL, SCH PUB HEALTH, 79- *Concurrent Pos:* Consult, Radiol Health Res Br, USPHS, 63-67, Nat Inst Arthritis & Metab Dis spec fel, 63-66; res geog epidemiol sect, Vet Admin, 64-66 & 78-80; mem subcomt epidemiol use of hosp data, Nat Comt Health & Vital Statist, 65-69; consult, US Food & Drug Admin, 65-70; sr investr, Arthritis Found, 66-71; Russell L Cecil fel award, 70-71; mem arthritis training grant comt, Nat Inst Arthritis & Metab Dis, 71-73. *Mem:* Am Fedn Clin Res; Am Rheumatism Asn; fel Am Pub Health Asn; fel Am Col Physicians. *Res:* Application of epidemiologic methods, such as population studies, community-wide hospital surveys and case-control investigations to research in chronic diseases in order to define better their causes and pathogenesis. *Mailing Add:* Dept of Med 123 SW Glendale Ave Peoria IL 61605

MASI, JAMES VINCENT, b Norwalk, Conn, Sept 21, 38; m 64; c 6. PHYSICS, MATERIALS SCIENCE. *Educ:* Fairfield Univ, BS, 60; C W Post Col, MS, 70. *Prof Exp:* Physicist res & develop, Transitron Electronics Corp, 60-61; teacher/researcher, Boston Col, 61-62; sr physicist, Space Age Mat, 62-65, Servo Corp, 65-66 & Hartman Systs Co, 66-69; sr engr/corp consult, Bunker-Ramo Corp, 69-73; dir res & develop, Innotech Corp, 73-74; consult, Optix Corp, 74-75; vpres, UCE Inc, 75-77; PROG DEVELOP MGR, INST ENERGY CONVERSION, UNIV DEL, 77- *Mem:* Inst Elec & Electronics Engrs; Soc Info Display; Electrochem Soc; Am Soc Metals; AAAS. *Res:* Solid state electronic devices, materials; electro-optics devices and materials; solar energy; photovoltaic devices and materials. *Mailing Add:* Inst Energy Conversion 1 Pike Creek Ctr Wilmington DE 19808

MASKAL, JOHN, b Garfield, NJ, Sept 27, 18; m 43; c 2. PHYSICAL CHEMISTRY. *Educ:* Syracuse Univ, BS, 40; Mich State Univ, MS, 42. *Prof Exp:* Supvr anal lab, Evansville Ord Plant, 42-44; engr mat testing, Chrysler Corp, 44-45; high sch teacher, Mich, 46-47; mgr plating plant, Ludington Plating Co, 47-50; supvr, Denham Mfg Co, 50-51; supvr, Res Lab, Dow Chem USA, 51-60, dir, Gen Lab, 60-80; RETIRED. *Concurrent Pos:* Group leader, Ludington Prod Labs, 72, mgr environ qual control, 73. *Mem:* Tech Asn Pulp & Paper Indust; fel Am Inst Chemists; Am Chem Soc. *Res:* Analytical and physical chemical research involving inorganic chemical manufacture. *Mailing Add:* 712 Dexter Ludington MI 49431

MASKEN, JAMES FREDERICK, b Frederick, Md, Apr 4, 27; m 59; c 3. PHYSIOLOGY, BIOCHEMISTRY. *Educ:* NY Univ, BA, 53; Colo State Univ, MS, 60, PhD(physiol), 65. *Prof Exp:* Lab asst pharmacol, Wm R Warner Co, 50-52 & Nepera Chem Co, 52-53; res technician, Surg Dept, Sinai Hosp, Baltimore, Md, 54-55; lab technician, Biochem Div, Toni Co, 55; res asst endocrinol, 55-62; from instr to asst prof physiol, 62-69, assoc prof, 69-77, PROF PHYSIOL, COLO STATE UNIV, 77- *Concurrent Pos:* Vis assoc prof, Univ Calif, 70-71. *Mem:* AAAS; Am Physiol Soc; Can Physiol Soc; Soc Study Reproduction. *Res:* Reproductive physiology; neuroendocrinology. *Mailing Add:* Dept of Physiol & Biophys Colo State Univ Ft Collins CO 80521

MASKER, WARREN EDWARD, b Honesdale, Pa, July 8, 43. MOLECULAR BIOLOGY. *Educ:* Lehigh Univ, BS, 65; Univ Rochester, PhD(physics), 70. *Prof Exp:* Fel, Univ Rochester, 69-71; fel, Stanford Univ, 71-73; fel, Med Sch, Harvard Univ, 73-74; RES STAFF MEM, BIOL DIV, OAK RIDGE NAT LAB, 75- *Concurrent Pos:* Am Cancer Soc fel, 70; Helen Hay Whitney Found fel, 71. *Mem:* Am Phys Soc; Biophys Soc; Am Soc Microbiol; Am Soc Photobiol. *Res:* Study of DNA replication and the molecular mechanism of DNA repair in bacteria and bacteriophage. *Mailing Add:* Div of Biol Oak Ridge Nat Lab PO Box Y Oak Ridge TN 37830

MASKIT, BERNARD, b New York, NY, May 27, 35; div; c 3. MATHEMATICS. *Educ:* NY Univ, AB, 57, MS, 62, PhD(math), 64. *Prof Exp:* Mem, Inst Advan Study, 63-65; from asst prof to assoc prof math, Mass Inst Technol, 65-70, Sloan Found fel, 70-71; chmn dept, 74-75, PROF MATH, STATE UNIV NY STONY BROOK, 71- *Mem:* Am Math Soc. *Res:* Riemann surfaces; Kleinian groups and surface topology. *Mailing Add:* Dept of Math State Univ of NY Stony Brook NY 11794

MASLACH, GEORGE JAMES, b San Francisco, Calif, May 4, 20; m 43; c 3. AERONAUTICAL ENGINEERING. *Educ:* Univ Calif, Berkeley, BS, 42. *Prof Exp:* Staff mem, Radiation Lab, Mass Inst Technol, 42-45 & Gen Precision Labs, NY, 45-49; res engr, 49-52, assoc prof mech design, 52-58, asst dir, Inst Eng Res, 56-58, assoc prof aeronaut eng, 58-59, chmn, Div Aeronaut Sci, 60-63, actg dean, Col Eng, 63, dean, 63-72, provost, Prof Schs & Cols, 72-81, PROF AERONAUT ENG, UNIV CALIF, BERKELEY, 59-, VCHANCELLOR, RES & ACAD SERV, 81- *Concurrent Pos:* Consult, Wright Air Develop Ctr, US Air Force, 54-55, Martin Aircraft Co, 58-60, Missile & Space Vehicles Dept, Gen Elec Co, 58-62 & Aeronaut Div, Ford Motor Co, 60-63; mem, Adv Group for Aeronaut Res & Develop, NATO, 60-; mem adv comt, US Naval Postgrad Sch, 64-65, US Naval Acad, 66-; mem tech adv bd, US Dept Commerce, 64- *Mem:* Am Soc Mech Engrs. *Res:* Rarefied gas dynamics and heat transfer; fluid mechanics; low density aerodynamics facilities. *Mailing Add:* 265 Panoramic Way Berkeley CA 94704

MASLAND, RICHARD HARRY, b Philadelphia, Pa, June 12, 42. NEUROBIOLOGY, PHYSIOLOGY. *Educ:* Harvard Univ, AB, 64; McGill Univ, PhD, 68. *Prof Exp:* Fel neurophysiol, Med Sch, Stanford Univ, 68-71; res assoc, 71-75, asst prof, 75-81, ASSOC PROF PHYSIOL, HARVARD MED SCH, 81- *Concurrent Pos:* Asst neurophysiologist, Mass Gen Hosp, 71-74, assoc, 74-; NIH res career develop award, 77- *Mem:* Asn Res Vision & Ophthal; Neurosci Soc; Am Physiol Soc. *Res:* Physiology of the retina; central nervous system development. *Mailing Add:* Mass Gen Hosp Boston MA 02114

MASLAND, RICHARD LAMBERT, b Philadelphia, Pa, Mar 24, 10; m 40; c 4. PSYCHIATRY, NEUROLOGY. *Educ:* Haverford Col, BA, 31; Univ Pa, MD, 35; Am Bd Neurol & Psychiat, dipl, 43, cert psychiat, 48. *Hon Degrees:* LLD, Haverford Col, 75. *Prof Exp:* Intern, Pa Hosp, 35-37, fel neurol, Hosp Univ Pa, 37-39, asst neurologist, 39-47, assoc, Univ, 40-46; from asst prof to prof psychiat & neurol, Bowman Gray Sch Med, 47-57, from asst prof to assoc prof physiol, 48-57; from asst dir to dir, Nat Inst Neurol Dis & Blindness, Md, 57-68; prof, 68-70, chmn dept, 68-73, Moses prof neurol, 70-73, H Houston Merritt prof, 73-76, EMER PROF NEUROL, COL PHYSICIANS & SURGEONS, COLUMBIA UNIV, 76- *Concurrent Pos:* Fel, Univ Pa, 40-46; res dir sci adv bd, Nat Asn Retarded Children, 55-56; fel psychiat, Pa Inst Ment Hyg, 56-57; mem med adv bd, Myasthenia Gravis Found, Inc, 57-; trustee, Nat Easter Seal Res Found, 59-71; mem res adv comt, United Cerebral Palsy Res & Educ Found, 61-; mem adv bd, Muscular Dystrophy Asn Am, 65-73; dir neurol serv, Neurol Inst, Presby Hosp, 68-73; mem policy comt, World Fedn Neurol, mem res group develop in dyslexia & world illiteracy, 68-76, vpres, 69; mem adv comt epilepsies, Dept Health, Educ & Welfare, 69-73, chmn, 70; regional chmn, Epilepsy Found Am, 71-76; mem NY State Develop Disabilities Coun, 73-76; exec dir, Comn Control Epilepsy & Consequences, HEW, 76-77; mem prof adv bd, Epilepsy Fedn Am. *Mem:* Fel Am Acad Neurol; hon mem Am Acad Cerebral Palsy; assoc Am Asn Neurol Surg; Am Epilepsy Soc (pres, 54); Am Neurol Asn (vpres, 64). *Res:* Neurophysiology; clinical neurology. *Mailing Add:* Neurol Inst Presby Hosp 710 W 168th St New York NY 10032

MASLEN, STEPHEN HAROLD, b Cleveland, Ohio, Jan 28, 26; m 51; c 5. APPLIED MATHEMATICS. *Educ:* Rensselaer Polytech Inst, BAeroEng, 45, MAeroEng, 47; Brown Univ, PhD(appl math), 52. *Prof Exp:* Aeronaut res scientist, Nat Adv Comt Aeronaut, 47-58, chief plasma physics br, Advan Propulsion Div, Lewis Res Ctr, NASA, 58-60; prin res scientist, Martin Co, 60-67, ASSOC DIR, MARTIN MARIETTA LABS, 67- *Mem:* Am Phys Soc; Am Inst Aeronaut & Astronaut. *Res:* Fluid dynamics. *Mailing Add:* Martin Marietta Labs 1450 S Rolling Rd Baltimore MD 21227

MASLIN, THOMAS PAUL, b Hankow, China, Oct 27, 09; US citizen; m 34; c 3. HERPETOLOGY. *Educ:* Univ Calif, BA, 33, MA, 39; Stanford Univ, PhD(zool), 45. *Prof Exp:* Asst prof zool, Colo Agr & Mech Col, 45-47; from asst prof to prof biol, 47-74, EMER PROF BIOL, UNIV COLO, BOULDER, 75-, CUR ZOOL, UNIV MUS, 66- *Concurrent Pos:* Off Coord Fisheries, Calif, 43-45. *Mem:* Fel Am Soc Ichthyologists & Herpetologists (pres, 77-79). *Res:* Anatomy, phylogeny and taxonomy of reptiles. *Mailing Add:* Univ of Colo Museum Boulder CO 80302

MASLOW, DAVID E, b Brooklyn, NY, July 6, 43. ONCOLOGY, CELL BIOLOGY. *Educ:* Brooklyn Col, BS, 63; Univ Pa, PhD(zool), 68. *Prof Exp:* Cancer res scientist, 68-73, cancer res scientist II, 73-77, CANCER RES SCIENTIST IV, ROSWELL PARK MEM INST, 77-; ASST PROF, DEPT BIOPHYSICS, STATE UNIV NY BUFFALO, 78- *Mem:* Soc Develop Biol; Am Soc Zoologists; Am Asn Cancer Res; AAAS. *Res:* Cell specificity in developing and neoplastic systems. *Mailing Add:* Dept of Exp Path Roswell Park Mem Inst Buffalo NY 14263

MASLOW, PHILIP HERMAN, b New York, NY, July 27, 18; m 43; c 3. ORGANIC CHEMISTRY. *Educ:* City Col, New York, BS, 38, MS, 41. *Prof Exp:* Control chemist paint lab, Monroe Sander Corp, 38-42; assoc chemist, Norfolk Naval Shipyard, Va, 42-45; chief chemist, Red Hand Marine Paint Co, NJ, 45-56; supvr coatings tech serv lab, Ciba Prods Corp, 56-59; tech dir, Permagile Corp Am, 59-61; tech dir & tech serv mgr, Dewey & Almy Chem Div, W R Grace & Co, 61-69; tech serv mgr, Preco Chem Corp, 70-73; vpres, Master Mastics Co Inc, 73-76; PRES, MASLOW ASSOCS, 76- *Concurrent Pos:* Mem, Concrete Indust Bd; lectr, Univ Mo-Rolla, Harvard Univ, New York City Community Col, Pratt Inst & Univ Wis-Madison; consult pvt pract, currently; fel, Construct Specif Inst. *Mem:* Am Concrete Inst; Am Chem Soc; Am Soc Testing & Mat; Fedn Soc Paint Technol; fel Construct Specifications Inst. *Res:* Paint technology, especially marine paints; epoxy technology, especially coatings and plastics applications; sealant, concrete, adhesive and building materials technology. *Mailing Add:* 739 E 49th St Brooklyn NY 11203

MASNARI, NINO A(NTONIO), b Three Rivers, Mich, Sept 20, 35; m 57; c 3. ELECTRICAL ENGINEERING. *Educ:* Univ Mich, BS, 58, MS, 59, PhD(elec eng), 64. *Prof Exp:* Res asst elec eng, Electron Physics Lab, Univ Mich, Ann Arbor, 57-60, res assoc, 60-64, assoc res engr, Electron Physics Lab & lectr elec eng univ, 64-67; electronic engr, Gen Elec Res & Develop Ctr, NY, 67-69; assoc prof elec eng, Univ Mich, Ann Arbor, 69-77 prof, 77-79, dir, Elec Physics Lab, 73-79; PROF ELEC ENG & HEAD DEPT, NC STATE UNIV, RALEIGH, 79- *Mem:* Inst Elec & Electronics Engrs. *Res:* Solid state physics and semiconductor electronics; integrated circuits and microelectronics; ion implantation; plasma and arc physics. *Mailing Add:* North Carolina State Univ PO Box 5275 Raleigh NC 27650

MASNER, LUBOMIR, b Prague, Czech, Apr 18, 34; Can citizen; m 61; c 2. ENTOMOLOGY. *Educ:* Charles Univ, BSc, 54, MSc, 57; Czech Acad Sci, PhD(entom), 62. *Prof Exp:* Res scientist, Inst Entom, Czech Acad Sci, 57-68; RES SCIENTIST ENTOM, BIOSYST RES INST, AGR CAN, 69- *Concurrent Pos:* Vis scientist, Brit Mus Natural Hist, London, 61, Smithsonian Inst, 64 & Harvard Univ, 66; Nat Res Coun Can fels, 65-66 & 68-69. *Mem:* Entom Soc Can. *Res:* Biosystematics of parasitic wasps of the superfamily Proctotrupoidea (Hymenoptera); taxonomy; evolution; geological history; ecology. *Mailing Add:* Biosyst Res Inst Agr Can Ottawa ON K1A 0C6 Can

MASNICK, BURT J, b New York, NY, June 3, 39; m 61. COMPUTER SCIENCE. *Educ:* Cooper Union, BSME, 60; NY Univ, MEE, 63, PhD(elec eng), 66. *Prof Exp:* Jr engr, Bulova Res & Develop Labs, 60-61; engr, Airborne Instruments Lab, 61-62; res engr, Grumman Aircraft Eng Corp, NY, 66-71, SR SYSTS ENGR, DIGITRONICS CORP, ALBERTSON, 71- *Mem:* Inst Elec & Electronics Engrs. *Res:* Communication theory; unequal error protection codes; optimal control computation; novel computing methods for new problems; time-sharing computing; computer aided design; microprocessors and microcomputers; real time systems; software and hardware architecture; logic design. *Mailing Add:* Digitron Inc 175 I U Willets Rd Albertson NY 11507

MASO, HENRY FRANK, b Perth Amboy, NJ, Nov 20, 19; m 44; c 3. COSMETIC CHEMISTRY. *Educ:* City Col New York, BS, 40. *Prof Exp:* Asst bur biol res, Rutgers Univ, 41; jr chemist, Philadelphia Navy Yd, 41-44; sr res chemist, Johnson & Johnson, 44-57; dir tech serv, Am Cholesterol Prod, Inc, 57-70, vpres, 70-79, SR VPRES, MKT & TECHNOL, AMERCHOL, CPC INT INC, 80- *Concurrent Pos:* Mem, Praesidium Int Fedn Socs Cosmetic Chemists rep USA Soc, 78. *Honors & Awards:* Medalist, Soc Cosmetic Chemists, 71. *Mem:* Am Chem Soc; Soc Cosmetic Chemists (pres-elect, 66, pres, 67). *Res:* Manufacture of raw materials for cosmetics, dermatologicals and pharmaceuticals. *Mailing Add:* Amerchol Corp PO Box 351 Edison NJ 08818

MASON, ALLEN SMITH, b Tulsa, Okla, Dec 9, 32; m 55; c 1. ATMOSPHERIC CHEMISTRY. *Educ:* Kans State Univ, BS, 54; Fla Inst Technol, MS, 67; Univ Miami, PhD(marine & atmospheric sci), 74. *Prof Exp:* Chemist inorg chem, FMC Labs, 60; mem tech staff, RCA Labs, 61-63; supt tech eval, Pan Am World Airways, 63-69; res assoc prof marine & atmospheric chem, Univ Miami, 74-80; STAFF MEM, LOS ALAMOS NAT LAB, 81- *Mem:* Am Chem Soc; Am Geophys Union. *Res:* Atmospheric tracer studies using radioactive and stable chemical species for estimation of large-scale mixing and transport processes. *Mailing Add:* Los Alamos Nat Lab, MS 514 PO Box 1663 Los Alamos NM 87545

MASON, ARTHUR ALLEN, b St Louis, Mo, May 6, 25; m 64. MOLECULAR SPECTROSCOPY. *Educ:* Univ Okla, BS, 51; Univ Tenn, PhD(physics), 63. *Prof Exp:* From asst prof to assoc prof physics, 64-74, asst dean, 76-80, PROF PHYSICS, SPACE INST, UNIV TENN, 74-, PROF, DEPT PHYSICS & ASTRON, 80- *Mem:* Am Phys Soc; Optical Soc Am. *Res:* Intensity spectroscopy of gases. *Mailing Add:* Space Inst Univ of Tenn Tullahoma TN 37388

MASON, BERYL TROXELL, b Victoria, BC, Jan 21, 07; US citizen; m 35; c 2. NEUROLOGY, PSYCHIATRY. *Educ:* Univ Wash, BS, 29; Univ Chicago, MS, 32, MD, 36. *Prof Exp:* Resident, Univ Chicago, 36; intern, St Margaret's Hosp, Pittsburgh, 36-37; instr bact, Col Med, Univ Ill, 37-38; instr phys diag, Univ NC, 42-44; pvt pract, NC, 42-44 & Ill, 45-53; res assoc neurol & neurosurg, Col Med, Univ Ill, 53-58, consult, 58-61; actg chief neurol, Vet Admin Hosp, Topeka, Kans, 61-64; clin dir, Ark Rehab Serv, 64-69; study of Mid-East dis, Istanbul, Turkey, 69-71; CONSULT IN RES, MATROX LABS, 71- *Concurrent Pos:* Consult to planning coun, Found of Viet-Nam Inst Technol, 74 & 75. *Res:* Central nervous system; epilepsy; brain x-radiation; public health; radiation; neurological disorders. *Mailing Add:* 5059 N Jones Rd Oak Harbor WA 98277

MASON, BRIAN HAROLD, b Port Chalmers, NZ, Apr 18, 17; m 43. GEOCHEMISTRY. *Educ:* Univ NZ, MSc, 38; Univ Stockholm, PhD(mineral), 43. *Prof Exp:* Res officer, NZ Govt, 43-44; sr lectr geol, Univ NZ, 44-47; assoc prof mineral, Ind Univ, 47-53; cur phys geol & mineral, Am Mus Natural Hist, 53-65; RES CUR, DIV METEORITES, US NAT MUS, 65- *Mem:* Fel Mineral Soc Am (pres, 65-66); Geochem Soc (pres, 64-65); Royal Soc NZ; Swedish & Norweg Geol Soc. *Res:* Geochemistry; petrology; regional geology; meteorites. *Mailing Add:* Smithsonian Inst Div of Meteorites Washington DC 20560

MASON, CAROLINE FAITH VIBERT, b Harrogate, Eng, Feb 24, 42; US citizen; m 69; c 2. INORGANIC CHEMISTRY. *Educ:* Univ London, BSc, 64, PhD(chem), 67. *Prof Exp:* Fel, State Univ NY Buffalo, 67-68; chemist, Howmet Corp, Dover, NJ, 69-70; assoc scientist chem, Ortho Res Found, Raritan, NJ, 70-71; biochemist, Los Alamos Med Ctr, 72-74, STAFF MEM CHEM, LOS ALAMOS NAT LAB, 75- *Concurrent Pos:* Consult, Particle Technol Inc, Coulter Electronics, 73-75. *Mem:* The Chem Soc; Am Chem Soc. *Res:* Thermochemical cycles for the decomposition of water to hydrogen and oxygen and related problems such as catalysis, separation of gases, kinetics and materials problems. *Mailing Add:* CMB 3 Los Alamos Sci Lab Los Alamos NM 87545

MASON, CHARLES EUGENE, b Brighton, Colo, Aug 28, 43; m 70; c 3. PEST MANAGEMENT, APICULTURE. *Educ:* Colo State Univ, BS, 68; Univ Mo, MS, 71; Kans State Univ, PhD(entom), 73. *Prof Exp:* Res asst entom, Univ Mo, 68-71 & Kans State Univ, 71, asst instr, 72-73; asst entomologist, Univ Ariz, 73-75; ASSOC PROF ENTOM, UNIV DEL, 75- *Mem:* Entom Soc Am; AAAS; Int Bee Res Asn; Ecol Soc Am; Am Entom Soc (vpres, 80). *Res:* Economic threshold of pest insects in crops, phenology models, genetics and ecology of European corn borer; pollination of crops by honey bees; ecology of soybean pollination. *Mailing Add:* Dept of Entom Univ of Del Newark DE 19711

MASON, CHARLES MORGAN, b Kenora, Ont, July 7, 06; US citizen; m 29; c 3. PHYSICAL CHEMISTRY. *Educ:* Univ Ariz, BS, 28, MS, 29; Yale Univ, PhD(phys chem), 32. *Prof Exp:* Asst, Yale Univ, 29-31; from asst prof to assoc prof, Univ NH, 32-41; phys chemist, US Bur Mines, 41-43; res chemist, Tenn Valley Authority, 43-48; phys chemist, US Bur Mines, 48-50, chief explosives res sect, 50-56, phys res sect, 56-60, proj coordr explosive res ctr, 60-69, supvry res chemist, Pittsburgh Mining & Safety Res Ctr, 69-77. *Concurrent Pos:* Explosives consult, Aluminum Co Am, 72- *Honors & Awards:* Meritorious Silver Medal, Dept Interior, 72. *Mem:* Am Chem Soc. *Res:* Thermodynamic properties of phosphates, rare earths and barium salts; water adsorption of glue; metallurgy of aluminum and lithium; magneto chemistry; non-metallic minerals; ignition of fire-damp; explosives and explosion phenomena; hazardous chemicals; ammonium nitrate. *Mailing Add:* 5 Dorchester Dr Apt 502 Pittsburgh PA 15241

MASON, CHARLES PERRY, b Newport, RI, Aug 12, 32; m 58; c 2. BOTANY. *Educ:* Univ RI, BS, 54; Univ Wis, MS, 58; Cornell Univ, PhD(bot), 61. *Prof Exp:* Instr bot, Univ Wis, Milwaukee, 57-58; from asst prof to assoc prof biol, Hamline Univ, 61-67; assoc prof, 67-80, PROF BIOL, GUSTAVUS ADOLPHUS COL, 80- *Mem:* Sigma Xi; Phycol Soc Am; Int Phycol Soc. *Res:* Toxins produced by blue-green algae; unialgal growth of Anabaena and Dictyosphaerium in Lake Itasca; algal protein studies using acrylamide gelectrophoresis; ecology of Cladophora in farm ponds; effect of temperature shock on DNA content of beta-chromosome containing nuclei in maize. *Mailing Add:* Dept of Biol Gustavus Adolphus Col St Peter MN 56082

MASON, CHARLES THOMAS, JR, b Joliet, Ill, Mar 26, 18; m 43; c 1. BOTANY. *Educ:* Univ Chicago, BS, 40; Univ Calif, MA, 42, PhD(bot), 49. *Prof Exp:* Instr bot, Univ Wis, 49-53; from asst prof to assoc prof, 53-62, PROF BOT, UNIV ARIZ, 62-, BOTANIST & CUR, HERBARIUM, 53- *Mem:* Fel AAAS; Sigma Xi; Am Soc Plant Taxon; Int Asn Plant Taxon; Soc Botanica Mex. *Res:* Cytotaxonomy of angiosperms, Limnanthaceae and Gentianaceae. *Mailing Add:* Herbarium-113 Agr Sci Univ Ariz Tucson AZ 85721

MASON, CONRAD JEROME, b Detroit, Mich, Jan 12, 32. MICROMETEOROLOGY, BIOMETEOROLOGY. *Educ:* Univ Mich, BS, 53; Univ Calif, Berkeley, MA, 55, PhD(physics), 60. *Prof Exp:* Assoc res physicist, Radiation Lab, 60-63 & High Altitude Eng Lab, 63-70, lectr, Dept Meteorol & Oceanog, 70-74, RES SCIENTIST & LECTR, DEPT ATMOSPHERIC & OCEANIC SCI, UNIV MICH, ANN ARBOR, 74-, RES SCIENTIST, BIOL STA, 79- *Concurrent Pos:* Pres, Aeromatrix Inc, Ann Arbor, 76-; vis prof dept plant physiol & entomol, Univ RI, 77-78; adj prof dept entomol, Mich State Univ, East Lansing, 79- *Mem:* Am Phys Soc; Am Geophys Union; Am Meteorol Soc; Air Pollution Control Asn; Int Asn Aerobiol. *Res:* Atmospheric science; air pollution; interaction of biological organisms with their physical environment. *Mailing Add:* 3640 E Huron River Dr Ann Arbor MI 48104

MASON, CURTIS LEONEL, b Daingerfield, Tex, Oct 9, 19; m 42; c 2. PESTICIDES. *Educ:* Tex Agr & Mech Col, BS, 40, MS, 42; Univ Ill, PhD(plant path), 47. *Prof Exp:* Agent bur plant indust, soils & agr eng, USDA, Tex, 39-42; asst, Univ Wis, 42-43; spec asst, Univ Ill, 46-47; assoc pathologist, Tex A&M Univ, 47-48; asst prof plant path, Univ Ark, 48-52; plant pathologist, Niagara Chem Div, Food Mach & Chem Corp, 52-54; asst sales mgr, 54-57, mgr tech serv, 57-59, regional mgr, 59-62; microbiologist, Buckman Labs, Inc, 62-65, area mgr, 65-70; exten plant pathologist, 71-77, PESTICIDE COORDR, AGR EXTEN SERV, UNIV ARK, LITTLE ROCK, 77-; SOUTHERN REGIONAL COORDR, NAT AGR PESTICIDE IMPACT ASSESSMENT PROG, ARK AGR EXP STA, USDA, 77- *Mem:* Am Phytopath Soc. *Res:* Diseases of cotton, orchard crops and peaches; testing of fungicides; fungicidal action of 8-quinolinol and some of its derivatives; industrial microorganism control. *Mailing Add:* Coop Exten Serv USDA 1201 McAlmont Box 391 Little Rock AR 72114

MASON, D(AVID) M(ALCOLM), b Los Angeles, Calif, Jan 7, 21; m 53. CHEMICAL ENGINEERING, CHEMISTRY. *Educ:* Calif Inst Technol, BS, 43, MS, 47, PhD(chem eng), 49. *Prof Exp:* Chem engr, Standard Oil Co, 43-46; instr chem eng, Calif Inst Technol, 49-51, supvr appl phys chem group, Jet Propulsion Lab, 52-55; assoc prof chem eng, 55-57, chmn dept, 55-72, assoc dean undergrad studies, 73-76, PROF CHEM ENG, STANFORD UNIV, 57-, ASSOC DEAN ENG, 79- *Concurrent Pos:* NSF fel, Imp Col, Univ London, 64-65. *Mem:* Fel Am Inst Chem Engrs; Am Chem Soc; Am Soc Eng Educ; Am Electrochem Soc. *Res:* Applied chemical kinetics and thermodynamics; transport processes in reacting systems; electrochemical engineering. *Mailing Add:* 148 Doud Dr Los Altos CA 94022

MASON, D(ONALD) R(OMAGNE), b Urbana, Ill, Aug 19, 20; m; c 3. CHEMICAL ENGINEERING. *Educ:* Univ Ill, BS, 42; Univ Minn, PhD(chem eng), 49. *Prof Exp:* Chem engr, Plastics Dept, E I du Pont de Nemours & Co, 42-44; asst chem eng, Univ Minn, 46-48; mem tech staff, Bell Tel Labs, Inc, NJ, 49-52, 53-56; assoc prof chem eng, Univ Mich, 56-61, prof, 61-65; sr scientist, Phys Electronics Div, Radiation, Inc, 65-67, Microelectronics Div, 67-70, sr scientist, Harris Semiconductor Div, Harris-Intertype Corp, 70-77; PROF & HEAD, DEPTS CHEM ENG & ENVIRON SCI & ENG, FLA INST TECHNOL, 78- *Concurrent Pos:* Fulbright scholar, Univ Nancy, 52-53; adj asst prof, NY Univ, 53-54; adj instr, Polytech Inst Brooklyn, 54-56; exchange prof, Ecole Normale Superieure, Paris, 63-64; adj prof, Fla Inst Technol, 66-77; indust consult, 77- *Mem:* AAAS; Am Chem Soc; Electrochem Soc; Inst Elec & Electronics Engrs; Am Inst Chem Engrs. *Res:* Continuous flow stirred tank reactor systems; electrical capacitors; transistor processing; semiconducting materials; chemical process dynamics; integrated circuits. *Mailing Add:* Dept Chem & Chem Eng Fla Inst Technol Melbourne FL 32901

MASON, DAVID DICKENSON, b Adingdon, Va, Jan 22, 17; m 44; c 2. APPLIED STATISTICS. *Educ:* King Col, BA, 36; Va Polytech Inst, MS, 38; NC State Col, PhD(agron), 48. *Prof Exp:* Asst agronomist, Exp Sta, Va Polytech Inst, 38-39 & Miss State Col, 41; asst, NC State Col, 41 & 45-47; asst prof agron, Ohio State Univ, 47-49; biometrician, Bur Plant Indust, USDA, 49-53; prof statist, 53-81, EMER PROF STATIST, NC STATE UNIV, 81-, HEAD DEPT & HEAD, INST STATIST, 63- *Concurrent Pos:* Statist consult, Res Div, United Fruit Co, Mass, 57-; chmn, Southern Regional Ed Bd Comt on Statist, 73-75. *Mem:* Fel Soil Sci Soc Am; fel Am Soc Agron; fel Am Statist Asn; Biomet Soc. *Res:* Applied statistics; soil and plant science. *Mailing Add:* Dept of Statist NC State Univ Box 5457 Raleigh NC 27650

MASON, DAVID LAMONT, b Warren, Pa, Dec 24, 34; m 63; c 1. BOTANY. *Educ:* Edinboro State Col, BS, 63; Univ Wis, MS, 67, PhD(bot), 70. *Prof Exp:* Teaching asst gen bot, Univ Wis, 63-64, teaching assoc, 64-65, res asst mycol, 65-69; from asst prof to assoc prof, 69-80, PROF BIOL, WITTENBURG UNIV, 80- *Mem:* Am Phytopath Soc; Sigma Xi. *Res:* Fungal parasitism; electron microscopy of human tumors, cancers and autoimmune diseases. *Mailing Add:* Dept of Biol Wittenburg Univ Springfield OH 45501

MASON, DAVID M(CARTHUR), b Sidney, Mont, Jan 6, 12; m 38; c 4. CHEMICAL ENGINEERING, PHYSICAL CHEMISTRY. *Educ:* Mont State Col, BS, 34; Univ NDak, MS, 35. *Prof Exp:* Asst chemist, Socony-Vacuum Oil Co, 37-38; analyst, Standard Oil Develop Co Div, Standard Oil Co, 38-40, anal chemist, 40-52; supvr, Anal Lab, 52-62, sr chemist, 62-77, SR CONSULT, INST GAS TECHNOL, 77- *Mem:* Am Chem Soc; Am Soc Testing & Mat. *Res:* Correlation of coal properties; coal petrography; properties of gaseous fuels; coal ash chemistry. *Mailing Add:* 5434 S Blackstone Ave Chicago IL 60615

MASON, DAVID THOMAS, b Berkeley, Calif, Jan 7, 37. LIMNOLOGY. *Educ:* Reed Col, BA, 58; Univ Calif, Davis, MA, 61, PhD(zool), 66. *Prof Exp:* Lectr zool, Univ Calif, Davis, 65; asst prof biol, 66-70, ASSOC PROF BIOL, FAIRHAVEN COL, WESTERN WASH UNIV, 71- *Concurrent Pos:* Asst prof, Univ Calif, Berkeley, 69-71. *Mem:* Am Soc Limnol & Oceanog; Sigma Xi; Int Soc Limnol. *Res:* Physical and biological limnology; saline lakes. *Mailing Add:* Fairhaven Col Western Wash Univ Bellingham WA 98225

MASON, DEAN TOWLE, b Berkeley, Calif, Sept 20, 32; m 57; c 2. CARDIOVASCULAR DISEASES. *Educ:* Duke Univ, BA, 54, MD, 58; Am Bd Internal Med, dipl, 65; Am Bd Cardiovasc Dis, dipl, 66. *Prof Exp:* From intern to asst resident, Osler Med Serv, Johns Hopkins Hosp, 58-61; asst resident med, Med Ctr, Duke Univ, 59-60; clin assoc, Cardiol Br, Nat Heart Inst, 61-63, asst sect chief cardiovasc diag, sr investr & attend physician, 63-68; PROF MED & PHYSIOL & CHIEF SECT CARDIOVASC MED, SCH MED, UNIV CALIF, DAVIS, 68- *Concurrent Pos:* Consult, Surg Br, Nat Heart Inst & Clin Ctr, NIH, 61-68; from clin asst prof to clin assoc prof med, Sch Med, Georgetown Univ, 65-68; fel, Coun on Circulation, Am Heart Asn, 66-, fel, Coun Clin Cardiol, 67-; consult, US Naval Med Ctr, Bethesda, Md, 67-68, Letterman Army Gen Hosp, San Francisco, Calif, 68-, David Grant Med Ctr, Travis AFB, Calif, NIH, Nat Aeronaut & Space Admin, Vet Admin & NSF; mem, Am Bd Internal Med; mem adv comt, US Pharmacopeia, 70, NIH Lipid Metab, 71 & NASA Life Sci, 73-; ed-in-chief, Am Heart J, 80- *Honors & Awards:* Am Therapeut Soc Award, 65 & 73. *Mem:* Am Soc Clin Invest; Am Physiol Soc; fel Royal Soc Med; Am Soc Pharmacol & Exp Therapeut; Am Col Cardiol (pres-elect). *Res:* Adult and pediatric clinical cardiology; cardiac catheterization and diagnosis; cardiovascular medicine, physiology, biochemistry and pharmacology; author or coauthor of over 750 publications. *Mailing Add:* Ed Off Suite 3E 132 E St Davis CA 95616

MASON, DONALD FRANK, b Chicago, Ill, Mar 17, 26; m; c 4. PHYSICAL CHEMISTRY. *Educ:* Univ Ill, BS, 49; Univ Wis, PhD(chem), 53. *Prof Exp:* Asst, Naval Res Lab, Univ Wis, 49-52; res assoc chem eng, Northwestern Univ, 52-55, asst prof, 55-58; assoc chemist, Argonne Nat Lab, 58-62; assoc prof chem, Natural Sci Div, Ill Teachers Col, Chicago-North, 62-68; PROF CHEM, NORTHEASTERN ILL UNIV, 68- *Concurrent Pos:* Consult, Vern Alden Co, 54-55. *Mem:* AAAS; Am Chem Soc; Sigma Xi. *Res:* Heterogeneous reaction kinetics; mass spectrometry; instrumentation. *Mailing Add:* Dept of Chem Northeastern Ill Univ Chicago IL 60625

MASON, DONALD JOSEPH, b Kokomo, Ind, July 24, 31; m 53; c 4. MICROBIOLOGY. *Educ:* Purdue Univ, BS, 53, MS, 55, PhD, 58. *Prof Exp:* Res assoc microbiol, 58-66, sect head anal microbiol, 66-68, MGR FED DRUG ADMIN, UPJOHN CO, 68- *Mem:* Am Soc Microbiol; AAAS; Am Fedn Clin Res. *Res:* Microbial cytology and biochemistry; antibiotic production. *Mailing Add:* Upjohn Co Kalamazoo MI 49001

MASON, EARL JAMES, b Marion, Ind, Aug 26, 23; m 46; c 2. PATHOLOGY, MICROBIOLOGY. *Educ:* Ind Univ, BS, 44, AB & MA, 47; Ohio State Univ, PhD(bact), 50; Western Reserve Univ, MD, 54. *Prof Exp:* Damon Runyon Cancer fel, 54-56; fel path, Postgrad Sch Med, Univ Tex, 58-59; asst prof path, Col Med, Baylor Univ, 59-60; asst pathologist, Michael Reese Hosp, Chicago, 60-61; assoc pathologist, Mercy Hosp, Chicago, 61-65, chmn dept biol sci, 62-65; DIR LABS, ST MARY MERCY HOSP, 65-; CLIN PROF PATH, SCH MED, INDIANA UNIV, 76- *Concurrent Pos:* From intern to resident, Case Western Reserve Univ, 54-56; assoc prof, Dept Path, Chicago Med Sch, 65- *Mem:* Am Asn Path & Bact; Am Asn Cancer Res; Am Soc Exp Path; Am Soc Hemat. *Res:* Mechanism of action of viruses on cells; cellular production of antibodies; thrombocytopathic action of viruses. *Mailing Add:* St Mary Mercy Hosp 540 Tyler St Gary IN 46402

MASON, EARL SEWELL, b Grand Forks, NDak, June 9, 35; m 58; c 3. CIVIL ENGINEERING, LAW. *Educ:* Univ NDak, BSCE, 57, JurD, 73; Utah State Univ, PhD(civil eng), 65. *Prof Exp:* Civil engr, Bur Reclamation, US Dept Interior, 57, hydraul engr, 63; design engr, Aerospace Div, Boeing Airplane Co, 60; res asst meteorol, Colo State Univ, 60-61; asst prof civil eng, Univ Utah, 64-68; assoc prof, 68-75, PROF CIVIL ENG, UNIV NDAK, 75- *Concurrent Pos:* Prin investr, NSF res initiation grant, Univ Utah, 66-68; assoc dir, NDak Water Resources Res Inst, 75- *Mem:* Am Soc Civil Engrs; Am Soc Eng Educ; Nat Soc Prof Engrs. *Res:* Large open channel roughness; groundwater and surface water hydrology; meteorology; law. *Mailing Add:* Dept of Civil Eng Univ of NDak Grand Forks ND 58202

MASON, EDWARD ALLEN, b Atlantic City, NJ, Sept 2, 26; m 52; c 4. CHEMICAL PHYSICS. *Educ:* Va Polytech Inst, BS, 47; Mass Inst Technol, PhD(phys chem), 51. *Prof Exp:* Res assoc chem, Mass Inst Technol, 50-52; Nat Res Coun fel, Univ Wis, 52-53; asst prof chem, Pa State Univ, 53-55; from assoc prof to prof molecular physics, Inst Molecular Physics, Univ Md, 55-67, dir, 66-67; PROF CHEM & ENG, BROWN UNIV, 67- *Concurrent Pos:* Vis prof, Harvard, Mass Inst Technol, 75, Leiden, 81-82. *Honors & Awards:* Sci achievement Award, Wash Acad Sci, 62. *Mem:* AAAS; Am Asn Physics Teachers; fel Am Phys Soc. *Res:* Molecular and ionic scattering and transport; equation of state of gases; theory of transport phenomena; membrane transport; intermolecular forces; statistical mechanics. *Mailing Add:* Dept of Chem Brown Univ Providence RI 02912

MASON, EDWARD ARCHIBALD, b Rochester, NY, Aug 9, 24; m 50; c 6. NUCLEAR ENGINEERING. *Educ:* Univ Rochester, BS, 45; Mass Inst Technol, SM, 48, ScD(chem eng), 50. *Prof Exp:* From instr to asst prof chem eng, Mass Inst Technol, 49-53; sr engr, Ionics, Inc, 53-54, dir res, 54-57; from assoc prof to prof nuclear eng, Mass Inst Technol, 57-75, head dept, 71-75; comnr, US Nuclear Regulatory Comn, 75-77; V PRES RES, STANDARD OIL CO, IND, 77- *Concurrent Pos:* NSF sr fel, 65-66; consult govt agencies & indust co. *Mem:* Nat Acad Eng; Am Chem Soc; fel Am Acad Arts & Sci; fel Am Nuclear Soc; fel Am Inst Chem. *Res:* Research management; nuclear fuel and power systems. *Mailing Add:* Standard Oil Co Inc 200 E Randolph Dr PO Box 5910A Chicago IL 60680

MASON, EDWARD EATON, b Boise, Idaho, Oct 16, 20; m 44; c 4. SURGERY. *Educ:* Univ Iowa, BA, 43, MD, 45; Univ Minn, PhD(surg), 53. *Prof Exp:* Intern surg, Univ Minn Hosps, 45-46, fel surg, 48-52; from asst prof to assoc prof, 53-60, PROF SURG, COL MED & UNIV HOSPS, UNIV IOWA, 60-, CHMN GEN SURG, 78-, ACTG HEAD, 81- *Mem:* AAAS; Soc Univ Surgeons; Soc Exp Biol & Med; AMA; Am Col Surgeons. *Res:* Diseases of thyroid, parathyroid and gastrointestinal tract; pneumoperit- oneum in giant hernia repair; side-to-side spenorenal shunt; fluid, electrolyte and nutritional balance; gastric bypass for obesity; fatty acid toxicity; vertical banded gastroplasty for obesity. *Mailing Add:* Dept of Surg Univ of Iowa Hosps Iowa City IA 52242

MASON, ELLIOTT BERNARD, b Detroit, Mich, July 29, 43; m 71; c 3. PHYSIOLOGY. *Educ:* Loyola Univ, Chicago, BS, 65; Wayne State Univ, MS, 69, PhD(biol), 72. *Prof Exp:* Asst prof biol, George Mason Col, Univ Va, 71-73; asst prof, 73-75, ASSOC PROF BIOL, STATE UNIV NY COL CORTLAND, 75- *Mem:* AAAS; Am Soc Zool. *Res:* Physiology and endocrinology of vertebrates; stress responses of vertebrates. *Mailing Add:* Dept of Biol Sci State Univ of NY Col Cortland NY 13045

MASON, GEORGE ROBERT, surgery, physiology, see previous edition

MASON, GRANT WILLIAM, b Waialua, Hawaii, Aug 8, 40; m 64; c 5. COSMIC RAY PHYSICS. *Educ:* Brigham Young Univ, BA, 61; Univ Utah, PhD(physics), 69. *Prof Exp:* Res assoc & assoc instr physics, Univ Utah, 68-69; sci co-worker, Physics Inst, Aachen Tech Univ, 69-70; asst prof, 70-74, assoc prof, 74-79, PROF PHYSICS, BRIGHAM YOUNG UNIV, 79- *Mem:* Am Phys Soc; Am Asn Physics Teachers; Sigma Xi. *Res:* High energy cosmic ray studies. *Mailing Add:* Dept Physics & Astron Brigham Young Univ Provo UT 84602

MASON, GRENVILLE R, b Sask, 34. INTERMEDIATE-ENERGY PHYSICS. *Educ:* Univ BC, BASc, 56; McMaster Univ, MEng, 59; Univ Alberta, PhD(physics), 64. *Prof Exp:* Engr, Can Westinghouse Co, Ltd, 56-58; lectr physics, 62-64, from instr to assoc prof, 64-80, PROF PHYSICS, UNIV VICTORIA, BC, 80- . *Mem:* Can Asn Physicists. *Res:* Mesonic atoms; pion production cross-sections. *Mailing Add:* Dept of Physics Univ of Victoria Victoria BC V8W 2Y2 Can

MASON, HAROLD FREDERICK, b Porterville, Calif, Feb 15, 25; m 54; c 3. PHYSICAL CHEMISTRY. *Educ:* Cornell Univ, BChE, 50; Univ Wis, PhD(phys chem), 55. *Prof Exp:* Chem engr, Rohm & Haas Co, Pa, 50-51; res chemist, Chevron Res Co Div, Standard Oil Co Calif, 54-59, group supvr, 59-64, sect supvr, 64-67, mgr petrol process develop div, 67-71, MGR PETROL PROCESS RES DIV, CHEVRON RES CO DIV, STANDARD OIL CO, CALIF, 71- *Mem:* Am Chem Soc; Am Inst Chem Eng. *Res:* Chemical reaction kinetics; catalysis; petroleum processing; hydrogenation and hydrocracking; solid state reactions. *Mailing Add:* Chevron Res Co 576 Standard Ave Richmond CA 94802

MASON, HAROLD G, b Seattle, Wash, Apr 26, 24; m; c 3. CIVIL & INDUSTRIAL ENGINEERING. *Educ:* Univ Wash, BSCE, 47, BSIE, 48, MSCE, 50. *Prof Exp:* Resident engr, M O Sylliassen, Consult Engr, Wash, 47-48; soils engr, US Army Corps Engrs, 48-50; sr soils res engr, US Naval Eng Lab, Calif, 50-58; dep chief soil & rock dynamics br, US Air Force Spec Weapons Ctr, NMex, 58-61; mgr soil & struct mech div, Burlingame Res Ctr, URS Corp, 61-69, mem bd dirs, 62-63; PRES, MASON RES CONSULTS, 69- *Honors & Awards:* Hogentogler Award, Am Soc Testing & Mat, 55. *Mem:* Am Soc Testing & Mat. *Res:* Soil mechanics and foundation engineering, especially stress wave propagation in soil and its interaction with buried structures; lateral loads on pile foundations; soil instrumentation design; solid waste management. *Mailing Add:* Mason Res Consults 1550 Dominion Ave Sunnyvale CA 94087

MASON, HARRY LOUIS, b Louisville, Ky, May 1, 35; m 57. MECHANICAL ENGINEERING. *Educ:* Univ Ky, BS, 56, MS, 59. *Prof Exp:* Engr, Gen Elec Co, 56-57; instr mech eng, 57-59, ASST PROF MECH ENG, UNIV KY, 59- *Concurrent Pos:* Consult, Stephen Watkins Inc, 65-, Minister Press Co, 79, Allis Chalmers, 80. *Mem:* Am Soc Eng Educ. *Res:* Machine design and mechanisms; dynamic valve; nuclear blast closure device. *Mailing Add:* Dept Mech Eng Univ Ky Lexington KY 40506

MASON, HENRY LEA, b Trenton, NJ, Aug 22, 00; m 28. MECHANICAL ENGINEERING. *Educ:* Rutgers Univ, BS, 21, ME, 26; Univ Mich, DSc(eng mech), 34. *Prof Exp:* Asst engr, Westinghouse Elec & Mfg Co, 22-25; instr & asst prof mech eng, Rutgers Univ, 25-31; asst prof, Columbia Univ, 31-34; res engr, Taylor Instrument Co, 34-38, dir res, 38-45; res prof mech eng, Iowa State Col, 45-52; basic instrumentation, Nat Bur Standards, 52-54, supvry engr, Data Processing Systs, 55-62; assoc dir res support ctr, Mt Alto Vet

Hosp, 63; phys sci adminr, Nat Bur Standards, 64-70, consult, Off Int Rels, 70-72, gen phys scientist, Off Info Activities, 73-76; CONSULT ENGR, 76- *Concurrent Pos:* Vchmn terminol & standards comt, Int Fedn Automatic Control, 78-81. *Mem:* Am Soc Mech Engrs; Am Soc Eng Educ; Instrument Soc Am. *Res:* Dynamics of automatic controls; physical measurement standardization; development industrialization. *Mailing Add:* 7008 Meadow Lane Chevy Chase MD 20015

MASON, HERMAN CHARLES, b Chicago, Ill, Sept 26, 10. PUBLIC HEALTH, IMMUNOLOGY. *Educ:* Univ Chicago, BS, 32; Univ Ill, MS, 37, PhD, 39. *Prof Exp:* Instr in chg lab med, dent & grad students, Dept Bact & Pub Health, Univ Ill Col Med, 35-39; fel, Johns Hopkins Univ, 39-40; bacteriologist venereal dis, Health Dept, Chicago, Ill, 40-41; asst prof bact, State Col Wash, 41-42; assoc prof bact & immunol, Sch Med, Univ NC, 42-45; in chg of bact & immunol, Schering Corp, 45; consult, Chicago, Ill, 46-49; dir labs, Navy Med Res Unit 4, Ill, 49-50; head bact & consult, State Dept Pub Welfare, Ill & Psychopath Inst, 50-57; head labs, State Dept Health, Wash, 57-59; res prof, Univ Wash, 59; sr pathologist & chief med serv group, Space Med Off, Boeing Ariplane Co, 59-61; adminr labs & res biochemist, Vet Admin Hosp, Topeka, Kans, 61-64; dir res labs, Ark State Hosp, 64-69; vis prof, Int Atomic Energy Agency, Cekmece Nuclear Reactor, Istanbul Univ, 69-71. *Concurrent Pos:* Spec lectr, Cook County Sch Nursing, 38 & Grinnell Col, 41; chief adv, Korean Nat Labs, Seoul, 47-48. *Mem:* Fel Am Geog Soc; fel Am Pub Health Asn; fel Royal Soc Health; fel Royal Soc Trop Med & Hyg. *Res:* Filtrable viruses; laboratory methods; central nervous system infections; behavioral sciences; radiobiology. *Mailing Add:* 5059 N Jones Rd Oak Harbor WA 98277

MASON, J(OHN) PHILIP HANSON, JR, b Richmond, Va, May 8, 30; m 53; c 3. AGRICULTURAL ENGINEERING. *Educ:* Va Polytech Inst, BS, 51, BS, 55, MS, 56; Univ Mo, PhD(agr eng), 62. *Prof Exp:* From asst prof to assoc prof, 55-71, head dept, 69-79, PROF AGR ENG, VA POLYTECH INST & STATE UNIV, 71- *Mem:* Am Soc Agr Engrs. *Res:* Farm structures; alternate sources of energy for agriculture; temporary storage of hay. *Mailing Add:* Dept of Agr Eng Seitz Hall Blacksburg VA 24060

MASON, JAMES IAN, b Skipton, Yorkshire, Eng, Dec 1, 44; m 68; c 4. BIOCHEMISTRY. *Educ:* Univ Edinburgh, BSc, 66, PhD(biochem), 70. *Prof Exp:* Res fel, Southwestern Med Sch, Univ Tex, 70-72, asst prof biochem, 72-73; res fel, Univ Edinburgh, 73-77; staff scientist biochem, Worcester Found Exp Biol, 77-80; RES ASST PROF BIOCHEM & OBSTET-GYNEC, UNIV TEX HEALTH SCI CTR, DALLAS, 80- *Concurrent Pos:* Prin investr, Nat Cancer Inst grant, 77- *Mem:* Biochem Soc; Soc Endocrinol; Endocrine Soc; Am Soc Biol Chemists. *Res:* Membrane-bound hydroxylation enzymes; mechanism of tropic hormone action; steroid biosynthesis. *Mailing Add:* Biochem & Obstet-Gynec Depts Univ Tex Health Sci Ctr Dallas TX 75235

MASON, JAMES MICHAEL, b Kingsport, Tenn, Mar 19, 43; m 69. IMMUNOLOGY, EXPERIMENTAL PATHOLOGY. *Educ:* Memphis State Univ, BS, 66; Univ Tenn, PhD(exp path), 71. *Prof Exp:* Instr, 71-74, ASST PROF PATH, CTR HEALTH SCI, UNIV TENN, MEMPHIS, 74- *Concurrent Pos:* Consult, Chief Med Examr, State of Tenn, 71-; lectr, Nat Inst Child Health & Human Develop, 74- *Mem:* AAAS; Reticuloendothelial Soc. *Res:* Infectious disease aspects of sudden infant death syndrome; control of cell division; immunology of carcinogenesis. *Mailing Add:* Dept of Path Univ Tenn Ctr Health Sci Memphis TN 38163

MASON, JAMES WILLARD, b Hollywood, Calif, Apr 5, 33; m 56; c 2. POLYMER CHEMISTRY. *Educ:* Univ Calif, BS, 56, PhD(org chem), 60. *Prof Exp:* Chemist, Papermate Pen Co, 56; res assoc med chem, Merck Sharp & Dohme Res Labs, 60-64; sr scientist, Aeronutronic Div, Philco-Ford Corp, 64-69; scientist, Havens Int, 69; prin scientist & consult, Aeronutronic Div, Aeronutronic-Ford Corp, 69-77, supvr process control, Aeronutronic Div, Ford Aerospace & Commun Corp, 77-78; tech dir, Am Thermoform Corp, 78-80; PRES, J MASON ASSOCS, INC, 80- *Mem:* Am Inst Chem; Am Chem Soc; Soc Plastic Engrs. *Res:* Polymer chemistry; adhesives; water and waste treatment; membrane processes. *Mailing Add:* President J Mason Assocs Inc Los Alamites CA 90720

MASON, JERRY D, chemical engineering, see previous edition

MASON, JESSE DAVID, US citizen. MATHEMATICS. *Educ:* Univ Mo, Kansas City, BS, 62; Univ Calif, Riverside, PhD(math), 68. *Prof Exp:* Prod designer, Vendo Co, 58-62; dynamics engr, Gen Dynamics, Pomona, 62-65; res assoc math, Univ Calif, Riverside, 65-67; asst prof, Calif State Univ, San Bernardino, 67-68; asst prof, Univ Ga, 68-71; ASSOC PROF MATH, UNIV UTAH, 71-, ADJ ASSOC PROF INDUST ENG, 80- *Concurrent Pos:* Adj assoc prof indust eng, Univ Utah, 77- *Mem:* Inst Math Statist; Math Asn Am. *Res:* Limit theorems in probability theory and stochastic differential equations. *Mailing Add:* Dept of Math Univ of Utah Salt Lake City UT 84112

MASON, JOHN CHRISTOPHER, ecology, fisheries biology, see previous edition

MASON, JOHN FREDERICK, b Los Angeles, Calif, Nov 25, 13; m 39; c 4. PETROLEUM GEOLOGY. *Educ:* Univ Southern Calif, AB, 34, AM, 35; Princeton Univ, PhD(geol), 41. *Prof Exp:* Field geologist, Socony-Vacuum Oil Co, Egypt, 37-40; instr earth sci, Univ Pa, 41-42; field geologist, Venezuelan Atlantic Ref Co, Barcelona & Caracas, 42-46; geologist, Foreign Prod Dept, Atlantic Ref Co, Pa, 46-51; asst to gen mgr, Foreign Opers Dept, Union Oil Co, Calif, 52-54; mgr explor, Standard Vacuum Oil Co, India, 54-56, resident mgr, Prod Div, Pakistan, 56-59; staff geologist, Foreign Dept, Continental Oil Co, 59-65, sr explor adv, 65-75; CONSULT, 75- *Concurrent Pos:* Field geologist, Pa Geol & Topog Surv, 41- *Mem:* Fel Am Asn Petrol Geologists; Am Geol Inst. *Res:* Sedimentary basins of the world as to petroleum prospects. *Mailing Add:* 240 Fisher Place Princeton NJ 08540

MASON, JOHN GROVE, b Louisville, Ky, Dec 4, 29; m 56; c 2. ANALYTICAL CHEMISTRY. *Educ:* Univ Louisville, BS, 50; Ohio State Univ, PhD(chem), 55. *Prof Exp:* Instr chem, Ill Inst Technol, 56-59; assoc prof, 59-66, PROF CHEM, VA POLYTECH INST & STATE UNIV, 66- *Mem:* Am Chem Soc. *Res:* Polarography; electrode processes. *Mailing Add:* Dept of Chem Va Polytech Inst & State Univ Blacksburg VA 24061

MASON, JOHN HUGH, b Batavia, NY, Mar 8, 29; m 53; c 2. POLYMER CHEMISTRY, ABRASIVES TECHNOLOGY. *Educ:* Univ Rochester, BS, 50; Carnegie Inst Technol, PhD(org chem), 55. *Prof Exp:* Res chemist, Union Carbide Plastics Co Div, Union Carbide Corp, 54-61; sr res assoc, 62-70, projs mgr, 70-73, sr develop assoc, 73-75, MGR ABRASIVE BOND DEVELOP, CARBORUNDUM CO, 75- *Honors & Awards:* IR-100 Award, 70, 73 & 75. *Mem:* Soc Advan Mat & Process Eng; Am Cancer Soc. *Res:* Inorganic fibers and composites; analytical chemistry; resin development and characterization; abrasive development and characterization. *Mailing Add:* 5205 Brookfield Lane Clarence NY 14031

MASON, JOHN L(ATIMER), b Los Angeles, Calif, Nov 8, 23; m 54; c 4. CHEMICAL ENGINEERING. *Educ:* Univ Chicago, BS, 44; Calif Inst Technol, BS, 47, MS, 48, PhD(chem eng), 50. *Prof Exp:* Group supvr preliminary design, AiResearch Mfg Co Div, 50-57, sr proj engr heat transfer systs, 57-58, chief preliminary design, 58-60, chief engr, 60-68, dir eng, 68-72, VPRES ENG, AIRESEARCH MFG CO DIV, GARRETT CORP, 72- *Concurrent Pos:* Mem NASA res adv comt mech power plant systs, 59-60, comt nuclear systs, 60-62 & comt biotech & human res, 63-67; vchmn, Cryogenic Eng Conf Planning Bd, 64-67, chmn, 68; mem cryogenics evaluation panel, Nat Bur Standards, 68- *Mem:* Assoc fel Am Inst Aeronaut & Astronaut; Soc Automotive Engrs. *Res:* Heat transfer; power and propulsion; systems engineering. *Mailing Add:* Garrett Corp 9851 Sepulveda Blvd Los Angeles CA 90009

MASON, JOHN WAYNE, b Chicago, Ill, Feb 9, 24; m 50; c 3. NEUROENDOCRINOLOGY. *Educ:* Ind Univ, AB, 44, MD, 47. *Prof Exp:* Asst physiol, Ind Univ, 43-45; intern surg, NY Hosp-Cornell Med Ctr, 47-48, resident path, 48-50; pathologist, Ft Riley, Kans & Brooke Army Hosp, Tex, 50-53; chief neuroendocrinol dept, Walter Reed Army Inst Res, 53-74, sci adv, Div Neurpsychiat, 74-77; PROF DEPT PSYCHIAT, SCH MED, YALE UNIV, 77- *Mem:* Endocrine Soc; Am Psychosom Soc (pres, 70). *Res:* Stress, psychoendocrine and psychosomatic mechanisms. *Mailing Add:* Vet Admin Hosp 116A West Haven CT 06516

MASON, KARL ERNEST, anatomy, nutrition, deceased

MASON, LARRY GORDON, b Wyandotte, Mich, Jan 19, 37. POPULATION BIOLOGY. *Educ:* Univ Mich, BS, 58, MA, 59, Univ Kans, PhD(entom), 64. *Prof Exp:* Res assoc biol, Stanford Univ, 64-65; asst prof, 66-72, ASSOC PROF BIOL, STATE UNIV NY ALBANY, 72- *Mem:* Soc Study Evolution; Am Soc Nat. *Res:* Population phenomena, especially quantitative aspects, in natural animal populations. *Mailing Add:* Dept of Biol State Univ of NY at Albany Albany NY 12203

MASON, MARCUS M, b New York, NY, Mar 23, 11; m 32; c 3. VETERINARY PATHOLOGY. *Educ:* Cornell Univ, BS, 33, MS, 34; NY State Col Vet Med, DVM, 38. *Prof Exp:* Vet, Lederle Lab, Am Cyanamid Co, 38-39 & US Bur Animal Indust, 39-40; asst prof path, Vet Col, Middlesex Univ, 40-41; vet, Civilian Conserv Corps, 41& Animal Clin, Mass, 46-57; dir biol res, Biologics Testing Lab, 57-60 & Mason Res Inst, Inc, 60-75; dir, Worcester Found for Exp Biol, 75-76; PROF ANIMAL SCI & HEAD VET ASST PROG, BECKER JR COL, 76- *Concurrent Pos:* Partic cycad conf, NIH, 65; mem geriat comt, Inst Lab Animal Resources, Nat Acad Sci, 65-; vis prof & consult, Worcester Polytech Inst, 80- *Mem:* Am Vet Med Asn; Endocrine Soc; Am Asn Lab Animal Sci; Soc Toxicol; Am Asn Lab Animal Sci. *Res:* Prostatic biology; comparative neuropathology; mammalian endocrinology bioassay and immunoassay; toxicology, viral oncology, carcinogenesis and cancer chemotherapy. *Mailing Add:* Dept of Animal Sci 1003 Old Main St Leicester MA 01524

MASON, MARION, b Toronto, Ont, Nov 29, 33; US citizen. NUTRITION. *Educ:* Miami Univ, BS, 55; Ohio State Univ, MS, 59; Cornell Univ, PhD(nutrit), 69. *Prof Exp:* Instr nutrit, Univ Rochester, 56-58; consult, Vis Nurse Asn, Chicago, 59-63; asst prof, Univ Rochester, 63-66; assoc prof med dietetics, Ohio State Univ, 69-72; RUBY WINSLOW LINN PROF NUTRIT, SIMMONS COL, 73- *Concurrent Pos:* Clin consult dietetics, Peter Bent Brigham Hosp, Boston, 73-77; res assoc, Eastman Dent Ctr, Rochester, NY, 74-75; vis prof, Univ Rochester, 75-77. *Mem:* Am Dietetic Asn; Sigma Xi; Soc Nutrit Educ. *Res:* Health care compliance and intervention; clinical dietetic practice; cost and benefit methodology in clinical dietetics. *Mailing Add:* Simmons Col 300 The Fenway Boston MA 02115

MASON, MARTIN A(LEXANDER), b Washington, DC, Apr 23, 07; m 32; c 2. HYDRAULIC ENGINEERING. *Educ:* George Washington Univ, BS, 31; Univ Grenoble, Ing Dr, 38. *Prof Exp:* Engr, Nat Bur Standards, 31-37, 38-40; chief engr, Beach Erosion Bd, 40-51; dean, Sch Eng, George Washington Univ, 51-67; pres, Capitol Inst Technol, DC, 68-71; CONSULT ENGR, 71- *Honors & Awards:* Memorial Eng Found Bd War Dept Exceptional Civilian Serv Award, 45. *Mem:* Nat Soc Prof Engrs; Am Soc Mech Engrs; Am Soc Civil Engrs; Am Soc Eng Educ; Geophys Union. *Res:* Water wave phenomena; shore processes; fluid dynamics; erosion control. *Mailing Add:* 3621 Raymond St Chevy Chase MD 20015

MASON, MAX GARRETT, b Roanoke, Va, Jan 15, 44; m 67; c 2. SURFACE PHYSICS. *Educ:* Johns Hopkins Univ, BA, 65, PhD(chem), 70. *Prof Exp:* Sr res assoc chem, Univ Southern Calif, 70-72; sr res chemist, 72-78, RES ASSOC, KODAK RES LABS, EASTMAN KODAK CO, 78- *Mem:* Am Vacuum Soc. *Res:* Ultraviolet and x-ray photoemission studies of solid surfaces; chemistry and physics of adsorbed species. *Mailing Add:* Kodak Res Labs Kodak Park Rochester NY 14650

MASON, MERLE, b Coldspring, Mo, Aug 9, 20; m 42; c 1. BIOCHEMISTRY. *Educ:* Univ Iowa, BS, 47, PhD(biochem), 50. *Prof Exp:* From instr to assoc prof, 50-79, PROF BIOCHEM, UNIV MICH, ANN ARBOR, 79- *Mem:* Am Chem Soc; Am Soc Biol Chemists. *Res:* Amino acid metabolism; steroid metabolism. *Mailing Add:* Dept Biol Chem Univ Mich Ann Arbor MI 48109

MASON, MORTON FREEMAN, b Pasadena, Calif, Nov 12, 02; m 29; c 2. BIOCHEMISTRY. *Educ:* Ore State Col, BSc, 25; Duke Univ, PhD(biochem), 34. *Prof Exp:* Asst chem, Exp Sta, Mich State Col, 26-30; asst biochem, Sch Med, Duke Univ, 32-34; from instr to assoc prof, Sch Med, Vanderbilt Univ, 34-44; prof path chem, 44-55, prof forensic med & toxicol, 55-78, EMER PROF FORENSIC MED & TOXICOL, UNIV TEX HEALTH SCI CTR DALLAS, 78- *Concurrent Pos:* Toxicologist, Dallas City-County, 44-74, dir, Criminal Invest Lab, 55-74; chemist, Parkland Mem Hosp, 44-74; sr consult, US Vet Admin, 46-74. *Mem:* Am Soc Biol Chem; Am Chem Soc; Am Acad Forensic Sci (pres, 73-74); Am Asn Clin Chem; Am Indust Hyg Asn. *Res:* Analytical toxicology. *Mailing Add:* 3172 Brookhollow Dr Dallas TX 75234

MASON, NORBERT, b Karlsruhe, Ger, Feb 10, 30; US citizen; m 56; c 2. CHEMICAL ENGINEERING. *Educ:* Univ Minn, BS, 54, MS, 55; Case Western Reserve Univ, PhD, 69. *Prof Exp:* Res engr, B F Goodrich Res Ctr, 55-64; proj engr, Case Western Reserve Univ, 64-66, asst, 66-68, res assoc, 68-70, sr res assoc, 70-72; SR RES ASSOC, WASH UNIV, 72- *Mem:* Am Inst Chem Engrs; Am Chem Soc. *Res:* Polymerization technology; chemical processes; process instrumentation; membrane and adsorbent technology for biomedical water pollution and desalination applications; microencapsulation; bioengineering. *Mailing Add:* 645 Longton Dr Clayton MO 63105

MASON, NORMAN RONALD, b Rochester, Minn, Nov 20, 29; m 53; c 2. BIOCHEMISTRY. *Educ:* Univ Chicago, AB, 50, BS, 53; Univ Utah, MA, 56, PhD(biochem), 59. *Prof Exp:* From res instr to res asst prof biochem, Endocrinol Lab, Sch Med, Univ Miami, 59-64; SR SCIENTIST, RES LABS, ELI LILLY & CO, 64- *Concurrent Pos:* Investr, Howard Hughes Med Inst, 59-64. *Mem:* AAAS; Endocrine Soc; Am Chem Soc. *Res:* Endocrinology; ovarian function; gonadotropin action; cyclic nucleotides; prostaglandins; steroid hormone synthesis and metabolism; neurotransmitter receptor binding; hormone action. *Mailing Add:* Lilly Res Labs Eli Lilly & Co Indianapolis IN 46285

MASON, PERRY SHIPLEY, JR, b Lubbock, Tex, Oct 2, 38; m 60; c 2. ORGANIC CHEMISTRY. *Educ:* Harding Col, BS, 59; La State Univ, PhD(org chem), 63. *Prof Exp:* Asst prof sci, Okla Christian Col, 63-64; res assoc chem, Grad Inst Technol, Univ Ark, 64-66; asst prof, Ark State Col, 66-71; PROF CHEM & HEAD DEPT, LUBBOCK CHRISTIAN COL, 71- *Concurrent Pos:* NIH fel, 63-66. *Mem:* Am Chem Soc. *Res:* Organometallic chemistry; reaction mechanism; gas chromatography. *Mailing Add:* Dept of Chem Lubbock Christian Col Box 7111 Lubbock TX 79407

MASON, REGINALD G, JR, b Washington, NC, July 9, 33; m 64; c 1. PATHOLOGY, BIOCHEMISTRY. *Educ:* Univ NC, BS, 57, MD, 62, PhD(exp path), 64. *Prof Exp:* From intern to resident path, 62-64, from instr to prof path, Sch Med, Univ NC, Chapel Hill, pathologist-in-chief, Mem Hosp, Pawtucket, RI, 75-77; prof path, Brown Univ, 75-77; PROF & CHMN DEPT PATH, UNIV S FLA, 77- *Concurrent Pos:* Mem, Path A Study AMA; Col Am Path; Am Soc Clin Pathologists; Am Asn Pathologists; NIH; fel exp path, Sch Med, Univ NC, Chapel Hill, 62-65, Markle scholar acad med, 65. *Mem:* AAAS. *Res:* Thrombosis and hemorrhage; blood coagulation; blood platelet agglutination and white thrombus formation; endothelial cell function; cellular cohesion and adhesion. *Mailing Add:* Dept of Path 12901 N 30th St Tampa FL 33612

MASON, RICHARD CANFIELD, b Indianapolis, Ind, Aug 12, 23; m 44; c 2. PHYSIOLOGY. *Educ:* Ind Univ, AB, 48, PhD(zool), 52. *Prof Exp:* Asst, Ind Univ, 48-49; res assoc, Merck Inst Therapeut Res, 52-56; asst prof physiol, Seton Hall Col Med & Dent, 56-61; asst prof, Col Physicians & Surgeons, Columbia Univ, 61-71, asst dean student affairs, 70-71; assoc prof physiol & assoc dean admis & student affairs, 71-76, ASST PROF PHYSIOL & BIOPHYSICS, COL MED & DENT NJ-RUTGERS MED SCH, 77- *Concurrent Pos:* Actg dean admis, NJ Sch Osteop Med, 76-77. *Mem:* AAAS; Am Soc Zool; Am Physiol Soc; Harvey Soc. *Res:* Renal physiology. *Mailing Add:* Col of Med & Dent NJ Rutgers Med Sch PO Box 101 Piscataway NJ 08854

MASON, RICHARD RANDOLPH, b St Louis, Mo, Oct 3, 30; m 56; c 4. FORESTRY, ENTOMOLOGY. *Educ:* Univ Mich, BS, 52, MF, 56, PhD(forestry), 66. *Prof Exp:* Forest entomologist, Bowaters Southern Paper Corp, 56-58, res forester, 58-65; RES ENTOMOLOGIST, FORESTRY SCI LAB, US FOREST SERV, 65- *Mem:* Soc Am Foresters; Entom Soc Am; AAAS; Entom Soc Can; Ecol Soc Am. *Res:* Protection of commercial forests from destructive insect pests, emphasizing their detection, evaluation and population dynamics. *Mailing Add:* Forestry Sci Lab US Forest Serv Corvallis OR 97331

MASON, ROBERT C, b Anthony, Idaho, July 9, 20; m 46; c 3. PHARMACOLOGY, MEDICINAL CHEMISTRY. *Educ:* Univ Utah, BS, 50; Univ Wis, PhD(pharmaceut chem), 54. *Prof Exp:* PROF MED CHEM, UNIV UTAH, 54- *Mem:* Am Chem Soc; Am Pharmaceut Asn. *Res:* Isolation, characterization and synthesis of natural products and related substances. *Mailing Add:* Col of Pharm Univ of Utah Salt Lake City UT 84112

MASON, ROBERT EDWARD, b Thunder Bay, Ont, Jan 21, 34; m 57; c 3. STATISTICS, ECOLOGY. *Educ:* Univ Toronto, BSA, 57, MSA, 62; NC State Univ, PhD(statist), 71. *Prof Exp:* Dist biologist, Ont Dept Lands & Forests, 57-59, fish & wildlife supvr, 59-64; from asst statistician to assoc statistician, NC State Univ, 65-71; statistician, 71-73, SR STATISTICIAN, RES TRIANGLE INST, 73- *Mem:* Ecol Soc Am; Biomet Soc. *Res:* Design and analysis of probability samples; nonlinear variance estimation; statistical ecology. *Mailing Add:* Res Triangle Inst PO Box 12194 Research Triangle Park NC 27709

MASON, RODNEY JACKSON, b New York, NY, Feb 27, 39; m 69. PLASMA PHYSICS, COMPUTER SIMULATION. *Educ:* Cornell Univ, BA, 60, PhD, 64. *Prof Exp:* Fulbright grant, Inst Plasma Physics, Garching, WGer, 64-65; asst prof aeronaut & astronaut, Mass Inst Technol, 65-67; mem tech staff, Bell Tel Labs, 67-72; STAFF MEM, LOS ALAMOS NAT LAB, 72- *Mem:* AAAS; Am Phys Soc. *Res:* Kinetic theory of shock formation and structure; computer simulation of ion-acoustic and magnetosonic collisionless shocks; computational physics; laser-plasma interaction studies; transport in laser fusion pellets; pellet design implosion and thermonuclear burn physics; long time scale, collisional plasma simulation in one and two dimensions; collisional plasma simulation in one and two dimensions. *Mailing Add:* Div X Los Alamos Nat Lab Los Alamos NM 87545

MASON, RONALD GEORGE, b Southampton, Eng, Dec 24, 16; m 46. GEOPHYSICS. *Educ:* Univ London, BSc, 38, MSc, 39, PhD(geophys), 51. *Prof Exp:* Lectr geophys, Imp Col, London, 47-63; asst res geophysicist, Scripps Inst, Univ Calif, 52-62; reader, 63-65, PROF GEOPHYS, IMP COL, UNIV LONDON, 67-; RES AFFIL, HAWAII INST GEOPHYS, UNIV HAWAII, 63- *Mem:* AAAS; Seismol Soc Am; Soc Explor Geophys; Am Geophys Union; Europ Asn Explor Geophys. *Res:* Crustal and upper mantle structure of the earth; earthquake and volcano mechanisms. *Mailing Add:* Dept of Geophys Imp Col London SW7 2BP England

MASON, S(TANLEY) G(EORGE), b Montreal, Que, Mar 20, 14; m 43; c 2. PHYSICAL CHEMISTRY. *Educ:* McGill Univ, BE, 36, PhD(phys chem), 39. *Prof Exp:* Instr phys chem, Trinity Col, Conn, 39-41; res engr, Suffield Exp Sta, Dept Nat Defence, Alta, 41-45; assoc res chemist, Div Atomic Energy, Nat Res Coun Can, 45-46; res assoc, 46-66, PROF, DEPT CHEM, MCGILL UNIV, 66-, OTTO MAASS PROF CHEM, 79- *Concurrent Pos:* Dir, Applied Chem Div & head, Phys Chem Sect, Pulp & Paper Res Inst Can, 46-79, consult, 79- *Honors & Awards:* Howard N Potts Medal, Franklin Inst, 80. *Mem:* Foreign assoc Nat Acad Eng; fel Royal Soc Can; assoc Can Pulp & Paper Asn; fel Chem Inst Can; fel Tech Asn Pulp & Paper Indust. *Res:* Colloids; cellulose; rheology; hemodynamics; pulp and paper. *Mailing Add:* Dept of Chem McGill Univ Montreal PQ H3A 2T5 Can

MASON, THOMAS JOSEPH, b St Louis, Mo, Aug 8, 42. BIOSTATISTICS, EPIDEMIOLOGY. *Educ:* St Bernard Col, BA, 64; Univ Ga, MS, 68, PhD(statist & comput sci), 73. *Prof Exp:* Aerospace engr, NASA Manned Spacecraft Ctr, 64-65; statistician epidemiol, Ctr Dis Control, 67-69; STATISTICIAN EPIDEMIOL, NIH NAT CANCER INST, 71-, CHIEF, POP STUDIES SECT, 78- *Mem:* Sigma Xi; Soc Epidemiol Res; AAAS. *Res:* Assessing carcinogenic exposures among residents of areas in the United States which have a markedly different cancer experience from that of this country as a whole. *Mailing Add:* Rm 3C29 Landow Bldg NIH Nat Cancer Inst Bethesda MD 20205

MASON, THOMAS OLIVER, b Cleveland, Ohio, Oct 14, 52; m 74. MATERIALS SCIENCE, CERAMICS ENGINEERING. *Educ:* Pa State Univ, BS, 74; Mass Inst Technol, PhD(mat sci & eng), 77. *Prof Exp:* ASST PROF MAT SCI & ENG, NORTHWESTERN UNIV, 78- *Concurrent Pos:* NATO fel, Inst Phys Chem & Electrochem, Tech Univ Hannover, W Ger, 77-78. *Mem:* Am Ceramic Soc; Am Chem Soc; Am Soc Eng Educ; Am Sci Affil; Nat Inst Ceramic Engrs. *Res:* Bulk and point defect thermodynamics in the solid state including phase equilibria; high temperature electrical properties of materials; ceramic processing. *Mailing Add:* Dept of Mat Sci & Eng Technol Inst Northwestern Univ Evanston IL 60201

MASON, TIM ROBERT, b Hereford, Tex, Apr 26, 30; m 53; c 3. ANIMAL NUTRITION, REPRODUCTIVE PHYSIOLOGY. *Educ:* Abilene Christian Col, BS, 53; Tex Tech Col, MS, 55; Tex A&M, PhD(animal nutrit), 63. *Prof Exp:* High sch teacher, Tex, 55-56; instr animal husb, Abilene Christian Col, 56-59, asst prof, 63-64; res asst, Tex A&M, 59-61 & 62-63; dir agr develop, Tex Power & Light Co, 61-62; dir livestock res, Beacon Div, Textron, Inc, 64-65; dir tech serv, 65-66; assoc prof animal husb, 66-68, prof agr, Tarleton State Univ, 68-77; CONSULT, SPAN-TEX CONSULT SERV, 77- *Mem:* Am Dairy Sci Asn; Am Soc Animal Sci. *Res:* Beef cattle; sheep, dairy and swine nutrition research. *Mailing Add:* Rt 3 Box 42A Stephenville TX 76401

MASON, V BRADFORD, b Boston, Mass, Nov 19, 42; m 65; c 2. ELECTRICAL ENGINEERING. *Educ:* Univ Mass, BS, 69; Univ Mich, MS, 70, PhD(elec eng), 72. *Prof Exp:* Sr res geophysicist, Shell Develop Co, 72-77; SR RES ENGR ELECTROMAGNETICS, SRI INT, 77- *Mem:* Inst Elec & Electronics Engrs; AAAS; Soc Explor Geophysicists. *Res:* Digital signal processing; geophysics; radar; sonar. *Mailing Add:* 2564 Greer Rd Palo Alto CA 94303

MASON, W ROY, III, b Charlottesville, Va, Feb 6, 43; m 63; c 3. INORGANIC CHEMISTRY. *Educ:* Emory Univ, BS, 63, MS & PhD(chem), 66. *Prof Exp:* Instr chem, Emory at Oxford, summer 64; res fel, Calif Inst Technol, 66-67; from asst prof to assoc prof, 67-80, PROF CHEM, NORTHERN ILL UNIV, 80- *Concurrent Pos:* Vis res fel, H C Orsted Inst, Univ Copenhagen, Denmark, 74-75. *Mem:* Am Chem Soc; Sigma Xi. *Res:* Heavy metal coordination compounds; electronic structure and reactivity; molecular orbital and ligand field theory. *Mailing Add:* Dept of Chem Northern Ill Univ DeKalb IL 60115

MASON, WARREN PERRY, b Colorado Springs, Colo, Sept 28, 00; m 29, 52, 56; c 1. ACOUSTICS. *Educ:* Univ Kans, BSEE, 21; Columbia Univ, MA, 24, PhD(physics), 28. *Prof Exp:* Mem tech staff, Bell Tel Labs, 21-31, head piezoelec res, 31-48, head mech res, 48-65; sr res assoc, Metallurgical Dept, 69-77, VIS PROF CIVIL ENG & ENG MECH, COLUMBIA UNIV, 65- *Concurrent Pos:* Res prof, George Washington Univ, 69-73. *Honors & Awards:* Arnold O Beckman Award, Instrument Soc Am; Benjamin Lamme Award, Inst Elec & Electronics Eng, 67; Gold Medal, Acoust Soc Am, 71; First Hon Mem, Brit Inst Acoust. *Mem:* AAAS; fel Acoust Soc Am (pres, 55-56); fel Am Phys Soc; fel Inst Elec & Electronics Eng; Instrument Soc Am. *Res:* Physical acoustics and the properties of materials; piezoelectricity and ferroelectricity; internal friction, acoustic emission and fatigue in metals. *Mailing Add:* 50 Gilbert Pl West Orange NJ 07052

MASON, WILLIAM BURKETT, b Warren, Ohio, Aug 20, 20; m 47, 70. CLINICAL CHEMISTRY. *Educ:* Univ Rochester, BS, 42, MD, 50; Princeton Univ, MA, 44, PhD(chem), 46; Am Bd Clin Chem, Dipl, 56. *Prof Exp:* Asst, Princeton Univ, 42-46, instr, 46; asst, Atomic Energy Proj, Univ Rochester, 46-47, assoc, 47-51, instr biochem, Sch Med & Dent, 51-57, from asst prof to assoc prof biochem & med, 57-70, path, 61-70; dir affil labs, 70-73, VPRES, BIO-SCI ENTERPRISES, 73- *Concurrent Pos:* Anal chemist, Manhattan Dist, Princeton Univ, 44-46; intern, Strong Mem Hosp, Rochester, 50-51, asst resident, 51-52; fel clin path, Clin Ctr, NIH, 61-62; chief med scientist, Med Diag Opers, Xerox Corp, 68-70. *Mem:* Am Chem Soc; Am Asn Clin Chem (pres, 67); Acad Clin Lab Physicians & Scientists. *Res:* Applications of analytical chemistry to medicine; quantitative analytical procedures; infrared microspectrophotometry. *Mailing Add:* Bio-Sci Enterprises 7600 Tyrone Ave Van Nuys CA 91405

MASON, WILLIAM C, US citizen. CIVIL ENGINEERING. *Educ:* Mont State Univ, BS, 63; Univ Wash, MS, 69; Am Acad Environ Engrs, dipl. *Prof Exp:* Mfg engr, Gen Elec Co, 63-67; res asst, Univ Wash, 67-69; environ engr, Ga Environ Protection Div, 69-72; applicatons engr, Gen Environ Equip Inc, 72-73; MEM STAFF, WESTON, 73- *Mem:* Water Pollution Control Fedn; Am Soc Civil Engrs; Am Water Works Asn. *Res:* Industrial treatment; pollution abatement; sludge dewatering and disposal; hazardous waste disposal. *Mailing Add:* Weston Weston Way West Chester PA 19380

MASON, WILLIAM HICKMON, b Bradford, Ark, June 16, 36; m 55; c 3. ZOOLOGY. *Educ:* Ark Polytech Col, BS, 58; Univ Ga, MEd, 64, DEd(sci educ), 66. *Prof Exp:* From asst prof to assoc prof, 66-75, PROF ZOOL & ENTOM, AUBURN UNIV, 75-, COORDR GEN BIOL, 68- *Mem:* Am Inst Biol Sci; AAAS; Entom Soc Am; Ecol Soc Am. *Res:* Ecosystem analysis through the use of radionuclide cycling and improvement of undergraduate teaching through the use of audiotutorial and modular concepts. *Mailing Add:* Dept Gen Biol Auburn Univ Auburn AL 36830

MASON, WILLIAM RICHARDSON MILES, b Lucknow, India, Nov 29, 21; Can citizen; m 51; c 2. SYSTEMATIC ENTOMOLOGY. *Educ:* Univ Alberta, BSc, 42; Cornell Univ, PhD(entomol), 53. *Prof Exp:* Seasonal agr res officer, 46-49, AGR RES OFFICER, CAN DEPT AGR, 49- *Concurrent Pos:* Ed, Can Entomologist, 61-64. *Mem:* Entom Soc Can. *Res:* Taxonomy of Hymenoptera, Ichneumonidae and Braconidae; systematics of Braconidae, especially Microgasterinae. *Mailing Add:* Biosyst Res Inst Can Agr Ottawa ON K1A 0C6 Can

MASON, WILLIAM VAN HORN, b Pittsburgh, Pa, Jan 8, 30; m 65; c 2. AEROSPACE MEDICINE. *Educ:* Harvard Univ, AB, 51; Baylor Univ, MD, 61. *Prof Exp:* Jr geophysicist, Humble Oil & Refining Co, 54-56; physician, Hood River Med Group, 62-65; RES PHYSICIAN, LOVELACE FOUND, 65- *Concurrent Pos:* NIH grants, 65- *Res:* Advanced diagnostic instrumentation; physiology of unusual environments. *Mailing Add:* Lovelace Found 5200 Gibson Blvd SE Albuquerque NM 87108

MASORO, EDWARD JOSEPH, b Oakland, Calif, Dec 28, 24; m 47. PHYSIOLOGY. *Educ:* Univ Calif, AB, 47, PhD(physiol), 50. *Prof Exp:* Asst physiol, Univ Calif, 47-48; asst prof, Queens Univ, 50-52; from asst prof to assoc prof, Med Sch, Tufts Univ, 52-62; from res assoc prof to res prof, Univ Wash, 62-64; prof & chmn dept, Med Col Pa, 64-73; PROF PHYSIOL & CHMN DEPT, UNIV TEX HEALTH SCI CTR, SAN ANTONIO, 73- *Mem:* Am Physiol Soc; Am Chem Soc; Can Biochem Soc; Can Physiol Soc; Am Soc Biol Chemists. *Res:* Intermediary metabolism; environmental physiology; muscle physiology; gerontology; membrane transport. *Mailing Add:* Dept of Physiol Univ of Tex Health Sci Ctr San Antonio TX 78284

MASOUREDIS, SERAFEIM PANOGIOTIS, b Detroit, Mich, Nov 14, 22; m 43; c 2. HEMATOLOGY, IMMUNOHEMATOLOGY. *Educ:* Univ Mich, AB, 44, MD, 48; Univ Calif, Berkeley, PhD(med physics), 52. *Prof Exp:* Clin instr med, Univ Calif, San Francisco, 50-52, res assoc med physics, Donner Lab, Berkeley, 54; from asst prof to assoc prof path, Sch Med, Univ Pittsburgh, 55-59, asst dir cent blood bank, 55-59; assoc prof prev med, Sch Med, Univ Calif, San Francisco, 59-62, assoc prof med, 62-66, assoc prof clin path & lab med, 66-67; prof med & microbiol, Sch Med, Marquette Univ, 67-69; PROF PATH & DIR UNIV HOSP BLOOD BANK, SCH MED, UNIV CALIF, SAN DIEGO, 69- *Concurrent Pos:* Res assoc, Cancer Res Inst, 59-67; chief H C Moffitt Blood Bank, 62-67; spec fel, Univ Lausanne, 65-66; exec dir, Milwaukee Blood Ctr, 67-69. *Honors & Awards:* Emily Cooley Mem lectr, 73; Karl Landsteiner Mem Award, 79. *Mem:* Am Asn Cancer Res; Am Asn Immunol; Am Soc Hemat; Soc Exp Biol & Med; Int Soc Hemat. *Res:* Blood group antigens; red cell membranes; membrane ultrastructure; immunological reactions involving red cell, hemolytic anemias. *Mailing Add:* Dept of Path Univ of Calif Sch of Med T-003 La Jolla CA 92037

MASOVER, GERALD K, b Chicago, Ill, May 12, 35; m 59; c 3. MICROBIOLOGY, PHARMACY. *Educ:* Univ Ill, BS, 57, MS, 70; Stanford Univ, PhD(med microbiol), 73. *Prof Exp:* Res assoc med microbiol, Med Sch, Stanford Univ, 73-76, res assoc surg, 76-80; MEM STAFF, BRUCE LYON MEM RES LABS, CHILDREN'S HOSP & MED CTR, 80- *Concurrent Pos:* NSF fel, Stanford Univ, 70-73; consult, Durrum Chem Corp, 75, Bactilabs, Inc, 76 & WHO, 75-; asst, Univ Ill Chicago Circle, 69 & Stanford Univ, 72; researcher, Univ Ill, 69; pharmacist, Calif & Ill, 57- *Mem:* Am Soc Microbiol; AAAS; Int Orgn Mycoplasmologists; Sigma Xi; Fedn Am Scientists. *Res:* Definition of life using smallest free living cell as model; host-parasite interaction; aging and development; cell culture. *Mailing Add:* Bruce Lyon Mem Res Labs 51st & Grove St Oakland CA 94609

MASRI, MERLE SID, b Jerusalem, Palestine, Sept 12, 27; nat US; m 52; c 4. AGRICULTURAL CHEMISTRY, MAMMALIAN PHYSIOLOGY. *Educ:* Univ Calif, AB, 50, PhD(physiol), 53. *Prof Exp:* Res assoc hemat, Michael Reese Hosp, Chicago, Ill, 54-56; res chemist pharmacol, 56-71, RES CHEMIST FIBER SCI, WESTERN REGIONAL RES LAB, USDA, 71- *Honors & Awards:* Spec Serv Merit Award, USDA, 66. *Mem:* AAAS; Am Asn Cereal Chem; NY Acad Sci. *Res:* Chemistry metabolism and pharmacology of mycotoxins; toxicology; fiber science, especially wool; protein chemistry; metallic ion interactions with proteins and bio polymers; polymers and enzyme immobilization; pollution abatement. *Mailing Add:* Western Regional Res Lab US Dept of Agr Berkeley CA 94710

MASRI, SAMI F(AIZ), b Beirut, Lebanon, Dec 9, 39; m 64; c 3. MECHANICAL ENGINEERING. *Educ:* Univ Tex, BS, 60, MS, 61; Calif Inst Technol, MS, 62, PhD(mech eng), 65. *Prof Exp:* Res fel mech eng, Calif Inst Technol, 65-66; from asst prof to assoc prof eng, 66-76, PROF ENG, UNIV SOUTHERN CALIF, 76- *Mem:* Am Soc Civil Engrs; Am Soc Mech Engrs. *Res:* Applied mechanics; shock and vibration; structural dynamics. *Mailing Add:* Dept of Civil Eng Univ of Southern Calif Los Angeles CA 90007

MASRY, SALEM EL, b Aug 2, 38; Can citizen. PHOTOGRAMMETRY. *Educ:* Ain Shams Univ, Cairo, BSc, 60; Univ Col, dipl, 62 & 63, Univ London, PhD(photogram), 66. *Prof Exp:* Fel photogram, 66-67, res assoc, 67-70, asst prof, 70-77, ASSOC PROF PHOTOGRAM, UNIV NB, FREDERICTON, 77- *Mem:* Am Soc Photogram. *Res:* Applications of real-time control to photogrammetric instruments. *Mailing Add:* Dept of Surveying Eng Univ of NB Fredericton NB E3B 5A3 Can

MASSA, DENNIS JON, b Myrtle Beach, SC, Sept 29, 45; m 66; c 3. PHYSICAL CHEMISTRY, POLYMER PHYSICS. *Educ:* Bradley Univ, BA, 66; Univ Wis-Madison, PhD(phys chem), 70. *Prof Exp:* NSF fel phys biochem, Univ Calif, San Diego, 70-71; sr res chemist, 71-78, RES ASSOC, RES LABS, EASTMAN KODAK CO, 79- *Mem:* Am Chem Soc; Am Phys Soc; Soc Rheol. *Res:* Polymer physics; physical chemistry of polymers and biopolymers; molecular motion in the solid state; polymer rheology. *Mailing Add:* Res Labs Eastman Kodak Co Rochester NY 14650

MASSA, LOUIS, b Aug 4, 40; US citizen. CHEMICAL PHYSICS. *Educ:* LeMoyne Col, BS, 61; Clarkson Col, MS, 62; Georgetown Univ, PhD(physics), 66. *Prof Exp:* Res fel chem, Brookhaven Nat Lab, 66-69; assoc prof, 69-76, PROF CHEM, HUNTER COL, 76- *Concurrent Pos:* Petrol Res Fund grant, Hunter Col, 70-, City Univ New York Res Found grant, 71- *Mem:* AAAS; Am Phys Soc; Am Chem Soc. *Res:* Theoretical chemical physics; quantum mechanics. *Mailing Add:* Dept of Chem Hunter Col 695 Park Ave New York NY 10021

MASSALSKI, T(ADEUSZ) B(RONISLAW), b Warsaw, Poland, June 29, 26; nat US; m 53; c 3. PHYSICAL METALLURGY. *Educ:* Univ Birmingham, BSc, 52, PhD, 54, DSc, 64. *Hon Degrees:* DSc, Univ Warsaw, 73. *Prof Exp:* Res fel, Inst Study Metals, Univ Chicago, 54-56; lectr phys metall, Univ Birmingham, 56-59; sr res fel, 59-61, STAFF FEL & HEAD METAL PHYSICS, MELLON INST, 61-, PROF METALL PHYSICS & MAT SCI, CARNEGIE-MELLON UNIV, 68- *Concurrent Pos:* Vis prof, Univ Buenos Aires, 62, Calif Inst Technol, 62, Stanford Univ, 63 & Univ Calif, 64 & 66; Guggenheim fel, Oxford Univ, 65-66; vis prof, Inst Physics Bariloche, Arg, 66 & 70 & Harvard Univ, 69; exchange prof, Krakov, Poland, 68. *Mem:* Am Phys Soc; Am Inst Mining, Metall & Petrol Engrs; fel Am Soc Metals; fel Brit Inst Physics; fel Brit Inst Metals. *Res:* Theory of alloy phases; transformations and crystallographic relationships in metals and alloys; metal physics. *Mailing Add:* Sci Hall 4311 Schenley Park Pittsburgh PA 15213

MASSARO, DONALD JOHN, b Jamaica, NY, Aug 7, 32; m 57; c 2. MEDICINE. *Educ:* Hofstra Col, BA, 53; Georgetown Univ, MD, 57. *Prof Exp:* Am Thoracic Soc fel, 60-62; from isntr to asst prof med, Georgetown Univ, 62-67; assoc prof, Duke Univ, 67-68; assoc prof, George Washington Univ, 68-72, prof med, 72-76; chief chest sect, Vet Admin Hosp, 68-76; PROF MED & PHYSIOL, SCH MED, UNIV MIAMI, 76- *Concurrent Pos:* fel physiol chem, Johns Hopkins Univ, 64-65; med investr, Vet Admin, 70- *Mem:* Am Physiol Soc; Am Soc Clin Invest; Soc Exp Biol & Med; Am Fedn Clin Res; Am Thoracic Soc. *Res:* Pulmonary diseases; lung biochemistry; phagocytosis; pulmonary physiology. *Mailing Add:* Univ Miami Sch of Med R-120 PO Box 016960 Miami FL 33101

MASSARO, EDWARD JOSEPH, b Passaic, NJ, June 7, 33; m 78; c 4. ENVIRONMENTAL TOXICOLOGY, BIOCHEMISTRY. *Educ:* Rutgers Univ, AB, 55; Univ Tex, MA, 58, PhD(biochem), 62. *Prof Exp:* Instr biol, Blinn Col, Tex, 56-57; USPHS fel biochem, Univ Tex, 62-63; USPHS fel physiol chem & biol, Med Sch, Johns Hopkins Univ, 63-65, res assoc biol, 65; res assoc, Yale Univ, 65-68; from asst prof to prof biochem, State Univ NY Buffalo, 68-78, res prof, 78; PROF TOXICOL, DEPT VET SCI & DIR CTR AIR ENVIRON STUDIES, PA STATE UNIV, 78- *Concurrent Pos:* Fel Rachel Carson Col, State Univ NY Buffalo, 68-78; dir chem carcinogenesis, Mason Res Inst, Mass, 77-78, dir toxicol, 78. *Mem:* AAAS; Am Soc Biol Chemists; Am Asn Pathologists; Am Soc Pharmacol & Exp Therapeut; Teratology Soc. *Res:* Environmental, developmental and comparative toxicology, biochemistry, physiology and pathology. *Mailing Add:* 226 Fenske Lab Pa State Univ University Park PA 16802

MASSE, ARTHUR N, b Columbus, Ohio, May 1, 28; m 55; c 3. CHEMICAL ENGINEERING. *Educ:* Ohio State Univ, BS, 51. *Prof Exp:* Jr engr, Raw Mat Lab, BF Goodrich Co, Ohio, 51 & 53, shift foreman acrylonitrile prod, Ky, 53-56, mem tech dept, 56-61; chem engr, res & develop water pollution control, 61-68, chief pilot plants, US Dept Interior, 68-77; chief prod control, Environ Protection Agency, 77-80, ENVIRON ENGR, TECH EVAL SERV, NAT ENFORCEMENT INVEST CTR, 80- *Mem:* Am Inst Chem Eng; Water Pollution Control Fedn. *Res:* Research and development work on physical and chemical processes to supplement or replace conventional biological treatment of municipal wastewaters. *Mailing Add:* Environ Protection Agency Denver Fed Ctr Denver CO 80225

MASSEE, TRUMAN WINFIELD, b Joseph, Ore, May 5, 30; m 51; c 3. SOIL FERTILITY. *Educ:* Ore State Univ, BS, 52, AgM, 53; Mont State Univ, PhD, 73. *Prof Exp:* Soil scientist, Northern Mont Br Exp Sta, Agr Res Serv, 55-57, res soil scientist, Tetonia Br Exp Sta, Univ Idaho, 58-64, RES SOIL SCIENTIST, SNAKE RIVER RES CTR, AGR RES SERV, USDA, 65- *Mem:* Am Soc Agron; Soil Conserv Soc Am; Soil Sci Soc Am; Sigma Xi. *Res:* Dryland soil moisture-fertility-plant growth relationships. *Mailing Add:* Snake River Conserv Res Ctr Rte 1 Box 186 Kimberly ID 83341

MASSEL, GARY ALAN, b Trenton, NJ, May 5, 39; m 59; c 2. TECHNICAL MANAGEMENT, SYSTEMS SCIENCE. *Educ:* NC State Univ, BS, 61, PhD(physics), 67. *Prof Exp:* Asst physics, NC State Univ, 61 & 63; Aerospace engr, Langley Res Ctr, NASA, Va, 65-67; res staff mem, Inst Defense Anal, 67-70; dir land force progs, 70-72 & naval force progs, Off Asst Secy Defense Systs Anal, 72-73; assoc adminr, Social & Rehabilitation Serv, Off Health, Educ & Welfare, 73-75; vpres, JRB Assocs, 75-77; corp vpres, Sci Appln Inc, 77-79, sr vpres, 79-81; DIR TECH PLANNING & EVAL, INT PAPER CO, 81- *Concurrent Pos:* Consult, Defense Atomic Support Agency, 68-; chmn, Comsysts Corp, 78-80; dir, JRB Assocs, 78- *Mem:* Am Phys Soc; Opers Res Soc Am; Am Pub Health Asn. *Res:* Computer modeling of many-body systems; high-temperature hydrodynamics; weapon systems analysis; health systems planning; energy systems analysis and planning; solar energy. *Mailing Add:* 8020 Birnam Wood Dr McLean VA 22101

MASSELL, PAUL BARRY, b Boston, Mass, June 26, 48. NUMBER THEORY. *Educ:* Univ Chicago, AB, 70; City Univ New York, PhD(math), 75. *Prof Exp:* Sr programmer, Nat Bur Econ Res, 74-75; res analyst, JWK Int Corp, 75-77; statist programmer, Battelle Mem Inst, 77-80; ASST PROF, US NAVAL ACAD, 80- *Concurrent Pos:* Lectr math, Brooklyn Col, 71-74. *Mem:* Am Math Soc; Math Asn Am. *Res:* Class field theory, especially examination of class groups of real quadratic number fields; relationship between class field theory and theorems of elementary number theory. *Mailing Add:* 9659 Basken Ring Rd Apt 3 Columbia MD 21045

MASSENGALE, MARTIN ANDREW, b Monticello, Ky, Oct 25, 33; m 59; c 2. AGRONOMY, CROP PHYSIOLOGY. *Educ:* Western Ky Univ, BS, 52; Univ Wis, MS, 54, PhD(agron), 56. *Prof Exp:* Asst agron, Univ Wis, 52-56; from asst prof & asst agronomist to assoc prof & assoc agronomist, Univ Ariz, 58-65, head dept agron & plant genetics, 66-74, prof & agronomist, 65-76, assoc dean col agr & assoc dir Ariz Agr Exp Sta & Coop Ext Serv, 74-76; prof agron & vchancellor agr & natural resources, 76-81, CHANCELLOR, UNIV NEBR-LINCOLN, 81- *Concurrent Pos:* Assoc ed, Agron J & Crop Sci, 69-72; consult in Brazil, Saudi Arabia, & USSR; mem nat coord comt for cotton res, 74. *Mem:* Fel AAAS; fel Am Soc Agron; Crop Sci Soc Am (pres, 72-73); Am Soc Plant Physiol; Soil Sci Soc Am. *Res:* Forage crops physiology, production and management; water-use efficiency, photosynthesis, respiration and dry-matter production. *Mailing Add:* Off Chancellor Univ of Nebr Lincoln NE 68588

MASSENGILL, RAYMOND, b Bristol, Va, Dec 8, 37; m 59; c 4. SPEECH PATHOLOGY, AUDIOLOGY. *Educ:* Univ Tenn, BS, 58, MS, 59; Univ Va, EdD(speech path & audiol), 68. *Prof Exp:* Dir speech path, audiol & speech sci, Palmer Rehab Ctr, Tenn, 60-62; dir speech path & speech sci & dir speech sci lab, Med Ctr, Duke Univ, 64-77; ASST DEAN & DIR MED EDUC, SCH MED, E TENN STATE UNIV, 78- *Concurrent Pos:* NIH grant, 67-; United Med Res Found grant, 67-68; Nat Inst Dent Res grant; consult speech path, audiol & speech sci, Univ Tenn, 67- & Nat Inst Dent Res, 68- *Mem:* AAAS; Am Speech & Hearing Asn; Am Inst Physics; Int Asn Rehab Facil; Int Asn Logopedics & Phoniatrics. *Res:* Speech physiology as it relates to oral and pharyngeal mechanisms and how this mechanism is altered due to certain plastic surgery procedures. *Mailing Add:* Sch of Med E Tenn State Univ Bristol TN 37620

MASSERMAN, JULES HOMAN, b Chudnov, Poland, Mar 10, 05; nat US; m 43. NEUROPHYSIOLOGY, PSYCHOANALYSIS. *Educ:* Wayne State Univ, MB, 30, MD, 31. *Prof Exp:* Resident neurol, Stanford Univ, 31-32; asst psychiatrist, Johns Hopkins Univ, 32-35; resident psychiat, Univ Chicago, 35-36, from instr to asst prof, 36-46; assoc prof, 46-50, PROF NEUROL & PSYCHIAT, NORTHWESTERN UNIV, CHICAGO, 50-, CO-CHMN DEPT, 64- *Concurrent Pos:* Chief consult, Downey Vet Hosp, 46-; sci dir, Nat Found Psychiat Res, 46-; consult, Great Lakes Naval Hosp, 47- & WHO, 50-; H M Camp lectr, 64; Karen Horney lectr, 65; dir ed, Ill State Psychiat Inst; vis prof psychiat, Univ Louis, Univ Zagreb. *Honors & Awards:* Lasker Award, Am Pub Health Asn, 47; Taylor Manor Award, 73; Sigmund Freud Award, 74. *Mem:* Soc Biol Psychiat (pres, 57-58); Int Asn Social Psychiat (pres, 69-); Am Asn Social Psychiat (pres, 78-79); fel Am Psychiat Asn (vpres, 74-75, secy, 75-77, pres, 78-79); Acad Psychoanal (pres, 57-58). *Res:* Experimental neuroses; physiology of emotion; music; occultisms; dynamics of language; dynamics of phantasy; dynamics of political action. *Mailing Add:* 8 S Mich Ave Chicago IL 60603

MASSEY, BARBARA W, b New Brunswick, NJ, Nov 8, 23; m 45; c 3. FIELD BIOLOGY, ORNITHOLOGY. *Educ:* Mt Holyoke Col, BA, 44; Calif State Univ, Long Beach, MA, 72. *Prof Exp:* Res technician, Argonne Nat Lab, Chicago, 50-52; res assoc, Med Sch, Univ Chicago, 52-55; res biologist, Univ Calif, Los Angeles, 55-60; res biochemist, Med Sch, Univ Southern Calif, 64-68; FIELD BIOLOGIST & CONSULT, 72- *Concurrent Pos:* Consult, 75-; res assoc, Los Angeles County Mus Nat Hist, 77- *Mem:* Am Ornith Union; Cooper Ornith Soc; Nat Audubon Soc. *Res:* Breeding biology, behavior and vocalizations of small terns, genus Sterna, worldwide; problems of endangered species of birds, mammals and plants in California; restoration of coastal salt marshes. *Mailing Add:* 1825 Knoxville Ave Long Beach CA 90815

MASSEY, DOUGLAS GORDON, b Clinton, Ont, Oct 14, 26; m 66; c 3. MEDICINE. *Educ:* Univ Toronto, MD, 51; MRCP, 61; McGill Univ, MSc, 63; FRCP(C), 63; FACP, 68; FRCPE, 79. *Prof Exp:* Consult, Estab Pulmonary Labs, Repatriation Dept, Australia, 55-57; dir pulmonary lab, Hosp St Luke, Montreal, Que, 64-66; from asst prof to assoc prof med, Univ Sherbrooke, 66-73, dir serv pneumology, Univ Hosp, 66-72; PROF MED, SCH MED, UNIV HAWAII, MANOA, 73- *Concurrent Pos:* Sir Edward Beatty fel, McGill Univ, 62-63; grants, Med Res Coun Can, 66-68, Nat Cancer Inst, 66-68, Inst Occup & Environ Health, 67-68 & Minister of Educ, 67-69. *Mem:* Fel Am Col Chest Physicians. *Res:* Medical education, curriculum development, programmed texts; asthma; asbestosis. *Mailing Add:* Univ of Hawaii Sch Med 2230 Liliha St Honolulu HI 96817

MASSEY, EDDIE H, b Canadian, Tex, July 14, 39; m 57; c 2. PHARMACEUTICAL CHEMISTRY. *Educ:* McMurry Col, BA, 61; Vanderbilt Univ, PhD(org chem), 66. *Prof Exp:* sr pharmaceut chemist 66-72, RES SCIENTIST, DEPT PHARMACEUT RES, ELI LILLY & CO, 72- *Mem:* Am Chem Soc. *Res:* chemistry and chemical modification of macrolide antibiotics. *Mailing Add:* 8337 Hi Vu Dr Indianapolis IN 46227

MASSEY, FRANK JONES, JR, b Portsmouth, NH, Nov 22, 19; m 43; c 2. MATHEMATICAL STATISTICS. *Educ:* Univ Calif, AB, 41, MA, 44, PhD(math statist), 47. *Prof Exp:* Asst prof math, Univ Md, 47-48; from asst prof to assoc prof, Univ Ore, 48-56; prof prev med & pub health, 59-80, PROF BIOSTATIST, UNIV CALIF, LOS ANGELES, 59-, PROF BIOMATH, 70- *Concurrent Pos:* Ford fel, 53-54. *Mem:* Am Statist Asn; Am Math Asn; Inst Math Statist; Biomet Soc. *Res:* Non-parametric statistical analysis. *Mailing Add:* Dept of Pub Health Univ of Calif Los Angeles CA 90024

MASSEY, FREDRICK ALAN, b Birmingham, Ala, Dec 20, 38; m 67; c 1. APPLIED MATHEMATICS. *Educ:* Samford Univ, BS, 61; Auburn Univ, 63, PhD(math), 66. *Prof Exp:* Asst prof math, Auburn Univ, 66-67; from asst prof to assoc prof, 67-74, interim chmn dept, 77-78, PROF MATH, GA STATE UNIV, 74-, CHMN DEPT, 78- *Concurrent Pos:* Mem Urban Life Fac, Ga State Univ, 77-81, Pub & Urban Affairs Fac, 81. *Mem:* Am Math Soc; Math Asn Am; Soc Indust & Appl Math. *Res:* Theoretical physics; economic theory; nonlinear programming. *Mailing Add:* Dept of Math Ga State Univ Atlanta GA 30303

MASSEY, GAIL AUSTIN, b El Paso, Tex, Dec 2, 36; m 60. LASERS. *Educ:* Calif Inst Technol, BS, 59; Stanford Univ, MS, 67, PhD(elec eng), 70. *Prof Exp:* Engr, Raytheon Co, Santa Barbara, 59-63; sr eng specialist, Electro-optics orgn, GTE Sylvania, 63-72; prof appl physics, Ore Grad Ctr, 72-80; PROF ELEC ENG, SAN DIEGO STATE UNIV, 81- *Concurrent Pos:* Consult laser fusion group, Lawrence Livermore Lab, Univ Calif, 75- *Mem:* Fel Optical Soc Am; Acoust Soc Am; Inst Elec & Electronics Engrs; Soc Photo-Optical Instrumentation Engrs. *Res:* Nonlinear optical devices; ultraviolet and wavelength-tunable lasers; ultrafast optical pulse techniques; electron beams and microscopy. *Mailing Add:* Dept Elec Eng San Diego State Univ San Diego CA 92182

MASSEY, HERBERT FANE, JR, b Kerrville, Tenn, Jan 23, 26; m 51. AGRONOMY, SOIL FERTILITY. *Educ:* Univ Tenn, BS, 49; Univ Wis, MS, 50, PhD(soils), 52. *Prof Exp:* Asst, Univ Wis, 49-52; res agronomist, Int Minerals & Chem Corp, 52-53; from asst prof to assoc prof, 53-60, PROF AGRON, UNIV KY, 60-, DIR DIV REGULATORY SERV, 70-, DIR OFF INT PROG AGR, 75- *Concurrent Pos:* Vis prof, San Carlos Univ, Guatemala, 59-60, Univ Indonesia, 61-64 & Thailand, 67-70. *Mem:* Soil Sci Soc Am; Am Soc Agron; Int Soc Soil Sci. *Res:* Soil chemistry and fertility; micro element studies; tropical agriculture. *Mailing Add:* Col of Agr Univ of Ky Lexington KY 40506

MASSEY, JAMES L, b Wauseon, Ohio, Feb 11, 34; m 58; c 4. ELECTRICAL ENGINEERING. *Educ:* Univ Notre Dame, BS, 56; Mass Inst Technol, SM, 60, PhD(elec eng), 62. *Prof Exp:* From asst prof to prof, Univ Notre Dame, 62-76, Frieimann prof elec eng, 76-80; MEM FAC, SWISS FED TECH UNIV, 80- *Concurrent Pos:* Consult, Codex Corp, Mass, 62; vis assoc prof, Mass Inst Technol, 66-67, guest prof, Tech Univ Denmark, 71-72. *Mem:* Fel Inst Elec & Electronics Engrs; Am Soc Eng Educ. *Res:* Information theory; coding theory; automata theory. *Mailing Add:* Swiss Fed Tech Univ Inst Fur Fernmeldetechnik Eth Zentrum Zurich 46556 Switzerland

MASSEY, JIMMY R, b Mart, Tex, July 9, 40; m 62. BOTANY, PLANT TAXONOMY. *Educ:* NTex State Univ, BSEd, 62; Tex A&M Univ, MS, 65; Univ Okla, PhD(bot), 71. *Prof Exp:* Instr bot, Tex A&M Univ, 64-65; vis scholar bot & genetics, Okla Col Lib Arts, 70-71; CUR HERBARIUM, UNIV NC, CHAPEL HILL, 71-, HERBARIUM ADMINR, 73-, ADJ ASSOC PROF, 80- *Mem:* Int Asn Plant Taxon; Am Soc Plant Taxonomists; Sigma Xi. *Res:* Vascular flora of southeastern United States; monograph polygalaceae; pollination-reproductive biology; species biology of threatened and endangered plant species. *Mailing Add:* Cur Herbarium Univ NC Dept Bot Chapel Hill NC 27514

MASSEY, JOE THOMAS, b Raleigh, NC, Apr 22, 17; m 41; c 2. BIOMEDICAL ENGINEERING. *Educ:* NC State Col, BS, 38; Johns Hopkins Univ, PhD(physics), 53. *Prof Exp:* Instr elec eng, Clemson Col, 38-39; instr eng mech, NC State Col, 39-41; asst to dir, 72-74, DIR BIOMED PROGS, JOHNS HOPKINS UNIV, 74-, PRIN STAFF MEM, APPL PHYSICS LAB, 46-, ASSOC PROF BIOMED ENG, SCH MED, 68- *Concurrent Pos:* Lectr, Johns Hopkins Univ, 57. *Mem:* NY Acad Sci; Inst Elec & Electronics Engrs. *Res:* Microwave plasma and physics; laser physics. *Mailing Add:* Appl Physics Lab Johns Hopkins Univ Laurel MD 20707

MASSEY, JOHN BOYD, b Memphis, Tenn, Feb 22, 50. LIPOPROTEIN METABOLISM, MEMBRANE PHYSICAL CHEMISTRY. *Educ:* Univ Tenn, BA, 72, PhD(biochem), 77. *Prof Exp:* Res assoc, 77-80, INSTR, BAYLOR COL MED, 80- *Res:* Dynamics and thermodynamics of lipid-protein associations in plasma lipoproteins; mechanisms of human plasma lipoprotein lipid transfer; role of plasma lipoproteins in vitamin E metabolism. *Mailing Add:* Baylor Col Med Mail Statium A601 6565 Fannin Houston TX 77030

MASSEY, L(ESTER) G(EORGE), b Madison, Wis, Dec 9, 18; m 42; c 3. CHEMICAL ENGINEERING. *Educ:* Univ Wis, BS, 42, MS, 47, PhD(chem eng), 50. *Prof Exp:* Instr chem eng, Univ Wis, 46-50; chem engr pilot plants, Am Cyanamid Co, 50-51; res chem engr, Universal Oil Prod Co, 51-55, process engr, 55-57, asst head comput dept, 57-59, head, 59-66, mgr, 66-67; assoc dir res, 67-77, MGR PROCESS DEVELOP, CONSOL NATURAL GAS SERV CO, INC, 77- *Concurrent Pos:* Proj adv, Am Gas Asn/US Govt Coal Gasification Prog, 72-76; chmn, Gordon Res Conf, Fuel Sci, 78-79. *Mem:* AAAS; Am Chem Soc; Am Inst Chem Engrs; fel Am Inst Chem; Sigma Xi. *Res:* Physical and chemical equilibrium; chemical thermodynamics; mass and heat transfer; heterogeneous catalysis and kinetics; coal conversion technology. *Mailing Add:* 11001 Cedar Ave Cleveland OH 44106

MASSEY, LINDA KATHLEEN LOCKE, b Oklahoma City, Okla, Aug 27, 45. HUMAN NUTRITION, LIPID METABOLISM. *Educ:* Univ Okla, BS, 66, PhD(microbiol), 71. *Prof Exp:* NIH fel microbiol, Health Sci Ctr, Univ Okla, 71-72, instr, 72-73; res assoc, Cancer Sect, Okla Med Res Found, 73-74; asst prof biochem, Okla Col Osteopath Med & Surg, 74-78; ASST PROF, HUMAN NUTRITION AND FOODS & ASST HOME ECONOMIST, HOME ECON RES CTR, WASH STATE UNIV, 78- *Concurrent Pos:* adj prof, foods, nutrit & inst mgt, Okla State Univ, 78. *Mem:* Am Dietetic Asn; AAAS; Soc Nutrit Educ. *Res:* Effects of dietary lactose and dairy products on human lipid metabolism. *Mailing Add:* Human Nutrit & Foods Wash State Univ Pullman WA 99164

MASSEY, LOUIS MELVILLE, JR, b Ithaca, NY, Apr 28, 23; m 49; c 2. PLANT BIOCHEMISTRY. *Educ:* Oberlin Col, AB, 47; Cornell Univ, PhD(biochem), 51. *Prof Exp:* Asst biochem, Cornell Univ, 47-51; res plant biochemist, US Army Biol Labs, Md, 51-57; from asst prof to assoc prof, 57-70, PROF BIOCHEM, NY STATE COL AGR & LIFE SCI, CORNELL UNIV, 70- *Mem:* AAAS; Am Chem Soc; Am Soc Plant Physiol; Am Soc Hort Sci; Inst Food Technol. *Res:* Post-harvest physiology of fruits and vegetables; irradiation effects on the physiology of plant tissues; transportation of fruits and vegetables for processing; biochemistry of ripening; fungus physiology. *Mailing Add:* Dept Food Sci NY State Agr Exp Sta Cornell Univ Geneva NY 14456

MASSEY, MICHAEL JOHN, b Madison, Wis, July 7, 47; m 70. ENVIRONMENTAL MANAGEMENT, FUEL TECHNOLOGY. *Educ:* Univ Wis-Madison, BS, 70; Carnegie-Mellon Univ, MS, 72, PhD(eng), 74. *Prof Exp:* Res asst gas chromatography, Dept Chem Eng, Univ Wis-Madison, 66-70; instr chem eng, 70-74, ASST PROF CHEM ENG & PUB AFFAIRS, CARNEGIE-MELLON UNIV, 74- *Concurrent Pos:* Alt mem, Allegheny County Air Pollution Adv Bd, 73-; consult, US Dept Com, Tech Adv Bd, 70-71, US Environ Protection Agency, Econ & Eval Br, 71, Alan Wood Steel Co, 73-74, Ill Inst Technol, 75- & Conoco Coal Develop Co, 75- *Mem:* Am Inst Chem Eng; Am Soc Eng Educ. *Res:* Environmental management; technology assessment; fossil-fuels processing, iron & steel processing; analysis of problems at the interface between technology and public policy. *Mailing Add:* Dept of Chem Eng Carnegie-Mellon Univ Pittsburgh PA 15213

MASSEY, PEYTON HOWARD, JR, b Zebulon, NC, Oct 4, 22; m 42; c 3. OLERICULTURE, ACADEMIC ADMINISTRATION. *Educ:* NC State Col, BS, 47, MS, 51; Cornell Univ, PhD(veg crops), 52. *Prof Exp:* Res asst, Cornell Univ, 49-52; from assoc prof to prof hort, Va Polytech Inst & State Univ, 52-65, assoc dean grad sch, 64-65, assoc dir res, Agr Exp Sta, 65-66 & res div, 66-68, assoc dean res & grad studies, 68-69, ASSOC DEAN, COL AGR & LIFE SCI, VA POLYTECH INST & STATE UNIV, 69- *Honors & Awards:* Medal of City, Paris, France, 68. *Mem:* AAAS; Am Soc Hort Sci; Int Soc Hort Sci; Am Inst Biol Sci. *Res:* Vegetable production and breeding; agricultural uses of plastics; research administration. *Mailing Add:* Va Polytech Inst & State Univ Blacksburg VA 24061

MASSEY, PHILIP LOUIS, b New York, NY, Feb 28, 52. STELLAR ASTRONOMY. *Educ:* Calif Inst Technol, BS & MS, 75; Univ Colo, Boulder, PhD(astrophysics), 80. *Prof Exp:* Teaching asst, Dept Astro-geophysics, Univ Colo, 75-76, res asst, Joint Inst Lab Astrophysics, 77-80; RES ASSOC ASTRON, DOMINION ASTROPHYS OBSERV, NAT RES COUN, 80- *Mem:* Am Astron Soc; Am Asn Variable Star Observers. *Res:* Observational studies of very hot and massive stars, particularly Wolf-Rayets and O stars in both the Milky Way and the neighboring galaxies of the local group. *Mailing Add:* Dominion Astrophys Observ 5071 W Saanid Rd Victoria BC V8X 4M6 Can

MASSEY, ROBERT UNRUH, b Detroit, Mich, Feb 23, 22; m 43; c 2. INTERNAL MEDICINE. *Educ:* Wayne Univ, MD, 46. *Prof Exp:* From intern to resident med, Henry Ford Hosp, 46-50; assoc, Lovelace Clin, 50-68, chmn dept, 58-68; clin assoc, Sch Med & Res, Univ NMex, 62-68; assoc dean, 68-71, actg exec dir & actg vpres health affairs, 75-76, PROF MED, MED SCH, UNIV CONN, 68-, DEAN, 71- *Concurrent Pos:* Consult, West Interstate Comn Higher Educ, 58-60; dir educ, Lovelace Found Med Educ, 60-68; consult, NMex Regional Med Prog, 65-68; mem accreditation comn, Am Asn Med Clins, 66-72. *Mem:* AAAS; Sigma Xi; Am Col Physicians; Am Diabetes Asn; Asn Am Med Cols. *Res:* Clinical endocrinology and diabetes; medical education; medical care and medical administration. *Mailing Add:* Sch of Med Univ of Conn Farmington CT 06032

MASSEY, VINCENT, b Berkeley, Australia, Nov 28, 26; m 50; c 3. BIOCHEMISTRY. *Educ:* Univ Sydney, BSc, 47; Cambridge Univ, PhD(biochem), 53. *Prof Exp:* Res officer biochem, Commonwealth Sci & Indust Res Orgn, Australia, 47-50; Imp Chem Industs Res fel, 53-55; mem res staff, Edsel B Ford Inst, Mich, 55-57; from lectr to sr lectr, Univ Sheffield, 57-63; PROF BIOL CHEM, SCH MED, UNIV MICH, ANN ARBOR, 63- *Concurrent Pos:* Humboldt award, 73. *Mem:* Fel Royal Soc London; Am Soc Biol Chemists; Am Chem Soc; Biochem Soc. *Res:* Basic enzymology; mechanisms of enzyme reactions, especially of flavoproteins and metalloflavoproteins; role of sulfide in biological oxidations. *Mailing Add:* Dept of Biol chem Univ of Mich Sch Med Ann Arbor MI 48104

MASSEY, WALTER EUGENE, b Hattiesburg, Miss, Apr 5, 38. THEORETICAL SOLID STATE PHYSICS. *Educ:* Morehouse Col, BS, 58; Wash Univ, MA & PhD(physics), 66. *Prof Exp:* Instr physics, Morehouse Col, 58-59; from fel to physicist, Argonne Nat Lab, 66-68; asst prof, Univ Ill, Urbana, 69-70; assoc prof, Brown Univ, 70-75, prof physics & dean col, 75-79; PROF PHYSICS, UNIV CHICAGO, & DIR, ARGONNE NAT LAB, 79- *Concurrent Pos:* Fel, Wash Univ, 66; mem, Nat Sci Bd. *Mem:* Am Phys Soc; Am Asn Physics Teachers. *Res:* Many-body problem; quantum liquids and solids; theory of classical liquids; solid state theory. *Mailing Add:* Argonne Nat Lab 9700 S Cass Ave Argonne IL 60439

MASSEY, WILLIAM S, b Granville, Ill, Aug 23, 20; m 53; c 3. MATHEMATICS. *Educ:* Univ Chicago, BS, 41, MS, 42; Princeton Univ, PhD(math), 48. *Prof Exp:* Off Naval Res fel, Princeton Univ, 48-50; from asst prof to assoc prof math, Brown Univ, 50-54; vis assoc prof, Princeton Univ, 54-55; prof, Brown Univ, 55-60; chmn dept, 68-71, PROF MATH, YALE UNIV, 60- *Concurrent Pos:* Assoc ed, Ind Univ Math J, 75- *Mem:* Am Acad Arts & Sci; Am Math Soc; Math Asn Am. *Res:* Algebraic topology. *Mailing Add:* Dept Math Yale Univ Box 2155 Yale Sta New Haven CT 06520

MASSIAH, THOMAS FREDERICK, b Montreal, Que, Aug 26, 26; m 51; c 1. ORGANIC CHEMISTRY. *Educ:* Sir George Williams Univ, BSc, 47; McGill Univ, MSc, 56; Univ Montreal, PhD(org chem), 62. *Prof Exp:* Chief control chemist, Dewey & Almy Chem Co, Que, 47-53; demonstr chem, McGill Univ, 53-56; res chemist, Merck & Co Ltd, Que, 56-59; sr demonstr chem, Univ Montreal, 59-62; chemist, Ayerst, McKenna & Harrison Ltd, 62-66; GROUP LEADER CHEM DEVELOP, CAN PACKERS LTD, 66- *Concurrent Pos:* Lectr, Sir George Williams Univ, 49-64. *Mem:* Chem Inst Can. *Res:* Organic, biochemical and medicinal chemistry; antibiotics, bile acids, enzymes; pharmaceuticals; steroids. *Mailing Add:* Res Ctr Can Packers Ltd 2211 St Clair Ave Toronto ON M6N 1K4 Can

MASSIE, EDWARD, b St Louis, Mo, Nov 21, 10; m 40; c 2. CARDIOLOGY. *Educ:* Wash Univ, AB, 31, MD, 35. *Prof Exp:* Assoc prof, 53-68, PROF CLIN MED, SCH MED, WASH UNIV, 68- *Concurrent Pos:* Consult, Heart Sta, Barnes Hosp, 41 & Heart Sta, Jewish Hosp, 70- *Mem:* Am Heart Asn; Am Fedn Clin Res; fel Am Col Physicians; fel Am Col Cardiol. *Res:* Cardiology and cardiovascular diseases. *Mailing Add:* Queeny Tower Suite 4104 4989 Barnes Hosp Plaza St Louis MO 63110

MASSIE, HAROLD RAYMOND, b Brisbane, Australia, Jan 31, 43; US citizen; m 70; c 3. MOLECULAR BIOLOGY. *Educ:* San Diego State Col, AB, 64; Univ Calif, San Diego, PhD(chem), 67. *Prof Exp:* NIH res fel chem & tutor biochem, Harvard Univ, 67-70; RES SCIENTIST, MASONIC MED RES LAB, 70- *Mem:* AAAS; Biophys Soc; Am Soc Biol Chemists; Am Aging Asn; Am Soc Microbiol. *Res:* DNA replication and structural changes; cell synchrony; animal cell culture; aging. *Mailing Add:* Masonic Med Res Lab 2150 Bleecker St Utica NY 13503

MASSIE, SAMUEL PROCTOR, b North Little Rock, Ark, July 3, 19; m 47; c 3. CHEMISTRY. *Educ:* Agr Mech & Normal Col, Ark, BS, 38; Fisk Univ, MA, 40; Iowa State Univ, PhD(org chem), 46. *Hon Degrees:* LLD, Univ Ark, 70. *Prof Exp:* Lab asst chem, Fisk Univ, 39-40; assoc prof math, Agr Mech & Normal Col, Ark, 40-41; res assoc chem, Iowa State Univ, 43-46; instr, Fish Univ, 46-47; prof & head dept, Langston Univ, 47-53, Fisk Univ, 53-60 & Howard Univ, 62-63; assoc prog dir, NSF, 60-63; pres, NC Col Durham, 63-66; PROF CHEM, US NAVAL ACAD, 66-, CHMN DEPT, 77- *Concurrent Pos:* Sigma Xi lectr, Swarthmore Col, 57. *Honors & Awards:* Mfg Chem Asn Award, 61. *Mem:* Am Chem Soc. *Mailing Add:* Dept of Chem US Naval Acad Annapolis MD 21402

MASSINGILL, JOHN LEE, JR, b Lufkin, Tex, Aug 18, 41; m 63; c 2. INDUSTRIAL ORGANIC CHEMISTRY. *Educ:* Tex Christian Univ, BA, 63, MS, 65, PhD(chem), 68. *Prof Exp:* Sr res chemist, Basic Res Dept, 68 & Hydrocarbon Process Res Dept, 70-73, res specialist, Hydrocarbon Process Res Dept, 73-76, RES SPECIALIST, RESINS RES DEPT, TEX DIV, DOW CHEM USA, FREEPORT, 76- *Concurrent Pos:* Consult, Ionics Res, Inc, 71-72. *Mem:* AAAS; Am Chem Soc; Sigma Xi. *Res:* Hydrocarbon utilization; new product research and development; new process research and development. *Mailing Add:* Dow Chem Co Bldg B-251 Freeport TX 77541

MASSION, WALTER HERBERT, b Eitorf, Ger, June 4, 23; nat US; m 56; c 3. ANESTHESIOLOGY, PHYSIOLOGY. *Educ:* Univ Cologne, BS, 47; Univ Heidelberg, MD, 51; Univ Bonn, DrMed, 51. *Prof Exp:* Intern med, Med Ctr, Univ Zurich, 51-52; trainee anesthesiol, Anesthesiol Ctr, WHO, Denmark, 52-53; asst prof physiol, Med Sch, Univ Basel, 53-54; asst resident anesthesiol, Med Sch, Univ Rochester, 54-56; from asst prof to assoc prof anesthesiol, 58-67, assoc prof physiol & res surg, 66-71, PROF ANESTHESIOL, COL MED, UNIV OKLA, 67-, PROF PHYSIOL, BIOPHYS & RES SURG, 71-, ADJ PROF CARDIORESPIRATORY SCI, 75- *Concurrent Pos:* Fel physiol, Med Sch, Univ Rochester, 54-56; fel, Cardiovasc Res Inst, Sch Med, Univ Calif, 59-60; NIH res career develop award, 61-71; John A Hartford Found res grant, 67-71; Humboldt Prize, Tech Univ Munich, Ger, 74-75; mem sci coun, Am Heart Asn. *Mem:* AAAS; Am Physiol Soc; Am Soc Anesthesiol; Int Anesthesia Res Soc. *Res:* Respiration; circulation; shock; vasoactive polypeptides; extracorporeal circulation. *Mailing Add:* Dept of Anesthesiol Univ of Okla Hlth Sci Ctr Oklahoma City OK 73190

MASSLER, MAURY, b New York, NY, Mar 24, 12; m 47; c 3. DENTISTRY. *Educ:* NY Univ, BS, 32; Univ Ill, DDS, 39, MS, 41. *Prof Exp:* Instr dent histol, Col Dent, Univ Ill Med Ctr, 39-41, dir child res clin, 41-73, from asst prof to assoc prof histol, 43-46, prof pedodont, 46-73, supvr hosp dent clin, 43-53, asst dean postgrad & teacher educ, 65-73, assoc dean col dent, 69-73; chmn dept restorative dent, Col Dent Med, 73-77, EMER PROF, DIV ADVAN EDUC, TUFTS UNIV, 77- *Mem:* Am Soc Dent for Children; Am Pub Health Asn; Am Dent Asn; Int Asn Dent Res; Am Acad Pedodontics. *Res:* Pedodontics; oral medicine; gerodontics; dental education. *Mailing Add:* Tufts Univ Col of Dent Med One Kneeland St Boston MA 02111

MASSON, CHARLES ROBB, b Aberdeen, Scotland, Sept 8, 22; m 48; c 2. PHYSICAL CHEMISTRY. *Educ:* Aberdeen Univ, BS, 43, PhD(chem), 48. *Prof Exp:* Asst lectr, Aberdeen Univ, 43-45; fel, Nat Res Coun Can, 48-50; fel, Univ Rochester, 50-51; from asst res officer to sr res officer, 51-65, PRIN RES OFFICER, NAT RES COUN CAN, 65-, HEAD HIGH TEMPERATURE CHEM SECT, 54- *Concurrent Pos:* Vis scientist, Brit Iron & Steel Res Asn, 54; hon prof fac grad studies, Dalhousie Univ, 63-71; vis prof, Imp Col, Univ London, 63, Univ Strathclyde, 64 & Aberdeen Univ, 71; hon res assoc, Fac Grad Studies, Univ NB, 73-; adj prof, Tech Univ NS, 81- *Mem:* Am Chem Soc; fel Chem Inst Can; fel Chem Soc London; Can Inst Mining & Metall. *Res:* Kinetics and equilibria of chemical reactions at high temperatures; polymer, silicate and metallurgical chemistry. *Mailing Add:* Atlantic Res Lab Nat Res Coun Can 1411 Oxford St Halifax NS B3H 3Z1 Can

MASSON, D(OUGLAS) BRUCE, b Corvallis, Ore, Dec 19, 32; m 58; c 3. PHYSICAL METALLURGY. *Educ:* Wash State Univ, BS, 54; Univ Chicago, MS, 56, PhD(chem), 58. *Prof Exp:* Asst prof mech eng, Rice Inst, 58-60; assoc prof phys metall, 60-71, PROF PHYS METALL, WASH STATE UNIV, 71-, CHMN DEPT MAT SCI & ENG, 75- *Mem:* Am Soc Metals; Am Inst Mining, Metall & Petrol Engrs. *Res:* Phase equilibria and transformations in metals; solid-state reaction kinetics; x-ray diffraction; crystal chemistry; thermodynamics of alloys. *Mailing Add:* Dept Mat Sci & Eng Wash State Univ Pullman WA 99163

MASSON, DAVID J(ENKS), b Lorain, Ohio, May 8, 20; m 43; c 3. MECHANICAL ENGINEERING. *Educ:* Ohio State Univ, BME, 43, MSc, 46, PhD(mech eng), 52. *Prof Exp:* Instr mech eng, Ohio State Univ, 47-52; engr, Gen Elec Co, 52-56; res engr, Rand Corp, 56-60, group leader basing tech, 60-61; sci adv to dep chief staff, US Air Force, DC, 61-62; group leader spacecraft group, Rand Corp, Calif, 62-63, dep head aero-astronaut dept, 63-67; dir space sci ctr & asst to pres appl sci & technol div, Litton Industs, Inc, 67-68; PRES, TELIC CORP, 68- *Concurrent Pos:* Mach designer, Western Elec Co, 47; lectr, Univ Calif, Los Angeles, 65; consult, Rand Corp, 68- *Res:* Heat transfer; fluid mechanics; thermodynamics; machine design; thin film technology. *Mailing Add:* Telic Corp 1631 Colorado Ave Santa Monica CA 90404

MASSOPUST, LEO CARL, JR, b Milwaukee, Wis, Nov 12, 20; m 43; c 2. ANATOMY. *Educ:* Marquette Univ, BS, 43, MS, 47; Univ Colo, PhD, 53. *Prof Exp:* Asst prof biol, Westminster Col (Mo), 47-48; instr anat, Univ Colo, 48-54; neuroanatomist, NIH, 54-58; sr res physiologist, Southeast La Hosp, 58-60; dir div neurophysiol, Cleveland Psychiat Inst & Hosp, 60-73; ASSOC PROF ANAT, MED SCH, ST LOUIS UNIV, 74- *Mem:* Am Asn Anat; Am Physiol Soc; Soc Exp Biol & Med; Am Acad Neurol; Soc Neurosci. *Res:* Physiology of ergot alkaloid; hypothermia; electrophysiology of vision; psychophysiology of audition; neurophysiology of brain function; hodology of central nervous system pathways. *Mailing Add:* Sch of Med 1402 S Grand Blvd St Louis MO 63104

MASSOUD, MONIR FOUAD, b Fayoum, Egypt, June 13, 30; m 57; c 2. ENGINEERING, SOLID MECHANICS. *Educ:* Cairo Univ, BSc, 51, dipl higher study, 57; Rensselaer Polytech Inst, MSc, 61, PhD(mech eng), 63. *Prof Exp:* Design engr, Heliopolis Aircraft Factory, Egypt, 51-59; res asst design, Rensselaer Polytech Inst, 60-63; assoc prof solid mech, Cairo Polytech Inst, 63-67; Norweg AID fel & researcher, Tech Univ Norway, 67-68; assoc prof mech eng, 68-74, PROF MECH ENG, UNIV SHERBROOKE, 74- *Mem:* Am Soc Mech Engrs; Can Soc Mech Engrs; Am Acad Mech. *Res:* Applied dynamics; investigation of dynamic behavior of mechanical engineering elements and systems; methods and probabilistic approaches to improve the reliability and optimize the behavior of a mechanical design. *Mailing Add:* Dept of Mech Eng Univ of Sherbrooke Fac Appl Sci Sherbrooke PQ J1K 2R1 Can

MASSOVER, WILLIAM H, b Chicago, Ill, 41; m 69. CELL BIOLOGY, TUMOR BIOLOGY. *Educ:* Univ Chicago, AB, 63, MD, 67, PhD(cell biol), 70. *Prof Exp:* NATO fel electron micros, Lab Electronic Optics, CNRS, Toulouse, France, 71-72; res assoc dept physics, Ariz State Univ, 72-73; asst prof biol, Brown Univ, 73-79; ASSOC PROF ANAT, NJ MED SCH, UNIV MED & DENT NJ, 79- *Concurrent Pos:* Mem spec study sect, NIH, 75 & 77. *Mem:* Am Soc Cell Biol; Biophys Soc; Electron Micros Soc Am; Int Soc Oncoderel Biol Med; Electrophoresis Soc. *Res:* Form and function of normal and neoplastic ferritius; cancer cell biology; high-resolution ultrastructure of biological macromolecules and macromolecular systems. *Mailing Add:* Dept Anat NJ Med Sch Univ Med & Dent NJ Newark NJ 07103

MAST, CECIL B, b Chicago, Ill, Feb 21, 27; m 59; c 2. GEOMETRY, THEORETICAL PHYSICS. *Educ:* De Paul Univ, BS, 50; Univ Notre Dame, PhD(physics), 56. *Prof Exp:* Instr physics, 56-57, from instr to asst prof math, 59-63, ASSOC PROF MATH, UNIV NOTRE DAME, 63- *Concurrent Pos:* Vis lectr, St Andrews, 65-66. *Mem:* Am Phys Soc; Am Math Soc; Math Asn Am. *Res:* Nuclear physics and group representations as used in nuclear models; relativity theory; differential geometry and lie groups; foundations of physics. *Mailing Add:* Dept of Math Univ of Notre Dame Notre Dame IN 46556

MAST, MORRIS GLEN, b Kalona, Iowa, Dec 8, 40; m 64; c 2. FOOD SCIENCE. *Educ:* Goshen Col, BS, 62; Ohio State Univ, MS, 69, PhD(food sci), 71. *Prof Exp:* Diag parasitologist, Evanston Hosp, Evanston, Ill, 62-65; mgr qual control, V F Weaver, Inc, New Holland, Pa, 65-67; res assoc poultry sci, Ohio State Univ, 67-71; asst prof food sci, 71-76, ASSOC PROF FOOD SCI & EXTEN FOOD SCIENTIST, PA STATE UNIV, UNIVERSITY PARK, 76- *Mem:* Coun Agr Sci & Technol; Poultry & Egg Inst Am; Poultry Sci Asn; Inst Food Technologists. *Res:* Microbiological, biochemical, and organoleptic changes occurring in poultry and egg products during processing and storage. *Mailing Add:* Dept of Food Sci Pa State Univ University Park PA 16802

MAST, P(LESSA) EDWARD, b Burbon, Ind, Oct 18, 26; m 47; c 7. ELECTRICAL ENGINEERING. *Educ:* Purdue Univ, BSEE, 48, MSEE, 50; Univ Ill, PhD(elec eng), 58. *Prof Exp:* Assoc prof, 52-70, PROF ELEC ENG, UNIV ILL, URBANA, 70- *Concurrent Pos:* Sr scientist, Aeronutronic Div, Philco-Ford Corp, 64-65. *Mem:* Inst Elec & Electronics Engrs. *Res:* Antennas; electromagnetic theory and scattering. *Mailing Add:* Dept of Elec Eng Univ of Ill Urbana IL 61801

MAST, RICHARD F(REDERICK), b Chicago, Ill, Oct 4, 31; m 57; c 5. PETROLEUM ENGINEERING, GEOLOGY. *Educ:* Univ Ill, BS, 57, MS, 60. *Prof Exp:* Asst petrol engr, Ill State Geol Surv, 59-64; petrol engr, Co Francais des Petrol, 64 & Francore Labs, 64-65; assoc petrol engr, Ill State Geol Surv, 65-73; mem staff, 73-76, chief, OIl & Gas Resources Br, 76-81, REG GEOLOGIST, CENT REG, US GEOL SURV, 81- *Concurrent Pos:* Chmn subcomt, Future Gas Requirements & Supply Comt, 65-69; mem eng comt, Interstate Oil Compact Comn, 69-71. *Mem:* Am Inst Mining, Metall & Petrol Engrs; Am Asn Petrol Geologists; Geol Soc Am. *Res:* Properties of rocks; especially continuity, inhomogeneity, grain orientation and permeability; petroleum geochemistry; Tertiary recovery methods. *Mailing Add:* 8 Skyline Dr Denver CO 80215

MAST, ROY CLARK, b Wheeling, WVa, Nov 28, 24; m 48; c 3. PHYSICAL CHEMISTRY, INORGANIC CHEMISTRY. *Educ:* Univ Cincinnati, BS, 49, MS, 51, PhD(inorg chem), 53. *Prof Exp:* Student asst instr, Univ Cincinnati, 49-51; RES CHEMIST PHYS & INORG CHEM, MIAMI VALLEY LABS, PROCTER & GAMBLE CO, 52- *Mem:* Am Chem Soc. *Res:* Surfactant solutions; adsorption of surfactants; emulsion formation; surface chemistry; phase studies; fundamentals of detergency; micellar solubilization; diffusion studies; polymer properties. *Mailing Add:* Procter & Gamble Co Miami Valley Labs PO Box 39175 Cincinnati OH 45247

MAST, TERRY STEVEN, b Los Angeles, Calif, Jan 2, 43; m 69; c 2. EXPERIMENTAL PHYSICS. *Educ:* Calif Inst Technol, BS, 64; Univ Calif, Berkeley, PhD(physics), 71. *Prof Exp:* PHYSICIST, LAWRENCE BERKELEY LAB, 71- *Res:* Experimental elementary astrophysics; particle physics; optics. *Mailing Add:* Lawrence Berkeley Lab Univ of Calif Berkeley CA 94720

MASTALERZ, JOHN W, b Mass, Mar 16, 26; m 54; c 3. FLORICULTURE, HORTICULTURE. *Educ:* Univ Mass, BS, 48; Purdue Univ, MS, 50; Cornell Univ, PhD(floricult), 53. *Prof Exp:* Asst prof res floricult, Waltham Field Sta, Univ Mass, 52-56; PROF FLORICULT, PA STATE UNIV, 56- *Concurrent Pos:* Ed, Pa Flower Growers, 56- *Mem:* AAAS; Am Soc Agron; Crop Sci Soc Am; Am Soc Horticult Sci; Am Hort Soc. *Res:* Post-harvest life of cut flowers; photoperiodic, temperature, soil mixture and fertilization requirements of flower crops; growth regulators; greenhouse environment. *Mailing Add:* 103 Tyson Bldg Pa State Univ University Park PA 16802

MASTASCUSA, EDWARD JOHN, b Pittsburgh, Pa, June 27, 38; m 60; c 6. ELECTRICAL ENGINEERING. *Educ:* Carnegie Inst Technol, BS, 60, MS, 61, PhD(elec eng), 64. *Prof Exp:* Asst prof elec eng, Univ Wyo, 66-68; asst prof, 68-73, ASSOC PROF ELEC ENG, BUCKNELL UNIV, 73-, CHMN DEPT, 77- *Mem:* Soc Comput Simulation. *Res:* Digital computation of system and circuit response; engineering creativity. *Mailing Add:* RD 1 Spruce Hills Lewisburg PA 17837

MASTELLER, EDWIN C, b Independence, Iowa, Aug 11, 34; m 57; c 2. BIOLOGY, ENTOMOLOGY. *Educ:* Northern Iowa Univ, BS, 58; Univ SDak, MA, 61; Iowa State Univ, PhD(entom), 67. *Prof Exp:* Pub sch instr, Minn, 58-64; asst prof, 67-77, ASSOC PROF BIOL, BEHREND COL, PA STATE UNIV, 77- *Concurrent Pos:* Fulbright-Hays sr res fel, Ger, 74-75. *Mem:* Am Inst Biol Sci; Entom Soc Am; Am Micros Soc. *Res:* insect-arthropod survey in vineyards; aquatic insect emergence--phenology; Ephemeroptera, Plectoptera, Trichoptera and Diptera. *Mailing Add:* Behrend Col Pa State Univ Erie PA 16563

MASTEN, MICHAEL K, b Gainesville, Tex, Nov 11, 39; m 64; c 1. ELECTRICAL ENGINEERING. *Educ:* Univ Tex, Austin, BS, 63, MS, 65, PhD(elec eng), 68. *Prof Exp:* Teaching asst, Univ Tex, Austin, 64-68; MEM TECH STAFF ELEC ENG, TEX INSTRUMENTS, INC, 68- *Mem:* Inst Elec & Electronics Engrs. *Res:* System, control and sensitivity theory; pattern recognition; adaptive systems; operations research; physical electronics. *Mailing Add:* Equip Res & Develop Lab M/S 208 Tex Instruments Inc Dallas TX 75222

MASTENBROOK, S MARTIN, JR, b Ft Worth, Tex, Mar 24, 46. BIOINSTRUMENTATION, PULMONARY PHYSIOLOGY. *Educ:* Tex Tech Univ, BSEE, 69; Univ Wis, Madison, MS(physiol) & MS(elec eng), 73, PhD(elec eng, bioeng), 77. *Prof Exp:* Res asst elec eng, Univ Wis, Madison, 70-74, fel bioeng, 74-77, fel pulmonary physiol, 77-78; res fel pulmonary physiol, Univ Calif, San Diego, 78-79, asst res physiologist, 79-81; ASST PROF BIOMED ENG, BOSTON UNIV, 81- *Concurrent Pos:* NIH fel, Univ Wis, Madison, 77-78, Am Lung Asn fel, 74-76. *Mem:* Inst Elec & Electronics Engrs; Biomed Eng Soc; Am Thoracic Soc; Am Soc Eng Educ; Am Heart Asn. *Res:* Physiology of pulmonary gas exchange; mathematical modeling of the lung; biomedical instrumentation applied to pulmonary physiology and medicine. *Mailing Add:* 78 Bay State Rd #8 Boston MA 02215

MASTERS, BETTIE SUE SILER, b Lexington, Va, June 13, 37; m 60; c 2. BIOCHEMISTRY. *Educ:* Roanoke Col, BS, 59; Duke Univ, PhD(biochem), 63. *Prof Exp:* Res assoc biochem, Duke Univ, 65-67, assoc, 67-68; asst prof biochem, Univ Tex Health Sci Ctr, Dallas, 68-72, assoc prof, 72-76, prof, 79-82, prof surg & dir biochem burn res, 79-82; PROF & CHMN BIOCHEM, MEDICAL COL WIS, MILWAUKEE, 82- *Concurrent Pos:* Am Heart Asn estab investr, 68-73; ed bd, J Biol Chem, 76-81; mem pharmacol-toxicol prog res rev comt, Nat Inst Gen Med Sci, NIH, 75-79; Am Cancer Soc fel biochem, Duke Univ, 63-65, Am Heart Asn advan res fel, 66-68; vis prof, Japan Soc Promotion Sci, 78, Osaka Univ & Kyushu Univ. *Mem:* AAAS; Am Soc Biol

Chem; Am Chem Soc; Am Soc Pharmacol & Exp Therapeut; Am Burn Asn. *Res:* Microsomal electron transport in various tissues with specific reference to nicotinamide adenine dinucleotide phosphate-cytochrome c (P-450) reductase. *Mailing Add:* Dept Biochem Med Col Wis 8701 Watertown Plank Rd Milwaukee WI 53226

MASTERS, BRUCE ALLEN, b Terre Haute, Ind, Nov 3, 36; m 63. MICROPALEONTOLOGY. *Educ:* Univ Valparaiso, BS, 59; Univ Calif, Berkeley, MA, 62; Univ Ill, Urbana, PhD(geol), 70. *Prof Exp:* Jr geologist, Humble Oil & Ref Co, 62-63, asst geologist, 63-65, assoc geologist, 65; from asst prof to assoc prof geol, Hartwick Col, 69-74; sr res scientist, 74-77, STAFF RES SCIENTIST, AMOCO PROD CO, 77- *Mem:* Am Asn Petrol Geol; Paleont Res Inst; Paleont Soc; Soc Econ Paleont & Mineral; Swiss Geol Soc. *Res:* Morphology, taxonomy, phylogeny, paleoecology and biostratigraphy of Mesozoic and Cenozoic planktonic foraminifers, benthonic foraminifers, nannoconids, calcispheres and tintinnids. *Mailing Add:* Amoco Prod Co Res Ctr PO Box 591 Tulsa OK 74102

MASTERS, BURTON JOSEPH, b Casper, Wyo, Sept 8, 29; m 53; c 5. SOLID STATE SCIENCE. *Educ:* Univ Calif, Los Angeles, BS, 50; Ore State Col, PhD(chem), 54. *Prof Exp:* Staff mem, Los Alamos Sci Lab, 54-63; SR CHEMIST, IBM CORP, 63- *Mem:* Am Phys Soc. *Res:* Diffusion and ion implantation in silicon; development of silicon integrated circuits; alpha particle induced soft errors in silicon memories; silicon micromechanics; diffusion and ion implantation of semiconductor devices and circuits. *Mailing Add:* IBM Corp D171/B340 Hopewell Junction NY 12533

MASTERS, CHARLES DAY, b Pawhuska, Okla, Aug 4, 29; m 53; c 3. GEOLOGY. *Educ:* Yale Univ, BS, 51, PhD(geol), 65; Univ Colo, MS, 57. *Prof Exp:* Hydrographic officer, US Navy, 52-54; explor geologist, Pan Am Petrol Corp, 57-68, res geologist, 68-70; chmn div sci & math, WGa Col, 70-73; chief, Off Energy Resources & actg cheif, Off Marine Geol, 73-80, RES GEOLOGIST WORLD ENERGY RESOURCES, US GEOL SURV, 80- *Mem:* AAAS; Sigma Xi; Geol Soc Am; Am Asn Petrol Geologists. *Mailing Add:* US Geol Surv Nat Ctr MS 915 Reston VA 22092

MASTERS, CHRISTOPHER FANSTONE, b Ashridge, Eng, Dec 26, 42; US citizen; m 66; c 2. MATHEMATICS. *Educ:* Doane Col, AB, 64; Fla State Univ, MS, 66; Univ Northern Colo, DA, 74. *Prof Exp:* Instr math, Fla Southern Col, 66-68; asst prof, 68-77, ASSOC PROF MATH, DOANE COL, 77- *Mem:* Math Asn Am; Nat Coun Teachers Math. *Mailing Add:* Dept of Math Doane Col Crete NE 68333

MASTERS, EDWIN M, b Everette, Mass, Nov 21, 31; m 64; c 4. ANATOMY. *Educ:* Harvard Univ, AB, 52; Ind Univ, AM, 55; Univ Minn, PhD(anat), 65. *Prof Exp:* Instr anat, Univ Pittsburgh, 58-64; instr, 64-65, asst prof, 65-75, ASSOC PROF ANAT, JEFFERSON MED COL, 75- *Concurrent Pos:* NIH fel, 51-64. *Mem:* AAAS; Am Asn Anat; NY Acad Sci. *Res:* Physiology of fat cells in tissue cultrue; histogenesis of elastic tissue; survival of homologous grafts in the brain. *Mailing Add:* Dept of Anat Jefferson Med Col Philadelphia PA 19107

MASTERS, FRANK WYNNE, b Pittsburgh, Pa, Nov 1, 20; m; c 3. PLASTIC SURGERY. *Educ:* Hamilton Col, AB, 43; Univ Rochester, MD, 45; Am Bd Plastic Surg, dipl, 55; Am Bd Surg, dipl, 56. *Prof Exp:* Intern, Strong Mem Hosp, Rochester, NY, 45-46; trainee gen surg, 48-51; trainee plastic surg, Med Ctr, Duke Univ, 51-53, assoc, 53-54; chief plastic surg, Charleston Mem Hosp, WVa, 54-58; from asst prof to assoc prof, 58-67, vchmn dept surg, 72-77, assoc dean clin affairs, 73-76, chief sect plastic surg, 72-80, PROF PLASTIC SURG, UNIV KANS MED CTR, KANSAS CITY, 67-, CHMN DEPT SURG, 77- *Concurrent Pos:* Consult, Vet Admin Hosps, Kansas City, Mo & Wadsworth, Kans; mem, Am Bd Plastic Surg, 68-74, co-chmn exam comt, 68-69, chmn, 69-73, rep, Am Bd Med Spec, 71-74, mem exec comt, 72-74, chmn, 73-74. *Mem:* Am Burn Asn; Am Asn Surg Trauma; Am Cleft Palate Asn; Am Soc Plastic & Reconstruct Surg; fel Am Col Surg. *Mailing Add:* Dept of Surg Univ of Kans Med Ctr Kansas City KS 66103

MASTERS, JOHN ALAN, b Shenandoah, Iowa, Sept 20, 27; m 51; c 3. PETROLEUM GEOLOGY. *Educ:* Yale Univ, BA, 48; Univ Colo, MS, 51. *Prof Exp:* Dist geologist, AEC, 51-53; chief geologist, Kerr-McGee Oil Industs, Inc, 53-66, mgr Can explor, Kerr-McGee Corp, 66-69, pres, Kerr-McGee Can Ltd, 69-73; PRES, CAN HUNTER EXPLOR, 73- *Honors & Awards:* Mattson Award, Asn Petrol Geol, 57. *Mem:* Geol Soc Am; Am Asn Petrol Geol. *Res:* Stratigraphy; oil exploration by means of subsurface and surface geology. *Mailing Add:* Can Hunter Explor 700-435 Fourth Ave SW Calgary AB T2P 3A8 Can

MASTERS, JOHN EDWARD, b Greeneville, Tenn, June 20, 13; m 38; c 2. ORGANIC CHEMISTRY. *Educ:* Tusculum Col, AB, 36; Univ Tenn, MS, 38. *Prof Exp:* Resin chemist high polymers, Jones-Dabney Co, 39-46, chief chemist resin div, 46-49; res dir, Devoe & Raynolds Co, 49-65; mgr, Trade Sales Labs, Celanese Coatings Co, Jeffersontown, 65-69, sr res assoc, 69-79; RETIRED. *Mem:* Am Chem Soc. *Res:* Exploratory research in the field of high polymers and protective coatings. *Mailing Add:* 9207 Darley Dr Louisville KY 40222

MASTERS, JOHN MICHAEL, b Cincinnati, Ohio, Aug 29, 42; m 63; c 2. PETROLEUM GEOLOGY. *Educ:* Univ Cincinnati, BS, 64, MS, 66. *Prof Exp:* Geologist petrol, Chevron Oil Co, 66-71; asst geologist, 71-80, ASSOC GEOLOGIST INDUST MINERALS, ILL STATE GEOL SURV, 80- *Mem:* Soc Mining Engrs; Am Inst Mining, Metall & Petrol Engrs. *Res:* Geology of industrial minerals, specializing in sand and gravel resources, beneficiation and utilization. *Mailing Add:* 2005 Easy St Urbana IL 61801

MASTERS, LARRY WILLIAM, b Martinsburg, WVa, Nov 18, 41; m 63; c 2. MATERIALS SCIENCE. *Educ:* Shepherd Col, BS, 63; Am Univ, MS, 68. *Prof Exp:* chemist, Harleton Labs, Falls Church, Va, 63-64; res chemist, 64-77, GROUP LEADER, NAT BUR STANDARDS, 77- *Concurrent Pos:* Mem, Int Union Testing & Res Lab Mat & Struct, chmn, Prediction Serv Life Comt, 71-; mem, Solar Energy Core Comt & Tech Adv Group, Int Standardization Orgn, 81- *Mem:* Am Chem Soc; Am Soc Testing & Mat. *Res:* Service life prediction of polymeric building materials; materials for use in solar energy systems; author or coauthor of over 40 publications. *Mailing Add:* Rm B-348 Bldg 226 Nat Bur Standards Washington DC 20234

MASTERS, ROBERT WAYNE, b Ft Wayne, Ind, May 25, 14; m 41; c 1. ELECTRONICS. *Educ:* Univ Ala, BS, 38; Ohio State Univ, MS, 41; Univ Pa, PhD, 57. *Prof Exp:* Adv develop engr, RCA Victor Div, Radio Corp Am, 41-49; assoc supvr, Antenna Lab, Ohio State Univ, 49-58; staff engr res supvr, Boeing Airplane Co, 58-60; mgr, Antenna Dept, Melpar, Inc, 60-62, mem systs staff to vpres eng, 62-64; staff scientist, DECO Electronics, 65-67; fel engr, DECO Commun Dept, Westinghouse Elec Corp, 67-68; vpres res eng, 68-70, vpres & secy, 70-75, PRES & CHMN, ANTENNA RES ASSOCS, INC, 75- *Concurrent Pos:* Prof, Ohio State Univ, 56-58. *Mem:* Fel Inst Elec & Electronics Engrs. *Res:* Antennas, including television transmitting, antenna complexes, radio-frequency transmission systems; propagation. *Mailing Add:* 6423 Walters Woods Dr Falls Church VA 22044

MASTERS, WILLIAM HOWELL, b Cleveland, Ohio, Dec 27, 15; m 71; c 2. OBSTETRICS & GYNECOLOGY. *Educ:* Hamilton Col, BS, 38; Univ Rochester, MD, 43; Am Bd Obstet & Gynec, dipl, 51. *Hon Degrees:* ScD, Hamilton Col, 73. *Prof Exp:* Intern path, 44, asst obstet & gynec, 44-47, from instr to assoc prof, 47-63, dir, Div Reprod Biol, 60-63, assoc prof clin obstet & gynec, 64-69, PROF CLIN OBSTET & GYNEC, SCH MED, WASHINGTON UNIV, 69-, DIR CYTOL SERV, 67- *Concurrent Pos:* Intern, Barnes Hosp, 43-45, asst resident, 44, resident, 46-47, assoc obstetrician & gynecologist, 47-; intern, St Louis Maternity Hosp, 43, asst resident, 44, resident, 45-46, assoc obstetrician & gynecologist, 47; assoc obstetrician & gynecologist, Washington Univ Clins; assoc gynecologist, St Louis Children's Hosp; consult gynecologist, St Louis City Infirmary & Salem Mem Hosp, Ill; dir, Family & Children's Serv & Health & Welfare Coun; dir, Reprod Biol Res Found, 64-73, co-dir, 73-80; chmn bd, Masters & Johnson Inst, 81- *Honors & Awards:* Paul H Hoch Award, Am Psychopath Asn, 71; Sex Info & Educ Coun US Award, 72; Distinguished Serv Award, Am Asn Marriage & Family Counr, 76; Mod Med Award Distinguished Achievement, 77; Am Asn Sex Educr, Counr & Therapists Award, 78; Biomed Res Award, World Asn Sexology, 79; Edward Henderson Lect Award, Am Geriat Soc, 81. *Mem:* AAAS; Am Fertil Soc; Endocrine Soc; NY Acad Sci; Am Geriat Soc. *Res:* Infertility and sterility; geriatric endocrinology; sexual inadequacy. *Mailing Add:* 4910 Forest Park Blvd St Louis MO 63108

MASTERSON, EILEEN, physiology, see previous edition

MASTERSON, KLEBER SANLIN, JR, b San Diego, Calif, Sept 26, 32; m 57; c 2. OPERATIONS RESEARCH, SYSTEMS DESIGN & SCIENCE. *Educ:* US Naval Acad, BS, 54; US Navy Postgrad Sch, MS, 60; Univ Calif, PhD(physics), 63. *Prof Exp:* Comput programmer, US Navy Electronics Lab, San Diego, 58-59; dep dir combat data syst, US Navy Electronics Lab & USS Wright, 63-64; head, Sea Cont Forces Group, Syst Anal Div, Off Chief Naval Opers, 71-74; proj mgr develop & procurement combat syst, Naval Mat & Sea Syst Commands, Antiship Missile Defense Proj, 74-77, exec asst & naval aide to secy navy, Dept Navy, 77-79, dep complete design release naval sea systs command, antiair warfare & anti-ship combat systs, 79-81, CHIEF STUDIES ANAL & GAMES AGENCY, OFF JOINT CHIEFS STAFF, 81. *Concurrent Pos:* Mem, Bd Control, US Naval Inst, 73- *Mem:* Am Phys Soc; Sigma Xi. *Res:* Plasma physics; theoretical nuclear physics, many-body problem; compilers; radars; anti-aircraft and anti-missile systems; electronic warfare systems; gun systems, command missile and control systems; systems analysis, strategic and naval, ground, air forces. *Mailing Add:* 101 Pommander Walk Alexandria VA 22314

MASTERTON, WILLIAM LEWIS, b Conway, NH, July 24, 27; m 53; c 2. GENERAL CHEMISTRY. *Educ:* Univ NH, BS, 49, MS, 50; Univ Ill, PhD(chem), 53. *Prof Exp:* Instr chem, Univ Ill, 53-55; from instr to assoc prof, 55-66, PROF CHEM, UNIV CONN, 66- *Mem:* Am Chem Soc; Sigma Xi; Am Assoc Univ Prof. *Res:* Thermodynamics of solutions; activity coefficients of electrolytes; solubility of gases in salt solutions. *Mailing Add:* Dept of Chem Univ of Conn Storrs CT 06268

MASTIN, CHARLES WAYNE, b Salinas, Calif, Apr 23, 43; m 71; c 2. MATHEMATICAL ANALYSIS. *Educ:* Austin Peay State Col, BS, 64; Miami Univ, MS, 66; Tex Christian Univ, PhD(math), 69. *Prof Exp:* Asst prof math, Miss State Univ, 69-75; vis scientist, Inst Comput Appln Sci & Eng, NASA Langley Res Ctr, 75-76; ASSOC PROF MATH, MISS STATE UNIV, 76- *Mem:* Sigma Xi; Soc Indust & Appl Math; Asn Comput Mach. *Res:* Practical application of transformation methods to the solution of fluid dynamics problems. *Mailing Add:* Drawer MA Mississippi State MS 39762

MASTRANGELO, MICHAEL JOSEPH, b Phoenixville, Pa, Oct 3, 38; m 64; c 3. MEDICINE, IMMUNOLOGY. *Educ:* Villanova Univ, BS, 60; Johns Hopkins Univ, MD, 64. *Prof Exp:* Instr, Sch Med, Thomas Jefferson Univ, 70-73; asst prof, 74-77, ASSOC PROF MED, TEMPLE UNIV, 77-; RES PHYSICIAN & CHIEF MELANOMA UNIT, FOX CHASE CANCER CTR, 72- *Mem:* Am Asn Cancer. *Res:* Am Soc Clin Oncol; Am Fedn Clin Res; AAAS; Am Col Clin Pharmacol. Res: Tumor immunology; tumor biology; cancer therapy. *Mailing Add:* Fox Chase Cancer Ctr 7701 Burholme Ave Philadelphia PA 19111

MASTRANGELO, SEBASTIAN VITO ROCCO, b New York, NY, July 1, 25; m 49; c 2. PHYSICAL CHEMISTRY. *Educ:* Queens Col, NY, BS, 47; Pa State Univ, MS, 48, PhD(chem), 51. *Prof Exp:* Chemist, Barrett Div, Allied Chem Corp, 51-52; phys chemist, Dextran Corp, 52-53, dept supvr, 53-56; res chemist, Jackson Lab, E I du Pont de Nemours & Co, Inc, 56-62, res assoc, Exp Sta, 62-64, res supvr, 64-69, RES FEL, EXP STA, E I DU PONT DE NEMOURS & CO, INC, 69- *Mem:* Am Chem Soc; Am Phys Soc; Am Inst Chem. *Res:* Low temperature purification; third law thermodynamics; adsorption thermodynamics; adsorption thermodynamics at liquid helium temperatures; high temperature adiabatic calorimetry; molecular weight distribution of high polymers; raman and infrared spectroscopy; free radical chemistry; elctrochemistry. *Mailing Add:* 8 Yorkridge Trail PO Box 73 Hockessin DE 19707

MASTRO, ANDREA M, b Sewickley, Pa, Sept 8, 44; m 73. CELL BIOLOGY, CELL PHYSIOLOGY. *Educ:* Carlow Col, BA, 66; Pa State Univ, MS, 68, PhD(biol), 71. *Prof Exp:* Fel oncol, McArdle Lab, Univ Wis, 71-73; res fel cell biol, Imp Cancer Res Fund Lab, London, 74-75; res assoc biochem & biophys, 75-78, ASST PROF MICROBIOL, PA STATE UNIV, 79- *Concurrent Pos:* Res grants, NIH-Nat Inst Gen Med Sci, 76-81, NIH-Nat Can Inst, 78-86 & Off Naval Res, 79-80; Damon Runyon fel, Damon Runyon Mem Fund Cancer Res, 71-73. *Mem:* AAAS; Am Soc Cell Biol; Tissue Culture Asn; Am Asn Cancer Res; Am Asn Women Sci. *Res:* Role of the plasma membrane in the control of cell growth in mammalian cells; role of cell-cell interactions in cell growth and differentiation; lymphocyte proliferation. *Mailing Add:* 431 S Frear Pa State Univ University Park PA 16802

MASTROIANNI, LUIGI, JR, b New Haven, Conn, Nov 8, 25; m 57; c c 3. OBSTETRICS & GYNECOLOGY. *Educ:* Yale Univ, AB, 46; Boston Univ, MD, 50; Am Bd Obstet & Gynec, dipl, 59, 74. *Prof Exp:* From instr to asst prof obstet & gynec, Sch Med, Yale Univ, 55-61; prof, Univ Calif, Los Angeles, 61-65; PROF OBSTET & GYNEC & CHMN DEPT, UNIV PA, 65- *Concurrent Pos:* Ed, J Fertil & Steril; res fel infertility & endocrinol, Harvard Med Sch, 54-55. *Mem:* Endocrine Soc; Am Fertil Soc (pres, 76-77); Am Gynec Soc; fel Am Col Obstet & Gynec; fel Am Col Surg. *Res:* Human infertility; reproductive physiology. *Mailing Add:* Hosp Univ Pa 3400 Spruce St Philadelphia PA 19104

MASTROMARINO, ANTHONY JOHN, b Brooklyn, NY, June 13, 40; m 73; c 2. MEDICAL MICROBIOLOGY, CANCER. *Educ:* Iona Col, BS, 61; Syracuse Univ, MS, 71; Baylor Col Med, PhD(exp biol, microbiol), 75. *Prof Exp:* Res assoc microbiol, Naylor Dana Inst Dis Prev, Am Health Found, 74-76; asst dir sci opers, Nat Large Bowel Cancer Proj, 76-80, ASSOC SCI DIR, NAT LARGE BOWEL CANCER PROJ, UNIV TEX SYSTS CANCER CTR, M D ANDERSON HOSP & TUMOR INST, 80-, ASST BIOLOGIST, DEPT INTERNAL MED, GASTROENTEROL, 78- *Mem:* Am Soc Microbiol; Asn Gnotobiotics (vpres, 79-80, pres, 80-81); Soc Exp Biol & Med; AAAS; NY Acad Sci. *Res:* Analysis of bacterial enzyme systems potentially useful in prognosis of risk for colon carcinogenesis; interaction of diet, neutral and acid sterols, and intestinal anaerobes in metabolic epidemiology of colon cancer. *Mailing Add:* Univ of Tex Syst Cancer Ctr 1100 Holcombe Blvd HMB 850 Houston TX 77030

MASTROMATTEO, ERNEST, b Toronto, Ont, Dec 16, 23; m 49; c 7. MEDICINE. *Educ:* Univ Toronto, MD, 47, dipl pub health, 50, dipl indust health, 58, cert; Am Bd Prev Med, dipl & cert occup med, 58; Can Bd Occup Med, cert. *Prof Exp:* Jr intern med, St Michael's Hosp, Toronto, 47-48; sr intern, Ottawa Gen Hosp, 48-49; med dir pub health, Govt of Man, 49-52; physician, Govt of Ont Health Dept, 52-66; chief, Occup Health Serv, Ont, 66-68; dir environ health, Ont Health Dept, 68-74; ASSOC PROF OCCUP HEALTH, FAC MED, UNIV TORONTO, 58- *Concurrent Pos:* Consult, Workmen's Compensation Bd, 55-74; trustee, Am Bd Prev Med, 68-78; chief occup safety & health br, Int Labour Orgn, Geneva, 74-76; dir occup health, Inco, Ltd, 76- *Honors & Awards:* Can Centennial Medal, 67. *Mem:* Am Col Prev Med; Am Acad Occup Med; Am Indust Hyg Asn; Am Occup Med Asn; Can Med Asn. *Res:* Occupational, environmental and public health. *Mailing Add:* Inco Ltd First Canadian Pl Toronto ON M5X 1C4 Can

MASUBUCHI, KOICHI, b Otaru, Hokkaido, Japan, Jan 11, 24; m 50. MARINE ENGINEERING. *Educ:* Univ Tokyo, BS, 46, MS, 48, DEng(naval archit), 59. *Prof Exp:* Res engr, Shipbuilding Lab, Japan, 48-50; res engr, Transp Tech Res Inst, 50-53, chief methods fabrication sect, 53-58; vis fel & consult, Battelle Mem Inst, 58-62, res assoc, 62; chief methods fabrication sect, Transp Tech Res Inst, 62-63; chief welding mech sect, Ship Res Inst, 63; res assoc, Battelle Mem Inst, 63-64, fel, 65-66, tech adv technol div, 66-68; assoc prof naval archit, 68-71, PROF OCEAN ENG & MAT SCI, MASS INST TECHNOL, 71- *Honors & Awards:* Distinguished Serv Award, Transp Tech Res Inst, 59; R D Thomas Mem Award, Am Welding Soc, 77. *Mem:* Am Welding Soc; Am Soc Metals; Japanese Welding Soc; Japanese Soc Naval Archit; Am Soc Mech Engrs. *Res:* Naval architecture; welding fabrication of ships and other structures; strength of welded structures; residual stresses; brittle fracture; welding of high strength steels and other materials. *Mailing Add:* Dept of Ocean Eng Mass Inst of Technol Cambridge MA 02139

MASUDA, MINORU, psychophysiology, deceased

MASUELLI, FRANK JOHN, b Masio, Italy, Apr 16, 21; nat US; m 63; c 2. ORGANIC CHEMISTRY. *Educ:* Manhattan Col, BS, 42; Va Polytech Inst, MS, 48, PhD(chem), 53. *Prof Exp:* Instr chem, Va Polytech Inst, 46-53; chemist, 53-55, supvr chem, 55-60, CHIEF PROPELLANTS RES BR, PICATINNY ARSENAL, 60- *Mem:* Am Chem Soc; Tech Asn Pulp & Paper Indust; Am Inst Chemists. *Res:* Nitrocellulose chemistry; artillery and rocket propellants. *Mailing Add:* 344 Diamond Spring Rd Denville NJ 07834

MASUI, YOSHIO, b Kyoto, Japan, Oct 6, 31; m 59; c 2. DEVELOPMENTAL BIOLOGY. *Educ:* Kyoto Univ, BSc, 53, MS, 55, PhD(zool), 61. *Prof Exp:* Lectr biol, Konan Univ, Japan, 58-65, asst prof, 65-68; lectr, Yale Univ, 69; assoc prof, 69-78, PROF ZOOL, UNIV TORONTO, 78- *Mem:* Int Soc Develop Biol; Soc Develop Biol; Can Soc Cell Biol; Can Soc Zoologists. *Res:* Developmental biology relating to nucleocytoplasmic interactions in early development and gametogenesis. *Mailing Add:* Dept Zool Univ Toronto Toronto ON M5S 2R8 Can

MASUMURA, ROBERT AKIRA, materials science, metallurgy, see previous edition

MASUOKA, DAVID TAKASHI, b Los Angeles, Calif, Oct 13, 21; m 44; c 2. PHARMACOLOGY. *Educ:* Univ Southern Calif, BS, 48, PhD(pharmacol), 51. *Prof Exp:* Asst pharmacol, Univ Southern Calif, 49-51, res assoc, 51-52; asst res pharmacologist, Sch Med, Univ Calif, Los Angeles, 53-60; pharmacologist, 60-69, CHIEF NEUROPHARMACOL RES, VET ADMIN HOSP, 69- *Concurrent Pos:* Giannini Found fel, Univ Southern Calif, 52-53; Commonwealth Fund fel, Stockholm, 64-65. *Mem:* Am Soc Pharmacol & Exp Therapeut; Am Soc Neurochem. *Res:* Central and peripheral monoamines; amphetamine; aging. *Mailing Add:* Neuropharmacol Res Lab 151B7 Vet Admin Hosp Sepulveda CA 91343

MASUR, E(RNEST) F(RANK), b Berlin, Ger, July 15, 19; nat US; m 44; c 3. MECHANICS. *Educ:* Univ Pittsburgh, BS, 41; Ill Inst Technol, MS, 48, PhD(mech), 52. *Prof Exp:* Assoc prof civil eng, Ill Inst Technol, 52-55; assoc prof eng mech, Univ Mich, 55-58, prof, 58-64; PROF ENG MECH & HEAD DEPT MAT ENG, UNIV ILL, CHICAGO CIRCLE, 64- *Concurrent Pos:* Consult, NSF; ed, J Struct Mech. *Honors & Awards:* Laurie Prize, Am Soc Civil Engrs, 60. *Mem:* Am Soc Civil Engrs. *Res:* Structural mechanics, dynamics, buckling, optimization; elasticity; plates and shells. *Mailing Add:* 510 Elmwood Evanston IL 60680

MASUREKAR, PRAKASH SHARATCHANDRA, b Bombay, India, Jan 23, 41; m 68; c 2. INDUSTRIAL MICROBIOLOGY, BIOCHEMICAL ENGINEERING. *Educ:* Univ Bombay, BSc, Hons, 62, BSc, 64, MSc, 66; Mass Inst Technol, SM, 68, PhD(biochem eng), 73. *Prof Exp:* Sr res chemist biochem eng, Eastman Kodak Co, 73-80; sr res bioengr, W R Grace & Co, 80-81; SR RES FEL, MERCK SHARP & DOHME RES LABS, 81- *Mem:* Am Soc Microbiol. *Res:* Microbiology and engineering of industrial fermentations; microbial physiology and genetics; biological conversions and enzyme technology. *Mailing Add:* Merck Sharp & Dohme Res Labs PO Box 2000 Rahway NJ 07065

MASURSKY, HAROLD, b Ft Wayne, Ind, Dec 23, 22; m 52; c 4. ASTROGEOLOGY. *Educ:* Yale Univ, BS, 43, MS, 51; Northern Ariz Univ, DSc, 80. *Prof Exp:* Geologist, 51-67, chief br astrogeol studies, 67-71, chief scientist, 71-76, SR SCIENTIST, CTR ASTROGEOL, US GEOL SURV, 77- *Concurrent Pos:* Team leader & prin investr, TV exp, Mariner Mars, 71; co-investr, Appolo Field Geol Team, Apollo 16 & 17, mem Apollo Orbital Sci Photog Team, Apollo Site Selection Group, leader, Viking Landing Site Staff, dep team leader, Orbiter Visual Imaging System, Viking Mars 75; comt space res rep Inter-Union Comn for Studies of the Moon; Int Astron Union Working Group on Nomenclature; Moon, Mars, Venus del, USA-USSR planetary data exchange; radar team mem & chmn, Surface & Interiors Group, Venus Pioneer, 78; interdisciplinary scientist, Voyager Imaging Team, Galileo, 82. *Mem:* Geol Soc Am; Am Geophys Union; AAAS; Geochem Soc; Meteoritical Soc. *Res:* Geology of Owl Creek Mountains, Wyoming; uranium bearing coal in the Red Desert, Wyoming; structure stratigraphy and volcanic rocks in central Nevada; stratigraphy and structure of the moon; geology of Mars; crustal formation, eolian deposits, volcanic history, channel formation; geology of Mercury; impact history; geology of Venus and satellites of Jupiter and Saturn. *Mailing Add:* US Geol Surv 2255 N Gemini Dr Flagstaff AZ 86001

MATA, LEONARDO J, b Dota, Costa Rica, Dec 6, 33; m 56; c 4. PUBLIC HEALTH, VIROLOGY. *Educ:* Univ Costa Rica, BS, 56; Univ PR, dipl, 58; Harvard Univ, MS, 60, DSc(trop pub health), 62. *Prof Exp:* Chief bact & parasitol, San Juan de Dios Hosp, Costa Rica, 56-59; lab instr microbiol, Sch Nursing, Univ Costa Rica, 57-58; chief enteric bact, Inst Nutrit Cent Am & Panama, 59; lab instr parasitol, Harvard Med Sch, 61-62; chief microbiol, Inst Nutrit Cent Am & Panama, Guatemala, 62-75 & prof microbiol, Sch Nutrit, 66-75; DIR INST RES HEALTH & PROF, UNIV COSTA RICA, 75- *Concurrent Pos:* Nat Inst Allergy & Infectious Dis grant, Inst Nutrit Cent Am & Panama, Guatemala, 62-71; mem, Pan Am Health Orgn-WHO-Inst Nutrit Cent Am & Panama internal coun, 65-74; mem, US-Japan coop proj, NIH grant, Guatemala, 68-71; US Armed Forces Res & Develop Command grant, Cent Am, 68-71; vis prof, San Carlos Univ Guatemala, 65-70 & sch med, Univ El Salvador, 70-; mem informal study group, WHO, 71-; dir, Inst Res Health, 75-; vis lectr, Harvard Sch Pub Health; clin prof, Univ Wash. *Honors & Awards:* UNESCO Sci Prize, 80. *Mem:* AAAS; Am Soc Trop Med & Hyg; Latin Am Nutrit Soc; NY Acad Sci; Am Soc Microbiol. *Res:* Tissue culture and virology; enteric microbiology; nutrition and human growth; tropical public health; research on public health interventions. *Mailing Add:* Inst Res Health INISA Univ of Costa Rica San Pedro Costa Rica

MATALON, SADIS, b Athens, Greece, Oct 6, 48; US citizen; m 75. PULMONARY PHYSIOLOGY. *Educ:* Macalester Col, BA, 70; Univ Minn, Minneapolis, MS, 73, PhD(physiol), 75. *Prof Exp:* Syst analyst biomed sci, Univ Minn, Minneapolis, 73-75; assoc physiol & pediat, Children's Mem Hosp & Northwestern Univ, Chicago, 75-76; res asst prof physiol, 76-77, ASST PROF PHYSIOL, STATE UNIV NY, BUFFALO, 76- *Concurrent Pos:* Fulbright scholar, 66-70. *Mem:* Am Physiol Soc; Am Thoracic Soc; Sigma Xi; Undersea Med Soc. *Res:* Oxygen toxicity; solute transport across the alveolar capillary membrane; interaction between hyperventilation and cardiac output. *Mailing Add:* Dept Physiol State Univ NY Buffalo Buffalo NY 14214

MATANOSKI, GENEVIEVE M, b Salem, Mass, Aug 26, 30; m 56; c 5. PEDIATRICS, EPIDEMIOLOGY. *Educ:* Radcliffe Col, AB, 51; Johns Hopkins Univ, MD, 55, MPH, 62, DrPH, 64. *Prof Exp:* Intern & asst resident pediat, Johns Hopkins Hosp, 55-57, res assoc epidemiol, 57-60, from instr to assoc prof, 60-75, PROF EPIDEMIOL, JOHNS HOPKINS UNIV, 75- *Concurrent Pos:* Assoc prof, Schs Med & Dent, Univ Md; NIH grants, 65-66 & 70- *Mem:* AAAS; NY Acad Sci; Soc Epidemiol Res; Int Epidemiol Asn; Am Pub Health Asn. *Res:* Cancer risks from occupational and environmental exposures to radiation and other agents; evaluation of health programs; family-based population studies; dental disease, especially oral cancer and the role of immunology in periodontal disease; rheumatic fever and streptococcal infections; infant mortality and congenital malformations. *Mailing Add:* Sch of Hyg & Pub Health Johns Hopkins Univ Baltimore MD 21205

MATARE, HERBERT FRANZ, b Aachen, W Ger, US citizen. SOLID STATE PHYSICS, ELECTRONICS. *Educ:* Aachen Tech Univ, MS, 39; Tech Univ Berlin, PhD(electronics), 42; Ecole Normale Superieure Univ, Paris, PhD(solid state), 50. *Prof Exp:* Pres, Intermetall Corp, 52-57; head, Dept Semiconductors, Gen Tel & Electronics Labs, Inc, 59-61; head quantum physics, Bendix Res Labs, 61-65; asst chief engr, McDonnell-Douglas Corp, 64-66; sci adv solid state, Rockwell Int, 66-69; CONSULT ELECTRONICS, INT SOLID STATE ELECTRONICS CONSULTS, 71- *Concurrent Pos:* Consult, Intermetall Corp, 53-55 & US Army Electronics Command, 53-56; vis prof, Univ Calif, Los Angeles, 68-69 & Calif State Univ, Fullerton, 69-70. *Mem:* AAAS; Am Phys Soc; Electrochem Soc; NY Acad Sci; fel Inst Elec & Electronics Engrs. *Res:* Compound semiconductors; crystal growth; III-V-ternary compounds; epitaxy; solid state electronics; solar cells; author of over 100 publications. *Mailing Add:* PO Box 7610 Van Nuys CA 91409

MATCHA, ROBERT LOUIS, b Omaha, Nebr, Oct 22, 38; m 80; c 3. THEORETICAL CHEMISTRY. *Educ:* Univ Omaha, BA, 60; Univ Wis-Madison, PhD(theoret chem), 65. *Prof Exp:* Fel, IBM Corp, Calif, 65-66 & Battelle Inst, 66-67; from asst prof to assoc prof, 67-80, PROF THEORET CHEM, UNIV HOUSTON, 80- *Concurrent Pos:* Consult, Battelle Inst, 70-74, Exxon Prod Res, 80-81. *Mem:* AAAS; Am Phys Soc; Am Chem Soc; fel Am Inst Chemists. *Res:* Theoretical study of electromagnetic interactions; effects of nuclear motion on expectation values, molecular Hartree Fock calculations; compton profiles; interactions between molecular ions and surfaces. *Mailing Add:* Dept of Chem Univ of Houston Cullen Blvd Houston TX 77004

MATCHES, ARTHUR GERALD, b Portland, Ore, Jan 28, 29; m 52; c 3. AGRONOMY. *Educ:* Ore State Univ, BS, 52, MS, 54; Purdue Univ, PhD(crop physiol & ecol), 60. *Prof Exp:* Asst farm crops, Ore State Univ, 52-54; instr agron, Purdue Univ, 56-60; asst prof, Southeastern Substa, NMex State Univ, 60-61; prof agron, Univ Mo-Columbia, 61-81; JESSIE W THORNTON DISTINGUISHED PROF PLANT & SOIL SCI, TEX TECH UNIV, 81- *Concurrent Pos:* Res agronomist, Agr Res Serv, USDA, 61-81. *Mem:* Am Forage & Grassland Coun (pres, 77); Soc Range Mgt; fel Am Soc Agron; Crop Sci Soc Am; Am Soc Animal Sci. *Res:* Pasture systems for nearly year long grazing; use of multiple assignment tester animals in grazing trials; pasture research methods. *Mailing Add:* Dept Plant & Soil Sci Texas Tech Univ Box 4169 Lubbock TX 79409

MATCHES, JACK RONALD, b Portland, Ore, May 20, 30; m 54; c 2. FOOD SCIENCE, FISH TECHNOLOGY. *Educ:* Ore State Univ, BS, 57, MS, 58; Iowa State Univ, PhD(microbiol), 63. *Prof Exp:* Res assoc microbiol & food sci, Iowa State Univ, 58-63; sr microbiologist, 63-65, asst prof microbiol & food sci, 65-68, assoc prof, 68-75, PROF FISHERIES, COL FISHERIES, UNIV WASH, 75- *Mem:* Inst Food Technologists; Am Soc Microbiol; Int Asn Milk, Food & Environ Sanit. *Res:* Food microbiology; low temperature microbiology; anaerobic microbiology; Fish Technology and decomposition. *Mailing Add:* Inst for Food Sci & Technol Univ Wash Col Ocean & Fisheries Sci Seattle WA 98195

MATCHETT, ANDREW JAMES, b Chicago, Ill, Jan 30, 50; m 76; c 1. ALGEBRA, FUNCTIONAL ANALYSIS. *Educ:* Univ Chicago, BS, 71; Univ Ill, PhD(math), 76. *Prof Exp:* Teaching fel math, Univ Ill, Urbana-Champaign, 71-73, asst, 73-76; ASST PROF MATH, TEX A&M UNIV, 76- *Mem:* AAAS; Am Math Soc; Math Asn Am. *Res:* Group representation theory, operatory theory, K-theory; respresentations of the symmetric groups. *Mailing Add:* Dept of Math Tex A&M Univ College Station TX 77843

MATCHETT, WILLIAM H, b Pinehurst, NC, Jan 4, 32; m 54; c 2. MICROBIAL PHYSIOLOGY. *Educ:* Univ Ill, BS, 53, MS, 58, PhD(plant physiol), 60. *Prof Exp:* Asst bot, Univ Ill, 57-60; NSF fel microbiol, Sch Med, Yale Univ, 60-61; res fel, Univ Calif, San Diego, 61-63; res scientist biol, Hanford Labs, Gen Elec Co, 63-65; mgr cell biol, Pac Northwest Lab, Battelle Mem Inst, 65-69, coordr life sci, Seattle Res Ctr, 69-70; prof bot & biol sci, Wash State Univ, 70-77, assoc dean grad sch, 71-74, chmn dept bot, 71-76; DEAN GRAD SCH, N MEX STATE UNIV, 77- *Concurrent Pos:* Vis lectr, Wash State Univ, 65, adj assoc prof chem, 67-71. *Mem:* AAAS; Am Soc Microbiol; Am Soc Biol Chemists; Sigma Xi. *Res:* Biochemical genetics of Neurospora crassa; metabolism of tryptophan in Neurospora; enzymology of tryptophan biosynthetic enzymes. *Mailing Add:* Grad Sch Box 3G NMex State Univ Las Cruces NM 88001

MATCOVICH, THOMAS J(AMES), b New York, NY, Jan 15, 29; m 55; c 3. PHYSICS, ELECTRICAL ENGINEERING. *Educ:* Cooper Union, BEE, 50; Univ Pa, MS, 56; Temple Univ, PhD(physics), 61. *Prof Exp:* Mem staff, Gen Elec Co, NY, 50-53 & Philco Corp, Pa, 53-55; eng mgr, Molecular Systs Dept, Univac Div, Sperry Rand Corp, 55-66; assoc prof, 66-71, PROF ELEC ENG & CHMN ELECTROPHYS ADVAN STUDY GROUP, DREXEL UNIV, 71- *Concurrent Pos:* Lectr, St Joseph's Col, Pa, 64-66; partner, C&M Assocs, 67- *Mem:* Am Inst Physics; Inst Elec & Electronics Engrs. *Res:* Microelectronics; computer memory systems; magnetism. *Mailing Add:* 1667 Ludwell Dr Maple Glen PA 19002

MATEER, FRANK MARION, b Pittsburgh, Pa, June 21, 21; m 44; c 3. MEDICINE. *Educ:* Univ Pittsburgh, BS, 41, MD, 44; Am Bd Internal Med, dipl, 52. *Prof Exp:* From instr to asst prof res med, Univ Pittsburgh, 50-62; dir, 65-70, mem sr staff & chief div med educ & res, 70-73, DIR RENAL UNIT, WESTERN PA HOSP, 73-; CLIN PROF MED, UNIV PITTSBURGH, 60- *Concurrent Pos:* Am Heart Asn estab investr, Univ Pittsburgh, 54-59; clin asst prof med, Univ Pittsburgh, 62-72; sr teaching fel physiol, Univ Pittsburgh, 47-48, res fel med, 48-50, Am Heart Asn res fel, 52-54. *Mem:* AAAS; Am Diabetes Asn; Am Fedn Clin Res; fel Am Col Physicians; Am Heart Asn. *Res:* Renal disease; endocrinology. *Mailing Add:* 4815 Liberty Ave Pittsburgh PA 15224

MATEER, NIALL JOHN, b Gerrards Cross, UK, Nov 17, 50. PALEONTOLOGY. *Educ:* Durham Univ, BSc Hons, 73; Uppsala Univ, FD, 78. *Prof Exp:* Res asst geol, Uppsala Univ, 73-78; high sch instr biol & geog, Enkoping, Sweden, 78-80; DEPT CHMN GEOL, MCMURRY COL, ABILENE, 81- *Concurrent Pos:* Lectr, Benin Univ, Nigeria, 78; res asst, NMex Bur Mines & Mineral Res, 80. *Mem:* Soc Econ Paleontologists & Mineralogists; Geol Soc Am; Soc Vert Paleontologists; Paleont Soc. *Res:* Paleoenvironment analysis and paleoecology of the cretaceous basins of the western interior, concentrating primarily on fossil vertebrates. *Mailing Add:* Dept Geol McMurry Col Abilene TX 79697

MATEER, RICHARD AUSTIN, b Ashland, Ky, July 30, 40; m 62; c 2. PHYSICAL ORGANIC CHEMISTRY. *Educ:* Centre Col, BA, 62; Tulane Univ, PhD, 66. *Prof Exp:* ASSOC PROF CHEM, UNIV RICHMOND, 66-, DEAN, 75- *Mem:* Sigma Xi. *Res:* Synthetic photochemistry; organic reaction mechanisms; nuclear magnetic resonance and infrared spectroscopy; organometallics. *Mailing Add:* Robins Hall Univ of Richmond Richmond VA 23173

MATEER, RICHARD S(HELBY), b Fredericktown, Mo, Sept 2, 23; m 52; c 3. METALLURGICAL ENGINEERING. *Educ:* Mo Sch Mines, BS, 44; Carnegie Inst Technol, MS, 47; Univ Pittsburgh, PhD(metall eng), 50. *Prof Exp:* Jr engr, Western Elec Co, 44-45; res fel, Mellon Inst, 50-52; res engr, Kaiser Aluminum & Chem Corp, 52-54; assoc prof metall eng, Univ Pittsburgh, 54-58; head dept mining & metall eng, 58-69, prof metall eng, 58-80, PROF DEPT CIVIL ENG, UNIV KY, 80- *Concurrent Pos:* Consult, Oak Ridge Nat Lab, 58-; vis prof, Imp Col, Univ London, 65. *Mem:* Am Soc Metals; Am Soc Eng Educ; Nat Soc Prof Engrs; Am Inst Mining, Metall & Petrol Engrs. *Res:* Surface tension of molten metals; powder metallurgy; nuclear and dental amalgam alloys. *Mailing Add:* Dept of Civil Eng Univ of Ky Lexington KY 40506

MATEJA, JOHN FREDERICK, b New Castle, Pa, June 3, 50; m 78. NUCLEAR PHYSICS. *Educ:* Univ Notre Dame, BS, 72, PhD(nuclear physics), 76. *Prof Exp:* Res assoc nuclear physics, Fla State Univ, 76-78; ASST PROF PHYSICS, TENN TECHNOL UNIV, 78- *Concurrent Pos:* Sigma Xi res award, Tenn Technol Univ. *Mem:* Am Phys Soc; Sigma Xi. *Res:* Low energy nuclear physics with a current emphasis on heavy ion induced reactions. *Mailing Add:* Dept of Physics Tenn Technol Univ Cookeville TN 38501

MATEKER, EMIL JOSEPH, JR, b St Louis, Mo, Apr 25, 31; m 54; c 3. GEOPHYSICS. *Educ:* St Louis Univ, BS, 56, MS, 59, PhD(geophys), 64. *Prof Exp:* Geophysicist, Standard Oil Co Calif, 57-60; instr geophys, St Louis Univ, 60-63; from asst prof to assoc prof geophys, Washington Univ, 63-69; mgr geophys res, 69-70, vpres res & develop, 70-74, vpres, 74-78, PRES, AERO SERV DIV, WESTERN GEOPHYS CO AM, HOUSTON, 78- *Concurrent Pos:* pres, Litton Resources Systs, 77 & Westrex Limited, 74-77. *Mem:* AAAS; Am Geophys Union; Seismol Soc Am; Soc Explor Geophys; Europ Asn Explor Geophys. *Res:* Generation of seismic waves; seismic vibrations; tectonics of stable interior; exploration geophysics; inertial guidance for marine exploration; lithology measurements from seismic reflections; marine seismic energy sources; deep solid earth geophysics. *Mailing Add:* 419 Hickory Post Houston TX 77079

MATELES, RICHARD I, b New York, NY, Sep 11, 35; m 56; c 3. FOOD SCIENCE & TECHNOLOGY. *Educ:* Mass Inst Technol, BS, 56, MS, 57, ScD, 59. *Prof Exp:* Fel, Microbiol Lab, Delft Univ Technol, 59-60; from instr biochem engr to assoc prof, Dept Nutrit & Food Sci, Mass Inst Technol, 60-70; prof appl microbiol, Inst Microbiol, Hebrew Univ, 68-80; asst dir & dir res, 80-81, VPRES RES, STAUFFER CHEM CO, 81- *Concurrent Pos:* Vis lectr, Dept Chem Eng, Univ Calif, Berkeley, 65; consult, Nat Coun Res & Develop, Israel, 65-80; mem, Panel World Food Supply, Presidents' Sci Adv Comt, 66-67; dir, Fermentation Unit, Jerusalem, 68-77; co-ed, Microbiol Series, Marcel Dekker Inc, 78- *Mem:* Am Chem Soc; Am Soc Microbiol; Soc Gen Microbiol; Inst Food Technologists; Am Inst Chem Eng. *Mailing Add:* Stauffer Chem Co Westport CT 06881

MATES, ROBERT EDWARD, b Buffalo, NY, May 19, 35; m 60; c 3. BIOENGINEERING, MECHANICAL ENGINEERING. *Educ:* Univ Rochester, BS, 57; Cornell Univ, MS, 59, PhD(mech eng), 63. *Prof Exp:* Instr, Cornell Univ, 58-61; from asst prof to assoc prof, 62-69, chmn, Dept Mech Eng, 67-70, 79-82, PROF MECH & AEROSPACE ENG, STATE UNIV NY BUFFALO, 69-, RES ASSOC PROF, DEPT MED, 72- *Concurrent Pos:* NIH spec res fel, Dept Med, State Univ NY Buffalo, 70-71; consult, Cornell Aeronaut Lab, 62-69, chmn mech eng, 67-70, 79-82; assoc ed, J Biomech Eng, 76-; NIH fel, State Univ NY Buffalo, 78-79. *Mem:* Am Soc Mech Engrs; Am Soc Eng Educ; Am Heart Asn; Am Physiol Soc. *Res:* Biomechanics of the cardiovascular and pulmonary systems, particularly coronary blood flow and its regulation. *Mailing Add:* 153 Bidwell Pkwy Buffalo NY 14222

MATESE, JOHN J, b Chicago, Ill, May 1, 38; m 66; c 3. THEORETICAL PHYSICS. *Educ:* DePaul Univ, BS, 60; Univ Notre Dame, PhD(physics), 66. *Prof Exp:* Lectr physics, Univ Notre Dame, 65-66; asst prof, La State Univ, Baton Rouge, 66-74; asst prof, 74-77, ASSOC PROF PHYSICS, UNIV SOUTHWESTERN LA, 77- *Mem:* Am Phys Soc. *Res:* Atomic physics. *Mailing Add:* Dept of Physics Univ of Southwestern La Lafayette LA 70501

MATESICH, MARY ANDREW, b Zanesville, Ohio, May 5, 39. PHYSICAL CHEMISTRY. *Educ:* Ohio Dominican Col, BA, 62; Univ Calif, Berkeley, MS, 63, PhD(chem), 66. *Prof Exp:* Asst prof chem, 65-70, chmn dept, 65-73, acad dean, 73-78, ASSOC PROF CHEM, OHIO DOMINICAN COL, 70-, PRES, 78- *Concurrent Pos:* Petrol Res Fund grant, Ohio Dominican Col, 65-68; NSF grant, Case Western Reserve Univ & Ohio Dominican Col, 69-72. *Mem:* Am Chem Soc. *Res:* Ion transport in membranes; nonaqueous solvents; transport processes in solution; solution thermodynamics. *Mailing Add:* Ohio Dominican Col Columbus OH 43219

MATEY, JAMES REGIS, b McKeesport, Pa, June 30, 51; m 73; c 2. PHYSICS. *Educ:* Carnegie-Mellon Univ, BS, 73; Univ Ill, Urbana, MS, 74, PhD(physics), 78. *Prof Exp:* MEM TECH STAFF RES & DEVELOP, DAVID SARNOFF RES CTR, RCA CORP, 78- *Mem:* Am Phys Soc. *Res:* Development of new hardware and software tools to study material surfaces. *Mailing Add:* RCA Labs Princeton NJ 08540

MATHAI, ARAKAPARAMPIL M, b Palai, India, Apr 28, 35; m 64; c 2. MATHEMATICAL STATISTICS. *Educ:* Univ Kerala, BSc, 57, MSc, 59; Univ Toronto, MA, 62, PhD(math statist), 64. *Prof Exp:* Lectr math, St Thomas Col, Univ Kerala, 59-61; Commonwealth scholar statist, Univ Toronto, 61-64; asst prof, 64-68, assoc prof, 68-78, PROF MATH, MCGILL UNIV, 79- *Concurrent Pos:* Ed, Can J Statist, 74-77. *Honors & Awards:* Gold Medal, Univ Kerala, 59. *Mem:* Exec mem Statist Sci Asn Can (secy, 72-74); Inst Math Statist; Statist Soc Can. *Res:* Statistical distributions; multivariate analysis; axiomatic foundations of statistical concepts; special functions and complex analysis; functional equations. *Mailing Add:* Dept Math McGill Univ 805 Sherbrooke St W Montreal PQ H3A 2K6 Can

MATHAY, WILLIAM LEWIS, b Greenville, Pa, Dec 1, 24; m 48; c 1. APPLIED CHEMISTRY, CORROSION. *Educ:* Thiel Col, BS, 47. *Prof Exp:* Res chemist, Calgon Inc, 47-54; head, Chem & Process Corrosion Sect, Appl Res Lab, 54-58, chief res engr, 58-64, mgr process indust mkt, 64-74, SR INDUST REP PROCESS INDUST, US STEEL CORP, 74- *Mem:* Nat Asn Corrosion Eng; fel Am Inst Chem; Am Inst Chem Eng; Tech Asn Pulp & Paper Indust; Am Soc Testing & Mat. *Res:* Steels for process industries; pollution control equipment of synfuels industry. *Mailing Add:* US Steel Corp 600 Grant St Pittsburgh PA 15230

MATHE, CLARENCE EUGENE, JR, b Carlstadt, NJ, July 16, 15; m 40; c 3. CHEMISTRY. *Educ:* Ohio Univ, BS, 39. *Prof Exp:* Develop chemist, Nat Oil Prod Co, NJ, 39-42; plant mgr, Metal Organics, Inc, 46-47; plant mgr, Metallic Stearates Div, Witco Chem Co, NY, 47-50; pres, Mathe Chem Co, NJ, 50-65; gen mgr, Berkeley Chem Dept, Millmaster Chem Co, 65-77; RETIRED. *Concurrent Pos:* Admin facil, Bergen Community Col, 72. *Mem:* Am Chem Soc. *Res:* Derivatives of fatty acids including esters, amides, amines and metallic soaps; lubricant additives; plasticizers and stabilizers. *Mailing Add:* 1529 Lake Francis Dr Errol Estate Apopka FL 32703

MATHENY, ADAM PENCE, JR, b Stanford, Ky, Sept 6, 32; m 67; c 2. DEVELOPMENTAL PSYCHOLOGY, PSYCHOBIOLOGY. *Educ:* Columbia Univ, BS, 58; Vanderbilt Univ, PhD(psychol), 62. *Prof Exp:* Sr engr human factors, Martin Aerospace Systs, 62-63; instr pediat, Med Sch, Johns Hopkins Univ, 63-65; staff fel, Nat Inst Child Health & Human Develop, 65-67; from asst prof to assoc prof, 67-76, PROF PEDIAT, MED SCH, UNIV LOUISVILLE, 76- *Concurrent Pos:* Out patient psychologist, Johns Hopkins Hosp, 63-65; clin instr, Georgetown Univ, 65-67; instr, Univ Louisville Col, 68-; chmn, Ky Task Force Except Children, 71-72; consult, Southeastern Ind Rehab Ctr, 72-75; bd mem, Ky Examr Speech & Hearing, 75-78. *Mem:* AAAS; Am Psychol Asn; Soc Res Child Develop; Int Soc Twin Studies; Sigma Xi. *Res:* Cognitive and affective development; children; behavioral genetics; medical counseling; studies of attention. *Mailing Add:* Dept of Pediat Sch of Med Univ Louisville Louisville KY 40202

MATHENY, ELLIS LEROY, JR, b Harrisonburg, Va, Nov 9, 39; div; c 3. ENTOMOLOGY. *Educ:* James Madison Univ, BS, 65; Univ Tenn, MS, 68, PhD(entom), 71. *Prof Exp:* Asst prof biol, Motlow State Col, Tullahoma, Tenn, 71-76; asst prof, 76-80, ASSOC PROF ENTOM, UNIV FLA, GAINESVILLE, 80- *Concurrent Pos:* NSF grant, Univ Fla, 77-79. *Mem:* Entom Soc Am. *Res:* Turf insects; mole crickets; sod webworms; development of innovative materials for teaching entomology. *Mailing Add:* Dept of Entom & Nematol Univ of Fla Gainesville FL 32611

MATHENY, JAMES DONALD, b Jackson, Miss, Dec 22, 25; m; c 2. MECHANICAL ENGINEERING. *Educ:* Univ SC BS, 45; Univ Tex, BS, 50, MS, 56, PhD (mech eng), 59. *Prof Exp:* Instr mech eng, Univ Tex, 52-56; asst prof, La Polytech Inst, 56-57; sr res engr, Convair, Tex, 57-58; assoc prof mech eng, Univ Ala, 58-63, prof, eng mech, 63-69; prof mech eng & head dept, Col Eng, Univ Wyo, 70-77; DEAN & PROF ENG, CALIF STATE UNIV, FRESNO, 77- *Mem:* Am Soc Mech Eng; Am Inst Aeronaut & Astronaut; Am Soc Eng Educ; Soc Natural Philos. *Res:* Heat transfer; naval aircraft landing systems; stress analysis of landing field materials; restrained buried pipe. *Mailing Add:* Calif State Univ Sch of Eng Fresno CA 93740

MATHENY, JAMES LAFAYETTE, b Vicksburg, Miss, Aug 28, 43; m 65. PHARMACOLOGY. *Educ:* Delta State Col, BS, 67; Univ Miss, PhD(pharmacol), 71. *Prof Exp:* Asst prof pharmacol, Med Col Ga, 71-77; ASSOC PROF BIOL, COL DENT, UNIV KY, 78- *Concurrent Pos:* NIH, Ga Heart Assoc, Fight for Sight Inc grant, 71-72. *Mem:* AAAS; NY Acad Sci; fel Am Col Clin Pharmacol; Am Heart Asn; Am Soc Pharmacol & Exp Therapeut. *Res:* Autonomic-cardiovascular pharmacology. *Mailing Add:* Dept of Oral Biol Univ of Ky Col of Dent Lexington KY 40506

MATHER, ALAN, b Alton, Ill, Oct 31, 10; m 40; c 2. CLINICAL BIOCHEMISTRY. *Educ:* Shurtleff Col, BS, 32; St Louis Univ, PhD(biochem), 39. *Prof Exp:* Biochemist, Neuroendocrine Found, Worcester, Mass, 39-42; res assoc, Clark Univ, 42-45; asst prof biochem, Dartmouth Med Sch, 45-55; biochemist, Mem Hosp, Wilmington, Del, 55-65; chief coronary drug proj lab, Commun Dis Ctr, USPHS, 65-67, chief clin chem sect, Ctr Dis Control, 67-73, ASSOC DIR CLIN CHEM, CTR DIS CONTROL, USPHS, 73- *Mem:* Am Asn Clin Chem. *Res:* Analytical methodology and instrumentation in clinical chemistry. *Mailing Add:* Clin Chem Div NH Communicable Dis Ctr Atlanta GA 30333

MATHER, BRYANT, b Baltimore, Md, Dec 27, 16; m 40. CIVIL ENGINEERING. *Educ:* Johns Hopkins Univ, AB, 36. *Hon Degrees:* DSc, Clarkson Col, 78. *Prof Exp:* Asst cur mineral, Chicago Mus Natural Hist, 39-41; geologist, Cent Concrete Lab, US War Dept, NY, 41-42, concrete res engr, 42-46; chief, Spec Invest Br, Concrete Div, Waterways Exp Sta, 46-65, from asst chief to chief, 65-78, CHIEF, STRUCT LAB, CORPS OF ENGRS, 78- *Concurrent Pos:* Mem comts, Transp Res Bd, Nat Acad Sci-Nat Res Coun & US Comt Large Dams; res assoc, Fla Dept Agr, 68-, Am Mus Natural Hist, Miss Mus Natural Sci & Miss Entom Mus, 80- & Miss Mus Coun, 81- *Honors & Awards:* Except Civilian Serv Award, Dept Army, 68. *Mem:* Fel AAAS; Am Soc Testing & Mat (pres, 75-76); Meteoritical Soc; Lepidop Soc; Am Concrete Inst (pres, 64). *Res:* Structural geology; composition and properties of concrete and concrete aggregates; methods of testing; butterflies and moths of Mississippi. *Mailing Add:* 213 Mt Salus Dr Clinton MS 39056

MATHER, EDWARD CHANTRY, b Iowa City, Iowa, Apr 7, 37; m 58; c 2. VETERINARY MEDICINE, ACADEMIC ADMINISTRATION. *Educ:* Iowa State Univ, DVM, 60, Univ Mo, MS, 68, PhD(reprod physiol), 70. *Prof Exp:* Pvt vet pract, 60-66; instr vet med, Univ Mo-Columbia, 66-68, res assoc, 68-70, from asst prof to assoc prof, 70-74, dir theriogenology lab, 68-73; assoc prof vet med, 74-78, head div theriogenology, 74-78, PROF & CHMN LARGE ANIMAL SURG & MED, MICH STATE UNIV, EAST LANSING, 78- *Concurrent Pos:* Adv prog appl res on fertil regulation, AID, 74-80; external examr, Nigeria, 78. *Honors & Awards:* Dipl, Am Col Theriogenology. *Mem:* Soc Theriogenology; Am Asn Vet Med Cols. *Res:* Effect of seminal constituents on endometrial metabolism; endocrinological variations in large mammals as affected by reproductive pathology; cost and benefits of animal health programs. *Mailing Add:* Vet Clinical Ctr Mich State Univ East Lansing MI 48824

MATHER, FRANCES JEAN, biostatistics, computer science, see previous edition

MATHER, IAN HEYWOOD, b Cheadle, Cheshire, Eng, June 24, 45; m 74; c 2. BIOCHEMISTRY, CELL BIOLOGY. *Educ:* Univ Wales, BSc, 66, PhD(biochem), 71. *Prof Exp:* Res fel biochem, Univ Kent, Canterbury, 70-72; res assoc, Purdue Univ, 73-75; asst prof, 75-80, ASSOC PROF BIOCHEM & CELL BIOL, UNIV MD, 80- *Concurrent Pos:* NSF grants, 78-79 & 79-81. *Mem:* AAAS; Am Dairy Sci Asn; Brit Biochem Soc. *Res:* Biochemistry and physiology of milk synthesis and secretion. *Mailing Add:* Dept of Dairy Sci Univ of MD College Park MD 20742

MATHER, JANE H, b Green Bay, Wis, July 16, 22. BIOCHEMISTRY. *Educ:* Univ Wis, BA, 44; Univ Chicago, PhD(biochem), 63. *Prof Exp:* Chem analyst, Western Elec Co, Ill, 44-45; res chemist, Armour Res Labs, Ill, 45-53; electron microscopist, Northwestern, 54-56, res asst, Univ Chicago, 56-62; asst prof biochem, Ill Inst Technol, 62-65; ASSOC PROF CHEM, GA STATE UNIV, 65- *Concurrent Pos:* Consult, Armour Res Labs, 53-57; USPHS res grants, Ill Inst Technol & Ga State Univ, 65-68. *Mem:* AAAS; Am Chem Soc. *Res:* Biochemical intermediary metabolism and enzymology; analytical chemistry. *Mailing Add:* Dept of Chem Ga State Univ Atlanta GA 30303

MATHER, JOHN CROMWELL, b Roanoke, Va, Aug 7, 46; m 80. ASTROPHYSICS, INFRARED SPECTROSCOPY. *Educ:* Swarthmore Col, BA, 68; Univ Calif, Berkeley, PhD(physics), 74. *Prof Exp:* Nat Res Coun fel astrophysics, Goddard Inst Space Studies, 74-76, ASTRONOMER ASTROPHYSICS, GODDARD SPACE FLIGHT CTR, NASA, 76- *Concurrent Pos:* Lectr astron, Columbia Univ, 75-76; prin investr, far infrared absolute spectrophotom & proj scientist, Cosmic Background Explorer Satellite, 76- *Mem:* Optical Soc Am; Am Phys Soc; Am Astron Soc; Soc Photo Optical Instrumentation Engrs; Sigma Xi. *Res:* Cosmology; the Big Bang. *Mailing Add:* NASA Goddard Space Flight Ctr Code 693-2 Greenbelt MD 20771

MATHER, JOHN NORMAN, b Los Angeles, Calif, June 9, 42; m 71; c 2. DYNAMICAL SYSTEMS. *Educ:* Harvard Univ, BA, 64; Princeton Univ, PhD(math), 67. *Prof Exp:* Assoc prof, Inst Higher Studies Sci, 67-69; from assoc prof to prof, Harvard Univ, 69-75; PROF MATH, PRINCETON UNIV, 75- *Concurrent Pos:* Vis prof math, Princeton Univ, 74-75. *Honors & Awards:* John J Carty Medal, Nat Acad Sci, 78. *Mem:* Am Math Soc. *Res:* Study of dynamical systems especially in dimension 2 with reference to questions of transitivity, ergodicity and kinematic analysis method theory. *Mailing Add:* Fine Hall Princeton Univ Princeton NJ 08544

MATHER, JOHN RUSSELL, b Boston, Mass, Oct 9, 23; m 46; c 3. CLIMATOLOGY. *Educ:* Williams Col, BA, 45; Mass Inst Technol, BS, 47, MS, 48; Johns Hopkins Univ, PhD(climat), 51. *Prof Exp:* Instr, McCoy Col, 49-51; asst prof, Johns Hopkins Univ, 51-53; adj assoc prof, Drexel Inst Technol, 57-60; PROF GEOG, UNIV DEL, 61-, CHMN, 65-, DIR, CTR CLIN RES, 79- *Concurrent Pos:* Res assoc climatologist, Lab Climat, 48-55, prin res scientist, 55-63; pres, C W Thornthwaite Assocs, 63-72; consult, World Meteorol Orgn, Yugoslavia, 57; vis lectr, Univ Chicago, 57-61; consult atmosphere & hydrol hazards from nuclear reactors, US, Iran, Italy & Israel. *Mem:* Am Meteorol Soc; Am Geog Soc; Am Geophys Union; Asn Am Geog. *Res:* Water budget; evaporation; transpiration; applied climatology. *Mailing Add:* Dept Geog Univ Del Newark DE 19711

MATHER, KATHARINE KNISKERN, b Ithaca, NY, Oct 21, 16; m 40. GEOLOGY. *Educ:* Bryn Mawr Col, AB, 37. *Hon Degrees:* Dsc, Clarkson Col Technol, 78. *Prof Exp:* Geologist, Cent Concrete Lab, NY, 42-44, engr concrete res, 44-46; chief petrog & x-ray br, 48-76, chief eng sci div, 76-78, GEOLOGIST, CONCRETE LAB, WATERWAYS EXP STA, US ARMY CORPS ENGRS, 46-, SPEC TECH ASST, STRUCTURES LAB, 78- *Concurrent Pos:* Chmn comt basic res cement & concrete, Transp Res Bd, Nat Acad Sci-Nat Res Coun. *Honors & Awards:* Thompson Award, Am Soc Testing & Mat, 53; Wason Res Medal, Am Concrete Inst, 53; Arthur R Anderson Award, Am Concrete Inst, 82; Fed Woman's Award, 63; Distinguished Civilian Serv Award, Secy Defense, 64. *Mem:* Fel Mineral Soc Am; Am Ceramic Soc; Am Concrete Inst fel, 68-71; Am Inst Mining, Metall & Petrol Eng; Clay Minerals Soc (secy, 64-67, pres, 73). *Res:* Constitution and microstructure of concrete, its constituents and alteration products; effects of variation in composition and exposure on properties of concrete. *Mailing Add:* PO Box 631 Vicksburg MS 39180

MATHER, KEITH BENSON, b Adelaide, S Australia, Jan 6, 22; m 46; c 2. GEOPHYSICS, NUCLEAR PHYSICS. *Educ:* Univ Adelaide, BSc, 42, MSc, 44. *Hon Degrees:* DSc, Univ Alaska, 68. *Prof Exp:* Demonstr physics, Univ Adelaide, 43-45, lectr, 46; Sci & Indust Endowment Fund stud & asst, Wash Univ, 46-48; Imp Chem Indust fel, Birmingham, 49-50; lectr, Ceylon, 50-51; res officer, Commonwealth Sci & Indust Res Org Australia, 52-54; sr res officer, Australian AEC, 54-56, physicist-in-chg Antarctic Div, 56-58; lectr physics, Melbourne, 58-61; assoc prof geophys, Geophys Inst, Univ Alaska, 61-62, asst dir, 63, prof physics & dir geophys, 63-76, VICE CHANCELLOR RES & ADVAN STUDY, UNIV ALASKA, 76- *Concurrent Pos:* Sci corresp, Melbourne AGE, 54-61; Fulbright travel grant, 61-62; mem polar res bd, Nat Acad Sci/Nat Res Coun, 70, vchmn, 72-77; mem, Rhodes Scholar selection comt, Alaska, 71, state secy, 77- *Mem:* Am Geophys Union; Nat Coun Univ Res Adminrs; Inst Physics & Phys Soc London; Australian Inst Physics; Archaeol Inst Am. *Res:* Optical spectroscopy; nuclear scattering and reaction studies; cosmic radiation; geomagnetism and aurora; katabatic winds; polar geophysics; theory of road corrugation and relaxation oscillations; university research administration. *Mailing Add:* Univ Alaska Rm 10 AHRB 901 Koyukuk Ave S Fairbanks AK 99701

MATHER, ROBERT EUGENE, b Goigoi Mission Station, Portuguese E Africa, Nov 12, 18; US citizen; m 43; c 2. ANIMAL BREEDING, STATISTICAL ANALYSIS. *Educ:* Purdue Univ, BS, 39; Univ Md, MS, 41; Univ Wis, PhD(dairy husb, genetics), 46. *Prof Exp:* Asst dairy husb, Univ Md, 39-41; from asst dairy husbandman to assoc dairy husbandman, Exp Sta, Va Polytech Inst, 45-48; assoc prof dairy husb, Rutgers Univ, New Brunswick, 48-59, from assoc res specialist to res specialist, Dairy Res Ctr, Exp Sta, 48-70, asst to dir, Agr Exp Sta for Statist & Comput Consult, 70-77, PROF STATISTICAL GENETICS, RUTGERS UNIV, NEW BRUNSWICK, 59-, MGT INFO SERV, COOK COL, 79- *Mem:* Am Soc Animal Sci; Am Dairy Sci Asn. *Res:* Dairy cattle genetics; use of statistics and computers in agricultural research. *Mailing Add:* Dept of Statist & Comput Sci PO Box 231 New Brunswick NJ 08903

MATHER, ROBERT LAURANCE, b Clarksville, Iowa, Oct 1, 21; m 56; c 2. PHYSICS. *Educ:* Iowa State Univ, BS, 42; Columbia Univ, AM, 47; Univ Calif, PhD(physics), 51. *Prof Exp:* Physicist, Naval Ord Lab, 42-44, Radio Corp Am, 44-46 & Nevis Cyclotron Lab, Columbia Univ, 46-47; asst physics, Univ Calif, 47-48, physicist, Lawrence Radiation Lab, 48-51; physicist, Atomic Energy Div, NAm Aviation, Inc, 51-52; physicist, Nuclear Radiation Physics Br, US Naval Radiol Defense Lab, 52-69, ENG PHYSICIST, NAVAL ELECTRONICS LAB, 69- *Mem:* Am Phys Soc; Inst Elec & Electronics Engrs. *Res:* Radar and communications; electronics; accelerators; Cerenkov radiation; nuclear weapon residual radiation; radiation physics. *Mailing Add:* 755 Cordova St San Diego CA 92107

MATHERS, ALEXANDER PICKENS, b Matherville, Miss, Sept 17, 09; m 33; c 1. ORGANIC CHEMISTRY. *Educ:* Univ Fla, BS, 31; Tulane Univ, MS, 46; George Washington Univ, PhD(chem), 56. *Prof Exp:* Self employed, 31-38; teacher high sch, Miss, 38-41; chemist, 41-55, from asst chief to chief Alcohol & Tobacco Tax Lab, US Treas Dept, 55-73; CONSULT WINE & DISTILLED SPIRITS INDUSTS, 73- *Concurrent Pos:* Owner & operator, Exp Winery & Vineyard, 74-81. *Mem:* AAAS; Am Inst Chemist (pres elect, 74-75, pres, 75-76); Asn Official Anal Chem (vpres, 65-66, pres, 66-67); Am Chem Soc. *Res:* Analytical chemistry; effect of skins, seed and pulp on the fermentation of juice of vitis Rotundifolia. *Mailing Add:* 1000 Frost Bridge Road Shubuta MS 39360

MATHERS, AUBRA CLINTON, b Smithville, WVa, June 28, 23; m 53; c 4. SOIL SCIENCE. *Educ:* Univ Mo, BS, 52, MS, 53; NC State Univ, PhD(soil chem), 56. *Prof Exp:* soil scientist, Southwestern Great Plains Res Ctr, Sci Educ Admin, 56-80, SOIL SCIENTIST, CONSERV & PROD RES LAB, AGR RES SERV, USDA, 80- *Mem:* Am Soc Agron. *Res:* Soil chemistry and fertility; fertility status of soils; iron chlorosis studies and effect of fertilizers on plant nutrition; use or disposal of feedlot wastes to prevent pollution; effect of moisture stress on crop growth and yield. *Mailing Add:* Conserv & Prod Res Lab Agr Res Serv USDA PO Drawer 10 Bushland TX 79012

MATHES, MARTIN CHARLES, b Amherst, Ohio, Feb 18, 35; m 57; c 3. PLANT PHYSIOLOGY. *Educ:* Miami Univ, BA, 57; Univ Md, MS, 59, PhD(plant physiol), 61. *Prof Exp:* Asst bot, Univ Md, 57-61; res aide plant physiol, Inst Paper Chem, Lawrence Univ, 61-64; asst prof, Univ Vt, 64-67; assoc prof, 67-74, PROF BIOL COL WILLIAM & MARY, 74- *Mem:* AAAS; Am Soc Plant Physiol. *Res:* Growth regulators; plant tissue cultures. *Mailing Add:* Dept of Biol Col of William & Mary Williamsburg VA 23185

MATHESON, ALASTAIR TAYLOR, b Vancouver, BC, Can, Oct 10, 29; m 59; c 2. BIOCHEMISTRY, CELL BIOLOGY. *Educ:* Univ BC, BA, 51, MSc, 53; Univ Toronto, PhD(biochem), 58. *Prof Exp:* Res fel enzymol, Nat Res Coun Can, 58-59; res assoc biophys, Johns Hopkins Univ, 59-60; from asst res officer to assoc res officer, Nat Res Coun Can, 60-70, sr res officer cell biochem, 70-77; PROF & CHMN DEPT BIOCHEM & MICROBIOL, UNIV VICTORIA, 77- *Concurrent Pos:* Adj prof biol, Carleton Univ, Ottawa, 74-77. *Mem:* Am Soc Biol Chem; Can Biochem Soc; Brit Biochem Soc; Can Soc Cell Biol; Can Soc Microbiol. *Res:* The structure and function of ribosomes in organisms that grow under extreme conditions; molecular evolution and molecular biology. *Mailing Add:* Dept of Biochem & Microbiol Univ of Victoria Victoria BC V8W 2Y2 Can

MATHESON, ARTHUR RALPH, b Kansas City, Mo, Oct 7, 15; m 41. INORGANIC CHEMISTRY. *Educ:* Univ Ill, BS, 40, MS, 47, PhD(inorg chem), 48. *Prof Exp:* Anal chemist, Univ Ill, 38-40; control chemist synthetic paints, Cook Paint & Varnish Co, Mo, 40; asst chem, Univ Ill, 46-47, asst, Off Naval Res Contract, 47-48; res chemist, Hanford Works, Gen Elec Co, 48-51; dir tech admin div, Schenectady Opers Off, US AEC, 51-54; mgr contract admin dept & asst to pres, M & C Nuclear, Inc, Mass, 54-59; mgr reprocessing, Sylvania-Corning Nuclear Corp, 59-60; sales mgr nuclear fuels dept, Spencer Chem Co, Mo, 60-61; mgr mat appln, Gen Atomic Div, Gen Dynamics Corp, 61-70, asst mgr uranium mkt, Gulf Gen Atomic Co, 70-72, mgr indust & govt activities, Uranium Supply & Distrib, Gulf Energy & Environ Systs, 72-73; CONSULT, SCI APPLNS, INC, 73-, BATTELLE MEM INST, 74- & ENERGY, INC, 75-, GEN ATOMIC CO, 76-, MAGNESEP CORP, 78- *Mem:* Fel AAAS; Fel Am Inst Chemists; Am Chem Soc; Am Nuclear Soc. *Res:* Nuclear fuels; reprocessing; coated particle fuels. *Mailing Add:* Rte 1, M3 Del Mar CA 92014

MATHESON, BALLEM HOWARD, bacteriology, see previous edition

MATHESON, DE LOSS H(EALY), b Ont, Feb 3, 08; m 42; c 1. ENGINEERING. *Educ:* Univ Toronto, BASc, 29, MASc, 31. *Prof Exp:* Chemist & bacteriologist, Hamilton Filtration Plant, 33-55; dir, Munic Labs, City Hamilton, 55-72; CONSULT, 72- *Mem:* Am Chem Soc; Am Water Works Asn; Air Pollution Control Asn; fel Chem Inst Can. *Res:* Water purification; water and air pollution. *Mailing Add:* 78 Mountain Ave Hamilton ON L8P 4G2 Can

MATHESON, WILLARD EDWARD, b Penticton, BC, Mar 6, 19; nat US; m 53; c 2. PHYSICS. *Educ:* Univ BC, BA & BASc, 47; Purdue Univ, MS, 49, PhD(physics), 54. *Prof Exp:* Res engr, Powell River Paper Co, Can, 47; asst physics, Purdue Univ, 47-48; res engr, Linde Air Prod Co Div, Union Carbide Corp, 54-56; engr, Douglas Aircraft Co, Inc, 56-58, adv systs engr, 58-60, exec adv, 60-61; dir eng, Acoustica Assocs, Inc, 61, vpres & gen mgr, 62-63; chief adv systs engr nuclear proj, Douglas Aircraft Co, Inc, 63-64, chief engr future systs, 64, dir new bus develop, 64-65, dir, Donald W Douglas Labs, Douglas Aircraft Co, Inc, 65-75; pres Life Systs Inc, 73-79; PRES SPINOR CORP, RICHLAND, WASH, 79- *Concurrent Pos:* Mem, Atomic Indust Forum; mem, Wash State Adv Coun Nuclear Energy & Radiation, & 68-; consult engr, 73- *Mem:* Am Phys Soc; Am Nuclear Soc; Sigma Xi. *Res:* Nuclear power systems; space systems development; electrical engineering; solid state energy conversion. *Mailing Add:* 119 Jackson Ct Richland WA 99352

MATHEW, MATHAI, b Mavelikara, India; US citizen; m 67. X-RAY CRYSTALLOGRAPHY, INORGANIC CHEMISTRY. *Educ:* Univ Kerala, India, BS, 53; Univ Agra, India, MS, 56; Univ Western Ont, PhD(chem), 66. *Prof Exp:* Lectr chem, Cath Col, India, 56-58 & 60-62; res asst, Atomic Energy Estab, India, 58-60; fel, Nat Res Coun Can, 65-67, Univ Waterloo, 67-70; res assoc, Univ Fla, 70-74; res assoc chem, 75-77, CHIEF RES SCIENTIST, DIV CRYSTALLOG, AM DENT ASN HEALTH FOUND, RES UNIT, NAT BUR STANDARDS, 77- *Mem:* Am Chem Soc; Am Crystallog Asn; Int Asn Dent Res. *Res:* X-ray crystallographic structural studies of dental materials and of compounds related to constituents of tooth, bone and dental calculus; phosphate minerals; substituted apatites. *Mailing Add:* Am Dent Asn Health Found Nat Bur of Stand Washington DC 20234

MATHEWES, DAVID A, b Gastonia, NC, Sept 22, 31; m 57; c 4. ORGANIC CHEMISTRY. *Educ:* Davidson Col, BS, 53; Univ Kans, MS, 55; Duke Univ, PhD(chem), 63. *Prof Exp:* Teaching asst chem, Univ Kans, 53-55; instr, Ga Inst Technol, 55-57; instr, Hampden-Sydney Col, 57-58; res asst, Duke Univ, 58-62; asst prof, 62-67, head dept, 67-69, PROF CHEM, WESTERN CAROLINA UNIV, 67- *Concurrent Pos:* Instr, Westminster Schs, 56-57; vis prof, Univ Stirling, 77-78. *Mem:* AAAS; Am Chem Soc; Sigma Xi; Royal Soc Chem. *Res:* Organophosphorus and organo-metallic chemistry; curriculum development; science education. *Mailing Add:* Dept of Chem Western Carolina Univ Cullowhee NC 28723

MATHEWES, ROLF WALTER, b Berleburg, WGer, Nov 11, 46; Can citizen; m 72. PALYNOLOGY. *Educ:* Simon Fraser Univ, B C, Can, BSc; Univ BC, PhD(bot). *Prof Exp:* Vis asst prof biogeog, Simon Fraser Univ, 73; Nat Res Coun fel palynology, Sch Bot, Cambridge Univ, Eng, 74; environ consult plant ecol, F F Slaney & Co Ltd, Vancouver, 74-75; vis asst prof, 74, ASST PROF BIOL, SIMON FRASER UNIV, 75- *Concurrent Pos:* Environ consult plant ecol, F F Slaney & Co Ltd, Vancouver, 74-75. *Mem:* Brit Ecol Soc; Can Bot Asn. *Res:* Palynology and paleoecology of postglacial vegetation; application of pollen analysis to archaeological and zoological problems. *Mailing Add:* Simon Fraser Univ Burnaby BC V5A 1S6 Can

MATHEWS, A L, b Whittier, NC, Mar 28, 40; m 60; c 3. CHEMISTRY. *Educ:* Western Carolina Univ, BS, 61; Univ Miss, PhD(phys chem), 65. *Prof Exp:* Asst prof phys chem, Western Carolina Univ, 65-69; admin asst biochem, Mich State Univ, 69-76; ADMIN MGR, DEPT CHEM, OHIO STATE UNIV, 76- *Mem:* AAAS; Am Chem Soc. *Res:* Research administration; communication and information exchange in solving significant problems; use of computers in designing experiments; thermodynamics of multiple phase systems. *Mailing Add:* Dept of Chem Ohio State Univ Columbus OH 43210

MATHEWS, BRUCE EUGENE, b Peru, Ill, June 1, 29; m 58; c 4. ELECTRICAL ENGINEERING. *Educ:* Univ Fla, BEE, 52, MSE, 53, PhD(elec eng), 64. *Prof Exp:* Engr, NAm Aviation, Inc, 55-56; asst prof elec eng, Univ Fla, 56-57, res assoc, 57-64, assoc prof, 64-69; chmn dept elec eng & commun sci, 69-78, PROF ELEC ENG & COMMUN SCI, UNIV CENTRAL FLA, 69-, ASST DEAN ENG, 78- *Concurrent Pos:* Consult, Vitro Corp Am, 57, Ohio State Res Found, 58, Northrop Corp, 59, Lockheed Missile & Space Co, 60 & Scott Aviation Corp, 62-63. *Mem:* Inst Elec & Electronics Engrs. *Res:* Electromagnetic fields; sensory aids for the handicapped; hybrid computers; creative problem solving. *Mailing Add:* Col Eng Univ Central Fla Orlando FL 32816

MATHEWS, CHRISTOPHER KING, b New York, NY, May 5, 37; m 60; c 2. BIOCHEMISTRY. *Educ:* Reed Col, BA, 58; Univ Wash, PhD(biochem), 62. *Prof Exp:* Asst prof biol, Yale Univ, 63-67; assoc prof, Univ Ariz, 67-73, prof biochem, Col Med, 73-77; PROF & CHMN DEPT BIOCHEM & BIOPHYSICS, ORE STATE UNIV, 78- *Concurrent Pos:* USPHS fel biochem, Univ Pa, 62-63; Am Cancer Soc scholar, Univ Calif, San Diego, 73-74; mem & chmn, virol & microbiol chem study sect, NIH, 73-81. *Mem:* AAAS; Am Soc Biol Chem; Am Soc Cell Biol; Am Soc Microbiol; Am Chem

Soc. *Res:* Microbial and viral enzymology; DNA precursor metabolism and its regulation; mechanism of action of antimetabolites; enzymatic aspects of bacteriophage structure and replication; metabolism of coenzymes, nucleotides, and nucleic acids. *Mailing Add:* Dept of Biochem & Biophysics Ore State Univ Corvallis OR 97331

MATHEWS, COLLIS WELDON, b Troy, Ala, July 19, 38; m 59; c 2. PHYSICAL CHEMISTRY, MOLECULAR SPECTROSCOPY. *Educ:* Univ Ala, BS, 60; Vanderbilt Univ, PhD(phys chem), 65. *Prof Exp:* Res assoc ultraviolet spectros, Vanderbilt Univ, 64-65; fel div pure physics, Nat Res Coun Can, 65-67; asst prof, 67-72, ASSOC PROF PHYS CHEM, OHIO STATE UNIV, 72- *Mem:* Am Chem Soc; fel Optical Soc Am. *Res:* Investigations of high-resolution visible and ultraviolet molecular spectra for the purposes of obtaining their geometric and electronic structures especially of unstable molecular species. *Mailing Add:* Dept of Chem Ohio State Univ 140 W 18th Ave Columbus OH 43210

MATHEWS, DONALD R(ICHARD), b Madera, Calif, Nov 23, 31; m 58; c 3. NUCLEAR ENGINEERING. *Educ:* Univ Calif, Berkeley, BS, 58, MS, 59; Mass Inst Technol, PhD(nuclear eng), 66. *Prof Exp:* Nuclear engr, Aerojet Gen Nucleonics, Calif, 59-61, sr nuclear engr, Univ Idaho, 61-62; staff assoc thermionic reactor design, Gen Atomic Div, Gen Dynamics Corp, 66-67; staff mem, Gulf Gen Atomic Inc, 67-70, mgr, 70-72, mem staff, 72-78, SR STAFF MEM, REACTOR PHYSICS METHODS DEVELOP BR, GULF GEN ATOMIC CO, 78- *Mem:* Am Nuclear Soc. *Res:* Nuclear reactor physics methods development, both analytic and computational aspects; neutron cross section evaluation and processing; gas-cooled thermal and fast reactor design; thermionic reactor design. *Mailing Add:* 4961 Lamont Pacific Beach CA 92109

MATHEWS, FRANCIS SCOTT, b Albany, Ore, Mar 2, 34; m 59; c 3. BIOCHEMISTRY. *Educ:* Univ Calif, BS, 55; Univ Minn, Minneapolis, PhD(phys chem), 59. *Prof Exp:* Corp fel chem, Harvard Univ, 59-61; USPHS res fel biol, Mass Inst Technol, 61-63; spec fel protein crystallog, Lab Molecular Biol, 63-65, assoc 66-80, PROF PHYSIOL & BIOPHYS, SCH MED, WASHINGTON UNIV, 80- *Mem:* Am Crystallog Asn; Biophys Soc; Am Chem Soc. *Res:* X-ray crystallographic study of biological materials, especially the structure and function of cytochromes and flavoenzymes. *Mailing Add:* Dept of Physiol & Biophys Wash Univ Sch of Med St Louis MO 63110

MATHEWS, FREDERICK JOHN, b Columbus, Wis, Dec 20, 18; m 52; c 2. ORGANIC CHEMISTRY. *Educ:* Carroll Col, BA, 40; Univ Wis, PhD(org chem), 43. *Prof Exp:* Asst, Univ Wis, 41-43; res chemist, Rohm & Haas Co, Pa, 43-46; asst prof chem, Kent State Univ, 46-47; from asst prof to assoc prof, Beloit Col, 47-59; PRES, LAB CRAFTSMEN INC, 59- *Mem:* Am Chem Soc. *Res:* Benzoquinoline compounds synthesis; silicones; design and manufacture of scientific equipment. *Mailing Add:* 2925 Bartells Dr Beloit WI 53511

MATHEWS, GEOFFREY WILLIAM, b Urbana, Ill, July 28, 38; m 61; c 2. PETROLOGY, GEOLOGY. *Educ:* Lawrence Univ, BA, 60; Case Western Reserve Univ, PhD(geol), 69. *Prof Exp:* Teacher pub sch, Conn, 62-64; asst prof, 67-74, assoc prof geol, Ind Univ, Ft Wayne, 74-77; geoscientist, Bendix Field Eng Corp, 77-78, asst dir, 78-81; VPRES, TERRADATA, GOLDEN, CO, 81- *Res:* Geochemical variability in epizonal igneous plutons. *Mailing Add:* 7555 W 10th Ave Ste 200 Lakewood CO 80215

MATHEWS, HARRY T, b Atlanta, Ga, Nov 13, 31; m 59; c 3. MATHEMATICS. *Educ:* Ga Inst Technol, BS, 59; Tulane Univ, PhD(math), 64. *Prof Exp:* Asst prof math, Wayne State Univ, 63-65; from asst prof to prof, math & head dept, 65-73, PROF MATH, UNIV TENN, KNOXVILLE, 73- *Mem:* Am Math Soc; Math Asn Am. *Res:* Boundary behavior of functions of a complex variable. *Mailing Add:* Dept of Math Univ of Tenn Knoxville TN 37916

MATHEWS, HENRY MABBETT, b Thomasville, Ga, May 19, 40; m 62; c 3. MEDICAL PARASITOLOGY. *Educ:* Univ Ga, BS, 62; Emory Univ, MS, 65, PhD(biol), 67. *Prof Exp:* Resident microbiol, Nat Commun Dis Ctr, 67-69; RES MICROBIOLOGIST, CTR DIS CONTROL, 69- *Mem:* Am Soc Parasitologists; Am Soc Trop Med & Hyg; Sigma Xi. *Res:* Serology and sero-epidemiology of parasitic diseases. *Mailing Add:* 1192 Denison Dr Clarkstown GA 30021

MATHEWS, JEROLD CHASE, b Des Moines, Iowa, Sept 12, 30; m 59; c 2. MATHEMATICS. *Educ:* Iowa State Univ, BS, 55, MS, 57, PhD(math), 59. *Prof Exp:* Asst prof math, Univ Okla, 60-61; mathematician, Mathematica, Inc, NJ, 61-62; from asst prof to assoc prof, 62-65, PROF MATH, IOWA STATE UNIV, 70- *Mem:* AAAS; Math Asn Am; Am Math Soc; Hist Sci Soc. *Res:* History of mathematics. *Mailing Add:* Dept of Math Iowa State Univ Ames IA 50011

MATHEWS, JOHN DAVID, b Kenton, Ohio, Apr 3, 47; m 69; c 2. IONOSPHERIC PHYSICS, RADAR SIGNAL PROCESSING. *Educ:* Case Inst Technol, BS, 69; Case Western Reserve Univ, MS, 72, PhD(elec eng), 72. *Prof Exp:* Res assoc, 72-73, sr res assoc, 73-75, asst prof, 75-79, ASSOC PROF ELEC ENG & APPL PHYSICS, CASE WESTERN RESERVE UNIV, 79- *Concurrent Pos:* Vis scientist, Nat Astron & Ionosphere Ctr, Puerto Rico, 72-75; adj prof & asst mem grad fac, Elec Eng Dept & Ionosphere Res Lab, Pa State Univ, 78-; consult, Nat Astron & Ionosphere Ctr, 78-; Sigma Xi Res Award, Case Western Reserve Univ, 79. *Mem:* Am Geophys Union; Sigma Xi; Int Union Radio Scientists. *Res:* Experimental and theoretical investigation of the physics and chemistry of the earth's upper atmosphere and ionosphere; radar scattering theory and signal processing; electromagnetic theory. *Mailing Add:* Glennan Bldg Rm 515 Case Western Reserve Univ Cleveland OH 44106

MATHEWS, JON, theoretical physics, deceased

MATHEWS, JOSEPH F(RANKLIN), b Rochester, NY, Nov 28, 33; m 67; c 2. CHEMICAL ENGINEERING. *Educ:* Univ Rochester, BS, 55; Univ Tex, MS, 57, PhD(chem eng), 60. *Prof Exp:* Res engr, Synthetic Rubber Div, Shell Chem Co, 60-66; asst prof chem & chem eng, 66-68, assoc prof, 68-74, PROF CHEM ENG, UNIV SASK, 74- *Mem:* Am Inst Chem Engrs; Am Chem Soc; Can Soc Chem Engrs. *Res:* Reaction kinetics and catalysis; reactor design; alternative uses for bio-mass. *Mailing Add:* Dept of Chem & Chem Eng Univ of Sask Saskatoon OK S7N 0W0 Can

MATHEWS, KENNETH PINE, b Schenectady, NY, Apr 1, 21; m 52, 75; c 3. ALLERGY, INTERNAL MEDICINE. *Educ:* Univ Mich, AB, 41, MD, 43. *Prof Exp:* From asst prof to assoc prof, 51-61, PROF INTERNAL MED, UNIV MICH, 61- *Concurrent Pos:* Consult, Ann Arbor Vet Admin Hosp & Wayne County Gen Hosp, 60-; ed, J Allergy & Clin Immunol, 68-72; mem training grant comt, Nat Inst Allergy & Infectious Dis, 71-73; chmn allergy & immunol res comt, NIH, 73-75; mem, Am Bd Allergy & Immunol, 77- *Honors & Awards:* Distinguished Serv Award, Am Acad Allergy, 76. *Mem:* Am Acad Allergy (pres, 64-65); Am Col Physicians; Am Asn Immunologists; Am Thoracic Soc. *Res:* Basic and clinical research in allergy; mechanisms of urticaria and augioedema; nasal responses to allergens and irritants; clinical pharmacology of drugs used in allergy. *Mailing Add:* Univ of Mich Med Ctr Box 27 D3259 S A C B Ann Arbor MI 48109

MATHEWS, LARRY ARTHUR, b Bremerton, Wash, Mar 23, 36; m 71; c 2. ATMOSPHERIC SCIENCES, AEROSOL PHYSICS. *Educ:* Univ Wash, BS, 59; Univ Utah, ME, 69, PhD(chem eng), 70. *Prof Exp:* Asst engr, Ga-Pac Corp, 58; technologist, Shell Oil Co, 59-60; assoc engr chem milling res, Boeing Co, 61; res assoc chem eng, Univ Utah, 64-69; res chem engr atmospheric & aerosol physics, 70-79, RES PHYS CHEMIST AEROSOL CHEM & PHYS, NAVAL WEAPONS CTR, 80- *Concurrent Pos:* Consult dust storms, Great Basin Unified Air Pollution Control Dist & Inyo County Dist Atty Off, 76-78. *Mem:* Sigma Xi; AAAS; Am Asn Aerosol Res. *Res:* Weather modification; rate of solution of ice nuclei in water drops; collection efficiencies of cloud drops; cloud and aerosol physics; air pollution; desert dust storms; fluid flow; earth sciences; both theoretical and experimental work; military smoke and obscurants. *Mailing Add:* Detonation Physics Div Naval Weapons Ctr Code 383 China Lake CA 93555

MATHEWS, M(AX) V(ERNON), b Columbus, Nebr, Nov 13, 26; m 47; c 3. ELECTRICAL ENGINEERING, COMPUTER SCIENCES. *Educ:* Calif Inst Technol, BS, 50; Mass Inst Technol, ScD, 54. *Prof Exp:* mem tech staff, 55-61, head, 61-62, DIR, BELL LABS, 62- *Concurrent Pos:* Sci adv, Inst de Recherche et Coord Acoustique/Musique, Paris, France, 74-80. *Honors & Awards:* David Sarnoff Gold Medal, Inst Elec & Electronics Engrs, 73. *Mem:* Nat Acad Sci; Nat Acad Eng; Inst Elec & Electronics Engrs; Audio Eng Soc; Acoust Soc Am. *Res:* Speech coding; computer music; digital computer technology. *Mailing Add:* Bell Tel Labs Murray Hill NJ 07974

MATHEWS, ROBERT THOMAS, b Indianapolis, Ind, Aug 30, 19; m 52; c 4. ASTRONOMY. *Educ:* Wesleyan Univ, BA, 40; Univ Calif, MA, 54. *Prof Exp:* From jr astronr to asst astronr, US Naval Observ, 42-44; observing asst, Lick Observ, Mt Hamilton, 47-48; instr astron, Wesleyan Univ, 48-54; from instr to asst prof astron & math, 54-67, assoc prof, 67-81, PROF ASTRON, CARLETON COL, 81- *Mem:* AAAS; Am Astron Soc; Sigma Xi; Am Asn Univ Professors. *Res:* Stellar parallax; photoelectric and spectroscopic study of galactic star clusters; visual double stars; history of science. *Mailing Add:* Dept of Physics & Astron Carleton Col Northfield MN 55057

MATHEWS, W(ARREN) E(DWARD), b Osborne, Kans, Nov 10, 21; m 49, 71; c 3. PHYSICS, ELECTRICAL ENGINEERING. *Educ:* Ohio Wesleyan Univ, AB, 42; Mass Inst Technol, BS & MS, 44; Calif Inst Technol, PhD(physics), 53. *Prof Exp:* Mem tech staff, Radio Res Dept, Bell Tel Labs, Inc, NJ, 46-49; mem tech staff, 50-54, head adv planning staff, 54-57, corp dir planning, 57-60, dir infrared labs, 60-66, assoc dir res & develop div, 62-66, mgr missile systs div, 66-70, assoc mgr systs div, 70-71, mgr equip eng div, 71-74, asst group exec, Electro-Optical & Data Systs Group, 74-75, corp dir, 75-82, STAFF VPRES, PROD EFFECTIVENESS, HUGHES AIRCRAFT CO, 82- *Concurrent Pos:* Mem nat exec comt, Infrared Info Symp, 60-65; mem bd dir, Santa Barbara Res Ctr, 60-66; gen chmn, Winter Conv Aerospace & Electronic Systs, 71; mem bd gov, Electronic Indust Asn, 76- *Mem:* Fel Inst Elec & Electronics Engrs; assoc fel Am Inst Aeronaut & Astronaut. *Res:* Guided missile systems analysis; infrared systems; microwave communication; traveling-wave amplification. *Mailing Add:* 1010 Centinela Ave Santa Monica CA 90403

MATHEWS, WALTER KELLY, b Columbus, Ga, Jan 16, 37; m; c 3. ORGANIC CHEMISTRY, BIOCHEMISTRY. *Educ:* Univ Ga, BS, 60, MS, 61; Univ Louisville, PhD(chem), 67. *Prof Exp:* Chemist, Sinclair Res, Inc, Ill, 61-63; instr gen chem, Wingate Col, 63-64; vis instr org chem, Univ Louisville, 65-66; ASSOC PROF ORG CHEM, GA SOUTHWESTERN COL, 67- *Mem:* Am Chem Soc. *Res:* Cationic polymerization mechanisms; selected oxidation processes; mechanisms of counterion binding to colloids and surfactants. *Mailing Add:* Dept of Org Chem Ga Southwestern Col Americus GA 31709

MATHEWS, WILLIAM HENRY, b Vancouver, BC, Feb 2, 19; m 48; c 3. GEOLOGY. *Educ:* Univ BC, BASc, 40, MASc, 41; Univ Calif, PhD(geol), 48. *Prof Exp:* Assoc mining engr, BC Dept Mines, Can, 42-49; asst prof geol, Univ Calif, 49-51; assoc prof, 51-59, head dept, 64-71, PROF GEOL, UNIV BC, 59- *Concurrent Pos:* Nat Res Coun Can sr fel, 63-64; mem, Can Nat Comt for Int Hydrologic Decade, 64-; mem, Int Comt Marine Geol, 66-; mem, Can Nat Adv Comt Res Geol Sci, 67-69; chmn standing comt solid earth sci, Pac Sci Asn, 67-71; Killam sr fel, 71-72. *Mem:* Fel Geol Soc Am; Am Asn Petrol Geologists; Royal Soc Can; Geol Asn Can; Glaciol Soc; Int Soc Soil Mech & Found Eng. *Res:* Geomorphology and glacial geology; glaciology, sedimentology and geological oceanography; sub-glacial vulcanism. *Mailing Add:* Dept of Geol Univ of BC Vancouver BC V6T 1W5 Can

MATHEWS, WILLIS WOODROW, b Wendling, Ore, May 27, 17; m 42; c 3. EMBRYOLOGY. *Educ:* Ore State Col, BA, 40; Univ Wis, PhD(zool), 45. *Prof Exp:* Asst zool, Univ Wis, 40-44; from instr to asst prof biol, Univ Chattanooga, 44-47; asst prof, 47-56, from actg chmn dept to chmn dept, 62-65, ASSOC PROF BIOL, WAYNE STATE UNIV, 56- *Concurrent Pos:* Vis lectr, Oakland Univ, 74-75 & 82. *Mem:* AAAS; Am Soc Zool. *Res:* Experimental embryology of chick; microscopy; growth factors; descriptive embryology. *Mailing Add:* Dept of Biol Wayne State Univ Detroit MI 48202

MATHEWSON, CHRISTOPHER COLVILLE, b Plainfield, NJ, Aug 12, 41; c 2. GEOLOGY. *Educ:* Case Inst Technol, BS, 63; Univ Ariz, MS, 65, PhD(geol eng), 71. *Prof Exp:* Asst prof, 71-77, assoc prof, 77-82, PROF GEOL, TEX A&M UNIV, 82- *Concurrent Pos:* Instr geol eng, Univ Ariz, 71; consult, 71- *Honors & Awards:* Claire P Holdredge Award, Asn Eng Geologists, 81. *Mem:* Asn Eng Geologists; Am Soc Civil Engrs; Geol Soc Am; Am Inst Mining Engrs; Am Geophys Union. *Res:* Engineering geology applied to coal mining, urban development, hazardous geologic processes, and natural resources. *Mailing Add:* Dept Geol Tex A&M Univ College Station TX 77843

MATHEWSON, FRANCIS ALEXANDER LAVENS, b New Westminster, BC, Feb 1, 05; m 36; c 2. INTERNAL MEDICINE. *Educ:* Univ Man, MD, 31, BSc, 33; Am Bd Prev Med, dipl & cert aviation med, 54; FRCP, 81. *Prof Exp:* ASSOC PROF MED, FAC MED, UNIV MAN, 45- *Concurrent Pos:* Physician, Winnipeg Gen Hosp, mem attend staff, 35, chmn, 51-52; mem asn comt aviation med res, Nat Res Coun Can, 42-44; mem panel aviation med res, Defense Res Bd, Can, 50-54; chmn, Royal Can Air Force Med Adv Comt, 54; fel coun clin cardiol, Am Heart Asn; Col Physicians & Surgeons Man Gordon Bell res fel, 33-34. *Honors & Awards:* Medal of Courage, Order Can. *Mem:* Fel Am Col Cardiol; Asn Life Ins Med Dirs (pres, 68-69); Can Cardiovasc Soc (pres, 57-58); Can Life Ins Med Off Asn (pres, 55-56); Defense Med Asn Can (pres, 54-55). *Res:* Cardiology; prospective epidemiological study of coronary heart disease. *Mailing Add:* 711 Med Arts Bldg 233 Kennedy St Winnipeg MB R3C 3J5 Can

MATHEWSON, JAMES H, b Norwalk, Conn, Nov 24, 29; m 58; c 3. BIO-ORGANIC CHEMISTRY, OCEANOGRAPHY. *Educ:* Harvard Univ, AB, 51; Johns Hopkins Univ, MA, 57, PhD(org chem), 59. *Prof Exp:* Res assoc chem, Johns Hopkins Univ, 59-60; guest investr, Rockefeller Inst, 60-61; res fel, Univ Calif, Berkeley, 61-63; asst prof chem, Western Wash State Col, 63-64; from asst prof to assoc prof, 64-72, PROF CHEM, SAN DIEGO STATE UNIV, 72- *Concurrent Pos:* USPHS fel, 60-63; Nat Inst Arthritis & Metab Dis res grant, 65-68, NSF sea grant prog res grant, 69-70; Nat Oceanic & Atmospheric Admin res grant, 70-71; actg dir, Bur Marine Sci, San Diego State Univ, 67-70; vis scientist, Lab Chem Enzyme Shell Res, Sittingbourne, Kent, UK, 74-75. *Mem:* AAAS; Am Chem Soc. *Res:* Organic and biological chemistry, especially tetrapyrroles; environmental chemistry, especially oceanic; science education, especially general education and interdisciplinary courses; chlorophyll chemistry; marine biochemistry; pollution measurement. *Mailing Add:* Dept of Chem San Diego State Univ San Diego CA 92182

MATHEWSON, WILFRED FAIRBANKS, JR, b Quincy, Mass, July 25, 33; m 53; c 4. CHEMICAL ENGINEERING, PHYSICAL CHEMISTRY. *Educ:* Univ NH, BS, 55; Rensselaer Polytech Inst, MS, 58; Cornell Univ, PhD(chem eng, phys chem), 62. *Prof Exp:* Engr, Gen Elec Co, 55-58; instr chem eng, Cornell Univ, 60-61; asst prof, State Univ NY Buffalo, 61-64; sr develop engr, Specialty Mat Dept, Gen Elec Co, 64-66, mgr abrasive systs, 66-67, mgr mkt develop man-made diamond, 67-68, mgr electrochem eng projs, Res & Develop Ctr, 68-69, mgr cardiopulmonary support systs, Med Develop Oper, 69-77; venture mgr, 77-78, vpres res & develop, Med Prod Div, Sybron Corp, 78- *Concurrent Pos:* Consult, Carborundum Co, NY, 61-63. *Mem:* Am Inst Chem Engrs; Asn Adv Med Inst; AAAS; NY Acad Sci. *Res:* Mass and heat transfer in reaction processes; surface chemistry. *Mailing Add:* 81 Ann Lee Dr North Rose NY 14516

MATHEWS-ROTH, MICHELINE MARY, b Mineola, NY, July 26, 34; m 66; c 1. DERMATOLOGY, MICROBIOLOGY. *Educ:* Col St Elizabeth, BS, 56; NY Univ, MD, 61. *Prof Exp:* Res assoc med & microbiol, 65-69, assoc microbiol & molecular genetics, 69-74, PRIN RES ASSOC MED, CHANNING LAB, HARVARD MED SCH, 74- *Concurrent Pos:* Borden res award, Sch Med, NY Univ, 61; NSF fel, Univ Calif, Berkeley, 61-62 & Harvard Univ, 63-65; intern path, Boston City Hosp, 62-63; grants, Med Found, 66-69, NSF, 68-71, NIH, 70, 78 & 75-; assoc ed, Photochem & Photobiol J, Am Soc Photobiol, 74- *Mem:* Am Soc Photobiol; Am Soc Microbiol; Soc Invest Dermat; Am Fedn Clin Res; Am Soc Clin Invest. *Res:* Photobiology; porphyrias; carotenoid pigments. *Mailing Add:* Channing Lab 180 Longwood Ave Boston MA 02115

MATHIAS, JOSEPH SIMON, b Bombay, India, Oct 28, 25; US citizen; m 56. METALLURGY. *Educ:* Univ Bombay, BS, 44, AB, 46, MS, 48; Univ Calif, MMetE, 51; Lehigh Univ, PhD(metall), 56. *Prof Exp:* Teaching asst physics, Univ Bombay, 44-48; res asst chem, Lehigh Univ, 51-52, res assoc metall, 52-54; chief metallurgist, Superior Metal Corp, 55-56; sr res engr, Jones & Laughlin Steel Corp, 56; group supvr metall, Foote Mineral Co, 56-59; sect mgr mat & processes, 59-66, dept mgr physics & mat, 66-67, dir res, 67-68, dir res & adv techniques, Univac Div, Sperry Rand Corp, 68-79, DIR MFG & HARDWARE RES, SPERRY-UNIVAC, 79- *Concurrent Pos:* Consult, Superior Metal Co, 52-55 & F J Stokes Mach Co, 57-58; lectr, Lehigh Univ, 55-56. *Mem:* Electrochem Soc; Inst Elec & Electronics Engrs; NY Acad Sci. *Res:* Materials and devices for computer memories and peripherals; manufacturing technologies involving electrodeposition, vacuum deposition and sputtering. *Mailing Add:* Sperry Univac PO Box 500 Blue Bell PA 19424

MATHIAS, MELVIN MERLE, b Columbia City, Ind, Feb 22, 39; m 63; c 3. NUTRITION. *Educ:* Purdue Univ, BS, 61; Cornell Univ, PhD(nutrit), 67. *Prof Exp:* Asst nutrit, Cornell Univ, 62-66; asst prof, 68-77, assoc prof, 77-81, PROF NUTRIT, COLO STATE UNIV, 81- *Concurrent Pos:* Fac partic, AEC prog, Donner Lab, Univ Calif, Berkeley, 71; sabbatical, Dept Biochem Nutrit, Hoffmann-La Roche, 74-75 & Dept Human Nutrit, Unilever Res Lab, Netherlands, 81. *Mem:* AAAS; Am Inst Nutrit; Am Oil Chem Soc; Sigma Xi. *Res:* Effects of diet and vitamin deficiencies on intermediary and prostaglandin metabolism. *Mailing Add:* Dept Food Sci & Nutrit Colo State Univ Ft Collins CO 80523

MATHIAS, MILDRED ESTHER (MRS GERALD L HASSLER), b Sappington, Mo, Sept 19, 06; m 30; c 4. BOTANY. *Educ:* Wash Univ, AB, 26, MS, 27, PhD(syst bot), 29. *Prof Exp:* Asst, Mo Bot Garden, 29-30; res assoc, NY Bot Garden, 32-36 & Univ Calif, 37-42; herbarium botanist, 47-51, lectr bot, 51-55, from asst prof to prof, 55-74, dir bot garden, Exp Sta, 56-74, EMER PROF BOT, UNIV CALIF, LOS ANGELES, 74- *Concurrent Pos:* Asst specialist, Bot Garden, Exp Sta, Univ Calif, Los Angeles, 51-55, asst plant systematist, 55-57, vchmn bot garden, 55-62 & assoc plant systematist, 57-62; pres, Orgn Trop Studies, 68-70; Secy, Bd of Trustees, Inst Ecol, 75-77. *Honors & Awards:* Merit Award, Bot Soc Am, 73; Sci Citation, Am Hort Soc, 74; Liberty Hyde Bailey Medal, Am Hort Soc, 80. *Mem:* AAAS; Bot Soc Am; Am Soc Plant Taxon (pres, 64); Soc Study Evolution; Am Soc Naturalists. *Res:* Classification of plants of western United States; monographic studies of the Umbelliferae, especially of North and South America; subtropical ornamental plants; tropical medicinal plants. *Mailing Add:* Dept of Biol Univ of Calif Los Angeles CA 90024

MATHIAS, ROBERT A(DDISON), b Monte Vista, Colo, Jan 14, 27; m 48; c 2. ELECTRICAL ENGINEERING. *Educ:* Univ Colo, BS, 47; Univ Pittsburgh, MS, 49; Carnegie Inst Technol, PhD(elec eng), 55. *Prof Exp:* Engr, Spec Prod Dept, Westinghouse Elec Corp, 47-49; from instr to asst prof elec eng, Carnegie Inst Technol, 51-61; consult, 59-61, adv engr, 61-67, MGR SYST SCI, WESTINGHOUSE RES LABS, 61-, MGR SYSTS SIMULATION & CONTROL, 67- *Concurrent Pos:* NSF fel, 57-59. *Mem:* Sr mem Inst Elec & Electronics Engrs; Inst Mgt Sci; NAm Soc Corp Planning; Am Forestry Asn. *Res:* Magnetic amplifiers; switching and logic control; computer control of real-time systems; systems engineering; planning techniques for urban and social systems; business and technology analysis; industrial strategy planning; image understanding. *Mailing Add:* 216 Thornberry Dr Pittsburgh PA 15235

MATHIASON, DENNIS R, b Fairmont, Minn, Feb 6, 41; m 63; c 2. INORGANIC CHEMISTRY, INSTRUMENTAL ANALYSIS. *Educ:* Mankato State Col, BS, 62; Univ SDak, PhD(chem), 66. *Prof Exp:* PROF CHEM, MOORHEAD STATE UNIV, 66- *Mem:* Am Chem Soc. *Res:* Analytical studies. *Mailing Add:* Dept of Chem Moorhead State Univ Moorhead MN 56560

MATHIES, ALLEN WRAY, JR, b Colorado Springs, Colo, Sept 23, 30; m 56; c 2. PEDIATRICS, INFECTIOUS DISEASES. *Educ:* Colo Col, BA, 52; Columbia Univ, MS, 56, PhD(parasitol), 58; Univ Vt, MD, 61. *Prof Exp:* Res assoc path, Col Med, Univ Vt, 57-61, from intern to resident pediat, Los Angeles Co Gen Hosp, 61-64; res assoc, 63-64, from asst prof to prof, 64-71, assoc dean, Sch Med, 70-74, interim dean, 74-75, DEAN SCH MED, UNIV SOUTHERN CALIF, 75-, PROF PEDIAT, 71- *Concurrent Pos:* Head physician commun dis, Los Angeles Co Gen Hosp, 64-75. *Mem:* Am Soc Parasitol; Am Soc Trop Med & Hyg; Soc Pediat Res; Infectious Dis Soc Am; Royal Soc Trop Med & Hyg. *Res:* Infectious diseases; central nervous system infections; tropical medicine. *Mailing Add:* 2025 Zonal Ave Los Angeles CA 90033

MATHIES, JAMES CROSBY, b Seattle, Wash, July 20, 19; m 42; c 2. BIOCHEMISTRY. *Educ:* Univ Wash, BS, 42, PhD(biochem), 48; Wayne State Univ, MS, 46. *Prof Exp:* Develop & res chemist, US Rubber Co, 42-45; assoc, Med Sch, Univ Wash, 46-48; biochemist, Edsel B Ford Inst Med Res, Henry Ford Hosp, 48-54; sr biochemist, Baxter Labs, Inc, 54-56; chief biochemist, Swedish Hosp, Seattle, 56-66; dir lab serv div, Enzomedic Labs, Inc, Wash, 66-67; CLIN BIOCHEMIST, PATH LAB, ST JOSEPH HOSP, 67- *Concurrent Pos:* Res biochemist, Pac Northwest Res Found, 56-66; consult, Philips Electronics, 61-65. *Mem:* AAAS; Am Chem Soc; Am Soc Biol Chem; Am Asn Clin Chem; NY Acad Sci. *Res:* Hormones and tissue enzymes; proteolytic enzymes; purification and characteristics of phosphatases; clinical chemistry; x-ray spectrochemical analysis. *Mailing Add:* Path Lab St Joseph Hosp 1845 Franklin St Denver CO 80218

MATHIES, MARGARET JEAN, b Colorado Springs, Colo, June 9, 35. MICROBIOLOGY, IMMUNOLOGY. *Educ:* Colo Col, BA, 57; Case Western Reserve Univ, PhD(microbiol), 63. *Prof Exp:* Asst prof biol, Haverford Col, 62-64; vis asst prof zool, Pomona Col, 64-65; from asst prof to assoc prof biol, 65-74, PROF BIOL, JOINT SCI DEPT, CLAREMONT MEN'S, PITZER & SCRIPPS COLS, 74-, CHMN JOINT SCI DEPT, 77- *Mem:* AAAS; Am Soc Microbiol. *Res:* Antibody formation and physico-chemical characterization of antibodies, using bacteriophage antigens; cellular immunology, T and B cell interactions; biochemistry; genetics. *Mailing Add:* Joint Sci Dept 11th & Dartmouth Claremont CA 91711

MATHIESON, ALFRED HERMAN, b Union City, NJ, July 6, 17; m 41; c 5. PHYSICS. *Educ:* Pa State Teachers Col, BS, 38; Columbia Univ, MA, 39. *Prof Exp:* Instr physics, Springfield Col, 39-40; asst prof, 46-81, ASSOC PROF PHYSICS, UNIV MASS, AMHERST, 81-, ASST HEAD DEPT PHYSICS & ASTRON, 65-, SPEC ASST TO DEAN FAC NAT SCI & MATH, 79- *Concurrent Pos:* NSF grant, 64. *Mailing Add:* Dept Physics & Astron Univ Mass Amherst MA 01003

MATHIESON, ARTHUR C, b Los Angeles, Calif, Dec 26, 37; m 58; c 3. BOTANY. *Educ:* Univ Calif, Los Angeles, BA, 60, MA, 61; Univ BC, PhD, 65. *Prof Exp:* From asst prof to assoc prof, 65-74, PROF BOT, UNIV NH, 74-, DIR, JACKSON ESTUARINE LAB, 72- *Mem:* Phycol Soc Am; Int Phycol Soc. *Res:* Morphology; distribution and ecology of marine plants in relation to oceanographic factors. *Mailing Add:* Dept of Bot Jackson Estuarine Lab Univ of NH Durham NH 03824

MATHIEU, LEO GILLES, b Nicolet, Que, Jan 7, 32; m 56; c 1. BIOCHEMISTRY, MICROBIOLOGY. *Educ:* Univ Montreal, DVM, 56; Cornell Univ, MSc, 58, PhD(nutrit), 60. *Prof Exp:* Asst prof biochem, Col Vet Med, 60-65, asst prof molecular biol, Fac Med, 65-69, assoc prof microbiol, 69-72, PROF MICROBIOL, FAC MED, UNIV MONTREAL, 72- *Concurrent Pos:* Mem exec coun, Grad Sch, Univ Montreal, 71-73. *Mem:* Soc Gen Microbiol; Can Soc Microbiol; Can Vet Med Asn; Am Soc Microbiol. *Res:* Microbial physiology. *Mailing Add:* Dept of Microbiol Univ of Montreal Fac of Med Montreal PQ H3Z 3J1 Can

MATHIEU, RICHARD D(ETWILER), b Trappe, Pa, June 23, 26; m 50; c 3. COMPUTER LITERACY, RESEARCH ADMINISTRATION. *Educ:* Pa State Univ, BS, 52, MS, 54, PhD(aeronaut eng), 61. *Prof Exp:* Instr aeronaut eng, Pa State Univ, 53-61, asst prof, 61; res engr, Space Sci Lab, Missiles & Space Div, Gen Elec Co, 61-63, specialist, 63-64, supvr engr reentry data anal, Reentry Systs Dept, 64-65; prof aerospace eng & chmn, US Naval Acad, 65-67, sr prof eng, 67-70; liaison scientist, Off Naval Res London, 70-71; dir res, 71-81, DIR RES & ASSOC DEAN, US NAVAL ACAD, 81- *Concurrent Pos:* Consult, HRB-Singer, Inc, 60-61, 65-; adj prof grad ctr, Pa State Univ, 63-65. *Mem:* Am Soc Eng Educ; Sigma Xi; Nat Coun Univ Res Adminr; Soc Res Adminr. *Res:* Computers in education; reentry aerodynamics; research and development management; educational technology. *Mailing Add:* 426 Ferry Point Rd Wild Rose Shores Annapolis MD 21403

MATHIEU, ROGER MAURICE, b Montreal, Que, Aug 4, 24; m 49; c 2. RADIOLOGY, PHYSICS. *Educ:* Univ Montreal, BSc, 46, MSc, 48, PhD(physics), 52. *Prof Exp:* Radiation physicist & biophysicist, Montreal Cancer Inst & X-Ray Dept, Hosp Notre Dame, 49-69; RADIATION PHYSICIST & BIOPHYSICIST, DEPT RADIOTHER & NUCLEAR MED, MAISONNEUVE-ROSEMONT HOSP, 69-; CLIN PROF RADIOL, FAC MED, UNIV MONTREAL, 70- *Honors & Awards:* Croix de Commandeur, France. *Mem:* Fr-Can Soc Radiol; Can Asn Physicists; Can Asn Radiol. *Res:* Radiological physics; biophysics; radiotherapy; nuclear medicine. *Mailing Add:* Dept of Radiother & Nuclear Med 5415 Blvd L'Assomtion Montreal PQ H1T 2M4 Can

MATHIPRAKASAM, BALAKRISHNAN, b Virudhunagar, India, Jan 3, 42; m 72; c 1. HEAT TRANSFER, THERMODYNAMICS. *Educ:* Virudhunagar Polytech, India, LME, 61; Univ Mysore, ME, 76; Ill Inst Technol, PhD(mech eng), 80. *Prof Exp:* Lectr mech eng, Virudhunagar Polytech, India, 61-68, workshop supt, 68-74; res asst, Ill Inst Technol, 76-79; assoc energy engr, 80-81, SR ENERGY ENGR, MIDWEST RES INST, KANSAS CITY, 81- *Mem:* Assoc mem Am Soc Mech Engrs; Sigma Xi. *Res:* Heat transfer and thermodynamic analyses of new concepts and processes; energy related research in space conditioning systems and thermal energy storage devices; thermoelectric cooling applications. *Mailing Add:* 6709 W 87th St #201 Overland Park KS 66212

MATHIS, BILLY JOHN, b Henryetta, Okla, Sept 12, 32; m 57; c 2. LIMNOLOGY. *Educ:* Okla State Univ, BS, 59, MS, 63, PhD(zool), 65. *Prof Exp:* Sci teacher pub schs, Tex, 59-62; from asst prof to assoc prof, 65-72, PROF BIOL, BRADLEY UNIV, 72-, CHMN DEPT, 70- *Mem:* Am Soc Limnol & Oceanog; Ecol Soc Am. *Res:* Stream pollution; primary productivity; distribution of heavy metals in aquatic environments. *Mailing Add:* 6600 Toronado Ct Peoria IL 61614

MATHIS, H(AROLD) F(LETCHER), b Wichita Falls, Tex, July 19, 16; m 42; c 2. ELECTRICAL ENGINEERING. *Educ:* Univ Okla, BS, 39, EE, 54; Agr & Mech Col, Tex, MS, 41, EE, 52; Northwestern Univ, PhD(elec eng), 53; Western Reserve Univ, PhD, 61. *Prof Exp:* Asst, Agr & Mech Col, Tex, 40-41 & Iowa State Univ, 41; mat inspector, US Navy, 41-42; asst, Univ Chicago, 46; res elec engr, Northwestern Univ, 46-49; assoc prof elec eng, Univ Okla, 49-54; res engr, Goodyear Aircraft Corp, Ohio, 54-60; PROF ELEC ENG, OHIO STATE UNIV, 60- *Concurrent Pos:* Sr tech specialist, Rockwell Int, 62-70. *Mem:* Am Soc Eng Educ; Inst Elec & Electronics Engrs. *Mailing Add:* 2905 Halstead Rd Columbus OH 43221

MATHIS, JAMES FORREST, b Dallas, Tex, Sept 28, 25; m 48; c 2. CHEMICAL ENGINEERING. *Educ:* Tex A&M Univ, BS, 46; Univ Wis, Madison, MS, 51, PhD(chem eng), 53. *Prof Exp:* Chemist, Humble Oil & Refining, 46-50, mem staff, Exxon Co, USA, 53-61, mgr labs, 61-63, mgr spec prods, 63-66, vpres petrol res, Exxon Res & Eng, 66-68; sr vpres petrochem opers, Imp Oil Ltd, Toronto, 68-71; vpres chem res, 71-73, V PRES TECHNOL, EXXON CHEM CO, 73- *Concurrent Pos:* Dir & treas, Chem Indust Inst Toxicol, 74-; chmn mgt prog, Am Inst Chem Engrs, 78- *Mem:* Soc Chem Indust; Am Chem Soc; AAAS; Am Inst Chem Engrs; Indust Res Inst. *Res:* Petrochemical process and product technology. *Mailing Add:* Exxon Chem Co PO Box 271 Florhan Park NJ 07932

MATHIS, JAMES L, b Dayton, Tenn, Jan 30, 25; m 48; c 4. PSYCHIATRY. *Educ:* Univ Mo, 44-45; St Louis Univ, MD, 49; Am Bd Psychiat & Neurol, dipl, 68. *Prof Exp:* Rotating intern, Fitzsimons Gen Hosp, 49-50; resident, Elk City Community Hosp-Clin, Okla, 50-51; gen practr, Crossett Health Ctr, Ark, 51-52; surg asst, Elk City Community Hosp, 52-55; pvt pract, Dayton, Tenn, 55-60; resident psychiat, Med Ctr, Univ Okla, 60-63; from instr to assoc prof, Med Sch, Rutgers Univ, 68-70; prof psychiat & chmn dept, Med Col Va, 70-76; PROF & CHMN DEPT PSYCHIAT, MED SCH, E CAROLINA UNIV, 76- *Concurrent Pos:* Asst chief psychiat serv, Vet Admin, Oklahoma City, 63-64; consult, Peace Corps, 65-69, Job Corps, 68-70 & NJ Correctional Syst, 68-70; asst examr, Am Bd Psychiat & Neurol, 71-; ed, Sexuality, 72-73 & Hosp Physician, 73- *Mem:* Am Psychiat Asn; Am Psychosom Soc; Am Col Psychiat; Am Asn Prof Psychiat. *Res:* Sexuality in medicine; death and dying; drug abuse; sleep and dreams. *Mailing Add:* Dept of Psychiat Med Sch E Carolina Univ Greenville NC 27834

MATHIS, JOHN SAMUEL, b Dallas, Tex, Feb 7, 31; m 54; c 5. ASTROPHYSICS. *Educ:* Mass Inst Technol, BS, 53; Calif Inst Technol, PhD(astron), 56. *Prof Exp:* NSF res fel, Yerkes Observ, Chicago, 56-57; asst prof astron, Mich State Univ, 57-59; from asst prof to assoc prof, 59-68, PROF ASTRON, UNIV WIS-MADISON, 68- *Concurrent Pos:* Sr sci awardee, Alexander-Von-Humboldt Found, Ger, 75-76. *Mem:* Int Astron Union; Am Astron Soc; Astron Soc Pac. *Res:* Inter- stellar matter. *Mailing Add:* Dept of Astron Univ of Wis Madison WI 53706

MATHIS, PHILIP MONROE, b Paducah, Ky, June 2, 42; m 64; c 1. BIOLOGY, SCIENCE EDUCATION. *Educ:* Murray State Univ, BS, 64; Mid Tenn State Univ, MS, 67; George Peabody Col, EdS, 71; Univ Ga, EdD(sci educ), 73. *Prof Exp:* Teacher & coord sci, Illmo-Scott City Sch, Mo, 64-67; instr biol, 67-73, asst prof, 73-78, ASSOC PROF BIOL, MID TENN STATE UNIV, 78- *Concurrent Pos:* Consult, Sci Manpower, King Personnel, Inc, Tenn, 69-70; Mid Tenn State Univ grant, proj dir, Instructional Develop Proj Biol, 77-81; ed, Soc Col Sci Teachers Publ; mem, Nat Steering Comt, Soc Col Sci Teachers. *Mem:* Nat Asn Biol Teachers; Nat Sci Teachers Asn; Soc Col Sci Teachers; Nat Asn Res Sci Teaching; AAAS. *Res:* Lichens as pollution indicators; instructional development in biology; vertebrate karyology; statistical genetics. *Mailing Add:* Dept Biol Mid Tenn State Univ Murfreesboro TN 37132

MATHIS, ROBERT FLETCHER, b Wheeling, WVa, Jan 22, 46; m 71; c 1. COMPUTER SCIENCE, COMPUTER SOFTWARE SYSTEMS. *Educ:* Ohio State Univ, BSc, 65, MSc, 66, PhD(math), 69. *Prof Exp:* Asst prof comput & info sci, Ohio State Univ, 69-75, asst dean grad sch, 74-75; ASSOC PROF MATH & COMPUT SCI, OLD DOMINION UNIV, 75- *Concurrent Pos:* Consult, Robert Corp & System Develop Corp, 81- *Mem:* Inst Elec & Electronics Engrs; Asn Comput Mach; Sigma Xi. *Res:* software engineering; computer programming languages; realtime and concurrent programming; computer algorithms; functional and numerical analysis. *Mailing Add:* Dept Comput Sci Old Dominion Univ Norfolk VA 23508

MATHIS, WAYNE NEILSEN, b Price, Utah, July 10, 45; m 70; c 3. DIPTERA, SYSTEMATICS. *Educ:* Brigham Young Univ, BS, 69; Ore State Univ, PhD(entomol), 76. *Prof Exp:* Assoc cur, 76-81, CHMN, ENTOMOL, SMITHSONIAN INST, 81- *Mem:* Entomol Soc Am; Soc Systs Zool; Am Entomol Soc; Great Basin Naturalist. *Res:* Systematics of shore flies (diptera, ephydridae) and other Drosophiloidea families, with emphasis on the Neotropics and Old World. *Mailing Add:* Dept Entomol NHB 169 Smithsonian Inst Washington DC 20560

MATHISEN, OLE ALFRED, b Oslo, Norway, Feb 9, 19; nat US; m 48; c 2. POPULATION STUDIES. *Educ:* Univ Oslo, Cand Mag, 41, Cand Real, 45; Univ Wash, PhD, 55. *Prof Exp:* Assoc prof, 64-68, PROF, FISHERIES RES INST, UNIV WASH, 68- *Concurrent Pos:* Inter-Univ Comt Travel Grants fel, Moscow, 60-61; Fulbright res fel, Oslo, 65-66; consult, Food & Agr Orgn of UN, 73- *Mem:* Am Fisheries Soc; Biomet Soc; Inst Fishery Res Biol; Am Soc Limnol & Oceanog; Sigma Xi. *Res:* Population dynamics, especially of salmonoids; acoustical stock estimation; nekton in upwelling systems; Antarctic krill. *Mailing Add:* Univ of Wash Fisheries Res Inst WH-10 Seattle WA 98195

MATHISON, IAN WILLIAM, b Liverpool, Eng, Apr 17, 38. ORGANIC & MEDICINAL CHEMISTRY. *Educ:* Univ London, BPharm, 60, PhD(pharmaceut chem), 63, DSc, 76. *Prof Exp:* Res assoc pharmaceut & med chem, Col Pharm, Univ Tenn, Memphis, 63-65, from asst prof to assoc prof med chem, 65-72, prof med chem, Ctr for Health Sci, 72-76; prof med chem, 76-80, DEAN, SCH PHARM, FERRIS STATE COL, 76- *Concurrent Pos:* Prin investr, Marion Labs grant, 65-74 & Beecham Pharmaceut Res grant, 74-79; sr investr grants, NSF, 68-72 & Molecular Design Inc, 81-83. *Mem:* Royal Soc Chem; Am Acad Pharmaceut Sci; Brit Pharmaceut Soc; Am Chem Soc; Royal Inst Chem, London. *Res:* Design and synthesis of organic compounds with potential pharmacodynamic activity; influence of stereochemistry and physicochemical parameters on pharmacological potency. *Mailing Add:* Sch of Pharm Ferris State Col Big Rapids MI 49307

MATHRE, DONALD EUGENE, b Frankfort, Kans, Jan 5, 38; m 61; c 2. PLANT PATHOLOGY. *Educ:* Iowa State Univ, BS, 60; Univ Calif, Davis, PhD(plant path), 64. *Prof Exp:* Asst prof plant path, Univ Calif, Davis, 64-67; from asst prof to assoc prof, 67-72, PROF PLANT PATH, MONT STATE UNIV, 72- *Mem:* Am Phytopath Soc; Am Soc Agron. *Res:* Soil-borne diseases of cereals and forages. *Mailing Add:* Dept Plant Path Mont State Univ Bozeman MT 59717

MATHRE, OWEN BERTWELL, b Kendall Co, Ill, Nov 26, 29; m 55; c 3. ANALYTICAL CHEMISTRY. *Educ:* Harvard Univ, AB, 51; Univ Minn, PhD(anal chem), 58. *Prof Exp:* Lab helper, Minn Mining & Mfg Co, Minn, 54; res chemist, Electrochem Dept, Del, 56-58, NY, 58-63, Tenn, 63-65, Del, 65-72, staff chemist, Indust Chems Dept, 72-77, RES ASSOC CHEM FIGMENTS DEPT, E I DU PONT DE NEMOURS & CO, INC, 77- *Mem:* Am Chem Soc; Am Soc Testing & Mat; Water Pollution Control Fedn. *Res:* Electrochemistry; instrumental and colorimetric analysis; gas phase catalysis; environmental pollution monitoring. *Mailing Add:* Chem Pigments Dept E I du Pont de Nemours & Co Wilmington DE 19898

MATHSEN, RONALD M, b Minneapolis, Minn, Oct 6, 38; m 62; c 2. MATHEMATICS. *Educ:* Concordia Col, Moorhead, Minn, BA, 60; Univ Nebr, MA, 62, PhD(math), 65. *Prof Exp:* Asst prof math, Concordia Col, Moorhead, Minn, 65-67; fel, Univ Alta, 67-68, asst prof, 68-69; ASSOC PROF MATH, NDAK STATE UNIV, 69- *Concurrent Pos:* Fulbright lectr, Liberia, 73-74. *Mem:* Math Asn Am; Am Math Soc. *Res:* Boundary value problems for ordinary differential equations; generalized convex functions. *Mailing Add:* Dept of Math NDak State Univ Fargo ND 58102

MATHUR, BHAGWAN PRAKASH, chemical physics, engineering physics, see previous edition

MATHUR, CAROLYN FRANCES, b Philadelphia, Pa, Mar 12, 47; m 68; c 2. BIOCHEMISTRY, MICROBIOLOGY. *Educ:* Millersville State Col, BA, 69; Auburn Univ, PhD(biochem), 73. *Prof Exp:* Asst prof biol, Millersville State Col, 74-75; chem, Pa State Univ, Capitol Campus, 76-77; asst prof, 77-80, ASSOC PROF BIOL, YORK COL PA, 80- *Mem:* Am Soc Microbiol; Environ Mutagen Soc. *Res:* Aflatoxin B-1, mode of action, effects on microorganisms, relation to in vitro ageing of human cells, role of dimethyl sulfoxide as a reversing agent. *Mailing Add:* York Col of Pa Country Club Rd York PA 17405

MATHUR, DILIP, b Agra, India, Feb 11, 41; m 68; c 2. FISH BIOLOGY. *Educ:* Univ Delhi, India, BSc, 61, MSc, 64; Cornell Univ, MS, 68; Auburn Univ, PhD(fishery mgt), 72. *Prof Exp:* Sr fishery biologist, 67-69, fisheries sect leader, 72-80, PROJ DIR & CHIEF RES OFFICER, ICHTHYOL ASN INC, 80- *Mem:* Am Fisheries Soc; Am Inst Fishery Res Biologist. *Res:* Effects of thermal discharges and pumped storage facilities on fishes and fish food organisms; impact of impingement and entrainment of fishes and fish larvae; ecology of fishes. *Mailing Add:* Radiation Mgt Corp PO Box 10 Drumore PA 17518

MATHUR, KISHAN BAHADUR, chemical engineering, see previous edition

MATHUR, MAYA SWARUP, b Amorha, India, July 1, 39; m 64; c 1. EXPERIMENTAL ATOMIC PHYSICS, EXPERIMENTAL MOLECULAR PHYSICS. *Educ:* Univ Allahabad, BSc, 57, MSc, 60, PhD(physics), 69. *Prof Exp:* res assoc atomic & molecular spectros, Dept Physics, 76-80, ASST PROF, DEPT ELEC ENG, UNIV MAN, 81- *Concurrent Pos:* Sr res fel, Univ Allahabad & res grant, Sigma Xi, 69; fel, Dept Chem, Lakehead Univ, 71-72; fel, Dept Physics, Univ Man, 72-76. *Res:* Dielectric and microwave spectroscopy and zero-field-level crossing atomic spectroscopy for the determination of the excited state lifetimes and oscillator strengths; study of collision cross-sections; far infrared, laser Raman and collision-induced light scattering by molecules; inelastic light scattering from surfaces of semiconductors. *Mailing Add:* Dept of Physics Univ of Man Winnipeg MB R3T 2N2 Can

MATHUR, PERSHOTTAM PRASAD, b Delhi, India, Jan 19, 38; US citizen; m 72. PHARMACOLOGY. *Educ:* Univ Delhi, BS, 57; Univ Fla, Gainesville, PhD(pharmacol), 68. *Prof Exp:* Res asst, Univ Fla, 63-68; res assoc, Med Col SC, 68-69 & Univ Ga, 69-70; head clin chemist & sr pharmacologist, Dept Path, St Barnabas Hosp, 72, group leader, 73-75, sect head biochem pharmacol, William H Rorrer, Inc Res Div, 75-76; group mgr cardiovasc & autonomic pharmacol, 77-79, SR PROJ COORDR CLIN PHARMACOL, A H ROBINS CO, 79- *Concurrent Pos:* NIH fel cardiol, St Luke's Hosp Ctr, NY, 69-72; adj asst prof pharmacol, Med Col Va, 77- *Mem:* Fel Am Col Clin Pharmacol; Am Soc Pharmacol & Exp Therapeut; Am Fedn Clin Res; Am Heart Asn; Clin Radioassay Soc. *Res:* Cardiovascular pharmacology with emphasis on myocardial ischemia; coronary blood flow, anti-arrhythmics, anti-hypertensives and adrenergic agents; biochemical mechanisms of drug action, drug metabolism, microsomal mixed function oxidases, adjuvant disease and anti-inflammatory agents. *Mailing Add:* Res Div A H Robins Co 1211 Sherwood Ave Richmond VA 23220

MATHUR, R(ADHEY) M(OHAN), b Alwar, India, Feb 2, 36; m 65; c 1. ELECTRICAL ENGINEERING, ELECTROMAGNETICS. *Educ:* Univ Rajasthan, BSc, 56; Indian Inst Technol, Kharagpur, BTech, 60; Univ Leeds, PhD(elec eng), 69. *Prof Exp:* Lectr elec eng, Univ Jodhpur, 60-64, Malaviya Regional Eng Col, 64-65 & Indian Inst Technol, New Delhi, 65-66; Nat Res Coun Can fel, 69-70, from asst prof to assoc prof, 70-78, PROF ELEC ENG, UNIV MAN, 78-, HEAD ELEC ENG, 80- *Concurrent Pos:* Nat Res Coun Can res grant & fel, Univ Man, 71-72. *Honors & Awards:* Indian Inst Eng Prize, 64. *Mem:* Indian Inst Eng; Brit Inst Elec Engrs; Inst Elec & Electronics Engrs. *Res:* Rotating machines; reluctance and stepper motors, transient and steady state performance and design optimization; power systems modeling; HVDC systems; static compensators. *Mailing Add:* Dept of Elec Eng Univ of Man Winnipeg MB R3T 2N2 Can

MATHUR, SUKHDEV PRASHAD, b Ajmer, Rajasthan, India, Dec 28, 34; Can citizen; m 60; c 3. SOIL SCIENCE, MICROBIAL BIOCHEMISTRY. *Educ:* Univ Delhi, BSc, 57; Ind Agr Res Inst, Assoc, 59; Univ Sask, PhD(soil microbiol), 66. *Prof Exp:* Dist supvr plant protection, Govt Rajasthan, India, 57; lectr chem, Dayanand Agr Col, Ajmer, India, 59-62; RES SCIENTIST SOIL BIOCHEM, RES BR, AGR CAN, 66- *Mem:* Can Soc Soil Sci; Soil Sci Soc Am; Int Soc Soil Sci; Am Soc Microbiol; Int Peat Soc. *Res:* Nature and behaviour of humus and organic soils, peats, mucks; soil pesticides and soil pollutants; mitigating decomposition and subsidence of organic soils and classification of organic deposits and terrains. *Mailing Add:* Land Resource Res Inst Res Br Agr Can Ottawa ON K1A 0C6 Can

MATHUR, SURESH CHANDRA, b Fatehgarh, India, Mar 23, 30; m 63; c 1. NUCLEAR PHYSICS. *Educ:* Univ Lucknow, BS, 48, MS, 50; Univ Tex, PhD(physics), 65. *Prof Exp:* Asst physicist, Dept Atomic Energy, Govt India, 50-58; sr res scientist, Tex Nuclear Corp, 62-67; PROF PHYSICS, UNIV LOWELL, 67-, DIR COMPUT CTR, 71- *Mem:* Am Phys Soc. *Res:* Nuclear radiation detection techniques and instrumentation; nuclear scattering theory and experiments; nuclear particle accelerators; computer programming. *Mailing Add:* Dept Physics & Appl Physics Univ Lowell Lowell MA 01854

MATHUR, VISHNU SAHAI, b Asansol, India, Apr 28, 34; m 61; c 3. WEAK INTERACTION THEORY. *Educ:* Delhi Univ, India, BSc, 53, MSc, 55, PhD(physics), 58. *Prof Exp:* Reader, Ctr Advan Studies Theoret Physics & Astrophysics, Delhi Univ, 63-65; vis sr res assoc, 65-68, SR RES ASSOC, UNIV ROCHESTER, 68-, PROF PHYSICS, 70- *Mem:* Am Phys Soc. *Res:* Theoretical particle physics; symmetry principles and group theory; author or coauthor of over 100 publications. *Mailing Add:* 45 Hampshire Dr Rochester NY 14618

MATHUR, VISHWA NATH PRASAD, forest products, see previous edition

MATICK, RICHARD EDWARD, b Pittsburgh, Pa, Nov 25, 33; m 62; c 1. ELECTRICAL ENGINEERING. *Educ:* Carnegie Inst Technol, BS, 55, MS, 56, PhD(elec eng), 58. *Prof Exp:* Staff engr memory res, 58-66, mem tech staff dir res, 66-70, tech asst dir res, 70-80, SR STAFF ENGR, IBM RES CTR, 80- *Mem:* Inst Elec & Electronics Engrs. *Res:* Direct current corona fields; high speed memory devices and systems; ferroelectric-ferromagnetic materials; thin magnetic films; read only memories. *Mailing Add:* 137 Lakeview Ave E Peckskill NY 10566

MATIJEVIC, EGON, b Otocac, Yugoslavia, Apr 27, 22; nat US; m 47. PHYSICAL CHEMISTRY, COLLOID CHEMISTRY. *Educ:* Univ Zagreb, Chem eng, 44, Dr Chem, 48, Dr habil, 52. *Hon Degrees:* DSci, Lehigh Univ, 77. *Prof Exp:* Instr chem, Fac Pharm, Univ Zagreb, 44-47, sr instr, Fac Sci, 48-52, privat-docent colloid chem, 52-54, docent phys & colloid chem, 55-56; res fel colloid sci, Cambridge Univ, 56-57; vis prof, 57-60, assoc prof chem, 60-62, dir, Inst Colloid & Surface Sci, 66-81, PROF CHEM, CLARKSON COL TECHNOL, 62- *Concurrent Pos:* Chmn, Gordon Conf Chem at Interfaces, 65, Div Colloid & Surface Chem, Am Chem Soc, 69-70 & 49th Nat Colloid Symp, NY, 75; vis prof, Unilever Res Lab, Port Sunlight, Eng, 71, Swedish Inst Surface Chem, Stockholm, 71 & Japan Soc Prom Sci, 73; ed, Surface & Colloid Sci; vis prof & lectr, Univ of Melbourne, 76; distinguished teaching award, Clarkson Col Technol, 75; guest lectr, Fed Polytech Sch, Lausanne, Switz, 81; vis prof, Sci Univ Tokyo, 79; referee, NATO Advan Study Inst. *Honors & Awards:* Kendall Award, Am Chem Soc, 72; Gold Medal, Am Electroplaters Soc, 76. *Mem:* Am Chem Soc; Colloid Soc Ger; Croatian Chem Soc; Am Water Works Asn; Int Asn Colloid & Interface Scientists (vpres elect). *Res:* Precipitation processes; coagulation; metal corrosion; photogalvanic phenomena; complex ionic species; heteropoly compounds; ionized monolayers; light scattering; aerosols; monodispersed colloidal metal hydrous oxides. *Mailing Add:* Dept of Chem Clarkson Col of Technol Potsdam NY 13676

MATILSKY, TERRY ALLEN, b Brooklyn, NY, Mar 29, 47; m 73. ASTROPHYSICS. *Educ:* Univ Mich, BS, 67; Princeton Univ, AM, 69, PhD(astrophys sci), 71. *Prof Exp:* Sr scientist x-ray astron, 71-73, proj scientist, Uhuru Satellite, Am Sci & Eng, 73; res staff x-ray astron, Mass Inst Technol, 74-76; asst prof, 76-81, ASSOC PROF PHYSICS & ASTRON, RUTGERS UNIV, 81- *Concurrent Pos:* Consult, Smithsonian Inst, 78-; prin investr, NASA grant, 77-82; co-investr, NASA satellite proj, 74- *Mem:* Am Astron Soc; AAAS. *Res:* X-ray astrophysics; stellar atmospheres of hot stars. *Mailing Add:* Dept of Physics Rutgers Univ New Brunswick NJ 08903

MATIN, SHAIKH BADARUL, b Agra, India, Feb 21, 44. PHARMACEUTICAL CHEMISTRY, CLINICAL PHARMACOLOGY. *Educ:* Univ Karachi, BSc, 63; Columbia Univ, MS, 65; Univ Calif, PhD(pharmaceut chem), 70. *Prof Exp:* Fel chem, Univ Calif, San Francisco, 70-74; RES SCIENTIST, SYNTEX RES, 74- *Mem:* Am Chem Soc; Am Pharmaceut Asn; Am Soc Mass Spectros; NY Acad Sci. *Res:* Investigation of the pharmacologic profile and time course of action, interaction and mechanism of action of synthetic drugs and naturally occurring compounds on animals and man. *Mailing Add:* 3372 N Millbrook Ave Fresno CA 93726

MATIS, JAMES HENRY, b Chicago, Ill, Mar 3, 41; m 63; c 4. STATISTICS, MATHEMATICAL STATISTICS. *Educ:* Weber State Col, BS, 65; Brigham Young Univ, MS, 67; Tex A&M Univ, PhD(statist), 70. *Prof Exp:* Math statistician, Intermountain Forest & Range Exp Sta, US Forest Serv, 65-67; res assoc statist, 70, asst prof, 70-74, ASSOC PROF STATIST, TEX A&M UNIV, 74- *Mem:* Am Statist Asn; Biomet Soc; Soc Math Biol; Sigma Xi; AAAS. *Res:* Applied stochastic processes; compartmental analysis; time series models of fish behavior; statistical ecology. *Mailing Add:* Inst of Statist Tex A&M Univ College Station TX 77843

MATISOFF, GERALD, b Boston, Mass, Apr 27, 51; m 74; c 1. GEOCHEMISTRY, ENVIRONMENTAL SCIENCES. *Educ:* Mass Inst Technol, SB, 73; Johns Hopkins Univ, MA, 75, PhD(geochem), 78. *Prof Exp:* ASST PROF EARTH SCI, CASE WESTERN RESERVE UNIV, 77- *Concurrent Pos:* Consult, Madison & Madison Int & Ecotech, Inc, 81-; assoc ed, J Great Lake Res, 81- *Mem:* Geochem Soc; Am Soc Limnol & Oceanog; Am Geophys Union; Int Asn Great Lakes Res. *Res:* Early diagenetic reactions and chemical fluxes; bioturbation; chemical weathering; solid-aqueous solution interactions; chemical cycles on a global scale; chemical mass balances. *Mailing Add:* Dept Geol Sci Case Western Reserve Univ Cleveland OH 44106

MATJEKA, EDWARD RAY, b San Antonio, Tex, Jan 3, 43; m 71. ORGANIC CHEMISTRY. *Educ:* St Mary's Univ, Tex, BS, 65; Iowa State Univ, PhD(org chem), 74. *Prof Exp:* Proj officer phys sci, US Army Watervliet Arsenal, 70-72; instr chem, Bowling Green State Univ, 73-74; fel org chem, Univ Mass, Amherst, 74-76; asst prof, 76-80, PROF CHEM, BOISE STATE UNIV, 80- *Mem:* Am Chem Soc. *Res:* Chemistry of natural products; organosilicon chemistry and carbene chemistry. *Mailing Add:* Dept of Chem Boise State Univ Boise ID 83725

MATKIN, ORIS ARTHUR, b Powell, Wyo, Jan 14, 17; m 42; c 3. HORTICULTURE. *Educ:* Univ Calif, Los Angeles, BA, 40. *Prof Exp:* OWNER & DIR, SOIL & PLANT LAB, INC, 46- *Honors & Awards:* Res Award, Calif Asn Nurserymen, 74. *Mem:* Am Soc Plant Physiol; Am Soc Hort Sci; Soil Sci Soc Am; Am Soc Agron; Int Plant Propagators Soc. *Res:* Soil, plant, water and pathology analyses. *Mailing Add:* Soil & Plant Lab Inc Southern Calif Off PO Box 11744 Santa Ana CA 92711

MATKOVICH, VLADO IVAN, b Vrboska, Yugoslavia, Feb 17, 24; nat US; m 51; c 2. ENGINEERING & MATERIALS. *Educ:* Univ Zagreb, dipl, 51; Univ Toronto, PhD, 56. *Prof Exp:* Supvr, Aluminum Labs, Ltd, Can, 55-57; eng scientist, Allis-Chalmers Mfg Co, 57-61; res assoc, Carborundum Co, NY, 61-69, proj mgr, Eng Br, 69-75, mgr tech br, 75-78; VPRES ENG, PALL BIOMED PROD CORP, 78- *Mem:* Am Chem Soc. *Res:* Crystal chemistry; synthesis and development of high temperature materials; plastics engineering development; plant design and construction; filtration and filter design. *Mailing Add:* Pall Biomed Prods Corp Glen Cove NY 11542

MATKOWSKY, BERNARD J, b New York, NY, Aug 19, 39; m 65; c 3. COMBUSTION, STOCHASTIC DIFFERENTIAL EQUATIONS. *Educ:* City Col New York, BS, 60; New York Univ, MEE, 61, MS, 63, PhD(math), 66. *Prof Exp:* Prof math, Rensselaer Polytech Inst, 66-77; PROF APPL MATH & PROF MATH, NORTHWESTERN UNIV, 77- *Concurrent Pos:* Fulbright-Hayes fel, US Govt, 72-73; vis prof, Tel-Aviv Univ, 72-73, 76 & 80, Weizmann Inst Sci, 76 & 80; consult, Argonne Nat Lab, 78-, Sandia Nat Lab & Exxon Res & Eng Corp, 80-; Guggenheim fel, 82-83; ed, SIAM J Appl Math, 76-78, assoc managing ed, 78-, ed, Wave Motion, 79- *Mem:* Soc Indust & Appl Math; Am Math Soc; AAAS; Combustion Inst. *Res:* Asymptotic and perturbation methods for ordinary and partial differential equations; nonlinear stability and bifurcation theory; stochastic differential equations; applications to fluid dynamics, elasticity, combustion theory and flame propagation; solid state physics. *Mailing Add:* Dept Eng Sci & Appl Math Technol Inst Northwestern Univ Evanston IL 60201

MATLACK, ALBERT SHELTON, organic polymer chemistry, deceased

MATLACK, GEORGE MILLER, b Pittsburgh, Pa, June 14, 21; m 43; c 4. RADIOCHEMISTRY. *Educ:* Grinnell Col, AB, 43; Univ Iowa, MS, 46, PhD(chem), 49. *Prof Exp:* Chemist, Iowa Geol Surv, 43-46; asst chem, Univ Iowa, 46-47, res assoc, 47-49; MEM STAFF, LOS ALAMOS SCI LAB, UNIV CALIF, 49- *Mem:* Fel AAAS; fel Am Inst Chem; Am Chem Soc; NY Acad Sci; Am Nuclear Soc. *Res:* Radiochemistry of plutonium and fission products; radiation properties of plutonium-238 fuels and environmental effects. *Mailing Add:* Los Alamos Sci Lab Univ of Calif Los Alamos NM 87545

MATLIS, EBEN, b Pittsburgh, Pa, Aug 28, 23; m 42; c 2. MATHEMATICS. *Educ:* Univ Pittsburgh, BS, 48; Univ Chicago, MS, 56, PhD(algebra), 58. *Prof Exp:* From instr to assoc prof, 58-67, PROF MATH, COL ARTS & SCI, NORTHWESTERN UNIV, ILL, 67- *Concurrent Pos:* Mem, Inst Advan Study, 62-63. *Mem:* Am Math Soc. *Res:* Homological algebra; theory of rings and modules. *Mailing Add:* Dept of Math Northwestern Univ Col of Arts & Sci Evanston IL 60201

MATLOCK, DANIEL BUDD, b Seattle, Wash, Aug 6, 47; m 75; c 1. SOMATIC POLYPLOIDY, MOLECULAR EVOLUTION. *Educ:* Univ Calif, Davis, BS, 69; Ore State Univ, MS, 74, PhD(zool), 78. *Prof Exp:* Instr zool, Ore State Univ, 76; instr biol, Cent Ore Community Col, 77-78; ASST PROF BIOL, UNIV GUAM, 78- *Concurrent Pos:* Proj dir, Instrnl Sci Equip Prog grant, NSF, 79-82; co-prin investr, Contract US Navy, 79-80 & Sea Grant, Univ Hawaii, 80-81; prin investr, Hatch grant, USDA, 80-83. *Mem:* Sigma Xi; Am Soc Zoologists; Soc Study Evolution; AAAS. *Res:* Cytophotometric and autoradiographic studies of nuclear DNA content and the development of somatic polyploidy, including the effect of molting hormone on DNA synthesis in polyploid nuclei; biochemical population genetics of tropical island species. *Mailing Add:* Dept Biol Univ Guam Mangilao GU 96913

MATLOCK, GIBB B, b Tom Green Co, Tex, Nov 27, 31; m 57; c 4. SYSTEMS ENGINEERING, MATHEMATICS. *Educ:* Univ Tex, Austin, BA, 57, MS, 59; Southern Methodist Univ, PhD(math statist), 70. *Prof Exp:* Res scientist math, Military Physics Res Lab, Balcomes Res Ctr, 58-59; electron engr, LTV Corp, 59-62; SR MEM TECH STAFF, SYST ENG, TEX INSTRUMENTS, INC, 62- *Mem:* Inst Elec & Electron Engrs; Am Statist Asn; Am Inst Navig. *Mailing Add:* 9521 Fieldcrest Dr Dallas TX 75238

MATLOCK, (LEE) HUDSON, b Floresville, Tex, Dec 9, 19; m 42; c 2. CIVIL ENGINEERING. *Educ:* Univ Tex, BS, 47, MS, 50. *Prof Exp:* From instr to assoc prof civil eng, 48-66, chmn dept, 72-77, PROF CIVIL ENG, UNIV TEX, AUSTIN, 66- *Mem:* Am Soc Civil Engrs; Soc Exp Stress Anal; Am Concrete Inst. *Res:* Soil mechanics and foundations; materials of engineering; experimental stress analysis. *Mailing Add:* Dept of Civil Eng 236 Eng-Sci Bldg Univ of Tex Austin TX 78712

MATLOCK, JOSEPH RAY, b Mt Enterprise, Tex, Apr 28, 03; m 27; c 2. CIVIL ENGINEERING. *Educ:* Univ Okla, BS, 25. *Prof Exp:* From asst to assoc prof civil eng, 25-51, prof 51-70, dir sch, 44-49, EMER PROF CIVIL ENG, UNIV OKLA, 70- *Concurrent Pos:* Mem, Nat Coun State Bds Eng Exam, 58-; secy, Okla State Bd Registr Prof Eng, 63-80. *Mem:* Fel Am Soc Civil Engrs; Nat Soc Prof Engrs; Am Concrete Inst; Am Inst Steel Construct. *Res:* Structural engineering and steel design; highway bridge design. *Mailing Add:* 633 Okmulgee St Norman OK 73071

MATLOCK, REX LEON, b Plain Dealing, La, Nov 27, 34; m 55; c 3. PHYSICS. *Educ:* Northwestern State Univ, BS, 60; La State Univ, Baton Rouge, MS, 65, PhD(physics), 67. *Prof Exp:* Asst prof, 67-70, assoc prof physics, 70-77, CHMN DEPT PHYSICS, LA STATE UNIV, SHREVEPORT, 69-, PROF, 75- *Concurrent Pos:* Grant, La State Univ, Shreveport, 70-71. *Mem:* Am Phys Soc. *Res:* High energy interactions and cosmic ray physics. *Mailing Add:* Dept of Physics La State Univ Shreveport LA 71105

MATLOCK, ROBERT GOLDEN, nuclear power, energy, see previous edition

MATLOW, SHELDON LEO, b Chicago, Ill, Aug 24, 28; m 58; c 3. CHEMICAL PHYSICS. *Educ:* Univ Chicago, PhB, 48, BS, 49, PhD(chem), 53. *Prof Exp:* Asst chem, Univ Chicago, 50-52; res assoc, Brookhaven Nat Lab, 53-54; dir chem res, Jefferson Elec Co, Ill, 55; sr physicist, Hoffman Electronics Corp, 57, unit supvr, 57-59, sect mgr, 59, tech coordr, 60; dir res & develop, Intellux, Inc, Calif, 61; pres, Inst Study Solid State, 62; sr scientist, Korad Corp, 63; mgr develop eng, Clevite Corp, 64; consult, 65-75; pres, Parodox Chems, Inc, 75-79; dir polymer res, Southwall Corp, 79-81; PRES, CONDUCTIMER CORP, 81- *Mem:* Am Chem Soc; Am Phys Soc; Electrochem Soc; NY Acad Sci. *Res:* Quantum mechanics; solid state physics; materials science and technology; philosophy of science; skin science. *Mailing Add:* Conductimer Corp 235 Ferne Ave Palo Alto CA 94306

MATNEY, THOMAS STULL, b Kansas City, Mo, Sept 21, 28; m 54; c 3. BACTERIOLOGY. *Educ:* Trinity Univ, BS, 48, BA, 49, MA, 51; Univ Tex, PhD(bact), 58. *Prof Exp:* Asst res biochemist, Southwest Res Inst, 50-52; med bacteriologist, Res & Develop Lab, US Dept Army, 52-55; assoc biologist & assoc prof biol, Univ Tex M D Anderson Hosp & Tumor Inst, 62-69; assoc prof, 63-70, assoc dean, 70-78, PROF MED GENETICS, UNIV TEX GRAD SCH BIOMED SCI HOUSTON, 70- *Concurrent Pos:* Instr, Trinity Univ (Tex), 50-51. *Mem:* Am Soc Microbiol; Genetics Soc Am; Environ Mutagen Soc; AAAS. *Res:* Bacterial genetics; radiobiology; biochemistry. *Mailing Add:* Univ Tex Grad Sch Biomed Sci PO Box 20334 Houston TX 77025

MATOCHA, CHARLES K, b Hondo, Tex, Aug 13, 29; m 53; c 2. SPECTROCHEMISTRY. *Educ:* St Marys Univ, Tex, BS, 49. *Prof Exp:* From anal chemist to group leader, Aluminum Co Am, Tex & Pa, 49-73, SCI ASSOC CHEM, ALCOA TECH CTR, ALUMINUM CO AM, 73- *Mem:* Sigma Xi; Soc Appl Spectros. *Res:* Analytical methods for x-ray fluorescence analysis with emphasis on nonmetallic samples; automation of analytical procedures; development of computer systems for mathematical correlation, data handling and automation; chemical analytic automation. *Mailing Add:* Alcoa Tech Ctr Alcoa Center PA 15069

MATOLTSY, ALEXANDER GEDEON, b Kaposvar, Hungary, Feb 27, 20; nat US; m. DERMATOLOGY. *Educ:* Univ Budapest, MD, 44. *Prof Exp:* Asst prof histol, Med Sch, Univ Budapest, 43-45; res assoc, Hungarian Biol Res Inst, Tihany, 45-47; asst prof cytol, Inst Muscle Res, Woods Hole, 49; res assoc dermat, Harvard Med Sch & Mass Gen Hosp, 49-59; asst prof, Rockefeller Inst, 56-59; res prof dermat, Med Sch, Univ Miami, 59-61; res prof path, 61-80, RES PROF DERMAT & BIOCHEM, SCH MED, BOSTON UNIV, 61- *Concurrent Pos:* Spec res fel, Karolinska Inst, Sweden, 47-49. *Honors & Awards:* Mr & Mrs J N Taub Intern Mem Award. *Mem:* European Soc Comp Skin Biol; Am Soc Cell Biol; Soc Invest Dermat; Soc Cutaneous Ultra Structure Res. *Res:* Keratin and keratinization. *Mailing Add:* Dept Dermat & Anat Sch Med Boston Univ Boston MA 02118

MATOLYAK, JOHN, b Johnstown, Pa, June 26, 39; m 63; c 2. MAGNETISM. *Educ:* St Francis Col, Pa, BS, 63; Univ Toledo, MS, 66; WVa Univ, PhD(physics), 75. *Prof Exp:* Instr math & physics, St Francis Col, Pa, 63-64; ASSOC PROF PHYSICS, IND UNIV, PA, 66- *Mem:* Am Phys Soc. *Res:* Magnetic properties of crystals particularly the magnetostriction of antiferromagnets, weak ferromagnets and amorphous solids. *Mailing Add:* Dept of Physics Ind Univ of Pa Indiana PA 15701

MATON, GILBERT L(OUIS), b East Hampton, Conn, Mar 17, 25; m 51; c 4. MATHEMATICAL STATISTICS. *Educ:* George Washington Univ, BS, 50. *Prof Exp:* Proj engr instrumentation, Picker X-ray Corp, 48-50; proj engr electronic instruments, Kenneth E Hughes Co, 50-51; proj engr, Sylvania Elec Prod Corp, Gen Tel & Electronics Corp, 51-52; proj engr, vpres & dir eng & res, John I Thompson & Co, 52-64, exec vpres, 64-68, pres, 68-76; vpres, Tracor Inc, 70-76, PRES, TRACOR JITCO, 76- *Mem:* Marine Technol Soc (secy-treas, 64-66); Am Soc Qual Control; Inst Math Statist; Biomet Soc; Am Soc Testing & Mat. *Res:* Industrial statistics; marine sciences; technological forecasting; research and development planning. *Mailing Add:* Tracor Jitco 1776 E Jefferson St Rockville MD 20852

MATONIS, VICTOR ARVIDAS, b Kaunas, Lithuania, May 15, 28; m 54; c 2. PLASTICS SCIENCE & TECHNOLOGY, MECHANICAL ENGINEERING. *Educ:* Worcester Polytech Inst, BS, 54; Univ Conn, MS, 60, PhD(appl mech), 67. *Prof Exp:* Res engr, Olin Mathieson Chem Co, 56-59; res eng mgt, Res & Develop, 70-80, SR RES SPECIALIST, NEW PROD DEVELOP, PLASTICS DIV, MPR PLASTICS DIV, MONSANTO CO, 70- *Mem:* Am Soc Mech Engr; Am Soc Testing & Mat. *Res:* Rubber modified styrenic polymers; plastic alloys; reinforcement; response of plastics to high speed impact; long term creep and fatigue of high polymers; polymeric foams; laminates. *Mailing Add:* Monsanto Co 730 Worcester St Indian Orchard MA 01151

MATOVICH, EDWIN, b New Chicago, Ind, Aug 29, 35; m 56; c 3. PHYSICAL CHEMISTRY. *Educ:* Ariz State Univ, BS, 56. *Prof Exp:* Anal chemist, Nat Lead Co, Utah, 56-57; res chemist, Motorola Semiconductor Prod, Inc, 57-59; device develop engr, Semiconductor Div, Hughes Aircraft Co, Calif, 59-62; electro-optical res chemist, Quantum Tech Lab, Calif, 62-63; res specialist, Autonetics Div, NAm Rockwell Corp, 63-72; CONSULT PHYS CHEM, 72- *Mem:* Sigma Xi. *Res:* Semiconductor devices and lasers; quantum behavior of fluorescent fluids; radiation devices; high temperature chemistry, particularly with regard to fuel processing, fuel gasification and desulfurization; petroleum and petrochemical engineering; chemical process systems, analysis and engineering; economic analyses. *Mailing Add:* 250 Verbena Lane Brea CA 92621

MATOVINOVIC, JOSIP, b Licko Cerje, Yugoslavia, Dec 22, 14; US citizen; m 43. MEDICINE. *Educ:* Univ Zagreb, MD, 39. *Prof Exp:* Resident internal med, State Gen Hosp, Zagreb, 40-45; asst prof, Med Sch, Univ Zagreb, 45-46; clin & res fel, Mass Gen Hosp, Harvard Med Sch, 47-48; chief div endocrinol, Univ Zagreb, 48-56, docent, 51-56; res assoc thyroid clin, Mass Gen Hosp, Harvard Med Sch, 56-58, res assoc diabetes clin, 59; from instr to assoc prof, 59-70, PROF INTERNAL MED, MED SCH, UNIV MICH, ANN ARBOR, 70- *Concurrent Pos:* Consult study group on endemic goiter, WHO, 52, Pakistan & Lebanon, 60; mem, Yugoslav Comn Prev Endemic Goiter, 53; ed bd, Yugoslav Encycl Med, 56; dir Mich study endemic goiter & iodine nutriture, Ctr Dis Control, 71; consult, Radiation Ctr, WHO, Bombay, India, 73. *Mem:* Endocrine Soc; Am Thyroid Asn. *Res:* Transplantable thyroid tumor of the rat; proliferation and differentiation of thyroid carcinoma in cell culture; iodine deficient goiter in human and experimental animals. *Mailing Add:* Dept of Internal Med Univ Hosp Univ of Mich Med Sch Ann Arbor MI 48109

MATSCH, CHARLES LEO, b Hastings, Minn. GEOLOGY, GLACIAL GEOLOGY. *Educ:* Univ Maine, BA, 59; Univ Minn, MS, 62; Univ Wis-Madison, PhD(geol), 71. *Prof Exp:* Explor geologist petrol, Stand Oil Co Tex, 61-64; instr geol, Univ Minn, Minneapolis, 64-66, asst prof, 66-70; from asst prof to assoc prof, 70-81, PROF & HEAD GEOLOGY DEPT, UNIV MINN, DULUTH, 81- *Concurrent Pos:* Secy, INQUA Comn, Genesis Glacial Sediments, 73-77. *Mem:* Geol Soc Am; Am Quaternary Asn; Nat Asn Geol Teachers. *Res:* Glacial geology of the midcontinent of North America; origin of quaternary continental sediments; environmental geology of glaciated terrains; glacial marine sediments. *Mailing Add:* Dept of Geol Univ of Minn Duluth MN 55812

MATSCH, L(EE) A(LLAN), b Chicago, Ill, Feb 21, 35; m 57; c 3. MECHANICAL ENGINEERING. *Educ:* Univ Ariz, BSME, 57; Univ Pittsburgh, MSME, 61; Ariz State Univ, PhD(eng sci), 67. *Prof Exp:* Assoc engr, Atomic Power Dept, Westinghouse Elec Corp, 57-61; supvr, AiRes Mfg Co, Div Garrett Corp, 61-70; mem res staff, Res Div, Ampex Corp, 70-71, eng mgr, Magnetic Tape Mfg Div, 71-76; sr supvr, Aires Mfg Co Ariz, 76-80; CHIEF MECH COMPONENT DESIGN, GARRETT TURBINE ENG CO, 80- *Concurrent Pos:* Fac assoc, Ariz State Univ, 67-68 & 78- *Mem:* Am Soc Mech Engrs. *Res:* Fluid mechanics; fluid film lubrication; engineering mechanics. *Mailing Add:* AiRes Mfg Co of Ariz PO Box 5217 Phoenix AZ 85010

MATSCHINER, JOHN THOMAS, b Portland, Ore, Dec 2, 27; m 49; c 5. BIOCHEMISTRY. *Educ:* Univ Portland, BS, 50, MS, 51; St Louis Univ, PhD, 57. *Prof Exp:* Res assoc, Univ Va, 51-52; from instr to assoc prof biochem, Sch Med, St Louis Univ, 58-70; PROF BIOCHEM, SCH MED, UNIV NEBR, 70- *Concurrent Pos:* Jane Coffin Childs Fund res fel, Univ Calif, 57-58. *Mem:* Am Soc Biol Chem; Am Inst Nutrit. *Res:* Biochemistry and nutrition of vitamin K. *Mailing Add:* 3554 Davenport St Omaha NE 68131

MATSCHKE, DONALD EDWARD, b Chicago, Ill, Mar 10, 33; m 68; c 4. CHEMICAL & ENVIRONMENTAL ENGINEERING. *Educ:* Northwestern Univ, BS, 55, MS, 57, PhD(chem eng), 65. *Prof Exp:* Consult, Chicago Bridge & Iron Co, 65, dir process res, 66-67, dir environ res, 67-70; partner, Bauer Eng, Inc, 70-75; PRES, D E MATSCHKE CO, 75- *Concurrent Pos:* Gen chmn, Cook County Clean Streams Comt, 64- *Mem:* Am Inst Chem Engrs; Am Chem Soc; Water Pollution Control Fedn; Am Water Works Asn; Am Inst Mining, Metall & Petrol Engrs. *Res:* Processes for utilization of water, air, land and natural resources; efforts directed at water and wastewater treatment; air pollution control; sludge or liquid and solid waste management; fossil fuel development. *Mailing Add:* D E Matschke Co Two Salt Creek Lane Hinsdale IL 60521

MATSEN, JOHN M(ORRIS), b Neenah, Wis, May 30, 36; m 71. CHEMICAL ENGINEERING, FLUIDIZATION. *Educ:* Princeton Univ, BSE, 57; Columbia Univ, MS, 59, PhD(chem eng), 63. *Prof Exp:* Instr chem eng, Columbia Univ, 60-61; engr, Esso Res & Eng Co, 61-71, ENG ASSOC, EXXON RES & ENG CO, 71- *Concurrent Pos:* Ed adv bd mem, Advan Environ Sci & Eng, 77-; tech comt mem, Particulate Solids Res Inc, 78-; chmn, Int Fluidization Conf, 80; co ed, Fluidization, 80. *Mem:* Am Chem Soc; Am Inst Chem Engrs; Air Pollution Control Asn; Sigma Xi. *Res:* Fluidization; pneumatic transport; gas cleaning; particulate emissions and air pollution; separations processes; fluid catalytic cracking; fluidized bed combustion; synthetic fuels. *Mailing Add:* Eng Technol Dept PO Box 101 Exxon Res & Eng Co Florham Park NJ 07932

MATSEN, JOHN MARTIN, b Salt Lake City, Utah, Feb 7, 33; m 59; c 10. MEDICINE, MICROBIOLOGY. *Educ:* Brigham Young Univ, BA, 58; Univ Calif, Los Angeles, MD, 63. *Prof Exp:* From intern to resident pediat, Univ Calif, Los Angeles, 63-66; from asst prof to prof lab med & path, pediat & microbiol, Univ Minn, Minneapolis, 68-74; assoc dean, 79-81, PROF PATH & PEDIAT & DIR CLIN MICRO LAB, UNIV UTAH, 74-, CHMN PATH, 81- *Concurrent Pos:* Fel pediat infectious dis, Univ Minn, Minneapolis, 66-68. *Mem:* Soc Pediat Res; fel Am Acad Microbiol; fel Col Am Pathologists; fel Am Acad Pediat; fel Am Soc Clin Path. *Res:* Pediatric enteric infections; antibiotic evaluation and evaluation of procedures in diagnostic microbiology. *Mailing Add:* Dept Path & Pediat Univ Utah Hosp Salt Lake City UT 84132

MATSON, DENNIS LUDWIG, b San Diego, Calif, Sept 29, 42. PLANETARY SCIENCES. *Educ:* San Diego State Univ, AB, 64; Calif Inst Technol, PhD(planetary sci), 72. *Prof Exp:* Res assoc planetology, 72-74, sr scientist planetology, 74-76, mem tech staff, 76-80, RES SCIENTIST & GROUP SUPVR, JET PROPULSION LAB, CALIF INST TECHNOL, 80- *Mem:* Am Geophys Union; Am Astron Soc; AAAS; Int Astron Union; Sigma Xi. *Res:* Composition and morphology of planetary surfaces; astronomical photometry and spectroscopy over the entire spectral range from the vacuum ultra-violet through the visible, long wavelength, infrared; two-dimensional photometry and imaging of solar system bodies; theoretical studies of the interactions between planetary surfaces, atmospheres and magnetospheres; spacecraft instrument development. *Mailing Add:* Mail Code 183-501 Jet Propulsion Lab Pasadena CA 91103

MATSON, HOWARD JOHN, b Monmouth, Ill, June 8, 21; m 46; c 4. ORGANIC CHEMISTRY, PETROLEUM CHEMISTRY. *Educ:* Monmouth Col, Ill, BS, 43; Pa State Univ, MS, 47. *Prof Exp:* Res asst petrol refining, Pa State Univ, 43-47, res instr, 47-50; chemist, Sinclair Res Labs, 50-53, group leader, 53-55, sect leader, 55-63, res scientist, 63-69, asst mgr prod qual, Atlantic Richfield Co, 69-70, supvr, 70-74, mgr prod specialities, 74-77, MGR SPECIF, SAFETY & REGULATORY SERV PROD, ATLANTIC RICHFIELD CO, 77- *Mem:* Am Chem Soc; Am Inst Chemists; Am Soc Lubrication Engrs; Am Soc Testing & Mat. *Res:* Petroleum product research and development. *Mailing Add:* Harvey Tech Ctr Atlantic Richfield Co Harvey IL 60426

MATSON, LESLIE EMMET, JR, b Evanston, Ill, Nov 14, 20; m 46; c 1. ELECTRICAL ENGINEERING, AEROSPACE SYSTEMS. *Educ:* Univ Mich, BSE, 42; Univ Pa, MS, 55, PhD, 61. *Prof Exp:* Engr, RCA Corp, 42-55, leader dynamics group, 55-59, mgr systs anal, Missile & Surface Radar Dept & Systs Eng Eval & Res, 59-63; mgr space systs anal, 63-66, mgr info & space systs, 66-71, mgr advan systs develop, Aerospace Systs Div, 71-75; MEM TECH STAFF, CHARLES STARK DRAPER LAB, INC, 75- *Mem:* Inst Elec & Electronics Engrs; Am Inst Aeronaut & Astronaut. *Res:* Analysis and synthesis of aerospace electronics systems; tracking and surveillance radar and electro-optical systems; decision and control systems; optimal navigation and information processing systems. *Mailing Add:* Charles Stark Draper Lab Inc 555 Technology Sq Cambridge MA 02139

MATSON, MICHAEL STEVEN, b Ft Wayne, Ind, June 3, 48; m 73; c 2. INORGANIC CHEMISTRY. *Educ:* Purdue Univ, BS, 70; Ind Univ, PhD(chem), 76. *Prof Exp:* Asst chemist, Ames Lab, 75-77; RES CHEMIST, CATALYTIC CHEM, PHILLIPS PETROL CO, 77- *Mem:* Am Chem Soc. *Res:* Catalytic synthesis of specialty chemicals via oxidation, carbonylation, reduction and/or reductive-amination reactions. *Mailing Add:* Phillips Res Ctr Bldg 87-G Phillips Petrol Co Bartlesville OK 74004

MATSON, TED P, b Ponca City, Okla, Jan 5, 29; m 51; c 3. APPLIED CHEMISTRY, SURFACE CHEMISTRY. *Educ:* Univ Okla, BS, 49, EdM, 51; Okla State Univ, MS, 67. *Prof Exp:* Teacher & coach pub schs, Okla, 51-56; asst res chemist, Res & Develop Dept, Continental Oil Co, 57-59, assoc res chemist, 59-62, res chemist, 62-64, tech adv to managing dir, Condea Petrochem GmbH, Hamburg, Ger, 64-65; res chemist, Res & Develop Dept, Continental Oil Co, 65-66, prod develop coordr, Conoco Chem, 66-72, RES GROUP LEADER SURFACTANTS, CONTINENTAL OIL CO, 72- *Mem:* Am Oil Chem Soc; Am Soc Testing & Mat; Chem Specialties Mfrs Asn. *Res:* New product development; oil field chemicals; study of applications and synthesis of surfactants and research and development of evaluation techniques. *Mailing Add:* Continental Oil Co Drawer 1267 Ponca City OK 74601

MATSUDA, KEN, b Napa, Calif, Nov 30, 20; m 46; c 2. ORGANIC CHEMISTRY. *Educ:* Univ Md, BS, 44, PhD(chem), 51. *Prof Exp:* Res chemist, 51-57, sr res chemist, 57-62, group leader, 61-71, proj mgr, 71-74, mgr chem sect, 74-77, mgr water treating & mining chem res & develop, 77-79, mgr catalyst res, 79-80, DIR TECHNOL ASSESSMENT, STAMFORD LABS, AM CYANAMID CO, 80- *Mem:* Am Chem Soc. *Res:* Catalysts; organic flocculents; mining reagents; fluorinated compounds; polynuclear aromatics; photochromic products; vinyl monomers and polymers; cyanogen derivatives; high temperature reaction; coal liquefaction. *Mailing Add:* Stamford Labs Am Cyanamid Co Stamford CT 06904

MATSUDA, SEIGO, b Tokyo, Japan, Feb 26, 25; m 51; c 1. METALLURGY. *Educ:* Yokohama Nat Univ, BEng, 46; Tohoku Univ, Japan, BEng, 50; Mass Inst Technol, ScD(metall), 61. *Prof Exp:* Instr electrochem, Tech High Sch, Japan, 46-47; mem bd dir, Nambu Lumber Co, 47-51; dept res asst, Govt Dept Educ, Tohoku Univ, Japan, 50-51, dept asst, 51-56; res asst, Mass Inst Technol, 56-60; sr metallurgist, Ilikon Co, 60-61; exec vpres & tech dir, Cambridge Metal Res Inc, 61-64; sr res specialist, Monsanto Res Corp, 64-67, advan technologist, 67-69; sr scientist, Biomed Res Lab, Am Hosp Supply Co, 69-70; CHIEF METALLURGIST, THERMO ELECTRON CORP, 70-, DEPT MGR, 75- *Concurrent Pos:* Lectr, Ctr Continuing Educ, Northeastern Univ, 69-71. *Mem:* Electrochem Soc; Nat Asn Corrosion Engrs; Am Soc Metals; Japan Inst Metals; Electrochem Soc Japan. *Res:* Electrochemistry; corrosion catalysis; technical consulting. *Mailing Add:* Thermo Electron Corp 85 First Ave Waltham MA 02254

MATSUDA, YOSHIYUKI, b Manchuria, China, Dec 7, 43; Japanese citizen; m 71. PLASMA PHYSICS. *Educ:* Kyoto Univ, BS, 66, MS, 68; Stanford Univ, PhD(elec eng), 74. *Prof Exp:* Res assoc plasma physics, Plasma Physics Lab, Princeton Univ, 74-78; PHYSICIST, LAWRENCE LIVERMORE LAB, 78- *Mem:* Am Phys Soc; Inst Elec & Electronics Engrs; AAAS. *Res:* Theoretical and computational study of plasma physics and controlled thermonuclear fusion. *Mailing Add:* L-439 Lawrence Livermore Lab Univ of Calif Livermore CA 94550

MATSUGUMA, HAROLD JOSEPH, b Honolulu, Hawaii, Oct 15, 28; m 63; c 1. INORGANIC CHEMISTRY. *Educ:* Univ Hawaii, BA, 51; Univ Ill, MS, 52, PhD(chem), 55. *Prof Exp:* Res assoc chem, Univ Ill, 52-55, assoc, 55; chemist, Explosives Res Sect, 55-57, chief, Synthesis Unit, 57-59, chief, Off Reactor Requirements & Explosives Res Sect, 59-63, actg chief, Explosives Lab, 63-66, CHIEF CHEM BR, ENERGETIC MAT DIV, ARRADCOM, US DEPT ARMY, 66- *Mem:* Am Chem Soc; Royal Soc Chem; Am Defense Preparedness Asn. *Res:* Synthesis of hydrazine; hydroxylamine derivatives; chemistries of nitrogen, phosphorus and sulfur compounds; chemistry of explosives; explosives safety; relation of chemical constitution to explosive properties. *Mailing Add:* US Army ARRADCOM DRDAR-LCE-C Dover NJ 07801

MATSUMOTO, CHARLES, b San Jose, Calif, Mar 25, 32; m 61; c 1. PHARMACOLOGY, BIOCHEMISTRY. *Educ:* San Jose State Col, BA, 53; Univ Idaho, MS, 55; Univ Wash, PhD(pharmacol), 63. *Prof Exp:* Chemist biol lab, US Fish & Wildlife Serv, 58-70; RES ASSOC, LILLY RES LAB, ELI LILLY & CO, 65- *Concurrent Pos:* Exec ed, Life Sci, 70-73; NIH fel, Lab Chem Pharmacol, Nat Heart Inst, 63-65. *Mem:* AAAS; Drug Info Asn; Am Soc Pharmacol & Exp Therapeut; Am Soc Clin Pharmacol & Therapeut; Sigma Xi. *Res:* Autonomic, cardiovascular and biochemical pharmacology. *Mailing Add:* Eli Lilly Res Labs Indianapolis IN 46206

MATSUMOTO, HIROMU, b Honolulu, Hawaii, Mar 28, 20. AGRICULTURAL BIOCHEMISTRY. *Educ:* Univ Hawaii, BS, 44, MS, 45; Purdue Univ, PhD(biochem), 55. *Prof Exp:* Asst chem, Exp Sta, Univ Hawaii, 45-49, jr chemist, 49-51; asst biochem, Purdue Univ, 51-54; from asst biochemist to assoc biochemist, 55-66, BIOCHEMIST, EXP STA, UNIV

HAWAII, 66- *Concurrent Pos:* Fel, Japan Soc Advan Sci, 75-76. *Mem:* Am Chem Soc; Soc Toxicol; Am Asn Cancer Res. *Res:* Effect of toxic plant constituents on animal metabolism; mimosine, 3-nitropropanoic acid, methylazoxymethanol; metabolic fate in animals of naturally occurring toxicants; cycasin methylazoxymethanol-glucosiduronic acid; toxicology; chemical carcinogenesis. *Mailing Add:* Dept of Agr Biochem 1800 East-West Rd Honolulu HI 96822

MATSUMOTO, HIROYUKI, b Nagasaki, Japan, May 5, 48. NEUROPHYSIOLOGY. *Educ:* Kyoto Univ, BS, 72, MS, 74, PhD(biophysics), 77. *Prof Exp:* Jr researcher, Dept Chem, Univ Hawaii, 77-79; res assoc, 79-80, ASST RES SCIENTIST, DEPT BIOL SCI, PURDUE UNIV, 80- *Concurrent Pos:* Asst researcher, Dept Chem, Univ Hawaii, 81. *Mem:* Asn Res Vision & Opthalmol. *Res:* Study of molecular mechanisms of sensory transduction in bovine and fruitfly visual photoreceptor systems; chromophore-protein interaction in rhodopsin and protein modifications involved in visual transduction. *Mailing Add:* Dept Biol Sci Purdue Univ West Lafayette IN 47907

MATSUMOTO, KEN, b San Bernadino, Calif, Sept 8, 41; m 67; c 2. ORGANIC CHEMISTRY, MEDICINAL CHEMISTRY. *Educ:* Ariz State Univ, BS, 63; Univ Calif, Berkeley, PhD(org chem), 67. *Prof Exp:* Teaching asst, Univ Calif, Berkeley, 63-64; sr org chemist, 69-75, sr res scientist, 75-81, RES ASSOC, LILLY RES LABS, 82- *Mem:* Am Chem Soc; Sigma Xi. *Mailing Add:* Lilly Res Labs Eli Lilly & Co Indianapolis IN 46285

MATSUMOTO, STEVEN G, b Seattle, Wash, May 31, 49; m 72. NEUROBIOLOGY. *Educ:* Univ Wash, BA, 73; State Univ NY, Albany, PhD(biol), 77. *Prof Exp:* Res asst neurobiol, Univ Iowa, 74, Univ Ore, 75 & State Univ NY, Albany, 75-77; FEL NEUROBIOL, HARVARD MED SCH, 77- *Mem:* Soc Neurosci. *Res:* Developmental neurobiology; invertebrate sensory physiology. *Mailing Add:* Dept of Neurobiol 25 Shattuck St Boston MA 02115

MATSUMOTO, YORIMI, b Yuba City, Calif, July 29, 26. PHYSIOLOGY. *Educ:* Whittier Col, AB, 50; Univ Calif, Los Angeles, PhD(zool), 64. *Prof Exp:* Instr biophys, Univ Ill, Urbana, 63-66, from asst prof to assoc prof, 66-69; ASSOC PROF PHYSIOL, EMORY UNIV, 69- *Mem:* AAAS; Biophys Soc; Am Soc Zoologists. *Res:* Mechanical analysis of muscular contraction; heat analysis of muscle-contraction; nerve-heat; birefrigency study of invertebrate muscle. *Mailing Add:* Dept of Physiol Emory Univ Sch of Med Atlanta GA 30322

MATSUMURA, KENNETH N, b Bangkok, Thailand, May 15, 45. MEDICAL & HEALTH SCIENCE. *Educ:* Univ Calif, Berkeley, BS, 66; Univ Calif, San Francisco, MD, 70. *Prof Exp:* DIR & COORDR, ARTIFICIAL LIVER PROJ, GLOBAL DEVELOP, ALIN-ACI, 70-, DIR, RES & DEVELOP, IMMUNITY RES LAB, 77- *Concurrent Pos:* Consult, Univ Calif, Berkeley, 74-75. *Res:* Artificial liver; artificial pancreas; transplantation immunology; biology of aging; cancer chemotherapy; emergency medical data systems. *Mailing Add:* One Alin Plaza 2107 Dwight at Shattuck Berkeley CA 94704

MATSUMURA, PHILIP, b San Jose, Calif, Aug 15, 47. MOLECULAR BIOLOGY. *Educ:* Univ Santa Clara, BS, 69; Univ Rochester, PhD(microbiol), 75. *Prof Exp:* Fel, Univ Calif, San Diego, 75-79; ASST PROF, UNIV ILL, CHICAGO, 79- *Mem:* AAAS; Sigma Xi; Soc Gen Microbiol; Am Soc Microbiol. *Res:* Microbial motility and chemotaxis. *Mailing Add:* Univ Ill Chicago IL 60680

MATSUO, KEIZO, b Osaka, Japan, Apr 23, 42. POLYMER CHEMISTRY. *Educ:* Kyoto Univ, BS, 66, MS, 68; Dartmouth Col, PhD(chem), 72. *Prof Exp:* Res assoc chem, 72-74, res instr chem, 74-77, SR RES ASSOC, DARTMOUTH COL, 78- *Mem:* Am Chem Soc; Japan Chem Soc. *Res:* Synthesis of new polymer; characterization; equilibrium and non-equilibrium study of polymer solution; kinetics; play with rotational state model. *Mailing Add:* Dept of Chem Dartmouth Col Hanover NH 03755

MATSUO, ROBERT R, b Duncan, BC, Feb 28, 32; m 61; c 2. BIOCHEMISTRY. *Educ:* Univ Man, BSc, 57; Univ Alta, PhD(plant biochem), 62. *Prof Exp:* Chemist I, Grain Res Lab, 57-59, chemist III, Durum Wheat Res, 62-66, RES SCIENTIST, GRAIN RES LAB, CAN DEPT AGR, 66- *Mem:* AAAS; Am Asn Cereal Chemists; Chem Inst Can; Prof Inst Pub Serv Can; Can Inst Food Sci & Technol. *Res:* Cereal chemistry; basic and applied research on durum wheat and durum wheat products. *Mailing Add:* Grain Res Lab 1404 303 Main St Winnipeg MB R3C 3G9 Can

MATSUOKA, SHIRO, b Kobe, Japan, May 1, 30; m 57; c 3. POLYMER PHYSICS, PLASTICS ENGINEERING. *Educ:* Stevens Inst Technol, ME, 55; Princeton Univ, MSE, 57, PhD(mech eng), 59. *Prof Exp:* Asst, Princeton Univ, 55-57; supvr res rheol, 63-71, supvr plastics develop, 71-74, HEAD PLASTICS RES & DEVELOP DEPT, BELL TEL LABS, INC, 74-, MEM TECH STAFF, 59- *Concurrent Pos:* Vis lectr, Stevens Inst Technol, 62-64, vis prof, 64-71; vis prof, Rutgers Univ, 77- *Honors & Awards:* Int Award, Soc Plastics Engrs, 80. *Mem:* Fel Am Phys Soc; Am Chem Soc; Soc Rheol; Soc Plastics Engrs. *Res:* Mechanical, electrical and morphological properties of high polymers; molecular relaxation phenomena. *Mailing Add:* Bell Tel Labs Inc Murray Hill NJ 07974

MATSUOKA, TATS, b Seattle, Wash, Aug 24, 29; m 64; c 1. VIROLOGY. *Educ:* Univ Minn, BA, 52; State Col Wash, DVM, 59. *Prof Exp:* Asst bacteriologist, Mont State Col, 52-55, asst bacteriologist & virologist, Vet Res Lab, 61-63; practicing vet, Idaho, 59-60; vet diagnostician, Mont Livestock Sanit Bd, 60-61; res vet, 63-67, sr virologist, 67-74, RES SCIENTIST, GREENFIELD LABS, ELI LILLY & CO, 74- *Mem:* Am Vet Med Asn; Am Soc Microbio; US Animal Health Asn; Conf Res Workers Animal Dis. *Res:* Anaerobic bacteria pathogenic to animals; animal viruses, particularly viral diseases of bovine. *Mailing Add:* Lilly Res Labs Box 708 Greenfield IN 46140

MATSUSAKA, TERUHISHA, b Kyoto, Japan, Apr 5, 26; m 50; c 5. GEOMETRY. *Educ:* Kyoto Univ, MS, 49, PhD(math), 54. *Prof Exp:* Instr math, Ochanomizu Univ, Japan, 52-53, asst prof, 53-54; res assoc, Univ Chicago, 54-57; from assoc prof to prof, Northwestern Univ, 57-61; prof math, 61-81, IRVING SCHNEIDER PROF, BRANDEIS UNIV, 81- *Concurrent Pos:* Guggenheim fel, 59. *Mem:* Am Math Soc; Am Acad Arts & Sci. *Res:* Algebra; algebraic geometry. *Mailing Add:* Dept of Math Brandeis Univ Waltham MA 02154

MATSUSHIMA, JOHN K, b Denver, Colo, Dec 24, 20; m 43; c 2. ANIMAL NUTRITION. *Educ:* Colo State Univ, BS, 43, MS, 45; Univ Minn, PhD, 49. *Prof Exp:* Asst animal husb, Colo State Univ, 43-45; from asst prof to prof, Univ Nebr, 49-61; PROF ANIMAL SCI, COLO STATE UNIV, 61- *Mem:* Am Soc Animal Sci; Soc Range Mgt; Am Dairy Sci Asn; Am Inst Nutrit. *Res:* Beef cattle nutrition, feeding and management. *Mailing Add:* Dept of Animal Sci Colo State Univ Ft Collins CO 80521

MATSUSHIMA, SATOSHI, b Fukui, Japan, May 6, 23; nat US; m 55; c 2. ASTRONOMY, ASTROPHYSICS. *Educ:* Univ Kyoto, MS, 46; Univ Utah, PhD(astrophys), 54; Univ Tokyo, DSc, 66. *Prof Exp:* Asst astron, Univ Kyoto, 46-50; res fel & asst, High Altitude Observ & Harvard Col Observ, 50-54; res assoc physics, Univ Pa & Strawbridge Observ, Haverford Col, 54-55; vis astronr, Astrophys Inst & Meudon Observ, Paris, France, 56-57; Humboldt fel, Inst Theoret Physics, Univ Kiel, 57-58; asst prof physics, Fla State Univ, 58-60; assoc prof astron, Univ Iowa, 60-67; actg head, Physics Dept, 81-82, PROF ASTRON, PA STATE UNIV, 67-, HEAD DEPT, 76- *Concurrent Pos:* Travel grants, Int Astron Union, 56 & 57, Ger Astron Soc, 57, US Res Coop, 58 & NSF, 65-82; guest astronr, Utrecht Observ, Neth, 56; sr res fel, Calif Inst Technol, 59-61; vis prof, US-Japan Coop Sci Prog, Univs Tokyo & Kyoto, 65-66; consult, Naval Res Lab, 62; mem, Int Astron Union Comns 12 & 36. *Mem:* Am Astron Soc; fel Royal Astron Soc; Am Geophys Union. *Res:* Theory of stellar atmospheres; solar and planetary physics; spectroscopy and spectrophometry; space and upper atmosphere physics. *Mailing Add:* 525 Davey Lab Pa State Univ University Park PA 16802

MATSUSHITA, SADAMI, b Ehime, Japan, Feb 12, 20; m; c 2. GEOPHYSICS. *Educ:* Kyoto Univ, MSc, 44, DrSc, 51. *Prof Exp:* Asst geophys, Kyoto Univ, 45, lectr, 45-54; mem res staff physics, Univ Col, London, 54-55; mem sr res staff, High Altitude Observ, Nat Ctr Atmospheric Res, 55-56; PROF ASTROGEOPHYS, UNIV COLO & MEM SR RES STAFF, HIGH ALTITUDE OBSERV, NAT CTR ATMOSPHERIC RES, 57- *Concurrent Pos:* Guest worker, Nat Bur Standards, 55-56 & 57-; consult, Environ Sci Serv Admin; mem, Int Sci Radio Union & Int Union Geod & Geophys. *Honors & Awards:* Scientist Award, Sigma Xi, 63. *Mem:* Fel AAAS; Meteorol Soc Am; Am Geophys Union; Sigma Xi. *Res:* Relations among geomagnetism, ionosphere, space and the sun. *Mailing Add:* High Altitude Observ PO Box 3000 Boulder CO 80307

MATSUSHITA, TATSUO, b Kearny, NJ, July 29, 37; m 67; c 1. BIOCHEMICAL GENETICS. *Educ:* Cornell Univ, AB, 60; Rutgers Univ, PhD(biochem), 70. *Prof Exp:* Teaching asst biochem, Rutgers Univ, 67-68; res assoc microbial genetics, Princeton Univ, 70-72; asst geneticist, 72-76, GENETICIST, ARGONNE NAT LAB, 76- *Concurrent Pos:* NIH fel, Princeton Univ, 71-72. *Mem:* Genetics Soc Am; Am Soc Microbiol; Biophys Soc. *Res:* DNA repair; sister chromatid exchanges; somatic cell mutation in mouse myelomas. *Mailing Add:* Div of Biol & Med Res Argonne Nat Lab Argonne IL 60439

MATSUURA, SHUJI, biochemistry, endocrinology, see previous edition

MATSUURA, TAKESHI, b Shizuoka, Japan, Dec 22, 36; Can citizen; m 68; c 1. CHEMICAL ENGINEERING. *Educ:* Univ Tokyo, BSc, 61, MSc, 63; Tech Univ Berlin, Dr Ing (chem eng), 65. *Prof Exp:* Staff asst synthetic chem, Univ Tokyo, 66-67; res assoc chem eng, Univ Calif, Davis, 67-69; res fel, 69-71, asst res officer, 71-75, assoc res officer, 75-80, SR RES OFFICER CHEM ENG, NAT RES COUN CAN, 81- *Mem:* Can Soc Chem Eng; Chem Soc Japan. *Res:* Reverse osmosis; separation by synthetic membranes; water treatment by reverse osmosis; food processing by reverse osmosis. *Mailing Add:* Div Chem Nat Res Coun Can Ottawa ON K1A 0R9 Can

MATSUYAMA, GEORGE, b Fresno, Calif, Nov 20, 18; m 45; c 2. ELECTROANALYTICAL CHEMISTRY. *Educ:* Univ Calif, BS, 40; Univ Minn, PhD(phys chem), 48. *Prof Exp:* Asst chem, Fresno State Col, 36-38; asst, Univ Minn, 40-43, instr, 43-48; asst prof, Wesleyan Univ, 48-52; res chemist, Union Oil Co, Calif, 52-55, sr res chemist, 55-57, res assoc, 57-59; sr chemist, Beckman Instruments Inc, 59-64, eng specialist, 64-69, res scientist, 70-79; sr staff scientist, 79-81, DIR RES, LONETICS, INC, 81- *Mem:* AAAS; Am Chem Soc; Am Asn Clin Chemists; Electrochem Soc. *Res:* Electrometric and volumetric analysis; electroanalytical instrumentation; ion-selective electrodes; gas sensors; enzyme electroanalytical methods. *Mailing Add:* 548 N Stanford Ave Fullerton CA 92631

MATT, JOSEPH, b Minneapolis, Minn, Jan 10, 20; m 61; c 2. ORGANIC CHEMISTRY. *Educ:* Univ Pa, BS, 41; Pa State Univ, MS, 42; Purdue Univ, PhD(chem), 49. *Prof Exp:* Res chemist, Sharp & Dohme Div, Merck & Co, Inc, 43-45 & Armour & Co, 48-54; sr res chemist, Va-Carolina Chem Corp, 54-56; res chemist, Alkydol Labs, Inc, 56-58 & Velsicol Chem Corp, 59-62; SR RES CHEMIST, NALCO CHEM CO, 62- *Mem:* Am Chem Soc. *Res:* Organic polymers; coating resins; organophosphorus and organofluorine compounds; fatty acid derivatives; microbiocides. *Mailing Add:* Nalco Chem Co Napervill Tech Ctr 1801 Diehl Rd Naperville IL 60540

MATTA, JOSEPH EDWARD, b Philadelphia, Pa, July 29, 48. ENVIRONMENTAL PHYSICS. *Educ:* St Joseph's Col, Philadelphia, BS, 70; Lehigh Univ, MS, 72, PhD(physics), 74. *Prof Exp:* Fel physics, Lehigh Univ, 74-75; res physicist, Mines Safety Res Ctr, 75-80; MEM STAFF, CHEM SYST LAB, ARMY RES & DEVELOP COMMAND, ABERDEEN PROVING GROUND, 80- *Mem:* Am Phys Soc. *Res:* Investigate various dust and methane control techniques for underground coal mines. *Mailing Add:* Chem Syst Lab DAR-C16-PO Army Res & Develop Command Aberdeen MD 21010

MATTA, MICHAEL STANLEY, b Dayton, Ohio, Feb 22, 40; m 62; c 3. BIOLOGICAL CHEMISTRY, ORGANIC CHEMISTRY. *Educ:* Univ Dayton, BS, 62; Ind Univ, PhD(org chem), 66. *Prof Exp:* Sr res chemist, Mound Lab, Monsanto Res Corp, Ohio, 66-68; res assoc biol chem, Amherst Col, 68-69; asst prof, 69-74, assoc prof, 74-77, PROF CHEM, SOUTHERN ILL UNIV, EDWARDSVILLE, 78- *Mem:* AAAS; Am Chem Soc. *Res:* Kinetics and mechanism of enzyme action; transfer reactions of borazines, free radical rearrangement and participation. *Mailing Add:* Dept Chem Southern Ill Univ Edwardsville IL 62025

MATTANO, LEONARD AUGUST, b Tampa, Fla, July 8, 17; m 41; c 5. ORGANIC CHEMISTRY. *Educ:* Univ Wis, BS, 41; Mich State Univ, PhD, 48. *Prof Exp:* Chemist, Allis-Chalmers Co, Wis, 41-42 & Dow Chem Co, Mich, 42-45; res chemist, Standard Oil Co, Ind, 48-56; sr res chemist, Dow Chem Co, 56-69; DIR CHEM RES, BISSELL, INC, 69- *Mem:* Am Chem Soc. *Res:* Motor oil additives; chelate resins; surfactants; general syntheses; chemical specialties; aerosols. *Mailing Add:* 2325 Ducoma Dr NW Grand Rapids MI 49504

MATTAR, FARRES PHILLIP, b Cairo, Egypt, Dec 21, 47; US citizen. QUANTUM ELECTRONICS, COMPUTATIONAL PHYSICS. *Educ:* Col des Freres de la Salle, Cairo, Baccalaureat, 64; Ain Shams Univ, Cairo, BScEE, 69; Polytech Inst, Brooklyn, MScEE, 70, PhD(electrophys & quantum elec), 75. *Prof Exp:* Fel, Lab Laser Energetics, nonlinear optics laser fusion feasability proj, Univ Rochester, 76-77, res assoc, quantum optics, Physics & Astron, 77; external res consult thermal blooming nonlinear propagation, Plasma Physics Group, Univ Montreal, 77-78; asst res prof computational physics, Polytech Inst of NY, Aerodynamics Lab, 78-81; ASSOC RES PROF, POLYTECH INST OF NY, 81- *Concurrent Pos:* External res consult, Aerodynamic Lab, Polytech Inst of NY, 78, physics Univ Montreal, 78, physics & astron, Univ Rochester, NY, 77- & physics, Univ Southern Calif, 79; vis res scientist, Spectroscopy Lab, Mass Inst Technol, 80-; consult, Battelle Mem Inst & Los Alamos Nat Lab, 80- *Mem:* Sigma Xi; Am Phys Soc; Optical Soc Am; Inst Elec & Electronic Engrs; NY Acad Sci. *Res:* Simulation of nonlinear physical processes to understand fundamental phenomena; coherent self lensing phenomena; swept gain super radiance; self focusing in multiphoton sonisation processes; fluid analogy of light propagation. *Mailing Add:* 73 Cranberry St Brooklyn NY 11201

MATTAUCH, ROBERT JOSEPH, b Rochester, Pa, May 30, 40; m 62; c 2. ELECTRICAL ENGINEERING. *Educ:* Carnegie Inst Technol, BSEE, 62; NC State Col, MEE, 64; NC State Univ, PhD(elec eng), 67. *Prof Exp:* Assoc prof, 66-72, PROF ELEC ENG, UNIV VA, 72-, DIR SEMICONDUCTOR DEVICE LAB, 70- *Mem:* Inst Elec & Electronics Engrs; Sigma Xi. *Res:* Solid state electrical engineering; semiconductor devices and insulator studies; millimeter wave mixer elements. *Mailing Add:* Dept Elec Eng Univ Va Charlottesville VA 22901

MATTAX, CALVIN COOLIDGE, b Sallisaw, Okla, Feb 4, 25; m 49; c 4. PHYSICAL CHEMISTRY. *Educ:* Univ Tulsa, BChem, 50; La State Univ, MS, 52, PhD(phys chem), 54. *Prof Exp:* Eng supvr, Esso Prod Res Co, 55-75, DIV MGR, EXXON PROD RES CO, 76- *Mem:* Am Chem Soc; Am Inst Mining, Metall & Petrol Eng. *Res:* Electrochemical kinetics; properties of polymer solutions; fluid mechanics in porous media; reservoir engineering. *Mailing Add:* PO Box 2189 Houston TX 77001

MATTE, JOSEPH, III, b Detroit, Mich, Feb 14, 16; m 56; c 3. NUCLEAR ENGINEERING, MECHANICAL ENGINEERING. *Educ:* Wayne State Univ, BSME, 38. *Prof Exp:* Mech engr, Ternsted Mfg Div, Gen Motors Corp, 40-42 & 47-48, Ford Motor Co, 48, Budd Co, 48-57; mech engr, Atomic Power Develop Assoc Inc, 57-63, unit leader mech group, 63-66, sect head, 66-72; proj qual assurance engr, Detroit Edison Co, 73-75; PROG MGR, ELEC POWER RES INST, 75- *Mem:* Am Inst Plant Engrs; Am Nuclear Soc; Am Soc Mech Engrs. *Res:* Mechanisms for large sodium-cooled fast reactors; physical and chemical fundamentals basic to design of sodium system components; inspection and repair of nuclear reactors; management of nuclear plant design projects. *Mailing Add:* Elec Power Res Inst PO Box 10412 Palo Alto CA 94303

MATTEI, JANET AKYÜZ, b Bodrum, Turkey, Jan 2, 43; m 72. ASTRONOMY. *Educ:* Brandeis Univ, BA, 65; Ege Univ, Turkey, Yüksek Lisans, 70; Univ Va, MS, 72. *Prof Exp:* Teacher physics, astron & phys sci, Am Col Inst, Turkey, 67-69; teaching asst astron, Ege Univ, Turkey, 69-70; asst dir, 72-73, DIR ASTRON, AM ASN VARIABLE STAR OBSERVERS, 73- *Mem:* Int Astron Union; Am Asn Variable Star Observers; Am Astron Soc. *Res:* Visual and photometric studies of variable stars, particularly dwarf novae, T Tauri stars and long period variables. *Mailing Add:* Am Asn Variable Star Observers 187 Concord Ave Cambridge MA 02138

MATTEN, LAWRENCE CHARLES, b Newark, NJ, Sept 1, 38; m 59; c 4. PALEOBOTANY, PLANT MORPHOLOGY. *Educ:* Rutgers Univ, BA, 59; Cornell Univ, PhD(bot), 65. *Prof Exp:* Instr biol, State Univ NY Col Cortland, 64-65; asst prof, 65-70, assoc prof, 70-77, PROF BOT, SOUTHERN ILL UNIV, CARBONDALE, 77- *Concurrent Pos:* Assoc ed, Palaeontographica. *Mem:* Int Orgn Paleobot; Linnean Soc London; Bot Soc Am; Paleont Soc; Palaeont Asn. *Res:* Elucidation of Paleozoic flora, especially Devonian plants from eastern United States and Devonian/Missippian transition floras. *Mailing Add:* Dept of Bot Southern Ill Univ Carbondale IL 62901

MATTENHEIMER, HERMANN G W, b Berlin, Ger, Mar 29, 21; m 43; c 3. BIOCHEMISTRY. *Educ:* Univ Gottingen, MD, 47. *Prof Exp:* Asst physician, Helmstedt Dist Hosp, Ger, 45-49; res asst, Berlin, 49-51; res asst, Free Univ Berlin, 51-55, privat-docent, 55-59; from asst prof to assoc prof biochem, Univ Ill, 59-71, PROF BIOCHEM, RUSH MED COL, 71-, ASSOC CHAIRPERSON, 81- *Concurrent Pos:* Dir clin chem, Presby-St Luke's Hosp, 59-; res fel, Theodor Kocher Inst, Switz, 51-53; Rusk Orsteel Found fel, Carlsberg Lab, Denmark, 55, WHO fel, 56-57. *Mem:* AAAS; Am Chem Soc; NY Acad Sci; Am Soc Biol Chem; Ger Soc Biol Chem. *Res:* Cell metabolism; ultramicrotechniques for enzyme determinations in single cells; clinical chemistry; clotting of casein; renal biochemistry. *Mailing Add:* Med Dept Tissue Lab St Lukes Hosp 1753 W Congress Pkwy Chicago IL 60612

MATTEO, MARTHA R, biochemistry, see previous edition

MATTERN, MICHAEL ROSS, b Palmerton, Pa, Oct 29, 47. BIOCHEMISTRY, MOLECULAR BIOLOGY. *Educ:* Muhlenberg Col, BS, 69; Princeton Univ, MA, 72, PhD(biochem), 75. *Prof Exp:* Fel biochem lab radiobiol, Univ Calif, San Francisco, 75-78; SR STAFF FEL BIOCHEM, LAB MOLECULAR CARCINOGENESIS, NAT CANCER INST, NIH, 78- *Mem:* Radiation Res Soc; Biophys Soc. *Res:* Molecular and cell biology of DNA replication and DNA repair in mammalian cells; chromosome structure and function. *Mailing Add:* Nat Cancer Inst NIH Bldg 37 Rm 3C27 Bethesda MD 20014

MATTERN, PAUL JOSEPH, b Winnetoon, Nebr, Jan 26, 22; m 56; c 4. ANALYTICAL CHEMISTRY. *Educ:* Univ Northern Iowa, BA, 47; Univ Wis, MS, 51. *Prof Exp:* Instr biochem & nutrit, 53-59, from asst prof to assoc prof agron, 59-70, PROF AGRON, UNIV NEBR, LINCOLN, 71- *Mem:* Sigma Xi; Am Asn Cereal Chemists. *Res:* Environmental and genetic effects on the chemical, physical and nutritional properties of wheat constituents. *Mailing Add:* Dept of Agron Univ of Nebr Lincoln NE 68583

MATTES, FREDERICK HENRY, b Sheboygan, Wis, Feb 18, 41; m 64; c 2. ANALYTICAL CHEMISTRY. *Educ:* Carroll Col, BS, 63; Ind Univ, PhD(chem), 68. *Prof Exp:* From instr to asst prof chem, Willamette Univ, 67-76; asst prof, 76-79, ASSOC PROF CHEM, HASTINGS COL, 79- *Mem:* Am Chem Soc. *Res:* Electroanalytical chemistry, particularly polarography and other voltammetric methods. *Mailing Add:* Dept of Chem Hastings Col Hastings NE 68901

MATTES, HANS GEORGE, b Washington, DC, Jan 27, 43; m 68; c 3. ELECTRICAL ENGINEERING, PHYSICS. *Educ:* Calif Inst Technol, BS, 64; Univ Southern Calif, MS, 66, PhD(elec eng), 68. *Prof Exp:* Mem tech staff electronics, Bell Tel Lab, 68-70; vis assoc prof, elec eng, Nat Taiwan Univ, 70-71; MEM TECH STAFF ELECTRONICS, BELL TEL LAB, 72- *Concurrent Pos:* Fel NSF, 64-68. *Res:* Man and machine interaction; telecommunications input-output technology. *Mailing Add:* Bell Tel Lab Indianapolis IN 46256

MATTESON, DONALD STEPHEN, b Kalispell, Mont, Nov 8, 32; m 53, 71; c 2. ORGANOMETALLIC CHEMISTRY. *Educ:* Univ Calif, BS, 54; Univ Ill, PhD(chem), 57. *Prof Exp:* Res chemist, E I du Pont de Nemours & Co, 57-58; from instr to assoc prof, 58-69, PROF CHEM, WASH STATE UNIV, 69- *Concurrent Pos:* Sloan Found fel, 66-68; mem comt examrs, Advan Chem Test, Grad Record Exam, 70- *Mem:* Am Chem Soc; AAAS. *Res:* Boron-substituted carbanions as synthetic intermediates; directed chiral synthesis with boronic esters as intermediates; organometallic reaction mechanisms; amino and amido boronic acids as enzyme inhibitors; tetrametallomethane chemistry; carboranes. *Mailing Add:* Dept of Chem Wash State Univ Pullman WA 99164

MATTESON, JOHN WARREN, b Flint, Mich, Nov 6, 32; m 58; c 3. ECONOMIC ENTOMOLOGY. *Educ:* Univ Ill, AB, 54, MS, 56, PhD, 59. *Prof Exp:* Asst entom, State Natural Hist Surv, Ill, 54-56; res assoc, Univ Ill, 56-58; entomologist, Entom Res Div, Agr Res Serv, USDA, 59-63 & Develop Dept, Monsanto Co, Mo, 63-67; ENTOMOLOGIST, AGRICHEM RES LAB, MINN MINING & MFG CO, 67- *Mem:* Entom Soc Am. *Res:* Plant resistance to insects; insecticide residues; insect physiology; toxicology; taxonomy. *Mailing Add:* Agrichem Res Lab Minn Mining & Mfg Co St Paul MN 55101

MATTESON, MICHAEL JUDE, b Everett, Wash, Dec 25, 36; m 63; c 3. AEROSOLS, MASS TRANSFER. *Educ:* Univ Wash, BS, 58, MS, 60; Clausthal Tech Univ, DrEng, 67. *Prof Exp:* USPHS fel radiation biol & biophys, Univ Rochester, 67-69; from asst prof to assoc prof, 69-79, PROF CHEM ENG, GA INST TECHNOL, 79- *Concurrent Pos:* NSF res grants, Sch Chem Eng, Ga Inst Technol, 70-72 & 77-81; Environ Protection Agency air pollution training grant, 70-76; Fulbright-Hays lectureship, Inst Exp Physics, Univ Vienna, Austria, 74-75; res grant, Dept of Energy, 77-79. *Mem:* Am Inst Chem Engrs; Am Chem Soc; Air Pollution Control Asn; Fine Particle Soc. *Res:* Aerosol characteristics; particle-gas reactions; nucleation; atomization; atmospheric chemistry. *Mailing Add:* Sch of Chem Eng GA Inst of Technol Atlanta GA 30332

MATTFELD, GEORGE FRANCIS, b Port Jefferson, NY, May 2, 41. WILDLIFE ECOLOGY, PHYSIOLOGICAL ECOLOGY. *Educ:* State Univ NY Col Forestry, BS, 62, Col Environ Sci & Forestry, PhD(zool), 74; Univ Mich, MWM, 64. *Prof Exp:* Instr, State Univ NY Col Forestry, 62; res asst, Univ Mich, 64-65; res asst, State Univ NY Col Environ Sci & Forestry, 65-72, res assoc, 72-77, sr res assoc, 77-78; supvry wildlife biologist, 78-81, ENVIRON MGT SPECIALIST, NY STATE DEPT ENVIRON CONSERV, 81- *Concurrent Pos:* Adj assoc prof, State Univ NY Col Environ Sci & Forestry, 78- *Mem:* Wildlife Soc. *Res:* Wildlife ecology and management; energetics of foraging; deer forest relationships. *Mailing Add:* 24 Crow Ridge Rd Voorheesville NY 12186

MATTHAEI, GEORGE L(AWRENCE), b Tacoma, Wash, Aug 28, 23; m 53; c 2. ELECTRICAL ENGINEERING. *Educ:* Univ Wash, BS, 48; Stanford Univ, MS, 49, EE, 51, PhD(elec eng), 52. *Prof Exp:* Asst, Stanford Univ, 49-51; from instr to asst prof elec eng, Univ Calif, 51-55; mem tech staff, Ramo-Woolridge Corp, 55-58; sr res engr, Stanford Res Inst, 58-60, asst head microwave group, 60-62, mgr electromagnetic tech lab, 62-64; PROF ELEC ENG, UNIV CALIF, SANTA BARBARA, 64- *Honors & Awards:* Microwave Prize, Inst Elec & Electronics Engrs, 61. *Mem:* Fel Inst Elec & Electronics Engrs. *Res:* Microwave device research; acoustic devices for electric signal processing; electric circuit synthesis. *Mailing Add:* Dept of Elec Eng & Comput Sci Univ of Calif Santa Barbara CA 93106

MATTHEIS, EULA BINGHAM, b Covington, Ky, July 9, 29; m 59; c 3. ENVIRONMENTAL HEALTH. *Educ:* Eastern Ky Univ, BS, 51; Univ Cincinnati, MS, 54, PhD(zool), 58. *Prof Exp:* Res asst deep mycoses, Jewish Hosp, Cincinnati, Ohio, 54-55; res assoc indust health, 57, asst prof environ health, 62-70, ASSOC PROF ENVIRON HEALTH, COL MED, UNIV CINCINNATI, 70- *Res:* Bioassay of chemical carcinogens in human environment, factors altering potency; role of alveolar macrophages in pulmonary defense; effect of metallic and carcinogenic particulates on lung; modification of toxicity by aging. *Mailing Add:* 922 Edwards Rd Cincinnati OH 45208

MATTHEIS, FLOYD E, b Ellendale, NDak, Dec 21, 31; m 55; c 5. SCIENCE EDUCATION. *Educ:* Univ NDak, BS, 52; Univ NC, MEd, 59, EdD, 62. *Prof Exp:* Teacher high sch, Minn, 54-58; from asst prof to assoc prof, 60-66, PROF SCI EDUC & CHMN DEPT, E CAROLINA UNIV, 66- *Concurrent Pos:* Dir NSF In-serv Inst Earth Sci for Elem Sch Teachers, 64-65 & Dist IV Nat Sci Teachers Asn, 72-74. *Mem:* AAAS; Asn Educ Teachers Sci; Nat Educ Asn; Nat Asn Res Sci Teaching; Nat Sci Teachers Asn (dir, 72-74). *Res:* Experimental studies in science teaching. *Mailing Add:* Dept Sci Educ E Carolina Univ Greenville NC 27834

MATTHES, RALPH KENNETH, JR, b Conway, SC, July 27, 35; m 56; c 3. AGRICULTURAL & BIOLOGICAL ENGINEERING. *Educ:* NC State Univ, BS, 56, MS, 61, PhD(biol & agr eng), 65. *Prof Exp:* From asst to assoc agr eng, NC State Univ, 59-65; asst prof, 65-68, assoc prof agr & biol eng, 68-72, PROF AGR & BIOL ENG, MISS STATE UNIV, 72- *Mem:* Am Soc Agr Engrs; Nat Soc Prof Engrs; Am Soc Eng Educ; Soc Am Forestry. *Res:* Drying and storage of seed under tropical condition; forest engineering research with emphasis in tree harvesting systems, site preparation for tree plantings, and fuel use during forestry operations. *Mailing Add:* Dept of Agr & Biol Eng Miss State Univ Box 5465 Mississippi State MS 39762

MATTHEWS, BRIAN WESLEY, b SAustralia, May 25, 38; m 63; c 2. MOLECULAR BIOLOGY, X-RAY CRYSTALLOGRAPHY. *Educ:* Univ Adelaide, BSc, 59, Hons, 60, PhD(physics), 64. *Prof Exp:* Mem staff, Med Res Coun Lab Molecular Biol, Eng, 63-66; vis assoc molecular biol, NIH, 67-68; assoc prof, 69-72, PROF & RES ASSOC PHYSICS & MOLECULAR BIOL, UNIV ORE, 72-, DIR, INST MOLECULAR BIOL, 80- *Concurrent Pos:* Sloan Res Found fel, 71; Guggenheim Mem Found fel, 77; mem, US Nat Comt Crystallog, 80- *Mem:* Am Crystallog Asn. *Res:* Protein structure and function; crystallography. *Mailing Add:* Inst Molecular Biol Univ Ore Eugene OR 97403

MATTHEWS, BURTON CLARE, b Kerwood, Ont, Dec 16, 26; m 51; c 2. SOIL CHEMISTRY. *Educ:* Ont Agr Col, BSA, 47; Univ Mo, AM, 48; Cornell Univ, PhD, 52. *Prof Exp:* From asst prof to assoc prof soil classification, Ont Agr Col, Guelph, 48-55, prof soil fertil & chem, 55-62, head dept soil sci, 62-66, acad vpres, 66-70; pres, Univ Waterloo, 70-81, vchancellor, 78-81; CHMN, ONT COUN UNIV AFFAIRS, 81- *Concurrent Pos:* Fel natural sci, Nuffield Found, 60-61; dir, Ont Educ Commun Authority, 72-78, Campbell Soup Co Ltd, 79- *Mem:* AAAS; Can Soil Sci Soc. *Res:* Soil genesis, classification and fertility. *Mailing Add:* 245 Old Post Rd Waterloo ON N2L 5B8 Can

MATTHEWS, CHARLES ROBERT, b Philadelphia, Pa, May 12, 46; m 68; c 3. BIOPHYSICAL CHEMISTRY. *Educ:* Univ Minn, BS, 68; Stanford Univ, MS, 69, PhD(chem), 74. *Prof Exp:* Fel biochem, Stanford Univ, 74-75; ASST PROF CHEM, PA STATE UNIV, UNIVERSITY PARK, 75- *Mem:* Am Chem Soc. *Res:* Conformational changes in biological macromolecules; mechanisms of reversible unfolding transitions in proteins; effect of missense mutations on protein folding and stability; chemical trapping of intermediates in protein folding. *Mailing Add:* Dept of Chem 152 Davey Lab Pa State Univ University Park PA 16802

MATTHEWS, CHARLES SEDWICK, b Houston, Tex, Mar 27, 20; m 45; c 2. EARTH SCIENCES. *Educ:* Rice Inst, BS, 41, MS, 43, PhD(phys chem), 44. *Prof Exp:* Engr chem plant design, Shell Develop Co, 44-48, chemist, 48-56, sr res assoc, 56-66, mgr exploitation eng, Shell Oil Co, 66-67, dir prod res, Shell Develop Co, 67-72; mgr eng, 72-73, SR CONSULT PETROL ENGR, SHELL OIL CO, 73- *Honors & Awards:* Lester C Uren Award, Soc Petrol Engrs, 75. *Mem:* Soc Petrol Engrs; Am Petrol Inst. *Res:* New methods for recovery of petroleum; behavior of petroleum reservoirs; geothermal energy; recovery from tar sands and oil shale. *Mailing Add:* Shell Oil Co PO Box 2463 Houston TX 77001

MATTHEWS, CLIFFORD NORMAN, b Hong Kong, China, Dec 20, 21; nat US; m 47; c 2. ORGANIC CHEMISTRY. *Educ:* Univ London, BSc, 50; Yale Univ, PhD(chem), 55. *Prof Exp:* Lab supt, Birkbeck Col, London, 46-48; res chemist, Conn Hard Rubber Co, 50-51, Diamond Alkali Co, 55-59 & Monsanto Co, 59-69; PROF CHEM, UNIV ILL, CHICAGO CIRCLE, 69- *Mem:* AAAS; Am Chem Soc; Royal Soc Chem. *Res:* Chemical evolution: origin of molecules in biochemistry, geochemistry and galactochemistry. *Mailing Add:* Dept of Chem Univ of Ill at Chicago Circle Chicago IL 60680

MATTHEWS, DAVID ALLAN, b Washington, DC, Feb 5, 43; m 67; c 2. BIOPHYSICAL CHEMISTRY. *Educ:* Earlham Col, AB, 65; Univ Ill, PhD(chem), 71. *Prof Exp:* Fel chem, 71-76, ASSOC RES CHEMIST, UNIV CALIF, SAN DIEGO, 76- *Concurrent Pos:* Jane Coffin Childs Mem Fund Med Res fel, 72-74; Nat Cancer Inst fel, 74-76. *Res:* X-ray crystallographic studies on the molecular structure and mechanism of action of dihydrofolate reductase; design of species specific reductase. *Mailing Add:* Dept Chem Univ Calif San Diego La Jolla CA 92093

MATTHEWS, DAVID LESUEUR, b Ottawa, Ont, May 10, 28; m 56; c 3. PLASMA PHYSICS, SPACE PHYSICS. *Educ:* Queen's Univ, Ont, BSc, 49; Princeton Univ, PhD(physics), 59. *Prof Exp:* Res officer, Nat Res Coun Can, 49-53; instr physics, Princeton Univ, 57-59; lectr, Carleton Univ, 59-60; sci officer, Defense Res Telecommun Estab, 60-66; RES ASSOC PROF, INST PHYS SCI & TECHNOL, UNIV MD, COLLEGE PARK, 66- *Concurrent Pos:* Rocket sect leader, Defense Res Telecommun Estab, 63-65. *Mem:* Am Geophys Union; Am Phys Soc; Inst Elec & Electronics Engrs. *Res:* Space and upper atmosphere physics. *Mailing Add:* Inst for Phys Sci & Technol Univ of Md College Park MD 20742

MATTHEWS, DAVID LIVINGSTONE, b New York, NY, Mar 13, 22; m 44; c 4. AGRONOMY, PLANT BREEDING. *Educ:* Rutgers Univ, BS, 48, MS, 50. *Prof Exp:* Asst farm crops, Rutgers Univ, 48-50; tech specialist radiation genetics, Brookhaven Nat Lab, 50-52; plant breeder, Eastern State Farmers Exchange, 52-54, mgr corn res, 55-64; mgr seed res, 65-66, dir farm eval & seed res, 66-68, dir crops res, 68-81, DIR CROPS RES & DEVELOPMENT, AGWAY INC, 81- *Concurrent Pos:* Dir, Farmers Forage Res Coop, 65-68. *Mem:* Genetics Soc Am; Am Soc Agron; Crop Sci Soc Am; Am Soc Hort Sci; Coun Agr Sci & Technol. *Res:* Mulch and irrigation management of vegetables; dairy and poultry manure management for optimum crop returns; forage nutrient conservation through crop management and use of chemical preservatives; high yield research with corn cereals, alfalfa and potatoes; computer applications to crop input recommendations and field history records. *Mailing Add:* Agway Inc Box 4933 Syracuse NY 13221

MATTHEWS, DEMETREOS NESTOR, b Portchester, NY, June 28, 28; m 53; c 2. ORGANIC CHEMISTRY. *Educ:* Rutgers Univ, BS, 49; Polytech Inst Brooklyn, PhD(chem), 60. *Prof Exp:* Chemist, Res Labs, Air Reduction Co, Inc, 52-54; res scientist org chem, Res Ctr, US Rubber Co, 59-67, SR RES SCIENTIST ORG CHEM, UNIROYAL RES CTR, 67- *Mem:* Am Chem Soc. *Res:* Organic reaction mechanisms; Diels-Alder reactions; solution polymerization; free radical reactions; correlation of mechanism with structure. *Mailing Add:* 40 Brookwood Rd Bethany CT 06525

MATTHEWS, DOYLE JENSEN, b Liberty, Idaho, Apr 13, 26; m 46; c 5. ANIMAL BREEDING. *Educ:* Utah State Univ, BS, 50, MS, 51; Kans State Univ, PhD, 59. *Prof Exp:* From instr to assoc prof animal husb, 51-65, asst dean, Col Agr, 65-69, assoc dean, 69-71, PROF ANIMAL, DAIRY & VET SCI, UTAH STATE UNIV, 66-, DEAN, COL AGR, 71-, DIR, AGR EXP STA, 74- *Mem:* Am Soc Animal Sci. *Res:* Improvement of carcass characteristics and productivity of meat animals through application of breeding techniques and methods. *Mailing Add:* Col of Agr Utah State Univ Logan UT 84321

MATTHEWS, E(DWARD) K, mechanical engineering, see previous edition

MATTHEWS, E(DGAR) W(ESLEY), JR, b Johnstown, Pa, May 19, 25; m 49; c 2. ELECTRICAL ENGINEERING. *Educ:* Rensselaer Polytech Inst, BEE, 46, MEE, 50; Harvard Univ, PhD(appl physics), 54. *Prof Exp:* Jr engr, Westinghouse Res Labs, 46-47; instr elec eng, Rensselaer Polytech Inst, 47-49; proj engr, Sperry Gyroscope Co, 53-54, sr engr, 54-55; from asst prof to assoc prof elec eng, Rensselaer Polytech Inst, 55-58; engr microwave res, Radio Corp Am, 58-60, eng leader, 60-62; dept head, Sperry Microwave Electronics Corp, 62-65; mgr solid state component res & develop, Watkins-Johnson Co, 65-66; sr staff specialist, Sylvania Electronic Systs-W, 66-68; independent consult, 68-70; staff scientist, Philco-Ford Corp, 70-76, PRIN ENGR, FORD AEROSPACE & COMMUN CORP, 76- *Mem:* Sr mem Inst Elec & Electronics Engrs. *Res:* Microwave theory and techniques; microwave devices and antennas. *Mailing Add:* 1264 Via Huerta Los Altos CA 94022

MATTHEWS, EDWARD WHITEHOUSE, b Annapolis, Md, Mar 7, 36. ANALYTICAL CHEMISTRY, ORGANIC CHEMISTRY. *Educ:* US Mil Acad, BS, 58; Univ Tex, MS, 71; Rutgers Univ, PhD(environ sci), 78. *Prof Exp:* Res chemist org chem, 76-81, RES CHEMIST TRACE METALS, US GEOL SURV, 81- *Concurrent Pos:* Res fel, Rutgers Univ, 70-71. *Mem:* Am Chem Soc; Asn Off Anal Chem; Am Soc Testing & Mat; Sigma Xi. *Res:* Organic chemicals found in association with waters, wastewaters, fish, plant tissues and sedimentary deposits. *Mailing Add:* 205 Parkmont Ct Roswell GA 30076

MATTHEWS, FLOYD V(ERNON), JR, b Parksley, Va, Aug 4, 27; m 46; c 6. AGRICULTURAL ENGINEERING. *Educ:* Va Polytech Inst, BS, 51; Okla State Univ, MS, 51; Mich State Univ, PhD, 66. *Prof Exp:* Layout draftsman, Int Harvester Co, 51-55; from asst prof to assoc prof agr eng, Univ Md, College Park, 55-68; assoc prof, 68-70, PROF AGR ENG & CHMN DEPT, CALIF STATE POLYTECH UNIV, POMONA, 70- *Concurrent Pos:* Agr consult, Ministry Educ, Greece, 72. *Mem:* Am Soc Agr Engrs; Am Soc Eng Educ. *Res:* Agricultural and food processing. *Mailing Add:* Dept of Agr Eng 3801 W Temple Ave Pomona CA 91768

MATTHEWS, FREDERICK WHITE, b Carbonear, Nfld, Nov 27, 15; m 43; c 4. CHEMISTRY, INFORMATION SCIENCE. *Educ:* Mt Allison Univ, BSc, 36; McGill Univ, PhD(phys chem), 41. *Prof Exp:* Res chemist, Can Industs Ltd, Montreal, 41-51, asst mgr prod, 51-56, mgr info serv, 56-69; mgr, Cent Tech Info Unit, Imp Chem Industs, Ltd, Eng, 69-72; PROF INFO SCI, SCH LIBR SERV, DALHOUSIE UNIV, 72- *Concurrent Pos:* Chmn data comn, Int Union Crystallog, 48-72; mem adv bd sci & tech info, Nat Res Coun Can, 72-77; consult, Info Systs, Imp Chem Industs, Eng, 72-76, Indexing Systs, Inst Jamaica, Kingston, 74-76 & Dartmouth Regional Libr, NS, 75. *Mem:* Chem Inst Can; Can Asn Info Sci; Am Soc Info Sci. *Res:* Library catalogue systems; x-ray diffraction powder data; systems for data retrieval; systems for storage and retrieval of information on computers. *Mailing Add:* Sch Libr Serv Dalhousie Univ Halifax NS B3H 4H8 Can

MATTHEWS, GARY JOSEPH, b Denver, Colo, Aug 6, 42; m 64; c 3. ORGANIC CHEMISTRY. *Educ:* Colo State Univ, BS, 64; Univ Colo, Boulder, PhD(org chem), 68. *Prof Exp:* Syntex res grant, Inst Org Chem, Syntex Res, Palo Alto, 68-69, res chemist, Arapahoe Chems Div, Syntex Corp, 69-72, group leader, 72, mgr res, 72-76, DIR RES & DEVELOP, ARAPAHOE CHEMS INC, 76- *Mem:* Am Chem Soc. *Res:* Process research and development on the production of fine organic chemicals. *Mailing Add:* Res Dept Arapahoe Chems Inc 2075 N 55th St Boulder CO 80301

MATTHEWS, HAZEL BENTON, JR, b Hertford, NC, Feb 8, 40; m 65; c 2. BIOCHEMICAL PHARMACOLOGY. *Educ:* NC State Univ, BS, 63, MS, 65; Univ Wis-Madison, PhD(entom), 68. *Prof Exp:* NIH grant, Univ Calif, Berkeley, 68-70; staff fel chem, 70-71, sr staff fel, 71-74, RES CHEM, NAT INST ENVIRON HEALTH SCI, NIH, 74- *Mem:* Soc Toxicol. *Res:* Development of kinetic parameters to describe absorption, tissue distribution, metabolism and excretion of lipid soluble chemicals in laboratory animals; use of kinetics to extrapolate laboratory data to man. *Mailing Add:* Lab of Pharmacokinetics Nat Inst Environ Health Sci NIH Research Triangle Park NC 27709

MATTHEWS, HERBERT MAURICE, physics, see previous edition

MATTHEWS, HEWITT WILLIAM, b Pensacola, Fla, Dec 1, 44; m 69; c 1. PHARMACEUTICAL CHEMISTRY. *Educ:* Clark Col, BS, 66; Mercer Univ, BS, 68; Univ Wis, MS, 71, PhD(pharm, biochem), 73. *Prof Exp:* Asst prof, 73-75, assoc prof & dir res, 75-81, PROF PHARM & ASST DEAN SERV, 81- *Mem:* Sigma Xi; AAAS; Am Asn Cols Pharm; Nat Inst Sci. *Res:* Pharmacologically active agents from microbial origin; screening for agents from fermentation broths that have anti inflamatory properties. *Mailing Add:* Mercer Univ Sch Pharm 345 Boulevard Ave NE Atlanta GA 30312

MATTHEWS, JAMES B, b Ft Benning, Ga, May 15, 33; m 53; c 3. AEROSPACE & MECHANICAL ENGINEERING. *Educ:* Rose Polytech Inst, BS, 54; Mass Inst Technol, MS, 59; Univ Ariz, PhD(aerospace eng), 66. *Prof Exp:* Design engr, Collins Radio Co, 54; instr mech eng, Rose-Hulman Inst Technol, 56-58, asst prof, 59-63, prof & chmn dept, 66-78, dean fac, 70-78; PROF MECH ENG & CHMN DEPT, WESTERN MICH UNIV, 78- *Mem:* Am Soc Mech Engrs; Am Soc Eng Educ; Soc Automotive Engrs. *Res:* Vibrations and structural dynamics. *Mailing Add:* Dept of Mech Eng Western Mich Univ Kalamazoo MI 49008

MATTHEWS, JAMES FRANCIS, b Winston-Salem, NC, Sept 14, 35; m 61; c 2. CYTOLOGY, PLANT TAXONOMY. *Educ:* Atlantic Christian Col, BA, 57; Cornell Univ, MS, 60; Emory Univ, PhD(cytol), 62. *Prof Exp:* Asst prof biol, Western Ky State Col, 62-64; from asst prof to assoc prof, 64-72, PROF BIOL, UNIV NC, CHARLOTTE, 72- *Mem:* Int Asn Plant Taxon; Am Inst Biol Sci; Am Asn Plant Taxon. *Res:* Speciation of plants endemic to the granite outcrops of the southeastern Piedmont; endangered and threatened plant species and habitats; floristics of urban areas. *Mailing Add:* Dept of Biol Univ of NC Charlotte NC 28223

MATTHEWS, JAMES HORACE, b Campbellton, NB, Mar 1, 30; m 54; c 5. NUCLEAR PHYSICS. *Educ:* Mt Allison Univ, BSc & cert eng, 51; Dalhousie Univ, MSc, 54; Univ London, PhD(physics), 57. *Prof Exp:* From asst prof to assoc prof, 57-69, PROF PHYSICS, MT ALLISON UNIV, 69- *Concurrent Pos:* Marjorie Young Bell fel, Univ Sussex, 66-67; vis prof, Univ Toronto, 74-75. *Mem:* Can Asn Physicists; Brit Inst Physics. *Res:* Theoretical nuclear physics; nuclear models; microwave gas discharge; picture enhancement. *Mailing Add:* Dept of Physics Mt Allison Univ Sackville NB E0A 3C0 Can

MATTHEWS, JAMES LESTER, b Denton, Tex, July 3, 26; m 50; c 3. MICROSCOPIC ANATOMY. *Educ:* NTex State Col, BS, 48, MS, 49; Univ Ill, PhD, 55. *Prof Exp:* Asst biol, NTex State Col, 47-48; instr biol & chem, Cisco Jr Col, 49-52; asst physiol, Univ Ill, 52-55; from res asst to assoc prof anat & physiol, 55-60, PROF MICROS ANAT & CHMN DEPT HISTOLMICROS ANAT, BAYLOR COL DENT, 60-, ASSOC DEAN, BAYLOR UNIV MED CTR, 74- *Mem:* Am Physiol Soc; assoc Soc Exp Biol & Med; Int Asn Dent Res; Am Asn Anat. *Res:* Physiology and fine structure of bone and connective tissues. *Mailing Add:* Dept Path 3500 Gaston Ave Dallas TX 75246

MATTHEWS, JERRY LEE, marine geology, see previous edition

MATTHEWS, JOHN BRIAN, b Glazebrook, Eng, Feb 15, 38; m 67. OCEANOGRAPHY. *Educ:* Univ London, BSc & ARCS, 60, PhD(cloud physics), 63, Imp Col, London, dipl, 63. *Prof Exp:* Res asst cloud physics, Imp Col, London, 57-63; res assoc, Inst Atmospheric Physics, Univ Ariz, 63-66; asst prof phys oceanog, Inst Marine Sci, 66-69, assoc prof, 69-76, PROF MARINE SCI, GEOPHYS INST, UNIV ALASKA, FAIRBANKS, 76- *Concurrent Pos:* Eckert fel environ sci, IBM-Watson Res Ctr, 73-74; res scientist, Bedford Inst Oceanog, Dartmouth, Can, 75-76; chmn, Working Group Coastal & Estuarine Regimes, Int Asn Phys Sci of the Ocean, 75-; mem, Int Comt Water Resources, 77- *Mem:* Assoc Am Geophys Union; fel Royal Meteorol Soc; fel Royal Geog Soc; Am Soc Limnol & Oceanog; Estuarine & Brackish Water Res Asn. *Res:* Environmental physics; physical oceanography; coastal and estuarine dynamics; tidal and storm surge analysis; hydrodynamical numerical modeling; fjord estuary research; arctic research. *Mailing Add:* Geophys Inst Univ of Alaska Fairbanks AK 99701

MATTHEWS, JUNE LORRAINE, b Cambridge, Mass, Aug 1, 39. NUCLEAR PHYSICS, INTERMEDIATE ENERGY PHYSICS. *Educ:* Carleton Col, BA, 60; Mass Inst Technol, SM, 62, PhD(physics), 67. *Prof Exp:* NSF fel physics, Glasgow Univ, 68-71; res assoc, Rutgers Univ, 71-72; asst prof, 72-75, ASSOC PROF PHYSICS, MASS INST TECHNOL, 75- *Concurrent Pos:* Mem prog adv comt, Los Alamos Meson Physics Facil, 82-84. *Mem:* Am Phys Soc; Sigma Xi. *Res:* Interactions of photons with nuclei; study of nucleon momentum distributions, short-range correlations and meson exchange effects; few-body problems; pion-nucleus interaction mechanisms. *Mailing Add:* Dept Physics Mass Inst Technol Cambridge MA 02139

MATTHEWS, KATHLEEN SHIVE, b Austin, Tex, Aug 30, 45; m 67. BIOCHEMISTRY. *Educ:* Univ Tex, Austin, BS, 66; Univ Calif, Berkeley, PhD(biochem), 70. *Prof Exp:* Am Asn Univ Women fel, Sch Med, Stanford Univ, 70-71, Giannini Found fel, 71-72; asst prof, 72-77, ASSOC PROF BIOCHEM, RICE UNIV, 77- *Concurrent Pos:* NSF fel. *Mem:* Am Soc Biol Chemists; AAAS; Soc Neurosci. *Res:* Chemistry and molecular biology of proteins; studies on the lactose repressor protein from Escherichia coli, including chemical modification, spectroscopy and other physical methods. *Mailing Add:* Dept of Biochem Rice Univ Houston TX 77001

MATTHEWS, LEE DREW, b Platteville, Wis, Mar 10, 43; m 69; c 1. PHYSICS. *Educ:* Wis State Col, BS, 64; Univ Vt, MS, 67, PhD(physics), 69. *Prof Exp:* Asst prof, 69-77, ASSOC PROF PHYSICS, SOUTHERN CONN STATE COL, 77- *Mem:* Am Inst Physics; Am Phys Soc; Am Asn Physics Teachers. *Res:* Surface physics; physics education. *Mailing Add:* Dept of Physics Southern Conn State Col New Haven CT 06515

MATTHEWS, MARTIN DAVID, b Elizabeth, NJ, Dec 10, 38; m 64; c 1. GEOLOGY, GEOCHEMISTRY. *Educ:* Allegheny Col, BS, 60; WVa Univ, MS, 63; Northwestern Univ, PhD(geol), 73. *Prof Exp:* Asst prof geol, Wash State Univ, 72-74; res geologist, 74-76, sr res geologist, 76-77, dir geol sect, 77-79, sr staff geologist, Gulf Oil, 79-81, sr res assoc, Gulf Res & Develop Co, 81, MISSION COORDR SUBSURFACE PROCESSES GEOCHEM, GULF RES & DEVELOP CO, 81- *Concurrent Pos:* Test site dir, Geosat, Inc, 77- *Mem:* Am Soc Photogram; Soc Econ Paleonotol & Mineral; Geol Soc Am; Clay Mineral Soc; Int Asn Sedimentol. *Res:* Flocculation of river sediments; sedimentology; clay mineralogy; geostatistics; remote sensing; basin evaluation; inorganic and petroleum geochemistry. *Mailing Add:* Gulf Res & Develop Co PO Drawer 2038 Pittsburgh PA 15230

MATTHEWS, MARY EILEEN, b Rochester, NY, May 22, 38. FOOD SCIENCE, NUTRITION. *Educ:* Drexel Univ, BS, 60; Okla State Univ, dipl, 61, MS, 62; Univ Wis-Madison, PhD(food sci), 70. *Prof Exp:* Asst nutritionist, Nat Diet Heart Study, Johns Hopkins Hosp, 63-65; res asst, 65-67, asst prof, 70-74, assoc prof, 74-79, PROF FOOD SCI, UNIV WIS-MADISON, 79- *Concurrent Pos:* USPHS grant, 72-73; Am Dietetic Asn & Dept Health, Educ & Welfare grant, Loma Linda Univ, 73-74; prog planning chair, Symposium, Hosp Patient Feeding Syst, US Army Natick Res & Develop Labs, 81. *Mem:* Am Dietetic Asn; Am Sch Food Serv Asn; Inst Food Technol. *Res:* Quality and safety of food produced and served in foodservice systems; optimal use of management resources in foodservice systems. *Mailing Add:* Dept of Food Sci 42 Agr Hall Madison WI 53706

MATTHEWS, MURRAY ALBERT, b Houston, Tex, June 16, 43; m 69; c 1. ANATOMY, NEUROPATHOLOGY. *Educ:* Univ St Thomas, BA, 65; Univ Tex Med Br, MA, 67, PhD(anat), 70. *Prof Exp:* ASST PROF ANAT, MED CTR, LA STATE UNIV, NEW ORLEANS, 72- *Concurrent Pos:* NIH trainee, Brain Res Inst, Med Sch, Univ Calif, Los Angeles, 70-72; Schlieder Educ Found res grant, 74; Nat Inst Neurol & Commun Disorders & Stroke grant. *Mem:* Am Asn Anat; Soc Neurosci. *Res:* Central nervous system trauma; spinal cord injury; reaction of neurons to mechanical or ischemic injury; reactive changes in nonneuronal, vascular elements. *Mailing Add:* Dept of Anat La State Univ Med Ctr New Orleans LA 70119

MATTHEWS, N(EELY) F(ORSYTH) J(ONES), b Clinton, NC, Aug 9, 31. SOLID STATE PHYSICS, ELECTRICAL ENGINEERING. *Educ:* George Washington Univ, BS, 57, MS, 59; Princeton Univ, MA, 62, PhD(solid state physics), 64. *Prof Exp:* Instr elec eng, George Washington Univ, 57-59; from asst prof to assoc prof, 64-76, PROF ELEC ENG, NC STATE UNIV, 76- *Mem:* Inst Elec & Electronics Engrs. *Res:* Electronic and optical properties of cadmium sulfide; photoconductivity; recombination and generation of charge; optical absorption; luminescence. *Mailing Add:* Dept of Elec Eng 232 Daniels Hall Raleigh NC 27607

MATTHEWS, R(OBERT) B(RUCE), b Redbank, NJ, Mar 7, 42; m 66; c 2. CERAMICS, NUCLEAR FUELS. *Educ:* Pa State Univ, BS, 64; Univ Denver, MS, 66; Univ Col Swansea, Wales, PhD(mat sci), 70. *Prof Exp:* Mem staff, Atomic Energy of Can Ltd, 70-78; res scientist, Northwest Labs, Battelle Mem Inst, 78-80; RES SCIENTIST, LOS ALAMOS NAT LABS, 80- *Mem:* Am Ceramic Soc. *Res:* Fabrication development properties and irradiation performance of ceramics and nuclear fuels, oxides, labrbides and silicides. *Mailing Add:* Los Alamos Nat Lab MS505 Los Alamos NM 87544

MATTHEWS, RICHARD FINIS, b Cullman, Ala, June 1, 29; m 55; c 2. FOOD CHEMISTRY, BIOCHEMISTRY. *Educ:* Univ Fla, BSA, 52; Cornell Univ, MS, 57, PhD(food sci), 60. *Prof Exp:* Assoc technologist, Res Ctr, Gen Foods Corp, 60-63; group leader tea chem, T J Lipton Res Ctr, NJ, 63-65; assoc prof, 65-73, PROF FOOD TECHNOL, UNIV FLA, 73- *Mem:* Am Chem Soc; Inst Food Technologists. *Res:* Natural products chemistry; flavor chemistry; processing horticultural crops. *Mailing Add:* Dept of Food Sci Univ of Fla Gainesville FL 32601

MATTHEWS, RICHARD JOHN, JR, b Scranton, Pa, Apr 11, 27; m 53; c 4. PHARMACOLOGY. *Educ:* Philadelphia Col Pharm, BS, 51; Jefferson Med Col, MS, 53, PhD(pharmacol), 55. *Prof Exp:* Head pharmacol res sect, Upjohn Co, Mich, 56-62; pres, Pharmakon, Inc, Pa, 62-65; dir pharmacol, Union Carbide Corp, 65-69; DIR RES, PHARMAKON LABS, 69- *Mem:* Am Soc Pharmacol & Exp Therapeut. *Res:* Action of drugs on synapse in peripheral and central nervous system, especially neurohumoral agents; neuropharmacology of psychotherapeutic drugs and effects of extracts of blood from schizophrenics on the central nervous system. *Mailing Add:* Res Dept Pharmakon Labs Waverly PA 18471

MATTHEWS, ROBERT WENDELL, b Detroit, Mich, Feb 17, 42; m 63; c 5. ENTOMOLOGY. *Educ:* Mich State Univ, BS, 63, MS, 65; Harvard Univ, PhD(biol), 69. *Prof Exp:* Asst prof, 69-74, assoc prof, 74-79, PROF ENTOM, UNIV GA, 79- *Concurrent Pos:* NSF res assoc, Commonwealth Sci & Indust Res Orgn, Canberra, Australia, 69-70 & Inst Miguel Lillo, Tucuman, Arg, 72; prin investr, NSF res grant, 75 & 78. *Mem:* AAAS; Entom Soc Am; Animal Behav Soc; Int Union Study Social Insects. *Res:* Behavior; systematics; ecology and evolution of Hymenoptera, especially Braconidae, Sphedidae and Vespidae; social insects. *Mailing Add:* Dept of Entom Univ of Ga Athens GA 30602

MATTHEWS, ROBLEY KNIGHT, b Dallas, Tex, Oct 6, 35; m 59; c 4. SEDIMENTOLOGY. *Educ:* Rice Univ, BA, 57, MA, 63, PhD(geol), 65. *Prof Exp:* Petrol geologist, Pan Am Petrol Corp, 57-58 & Am Int Oil Co, Libya, 58-60; geologist, Marine Geophys Serv, 60-63; asst prof, 64-71, chmn dept, 71-77, PROF GEOL, BROWN UNIV, 71- *Mem:* Geol Soc Am; Am Asn Petrol Geologists; Soc Econ Paleont & Mineral. *Res:* Sedimentary petrology; physical and chemical aspects of carbonate deposition and diagenesis; dynamics of climate change; mesozoic and cenozoic sea level history; finite resources. *Mailing Add:* Dept of Geol Sci Brown Univ Providence RI 02912

MATTHEWS, ROWENA GREEN, b Cambridge, Eng, Aug 20, 38; US citizen; m 60; c 2. ENZYMOLOGY, METABOLIC REGULATION. *Educ:* Radcliffe Col, BA, 60; Univ Mich, Ann Arbor, PhD(biophys), 69. *Prof Exp:* Instr biol, Univ SC, 63-64; fel biol chem, 71-74, res investr, 74-75, res chemist, Vet Admin Hosp, 75-78, asst prof, 75-81, ASSOC PROF BIOL CHEM, UNIV MICH, ANN ARBOR, 81- *Concurrent Pos:* Estab investr, Am Heart Asn, 78-83. *Mem:* Am Chem Soc; Biophys Soc; Sigma Xi; AAAS; Am Soc Biol Chemists. *Res:* Catalytic mechanisms of folate-dependent enzymes; catalytic mechanisms of flavoprotein dehydrogenases; regulation of folate metabolism. *Mailing Add:* Dept of Biol Chem Univ of Mich Ann Arbor MI 48109

MATTHEWS, THOMAS ROBERT, b Deadwood, SDak, Dec 24, 39; m 63; c 3. MICROBIOLOGY, BIOCHEMISTRY. *Educ:* Univ Wyo, BS, 64, MS, 66; Univ Ind, PhD(microbiol), 72. *Prof Exp:* Microbiologist antifungal chemother, Eli Lilly & Co, 66-69; div dir antimicrobial & antiviral chemother, ICN Parmaceut, 72-77; HEAD ANTIMICROBIAL ANTIVIRAL CHEMOTHER, SYNTEX RES, 77- *Mem:* Am Soc Microbiol. *Res:* Experimental antimicrobial and antiviral chemotherapy; immunomodulation of infectious disease. *Mailing Add:* Syntex 3401 Hillview Ave Palo Alto CA 94304

MATTHEWS, VIRGIL EDISON, b LaFayette, Ala, Oct 5, 28; m 60; c 3. ORGANIC & POLYMER CHEMISTRY. *Educ:* Univ Ill, BS, 51; Univ Chicago, SM, 52, PhD(chem), 55. *Prof Exp:* Teaching asst org chem, Univ Chicago, 51-52; res chemist, Res & Develop Dept, Chem Div, 54-67, Chem & Plastics Div, 67, proj scientist, 67-75, DEVELOP SCIENTIST, CHEM & PLASTICS DIV, UNION CARBIDE CORP, 75- *Concurrent Pos:* Instr, WVa State Col, 55-60, part-time assoc prof & prof, 60-70. *Mem:* Fel AAAS; Am Chem Soc; Royal Soc Chem; fel Am Inst Chemists; Sigma Xi. *Res:* Synthesis, structure properties and uses of polymers; free radical chemistry; organic synthesis; elastomers and polyurethanes; polymeric composites; fibers; synthetic hydrogels; polymer-anchored catalysts; organometallic chemistry. *Mailing Add:* 2106 Kan Blvd E Apt B-626 Charleston WV 25311

MATTHEWS, WILLIAM HENRY, III, b Henrietta, Okla, Mar 1, 19; m 40; c 2. GEOLOGY. *Educ:* Tex Christian Univ, BA, 48, MA, 49. *Prof Exp:* Asst prof geol, Tex Christian Univ, 51-52; subsurface geologist, Tex Co, 52-55; from asst prof to assoc prof, 55-62, PROF GEOL, LAMAR UNIV, 62- *Concurrent Pos:* Consult, Tex Hwy Dept, 58-59, Tex Portland Cement Co, 59-, Earth Sci Curriculum Proj, 62- & Tex Ed Agency, 64-; dir educ, Am Geol Inst, 72-; chief tech adv, Encycl Britannica Earth Sci films, 73-; Regents Prof, Lamar Univ, 74; ed, ref series, Earth Sci Curriculum Proj. *Honors & Awards:* Neil Miner Award, Nat Asn Geol Teachers, 64. *Mem:* AAAS; Geol Soc Am; Soc Econ Paleont & Mineral; Paleont Soc; Am Asn Petrol Geologists; Nat Asn Geol Teachers. *Res:* Invertebrate paleontology; historical petroleum and subsurface geology; paleoecology; stratigraphy; earth science teaching. *Mailing Add:* Dept of Geol Lamar Univ Beaumont TX 77710

MATTHEWS, WILLIAM JOHN, b Memphis, Tenn, Nov 11, 46; m 68; c 2. ICHTHYOLOGY, FISH ECOLOGY. *Educ:* Ark State Univ, BSE, 68, MS, 73; Univ Okla, PhD(zool), 77. *Prof Exp:* Asst prof biol, Roanoke Col, 77-79; RES ASSOC & ASST PROF ICHTHYOL & FISH ECOL, ZOOL DEPT & BIOL STA, UNIV OKLA, 79- *Concurrent Pos:* Assoc ed, Lower Vertebrates, Southwestern Asn Naturalists, 80-; cur fish, Stovall Mus Sci & Hist, Univ Okla, 81- *Mem:* Am Soc Ichthyologists & Herpetologists; Ecol Soc Am; Sigma Xi; Southwestern Asn Naturalists; Am Fisheries Soc. *Res:* Ecology and systematics of North American freshwater fishes, with emphasis on adaptation of fishes to harsh environments, fish community structure, resource use in fish communities, distributional ecology of fishes, and predator-prey interactions in reservoir fisheries to include larval and adult fish. *Mailing Add:* Univ Okla Biol Sta Kingston OK 73439

MATTHIAS, BERND T, physics, deceased

MATTHIAS, JUDSON S, b Schofield Barracks, Hawaii, Oct 6, 31; m 56; c 4. CIVIL ENGINEERING. *Educ:* US Mil Acad, BS, 54; Ore State Univ, MS, 63; Purdue Univ, PhD(civil eng, transp), 67. *Prof Exp:* Instr civil eng, Ore State Univ, 62-64 & Purdue Univ, 64-67; asst prof eng, 67-71, assoc prof, 71-81, PROF ENG, ARIZ STATE UNIV, 81- *Concurrent Pos:* Mem, Hwy Res Bd, Nat Acad Sci-Nat Res Coun, 64- *Mem:* Am Soc Civil Engrs; Inst Traffic Engrs; Sigma Xi. *Res:* Transportation planning; urban transportation problems. *Mailing Add:* Dept Eng Ariz State Univ Tempe AZ 85281

MATTHIES, DENNIS LEE, physics, electrical engineering, see previous edition

MATTHIJSSEN, CHARLES, b Amsterdam, Holland, July 26, 31; nat US; m 57; c 2. MICROBIOLOGY, BIOCHEMISTRY. *Educ:* Upsala Col, BS, 51; Rutgers Univ, MS, 55, PhD(microbiol), 57. *Prof Exp:* Res chemist, P Ballentine & Sons, 57-59; vchmn dept endocrinol, Southwest Found Res & Educ, 59-74, assoc scientist, 65-74; asst dir clin res endocrinol, 74-78, ASSOC DIR RES METABOLIC & INFECTIOUS DIS, HOECHST-ROUSSEL PHARM INC, 78- *Mem:* AAAS; Am Chem Soc; NY Acad Sci; fel Am Inst Chemists; Am Soc Microbiol. *Res:* Clinical. *Mailing Add:* Hoechst-Roussel Pharm Inc Rte 202-206 N Somerville NJ 08876

MATTHYSSE, ANN GALE, b Chicago, Ill, Oct 25, 39; m 62; c 1. MICROBIOLOGY. *Educ:* Radcliffe Col, AB, 61; Harvard Univ, PhD(biol), 66. *Prof Exp:* Lectr biol, Harvard Univ, 70-71; asst prof microbiol, Sch Med, Ind Univ Indianapolis, 71-75; asst prof bot, 75-77, ASSOC PROF BOT, UNIV NC, 77- *Concurrent Pos:* NIH fel, Calif Inst Technol, 66-69 & Harvard Med Sch, 69-70. *Mem:* AAAS; Am Soc Microbiol; Am Soc Plant Physiol; Am Phytopathol Soc. *Res:* Eukaryote-prokaryote interactions; molecular regulatory mechanisms; molecular biology of plants and of plant diseases. *Mailing Add:* Dept Bot Univ NC Chapel Hill NC 27514

MATTHYSSE, STEVEN WILLIAM, b New York, NY, Aug 27, 39; m 62; c 1. PSYCHOBIOLOGY, PSYCHIATRY. *Educ:* Yale Univ, BS, 59, BA, 60; Harvard Univ, PhD(clin psychol), 67. *Prof Exp:* Asst prof, Pitzer Col, 66-69; asst prof, 70-78, ASSOC PROF PSYCHOBIOL, HARVARD MED SCH, 78- *Concurrent Pos:* Marks Found fel, Harvard Univ, 70-71; res dir, Schizophrenia Res Prog, Scottish Rite, 72- *Mem:* AAAS; Soc Neurosci; Am Soc Neurochem; Asn Res Nerv & Ment Dis. *Res:* Mathematical neuroanatomy; biological aspects of schizophrenia; theoretic genetics. *Mailing Add:* Mailman Res Ctr McLean Hosp Belmont MA 02178

MATTICE, JACK SHAFER, b Hobart, NY, Aug 25, 41; m 67. AQUATIC ECOLOGY, ENVIRONMENTAL TOXICOLOGY. *Educ:* State Univ NY Stony Brook, BS, 63; Syracuse Univ, PhD(invert zool), 71. *Prof Exp:* RES ECOLOGIST AQUATIC ECOL, OAK RIDGE NAT LAB, UNION CARBIDE CORP, 72- *Mem:* Ecol Soc Am; Int Soc Limnol; Malacol Soc London; Sigma Xi. *Res:* Physiological ecology of invertebrates; impacts of power plant effluents on aquatic biota with particular reference to chlorine and temperature. *Mailing Add:* Environ Sci Div Oak Ridge Nat Lab Oak Ridge TN 37830

MATTICE, WAYNE LEE, b Cherokee, Iowa, July 9, 40; m 65; c 1. PHYSICAL BIOCHEMISTRY. *Educ:* Grinnell Col, BA, 63; Duke Univ, PhD(biochem), 68. *Prof Exp:* USPHS fel, Fla State Univ, 68-70; from asst prof to assoc prof, 70-79, PROF CHEM, LA STATE UNIV, BATON ROUGE, 79- *Mem:* AAAS; Am Chem Soc; Biophys Soc. *Res:* Physical chemistry of biopolymers. *Mailing Add:* Dept of Chem La State Univ Baton Rouge LA 70803

MATTICK, JOSEPH FRANCIS, b Hudson, Pa, Nov 16, 18; m 52; c 1. BIOCHEMISTRY, BACTERIOLOGY. *Educ:* Pa State Univ, BS, 42, PhD(dairy technol), 50. *Prof Exp:* Asst prof dairy technol, Univ Md, 50-52, assoc prof, 53-58; tech consult, Venezuela, 58-60; assoc prof dairy technol, 60-65, PROF DAIRY SCI, UNIV MD, COLLEGE PARK, 65-, CHMN DEPT, 74-, CHMN FOOD SCI PROG, 78- *Concurrent Pos:* Consult, Interam Develop Bank & World Bank. *Mem:* Am Dairy Sci Asn; Inst Food Technol. *Res:* Products development; curriculum of food science; food processing waste disposal acid whey utilization. *Mailing Add:* Dept of Dairy Sci Univ of Md Animal Sci Bldg College Park MD 20742

MATTICS, LEON EUGENE, b Butte, Mont, Mar 2, 40; m 67; c 2. NUMBER THEORY. *Educ:* Mont State Univ, BS, 63, PhD(math), 67. *Prof Exp:* Instr math, Mont State Univ, 66-67; PROF MATH, UNIV SOUTH ALA, 67- *Mem:* Math Asn Am. *Res:* Problem solving; number theory. *Mailing Add:* Dept of Math Univ South Ala Mobile AL 36688

MATTINA, CHARLES FREDERICK, JR, b Elizabeth, NJ, Dec 5, 44; m 69; c 3. PHYSICAL CHEMISTRY. *Educ:* Providence Col, BS, 66; Yale Univ, PhD(phys chem), 69. *Prof Exp:* Asst prof chem, Albertus Magnus Col, 69-71; res chemist, 71-74, HEAD CHEM SECT, SCHWEITZER DIV, KIMBERLY-CLARK CORP, 74- *Mem:* Am Chem Soc. *Res:* Electrolytic conductance; viscosity of ionic solutions; tobacco chemistry; condenser paper; cigarette paper. *Mailing Add:* Schweitzer Div Kimberly-Clark Corp Lee MA 01238

MATTINGLY, GLEN E, b Provo, Ark, Oct 31, 32; m 54; c 2. MATHEMATICS. *Educ:* Sam Houston State Univ, BS, 56, MS, 57; NMex State Univ, PhD(math), 65. *Prof Exp:* From instr to assoc prof, 56-67, PROF MATH & DIR DEPT, SAM HOUSTON STATE UNIV, 67- *Mem:* Am Math Soc; Math Asn Am. *Res:* Topological semi-groups; semi-topological groups; topological modules. *Mailing Add:* Dept of Math Sam Houston State Univ Huntsville TX 77340

MATTINGLY, MARY ELLEN, b Louisville, Ky, Jan 31, 32. BIOLOGY. *Educ:* Brescia Col, Ky, AB, 58; Cath Univ Am, PhD(biol), 62. *Prof Exp:* Asst prof biol, Brescia Col, Ky, 62-64; cytologist, Biol Div, Oak Ridge Nat Lab, 64-69; ASSOC PROF ZOOL, UNIV GA, 69- *Mem:* AAAS; Am Soc Cell Biol. *Res:* Physiological phenomena associated with the cell cycle. *Mailing Add:* Dept of Zool Univ of Ga Athens GA 30602

MATTINGLY, RICHARD FRANCIS, b Zanesville, Ohio, Oct 25, 25; m 48; c 7. OBSTETRICS & GYNECOLOGY. *Educ:* Ohio State Univ, AB, 49; Cornell Univ, MD, 53; Am Bd Obstet & Gynec, dipl, cert gynec oncol, 74. *Prof Exp:* Intern obstet & gynec, Univ Hosp, Johns Hopkins Univ, 53-54, asst resident obstet & gynec, Univ, 54-57, res gynecologist & sr resident gynec, 57-58, asst dir gynec endocrine clin, 57-61, from instr to asst prof gynec & obstet, 58-61, obstetrician-gynecologist in charge, outpatient dept, 59-61; PROF GYNEC & OBSTET & CHMN, MED COL WIS, 61-; DIR DEPT, MILWAUKEE CO HOSP, 61- *Concurrent Pos:* Consult staff, Columbia, Milwaukee, Mt Sinai, St Joseph's, St Luke's, & St Mary's Hosps, 61-; ed, Obstet & Gynec, Am Col Obstet & Gynec. *Mem:* Fel Am Col Obstet & Gynec; Am Gynec Soc; Am Asn Obstet & Gynec; Am Soc Cytol; Am Fertil Soc. *Mailing Add:* 8700 W Wisconsin Ave Milwaukee WI 53226

MATTINGLY, STEELE F, b Trinity, Ky, Aug 28, 27; m 49; c 2. ANIMAL HUSBANDRY, VETERINARY MEDICINE. *Educ:* Berea Col, BS, 50; Auburn Univ, DVM, 55; Am Col Lab Animal Med, dipl, 64. *Prof Exp:* Assoc teacher high sch, Ky, 50-51; mem staff primate test animals, Allied Labs, Pitman Moore Co Div & Dow Chem Co, 55-57, unit head test animals, 57-62;

prod mgr, Lab Supply Co, 62-65; DIR DEPT LAB ANIMAL MED, COL MED, UNIV CINCINNATI, 65- *Concurrent Pos:* Consult, Vet Admin, Ohio, 65- *Mem:* Am Vet Med Asn; Am Asn Lab Animal Sci; NY Acad Sci. *Res:* Husbandry of laboratory animals; laboratory animal medicine; germ free life and its relationship to other animal research. *Mailing Add:* Dept of Lab Animal Med Univ of Cincinnati Cincinnati OH 45219

MATTINGLY, STEPHEN JOSEPH, b Evansville, Ind, Mar 3, 43; m 63; c 4. MICROBIAL PHYSIOLOGY. *Educ:* Univ Tex, Austin, BA, 65; Villanova Univ, MS, 68; Med Col Ga, PhD(microbiol), 72. *Prof Exp:* Microbiologist, US Food & Drug Admin, 65-66; microbiologist, Valley Forge Gen Hosp, 66-68; microbiologist, Naval Med Field Res Lab, Camp LeJeune, 68-69; res assoc, Sch Med, Temple Univ, 72-74; asst prof, 74-79, ASSOC PROF MICROBIOL, UNIV TEX HEALTH SCI CTR, 79- *Concurrent Pos:* Nat Inst Dent Res fel, 74. *Mem:* Am Soc Microbiol; Sigma Xi. *Res:* Bacterial physiology; regulation of cell wall and polysaccharide biosynthesis; physiology of cariogenic streptococci and group B streptococci. *Mailing Add:* Dept of Microbiol Univ of Tex Health Sci Ctr San Antonio TX 78284

MATTINGLY, SUSAN CAROL, audiology, see previous edition

MATTINSON, JAMES MEIKLE, b Maracaibo, Venezuela, Aug 28, 44; US citizen. GEOCHRONOLOGY, PETROLOGY. *Educ:* Univ Calif, Santa Barbara, BA, 66, PhD(geol), 70. *Prof Exp:* Fel geochronology, Geophys Lab, Carnegie Inst, Washington, 70-73; lectr geol, 73-76, asst prof, 77-81, ASSOC PROF GEOL, UNIV CALIF, SANTA BARBARA, 81- *Mem:* Am Geophys Union; Geol Soc Am; AAAS; Sigma Xi. *Res:* Igneous rocks, especially calc-alkaline ingeous complexes and ophiolitic complexes. *Mailing Add:* Dept of Geol Sci Univ of Calif Santa Barbara CA 93106

MATTIS, ALLEN FRANCIS, b Spooner, Wis, May 3, 47; m 75. PETROLEUM GEOLOGY. *Educ:* Univ Wis-Superior, BS, 69; Univ Minn, Duluth, MS, 72; Rutgers Univ, MPhil, 74, PhD(geol), 75. *Prof Exp:* GEOLOGIST, TEXACO INC, 75- *Mem:* Geol Soc Am; Am Asn Petrol Geologists; Am Inst Mining, Metall & Petrol Engrs. *Res:* Sedimentation; provenance; regional tectonics. *Mailing Add:* 9279 E 58th St South Tulsa OK 74145

MATTIS, DANIEL CHARLES, b Brussels, Belg, Sept 8, 32; nat US; m 58. SOLID STATE PHYSICS. *Educ:* Mass Inst Technol, BS, 53; Univ Ill, MS, 54, PhD(physics), 57. *Prof Exp:* Asst, Univ Ill, 54-57; asst, Nat Ctr Sci Res, France, 57-58; physicist, Res Ctr, Int Bus Mach Corp, 58-65; from assoc prof to prof physics, Belfer Grad Sch Sci, Yeshiva Univ, 65-78; Thomas Potts Prof physics, Polytech Inst NY, 78-81; PROF PHYSICS, UNIV UTAH, 80- *Concurrent Pos:* Adj prof physics, State Univ NY Buffalo & Univ Utah, 78- *Mem:* NY Acad Sci; fel Am Phys Soc. *Res:* Theoretical investigation of electronic properties, especially the theory of electrical conduction, with applications to metals and semiconductors; many-body theory of metal alloys; theory of magnetism. *Mailing Add:* Dept Physics Univ Utah Salt Lake City UT 84112

MATTISON, LOUIS EMIL, b Lincoln, Nebr, Oct 3, 27; m 49; c 3. CHEMISTRY. *Educ:* La State Univ, BS, 49; Univ Del, MS, 50, PhD(org chem), 52. *Prof Exp:* Res chemist, Carothers Lab, Exp Sta, E I du Pont de Nemours & Co, 52-54; from assoc prof to prof chem, Davis & Elkins Col, 56-62; PROF CHEM & CHMN DEPT, KING COL, 63- *Concurrent Pos:* Cottrell res grant, 56-60; chmn dept chem, Davis & Elkins Col, 56-62; res assoc, Univ Ariz, 62-63. *Mem:* AAAS; Am Chem Soc; Sigma Xi; NY Acad Sci; Am Inst Chemists. *Res:* Organic synthesis of chelating agents; metal chelates; coordination compounds; photochemistry. *Mailing Add:* 323 Poplar St Bristol TN 37620

MATTISON, PHILLIP LEROY, organic chemistry, see previous edition

MATTMAN, LIDA HOLMES, b Denver, Colo, July 31, 12; m 44; c 2. BACTERIOLOGY. *Educ:* Univ Kans, AB, 33, MA, 34; Yale Univ, PhD(bact), 40. *Prof Exp:* Bacteriologist, Med Dept, Endicott Johnson, NY, 34; asst, Iowa Hosp, 40-42; res bacteriologist, Nat Res Coun, 42-44, comn airborne infection, 45; mycologist, Santa Rosa Hosp, San Antonio, Tex, 46-47; sr bacteriologist, State Health Labs, Mass, 47-49; from asst prof to assoc prof bact, 49-74, PROF BIOL, WAYNE STATE UNIV, 74- *Concurrent Pos:* Nat Res Coun fel, Univ Pa, 43-44. *Mem:* Am Soc Microbiol; NY Acad Sci. *Res:* Surface tension depressants in immunological systems; pathogenic anaerobes; L variants and mycoplasmae. *Mailing Add:* 1500 Seminole St Detroit MI 48214

MATTOON, JAMES RICHARD, b Loveland, Colo, Dec 9, 30; m 53; c 2. MOLECULAR BIOLOGY. *Educ:* Univ Ill, BS, 53; Univ Wis, MS, 54, PhD(biochem), 57. *Prof Exp:* From instr to asst prof chem, Univ Nebr, 57-62; asst prof physiol chem, Sch Med, Johns Hopkins Univ, 64-70, assoc prof, 70-79; PROF BIOL, UNIV COLO, COLORADO SPRINGS, 79- *Concurrent Pos:* Fel, Sch Med, Johns Hopkins Univ, 62-64. *Mem:* Am Chem Soc; Am Soc Biol Chemists; Am Soc Microbiol; Genetics Soc Am; AAAS. *Res:* Genetics of mitochondria; yeast molecular biology; mitochondrial biogenesis; oxidative phosphorylation; yeast respiration and mitochondria; lysine biosynthesis. *Mailing Add:* Dept Biol Univ Colo Colo Springs CO 80907

MATTOR, JOHN ALAN, b Oxford, Maine, Jan 15, 32; m 58; c 3. SYNTHETIC ORGANIC CHEMISTRY. *Educ:* Bates Col, BS, 58; Lawrence Univ, MS, 60, PhD(chem), 63. *Prof Exp:* Mem staff, 62-75, SR RES ASSOC, S D WARREN CO, SCOTT PAPER, WESTBROOK, 75- *Mem:* Am Chem Soc; AAAS; Soc Photog Scientists & Engrs. *Res:* Photochemistry; organic photoconductivity; dye sensitization. *Mailing Add:* Box 85 Bar Mills ME 04004

MATTOX, DOUGLAS MILTON, b Plainfield, NJ, Jan 2, 41; m 62; c 3. CERAMICS, GLASS TECHNOLOGY. *Educ:* Rutgers Univ, BS, 62, PhD(ceramics), 66. *Prof Exp:* Adv res scientist glass technol, PPG Indust, 65-67; sr scientist, 67-74, MGR CERAMIC SYST, WESTINGHOUSE RES & DEVELOP CTR, 74- *Mem:* Am Ceramic Soc; Illum Eng Soc. *Res:* Glass technology; ceramics; technological forecasting; lamps and lighting. *Mailing Add:* Westinghouse Res & Develop Ctr 1310 Beulah Rd Pittsburgh PA 15235

MATTOX, KARL, b Cincinnati, Ohio, Aug 22, 36; m 57; c 3. PHYCOLOGY. *Educ:* Miami Univ, BS, 58, MA, 60; Univ Tex, PhD(bot), 62. *Prof Exp:* Asst prof bot, Univ Toronto, 62-66; from asst prof to assoc prof, 66-75, PROF BOT, MIAMI UNIV, 75-, CHMN DEPT, 77- *Concurrent Pos:* Res assoc, Great Lakes Inst, 62- *Mem:* Bot Soc Am; Phycol Soc Am. *Res:* Morphology; cytology and evolution of algae. *Mailing Add:* Dept of Bot Miami Univ Oxford OH 45056

MATTOX, RICHARD BENJAMIN, b Middletown, Ohio, May 15, 21; m 48. GEOLOGY. *Educ:* Miami Univ, BA, 48, MS, 49; Univ Iowa, PhD(geol), 54. *Prof Exp:* Instr geol, Miami Univ, 49-50; petrol geologist, Magnolia Petrol Co, 50; asst instr geol, Univ Iowa, 50-52; asst prof, Miss State Col, 52-54; assoc prof, 54-57, PROF GEOL, TEX TECH UNIV, 57- *Concurrent Pos:* Head dept geol, Tex Tech Univ, 64-70. *Mem:* AAAS; Nat Asn Geol Teachers; Geol Soc Am; Am Asn Petrol Geologists. *Res:* Eolian geology; stratigraphy; geology of Colorado plateau. *Mailing Add:* Dept Geosci Tex Tech Univ Lubbock TX 79409

MATTSON, DALE EDWARD, b Newberry, Mich, Apr 5, 34; m 57; c 2. BIOMETRICS. *Educ:* Colo Col, BA, 59; Univ Ill, MA, 61, PhD(educ psychol), 63. *Prof Exp:* Asst prof educ measurement, Univ Wash, 63-64; dir educ res, Am Asn Dent Schs, 64-66 & Asn Am Med Cols, 66-69; dir admis & rec, 69-72, PROF BIOMET, SCH PUB HEALTH, UNIV ILL, 72- *Mem:* Am Pub Health Asn; Am Statist Asn. *Res:* Indices of serial correlation with applications to measures of health statistics; epidemiology of sports injuries. *Mailing Add:* 5243 N Mason Ave Chicago IL 60630

MATTSON, DONALD EUGENE, b Chatsworth, Calif, May 19, 34; m 59; c 3. VETERINARY VIROLOGY. *Educ:* Univ Calif, Davis, BS, 57, DVM, 59; Wash State Univ, PhD(microbiol), 66. *Prof Exp:* Asst prof, 67-69, ASSOC PROF VET MED, ORE STATE UNIV, 69- *Mem:* Am Vet Med Asn. *Res:* Physical, chemical and serological properties of viruses; virus diseases of the newborn, especially bovine. *Mailing Add:* Sch of Vet Med Ore State Univ Corvallis OR 97331

MATTSON, FRED HUGH, b Spokane, Wash, Dec 16, 18; m 43; c 5. BIOCHEMISTRY. *Educ:* Loyola Univ, Calif, BS, 40; Univ Southern Calif, MS, 42, PhD(biochem), 48; Am Soc Clin Nutrit, cert specialist human nutrit, 71. *Prof Exp:* Res chemist, Procter & Gamble Co, 48-78; PROF MED & DIR, LIPID RES CLIN, UNIV CALIF, SAN DIEGO, 79- *Concurrent Pos:* Adj prof, Univ Cincinnati, 70-78; mem coun arteriosclerosis, Am Heart Asn. *Honors & Awards:* Am Chem Soc Award, 69. *Mem:* Am Chem Soc; Am Soc Biol Chem; Am Inst Nutrit. *Res:* Digestion and absorption of fat; nutritive value of fat; diet and cardio-vascular disease. *Mailing Add:* Lipid Res Clin M-020 Univ of Calif at San Diego La Jolla CA 92093

MATTSON, GUY C, b Bloomfield, NJ, Jan 3, 27; m 50; c 4. ORGANIC CHEMISTRY. *Educ:* Union Col, NY, BS, 49; Univ Fla, PhD(chem), 55. *Prof Exp:* Chemist, Warner-Chilcott Labs, NJ, 49-52; instr chem, Univ Fla, 52-55; res chemist, Dow Chem Co, Mich, 55-60, facil mgr, Fla, 60-64, prod engr, Saginaw Bay, 64-65, proj mgr, Tex, 65-66, dept head, Ind, 66-71; PROF CHEM, UNIV CENT FLA, 70-, CHMN DEPT, 78- *Mem:* Am Chem Soc. *Res:* Organic synthesis; process development. *Mailing Add:* Dept of Chem Univ Cent Fla Orlando FL 32816

MATTSON, HAROLD F, JR, b Ann Arbor, Mich, Dec 7, 30. APPLIED MATHEMATICS. *Educ:* Oberlin Col, AB, 51; Mass Inst Technol, PhD(math), 55. *Prof Exp:* Mathematician, Air Force Cambridge Res Ctr, 55-60; mathematician, Appl Res Lab, Sylvania Elec Prod, Inc, Gen Tel & Electronics Corp, 60-70, Eastern Opers, 70-71; PROF COMPUT & INFO SCI, SYRACUSE UNIV, 71- *Concurrent Pos:* Ed, Review, Soc Indust & Appl Math, 70-79. *Mem:* Am Math Soc; Math Asn Am; Soc Indust & Appl Math. *Res:* Combinatorial analysis; error-correcting codes. *Mailing Add:* Link 313 CIS Syracuse Univ Syracuse NY 13210

MATTSON, JAMES STEWART, chemical oceanography, surface chemistry, see previous edition

MATTSON, MARGARET ELLEN, b Philadelphia, Pa, May 13, 47. BEHAVIORAL MEDICINE, EPIDEMIOLOGY. *Educ:* Holy Family Col, BA, 69; Cornell Univ, PhD(neurobiol), 75. *Prof Exp:* Investr environ health, Environ Control, Inc, 76-78; PROJ OFFICER BEHAV MED & CLIN TRAITS, NAT HEART, LUNG & BLOOD INST, 78- *Mem:* Soc Neurosci; Am Psychol Asn; Soc Clin Traits; Soc Behav Med. *Res:* Psychobiology. *Mailing Add:* Nat Heart, Lung & Blood Inst Fed Bldg Bethesda MD 20205

MATTSON, MARLIN ROY ALBIN, b Bellingham, Wash, Apr 25, 39. PSYCHIATRY. *Educ:* Univ Wash, BA, 61, MD, 65. *Prof Exp:* Intern & resident med, Cornell's Combined Prog Med, Bellevue Hosp & Mem Hosp, New York, 65-67; Capt US Army Med Corps med & obstet, 67-69; residency chief resident psychiat, Payne Whitney Clin, NY Hosp, 69-73, act med dir, 74, ASST MED DIR, PAYNE WHITNEY PSYCHIAT CLIN, 73-; assoc prof clin psychiat, Med Col, Cornell Univ, 70-79; asst attending psychiatrist, 73-79, ASSOC ATTENDING PSYCHIATRIST, NEW YORK HOSP, 79-, ASST MED DIR QUAL ASSURANCE, WESTCHESTER DIV, 80- *Concurrent Pos:* Ginsberg fel, Group Advan Psychiat, 71-73; mem hosp rev comt, NY County Health Serv Rev Orgn, 76- *Mem:* Am Psychiat Asn; NY Acad Sci; Am Acad Psychiat & Law. *Res:* Quality assurance and utilization review; aspects of hospital psychiatry. *Mailing Add:* Payne Whitney Clin 525 E 68th St New York NY 10021

MATTSON, PETER HUMPHREY, b Evanston, Ill, Apr 3, 32; m 54; c 3. GEOLOGY. *Educ:* Oberlin Col, BA, 53; Princeton Univ, PhD(geol), 57. *Prof Exp:* Geologist, US Geol Surv, 57-64; from asst prof to assoc prof, 64-72, PROF EARTH & ENVIRON SCI, QUEENS COL, NY, 73- *Concurrent Pos:* Chmn dept geol & geog, Queens Col, NY, 65-68; consult, Commonwealth PR, 65-69 & Venezuela, 77-; indust consult, 67- *Mem:* Geol Soc Am; Am Geophys Union. *Res:* Igneous petrology; volcanic rocks; structural geology; geology of Puerto Rico and the Caribbean area; island arcs. *Mailing Add:* Dept of Earth & Environ Sci Queens Col Flushing NY 11367

MATTSON, RAYMOND HARDING, b Matchwood, Mich, Oct 10, 20; m 51; c 4. ORGANIC CHEMISTRY. *Educ:* Univ Mich, BS, 43; Univ Ill, PhD(chem), 51. *Prof Exp:* Res chemist, Rohm and Haas Co, 43-44, Am Cyanamid Co, 50-52 & mkt develop, Jefferson Chem Co, 52-55; sr mkt res analyst, Am Cyanamid Co, 55-59, tech rep, 59-62, mgr sales develop rubber chem, 62-63; mkt res assoc, Glidden Co, SCM Corp, 63-71, mgr group mkt res, Glidden-Durkee Div, 71-76, dir bus develop, Org Chem Div, 76-78, mkt res assoc, Durkee Foods Div, group mkt res, Glidden Durkee Div, 78-81; PRES, POLARIS ASSOC CONSULT ORGN, 82- *Mem:* Am Chem Soc. *Res:* Restricted rotation in aryl amines. *Mailing Add:* 7396 Ober Lane Chagrin Falls OH 44022

MATTSON, RICHARD LEWIS, b Greeley, Colo, May 29, 35; m 57; c 2. COMPUTER SCIENCE, ELECTRICAL ENGINEERING. *Educ:* Univ Calif, Berkeley, BS, 57; Mass Inst Technol, MS, 59; Stanford Univ, PhD(elec eng), 62. *Prof Exp:* Res engr, Lockheed Aircraft Corp, 59-62; asst prof elec eng, Stanford Univ, 62-64; RES STAFF MEM, IBM CORP, 65- *Concurrent Pos:* Assoc prof, Stanford Univ, 64-65. *Mem:* AAAS; Asn Comput Mach; Inst Elec & Electronics Engrs. *Res:* Switching theory; computer system design. *Mailing Add:* 6838 Rockview Ct San Jose CA 95120

MATTSON, ROY HENRY, b Chisholm, Minn, Dec 26, 27; m 48; c 7. ELECTRICAL ENGINEERING. *Educ:* Univ Minn, BEE, 51, MS, 52; Iowa State Univ, PhD(elec eng), 59. *Prof Exp:* Mem tech staff, Bell Tel Labs, Inc, 52-56; from asst prof to assoc prof elec eng, Iowa State Univ, 56-61; assoc prof, Univ Minn, 61-66; PROF ELEC ENG & HEAD DEPT, UNIV ARIZ, 66- *Concurrent Pos:* Electronics consult, NStar Res & Develop Inst, 63-65 & MacMillan Bk Co, 63-64; mem, Amphitheater Sch Bd; ed, Trans on Educ, Inst Elec & Electronics Engrs. *Mem:* Fel AAAS; Am Soc Eng Educ; fel Inst Elec & Electronics Engrs. *Res:* Solid state and biomedical electronics; electrical engineering education; microelectronics, solar energy, and biomedical instrumentation. *Mailing Add:* Dept of Elec Eng Univ of Ariz Tucson AZ 85721

MATTSON, VERNON (LINNNAEUS), b Chicago, Ill, July 12, 02; m 28; c 1. MINING, METALLURGY. *Educ:* Colo Sch Mines, EM, 26. *Prof Exp:* Vpres & gen mgr, Celo Mines, Inc, 30-44; chief engr, Consol Feldspar Corp, 44-49; dir, Res Found, Colo Sch Mines, 49-55; vpres & tech adv to pres, Kerr-McGee Corp, 55-68, vpres res, 68-71; CONSULT, 71- *Mem:* AAAS; Am Inst Mining, Metall & Petrol Engrs; Am Nuclear Soc; Geol Soc Am. *Res:* Mineral economics; geophysics; mineralogy; applied geology. *Mailing Add:* PO Box 2690 Estes Park CO 80517

MATTSON, VICTOR FRANK, chemistry, see previous edition

MATTUCK, ARTHUR PAUL, b Brooklyn, NY, June 11, 30; div; c 1. GEOMETRY. *Educ:* Swarthmore Col, AB, 51; Princeton Univ, PhD(math), 54. *Prof Exp:* Res fel math, Harvard Univ, 54-55; C L E Moore instr, 55-57, lectr, 57-58, from asst prof to prof, 58-73, CLASS OF 1922 PROF MATH, MASS INST TECHNOL, 73- *Mem:* Am Math Soc; Math Asn Am. *Res:* Algebraic geometry. *Mailing Add:* Dept of Math Mass Inst Technol Cambridge MA 02139

MATUKAS, VICTOR JOHN, b Freeport, Tex, Oct 20, 33; m 61; c 3. EXPERIMENTAL PATHOLOGY. *Educ:* Loyola Univ, La, DDS, 56; Univ Rochester, PhD(path), 66; Univ Colo, Denver, MD, 73. *Prof Exp:* Resident oral surg, Charity Hosp, New Orleans, La, 58-61; asst prof path, Loyola Univ, La, 61-62 & Univ Pa, 66-68; prof stomatol & chmn dept, Sch Dent, Univ Colo, Denver, 71-74; med internship, Univ Ala Hosps, 74-75, investr dent res, 74-80, dir advan educ prog oral & maxillofacial surg, 75-80, ASSOC DEAN, SCH DENT, UNIV ALA, BIRMINGHAM, 78-, SR SCIENTIST, INST DENT RES, 80-, PROF DENT & CHMN DEPT ORAL & MAXILLOFACIAL SURG, 81- *Concurrent Pos:* Spec res fel, Nat Inst Dent Res, 68-71. *Mem:* AAAS; Am Dent Asn. *Res:* Synthesis, metabolism and ultrastructure of collagen and protein-polysaccharide; biological mineralization. *Mailing Add:* Inst Dent Res Sch Dent Univ Ala Birmingham AL 35294

MATULA, DAVID WILLIAM, b St Louis, Mo, Nov 6, 37; m 66; c 3. COMPUTER ARITHMETIC, DATA STRUCTURE. *Educ:* Wash Univ, BS, 59; Univ Calif, Berkeley, PhD(eng sci & operation res), 66. *Prof Exp:* Asst prof comput sci, Wash Univ, 66-69, assoc prof, 69-74; dept chmn, 74-79, PROF COMPUT SCI, SOUTHERN METHODIST UNIV, 74- *Concurrent Pos:* Prin investr, NSF, 73-; vis prof, Univ Karlsruhe, Ger, 74; consult, Control Data, 76-80; distinguished vis prof, Naval Postgrad Sch, 78; vis prof, Stanford Univ, 80; vis researcher, Aarhus Univ, Denmark, 80-81. *Mem:* Asn Comput Mach; Soc Indust & Appl Math; Operations Res Soc Am; Math Asn Am; Sigma Xi. *Res:* Computer arithmetic has emphasized the nature of computer number systems and the best procedures for computation subject to finite precision limitation; cluster analysis and classification emphasizing graph theoretic approaches and efficient algorithms for identifying clusters in data. *Mailing Add:* Dept Comput Sci Southern Methodist Univ Dallas TX 75275

MATULA, RICHARD A, b Chicago, Ill, Aug 22, 39; m 59; c 4. MECHANICAL ENGINEERING, COMBUSTION. *Educ:* Purdue Univ, BS, 61, MS, 62, PhD(thermodyn), 64. *Prof Exp:* Instr mech eng, Purdue Univ, 63-64; asst prof mech eng, Univ Calif, Santa Barbara, 64-66; asst prof mech eng, Univ Mich, 66-68; assoc prof mech eng, Drexel Univ, 68-70, prof, 70-76; PROF MECH ENG, & DEAN, COL ENG, LA STATE UNIV, BATON ROUGE, 76- *Mem:* Am Soc Mech Eng; AAAS; Combustion Inst; Soc Automotive Engrs; Am Soc Eng Educ. *Res:* Combustion kinetics and energy conversion. *Mailing Add:* Col of Eng La State Univ Baton Rouge LA 70803

MATULA, RICHARD ALLEN, b Newark, NJ, Jan 12, 38; m 75; c 1. PHYSICS, INFORMATION SCIENCE. *Educ:* Newark Col Eng, BSEE, 60, MSEE, 63; Purdue Univ, MS, 65; PhD(physics), 73. *Prof Exp:* Asst instr elec eng, Newark Col Eng, 60-63; res assoc, Ctr Info & Numerical Data Anal & Synthesis, 73-75, asst sr researcher, 75-78, assoc sr reseacher, 78-80; INFO SCIENTIST, BELL LABS, 80- *Mem:* Am Phys Soc. *Res:* Information retrieval using online searching; development of bibliographies from online searches; development of evaluated data for physical properties of materials. *Mailing Add:* Bell Labs 600 Mountain Ave Murray Hill NJ 07974

MATULEVICIUS, EDWARD S(TEPHEN), b Montreal, Que, Sept 4, 42; m 70; c 2. CHEMICAL ENGINEERING. *Educ:* McGill Univ, BEng, 64; Mass Inst Technol, SM, 66, ScD(chem eng), 70. *Prof Exp:* Res assoc, 69-76, sect mgr process technol, Air Prods & Chem Div, 76-78, mgr fuel utilization eng, 78-81, SECT HEAD THERMAL FLUIDS, EXXON RES & ENG CO, 81- *Mem:* Am Inst Chem Engrs. *Res:* Fuel utilization, especially coal, fluidized bed combustion; combustion; heat transfer; fluid mechanics. *Mailing Add:* RD 2 Coopersburg PA 18036

MATULIC, LJUBOMIR FRANCISCO, b Potosi, Bolivia, May 8, 23; US citizen; m 53; c 3. QUANTUM OPTICS. *Educ:* State Gym, Yugoslavia, BA, 42; Univ Chile, Lic Math & Physics, 49; Ind Univ, Bloomington, MS, 63; Univ Rochester, PhD(physics), 71. *Prof Exp:* Teacher high sch, Bolivia, 49-50; prof math, Collegio Normal Superior, Bolivia, 50-54; prof math & physics, Leguerrier Classical Inst, Montreal, 54-58; lectr math, Royal Mil Col, Que, 58-60; assoc prof, 63-68 & 70-73, PROF PHYSICS, ST JOHN FISHER COL, 73- *Concurrent Pos:* Instr, Univ San Simon, Bolivia, 49-50; vis scientist, Inst Ruder Boskovic, Univ Zagreb, Yugoslavia, 74; vis scientist, Ctr Invest Optom, Leon, Mex, 81-82. *Mem:* Arg Math Union; Am Asn Physics Teachers; Optical Soc Am; Am Phys Soc. *Res:* Theoretical investigation of distortionless propagation of electromagnetic fields through nonlinear absorbers, especially the phase modulation of this field due to the interaction with resonant atoms and to the bulk host medium. *Mailing Add:* Dept of Physics St John Fisher Col Rochester NY 14618

MATULIONIS, DANIEL H, b Lithuania, Oct 2, 38; US citizen; m 60; c 2. ANATOMY, EMBRYOLOGY. *Educ:* Wis State Univ-Whitewater, BEd, 63; Univ Ill, Urbana, MS, 65; Tulane Univ, PhD(anat), 70. *Prof Exp:* Instr biol, Eastern Ky Univ, 65-67; instr, 70-71, ASST PROF ANAT, COL MED, UNIV KY, LEXINGTON, 71- *Concurrent Pos:* Gen Res Support grant, Univ Ky, 70-71; Ky Tobacco Res Inst grant, 71-72. *Mem:* Am Asn Anat. *Res:* Ultrastructural analysis of keratin precursors; glycogen synthesis; ultrastructural analysis of cigarette smoke effects on the respiratory system. *Mailing Add:* Dept of Anat Col Med Univ of Ky Lexington KY 40506

MATULIS, RAYMOND M, analytical chemistry, see previous edition

MATUMOTO, TOSIMATU, b Tokyo, Japan, Aug 3, 26; m 55; c 2. GEOPHYSICS. *Educ:* Tokyo Univ, MS, 51, PhD(seismol), 60. *Prof Exp:* Res asst geophys, Earthquake Res Inst, Univ Tokyo, 51-61; res assoc, Lamont-Doherty Geol Observ, Columbia Univ, 60-65, sr res assoc, 66-74; mem staff, Marine Sci Inst, Galveston, Tex, 74-81; PROF GEOL SCI, UNIV TEX, AUSTIN, 81-, MEM STAFF, INST GEOPHYS, 81- *Mem:* Seismol Soc Am; Am Geophys Union. *Res:* Spectral analysis of seismic waves and its relation to magnitude; study of seismicity and microearthquake in Alaska and central and South America. *Mailing Add:* Dept Geol Sci Univ Tex Austin TX 78712

MATURI, VINCENT FRANCIS, b New York, NY, Oct 23, 16; c 5. HEALTH SCIENCES, HOSPITAL ADMINSTRATION. *Educ:* Cooper Union, BS, 39; NY Univ, MS, 43; Polytech Inst Brooklyn, PhD(chem eng), 48; George Washington Univ, MHCA, 72. *Prof Exp:* Asst div head res biochem, Standard Brands Inc, Stamford, Conn, 49-54; asst dir indust appln, Am Cyanamid Co, New York, 54-60; biochemist, Food & Drug Admin, 60-62; life sci specialist, NASA, 62-64; dep chief sci div, Smithsonian Inst, 64-68; exec secy, Ctr Demonstration Grants, HEW, Washington, DC, 68-71, HEALTH SCIENTIST ADMINR, HEALTH CARE TECHNOL DIV, NAT CTR HEALTH SERV RES, DEPT HEALTH & HUMAN SERV, 71- *Concurrent Pos:* Consult, Nat Ctr Health Serv Res & Develop, HEW, 68-69. *Mem:* Am Hosp Asn; Am Pub Health Asn; Am Asn Clin Chemists; Am Chem Soc. *Res:* Health care administration; health care technology; medical information systems, medical devices, computerized scientific data handling; drugs; biochemistry; clinical chemistry. *Mailing Add:* Dept Health & Human Serv 3700 East West Hwy Hyattsville MD 20782

MATURO, FRANK JUAN SARNO, JR, b Nashville, Tenn, Apr 28, 29; m 60; c 3. MARINE BIOLOGY. *Educ:* Univ Ky, BS, 51; Duke Univ, MA, 53, PhD(marine ecol), 56. *Prof Exp:* Instr zool, Duke Univ, 55-57; vis asst prof, Univ NC, 57-58; asst prof biol, 58-64, assoc prof zool, 64-72, PROF ZOOL, UNIV FLA, 72-, DIR MARINE LAB, 70- *Concurrent Pos:* Nat Acad Sci-Nat Res Coun sr vis res assoc, Smithsonian Inst Mus Natural Hist, 65-66. *Mem:* Am Soc Zoologists; Estuarine Res Fedn; Sigma Xi; fel AAAS; Int Bryozool Asn (pres, 71-74). *Res:* Seasonal distribution and settling rates of marine invertebrates; zoogeography, ecology, and systematics of marine Bryozoa; larval behavior, metamorphosis, and astogeny of Bryozoa. *Mailing Add:* Dept of Zool Univ of Fla Gainesville FL 32611

MATURO, JOSEPH MARTIN, III, b Bridgeport, Conn, Nov 15, 42; m 66; c 2. BIOCHEMISTRY, PHYSIOLOGY. *Educ:* Fairfield Univ, BS, 64; Boston Col, PhD(biol), 69. *Prof Exp:* from asst prof to assoc prof, 69-77, PROF BIOL, C W POST COL, LONG ISLAND UNIV, 77- *Concurrent Pos:* NIH fel, Sch Med, Johns Hopkins Univ, 76-77; vis prof, Johns Hopkins Hosp, Baltimore, Md, 77 & St Georges Sch Med, Granada, WIndies & Sch Med, Univ Calgary, Alberta, 81; consult, Nat Cancer Cynology Ctr, Melville, NY,

75-77, Howard Hughes Med Inst, Miami, Fla, 78- *Mem:* AAAS; Sigma Xi (pres 77-78 & 81-); NY Acad Sci. *Res:* Mechanism of action of insulin. *Mailing Add:* Dept of Biol CW Post Col Long Island Univ P O Greenvale NY 11548

MATUSZAK, ALICE JEAN BOYER, b Newark, Ohio, June 22, 35; m 55; c 2. MEDICINAL CHEMISTRY, PHARMACY. *Educ:* Ohio State Univ, BS, 58, MS, 59; Univ Kans, PhD(pharmaceut chem), 63. *Prof Exp:* Asst prof pharmaceut chem, 63-67, assoc prof med chem, 75-78, PROF MED CHEM, UNIV OF THE PAC, 78- *Concurrent Pos:* Chief investr, NIMH grant, 65-66. *Mem:* Am Chem Soc; Am Pharmaceut Asn; AAAS; Acad Pharmaceut Sci; Am Asn Col Pharm. *Res:* Synthesis of small heterocyclic compounds and their biochemical and pharmacological effects; use of audiovisual techniques to improve the teaching of medicinal chemistry; drug biotransformation. *Mailing Add:* Sch of Pharm Univ of the Pac Stockton CA 95211

MATUSZAK, CHARLES A, b Pittsburgh, Pa, Jan 7, 32; m 55; c 2. PHYSICAL ORGANIC CHEMISTRY. *Educ:* Univ Okla, BS, 52, MS, 53; Ohio State Univ, PhD(org chem), 57. *Prof Exp:* Asst org chem, Ohio State Univ, 53-57; res chemist, Owens-Corning Fiberglas Corp, 57-58; fel org chem, Ohio State Univ, 58-59, Univ Wis, 59-60 & Univ Kans, 60-61 & 62-63; asst prof, Washburn Univ, 61-62; from asst prof to assoc prof, 63-77, PROF ORG CHEM, UNIV OF THE PAC, 77- *Mem:* Am Chem Soc; Royal Soc Chem; Sigma Xi. *Res:* Mechanisms; Birch reduction; imidazole compounds; biphenylenes. *Mailing Add:* Dept of Chem Univ of the Pac Stockton CA 95211

MATUSZAK, DAVID ROBERT, b Oct 2, 34; US citizen; m 53; c 3. GEOLOGY. *Educ:* Univ Okla, BS, 55, MS, 57; Northwestern Univ, PhD(geol), 61. *Prof Exp:* Lab asst geol, Univ Okla, 56-57; geologist, Kerr-McGee Oil Industs, Inc, 57-58; lab asst geol, Northwestern Univ, 58-60; res engr, Pan Am Petrol Corp, 61-63, sr res scientist, 63-68, res group supvr, 68-71, sr staff geologist, 71-76, geol assoc, 76-78, supvr explor systs, 78-80, DIR EXPLOR SYSTS, AMOCO PROD CO, 80- *Mem:* Am Asn Petrol Geologists; Soc Prof Well Log Analysts. *Res:* Use of subsurface data and computers in oil exploration. *Mailing Add:* Amoco Prod Co PO Box 591 Tulsa OK 74102

MATUSZEK, JOHN MICHAEL, JR, b Worcester, Mass, Apr 16, 35; m 57; c 4. RADIOLOGICAL HEALTH, RADIOCHEMISTRY. *Educ:* Worcester Polytech Inst, BS, 57; Clark Univ, PhD(nuclear chem), 62. *Prof Exp:* Scientist, Southeastern Radiol Health Lab, USPHS, 62-64; asst mgr measurements div, Isotopes, Inc, 64-67; mgr physics dept, Teledyne Isotopes, 67-71; DIR RADIOL SCI LAB, NY STATE HEALTH DEPT, 71- *Mem:* Am Nuclear Soc; Health Physics Soc. *Res:* Nuclear reaction mechanisms for intermediate energy interactions; nuclear spectroscopy; radiological health; radiochemical procedures; fission research. *Mailing Add:* NY State Health Dept Empire State Plaza Albany NY 12201

MATUSZKO, ANTHONY JOSEPH, b Hadley, Mass, Jan 31, 26; m 56; c 4. ORGANIC CHEMISTRY, INORGANIC CHEMISTRY. *Educ:* Amherst Col, AB, 46; Univ Mass, MS, 51; McGill Univ, PhD(org chem), 53. *Prof Exp:* Demonstr chem, McGill Univ, 50-52; instr, Lafayette Col, 52-53, from asst prof to assoc prof, 53-58; assoc head chem div, Res & Develop Dept, US Naval Propellant Plant, 58-59, head fundamental processes div, 59-62, polymer div, 62; chief org chem prog, 62-71, PROG MGR, CHEM SCI DIRECTORATE, AIR FORCE OFF SCI RES, 71- *Concurrent Pos:* Hon fel, Univ Wis, 67-68. *Mem:* Fel AAAS; Am Chem Soc; fel Am Inst Chemists; Am Ord Asn; Sigma Xi. *Res:* Organometallics; reactions with nitriles; pyridine derivatives; modifications and properties of cellulose nitrates; phosphonitrilic derivatives; high nitrogen compounds. *Mailing Add:* Chem Sci Directorate Air Force Off Sci Res Bolling AFB Washington DC 20332

MATWIYOFF, NICHOLAS ALEXANDER, b Ann Arbor, Mich, Aug 19, 37; m 62; c 1. BIOPHYSICAL CHEMISTRY. *Educ:* Mich Col Mining & Technol, BS, 59; Univ Ill, MS, 61, PhD(chem), 62. *Prof Exp:* Fel chem, Stanford Univ, 62-63; asst prof chem, Pa State Univ, 63-68; sect leader nuclear magnetic resonance spectros, 68-72, alternate group leader inorg & phys chem, 72-78, MGR STABLE ISOTOPES RESOURCE, LOS ALAMOS NAT LAB, 75-, DEP DIV LEADER, CHEM DIV, 78- *Mem:* Am Soc Biol Chem; Am Chem Soc. *Res:* Study of structure and dynamics of peptides, enzymes, nucleic acids, and cellular systems; nuclear magnetic resonance. *Mailing Add:* Group CNC-4 Los Alamos Nat Lab Los Alamos NM 87545

MATYAS, E(LMER) LESLIE, b Hamilton, Ont, June 28, 32; m 54; c 2. GEOTECHNICAL ENGINEERING. *Educ:* Univ Toronto, BASc, 54; Univ London, PhD(soil mech), 63, Imp Col, dipl, 63. *Prof Exp:* Soils engr, Ont Hydro, 54-60; asst prof eng, Carleton Univ, 63-65; ASSOC PROF CIVIL ENG, UNIV WATERLOO, 65- *Concurrent Pos:* Assoc consult, Golder Assocs, 78- *Honors & Awards:* Hogentogler Award, Am Soc Testing & Mat, 69. *Mem:* Can Geotech Soc; Am Soc Civil Engrs. *Res:* Settlement of foundations on layered soils; earth loads on buried pipes; static and dynamic properties of mine tailings. *Mailing Add:* Dept Civil Eng Univ Waterloo Waterloo ON N2L 3G1 Can

MATZ, JOHN J, JR, nutrition, biochemistry, see previous edition

MATZ, ROBERT, b New York, NY, Aug 5, 31; m 55; c 3. INTERNAL MEDICINE. *Educ:* NY Univ, BA, 52, MD, 56. *Prof Exp:* From intern to resident, Bronx Municipal Hosp Ctr, 56-60; consult, Obstet Serv, Lincoln Hosp, Bronx, 62-63; NIH trainee metab, 63-64, assoc prof, 71-79, PROF MED, ALBERT EINSTEIN COL MED, 79-; DIR MED, MONTEFIORE-NORTH CENT BRONX AFFIL, 77-, CO-DIR, PRIMARY CARE RESIDENCY PROG INTERNAL MED, 80- *Concurrent Pos:* Vis physician, Montefiore-Morrisania Affil, 64-76, assoc dir med, 64-, head endocrinol & metab, 75-76, attend physician, Montefiore Hosp & Med Ctr, 75-76; attend physician, Bronx Munic Hosp Ctr, 71-76, co-dir, Diabetes Clin, 73-76; mem, Endocrine Dis Adv Comt, New York Dept Health, 72; consult, Health, Educ & Welfare Eval Unit, Albert Einstein Col Med, 73-76. *Mem:* Am Diabetes Asn; Harvey Soc; Am Fedn Clin Res; Am Col Physicians; Am Heart Asn. *Res:* Clinical research in diabetes mellitus, diabetic coma, and metabolic acidoses; clinical investigation of methods to improve delivery of health care. *Mailing Add:* 32 Buena Vista Dr Hastings-on-Hudson NY 10706

MATZ, SAMUEL ADAM, b Carmi, Ill, July 1, 24; m 51; c 4. FOOD SCIENCE. *Educ:* Evansville Col, BA, 48; Kans State Col, MS, 50; Univ Calif, PhD(agr chem), 58. *Prof Exp:* Instr, Kans State Col, 50; chief chemist, Harvest Queen Mill & Elevator Co, 50-51; food technologist cereal & gen prod & chief br, Armed Forces Qm Food & Container Inst, 51-59; supvr refrig dough invests, Borden Foods Co, 59-65; vpres res & develop, Robert A Johnston Co, Wis, 65-69; vpres, Ovaltine Food Prod, Ill, 69-71, VPRES RES & DEVELOP & REGULATORY AFFAIRS, OVALTINE PROD INC, 71- *Concurrent Pos:* Dir, Avi Publ Co, 73- *Mem:* Am Chem Soc; Inst Food Technologists. *Res:* Food preservation methods and texture; cereal and flavor chemistry; permeability mechanisms; nutrition; regulatory affairs. *Mailing Add:* Ovaltine Prod Div Sandoz-Wander Inc Villa Park IL 60181

MATZEN, VERNON CHARLES, b Petaluma, Calif. STRUCTURAL DYNAMICS, SYSTEM IDENTIFICATION. *Educ:* Univ Colo, BSCE, 66; Purdue Univ, MSCE, 68; Univ Calif, Berkeley, PhD(struct mech), 76. *Prof Exp:* Res & develop engr, Elec Boat Div, Gen Dynamics, Groton, Conn, 67-70; asst res engr, Univ Calif, Berkeley, 76-77; ASST PROF STRUCT MECH, NC STATE UNIV, 77- *Concurrent Pos:* Consult, Acures Corp, 75; lectr, Univ Calif, Berkeley, 76-77; consult, Brandt Indust, NC, 78-; prin investr, NSF, 80-82. *Mem:* Am Soc Civil Eng; Am Acad Mech; Earthquake Eng Res Inst; Sigma Xi. *Res:* Formulation of mathematical models of structures using measure response to known time-varying excitations; relationship between size of model, number and placement of sensors; uniqueness of parameters. *Mailing Add:* NC State Univ PO Box 5993 Raleigh NC 27650

MATZEN, WALTER T(HEODORE), b Columbus, Nebr, Sept 30, 22; m 43; c 3. ELECTRICAL ENGINEERING. *Educ:* Iowa State Univ, BS, 43; Agr & Mech Col, Tex, MS, 50, PhD(elec eng), 54. *Prof Exp:* Electronic engr, Stromberg Carlson Co, 46-48; assoc prof elec eng, Agr & Mech Col, Tex, 48-57, res assoc, 53-57; MGR ADVAN COMPONENTS, TEX INSTRUMENTS, INC, 57- *Mem:* Inst Elec & Electronics Engrs. *Res:* Design and technology of new semiconductor components. *Mailing Add:* 209 Thompson Richardson TX 75080

MATZINGER, DALE FREDERICK, b Alleman, Iowa, Apr 14, 29; m 60; c 2. QUANTITATIVE GENETICS. *Educ:* Iowa State Univ, BS, 50, MS, 51, PhD(plant breeding), 56. *Prof Exp:* Asst plant breeding, Iowa State Univ, 53-56; asst statistician, 56-57, asst prof statist, 57-58, statist & genetics, 58-60, assoc prof genetics, 60-64, PROF GENETICS, NC STATE UNIV, 64- *Honors & Awards:* Philip Morris Award Distinguished Achievement Tobacco Sci, 71. *Mem:* Fel Am Soc Agron; Crop Sci Soc Am; Genetics Soc Am; Biomet Soc; AAAS. *Res:* Statistical genetic theory and breeding methodology of self-pollinated plants; appled statistics; plant science. *Mailing Add:* Dept of Genetics NC State Univ Raleigh NC 27650

MATZKANIN, GEORGE ANDREW, b Chicago, Ill, June 30, 38; m 63; c 2. NONDESTRUCTRIVE EVALUATION, MATERIALS SCIENCE. *Educ:* St Mary's Col, AB, 60; Univ Fla, MS, 62, PhD(physics), 66; Trinity Univ, MBA, 77. *Prof Exp:* Res assoc metals physics, Argonne Nat Lab, 66-68; vis asst prof physics, Univ Ill, Chicago Circle, 68-69; SR RES PHYSICIST INSTRUMENTATION DIV, SOUTHWEST RES INST, 69- *Mem:* AAAS; Am Phys Soc; Am Soc Nondestructive Testing; Sigma Xi. *Res:* Nondestructive evaluation research; instrumentation research; nuclear magnetic resonance; magnetic and mechanical properties of materials; Barkhausen phenomena; residual stress; evaluation of metal fatigue; moisture measurement; composite materials. *Mailing Add:* Southwest Res Inst PO Drawer 28510 San Antonio TX 78284

MATZKE, HOWARD ARTHUR, neuroanatomy, see previous edition

MATZNER, EDWIN ARTHUR, b Vienna, Austria, May 14, 28; m 53; c 1. ORGANIC CHEMISTRY. *Educ:* Calif Inst Technol, BS, 51; Yale Univ, PhD(org chem), 58. *Prof Exp:* Res chemist, 58-63, sr res group leader, 63-67, mgr res & develop, 66-77, MEM STAFF INORG RES DEPT, MONSANTO CO, 77- *Mem:* Am Chem Soc; Soc Chem & Indust; Res & Eng Soc Am. *Res:* Synthetic organic chemistry; solvent extraction; chemistry of phosphates; electrochemistry; chemistry of detergents and surfactants. *Mailing Add:* Monsanto Co 800 N Lindbergh Blvd St Louis MO 63166

MATZNER, MARKUS, b Biala, Poland, Mar 19, 29; nat US; m 54; c 1. ORGANIC CHEMISTRY. *Educ:* Univ Brussels, MS, 50, PhD, 53. *Prof Exp:* Res chemist, Tirlemont Refinery, Belg, 53-54 & Probel Labs, 54-56; res & control chemist, Belg Petrol Refinery, 56-59; res chemist, Plastics Div, Union Carbide Corp, 59-63, proj scientist, 63-66, res scientist, 66-68, sr res scientist, 68-71, RES ASSOC CHEM & PLASTICS RES & DEVELOP DEPT, UNION CARBIDE CORP, 71- *Honors & Awards:* Prix, Belgian Acad Sci, 53. *Mem:* Am Chem Soc; Sigma Xi. *Res:* Organic synthesis; mechanisms of reactions; polymer chemistry. *Mailing Add:* 23 Marshall Dr Edison NJ 08817

MATZNER, RICHARD ALFRED, b Ft Worth, Tex, Jan 2, 42; m 67; c 1. PHYSICS. *Educ:* Univ Notre Dame, BS, 63; Univ Md, College Park, PhD(physics), 67. *Prof Exp:* NSF fac assoc physics, 67-69, asst prof, 69-73, res physicist, Ctr Relativity Theory, 73-77, ASSOC PROF PHYSICS, UNIV TEX, AUSTIN, 73- *Concurrent Pos:* Res fel physics, Wesleyan Univ, 69-70. *Mem:* AAAS. *Res:* General relativity; cosmology; gravitational collapse; geometrical optics; canonical formulations; statistical mechanics. *Mailing Add:* Dept of Physics Univ of Tex Austin TX 78712

MAUCH, HANS A, b 1906. ENGINEERING. *Prof Exp:* Mem staff, E Zwietusch & Co, Berlin, 30-35 & Ger Air Ministry, Berlin, 35-39; head eng off, Berlin, 39-48; mem staff, Aeromed Ctr, US Air Force, Heidelberg, 45-46 & Aeromed Lab, Wright Field, Dayton Ohio, 46-57; PRES, MAUCH LABS INC, 57- *Honors & Awards:* Outstanding Civil Serv Commendation, US Air Force, 56, Outstanding Inventor Award, 60. *Mem:* Nat Acad Eng. *Mailing Add:* Mauch Labs Inc 3035 Dryden Rd Dayton OH 45439

MAUCK, HENRY PAGE, JR, b Richmond, Va, Feb 3, 26; c 2. CARDIOLOGY. *Educ:* Univ Va, BA, 48, MD, 52; Am Bd Internal Med, dipl, 59. *Prof Exp:* DIR CARDIAC CATHETERIZATION LAB, MED COL VA, 70-, PROF MED & PEDIAT, 72- *Concurrent Pos:* Am Heart Asn fel, 56-57; consult pediat cardiol, Langley Air Force Hosp; ed consult, Am Heart J. *Mem:* AMA; fel Am Col Physicians; fel Am Col Cardiol; Am Fedn Clin Res; fel Am Heart Asn. *Res:* Neural control of the circulation. *Mailing Add:* Dept of Med Med Col of Va Richmond VA 23298

MAUDERLI, WALTER, b Aarau, Switz, Mar 8, 24; nat US; m 50; c 5. NUCLEAR PHYSICS. *Educ:* Swiss Fed Inst Technol, MS, 49, DSc(physics), 56. *Prof Exp:* Physicist & asst radiol, Univ Zurich, 50-56; physicist, asst prof & head isotope labs, Sch Med, Univ Ark, 56-60; assoc prof radiation physics, 60-64, PROF RADIATION PHYSICS, J HILLIS MILLER HEALTH CTR, COL MED, UNIV FLA, 65-, PHYSICIST, 60-, PROF ENVIRON ENG SCI, 74- *Concurrent Pos:* Lectr, Grad Inst Technol & Med Ctr, Univ Ark; consult, Vet Admin Hosp, Little Rock. *Mem:* Am Asn Physicists in Med; Simulation Coun; Soc Nuclear Med; AMA; Asn Comput Mach. *Res:* Radiation physics; computer applications in radiology; electronic instrumentation in radiation physics. *Mailing Add:* Dept of Radiol Univ of Fla Gainesville FL 32601

MAUDERLY, JOE L, b Strong City, Kans, Aug 31, 43; m 65; c 2. PULMONARY PHYSIOLOGY. *Educ:* Kans State Univ, BS, 65, DVM, 67. *Prof Exp:* PHYSIOLOGIST, LOVELACE BIOMED & ENVIRON RES INST, 69- *Mem:* Am Vet Med Asn; Am Soc Vet Physiol & Pharmacol; Am Physiol Soc; World Asn Vet Physiol, Pharmacol & Biochem; Am Soc Vet Anesthesiol. *Res:* Comparative cardiopulmonary physiology; pulmonary function measurements in animals; lung disease from inhaled toxic materials; animal models of lung disease; age effects on lung; bronchopulmonary lavage; anesthesiology of animals. *Mailing Add:* Inhal Toxicol Res Inst PO Box 5890 Albuquerque NM 87115

MAUDLIN, LLOYD Z, b Miles City, Mont, Feb 20, 24; m 46; c 4. PHYSICS. *Educ:* Univ Calif, Los Angeles, AB, 49; Univ Southern Calif, MS, 52. *Prof Exp:* Electronic scientist, US Naval Ord Test Sta, 51-56, supvry electronic scientist & head simulation br, 56-59, supvry physicist & dir simulation & comput ctr, 59-67, head simulation & anal div, Naval Undersea Warfare Ctr, 67-71, supvry physicist & head comput sci & simulation div, Naval Undersea Res & Develop Ctr, 71-77, SUPVRY PHYSICIST & HEAD COMPUT SCI & SIMULATION DEPT, NAVAL OCEAN SYSTS CTR, 77- *Mem:* Inst Elec & Electronics Engrs; NY Acad Sci. *Res:* Anti-submarine warfare, particularly guidance and control of underwater weapons; computer and simulation analysis of anti-submarine warfare weapons systems; analog and digital computing techniques. *Mailing Add:* Naval Ocean Systs Ctr Code 91 San Diego CA 92152

MAUDSLEY, DAVID V, b Blackburn, Eng, Dec 13, 40. BIOCHEMICAL PHARMACOLOGY. *Educ:* Univ London, BP, 62, PhD(pharmacol), 66. *Prof Exp:* Lectr pharmacol, Sch Pharm, Univ London, 64-66; staff scientist, 66-75, SR SCIENTIST, WORCESTER FOUND FOR EXP BIOL, SHREWSBURY, 75- *Concurrent Pos:* Assoc res prof biochem, Univ Mass Med Sch, 77- *Mem:* Am Soc Pharmacol & Exp Therapeut; NY Acad Sci. *Res:* Regulation of diamine and polyamine metabolism in proliferating systems. *Mailing Add:* Worcester Found for Exp Biol Shrewsbury MA 01545

MAUE-DICKSON, WILMA, developmental anatomy, see previous edition

MAUER, ALVIN MARX, b Le Mars, Iowa, Jan 10, 28; m 50; c 4. MEDICINE. *Educ:* Univ Iowa, BA, 50, MD, 53. *Prof Exp:* Intern, Cincinnati Gen Hosp, 53-54; from jr resident to chief resident pediat, Cincinnati Children's Hosp, 54-56; from asst prof to assoc prof pediat, Col Med, Univ Cincinnati, 59-69, prof, 69-73; PROF PEDIAT, UNIV TENN, MEMPHIS, 73-; DIR, ST JUDE CHILDREN'S RES HOSP, 73- *Concurrent Pos:* Dir div hemat, Children's Hosp Res Found, 59-; attend pediatrician & dir div hemat & hemat clin, Children's Hosp, Cincinnati, 59-; attend pediatrician, Cincinnati Gen Hosp, 59-; attend hematologist, Vet Admin Hosp, 60-; NIH fel, 56-58; res fel hemat, Univ Utah, 56-59; Am Cancer Soc fel, 58-59; NIH res career develop award, 62-; fel, Div Hemat, Children's Hosp Res Found, 63- *Mem:* Am Asn Cancer Res; Am Pediat Soc; Am Soc Clin Invest; Am Soc Hemat (pres); Asn Am Physicians. *Res:* Labeling techniques with radioactive materials to study leukocyte kinetics in patients with acute leukemia and disorders of granulopoiesis. *Mailing Add:* St Jude Children's Res Hosp PO Box 318 Memphis TN 38101

MAUER, IRVING, b Montreal, Que, Feb 7, 27; nat US; m 52; c 3. GENETICS, MUTAGENESIS. *Educ:* McGill Univ, PhD(genetics), 60. *Prof Exp:* Asst cytol, Sci Serv, Can Dept Agr, 48-49; demonstr genetics, McGill Univ, 54-56, asst, 55-56; res assoc animal genetics, Storrs Agr Exp Sta, Univ Conn, 56-57; sr med writer, Squibb Inst Med Res Div, Olin Mathieson Chem Corp, 57-60; psychiat res fel, NY State Dept Ment Health, 61-62, sr res scientist, 62-67, lectr, 62 & 65; head cytogenetics group, Dept Exp Path, Hoffmann-La Rocke Inc, 67-77; GENETICIST, HAZARD EVAL DIV, OFF PESTICIDE PROGS, ENVIRON PROTECTION AGENCY, 78- *Mem:* AAAS; Am Acad Ment Retardation; Genetics Soc Am; Am Soc Human Genetics; Am Genetic Asn. *Res:* Cytogenetics of man; mutagenicity testing; teratology; experimental cytogenetics; mutagenicity testing. *Mailing Add:* 4300 Old Dominion Dr Arlington VA 22207

MAUER, PAUL BERNARD, optical physics, see previous edition

MAUERSBERGER, KONRAD, b Lengefeld, Ger, Apr 28, 38; m 64; c 2. AERONOMY. *Educ:* Univ Bonn, Dipl, 64, PhD(physics), 68. *Prof Exp:* Res assoc physics, Univ Bonn, 68-69; res assoc, 69-74, asst prof, 74-77, ASSOC PROF PHYSICS, UNIV MINN, MINNEAPOLIS, 77- *Mem:* Am Geophys Union. *Res:* Composition and dynamics of Earth's upper atmosphere using mass spectrometers carried on balloons, rockets and satellites; solar-atmospheric interactions at altitudes above twenty kilometers. *Mailing Add:* 148 Physics Bldg Univ of Minn Minneapolis MN 55455

MAUGER, JOHN WILLIAM, b Scranton, Pa, Aug 10, 42; m 65; c 1. PHARMACEUTICS. *Educ:* Union Univ, NY, BS, 65; Univ RI, MS, 68, PhD(pharmaceut sci), 71. *Prof Exp:* Instr pharm, Univ RI, 69-71; asst prof, 71-80, ASSOC PROF PHARM, SCH PHARM, WVA UNIV MED CTR, 80- *Mem:* Am Pharmaceut Asn. *Res:* Nonelectrolyte solubility; aqueous solutions of pharmaceutical solutes; convective diffusion. *Mailing Add:* Marion Meadows Morgantown WV 26505

MAUGER, RICHARD L, b Fairdale, Pa, Sept 20, 36; m 63; c 1. GEOLOGY. *Educ:* Franklin & Marshall Col, BS, 58; Calif Inst Technol, MS, 60; Univ Ariz, PhD(geol), 66. *Prof Exp:* Asst prof geol, Univ Utah, 66-69; from asst prof to assoc prof, 69-76, PROF GEOL, EAST CAROLINA UNIV, 76- *Mem:* AAAS; Geol Soc Am; Am Geophys Union. *Res:* Mineral deposits; isotopic dating and stable isotopes. *Mailing Add:* Dept of Geol ECarolina Univ Greenville NC 27834

MAUGHAN, EDWIN KELLY, b Glendale, Calif, Oct 13, 26; m 51; c 4. GEOLOGY. *Educ:* Utah State Univ, BS, 50. *Prof Exp:* Geologist, Corps Engrs, US Dept Army, 51; GEOLOGIST, US GEOL SURV, 51- *Concurrent Pos:* Tech adv phosphate deposits, Inventario Minero Nacional Colombia, 67-69 & stratig, Struct & Coal Resources Southeast Ky, 69-72. *Mem:* Geol Soc Am; Am Asn Petrol Geologists; Colombian Asn Advan Sci; Soc Econ Paleont & Mineral. *Res:* Areal geology vicinity of Great Falls, Mont, Thermopolis, Wyo, Middlesboro, Ky; stratigraphy and phosphate resources in Cretaceous of Colombia; stratigraphy, paleogeography and mineral resources (petroleum, salt, phosphate) in Permian, Pennsylvanian and Mississippian rocks of northern Rocky Mountains and Great Basin. *Mailing Add:* US Geol Surv (MS 940) Fed Ctr Box 25046 Denver CO 80225

MAUGHAN, GEORGE BURWELL, b Toronto, Ont, May 8, 10; m 67; c 6. OBSTETRICS & GYNECOLOGY. *Educ:* McGill Univ, MD & CM, 34, MSc, 38; FRCS(C), 52; FRCOG, 57. *Prof Exp:* Demonstr path & bact, McGill Univ, 34-35, demonstr anat, 39-40, from demonstr to asst prof obstet & gynec, 40-56, prof & chmn dept, 56-77, EMER PROF OBSTET & GYNEC, McGILL UNIV, 77- *Concurrent Pos:* Obstetrician & gynecologist-in-chief, Royal Victoria Hosp, 56-75, hon consult obstet & gynec, 75-; consult obstetrician & gynecologist, Montreal Gen, Reddy Mem, Queen Elizabeth, St Mary's & Jewish Gen, Lakeshore Gen, Montreal Chinese. *Mem:* Can Med Asn; fel Am Col Surg; Soc Obstet & Gynaec Can (past pres); fel Am Asn Obstet & Gynec; Can Gynaec Soc. *Res:* Intensive care in high risk pregnancy. *Mailing Add:* Apt F-61 1321 Sherbrooke St W Montreal PQ H3G 1J4 Can

MAUGHAN, OWEN EUGENE, b Preston, Idaho, Jan 3, 43; m 62; c 4. FISH BIOLOGY, AQUATIC ECOLOGY. *Educ:* Utah State Univ, BS, 66; Univ Kans, MA, 68; Wash State Univ, PhD(zool), 72. *Prof Exp:* Proj leader, Nat Res Planning Div, River Basin Studies, 71-72, asst leader & assoc prof fisheries, Va Coop Fishery Res Unit, 72-77, UNIT LEADER & ASSOC PROF FISHERIES, OKLA COOP FISHERY RES UNIT, US FISH & WILDLIFE SERV, 77- *Concurrent Pos:* Fisheries sect leader, Va Polytech Inst & State Univ, 76-77. *Mem:* Am Fisheries Soc; Am Soc Ichthyol & Herpetol; Can Soc Zool. *Res:* Fisheries biology and aquatic ecology; particularly the effects of man caused development on aquatic ecosystems. *Mailing Add:* US Fish & Wildlife Serv Okla State Univ Stillwater OK 74074

MAUGHAN, PAUL MCALPINE, marine sciences, remote sensing, see previous edition

MAUK, MARCIA ROKUS, b Wisconsin Rapids, Wis, July 11, 47; m 70. BIOCHEMISTRY. *Educ:* Ripon Col, AB, 69; Med Col Wis, Milwaukee, PhD(biochem), 74. *Prof Exp:* Fel biochem, Med Col Wis, 74-76; res fel, Calif Inst Technol, 76-79; RES ASSOC BIOCHEM, UNIV BC, 81- *Res:* Structure-function relationships in hemeproteins; mechanisms of protein-protein interaction; targeting of lipid vesicles. *Mailing Add:* Dept Biochem Univ BC Vancouver BC V6T 1W5 Can

MAUL, JAMES JOSEPH, b Buffalo, NY, Nov 3, 38; m 62; c 2. ORGANIC CHEMISTRY. *Educ:* Canisius Col, BS, 60; Wayne State Univ, PhD(org chem), 66. *Prof Exp:* Sr chemist, 68-75, SR RES CHEMIST, HOOKER CHEM CORP, 75- *Mem:* Am Chem Soc. *Res:* Organo-fluorine chemistry; organo-halogen chemistry. *Mailing Add:* 15 Beaver Ln Grand Island NY 14072

MAUL, STEPHEN BAILEY, b Parkersburg, WVa, Jan 11, 42; m 67. INDUSTRIAL MICROBIOLOGY. *Educ:* Abilene Christian Col, BS, 63; Univ Tex, Austin, PhD(biochem), 69. *Prof Exp:* Res assoc nutrit & food sci, Mass Inst Technol, 69-70; sr biochemist, Antibiotic Develop Dept, Eli Lilly & Co, 70-74; sr scientist, Schering Corp, 74-76; SCIENTIST, BUTLER COUNTY MUSHROOM FARM, INC, 76- *Mem:* AAAS; Am Chem Soc; Am Soc Microbiol; Soc Indust Microbiol. *Res:* Antibiotic fermentations; new fermentation technology; enzyme applications; biological control mechanisms; mineral requirements in fermentations; computer control of fermentations; soild state fermentation; composting; mycorrhizae. *Mailing Add:* Butler County Mushroom Farm Inc Worthington PA 16262

MAULBETSCH, JOHN STEWART, b Brooklyn, NY, May 25, 39; m 75. MECHANICAL ENGINEERING. *Educ:* Mass Inst Technol, SB, 60, SM, 62, PhD(mech eng), 65. *Prof Exp:* Asst prof mech eng, Mass Inst Technol, 65-67; proj engr, Dynatech Res & Develop Co, 67-70, prin engr, 70-75; PROG MGR HEAT, WASTE & WATER MGT, ELEC POWER RES INST, 75- *Concurrent Pos:* Ford fel, 65-67. *Mem:* Am Soc Mech Engrs. *Res:* Two-phase flow and boiling; environmental control. *Mailing Add:* 90 Lloyden Dr Atherton CA 94025

MAULDIN, JOE KENNON, entomology, biochemistry, see previous edition

MAULDIN, RICHARD DANIEL, b Longview, Tex, Jan 17, 43; m 74; c 1. MATHEMATICS. *Educ:* Univ Tex, BA, 65, MA, 66, PhD(math), 69. *Prof Exp:* From asst prof to assoc prof math, Univ Fla, 69-77; ASSOC PROF MATH, NORTH TEX STATE UNIV, 77- *Mem:* Am Math Soc. *Res:* Descriptive set theory, measure theory and point set topology and the interaction of these three areas. *Mailing Add:* Dept of Math N Tex State Univ Denton TX 76203

MAULDING, DONALD ROY, b Evansville, Ind, Aug 15, 36; m 58; c 1. SYNTHETIC ORGANIC CHEMISTRY. *Educ:* Evansville Col, AB, 58; Univ Ind, PhD(org chem), 62. *Prof Exp:* Fel, Ohio State Univ, 62-64; RES CHEMIST, AM CYANAMID CO, 64- *Mem:* Am Chem Soc. *Res:* Organic mechanisms; photochemistry and chemiluminescence; fluorescence; rubber chemicals and polyurethanes; agricultural chemicals; synthesis; process development. *Mailing Add:* Org Chems Div Am Cyanamid Co Bound Brook NJ 08805

MAULDING, HAWKINS VALLIANT, JR, b Foreman, Ark, Dec 21, 35; m 59; c 3. PHYSICAL CHEMISTRY, PHYSICAL PHARMACY. *Educ:* Univ Ark, Little Rock, BS, 58; Univ Minn, Minneapolis, PhD(med chem), 64. *Prof Exp:* Asst prof pharm, Univ Houston, 64-66; SR SCIENTIST & GROUP LEADER PHYS CHEM & PHYS PHARM, SANDOZ PHARMACEUT, EAST HANOVER, 66- *Mem:* Am Pharmaceut Asn. *Res:* Theoretical and applied kinetics; complexation; reaction mechanisms; stability of solid products; dosage form design. *Mailing Add:* Sandoz Pharmaceut Rte 10 East Hanover NJ 07936

MAULDON, JAMES GRENFELL, b London, Eng, Feb 9, 20; m 53; c 4. PURE MATHEMATICS. *Educ:* Oxford Univ, BA & MA, 47. *Hon Degrees:* MA, Amherst Col, 70. *Prof Exp:* Lectr math, Oxford Univ, 47-68; prof math, 68-80, WALKER PROF, AMHERST COL, 80- *Concurrent Pos:* Lectr, St John's Col, Oxford Univ, 50-59, fel, Corpus Christi Col, 50-68; vis prof, Univ Calif, Berkeley, 60-61; chmn fac, Oxford Univ, 66-68; consult, IBM Corp, 74-75. *Mem:* Royal Statist Soc; Inst Math Statist; Am Math Soc. *Res:* Mathematics, including probability, algebra, analysis, geometry and combinatorics; computer languages. *Mailing Add:* Dept of Math Amherst Col Amherst MA 01002

MAUNDER, A BRUCE, b Holdrege, Nebr, May 13, 34; m 78; c 1. GENETICS, PLANT BREEDING. *Educ:* Univ Nebr, BS, 56; Purdue Univ, MS, 58, PhD(genetics), 60. *Prof Exp:* Plant breeder, 59-61, sorghum res dir, 61-78, actg agron res dir, 78-79, AGRON RES DIR, DEKALB AGRESEARCH INC, 79- *Honors & Awards:* Gerald Thomas Award, Am Soc Agron. *Mem:* Fel Am Soc Agron. *Res:* Inheritance of male sterility; heterosis as regards sorghum; disease and insect resistance; genetic advances; evolution. *Mailing Add:* DeKalb AgResearch Inc Route 2 Lubbock TX 79415

MAUNDER, DUANE THAYER, microbiology, see previous edition

MAUNE, DAVID FRANCIS, b Washington, Mo, July 12, 39; m 61; c 2. PHOTOGRAMMETRY, RESEARCH ADMINISTRATION. *Educ:* Univ Mo-Rolla, BSc, 61; Ohio State Univ, MSc, 70, PhD(geod, photogram), 73. *Prof Exp:* Mech engr, Union Elec Co, St Louis, 61; US Army, 63-, co comdr & opers officer, 656 Eng Topog Battalion, US Army, Ger, 63-66, mapping officer, Hq, Vietnam, 66-67, opers officer, 36 Engr Group, Korea, 70-71, officer-in-charge prod, Mapping & Charting Estab, Royal Engrs, Eng, 73-74, staff officer, Directorate Army Res, Washington, DC, 74-76, topog plans officer, 77-78, battalion comndr, 652 Eng Topog Battalion, Hawaii, 78-80, CHIEF TRAINING DEVELOP & EVAL, DEFENSE MAPPING SCH, US DEPT ARMY, FT BELVOIR, VA, 81- *Mem:* Am Soc Photogram; Soc Am Military Engrs. *Res:* Photogrammetric calibration of scanning electron microscopes; analytical photogrammetry; satellite geodesy; operations research systems analysis; military research and development management; mapping, charting and geodesy training. *Mailing Add:* 801 Fieldcrest Dr Washington MO 63090

MAUNSELL, CHARLES DUDLEY, b Victoria, BC, Mar 29, 24. PHYSICS. *Educ:* Univ BC, BA, 45, MA, 47; Univ Calif, PhD(physics), 55. *Prof Exp:* Sci officer, Pac Naval Lab, 55-63; SR SCI OFFICER, BEDFORD INST OCEANOG, CAN DEPT ENERGY, MINES & RESOURCES, 63- *Mem:* Am Phys Soc; assoc Acoust Soc Am; Can Asn Physicists. *Res:* Physical oceanography; underwater acoustics; scientific computing. *Mailing Add:* Suite 801 139 Clarence St Victoria BC V8V 2J1 Can

MAURER, ARTHUR JAMES, b Winfield, Pa, Apr 16, 42; m 66; c 2. POULTRY SCIENCE, FOOD SCIENCE. *Educ:* Pa State Univ, BS, 64; Cornell Univ, MS, 66, PhD(food Sci), 71. *Prof Exp:* Asst county agent, Pa State Univ, 63-64; res asst, Cornell Univ, 64-70; asst prof, 70-75, assoc prof, 75-81, PROF POULTRY SCI, UNIV WIS, 81- *Concurrent Pos:* NIH fel, 64-68; poultry consult, Wis Nicaragua Partners Prog, 77; consult, Vol Tech Asst, 76. *Mem:* Poultry Sci Asn; Inst Food Technol; Int Asn Milk, Food & Environ Sanitarians; World Poultry Sci Asn. *Res:* Poultry products technology; processing, preservation, product development and marketing of poultry meat and eggs. *Mailing Add:* Dept Poultry Sci Univ Wis Madison WI 53706

MAURER, BRUCE ANTHONY, b Springfield, Mass, Oct 22, 36; c 3. RESEARCH ADMINISTRATION. *Educ:* St Michael's Col, BA, 58; Univ Mass, MS, 60; Univ Ariz, PhD(microbiol), 66. *Prof Exp:* Asst prof microbiol, Miami Univ, 66-68; sr cancer res scientist, Roswell Park Mem Inst, 68-71; asst res prof virol, Roswell Park Div, State Univ NY Buffalo, 69-71; dir biol, Assoc Biomedic Systs, 71-73; res scientist immunol, Litton-Bionetics, Inc, Md, 73-78; grants assoc, NIH, 78-79, prog dir immunol, Nat Inst Aging, 79-81, PROG DIR IMMUNOL, NAT CANCER INST, 81- *Mem:* Sigma Xi. Microbiol. *Res:* Biochemistry of polyona virus infection in vitro; cell virus interaction of Epstein-Barr virus and human lymphoblastoid cell lines; cellular immunology of human and animal neoplasias; lymphocyte alloantigens of rhesus monkey major histocompatibility complex. *Mailing Add:* Immunol Prog Nat Cancer Inst NIH Westwood Bldg Rm 2A03 Bethesda MD 20205

MAURER, DONALD LEO, b Chicago, Ill, Sept 3, 34; m 67; c 4. MARINE ECOLOGY, POLLUTION BIOLOGY. *Educ:* Univ Ill, BS, 56; Univ Wash, MS, 58; Univ Chicago, PhD(paleozool), 64. *Prof Exp:* Res assoc marine ecol, Pac Marine Sta, Calif, 64-65; assoc prof biol, Old Dom Col, 65-67; asst prof, 67-73, ASSOC PROF MARINE BIOL, UNIV DEL, 73- *Mem:* Soc Econ Paleont & Mineral; Soc Limnol & Oceanog; Atlantic Estuarine Res Soc; Sigma Xi. *Res:* Ecology of marine invertebrates; paleoecology; description of macroscopic Benthic invertebrate communities in the Delaware bay and adjacent coastal zones; determination of community and specific response to pollutants in the aforementioned areas. *Mailing Add:* Field Sta Col of Marine Stud Univ of Del Lewes DE 19958

MAURER, EDWARD ROBERT, b San Francisco, Calif, Jan 3, 21; m 55; c 2. PHYSICAL SCIENCE, HISTORY OF SCIENCE. *Educ:* Stanford Univ, BS, 48, MS, 50, PhD(phys sci), 64. *Prof Exp:* Instr phys sci, Chico State Col, 52-55, asst prof, 55-56; vis asst prof, Stanford Univ, 56-58; assoc prof, 58-65, head dept phys sci, 58-67, dean, Sch Prof Studies, 70-74, asst dean acad affairs, 75, PROF PHYS SCI, CALIF STATE UNIV, CHICO, 65- *Mem:* Fel AAAS; Hist Sci Soc; Soc Hist Technol; Sigma Xi; Soc Hist Alchemy & Chem. *Res:* History of science and technology, with special interest in the development of British chemistry during the 18th and 19th centuries; the role of the physical sciences in general education. *Mailing Add:* Dept of Geol & Phys Sci Calif State Univ Chico CA 95929

MAURER, FRED DRY, b Moscow, Idaho, May 4, 09; m 35; c 2. VETERINARY PATHOLOGY. *Educ:* Univ Idaho, BS, 34; State Col Wash, BS & DVM, 37; Cornell Univ, PhD(path bact), 48. *Prof Exp:* Jr veterinarian dis control, Bur Animal Indust, USDA, 37; asst prof, Univ Idaho & asst bacteriologist, Exp Sta, 37-38; instr path & bact, Vet Col, Cornell Univ, 38-41; staff mem, Vet Res Lab, Vet Corps, US Army, Va, 41-43, lab officer, War Dis Control Sta, Can & Africa, 43-46, Res & Grad Sch, Army Med Ctr, 47-51, chief, Vet Path Div, Armed Forces Inst Path, 54-61, dir, Div Med, Army Med Res Lab, Ft Knox, Ky, 61-64; dir, Inst Trop Vet Med, 74-76, distinguished prof path, 64-76, EMER DIR, INST TROP VET MED, COL VET MED, TEX A&M UNIV, 76- *Concurrent Pos:* Assoc dean, Col Vet Med, Tex A&M Univ, 64-74. *Honors & Awards:* 12th Int Vet Cong Prize, 68. *Mem:* Am Vet Med Asn; US Animal Health Asn; Am Col Vet Path (pres, 64); Conf Res Workers Animal Dis; Am Asn Lab Animal Sci. *Res:* Virology and pathology of infectious diseases of animals. *Mailing Add:* Col Vet Med Tex A&M Univ College Station TX 77843

MAURER, HANS ANDREAS, b Frankfurt, Ger, May 7, 13; US citizen. PHYSICS. *Educ:* Univ Munich, BSc, 33; Univ Frankfurt, PhD(appl physics), 37. *Prof Exp:* Sr proj engr, Missile Systs Div, Raytheon Co, 57-61, mgr advan weapons systs, 61-63, mgr Advan Syst Ctr, 63-64, chief engr, 64-65; tech dir to asst div mgr, Missile Div, Aerospace Group, 66-76, TECH DIR, MISSILE SYSTS GROUP, HUGHES AIRCRAFT CO, 76- *Mem:* AAAS; Ger Oberth Soc; fel Inst Elec & Electronics Engrs. *Mailing Add:* Hughes Aircraft Co Missile Systs Group 8433 Fallbrook Ave Canoga Park CA 91304

MAURER, JOHN EDWARD, b Matherville, Ill, Apr 3, 23; m 46; c 4. ORGANIC CHEMISTRY. *Educ:* Augustana Col, AB, 47; Univ Iowa, MS, 48, PhD(org chem), 50. *Prof Exp:* Res assoc, Northwestern Univ, 50-52; res chemist, Rock Island Arsenal, 52-53; from asst prof to assoc prof, 53-66, asst head dept, 68-77, PROF CHEM, UNIV WYO, 66-, ACTG HEAD DEPT, 77- *Mem:* AAAS; Am Chem Soc. *Res:* Halogenations; Van Slyke reactions; naturalproducts. *Mailing Add:* Dept of Chem Univ of Wyo Box 3838 Laramie WY 82071

MAURER, JOHN FREDERICK, b Rochester, NY, Sept 22, 23. ENGINEERING. *Educ:* Univ Mich, BSE, 45, MSE, 47, PhD(chem eng), 51. *Prof Exp:* Res engr, 51-60, sr res engr, 60-62, res assoc, 62-67, res supvr, 67-71, ASSOC ENGR, E I DU PONT DE NEMOURS & CO, INC, 71- *Res:* Chemical kinetics; metallurgy; semiconductors. *Mailing Add:* 306 Glen Berne Dr Wilmington DE 19804

MAURER, KARL GUSTAV, b Philadelphia, Pa, Aug 25, 29; m 55; c 3. ENGINEERING MECHANICS, MECHANICAL ENGINEERING. *Educ:* Drexel Inst Technol, BSME, 59; Univ Kans, MS, 62, PhD(fluid mech), 66. *Prof Exp:* Design engr, Gen Dynamics/Astronaut Div, 59-60; asst instr eng mech, Univ Kans, 60-65; asst prof civil eng, Rose Polytech Inst, 66-67; assoc prof mech eng & asst dean col eng & archit, 67-72, PROF MECH ENG & CHMN DEPT, NDAK STATE UNIV, 72- *Mem:* Am Soc Mech Engrs; Am Soc Eng Educ. *Res:* Classical fluid mechanics and boundary layer theory. *Mailing Add:* 3001 Ninth St N Fargo ND 58102

MAURER, PAUL HERBERT, b New York, NY, June 29, 23; m 48; c 3. IMMUNOLOGY. *Educ:* City Col New York, BS, 44; Columbia Univ, PhD(immunochem), 50. *Prof Exp:* Res biochemist, Gen Foods Corp, 44 & 46; instr, City Col New York, 46-51; res assoc, Col Physicians & Surgeons, Columbia Univ, 50-51; asst res prof, Sch Med, Univ Pittsburgh, 51-54, assoc prof immunochem, 54-60; prof microbiol, NJ Col Med & Dent, 60-66; PROF BIOCHEM & HEAD DEPT, JEFFERSON MED COL, 66- *Concurrent Pos:* NIH res career award, 62- *Mem:* Am Chem Soc; Am Asn Immunol; NY Acad Sci; Brit Biochem Soc. *Res:* Immunochemistry; biochemistry; protein chemistry. *Mailing Add:* Dept of Biochem Jefferson Med Col Philadelphia PA 19107

MAURER, RALPH RUDOLF, b Monroe, Wis, Feb 28, 41; m 63; c 3. REPRODUCTIVE PHYSIOLOGY, REPRODUCTIVE ENDOCRINOLOGY. *Educ:* Univ Wis, BS, 63; Cornell Univ, MS, 66, PhD(physiol), 69. *Prof Exp:* RES PHYSIOLOGIST, ROMAN L HRUSKA

US MEAT ANIMAL RES CTR, 76- *Concurrent Pos:* Alexander von Humboldt Fel, 69-71; sr staff fel, Nat Inst Environ Health Sci, 71-76. *Honors & Awards:* Lalor Found Award, 69. *Mem:* Soc Study Reprod; Brit Soc Study Fertil; Am Soc Animal Sci; Am Inst Biol Sci; Teretology Soc. *Res:* Early embryonic development in swine and cattle; environmental factors affecting reproduction; maternal aging and embryonic mortality; storage of gametes and embryos. *Mailing Add:* Roman L Hruska US Meat Animal Res PO Box 166 Clay Center NE 68933

MAURER, RICHARD ALLEN, b Long Beach, Calif, Mar 21, 47; m 68. PHYSIOLOGY. *Educ:* Univ Calif, Irvine, BS, 69; Univ Calif, Davis, PhD(physiol), 73. *Prof Exp:* Fel, Univ Wis, Madison, 73-77; asst prof, 77-81, ASSOC PROF PHYSIOL, UNIV IOWA, 81- *Mem:* Endocrine Soc; Am Soc Biol Chemists. *Res:* The molecular basis for the endocrine control of prolactin synthesis and secretion; analysis of the rate limiting factors in the processes of prolactin gene transcription; hormonal control of DNA synthesis and cell differentiation in the anterior pituitary. *Mailing Add:* Dept Physiol Univ Iowa Iowa City IA 52242

MAURER, ROBERT DISTLER, b St Louis, Mo, July 20, 24; m 51; c 3. APPLIED PHYSICS. *Educ:* Univ Ark, BS, 48; Mass Inst Technol, PhD(physics), 51. *Hon Degrees:* LLD, Univ Ark, 80. *Prof Exp:* Mem physics staff, Mass Inst Technol, 51-52; physicist, 52-62, sr res assoc, 62-63, mgr fundamental physics res, 63-70, mgr appl physics res, 70-78, RES FEL, CORNING GLASS WORKS, 78- *Honors & Awards:* George W Morey Award, Am Ceramic Soc, 76; Morris N Liebmann Award, Inst Elec & Electronics Engrs, 78; Ericsson Int Prize, telecommun, 79; Prize, Am Inst Physics. *Mem:* Nat Acad Eng; fel Am Ceramic Soc; sr mem Inst Elec & Electronics Engrs; Am Phys Soc. *Res:* Physical behavior of glasses; optical communications. *Mailing Add:* Corning Glass Works Sullivan Park Corning NY 14830

MAURER, ROBERT EUGENE, b Uhrichsville, Ohio, 25; m 53; c 1. GEOLOGY. *Educ:* Ohio State Univ, BS, 50; Univ Utah, PhD, 70. *Prof Exp:* Geologist, Texaco, Inc, 52-56; instr geol, Westminster Col, Utah, 57-59, asst prof, 59-66; asst prof, 66-70, ASSOC PROF GEOL, STATE UNIV NY COL OSWEGO, 70- *Concurrent Pos:* Chmn sci div, Westminster Col, Utah, 62-66; chmn dept earth sci, State Univ NY Col Oswego, 67-72. *Mem:* AAAS; Geol Soc Am. *Res:* Surface and subsurface geologic mapping. *Mailing Add:* Dept of Earth Sci State Univ of NY Col Oswego NY 13126

MAURER, ROBERT JOSEPH, b Rochester, NY, Mar 26, 13; m 40. SOLID STATE PHYSICS, RESEARCH ADMINISTRATION. *Educ:* Univ Rochester, BS, 34, PhD(physics), 39. *Prof Exp:* Res assoc, Mass Inst Technol, 39-42; instr physics, Univ Pa, 42-43; from asst prof to assoc prof, Carnegie Inst Technol, 43-49; assoc prof, 49-51, prof, 51-81, dir, Mat Res Lab, 63-78, EMER PROF PHYSICS, UNIV ILL, URBANA, 81- *Concurrent Pos:* Physicist, Metall Lab, Univ Chicago, 44-45; head physics br, Off Naval Res, 48. *Mem:* Am Phys Soc. *Res:* Self diffusion in solids; electrical prerties of solids; photoelectric properties of metals; optical properties of solids. *Mailing Add:* Dept of Physics Univ of Ill Urbana IL 61801

MAURICE, DAVID MYER, b London, Eng, Apr 3, 22; m 54; c 3. PHYSIOLOGY. *Educ:* Univ Reading, BSc, 41; Univ London, PhD(physiol), 51. *Prof Exp:* Jr sci officer, Telecommun Res Estab, Ministry Aircraft Prod, 41-46; staff mem ophthal res unit, Med Res Coun, 46-63; reader physiol, Inst Ophthal, Univ London, 63-68; SR SCIENTIST OPHTHAL, MED SCH, STANFORD UNIV, 68-, ADJ PROF SURG, 74- *Concurrent Pos:* Ital Govt fel, Univ Rome, 51-52; Fulbright fel, Univ Calif, San Francisco, 57-58; vis prof, Hadassah Med Sch, 63-64; lectr ophthal, Harvard Med Sch, 74- *Honors & Awards:* Friedenwald Medal, Asn Res Vision & Ophthal, 67. *Mem:* AAAS; Asn Eye Res; Am Physiol Soc; Biophys Soc; Asn Res Vision & Ophthal. *Res:* Vegetative physiology of the eye; physiology and biochemistry of cornea; transport mechanisms. *Mailing Add:* Div of Ophthal Stanford Univ Med Ctr Stanford CA 94305

MAURIELLO, DAVID ANTHONY, ecology, see previous edition

MAURO, ALEXANDER, b New Haven, Conn, Aug 14, 21; m 55. BIOPHYSICS. *Educ:* Yale Univ, BE, 42, PhD(biophys), 50. *Prof Exp:* Instr physiol, Sch Med, Yale Univ, 51-52, asst prof, 52-59; from asst prof to assoc prof, 59-71, PROF BIOPHYS, ROCKEFELLER UNIV, 71- *Mem:* Am Physiol Soc; Biophys Soc; Inst Elec & Electronics Eng. *Res:* Nerve and muscle physiology; fundamental mechanisms in electrophysiological systems; physico-chemical studies of ionic membranes and their relationship to physiological membranes; experimental and theoretical study of semipermeability and membrane transport. *Mailing Add:* 392 Central Park West New York NY 10025

MAURO, JACK ANTHONY, b Brooklyn, NY, Feb 21, 16; m 37; c 3. OPTICAL PHYSICS, PHYSIOLOGICAL OPTICS. *Educ:* Columbia Univ, BS & cert, 47; Phila Optical Col, OD, 51. *Prof Exp:* Mgr optics, Equitable Optical Co, 34-43; chief instr theoret optics & math, NY Inst Optics, 47-53; dir eng, Saratoga Div, Espey Mfg Co, 50-55; engr, Gen Eng Lab, Gen Elec Co, 55-60, consult optics engr, Ord Dept, Defense Electronics Div, 60-65, consult engr, Missile & Space Vehicle Div, 65-70; dir res, Shuron Continental Div, Textron Inc, 70-74; CONSULT HIGH ENERGY LASER OPTICAL SYSTS, BATTELLE MEM INST, UNIV DAYTON RES INST & US AIR FORCE LASER WEAPONS LAB, 74- *Concurrent Pos:* Consult, NY Inst Optics, 47-55 & Navigational Inst Am, 47-52; mem, Bd Dirs, Columbia Univ, 48-51; consult, US Army & US Navy Ord Off, 50-51; chmn, Man-Mach Symp, US Army-Gen Elec Co, 58; mem, High Energy Laser Weapons Ad Hoc Comt, US Army Missile Command, US Air Force Weapons Lab & Univ Dayton Res Inst. *Mem:* Am Phys Soc; Optical Soc Am; fel Am Acad Optom; Soc Photo-Optical Instrument Eng; NY Acad Sci. *Res:* Optics and electronics; physical and geometrical optics; optical design. *Mailing Add:* 4949 San Pedro Dr NE Albuquerque NM 87109

MAURY, LUCIEN GARNETT, b Hoisington, Kans, Aug 14, 23; m 47; c 3. PHYSICAL CHEMISTRY, ORGANIC CHEMISTRY. *Educ:* Ill Inst Technol, BS, 48; Northwestern Univ, PhD(chem), 52. *Prof Exp:* Res chemist, Hercules Inc, Del, 51-56, supvr, 56-58, mgr explosives res & high pressure lab, 58-61, mgr synthetics res, 61-64, mgr cent res, 64-67, proj mgr, 67-68, dir develop fibers & film, 68-71, dir fibers, 71-73; gen mgr, Hercules Int Dept, 73-74; pres, 74-78, VPRES RES & DEVELOP, HERCULES EUROPE, 78- *Res:* Homogeneous and heterogeneous catalysis; nitrogen chemistry. *Mailing Add:* Hercules Inc 910 Market St Wilmington DE 19899

MAUSEL, PAUL WARNER, b Minneapolis, Minn, Jan 2, 36; m 66; c 3. REMOTE SENSING. *Educ:* Univ Minn, BA(chem) & BA(geog), 58, MA, 61; Univ NC, PhD(geog), 66. *Prof Exp:* Instr geog, Mankato State Col, 61-62; from asst prof to assoc prof, Eastern Ill Univ, 65-71; assoc prof, 72-76, PROF GEOG & DIR REMOTE SENSING LAB, IND STATE UNIV, TERRE HAUTE, 76- *Concurrent Pos:* Res grants, Eastern Ill Univ, 67-68 & 69-70; researcher, Lab Appln Remote Sensing, Purdue Univ, 72-74; res grants, NSF, 76, Environ Protection Agency, 77, US Forest Serv, 77 & Ind State Univ, 77; training grants, NSF, 78; res grants, Northern Ky Area Develop Dist, 80 & Able Energy Co, 80. *Mem:* Asn Am Geog; Am Soc Photogram; Soil Sci Soc Am. *Res:* Remote sensing of the environment using automatically data processed multispectral sensor data, stressing land use and mineral resources; soils geography. *Mailing Add:* Dept of Geog & Geol Ind State Univ Terre Haute IN 47809

MAUSNER, JUDITH S, b New York, NY, Oct 11, 24; m 44; c 2. EPIDEMIOLOGY, PUBLIC HEALTH. *Educ:* Queens Col (NY), BA, 44; NY Med Col, MD, 48; Univ Pittsburgh, MPH, 61. *Prof Exp:* Asst prof epidemiol, Grad Sch Pub Health, Univ Pittsburgh, 61-62; from asst prof to assoc prof, 63-77, PROF EPIDEMIOL, MED COL PA, 77- *Mem:* Am Pub Health Asn; Soc Epidemiol Res; Asn Teachers Prev Med. *Res:* Chronic disease epidemiology. *Mailing Add:* Dept of Community & Prev Med Med Col of Pa Philadelphia PA 19129

MAUSNER, LEONARD FRANKLIN, b New York, NY, Mar 6, 47; m 69; c 3. NUCLEAR CHEMISTRY. *Educ:* Mass Inst Technol, BS, 68; Princeton Univ, MA, 72, PhD(chem), 75. *Prof Exp:* Instr chem, Princeton Univ, 74-75; fel chem, Los Alamos Sci Lab, 75-77; mem staff, Argonne Nat Lab, 77-81; MEM STAFF, BROOKHAVEN NAT LAB, 81- *Concurrent Pos:* Consult, Princeton Gamma Tech, 73. *Mem:* Am Phys Soc; Am Chem Soc; Sigma Xi. *Res:* Alpha spectra of radium in bone; radionuclide production and research for nuclear medicine. *Mailing Add:* Med Dept Bldg 801 Brookhaven Nat Lab Upton NY 11973

MAUSTELLER, JOHN WILSON, b West Milton, Pa, May 14, 22; m 44; c 4. PHYSICAL CHEMISTRY. *Educ:* Bucknell Univ, BS, 44; Pa State Univ, MS, 49, PhD(phys chem), 51. *Prof Exp:* Chemist, E I du Pont de Nemours & Co, 44-46; asst, Fluorine Labs, Pa State Univ, 47-50; res chemist, Callery Chem Co, 50-51; engr, Mine Safety Appliances Co, 51-52, proj engr, 52-57; res mgr, 57-60, assoc dir res, 60-74, GEN MGR, MSA RES CORP, 74- *Mem:* Am Chem Soc; Am Nuclear Soc. *Res:* Chemical oxygen; air and water pollution; safety and handling hazardous materials; life support systems; liquid metals technology; reactor coolants; chemical warfare protective technology. *Mailing Add:* MSA Res Corp Evans City PA 16033

MAUSTON, GLENN WARREN, b St Paul, Minn, Oct 22, 35; m 57; c 3. ENTOMOLOGY. *Educ:* Gustavus Adolphus Col, BS, 57; Iowa State Univ, MS, 59; NDak State Univ, PhD(entom), 69. *Prof Exp:* INSTR BIOL, MESABI COMMUNITY COL, 59- *Res:* Taxonomy and biology of the subfamily Crambinae. *Mailing Add:* Dept of Biol Mesabi Community Col Virginia MN 55792

MAUTE, ROBERT LEWIS, b Springfield, Ohio, July 1, 24; m 46; c 2. ANALYTICAL CHEMISTRY. *Educ:* Colo Col, BS, 49; Univ Houston, MS, 50. *Prof Exp:* Chemist, Phillips Petrol Co, 50-51; res chemist, Monsanto Co, 51-55, asst group leader, Anal Group, 55-58, group leader, 58-64, mgr anal sect, Tex, 64-78; MGR ANAL TECHNOL, MONSANTO RES CORP, 78- *Mem:* Am Chem Soc; Am Inst Chem Engrs; Royal Soc Chem; Am Inst Chemists; Sigma Xi. *Res:* Instrumental and chemical analyses; physical chemistry; trace environmental analysis of hazardous material; bioanalytical characterization. *Mailing Add:* Monsanto Res Corp Sta B PO Box 8 Dayton OH 45407

MAUTNER, HENRY GEORGE, b Prague, Czech, Mar 30, 25; nat US; m 67; c 3. BIOCHEMISTRY, PHARMACOLOGY. *Educ:* Univ Calif, Los Angeles, BS, 46; Univ Southern Calif, MS, 49; Univ Calif, PhD(chem), 55. *Hon Degrees:* MS, Yale Univ, 67. *Prof Exp:* Lab asst, Univ Southern Calif, 47-49; res chemist, Productol Co, 50; sr res technician, Univ Calif, 51-53, asst, 53-55; from instr to assoc prof pharmacol, Sch Med, Yale Univ, 56-67, prof pharmacol & head sect med chem, 67-70; PROF BIOCHEM & PHARMACOL & CHMN DEPT, SCH MED, TUFTS UNIV, 70- *Concurrent Pos:* Squibb fel pharmacol, Sch Med, Yale Univ, 55-56; mem, Neurobiol Panel, NSF, 77-80. *Mem:* Am Chem Soc; Am Asn Cancer; Royal Soc Chem; Am Soc Biol Chemists; Biophys Soc. *Res:* Heterocyclic chemistry; purines; pyrimidines; pteridines; chemistry of selenium compounds; coenzyme analogs; choline acetyltransferase; electrically excitable membranes; antimetabolites; comparative kinetics of reactions of oxygen, sulfur and selenium isologs; molecular basis of nerve conduction. *Mailing Add:* Dept Biochem & Pharmacol Sch Med Tufts Univ Boston MA 02111

MAUTZ, CHARLES WILLIAM, b St Elmo, Ill, Apr 27, 17; m 45; c 1. PHYSICS. *Educ:* Univ Ill, BS, 41, MS, 43; Univ Mich, PhD(physics), 49. *Prof Exp:* Mem staff, Radiation Lab, Mass Inst Technol, 44-45 & Los Alamos Sci Lab, 49-60; mem staff, Gulf Gen Atomic Co, 60-76; MEM STAFF, LOS ALAMOS SCI LAB, 76- *Concurrent Pos:* Vis assoc prof, Univ Mich, 61-62. *Mem:* AAAS; Am Phys Soc. *Res:* Gas dynamics; explosives; lasers; shockwaves; detonation. *Mailing Add:* Los Alamos Sci Lab PO Box 1663 M-3 MS-960 Los Alamos NM 87545

MAUTZ, WILLIAM WARD, b Eau Claire, Wis, Apr 13, 43; m 65; c 3. WILDLIFE RESEARCH, WILDLIFE ECOLOGY. *Educ:* Wis State Univ-Eau Claire, BS, 65; Mich State Univ, MS, 67, PhD(wildlife ecol & physiol), 69. *Prof Exp:* From asst prof to assoc prof wildlife ecol, Inst Natural & Environ Resources, Univ NH, 69-75; asst unit leader, Colo Coop Wildlife Res Unit, Colo State Univ, 75-76; assoc prof, 76-78, PROF WILDLIFE ECOL, INST NATURAL & ENVIRON RESOURCES, UNIV NH, 79- *Concurrent Pos:* Wildlife consult, 76. *Mem:* Wildlife Soc; Ecol Soc Am. *Res:* Ecological energetics; energy flow studies with wildlife species involving energy requirements and efficiency of food energy utilization; development of procedures for the determination of energy utilization and requirements in wildlife species. *Mailing Add:* Inst Natural & Environ Resources Univ of NH Durham NH 03824

MAUZERALL, DAVID CHARLES, b Sanford, Maine, July 22, 29; m 59; c 2. BIOPHYSICS. *Educ:* St Michael's Col, BS, 51; Univ Chicago, PhD(chem), 54. *Prof Exp:* Res assoc, 54-59, from asst prof to assoc prof, 59-69, PROF BIOPHYS, ROCKEFELLER UNIV, 69- *Concurrent Pos:* Vis assoc prof, Univ Calif, San Diego, 65-68, adj prof, 68-; Guggenheim fel, 66. *Mem:* AAAS; Am Chem Soc; Am Soc Biol Chemists. *Res:* Mechanism of photochemical and photobiological reactions; porphyrin biochemistry; photosynthesis. *Mailing Add:* Rockefeller Univ New York NY 10021

MAUZEY, PETER T, b Poughkeepsie, NY, Nov 16, 30. ELECTRICAL ENGINEERING. *Educ:* Columbia Univ, BSEE, 52, MSEE, 54, EE, 58. *Prof Exp:* Asst elec eng, Columbia Univ, 52-54, instr, 54-59, assoc elec eng, 59-62; mem tech staff, Data Commun Dept, 62-77, mem tech staff, Data Terminals Dept, 77-81, MEM TECH STAFF, DATA APPL ENG DEPT, BELL LABS, 81- *Concurrent Pos:* Dir eng, Electronic Music Ctr, Columbia Univ & Princeton Univ, 59-62. *Mem:* Inst Elec & Electronics Engrs; Acoust Soc Am; Audio Eng Soc; assoc Soc Motion Picture & TV. *Res:* Electronic circuitry for high-quality recording and reproduction of speech and music; hardware and software design for office system planning; data commmunications systems engineering; project planning. *Mailing Add:* Bell Tel Labs Holmdel NJ 07733

MAUZY, MICHAEL P, US citizen. TECHNICAL MANAGEMENT. *Educ:* Va Polytech Inst, BS; Univ Tenn, MS. *Prof Exp:* Dir eng & mfg, Monsanto Co, St Louis, 51-71; mem staff, Kummer Corp, St Louis, Mo, 71-72; dir, Ill Environ Protection Agency, Springfield, Ill, 72-81; VPRES, WESTON, 81- *Concurrent Pos:* Mem, Water Mgt Subcomt, Mgt Adv Group & Ohio River Valley Sanit Comm; Judge, Am Consult Engrs Coun Excellence Award, 81. *Mem:* Asn State & Interstate Water Pollution Control Admin (pres, 77 & 80); Am Inst Chem Engrs; Am Pub Works Asn; Water Pollution Control Asn. *Res:* Planning, design, construction and operation of research, development and manufacturing facilities; program planning and management, strategy, policy development and evaluation, fiscal control, personnel training, employee development and public involvement; environmental and resource management at state and federal level; compliance evaluation and management. *Mailing Add:* Weston Weston Way West Chester PA 19380

MAVERICK, ANDREW WILLIAM, b Los Angeles, Calif, Mar 21, 55. PHOTOCHEMISTRY. *Educ:* Carleton Col, BA, 75; Calif Inst Technol, PhD(inorg chem), 82. *Prof Exp:* ASST PROF CHEM, WASHINGTON UNIV, 81- *Mem:* Am Chem Soc. *Res:* Inorganic chemistry; transition-metal complexes; redox reactions and photochemistry; spectroscopy and electronic structure. *Mailing Add:* Washington Univ Box 1134 St Louis MO 63130

MAVIS, JAMES OSBERT, b Mansfield, Ohio, Aug 6, 25; m 53; c 2. FOOD TECHNOLOGY. *Educ:* Ohio State Univ, BSc, 50, MSc, 53, PhD(food technol), 55. *Prof Exp:* Asst, Food Technol, Agr Exp Sta, Univ Ohio, 48-50; area rep, Topco Assocs, Inc, Ill, 50-52; chief customer res, Heekin Can Co, Ohio, 56-57; sect chief, Non-milk Frozen Foods, Pet Milk Co, 58-61, group mgr, Bakery & Hort Prods, 61-65, assoc dir res, 65-68, tech dir, Frozen Foods Div, Pet Inc, 68-69; dir res & develop, Fairmont Foods, Co, Nebr, 69-70, vpres, 70-72; dir res & develop, Interstate Brands Corp, 72-77; V PRES TECH SERV, BANQUET FOODS CORP, 77- *Mem:* Am Hort Soc; Am Soc Qual Control; Inst Food Technol. *Res:* New bakery and horticultural food products development and engineering and packaging research. *Mailing Add:* Banquet Foods Corp PO Box 70 Ballwin MO 63011

MAVIS, RICHARD DAVID, b Fergus Falls, Minn, Aug 7, 43; m 66; c 2. BIOCHEMISTRY. *Educ:* St Olaf Col, BA, 65; Univ Iowa, PhD(biochem), 70. *Prof Exp:* Asst prof biochem, Dent Med Sch, Northwestern Univ, Chicago, 72-75; asst prof, 75-81, ASSOC PROF, DEPT RADIATION BIOL, BIOPHYS & BIOCHEM, SCH MED & DENT, UNIV ROCHESTER, 81- *Concurrent Pos:* USPHS fel, Wash Univ, 69-72; NIH res grant, 73. *Mem:* AAAS. *Res:* Membrane structure and function; phospholipid metabolism; effect of toxic agents on metabolism and peroxidation of lipids of lung and other tissues; antioxidant protection of lung by vitamin E; mechanism of lipid peroxidation. *Mailing Add:* Dept Radiation Biol & Biophys Sch Med & Dent Univ Rochester Rochester NY 14642

MAVITY, VICTOR T(HOMAS), JR, b Sewell, Chile, Mar 14, 20; US citizen. CHEMICAL ENGINEERING. *Educ:* Purdue Univ, BS, 41. *Prof Exp:* Trainee, Ashland Oil & Refining Co, 41-42; chem engr, Lago Oil & Transport Co, Ltd, 42-45 & Esso Standard Oil Co, 45-55; tech analyst & writer, Ethyl Corp, 58-59; chem engr oil refining, Res Ctr, Pure Oil Co, 60-65; CHEM ENGR OIL REFINING, RES CTR, UNION OIL CO CALIF, 65- *Mem:* Am Chem Soc; Am Asn Cost Engrs. *Res:* Process analysis and development; engineering and economics; manufacture of petroleum and petrochemical products; technical writing and editing. *Mailing Add:* Res Dept Union Oil Co Calif PO Box 76 Brea CA 92621

MAVKO, GEORGE EDWARD, astronomy, optics, see previous edition

MAVOR, HUNTINGTON, b Schenectady, NY, Mar 26, 27; m 56; c 4. NEUROLOGY. *Educ:* Harvard Col, AB, 48; Univ Rochester, MD, 55; Am Bd Psychiat & Neurol, dipl, 62. *Prof Exp:* From instr to assoc prof neurol, Univ Utah, 61-69, instr med, 61-69; assoc prof, Univ Vt, 69-74; ASSOC PROF NEUROL, UNIV UTAH, 74- *Concurrent Pos:* Fel EEG & clin neurophys, Montreal Neurol Inst, 59-61; asst chief neurol, Salt Lake City Vet Admin Hosp, 63-69 & 74- *Mem:* Am Acad Neurol; Am Electroencephalog Soc. *Res:* Clinical electroencephalography and neurophysiology. *Mailing Add:* Dept of Neurol Univ of Utah Salt Lake City UT 84114

MAVRETIC, ANTON, b Slovenia, Yugoslavia, Dec 11, 34; m 64; c 2. ATMOSPHERIC SCIENCES. *Educ:* Denver Univ, BS, 59, MS, 61; Pa State Univ, PhD(elec eng), 68. *Prof Exp:* Proj engr elec eng, Mass Inst Technol, 68-78; sr res engr, Harvard Univ, 78-80; ASSOC PROF ELEC ENG, BOSTON UNIV, 80- *Concurrent Pos:* Sr lectr, Northeastern Univ, 69-82; consult, Div Appl Sci, Harvard Univ, 81-; co-prin investr, Air Force Geophys Lab, 82- *Mem:* Inst Elec & Electronics Engrs. *Res:* Space instrumentation and sophisticated electronic curcuit design; chip design. *Mailing Add:* Col Eng Boston Univ 110 Cummington St Boston MA 02215

MAVRIDES, CHARALAMPOS, b Greece, June 25, 26; Can citizen. BIOCHEMISTRY. *Educ:* Nat Univ Athens, BSc, 53; Univ Ottawa, PhD(biochem), 64. *Prof Exp:* Fel pharmacol, NY Univ, from asst prof to assoc prof, 66-76, PROF BIOCHEM, UNIV OTTAWA, 76- *Mem:* Can Biochem Soc. *Res:* Regulation of enzymes in higher cells; enzymology of transamination in procaryotes. *Mailing Add:* Dept of Biochem Univ of Ottawa Ottawa ON K2P 2G2 Can

MAVRIPLIS, F, b Thessaloniki, Greece, Jan 31, 20; Can citizen; m 55; c 3. COMPUTATIONAL AERODYNAMIC DESIGN, EXPERIMENTAL AERODYNAMICS. *Educ:* Munich Tech Inst, DiplIng, 41. *Prof Exp:* Sr engr, 52-58, group leader thermodyn, 58-61, mem sr staff in charge space systs res & develop, 61-66, mem sr staff in charge tech develop aerothermodyn, 66-76, sr staff specialist, CL-600 aerodyn develop, 76-80, SECT CHIEF CHALLENGER AERODYN DEVELOP, CANADAIR LTD, 80- *Concurrent Pos:* Mem & chmn assoc comt aerodyn, Nat Res Coun Can, 73. *Honors & Awards:* F C Baldwin Medals, Can Aeronaut & Space Inst, 71 & 73. *Mem:* Fel Can Aeronaut & Space Inst; assoc fel, Am Inst Aeronaut & Astronaut. *Res:* Transonic transport aircraft aerodynamic configuration design and development; supercritical wing aerodynamics. *Mailing Add:* 11455 Pasteur St Montreal PQ H3M 2N8 Can

MAVROIDES, JOHN GEORGE, b Ipswich, Mass, Dec 29, 22; m 52; c 2. PHYSICS. *Educ:* Tufts Col, BS, 44; Brown Univ, MS, 51, PhD(physics), 53. *Prof Exp:* Proj engr, US Naval Underwater Sound Lab, 46-49; fel Brown Univ, 50-51; mem staff, 52-60, group leader, 60-74, SR STAFF, LINCOLN LAB, MASS INST TECHNOL, 74- *Mem:* Electrochem Soc; Fel Am Phys Soc. *Res:* Solid state physics, especially galvanometric effects; magneto-optical studies; magneto-piezo-optics; magneto-acoustic effects; cyclotron resonance; electronic bandstructure; Fermi surfaces; infrared; lasers; electrochemistry; energy conversion. *Mailing Add:* Lincoln Lab Mass Inst Technol Lexington MA 02173

MAVROYANNIS, CONSTANTINE, b Athens, Greece, Nov 13, 27; Can citizen; m 61; c 2. THEORETICAL SOLID STATE PHYSICS. *Educ:* Athens Tech Univ, BS, 57; McGill Univ, PhD(phys chem), 61; Oxford Univ, DPhil(math), 63. *Prof Exp:* Nat Res Coun Can NATO sci overseas fel, 61-63; Nat Res Coun Can fel, 63-64; asst res officer, 64-65, assoc res officer, 66-73, SR RES OFFICER, NAT RES COUN CAN, 74- *Mem:* Am Phys Soc; Can Asn Physicists; fel Chem Inst Can. *Res:* Optical properties and many-body interactions in solids; modern quantum chemistry; spin wave theory; electromagnetic interactions in solids; quantum optics. *Mailing Add:* Div of Chem Sussex Dr Ottawa ON K1A 0R6 Can

MAWARDI, OSMAN KAMEL, b Cairo, Egypt, Dec 12, 17; nat US; m 50. PLASMA PHYSICS, ACOUSTICS. *Educ:* Fuad I Univ, Egypt, BSc, 40, MSc, 46; Harvard Univ, AM, 47, PhD(acoust), 48. *Prof Exp:* Transmission engr, Egyptian State Tel & Tel Co, 40-41; lectr physics, Fuad I Univ, 41-46; asst prof elec eng, Mass Inst Technol, 51-56, assoc prof mech & elec eng & mem res lab electronics, 56-60; chmn, Plasma Dynamics & Nuclear Eng, 60-66, dir, Plasma Res Prog, 66-75, energy coordr, 75-77, dir, Energy Res Off, 77-81, PROF ENG, CASE WESTERN RESERVE UNIV, 60-; PRES, COLLAB PLANNERS, 73- *Concurrent Pos:* Consult, Bolt, Beranek & Newman, Inc, 50-54, Nat Prod Corp, 51-52, Res Found, Lowell Tech Inst, 53-54, Philco Corp, 53-64, Gen Ultrasonics Corp, 55-57, Boeing Airplane Co, 55-57, Pratt & Whitney Div, United Aircraft Corp, 58-64, Conesco, 58-61, Los Alamos Sci Lab, 59-61, 66- & Amoco Res Lab, 69-71; Guggenheim fel, 54-55; mem, Inst Advan Study, 69-70; vpres, Auctor Assocs Inc, 70-73; mem, Adv Energy Task Force to Gov, Ohio, 73-74. *Honors & Awards:* Biennial Award, Acoust Soc Am, 52. *Mem:* Fel AAAS; fel Acoust Soc Am; fel Am Phys Soc; fel Inst Elec & Electronics Engrs; NY Acad Sci. *Res:* Controlled fusion research; acoustic holography; electric power systems. *Mailing Add:* Case Western Reserve Univ Cleveland OH 44106

MAWBY, JOHN EVANS, b Dayton, Ohio, Dec 7, 35; m 67. VERTEBRATE PALEONTOLOGY. *Educ:* Cornell Univ, BA, 58; Univ Calif, Berkeley, MA, 60, PhD(paleont), 65. *Prof Exp:* Instr biol & geol, Deep Springs Col, 64-67; asst prof biol, Calif State Col, Long Beach, 67-69; actg dir/dean, 75-76, ASST DEAN, DEEP SPRINGS COL, 69- *Concurrent Pos:* Res assoc, Los Angeles County Mus Natural Hist, 68- *Mem:* Soc Vert Paleont; Am Soc Mammal; Geol Soc Am; Paleont Soc; Am Soc Zoologists; Soc Study Evolution. *Res:* Evolution of later Cenozoic mammals; fossil mammals of the Great Basin area; paleontology of early man sites. *Mailing Add:* Deep Springs Col Deep Springs Calif via Dyer NV 89010

MAWE, RICHARD C, b Apr 17, 29; US citizen. CELL PHYSIOLOGY. *Educ:* Fordham Univ, BS, 50, MS, 51; Princeton Univ, PhD(cell physiol), 54. *Prof Exp:* Asst biol, Fordham Univ, 50-51; asst, Princeton Univ, 51-54, res assoc physiol, 54-55; lectr zool, Columbia Univ, 60-61; from instr to assoc prof biol, 61-71, chmn, Dept Biol Sci, 65-80, actg dean sci & math, 80-81, PROF BIOL, HUNTER COL, 71-, DEAN SCI & MATH, 81- *Concurrent Pos:* NSF grants, 62-70; vis scientist, Off Health Affairs, Food & Drug Admin, 78-79. *Mem:* AAAS; Soc Gen Physiol. *Res:* Transport; membrane structure. *Mailing Add:* Dean Sci & Math Hunter Col New York NY 10021

MAWHINNEY, MICHAEL G, b Honolulu, Hawaii, Aug 29, 45; m 69; c 2. PHARMACOLOGY. *Educ:* Grove City Col, BS, 67; WVa Univ, MS, 69, PhD(pharmacol), 70. *Prof Exp:* Asst prof, 71-75, ASSOC PROF PHARMACOL & UROL, MED CTR, WVA UNIV, 75- *Concurrent Pos:* Consult, Albert Gallatin Sch Dist, 73- & J Urol, 75- *Honors & Awards:* Award, Pharmaceut Mfg Asn Found, 74 & 76. *Mem:* Am Soc Pharmacol & Exp Therapeut; Endocrine Soc. *Res:* Hormonal regulation of the epithelial and stromal elements of normal, aged and neoplastic male accessory sex organs. *Mailing Add:* Dept of Pharmacol Med Ctr WVa Univ Morgantown WV 26506

MAX, CLAIRE ELLEN, b Boston, Mass, Sept 29, 46; m 74. PLASMA PHYSICS, ASTROPHYSICS. *Educ:* Radcliffe Col, AB, 68; Princeton Univ, PhD(astrophys sci), 72. *Prof Exp:* Res assoc physics, Univ Calif, Berkeley, 72-74; PHYSICIST, LAWRENCE LIVERMORE LAB, UNIV CALIF, 74- *Concurrent Pos:* Mem physics adv comt, NSF, 78-82; consult progs to interest young women entering sci careers; sabbatical leave, Ecole Polytech, Paris, 81. *Mem:* Fel Am Phys Soc; Am Astron Soc; AAAS. *Res:* Laser-plasma interactions; applications of plasma physics to astronomical problems. *Mailing Add:* L-477 Lawrence Livermore Lab Livermore CA 94550

MAX, STEPHEN RICHARD, b Providence, RI, Dec 25, 40; m; c 1. BIOCHEMISTRY. *Educ:* Univ RI, BS, 62, PhD(biochem), 66. *Prof Exp:* Asst prof, Col Med, Howard Univ, 67-70; assoc prof neurol, 70-81, PROF NEUROL, SCH MED, UNIV MD, BALTIMORE, 81-, ASST PROF, DEPT PEDIAT & PATH & ASSOC PROF, DEPT BIOCHEM, 70- *Concurrent Pos:* Nat Inst Neurol Dis & Stroke fel, 68-70; Dysautonomia Found & Frank G Bressler Reserve Fund res grants, 71-72; res grants, Muscular Dystrophy Asn, 75-76, NIH, 75-, NASA, 81-; guestworker neurochem, Nat Inst Neurol Dis & Stroke, 68-70; lectr fac grad sch, NIH, 72- *Mem:* Am Chem Soc; Soc Neurosci; Am Soc Neurochem; Int Soc Neurochem; Am Acad Neurol. *Res:* Neurochemistry; muscle metabolism; neuromuscular diseases; sex hormones and muscle; muscle regeneration. *Mailing Add:* Dept of Neurol Univ of Md Sch of Med Baltimore MD 21201

MAXCY, RUTHFORD BURT, food science, microbiology, see previous edition

MAXEY, BRIAN WILLIAM, b Michigan City, Ind, Sept 13, 39. VETERINARY PHARMACEUTICALS, RESEARCH MANAGEMENT. *Educ:* Purdue Univ, West Lafayette, BS, 61; Mich State Univ, PhD(anal chem), 68. *Prof Exp:* Chemist, Dow Chem Co, 61-65; from sr scientist to sr res scientist, 68-73, proj leader, 73-75, res head vet therapeut, 75-76, RES MGR VET PARASITOL & THERAPEUT, UPJOHN CO, 76- *Mem:* AAAS; Am Chem Soc; Sigma Xi. *Res:* Agricultural science; veterinary therapeutics; research and development of veterinary pharmaceuticals. *Mailing Add:* Upjohn Co 9650-190-1 Kalamazoo MI 49001

MAXFIELD, BRUCE WRIGHT, b Coronation, Alta, July 15, 39. SOLID STATE PHYSICS, NON DESTRUCTIVE TESTING. *Educ:* Univ Alta, BSc, 61; Rutgers Univ, PhD(physics), 64. *Prof Exp:* Res assoc, Cornell Univ, 64-66, actg asst prof, 66-67, asst sr res assoc physics, 71-76; engr, 76-81, SECT LEADER & HEAD, NONDESTRUCTIVE TESTING FACIL, LAWRENCE LIVERMORE NAT LAB, 81- *Concurrent Pos:* Sloan Found res fel. *Mem:* Am Phys Soc; Inst Elec & Electronics Engrs. *Res:* Transport properties in pure metals and alloys, ultrasonic studies in metals and nondestructive testing research and development including ultrasonics, optical holography and eddy currents. *Mailing Add:* Lawrence Livermore Lab Mail Code L333 Livermore CA 94550

MAXFIELD, JOHN EDWARD, b Los Angeles, Calif, Mar 17, 27; m 48; c 2. ALGEBRA. *Educ:* Mass Inst Technol, BS, 47; Univ Wis, MS, 49; Univ Ore, PhD(math), 51. *Prof Exp:* Instr math, Univ Ore, 50-51; mathematician, Naval Ord Test Sta, 51-58, head math div, 58-60; prof math & head dept, Univ Fla, 60-67; prof math & head dept, Kans State Univ, 67-81; DEAN, GRAD SCH & UNIV RES, LA TECH UNIV, 81- *Mem:* Am Math Soc; Sigma Xi; Soc Indust & Appl Math; Math Asn Am; Asn for Women Math. *Res:* Number theory; analog and digital computing techniques; numerical analysis. *Mailing Add:* Grad Sch La Tech Univ Ruston LA 71270

MAXFIELD, MARGARET WAUGH, b Conn, Feb 23, 26; m 48; c 4. MATHEMATICS. *Educ:* Oberlin Col, BA, 47; Univ Wis, MS, 48; Univ Ore, PhD(algebra), 51. *Prof Exp:* Mathematician, Naval Ord Test Sta, Calif, 49-53 & 55-60, consult, 60-65; pvt res & writing, 65-75; asst prof, Dept Statist, 75-77, ASST PROF, COL BUS AD, KANS STATE UNIV, MANHATTAN, 77- Prof Exp: Instr & lectr, Univ Calif, Los Angeles, 57-60; vis assoc prof, Univ NB, 74-75. *Honors & Awards:* Lester R Ford Award, 67. *Res:* Number theory; statistics. *Mailing Add:* Col of Bus AD Kans State Univ Manhattan KS 66506

MAXIM, LESLIE DANIEL, b New York, NY, Feb 27, 41; m 62; c 2. OPERATIONS RESEARCH. *Educ:* Manhattan Col, BChE, 61; State Univ NY, MSc, 63; Stevens Inst Technol, MMS, 66; NY Univ, PhD(opers res), 73. *Prof Exp:* Jr chemist, Nat Starch & Chem Corp, Plainfield, 60-61, res chemist, 61-65, proj supvr phys chem res, 65-68; staff consult, Mathmatica Inc, 68-69, asst dir opers res, 69-71, dir, 71-73, vpres, Mathtech Div, 73-76, sr vpres & mem bd dirs, 76-79; PRES & CHMN, EVEREST CONSULT ASSOCS, 80- *Concurrent Pos:* Vis lectr, Grad Dept Mgt Sci, Stevens Inst Technol, 66-70, adj prof, Newark Col Eng, 70-75; adj fac, Polytech Inst NY, Brooklyn, 74-77. *Mem:* AAAS; Am Inst Chem Eng; Opers Res Soc Am; Am Statist Asn; NY Acad Sci. *Res:* Physical chemistry of polymers; statistics; statistical systems analysis. *Mailing Add:* Everest Consult Assocs Inc PO Box 786 Princeton Junction NJ 08550

MAXON, MARSHALL STEPHEN, b Syracuse, NY, June 21, 37; m 58; c 2. PLASMA PHYSICS. *Educ:* Syracuse Univ, BS, 58; Ind Univ, MS, 60, PhD(physics), 64. *Prof Exp:* Physicist, 63-69, group leader, 69-71, SR PHYSICIST, LAWRENCE LIVERMORE NAT LAB, UNIV CALIF, 71- *Mem:* AAAS; Am Phys Soc. *Res:* X-ray emission from plasmas; solvable models in quantum field theory; thermonuclear physics; nonlinear plasma waves; magnetohydrodynamics. *Mailing Add:* Lawrence Livermore Nat Lab L-71 Univ of Calif PO Box 808 Livermore CA 94550

MAXON, WILLIAM DENSMORE, b Detroit, Mich, Dec 8, 26; m 50; c 4. BIOCHEMISTRY. *Educ:* Yale Univ, BE, 48; Univ Wis, MS, 51, PhD(biochem), 53. *Prof Exp:* Asst biochem, Univ Wis, 49-53; res scientist antibiotics, 53-56, sect head, 56-67, GROUP MGR, FERMENTATION RES & DEVELOP, UPJOHN CO, 67- *Mem:* AAAS; Am Chem Soc; Am Soc Microbiol. *Res:* Fermentation technology and kinetics; continuous fermentation; aeration-agitation in fermentations. *Mailing Add:* 400 Burrows Rd Kalamazoo MI 49007

MAXSON, CARLTON J, b Cortland, NY, Apr 19, 36; m 57; c 2. MATHEMATICS. *Educ:* State Univ NY Albany, BS, 58; Univ Ill, MA, 61; State Univ NY Buffalo, PhD(math), 67. *Prof Exp:* Math teacher, Hammondsport Cent Sch, 58-61; asst prof math, State Univ NY Col Fredonia, 61-66, assoc prof, 66-69; assoc prof, 69-74, PROF MATH, TEX A&M UNIV, 74- *Concurrent Pos:* Fac res awards, State Univ NY Col Fredonia, 67 & 68. *Mem:* Am Math Soc; Math Asn Am; Edinburgh Math Soc; AAAS. *Res:* Algebra; semigroups; rings; near-rings; applications of algebraic structures to study of discrete structures. *Mailing Add:* Dept of Math Tex A&M Univ College Station TX 77840

MAXSON, DONALD ROBERT, b Claremont, NH, Jan 19, 24; m 57; c 2. PHYSICS. *Educ:* Bowdoin Col, BS, 44; Univ Ill, MS, 48, PhD(physics), 54. *Prof Exp:* Radio engr, US Naval Res Lab, DC, 44-47; res assoc physics, Univ Ill, 54-55; instr, Princeton Univ, 55-58, res assoc, 58-59; from asst prof to assoc prof, 59-67, PROF PHYSICS, BROWN UNIV, 67- *Mem:* Am Phys Soc. *Res:* Neutrino recoil experiments for identification of beta decay interaction; experimental studies of nuclear reactions induced by charged particles and fast neutrons; reaction mechanics and nuclear structure. *Mailing Add:* Dept of Physics Brown Univ Providence RI 02912

MAXSON, LINDA ELLEN R, b New York, NY, Apr 24, 43; m 64; c 1. EVOLUTIONARY BIOLOGY, GENETICS. *Educ:* Univ San Diego, BS, 64, MA, 66; Univ Calif, Berkeley, PhD(genetics), 73. *Prof Exp:* Instr biol, San Diego State Univ, 66-68; gen sci teacher, San Diego Unified Sch Dist, 68-69; instr biochem, Univ Calif, Berkeley, 74; asst prof zool, 74-76, asst prof genetics, 76-79, ASSOC PROF GENETICS, DEVELOP, ECOL, ETHOLOGY & EVOLUTION, UNIV ILL, URBANA, 79- *Concurrent Pos:* Res biochemist, Univ Calif, Berkeley, 73-74; prin investr, NSF Grant, 76-78; res assoc, Dept Vert Zool, Smithsonian Inst, 80-83. *Mem:* AAAS; Soc Study Evolution; Soc Syst Zool; Sigma Xi; Am Soc Ichthyol & Herpetol. *Res:* Evolutionary biology; biochemical and quantitative immunological studies of protein evolution in amphibian phylogeny and systematics; use of molecules as evolutionary clocks and as probes of population structure and evolution. *Mailing Add:* Dept of Genetics & Develop Univ of Ill Urbana IL 61801

MAXSON, ORWIN G(ENE), b Arkansas City, Kans, Feb 14, 27; m 50; c 5. MECHANICAL ENGINEERING. *Educ:* Okla State Univ, BS, 51. *Prof Exp:* Tech serv engr, Dow Chem Co, 51-60; plant mgr, Luma Industs, 60-61; plant engr, Sani-Gard Plastics, 61-62; RES ENGR, CONOCO INC, 62- *Mem:* Soc Plastics Engrs. *Res:* Materials research. *Mailing Add:* Mat Sci Bldg Conoco Inc Ponca City OK 74601

MAXSON, ROBERT E, JR, b San Francisco, Calif, June 12, 51. MOLECULAR BIOLOGY. *Educ:* Univ Calif, Berkeley, AB, 73, PhD(zool), 78. *Prof Exp:* FEL, DEPT MED, SCH MED, STANFORD UNIV, 78- *Mem:* Soc Develop Biol. *Res:* Structure and function of the histone gene family in the sea urchin. *Mailing Add:* Dept Med 151 M Vet Admin Hosp 3801 Miranda Ave Palo Alto CA 94304

MAXSON, STEPHEN C, b Newport, RI, Apr 13, 38; m 80. PSYCHOBIOLOGY, BEHAVIOR GENETICS. *Educ:* Univ Chicago, SB, 60, PhD(biopsychol), 66. *Prof Exp:* Instr biol & res assoc behav genetics, Univ Chicago, 66-69; asst prof, 69-74, ASSOC PROF BIO-BEHAV SCI, UNIV CONN, 74- *Mem:* Behav Genetics Asn; Soc Neurosci; fel Int Soc Res Aggression. *Res:* Inheritance of behavior in mice and genetic mapping of behavioral loci; genotype-environment interactions in neurobehavioral development; pharmacogenetics of behavior; genetics, development, physiology and pharmacology of aggressive behavior; behavior as an assay for potentially mutagenic and teratogenic substances; genetics, development, physiology and pharmacology of audiogenic and spontaneous seizures. *Mailing Add:* Dept of Bio-Behav Sci Univ of Conn Storrs CT 06268

MAXUM, BERNARD J, b Bremerton, Wash, Nov 4, 31; m 59; c 5. ELECTROMAGNETICS, ENERGY SYSTEMS. *Educ:* Univ Wash, BS, 55; Univ Southern Calif, MS, 57; Univ Calif, Berkeley, PhD(cyclotron wave instabilities), 63. *Prof Exp:* Teaching, res & mgt of res & eng, 55-80; PRES, ENERGY SYSTS DESIGN & LECTURING, SEMCOR ENTERPRISES, INC, 70- *Concurrent Pos:* Hughes fel, Univ Southern Calif & Ford Found fel, Univ Calif, Berkeley. *Mem:* Am Phys Soc; Inst Elec & Electronics Engrs; Nat Energy Resources Orgn; Solar Energy Indust Asn; Am Soc Heating, Refrigeration & Airconditioning. *Res:* Electromagnetic, acoustic electronic and energy systems; business modeling. *Mailing Add:* 25675 Taledvo Circle Suite E Mission Viejo CA 92691

MAXWELL, ARTHUR EUGENE, b Maywood, Calif, Apr 11, 25; m 46, 64; c 5. OCEANOGRAPHY. *Educ:* NMex State Univ, BS, 49; Univ Calif, MS, 52, PhD(oceanog), 59. *Prof Exp:* Asst, Scripps Inst, Univ Calif, 49-50, asst oceanog, 50-52, jr res geophysicist, 52-55; head oceanogr, Geophys Br, Off Naval Res, 55-59, head, 59-65; assoc dir, Woods Hole Oceanog Inst, 65-69, dir res, 69-71, provost, 71-82; DIR, INST GEOPHYS, UNIV TEX AUSTIN, 82- *Concurrent Pos:* Mem, Nat Adv Comt Oceans & Atmosphere, 72-75. *Honors & Awards:* Civilian Meritorious Serv Award, US Navy, 58, Superior Civilian Serv Award, 63 & Distinguished Civilian Serv Award, 64. *Mem:* AAAS; Marine Technol Soc (vpres, 64-65, pres, 81-82); Sigma Xi; fel Am Geophys Union (pres, 76-78). *Res:* Physical oceanography and geophysics, particularly the measurement and interpretation of heat flow through the ocean floor. *Mailing Add:* Inst Geophys Univ Tex Austin TX 78712

MAXWELL, BRYCE, b Glen Cove, NY, July 26, 19; Wid; c 3. POLYMERS. *Educ:* Princeton Univ, BS, 43, MS, 48. *Prof Exp:* Res assoc, Plastics Lab, 48-53, from asst prof to assoc prof mech eng, 53-63, assoc prof chem eng, 63-68, asst dean, 63-69, PROF CHEM ENG, PRINCETON UNIV, 68-, . *Concurrent Pos:* Ed, Soc Rheol Jour, 56-58. *Honors & Awards:* Gold Medal an Int Award in Plastics Sci & Eng, Soc Plastics Engrs, 76. *Mem:* Soc Plastics Engrs; Soc Rheol; Am Soc Testing & Mat; Am Soc Eng Educ; Am Soc Mech Engrs. *Res:* Mechanical properties of polymers; fabrication and materials processing; rheology. *Mailing Add:* Polymer Mat Lab Eng Quandrangle Princeton Univ Princeton NJ 08540

MAXWELL, CHARLES HENRY, b Las Palomas, NMex, July 9, 23; m 52; c 3. GEOLOGY. *Educ:* Univ NMex, BS, 50, MS, 52. *Prof Exp:* Geologist, Shell Oil Co, 51-52; geologist, Br Mineral Deposits, 52-56, Br Foreign Geol, Brazil, 56-61, Br Regional Geol, Ky, 61-63, Br Mil Geol, 63-66 & Br Radioactive Mat, 66-69, GEOLOGIST, BR CENT MINERAL RESOURCES, US GEOL SURV, 69- *Mem:* AAAS; Geol Soc Am. *Res:* Geologic mapping; field interpretive and engineering geology. *Mailing Add:* US Geol Surv Fed Ctr Denver CO 80225

MAXWELL, CHARLES NEVILLE, b Tuscaloosa, Ala, Oct 27, 27; m 52; c 4. MATHEMATICS. *Educ:* Univ Chicago, BS, 49, MS, 51; Univ Ill, PhD(math), 55. *Prof Exp:* Instr math, Univ Mich, 55-58; assoc prof, Univ Ala, 58-63; PROF MATH, SOUTHERN ILL UNIV, CARBONDALE, 63- *Mem:* Am Math Soc. *Res:* Topology; topological transformation groups; algebraic topology. *Mailing Add:* Dept of Math Southern Ill Univ Carbondale IL 62901

MAXWELL, DAVID SAMUEL, b Bremerton, Wash, Feb 13, 31; m 57; c 3. ANATOMY. *Educ:* Westminster Col (Mo), AB, 54; Oxford Univ, BA, 57; Univ Calif, Los Angeles, PhD, 60. *Prof Exp:* From instr to assoc prof, 59-68, PROF ANAT, SCH MED, UNIV CALIF, LOS ANGELES, 68-, VCHMN DEPT, 73-, PROF SURG/ANAT, CHARLES DREW POSTGRAD MED SCH, 74- *Mem:* AAAS; Am Asn Anat; Electron Micros Soc Am; Am Soc Cell Biol; Soc Neurosci; Asn Am Med Cols. *Res:* Electron microscopy; histochemistry and cytochemistry of the nervous system and eye. *Mailing Add:* Dept of Anat Univ of Calif Sch of Med Los Angeles CA 90024

MAXWELL, DONALD A, b Austin, Tex, Apr 23, 38; m 63; c 4. CIVIL ENGINEERING. *Educ:* Univ Tes, Austin, BS, 62, MS, 64; Tex A&M Univ, PhD(civil eng), 68. *Prof Exp:* Highway engr, Fed Highway Admin, 62-68; mem tech staff, Comput Sci Corp, 69-71; sr assoc, Alan M Voorhers & Assocs, 71-77; assoc prof, 77-83, PROF CIVIL ENG, TEX A&M UNIV, 83- *Mem:* Am Soc Civil Engrs. *Res:* Design and implementation of paratransit systems; evalvation of cost effectiveness of engineered solutions; applied statistics and simulation. *Mailing Add:* 2601 Wayside Dr Bryan TX 77821

MAXWELL, DONALD ROBERT, b Paris, France, Mar 30, 29; US citizen; m 56; c 8. PHARMACOLOGY. *Educ:* Cambridge Univ, BA, 52, MA, 56, PhD(pharmacol), 55. *Prof Exp:* Res attache, Pasteur Inst, Paris, 55-56; pharmacologist, May & Baker Ltd, Dagenham, Eng, 56-69, mgr pharmacol res, 69-74; VPRES PRECLIN RES, WARNER-LAMBERT/PARKE-DAVIS RES, 74- *Mem:* Fel Royal Soc Med; fel Brit Inst Biol; Brit Pharmacol Soc; Brit Physiol Soc; Int Col Neuropsychopharmacol. *Res:* Psychopharmacology and neuropharmacology in relation to development of new drugs; cardiovascular drugs; anti-allergic drugs. *Mailing Add:* Warner-Lambert/Parke-Davis Pharmaceut Res Ann Arbor MI 48105

MAXWELL, DOUGLAS PAUL, b Norfolk, Nebr, Feb 12, 41; m 64; c 2. PLANT PATHOLOGY. *Educ:* Nebr Wesleyan Univ, BA, 63; Cornell Univ, PhD(plant path), 68. *Prof Exp:* From asst prof to assoc prof, 68-77, PROF PLANT PATH, UNIV WIS-MADISON, 77-, CHMN, 80- *Mem:* Am Phytopath Soc. *Res:* Ultrastructure of fungi; function of fungal microbodies; breeding for disease resistance in forages. *Mailing Add:* Dept Plant Path Univ Wis Madison WI 53706

MAXWELL, DWIGHT THOMAS, b Manhattan, Kans, Aug 25, 37; m 64. MINERALOGY. *Educ:* Univ Kans City, BS, 59; Mont State Univ, PhD(geol), 65. *Prof Exp:* Asst prof geol, Univ Mo-Kansas City, 64-67 & Northeast La State Col, 67-70; ASSOC PROF EARTH SCI, NORTHWEST MO STATE COL, 70-, ASSOC PROF GEOL, 81- *Mem:* Clay Minerals Soc; Mineral Soc Am. *Res:* Clay mineralogy. *Mailing Add:* Dept of Earth Sci Northwest Mo State Col Maryville MO 64468

MAXWELL, EMANUEL, b Brooklyn, NY, Dec 16, 12; m. PHYSICS. *Educ:* Columbia Univ, BS, 34, EE, 35; Mass Inst Technol, PhD(physics), 48. *Prof Exp:* Patent examr, US Patent Off, 37; geophysicist, Shell Oil Co, Inc, Tex, 37-41; staff mem, Radiation Lab, Mass Inst Technol, 41-45, res assoc physics, 45-48; physicist, Nat Bur Standards, 48-53; mem staff, Lincoln Lab, 53-63, vis assoc prof physics, 58-63, prof leader, 63-80, SR SCIENTIST, FRANCIS BITTER NAT MAGNET LAB, MASS INST TECHNOL, 63- *Mem:* Fel Am Phys Soc. *Mailing Add:* 24 Bates St Cambridge MA 02140

MAXWELL, FOWDEN GENE, entomology, see previous edition

MAXWELL, GEORGE RALPH, II, b Morgantown, WVa, Mar 27, 35; m 59; c 3. ECOLOGY, ORNITHOLOGY. *Educ:* WVa Univ, AB, 57, MS, 61; Ohio State Univ, PhD(zool), 65. *Prof Exp:* Asst prof biol, The Citadel, 65-66; dir, Rice Creek Biol Field Sta, 66-79, PROF ZOOL, STATE UNIV NY COL OSWEGO, 66- *Concurrent Pos:* NSF instrnl sci equipment prog res grant, 67-69; State Univ NY Res Found grant-in-aid, 68-70; fel, Univ NC, Chapel Hill, 70; vis scientist, Fla Med Entom Lab, 73. *Mem:* Am Ornithologists Union; Wilson Ornith Soc. *Res:* Growth of stream mayflies; maintenance behavior of herons; breeding biology of the grackle; impact of winter navigation on the birds of the St Lawrence River; heron and mosquito ecology. *Mailing Add:* Dept Zool State Univ NY Oswego NY 13126

MAXWELL, GLENN, b Kent, Ohio, May 20, 31; m 59; c 3. MATHEMATICS. *Educ:* Kent State Univ, BS, 53, MA, 54; Ohio State Univ, PhD(math), 64. *Prof Exp:* Teacher high sch, Ohio, 54-56; instr, 63-64, ASST PROF MATH, KENT STATE UNIV, 64- *Mem:* Math Asn Am; Am Math Soc. *Res:* Mathematical foundations of set theory and logic. *Mailing Add:* Dept of Math Kent State Univ Kent OH 44242

MAXWELL, JAMES DONALD, plant breeding, see previous edition

MAXWELL, JOHN ALFRED, b Hamilton, Ont, Aug 28, 21; m 53. GEOCHEMISTRY, ANALYTICAL CHEMISTRY. *Educ:* McMaster Univ, BSc, 49, MSc, 50; Univ Minn, PhD(geol, mineral & anal chem), 53. *Prof Exp:* Metall chemist, Burlington Steel Co, 39-45; asst chem, McMaster Univ, 48-50; asst petrol, Univ Minn, 51, analyst, Rock Anal Lab, 51-53; geochemist, 53-74, DIR CENT LABS & TECH SERV, GEOL SURV OF CAN, 74- *Mem:* Geol Asn Can; fel Royal Soc Can; Geochem Soc; Chem Inst Can; Mineral Asn Can. *Res:* Methods of rock and mineral analysis; compilation of geochemical data; meteorites; lunar samples. *Mailing Add:* Geol Surv of Can 601 Booth St Ottawa ON K1A 0E8 Can

MAXWELL, JOHN CRAWFORD, b Xenia, Ohio, Dec 28, 14; m 39; c 2. GEOLOGY, TECTONICS. *Educ:* DePauw Univ, BA, 36; Univ Minn, MA, 37; Princeton Univ, PhD(geol), 46. *Prof Exp:* Reflections seismograph comput, Tex Co, 37; subsurface geologist, Sun Oil Co, 37-40; from instr to assoc prof geol, Princeton Univ, 46-55, prof geol eng, 55-70, chmn dept, 55-66, chmn dept geol, 66-70, chmn interdept prog water resources, 64-70; WILLIAM STAMPS FARISH PROF GEOL SCI, UNIV TEX, AUSTIN, 70- *Concurrent Pos:* Fulbright scholar, Italy, 52-53, NSF fel, 61-62; chmn earth sci div, Nat Res Coun, 70-72; consult, Adv Comt Reactor Safeguards, Nuclear Regulatory Comn, 74-; chmn, US Nat Comt Geodynamics, 79- *Mem:* Geol Soc Am (pres, 72-73); Am Asn Petrol Geologists; Am Geophys Union; Am Geol Inst (pres, 71-72); Ital Geol Soc. *Res:* Geology of Caribbean area and Montana-Wyoming; gravity tectonics in Italian Apennines and California coast ranges; high temperature high pressure on limestone, quartz sand, and sandstone; origin of rock cleavage. *Mailing Add:* Dept Geol Sci Univ Tex Austin TX 78712

MAXWELL, JOHN GARY, b Salt Lake City, Utah, Oct 5, 33; m 80; c 6. SURGERY. *Educ:* Univ Utah, BS, 54, MD, 58. *Prof Exp:* From instr to asst prof, 66-73, ASSOC PROF SURG, COL MED, UNIV UTAH, 73- *Concurrent Pos:* Asst chief, Vet Admin Hosp, 66-76. *Mem:* Am Col Surg; Asn Acad Surg. *Res:* Gastrointestinal surgery; transplantation; vascular surgery. *Mailing Add:* Dept Surg Univ Utah Col Med Salt Lake City UT 84112

MAXWELL, JOYCE BENNETT, b Merced, Calif, June 18, 41; m 68; c 2. GENETICS. *Educ:* Univ Calif, Los Angeles, AB, 63; Calif Inst Technol, PhD(genetics, biochem), 70. *Prof Exp:* Res asst neurohistochem, Camarillo State Hosp, 69; asst prof, 70-81, ASSOC PROF BIOL, CALIF STATE UNIV, NORTHRIDGE, 81- *Mem:* AAAS; Am Women in Sci. *Res:* Biochemical genetics; synthesis of serine and glycine by Neurospora crassa; multiple electrophoretic forms of tyrosinase in Neurospora crassa; high mutable serine-dependent strain of Neurospora. *Mailing Add:* Dept of Biol Calif State Univ Northridge CA 91324

MAXWELL, KENNETH EUGENE, b Huntington Beach, Calif, Sept 27, 08; m 41; c 3. ENTOMOLOGY. *Educ:* Univ Calif, BS, 33; Cornell Univ, PhD(entom), 37. *Prof Exp:* Jr entomologist, Univ Calif, Riverside, 37-39; technologist, Shell Oil Co, 39-42; mgr agr div, Chemurgic Corp, 45-47; consult, Maxwell Labs, 47-49; entomologist, E I du Pont de Nemours & Co, 49-50; mgr, Insecticide Dept, Agriform Co, 50-53; entomologist, Monsanto Chem Co, 53-59; tech dir, Moyer Chem Co, 59-63; from assoc prof to prof, 63-74, EMER PROF ENTOM, CALIF STATE UNIV, LONG BEACH, 74- *Mem:* AAAS; Entom Soc Am; Am Chem Soc; Sigma Xi. *Res:* Toxicology of pesticides; environmental toxicology. *Mailing Add:* 16751 Greenview Lane Huntington Beach CA 92649

MAXWELL, LEE M(EDILL), b Los Angeles, Calif, July 17, 30; m 52; c 4. ELECTRICAL ENGINEERING. *Educ:* Univ Okla, BS, 56; Univ Idaho, MS, 59; Univ Colo, PhD(elec eng), 63. *Prof Exp:* From instr to asst prof elec eng, Univ Idaho, 57-63; assoc prof, 63-69, PROF ELEC ENG, COLO STATE UNIV, 69- *Mem:* Inst Elec & Electronics Engrs; Am Soc Eng Educ. *Res:* Network and graph theory. *Mailing Add:* Dept of Elec Eng Colo State Univ Ft Collins CO 80523

MAXWELL, RICHARD ELMORE, biochemistry, see previous edition

MAXWELL, ROBERT ARTHUR, b Union City, NJ, Oct 6, 27; m 56; c 3. PHARMACOLOGY. *Educ:* Princeton Univ, PhD(biol), 54. *Prof Exp:* Assoc pharmacologist, Ciba Pharmaceut Co, 54-60, assoc dir pharmacol, 60-62; assoc prof, Col Med, Univ Vt, 62-65; HEAD PHARMACOL, WELLCOME RES LABS, 66- *Concurrent Pos:* Vis prof, Col Med, Univ Vt, 66-; adj prof pharmacol & exp med, Med Ctr, Duke Univ, 70-; adj prof pharmacol, Sch Med, Univ NC, Chapel Hill, 73- *Mem:* AAAS; Am Soc Pharmacol & Exp Therapeut; Pharmacol Soc Can; NY Acad Sci. *Res:* Cardiovascular and autonomic pharmacology. *Mailing Add:* Wellcome Res Labs 3030 Cornwallis Rd Research Triangle Park NC 27709

MAXWELL, ROBERT L(OUIS), b Lexington, Tenn, Feb 24, 20; m 46; c 2. MECHANICAL ENGINEERING. *Educ:* Univ Tenn, BS, 44; Case Western Reserve Univ, MS, 46. *Prof Exp:* Mech engr, Nat Adv Comt Aeronaut, 44-46; instr mech eng, Case Western Reserve Univ, 46; from instr to assoc prof, 46-70, PROF MECH ENG, UNIV TENN, KNOXVILLE, 70- *Concurrent Pos:* Consult, Redstone Arsenal, 52-54 & Union Carbide Co, 52- *Mem:* Am Soc Mech Engrs; Soc Exp Stress Anal; Am Soc Eng Educ. *Res:* Stress analysis; vibrations. *Mailing Add:* Dept of Mech & Aeronaut Eng Univ of Tenn Knoxville TN 37916

MAXWELL, WILLIAM HALL CHRISTIE, b Coleraine, Northern Ireland, Jan 25, 36; US citizen; m 60; c 4. CIVIL ENGINEERING, FLUID MECHANICS. *Educ:* Queen's Univ Belfast, BSc, 56; Queen's Univ, Ont, MSc, 58; Univ Minn, PhD(civil eng), 64. *Prof Exp:* Res asst hydromech, Nat Res Coun Can, 58; res fel, St Anthony Falls Hydraul Lab, Univ Minn, 61-63; asst prof civil eng, 64-70, ASSOC PROF CIVIL ENG, UNIV ILL, URBANA, 70- *Concurrent Pos:* NSF res initiation grant, 66-67; tech ed, Water Int, Int Water Resources Asn, 76-; mem, Am Soc Civil Engrs Hydraul Div Res Comt, 80- & Am Soc Civil Engrs Eng Mech Div Fluids Comt, 80- *Mem:* Am Soc Civil Engrs; Am Geophys Union; Int Asn Hydraul Res; Int Water Resources Asn. *Res:* Hydraulic and water resources engineering; bubble screens; hydraulic models; jet diffusion; surface tension. *Mailing Add:* B114 Civil Eng Bldg Univ Ill 208 N Romine St Urbana IL 61801

MAXWELL, WILLIAM L, b Philadelphia, Pa, July 11, 34; m 69; c 4. OPERATIONS RESEARCH, INDUSTRIAL ENGINEERING. *Educ:* Cornell Univ, BME, 57, PhD(opers res), 61. *Prof Exp:* Asst prof indust eng, 61-64, assoc prof indust eng & opers res, 64-69, PROF OPERS RES, CORNELL UNIV, 69-, ASSOC DIR DEPT, 78- *Mem:* Asn Comput Mach; Opers Res Soc Am; Inst Mgt Sci. *Res:* Scheduling theory; digital simulation; production control and data processing systems; education computing languages. *Mailing Add:* Upson Hall Cornell Univ Ithaca NY 14853

MAXWORTHY, TONY, b London, Eng, May 21, 33; US citizen; m 56; c 2. AEROSPACE & MECHANICAL ENGINEERING. *Educ:* Univ London, BSc, 54; Princeton Univ, MSE, 55; Harvard Univ, PhD(mech eng), 60. *Prof Exp:* Scientist, Jet Propulsion Labs, 60-62, sr scientist, 63-65, group supvr, 66-67; assoc prof, 67-70, PROF AEROSPACE & MECH ENG, UNIV SOUTHERN CALIF, 70- *Concurrent Pos:* Mem comt fluid mech, NASA, 66-67; consult, Jet Propulsion Labs, 68-; vpres, Univ Consult Inc, 71-, consult, Xonics, Inc & Sci, Systs & Software, Inc, 72- *Mem:* Am Phys Soc; Am Geophys Union; Am Meteorol Soc. *Res:* Application of basic principles of fluid mechanics to problems of technological and geophysical significance. *Mailing Add:* Dept of Aerospace Eng OHE 300 Univ of Southern Calif Los Angeles CA 90007

MAY, ADOLF D(ARLINGTON), JR, b Little Rock, Ark, Mar 25, 27; m 48; c 4. ENGINEERING. *Educ:* Southern Methodist Univ, BS, 49; Iowa State Univ, MS, 50; Purdue Univ, PhD, 55. *Prof Exp:* Instr civil eng, Iowa State Univ, 49-50; res asst, Purdue Univ, 50-52; assoc prof, Clarkson Col Technol, 52-56 & Mich State Univ, 56-59; mem tech staff traffic control, Thompson-Ramo-Wooldridge, Inc, 59-62; dir, Chicago Expressway Surveillance Proj, 62-65; assoc prof, 65-67, PROF TRANSP ENG, UNIV CALIF, BERKELEY, 67- *Concurrent Pos:* Mem Hwy Res Bd, Nat Acad Sci-Nat Res Coun, 50- *Mem:* Am Soc Eng Educ; Inst Traffic Engrs. *Res:* Electronic control systems; theory of traffic flow; highway geometric design and planning; traffic operations. *Mailing Add:* Dept of Civil Eng Rm 114 McLaughlin Hall Univ of Calif Berkeley CA 94720

MAY, CHARLES EDWARD, b Hamilton, Ohio, Dec 16, 25; m 66; c 2. PHYSICAL CHEMISTRY. *Educ:* Xavier Univ, BS, 47, MS, 49; Purdue Univ, PhD, 53. *Prof Exp:* Head chem sect, 53-81, TECH CONSULT, NASA, 81- *Res:* High temperature chemistry; x-ray and electron diffraction; Raman and infrared spectroscopy; electrochemistry. *Mailing Add:* Lewis Res Ctr NASA 21000 Brookpark Rd Cleveland OH 44135

MAY, DONALD CURTIS, JR, b Ann Arbor, Mich, May 31, 17; m 42. OPERATIONS RESEARCH. *Educ:* Univ Mich, AB, 38; Princeton Univ, AM, 40, PhD(math), 41. *Prof Exp:* Instr math, Princeton Univ, 39-40; mathematician, Bur Naval Weapons, 41-63, mathematician opers res, Surface Missile Systs Proj, US Dept Navy, 63-75; systs analyst, Shipbuilding Proj, 75-80; NAVAL SYST ANALIST, APPL PHYSICS LAB, JOHNS HOPKINS UNIV, 81- *Res:* Evaluation of Navy weapon systems. *Mailing Add:* 5931 Oakdale Rd McLean VA 22101

MAY, EDWIN ANTHONY, b Tuckahoe, NY, Nov 22, 23; m 49; c 5. MECHANICAL ENGINEERING. *Educ:* Stevens Inst Technol, ME, 47. *Prof Exp:* Proj engr, Prod Develop Div, Becton, Dickinson & Co, 47-57, asst to dir, 58-59, asst to vpres, Cent Res Div, 59-60, asst dir res & develop, Cardiovasc & Spec Instrument Div, 61-65, mgr bioeng, Corp Res Ctr, 66-68; dir res & mkt, Bio-Med Syst, Inc, 68-70; group dir biomed eng, Corp Res & Develop Div, 70-76, mgr prod develop, Davol Inc, 76-77, mgr prod planning, 77-78, MGR NEW PROD VENTURES, DAVOL INC DIV, INT PAPER CO, 78- *Mem:* Am Soc Artificial Internal Organs; Am Soc Mech Engrs; Inst Elec & Electronic Engrs; AAAS. *Res:* Diagnostic, surgical, laboratory instrumentation; hospital systems; surgical research; artificial organs; cardiovascular instrumentation; biomedical research; biomaterials research; health care systems; advanced technology applications. *Mailing Add:* 30 Devon Ct East Greenwich RI 02818

MAY, EVERETTE LEE, b Timberville, Va, Aug 1, 14; m 40, 65; c 4. MEDICINAL CHEMISTRY. *Educ:* Bridgewater Col, AB, 35; Univ Va, PhD(org chem), 39. *Prof Exp:* Res chemist, Nat Oil Prods Co, 39-41; from assoc chemist to sr chemist, NIH, 41-53, from scientist to sr scientist, Commissioned Corps, 53-58, scientist dir, 59, chief sect med chem, Nat Insts Arthritis & Metabolic Dis, USPHS, 60-78; adj prof pharmacol, 74-77, PROF PHARMACOL, MED COL VA, 77- *Concurrent Pos:* Mem expert adv panel drugs liable to cause addiction & comt probs drug dependence, 58-78; chem adv panel mem, Walter Reed Army Inst, 65-; mem ad hoc rev comt, Nat Cancer Inst, 78. *Honors & Awards:* E E Smissman Award Med Chem, Am Chem Soc, 79. *Mem:* Am Chem Soc. *Res:* Surface active agents; vitamins of the B complex; antimalarial agents; analgesic drugs; antitubercular compounds; carcinolytic agents; chemical and pharmacological investigations on central nervous system and anti-inflammatory agents. *Mailing Add:* Dept of Pharmacol Med Col of Va Richmond VA 23298

MAY, EVERETTE LEE, JR, b Bethesda, Md, May 26, 44; m 65; c 2. MATHEMATICS, COMPUTER SCIENCE. *Educ:* Wake Forest Col, BS, 66; Emory Univ, PhD(math), 71. *Prof Exp:* Asst prof math, Kennesaw Jr Col, 72; asst prof, 72-75, ASSOC PROF, SALISBURY STATE COL, 75- *Concurrent Pos:* Comput consult, 79-; vis assoc prof, Wake Forest Univ, 80-81. *Mem:* Am Math Soc; Math Asn Am. *Res:* Search for a viable notion of spectrum for a nonlinear transformation viable in the sense of yielding useful analytical tools; applying mathematics along with programming principles to the construction of database systems and the solving of problems for small businesses. *Mailing Add:* 606 Irene Ave Salisbury MD 21801

MAY, FRANK PIERCE, b Quincy, Fla, Oct 2, 20; m 45; c 3. CHEMICAL ENGINEERING. *Educ:* Univ Fla, BChE, 48, MSE, 58, PhD(chem eng, math), 61. *Prof Exp:* Chem engr, Am Oil Co, Tex, 48-50; chem engr, US Phosphoric Prod Div, Tenn Corp, Fla, 50-53, night supt, 53-54, dept supvr, 54-55; from instr to assoc prof chem eng, 55-69, PROF CHEM ENG, UNIV FLA, 69- *Mem:* AAAS; Am Inst Chem Engrs; Nat Soc Prof Engrs; Am Chem Soc. *Res:* Chemical process dynamics and optimization; chemical processing by by-product recovery and pollution abatement in the citrus processing industry. *Mailing Add:* Dept of Chem Eng Univ of Fla Gainesville FL 32601

MAY, FRED EUGENE, palynology, stratigraphy, see previous edition

MAY, GERALD WARE, b Warrenton, Ga, Feb 27, 40; m 62. MECHANICAL ENGINEERING, STRUCTURAL MECHANICS. *Educ:* Ga Inst Technol, BS, 63, MS(eng mech), 65, MS, 67, PhD(mech eng), 69. *Prof Exp:* Engr, E I du Pont de Nemours & Co, Inc, 63; res engr, Burlington Industs, Inc, Greensboro, NC, 69-72; lead stress analyst on nuclear reactor, Westinghouse Elec Corp, 72-76; PROG MGR NUCLEAR SHIPPING CASK DEVELOP, DEPT ENERGY, US GOVT, 76- *Mem:* Am Soc Mech Engrs. *Res:* Noise abatement engineering; thermal and solid mechanics research. *Mailing Add:* 3597 Pebble Beach Dr Martinez GA 30907

MAY, HAROLD E(DWARD), b New York, NY, Oct 18, 20; m 43; c 2. MECHANICAL ENGINEERING. *Educ:* Columbia Univ, AB, 41, BS, 42. *Prof Exp:* Supvr, Eng Field Group, 42-50, area supt prod, 50-55, tech mgr, 55-58, asst dir prod, 58-62, asst dir res, Electrochem Dept, 62-68, mgr, Electronic Prod Div, 68-71, dir, Chem Prod Div, 71-72, dir, Indust Specialties Div, 72-74, dir corp purchusing, 74-76, gen mgr energy & mat, 76-77, VPRES MAT & LOGISTICS, E I DU PONT DE NEMOURS & CO, INC, 77- *Mailing Add:* 2007 Greenbriar Dr Holly Oak DE 19810

MAY, IRVING, b New York, NY, Feb 16, 18; m 40; c 1. ANALYTICAL CHEMISTRY, GEOCHEMISTRY. *Educ:* City Col New York, BS, 38; George Washington Univ, MS, 48. *Prof Exp:* Testing technician, Panama Canal, 39-41; anal chemist, USPHS, NIH, 41-48; anal chemist, US Geol Surv, 48-71, chief, Br Anal Labs, 71-76, chief chemist, 76-80; RETIRED. *Mem:* Am Chem Soc; Geochem Soc; Sigma Xi; AAAS. *Res:* Geochemical analysis, particularly determination of trace elements. *Mailing Add:* 917 Brentwood Lane Silver Spring MD 20902

MAY, JAMES AUBREY, JR, b Houston, Tex, July 15, 42; m 68; c 2. POLYMER CHEMISTRY, ORGANOMETALLIC CHEMISTRY. *Educ:* Tex Christian Univ, BS, 64, PhD(org chem), 68. *Prof Exp:* Sr res chemist, 68-72, res specialist, 72-76, group leader, 76-81, RES MGR, DOW CHEM CO, USA, 81- *Mem:* Am Chem Soc; Sigma Xi; NY Acad Sci. *Res:* Polymer characterization; gel permeation chromatography; polyolefins; Ziegler catalysis; product research; specialty polyolefin copolymers; process research; free radical catalysis kinetics; electrochemistry. *Mailing Add:* B-2234 Bldg Dow Chem Co USA Freeport TX 77541

MAY, JAMES DAVID, b Blue Mountain, Miss, Aug 21, 40; m 61; c 3. POULTRY PHYSIOLOGY. *Educ:* Miss State Univ, BS, 61, MS, 63; NC State Univ, PhD(physiol), 70. *Prof Exp:* Res physiologist, SCent Poultry Res Lab, Agr Res Serv, 69-78, RES PHYSIOLOGIST, POULTRY RES LAB, SCI & EDUC ADMIN-FED RES, USDA, 78- *Concurrent Pos:* Adj asst prof, Miss State Univ, 70. *Mem:* Poultry Sci Asn; World Poultry Sci Asn; AAAS; Am Physiol Soc. *Res:* Poultry environmental physiology; thyroid metabolism; amino acid metabolism. *Mailing Add:* US Dept Agr Sci & Educ Admin-Fed Res Georgetown DE 19947

MAY, JOAN CHRISTINE, b Buffalo, NY. ANALYTICAL CHEMISTRY, INORGANIC CHEMISTRY. *Educ:* Nazareth Col Rochester, BS, 65; Univ Wis-Madison, MS, 68; Univ Notre Dame, PhD(anal-inorg chem), 71. *Prof Exp:* Sr chemist anal chem, 73-74, DIR, ANAL CHEM BR, BUR BIOLOGICS, DEPT HEALTH, EDUC & WELFARE, USPHS & FOOD & DRUG ADMIN, 74- *Concurrent Pos:* Chemist, Roswell Park Mem Inst, 71-72 & Anal Chem Div, Nat Bur Standards, Washington, DC, 72-73. *Mem:* Am Chem Soc; Asn Off Anal Chemists; Sigma Xi; Int Asn Biol Standardization. *Res:* Accurate analytical methods for the determination of trace and macro amounts of organic and inorganic additives, preservatives and other impurities or constituent materials found in vaccines and other biological products. *Mailing Add:* Bur of Biologics 8800 Rockville Pike Bethesda MD 20014

MAY, JOHN E(DWARD), b New York, NY, Sept 27, 27; m 50; c 3. METALLURGY, CERAMICS. *Educ:* City Col New York, BS, 49; Mo Sch Mines, MS, 51; Rensselaer Polytech Inst, MS, 62. *Prof Exp:* Res metallurgist-ceramist, Res Lab, 51-59, Power Transformer Dept, 59-61 & Metallurgist Semiconductor Prod, 61-68, process scientist, Integrated Circuits Ctr, 68-72,

CERAMIST, SEMICONDUCTOR PROD DEPT, GEN ELEC CO, 72- *Mem:* AAAS; Electrochem Soc; Am Soc Metals; Am Ceramic Soc. *Res:* Epitaxial deposition; metal-semiconductor contacts; physical chemistry of semiconductor technology; recrystallization and crystal growth; kinetics of metallurgical and ceramic processes; sintering; physical ceramics; mechanical properties; deformation mechanisms; development of zinc oxide varistors and electronic ceramics, microstructure and mechanisms of operation. *Mailing Add:* Gen Elec Co Semiconductor Prod Div Electronics Park Syracuse NY 13220

MAY, JOHN ELLIOTT, JR, b Meriden, Conn, June 4, 21; m 45; c 2. PHYSICS. *Educ:* Wesleyan Univ, BA, 43; Tufts Col, MS, 49; Yale Univ, PhD(physics), 53. *Prof Exp:* Electronics physicist, US Naval Res Lab Field Sta, Mass, 46-49; mem tech staff, Bell Tel Labs, Inc, 52-59, supvr explor develop delay devices, 59-62, ultrasonic amplifier & evaporated film transducer develop, 62-65, head ultrasonic device dept, 65-71, head process capability dept, 71-77, supvr eval digital transmission equip, 77-79, PHYSICIST, BELL LABS, 79- *Mem:* Am Phys Soc; Inst Elec & Electronics Engrs; fel Acoust Soc Am. *Res:* Research and development in ultrasonic devices including delay line geometry, ceramic transducers; elastic wave guide effects; piezoelectric materials; ultrasonic amplification; mechanical filters; microphones; thin film circuits; conductors, resistors and capacitors. *Mailing Add:* Bell Labs 1600 Osgood St North Andover MA 01845

MAY, JOHN WALTER, b London, Eng, June 25, 36; Can citizen; m 66; c 2. SURFACE PHYSICS, SURFACE CHEMISTRY. *Educ:* Univ BC, BA, 57, MS, 60; Oxford Univ, PhD(chem), 63. *Prof Exp:* Res assoc, Dept Appl Physics, Cornell Univ, 64-68; physicist, Bartol Res Found, Franklin Inst, 68-72; sr res chemist, 72-80, RES ASSOC, EASTMAN KODAK RES LABS, 80- *Mem:* Am Vacuum Soc; Sigma Xi. *Res:* Surface science, including adsorption, catalysis, surface structure, surface electrostatics, triboelectrification, low energy electron diffraction, auger and x-ray photoelectron spectroscopies; electrophotography. *Mailing Add:* Eastman Kodak Res Labs Kodak Park Rochester NY 14650

MAY, KENNETH NATHANIEL, b Livingston, La, Dec 24, 30; m 53; c 2. FOOD TECHNOLOGY. *Educ:* La State Univ, BS, 52, MS, 55; Purdue Univ, PhD(food technol), 59. *Prof Exp:* Asst poultry sci, La State Univ, 52-54, res assoc, 54-56; asst state poultry supvr, State Livestock Sanit Bd, La, 54; asst poultry husb, Purdue Univ, 56-58; from asst prof to prof, Univ Ga, 58-68; prof, Miss State Univ, 68-70; dir res & qual assurance, 70-73, VPRES RES & QUAL ASSURANCE, HOLLY FARMS POULTRY INDUSTS, INC, 73- *Concurrent Pos:* Mem salmonella adv comt, Secy Agr, 75-78; adj prof, NC State Univ, Raleigh, 75-; mem, Nat Adv Comt, Meat & Poultry Insp, 79-81. *Honors & Awards:* Res Award, Inst Am Poultry Industs, 63; Res Award, Ga Egg Comn, 64; Indust Serv Award, Poultry & Egg Inst Am, 71. *Mem:* Am Poultry Sci Asn; Inst Food Technol; World Poultry Sci Asn. *Res:* Meat yields and processing losses of poultry; nutritive value and bacteriology of poultry products; biochemistry of bruised tissue. *Mailing Add:* Res Dept Holly Farms Poultry Industs Inc Wilkesboro NC 28697

MAY, LEOPOLD, b Brooklyn, NY, Nov 26, 23; m 47; c 2. PHYSICAL BIOCHEMISTRY. *Educ:* City Col New York, BChE, 44; Polytech Inst Brooklyn, MS, 48, PhD, 51. *Prof Exp:* Instr, Polytech Inst Brooklyn, 49-50; res chemist, Columbia Univ, 50-54; res assoc, Univ Md, 54-56, instr, 56-59; asst prof, 59-61, ASSOC PROF CHEM, CATH UNIV AM, 61- *Concurrent Pos:* Lectr, Brooklyn Col, 53; instr, Johns Hopkins Univ, 54-57; ed-in-chief, Appl Spectros, 61-64; vis assoc prof, Tel-Aviv Univ, 72-73; vis scientist, Soreg Nuclear Physics Ctr, Israel, 72-73; Nat Acad Sci exchange scientist, Inst Chem Physics, Moscow, USSR, 76-78; vis prof chem, Bamoras Hindu Univ, India, 78; vis res prof, Armed Forces Radiobiol Res Inst, Bethesda, Md, 78-; Fulbright-Hays Award, Lima, Peru, 80. *Mem:* Am Chem Soc; Soc Appl Spectros (pres, 71). *Res:* Infrared and Mossbauer spectroscopy of biological materials and chemicals. *Mailing Add:* Dept of Chem Cath Univ of Am Washington DC 20064

MAY, MICHAEL MELVILLE, b Marseilles, France, Dec 23, 25; nat US; m 52; c 4. PHYSICS. *Educ:* Whitman Col, BA, 44; Univ Calif, PhD(physics), 52. *Hon Degrees:* DSc, Whitman Col, Walla Walla, WA, 76. *Prof Exp:* Res physicist, Lawrence Livermore Lab, Univ Calif, 52-57; vpres, E H Plesset Assocs, 57-60; res physicist, 60-61, div leader, 61-62, assoc dir, 62-64, lectr appl sci, 64-65, dir, 65-71, RES PHYSICIST & ASSOC DIR-AT-LG, LAWRENCE LIVERMORE LAB, UNIV CALIF, 72- *Concurrent Pos:* Vis physicist, Princeton Univ, 71-72; sr personal adv to Secy of Defense for Strategic Arms Limitation Talks & mem US deleg, 74-76. *Honors & Awards:* E O Lawrence Mem Award, Atomic Energy Comn, 70. *Mem:* Am Phys Soc. *Res:* Nuclear explosions; heat and radiation; relativity. *Mailing Add:* 728 E Angela St Pleasanton CA 94566

MAY, MORTON, range conservation, see previous edition

MAY, PAUL DAVID, polymer chemistry, bio-organic chemistry, see previous edition

MAY, PAUL S, b Brooklyn, NY, July 12, 31; m 56; c 3. MICROBIOLOGY. *Educ:* City Col New York, BS, 51; Syracuse Univ, MS, 52; Phila Col Pharm, DSc(indust microbiol), 55; Columbia Univ, MPH, 70. *Prof Exp:* Instr bact, Phila Col Pharm, 52-53, instr zool, 54-55; sr res microbiologist, S B Penick & Co, 55-58; asst microbiologist, Beth Israel Hosp, NY, 58-62; sr scientist microbiol, Life Sci Lab, Melpar, Inc, 62-64; lectr, Sch Pub Health, Columbia Univ, 64; asst dir bur Labs, 64-71, DEP ASST COMN BUR LABS, NEW YORK DEPT HEALTH, 71-; ADJ ASST PROF, SCH PUB HEALTH & ADMIN MED, COLUMBIA UNIV & HUNTER COL, 78- *Mem:* Am Soc Microbiol; Am Pub Health Asn. *Res:* Antibiotics; fermentations; medical bacteriology, parasitology and mycology; public health microbiology; laboratory and public health administration; epidemiology. *Mailing Add:* 23 Fairview Lane Orangeburg NY 10962

MAY, PHILIP REGINALD ALDRIDGE, b Weymouth, Eng, May 30, 20; nat US; m 59. PSYCHIATRY. *Educ:* Cambridge Univ, BA, 41, MB, BCh, 44, MA, 46; Stanford Univ, MD, 44; Royal Col Physicians & Surgeons, dipl psychol med, 47; Am Bd Psychiat & Neurol, dipl, 51. *Prof Exp:* Resident med & neurol, Guy's Hosp, London, 45, resident psychiat, 45-46; resident, Bexley Hosp, 46-47 & Sch Med, Univ Colo, 49-50; from instr to asst prof, 50-53, from asst clin prof to assoc clin prof, 56-68, clin dir neuropsychiat inst, 62-73, PROF PSYCHIAT, UNIV CALIF, LOS ANGELES, 69-; CHIEF HEALTH SERV RES & DEVELOP LAB, BRENTWOOD VET ADMIN HOSP, LOS ANGELES, 70- *Concurrent Pos:* Chief male inpatient serv, Colo Psychopathic Hosp, 50-51, asst dir, Hosp, 51-53; consult, Fitzsimmons Army Hosp, Denver & US Armed Forces Epidemiol Bd, 51-53, Vet Admin Hosps, Denver, 51-53 & Los Angeles, 66-70; clin dir, Camarillo State Hosp, Calif, 55-59, chief res, 59-62; consult, Superior Ct, Santa Barbara & Ventura Counties & Probation Dept, Ventura, Calif, 58-66. *Honors & Awards:* Bronze Award, Am Psychiat Asn, 63; Paul Hoch Award, Am Psychopath Asn, 74. *Mem:* Fel Am Psychiat Asn; AMA; fel Am Col Neuropsychopharmacol (pres, 75); Int Col Psychopharmacol; Royal Col Physicians. *Res:* Outcome and treatment of schizophrenia; development and evaluation of treatment and other programs; head injury. *Mailing Add:* Dept of Psychiat Univ of Calif Los Angeles CA 90024

MAY, RALPH FORREST, b Idaho, Ohio, Oct 1, 41; m 63, 78. AGRICULTURAL CHEMISTRY. *Educ:* Wilmington Col, AB, 63; Ind Univ, Bloomington, MA, 66, PhD(org chem), 67. *Prof Exp:* res chemist, 67-80, SR RES CHEMIST AGR CHEM, BIOCHEM DEPT, E I DU PONT DE NEMOURS & CO, INC, 80- *Mem:* Am Chem Soc. *Res:* Formulation and development of insecticides. *Mailing Add:* Biochem Dept E324/111 Du Pont Exp Sta Wilmington DE 19898

MAY, ROBERT CARLYLE, b San Francisco, Calif, Feb, 4, 43; m 79; c 1. AQUACULTURE, DEVELOPING COUNTRIES. *Educ:* Univ Calif, Berkeley, BA, 64; Univ Hawaii, MS, 67; Univ Calif, San Diego, PhD(marine biol), 72. *Prof Exp:* Asst marine biologist, Univ Hawaii, 72-77; AQUACULT SPECIALIST, ASIAN DEVELOP BANK, 78- *Mem:* AAAS; Am Fisheries Soc; Am Soc Ichthyologists & Herpetologists. *Res:* Cultivation of marine fishes; factors influencing larval survival in marine fishes. *Mailing Add:* Asian Develop Bank PO Box 789 Manila Philippines

MAY, ROBERT MCCREDIE, b Sydney, Australia, Jan 8, 36; m 62; c 1. ECOLOGY. *Educ:* Univ Sydney, BSc, 57, PhD(physics), 60. *Prof Exp:* Gordon MacKay lectr appl math, Harvard Univ, 59-61; sr lectr & reader physics, Univ Sydney, 62-69, prof, 70-73; prof biol, 73-75, CLASS OF 1877 PROF ZOOL, PRINCETON UNIV, 75- *Concurrent Pos:* Vis prof physics, Calif Inst Technol, 67 & Magdalene Col, Oxford, 71; vis mem, Inst Advan Study, 71-72 & King's Col, Cambridge, 76; mem comt ecosyst anal, Nat Acad Sci, 73-75; assoc ed, Theoret Pop Biol & Math Biosci, 74- & SIAM J Appl Math & Appl Ecol Abstr, 75- *Honors & Awards:* Pawsey Medal, Australian Acad Sci, 67. *Mem:* Brit Ecol Soc; Am Soc Naturalists; fel Royal Soc; Asn Arts & Sci. *Res:* Theoretical models which give insights into the dynamics of single populations, pairs of populations, or of entire communities of interacting populations. *Mailing Add:* Dept of Biol Princeton Univ Princeton NJ 08540

MAY, SHELDON WILLIAM, b Minneapolis, Minn, June 27, 46; m 68; c 3. BIOCHEMISTRY. *Educ:* Roosevelt Univ, BS, 66; Univ Chicago, PhD(chem), 70. *Prof Exp:* Sr res chemist, Corp Res Lab, Exxon Res & Eng Co, 70-73; from asst prof to assoc prof, 74-80, PROF CHEM, GA INST TECHNOL, 80- *Concurrent Pos:* NSF fel, 67-70, NIH, 70; fel, A P Sloan Found, 77-79; vis prof, Centre de Neurochimie, Strashourg, Fr, 79. *Mem:* Am Soc Biol Chemists; AAAS; Am Chem Soc. *Res:* Enzyme chemistry; mechanisms of biochemical reactions; biochemical oxidations; molecular neurochemistry; immobilized enzymes; enzyme and biochemical technology. *Mailing Add:* Sch of Chem Ga Inst Technol Atlanta GA 30332

MAY, SHERRY JAN, Can citizen. MATHEMATICAL ANALYSIS. *Educ:* Univ Sask, BA, 68, dipl math, 69; Univ Waterloo, NM, 70, PhD(appl math), 74. *Prof Exp:* Nat Res Coun Can fel, Univ Sask, 74-77; ASST PROF MATH, MEM UNIV NFLD, 77- *Concurrent Pos:* Res grant, Can Coun, 75. *Mem:* Am Math Soc. *Res:* Rational belief change in philosophy, such as probability kinematics, as constrained optimization problems. *Mailing Add:* 52 Whiteway St St Johns NF A1B 1K4 Can

MAY, SHERRY JAN, Can citizen. MATHEMATICAL ANALYSIS. *Educ:* Univ Sask, Ba, 68, dipl math, 69; Univ Waterloo, MM, 70, PhD(appl math), 74. *Prof Exp:* Nat Res Coun Can fel, Univ Sask, 74-77; ASST PROF MATH, MEM UNIV NFLD, 77- *Concurrent Pos:* Res grant, Can Coun 75. *Mem:* Am Math Soc. *Res:* Probability kinematics; constrained optimiation problems. *Mailing Add:* 52 Whiteway St St John's NF A1B 1K4 Can

MAY, WALTER GRANT, b Saskatoon, Sask, Nov 28, 18; US citizen; wid; c 3. CHEMICAL ENGINEERING, PHYSICAL CHEMISTRY. *Educ:* Univ Sask, BSc, 39, MSc, 42; Mass Inst Technol, ScD(chem eng), 48. *Prof Exp:* Asst chemist, Brit Am Oil Co, 39-40; asst prof chem eng, Univ Sask, 43-46; res assoc, Esso Res & Eng Co, 48-59; engr rocket propellants, Inst Defense Anal, 59-60; sr res assoc, Esso Res & Eng Co, 60-67; prof mech eng, Stevens Inst Technol, 67-77; SR SCI ADVISOR, EXXON RES & ENG CO, 77- *Concurrent Pos:* Mem panel thermodyn, Interagency Chem Rocket Propulsion Group, 59-66; sr sci advisor, Exxon Nuclear, 73-77; prof, Rensselaer Polytech Inst, 74-77. *Mem:* Am Inst Chem Engrs; Am Soc Mech Engrs; Combustion Inst; Nat Acad Eng. *Res:* Chemical reaction kinetics; solid rocket propellants; combustion; thermodynamics; chemical reactor engineering; isotope separations. *Mailing Add:* Exxon Res & Eng Co PO Box 45 Linden NJ 07036

MAY, WALTER RUCH, b Senath, Mo, Aug 4, 37; m 57; c 3. PHYSICAL INORGANIC CHEMISTRY. *Educ:* Memphis State Univ, BS, 59; Vanderbilt Univ, PhD(chem), 62. *Prof Exp:* Instr chem, Vanderbilt Univ, 59-62; res chemist, Monsanto Co, 62-65, sr res chemist, 65-66; res chemist, Tretolite Div, Petrolite Corp, 66-67, res group leader, Corp Lab, 67-73, indust chem group leader, 73-75, mgr indust & water res, 75-76, mgr indust fuels res, 76-77, mgr indust fuel additives sales, For Oper Dept, 77-78; gen mgr, Specialty Fuel Additives Div, Perolin Co, Inc, 78-80; PRES, SFA TECHNOL, INC, GEORGETOWN, CONN, 80- *Mem:* Am Chem Soc; Nat Asn Corrosion Engrs; Sigma Xi; Am Soc Mech Engrs. *Res:* High temperature corrosion; hydrocarbon oxidation; thermal analysis; coordination compounds; heavy petroleum fuel additives. *Mailing Add:* SFA Tech Inc 4 Old Mill Rd Ste 3 Georgetown CT 06829

MAY, WILLIAM G(AMBRILL), b St Louis, Mo, Dec 30, 37. ELECTRICAL ENGINEERING, INTEGRATED CIRCUITS. *Educ:* Mass Inst Technol, SB & SM, 60, PhD(elec eng), 64. *Prof Exp:* Asst elec eng, Mass Inst Technol, 60-62, from instr to asst prof, 62-66; asst prof, 66-69, assoc prof, 70-77, PROF ELEC ENG, UNIV COLO, BOULDER, 78- *Concurrent Pos:* Ford fel eng, 64-66. *Mem:* Am Phys Soc. *Res:* Semiconductor devices and device physics; electrical properties of semiconductors and semimetals; integrated circuit design and fabrication; optical and microwave plasma devices. *Mailing Add:* Dept Elec Eng Univ Colo Boulder CO 80309

MAYA, LEON, b Mexico City, Mex, Mar 23, 38; US citizen; m 60; c 2. INORGANIC CHEMISTRY. *Educ:* Nat Univ Mex, BS, 60; Univ Southern Calif, PhD(inorg chem), 73. *Prof Exp:* Supvr qual control lab, Monsanto Mexicana SA, 60-62; sr chemist, Israel Mining Industs Res Inst, 62-68; chemist, Rainbow Beauty Supply, 68-69; fel inorg chem, Univ Southern Calif, 73-74; MEM RES STAFF, OAK RIDGE NAT LAB, 74- *Mem:* AAAS; Am Chem Soc; Sigma Xi. *Res:* Synthetic inorganic chemistry; use of physical methods for structural determination; chemistry of main group elements, particularly boron, silicon, phosphorus and fluorine; transition of metal elements ruthenium, zirconium and niobium, with emphasis on uranium and neptunium. *Mailing Add:* Oak Ridge Nat Lab PO Box X Oak Ridge TN 37830

MAYA, WALTER, b New York, NY, Oct 25, 29; m 77; c 4. ORGANIC CHEMISTRY, INORGANIC CHEMISTRY. *Educ:* Univ Calif, Los Angeles, BS, 54, PhD(org chem), 58. *Prof Exp:* Res chemist, E I du Pont de Nemours & Co, 58-59; specialist fluorine chem, Rocketdyne Div, NAm Aviation, Inc, 59-70; lectr, 71-72, from asst prof to assoc prof, 72-81, PROF CHEM, CALIF STATE POLYTECH UNIV, POMONA, 81- *Concurrent Pos:* Pfizer fel, Univ Ill, 58-59. *Mem:* AAAS; Am Chem Soc; Sigma Xi; Fedn Am Scientists. *Res:* Synthesis of fluorine compounds; physical-organic chemistry. *Mailing Add:* Dept of Chem Calif State Polytech Univ Pomona CA 91768

MAYADAS, A FRANK, b Ferozepore, India, Dec 7, 39; US citizen; m 62; c 2. SOLID STATE PHYSICS, PHYSICAL METALLURGY. *Educ:* Colo Sch Mines, MetE, 61; Cornell Univ, PhD, 66. *Prof Exp:* Mem res staff, 65-71, mgr thin film & metall group, 71-75, mgr memory & storage res, 75-77, mgr tech planning staff, Watson Res Ctr, 77-79, mgr storage systs & technol, San Jose, Calif, Res Lab, 79-81, DIR, TECH PLANNING & CONTROLS, WATSON RES CTR, IBM CORP, 81- *Mem:* Am Phys Soc; Inst Elec & Electronics Engrs. *Res:* Electron microscopy; dislocation relaxation in metals; microwave resonance; anisotropy studies in magnetic thin films; electron scattering mechanisms in thin metal films. *Mailing Add:* Watson Res Ctr IBM Corp PO Box 218 Yorktown Heights NY 10598

MAYALL, BRIAN HOLDEN, b Nelson, Eng, Nov 14, 32; US citizen; m 55; c 4. ANALYTICAL CYTOLOGY, CYTOMETRY. *Educ:* Cambridge Univ, BA, 54, MA, 58; Univ Western Ont, MD, 61. *Prof Exp:* Res assoc, Wistar Inst, 62-64; from instr radiol to asst prof radiol sci, Med Sch, Univ Pa, 64-71, assoc prof radiol, 71-72; SECT LEADER CYTOGENETICS & CYTOMORPHOMETRY, BIOMED DIV, LAWRENCE LIVERMORE NAT LAB, UNIV CALIF, 72- *Concurrent Pos:* Pa Plan scholar, Wistar Inst & Univ Pa, 63-65; consult, Med Res Coun, UK, 68 & Nat Cancer Inst, 70-; adj assoc prof radiol, Univ Calif, Davis, 74-; ed, Cytometry, 80- *Mem:* AAAS; Histochem Soc; Am Soc Cell Biol; Soc Anal Cytol; Sigma Xi. *Res:* Quantitative cytochemistry; image cytometry; automated cytology; image analysis of cells and chromosomes. *Mailing Add:* Biomed Div L-452 Lawrence Livermore Nat Lab PO Box 5507 Livermore CA 94550

MAYALL, NICHOLAS ULRICH, b Moline, Ill, May 9, 06; m 34; c 2. ASTRONOMY. *Educ:* Univ Calif, AB, 28, PhD(astron), 34. *Prof Exp:* Asst, Univ Calif, 28-29; asst comput, Mt Wilson Observ, 29-31; observing asst, Lick Observ, 33-35, asst astronr, 35-42; mem staff radiation lab, Mass Inst Technol, 42-43; res assoc, Calif Inst Technol, 43-45; from assoc astronr to astronr, Lick Observ, 45-60; dir, Kitt Peak Nat Observ, 60-71; RETIRED. *Mem:* Nat Acad Sci; Am Philos Soc; Am Astron Soc; Am Acad Arts & Sci; Int Astron Union. *Res:* Nebular spectroscopy; photography; radial velocities of galactic nebulae, globular star clusters; red shifts and internal motions of extragalactic nebulae. *Mailing Add:* 7206 E Camino Vecino Tucson AZ 85715

MAYBANK, JOHN, b Winnipeg, Man, Jan 23, 30; m 52; c 2. ATMOSPHERIC PHYSICS. *Educ:* Univ Man, BSc, 52; Univ BC, MSc, 54; Univ London, PhD(meteorol), 59. *Prof Exp:* Sci officer, Physics & Meteorol Sect, Defence Res Bd, 54-61; res officer, Physics Div, Sask Res Coun, 61-70; climatologist, Caribbean Meteorol Inst, Barbados, 70-71; HEAD PHYSICS DIV, SASK RES COUN, 72- *Concurrent Pos:* Res assoc, Univ Sask, 62-66, adj prof, 68- *Mem:* Can Asn Physicists; Royal Meteorol Soc; Can Meteorol Soc. *Res:* Cloud physics; ice nucleation phenomena; atmospheric pollution; agrometeorology. *Mailing Add:* Sask Res Coun Saskatoon SK S7N 0X1 Can

MAYBEE, JOHN STANLEY, b Washington, DC, Mar 23, 28; m 55; c 6. MATHEMATICS. *Educ:* Univ Md, BS, 50; Univ Minn, PhD, 56. *Prof Exp:* Mathematician, David Taylor Model Basin, US Dept Navy, 50-52; asst math, Univ Minn, 52-56; from instr to asst prof, Univ Southern Calif, 56-59; asst prof, Univ Ore, 59-61; from asst prof to assoc prof, Purdue Univ, 61-67; PROF MATH & COMPUT SCI, UNIV COLO, BOULDER, 67- *Concurrent Pos:* Mem, Inst Math Sci, NY Univ, 58-59. *Mem:* Am Math Soc; Soc Indust & Appl Math. *Res:* Differential equations; applied mathematics; matrix theory; numerical analysis. *Mailing Add:* Dept of Math Univ of Colo Boulder CO 80309

MAYBERGER, HAROLD WOODROW, b New York, NY, Aug 28, 19; m 51; c 3. OBSTETRICS & GYNECOLOGY. *Educ:* Univ Ala, BA, 41; Long Island Col Med, MD, 44; Am Bd Legal Med, dipl, 56; Am Bd Obstet & Gynec, dipl, 61. *Prof Exp:* Intern, St John's Episcopal Hosp, 44-45 & 47-48, resident obstet & gynec, 48-51; mem courtesy staff, 53, clin asst, 53-55, from asst attend obstetrician & gynecologist to assoc attend obstetrician & gynecologist, 55-58, attend obstetrician & gynecologist & asst attend pathologist, 58-64, CHIEF DIV OBSTET & GYNEC, COMMUNITY HOSP, GLEN COVE, NY, 64- *Concurrent Pos:* Res fel neonatal path, Beth El Hosp, 51-53; assoc prof clin obstet & gynec, State Univ NY Stony Brook; consult, St John's Episcopal Hosp, Brooklyn, 65, Nassau Hosp, Mineola. *Mem:* AAAS; fel Am Col Legal Med; fel Am Col Surg; fel Am Col Obstet & Gynec; NY Acad Sci. *Res:* Neonatal pathology; forensic obstetrics. *Mailing Add:* 4 Bear Lane Locust Valley NY 11560

MAYBERRY, JOHN PATTERSON, b New Haven, Conn, July 17, 29; m 54; c 3. OPERATIONS RESEARCH. *Educ:* Univ Toronto, BA, 50; Princeton Univ, MA, 54, PhD(math), 55. *Prof Exp:* Asst econ, Princeton Univ, 50-52, asst appl math, Anal Res Group, 53-55; engr, Defense Electronic Prod Dept, Radio Corp Am, 55-58; opers analyst, Hq Fifth Air Force, Japan, 58-61, opers analyst, Hq, US Air Force, Washington, DC, 61-64, chief res group mil opers res, 64-67; mathematician, Mathematica Inc, 67, dir math res serv, 67-69; mathematician, Lambda Corp, Va, 69-71; chmn dept, 72-75, PROF MATH, BROCK UNIV, 71-; CONSULT, JOHN P MAYBERRY ASSOCS, 71- *Mem:* Asn Comput Mach; Am Math Soc; Math Asn Am; Soc Indust & Appl Math; Opers Res Soc Am. *Res:* Topology; graph theory; decision theory; systems analysis; game theory. *Mailing Add:* Dept of Math Brock Univ St Catharines ON L2N 3A1 Can

MAYBERRY, LILLIAN FAYE, b Portland, Ore, May 19, 43; m 75. CELL BIOLOGY, PARASITOLOGY. *Educ:* San Jose State Col, AB, 67; Univ Nev, Reno, MS, 70; Colo State Univ, PhD(zool), 73. *Prof Exp:* Res assoc cell biol, Colo State Univ, 73-74 & Univ Colo, Boulder, 74-76; RES AFFIL BIOL SCI, UNIV TEX, EL PASO, 76-, INSTR, NURSING DEPT, 77- *Concurrent Pos:* Protozoologist, Yugoslavian Int Biol Prog, 75-76. *Mem:* Am Soc Parasitologists; Am Soc Zoologists; Soc Protozoologists; AAAS; Am Inst Biol Sci. *Res:* Physiology and ecology of host-parasite relationships. *Mailing Add:* Dept Biol Sci Univ Tex El Paso TX 79968

MAYBERRY, THOMAS CARLYLE, b Nashville, Tenn, Oct 16, 25; m 53; c 2. POLYMER CHEMISTRY, ORGANIC CHEMISTRY. *Educ:* Vanderbilt Univ, BA, 49, MS, 51; Univ Del, PhD(chem), 62. *Prof Exp:* Chemist, Old Hickory Textile Fibers, 51-53, res chemist, Rayon Res Lab, 53-57, res supvr, Indust Prod Res Lab, 58-69 & Dacron Res Lab, 69-72, sr res chemist, Carothers Res Lab, 72-76, DEVELOP ASSOC, CHATTANOOGA RES & DEVELOP SECT, E I DU PONT DE NEMOURS & CO, INC, 76- *Mem:* Am Chem Soc. *Res:* Polymer and fiber chemistry; physics; engineering. *Mailing Add:* E I du Pont de Nemours & Co Inc PO Box 71 Chattanooga TN 37401

MAYBERRY, WILLIAM EUGENE, b Cookeville, Tenn, Aug 22, 29; m 53; c 2. ENDOCRINOLOGY. *Educ:* Univ Tenn, MD, 53, Univ Minn, MS, 53; Am Bd Internal Med, dipl. *Prof Exp:* First asst & asst to staff internal med, 56-59, from instr to assoc prof med, Mayo Grad Sch Med, Univ Minn, 60-74, chmn dept lab med, Mayo Clin, 71-75, PROF LAB MED, MAYO MED SCH, 74- *Concurrent Pos:* Fel internal med, Mayo Grad Sch Med, Univ Minn, 56-59; Nat Inst Arthritis & Metab Dis trainee & res fel endocrinol, New Eng Ctr Hosp, 59-60; Am Cancer Soc fel, Nat Inst Arthritis & Metab Dis, 62-64; asst, Sch Med, Tufts Univ, 59-60; consult, Mayo Clin, 60-62, mem bd gov, 71-, vchmn, 73-75, chmn, 76-; consult, Mayo Clin, 64-, mem bd trustees, Mayo Found, 71-, vchmn, 75- *Mem:* Endocrine Soc; Am Thyroid Asn; Am Chem Soc; Am Fedn Clin Res; fel Am Col Physicians. *Res:* Biochemistry and physiology of the thyroid gland; biosynthesis of thyroxine. *Mailing Add:* Dept of Lab Med Mayo Clin Rochester MD 55901

MAYBERRY, WILLIAM ROY, b Grand Junction, Colo, Nov 30, 38; m 67. MICROBIOLOGY, ANALYTICAL BIOCHEMISTRY. *Educ:* Univ Colo, BA, 61; Western State Col Colo, MA, 64; Univ Ga, PhD(microbiol & biochem), 66. *Prof Exp:* Chemist, AEC, Lucius Pitkin, Inc, Colo, 60-61; asst instr chem, Mesa Col, 62; res assoc microbiol, Univ Ga, 66-67; res assoc, 67-68, asst prof, 68-75, assoc prof, Sch Med, Univ SDak, 75-78; ASSOC PROF MICROBIOL, COL MED, E TENN STATE UNIV, 78- *Mem:* AAAS; Am Chem Soc; NY Acad Sci; Am Soc Microbiol; Am Inst Biol Sci. *Res:* Gas chromatographic analysis of biological materials; growth yields and energy relationships of bacteria; membrane structure and function. *Mailing Add:* Dept of Microbiol E Tenn State Univ Col of Med Johnson City TN 37601

MAYBURG, SUMNER, b Boston, Mass, Feb 21, 26. SOLID STATE PHYSICS. *Educ:* Harvard Univ, BS, 46; Univ Chicago, MS, 48, PhD(physics), 50. *Prof Exp:* Asst, Univ Chicago, 49-50; sr scientist radiation damage to solids, Atomic Power Div, Westinghouse Elec Corp, 50-52; sr engr, Res Labs, Sylvania Elec Prod, Inc, 52-55, engr mgr & chief engr, Semiconductor Div, 55-59; sr eng specialist, Gen Tel & Electronics Lab Div, 59-64; dir radiation effects div, Controls for Radiation, 64-67; CO-FOUNDER, TREAS & MEM TECH STAFF, SEMICONDUCTOR PROCESSING CO, INC, 67- *Mem:* Am Phys Soc; Electrochem Soc; sr mem Inst Elec & Electronics Engrs; NY Acad Sci; Am Inst Physics. *Res:* Dielectric constants; photoconductivity in insulators and semiconductors; lattice defects in semiconductors; semiconductor devices; intermetallic semiconductors; semiconductor lasers; radiation effects in semiconductor materials and devices; surface preparation of crystalline materials. *Mailing Add:* 409 E First St 10 Industrial Park Rd Boston MA 02127

MAYBURY, PAUL CALVIN, b Rio Grande, NJ, July 20, 24; m 49; c 5. PHYSICAL CHEMISTRY. *Educ:* Eastern Nazarene Col, BS, 47; Johns Hopkins Univ, PhD(chem), 52. *Prof Exp:* Sr staff chemist missiles, Appl Physics Lab, Johns Hopkins Univ, 51-52, res assoc chem, Univ, 52-54; from asst prof to assoc prof, Eastern Nazarene Col, 54-61, chmn dept, 56-61; assoc prof, 61-63, chmn dept, 62-74, PROF CHEM, UNIV SFLA, 64- *Concurrent Pos:* Res assoc, Tufts Univ, 54, vis prof, 66; vis scholar, Univ Calif, Los Angeles, 73-74; consult, Belmac Corp, St Petersburg & Diamond Prod Co, Tampa. *Mem:* AAAS; Am Chem Soc; fel Am Inst Chemists. *Res:* Boron hydride chemistry, including isotopic exchange studies; high energy particle tracks; heterogenous catalysis; reactions of metal borohydrides; methanation. *Mailing Add:* Dept of Chem Univ of SFla Tampa FL 33620

MAYCOCK, JOHN NORMAN, b Ripley, Eng, Dec 27, 37; m 62; c 2. SOLID STATE PHYSICS, CHEMICAL PHYSICS. *Educ:* Univ London, BS, 59, PhD(solid state chem), 62. *Prof Exp:* Scientist, Rias Div, Martin Co, 62-67, sr scientist, 67-69, head chem physics dept, 69-74, assoc dir, 71-74; head energy technol ctr, Martin Marietta Labs & corp dir energy affairs, 74-77, tech dir, Martin Marietta Cement, 77-78, V PRES TECH SERV, MARTIN MARIETTA CEMENT, 78- *Mem:* Am Phys Soc; The Chem Soc. *Res:* Charge transport in alkali halides; physics of explosives and oxidizers; energy conservation as related to industry. *Mailing Add:* Martin Marietta Corp 6801 Rockledge Dr Bethesda MD 20034

MAYCOCK, PAUL DEAN, b Sioux City, Iowa, Sept 2, 35; m 59; c 5. SOLID STATE PHYSICS, SCIENCE ADMINISTRATION. *Educ:* Iowa State Univ, BS, 57, MS, 62. *Prof Exp:* Res asst physics, Ames Lab, AEC, 60-62; mem tech staff, Tex Instruments Inc, 62-67, mgr new prod develop, 67-69, mgr bus develop, 69-71, sr bus analyst mat & elec prod group, 71-75; br chief econ anal, Solar Energy, Energy Res & Develop Admin, 75-76, dir solar energy planning, 76-77; asst dir, 77-80, PRES, PHOTOVOLTAIC ENERGY SYSTS, DEPT ENERGY, 80- *Mem:* Am Phys Soc; Inst Elec & Electronics Engrs. *Res:* Thermal properties of solids; energy economics. *Mailing Add:* 2401 Childs Lane Alexandria VA 22308

MAYCOCK, PAUL FREDERICK, b Hamilton, Ont, Aug 13, 30; m 53; c 3. PLANT ECOLOGY. *Educ:* Queen's Univ, Ont, BA, 54; Univ Wis, MSc, 55, PhD(bot), 57. *Prof Exp:* Demonstr bot & zool, Queen's Univ, Ont, 52-54; lectr bot, McGill Univ, 57-58, from asst prof to assoc prof, 58-69; PROF BOT, ERINDALE COL, UNIV TORONTO, 69- *Concurrent Pos:* Mem staff, Polish Acad Sci, Cracow, 64-65; mem grant selection comt pop biol, Nat Res Coun, Can, 73-75; assoc ed ecology, Can J Bot, 80- *Mem:* Arctic Inst NAm; Ecol Soc Am; Can Bot Asn. *Res:* Phytosociology; boreal forests of North America and world; vegetation of central Canada; synecology and autecology of forest species; nature reserves and conservation research. *Mailing Add:* Ecol Lab Erindale Col Univ Toronto 3359 Mississauga Rd Clarkson ON M5S 1A1 Can

MAYDAN, DAN, b Tel Aviv, Israel, Dec 20, 35; m 60; c 3. APPLIED PHYSICS, ELECTROOPTICS. *Educ:* Israel Inst Technol, BSc, 57, MSc, 62; Univ Edinburgh, PhD(physics), 65. *Prof Exp:* Supvr instrumentation, Soreq Res Estab, Israel AEC, 57-62, group leader devices, 65-67; mem tech staff, Bell Labs, 67-71, supvr optical scanning & modulation, 71-72, supvr new exposure syst group, 72-80; MEM STAFF, APPL MAT INC, 80- *Mem:* Inst Elec & Electronics Engrs. *Res:* X-ray lithography; acoustooptical devices; high resolution laser recording; display devices. *Mailing Add:* Appl Mat Inc 3001 Oakmead Village Dr Santa Clara CA 95051

MAYDEW, RANDALL C, b Lebanon, Kans, Jan 29, 24; c 3. AERODYNAMICS. *Educ:* Univ Colo, BS, 48, MS, 49. *Prof Exp:* Asst aerodyn, Eng Exp Sta, Univ Colo, 48-49; aeronaut res scientist, Ames Aeronaut Lab, Nat Adv Comt Aeronaut, 49-52; mem staff, Sandia Corp, 52-57, supvr, Exp Aerodyn Div, 57-64, MGR AERODYN DEPT, SANDIA NAT LABS, 64- *Mem:* Assoc fel Am Inst Aeronaut & Astronaut; Sigma Xi; Supersonic Tunnel Asn (pres, 69-70). *Res:* Transonic, supersonic and hypersonic experimental aerodynamics; wind tunnel design and operation; boundary layer phenomena; heat transfer; ballistics; re-entry phenomena; decelerators; darrieus wind turbines. *Mailing Add:* Dept 5630 Sandia Nat Labs Albuquerque NM 87110

MAYEDA, KAZUTOSHI, b Santa Monica, Calif, June 17, 28; m 49; c 3. GENETICS. *Educ:* Univ Utah, BS, 57, MS, 58, PhD(genetics), 61. *Prof Exp:* From asst prof to assoc prof, 61-73, PROF BIOL, WAYNE STATE UNIV, 73-, GENETIC COUNR, DEPT GYNEC & OBSTET, SCH MED, 77- *Concurrent Pos:* Res assoc, Nat Inst Genetics Japan, Mishima, Shizuoka-Ken, 70-71. *Mem:* AAAS; Am Soc Human Genetics; Am Genetics Soc; Am Genetic Asn; Sigma Xi. *Res:* Immunogenetics of Drosophila and human; linkages of human genes and DNA analyses; genetics of human serum proteins; biochemical studies of amniotic fluids and cells. *Mailing Add:* Dept of Biol Wayne State Univ Detroit MI 48202

MAYEDA, WATARU, b Shizuoka, Japan, June 21, 28; m 57; c 2. ELECTRICAL ENGINEERING. *Educ:* Utah State Univ, BS, 54; Univ Utah, MS, 55; Univ Ill, PhD(elec eng), 58; Tokyo Inst Technol, PhD(eng), 65. *Prof Exp:* Asst prof elec eng, Univ Ill, 58-59; staff engr, IBM Res Ctr, 59-60; assoc prof elec eng, 60-65, PROF ELEC ENG, UNIV ILL, URBANA, 65- *Mem:* Inst Elec & Electronics Engrs; Inst Elec Commun Eng Japan. *Res:* Linear graph theory especially application of linear graphs to engineering problems such as electrical networks, communication nets, switching networks. *Mailing Add:* Coord Sci Lab Univ of Ill Urbana IL 61801

MAYER, BROMLEY MORGAN, b Los Angeles, Calif, Sept 28, 18; c 3. MICROBIOLOGY. *Educ:* Univ Southern Calif, BA, 40, MS, 42. *Prof Exp:* Microbiologist, 46-67, DIR RES, KNUDSEN CORP, 67- *Mem:* Inst Food Technol; Am Soc Microbiol; Am Dairy Sci Asn. *Res:* Fermented dairy products; whey utilization; yeast fermentation. *Mailing Add:* Knudsen Corp PO Box 2335 Terminal Annex Los Angeles CA 90054

MAYER, CORNELL HENRY, b Ossian, Iowa, Dec 10, 21; m 46; c 2. ASTRONOMY. *Educ:* Univ Iowa, BS, 43; Univ Md, MS, 51. *Prof Exp:* Electronic engr, 43-49, physicist, 49-68, head radio astron, 68-80, CONSULT, NAVAL RES LAB, 80- *Concurrent Pos:* Mem vis comt, Nat Radio Astron Observ, 69-72; mem nat adv comt, Owens Valley Radio Observ, Calif Inst Technol, 70-75; mem, Arecibo Adv Bd, Nat Astron & Ionosphere Ctr, 75-78. *Mem:* Int Astron Union; Am Astron Soc; Royal Astron Soc; Int Sci Radio Union; Inst Elec & Electronic Engrs. *Res:* Physical studies of space molecule regions and of the planets and satellites. *Mailing Add:* Space Sci Div Naval Res Lab Washington DC 20375

MAYER, DAVID JONATHAN, b Mt Vernon, NY, July 18, 42; m 72. NEUROPHYSIOLOGY. *Educ:* City Univ New York, BA, 66; Univ Calif, Los Angeles, PhD(psychol), 71. *Prof Exp:* Asst prof, 72-75, assoc prof physiol, 75-78, PROF PHYSIOL, MED COL VA, 78- *Concurrent Pos:* NIH fel, Brain Res Inst, Univ Calif, Los Angeles, 71-72. *Mem:* Soc Neurosci; Am Physiol Soc; Int Asn Study Pain. *Res:* Neurophysiology of pain and pain inhibitory systems; neuropharmacology of narcotic analgesics. *Mailing Add:* Dept of Physiol Med Col of Va Richmond VA 23298

MAYER, ERNEST, JR, chemical engineering, see previous edition

MAYER, EUGENE STEPHEN, b Norwalk, Conn, June 5, 38; m 63; c 1. MEDICAL EDUCATION. *Educ:* Tufts Univ, BS, 60; Columbia Univ, MD, 64; Yale Univ, MPH, 71. *Prof Exp:* Physician, USPHS & US Peace Corps, Ankara, Turkey, 65-67 & Washington, DC, 67-68; dep dir & assoc prof family med & internal med, 71-78, DIR & PROF FAMILY MED & INTERNAL MED, AREA HEALTH EDUC CTR PROG, SCH MED, UNIV NC, CHAPEL HILL, 78-, ASSOC DEAN SCH MED, 78- *Concurrent Pos:* Consult, Bur Health Manpower, 74- *Mem:* Asn Am Med Cols; Asn Teachers Prev Med; AMA. *Res:* Distribution of health manpower and the effect of medical education on this distribution. *Mailing Add:* 618 Wells Ct Chapel Hill NC 27514

MAYER, FLORENCE E, b Karuizawa, Japan, Sept 26, 23; US citizen. MEDICINE, PEDIATRICS. *Educ:* NCent Col, BA, 45; Northwestern Univ, Chicago, MD, 50. *Prof Exp:* Rotating intern, Cincinnati Gen Hosp, 50-51; resident pediat, Cincinnati Children's Hosp, 51-53; resident, Children's Med Ctr, Boston, 53-54; instr pediat, Med Ctr, NY Univ, 59-60, asst clin prof, 60-61; med officer, Nat Inst Child Health & Human Develop, 63-72; SR STAFF SCIENTIST, NAT HEART, LUNG & BLOOD INST, NIH, 72- *Concurrent Pos:* Fel cardiol, Children's Med Ctr, Boston, 53-54; NIH res fel, Hosp Sick Children, London, 57-58; Med Res Fund Australia res fel, Royal Alexandra Hosp Children, Sydney, 61-62. *Mem:* AAAS; Am Heart Asn; Am Acad Pediat. *Res:* Physiology of growth and development. *Mailing Add:* Nat Heart Lung & Blood Inst Bethesda MD 20014

MAYER, FOSTER LEE, JR, b Fletcher, Okla, Nov 17, 42; m 62; c 2. TOXICOLOGY, AQUATIC ECOLOGY. *Educ:* Southwestern State Col, BS, 65; Utah State Univ, MS, 67, PhD(toxicol), 70. *Prof Exp:* Leader res sect, US Fish & Wildlife Serv, 70-74, chief biologist, Fish-Pesticide Res Lab, 74-81; RES SCIENTIST, COLUMBIA NAT FISH RES LAB, 81- *Concurrent Pos:* Res assoc sch forestry, fisheries & wildlife, Univ Mo-Columbia, 71- *Mem:* Soc Environ Toxicol & Chem; Am Chem Soc; Am Fisheries Soc; Am Soc Testing & Mat; Soc Toxicol. *Res:* Toxicology of chemical contaminants in aquatic organisms, including biochemical and physiological aspects; formulation of mathematical models appropriate for prediction of contaminant effects in natural aquatic ecosystems. *Mailing Add:* Columbia Nat Fisheries Res Lab Rte 1 Columbia MO 65201

MAYER, FRANCIS X(AVIER), b Muskogee, Okla, Mar 20, 30; m 54; c 5. CHEMICAL ENGINEERING, CHEMISTRY. *Educ:* Univ Tulsa, BCh, 52. *Prof Exp:* Asst lab instr chem, Univ Tulsa, 50-52; chem engr res & develop, 52-55, 57-60, sr engr, 60-64, eng assoc, 64-66, sect head eng design & math sect, 66-67, asst dir design & math sect & desulfurization, 67-71, mgr lab serv, 71-73, res coordr, 73-78, ENGR ADV, EXXON RES & DEVELOP LABS, 78- *Mem:* Am Chem Soc; Am Inst Chem Engrs. *Res:* Fluid hydroforming; petrochemicals; instrumentation and automation; fluid iron ore reduction; hydroconversion; hydrotreating; hydrodesulfurization; magnetically stabilized beds; hydroconversion. *Mailing Add:* Exxon Res & Develop Labs PO Box 2226 Baton Rouge LA 70821

MAYER, FREDERICK JOSEPH, b Lock Haven, Pa, May 24, 40; m 65; c 2. PHYSICS. *Educ:* Pa State Univ, BS, 62; Case Inst Technol, MS, 65; Case Western Reserve Univ, PhD(physics), 68. *Prof Exp:* Sr res assoc plasma physics, Case Western Reserve Univ, 69-71; res scientist laser fusion, 71-75, sr scientist, 75-76, MGR LASER FUSION, KMS FUSION, INC, 76-, DIR, FUSION EXP DIV, 78-, SCIENTIST-AT-LARGE, 80- *Concurrent Pos:* Adj res scientist, Dept Nuclear Eng, Univ Mich, 78- *Mem:* AAAS; fel Am Phys Soc; Sigma Xi. *Res:* Experimental and theoretical laser plasma physics; thermonuclear fusion physics; plasma diagnostic techniques and instrumentation; similarity hydrodynamics; research and development funding and science policy. *Mailing Add:* 1417 Dickens Dr Ann Arbor MI 48103

MAYER, GARRY FRANKLIN, b New York, NY, Oct 11, 45; m 71; c 2. POLLUTION ECOLOGY. *Educ:* Queens Col, BA, 66; Harvard Univ, MA, 70, PhD(biol), 72. *Prof Exp:* Res asst biol, Queens Col, 65-66; res asst, Woods Hole Oceanog Inst, 67; teaching asst, Harvard Univ, 68-70; asst prof biol & natural sci, Boston Univ, 72-74; res assoc marine sci, Univ SFla, 74-76; ecologist & oceanographer marine ecosyst anal, New York Bight Proj, 76-80,

SR ECOLOGIST, OFFICE MARINE POLLUTION ASSESSMENT, NAT OCEANOG & ATMOSPHERIC ADMIN, 80- *Concurrent Pos:* NSF fel biol, Harvard Univ, 66-71, res assoc icthyol, Mus Comparative Zool, 73-75; adj prof, Marine Sci Res Ctr, State Univ NY, Stony Brook, 79- *Mem:* Am Soc Limnol & Oceanog; Am Soc Icthyologists & Herpetologists; AAAS; Sigma Xi. *Res:* Effects of pollution on estuarine, coastal ecosystems for applications problems in environmental management; develop marine educational materials; investigate ecology, evolution, and systematics of marine fishes. *Mailing Add:* Off Marine Pollution Assessment Nat Atmospheric & Oceanic Admin State Univ Stony Brook NY 11794

MAYER, GEORGE, b Gyor, Hungary, Feb 10, 34; US citizen; m 61; c 1. MATERIALS SCIENCE, METALLURGICAL ENGINEERING. *Educ:* Boston Univ, BS, 57; Univ Okla, MMetE, 63; Mass Inst Technol, PhD(metall), 67. *Prof Exp:* Develop engr, Missile Div, Chrysler Corp, Mich, 57-58; sr res metallurgist, Ilikon Corp, Mass, 61-63; res asst metall, Mass Inst Technol, 63-67; sr res metallurgist, New Enterprise Div, Monsanto Co, 66-68; chief, Phys Mech Br, 68-72, assoc dir, 72-74, DIR, METALL-MAT SCI DIV, US ARMY RES OFF, 74- *Concurrent Pos:* Adj assoc prof, NC State Univ, 69-75, adj prof, 75-; adj assoc prof, Duke Univ, 74-75; mem, Joint US/USSR Comn Electrometall & Mat, 78- *Mem:* Am Soc Metals; Am Inst Mining, Metall & Petrol Engrs; fel Am Inst Chemists. *Res:* Mechanical behavior of materials; environment-sensitive properties; crystal growth, characterization and plasticity; corrosion of metals; nondestructive testing; materials processing; deformation processing; deformation and fracture of polymers. *Mailing Add:* Army Res Off PO Box 12211 Research Triangle Park NC 27709

MAYER, GERALD DOUGLAS, b Crowley, La, Jan 2, 33; m 79; c 4. MICROBIOLOGY. *Educ:* Southwestern La Univ, BS, 58, MS, 60; Iowa State Univ, PhD(bact), 64. *Prof Exp:* Res assoc virol, Charles Pfizer & Co, 64-66; sect head, Dept Infectious Dis, 66-74, DEPT HEAD CHEMOTHERAPEUT, MERRELL RES CTR, MERRELL-DOW PHARMACEUTICALS INC, 74- *Mem:* Am Soc Microbiol; Soc Exp Biol & Med; NY Acad Sci. *Res:* Interferon and interferon inducers; antimicrobial chemotherapy; virology. *Mailing Add:* Dept of Infectious Dis 2110 E Galbraith Rd Cincinnati OH 45215

MAYER, HARRIS LOUIS, b New York, NY, Feb 15, 21; m 46; c 3. THEORETICAL PHYSICS. *Educ:* NY Univ, BA, 40; Columbia Univ, MS, 41; Univ Chicago, PhD(physics), 47. *Prof Exp:* With Div War Res, Columbia Univ, 41-46; group leader theoret physics, Los Alamos Sci Lab, 47-56; dept head, Aeronutronic Systs, Inc, 56-58; vpres, E H Plesset Assoc, Inc, 58-64; spec asst to vpres res, Inst Defense Anal, 64-68; group dir survivability, 68-71, MEM TECHNOL PLANNING STAFF, AEROSPACE CORP, 71- *Concurrent Pos:* Consult, Avco Mfg Co, 55; consult, Los Alamos Sci Lab, 56-; mem nuclear panel, Sci Adv Bd, US Air Force, 58-62 & Lawrence Radiation Lab, Livermore, 60; mem weapons effects bd, Defense Atomic Support Agency, 60; dir nuclear technol seminar study, Advan Res Projs Agency, 68; mem space task group, Aerospace Corp, 69; study utilization space transp syst, NASA, 71. *Mem:* Fel Am Phys Soc. *Res:* Atomic physics; strategic support systems and space systems; energy management and reactor waste disposal; historical projections to year 2000; future space applications; large space structures; manned space operations; macro-engineering principles; meta-program engineering; space power systems. *Mailing Add:* Aerospace Corp PO Box 92957 Los Angeles CA 90009

MAYER, J(OHN) K(ING), b Amite, La, Dec 2, 07; m 39. CIVIL ENGINEERING. *Educ:* Tulane Univ, BE, 30, ME, 37. *Prof Exp:* Lab asst, Tulane Univ, 29-30; jr engr, Standard Oil Co, NJ, 30-31; engr, Smith & Kanzler, Inc, 31; instr exp eng, 32-38, head dept, 38-40, from asst prof to prof, 38-49, prof mech eng, 49-60, prof civil eng, 60-73, EMER PROF CIVIL ENG, TULANE UNIV, 73- *Concurrent Pos:* Consult engr, 44- *Mem:* Am Soc Mech Engrs; Am Soc Eng Educ. *Res:* Soil mechanics and testing; engineering materials; material testing; experimental stress analysis. *Mailing Add:* 2419 Audubon St New Orleans LA 70125

MAYER, JAMES W(ALTER), b Chicago, Ill, Apr 24, 30; m 52; c 5. PHYSICS, ELECTRICAL ENGINEERING. *Educ:* Purdue Univ, BS, 52, PhD(physics), 60. *Prof Exp:* Mem tech staff, Hughes Res Labs, 59-62, sect head solid state studies, 62-67; assoc prof elec eng, Calif Inst Technol, 67-71, prof, 71-80; BARD PROF MAT SCI, CORNELL UNIV, 80- *Honors & Awards:* Von Hippel Award, Mat Res Soc, 81. *Mem:* Fel Am Phys Soc; fel Inst Elec & Electronics Engrs; Bonmische Phys Soc. *Res:* Characteristics of semiconductor junction nuclear particle detectors; diffusion and ion drift processes in semiconductors; transport phenomena and ion implantation in semiconductors; channeling of million electron volts particles. *Mailing Add:* Dept Mat Sci Bard Hall Cornell Univ Ithaca NY 14853

MAYER, JEAN, b Paris, France, Feb 19, 20; nat US; m 42; c 5. PHYSIOLOGY, NUTRITION. *Educ:* Univ Paris, BLitt, 37, MSc, 39 & 40; Yale Univ, PhD(physiol chem), 48; Sorbonne, DSc(physiol), 50. *Hon Degrees:* Various from several US & foreign Col & Univ, 65-81. *Prof Exp:* Demonstr physiol chem, Yale Univ, 46-48; mem nutrit div, Food & Agr Orgn, UN, 48-49; res assoc pharmacol, George Washington Univ, 49; from asst prof to assoc prof, 50-65, prof nutrit, Harvard Univ, 65-76, lectr hist pub health, 68-76; PRES, TUFTS UNIV, 76- *Concurrent Pos:* Consult, Spec Div, UN, 48; tech secy, Int Comt Calorie Requirements, Food & Agr Off & WHO, 50 & 57, tech secy, Comt Protein Requirements, 57; assoc ed, Nutrit Revs, 51-54; consult, Children's Hosp, Boston, 57-, Ghana Govt, 58 & Ivory Coast Govt, 59; Severinghouse lectr, Med Sch, Univ Ga, 58; nutrit ed, Postgrad Med, 59-; Phi Beta Kappa scholar, 68-69; mem, Ctr Pop Studies, 68-, Consumer Adv Coun, US Dept Energy, 79-, Adv Comt, Oceans & Int Environ Sci Affairs, US State Dept, 79-; spec consult to the President, 69-70; chmn, White House Conf Food, Nutrit & Health, 69; mem, President's Consumer Adv Coun, 70-77; chmn nutrit div, White House Conf on Aging, 71; W O Atwater Mem lectr, Agr Res Serv, USDA, 71; mem, Protein Adv Group, UN, 73-75; gen coordr, US Sen Nat Nutrit Policy Study, 74; vchmn, President's Comn World Hunger, 78- *Honors & Awards:* Silver Medal, Int Physiol Cong, 56; Alvarenga Prize, Col Physicians Philadelphia, 68; Conrad A Elvehjem Award, Am Inst Nutrit, 78; Atwater Medal, 71; Presidential Honor Citation, Am Asn Health, Phys Educ & Recreation, 72; Bradford Washburn Award, Boston Mus Sci, 75; Sarah L Poiley Mem Award, NY Acad Sci, 75; Bolton L Corson Medal, Franklin Inst, 78; Lemuel Shattuck Award, Mass Pub Health Asn, 80- *Mem:* AAAS; Am Physiol Soc; Am Inst Nutrit; Am Fedn Clin Res; fel Am Acad Arts & Sci. *Res:* Regulation of food and water intake; obesity; general nutrition. *Mailing Add:* Ballou Hall Tufts Univ Medford MA 02155

MAYER, JEROME F, b Milwaukee, Wis, Jan 20, 47; m 78; c 1. PETROLEUM REFINING, HYDROPROCESSING. *Educ:* Univ Wis, BS, 70; Mass Inst Technol, MS, 71, PhD(chem eng), 74. *Prof Exp:* SR RES ENG, CHEVRON RES CO, STANDARD OIL CO CALIF, 74- *Mem:* Am Inst Chem Engrs; Am Chem Soc; Sigma Xi. *Res:* Petroleum refining catalysts and processes, particularly in the area of hydroprocessing. *Mailing Add:* Chevron Res Co PO Box 1627 Richmond CA 94802

MAYER, JOERG WERNER PETER, b Munich, Ger, Aug 4, 29; nat US; m 55, 65; c 5. MATHEMATICS. *Educ:* Univ Giessen, dipl, 53, Dr rer nat, 54. *Prof Exp:* Lectr math, Univ Malaya, 54-57; from asst prof to assoc prof, Univ NMex, 57-68; chmn dept, George Mason Col, 68-70; dir, Comput Ctr, 74-76, CHMN DEPT MATH, LEBANON VALLEY COL, 70- *Mem:* Oper Soc Am; Asn Comput Mach; Am Math Soc; Math Asn Am. *Res:* Philosophy of technology. *Mailing Add:* Dept Math Lebanon Valley Col Annville PA 17003

MAYER, JOHN P(ROSPER), b Binghamton, NY, May 10, 22; m 49; c 3. ASTRODYNAMICS. *Educ:* Univ Mich, BS, 44. *Prof Exp:* Aeronaut res scientist, Aeronaut Lab, Nat Adv Comt Aeronaut, Langley AFB, Va, 44-47 & High Speed Flight Sta, Edwards AFB, Calif, 47-50, aeronaut res engr, Langley AFB, Va, 50-58, space task group, NASA, 58-59, head mission anal br, Hampton, 59-62, asst chief mission planning & flight opers, Manned Spacecraft Ctr, Tex, 62-63, chief mission planning & anal div, 63-74, ASST DIR DATA SYSTS, JOHNSON SPACE CTR, HOUSTON, 74- *Mem:* Assoc fel Am Inst Aeronaut & Astronaut; AAAS. *Mailing Add:* 1018 Willovale Seabrook TX 77586

MAYER, JOSEPH EDWARD, b New York, NY, Feb 5, 04; m 30; c 2. CHEMICAL PHYSICS. *Educ:* Calif Inst Technol, BS, 24; Univ Calif, PhD(phys chem), 27. *Hon Degrees:* ScD, Free Univ Brussels, 62. *Prof Exp:* Asst, Univ Calif, 27-28; Int fel, Univ Gottingen, 29-30; assoc chem, Johns Hopkins Univ, 30-37, assoc prof, 37-39; assoc prof, Columbia Univ, 39-45; prof, Univ Chicago, 45-56, Eisendrath prof, 56-60; prof, 60-72, chmn dept, 63-66, EMER PROF CHEM, UNIV CALIF, SAN DIEGO, 72- *Concurrent Pos:* Gibbs lectr, Am Math Soc, 55; Kennedy lectr, Washington Univ, 67. Consult & mem adv comt, Ballistics Res Lab, 42-60, mem adv comt, 73-; consult, Los Alamos Sci Lab, 46-49, US Air Force & Midway Lab, Korea, 51 & Rand Corp, 63- Chmn div phys chem, Nat Res Coun, 51-56; pres comn thermodyn & statist mech, Int Union Pure & Appl Physics, 52-56; vpres tables of constants, Int Union Pure & Appl Chem, 55-; mem sci comn, Solvay Int Inst, 60- *Honors & Awards:* G N Lewis Medal, Am Chem Soc, 58, Peter Debye Award, 67; Chandler Medal, Columbia Univ, 66; J G Kirkwood Medal, Yale Univ, 67; James Flack Norris Award, 69. *Mem:* Nat Acad Sci (pres, Class I, 65); Am Chem Soc; fel Am Phys Soc (vpres, 72, pres, 74); Am Acad Arts & Sci; Philos Soc. *Res:* Statistical and quantum mechanics. *Mailing Add:* 2345 via Siena La Jolla CA 92037

MAYER, JULIAN RICHARD, b New York, NY, Feb 12, 29; m 49; c 4. ENVIRONMENTAL MANAGEMENT, ENVIRONMENTAL CHEMISTRY. *Educ:* Union Univ, NY, BS, 50; Columbia Univ, MA, 51; Yale Univ, PhD(chem), 55. *Prof Exp:* Res assoc, Sterling-Winthrop Res Inst, Sterling Drug Co, 54-60, assoc mem, 60-61, group leader, 61-62; asst prog dir, NSF, 62-63; asst dir, Atmospheric Sci Res Ctr, State Univ NY, 63-64; staff assoc, NSF, 64-70; dir environ resources ctr, State Univ NY Col Fredonia, 70-78; DEAN, HUXLEY COL ENVIRON STUDIES, WESTERN WASH UNIV, BELLINGHAM, 78- *Concurrent Pos:* Spec consult, NSF, 63; consult, Environ Protection Agency, 72-73 & Union Carbide Corp, 75-78. *Mem:* AAAS; Am Chem Soc. *Res:* Science administration; science policy planning; environmental problems; water quality research and management; chemical and physical limnology; water chemistry. *Mailing Add:* Huxley Col of Environ Studies Western Wash Univ Bellingham WA 98225

MAYER, KLAUS, b May 21, 24; US citizen; m 50; c 2. INTERNAL MEDICINE, HEMATOLOGY. *Educ:* Queens Col, BS, 45; Univ Zurich & Groningen, MD, 50; Am Bd Internal Med, cert, 64. *Prof Exp:* Intern, Hosp St Raphael, New Haven, Conn, 50-51; staff mem, Dept Med, Brookhaven Nat Lab, 51-52; resident, Mem Hosp Cancer & Allied Dis, 52-55; res assoc cancer anemia, Sloan-Kettering Inst, 58-59, asst, 59-60; from instr to clin assoc prof, 58-80, PROF CLIN MED, MED COL, CORNELL UNIV, 80-; ASSOC, SLOAN-KETTERING INST, 60- *Concurrent Pos:* Spec fel med, Mem Hosp, 55-56; Damon Runyon fel, Sloan-Kettering Inst, 55-58; clin asst med, Mem Hosp Cancer & Allied Dis, 56-60, from asst attend physician to assoc attend physician, 60-72, attend physician, 72-, dir, Blood Bank & Serol Lab, 66-, dir, Hemat Lab, 71-, assoc chmn, Dept Med Clin Labs, 81; attend hematologist, Hosp Spec Surg, 57-, res hematologist, 58-62, dir blood bank, 58-, assoc scientist, 62-63, sr scientist, 63-; physician to outpatients, New York Hosp, 58-68, assoc attend physician, 68-; from asst vis physician to assoc vis physician, James Ewing Hosp, 59-68; asst vis physician, Bellevue Hosp, 62-68; res collabr, Brookhaven Nat Lab, 65-66; pres, Am Asn Blood Bank, 73-74; prin, ad hoc comt to form Am Blood Comn, 74-75, secy-treas, 75- *Mem:* Am Soc Nuclear Med; Am Soc Hematol; Harvey Soc; fel Am Col Physicians; Int Soc Hemat. *Res:* Application of radioisotopic technique to hematology and transfusion therapy; quantitation of reticuloendothelial function. *Mailing Add:* Mem Sloan-Kettering Cancer Ctr Box 45 1275 York Ave New York NY 10021

MAYER, LAWRENCE MICHAEL, b Laredo, Tex, July 26, 49; m 73. GEOCHEMISTRY, CHEMICAL OCEANOGRAPHY. *Educ:* Case Western Reserve Univ, BS, 71; Dartmouth Col, AM, 74, PhD(geol), 76. *Prof Exp:* ASST PROF OCEANOG, UNIV MAINE, ORONO, 76- *Mem:* Clay Minerals Soc; Am Soc Limnol & Oceanog; Am Geophys Union. *Res:* Biogeochemical cycling of nutrients, organic compounds, and trace metals; mineral-water interactions. *Mailing Add:* Prog Oceanog Univ Maine Orono Walpole ME 04573

MAYER, MANFRED MARTIN, b Frankfurt, Ger, June 15, 16; US citizen; m 42; c 4. IMMUNOLOGY, BIOCHEMISTRY. *Educ:* City Col New York, BS, 38; Columbia Univ, PhD(biochem), 46. *Hon Degrees:* MD, Univ Mainz, 69. *Prof Exp:* From asst prof to assoc prof bacteriol, Sch Hyg & Pub Health, 46-59, assoc prof microbiol, Sch Med, 59-60, PROF MICROBIOL, SCH MED, JOHNS HOPKINS UNIV, 60- *Concurrent Pos:* Consult, USPHS, NSF, Off Naval Res & Plum Island Animal Dis Lab, USDA; assoc ed, Biol Abstracts, J Immunol & Anal Biochem; adv ed, Immunochem. *Honors & Awards:* Kimble Award Methodology, 53; Selman Waksman Lectr Award, 57; Karl Landsteiner Award, Am Asn Blood Banks, 74. *Mem:* Fel AAAS; Am Soc Biol Chem (pres, 76-77); Am Asn Immunol; Soc Exp Biol & Med; Biochem Soc. *Res:* Complement, an immunopathologic mediator system; properdin system; lymphokines. *Mailing Add:* Dept of Microbiol Johns Hopkins Univ Sch of Med Baltimore MD 21205

MAYER, MARION SIDNEY, b New Orleans, La, July 25, 35. ENTOMOLOGY, BIOCHEMISTRY. *Educ:* La State Univ, BS, 57; Tex A&M Univ, MS, 61, PhD(entom), 63. *Prof Exp:* RES ENTOMOLOGIST, AGR RES SERV, USDA, 63- *Mem:* AAAS. *Res:* Insect attractants, isolation and behavioral characteristics leading to host or mate location; electrophysiological studies to demonstrate details of nervous activity leading to host or mate locations and thresholds. *Mailing Add:* USDA Agr Res Serv PO Box 14565 Gainesville FL 32604

MAYER, MEINHARD EDWIN, b Seletin, USSR, Mar 18, 29; m 54; c 2. MATHEMATICAL PHYSICS. *Educ:* Bucharest Polytech Inst, Dipl Ing, 51; Parhon Univ, PhD, 57. *Prof Exp:* From instr to assoc prof math physics, Parhon Univ, 49-61; sr res worker theoret physics, Joint Inst Nuclear Res, USSR, 57-58; vis prof theoret physics, Univ Vienna, 61-62 & Imp Col, Univ London, 62; vis physicist, Europ Orgn Nuclear Res, Switz, 62; vis assoc prof physics, Brandeis Univ, 62-64; assoc prof theoret physics, Ind Univ, 64-66; PROF MATH & PHYSICS, UNIV CALIF, IRVINE, 66- *Concurrent Pos:* Asst prof, Bucharest Polytech Inst, 50-52; sr res worker, Inst Atomic Physics, Acad Rumania, 51-58; vis assoc physicist, Brookhaven Nat Lab, NY, 63-; vis prof, Inst Advan Sci Studies, Bures-sur-Yvette, France, 70-71 & 78, Tel-Aviv Univ, 71 & Swiss Fed Inst Technol, 77-78. *Mem:* Am Math Soc; fel Am Phys Soc. *Res:* Quantum field theory and statistical mechanics; differential-geometric approach to gauge theory; relativistic statistical mechanics. *Mailing Add:* Dept of Physics Univ of Calif Irvine CA 92717

MAYER, PAUL G(USTAV) WILHELM, b Frankfurt, Ger, Nov 3, 23; nat US; m 55; c 4. CIVIL ENGINEERING. *Educ:* Univ Cincinnati, CE, 53; Cornell Univ, MS, 55, PhD(hydraul), 57. *Prof Exp:* Asst prof hydraul, Cornell Univ, 57-59; from assoc prof to prof hydraul, 59-74, REGENTS' PROF, GA INST TECHNOL, 74- *Concurrent Pos:* Vis prof, Univ Wales, 64-65. *Mem:* Nat Soc Prof Engrs; Am Soc Civil Engrs; Am Soc Eng Educ; Int Asn Hydraul Res. *Res:* Steady and unsteady phenomena in open channel flow; turbulence energy and momentum relationships in incompressible, free surface flows; hydraulic model studies; mathematical modeling. *Mailing Add:* Sch of Civil Eng Ga Inst of Technol Atlanta GA 30332

MAYER, RAMONA ANN, b Algona, Iowa, May 9, 29. CHEMISTRY. *Educ:* Iowa State Univ, BA, 56. *Prof Exp:* Info specialist, 56-59, res scientist, 59-77, QUAL ASSURANCE UNIT DIR DEPT BIOL, ECOL, MED SCI, BATTELLE-COLUMBUS LABS, 77- *Concurrent Pos:* Abstractor, Chem Abstr Serv, 58- *Mem:* AAAS; Am Chem Soc; Am Inst Chemists; Nat Soc Med Res; Am Soc Qual Contol. *Res:* Director of quality assurance on programs dealing with toxicology, biochemistry, immunology, teratology, chemotherapy, animal behavior, ecology. *Mailing Add:* Battelle-Columbus Labs 505 King Ave Columbus OH 43201

MAYER, RICHARD F, b Olean, NY, June 2, 29; m 59; c 5. NEUROLOGY. *Educ:* St Bonaventure Col, BS, 50; Univ Buffalo, MD, 54. *Prof Exp:* Intern med, Boston City Hosp, 54-55; resident neurol, Mass Gen Hosp, 56-57, resident neuropath, 58; res asst, Inst Neurol, Univ London, 57-58; instr neurol, Harvard Med Sch, 61-65, assoc, 65-66; assoc prof, 66-68, PROF NEUROL, SCH MED, UNIV MD, BALTIMORE, 68-, DIR NEUROMUSCULAR CLIN & EMG LAB, UNIV HOSP, 69- *Concurrent Pos:* Fel neurol, Mayo Found, Univ Minn, 55-56; NIH res fel, Harvard Med Sch, 60-61; NIH res grant, Boston City Hosp, 60-64; Nat Multiple Sclerosis Soc res grant, 66-67. *Mem:* AAAS; Am Neurol Asn; Am Electroencephalog Soc; Am Acad Neurol; Soc Neurosci. *Res:* Clinical neurophysiology; clinical and experimental animal studies of motor dysfunction; nerve and reflex activity in man; myasthenia gravis-neuromuscular transmission and ultra structure. *Mailing Add:* Dept of Neurol Univ of Md Med Sch Baltimore MD 21201

MAYER, RICHARD THOMAS, b Pensacola, Fla, May 11, 45; m 66; c 2. TOXICOLOGY. *Educ:* Univ Ga, BS, 67, PhD(entom), 70. *Prof Exp:* Fel entom, Univ Ga, 70-71; res entomologist, 71-77, RES LEADER PHYSIOL & BIOCHEM, LIVESTOCK INSECTS RES UNIT, VET TOXICOL ENTOM RES LAB, SCI & EDUC ADMIN, AGR RES, USDA, 77- *Concurrent Pos:* Alexander von Humboldt Award, 81. *Mem:* Sigma Xi; Am Registry Prof Entomologists; Am Chem Soc; Am Entom Soc. *Res:* Insecticide and hormone metabolism by insects; isolation and characterization of insect metabolic systems; enzyme assay development. *Mailing Add:* Vet Toxicol & Entom Res Lab USDA Sci & Educ Admin-Agr Res PO Drawer GE College Station TX 77840

MAYER, STANLEY WALLACE, b New York, NY, Mar 29, 16; m 45; c 2. PHYSICAL CHEMISTRY, BATTERY ELECTEOCHEMISTRY. *Educ:* City Col New York, BS, 38; Univ Calif, Los Angeles, PhD(chem), 53. *Prof Exp:* Res scientist, NY Water Dept, 39-41 & US War Dept, 41-43; sr sci staff, Columbia Univ, 43-46, Oak Ridge Nat Lab, 46-48, US Naval Radio Lab, 48-53, US Radioisotope Res Univ, 53-56 & NAm Aviation Inc, 56-61; SR SCIENTIST, PHYS CHEM DEPT, CHEM & PHYSICS LAB, AEROSPACE CORP, 61-; CONSULT BATTERIES CO & ENERGY ASN, 77- *Mem:* Am Chem Soc; Am Nuclear Soc; Am Inst Aeronaut & Astronaut; Am Phys Soc; Combustion Inst. *Res:* High temperature reactions and propulsion; nuclear power; properties of propellants; electrochemistry; biomedical physics; research with electronic computers; lasers. *Mailing Add:* 2235 Malcolm Ave Los Angeles CA 90064

MAYER, STEVEN EDWARD, b Frankfurt am Main, Ger, Feb 11, 29; nat US; m 51; c 2. PHARMACOLOGY, BIOCHEMISTRY. *Educ:* Univ Chicago, BA, 47, BS, 49; Univ Ill, MS, 52, PhD(pharmacol), 54. *Prof Exp:* Sr asst scientist, Lab Chem Pharmacol, Nat Heart Inst, 54-56; from asst prof to prof pharmacol, Emory Univ, 57-69; PROF PHARMACOL & CHIEF DIV, UNIV CALIF, SAN DIEGO, 69- *Concurrent Pos:* Fel pharmacol, Wash Univ, 56-57; asst ed, J Am Soc Pharmacol & Exp Therapeut, 61-64; vis scholar, Univ Wash, 65; mem pharmacol study sect, NIH, 65-69, mem neurosci res training B comt; ed, Molecular Pharmacol, 71-74; chmn, Gordon Res Conf Heart Muscle, 72; mem res comt, Am Heart Asn, 73-; mem, USUSSR Working Group Myocardial Metab, 73-78; A J Carlson Lectr, Univ Chicago, 75; fel, Coun Circulation, Am Heart Asn, 79. *Honors & Awards:* John J Abel Award, Am Soc Pharmacol & Exp Therapeut, 63. *Mem:* AAAS; Am Soc Pharmacol & Exp Therapeut (pres, 77-78); Am Physiol Soc; Am Soc Biol Chemists; Fedn Am Scientists. *Res:* Drug and hormone action on metabolic control mechanisms. *Mailing Add:* Div Pharmacol Univ Calif San Diego La Jolla CA 92093

MAYER, THEODORE JACK, b Bridgewater, SDak, Feb 13, 33; m 59; c 4. PETROLEUM CHEMISTRY. *Educ:* Univ SDak, BA, 55; Pa State Univ, MS, 61; Carnegie Inst Technol, PhD(phys chem), 63; Widener Col, MBA, 77. *Prof Exp:* Res asst petrol chem, Petrol Ref Lab, Pa State Univ, 55-59; res chemist, Res & Develop Div, Sun Oil Co, 63-65, group leader anal, 65-75, supvr, Indus Hyg Lab, 75-78, supvr gasoline prod develop, Suntech, Inc, Sun Oil Co, 78-80, asst prod mgr white oils, 80-81, MGR SPEC OIL TECHNOL, SUNTECH, INC, SUN CO, INC, 81- *Mem:* Am Chem Soc; Am Soc Testing & Mat; Am Soc Heating, Refrigerating & Airconditioning Engrs. *Res:* Composition of petroleum; analysis of petroleum fractions by instrumental methods; laboratory automation; industrial hygiene analytical methods; gasoline additives; gasoline product quality; technology of white oils; technology of refrigeration, electrical and insulating oils. *Mailing Add:* 410 Bickmore Dr Wallingford PA 19086

MAYER, THOMAS C, b Pittsburgh, Pa, Nov 30, 31; m 58. DEVELOPMENTAL BIOLOGY. *Educ:* Univ Tenn, AB, 53; Johns Hopkins Univ, MA, 57; La State Univ, PhD(embryol), 62. *Prof Exp:* Asst prof biol, Greensboro Col, 57-60; from asst prof to assoc prof, 62-67, PROF BIOL, RIDER COL, 67- *Concurrent Pos:* NSF res grants, 63-72. *Mem:* AAAS; Soc Develop Biol; Am Soc Zool. *Res:* Embryogenesis of spotting patterns in mice. *Mailing Add:* Dept of Biol Rider Col Trenton NJ 08602

MAYER, VERNON WILLIAM, JR, b Newark, NJ, Mar 29, 39; c 2. MICROBIOLOGY, GENETICS. *Educ:* Univ Md, BS, 63, MS, 65, PhD(microbiol), 67. *Prof Exp:* Nat Res Coun-Nat Acad Sci res assoc, 67-68, RES MICROBIOLOGIST, FOOD & DRUG ADMIN, 68- *Mem:* AAAS; Am Soc Microbiol; Environ Mutagen Soc; Genetics Soc Am. *Res:* Yeast genetics; chemical mutagenesis. *Mailing Add:* HFF 170 Genetic Toxicol Br Div Toxicol Food & Drug Admin Washington DC 20204

MAYER, VICTOR JAMES, b Mayville, Wis, Mar 25, 33; m 65; c 2. EARTH SCIENCES, SCIENCE EDUCATION. *Educ:* Univ Wis, BS, 56; Univ Colo, MS, 60, PhD(sci educ), 66. *Prof Exp:* Pub sch teacher, Colo, 60-62; asst prof earth sci, State Univ NY Col Oneonta, 65-67; from asst prof to assoc prof, 67-75, PROF GEOL & SCI EDUC, OHIO STATE UNIV, 75- *Concurrent Pos:* Consult, NY State Dept Educ, 66-67, Pedag Inst Caracas, 71 & UNESCO, 75- *Mem:* Fel AAAS; Nat Sci Teachers Asn; Am Educ Res Asn; Nat Asn Res Sci Teaching; Nat Asn Geol Teachers. *Res:* Research designs; curriculum evaluation. *Mailing Add:* 111 W Dominion Columbus OH 43214

MAYER, WALTER GEORG, b Silberbach, Czech, Mar 13, 27; nat US; m 59. PHYSICS. *Educ:* Hope Col, AB, 53; Mich State Univ, MS, 55, PhD(physics), 58. *Prof Exp:* Physicist high temperature res, Siemens Res Lab, Ger, 58-59; res asst prof ultrasonics, Dept Physics & Astron, Mich State Univ, 59-65; from asst prof to assoc prof, 65-72, PROF PHYSICS, GEORGETOWN UNIV, 72- *Concurrent Pos:* Assoc ed, Inst Elec & Electronics Engrs Trans Sonics & Ultrasonics, 72- & J Acoust Soc Am, 74- *Honors & Awards:* Humboldt Prize, 80. *Mem:* Fel Brit Acoust Soc; fel Acoust Soc India; fel Acoust Soc Am. *Res:* Ultrasonics, particularly measurements of wave characteristics by optical methods; application of ultrasonics to solid and liquid state; surface and interfacial waves; nonlinear acoustics. *Mailing Add:* Dept of Physics Georgetown Univ Washington DC 20057

MAYER, WARREN CLIFFORD, food science, engineering, see previous edition

MAYER, WILLIAM DIXON, b Beaver Falls, Pa, Oct 5, 28. MEDICINE. *Educ:* Colagte Univ, AB, 51; Univ Rochester, MD, 57. *Prof Exp:* Intern path, Sch Med, Univ Rochester, 57-58, resident, 58-59, instr, 58-61; from asst prof to assoc prof path, 61-67, from asst dean to assoc dean, Sch Med, 61-67, dean, Sch Med & dir Med Ctr, 67-74, prof path, Univ Mo-Columbia, 67-76, dir Health Serv Res Ctr, 75-76; asst chief med dir acad affairs, Vet Admin Cent Off, 76-79; PRES, EASTERN VA MED AUTHORITY, 79- *Concurrent Pos:* Boswell fel, Univ Rochester, 59-61; Markle scholar, 62-67; assoc dir div regional med progs, NIH, 66-67. *Mem:* AAAS; Am Soc Exp Path; Col Am Path; Asn Am Med Cols; AMA. *Mailing Add:* Eastern Va Med Authority PO Box 1980 Norfolk VA 23501

MAYER, WILLIAM JOHN, b Detroit, Mich, Mar 29, 21; m 51; c 6. PHYSICAL CHEMISTRY. *Educ:* Wayne State Univ, BS, 44, PhD(chem), 50. *Prof Exp:* Anal control chemist, Gelatin Prod Corp, 44-45; lab asst phys chem, Wayne State Univ, 48-50; res chemist, Argonne Nat Lab, 50-56; STAFF RES SCIENTIST, RES LABS, GEN MOTORS CORP, 56- *Honors & Awards:* Arch T Colwell Award, Soc Automotive Engrs, 67. *Mem:* Am Chem Soc; Soc Automotive Engrs; Combustion Inst. *Res:* Radiochemistry and isotopes; chemistry of surfaces; combustion chemistry; radiometric methods applied to automotive engines. *Mailing Add:* Chem Dept Res Labs Gen Motors Tech Ctr Warren MI 48090

MAYER, WILLIAM JOSEPH, b Springfield, Ohio, Sept 30, 39; m 71. INFORMATION SCIENCE. *Educ:* Xavier Univ, Ohio, BS, 61; Univ Mich, MS, 63, PhD(pharmaceut chem), 65. *Prof Exp:* Patent chemist, Res Labs, Parke Davis & Co, 65-71; res info assoc, Olin Corp, 71-74; mgr, Tech Info Serv, James Ford Bell Tech Ctr, Gen Mills, Inc, 74-81; PRES, B-K ASSOCS, 81- *Concurrent Pos:* Consult, Inst Food Technologists & Info Connection. *Mem:* Inst Food Technologists; Am Chem Soc. *Res:* Synthesis of organic medicinals; patent development; computerized information search services; technology assessment; technical writing and editing; food technology futures; records and file management systems; identification of emerging scientific specialties and technologies. *Mailing Add:* 2024 Crosby Rd Wayzata MN 55391

MAYER, WILLIAM VERNON, b Vancouver, BC, Mar 25, 20; nat US; m 41; c 2. ZOOLOGY. *Educ:* Univ Calif, AB, 41; Stanford Univ, PhD(biol), 49. *Prof Exp:* Res observer, Francis Simes Hastings Natural Hist Reserve, 41; asst zool, anat & physiol, Mont State Col, 41-42; asst comp anat, Stanford Univ, 46-48, instr, 48; from instr to assoc prof anat & zool, Univ Southern Calif, 48-57, actg head dept biol, 56-57; prof biol & chmn dept, Wayne State Univ, 57-67, actg assoc dean col liberal arts, 60-61, assoc dean, 62-65; PROF BIOL, UNIV COLO, BOULDER, 67- *Concurrent Pos:* Writer biol sci curric study, Am Inst Biol Sci, 60-, assoc dir, 63-64, dir, 65, chmn test construct comt, 60-66; mem bd dirs, Kresge Libr Assocs; mem res adv coun & res adv comt, Mich Cancer Found; assoc mem region 8 selection comt, Woodrow Wilson Fel Found, 61-63; assoc dir biol sci curric study, Univ Colo, Boulder, 63-65, dir, 65-; consult, Nat Sci Develop Bd Philippines, 64 & DC Heath & Co; mem exec comt, Mich Comn Col Accreditation, 64-65; mem coun, Assoc Midwestern Univs, 65-; pres, Educ Progs Improv Corp, 70; mem panel eval & testing, Comn Undergrad Educ Biol Sci, NSF, chmn tundra biome adv panel, 71; mem, Educ Adv Bd, Decision Making Coun, Nat Media Mat Ctr for Severley Handicapped Persons, Comn Biol Educ, Int Union Biol Sci. *Mem:* Fel AAAS; Am Soc Mammal; Am Soc Zool; Soc Syst Zool; hon mem Nat Asn Biol Teachers (pres elect, 65, pres, 66-67). *Res:* Comparative vertebrate anatomy; mammalian ecology; arctic biology; hibernation; temperature phenomena; evolutionary biology. *Mailing Add:* Biol Sci Curric Study 833 W South Boulder Rd Louisville CO 80027

MAYERI, EARL MELCHIOR, b Berkeley, Calif, Dec 10, 40; m 68; c 1. NEUROBIOLOGY. *Educ:* Univ Calif, Berkeley, BA, 63, PhD(biophys), 69. *Prof Exp:* ASST PROF PHYSIOL, UNIV CALIF, SAN FRANCISCO, 71- *Concurrent Pos:* USPHS fel neurophysiol, Med Sch, NY Univ, 59-71; fel, Pub Health Res Inst, New York, 69-71. *Mem:* AAAS; Am Physiol Soc; Soc Neurosci. *Res:* Invertebrate neurobiology and behavior. *Mailing Add:* Dept of Physiol Univ of Calif San Francisco CA 94143

MAYERLE, JAMES JOSEPH, b Grand Rapids, Minn, Dec 16, 45; m 75; c 2. SOLID STATE CHEMISTRY, INORGANIC CHEMISTRY. *Educ:* St John's Univ, Minn, BA, 67; Columbia Univ, PhD(inorg chem), 72. *Prof Exp:* Res assoc inorg chem, Mass Inst Technol, 72-74; MEM RES STAFF CHEM, IBM RES LAB, 74- *Mem:* AAAS; Am Chem Soc; Am Crystallog Asn. *Res:* Organic and inorganic solid state chemistry. *Mailing Add:* Dept K32 IBM Res Lab San Jose CA 95193

MAYERNIK, JOHN JOSEPH, b Manville, NJ, July 6, 16; m 46; c 1. MICROBIOLOGY. *Educ:* Rutgers Univ, BSc, 39, PhD(soil chem), 44; Univ Vt, MS, 41. *Prof Exp:* Chief microbiol & sterile prod control lab, 46-75, MGR MICROBIOL SERV, MERCK & CO, INC, 75- *Concurrent Pos:* Mem, US Pharmacopoeia Adv Panel on Biol Indicators. *Mem:* Am Soc Microbiol; Am Chem Soc; fel Asn Off Anal Chemists. *Res:* Microbiological assays of antibiotics, vitamins and amino acids; quality control of pharmaceutical products; evaluation of methods of sterilization and product sterility; evaluation of preservatives and disinfectants; bacterial monitoring of electron irradiation. *Mailing Add:* 42 Jefferson Ave New Brunswick NJ 08901

MAYERS, GEORGE LOUIS, b New York, NY, Feb 22, 38; m 66; c 2. BIO-ORGANIC CHEMISTRY, IMMUNOCHEMISTRY. *Educ:* City Col New York, BS, 60, MA, 64; City Univ New York, PhD(org chem), 67. *Prof Exp:* Fel peptide chem, St John's Univ, NY, 67-70; CANCER RES SCIENTIST IV, ROSWELL PARK MEM INST, 70- *Concurrent Pos:* Asst res prof, Roswell Park Div, State Univ NY Buffalo, 75-; res prof, Niagara Univ, 77- *Mem:* Am Chem Soc; Royal Soc Chem. *Res:* Structure of the antibody site; auto-idiotype control of the immune response; characterization and function of cell surface receptors; homogeneous antibody responses; tumor immunology. *Mailing Add:* Immunol Res Roswell Park Mem Inst 666 Elm St Buffalo NY 14203

MAYERS, JEAN, b New York, NY, June 8, 20; m 45; c 2. NONLINEAR STRUCTURAL MECHANICS. *Educ:* Polytech Inst Brooklyn, BAeroEng, 42, MAeroEng, 48. *Prof Exp:* Aeronaut res scientist, Nat Adv Comt Aeronaut, 48-56; prin engr, Sperry Utah Co, 56-57, eng sect head, 57-59, eng dept head, 59-61; vis assoc prof aerospace struct, 61-63, assoc prof, 63-67, vchmn dept aeronaut & astronaut, 66-71, PROF AEROSPACE STRUCT, STANFORD UNIV, 67- *Concurrent Pos:* Sci adv, US Army Res Off, 62-74; assoc ed, Am Inst Aeronaut & Astronaut J, 67-70; vis prof, Israel Inst Technol, 70; Naval Air Systs Command res chair, US Naval Acad, 78-79. *Honors & Awards:* Outstanding Civilian Serv Medal, US Army, 72. *Mem:* Assoc fel Am Inst Aeronaut & Astronaut. *Res:* Theoretical aerospace structures; aerospace systems synthesis and analysis; optimum structural design; design criteria for high-strength, high-stiffness, light-weight aerospace structures; conventional, sandwich and composite structures. *Mailing Add:* Dept Aeronaut & Astronaut Stanford Univ Stanford CA 94305

MAYERS, RICHARD RALPH, b West Brownsville, Pa, July 6, 25; m 49; c 2. NUCLEAR PHYSICS. *Educ:* Dartmouth Col, AB, 47; Wesleyan Univ, MA, 57. *Prof Exp:* Instr physics, Hood Col, 47-49; physicist, Nat Bur Standards, 49-50 & Glenn L Martin Co, 55-56; asst prof physics, Colby Col, 56-61, actg chmn dept, 57-59; from assoc prof to prof & chmn dept, Defiance Col, 61-74; RES, SURFACE COMBUSTION CO, 74- *Concurrent Pos:* Vis prof, Univ Surrey, 67-68; vis lectr, Tex A&M Univ, 68. *Mem:* AAAS; Am Phys Soc; Am Phys Soc. *Res:* Neutron activation analysis and gamma ray spectroscopy; industrial combustion systems. *Mailing Add:* 415 Monroe St Delta OH 43515

MAYERSON, HYMEN SAMUEL, b Providence, RI, Sept 10, 00; m 30; c 2. PHYSIOLOGY. *Educ:* Brown Univ, AB, 22; Yale Univ, PhD(physiol), 25. *Hon Degrees:* DSc, Brown Univ, 62. *Prof Exp:* Asst biol, Brown Univ, 21-22; asst physiol, Yale Univ, 22-25, instr, Sch Med, 25-26; from instr to prof & chmn dept, 26-65, EMER PROF PHYSIOL, SCH MED, TULANE UNIV, 65- *Concurrent Pos:* Consult, Touro Infirmary, 59-65, assoc dir prof serv & educ, 65-75; consult, Vet Hosp, 53-65; mem comt shock, Nat Res Coun, 54-61, rep biol & agr rev comt, Int Exchange Persons, 55-57; mem, Nat Bd Med Examrs, 56-60, chmn physiol test comt, 58-60; mem US nat comt, Int Union Physiol Sci, 61-65; fel panel, NSF Grad Fel Prog, Nat Acad Sci, 63-65; pres, Fedn Am Socs Exp Biol, 63. *Mem:* Am Physiol Soc (pres, 62); Soc Exp Biol & Med; Am Heart Asn; hon mem Int Soc Lymphology. *Res:* Cardiovascular effects of posture; blood volume changes in health and disease; capillary permeability to large molecules; lymph and lymphatics. *Mailing Add:* 1140 Seventh St New Orleans LA 70115

MAYES, BILLY WOODS, II, b Port Arthur, Tex, Feb 6, 41; m 60; c 1. PHYSICS. *Educ:* Univ Houston, BS, 63, MS, 65; Mass Inst Technol, PhD(physics), 69. *Prof Exp:* Fel, 68-69, asst prof, 69-73, ASSOC PROF PHYSICS, UNIV HOUSTON, 73- *Mem:* Am Phys Soc. *Res:* Experimental pion nucleus cross sections. *Mailing Add:* 15514 Baybrook Dr Houston TX 77062

MAYES, JAMES H(UGH), b Lauann, Ark, Sept 19, 24; m 45; c 2. CHEMICAL ENGINEERING. *Educ:* Tex Col Arts & Indust, BS(chem eng) & BS(chem), 49; Johns Hopkins Univ, MS, 51, DEng(chem eng), 52. *Prof Exp:* Chem engr, Sinclair Res Labs, Inc, 53-55 & Crown Cent Petrol Co, 55-57; tech supt, Foster Grant Co, 57-64; tech dir, First Miss Corp, 64-67, vpres & dir, First Chem, 67; CHEM CONSULT, 67- *Res:* Adsorption; process design. *Mailing Add:* 10275 Kenlee St Baton Rouge LA 70815

MAYES, JARY S, b Walters, Okla, Oct 19, 38; m 58; c 3. BIOCHEMISTRY, HUMAN GENETICS. *Educ:* Okla State Univ, BS, 60; Mich State Univ, PhD(biochem), 65. *Prof Exp:* Asst prof biochem, 67-70, ASST PROF RES PEDIAT & ASSOC PROF BIOCHEM, HEALTH SCI CTR, UNIV OKLA, 70- *Concurrent Pos:* Fel, State Univ NY Buffalo, 65-67. *Mem:* AAAS; Am Chem Soc; Am Soc Human Genetics. *Res:* Inborn errors of metabolism; galactose metabolism; regulation of enzyme activity. *Mailing Add:* Dept of Biochem Univ Okla Health Sci Ctr Oklahoma City OK 73190

MAYES, MCKINLEY, b Oxford, NC, Oct 7, 30; m 59; c 1. AGRONOMY. *Educ:* NC Agr & Tech Col, BS, 53, MS, 56; Rutgers Univ, PhD(agron), 59. *Prof Exp:* Prof agron, Southern Univ, Baton Rouge, 59-67, dean & coordr CRS res progs, 74-76; COORDR SPEC PROGS, SCI & EDUC ADMIN-COOP RES, USDA, 76- *Mem:* Am Soc Agron; Soil Conserv Soc Am. *Res:* Plant breeding, especially field corn and sweet corn improvement. *Mailing Add:* 9012 Lake Braddock Dr Burke VA 22015

MAYES, PAUL E(UGENE), b Frederick, Okla, Dec 21, 28; m 50; c 6. ELECTRICAL ENGINEERING. *Educ:* Univ Okla, BS, 50; Northwestern Univ, MS, 52, PhD(elec eng), 55. *Prof Exp:* Res assoc, Northwestern Univ, 50-54; res asst prof elec eng, 54-58, assoc prof, 58-63, PROF ELEC ENG, UNIV ILL, 63- *Concurrent Pos:* Consult, Mark Prod Co, Ill, JFD Electronics Corp, 62-, TRW Inc, Calif & Avanti Res & Develop, Ill; mem comn six, Int Union Radio Sci. *Mem:* Fel Inst Elec & Electronics Engrs. *Res:* Electromagnetic theory; antennas, particularly extremely broadband and superdirective types. *Mailing Add:* Col Eng Univ Ill 1406 W Green St Urbana IL 61801

MAYES, RICHARD ALAN, systematic botany, see previous edition

MAYES, TERRILL W, b Evansville, Ind, Sept 4, 41; m 59; c 3. PLASMA PHYSICS, ATOMIC SPECTROSCOPY. *Educ:* Western Ky Univ, BS, 63; Vanderbilt Univ, MA, 65, PhD(physics), 67. *Prof Exp:* Asst prof, 67-74, ASSOC PROF PHYSICS, UNIV NC, CHARLOTTE, 74- *Mem:* Am Phys Soc; Am Asn Physics Teachers. *Res:* Radiation and atomic physics; electricity and magnetism; classical mechanics; optics. *Mailing Add:* Dept of Physics Univ of NC Charlotte NC 28223

MAYEUX, JERRY VINCENT, b Mamou, La, Apr 22, 37; m 81; c 2. MICROBIOLOGY, PLANT GROWTH REGULATORS. *Educ:* La State Univ, Baton Rouge, BS, 60, MS, 61; Ore State Univ, PhD(microbiol), 64. *Prof Exp:* Nat Acad Sci-Nat Res Coun res assoc exobiol, NASA Ames Res Ctr, 65-66; asst prof microbiol, Colo State Univ, 66-70; sr res scientist, Manned Exp & Life Sci Dept, Martin Marietta Corp, 70-72, chief, Life Sci, 72-74; dir, Res & Develop, Ferma Gro Corp, 74-75; lectr microbiol, Buena Vista Col, Storm Lake, Iowa, 75-76; founder, pres & chmn bd, Dawn Corp, 76-80; FOUNDER & PRES, BURST PROD, INC, 80- *Concurrent Pos:* Asst prof range sci, Colo State Univ, 69-70, affil prof microbiol, 70-76, col eng, 71; consult, NASA Life Sci Shuttle Planning Panel, 74-; consult, Martin Marietta Aerospace, 74-75. *Mem:* Soc Indust Microbiol; AAAS; Am Soc Microbiol; Am Chem Soc; Sigma Xi. *Res:* Microbial ecology; soil and water pollution; microbial/plant interaction; plant growth regulators; aerospace biology; waste reutilization; biological control of plant disease. *Mailing Add:* 4201 W 99th St Overland Park KS 66207

MAYEWSKI, PAUL ANDREW, b Edinburgh, Scotland, July 5, 46; US citizen; m 69. GLACIAL GEOLOGY, GEOMORPHOLOGY. *Educ:* State Univ NY, Buffalo, BA, 68; Ohio State Univ, PhD(geol), 73. *Prof Exp:* Res assoc geol, Inst Polar Studies, Ohio State Univ, 68-73; fel, Inst Quaternary Studies, Univ Maine, Orono, 73-75; ASST PROF GEOL, UNIV NH, 75- *Concurrent Pos:* Mem res team, Climate-Long Range Invest Mapping & Prediction, 73-; panel mem, W Antarctic Ice Sheet Proj, 75- *Honors & Awards:* Antarctic Serv Medal, US Govt, 74. *Mem:* Glaciol Soc. *Res:* Holocene glaciation in the Himalayas; mass balance reconstructions for the Athabasca Glacier, Columbia Icefield, Alberta; reconstruction and synthesis of the late Wisconsin glacial history of North America; former glacier flowline study in the Cocheco River drainage, New Hampshire; study of Antarctic weathering and mass wasting phenomena. *Mailing Add:* Dept of Earth Sci James Hall Univ of NH Durham NH 03824

MAYFIELD, DARWIN LYELL, b Somerset, Ky, Feb 22, 20; m 45; c 2. ORGANIC CHEMISTRY. *Educ:* Bowling Green State Univ, AB & BS, 41; Univ Chicago, MS, 44; Univ Wis, PhD(org chem), 50. *Prof Exp:* Res chemist, Nat Defense Res Comt, 42-43, Off Sci Res & Develop, 43-45 & Rubber Res Bd, 45-47; asst, Univ Wis, 47-50; from asst prof to assoc prof chem, Univ Idaho, 50-56; from asst prof to assoc prof, 56-62, chmn dept, 64-66, dir res, 67-81, PROF CHEM, CALIF STATE UNIV, LONG BEACH, 62- *Concurrent Pos:* Fulbright lectr, Kasetsart Univ, Bangkok, 55-56 & Ain Shams Univ, Cairo, 66-67; NIH res fel, Nat Sci Res Ctr, France, 62-63. *Mem:* AAAS; Am Chem Soc. *Res:* Chemistry of plant hormones responsible for floral initiation; research administration and federal relations. *Mailing Add:* Dept Chem Calif State Univ Long Beach CA 90840

MAYFIELD, EARLE BYRON, b Oklahoma City, Okla, Jan 31, 23; m 52; c 7. SPACE PHYSICS. *Educ:* Univ Calif, Los Angeles, BA, 50; Univ Utah, MA, 54, PhD(physics), 59. *Prof Exp:* Physicist, Res Dept, US Naval Ord Test Sta, Calif, 50-59; mem tech staff, Phys Res Lab, Space Tech Labs, Inc, Thompson-Ramo-Wooldridge, Inc, 59-60; MEM TECH STAFF, AEROSPACE CORP, 60- *Concurrent Pos:* Asst, Univ Utah, 54-55. *Mem:* Am Phys Soc; Am Astron Soc; Int Astron Union. *Res:* Plasma and solar physics. *Mailing Add:* 5536 Michelle Dr Torrance CA 90503

MAYFIELD, HAROLD FORD, b Minneapolis, Minn, Mar 25, 11; m 36; c 4. ORNITHOLOGY. *Educ:* Shurtleff Col, BS, 33; Univ Ill, MA, 34. *Hon Degrees:* DSc, Occidental Col, 68 & Bowling Green State Univ, 75. *Prof Exp:* Secy, Wilson Ornith Soc, 48-52, vpres, 53-54 & 58-59, pres, 60-61; secy, Am Ornith Union, 53-58, vpres, 64-66, pres, 66-68; vpres, Cooper Ornith Soc, 73, pres, 74-76. *Concurrent Pos:* Adj prof biol, Univ Toledo, 82. *Honors & Awards:* Brewster Mem Award for work on birds of Western Hemisphere, Am Ornithologists Union, 61. *Mem:* Fel AAAS; Cooper Ornith Soc; Wilson Ornith Soc; fel Am Ornithologists Union. *Res:* Bird reproduction and mortality, social parasitism and ecology. *Mailing Add:* 9235 River Rd Waterville OH 43566

MAYFIELD, JOHN EMORY, b Thomasville, NC, Aug 30, 37; m 60; c 2. MYCOLOGY. *Educ:* Livingstone Col, BS, 59; State Univ NY Buffalo, MA, 71, PhD(biol), 72. *Prof Exp:* Teacher sci, Southside Sch, 59-63; teacher driver educ, Rowan Co Schs, 63-64; teacher sci, J F Kennedy Jr High Sch, 64-67; res botanist mycol, Agr Res Serv, USDA, 72-73; asst prof biol, Ala State Univ, 73-76; ASSOC PROF BIOL, ATLANTA UNIV, 76- *Mem:* NY Acad Sci; Mycol Soc Am; Am Phytopath Soc; Electron Micros Soc Am. *Res:* Fungal development and differentiation at the ultrastructural level. *Mailing Add:* Dept of Biol Atlanta Univ Atlanta GA 30314

MAYFIELD, LEWIS G, b Forsyth, Mont, Oct 23, 22; m 47; c 2. CHEMICAL ENGINEERING. *Educ:* Mont State Col, BS, 44, MS, 50. *Prof Exp:* Jr engr, Enzymes, Inc, 46-48; chem engr oil shale & petrol exp, US Bur Mines, 49-51; from asst prof to assoc prof chem eng, Mont State Col, 51-62; asst prog dir eng, 62-64, prog dir, 64-71, dep dir, Advan Technol Applns Div, 71-75, sr scientist, Resources Div, 75-78, dep dir, Integrated Basic Res Div, 78-81, DEP DIV DIR, CHEM & PROCESS ENG DIV, NAT SCI FOUND, 81- *Concurrent Pos:* Asst prog dir eng, Nat Sci Found, 60-61. *Mem:* Am Inst Chem Engrs; Am Soc Eng Educ; Sigma Xi. *Res:* Catalysis; hydrogenation of shale-oil; reaction kinetics; mass transfer; enzyme technology; mineral benefication. *Mailing Add:* Integrated Basic Res Nat Sci Found Washington DC 20550

MAYFIELD, MELBURN ROSS, b Island, Ky, Aug 24, 21; m 50; c 1. PHYSICS, SCIENCE EDUCATION. *Educ:* Western Ky State Col, AB & BS, 48; Univ Fla, MS, 50. *Prof Exp:* From instr to asst prof physics, Mercer Univ, 50-55, asst prof math & physics, 55-57; assoc prof physics, 57-61, chmn dept, 58-70, dir prog teachers, 68, PROF PHYSICS, AUSTIN PEAY STATE UNIV, 61-, DIR CTR FOR TEACHERS, 70-, VPRES DEVELOP & FIELD SERV, 74- *Concurrent Pos:* Consult under NSF grant, Acad Yr Inst Jr Col Teachers, Univ Fla, 66-67, consult, 67-68; consult, Proj Reachigh, 68, Inst Energy Anal, 79- *Mem:* Fel AAAS; Am Asn Physics Teachers. *Res:* Radioactive fallout measurement and identification; physics education at high school and college level. *Mailing Add:* 113 Morgan Ct Clarksville TN 37040

MAYHALL, JOHN TARKINGTON, b Greencastle, Ind, Apr 7, 37; m 60. DENTAL ANTHROPOLOGY. *Educ:* DePauw Univ, BA, 59; Ind Univ, Indianapolis, DDS, 63; Univ Chicago, MA, 68, PhD, 76. *Prof Exp:* Res assoc, 71-72, res assoc prof anthrop, 71-76, assoc prof, 76-81, asst prof dent anat, 72-76, assoc prof, 76-81, PROF DENT ANAT, FAC DENT & PROF ANTHROP, UNIV TORONTO, 81- *Concurrent Pos:* Res fel dent anthrop, Fac Dent, Univ Toronto, 71-73; abstractor, Oral Res Abstr, 71-78. *Mem:* Can Asn Dent Res; Soc Study Human Biol; Human Biol Coun; Am Asn Phys Anthrop; Fr Soc Anthrop & Dent-Facial Genetics. *Res:* Dental morphology, genetics and craniofacial growth and development of North American Eskimos and Indians; dental anatomy; forensic odontology; osteology. *Mailing Add:* Fac of Dent Univ of Toronto Toronto ON M5G 1G6 Can

MAYHAN, ROBERT J(OSEPH), b Omaha, Nebr, Dec 22, 38. ELECTRICAL ENGINEERING. *Educ:* Purdue Univ, BSEE, 60, MSEE, 62, PhD(elec eng), 66. *Prof Exp:* Instr elec eng, Purdue Univ, 62-65; sr staff scientist, Space Systs Div, Avco Corp, 65-67; asst prof, 67-76, ASSOC PROF ELEC ENG, OHIO STATE UNIV, 76- *Mem:* Inst Elec & Electronics Engrs. *Res:* Electromagnetic scattering from plasma coated obstacles; scattering from turbulent media; electromagnetic wave interaction with plasmas as a diagnostic tool and for reentry vehicle communications; highway research, especially automatic guidance systems and vehicular communications. *Mailing Add:* Dept Elec Eng Ohio State Univ 2015 Neil Ave Columbus OH 43210

MAYHEW, DENNIS ED, plant pathology, plant virology, see previous edition

MAYHEW, ERIC GEORGE, b London, Eng, June 22, 38; m; c 2. CELL BIOLOGY, DRUG CARRIERS. *Educ:* Univ London, BSc, 60, MSc, 63, PhD(zool), 67. *Prof Exp:* Res asst cell biol, Chester Beatty Res Inst, London, Eng, 60-64; cancer res scientist, 64-68, sr cancer res scientist, 68-72, assoc cancer res scientist, 72-79, CANCER RES SCIENTIST V, ROSWELL PARK MEM INST, 79- *Concurrent Pos:* Vis scientist, Int Inst Cellular & Molec Path, Brussels, 77-78; assoc res prof biophysics, State Univ NY, Buffalo, 79- *Mem:* NY Acad Sci; AAAS; Am Asn Cancer Res. *Res:* Role of the cell periphery in cellular interactions; possible differences between normal and cancer cells and possible exploitation in chemotherapy; use of liposomes and other macromolecular structures as drug delivery systems. *Mailing Add:* Dept Exp Path Roswell Park Mem Inst Buffalo NY 14263

MAYHEW, THOMAS R, b Monongahela, Pa, Feb 11, 35; m 55; c 2. ELECTRICAL ENGINEERING, PHYSICS. *Educ:* Univ Fla, BEE, 56; Univ Pa, MSEE, 62. *Prof Exp:* Engr, Radio Corp Am, 56-68, group leader electronics, 68-69, eng leader, Defense Microelectronics Dept, 69-76, mgr monolithic arrays, 76-79, MGR LSI APPLN, SOLID STATE TECH CTR, RCA CORP, 79- *Mem:* Inst Elec & Electronics Engrs. *Res:* Microelectronics; circuits; digital analytical systems. *Mailing Add:* RCA Corp Hwy 202 S Somerville NJ 08876

MAYHEW, WILBUR WALDO, b Yoder, Colo, Mar 17, 20; m 48; c 3. VERTEBRATE BIOLOGY, DESERT ECOLOGY. *Educ:* Univ Calif, AB, 48, MA, 51, PhD(zool), 53. *Prof Exp:* Assoc zool, Univ Calif, Davis, 48-50 & 51-53; jr res biologist, Atomic Energy Proj, Univ Calif, Los Angeles, 53-54; instr biol, 54-56, from asst prof to assoc prof zool, 56-69, PROF ZOOL, UNIV CALIF, RIVERSIDE, 69- *Concurrent Pos:* Fulbright lectr, UAR, 65-66; Am consult, All-Indian Inst Ecol, Saurashtra Univ, India, 70; mem US deleg, Binational Conf Educ & Res Life Sci, India, 71; mem adv comt, Calif Desert Conserv Area, US Bur Land Mgt, 77-81. *Mem:* AAAS; Am Soc Ichthyologists & Herpetologists; Herpetologists' League; Soc Study Amphibians & Reptiles. *Res:* Ecology and physiology of avian and reptilian reproduction; cliff swallow nesting and migration; ecology of deserts. *Mailing Add:* Dept of Biol Univ of Calif Riverside CA 92521

MAYKUT, MADELAINE OLGA, b Toronto, Ont, July 8, 25. CLINICAL PHARMACOLOGY. *Educ:* Univ Toronto, BA, 48, MA, 50, PhD(pharmacol), 57, MD, 64. *Prof Exp:* Asst cancer res, Univ Toronto, 48-49; asst biochemist, Henry Ford Hosp, Detroit, Mich, 50-51; pharmacologist, Univ Toronto, 51-59; sr pharmacologist, Res Ctr, Pitman-Moore Co Div, Dow Chem Co, Ind, 59-60; rotating intern, Univ Toronto, 64-65, Locum asst surg, Shouldice Surg, 65-66; asst dir clin res, Wm S Merrell Co, 66-67; asst dir med res, Bristol Labs, 67-72; adv, Bur Drugs, 72-73, chief biomed res, Nonmed Use Drugs Directorate, 73-78, CHIEF BIOMED RES, BUR TOBACCO CONTROL & BIOMETRICS, HEALTH PROTECTION BR, HEALTH & WELFARE, 78- *Mem:* Pharmacol Soc Can; NY Acad Sci; Drug Info Asn. *Res:* Local anesthetics; biometrics; drug combinations; anti-arrythmics; anti-inflammatory agents; narcotic antagonists; analgesics; anti-anginal agents; anti-hypertensives; drugs of abuse. *Mailing Add:* Rm 141 HPB Bldg Health & Welfare Tunney's Pasture ON K1A 0L2 Can

MAYKUTH, D(ANIEL) J(OHN), b Detroit, Mich, Sept 29, 23; m 50; c 4. METALLURGICAL ENGINEERING. *Educ:* Mich Col Mining, BS, 46; Ohio State Univ, MS, 53. *Prof Exp:* Res engr, Nonferrous Phys Metall Div, Battelle Mem Inst, Columbus, 47-54, asst chief, 54-71, dir, Cobalt Info Ctr, 72-75, prin scientist, Materials Develop Sect, 75-80; MGR, TIN RES INST, COLUMBUS, 80- *Concurrent Pos:* Consult, Mat Adv Bd, Nat Acad Sci, 58-59. *Mem:* Am Soc Metals; Am Inst Mining, Metall & Petrol Engrs. *Res:* Nonferrous physical metallurgy of tungsten, rhenium, chromium, molybdenum, titanium, zirconium, columbium, tantalum, cobalt and their alloys. *Mailing Add:* TIN Res Inst 1353 Perry St Columbus OH 43201

MAYLAND, BERTRAND JESSE, b Racine, Wis, Aug 31, 16; m 40; c 3. CHEMICAL ENGINEERING, CHEMISTRY. *Educ:* Univ Wis, BS, 40; Univ Ill, MS, 42, PhD(chem eng), 43. *Prof Exp:* Asst, Eng Exp Sta, Univ Ill, 40-43; sr chem engr, Phillips Petrol Co, 43-51; sr develop engr, Girdler Construct Div, Chemetron Corp, 51-60, dir res & develop, C & I Girdler Inc, 60-71; vpres, 71-73, PRES & CONSULT, CHENOWETH DEVELOP LABS, 73- *Concurrent Pos:* Sanit engr, City Water Dept, Springfield, Ill, 42; spec lectr, Okla Agr & Mech Col, 47-51; consult, 60- *Mem:* Am Chem Soc; Am Inst Chem Engrs. *Res:* Petroleum and chemical process development and design; physical properties; separations; catalytic engineering and catalysts; synthetic fuels and fertilizers; computer applications and process control; catalytic reactions and purification in pollution abatement. *Mailing Add:* 4901 Chenoweth Run Rd PO Box 99254 Louisville KY 40299

MAYLAND, HENRY FREDERICK, b Greybull, Wyo, Dec 31, 35; m 57; c 2. SOIL SCIENCE. *Educ:* Univ Wyo, BS, 60, MS, 61; Univ Ariz, PhD(agr chem & soils), 65. *Prof Exp:* Soil SCI & EDUC ADMIN-AGR RES, USDA, 73- *Concurrent Pos:* Fed collabr, Utah State Univ, 67-; affil prof, Univ Idaho, 68-; vis fel, Plant, Soil & Nutrit Lab, USDA & Cornell Univ, 73-74. *Mem:* Am Soc Agron; Soil Sci Soc Am; Soc Range Mgt. *Res:* Soil-water-plant-animal relations on rangelands. *Mailing Add:* Sci & Educ Admin-Agr Res USDA Kimberly ID 83341

MAYNARD, CARL WESLEY, JR, b Eveleth, Minn, June 18, 13; m 37. ORGANIC CHEMISTRY. *Educ:* Colo Col, AB, 34; Mass Inst Technol, PhD(org chem), 38. *Prof Exp:* Anal chemist, Dow Chem Co, Mich, 35-36; res chemist, Jackson Lab, E I Du Pont de Nemours & Co, Inc, 38-52, sr supvr intel, 52-77; CONSULT SYNTHETIC DYES, 77- *Concurrent Pos:* Civilian with Manhattan Proj, 42-44. *Mem:* Am Chem Soc; Am Asn Textile Chemists & Colorists. *Res:* Chemistry and toxicology of synthetic dyes; chemical literature. *Mailing Add:* 114 Cambridge Dr Wilmington DE 19803

MAYNARD, CHARLES ALVIN, b Des Moines, Iowa, Mar 25, 51; m 71. NITROGEN FIXATION, TREE IMPROVEMENT. *Educ:* Iowa State Univ, BS, 74, MS, 77, PhD(forest genetics), 80. *Prof Exp:* Extension asst forestry, Forestry Dept, Iowa State Univ, 75-77, res asst forest genetics, 77-80; RES ASSOC FOREST GENETICS, COL ENVIRON SCI, STATE UNIV NY, 80- *Concurrent Pos:* Consult forestry mgt, YMCA Camp, Boone, Iowa, 77; fel, Int Agr Ctr, Wageninger, Neth, 78. *Mem:* Soc Am Foresters. *Res:* Non-legume host and symbiont selection for enhanced nitrogen fixation and improved plant growth; improving site quality through the use of nitrogen fixing species; short rotation silviculture for biomass production. *Mailing Add:* Sch Forestry 216 Marshall Hall State Univ NY Syracuse NY 13210

MAYNARD, CHARLES DOUGLAS, b Atlantic City, NJ, Sept 11, 34; m 58; c 3. NUCLEAR MEDICINE. *Educ:* Wake Forest Univ, BS, 55; Bowman Gray Sch Med, MD, 59. *Prof Exp:* Dir nuclear med, NC Baptist Hosp, Winston-Salem, 66-77, chmn dept radiol, 77; from instr to assoc prof radiol, 66-73, assoc dean admis, 66-71, assoc dean student affairs, 71-75, PROF RADIOL, BOWMAN GRAY SCH MED, WAKE FOREST UNIV, 73- *Concurrent Pos:* Am Cancer Soc fel, 64-66; James Picker Found scholar radiol res, 66-68; consult ed, J Nuclear Med & Technol, 74; consult nuclear med, Am Registry Radiologic Technologists, 74; guest examr, Am Bd Radiol, 75. *Mem:* Soc Nuclear Med (vpres, 76, pres, 78); Asn Univ Radiologists; Radiol Soc NAm; Am Col Nuclear physicians; Am Col Radiol. *Res:* Clinical applications of radionuclides in the diagnoses of disease. *Mailing Add:* Dept of Radiol Bowman Gray Sch of Med Winston-Salem NC 27103

MAYNARD, DONALD EARLE, b Toronto, Ont, Nov 2, 33; US citizen; m 59; c 2. BIOCHEMISTRY, CLINICAL RESEARCH. *Educ:* Univ Buffalo, BA, 55; Univ Ky, MSc, 58; Ohio State Univ, PhD(biochem), 61. *Prof Exp:* Res assoc med, asst prof physiol chem & dir clin endocrinol labs, Med Col, Ohio State Univ, 62-65; sr biochemist, Dept Clin Pharmacol, Hoffmann-La Roche, Inc, 66-67 & Chem Res Dept, 68-71, sr biochemist, Dept Biochem & Drug Metab, 72-78; asst dir, Dept Clin Pharmacol, 78-79, ASST DIR, DEPT CLIN RES, USV LABS, 79-81; ASSOC DIR, CLIN RES, GLAXO, INC, 81- *Mem:* Am Chem Soc; Am Asn Clin Chemists; Endocrine Soc; Am Soc Clin Pharmacol Therapeut; Am Acad Allergy. *Res:* Biochemistry of steroid hormones; metabolism of tetrahydrocannabinols and alkaloids; biopharmaceutics; pharmacokinetics; clinical pharmacology of antiallergics and antidepressants; clinical pharmatopical and systemic steroids. *Mailing Add:* Dept Clin Res Glaxo, Inc Research Triangle Park NC 27709

MAYNARD, DONALD NELSON, plant physiology, see previous edition

MAYNARD, JERRY ALLEN, b Reedsburg, Wis, Apr 22, 37; m 57; c 2. CELL BIOLOGY. *Educ:* Univ Northern Iowa, BA, 58; Ind Univ, MS, 61; Univ Iowa, PhD(phys educ, anat & kinesiology), 70. *Prof Exp:* Fel exercise physiol, Univ Iowa, 68-69, res asst, cytol, Dept Orthop, 69-71, res assoc, 71-72, asst prof anat, 72-76, assoc prof anat, Depts Orthop, Phys Educ & Anat, 76-81, PROF ANAT, DEPTS ORTHOP & PHYS EDUC, UNIV IOWA, 81- *Concurrent Pos:* Fel Dept Orthop Surg, Univ Iowa, 68-71. *Mem:* Am Asn Anat; Anat Soc Gr Brit & Ireland; Orthop Res Soc. *Res:* Ultrastructure, cytochemistry and light microscopy of the musculoskeletal system during growth and development and as it is affected by hyperactivity, inactivity and skeletal growth dysplasias. *Mailing Add:* Dept of Orthop Surg Univ of Iowa Iowa City IA 52242

MAYNARD, JULIAN DECATUR, b Newport News, Va, Nov 18, 45. SOLID STATE PHYSICS. *Educ:* Univ Va, BS, 67; Princeton Univ, MA, 69, PhD(physics), 74. *Prof Exp:* Instr physics, Princeton Univ, 73-74; adj asst prof, Univ Calif, Los Angeles, 74-77; ASST PROF PHYSICS, PA STATE UNIV, 77- *Mem:* Am Phys Soc; Acoustical Soc Am; Sigma Xi. *Res:* Quantum liquids and solids and critical phenomena with extensive application of acoustic techniques. *Mailing Add:* Dept Physics 104 Davey Lab Pa State Univ University Park PA 16802

MAYNARD, NANCY GRAY, marine ecology, pollution biology, see previous edition

MAYNARD, ROBERT G, b Memphis, Tenn, Feb 3, 19; m 49; c 4. GEOLOGY. *Educ:* Univ Calif, Los Angeles, AB, 41, MA, 48. *Prof Exp:* Petrol geologist, Richfield Oil Corp, 45-47; petrol geologist, Sunray Oil Corp, 47-65, mgr hard mineral explor, D-X Sunray Oil Co, 65-68, Alaska area geologist, 68-75, mgr geol & geochem, Suntech Co, 75-77, CONSULT TO MGR EXPLOR URANIUM, SUNEDCO, SUN OIL CO, 77- *Mem:* Fel Geol Soc Am; Am Asn Petrol Geol; Soc Mining Engrs; Am Inst Mining Metall & Petrol Engrs. *Res:* Structural geology; economic mineral deposits; marine geology; remote sensing. *Mailing Add:* 9819 Elmcrest Dallas TX 75238

MAYNARD, RUSSELL MILTON, b Monmouth, Ill, June 6, 16; m 41; c 7. PATHOLOGY. *Educ:* Monmouth Col, BS, 38; Univ Ill, MD, 42; Am Bd Path, dipl, 50. *Prof Exp:* Instr path, Univ Colo, 54-57; asst prof, Sch Med, Marquette Univ, 57-62; pathologist, Vet Admin Hosp, Phoenix, Ariz, 62-64; clin pathologist, Good Samaritan Hosp, 64-67; chief lab serv, Vet Admin Hosp, Vancouver, 67-79; RETIRED. *Concurrent Pos:* Asst chief lab serv, Vet Admin Hosp, Denver, Colo, 54-57 & chief, Wood, Wis, 57-62. *Mem:* Am Soc Clin Path; Col Am Path; Am Col Physicians. *Res:* Anatomic and clinical pathology. *Mailing Add:* 56305 Spruce Rd Otis OR 97368

MAYNARD, THEODORE ROBERTS, b Denver, Colo, Dec 4, 38; m 66; c 2. GEOTECHNICAL ENGINEERING. *Educ:* Colo Sch Mines, BS, 62; Univ Ill, MS, 65. *Prof Exp:* CHIEF SOILS ENGR, DEPT PUBLIC WORKS, BUR ENG, CITY CHICAGO, 65- *Concurrent Pos:* Guest lectr, various univs & socs, 66-; mem, Ill Highway Res Coun, 77- *Mem:* Asn Eng Geologists; Am Soc Engrs; Nat Soc Prof Engrs; Int Soc Soil Mech & Found Engrs; Int Asn Eng Geologists. *Res:* Soil-structure interaction; performance of earth retention systems and deep foundation elements; pavement evaluation and design. *Mailing Add:* 6261 N Oriole Ave Chicago IL 60631

MAYNARD, WILLIAM ROSE, JR, b Portsmouth, Va, May 31, 19; m 42. ANALYTICAL CHEMISTRY, BIOCHEMISTRY. *Educ:* Univ Richmond, BA, 41; Med Col Va, BS, 53. *Prof Exp:* Supvr drug lab, Va Dept Agr, 46-62; anal res chemist, 63-65, sr res chemist, 65-77, GROUP MGR DRUG METAB, A H ROBINS CO, INC, 77- *Concurrent Pos:* Mem revision comt, US Pharmacopoeia, 60-; mem, Va Bd Pharm, 67- *Mem:* Am Pharmaceut Asn; Am Chem Soc; fel Am Inst Chemists. *Res:* Metabolite study of clinical drugs under investigation; instrumentation and development of analytical methods for pharmaceuticals. *Mailing Add:* 7711 Brentford Dr Richmond VA 23225

MAYNE, BERGER C, b Towner, Colo, July 10, 20; m 56; c 2. PLANT PHYSIOLOGY. *Educ:* Western State Col Colo, AB, 46; Univ Utah, PhD(physiol), 58. *Prof Exp:* Res assoc, Univ Minn, 58-62; staff scientist, 62-67, INVESTR, CHARLES F KETTERING RES LAB, 67- *Mem:* Am Soc Plant Physiologists; Biophys Soc. *Res:* Photosynthesis. *Mailing Add:* Charles F Kettering Res Lab 150 E South College St Yellow Springs OH 45387

MAYNE, WILLIAM HARRY, b Austin, Tex, Apr 29, 13; m 39; c 1. GEOPHYSICS. *Educ:* Univ Tex, BS & MS, 35. *Prof Exp:* Asst observer, Petty Geophys Eng Co, 35, observer, 36, observer-field mgr, 36-38, res engr seismic & med instrumentation, Petty Labs, Inc, 39-57, sales coordr, Petty Geophys Eng Co, 58, vpres tech serv, 58-75; corp mgr, 75-78, CONSULT NEW TECHNOL DEVELOP, GEOSOURCE INC, 78- *Concurrent Pos:* Mem adv bd, Exp Comt, Int Oil & Gas Educ Ctr, 69; guest lectr geophysics, Univ Tex, Austin & Univ Houston. *Honors & Awards:* Reginald Fessenden Medal, 65; William Smith Medal, Geol Soc London, 79. *Mem:* Am Geophys Union; Am Asn Petrol Geol; Am Geol Inst; Mex Soc Explor Geophys; hon mem Soc Explor Geophys (1st vpres, 66-67, pres, 68-69, past pres, 69-70). *Res:* Geophysics and geophysical instrumentation; exploration seismology; underwater sound; optimum utilization of seismographic instruments and techniques. *Mailing Add:* PO Box 36306 Houston TX 77036

MAYNERT, EVERETT WILLIAM, b Providence, RI, Mar 18, 20. PHARMACOLOGY, CHEMISTRY. *Educ:* Brown Univ, ScB, 41; Univ Ill, PhD(org chem), 45; Johns Hopkins Univ, MD, 57. *Prof Exp:* Res chemist, Interchem Corp, NY, 45-47; res assoc pharmacol, Columbia Univ, 47-51, assoc, 51-52, asst prof, 52; assoc prof pharmacol & exp therapeut, Johns Hopkins Univ, 52-65; PROF PHARMACOL, COL MED, UNIV ILL MED CTR, 65- *Concurrent Pos:* Am Cyanamid fel, Johns Hopkins Univ, 52-57. *Mem:* Fel AAAS; Am Chem Soc; Harvey Soc; Am Soc Pharmacol. *Res:* Neuropharmacology; drug metabolism; toxicology. *Mailing Add:* Dept Pharmacol Col Med Univ Ill Med Ctr Chicago IL 60680

MAYNES, ALBION DONALD, b Buffalo, NY, Jan 21, 29; Can citizen; m 52; c 2. ANALYTICAL CHEMISTRY. *Educ:* Univ Toronto, BA, 52, MA, 53, PhD(inorg & anal chem), 56. *Prof Exp:* Res assoc, Dept Physics, Univ Toronto, 56-58; anal chemist, Div Geol Sci, Calif Inst Technol, 58-65; asst prof, 65-66, ASSOC PROF CHEM, UNIV WATERLOO, 66- *Concurrent Pos:* Eldorado Mining & Refining Co res grant, 56-58. *Mem:* Chem Inst Can; Meteoritical Soc. *Res:* Trace analysis; analysis of silicate rocks and minerals; analysis of meteorities. *Mailing Add:* Dept of Chem Univ of Waterloo Waterloo ON N2L 3G1 Can

MAYNES, GORDON GEORGE, b Freeport, NY, Nov 4, 46; m 69; c 1. ORGANIC CHEMISTRY, POLYMER CHEMISTRY. *Educ:* St Lawrence Univ, BS, 68; Univ Ill-Champaign, PhD(org chem), 72. *Prof Exp:* Teaching asst chem, Univ Ill, 68-72; res chemist polymer chem, 72-76, sr res chemist, 76-80, SUPVR RES & DEVELOP, E I DU PONT DE NEMOURS & CO INC, 80- *Mem:* Am Chem Soc. *Res:* Physical organic chemistry; free radical mechanisms; small ring compounds; dye chemistry; condensation polymerization; polymer melt spinning. *Mailing Add:* Seaford Nylon Plant E I du Pont de Nemours & Co Inc Seaford DE 19973

MAYO, BARBARA SHULER, b Tallahassee, Fla; Jan 5, 45; m 72; c 1. MARINE BIOLOGY. *Educ:* Mary Baldwin Col, BA, 67; Univ Miami, MS, 70, PhD(marine sci), 74. *Prof Exp:* Teaching asst oceanog, Univ Miami, 70-74; consult biologist, marine biol, Consult Marine Biologists, 74-76; dir, 76-78, INSTR MARINE ECOL, PROVINCETOWN CTR FOR COASTAL STUDIES, 75-, ASSOC SCIENTIST, 76- *Concurrent Pos:* Mem Cape Cod Nat Seashore Adv Comn, 77- *Mem:* Sigma Xi. *Res:* Coastal marine ecology; systematics of decapod crustaceans. *Mailing Add:* Provincetown Ctr for Coastal Studies 59 Commercial St Box 826 Provincetown MA 02657

MAYO, CHARLES ATKINS, III, b Washington, DC, Mar 13, 43; m 72; c 1. MARINE BIOLOGY, MARINE FISHERIES SCIENCE. *Educ:* Dartmouth Col, BA, 65; Univ Miami, MS, 69, PhD(marine biol), 73. *Prof Exp:* Fish biologist, SE Fisheries Ctr, Nat Marine Fish Serv, 72-74; chief biologist, marine ecol, Barceloneta Proj, PRASA, PR, 74-75; CHIEF NATURALIST CETACEAN STUDIES, DOLPHIN III, PROVINCETOWN CTR FOR COASTAL STUDIES, 74-, ASSOC SCIENTIST MARINE BIOL, 76-, DIR, CETACEAN RES PROG, 80- *Res:* Ecology of coastal marine systems and effects of pollutants; pollutants; early life histories of marine fishes and applied rearing studies; field studies of great whales. *Mailing Add:* Ctr for Coastal Studies Box 826 Provincetown MA 02657

MAYO, DANA WALKER, b Bethlehem, Pa, July 20, 28; m 62; c 3. ORGANIC CHEMISTRY. *Educ:* Mass Inst Technol, BS, 52; Ind Univ, PhD(chem), 59. *Prof Exp:* Res chemist, Polychem Dept, Exp Sta, E I du Pont de Nemours & Co, Del, 52; asst, Univ Pa, 52-53 & Ind Univ, 53-55 & 56-57; res assoc, Mass Inst Technol, 59-60, NIH fel, 60-62, fel, Sch Advan Study, 60-62; from asst prof to prof, 62-70, CHARLES WESTON PICKARD PROF CHEM, BOWDOIN COL, 70-, CHMN DEPT, 69- *Concurrent Pos:* Vis lectr, Mass Inst Technol, 62-71; NIH spec fel chem, Univ Md, 67 & 69-70; consult, Perkin-Elmer Corp; vis scientist, Explosives Res & Develop Estab, Waltham-Abbey, UK, 75. *Mem:* Am Chem Soc; Soc Appl Spectros; Coblentz Soc. *Res:* Natural products; applications of infrared spectroscopy to organic chemistry; oil pollution; animal and plant chemical communication substances. *Mailing Add:* Dept Chem Bowdoin Col Brunswick ME 04011

MAYO, FRANK REA, b Chicago, Ill, June 23, 08; m 33; c 2. PHYSICAL ORGANIC CHEMISTRY, POLYMER CHEMISTRY. *Educ:* Univ Chicago, BS, 29, PhD(chem), 31. *Prof Exp:* Lilly fel, Univ Chicago, 31-32; res chemist, E I du Pont de Nemours & Co, 33-35; instr org chem, Univ Chicago, 36-42; res chemist, US Rubber Co, 42-50; res assoc, Res Lab, Gen Elec Co, 50-56; SCI FEL, SRI INT, 56- *Concurrent Pos:* Lectr, Stanford Univ, 57-65. *Honors & Awards:* Award in Polymer Chem, Am Chem Soc, 67. *Mem:* Am Chem Soc; Royal Soc Chem. *Res:* Oxidation of hydrocarbons; aging of polymers; coal chemistry; free radical reactions. *Mailing Add:* 89 Larch Dr Atherton CA 94025

MAYO, JOHN S, b Greenville, NC, Feb 26, 30; m 57; c 4. ELECTRICAL ENGINEERING. *Educ:* NC State Univ, BS, 52, MS, 53, PhD(elec eng), 55. *Prof Exp:* Photoelectric analyzer, NC State Univ, 54-55; mem tech staff comput res, 55-58, supvr, T1 carrier syst, 58-60, head, High-Speed Pulse Code Modulation Terminal Dept, 60-67, dir, Underwater Systs Lab, 67-71, exec dir, Ocean Systs Div, 71-73, exec dir, Toll Electronic Switching Div, 73-75, pres elec technol, 75-79, EXEC VPRES NETWORK SYSTS, BELL LABS, 79- *Concurrent Pos:* Mem prog comt, Int Solid State Circuits Conf, 61-, chmn, 67, gen chmn, 68; mem prog comt, Northeast Electronics Res & Eng Meeting, 65 & 66. *Honors & Awards:* Alexander Graham Bell Award, Inst Elect & Electronics Engrs, 78. *Mem:* Nat Acad Eng; fel Inst Elec & Electronics Engrs. *Res:* Research and development of communications devices, circuitry and systems. *Mailing Add:* Bell Labs Murray Hill NJ 07974

MAYO, JOSEPH WILLIAM, b Greenfield, Mass, Sept 22, 41; m 69; c 2. BIOCHEMISTRY, PEDIATRICS. *Educ:* Univ Mass, Amherst, BS, 63; Mich State Univ, PhD(biochem), 68; Case Western Reserve Univ, MD, 76. *Prof Exp:* Asst prof biochem in pediat, Med Sch, Case Western Reserve Univ, 70-76; intern pediat, Cleveland Metr Gen Hosp & Rainbow Babies & Children's Hosp, 76-77; resident pediat, 77-78, chief resident, 78-79, ASST PROF PEDIAT, DEPT CHILD HEALTH, UNIV MO MED CTR, 79- *Concurrent Pos:* Nat Cystic Fibrosis Res Found fel, Sch Med, Case Western Reserve Univ, 68-70. *Res:* Carbohydrate metabolism; glycoproteins; composition and regulation of human exocrine secretions; primary care pediatrics. *Mailing Add:* Dept of Child Health Univ of Mo Med Ctr Columbia MO 65201

MAYO, RALPH ELLIOTT, b Greenville, NC, May 9, 40; m 64; c 2. PHYSICAL CHEMISTRY. *Educ:* Emory Univ, BS, 63, PhD(phys chem), 66. *Prof Exp:* Sr res chemist, Perkin Elmer Corp, 66-68; supvr method develop lab, 68-78, mgr anal serv, Linwood, 78-81, MGR, RES & DEVELOP SYSTS & PRODUCTIVITY, ALLENTOWN, AIR PROD & CHEM, INC, 81- *Mem:* AAAS; Catalysis Soc; Am Chem Soc; Soc Appl Spectros. *Res:* Nuclear magnetic resonance spectroscopy; analytical instrumentation design; laboratory automation and process control; digital processing of scientific data; analytical methods development; mass spectrometry; spectrophotometric analyses. *Mailing Add:* Air Prod & Chem Inc PO Box 538 Allentown PA 18105

MAYO, SANTOS, b Buenos Aires, Arg, June 10, 28; m 59; c 3. MICROELECTRONICS. *Educ:* La Plata Univ, PhD(physics), 54. *Prof Exp:* Assoc res nuclear spectros, Arg AEC, 53-55, head synchrocyclotron lab, 55-68; mgr res & develop, Fate, 68-71; res mem, Cyclotron Lab, Arg AEC, 71-72; head planning, Arg Inst Indust Technol, 72-73; SOLID STATE PHYSICIST, NAT BUR STANDARDS, 74- *Concurrent Pos:* Instr, La Plata Univ, 50-60, assoc prof, 60-61; guest physicist, Brookhaven Nat Lab, 57; assoc res, Radiation Lab, Univ Pittsburgh, 58-59; head nuclear physics dept, Arg AEC, 62-63; Arg rep, Latin Am Physics Ctr, Brazil, 63-; consult physicist, Nat Res Coun, Arg, 64-; res fel, UN Develop Orgn, Nat Bur Standards, 73-74. *Mem:* Arg Physics Asn (gen secy, 68-70, pres, 70-72). *Res:* Beta and gamma nuclear spectroscopy; low and medium energy nuclear reactions; laser induced resonance ionization spectroscopy; charged particle spectroscopy; accelerator techniques; microelectronic technology; surface probe analysis; physics of microelectronic devices; x-ray topography. *Mailing Add:* Nat Bur of Standards Washington DC 20234

MAYO, THOMAS TABB, IV, b Radford, Va, June 15, 32; m 57; c 3. PHYSICS. *Educ:* Va Mil Inst, BS, 54; Univ Va, MS, 57, PhD(physics), 60. *Prof Exp:* Asst instr physics, Va Mil Inst, 54-55; sr scientist res lab eng sci, Univ Va, 60-61; from asst prof physics to assoc prof physics & math, 62-67, asst acad dean, 71-73, assoc acad dean, 73-75 & 76-77, actg acad dean, 75-76, PROF PHYSICS, HAMPDEN-SYDNEY COL, 67- *Concurrent Pos:* Res assoc quantum theory proj, Univ Fla, 69-70. *Mem:* Am Phys Soc; Am Asn Physics Teachers; Sigma Xi. *Res:* Teaching physical theory and applied mathematics at undergraduate level; classical and quantum mechanics; history of physics; quantum theory of atoms, molecules, and solids. *Mailing Add:* Dept Physics Hampden-Sydney Col Hampden-Sydney VA 23943

MAYO, Z B, b Lubbock, Tex, Mar 29, 43; m 71. ENTOMOLOGY. *Educ:* Tex Tech Univ, BS, 67; Okla State Univ, MS, 69, PhD(entom), 71. *Prof Exp:* Res assoc entom, Okla State Univ, 71-72; asst prof, 72-76, ASSOC PROF ENTOM, UNIV NEBR-LINCOLN, 76- *Mem:* Entom Soc Am; Am Registry Prof Entomologists; Sigma Xi. *Res:* Development of pest management procedures for insect pest associated with corn production. *Mailing Add:* Dept of Entom 202 P I Univ of Nebr Lincoln NE 68583

MAYOL, ROBERT FRANCIS, b Springfield, Ill, Nov 11, 41; m 62; c 4. BIOCHEMISTRY, IMMUNOCHEMISTRY. *Educ:* Southern Ill Univ, Carbondale, BA, 64; St Louis Univ, PhD(biochem), 68. *Prof Exp:* USPHS fel, Calif Inst Technol, 68-70; sr scientist biochem endocrinol, 70-75, sr investr drug metab, 75-78, PRIN RES SCIENTIST, MEAD JOHNSON RES CTR, 78- *Concurrent Pos:* Mem assoc fac, Sch Med, Ind Univ, Evansville Ctr, 71- *Mem:* Sigma Xi; Endocrine Soc; AAAS; Am Soc Pharm & Exp Therapeut. *Res:* Protein chemistry; development of radioimmunoassays; drug metabolism. *Mailing Add:* 1900 Tree Lane Dr Evansville IN 47712

MAYOR, GILBERT HAROLD, b Detroit, Mich, Sept 12, 39; m 68; c 3. NEPHROLOGY, INTERNAL MEDICINE. *Educ:* Wayne State Univ, BS, 61, MD, 65. *Prof Exp:* Intern med, 65-66, asst resident med, Barnes Hosp, 68-69; resident med, 69-70, fel endocrinol & metab, 70-71, fel nephrol, 71-72, instr internal med, 72-73, asst prof internal med, Univ Mich Med Ctr, 73-75; asst prof med & surg, 76-78, ASSOC PROF MED & SURG, MICH STATE UNIV, 78-; VIS RES SCIENTIST GROWTH & DEVELOP, CTR HUMAN GROWTH & DEVELOP, UNIV MICH, 77- *Concurrent Pos:* Med asst, Sch Med, Wash Univ, 65 & 69; consult, Saginaw Gen Hosp, 77-; prin investr, Dept Health Mich, NIH, Kidney Found Mich & Mich State Univ grants. *Honors & Awards:* Physicians Recognition Award, AMA, 71. *Mem:* Am Soc Nephrol; Int Soc Nephrol; Am Fedn Clin Res; fel Am Col Physicians; NY Acad Sci. *Res:* Bone mineral and divalent ion metabolism; effects of hormones on metal metabolism; especially aluminum; hepatitis epidemiology. *Mailing Add:* Dept Med & Surg Mich State Univ East Lansing MI 48824

MAYOR, HEATHER DONALD, b Melbourne, Australia, July 6, 30; m 56; c 2. VIROLOGY, MOLECULAR BIOLOGY. *Educ:* Univ Melbourne, BS, 48, MSc, 50, DSc, 70; Univ London, PhD(biophys), 54. *Prof Exp:* Res officer crystal physics, Defense Res Labs, Melbourne, Australia, 50-51; electron microscopist, Nat Inst Med Res, London, 52-55; res assoc virol, Walter & Eliza Hall Inst Med Res, Melbourne, 55-56; res assoc bacteriol & immunol, Harvard Med Sch, 56-59; from asst prof to assoc prof virol, 60-71, assoc prof microbiol, 71-74, PROF MICROBIOL, BAYLOR COL MED, 74- *Concurrent Pos:* Consult, Res Resources Br, NIH, 70-, AEC, 71- & Univ Tex M D Anderson Hosp & Tumor Inst, Houston, 73- *Honors & Awards:* Award, Ctr Interaction, Man, Sci & Cult, 73. *Mem:* Am Asn Immunol; Am Soc Microbiol; Am Asn Cancer Res; Am Soc Cell Biol (treas); Sigma Xi (secy-treas). *Res:* Molecular biology of the growth and development of animal viruses with particular emphasis on viruses which cause cancer and on extremely small DNA-containing viruses; recombinant DNA technology in viral systems. *Mailing Add:* Dept of Microbiol & Immunol Baylor Col of Med Houston TX 77030

MAYOR, JOHN ROBERTS, b La Harpe, Ill, July 9, 06; m 34; c 2. MATHEMATICS. *Educ:* Knox Col, BS, 28; Univ Ill, AM, 29; Univ Wis, PhD(math), 33. *Hon Degrees:* LLD, Knox Col, 59. *Prof Exp:* Instr math, Univ Wis, 29-31, 32-35 & Milwaukee Exten Div, 35; prof & chmn dept, Southern Ill Univ, 35-47; assoc prof math & educ, Univ Wis, 47-51, prof math & educ & chmn dept educ, 51-54, actg dean sch educ, 54-55; dir educ, Am Asn Advan Sci, 55-74; ASST PROVOST RES, DIV HUMAN & COMMUNITY RESOURCES, UNIV MD, COLLEGE PARK, 74- *Concurrent Pos:* Dir math proj & prof, Univ Md, 57-67; dir study accreditation in teacher educ, Nat Comn Accrediting, 63-65; mem adv comt, Sch Math Study Group; consult, Knox Col. *Mem:* AAAS; Am Math Soc; Math Asn Am; Nat Asn Res Sci Teaching; Conf Bd Math Sci (secy, 60-71, treas, 61-71). *Res:* Mapping rational varieties; multiple correspondences in space and hyperspace. *Mailing Add:* 411 Windsor St Silver Spring MD 20910

MAYOR, ROWLAND HERBERT, b Eng, Nov 5, 20; US citizen; m 48; c 3. RUBBER CHEMISTRY. *Educ:* Univ NH, BS, 42, MS, 44; Univ Conn, PhD(org chem), 49. *Prof Exp:* Instr org chem, Univ RI, 48-51; res chemist, 51-55, res sect head, 55-63, mgr stereorubber res, 64-75, asst mgr synthetic rubber res, 75-76, MGR ELASTOMER RES, GOODYEAR TIRE & RUBBER CO, 76- *Mem:* Am Chem Soc. *Res:* Molcular rearrangements; synthesis of diamines; condensation polymerization; synthetic rubber. *Mailing Add:* Res Div Goodyear Tire & Rubber Co Akron OH 44316

MAYOR, STEPHEN JOSEPH, neurophysiology, see previous edition

MAYPER, V(ICTOR), JR, b New York, NY, June 12, 28; m 58; c 2. PHYSICS, ELECTRONICS. *Educ:* Mass Inst Technol, BS, 47, PhD(physics), 53. *Prof Exp:* Res asst, Mass Inst Technol, 47-53; res engr, Newmont Explor Ltd, 53-55; mem tech staff, Hughes Aircraft Co, 55-64; pres, Mayper Assocs, 64-67; chief engr, Jacobi Systs Corp, 67-70; pres, Mayper Assocs, 70-72; jr staff engr, Compata Inc, 72-77; SR STAFF ENGR, OPERATING SYSTS INC, 77- *Concurrent Pos:* Sr engr, Holmes & Narver, Inc, 50-51. *Mem:* Am Phys Soc; Inst Elec & Electronics Engrs; Asn Comput Mach. *Res:* Electronic systems; computer applications; automation. *Mailing Add:* 4640 St Clair Ave North Hollywood CA 91607

MAYR, ERNST, b Kempten, Ger, July 5, 04; m 35; c 2. EVOLUTIONARY BIOLOGY, HISTORY OF SCIENCE. *Educ:* Univ Berlin, PhD(zool), 26. *Hon Degrees:* DPhil, Univ Uppsala, 57 & Univ Paris, 75; DSc, Yale Univ, 59, Univ Melbourne, 59, Oxford Univ, 66, Univ Munich, 68 & Harvard Univ, 70. *Prof Exp:* Asst cur zool mus, Univ Berlin, 26-32; from assoc cur to cur, Whitney-Rothschild Collection, Am Mus Natural Hist, 32-53; Agassiz prof zool, 53-75, dir mus comp zool, 61-70, EMER PROF ZOOL, HARVARD UNIV, 75- *Concurrent Pos:* Mem exneds, Dutch New Guinea, 28, Mandate Territory, New Guinea, 29 & Solomon Islands, 29-30; Jesup lectr, Columbia Univ, 41; ed, Soc Study Evolution, 47-49; vpres, 11th Int Zool Cong; pres, 13th Int Ornith Cong. *Honors & Awards:* Leidy Medal, 46; Darwin-Wallace Medal, 58; Brewster Medal, 65; Verrill Medal, 66; Daniel Giraud Eliot Medal, 67; Nat Medal of Sci, 70; Gregor Mendel Medal, 80. *Mem:* Nat Acad Sci; Am Soc Naturalists; Am Soc Zool; Soc Syst Zool (pres, 66); Soc Study Evolution (secy, 46, pres, 50). *Res:* Ornithology; evolution; systematics; history and philosophy of biology. *Mailing Add:* Mus of Comp Zool Harvard Univ Cambridge MA 02138

MAYRON, LEWIS WALTER, b Chicago, Ill, Sept 20, 32; m 58; c 2. BIOLOGICAL CHEMISTRY, NUCLEAR MEDICINE. *Educ:* Univ Ill, MS, 56, PhD(biol chem), 59. *Prof Exp:* Chemist, Qm Food & Container Inst, 54; asst biochem, Univ Ill, 54-59; res assoc, Univ Southern Calif, 59-61; asst biochemist, Presby-St Lukes Hosp, 61-62, Tardanbek Labs, 62-63 & Abbott Labs, 63; res assoc, Michael Reese Hosp & Med Ctr, 64-66; consult, 66-68; res chemist, Hines Vet Admin Hosp, 68-80; MEM STAFF, NUCLEAR MED SERV, WADSWORTH MED CTR, 80- *Concurrent Pos:* Guest investr, Argonne Nat Lab, 73- *Honors & Awards:* Laureat, Genia Czerniak Prize Nuclear Med & Radiopharmacol, Ahavot Zion Found of Israel, 74. *Mem:* Soc Exp Biol & Med; Soc Nuclear Med; AAAS; Brit Biochem Soc; Am Asn Clin Chemists. *Res:* Biochemistry of immune mechanisms; nuclear biochemistry for medical diagnosis. *Mailing Add:* Nuclear Med Serv Wadsworth Med Ctr Los Angeles CA 90073

MAYS, LAURA LIVINGSTON, see Hoopes, Laura Livingston Mays

MAYS, CHARLES EDWIN, b Lincoln, Nebr, May 6, 38; m 63; c 2. PHYSIOLOGY, HERPETOLOGY. *Educ:* Univ Nebr, BS, 63, MS, 65; Ariz State Univ, PhD(zool), 68. *Prof Exp:* Asst prof, 68-74, assoc prof, 74-80, PROF ZOOL, DEPAUW UNIV, 80- *Concurrent Pos:* Du Pont & Nat Sci Found grants, 69-70; Ind Acad Sci grants, 69, 71, 74 & 77. *Mem:* AAAS; Herpetologists League; Sigma Xi; Am Soc Ichthyologists & Herpetologists; Soc Study Amphibians & Reptiles. *Res:* Natural history and physiological studies of the hellbender salamander and map turtle; growth studies on fish; effects of cigarette smoke on murine reproduction and development. *Mailing Add:* Dept Zool DePauw Univ Greencastle IN 46135

MAYS, CHARLES WILLIAM, b Corsicana, Tex, March 17, 30; m 51, 72; c 5. RADIATION RISK, CHELATION THERAPY. *Educ:* Univ Utah, BS, 51, PhD(physics), 58. *Prof Exp:* Res assoc, 57-62, asst res prof, 62-66, assoc res prof, 66-75, RES PROF ANAT, UNIV UTAH, 75-, ADJ PROF PHYSICS, 79-, RES PROF PHARMACOL, 79- *Concurrent Pos:* Mem, US Nat Coun Radiation Protection, 66-, Int Com Radiol Protection Comt #2, 72-, Nat Acad Sci Biol Effects Ionizing Radiation Comt, 76-80; chmn, Adv Comt US Transuranium Registry, 78- *Mem:* Health Physics Soc; Radiation Res Soc; AAAS. *Res:* Internally deposited radioactivity; risk from radiation induced cancer; removal of radioactivity from the body; author or coauthor of 127 published scientific papers. *Mailing Add:* Radiobiol Div Bldg 351 Univ Utah Salt Lake City UT 84112

MAYS, DAVID LEE, b Lafayette, Ind, Sept 30, 42; m 64. ANALYTICAL CHEMISTRY. *Educ:* Taylor Univ, BA, 64; Purdue Univ, MS, 66, PhD(bionucleonics), 68. *Prof Exp:* Res scientist anal chem, Bristol Labs Div, Bristol-Myers Co, 68-72, sr res scientist, 72-78; group leader pharmaceut anal, 78-80, SECT MGR NUTRIT ANAL, MEAD JOHNSON CO, DIV BRISTOL-MYERS CO, 80- *Mem:* Am Chem Soc. *Res:* Analytical separations and instrumental analyses of pharmaceuticals and nutritionals. *Mailing Add:* Mead Johnson & Co Pharmaceut Qual Control Evansville IN 47721

MAYS, JOHN RUSHING, b Jasper, Tex, Apr 22, 34; m 65; c 2. CIVIL ENGINEERING. *Educ:* Lamar Univ, BS, 56; Univ Colo, MS, 60, PhD(civil eng), 67. *Prof Exp:* From instr to assoc prof, Lamar Univ, 56-67; assoc prof, 67-75, PROF CIVIL ENG, UNIV COLO, 75- *Concurrent Pos:* Consult, US Bur Reclamation, 75- *Mem:* Am Soc Civil Engrs; Am Soc Eng Educ; Sigma Xi. *Res:* Dynamic response of nonlinear structures to shock loads. *Mailing Add:* Univ of Colo 1100 14th St Denver CO 80202

MAYS, LARRY WESLEY, b Pittsfield, Ill, Feb 7, 48; div. CIVIL ENGINEERING, WATER RESOURCES. *Educ:* Univ Mo, Rolla, Mo Sch Mines, BS, 70, MS, 71; Univ Ill, PhD(civil eng), 76. *Prof Exp:* Civil eng, US Army Eng Explosive Excavation Res Lab, 71-73; res asst water resources, 73-76, vis res asst prof, Univ Ill, 76; asst prof, 76-80, ASSOC PROF CIVIL ENG, WATER RESOURCES, UNIV TEX, 80- *Concurrent Pos:* Consult, US Army Construct Eng Res Lab, 76-77. *Mem:* Am Soc Civil Eng; Am Geophys Union; Am Water Resources Asn; Sigma Xi. *Res:* Field of applications of systems analysis techniques to water resources problems; in particular the application of operations research, probability and statistics to hydraulic design and hydrologic analysis. *Mailing Add:* Dept Civil Eng Univ Tex Austin TX 78712

MAYS, ROBERT, JR, b El Paso, Tex, Jan 13, 47; m 68; c 2. NONLINEAR OPTICS, LASER PHYSICS. *Educ:* Tex Tech Univ, BS, 69, MS, 71; Tex Christian Univ, PhD(physics), 79. *Prof Exp:* Systs engr, Tex Instruments, Inc, 71-77; tech staff, Avionics Div, Int Tel & Tel, 77-78; mem tech staff, Tex Instruments, Inc, 79-82; SR ENG SPECIALIST, VOUGHT CORP-LTV CO, 82- *Mem:* Inst Elec & Electronics Engrs; Am Phys Soc; Sigma Xi. *Res:* Electromagnetic and high energy beam interactions with matter; electro-optics, quantum electronics and solid state physics. *Mailing Add:* Vought Corp Box 225907 MS 220-13 Dallas TX 75265

MAYS, ROLLAND LEE, b Buffalo, NY, Feb 21, 20; m 44; c 4. ANALYTICAL CHEMISTRY. *Educ:* Univ Buffalo, BA, 52. *Prof Exp:* Chemist, Bliss & Laughlin Co, Inc, 42-48, supvr & chief chemist, 48-52; chemist, Linde Div, Union Carbide Corp, 52-58, develop supvr, 58-63, develop mgr, 63-71, mgr technol, Molecular Sieve Dept, Mat Systs Div, 71-75, dir technol, Molecular Sieve Dept, 75-78 & 79-81, dir res, Linde Div, 78-81. *Mem:* AAAS; Am Chem Soc; Sigma Xi. *Res:* Sorption on solid sorbents and heterogeneous catalysis, particularly in zeolites; sorption, catalytic and ion exchange products; process development and process design. *Mailing Add:* Union Carbide Tech Ctr Tarrytown NY 10591

MAYSILLES, JAMES HOWARD, b Grafton, WVa, Aug 23, 21. TAXONOMY, PLANT ECOLOGY. *Educ:* Univ Mich, BS, 47, MS, 48, PhD, 59. *Prof Exp:* Asst, Herbarium, Univ Mich, 47-48; asst prof bot, 49-56, ASSOC PROF BIOL, HANOVER COL, 56- *Mem:* Am Soc Plant Taxon. *Res:* Taxonomy and ecology of vascular plants of Durango, Mexico and floral relationships of the pine forests of western Durango. *Mailing Add:* Box 163 Hanover Col Dept Bot Hanover IN 47243

MAZAC, CHARLES JAMES, b Deming, NMex, May 4, 40; m 57; c 3. SYNTHESIS GAS CHEMISTRY, HYDROFORMULATION CHEMISTRY. *Educ:* NMex State Univ, BS, 62; MS, 66, PhD(phys chem), 68. *Prof Exp:* Engr res chem, Rocketdyne, 62-64; grad asst chem, NMex State Univ, 64-68; supvr photochem, Phys Sci Lab, 64-65; sr res chemist, Corp US Christi Tech Ctr, PPG Indust, 68-75, sr res supvr chem, 75-79, head gen res dept, 74-80; SECT LEADER, RES DEPT, TECH CTR, CELANESE CHEM CO, 79- *Concurrent Pos:* Adj prof math, Del Mar Jr Col, 69-81. *Mem:* Am Chem Soc. *Res:* Heterogeneous and homogeneous catalysis; gas phase kinetics of organosilanes; photochemistry; iodine chemistry; synthesis of olefin oxides; carbonylation chemistry at high pressures; thermochemistry. *Mailing Add:* Celanese Chem Co PO Box 9077 Corpus Christi TX 78408

MAZADE, NOEL ANDRE, public health administration, see previous edition

MAZARAKIS, MICHAEL GERASSIMOS, b Volos, Greece, Apr 25, 37; US citizen. PARTICLE BEAM PHYSICS, INERTIAL FUSION. *Educ:* Univ Athens, BS, 60; Univ Paris, PhD(physics), 65; Univ Pa, PhD(physics), 71; Mass Inst Technol, cert, 76. *Prof Exp:* Sr res assoc physics, Rutgers Univ, 71-73; vpres & dir exp prog, Fusion Energy Corp, 74-77; physicist, Argonne Nat Lab, Univ Chicago, 78-81; PHYSICIST, HIGH ENERGY BEAM PHYSICS DIV, SANDIA NAT LABS, 81- *Concurrent Pos:* Dir, Fusion Energy Corp, 72-77. *Mem:* Am Phys Soc; Inst Elec & Electronics Engrs; Sigma Xi. *Res:* Nuclear fusion; plasma physics; nuclear physics; nuclear astrophysics; accelerator physics; nuclear reactor physics and engineering; pulsed power technology. *Mailing Add:* Sandia Nat Labs Div 4255 PO Box 5800 Albuquerque NM 87185

MAZE, JACK REISER, b San Jose, Calif, Sept 28, 37; m 61. BOTANY. *Educ:* Humboldt State Col, BA, 60; Univ Wash, MS, 63; Univ Calif, Davis, PhD(bot), 65. *Prof Exp:* Lectr bot, Univ Calif, Davis, 65-66; asst prof, Univ Toronto, 66-68; asst prof, 68-73, ASSOC PROF BOT & CUR VASCULAR PLANTS, UNIV BC, 73- *Mem:* AAAS; Am Inst Biol Sci; Am Soc Plant Taxon; Bot Soc Am; Ecol Soc Am. *Res:* Plant evolution and taxonomy; embryology and floret development in grasses; evolution of higher taxa; ecological morphogenesis. *Mailing Add:* Dept of Bot Univ of BC Vancouver BC V6T 1W5 Can

MAZE, ROBERT CRAIG, b Galveston, Ind, May 24, 34; m 54; c 3. CHEMICAL ENGINEERING, SURFACE CHEMISTRY. *Educ:* Purdue Univ, BS, 59; Iowa State Univ, MS, 67, PhD(chem eng), 70. *Prof Exp:* Supvr qual control, Hercules, Inc, 59-60; mat engr, Martin Marietta Corp, 60-65; sect mgr, Motorola, Inc, 70-78; MEM STAFF, HEWLITT PACKARD, INC, 78- *Concurrent Pos:* US Atomic Energy Comn assistantship, Iowa State Univ, 66-70. *Mem:* Am Inst Chem Eng; Am Chem Soc. *Res:* Thermal analysis; liquid crystals. *Mailing Add:* Hewlitt Packard Inc 1000 NE Circle Blvd Corvallis OR 97330

MAZE, THOMAS HAROLD, b St Paul, Minn, June 1, 51; m 79; c 2. TRANSPORTAION ENGINEERING. *Educ:* Iowa State Univ, BS, 75; Univ Calif, Berkeley, ME, 77; Mich State Univ, PhD(civil eng), 82. *Prof Exp:* Field engr, Blasi Construct Co, 75; intern, Metropolitan Transit Comn, 76-77; res assoc, Univ Fla, 77-79; ASST PROF CIVIL ENG, WAYNE STATE UNIV, 79- *Concurrent Pos:* Prin investr, Southeastern Transp Authority, 80-81 & Urban Mass Transp Admin, 80- *Mem:* Inst Transp Engrs; Am Soc Civil Engrs; Regional Sci Asn. *Res:* Transit plan and operations; operations and planning of transit maintenance and storage facilities. *Mailing Add:* Dept Civil Eng Wayne State Univ Detroit MI 48202

MAZEL, PAUL, b Norfolk, Va, Nov 27, 25; m 55; c 3. PHARMACOLOGY, BIOCHEMISTRY. *Educ:* Med Col Va, BS, 46; Trinity Univ, MS, 55; Vanderbilt Univ, PhD(pharmacol), 60. *Prof Exp:* Res asst biol, Southwest Found Res & Educ, 54-55; res asst pharmacol, Yale Univ, 55-56; res asst, Vanderbilt Univ, 56-60, instr, 60-61; from asst prof to assoc prof, 61-71, PROF PHARMACOL, GEORGE WASHINGTON UNIV, 71-, PROF ANESTHESIOL, 74- *Concurrent Pos:* USPHS fel, 60-61; lectr, US Naval Dent Sch, 61-62; consult, Datatrol Corp & Mediphone, Inc, 62-63 & Wallace Labs, 65-; vis prof, Fed City Col, 72-74 & Catholic Univ Am, 80-82; dir, Nurse Anesthetists Prog, George Washington Univ Med Ctr. *Mem:* Soc Toxicol; Am Soc Pharmacol & Exp Therapeut. *Res:* Pharmacology of central nervous system acting drugs; physiological disposition of drugs; barbiturate metabolism; adaptive enzyme formation; membrane permeability; microsomal enzymes; blood-brain barrier; immunochemistry. *Mailing Add:* Dept Pharmacol George Washington Univ Washington DC 20037

MAZELIS, MENDEL, b Chicago, Ill, Aug 31, 22; m 69; c 1. PLANT BIOCHEMISTRY. *Educ:* Univ Calif, BS, 43, PhD(plant physiol), 54. *Prof Exp:* Jr res biochemist, Univ Calif, 54-55; res assoc & instr, Univ Chicago, 55-57; assoc chemist, Western Regional Res Lab, USDA, 57-61; lectr, 61-65, asst biochemist, 61-64, assoc biochemist, 64-73, assoc prof food sci & technol, 65-73, PROF FOOD SCI & TECHNOL, UNIV CALIF, DAVIS, 73-, BIOCHEMIST, 73- *Mem:* Am Soc Biol Chemists; Am Soc Plant Physiol; Brit Biochem Soc; Phytochem Soc Eur; Phytochem Soc NAm. *Res:* Intermediary metabolism of higher plants; enzymology. *Mailing Add:* Dept of Food Sci & Technol Univ of Calif Davis CA 95616

MAZELSKY, ROBERT, b Middletown, NY, Mar 11, 33; m 56; c 4. SOLID STATE CHEMISTRY. *Educ:* Hofstra Univ, BS, 54; Univ Conn, PhD(chem), 58. *Prof Exp:* Res scientist solid state, 58-64, MGR CRYSTAL SCI & TECHNOL, WESTINGHOUSE RES, 64- *Mem:* Am Asn Crystal Growth. *Res:* Direct research programs on inorganic materials including synthesis, crystal growth and characterization; primary emphasis has been on optical, acoustic and semiconducting materials. *Mailing Add:* Westinghouse Res Beulah Rd Pittsburgh PA 15235

MAZENKO, GENE FRANCIS, statistical mechanics, see previous edition

MAZER, MILTON, b New York, NY, March 5, 11; m 49; c 2. PSYCHIATRY. *Educ:* Univ Pa, BA, 32, MD, 35; William A White Inst NY, cert, 51. *Prof Exp:* Intern, Mt Sinai Hosp, Philadelphia, 35-36; resident internal med, Montefiore Hosp, New York, 36-37; clin asst, Mt Sinai Hosp, Philadelphia, 37-39; from internist to chief cardiac res unit, US Vet Admin, 39-43, resident psychiat, Vet Admin Hosp, 46-49; attend psychiatrist, Presby Hosp, 53-56; DIR PSYCHIAT, MARTHA'S VINEYARD MENT HEALTH CTR, 61-; ASST PSYCHIATRIST, MASS GEN HOSP, 63- *Concurrent Pos:* Pvt pract, 46-61; consult psychiat, Vet Admin, 49-55; fel, William White Inst, 52-; NIMH res grant, Martha's Vineyard Ment Health Ctr, 64-69; clin instr, Harvard Med Sch, 66-75, asst clin prof psychiat, 75-77; NIMH res grant, 73-75. *Mem:* AAAS; Am Psychiat Asn; Am Acad Psychoanal. *Res:* Social factors in mental disorder; community mental health practice; epidemiology of psychiatric disorders. *Mailing Add:* Martha's Vineyard Ment Health Ctr Edgartown MA 02539

MAZERES, REGINALD MERLE, b Metairie, La, Feb 15, 34; m 57; c 3. ALGEBRA. *Educ:* Univ Southwestern La, BS, 59; Auburn Univ, MS, 60, PhD(math), 69. *Prof Exp:* Instr math, Auburn Univ, 62-63; from asst prof to assoc prof, 63-71, PROF MATH, TENN TECHNOL UNIV, 71- *Res:* Inflations and enlargements of semigroups. *Mailing Add:* Box 5054 Tenn Technol Univ Cookeville TN 38501

MAZESS, RICHARD B, b Philadelphia, Pa, June 10, 39. MEDICAL PHYSICS. *Educ:* Pa State Univ, BA, 61, MA, 63; Univ Wis-Madison, PhD(anthrop), 67. *Prof Exp:* NIH fel, 67-68, asst prof anthrop, 67-69, asst prof radiol, 69-76, ASSOC PROF RADIOL, UNIV WIS-MADISON, 77- *Mem:* Am Asn Physicists Med. *Res:* Radionuclide measurements of skeleton and body composition; growth and aging. *Mailing Add:* Dept Radiol Univ Wis Hosp Madison WI 53706

MAZIA, DANIEL, b Scranton, Pa, Dec 18, 12; m 38; c 2. ZOOLOGY. *Educ:* Univ Pa, AB, 33, PhD(zool), 37. *Prof Exp:* Instr zool, Univ Pa, 35-36; Nat Res Coun fel, Princeton Univ & Marine Biol Labs, Woods Hole, 37-38; from asst prof to prof, Univ Mo, 38-50; assoc prof, 51-53, PROF ZOOL, UNIV CALIF, BERKELEY, 53- *Concurrent Pos:* Trustee, Marine Biol Lab, Univ Calif, Berkeley, 50-58, head physiol, 52-56. *Mem:* Nat Acad Sci; Am Soc Zool; Soc Gen Physiol (pres, 57-58); Am Acad Arts & Sci. *Res:* Ionic changes in stimulation; ion accumulation and exchange; chemistry of chromosomes; nuclear and cellular physiology; surface chemistry of enzymes; biochemistry of mitosis. *Mailing Add:* Dept of Zool Univ of Calif Berkeley CA 94720

MAZO, JAMES EMERY, b Bernardsville, NJ, Jan 15, 37; m 59; c 2. APPLIED MATHEMATICS. *Educ:* Mass Inst Technol, BS, 58; Syracuse Univ, MS, 60, PhD(physics), 63. *Prof Exp:* Res assoc physics, Ind Univ, 63-64; MEM TECH STAFF APPL MATH, BELL LABS, 64- *Mem:* Am Phys Soc; Inst Elec & Electronics Engrs. *Res:* Communication theory, noise theory and information theory. *Mailing Add:* Bell Labs Mountain Ave Murray Hill NJ 07974

MAZO, ROBERT MARC, b Brooklyn, NY, Oct 3, 30; m 54; c 3. THEORETICAL CHEMISTRY. *Educ:* Harvard Univ, AB, 52; Yale Univ, MS, 53, PhD(chem), 55. *Prof Exp:* NSF res fel, Univ Amsterdam, 55-56; res assoc, Univ Chicago, 56-58; asst prof chem, Calif Inst Technol, 58-62; assoc prof chem, 62-65, dir inst theoret sci, 64-67, assoc dean grad sch, 67-71, PROF CHEM, UNIV ORE, 65- *Concurrent Pos:* NSF sr fel & vis prof, Free Univ Brussels, 68-69. *Mem:* AAAS; Am Phys Soc. *Res:* Statistical mechanics; kinetic theory; irreversible thermodynamics; intermolecular forces. *Mailing Add:* Dept of Chem Univ of Ore Eugene OR 97403

MAZUMDAR, MAINAK, b Calcutta, India, Nov 19, 35; m 60; c 3. OPERATIONS RESEARCH, STATISTICS. *Educ:* Univ Calcutta, BS, 54, MS, 56; Cornell Univ, PhD(appl probability & statist), 66. *Prof Exp:* Res asst & res assoc opers res, Cornell Univ, 62-66; sr mathematician, 66-70, fel mathematician, 70-74, ADV MATHEMATICIAN, WESTINGHOUSE RES LABS, 74- *Concurrent Pos:* Lectr, Univ Pittsburgh, 67- *Mem:* Am Statist Asn; Inst Math Statist. *Res:* Mathematical theory of reliability; application of reliability methods to nuclear engineering. *Mailing Add:* Dept of Math Westinghouse Res Labs Pittsburgh PA 15235

MAZUMDAR, PURABI, experimental solid state physics, see previous edition

MAZUMDER, BIBHUTI R, b July 1, 24; Indian citizen; m 51; c 3. SURFACE CHEMISTRY, SOLID STATE CHEMISTRY. *Educ:* Univ Calcutta, BS, 44; Univ Dacca, MS, 47; Howard Univ, PhD(phys chem), 58; FRIC. *Prof Exp:* Chemist, Standard Pharmaceut, India, 48-54; res assoc chem, Cornell Univ, 58-59; chemist, Unilever, Eng, 59-60; head phys chem, Lever Bros, India, 60-67; PROF CHEM, MORGAN STATE UNIV, 67- *Mem:* Sr mem Am Chem Soc. *Res:* Research and development of soaps, detergents and cosmetics. *Mailing Add:* Dept of Chem Morgan State Univ Baltimore MD 21212

MAZUMDER, RAJARSHI, b Dacca, Bangladesh. BIOCHEMISTRY. *Educ:* Univ Calcutta, BSc, 51, MSc, 53; Univ Calif, Berkeley, PhD(biochem), 59. *Prof Exp:* Pool officer biochem, All-India Inst Med Sci, New Delhi, 64-65, asst prof, 65-67; asst prof, 67-73, ASSOC PROF BIOCHEM, MED SCH, NY UNIV, 73- *Concurrent Pos:* Fel biochem, Med Sch, NY Univ, 60-63. *Mem:* Am Soc Biol Chem; Harvey Soc. *Res:* Mechanism of protein synthesis. *Mailing Add:* Dept of Biochem NY Univ Med Sch New York NY 10016

MAZUR, ABRAHAM, b New York, NY, Oct 8, 11; m 40; c 2. BIOCHEMISTRY. *Educ:* City Col New York, BS, 32; Columbia Univ, AM, 34, PhD(biochem), 38. *Prof Exp:* Tutor, 36-38, from instr to prof chem, City Col New York, 38-75, chmn dept, 69-72; VPRES RES, LINDSLEY F KIMBALL RES INST, NEW YORK BLOOD CTR, 75- *Concurrent Pos:* Carnegie Corp fel, Col Physicians & Surgeons, Columbia Univ, 38-39; Guggenheim fel, 49-50; res assoc biochem, Med Col, Cornell Univ, 41-49, asst prof, 49-66. *Mem:* AAAS; fel Soc Exp Biol & Med; Am Chem Soc; Am Soc Biol Chemists; Harvey Soc. *Res:* Acetylation mechanism; fat metabolism hormone; stilbestrol; components of autotrophic organisms; anticholinesterases; chemical factor in shock; ferritin; iron metabolism. *Mailing Add:* Lindsley F Kimball Res Inst 310 E 67th Ct New York NY 10021

MAZUR, BARBARA JEAN, molecular biology, see previous edition

MAZUR, JACOB, b Lodz, Poland, Dec 17, 21; nat US; m 51; c 2. POLYMER PHYSICS. *Educ:* Hebrew Univ, MSc, 45, PhD(phys chem), 48. *Prof Exp:* Res fel, Calif Inst Technol, 48-50; vis fel, Univ Chicago, 50-51; res scientist, Weizmann Inst Sci, Israel, 51-55; res assoc, Univ Ill, 55-57; res chemist, Dow Chem Co, 57-60; PHYS CHEMIST, NAT BUR STAND, 60- *Concurrent Pos:* Rockefeller Found fel, 49-50. *Honors & Awards:* Morrison Award, NY Acad Sci, 59. *Mem:* Fel Am Phys Soc. *Res:* Theoretical physical chemistry; high polymer physics; statistical mechanics. *Mailing Add:* Nat Bur of Stand Washington DC 20234

MAZUR, PETER, b New York, NY, Mar 3, 28; m 53; c 1. CELL PHYSIOLOGY, CRYOBIOLOGY. *Educ:* Harvard Univ, AB, 49, PhD(biol), 53. *Prof Exp:* Mem staff, Hq, Air Res & Develop Command, US Air Force, 53-57; NSF fel, Princeton Univ, 57-59; BIOLOGIST, OAK RIDGE NAT LAB, 59- *Concurrent Pos:* Mem, Am Inst Biol Sci Adv Comt, Biol & Med Br, Off Naval Res, 63-66 & Environ Biol Br, NASA, 66-; mem adv bd, Am Type Cult Collection, 66-70; vis lectr, Duke Univ, 67; chmn long-range planning off, Oak Ridge Nat Lab, 70, sci dir biophys & cell physiol, 74-75; prof, Univ Tenn-Oak Ridge Grad Sch Biomed Sci, 70-; mem, Harvard Bd Overseers Vis Comt Biol, 70- ; mem space sci bd, Nat Acad Sci, 75- *Mem:* Fel AAAS; Soc Gen Physiol; Biophys Soc; Bot Soc Am; Soc Cryobiol (pres, 73-74). *Res:* Low temperature biology; freezing and drying; cell water, membranes and permeability. *Mailing Add:* Biol Div Oak Ridge Nat Lab PO Box Y Oak Ridge TN 37830

MAZUR, ROBERT HENRY, b Indianapolis, Ind, June 15, 24; m 54; c 3. PEPTIDE SYNTHESIS, MEDICINAL CHEMISTRY. *Educ:* Mass Inst Technol, BS, 48, PhD(org chem), 51. *Prof Exp:* NIH fel, Swiss Fed Inst Technol, 51-52; RES CHEMIST, G D SEARLE & CO, 52- *Concurrent Pos:* Nat Cancer Inst fel, Cambridge, 56-57. *Mem:* Am Chem Soc. *Res:* Molecular rearrangements; reaction mechanisms; alkaloids; steroids; peptides. *Mailing Add:* 5445 S Cornell Chicago IL 60615

MAZUR, STEPHEN, b Baltimore, Md, Apr 9, 45; m 69. ORGANIC CHEMISTRY. *Educ:* Yale Univ, BS, 67; Univ Calif, Los Angeles, MS, 69, PhD(chem), 71. *Prof Exp:* Assoc chem, Univ Calif, Los Angeles, 69-70; NSF fel & res assoc, Columbia Univ, 71-72, lectr, 72-73; asst prof chem, Univ Chicago, 73-79; MEM STAFF, CENT RES DEPT, E I DU PONT DE NEMOURS & CO, INC, 79- *Mem:* Sigma Xi. *Res:* Physical organic chemistry; polymers; electron transfer processes. *Mailing Add:* Cent Res Dept E I DuPont de Nemours & Co Inc Wilmington DE 19898

MAZURKIEWICZ, JOSEPH EDWARD, b Brooklyn, NY, Mar 19, 42. CELL BIOLOGY, HISTOCHEMISTRY. *Educ:* Univ Mass, BS, 66; Ariz State Univ, MS, 70; Univ Colo Med Ctr, PhD(exp path), 73. *Prof Exp:* NIH res fel anat, Yale Univ Sch Med, 73-75, res assoc cytol & cell biol, 75-78; asst prof, 78-81, ASSOC PROF ANAT, ALBANY MED COL, UNION UNIV, 81- *Concurrent Pos:* NIH fel Gen Med Sci, 73-75; NSF instrumentation grant, 80-82; NIH res grant, 81-84. *Mem:* Am Soc Cell Biol; Electron Micros Soc Am; Histochem Soc; Sigma Xi. *Res:* Structure and function of biomembranes especially of ion and water transporting epithelia; immunocytochemistry; electron microscopy; cytochemistry; detection and measurement of intracellular ion concentrations utilizing electron probe microanalysis. *Mailing Add:* Dept of Anat 47 New Scotland Ave Albany NY 12208

MAZURKIEWICZ-KWILECKI, IRENA MARIA, b Tarnow, Poland, May 14, 24; nat Can; m; c 1. PHARMACOLOGY. *Educ:* Jagellonian Univ, MPharm, 47; McGill Univ, MSc, 55, PhD(pharmacol), 57. *Prof Exp:* Res asst pharmacol, Sch Med, Jagellonian Univ, 47-48; res asst, McGill Univ, 53-57; res pharmacologist, Food & Drug Labs, Dept Nat Health & Welfare, Ont, 57-59; res pharmacologist, Prov Labs, Ministry of Health, Que, 59-60; asst prof, 60, assoc prof, 64, actg head dept, 64-65, PROF PHARMACOL, FAC MED, UNIV OTTAWA, 72- *Concurrent Pos:* Am Med Life Ins Fund Med Res Found fel, 57. *Mem:* AAAS; Fr-Can Asn Advan Sci; NY Acad Sci; Am Soc Pharmacol & Exp Therapeut; Pharmacol Soc Can. *Res:* Pharmacology of autonomic nervous system; neuropharmacology; catecholamines; histamine; psychoactive drugs; drugs of abuse; cardiovascular pharmacology. *Mailing Add:* Dept of Pharmacol 275 Nicholas St Ottawa ON K1N 9A9 Can

MAZZAWY, ROBERT SALEM, engineering, see previous edition

MAZZENO, LAURENCE WILLIAM, b New Orleans, La, Sept 4, 21; m 44; c 4. ORGANIC CHEMISTRY. *Educ:* Loyola Univ, La, BS, 42; Univ Detroit, MS, 44. *Prof Exp:* Asst chem, Univ Detroit, 42-44; chemist, Southern Regional Res Lab, Bur Agr & Indust Chem, USDA, 44-53 & Southern Utilization Res Br, 53-58, head new prod invests, Southern Utilization Res Div, 58-59, head chem modification invests, 59-61, asst to dir indust develop, 61-69, res chemist, Cotton Finishes Lab, Southern Mkt & Nutrit Res Div, 69-74, head Tech & Econ Anal Res, Southern Regional Res Ctr, 74-78. *Concurrent Pos:* Lectr chem, Our Lady Holy Cross Col, 78- *Mem:* Am Chem Soc; Sigma Xi; Asn Textile Chem & Colorists. *Res:* Textile finishing, including chemical modification and resin finishing of cotton; flame and weather resistant finishes for cotton textiles. *Mailing Add:* Our Lady Holy Cross Col 4123 Woodland Dr New Orleans LA 70114

MAZZITELLI, FREDERICK R(OCCO), b Pittston, Pa, Mar 4, 24; m 47; c 9. AERONAUTICAL ENGINEERING, OPERATIONS ANALYSIS. *Educ:* Pa State Univ, BS, 47. *Prof Exp:* Proj engr, Convertawings, Inc, 53-55; chief res aerodynamicist, Vertol Aircraft Corp, 55-57, chief design anal, 57-58; preliminary design engr, 59-61, chief transp, logistics opers anal, 61-67, mgr transp systs, 67-76, MGR ADVAN STUDIES & ANAL, OPERS ANAL, GRUMMAN AEROSPACE CORP, 76- *Concurrent Pos:* Consult transp adv comt, Huntington Town Planning Bd, 67-69 & Aviation Adv Comn, 71. *Mem:* Am Helicopter Soc; assoc fel Am Inst Aeronaut & Astronaut. *Res:* Design of vertical take-off and landing aircraft; transportation systems and logistic functions of commercial and military aircraft systems; business analysis of domestic and international airlines. *Mailing Add:* 10 Montana Pl Huntington Station NY 11746

MAZZOCCHI, PAUL HENRY, b New York, NY, May 6, 39; m 61. ORGANIC CHEMISTRY. *Educ:* Queens Col, NY, BS, 61; Fordham Univ, PhD(org chem), 66. *Prof Exp:* NIH fel org chem, Cornell Univ, 65-67; from asst prof to assoc prof, 67-77, PROF ORG CHEM, UNIV MD, COLLEGE PARK, 77- *Mem:* Interam Photochem Soc; Am Chem Soc. *Res:* Organic photochemistry; synthetic chemistry. *Mailing Add:* Dept of Chem Univ of Md College Park MD 20740

MAZZOLENI, ALBERTO, b Milan, Italy, Sept 12, 27; US citizen; m; c 2. CARDIOLOGY. *Educ:* Univ Milan, MD, 52; Am Bd Internal Med, dipl, 63; Am Bd Cardiovasc Dis, dipl, 68; Am Bd Internal Med, dipl, 77. *Prof Exp:* Intern med, Miriam Hosp, Providence, RI, 57-58; res asst, Lemuel Shattuck Hosp, Boston, 58-59; res asst, Boston City Hosp, 59-60; from asst prof med to assoc prof clin med, Sch Med, Univ Ky, 61-72; asst chief internal med, 64-73, chief cardiol, 67-72, DIR CORONARY CARE UNIT, VET ADMIN HOSP, LEXINGTON, 73-; ASSOC PROF MED, SCH MED, UNIV KY, 72- *Concurrent Pos:* Res fel cardiol, Beth Israel Hosp, Boston, 55-57 & 60-61. *Mem:* Fel Am Col Cardiol; fel Am Col Physicians. *Res:* Electrocardiogram diagnosis of cardiac hypertrophy; component heart weights. *Mailing Add:* 3772 Gloucester Dr Lexington KY 40511

MAZZONE, HORACE M, b Franklin, Mass, May 19, 30; m 62; c 1. BIOCHEMISTRY. *Educ:* Boston Col, BS, 51, MS, 53; Univ Wis, PhD(biochem), 59. *Prof Exp:* Res assoc biochem, Long Island Biol Asn & dept genetics, Carnegie Inst, 59; fel pharmacol, Harvard Med Sch, 59-61; res assoc path, Children's Hosp Med Ctr & Children's Cancer Res Found, Boston, 61-63; res assoc biol, Mass Inst Technol, 63-65; BIOCHEMIST, FOREST INSECT & DIS LAB, USDA, 65- *Concurrent Pos:* Res assoc physics, Mass Gen Hosp, 64-65; lectr, Yale Univ, 72- *Mem:* AAAS; Am Chem Soc; Am Soc Cell Biol; Tissue Cult Asn. *Res:* Viruses; properties of infectious agents; tissue culture. *Mailing Add:* US Dept Agr 51 Mill Pond Rd Hamden CT 06514

MAZZUCATO, ERNESTO, b Padova, Italy, July 7, 37; m 64; c 3. PLASMA PHYSICS. *Educ:* Univ Padova, Dr phys, 60; Univ Roma, Libero Docente (plasma physics), 70. *Prof Exp:* Sr res physicist plasma physics, Univ Padova, 60-62 & Comt Nat Nuclear Energy, 62-72; RES PHYSICIST PLASMA PHYSICS, PRINCETON UNIV, 72- *Mailing Add:* Princeton Univ PO Box 451 Princeton NJ 08540

MAZZUR, SCOTT RUIGH, microbiology, medical anthropology, deceased

MCURDY, ORVILLE L, polymer chemistry, organic chemistry, see previous edition

MEACHAM, ROBERT COLEGROVE, b Moultrie, Ga, May 1, 20; m 43; c 4. MATHEMATICS. *Educ:* Southwestern Univ, Memphis, AB, 42; Brown Univ, ScM, 48, PhD(appl math), 49. *Prof Exp:* Instr math, Carnegie Inst Technol, 49-50, asst prof, 50-54; assoc prof, Univ Fla, 54-60; PROF MATH, ECKERD COL, 60- *Concurrent Pos:* Consult, RCA Serv Co, 58-64; NSF fel comput sci, Stanford Univ, 65-66; mem panel on res, Sch Math Study Group, 68-72. *Mem:* Math Asn Am; Soc Indust & Appl Math. *Res:* Mechanics; numerical analysis; differential equations. *Mailing Add:* Dept of Math Eckerd Col PO Box 12560 St Petersburg FL 33733

MEACHAM, ROGER HENING, JR, b Richmond, Va, Sept 10, 42; m 65; c 5. PHARMACOLOGY, DRUG METABOLISM. *Educ:* Univ Richmond, BS, 65, MS, 67; Med Col Va, PhD(pharmacol), 71. *Prof Exp:* Sr scientist metab chem, 71-77, SUPVR, BIOCHEM PHARM UNIT, DRUG DISPENSARY SECT, WYETH LABS, 77- *Concurrent Pos:* mem steering comt, Delaware Valley Drug Metabol Discussion Group, 79- *Mem:* Sigma Xi; Int Soc Study Xenobiosis. *Res:* Drug biotransformation; drug analysis; pharmacokinetics; drug-drug interaction. *Mailing Add:* Wyeth Labs Inc Metab Chem Sect PO Box 8299 Philadelphia PA 19101

MEACHAM, WILLIAM FELAND, b Washington, DC, Dec 12, 13; m 44; c 4. SURGERY. *Educ:* Western Ky State Col, BS, 36; Vanderbilt Univ, MD, 40; Am Bd Surg, dipl, 47; Am Bd Neurol Surg, dipl, 48. *Prof Exp:* Intern surg, Univ Hosp, 40-41, asst surg, Sch Med, 41-43, instr, 43-44, from asst prof to assoc prof clin surg, 47-53, assoc prof neurol surg, 53, CLIN PROF NEUROL SURG & CHMN DEPT, SCH MED, VANDERBILT UNIV, 54-, ASSOC DIR, SURG SERV SECT, 75- *Concurrent Pos:* Howe fel neurosurg, Sch Med, Vanderbilt Univ, 45-47; asst resident, Vanderbilt Univ Hosp, 41-43, resident surgeon, 43-44, asst vis surgeon, 44-, assoc vis surgeon, Outpatient Serv, 44-, neurosurgeon-in-chief; vol asst, Montreal Neurol Inst, 47-; asst prof, Meharry Med Col, 50; attend neurosurgeon & consult, hosps; chmn, Dept Neurol Surg. *Mem:* Neurosurg Soc Am (pres, 52); Am Asn Neurol Surg; Soc Univ Surg; AMA; Am Col Surg. *Res:* Intracranial tumors and aneurysms; steroatactic surgery. *Mailing Add:* Dept of Neurol Surg Vanderbilt Univ Hosp Nashville TN 37232

MEACHAM, WILLIAM ROSS, b Ft Worth, Tex, Jan 12, 23; m 50; c 3. VERTEBRATE ZOOLOGY. *Educ:* Agr & Mech Col, Tex, BS, 48; NTex State Col, MS, 50; Univ Tex, PhD(vert zool), 58. *Prof Exp:* From asst prof to assoc prof, 50-63, head dept, 63-77, PROF BIOL 77- *Res:* Animal ecology; evolution; genetics; vertebrate population dynamics. *Mailing Add:* Dept of Biol Univ of Tex Arlington TX 76010

MEAD, ALBERT RAYMOND, b San Jose, Calif, July 17, 15; m; c 2. MALACOLOGY. *Educ:* Univ Calif, BS, 38; Cornell Univ, PhD(zool), 42. *Prof Exp:* With Marine Biol Lab, 41-42; instr, US Army Col, Brit WAfrica, 44-45; from instr to assoc prof, 46-52, head dept zool, 56-67, coordr marine sci prog, 67-70, cur invert 67-70, prof zool, Univ Ariz, 52-76, coordr undergrad prog, Biol Sci, 70-76, assoc dean, Liberal Arts Col, 76-80, PROF GEN BIOL, UNIV ARIZ, 80- *Concurrent Pos:* Res fel, Univ Calif, 46; res assoc, Pac Sci Bd, nat Res Coun, 48 & 49 & NSF, 54; Pac Sci Coun observer, UNESCO Adv Comt Humid Tropics Res, 61; mem, Invert Consults Comt Pac, Pac Sci Bd, Nat Res Coun-Nat Acad Sci, 63-; guest scientist, Royal Mus Cent Africa, Tervuren, Belg, 74-75, 77 & 81. *Mem:* Soc Invert Path; AAAS; Am Soc Zool; Am Malacol Union (pres, 63). *Res:* Giant African snail ecology and control; comparative genital anatomy and physiology of Gastropoda; speciation and toxonomy of Gastropoda; economic malacology; molluscan pathology. *Mailing Add:* Dept Gen Biol Univ Ariz Tucson AZ 85721

MEAD, CARVER ANDRESS, b Bakersfield, Calif, May 1, 34; m 54; c 3. ELECTRICAL ENGINEERING, COMPUTER SCIENCE. *Educ:* Calif Inst Technol, BS, 56, MS, 57, PhD, 59. *Prof Exp:* From instr to assoc prof elec eng, 57-67, PROF ELEC ENG & COMPUT SCI, CALIF INST TECHNOL, 67- *Concurrent Pos:* Consult, NASA Adv Coun & Comt, 78. *Mem:* Fel Am Phys Soc. *Res:* Electron transport in thin films; semiconductor surface barriers. *Mailing Add:* Dept of Comput Sci Calif Inst of Technol Pasadena CA 91125

MEAD, CHESTER ALDEN, b St Louis, Mo, Dec 9, 32. THEORETICAL CHEMISTRY. *Educ:* Carleton Col, BA, 54; Wash Univ, PhD, 57. *Prof Exp:* Res assoc chem, Brookhaven Nat Lab, 57-58; from asst prof to assoc prof phys chem, 58-66, PROF PHYS CHEM, UNIV MINN, MINNEAPOLIS, 66- *Concurrent Pos:* Consult, Brookhaven Nat Lab, 59-63. *Mem:* Am Phys Soc; Am Chem Soc. *Res:* Quantum mechanics; quantum theory of dispersion and absorption line shapes; theory of excitons in solids; gravitation and quantum theory; algebraic techniques in theoretical chemistry; molecular quantum mechanics, especially corrections to adiabatic approximation; generalized entropy in irreversible thermodynamics. *Mailing Add:* Dept of Chem Univ of Minn Minneapolis MN 55455

MEAD, DARWIN JAMES, b Dowagiac, Mich, June 27, 10; m 36; c 3. CHEMISTRY. *Educ:* Kalamazoo Col, AB, 32; Brown Univ, ScM, 33, PhD(chem), 36. *Prof Exp:* Instr chem, Colby Col, 36-38; res chemist, Gen Elec Co, 38-46; ASSOC PROF PHYSICS, UNIV NOTRE DAME, 46- *Mem:* Am Phys Soc. *Res:* Conductance of electrolytes; properties of high polymers; dielectric properties of polymers. *Mailing Add:* 1101 Cleveland Ave South Bend IN 46628

MEAD, EDWARD JAIRUS, b Cleveland, Ohio, Oct 3, 28; m 59; c 2. INORGANIC CHEMISTRY. *Educ:* Va Mil Inst, BS, 49; Purdue Univ, MS, 52, PhD(inorg chem), 55. *Prof Exp:* Instr chem, Va Mil Inst, 49-50; res chemist, 54-63, res supvr, 64-65, prod develop mgr, 65-73, dir lab, Dept Pigments, Exp Sta, 74-78, MGR NEW BUS DEVELOP, DEPT PHOTOPROD, E I DU PONT DE NEMOURS & CO, INC, 78- *Mem:* Am Chem Soc. *Res:* Substituted borohydrides; textile fibers; synthesis and properties of organic and inorganic pigments. *Mailing Add:* Dept Photoprod E I du Pont de Nemours & Co Inc Wilmington DE 19898

MEAD, FRANK WALDRETH, b Columbus, Ohio, June 11, 22; m 45; c 2. ENTOMOLOGY. *Educ:* Ohio State Univ, BS, 47, MS, 49; NC State Univ, PhD(entom), 68. *Prof Exp:* Asst entom, Ohio State Univ, 48-49; scout Japanese beetle control proj, Bur Entom & Plant Quarantine, USDA, 48, biol aid, Div Forest Insect Invest, 50-53; entomologist, 53-71, TAXONOMIC ENTOMOLOGIST, DIV PLANT INDUST, FLA DEPT AGR & CONSUMER SERV, 71- *Concurrent Pos:* Res asst insect mus, NC State Univ, 58-60; courtesy assoc prof, Dept Entom & Nematol, Univ Fla; adj assoc prof,Dept Entom, Fla A&M Univ. *Honors & Awards:* Cert Appreciation for Serv Rendered in Field of Entom, Fla Entom Soc, 75. *Mem:* Entom Soc Am; Am Registry Prof Entomologists; Soc Syst Zool; Am Mosquito Control Asn; Am Breeding Asn. *Res:* Fulgoroidea, especially Oliarus and other Cixiidae; Auchenorhynchus Homoptera; Culicidae. *Mailing Add:* Div Plant Indust PO Box 1269 Fla Dept Agr & Consumer Serv Gainesville FL 32602

MEAD, GILBERT DUNBAR, b Madison, Wis, May 31, 30; m 51, 68; c 4. GEOPHYSICS. *Educ:* Yale Univ, BS, 52, MA, 53; Univ Calif, Berkeley, PhD(physics), 62. *Prof Exp:* Instr sci high sch, Calif, 53-55; res asst, Lawrence Radiation Lab, Univ Calif, 57-62; physicist lab theoret studies, 62-68, physicist lab space physics, 68-73, head, Geophys Br, 73-80, GEOPHYSICIST, CRUSTAL DYNAMICS PROJ, GODDARD SPACE FLIGHT CTR, NASA, 80- *Concurrent Pos:* Lectr dept space sci & appl physics, Cath Univ Am, 64-67. *Mem:* Fel Am Phys Soc; Am Geophys Union; Seismol Soc Am. *Res:* Experimental high energy physics; space and magnetospheric physics; Jupiter's magnetosphere; geomagnetism; magnetospheric models; plate tectonics; models of plate motion; geodesy. *Mailing Add:* Geophys Br Code 922 NASA Goddard Space Flight Ctr Greenbelt MD 20771

MEAD, GILES WILLIS, b New York, NY, Feb 5, 28. ICHTHYOLOGY. *Educ:* Stanford Univ, AB, 49, AM, 52, PhD(biol), 53. *Prof Exp:* Fishery res biologist, US Fish & Wildlife Serv, 49-51, syst zoologist, 51-54, dir ichthyol lab, 56-60; cur fishes, Mus Comp Zool, Harvard Univ, 60-70; DIR, LOS ANGELES COUNTY MUS NATURAL HIST, 70- *Concurrent Pos:* Chmn, Calif Natural Areas Coord Coun, 70- *Res:* Systematics, distribution and ecology of oceanic fishes. *Mailing Add:* Los Angeles County Mus of Natural Hist 900 Exposition Blvd Los Angeles CA 90007

MEAD, JAMES FRANKLYN, b Evanston, Ill, Oct 24, 16; m 42; c 3. BIOCHEMISTRY. *Educ:* Princeton Univ, AB, 38; Calif Inst Technol, PhD(org chem), 42. *Prof Exp:* Asst, Calif Inst Technol, 42; from instr to asst prof, Occidental Col, 45-48; res coordr, Off Naval Res, Calif, 48; head synthetic br, Biochem Dept, Atomic Energy Proj, 48-50, res biochemist &

chief biochem div, 50-69, assoc clin prof physiol chem, 51-56, prof, 56-63, prof biol chem & biophys, Med Sch, 63-69, PROF BIOL CHEM, MED SCH & ASSOC DIR LABS NUCLEAR MED & RADIATION BIOL, UNIV CALIF, LOS ANGELES, 69-, PROF PUB HEALTH, 73- *Concurrent Pos:* NIH career res award. *Honors & Awards:* E A Bailey Award, 71; Am Oil Chem Soc Award, 80. *Mem:* Am Chem Soc; Am Soc Biol Chem; Am Oil Chem Soc. *Res:* Lipid, brain lipid and fatty acid metabolism; essential fatty acids; lipid and membrane peroxidation. *Mailing Add:* Dept of Biol Chem Univ of Calif Sch of Med Los Angeles CA 90024

MEAD, JAYLEE MONTAGUE, b Clayton, NC, June 14, 29; m 68. ASTRONOMY. *Educ:* Univ NC, BA, 51; Stanford Univ, MA, 54; Georgetown Univ, PhD(astron), 70. *Prof Exp:* Eng asst math, Knolls Atomic Power Lab, Gen Elec Co, 51-52; teacher, Van Antwerp Sch, NY, 52-53; counsr & instr, Univ NC, 54-56; mathematician opers res off, Johns Hopkins Univ, 57-59; mathematician, 59-68, astronomer lab theoret studies, 68-71, astronomer lab optical astron, 71-77, ASST CHIEF LAB ASTRON & SOLAR PHYSICS, GODDARD SPACE FLIGHT CTR, NASA, 77- *Mem:* Am Astron Soc; Am Geophys Union; Int Astron Union; Sigma Xi. *Res:* Statistical astronomy; stellar dynamics; planetary atmospheres; planet Mars; star catalogues and computerized astronomy data retrieval systems. *Mailing Add:* Lab Astron & Solar Physics Code 680 NASA Goddard Space Flight Ctr Greenbelt MD 20771

MEAD, JUDSON, b Madison, Wis, Sept 16, 17; m 44; c 3. GEOPHYSICS. *Educ:* Mass Inst Technol, BS, 40, PhD(geophys), 49. *Prof Exp:* Proj supvr, Airborne Instruments Lab, 41-45; from asst prof to assoc prof, 49-60, dir geol field sta, 65-70, PROF GEOPHYS, IND UNIV, BLOOMINGTON, 60-, DIR GEOL FIELD STA, 74- *Mem:* Geol Soc Am; Am Geophys Union; Am Inst Mining, Metall & Petrol Eng. *Res:* Structure of the crust; exploration geophysics. *Mailing Add:* Dept of Geol Ind Univ Bloomington IN 47401

MEAD, MARSHALL WALTER, b Franklin, Ind, Jan 15, 21; m 47; c 3. ANALYTICAL CHEMISTRY. *Educ:* Franklin Col, AB, 42. *Prof Exp:* Anal chemist, Ala Ord Works, E I du Pont de Nemours & Co, 42-43; chief anal chemist, Oldbury Electrochem Co, 48-54, prod supt, Miss Works, 54-55; admin asst res & develop, Nat Aniline Div, Allied Chem Corp, 55-62; mgr local sect activ off, 62-69, asst dir mem activ div, 69-71, HEAD, MEM ACTIV DEPT, AM CHEM SOC, 71- *Mem:* Am Chem Soc . *Res:* Analytical chemistry of chlorates; phosphorus compounds; perchlorates; instrumental methods of analysis; research management. *Mailing Add:* 1507 Milestone Dr Silver Spring MD 20904

MEAD, RICHARD WILSON, b Los Angeles, Calif, Jan 7, 41; m 64; c 2. HYDROMETALLURGY. *Educ:* Univ Denver, BChemE, 63, MS, 66; Univ Ariz, PhD(chem eng), 71. *Prof Exp:* Process engr, Shell Chem Co, 63-65; asst instr chem eng, Univ Ariz, 66-68, instr, 68-71, res assoc, 71-72; res engr, Phelps Dodge Corp, 72-74; asst prof, 74-78, ASSOC PROF CHEM ENG, UNIV NMEX, 78- *Concurrent Pos:* Consult, Los Alamos Nat Lab, 79-81, Extraction Res & Develop, Inc, 80-81, Bur Bus & Econ Res, Univ NMex, 75-80 & NMex Environ Improvement Agency, 75-76. *Mem:* Am Inst Chem Engrs; Am Inst Mining, Metall & Petrol Engrs. *Res:* Development of new processes or units which facilitate the recovery of metals from novel sources or waste streams; leaching studies and metalion mass transfer. *Mailing Add:* Dept Chem & Nuclear Eng Univ NMex Albuquerque NM 87131

MEAD, ROBERT WARREN, b Yonkers, NY, Mar 3, 40; m 61; c 3. ANIMAL PARASITOLOGY, INVERTEBRATE ZOOLOGY. *Educ:* Colo State Univ, BS, 62, MS, 63, PhD(zool), 68. *Prof Exp:* Asst prof biol, Davis & Elkins Col, 65-67; NIH fel, Univ Mass, Amherst, 68-70; asst prof, 70-74, assoc prof, 74-81, chmn dept, 76-79, PROF BIOL, SCH MED, UNIV NEV, RENO, 81- *Mem:* AAAS; Am Soc Zool; Am Soc Parasitol; Rocky Mountain Conf Parasitologists (pres, 78-79); Sigma Xi. *Res:* Cell and developmental biology of parasitic and free living invertebrates; host-parasite interactions; invertebrate zoology. *Mailing Add:* Dept Biol Univ Nev Reno NV 89557

MEAD, RODNEY A, b Moline, Ill, Apr 28, 38; m 61; c 2. REPRODUCTIVE PHYSIOLOGY, ENDOCRINOLOGY. *Educ:* Univ Calif, Davis, AB, 60, MA, 62; Univ Mont, PhD(zool), 66. *Prof Exp:* USPHS fel steroid biochem, Col Med, Univ Utah, 66-68; from asst prof to assoc prof, 68-76, PROF ZOOL, UNIV IDAHO, 76- *Concurrent Pos:* Mem biol reprod study sect, Inst Child Health & Human Develop, 75-79. *Honors & Awards:* A Brazier Howell Award, Am Soc Mammalogists, 66. *Mem:* AAAS; Soc Study Reproduction; Am Soc Mammal; Am Soc Zool. *Res:* Hormonal control of delayed implantation in mustelids. *Mailing Add:* Dept Biol Sci Univ Idaho Moscow ID 83843

MEAD, SYLVESTER WARREN, III, b New Brunswick, NJ, Jan 26, 23; m 54; c 3. PHYSICS. *Educ:* Univ Calif, BA, 48, PhD(physics), 57. *Prof Exp:* Assoc math, 49-50, PHYSICIST, LAWRENCE LIVERMORE LAB, UNIV CALIF, 57- *Mem:* Am Phys Soc. *Res:* Lasers; laser-produced plasmas; environmental sciences. *Mailing Add:* Lawrence Livermore Lab Univ of Calif PO Box 808 Livermore CA 94550

MEAD, THOMAS EDWARD, b Norwalk, Conn, Jan 9, 33; m 60; c 2. ORGANIC CHEMISTRY, MASS SPECTROMETRY. *Educ:* Ohio Wesleyan Univ, AB, 55; Brown Univ, MS, 58. *Prof Exp:* Chemist 57-65, group leader mass spectrometry, 65-70, SR RES SCIENTIST, STAMFORD RES LABS, AM CYANAMID CO, 70- *Mem:* Am Chem Soc; Am Soc Mass Spectrometry. *Res:* Acid-base reactions in nonaqueous solvents; countercurrent distribution; gas-liquid chromatography and high resolution mass spectrometry. *Mailing Add:* Stamford Res Labs Am Cyanamid Co 1937 W Main St Stamford CT 06904

MEAD, WILLIAM C, b Hazleton, Pa, Dec 6, 46; m 69; c 1. LASER PLASMA INTERACTIONS, HYDRODYNAMICS SIMULATIONS. *Educ:* Syracuse Univ, BS, 68; Princeton Univ, MA, 70, PhD(physics), 74. *Prof Exp:* PHYSICIST, LAWRENCE LIVERMORE NAT LAB, 73- *Mem:* Am Phys Soc. *Res:* Behavior of laser-plasma coupling processes and their effects on inertial confinement fusion targets: instabilities, thermal transport, radiative processes, and hydrodynamics; design, analysis and numerical simulations of experiments. *Mailing Add:* Lawrence Livermore Nat Lab PO Box 5808 L-477 Livermore CA 94550

MEAD, WILLIAM J(ASPER), b Columbus, Ohio, Dec 29, 27; m 50, 75; c 2. CHEMICAL ENGINEERING. *Educ:* Ohio State Univ, BChE, 48, ChE, 62; Stevens Inst Technol, MS, 61. *Prof Exp:* Chem engr, Colgate Palmolive Co, 50-51; chem engr, Whitehall Labs, Inc, Am Home Prod Corp, 51-56, asst tech dir, Home Prod Int, Ltd, 56-58, tech dir, 58-65; dir mfg, Alberto-Culver Co, Ill, 65-67, vpres, 66-67; DIR MFG, COMBE, INC, 69-, VPRES, 77- *Concurrent Pos:* Ed-in-chief, Encyclop Chem Process Equip, 64- *Mem:* AAAS; Am Inst Chem Engrs; Am Chem Soc; Soc Cosmetic Chemists; Am Inst Chemists. *Res:* Manufacture, formulation, quality control, plant design, packaging, equipment selection and layout for pharmaceuticals; cosmetics, insecticides, waxes, polishes and other household chemical specialty products. *Mailing Add:* Combe Inc 1101 Westchester Ave White Plains NY 10604

MEADE, ALSTON BANCROFT, b Jamaica, WI, June 28, 30; m 57; c 5. ENTOMOLOGY. *Educ:* Fisk Univ, BA, 56; Univ Minn, MS, 59, PhD(entom), 62. *Prof Exp:* Res biologist, 64-71, sr res biologist, 71-81, RES ASSOC, BIOCHEM DEPT, E I DU PONT DE NEMOURS & CO INC, 81- *Mem:* Entom Soc Am; Royal Entom Soc London; Sigma Xi. *Res:* Resistance of plants to insect attack; ecology of Empoasca fabae and Macrosteles fascifrons; insecticidal controls of vegetable pests; development of new insecticides; insect attractants. *Mailing Add:* Exp Sta Bldg 268 E I DuPont de Nemours & Co Inc Wilmington DE 19898

MEADE, DALE M, b Portage, Wis, Aug 7, 39; m 58; c 2. PLASMA PHYSICS. *Educ:* Univ Wis, BA, 61, MS, 62, PhD(physics), 65. *Prof Exp:* Res assoc physics, Univ Wis, 65-66; res assoc, Princeton Univ, 66-67; from asst prof to prof physics, Univ Wis-Madison, 67-73; res physicist, 73-78, sr res physicist, 78-80, HEAD, EXP DIV, PLASMA PHYS LAB, PRINCETON UNIV, 80- *Mem:* Fel Am Phys Soc. *Res:* Experimental studies of equilibrium and stability of plasma confined by magnetic fields with emphasis on applications in controlled thermonuclear fusion. *Mailing Add:* Plasma Physics Lab PO Box 451 Princeton NJ 08544

MEADE, GRAYSON EICHELBERGER, b Palacios, Tex, Apr 8, 12; m 37; c 4. GEOLOGY. *Educ:* Univ Nebr, AB, 35, MA, 37; Univ Chicago, PhD(geol), 46. *Prof Exp:* From instr to assoc prof geol, Tex Tech Col, 41-46; asst geologist, Bur Econ Geol, Tex, 44-45; geologist, Tex Mem Mus, 46-49; assoc prof, Tex Tech Col, 49-52; geologist, Union Oil Co, Calif, 52-58, chief geologist, Union Oil Co Can, 58-61, staff geologist, 61-72; CONSULT GEOLOGIST, 72- *Concurrent Pos:* Sessional instr, Dept Archaeol, Univ Calgary, 68-72. *Mem:* Fel Geol Soc Am; Soc Vert Paleont; Am Asn Petrol Geol. *Res:* Cenozoic and petroleum geology; vertebrate paleontology; Devonian stratigraphy. *Mailing Add:* Agate Springs Ranch Harrison NE 69346

MEADE, JAMES HORACE, JR, b Vicksburg, Miss, Nov 1, 32; m 58; c 3. BIOMETRICS. *Educ:* Miss State Univ, BS, 54, MS, 59; Univ Fla, PhD(animal genetics), 61. *Prof Exp:* Fel biomath, NC State Col, 61-62, asst statistician, 62-63; from asst prof to assoc prof biostatist, Med Ctr, Univ Ala, 63-65, sr biostatistician, 63-65; assoc prof biomet, 65-69, head biomet div, 69-77, PROF BIOMET, MED SCH, UNIV ARK, LITTLE ROCK, 69- *Concurrent Pos:* Consult, Vet Admin, 66- *Mem:* Biomet Soc; Am Statist Asn. *Res:* Applications of mathematics and statistics in medical research; use of computers in medicine; teaching statistics to biologists. *Mailing Add:* Div Biomet Univ of Ark Med Ctr 4301 W Markham Little Rock AR 72201

MEADE, JOHN ARTHUR, b Coldwater, Mich, Aug 29, 28; m 49; c 2. AGRONOMY. *Educ:* Univ Md, BS, 54, MS, 55; Iowa State Col, PhD(plant physiol), 58. *Prof Exp:* From asst prof to assoc prof agron, Univ Md, 58-66; EXTEN SPECIALIST, RUTGERS UNIV, NEW BRUNSWICK, 66- *Mem:* Weed Sci Soc Am. *Res:* Herbicides. *Mailing Add:* Dept of Soils & Crops Rutgers Univ New Brunswick NJ 08903

MEADE, LINDA CELIDA, biochemical genetics, see previous edition

MEADE, REGINALD ESON, b Great Bend, Kans, Mar 1, 11; m 52; c 2. FOOD SCIENCE, FOOD TECHNOLOGY. *Prof Exp:* Engr process develop, Western Condensing Co, 33-42, vpres res & develop process & prod develop, 43-48, exec vpres & gen mgr, 49-52; independent eng consult process & prod develop, 53-62; engr & res assoc process eng & food process res, Pillsbury Co, 63-72, sr res assoc food res, 73-76; PROCESS CONSULT, 76- *Concurrent Pos:* Exec consult, Int Exec Serv Corps, Manila, Philippines, 71-72; mem adv bd & consult proj, Dept Energy Conserv in Milk Processing, Jet Propulsion Lab, Calif Inst Technol, 81. *Honors & Awards:* Cert Appreciation, Nat Inst Sci & Technol, Repub Philippines, 72; USAID, life mission to SE Asia, 76. *Mem:* Am Dairy Sci Asn; AAAS; NZ Soc Dairy Sci & Technol; Inst Food Technol; Am Asn Cereal Chemists. *Res:* Thermal processes and water activity in food dehydration and evaporation processes; prevention and recovery of liquid and solid wastes in food processing; industrial fermentations; plant nutrition. *Mailing Add:* 551 Gem Ave Tulare CA 93274

MEADE, ROBERT HEBER, JR, b Brooklyn, NY, Dec 27, 30; m 56; c 3. GEOLOGY. *Educ:* Univ Okla, BS, 52; Stanford Univ, MS, 57, PhD(geol), 60. *Prof Exp:* Geologist, Calif Co, 52 & 55-56; GEOLOGIST, US GEOL SURV, 57- *Concurrent Pos:* Assoc ed, J Geophys Res, 74-76; adj prof, State Univ NY, Stony Brook, 75- *Mem:* Soc Econ Paleont & Mineral; Int Asn Sedimentol; Am Geophys Union; Am Soc Civil Eng; fel Geol Soc Am. *Res:* Sedimentology; erosion, transport, deposition and compaction of sediments; river morphology; coastal hydrology and oceanography. *Mailing Add:* US Geol Surv Denver CO 80225

MEADE, THOMAS GERALD, b Pound, Va, Sept 3, 37. PARASITOLOGY, INVERTEBRATE ZOOLOGY. *Educ:* Whitman Col, BA, 59; Purdue Univ, MS, 62; Ore State Univ, PhD(zool), 65. *Prof Exp:* Grad coun fel, Ore State Univ, 64-65; from asst prof to assoc prof parasitol, 65-75, PROF PARASITOL, SAM HOUSTON STATE UNIV, 75- *Mem:* Am Soc Parasitol; Helminthol Soc Washington. *Res:* Helminth parasites of fishes; immuno-parasitology; larval trematode snail interaction. *Mailing Add:* Dept of Life Sci Sam Houston State Univ Huntsville TX 77340

MEADE, THOMAS LEROY, b Center Junction, Iowa, July 4, 20; m 42; c 2. ANIMAL NUTRITION. *Educ:* Univ Fla, BS, 50, MS, 51, PhD, 53. *Prof Exp:* Asst animal nutritionist, Univ Fla, 53-54; animal nutritionist, Chas Pfizer & Co, 54-55; vpres & dir res, Hayne Prod Inc, 55-63; dir res, J Howard Smith, Inc, 63-68; assoc prof, 68-74, prof fisheries & marine technol, 74-77, prof animal sci, 77-81, PROF AQUACULT SCI & PATH, UNIV RI, 81- *Res:* Marine resource utilization, primary efforts in process and product development for industrial fisheries; aquaculture systems development, including nutrition and physiology of salmonoids. *Mailing Add:* Dept of Animal Sci Univ of RI Kingston RI 02881

MEADER, ARTHUR LLOYD, JR, b Clarksville, Tenn, Dec 13, 20; m 43; c 2. PETROLEUM CHEMISTRY. *Educ:* Univ Ky, BS, 41; Univ Wis, MS, 44, PhD(chem), 47. *Prof Exp:* From assoc res chemist to res chemist, Calif Res Corp Div, Standard Oil Co, Calif, 47-62, sr res chemist, Chevron Res Co, 62-67, SR RES ASSOC, CHEVRON RES CO, 67- *Mem:* Am Chem Soc. *Res:* Surface-active chemicals; plastics; fibers; surface coatings; elastomers; asphalt specialties. *Mailing Add:* 2023 Los Angeles Ave Berkeley CA 94707

MEADER, RALPH GIBSON, b Eaton Rapids, Mich, Sept 6, 04; m 28; c 1. ANATOMY. *Educ:* Ohio Wesleyan Univ, AB, 25; Hamilton Col, AM, 27; Yale Univ, PhD(comp anat), 32. *Hon Degrees:* LLD, Philadelphia Col Osteop Med, 56; ScD, Ohio Wesleyan Univ, 58. *Prof Exp:* From instr to asst prof biol, Hamilton Col, 25-28; instr, Wesleyan Univ, 28-29; from instr to assoc prof anat, Sch Med, Yale Univ, 31-48; chief, Cancer Res Grants Br, Nat Cancer Inst, 48-53, chief, Res Grants & Fels Br, 53-60, assoc dir grants & training, 60-65; dep dir res admin, Mass Gen Hosp, 65-76; CONSULT, NAT CANCER INST, 65-, CONSULT ON GRANTS CONTRACTS, 76- *Concurrent Pos:* Biologist, State Biol Surv, NY, 29-30; Blossom fel neuroanat, Yale Univ, 29-31; mem corp, Bermuda Biol Sta, 32-; Rockefeller Found fel neurol, Univ Amsterdam & Ctr Inst for Brain Res, 38-39; asst to dir bd sci advs, Jane Coffin Childs Mem Fund Med Res, 42-43, asst dir, 43-48; exec secy, Nat Adv Cancer Coun, 47-65; mem selection & scheduling comt, Gordon Res Conf, 65-80; incorporator & trustee, Eunice Kennedy Shriver Ctr for Ment Retardation Inc, 69-, pres, 77-, Spaulding Youth Ctr Inc, 66-, pres, 72-75; mem biomed libr review comt, Nat Libr of Med, 74-76, chmn, 75-76. *Honors & Awards:* Super Serv Award, HEW, 59. *Mem:* Fel AAAS; Soc Develop & Growth; Sigma Xi; Am Asn Anat; Am Asn Cancer Res. *Res:* Comparative anatomy of nervous system; neuroanatomy of teleosts; electrical characteristics of living organisms; history of medicine; sequence of nerve degeneration. *Mailing Add:* Calef Farm Rd 1 Franklin NH 03235

MEADOR, NEIL FRANKLIN, b Sweet Springs, Mo, Sept 19, 38; m 58; c 2. AGRICULTURAL ENGINEERING. *Educ:* Univ Mo, Columbia, BSc, 61; Va Polytech Inst, MSc, 63; Mich State Univ, PhD(agr eng), 68. *Prof Exp:* Instr agr eng, Va Polytech Inst, 61-62; instr, Mich State Univ, 63-67; assoc prof, 67-72, PROF AGR ENG, UNIV MO-COLUMBIA, 72- *Mem:* Am Soc Agr Engrs. *Res:* Structural research concerning farm and light industrial buildings. *Mailing Add:* Dept of Agr Eng Univ of Mo Columbia MO 65201

MEADOWS, ANNA T, b Cherbourg, France, Apr 30, 31; US citizen. PEDIATRICS, EPIDEMIOLOGY. *Educ:* Queens Col, BA, 52; NY Univ, MA, 53; Med Col Pa, MD, 69. *Prof Exp:* Instr, 72-74, assoc, 74-75, asst prof pediat, 75-80, ASSOC PROF PEDIAT, SCH MED, UNIV PA, 80- *Concurrent Pos:* Asst physician oncol, Children's Hosp Philadelphia, 74-76, assoc physician med, 76-79, sr physician, Dept Med, 79-; dir epidemiol, etiol & genetics, Children's Cancer Res Ctr, 80- *Mem:* Am Acad Pediat; Am Soc Clin Oncol; Int Soc Pediat Oncol; Am Asn Cancer Res; Am Soc Pediat Hematol-Oncol. *Res:* Investigations of pediatric cancer etiology, epidemiology, late effects of cancer therapy, and information exchange, utilizing tumor registries originating from a pediatric cancer center, a geographic region, and an international group. *Mailing Add:* Children's Hosp of Philadelphia 34th & Civic Center Blvd Philadelphia PA 19104

MEADOWS, BRIAN T, b London, Eng, May 20, 40; m 63. HIGH ENERGY PHYSICS. *Educ:* Oxford Univ, BA, 62, MA, 67, PhD(physics), 67. *Prof Exp:* Sci Res Coun Gr Brit res fel high energy physics, Oxford Univ, 66-67; res assoc, Syracuse Univ, 67-68, vis asst prof, 68-69, asst prof, 69-72; ASSOC PROF HIGH ENERGY PHYSICS, UNIV CINCINNATI, 72- *Res:* Experimental high energy physics. *Mailing Add:* Dept of Physics Univ of Cincinnati Cincinnati OH 54221

MEADOWS, CHARLES MILTON, b Merryville, La, Nov 8, 12; m 41; c 2. ENTOMOLOGY. *Educ:* La State Norm Col, AB, 36; La State Univ, MS, 38; Ohio State Univ, PhD, 42. *Prof Exp:* Asst entom, Ohio State Univ, 38-42; in-charge cotton insect invest, 42-44; tech rep, Sherwin-Williams Co, 46-50; PRES & GEN MGR, SOUTHWEST SPRAYER & CHEM CO, 50- *Concurrent Pos:* Consult, Tenneco Oil Co, Tex, 64- *Mem:* AAAS; Nat Agr Chem Asn; Entom Soc Am. *Res:* Toxicity of insecticides; development and application of selective weed killers; spray machinery. *Mailing Add:* Southwest Sprayer & Chem Co 2632 Cedar Ridge Waco TX 76708

MEADOWS, GARY GLENN, b American Falls, Idaho, June 6, 45; m 68; c 2. PHARMACY, PHARMACOGNOSY. *Educ:* Idaho State Univ, BS, 68, MS, 72; Univ Wash, PhD(pharmaceut sci), 76. *Prof Exp:* ASST PROF PHARMACOG, COL PHARM, WASH STATE UNIV, 76- *Mem:* Sigma Xi; Am Soc Pharmacog. *Res:* Isolation and use of amino acid degrading enzymes in cancer treatment; metabolism of pyridoxal phosphate-requiring enzymes; nutrition and carcinogenesis and in cancer chemotherapy; food-drug interactions. *Mailing Add:* Col of Pharm Wash State Univ Pullman WA 99164

MEADOWS, GEOFFREY WALSH, b Bury, Eng, Jan 16, 21; m 45; c 3. INDUSTRIAL CHEMISTRY. *Educ:* Univ Manchester, BSc, 42, MSc, 43, PhD(chem), 48. *Prof Exp:* Res chemist, Shell Co, Eng, 43-45; asst lectr, Univ Manchester, 45-49; Nat Res Coun Can fel, 49-51; res chemist, E I Du Pont de Nemours & Co, Inc, 51-65, res assoc, 65-66, res supvr, 66-72, res assoc, 72-80; RETIRED. *Mem:* Am Chem Soc; Sigma Xi. *Res:* Ionic catalysed polymerization; physical properties of polymers; reaction kinetics; high temperature synthesis. *Mailing Add:* 139 E Sickles St Kennett Square PA 19348

MEADOWS, GUY ALLEN, b Detroit, Mich, May 5, 50; m 73. PHYSICAL OCEANOGRAPHY. *Educ:* Mich State Univ, BS, 72, MS, 74; Purdue Univ, PhD(marine sci), 77. *Prof Exp:* Prod design engr, Ford Motor Co, 72; res instr, Great Lakes Coastal Res Lab, Purdue Univ, 73-77, res coordr phys oceanog, 74-77; ASST PROF PHYS OCEANOG, UNIV MICH, ANN ARBOR, 77- *Concurrent Pos:* Instr, Purdue Univ, 74-76. *Mem:* Sigma Xi; Am Geophys Union; Int Asn Great Lakes Res. *Res:* Coastal hydrodynamics; nearshore dynamics and thermally driven circulations. *Mailing Add:* Dept of Atmospheric & Oceanic Sci Univ of Mich Ann Arbor MI 48109

MEADOWS, HENRY E(MERSON), JR, b Atlanta, Ga, May 27, 31; m. ELECTRICAL ENGINEERING. *Educ:* Ga Inst Technol, BEE, 52, MSEE, 53, PhD(elec eng), 59. *Prof Exp:* Asst elec eng, Ga Inst Technol, 54-55, instr, 55-58; mem tech staff, Bell Tel Labs, Inc, 59-62; from asst prof to assoc prof, 62-70, PROF ELEC ENG, COLUMBIA UNIV, 70- *Concurrent Pos:* Consult, 62-; consult & vpres, Technol Consult, Inc, 63-70; NSF grants, 64-66 & 67-71; prin investr, Off Naval Res contract, 64-67; NASA grant, 67-72; Ford Found eng resident, Western Develop Labs Div, Philco-Ford Corp, 68-69. *Mem:* Inst Elec & Electronics Engrs; Tensor Soc; Simulation Coun. *Res:* Systems engineering, controls, network theory, simulation, applied mathematics, mathematical economics. *Mailing Add:* Dept of Elec Eng & Comput Sci Columbia Univ New York NY 10027

MEADOWS, JAMES WALLACE, JR, b Meridian, La, Aug 16, 23; m 50; c 2. NUCLEAR PHYSICS. *Educ:* La Polytech Inst, BS, 44; La State Univ, MS, 48, PhD(chem), 50. *Prof Exp:* Anal chemist, Cities Serv Refining Corp, La, 44-46; asst, La State Univ, 46-50; tech asst, Harvard Univ, 50-58; assoc chemist, 58-70, CHEMIST, ARGONNE NAT LAB, 70- *Mem:* Am Chem Soc; Am Phys Soc; Am Nuclear Soc. *Res:* Nuclear reactions; neutron diffusion; fission; neutron physics. *Mailing Add:* Appl Physics Div Argonne Nat Lab Bldg 316 9700 S Cass Ave Argonne IL 60439

MEADOWS, JERRIANE KUJIE STAFFORD, b Staten Island, NY, Oct 9, 43; m 66. NUTRITION. *Educ:* Mich State Univ, BS, 65; Univ Ga, MS, 68; Univ NC, Greensboro, PhD(nutrit), 74. *Prof Exp:* Jr high teacher sci, Telfair County High Sch, McRae, Ga, 68-69; instr, 69-71, asst prof foods & nutrit, Div Home Econ, Ga Southern Col, 74-76; ASSOC PROF FOODS & NUTRIT, DEPT HOME ECON, JACKSONVILLE STATE UNIV, 76- *Mem:* Am Dietetic Asn; Am Home Econ Asn; Soc Nutrit Educ; Nutrit Today Soc; Inst Food Technologists. *Res:* Determination of palatability, tenderness, and vitamin retention of meat cooked in a selected oven film. *Mailing Add:* Box 68 Mt Berry GA 30149

MEADOWS, W ROBERT, b Chicago, Ill, Feb 3, 19. INTERNAL MEDICINE, CARDIOLOGY. *Educ:* Northwestern Univ, BS, 41, MD, 44. *Prof Exp:* Intern, Cook County Hosp, 44, resident med, 47-48, 49-50; ward physician med, Livermore, Calif, 53-55, ward physician, Palo Alto, 55-60, asst chief cardiopulmonary lab, Hines, Ill, 60-72, chief cardiac catheterization lab, 72-74, CHIEF GRAPHICS SECT CARDIOL, VET ADMIN HOSP, HINES, 74- *Concurrent Pos:* Fel hemat, Cook County Hosp, Chicago, Ill, 50-51; fel cardiol, New Eng Deaconess Hosp, Boston, Mass, 59-60; asst clin prof, Stritch Sch Med, Loyola Univ Chicago, 61-62, asst prof, 62-65, assoc prof, 65- *Mem:* Fel Am Col Physicians; fel Am Col Cardiol. *Mailing Add:* Cardiol Sect Vet Admin Hosp Hines IL 60141

MEADS, MANSON, b Oakland, Calif, Mar 25, 18; m 45; c 1. MEDICINE. *Educ:* Univ Calif, AB, 39; Temple Univ, MD, 43. *Hon Degrees:* DSc, Temple Univ, 56. *Prof Exp:* Asst med, Thorndike Mem Lab, Harvard Med Sch, 44-46, asst bact & immunol, 46-47; instr med, 47-50, asst prof internal med, 51-56, from assoc prof to prof prev med, 51-57, dir dept, 51-57, assoc dean, 55-58, acad dean, 58-59, exec dean, 59-63, dean, 63-71, PROF INTERNAL MED, BOWMAN GRAY SCH MED, 57-, VPRES HEALTH AFFAIRS, 67-, DIR MED CTR, 74- *Concurrent Pos:* Ernst fel, Thorndike Mem Lab, Harvard Med Sch, 46-47; Markle scholar, 48-53; med officer, vis prof & adv, USPHS, Thailand, 53-55. *Mem:* Am Soc Clin Invest; AMA; fel Am Col Physicians. *Res:* Medical school administration. *Mailing Add:* Off of VPres Bowman Gray Sch of Med Winston-Salem NC 27103

MEADS, PHILIP F, b Oakland, Calif, Dec 4, 07; m 36; c 3. PHYSICAL CHEMISTRY. *Educ:* Univ Calif, Berkeley, BS, 28, PhD(chem), 32. *Prof Exp:* Chief chemist, Calif & Hawaiian Sugar Co, 53-59; tech dir, Calif & Hawaiian Sugar Co, Crockett, 59-72, asst refinery mgr environ affairs, 72-76; RETIRED. *Concurrent Pos:* Partic cane sugar refiners res proj, US Nat Comt Sugar Anal. *Honors & Awards:* Hon Award, Sugar Indust Technicians, 69. *Mem:* Am Chem Soc; Inst Food Technol; Sugar Indust Technologists (pres, 71-72). *Res:* Refining of cane sugar; sugar analysis and products; sugar refinery wastewater treatment. *Mailing Add:* 33 Linda Ave 2603 Oakland CA 94611

MEADS, PHILIP FRANCIS, JR, b Oakland, Calif, May 19, 37; m 66; c 3. THEORETICAL PHYSICS, COMPUTER SCIENCE. *Educ:* Univ Calif, Berkeley, AB, 58, PhD(physics), 63. *Prof Exp:* Asst physics, Lawrence Radiation Lab, Univ Calif, 59-63; physicist, Midwest Univ Res Asn, Wis, 63-65; physicist, William M Brobeck & Assocs, 65-79; CONSULT, 79- *Concurrent Pos:* Consult, William M Brobeck & Assocs, 60, Argonne Nat Lab, Lawrence Radiation Lab, Univ Calif, 65-, Los Alamos Sci Lab, 70-, Hanford Eng Develop Lab, 75- & Fermi Nat Accelerator Lab, 78- *Mem:* AAAS; Health Physics Soc; Am Phys Soc; Audio Eng Soc. *Res:* Aberrations of quadrupole focusing magnets; accelerator design, particularly injection and extraction studies; optical design of beam transport systems; digital computer systems and subsystems, particularly microprocessors. *Mailing Add:* 7053 Shirley Dr Oakland CA 94611

MEAGHER, JAMES FRANCIS, physical chemistry, see previous edition

MEAGHER, MICHAEL DESMOND, b Nelson, BC, Nov 27, 33; m 65; c 2. FORESTRY. *Educ:* Univ BC, BSF, 57, PhD(forestry), 76; Univ Toronto, MScF, 63. *Prof Exp:* Forester-in-training silvicult, BC Forest Serv, 57-61; lectr dendrol, silvicult & urban forestry, Univ Toronto, 63-67, forestry, Univ BC, 70-71; FORESTER SILVICULT & GENETICS, BC FOREST SERV, 72- *Res:* Genetics research and breeding of western hemlock (tsunga heterophyllic pinaceal) for reforestation in coastal British Columbia. *Mailing Add:* Res Br BC Forest Serv 1450 Govt St Victoria BC V8W 3E7 Can

MEAGHER, RALPH E, b Chicago, Ill, Sept 22, 17; m 41; c 1. APPLIED PHYSICS, COMPUTER SCIENCE. *Educ:* Univ Chicago, BS, 38; Mass Inst Technol, MS, 39; Univ Ill, PhD(physics), 49. *Prof Exp:* Mem staff radiation lab, Mass Inst Technol, 41-45; res asst prof physics, Univ Ill, 48-50, res assoc prof, 50-51, res prof, 51-57, res prof physics & elec eng, 57-58; CONSULT, 58- *Concurrent Pos:* Head digital comput lab, Univ Ill, 57-58. *Honors & Awards:* President's Cert of Merit, 47. *Mem:* Fel Am Phys Soc; Asn Comput Mach; fel Inst Elec & Electronics Eng. *Res:* Radar and radar indicators; nuclear physics; electronics; proton-proton scattering; electronic computers. *Mailing Add:* PO Box 356 South Bend IN 46624

MEAGHER, RICHARD BRIAN, b Chicago, Ill, Sept 30, 47; m 68; c 1. MOLECULAR GENETICS, ENZYMOLOGY. *Educ:* Univ Ill, BS, 69; Yale Univ, MPhil, 71, PhD(biol), 73. *Prof Exp:* Am Cancer Soc fel biochem, Univ Calif, Berkeley, 73-74, lectr, 73-74; NIH res fel biochem & microbiol, Univ Calif, San Francisco, 74-76; MEM STAFF MICROBIOL, UNIV GA, 76- *Mem:* Am Chem Soc; Plant Molecular Biol Asn; Am Soc Microbiol. *Res:* Evolution of biochemical pathways and their regulation; molecular cloning and expression of higher plant genes; techniques of genetic engineering applied to the developing of new plant phenotypes. *Mailing Add:* Dept of Microbiol Univ of Ga Athens GA 30602

MEAKIN, JAMES WILLIAM, b Smith Falls, Ont, May 28, 29; m 53; c 2. INTERNAL MEDICINE. *Educ:* Queen's Univ, Ont, MD, CM, 53; Univ Toronto, MA, 57; FRCP(C), 60. *Prof Exp:* Fel med, Harvard Univ & asst med, Peter Bent Brigham Hosp, 57-59; clin teacher, 60-65, assoc, 65-68, ASSOC PROF MED, FAC MED, UNIV TORONTO, 68-; PHYSICIAN, ONT CANCER INST & PRINCESS MARGARET HOSP, 60- *Concurrent Pos:* Am Col Physicians fel, Harvard Univ, 57-58, Life Ins Med Res Fund fel, 58-59. *Honors & Awards:* Starr Medal, 57. *Mem:* Can Med Asn; Can Biochem Soc; Can Soc Clin Invest; Endocrine Soc. *Res:* Effect of steroid hormones on cells, particularly tumour cell growth in animals and man. *Mailing Add:* 4 Aldenham Cres Toronto PQ M3A 1S2 Can

MEAKIN, JOHN DAVID, b Nottingham, Eng, Feb 11, 34; m 57; c 5. METALLURGY. *Educ:* Univ Leeds, BSc, 55, PhD(metall), 57. *Prof Exp:* Vis res assoc, Franklin Inst, 58-60; res fel, King's Col, Durham, 60-61, Imp Chem Indust sr res fel, 61-62; sr res scientist, Res Labs, Franklin Inst, 62-65, sr staff scientist, 65-66, prin staff scientist, 66-69, lab mgr, 69-74; PROF MAT SCI, MECH & AEROSPACE ENG & DIR SOLAR CELL DEVELOP, INST ENERGY CONVERSION, UNIV DEL, 74- *Concurrent Pos:* Vis assoc prof, Univ Del, 67. *Mem:* Int Solar Energy Soc; sr mem Inst Elec & Electronics Engrs. *Res:* Structure and properties of materials; thin film solar cells; solar energy utilization. *Mailing Add:* Inst of Energy Conversion Univ of Del Newark DE 19711

MEAKIN, PAUL, b Burton-on-Trent Staffs, Eng, Mar 29, 44. PHYSICAL CHEMISTRY. *Educ:* Manchester Univ, BSc, 65; Univ Calif, Santa Barbara, PhD(chem), 69. *Prof Exp:* Chemist, 69-75, groupleader, 75-76, RES SUPVR, E I DU PONT DE NEMOURS & CO INC, 76- *Res:* Magnetic resonance, nuclear magnetic resonance and electron spin resonance; polymer chemistry and physics; chemical dynamics of transition metal complexes; solid state chemistry and physics, solid electrolytes; atmospheric chemistry. *Mailing Add:* Cent Res & Develop Dept Exp Sta E I du Pont de Nemours & Co Inc Wilmington DE 19898

MEAL, HARLAN C, b Rush Co, Ind, Jan 31, 25; m 53; c 3. OPERATIONS MANAGEMENT. *Educ:* Harvard Univ, AB, 50, MA, 53, PhD(phys chem), 54. *Prof Exp:* Opers analyst oper res off, Johns Hopkins Univ, 53-57; opers analyst, Dunlap & Assocs, Inc, 57-59; opers analyst, Arthur D Little, Inc, 59-72, head logistics unit, 72-76; SR LECTR, SLOAN SCH OF MGT, MASS INST TECHNOL, 76- *Concurrent Pos:* mgt consult, 76- *Mem:* Inst Mgt Sci; Am Prod & Inventory Control Soc; Opers Res Soc Am; Am Inst Decision Sci. *Res:* Industrial operations research; management of production; distribution and service operations; industrial logistics; management systems for industrial operations; decision rules, control systems and organizational structures. *Mailing Add:* Sloan Sch of Mgt 50 Memorial Dr Cambridge MA 02139

MEAL, LARIE L, b Cincinnati, Ohio, June 15, 39. PHYSICAL CHEMISTRY, ANALYTICAL CHEMISTRY. *Educ:* Univ Cincinnati, BS, 61, PhD(phys chem), 66. *Prof Exp:* Res chemist, US Indust Chem Co, Nat Distillers & Chem Corp, 66-67; instr chem, Ohio Col Appl Sci, 68-69; asst prof chem technol, 69-75, ASSOC PROF CHEM TECHNOL, UNIV CINCINNATI, 75- *Concurrent Pos:* Consult & chem analyst, Cincinnati Fire Div, 74- *Mem:* AAAS; Am Chem Soc; NY Acad Sci. *Res:* Ethylenediaminetetraacetic acid titrations; chemical analysis of arson debris. *Mailing Add:* 2231 Slane Ave Norwood OH 45212

MEALEY, EDWARD H, b Boston, Mass, July 28, 25; m 51; c 3. BIOCHEMISTRY. *Educ:* Tufts Col, BS, 48; Univ Kans, PhD(biochem), 60. *Prof Exp:* Supvr chem test unit lab blood & blood prod, Div Biologics Standards, NIH, 60-63, chief blood & blood derivatives sect, 64-67; dir qual assurance, Hyland Labs, 67-70; sr vpres & tech dir, Int Clin Lab Sci, 70-80; VPRES QUALITY ASSURANCE, ALPHA THERAPEUT CORP, 81- *Mem:* AAAS; Am Pub Health Asn; NY Acad Sci; Am Chem Soc. *Res:* Physical and chemical studies on whole blood; plasma and plasma protein solutions. *Mailing Add:* 17646 Fremont St Fountain Valley CA 92708

MEALEY, JOHN, JR, b Providence, RI, Aug 30, 28; m 52; c 3. NEUROSURGERY. *Educ:* Brown Univ, BA, 49; Johns Hopkins Univ, MD, 52; Am Bd Neurol Surg, dipl, 62. *Prof Exp:* Intern surg, Johns Hopkins Hosp, 52-53; clin & res fel neurosurg, Harvard Sch Med, 55-56; from asst resident to resident, Mass Gen Hosp, 56-60; from instr to assoc prof surg, 60-68, PROF NEUROL SURG, SCH MED, IND UNIV, INDIANAPOLIS, 69- *Mem:* AMA; Am Asn Neurol Surg; Cong Neurol Surg; Am Col Surg. *Res:* Brain tumors; radioactive methods; chemotherapy; head injuries. *Mailing Add:* 1100 W Michigan St Indianapolis IN 46202

MEANS, ANTHONY R, b Bartlesville, Okla, May 7, 41. ENDOCRINOLOGY, CELL BIOLOGY. *Educ:* Okla State Univ, BA, 63, MS, 64; Univ Tex, Austin, PhD(physiol), 67. *Prof Exp:* Res assoc molecular biol, Southwest Found Res & Educ, 68-69; asst prof obstet & gynec, Med Sch, Vanderbilt Univ, 69-72, asst prof physiol & asst dir, Ctr Pop Res, 71-72; assoc prof, 73-75; PROF CELL BIOL & ASSOC DIR, CTR POP RES, BAYLOR COL MED, 75- *Concurrent Pos:* Res fel, Australian Res Coun, Russell Grimwade Sch Biochem, Univ Melbourne, 67-68. *Honors & Awards:* Edwin B Astwood Award, Endocrine Soc, 80. *Mem:* Soc Study Reproduction; Am Soc Cell Biol; Endocrine Soc; Am Soc Biol Chem. *Res:* Calmodulin and cyclic nucleotide regulation of cell function. *Mailing Add:* Dept of Cell Biol Baylor Col of Med Houston TX 77030

MEANS, CRAIG RAY, b Shreveport, La, Aug 16, 22; div. PROSTHODONTICS. *Educ:* Southern Univ, BS, 50; Howard Univ, DDS, 54; Ohio State Univ, MSc, 63. *Prof Exp:* Asst prof prosthodont, 61-62 & 64-66, supvr dent technicians, 64-67, assoc prof & chief div removable partial & complete dentures, 66-68, actg chmn dept removable prosthodont, 68-69, assoc prof & chmn dept, 69-70, assoc dean undergrad affairs, 70-81, PROF REMOVABLE PROSTHODONT, COL DENT, HOWARD UNIV, 70- *Mem:* Am Dent Asn; Nat Dent Asn; Am Prosthodont Soc. *Res:* Damage to the oral tissues resulting from the use of home reline denture materials; temporomandibular joint function in complete denture patients. *Mailing Add:* Dept Removable Prosthodontics Col Dent Howard Univ Washington DC 20059

MEANS, D BRUCE, b Los Angeles, Calif, Mar 9, 41; div; c 2. ECOLOGY, HERPETOLOGY. *Educ:* Fla State Univ, BS, 68, MS, 72, PhD(ecol), 75. *Prof Exp:* Teaching asst, Fla State Univ, 68-70; Gerald Beadel res scholar, 70-75; asst dir, 75-77, DIR, TALL TIMBERS RES STA, 78- *Concurrent Pos:* Adj asst prof, Fla State Univ, 76- *Mem:* AAAS; Ecol Soc Am; Soc Study Evolution; Am Soc Naturalists; Am Soc Ichthyologists & Herpetologists. *Res:* Population biology; ecology of reproduction and life history phenomena; evolution at the species and population level; geographical ecology. *Mailing Add:* Tall Timbers Res Sta Rte 1 Box 160 Tallahasse FL 32312

MEANS, GARY EDWARD, b Wykoff, Minn, Aug 31, 40. BIOCHEMISTRY. *Educ:* San Jose State Col, BS, 64; Univ Calif, Davis, PhD(biochem), 68. *Prof Exp:* USPHS fel, Virus Lab, Univ Calif, Berkeley, 68-70; instr, 71-73, asst prof, 74-79, ASSOC PROF BIOCHEM, OHIO STATE UNIV, 79-, ACTG CHMN DEPT, 80- *Mem:* Am Chem Soc; Am Soc Biol Chemists. *Res:* Protein chemistry; structure-function relationships of proteins, enzyme mechanisms. *Mailing Add:* Dept of Biochem Ohio State Univ 484 W 12th Ave Columbus OH 43210

MEANS, JEFFREY LYNN, b Hinsdale, Ill, July 16, 52; m 75. GEOCHEMISTRY, GEOLOGY. *Educ:* Bucknell Univ, BS, 74; Princeton Univ, MA, 76, PhD(geol), 81. *Prof Exp:* Res asst geochem, Oak Ridge Nat Lab, 74 & Princeton Univ, 74-78; RES SCIENTIST GEOCHEM, COLUMBUS LABS, BATTELLE MEM INST, 78- *Concurrent Pos:* Prin investr, Battelle Columbus Lab, contract, 79-; consult, Oak Ridge Nat Lab, 75-77. *Mem:* Geochem Soc; Sigma Xi. *Res:* Organic, trace element, isotope and aqueous geochemistry, especially radioactive waste management and environmental geochemistry of natural waters. *Mailing Add:* Battelle Columbus Labs 505 King Ave Columbus OH 43201

MEANS, LYNN L, b Kansas City, Mo, Jan 26, 14; m 36; c 4. METEOROLOGY, PHYSICAL SCIENCE. *Educ:* Univ Chicago, BS, 42, MS, 44. *Prof Exp:* Instr & res assoc, Univ Chicago, 42-45; forecaster, Chicago Forecast Ctr, US Weather Bur, Nat Oceanic & Atmospheric Admin, 45-47, res forecaster, 47-55, leading analyst, Nat Weather Anal Ctr, 55-59, chief pub & agr forecast sect, 59-65, dep to dir user affairs, Environ Sci Serv Admin, 65-68, sr prog analyst, 68-74, consult & gen phys scientist, 75-79; RETIRED. *Concurrent Pos:* Consult air weather serv, US Army Air Force, 44-46. *Mem:* Am Meteorol Soc. *Res:* Applied meteorology; forecast improvement; economic benefits of science services. *Mailing Add:* 4901 Stan Haven Rd Camp Springs MD 20031

MEANY, JOHN EAGLETON, b Brooklyn, NY, Sept 28, 37; m 59; c 2. CHEMISTRY. *Educ:* Seattle Univ, BS, 62; Univ Wash, PhD, 66. *Prof Exp:* Anal chemist, Wash State Horse Racing Comn, 60-62; res assoc acid-base catalysis, Univ Wash, 66-67; asst prof chem, Loyola Univ, 67-68; from asst prof to assoc prof chem, Cent Wash State Col, 68-76; ASSOC PROF CHEM, CENT WASH UNIV, 76- *Concurrent Pos:* NIH fel, 66-67; NSF grant, Sci Fac Prof Develop, 77-78. *Mem:* Am Chem Soc. *Res:* Chemical and enzymatic catalysis in organic reactions. *Mailing Add:* Dept of Chem Cent Wash Univ Ellensburg WA 98926

MEARES, CLAUDE FRANCIS, b Wilmington, NC, Sept 25, 46; m 63; c 3. PHYSICAL CHEMISTRY, BIOLOGICAL CHEMISTRY. *Educ:* Univ NC, BS, 68; Stanford Univ, PhD(phys chem), 72. *Prof Exp:* Asst prof, 72-78, ASSOC PROF CHEM, UNIV CALIF, DAVIS, 78- *Concurrent Pos:* Nat

Cancer Inst grant, 74-; Nat Inst Med Sci grant, 78-; res career develop award, Nat Cancer Inst, NIH, 79-84. *Honors & Awards:* Von Hevesy Prize for Nuclear Med, Von Hevesy Comt & Soc Nuclear Med, 74. *Mem:* Am Chem Soc; Am Soc Biol Chemists; Biophys Soc. *Res:* Metals and bifunctional chelating agents in biology and medicine; structure and mechanism of ribonucleic acid polymerases; photo affinity labelling, fluorescence, energy transfer, radiopharmaceuticals, bleomycin. *Mailing Add:* Dept Chem Univ Calif Davis CA 95616

MEARNS, ALAN JOHN, b Los Angeles, Calif, Oct 4, 43; m; m 74; c 1. FISHERIES, POLLUTION BIOLOGY. *Educ:* Calif State Univ, Long Beach, BS, 65, MA, 68; Univ Wash, PhD(fisheries), 71. *Prof Exp:* Biologist, Allan Hancock Found, Univ Southern Calif, Los Angeles/Arctic Res Lab, Barrow, Alaska, 65-66; res assoc, Fisheries Res Inst, Univ Wash, 68-70; consult physiol, Auke Bay Lab, Nat Marine Fisheries Serv, 70; sr environ scientist pollution biol, Southern Calif Coastal Water Res Proj, 71-73, dir, Biol Div, 73-80; SR ECOLOGIST, OFFICE MARINE POLLUTION ASSESSMENT, NAT OCEANIC & ATMOSPHERIC ADMIN, SEATTLE, 80- *Concurrent Pos:* Environ Protection Agency grant, Corvallis, Ore, 72-75; consult, Calif State Water Resources Control Bd, 75-; Nat Oceanog & Atmospheric Admin grant & NY Bight Mesa Proj grant, 77; water qual comt, Am Fisheries Soc, 77-; Bur of Land Mgt subcontract, 77-78; mem res comt, Water Pollution Control Fedn, 78-; NSF grant, 78-81. *Mem:* Am Inst Fishery Res Biologists; Am Fisheries Soc; Sigma Xi. *Res:* Planning and coordinating national and United States west coast marine pollution and monitoring programs; developing alternative strategies for marine sewage and sludge disposal; conducting research on marine pollution in Puget Sound and on pollutant flow through marine food webs. *Mailing Add:* Off Marine Pollution Assessment Nat Oceanic & Atmospheric Admin 7600 Sand Pt Way NE Seattle WA 98115

MEARS, BRAINERD, JR, b Williamstown, Mass, June 24, 21; m 48; c 4. GEOMORPHOLOGY. *Educ:* Williams Col, AB, 43; Columbia Univ, PhD(geol), 50. *Prof Exp:* Lectr geomorphol, Columbia Univ, 47-49; from asst prof to assoc prof, 49-63, PROF GEOL, UNIV WYO, 63- *Mem:* AAAS; Geol Soc Am; Int Union Quaternary Res. *Res:* Pleistocene geology. *Mailing Add:* Dept of Geol Univ of Wyo Laramie WY 82071

MEARS, DANA CHRISTOPHER, b Pittsburgh, Pa, Sept 4, 40; m 64; c 2. CHEMICAL METALLURGY, MEDICINE. *Educ:* Cornell Univ, BA, 62, Cambridge Univ, PhD(metall), 65; Oxford Univ, MD, 69; MRCP, UK, 72. *Prof Exp:* Res asst metall, Cent Res Lab, Broken Hill Proprietary Co, Ltd, 62; res worker, Cambridge Univ, 62-66; res fel physiol, Nuffield Dept Orthop Surg, Oxford Univ, 66-70, house physician, Radcliffe Infirmary, 70; intern surg, Univ Pittsburgh, 70-71; sr house officer rheumatol, Nuffield Orthop Ctr, Oxford Univ, 71-72, registr in metab med, Nuffield Dept Orthop Surg, 72; resident orthop surg, Children's Hosp Pittsburgh, 72-75; ASST PROF ORTHOP SURG, UNIV PITTSBURGH, 75- *Concurrent Pos:* Mem, Brit Standards Comt Surg Implants, 64- *Mem:* Am Soc Metals; Brit Corrosion & Protection Asn; Brit Corrosion Sci Soc. *Res:* Corrosion and passivity; selection of materials for surgical implants; bone physiology, the relationship between mechanical stress on bone and bone cell metabolism. *Mailing Add:* Children's Hosp Pittsburgh De Sota St Pittsburgh PA 15213

MEARS, DAVID ELLIOTT, b Hamilton, Ohio, Feb 26, 39; m 66; c 1. CHEMICAL ENGINEERING, CATALYSIS. *Educ:* Carnegie Inst Technol, BS, 61; Univ Calif, Berkeley, PhD(chem eng), 65. *Prof Exp:* Res asst chem eng, Univ Calif, Berkeley, 61-65; res engr, 65-68, sr res engr, 68-71, technol sales engr, 71-74, res assoc, 74-75, SUPVR PETROCHEM PROCESS RES, RES CTR, UNION OIL CO CALIF, 76- *Mem:* Am Chem Soc; Am Inst Chem Engrs. *Res:* Heterogeneous chemical kinetics; catalysis; transport effects; petrochemical and refining processes. *Mailing Add:* Res Dept Union Oil Co of Calif PO Box 76 Brea CA 92621

MEARS, DAVID R, b Brooklyn, NY, May 1, 36; m 68; c 2. BIOLOGICAL & AGRICULTURAL ENGINEERING. *Educ:* Rutgers Univ, BS, 58, MS, 61, PhD(eng mech), 68. *Prof Exp:* Asst instr agr eng, Rutgers Univ, 58-60; asst prof sci, Cuttington Col, Liberia, 60-64; teaching asst eng, Univ Calif, Davis, 64-65; res assoc agr eng, 65-69, from asst prof to assoc prof biol & agr eng, 69-78, PROF BIOL & AGR ENG, RUTGERS UNIV, 78-; ASSOC DIR PROG PLANNING & DEVELOP, NJ AGR EXP STA, 81- *Mem:* Am Soc Agr Engrs. *Res:* Mechanical properties of biological materials; mechanization of fruit and vegetable harvesting; engineering agricultural systems for livestock housing, forage production and greenhouses; solar energy for greenhouses; greenhouse engineering; waste heat for greenhouses. *Mailing Add:* Dept of Biol & Agr Eng Cook Col Rutgers Univ New Brunswick NJ 08903

MEARS, GERALD JOHN, b Peace River, Alta, Nov 25, 38; m 63; c 3. ANIMAL PHYSIOLOGY, ENDOCRINOLOGY. *Educ:* Univ Alta, BSc, 63, MSc, 66; Univ Calif, Davis, PhD(physiol), 71. *Prof Exp:* Res asst animal physiol, Univ Calif, Davis, 63-71; fel med physiol, Univ Calgary, 71-73, res assoc fetal pharmacol, 73-74, Med Res Coun Can prof asst, 74-78; RES SCIENTIST ANIMAL PHYSIOL, RES BR, AGR CAN, 78- *Concurrent Pos:* Res fel animal physiol, Univ Calif, Davis, 67-68; fel med physiol, Univ Calgary, 71-73. *Mem:* Agr Inst Can; Can Soc Animal Prod; Can Physiol Soc; Can Fedn Biol Socs. *Res:* The placental transfer of drugs and hormones between the fetus and mother, development of the fetal endocrine system, the relationship between hormones and growth, and ovine reproduction. *Mailing Add:* Animal Sci Sect Agr Can Res Sta Lethbridge AB T1J 4B1 Can

MEARS, JAMES AUSTIN, b Baytown, Tex, May 18, 44; m 66; c 3. BIOCHEMISTRY, SYSTEMATICS. *Educ:* Univ Tex, Austin, BA, 66, PhD(biol), 70. *Prof Exp:* asst cur, 70-80, ASSOC CUR, DEPT BIOL, ACAD NATURAL SCI PHILADELPHIA, 80- *Concurrent Pos:* Adj asst prof, Univ Pa, 70-80, adj assoc prof, 80-; NSF grants, Smithsonian Inst, 71 & Acad Natural Sci, 71-72, 72-73, 74-76, 76-78 & 72-77; res assoc, Morris Arboretum, Philadelphia, 71-; Am Philos Soc grants, 75 & 80; mem bd dirs, Henry Found Bot Res; ed & publ, Chem Plant Taxon Newsletter. *Mem:* Am Soc Plant Taxon; Phytochem Soc NAm; Am Inst Biol Sci; Sigma Xi. *Res:* Studies of the processes of organism and molecule evolution, primarily through analyses of morphological and biochemical characteristics. *Mailing Add:* Dept of Bot Acad Natural Sci 19th & Pkwy Philadelphia PA 19103

MEARS, WHITNEY HARRIS, b Williamstown, Mass, June 8, 12; m; c 2. CHEMISTRY. *Educ:* Williams Col, BA, 33; Harvard Univ, AM, 35, PhD(phys chem), 37. *Prof Exp:* Rockefeller grant, Mt Sinai Hosp, New York, 37-38; Am Philos Soc grant, Univ Pa, 38-39; res chemist, Interchem Co, NY, 40; res chemist, Specialty Chem Div, Allied Chem Corp, 41-43 & 46-70, res assoc, 70-76; RETIRED. *Mem:* Am Chem Soc; Am Soc Heat, Refrig & Air Conditioning Eng; Inst Elec & Electronics Engrs. *Res:* Thermodynamic properties of fluorine compounds; gaseous dielectrics, mixtures; sexagesimo-quarto properties. *Mailing Add:* 45 Dan Ave Pittsfield MA 01201

MEASAMER, S(CHUBERT) G(ERNT), b Wilder, Tenn, Aug 7, 13; m 39; c 2. CHEMICAL ENGINEERING. *Educ:* Tenn Polytech Inst, BS, 35; Iowa State Col, MS, 37, PhD(chem eng), 41. *Prof Exp:* Instr chem, Eng Unit Opers Lab, Iowa State Col, 38-41; res chem engr, Plastics Dept, E I du Pont de Nemours & Co, Inc, NJ, 41-47, group leader, 47-49, res supvr, Film Dept, NY, 49-53, process develop supvr, Ohio, 53-64, process develop supt, E I du Pont de Nemours, Luxembourg SA, 64-70, staff engr expansion, 70-72, staff engr, Circleville Lab, 72-73, sr engr Teflon, 73-78; RETIRED. *Mem:* Am Chem Soc; Am Inst Chem Engrs. *Res:* Extraction of oil from soybeans; product and process development work on plastics; polymer films formation; handling and coating. *Mailing Add:* 1315 Bristol Ct Circleville OH 43113

MEASEL, JOHN WILLIAM, b Texarkana, Tex, Sept 12, 40; m 65; c 1. IMMUNOLOGY, MEDICAL MICROBIOLOGY. *Educ:* Henderson State Univ, BA, 63; ETex State Univ, MA, 64; Univ Okla, PhD(microbiol), 70. *Prof Exp:* Fel vet path, Purdue Univ, 70-72; sr res scientist biochem, Armour Pharm Co, 72-75; asst prof microbiol, Kirksville Col Osteop Med, 75-78; ASST PROF MICROBIOL, TEX COL OSTEOP MED, 78- *Mem:* Am Soc Microbiol; Am Rheumatism Asn; Am Osteop Col Rheumatology. *Res:* Immunology, particularly rheumatoid arthritis and autoimmune diseases. *Mailing Add:* Dept of Microbiol & Immunol 3516 Camp Bowie Blvd Ft Worth TX 76102

MEASURES, RAYMOND MASSEY, b London, Eng, Feb 17, 38; m 62; c 3. LASER PHYSICS. *Educ:* Univ London, BSc, 60, Imp Col, dipl, PhD(physics), 64. *Prof Exp:* From asst prof to assoc prof physics, 64-77, PROF APPL SCI & ENG, INST AEROSPACE STUDIES, UNIV TORONTO, 77- *Res:* Laser environmental sensing; laser studies of plasmas; laser ionization by resonance saturation, development of laser trace element microprobe. *Mailing Add:* Inst Aerospace Studies Univ Toronto 4925 Dufferin St Downsview ON M3H 5T6 Can

MEATH, WILLIAM JOHN, b Toronto, Ont, Apr 8, 36; m 60; c 2. THEORETICAL CHEMISTRY. *Educ:* Carleton Univ, BSc, 60; Univ Wis, PhD(chem), 65. *Prof Exp:* Proj assoc theoret chem inst, Univ Wis, 65; from asst prof to assoc prof chem, 65-71, PROF CHEM, UNIV WESTERN ONT, 71- *Concurrent Pos:* Vis asst prof, Theoret Chem Inst, Univ Wis, 66 & Inst Perla Ricerca Sci E Technol, Univ Di Trento, 79. *Mem:* Am Phys Soc; fel Chem Inst Can. *Res:* Atomic and molecular quantum mechanics; intermolecular forces; stationary state and time dependent atomic and molecular properties. *Mailing Add:* Dept Chem Univ Western Ont London ON N6A 5B8 Can

MEBUS, CHARLES ALBERT, b Paterson, NJ, Sept 10, 32; m 55; c 3. VETERINARY PATHOLOGY. *Educ:* Cornell Univ, DVM, 56; Kans State Univ, MS, 62, PhD(vet path), 63. *Prof Exp:* Pvt pract, Del, 58-60; assoc prof vet path, Kans State Univ, 63-65; prof vet sci, Univ Nebr, Lincoln, 65-77; LAB CHIEF PATH, PLUM ISLAND ANIMAL DIS CTR, 77- *Mem:* Am Vet Med Asn; Am Col Vet Path. *Res:* Viral animal diseases. *Mailing Add:* Plum Island Dis Ctr PO Box 848 Greenport NY 11944

MECCA, CHRISTYNA EMMA, b Brooklyn, NY, Oct 23, 36. BIOLOGY, BIOCHEMISTRY. *Educ:* George Washington Univ, BS, 60, MS, 63, PhD(biol), 69. *Prof Exp:* Med biol technician, NIH, 58-60, biologist, 60-62, chemist, 62-65; instr gen biol, Montgomery Col, 68-69; res biologist, Bur Radiol Health, USPHS, 69-70; staff biologist, Coastal Plains Ctr Marine Develop Serv, Washington, DC, 70-72; prog analyst, NIH, 72-74; analyst-biologist, Smithsonian Inst Sci Info Exchange, 75-76; lectr biol, Wheeling Col, 78; RES ASSOC DEPT BIOCHEM, SCH MED, WVA UNIV, 79- *Mem:* AAAS. *Res:* Qualitative biochemical characteristics of cellular and organismic systems. *Mailing Add:* Dept Biochem WVa Univ Morgantown WV 26506

MECCA, STEPHEN JOSEPH, b New York, NY, Jan 15, 43; m 64; c 3. ENERGY SYSTEMS, SOFTWARE ENGINEERING. *Educ:* Providence Col, BS, 64, MS, 66; Rensselaer Polytech Inst, PhD(physics), 69. *Prof Exp:* Assoc prof physics, 69-80, PROF ENG PHYSICS SYSTEMS, PROVIDENCE COL, 80- *Mem:* Am Phys Soc; Am Inst Physics; Am Asn Physics Teachers. *Res:* Nuclear physics; especially nuclear spectroscopy and photonuclear physics; systems approach to complex problem solving; systems analysis, systems science and engineering; energy management; solar systems. *Mailing Add:* Dept Physics Providence Col Providence RI 02918

MECH, LUCYAN DAVID, b Auburn, NY, Jan 18, 37; m 58; c 4. WILDLIFE ECOLOGY. *Educ:* Cornell Univ, BS, 58; Purdue Univ, PhD(vert ecol), 62. *Prof Exp:* NIH fel animal movements & telemetry, Univ Minn, Minneapolis, 63-64, res assoc, 64-66; res assoc biol, Macalester Col, 66-69; WILDLIFE RES BIOLOGIST, US FISH & WILDLIFE SERV, 69- *Honors & Awards:* Spec Achievement Award, US Fish & Wildlife Serv, 70 & Civil Servant of the Year Award, 73; Terrestrial Wildlife Publ Award, Wildlife Soc, 72. *Mem:* Am Soc Mammal; Ecol Soc Am; Sigma Xi; Wildlife Soc. *Res:* Predator-prey relations; mammal behavior and natural history; animal movements and factors affecting them; ecology, behavior and sociology of wolves; spatial organization of mammals; telemetry and radio-tracking. *Mailing Add:* US Fish & Wildlife Serv NCent Forest Exp Sta Folwell Ave St Paul MN 55108

MECH, WILLIAM PAUL, b La Crosse, Wis, Mar 10, 42; m 64; c 3. MATHEMATICS. *Educ:* Wash State Univ, BA, 64; Univ Ill, MS, 65, PhD(math), 70. *Prof Exp:* From asst prof to assoc prof, 70-78, chmn dept, 75-80, PROF MATH, BOISE STATE UNIV, 78- *Concurrent Pos:* Dir honors prog, Boise State Univ, 70-; pres, Nat Collegiate Honors Coun, 80-81. *Mem:* AAAS; Math Asn Am; Am Math Soc. *Res:* Analysis and functional analysis; extension of positive operators; graphs of groups; spectral analysis. *Mailing Add:* Dept of Math Boise State Univ Boise ID 83725

MECHAM, JOHN STEPHEN, b Austin, Tex, Feb 29, 28; m 50; c 2. HERPETOLOGY, EVOLUTIONARY BIOLOGY. *Educ:* Univ Tex, BA, 50, PhD(zool), 55; Univ Fla, MS, 52. *Prof Exp:* Asst prof zool, Univ Tulsa, 55-56; from asst prof to assoc prof, Auburn Univ, 56-65; assoc prof, 65-69, PROF ZOOL, TEX TECH UNIV, 69- *Concurrent Pos:* NSF res grants, 58-61, 62-65, 67-68 & 69-71. *Mem:* Am Soc Ichthyol & Herpet; Soc Study Evolution; Soc Syst Zool. *Res:* Systematics and evolutionary mechanisms of anuran amphibians. *Mailing Add:* Dept of Biol Sci Tex Tech Univ Lubbock TX 79409

MECHAM, MERLIN J, b Neola, Utah, Jan 31, 23; m 47; c 2. SPEECH PATHOLOGY, AUDIOLOGY. *Educ:* Brigham Young Univ, BA, 48; Utah State Univ, MS, 49; Ohio State Univ, PhD(speech path, audiol), 54. *Prof Exp:* Instr speech, Utah State Univ, 49-50; instr, Ohio State Univ, 52-54; assoc prof speech path, Brigham Young Univ, 54-61; dir speech path & audiol, 61-76, actg chmn dept speech, 69-70, PROF SPEECH, UNIV UTAH, 61- *Concurrent Pos:* Book abstractor, DSH Abstracts, 60-; consult, Utah State Training Sch, American Fork, 68-; Am Speech & Hearing Asn accrediting site visitor, Am Bd Examr, 70-77; consult ed, J Speech & Hearing Disorders, 74-77. *Mem:* Fel Am Speech & Hearing Asn; Am Asn Mental Retardation. *Res:* Developmental aspects of normal and disordered audiolinguistic skills in children; exploratory model of neurolinguistic dysfunction. *Mailing Add:* Div of Speech Path & Audiol Univ of Utah Salt Lake City UT 84112

MECHANIC, GERALD, b New York, NY, Jan 7, 27; m 52; c 2. ORGANIC CHEMISTRY, BIOCHEMISTRY. *Educ:* City Col New York, BS, 51; NY Univ, MS, 53, PhD(chem), 58. *Prof Exp:* Asst acetylene chem, NY Univ, 52-53, res chemist biochem, 57-58; head biochem res lab, Manhattan State Hosp, 58-59; res assoc, Inst Med Res & Studies, NY, 59-60; res fel orthop surg, Mass Gen Hosp, 60-69, asst biochem, 66-69; res assoc biol chem, Harvard Med Sch, 63-69; assoc prof, 69-72, PROF ORAL BIOL, SCH DENT & PROF BIOCHEM, SCH MED, UNIV NC, CHAPEL HILL, 72- *Mem:* AAAS; Am Chem Soc; NY Acad Sci; Royal Soc Chem; Am Soc Biol Chemists. *Res:* Chemistry of amino acids, peptides and proteins, with special reference to connective tissue. *Mailing Add:* Dent Res Ctr Univ of NC Chapel Hill NC 27514

MECHERIKUNNEL, ANN T, b Pottanat Vempally, India, Dec, 28, 34; US citizen; m 61; c 2. SPACE SCIENCE. *Educ:* Univ Madras, BS, 55; Univ Kerala, MS, 58; George Washington Univ, PhD(chem), 70. *Prof Exp:* Chemist, Health Serv Div, USV Pharmaceut Corp, 72-74; res assoc chem, Col Pharm, Howard Univ, 74-75; res assoc solar studies, 75-78, ASST SPACE OPTICS, GODDARD SPACE FLIGHT CTR, NASA, 78- *Concurrent Pos:* Lectr chem, George Washington Univ, 70-71; instr chem, Prince Georges Col, Md, 72-73. *Mem:* Am Chem Soc; Illum Eng Soc; AAAS. *Res:* Total and spectral irradiance of the sun and its variability; earth radiation budget studies; ultraviolet-visible, infrared calibration of sensors for experiments from space; atmospheric radiative transfer models; effect of aerosol, water vapor, ozone and carbondioxide on the solar radiation received at ground surface and at the upper atmosphere. *Mailing Add:* Code 972 Goddard Space Flight Ctr Greenbelt MD 20771

MECHLER, MARK VINCENT, b Fredericksburg, Tex, Feb 5, 25; m 57; c 3. PHYSICS. *Educ:* Univ Tex, BA, 51, MA, 57, PhD(physics), 67. *Prof Exp:* Res scientist, Defense Res Lab, Univ Tex, 51-57; res engr, Collins Radio Co, 57-58; from res scientist to head underwater missile div, Defense Res Lab, Univ Tex, Austin, 58-69; SR SCIENTIST RES DIV, UNITECH, INC, 69- *Mem:* Acoust Soc Am. *Res:* Underwater sound; electro-acoustic transducers; sound propagation and scattering; electronics. *Mailing Add:* Unitech Inc 1005 St Elmo Rd Austin TX 78745

MECHLIN, GEORGE FRANCIS, JR, b Pittsburgh, Pa, July 23, 23; m 49. PHYSICS. *Educ:* Univ Pittsburgh, BS, 44, MS, 47, PhD(physics), 50. *Prof Exp:* Sr scientist, Bettis Atomic Power Div, 49-57, dir adv systs eng, Sunnyvale Div, Calif, 57-64, mgr missile launching & handling, 64-68, gen mgr, Underseas Div, Md, 68-71, gen mgr astronuclear & oceanic div, Md, 71-73, VPRES, RES & DEVELOP, WESTINGHOUSE ELEC CORP, 73- *Concurrent Pos:* Mem, Res Adv Comt, US Coast Guard, 73-75; vchmn, Marine Bd, Nat Res Coun, 75-79; mem naval res adv comt, Lab Adv Bd for Naval Ships, 75-78; dir, Pittsburgh Broadcasting Co, 80- *Honors & Awards:* Order of Merit, Westinghouse Elec Corp, 61. *Mem:* Nat Acad Eng; Am Phys Soc; Am Inst Aeronaut & Astronaut; Marine Technol Soc; Nat Soc Aerospace Prof. *Mailing Add:* Res & Develop Ctr Westinghouse Elec Corp Pittsburgh PA 15235

MECHOLSKY, JOHN JOSEPH, JR, b Philadelphia, Pa, July 24, 44; m 66; c 3. MATERIALS SCIENCE ENGINEERING. *Educ:* Catholic Univ Am, BCE, 66, MCE, 68, PhD(mats sci), 73. *Prof Exp:* Civil engr, Naval Fac Eng Command, Washington, DC, 66-67; structural engr, Naval Ship Res & Develop Ctr, 67-72; ceramic res engr, Naval Res Labs, DC, 72-79; MEM TECH STAFF, SANDIA NAT LABS, 79- *Concurrent Pos:* Res asst mat sci, Cath Univ Am, 68-73. *Mem:* Am Soc Testing & Mat; Am Ceramic Soc; Sigma Xi. *Res:* Quantitative fracture surface analysis of brittle materials; identification of toughening mechanisms in glass ceramics; production of reinforced glasses; understanding environmentally assisted stress corrosion in glasses; author or coauthor of over 90 publications. *Mailing Add:* Orgn 5845 Sandia Nat Labs Albuquerque NM 87185

MECHTLY, EUGENE A, b Red Lion, Pa, Feb 14, 31; m 65; c 3. RADIOPHYSICS. *Educ:* Western Md Col, BS, 52; Pa State Univ, MS, 58, PhD(physics), 62. *Prof Exp:* Physicist, Army Missile Labs & Marshall Space Flight Ctr, NASA, 54-65; res assoc elec eng, 65-67, asst prof, 67-69, asst dean col eng, 75-76 & 78-79, ASSOC PROF ELEC ENG, UNIV ILL, URBANA, 69- *Concurrent Pos:* Mem comn G, US Nat Comt, Int Union Radio Sci; chmn metrication comt, Am Soc Eng Educ, 78- *Mem:* Am Geophys Union; Am Soc Eng Educ; Am Soc Testing & Mat; Int Union Radio Sci. *Res:* Propagation of radio waves in the ionosphere; physics of the upper atmosphere; metrology. *Mailing Add:* 804 Mumford Dr Urbana IL 61801

MECKEL, ALFRED HANS, b Munich, Ger, Mar 12, 24; US citizen; m 51; c 1. DENTISTRY. *Educ:* Univ Munich, Dr med dent, 49; Northwestern Univ, DDS, 57. *Prof Exp:* Dentist, US Army, Ger, 49-54; RES DENTIST, PROCTER & GAMBLE CO, 54- *Mem:* Am Dent Asn; Int Dent Fedn; Int Asn Dent Res. *Res:* Organic films on teeth; reactions of tin and fluorides; enamel structure; electron microscopy; clinical investigations. *Mailing Add:* 6110 Center Hill Rd Cincinnati OH 45224

MECKLENBORG, KENNETH THOMAS, organic chemistry, deceased

MECKLENBURG, ROY ALBERT, b Elmhurst, Ill, Feb 10, 33; m 60; c 3. PLANT PHYSIOLOGY, MICROCLIMATOLOGY. *Educ:* Mich State Univ, BS, 58; Cornell Univ, MS, 61, PhD(agr), 63. *Prof Exp:* Asst ornamental hort, Cornell Univ, 58-63; asst prof landscape hort, Mich State Univ, 63-70, assoc prof hort, 70-76, prof, 76-77; PRES, CHICAGO HORT SOC & DIR, CHIGAGO BOT GARDEN, 77- *Mem:* Am Asn Bot Gardens & Arboreta; Am Soc Hort Sci. *Res:* Physiology of low temperature hardiness in higher plants; the effect of plants on urban noise, dust and microclimate. *Mailing Add:* Bot Garden PO Box 400 Glencoe IL 60022

MECKLER, ALVIN, b New York, NY, Apr 20, 26; m 47; c 3. THEORETICAL PHYSICS. *Educ:* City Col New York, BS, 47; Mass Inst Technol, PhD(physics), 52. *Prof Exp:* Mem staff solid state physics, Lincoln Lab, Mass Inst Technol, 52-55; chief div phys sci, Nat Security Agency, Md, 55-67; ASSOC PROF PHYSICS, UNIV MD, BALTIMORE COUNTY, 67- *Mem:* Am Phys Soc. *Mailing Add:* 5234 Hesperus Dr Columbia MD 21043

MECKLOSKY, MORTON, b New York, NY, Apr 13, 32; m 52; c 2. MATHEMATICS. *Educ:* Hunter Col, AB, 59; Columbia Univ, MA, 61, prof dipl math, 65; Rutgers Univ, MA, 63. *Prof Exp:* PROF MATH, SUFFOLK COUNTY COMMUNITY COL, 63- *Concurrent Pos:* Lectr, State Univ NY Stony Brook, 68- *Mem:* Math Asn Am. *Res:* Logic. *Mailing Add:* 35 Shelbourne Lane Stony Brook NY 11790

MECKSTROTH, GEORGE R, b Cincinnati, Ohio, Aug 26, 35; m 57; c 2. RADIOLOGICAL PHYSICS. *Educ:* Univ Cincinnati, BS, 58, MS, 60; PhD(radiol physics), 63. *Prof Exp:* ADJ PROF RADIOL, SCH MED, TULANE UNIV, 64- *Concurrent Pos:* Consult, Charity Hosp La, New Orleans, 65-, USPHS Hosp, 65-, Vet Admin Hosp, 65-, West Jefferson Gen Hosp, 68-, Hotel Dieu Hosp, 68-, East Jefferson Gen Hosp, 70- & St Charles Gen Hosp, 73- *Mem:* Am Col Radiol; Am Asn Univ Prof; Am Asn Physicists in Med; Health Physics Soc; Soc Nuclear Med. *Mailing Add:* Dept of Radiol Tulane Univ Sch of Med New Orleans LA 70112

MEDAK, HERMAN, b Vienna, Austria, Apr 26, 14; nat US; m 45; c 4. ORAL PATHOLOGY. *Educ:* Univ Toledo, BS, 43; Northwestern Univ, MS & DDS, 46; Univ Ill, PhD(anat), 59; Am Bd Oral Path, dipl, 64; Univ Vienna, MD, 73. *Prof Exp:* Med technician, Flower Hosp, Toledo, Ohio, 39-43; med technician, Chicago Wesley Mem Hosp, 43-47; res asst histol, 48-51, from instr to prof oral path, 53-67, actg head dept, 64-67, PROF PREV MED & COMMUNITY HEALTH, COL MED, UNIV ILL MED CTR, 67-, CHIEF CLIN ORAL PATH, DEPT ORAL DIAG, COL DENT, 67-, HEAD DEPT ORAL DIAG, 77- *Concurrent Pos:* Dent consult, Ill Res Hosp & Tumor Clin, 48-53. *Mem:* AAAS; Am Dent Asn; Am Soc Clin Path; Am Acad Dent Med; Am Acad Oral Path. *Res:* Effect of irradiation on teeth and oral structures; epithelium of the oral mucosa; oral cytology. *Mailing Add:* Dept of Oral Diag Col of Dent Univ of Ill Med Ctr Chicago IL 60680

MEDALIA, AVROM IZAK, b Boston, Mass, Feb 3, 23; m 43, 56; c 4. COLLOID CHEMISTRY, RUBBER CHEMISTRY. *Educ:* Harvard Univ, AB, 42; Univ Minn, PhD(anal chem), 48. *Prof Exp:* Asst, Cornell Univ, 42-43; chemist, Brookhaven Nat Lab, 49-52; asst dir polymer res, Boston Univ, 52-55; sr res chemist, Godfrey L Cabot, Inc, 56-58, head fundamental res sect, 59-62, assoc dir res carbon black div, 63-70, group leader, Res & Develop Div, 70-80, SR SCIENTIST, CABOT CORP, 80- *Mem:* Am Chem Soc; Soc Rheology. *Res:* Colloids; polymers. *Mailing Add:* Cabot Corp Concord Rd Billerica MA 01821

MEDARIS, L GORDON, JR, b Memphis, Tenn, July 14, 36; m 58; c 3. PETROLOGY. *Educ:* Stanford Univ, BS, 58; Univ Calif, Los Angeles, PhD(geol), 66. *Prof Exp:* Assoc prof, 71-77, PROF GEOL, UNIV WIS-MADISON, 77- *Mem:* AAAS; Geol Soc Am; Mineral Soc Am; Geochem Soc; Am Geophys Union. *Res:* Igneous and metamorphiz petrology; petrology of alpine peridotites; areal geology of northwest California and southwest Oregon; precambrian geology of Wisconsin; crustal garnet peridotites in Norway. *Mailing Add:* Dept of Geol & Geophys Univ of Wis Madison WI 53706

MEDCALF, DARRELL GERALD, b Tillamook, Ore, Feb 10, 37; m 60; c 3. CARBOHYDRATE CHEMISTRY. *Educ:* Lewis & Clark Col, BA, 59; Purdue Univ, MS, 62, PhD(biochem), 64. *Prof Exp:* Asst prof cereal technol, NDak State Univ, 63-67; from assoc prof to prof chem, Univ Puget Sound, 67-78; lab mgr, 78-80, SR LAB MGR, GEN FOODS CORP, 80- *Mem:* Am Chem Soc; Am Asn Cereal Chemists. *Res:* Organic chemistry of carbohydrates, particularly polysaccharides; plant biochemistry, cereal chemistry. *Mailing Add:* Gen Foods Corp 250 North St White Plains NY 10625

MEDEARIS, DONALD N, JR, b Kansas City, Kans, Aug 22, 27; m 56; c 3. PEDIATRICS, MICROBIOLOGY. *Educ:* Univ Kans, AB, 49; Harvard Med Sch, MD, 53. *Prof Exp:* Intern internal med, Barnes Hosp, St Louis, Mo, 53-54; resident pediat, Children's Hosp, Cincinnati, Ohio, 54-56; res fel, Harvard Med Sch & Res Div Infectious Dis, Children's Med Ctr, Boston, 56-58; asst prof pediat, Sch Med, Johns Hopkins Univ, 58-63, asst prof microbiol, 59-63, assoc prof pediat & microbiol, 63-65; prof pediat, Sch Med, Univ Pittsburgh, 65-75, chmn dept, 65-69, dean, 69-75; PROF PEDIAT, HARVARD MED SCH & CHIEF, CHILDREN'S SERVS, MASS GEN HOSP, 75- *Concurrent Pos:* Med dir, Children's Hosp Pittsburgh, 65-69. *Mem:* AAAS; Am Asn Immunol; Soc Pediat Res; Infectious Dis Soc Am; Soc Exp Biol & Med. *Res:* Pathogenesis of infection in immature animals. *Mailing Add:* Burnham Div Mass Gen Hosp 32 Fruit St Boston MA 02114

MEDEARIS, KENNETH GORDON, b Peoria, Ill, Aug 5, 30; m 53; c 3. CIVIL ENGINEERING, ENGINEERING MECHANICS. *Educ:* Univ Ill, BS, 52, MS, 53; Stanford Univ, PhD(eng), 62. *Prof Exp:* Stress analyst, Sandia Corp, NMex, 57-58; from asst prof to assoc prof civil eng, Univ NMex, 58-62; assoc prof eng, Ariz State Univ, 62-63; eng consult, 62-66; prof & dir comput ctr, Colo State Univ, 66-69; PRES, KENNETH MEDEARIS & ASSOCS, RES, ENG & COMPUT CONSULTS, 69- *Concurrent Pos:* State of Calif res grants, 61-65; affiliate prof, Colo State Univ, 69-; chmn, Larimer Co Comput Comn, 74- *Mem:* Seismol Soc Am; Am Soc Civil Engrs; Asn Comput Mach; Sigma Xi. *Res:* Structural dynamics; applied mathematics; computers. *Mailing Add:* 1901 Seminole Dr Ft Collins CO 80525

MEDEIROS, ROBERT WHIPPEN, b Newburgh, NY, Mar 10, 31; m 59; c 2. ORGANIC CHEMISTRY. *Educ:* Univ Maine, BS, 52, Univ Del, MS, 57, PhD(org chem), 60. *Prof Exp:* Res chemist, Scott Paper Co, Pa, 52-55; res chemist, Newburgh Res Lab, E I du Pont de Nemours & Co, NY, 59-60 & Armstrong Cork Co, Pa, 60-63; asst prof chem, PMC Cols, 63-68; assoc prof, 68-74, PROF CHEM, WEST CHESTER STATE COL, 74- *Concurrent Pos:* Petrol Res Fund grant, 67-69. *Mem:* Am Chem Soc. *Res:* Chemistry of heterocyclic nitrogen compounds and vinyl polymers. *Mailing Add:* West Chester State Col West Chester PA 19380

MEDERSKI, HENRY JOHN, b Chicago, Ill, Jan 24, 22; m 48; c 3. PLANT PHYSIOLOGY. *Educ:* Mich State Col, BS, 47; Ohio State Univ, PhD(soils, agron), 50. *Prof Exp:* From asst prof to assoc prof agron, Agr Res & Develop Ctr, 50-59, PROF AGRON, AGR RES & DEVELOP CTR, UNIV OHIO, 59- *Concurrent Pos:* Consult, Farm Bur Coop Asn, 57- & Int Atomic Energy Agency, 63 & 66. *Mem:* Fel AAAS; Am Soc Plant Physiol; Soil Sci Soc Am; Am Soc Agron. *Res:* Soil-plant-water relations; internal plant water relations; photosynthesis; plant-climate relations; plant nutrition. *Mailing Add:* Ohio Agr Res & Develop Ctr Wooster OH 44691

MEDICI, PAUL T, b New York, NY, May 10, 19; m 43; c 3. HEMATOLOGY, ENDOCRINOLOGY. *Educ:* St John's Univ, NY, BS, 42 & 48, MS, 51; NY Univ, PhD, 56. *Prof Exp:* Instr biol sci, Col Pharm, 48-52, asst prof bact & pub health, 52-56, from assoc prof to prof, Grad Sch, 56-65, PROF HEMAT & ENDOCRINOL, GRAD SCH, ST JOHN'S UNIV, NY, 65-, CHMN DEPT BIOL, 65-, DEAN GRAD SCH ARTS & SCI, 69- *Concurrent Pos:* Lectr, Guggenheim Dent Clin, New York, 51-53. *Mem:* Fel AAAS; fel NY Acad Sci; Soc Study Blood; Am Soc Hemat. *Res:* Endocrinology of blood. *Mailing Add:* Grad Sch of Art & Sci St John's Univ Jamaica NY 11439

MEDICK, MATTHEW A, b New York, NY, Jan 20, 27; m 53; c 5. ENGINEERING MECHANICS, APPLIED MATHEMATICS. *Educ:* Univ Ill, BS, 48; NY Univ, MS, 50, PhD(eng mech), 58. *Prof Exp:* Lectr math, Pace Col, 50-51; appl sci rep, Int Bus Mach Corp, 51-53; lectr math, City Col New York, 53-55; res assoc civil eng & eng mech, Columbia Univ, 55-57; sr staff scientist, Res & Advan Develop Div, Avco Corp, 57-62; PROF MECH ENG, MICH STATE UNIV, 62- *Mem:* Am Soc Mech Engrs; Am Math Soc; Math Asn Am; Soc Indust & Appl Math; Soc Eng Sci. *Res:* Wave motion; impact and vibrations in solids; continuum mechanics; asymptotic phenomena; functional analysis; biomechanics. *Mailing Add:* Col of Eng Mich State Univ East Lansing MI 48824

MEDICUS, HEINRICH ADOLF, b Zurich, Switz, Dec 24, 18; m 61. NUCLEAR PHYSICS. *Educ:* Swiss Fed Inst Technol, DrScNat(physics), 49. *Prof Exp:* Res assoc physics, Swiss Fed Inst Technol, 43-50; visitor radiation lab, Univ Calif, 50-51; guest, Mass Inst Technol, 51-52, instr physics, 52-54, vis asst prof, 54-55; assoc prof, 55-72, PROF PHYSICS, RENSSELAER POLYTECH INST, 72- *Concurrent Pos:* Swiss Nat Scholarship, 50-52; vis scientist, Atomic Energy Res Estab, Harwell, Eng, 67-68 & Swiss Inst Nuclear Res, Villigen, 75-76. *Mem:* Am Phys Soc; Swiss Phys Soc. *Res:* Radioactivity; meson physics; photonuclear reactions; nuclear structure; history of physics. *Mailing Add:* Dept of Physics Rensselaer Polytech Inst Troy NY 12181

MEDIN, A(ARON) LOUIS, b Baltimore, Md, Oct 2, 25; m 50; c 4. CHEMICAL ENGINEERING, DATA PROCESSING SYSTEMS. *Educ:* Johns Hopkins Univ, BE, 48; Ohio State Univ, PhD(chem eng), 51. *Prof Exp:* Asst, USPHS, Ohio State Univ, 49-50; chem engr, US Atomic Energy Comn, 51-53; res engr, Ford Motor Co, 53-55; chief nuclear chem technol, Alco Prod, Inc, 55-58; res engr nuclear appln, US Steel Corp, 58-62; sr proj scientist, Avco Corp, 63-65; mgr sci applns dept, Int Bus Mach Corp, 65-67, mgr advan med applns, IBM Corp, 67-70, mgr environ & health sci, 70-72; dir environ & life sci, Off Dir Defense Res & Eng, Dept Defense, 72-74; sr govt analyst, 75-78, MGR DEVELOP PROG, IBM CORP, 79- *Honors & Awards:* Outstanding Contrib Award, IBM Corp, 69. *Mem:* Am Inst Chem Engrs; Am Inst Aeronaut & Astronaut; Nat Security Indust Asn; Am Defense Preparedness Asn. *Res:* Aerospace applications; space experimentations; nuclear power technology; corrosion, materials and water technology, data processing and medical applications; defense systems; command and control systems; training device systems; advanced semi-conductor applications. *Mailing Add:* 10912 Candlelight Lane Potomac MD 20854

MEDINA, DANIEL, b New York, NY, Mar 6, 41; m 63; c 3. ONCOLOGY. *Educ:* Univ Calif, Berkeley, BA, 63, MA, 66, PhD(zool), 69. *Prof Exp:* PROF CELL BIOL, BAYLOR COL MED, 69- *Concurrent Pos:* USPHS res grant chem carcinogenesis, Baylor Col Med, 71-82; assoc ed, Cancer Res, Breast Cancer Res & Treat. *Mem:* AAAS; Am Asn Cancer Res; Am Soc Cell Biol. *Res:* Tumor biology; chemical carcinogenesis of mouse mammary glands; chemical-virus interactions; biology of preneoplastic lesions. *Mailing Add:* Dept of Cell Biol Baylor Col of Med Houston TX 77030

MEDINA, JOSE ENRIQUE, b Santurce, PR, May 1, 26; m 48; c 3. DENTISTRY. *Educ:* Univ Md, DDS, 48. *Prof Exp:* From instr to prof oper dent, Baltimore Col Dent Surg, Sch Dent, Univ Md, 48-67, from actg head dept to head dept, 57-67, asst dean col, 63-67; from assoc dean to dean, Col Dent, 67-74, dir health ctr space planning & utilization, 74-76, PROF CLIN DENT, UNIV FLA, 67-, ASST V PRES FACIL PLANNING & OPER, 76- *Concurrent Pos:* Spec lectr, Walter Reed Army Med Ctr, Washington, DC, 58-64; consult, Univ Md Hosp, 58-67, USPHS Hosp, 60-67 & US Naval Dent Sch, 64-67; hon prof, San Carlos Univ Guatemala, 60. *Honors & Awards:* Distinguished Serv Award, Fla Dent Asn, 78- *Mem:* Fel AAAS; fel Int Col Dentist; fel Am Col Dent; Int Asn Dent Res; hon Dent Soc Guatemala. *Res:* Restorative procedures; new materials for dental use. *Mailing Add:* J Hillis Miller Health Ctr Univ of Fla Col of Dent Gainesville FL 32610

MEDINA, MARJORIE B, b Capiz, Philippines, Dec 29, 45; US citizen. FOOD SCIENCE, NUTRITION. *Educ:* Univ Santo Tomas, Manila, BS, 64; Rutgers Univ, MS, 74, PhD(food sci), 78. *Prof Exp:* Res chemist textile, Consolidated Textile Mills, 64-65; res assoc labor res, Univ Philippines, 65-68; sr res technician endocrinol, Med Ctr, Cornell Univ, 68-71; lectr food sci, Univ Vt, 77-80; MEM STAFF, US DEPT AGR, 80- *Mem:* Inst Food Technologists; Am Chem Soc; NY Acad Sci; AAAS; Res & Develop Assocs Mil Foods & Packaging Systs. *Res:* Protein quantitation and protein quality analysis; applications of scanning electron microscopy and x-ray fluorescent analysis food systems; carbohydrate analysis; leaf protein analysis; food chemistry. *Mailing Add:* USDA ERRC 600 E Mermaid Lane Philadelphia PA 19141

MEDINA, MIGUEL ANGEL, b Laredo, Tex, July 5, 32; m 63; c 3. PHARMACOLOGY, BIOCHEMISTRY. *Educ:* St Mary's Univ, Tex, BS, 57, MS, 63; Univ Tex, Dallas, PhD(pharmacol), 68. *Prof Exp:* Jr chemist, Res & Develop Div, Am Oil Co, Tex, 57-59; res biochemist, Sch Aerospace Med, Brooks AFB, 59-64, res pharmacologist, 67-70; PROF PHARMACOL, UNIV TEX HEALTH SCI CTR, SAN ANTONIO, 70- *Concurrent Pos:* Lectr, St Mary's Univ, Tex, 67-70. *Mem:* Am Chem Soc; Am Soc Pharmacol & Exp Therapeut; Int Soc Biochem Pharmacol. *Res:* Brain and drug metabolism; histamine. *Mailing Add:* 120 West Summit San Antonio TX 78212

MEDINA, MIGUEL ANGEL, JR, b Havana, Cuba, Dec 9, 46; US citizen; m 76; c 1. WATER RESOURCES, ENVIRONMENTAL ENGINEERING. *Educ:* Univ Ala, BSCE, 68, MSCE, 72; Univ Fla, PhD(water resources & environ eng), 76. *Prof Exp:* Asst post engr design & construct, 3rd US Army Hq, Ft McPherson, Ga, 70-71; researcher water pollution, Univ Ala, 71-72; researcher urban stormwater, Univ Fla, 72-76; asst prof, 76-80, PROF CIVIL ENG, DUKE UNIV, 80- *Concurrent Pos:* Prin investr, US Environ Protection Agency, 77-79, consult, 78-; rep, Nat Water Data Exchange, US Geol Surv, 77-; prin investr, NSF, 78-80; consult, Univ Fla Indust & Exp Sta, 78- & Tech Adv Serv for Atty, 78- & Technol Dept & Appln Br, Environ Protection Agency, Athens, Ga; prin investr, Off Water Res & Technol, 80-81 & NC Water Resources Res Inst, 81-82. *Mem:* Am Geophys Union; Am Soc Civil Engrs; Am Water Resources Asn; Asn Environ Eng Prof; Sigma Xi. *Res:* Mathematical modeling and computer simulation of pollutant transport systems, natural and man-made, throughout hydrologic cycle; operational hydrology. *Mailing Add:* Dept Civil Eng Duke Univ Durham NC 27706

MEDITCH, JAMES S, b Indianapolis, Ind, July 30, 34; m 64; c 2. ELECTRICAL ENGINEERING. *Educ:* Purdue Univ, BSEE, 56, PhD, 61; Mass Inst Technol, SM, 57. *Prof Exp:* Mem tech staff, Aerospace Corp, Calif, 61-65; assoc prof elec eng, Northwestern Univ, 66-67; staff mem, Boeing Sci Res Labs, Wash, 67-70; from assoc prof to prof, Elec Eng, Univ Calif, Irvine, 70-77; PROF & CHMN, DEPT ELEC ENG, UNIV WASH, SEATTLE, 77- *Concurrent Pos:* Adj prof comput sci, Univ Wash, Seattle, 80- *Mem:* Fel Inst Elec & Electronics Engrs; Asn Comput Mach; AAAS. *Res:* Computer networks; telecommunications; optimization theory. *Mailing Add:* Dept of Elec Eng FT-10 Univ of Wash Seattle WA 98195

MEDLER, JOHN THOMAS, b Las Cruces, NMex, May 28, 14; m 64; c 4. ENTOMOLOGY. *Educ:* NMex State Col, BS, 36, MS, 37; Univ Minn, PhD(entom), 40. *Prof Exp:* Asst entom, Univ Minn, 37-40; res fel exp sta, NMex State Col coop with Tex Gulf Sulfur Co, 41; Guggenheim Mem Found fel, Univ Calif, 42; asst entomologist, USPHS, 42-43; from asst prof to prof, 46-79, EMER PROF ENTOM, UNIV WIS-MADISON, 79-; HON ASSOC, BERNICE P BISHOP MUS, 79- *Concurrent Pos:* Chmn dept plant sci, chief party Wis-USAID contract, Fac Agr, Univ Nigeria, 68-75; proj dir, Midwest Univ Consortium Int Activ-USAID-Govt Indonesia Higher Educ contracts, Indonesia, 76-79. *Res:* taxonomy and biology of Homoptera; ecology of bumblebees and native wild bees; classification and faunal list of Nigerian insects; research and development of Nigerian agriculture; higher agricultural education development in Indonesia. *Mailing Add:* Dept Entom Bernice P Bishop Mus PO Box 19000-A Honolulu HI 96819

MEDLIN, GENE WOODARD, b Greensboro, NC, Oct 5, 25; m 45; c 5. MATHEMATICS. *Educ:* Wake Forest Col, BS, 48; Univ NC, MA, 50, PhD(math), 53. *Prof Exp:* Assoc prof math, Wake Forest Col, 52-56; mathematician, Oak Ridge Nat Lab, 56-57; NSF grant, Swiss Fed Inst Tech, 57-58; assoc prof, 58-65, PROF MATH, STETSON UNIV, 65-, CHMN DEPT, 58- *Concurrent Pos:* Vis lectr grad sch, Univ Tenn, 56-57. *Mem:* Am Math Soc; Math Asn Am; Asn Comput Mach. *Res:* Matrix theory. *Mailing Add:* 600 N McDonald Ave Deland FL 32720

MEDLIN, JULIE ANNE, b Battlecreek, Mich, Apr 30, 36. ENVIRONMENTAL SCIENCES. *Educ:* Univ Mich, BS, 58; Western Mich Univ, MA, 63, PhD(environ sci), 80. *Prof Exp:* Instr ecol & oceanog, Western Mich Univ, 78-80; ASST PROF ECOL & PHYSIOL, NAZARETH COL, 81- *Concurrent Pos:* Consult, Geol Dept, Western Mich Univ, 80- *Mem:* AAAS. *Res:* Uptake of heavy metals in plants; distribution of heavy metals and ions that affect the uptake in the plant; use of lichens as indicators of air pollution. *Mailing Add:* 1424 Hillcrest Kalamazoo MI 49008

MEDLIN, WILLIAM LOUIS, b Harlingen, Tex, Aug 25, 28; m 58. SOLID STATE PHYSICS. *Educ:* Univ Tex, BS, 51, MS, 54, PhD(physics), 56. *Prof Exp:* Res assoc, Mobil Oil Corp, 56-57, RES ASSOC, FIELD RES LAB, MOBIL RES & DEVELOP CORP, 67- *Res:* Rock mechanics; geophysics; luminescence; color centers. *Mailing Add:* Field Res Lab Mobil Res & Develop Corp Dallas TX 75221

MEDNICK, MORTON L, organic chemistry, see previous edition

MEDOFF, GERALD, b New York, NY, Nov 9, 36; m 60; c 2. MICROBIOLOGY. *Educ:* Columbia Univ, AB, 58; Wash Univ, MD, 62; Am Bd Internal Med, dipl. *Prof Exp:* Fel infectious dis, Mass Gen Hosp, Boston, 65-68, instr med & pediat, Harvard Med Sch, 68-70; from asst prof to assoc prof med, 70-76, asst prof microbiol, 71-76, PROF MED & ASSOC PROF MICROBIOL & IMMUNOL, SCH MED, WASH UNIV, 76-, CHIEF INFECTIOUS DIS DIV, 72- *Res:* Mycology; infectious diseases; medicine. *Mailing Add:* Dept of Med Box 8051 Wash Univ Sch of Med St Louis MO 63110

MEDORA, RUSTEM SOHRAB, b Deolali, India, May 4, 34; m 64; c 2. PHARMACOGNOSY, BIOLOGY. *Educ:* Gujarat Univ, India, BPharm, 58, MPharm, 60; Univ RI, PhD(pharmaceut sci), 65. *Prof Exp:* Tutor pharmacog, L M Col Pharm, Gujarat Univ, 58-61; asst, Univ RI, 61-65; asst prof, Idaho State Univ, 65-66; Nat Res Coun Can fel bot, McGill Univ, 66-67; asst prof pharmacog, 67-72, assoc prof, 72-79, PROF PHARM, SCH PHARM, UNIV MONT, 79- *Concurrent Pos:* Smith Kline Found, Mont Heart Asn & Miles Lab, Title I, HEA, res grants. *Mem:* Int Tissue Cult Asn; Sigma Xi; Am Soc Pharmacog; Soc Econ Bot; Tissue Cult Asn. *Res:* Pharmacognosy, tissue culture of plants of medicinal interest and gerontology. *Mailing Add:* Sch of Pharm Univ of Mont Missoula MT 59801

MEDRUD, RONALD CURTIS, b Tracy, Minn, July 9, 34; m 59; c 2. X-RAY CRYSTALLOGRAPHY. *Educ:* Augustana Col, SDak, BA, 56; Univ Iowa, PhD(phys chem), 63. *Prof Exp:* Nat Acad Sci-Nat Res Coun res assoc, US Naval Ord Lab, 63-64; sr res chemist, Corning Glass Works, 64-77; SR RES CHEMIST, CHEVRON RES CO, 77- *Mem:* Am Crystallog Asn; Am Chem Soc; Am Ceramic Soc; Electron Microsc Soc Am. *Res:* X-ray crystallography and microscopy for materials evaluation; laboratory automation. *Mailing Add:* Chevron Res Co 576 Standard Ave Richmond CA 94802

MEDSKER, LARRY ROBERT, experimental nuclear physics, see previous edition

MEDVE, RICHARD J, b California, Pa, Jan 28, 36; m 58; c 5. PLANT ECOLOGY. *Educ:* California State Col, Pa, BS, 57; Kent State Univ, MA, 59; Ohio State Univ, PhD(bot), 68. *Prof Exp:* Counr, Kent State Univ, 57-58; teacher pub schs, 58-66; TEACHER BIOL, SLIPPERY ROCK STATE COL, 66- *Concurrent Pos:* Consult, Aquatic Ecol Assocs. *Mem:* Torrey Bot Club; Ecol Soc Am; Nat Sci Teachers Asn; Nat Asn Biol Teachers. *Res:* Mycorrhizae; stripmine revegetation. *Mailing Add:* Dept Biol Slippery Rock State Col Slippery Rock PA 16057

MEDVED, DAVID BERNARD, b Philadelphia, Pa, Feb 21, 26; m 47; c 4. ELECTROOPTICS. *Educ:* Univ Pa, BA, 49, MSc, 51, PhD(physics), 55. *Prof Exp:* Res physicist, Philco Corp, 49-51; sr res engr, Gen Dynamics/Convair, 54-57, head solid state physics group, 57-63; mgr advan concept, Electro-Optical Systs, Inc, Calif, 63-67, chief scientist, Measurement Systs Div, 67-68, chief scientist, Advan Systs & Requirements, 68-69; pres & tech dir, Meret Co, 69-72, PRES & TECH DIR, MERET INC, 72- *Concurrent Pos:* Consult, Remington Rand & Univac Divs, Sperry Rand Corp, 52; vis asst prof & lectr, Univ Calif, Los Angeles, 56-; assoc prof, San Diego State Col, 58- *Mem:* Am Phys Soc; Inst Elec & Electronics Eng. *Res:* Experimental solid state and plasma physics, especially particle-surface interactions, physical electronics, electronic properties of semiconductors and interaction of electromagnetic radiation with matter. *Mailing Add:* Meret Inc 1815 24th St Santa Monica CA 90404

MEDWAY, WILLIAM, b Man, Can, Feb 23, 27; m 71. VETERINARY MEDICINE, CLINICAL MEDICINE. *Educ:* Univ Man, BS, 47; Ont Vet Col, DVM, 54; Cornell Univ, PhD(physiol), 58. *Hon Degrees:* MA, Univ Pa, 71. *Prof Exp:* Instr biochem, Ont Agr Col, Univ Toronto, 48-49; asst physiol chem, Cornell Univ, 54-58; assoc med, Univ Pa, 58-60; asst prof physiol & res assoc, Ont Vet Col, 60-62; from asst prof to assoc prof, 62-68, PROF CLIN LAB MED, UNIV PA, 68- *Concurrent Pos:* Ed newsletter, Int Asn Aquatic Animal Med, 77- *Mem:* Am Soc Vet Clin Path (pres, 68-69); Int Asn Aquatic Animal Med (secy-treas, 69-74, pres, 74-75); Am Soc Vet Physiol & Pharmacol; Am Physiol Soc; Am Vet Med Asn. *Res:* Clinical chemistry; clinical pathology as applied to aquatic animals; veterinary diagnostics; veterinary physiology. *Mailing Add:* Dept of Clin Studies Univ of Pa Philadelphia PA 19104

MEDWICK, THOMAS, b Jersey City, NJ, Oct 15, 29. ANALYTICAL CHEMISTRY. *Educ:* Rutgers Univ, BS, 52, MS, 54; Univ Wis, PhD(pharmaceut chem), 58. *Prof Exp:* Res analyst, Merck & Co, Inc, NJ, 58-60; asst prof pharmaceut chem, Col Pharm, Rutgers Univ, Newark, 60-63, from assoc prof to prof, 63-71, PROF PHARMACEUT CHEM, COL PHARM, RUTGERS UNIV, NEW BRUNSWICK, 71- *Concurrent Pos:* Sci adv, NY Dist, Food & Drug Admin, 70- *Mem:* Am Pharmaceut Asn; Am Chem Soc; fel Am Inst Chemists. *Res:* Theoretical analytical and hydrazine chemistry; acid-base reactions in nonaqueous solvents; analysis of pharmaceuticals. *Mailing Add:* Col of Pharm Rutgers Univ Busch Campus New Brunswick NJ 08903

MEDWIN, HERMAN, b Springfield, Mass, Apr 9, 20; m 45. UNDERWATER ACOUSTICS. *Educ:* Worcester Polytech Inst, BS, 41; Univ Calif, Los Angeles, MS, 48, PhD(physics), 54. *Prof Exp:* Asst physics, Univ Calif, Los Angeles, 46-53, res assoc, 53-54; consult acoustics, Bolt, Beranek & Newman, Inc, 54-55; assoc prof physics, 55-60, PROF PHYSICS, US NAVAL POSTGRAD SCH, 60- *Concurrent Pos:* Instr, Los Angeles City Col, 48-54; liaison scientist, Off Naval Res, London, 61-62, ed, Europ Sci Notes, 62; consult, Hudson Labs, Columbia Univ, 64-68; vis prof, Imp Col, Univ London, 65-66 & Nat Defense Acad, Yokosuka, Japan, 81; vchmn acoustics panel, Nat Acad Sci-Nat Res Coun Physics Surv Comt, 70-71; vis scientist, Royal Australian Naval Res Lab, 72-73. *Honors & Awards:* Res Award, Naval Postgrad Sch Chap, Sigma Xi, 72. *Mem:* Fel Acoust Soc Am; Am Geophys Union; Inst Noise Control Eng. *Res:* Microbubbles at sea; surface and volume scattering of sound in the sea; effects of high intensity sounds; acoustic diffraction. *Mailing Add:* Dept of Physics US Naval Postgrad Sch Monterey CA 93940

MEDZ, ROBERT B, b Los Angeles, Calif, Nov 7, 19; m 66. ENVIRONMENTAL MANAGEMENT. *Educ:* Univ Calif, BA, 42, MA, 47; Univ Wash, PhD, 64. *Prof Exp:* Fel, Univ Wash, 64, instr chem, 64-65; res chemist, Southeast Water Lab, Fed Water Pollution Control Admin, 65-67; phys sci adminr, Bur Dis Prev & Environ Controls, USPHS, 68-69, phys sci adminr, Environ Health Serv, 70, assoc dir, Lab Opers Div, 70-72, chief standardization br, Qual Assurance Div, Off Res & Develop, 72-75, sr prog adv monitoring qual assurance, Monitoring Technol Div, Off Res & Develop, 75-77, chief water qual, Pesticides & Toxic, Measurement Systs & Qual Assurance, 77-79, ASSOC DIR, WATER & WASTE MGT MONITORING RES DIV, ENVIRON PROTECTION AGENCY, 79- *Concurrent Pos:* Tech adv, Pilot Secretariat Pollution Measurement, Int Orgn Legal Metrol, 74- *Mem:* AAAS; Am Chem Soc; NY Acad Sci. *Res:* Impact of chemical pollutants on the quality of the environment and upon human health and the well being of all life forms. *Mailing Add:* Off Res & Develop Environ Protection Agency Washington DC 20460

MEDZIHRADSKY, FEDOR, b Kikinda, Yugoslavia, Feb 4, 32; m 67; c 2. NEUROCHEMISTRY. *Educ:* Munich Tech Univ, MS, 61, PhD(biochem), 65. *Prof Exp:* Instr biochem, Univ Munich, 65-66; asst prof, 69-73, assoc prof biochem, 73-81, assoc prof pharmacol, 75-81, PROF BIOCHEM, MED SCH, UNIV MICH, ANN ARBOR, 73- *Concurrent Pos:* NIH fel, Univ Wis, 66-67; Nat Inst Neurol Dis & Blindness trainee, Wash Univ, 67-69; vis assoc prof pharmacol, Stanford Univ Med Ctr, 75-76; Nat Res Serv Award, USPHS-Alcohol, Drug Abuse & Mental Health Admin, 75-76. *Mem:* Ger Soc Biol Chemists; Am Soc Neurochem; Am Chem Soc; Am Soc Biol Chemists; Am Soc Pharmacol & Exp Therapeut. *Res:* Neurochemistry; biochemical pharmacology; molecular mechanisms of drug-membrane interactions: cellular transport, membrane receptors and neuron-glia interrelation. *Mailing Add:* Dept Biol Chem Med Sch Med Sci Bldg 1 Univ Mich Ann Arbor MI 48109

MEDZON, EDWARD LIONEL, b Winnipeg, Man, May 26, 36; m 61; c 3. VIROLOGY. *Educ:* Univ Man, BSc, 57, MSc, 60; McGill Univ, PhD(virol, immunol), 64. *Prof Exp:* Instr microbiol, Univ Mich, 63-65; asst prof, 65-69, ASSOC PROF MICROBIOL, UNIV WESTERN ONT, 69- *Concurrent Pos:* Vis lectr, Eastern Mich Univ, 64-65; ed-in-chief, Dict Microbiol, Am Soc Microbiol, 73- *Mem:* AAAS; Am Soc Microbiol; Can Soc Microbiol; Can Soc Cell Biol; NY Acad Sci. *Res:* Virus infection, replication, and immunity; early detection of virus infection in vitro; effect of aging on infection and immunity. *Mailing Add:* Dept of Microbiol & Immunol Health Sci Ctr Univ Western Ont London ON N6A 5B8 Can

MEE, JACK EVERETT, b Brainerd, Minn, July 6, 30; m 52; c 3. INORGANIC CHEMISTRY, SOLID STATE ELECTRONICS. *Educ:* Dakota Wesleyan Univ, BA, 52; Iowa State Univ, PhD(inorg chem), 62. *Prof Exp:* Jr chemist, Gen Elec Co, Wash, 52-57; res asst inorg chem, Inst Atomic Res, Iowa State Univ, 57-62; sr res engr, Autonetics Div, NAm Rockwell Corp, 62-64, specialist res, 64-67, supvr, 67-74, MGR SOLID STATE MAT RES BR, AUTONETICS GROUP, ROCKWELL INT, 74- *Mem:* Am Chem Soc; Inst Elec & Electronics Engrs; Sigma Xi. *Res:* Chemical vapor deposition; liquid phase epitaxy; epitaxial garnets; bubble domain materials; epitaxial III-V's. *Mailing Add:* Rockwell Int Electronics Res Div 3370 Miraloma Ave Anaheim CA 92803

MEECE, W(ILLIAM) E(RVIN), b Dayton, Ohio, Mar 29, 25; m 51; c 4. CHEMICAL ENGINEERING. *Educ:* Cooper Union, BChE, 48; Univ Del, MChE, 49. *Prof Exp:* Develop engr, 50-55, supvr chem group, 55-59, chief supvr, 59-66, chief supvr mfg azo dyes, NJ, 66-69, mkt planning mgr, 70-72, planning assoc, Int Dept, 73-76, eng mgr, Orchem Dept, 76-77, staff engr, 77-79, PLANNING ASSOC, CHEM & PIGMENTS DEPT, E I DU PONT DE NEMOURS & CO, INC, 79- *Res:* Organic chemicals. *Mailing Add:* E I du Pont de Nemours & Co Inc 1007 Market St Wilmington DE 19898

MEECH, JOHN ATHOL, b Toronto, Ont, Jan 16, 47; m 72; c 2. SURFACE CHEMISTRY. *Educ:* McGill Univ, BEng, 70; Queen's Univ, MSc, 75, PhD(mineral eng), 79. *Prof Exp:* Sr asst metal eng, Roan Consolidated Mines Ltd, Zambia, 70-73; lectr, 74-77, asst prof, 77-82, ASSOC PROF MINERAL PROCESSING, QUEEN'S UNIV, ONT, 82- *Mem:* Can Inst Mining & Metall; Am Inst Mining Engrs. *Res:* Flotation and surface chemistry; chrysocolla ores; process develoment and feasibility studies; computer simulation; iron ore agglomeration; fine particle recovery techniques; environmental control of mining effluents; pyrrhotite oxidation. *Mailing Add:* Dept Mining Eng Queen's Univ Goodwin Hall Kingston ON K7L 5Y8 Can

MEECHAM, WILLIAM CORYELL, b Detroit, Mich, June 17, 28; m 48; c 2. MATHEMATICAL PHYSICS, CLASSICAL PHYSICS. *Educ:* Univ Mich, BS & MS, 48, PhD(physics), 54. *Prof Exp:* Asst physics, Univ Mich, 48-53 & Brown Univ, 53-54; res assoc, Univ Mich, 54-55, assoc res physicist, 55-56, instr, 56-57, asst prof, 57-60, res physicist & head fluid & solid mech lab, 59-60; prof fluid mech, Univ Minn, Minneapolis, 60-66; sr scientist, Lockheed

Palo Alto Res Labs, 66-67; head div appl mech, Col Eng, 68-69, PROF FLUID MECH & ACOUST, UNIV CALIF, LOS ANGELES, 67- *Concurrent Pos:* Res assoc, Univ Calif, San Diego, 63; consult, TRW, Inc, 59-65, Rand Corp, Calif, 64-72, Inst Sci & Technol, Univ Mich, 60-67 & Bolt, Beranek & Newman, Inc, 68-74; consult, Aerospace Corp, 75- res & develop assoc, 74-76. *Mem:* Am Phys Soc; fel Acoust Soc Am; assoc fel Am Inst Aeronaut & Astronaut. Mem: Fluid dynamics; acoustics; diffraction theory; stochastic processes; wave propagation problems. *Mailing Add:* Sch Eng & Appl Sci Univ of Calif Los Angeles CA 90024

MEECHAN, CHARLES JAMES, b Usk, Wash, Aug 7, 28; m 51; c 6. SOLID STATE PHYSICS. *Educ:* Ore State Col, BS, 51. *Prof Exp:* Res physicist, Atomics Int Div, NAm Aviation, Inc, 51-61, staff physicist, Sci Ctr, 61-63, res adv, Corp Off, 63-67, exec dir res & eng, NAm Rockwell Corp, 67-69, vpres indust systs, 69-71, vpres & dir, Sci Ctr, 71-72, vpres res & eng, 72-78, EXEC VPRES ENERGY SYSTS GROUP, ROCKWELL INT CORP, 78- *Mem:* Am Phys Soc; Sigma Xi. *Res:* Experimental research in study of lattice imperfections; radiaton damage and diffusion phenomena in solids; Mossbauer spectroscopy. *Mailing Add:* Rockwell Int Corp 8900 DeSoto Ave Canoga Park CA 91304

MEECHAN, ROBERT JOHN, b Newport, Wash, Aug 25, 26; m 53; c 3. PEDIATRICS. *Educ:* Ore State Col, BA, 51; Univ Ore, MS & MD, 53. *Prof Exp:* From instr to assoc prof, 57-68, PROF PEDIAT, MED SCH, UNIV ORE, 68-, ASST DEAN, MED SCH ADMIS, 80- *Mailing Add:* Dept of Pediat Univ of Ore Sch of Med Portland OR 97201

MEEGAN, CHARLES ANTHONY, b Buffalo, NY, Sept 24, 44. ASTROPHYSICS. *Educ:* Rensselaer Polytech Inst, BS, 66; Univ Md, PhD(physics), 73. *Prof Exp:* Res assoc astrophys, Rice Univ, 74-75, Univ Ala, Huntsville, 76 & Nat Res Coun, 76-78; SPACE SCIENTIST ASTROPHYS, NASA MARSHALL SPACE FLIGHT CTR, 78- *Mem:* Am Phys Soc; Am Astron Soc. *Res:* Cosmic ray astrophysics and medium-energy gamma-ray astronomy. *Mailing Add:* Mail Code ES-62 Marshall Space Flight Ctr Huntsville AL 35812

MEEHAN, EDWARD JOSEPH, b Oakland, Calif, July 21, 12; m 45; c 3. CHEMISTRY. *Educ:* Univ Calif, BS, 33, PhD(phys chem), 36. *Prof Exp:* Instr chem, Univ Calif, 36-39; from instr to assoc prof, 39-52, PROF CHEM, UNIV MINN, MINNEAPOLIS, 52- *Concurrent Pos:* With Off Rubber Reserve, 44. *Mem:* Am Chem Soc; Optical Soc Am. *Res:* Absorption spectra of solids; spectrophotometry; physical and chemical properties of high polymers; light scattering; reaction mechanisms. *Mailing Add:* Dept of Chem Univ of Minn Minneapolis MN 55455

MEEHAN, JOHN PATRICK, b San Francisco, Calif, May 22, 23; m 49; c 4. PHYSIOLOGY. *Educ:* Univ Southern Calif, MD, 48. *Prof Exp:* Instr, 47-49, asst prof, 49-51 & 54-55, assoc prof, 55-62, PROF PHYSIOL, SCH MED, UNIV SOUTHERN CALIF, 62-, CHMN DEPT, 66- *Mem:* AAAS; Aerospace Med Asn. *Res:* Aviation physiology; central nervous system control of the vascular system; cardiovascular and respiratory physiology; aerospace medicine. *Mailing Add:* Dept of Physiol Sch of Med Univ of Southern Calif Los Angeles CA 90033

MEEHAN, THOMAS DENNIS, b Youngstown, Ohio. BIOLOGICAL CHEMISTRY, BIOPHYSICS. *Educ:* Univ Akron, BS, 65; St Louis Univ, PhD(biochem), 73. *Prof Exp:* Researcher chem carcinogenesis, Lab Chem Biodynamics, Univ Calif, 74-76, jr staff biochemist, 76-78; sr res assoc, 78-80, ASST PROF BIOCHEM, MICH MOLECULAR INST, 80- *Concurrent Pos:* NIH fel, Univ Calif, 74-75. *Mem:* AAAS; Am Chem Soc; Biophys Soc; Am Asn Cancer Res. *Res:* Mutation mechanisms of mutagenesis; alteration of gene expression by chemical carcinogens; physical and chemical interactions between carcinogens and DNA. *Mailing Add:* Mich Molecular Inst 1910 W St Andrews Dr Midland MI 48640

MEEHAN, WILLIAM ROBERT, b Buffalo, NY, Apr 9, 31. FISH BIOLOGY. *Educ:* Univ Buffalo, BA, 52; Univ Ore, MA, 55; Mich State Univ, PhD(fisheries, wildlife), 58. *Prof Exp:* Res biologist, Alaska Dept Fish & Game, 58-66; FISHERY RES BIOLOGIST, FORESTRY SCI LAB, US FOREST SERV, 66- *Mem:* Am Fisheries Soc; Am Soc Limnol & Oceanog; Pac Fishery Biologists; Am Inst Fishery Res Biologists. *Res:* Wildlife biology; salmon investigations; aquatic entomology. *Mailing Add:* Forestry Sci Lab US Forest Serv PO Box 909 Juneau AK 99802

MEEK, BURL DEAN, soil chemistry, see previous edition

MEEK, DEVON WALTER, b River, Ky, Feb 24, 36; m 65. INORGANIC CHEMISTRY. *Educ:* Berea Col, BA, 58; Univ Ill, MS, 60, PhD(chem), 61. *Prof Exp:* Asst chem, Univ Ill, 58-60, res fel, 60-61; from asst prof to assoc prof inorg chem, 61-69, chmn dept, 77-81, PROF INORG CHEM, OHIO STATE UNIV, 69- *Concurrent Pos:* Vis assoc prof, Northwestern Univ, 67; sr res fel, Univ of Sussex, England, 74. *Mem:* Am Chem Soc; The Chem Soc; Sigma Xi. *Res:* Studies of the syntheses, electronic and magnetic properties and structures of transition metal complexes with unusual coordination number; homogeneous catalysis and activition and/or stabilization of small molecules. *Mailing Add:* Dept Chem Ohio State Univ Columbus OH 43210

MEEK, EDWARD STANLEY, b Bristol, Eng, Oct 9, 19; m 46; c 2. PATHOLOGY, BIOLOGY. *Educ:* Univ St Andrews, MB, ChB, 51, MD, 55. *Prof Exp:* Res fel cancer, Univ Bristol, 56-67, lectr cytogenetics, 65-68, sr clin lectr microbiol, 69-70; prof Microbiol, 70-73, PROF PATH & OPHTHAL, UNIV IOWA, 73- *Concurrent Pos:* Hon consult virol, United Bristol Hosps, Eng, 68-70; consult physician virol, Vet Admin Hosp, Iowa City, 71-; consult pathologist microbiol, Univ Hosp, Iowa City, 73-; reviewer, NSF, 78- *Mem:* Fel Am Acad Microbiol; fel Royal Col Pathologists; fel Sigma Xi; Am Asn Immunologists; NY Acad Sci. *Res:* Cancer cell biology; virology. *Mailing Add:* Col of Med Univ of Iowa Iowa City IA 52242

MEEK, JACK HENRY, b Toronto, Ont, July 30, 18; m 41; c 7. PHYSICS. *Educ:* Univ Toronto, BA, 40; Univ Sask, MA, 53, PhD, 55. *Prof Exp:* Forecaster, Meteorol Serv Can, 40-42; with radio physics lab, Defense Res Bd Can, 47-51, with physics dept, Saskatchewan, 51-56, dep dir phys res, 56-59, supt commun lab, 60-67, mem plans staff, 68-72, DIR SCI & TECHNOL INFO ANAL, DEPT NAT DEFENCE, 73- *Mem:* Am Geophys Union; Inst Elec & Electronics Eng; Can Asn Physicists. *Res:* Upper atmospheric physics and meteorology; geomagnetism; oceanography; radio communications; cybernetics; technological forecasting. *Mailing Add:* 2365 Ridgecrest Pl Ottawa ON K1H 7V4 Can

MEEK, JAMES LATHAM, b San Antonio, Tex, Apr 10, 37; m 56; c 3. MATHEMATICS. *Educ:* Univ Tex, BA, 62, MA, 63, PhD(math), 67. *Prof Exp:* Instr math, San Antonio Col, 63-64; res assoc acoust & math, Defense Res Lab, Univ Tex, Austin, 67; asst prof, 67-74, ASSOC PROF MATH, UNIV ARK, FAYETTEVILLE, 74- *Concurrent Pos:* Consult, Defense Res Lab, Univ Tex, Austin, 67-68. *Mem:* Am Math Soc; Math Asn Am. *Res:* Underwater acoustics; boundary behavior of analytic, harmonic, and subharmonic functions; harmonic analysis. *Mailing Add:* Dept of Math Univ of Ark Fayetteville AR 72701

MEEK, JOHN SAWYERS, b Madison, Wis, Aug 12, 18; m 45; c 2. ORGANIC CHEMISTRY. *Educ:* Univ Wis, BA, 41; Univ Ill, MS, 44, PhD(org chem), 45. *Prof Exp:* Asst inorg chem, Univ Ill, 41-44, Allied Chem & Dye fel, 45; from instr to assoc prof, 45-60, PROF ORG CHEM, UNIV COLO, BOULDER, 60- *Concurrent Pos:* Asst, Univ Wis, 43. *Mem:* Am Chem Soc. *Res:* Diels-Alder reactions; Bridgehead compounds. *Mailing Add:* Dept of Chem Univ of Colo Boulder CO 80309

MEEK, JOSEPH CHESTER, JR, b Sabetha, Kans, July 16, 31; m 54; c 3. INTERNAL MEDICINE, ENDOCRINOLOGY. *Educ:* Univ Kans, AB, 54, MD, 57. *Prof Exp:* Intern, San Diego County Gen Hosp, Calif, 57-58; resident, Univ Kans Med Ctr, Kansas City, 58-60; res asst space med, US Naval Sch Aviation Med, 60-62; from instr to asst prof, 64-69, assoc prof med, 69-75, PROF MED, UNIV KANS MED CTR, KANSAS CITY, 75-, VCHANCELLOR ACADEMIC AFFAIRS, 81- *Concurrent Pos:* Am Col Physicians Mead Johnson scholar, Univ Kans, 59-60; fel endocrinol, Scripps Clin & Res Found, La Jolla, Calif, 62-63, trainee, 63-64; attending physician, Vet Admin Hosp, 64- *Mem:* Am Fedn Clin Res; Am Thyroid Asn; Am Diabetes Asn; fel Am Col Physicians; Endocrine Soc. *Res:* Metabolism; long acting throid stimulator; insulin A and B chains. *Mailing Add:* Dept of Med Univ of Kans Med Ctr Kansas City KS 66103

MEEK, PAUL D(ERALD), b McAllen, Tex, Aug 15, 30; m 54; c 4. CHEMICAL ENGINEERING. *Educ:* Univ Tex, BSChE, 53. *Prof Exp:* Asst chem engr tech serv, Humble Oil & Refining Co, 53-55; mgr tech dept, Cosden Oil & Chem Co, 55-60, vpres chem, 62-68, pres, 68-76; vpres, 68-76, PRES & CHIEF OPERATING OFFICER, AM PETROFINA, INC, 76-, DIR, 68- *Mem:* Am Inst Chem Engrs; Am Petrol Inst. *Res:* Refinery technology, especially aromatics, styrene monomers and polystyrenes. *Mailing Add:* Am Petrofina Inc Box 2159 Dallas TX 75221

MEEK, RICHARD L(EE), b Smyrna, Ga, May 5, 25. CHEMICAL ENGINEERING. *Educ:* Ga Inst Technol, BS, 48, MS, 50, PhD(chem eng), 52. *Prof Exp:* Res engr, Phillips Petrol Co, Tex, 48; sr res engr, Lion Oil Co, Ark, 52-55; dir chem res, Scripto, Inc, Ga, 55-62; dir develop, Tenn Corp, 62-65, asst dir res & develop, Chem & Metals Group, 65-71; res coordr, Cities Serv Co, 71-74; head, Chem Processing Sect, Southern Res Inst, 74-80; ASSOC DIR, PHYS & ENG SCI DIV, GULF SOUTH RES INST, 80- *Mem:* Am Inst Chem Engrs; Am Chem Soc; Am Inst Mining, Metall & Petrol Engrs; Am Inst Chemists. *Res:* Reaction kinetics; pilot plant development; research planning and evaluation; air and water environmental control; fiber, film and membrane processing. *Mailing Add:* Phys & Eng Sci Div Gulf South Res Inst PO Box 26518 New Orleans LA 70186

MEEK, VIOLET IMHOF, b Geneva, Ill, June 12, 39; m 65; c 2. INORGANIC CHEMISTRY. *Educ:* St Olaf Col, BA, 60; Univ Ill, MS, 62, PhD(inorg chem), 64. *Prof Exp:* Instr chem, Mt Holyoke Col, 64-65; asst prof, 65-70, chmn dept, 75-79, ASSOC PROF CHEM, OHIO WESLEYAN UNIV, 70-, DEAN EDUC SERV, 80- *Mem:* AAAS; Am Chem Soc; Royal Soc Chem. *Res:* Preparation of coordination compounds of transition metals and studies of their structures and properties using physical methods. *Mailing Add:* Dept Chem Ohio Wesleyan Univ Delaware OH 43015

MEEKER, RALPH DENNIS, b Chicago, Ill, Nov 15, 45; m 68; c 2. PHYSICS. *Educ:* Ill Benedictine Col, BS, 67; Iowa State Univ, PhD(physics), 70. *Prof Exp:* From asst prof to assoc prof physics, 70-79, PROF PHYSICS, ILL BENEDICTINE COL, 79-, CHMN DEPT, 72-75 & 78-, CHMN SCI DIV, 81- *Concurrent Pos:* Resident assoc, Argonne Nat Lab, consult, 71-76; pres, Exradin, Inc, 78- *Mem:* Am Phys Soc; Am Asn Physics Teachers. *Res:* Medical physics (radiation dosimetry). *Mailing Add:* Dept Physics Ill Benedictine Col Lisle IL 60532

MEEKER, ROBERT ELDON, b Moline, Ill, Sept 6, 30; m 51; c 3. PHYSICAL CHEMISTRY. *Educ:* Ill Wesleyan Univ, BS, 52; Northwestern Univ, PhD(phys chem), 55. *Prof Exp:* Mgt res & develop, Shell Oil Co, 55-76; VPRES & GEN MGR, ENERGY SYSTS MGT DIV, TRW, INC, 76-, VPRES & GEN MGR MAJ PROGS, 79- *Mem:* Am Chem Soc. *Mailing Add:* Energy Develop Group TRW Inc One Space Park Redondo Beach CA 90278

MEEKER, THRYGVE RICHARD, b Pottstown, Pa, Mar 9, 29; m 54; c 3. PHYSICAL CHEMISTRY. *Educ:* Ursinus Col, BS, 51; Univ Del, MS, 54, PhD(phys chem), 56. *Prof Exp:* MEM TECH STAFF, BELL LABS, 55- *Mem:* Am Chem Soc; Am Phys Soc; Am Inst Chemists; Inst Elec & Electronics Eng; NY Acad Sci. *Res:* Chemical kinetics; spectroscopy; ultrasonics and elastic properties; piezoelectric, dielectric and ferroelectric phenomena; applied mathematics; quantum mechanics; thermodynamics; wave phenomena. *Mailing Add:* 2956 Lindberg Ave Allentown PA 18103

MEEKER, WILLIAM QUACKENBUSH, JR, b New York, NY, Nov 28, 49; m 75; c 1. STATISTICS. *Educ:* Clarkson Col Technol, BS, 72; Union Col, MS, 73, PhD(admin & eng systs), 75. *Prof Exp:* Res fel statist, Inst Admin & Mgt, Union Col, 73-75; asst prof, 75-78, assoc prof, 78-81, PROF STATIST, IOWA STATE UNIV, 81- *Concurrent Pos:* Statistician, Corp Res & Develop, Gen Elec Co, 73-75; statist consult, Bell Lab, 78-81. *Mem:* Am Soc Qual Control; Am Statist Asn; Inst Math Statist; Biomet Soc; AAAS. *Res:* Applied areas of statistics, including life data analysis, time series analysis,, sequential analysis statistical computing and experimental design. *Mailing Add:* Dept Statist Snedecor Hall Iowa State Univ Ames IA 50011

MEEKINS, JOHN FRED, b Boston, Mass, Oct 4, 37; m 61; c 2. X-RAY ASTRONOMY, SOLAR PHYSICS. *Educ:* Bowdoin Col, BA, 59; Cath Univ Am, PhD(physics), 73. *Prof Exp:* RES PHYSICIST, NAVAL RES LAB, 59- *Mem:* Am Astron Soc; Sigma Xi. *Res:* Astrophysics, especially concerning high temperature astrophysical plasmas. *Mailing Add:* Naval Res Lab Code 4125 Washington DC 20375

MEEKS, BENJAMIN SPENCER, JR, b Florence, SC, Nov 17, 24; m 49; c 2. ORGANIC CHEMISTRY. *Educ:* Univ SC, BS, 44; Cornell Univ, PhD(org chem), 51. *Prof Exp:* Res chemist, US Rubber Co, 51-52 & Tenn Eastman Co, 52-56; assoc prof chem, Mercer Univ, 56-58; Univ Ky Contract Team, Bandung Tech Inst, 58-62; assoc prof, 62-65, chmn dept, 74-81, PROF CHEM, MOORHEAD STATE UNIV, 65-, DIR PROG INDUST CHEM, 81- *Concurrent Pos:* Res grant, Univ Col, London, 69-70; res assoc, Univ Minn, 77-78. *Mem:* AAAS; Am Chem Soc; Royal Soc Chem; Sigma Xi. *Res:* Synthesis of pteridines; general organic synthesis; condensation polymerization; ionic reaction mechanisms; diazo ring enlargements. *Mailing Add:* Dept of Chem Moorhead State Univ Moorhead MN 56560

MEEKS, FRANK ROBERT, b Ft Worth, Tex, Dec 5, 28. PHYSICAL CHEMISTRY. *Educ:* Tex Christian Univ, BA, 49; Polytech Inst of NY, PhD, 56. *Prof Exp:* From asst prof to assoc prof, 57-77, PROF PHYS CHEM, UNIV CINCINNATI, 77- *Concurrent Pos:* Res scholar, Univ Montpellier, France, 63-64. *Mem:* Am Chem Soc; Sigma Xi. *Res:* Periodic precipitation and condensation kinetics; critical phenomena in binary liquid systems; statistical mechanics; thermodynamics of irreversible processes. *Mailing Add:* Dept of Chem Univ of Cincinnati Cincinnati OH 45221

MEEKS, MARION LITTLETON, b Gainesville, Ga, Oct 1, 23; m 44, 70; c 5. RADIO ASTRONOMY. *Educ:* Ga Inst Technol, BS, 43, MS, 48; Duke Univ, PhD(physics), 51. *Prof Exp:* Instr physics, Ga Inst Technol, 46-47 & Duke Univ, 48-49; asst prof, Clemson Col, 50-51; from asst prof to assoc prof, Ga Inst Technol, 51-61; staff mem, Lincoln Lab, 61-72, staff mem, Haystack Observ, 72-78, STAFF MEM, LINCOLN LAB, MASS INST TECHNOL, 78- *Concurrent Pos:* Physicist, Harvard Observ, 59-60; vis prof, Univ Mass, Amherst, 71; mem comn J, Int Union Radio Sci; mem comn 40, Int Astron Union; adj prof, Five Col Astron Dept, 74-76; assoc, Harvard Col Observ, 64-81. *Mem:* Am Sci Film Asn; Am Astron Soc. *Res:* Microwave spectral lines; computer control and data processing in radio astronomy; computer graphics and animation; microwave propagation. *Mailing Add:* Mass Inst Technol PO Box 73 Lexington MA 02173

MEEKS, ROBERT G, b Columbus, Ohio, Jan 24, 42; m 62; c 1. TOXICOLOGY. *Educ:* Otterbein Col, BSc, 72; Ohio State Univ, PhD(pharmacol & toxicol), 77. *Prof Exp:* Med technologist, Childrens Hosp, 62-66; head, Protein Hormone & Radioimmunoassay Res & Develop Sect, G D Searle Reference Lab, 66-72; sr staff fel, Dept Health, Educ & Welfare Nat Inst Health, Nat Cancer Inst, 77-80; SR TOXICOLOGIST, SOUTHERN RES INST, 80-, HEAD TOXICOL, 81- *Concurrent Pos:* Adj asst prof, Dept Pub Health, Sch Med & Sch Community Health, Univ Ala, Birmingham, 80- *Mem:* Am Asn Clin Chemists; AAAS; Am Chem Soc; NY Acad Sci; Biophys Soc. *Res:* In vivo and in vitro toxicity of antitumor drugs, anticonvulsants and retinoids as well as other compounds under development for potential use in man. *Mailing Add:* Southern Res Inst PO Box 3307-A Birmingham AL 35255

MEEKS, WILKISON (WINFIELD), b Pittsburgh, Pa, Apr 4, 15; m 46; c 2. ACOUSTICS. *Educ:* Maryville Col, AB, 37; Northwestern Univ, MS, 39, PhD(physics), 41. *Prof Exp:* Contract employee, US Naval Ord Lab, 41-44; staff physicist, Haskins Labs, Inc, NY, 44-46; assoc prof physics, Western Md Col, 46-47 & Southern Ill Univ, 47-48; asst prof, Western Reserve Univ, 48-55; physicist res ctr, B F Goodrich Co, Ohio, 55-58; assoc prof physics, 58-60, chmn dept, 60-68, PROF PHYSICS, ROSE-HULMAN INST TECHNOL, 60- *Mem:* Am Phys Soc; Acoust Soc Am; Am Asn Physics Teachers. *Res:* Magneto-mechanical effects; underwater sound. *Mailing Add:* Dept of Physics Rose-Hulman Inst of Technol Terre Haute IN 47803

MEELHEIM, RICHARD YOUNG, b Cape Charles, Va, Aug 30, 25; m 51; c 3. PHYSICAL CHEMISTRY. *Educ:* Univ Va, BS, 50, PhD(chem), 58. *Prof Exp:* Anal chemist, Monsanto Chem Co, 50-54; res chemist fiber surface res, 58-62, chemist, Dacron Res Lab, 62-67, SR RES CHEMIST, DACRON RES LAB, E I DU PONT DE NEMOURS & CO, INC, 67- *Mem:* Sigma Xi. *Res:* Research and development fibers. *Mailing Add:* 1218 Stockton Rd Kinston NC 28501

MEEM, J(AMES), LAWRENCE, JR, b Brooklyn, NY, Dec 24, 15; m 40; c 2. NUCLEAR ENGINEERING. *Educ:* Va Mil Inst, BS, 39; Univ Ind, MS, 47, PhD(physics), 49. *Prof Exp:* Instr chem, Va Mil Inst, 39-40; aeronaut res scientist, Nat Adv Comt Aeronaut, Va, 41-43, Ohio, 44-46; reactor physicist, Oak Ridge Nat Lab, 50-55; chief reactor scientist, Alco Prod, Inc, 55-57; prof, 57-81, chmn dept, 57-77, EMER PROF NUCLEAR ENG, UNIV VA, 81- *Concurrent Pos:* Consult, NASA, 60-67 & Westinghouse Elec Corp, 63-67; vis mem staff, Los Alamos Sci Lab, 67-68; vis consult, Sandia Labs, NMex, 77-78. *Mem:* Am Phys Soc; fel Am Nuclear Soc; Am Soc Eng Educ. *Res:* Alternative nuclear fuel cycles; plutonium proliferation risk. *Mailing Add:* Dept of Nuclear Eng Univ of Va Charlottesville VA 22901

MEEN, RONALD HUGH, b Can, Nov 25, 25; m 68. SYNTHETIC ORGANIC CHEMISTRY. *Educ:* Univ Toronto, BA, 47, MA, 49, PhD(chem), 53. *Prof Exp:* Fel & res assoc org chem, Iowa State Col, 53-54; RES CHEMIST, TENN EASTMAN CO, 54- *Mem:* Am Chem Soc. *Res:* Chemistry; organic chemical development. *Mailing Add:* 2121 Cypress St Kingsport TN 37664

MEENAGHAN, G(EORGE) F(RANCIS), chemical engineering, see previous edition

MEENAN, PETER MICHAEL, b New York, NY, Nov 20, 42; m 70. SYSTEMS ENGINEERING, COMPUTER SCIENCE. *Educ:* Manhattan Col, BS, 64; Univ Ariz, MS, 66; Union Col, NY, MS, 70, PhD(admin, eng systs), 74. *Prof Exp:* Nuclear engr, Knolls Atomic Power Lab, 66-70; syst engr, 70-71, mgr syst anal & simulation tech, 72-77, mgr indust info systs, 78-79, MGR ELECTRONIC PLANNING & RES, GEN ELEC RES & DEVELOP CTR, 80- *Concurrent Pos:* Adj prof comput sci, State Univ NY Albany, 76- *Mem:* Inst Elec & Electronics Engrs; Soc Comput Simulation. *Res:* Use of computer science and systems engineering techniques to improve engineering and manufacturing productivity, design new products and improve existing products. *Mailing Add:* Gen Elec Res & Develop Ctr PO Box 8 Schenectady NY 12301

MEENTEMEYER, VERNON GEORGE, b Centralia, Ill, Nov 7, 42; m 66; c 2. CLIMATOLOGY. *Educ:* Southern Ill Univ, BA, 65, MA, 68, PhD(climat), 71. *Prof Exp:* Asst prof phys geog, Southern Ill Univ, 73; asst prof, 73-80, ASSOC PROF PHYS GEOG, UNIV GA, 80- *Mem:* Asn Am Geogrs; AAAS; Ecol Soc Am. *Res:* Climatic influences on decomposer food chains; atmospheric hazards; impact on natural ecosystems, and probability mapping; radiant energy flows in forests; terretrial carbon balance; computer mapping of ecosystem dynamics. *Mailing Add:* Dept of Geog Univ of Ga Athens GA 30602

MEERBOTT, WILLIAM KEDDIE, b Jersey City, NJ, Aug 31, 18; m 43; c 2. PETROLEUM CHEMISTRY. *Educ:* St Peters Col, BS, 40; Lehigh Univ, MS, 42. *Prof Exp:* Sr res chemist, Shell Oil Co, 49, group leader, 51-66, staff res chemist, 66-72; staff res chemist, Shell Develop Co, 72-78, sr staff res chemist, 78-81; RETIRED. *Mem:* Am Chem Soc. *Res:* Catalysis in the field of petroleum chemistry and related to hydro processing, desulfurization and catalytic reforming. *Mailing Add:* 3006 Winslow Houston TX 77025

MEEROVITCH, EUGENE, b Vladivostok, Russia, July 11, 19; Can citizien; m 61; c 2. PARASITOLOGY. *Educ:* St John's Univ, China, BSc, 47; McGill Univ, MSc, 53, PhD(parasitol), 57. *Prof Exp:* Res asst parasitol, Hebrew Univ, Israel, 48-53; res asst, 53-57, from asst prof to assoc prof, 57-71, PROF PARASITOL, MACDONALD COL, McGILL UNIV, 71-, DIR, INST PARASITOL, 78- *Concurrent Pos:* US Acad Sci Donner fel, Nat Inst Med Res, Eng, 58-59; consult, WHO, 69-; vis sr scientist, Wellcome Res Labs, Eng, 75-76. *Mem:* AAAS; Am Soc Parasitol; Am Soc Trop Med & Hyg; Royal Soc Trop Med & Hyg; Can Soc Zoologists. *Res:* Amoebiasis, especially immunology, serology and host-parasite relations; trichinosis, especially bionomics and strain variation; in vitro cultivation of parasites; experimental concomitant helminth-protozoal infections; effects of parasites on tumors. *Mailing Add:* Inst of Parasitol MacDonald Campus of McGill Univ MacDonald College PQ H9X 1C0 Can

MEERS, JOSEPH TINSLEY, b Hardin Co, Ky, June 20, 23; m 47; c 3. RESEARCH ADMINISTRATION. *Educ:* Western Ky State Teachers Col, BS, 44; Univ Ky, MS, 47; Univ NC, PhD(physics), 54. *Prof Exp:* Staff scientist, Nat Carbon Co, 54-60, group leader physics, 60-67, asst dir process eng, 67-70, dir electrode technol, 70-74, DIR RES, CARBON PROD DIV, UNION CARBIDE CORP, 74- *Mem:* Am Carbon Soc. *Res:* Formulation and administration of research programs on carbon and its precursors, with special emphasis on the growth and motivation of scientists. *Mailing Add:* Parma Tech Ctr Union Carbide 12900 Snow Rd Parma OH 44130

MEESE, JON MICHAEL, b Indianapolis, Ind, Aug 5, 38; m 63; c 1. SOLID STATE PHYSICS. *Educ:* Univ Cincinnati, BS, 61; Purdue Univ, Lafayette, MS, 64, PhD(physics), 70. *Prof Exp:* Jr physicist, Wabash Magnetics, 60-61; asst instr solid state physics, Purdue Univ, Lafayette, 61-62, assoc instr, 62-65, res asst, 65-70; res physicist, Univ Dayton, 70-76; asst prof physics, 76-80, SR RES PHYSICIST & GROUP LEADER RADIATION EFFECTS, RES REACTOR FACIL, UNIV MO, 76-, ASSOC PROF ELEC ENG, 81- *Concurrent Pos:* In-house contractor, Aerospace Res Labs, Wright-Patterson AFB, 70-72; adj prof physics, Wright State Univ, 75- *Mem:* Am Phys Soc. *Res:* Radiation damage and ion implantation in semiconductors; luminescence; electro-optical devices; solar cells; neutron transmutation doping of semiconductors. *Mailing Add:* Res Reactor Facil Univ of Mo Columbia MO 65211

MEETER, DUANE ANTHONY, b Hammond, Ind, Apr 20, 37; m 60; c 2. STATISTICS. *Educ:* Univ Mich, Ann Arbor, AB, 60; Univ Wis-Madison, MS, 61 & 62, PhD(statist), 64. *Prof Exp:* From asst prof to assoc prof, 64-76, PROF STATIST, FLA STATE UNIV, 76-, DIR DEPT, 75- *Concurrent Pos:* Vis prof statist, Univ Victoria, BC, 76-77. *Mem:* Am Statist Asn. *Res:* Biostatistics; sequential design of experiments; nonlinear design; computer applications. *Mailing Add:* Dept of Statist Fla State Univ Tallahassee FL 32306

MEETZ, GERALD DAVID, b Aurora, Ill, Aug 22, 37; m 81. IMMUNOLOGY, CELL BIOLOGY. *Educ:* NCent Col, Ill, BA, 59; Univ Ill, MS, 67, PhD(anat), 69. *Prof Exp:* USPHS fel cellular, molecular & develop biol, Univ Colo, 69-70; fel pediat, Univ Minn, Minneapolis, 70-71, fel path, 71-72; asst prof anat, Med Col Va, 72-75; asst prof anat, Sch Dent, Marquette Univ, 73-79; ASST PROF ANAT, SOUTHERN CALIF COL OPTOM, 79- *Mem:* Am Soc Cell Biol; Am Asn Anatomists; Am Soc Microbiol; Reticuloendothelial Soc. *Res:* Role of histones in development of avian erythrocyte; gene activation in lymphoid cells; immunobiology of rheumatoid arthritis; anti-tumor activity of shark serum. *Mailing Add:* 2001 Assoc Rd Fullerton CA 92631

MEEUWIG, RICHARD O'BANNON, b St Louis, Mo, Dec 8, 27; m 67; c 2. FOREST ECOLOGY. *Educ:* Univ Calif, Berkeley, BS, 51, MS, 60; Utah State Univ, PhD(soil physics), 64. *Prof Exp:* Forester timber mgt, US Forest Serv, 51-55, forester watershed mgt, 56-64, soil scientist, 64-75, RES FORESTER, INTERMOUNTAIN FOREST & RANGE EXP STA, 75- *Concurrent Pos:* Adj prof, Univ Nev, Reno. *Mem:* Soc Range Mgt. *Res:* Ecology and management of pinyon-juniper woodlands. *Mailing Add:* 1200 Monroe Reno NV 89509

MEEZAN, ELIAS, b New York, NY, Mar 5, 42; m 67; c 3. BIOCHEMISTRY, PHARMACOLOGY. *Educ:* City Col New York, BS, 62; Duke Univ, PhD(biochem), 66. *Prof Exp:* Asst prof pharmacol, Duke Univ, 69-70; from asst prof to assoc prof pharmacol, Univ Ariz Med Sch, 70-79; PROF & CHMN PHARMACOL, UNIV ALA, BIRMINGHAM, 79- *Concurrent Pos:* Helen Hay Whitney fel, 66-69. *Mem:* AAAS; Am Soc Pharmacol & Exp Therapeut; NY Acad Sci. *Res:* Biochemical pharmacology of diabetes; insulin receptors and action and basement membrane structure and matabolism in isolated renal glomeroli and tubules and brain and retinal microvessels. *Mailing Add:* Dept Pharmacol Univ Ala Birmingham AL 35294

MEFFORD, DAVID ALLEN, b Keokuk, Iowa, Dec 28, 28; m 51; c 3. ANALYTICAL CHEMISTRY. *Educ:* Randolph-Macon Col, BS, 51. *Prof Exp:* Asst biol, Randolph-Macon Col, 50; chemist, 53-73, with qual assurance, 57-62, DIR QUAL ASSURANCE, A H ROBINS CO, INC, 73- *Mem:* AAAS; Am Chem Soc; Am Soc Qual Control; Pharmaceut Mfrs Asn. *Res:* Microelemental analysis; analytical problems related to pharmaceutical products; automated analysis, computer automation. *Mailing Add:* Qual Assurance A H Robins Co Inc 1407 Cummings Dr Richmond VA 23220

MEGARD, ROBERT O, b Garretson, SDak, Dec 4, 33; m 58. LIMNOLOGY, PLANKTON. *Educ:* St Olaf Col, BA, 56; Univ NMex, MS, 58; Ind Univ, PhD(zool), 62. *Prof Exp:* Res fel limnol, Univ Minn, Minneapolis, 61-64, res assoc, 64-67, asst prof ecol, 67-71, asst prof, Col Biol Sci, St Paul, 71-72, ASSOC PROF ECOL, COL BIOL SCI, UNIV MINN, MINNEAPOLIS, 72- *Mem:* AAAS; Am Soc Limnol & Oceanog; Ecol Soc Am. *Res:* Limnology ecology of plankton; paleolimnology; biology and ecology of plankton populations. *Mailing Add:* Dept of Ecol & Behav Biol 108 Zool Bldg Univ of Minn Minneapolis MN 55455

MEGARGLE, ROBERT G, b Flushing, NY, Oct 11, 41; m 63. ANALYTICAL CHEMISTRY. *Educ:* Clarkson Col, BS, 63, PhD(chem), 68. *Prof Exp:* NSF fel chem, Univ Minn, Minneapolis, 66-67; asst prof, Univ Mo-Columbia, 67-72; ASSOC PROF CHEM, CLEVELAND STATE UNIV, 72- *Mem:* AAAS; Am Chem Soc. *Res:* Development of instrumentation and laboratory computers for measurement and control of experiments; distributed networks for laboratory experimentation; titration methods of analysis; chromatographic/mass spectroscopic analysis. *Mailing Add:* Dept of Chem Cleveland State Univ Cleveland OH 44115

MEGAW, WILLIAM JAMES, b Belfast, Northern Ireland, July 8, 24; m 46; c 3. ATMOSPHERIC PHYSICS. *Educ:* Univ Liverpool, BSc, 51, DSc(physics), 73. *Prof Exp:* Sci officer, UK Atomic Energy Authority, 51-53; sr sci officer, Atomic Energy Res Estab, Eng, 53-57, prin sci officer, 57-61, sr prin sci officer, 61-71; PROF PHYSICS, YORK UNIV, 71-, DIR, CTR RES ENVIRON QUAL, 74-, CHMN DEPT, 79- *Concurrent Pos:* Mem, Comt Nucleation, Comn Cloud Physics, Int Asn Meteorol & Atmospheric Physics, 65-; subcomn ions, aerosols & radioactivity, Int Comn Atmospheric Elec, 67-; consult, Danish AEC, 69- *Mem:* Fel Brit Inst Physics. *Res:* Physics of particles in the atmosphere; inhibition of condensation on cloud nuclei; fog modification; environmental protection. *Mailing Add:* Dept of Physics York Univ 4700 Keele St Downsview ON M3J 2R3 Can

MEGEL, HERBERT, b Newark, NJ, Nov 10, 26; m 51; c 2. TOXICOLOGY. *Educ:* NY Univ, BS, 48, MS, 50, PhD(exp biol), 54. *Prof Exp:* Res physiologist endocrine physiol, Princeton Labs, 54-59; res physiologist environ physiol, Boeing Co, 59-62; res biochemist, Nat Drug Co, 62-70; sect head immunol, Merrell Res Ctr, Merell Nat Lab, Richardson-Merrell Inc, 70-78, SECT HEAD PATH & TOXICOL DEPT, MERRELL-DOW PHAMACEUT INC, 78- *Mem:* AAAS; Soc Toxicol; Am Soc Pharmacol & Exp Therapeut; Soc Exp Biol & Med; Am Asn Immunol. *Res:* Immunopharmacology; immunotoxicology; biochemical pharmacology; endocrine physiology; toxicology. *Mailing Add:* Merrell Res Ctr Div of Richardson-Merrell Inc Cincinnati OH 45215

MEGGERS, WILLIAM F(REDERICK), JR, b Washington, DC, May 12, 24; m 50; c 2. ELECTRONIC ENGINEERING, PHYSICS. *Educ:* Univ Wis, BS, 50, MS, 51. *Prof Exp:* Electronic scientist, Microwave Systs Div, US Naval Ord Lab, Corona, 51-55, head, Talos Missile Countermeasures Br, Countermeasures Div, 55-59, head, Counter-countermeasures Tech Br, 59-61, head, Guide Div, Missile Systs Dept, 61-71; consult, Electronic Systs Dept, Naval Weapons Ctr, 71-75, head of staff, Electronic Warfare Dept, 75-80; RETIRED. *Res:* Electronic systems analysis; missile guidance systems design; microwave and electro-optical components and techniques. *Mailing Add:* 609 W Coral Ave Ridgecrest CA 93555

MEGGISON, DAVID LAURENCE, b Lynn, Mass, Dec 24, 28; m 52; c 4. FOOD TECHNOLOGY. *Educ:* Johns Hopkins Univ, BA, 48; Univ Mass, MS, 50, PhD(food sci), 53. *Prof Exp:* Assoc technologist cent labs, Gen Foods Corp, 52-55, proj leader frozen foods, Birds Eye Labs, 55-59; food prod res lab, Borden Foods Co, NY, 59-62; sect chief, Hunt Foods & Industs, Inc, 62-64, assoc dir res, Prod Develop, Hunt-Wesson Foods, 64-74; vpres res & develop, United Vintners, Inc, 74-75; vpres tech serv, RJR Foods, 75-80; VPRES CORP RES & TECH SERV, DEL MONTE CORP, 80- *Mem:* Inst Food Technol. *Res:* Development of new products and processes in instant foods; frozen and canned foods; wines. *Mailing Add:* Del Monte Corp One Mkt Plaza Box 3575 San Francisco CA 94119

MEGGITT, WILLIAM FREDRIC, b Green Springs, Ohio, Feb 9, 28; m 48; c 1. AGRONOMY. *Educ:* Ohio State Univ, BS, 50, MS, 51; Rutgers Univ, PhD(weed control, farm crops), 54. *Prof Exp:* Res agronomist, Agr Res Serv, USDA, 57-58; asst prof farm crops & weed control, Rutgers Univ, 58-60; assoc prof crop sci & weed control, 60-66, PROF CROP SCI, MICH STATE UNIV, 66- *Mem:* Am Soc Agron; Crop Sci Soc Am; Weed Sci Soc Am. *Res:* Weed control, chemical and cultural means; weed life cycles and competition; soil residues, penetration, translocation, accumulation and sites of action of herbicides. *Mailing Add:* Dept of Crop & Soil Sci Mich State Univ East Lansing MI 48824

MEGHREBLIAN, ROBERT V(ARTAN), b Cairo, Egypt, Sept 6, 22; nat US; c 2. RESEARCH & ENGINEERING MANAGEMENT. *Educ:* Rensselaer Polytech Inst, BAeE, 43; Calif Inst Technol, MS, 50, PhD(aeronaut, math), 53. *Prof Exp:* Struct engr, Consol Vultee Corp, 46-47; civil engr, Fluor Corp, 47; asst proj engr, Guided Missile Develop, Jet Propulsion Lab, Calif Inst Technol, 47-52; sr res engr & lectr, Oak Ridge Sch Reactor Technol, 52-55; chief appl mech group, Aircraft Nuclear Propulsion Proj, Oak Ridge Nat Lab, 55-57, assoc dir gas cooled power reactor proj, 57-58; chief physics sect, Jet Propulsion Lab, Calif Inst Technol, 58-60, chief phys sci div, 60-62, mgr space sci div, 62-68, dep asst lab dir tech div, 68-71; VPRES, CABOT CORP, 71-; PRES, DISTRIGAS CORP, 79- *Concurrent Pos:* Assoc prof, Calif Inst Technol, 60-61. *Mem:* Fel Am Nuclear Soc; Am Inst Aeronaut & Astronaut; Indust Res Inst; Am Gas Asn; New Eng Gas Asn. *Res:* High temperature thermodynamics; reactor analysis. *Mailing Add:* 50 Longwood Ave 815 Brookline MA 02146

MEGIBBEN, CHARLES KIMBROUGH, b Lexington, Ky, Oct 22, 36; m 57; c 4. MATHEMATICS. *Educ:* Southern Methodist Univ, BS, 59; Auburn Univ, PhD(math), 63. *Prof Exp:* Asst prof math, Tex Tech Col, 63-64; res assoc, Off Naval Res, Univ Wash, 64-65; asst prof, Univ Houston, 65-67; assoc prof, 67-81, PROF MATH, VANDERBILT UNIV, 81- *Concurrent Pos:* NSF res grants, 66-72. *Mem:* Am Math Soc. *Res:* Theory of Abelian groups; rings and modules. *Mailing Add:* Box 1589 Vanderbilt Univ Nashville TN 37235

MEGILL, LAWRENCE REXFORD, b Potsdam, Ohio, July 5, 25; m 46; c 2. PHYSICS. *Educ:* Univ Nebr, BSc, 49, MA, 51; Univ Colo, PhD(physics), 59. *Prof Exp:* Mem staff, Los Alamos Sci Lab, Univ Calif, 51-53; physicist inst telecommun sci & aeronomy, Environ Sci Serv Admin, Colo, 55-69; PROF PHYSICS & ELEC ENG, UTAH STATE UNIV, 69-, DIR, CTR ATMOSPHERIC & SPACE SCI, 77- *Concurrent Pos:* Prog dir aeronomy, NSF, 74-75. *Res:* Atmospheric physics, particularly photometry and spectroscopy. *Mailing Add:* Ctr Atmospheric & Space Sci Utah State Univ Logan UT 84322

MEGIRIAN, ROBERT, b New York, NY, June 18, 26; m 57; c 1. PHARMACOLOGY. *Educ:* Colgate Univ, AB, 51; Univ Rochester, MS, 53; Boston Univ, PhD(pharmacol), 57. *Prof Exp:* Res assoc pharmacol, Univ Rochester, 51-53; asst, Boston Univ, 53-56; pharmacologist, US Food & Drug Admin, 57-61; asst prof, 61-68, assoc prof, 68-74, PROF PHARMACOL, ALBANY MED COL, 75- *Concurrent Pos:* Res fel, Boston City Hosp, Mass, 57. *Mem:* Reticuloendothelial Soc; Am Soc Pharmacol & Exp Therapeut; Soc Exp Biol & Med; Am Soc Clin Pharmacol & Exp Therapeut. *Res:* Effect of drugs on the reticuloendothelial system. *Mailing Add:* Dept Physiol Albany Med Col Albany NY 12208

MEGLA, GERHARD KARL, b Berlin, Ger, Jan 22, 18; US citizen; m 41; c 1. ELECTRONICS, OPTICS. *Educ:* Univ Berlin, BS, 38; Dresden Tech Univ, PhD(elec eng), 54. *Prof Exp:* Design engr, C Lorenz AG, Ger, 39-44, lab mgr, 44-47; res dir commun, Sachsenwork, Radleberg, 47-55; prof, Ilmenau Tech Univ, 55-59; sr scientist, Martin Co, Fla, 60-61; group leader, Hoffmann Sci Ctr, Calif, 61-63; res mgr electrooptics, 63-66, dir electronics res, 66-76, MGR INT LIAISON, CORNING GLASS WORKS, 76-; PROF ELEC ENG, NC STATE UNIV, 63- *Mem:* Fel Inst Elec & Electronics Engrs; Optical Soc Am; Soc Photog Sci & Eng; NY Acad Sci. *Res:* Information and communication theory; wave propagation; antenna theory; optical information processing. *Mailing Add:* Corning Glas GmbH Hoehenstrasse 28a 6200 Wiesbaden Federal Republic of Germany

MEGNA, JOHN C(OSIMO), b Milwaukee, Wis, Oct 22, 27; m 50; c 5. CHEMICAL & BIOCHEMICAL ENGINEERING. *Educ:* Univ Wis, BS, 51. *Prof Exp:* Chem engr, Develop Div, Parke, Davis & Co, Mich, 51-52; head fermentation pilot plant, Res Labs, Pabst Brewing Co, Wis, 52-54; asst dept head fermentation develop div, Bristol Labs Div, Bristol-Myers Co, 54-57; from dir develop to plant mgr bioferm div, Int Minerals & Chem Corp, 57-67; vpres, Rahr Bio-Tech Labs, 67-71; VPRES MFG, DADE DIV, AM HOSP SUPPLY CORP, 71- *Mem:* Am Chem Soc; Am Inst Chem Engrs; Soc Indust Microbiol; Am Soc Microbiol. *Res:* Development and application of bioengineering principles to industrial fermentation; application and substitution of fermentation for existing technologies for the commercial production of useful new and existing products. *Mailing Add:* Am Hosp Supply Corp Dade Div PO Box 520672 Miami FL 33152

MEGO, JOHN L, b Pukwana, SDak, Sept 29, 22; m 53; c 2. BIOCHEMISTRY. *Educ:* Johns Hopkins Univ, PhD(biol), 60. *Prof Exp:* Res assoc plant physiol, Johns Hopkins Univ, 60; res asst neurosurg, Baltimore City Hosps, 60-62, res assoc, 62-65, res chief, 65-67; assoc prof biol, 67-73, PROF BIOL, UNIV ALA, TUSCALOOSA, 73- *Concurrent Pos:* Co-prin investr, NIH-AEC grant, 64-; Nat Acad Sci exchange fel, Univ Bratislava, 67; Nat Inst Environ Health Sci grant award, 71-74; Nat Inst Gen Med Sci res grant, 75-78; res grant award, Univ de Provence, Marseille, France, Nat Ctr Sci Res, 79. *Mem:* AAAS; Am Soc Cell Biol; Am Chem Soc. Res; Biochemical properties of lysosomes and related subcellular particles; Am Soc Biol Chemists. *Mailing Add:* Dept of Biol Box 1927 Univ of Ala in Tuscaloosa University AL 35486

MEGRAW, ROBERT ARTHUR, b Rochester, Minn, Dec 5, 39; m 69. FORESTRY, WOOD TECHNOLOGY. *Educ:* Univ Minn, BS, 62, PhD(forest prod eng), 66. *Prof Exp:* Res scientist pioneering dept, Res Div, 66-68, sr scientist, Res & Eng Div, 68-74, mgr, Wood Sci & Morphol Sect, 74-76, MGR, MICROSTRUCT & WOOD SCI SECT, RES & ENG DIV, WEYERHAEUSER CO, 76- *Honors & Awards:* Wood Award, 67. *Mem:* Forest Prod Res Soc; Soc Wood Sci & Technol; Tech Asn Pulp & Paper Indust. *Res:* Wood and fiber properties; tree growth-fiber property relationships; flame spread control in wood and fiber products; x-ray transmission as a wood and fiber research tool; scanning electron microscopy. *Mailing Add:* Weyerhaeuser Co Weyerhaeuser Technol Ctr Tacoma WA 98401

MEGRAW, ROBERT ELLIS, b Philadelphia, Pa, Feb 10, 30; m 71; c 5. CLINICAL CHEMISTRY. *Educ:* Fla State Univ, BA, 56, MS, 60; Iowa State Univ, PhD(bact), 64; Am Bd Clin Chem, dipl. *Prof Exp:* Fel biochem, Albert Einstein Med Ctr, 64-66; scientist, Warner-Lambert Res Inst, 66-71; res biochemist, Sigma Chem Co, 71-73; mgr unitest chem, Bio-dynamics/bmc, 73-80; MGR RES, ORTHO DIAGNOSTIC SYSTS INC, 81- *Concurrent Pos:* Lectr chem, Butler Univ, 81. *Mem:* AAAS; Am Chem Soc; Sigma Xi; Soc Exp Biol & Med; Am Asn Clin Chemists. *Res:* Research and development of clinical diagnostic reagents. *Mailing Add:* 14442 Deerfield Ave Tustin CA 92680

MEGRUE, GEORGE HENRY, b Jamaica, NY, Mar 23, 36; m 58; c 4. GEOCHEMISTRY, RESEARCH ADMINISTRATION. *Educ:* Amherst Col, BA, 57; Columbia Univ, MA, 59, PhD(geol), 62. *Prof Exp:* Res assoc chem, Brookhaven Nat Lab, 62-64, assoc chemist, 64-66; geochemist & cosmochemist, Smithsonian Inst Astrophys Observ & Harvard Col Observ, 66-74; FOUNDER & PRES, MEGRUE MICROANAL SYSTS CO, 74- *Concurrent Pos:* Sci leader, Nat Geog Ethiopian Rift Valley Exped, 69; prin investr, Apollo 12, 14 & 15 Manned Space Flights, NASA, 71-73. *Mem:* AAAS; Explorers Club; Am Geophys Union; Am Chem Soc. *Res:* Thermal history of meteorites; tectonic history of Ethiopian Rift Valley; distribution and origin of helium, neon, and argon isotopes in meteorites and lunar rocks; laser probe mass spectrometry; chemistry of cosmic dust; application of laser microchemical analyses to scientific research and development. *Mailing Add:* Megrue Microanal Systs Co Box 523 New Canaan CT 06840

MEGUERIAN, GARBIS H, b Turkey, Sept 10, 22; nat US; m 51; c 2. PHYSICAL ORGANIC CHEMISTRY. *Educ:* Am Univ, Beirut, BS, 47; Brown Univ, PhD(chem), 50. *Prof Exp:* Fel & res chemist, Harvard Univ, 50-52; chemist, Standard Oil Co Ind, 52-58, group leader, 58-64, RES ASSOC AMOCO OIL CO, 64- *Mem:* Am Chem Soc. *Res:* Reactions of elementary sulfur; oxidation of mercaptans; high temperature oxidation of hydrocarbons; nitrogen oxides control in automotive emissions. *Mailing Add:* Amoco Oil Co PO Box 400 Naperville IL 60540

MEHENDALE, HARIHARA MAHADEVA, b Philya, India, Jan 12, 42; m 68; c 2. ENVIRONMENTAL TOXICOLOGY. *Educ:* Karnatak Univ, India, BSc, 63; NC State Univ, MS, 66, PhD(physiol), 69. *Prof Exp:* Fel entom, Univ Ky, 69-71; NIH vis fel, Anal & Synthetic Chem Br, Nat Inst Environ Health Sci, 71-72, staff fel, Environ Pharmacol & Toxicol Br, 72-75; asst prof, 75-78, assoc prof, 78-80, PROF PHARMACOL & TOXICOL, UNIV MISS MED CTR, 80- *Concurrent Pos:* mem, Res Adv & Policy Comt, Miss Heart Asn, 79- & Toxicol Study Sect, NIH, 81-84. *Mem:* Soc Toxicol; Am Chem Soc; Entom Soc India; Am Soc Pharmacol & Exp Therapeut; Am Thoracic Soc. *Res:* Use of isolated perfused organs in studies of environmental toxicology; pharmacokinetics of environmental agents; effect of toxic agents on hepatobiliary and pulmonary systems. *Mailing Add:* Dept of Pharmacol & Toxicol Univ of Miss Med Ctr Jackson MS 39216

MEHERIUK, MICHAEL, b Derwent, Alta, June 5, 36; m 63. PLANT BIOCHEMISTRY. *Educ:* Univ Alta, BSc, 57, BEd, 59, PhD(biochem), 65. *Prof Exp:* RES SCIENTIST, CAN DEP AGR, 65- *Res:* Post-harvest physiology; storage of tree fruits, especially pears and apples. *Mailing Add:* RR 2 Summerland BC V0H 1C0 Can

MEHL, JAMES BERNARD, b Minneapolis, Minn, May 5, 39; m 61; c 2. PHYSICAL ACOUSTICS. *Educ:* Univ Minn, BPhys, 61, MS, 64, PhD(physics), 66. *Prof Exp:* Res assoc physics, Univ Ore, 66-68; asst prof, 68-74, ASSOC PROF PHYSICS, UNIV DEL, 74- *Concurrent Pos:* Physicist, Nat Bur Standards, 80. *Mem:* Acoustical Soc Am; Am Asn Physics Teachers; Am Phys Soc; AAAS. *Res:* physical acoustics of gases; low temperature physics; thermophysical properties of matter. *Mailing Add:* Dept of Physics Univ of Del Newark DE 19711

MEHLER, ALAN HASKELL, b St Louis, Mo, May 24, 22; m 43; c 4. BIOCHEMISTRY. *Educ:* Wash Univ, AB, 42; NY Univ, PhD(biochem), 48. *Prof Exp:* Res assoc, Rheumatic Fever Res Inst, Northwestern Univ, 49; asst prof, Inst Radiobiol & Biophys, Univ Chicago, 49-51; vis scientist, NIH, 51-52, chemist, 52-60, chief enzyme chem sect, Nat Inst Dent Res, 60-65; prof chem & chmn, Dept Med, 65-80, DIR, LAB ENZYMOL, MED COL WIS, 80- *Concurrent Pos:* Mem, Weizmann Inst, 48; NSF sr fel, Dept Genetics, Sorbonne, 58-59; Guggenheim fel, Inst Molecular Biol, Univ Paris, 72-73. *Mem:* AAAS; Am Chem Soc; Am Soc Biol Chem; Soc Gen Physiol; Biochem Soc. *Res:* Enzyme chemistry; transfer ribonucleic acid; intermediary metabolism. *Mailing Add:* Lab Enzym 8701 Watertown Plank Rd Milwaukee WI 53226

MEHLER, ERNEST LOUIS, b Amsterdam, Holland, Sept 25, 38; US citizen; m 64; c 2. THEORETICAL STRUCTURAL BIOLOGY. *Educ:* Ill Inst Technol, BS, 60; Johns Hopkins Univ, MA, 64; Iowa State Univ, PhD(theoret chem), 68. *Prof Exp:* Instr theoret chem, Univ Groningen, 71-73; sr res assoc theoret biochem, 74-79, PRIVAT DOZENT, UNIV BASEL, 79- *Concurrent Pos:* Fel, Univ Wash, 68-70. *Mem:* Am Chem Soc; Int Soc Quantum Biol. *Res:* Ab initio methods for large molecules; structure of proteins; molecular aspects of drug reactivity; computerized molecular modelling; computer graphics for molecular modelling. *Mailing Add:* Biocenter Univ of Basel Klingelbergstr 70 Basel Switzerland

MEHLER, WILLIAM RAPHAEL, neuroanatomy, see previous edition

MEHLHAFF, LEON CURTIS, b Lodi, Calif, Apr 28, 40; m 65; c 3. ANALYTICAL CHEMISTRY, POLYMER CHEMISTRY. *Educ:* Univ Calif, Berkeley, BS, 61; Univ Wash, PhD(anal chem), 65. *Prof Exp:* Chemist plastics dept, E I du Pont de Nemours & Co, 65-68; asst prof anal chem, 68-71, ASSOC PROF ANAL CHEM, UNIV PUGET SOUND, 71- *Concurrent Pos:* Regional coordr, Wash Shoreline Tech Adv Bd, 71-73; mem, Hazardous Waste Sect, Wash State Dept Ecol, 76-77. *Mem:* Am Chem Soc; Electrochem Soc. *Res:* Analytical chemistry of polymer systems; instrumental analytical chemistry; electrochemistry; environmental science program; hazardous waste. *Mailing Add:* Dept Chem Univ Puget Sound Tacoma WA 98416

MEHMEDBASICH, ENVER, organic chemistry, see previous edition

MEHNER, JOHN FREDERICK, b Grove City, Pa, July 15, 21. ORNITHOLOGY. *Educ:* Grove City Col, BS, 42; Univ Pittsburgh, MS, 50; Mich State Univ, PhD(zool), 58. *Prof Exp:* Teacher high sch, Pa, 42-59; assoc prof biol, Edinboro State Col, 59-63; assoc prof, 63-66, PROF BIOL, MARY BALDWIN COL, 66-, CHMN DEPT, 63- *Mem:* Am Ornith Union; Ecol Soc Am; Wilson Ornith Soc; AAAS; Am Inst Biol Sci. *Res:* Effects of insecticides on passerine bird populations; ecology and ethology of the evening grosbeak; a checklist of the birds of Augusta County, Virginia; breeding biology of the house finch in Virginia. *Mailing Add:* Dept of Biol Mary Baldwin Col Staunton VA 24401

MEHR, CYRUS B, b Tehran, Iran, July 7, 27; US citizen; m 55; c 4. MATHEMATICS, ELECTRICAL ENGINEERING. *Educ:* La State Univ, BS, 52; Purdue Univ, MS, 53, PhD(math, elec eng), 64. *Prof Exp:* Develop engr, Elec Prod Co, 53-55; systs engr, Gen Elec Co, 55-57; mem develop lab, Square D Elec Co, 57-59; mem res staff, Int Bus Mach Corp, 63-65; asst prof, 65-67, ASSOC PROF MATH, OHIO UNIV, 67- *Mem:* Math Asn Am. *Res:* Functional analysis; probabicity. *Mailing Add:* Dept of Math Ohio Univ Athens OH 45701

MEHRA, MOOL CHAND, b Lahore, Pakistan, July 31, 36; Can citizen; m 64; c 2. RADIOCHEMISTRY, INORGANIC CHEMISTRY. *Educ:* Univ Rajasthan, BSc. 55, MSc, 57; Laval Univ, DSc(chem), 68. *Prof Exp:* Asst prof chem, Univ Rasjasthan, 57-59; sci off radiochem, Atomic Energy Estab, India, 59-65; from asst prof to assoc prof, 68-74, head dept, 69-72, PROF CHEM, UNIV MONCTON, 74- *Concurrent Pos:* Univ Moncton rep, Atlantic Prov Inter-Univ Comt Sci, Chem & Water Resources, 70-72 & Chem Inst Can, 75-79. *Mem:* Fel Chem Inst Can; fel Am Inst Chem; fel Indian Chem Soc. *Res:* Radioanalytical chemistry; analytical chemistry of metals coordination complexes in solution. *Mailing Add:* Dept of Chem Univ of Moncton Moncton NB E1A 3E9 Can

MEHRA, VINODKUMAR S, b Lahore, Pakistan, Oct 26, 35; m 65; c 2. CHEMICAL ENGINEERING. *Educ:* Univ Bombay, BChemEng, 56; Northwestern Univ, PhD(chem eng), 63. *Prof Exp:* Res engr, 63-71, SR RES ENGR, PLASTIC PROD & RESINS DEPT, E I DU PONT DE NEMOURS & CO, INC, 71- *Res:* Chemical engineering thermodynamics; processing equipment; economic analysis; process development; plastics; plastics processing; polymer synthesis; plastics product development. *Mailing Add:* Plastic Prod & Resins Dept E I du Pont de Nemours & Co Inc Wilmington DE 19898

MEHRABIAN, ROBERT, b Tehran, Iran, July 31, 41; US citizen; m 77. METALLURGY. *Educ:* Mass Inst Technol, BS, 64, PhD(metall), 68. *Prof Exp:* From asst prof to assoc prof metall & mat sci, Mass Inst Technol, 72-75; assoc prof, 75-78, prof, 78-79, ADJ PROF METALL, DEPT METALL & MINING & DEPT MECH & INDUST ENG, UNIV ILL, URBANA-CHAMPAIGN, 79-; CHIEF METALL, NAT BUR STANDARDS, DEPT COMMERCE, 80- *Concurrent Pos:* Consult, Rheocast Corp, 74-, Army Mat & Mech Res Ctr, 75-, Univ Space Res Admin, 75-, United Technol, 76-, Sandia Labs, 76- & Phrasor Technol, 77-; mem, Nat Mat Adv Bd Amorphous & Metastable Mat, 78. *Honors & Awards:* George Kimball Burgess Mem lectr, Washington, DC, 80. *Mem:* Am Inst Metall Engrs; Am Soc Metals; Soc Rheol; Am Foundrymen's Soc; Am Soc Testing & Mat. *Res:* Foundry solidification, powder metallurgy, metal matrix composites and refining of alloy scrap; co-inventor of rheocasting and several associated processes. *Mailing Add:* Dept Metall & Mining Eng Univ Ill at Urbana-Champaign Urbana IL 61801

MEHRAN, FARROKH, b Tehran, Iran, June 29, 36; m 63; c 2. PHYSICS. *Educ:* Univ Calif, Berkeley, BS, 59; Harvard Univ, PhD(physics), 64. *Prof Exp:* Fel, Harvard Univ, 64-65; asst prof physics, Sacramento State Col, 65-67; staff physicist, 67-70, MEM RES STAFF, IBM CORP, 70- *Mem:* Am Phys Soc. *Res:* Molecular beams; quantum electronics; electron paramagnetic resonance. *Mailing Add:* Dept of Phys Sci IBM Corp PO Box 218 Yorktown Heights NY 10598

MEHRING, ARNON LEWIS, JR, b Washington, DC, Apr 24, 15; m 36; c 3. POULTRY NUTRITION. *Educ:* Univ Md, BS, 36. *Prof Exp:* Mkt inspector eggs, State Dept Mkt, Exten Serv, Univ Md, 36-39; farm owner, 39-43; farm mgr, 43-45; poultryman in-chg nutrit & breeding invests, Lime Crest Res Lab, 45-63; nutritionist, Limestone Prod Corp, 63-70, qual supvr, 70-79; RETIRED. *Mem:* Poultry Sci Asn; Am Soc Animal Sci; Am Dairy Sci Asn; Am Soc Testing & Mat. *Res:* Mineral nutrition of livestock and poultry. *Mailing Add:* Limestone Prod Corp PO Box 217 Sparta NJ 07871

MEHRING, JEFFREY SCOTT, b Cleveland, Ohio, July 6, 42; m 65; c 3. NUTRITION, TOXICOLOGY. *Educ:* Ohio State Univ, BS, 64, MS, 66, PhD(nutrit), 69. *Prof Exp:* Lectr nutrit, Ohio State Univ, 69; lab mgr nutrit, Gaines Nutrit Ctr, Gen Foods Corp, 69-77; dir large animal toxicol, Int Res & Develop Corp, 77-79; consult, Occup Health & Safety & Gen Toxicol, 80-81; VPRES, RES LAB, RES ENTERPRISES, INC, 81- *Concurrent Pos:* Mem subcomt lab animal nutrit, Nat Acad Sci-Nat Res Coun, 74-78. *Mem:* Animal Nutrit Res Coun; Am Soc Animal Sci; Inst Food Technologists. *Res:* Comparative animal nutrition; quantification of nutrient requirements; clinical assessment of nutritional status and applied toxicology; safety evaluation and regulatory compliance. *Mailing Add:* 5767 West R Ave Schoolcraft MI 49087

MEHRINGER, PETER JOSEPH, JR, b Lawrence, Kans, Dec 9, 33; m 54; c 3. PALEOECOLOGY, PALYNOLOGY. *Educ:* Calif State Col, Los Angeles, BA, 59, MA, 62; Univ Ariz, PhD, 68. *Prof Exp:* Instr biol, Glendale Jr Col, 60-61; res assoc geochronology, Univ Ariz, 64-68, asst prof earth sci, 68-69; asst prof anthrop, Univ Utah, 69-71; assoc prof anthrop, 71-78, PROF ANTHROP & GEOL, WASH STATE UNIV, 78- *Honors & Awards:* Roald Tryxell Award, Soc Am Archaeol, 79. *Mem:* AAAS; Ecol Soc Am; Soc Am Archael; Am Quaternary Asn. *Res:* Quaternary biogeography, paleoecolgy, chronology and geology of North America, Egypt and the Sudan. *Mailing Add:* Lab Anthrop Wash State Univ Pullman WA 99164

MEHRLE, PAUL MARTIN, JR, b Caruthersville, Mo, Dec 13, 45; m 64; c 2. BIOCHEMISTRY, PHYSIOLOGY. *Educ:* Southwestern at Memphis, BA, 67; Univ Mo-Columbia, MA, 69, PhD(biochem), 71. *Prof Exp:* physiologist, Fish-Pesticide Res Lab, 71-81, CHIEF BIOLOGIST, NAT FISH RES LAB, US DEPT INTERIOR, 81- *Concurrent Pos:* Res assoc, Univ Mo-Columbia, 73- *Mem:* Am Chem Soc; Sigma Xi; Am Fish Soc; Soc Toxicol. *Res:* Directing research concerned with evaluating the biochemical and physiological effects of pesticides and other xenobiotics on fish; major areas of interest are enzymatic metabolism of xenobiotics, amino acid metabolism and nutrition; coordination of integrated aquatic toxicology programs to assess the impacts of cantaminants on aquatic resources. *Mailing Add:* Nat Fish Res Lab Rte 1 Columbia MO 65201

MEHRLICH, FERDINAND PAUL, b Cincinnati, Ohio, 05; m 33; c 3. FOOD SCIENCE. *Educ:* Butler Univ, AB, 27; Univ Wis, PhD(plant physiol), 30. *Prof Exp:* Asst plant physiol, Univ Wis, 28-30; assoc pathologist pineapple res, Pineapple Producers Coop Asn, Hawaii, 30-35; sci adv, Hawaiian Pineapple Co, Ltd, 35-43, dir res, 43-44, asst vpres in-charge res, 44-49; vpres, Res Inst, Int Basic Econ Corp, 50-54, trustee & dir res div, 54-58; sci dir, Qm Food & Container Inst Armed Forces, 58-63, dir, Food Labs, US Army Natick Labs, 63-75; CONSULT & TECH WRITER, 75- *Concurrent Pos:* Consult, Cocoa Res Inst, DC, 56-, Nat Planning Asn, 56- & Arthur D Little, Inc, Mass, 56-; consult to vpres res, Gen Foods Corp, NY, 56-57; mem survs, WAfrica, Belgian Cong, Brazil, Costa Rica, Cuba, Mex, PR, Venezuela & Peru. *Honors & Awards:* Meritorious Civilian Serv award, 64. *Mem:* Fel AAAS; Am Soc Plant Physiol; Inst Food Technol; Nutrit Today; NY Acad Sci. *Res:* Food technology including radiation preservation of food; product and process development; agricultural research and planning; pineapple and coffee production and processing; tropical and subtropical crop production and upgrading. *Mailing Add:* 96 Pilgrim Rd Wellesley MA 02181

MEHROTRA, BAM DEO, b Meerut, India, Sept 4, 33; m 65; c 1. BIOCHEMISTRY. *Educ:* Agra Univ, BSc, 50, MSc, 52; Ind Univ, Bloomington, PhD(biochem), 64. *Prof Exp:* Lectr org chem, J V Col, India, 52-58; fel biochem, Inst Enzyme Res, Univ Wis-Madison, 62-64; asst prof, All-India Inst Med Sci, New Delhi, 65-66; res assoc, Ind Univ, Bloomington, 67-69; PROF CHEM, TOUGALOO COL, 69- . *Mem:* Am Chem Soc. *Res:* Chemistry of nucleic acids, their interactions with small ions, and their physical, chemical and biological characteristics; effect of pesticides on mammalian systems. *Mailing Add:* Dept of Chem Tougaloo Col Tougaloo MS 39174

MEHROTRA, KISHAN GOPAL, b Kashipur, India, Dec 9, 41; m 71; c 1. MATHEMATICAL STATISTICS. *Educ:* Univ Lucknow, BSc, 60, MSc, 62; Univ Wis-Madison, MS, 69, PhD(statist), 71. *Prof Exp:* Lectr statist, Banaras Hindu Univ, 62-66; asst prof, 71-72, assoc prof, 72-77, PROF STATIST, SYRACUSE UNIV, 77- *Mem:* Inst Math Statist; Am Statist Asn. *Res:* Nonparametric statistics; pattern recognition. *Mailing Add:* Sch Comput & Info Sci Syracuse Univ Syracuse NY 13210

MEHS, DOREEN MARGARET, b Buffalo, NY, July 27, 44. ANALYTICAL CHEMISTRY, INORGANIC CHEMISTRY. *Educ:* Harpur Col, BA, 66; State Univ NY Binghamton, MA, 72; Univ NMex, PhD(chem), 80. *Prof Exp:* Admin asst & asst instr chem, State Univ NY Binghamton, 66-73; instr, 73-75, asst prof, 75-81, ASSOC PROF CHEM & CHMN, FT LEWIS COL, 81- *Concurrent Pos:* Consult, Four Corners Environ Res Inst, 73- *Mem:* Am Chem Soc; Soc Appl Spectros. *Res:* Environmental analysis; high pressure liquid chromatographic analysis. *Mailing Add:* Dept of Chem Ft Lewis Col Durango CO 81301

MEHTA, ATUL MANSUKHBHAI, b Jamnagar, India, May 4, 49; m 77; c 1. INDUSTRIAL PHARMACY, BIOPHARMACEUTICS. *Educ:* Shivaji Univ, India, BPharm, 72; Univ Md, MS, 75, BS, 76, PhD(pharmaceut), 81. *Prof Exp:* Pharmaceut chemist, Roche Prod Ltd, 72-73; asst instr, Univ Md, 74-75; mem packaging-in-charge staff, US Pharmacoepia, 74-78; GROUP LEADER, AYERST LABS, 81- *Concurrent Pos:* Staff pharmacist, St Agnes Hosp, 77-81. *Mem:* Am Pharmaceut Asn; Acad Pharmaceut Sci. *Res:* Formulation and process variable effects on the performance of a solid dosage form (pharmaceutical) in vitro and in vivo including stability of such dosage forms; design and development of sustained release dosage forms. *Mailing Add:* 3 Terrace West 18 Plattsburgh NY 12901

MEHTA, AVINASH C, b Rehlu, India, Nov 1, 31; m 70; c 1. ORGANIC CHEMISTRY. *Educ:* Panjab Univ, India, BSc, 52, MSc, 54; Univ Delhi, PhD(org chem), 58. *Prof Exp:* Lectr chem, Deshbandhu Col, New Delhi, India, 57-58 & Univ Delhi, 59-62; res assoc org chem, Univ Mich, 62-64; res scientist, Uniroyal Res Labs, Ont, 64-67; sr org chemist, Arthur D Little, Inc, 68-70; scientist, 70-74, res group leader, 74, RES ASSOC, POLAROID CORP, 74- *Mem:* Am Chem Soc; Royal Soc Chem. *Res:* Organic chemical reaction mechanisms; organic synthesis, polymer chemistry and photographic chemistry; synthesis of novel monomers and polymers. *Mailing Add:* 12 Brookside Ave Belmont MA 02178

MEHTA, BIPIN MOHANLAL, b Bombay, India, July 25, 35; m 60. MICROBIAL GENETICS, MICROBIAL PHYSIOLOGY. *Educ:* Univ Bombay, BSc, 55, BSc, 57, PhD(microbial genetics & nutrit), 63. *Prof Exp:* Teaching asst microbiol & biochem, Univ Bombay, 60-61; sr res asst microbial genetics, Coun Sci & Indust Res, Govt India, 61-65; teaching asst & res assoc molecular biol, State Univ NY Downstate Med Ctr, 65-66; vis res fel molecular genetics, Sloan-Kettering Inst Cancer Res, 66-69; res assoc microbiol, Univ Ottawa, 69-72; res assoc, 72-74, assoc, 74-81, ASST, MEM SLOAN-KETTERING INST CANCER RES, 74-81; ASST PROF, SLOAN-KETTERING DIV, GRAD SCH MED SCI, CORNELL UNIV, 75- *Mem:* Am Soc Microbiol; Soc Gen Microbiol; Can Soc Cell Biol; Am Asn Cancer Res; Am Soc Clin Oncol. *Res:* Study of the distribution kinetics of cancer chemotherapeutic agents in body fluids and tissues of patients and experimental animals; study of mechanism of resistance to drugs; pharmacokinetics of anticancer agents; genetic recombination in microorganisms. *Mailing Add:* Sloan-Kettering Inst Cancer Res 145 Boston Post Rd Rye NY 10580

MEHTA, GURMUKH D, b India, Aug 27, 45; m 73; c 1. FLUID MECHANICS, ENERGY SYSTEMS. *Educ:* Guru Nanak Eng Col, BSc, 67; Indian Inst Technol, MS, 69; Brown Univ, PhD(eng), 74. *Prof Exp:* Res scientist, Bhabha Atomic Res Ctr, Bombay, India, 67; grad eng, Duragapur Steel Plant, India, 67; res scholar mech eng, Indian Inst Technol, 68-69, sr res assoc, 69-70; res asst, Div Eng, Brown Univ, 70-74; res scientist, Dept Appl Sci, Hydronautics Inc, 74-77; SR ENGR, INTERTECHNOL SOLAR CORP, 77-, MGR ADVAN THERMAL SYST, 78- *Concurrent Pos:* Teaching asst, Div Eng, Brown Univ, 71-74. *Mem:* Am Soc Mech Engrs; Am Inst Aeronaut & Astronaut; Int Solar Energy Soc; Sigma Xi. *Res:* Water jets; membrane transport; cavitation; thermodynamics and heat transfer; alternate power and energy systems development; solar energy; salinity power; heat pumps; systems engineering and optimization; advanced air conditioning systems; ocean energy conversion systems. *Mailing Add:* InterTechnol Solar Corp 100 Main St War renton VA 22186

MEHTA, JATINDER S, b Amritsar, India, Oct 4, 39; US citizen. STATISTICAL ESTIMATION, STATISTICAL TESTING. *Educ:* Panjab Univ, India, BA, 59, MA, 61; Wis Univ, MS, 65, PhD(statist), 68. *Prof Exp:* From asst prof to assoc prof, 68-78, PROF MATH, TEMPLE UNIV, 78- *Mem:* Am Statist Asn. *Res:* Statistical estimation and testing; econometrics; author or coauthor of over 40 publications. *Mailing Add:* Dept Math Temple Univ Philadelphia PA 19122

MEHTA, MAHESH J, physical chemistry, see previous edition

MEHTA, N(AVNIT) C(HHAGANLAL), b Bombay, India, Feb 21, 38; m 69. MECHANICAL ENGINEERING, MATHEMATICS. *Educ:* Univ Baroda, India, BEMech, 60; Mo Sch Mines, MS, 62; Univ Mo-Rolla, PhD(mech), 67. *Prof Exp:* Trainee engr, Ex-Cell-O Pvt Ltd, India, 60; proj engr, Olin Mathieson Chem Corp, 62-64; spec consult new plastic prod develop, K V Industs, Bombay, 64; res engr, Shell Oil Co, 67-68; assoc prof vibrations & eng mech, Tri-State Col, 68-73; mgr vehicle dynamics, 73-80, CHIEF ENGR, VEHICLE DYNAMICS & TEST, TRUCK GROUP ENG, INT HARVESTER, 80- *Concurrent Pos:* Consult, Magnavox Co, 70 & Hendrickson Tandem Corp, 71- *Honors & Awards:* Ralph R Teetor Award, Soc Automotive Engrs, 71. *Mem:* Soc Automotive Engrs; Am Soc Mech Engrs; Am Soc Eng Educ. *Res:* Nonlinear vibrations of automotive vehicles and other structures. *Mailing Add:* 7710 Wishing Well Ct Ft Wayne IN 46815

MEHTA, NARIMAN BOMANSHAW, b Bombay, India, Apr 8, 20; nat US; m 54; c 3. MEDICINAL & PHARMACEUTICAL CHEMISTRY. *Educ:* Univ Bombay, BSc, 41, BA, 42; Univ Kans, PhD, 52. *Prof Exp:* Lectr physics, Univ Bombay, 41-46; trainee, J E Seagram & Sons, Inc, Ky, 47-48; fel, Univ Toronto, 53-54; prof chem, Cent State Col, 54-57; sr res scientist, 57-76, PRIN SCIENTIST, WELLCOME RES LABS, BURROUGHS WELLCOME & CO, INC, 77- *Concurrent Pos:* Consult, Charles F Kettering Found, Ohio, 55-57. *Mem:* Am Chem Soc; Royal Soc Chem; fel Indian Chem Soc. *Res:* Organo-physical and heterocyclic chemistry; reaction mechanisms and kinetics; high vacuum techniques; medicinal chemistry; structure-activity studies in design of drugs of central nervous system; mechanism of reactions. *Mailing Add:* 3030 Cornwallis Rd Research Triangle Park NC 27709

MEHTA, POVINDAR KUMAR, b Panjab, India. MATERIALS SCIENCE. *Educ:* Delhi Polytech Inst, Nat dipl, 52; NC State Univ, MS, 62; Univ Calif, Berkeley, DE(mat sci & eng), 64. *Prof Exp:* Chem engr, Rohtas Industs, India, 52-61; works mgr, Jaipur Udyog, 66-68; asst prof civil eng, 64-66, assoc prof eng sci, 68-74, PROF ENG SCI, UNIV CALIF, BERKELEY, 74- *Concurrent Pos:* Consult cement chem. *Mem:* Am Soc Testing & Mat; Am Ceramic Soc; Am Concrete Inst; Int Union Testing & Res Labs Mat & Struct. *Res:* Physical chemistry of cement and concrete; cement technology; expansive cements; high alumina cements and blended cements; utilization of industrial and agricultural wastes for making cementitious materials. *Mailing Add:* Dept of Civil Eng 537 Davis Hall Univ of Calif Berkeley CA 94720

MEHTA, RAJEN SUMATILAL, b Mahlaing, Burma, Sept 16, 50; m 80. DAIRY PRODUCTS, FOOD ENZYMES. *Educ:* Col Ag, Poona, India, BSc, 71, Kans State Univ, Manhattan, MS, 73, PhD(food sci), 77. *Prof Exp:* Res asst dairy sci, Kans State Univ, 77; prod develop tech, dairy & food, Dederich Corp, 78; TECH DEVELOP REP, INGREDIENTS, PFIZER INC, 78- *Mem:* Inst Food Technologists; Am Dairy Sci Asn; Int Asn Milk Food & Environ Sanitarians. *Res:* Application of enzyme and other ingredients in dairy and other foods; ultra high temperature sterilization of milk; flavor enhancement and chemistry of cheeses; direct acidification production of dairy products; author or coauthor of numerous papers and publications. *Mailing Add:* 1230 E Singer Circle 208 Milwaukee WI 53212

MEHTA, SUDHIR, b Dhoraji, India, Nov 10, 46; m 75. MATERIALS SCIENCE, EARTH SCIENCES. *Educ:* Indian Inst Technol, BSc, 67, MSc, 69; Lehigh UniY, MS, 71, PhD(geol), 73. *Prof Exp:* Res assoc metall, Lehigh Univ, 74-76, res assoc chem, 76-77, res scientist mat sci, 78-80; RES ENGR, BETHLEHEM STEEL CORP, 80- *Concurrent Pos:* Fel, Pa Sci & Eng Found & NSF grants, 76-77; co-investr, Lunar Sci grant, NASA, 78- *Mem:* Microbeam Anal Soc; Sigma Xi. *Res:* Basic and applied research with the application of modern electron optical techniques, (scanning electron microscope, scanning transmission electron microscope, & transmission electron microscope), to problems in lunar science, catalysis, coal carbonization and ceramic materials. *Mailing Add:* 3 Adams Lane RD 5 Bethlehem PA 18015

MEI, CHIANG C(HUNG), b Wuhan, China, Apr 4, 35; m 65; c 1. FLUID MECHANICS, CIVIL ENGINEERING. *Educ:* Nat Taiwan Univ, BS, 55; Stanford Univ, MS, 58; Calif Inst Technol, PhD(eng sci), 63. *Prof Exp:* Res fel eng sci, Calif Inst Technol, 63-65; mem tech staff, Nat Eng Sci Co, Calif, 65; from asst prof to assoc prof, 65-76, PROF CIVIL ENG, MASS INST TECHNOL, 76- *Mem:* Sigma Xi; Am Soc Civil Engrs. *Res:* Hydrodynamics; coastal and ocean engineering; applied mechanics. *Mailing Add:* Dept of Civil Eng Mass Inst of Technol Cambridge MA 02139

MEI, KENNETH K, b Shanghai, China, May 19, 32; m 68; c 2. ELECTROMAGNETIC SCATTERING & RADIATION. *Educ:* Univ Wis, BSEE, 59, MS, 60, PhD(elec eng), 62. *Prof Exp:* From asst prof to assoc prof, 62-76, PROF ELEC ENG, UNIV CALIF, BERKELEY, 76- *Concurrent Pos:* Mem US Nat Comt, Comn 6, Int Union Radio Sci, 70-; ed, J Electromagnetics. *Mem:* Inst Elec & Electronics Engrs; Electromagnetics Soc (pres). *Res:* Electromagnetic theory, wave radiation and propagation. *Mailing Add:* Dept of Elec Eng & Comput Sci Univ of Calif Berkeley CA 94720

MEIBACH, RICHARD C, NEUROSCIENCE. *Educ:* Brooklyn Col, City Univ NY, BA, 72; NJ Med Col, PhD(anat), 76. *Prof Exp:* Fel res, Albert Einstein Col Med, 76-78; ASST PROF PHARMACOL, MT SINAI SCH MED, CITY UNIV NY, 78- *Concurrent Pos:* Vis prof, Neurosci Dept, NJ Col Med, 78-79; Reviewer, NSF, 79- *Mem:* Am Asn Anatomists; Soc Neurosci. *Res:* Neuroanatomy of the limbic system- determining the connections of the hippocampal formation and amygdala; morphological pharmacology--the use of biochemical techniques to anatomically determine sites of action of drugs and neurotransmitters in brain. *Mailing Add:* Dept Pharmacol Mt Sinai Sch Med One Gustave L Levy Pl New York NY 10029

MEIBOHM, EDGAR PAUL HUBERT, b New Orleans, La, Dec 13, 15; m 55; c 4. POLYMER SCIENCE. *Educ:* Guilford Col, BS, 36; Univ NC, MS, 39; Ohio State Univ, PhD(phys chem), 47. *Prof Exp:* Instr chem, Kans State Univ, 41-42; group leader, Nat Defense Res Comt Div Eight, Explosive Res Lab, Pa, 42-45, res sect leader, Los Alamos Sci Lab, 45; res chemist, Cent Res Dept, E I Du Pont De Nemours & Co, Inc, Philadelphia, 47-55, sr res chemist, Rayon Res Lab, 55-57, sr res chemist, Dacron Res Lab, 57-62, sr res chemist, Kinston Plant Tech, 62-67, staff chemist, Marshall Lab, 67-81; RETIRED. *Mem:* Am Chem Soc; Am Crystallog Asn. *Res:* Small-angle scattering of x-rays; crystal structures; applications of x-ray diffraction to high polymers; physics and physical chemistry of polymers; polymer characterization. *Mailing Add:* 521 Shadeland Ave Drexel Hill PA 19026

MEIBOOM, SAUL, b Antwerp, Belg, Apr 7, 16; US citizen; m 46; c 2. PHYSICS OF LIQUID CRYSTALS. *Educ:* Univ Delft, PhysEng, 39; Hebrew Univ, Israel, PhD(physics), 55. *Prof Exp:* Instr physics, Hebrew Univ, Israel, 40-48; sr scientist, Weizmann Inst, 48-58; MEM TECH STAFF, BELL LABS, 58- *Mem:* Am Phys Soc. *Res:* Physical properties of liquid crystals, including surface interactions, flow properties and phase transitions. *Mailing Add:* Bell Labs PO Box 261 1B-308 Murray Hill NJ 07974

MEIBUHR, STUART GENE, b Cleveland, Ohio, Jan 6, 34; m 60. ELECTROCHEMISTRY. *Educ:* Western Reserve Univ, BS, 55, MS, 58, PhD(electrochem), 60. *Prof Exp:* Chemist, Harshaw Chem Co, Ohio, 54-57; technologist appl res lab, US Steel Corp, Pa, 60-63; sr res chemist, Fuel Cell Corp, Mo, 63-64; assoc sr res chemist, Res Lab, 64-65, sr res chemist, 65-81, STAFF SCIENTIST, RES LAB, GEN MOTORS CORP, 81- *Mem:* Am Chem Soc; Sigma Xi; Electrochem Soc; Prof Photog Am; Am Asn Zool Parks & Aquiariums. *Res:* Electrodeposition; electrode kinetics; fuel cells; batteries; organic electrolytes; scanning electron microscope x-ray. *Mailing Add:* Gen Motors Res Lab Electrochem Dept RCEL Bldg Warren MI 48090

MEIENHOFER, JOHANNES ARNOLD, b Dresden, Ger, Mar 3, 29; c 2. BIOCHEMISTRY, ORGANIC CHEMISTRY. *Educ:* Univ Heidelberg, dipl, 54, PhD(chem), 56. *Prof Exp:* Res assoc, Med Sch, Cornell Univ, 57-59; res assoc, Univ Calif, Berkeley, 59-60; proj chief, Ger Wool Res Inst, Aachen, 61-64; head peptide & protein chem lab, Children's Cancer Res Found, Boston, 65-73; sect chief, 73-80, DIR, CHEM RES DEPT, HOFFMANN-LA ROCHE, INC, NUTLEY, 80- *Concurrent Pos:* Fulbright travel grant, 57-61; res assoc, Farbenfabriken Bayer, A G, Ger, 61-64; assoc, Harvard Med Sch, 69-71, lectr, 71- *Mem:* AAAS; Am Chem Soc; Am Soc Biol Chem; Ger Chem Soc; Ger Soc Biol Chem. *Res:* Peptide and protein chemistry; hormones; antibiotics; antitumor agents. *Mailing Add:* Chem Res Dept Hoffmann-La Roche Inc Nutley NJ 07110

MEIER, ALBERT HENRY, b New Haven, Mo, June 29, 29; m 54; c 3. ZOOLOGY, PHYSIOLOGY. *Educ:* Washington Univ, AB, 56; Univ Mo, MA, 59, PhD(zool), 62. *Prof Exp:* NIH fel, Wash State Univ, 62-64; from asst prof to assoc prof zool, 64-72, PROF ZOOL, LA STATE UNIV, 72- *Concurrent Pos:* NIH res career develop award, 69-74. *Honors & Awards:* Distinguished Res Master, La State Univ, 73. *Mem:* Am Soc Zool; Am Ornith Union; Ecol Soc Am; Soc Exp Biol & Med; Int Soc Chronobiol. *Res:* Comparative endocrinology and physiology of vertebrates; biological rhythms in hormonal control of seasonal and developmental conditions. *Mailing Add:* Dept of Zool La State Univ Baton Rouge LA 70803

MEIER, CHARLES FREDERICK, JR, b Cincinnati, Ohio, Feb 14, 49; m 76; c 2. ELECTROPHYSIOLOGY. *Educ:* Univ Cincinnati, BS, 71; Univ Miami, PhD(pharmacol), 77. *Prof Exp:* Res pharmacologist, Dept Pharmacol, Col Med, Univ Calif, San Francisco, 77-79; ASST PROF PHARMACOL, COL MED, UNIV OKLA, 79- *Concurrent Pos:* Mem, Am Heart Asn. *Mem:* Sigma Xi; Int Soc Heart Res. *Res:* Normal and abnormal cardiac excitation contraction coupling, transmembrane ionic currents and drug effects on these phenomena using isolated adult cardiac cell preparations and voltage clamp techniques. *Mailing Add:* Dept Pharmacol BMSB 753 Health Sci Ctr Univ Okla PO Box 26901 Oklahoma City OK 73190

MEIER, DALE JOSEPH, b The Dalles, Ore, Apr 21, 22; m 48; c 2. POLYMER PHYSICS. *Educ:* Calif Inst Technol, BS, 47, MS, 48; Univ Calif, Los Angeles, PhD(chem), 51. *Prof Exp:* Chemist, Shell Develop Co, 51-55, supvr res, 55-68, exchange scientist, Shell Lab, Amsterdam, 68-69, proj leader, Shell Chem Co, 69-71, supvr res, Shell Develop Co, 71-72; sr res scientist, Midland Macromolecular Inst, 72-78, SR SCIENTIST & PROF POLYMER PHYSICS, MICH MOLECULAR INST, 78- *Concurrent Pos:* Consult, Alza Corp, 73-, Dynapol, 73-, Lawrence Livermore Lab, 76-, AMP, Inc, 76-, Dow Chem Co, 79-, Coopervision, 80- & Nuclear Div, Union Carbide, 81-; adj prof, Case Western Reserve Univ, 78-, Cent Mich Univ, 79-; vis prof, Univ Kyoto, 81. *Mem:* Am Phys Soc; Am Chem Soc; Soc Rheology. *Res:* Physics of high polymers and polymer solutions; rheology; statistical mechanics; physics of interfaces. *Mailing Add:* Mich Molecular Inst 1910 St Andrews Dr Midland MI 48640

MEIER, EUGENE PAUL, b Rosenberg, Tex, Oct 3, 42; m 63; c 2. ENVIRONMENTAL CHEMISTRY, ANALYTICAL CHEMISTRY. *Educ:* Tex A&M Univ, BS, 65; Univ Colo, Boulder, PhD(anal chem), 69. *Prof Exp:* Biochemist protein chem br, Med Res Labs, Edgewood Arsenal, 69-70, chemist, Phys Protection Br, Defense Eng & Develop, Defense Systs Div, 71-72; res chemist, Environ Protection Res Br, US Army Med Biomech Res & Develop Lab, 72-78, chief, Anal Support Br, Las Vegas, 78-79, DIR, QUAL ASSURANCE DIV, ENVIRON MONITORING SYSTS LAB, LAS VEGAS, 79- *Mem:* Am Chem Soc. *Res:* Gas chromatography; tr trace analysis; metals and organics in water; environmental analysis. *Mailing Add:* Environ Monitoring Syst Lab US EPA PO box 15027 Las Vegas NV 89114

MEIER, FRANCE ARNETT, b Lubbock, Tex, Aug 11, 28; m 58; c 3. INDUSTRIAL ENGINEERING, PRODUCTION SYSTEMS. *Educ:* Tex Tech Univ, BS, 51; Univ Houston, MS, 59; Wash Univ, DSc(eng), 66. *Prof Exp:* Indust engr, Ideco of Dresser Industs, 51-55; instr indust eng, Lamar State Col, 55-59, asst prof, 59-61; teaching asst, Wash Univ, 61-64; assoc prof, 65-69, head dept, 67-77, PROF INDUST ENG, UNIV TEX, ARLINGTON, 69- *Concurrent Pos:* Consult gen dynamics, Tex Instruments. *Mem:* Am Inst Indust Engrs; Soc Mfg Engrs; Int Mat Mgt Soc; Am Soc Eng Educ. *Res:* Reliability design and testing of the exponential and non-exponential cases; applications of probability and statistics to industrial decisions; productivity improvement for handicapped; computer applications. *Mailing Add:* Dept Indust Eng Box 19017 Univ of Tex Arlington TX 76019

MEIER, GERALD HERBERT, b Pittsburgh, Pa, Nov 22, 42; m 66; c 3. METALLURGY. *Educ:* Carnegie Inst Technol, BS, 64; Ohio State Univ, PhD(metall eng), 68. *Prof Exp:* Res grant, Univ Münster, 68-69; asst prof, 69-77, ASSOC PROF METALL, UNIV PITTSBURGH, 77- *Mem:* Am Soc Metals; Am Inst Metall Engrs; Electrochem Soc. *Res:* Physical metallurgy, particularly oxidation of metals and alloys, strengthening of metals, chemical vapor deposition, thermodynamics of point defects. *Mailing Add:* Dept of Metall & Mat Eng Univ of Pittsburgh Pittsburgh PA 15213

MEIER, HANS, b Ruemlang, Switz, July 21, 29; nat US; m 57, 65; c 2. EXPERIMENTAL PATHOLOGY. *Educ:* Univ Zurich, DVM, 54, PhD, 57. *Prof Exp:* Asst path, Angel Mem Hosp, Boston, Mass, 54-55, resident, 55-56, head dept, 56-57; asst path, Harvard Med Sch, 57-60; assoc staff scientist, 60-62, staff scientist, 62-70, SR STAFF SCIENTIST, JACKSON LAB, 70- *Concurrent Pos:* Asst, Children's Cancer Res Found & asst pathologist, Children's Hosp, 57-59, res assoc, Children's Med Ctr, 59-60; consult, Charles River Breeding Labs, 58-60, Worcester Biol Testing Labs, 59-60 & Nat Cancer Inst, 70-; consult sci adv bd, Coun Tobacco Res, 71-; mem breast cancer virus working group, Nat Cancer Inst, 72-; mem sci adv bd, Inst de la Vie, 74- *Mem:* Am Soc Exp Path; NY Acad Sci; Am Vet Med Asn; Am Asn Cancer Res; Am Asn Lab Animal Sci. *Res:* Histochemistry; metabolic disorders; diabetes; cancer; infectious diseases; immunopathology. *Mailing Add:* Jackson Lab Bar Harbor ME 04609

MEIER, JAMES ARCHIBALD, b New Salem, NDak, May 6, 36; m 67. POLYMER CHEMISTRY. *Educ:* NDak State Univ, BS, 59, PhD(phys chem), 71. *Prof Exp:* sr chemist resins, Inmount Corp, 71-74, supvr resin develop, 74-76, tech mgr, Automotive Develop Ctr, 76-81; TECH COORDR, AUTOMOTIVE FINISHES, PPG INDUSTS, 81- *Mem:* Am Chem Soc; Fedn Socs Coatings Technol. *Res:* Automotive coatings development. *Mailing Add:* PPG Industs 3800 W 143rd St Cleveland OH 44111

MEIER, JOSEPH FRANCIS, b Sharon, Pa, Nov 7, 36. POLYMER CHEMISTRY. *Educ:* John Carroll Univ, BS, 58; Univ Akron, MS, 60, PhD(polymer chem), 63. *Prof Exp:* Res chemist, Gen Tire & Rubber Co, 62-63 & 64-66; sr res chemist, 66-72, mgr elastomers group, 73-78, MGR PLASTICS & ELASTOMERS, WESTINGHOUSE ELEC CORP, 78- *Honors & Awards:* Mat Eng Awards, Mat Eng Mag, 67, 68 & 78. *Res:* Development of rigid-brittle phenolic foam for energy absorbing applications; phenolic and melamine resins for high pressure decorative laminates; molded and cast elastomers for missile launch systems, including dynamic and static compressive testing and creep measurements on missile support pads, and both launch tube and missile mounted launch seals. *Mailing Add:* Westinghouse Elec Corp Beulah Rd Pittsburgh PA 15235

MEIER, MANFRED JOHN, b Milwaukee, Wis, July 17, 29; m 54; c 2. NEUROPSYCHOLOGY. *Educ:* Univ Wis, BA, 52, MS, 53, PhD(psychol), 56. *Prof Exp:* Instr psychol, Univ Wis, 56-57; from asst prof to assoc prof, 57-66, PROF PSYCHOL & DIR NEUROPSYCHOL LAB, UNIV MINN, MINNEAPOLIS, 66- *Concurrent Pos:* Staff psychologist, Clin Psychol, Vet Admin Hosp, Wood, Wis, 56-57; Nat Inst Neurol Dis & Blindness res career develop award, 62-72. *Mem:* Am Psychol Asn; Am Acad Neurol; Am Heart Asn. *Res:* Effects of brain lesions on behavior in man. *Mailing Add:* Box 390 Mayo Med Sch Univ of Minn Minneapolis MN 55455

MEIER, MARK FREDERICK, b Iowa City, Iowa, Dec 19, 25; m 55; c 3. GLACIOLOGY. *Educ:* Univ Iowa, BS, 49, MS, 51; Calif Inst Technol, PhD(geol, appl mech), 57. *Prof Exp:* Engr geol, US Bur Reclamation, Wash, 48-49; geologist, US Geol Surv, Alaska, 51; instr geol, Occidental Col, 52-55; Fulbright grant, Innsbruck Univ, 55-56; GEOLOGIST, US GEOL SURV, 56-; RES PROF GEOPHYS, UNIV WASH, 64- *Concurrent Pos:* Mem tech panel, US Nat Comt, Int Geophys Year, 57-59; mem glaciol panel, Comt Polar Res, Nat Acad Sci, 59-68; vis assoc prof, Dartmouth Col, 64; US Nat Comt Int Hydrol Decade, 64-66, chmn working group combined balances & glacial basins, 65-71; pres, Int Comn Snow & Ice, 67-71; dir, World Data Ctr A, Glaciol, 70-76; mem gov bd, Permanent Serv Glacier Fluctuations, Zurich, 65-71; mem, comt geophys data, Geophys Res Bd, Nat Acad Sci, chmn, Glacial Comt Polar Res Bd, 80-84; mem, Climate Coord Forum, Int Ccun Sci Unions, 81- *Honors & Awards:* Distinguished Serv Award, Us Dept Interior, 68; Medal of 150th Anniversary of Discovery of Antarctica & Medal of Inst Geog, Acad Sci, USSR, US Antarctic Serv Medal. *Mem:* Fel AAAS; fel Geol Soc Am; fel Am Geophys Union; fel Arctic Inst NAm; hon mem, Int Glaciol Soc (vpres, 66-69). *Res:* Seasonal snowcover, glaciers, remote sensing of snow and ice, mountain and arctic hydrology, structural glaciology, flow of ice and rock. *Mailing Add:* US Geol Surv 1201 Pacific Ave Suite 850 Tacoma WA 98402

MEIER, MICHAEL MCDANIEL, b Chicago, Ill, Oct 14, 40; m 70. NUCLEAR ENGINEERING, SOFTWARE SYSTEMS. *Educ:* St Procopius Col, BS, 62; Duke Univ, PhD(nuclear physics), 69. *Prof Exp:* Teaching asst physics, Duke Univ, 62-63, res asst nuclear physics, 63-69, res assoc, 69-70; physicist, Nat Bur Standands, 70-80; MEM STAFF, LOS ALAMOS NAT LAB, 80- *Mem:* Am Phys Soc; AAAS. *Res:* Neutron polarization; neutron standards. *Mailing Add:* MS 805 Los Alamos Nat Lab Los Alamos NM 87545

MEIER, PAUL, b New York, NY, July 24, 24; m 48; c 3. STATISTICS. *Educ:* Oberlin Col, BS, 45; Princeton Univ, MA, 47, PhD(math), 51. *Prof Exp:* Asst prof math, Lehigh Univ, 48-49; res secy, Philadelphia Tuberc & Health Asn, 49-51; res assoc math anal, Forrestal Res Ctr, Princeton Univ, 51-52; biostatist, Sch Hyg & Pub Health, Johns Hopkins Univ, 52-53, from asst prof to assoc prof, 53-57; assoc prof statist, 57-62, chmn dept statist, 60-66, dir biol sci comput ctr, 62-69, actg chmn dept statist, 70-71, prof theoret biol, 68-76, PROF PHAR & PHYSIOL SCI, UNIV CHICAGO, 74-, PROF STATIST, 62- *Concurrent Pos:* Mem spec study sect biomath & statist, Nat Inst Gen Med Sci, 65-70, therapeut eval comt, Nat Heart Inst, 67-71 & diet-heart feasibility study rev comt, 68; comt biol effects of atmospheric pollution, Nat Acad Sci-Nat Inst Health spec fel, Sch Hyg & Trop Med, Imp Col, Univ London, 66-67; consult, statist probs to indust & govt. *Mem:* Fel AAAS; fel Am Statist Asn (vpres, 65-67); Inst Math Statist; Soc Indust & Appl Math; fel Am Thoracic Soc. *Res:* Estimation from incomplete observations. *Mailing Add:* Dept of Statist Univ of Chicago 5801 S Ellis Ave Chicago IL 60637

MEIER, PETER GUSTAV, b Jaegerndorf, Ger, Aug 18, 37; US citizen; m 66; c 2. AQUATIC ECOLOGY, AQUATIC TOXICOLOGY. *Educ:* Univ Mich, BA, 62, PhD(environ health), 70; Cent Mich Univ, MA, 64. *Prof Exp:* Instr aquatic entom, 68-70, res scientist water qual, 69-70, lectr water pollution, 70-72, asst prof, 72-78, ASSOC PROF WATER QUAL, UNIV MICH, ANN ARBOR, 78- *Concurrent Pos:* Consult, Egyptian Acad Sci, 75-, UNESCO, Brazil, 75-, Pan Am Health Orgn, 76- & Ethyl Corp, Manila Bay, Philippines, 78-; Fulbright Hays fel, Yugoslavia, 79. *Mem:* Am Soc Limnol & Oceanog; Int Asn Theoret & Appl Limnol; Am Entom Soc. *Res:* Water quality monitoring with the use of macroinvertebrates; polychlorinated biphenyl uptake by aquatic insects an excretion; methodology of sampling aquatic communities; aquatic bioassays techniques. *Mailing Add:* 2516 SPH I Univ of Mich Ann Arbor MI 48109

MEIER, PETER M, biomedical engineering, see previous edition

MEIER, ROBERT R, b Pittsburgh, Pa, Nov 21, 40; m 63; c 2. AERONOMY. *Educ:* Duquesne Univ, BS, 62; Univ Pittsburgh, PhD(physics), 66. *Prof Exp:* Res asst physics, Univ Pittsburgh, 62-66, res assoc, E O Hulburt Ctr Space Res, US Naval Res Lab & Univ Pittsburgh, 66-68, RES PHYSICIST, US NAVAL RES LAB, 68- *Concurrent Pos:* Assoc ed, J Geophycical Res, Am Geophys Union, 73-75. *Mem:* Am Phys Soc; Am Geophys Union; Sigma Xi. *Res:* Aeronomy, especially airglow, radiative transfer theory, ionospheric physics and model atmospheres; interplanetary medium; comets. *Mailing Add:* Code 4141 Naval Res Lab Washington DC 20375

MEIER, RUDOLF H, b Heiligenstadt, Ger, Feb 27, 18; US citizen; m 52; c 1. OPTICAL PHYSICS. *Educ:* Univ Gottingen, Vordiplom, 46; Univ Jena, dipl physics, 49, Dr rer nat(physics), 51. *Prof Exp:* Assoc res scientist, Zeiss Werke, Ger, 49-53; physicist with Dr J & H Krautkramer, Cologne, 53-54; consult engr, Sperry Prod, Conn, 54-55; sr physicist & group leader, Perkin-Elmer Corp, 55-60; sect supvr, Aeronutronic Div, Philco Corp, Calif, 60-66; br chief, Electro-Optics, 66-73, PRIN SCIENTIST TECH STAFF, McDONNELL DOUGLAS ASTRONAUTICS CO, HUNTINGTON BEACH, 73- *Mem:* Fel Optical Soc Am; Ger Soc Appl Optics. *Res:* Space optics; radiometry; infrared physics; design of ground test facilities for space optical systems. *Mailing Add:* 11001 Limetree Dr Santa Ana CA 92705

MEIER, WILBUR L(EROY), JR, b Elgin, Tex, Jan 3, 39; m 58; c 3. INDUSTRIAL ENGINEERING, OPERATIONS RESEARCH. *Educ:* Univ Tex, Austin, BS, 62, MS, 64, PhD(opers res), 67. *Prof Exp:* Planning engr, Tex Water Develop Bd, Austin, 62-66; res engr, Univ Tex, Austin, 66-67; from asst prof to prof indust eng, Tex A&M Univ, 67-73, asst head dept, 72-73; prof & chmn dept, Iowa State Univ, Ames, 73-74; prof & head, Dept Indust Eng, Purdue Univ, West Lafayette, 74-81; PROF INDUST ENG & DEAN, COL ENG, PA STATE UNIV, 81- *Concurrent Pos:* Off Water Resources res grants, Tex A&M Univ, 67-71, US Post Off Dept contract, 70-71; consult, govt & indust, 67- *Mem:* Inst Indust Engrs; Opers Res Soc Am; Am Soc Civil Engrs; Am Soc Eng Educ; Nat Soc Prof Engrs. *Res:* Systems engineering; application of operations research techniques in solving public planning problems; development of optimization methods; operations research and optimization; systems engineering; engineering and public policy. *Mailing Add:* Col Eng Pa State Univ 101 Hammond Bldg University Park PA 16802

MEIERAN, EUGENE STUART, b Cleveland, Ohio, Dec 23, 37; m 62; c 2. PHYSICAL METALLURGY, CRYSTALLOGRAPHY. *Educ:* Purdue Univ, BS, 59; Mass Inst Technol, MS, 61, ScD(metall), 63. *Prof Exp:* Sr mem res staff semiconductor technol, Res & Develop Labs, Fairchild Camera & Instrument Corp, Palo Alto, 63-73; MRG QUAL ASSURANCE, INTEL CORP, 73- *Concurrent Pos:* Res assoc, H H Wills Physics Lab, Bristol Univ, 70-71; lectr, Israel Inst Technol, 71. *Mem:* Electron Micros Soc Am; Am Inst Mining, Metall & Petrol Engrs. *Res:* Effects of crystal defects on properties of semiconductor materials; development of advanced x-ray and electron microscopy techniques for studying semiconductor materials; packaging materials; reliability; semiconductors. *Mailing Add:* 27610 Natoma Rd Los Altos Hills CA 94022

MEIERE, FORREST T, b Atlanta, Ga, Oct 12, 37; m 57; c 2. THEORETICAL PHYSICS. *Educ:* Carnegie Inst Technol, BS(math) & BS(physics), 59; Mass Inst Technol, PhD(physics), 64. *Prof Exp:* Res assoc physics, Mass Inst Technol, 64; asst prof, Purdue Univ, Lafayette, 64-69; assoc prof, 69-72, PROF PHYSICS, IND UNIV-PURDUE UNIV, INDIANAPOLIS, 72-, CHMN DEPT, 69- *Mem:* Am Phys Soc; Am Asn Physics Teachers. *Res:* Theory of elementary particles; biophysics; imaging. *Mailing Add:* 1201 E 38th St Indianapolis IN 46205

MEIGHEN, EDWARD ARTHUR, b Vancouver, BC, Dec 27, 42; m 62; c 2. BIOCHEMISTRY. *Educ:* Univ Alta, BSc, 64; Univ Calif, Berkeley, PhD(biochem), 69. *Prof Exp:* Res fel biochem, Dept Molecular Biol & Virol, Univ Calif, Berkeley, 69; res fel biol, Biol Labs, Harvard Univ, 69-71; asst prof, 71-76, PROF BIOCHEM, MCGILL UNIV, 76- *Mem:* Am Soc Biol Chemists; Can Fedn Biol Socs. *Res:* Enzyme regulation and relationship to subunit structure; mechanisms and control of enzyme induction in bioluminescent bacteria. *Mailing Add:* Dept of Biochem McGill Univ 3655 Drummond St Montreal PQ H3A 2T5 Can

MEIGS, FREDERICK MADISON, b Quincy, Ill, Apr 26, 06; m 41; c 3. CHEMISTRY. *Educ:* Univ Chicago, BS, 27, PhD(org chem), 30. *Prof Exp:* Res chemist, E I du Pont de Nemours & Co, 30-36, res chemist mkt develop, 37-40, res chemist develop, 40-42; dir develop dept, Gen Aniline & Film Corp, 42-53, gen mgr foreign opers, 53-58; exec dir indust res, Merck Sharp & Dohme Res Labs, 58-65; consult, 65-67; pres, Oxford Chem Res, Inc, 67-77. *Mem:* Am Chem Soc; fel Am Inst Chem. *Res:* Amino acid chemistry; polypeptides; synthetic fibers, films and coatings; surfactants; acetylene chemistry; organic specialties; organic synthesis. *Mailing Add:* Oxford MD 21654

MEIJER, AREND, b Berg en Dal, Neth, Aug 27, 47; US citizen; m 68; c 1. GEOLOGICAL SCIENCES, GEOCHEMISTRY. *Educ:* Univ Calif, Santa Barbara, BA, 69, MA, 71, PhD(geol), 74. *Prof Exp:* Fel geochem, Va Polytech Inst & State Univ, 74-75; fel, Calif Inst Technol, 75-76; ASST PROF GEOSCI, UNIV ARIZ, 76- *Mem:* Am Geophys Union; Sigma Xi; Geol Soc Am. *Res:* Isotope and trace element geochemistry; origin and evolution of volcanic arc magmas; geochemistry as applied to problems in tectonics. *Mailing Add:* Dept of Geosci Univ of Ariz Tucson AZ 85721

MEIJER, PAUL HERMAN ERNST, b The Hague, Neth, Nov 14, 21; nat US; m 49; c 4. THEORETICAL PHYSICS, APPLIED MATHEMATICS. *Educ:* Delft Technol Univ, BS, 42; Univ Leiden, PhD(physics), 51. *Prof Exp:* Vis lectr physics, Case Univ, 53-54; res assoc, Duke Univ, 54-55; asst prof, Univ Del, 55-56; assoc prof, 56-60, PROF PHYSICS, CATH UNIV AM, 60-, CHMN, 80- *Concurrent Pos:* Fulbright grant, 53-55 & 78; consult, Nat Bur Standards, 58-, Naval Ord Lab, Naval Res Lab, Ft Belvoir & Lawrence Radiation Lab; Guggenheim Mem Found grant, Lab Magnetic Resonance, Univ Paris, 64-65; vis prof, Univ Paris, 78. *Mem:* Am Phys Soc; Europ Phys Soc; Neth Phys Soc; Sigma Xi; Int Asn Math Physics. *Res:* Statistical mechanics; critical phenomena; phase transitions; irreversible thermodynamics; solid state; magnetism; paramagnetic resonance; surface phenomena; superconductivity; mathematical physics; group theory; liquid state. *Mailing Add:* Dept Physics Cath Univ Am Washington DC 20064

MEIKLE, MARY B, b Springfield, Mass, Aug 30, 34. AUDITORY PHYSIOLOGY. *Educ:* Vassar Col, AB, 54; Univ Ore Med Sch, MS, 67, PhD(physiol psychol), 69. *Prof Exp:* NIH res fel, Kresge Hearing Res Lab, 69-71, res assoc physiol of the ear, 71-72, asst prof otolaryngol & med psychol, 72-76, ASSOC PROF OTOLARYNGOL & MED PSYCHOL, KRESGE HEARING RES LAB, ORE HEALTH SCI UNIV, 76- *Concurrent Pos:* Vis lectr, Reed Col, 70. *Mem:* Sigma Xi; Acoustical Soc Am; Asn Res Otolaryngol; AAAS; Soc Neurosci. *Mailing Add:* Kresge Lab Dept of Otolaryngol Univ of Ore Health Sci Ctr Portland OR 97201

MEIKLE, RICHARD WILLIAM, b Chicago, Ill, June 15, 22; m 50; c 4. ORGANIC CHEMISTRY, BIOCHEMISTRY. *Educ:* Ill Wesleyan Univ, BS, 43; Univ Ill, MS, 47, PhD(chem), 50. *Prof Exp:* Res assoc org chem, Univ Wash, 50; sr res chemist, 51-79, RES LEADER BIOPROD RES, DOW CHEM CO, 79- *Mem:* Am Chem Soc; Sigma Xi. *Res:* Agricultural research. *Mailing Add:* Agr-Prod Res Dow Chem Co Walnut Creek CA 94598

MEIKSIN, ZVI H(ANS), b Dessau, Ger, July 9, 26; nat US; m 55; c 4. ELECTRICAL ENGINEERING. *Educ:* Israel Inst Technol, Dipl, 51; Carnegie Inst Technol, MS, 53; Univ Pittsburgh, PhD(elec eng), 59. *Prof Exp:* Design & maintenance engr, Israel, 51-52; design engr, Pa Transformer Co, 53-54; from instr to assoc prof, 54-67, PROF ELEC ENG, UNIV PITTSBURGH, 67- *Concurrent Pos:* Proj engr, Westinghouse Elec Corp, 56-59, sr engr, 63, adv engr, 68; consult, Ohio Med Prod, Bell & Howell Co, RCA, Medrad, IBM, Union Carbide, Essex Int, Bendix & Westinghouse Elec Corp, 59-78. *Mem:* Inst Elec & Electronics Engrs. *Res:* Servo-mechanisms; non-linear magnetics and magnetic amplifiers; thin film electronics; transistor circuits; biomedical instrumentation. *Mailing Add:* Dept of Elec Eng Univ of Pittsburgh Pittsburgh PA 15261

MEILING, GERALD STEWART, b Provo, Utah, Sept 12, 36; m 62; c 3. CERAMICS, GLASS SCIENCE & TECHNOLOGY. *Educ:* Univ Utah, BS, 58; Mass Inst Technol, SM, 59, ScD(ceramics), 66. *Prof Exp:* Atomic Energy Comn res grant, Mass Inst Technol, 62-66; res ceramist, res lab, 66-67, Ion Physics, 67-69, Signetics Res Lab, 69-70, res lab, 71-75, res assoc, 75-77, MGR OPTICAL PROD DEVELOP, CORNING GLASS WORKS, 77- *Mem:* Am Ceramic Soc; Electrochem Soc; Brit Soc Glass Technol. *Res:* Glass and glass ceramic research; crystal growth; photochromic glass; luminescence. *Mailing Add:* Sullivan Sci Park Corning Glass Works Corning NY 14830

MEILING, RICHARD L, b Springfield, Ohio, Dec 21, 08; m 40; c 1. OBSTETRICS & GYNECOLOGY. *Educ:* Wittenberg Col, AB, 30; Univ Munich, MD, 37; Am Bd Obstet & Gynec, dipl, 47; Am Bd Prev Med, dipl aviation med, 53. *Hon Degrees:* DSc, Wittenberg Col, 50; LHD, Ohio State Univ, 77. *Prof Exp:* Demonstr gynec, Western Reserve Univ, 46-47; clin asst prof obstet & gynec, 47-51, clin instr path, 47-60, assoc med dir, Health Ctr, 51-60, from assoc prof to prof obstet & gynec, 51-67, from assoc dean to dean, Col Med, 51-70, dir, Univ Hosps, 61-72, vpres med affairs, 70-74, PROF ALLIED MED PROFESSIONS, OHIO STATE UNIV, 67-, EMER VPRES MED AFFAIRS, 74- *Concurrent Pos:* Med adv, Comn Reorgn Exec Br Govt, Nat Security Comt, 48; mem, Armed Forces Med Adv Comt, 48-49; consult, Surgeon Gen, US Dept Air Force, 48-49, 51-53; asst secy med & health affairs, US Dept Defense, 49-51, consult, 51-53; mem US deleg world health assembly, WHO, Geneva, 50-51, mem coun, NIH, 50-51; med adv, Fed Civil Defense Adminr, 53. *Honors & Awards:* Commendation Award, Secy War; Cert, US Dept Defense, 51. *Mem:* AMA; fel Aerospace Med Asn; fel Am Col Surg; fel Col Obstet & Gynec. *Mailing Add:* 91 N Columbia Ave Columbus OH 43209

MEIMAN, JAMES R, b Louisville, Ky, Dec 10, 33. WATERSHED MANAGEMENT. *Educ:* Univ Ky, BS, 55, MS, 59; Colo State Univ, PhD(watershed mgt), 62. *Prof Exp:* Soil conservationist, Soil Conserv Serv, USDA, 55, 57-58 & 59; soil conservationist, Forest Serv, 62; from instr to assoc prof, 62-74, prof watershed mgt, 74-75, dean grad sch, 75-81, DIR INT PROGS, COLO STATE UNIV, 75-, ASSOC VPRES RES, 81- *Concurrent Pos:* Assoc ed, Water Resources Res; hydrologist, Rocky Mountain Forest & Range Exp Sta, US Forest Serv, Ft Collins, Colo, 75-; mem, Snow Res Working Group, NASA, 80- *Mem:* Am Geophys Union; Glaciol Soc. *Res:* Water yields and quality of wildland watersheds and impact of land use thereon; snow hydrology. *Mailing Add:* Off VPres Res 202 Admin Colo State Univ Ft Collins CO 80521

MEINCKE, P P M, b Winnipeg, Man, Jan 21, 36; m 58; c 2. PHYSICS. *Educ:* Queen's Univ, Ont, BSc, 59; Univ Toronto, MA, 60, PhD(physics), 63. *Prof Exp:* Asst prof physics, Royal Mil Col, Ont, 62-65; mem tech staff, Bell Tel Labs, 65-67; from asst prof to prof physics, Univ Toronto, 66-77, assoc dean, Erindale Col, 70-72, vprovost, 72-76; PRES, UNIV PRINCE EDWARD ISLAND, 78- *Mem:* Am Phys Soc. *Res:* Low temperature solid state physics; thermal expansion of solids at low temperatures; magnetism; superconductivity. *Mailing Add:* Off of Pres Univ of Prince Edward Island Charlottetown PE C1A 4P3 Can

MEINDL, JAMES D, b Pittsburgh, Pa, Apr 20, 33; m 61. SOLID STATE ELECTRONICS. *Educ:* Carnegie Inst Technol, BS, 55, MS, 56, PhD(elec eng), 58. *Prof Exp:* Engr, New Prod Dept, Westinghouse Elec Corp, 58-59; leader microelectronics develop & circuits area, US Army Electronics Command, 59-62, chief semi-conductor & microelectronics br, 62-64, chief integrated electronics div, 64-67; assoc prof elec eng, 67-70, PROF ELEC ENG, STANFORD UNIV, 70-, DIR, INTEGRATED CIRCUITS LAB, 71-, DIR, STANFORD ELECTRONICS LABS, 72-, DIR CTR INTEGRATED SYSTS, 81- *Concurrent Pos:* Chmn, Int Solid State Circuits Conf, 69; chmn, 28th Ann Conf Eng in Med & Biol, 76; consult surg & bioeng study sect, NIH, 78- *Honors & Awards:* J J Ebers Award, Inst Elec & Electronics Engrs, 80. *Mem:* Nat Acad Eng; fel Inst Elec & Electronics Engrs; fel AAAS; Electrochem Soc; Am Inst Ultrasound Med. *Res:* Microelectronics; micropower circuits; integrated electronics; medical electronics. *Mailing Add:* 118 AEL Bldg Stanford Univ Stanford CA 94305

MEINECKE, EBERHARD A, b Braunschweig, Ger, June 7, 33; m 63; c 1. POLYMER ENGINEERING. *Educ:* Brunswick Tech Univ, DrIng, 59. *Prof Exp:* Res assoc wood prod, Inst Wood Prod, Brunswick Tech Univ, 57-59; asst dir res & develop, Joh Kleinewefers Sohne, Germany, 59-60; NATO res fel forest prod, Wis, 60; fel polymer sci, Polymer Res Inst, Univ Mass, 60-63; from asst prof to assoc prof, 63-72, PROF POLYMER SCI, INST POLYMER SCI, UNIV AKRON, 72-, RES ASSOC, 63- *Res:* Mechanical and optical properties of polymers; rheology; properties of engineering materials. *Mailing Add:* Dept of Mech Eng Univ of Akron Akron OH 44304

MEINEKE, HOWARD ALBERT, b Cincinnati, Ohio, July 2, 21; m 46; c 5. ANATOMY. *Educ:* Maryville Col, BA, 47; Univ Cincinnati, MS, 49, PhD(zool), 53. *Prof Exp:* Asst zool, 47-49, 50-51, instr, 49-50, from instr to assoc prof anat, 51-69, PROF ANAT, COL MED, UNIV CINCINNATI, 69- *Mem:* AAAS; Am Asn Anat. *Mailing Add:* 1339 Delta Ave Cincinnati OH 45208

MEINEL, ADEN BAKER, b Pasadena, Calif, Nov 25, 22; m 44; c 7. ENERGY ECONOMICS, ASTRONOMY. *Educ:* Univ Calif, AB, 47, PhD(astron), 49. *Prof Exp:* From instr to assoc prof astrophys, Univ Chicago, 50-53; assoc dir, Yerkes & McDonald Observ, 53-56; dir, Kitt Peak Nat Observ, 56-60; chmn dept astron, 61-65, dir, Steward Observ, 62-67, dir, Optical Sci Ctr, 67-73, PROF ASTRON & OPTICAL SCI, UNIV ARIZ, 61- *Concurrent Pos:* Regent, Calif Lutheran Col, 62-71; mem pres comn 9, Int Astron Union, 73-76; consult, Energy Res & Develop Admin, 75-79. *Honors & Awards:* Lomb Medal, Optical Soc Am, 52; Warner Prize, Am Astron Soc, 54; Ives Medal, Optical Soc Am, 80. *Mem:* AAAS; Am Acad Arts & Sci; Optical Soc Am (pres, 72); Solar Energy Soc. *Res:* Energy/gross national product dynamics; solar energy; history of technology; volcanic eruptions; astronomical optics; stellar classification; engineering optics; aurora and airglow physics. *Mailing Add:* Dept Astron & Optical Sci Univ Ariz Tucson AZ 85721

MEINEL, MARJORIE PETTIT, b Pasadena, Calif, May 13, 22; m 44; c 7. SOLAR ENERGY, ASTRONOMY. *Educ:* Pomona Col, BA, 43; Claremont Col, MA, 44. *Prof Exp:* Ed rocketry, Calif Inst Technol, 44-45; RES ASSOC SOLAR ENERGY, UNIV ARIZ, 74- *Concurrent Pos:* Consult, Off Technol Assessment, US Cong, 74-80; consult, Ariz Solar Energy Res Comn, 75-81; adv coun mem, Am Energy Independence, 78- *Mem:* NY Acad Sci; Solar Thermal Test Facil Users Asn. *Res:* Solar energy applications; upper atmospheric phenomena; volcanic eruptions; astronomy, solar and variable stars; astronomical optics. *Mailing Add:* Optical Sci Ctr Univ Ariz Tucson AZ 85721

MEINERS, HENRY C(ITO), b Pendleton, Ore, Feb 11, 16; m 38; c 3. CHEMICAL ENGINEERING. *Educ:* Ore State Col, BS, 38; Mass Inst Technol, DSc, 42. *Prof Exp:* Asst, Mass Inst Technol, 38-42; proj engr, Union Oil Co Calif, 42, process supvr oleum, 42-44, group leader, La, 44, process supvr, Mfg Dept, Calif, 45, supt cracking, La, 45-49, asst refinery mgr oleum, 49-52, refinery mgr, 52-53, Los Angeles, 53-56, RES PROCESS CONSULT, UNION OIL CO CALIF, LOS ANGELES, 56- *Mem:* AAAS; Am Chem Soc; Am Inst Chem Engrs; Am Inst Chemists. *Res:* Design and operation of petroleum refining equipment. *Mailing Add:* 3909 Via Picaposte Palos Verdes Estates CA 90275

MEINERS, JACK PEARSON, b Walla Walla, Wash, Sept 9, 19; m 45; c 3. PHYTOPATHOLOGY. *Educ:* Wash State Univ, BS, 42, PhD(plant path), 49. *Prof Exp:* Jr pathologist, Forage Div, Bur Plant Indust, USDA, Wash, 46-49, assoc pathologist, Fruit & Veg Div, Idaho, 49-50; from asst prof to assoc prof plant path, Wash State Univ, 50-53; pathologist, Cereal Crops Res Br, Wash, Agr Res Serv, USDA, 53-58, asst chief Md, 58-65, asst dir crops res div, 65-70, leader bean & pea invests, Veg & Ornamentals Res Br, Plant Sci Res Div, 70-72, chmn, Plant Protection Inst, Beltsville Agr Res Ctr, 72-74, chief appl Plant Path Lab, 74-80; RETIRED. *Mem:* Am Phytopath Soc. *Res:* Diseases, breeding and physiology of beans, peas and other edible legumes. *Mailing Add:* Appl Plant Path Lab Beltsville Agr Res Ctr W Beltsville MD 20705

MEINERT, CURTIS L, b Sleepy Eye, Minn, June 30, 34; m 57; c 3. BIOSTATISTICS. *Educ:* Univ Minn, BA, 56, MS, 59, PhD(biostatist), 64. *Prof Exp:* Res assoc, Sch Pub Health, Univ Minn, 60-62; res assoc, Inst Int Med, Univ Md, Baltimore, 62-65, from asst prof to assoc prof, 65-72, prof epidemiol & prev med, 72-78; PROF EPIDEMIOL, JOHNS HOPKINS UNIV, 78- *Concurrent Pos:* Ed, J Controlled Clin Trials. *Mem:* Am Heart Asn; Am Pub Health Asn; Am Statist Asn; Biomet Soc; Soc Epidemiol Res. *Res:* Design and conduct of long-term multicenter trials; development of the methods for clinical trials. *Mailing Add:* Dept Epidemiol John Hopkins Univ Baltimore MD 21204

MEINERT, WALTER THEODORE, b Walcott, Iowa, May 18, 22; m 46; c 3. ORGANIC CHEMISTRY. *Educ:* St Ambrose Col, BS, 47; Univ Va, MS, 49. *Prof Exp:* Tech serv rep, Emery Industs, Inc, 49-51, develop rep, 51-53, asst dir develop & tech serv, 53-56, dir, 56-65, gen mgr, Western Opers, Org Chem Div, 65-67, dir int opers, 67-69, vpres int opers, 69-79; PRES, DM INT, INC, 79- *Concurrent Pos:* Adv to pres, Unilever-Emery NV, Neth, 63-65. *Mem:* Am Chem Soc; Am Inst Chemists; Commercial Develop Asn. *Res:* Markets and uses for chemicals derived from fat sources; ozone oxidation and polymerization of unsaturated fatty chemicals; fatty acids. *Mailing Add:* DN Int Inc PO Box 6368 Cincinnati OH 45206

MEINHARD, JAMES EDGAR, b Ill, 1919; m 45; c 3. APPLIED CHEMISTRY, EXPERIMENTAL SOLID STATE PHYSICS. *Educ:* Univ Wis, BS, 47, PhD(chem), 50. *Prof Exp:* Prob leader anal separations, Hanford Atomic Prod Oper, Gen Elec Co, 50-56; with Nat Cash Register Co, 56-57 & Hughes Aircraft Co, 57-59; pres, Crystech, Inc, 59-69; PRES, J E MEINHARD ASSOCS, 69- *Concurrent Pos:* Mem staff, Astropower Lab, Douglas Aircraft Co, 62-64, NAm Aviation, Inc, 64-71, NAm Rockwell Corp, 71-73 & Dept Physics, Calif State Col, Fullerton, 66-69. *Mem:* Fel AAAS; fel Am Inst Chemists. *Res:* Solid state physics; chemistry; organic semiconductors; development of analytical instrument components; solid state devices. *Mailing Add:* 12472 Ranchwood Rd Santa Ana CA 92705

MEINHARDT, NORMAN ANTHONY, b Davenport, Iowa, Jan 19, 19; m 51; c 5. ORGANIC POLYMER CHEMISTRY. *Educ:* St Ambrose Col, BS, 40; Univ Iowa, PhD(org chem), 49. *Prof Exp:* Asst chemist ferrous anal, Rock Island Arsenal, 40-44; fel rubber res, Univ Ill, 49-50; res chemist org phosphorous compounds, Lubrizol Corp, 50-53, res supvr develop group, 53-56, fundamental group, 56-61 & lubricant additives sect, 61-65, res supvr ashless dispersants, 65-71, res supvr polymer res, 71-79, proj mgr Japanese motor oil additives, 79-81; RETIRED. *Res:* Highly arylated ethylenes; initiation systems for emulsion polymerization; sulfinic acid reactions; organic phosphorous reactions; additive systems and intermediates for diesel engine lubricants; ashless inhibitor systems. *Mailing Add:* 1884 Dunellon Dr Lyndhurst OH 44124

MEINHOLD, CHARLES BOYD, b Boston, Mass, Nov 1, 34; m 56; c 5. HEALTH PHYSICS. *Educ:* Providence Col, BS, 56; Am Bd Health Physics, cert. *Prof Exp:* AEC fel radiol physics, 56; from jr scientist to sr scientist health physics, 57-71; HEAD, SAFETY & ENVIRON PROTECTION DIV, ASSOC UNIVS, BROOKHAVEN NAT LAB, 72- *Concurrent Pos:* Chmn sci comt oper radiation safety, Nat Coun Radiation Protection & Measurements, 73, mem Coun, 78-; mem, Main Comn & Comn 3 Protection in Med, Int Comn Radiol Protection, 77- *Mem:* Health Physics Soc (treas, 75-77, pres, 81); Am Nuclear Soc; AAAS. *Res:* Radiation dosimetry and radiation protection standards development. *Mailing Add:* Safety & Environ Protection Div Brookhaven Nat Lab Upton NY 11973

MEINKE, GERALDINE CHCIUK, b Detroit, Mich, Jan 21, 44; m 69; c 2. IMMUNOLOGY. *Educ:* Madonna Col, BS, 65; Wayne State Univ, PhD(microbiol), 70. *Prof Exp:* Res fel immunol, Dept Immunopath, Scripps Clin & Res Found, 70-74, res assoc immunol, 75-78; vis asst prof, Dept

Microbiol, 78-79, ADJ ASST PROF, DEPT MED & MOLECULAR MICROBIOL, COL MED, UNIV ARIZ, 80- *Concurrent Pos:* Leukemia Soc Am spec fel, Scripps Clin & Res Found, 73-75. *Mem:* Am Asn Immunologists. *Res:* Immunological and structural studies of bovine papilloma viral proteins; isolation and characterization of crystallizable fragment receptors for immunoglobulin E from human lymphoblastoid cells. *Mailing Add:* 3960 N Calle Hondonada Tucson AZ 85715

MEINKE, WILLIAM JOHN, b Troy, Mich, May 16, 42; m 69. MICROBIOLOGY, VIROLOGY. *Educ:* Albion Col, BA, 64; Wayne State Univ, MS, 67, PhD(microbiol), 69. *Prof Exp:* Nat Cancer Inst fel, Scripps Clin & Res Found, 69-72, assoc microbiol, 72-77; ASSOC PROF MOLECULAR & MED MICROBIOL, COL MED, UNIV ARIZ, 77- *Mem:* AAAS; Am Soc Microbiol; Biophys Soc; Tissue Cult Asn; NY Acad Sci. *Res:* Cell regulation in normal and neoplastic cells; mechanisms of virus replication. *Mailing Add:* Dept of Microbiol Univ of Ariz Col Med Tucson AZ 85724

MEINKE, WILLIAM WAYNE, radiation applications, see previous edition

MEINKEN, R(OBERT) H, b Long Branch, NJ, July 29, 28; m 53; c 4. CERAMICS, PHYSICAL CHEMISTRY. *Educ:* Rutgers Univ, BSc, 49, MSc, 51, PhD(ceramics), 54. *Prof Exp:* Mem tech staff, Bell Tel Labs, 54-59, supvr electro-optical devices, 59-61, dept head magnetic mat & memory devices, 61-69; DEPT MGR MAT & METALL, SANDIA LABS, LIVERMORE, 69- *Mem:* Am Ceramic Soc. *Res:* Research and development related to electrical and magnetic properties of solid state materials and devices; semiconductor properties of IV-V compounds including electro-optical properties; magnetic properties of ferrites, garnets and alloys. *Mailing Add:* 638 Escondido Circle Livermore CA 94550

MEINKOTH, NORMAN AUGUST, b New Baden, Ill, Jan 29, 13; m 38; c 1. ZOOLOGY. *Educ:* Southern Ill Normal Univ, BEd, 38; Univ Ill, MS, 44, PhD(zool), 47. *Prof Exp:* Pub sch instr, Ill, 38-41; asst zool, Univ Ill, 41-47; from instr to prof, 47-78, EMER PROF ZOOL & CHMN DEPT BIOL, SWARTHMORE COL, 78- *Concurrent Pos:* With Marine Biol Lab Corp; Fulbright lectr, Chulalongkorn Univ, Bangkok, 57-58; mem staff, Univ NH, 59, 60, 63-65, 67-79 & 81. *Mem:* AAAS; Am Soc Zoologists; Am Soc Parasitologists; Am Micros Soc. *Res:* Parasitology; cestodes; bird blood protozoa; invertebrate zoology; free-living flatworms; nemerteans; Stauromedusae. *Mailing Add:* Dept Biol Swarthmore Col Swarthmore PA 19081

MEINS, FREDERICK, JR, b New York, NY, May 31, 42; m 70. DEVELOPMENTAL BIOLOGY, BIOCHEMISTRY. *Educ:* Univ Chicago, BS, 64; Rockefeller Univ, PhD(life sci), 69. *Prof Exp:* Asst prof biol, Princeton Univ, 69-76; assoc prof bot & genetics & develop, 76-81, PROF, DEPT BIOL, UNIV ILL, URBANA, 81- *Mem:* NY Acad Sci; Soc Develop Biol; Ger Soc Biol Chem; Am Soc Plant Physiol. *Res:* Studies of cell heredity and the stability of the differentiated state using chemical approaches and crown gall tumors as test objects. *Mailing Add:* Dept of Bot Univ of Ill Urbana IL 61801

MEINSCHEIN, WARREN G, b Slaughters, Ky, Nov 12, 20; m 44; c 3. ORGANIC CHEMISTRY. *Educ:* Univ Mich, BS, 48; Univ Tex, PhD, 51. *Prof Exp:* Res assoc geochem, Field Res Lab, Magnolia Petrol Co Div, Socony Mobil Oil Co, Inc, 51-58; sr chemist, Esso Res & Eng Co, NJ, 58-61, res assoc, 61-66; assoc dean acad progs, Sch Pub & Environ Affairs, 75-80, PROF GEOCHEM, IND UNIV, BLOOMINGTON, 66- *Concurrent Pos:* Vchmn, Comt Geochem, Nat Res Ctr, Nat Acad Sci, 68-70 & 70-72; mem, Lunar Sample Review Bd, NASA, 70-72. *Mem:* AAAS; Am Chem Soc; Am Geophys Union; Geol Soc Am; Geochem Soc. *Res:* Geochemistry; origin of petroleum composition of naturally occurring hydrocarbons; paleobiochemistry; evidence for life in Precambrian rocks and meteorites; intramolecular distribution of stable carbon isotopes in organic compounds. *Mailing Add:* Dept Geol Ind Univ Bloomington IN 47401

MEINTS, CLIFFORD LEROY, b Kansas City, Mo, May 23, 30; m 54; c 4. BACTERIAL METABOLISM. *Educ:* Purdue Univ, BS, 53; Ohio Univ, MS, 54; Univ Okla, PhD(biochem), 57. *Prof Exp:* Asst prof chem, 57-58, dir comput develop, 73-80, Kresge-Carver assoc prof natural sci, 58-64, KRESGE-CARVER PROF NATURAL SCI, SIMPSON COL, 64-, CHMN DIV, 59- *Concurrent Pos:* Consult, Armstrong Rubber Mfg Co, Nat Cancer Inst fel, Sci Res Inst, Ore State Univ, 64-65; vis prof chem, Univ Tex, Austin, 80-81. *Mem:* Am Chem Soc. *Res:* Computer applications in chemical education; Wiswesser line notation use in laboratory courses; computer applications in chemical education. *Mailing Add:* Dept of Chem Simpson Col Indianola IA 50125

MEINTS, RUSSEL H, b Clara City, Minn, Apr 13, 39; m 59; c 3. DEVELOPMENTAL BIOLOGY. *Educ:* Macalester Col, AB, 60; Kent State Univ, MA, 62, PhD(cell biol), 65. *Prof Exp:* Instr biol, Kent State Univ, 62-63; from asst prof to assoc prof, 65-74, PROF ZOOL, UNIV NEBR-LINCOLN, 74-, DIR SCH LIFE SCI, 75- *Concurrent Pos:* Res assoc, Dept Biochem, Univ Chicago & Argonne Cancer Res Hosp, 70-71; NIH fel, 71. *Mem:* AAAS; Am Soc Cell Biologists; Sigma Xi. *Res:* Developmental biology of cell surface recognition; hemopoietic stem cells; hydra-algae symbiotic associations. *Mailing Add:* Sch of Life Sci Univ of Nebr Lincoln NE 62508

MEINTS, VERNON W, b Beatrice, Nebr, Apr 20, 48; m 75; c 3. SOIL CHEMISTRY. *Educ:* Univ Nebr, Lincoln, BS, 70, MS, 71; UniV Ill, PhD(soil fertil & chem), 75. *Prof Exp:* Asst prof, Mont State Univ, 75-77; EXTEN SOILS SPECIALIST & ASST PROF SOILS, MICH STATE UNIV, 77- *Mem:* Am Soc Agron; Soil Sci Soc Am; Sigma Xi. *Res:* Soil and fertilizer nitrogen reactions; fertilizer use efficiency; soil testing and plant analysis. *Mailing Add:* Dept of Crop & Soil Sci Mich State Univ East Lansing MI 48824

MEINTZER, ROGER BRUCE, b Fargo, NDak, July 5, 27; m 54; c 6. BIOCHEMISTRY. *Educ:* NDak Agr Col, BS, 50, MS, 52; Univ Wis, PhD(biochem), 54. *Prof Exp:* Res assoc biochem, Univ Wis, 54-55; instr med sch, Northwestern Univ, 55-57; assoc prof, NDak State Univ, 57-67; assoc prof, 67-70, PROF CHEM & CHMN DEPT, UNIV LETHBRIDGE, 70-, COORDR CONTINUING EDUC, 74- *Mem:* AAAS; Am Chem Soc; NY Acad Sci. *Res:* Mechanism of action of vitamin D and parathyroid hormone; chemistry of citric acid and other organic acids; their assay and metabolism as related to vitamins and endocrine functions. *Mailing Add:* Dept Chem Univ Lethbridge 4401 University Dr Lethbridge AB T1K 3M4 Can

MEINWALD, JERROLD, b New York, NY, Jan 16, 27; m 55, 80; c 2. ORGANIC CHEMISTRY. *Educ:* Univ Chicago, PhB, 47, BS, 48; Harvard Univ, PhD(chem), 52. *Prof Exp:* Du Pont fel, Cornell Univ, 52, from instr to prof chem, 52-72; prof, Univ Calif, San Diego, 72-73; prof, 73-80, GOLDWIN SMITH PROF CHEM, CORNELL UNIV, 80- *Concurrent Pos:* Sloan Found fel, 58; Guggenheim fels, 60-61 & 76-77; NIH spec fel, 67-68; vis prof, Rockefeller Univ & Univ Calif, San Diego, 70; mem med chem study sect A, NIH, 64-68; chmn vis comt, Dept Chem, Brookhaven Nat Lab & res dir, Int Ctr Insect Physiol & Ecol, Nairobi, 70-77; consult, Schering Corp & Norwich Pharmacal Co; adv bd mem, Petrol Res Fund, 70-73, Res Corp, 78-, mem adv coun, Princeton Univ, 79- & mem, Chem Adv Comm, NSF, 79-; Louderman lectr, Wash Univ, 64; four-col lectr, Mt Holyoke Col, Smith Col, Amherst Col & Univ Mass, 65; Sigma Xi-Sci Res Soc Am nat lectr, 65 & 75; A Burger lectr, Univ Va, 66; Rennebohm lectr, Univ Wis, 67; F B Dains lectr, Univ Kans, 68; F P Venable lectr, Univ NC, 70; 70; Frontiers of Chem lectr, Case-Western Reserve Univ, 71; Julius Stieglitz lectr, Univ Chicago, 72; distinguished lectr, Howard Univ, 72; Reilly lectr, Univ Notre Dame, 73; Priestly lectr, Pa State Univ, 73; Inaugural Dow Lectr, Bucknell Univ, 74; Raymond Lemieux Lectr, Univ Ottawa, 76; del, 10th Int Biochmm Cong, Hamburg, Ger, 76; distinguished vis lectr, Univ NC, 77. *Mem:* Nat Acad Sci; AAAS; fel Am Acad Arts & Sci; Am Chem Soc; Royal Soc Chem. *Res:* Problems of structure, synthesis and reaction mechanism from the field of natural products; synthesis and reactions of highly strained systems; molecular rearrangements; photochemistry; chemical defense mechanisms of arthropods; chemistry of pheromones. *Mailing Add:* Dept Chem Baker Lab Cornell Univ Ithaca NY 14853

MEINWALD, YVONNE CHU, b Shanghai, China, Feb 24, 29; nat US; div; c 2. ORGANIC CHEMISTRY. *Educ:* Bryn Mawr Col, BA, 52; Cornell Univ, PhD(chem), 55. *Prof Exp:* Res assoc, 55-67, lectr chem, 71-76, RES ASSOC, CORNELL UNIV, 77- *Concurrent Pos:* Lectr chem, Univ Calif, San Diego, 72-73; mem comt scholarly relationships with People's Repub of China, Nat Acad Sci, 74- *Mem:* Am Chem Soc. *Res:* Synthesis, solvolysis and rearrangement reaction of medium-sized rings; synthesis of bisketenes; synthesis and reactions of highly unsaturated cyclobutane derivatives; 1, 2-cycloaddition reactions of tetracyanoethylene; nitrosyl chloride addition reactions; chemistry of arthropod defensive secretions and pheromones; peptide synthesis. *Mailing Add:* Dept of Chem Cornell Univ Ithaca NY 14853

MEIROVITCH, L(EONARD), b Maxut, Rumania, Nov 28, 28; nat US; m 60, 71. ENGINEERING. *Educ:* Israel Inst Technol, BS, 53; Univ Calif, Los Angeles, MS, 57, PhD(eng), 60. *Prof Exp:* Struct engr, Water Planning Israel, 53-55, asst head sect, 55-56; asst res engr, Univ Calif, Los Angeles, 56-58, assoc eng, 58-60; staff engr, Int Bus Mach Corp, 60-62; assoc prof eng, Ariz State Univ, 62-67; prof, Univ Cincinnati, 67-71; prof, 71-79, REYNOLDS METALS PROF ENG, VA POLYTECH INST & STATE UNIV, 79- *Concurrent Pos:* Am Soc Eng Educ-NASA res fel, 64; Nat Acad Sci sr res assoc, Space Mech Div, NASA Langley Res Ctr, 66-67; consult, Goodyear Aerospace Corp, 62-63, Draper Lab, 77- & Intelsat, 80- *Mem:* Am Inst Aeronaut & Astronaut; Am Soc Mech Engrs. *Res:* Astrodynamics; classical mechanics; vibrations; nonlinear analysis; control of structures. *Mailing Add:* Dept Eng Sci & Mech Va Polytech Inst & State Univ Blacksburg VA 24061

MEISEL, DAN, b Tel-Aviv, Israel, July 4, 43; m 65; c 2. PHYSICAL CHEMISTRY, RADIATION CHEMISTRY. *Educ:* Hebrew Univ, Jerusalem, BSc, 67, MSc, 69, PhD(phys chem), 74. *Prof Exp:* Res fel radiation chem, Carnegie-Mellon Univ, 74-76; res fel chem, 76-78, CHEMIST, ARGONNE NAT LAB, 78- *Res:* Photochemistry and radiation chemistry of organic and inorganic systems; fast kinetics in solutions; kinetic effects in micellar and polyelectrolyte solutions; electron spin resonance and radical reactions; electron-transfer reactions. *Mailing Add:* Argonne Nat Lab Chem Div 9700 S Cass Ave Argonne IL 60439

MEISEL, DAVID DERING, b Fairmont, WVa, Mar 28, 40; m 62; c 2. ASTRONOMY, ASTROPHYSICS. *Educ:* WVa Univ, BS, 61; Ohio State Univ, MS, 63, PhD(astron), 67. *Prof Exp:* From instr to asst prof astron, Univ Va, 65-70; asst prof, 70-74, ASSOC PROF ASTRON, COL ARTS & SCI, STATE UNIV NY COL GENESEO, 74-, DIR PLANETARIUM & OBSERV, 70- *Concurrent Pos:* Mem US nat comt & mem comn radio astron, Int Union Radio Sci; res assoc, C E K Mees Observ, Univ Rochester, 73-; consult, NASA, 74-; res assoc, Kellogg Observ, Buffalo Mus of Sci, 74-; guest investr, Copernicus Space Telescope, Princeton Univ, 74-; Nat Res Coun-Nat Acad Sci sr assoc, NASA Goddard Space Flight Ctr, 77-78. *Mem:* Fel AAAS; Am Astron Soc; Am Meteor Soc; Int Astron Union; fel Royal Astron Soc. *Res:* Astrophysical studies of early-type stars; comets and meteors; ionospheric radiowave propagation; studies of solar-terrestrial relations, especially during solar eclipses; astronomical time series analysis. *Mailing Add:* Dept of Physics & Astron State Univ of NY Geneseo NY 14454

MEISEL, JEROME, b Cleveland, Ohio, Aug 9, 34; m 57; c 2. ELECTRICAL ENGINEERING. *Educ:* Case Inst Technol, BS, 56, PhD(elec eng), 61; Mass Inst Technol, MS, 57. *Prof Exp:* Staff engr, Gilmore Indust Inc, 55-57; from instr to asst prof elec eng, Case Inst Technol, 57-64; mem tech staff, Bell Tel Labs, 65-66; assoc prof, 66-70, PROF ELEC ENG, WAYNE STATE UNIV, 70- *Concurrent Pos:* Consult, Encore Mfg, Inc, 59-, Linde Co, 61, Globe Indust Inc, 61-62, Flex Cable Corp, 62, Lear Siegler, Inc, 62-63 & M Zucker, Inc, 68- *Mem:* Inst Elec & Electronics Engrs; Int Conf Large High Tension

Elec Systs. *Res:* System theory; current instrument transformers; electromechanical energy conversions; real-time computer control systems for electronic telephone switching; stability of large interconnected power systems. *Mailing Add:* Dept of Elec Eng Wayne State Univ Detroit MI 48202

MEISEL, SEYMOUR LIONEL, b Albany, NY, Aug 19, 22; m 46; c 3. ORGANIC CHEMISTRY, RESEARCH ADMINISTRATION. *Educ:* Union Col, NY, BS, 44; Univ Ill, MS, 46, PhD(org chem), 47. *Prof Exp:* Res chemist, Socony-Vacuum Oil Co, 47-50; sr res chemist, 50-56, asst supvr, 56-58, supvr, 58-61, tech dir, 61-64, mgr appl res & develop div, 64-68, VPRES RES, MOBIL OIL CORP, 68- *Mem:* Nat Acad Eng; Am Chem Soc; Am Petrol Inst; Am Inst Chem Engrs; Soc Automotive Engrs. *Res:* Citronellal; azo dyes containing boron; thiophene chemistry; petrochemicals; hydrocarbon catalysis; petroleum composition; shale oil; combustion; lubrication; additives for fuels and lubricants; petroleum synthetic fuels from coal and chemical processes; exploration and producion of oil and gas. *Mailing Add:* 150 E 42nd St New York NY 10017

MEISELMAN, NEWTON, b Mineola, NY, Apr 5, 30; m 61; c 4. BOTANY, BIOLOGY. *Educ:* Syracuse Univ, AB, 51; Hofstra Univ, MS, 52; Rutgers Univ, PhD(bot), 56. *Prof Exp:* Asst, Rutgers Univ, 52-54; res assoc, Brookhaven Nat Lab, 55-56; from asst prof to assoc prof, 56-65, chmn dept, 68-74, PROF BIOL, C W POST COL, LONG ISLAND UNIV, 65- *Concurrent Pos:* Res collabr, Brookhaven Nat Lab, 59-62; researcher, Sect Biol Ultrastruct, Weizmann Inst, Israel, 65-66 & Plant Breeding Inst, Cambridge Univ, Eng, 75. *Mem:* AAAS; Bot Soc Am; Electron Micros Soc Am; Sigma Xi. *Res:* Morphogenesis; radiation morphology and cytology; electron microscopy; plant cytology. *Mailing Add:* 30 Kenswick Lane Huntington Station NY 11746

MEISELS, ALEXANDER, b Berlin, Ger, Feb 18, 26; Can citizen; m 53; c 5. CYTOLOGY. *Educ:* Nat Univ Mex, MD, 51; FRCP(C); Am Bd Path, dipl. *Prof Exp:* Asst dir lab cytol, Nat Cancer Inst, Mex, 56-60; dir lab clin cytol, 60-70, from asst prof to assoc prof path, 61-68, PROF PATH, UNIV LAVAL, 68-; DIR DEPT LAB MED & HEAD PATH & CYTOL, ST SACREMENT HOSP, QUEBEC, 78- *Concurrent Pos:* Consult cytopathologist, Hotel-Dieu Hosp, Levis, 64-; mem, Can Cytol Coun, vchmn, 65, chmn, 66 & 78; dir, Regional Cytodiag Ctr, St Sacrement Hosp, Quebec, 70-78. *Honors & Awards:* Maurice Goldblett Cytology Award, 76. *Mem:* Am Soc Cytol; Can Asn Path; Int Acad Cytol (secy-treas, 71-). *Res:* Clinical cytology, particularly hormone, urinary and vaginal cytology; carcinogenesis, particularly effect of sex hormones and flora on evolution of cancer of the cervix; condylomata acuminata of genital tract. *Mailing Add:* Dept of Lab Med 1050 Chemin Ste-Foy Quebec PQ G1S 4L8 Can

MEISELS, GERHARD GEORGE, b Vienna, Austria, May 11, 31; nat US; m 58; c 1. PHYSICAL CHEMISTRY, ANALYTICAL CHEMISTRY. *Educ:* Univ Notre Dame, MS, 52, PhD(phys chem), 56. *Prof Exp:* Res assoc, AEC, Univ Notre Dame, 53-56; radiation chemist, Gulf Res & Develop Co, 56-59; chemist, Union Carbide Nuclear Co, 59-63, asst group leader, 63-65; from assoc prof to prof chem, Univ Houston, 65-75, assoc chmn dept, 69-72, chmn dept, 72-75; prof chem & chmn dept, 75-81, INTERIM DEAN ARTS & SCI, UNIV NEBR-LINCOLN, 81- *Concurrent Pos:* Consult, Tech Div, Union Carbide Corp, 65; chmn gov bd, NSF Regional Instrumentation Ctr Mass Spectrometry, Univ Nebr, 78-; dir, Coun Chem Res, 81- *Mem:* AAAS; Am Chem Soc; Am Phys Soc; fel Am Inst Chemists; Am Soc Mass Spectrometry. *Res:* Radiation chemistry; mass spectrometry; photochemistry; ion molecule reactions and collision dynamics. *Mailing Add:* Dept Chem Univ Nebr Lincoln NE 68588

MEISEN, AXEL, b Hamburg, WGer, Oct 17, 43; m 69. CHEMICAL ENGINEERING. *Educ:* Univ London, BSc, 65; Calif Inst Technol, MSc, 66; McGill Univ, PhD(chem eng), 70. *Prof Exp:* Lectr chem eng, McGill Univ, 67-68; from asst prof to assoc prof, 74-79, PROF CHEM ENG, UNIV BC, 79-, ASSOC DEAN APPL SCI, 76- *Concurrent Pos:* Environ engr, Imp Oil Enterprises Ltd, 74-75. *Mem:* Can Soc Chem Eng. *Res:* Air pollution control; aerosol mechanics; natural gas processing; petroleum refining; sulphur. *Mailing Add:* Dept of Chem Eng Univ of BC Vancouver BC V6T 1W5 Can

MEISENHEIMER, JOHN LONG, b Olney, Ill, June 21, 33; m 56; c 2. ORGANIC CHEMISTRY. *Educ:* Evansville Col, BA, 54; Ind Univ, PhD(org chem), 63. *Prof Exp:* From asst prof to assoc prof, 63-68, PROF CHEM, EASTERN KY UNIV, 68- *Mem:* Am Chem Soc. *Res:* Medicinal and heterocyclic chemistry. *Mailing Add:* Dept of Chem Eastern Ky Univ Richmond KY 40475

MEISER, JOHN H, b Cincinnati, Ohio, Nov 21, 38; m 67; c 3. CHEMISTRY, PHYSICAL CHEMISTRY. *Educ:* Xavier Univ, BS, 61; Univ Cincinnati, PhD(chem), 66. *Prof Exp:* Asst prof chem, Univ Dayton, 66-69; asst prof, 69-74, assoc prof, 74-79, PROF CHEM, BALL STATE UNIV, 79- *Mem:* Am Chem Soc; Am Phys Soc. *Res:* Diffusion of metals; counterdiffusion of ions; enzyme kinetics; x-ray analysis; thermodynamics and material properties. *Mailing Add:* Dept of Chem Ball State Univ Muncie IN 47306

MEISER, K(ENNETH) D(ONALDSON), b Crafton, Pa, Nov 22, 09; m 34; c 4. CHEMICAL ENGINEERING. *Educ:* Univ Pittsburgh, BS, 31. *Prof Exp:* Process engr, Toledo Synthetic Prod, 31-34; chief chemist, Plaskon Co, 35-40, tech supt, 41-48, chief prod engr, Plaskon Div, Libbey-Owens-Ford Glass Co, 48-53; tech supvr, Toledo Opers, Allied Chem Corp, 54-59, asst dir eng, plastics & coal chem div, 59-61; VPRES RES & DEVELOP, PLASTICS MFG CO, 61- *Mem:* AAAS; Am Chem Soc; Am Inst Chem Engrs. *Res:* Plastics and resins; process and product development; process engineering and economics; plant design and operations. *Mailing Add:* Plastics Mfg Co 2700 S Westmoreland Ave Dallas TX 75233

MEISER, MICHAEL DAVID, b Reading, Pa, Sept 28, 53; c 1. MECHANICAL PROPERTIES. *Educ:* Pa State Univ, BS, 75, MS, 77, PhD(ceramic sci), 79. *Prof Exp:* RES CERAMIST, AIRCO CARBON, 79- *Mem:* Am Ceramic Soc; Am Carbon Soc. *Res:* Environmental effects on the mechanical properties of graphite and the oxidation behavior of graphite. *Mailing Add:* Airco Carbon PO Box 828 Niagra Falls NY 14302

MEISINGER, JOHN JOSEPH, b Aurora, Ill, Jan 3, 45; m 66; c 2. SOIL SCIENCE, APPLIED STATISTICS. *Educ:* Iowa State Univ, BS, 67; Cornell Univ, PhD(soil sci), 75. *Prof Exp:* SOIL SCIENTIST, SCI & EDUC ADMIN-AGR RES, USDA, 75- *Mem:* Soil Sci Soc Am; Am Soc Agron. *Res:* Nitrogen transformations in the soil-plant system, with emphasis on soil nitrogen aspects such as mineralization of organic matter, nitrogen fixation, and the study of nittogen turnover processes with stable isotopes. *Mailing Add:* Bldg 007 Rm 230 BARC-West Beltsville Agr Res Ctr Beltsville MD 20705

MEISKE, JAY C, b Hartley, Iowa, June 22, 30; m 56; c 4. ANIMAL HUSBANDRY. *Educ:* Iowa State Col, BS, 52; Okla State Univ, MS, 53; Mich State Univ, PhD, 57. *Prof Exp:* Asst animal husb, Okla State Univ, 52-53 & Mich State Univ, 53-57; from instr to assoc prof, 57-70, PROF ANIMAL HUSB, UNIV MINN, ST PAUL, 70- *Mem:* Am Soc Animal Sci; Am Inst Nutrit. *Res:* Ruminant nutrition; rumen microbiology and biochemistry. *Mailing Add:* Dept of Animal Sci Univ of Minn Inst of Agr St Paul MN 55108

MEISLER, HAROLD, b New York, NY, Feb 7, 31; m 54; c 2. HYDROGEOLOGY. *Educ:* City Col New York, BS, 52; Univ Mich, MS, 53. *Prof Exp:* Geophysicist, Carter Oil Co, 55-56; geologist, Ground Water Br, 56-75, CHIEF NJ DIST, US GEOL SURV, 75- *Mem:* Geol Soc Am. *Res:* Hydrogeology of carbonate rocks, sandstones and shales; geomorphology of limestone terrain; computer simulation modeling of aquifer systems. *Mailing Add:* US Geol Surv Fed Bldg PO Box 1238 Trenton NJ 08607

MEISLER, MIRIAM HOROWITZ, b New York, NY, Mar 28, 43; m 63; c 2. BIOCHEMICAL GENETICS. *Educ:* Queens Col, BA, 64; Ohio State Univ, PhD(biochem), 68. *Prof Exp:* Cancer res scientist, Roswell Park Mem Inst, 71-73; asst prof biochem, Sch Med, State Univ NY Buffalo, 73-77; ASSOC PROF HUMAN GENETICS, SCH MED, UNIV MICH, ANN ARBOR, 77- *Concurrent Pos:* NIH fel biochem, Roswell Park Mem Inst, 69-70; Nat Found March of Dimes res grant, 74-76 & 77-79; NIH proj grants, 74-77, 78-81 & 81-86; co-investr, Dept Energy contract, 77- *Mem:* Am Soc Biol Chemists; AAAS; Am Soc Human Genetics; NY Acad Sci. *Res:* Regulation of gene expression in mammals; developmental biochemistry; genetic polymophism of proteins and restriction fragments in human populations. *Mailing Add:* Dept of Human Genetics 1137 E Catherine Ann Arbor MI 48109

MEISLICH, HERBERT, b Brooklyn, NY, Mar 26, 20; m 55; c 3. ORGANIC CHEMISTRY. *Educ:* Brooklyn Col, AB, 40; Columbia Univ, AM, 47, PhD(chem), 51. *Prof Exp:* Chemist control & res, Edgewood Arsenal, 41-43; from teacher to assoc prof 46-68, PROF CHEM, CITY COL NEW YORK, 68- *Concurrent Pos:* Chemist, Med Sch, Columbia Univ, 50-52; fel, Med Sch, NY Univ, 52-53; lectr, Brooklyn Col, 52-58; Sloan-Kettering fel, 55-57. *Mem:* Am Chem Soc. *Res:* Mechanisms of organic reactions; heterocyclic chemistry; structure and reactivity of organic compounds. *Mailing Add:* Dept Chem City Col New York Convent Ave W New York NY 10031

MEISLING, TORBEN (HANS), b Copenhagen, Denmark, Feb 20, 23; nat US; m 52; c 1. COMPUTER SCIENCE, INDUSTRIAL AUTOMATION. *Educ:* Royal Tech Univ Denmark, MS, 48; Univ Calif, Berkeley, PhD(elec eng), 52. *Prof Exp:* Res engr microwave antennas, Royal Tech Univ Denmark, 48; res engr digital comput & lectr, Univ Calif, 49-52, asst prof, 52-54; mem staff, Digital Comput Div, Lincoln Labs, Mass Inst Technol, 54-56; mgr, Systs Eng Lab, Stanford Res Inst, 56-68, exec dir, 68-71, managing dir, SRI-Europe, 71-74, sr indust consult, 74-77; INT TECHNOL CONSULT, PALO ALTO, CALIF, 77-; PRES, TORBEN MEISLING INC, 77- *Mem:* Sr mem Inst Elec & Electronics Engrs. *Res:* Design and application of electronic digital computers; traffic analysis; design of microwave antennas. *Mailing Add:* 2110 Barbara Dr Palo Alto CA 94303

MEISNER, GERALD WARREN, b Mt Kisco, NY, Aug 16, 38; m 62; c 2. ELEMENTARY PARTICLE PHYSICS. *Educ:* Hamilton Col, AB, 60; Univ Calif, Berkeley, PhD(physics), 66. *Prof Exp:* Res assoc & guest lectr physics, Univ Mass, 66-70; ASSOC PROF PHYSICS, UNIV NC, GREENSBORO, 70- *Concurrent Pos:* Res Corp grant, 72. *Mem:* Am Phys Soc. *Res:* Experimental high-energy physics. *Mailing Add:* Dept of Physics Univ of NC Greensboro NC 27412

MEISS, ALFRED NELSON, b Philadelphia, Pa, Mar 27, 18; m 42; c 3. BIOLOGY. *Educ:* Rutgers Univ, BSc, 41, MSc, 43; Yale Univ, PhD(plant sci), 50. *Prof Exp:* Asst veg crops, Rutgers Univ, 43-44 & 46; asst bot, Yale Univ, 46-47; asst biochemist, Conn Agr Exp Sta, 49-52; asst res specialist soils, Rutgers Univ, 52-54, assoc prof, 54-57; sci adv, Ted Bates & Co, 57-68; sr assoc, Sidney M Cantor Assocs, Inc, 68-71, vpres, 71-74; CONSULT, FFE INT, 74- *Mem:* AAAS; Am Chem Soc. *Res:* Foods and nutrition; conservation; planning and management of natural resources; international development; industrial product development and marketing. *Mailing Add:* 14 N Main St Cranbury NJ 08512

MEISS, RICHARD ALAN, b Philadelphia, Pa, Aug 25, 43; m 65; c 1. PHYSIOLOGY. *Educ:* Univ Del, BA, 65; Univ Ill, Urbana, PhD(physiol), 69. *Prof Exp:* Asst prof physiol, asst prof obstet & gynec & asst prof med biophys, 71-77, ASSOC PROF PHYSIOL, ASSOC PROF OBSTET & GYNEC & ASSOC PROF MED BIOPHYS, MED CTR, IND UNIV, INDIANAPOLIS, 77- *Concurrent Pos:* Nat Heart Inst fel, Harvard Med Sch, 69-71. *Mem:* AAAS; Am Physiol Soc. *Res:* Physiology and mechanical properties of muscle, in particular, cardiac muscle and the smooth muscle of the female reproductive system. *Mailing Add:* Dept of Obstet & Gynec Ind Univ Med Ctr Indianapolis IN 46202

MEISSNER, CHARLES ROEBLING, JR, b Joliet, Ill, May 4, 23; m 44; c 5. GEOLOGY. *Educ:* Lehigh Univ, BA, 48. *Prof Exp:* Explor geologist, US Geol Surv, Colo, 48-49; field geologist, Gulf Oil Corp, Okla, 49-52, field coordr, 52, well-site geologist, 52-53; Foreign Opers Admin mutual security mission consult & petrol geologist, Chinese Petrol Corp, Taiwan, 53-55; asst area geologist, Stanolind Oil & Gas Co, Tex, 55-56; sr geologist, Standard-Vacuum Oil Co, Sumatra & India, 56-61; geologist adv, Pakistan, 61-66, econ geologist, Saudi Arabia, 66-70, proj geologist, Southwest Va & WVa, 70-80, CHIEF, GULF COAST LIGNITE PROJ, MISSISSIPPI EMBAYMENT, US GEOL SURV, 80- *Mem:* Am Asn Petrol Geologists. *Res:* Regional and detailed geologic mapping; mineral investigations; stratigraphy; petroleum geology; coal geology. *Mailing Add:* US Geol Surv 956 Nat Ctr Reston VA 22092

MEISSNER, HANS WALTER, b Berlin, Ger, Mar 19, 22; nat US; m 47; c 3. EXPERIMENTAL PHYSICS. *Educ:* Univ Munich, BS, 46, MS & PhD, 48. *Hon Degrees:* MS, Stevens Inst Technol, 62. *Prof Exp:* Res asst physics, Low Temperature Inst, Acad Sci, Bavaria, 48-52; res engr, Heat Transfer Lab, Ill Inst Technol, 52-53; asst prof physics, Johns Hopkins Univ, 53-59; assoc prof, 59-62, PROF PHYSICS, STEVENS INST TECHNOL, 62- *Honors & Awards:* Jess H Davis Award, Stevens Inst Technol, 74. *Mem:* Sigma Xi; Fel Am Phys Soc. *Res:* Low temperature physics; superconductivity; metal physics; time dependent phenomena in superconductivity; plasma etching. *Mailing Add:* Dept of Physics Stevens Inst of Technol Castle Point Hoboken NJ 07030

MEISSNER, LOREN PHILLIP, b Los Angeles, Calif, Nov 24, 28; m 49; c 3. COMPUTER SCIENCE, APPLIED MATHEMATICS. *Educ:* Univ Calif, Berkeley, BA, 49, MA, 63, PhD(appl math), 65. *Prof Exp:* lectr comput sci, 68-80, MATHEMATICIAN, LAWRENCE BERKELEY LAB, UNIV CALIF, 59- *Mem:* Asn Comput Mach. *Res:* Non-numeric applications of computers; programming languages. *Mailing Add:* Lawren Berkeley Lab Univ of Calif Berkeley CA 94720

MEISTER, ALTON, b New York, NY, June 1, 22; m 43; c 2. BIOCHEMISTRY. *Educ:* Harvard Univ, BS, 42; Cornell Univ, MD, 45. *Prof Exp:* From intern to asst resident, New York Hosp, 45-46; res worker, NIH, 46-55; prof biochem & chmn dept, Sch Med, Tufts Univ, 56-67; PROF BIOCHEM & CHMN DEPT, MED COL, CORNELL UNIV, 67-; BIOCHEMIST-IN-CHIEF, NEW YORK HOSP, 71- *Concurrent Pos:* Mem comt growth, Nat Res Coun, 54; mem biochem study sect, USPHS, 55-60, mem biochem training comt, 60-63; consult, Am Cancer Soc, 58-61 & 71-74; vis prof, Univ Wash, 59 & Univ Calif, Berkeley, 62; mem, US Nat Comt Biochem, 62-65 & 78-, chmn, 79-82; mem sci adv comn, New Eng Enzyme Ctr, 63-, chmn, 63-67; chmn physiol chem study sect, USPHS, 64-67; mem bd sci counr, Nat Cancer Inst, chmn, 72; ed, Advan Enzymol; assoc ed, J Biol Chem & Annual Review of Biochem. *Honors & Awards:* Paul-Lewis Award, Am Chem Soc, 54. *Mem:* Nat Acad Sci; Inst Med-Nat Acad Sci; Am Chem Soc; fel Am Acad Arts & Sci; Am Soc Biol Chemists (pres, 77-78). *Res:* Biochemistry of amino acids and proteins; enzymology, metabolism, glutamine, glutathione. *Mailing Add:* Med Col Dept of Biochem Cornell Univ 1300 York Ave New York NY 10021

MEISTER, CHARLES WILLIAM, b Hackensack, NJ, Oct 5, 40. PLANT PATHOLOGY, PLANT PHYSIOLOGY. *Educ:* Rutgers Univ, New Brunswick, BS, 63; Univ Nebr, Lincoln, MS, 66; Univ Ariz, PhD(plant path), 72. *Prof Exp:* Res asst, Boyce Thompson Inst Plant Res, 65-66; asst prof biol, Catawba Col, 67-69; res asst agr biochem, Univ Ariz, 72; citrus virologist, Peace Corps, USDA, Fiji, 72-74; plant virologist, USDA, Suva, Fiji, 74-76, IR-4 PROJ COORDR, SOUTHERN REGION, USDA, PESTICIDE RES LAB, UNIV FLA, 76- *Concurrent Pos:* Consult citrus virol, UNDP/Food Agr Org Surv Plant Pests & Dis in SPac, 75 & 76. *Mem:* Am Phytopath Soc; Am Inst Biol Sci. *Res:* Plant virology, pesticides; obtaining date required for the expansion of pesticide labels for new uses; established citrus-virus-indexing programs in Fiji and the Cook Islands; pesticides. *Mailing Add:* Pesticide Res Lab Univ Fla Gainesville FL 32611

MEISTER, PETER DIETRICH, b Schaffhausen, Switz, May 24, 20; m 51; c 2. ORGANIC CHEMISTRY. *Educ:* Swiss Fed Inst Technol, MSc, 44, PhD(chem), 47. *Prof Exp:* Fel, Swiss Fed Inst Technol, 47-49 & Nat Res Coun Can, 49-50; res chemist, 50-55, sect head, 56-63, mgr, 63-66, asst dir, 66-68, dir supportive res, 68-78, DIR PHARMACEUT DEVELOP LABS, UPJOHN CO, 78- *Concurrent Pos:* Mem bd dirs, Microlife Technics, 70- *Mem:* Am Chem Soc; Am Pharmaceut Asn. *Res:* Synthesis of steroids; degradation of lycopodium alkaloids; microbiological transformations of steroids; dosage forms. *Mailing Add:* 1001 Wilshire Blvd Kalamazoo MI 49008

MEISTER, ROBERT, b Brooklyn, NY, Feb 16, 25; m 48; c 3. ELECTRICAL ENGINEERING. *Educ:* Cath Univ Am, BSEE, 49, MS, 52, PhD(physics), 58. *Prof Exp:* Instr elec eng, Howard Univ, 51-55; PROF ELEC ENG, CATH UNIV AM, 55-, CHMN DEPT, 70- *Mem:* Inst Elec & Electronics Engrs; Am Soc Eng Educ. *Res:* The elastic and anelastic properties of solids using ultrasonic techniques; the dynamic properties of liquids using nuclear magnetic resonance techniques; dulectric properties of materials using optical techniques. *Mailing Add:* Dept of Elec Eng Cath Univ of Am Washington DC 20017

MEISTERS, GARY HOSLER, b Ottumwa, Iowa, Feb 17, 32; m 52; c 2. MATHEMATICS. *Educ:* Iowa State Univ, BS, 54, PhD(math), 58. *Prof Exp:* Instr math, Iowa State Univ, 57-58; res instr, Duke Univ, 58-59; from asst prof to assoc prof, Univ Nebr, 59-63; from assoc prof to prof, Univ Colo, Boulder, 63-72; PROF MATH, UNIV NEBR, LINCOLN, 72- *Concurrent Pos:* Res fel, Res Inst Advan Study, Md, 60-62. *Mem:* Am Math Soc; Math Asn Am. *Res:* Almost periodic functions; ordinary differential equations; abstract and functional analysis. *Mailing Add:* Dept of Math Univ of Nebr Lincoln NE 68508

MEISTRICH, MARVIN LAWRENCE, b Brooklyn, NY, Oct 10, 41. RADIATION BIOLOGY, BIOPHYSICS. *Educ:* Rensselaer Polytech Inst BS, 62; Cornell Univ, PhD(physics), 67. *Prof Exp:* Mem tech staff, Bell Tel Labs, 67-69; res assoc biophys, Ont Cancer Inst, 69-72; asst prof, 72-77, ASSOC PROF BIOPHYS, UNIV TEX M D ANDERSON HOSP & TUMOR INST, 77- *Mem:* Biophys Soc; Cell Kinetics Soc; Am Soc Cell Biol; Am Soc Andrology; Radiation Res Soc. *Res:* Biophysical methods for cell separation; biochemical mechanisms in cell differnedifferentiation; cytotoxic and mutagenic effects of radiation and chemicals on spermatogenic cells; spermatogenesis; nucleoproteins; cell biology. *Mailing Add:* Dept Exp Radiother Univ Tex M D Anderson Hosp Tex Med Ctr Houston TX 77030

MEITES, JOSEPH, b Kishinev, Russia, Dec 22, 13; nat US; m 43. PHYSIOLOGY, ENDOCRINOLOGY. *Educ:* Univ Mo, BS, 38, MA, 40, PhD(exp endocrinol), 47. *Prof Exp:* Asst, Exp Sta, Univ Mo, 40-42, 46-47; from asst prof to assoc prof, 47-53, PROF PHYSIOL, MICH STATE UNIV, 53-, MEM STAFF, AGR EXP STA, 47- *Concurrent Pos:* Weizmann fel, Weizmann Inst Sci, Israel, 55-56; mem subcomt, use hormones in domestic animals, Nat Acad Sci-Nat Res Coun, 60-; mem endocrinol study sect, NIH, 66-70, chmn comn endocrinol, Int Union Physiol Sci, 71-; pres, Int Soc Neuroendocrinol, 72-76; chmn comn endocrinol, Int Union Physiol Sci, 72-; mem coun, Int Brain Orgn, 76-; lectr, Kansas State Univ, 77; Pfizer lectr, Montreal Clin Res Inst, 77; assoc ed, Cancer Res, Am Asn Cancer Res; vis prof, Cairo Univ, 80. *Honors & Awards:* Carl G Hartman Award, Am Soc Study Reprod, 79; Georffrey Harris Mem lectr, Cambridge, Eng, 81. *Mem:* AAAS; Am Asn Cancer Res; Am Physiol Soc; Endocrine Soc; Soc Exp Biol & Med. *Res:* Endocrinology as related to nutrition, lactation, reproduction, aging and tumors; brain-pituitary relationships; author or coauthor of various publications. *Mailing Add:* Dept of Physiol Mich State Univ East Lansing MI 48823

MEITES, LOUIS, b Baltimore, Md, Dec 6, 26; m 78; c 3. PHYSICAL CHEMISTRY, ANALYTICAL CHEMISTRY. *Educ:* Middlebury Col, BA, 45; Harvard Univ, MA, 46, PhD(chem), 47. *Prof Exp:* Instr chem, Princeton Univ, 47-48; from instr to asst prof, Yale Univ, 48-55; from assoc prof to prof, Polytech Inst Brooklyn, 55-68; chmn dept, 68-81, PROF CHEM, CLARKSON COL TECHNOL, 68- *Concurrent Pos:* Founding ed, Critical Rev in Anal Chem, 69-74. *Res:* Thermochemical and electrochemical investigations of reaction kinetics and equilibria; differential thermometry and ebulliometry, controlled-potential electrolysis, polarography; titrimetric theory; chemical applications of non-linear regression; machine decisions. *Mailing Add:* Dept Chem Clarkson Col Technol Potsdam NY 13676

MEITES, SAMUEL, b St Joseph, Mo, Jan 3, 21; m 45; c 1. CLINICAL CHEMISTRY. *Educ:* Univ Mo, AB, 42; Ohio State Univ, PhD(biochem), 50; Am Bd Clin Chem, dipl. *Prof Exp:* Biochemist, Vet Admin Hosp, Poplar Bluff, Mo, 50-52 & Toledo Hosp, Ohio, 53; res asst prof, 54-66, assoc prof, 66-72, PROF PEDIAT, OHIO STATE UNIV, COL MED, 72-, PROF PATH, 74- *Concurrent Pos:* Clin chemist, Children's Hosp, Columbus, Ohio, 54- *Honors & Awards:* Bernard J Katchman Award, Am Asn Clin Chemists, 72; Fisher Award, Am Asn Clin Chemists, 81. *Mem:* Fel AAAS; Am Chem Soc; fel Am Asn Clin Chemists (secy, 75-77). *Res:* Amylase isoenzymes; pediatric micro methods; measurement of jaundice; reference values in pediatric clinical chemistry; history of clinical chemistry. *Mailing Add:* Clin Chem Lab 700 Children's Dr Columbus OH 43205

MEITIN, JOSE GARCIA, JR, b Havana, Cuba, Sept 22, 50; US citizen; m 73; c 2. METEOROLOGY. *Educ:* Fla State Univ, BS, 72, MS, 75. *Prof Exp:* Teaching asst meteorol, Fla State Univ, 72-75; res asst, Coastal Upwelling Ecosysts Prog, 73-75; support scientist meteorol, Nat Ctr Atmospheric Res, 76-79; PROF RES ASST, COOP INST RES ENVIRON SCI, UNIV COLO, 79- *Mem:* Am Meteorol Soc. *Res:* Satellite meteorology; mesoscale research. *Mailing Add:* NOAA/ERL Rx8 325 Broadway Boulder CO 80309

MEITZLER, ALLEN HENRY, b Allentown, Pa, Dec 16, 28; m 53; c 3. PHYSICS. *Educ:* Muhlenberg Col, BS, 51; Lehigh Univ, MS, 53, PhD, 55. *Prof Exp:* Asst physics, Lehigh Univ, 51-54; mem tech staff, Bell Tel Labs, Inc, NJ, 55-72; PRIN RES SCIENTIST, RES STAFF, FORD MOTOR CO, 72- *Mem:* Am Phys Soc; fel Acoust Soc Am; fel Inst Elec & Electronics Engrs. *Res:* Solid state physics; ultrasonic devices, ferroelectric ceramic and liquid crystal display devices; automotive emission control systems. *Mailing Add:* 3055 Foxcroft Ave Ann Arbor MI 48104

MEIXLER, LEWIS DONALD, b New York, NY, July 25, 41; m 64; c 2. ELECTRONIC DESIGN. *Educ:* City Col New York, BSEE, 64; Rutgers Univ, MSEE, 71. *Prof Exp:* Engr data commun, Western Union Tel Co, 64-67; design engr spacecraft electronics, Astro Electronics Div, RCA Corp, 67-75; MEM PROF TECH STAFF ELECTRONICS ENG, PLASMA PHYSICS LAB, PRINCETON UNIV, 75- *Concurrent Pos:* Adj asst prof, Mercer County Col, 78- *Mailing Add:* 11 Cheery Brook Lane East Windsor NJ 08520

MEIZEL, STANLEY, b New York, NY, May 1, 38; m 68; c 2. REPRODUCTIVE BIOLOGY, CELL BIOLOGY. *Educ:* Queens Col, NY, BS, 59; Univ Rochester, PhD(biochem), 66. *Prof Exp:* From asst prof to assoc prof, 67-80, PROF HUMAN ANAT, SCH MED, UNIV CALIF, DAVIS, 80- *Concurrent Pos:* NIH fel develop biol, Yale Univ, 65-67; assoc ed, J Exp Zool, 78- *Mem:* Am Asn Anat; Soc Study Reproduction; Am Soc Cell Biol; Histochem Soc; Am Soc Biol Chemists. *Res:* Biochemistry of mammalian fertilization, sperm enzymes, sperm capacitation and the acrosome reaction. *Mailing Add:* Dept of Human Anat Univ of Calif Sch of Med Davis CA 95616

MEKJIAN, ARAM ZAREH, b New York, NY, Sept 26, 41; m 69; c 2. NUCLEAR PHYSICS. *Educ:* Calif Inst Technol, BS, 63; Univ Md, College Park, PhD(physics), 68. *Prof Exp:* Fel, Rutgers Univ, 68-69; Alexander von Humboldt fel, Univ Heidelberg, 69-71; asst prof, 71-74, ASSOC PROF PHYSICS, RUTGERS UNIV, 74- *Concurrent Pos:* NSF grant, 71-72. *Res:* Nuclear structure; nuclear reactions; heavy ion physics; intermediate energy physics. *Mailing Add:* Dept of Physics Rutger Univ New Brunswick NJ 08903

MEKLER, ARLEN B, b New York, NY, May 4, 32; m 61; c 6. ORGANIC CHEMISTRY. *Educ:* San Jose State Col, BS, 53; Iowa State Univ, MS, 55; Ohio State Univ, PhD(phys org chem), 58; Temple Univ, JD, 72. *Prof Exp:* E I du Pont de Nemours & Co res fel, Ohio State Univ, 58-59; res chemist, Polychem Dept, E I du Pont de Nemours & Co, 59-61, res chemist, Explosives Dept, 61-63; sr res chemist, Arco Chem Res Div, Atlantic Richfield Co, 63-69; RES ASSOC, RCEO INC, 69- *Mem:* AAAS; Am Chem Soc; Sigma Xi; Royal Soc Chem. *Res:* Benzil-ammonia reaction; synthesis of steroid intermediates; steric effects in addition reaction; stereospecific polymerizations; selective oxidation and oxidative coupling reactions; transition metal-olefin complexes; synthesis and polymerization of small ring compounds; patent law; forensic science. *Mailing Add:* 1007 Barley Mill Rd Greenville DE 19807

MEL, HOWARD CHARLES, b Oakland, Calif, Jan 14, 26; m 49; c 3. BIOPHYSICS. *Educ:* Univ Calif, Berkeley, BS, 48, PhD(phys chem), 53. *Prof Exp:* Mem staff, Calo Dog Food Co, Calif, 48-50; asst chem, Univ Calif, Berkeley, 50-51, chemist radiation lab, 51-53; Fulbright fel, Free Univ Brussels, 53-54; instr chem, 55, USPHS fel, spec fel & lectr med physics & biophys, 55-59, from asst prof to assoc prof, 60-73, PROF BIOPHYS, UNIV CALIF, BERKELEY, 73-, STAFF MEM, DONNER RADIATION LAB, 60- *Concurrent Pos:* Am Inst Physics vis scientist, 63-; NSF sr fel, France, 65-66. *Mem:* AAAS; Biophys Soc; Am Chem Soc; Am Asn Physics Teachers. *Res:* Cellular and subcellular biophysics; biological separations including electrophoresis; cellular development and differentiation, hematopoiesis; thermodynamics of open and closed systems. *Mailing Add:* Div of Med Physics Donner Lab Univ of Calif Berkeley CA 94720

MELA, LEENA MARJA, b Viiala, Finland, Apr 5, 35. PHYSIOLOGY, BIOCHEMISTRY. *Educ:* Univ Helsinki, BSc, 60; Turku Univ, MD, 64. *Prof Exp:* USPHS fel, Johnson Res Found, Univ Pa, 65-69, res assoc, Harrison Dept Surg Res Hosp, 69-70, asst prof, 70-75, assoc prof phys biochem in surg, Harrison Dept Surg Res, 75-80; PROF PHYSIOL & SURG, MICH STATE UNIV, 80- *Concurrent Pos:* NIH career develop award, 71-76; mem prog proj adv comt, Nat Inst Neurol & Commun Disorders & Stroke, 74-78 & 79-83. *Mem:* AAAS; Am Soc Biol Chemists; Nat Soc Med Res; Biophys Soc; Shock Soc (secy, 80-). *Res:* Mitochondrial metabolism during shock and trauma; structural and functional damage of the cell after injury; mitochondrial membrane transport and energy-linked functions. *Mailing Add:* Dept Physiol Mich State Univ East Lansing MI 48824

MELACHOURIS, NICHOLAS, b Piraeus, Greece, May 24, 34; US citizen; m 67. FOOD SCIENCE, BIOCHEMISTRY. *Educ:* Col Agr Athens, Greece, BS, 58; Univ Ill, Urbana, MS, 63, PhD(food sci), 66. *Prof Exp:* Res chemist, Miles Labs, 67-69; MGR RES, STAUFFER CHEM CO, 69- *Mem:* Am Chem Soc; NY Acad Sci; Inst Food Technologists; Am Dairy Sci Asn. *Res:* Protein chemistry, yeasts, phosphates and biochemistry. *Mailing Add:* Eastern Res Ctr Stauffer Chem Co Dobbs Ferry NY 10522

MELACK, JOHN MICHAEL, b Pittsburgh, Pa, May 27, 47; m 77. AQUATIC ECOLOGY, LIMNOLOGY. *Educ:* Cornell Univ, AB, 69; Duke Univ, PhD(zool), 76. *Prof Exp:* NSF fel biol, Univ Mich, Ann Arbor, 76-77; ASST PROF BIOL, UNIV CALIF, SANTA BARBARA, 77- *Mem:* Am Soc Limnol & Oceanog; Ecol Soc Am; Soc Int Limnologie. *Res:* Phytoplankton ecology, especially in tropical African and saline lakes; paleolimnology; nutrient dynamics; alpine lakes. *Mailing Add:* Dept of Biol Sci Univ of Calif Santa Barbara CA 93106

MELAMED, MYRON ROY, b Cleveland, Ohio, Aug 9, 27; m 58; c 2. MEDICINE, PATHOLOGY. *Educ:* Western Reserve Univ, BS, 47; Univ Cincinnati, MD, 50. *Prof Exp:* From asst attend pathologist to assoc attend pathologist, 58-69, ATTEND PATHOLOGIST, MEM HOSP CANCER & ALLIED DIS, 69-, CHIEF CYTOL SERV, 73-; ASSOC PROF PATH, MED SCH, CORNELL UNIV, 73- *Concurrent Pos:* Mem, Sloan-Kettering Inst Cancer Res, 78-; consult, USPHS Hosp, Staten Island, NY, 61-64; med res consult, Int Bus Mach Corp, 64-68, NY State Dept Health, 65 & Col Dent, NY Univ, 65; asst vis pathologist, James Ewing Hosp, 65; consult, Hosp Spec Surg, 73- *Honors & Awards:* Papanicolaou Award, Am Soc Cytol, 75. *Mem:* AAAS; Am Asn Path; Am Soc Cytol; Am Soc Clin Path. *Res:* Pathology and cytology of cancer. *Mailing Add:* Sloan-Kettering Cancer Ctr 1275 York Ave New York NY 10021

MELAMED, NATHAN T, b Poland, May 1, 23; nat US; m 67; c 2. CHEMISTRY. *Educ:* City Col New York, BS, 43; Polytech Inst Brooklyn, PhD(chem), 49. *Prof Exp:* Res chemist, Manhattan Dist Proj, SAM Labs, Columbia Univ, 43-45; instr chem, Polytech Inst Brooklyn, 48; res physicist solid state physics, Horizons, Inc, 49-50; mgr optical electronics, 72-74, ADV SCIENTIST, WESTINGHOUSE RES LABS, 50- *Concurrent Pos:* Lectr, Univ Pittsburgh, 55-56; prof, Fed Univ Rio de Janeiro, 73 & 74. *Honors & Awards:* IR-100 Award, 65. *Mem:* Am Phys Soc; NY Acad Sci. *Res:* Luminescence of inorganic solids-fundamental theory; laser physics; semiconductors; spectroscopy. *Mailing Add:* 6636 Dalzell Pl Pittsburgh PA 15217

MELAMED, SIDNEY, b Philadelphia, Pa, Oct 5, 20; m 43; c 2. COATINGS, BIOPOLYMERS. *Educ:* Philadelphia Col Pharm, BSc, 41; Univ Ill, PhD(org chem), 44. *Prof Exp:* Res chemist, Univ Ill, 43-44; res chemist, Univ Md, 44-45, res chemist, Comt Med Res, 45-46; res chemist, US Navy, 46-47; res chemist, 47-58, lab head, 58-71, supvr new prod develop, Fibers Div, 71-73, pioneering life sci, 73-76, sr res assoc polymer technol, 73-81, DEPT MGR BIOCIDES, ROHM AND HAAS CO, 81- *Mem:* AAAS; Am Chem Soc. *Res:* Nylon, polyesters, elastic and antistatic fibers; vinyl and condensation polymers; monomers; polymers for paper, textiles, leather and coatings; ion-exchange resins and fibers; insecticides; fiber and fabric technology; biomedical research; agricultural chemicals; biocides. *Mailing Add:* 8270 Thomson Rd Elkins Park PA 19117

MELAMPY, ROBERT MAURICE, b Lebanon, Ohio, Apr 1, 09; m 37; c 1. PHYSIOLOGY. *Educ:* Wilmington Col, BS, 30; Haverford Col, MA, 31; Cornell Univ, PhD(animal nutrit), 35. *Prof Exp:* Asst animal nutrit, Cornell Univ, 31-35; asst physiologist, USDA, 36-41; asst prof physiol, La State Univ, 41-42, assoc prof, 42-46 & 48-49; assoc prof, Univ Ill, 46-48; assoc prof, 49-50, PROF ANIMAL SCI, IOWA STATE UNIV, 50- *Concurrent Pos:* Res fel, Cambridge Univ, 66-67; consult, NIH, 66-77. *Honors & Awards:* Award, Am Soc Animal Sci, 66. *Mem:* AAAS; Am Physiol Soc; Soc Exp Biol & Med; fel Am Soc Animal Sci; Soc Study Reproduction (pres, 67-68). *Res:* Physiology of reproduction. *Mailing Add:* Dept Animal Sci Iowa State Univ Ames IA 50011

MELANDER, WAYNE RUSSELL, b Watertown, SDak, Dec 2, 43. PHYSICAL CHEMISTRY, BIOPHYSICAL CHEMISTRY. *Educ:* Mich State Univ, BS, 65; Cornell Univ, PhD(phys chem), 70. *Prof Exp:* Asst prof biochem, Univ Wyo, 70-75; res assoc chromatography, Dept Eng & Appl Sci, Yale Univ, 75-77; chemist enzymol, Clinton Corn Processing Co, Iowa, 77; res assoc chromatography, Eng & Appl Sci Div, 78-81, RES ASSOC & LECTR, CHEM ENG DEPT, YALE UNIV, 81- *Mem:* AAAS; Am Chem Soc. *Res:* Chromatography, specifically the of theory of solvent effects in reversed-phase liquid chromatography and physical chemistry of separations; development and interpretation of novel separations; enzymology, especially basic studies and use of immobilized enzyme reactors. *Mailing Add:* Mason Lab Yale Univ New Haven CT 06520

MELBY, EDWARD C, JR, b Burlington, Vt, Aug 10, 29; m 53; c 4. VETERINARY MEDICINE. *Educ:* Cornell Univ, DVM, 54; Am Col Lab Animal Med, dipl, 67. *Prof Exp:* Pvt pract, Vt, 54-62; from instr to prof & dir dept, Lab Animal Med, Sch Med, Johns Hopkins Univ, 62-74; DEAN & PROF MED, NY STATE COL VET MED, CORNELL UNIV, 74- *Concurrent Pos:* Consult, Vet Admin, 64-74; mem, White House Conf on Health, 65; mem coun accreditation, Am Asn Accreditation Lab Animal Care, 66-73; mem, Inst Lab Animal Resources, Nat Res Coun-Nat Acad Sci, 75-; mem adv comt, Div Res Resources, NIH; consult, Nat Inst Child Health & Human Develop, 71-; pres, Am Col Lab Animal Med, 74-75. *Mem:* AAAS; Am Asn Lab Animal Sci; Am Vet Med Asn; NY Acad Sci; Asm Biomed Res (pres, 80-). *Res:* Laboratory animal medicine and comparative pathology, especially lymphoproliferative diseases and transplantation. *Mailing Add:* NY State Col Vet Med Cornell Univ Ithaca NY 14853

MELBY, JAMES CHRISTIAN, b Duluth, Minn, Feb 14, 28; m 55; c 2. MEDICINE. *Educ:* Univ Minn, BS, 51, MD, 53. *Prof Exp:* Lectr endocrine biochem, Med Sch, Univ Minn, 58, instr med & dir clin chem, 58-59; asst prof med & biochem, Sch Med, Univ Ark, 59-62; assoc prof, 62-69, PROF MED, SCH MED, BOSTON UNIV, 69-, PROF PHYSIOL, 71-, MEM FAC, DIV MED SCI, GRAD SCH, 71- *Concurrent Pos:* Consult, Merck & Co, 55-65; head sect endocrinol, Evans Mem Hosp, 62- *Mem:* AAAS; Am Soc Clin Invest; Asn Am Physicians; Am Chem Soc; Endocrine Soc. *Res:* Metabolism of steroid hormones, physical interaction of steroid hormones and macromolecules; endocrinology; internal medicine. *Mailing Add:* Univ Hosp Boston MA 02118

MELBY, L RUSSELL, b Calgary, Alta, Oct 9, 27; nat US; c 3. ORGANIC CHEMISTRY. *Educ:* Univ Alta, BS, 48, MS, 50; Univ Ill, PhD(chem), 53. *Prof Exp:* RES ORG CHEMIST, CENT RES & DEVELOP DEPT, E I DU PONT DE NEMOURS & CO, INC, 53- *Mem:* Am Chem Soc. *Res:* Synthetic oligonucleotides; coordination compounds, organic ligands and organic reactions of polymers; anionic polymerizations. *Mailing Add:* Cent Res & Develop Dept E I du Pont de Nemours & Co Inc Wilmington DE 19898

MELBYE, SUSANNE WARNER, biochemistry, dermatology, see previous edition

MELCER, IRVING, b Havana, Cuba, Nov 15, 31; nat US; m 54; c 5. BIOCHEMISTRY, FOOD SCIENCE. *Educ:* Wayne State Univ, BS, 53, PhD(biochem), 58. *Prof Exp:* USPHS res fel pharmacol, Yale Univ, 58-59; res chemist, Wilson Labs, 59-64; res chemist, 65-73, lab mgr chem processing res, 73-78, RES MGR, GRIFFITH LABS, USA INC, 79- *Mem:* Am Chem Soc; Inst Food Technol. *Res:* Soy proteins and protein hydrolysates; porphyrin and serotonin biosynthesis; isolation of enzymes, hormones, proteins and other natural products; chemistry of meat and meat processing; chemistry of liquid smoke. *Mailing Add:* Griffith Labs 1415 W 37th St Chicago IL 60609

MELCHER, ANTONY HENRY, Can Citizen; m 53; c 2. HISTOLOGY, CELL BIOLOGY. *Educ:* Univ Witwatersrand, BDS, 49, HDD, 58, MDS, 60; Univ London, PhD(morphol), 64. *Prof Exp:* PROF HISTOL, FAC DENT, UNIV TORONTO, 69-, DIR MED RES COUN GROUP PERIODONT PHYSIOL, 74- *Concurrent Pos:* Leverhulme Found res fel, Royal Col Surgeons Eng, 64-67, col res fel morphol, 67-69; assoc ed, J Gerodontics. *Mem:* Int Asn Dent Res (pres, 82-83); Am Soc Cell Biol; Tissue Culture Asn; Brit Bone & Tooth Soc. *Res:* Repair of bone; resorption of collagen; structure and function of periodontium. *Mailing Add:* MRC Group in Periodont Physiol Univ of Toronto Toronto ON Can

MELCHER, JAMES RUSSEL, b Giard, Iowa, July 5, 36; m 57; c 3. ELECTRICAL ENGINEERING. *Educ:* Iowa State Univ, BS, 57, MS, 58; Mass Inst Technol, PhD(elec eng), 62. *Prof Exp:* Systs engr, Martin Aircraft Co, 57; res engr, Boeing Airplane Co, 59; from instr to assoc prof, 61-69, PROF ELEC ENG, MASS INST TECHNOL, 69-, STRATTON CHAIR ELEC ENG & PHYSICS, 81- *Concurrent Pos:* Ford fel, 62-64; Guggenheim fel, 71-72. *Honors & Awards:* Mark Mills Award, Am Nuclear Soc, 59. *Mem:* Fel Inst Elec & Electronics Engrs; Am Phys Soc; Am Nuclear Soc; Am Chem Soc. *Res:* Continuum electromechanics; electrohydrodynamics; precipitation pollution control; electromechanics of biological systems. *Mailing Add:* Dept of Elec Eng Mass Inst of Technol Cambridge MA 02139

MELCHER, ROBERT LEE, b Marshalltown, Iowa, Jan 27, 40; m 66; c 2. SOLID STATE PHYSICS. *Educ:* Southern Methodist Univ, BS, 62; Wash Univ, MA, 65, PhD(physics), 68. *Prof Exp:* Res assoc physics, Cornell Univ, 68-70; MEM RES STAFF, WATSON RES CTR, IBM CORP, 70- *Mem:* Am Phys Soc. *Res:* Elastic and magnetoelastic properties of materials; nuclear spin-phonon interactions; elastic properties of materials undergoing phase transitions; polarization echoes in piezoelectric and magnetoelastic materials, echo holography in piezoelectric semiconductors; low temperature physics; photoacoustic and pyroelectric phenomenas. *Mailing Add:* IBM Watson Res Ctr PO Box 218 Yorktown Heights NY 10598

MELCHER, ULRICH KARL, b London, Eng, July 7, 45; US citizen; m 68; c 2. MOLECULAR BIOLOGY, IMMUNOCHEMISTRY. *Educ:* Univ Chicago, BS, 65; Mich State Univ, PhD(biochem), 70. *Prof Exp:* Fel molecular biol, Univ Aarhus, Denmark, 70-71; res scientist immunol, Med Ctr, NY Univ, 72; res asst microbiol, Univ Tex Health Sci Ctr, Dallas, 72-74, asst prof, 74-75; asst prof, 75-78, ASSOC PROF BIOCHEM, OKLA STATE UNIV, 78- *Concurrent Pos:* NATO fel, 70-71 & NIH fel, 73-74. *Mem:* Am Soc Plant Physiologists; Am Soc Biol Chemists; Am Asn Immunologist. *Res:* Genetic engineering of plants; control of protein synthesis in seed development; plant virology. *Mailing Add:* Dept of Biochem PS II Okla State Univ Stillwater OK 74078

MELCHING, J STANLEY, b New York, NY, Mar 4, 23; m 41; c 2. PLANT PATHOLOGY. *Educ:* Univ Maine, BS, 54, MS, 56; Cornell Univ, PhD(plant path), 61. *Prof Exp:* Res plant pathologist, Field Crops & Animal Prods Br, USDA, Watseka, Ill, 61-63 & Biol Br, Corps Div, US Army Biol Labs, Ft Detrick, Frederick, Md, 63-70; RES PLANT PATHOLOGIST, CROP RESPONSE FOREIGN DIS RES UNIT, PLANT DIS RES LAB, SCI & EDUC ADMIN-AGR RES, USDA, 70- *Mem:* Am Phytopath Soc; Am Soc Plant Physiologists; Am Inst Biol Sci; Sigma Xi. *Res:* Disease dynamics of the rusts of corn and the soybean rust; development of quantitative techniques for measurement of the infection process, disease spread and special instrumentation for assessment of environmental factors. *Mailing Add:* Plant Dis Res Lab Sci & Educ Admin-Agr Res USDA Box 1209 Frederick MD 21701

MELCHIOR, JACKLYN BUTLER, b Sacramento, Calif, May 19, 18; m 39; c 2. BIOCHEMISTRY. *Educ:* Univ Calif, BS, 40, PhD(biochem), 46. *Prof Exp:* Res assoc chem, Northwestern Univ, 46-49; from instr to asst prof biochem, Sch Med, Loyola Univ, Ill, 49-57, assoc prof pharmacol, 57-59; asst dean, Chicago Col Osteop Med, 59-77, prof biochem & chmn, Dept Basic Sci, 59-80, dean, 77-80; RETIRED. *Concurrent Pos:* Lederle Med Fac Award, 57. *Mem:* Am Chem Soc; Am Soc Biol Chem. *Res:* Enzyme chemistry; protein conformation. *Mailing Add:* 2601 Col Ave #212 Berkeley CA 94704

MELCHIOR, ROBERT CHARLES, b Fargo, NDak, July 22, 33; m 58; c 3. PALEOBOTANY, STRATIGRAPHY. *Educ:* Moorhead State Col, BS, 58; Univ Minn, MS, 60, PhD(paleobot), 65. *Prof Exp:* PROF BIOL, BEMIDJI STATE UNIV, 64- *Concurrent Pos:* Res assoc, Sci Mus of Minn, 74- *Mem:* Paleont Soc; Am Bot Soc; Sigma Xi; Am Asn Stratig Palynologists. *Res:* Paleoecology of the Paleocene, Glacial and Pleistocene stratigraphy of northern Minnesota. *Mailing Add:* Dept of Biol Bemidji State Univ Bemidji MN 56601

MELCHOR, JACK L, b Mooresville, NC, July 6, 25; m 46; c 4. PHYSICS. *Educ:* Univ NC, BS, 48, MS, 50; Univ Notre Dame, PhD(physics), 53. *Prof Exp:* Group leader, Sylvania Elec Co, 53-56; pres & treas, Melabs, Inc, 56-61; pres, HP Assocs, 61-67; gen mgr, Palo Alto Div, Hewlett Packard Co, 67-68; CHMN BD, PALO ALTO INVEST CO, 69- *Concurrent Pos:* Consult, Triad Am Capital Mgt, 74- *Honors & Awards:* Notre Dame Centennial of Sci Award, 67. *Mem:* Fel Inst Elec & Electronics Engrs; Sigma Xi. *Res:* Microwave ferrites; semiconductor devices; photo conductors; microwave semiconductors; small company development in the Middle East. *Mailing Add:* 26000 Westwind Way Los Altos Hills CA 94022

MELDAU, R(OBERT) F(REDERICK), b Pasadena, Calif, Feb 6, 29; m 51; c 3. THERMAL OIL RECOVERY, RESERVOIR ENGINEERING. *Educ:* Univ Calif, BS, 50; Calif Inst Technol, MS, 55. *Prof Exp:* Res engr, La Habra Lab, Chevron Res Corp, Standard Oil Co Calif, 55-61, sec recovery engr, 61-64; res eng, Phillips Petrol Co, Okla, 64-69, sect mgr pilot projs, 69-70, chief engr, Venezuela, 70-73, staff dir improved oil recovery, 73-76; mgr enhanced oil recovery, Husky Oil Co, 76-78; ENG CONSULT, 78- *Mem:* Soc Petrol Engrs. *Res:* Enhanced recovery of crude oil by steam flooding, underground combustion and chemical flooding. *Mailing Add:* Husky Oil Co PO Box 1869 Santa Maria CA 93456

MELDNER, HEINER WALTER, b Koenigsberg/Prussia, Ger, May 21, 39; US citizen; m 76; c 2. PHYSICS. *Educ:* Univ Frankfurt, PhD(theoret physics), 65. *Prof Exp:* NATO fel theoret physics, Lawrence Radiation Lab, Univ Calif, Berkeley, 65-67; pvt univ lectr, Univ Berlin, 67-69; assoc prof, Univ Calif, San Diego, 69-75; PHYSICIST NUCLEAR WEAPONS DESIGN, LAWRENCE LIVERMORE NAT LAB, UNIV CALIF, 76- *Concurrent Pos:* Pres, Cordtran Corp, Moss Beach, Calif, 79-; tech consult. *Mem:* Am Phys Soc. *Res:* Inertial confinement fusion and fission; nuclear theory; computer modeling of complex physical processes. *Mailing Add:* Lawrence Livermore Nat Lab L-22 PO Box 808 Livermore CA 94550

MELDON, JERRY HARRIS, b New York, NY, Oct 23, 47. MASS TRANSFER, MEMBRANE PROCESSES. *Educ:* Cooper Union, BE, 68; Mass Inst Technol, PhD(chem eng), 73. *Prof Exp:* Res fel physiol, Odense Univ, Denmark, 73-77; ASST PROF CHEM ENG, TUFTS UNIV, 77- *Concurrent Pos:* Consult, Prototech Co, Newton Highlands, Mass, 80, US Army Mat & Mech Res Ctr, Watertown, Mass, 82. *Mem:* Inst Chem Engrs; AAAS; Sigma Xi. *Res:* Analysis of mass transfer and separation processes; diffusion and chemical reaction in absorber and membrane systems; physiological transport processes; electrochemical systems; polymer membrane permeation; blood gas chemistry. *Mailing Add:* Dept Chem Eng Tufts Univ Medford MA 02155

MELDRIM, JOHN WALDO, b Glendale, Calif, Sept 29, 41; m 64; c 2. FISH BIOLOGY, ICHTHYOLOGY. *Educ:* Occidental Col, BA, 63; Univ Wash, PhD(fisheries), 68. *Prof Exp:* Sr res biologist, 68-76, TECH DIR EXP STUDIES, ICHTHYOL ASSOCS, INC, 76- *Mem:* Am Fisheries Soc; Am Soc Ichthyol & Herpet; Sigma Xi; Soc Syst Zool; Soc Study Evolution. *Res:* Tolerance and behavioral responses of estuarine, freshwater and marine fishes and motile macroinvertebrates to temperature and to chemicals. *Mailing Add:* Ichthyol Assocs Inc 100 S Cass St Middletown DE 19709

MELDRUM, ALAN HAYWARD, b Lethbridge, Alta, Can, May 24, 13; nat US; m 47. INDUSTRIAL ENGINEERING. *Educ:* Univ Alta, BS, 38; Univ Okla, BS, 46, MS, 49; Pa State Univ, PhD(petrol eng), 54. *Prof Exp:* Coke oven chemist, Algoma Steel Corp, Can, 38-44; ref chemist, Brit Am Oil Ref Co, Ltd, 44-45; res assoc, Pa State Univ, 47-54; from assoc prof to prof petrol eng, 54-61, prof indust eng, 62-80, EMER PROF INDUST ENG, UNIV NDAK, 80- *Mem:* Am Inst Indust Engrs; Nat Soc Prof Engrs. *Res:* Three phase equilibria for carbon dioxide-hydrocarbon mix- tures; petroleum consulting; industrial consulting for plant layout, organization and wage administration. *Mailing Add:* Dept of Indust Eng Univ of NDak Box 8144 University Sta Grand Forks ND 58202

MELECA, C BENJAMIN, b Batavia, NY, Nov 8, 37; m 58; c 4. MEDICAL EDUCATION. *Educ:* State Univ NY Col Brockport, BS, 63; Syracuse Univ, MS, 66, PhD(sci educ), 68. *Prof Exp:* High sch teacher, NY, 63-65; instr biol, Syracuse Univ, 67-68; asst dir, Biol Core Prog, 68-70, asst prof biochem, 68-72, dir introductory biol prog, 70-74, assoc prof prev med, 74-78, ASSOC PROF BIOCHEM, OHIO STATE UNIV, 72-, PROF, DEPT FAMILY MED, 78-, DIR DIV RES & EVAL IN MED EDUC, COL MED, 74- *Concurrent Pos:* Pres, Int Cong Individualized Audio Instrn, 70-72; chmn, Audio-Tutorial Conf, 71, chmn conf comt, 71; chmn, Promotion & Tenure Comt, Dept Family Med, 80-; mem, Nat Adv Coun, Am Podiat Asn, 79- *Mem:* Am Educ Res Asn; Am Chem Soc; Eastern Educ Res Asn; Am Asn Med Cols. *Res:* Medical education; biological sciences education; independent study and computer based education; pre and post MD education; research, evaluation, and development in undergraduate medical education; instructional study of clinical teaching skills and strategies; development; academic and curricular affairs. *Mailing Add:* 3190 Graves Hall Ohio State Univ Col of Med Columbus OH 43210

MELECHEN, NORMAN EDWARD, b New York, NY, Jan 26, 24; m 53; c 3. GENETICS. *Educ:* Columbia Univ, AB, 44; Univ Pa, PhD(zool), 54. *Prof Exp:* Spec investr genetics, Carnegie Inst Wash, 54-56; instr, 56-57, sr instr, 57-58, from asst prof to assoc prof, 58-64, PROF MICROBIOL, SCH MED, ST LOUIS UNIV, 64- *Concurrent Pos:* Commonwealth Fund fel, Stanford Univ, 66-67. *Mem:* Genetics Soc Am; Am Soc Microbiol; Brit Soc Gen Microbiol. *Res:* Structure and function of bacteriophage chromosomes; genetics and chemistry of bacteriophage infection and induction. *Mailing Add:* Dept of Microbiol St Louis Univ Sch of Med St Louis MO 63104

MELEHY, MAHMOUD AHMED, b Egypt, June 10, 26; nat US; m 57; c 3. ELECTRICAL ENGINEERING. *Educ:* Cairo Univ, BS, 47; Ohio State Univ, MS, 49; Univ Ill, MS, 50, PhD(elec eng), 52. *Prof Exp:* Asst prof elec eng, Univ Ark, 52-53; lectr, Ain Shams Univ, Cairo, 53-54; assoc prof, Univ Alaska, 54-55; asst prof, Mich State Univ, 55-58; from asst prof to assoc prof, 58-71, PROF ELEC ENG, UNIV CONN, 71- *Concurrent Pos:* Consult, Shockley Transistor, 60 & Elec Boat Div, Gen Dynamics Corp, 64- *Mem:* AAAS; Am Phys Soc; Inst Elec & Electronics Engrs. *Res:* Consequences of new thermodynamic theory, especially unified theories for p-n junctions, heterojunctions, Schottky diodes, thermoelectricity, superconductivity and superfluidity. *Mailing Add:* Dept of Elec Eng Univ of Conn Storrs CT 06268

MELENDEZ, LUIS VARGAS, virology, see previous edition

MELENEY, WILLIAM PHELPS, b Peking, China, Dec 24, 21; US citizen; m 46, 70; c 2. VETERINARY PARASITOLOGY, MEDICAL ENTOMOLOGY. *Educ:* Cornell Univ, DVM, 51. *Prof Exp:* Assoc vet med, Glasgow Animal Clin, Ky, 51-52; vet, Hope, NJ, 52-56; area vet, Animal Dis Eradication Div, Woodward, Okla, 56-57, vet, Animal Dis & Parasite Res Div, Agr Res Serv, Albuquerque, NMex, 57-59, parasitologist, 59-62, res vet, 62-63, vet med officer, Agr Res Serv, Western Region, 63-67, supv vet med officer, Sci & Educ Adm, 77-81, SUPV VET MED OFFICER, AGR RES SERV, USDA, 81- *Concurrent Pos:* Reviewer, Merck Vet Manual, Merck Sharp & Dohme, NJ, 77- *Mem:* Am Vet Med Asn; Am Asn Vet Parasitologists; Am Soc Parasitologists; Acarological Soc Am; US Animal Health Asn. *Res:* Biology and control of arthropod parasites of domestic animals and wildlife, especially scabies and mange-producing mites of the genera Psoroptes, Chorioptes, Sarcoptes and Psorergates, and the sucking lice, Anoplura. *Mailing Add:* 803 Bluebonnet Dr Kerrville TX 78028

MELERA, PETER WILLIAM, b Union City, NJ, Feb 19, 42; m 63; c 2. CELL BIOLOGY, BIOCHEMISTRY. *Educ:* Univ Ga, BS, 65, PhD(bot), 69. *Prof Exp:* Asst prof biochem, Cornell Grad Med Sch, 76-78; res assoc, 72-75, ASSOC, WALKER LAB, SLOAN-KETTERING INST CANCER RES, 75-, LAB HEAD, 76- *Concurrent Pos:* NIH fel, McArdle Lab Cancer Res, Univ Wis-Madison, 69-72. *Mem:* Am Chem Soc; Am Soc Cell Biol. *Res:* Ribonucleic acid synthesis and regulation; mechanisms of somatic cell gene amplification in anti-tumor drug resistant mammalian cells and in human neuroblastoma cells; recombinent DNA technology. *Mailing Add:* Walker Lab Sloan-Kettering Inst Cancer Res Rye NY 10580

MELESE D' HOSPITAL, GILBERT B(ERNARD), b Paris, France, Oct 17, 26; m 54; c 4. NUCLEAR ENGINEERING. *Educ:* Univ Paris, AeroEng, 49; Johns Hopkins Univ, PhD(fluid mech), 54. *Prof Exp:* Asst aeronaut, Johns Hopkins Univ, 50-51, 52-54; group leader, Saclay Nuclear Res Ctr, France, 54-57; from asst prof to assoc prof mech eng, Columbia Univ, 57-60; mem res staff, Gen Atomic Div, Gen Dynamics Corp, 60-67; SR TECH ADV, GEN ATOMIC CO, 67- *Concurrent Pos:* Consult, Repub Aviation Corp, 58-60; adj assoc prof, Columbia Univ, 60-61; lectr, exten, Univ Calif, San Diego, 60-62.

Mem: AAAS; fel Am Nuclear Soc; Am Soc Mech Engrs; assoc fel Am Inst Aeronaut & Astronaut. *Res:* Heat transfer in nuclear reactors; conduction heat transfer; design of thermal and fast gas-cooled power reactors. *Mailing Add:* Gen Atomic Co PO Box 81608 San Diego CA 92138

MELFI, LEONARD THEORDORE, JR, b Charleston, SC, Sept 8, 37; m 60; c 2. PHYSICS, ATMOSPHERIC SCIENCES. *Educ:* The Citadel, BS, 59; Col William & Mary, MA, 64; Fla State Univ, PhD(meteorol), 71. *Prof Exp:* AEROSPACE TECHNOLOGIST & PHYSICIST, NASA LANGLEY RES CTR, 59- *Concurrent Pos:* Adj assoc prof physics, Old Dominion Univ, 78- *Mem:* Sigma Xi; Am Vacuum Soc. *Res:* Atmospheric physics as applied to the terrestrial thermosphere; materials science for space application; vacuum instrumentation and technology, particularly mass spectrometry. *Mailing Add:* MC 160 NASA Langley Res Ctr Hampton VA 23665

MELFORD, SARA STECK, b Greenville, Ohio, Feb 3, 42; m 71. INORGANIC CHEMISTRY, MASS SPECTROMETRY. *Educ:* Bowling Green State Univ, BS, 64; Northwestern Univ, PhD(chem), 68. *Prof Exp:* NSF fel chem, Rice Univ, 68-70; asst prof, 70-81, ASSOC PROF CHEM, DEPAUL UNIV, 81- *Mem:* Am Chem Soc; Am Asn Mass Spectrometry; AAAS. *Res:* High temperature inorganic chemistry, mass spectrometry and solid waste chemistry. *Mailing Add:* Dept of Chem DePaul Univ Chicago IL 60614

MELGARD, RODNEY, b Carrington, NDak, Feb 24, 36; m 60; c 3. RADIOCHEMISTRY, NUCLEAR PHYSICS. *Educ:* Jamestown Col, BS, 57. *Prof Exp:* Actinide element group leader, Tracerlab Inc, 58-61; supvr radiactivity measurement, 61-73, mgr lab opers, 74-79, GEN MGR, ENVIRON DIV, FLE CORP, RICHMOND, 80- *Mem:* Am Chem Soc; Am Inst Chemists; Am Nuclear Soc; Health Physics Soc. *Res:* High sensitivity studies of natural and man-made radiation related to environmental surveillance programs; geothermal radiochemistry; reactor coolant chemistry; nuclear rocket ablation studies; snap devices; alpha and gamma spectroscopy; tranuranic translocation and uptake studies. *Mailing Add:* 1000 Alberdan Circle Pinole CA 94564

MELGES, FREDERICK TOWNE, b Battle Creek, Mich, Dec 2, 35; m 58; c 2. PSYCHIATRY, EXPERIMENTAL PSYCHOLOGY. *Educ:* Princeton Univ, AB, 57; Columbia Univ, MD, 61. *Prof Exp:* Med intern, Univ Mich, 61-62; res psychiat, Strong Mem Hosp, Univ Rochester, 62-64, chief res & instr, 64-65; NIMH spec fel, Sch Med, Stanford Univ, 65-67, asst prof, 67-77, chmn psychiat dept, 77-80; MEM FAC, DEPT PSYCHIAT, MED CTR, DUKE UNIV, 80- *Concurrent Pos:* Dir psychiat educ & res, Stanford Univ Prog at Santa Clara Valley Med Ctr, San Jose, Calif. *Mem:* Am Psychiat Asn. *Res:* Time sense, identification and emotion in mental illness; hormones and behavior. *Mailing Add:* 506 E Forest Hills Blvd Durham NC 27707

MELHORN, WILTON NEWTON, b Sistersville, WVa, July 8, 20; m 61. GEOMORPHOLOGY, QUATERNARY GEOLOGY. *Educ:* Mich State Univ, BS, 42, MS, 51; NY Univ, MS, 43; Univ Mich, PhD(geol), 55. *Prof Exp:* Hydrogeologist, Geol Surv, Mich, 46-49; meteorologist, US Weather Bur, 49-50; from asst prof to assoc prof eng geol, 55-67, head dept geosci, 67-71, PROF ENG GEOL, PURDUE UNIV, WEST LAFAYETTE, 67- *Concurrent Pos:* Vis prof, Univ Ill, 60-61; vis prof, Univ Nev, Reno, 71-72, adj prof, Mackay Sch Mines, 73- *Mem:* Fel AAAS; fel Geol Soc Am; Am Meteorol Soc; Soc Econ Paleontologists & Mineralogists; Am Asn Petrol Geologists. *Res:* Geomorphology and Pleistocene geology; archaeological geology; remote sensing; geomorphology of arid lands. *Mailing Add:* Dept of Geosci Purdue Univ West Lafayette IN 47907

MELI, ALBERTO L G, b Florence, Italy, Sept 19, 21; US citizen; m 55; c 1. PHYSIOLOGY. *Educ:* Univ Pisa, DVM, 47; Univ Milan, PhD(physiol), 58, PhD(pharmacol), 69. *Prof Exp:* Lectr physiol, Univ Pisa, 47-49; group leader pharmacol, C Erba Res Inst, Italy, 50-57; group leader endocrinol, Vister Labs, 58-59; group leader pharmacol, Sterling-Winthrop Res Inst, NY, 60-61; sr res assoc physiol, Warner-Lambert Res Inst, NJ, 61-67; dir pharmacol dept, Vister Labs, Italy, 67-68, dir biol res, 68-69; DIR RES, MANARINI LABS, 69- *Mem:* AAAS; Soc Study Reproduction; Endocrine Soc; NY Acad Sci; Soc Exp Biol & Med. *Res:* General endocrinology and pharmacology; reproductive physiology; metabolism. *Mailing Add:* Lab Chimico Farmaceutico A Menarini Via Sette Santi 1 Florence 50131 Italy

MELIA, MICHAEL BRENDAN, b Blackpool, Eng, Jan 20, 49; US citizen; m 70; c 2. PALYNOLOGY. *Educ:* Northwestern State Univ, BS, 73; State Univ NY, Oneonta, MA, 75; Mich State Univ, PhD(geol), 80. *Prof Exp:* SR GEOLOGIST, EXXON CO, USA, 79- *Mem:* Sigma Xi; Am Asn Stratigraphic Palynologists. *Res:* Distribution of palynomorphs in aerosols and deep-sea sediments off the coast of Northwest Africa; palynological age determination of rocks drilled by oil companies. *Mailing Add:* Exxon Co USA PO Box 2189 Houston TX 77001

MELICK, WILLIAM F, b St Louis, Mo, Nov 9, 14; m 39; c 4. UROLOGY. *Educ:* Wash Univ, MD, 39; St Louis Univ, MS, 43. *Prof Exp:* From asst prof to assoc prof, 53-60, dir dept, 59-66, PROF CLIN UROL, ST LOUIS UNIV, 60- *Mem:* Am Urol Asn; Am Col Surg. *Res:* Renal arteriography; urographic media; cancer of bladder; ureteral physiology. *Mailing Add:* 911 S Brentwood Blvd St Louis MO 63105

MELILLO, DAVID GREGORY, b Newark, NJ, Dec 3, 47; m 71. ORGANIC CHEMISTRY. *Educ:* Rutgers Univ, BA, 69; Mass Inst Technol, PhD(org chem), 73. *Prof Exp:* RES FEL PROCESS RES, MERCK SHARP & DOHME RES LABS, 72- *Mem:* Am Chem Soc. *Res:* Discovery and development of commercially viable syntheses of biologically active organic compounds, including beta-lactam antibiotics, amino acids, steroids and heterocycles. *Mailing Add:* 2637 Crest Lane Scotch Plains NJ 07076

MELIN, BRIAN EDWARD, b Berwyn, Ill, Dec 10, 43; m 68; c 2. INSECT PATHOLOGY. *Educ:* Carthage Col, AB, 58; Bowling Green State Univ, AM, 69; Univ Ill, PhD(entom), 78. *Prof Exp:* Entomologist, Velsicol Chem Corp, 78-79; res entomologist, Crop Protection Div, Sandoz, Inc, 79-80; RES ENTOMOLOGIST, AGR CHEM DIV, ABBOTT LABS, 80- *Mem:* Soc Invertebrate Path; Entom Soc Am. *Res:* Microbial insect pathogens and the development of these agents into commercial insecticides and miticides. *Mailing Add:* D-912 Chem & Agr Prod Div Abbott Labs North Chicago IL 60064

MELINE, ROBERT S(VEN), b Braham, Minn, Mar 29, 19; m 52; c 2. CHEMICAL ENGINEERING. *Educ:* Univ Minn, BChE, 41. *Prof Exp:* Pub health engr, USPHS, 41; develop engr, 41-65, GROUP LEADER, TENN VALLEY AUTHORITY, 65- *Mem:* Am Chem Soc; Am Inst Chem Engrs. *Res:* Development of processes for fertilizer production. *Mailing Add:* Tenn Valley Authority Wilson Dam AL 35660

MELISSINOS, ADRIAN CONSTANTIN, b Thessaloniki, Greece, July 28, 29; m 60; c 2. PARTICLE PHYSICS. *Educ:* Mass Inst Technol, MS, 56, PhD, 58. *Prof Exp:* Asst, Univ Athens, Greece, 54-55 & Mass Inst Technol, 55-58; from instr to assoc prof, 58-67, chmn dept physics & astron, 74-77, PROF PHYSICS, UNIV ROCHESTER, 67- *Concurrent Pos:* Guest physicist, Brookhaven Nat Lab, 63-; vis scientist, Europ Orgn Nuclear Res, 68-69 & 77-78. *Mem:* Fel Am Phys Soc; Nat Acad Greece. *Mailing Add:* Dept of Physics & Astron Univ of Rochester Rochester NY 14627

MELIUS, PAUL, b Livingston, Ill, Nov 21, 27; m 53; c 4. BIOCHEMISTRY. *Educ:* Bradley Univ, BS, 50; Univ Chicago, MS, 52; Loyola Univ, Ill, PhD(biochem), 56. *Prof Exp:* Chemist, Nat Aluminate Corp, 52-53; biochemist, Med Sch, Northwestern Univ, 56-57; assoc prof, 57-65, PROF BIOCHEM, AUBURN UNIV, 65- *Concurrent Pos:* NIH spec fel biochem, Univ Ky, 62 & Univ Calif, Los Angeles, 68; vis prof, Univ Athens, Greece & Univ Miami, 76. *Mem:* Am Chem Soc; Brit Biochem Soc; Am Soc Biol Chemists. *Res:* Thermal polymerization of amino acids, pyridoxine analogs, platinum complexes and enzymes and protein chemistry; metabolism of polyaromatic. *Mailing Add:* Dept Chem Auburn Univ Auburn AL 36830

MELKANOFF, MICHEL ALLAN, b Russia, July 3, 23; nat US; wid; c 1. DATA BASES, COMPUTER-AIDED DESIGN. *Educ:* NY Univ, BS, 43; Univ Calif, Los Angeles, MA, 50, PhD(physics), 55. *Prof Exp:* Aeronaut engr, 43-44 & 46-47; vis asst prof physics, 56-58, from asst res physicist to assoc res physicist, 58-61, assoc prof eng, 62-66, chmn dept, 69-77, PROF ENG, UNIV CALIF, LOS ANGELES, 66-, DIR MFG ENG PROG, 81- *Concurrent Pos:* Vis physicist, Saclay Nuclear Res Ctr, France, 61-62; consult, Thompson Ramo Wooldridge, Inc, 59-60, Opers Res Ctr, France, 62, Mass Inst Technol, 63, Univ Hawaii, 64, Univ Md, 65, Douglas Aircraft Inc, 65, Rand Corp, 65-66, Nat Bank of Mex, 71, US Army Comput Syst Command, 71, IBM, IBM World Trade, Lockheed, Hughes & Nat Acad Eng. *Mem:* Asn Comput Mach. *Res:* Digital computers; computer languages, compilers, design automated design; file organization; management; information systems. *Mailing Add:* Dept Comput Sci Univ of Calif Los angeles CA 90024

MELKONIAN, EDWARD, b Alexandria, Egypt, June 29, 20; US citizen; m 54; c 3. PHYSICS. *Educ:* Columbia Univ, AB, 40, AM, 41, PhD(physics), 49. *Prof Exp:* Asst physics, Columbia Univ, 41-42; tech engr, Carbide & Carbon Chem Corp, Tenn, 45-46; res scientist, Atomic Energy Comn Contract, 46-63, assoc prof, 63-68, PROF NUCLEAR SCI & ENG, COLUMBIA UNIV, 68- *Concurrent Pos:* Res scientist, Nat Defense Res Comt, Off Sci Res & Develop & Manhattan Dist, Columbia Univ, 41-44; res assoc, Atomic Energy Res Estab, Harwell, Eng, 58-59. *Mem:* AAAS; fel Am Phys Soc; Am Nuclear Soc. *Res:* Porous membranes; gas flow; mathematical study of diffusion cascade; neutron spectroscopy of gases; neutron resonances and physics; fission and nuclear reactor physics; application of computers to scientific problems; nuclear engineering. *Mailing Add:* Dept of Appl Physics & Nuclear Eng Columbia Univ New York NY 10027

MELL, GALEN P, b Modesto, Calif, Sept 20, 34; m 61; c 3. BIOCHEMISTRY. *Educ:* Univ Idaho, BS, 56; Univ Wash, PhD(biochem), 61. *Prof Exp:* Res fel folic acid, Scripps Clin & Res Found, 64-68; from asst prof to assoc prof biochem, 68-80, Am Cancer Soc grant, 70-72, PROF BIOCHEM, UNIV MONT, 80- *Mem:* Am Chem Soc. *Res:* Enzymology; clinical biochemistry; role of folic acid coenzymes in intermediary metabolism; proteases from plant tissue cultures. *Mailing Add:* Dept of Chem Univ of Mont Missoula MT 59812

MELL, LEROY DAYTON, JR, analytical chemistry, see previous edition

MELLBERG, JAMES RICHARD, b Manitowac, Wis, June 3, 32; m 56; c 3. DENTAL CHEMISTRY, CHEMISTRY. *Educ:* Wis State Col, Oshkosh, BS, 55; Loyola Univ Chicago, MS, 60. *Prof Exp:* Res chemist med, Kendall Co, 58-68, head dent res, 68-75; res assoc dent, 75-81, SR SCIENTIST, COLGATE-PALMOLIVE CO, PISCATAWAY, 81- *Concurrent Pos:* Consult, Great Lakes Naval Dent Res Inst, 72- *Mem:* AAAS; Int Asn Dent Res; Am Chem Soc. *Res:* Use of topical and systemic fluoride for dental ca ries. inhibition; dental calculus and plaque; dental abrasives. *Mailing Add:* 6 Addison Dr Pottersville NJ 07979

MELLBERG, LEONARD EVERT, b Springfield, Mass, Dec 18, 35. ACOUSTICS. *Educ:* Univ Mass, BS, 61; Trinity Col, MS, 68. *Prof Exp:* Res physicist, Navy Underwater Sound Lab, 61-68, NATO Saclant ASW Res Ctr, Italy, 68-72, RES PHYSICIST, NAVAL UNDERWATER SYSTS CTR, 72- *Mem:* Acoust Soc Am; Am Geophys Union; Inst Elec & Electronics Engrs. *Res:* Theoretical and experimental studies of the relationships between underwater acoustic propagation and the environment; author of over 40 scientific publications. *Mailing Add:* Naval Underwater Systs Ctr Newport RI 02840

MELLEN, DAVID L, b Omaha, Nebr, Aug 15, 25; m 48; c 3. AERONAUTICAL ENGINEERING. *Educ:* Iowa State Univ, BS, 45, MS, 47. *Prof Exp:* Dynamics engr, Chance Vought Aircraft, 47-50; res engr automatic flight control, Minneapolis-Honeywell Regulator Co, 50-54, res proj engr, 54-56, res supvr, 56-57, proj engr automatic flight control anal, 57-58, head, Anal & Thermodyn Sect, 58-59, staff engr, 59, proj mgr X-15 adaptive flight control, 59-62, Athena attitude control syst, 62-64, mgr all weather landing syst develop, Honeywell, Inc, 64-66, proj mgr adv flight control, 66-67, sect head advan flight control syst & fixed wing systs, 67-70, mgr space shuttle flight control, 70-71; staff specialist space guid & navig, Control Data Corp, 71-72, dept mgr, 72-78; STAFF ENGR & PROG MGR, DEFENSE SYSTS DIV, HONEYWELL INC, 78- *Mem:* Assoc fel Am Inst Aeronaut & Astronaut; Soc Automotive Eng. *Res:* Automatic flight control, guidance and analysis; electronic component development. *Mailing Add:* Defense Systs Div Honeywll Inc 600 Second St Hopkins MN 55343

MELLEN, GILBERT EMERY, b Akron, Iowa, Mar 16, 21; m 44; c 3. PHYSICS. *Educ:* Iowa State Col, BS, 43. *Prof Exp:* Physicist, Radiation Lab, Univ Calif, 43-45, Tenn Eastman Corp, Oak Ridge, 45-47 & Carbide & Carbon Chem Co, 47-61; PHYSICIST, CHEM & PLASTICS DIV, UNION CARBIDE CORP, 61- *Mem:* Am Soc Mass Spectrometry. *Res:* Development of calutron ion source; mass spectrometer analysis; data processing systems; analytical and preparative gas chromatography. *Mailing Add:* SUI Div Bldg 106 Union Carbide Corp PO Box 8004 South Charleston WV 25303

MELLEN, ROBERT HARRISON, b New Haven, Conn, Nov 12, 19; m 42; c 2. PHYSICS. *Educ:* Wesleyan Univ, BA, 41; Univ Conn, MA, 53, PhD, 55. *Prof Exp:* Res physicist, US Naval Res Lab, DC, 41-46, Underwater Sound Lab, Conn, 46-64; marine electronics off, Avco Corp, 64-67; mem staff, Naval Underwater Systs Ctr, New London, 67-81; RES PHYSICIST, MAR INC, EAST LYME, CONN, 81- *Mem:* AAAS; Am Phys Soc; Acoust Soc Am. *Res:* Underwater sound. *Mailing Add:* RD 3 Old Lyme CT 06371

MELLEN, WALTER ROY, b Newark, NJ, Mar 10, 28; m 50; c 5. ELEMENTARY PARTICLE PHYSICS, THEORETICAL PHYSICS. *Educ:* Mass Inst Technol, SB, 48; Lowell Technol Inst, MS, 62. *Prof Exp:* Tech writer, Sperry Gyroscope Co, 50-53; instr physics, Adelphi Col, 53-55; tech writer, Sperry Gyroscope Co, 55-56; asst prof, Alfred Univ, 56-59; asst prof elec eng, 59-63, ASSOC PROF PHYSICS, LOWELL TECHNOL INST & UNIV LOWELL, 63- *Mem:* AAAS; Am Asn Physics Teachers; Am Phys Soc. *Res:* Relativistic electromagnetic wave theory and its applications to standing waves, de Broglie waves, the compton effect and the fine structure constant. *Mailing Add:* Dept of Physics Univ of Lowell Lowell MA 01854

MELLENTHIN, WALTER M, b Ririe, Idaho, July 10, 20; m 46; c 3. HORTICULTURE. *Educ:* Ore State Univ, BS, 50, MS, 51. *Prof Exp:* Instr hort, 51-52, from asst prof & supt to assoc prof & supt, 52-65, PROF HORT & SUPT, MID-COLUMBIA BR EXP STA, ORE STATE UNIV, 65- *Mem:* Am Pomol Soc; Am Soc Hort Sci. *Res:* Pome fruit rootstocks; effects of environment on growth and maturity of pears; effect of environments on quality; physiological disorders of pears and apples. *Mailing Add:* Mid-Columbia Br Exp Sta 3005 Experiment Station Dr Hood River OR 97031

MELLETT, JAMES SILVAN, b New York, NY, July 12, 36; m 61; c 2. PALEOBIOLOGY, MAMMALOGY. *Educ:* Iona Col, BS, 59; Columbia Univ, MA, 64, PhD(geol), 66. *Prof Exp:* Asst prof biol, Iona Col, 63-67; asst prof, 67-71, ASSOC PROF GEOL, NY UNIV, 71- *Mem:* Am Soc Mammalogists; Sigma Xi; AAAS; Soc Vert Paleont. *Res:* Paleobiology of fossil mammals; functional morphology of the mammalian feeding mechanism; taphonomy of vertebrate fossil assemblages; landsat imagery in geologic mapping; environmental geology; history of geology and paleontology. *Mailing Add:* Dept Biol NY Univ New York NY 10003

MELLETT, LAWRENCE B, b Detroit, Mich, Mar 13, 24; m 51; c 8. PHARMACOLOGY. *Educ:* Univ Detroit, BS, 48, MS, 51; Univ Mich, PhD(pharmacol), 57. *Prof Exp:* Asst, Univ Mich, 52-56, from instr to asst prof pharmacol, Med Sch, 57-65; head pharmacol sect, 65-68, head biochem pharmacol div, Southern Res Inst, 68-76; dir biol res, USV Pharmaceut Corp, 76-80, DIR, SCI LIAISON & COMPLIANCE, REVLON HEALTH CARE GROUP, 80- *Concurrent Pos:* Mem cancer chemother collab rev comt, Nat Cancer Inst, 67-69; assoc, Med Ctr, Univ Ala, 65-74; prof, Med Ctr, Univ Ala, Birmingham, 74-76. *Mem:* AAAS; Am Soc Pharmacol; NY Acad Sci; Am Asn Cancer Res; Am Soc Microbiol. *Res:* Drug metabolism; biological disposition of narcotic analgesics and antitumor agents; biochemical mechanisms of drug action. *Mailing Add:* USV Pharmaceut Corp One Scarsdale Rd Tuckahoe NY 10707

MELLETTE, RUSSELL RAMSEY, JR, b Orangeburg, SC, Dec 11, 27; m 51; c 5. CHILD PSYCHIATRY. *Educ:* Clemson Col, BS, 46; Med Col SC, MD, 50. *Prof Exp:* Intern, Wayne County Gen Hosp, Eloise, Mich, 50-51; resident psychiat, Edgewood Sanatorium, Orangeburg, SC, 51-52, clin dir, 52, med dir, 53; staff psychiatrist, US Army Hosp, Ft Sam Houston, Tex, 53-54; resident med neuropsychiat, Med Ctr Hosps, Charleston, SC, 55-56; from asst resident to resident & jr clin instr, Neuropsychiat Inst & Children's Psychiat Hosp, Sch Med, Univ Mich, Ann Arbor, 56-58, instr neuropsychiat, 58; asst prof psychiat, 58-65, chief child psychiat sect, 63-73, actg dir youth serv div, Dept Psychiat & Behav Sci, 73-74, ASSOC PROF PSYCHIAT, MED UNIV SC, 65-, ASSOC PROF PEDIAT, 67-, ASSOC PROF BEHAV SCI, 73-, DIR YOUTH OUTPATIENT SERV, DEPT PSYCHIAT & BEHAV SCI, 74- *Concurrent Pos:* Dir, Charleston County Ment Health Clin, SC, 58-60; sr teaching fel & chief children's psychiat unit, Sch Med, Univ NC, Chapel Hill, 60-61; consult child psychiat, Child Develop Clin, Dept Pediat, Med Univ SC, 61-66; consult, SC Dept Ment Health, 61-69 & NIMH Sch Proj, Sumter, SC, 61-74; consult & lectr, SC State Hosp, Columbia, 61-; NIMH GP educ grant, 64-74. *Mem:* Fel Am Geriat Soc; fel Am Orthopsychiat Asn; fel Am Psychiat Asn; fel Am Acad Child Psychiat; AMA. *Res:* Inpatient child psychiatry sevices; postgraduate education of nonpsychiatric physicians; voodoo; bromism; iatrogenic illnesses; involutional depressive states; infectious mononucleosis. *Mailing Add:* Dept of Psychiat & Behav Sci Med Univ of SC Charleston SC 29403

MELLICK, PAUL WAYNE, b Shelby, Ohio, July 11, 38; m 60; c 3. VETERINARY PATHOLOGY, COMPARATIVE MEDICINE. *Educ:* Ohio State Univ, DVM, 62; Cornell Univ, MS, 64; Univ Calif, Davis, PhD(comp path), 75. *Prof Exp:* Vet pathologist, Armed Forces Inst Path, 66-67 & 68-70; vet pathologist, Nat Inst Bact, Repub of Vietnam, 67-68; chief toxicol div, US Army Environ Hyg Agency, 70-72; CHIEF PATH SERV, LETTERMAN ARMY INST RES, 76- *Mem:* Am Vet Med Asn; Am Col Vet Pathologists; Int Acad Path. *Res:* Pulmonary pathology; environmental toxicology; inhalation toxicology; ultrastructural research to determine effects of non-sanguinous acellular blood replacement materials. *Mailing Add:* Path Serv Group Letterman Army Inst of Res Presidio of San Francisco CA 94129

MELLIERE, ALVIN L, b Praire du Rocher, Ill, Aug 9, 39; m 61; c 3. NUTRITION. *Educ:* Univ Ill, BS, 61, MS, 64, PhD(nutrit biochem), 65. *Prof Exp:* Asst prof nutrit, Univ Minn, 65-67; res scientist, 67-79, RES MGR, LILLY RES LABS, ELI LILLY & CO, 79- *Mem:* AAAS; Am Soc Animal Sci. *Res:* Dietary and chemical factors affecting the metabolism of nutrients in monogastric animals. *Mailing Add:* 1710 Chapman Dr Greenfield IN 46140

MELLIN, GILBERT WYLIE, b Manorville, Pa, Sept 22, 25; m 55; c 2. MEDICINE, PEDIATRICS. *Educ:* Bethany Col, BS, 45; Johns Hopkins Univ, MD, 49; Am Bd Pediat, dipl, 54. *Prof Exp:* Intern med, Med Ctr, Univ Pittsburgh, 49-50; from jr resident to sr resident pediat, Bellevue Hosp, New York, 50-52; instr, Med Sch, NY Univ, 52-53; clin instr, Med Sch, Georgetown Univ, 53-55; actg chmn dept, 70-71, instr, 55-57, assoc, 57-58, asst prof, 58-67, ASSOC PROF PEDIAT, COL PHYSICIANS & SURGEONS, COLUMBIA UNIV, 67- *Concurrent Pos:* Dir fetal life study, Columbia-Presby Med Ctr; chief resident, Bellevue Hosp, 52-53; jr assoc, Children's Hosp, Washington, DC, 53-55; asst pediatrician, Babies Hosp & Vanderbilt Clin, Presby Hosp, New York, 55-57, asst attend pediatrician, 57-67, assoc attend pediatrician, 67-, actg dir pediat serv, 70-71, dir qual assurance, 77-; mem tech adv comt cleft palate, City New York Dept Health, 61-; proj consult, Children's Bur, US Dept Health, Educ & Welfare & Govt Pakistan, 67- *Mem:* AAAS; Am Acad Pediat; fel Am Pub Health Asn; Am Statist Asn; Soc Pediat Res. *Res:* Epidemiological approach to fetal life and pregnancy outcome by means of direct prospective observation; establishment of documented magnetic tape data set banks for rapid data tabulation and analysis by electronic computer. *Mailing Add:* Col of Physicians & Surgeons Columbia Univ New York NY 10032

MELLIN, THEODORE NELSON, b Paterson, NJ, Dec 24, 37; m 59; c 3. PHYSIOLOGY, BIOCHEMISTRY. *Educ:* Univ Vt, BS, 59; Univ Maine, MS, 61; Purdue Univ, PhD(reproductive physiol), 65. *Prof Exp:* Res asst animal sci, Univ Maine, 59-61; res asst reproductive physiol, Wash State Univ, 61-62; res asst, Purdue Univ, 62-63, res fel, 63-65; RES FEL, MERCK INST THERAPEUT RES, 66- *Concurrent Pos:* Nat Cancer Inst fel steroid biochem, Worcester Found Exp Biol, 64-66; trainee electrophysiol methods, Cold Spring Harbor Lab, NY, 79. *Mem:* Am Dairy Sci Asn; Am Soc Animal Sci; Soc Study Reproduction; Soc Neurosci; Sigma Xi. *Res:* Reproductive physiology and endocrinology of animals; metabolism of steroid sex hormones; development and application of steroid sex hormone assays to the bovine; rumen microbiology; animal growth promotion; invertebrate neurophysiology; schistosome neuropharmacology; biochemistry of protozoan parasites. *Mailing Add:* Dept Biochem Merck Inst Therapeut Res Rahway NJ 07065

MELLINGER, CLAIR, b Ephrata, Pa, Mar 29, 42; m 66; c 1. PLANT ECOLOGY. *Educ:* Eastern Mennonite Col, BS, 64; Univ NC, Chapel Hill, PhD(bot), 72. *Prof Exp:* Asst instr, 64-65, assoc prof, 70-81, PROF BIOL, EASTERN MENNONITE COL, 81- *Mem:* AAAS; Ecol Soc Am; Am Inst Biol Sci. *Res:* Population dynamics of plant species under environmental stress. *Mailing Add:* Biol Dept Eastern Mennonite Col Harrisonburg VA 22801

MELLINGER, DONALD LEE, b Terre Hill, Pa, July 28, 36; m 65; c 2. AQUATIC ECOLOGY. *Educ:* Eastern Mennonite Col, BS, 58; Pa State Univ, MEd, 65; Mich State Univ, PhD(zool), 74. *Prof Exp:* Sec sch teacher sci, Musoma Alliance Sec Sch, Musoma, Tanzania, 58-61 & biol, Lancaster Mennonite Sch, 62-64; instr, Eastern Mennonite Col, 65-69; fel ecol, 74-76, ASST ECOLOGIST AQUATIC ECOL, ARGONNE NAT LAB, 76- *Mem:* Am Sci Affil; Am Soc Limnol & Oceanog; Soc Internationalis Limnologiae; Int Asn Great Lakes Res. *Res:* Effects of environmental pollutants on freshwater zooplankton. *Mailing Add:* Argonne Nat Lab 9700 S Cass Ave Argonne IL 60439

MELLINGER, GARY ANDREAS, b De Kalb, Ill, Apr 27, 43; m 67; c 2. CHEMICAL ENGINEERING, POLYMER ENGINEERING. *Educ:* Northwestern Univ, BS, 66; Mass Inst Technol, SM, 68, ScD(chem eng), 71. *Prof Exp:* Mem res staff, Corp Res & Develop, 71-75, mgr polymer processing, 75-77, mgr plastics processing technol, Maj Appln Labs, 77-81, MGR PLASTICS LAB & APPL CTR, GEN ELEC CO, 81- *Mem:* Soc Plastics Engrs. *Res:* Determination of plastics processing-property relationships and their application to design and fabrication of plastic components. *Mailing Add:* Gen Elec Co Appliance Park Bldg 35-1010 Louisville KY 40225

MELLINGER, GEORGE T, b New Orleans, La, Nov 8, 19; m 45; c 2. UROLOGY. *Educ:* Tulane Univ, BS, 41, MD, 43; Am Bd Urol, dipl, 52. *Prof Exp:* Chief urol, Vet Admin Hosp, Cincinnati, 55-60, chief urol, Minneapolis, 60-69, chief staff, Kansas City, 69-72, mem staff, Wichita, 72-79; PROF UROL, UNIV SDAK, 79- *Concurrent Pos:* Chmn, Vet Admin Coop Urol Res Group, 59-75; assoc prof, Med Sch, Univ Minn, Minneapolis, 60-69; prof urol & asst dean sch, Univ Kans, 69-72. *Mem:* Am Urol Asn; Am Col Surg; Pan-Am Med Asn; Asn Mil Surg US; Asn Univ Urologists. *Res:* Carcinoma of the prostate. *Mailing Add:* 1200 S Euclid Sioux Falls SD 57106

MELLINGER, MELVIN WAYNE, b Quincy, Ill, Mar 10, 41; m 65; c 3. NEUROPSYCHOLOGY. *Educ:* Univ Mo-Kansas City, BA, 68, MA, 70; Univ Kans, PhD(anat), 75. *Prof Exp:* ASST PROF ANAT, UNIV TEX MED BR, GALVESTON, 75- *Mem:* Sigma Xi; Soc Neurosci. *Res:* Forebrain regeneration and behavioral implications in lower vertebrates. *Mailing Add:* Dept of Anat Univ of Tex Med Br Galveston TX 77550

MELLINGER, MICHAEL VANCE, b Harrisburg, Pa, Dec 21, 45; m 68; c 2. ECOLOGY, ENVIRONMENTAL MANAGEMENT. *Educ:* Bloomsburg State Col, BA, 67; Syracuse Univ, PhD(plant ecol), 72. *Prof Exp:* Ecologist & proj coordr, Sargent & Lundy Engrs, 72-80; PRIN ECOLOGIST, WESTON, 80- *Mem:* Ecol Soc Am; Brit Ecol Soc; Am Inst Biol Sci; AAAS; Sigma Xi. *Res:* Structure and function of terrestrial communities; analysis of environmental effects of electric power facilities. *Mailing Add:* Sargent & Lundy Engrs 55 E Monroe St Chicago IL 60603

MELLINKOFF, SHERMAN MUSSOFF, b McKeesport, Pa, Mar 23, 20; m 44; c 2. MEDICINE. *Educ:* Stanford Univ, BA, 41, MD, 44. *Prof Exp:* Intern med, Stanford Univ Hosp, 44, asst resident, 44-45; asst resident, Osler Serv, Johns Hopkins Hosp, 47-49, resident & instr, 50-51, physician in charge gastroenterol, Outpatient Dept, 51-53; from asst prof to assoc prof, 53-62, PROF MED & DEAN, SCH MED, UNIV CALIF, LOS ANGELES, 62- *Concurrent Pos:* Fel, Hosp Univ Pa, 49-50; instr med, Johns Hopkins Univ, 51-53; attend consult, Wadsworth Gen Hosp, Vet Admin Ctr, 53-; sr attend physician, Harbor Gen Hosp, Torrance, 53-; sci adv panel, Res Prevent Blindness, Inc, 75-78. *Mem:* Nat Inst Med; AAAS; Am Gastroenterol Asn; Am Fedn Clin Res; Am Col Physicians. *Res:* Gastroenterology. *Mailing Add:* Univ of Calif Sch of Med Los Angeles CA 90024

MELLINS, HARRY ZACHARY, b New York, NY, May 23, 21; m 50; c 3. RADIOLOGY. *Educ:* Columbia Univ, AB, 41; Long Island Col Med, MD, 44; Univ Minn, MS, 51; Am Bd Radiol, dipl. *Hon Degrees:* AM, Harvard Univ, 69. *Prof Exp:* From instr to asst prof radiol, Med Sch, Univ Minn, 50-53; clin asst prof, Col Med, Wayne State Univ, 53-56; prof & chmn dept, Col Med, State Univ NY Downstate Med Ctr, 56-69; PROF RADIOL, HARVARD MED SCH, 69- *Concurrent Pos:* AEC-Nat Res Coun fel, Rice Inst, 49-50; nat consult, Surgeon-Gen, US Air Force, 65-79; consult, Vet Admin Hosp, West Roxbury; dir, Div Diag Radiol, Peter Bent Brigham Hosp, Boston, 69-80, dir diag radiol, Brigham & Women's Hosp, 80- *Mem:* Am Roentgen Ray Soc (pres, 77-79); Am Col Radiol; Asn Univ Radiol (pres, 69); Radiol Soc NAm. *Res:* Intestinal obstruction; renal medullary function. *Mailing Add:* 25 Shattuck St Boston MA 02115

MELLINS, ROBERT B, b New York, NY, Mar 6, 28; m 59; c 2. PEDIATRICS, CARDIOPULMONARY PHYSIOLOGY. *Educ:* Columbia Univ, AB, 48; Johns Hopkins Univ, MD, 52; Am Bd Pediat, dipl. *Prof Exp:* Intern pediat, Johns Hopkins Hosp, 52-53; clin instr, Col Med, Univ Ill, 54-55; asst resident pediat, New York Hosp, 55-56; asst resident, Columbia-Presby Med Ctr, 56-57, asst, 57-60, instr, 60-65, assoc, 65-66, asst prof, 66-70, assoc prof pediat, 70-75, PROF PEDIAT, COL PHYSICIANS & SURGEONS, COLUMBIA UNIV, 75-, DIR PEDIAT PULMONARY DIV, 72- *Concurrent Pos:* NY Heart Asn trainee, 61-63, res fel, 63-66; NIH career develop award, 66-71; founder & dir, Chicago Poison Control Ctr, 53-55; mem subcomt poisoning, Am Standards Asn, 54-55; asst pediatrician, Presby Hosp, 57-65, asst attend pediatrician, 65-70, assoc attend pediatrician, 70-75, attend pediatrician, 75; Stevens Triennial Award, Columbia Univ Col Physicians & Surgeons, 80. *Mem:* Am Fedn Clin Res; Soc Pediat Res; Am Thoracic Soc (pres, 82-83); Am Physiol Soc; NY Acad Sci. *Res:* Cardiopulmonary research; lung mechanics; regulation of respiration and transcapillary exchange of fluid in lung and the role of vasoactive chemical mediators; metabolic functions of the lung. *Mailing Add:* Col of Physicians & Surgeons 622 W 168th St New York NY 10032

MELLITS, E DAVID, b Philadelphia, Pa, Sept 5, 37; m 58; c 2. BIOSTATISTICS. *Educ:* Johns Hopkins Univ, BES, 59, ScD(biostatist), 65. *Prof Exp:* Systs analyst, Strong Mem Hosp, Rochester, NY, 59-61; asst prof, 65-71, ASSOC PROF BIOSTATIST, SCHS HYG & MED, JOHNS HOPKINS UNIV, 71- *Mem:* Am Statist Asn; Biomet Soc; Am Inst Math Statist; NY Acad Sci; Soc Pediat Res. *Res:* Application of statistics in the biological and medical sciences. *Mailing Add:* Dept of Pediat Johns Hopkins Hosp Baltimore MD 21218

MELLON, DEFOREST, JR, b Cleveland, Ohio, Dec 18, 34; m. NEUROPHYSIOLOGY. *Educ:* Yale Univ, BS, 57; Johns Hopkins Univ, PhD(biol), 61. *Prof Exp:* Air Force Off Sci Res-USPHS fel neurophysiol, Stanford Univ, 61-63; asst prof, 63-68, assoc prof, 68-78, PROF BIOL, UNIV VA, 78- *Concurrent Pos:* Guggenheim Mem fel, 66-67. *Mem:* Fel AAAS; Soc Gen Physiol; Soc Neurosci; Am Soc Zoologists. *Res:* Comparative neurophysiology; nerve-muscle interactions in development; crayfish oculomotor organization. *Mailing Add:* Dept of Biol Gilmer Hall Univ of Va Charlottesville VA 22903

MELLON, EDWARD KNOX, JR, b Rochester, NY, Oct 8, 36; m 66. INORGANIC CHEMISTRY, SCIENCE EDUCATION. *Educ:* Univ Tex, BS, 59, PhD(chem), 63. *Prof Exp:* Instr chem, St Edward's Univ, 62-63; fel, Univ Mich, 63-65, lectr, 65-66; from asst prof to assoc prof, 66-80, PROF CHEM, FLA STATE UNIV, 80- *Mem:* Am Chem Soc; Royal Soc Chem. *Res:* Chemical education; synthesis and structure of organometallic compounds. *Mailing Add:* Dept of Chem Fla State Univ Tallahassee FL 32306

MELLON, GEORGE BARRY, b Edmonton, Alta, Aug 5, 31. GEOLOGY. *Educ:* Univ Alta, BSc, 54, MSc, 55; Pa State Univ, PhD(mineral, petrol), 59. *Prof Exp:* Sr res off & head geol div, Res Coun Alta, 58-74; MEM STAFF, ALTA ENERGY & NATURAL RESOURCES, DEP MINISTER ENERGY RESOURCES, 74- *Mem:* Geol Asn Can; Can Soc Petrol Geol. *Res:* Sedimentary petrology and applied statistics in geology. *Mailing Add:* Alta Energy & Nat Resources Dep Minister Energy Resources Edmonton AB T5K 2C9 Can

MELLOR, ARTHUR M(CLEOD), b Elmira, NY, Jan 1, 42. MECHANICAL ENGINEERING. *Educ:* Princeton Univ, BSE, 63, MA, 65, PhD(aerospace & mech sci), 68. *Prof Exp:* From asst prof to assoc prof, 67-75, PROF MECH ENG, PURDUE UNIV, 75- *Mem:* Air Pollution Control Asn; Combustion Inst; Soc Automotive Engrs. *Res:* Chemical kinetics of combustion-generated air pollution; metal combustion; gas turbine combustor design. *Mailing Add:* Sch of Mech Eng Purdue Univ Lafayette IN 47907

MELLOR, CLIVE SIDNEY, psychiatry, see previous edition

MELLOR, DAVID BRIDGWOOD, b Brockton, Mass, June 25, 29; div. POULTRY SCIENCE, FOOD TECHNOLOGY. *Educ:* Pa State Univ, BS, 56; Tex A&M Univ, MS, 57; Purdue Univ, PhD(food tech), 65. *Prof Exp:* Overseas trainee, Int Coop Admin, 57-58, livestock adv, Agency Int Develop, 58-62; poultry adv, IRI Res Inst Inc, 65-67; assoc prof poultry mkt, 67-77, POULTRY MKT SPECIALIST, TEX AGR EXTEN SERV, TEX A&M UNIV, 67- *Concurrent Pos:* Consult, UN Develop Prog, Poultry Res Ctr, Pakistan, 72, Fed Univ Minas Gerias Poultry Mkt Prog, Brazil, 75 & Egg Qual & Control Prog, SAfrica, 78- *Mem:* Poultry Sci Asn; Inst Food Technol. *Res:* Egg quality; broiler yield and evaluation consumer opinion. *Mailing Add:* Dept of Poultry Sci Tex A&M Univ College Station TX 77843

MELLOR, GEORGE LINCOLN, JR, b Yonkers, NY, May 12, 29; m 54; c 2. PLANETARY BOUNDARY LAYERS. *Educ:* Mass Inst Technol, SB, 52, SM, 54, ScD(mech eng), 57. *Prof Exp:* Anal engr, Pratt & Whitney Aircraft Div, United Aircraft Corp, 52-53; res fel, Gas Turbine Lab, Mass Inst Technol, 53-57; aerodyn specialist, Curtiss-Wright Corp, 57; dir, Geophys Fluid Dynamics Prog, 69-76, PROF FLUID MECH, PRINCETON UNIV, 57- *Concurrent Pos:* Consult, Dynalysis & other industs; Nat Sci Found fel, Cambridge Univ, 62-63; Nat Acad Sci sci exchange fel, Inst Oceanol, Moscow, 70-71. *Honors & Awards:* Robert Knapp Award, Am Soc Mech Engrs, 59. *Mem:* Am Soc Mech Engrs; Am Geophys Union; Am Meteorol Soc. *Res:* Aerodynamics of turbomachinery; boundary layer mechanics; physical oceanography; meteorology. *Mailing Add:* Dept of Mech & Aerospace Eng Princeton Univ Princeton NJ 08540

MELLOR, JESSE LYNN, b Manti, Utah, Aug 5, 20; m 47; c 2. SOILS. *Educ:* Utah State Agr Col, BS, 47; Colo Agr & Mech Col, MS, 50; NC State Col, PhD(soils), 53. *Prof Exp:* Asst prof, Colo Agr & Mech Col, 47-50; agt & soil scientist, Bur Plant Indust, Soils & Agr Eng, USDA, 53; asst prof agron, Univ Wyo, 53-55; dir plant foods, Olin Corp, 55-79; RETIRED. *Mem:* Am Soc Agron. *Res:* Soil chemistry and ferility. *Mailing Add:* Olin Corp PO Box 991 Little Rock AR 77203

MELLOR, JOHN, b Guilford, Conn, Apr 28, 33; m 56; c 3. PHYSICAL CHEMISTRY. *Educ:* Univ Conn, BA, 56; Tufts Univ, MS, 58; Mass Inst Technol, PhD(phys chem), 62. *Prof Exp:* Chemist, Gen Elec Co, Conn, 56; res asst phys chem, Tufts Univ, 58; asst chemist, Arthur D Little, Inc, Mass, 59, consult physics, 60-62; res assoc, Brookhaven Nat Lab, 62-64; asst prof, 64-74, ASSOC PROF PHYS CHEM, UNIV BRIDGEPORT, 74-, CHMN DEPT, 77- *Concurrent Pos:* Vis asst physicist, Brookhaven Nat Lab, 65, res collabr, 65-66. *Mem:* Am Crystallog Asn. *Res:* Crystal structure analysis by x-ray and neutron diffraction; molecular motions and lattice dynamics by neutron inelastic scattering. *Mailing Add:* Dept of Chem Univ of Bridgeport Bridgeport CT 06602

MELLOR, MALCOLM, b Stalybridge, Eng, May 24, 33; m 58; c 2. APPLIED PHYSICS, ENGINEERING. *Educ:* Univ Nottingham, BS, 55; Univ Melbourne, MS, 59, DSc(appl sci), 69; Univ Sheffield, PhD(civil & struct eng), 70. *Prof Exp:* Asst engr, State Rivers & Water Supply Comn, Australia, 56; glaciologist, Australian Nat Antarctic Res Expeds, Dept External Affairs, 56-59; contract engr, Snow, Ice & Permafrost Res Estab, US Dept Army, Thayer Sch Eng, Dartmouth Col, 59-61, res engr, Cold Regions Res Lab, 61-75, RES PHYS SCIENTIST, COLD REGIONS RES & ENG LAB, US DEPT ARMY, 75- *Concurrent Pos:* Assoc consult, Creare Inc, 70-74; mem ed bd, Int Glaciological Soc, 72-; mem comt glaciol, Polar Res Bd, 74-78; secy, Int Comn Snow & Ice, 75-; ed, Cold Regions Sci & Technol, 78-; consult, 70- *Honors & Awards:* Brit Polar Medal, 59; Antarctic Medal, 67; Spec Award, Nat Res Coun, Nat Acad Sci-Nat Acad Eng, 72. *Mem:* Int Glaciological Soc; Glaciol Soc. *Res:* Applied mechanics; explosives; physics and mechanics of snow, ice and frozen ground; cold regions engineering; glaciology; ocean engineering; machine design. *Mailing Add:* Cold Regions Res & Eng Lab Hanover NH 03755

MELLOR, ROBERT SYDNEY, b Casper, Wyo, June 25, 31; m 60; c 3. PLANT PHYSIOLOGY. *Educ:* Colo State Univ, BS, 54, MS, 59, PhD(plant physiol), 62. *Prof Exp:* Asst prof, 62-67, ASSOC PROF BIOL, UNIV ARIZ, 67- *Mem:* Am Soc Plant Physiologists; Sigma Xi. *Res:* Plant-water relations; plant biochemistry. *Mailing Add:* Dept of Biol Sci Univ of Ariz Tucson AZ 85721

MELLORS, ALAN, b Mansfield, Eng, Feb 26, 40. BIOCHEMISTRY. *Educ:* Univ Liverpool, BSc, 61, PhD(biochem), 64. *Prof Exp:* Res biochemist, Univ Calif, Davis, 64-67; res scientist, Food Res Inst, Can Dept Agr, 67-68; asst prof, 68-71, assoc prof, 71-79, PROF CHEM, UNIV GUELPH, 79- *Concurrent Pos:* Fulbright scholar, 64-67; Nuffield Found scholar, 75-76. *Mem:* Am Soc Biol Chemists; Brit Biochem Soc; Can Biochem Soc; Can Soc Cell Biologists. *Res:* Phospholipases; trypanosomal enzymes; enzymes of pathogens; drug design; structure-activity relationships; molar volume relationships and physical toxicity; membrane events in cell activation. *Mailing Add:* Dept of Chem Univ of Guelph Guelph ON N1G 2W1 Can

MELLORS, ROBERT CHARLES, b Dayton, Ohio, June 18, 16; m 44; c 4. PATHOLOGY. *Educ:* Western Reserve Univ, AB, 37, MA, 38, PhD(biochem), 40; Johns Hopkins Univ, MD, 44. *Prof Exp:* Instr biochem, Western Reserve Univ, 40-42; asst epidemiol, Sch Hyg & Pub Health & asst poliomyelitis, Res Ctr, Johns Hopkins Univ, 42-44; assoc prof path, 53-58, assoc dir res, 58-69, PROF PATH, MED COL, CORNELL UNIV, 61-, DIR

RES, HOSP SPEC SURG, 69-, PATHOLOGIST-IN-CHIEF & DIR LABS, 58- *Concurrent Pos:* Spec fel med, Mem Hosp Ctr, New York, 46-47, Am Cancer Soc sr fel, 47-50, Runyan Fund sr fel, 50-53; ed, Anal Cytol & Anal Path Mem, Nat Found Infantile Paralysis Res, 43; assoc, Sloan-Kettering Inst, 50-53; assoc attend pathologist, Mem Hosp & Ewing Hosp, 53-58; mem res adv comt, USPHS, 62-66; attend pathologist, New York Hosp, 71- *Mem:* Am Asn Path; Am Soc Biol Chem; Am Asn Immunol; fel Am Soc Clin Path; fel Royal Col Path. *Res:* Experimental pathology; immunopathology; glomerulonephritis; rheumatoid arthritis; autoimmune diseases; systemic lupus erythematosus; cancer; viruses in cancer. *Mailing Add:* Hosp for Spec Surg Dept of Res 535 E 70th St New York NY 10021

MELLOW, ERNEST W(ESLEY), b St Louis, Mo, Feb 20, 18; m 48; c 3. CHEMICAL ENGINEERING. *Educ:* Univ Mo, BS, 40, MS, 46; Univ Ill, PhD(chem eng), 50. *Prof Exp:* Asst chem eng, Univ Mo, 40-41; chem engr, E I du Pont de Nemours & Co, Inc, 41-42; asst chem eng, Univ Ill, 46-49; asst prof, Univ Mo, 49-52; proj supvr, Callery Chem Co, 52-53; staff chem engr, Res & Develop Dept, Phillips Petrol Co, 52-56, sect mgr, 56-65, asst to mgr eng & test br, Atomic Energy Div, 65-69; PROF CHEM ENG, W VA INST TECHNOL, 69- *Concurrent Pos:* Vis prof, Okla State Univ, 67-68. *Mem:* Am Chem Soc; Am Soc Eng Educ; fel Am Inst Chem Engrs. *Res:* Environmental studies; technology assessment; relations between technology and society. *Mailing Add:* Dept of Chem Eng WVa Inst of Technol Montgomery WV 25136

MELLOW, GEORGE HENRY, b Brooklyn, NY, Aug 5, 54; m 81. PARASITOLOGY. *Educ:* Univ Notre Dame, BS, 75, MS, 77; Sch Med, NY Univ, PhD(parasitol), 81. *Prof Exp:* FEL ASSOC, SCH MED, NY UNIV, 81-, ASST RES SCIENTIST, 82- *Mem:* Am Soc Trop Med & Hyg; Am Soc Parasitologists. *Res:* Study of the enhanced immological protection to trypanosome infections (T lewisi and T cruzi) seen during host lactation and its association with concurrent rheumatoid factor production. *Mailing Add:* Div Parasitol Sch Med NY Univ 550 First Ave New York NY 10016

MELMON, KENNETH LLOYD, b San Francisco, Calif, July 20, 34; m 58; c 2. CLINICAL PHARMACOLOGY. *Educ:* Stanford Univ, AB, 56; Univ Calif, MD, 59; Am Bd Internal Med, dipl, 66. *Prof Exp:* Intern internal med, Moffitt Hosp, Univ Calif, San Francisco, 59-60, asst resident, 60-61; clin assoc exp therapeut, Nat Heart Inst, 61-64; chief resident med, King County Hosp, Seattle, Wash, 64-65; chief sect clin pharmacol, asst prof med & pharmacol & assoc mem cardiovasc res inst, 65-68, chief div clin pharmacol, sr staff cardiovasc res inst & prof med & pharmacol, Sch Med, Univ Calif, San Francisco, 68-78; BLOOMFIELD PROF MED & CHMN DEPT, SCH MED, STANFORD UNIV, 78- *Concurrent Pos:* Mosby scholar, 59; consult, NIH, 65-; Burroughs Wellcome scholar clin pharmacol, 66-71; mem consult comt, Food & Drug Admin, Senate Subcomt on Health, House Ways & Means Comt; mem coun basic scis, high blood pressure, res & circulation, Am Heart Asn; mem bd, Am Bd Internal Med, 68; Guggenheim fel exp studies clin biochem & immunopharmacol, 71; NIH spec fel, 71. *Mem:* Inst Med-Nat Acad Sci; Am Fedn Clin Res; Am Soc Pharmacol & Exp Therapeut; fel Am Col Physicians; Am Physiol Soc. *Res:* Mechanism of action cyclic amp on cell growth and death; hormone receptors on cells; leukocyte; role of vasoactive amines in immunology; carcinoid syndrome. *Mailing Add:* Dept of Med Stanford Univ Sch of Med Stanford CA 94305

MELNGAILIS, IVARS, b Riga, Latvia, Nov 13, 33; US citizen; m 64; c 2. SOLID STATE PHYSICS, ELECTRICAL ENGINEERING. *Educ:* Carnegie Inst Technol, BS, 56, PhD(elec eng), 61. *Prof Exp:* Instr elec eng, Carnegie Inst Technol, 59-60; staff mem, Appl Physics Group, 61-65, asst group leader, 65-71, group leader, 71-75, ASSOC DIV HEAD, SOLID STATE DIV, LINCOLN LAB, MASS INST TECHNOL, 75- *Mem:* Inst Elec & Electronics Engrs; Am Phys Soc. *Res:* Infrared detectors; physics of semiconductor devices; impact ionization in semiconductors at low temperatures; magnetic field effects on plasmas in semiconductors; semiconductor lasers and detectors; integrated optics. *Mailing Add:* Lincoln Lab Mass Inst of Technol Lexington MA 02173

MELNGAILIS, JOHN, b Riga, Latvia, Feb 4, 39; US citizen; m 68; c 2. APPLIED PHYSICS. *Educ:* Carnegie Inst Technol, BS, 60, MS, 62, PhD(solid state theory), 65. *Prof Exp:* Assoc engr, Westinghouse Res Lab, 60-65; staff mem, 67-80, PRIN RES SCIENTIST, LINCOLN LAB, MASS INST TECHNOL, 80- *Concurrent Pos:* NSF fel, Max Planck Inst Metall Res, Stuttgart, Ger, 65; res attache, Nat Ctr Sci Res, Bellevue, France, 66-67. *Mem:* Am Phys Soc; Inst Elec & Electronics Engrs. *Res:* Surface acoustic wave devices; solid state physics; microstructure fabrication technology. *Mailing Add:* Mass Inst Technol Rm 13-3065 Lexington MA 02173

MELNICK, EDWARD LAWRENCE, b Ann Arbor, Mich, Dec 12, 38; m 63; c 2. MATHEMATICS, STATISTICS. *Educ:* Lehigh Univ, BA, 60; Va Polytech Inst & State Univ, MS, 63; George Washington Univ, PhD(math statist), 70. *Prof Exp:* Math statistician, US Census Bur, Dept of Com, 63-69; asst prof, 69-73, assoc prof, 73-79, PROF STATIST, GRAD SCH BUS ADMIN, NY UNIV, 73-, FAC RES GRANT, 69- *Concurrent Pos:* Lectr, Grad Sch, USDA, 64-69; statist consult, Bellevue Hosp & others, 69- *Mem:* Am Statist Asn; fel Royal Statist Soc; Inst Math Statist. *Res:* Time series analysis with emphasis upon signal detection and prediction theory; collection and analysis of data. *Mailing Add:* GBA Quantitative Anal Area NY Univ Grad Sch of Bus Admin New York NY 10006

MELNICK, JOSEPH LOUIS, b Boston, Mass, Oct 9, 14; m 36; c 1. VIROLOGY. *Educ:* Wesleyan Univ, BA, 36, Yale Univ, PhD(biochem), 39; Am Bd Med Microbiol, dipl. *Hon Degrees:* DSc, Wesleyan Univ, 71. *Prof Exp:* Asst physiol chem, Sch Med, Yale Univ, 37-39, from instr to asst prof prev med, 42-49, assoc prof microbiol, 49-54, prof epidemiol, 54-57; chief virus labs, Div Biologics Standards, NIH, 57-58; PROF VIROL & EPIDEMIOL & CHMN DEPT, BAYLOR COL MED, 58-, DEAN GRAD SCI, 68-, DISTINGUISHED SERV PROF, 74- *Concurrent Pos:* Finney-Howell Res Found fel, Sch Med, Yale Univ, 39-41, Nat Res Coun fel prev med & pediat, 41-42; Am-Scand Found fel viruses, Karolinska Inst, Sweden, 49; mem, Viral & Rickettsial Registry Comt & Exec Comt, 57-60; mem panel virol & immunol, Comt on Growth, Nat Res Coun, 52-56 & Comt Viral Hepatitis, 71-75; chmn comt echoviruses, Nat Found, 55-57, chmn comt enteroviruses, 57-60; expert adv panel virus dis, WHO, 57-, dir int reference ctr enteroviruses, 61-74, mem comt polio vaccine, 72-, dir Collaborating Ctr Virus Reference & Res, 74-; mem comt live polio virus vaccine, USPHS, 58-61, mem nat adv cancer coun, 65-69; mem viruses & cancer bd, Nat Cancer Inst, 60-62, mem human cancer virus task force, 62-66, mem etiology prog adv comt, 70-73; chmn comt enteroviruses, NIH, 60-63; mem bd virus reference reagents, Nat Inst Allergy & Infectious Dis, 62-65, mem allergy & infectious dis training grant comt, 62-65, mem panel picornaviruses, 63-65; nat lectr, Found for Microbiol, 63-64 & 66-67; trustee, George Washington Carver Res Found, Tuskegee Inst, 64-; mem, Int Comt Nomenclature of Viruses, 66-74; chmn, Picornavirus & Papovavirus Comts, 68-81; mem, Surgeon Gen Comt Hepatitis, Dept Army, 66-73; secy-gen, Int Congs Virol, Helsinki, 68 & Budapest, 71; chmn virol sect & mem exec bd, Int Asn Microbiol Socs, 70-75, mem int comt microbial ecology, 72-; mem coun res & clin invest, Am Cancer Soc, 71-75; chmn task group active immunization against viral hepatitis, NIH, 73-74; co-chmn, Duran-Reynals Int Symp Viral Oncol, Barcelona, Spain, 73; ed-in-chief, Progress Med Virol, 58-, Monographs in Virol, 60-, Intervirol, 73-; chmn int conf viruses in water, Am Pub Health Asn & WHO, Mexico City, 74; mem, Int Comt Taxon Viruses, 74-; lectr virol, Chinese Acad Med Sci, 78 & Shanghai First Med Col, 79; Latin Am prof microbiol, Buenos Aires, 77 & Santiago, 79. *Honors & Awards:* Int Gold Medal, Arg Found Against Infantile Paralysis, 49; Polio Hall of Fame, 58; Mod Med Distinguished Achievement Award, 65; Indust Res-100 Award, 71; Inventor of Year Award, 72; Freedman Found Award Res Virol, NY Acad Sci, 73; Maimonides Award, State Israel, 80. *Mem:* Fel AAAS; Am Epidemiol Soc; Soc Exp Biol & Med; Am Asn Immunol; Am Soc Microbiol. *Res:* Virology, especially infectious diseases and cancer. *Mailing Add:* Dept Virol & Epidemiol Baylor Col Med Houston TX 77030

MELNICK, LABEN MORTON, b Pittsburgh, Pa, June 10, 26; m 49; c 2. ANALYTICAL CHEMISTRY. *Educ:* Univ Pittsburgh, BS, 49, MS, 50, PhD(anal chem), 54. *Prof Exp:* Anal chemist, Res Lab, Jones & Laughlin Steel Corp, 50, x-ray diffractionist & spectroscopist, 51-52; technologist, 53-56, supv technologist, 56-58, sect supvr anal chem, 58-75, DIV CHIEF PHYSICS & ANAL CHEM, RES LAB, US STEEL CORP, 75- *Concurrent Pos:* Mem, Nat Acad Sci-Nat Res Coun adv panels to anal chem div, Nat Bur Standards, 69-71 & measures for air qual off, 71-73. *Mem:* AAAS; Israel Chem Soc; Am Chem Soc. *Res:* Analysis of raw materials and metals; determination of gases and second phase inclusions in steel; analysis of water. *Mailing Add:* Res Lab Physics & Anal Chem Div US Steel Corp Mail Sta 15 Monroeville PA 15146

MELNICK, RONALD L, cell physiology, see previous edition

MELNYK, JOHN H, cytogenetics, see previous edition

MELNYKOVYCH, GEORGE, b Halych, Ukraine, Oct 14, 24; nat US; m 49; c 2. CELL BIOLOGY. *Educ:* Univ Minn, MS, 53, PhD, 56. *Prof Exp:* Res chemist, Elgin State Hosp, Ill, 58 & Lederle Labs Div, Am Cyanamid Co, 58-63; asst prof microbiol, 63-70, PROF MICROBIOL, SCH MED, UNIV KANS, 70-; RES CAREER SCIENTIST, VET ADMIN HOSP, 63- *Concurrent Pos:* USPHS fel biochem, Univ Tex, 56 & Univ Calif, 56-58. *Mem:* AAAS; Am Soc Cell Biol; Tissue Cult Asn; Am Soc Biol Chem; Am Soc Exp Path. *Res:* Tissue culture nutrition and metabolism; steroid hormones; membrane biochemistry. *Mailing Add:* US Vet Admin Hosp 4801 Linwood Blvd Kansas City MO 64128

MELOAN, CLIFTON E, b Bettendorf, Iowa, Aug 4, 31; m 57; c 3. ANALYTICAL CHEMISTRY. *Educ:* Iowa State Univ, BS, 53; Purdue Univ, PhD(anal chem), 59. *Prof Exp:* From asst prof to assoc prof, 59-68, PROF CHEM, KANS STATE UNIV, 68- *Concurrent Pos:* Sci adv, Food & Drug Admin, 66- *Mem:* Am Chem Soc. *Res:* Liquid-liquid extractions; metal chelates; infrared; gas chromatography; spectrophotometry. *Mailing Add:* Dept of Chem Kans State Univ Manhattan KS 66502

MELOCHE, HENRY PAUL, b Detroit, Mich, Nov 15, 28; div; c 6. MICROBIOLOGY, PUBLIC HEALTH. *Educ:* Univ Detroit, BS, 51; Mich State Univ, MS, 53, PhD(microbiol), 56. *Prof Exp:* Food chemist, Swift & Co, 56-57; microbiologist, Fermentation Lab, Agr Res Serv, USDA, 57-60; res assoc agr chem, Mich State Univ, 60-64; res assoc, Inst Cancer Res, 64-69, asst mem, 69-76; SR RES SCIENTIST & ASSOC DIR, PAPANICOLAOU CANCER RES INST, 77- *Concurrent Pos:* NIH fel, 62-63; adj assoc prof biochem, Papanicloaou Cancer Res Inst, Univ Miami, 77- *Mem:* AAAS; Am Chem Soc; Am Soc Microbiol; Am Soc Biol Chem. *Res:* Enzyme chemistry active site chemistry, sterochemistry. *Mailing Add:* Papanicolaou Cancer Res Inst 1155 NW 14th St Miami FL 33136

MELONI, EDWARD GEORGE, b East Boston, Mass, Aug 2, 32; m 59; c 2. INORGANIC CHEMISTRY. *Educ:* Columbia Univ, AB, 53; Tufts Univ, MS, 55; Rutgers Univ, PhD(chem), 61, Northeastern Univ, MBA, 72. *Prof Exp:* Res chemist, Pennsalt Chem Corp, 60-63; res chemist, Esso Res & Eng Co, 63-65; chief chemist, Alfa Inorg Inc, 65-71; tech dir, Ventron Corp, 71-80; TECHNOL SPECIALIST, COMBUSTION ENG CO, 81- *Mem:* Am Inst Chem; Am Chem Soc. *Res:* Synthetic inorganic chemistry; inorganic polymers. *Mailing Add:* Alfa Prods Arlington MA 02174

MELOON, DANIEL THOMAS, JR, b Buffalo, NY, Aug 13, 35; m 59; c 5. ANALYTICAL CHEMISTRY. *Educ:* Univ Buffalo, BA, 57, MA, 60, PhD(inorg chem), 63. *Prof Exp:* Sr chemist, Carborundum Co, Niagara Falls, 63-66; asst prof, 66-68, assoc prof, 68-80, PROF CHEM, STATE UNIV NY COL BUFFALO, 80- *Mem:* Am Chem Soc; Sigma Xi; Creation Res Soc. *Res:* High temperature oxidation catalysts; water pollution and inorganic complex ions. *Mailing Add:* 186 Calvert Blvd Tonawanda NY 14150

MELOON, DAVID RAND, b Buffalo, NY, July 20, 48; m 75. INORGANIC CHEMISTRY, PHYSICAL CHEMISTRY. *Educ:* State Univ NY Buffalo, BA, 70, PhD(chem), 75. *Prof Exp:* Res fel chem, State Univ NY Buffalo, 74-75, lectr, 75-76; res chemist, 76-79, MGR RES & DEVELOP, GEN ABRASIVE DIV, DRESSER INDUSTS, 79- *Mem:* Am Chem Soc; Sigma Xi; Am Inst Chemists. *Res:* Abrasive and refractory materials; kinetics and mechanisms of inorganic and bio-inorganic reactions. *Mailing Add:* Gen Abrasive Div 2000 College Ave Niagara Falls NY 14305

MELOSH, HENRY JAY, IV, b Paterson, NJ, June 23, 47; m 69; c 2. PLANETARY SCIENCES, GEOPHYSICS. *Educ:* Princeton Univ, AB, 69; Calif Inst Technol, MS, 71, PhD(physics), 73. *Prof Exp:* Res assoc physics, Univ Chicago, 73-74; instr geophys & planetary sci, Calif Inst Technol, 74-76, asst prof planetary sci, 76-78, assoc prof, 78-79; ASSOC PROF GEOPHYS, STATE UNIV NY STONY BROOK, 79- *Concurrent Pos:* Geophysicist, US Geol Surv, 77-79; consult geosci, Los Alamos Nat Lab, 80- *Mem:* Am Geophys Union. *Res:* Tectonics of planetary lithospheres; crater mechanics; dynamics of earth's lithosphere, especially spreading centers, subduction zones, anelastic response of the earth, rheology; physics of earthquakes and large landslides. *Mailing Add:* Earth & Space Sci Dept State Univ NY Stony Brook NY 11794

MELOY, CARL RIDGE, b Detroit, Mich, Sept 21, 12; m 32, 65; c 4. ORGANIC CHEMISTRY. *Educ:* Univ Mich, BS, 32, MS, 34; Mich State Univ, PhD(org chem), 42. *Prof Exp:* Instr chem, Highland Park Jr Col, Mich, 34-42; res chemist, Stamford Res Lab, Air Reduction Co, Conn, 42-43; asst prof chem & physics, Baldwin-Wallace Col, 43-45; asst prof phys sci, Mich State Univ, 45-47; from asst prof to prof phys sci & head dept, Univ Ill, 47-64; chmn div sci, 64-69, prof chem, Grand Valley State Col, 64-78; PROF PHYS SCI, URBANA COL, 78- *Concurrent Pos:* Chemist, Process Chem Co, Mich, 39-40 & McGean Chem Co, Ohio, 45; res consult, Culligan, Inc, 51-53; Smith-Mundt exchange prof, Kabul Univ, Afghanistan, 61-62; fel, Imp Col, Univ London, 62; vis prof, Univ Kent, 71. *Mem:* AAAS; Am Chem Soc; Royal Soc Chem. *Res:* Organic synthesis; aromatic and heterocyclic compounds. *Mailing Add:* Urbana Col 635 Boyce St Urbana OH 43078

MELOY, THOMAS PHILLIPS, b New York, NY, Sept 14, 25; m 57; c 1. PHYSICS, METALLURGY. *Educ:* Harvard Univ, AB, 49; Mass Inst Technol, BS, 51, PhD(metall), 60. *Prof Exp:* Metall engr, Gen Elec Co, 51-52, 53-54, instr chem eng, 52-53, dept specialist jet eng, 54-57; from instr to asst prof metall, Mass Inst Technol, 57-61, vis scientist, Lincoln Lab, 61; sr staff scientist, Allis-Chalmers Mfg Co, Wis, 61-67; staff scientist, Westinghouse Airbrake Co & mgr environ & appl sci ctr, Melpar Co, 67-70; VPRES RES & DEVELOP, MELOY LABS, 70-; CLAUDE WORTHINGTON BENEDUM PROF MINERAL PROCESSING, W VA UNIV, 67- *Concurrent Pos:* Consult, Mat Tech Co, 58-62, US Coast & Geod Surv, 65-, Off Sci & Technol, 65- & ITT Res Inst, 68-; Ford Found fel, 60-61; instr, Boston Univ, 61-62 & Univ Wis-Milwaukee, 63-64; ed, J Marine Technol, 64-71; dir, Eng Div, Nat Sci Found, 64-66; chmn interagency comt oceanog, Nat Securities Industs Asn Continental Shelf Study, 65-66; dir indust extractive & process res div, Environ Protection Agency, 66-67; chmn, Eng Found Conf Particulate Systs, 66, 69, Rapid Excavation, 70, Coal Mine Safety & Survival, 71; Nat Sci Found travel fel, Poland & Yugoslavia, 71. *Mem:* AAAS; Am Inst Aeronaut & Astronaut; Am Inst Mining, Metall & Petrol Engrs; fel Marine Technol Soc; Am Inst Chem Engrs. *Res:* Behavior of particulate systems involving comminution and accretion; origin of solar system; aerosols, modeling of industrial process, air, water, and oil pollution; oil tagging; particle morphology; separation of particulates; coal cleaning; mineral processing; relating particle shape to behavior in industrial processes. *Mailing Add:* 138 Hodges Hall Dept of Physics WVa Univ Morgantown WV 26506

MELROSE, JAMES C, b Spokane, Wash, Mar 27, 22; m 52; c 1. PHYSICAL CHEMISTRY. *Educ:* Harvard Univ, SB, 43; Stanford Univ, PhD(chem), 58. *Prof Exp:* Jr res chemist, Shell Oil Co, 43-46; res chemist, Mobil Oil Corp, 47-49, sr res chemist, 49-51 & 54-58, res assoc, 58-65, sr res assoc, 65-67; SR RES ASSOC, MOBIL RES & DEVELOP CORP, 67- *Concurrent Pos:* Vis lectr, Univ Tex, 64; vis assoc, Calif Inst Technol, 65. *Mem:* Fel AAAS; Am Chem Soc; fel Am Inst Chemists; Soc Petrol Engrs. *Res:* Thermodynamics of interfaces; capillary phenomena in porous media; properties of petroleum reservoir rocks and fluids; processes for enhanced oil recovery. *Mailing Add:* Field Res Lab Mobil Res & Develop Corp PO Box 900 Dallas TX 75221

MELROSE, RAYMOND JOHN, b Chicago, Ill, Nov 27, 36; m 81. ORAL PATHOLOGY. *Educ:* Northwestern Univ, DDS, 62. *Prof Exp:* Intern dent, Vet Admin Hosp, Long Beach, Calif, 64-65; spec lectr path, 66-68, asst prof, 68-72, assoc prof path, 72-78, assoc dean, 80, PROF PATH & CHMN DIAG SCI DIV, SCH DENT, UNIV SOUTHERN CALIF, 78- *Concurrent Pos:* Resident oral path, Vet Admin Hosp, Long Beach, 65-68, consult & oral pathologist, 68-; consult test construct comt path & microbiol, oral path & radiol, Nat Bd Dent Examr-Am Dent Asn. *Mem:* Am Dent Asn; Am Acad Oral Path; Am Soc Clin Path. *Res:* Oral cancer; odontogenic tumors; minor salivary gland tumors of the oral cavity. *Mailing Add:* Sch Dent Dept Path Univ Southern Calif Los Angeles CA 90007

MELSA, JAMES LOUIS, b Omaha, Nebr, July 6, 38; m 60; c 6. CONTROL ENGINEERING, DIGITAL SIGNAL PROCESSING. *Educ:* Iowa State Univ, BSEE, 60; Ariz Univ, MSEE, 62, PhD(elec eng), 65. *Prof Exp:* Assoc mem tech staff, Radio Corp Am, 60-61; instr elec eng, Ariz Univ, 61-65, asst prof, 65-67; from assoc prof to prof info & control sci, South Methodist Univ, 67-73; PROF & CHMN ELEC ENG DEPT, UNIV NOTRE DAME, 73- *Concurrent Pos:* Consult, Los Alamos Nat Lab, 65- & Tellabs, Inc, 80- *Mem:* Fel Inst Elec & Electronics Engrs. *Res:* Applications of optimal control and estimation theory to the problem of systems control. *Mailing Add:* Dept of Elec Eng Univ Notre Dame Notre Dame IN 46556

MELSHEIMER, FRANK MURPHY, b Alhambra, Calif, Dec 9, 40; c 1. MECHANICAL ENGINEERING, ASTRONOMICAL INSTRUMENTATION. *Educ:* Univ Calif, Berkeley, BS, 63, MSME, 68, DEng, 72. *Prof Exp:* Electrometer engr, Appl Physics Corp, 62-64; instrumentation engr aircraft flight test, Douglas Aircraft Co, 65-67; chief engr astron, Lick Observ, Univ Calif, 72-76; proj prof eng, McDonald Observ, 76; asst prof eng design, Univ Colo, 76-78; ENGR & CONSULT ASTRON, DFM ENG, 79- *Concurrent Pos:* Design engr, T Melsheimer Co, 76-77; instrument designer, Monterey Inst Res Astron, 77-79. *Res:* Digital control; micro computer applications. *Mailing Add:* 4380 Ludlow St Boulder CO 80303

MELSHEIMER, STEPHEN SAMUEL, b Baton Rouge, La, Feb 23, 43; m 65; c 2. CHEMICAL ENGINEERING. *Educ:* La State Univ, Baton Rouge, BS, 65; Tulane Univ, PhD(chem eng), 69. *Prof Exp:* Asst prof, 69-77, assoc prof, 77-81, PROF CHEM ENG, CLEMSON UNIV, 81- *Mem:* Am Inst Chem Engrs. *Res:* Process dynamics and control; applied mathematics. *Mailing Add:* Dept of Chem Eng Clemson Univ Clemson SC 29631

MELSON, GORDON ANTHONY, b Sheffield, Eng, July 6, 37; m 62; c 2. INORGANIC CHEMISTRY. *Educ:* Univ Sheffield, BSc, 59, PhD(chem), 62. *Prof Exp:* Res assoc chem, Ohio State Univ, 62-64; lectr, Univ Strathclyde, 64-69; asst prof, Mich State Univ, 69-75; assoc prof, 75-80, PROF CHEM, VA COMMONWEALTH UNIV, 80- *Mem:* Am Chem Soc; Royal Soc Chem. *Res:* Catalysis of coal liquefaction; mechanisms of macrocyclic ligand formation. *Mailing Add:* Dept of Chem Va Commonwealth Univ Richmond VA 23284

MELSON, WILLIAM GERALD, b Washington, DC, Oct 23, 38; m 61; c 1. PETROLOGY, GEOCHEMISTRY. *Educ:* Johns Hopkins Univ, AB, 61; Princeton Univ, MA, 63, PhD(petrol), 64. *Prof Exp:* Instr geol, Johns Hopkins Univ, 60-61; geologist, US Geol Surv, 61; NSF fel, 61-64; CUR PETROL, SMITHSONIAN INST, US NAT MUS, 64- *Mem:* Am Geophys Union; Am Mineral Soc; fel Geol Soc Am. *Res:* Inorganic geochemistry; phase equilibria in metamorphic rocks; petrology of oceanic rocks, particularly those from the mid-Atlantic ridge; studies of active volcanoes. *Mailing Add:* US Nat Mus Smithsonian Inst Washington DC 20560

MELSTED, SIGURD WALTER, b Gardar, NDak, Nov 23, 11. AGRONOMY, SOILS. *Educ:* NDak State Col, BS, 38; Rutgers Univ, MS, 40; Univ Ill, PhD(soil chem), 43. *Prof Exp:* Asst, NDak State Col, 36-38 & Rutgers Univ, 38-40; soil surv anal, Univ Ill, Urbana, 40-43, from asst prof to prof soils, 46-75; RES SCIENTIST IN SOILS, NDAK STATE UNIV, 75- *Concurrent Pos:* Guggenheim fel, 56-57; guest lectr, Mid East Tech Univ Ankara, 63-64; AID adv, Njala Univ Col, Sierra Leone, 65-67, adv soils, 71; adv agr, US State Dept Atoms for Peace Exhib, Tehran, Iran, 67; AID-A T Kearndy Co consult fertilizer technol, Chile, 69- *Mem:* AAAS; Am Chem Soc; Soil Sci Soc Am; fel Am Soc Agron; Instrument Soc Am; fel Am Inst Chemists. *Res:* Soil colloids; fertilizer use; soil testing methods and calibration; spectrographic analysis of soils and plants; waste disposal on land; heavy metal toxicity in soils; phosphorus pollution of waters; international agriculture. *Mailing Add:* Dept of Soils NDak State Univ Fargo ND 58102

MELTER, ROBERT ALAN, b New York, NY, Mar 20, 35; m 65; c 1. MATHEMATICS, BOOLEAN ALGEBRA. *Educ:* Cornell Univ, AB, 56; Univ Mo, AM, 60, PhD(math), 62. *Prof Exp:* Instr math, Univ Mo, 58-62; asst prof, Univ RI, 62-64 & Univ Mass, 64-67; assoc prof, Univ SC, 67-71; assoc prof, 71-80, PROF MATH, SOUTHAMPTON COL, LONG ISLAND UNIV, 80- *Concurrent Pos:* Vis asst prof, Amherst Col, 67; Fulbright lectr, Univ Niamey, Niger, 74-75; ed consult, Math Rev, 78-80, assoc ed, 80- *Mem:* Am Math Soc; Math Asn Am; Sigma Xi. *Res:* Algebra; abstract distance spaces and valuations; graph theory; binary images. *Mailing Add:* Dept Math Southampton Col Long Island Univ Southampton NY 11968

MELTON, ARTHUR RICHARD, b Ysleta, Tex, Apr 28, 43; m 65; c 2. PUBLIC HEALTH & EPIDEMIOLOGY. *Educ:* Univ Utah, BS, 69; Univ NC, MPH, 74, DrPH, 76. *Prof Exp:* Microbiologist, Div Health, Bur Labs, Utah Dept Social Serv, 70-73; DIR, LAB PROG, SDAK DEPT HEALTH, 76- *Mem:* Am Public Health Asn; Am Soc Microbiol. *Mailing Add:* Health Lab Bldg SDak Dept Health Pierre SD 57501

MELTON, BILLY ALEXANDER, JR, b Wheeler, Tex, Aug 21, 32; m 51; c 2. PLANT BREEDING. *Educ:* NMex Col Agr & Mech Arts, BS, 54; Univ Ill, MS, 56, PhD, 58. *Prof Exp:* Asst plant breeding, Univ Ill, 54-58; from asst prof to assoc prof, 58-69, PROF AGRON, N MEX STATE UNIV, 69- *Mem:* Am Soc Agron. *Res:* Genetics of sorghum and forage crops, primarily alfalfa. *Mailing Add:* Dept of Agron NMex State Univ Las Cruces NM 88001

MELTON, CARL WESLEY, b Barnesville, Ohio, July 7, 21; m 45; c 3. ZOOLOGY, ELECTRON MICROSCOPY. *Educ:* Kent State Univ, AB, 47. *Prof Exp:* Sr microscopist, 47-74, SR RES SCIENTIST, COLUMBUS LAB, BATTELLE MEM INST, 74- *Mem:* AAAS; Electron Micros Soc Am. *Res:* Light and electron microscopy coupled with chemical analysis to relate microstructer and chemical composition in various sample types for the purpose of product or process development or improvement. *Mailing Add:* Columbus Lab Battelle Mem Inst 505 King Ave Columbus OH 43201

MELTON, CARLTON EARL, JR, b Allen, Tex, June 1, 24; m 57; c 3. PHYSIOLOGY. *Educ:* NTex State Col, BS, 48; Univ Ill, MS, 50, PhD(physiol), 53. *Prof Exp:* Asst elec eng, Univ Ill, 49-51, asst physiol, 51-53; instr, Sch Med, Western Reserve Univ, 53-55; from instr to asst prof, Univ Tex Southwestern Med Sch Dallas, 55-61; assoc prof, 61-66, PROF RES PHYSIOL, SCH MED, UNIV OKLA, 66-, ADJ PROF ZOOL, 73-; CHIEF, PHYSIOL LAB, CIVIL AEROMED INST, FED AVIATION ADMIN, 61- *Honors & Awards:* Arnold D Tuttle Award, Aerospace Med Asn, 79. *Mem:* Am Physiol Soc; Soc Exp Biol & Med; Am Asn Anat. *Res:* Physiology of muscle and nerve; special senses; stress. *Mailing Add:* Civil Aeromed Inst AAC-115 Fed Aviation Admin PO Box 25082 Oklahoma City OK 73125

MELTON, CHARLES ESTEL, b Fancy Gap, Va, May 18, 24; m 46; c 3. CHEMICAL PHYSICS. *Educ:* Emory & Henry Col, BA, 52; Vanderbilt Univ, MS, 54; Univ Notre Dame, PhD(phys chem), 64. *Hon Degrees:* DSc, Emory & Henry Col, 67. *Prof Exp:* Physicist, Oak Ridge Nat Lab, 54-67; head dept, 72-77, PROF CHEM, UNIV GA, 67- *Honors & Awards:* DeFriece Award Physics, Emory & Henry Col, 59. *Mem:* Fel AAAS; Am Chem Soc; Sigma Xi. *Res:* Chemical kinetics; mass spectrometry; atmospheric chemistry and physics; catalysis; theoretical chemistry and geochemistry. *Mailing Add:* Rte 2 Box 18 Hull GA 30646

MELTON, JAMES RAY, b Paris, Tex, Aug 24, 40; m 62; c 2. ANALYTICAL CHEMISTRY, SOIL CHEMISTRY. *Educ:* Tex Tech Col, BS, 62; Mich State Univ, MS, 64, PhD(soil sci), 68. *Prof Exp:* ASSOC PROF AGR ANAL SERV, TEX A&M UNIV, 68- *Mem:* Sigma Xi; Asn Off Anal Chemists; Am Soc Agron; Soil Sci Soc Am. *Res:* Use of microwave for garimetric phosphoras method; movement and availability of heavy metals in soils; development of methods for determination of heavy metals by atomic absorption and atomic emission. *Mailing Add:* Agr Anal Serv Tex A&M Univ College Station TX 77843

MELTON, LEE JOSEPH, III, b Pensacola, Fla, May 17, 44. EPIDEMIOLOGY, MEDICINE. *Educ:* La State Univ, BS, 65, MD, 69; Univ Mich, MPH, 71. *Prof Exp:* Epidemiologist, US Navy, 67-77; CONSULT EPIDEMIOL, MAYO CLIN, 77-, ASST PROF, MAYO MED SCH, 78- *Concurrent Pos:* Asst prof epidemiol, Uniformed Serv Univ Health Sci, 76-77. *Honors & Awards:* Gaylor Award, Asn Mil Surgeons of US, 76. *Mem:* Am Col Prev Med; Soc Epidemiol Res; Am Pub Health Asn; Int Epidemiol Asn; Sigma Xi. *Res:* Epidemiology of diabetes mellitus, osteoporosis and breast cancer. *Mailing Add:* Dept of Epidemiol & Med Statist Mayo Clin Rochester MN 55901

MELTON, LYNN AYRES, b Huntsville, Tex, Aug 7, 44; m 67; c 2. PHYSICAL CHEMISTRY, SCIENCE EDUCATION. *Educ:* Calif Inst Technol, BS, 66; Harvard Univ, MA & PhD(chem), 72. *Prof Exp:* Asst prof, 71-76, head prog, 76-79, head sci educ, 79-81, ASSOC PROF CHEM, UNIV TEX, DALLAS, 76- *Concurrent Pos:* Consult, United Technologies Res Ctr, East Hartford, Conn, 81-82. *Mem:* Am Chem Soc; Am Phys Soc; AAAS. *Res:* Gas phase energy transfer, detailed state-to-state rate measurements by laser excited fluorescence. *Mailing Add:* Dept Chem Univ Tex at Dallas Box 688 Richardson TX 75080

MELTON, REX EUGENE, b Ozark, Mo, Dec 4, 21; m 42; c 4. FORESTRY. *Educ:* Univ Mo, BS, 46; Univ Mich, BS & MF, 47. *Prof Exp:* Asst prof forestry, 47-58, dir exp forest, 58-78, assoc prof, 58-76, PROF FORESTRY, 76- ASST TO DIR SCH FOREST RESOURCES, 74- *Mem:* Soc Am Foresters. *Res:* Forest entomology and management; watershed management; silviculture. *Mailing Add:* Sch of Forest Resources 107 Ferguson Bldg Pa State Univ University Park PA 16802

MELTON, THOMAS MASON, b Rockville, Va, Jan 8, 27; m 49, 57; c 2. ORGANIC CHEMISTRY, INDUSTRIAL HYGIENE. *Educ:* Col William & Mary, BS, 48; Am Acad Indust Hyg, dipl. *Prof Exp:* Res chemist, Sterling-Winthrop Res Inst, 48-51; sr chemist, Va-Carolina Chem Corp, 51-65; group leader agr chem, Mobil Chem Co, 65-71; CHEM SPECIALIST & CONSULT CHEM & INDUST HYG & SAFETY, TRAVELERS CORP, 71- *Mem:* Am Chem Soc. *Res:* Synthesis of insecticides; organic phosphorus and organic medicinal chemicals. *Mailing Add:* 1914 LeSuer Rd Richmond VA 23229

MELTON, WILLIAM GROVER, JR, b Oakland, Calif, Jan 1, 23; m 56; c 5. VERTEBRATE PALEONTOLOGY. *Educ:* Univ Mont, BA, 53; Univ Mich, MS, 69. *Prof Exp:* Geologist, US Geol Surv, 53-56; preparator vert paleont, Univ Mich, 57-66; asst, 66-69, lectr, 69-75, CUR GEOL, UNIV MONT, 66-, ADJ ASSOC PROF, 75- *Mem:* Soc Vert Paleont. *Res:* Paleozoic ray finned fish; conodonts and conodont bearing animals; soft anatomy and classification. *Mailing Add:* Dept of Geol Univ of Mont Missoula MT 59801

MELTZ, MARTIN LOWELL, b New York, NY, Dec 22, 42; m 70; c 1. EXPERIMENTAL ONCOLOGY, GENETIC TOXICOLOGY. *Educ:* State Univ NY Stony Brook, BS, 63; Univ Rochester, PhD(biophys), 70. *Prof Exp:* AEC fel, Lab Radiobiol, Univ Calif, San Francisco, 69-70, res biophysicist, 70-71; assoc scientist, Southwest Found Res & Educ, 71-79; ASST PROF RADIOL, UNIV TEX HEALTH SCI CTR, 79- *Mem:* AAAS; Biophys Soc; Radiation Res Soc; Environ Mutagen Soc; Am Soc Cell Biol. *Res:* Mammalian cell mutagenicity; DNA damage and repair; mammalian cell chemical transformation; combined modality chemotherapy-radiotherapy studies in mammalian cells. *Mailing Add:* Dept Radiol Univ Tex Health Sci Ctr San Antonio TX 78284

MELTZER, ALAN SIDNEY, b New York, NY, Apr 26, 32; m 57. ASTRONOMY. *Educ:* Syracuse Univ, BS, 53; Princeton Univ, PhD(astron), 56. *Prof Exp:* Res assoc observ, Harvard Col, 56; physicist, Smithsonian Astrophys Observ, 56-57; assoc prof, 57-74, assoc prof, 74-78, PROF ASTRON, RENSSELAER POLYTECH INST, 78-, COORDR, LEARNING CTR, 80- *Mem:* Fel AAAS; Am Astron Soc. *Res:* Solar and stellar spectroscopy; interstellar extinction of polarization; science education; developmental education; administration. *Mailing Add:* Dept of Physics Rensselaer Polytech Inst Troy NY 12181

MELTZER, ARNOLD CHARLES, b New York, NY, May 9, 36; m 61; c 2. COMPUTER SCIENCE, ELECTRICAL ENGINEERING. *Educ:* George Washington Univ, BS, 58, MSE, 61, DSc(network synthesis), 67. *Prof Exp:* Student trainee elec rates, Fed Power Comn, 56-58, rate engr, 58-60; from instr to assoc prof, 60-74, actg chmn dept elec eng & comput sci, 69-70, chmn, 74-78, PROF COMPUT SCI, GEORGE WASHINGTON UNIV, 74- *Concurrent Pos:* Consult, Fed Power Comn, 61-63 & US govt, 75-; NASA grant, 69-70; Am Soc Eng Educ-Ford Found fac resident, IBM Corp, NY, 70-71. *Mem:* Inst Elec & Electronics Engrs; Asn Comput Mach. *Res:* Synthesis of active filters using distributed parameter networks and a minimum number of active devices; computer architecture; multiprocessors; distributed processing. *Mailing Add:* Sch of Eng & Appl Sci 725 23rd St NW Washington DC 20052

MELTZER, HERBERT LEWIS, b New York, NY, Apr 23, 21; m 49; c 2. BIOCHEMISTRY. *Educ:* Long Island Univ, BS, 42; Columbia Univ, PhD, 50. *Prof Exp:* Res assoc, 51-56, ASST PROF BIOCHEM, COL PHYSICIANS & SURGEONS, COLUMBIA UNIV, 56-; RES SCIENTIST, NY STATE PSYCHIAT INST, 77- *Concurrent Pos:* Assoc res scientist, NY State Psychiat Inst, 52-77. *Mem:* Fel Am Col Clin Pharmacol; Am Soc Biol Chem. *Res:* Neurochemical and behavioral effects of rubidium; membrane transport systems; lithium kinetics in manic-depressive illnes; calcium transport in psychiatric illness. *Mailing Add:* NY State Psychiat Inst New York NY 10032

MELTZER, HERBERT YALE, b Brooklyn, NY, July 29, 37; m 60; c 2. PSYCHIATRY. *Educ:* Cornell Univ, BA, 58; Harvard Univ, MA, 59; Yale Univ, MD, 63. *Prof Exp:* Res assoc pharmacol & anat, Sch Med, Yale Univ, 59-63; clin assoc, Lab Clin Sci, NIH, 66-68, instr grad training prog, 67-68; from asst prof to assoc prof, 68-74, PROF PSYCHIAT, UNIV CHICAGO, 74-; RES ASSOC, ILL STATE PSYCHIAT INST, 68-, DIR, LAB BIOL PSYCHIAT, 75- *Concurrent Pos:* Teaching fel psychiat, Harvard Med Sch, 64-66; consult, Peter Bent Brigham Hosp & Mass Ment Health Ctr, 65-66 & VISTA, 68-; assoc ed, Schizophrenia Bull. *Mem:* Am Col Neuropsychopharmacol. *Res:* Biological study of mental illness; neuroendocrinology; biochemical and behavioral pharmacology of psychotomimetic drugs. muscle physiology and ultrastructure. *Mailing Add:* Pritzker Sch of Med Univ of Chicago Chicago IL 60637

MELTZER, ROBERT ISRAEL, organic chemistry, see previous edition

MELVEGER, ALVIN JOSEPH, b New York, NY, July 9, 37; m 61; c 1. CHEMISTRY, ANALYTICAL CHEMISTRY. *Educ:* Brooklyn Col, BS, 59; Northeastern Univ, MS, 64; Univ Md, College Park, PhD(chem), 68. *Prof Exp:* Scientist mat, Avco Corp, Mass, 60-64; grant, Ctr Mat Res, Univ Md, College Park, 68-69; res chemist, Allied Chem Corp, 69-72; sect mgr instrumental anal, 72-78, MGR ANAL CHEM DEPT, ETHICON, INC, 78- *Mem:* AAAS; Am Chem Soc; Am Phys Soc; Soc Appl Spectros; Am Soc Testing & Mat. *Res:* Molecular, analytical and high pressure spectroscopy; laser-Raman and infrared spectroscopy of polymers and inorganic materials; structure-property relationships of polymers; polymer characterization. *Mailing Add:* Ethicon Inc Somerville NJ 08876

MELVILLE, DONALD BURTON, b Netherton, Eng, Jan 30, 14; nat US; m 40; c 2. BIOCHEMISTRY. *Educ:* Univ Ill, BS, 36, MS, 37, PhD(biochem), 39. *Prof Exp:* Asst biochem, Univ Ill, 36-38; res assoc, Med Col, Cornell Univ, 39-46, from asst prof to assoc prof, 46-60; chmn dept, Biochem, Col Med, Univ Vt, 60-76, prof, 60-79. *Mem:* Am Chem Soc; Am Soc Biol Chem; NY Acad Sci. *Res:* Determination of structure and study of biological effects of biotin; chemistry of penicillin; syntheses with radio isotopes; biochemistry of ergothioneine. *Mailing Add:* 1 Fern St Burlington VT 05401

MELVILLE, JOEL GEORGE, b Meadville, Pa, Feb 5, 43; m 67; c 2. GROUNDWATER HYDRAULICS. *Educ:* Univ Tex, MS, 67; Pa State Univ, BS, 65, PhD(eng mech), 72. *Prof Exp:* Adj asst prof hydraulics, Univ Iowa, 72-76; asst prof, Univ Fla, 76-79; ASSOC PROF HYDRAULICS, AUBURN UNIV, 79- *Mem:* Am Asn Civil Engrs; Am Water Well Asn. *Res:* Fluid mechanical aspects of flow in the small intestine; hydraulic modelling; aquifer thermal energy storage. *Mailing Add:* Dept Civil Eng Auburn Univ Auburn AL 36849

MELVILLE, MARJORIE HARRIS, b Baltimore, Md, Aug 30, 27; m 48; c 3. ORGANIC CHEMISTRY. *Educ:* Agnes Scott Col, BA, 47; Johns Hopkins Univ, MA, 49, PhD(chem), 53. *Prof Exp:* From asst prof to assoc prof, 64-75, PROF CHEM, SAN ANTONIO COL, 75- *Mem:* Am Chem Soc; Sigma Xi. *Mailing Add:* 110 Chesterfield Dr San Antonio TX 78223

MELVIN, CRUSE DOUGLAS, b Woodville, Tex, June 5, 42; m 64; c 2. PHYSICS, MATHEMATICS. *Educ:* Stephen F Austin State Univ, BS, 64, MS, 65; Tulane Univ, PhD(physics), 71. *Prof Exp:* Instr physics, Stephen F Austin State Univ, 65-66; asst prof, Nicholls State Univ, 66-70; sr res scientist phys anal, Sci Res Lab, Ford Motor Co, 71-72, supvr eng res staff, 72-77; assoc prof, 77-80, PROF PHYSICS, DELTA STATE UNIV, 80- *Mem:* Am Asn Physics Teachers. *Res:* Scanning and transmission electron microscopy; surface analysis, x-ray analysis and neutron analysis methods; computer science. *Mailing Add:* Dept of Phys Sci Delta State Univ Cleveland MS 38733

MELVIN, DONALD WALTER, b Manchester, NH, Sept 17, 29; m 59; c 1. ELECTRICAL ENGINEERING. *Educ:* Univ NH, BS, 55; Yale Univ, MEng 57; Syracuse Univ, PhD(elec eng), 71. *Prof Exp:* From instr to asst prof, 57-65, asst dean, Col Eng & Phys Sci, 77-78, ASSOC PROF ELEC ENG, UNIV NH, 65-, ASSOC DEAN, COL ENG & PHYS SCI, 78- *Concurrent Pos:* Instr, Syracuse Univ, 61-63. *Mem:* Inst Elec & Electronics Engrs. *Res:* Ocean engineering; energy systems. *Mailing Add:* Dean's Off Kingsbury Hall Univ of NH Durham NH 03824

MELVIN, DOROTHY MAE, b Fayetteville, NC. MEDICAL PARASITOLOGY. *Educ:* Univ NC, Greensboro, AB, 42; Univ NC, Chapel Hill, MS, 45; Rice Univ, PhD(parasitol), 51. *Prof Exp:* Training officer & med parasitologist, 45-49, 51-62, chief parasitol training unit, 62-74, CHIEF PARASITOL TRAINING BR, CTR DIS CONTROL, 74- *Concurrent Pos:* La State Univ fel trop med, PR & Haiti, 58; asst prof, Sch Med, Emory Univ, 67- *Honors & Awards:* Super Performance Award, Ctr Dis Control, 58. *Mem:* Am Soc Trop Med & Hyg; Am Soc Parasitol. *Res:* Methodology of technical training for health care personnel. *Mailing Add:* Parasitol Training Sect Ctr for Dis Control Atlanta GA 30333

MELVIN, E(UGENE) A(VERY), b Baltimore, Md, Oct 11, 19; m 46; c 3. ELECTRICAL ENGINEERING. *Educ:* Johns Hopkins Univ, BE, 41; State Univ NY Buffalo, MS, 50. *Prof Exp:* Elec designer, Glenn L Martin, 41; instr electronics, State Univ NY Buffalo, 47-50; proj engr, Frederick Res Corp, 50-58, tech dir, 58-59; eng mgr, Martin Co, Fla, 59-67; dir, Tech Support Div,

67-75, STAFF ASST RESOURCES, NAVAL AIR TESTING CTR, 75- *Concurrent Pos:* Instr, Millard Fillmore Col, 48; res engr, Fredric Flader, Inc, 48-50. *Mem:* Am Soc Eng Educ; Am Ord Asn; Inst Elec & Electronics Engrs; Am Inst Aeronaut & Astronaut. *Res:* Electrical analogs; servomechanisms; ground-support equipment and checkout; instrumentation. *Mailing Add:* CT-251 Staff NATC Patuxent River MD 20670

MELVIN, JOHN LEWIS, b Columbus, Ohio, May 26, 35; m 57; c 4. PHYSICAL MEDICINE & REHABILITATION, ELECTROMYOGRAPHY. *Educ:* Ohio State Univ, BSc, 55, MD, 60, MMSc, 66; Am Bd Phys Med & Rehab, Cert, 68. *Prof Exp:* From asst prof to assoc prof phys med, Col Med, Ohio State Univ, 66-73; PROF PHYS MED & REHAB & CHMN DEPT, MED COL WIS, 73- *Concurrent Pos:* Mem adv comt, Joint Comt Stroke Facil, 69-77; med dir, Curative Rehab Ctr Milwaukee, 73-; sr attend staff, Milwaukee County Med Complex, 73-; dir phys med, Sacred Heart Rehab Hosp, 74-; mem consult staff, Milwaukee Children's Hosp, 73-, St Luke's Hosp, 73- & West Allis Mem Hosp, 74-, Good Samaritan Med Ctr, 77-; staff physician, Wood Vet Admin Ctr, 76-; consult, Brown Univ, 78, Nat Cancer Inst, 78-79 & Univ Calif, San Francisco, 80. *Honors & Awards:* Sci Exhib-Gold Medal Award, Am Cong Rehab Med, 71. *Mem:* Am Acad Phys Med & Rehab; Am Cong Rehab Med (5th pres, 80); Am Asn Electromyog & Electrodiag (pres, 79); Am Asn Acad Physiatrists (secy, 75, vpres 81-); Int Fedn Phys Med & Rehab. *Res:* Testing models for delivery of rehabilitation services; conceptualizing, classifying, and describing disability states; identifying electrophysiologic responses associated with diseases of the peripheral nervous system. *Mailing Add:* Med Col of Wis 9001 W Watertown Plank Rd Milwaukee WI 53226

MELVIN, JONATHAN DAVID, b New York, NY, Apr 7, 47. ATOMIC PHYSICS, GEOPHYSICS. *Educ:* Yale Univ, BA & MA, 68; Calif Inst Technol, PhD(physics), 74. *Prof Exp:* Instr math, Albertus Magnus Col, 68-69; res physicist, Lab Nuclear Med & Radiation Biol, Univ Calif, Los Angeles, 74-75; Robert A Milliken res fel, Kellogg Lab, 75-76, Richard Chase Toleman fel, 76-77, SR SCIENTIST IN PHYSICS, CALIF INST TECHNOL, 77- *Concurrent Pos:* Mem res staff, Hughes Res Lab, 71-74; consult physicist, Technion, Inc, 74-75; vis scientist, Nat Univ Mex & INEN, Mexico City, 76; consult, physicist, Phrasar Technol, Inc, 78-, computer specialist, Hughes Res Labs, 80- *Mem:* AAAS; Am Geophys Union; Am Phys Soc. *Res:* Application of nuclearphysics to earthquake prediction; computer network systems for nuclear data acquisition. *Mailing Add:* Calif Inst Technol 106-38 Pasadena CA 91125

MELVIN, LAWRENCE SHERMAN, JR, b Chicago, Ill, Feb 1, 47; m 66; c 2. ORGANIC CHEMISTRY, MEDICINAL CHEMISTRY. *Educ:* Univ Ill, BS, 69; Univ Wis, PhD(org chem), 73. *Prof Exp:* Fel chem, Harvard Univ, 73-75; SR RES INVESTR, PFIZER INC CENT RES, 75- *Mem:* Am Chem Soc. *Res:* Synthetic organic chemistry; medicinal chemistry; natural product chemistry. *Mailing Add:* Pfizer Inc Cent Res Eastern Point Rd Groton CT 06340

MELVIN, MAEL AVRAMY, b Palestine, Mar 27, 13; US citizen; m 46; c 2. PHYSICS. *Educ:* Univ Chicago, BS, 33, MS, 35, PhD(physics), 38. *Prof Exp:* Metallurgist, Carnegie Ill Steel Corp, 37-38; assoc metall, Columbia Univ, 38-40, instr, 40-42, instr physics, 42-46, asst prof metal physics, 46-47, assoc prof, 47-48; vis prof, Univ Ore, 51; Guggenheim fel, Princeton Univ, 51-52; prof physics, Fla State Univ, 52-66; PROF PHYSICS, TEMPLE UNIV, 66- *Concurrent Pos:* Guggenheim fel & vis prof, Univ Upsala, 57-58; Int Atomic Energy Agency exchange prog vis prof, Inst Physics, Bariloche, Arg, 59-60; Nat Res Coun sr resident res assoc, Jet Propulsion Lab, Calif Inst Technol, 71-72; consult, Chem Warfare Serv, US Dept Army, 41, Nat Defense Res Comt, 42, Hazeltine Serv Corp, NY, 43, Heat Transfer Res Lab, 43 & Off Sci Res & Develop, 43-45. *Mem:* Fel Am Phys Soc. *Res:* Symmetry methods in physics; elementary particles and fields; relativity; astrophysics; cosmology; homogeneous and anisotropic cosmologies. *Mailing Add:* Dept of Physics Temple Univ Philadelphia PA 19122

MELVIN, STEWART WAYNE, b Bloomfield, Iowa, Nov 24, 41; m 71; c 2. AGRICULTURAL ENGINEERING. *Educ:* Iowa State Univ, BS, 64, MS, 67, PhD(agr eng), 70. *Prof Exp:* Field engr, Soil Conserv Serv, USDA, 64; asst prof agr eng, Colo State Univ, 70; asst prof, 70-74, assoc prof, 74-78, PROF AGR ENG, IOWA STATE UNIV, 78- *Concurrent Pos:* private consult, Soil Water & Waste Mgt. *Mem:* Am Soc Agr Engrs; Soil Conserv Soc Am. *Res:* Soil and water conservation; animal waste management; rural water and waste systems. *Mailing Add:* 2802 Torrey Pines Circle Ames IA 50010

MELVOLD, ROGER WAYNE, b Henning, Minn, Mar 21, 46. GENETICS. *Educ:* Moorhead State Col, BS, 68; Univ Kans, PhD(genetics), 73. *Prof Exp:* Prin res assoc radiation biol (genetics), Med Sch, Harvard Univ, 72-79; ASST PROF MED & MICROBIOL IMMUNOL, NORTHWESTERN UNIV, 79- *Mem:* Am Soc Immunologists; Transplantation Soc. *Res:* Identifying and utiliing mutations of genes affecting tissue transplantation to explore the fine level genetic influences on the mammalian immune system; special emphasis on mouse system. *Mailing Add:* Dept Microbiol Immuniol Med Sch Northwestern Univ 303 E Chicago Ave Chicago IL 60611

MEMEGER, WESLEY, JR, b Riverdale, Fla, Sept 21, 39; m 63; c 2. ORGANIC CHEMISTRY, ANALYTICAL CHEMISTRY. *Educ:* Clark Col, BS, 61; Adelphi Univ, PhD(org chem), 66. *Prof Exp:* Res cemist, 65-71, sr res chemist, 71-80, RES ASSOC, E I DU PONT DE NEMOURS & CO INC, 80- *Mem:* Am Chem Soc; Sigma Xi; NY Acad Sci. *Res:* Field effects in nucleophilic substitution reactions; reaction kinetics; synthesis and characterization of addition and condensation polymers; high temperature fibers; basic research aimed at new high strength high modulus polymers and fibers; basic and applied research on high temperature insulating cellular materials, mainly aramids. *Mailing Add:* 109 Hoiland Dr Shipley Heights Wilmington DE 19803

MEMORY, JASPER DURHAM, b Raleigh, NC, Dec 10, 36; m 61; c 2. PHYSICS. *Educ:* Wake Forest Col, BS, 56; Univ NC, PhD(physics), 60. *Prof Exp:* From asst prof to assoc prof physics, Univ SC, 60-64; assoc prof, 64-67, PROF PHYSICS, NC STATE UNIV, 67-, ASSOC DEAN SCH PHYS & MATH SCI, 68- *Mem:* Am Phys Soc. *Res:* Nuclear magnetic resonance, quantum theory of molecular electronic structure; molecular biophysics. *Mailing Add:* 116 Cox Hall NC State Univ Raleigh NC 27650

MENA, ROBERTO ABRAHAM, b Merida, Mex, Mar 12, 46; m 69. ALGEBRA. *Educ:* Univ Houston, BS, 68, MS, 71, PhD(math), 73. *Prof Exp:* asst prof, 73-77, ASSOC PROF MATH, UNIV WYO, 77- *Concurrent Pos:* Nat Acad Sci fel, Calif Inst Technol, 80-81. *Res:* Matrix theory and combinatorics. *Mailing Add:* Dept of Math Univ of Wyo Laramie WY 82071

MENAKER, MICHAEL, b Vienna, Austria, May 19, 34; US citizen; m 55; c 2. COMPARATIVE PHYSIOLOGY. *Educ:* Swarthmore Col, BA, 55; Princeton Univ, MA, 58, PhD(biol), 60. *Prof Exp:* NSF fel, Harvard Univ, 59-61, NIH fel, 61-62; from asst prof to assoc prof, Univ Tex, Austin, 62-72, prof zool, 72-79; PROF BIOL & DIR, INST NEUROSCI, UNIV ORE, 79- *Concurrent Pos:* Guggenheim Mem Found fel, 71. *Mem:* Am Physiol Soc; Am Soc Photobiol; Soc Neurosci. *Res:* Biological clocks; celestial orientation in animals; time measurement in animal photoperiodism; annual cycles; physiology of mammalian hibernation; brain photoreception and pineal physiology. *Mailing Add:* Inst Neurosci Univ Ore Eugene OR 97403

MENAPACE, LAWRENCE WILLIAM, b Brooklyn, NY, Apr 13, 37; m 60; c 3. ORGANIC CHEMISTRY. *Educ:* St Peter's Col, BS, 60; Univ NH, PhD(org chem), 64. *Prof Exp:* Chemist, Texaco Exp, Inc, 63-65, sr chemist, Texaco, Inc, 65-68; asst prof, 68-71, ASSOC PROF CHEM, MARIST COL, 71-; VPRES, R-2 ENVIRON CONSULTS, 73- *Concurrent Pos:* Mem, Environ Adv Comt, 73- *Mem:* Am Chem Soc. *Res:* Mechanism and scope of organotin hydride reductions; fundamentals of chemical vapor plating; synthesis of petroleum based chemicals. *Mailing Add:* Dept of Chem Marist Col Poughkeepsie NY 12601

MENARD, ALBERT ROBERT, III, b Boston, Mass, July 17, 43; m 70; c 2. THERMAL PHYSICS. *Educ:* Amherst Col, BA, 65; Univ Minn, Minnea;;olis, MS, 69; Univ Fla, PhD(physics), 74. *Prof Exp:* Asst prof physics, WVa State Col, 74-75, Bloomsburg State Col, 75-76 & Washington Col, 76-77; asst prof physics & geol, Washington & Jefferson Col, 77-80; ASST PROF PHYSICS, SAGINAW VALLEY STATE COL, 80- *Concurrent Pos:* Res grant, US Air Force, 81-82. *Mem:* Am Phys Soc; Am Asn Physics Teachers. *Res:* Properties of superfluid helium at ultralow temperatures; transient heat transfer at low temperatures; climatic history of the earth. *Mailing Add:* Dept Physics Saginaw Valley State Col Univ Ctr MI 48710

MENARD, HENRY WILLIAM, JR, b Calif, Dec 10, 20; m 46; c 3. GEOLOGY. *Educ:* Calif Inst Technol, BS, 42, MS, 47; Harvard Univ, PhD(geol), 49. *Prof Exp:* Oceanogr, US Navy Electronics Lab, 49-55; assoc prof, 55-60, prof geol, Inst Marine Resources & Scripps Inst Oceanog, Univ Calif, 61-78, DIR, US GEOL SURV, RESTON, VA, 78- *Concurrent Pos:* Dir, Geol Diving Consults, Inc, 54-58; vis prof, Calif Inst Technol, 59; Guggenheim fel, 62; tech asst, Off Sci & Technol, 65; fel, Churchill Col, Cambridge Univ, 70. *Mem:* Nat Acad Sci; Am Acad Arts & Sci; fel Geol Soc Am; Am Geophys Union; Am Asn Petrol Geologists. *Res:* Marine geology; tectonics; sedimentation; sociology of science; mineral resources and environment. *Mailing Add:* US Geol Surv Nat Ctr Reston VA 22092

MENASHE, VICTOR D, b Portland, Ore, July 13, 29; m 52; c 2. PEDIATRICS, CARDIOLOGY. *Educ:* Univ Ore, BS, 51, MD, 53. *Prof Exp:* Intern gen med, Univ Hosps & Clins, 53-54, resident pediat, 54-56, from instr to assoc prof, Med Sch, 58-71, asst dean, 72-77, PROF PEDIAT, MED SCH, UNIV ORE, 71-, DIR CRIPPLED CHILDREN'S DIV, HEALTH SCI CTR, 72- *Concurrent Pos:* Pediat consult, Shriners Hosp Crippled Children, 59- *Mem:* Am Acad Pediat; Am Heart Asn. *Res:* Epidemiology of congenital heart disease. *Mailing Add:* Crippled Children's Div PO Box 574 Portland OR 97207

MENASHI, JAMEEL, b Teheran, Iran, Apr 1, 38; m 64; c 1. INORGANIC CHEMISTRY, PHYSICAL CHEMISTRY. *Educ:* Univ London, BS, 60, PhD(phys chem), 63. *Prof Exp:* Fel chem, 63-64; group leader, Harshaw Chem Co, 64-68; mem tech staff, 68-80, GROUP LEADER, CABOT CORP, 80- *Mem:* Am Chem Soc. *Res:* Kinetics of electron exchange reactions; inorganic and organic pigment systems; thermodynamic constants of complexes; synthesis and kinetics of catalytic systems; hydrometallurgy. *Mailing Add:* 68 Gleason Rd Lexington MA 02173

MENCH, PATRICIA ANN, see Ellis, Patricia Mench

MENCHER, ALAN GEORGE, b New York, NY, May 17, 25; m 46, 64; c 5. SCIENCE AND TECHNOLOGY POLICY. *Educ:* Mass Inst Technol, SB, 45; Yale Univ, ME, 47; Univ Calif, Los Angeles, PhD(physics), 52. *Prof Exp:* Engr, Airborne Instruments Lab, Inc, 47-48; asst physics, Univ Calif, Los Angeles, 48-52, instr, 53-54; mem tech staff, Hughes Aircraft Co, 52-53; Swiss Govt-Inst Int Educ fel, Swiss Fed Inst Technol, 54-55, Swiss-Am Found Sci Exchange fel physics, 55-56; mem tech staff, Missile Systs Div, Ramo-Wooldridge Corp, 56-57; foreign serv officer, Am Embassy, Paris, 57-60, dep sci attache, London, 61-63, Paris, 63-65, actg sci attache, 65-66, sci attache, 66-67, sci attache, London, 67-73; vis fel, London Grad Sch Bus Studies, 73-75; dup dir, Off Strategic Affairs, Bur Intel & Res, Dept of State, 75-76, ADV ON INT TECH & BUS AFFAIRS, 76- *Concurrent Pos:* Consult, Ctr Policy Alternatives, Mass Inst Technol, 73-74; prin investr, NSF, 73-75. *Mem:* Am Phys Soc. *Res:* Semiconductor physics; optical properties of solids; international scientific and technological affairs; science and government; national and international science policy. *Mailing Add:* 137 Kellogg Dr Wilton CT 06897

MENCZEL, JEHUDA H, b Vienna, Austria, Jan 29, 36; US citizen; m 71. ENVIRONMENTAL CHEMISTRY. *Educ:* Univ Minn, Minneapolis, BA, 61; Rutgers Univ, PhD(phys chem), 67. *Prof Exp:* NSF res asst, Rutgers Univ, 65-66; staff scientist, Aerospace Res Ctr, Singer-Gen Precision, Inc, 66-69 & Res Labs, Olivetti Corp, Am, 69-71; chemist, 71-73, SECT CHIEF AIR FACIL BR, US ENVIRON PROTECTION AGENCY, 73- *Mem:* Am Chem Soc; Air Pollution Control Asn. *Res:* Photochemistry and gas phase kinetics; photoconductivity; thermochromic phenomena; electrochemical processes in conjunction with non-impact printing; waste water treatment; air pollution. *Mailing Add:* Environ Protection Agency 26 Fed Plaza New York NY 10278

MENDALL, HOWARD LEWIS, b Augusta, Maine, Nov 21, 09; m 33. WILDLIFE BIOLOGY, ORNITHOLOGY. *Educ:* Univ Maine, BA, 31, MA, 34. *Prof Exp:* Asst zool, Univ Maine, 34-36; wildlife technician, US Resettlement Admin, 36-37; asst leader, Maine Coop Wildlife Res Unit, US Bur Sport Fisheries & Wildlife & prof wildlife resources, 37-42, leader, 42-77, EMER PROF, UNIV MAINE, ORONO, 77- *Honors & Awards:* Terrestrial Pub Award, Wildlife Soc, 59 & John Pearce Mem Award, 66. *Mem:* Wildlife Soc; fel Am Ornithologists Union. *Res:* Field ornithology and general wildlife ecology, especially food habits; habitat influences and breeding biology; fish-eating birds, woodcock and waterfowl. *Mailing Add:* 97 Eastern Ave Box 133 Brewer ME 04412

MENDE, THOMAS JULIUS, b Budapest, Hungary, Oct 3, 22; m 49; c 2. BIOCHEMISTRY. *Educ:* Univ of Sciences, Budapest, PhD(org chem), 48. *Prof Exp:* Res assoc chem embryol, NY Univ, 49-50; res asst prof biochem, 54-58, asst prof, 58-60, assoc prof, 60-74, PROF BIOCHEM, SCH MED, UNIV MIAMI, 74- *Concurrent Pos:* Res fel enzymol, Med Sch, Univ Budapest, 48; res fel, Lobund Inst, Univ Notre Dame, 50-54. *Mem:* Am Chem Soc; Am Soc Pharmacol & Exp Therapeut; Int Soc Haemostasis & Thrombosis; Sigma Xi; fel Gerontological Soc. *Res:* Natural products chemistry; blood coagulation; thrombosis. *Mailing Add:* PO Box 520875 Sch of Med Univ Miami Miami FL 33124

MENDEL, ARTHUR, b Ger, Dec 14, 31; nat US; m 56; c 1. ORGANIC CHEMISTRY. *Educ:* Univ Ill, BS, 54; Univ Mo, MA, 56, PhD, 58. *Prof Exp:* Res chemist, Petrol chem, Inc, 58-60; res chemist, Minn Mining & Mfg Co, St Paul, 60-76, sr environ specialist environ chem, 76-81; PATENT LIAISON, 3-M CO, 81- *Mem:* Am Chem Soc. *Res:* Organic synthesis; medicinals; organometallic and analytical organic chemistry; chromatography; electrophoresis. *Mailing Add:* 4525 Oak Leaf Dr White Bear Lake MN 55110

MENDEL, FRANK C, b Cheyenne, Wyo, Dec 2, 46; m 68; c 2. ANATOMY. *Educ:* Calif State Univ, San Diego, BA, 69; Univ Calif, Davis, MA, 71, PhD(anthrop), 76. *Prof Exp:* ASST PROF ANAT, STATE UNIV NY BUFFALO, 76- *Concurrent Pos:* Adj asst prof, State Univ NY Buffalo, 77- *Mem:* Am Asn Phys Anthropologists; Am Asn Anatomists; Am Soc Mammalogists; Sigma Xi. *Res:* Adaptive advantages of suspensory behavior; form and function in masticatory apparatus of primitive mammals. *Mailing Add:* Dept Anat Sci 317 Farber Hall Sch Med State Univ NY Buffalo NY 14214

MENDEL, GERALD ALAN, b New York, NY, May 9, 29; m 69; c 4. INTERNAL MEDICINE, HEMATOLOGY. *Educ:* Col William & Mary, BS, 50; Washington Univ, MD, 54; Am Bd Internal Med, dipl, 62; Am Bd Hematol, dipl, 80. *Prof Exp:* Intern, Univ Chicago, 54-55, resident med, 57-60, from instr to asst prof, 60-66; ASST PROF MED, SCH MED, NORTHWESTERN UNIV, EVANSTON, 66- *Concurrent Pos:* Schweppe Found grant, 62-65. *Honors & Awards:* Joseph A Capps Prize, 61. *Mem:* Am Fedn Clin Res; Am Soc Hemat. *Res:* Iron metabolism. *Mailing Add:* Dept of Med Sch of Med Northwestern Univ Evanston IL 60201

MENDEL, JERRY M, b New York, NY, May 14, 38; m 60; c 2. CONTROL THEORY, EXPLORATION GEOPHYSICS. *Educ:* Polytech Inst Brooklyn, BME, 59, MEE, 60, PhD(elec eng), 63. *Prof Exp:* Instr elec eng, Polytech Inst Brooklyn, 60-63; res specialist, McDonnell Douglas Astronaut Co, Huntington Beach, 63-66, sr engr, 66-74; res assoc prof, 74-79, res prof, 79-80, PROF ELEC ENG, UNIV SOUTHERN CALIF, 80-, DIR, GEO-SIGNAL PROCESSING PROG, 80- *Concurrent Pos:* Lectr, Univ Calif, Los Angeles, 64-71; ed, Inst Elec & Electronics Engrs on Automatic Control, 72-74. *Mem:* Fel Inst Elec & Electronics Engrs; Control Systs Soc; Soc Explor Geophysicists; Europ Asn Exp Geophysicists. *Res:* Estimation and identification theories as applied to problems in reflection seismology; modeling of layered media systems. *Mailing Add:* Dept of Elec Eng University Park Los Angeles CA 90007

MENDEL, JOHN RICHARD, b St Paul, Minn, Nov 24, 36; m 68. COLLOID CHEMISTRY, POLYMER CHEMISTRY. *Educ:* Univ Wash, BS, 58; Boston Col, MS, 69. *Prof Exp:* Chemist adhesives, Am Marietta Co, 59-61; chemist dispersions, Hercules Inc, 68-70; SR RES CHEMIST PHOTO DEVELOP, EASTMAN KODAK CO, 70- *Mem:* Am Chem Soc; Soc Photog Scientists & Engrs. *Res:* Polymer colloids; synthesis, characterization and determination of all physical and chemical properties; physical and chemical properties of silver halide chemistry; precipitation, sensitization and sensitometric response of light sensitive materials. *Mailing Add:* 158 Lake Lea Rd Rochester NY 14617

MENDEL, JULIUS LOUIS, b Amarillo, Tex, Jan 13, 25. CLINICAL CHEMISTRY. *Educ:* Univ Tex, BA, 46; Univ Southern Calif, MS, 49, PhD(biochem), 50. *Prof Exp:* Biochemist, US Vet Admin, 51-63; res chemist, US Vet Admin, 51-63 & US Food & Drug Admin, Washington, DC, 63-66; asst to dir path, Cent Off, Vet Admin, 66-81; RETIRED. *Mem:* AAAS; Am Asn Clin Chemists; NY Acad Sci; Am Inst Chemists. *Res:* Hematology; data processing in clinical laboratories. *Mailing Add:* 16202 Fallkiak Dr Dallas TX 75248

MENDEL, MARYANN MADELIENE, photographic chemistry, synthetic organic chemistry, see previous edition

MENDEL, VERNE EDWARD, b Lewistown, Mont, Apr 28, 23; m 46, 73; c 5. PHYSIOLOGY. *Educ:* Univ Idaho, BSc, 55, MSc, 58; Univ Calif, PhD(animal physiol), 60. *Prof Exp:* Asst prof animal physiol, Univ Alta, 60-63; asst physiologist & lectr, 63-71, assoc prof, 71-75, chmn dept, 73-78, PROF ANIMAL PHYSIOL, UNIV CALIF, DAVIS, 75- *Mem:* Am Physiol Soc; Endocrine Soc; Soc Neurosci. *Res:* Chemical and physiological basis of food intake control. *Mailing Add:* Dept of Animal Physiol Univ of Calif Davis CA 95616

MENDEL, WERNER MAX, b Hamburg, Ger, June 11, 27; US citizen; c 2. PSYCHIATRY. *Educ:* Univ Calif, Los Angeles, BA, 48; Stanford Univ, MA, 49, MD, 53; Am Bd Psychiat & Neurol, cert psychiat, 59; Southern Calif Psychoanal Inst, dipl, 64. *Prof Exp:* Intern, Los Angeles County Gen Hosp, 53-54; resident psychiat, St Elizabeth's Hosp, Washington, DC, 54-55 & Winter Vet Admin Hosp, Topeka, Kans, 55-57; staff psychiatrist & dir rehab proj, Metrop State Hosp, Norwalk, Calif, 57-58; clin instr, 58-60, from asst prof to assoc prof, 60-67, PROF PSYCHIAT, SCH MED, UNIV SOUTHERN CALIF, 67- *Concurrent Pos:* Fel, Menninger Sch Psychiat, 55-57; dir outpatient serv, Metrop State Hosp, Norwalk, Calif, 58-60; chief sr clerkship psychiat, Sch Med, Univ Southern Calif, 60-62; consult, Calif State Dept Ment Hyg, 60-, mem spec residency training rev bd, 65 & res adv comt, 70-74; mem attend staff, Los Angeles County Gen Hosp Psychiat Unit, 60-; chief teaching serv, Psychiat Hosp, Los Angeles County-Univ Southern Calif Med Ctr, 62-65, clin dir, Adult Inpatient Serv, 65-67, dir, Div Prof & Staff Develop, 67-; consult, Ment Health Comt, Am Acad Gen Pract, 63-66; asst examr, Am Bd Neurol & Psychiat, 64-68; spec proj ed, Basic Bks, Inc, 66-69; mem exp & spec training rev comt, NIMH, 68-72; ed-in-chief, Mara Bks, Inc, 69-; chmn med adv bd, Human Resource Inst, Inc, 70-74; Calif State Dept Ment Hyg grant; Attend Staff Fund grants, Los Angeles County-Univ Southern Calif Med Ctr; Vet Admin grant; NIMH grants. *Mem:* AMA; Am Psychiat Asn; Asn Am Med Cols; Am Psychoanal Asn. *Res:* Determinants of the decision for psychiatric hospitalization; reversal of soft neurological signs in brain-damaged patients; perceptual changes in schizophrenic patients; effectiveness of outpatient treatment in chronic schizophrenia; phenomenological theory of schizophrenia; mental health care delivery systems. *Mailing Add:* Dept of Psychiat Univ of Southern Calif Sch of Med Los Angeles CA 90033

MENDELHALL, VON THATCHER, b Soda Springs, Idaho, Nov 1, 37; m 56; c 4. FOOD SCIENCE. *Educ:* Utah State Univ, BS, 62, MS, 67; Ore State Univ, PhD(food sci), 70. *Prof Exp:* Asst prof food sci, Univ Fla, 70-72; asst prof, 72-77, ASSOC PROF FOOD SCI, UTAH STATE UNIV, 77- *Mem:* Inst Food Technologists. *Res:* Protein degradation in shellfish; formaldehyde production in frozen fish tissue; lipid oxidation in Florida mullet and turkey products. *Mailing Add:* Dept of Food Sci Utah State Univ Logan UT 84322

MENDELL, JAY STANLEY, b New York, NY, Mar 13, 36; m 61; c 2. TECHNOLOGICAL INNOVATION. *Educ:* Rensselaer Polytech Inst, BS, 56, PhD(physics), 64; Vanderbilt Univ, MA, 58. *Prof Exp:* Health physicist, Oak Ridge Nat Lab, 57-58; asst physics, Rensselaer Polytech Inst, 58-60, asst elec eng, 60-63; asst proj engr, Pratt & Whitney Aircraft Div, United Aircraft Corp, 63-68, sr staff analyst, Advan Planning, 68-73; assoc prof, Sch Technol, Fla Int Univ, 73-76; PROF, COL BUS, FLA ATLANTIC UNIV, 76- *Concurrent Pos:* Consult, Jay S Mendell & Assoc, 73- innovation ed, The Futurist, World Future Soc, 69-; contrib ed, Planning Digest, 71-74 & Planning Rev, 74-; mem adv bd, Technol Forecasting & Social Change, 71-; ed chmn, Bus Tomorrow, 78-81; contrib ed, Brain & Strategy, 79- *Mem:* World Future Soc; Inst Elec & Electronics Engrs; fel Am Asn Psychiat. *Res:* Creativity; corporate planning; technological innovation; futures research. *Mailing Add:* 11295 NW 38th St Coral Springs FL 33065

MENDELL, LORNE MICHAEL, b Montreal, Que, Nov 6, 41; m 67. NEUROPHYSIOLOGY. *Educ:* McGill Univ, BSc, 61; Mass Inst Technol, PhD(neurophysiol), 65. *Prof Exp:* Asst prof, 68-73, ASSOC PROF PHYSIOL, MED CTR, DUKE UNIV, 73- *Concurrent Pos:* USPHS fel, Harvard Med Sch, 65-68; USPHS grant, Med Ctr, Duke Univ, 69-; NIH career develop award, 71; mem staff, dept anat, Univ Col London, 76-77; mem neurobiol adv panel, NSF, 75-78. *Mem:* AAAS; Am Physiol Soc; Soc Neurosci; Soc Gen Physiol. *Res:* Neuroembryology. *Mailing Add:* Dept of Physiol Duke Univ Med Ctr Durham NC 27710

MENDELL, NANCY ROLE, b Boston, Mass, June 12, 44; m 67; c 1. BIOSTATISTICS, GENETICS. *Educ:* Smith Col, BA, 66; Harvard Univ, MSc, 68; Univ NC, PhD(biostat), 72. *Prof Exp:* Fel immunol, 72-73, instr, 73-74, assoc immunol & community health sci, 74-77, lectr, Sch Nursing, 75-78, MED RES ASST PROF IMMUNOL & COMMUNITY HEALTH SCI, DUKE UNIV, 77- *Concurrent Pos:* Mem transplantation & immunol adv comt, NIH, 75-79; hon res fel, London Hosp Med Col, 76-77. *Mem:* Am Soc Human Genetics; Royal Stat Soc; Sigma Xi. *Res:* Statistical genetics; quantitative immunology. *Mailing Add:* 8 Market St Setauket NY 22733

MENDELL, ROSALIND B, b New York, NY, Oct 20, 20; m 41; c 2. COSMIC RAY PHYSICS. *Educ:* Hunter Col, BA, 40; NY Univ, PhD(physics), 63. *Prof Exp:* Instr physics, NY Univ, 42-43; physicist, US Bur Standards, 44-46; assoc res scientist, 63-74, adj assoc prof, 72-75, RES SCIENTIST, NY UNIV, 74-, ASSOC RES PROF, 75- *Mem:* Am Phys Soc; Am Geophys Union. *Res:* Study of neutrons in cosmic radiation; cosmic ray modulation. *Mailing Add:* Dept of Physics NY Univ 4 Washington Pl New York NY 10003

MENDELSOHN, LAWRENCE BARRY, b Brooklyn, NY, Apr 19, 34; m 58; c 3. PHYSICS. *Educ:* Brooklyn Col, BS, 55; Columbia Univ, MA, 59; NY Univ, PhD(physics), 65. *Prof Exp:* Physicist, Combustion Eng, Conn, 56-57, Walter Kidde Nuclear Labs, 58-59 & Tech Res Group, Inc, 59-62; instr physics, Cooper Union, 62-65; from asst prof to assoc prof, Polytech Inst Brooklyn, 65-73; prof physics, New Sch Lib Arts, Brooklyn Col, 73-80; adj res prof physics, Polytech Inst Ny, 73-79; PROF PHYSICS, BROOKLYN COL, 80- *Concurrent Pos:* Consult, Sandia Corp, 69-75. *Mem:* Am Phys Soc.

Res: Many body problem, particularly calculation of correlation effects in atoms and molecules; industrial experience comprises; nuclear reactor and shielding calculations; x-ray scattering cross sections. *Mailing Add:* Physics Dept Brooklyn Col Bedford Ave & Ave H Brooklyn NY 11210

MENDELSOHN, MARSHALL H, b Chicago, Ill, Apr 5, 46. INORGANIC CHEMISTRY. *Educ:* Ill Inst Technol, BS, 67; Univ Calif, Berkeley, PhD(chem), 72. *Prof Exp:* Res asst metal hydrides, Univ Conn, 72; chemist phosphors, US Radium Corp, 73-74 & Zipcor, Inc, 75; ASST CHEMIST METAL HYDRIDES, ARGONNE NAT LAB, 75- *Mem:* Am Chem Soc; Int Asn Hydrogen Energy; Sigma Xi. *Res:* Preparation and characterization of stable and unstable solid state metallic hydrides; thermodynamic and structural relationships of metal hydrides. *Mailing Add:* Argonne Nat Lab 9700 S Cass Argonne IL 60439

MENDELSOHN, MORRIS A, b Pittsburgh, Pa, Nov 13, 28; m 51; c 8. CHEMISTRY, CHEMICAL ENGINEERING. *Educ:* Univ Pittsburgh, BS, 48, MS, 54, PhD(chem), 60. *Prof Exp:* Engr, US Bur Mines, 48-52 & Shell Chem Corp, 52-53; res engr, 53-61, sr engr, 61-64, fel scientist, 64-70, ADV SCIENTIST, RES & DEVELOP CTR, WESTINGHOUSE ELEC CORP, 70- *Honors & Awards:* Soc Plastics Engrs Awards, 68 & 70; Mat Sci & Eng Citation, Mat Eng Mag, 78. *Mem:* Am Inst Chem Engrs; Am Chem Soc; Soc Plastics Engrs. *Res:* composites of inorganic glasses and organic polymers; autoxidation of metal chelates; kinetics of hydrolytic and oxidative degradation of polymers; electrical insulating materials; solar collector sealants; shock isolation systems; vibration damping materials; relationships between mechanical properties and chemical composition of polymers. *Mailing Add:* Res & Develop Ctr Westinghouse Elec Corp 1310 Beulah Rd Churchill Boro Pittsburgh PA 15235

MENDELSOHN, MORTIMER LESTER, b New York, NY, Dec 1, 25; m 48; c 3. BIOPHYSICS, CANCER. *Educ:* Harvard Univ, MD, 48; Cambridge Univ, PhD, 58. *Prof Exp:* Intern med, Mass Gen Hosp, 48-49; resident, Mem Ctr, NY, 49-52; from asst prof to prof radiol, Sch Med, Univ Pa, 57-72; dir biomed div, 72-76, ASSOC DIR BIOMED & ENVIRON RES, LAWRENCE LIVERMORE LAB, UNIV CALIF, 76- *Concurrent Pos:* Res fel, Sloan-Kettering Inst Cancer Res, 52-53; Am Cancer Soc Brit-Am exchange fel, 55-57; mem, comput res study sect, NIH, 67-70, chmn, 70-71. *Mem:* Radiation Res Soc; Histochem Soc; Soc Anal Cytol (pres, 78); Am Asn Cancer Res; Environ Mutagen Soc (pres-elect, 78, pres, 79). *Res:* Experimental and clinical cancer research; radiation effects; cell division; biophysical cytology; flow cytometry; computer analysis of cell images; environmental mutagenesis. *Mailing Add:* Lawrence Livermore Lab Univ of Calif Livermore CA 94550

MENDELSOHN, NATHAN SAUL, b Brooklyn, NY, Apr 14, 17; m 40; c 2. MATHEMATICS. *Educ:* Univ Toronto, BA, 39, MA, 40, PhD, 42. *Prof Exp:* Supvr munitions gauge lab, Nat Res Coun Can, 42; scientist, Proof & Develop Estab, Que, 42-45; lectr math, Queen's Univ, Ont, 45-47; PROF, UNIV MAN, 47-, HEAD DEPT, 63- *Honors & Awards:* Henry Marshall Tory Gold Medal, Royal Soc Can. *Mem:* Soc Indust & Appl Math; Am Math Soc; Math Asn Am; fel Royal Soc Can; Can Math Cong (pres). *Res:* Abstract algebra and geometry; combinatory statistics; a group-theoretic characterization of the general projective collineation group; ballistics; theory of error in computing machines; graph and matroid theory. *Mailing Add:* Dept of Math Univ of Man Winnipeg MB R3T 2N2 Can

MENDELSON, BERT, b Brooklyn, NY, Jan 3, 26; m 52; c 3. MATHEMATICS. *Educ:* Columbia Univ, BA, 45, PHD(math), 59; Univ Nebr, MA, 51. *Prof Exp:* PROF MATH, SMITH COL, 57-, DIR COMPUT CTR, 74- *Mem:* Am Math Soc; Math Asn Am. *Res:* Algebraic topology. *Mailing Add:* Dept of Math Smith Col Northampton MA 01063

MENDELSON, ELLIOTT, b New York, NY, May 24, 31; m 59; c 3. MATHEMATICAL LOGIC. *Educ:* Columbia Univ, AB, 52; Cornell Univ, MA, 54, PhD(math), 55. *Prof Exp:* Instr math, Univ Chicago, 55-56; jr fel, Harvard Univ, 56-58; J F Ritt instr, Columbia Univ, 58-61; assoc prof, 61-64, PROF MATH, QUEENS COL, NY, 64- *Mem:* Am Math Soc; Math Asn Am; Asn Symbolic Logic. *Res:* Axiomatic set theory. *Mailing Add:* Dept of Math Queens Col Flushing NY 11367

MENDELSON, JACK H, b Baltimore, Md, Aug 30, 29; m 52; c 3. MEDICINE, PSYCHIATRY. *Educ:* Univ Md, MD, 55. *Prof Exp:* Intern med serv, Boston City Hosp, 55-56; asst, 59-71, PROF PSYCHIAT, HARVARD MED SCH, 71-; DIR, ALCOHOL & DRUG ABUSE RES CTR, McLEAN HOSP, 73- *Concurrent Pos:* Teaching fel psychiat, Harvard Med Sch, 56-59; res fel psychiat, Boston City & Mass Gen Hosps, 56-59; consult, Washingtonian Hosp, Boston, 58-59; consult, psychiat res labs, Sch Med, Univ Md, 59-; asst, Mass Gen Hosp, 59-; dir dept psychiat, Boston City Hosp, 71-73. *Mem:* Am Psychiat Asn; Asn Res Nerv & Ment Dis; Endocrine Soc; Am Soc Pharmacol & Exp Therapeut. *Res:* Psychiatric research, especially in alcohol and drug abuse. *Mailing Add:* Alcohol & Drug Abuse Res Ctr McLean Hosp Belmont MA 02178

MENDELSON, KENNETH SAMUEL, b Chicago, Ill, Aug 24, 33; m 61; c 3. PHYSICS. *Educ:* Ill Inst Technol, BS, 55; Purdue Univ, MS, 57, PhD(physics), 63. *Prof Exp:* Assoc physicist, IIT Res Inst, 62-65; asst prof, 65-70, assoc prof, 70-81, PROF PHYSICS, MARQUETTE UNIV, 81- *Concurrent Pos:* Sr sci fel, NATO, 74. *Mem:* Am Phys Soc. *Res:* Theory of inhomogeneous media; effective constants; field fluctuations; percolation theory; rock physics. *Mailing Add:* Physics Dept Marquette Univ Milwaukee WI 53233

MENDELSON, MARTIN, b New York, NY, Apr 16, 37; m 58; c 2. PHYSIOLOGY. *Educ:* Cornell Univ, AB, 58; Calif Inst Technol, PhD(biol), 62; State Univ NY Stony Brook, MD, 76. *Prof Exp:* Res assoc physiol, Col Physicians & Surgeons, Columbia Univ, 61-63; from instr to assoc prof, Sch Med, NY Univ, 63-71; assoc prof physiol, Health Sci Ctr, State Univ NY, Stony Brook, 71-76, mem adj staff, Dept Med, Div Neurol, Nassau County Med Ctr, 76-77; RESIDENT FAMILY PRACT, EMANUEL HOSP, PORTLAND, 77- *Concurrent Pos:* Mem, Corp Marine Biol Lab, Woods Hole, Mass. *Mem:* Soc Neurosci; Am Acad Family Physicians; Am Soc Zool; Soc Gen Physiol. *Res:* Sensory mechanisms in Crustacea and mammals; neuromuscular transmission in Crustacea; central nervous mechanisms of rhythmicity and integration in Curstacea. *Mailing Add:* Family Pract Med Ctr 501B N Graham Portland OR 97227

MENDELSON, MYER, b Lithuania, Dec 5, 20; nat US; m 56; c 1. PSYCHIATRY. *Educ:* Dalhousie Univ, BA, 45, BSc, 46, MD, CM, 50. *Prof Exp:* Instr psychiat, Johns Hopkins Univ, 54-56; asst prof, Dalhousie Univ, 56-58; from asst prof to assoc prof, 58-71, PROF CLIN PSYCHIAT, SCH MED, UNIV PA, 71- *Mem:* Am Psychiat Asn; Can Psychiat Asn. *Res:* Theoretical models in psychoanalysis; depression; manic-depressive illness; psychopharmacology; obesity. *Mailing Add:* 1220 Wyngate Rd Wynnewood PA 19096

MENDELSON, NEIL HARLAND, b New York, NY, Nov 15, 37; m 59; c 2. GENETICS, CELL BIOLOGY. *Educ:* Cornell Univ, BS, 59; Ind Univ, PhD(genetics, bact), 64. *Prof Exp:* Asst prof biol sci, Univ Md, Baltimore County, 66-69; assoc prof, 69-74, prof microbiol & med technol, 74-78, PROF CELLULAR & DEVELOP BIOL, UNIV ARIZ, 78-, HEAD DEPT, 79- *Concurrent Pos:* NSF fel, Med Res Coun Microbial Genetics Res Unit, Hammersmith Hosp, London, Eng, 65-66; vis scientist, Unite de physiol cellulaire, dept de biochimie et genetique microbienne, Inst Pasteur, Paris, 76-77; Nat Inst Gen Med Sci res career develop award, 73-77; prin investr res grant, Div Biol & Med Sci, NSF, 67-69, 69-71 & 82-84 & Nat Inst Gen Med Sci, 71-82. *Mem:* Fel AAAS; Am Soc Microbiol; Genetics Soc Am; Sigma Xi; fel Am Acad Microbiol. *Res:* Molecular and microbial genetics; genetic control of DNA replication, growth and cell division in Bacillus subtilis; helical growth of Bacillus subtilis, the theory of helical clocks and DNA segregation in bacteria. *Mailing Add:* Dept Cellular & Develop Biol Univ of Ariz Tucson AZ 85721

MENDELSON, ROBERT ALEXANDER, JR, b Los Angeles, Calif, Jan 24, 41. NUCLEAR PHYSICS, MOLECULAR BIOLOGY. *Educ:* Occidental Col, AB, 62; Univ Iowa, MS, 64, PhD(physics), 68. *Prof Exp:* Res assoc physics, Lawrence Berkeley Lab, Univ Calif, 68-71; res assoc biophys, 71-79, ASSOC PROF BIOPHYS, UNIV CALIF, SAN FRANCISCO, 79- *Mem:* Am Phys Soc; Biophys Soc. *Res:* Nuclear structure physics. *Mailing Add:* 127 Lower Terrace San Francisco CA 94114

MENDELSON, ROBERT ALLEN, b Cleveland, Ohio, Dec 17, 30; m 71. POLYMER SCIENCE, RHEOLOGY. *Educ:* Case Western Reserve Univ, BS, 52, PhD(chem), 56. *Prof Exp:* Res chemist, Monsanto Chem Co, 56-61, res specialist, 61-69, SCI FEL, MONSANTO CO, 69- *Mem:* AAAS; Am Chem Soc; Soc Rheol (secy, 74-78). *Res:* Polymer solution properties; polymer molecular weight and structure characterization; polymer rheology and processing; polymer mechanical properties. *Mailing Add:* Technol Dept Monsanto Co 730 Worcester St Indian Orchard MA 01151

MENDELSON, WILFORD LEE, b Baltimore, Md, July 8, 37. ORGANIC CHEMISTRY. *Educ:* Johns Hopkins Univ, AB, 58, MA, 60, PhD(chem), 63. *Prof Exp:* Sr chemist, 63-75, SR INVESTR, SMITH KLINE & FRENCH LABS, 75- *Mem:* Am Chem Soc; Royal Soc Chem. *Res:* Incorporation of C-14 and H-3 into existing and potential pharmaceuticals; organic synthesis with isotopes; process chemistry. *Mailing Add:* 592 General Learned Rd King of Prussia PA 19406

MENDELSSOHN, ROY, b Philadelphia, Pa, Dec 13, 49. OPERATIONS RESEARCH. *Educ:* Harvard Univ, BA, 71; Yale Univ, MFS, 73, MPhil, 75, PhD(environ studies), 76. *Prof Exp:* opers res analyst, Honolulu Lab, 76-81, OPERS RES ANALYST, PAC ENVIRON GROUP, SOUTHWEST FISHERIES CTR, NAT MARINE FISHERIES SERV, MONTEREY, CALIF, 81- *Mem:* Opers Res Soc Am; Inst Mgt Sci; Am Statist Asn; Biomet Soc; Soc Indust & Appl Math. *Res:* Dynamic programming and the optimal management of renewable resources; multi-objective decision making; statistical analysis of population dynamics. *Mailing Add:* PO Box 831 Pac Environ Group Monterey CA 93942

MENDENHALL, GEORGE DAVID, b Iowa City, Iowa, Feb 12, 45; m 73; c 2. PHYSICAL ORGANIC CHEMISTRY, POLYMER CHEMISTRY. *Educ:* Univ Mich, BS, 66; Harvard Univ, PhD(chem), 71. *Prof Exp:* Fel, Nat Res Coun Can, 71-73; fel, Stanford Res Inst, 73-74; mem staff chem, Columbus Labs, Battelle Mem Inst, 74-80; ASSOC PROF, MICH TECHNOL UNIV, 80- *Mem:* Am Chem Soc; Int Photochem Soc. *Res:* Reactions of ozone, singlet molecular oxygen; electron spin resonance studies of organic radicals; kinetics of smog-producing reactions; composition of atmospheric aerosols; autoxidation processes studied by chemiluminescence. *Mailing Add:* Chem Dept Mich Technol Univ Haughton MI 49931

MENDENHALL, ROBERT VERNON, b Geneva, Ind, Dec 27, 20; m 44; c 3. MATHEMATICAL LOGIC. *Educ:* Ohio State Univ, BA, 47, MA, 49, PhD(math), 52. *Prof Exp:* Instr math, Ohio State Univ, 47-53; mathematician, NAm Aviation, Inc, 53-55 & Vitro Labs, Inc, 55; asst prof math, Univ Miami, 55-62; assoc prof, 62-66, PROF MATH, OHIO WESLEYAN UNIV, 66- *Concurrent Pos:* Consult, NSF Math Insts, India, 65, 66 & 70. *Mem:* AAAS; Am Math Soc; Math Asn Am; Indian Math Soc. *Res:* Measure theory; integration. *Mailing Add:* Dept of Math Ohio Wesleyan Univ Delaware OH 43015

MENDENHALL, WILLIAM, III, b Pa, Apr 20, 25; m 49; c 2. STATISTICS. *Educ:* Bucknell Univ, BS, 45, MS, 50; NC State Col, PhD(statist), 57. *Prof Exp:* Asst prof statist, NC State Col, 58-59; assoc prof math, Bucknell Univ, 59-63; PROF STATIST, UNIV FLA, 63- *Concurrent Pos:* Assoc statistician, London Sch Econ, 57-58; consult, Westinghouse Elec Co, Pa, 59-60, Armstrong Cork Co, Pa, 60-, Burroughs Corp, Mich, 60-61, Lewis Res Ctr,

NASA, Ohio, 60-61, Merck & Co, Pa, 61-62 & WVa Pulp & Paper Co, 65. *Mem:* Am Statist Asn; Inst Math Statist; Royal Statist Soc. *Res:* Design of experiments; distribution theory. *Mailing Add:* Dept of Statist 507 NSC Univ of Fla Gainesville FL 32601

MENDES, ROBERT W, b Fall River, Mass, Apr 6, 38; m 60. INDUSTRIAL PHARMACY. *Educ:* New Eng Col Pharm, BS, 60; Univ NC, MS, 64, PhD(pharm), 66. *Prof Exp:* Asst prof pharm, 65-73, assoc prof, 73-78, PROF INDUST PHARM, MASS COL PHARM, 79-, DIR, PFEIFFER LABS, 79- *Concurrent Pos:* Consult & grantee, several material suppliers and mfg concerns, 71-; mem, Eastern Regional Indust Pharmaceut Technol Sect Planning Comt, 80-, Tableting Specifications Comt, Acad Pharmaceut Sci, 79-81. *Mem:* Am Pharmaceut Asn; Acad Pharmaceut Sci; Soc Cosmetic Chemists. *Res:* Development and evaluation of pharmaceutical dosage forms nd excipient materials; effect of formulation and process variables on bioavailability and bioequivalence of drug products. *Mailing Add:* Dept Pharm Mass Col of Pharm 179 Longwood Ave Boston MA 02115

MENDEZ, EUSTORGIO, b Panama City, Panama, Mar 1, 27; m 60; c 2. ZOOLOGY, MEDICAL ENTOMOLOGY. *Educ:* Univ Panama, BS, 50; Univ Calif, Berkeley, MS, 54; Mich State Univ, PhD(zool), 76. *Prof Exp:* Entomologist, Ministry of Health, Panama, 55-57; ZOOLOGIST, GORGAS MEM LAB, 57-; PROF ZOOL, UNIV PANAMA, 65- *Concurrent Pos:* Guggenheim Mem Found fel, 61-62; mem, Panama Nat Comn Wildlife Conserv, 66-; consult, Int Union Conserv Nature & Natural Resources, 72-; fel, Orgn Am States, 74-75. *Mem:* Sigma Xi. *Res:* Mammalogy; entomology; wildlife conservation; applied ecology. *Mailing Add:* Gorgas Mem Lab Apartado 6991 Zona 5 Panama

MENDEZ, JOSE DE LA VEGA, b Tapachula, Mex, Aug 17, 21; m 57; c 5. PHYSIOLOGY. *Educ:* San Carlos Univ Guatemala, BS, 47; Univ Ill, MS, 48; Univ Minn, PhD(physiol), 57. *Prof Exp:* Chief spec projs, Inst Nutrit Cent Am & Panama, Guatemala, 49-53, dir training progs & co-chief physiol, 59-65; assoc prof nutrit, Mass Inst Technol, 65-66; PROF HEALTH & APPL PHYSIOL, LAB HUMAN PERFORMANCE RES, PA STATE UNIV, 66- *Concurrent Pos:* Adv, Sch Med, San Carlos Univ Guatemala, 59-60. *Mem:* AAAS; Am Inst Nutrit; NY Acad Sci; Guatemala Soc Natural Sci & Pharm; Latin Am Nutrit Soc. *Res:* Nutritional studies and nutrition training in developing countries; body composition and anthropology; fat metabolism and nutritional factors in atherosclerosis; physiology of work and nutrition; adaptation of man to different environmental stresses. *Mailing Add:* Lab of Human Performance Res Pa State Univ University Park PA 16802

MENDEZ, VICTOR MANUEL, b San Antonio, Tex, May 14, 44; c 3. ORGANIC CHEMISTRY, ANALYTICAL CHEMISTRY. *Educ:* St Mary's Univ, Tex, BS, 66; Univ Tex, Austin, MA, 77. *Prof Exp:* Asst res chemist, Southwest Res Inst, 66-67; chem officer, US Army Chem Corps, 68-71; res chemist, Southwest Res Inst, 71-73; RES CHEMIST, SOUTHWEST FOUND RES & EDUC, 73- *Mem:* Am Chem Soc. *Res:* Production and monitoring of pollutant atmospheres used in toxicological studies; automation of laboratory experiments through the use of microcomputers. *Mailing Add:* Southwest Found for Res & Educ 8848 W Commerce St PO Box 28147 San Antonio TX 78284

MENDICINO, JOSEPH FRANK, b Cleveland, Ohio, Nov 22, 30; m 52; c 4. BIOCHEMISTRY. *Educ:* Case Western Reserve Univ, BS, 53; PhD, 57. *Prof Exp:* NSF res fel, Inst Biochem Invest, Argentina, 59-60 & Case Western Reserve Univ, 60-62; asst prof agr biochem, Ohio State Univ, 62-68; ASSOC PROF BIOCHEM, UNIV GA, 68- *Mem:* Am Chem Soc; Am Soc Biol Chem. *Res:* Enzymology. *Mailing Add:* Dept of Biochem Univ of Ga Athens GA 30602

MENDILLO, MICHAEL, b Providence, RI, Aug 22, 44; m 70; c 2. SPACE PHYSICS, ASTRONOMY. *Educ:* Providence Col, BS, 66; Boston Univ, MA, 68, PhD(physics & astron), 71. *Prof Exp:* Asst prof astron, Boston Univ, 71-72; Nat Acad Sci-Nat Res Coun resident res assoc space sci, Air Force Cambridge Res Lab, Bedford, Mass, 72-74; from asst prof to assoc prof astron, 74-78, ASSOC DEAN GRAD SCH, BOSTON UNIV, 78- *Mem:* AAAS; Am Geophys Union; Am Astron Soc; Int Union Radio Sci; Sigma Xi. *Res:* Solar-terrestrial relations; artificial modification of ionosphere, history of astronomy and geophysics. *Mailing Add:* Dept of Astron Boston Univ Boston MA 02215

MENDIS, EUSTACE FRANCIS, b Colombo, Ceylon, June 22, 37; m 71. SOLID STATE PHYSICS. *Educ:* Univ Ceylon, BSc, 58; Univ Wis, PhD(physics), 68. *Prof Exp:* Fel physics, Univ NB, 69-70; lectr, Univ of Toronto, 70-75; head physics dept, 75-78, CHIEF SCIENTIST, ONTARIO SCI CTR, 78- *Mem:* Am Phys Soc; Can Asn Physicists; Ceylon Asn Advan Sci. *Res:* Nuclear magnetic resonance in ferromagnets. *Mailing Add:* Ontario Sci Ctr 770 Don Mills Rd Toronto ON M3C 1T3 Can

MENDLER, J(OHN) OLIVER, b Bacsalmas, Hungary, June 21, 27; US citizen; m 57; c 3. MECHANICAL ENGINEERING. *Educ:* Mass Inst Technol, SB, 55; Univ Pittsburgh, MS, 59, PhD(mech eng), 63. *Prof Exp:* Engr, Bettis Atomic Power Lab, West Mifflin, 55-81, PRIN ENGR, WESTINGHOUSE ELEC CORP, PITTSBURGH, 81- *Res:* Heat transfer and fluid flow; thermal design of nuclear reactors; natural-circulation tests with water at 800 to 2000 psia under nonboiling, local boiling and bulk boiling conditions; sudden expansion losses in single-phase and two-phase flow; steam generator performance under steady-state and accident transient conditions. *Mailing Add:* 134 Carnold Dr Munhall PA 15120

MENDLOWITZ, HAROLD, b New York, NY, Aug 23, 27; m 50; c 3. THEORETICAL PHYSICS. *Educ:* City Col New York, BS, 47; Columbia Univ, AM, 48; Univ Mich, PhD(physics), 54. *Prof Exp:* Asst prin & chmn dept, Beth Yehudah Schs, Mich, 48-49; asst exp physics, Columbia Univ, 49-50; physicist, Nat Bur Standards, 51-52; instr aeronaut eng, Univ Mich, 52-53, asst theoret physics, 53-54; theoret physicist, Nat Bur Standards, 54-65; PROF PHYSICS, HOWARD UNIV, 65- *Concurrent Pos:* Sr res fel, Hebrew Univ, Israel, 61-62; consult, Nat Bur Standards; vis prof, Hebrew Univ, Israel, 71-72; mem staff, Nat Bur Standards, 78-79. *Mem:* Fel Am Phys Soc; Sigma Xi. *Res:* Photomeson production; electron physics, scattering, interference and polarization; Dirac theory; optical properties of solids; magnetic moment of electron; characteristic electron energy losses in solids; atomic spectroscopy; transition probabilities; radiation theory, cerenkov radiation, channeling radiation. *Mailing Add:* Dept Physics & Astron Howard Univ Washington DC 20001

MENDLOWITZ, MILTON, b New York, NY, Dec 30, 06; m 40; c 3. INTERNAL MEDICINE, CARDIOLOGY. *Educ:* City Col New York, AB, 27; Univ Mich, MD, 32. *Prof Exp:* Clin asst, 39-40, sr asst, 40-42, adj physician, 46-53, assoc attend physician, 53-59, Joe Lowe & Louis Price prof, Med Sch, 72-77, ATTEND PHYSICIAN, MT SINAI HOSP, 59-, EMER PROF MED, MT SINAI MED SCH, 77- *Concurrent Pos:* Blumenthal fel, Mt Sinai Hosp, 36; Libman fel, Michael Reese Hosp, Chicago, Ill, 37 & Univ Col Hosp, London, 38; Dazian fel, Mt Sinai Hosp, 42; res fel, Goldwater Mem Hosp, 51-; Pvt pract, 39-42 & 46-; sr physician, NY Regional Off, US Vet Admin, 46-52; asst clin prof med, Columbia Univ, 56-61, assoc clin prof, 66-; assoc clin prof, Mt Sinai Med Sch, 66- *Mem:* Fel AAAS; Am Soc Clin Invest; Am Physiol Soc; Soc Exp Biol & Med; AMA. *Res:* Physiology and pathological physiology of digital circulation; mechanism of heart failure; physiological effects of coronary occlusion and pulmonary embolism; mechanism and treatment of hypertension. *Mailing Add:* 1200 Fifth Ave New York NY 10029

MENDLOWSKI, BRONISLAW, b Tarnopol, Poland, June 28, 14; US citizen; m 50; c 3. PATHOLOGY, IMMUNOLOGY. *Educ:* Univ Lwow, Poland, DVM, 44; Univ Edinburgh, MRCVS, 47; Univ Ill, MS, 63. *Prof Exp:* Pathologist, West of Scotland Agr Col, 45-46, Wis State Diag Lab, 51-60 & Univ Ill, 60-63; res fel path, 63-74, SR RES FEL PATH, MERCK INST THERAPEUT RES, 74- *Mem:* Am Vet Med Asn; NY Acad Sci. *Res:* Etiologic and immunologic aspects of arthritides in animals; effects of interferon inducers and of thymic factors in autoimmune disease of animals; immunopathologic approach for determining a possible toxicity in animals caused by chemical compounds. *Mailing Add:* Merck Inst for Therapeut Res West Point PA 19486

MENDOZA, CELSO ENRIQUEZ, b Bocaue, Bulacan, Philippines, Mar 28, 33; m 68; c 3. BIOCHEMISTRY, ENTOMOLOGY. *Educ:* Univ Philippines, BS, 59; Iowa State Univ, MS, 61, PhD(entom), 64. *Prof Exp:* Res assoc med entom, Cornell Univ, 64-65; Nat Res Coun Can fel pesticide residue anal, Health Protection Br, Nat Health & Welfare Dept, Can, 65-67, res scientist I, 67-69, res scientist II, 69-79. *Concurrent Pos:* Assoc referee esterase methods, Asn Off Anal Chem, 70-; NATO spec study travel grant, Alta, Can, 71; vis scientist, Biochem Dept, Arrhenius Lab, Stockholm Univ, 73-74; NATO ecotoxicol travel grant, Univ Surrey, Guilford, Eng, 77. *Mem:* AAAS; Am Chem Soc; Entom Soc Am; Philippine Entom Soc; NY Acad Sci. *Res:* Development of analytical method for pesticide residues in foods; chromatographic-enzyme inhibition techniques for insecticides; toxicological and biochemical determination of pesticide effects on animals particularly neonates; evaluation of toxicological data in support of submission for pesticide registration. *Mailing Add:* 570 Prospect Dr SW Medicine Hat AB T1A 4C1 Can

MENDUKE, HYMAN, b Warsaw, Poland, Aug 20, 21; US citizen; m 46; c 1. BIOSTATISTICS. *Educ:* Univ Pa, BA, 43, MA, 48, PhD(econ statist), 52. *Prof Exp:* Instr soc & econ statist, Univ Pa, 47-53; asst prof biostatist, 53-58, assoc prof, 58-63, prof community health & prev med, 63-79, DIR SPONSORED PROGS, JEFFERSON MED COL, 63-, PROF PHARMACOL, 78- *Concurrent Pos:* Lectr statist eval clin data, Philadelphia Col Pharm, 75- *Mem:* Am Statist Asn; Biomet Soc; Sigma Xi. *Res:* Applied statistics in the design of surveys, clinical trials and laboratory experiments and in the analysis, interpretation and presentation of results. *Mailing Add:* Jefferson Med Col 1025 Walnut St Philadelphia PA 19107

MENEES, JAMES H, b Checotak, Okla, Nov 24, 29; m 53; c 1. HISTOLOGY, EMBRYOLOGY. *Educ:* San Jose State Col, AB, 53; Cornell Univ, MS, 57, PhD(entom), 59. *Prof Exp:* Asst, Cornell Univ, 56-59; PROF ENTOM, LONG BEACH STATE COL, 59- *Concurrent Pos:* Res grants, USDA, 56-59 & Univ Southern Calif, 79-81. *Mem:* Entom Soc Am; Am Soc Parasitol. *Res:* Insect anatomy; arthropod histology, embryology and physiology. *Mailing Add:* Dept of Biol Sci Calif State Col Long Beach CA 90804

MENEFEE, EMORY, b Wichita Falls, Tex, June 30, 29; m 53; c 3. PHYSICAL CHEMISTRY, POLYMER CHEMISTRY. *Educ:* Tex Tech Col, BS, 50; Mass Inst Technol, PhD(phys chem), 56. *Prof Exp:* Chem engr, Amarillo Helium Plant, US Bur Mines, Tex, 50-52; chemist, Plastics Dept, E I du Pont de Nemours & Co, Del, 56-60; CHEMIST WOOL LAB, WESTERN REGIONAL RES LAB, US DEPT AGR, 60- *Mem:* Soc Rheol. *Res:* Viscoelasticity of molten polymers; rheology and physical chemistry of wool fibers; crosslinking. *Mailing Add:* Western Regional Res Lab 800 Buchanan St Albany CA 94710

MENEFEE, MAX GENE, b Perry, Mo, Mar 30, 25; m 51; c 3. FAMILY MEDICINE. *Educ:* Wash Univ, PhD(anat), 56; State Univ NY, MD, 61. *Prof Exp:* Spec lectr surg, Col Med, State Univ NY Upstate Med Ctr, 57-61; asst prof anat, 61-66, assoc prof path & anat, 66-81, PRECEPTOR FAMILY MED, COL MED, UNIV CINCINNATI, 81- *Concurrent Pos:* USPHS fel, 56-57; consult, US Vet Admin Hosp, 71-81; spec residency family med, Univ Hosp, Univ Cincinnati, 80-81. *Mem:* Am Asn Anat; Sigma Xi. *Res:* Morphological aspects of vascular transport and disease; arthritis and rheumatism. *Mailing Add:* 10150 Harrison Ave Harrison OH 45030

MENEFEE, ROBERT WILLIAM, b Akron, Ohio, Aug 8, 29; m 54; c 3. SCIENCE EDUCATION. *Educ:* Univ Akron, BS, 52; Kent State Univ, ME, 57; Ohio State Univ, PhD(sci ed), 65. *Prof Exp:* Teacher pub schs, Ohio, 54-62; instr unified sci, Ohio State Univ Sch, 63-65, asst prof zool, Ohio State Univ, 65-67, core prog dir biol, 67-68, asst dean & core dir biol sci, 68-69; assoc prof of sci teaching, Univ Md, College Park, 69-71; chmn div math sci, 71-78, DEAN INST NATURAL SCI, MONTGOMERY COL, TAKOMA PARK, 78- *Mem:* Fel AAAS; Am Inst Biol Sci; Nat Asn Res Sci Teaching; Nat Sci Teachers Asn. *Res:* Televised biology instruction; individualized instruction in biology; unified science; Nat Science Foundation-science education. *Mailing Add:* Inst Natural Sci Montgomery Col Takoma Park MD 20912

MENEGHETTI, DAVID, b Chicago, Ill, May 8, 23; m 50; c 2. NUCLEAR PHYSICS. *Educ:* Univ Chicago, BS, 44; Ill Inst Technol, PhD(physics), 54. *Prof Exp:* Asst physicist, Argonne Nat Lab, 46-49 & 52-54; lab asst nuclear physics, Med Sch, Univ Ill, 51-52; assoc physicist, Armour Res Found, Ill Inst Technol, 54-55; SR PHYSICIST, ARGONNE NAT LAB, 55- *Concurrent Pos:* Consult, Centro di Calcolo & lectr, Univ Bologna, 62-63. *Mem:* Am Phys Soc; fel Am Nuclear Soc. *Res:* Neutron physics; neutron diffraction; magnetics and antiferromagnetics; reactor physics. *Mailing Add:* Argonne Nat Lab 9700 Cass Ave Argonne IL 60439

MENENDEZ, MANUEL GASPAR, b New York, NY, June 15, 35; m 58; c 3. ATOMIC PHYSICS, MOLECULAR PHYSICS. *Educ:* Univ Fla, BChE, 58, PhD(chem physics), 63. *Prof Exp:* Fel chem physics, Oak Ridge Nat Lab, 63-65; atomic physicist, Nat Bur Standards, 65-66; staff scientist, Martin Marietta Corp, 66-69; assoc prof, 69-81, PROF PHYSICS, UNIV GA, 81- *Concurrent Pos:* Consult, Martin Marietta Corp, 70-72. *Mem:* Am Phys Soc. *Res:* Ionization mechanisms at intermediate and low energies; molecular aspects of ion-atom collisions. *Mailing Add:* Dept Physics & Astron Univ Ga Athens GA 30602

MENENDEZ, MARIA ANTONIA, b Sancti-Spiritus, Cuba, Mar 3, 50. ELECTRONICS ENGINEERING. *Educ:* Wright State Univ, BS, 73; Univ Ill, Urbana, MS, 74, PHD(physics), 79. *Prof Exp:* MEM TECH STAFF, BELL LABS, 79- *Mem:* Am Phys Soc. *Res:* Reliability of high voltage integrated circuits. *Mailing Add:* Bell Labs Rm 7C-313 600 Mountain Ave Murray Hill NJ 07974

MENES, MEIR, b Berlin, Ger, Oct 3, 25; nat US. PHYSICS. *Educ:* Cooper Union, BE, 48; NY Univ, PhD(physics), 52. *Prof Exp:* Physicist, Res Labs, Westinghouse Elec Corp, 52-60; ASSOC PROF PHYSICS, POLYTECH INST BROOKLYN, 60- *Mem:* Am Phys Soc. *Res:* Electrical discharges through gases; nuclear magnetic resonance; acoustic studies of solids. *Mailing Add:* Dept of Physics Polytech Inst Brooklyn Brooklyn NY 11201

MENEZ, ERNANI GUINGONA, b Manila, Philippines, Aug 15, 31; m 61; c 2. MARINE PHYCOLOGY. *Educ:* Univ Philippines, BS, 54; Univ Hawaii, MS, 62; Univ NH, PhD, 80. *Prof Exp:* Res asst bot, Univ Philippines, 53-54; instr bot & zool, Southeastern Col, Philippines, 54-58; asst bot, Univ Hawaii, 58-61 & Univ BC, 62-64; SUPVR ALGAE, SMITHSONIAN OCEANOG SORTING CTR, SMITHSONIAN INST, 64- *Concurrent Pos:* Dir, Mediterranean Marine Sorting Ctr, Tunisia, 73-75. *Mem:* Phycol Soc Philippines; Int Phycol Soc. *Res:* Taxonomy and ecology of tropical marine benthic algae; marine floristics of Tunisia. *Mailing Add:* Smithsonian Oceanog Sorting Ctr Smithsonian Inst Washington DC 20560

MENEZES, JOSE PIEDADE CAETANO AGNELO, b Curtorim, India, July 25, 39; Can citizen; m 70. MICROBIOLOGY, IMMUNOLOGY. *Educ:* Nat Col Goa, India, dipl, 58; Univ Perugia, DVM, 63; Pasteur Inst, Paris, dipl bact, 65; Univ Montreal, MS, 67; Univ Ottawa, PhD(microbiol), 71. *Prof Exp:* Asst prof, 73-77; res assoc prof microbiol & immunol & heal lab immunovirol, 77-81, RES PROF & HEAD LAB IMMUNOVIROL, PEDIAT RES CTR, FAC MED, UNIV MONTREAL, 81- *Concurrent Pos:* Sr res scholar, Med Res Coun Quebec, Med Res Coun Can fel, 67-73, Univ Ottawa, 68-71 & Dept Tumor Biol, Karolinska Inst, Sweden, 71-73; Med Res Coun Can scholar, Univ Montreal, 73-78. *Mem:* Am Soc Microbiol; Int Asn Comp Res Leukemia & Related Dis; Fr Soc Microbiol; NY Acad Sci; Tissue Cult Asn. *Res:* Virology; cellular immunology; tumor biology; cell culture; cell biology; electron microscopy. *Mailing Add:* Dept of Microbiol & Immunol Ste-Justine Hosp Montreal PQ H3T 1C5 Can

MENG, HEINZ KARL, b Baden, Ger, Feb 25, 24; nat US; m 53. BIOLOGY. *Educ:* Cornell Univ, BS, 47, PhD(ornith), 51. *Prof Exp:* Asst prof, 51-56, assoc prof, 56-61, PROF BIOL, STATE UNIV NY COL NEW PALTZ, 61- *Mem:* Assoc Wildlife Soc; Assoc Cooper Ornith Soc; assoc Wilson Ornith Soc; assoc Am Ornith Union. *Res:* Ornithology; entomology; falconry; vertebrate zoology. *Mailing Add:* Dept Biol State Univ New York Col New Paltz NY 12561

MENG, KARL H(ALL), b Rochester, NY, Nov 7, 11; m 43; c 3. CHEMICAL ENGINEERING. *Educ:* Univ Rochester, BS, 34, MS, 36, PhD(org chem), 39. *Prof Exp:* Asst chem, Univ Rochester, 34-38; instr, Nazareth Col, 39-41; chemist, Distillation Prod, Inc, Eastman Kodak Co, 41-42, chem engr & chem plant supvr, Distillation Prod Industs Div, 42-65, staff asst, Photomat Div, 65-69, staff asst, Res Labs, Admin Div, 70-76; RETIRED. *Mem:* Am Chem Soc. *Res:* Sources and methods for making fish liver oils; stability of vitamin concentrates; adsorption processes; manufacturing methods for Vitamin A and E and derivatives; production of synthetic vitamin A and fine chemicals; process and product development; finance. *Mailing Add:* 40 Hollyvale Rochester NY 14618

MENG, SHIEN-YI, b Kirin, China, Oct 19, 29; m 70; c 2. ELECTRICAL ENGINEERING, RADIO ASTRONOMY. *Educ:* Cheng Kung Univ, Taiwan, BS, 53; Okla State Univ, MS, 58; Ohio State Univ, PhD(elec eng), 68. *Prof Exp:* Jr engr, Taiwan Prov Govt, China, 54-56; designer, Ramseyer & Miller, Inc, NY, 58-59; res assoc radio astron, Radio Observ, Ohio State Univ, 66-68; asst prof, 68-74, assoc prof, 74-80, PROF ELEC ENG, CALIF POLYTECH STATE UNIV, SAN LUIS OBISPO, 80- *Concurrent Pos:* Res engr, SRI Int, Menlo Park, Calif, 79. *Mem:* Inst Elec & Electronics Engrs; Am Astron Soc; Am Soc Eng Educ. *Res:* Electromagnetic theory; antennas; radio wave propagation. *Mailing Add:* Dept of Elec Eng Calif State Polytech Univ San Luis Obispo CA 93407

MENGE, ALAN C, b Marengo, Ill, Apr 8, 34; m 57; c 4. REPRODUCTIVE PHYSIOLOGY. *Educ:* Univ Ill, BSc, 56; Univ Wis, MSc, 58, PhD(endocrinol), 61. *Prof Exp:* Asst prof animal sci, Rutgers Univ, 61-65, assoc prof, 65-67; ASSOC PROF REPROD BIOL, MED CTR, UNIV MICH, ANN ARBOR, 67- *Concurrent Pos:* Mem, Int Coord Comt Immunol of Reprod USA, 58; vis scientist, Uppsala Univ, Sweden, 79-80. *Mem:* Soc Study Reproduction; Int Soc Immunol Reproduction (vpres, 78-82); Brit Soc Study Fertil; Sigma Xi; Soc Exp Biol & Med. *Res:* Problems related to endocrine and immunologic causes of infertility. *Mailing Add:* Dept of Obstet & Gynec Univ of Mich Med Ctr Ann Arbor MI 48104

MENGE, BRUCE ALLAN, b Minneapolis, Minn, Oct 5, 43; m 71. ECOLOGY. *Educ:* Univ Minn, Minneapolis, BA, 65; Univ Wash, PhD(ecol), 70. *Prof Exp:* Ford Found fel, Univ Calif, Santa Barbara, 70-71; asst prof biol, Univ Mass, Boston, 71-76; asst prof, 76-79, ASSOC PROF ZOOL, ORE STATE UNIV, 79- *Concurrent Pos:* Vis prof, Univ Guam, 80. *Mem:* Ecol Soc Am; Am Soc Nat; Am Soc Zool; Soc Study Evolution. *Res:* Population and community ecology in the marine environment; effect of biological interactions; life history strategies tropical marine ecology. *Mailing Add:* Dept of Zool Ore State Univ Corvallis OR 97331

MENGE, JOHN ARTHUR, b Minneapolis, Minn, Feb 24, 45; m 68; c 2. PLANT PATHOLOGY, MYCOLOGY. *Educ:* Univ Minn, BS, 67, MS, 69; NC State Univ PhD(plant path), 75. *Prof Exp:* ASST PROF PLANT PATH, UNIV CALIF, RIVERSIDE, 74- *Mem:* Am Phytopath Soc; Mycol Soc Am. *Res:* Fungus diseases of citrus; the mycorrhizal association of plants. *Mailing Add:* Dept of Plant Path Univ of Calif Riverside CA 92521

MENGEBIER, WILLIAM LOUIS, b New York, NY, Dec 2, 21; m; c 3. PHYSIOLOGY. *Educ:* The Citadel, BS, 43; Oberlin Col, MA, 49; Univ Tenn, PhD(zool), 53. *Prof Exp:* Instr chem & biol, The Citadel, 46-49, asst prof, 49-54; prof biol, Madison Col, Va, 54-67; PROF BIOL, BRIDGEWATER COL, 67- *Res:* Effects of anoxia on cellular respiration; relative survival times of hibernators and mammals to anoxia; cellular physiology; effect of vertebrate hormones on invertebrates. *Mailing Add:* Dept of Biol Bridgewater Col Bridgewater VA 22812

MENGEL, CHARLES E, b Baltimore, Md, Nov 29, 31; m; c 5. MEDICINE, HEMATOLOGY. *Educ:* Lafayette Col, AB, 53; Johns Hopkins Univ, MD, 57. *Prof Exp:* Intern, Osler Ward Med Serv, Johns Hopkins Hosp, 57-58; asst resident med, Duke Univ Hosp, 58-59; clin assoc exp pharmacol & therapeut, Leukemia Serv, Nat Cancer Inst, 59-61; chief resident & instr med, Duke Univ Hosp, 61-62, assoc med, sr staff & fac, Med Ctr & dir, Med Emergency Room Facilities, 62-65, organizer & dir med educ, Lincoln Hosp, 62-65; assoc prof med, Ohio State Univ & dir, Div Hemat & Oncol, Univ Hosp, 65-70; assoc prof med, Univ Mo, Columbia, 68-82; MEM STAFF, MOBERLY REGIONAL MED CTR, 82- *Concurrent Pos:* Markle scholar acad med, 63-68. *Mem:* Am Fedn Clin Res; Am Soc Hemat; Am Asn Cancer Res; NY Acad Sci; Am Soc Clin Investr. *Res:* Nonimmune hemolytic mechanisms; abnormalities of tryptophan metabolism; adult and childhood leukemia; medical education programs, particularly bridging of preclinical and clinical areas and student and fellow research training. *Mailing Add:* Moberly Regional Med Ctr Moberly MO 65270

MENGEL, DAVID BRUCE, b East Chicago, Ind, May 1, 48; m 68; c 2. SOIL FERTILITY, CROP PRODUCTION. *Educ:* Purdue Univ, BS, 70, MS, 72; NC State Univ, PhD(soils), 75. *Prof Exp:* Asst prof soil fertility & plant nutrit, Rice Exp Sta, La State Univ, 75-79; asst prof, 79-82, ASSOC PROF SOIL FERTILITY & PLANT NUTRIT, DEPT AGRON, PURDUE UNIV, 82- *Mem:* Soil Sci Soc Am; Am Soc Agron. *Res:* Nitrogen fertilization of cereal crops (corn, wheat), particularly as related to reduced tillage systems; soil testing; cropping systems and irrigation. *Mailing Add:* Dept Agron Purdue Univ West Lafayette IN 47907

MENGEL, JOHN GEIST, astronomy, see previous edition

MENGEL, ROBERT MORROW, b Glenview, Ky, Aug 19, 21; m 63. ZOOLOGY. *Educ:* Cornell Univ, BS, 47; Univ Mich, MA, 50, PhD, 58. *Prof Exp:* Ornith bibliographer, univ libr & res assoc, 53-65, lectr zool, 65-67, assoc prof, 67-71, instr, 58-65, assoc cur birds, 67-68, PROF SYST & ECOL, UNIV KANS, 72-, CUR BIRDS, MUS NAT HIST, 69- *Concurrent Pos:* Ed, The Auk, Am Ornith Union, 63-67, ed, monogr, 69-74; ed, various publ, Mus Natural History, Univ Kans, 80- *Mem:* Fel Am Ornith Union; Wilson Ornith Soc; Cooper Ornith Soc; Soc Systs Zool; Soc Study Evolution. *Res:* Distribution, ecology, evolution, systematics and paleontology of birds and mammals; bibliography of ornithology. *Mailing Add:* Dept of Syst & Ecol Univ of Kans Lawrence KS 66044

MENGEL, W(ILLIAM) E(DWARD), b Poplar Bluff, Mo, Feb 28, 18; m 42; c 1. MECHANICAL ENGINEERING, APPLIED MECHANICS. *Educ:* Washington Univ, BS & MS, 47, MEngAdmin, 63. *Prof Exp:* Assembler & riveter, 41-43, lead inspector, 43-45, struct test engr, 47-52, asst chief struct lab, 52-56, mgr, 56-62, mgr, Space Simulation & Systs Labs, 65-68, mgr lab projs, 68-77, CHIEF TEST ENGR, STRUCT & SYSTS LABS, MCDONNELL AIRCRAFT CO, 77- *Mem:* Assoc fel Am Inst Aeronaut & Astronaut; Am Soc Testing & Mat; Inst Environ Sci. *Res:* Testing structures, space simulation and aircraft and spacecraft systems. *Mailing Add:* McDonnell Aircraft Co PO Box 516 St Louis MO 63166

MENGELING, WILLIAM LLOYD, b Elgin, Ill, Apr 1, 33; m 58; c 2. VETERINARY VIROLOGY. *Educ:* Kans State Univ, BS, 58, DVM, 60; Iowa State Univ, MS, 66, PhD(microbiol, biochem), 69; Am Col Vet Microbiol; Dipl. *Prof Exp:* Vet, St Francis Animal Hosp, Albuquerque, NMex, 60-61; res vet, 61-76, CHIEF VIROL RES LAB, NAT ANIMAL DIS CTR, 76- *Concurrent Pos:* Collaborative prof, Iowa State Univ; co ed, Dis of Swine, Iowa State Univ Press, 81. *Mem:* Am Vet Med Asn; Animal Health Asn. *Res:* Respiratory and reproductive diseases of swine; virology. *Mailing Add:* Virol Dept Nat Animal Dis Lab Ames IA 50010

MENGENHAUSER, JAMES VERNON, b Armour, SDak, Oct 12, 33; m 60; c 1. PHYSICAL CHEMISTRY, PETROLEUM CHEMISTRY. *Educ:* Univ SDak, BA, 54; NMex State Univ, MS, 64; Univ Colo, PhD(chem), 69. *Prof Exp:* Chemist, Ames Lab, AEC, 54-55; chemist, El Paso Natural Gas Co, 59-61; CHEMIST, US ARMY MOBILITY EQUIP RES & DEVELOP COMMAND, FT BELVOIR, 68- *Mem:* Am Chem Soc; Sigma Xi. *Res:* Petroleum-water emulsions; nuclear magnetic resonance; pyrolysis chromatography; solubility of hydrocarbon fuels in water; turbulent drag reduction. *Mailing Add:* Res & Develop Command US Army Mobility Equip Ft Belvoir VA 22060

MENGER, EVA L, b South Bend, Ind, Feb 18, 43; m 64, 77; c 2. CHEMICAL PHYSICS. *Educ:* Carleton Col, BA, 64; Harvard Univ, MA, 65, PhD(chem), 68. *Prof Exp:* Asst ed, Accts Chem Res, 69-74; asst prof chem, Univ Calif, Santa Cruz, 74-78; sr res chemist, Allied Chem Corp, 78-80, ASSOC DIR FORWARD RES, ALLIED CORP, 80- *Mem:* Am Chem Soc; Sigma Xi. *Res:* Special interest focuses on nonsteady state effects in diffusion controlled processes and excited state reactions; heterogeneous catalysis; industrial chemicals and processes. *Mailing Add:* Allied Corp PO Box 1087R Morristown NJ 07960

MENGER, FRED M, b South Bend, Ind, Dec 13, 37; m 62. ORGANIC CHEMISTRY. *Educ:* Johns Hopkins Univ, AB, 58; Univ Wis, PhD(chem), 63. *Prof Exp:* NIH fel, Northwestern Univ, 64-65; from asst prof to assoc prof, 65-72, PROF CHEM, EMORY UNIV, 72- *Honors & Awards:* Camille & Henry Dreyfus teacher-scholar award, 70; NIH career develop award, 70-75. *Res:* Bio-organic and physical organic chemistry; interfaces and colloidal systems; reaction mechanisms; enzyme models. *Mailing Add:* Dept of Chem Emory Univ Atlanta GA 30322

MENGOLI, HENRY FRANCIS, b Plymouth, Mass, June 8, 28; m 54; c 2. IMMUNOLOGY. *Educ:* Boston Univ, AB, 50; Cath Univ, MS, 53, PhD(biol), 57. *Prof Exp:* Bacteriologist, Clin Ctr, NIH, 57-59, res biologist, Peripheral Blood Proj, Collab Area, Diag Res Br, Nat Cancer Inst, 59-63; instr, Cancer Res Lab, 63-65, asst prof path & microbiol, 65-73, asst prof microbiol, 73-75, ASSOC PROF MICROBIOL, IMMUNOL RES LAB, MED CTR, WVA UNIV, 75- *Mem:* NY Acad Sci; Am Chem Soc; Am Asn Microbiol; Sigma Xi. *Res:* Non-immunological mechanisms of host tissue destruction; host-microbial interactions in oral disease; cationic proteins of host tissues. *Mailing Add:* Dept of Microbiol WVa Univ Med Ctr Morgantown WV 26506

MENGUY, RENE, b Prague, Czech, Feb 4, 26; nat US; m; c 2. MEDICINE. *Educ:* Univ Paris, MD, 51, Univ Minn, PhD, 57. *Prof Exp:* Fulbright grant, Am Hosp Chicago, Ill, 51-52, fel, Mayo Clin, 52-57; from instr to asst prof surg, Med Ctr, Univ Okla, 57-58; from assoc prof to prof, Med Ctr, Univ Ky, 61-65, assoc prof physiol, 64-65; prof surg & chmn dept, Univ Chicago, 65-71; PROF SURG, SCH MED & DENT, UNIV ROCHESTER, 71-; SURGEON-IN-CHIEF, EMER GENESEE HOSP, 77- *Concurrent Pos:* Markle scholar, 58; asst chief surgeon Vet Admin Hosp, Okla, 59-61; surgeon-in-chief, Genesee Hosp, 71-77. *Mem:* Soc Exp Biol & Med; Am Gastroenterol Asn; AMA; Am Fedn Clin Res; Am Asn Cancer Res. *Res:* Surgery; gastroenterological surgery; experimental biology. *Mailing Add:* Genesee Hosp 224 Alexander St Rochester NY 14607

MENHINICK, EDWARD FULTON, b Cambridge, Mass, May 18, 35; m 61; c 3. ECOLOGY, PHYSIOLOGY. *Educ:* Emory Univ, BA, 57; Cornell Univ, MS, 60; Univ Ga, PhD(zool), 62-63; fel, Health Physics Div, Oak Rdige Nat Lab, 63-65; from asst prof to assoc prof, 65-77, PROF BIOL, UNIV NC, CHARLOTTE, 77- *Mem:* Ecol Soc Am; Entom Soc Am. *Res:* Ichthyology; water pollution; radiation ecology; environmental physiology; statistical analysis of density, diversity and energy flow. *Mailing Add:* Dept of Biol Univ of NC Charlotte NC 28213

MENKART, JOHN, b Prague, Aug 20, 22; m; c 4. COSMETIC CHEMISTRY, RESEARCH ADMINISTRATION. *Educ:* Univ Leeds, BSc, 44, PhD(textile chem), 46. *Prof Exp:* Res chemist, Denham & Hargrave, Ltd, 46-48; sci liaison officer, Int Wool Secretariat, Eng, 48-50; res chemist, Patons Baldwins, Ltd, 50-53; asst dir res, Textile Res Inst, Princeton Univ, 54-58; group leader, Harris Res Labs Inc, Gillette Co, 58-65, from asst dir to assoc dir, 65-67, vpres, Gillette Res Inst, 67-68, pres, 68-71; vpres, 71-77, SR VPRES TECHNOL, CLAIROL, INC, 77- *Honors & Awards:* CBS Award, Cosmetics, Toiletries & Fragrances Asn, 79. *Mem:* Soc Cosmetic Chem; Am Chem Soc; Fiber Soc; fel Brit Textile Inst. *Res:* Chemistry and physical properties of fibers; formulation and properties of topical products. *Mailing Add:* Clairol Inc 2 Blachley Rd Stamford CT 06902

MENKE, ANDREW G, b Lithuania, Aug 24, 44; US citizen; m 71; c 1. ORGANOMETALLIC CHEMISTRY. *Educ:* Wayne State Univ, BS, 67; Univ Toledo, MS, 73. *Prof Exp:* Asst chem, Wayne State Univ, 63-67; sr res chemist, Libbey-Owens-Ford Co, Ohio, 68-75; dir res & develop, Anglass Indust Inc, 75-77; sr prod & process engr, Donnelly Mirrors, 77-78; mgr glass technol, 78-80, VPRES RES, DEVELOP, TEMPERING & COATINGS DIV, ARDCO INC, 80- *Mem:* Int Solar Energy Soc; Am Chem Soc; Am Vacuum Soc. *Res:* Selective coating for solar collectors; low emissivity coatings for different applications; work on organotin compounds used to produce conductive tin oxide by pyrolysis of same; properties of these compounds and other related organometallic compounds; transparent conductive coatings on glass. *Mailing Add:* Ardco Inc 12400 S Laramie Ave Chicago IL 60658

MENKE, ARNOLD STEPHEN ERNST, b Glendale, Calif, Nov 22, 34; div; c 1. ENTOMOLOGY. *Educ:* Univ Calif, Berkeley, BS, 57; Univ Calif, Davis, MS, 59, PhD(entom), 65. *Prof Exp:* Asst res entomologist, Univ Calif, Davis, 65-67; RES ENTOMOLOGIST, US DEPT AGR, 68- *Concurrent Pos:* Res assoc, Los Angeles County Mus Natural Hist, 66- & Smithsonian Inst, Washington, DC, 78- *Mem:* Polish Entom Soc. *Res:* Systematics of aculeate hymenoptera, especially Sphecidae and Belostomatidae. *Mailing Add:* Syst Entomol Lab USDA c/o US Nat Mus Washington DC 20560

MENKES, EDGAR GEBRATH, aeronautical & mechanical engineering, see previous edition

MENKES, JOHN H, b Vienna, Austria, Dec 20, 28; US citizen; m 57; c 3. PEDIATRICS, NEUROLOGY. *Educ:* Univ Southern Calif, AB, 47, MS, 51; Johns Hopkins Univ, MD, 52. *Prof Exp:* Intern & asst resident pediat, Boston Children's Hosp, Mass, 52-54; asst prof neurol med & assoc prof pediat, Johns Hopkins Univ, 60-66; prof pediat & neurol, 66-70, CLIN PROF PEDIAT, NEUROL, UNIV CALIF, LOS ANGELES, 70- *Concurrent Pos:* Fel pediat neurol, NY, 57-60; Joseph P Kennedy, Jr scholar ment retardation, 60-66. *Mem:* AAAS; fel Am Acad Neurol; fel Am Neurol Asn; Am Pediat Soc; Soc Pediat Res. *Res:* Metabolic disorders of the nervous system; child neurology. *Mailing Add:* 9615 Brighton Way Beverly Hills CA 90210

MENKES, JOSHUA, b Vienna, Austria, Aug 14, 25; US citizen; m 61; c 2. APPLIED MATHEMATICS. *Educ:* Polytech Inst Brooklyn, BS, 53, MS, 54; Univ Mich, Ann Arbor, PhD(appl math), 56. *Prof Exp:* Analyst physics, Jet Propulsion Lab, Calif Inst Technol, 57-61; sr staff mem systs anal, Inst Defense Anal, 62-70; prof eng, Univ Colo, Boulder, 70-75; dir div systs anal, 75-77, GROUP LEADER TECHNOL ASSESSMENT & RISK ANAL, DIV POLICY RES & ANAL, NSF, 77- *Res:* Resource allocation and policy analysis. *Mailing Add:* NSF 1800 G St NW Washington DC 20550

MENKES, SHERWOOD BRADFORD, b Bradford, Pa, Mar 14, 21; m 50; c 4. MACHINE DESIGN. *Educ:* Columbia Col, BA, 41; Columbia Univ, BS, 42, MS, 54. *Prof Exp:* Engr, Western Elec Co, 42-49; PROF MECH ENG, CITY COL NEW YORK, 49- *Concurrent Pos:* Consult, 50-; forensic engr, 72-; ed, Marcel Dekker, Inc, 78- *Mem:* Am Soc Mech Eng; Am Soc Eng Educ. *Res:* Structural dynamics, especially in those situations in which the loads exceed the elastic limit for the structure, to the point of prompt failure. *Mailing Add:* Mech Eng Dept City Col New York NY 10031

MENLOVE, HOWARD OLSEN, b Mayfield, Utah, Oct 23, 36; m 58; c 4. NUCLEAR ENGINEERING, PHYSICS. *Educ:* Univ Calif, Berkeley, BS, 59; Univ Mich, Ann Arbor, MS, 61; Stanford Univ, PhD(nuclear eng), 66. *Prof Exp:* Physicist, Lockheed Palo Alto Res Lab, 61-66; scientist, Nuclear Res Ctr, Karlsruhe, Ger, 66-67; group leader nuclear safeguards, 67-80, PROJ MGR INT SAFEGUARDS, LOS ALAMOS NAT LAB, 80- *Concurrent Pos:* Consult, Int Atomic Energy Agency, 74-77. *Mem:* Am Nuclear Soc; Am Phys Soc; Inst Nuclear Mat Mgt. *Res:* Neutron cross-section measurements; fission physics; nondestructive assay instrumentation research and development; international safeguards research. *Mailing Add:* Los Alamos Nat Lab PO Box 1663 Los Alamos NM 87545

MENN, JULIUS JOEL, b Free City of Danzig, Feb 20, 29; m 52; c 3. INSECT TOXICOLOGY, BIOCHEMISTRY. *Educ:* Univ Calif, BS, 53, MS, 54, PhD(toxicol), 58. *Prof Exp:* Res asst, Univ Calif, 53-57; head entom & insecticide biochem sect, Agr Res Ctr, Stauffer Chem Co, 57-67, sr sect mgr, Biochem & Entom, 67-69, sr sect mgr, Insecticide Res & Biochem, 69-74, mgr biochem dept, 74-81; MEM STAFF, ZOECON CORP, 81- *Concurrent Pos:* NSF lectr, Univ Calif, Davis, 65; invited speaker spec conf fate of pesticides in environ, Nat Acad Sci-Nat Res Coun, 71; mem proj, Forms & Mechanisms by which Pesticides are transported in the environ, US/USSR, 74- *Honors & Awards:* Burdick & Jackson Int Award, 78. *Mem:* AAAS; Am Chem Soc; Entom Soc Am; NY Acad Sci; Soc Toxicol. *Res:* Metabolism and mode of action of pesticides; development of pesticides. *Mailing Add:* Zoecon Corp 975 Calif Ave Palo Alto CA 94304

MENNE, THOMAS JOSEPH, b St Louis, Mo, May 13, 34; m 56; c 1. THEORETICAL PHYSICS. *Educ:* St Louis Univ, BS, 56; Univ Calif, Los Angeles, MS, 58, PhD(physics), 63. *Prof Exp:* Mem tech staff, Hughes Aircraft Co, 56-59; lectr physics, Loyola Univ Los Angeles, 60-62; res scientist, 62-65, assoc scientist, 65-69, scientist, 69-70, MGR RES, McDONNELL DOUGLAS CORP, 70- *Concurrent Pos:* Lectr, Washington Univ, 65-67. *Mem:* Am Phys Soc; Sigma Xi. *Res:* Theoretical research on laser dynamics, electron spin resonance spectroscopy, crystal field theory and paramagnetic ion-lattice phonon interactions; magnetic and inertial confinement fusion; particle beams, cosmic rays and magnetic resonance characterization of polymers; research direction in chemical and molecular laser development. *Mailing Add:* McDonnell Douglas Corp PO Box 516 Dept E230 St Louis MO 63166

MENNEAR, JOHN HARTLEY, b Flint, Mich, Apr 25, 35; m 56; c 4. PHARMACOLOGY. *Educ:* Ferris Inst, BS, 57; Purdue Univ, MS, 60, PhD(pharmacol), 62. *Prof Exp:* Pharmacologist, Hazleton Labs, Inc, 62-63; Pitman-Moore Div, Dow Chem Co, 63-66; from asst prof to assoc prof, Purdue Univ, 66-72, prof toxicol, 72-76; TOXICOLOGIST, CHEM INDUST INST TOXICOL, 76- *Mem:* Am Soc Pharmacol & Exp Therapeut; Soc Toxicol. *Res:* Toxicology; applied pharmacology. *Mailing Add:* Chem Indust Inst of Toxicol Box 12137 Research Triangle Park NC 27709

MENNEGA, AALDERT, b Assen, Netherlands, July 3, 30; US citizen; m 58; c 5. ANATOMY, PHYSIOLOGY. *Educ:* Calvin Col, AB, 57; Mich State Univ, MA, 60, PhD(anat, zool), 64. *Prof Exp:* Lab technologist, Grand Rapids Osteop Hosp, Mich, 58-59; med technologist, E W Sparrow Hosp, Lansing, 59-64; from asst to assoc prof, 64-75, PROF BIOL, DORDT COL, 75-, CHMN DEPT, 70- *Mem:* Creation Res Soc. *Res:* Respiratory system, especially of birds; histology and gross anatomy of birds, mammals and snakes; embryology. *Mailing Add:* Dept Biol Dordt Col Sioux Center IA 51250

MENNINGA, CLARENCE, b Otley, Iowa, Apr 6, 28; m 49; c 7. NUCLEAR CHEMISTRY, PHYSICAL CHEMISTRY. *Educ:* Calvin Col, BA, 49; Western Mich Univ, MA, 59; Purdue Univ, PhD(chem), 66. *Prof Exp:* Chemist, Maytag Co, 50-56; teacher, Grand Rapids Christian High Sch, 56-61; chemist, Lawrence Radiation Lab, 66-67; ASST PROF GEOL, CALVIN COL, 67- *Mem:* Geochem Soc; Am Sci Affil; Meteoritical Soc. *Res:* Composition of meteorites; geochemistry. *Mailing Add:* Dept of Geol Calvin Col Grand Rapids MI 49506

MENNINGA, LARRY DEAN, computer science, see previous edition

MENNINGER, FLORIAN FRANCIS, JR, b Brooklyn, NY, Aug 18, 37; m 60; c 3. IMMUNOLOGY, IMMUNOCHEMISTRY. *Educ:* St Michael's Col, BA, 59; St John's Univ, NY, MS, 62, PhD(microbiol), 65. *Prof Exp:* Res assoc bact & immunol, State Univ NY Buffalo, 64-67; res immunologist, Mason Res Inst, 67-73; mgr immunochem reagent develop & prod, 73-74, mgr immunodiag pilot prod, Biomedica Div, 74-75, prod mgr immunol res & develop, 75-76, quality engr immunodiag, 76-78, proj mgr res & develop, Lab Prod Div, 78-80; TECH MKT DIR, SERAGEN INC, BOSTON, 80- *Concurrent Pos:* Res assoc, Urol Res Lab & head immunol & biochem div, Millard Fillmore Hosp Res Inst, Buffalo, NY, 65-66; instr, Clark Univ, 69. *Mem:* AAAS; Soc Indust Microbiol; NY Acad Sci; Am Pub Health Asn. *Res:* Applied immunology and immunochemistry; radioimmunoassay of protein hormones; tumor immunology; cancer specific antigens; non-specific enhancement of immune response; immunosuppression by anti-cancer agents. *Mailing Add:* 4 Underwood Ct Westborough MA 01581

MENNINGER, JOHN ROBERT, b Columbus, Ohio, July 29, 35; m 60; c 2. MOLECULAR BIOLOGY. *Educ:* Harvard Univ, AB, 57, PhD(biochem), 64. *Prof Exp:* Whitney Found vis res fel molecular genetics, Med Res Coun Lab Molecular Biol, Cambridge Univ, 63-66; asst prof biol, Univ Ore, 66-72, res assoc molecular biol, Inst Molecular Biol, 66-72; assoc prof, 72-78, PROF ZOOL, UNIV IOWA, 78- *Concurrent Pos:* Prog dir, Cellular & Molecular Biol Training Grant, Univ Iowa Grad Col, 75- *Mem:* Am Soc Biol Chemists. *Res:* Mechanism and control of information transfer in biological systems; protein biosynthesis; peptidyl-tRNA metabolism; mechanisms of cellular aging; accuracy of protein synthesis. *Mailing Add:* Dept of Zool Univ of Iowa Iowa City IA 52242

MENNINGER, KARL AUGUSTUS, b Topeka, Kans, July 22, 93; m 16, 41; c 4. PSYCHIATRY. *Educ:* Univ Wis, AB, 14, MS, 15; Harvard Univ, MD, 17. *Hon Degrees:* DSc, Washburn Univ, 49, Univ Wis, 65; LHD, Park Col, 55, St Benedict's Col, Kans, 63; LLD, Jefferson Med Col, 56, Parsons Col, 60, Kans State Univ, 62, Baker Univ, 65. *Prof Exp:* Intern, Kansas City Gen Hosp, Mo, 17-18; asst neuropath, Harvard Med Sch, 18-20; prof ment hyg, criminol & abnormal psychol, Washburn Col, 23-40; dean, Menninger Sch Psychiat, 46-70, dir educ, Menninger Found, 46-70, chmn bd trustees, 54-70, mem educ comt, 67-70, chief staff, Menninger Clin, 25-46, 52-70; prof med, 70-76, UNIV PROF AT LARGE, SCH MED, UNIV KANS, 76- *Concurrent Pos:* Asst, Med Col, Tufts Univ, 18-19; from asst to instr, Boston Psychopathic Hosp, 19; ed-in-chief, Bull, Menninger Clin, 20-; col asst, Topeka State Hosp, Kans, 20, chief consult, 48-; adv, Surg Gen, US Army, 45; consult, Fed Bur Prisons, Off Voc Rehab, Dept Health, Educ & Welfare, 48-; consult, Vet Admin Hosp, Topeka, 48-; mgr, Winter Vet Admin Hosp, 45-48, chmn, Dean's Comt & sr consult, 48-55; consult, Forbes AFB Hosp, 58- & Stone-Brandel Ctr, Chicago; dir, Topeka Inst Psychoanal, 60-; mem, Adv Comt, Int Surv Correctional Res & Pract, Calif, 60-; prof-at-large, Univ Kans; neuropsychiatrist, Stormont-Vail Hosp, Topeka; vis prof, Med Sch, Univ Cincinnati, trustee, Albert Deutsch Mem Found, 61; trustee, Aspen Inst Humanistic Studies, 61-64; consult, Inst Mgt Bd Social Welfare, State Kans; consult, Res Inst, Boston Univ, Europ Educ Ctr, Asn Migros Schs, Zurich; mem, Nat Cong Am Indian; mem, Kans Bd, John F Kennedy Mem Libr, Bd Overseers, Lemberg Ctr Study Violence, Brandeis Univ & Spec Comt Psychiat, Off Sci Res & Develop. *Honors & Awards:* Distinguished Serv Award, Am Psychiat Asn, 65. *Mem:* Fel AMA; fel Am Psychiat Asn; fel Am Psychoanal Asn (pres, 41-43); fel Am Col Physicians; Am Orthopsychiat Asn (secy, 26, pres, 27); hon fel Am Asn Suicidology. *Res:* Influenza and mental diseases; psychological factors in somatic disease; suicide; hypertension; industrial and military psychiatry; psychiatric education; criminology; penology; religion. *Mailing Add:* Menninger Found Box 829 Topeka KS 66601

MENNINGER, WILLIAM WALTER, b Topeka, Kans, Oct 23, 31; m 53; c 6. PSYCHIATRY. *Educ:* Stanford Univ, AB, 53; Cornell Univ, MD, 57; Am Bd Psychiat & Neurol, dipl, Am Bd Forensic Psychiatry, dipl. *Prof Exp:* Intern, Harvard Med Serv & Boston City Hosp, 57-58; resident psychiat, Menninger Sch Psychiat, 58-61; comdg med officer, USPHS, 61; chief med officer & psychiatrist, Fed Reformatory, El Reno, Okla, 61-63; assoc psychiatrist, Peace Corps, 63-64; coordr develop, 67-69, STAFF PSYCHIATRIST, MENNINGER FOUND, 65- *Concurrent Pos:* Mem staff, USPHS, 59-64; mem nat adv health coun, HEW, 67-71; mem, Nat Comn Causes & Prevention Violence, 68-69; clin supvr, Topeka State Hosp, 69-70, sect dir, 70-72, asst supt, clin dir & dir residency training, 72-81; mem, Fed Prison Facil Planning Coun, 70-73; ed, Psychiat Digest, 71-74; mem adv bd, Nat Inst Corrections, 74-, chmn, 80-82; adj prof, Washburn Univ & San Francisco Theol Sem; lectr, Menninger Sch Psychiat, Topeka Inst Psychoanalysis; consult, US Bur Prisons. *Mem:* Inst of Med of Nat Acad Sci; AMA; Am Acad Psychiat & Law; AAAS; fel Am Col Physicians. *Mailing Add:* Menninger Found Box 829 Topeka KS 66601

MENNITT, PHILIP GARY, b Battle Creek, Mich, Mar 29, 37; m 61; c 4. PHYSICAL CHEMISTRY. *Educ:* Providence Col, BS, 58; Mass Inst Technol, PhD(phys chem), 62. *Prof Exp:* From instr to asst prof, 64-73, ASSOC PROF CHEM, BROOKLYN COL, 73- *Mem:* Am Chem Soc. *Res:* Nuclear magnetic resonance spectroscopy. *Mailing Add:* Dept of Chem Brooklyn Col Brooklyn NY 11210

MENON, MANCHERY PRABHAKARA, b India, Aug 31, 28; m 55; c 2. NUCLEAR CHEMISTRY, RADIOCHEMISTRY. *Educ:* Univ Madras, BSc, 49; Agra Univ, MSc, 53; Univ Ark, PhD(nuclear chem, radiochem), 63. *Prof Exp:* Teacher sci, St Mary's CGH Sch, Kerala, India, 49-50; HS Vadayar, Kerala, 50-51; lectr chem, NSS Col, 53-55; lectr & head dept, Moulmein Col, Rangoon, 55-59; res asst, Univ Ark, 59-63; res assoc nuclear sci, Mass Inst Technol, 63-64; asst prof chem & asst res chemist, Activation Anal Lab, Tex A&M Univ, 64-67; assoc prof, 67-71, PROF CHEM, SAVANNAH STATE COL, 71- *Concurrent Pos:* Res grants, NSF, NASA, Am Chem Soc-PRF, Res Corp, Environ Protection Agency & NIH. *Mem:* Am Chem Soc. *Res:* Nuclear fission; natural radioactivity; fall-out from nuclear detonation; radio reagent methods of analysis for five elements; trace element release from sediments; lactate dehydrogenase iroenzymes in clinical chemistry; author or coauthor of forty publications. *Mailing Add:* 2 Friar Tuck Dr Savannah GA 31406

MENON, PREMACHANDRAN R(AMA), b Tapah, Malaysia, June 29, 31; US citizen; m 59; c 1. ELECTRICAL ENGINEERING, COMPUTER SCIENCE. *Educ:* Banaras Hindu Univ, BSc, 54; Univ Wash, PhD(elec eng), 62. *Prof Exp:* Apprentice engr, Delhi Cloth Mills, India, 54-56, asst engr, 56-57; asst prof elec eng, Univ Wash, 62-63; MEM TECH STAFF, BELL TEL LABS, 63- *Mem:* Inst Elec & Electronics Engrs. *Res:* Switching theory; diagnosis of digital circuits; computer applications. *Mailing Add:* Bell Tel Labs Naperville IL 60566

MENSAH, PATRICIA LUCAS, b Washington, DC, Feb 7, 48. NEUROANATOMY, NEUROSCIENCES. *Educ:* Howard Univ, BS, 70; Univ Calif, Irvine, PhD(biol sci), 74. *Prof Exp:* Psychologist neuropsychol, NIMH, 70; fel psychiat, State Univ NY Stony Brook, 74-75; instr neuroanat, Univ Calif, Irvine, 75, NIMH fel psychobiol, 75-76; ASST PROF ANAT, UNIV SOUTHERN CALIF, 76- *Concurrent Pos:* mem, Minority Women in Sci Network, AAAS. *Mem:* Am Asn Anatomists; Soc Neurosci. *Res:* Detailed neuroanatomical analyses of projection patterns within the caudate nuclei of the mammalian striatum; dendritic specialization: a look at the specific synaptic contacts of individual dendrites of the same neuron; neuronal cell death during development. *Mailing Add:* Dept of Anat Sch of Med Univ of Southern Calif Los Angeles CA 90033

MENSER, HARRY ALVIN, JR, b Pittsburgh, Pa, Dec 30, 30; m 60; c 2. PLANT PHYSIOLOGY. *Educ:* Univ Delaware, BS, 54; Univ Md, MS, 59, PhD(agron, bot), 62. *Prof Exp:* Asst county agent, Agr Exten Serv, Univ Md, 55-57, asst agron, Univ Md, 57-59; res technician, Tobacco Lab, Plant Genetics & Germplasm Inst, Sci & Educ Admin-Agr Res, US Dept Agr, 60-63, res plant physiologist, 63-80; ASSOC PROF HORT, UNIV IDAHO, 80- *Mem:* Sigma Xi; Am Soc Hort Sci; Am Soc Agron; Crop Sci Soc Am. *Res:* Analysis of heavy metals as environmental hazards; land recycling of municipal wastes; revegetation of lands disturbed by surface mining; fruit and vegetables; nursery and ornamentals; christmas trees; grain and forages; biomass for fuels; cooperative extension service. *Mailing Add:* Agr Exp Sta Univ Idaho Rte 3 Box 298 Sandpoint ID 83864

MENSING, RICHARD WALTER, b Hackensack, NJ, Sept 20, 36; m 57; c 3. STATISTICS. *Educ:* Valparaiso Univ, BS, 60; Iowa State Univ, MS, 65, PhD(statist), 68. *Prof Exp:* Engr, Gen Elec Co, 60-62; from instr to assoc prof statist, Iowa State Univ, 66-77; STATISTICIAN, LAWRENCE LIVERMORE LAB, 77- *Mem:* Inst Math Statist; Am Statist Asn. *Res:* Engineering and industrial statistics; applied probability. *Mailing Add:* Lawrence Livermore Lab PO Box 808 Livermore CA 94550

MENTE, GLEN ALLEN, b Wheatland, Iowa, Feb 25, 38; m 59; c 2. ANIMAL NUTRITION. *Educ:* Iowa State Univ, BS, 61, MS, 63. *Prof Exp:* Nutritionist, Farmers Coop Soc, 63-64; nutritionist, 64-67, mgr, 67-74, vpres, 74-81, BD DIRS & PRES NUTRIT & PROD DEVELOP, KENT FEEDS INC, 81- *Mem:* Am Soc Animal Sci; Agr Res Inst; Nutrit Coun Am Feed Mgrs; Nutrit Feed Ingredients Asn. *Res:* Continuous evaluation of nutrient requirements for swine, beef, dairy, poultry, turkeys, lambs, horses, fish, pets and miscellaneous animals; also genetic research with swine and beef. *Mailing Add:* Kent Feeds Inc 1600 Oregon St Muscatine IA 52761

MENTEL, THEODORE JOSEPH, systems analysis, see previous edition

MENTON, DAVID NORMAN, b Mankato, Minn, July 1, 38; m 61; c 2. ANATOMY, HISTOLOGY. *Educ:* Mankato State Col, BS, 59; Brown Univ, PhD(biol), 66. *Prof Exp:* Instr anat, 66-70, asst prof anat & path, 70-76, ASSOC PROF ANAT & PATH, SCH MED, WASH UNIV, 76- *Mem:* AAAS; Am Asn Anat; Soc Invest Dermat. *Res:* Fine structure of skin and its adnexa; barrier function of the stratum corneum; effects of essential fatty acid deficiency of skin. *Mailing Add:* Dept of Anat Wash Univ Sch of Med St Louis MO 63110

MENTON, ROBERT THOMAS, b Jamaica, NY, Dec 12, 42; m 67; c 1. ACOUSTICS. *Educ:* Cooper Union, BEng, 64; Univ Conn, MS, 67; Catholic Univ Am, PhD(eng acoustics), 73. *Prof Exp:* Mech engr, Naval Underwater Systems Ctr, 64-81; MECH ENGR, NAVAL RES LAB, 81- *Mem:* Acoust Soc Am. *Res:* Deterministic, random and turbulence excited responses of plate and shell structures with heavy fluid loading; performance of sonar systems in the noise field radiated by these structures. *Mailing Add:* Naval Res Lab Code 5844 4555 Overlook Ave SW Washington DC 20375

MENTONE, PAT FRANCIS, b Chicago, Ill, May 25, 42; m 70. INORGANIC CHEMISTRY, ELECTROCHEMISTRY. *Educ:* Col St Thomas, BS, 64; Univ Minn, PhD(inorg chem), 69. *Prof Exp:* Sr chemist, 69-73, plating prod mgr, 73-74, ENG SUPVR, BUCKBEE MEARS CO, 74- *Mem:* Am Chem Soc; Am Electroplaters Soc. *Res:* New product development and manufacturing engineering for microelectronic components. *Mailing Add:* 1756 Eleanor St Paul MN 55116

MENTZER, JOHN R(AYMOND), b Arch Spring, Pa, June 16, 16; m; c 2. PHYSICS. *Educ:* Pa State Univ, BS, 42, MS, 48; Ohio State Univ, PhD(physics), 52. *Prof Exp:* Res assoc antennas, Ohio State Univ, 48-52; mem staff propagation theory, Lincoln Lab, Mass Inst Technol, 52-54; from assoc prof to prof elec eng, 54-57, PROF ENG SCI, PA STATE UNIV, 57-, HEAD DEPT, 74- *Concurrent Pos:* Consult, Sandia Corp, 59- & Bell Tel Labs, 65- *Mem:* AAAS; sr mem Inst Elec & Electronics Engrs; Soc Indust & Appl Math; Am Soc Eng Educ. *Res:* Scattering and diffraction of electromagnetic waves; magnetoplasma dynamics; ionospheric and tropospheric propagation; high energy particle dynamics and interactions with electromagnetic fields. *Mailing Add:* Dept of Eng Sci & Mech Pa State Univ University Park PA 16802

MENZ, LEO JOSEPH, b Erie, Pa, Mar 7, 27; m 54; c 6. BIOPHYSICS, CRYOBIOLOGY. *Educ:* Gannon Col, BS, 49; St Louis Univ, MS, 52, PhD(biophys), 57. *Prof Exp:* Asst prof biol & dir dept, Gannon Col, 54-57; res assoc, Am Found Biol Res, 57-68; ASSOC PROF SURG, ST LOUIS UNIV, 68- *Concurrent Pos:* Consult, US Vet-Cochran Hosp, St Louis; adj assoc prof biol, St Louis Univ, 80- *Mem:* Sigma Xi; Soc Cryobiol; Electron Micros Soc Am; Biophys Soc; Soc Cell Biol. *Res:* Effects of low temperature on biological material; freeze-drying; correlation of ultrastructural changes and function of frozen-thawed tissues, such as mammalian nerve, heart and blood cells; toxicity of cryoprotectants; hypothermic perservation of mammalian heart and kidney; ultrastructure; nature of freezing injury. *Mailing Add:* Dept Surg 1402 S Grand Blvd St Louis Univ St Louis MO 63104

MENZ, WILLIAM WOLFGANG, b Zweibruecken, Ger, Mar 2, 17; m 41; c 2. ORGANIC CHEMISTRY, CHEMICAL LITERATURE. *Educ:* Univ Munich, Diplom Chemiker, 39. *Prof Exp:* Br chief, Intel Dept, US Army Air Force & US Air Force, 46-50; ed, USPHS, 50-51; info analyst, Gen Aniline & Film Corp, 51-52 & Ethyl Corp, 52-57; sect chief tobacco res, R J Reynolds Indust, 57-70; dir tech info, 70-75, dir res, 75-76, V PRES RES, DAIRY RES INC, 76- *Mem:* Am Dairy Sci Asn; Am Chem Soc. *Res:* Scientific information storage and retrieval; fats and oils; dairy chemistry. *Mailing Add:* Dairy Res Inc 6300 River Rd Rosemont IL 60018

MENZEL, BRUCE WILLARD, b Waukesha, Wis, Aug 23, 42; m 69; c 2. ICHTHYOLOGY, FISHERIES. *Educ:* Univ Wis, BS, 64; Marquette Univ, MS, 66; Cornell Univ, PhD(vert zool), 70. *Prof Exp:* Asst prof, 70-74, assoc prof, 74-80, PROF ZOOL, IOWA STATE UNIV, 80- *Mem:* Am Soc Ichthyol & Herpet; Am Fisheries Soc. *Res:* Systematics; ecology and behavior of North American freshwater fishes. *Mailing Add:* Dept of Animal Ecol Iowa State Univ Ames IA 50011

MENZEL, DANIEL B, b Cincinnati, Ohio, Sept 27, 34; m 56; c 1. TOXICOLOGY, PHARMACOLOGY. *Educ:* Univ Calif, Berkeley, BS, 56, PhD(biol chem), 61. *Prof Exp:* Asst specialist nutrit, Univ Calif, Berkeley, 62, 65, asst prof food sci & asst biochemist, Inst Marine Sci, 62-67, asst prof food sci, Univ & asst biochemist, Agr Exp Sta, 65-67; res assoc biol, Pac Northwest Labs, Battelle Mem Inst, Wash, 67-68, mgr nutrit & food technol sect, 68-69; dir clin res, Ross Labs Div, Abbott Labs, Ohio, 69-71; assoc prof, 71-78, head, Div Pharmacol, 75-77, PROF PHARMACOL & EXP MED, DUKE UNIV, 78-, COORDR, ENVIRON HEALTH AFFAIRS, 75- *Concurrent Pos:* Biochemist, US Bur Com Fisheries, 62-65; consult, Life Sci Div, Ames Res Ctr, NASA, 63-71; consult, Environ Protection Agency, 71-, mem, Sci Adv Bd, 78-; mem, Toxicol Study Sect, NIH, 75-80; mem, Acad Coun, Duke Univ, 77-78; ed, Toxicol Letts, 77- & Res Methods in Toxicol, 78-; mem, Nat Libr Med Adv Bd, 78-; Foggarty sr fel, 80; mem, Bd Toxicol & Environ Health Hazards & chmn, Comt Drinking Water & Health, Nat Acad Sci, 81; Alexander von Humboldt prize, 80. *Mem:* AAAS; Am Chem Soc; Am Oil Chem Soc; Entom Soc Am; NY Acad Sci. *Res:* Mechanisms of aging; lipid oxidation and vitamin E; biochemistry of fat soluble vitamins; environmental effects on the lung; chronic lung disease. *Mailing Add:* Dept Pharmacol Duke Univ Med Ctr Durham NC 27710

MENZEL, DAVID WASHINGTON, b India, Feb 22, 28; m 52. OCEANOGRAPHY. *Educ:* Elmhurst Col, BS, 49; Univ Ill, MS, 52; Univ Mich, PhD(fisheries), 58. *Prof Exp:* Res biologist, Bermuda Biol Sta, 57-63; assoc scientist, Woods Hole Oceanog Inst, 63-70; DIR, SKIDAWAY INST OCEANOG, 70- *Mem:* AAAS; Am Soc Limnol & Oceanog. *Res:* Ecology and physiology of marine plankton; marine chemistry and biology. *Mailing Add:* Skidaway Inst of Oceanog PO Box 13687 Savannah GA 31406

MENZEL, ERHARD ROLAND, US citizen. MOLECULAR SPECTROSCOPY. *Educ:* Wash State Univ, BS, 67, PhD(physics), 70. *Prof Exp:* Fels, Simon Frazer Univ, 70-72, Purdue Univ, 72-73 & Univ Ky, 73-74; mem sci staff physics, Xerox Res Centre Can Ltd, 75-79; ASST PROF PHYSICS, TEX TECH UNIV, 79- *Mem:* Am Chem Soc; Am Phys Soc. *Res:* Luminescence spectroscopy of pigments and dyes; electron spin resonance of free radicals and transition metal complexes; fingerprint detection with use of lasers. *Mailing Add:* Physics Dept Tex Tech Univ Lubbock TX 79409

MENZEL, JOERG H, b Kassel, Ger, July 27, 39; US citizen. NUCLEAR SCIENCE. *Educ:* Rensselaer Polytech Inst, BME, 62, MS, 64, PhD(nuclear sci), 68. *Prof Exp:* Staff mem res & develop safeguards, Los Alamos Sci Lab, 68-73; first officer int safeguards, Int Atomic Energy Agency, 73-75; staff mem res & develop safeguards, Los Alamos Sci Lab, 75-76; phys sci officer, 76-78, chief nuclear safeguards staff, 78-81, CHIEF NUCLEAR SAFEGUARDS & TECHNOL DIV, ARMS CONTROL & DISARMAMENT AGENCY, 81- *Honors & Awards:* Meritorious Honor Award, Arms Control & Disarmament Agency, 78. *Mem:* Inst Nuclear Mat Mgt; Am Nuclear Soc. *Res:* Non-destructive analysis of nuclear materials. *Mailing Add:* US Arms Control & Disarm Agency State Dept Bldg Washington DC 20451

MENZEL, MARGARET YOUNG, b Kerrville, Tex, June 21, 24; m 49; c 3. CYTOGENETICS. *Educ:* Southwestern Univ, Tex, BA, 44; Univ Va, PhD(biol), 49. *Prof Exp:* Instr chem & bact, Lamar Col, 44-45; instr agron, Agr & Mech Col, Tex, 49-54; res assoc, 55-63, assoc prof, 63-68, assoc chmn dept, 72-73, PROF BIOL SCI, FLA STATE UNIV, 68- *Concurrent Pos:* Plant geneticist, Agr Res Serv, USDA, 56-63; res grants, Am Philos Soc, 55-66, Sigma Xi, 55, Atomic Energy Comn, 65-75, Cotton, Inc, 74-75, USDA, 77-81, Southern Regulatory Educ Bd, 78, NSF, 78-81 & 82-84 & Agr Res Serv, USDA, 78-84. *Mem:* Soc Study Evolution; Bot Soc Am; Genetics Soc Am; Am Soc Plant Taxon; Am Soc Cell Biol. *Res:* Cytotaxonomy and cytogenetics of Hibiscus; cytogenetics of cotton; fine structure of meiotic chromosomes. *Mailing Add:* Dept of Biol Sci Fla State Univ Tallahassee FL 32306

MENZEL, ROBERT WINSTON, b Toano, Va, Jan 29, 20. MARINE BIOLOGY. *Educ:* Col William & Mary, BS, 40, MA, 43; Tex A&M Univ, PhD, 54. *Prof Exp:* Asst, Va Fisheries Lab, 40-42, asst biologist, 42-46; lab instr bot, Univ Va, 46-47; biologist, Res Found, Agr & Mech Col Tex, 47-52, asst prof wildlife mgt, 53, instr biol, 53-54; from asst prof to assoc prof, 54-70, PROF OCEANOG, FLA STATE UNIV, 70- *Mem:* AAAS; Am Fisheries Soc; Am Soc Limnol & Oceanog; Am Soc Ichthyol & Herpet; Nat Shellfisheries Asn (vpres, 71-72, pres, 72-73). *Res:* Clam and oyster biology; marine ecology; commercial fish. *Mailing Add:* Dept of Oceanog Fla State Univ Tallahassee FL 32306

MENZEL, RONALD GEORGE, b Independence, Iowa, Jan 23, 24; m 52; c 2. SOIL CHEMISTRY. *Educ:* Iowa State Col, BS, 47; Univ Wis, PhD(soil chem), 50. *Prof Exp:* Soil scientist, Agr Res Serv, 50-69, dir, 69-80, RES LEADER, WATER QUAL MGT LAB, US DEPT AGR, 77- *Concurrent Pos:* Ed, J Environ Qual, 77- *Mem:* AAAS; Soil Sci Soc Am; fel Am Soc Agron; Am Chem Soc. *Res:* Reactions of copper and zinc in soils and availability to plants; uptake of nuclear fission products by plants; relation of agricultural chemicals and fertilizers to water pollution. *Mailing Add:* Water Qual Mgt Lab US Dept Agr PO Box 1430 Durant OK 74701

MENZEL, WOLFGANG PAUL, b Heidenheim, Ger, Oct 5, 45; US citizen. THEORETICAL SOLID STATE PHYSICS. *Educ:* Univ Md, BS, 67; Univ Wis, MS, 68, PhD(physics), 74. *Prof Exp:* Res asst solid state physics, Univ, 72-74, proj asst, 74-75, proj assoc radiometry, 75-77, ASST SCIENTIST, SPACE SCI & ENG CTR, UNIV WIS-MADISON, 77- *Mem:* Sigma Xi. *Res:* Investigation of optical properties of solids using the method of linear combinations of atomic orbitals; real time analysis of the atmosphere with infrared radiometric satellite probing. *Mailing Add:* Space Sci & Eng Ctr 1225 Dayton St Madison WI 53706

MENZER, ROBERT EVERETT, b Wash, DC, Dec 21, 38; m 62; c 3. INSECT TOXICOLOGY. *Educ:* Univ Pa, BS, 60; Univ Md, MS, 62; Univ Wis, PhD(entom, biochem), 64. *Prof Exp:* Res asst entom, Univ Md, 61-62, instr, 62; instr, Univ Wis, 64; from asst prof to assoc prof, 64-73, assoc dean grad studies, 74-76, actg dean grad studies, 76-80, PROF ENTOM, UNIV MD, COLLEGE PARK, 73-, CHMN, GRAD PROG MARINE-ESTUARINE-ENVIRON SCI, 80-, DIR, WATER RESOURCES RES CTR, 81- *Concurrent Pos:* Mem toxicol study sect, NIH, 71-75, chmn, 73-75. *Mem:* AAAS; Am Chem Soc; Entom Soc Am; Soc Toxicol. *Res:* Pesticide chemistry and toxicology; metabolism of organophosphorus insecticides; insect biochemistry. *Mailing Add:* Dept of Entom Univ of Md College Park MD 20742

MENZIE, DONALD E, b DuBois, Pa, Apr 4, 22; m 46; c 4. ENGINEERING. *Educ:* Pa State Univ, BS, 42, MS, 48, PhD, 62. *Prof Exp:* Jr marine engr, Philadelphia Navy Yard, 43-46; asst petrol eng, Pa State Univ, 46-48, instr, 48-51; from asst prof to prof, 51-72, dir, Sch Petrol Eng, 63-72, dir petrol eng educ, 63-79, PROF PETROL & GEOL ENG, UNIV OKLA, 72-, ASSOC EXEC DIR, ENERGY RESOURCES CTR, 79- *Concurrent Pos:* Consult, 51-; Halliburton distinguished lectr award, Col Eng, Univ Okla, 81-84. *Mem:* Am Inst Mining, Metall & Petrol Engrs. *Res:* Petroleum, reservoir and geological engineering; secondary recovery. *Mailing Add:* 1503 Melrose Dr Norman OK 73069

MENZIES, CARL STEPHEN, b Menard, Tex, Mar 6, 32; m 52; c 2. ANIMAL HUSBANDRY. *Educ:* Tex Tech Col, BS, 54; Kans State Univ, MS, 56; Univ Ky, PhD(animal nutrit), 65. *Prof Exp:* Asst county agent, Tex Exten Serv, 54; res asst animal husb, Kans State Univ, 54-55, from instr to assoc prof, 55-68; prof animal sci & head dept, SDak State Univ, 68-72; PROF ANIMAL SCI & RESIDENT DIR RES, TAMU AGR RES & EXTEN CTR, TEX A&M UNIV, 72- *Mem:* Am Soc Animal Sci; Sigma Xi. *Res:* Nutrition and breeding of sheep. *Mailing Add:* Tex A&M Univ Res & Exten Ctr Box 950 Rte 1 San Angelo TX 76901

MENZIES, DONALD ROSS, agricultural engineering, see previous edition

MENZIES, ROBERT ALLEN, b San Francisco, Calif, Nov 13, 35; m 58; c 3. BIOCHEMISTRY. *Educ:* Univ Fla, BS, 60, MS, 62; Cornell Univ, PhD(phys biol), 66. *Prof Exp:* Res chemist, Aging Res Lab, Vet Admin Hosp, Baltimore, Md, 65-67; asst prof biochem, La State Univ Med Ctr, New Orleans, 67-73; asst prof, 73-74, assoc prof biochem & ocean sci, 77-79, ASSOC PROF BIOCHEM, LIFE SCI CTR, NOVA UNIV, 75-, PROF BIOCHEM & OCEANOG, 79- *Mem:* Am Soc Biol Chem; Am Chem Soc; Biophys Soc; NY Acad Sci; Am Soc Cell Biol. *Res:* Biochemical systematics with applications to evolution and fisheries; metabolism of organic pollutants by marine aguatic organisms; relationship of oceanic currents with gene flow and larval dispersal and recruitment. *Mailing Add:* Biol Lab Nova Univ Oceanog Ctr Dania FL 33004

MENZIES, ROBERT THOMAS, b San Francisco, Calif, Mar 31, 43; m 66; c 1. LASER SPECTROSCOPY, ATMOSPHERIC PHYSICS. *Educ:* Mass Inst Technol, BS, 65; Calif Inst Technol, MS, 67, PhD(physics), 70. *Prof Exp:* Scientist laser physics, 70-75, MEM TECH STAFF ATMOSPHERIC

STUDIES, JET PROPULSION LAB, CALIF INST TECHNOL, 75- *Concurrent Pos:* Vis assoc, Calif Inst Technol, 72-77; vis scientist, Chalmers Inst Technol, Goteborg, Sweden, 74. *Mem:* AAAS; Am Geophys Union; fel Optical Soc Am; Sigma Xi. *Res:* Atmospheric measurements with laser and heterodyne detection techniques; laser development. *Mailing Add:* Jet Propulsion Lab 4800 Oak Grove Dr Pasadena CA 91103

MENZIN, MARGARET SCHOENBERG, b New York, NY, Nov 17, 42; m 68; c 2. MATHEMATICS. *Educ:* Swarthmore Col, BA, 63; Brandeis Univ, MA, 67, PhD(math), 70. *Prof Exp:* From instr to asst prof, 69-73, chmn dept, 71-77, assoc prof, 73-80, PROF MATH, SIMMONS COL, 80-, CO-DIR, PROG APPL COMPUT SCI, 80- *Concurrent Pos:* Consult & dir, Design Technol Corp, 69- *Mem:* Am Math Soc; Math Asn Am; Asn Women in Math; Women in Sci & Eng; Sigma Xi. *Res:* Ring theory; linear programming; mathematical models. *Mailing Add:* Dept Math Simmons Col 300 The Fenway Boston MA 02115

MEOLA, ROBERT RALPH, b Newark, NJ, Jan 27, 27; m 48; c 2. ELECTRICAL ENGINEERING. *Educ:* Newark Col Eng, BS, 46; Stevens Inst Technol, MS, 49. *Prof Exp:* Jr engr, Nat Union Radio Corp, 46-47; instr elec eng, Newark Col Eng, 47-51; engr, Western Elec Co, 51-53; from instr to assoc prof, 53-69, PROF ELEC ENG, NEWARK COL ENG, NJ INST TECHNOL, 69- *Concurrent Pos:* Consult, Int Tel & Tel Corp, NJ, 58-60, Hewlett Packard Co, 61-64, 66, NJ Bell Tel Co, 65 & Calculagraph Co, 69-72. *Mem:* Am Soc Eng Educ; sr mem Inst Elec & Electronics Engrs; Nat Soc Prof Engrs. *Res:* Analysis and design of transistor circuits. *Mailing Add:* Dept Elec Eng Col Eng NJ Inst Technol Newark NJ 07102

MEOLA, ROGER WALKER, b Cleveland, Ohio, Aug 25, 34; m 56. INSECT PHYSIOLOGY, MEDICAL-VETERINARY ENTOMOLOGY. *Educ:* Ohio State Univ, BS, 56, MS, 58, Ph(entom), 63. *Prof Exp:* Entomologist, Fla State Bd Health, 64-69; res assoc, Univ Ga, 70-72; res assoc, Tex A&M Unniv, 73-74, lectr introductory entom, 75-77, asst prof vet entom, 78-81. *Mem:* AAAS; Am Mosquito Control Asn; Am Soc Zoologists; Entom Soc Am; Sigma Xi. *Res:* Endocrine regulation of mosquito reproduction and behavior; physiology of diapause and insect microsurgical techniques. *Mailing Add:* Dept Entom Tex A&M Univ College Station TX 77843

MEOLA, SHIRLEE MAY, b Canton, Ohio, Dec 7, 35; m 56. ENTOMOLOGY. *Educ:* Ohio State Univ, BSc, 58, MSc, 62, PhD(zool & entom), 70. *Prof Exp:* Res assoc entom, Entom Res Ctr, Vero Beach, Fla, 64-69 & Univ Ga, 69-72; RES ENTOMOLOGIST, TOXICOL & ENTOM RES LAB, SCI & EDUC ADMIN-AGR RES, USDA, 72- *Mem:* Am Soc Zoologist; Am Soc Cell Biologists; Entom Soc Am; Am Soc Electron Microscopists. *Res:* Histological and ultrastructural studies of the morphology of Diptera, especially the neuroendocrine and reproductive systems and growth regulators in insects. *Mailing Add:* Vet Toxicol & Entom Res Lab USDA PO Box GE College Station TX 77801

MERANZE, DAVID RAYMOND, b Philadelphia, Pa, Dec 25, 00; m 27; c 2. PATHOLOGY. *Educ:* Univ Pa, BS, 21, MA, 20; Jefferson Med Col, MD, 27. *Prof Exp:* Asst biochem, Jefferson Med Col, 22-23; instr path, Grad Sch Med, Univ Pa, 28-30; dir labs & pathologist, Mt Sinai Hosp, Philadelphia, 30-54; dir res & med educ, 54-55, pathologist & dir labs & res, South Div, 55-66, MEM & HEAD RES PATH, KORMAN RES INST, ALBERT EINSTEIN MED CTR, 66- *Concurrent Pos:* Asst, Jefferson Med Col, 31-33, assoc, 34-36; dep asst pathologist, Philadelphia Gen Hosp, 38-45; assoc mem, Med Adv Bd Philadelphia, 42-44; consult pathologist, Philadelphia Psychiat Hosp, 45-64; affiliate prof path, Hahnemann Med Col, 47-66; consult, Fels Res Inst, Med Sch, Temple Univ, 62-73 & NIH, 66-74; pathologist & dir labs, Philadelphia Geratric Ctr, 70-78. *Honors & Awards:* Highest Award, Int Cong Radiol, 37. *Mem:* AAAS; Am Soc Clin Path; Am Soc Microbiol; fel AMA; Col Am Path. *Res:* Toxic granulations of white blood cells; phosphatase content of the blood in jaundice; syphilis and tuberculosis in rabbits; role of liver in metabolism of estrogens; galactose tolerance test; coagulation of blood; testicular histopathology; pathogenesis of atherosclerosis; histopathology; experimental schistosomiasis; ovarian histology; experimental carcinogenesis and emphysema. *Mailing Add:* Pelham Park Apts 229 West Upsal St Philadelphia PA 19119

MERBS, CHARLES FRANCIS, b Neenah, Wis, Sept 3, 36; m 62; c 2. PHYSICAL ANTHROPOLOGY. *Educ:* Univ Wis-Madison, BS, 58, MS, 63, PhD(anthrop, genetics), 69. *Prof Exp:* From instr to assoc prof anthrop, Univ Chicago, 63-73; chmn dept, 73-79, assoc prof, 73-74, PROF ANTHROP, ARIZ STATE UNIV, 74- *Mem:* Fel Arctic Inst NAm; Soc Am Archaeol; Am Asn Phys Anthropologists; Soc Study Human Biol. *Res:* Physical anthropology, human osteology, paleopathology, medical genetics; Arctic populations of America and Siberia; southwestern United States and northeastern Africa. *Mailing Add:* Dept Anthrop Ariz State Univ Tempe AZ 85281

MERCADO-JIMENEZ, TEODORO, b Arecibo, PR, Jan 4, 35; m 58; c 5. ELECTRICAL ENGINEERING, CONTROL SYSTEMS. *Educ:* Univ PR, Mayaguez, BSEE, 57; Univ Mich, Ann Arbor, MS, 61; Tex A&M Univ, PhD(elec eng), 65. *Prof Exp:* Instr elec eng, Univ PR, Mayagüez, 57-60; instr, Tex A&M Univ, 62-64; asst prof, 64-67, assoc prof, 67-80, PROF ELEC ENG, UNIV PR, MAYAGUEZ, 80- *Concurrent Pos:* Am Soc Eng Educ summer fac fel, Goddard Space Flight Ctr, NASA, 65 & 66; vis prof, Univ Oriente, Venezuela, 70-71. *Mem:* Inst Elec & Electronics Engrs; PR Col Eng, Archit & Surveyors; PR Soc Elec Engrs. *Res:* Circuit theory; instrumentation; applied mathematics; education. *Mailing Add:* Dept Elec Eng Univ PR Mayaguez PR 00708

MERCER, EDWARD EVERETT, b Buffalo, NY, Mar 5, 34; m 57; c 6. PHYSICAL INORGANIC CHEMISTRY. *Educ:* Canisius Col, 55; Purdue Univ, PhD(phys chem), 60. *Prof Exp:* Res assoc chem, Lawrence Radiation Lab, Univ Calif, 60-61; from asst prof to assoc prof, 61-73, asst head dept, 73-74, PROF CHEM, UNIV SC, 73-, ASST DEAN SCI & MATH, 79- *Mem:* AAAS; Am Chem Soc. *Res:* Thermodynamics and kinetics of metal complexes in solution; chemistry of ruthenium. *Mailing Add:* Dept Chem Univ SC Columbia SC 29208

MERCER, EDWARD KING, b Santa Barbara, Calif, July 1, 31; m 63; c 2. PLANT NEMATOLOGY, FRESH WATER BIOLOGY. *Educ:* Univ Calif, Santa Barbara, BA, 58, MA, 62; Auburn Univ, PhD(plant nematol), 68. *Prof Exp:* Res asst plant nematol, Univ Calif, Riverside, 63-65; res asst, Auburn Univ, 65-68; assoc prof, 68-76, PROF BIOL SCI, CALIF STATE POLYTECH UNIV, POMONA, 76- *Mem:* AAAS; Am Inst Biol Sci; Am Soc Limnol & Oceanog; Soc Nematol; Asn Meiobenthologists. *Res:* Energy requirements and feeding behavior of free-living fresh water nematodes; nematodes in relation to water quality. *Mailing Add:* Dept of Biol Sci Calif State Polytech Univ Pomona CA 91768

MERCER, HENRY DWIGHT, b Blakely, Ga, Feb 20, 39; m 60; c 2. VETERINARY PHARMACOLOGY, VETERINARY TOXICOLOGY. *Educ:* Univ Ga, BS, 60, DVM, 63; Univ Fla, MS, 66; Am Bd Vet Toxicol, dipl, 73, Ohio State Univ, PhD, 76. *Prof Exp:* Practitioner vet med, Houston Animal Clin, Blakely, 63-64; NIH fel, Univ Fla, 65-66; br chief vet med, Div New Animal Drugs, Food & Drug Admin, 66-68, actg dir, Div Vet Res, 68-72 & 74-77, dept dir, 72-74; PROF, MISS STATE UNIV, 77- *Concurrent Pos:* Rating bd mem, Civil Serv Comn, 70-; mem res comt, Food & Drug Admin Task Force, 71 & Nat Mastitis Coun, 73-; fel, Ohio State Univ, 75-76; dir, Animal Health Ctr, Miss State Univ, 78-81, dir, Acad Prog, 79-80, admin officer, Col Vet Med, 79-82. *Honors & Awards:* Award of Merit, Food & Drug Admin, 74. *Mem:* Am Vet Med Asn; Sigma Xi; Am Soc Vet Physiol & Pharmacol; Am Col Vet Toxicol; Am Acad Pharmacol & Therapeut. *Res:* Clinical pharmacology in domestic animals, specifically, the metabolism kinetics and pharmacokinetics of veterinary drugs in food producing animals. *Mailing Add:* PO Drawer V Col Vet Med Mississippi State MS 39762

MERCER, JAMES WAYNE, b Panama City, Fla, Dec 23, 47; m 69. HYDROGEOLOGY. *Educ:* Fla State Univ, BS, 69; Univ Ill, MS, 72, PhD(geol), 73. *Prof Exp:* hydrologist, US Geol Surv, 72-79; PRES, GEOTRANS, INC, 79- *Concurrent Pos:* Asst prof, George Washington Univ, 80- *Mem:* Am Geophys Union; Soc Petrol Engrs; Am Soc Civil Engrs; Geological Soc Am; Am Water Resources Asn. *Res:* Development of theoretical and numerical models for simulating hydrogeologic processes, with emphasis on geothermal systems, hazardous waste, radioactive waste, and salt water intrusion. *Mailing Add:* Mail Stop 431 US Geol Surv Reston VA 22092

MERCER, LEONARD PRESTON, II, b Fort Worth, Tex, Jan 16, 41; m 63; c 3. NUTRITIONAL BIOCHEMISTRY. *Educ:* Univ Tex, Austin, BS, 68; La State Univ, PhD(biochem), 71. *Prof Exp:* NIH fel, Med Sch, Univ Ala, Birmingham, 71-73; instr, Univ S Ala, 73-74, asst prof biochem, 74-77; asst prof biochem, 77-79, ASSOC PROF & CHMN, SCH MED & DENT, ORAL ROBERTS UNIV, 79- *Mem:* Am Inst Nutrit; Nutrit Educ Soc; Am Chem Soc. *Res:* Mathematical analysis of biochemical responses to nutritional stimuli; prediction of nutritional responses of proteins and amino acids and comparison of biological efficacy of alternate nutrient sources. *Mailing Add:* Dept of Biochem Oral Roberts Univ Tulsa OK 74171

MERCER, MALCOLM CLARENCE, b St John's, Nfld, June 20, 44. FISHERIES MANAGEMENT, SYSTEMATIC ZOOLOGY. *Educ:* Mem Univ Nfld, BSc, 65, MSc, 68. *Prof Exp:* Scientist, Fisheries Res Bd Can, 65-69, res biologist, 69-74, sect head shellfish, 74-75, prog head marine fisheries mgt pelagic & shellfish, Nfld Biol Sta, 75-76, sr policy prog adv, Marine Mammals, Dept Environ Fish & Marine Serv, 76-78, assoc dir, Fisheries Res Br, Resource Serv Directorate, Fisheries Environ Fish & Oceans Serv, Ottawa, 78-79, dir, 79-81, DIR RES & RESOURCE SERV, DEPT FISHERIES & OCEANS, NFLD REGION, 81-; CAN WHALING COMNR, 78- *Concurrent Pos:* Vchmn, Int Whaling Comn, 78-81. *Mem:* Sigma Xi. *Res:* Research administration; resource management. *Mailing Add:* Dept Fisheries & Oceans PO Box 5667 St John's NF A1C 5X1 Can

MERCER, PAUL FREDERICK, b Guelph, Ont, Apr 21, 36; m 62; c 1. PHYSIOLOGY. *Educ:* Univ Toronto, DVM, 59; Cornell Univ, PhD(phys biol), 64. *Prof Exp:* Med Res Coun Can fel biol chem, Copenhagen Univ, 63-64; asst prof physiol, Univ Alta, 64-67; from asst prof to assoc prof, 67-80, PROF PHYSIOL, UNIV WESTERN ONT, 80- *Mem:* Soc Nephrology; Can Physiol Soc; Am Physiol Soc. *Res:* Renal physiology. *Mailing Add:* Dept of Physiol Univ of Western Ont London ON N6A 5B8 Can

MERCER, ROBERT ALLEN, b Providence, RI, Aug 2, 42; m 66; c 2. SYSTEMS ENGINEERING. *Educ:* Carnegie-Mellon Univ, BS, 64; Johns Hopkins Univ, PhD(physics), 69. *Prof Exp:* Res assoc physics, Johns Hopkins Univ, 69-70; asst prof, Ind Univ, Bloomington, 70-73; mem tech staff, Bell Labs, 73-75, tech supvr, 75-79; div mgr, AT&T Co, 79-81; DIR, BELL LABS, 81- *Mem:* Inst Elec & Electronics Engrs. *Res:* Telecommunications systems engineering. *Mailing Add:* Bell Labs Rm WB1L366 Crawford Corner Rd Holmdel NJ 07733

MERCER, ROBERT J, b Gordon, Nebr, Nov 28, 29; m 52; c 2. NUMERICAL ANALYSIS. *Educ:* Univ Calif, Berkeley, BA, 51, Los Angeles, MA, 56. *Prof Exp:* Mem tech staff, Space Tech Labs, 56-61; MEM TECH STAFF, AEROSPACE CORP, 61- *Concurrent Pos:* Lectr, Univ Calif, Los Angeles, 62-63 & Univ Southern Calif, 63-65. *Mem:* Soc Indust & Appl Math; Asn Comput Mach. *Res:* Satellite orbit reconstruction and tracking system analysis. *Mailing Add:* Aerospace Corp Box 92957 Los Angeles CA 90009

MERCER, ROBERT LEROY, b San Jose, Calif, July 11, 46; m 67; c 3. COMPUTER SCIENCE. *Educ:* Univ NMex, BSc, 68; Univ Ill, Urbana, MS, 70, PhD(comput sci), 72. *Prof Exp:* RES ASSOC AUTOMATIC CONTINUOUS SPEECH RECOGNITION, INT BUS MACH CORP, 72- *Mem:* Inst Elec & Electronics Engrs. *Res:* Theoretical nuclear physics at intermediate energies; automatic recognition of continuous speech. *Mailing Add:* Dept of Comput Sci IBM Res Ctr PO Box 218 Yorktown Heights NY 10598

MERCER, SAMUEL, JR, b Philadelphia, Pa, Sept 4, 20; m 44; c 8. MECHANICAL ENGINEERING. *Educ:* Drexel Inst Technol, BS, 43; Mich State Col, MS, 50; Purdue Univ, PhD(mech eng), 56. *Prof Exp:* Draftsman, Mech Design Sect, Glenn L Martin Co, 46-47; from instr to asst prof mech eng, Mich State Col, 47-53, from asst prof to assoc prof appl mech, 53-59; prof mech eng & head dept, 59-66, assoc dean col eng, 66-70, dir continuing educ, 71-72, dean continuing & coop educ, 72-77, DEAN CONTINUING EDUC, DREXEL UNIV, 77- *Mem:* Am Soc Mech Engrs; Am Soc Eng Educ. *Res:* Kinematics; dynamics; vibration; machine design; dynamics of cam actuated systems and automobile skid testing. *Mailing Add:* Off of Continuing Prof Educ Drexel Univ 32nd & Chestnut Sts Philadelphia PA 19104

MERCER, SHERWOOD ROCKE, b Manchester, Conn, June 27, 07; m 33; c 3. HISTORY OF MEDICINE, HISTORY OF SCIENCE. *Educ:* Wesleyan Univ, AB, 29, AM, 30. *Hon Degrees:* LLD, Philadelphia Col Textiles & Sci, 57. *Prof Exp:* Instr hist & eng, Pub Schs, Conn, 30-42; assoc, Harvard Univ, 42-44; chmn div appl sci, Elmira Col, 44-45; consult higher educ, Conn Dept Pub Instr, 45-46; dean fac, Muhlenberg Col, 46-54; prof hist med & osteop, 54-76, dean, 54-69, vpres educ affairs, 67-76, EMER PROF HIST MED & OSTEOP, PHILADELPHIA COL OSTEOP MED, 76- *Concurrent Pos:* Consult, Columbia Univ, 54-75. *Mem:* Am Osteop Asn; Am Asn Cols Osteop Med (secy-treas, 71-). *Res:* Nature, structure and teaching for a liberal education, particularly in a society heavily influenced by pure and applied science. *Mailing Add:* 13 Thompson Dr Havertown PA 19083

MERCER, THOMAS T, b Victoria, BC, Dec 30, 20; m 42; c 3. INDUSTRIAL HYGIENE, HEALTH PHYSICS. *Educ:* San Jose State Col, AB, 49; Univ Rochester, PhD(indust hyg), 57. *Prof Exp:* Health physicist & instr, Univ Wash, 53-55; res assoc aerosol physics, Atomic Energy Proj, Univ Rochester, 55-57, chief aerosol physics sect, 57-59; nuclear physicist, US Naval Radiol Defense Lab, San Francisco, 59-61; head dept aerosol physics, Lovelace Found Med Educ & Res, NMex, 61-65; assoc prof, 65-70, PROF RADIATION BIOL & BIOPHYS, UNIV ROCHESTER, 70- *Mem:* AAAS; Am Indust Hyg Asn; Health Phys Soc. *Res:* Production and characterization of airborne particulates; interaction of radioactive vapors with particles. *Mailing Add:* Dept Radiation Biol & Biophys Univ Rochester Rochester NY 14642

MERCEREAU, JAMES EDGAR, b Sharon, Pa, Apr 3, 30; m 50; c 3. PHYSICS. *Educ:* Pomona Col, BA, 53; Univ Ill, MS, 54; Calif Inst Technol, PhD, 59. *Hon Degrees:* DSc, Pomona Col, 68. *Prof Exp:* Asst, Univ Ill, 53-54; physicist, Hughes Res Labs, 54-59; asst prof, Calif Inst Technol, 59-62; prin scientist, Sci Labs, Ford Motor Co, Calif, 62-65, mgr cryogenics, 65-69; PROF APPL PHYSICS, CALIF INST TECHNOL, 69-, PROF PHYSICS, 80- *Concurrent Pos:* Consult, Hughes Aircraft Co, 59-60 & Aerospace Corp, 60-62; vis assoc, Calif Inst Technol, 64-65, res assoc, 65-; prof, Univ Calif, Irvine, 65-69. *Mem:* Fel Am Phys Soc. *Res:* Cryogenics; ferromagnetism. *Mailing Add:* Dept Physics Mail Code 63-37 Calif Inst Technol Pasadena CA 91109

MERCHANT, DONALD JOSEPH, b Biltmore, NC, Sept 7, 21; m 43; c 3. MICROBIOLOGY. *Educ:* Berea Col, AB, 42; Univ Mich, MS, 47, PhD(bact), 50. *Prof Exp:* From instr to prof bact, Univ Mich, 48-69; dir, W Alton Jones Cell Sci Ctr, Tissue Cult Asn, 69-73; PROF MICROBIOL & IMMUNOL & CHMN DEPT, EASTERN VA MED SCH, NORFOLK, 73-, DIR, TIDEWATER REGIONAL CANCER NETWORK, 77- *Concurrent Pos:* Mem working cadre, Nat Prostatic Cancer Proj, Nat Cancer Inst, 72-79. *Mem:* AAAS; Am Soc Microbiol; Soc Exp Biol & Med; Tissue Cult Asn (vpres, 60-64, pres, 64-66); Am Soc Cell Biol. *Res:* Tissue culture techniques; cell growth and metabolism; cancer cell biology; pathogenesis of infectious disease. *Mailing Add:* 2433 Spindrift Rd Virginia Beach VA 23451

MERCHANT, HENRY CLIFTON, b Washington, DC, Aug 7, 42; m 65; c 4. ECOLOGY, ZOOLOGY. *Educ:* Univ Md, College Park, BS, 64, MS, 66; Rutgers Univ, New Brunswick, PhD(zool), 70. *Prof Exp:* Instr zool, Rutgers Univ, 70; asst prof, 70-75, ASSOC PROF BIOL, GEORGE WASHINGTON UNIV, 75- *Mem:* AAAS; Ecol Soc Am; Am Inst Biol Sci. *Res:* Bioenergetics of species, populations and communities. *Mailing Add:* Dept of Biol Sci George Washington Univ Washington DC 20006

MERCHANT, HOWARD CARL, b Mt Vernon, Wash, Jan 9, 35; m 60; c 2. MECHANICAL ENGINEERING. *Educ:* Univ Wash, BS, 56; Mass Inst Technol, SM, 57; Calif Inst Technol, PhD(mech eng), 61. *Prof Exp:* Asst prof, Univ Wash, 61-63; tech staff mem, Livermore Lab, Sandia Corp, 63-65, anal tech group leader, 65; anal engr, Physics Int Co, 65-66, head vulnerability dept, 66-67; assoc prof, 67-74, PROF MECH ENG, UNIV WASH, 74- *Concurrent Pos:* Consult, Honeywell, Marine Systs Div, Wash, 67-, Electro Develop Corp, 72-, Terra Tech Corp, 73-, Columbia Eng Serv, 74-, Hanford Eng Develop Lab, 74- & Boeing Com Airplane Co, 80-; adj prof geophysics, Univ Wash, 74- *Mem:* Am Soc Mech Engrs; Acoust Soc Am; Am Soc Eng Educ; Marine Technol Soc; Earthquake Eng Res Inst. *Res:* Applied mechanics; vibration of equipment and structures; shock and vibration instrumentation and specifications; acoustics; engineering education. *Mailing Add:* 16334 84th Ave NE Bothell WA 98011

MERCHANT, MYLON EUGENE, b Springfield, Mass, May 6, 13; m 37; c 3. MANUFACTURING ENGINEERING, PHYSICS. *Educ:* Univ Vt, BS, 36; Univ Cincinnati, DSc(physics), 41. *Hon Degrees:* DSc, Univ Vt, 73; Univ Salford, Eng, 80. *Prof Exp:* Res physicist, 40-48, sr res physicist, 48-51, asst dir res eng physics, 51-57, dir physics res, 57-63, dir sci res, 63-69, dir res planning, 69-81, PRIN SCIENTIST MFG RES, CINCINNATI MILACRON INC, 81- *Concurrent Pos:* Adj prof mech eng, Univ Cincinnati, 64-69; vis prof, Univ Salford, Eng, 73- *Honors & Awards:* Richards Mem Award, Am Soc Mech Engrs, 59; Res Medal, Soc Mfg Engrs, 68; Tribology Gold Medal, Inst Mech Engrs, UK, 80; George Schlesinger Prize, City Berlin, 80; Otto Benedikt Prize, Comput & Automation Inst, Hungary, 81. *Mem:* Nat Acad Eng; Soc Mfg Engrs (pres, 76-77); Am Soc Mech Engrs (vpres, 73-75); Int Inst Prod Eng Res (pres, 68-69). *Res:* Physics of manufacturing processes, friction, lubrication and wear; systems approach to manufacturing; manufacturing systems; computer aided manufacturing; computer automated factory; future of manufacturing. *Mailing Add:* Cincinnati Milacron Inc Cincinnati OH 45209

MERCHANT, ROLAND SAMUEL, SR, b New York, NY, Apr 18, 29; m 70; c 3. BIOSTATISTICS, ECONOMIC STATISTICS. *Educ:* NY Univ, BA, 57, MA, 60; Columbia Univ, MS, 63, MSHA, 74. *Prof Exp:* Asst statistician, New York City Dept Health, 57-60, statistician, 60-63; statistician, NY Tuberc & Health Asn, 63-65; biostatistician, Inst Surg Studies, Montefiore Hosp & Med Ctr, 65-72; admin resident, Roosevelt Hosp, 73-74; dir health & hosp mgt, NY City Dept Health, 74-76; asst adminer & adminr, West Adams Community Hosp, 76; SPEC ASST TO ASSOC V PRES MED AFFAIRS, MED CTR, STANFORD UNIV, 77- *Mem:* AAAS; fel Am Pub Health Asn; Am Statist Asn; Biomet Soc; Inst Math Statist. *Res:* Application of biostatistical techniques to administrative methodology in health care delivery systems. *Mailing Add:* 953 Cheswick Dr San Jose CA 95121

MERCIER, PHILIP LAURENT, b Norwich, Conn, Oct 3, 26; m 55; c 5. PHYSICAL CHEMISTRY. *Educ:* Univ Conn, BA, 51; Brown Univ, PhD(chem), 55. *Prof Exp:* Res chemist, Esso Res & Eng Co, 55-61; supvr, Rexall Chem Co, 61-68; lab sect head, Borden Chem Co, 68; MGR PHYS CHEM GROUP, DART INDUSTS, 68- *Mem:* Am Chem Soc. *Res:* Conductance of electrolytes in aqueous and nonaqueous solvents; physical characterization of polymers. *Mailing Add:* Dart Industs 115 W Century Rd Paramus NJ 07652

MERCKEL, CHARLES GEORGE, b Detroit, Mich, Aug 21, 11; wid; c 2. MEDICINE. *Educ:* Wayne State Univ, AB, 33, MS, 38, MB, 40, MD, 41. *Prof Exp:* Asst dir student health serv, Wayne State Univ, 39-40; intern, Hosp Univ Pa, 40-42; instr med, Univ Southern Calif, 46-53; med dir, Sylvania Elec Prod, Inc Div, Gen Tel & Electronics Corp, 60-71; chief benefits exam sect, 71-74, ACTG CHIEF AMBULATORY CARE SECT, VET ADMIN HOSP, 74- *Concurrent Pos:* Pvt pract, Calif, 46-51; attend staff, Los Angeles County Gen Hosp, 46-60 & Hosp of Good Samaritan, Los Angeles, 51-60; mem med staff, Southern Calif Edison Co, 51-60. *Mem:* AAAS; Asn Mil Surg US; fel Indust Med Asn. *Res:* Physiology of reproduction; internal and preventive medicine. *Mailing Add:* Vet Admin Hosp 4150 Clement St San Francisco CA 94121

MERCKX, KENNETH R(ING), b Chicago, Ill, July 2, 26; m 54; c 4. ENGINEERING MECHANICS. *Educ:* Northwestern Univ, BS, 50; Stanford Univ, PhD(eng mech), 53. *Prof Exp:* Res assoc, Battelle-Northwest, 65-70; sr res assoc, Westinghouse Hanford Co, 70-72; STAFF CONSULT, EXXON NUCLEAR CO, INC, 72- *Concurrent Pos:* Affiliate assoc prof, Joint Ctr Grad Study, 57- *Mem:* Fel Am Soc Mech Engrs. *Res:* Material behavior; stress analysis; reactor fuel design. *Mailing Add:* Exxon Nuclear Co Inc 2101 Horn Rapids Rd Richland WA 99352

MERCURI, ARTHUR J, b Albany, NY, Mar 25, 23; m 56; c 4. FOOD MICROBIOLOGY, FOOD SCIENCE. *Educ:* San Jose State Col, AB, 48; Stanford Univ, PhD(bact), 54. *Prof Exp:* Bacteriologist, Consumer Yeast Co, Calif, 54-55; food technologist, Biol Sci Br, Agr Mkt Serv, USDA, 55-56, bacteriologist, Biol Sci Br, 56-62, leader poultry qual invests, Mkt Qual Res Div, 62-70, chief animal prod lab, Richard B Russell Agr Res Ctr, Sci & Educ Admin, USDA, Ga, 70-79; CONSULT. *Mem:* Inst Food Technol. *Res:* Bacterial physiology; food microbiology and technology; sanitation; Salmonellae; staph; clostridium; food poisoning; poultry and meat products technology; pollution; public health research administration. *Mailing Add:* 1775 S Milledge Ave #C USDA PO Box 5677 Athens GA 30605

MERDINGER, CHARLES J(OHN), b Chicago, Ill, Apr 20, 18; m 44; c 4. CIVIL ENGINEERING. *Educ:* US Naval Acad, BS, 41; Rensselaer Polytech Inst, BCE, 45, MCE, 46; Oxford Univ, PhD(phys sci), 49. *Prof Exp:* Officer-in-charge construct, US Navy, Panama, CZ, 46-47, design coordr, Bur Yards & Docks, Washington, DC, 49-51, asst pub works officer, Naval Shipyard, Wash, 51-53, pub works officer, Adak, Alaska, 53-54, Naval Air Sta Miramar, 54-56, commanding officer & dir, Naval Civil Eng Lab, 56-59, pub works officer, Fleet Activities, Yokosuka, Japan, 59-62, head dept Eng, hist & govt, US Naval Acad, 62-65, asst comdr opers & maintenance, Naval Facil Eng Command, 65-67, pub works officer, Da Nang, Vietnam, 67-68, commanding officer, Western Div, Naval Facil Eng Command, 68-70; pres, Washington Col, 70-73; vpres, Aspen Inst Humanistic Studies, Colo, 73-74; dep dir, Scripps Inst Oceanog, Calif, 74-80; DIR, AVCO CORP, 78- *Concurrent Pos:* Mem, Southern Regional Educ Bd, 71-73; mem, Nat Comn Hist & Heritage of Am Civil Eng; alumni trustee, US Naval Acad, 71-74; mem coun, Rensselaer Polytech Inst, 72; trustee, Found Ocean Res, 76-80; chmn bd trustees, Sierra Nev Col, 80- *Honors & Awards:* Toulmin Medal, Soc Am Mil Engrs, 52, 57 & 61; Nat Hist & Heritage Award, Am Soc Civil Engrs, 72. *Mem:* Fel Am Soc Civil Engrs; Nat Soc Prof Engrs; Soc Am Mil Engrs; fel Explorer's Club; Sigma Xi. *Mailing Add:* 321 Ski Way 190 PO Box 7249 Incline Village NV 89450

MERDINGER, EMANUEL, b Austria, Mar 29, 06; nat US; m 53. BIOCHEMISTRY. *Educ:* Prague Tech Univ, Master Pharmacol, 31; Univ Ferrara, Dr Pharm, 34, Dr Chem, 35, Dr Natural Sci, 39. *Prof Exp:* Prof sch eng, Univ Ferrara, 36-38, 45-47; from asst prof to prof chem, Roosevelt Univ, 47-72; BIOCHEM RESEARCHER, USDA & DISTINGUISHED PROF, DEPT ENTOM, UNIV FLA, GAINESVILLE, 77- *Concurrent Pos:* Mem res dept dermat, Univ Chicago; abstractor, Chem Abstr, 49-62; Abbott Labs annual res grants, Roosevelt Univ, 61-72, Ill State Acad Sci grants, 68-71; Nat Acad Sci exchange scientist, Romanian Acad Sci, 71-72, 75, 80; Nat Acad Sci exchange scientist, Bulgarian Acad Sci, 74-75; res assoc, Loyola Univ Stritch Sch Med, 72-, distinguished lectr, 74-76. *Mem:* Am Chem Soc; Am Soc Microbiol; hon mem Union Socs Med Sci Romania. *Res:* Microbiological biochemistry; lipid and carbohydrate metabolism and enzymology of yeasts and fungi; fungal pigments and some of their chemotherapeutic properties; relation between Pullularia pullulans, a fungus, and arthritis. *Mailing Add:* 4908 NW 16th Pl Gainsville FL 32605

MEREDITH, CHARLES EYMARD, hospital administration, psychiatry, see previous edition

MEREDITH, DALE DEAN, b Centralia, Ill, Mar 24, 40; m 65; c 2. CIVIL ENGINEERING, WATER RESOURCES. *Educ:* Univ Ill, Urbana, BS, 63, MS, 64, PhD(civil eng), 68. *Prof Exp:* Asst prof civil eng, Univ Ill, Urbana-Champaign, 68-73; assoc prof, 73-79, PROF CIVIL ENG, STATE UNIV NY, BUFFALO, 79- *Concurrent Pos:* Prin investr & US Dept Interior res grants, Univ Ill, Urbana-Champaign, 68-73 & State Univ NY, Buffalo, 73-; prin investr & US Dept Com res grant, State Univ NY, Buffalo, 76- *Mem:* Am Soc Civil Engrs; Am Geophys Union; Am Water Resources Asn; Water Pollution Control Fedn; Inst Mgt Sci. *Res:* Water resources system design; planning, operation management and optimization; hydrology. *Mailing Add:* Dept of Civil Eng State Univ of NY Buffalo NY 14260

MEREDITH, FARRIS RAY, b Denver, Colo, Mar 15, 29; m 50; c 3. BOTANY, SOILS. *Educ:* Colo State Univ, BS, 51; NMex Highlands Univ, MS, 58; Wash State Univ, PhD(bot, plant ecol), 65. *Prof Exp:* Asst prof bot, Humboldt State Col, 63-65; asst prof, NMex Highlands Univ, 65-66; from asst prof to assoc prof, 66-74, PROF BOT, HUMBOLDT STATE UNIV, 74- *Mem:* AAAS; Ecol Soc Am; Torrey Bot Club. *Res:* Plant autecology and synecology; autecology and physiology of coniferous trees. *Mailing Add:* Dept of Biol Humboldt State Univ Arcata CA 95521

MEREDITH, HARVEY L, b Nebraska City, Nebr, Mar 10, 31; m 69; c 2. SOIL PHYSICS. *Educ:* La State Univ, BS, 58, MS, 59; Purdue Univ, PhD(soil physics), 64. *Prof Exp:* Area dir, Tenn Valley Authority, Mich, 64-65; AGRICULTURIST, UNIV MINN, ST PAUL, 65- *Res:* Crop Production, particularly soil nutrition. *Mailing Add:* Dept of Soil Sci Univ of Minn St Paul MN 55101

MEREDITH, HOWARD VOAS, b Birmingham, Eng, Nov 5, 03; nat US; m 26; c 2. CHILD GROWTH, MORPHOLOGY. *Educ:* Univ Iowa, BA, 31, MA, 32, PhD(phys growth), 35. *Prof Exp:* Asst, Child Welfare Res Sta, Univ Iowa, 31-35, res assoc, 35-39, from asst prof to assoc prof, 39-48, prof phys growth, 48-49; prof, Sch Health & Phys Educ, Univ Ore, 49-52; prof, Child Welfare Res Sta, 52-63, consult Res Sta & Col Dent, 52-56, prof child somatol, Inst Child Behav & Develop, 63-72, actg dir, 71-72, EMER PROF CHILD SOMATOL, INST CHILD BEHAV & DEVELOP, UNIV IOWA, 72- TCPExchange fel, Harvard Univ, 35; vis lectr, Univ Southern Calif, 48, vis prof, 51; affil prof human somatology, Univ SC, 73- *Mem:* Soc Res Child Develop (pres, 53-55); Am Asn Phys Anthrop; Int Asn Human Biol; Sigma Xi; hon mem Am Asn Orthodontists. *Res:* Physical growth of the child. *Mailing Add:* Col of Health & Phys Educ Univ of SC Columbia SC 29208

MEREDITH, JESSE HEDGEPETH, b Fancy Gap, Va, Mar 19, 23; m; c 3. MEDICINE. *Educ:* Elon Col, BA, 43; Western Reserve Univ, MD, 51; Am Bd Surg, dipl, 58; Am Bd Thoracic Surg, dipl, 59. *Prof Exp:* Intern med, Bellevue Hosp, New York, 51-52; asst surgeon, NC Baptist Hosp, Winston-Salem, 52-56, resident gen & thoracic surg, 56-57, cardiovasc surg, 57-58; asst surgeon, 52-58, from instr to assoc prof, 58-70, PROF SURG, BOWMAN GRAY SCH MED, 70-, DIR SURG RES, 59- *Concurrent Pos:* NIH res fel, 56-57, spec res fel, 59-62; res fel, Bowman Gray Sch Med, 58. *Mem:* Fel Am Col Surgeons; Am Asn Thoracic Surgeons; AMA; Am Soc Artificial Internal Organs. *Res:* Cardiovascular surgery and physiology; cancer chemotherapy; biomedical engineering; cadaver blood in transfusions; kidney transplantation. *Mailing Add:* 2819 Bartram Rd Winston-Salem NC 27106

MEREDITH, LESLIE HUGH, b Birmingham, Eng, Oct 23, 27; m 48; c 3. SPACE PHYSICS. *Educ:* Univ Iowa, BA, 50, MS, 52, PhD(physics), 54. *Prof Exp:* Res assoc, Univ Iowa, 51-53; asst, Proj Matterhorn, Princeton Univ, 53-54; sect head, Naval Res Lab, 54-58, br head, 58; br head, 58-59, div chief space sci, 59-70, dep dir space & earth sci directorate, 70-72, asst dir, 72-79, DIR APPLN, GODDARD SPACE FLIGHT CTR, 79- *Mem:* AAAS; Am Phys Soc; Am Geophys Union (gen secy, 80-). *Mailing Add:* Goddard Space Flight Ctr Greenbelt MD 20771

MEREDITH, ORSELL MONTGOMERY, b Jamestown, NY, Oct 19, 23; m 49; c 1. RADIOLOGICAL HEALTH, RESEARCH ADMINISTRATION. *Educ:* Univ Chicago, BS, 48; Univ Southern Calif, MS, 51, PhD(pharmacol, toxicol), 53; Am Univ, Washington, DC, MS, 74. *Prof Exp:* Asst pharmacol & toxicol, Sch Med, Univ Southern Calif, 49-52; pharmacologist, Carlborg Labs, Calif, 52-53; chief nuclear physiol sect & asst res pharmacologist, Lab Nuclear Med & Radiation Biol, Med Ctr, Univ Calif, Los Angeles, 53-62; res scientist, Lockheed Missiles & Space Co, Calif, 62-66; tech mgr, US Naval Radiological Defense Lab, 66-69; Biologist, Nuclear Prog Off, Adv Planning & Anal Staff, Naval Ord Lab, 69-75; exec secy, Spec Progs Br, Div Res Grants, NIH, 74-78; EXEC SECY, NAT CANCER INST, 78- *Concurrent Pos:* Consult, Nuclear Div, Am Electronics Inc, Calif. *Mem:* AAAS; Health Physics Soc; Soc Nuclear Med; Radiation Res Soc; NY Acad Sci. *Res:* Catecholamine action on intestinal smooth muscle; anticholinesterase action of organic phosphate insecticides; inhalation toxicity of radioactive fallout debris; radioisotope clinical diagnosis; bioastronautics; mammalian radiation biology; operations research. *Mailing Add:* 5333 Westbard Ave Bethesda MD 20014

MEREDITH, ROBERT E(UGENE), b Santa Barbara, Calif, Feb 25, 28; m 53; c 4. CHEMISTRY, CHEMICAL ENGINEERING. *Educ:* Univ Calif, BS, 56, PhD(chem eng), 59. *Prof Exp:* Asst prof, 59-62, ASSOC PROF CHEM ENG, ORE STATE UNIV, 63- *Concurrent Pos:* Nat Acad Sci sr res assoc, Jet Propulsion Lab, 66-67; vis prof, Univ Calif, Berkeley, 71; consult, Comt Critical Mat Technol, Nat Res Coun, 73-74, Electric Power Res Inst, 75-78 & US Dept Energy, 81-82. *Mem:* Electrochem Soc; Am Inst Chem Engrs; Nat Asn Corrosion Engrs. *Res:* Electrochemical processes; fuel cells; mass transfer; thermodynamics and kinetics; chemical engineering plant design; corrosion. *Mailing Add:* Dept of Chem Eng Ore State Univ Corvallis OR 97331

MEREDITH, RUBY FRANCES, b Sedalia, Mo, Feb 6, 48. HEMATOLOGY, CANCER. *Educ:* Univ Mo, BA, 69; Ind Univ, AM, 71, PhD(genetics), 74. *Prof Exp:* Asst prof biol, Baylor Univ, 74-75; fel, 75-76, res assoc viral oncogenesis, Cancer Res Unit, 76-77, ASSOC HEAD, EXP HEMAT SECT, ALLEGHENY GEN HOSP, 77- *Honors & Awards:* Harold C Bold Award, Phycol Soc Am, 74; Outstanding Contrib Award, Health Res Serv Found, 78. *Mem:* Genetics Soc Am; Int Soc Exp Hemat; Phycol Soc Am; spec fel Leukemia Soc Am; Radiation Res Soc. *Res:* Pathology, genetics and treatment of murine viral leukemogenesis including chemotherapy, radiotherapy, bone marrow transplantation, immunotherapy and combinations of these. *Mailing Add:* Cancer Res Labs Allegheny Gen Hosp Pittsburgh PA 15212

MEREDITH, WILLIAM EDWARD, b Dennison, Ohio, Nov 30, 32; m 57; c 3. MICROBIOLOGY. *Educ:* Ohio Univ, BSc, 59; Ohio State Univ, MSc, 61, PhD(microbiol), 64. *Prof Exp:* Asst microbiol, Ohio State Univ, 59-62, Ohio State Univ Res Found, 62-64; microbiologist, Hess & Clark Div, Richardson-Merrell Inc, 64-68; PROF BIOL, ASHLAND COL, 68-, CHMN DEPT, 77- *Concurrent Pos:* Researcher, Ohio Agr Res & Develop Ctr, 69, 70, 73. *Mem:* AAAS; Am Soc Microbiol. *Res:* General microbiology; immunology; microbial physiology. *Mailing Add:* Dept of Biol Ashland Col Ashland OH 44805

MEREDITH, WILLIAM G, b Fairmont, WVa, May 16, 33; m 55; c 3. ECOLOGY. *Educ:* Fairmont State Col, AB, 55; WVa Univ, MS, 57; Univ Md, PhD(ecol), 67. *Prof Exp:* From instr to assoc prof, 57-71, chmn dept sci & math, 68-75, PROF BIOL, MT ST MARY'S COL, MD, 71-, ASSOC DEAN, 81- *Mem:* AAAS; Ecol Soc Am; Am Inst Biol Sci; Sigma Xi. *Res:* Comparative ecology and physiology of crayfishes; food habits of freshwater fishes; distribution of crayfishes. *Mailing Add:* Dept of Sci & Math Mt St Mary's Col Emmitsburg MD 21727

MERESZ, OTTO, b Rima-Sobota, Czech, Jan 16, 32; m 55; c 1. ANALYTICAL CHEMISTRY, ORGANIC CHEMISTRY. *Educ:* Budapest Tech Univ, Dipl org chem, 56; Univ London, PhD(org chem), 65. *Prof Exp:* Tech officer, Imp Chem Indust Ltd, 57-58; res chemist, Res Inst, May & Baker Ltd, 58-61, sect head synthetic perfumes, 61-65, dept head, 66-67; asst prof chem, Univ Toronto, 67-73; dir res, Kemada Res Corp, 73-74; MGR, ORG CHEM SECT, ONT MINISTRY OF THE ENVIRON, 74- *Concurrent Pos:* Fel, Univ Toronto, 65-66; consult, Addiction Res Found, Ont, 74- *Mem:* The Chem Soc; Am Chem Soc; Chem Inst Can. *Res:* Environmental chemistry; correlation between chemical structure and odor; synthetic and structural organic chemistry; trace-organic analysis. *Mailing Add:* 8 Wallingford Rd Don Mills ON M3A 2T9 Can

MEREU, ROBERT FRANK, b Alta, Nov 1, 30; m 61; c 3. GEOPHYSICS, SEISMOLOGY. *Educ:* Univ Western Ont, BSc, 52, PhD(physics), 62; Univ Toronto, MA, 53. prof. *Prof Exp:* From asst prof to assoc prof, 63-74, PROF GEOPHYS, UNIV WESTERN ONT, 74- *Mem:* Seismol Soc Am; Am Geophys Union; Can Geophys Union; Geol Asn Can; Soc Explor Geophysicists. *Mailing Add:* Dept of Geophys Univ of Western Ont London ON N6A 5B7 Can

MERGEN, FRANCOIS, b Redange, Luxembourg, May 1, 25; nat US; m 47; c 1. FOREST GENETICS. *Educ:* Univ NB, BSF, 50; Yale Univ, MF, 51, PhD(forest genetics), 54. *Prof Exp:* Forest geneticist, US Forest Serv, Fla, 52-54; asst prof forest genetics, J A Hartford Mem Res Ctr, 54-60, actg dir ctr, 55-58, from assoc prof to prof, 60-66, dean sch forestry & environ studies, 65-77, PINCHOT PROF FORESTRY, YALE UNIV, 66-, FEL, SAYBROOK COL, 74- *Concurrent Pos:* Res collab, Brookhaven Nat Lab, 60-70. *Honors & Awards:* Barrington Moore Award, Soc Am Foresters. *Mem:* Soc Am Foresters; Can Inst Forestry. *Res:* Effect of storms on trees; vegetative propagation of slash pine; physiology of flow of oleo-resin; forest genetics of southern pines; cytology of conifers; effect of radiation on forest trees. *Mailing Add:* Sch Forestry & Environ Yale Univ 205 Prospect St New Haven CT 06511

MERGENHAGEN, STEPHAN EDWARD, b Depew, NY, Apr 12, 30; m 55; c 3. IMMUNOLOGY, MICROBIOLOGY. *Educ:* Allegheny Col, BS, 52; Univ Buffalo, MA, 54; Univ Rochester, PhD(bact), 57. *Prof Exp:* Res microbiologist, 58-65, chief immunol sect, 65-69, CHIEF LAB MICROBIOL & IMMUNOL, NAT INST DENT RES, 69- *Concurrent Pos:* Fel, Univ Rochester, 57-58. *Honors & Awards:* US Sr scientist award, Alexander von Humboldt Found, WGer, 81. *Mem:* Am Soc Microbiol; Soc Exp Biol & Med; Infectious Dis Soc Am; Reticuloendothelial Soc; Am Asn Immunol. *Res:* Natural resistance mechanisms in oral and systemic disease; immunochemistry of bacterial antigens; endotoxic lipopolysaccharides; pathogenesis of mixed infections. *Mailing Add:* Lab Microbiol & Immunol Rm 332 Bldg 301 Nat Inst Dent Res Bethesda MD 20205

MERGENS, WILLIAM JOSEPH, b Queens, NY, July 26, 42; m 65; c 3. ANALYTICAL CHEMISTRY. *Educ:* St Johns Univ, BS, 64; Seton Hall Univ, MS, 70, PhD(chem), 76. *Prof Exp:* GROUP MGR PROD DEVELOP & APPLN, HOFFMANN-LA ROCHE INC, 64- *Mem:* Am Chem Soc. *Res:* Formulation and analysis of product development chemistry; chemical carcinogenesis. *Mailing Add:* Hoffmann LaRoche Inc 340 Kingsland St Nutley NJ 07110

MERGENTIME, MAX, b Brooklyn, NY, Apr 2, 14; m 50; c 4. FOOD CHEMISTRY. *Educ:* Cornell Univ, BS, 35, MS, 36; Ore State Col, PhD(food tech), 41. *Prof Exp:* Processed foods inspector, Prod & Mkt Admin, USDA, 41-45; chief chemist, Sunshine Packing Corp, Pa, 45-50; HEAD JUICE DEPT, FRIGID FOOD PROD, INC, 50- *Mem:* Inst Food Technol. *Res:* Low temperature studies rate; reaction proteolytic enzyme of peas. *Mailing Add:* 2685 Lahser Rd Bloomfield Hills MI 48103

MERGLER, H(ARRY) W(INSTON), b Chillicothe, Ohio, June 1, 24; m 48; c 3. ELECTRICAL ENGINEERING. *Educ:* Case Inst Technol, BS, 48, MS, 58, PhD(eng), 56. *Prof Exp:* Aeronaut res scientist, Nat Adv Comt Aeronaut, 48-56; from asst prof to assoc prof control eng, 56-61, prof eng, 62-73, LEONARD CASE PROF ELEC ENG, CASE WESTERN RESERVE UNIV, 73-, DIR, DIGITAL SYSTS LAB, 67- *Concurrent Pos:* Consult to various indust concerns; consult ed, Control Eng Mag; pres, Digital/Gen Corp, 68-71. *Honors & Awards:* Lamme Medal, Inst Elec & Electronic Engrs, 78. *Mem:* Nat Acad Eng; Indust Electronics & Control Instrumentation (pres, 76-78); fel Inst Elec & Electronics Engrs. *Res:* Application of digital computer techniques to problems of digital guidance and control systems. *Mailing Add:* Dept of Elec Eng Case Western Reserve Univ Cleveland OH 44106

MERIAM, JAMES LATHROP, b Columbia, Mo, Mar 25, 17; m 40; c 2. MECHANICAL ENGINEERING. *Educ:* Yale Univ, BE, 39, MEng, 41, PhD(mech eng), 42. *Prof Exp:* Asst mech eng, Yale Univ, 40-42; instr, Univ Calif, Berkeley, 42-44; from asst prof to prof, 44-54, asst dean, Col Eng, 52-56, asst to chancellor, 53-54, chmn div mech & design, 59-61; prof eng mech, Duke Univ, 63-72, dean, Sch Eng, 63-69; prof mech eng, Calif Polytech State Univ, San Luis Obsipo, 72-80; RETIRED. *Concurrent Pos:* Vis prof, Univ Calif, Santa Barbara, 80- *Mem:* Am Soc Eng Educ; fel Am Soc Mech Engrs; Sigma Xi. *Mailing Add:* Dept Mech Eng Calif Polytech State Univ San Luis Obispo CA 93407

MERIANOS, JOHN JAMES, medicinal chemistry, see previous edition

MERICLE, LEO WILLIS, b Weatherford, Okla, Oct 4, 15; m 53; c 1. GENETICS, RADIATION BIOLOGY. *Educ:* Southwestern State Col, Okla, BS, 34; Univ Okla, MS, 41; Univ Tex, PhD(bot), 49. *Prof Exp:* Instr high sch & jr col, Okla, 36-40; Naval Res fel, Univ Tex, 49-50, from asst prof to assoc prof, 50-60, PROF BOT & PLANT PATH, MICH STATE UNIV, 60- *Concurrent Pos:* Res collabr, Brookhaven Nat Lab, 57-70; res grants, AEC, NSF, Mich State Alumni Fund & Res Fund; ed, Radiation Bot. *Mem:* Genetics Soc Am; Am Genetic Asn; Radiation Res Soc. *Res:* Developmental genetics, gene expression, and radio-sensitivity; modification by environment and fine structure changes during development. *Mailing Add:* Dept of Bot & Plant Path Mich State Univ East Lansing MI 48823

MERICLE, MORRIS H, b Toledo, Iowa, Mar 26, 25; m 59. ELECTRICAL ENGINEERING. *Educ:* Iowa State Univ, BS, 47, MS, 56, PhD(elec eng), 63. *Prof Exp:* Elec engr, Repub Steel Corp, 47-51; from instr to asst prof elec eng, Iowa State Univ, 53-58; sr engr, Autonetics Div, NAm Aviation Inc, 58-60; asst prof, 60-63, ASSOC PROF ELEC ENG, IOWA STATE UNIV, 63- *Concurrent Pos:* Consult, Iowa Methodist Hosp, Des Moines, 62- *Mem:* Inst Elec & Electronics Engrs. *Res:* Pattern recognition of biological signals. *Mailing Add:* Dept of Elec Eng Iowa State Univ Ames IA 50012

MERICLE, R BRUCE, b Omaha, Nebr, June 4, 38; m 63; c 3. MATHEMATICS. *Educ:* Iowa State Univ, BS, 60; Univ Md, College Park, MS, 64; Wash State Univ, PhD(math), 70. *Prof Exp:* Instr math, Univ Maine, 64-66; instr, Wash State Univ, 66-70; asst prof, Mankato State Col, 70-74; dir acad comput serv, Mich Technol Univ, 74-77; ASSOC PROF, MANKATO STATE UNIV, 77- *Mem:* Am Math Soc; Math Asn Am. *Res:* Measure theory; measures in topological spaces. *Mailing Add:* Dept of Math Mankato State Univ Mankato MN 56001

MERICLE, RAE PHELPS, developmental genetics, deceased

MERICOLA, FRANCIS CARL, b Franklin, Md, Jan 27, 11; m 37. INORGANIC CHEMISTRY. *Educ:* Kent State Univ, BS, 33; Western Reserve Univ, PhD(inorg chem), 38. *Prof Exp:* Asst instr qual & quant anal, Western Reserve Univ, 35-38; staff mem, Res Dept, BASF Wyandotte Corp, 38-45, supvr plant res dept, 45-50, prod supt, S Works, 50-53, prod res dept, 53-55, mgr, 55-63, tech asst to vpres mfg opers, 63-66, tech asst to dir res opers, 66-68, process engr, Eng Dept, 68-73, consult, BASF Wyandotte Corp, 73-76; RETIRED. *Mem:* Am Chem Soc. *Res:* Chemical engineering. *Mailing Add:* 2071 17th St Wyandotte MI 48192

MERIDETH, CHARLES WAYMOND, physical inorganic chemistry, see previous edition

MERIFIELD, PAUL M, b Santa Monica, Calif, Mar 17, 32; m 68; c 2. GEOLOGY. *Educ:* Univ Calif, Los Angeles, AB, 54, MA, 58; Univ Colo, PhD(geol), 63. *Prof Exp:* Res scientist, Lockheed-Calif Co, 62-64; DIR GEOSCI, EARTH SCI RES CORP, 64- *Concurrent Pos:* Lectr, Univ Calif, Los Angeles; partner, Lamar-Merifield, 64- *Mem:* AAAS; Am Soc Photogram; Asn Eng Geol. *Res:* Interpretation of satellite photography; age and origin of the earth-moon system; remote sensing; engineering and environmental geology. *Mailing Add:* 1318 Second St Suite 25 Santa Monica CA 90401

MERIGAN, THOMAS CHARLES, JR, b San Francisco, Calif, Jan 18, 34; m 59; c 1. INFECTIOUS DISEASES, VIROLOGY. *Educ:* Univ Calif, Berkeley, BA, 55; Univ Calif, San Francisco, MD, 58; Am Bd Internal Med, dipl, 65. *Prof Exp:* Intern med, Boston City Hosp, Mass, 58-59, asst resident, 59-60; clin assoc, Nat Heart Inst, 60-62; assoc, Nat Insts Arthritis & Metab Dis, 62-63; from asst prof to assoc prof med, 63-72, dir diag microbiol lab, 66-72, prof med, 72-80, GEORGE E & LUCY BECKER PROF MED, SCH MED, STANFORD UNIV, 80-, CHIEF DIV INFECTIOUS DIS & HOSP EPIDEMIOLOGIST, 66-, DIR DIAG VIROL LAB, 69- *Concurrent Pos:* Mem microbiol training grant comt, Nat Inst Gen Med Sci, 69-73, mem virol study sect, Div Res Grants, NIH, 74-78. *Honors & Awards:* Borden Award for Outstanding Res, 73. *Mem:* Inst Med-Nat Acad Sci; Am Asn Immunol; Am Fedn Clin Res; Am Soc Clin Invest; Am Soc Microbiol. *Res:* Host responses to viral infections and antiviral agents. *Mailing Add:* Div of Infectious Dis Stanford Univ Sch of Med Stanford CA 94305

MERIJANIAN, ARIS, organic chemistry, see previous edition

MERILAN, CHARLES PRESTON, b Lesterville, Mo, Jan 14, 26; m 49; c 2. DAIRY HUSBANDRY. *Educ:* Univ Mo, BS, 48, AM, 49, PhD(dairy husb), 52. *Prof Exp:* Instr dairy husb, 50-52, bact & prev med, 52-53, from asst prof to assoc prof, 53-59, chmn dept, 61-62, assoc dir agr exp sta, 62-63, PROF DAIRY HUSB, UNIV MO-COLUMBIA, 59- *Mem:* AAAS; Am Chem Soc; Am Soc Animal Sci; Am Dairy Sci Asn; Soc Cryobiol. *Res:* Cellular physiology; biophysics; reproductive physiology. *Mailing Add:* 201 Eckles Hall Univ of Mo Columbia MO 65201

MERIN, ROBERT GILLESPIE, b Glens Falls, NY, June 16, 33; m 58; c 3. ANESTHESIOLOGY, PHARMACOLOGY. *Educ:* Swarthmore Col, BA, 54; Cornell Univ, MD, 58. *Prof Exp:* Instr anesthesiol, Albany Med Col, 63-66, res assoc pharmacol, 65-66; asst prof anesthesiol, Sch Med, Univ Rochester, 66-70, assoc prof, 70-76, prof, 76-81, assoc prof pharmacol, 72-81; PROF ANESTHESIOL, UNIV TEX HEALTH SCI CTR, HOUSTON, 81- *Concurrent Pos:* NIH career develop award, Sch Med, Univ Rochester, 72-77; consult, Vet Admin Hosp, Albany, 63-66. *Mem:* Am Soc Anesthesiol; Int Anesthesia Res Soc; NY Acad Sci; Am Soc Pharmacol & Exp Therapeut. *Res:* Effect of anesthesia on the cardiovascular system and metabolism. *Mailing Add:* Univ Tex Health Sci Ctr 6431 Fannin 5.020 MSMB Houston TX 77030

MERIWETHER, JOHN R, b Beaumont, Tex, May 22, 37; m 56; c 4. NUCLEAR PHYSICS. *Educ:* Univ Southwestern La, BS, 58, MS, 59; Fla State Univ, PhD(nuclear physics), 62. *Prof Exp:* Assoc, Lawrence Radiation Lab, 62-65, staff physicist, 65-66; asst prof nuclear physics & comput sci, 66-71, assoc prof, 71-75, chmn dept, 71-81, PROF PHYSICS, UNIV SOUTHWESTERN LA, 75-, DIR, CTR ENERGY STUDIES, 78- *Concurrent Pos:* Ed, Proc Third Geopressured-Geothermal Energy Conf, Lafayette, 78. *Mem:* Am Phys Soc; Sigma Xi. *Res:* Nuclear spectroscopy using inelastic scattering of particles from nuclei; application of computer based numerical analysis to physical problems; applied atomic physics-proton induced x-ray emission as an analytical method; analysis of fluids from a geopressured geothermal well. *Mailing Add:* Rte 3 Box 346 A Arnaudville LA 70512

MERIWETHER, JOHN WILLIAMS, JR, b Louisville, Ky, Apr 14, 42; m 73; c 1. AERONOMY. *Educ:* Mass Inst Technol, SB, 64; Univ Md, PhD(physics), 70. *Prof Exp:* Nat Acad Sci res assoc, Goddard Space Flight Ctr, 69-71; res assoc atmospheric physics, Univ Mich, 71-73; staff physicist atmospheric physics, PhotoMetrics, Inc, 73-74; res assoc ionospheric physics, Arecibo Observ, Cornell Univ, 75-79; ASSOC RES SCIENTIST SPACE PHYSICS, UNIV MICH, 79- *Mem:* Am Inst Physics; Am Geophys Union. *Res:* Aeronomy of the earth's atmosphere by means of high spectrol resolution observations of airglow and auroral emissions from remote ground-based statious as supplemented with incoherent scatter radar observations of the ionosphere. *Mailing Add:* Space Physics Res Lab Univ Mich Ann Arbor MI 48109

MERIWETHER, LEWIS SMITH, b Washington, DC, May 23, 30; m 53; c 3. PHYSICAL CHEMISTRY, ORGANIC CHEMISTRY. *Educ:* Harvard Univ, AB, 52; Univ Chicago, PhD(chem), 56. *Prof Exp:* Res chemist, 55-59, SR RES CHEMIST, AM CYANAMID CO, 59-, GROUP LEADER, 60- *Concurrent Pos:* Cyanamid Sr Award, 64-65. *Mem:* NY Acad Sci; Am Chem Soc. *Res:* Homogeneous catalysis; transition metal complexes; polymerization; photochemistry; enzyme model systems; membranes; surgical adhesives; artificial kidney systems; biomaterials; biocides; cosmetics; pharmaceuticals. *Mailing Add:* Chem Res Div Am Cyanamid Co 1937 W Main St Stamford CT 06904

MERKAL, RICHARD STERLING, b Lansing, Mich, Nov 12, 28; m 49; c 3. MICROBIOLOGY. *Educ:* Univ Md, BS, 53; Auburn Univ, MS, 61; Iowa State Univ, PhD(physiol bact), 65. *Prof Exp:* Bacteriologist regional animal dis res lab, Ala, 53-61, RES MICROBIOLOGIST, NAT ANIMAL DIS LAB, USDA, 61- *Mem:* Am Soc Microbiol. *Res:* Mycobacterial metabolism and nutrition; relationship of metabolic products to host; histochemistry; serology and immunology. *Mailing Add:* Nat Animal Dis Lab USDA Ames IA 50011

MERKEL, DANIEL LEE, b Rozel, Kans, Mar 8, 35; c 3. RANGE MANAGEMENT. *Educ:* Fort Hays Kans State Univ, BS, 57, MS, 58. *Prof Exp:* Range & district conservationist, Soil Conserv Serv, USDA, Nebr, 58-63, area & asst state range conservationist, NMex, 63-69, plant materials specialist, 69-75, state range conservationist, Ore, 75-77, RANGE CONSERVATIONIST, ROCK MOUNTAIN FOREST & RANGE EXP STA, SOIL CONSERV, USDA, 79- *Concurrent Pos:* Mem & co-chmn sub-comts, NMex Interagency Range Comt, USDA, US Dept Interior & NMex, Resource Agencies, 67-73; Ore task group for coord resource mgt mem, USDA & US Dept Interior, 76-77. *Honors & Awards:* Outstanding Achievement Award, Soc Range Mgt, 77. *Mem:* Fel Soc Range Mgt (pres, 79). *Res:* Land classification; renewable resource inventory techniques; authored or coauthored publications on range seeding, range improvement and management practices, selection of improved plants and critical area stabilization. *Mailing Add:* Rocky Mountain Forest & Range Exp Sta 240 W Prospect Ft Collins CO 80526

MERKEL, FREDERICK KARL, b Athens, Greece, May 27, 36; US citizen; m 76; c 2. TRANSPLANTATION, VASCULAR SURGERY. *Educ:* Univ Cincinnati, BS, 57; Johns Hopkins Univ, MD, 61; FACS, 72. *Prof Exp:* Instr surg, Med Ctr, Univ Colo, 69-70; asst prof & coordr transplantation, Med Sch, Northwestern Univ, 70-72; ASSOC PROF SURG, IMMUNOL & MED & DIR TRANSPLANTATION, RUSH-PRESBY-ST LUKE'S MED CTR, 72- *Concurrent Pos:* Chief gastrointestinal & transplant surg, Denver Gen Hosp, 69-70; dir transplantation, Children's Mem Hosp, Chicago, 70-72; consult surg, St Therese Hosp, Waukegan, Ill, 72-, Martha Washington Hosp, Chicago, 73-, Mt Sinai Hosp Med Ctr, Chicago, 74- & Ingalls Mem Hosp, Harvey, 78-; assoc attend surgeon & assoc attend physician, Rush-Presby-St Luke's Med Ctr, 73- *Honors & Awards:* Peter F Salisbury Award, Am Soc

Artificial Organs, 78. *Mem:* Am Soc Transplant Surgeons (pres, 78-79); Transplantation Soc; Brit Transplantation Soc; Am Col Surgeons; Europ Soc Surg Res. *Res:* Organ transplantation, especially pancreas and kidney; organ preservation; transplant immunology. *Mailing Add:* 151 Sheridan Rd Kenilworth IL 60043

MERKEL, GEORGE, b San Francisco, Calif, Sept 2, 29; m 59; c 1. NUCLEAR RADIATION EFFECTS, ANTENNA THEORY. *Educ:* Calif Inst Technol, BS, 51; Univ Calif, Berkeley, PhD(nuclear physics), 63; George Washington Univ, MS, 75I. *Prof Exp:* Res asst physicist, Lawrence Radiation Lab, 53-62; res assoc, Univ Rochester, 63-64; physicist, Gen Atomic, San Diego, 64-67; physicist, Off Naval Res, 67-68; PHYSICIST, DEPT DEFENSE, HARRY DIAMOND LABS, US ARMY ELECTRONICS RES & DEVELOP COMMAND, 68- *Concurrent Pos:* Reviewer, Nuclear & Plasma Soc, Inst Elec & Electronics Engrs, 80-81. *Mem:* Am Phys Soc; Inst Elec & Electronics Engrs; Sigma Xi; AAAS; Am Geophys Union. *Res:* Nuclear reactions; charged particle transport; nuclear structure program; theoretical and experimental investigations of antenna response in ionized media. *Mailing Add:* US Army Electronics Res & Develop Command Harry Diamond Lab 2800 Powder Mill Rd Adelphi MD 20783

MERKEL, GLENN JOSEPH, microbiology, membrane biology, see previous edition

MERKEL, JAMES ANTHONY, agricultural engineering, see previous edition

MERKEL, JOSEPH ROBERT, b Alburtis, Pa, Dec 21, 24; m 48; c 1. MICROBIAL BIOCHEMISTRY, MARINE MICROBIOLOGY. *Educ:* Moravian Col, BS, 48; Purdue Univ, MS, 50; Univ Md, PhD(bact), 52. *Prof Exp:* Waksman-Merck fel, Rutgers Univ, 52-53, res assoc, 53-54, res investr, Inst Microbiol, 54-55; dir, Ft Johnson Marine Biol Lab, Col Charleston, 55-62; assoc prof biochem, 62-65, PROF DEPT CHEM & MARINE MICROBIOLOGIST, CTR MARINE & ENVIRON STUDIES, LEHIGH UNIV, 65- *Mem:* Am Soc Biol Chem; Am Chem Soc; Am Soc Microbiol. *Res:* Proteolytic enzymes of marine bacteria; collagenases. *Mailing Add:* Seeley G Mudd Bldg Dept Chem Lehigh Univ Bethlehem PA 18015

MERKEL, PAUL BARRETT, b Rochester, NY, May 14, 45. PHOTOCHEMISTRY, PHOTOGRAPHIC CHEMISTRY. *Educ:* St John Fisher Col, BS, 67; Univ Notre Dame, PhD(chem), 70. *Prof Exp:* Res assoc chem, Univ Calif, Riverside, 70-71; SR RES CHEMIST, EASTMAN KODAK CO, 71- *Mem:* Am Chem Soc; Sigma Xi. *Res:* In photochemistry and photophysics, interests include laser and flash photolysis, photooxidation reactions, electronic excitation and luminescence; research in photographic chemistry involves kinetics and mechanisms, thermoanalytical methods and dye imaging. *Mailing Add:* Res Labs Eastman Kodak Co Rochester NY 14650

MERKEL, ROBERT ANTHONY, b Marshfield, Wis, Feb 7, 26; m 54; c 4. MEAT SCIENCE. *Educ:* Univ Wis-Madison, BS, 51, MS, 53, PhD(meat sci, biochem), 57. *Prof Exp:* From asst prof to assoc prof meat sci, Kans State Univ, 57-62; assoc prof, 62-67, prof meat sci, 67-77, PROF ANIMAL HUSB & FOOD SCI & HUMAN NUTRIT, MICH STATE UNIV, 77- *Concurrent Pos:* Sect ed meat sci & muscle biol, J Animal Sci, 74-76. *Mem:* AAAS; Am Meat Sci Asn; Am Soc Animal Sci; Inst Food Technologists. *Res:* Differentiation, histogenesis and growth of muscle and adipose tissues; biosynthesis of muscle proteins and subcellular and molecular study of meat tenderness. *Mailing Add:* Dept Animal Sci Mich State Univ East Lansing MI 48824

MERKEL, TIMOTHY FRANKLIN, b Jersey Shore, Pa, June 24, 42; m 66; c 2. ORGANIC POLYMER CHEMISTRY. *Educ:* Lycoming Col, AB, 64; Pa State Univ, MS, 66; Univ Mich, PhD(org chem), 73. *Prof Exp:* Res chemist, Whitmoyer Labs Inc, Rohm & Haas Co, 66-68; mgr prod develop, Sartomer Co, 73-78; mgr long range res & develop, 78-79, MGR FRICTION MATS RES, ABEX CORP, 79- *Mem:* Am Chem Soc; AAAS; Sigma Xi. *Res:* Specialty monomers, cyclic azo compounds; friction materials. *Mailing Add:* Abex Corp Valley Rd Mahwah NJ 07430

MERKELO, HENRI, b Borky, Ukraine, June 12, 39; US citizen. QUANTUM ELECTRONICS, OPTICAL ELECTRONICS. *Educ:* Univ Ill, BS, 60, MS, 62, PhD(elec eng, physics), 66. *Prof Exp:* Asst prof, 66-70, ASSOC PROF ELEC ENG, UNIV ILL, URBANA, 70- *Concurrent Pos:* NSF grants, Univ Ill, 67-, Cottrell Found grant, 68-70. *Mem:* Am Inst Physics; Inst Elec & Electronics Engrs. *Res:* Lasers; fluorescence; luminescence; photosynthesis; physical electronic devices; picosecond optical electronics. *Mailing Add:* Dept of Elec Eng Univ of Ill Urbana IL 61801

MERKEN, HENRY, b Peabody, Mass, Oct 14, 29; m 53; c 4. POLYMER CHEMISTRY. *Educ:* Northeastern Univ, BS, 53. *Prof Exp:* Asst engr, Res & Develop Dept, Am Polymer Corp, Mass, 49-53, develop engr, 53; develop engr, Polyco Dept, Borden Co, 55-56; develop engr, Polyvinyl Chem, Inc, 56-64, dir mfg, 64-68, asst to pres, 68-71, vpres int, 71-72; DIR INT OPER, BEATRICE CHEM, 72- *Concurrent Pos:* Instr, Lowell Tech Inst, 59-62. *Mem:* Am Chem Soc; Am Inst Chem Eng. *Res:* Organic chemistry; emulsion polymers; plasticizers. *Mailing Add:* 730 Main St Wilmington MA 01887

MERKEN, MELVIN, b Peabody, Mass, Jan 19, 27; m 56; c 3. CHEMISTRY, SCIENCE EDUCATION. *Educ:* Tufts Univ, BS, 50, AM, 51; Boston Univ, EdD(sci ed), 67. *Prof Exp:* Teacher high schs, Conn, 51-58; assoc prof, 58-67, PROF CHEM, WORCESTER STATE COL, 67-, CHMN DEPT, 58- *Mem:* Fel AAAS; fel Am Inst Chem; Am Chem Soc; Am Asn Physics Teachers. *Res:* Teaching science to non-scientists in general education program at college level; promotion of scientific literacy and understanding; environmental chemistry. *Mailing Add:* Dept Chem Worcester State Col Worcester MA 01602

MERKER, MILTON, b New York, NY, Sept 15, 41; m 63; c 2. NUCLEAR PHYSICS, COSMIC RAY PHYSICS. *Educ:* City Col New York, BS, 63; NY Univ, MS, 65, PhD(physics), 70. *Prof Exp:* Res asst physics, NY Univ, 65-70; res assoc, Univ Pa, 69-71, res asst prof astrophys, 71-73, asst prof & chmn dept, 73-77; STAFF SCIENTIST, SCI APPLNS, INC, 77- *Mem:* AAAS; Sigma Xi; Am Phys Soc; Am Geophys Union. *Res:* Nuclear radiation transport and effects; cosmic rays; astrophysical spallation and heavy-ion reactions; quasars; nuclear cascade; high-energy shielding and radiologic dosimetry; atmospheric neutrons. *Mailing Add:* Sci Applns Inc 1200 Prospect St La Jolla CA 92037

MERKER, PHILIP CHARLES, b New York, NY, July 23, 22; m 52; c 2. PHARMACOLOGY, TOXICOLOGY. *Educ:* Brooklyn Col, BA, 46; Long Island Univ, BS, 51; Purdue Univ, MS, 53, PhD, 55. *Prof Exp:* Lab asst physiol, Brooklyn Col, 46-47; teaching asst mat med, Long Island Univ, 48-51; asst pharm, Purdue Univ, 51-53; asst, Sloan-Kettering Inst Cancer Res, 56-62, head sect, 58-62, assoc mem, 62; prof pharmaceut, Col Pharm, Univ Tenn, 62-64; chmn dept pharmacol & animal sci, Col Pharmaceut Sci, Columbia Univ, 65, prof pharmacol & chmn div biol sci & pharmacol, 65-72; PHARMACOLOGIST, Arthur D Little, Inc, 72-77; assoc dir, 77-80, DIR, PHARMACOL & TOXICOL, VICK RES DIV, 80- *Concurrent Pos:* Res fel, Sloan-Kettering Inst Cancer Res, 54-56; asst prof, Sloan-Kettering Div, Cornell Univ, 58-62. *Mem:* AAAS; Am Asn Cancer Res; Am Soc Exp Path; Am Soc Pharmacol & Exp Therapeut; Soc Toxicol. *Res:* Experimental cancer chemotherapy; chemotherapy. *Mailing Add:* Vicks Res Ctr One Far Mill Crossing Shelton CT 06484

MERKES, EDWARD PETER, b Chicago, Ill, Apr 14, 29; m 56. MATHEMATICS. *Educ:* DePaul Univ, BS, 50; Northwestern Univ, PhD, 58. *Prof Exp:* Lectr math, De Paul Univ, 50-54, instr, 56-58, asst prof, 58-59; asst prof, Marquette Univ, 59-62, assoc prof, 62-63; assoc prof, 63-69, head dept, 70-77, PROF MATH, UNIV CINCINNATI, 69- *Concurrent Pos:* Vis assoc prof, Math Res Ctr, Univ Wis, 62-63. *Mem:* Am Math Soc; Math Asn Am. *Res:* Complex variable and continued fractions. *Mailing Add:* 3108 Hanna Cincinnati OH 45211

MERKL, MARVIN EUGENE, entomology, see previous edition

MERKLE, F HENRY, b Newark, NJ, Aug 31, 31; m; c 3. PHARMACEUTICAL CHEMISTRY. *Educ:* Rutgers Univ, BS, 54, MS, 61, PhD(pharmaceut sci), 64. *Prof Exp:* Instr pharm, Rutgers Univ, 58-62, lectr, 62-63; res scientist, Res Ctr, FMC Corp, NJ, 64-65; sr res scientist, 65-70, dept head pharmaceut prod develop, 70-75, MGR PHARM PROD DEVELOP, BRISTOL MYERS PROD, 75- *Mem:* Am Pharmaceut Asn; Am Chem Soc. *Res:* Pharmaceutical analysis, products, and development. *Mailing Add:* 2217 Shawnee Path Scotch Plains NJ 07076

MERKLE, OWEN GEORGE, b Meade, Kans, Nov 22, 29; m 52; c 5. PLANT BREEDING, GENETICS. *Educ:* Okla State Univ, BS, 51, MS, 54; Tex A&M Univ, PhD(plant breeding), 63. *Prof Exp:* Res agronomist, US Dept Agr, 57-80; MEM FAC, DEPT SOILS & CROP SCI, TEX A&M UNIV, 80- *Mem:* Am Soc Agron; Crop Sci Soc Am. *Res:* Plant breeding; breeding wheat for disease resistance; improved quality and agronomic characters and associated genetic studies. *Mailing Add:* Dept Soil & Crop Sci Tex A&M Univ Stillwater TX 77840

MERKLEY, DAVID FREDERICK, b Pipestone, Minn, Apr 23, 45; m 70; c 1. VETERINARY SURGERY. *Educ:* Univ SDak, BA, 67; Iowa State Univ, DVM, 71; Mich State Univ, MS, 75. *Prof Exp:* Asst prof vet surg, Mich State Univ, 75-80; MEM FAC, COL VET MED, IOWA STATE UNIV, AMES, 80- *Mailing Add:* Col Vet Med Iowa State Univ Ames IA 50010

MERKLEY, WAYNE BINGHAM, b Murray, Utah, Apr 1, 41; m 59; c 4. ECOLOGY OF REGULATED STREAMS, AQUATIC ECOLOGY. *Educ:* Univ Utah, BS, 63, MA, 66, PhD(limnol), 69. *Prof Exp:* Instr biol, Univ Utah, 68; from asst prof to assoc prof, 69-80, PROF BIOL, DRAKE UNIV, 80- *Mem:* Am Inst Biol Sci; Am Soc Limnol & Oceanog; Water Pollution Control Fedn; NAm Benthol Soc. *Res:* Ecological impact of impoundments and urban areas on aquatic environments in large prairie rivers. *Mailing Add:* Dept of Biol Drake Univ Des Moines IA 50311

MERLAN, STEPHEN JESSE, b Bay Shore, NY, Nov 14, 45. INFORMATION SCIENCE, PHYSICS. *Educ:* Univ Idaho, BS, 66; Yale Univ, PhD(physics), 72. *Prof Exp:* Staff mem, 73-77, asst for res, 77-78, PROG MGR, LOS ALAMOS SCI LAB, 78- *Mem:* Asn Symbolic Logic. *Res:* Coding; pattern recognition; data structures. *Mailing Add:* Los Alamos Sci Lab PO Box 1663 Los Alamos NM 87545

MERLIN, ROBERTO DANIEL, b Buenos Aires, Argentina, Aug 12, 50. INELASTIC LIGHT SCATTERING, OPTICAL PROPERTIES. *Educ:* Univ Buenos Aires, Licenciatura, 73; Univ Stuttgart, WGer, Dr rer nat, 78. *Prof Exp:* Res assoc, Univ Ill, Urbana, 78-80; ASST PROF PHYSICS, UNIV MICH, ANN ARBOR, 80- *Mem:* Am Phys Soc. *Res:* Semiconductor heterostructures, high-ionic mobility materials and glassy metals. *Mailing Add:* Dept Physics Univ Mich Ann Arbor MI 48109

MERLINO, GLENN T, b New York, NY, Aug 25, 53; m 75. DEVELOPMENTAL BIOLOGY. *Educ:* Adelphi Univ, NY, BA, 75; Univ Mich, Ann Arbor, PhD(biol sci), 80. *Prof Exp:* Grad fel biol sci, Univ Mich, 75-80; FEL, NAT CANCER INST, NIH, 80- *Concurrent Pos:* Fel, Cystic Fibrosis Found, 80 & Arthritis Found, 81- *Mem:* AAAS; Am Soc Zoologists; NY Acad Sci. *Res:* Regulations of enkaryotic genes during cellular differentiation; use of two model systems (viral-induced transformation of chicken embryo fibroblasts and early sea urlin development) to study the genes encoding collagen, tublin and actin. *Mailing Add:* Lab Molecular Biol Nat Cancer Inst Bldg 37 Rm 2D27 NIH Bethesda MD 20205

MERLIS, JEROME K, b New York, NY, Feb 24, 14; m 41; c 3. NEUROPHYSIOLOGY. *Educ:* Univ Louisville, BS, 33, MD, 37, MS, 38; Am Bd Psychiat & Neurol, dipl, 48. *Prof Exp:* Asst physiol, Sch Med, Univ Louisville, 37-38, from instr to asst prof, 38-46; neurologist in chg, Nat Vet Epilepsy Ctr, Cushing Vet Admin Hosp, Mass, 46-52, chief, 52-56; assoc prof physiol, 59-75, prof neurol & clin neurophysiol, 56-77, head EEG dept, Univ Hosp, 56-77, EMER PROF NEUROL, SCH MED, UNIV MD, BALTIMORE CITY, 77- *Concurrent Pos:* Coman fel, Univ Chicago, 39; Commonwealth Fund fel, Yale Univ, 40-41; ed, Epilepsia, 52-56; clin assoc neurol, Mass Gen Hosp, 53-56; asst, Harvard Univ, 53-54, instr, 54-56. *Mem:* Am Neurol Asn; Am Acad Neurol; Am Electroencephalog Soc (secy, 56-59, pres, 60); Am Epilepsy Soc (secy-treas, 51-55, pres, 57); Int League Against Epilepsy (treas, 57-65, vpres, 65-68, pres, 68-69). *Res:* Electroencephalography; experimental epilepsy; neurology. *Mailing Add:* EEG Dept Univ of Md Hosp Baltimore MD 21201

MERMAGEN, WILLIAM HENRY, b New York, NY, May 21, 35; m 60; c 4. PHYSICS, AERONAUTICS. *Educ:* Fordham Univ, BS, 57; Univ Del, MS, 66. *Prof Exp:* Res physicist aeroballistics, 57-67, PHYS SCI ADMINR AEROBALLISTICS, US ARMY BALLISTIC RES LAB, 67- *Concurrent Pos:* Fel, US Army Ballistic Res Lab, 75. *Mem:* Assoc fel Am Inst Aeronaut & Astronaut. *Res:* Aeroballistics including missile dynamics, flight mechanics, heat transfer, fluid flow, measurement systems and liquid-filled projectiles. *Mailing Add:* 4149 U-Way Havre de Grace MD 21078

MERMEL, THADDEUS WALTER, b Chicago, Ill, Sept 12, 07; m 30; c 3. ELECTRICAL ENGINEERING, CIVIL ENGINEERING. *Educ:* Univ Ill, BS, 30. *Prof Exp:* Engr, Bur Reclamation, US Dept Interior, 33-73, asst to comnr res, 64-71, asst to comnr sci affairs, 71-73; CONSULT CIVIL ENG, PROCUREMENT SPECIALTY, CONTRACT ADMIN ARBITRATION, 73- *Concurrent Pos:* Mem fed construct coun, Nat Acad Sci, 55-, mem comt on construct mgt, Hwy Res Bd & alt mem adv bd, Off Critical Tables; chmn comt world register of dams, Int Comn Large Dams, 60-; consult, Overseas Adv Assocs, 73-76 & World Bank, 73-81. *Mem:* AAAS; Am Soc Civil Engrs; Inst Elec & Electronics Engrs; Int Conf Large Elec Systs; Int Soc Rock Mech. *Res:* Dams; hydroelectric plant equipment; generators; turbines; underground high-voltage transmission; water resource development. *Mailing Add:* 4540 43rd St NW Washington DC 20016

MERMELSTEIN, ROBERT, b Mukacevo, Czech; Can citizen. POLYMER CHEMISTRY. *Educ:* Sir George Williams Univ, BSc, 57; Univ Alta, PhD(phys org chem), 64. *Prof Exp:* Fel, Brandeis Univ, 64-65 & Childrens' Cancer Res Found, Boston, 65-66; SCIENTIST POLYMER CHEM, XEROX CORP, 66- *Mem:* AAAS; Am Chem Soc; Environ Mutagen Soc. *Res:* Synthesis, characterization of vinyl and condensation polymers; biopolymers; structure-activity relationships; rheological behaviour; kinetics and mechanism of organic reactions; microbiology of nitroarnenes. *Mailing Add:* 345 Pelham Rd Rochester NY 14610

MERMIN, N DAVID, b New Haven, Conn, Mar 30, 35; m 57. PHYSICS. *Educ:* Harvard Univ, AB, 56, AM, 57, PhD(physics), 61. *Prof Exp:* NSF fel physics, Univ Birmingham, 61-63; res assoc, Univ Calif, San Diego, 63-64; from asst prof to assoc prof, 64-72, PROF PHYSICS, CORNELL UNIV, 72- *Concurrent Pos:* Alfred P Sloan Found fel, 66-70; John Simon Guggenheim Found fel, 70-71. *Mem:* Fel Am Phys Soc. *Res:* Theoretical solid state and statistical physics. *Mailing Add:* Dept of Physics Cornell Univ Ithaca NY 14853

MERNER, RICHARD RAYMOND, b Chicago, Ill, Sept 23, 18; m 51; c 2. INDUSTRIAL ORGANIC CHEMISTRY, SCIENCE ADMINISTRATION. *Educ:* Univ Ill, BS, 39; Northwestern Univ, PhD(chem), 49. *Prof Exp:* Asst chem, Univ Mo, 39-40; asst chem electrochem dept, Res & Develop, E I du Pont de Nemours & Co, Inc, 40-44, org chem dept, Res, 49-53, tech supvr process develop, 53-67, supvr tech employ & personnel develop, 67-76, mgr distrib regulatory compliance, 76-78; CONSULT & PRES, MERNER ASSOCS, INC, 77- *Concurrent Pos:* Adj prof & mgt lectr, Col Bus & Econs, Univ Del, 70- *Mem:* AAAS; Am Chem Soc; Am Inst Chem Eng; Sigma Xi. *Res:* Development research; intermediates; dyes and pigments; fluorocarbons; management science; behavior science. *Mailing Add:* RD 2 Box 326 Sullivan Rd Avondale PA 19311

MEROLA, A JOHN, b Freehold, NJ, July 21, 31; m 58; c 3. BIOCHEMISTRY, MICROBIOLOGY. *Educ:* Univ Tex, BA, 53; Rutgers Univ, MS, 59, PhD(bact), 61. *Prof Exp:* Fel biochem, Enzyme Inst, Univ Wis, 61-63; res biologist, Sterling-Winthrop Res Inst, 63-65; from asst prof to assoc prof, 66-73, PROF PHYSIOL CHEM, OHIO STATE UNIV, 73- *Res:* Energy conservation; drug and cholesterol metabolism; electron transport. *Mailing Add:* Dept of Physiol Chem Ohio State Univ Columbus OH 43210

MEROLA, JOSEPH SALVATORE, b Pittsburgh, Pa, Sept 27, 52; m 77; c 1. HOMOGENEOUS CATALYSIS. *Educ:* Carnegie-Mellon Univ, BS, 74; Mass Inst Technol, PhD(inorg chem), 78. *Prof Exp:* SR CHEMIST, CORP RES LABS, EXXON RES & ENG CO, 78- *Mem:* Am Chem Soc. *Res:* Synthesis of polymetallic transition metal complexes capable of producing unusual interactions with and reactions of carbon monoxide and hydrogen. *Mailing Add:* Corp Res Labs Exxon Res & Eng Co PO Box 45 Linden NJ 07036

MERONEY, ROBERT N, b Chicago, Ill, Oct 4, 37; m 65; c 2. MECHANICAL ENGINEERING, FLUID MECHANICS. *Educ:* Univ Tenn, BS, 60; Univ Calif, Berkeley, MS, 64, PhD(mech eng), 65. *Prof Exp:* Engr, US Naval Ord Lab, 60-65; from asst prof to assoc prof civil eng, 65-75, PROF CIVIL ENG, COLO STATE UNIV, FT COLLINS, 75- *Concurrent Pos:* Clean Air Act fel, 72-73; Fulbright Hays fel, 77-78; Erskine lectr, Univ Canterbury, 77-78; Alexander von Humboldt Award, 80-81. *Mem:* Am Soc Mech Engrs; Am Inst Aeronaut & Astronaut; Am Soc Eng Educ; Am Meteorol Soc; Am Soc Civil Engrs. *Res:* Heat transfer and transpiration of turbulent boundary layers; meteorological fluid mechanics; environmental simulation; air pollution. *Mailing Add:* Dept of Civil Eng Colo State Univ Ft Collins CO 80523

MERONEY, WILLIAM HYDE, III, b Murphy, NC, Dec 27, 17; m 52. INTERNAL MEDICINE. *Educ:* Univ NC, BS, 43; NY Univ, MD, 45; Am Bd Internal Med, dipl. *Prof Exp:* Instr pharmacol, Sch Med, Univ NC, 43; Med Corps, US Army, 46-75; instr internal med, Yale Univ, 50-51, lectr, 51-52, chief renal insufficiency ctr, Korea, 53, from res clinician to chief dept metab, Walter Reed Army Inst Res, 53-57, dep dir inst, 61-64, dir trop res med lab, San Juan, PR, 57-61, chief res div, Med Res & Develop Command, Washington, DC, 64-65, dep dir personnel & training directorate, Off Surgeon Gen, 66-68, dir & commandant, Walter Reed Army Inst Res, 68-71, commanding gen, Walter Reed Gen Hosp, 71-72, commanding gen, Madigan Army Med Ctr, Med Corps, US Army, 72-75; consult med, 75-77, DIR PROF SERV, DEPT HEALTH, PROVIDENCE, RI, 77- *Concurrent Pos:* Asst clin prof, Sch Med, Georgetown Univ, 57; clin assoc prof, Univ PR, 57-61; consult, Bayamon Dist Hosp, PR & Surgeon Gen, US Army. *Mem:* AAAS; Endocrine Soc; Soc Exp Biol & Med; AMA; fel Am Col Physicians. *Res:* Metabolic processes. *Mailing Add:* 602 Black Point Farm Portsmouth RI 02871

MEROW, WILLIAM WAYNE, b Sparta, Wis, Mar 22, 22; m 44; c 2. ORTHODONTICS. *Educ:* Univ Md, DDS, 51, Ohio State Univ, MS, 61. *Prof Exp:* Instr dent anat, Baltimore Col Dent Surg, Univ Md, 51-52; instr orthod, Col Dent, Ohio State Univ, 61-65; PROF ORTHOD & CHMN DEPT, SCH DENT, WVA UNIV, 65- *Concurrent Pos:* Orthod consult, Children's Hosp, Columbus, 61-65. *Mem:* Am Dent Asn; Am Asn Orthod. *Res:* Growth and development, including proportional growth changes in the facial and cranial skeleton of the growing child; force distribution accompanying rapid palatal expansion. *Mailing Add:* Sch of Dent WVa Univ Morgantown WV 26506

MERRELL, DAVID JOHN, b Bound Brook, NJ, Aug 20, 19; m 45; c 4. GENETICS. *Educ:* Rutgers Univ, BS, 41; Harvard Univ, MA, 47, PhD(zool), 48. *Prof Exp:* From instr to assoc prof, 48-64, PROF GENETICS & ECOL, UNIV MINN, MINNEAPOLIS, 64- *Mem:* Soc Study Evolution; Genetics Soc Am; Am Genetics Asn; Am Soc Nat; AAAS; Behav Genetics Asn. *Res:* Ecological and behavioral genetics. *Mailing Add:* 319 Zool Bldg Univ Minn Minneapolis MN 55455

MERRIAM, CHARLES WOLCOTT, III, b Birmingham, Ala, Mar 31, 31; m 54; c 2. ELECTRICAL ENGINEERING. *Educ:* Brown Univ, ScB, 53; Mass Inst Technol, MS, 55, ScD(elec eng), 58. *Prof Exp:* Asst prof elec eng, Mass Inst Technol, 58-64; prof, Cornell Univ, 64-71; PROF ELEC ENG & CHMN DEPT, UNIV ROCHESTER, RIVER CAMPUS, 71- *Concurrent Pos:* Consult, Air Res & Develop Command, US Air Force, 58-59; elec engr, Res Lab, Gen Elec Co, 59-64; adj prof, Rensselaer Polytech Inst, 60- *Mem:* Assoc Inst Elec & Electronics Engrs. *Res:* Optimization theory; computations; feedback control. *Mailing Add:* Dept of Elec Eng Univ of Rochester River Campus Rochester NY 14627

MERRIAM, DANIEL FRANCIS, b Omaha, Nebr, Feb 9, 27; m 46; c 5. GEOLOGY. *Educ:* Univ Kans, BS, 49, MS, 53, PhD, 61; Univ Leicester, MSc, 69, DSc, 75. *Prof Exp:* Geologist, Union Oil Co, Calif, 49-51; asst instr geol, Univ Kans, 51-53, instr, 54; geologist, Kans Geol Surv, 53-58, div head basic geol, 58-63, chief geol res, 63-71; Jessie Page Heroy prof geol, Syracuse Univ, 71-81, chmn dept, 71-80; ENDOWMENT ASN DISTINGUISHED PROF GEOL & CHMN DEPT, WICHITA STATE UNIV, 81- *Concurrent Pos:* Res assoc, Univ Kans, 63-71; vis vis res scientist, Stanford Univ, 63; Fulbright-Hays sr res fel, UK, 64-65; dir, Am Geol Inst Int Field Inst, Japan, 67; vis prof geol, Wichita State Univ, 68-70; Am Geol Inst Vis Geol Scientist, 69; mem, Sci Comt 4, 75-, chmn, 76-77 & 78-79; participant, Project COMPUTe, Dartmouth Col, 74; mem, US Nat Comn for Int Geol Correl Prog, 76-; vis prof, Ctr d'Info Geol, Ecole des Mines de Paris, 80. *Honors & Awards:* Erasmus Haworth Grad Award Geol, Univ Kans, 55. *Mem:* Fel AAAS; fel Geol Soc London; Int Asn Math Geol (pres, 76-); fel Geol Soc Am; Am Asn Petrol Geol. *Res:* Carboniferous and Mesozoic stratigraphy; geologic history of the mid-continent; cyclic sedimentation; petroleum geology; computers and computer applications in the earth sciences; quantitative stratigraphic analysis. *Mailing Add:* Dept Geol Wichita State Univ Wichita KS 67208

MERRIAM, ESTHER VIRGINIA, b Pittsburgh, Pa, Apr 9, 40; m 63; c 2. VIROLOGY, BIOCHEMISTRY. *Educ:* Elizabethtown Col, BS, 62; Univ Wash, PhD(biochem), 66. *Prof Exp:* USPHS fel biol div, Oak Ridge Nat Lab, 66-67; fel, Calif Inst Technol, 67-69; actg asst prof molecular biol in bact, Univ Calif, Los Angeles, 69-71; asst prof, Loyola Univ Los Angeles, 71-74, ASSOC PROF BIOL, LOYOLA MARYMOUNT UNIV, 74- *Mem:* Am Soc Microbiol; Genetics Soc Am. *Res:* Nucleic acid interactions, especially in connection with viral systems. *Mailing Add:* Dept of Biol Loyola Marymount Univ Los Angeles CA 90045

MERRIAM, GEORGE RENNELL, JR, b Harrisburg, Pa, May 22, 13; m 36; c 4. MEDICINE. *Educ:* Brown Univ, AB, 34; Columbia Univ, MD, 41; Am Bd Ophthal, dipl, 49. *Prof Exp:* Instr ophthal, 49-56, assoc, 56-59, prof, 59-68, EMER PROF CLIN OPHTHAL, COL PHYSICIANS & SURGEONS, COLUMBIA UNIV, 68- *Concurrent Pos:* Asst ophthalmologist, Presby Hosp, New York, 49-56, attend ophthalmologist, 56-; asst ophthalmologist, Mem Hosp, New York, 49-57, assoc ophthalmologist, 57-59, ophthalmologist, 59-69; assoc ophthalmologist, Francis Delafield Hosp, 51- *Mem:* Am Ophthal Soc; Am Radium Soc; Asn Res Ophthal; fel Am Col Surgeons; AMA. *Res:* Ophthalmic radiotherapy; cataracts; relative biological effectiveness of various qualities of radiation. *Mailing Add:* Edward S Harkness Eye Inst Columbia Univ New York NY 10032

MERRIAM, HOWARD GRAY, b Smithville, Ont, July 8, 32; m 56; c 2. ECOLOGY. *Educ:* Univ Toronto, BSA, 56; Cornell Univ, PhD, 60. *Prof Exp:* Asst gen zool, Cornell Univ, 56-58, asst animal ecol, 58-60; from asst prof to assoc prof animal ecol, Univ Tex, 60-68; ASSOC PROF BIOL, CARLETON UNIV, 68-, CHMN DEPT, 79- *Concurrent Pos:* Consult, Can Ministry State Urban Affairs, 73-74, Can Wildlife Serv, 74-75 & Parks Can, 75- *Mem:* Can

Soc Zoologists; Can Soc Environ Biologists; AAAS; Ecol Soc Am; Am Soc Mammal. *Res:* Population ecology and quantitative autecology; ecology of land isopods and marmots; ecology of decomposer ecosystems; heterogeneity in natural systems. *Mailing Add:* Dept Biol Carleton Univ Ottawa ON K1S 5B6 Can

MERRIAM, JOHN L(AFAYETTE), b Corona, Calif, Nov 27, 11; m 38; c 2. CIVIL ENGINEERING, AGRICULTURAL ENGINEERING. *Educ:* Calif Inst Technol, BSCE, 38. *Prof Exp:* Area engr, Soil Conserv Serv, USDA, 39-56; irrig engr, Ministry Agr, Saudi Arabia, 56-58; prof, 58-78, EMER PROF AGR ENG, CALIF STATE POLYTECH UNIV, 78-; CONSULT IRRIG ENG, 78- *Concurrent Pos:* Consult, Irrig & Drainage Proj, Siwa Oasis, Egypt, Ralph M Parsons Co, 62; consult irrig, Inst Fomento Nac, Managua, Nicaragua, 66; UN Food & Agr Orgn, Saudi Arabia, 69; US Overseas Mission, Thailand, 69-70; Peace Corps, 71; consult irrig, USAID, Tunisia, 75 & Govt Sri Lanka, 78-83. *Honors & Awards:* Royce J Tipton Award, Am Soc Civil Engrs, 79. *Mem:* Am Soc Civil Engrs; sr mem Am Soc Agr Engrs; Am Geophys Union; Int Comt Irrig & Drain. *Res:* On-farm irrigation efficiency; small project water supply systems; irrigation and drainage. *Mailing Add:* Dept of Agr Eng Calif State Polytech Univ San Luis Obispo CA 93401

MERRIAM, JOHN ROGER, b Kenosha, Wis, Jan 6, 40; m 63; c 2. GENETICS. *Educ:* Univ Wis, BS, 62; Univ Wash, MS, 63, PhD(genetics), 66. *Prof Exp:* USPHS fels biol, Oak Ridge Nat Lab, 66-67 & Calif Inst Technol, 67-69; asst prof, 69-74, ASSOC PROF GENETICS, UNIV CALIF, LOS ANGELES, 74- *Concurrent Pos:* Vis fel, Res Sch Biol Sci, Australian Nat Univ, 75-76 & genetics & develop, Cornell Univ, 80-81. *Mem:* AAAS; Genetics Soc Am. *Res:* Neurological genetics of Drosophila; gene regulation; chromosome mechanics; somatic crossing over and mosaic analysis of development. *Mailing Add:* Dept of Biol Univ of Calif Los Angeles CA 90024

MERRIAM, LAWRENCE CAMPBELL, JR, b Portland, Ore, Aug 31, 23; m 47; c 5. FOREST MANAGEMENT. *Educ:* Univ Calif, BS, 48; Ore State Univ, MF, 58, PhD(forest mgt), 63. *Prof Exp:* Log scaler-compassman, Shasta Forests Co, Calif, 48; forestry aide, Ore Bur Land Mgt, 49; retail sales millworker, Willamette Nat Lumber Co, 49-50; log pond foreman bookkeeper, M&M Woodworking Co, 50; state parks historian, planner & forester state parks div, Ore State Hwy Dept, 51-59; from asst prof to assoc prof forestry, Univ Mont, 59-66; PROF FORESTRY, UNIV MINN, ST PAUL, 66- *Concurrent Pos:* Consult, Bur Land Mgt, DC, 65-66 & UN Food & Agr Orgn, Paraguay, 69. *Mem:* Soc Am Foresters; fel Soc Park & Recreation Educr; Nat Parks Asn. *Res:* Park wilderness management and policy. *Mailing Add:* Col of Forestry Univ of Minn St Paul MN 55108

MERRIAM, MARSHAL F(REDRIC), b Ossining, NY, Apr 1, 32; m 53; c 5. ENERGY CONVERSION, MATERIALS SCIENCE. *Educ:* Mass Inst Technol, SB, 53; Carnegie Inst Technol, MS, 58, PhD(physics), 61. *Prof Exp:* Staff scientist, Gen Atomic Div, Gen Dynamics Corp, 60-61; res assoc physics, Univ Calif, San Diego, 61-62; asst prof, 62-66, ASSOC PROF ENG SCI, UNIV CALIF, BERKELEY, 66- *Concurrent Pos:* Staff consult, Gulf Gen Atomic, 61-71, IBM Corp, NY, 63 & United Aircraft Res Labs, Conn, 65; vis prof, Indian Inst Technol, Kanpur, 67-69 & Sch Eng, Univ Sao Paulo, 71; mem res staff, Technol & Develop Inst, East-West Ctr, Hawaii, 71-72; mem vis research staff, Niels Bohr Inst, 77-78. *Mem:* Am Phys Soc; Solar Energy Soc; Am Wind Energy Asn. *Res:* Solar energy devices; electric and magnetic properties of materials; wind energy. *Mailing Add:* Dept of Mat Sci & Eng Univ of Calif Hearst Mining Bldg Berkeley CA 94720

MERRIAM, ROBERT ARNOLD, b Keokuk, Iowa, Apr 30, 27; m 53; c 3. FOREST HYDROLOGY, BIOMASS ENERGY. *Educ:* Iowa State Univ, BS, 51; Univ Calif, Berkeley, MS, 57. *Prof Exp:* Range conservationist, Calif Forest & Range Exp Sta, 53-55, res forester, Pac Southwest Forest & Range Exp Sta, 55-60, Intermountain Forest & Range Exp Sta, 60-63 & Pac Southwest Forest & Range Exp Sta, 63-73, asst mgr Hawaii water resources regional study, State Hawaii, 73-76, RESOURCES MGT FORESTER, HAWAII DIV FORESTRY & WILDLIFE, US FOREST SERV, 76- . *Concurrent Pos:* Crown Zellerbach fel. *Mem:* Soc Am Foresters; Am Geophys Union; Sigma Xi; Int Soc Tropical Foresters. *Res:* Watershed management; soil moisture measurement techniques, including neutron probe; interception and fog drip; river basin surveys; biomass fuels; short rotation plantation silviculture. *Mailing Add:* 616 Pamaele St Kailua HI 96734

MERRIAM, ROBERT WILLIAM, b Waverly, Iowa, Nov 21, 23; m 50; c 2. DEVELOPMENTAL BIOLOGY. *Educ:* Univ Iowa, AB, 47; Ore State Univ, MS, 49; Univ Wis, PhD(zool), 53. *Prof Exp:* Asst zool, Ore State Univ, 47-50 & Univ Wis, 50-53; from instr to asst prof, Univ Pa, 53-59; ASSOC PROF BIOL, STATE UNIV NY STONY BROOK, 61- *Concurrent Pos:* Vis fel zool, Columbia Univ, 60-61; NIH spec fel, Oxford Univ, 67-68; vis scientist, Hubrecht Laboratorium, Netherlands, 82. *Honors & Awards:* Lalor Found Awards, 55 & 57. *Mem:* AAAS; Soc Develop Biol; Am Soc Cell Biol. *Res:* Cellular biology; nuclear-cytoplasmic interaction; control mechanisms in oogenesis; contrafile systems in egg cells. *Mailing Add:* Dept Neurobiol State Univ of NY Stony Brook NY 11790

MERRICK, ARTHUR WEST, b Great Falls, Mont, Dec 22, 17; m 45; c 5. PHYSIOLOGY. *Educ:* Univ Mont, AB & BS, 50; Univ Mo, MA, 52, PhD(physiol), 54. *Prof Exp:* Asst physiol, Univ Mo, 51-52, asst instr, 53-54; instr, Univ Kans, 54-55; from asst prof to assoc prof, Med Ctr, Univ Mo-Columbia, 55-68; prof, Ill State Univ, 68-72; HEALTH SCIENTIST ADMINR, NAT HEART, LUNG & BLOOD INST, 72- *Concurrent Pos:* Wyeth Drug Corp fel, 61-62; Nat Heart Inst grants; grant; exec secy, Rev Br, Div Extramural Affairs, Nat Heart, Lung & Blood Inst, 73- *Mem:* Fel AAAS; Am Physiol Soc; NY Acad Sci. *Res:* Carbohydrate metabolism of cardiac and nervous tissue; intrinsic nervous system of mammalian heart. *Mailing Add:* Rev Br Div Extramural Affairs Nat Heart Lung & Blood Inst Bethesda MD 20205

MERRICK, JOSEPH M, b Welland, Ont, Mar 20, 30; m 55; c 3. BIOCHEMISTRY, MICROBIOLOGY. *Educ:* Mich State Univ, BS, 51, MS, 53; Univ Mich, PhD(biochem), 58. *Prof Exp:* Arthritis & Rheumatism Found fel, Univ Calif, 59-61; assoc biochem, State Univ NY Buffalo, 61-62, asst prof, 62-65; assoc prof bact & bot, Syracuse Univ, 65-70; PROF MICROBIOL, STATE UNIV NY BUFFALO, 70- *Mem:* Am Soc Microbiol; Am Chem Soc; AAAS; Am Soc Biol Chem. *Res:* Bacterial transport; isolation and characterization of glycolipid and glycoprotein membrane antigens. *Mailing Add:* Dept of Microbiol State Univ of NY Buffalo NY 14214

MERRIELL, DAVID MCCRAY, b Minneapolis, Minn, Oct 25, 19; m 51; c 2. MATHEMATICS. *Educ:* Yale Univ, BA, 41; Univ Chicago, MS, 47, PhD(math), 51. *Prof Exp:* Instr math, Univ Chicago, 49-51; asst prof, Robert Col, Turkey, 51-54, assoc prof & head dept, 54-57; from asst prof to assoc prof, Univ Calif, Santa Barbara, 57-68; chmn dept math, 71-74, PROF MATH, VASSAR COL, 68-, CHMN DEPT, 77- *Mem:* Am Math Soc; Math Asn Am; Asn Women Math; Fedn Am Scientists. *Res:* Non-associative algebras; graph theory. *Mailing Add:* Dept of Math Vassar Col Poughkeepsie NY 12601

MERRIFIELD, D BRUCE, b Chicago, Ill, June 13, 21; m 49; c 3. PHYSICAL ORGANIC CHEMISTRY. *Educ:* Princeton Univ, BS, 42; Univ Chicago, MS, 48, PhD(phys org chem), 50. *Prof Exp:* Res chemist, Monsanto Co, 50-56; group leader res, Tex-US Chem Co, 56-60, mgr polymer res, 60-63; dir res, Petrolite Corp, 63-68; dir res, Res Ctr, Hooker Chem Corp, 68-70, vpres res & develop, 70-77; VPRES TECHNOL, CONTINENTAL GROUP, INC, 77- *Mem:* Fel AAAS; fel Am Inst Chemists; Indust Res Inst (pres elect); Res Dirs Asn; Am Chem Soc. *Res:* Mechanisms of free radical reactions; oxidation mechanisms; polymer and surface chemistry; electrochemistry and electronics. *Mailing Add:* Continental Group Inc 633 Third Ave New York NY 10017

MERRIFIELD, PAUL ELLIOTT, b Springvale, Maine, Dec 31, 22; m 44; c 4. COLLOID CHEMISTRY. *Educ:* Colby Col, AB, 47; Rice Inst, AM, 49, PhD(chem), 51. *Prof Exp:* Res chemist, Armstrong Cork Co, 51-59, plant chief chemist, 60-67, mgr felt mfg, 67-81; RETIRED. *Mem:* Am Chem Soc. *Res:* Colloidal properties of fibers; fiber products development. *Mailing Add:* PO Box 184 Springvale ME 04083

MERRIFIELD, RICHARD EBERT, b Seattle, Wash, Feb 18, 29; m 56; c 2. CHEMICAL PHYSICS. *Educ:* Mass Inst Technol, PhD(phys chem), 53. *Prof Exp:* Res chemist, 53-59, RES SUPVR CENT RES DEPT, E I DU PONT DE NEMOURS & CO, INC, 59- *Mem:* Am Phys Soc. *Res:* Molecular spectra and structure; solid state theory; exciton physics; physics of molecular crystals. *Mailing Add:* 2633 Longwood Dr Wilmington DE 19810

MERRIFIELD, ROBERT BRUCE, b Ft Worth, Tex, July 15, 21; m 49; c 6. BIOCHEMISTRY. *Educ:* Univ Calif, Los Angeles, BA, 43, PhD(chem), 49. *Hon Degrees:* DSc, Univ Colo, 69 & Yale Univ, 71; PhD, Uppsala Univ, 70. *Prof Exp:* Chemist, Philip R Park Res Found, 43-44; asst chem, Med Sch, Univ Calif, Los Angeles, 48-49; asst biochem, 49-53, assoc, 53-57, from asst prof to assoc prof, 57-66, PROF BIOCHEM, ROCKEFELLER UNIV, 66- *Concurrent Pos:* Nobel guest prof, Uppsala Univ, 68; assoc ed, Int J Peptide & Protein Res, 69- *Honors & Awards:* Lasker Award Basic Med Res, 69; Gairdner Award, 70; Intra-Sci Award, 70; Award for Creative Work in Synthetic Org Chem, Am Chem Soc, 72, Nichols Medal, 73. *Mem:* Nat Acad Sci. *Res:* Development of solid phase peptide synthesis, first synthesis of an enzyme; relation of structure to function in synthetic, biologically active peptides and proteins. *Mailing Add:* Rockefeller Univ 66th St & York Ave New York NY 10021

MERRIFIELD, ROBERT G, b Carthage, Mo, July 26, 30; m 52; c 4. SILVICULTURE. *Educ:* Ark Agr & Mech Col, BS, 53; La State Univ, MF, 58; Duke Univ, DF(silvicult), 62. *Prof Exp:* From asst prof to assoc prof forestry, La State Univ, 58-67; PROF FORESTRY, TEX A&M UNIV, 67-, HEAD DEPT FOREST SCI, 69- *Mem:* Soc Am Foresters. *Res:* Artificial regeneration and plantation management of southern pines; intensive culture of pulping hardwood species. *Mailing Add:* Dept of Forest Sci Tex A&M Univ College Station TX 77843

MERRIGAN, JOSEPH A, b Maryville, Mo, Feb 8, 40; m 62; c 2. PHOTOGRAPHIC CHEMISTRY. *Educ:* Northwest Mo State Col, BS, 62; Univ Nebr, MS, 65, PhD(phys chem), 66; Mass Inst Technol, SM, 74. *Prof Exp:* Sr res chemist, Eastman Kodak Co, 67-69, res assoc & head silver halide chem lab, 69-74, head radiography lab, Kodak Res Labs, 74-75, head spec processes lab, 75-79, DIR MAT COATING & ENG DIV, KODAK RES LABS, 79- *Res:* Hot atom reactions of neutron irradiated bromine with organic molecules; positronium interactions in solid systems; mechanisms of photographic recording; radiographic recording; photovoltaic cells. *Mailing Add:* Eastman Kodak Res Labs 1669 Lake Ave Rochester NY 14650

MERRIL, CARL R, b Brooklyn, NY, Dec 6, 36; m 61; c 2. MOLECULAR BIOLOGY, MEDICINE. *Educ:* Col William & Mary, BS, 58; Georgetown Univ, MD, 62. *Prof Exp:* Intern med, USPHS Hosp, Boston, Mass, 62-63; res assoc molecular biol, Lab Neurochem Sect, Phys Chem, 63-65, mem staff, 65-69, SR STAFF SCIENTIST, LAB GEN & COMP BIOCHEM, NIMH, 69- *Mem:* AAAS; Biophys Soc; NY Acad Sci; Electrophoresis Soc. *Res:* Bacteriophage interactions with eukaryotic systems, quantitative two dimensional electrophoresis of proteins, silver stains for proteins and DNA; galactose metabolism in prokaryotes; galactosemia; inborn metabolic diseases; gene transfer; primary structure of biopolymers. *Mailing Add:* Lab of Gen & Comp Biochem NIMH Bldg 36 Rm 3A15 Bethesda MD 20014

MERRILL, DOROTHY, b Abington, Mass, Jan 1, 27. ZOOLOGY. *Educ:* Mass State Col Bridgewater, BS, 47; Univ Mich, AM, 59, PhD(zool), 64. *Prof Exp:* Teacher high sch, Mass, 47-60; from instr to asst prof zool, Smith Col, 64-70; assoc prof biol, Western Col, 70-74; assoc prof, 74-79, PROF BIOL, KIRKHOF COL, GRAND VALLEY STATE COLS, 79- *Mem:* Am Soc Zool; Animal Behav Soc. *Res:* Neural mechanisms in insect behavior; biology of caddis larvae. *Mailing Add:* Kirkhof Col Grand Valley State Cols Allendale MI 49401

MERRILL, E(DWARD) W(ILSON), b New Bedford, Mass, Aug 31, 23; m 48. ENGINEERING. *Educ:* Harvard Univ, AB, 44; Mass Inst Technol, DSc, 47. *Prof Exp:* Res engr, Dewey & Almy Chem Co, 47-50; from asst prof to assoc prof chem eng, 50-64, PROF CHEM ENG, MASS INST TECHNOL, 64- *Concurrent Pos:* Consult, Mass Gen Hosp, Boston, 64- & Dept Surg, Beth Israel Hosp, Boston, 69-; consult to dir, Nat Inst Arthritis & Metab Diseases, 67-; vis res assoc surg, Children's Hosp Med Ctr, Boston, 70- *Mem:* Am Chem Soc; Soc Rheol; fel Am Acad Arts & Sci; Am Inst Chem Engrs. *Res:* Polymer chemistry; rheology; biomedical engineering. *Mailing Add:* Dept of Chem Eng Mass Inst of Technol Cambridge MA 02139

MERRILL, EDWIN THAYER, b Seattle, Wash, Feb 15, 23; m 45; c 4. CHEMICAL ENGINEERING. *Educ:* Univ Wash, BS, 44. *Prof Exp:* Sr engr, Gen Elec Co, 47-64; SR RES ENGR, ADVAN CONCEPTS ANAL SECT, MATH DEPT, PAC NORTHWEST LABS, BATTELLE MEM INST, 65- *Mem:* Am Inst Chem Engrs. *Res:* Spent fuel processing; solvent extraction; plutonium processing; fuel cycle analysis. *Mailing Add:* 1 Spout Rd Richland WA 99352

MERRILL, GLEN KENTON, b Columbus, Ohio, Aug 28, 35; m 64. GEOLOGY, PALEONTOLOGY. *Educ:* Ohio Univ, BS, 57; Univ Tex, Austin, MA, 64; La State Univ, PhD(geol), 68. *Prof Exp:* Instr geol, Northwestern La State Col, 64; asst prof, Monmouth Col, 68-71; asst prof, Univ Tex, Arlington, 71-74; asst prof, 74-76, ASSOC PROF GEOL, COL CHARLESTON, 77- *Concurrent Pos:* Consult, 77- *Mem:* Geol Soc Am; Paleont Soc; Soc Econ Paleontologists & Mineralogists; Nat Speleol Soc; Paleont Res Inst. *Res:* Biostratigraphy, paleoecology and systematics of late Paleozoic conodonts; carbonate petrography. *Mailing Add:* Dept Geol Col Charleston Charleston SC 29401

MERRILL, HOWARD EMERSON, b Laconia, NH, Aug 6, 30; m 53; c 4. PETROLEUM CHEMISTRY. *Educ:* Stetson Univ, BS, 52; Univ Pittsburgh, PhD(chem), 57. *Prof Exp:* Sr res chemist, Esso Res Labs, Exxon Co, USA, 57-75, SR STAFF CHEMIST, EXXON CHEM AMERICAS, 75- *Mem:* AAAS; Sigma Xi. *Res:* Catalysis. *Mailing Add:* Exxon Chem Americas Baton Rouge Chem Plant POB 241 Baton Rouge LA 70821

MERRILL, JAMES ALLEN, b Cedar City, Utah, Oct 27, 25; m 49; c 4. OBSTETRICS & GYNECOLOGY, PATHOLOGY. *Educ:* Univ Calif, Berkeley, AB, 45, Univ Calif, San Francisco, MD, 48. *Prof Exp:* Fel path, Harvard Med Sch, 50-51; fel, Cancer Res Inst, Univ Calif, San Francisco, 58-61; from instr to asst prof obstet & gynec, Sch Med, Univ Calif, San Francisco, 57-61, asst clin prof path, 59-61, res asst, Cancer Res Inst, 58-61; PROF GYNEC & OBSTET & HEAD DEPT, SCH MED, UNIV OKLA, 61-, CONSULT PROF PATH, 61-, PROF CYTOTECHNOL, COL HEALTH REL PROFESSIONS, 70- *Concurrent Pos:* Markle scholar med sci, 57-62; consult, Vet Admin Hosp, Oklahoma City, 61-, US Army Hosp, Ft Sill, Okla & Tinker AFB Hosp, Midwest City, 61-; nat consult, Air Force Hosp, Lackland AFB, San Antonio, Tex, 63. *Honors & Awards:* Aesculapian Award, Univ Okla Student Body, 63 & 69; Regents Award Superior Teaching, Univ Okla Bd Regents, 69. *Mem:* Am Asn Obstetricians & Gynecologists; Soc Gynec Invest; Asn Profs Gynec & Obstet (pres, 66-67); Int Soc Advan Humanistic Studies Gynec (pres, 72-73); Am Gynec Soc (treas, 70-75). *Res:* Gynecologic oncology. *Mailing Add:* Dept of Obstet & Gynec Univ of Okla Col of Med Oklahoma City OK 73190

MERRILL, JERALD CARL, b Las Vegas, Nev, Aug 12, 40; m 63; c 1. PHYSICAL CHEMISTRY. *Educ:* Univ Nev, Reno, BS, 62, PhD(phys chem), 71. *Prof Exp:* US AEC fel, Univ Calif, Davis, 71-72; presidential res intern, Brookhaven Nat Lab, 72-73; lectr chem, Univ Utah, 73-77; asst prof chem, Cent Mo State Univ, 77-78; DEVELOP CHEMIST, AMERSHAM CORP, 78- *Concurrent Pos:* Lectr, Univ Calif, Davis, 72. *Mem:* Am Chem Soc. *Res:* Radiochemistry; microemulsions; liquid scintillation counting. *Mailing Add:* Amersham Corp 2636 S Clearbrook Dr Arlington Heights IL 60005

MERRILL, JOHN ELLSWORTH, b Parsonsfield, Maine, May 10, 02; m 25; c 2. ASTRONOMY. *Educ:* Univ Boston, AB, 23; Case Inst Technol, MS, 27; Princeton Univ, AM, 29, PhD(astron), 31. *Prof Exp:* Instr math, Case Inst Technol, 24-28, Cleveland Col, 25-28 & Princeton Univ, 29-30; asst prof astron, Univ Ill, 31-32; cur, Buffalo Mus Sci, 32-36; asst, Princeton Univ, 36-37; instr, Hunter Col, 37-38, from asst prof to assoc prof, 38-50; from asst prof to assoc prof, Ohio Wesleyan Univ & Ohio State Univ, 50-51, prof, 51-59; sr staff engr, Franklin Inst, 59-61, prin scientist astron, 61-63; prof astron & math & dir, Morrison Observ, 64-67, Dearing prof astron, 67-69, EMER PROF ASTRON, CENT METHODIST COL, 69-; VIS PROF, UNIV FLA, 69- *Concurrent Pos:* Am Philos Soc grants, 41-42; dir pilot training prog, Princeton Univ, 42-43, vis asst prof, 43-45, res assoc, 47-63; adj prof, Univ Pa, 59-63; pres comn 42, Int Astron Union, 61-67; vis prof astron, Univ Fla, 69-73, adj prof astron, 73- *Mem:* AAAS; Am Astron Soc; Astronomical Union. *Res:* Photometry of eclipsing variables; solutions for orbits of eclipsing binaries; effects of eccentricity of orbit; tables for facilitating determinations of eccentricity. *Mailing Add:* 1838 1/2 Col Ave Conway AR 72032

MERRILL, JOHN JAY, b Nampa, Idaho, Jan 24, 33; m 53; c 6. PHYSICS. *Educ:* Calif Inst Technol, BS, 55, MS, 56, PhD(physics), 60. *Prof Exp:* Instr physics, Harvey Mudd Col, 59-60; med physicist, Dee Mem Hosp, Ogden, Utah, 60-62; assoc prof physics, Utah State Univ, 62-69; pres, Tronac, Inc, 69-71; PROF PHYSICS, BRIGHAM YOUNG UNIV, 70- *Mem:* Am Phys Soc; Am Asn Physics Teachers. *Res:* Instructional design. *Mailing Add:* 763 S 600 West Orem UT 84057

MERRILL, JOHN PUTNAM, b Hartford, Conn, Mar 10, 17; m 42; c 3. MEDICINE. *Educ:* Dartmouth Col, AB, 38; Harvard Med Sch, MD, 42; Am Bd Internal Med, dipl, 50. *Hon Degrees:* DSc, Colby Col, 69, Univ Paris, 74. *Prof Exp:* House officer med, Peter Bent Brigham Hosp, 42-43, asst resident physician, 47-48; instr, 50-52, assoc, 52-56, from asst prof to assoc prof, 56-69, PROF MED, HARVARD MED SCH, 69- *Concurrent Pos:* Milton fel med, Harvard Med Sch, 48-49, res fel, 49-50; Am Heart Asn res fel, 49-50; asst, Peter Bent Brigham Hosp, 48-50, jr assoc, 50-54, sr assoc, 55-63, physician, 63-; estab investr, Am Heart Asn, 50-57; investr, Howard Hughes Med Inst, 57-; consult, Surgeon Gen, US Air Force, 64 & Nat Inst Arthritis & Metab Dis, 65; res collab, Brookhaven Nat Labs, 65-66; mem Nat Adv Coun, Regional Med Prog Servs, 71; nat adv coun, Nat Inst Arthritis & Metabolic Dis, 71-75. *Honors & Awards:* Alvarenga prize, 60; Mod Med Distinguished Achievement Award, 65; Gairdner Int Award, 69; Valentine Medal, NY Acad Sci, 70; Rosenthal Award, Am Col Physicians, 78; Armory Prize, AAAS. *Mem:* Am Soc Clin Invest (pres, 63); Am Physiol Soc; Am Clin & Climat Asn; AMA; fel Am Col Physicians. *Res:* Internal medicine. *Mailing Add:* Brigham & Women's Hosp 75 Francis St Boston MA 02115

MERRILL, JOHN RAYMOND, b Englewood, NJ, Aug 25, 39; m 60; c 4. LOW TEMPERATURE PHYSICS, EDUCATIONAL DESIGN. *Educ:* Swarthmore Col, AB, 61; Cornell Univ, PhD(solid state physics), 66. *Prof Exp:* Instr & res assoc physics, Cornell Univ, 66-67; asst prof, Dartmouth Col, 67-73; assoc prof physics & dir ctr educ design, Fla State Univ, 73-76; instr, NATO Postgrad Inst, Belgium, 76; VPRES, DEAN & PROF PHYSICS, HENDRIX COL, 76- *Concurrent Pos:* Res Corp res grant, 68; AEC res grant, 70-73. *Mem:* AAAS; Am Phys Soc; Am Asn Physics Teachers; Sigma Xi; NY Acad Sci. *Res:* Computers in teaching; low temperature solid state physics; instructional design and development; science education. *Mailing Add:* VPres Hendrix Col Conway AR 72032

MERRILL, JOHN T, b Oakland, Calif, May 29, 46; m 76. ATMOSPHEERIC CHEMISTRY & PHYSICS, FLUID DYNAMICS. *Educ:* Univ Calif, Berkeley, AB, 68; Univ Ill, MS, 70; Univ Colo, PhD(atmospheric sci), 76. *Prof Exp:* Res assoc air sea interaction, Rosenstiel Sch Marine & Atmospheric Sci, Univ Miami, 76-77, asst prof meteorol & phys oceanog, 77-82; ASSOC MARINE SCIENTIST, UNIV RI, 81- *Mem:* Am Meteorol Soc; Am Geophys Union. *Res:* Atmospheric transport; geophysical boundary layers. *Mailing Add:* Ctr Atmospheric Chem Studies Grad Sch Oceanog Univ RI Narragansett, RI 02882

MERRILL, JOSEPH MELTON, b Andalusia, Ala, Dec 8, 23. MEDICAL CARE. *Educ:* Harvard Med Sch, MD, 48; Am Bd Internal Med, dipl, 56. *Prof Exp:* Intern, Louisville Gen Hosp, Mo, 48-49; intern, Vanderbilt Univ Hosp, 49-50, asst resident med, 50-51; instr med & attend physician, Med Col, Univ Ala, 53-54; asst resident med res, Vet Admin Hosp, Nashville, Tenn, 54-55; res assoc, Postgrad Med Sch, Univ London, 55-56; chief clin physiol, Vet Admin Hosp, 56-64; chief Gen Clin Res Ctrs Br, Div Res Facil, NIH, 64-67; PROF MED, BAYLOR COL MED, 67- *Concurrent Pos:* Clin investr, Vet Admin Hosp, Nashville, Tenn, 56-59, asst chief radioisotope serv, 57-64, asst dir, Prof Servs for Res, 60-64; instr, Med Sch, Vanderbilt Univ, 60-; Wellcome assoc, Royal Soc Med, 55-56. *Mem:* Am Physiol Soc; AMA; Am Heart Asn; Am Fedn Clin Res; fel Am Col Physicians. *Res:* Application of human factors (ergonomics) engineering to medicine. *Mailing Add:* Baylor Col of Med Houston TX 77030

MERRILL, LELAND (GILBERT), JR, b Danville, Ill, Oct 4, 20; m 49; c 2. ENVIRONMENTAL SCIENCE. *Educ:* Mich State Col, BS, 42; Rutgers Univ, MS, 48, PhD, 49. *Prof Exp:* Asst, Rutgers Univ, 46-49; asst prof entom, Mich State Col, 49-53; exten specialist, 53-59, res specialist, 59-61, dean col agr & environ sci, 61-71, dir inst environ studies, 71-76, PROF NATURAL RESOURCE POLICY STUDIES, CTR COASTAL & ENVIRON STUDIES, RUTGERS UNIV, NEW BRUNSWICK, 76- *Mem:* AAAS; Entom Soc Am. *Res:* Applied environmental studies; natural resource inventory applications to land use management. *Mailing Add:* Inst for Environ Studies Rutgers Univ New Brunswick NJ 08903

MERRILL, MALCOLM HENDRICKS, b Richmond, Utah, June 28, 03; m 26; c 3. PUBLIC HEALTH. *Educ:* Utah State Univ, BS, 25; St Louis Univ, MS, 27, MD, 32; Univ Calif, MPH, 47; Am Bd Prev Med & Pub Health, dipl, 49. *Prof Exp:* Asst bact, St Louis Univ, 25-32 & Rockefeller Inst, Princeton, 32-35; intern med, Univ Calif, 35-36; asst dermat & resident med, 36-37; chief bur venereal dis, Calif State Dept Pub Health, 37-41, chief div labs, 41-54, dep dir pub health, 44-54, actg dir, 51-52, dir, 54-65; dir health serv, Off Tech Coop & Res, AID, 65-68; dir community health action planning serv, Am Pub Health Asn, 68-71, dir div int health progs, 71-77. *Concurrent Pos:* Lectr sch pub health, Univ Calif, 46-65; mem exp therapeut study sect, NIH, 48-53, cancer control comt, 55-58, nat adv comt on pub health traineeships, 56-60, nat adv comt on community air pollution, 57-61 & nat adv health coun, 57-61; consult pub health for India, Tech Coop Admin, 52; mem tech adv comt, Inst Nutrit Cent Am & Panama, 55, 56, 58, 59; mem, US Pub Health Mission to Russia, 57. *Honors & Awards:* Bronfman Prize, Am Pub Health Asn, 64 & Sedgwick Mem Medal, 76. *Mem:* AAAS; Am Pub Health Asn (pres, 59-60); AMA; Asn State & Territorial Health Officers (pres, 61-62); Asn State & Territorial Pub Health Lab Dirs. *Res:* Virus diseases; etiology and transmission of virus encephalitides; immunology of virus diseases; metabolism of the mycobacteria; epidemiology of typhoid fever and Q fever; problems in financing public health administration; serology. *Mailing Add:* 3441 Tice Creek Dr 1 Walnut Creek CA 94595

MERRILL, ROBERT KIMBALL, b Lima, Peru, Oct 11, 45; US citizen; m 72. EXPLORATION GEOLOGY. *Educ:* Colby Col, AB, 67; Ariz State Univ, MS, 70, PhD(geol), 74. *Prof Exp:* Stratigr, Am Stratig Co, 69-70; instr geol, Ariz State Univ, 73-74; staff geologist, 74-78, tech asst vpres, Western Area, 78-81, EXPLOR GEOLOGIST, WESTERN REGION, CITIES SERV CO, 81- *Mem:* Sigma Xi; Geol Soc Am; Am Asn Petrol Geologists; Am Inst Prof Geologists. *Res:* Analysis of the tectonic development within the structural and stratigraphic framework of established hydrocarbon provinces and frontier areas to find oil and gas. *Mailing Add:* 7732 S Eudora Ct Littleton CO 80122

MERRILL, ROBERT P, b Salt Lake City, Utah, Nov 17, 34; m 58; c 6. CHEMICAL ENGINEERING. *Educ:* Cornell Univ, BChE, 60; Mass Inst Technol, ScD(chem eng), 64. *Prof Exp:* Consult, Raytheon Mfg Co, 61-63 & Abcor Inc, 63-64; instr chem eng, Mass Inst Technol, 64; from asst prof to assoc prof, Univ Calif, Berkeley, 64-73; prof, 73-76, HF JOHNSON PROF INDUST CHEM, CORNELL UNIV, 76- *Concurrent Pos:* Consult, Lockheed Missiles & Space Co, 65-72, Stauffer Chem Soc, 65-67, Universal Oil Prods, 66- & Gulf Gen Atomic, 70-73. *Mem:* AAAS; Am Vacuum Soc; Catalysis Soc; Am Chem Soc; Am Inst Chem Engrs. *Res:* Chemical kinetics; heterogeneous catalysis; physics and chemistry of solid surfaces; atomic and molecular beam scattering from solid surfaces; photoelectron spectroscopy; laser induced surface reactions. *Mailing Add:* 34 Blackstone Ave Ithaca NY 14850

MERRILL, RONALD EUGENE, b Salem, Ore, Aug 7, 47; m 74. SYNTHETIC ORGANIC CHEMISTRY. *Educ:* Mass Inst Technol, BS, 68; Univ Ore, PhD(chem), 73. *Prof Exp:* Fel chem, Syracuse Univ, 73-74; vis asst prof chem, Rochester Inst Technol, 74-77; sr chemist, Lifesysts Co, 77-79; PRES, REACTION DESIGN CORP, HILLSIDE, NJ, 79- *Concurrent Pos:* Exec comt enterprise forum, Mass Inst Technol. *Mem:* Am Chem Soc. *Res:* New synthetic reactions; organoborane chemistry; heterocyclic chemistry; nuclear magnetic resonance spectroscopy. *Mailing Add:* Reaction Design Corp 100 Hoffman Pl Hillside NJ 07205

MERRILL, RONALD THOMAS, b Detroit, Mich, Feb 5, 38; m 61; c 2. GEOPHYSICS. *Educ:* Univ Mich, BS, 59, MS, 61; Univ Calif, Berkeley, PhD(geophys), 67. *Prof Exp:* From asst prof to assoc prof, 67-77, PROF GEOPHYS, UNIV WASH, 77- *Concurrent Pos:* Hon vis fel, Res Sch Earth Sci, Australia Nat Univ, 75, 77 & 79. *Mem:* AAAS; Am Geophys Union; Soc Terrestrial Magnetism & Elec Japan. *Res:* Geomagnetism, especially paleomagnetism and rock magnetism. *Mailing Add:* Dept Oceanog Univ Wash Seattle WA 98195

MERRILL, SAMUEL, III, b New Orleans, La, Oct 27, 39; m 69; c 2. MATHEMATICS. *Educ:* Tulane Univ, BA, 61; Yale Univ, MA, 63, PhD(math), 65; Pa State Univ, MS, 80. *Prof Exp:* Instr math, Univ Rochester, 65-67, asst prof, 67-73; assoc prof, 73-81, PROF MATH/COMPUT SCI, WILKES COL, 81- *Mem:* Am Math Soc; Am Stat Assoc; Public Choice Soc; Math Asn Am. *Res:* Mathematical applications to political science, especially voting power and voting systems, statistical applications; functional analysis, especially Banach spaces of analytic functions. *Mailing Add:* Dept Math/Comput Sci Wilkes Col Wilkes-Barre PA 18766

MERRILL, STEPHEN DAY, b Canandaigua, NY, Mar 27, 39; m 61; c 3. SOIL SCIENCE, SOIL PHYSICS. *Educ:* Dartmouth Col, BA, 61, MA, 63; Univ Calif, Riverside, PhD(soil sci), 76. *Prof Exp:* Sci teacher chem & biol, Drew Sch, San Francisco, Calif, 64-65; chemist soil-plant water rels, USDA, Agr Res Serv, US Salinity Lab, 66-70, physicist, 70-77; RES SOIL SCIENTIST SOIL PHYSICS, NORTHERN GREAT PLAINS RES CTR, AGR RES SERV, USDA, 77- *Concurrent Pos:* Adj prof soils, NDak State Univ, 79- *Mem:* Am Soc Agron; Soil Sci Soc Am; Soil Conservation Soc Am. *Res:* Soil physics and soil chemistry; water, salt and heat transport in soil; reclamation of strip-mined land; soil physical conditions and crop root growth. *Mailing Add:* Northern Great Plains Res Ctr PO Box 459 Mandan ND 58554

MERRILL, STEWART HENRY, b Andover, Ohio, Sept 8, 26; m 50; c 4. ORGANIC POLYMER CHEMISTRY. *Educ:* Case Inst Technol, BS, 50; Ohio State Univ, PhD(chem), 53. *Prof Exp:* Res chemist, 53-64, res assoc, 64-79, SR RES ASSOC, RES LAB, EASTMAN KODAK CO, 79- *Res:* Synthesis and polymerization of monomers; reactions, structures and properties of polymers. *Mailing Add:* Eastman Kodak Co Bldg 82 Kodak Park Rochester NY 14650

MERRILL, WARNER JAY, JR, b Springfield, Ill, Jan 27, 23; m 45; c 2. STATISTICS. *Educ:* Univ Del, BA, 47; Ohio State Univ, PhD(statist), 56. *Prof Exp:* Asst psychol statist, Ohio State Univ, 49-51; staff statistician, Am Power Jet Co, 51-53; assoc math, IBM, Endicott, NY, 53-56; statistician, Gen Elec Co, NY, 56-61; prof mgt, Rensselaer Polytech Inst, 61-64; mgt scientist, Dunlap & Assocs, 64-65; mem tech staff, Hughes Aircraft Co, 65-66; sr assoc, Planning Res Corp, 66-68; OPERS RES ANALYST, NAT INST JUSTICE, DEPT JUSTICE, 68- *Concurrent Pos:* Prof lectr, George Washington Univ, 68-70; prof lectr, Am Univ, 69-70, adj prof, 70-72. *Mem:* Am Statist Asn; Inst Mgt Sci. *Res:* Applications of statistics to crime research; systems analysis, including human factors; statistical applications of computers; non-parametric statistics; operations research. *Mailing Add:* 9904 Inglemere Dr Bethesda MD 20817

MERRILL, WILLIAM, b Haverhill, NH, Sept 5, 33; m 61; c 2. FOREST PATHOLOGY, FOREST PRODUCTS. *Educ:* Univ NH, BS, 58; Univ Minn, MS, 61, PhD(plant path), 63. *Prof Exp:* Instr plant path, Univ Minn, 61-64; res staff pathologist & fel, Yale Univ, 64-65; from asst prof to assoc prof, 65-75, PROF PLANT PATH, PA STATE UNIV, UNIVERSITY PARK, 75- *Mem:* Am Phytopath Soc. *Res:* Etiology, epidemiology and control of forest tree pathogens; biodeterioration of wood. *Mailing Add:* 210 Buckhout Lab Pa State Univ University Park PA 16802

MERRILL, WILLIAM GEORGE, b Wilmington, Del, Oct 19, 31; m 58; c 3. ANIMAL NUTRITION. *Educ:* Univ Md, BS, 53; Univ Wis, MS, 54; Cornell Univ, PhD(animal nutrit), 59. *Prof Exp:* Asst prof, Exten Div, 59-64, assoc prof animal husb, Dairy Cattle Div, 64-79, PROF ANIMAL SCI & DAIRY MGT, CORNELL UNIV, 79- *Mem:* Am Soc Animal Sci; Am Dairy Sci Asn. *Res:* Dairy husbandry; dairy cattle management systems; manure handling, manure re-feeding; milking systems; feeding systems. *Mailing Add:* Dept of Animal Sci Cornell Univ Ithaca NY 14853

MERRILL, WILLIAM MEREDITH, b Detroit, Mich, Dec 1, 18; m 43; c 3. GEOLOGY. *Educ:* Mich State Univ, BS, 46; Ohio State Univ, MA, 48, PhD(geol), 50. *Prof Exp:* Geologist, Ohio Div Geol Surv, 46-50; from instr to assoc prof geol, Univ Ill, 50-58; prof & chmn dept, Syracuse Univ, 58-63; chmn dept, 63-72, PROF GEOL, UNIV KANS, 63- *Concurrent Pos:* Asst, Ohio State Univ, 47-48, res assoc, Res Found, 55-57; consult, Ohio Div Geol Surv, 50-60; geologist, Nfld Dept Mines, 54 & Res Coun Alta, 58-62; vis scientist, Am Geol Inst, 62 & 64; team capt, Geo-Study, 62-63; chmn panel earth sci teacher prep, Coun Educ Geol Sci, 64-67, mem steering comt, Earth Sci Curriculum Proj, 65-, mem writers conf, 66. *Mem:* Fel Geol Soc Am; Soc Econ Paleont & Mineral; Am Asn Petrol Geol; Int Asn Sedimentol; Int Asn Math Geol. *Res:* Mesozoic stratigraphy of western United States and Canada; computer simulation in geology. *Mailing Add:* Dept of Geol Univ of Kans Lawrence KS 66044

MERRIMAN, CHARLES RICHARD, biochemistry, see previous edition

MERRIMAN, DANIEL, b Cambridge, Mass, Sept 17, 08; m 34, 71. BIOLOGICAL OCEANOGRAPHY. *Educ:* Univ Wash, BS, 33, MS, 34; Yale Univ, PhD(zool), 39. *Prof Exp:* Aquatic biologist, Conn State Bd Fish & Game, 36-38; from instr to asst prof biol, Yale Univ, 38-46, dir, Bingham Oceanog Lab, 42-66, master, Davenport Col, 46-66, assoc prof biol, 46-76, dir Sears Found Marine Res & Oceanog Hist, 66-76, prof biol, 76-77, EMER PROF BIOL, YALE UNIV, 77- MARINE RES & OCEANOG HIST, 66- *Concurrent Pos:* Chmn comt food resources coastal waters, Nat Res Coun, 43-46; trustee, Bermuda Biol Sta & Woods Hole Oceanog Inst, 44-64; res assoc dept fishes & aquatic biol, Am Mus Natural Hist, 45-62; mem adv comt biol, Off Naval Res, 49-52; consult, NSF, 51-54 & President's Sci Adv Comt, 60 & 61; comnr, Conn State Bd Fish & Game, 53-56; mem adv comt, Susquehanna Fishery Study, 57-60; dir, Conn River Study, Conn Yankee Atomic Power Co, 64-74. *Mem:* Am Soc Limnol & Oceanog; Am Soc Zool; Hist Sci Soc; Am Soc Ichthyol & Herpet. *Res:* Ichthyology; fisheries biology; oceanography; morphology; history of sciences. *Mailing Add:* 298 Sperry Rd Bethany CT 06525

MERRIN, SEYMOUR, b Brooklyn, NY, Aug 13, 31; m 63; c 2. PHYSICAL CHEMISTRY, GEOCHEMISTRY. *Educ:* Tufts Univ, BS, 52; Univ Ariz, MS, 54; Pa State Univ, PhD(geochem), 62. *Prof Exp:* Geologist, US Geol Surv, 56-58; asst geochem, Pa State Univ, 59-62; sr assoc chemist, IBM Corp, 62-64; package develop dept mgr, Sperry Semiconductor Div, Sperry Rand Corp, 65-68; independent consult prod & prod develop electronics, 68-69; vpres technol, Innotech Corp, 69-74; div mgr, Exxon Enterprises, 74-78; PRES, COMPUTERWORKS, INC, 79- *Mem:* AAAS; fel Am Inst Chemists; Int Soc Hybrid Microelectronics; fel Geol Soc Am; Mineral Soc Am. *Res:* Glass; experimental petrology; microelectronic processing; phase equilibrium. *Mailing Add:* 235 Old Spring Rd Fairfield CT 06430

MERRINER, JOHN VENNOR, b Winchester, Va, Sept 13, 41. FISH BIOLOGY, MARINE BIOLOGY. *Educ:* Rutgers Univ, AB, 64; NC State Univ, MS, 67, PhD(zool), 73. *Prof Exp:* Assoc marine scientist, 70-74, actg head dept, 74-75, SR MARINE SCIENTIST & HEAD DEPT ICHTHYOL, VA INST MARINE SCI, 75- *Concurrent Pos:* Asst prof marine sci, Col William & Mary & Univ Va, 75-78, assoc prof, 78- *Mem:* Am Fisheries Soc; Am Soc Ichthyologists & Herpetologists. *Res:* Ecology and life history of estuarine and marine fishes; response of fishes to natural and pollution stress factors. *Mailing Add:* Dept of Ichthyol Va Inst of Marine Sci Gloucester Point VA 23062

MERRIS, RUSSELL LLOYD, b Calif, 1943. ALGEBRA. *Educ:* Harvey Mudd Col, BS, 64; Univ Calif, Santa Barbara, MA, 67, PhD(math), 69. *Prof Exp:* Nat Acad Sci-Mat Res Coun assoc, Nat Bur Stand, 69-71; from asst prof to assoc prof, 71-78, PROF MATH, CALIF STATE UNIV, HAYWARD, 78- *Mem:* Am Math Soc; Math Asn Am. *Res:* Multilinear algebra; group representation theory; combinatorics. *Mailing Add:* Dept Math Calif State Univ Hayward CA 94542

MERRITT, ALFRED M, II, b Boston, Mass, Apr 10, 37; m 63; c 2. GASTROENTEROLOGY, VETERINARY MEDICINE. *Educ:* Bowdoin Col, AB, 59; Cornell Univ, DVM, 63, Univ Pa, MS, 69. *Prof Exp:* Asst instr vet med, Sch Vet Med, Univ Calif, 63-64; instr vet med, Sch Vet Med, 64-66, fel, Grad Sch Arts & Sci, 66-69, asst prof vet med, 69-72, assoc prof vet med, Sch Vet Med, Univ Pa, 72-78; PROF MED, COL VET MED, UNIV FLA, 78- *Concurrent Pos:* Ed comp gastroenterol, Am J Digestive Dis, 72-77; mem res adv bd, Morris Animal Found, 79-82. *Mem:* Am Vet Med Asn; Comp Gastroenterol Soc (pres, 75); NY Acad Sci; Am Gastroenterol Asn. *Res:* Neurohumoral control of gastric and pancreatic secretion in swine; pathophysiology of chronic diarrhea in horses; gastrointestinal motility in animals. *Mailing Add:* Col Vet Med Box J-126 JHMHC Gainesville FL 32610

MERRITT, ARTHUR DONALD, b Shawnee, Okla, June 11, 25; m 53; c 2. INTERNAL MEDICINE. *Educ:* George Washington Univ, AB, 49, MD, 52; Am Bd Internal Med, dipl, 60. *Prof Exp:* Intern, Washington, DC Gen Hosp, 52-53; asst resident med, George Washington Univ Hosp, 53-54; asst resident med, Duke Univ Hosp, 54-55, chief resident & instr, 56-57; clin assoc, Nat Inst Arthritis & Metab Dis, 57-58, chief, 59-60; assoc prof med & biochem, 61-66, chmn med genetics prog, 62-66, chmn dept, 66-78, PROF MED & CHMN DEPT MED GENETICS, MED CTR, IND UNIV INDIANAPOLIS, 66- *Concurrent Pos:* Fel, Duke Univ Hosp, 55-56; consult, Durham Vet Admin Hosp, NC, 57-58; lectr & clin instr, Sch Med, George Washington Univ, 59-60. *Mem:* Am Soc Human Genetics (treas, 64-70); Genetics Soc Am; Am Fedn Clin Res; NY Acad Sci; Am Col Physicians. *Res:* Human genetics; medical education; intermediary metabolism. *Mailing Add:* Ind Univ Med Ctr 129 Riley Res Wing Indianapolis IN 46202

MERRITT, CHARLES, JR, b Lynn, Mass, Mar 15, 19; m 42; c 3. ANALYTICAL CHEMISTRY. *Educ:* Dartmouth Col, AB, 41; Univ Vt, MS, 48; Mass Inst Technol, PhD(anal chem), 53. *Prof Exp:* Finish engr, W Lynn Works Lab, Gen Elec Co, 41-46; instr chem, Univ Vt, 46-49; asst, Mass Inst

Technol, 49-53; res anal chemist, Nat Bur Stand, 53; asst prof anal chem, Polytech Inst Brooklyn, 53-56; supvry anal chemist, 56-57, HEAD ANAL CHEM LAB, US ARMY NATICK LABS, 57- *Concurrent Pos:* Mem staff grad sch arts & sci, Northeastern Univ, 56-; vis lectr, Mass Inst Technol, 65-; adj prof food sci, Univ Mass, 75-; mem subcomt stand ref mat, Nat Acad Sci-Nat Res Coun. *Mem:* AAAS; Inst Food Technol; Am Soc Mass Spectrometry; Am Chem Soc; Soc Appl Spectros. *Res:* Electrodeposition; spectrophotometry; gas chromatography; mass spectrometry; irradiation techniques; determination of the volatile components of foodstuffs; pollution and environmental studies. *Mailing Add:* US Army Natick Labs Natick MA 01760

MERRITT, CLAIR, b Quakertown, Pa, Jan 27, 22; m 43; c 3. FORESTRY. *Educ:* Univ Mich, BSF, 43, MF, 48, PhD(forestry), 59. *Prof Exp:* Asst dist forester, Md, 47; self-employed, 48; from instr to asst prof forestry, State Univ NY Col Forestry, Syracuse Univ, 49-56; assoc prof, 56-58, PROF FORESTRY, PURDUE UNIV, WEST LAFAYETTE, 68- *Concurrent Pos:* Vpres, Foresters, Inc. *Mem:* Soc Am Foresters. *Res:* Silvics and silviculture, light relationships in forest openings; establishment of hardwood regeneration. *Mailing Add:* Dept Forestry & Nat Resources Purdue Univ West Lafayette IN 47907

MERRITT, DORIS HONIG, b New York, NY, July 16, 23; m 53; c 2. RESEARCH ADMINISTRATION, PEDIATRICS. *Educ:* Hunter Col, BA, 44; George Washington Univ, MD, 52. *Prof Exp:* Exec secy cardiovasc & gen med dis, NIH, 57-60; from asst to assoc prof pediat, Ind Univ, Indianapolis, 61-73, from asst to assoc dean grants admin, 62-68, from asst to assoc dean sponsored prog, 65-70, dean sponsored progs, 70-78, prof pediat, 73-78; SPEC ASST TO DIR, NIH, 78- *Concurrent Pos:* Nat Heart Inst fel cardiovasc dis, Duke Univ, 56-57; Nat Heart & Lung Inst grant & interim dir, Indianapolis Sickle Cell Ctr, Sch Med, Ind Univ-Purdue Univ, 73-, Lilly endowment urban educ, 74-76; consult div res grants, Nat Heart & Lung Inst, 63-; mem regional adv group, Ind Regional Med Prog, 69-; mem & chmn biomed libr rev comt, Nat Libr Med, 70-73; chmn, Consortium for Urban Educ, Indianapolis, 71-75; mem, Nat Coun Univ Res Adminr. *Mem:* AAAS; Am Acad Pediat. *Res:* Genetic counseling; sickle cell disease; improvement of research administration. *Mailing Add:* Nat Inst of Health 9000 Rockville Pike Bethesda MD 20014

MERRITT, HARRY WARNER, JR, b Houston, Tex, Aug 25, 34. CHEMICAL ENGINEERING. *Educ:* Yale Univ, BS, 56; Univ Tex, BS, 61; Univ Minn, MS, 63; Univ Okla, PhD(chem eng), 67. *Prof Exp:* Cost engr, E I du Pont de Nemours & Co, Inc, 56-59, develop engr, 66-68, col rels rep, 68-69, res engr, 69-71; SR RES ENGR, HOUSTON RES, INC, 71- *Mem:* Am Inst Chem Engrs. *Res:* Fluid flow and mass transfer; heat transfer. *Mailing Add:* 1811 Sunset Blvd Houston TX 77005

MERRITT, J(OSHUA) L(EVERING), JR, b Dundalk, Md, July 28, 31; m 54; c 3. STRUCTURAL ENGINEERING, ROCK MECHANICS. *Educ:* Lehigh Univ, BS, 52; Univ Ill, MS, 55, PhD(eng), 58. *Prof Exp:* Asst civil eng, Univ Ill, Urbana, 52-54, res assoc, 54-58, from asst prof to prof, 58-68; mgr hard rock silo develop prog, TRW Systs Inc, 68-70, facilities eng, 70-71, asst prog mgr minuteman prog, 68-71; PRES, MERRITT CASES, INC, 71- *Concurrent Pos:* Consult, 58-; part-time prof, Univ Ill, Urbana, 68-69. *Mem:* AAAS; Am Soc Civil Engrs; Am Concrete Inst; Am Soc Testing & Mat; Earthquake Eng Res Inst. *Res:* Structural analysis and design; strength and behavior of materials and structural systems; behavior of structures and structural systems subjected to transient loads; experimental design and interpretation; tunnel and shaft design and support; shock isolation; earthquake engineering. *Mailing Add:* Merritt Cases Inc PO Box 1206 Redlands CA 92373

MERRITT, JACK, b Sacramento, Calif, May 2, 18; m 42; c 1. PHYSICS. *Educ:* Pomona Col, AB, 39; Univ Calif, PhD(physics), 53. *Prof Exp:* Admin analyst, US Bur Budget, 46-47; admin officer res div, AEC, 47-49; physicist radiation lab, Univ Calif, 53-54; instrumentation, Shell Develop Co Div, Shell Oil Co, 55-57, Spectros, 57-66; PROF PHYSICS, CLAREMONT MEN'S COL, 66- *Mem:* Am Phys Soc. *Res:* High energy nuclear physics; instrumentation; meson production; spectroscopy; x-rays. *Mailing Add:* Physics Dept Claremont Men's Col Claremont CA 91711

MERRITT, JAMES FRANCIS, b Wake Co, NC, July 21, 44; m 69; c 3. GENETICS, BOTANY. *Educ:* ECarolina Univ, BS, 66, MS, 68; NC State Univ, PhD(genetics), 73. *Prof Exp:* Asst prof, 73-79, actg chmn dept, 78-79, ASSOC PROF BIOL, UNIV NC, WILMINGTON, 79-, CHMN DEPT, 79- *Mem:* Am Genetic Asn. *Res:* Cytogenetics of Vaccinium species. *Mailing Add:* Dept of Biol Univ of NC Wilmington NC 28406

MERRITT, KATHARINE, b Bridgeport, Conn, Apr 11, 38; m 70. IMMUNOLOGY, MICROBIOLOGY. *Educ:* Vassar Col, AB, 60; Univ Mich, MS, 62, PhD(microbiol), 64. *Prof Exp:* Res assoc path & microbiol, Dartmouth Med Sch, 64-66, instr, 66-68, asst prof microbiol, 68-80; ASSOC PROF MICROBIOL, UNIV CALIF, DAVIS, 80- *Mem:* Am Soc Microbiol; Can Soc Immunol; Am Asn Immunol Res. *Res:* Pathogenesis of infectious diseases, host defense mechanisms; host response to orthopaedic implants. *Mailing Add:* Orthopaedic Res TB 139 Univ Calif Davis CA 95616

MERRITT, LAVERE BARRUS, b Afton, Wyo, Mar 11, 36; m 56; c 2. WATER QUALITY, COMPUTER ANALYSIS. *Educ:* Univ Utah, BS, 63, MS, 66; Univ Wash, PhD(civil eng), 70. *Prof Exp:* Civil engr, US Forest Serv, 63-64; instr civil eng, Brigham Young Univ, 64-67; Fed Water Qual Admin trainee, Univ Wash, 67-70; PROF CIVIL ENG, BRIGHAM YOUNG UNIV, 70- *Concurrent Pos:* Prin investr lake & stream water qual studies, 75- *Mem:* Am Soc Civil Engrs; Am Water Works Asn; Am Acad Environ Engrs; Am Soc Eng Educ; Water Pollution Control Fedn. *Res:* Water quality research and multidisciplinary investigations; computer applications in sanitary engineering; water quality modeling; sewer design; solid waste management. *Mailing Add:* 368-R Clyde Bldg Brigham Young Univ Provo UT 84602

MERRITT, LYNNE LIONEL, JR, b Alba, Pa, Sept 10, 15; m 37; c 4. ANALYTICAL CHEMISTRY. *Educ:* Wayne State Univ, BS, 36, MS, 37; Univ Mich, PhD(anal chem), 40. *Prof Exp:* Instr chem, Wayne State Univ, 36-37, 39-42; from asst prof to assoc prof chem, 42-53, assoc dean col arts & sci, 59-62, dir bur instnl res, 60-65, assoc dean faculties, 62-64, actg dean, 63-64, vpres & dean res & advan studies, 65-75, dean res coord & develop, 75-80, PROF CHEM, IND UNIV, BLOOMINGTON, 53-, SPEC ASST TO PRES, 75- *Concurrent Pos:* Vis prof, Calif Inst Technol, 49-50; Guggenheim fel & res assoc, 55-56; pres & dir, Ind Instrument & Chem Corp, 59-; Fulbright fel, Nat Sci Res Ctr, France, 63. *Mem:* AAAS; Am Chem Soc; Am Crystallog Asn; Am Inst Chemists. *Res:* Organic reagents; instrumental methods of analysis; x-ray diffraction crystal structure determinations. *Mailing Add:* Dept of Chem Ind Univ Bloomington IN 47405

MERRITT, MARGARET VIRGINIA, b Springfield, Ohio, June 30, 42. ANALYTICAL CHEMISTRY. *Educ:* Col Wooster, BA, 64; Cornell Univ, PhD(anal chem), 68. *Prof Exp:* Fel electrochem, Univ Calif, Riverside, 68-69; fel, Radiation Res Lab, Mellon Inst, 69-70; asst prof anal chem, Franklin & Marshall Col, 70-72; res chemist, 72-80, RES HEAD, UPJOHN CO, 80- *Mem:* Am Chem Soc; Sigma Xi. *Res:* High pressure liquid chromatography; trace organic analysis; electron spin resonance; spin labeling; spin trapping; lipid analysis; biomembrane characterization. *Mailing Add:* Phys & Anal Chem Upjohn Co Kalamazoo MI 49001

MERRITT, MELVIN LEROY, b Juneau, Alaska, Nov 12, 21; m 49; c 4. PHYSICS. *Educ:* Calif Inst Technol, BS, 43, PhD(physics), 50. *Prof Exp:* Test engr, Gen Elec Co, 43-46; mem staff, 50-56, mgr phys res dept, 56-61, DIV SUPVR, SANDIA NAT LABS, 61- *Mem:* AAAS; Am Phys Soc; Am Asn Physics Teachers; Arctic Inst NAm; Health Physics Soc. *Res:* Cosmic rays; shock waves; effects of nuclear weapons; environmental studies and assessments. *Mailing Add:* Div 4733 Sandia Nat Labs Albuquerque NM 87185

MERRITT, MICHAEL J, b Council Bluffs, Iowa, Dec 18, 38; m 64; c 1. COMPUTER SCIENCE, CONTROL THEORY. *Educ:* Univ Calif, Los Angeles, BS, 60, MS, 62; Univ Southern Calif, PhD(elec eng), 67. *Prof Exp:* Sr engr, Space & Info Div, N Am Rockwell, 64-66; asst prof aerospace eng, Univ Southern Calif, 67-78; SR SCIENTIST, METEOROLOGY RES, INC, 78- *Concurrent Pos:* Lectr, Univ Southern Calif, 64-67; consult, Systron Donner Corp, 65-, CBS TV Network, 65- & TRW Systs, Inc, 67-; mem steering comt, western region, Simulation Coun, 68. *Mem:* Inst Elec & Electronics Engrs. *Res:* Application of computer graphics to improvement in man-hybrid computer interface; analysis of hybrid computer systems. *Mailing Add:* 758 E Sacramento Meterology Res Inc Altadena CA 91001

MERRITT, PAUL EUGENE, b Watertown, NY, Oct 23, 20; m 46; c 2. ANALYTICAL CHEMISTRY. *Educ:* NY State Col Teachers, Albany, BA, 42, MA, 47; Rensselaer Polytech Inst, PhD, 54. *Prof Exp:* Line foreman, Gen Chem Defense Corp, 42-43; teacher pub sch, 47-48; asst gen chem, Rensselaer Polytech Inst, 48-51, instr anal chem, 53-54; from asst prof to assoc prof, St Lawrence Univ, 54-63; chmn dept chem, 70-73, PROF ANAL CHEM, STATE UNIV NY COL POTSDAM, 63- *Mem:* Fel Am Inst Chemists; Am Chem Soc; Sigma Xi; NY Acad Sci. *Res:* Physico-chemical methods of analysis; infrared analysis of inorganic complexes, minerals and ores; structure studies of complex-inorganic salts; trinitrotoluene. *Mailing Add:* Dept of Chem State Univ of NY Col Potsdam NY 13676

MERRITT, R(OBERT) W(ALTER), b St Joseph, Mich, Feb 2, 13; m 35; c 2. MANUFACTURING CHEMISTRY. *Educ:* Univ Mich, BS, 34, MS, 35, PhD(chem eng), 39. *Prof Exp:* From trainee to dir adhesive prod, Nat Starch Prod Inc, 37-51, asst vpres, 51-56, vpres, 56-63, dir, Nat Starch & Chem Corp, 58-77, exec vpres, 63-77; RETIRED. *Res:* Synthetic resin polymers; wood and starch chemistry; manufacturing of adhesive; chemical decomposition of wood by super heated steam at temperature below 270 degrees centigrade. *Mailing Add:* 3841 Greenleaf Circle Kalamazoo MI 49008

MERRITT, RICHARD FOSTER, b South Braintree, Mass, Nov 16, 34; m 56; c 3. ORGANIC CHEMISTRY. *Educ:* Bowdoin Col, AB, 56; Mass Inst Technol, PhD(org chem), 62. *Prof Exp:* Res chemist, Redstone Arsenal Res Div, 62-67, group leader, 67-70, LAB HEAD PROCESS RES & DEVELOP, ROHM AND HAAS CO, 70- *Concurrent Pos:* Guest lectr, St Bernard Col, 62-64. *Mem:* Am Chem Soc. *Res:* Fluorine and oxygen difluoride chemistry; fluorine nuclear magnetic resonance spectroscopy; strained smallring hydrocarbons. *Mailing Add:* Rohm and Haas Co Res Labs Spring House PA 19477

MERRITT, RICHARD HOWARD, b Jersey City, NJ, Mar 28, 33; m 55; c 4. HORTICULTURE, ACADEMIC ADMINISTRATION. *Educ:* Rutgers Univ, BSc, 55, MSc, 56, PhD(hort, plant physiol), 61. *Prof Exp:* Lectr pomol, 58-61, from asst prof ornamental hort to assoc prof hort, 61-70, dir res instr & assoc dean, Col Agr & Environ Sci, 62-73, dean instr, 74-81, PROF HORT, RUTGERS UNIV, 70-, ASSOC DEAN, COOK COL, 73- *Mem:* Am Soc Hort Sci; AAAS. *Res:* Educational research; post harvest studies on apples; physiological studies on Easter lily. *Mailing Add:* Cook College PO Box 231 New Brunswick NJ 08903

MERRITT, RICHARD WILLIAM, b San Francisco, Calif, July 26, 45; m 67; c 2. ENTOMOLOGY. *Educ:* Calif State Univ, San Jose, BA, 68; Wash State Univ, MS, 70; Univ Calif, Berkeley, PhD(entom), 74. *Prof Exp:* asst prof, 74-78, ASSOC PROF ENTOM, MICH STATE UNIV, 78- *Concurrent Pos:* Assoc ed, Freshwater Invert Biol, 81- *Mem:* Entom Soc Am; NAm Benthological Soc; Sigma Xi; Freshwater Biol Asn; Am Inst Biol Sci. *Res:* Aquatic and veterinary entomology and ecology; filter-feeding in aquatic insects; aquatic biting flies; degradation and processing of organic material by insects; floodplain ecology; biosystematics of Diptera. *Mailing Add:* Dept of Entom Mich State Univ East Lansing MI 48823

MERRITT, ROBERT BUELL, b Topeka, Kans, Nov 20, 42; m 65. POPULATION GENETICS. *Educ:* Univ Kans, BA, 64, PhD(zool), 70. *Prof Exp:* Trainee genetics, Univ Rochester, 70-72; asst prof, 72-77, ASSOC PROF BIOL, SMITH COL, 77- *Mem:* AAAS; Soc Study Evolution; Genetics Soc Am. *Mailing Add:* Dept of Biol Smith Col Northampton MA 01063

MERRITT, ROBERT EDWARD, b Coudersport, Pa, Aug 1, 30; m 73; c 2. LEATHER CHEMISTRY, INFORMATION SCIENCE. *Educ:* Hanover Col, AB, 51; Univ Cincinnati, MS, 53. *Prof Exp:* Dir res, Barrentan Testing & Res Corp, Pa, 53-59; asst ed, 59-63, assoc ed, 63-68, group leader, 68-71, sr assoc indexer, 71-72, SR ASSOC ED, CHEM ABSTRACTS SERV, OHIO STATE UNIV, 72- *Concurrent Pos:* Ed, The Chem Record, Am Chem Soc, 69-; assoc ed, J Am Leather Chemists Asn, 78- *Mem:* Am Chem Soc; Am Leather Chemists Asn. *Res:* Leather chemistry, especially synthetic tanning materials and lignosulfonates; polymer chemistry; information science. *Mailing Add:* 3468 Colchester Rd Columbus OH 43221

MERROW, RAYMOND THEODORE, b Allport, Pa, Aug 5, 20; m 43, 58; c 3. ORGANIC CHEMISTRY. *Educ:* Juniata Col, BS, 40; Univ Colo, PhD(chem), 51. *Prof Exp:* Teacher high sch, Pa, 40-41; analyst, Union Steel Castings Co, 41-42; chemist, Biochem Div, Eastern Regional Res Lab, USDA, 42-43, 46-47; org chemist, Res Dept, Naval Weapons Ctr, 51-58, head solid propellants br, 58-64, head systs anal br, 64-71, opers res analyst, weapons planning group, 71-80; RETIRED. *Res:* Mechanism of organic reactions; diene syntheses; chemistry of nitrate esters; solid propellants; military operations research. *Mailing Add:* 312 Howell St Ridgecrest CA 93555

MERRY, PAUL ROBERT, b Kansas City, Mo, May 15, 21; m 43; c 2. STATISTICS. *Educ:* Baker Univ, AB, 42; Univ Denver, MBA, 47; Northwestern Univ, PhD(mkt), 55. *Prof Exp:* From asst prof to assoc prof statist & res, 49-56, assoc prof mkt & statist, 56-60, asst dean, Col Bus Admin, 60-64, res fel, Bur Bus & Social Res, 46-47, res assoc, 49-51, assoc dir, 51-60, prof, 60-80, EMER PROF STATIST, UNIV DENVER, 80- *Concurrent Pos:* Ford Found fel, Inst Basic Math for Appl Bus, Harvard Univ, 59-60; mem, US Air Force Opers Anal Standby Unit, 55-77, dir, 64-71. *Mem:* Am Statist Asn. *Res:* Research methodology. *Mailing Add:* 1551 E Cornell Ave Englewood CO 80110

MERRYMAN, EARL LEWIS, physical chemistry, inorganic chemistry, see previous edition

MERRYMAN, JOHN, JR, b Baltimore, Md, Nov 10, 22; m 46; c 3; m 63; c 2. CHEMICAL ENGINEERING. *Educ:* Va Polytech Inst, BS, 43. *Prof Exp:* Prod foreman, Aluminum Co Am, Tenn, 43-44; tech supvr, Tenn Eastman Corp, 44-47; res engr, Davison Chem Co, 47-51, prod scheduler, 51-53, res eng supvr, 53-55, plant mgr, 56-58; chem engr, Southern Press & Filter Media Co, Ga, 58; develop planning engr, Davison Chem Co Div, 58-61, tech serv, Agr Chem Div, 61-63, prod mgr agr chem, 63-66, mgr tech servs & develop, Agr Prod Div, 66-68, works mgr, Curtis Bay Works, 68-72, gen mgr auto exhaust catalyst, 72-73, VPRES MFG INDUST CHEM, DAVISON CHEM DIV, W R GRACE & CO, 73- *Mailing Add:* W R Grace & Co Davison Chem Div 5500 Chemical Rd Baltimore MD 21226

MERSEREAU, RUSSELL MANNING, b Cambridge, Mass, Aug 29, 46; m 68; c 2. DIGITAL SIGNAL PROCESSING, IMAGE PROCESSING. *Educ:* Mass Inst Technol, SB & SM, 69, EE, 70. *Prof Exp:* Res assoc elec eng, Mass Inst Technol, 73-75; asst prof, 75-79, ASSOC PROF ELEC ENG, GA INST TECHNOL, 79- *Concurrent Pos:* Consult, Lincoln Lab, Mass Inst Technol, 73-80, KINEX Corp, 78-81; asoc ed, Tranactions Acoust, Speech & Signal Processing, Inst Elec & Electronics Engrs, 76-80; vpres & treas, Atlanta Signal Processors, Inc, 81- *Honors & Awards:* Browder J Thompson Award, Inst Elec & Electronics Engrs, 76. *Mem:* Sr mem Inst Elec & Electronics Engrs. *Res:* Development of efficient algorithms for digital processing of multi-dimensional data including sampled photographic images, seismic and sonar arrays, and computer aided tomography. *Mailing Add:* Sch Elec Eng Ga Inst Technol Atlanta GA 30332

MERSKEY, CLARENCE, b Alberton, SAfrica, July 20, 14; US citizen; m 39; c 3. PHYSIOLOGY, MEDICINE. *Educ:* Univ Cape Town, MB, ChB, 37, MD, 47; FRCP, 78. *Prof Exp:* Res asst, Radcliffe Infirmary, Oxford, Eng, 49-50; sr lectr med, Univ Cape Town, 50-59; from asst prof to assoc prof, 59-72, PROF MED, ALBERT EINSTEIN COL MED, 72-, PROF LAB MED, 74- *Concurrent Pos:* Cecil John Adams travelling fel, SAfrica, 49-50; Rockefeller travelling fel, 57; fel biol chem, Harvard Univ, 57; fel, Col Physicians & Surgeons, SAfrica, 58; fel, Univ Cape Town, 58. *Mem:* Am Physiol Soc; Soc Exp Biol & Med; Am Soc Hemat; Int Soc Hemat. *Res:* Internal medicine and hematology, especially blood coagulation, thrombosis and atheroma; congenital hemorrhagic disorders. *Mailing Add:* Dept Med Albert Einstein Col Med New York NY 10461

MERSKEY, HAROLD, b Sunderland, Eng, Feb 11, 29; UK & Can citizen; m 65; c 3. PSYCHIATRY. *Educ:* Oxford Univ, BA, 50, BM, BCh, 53, DM, 65; FRCP(C); FRCPsychiat. *Prof Exp:* Lectr, Univ Sheffield, 61-64; consult, Saxondale Hosp, Nottingham, 64-67, Nat Hosps, Nervous Dis, Queen Square, London, 67-76; assoc prof, 76-77, PROF PSYCHIAT, UNIV WESTERN ONT, 77-; DIR EDUC & RES, LONDON PSYCHIAT HOSP, 76- *Concurrent Pos:* Chmn, Comt Taxon, Int Asn Study Pain, 75-, Med & Sci Comt, Soviet Jewry, 71-76; mem, Ont Mental Health Found Res Adv Bd, 78-, Behav Sci Grants Comt, Med Res Coun, Can, 82- *Mem:* Fel Royal Col Physicians London; Int Asn Study Pain. *Res:* Psychiatric aspects of pain; organic aspects of psychiatry and psychopharmacology; hysteria; social psychiatry, especially abuses of psychiatry. *Mailing Add:* London Psychiat Hosp 850 Highbury Ave London ON N6A 4H1 Can

MERSMANN, HARRY JOHN, b St Louis, Mo, Nov 13, 36; m 59; c 2. BIOCHEMISTRY. *Educ:* St Louis Univ, BS, 58, PhD(biol), 63. *Prof Exp:* Res assoc biochem, Auburn Univ, 63-65, Univ Calif, San Francisco, 65-66 & State Univ NY Buffalo, 66-68; asst prof life sci, Ind State Univ, 68-69; biochemist, Shell Develop Co, 69-79; RES CHEMIST, MEAT ANIMAL RES CTR, USDA, CLAY CENTER, NEBR, 80- *Mem:* Am Soc Biol Chemists; Am Inst Nutrit; Soc Exp Biol Med. *Res:* Animal growth and development; lipid metabolism; neonatal biology. *Mailing Add:* Meat Res USDA Meat Animal Res Ctr PO Box 166 Clay Center NE 68933

MERSTEN, GERALD STUART, b Brooklyn, NY, Sept 28, 42; m 66; c 2. ELECTRICAL ENGINEERING, COMPUTER ENGINEERING. *Educ:* City Col New York, BE, 65, ME, 69; City Univ New York, PhD(elec eng), 78. *Prof Exp:* ENG SECT SUPVR COMPUT ENG, GUID SYSTS DIV, BENDIX CORP, 65- *Concurrent Pos:* Adj lectr elec eng, City Col New York, City Univ New York, 74-75, adj asst prof, 79- *Mem:* Sigma Xi; Inst Elec & Electronics Engrs. *Res:* Real Time computer systems; high performance general purpose processors; high performance parallel processors (parallel processing); multiprocessing systems; fault tolerant computing. *Mailing Add:* 37 Polhemus Terr Whippany NJ 07981

MERTE, HERMAN, JR, b Detroit, Mich, Apr 3, 29; m 52; c 5. MECHANICAL ENGINEERING. *Educ:* Univ Mich, BS, 50 & 51, MS, 56, PhD(mech eng), 60. *Prof Exp:* Instr & lectr mech eng, 59, from asst prof to assoc prof, 60-67, PROF MECH ENG, UNIV MICH, ANN ARBOR, 67- *Concurrent Pos:* NSF sr fel, Munich, Ger, 67-68; vis prof, Inst Reactor & Apparatus Construction, Tech Univ Munich, 74-75. *Mem:* Am Soc Mech Engrs; Am Soc Eng Educ. *Res:* Heat transfer and thermodynamics. *Mailing Add:* Dept of Mech Eng Univ of Mich Ann Arbor MI 48104

MERTEL, HOLLY EDGAR, b Springfield, Mo, Sept 26, 20; c 1. SYNTHETIC ORGANIC CHEMISTRY, NATURAL PRODUCTS CHEMISTRY. *Educ:* Drury Col, BS, 41; Univ Nev, MS, 43; Univ Southern Calif, PhD(org chem), 50. *Prof Exp:* Res assoc, Columbia Univ, 50-51; RES CHEMIST, MERCK SHARP & DOHME RES LABS DIV, MERCK & CO, INC, 51-, SR RES FEL, 70- *Mem:* AAAS; Am Chem Soc; Royal Soc Chem; Health Physics Soc. *Res:* Radiochemical preparations; cortical steroid hormones. *Mailing Add:* Merck Sharp & Dohme Res Lab PO Box 2000 Rahway NJ 07065

MERTEN, ALAN GILBERT, b Milwaukee, Wis, Dec 27, 41; m 67; c 2. COMPUTER SCIENCES, INFORMATION SYSTEMS. *Educ:* Univ Wis-Madison, BS, 63, PhD(comput sci), 70; Stanford Univ, MS, 65. *Prof Exp:* Asst prof indust & opers eng, 70-74, assoc prof, 74-81, PROF COMPUT & INFO SYST & BUS ADMIN, UNIV MICH, ANN ARBOR, 81- *Concurrent Pos:* Consult, Timken Co, US Navy & Tex Instruments; chmn, Adv Comt, Wang Inst Grad Studies. *Mem:* Asn Comput Mach; Soc Mgt Info Syst. *Res:* Management and internal control systems; effective use of computer-based information systems; education of managers on implementation and management of computer systems. *Mailing Add:* Grad Sch Bus Admin Univ Mich Ann Arbor MI 48109

MERTEN, HELMUT LUDWIG, organic chemistry, see previous edition

MERTEN, ULRICH, b Houston, Tex, Feb 27, 30; m 53; c 2. PHYSICAL CHEMISTRY. *Educ:* Calif Inst Technol, BS, 51; Wash Univ, PhD(chem), 55. *Prof Exp:* Mem staff chem, Knolls Atomic Power Lab, Gen Elec Co, 55-56; mem staff chem, Gen Atomic Div, Gen Dynamics Corp, 56-67, Gulf Gen Atomic, 67-71; VPRES CHEM & MINERALS, GULF RES & DEVELOP CO, 71- *Mem:* AAAS; Am Chem Soc. *Res:* High temperature chemistry; membrane phenomena; synthetic fuels. *Mailing Add:* 321 Wildberry Rd Pittsburgh PA 15238

MERTENS, DAVID ROY, b Jefferson City, Mo, Sept 11, 47; m 72; c 2. RUMINANT NUTRITION, DAIRY SCIENCE. *Educ:* Univ Mo-Columbia, BS, 69, MS, 70; Cornell Univ, PhD(nutrit), 73. *Prof Exp:* Asst prof animal sci, Iowa State Univ, 73-75; ASST PROF DAIRY SCI, UNIV GA, 75- *Mem:* Sigma Xi; Am Dairy Sci Asn; Am Soc Microbiol; Am Soc Animal Sci; AAAS. *Res:* Mathematical and chemical study of ruminal metabolism of forages and fibrous carbohydrates; development of optimal nutrition and management of dairy animals. *Mailing Add:* 322 Livestock-Poultry Bldg Univ of Ga Athens GA 30602

MERTENS, EDWARD WILLIAM, b White Sulphur Springs, Mont, Mar 12, 22; m 45; c 3. ORGANIC CHEMISTRY, MARINE BIOLOGY. *Educ:* Univ Calif, BS, 43. *Prof Exp:* Res chemist, Calif Res Corp Div, Stand Oil Co Calif, 45-59, group supvr, 59-63, sect supvr, Chevron Res Co, 63-67, mgr asphalts div, 67-69, sr staff engr, 69-73, sr res assoc, Chevron Res Co, Stand Oil Co Calif, 73-77; sr staff specialist marine environ, 77-81, MGR ECOL PROGS, CHEVRON USA INC, 81- *Mem:* Am Fisheries Soc; Am Chem Soc. *Res:* Asphalts and asphalt products; fundamental properties of asphalts; oil spill prevention, control and retrieval technology; fate and behavior of oil in marine waters; effect of oil on marine organisms. *Mailing Add:* Chevron USA Inc PO Box 3069 San Francisco CA 94119

MERTENS, FREDERICK PAUL, b Danbury, Conn, June 10, 35; m 62; c 1. PHYSICAL CHEMISTRY, CORROSION. *Educ:* Worcester Polytech Inst, BS, 57, PhD(chem), 65. *Prof Exp:* Res chemist, Columbia-Southern Chem Corp, 57-60; res asst, Worcester Polytech Inst, 60-64; chemist, 64-65, sr chemist, 65-69, res chemist, 69-72, proj chemist, 72-80, SR PROJ CHEMIST, TEXACO INC, PORT ARTHUR, 80- *Mem:* Am Chem Soc; Nat Asn Corrosion Engrs; Sigma Xi; Am Inst Chemists; Southwest Catalysis Soc. *Res:* Infrared reflectance study of metallic corrosion and adsorbed molecules; failure analysis; basic and applied catalysis research; evaluation and recommendation of corrosion inhibitors, antifoulants, coatings and materials of construction in petroleum industry; electron spectroscopic study of catalysts. *Mailing Add:* 3216 Lawrence Ave Nederland TX 77627

MERTENS, LAWRENCE E(DWIN), b New York, NY, Mar 6, 29. SYSTEMS ENGINEERING, OPTICAL OCEANOGRAPHY. *Educ:* Columbia Univ, BS, 51, MS, 52, DEngSci, 55. *Prof Exp:* Engr, Bendix Aviation Corp, 52; systs engr, Radio Corp Am, 52-57, staff engr, 57-59, mgr digital commun eng, 59-62, chief scientist, RCA Corp, 62-76, mgr aerostat systs, 76-81, MGR TECH ANAL, RCA SERV CO, 81- *Concurrent Pos:* Adj prof, Fla Inst Technol, 65- *Mem:* Inst Elec & Electronics Engrs; NY Acad Sci; Marine Technol Soc; Soc Photo-Optical Instrumentation Engrs. *Res:* Range instrumentation; systems engineering; information theory; data processing; oceanography. *Mailing Add:* RCA Serv Co Bldg 989 MU 645 Patrick AFB FL 32925

MERTENS, THOMAS ROBERT, b Ft Wayne, Ind, May 22, 30; m 53; c 2. GENETICS, SCIENCE EDUCATION. *Educ:* Ball State Univ, BS, 52; Purdue Univ, MS, 54, PhD(genetics), 56. *Prof Exp:* Res assoc genetics, Univ Wis, 56-57; from asst prof sci to assoc prof biol, 57-66, PROF BIOL, BALL STATE UNIV, 66-, ASSOC DIR, HUMAN GENETICS & BIOEHTNICS EDUC LAB, 77- *Concurrent Pos:* NSF fac fel, Stanford Univ, 63-64. *Mem:* AAAS; Nat Asn Biol Teachers; Genetics Soc Am; Am Genetic Asn. *Res:* Plant genetics and taxonomy; cytotaxonomy of genus Polygonum in North America; cytogenetics of Rhoeo; programmed instruction in biology education; needs assessments in human genetics education. *Mailing Add:* Dept of Biol Ball State Univ Muncie IN 47306

MERTES, DAVID H, b Pittsburg, Calif, Nov 22, 29; m 62. CHEMICAL EMBRYOLOGY. *Educ:* San Francisco State Col, BA, 52; Univ Calif, Berkeley, MA, 59, PhD(zool), 66. *Prof Exp:* Mem fac zool, San Joaquin Delta Col, 59-62; Am Cancer Soc Dernham res fel, Univ Calif, Berkeley, 66-68; chmn div sci, 68-69, acad dean, 69-71, pres, Col San Mateo, 71-78; supt pres, Santa Barbara City Col, 78-81; CHANCELLOR, LOS RIOS COMMUNITY COL DIST, 81- *Mem:* AAAS; Am Soc Zool; Am Inst Biol Sci; Soc Develop Biol. *Res:* Biochemical embryology; genetic read-off and protein synthesis during the early embryogenesis of invertebrate embryos, differentiation. *Mailing Add:* Chancellor Los Rios Community Col Dist Sacramento CA 95825

MERTES, FRANK PETER, JR, b Chicago, Ill, Apr 2, 35; m 59; c 1. NUCLEAR ENGINEERING, CHEMICAL ENGINEERING. *Educ:* Northwestern Univ, BS, 58; Iowa State Univ, MS, 59, PhD(nuclear eng), 62. *Prof Exp:* Nuclear engr, Anal Serv Inc, 62-68; MGR SYST ANAL OFF, TRW ENERGY SYST PLANNING, 68- *Mem:* Am Nuclear Soc; Am Inst Aeronaut & Astronaut. *Res:* Analysis of and computer simulation of competing energy system alternatives; determination of economic and technical feasibility of nuclear power plants, synthetic fuel facilities and solar energy installations. *Mailing Add:* 6722 Bellamy Ave Springfield VA 22150

MERTES, KRISTIN BOWMAN, b Philadelphia, Pa, June 4, 46; m 76. INORGANIC CHEMISTRY. *Educ:* Temple Univ, BA, 68, PhD(chem), 74. *Prof Exp:* Asst prof, 75-81, ASSOC PROF CHEM, UNIV KANS, 81- *Mem:* Am Chem Soc; Am Crystallographer's Asn. *Res:* Structure reactivity aspects of transition metal complexes particularly with macrocyclic ligand systems. *Mailing Add:* Dept Chem Univ Kans Lawrence KS 66045

MERTES, MATHIAS PETER, b Chicago, Ill, Apr 22, 32; c 5. MEDICINAL CHEMISTRY. *Educ:* Univ Ill, BS, 54; Univ Tex, MS, 56; Univ Minn, PhD(med chem), 60. *Prof Exp:* From asst prof to assoc prof, 60-68, PROF MED CHEM, SCH PHARM, UNIV KANS, 68- *Concurrent Pos:* NIH career develop award, 67-72. *Mem:* Am Chem Soc (chmn, Med Chem Div, 78). *Res:* Organic reaction mechanisms and drug-enzyme interactions. *Mailing Add:* Malott Hall Univ of Kans Sch of Pharm Lawrence KS 66045

MERTINS, JAMES WALTER, b Milwaukee, Wis, Feb 18, 43; m 79. ENTOMOLOGY. *Educ:* Univ Wis-Milwaukee, BS, 65; Univ Wis-Madison, MS, 67, PhD(entom), 71. *Prof Exp:* Res assoc entom, Univ Wis-Madison, 71-77; ASST PROF ENTOM, IOWA STATE UNIV, 77- *Concurrent Pos:* NSF fel, Univ Wis-Madison, 69-70. *Mem:* Int Orgn Biol Control; Entom Soc Am; Entom Soc Can. *Res:* Biological insect pest supression; insect pathology; parasitoid-complex interactions; parasitoid life histories and biologies. *Mailing Add:* Dept of Entom 10 Insectary Ames IA 50011

MERTS, ATHEL LAVELLE, b Paragould, Ark, Oct 14, 25; m 47; c 1. ATOMIC PHYSICS, ASTROPHYSICS. *Educ:* Univ Mo-Rolla, BS, 50, MS, 51; Univ Kans, PhD(physics), 57. *Prof Exp:* Instr physics, Univ Tulsa, 51-52; staff mem continuum physics, Los Alamos Sci Lab, 57-64; sr scientist, Gulf-Gen Atomics, staff mem, 65-76, assoc group leader, 76-80, DEP GROUP LEADER ATOMIC PHYSICS OPACITIES, LOS ALAMOS NAT LAB, 80- *Mem:* Am Phys Soc; Am Astrophys Soc; Sigma Xi. *Res:* Study of the effects of collisional excitation and dielectronic recombination processes on the radiative power loss from optically thin plasmas. *Mailing Add:* 125 Aztec Ave Los Alamos NM 87544

MERTZ, DAN, b Allen Co, Ohio, Sept 19, 28; m 56; c 1. PLANT PHYSIOLOGY. *Educ:* Ohio Univ, BA, 54; Univ Tex, PhD(plant physiol), 60. *Prof Exp:* Asst bot & biol, Univ Tex, 54-57, res scientist, 57-60; res assoc bot, 60-61, assoc prof, 61-71, PROF BIOL SCI, UNIV MO-COLUMBIA, 71- *Concurrent Pos:* Visitor, Univ Glasgow, 67-68. *Mem:* Am Soc Plant Physiol; Bot Soc Am; Scand Soc Plant Physiol. *Res:* Physiological and biochemical changes associated with growth and development. *Mailing Add:* Div of Biol Sci 110 Tucker Hall Univ of Mo Columbia MO 65201

MERTZ, DAVID B, b Sandusky, Ohio, July 10, 34; m 61. ANIMAL ECOLOGY. *Educ:* Univ Chicago, BS, 60, PhD(zool), 65. *Prof Exp:* NSF vis scholar statist, Univ Calif, Berkeley, 65-66; asst prof biol, Univ Calif, Santa Barbara, 66-69; assoc prof, 69-74, PROF BIOL SCI, UNIV ILL, CHICAGO CIRCLE, 74- *Mem:* AAAS; Am Soc Naturalists; Ecol Soc Am; Soc Study Evolution; Am Soc Zool. *Res:* Population ecology and ecological genetics of flour beetles. *Mailing Add:* Dept Biol Sci Univ Ill at Chicago Circle Chicago IL 60680

MERTZ, EARL RICHARD, b Clayton, Mo, Oct 1, 10; m 34, 68; c 2. METALLURGY, MECHANICAL ENGINEERING. *Educ:* Mo Sch Mines, BS, 33; Tex A&M Univ, MS, 39, Univ Calif, Los Angeles, PhD(theory of struct), 53. *Prof Exp:* Metallurgist, Jones & Laughlin Steel Corp, 34-36; from instr to asst prof mech eng, Tex A&M Univ, 36-39; asst prof gen eng, Bradley Univ, 39-40; teaching specialist mech eng, Stanford Univ, 40-42; chief metallurgist, US Spring & Bumper Co, 42 & Bendix Aviation Corp, 42-44; res engr, Lockheed Aircraft Corp, 44-45; assoc prof mech eng, Univ Southern Calif, 45-55; mgr mat eng dept, Liquid Rocket Plant, Aerojet-Gen Corp, 55-58, prin engr, 58-59 & 60-61, mgr mat res & develop, 59-60; mgr acceptance testing, Missile Div, Martin-Marietta Corp, 61-62; chief engr, NAm Aviation Corp, 62-63; prof struct eng, Univ Hawaii, 63-64; prof physics & math, Sacramento State Col, 64-65; consult design & metall, Electromec Corp, 66-67; assoc prof mech eng, Calif State Polytech Univ, Kellogg-Voorhis, 68-78; RETIRED. *Concurrent Pos:* Fulbright grant, Univ Adelaide, 53-54; consult mat adv bd, Nat Acad Sci-Nat Res Coun, 58; adv, Comput Div, Int Bus Mach Corp, 66 & Atomic Energy Div, Phillips Petrol Corp, 66-67. *Mem:* Am Soc Metals; Am Soc Eng Educ. *Res:* Optimum design of beams; crack propagation by acoustic emission detection and analysis. *Mailing Add:* 2408 Via Lucia Montebello CA 90640

MERTZ, EDWIN THEODORE, b Missoula, Mont, Dec 6, 09; m 36; c 2. BIOCHEMISTRY. *Educ:* Univ Mont, AB, 31; Univ Ill, MS, 33, PhD(biochem), 35. *Hon Degrees:* DAgr, Purdue Univ, 77; DSc, Univ Mont, 79. *Prof Exp:* Res chemist, Armour & Co, 35-37; instr biochem, Univ Ill, 37-38; res assoc path, Univ Iowa, 38-40; instr agr chem, Univ Mo, 40-43; res chemist, Exp Sta, Hercules Powder Co, Del, 43-46; from asst prof agr chem to prof biochem, 46-76, EMER PROF BIOCHEM, PURDUE UNIV, WEST LAFAYETTE, 76- *Concurrent Pos:* Consult, Ind State Hosps, 57- & US-Japan Malnutrit Panel, 70-73; vis prof Notre Dame Univ, 76-77; consult, Purdue Univ, 76- *Honors & Awards:* McCoy Award, 67; John Scott Award, 67; Hoblitzelle Award, 68; Cong Medal, Fed Land Banks, 68; Spencer Award, Am Chem Soc, 70; Osborne-Mendel Award, Am Inst Nutrit, 72; Distinguished Serv Award, Univ Mont, 73; Edward W Browning Award, Am Soc Agron, 74. *Mem:* Nat Acad Sci; Am Chem Soc; Am Soc Biol Chem; Am Inst Nutrit; Am Asn Cereal Chem. *Res:* Amino acid requirements of humans and animals; purification of plasminogens; biochemistry of mental retardation; opaque-2 and floury-2 high lysine maize and high lysine sorghum. *Mailing Add:* Dept of Biochem Purdue Univ West Lafayette IN 47907

MERTZ, JANET ELAINE, b Bronx, NY, Aug 9, 49; m 80. MOLECULAR BIOLOGY, BIOCHEMISTRY. *Educ:* Mass Inst Technol, BS(biol) & BS(elec eng), 70; Stanford Univ, PhD(biochem), 75. *Prof Exp:* Jane Coffin Childs Mem Fund fel, Med Res Coun Lab Molecular Biol, Cambridge, Eng, 75-76; ASST PROF ONCOL, McARDLE LAB CANCER RES, UNIV WIS-MADISON, 76- *Mem:* AAAS; Am Soc Microbiol; Fedn Am Scientists. *Res:* Molecular biology of tumor viruses; regulation of transcription and RNA processing in eucaryotes. *Mailing Add:* McArdle Lab Cancer Res Univ of Wis Madison WI 53706

MERTZ, ROBERT LEROY, b Milwaukee, Wis, Jan 4, 34; m 59; c 3. ELECTRICAL ENGINEERING. *Educ:* Marquette Univ, BEE, 56; Mass Inst Technol, SM, 57; Univ Wis, PhD(elec eng), 60. *Prof Exp:* Asst prof elec eng, Marquette Univ, 60-64; staff engr, AC Electronics Div, Gen Motors Corp, 64-68; mgr radiation effects eng, Gulf Gen Atomic, Inc, 68-70, dep mgr, Gulf Radiation Technol Div, Gulf Energy & Environ Systs Co, San Diego, 70-74; PRES, IRT CORP, 74- *Concurrent Pos:* Consult, AC Electronics Div, Gen Motors Corp, 62-64. *Mem:* Inst Elec & Electronics Engrs. *Res:* Theory of systems and automatic control; effects of radiation on electronic systems. *Mailing Add:* IRT Corp 7650 Convoy Ct San Diego CA 92111

MERTZ, ROBERT THEODORE, b Floral Park, NY, Jan 18, 28; m 53; c 2. APPLIED MATHEMATICS. *Educ:* Harvard Univ, AB, 48; Columbia Univ, AM, 51, PhD(appl math), 61. *Prof Exp:* MATHEMATICIAN & PROGRAMMER SYSTS ANAL, IBM CORP, 50- *Concurrent Pos:* Bus exec fel, Brookings Inst, 68-69. *Mem:* AAAS; Soc Indust & Appl Math; Am Math Soc; Math Asn Am; Opers Res Soc Am. *Res:* Large scale computer programming; applications in satellite orbits, missile trajectories; English-to-Braille translation; portfolio selection; linear, quadratic, non-linear programming and optimization; management information systems; econometric modelling. *Mailing Add:* 51 Mansfield Ave Darien CT 06820

MERTZ, WALTER, b Mainz, Ger, May 4, 23; m 53. NUTRITION, BIOCHEMISTRY. *Educ:* Univ Mainz, MD, 51. *Prof Exp:* Intern surg, County Hosp, Ger, 52-53; asst internal med, Univ Hosp, Univ Frankfurt, 53; res fel nutrit, NIH, 53-56, vis scientist, Exp Liver Dis Sect, 56-61; res biochemist, Walter Reed Army Inst Res, Washington, DC, 61-64, chief dept biol chem, 64-69; chief vitamin & mineral nutrit lab, Human Nutrit Res Div, 69-72, chmn nutrit inst, 72-80, DIR, HUMAN NUTRIT RES CTR, AGR RES SERV, USDA, 80- *Mem:* Am Soc Biol Chem; Am Inst Nutrit. *Res:* Biochemistry and nutrition of trace elements. *Mailing Add:* Human Nutrition Res Ctr Agr Res Serv USDA Beltsville MD 20705

MERVA, GEORGE E, b Guernsey Co, Ohio, Aug 20, 32; m 59; c 5. AGRICULTURAL ENGINEERING, HYDROLOGY. *Educ:* Ohio State Univ, BAE, 60, PhD(hydrol), 67. *Prof Exp:* Asst prof agron, Ohio Agr Res & Develop Ctr, 60-63; res asst agr eng, Ohio State Univ, 63-67; assoc prof, 68-74, PROF AGR ENG, MICH STATE UNIV, 74- *Mem:* Am Soc Agr Eng. *Res:* Plant-soil-water relationships and agricultural drainage of layered soils. *Mailing Add:* Dept of Agr Eng Mich State Univ East Lansing MI 48823

MERWIN, RUTH MINERVA, b Washington, DC, July 3, 16. ZOOLOGY. *Educ:* Mt Holyoke Col, AB, 37, AM, 39; Univ CHicago, PhD(zool), 44. *Prof Exp:* Asst, Mt Holyoke Col, 37-39; asst, Univ Chicago, 39-41; instr zool, Conn Col, 44-47; BIOLOGIST, NAT CANCER INST, 47- *Mem:* Am Soc Exp Path; Am Asn Cancer Res; Radiation Res Soc; Microcirc Soc. *Res:* Ecology; cancer study. *Mailing Add:* Viral Biol Br Nat Cancer Inst NIH Bldg 37 Rm 1D21 Bethesda MD 20205

MERWINE, NORMAN CHARLES, b Westerville, Ohio, Dec 27, 21; m 45; c 1. AGRONOMY, CROP SCIENCE. *Educ:* Ohio State Univ, BSc, 43; Miss State Univ, MS, 53, PhD(cytogenetics, plant breeding), 56. *Prof Exp:* Teacher pub schs, Ohio, 46-47 & Miss, 47-50; asst, 50-51, 52-54, asst agronomist, Exp Sta, 55-59, assoc agronomist & assoc prof agron, 59-62, dean col agr, 66-67, PROF AGRON & AGRONOMIST, MISS STATE UNIV, 62-66 & 67- *Mem:* Am Soc Agron; Sigma Xi. *Res:* Genetics and improvement of grain sorghum; intensive cropping systems; minimum tillage technology. *Mailing Add:* Dept of Agron Miss State Univ Box 5248 Mississippi State MS 39762

MERYMAN, HAROLD THAYER, b Washington, DC, Feb 5, 21; m 47; c 4. CRYOBIOLOGY, MEDICAL RESEARCH. *Educ:* Long Island Col Med, MD, 46. *Prof Exp:* Intern, US Naval Hosp, Md, 46-47; physiologist, Naval Med Res Inst, 47-54; Am Cancer Soc fel, Yale Univ, 54-56, res fel, Sch Med, 55-57; physiologist, Naval Med Res Inst, Md, 57-68; ASSOC RES DIR BLOOD PROG, AM NAT RED CROSS, 68- *Mem:* Am Physiol Soc; Biophys Soc; Am Soc Cell Biol; Electron Micros Soc Am; Cryobiol Soc (pres, 81-82). *Res:* Mechanism of freezing and drying injury in biological media; physiology of cold injury; preservation of cells and tissues by freezing; blood banking. *Mailing Add:* Am Red Cross Blood Serv Labs 9312 Old Georgetown Rd Bethesda MD 20814

MERZ, CHARLES JOSEPH, JR, mechanical engineering, deceased

MERZ, EARL H, b Chicago, Ill, Nov 26, 08; m 36; c 2. OPHTHALMOLOGY. *Educ:* Valparaiso Univ, BS, 38; Northwestern Univ, MD, 38; Am Bd Ophthal, dipl, 43. *Prof Exp:* Chmn dept ophthal, 66-69, SR ATTEND OPHTHALMOLOGIST, WESLEY MEM HOSP, CHICAGO, 69-; ASSOC PROF OPHTHAL, MED SCH, NORTHWESTERN UNIV, CHICAGO, 68- *Mem:* Am Acad Ophthal & Otolaryngol; AMA; Asn Res Vision & Ophthal; Pan-Am Asn Ophthal. *Mailing Add:* Dept of Ophthal Northwestern Univ Med Sch Chicago IL 60201

MERZ, EDMUND HERMAN, polymer chemistry, see previous edition

MERZ, JAMES L, b Jersey City, NJ, Apr 14, 36; m 62; c 4. SOLID STATE PHYSICS. *Educ:* Univ Notre Dame, BS, 59; Harvard Univ, MA, 61, PhD(appl physics), 67. *Prof Exp:* mem staff physics, Bell Labs, 66-78; PROF ELEC ENG, UNIV CALIF, SANTA BARBARA, 78- *Concurrent Pos:* Vis lectr, Harvard Univ, 72. *Mem:* Am Phys Soc. *Res:* Study of semiconducting compounds for optical communications and optoelectronic devices. *Mailing Add:* Dept Elec Eng Univ Calif Santa Barbara CA 93106

MERZ, KENNETH M(ALCOLM), b Philadelphia, Pa, July 28, 22; m 52; c 4. CHEMISTRY, CERAMICS. *Educ:* Susquehanna Univ, BA, 49; Bucknell Univ, MA, 50; Rutgers Univ, PhD(ceramics), 57. *Prof Exp:* Res chemist, Nat Lead Co, 50-53; sr res engr, Carborundum Co, 57-59; res ceramic engr, Cornell Aeronaut Lab, Inc, 59-60; assoc dir res & develop, IRC Inc, Pa, 60-69; MGR RES, PHILADELPHIA LAB, TRW INC, 69- *Mem:* Am Ceramic Soc; Am Chem Soc. *Res:* Electronic components; preparation and properties of resistive materials; electronic ceramics; thin films; thermal expansion; optical, x-ray and electron microscopy; inorganic pigments; electrolytic preparation of titanium; thick films; fiber optic devices; sensors. *Mailing Add:* 801 Youngsford Rd Gladwyne PA 19035

MERZ, PAUL LOUIS, b New Haven, Conn, June 1, 18; m 50; c 4. RUBBER CHEMISTRY, POLYMER CHEMISTRY. *Educ:* Union Col, NY, BS, 40; Yale Univ, PhD(org chem), 52. *Prof Exp:* Res chemist, Beech-Nut Packing Co, 40-43, head polymer lab, 45-47, consult, 47-51; sr res chemist, Naugatuck Chem Div, US Rubber Co, 51-56, group leader, 56-59, sr res specialist, 59-61, proj leader high temperature elastomers, 61-62; plastics chemist, Lawrence Radiation Lab, 62-64; staff scientist, 64-79, SR ENG SPECIALIST, GEN DYNAMICS/CONVAIR, 79- *Mem:* AAAS; Am Chem Soc; Soc Advan Mat & Process Eng; Sigma Xi. *Res:* Vinyl polymerization; antioxidant and antiozonant research; rubber reclaiming; high temperature and cryogenic seals for aerospace applications; polymeric systems for radiation shielding; advanced structural and thermoformable composites; advanced aerospace adhesives and sealants; materials science. *Mailing Add:* Gen Dynamics/Convair Mail Zone 43-6310 PO Box 80847 San Diego CA 92138

MERZ, TIMOTHY, b Philadelphia, Pa, Jan 11, 27; m 53; c 2. CYTOGENETICS, RADIOBIOLOGY. *Educ:* Johns Hopkins Univ, AB, 51, PhD, 58. *Prof Exp:* NIH fel, Johns Hopkins Univ, 58-60, res assoc, 60-61, from asst prof to assoc prof cytogenetics, 64-75; PROF RADIOL & CHMN DIV RADIATION BIOL, MED COL VA, VA COMMONWEALTH UNIV, 75- *Mem:* AAAS; Radiation Res Soc; Am Soc Cell Biol; Genetics Soc Am; Am Soc Human Genetics. *Res:* Chromosome structure and behavior. *Mailing Add:* Med Col Va Div Radiation Biol Box 87 1200 E Broad St Richmond VA 23298

MERZ, WALTER JOHN, b Cheadle Hulme, Eng, Oct 10, 20; US citizen; m 49; c 2. SOLID STATE PHYSICS. *Educ:* Swiss Fed Inst Technol, MS, 44, PhD(physics), 48. *Prof Exp:* Res asst solid state physics, Mass Inst Technol, 48-51; vis prof, Pa State Univ, 51; mem tech staff, Bell Tel Labs, Inc, 51-56; mem tech staff, RCA Labs, Inc, NJ, 56-57, mgr res, 57-68, DIR RES, LABS, RCA LTD, SWITZ, 68- *Mem:* Am Phys Soc. *Res:* Ferroelectrics; dielectrics; semiconductors; photoconductors. *Mailing Add:* Labs RCA Ltd Badenerstrasse 569 CH-8048 Zurich Switzerland

MERZ, WILLIAM GEORGE, b Orange, NJ, Dec 20, 41. MEDICAL MYCOLOGY, IMMUNOLOGY. *Educ:* Drew Univ, BA, 63; WVa Univ, MS, 65, PhD(microbiol), 68. *Prof Exp:* NIH fel microbiol, Columbia-Presby Med Ctr, 68-70; instr dermat, Col Physicians & Surgeons, Columbia Univ, 70-73; instr dermat, 73-75, asst prof lab med, 73-80, asst prof dermat & epidemiol, 75-80, ASSOC PROF LAB MED, DERMAT & EPIDEMIOL, JOHNS HOPKINS UNIV, 80-; CLIN MICROBIOLOGIST, DEPT LAB MED, JOHNS HOPKINS HOSP, 73- *Concurrent Pos:* Brown-Hazen grant dermat, Columbia Univ, 70-73. *Honors & Awards:* Bot Award, Ciba Pharmaceut Co, 63. *Mem:* Am Soc Microbiol; Mycol Soc Am; Med Mycol Soc of the Americas; Int Soc Human & Animal Mycoses. *Res:* Rapid techniques for the identification of fungi; immune responses to mycotic infections. *Mailing Add:* Dept Lab Med (Path) Johns Hopkins Hosp Baltimore MD 21205

MERZBACHER, CLAUDE F, b Philadelphia, Pa, Oct 29, 17; m 45; c 2. NATURAL HISTORY, CHEMICAL ENGINEERING. *Educ:* Univ Pa, BS, 39; Claremont Grad Sch, MA, 50; Univ Poitiers, cert, 51; Univ Calif, Los Angeles, EdD, 61. *Prof Exp:* Teacher math high sch, Fla, 45-46; instr math, physics & chem, Oceanside High Sch & Jr Col, 46-47; instr chem, 47-50, from asst prof to assoc prof phys sci, 50-65, chmn dept, 64-69, PROF PHYS SCI, SAN DIEGO STATE UNIV, 65-, PLANETARIUM LECTR, 53-, COUNR, 54- *Concurrent Pos:* Dir, NSF Coop Col-Sch Sci Prog, 67-69; pvt pract psychother; consult mgt & leadership creativity. *Mem:* AAAS; Am Psychol Asn; Am Soc Clin Hypnosis; Am Chem Soc; fel Am Inst Chemists. *Res:* Affective interference with mathematics performance; design of integrated courses in physical science; statistical methods; noncognitive processes; psychology. *Mailing Add:* Dept of Natural Sci San Diego State Univ San Diego CA 92182

MERZBACHER, EUGEN, b Berlin, Ger, Apr 9, 21; nat US; m 52; c 4. THEORETICAL PHYSICS. *Educ:* Istanbul Univ, Licentiate, 43; Harvard Univ, AM, 48, PhD(physics), 50. *Prof Exp:* Mem, Inst Advan Study, 50-51; vis asst prof physics, Duke Univ, 51-52; from asst prof to prof, 52-69, CHMN DEPT, 77-, KENAN PROF PHYSICS, UNIV NC, CHAPEL HILL, 69- *Concurrent Pos:* NSF fac fel, Inst Theoret Physics, Copenhagen, 59-60, vis prof, Univ Washington, Seattle, 67-68; Sr US Humboldt Award, Univ Frankfurt, Ger, 77. *Mem:* Fel AAAS; fel Am Phys Soc; Am Asn Physics Teachers. *Res:* Quantum mechanics; atomic and nuclear theory. *Mailing Add:* Dept Physics & Astron Univ NC Chapel Hill NC 27514

MERZENICH, MICHAEL MATTHIAS, b Lebanon, Ore, May 15, 42; m 66; c 2. NEUROPHYSIOLOGY, NEUROANATOMY. *Educ:* Univ Portland, BS, 64; Johns Hopkins Univ, PhD(physiol), 68. *Prof Exp:* NIH fel, Univ Wis, 68-71; asst prof, 72-75, assoc prof, 75-80, PROF PHYSIOL & OTOLARYNGOL, UNIV CALIF, SAN FRANCISCO, 80-; DIR, COLEMAN MEM LAB, 71- *Concurrent Pos:* Consult, NIH, 74. *Mem:* AAAS; Soc Res Otolaryngol; Acoust Soc Am; Soc Neurosci. *Res:* Auditory neurophysiology; aids for the profoundly deaf; sensation coding; anatomy and physiology of the central auditory nervous system. *Mailing Add:* Dept Physiol & Otolaryngol HSE 863 Univ of Calif San Francisco CA 94143

MES, HANS, b Eindhoven, Neth, July 1, 44; Can citizen; m 66; c 2. HIGH ENERGY PHYSICS, INTERMEDIATE ENERGY PHYSICS. *Educ:* Univ Ottawa, BSc, 65, PhD(physics), 68. *Prof Exp:* Fel physics, Univ Geneva, 68-69; fel, Carleton Univ, 69-70, res assoc, 70-72; RES OFFICER PHYSICS, NAT RES COUN CAN, 72- *Mem:* Am Phys Soc; Inst Elec & Electronics Engrs. *Res:* Elementary particle physics. *Mailing Add:* Div Physics Rm X55 Nat Res Coun Can Ottawa ON K1A 0R6 Can

MESCHAN, ISADORE, b Cleveland, Ohio, May 30, 14; m 43; c 4. RADIOLOGY. *Educ:* Case Western Reserve Univ, BA, 35, MA, 37, MD, 39; Am Bd Radiol, dipl, 57. *Prof Exp:* Intern, Cleveland City Hosp, 39-40; resident, Univ Hosps, Case Western Reserve Univ, 40-42, instr radiol, Univ, 46-47; prof & head dept, Sch Med, Univ Ark, 47-55; PROF RADIOL & DIR, BOWMAN GRAY SCH MED, WAKE FOREST UNIV, 55- *Concurrent Pos:* Consult, Walter Reed Army Hosp; chmn comt radiol, Nat Acad Sci-Nat Res Coun, 74. *Mem:* Radiol Soc NAm; Radiation Res Soc; Am Roentgen Ray Soc; Soc Nuclear Med; fel Am Col Radiol. *Res:* Radioisotopes and nuclear medicine; radiation biology; diagnostic and therapeutic clinical radiology. *Mailing Add:* Dept of Radiol Bowman Gray Sch Med Winston-Salem NC 27103

MESCHI, DAVID JOHN, b East Chicago, Ind, May 1, 24. HIGH TEMPERATURE CHEMISTRY. *Educ:* Univ Chicago, BA, 49, MS, 52; Univ Calif, PhD(chem), 56. *Prof Exp:* Asst res chemist, Inst Eng Res, Univ Calif, 56-59; resident res assoc, Argonne Nat Lab, 59-60; assoc res chemist, 60-65, CHEMIST, INORG MAT RES DIV, LAWRENCE BERKELEY LAB, UNIV CALIF, 65- *Mem:* Am Chem Soc; Am Phys Soc; Am Ceramic Soc. *Res:* High temperature physics. *Mailing Add:* Inorg Mat Res Div Bldg 62 Lawrence Berkeley Lab Berkeley CA 94720

MESCHIA, GIACOMO, b Milan, Italy, Feb 7, 26; nat US; m 61; c 3. PHYSIOLOGY. *Educ:* Univ Milan, MD, 50. *Prof Exp:* Asst prof physiol, Univ Milan, 51-53; Toscanini res fel, Sch Med, Yale Univ, 53-55; asst prof physiol, Univ Milan, 55-56; res fel, Josiah Macy Found, Sch Med, Yale Univ, 56-58, res asst, 58-59, asst prof, 59-65; assoc prof, 65-69, PROF PHYSIOL, MED CTR, UNIV COLO, DENVER, 69- *Mem:* AAAS; Am Physiol Soc; hon fel Am Gynecol Soc. *Res:* Fetal physiology. *Mailing Add:* Dept of Physiol Univ of Colo Med Ctr Denver CO 80220

MESCHINO, JOSEPH ALBERT, b Cranston, RI, Aug 23, 32; m 54; c 3. ORGANIC CHEMISTRY, MEDICINAL CHEMISTRY. *Educ:* Brown Univ, ScB, 54; Rice Univ, PhD(org chem), 58. *Prof Exp:* NIH fel org synthesis, Mass Inst Technol, 58-59; sr scientist, 59-61, group leader chem develop, 61-67, dir chem res, McNeil Labs, 67-80, DIR NEW PROD DEVELOP, JOHNSON & JOHNSON, EUROPE, 80- *Mem:* Am Chem Soc. *Res:* Design and synthesis of new biologically active agents; process development of fine organic chemicals. *Mailing Add:* 14 Sandy Knoll Dr Doylestown PA 18901

MESCON, HERBERT, b Toronto, Ont, Apr 3, 19; nat US; m 46; c 4. DERMATOLOGY. *Educ:* City Col New York, BS, 38; Boston Univ, MD, 42. *Prof Exp:* Resident, Mallory Inst, Boston City Hosp, 42-43; intern med, Lebanon Hosp, Bronx, NY, 46-47 & Tufts Med Serv, 47-48; asst instr dermat, Sch Med, Univ Pa, 48-52, instr, Grad Sch Med, 50-52; PROF DERMAT & CHMN DEPT, SCH MED, BOSTON UNIV, 52-; CHIEF DERMAT &

GENITO-INFECTIOUS DIS, UNIV HOSPS & MEM EVANS MEM DEPT PREV MED, 52- *Concurrent Pos:* Res fel, Hosp Univ Pa, 48-51; Runyon clin cancer res fel, 49-51; consult, Vet Admin Hosps, Wilmington, Del, 50-52 & Boston, Mass, 54- & Lemuel Shattuck Hosp, Jamaica Plain, 55-; area consult, Vet Admin, Boston, 59-64; mem comt cutaneous med, Nat Res Coun, 62-65; dir dermat, Boston City Hosp, 74- *Mem:* Soc Invest Dermat (vpres, pres); Histochem Soc; Am Asn Path & Bact; Am Dermat Asn; Am Acad Dermat (vpres). *Res:* Dermatopathology; clinical dermatology. *Mailing Add:* 720 Harrison Ave Boston MA 02118

MESECAR, RODERICK SMIT, b Hot Springs, SDak, May 24, 33; m 52; c 4. PHYSICAL OCEANOGRAPHY, ELECTRICAL ENGINEERING. *Educ:* Ore State Univ, BS, 56, MS, 58, EE, 64, PhD(oceanog), 67. *Prof Exp:* Design engr res lab, Raytheon Co, 58-61; asst prof comput res, 61-64, asst prof oceanog res, 64-74, ASSOC PROF OCEANOG RES, ORE STATE UNIV, 74-, ASST CHMN DEPT OCEANOG, 71- *Mem:* Inst Elec & Electronics Engrs; Marine Technol Soc. *Res:* Application of electronic circuit designs and instrumentation to computer development and oceanographic research. *Mailing Add:* Dept of Oceanog Ore State Univ Corvallis OR 97331

MESELSON, MATTHEW STANLEY, b Denver, Colo, May 24, 30; m 69; c 2. MOLECULAR BIOLOGY. *Educ:* Univ Chicago, PhB, 51; Calif Inst Technol, PhD, 57. *Hon Degrees:* DSc, Oakland Univ, 66, Columbia Univ, 71 & Univ Chicago, 75. *Prof Exp:* Asst prof chem, Calif Inst Technol, 58-60; from assoc prof to prof biol, 60-76, CABOT PROF NATURAL SCI, HARVARD UNIV, 76- *Concurrent Pos:* Consult, US Arms Control & Disarmament Agency, 63- *Honors & Awards:* Nat Acad Sci Prize Molecular Biol, 63; Eli Lilly Award Microbiol & Immunol, 64; Lehman Award, NY Acad Sci, 75; Leo Szilard Award, Am Physical Soc, 78. *Mem:* Coun on Foreign Relations; Academia Santa Chiara (Genoa); Nat Acad Sci; Inst of Med of Nat Acad Sci; fel Am Acad Arts & Sci. *Res:* Molecular biology of nucleic acids; mechanisms of DNA recombination and repair; gene control and evolution. *Mailing Add:* Dept Biol Biochem & Molecular Biol Harvard Univ 7 Divinity Ave Cambridge MA 02138

MESERVE, BRUCE ELWYN, b Portland, Maine, Feb 2, 17; m 61; c 3. MATHEMATICS. *Educ:* Bates Col, AB, 38; Duke Univ, AM, 41, PhD(math), 47. *Prof Exp:* Teacher, Moses Brown Sch, RI, 38-41; asst math, Duke Univ, 41-42, 45-46; instr, Univ Ill, 46-47, asst prof, 48-54; from assoc prof to prof, 54-Montclair State Col, 54-64, chmn dept, 57-63; PROF MATH, UNIV VT, 64- *Mem:* AAAS; Am Math Soc; Math Asn Am; Nat Coun Teachers Math. *Res:* Geometry; mathematical training of prospective teachers; historical evolution of mathematical sciences. *Mailing Add:* Dept of Math Univ of Vt Burlington VT 05405

MESERVE, LEE ARTHUR, b Saco, Maine, Mar 9, 44; m 68. ENDOCRINOLOGY, PHYSIOLOGY. *Educ:* Univ Maine, BS, 66; Rutgers Univ, PhD(zool), 72. *Prof Exp:* Vis asst prof biol, Vassar Col, 72-73; ASST PROF BIOL, BOWLING GREEN STATE UNIV, 73-, ADJ ASST PROF GERONT, HEALTH & COMMUNITY SERV, 77- *Mem:* AAAS; Am Aging Asn; Am Soc Zoologists; Geront Soc; Soc Study Reproduction. *Res:* Development of endocrine control; endocrine interactions; aging and endocrinology. *Mailing Add:* Dept of Biol Sci Bowling Green State Univ Bowling Green OH 43403

MESERVE, PETER LAMBERT, b Buffalo, NY, Sept 22, 45; m 69. ECOLOGY. *Educ:* Univ Calif, Davis, BA, 67; Univ Nebr-Lincoln, MS, 69; Univ Calif, Irvine, PhD(biol), 72. *Prof Exp:* Asst prof ecol, Cath Univ, Santiago, 73-75; asst prof zool, Univ Idaho, 75-76; ASST PROF BIOL, NORTHERN ILL UNIV, 76- *Mem:* Ecol Soc Am; Am Soc Mammalogists; Am Soc Naturalists. *Res:* Population and community ecology of vertebrates; biogeography; behavioral ecology. *Mailing Add:* Dept of Biol Sci Northern Ill Univ DeKalb IL 60115

MESERVEY, ROBERT H, b Hanover, NH, Apr 1, 21; m 53; c 2. SOLID STATE PHYSICS. *Educ:* Dartmouth Col, BA, 43; Yale Univ, PhD(physics), 61. *Prof Exp:* Physicist, US Army Eng Res & Develop Lab, 51-55; consult, Perkin Elmer Corp, 55-60; physicist, Lincoln Lab, 61-63, SR SCIENTIST, FRANCIS BITTER NAT MAGNET LAB, MASS INST TECHNOL, 63- *Mem:* Fel Am Phys Soc. *Res:* Superconductivity; magnetism; low temperature physics; fluid mechanics; optics. *Mailing Add:* Francis Bitter Nat Magnet Lab Mass Inst of Technol Cambridge MA 02139

MESETH, EARL HERBERT, b Chicago, Ill, Nov 29, 38; m 81; c 1. ZOOLOGY. *Educ:* Ill Col, BS, 61; Wash Univ, MA, 62; Southern Ill Univ, Carbondale, PhD(zool), 68. *Prof Exp:* From asst prof to assoc prof, 68-78, PROF BIOL, ELMHURST COL, 78- *Mem:* Sigma Xi; Am Ornithologists Union; Cooper Ornith Soc; Soc Study Evolution. *Res:* Behavior, ecology and biology of albatrosses, Diomedea immutabilis; relationship of courtship rituals to nest site selection and pair bonding. *Mailing Add:* Dept of Biol Elmhurst Col Elmhurst IL 60126

MESHII, MASAHIRO, b Hyogo, Japan, Oct 6, 31; m 59; c 2. MATERIALS SCIENCE. *Educ:* Osaka Univ, BEng, 54, MS, 56; Northwestern Univ, PhD(mat sci), 59. *Prof Exp:* Res assoc & lectr mat sci, 59-60, from asst prof to assoc prof, 60-67, PROF MAT SCI, NORTHWESTERN UNIV, EVANSTON, 67-, CHMN DEPT MAT SCI & ENG, 78- *Concurrent Pos:* Vis scientist, Nat Res Inst Metals, 70-71. *Honors & Awards:* Howe Medal, Am Soc Metals, 67. *Mem:* Am Soc Metals; Am Inst Mining, Metall & Petrol Engrs; Am Phys Soc; Electron Micros Soc Am; Japan Inst Metals. *Res:* Plastic deformation, fatigue and radiation damage in metals and alloys; electron microscopy. *Mailing Add:* Dept of Mat Sci & Eng Northwestern Univ Technol Inst Evanston IL 60201

MESHKOV, SYDNEY, b Philadelphia, Pa, June 5, 27; m 56; c 3. PHYSICS. *Educ:* Univ Pa, AB, 47, PhD(physics), 54; Univ Ill, MS, 49. *Prof Exp:* Asst physics, Univ Ill, 47-49; asst instr, Univ Pa, 49-54; asst prof, Univ Del, 54-55; lectr, Univ Pa, 55-56; asst prof, Univ Pittsburgh, 56-62; PHYSICIST, SR EXEC SERV, NAT BUR STANDARDS, 62- *Concurrent Pos:* Instr, LaSalle Col, 51-52; res assoc, Princeton Univ, 60; res assoc, Weizmann Inst, 61-62; vis assoc, Calif Inst Technol, 73; secy, Aspen Ctr Physics, 75-; vis prof theoret physics, Calif Inst Technol, 77-78 & 81-82; vis prof physics, Univ Calif, Irvine, 81-82. *Mem:* Fel Am Phys Soc. *Res:* Elementary particle theory. *Mailing Add:* 532 00 Nat Bur Standards Washington DC 20234

MESHRI, DAYALDAS TANUMAL, b Kaloi, WPakistan, Mar 11, 36; m 66; c 2. INORGANIC CHEMISTRY, PHYSICAL CHEMISTRY. *Educ:* Gujarat Univ, India, BSc, 58, MSc, 62; Univ Idaho, PhD(inorg & phys chem), 68. *Prof Exp:* Demonstr chem, St Xavier's Col, India, 58; demonstr, Gujarat Col, 58-61, asst lectr, 61-62; postdoc, assoc, Cornell Univ, 67-69; res chemist, 69-70, head fluorine res dept, 70-72, DIR FLUORINE & INORG RES, SPEC CHEM DIV, OZARK-MAHONING CO, 73- *Mem:* Fel Am Inst Chemists; Am Chem Soc; AAAS; Electrochem Soc; Sigma Xi. *Res:* Neutron activation analysis; coordination and fluorine chemistry; nitrogen-fluorine, oxygen fluorine chemistry; electrophilic substitution; hydrogen fluoride chemistry. *Mailing Add:* Ozark-Mahoning Co Spec Chem Div 1870 S Boulder Tulsa OK 74119

MESIROV, JILL PORTNER, b Philadelphia, Pa, May 12, 50. MATHEMATICS. *Educ:* Univ Pa, AB, 70; Brandeis Univ, MA, 71, PhD(math), 74. *Prof Exp:* lectr math, Univ Calif, Berkeley, 74-76; RES MATHEMATICIAN, IDA COMMUN RES DIV, 76- *Concurrent Pos:* Vis lectr, Princeton Univ, 80 & 81. *Mem:* Soc Indust & Appl Math; Am Math Soc; Asn Women in Math. *Res:* Global analysis; calculus of variations. *Mailing Add:* IDA-CRD Thanet Rd Princeton NJ 08540

MESKIN, LAWRENCE HENRY, b Detroit, Mich, July 21, 35; m 59; c 2. DENTAL EPIDEMIOLOGY. *Educ:* Univ Detroit, DDS, 61; Univ Minn, Minneapolis, MSD, 63, MPH, 64, PhD(epidemiol), 66. *Prof Exp:* Instr oral path, Sch Dent, Univ Minn, Minneapolis, 63-66, assoc prof prev dent & chmn div, 66-68, chmn, Div Health Ecol, 68-81, Hill res prof, Delivery Dent Health Serv, 70-81, lectr pediat, Sch Med, 63-81; DEAN, SCH DENT, UNIV COLO, 81- *Concurrent Pos:* USPHS fel epidemiol, 63-; consult, Cleft Palate Clin, Univ Ill, 64-; partic, Inst Advan Educ Dent Res, 64; WHO traveling fel, 68. *Mem:* Am Dent Asn; Am Acad Oral Path; Int Asn Dent Res; Am Pub Health Asn; Am Asn Dent Sch. *Res:* Preventive dentistry; dental public health; craniofacial malformations; health care delivery. *Mailing Add:* Sch Dent Univ Colo 4200 E 9th Ave Denver CO 80262

MESLER, R(USSELL) B(ERNARD), b Kansas City, Mo, Aug 24, 27; m 51; c 4. CHEMICAL ENGINEERING. *Educ:* Univ Kans, BS, 49; Univ Mich, MS, 53, PhD(chem eng), 55. *Prof Exp:* Process engr, Colgate-Palmolive Co, 49-51; asst Ford nuclear reactor, Univ Mich, 53-55, asst prof nuclear eng & proj engr, Ford nuclear reactor, 55-57; from assoc prof to prof, 57-70, WARREN S BELLOWS DISTINGUISHED PROF CHEM ENG, UNIV KANS, 70- *Concurrent Pos:* Resident res engr, Argonne Nat Lab, 58; consult, Spencer Chem Co, Kerr McGee, Westinghouse Elec & Farmland Industs; fac res participant, Savannah River Lab, E I du Pont de Nemours, Co, Inc, 81. *Honors & Awards:* Robert T Knapp Award, Am Soc Mech Engrs, 67. *Mem:* Am Chem Soc; fel Am Inst Chem Engrs; Am Soc Eng Educ; Am Nuclear Soc; Sigma Xi. *Res:* Heat transfer, especially nucleate boiling; nuclear technology; cavitation; high speed photography. *Mailing Add:* Dept of Chem & Petrol Eng Univ of Kans Lawrence KS 66044

MESLOW, E CHARLES, b Waukegan, Ill, Aug 25, 37; m 59; c 3. ECOLOGY, WILDLIFE RESEARCH. *Educ:* Univ Minn, BS, 59, MS, 66; Univ Wis, PhD(wildlife ecol), 70. *Prof Exp:* Asst prof zool & vet sci, NDak State Univ, 68-71; asst leader, 71-77, LEADER ORE COOP WILDLIFE RES UNIT, ORE STATE UNIV, 77-, ASSOC PROF WILDLIFE & ECOL, 77- *Mem:* Ecol Soc Am; Wildlife Soc; Am Soc Mammal; Am Ornith Union. *Res:* Population dynamics; predation; wildlife ecology. *Mailing Add:* Coop Wildlife Res Unit 104 Nash Hall Ore State Univ Corvallis OR 97331

MESNER, MAX H(UTCHINSON), b Meadville, Mo, Apr 16, 12; m 37; c 1. ELECTRONIC ENGINEERING. *Educ:* Univ Mo, BS, 40. *Prof Exp:* Design engr, RCA Corp, 40-41, res engr, labs, 41-58, proj engr, 58-60, eng group leader, 60-61, eng mgr, astro-electronics div, Princeton, 61-81; RETIRED. *Mem:* Fel Inst Elec & Electronics Engrs; Soc Photo-Optical Instrument Eng. *Res:* Television camera systems for space vehicles. *Mailing Add:* 9 Wynnewood Dr Cranbury NJ 08512

MESNIKOFF, ALVIN MURRAY, b Asbury Park, NJ, Dec 25, 25; m 52; c 4. PSYCHIATRY, PSYCHOANALYSIS. *Educ:* Rutgers Univ, BA, 48; Univ Chicago, MD, 54. *Prof Exp:* Asst chief male serv, NY State Psychiat Inst, 58-60, chief female psychiat serv, 60-65, dir, Washington Heights Community Serv, 65-68; dir, South Beach Psychiat Ctr, 68-75, NEW YORK CITY REGIONAL DIR, NY STATE OFF MENT HEALTH, 75-; PROF PSYCHIAT, STATE UNIV NY DOWNSTATE MED CTR, 68- *Concurrent Pos:* Assoc clin prof psychiat, Columbia Univ, 60-68; assoc attend psychiatrist, Columbia Presby Hosp, 68-69; lectr psychiatry, Columbia Univ, 68; attend psychiatrist, Kings County Hosp, 69- & St Vincent's Med Ctr, 70- *Mem:* AAAS; fel Am Psychiat Asn; NY Acad Sci. *Res:* Community psychiatry; design of programs; evaluation of mental health services. *Mailing Add:* 2 World Trade Ctr 56th Floor New York NY 10047

MESROBIAN, ROBERT BENJAMIN, b New York, NY, July 31, 24; m 50; c 5. CHEMISTRY. *Educ:* Princeton Univ, BA, 44, MS, 45, PhD(phys chem), 47. *Prof Exp:* Res assoc & proj adminr, Polytech Inst Brooklyn, 47-49, from asst prof to assoc prof polymer chem, 49-54, prof & assoc dir, Polymer Res Inst, 55-57; assoc dir res high polymer chem, Cent Res & Eng Div, 57-58, gen mgr, Gen Packaging Res & Develop Div, 59-64, gen mgr, Cent Res & Eng Div, 64-67, gen mgr res & eng, Continental Can Co, Inc, 67-69, VPRES RES & ENG, CONTINENTAL PACKAGING CO, 69- *Concurrent Pos:* Co-holder, Chaire Franqui lectr, Univ Liege, 47-48; US Educ Found vis prof, State Univ Groningen, 50; consult, Nuclear Eng Div, Brookhaven Nat Lab, 51-; US State Dept adv, Atoms for Peace Conf, Geneva, 58. *Mem:* Am Chem

Soc; Soc Plastics Eng; Am Inst Chem. *Res:* Synthesis and properties of polymers; oxidation of hydrocarbons; organic peroxides; effects of ionizing radiation on polymers; application of polymers for coatings, adhesives, inks and packaging. *Mailing Add:* Continental Packaging Co PO Box 10004 Stamford CT 06904

MESSAL, EDWARD EMIL, b Chicago, Ill, Nov 24, 37; m 67; c 3. MECHANICAL ENGINEERING. *Educ:* Ill Inst Technol, BS, 59, MS, 63, PhD(mech eng), 70. *Prof Exp:* Instr mech eng, Ill Inst Technol, 60-64 & 65-66; from instr to asst prof eng sci, Roosevelt Univ, 66-70; asst prof mech eng technol, 70-76, ASSOC PROF MECH ENG TECHNOL, IND UNIV-PURDUE UNIV, FT WAYNE, 76- *Concurrent Pos:* Tech writer, Central Soya Co, Inc, 77-78. *Mem:* Assoc Am Soc Mech Engrs. *Res:* Machine design; medical apparatus; hydraulics and pneumatics; stress analysis; rotor dynamics; mathematics. *Mailing Add:* Mfg Technol Ind Univ-Purdue Univ Ft Wayne IN 46805

MESSENGER, AUBREY STEVEN, soil science, forest ecology, see previous edition

MESSENGER, GEORGE CLEMENT, b Bellows Falls, Vt, July 20, 30; m 54; c 3. PHYSICS, ELECTRICAL ENGINEERING. *Educ:* Worcester Polytech Inst, BS, 51; Univ Pa, MS, 57. *Prof Exp:* Res scientist solid state physics, Philco Corp, 51-59; eng mgr semiconductor div, Hughes Aircraft Co, 59-61; div mgr transistor div, Transitron Corp, 61-62; staff scientist, Northrop Corp, 63-68; CONSULT ENGR SOLID STATE PHYSICS, 68- *Concurrent Pos:* Lectr, Univ Calif, Los Angeles, 69-74; consult, Defense Nuclear Agency, 70. *Mem:* Fel Inst Elec & Electronics Engrs; Am Phys Soc; Res Soc Am. *Res:* Radiation effects on electronic components and systems; research and development of solid state electronic components; development of quality control and hardness assurance programs for systems. *Mailing Add:* 3111 Bel Air Dr 7F Las Vegas NV 89109

MESSENGER, JOSEPH UMLAH, b Medicine Hat, Alta, Aug 5, 13; US citizen; m 41; c 3. INORGANIC CHEMISTRY, PHYSICAL CHEMISTRY. *Educ:* Univ Calif, Berkeley, AB, 35, BS, 39; Univ Southern Calif, MS, 42. *Prof Exp:* Res chemist, Nat Defense Res Coun, Univ Southern Calif, 41-42 & Univ Chicago, 42-43; from asst res chemist to res chemist, Field Res Lab, Socony Mobil Oil Co, Inc, 43-46, from sr chemist to sr res chemist, 46-50, sr res technologist, 50-54, drilling mud engr, Mobil Oil Can, Ltd, Alta, 54-58, sr staff engr, 58-60, chem eng sect chief, 60-62, eng specialist, Field Res Lab, Mobil Oil Corp, Tex, 62-67, eng assoc, Field Res Lab, Mobil Res & Develop Corp, 67-78; RETIRED. *Mem:* Soc Petrol Eng; Am Inst Mining, Metall & Petrol Eng; Sigma Xi; fel Am Inst Chemists. *Res:* Chemical and petroleum engineering; chemical well stimulation, drilling muds, cements, lost circulation, water injection and corrosion; contact catalysis; fluorine, boron and uranium chemistry. *Mailing Add:* 2906 Gladiolus Dallas TX 75233

MESSENGER, ROGER ALAN, b St Paul, Minn, Aug 26, 43; m 66; c 1. ELECTRICAL ENGINEERING. *Educ:* Univ Minn, BS, 65, MSEE, 66, PhD(elec eng), 69. *Prof Exp:* US Air Force Off Sci Res fel, 69-71, asst prof elec eng, 71-75, ASSOC PROF ELEC ENG, FLA ATLANTIC UNIV, 75- *Mem:* Inst Elec & Electronics Engrs. *Res:* Energy conservation technology. *Mailing Add:* Dept of Elec Eng Fla Atlantic Univ Boca Raton FL 33431

MESSER, CHARLES EDWARD, b Baltimore, Md, Aug 16, 15; m 58. PHYSICAL CHEMISTRY. *Educ:* Johns Hopkins Univ, AB, 36, PhD(phys chem), 40. *Prof Exp:* Res chemist, Biochem Res Found, Del, 41 & Nat Defense Res Comt, US Bur Mines, Pa, 41-42; instr chem, Clarkson Tech, 42-44 & Dartmouth Col, 44-46; from instr to asst prof, 46-53, assoc prof, 53-80, EMER PROF CHEM, TUFTS UNIV, 80- *Mem:* Am Chem Soc; AAAS; Sigma Xi. *Res:* Calorimetry; phase studies. *Mailing Add:* Dept of Chem Tufts Univ Medford MA 02155

MESSER, LOUISE BREARLEY, b Wolverton, UK, Mar 22, 40; Australian citizen; m 68; c 1. PEDIATRIC DENTISTRY, PREVENTIVE DENTISTRY. *Educ:* Univ Melbourne, BDSc & LDS, 62, MDSc, 68. *Prof Exp:* Dentist pediat, Melbourne Dent Hosp, Australia, 63; asst lectr, Dept Conserv Dent, Univ Melbourne, 63-65, lectr, 65-68; asst prof & dir clin, Div Pediat Dent, Univ Minn, 68-71, actg chmn div, 69-70, assoc prof, 71-72; vis lectr, Dept Oral Biol, Univ BC, 72-74; assoc prof, 74-80, PROF PEDIAT DENT, UNIV MINN, MINNEAPOLIS, 80- *Concurrent Pos:* USPHS grant, 68-70; res grant reviewer, Nat Health Res & Develop Prog, Health & Welfare, Can, 73-; clin dir, NIH, 75-80; res award, Int Asn Dent Res, 66; sr scientist award, NIH, 81. *Mem:* Am Asn Dent Sch; Int Asn Dent Res. *Res:* Growth and development of oro-facial structures and prevention of dental caries, with particular reference to the pediatric patient. *Mailing Add:* Div Pediat Dent Sch Dent Univ Minn Minneapolis MN 55455

MESSER, WAYNE RONALD, b Cedar Rapids, Iowa, Nov 7, 42; m 64; c 2. ORGANIC CHEMISTRY, PHOTOCHEMISTRY. *Educ:* Iowa State Univ, BS, 64; Univ Ill, PhD(chem), 68. *Prof Exp:* Res chemist, Cent Res Div, Hercules, Inc, 68-77; SR RES CHEMIST, CHEMICAL SCI DIV, HERCULES, INC, 77- *Mem:* Am Chem Soc; Inter-Am Photochem Soc; Sigma Xi. *Res:* Nitrogen heterocycles; cycloadditions; concerted reactions; physical organic chemistry; photopolymerization. *Mailing Add:* Res Ctr Hercules Inc Wilmington DE 19899

MESSERLE, LOUIS, b Jersey City, NJ, Apr 6, 53. ORGANOMETALLIC CHEMISTRY. *Educ:* Brown Univ, ScB, 75; Mass Inst Technol, PhD(inorg chem), 79. *Prof Exp:* Fel, 79-81, MICH SOC FELS SCHOLAR & ASST PROF INORG CHEM, DEPT CHEM, UNIV MICH, 81- *Concurrent Pos:* Lectr, Dept Chem, Univ Mich, 81 & 82-84. *Mem:* Am Chem Soc; Sigma Xi. *Res:* Synthetic and mechanistic organotransition metal chemistry; homogeneous catalysis; multinuclear magnetic resonance spectroscopy of transition metal complexes, particularly carbon 13 nuclear magnetic resonance. *Mailing Add:* Dept Chem Univ Mich Ann Arbor MI 48109

MESSERSMITH, DONALD HOWARD, b Toledo, Ohio, Dec 17, 28; m 57; c 4. ENTOMOLOGY, ORNITHOLOGY. *Educ:* Univ Toledo, BEd, 51; Univ Mich, MS, 53; Va Polytech Inst, PhD(entom), 62. *Prof Exp:* Prof biol, Radford Col, 57-64; PROF ENTOM, UNIV MD, COLLEGE PARK, 64- *Mem:* Entom Soc Am; Am Ornith Union. *Res:* Biology and taxonomy of Culicoides, Forcipomyia and Simuliidae; control of bird depredations. *Mailing Add:* Dept Entom Univ Md College Park MD 20742

MESSERSMITH, JAMES DAVID, b Paintsville, Ky, Sept 14, 31; m 60; c 4. FISHERIES MANAGEMENT. *Educ:* Ore State Univ, BS, 53, MS, 58. *Prof Exp:* Res fel, Ore Coop Wildlife Res, 56-58; fishery biologist, 58-60, marine biologist, 61-63, assoc marine biologist, 63-69, sr marine biologist, 69-72, coordr state-fed fisheries mgt progs, 72-75, conserv prog officer & legis coordr, 75-81, ASST DEP DIR OPER, CALIF DEPT FISH & GAME, 81- *Concurrent Pos:* Proj mgr, Dungeness Crab Mgt Proj, Pac Fishery Biol. *Mem:* Am Fisheries Soc; Am Inst Fishery Res Biol. *Res:* Legislation and management with reference to marine fauna of the northeastern Pacific Ocean with emphasis on fish, mollusks and crustaceans of sport and commercial importance. *Mailing Add:* Calif Dept of Fish & Game Rm 1236-4, 1416 Ninth St Sacramento CA 95814

MESSERSMITH, ROBERT E, b Trenton, NJ, Mar 15, 30; m 57; c 3. VETERINARY MEDICINE. *Educ:* Cornell Univ, DVM, 54. *Prof Exp:* Vet, pvt pract, 54-61; vet, Agr Div, Am Cyanamid Co, NJ, 61-63, mgr swine prog, 63-68; clin vet, Animal Health Res Dept, 68-74, PROF SERV VET, DEPT AGR & ANIMAL HEALTH, CHEM DIV, HOFFMANN-LA ROCHE, INC, 74- *Mem:* Am Vet Med Asn. *Res:* Cause of problems in animal production and development of practical methods of control. *Mailing Add:* Chem Div Hoffmann-La Roche Inc 1521 Angelina Bend Denton TX 76201

MESSICK, ROGER E, b Chicago, Ill, Jan 20, 29; m 50; c 2. APPLIED MATHEMATICS, ENGINEERING. *Educ:* Univ Ill, BS, 51, MS, 52; Calif Inst Technol, PhD(eng sci), 62. *Prof Exp:* Engr, Arnold Eng Develop Ctr, ARO, Inc, 52-53; instr eng math, Calif Inst Technol, 63; asst prof math, Case Western Reserve Univ, 63-67; ASSOC PROF ENG SCI & MATH, UNIV CINCINNATI, 67- *Concurrent Pos:* Consult, Aerojet-Gen Corp, Calif, 57-62; Fulbright grad fel & univ grant, Univ Sydney, 62-63. *Mem:* Am Math Soc; Math Asn Am; Am Asn Physics Teachers; Soc Indust & Appl Math; Am Acad Mech. *Res:* Partial differential equations; singular perturbations; asymptotic and numerical approximations; continuum mechanics; elastic shell theory; free surface gravity waves; boundary layer and edge effects. *Mailing Add:* Dept of Eng Sci Univ of Cincinnati Cincinnati OH 45221

MESSIER, BERNARD, b Montreal, Que, May 4, 26; m 53; c 4. EXPERIMENTAL PATHOLOGY. *Educ:* Univ Montreal, BS, 49; McGill Univ, MSc, 56, PhD(anat), 60. *Prof Exp:* Asst path, Col Physicians & Surgeons, Columbia Univ, 61-62; asst prof med, 64-67, from asst prof to assoc prof anat, 67-75, PROF ANAT, UNIV MONTREAL, 75- *Mem:* Am Asn Anatomists; Can Asn Anatomists. *Res:* Radioautography; cell renewal in normal tissues. *Mailing Add:* Dept of Anat Univ of Montreal Montreal PQ H3C 3T7 Can

MESSIER, DONALD ROYAL, b Springfield, Mass, Oct 3, 32. CERAMICS ENGINEERING. *Educ:* Alfred Univ, BS, 59; Univ Calif, Berkeley, MS, 61, PhD(eng), 64. *Prof Exp:* Asst ceramic engr, Argonne Nat Lab, 64-68; RES CERAMIC ENGR, ARMY MAT & MECH RES CTR, 68- *Mem:* Am Ceramic Soc. *Res:* High temperature behavior of inorganic materials; ceramic fabrication processes; nitrogen glass-ceramics. *Mailing Add:* Army Mat & Mech Res Ctr Watertown MA 02172

MESSIER, ROBERT LOUIS, b Worcester, Mass, Sept 13, 17. PATHOLOGY BIOCHEMISTRY COMMUNICATIONS. *Educ:* Worcester Polytech Inst, BS, 40; Univ Mass, MS, 41; Cornell Univ, PhD(biochem), 45. *Prof Exp:* Dir food packing, NGrafton State Hosp, Mass, 41; assoc ed, 45-59, SR ASSOC ED, CHEM ABSTR, 59- *Mem:* Am Chem Soc. *Res:* Chemical information. *Mailing Add:* Chem Abstr Dept 54 Ohio State Univ Columbus OH 43210

MESSIER, RUSSELL, b Nashua, NH, July 30, 44; m 69; c 2. THIN FILMS, RADIO FREQUENCY-SPUTTERING. *Educ:* Northeastern Univ, BS, 67; Pa State Univ, PhD(solid state sci), 73. *Prof Exp:* Res assoc, Pa State Univ, 73-74; advan res eng, GTE Sylvania, 74-76; res assoc, 76-79, sr res assoc, 79-81, ASSOC PROF MAT RES, PA STATE UNIV, 81- *Mem:* Inst Elec & Electronics Engrs; Am Vacuum Soc; Mat Res Soc. *Res:* Thin film preparation and characterization using the radio frequency-sputtering technique; characterization of the sputtering process; noncrystalline solid formation; thin films for solar energy conversion. *Mailing Add:* 265 Mat Res Lab Univ Park PA 16802

MESSINA, CARLA GRETCHEN, b Ames, Iowa, July 22, 37; m 62; c 2. COMPUTER SCIENCE, PHYSICS. *Educ:* Univ Md, BS, 59; George Washington Univ, MS, 62. *Prof Exp:* PHYSICIST, NAT BUR STANDARDS, 55- *Res:* Data processing; data transformation; scientific text typesetting; data book design. *Mailing Add:* Nat Bur of Standards Washington DC 20234

MESSINA, EDWARD JOSEPH, b Brooklyn, NY, May 28, 37; m 60; c 1. CARDIOVASCULAR PHYSIOLOGY. *Educ:* St John's Univ, BSc, 60; New York Med Col, PhD(physiol), 72. *Prof Exp:* NIH fel, 72-73; from instr to assoc prof, 73-81, PROF PHYSIOL, NEY YORK MED COL, 82- *Mem:* AAAS; Microcirc Soc; NY Acad Sci; Am Physiol Soc. *Res:* Understanding the interrelationships between those local factors which contribute to the regional regulation of blood flow. *Mailing Add:* Dept of Physiol New York Med Col Valhalla NY 10595

MESSINA, FRANK JAMES, b Lawrence, Mass, Jan 24, 55. INSECT ECOLOGY, INSECT BEHAVIOR. *Educ:* Clark Univ, BA, 76; Cornell Univ, PhD(ecol), 82. *Prof Exp:* Teaching asst intro biol, Cornell Univ, 76-78, res asst, 78-81; ASSOC, BOYCE THOMPSON INST PLANT RES, 82- *Mem:* Ecol Soc Am; Soc Study Evolution; Entom Soc Am. *Res:* Feeding and oviposition behavior of phytophagous insects, with reference to biological control; evolution of insect feeding habits and mating systems; insect dispersal. *Mailing Add:* Boyce Thompson Inst Plant Res Tower Rd Ithaca NY 14853

MESSINEO, LUIGI, b Bronte, Italy, May 25, 26; US citizen; m 68. BIOCHEMISTRY, BIOPHYSICS. *Educ:* Univ Palermo, Lic clas, 46, PhD(natural sci), 53; Inst Philos, Messina, Italy, lic philos, 49. *Prof Exp:* Vis investr biochem physiol, Univ Calif, Berkeley, 58-59; vis investr biophys, Univ Pittsburgh, 59-61; res chemist, Vet Admin Hosp, Buffalo, NY, 62-67; dir biochem res lab, Vet Admin Ctr, 67-70; PROF BIOL & CHEM, CLEVELAND STATE UNIV, 70- *Concurrent Pos:* Vis scientist, LaStazione Zoologica, Italy, 53; vis investr, Univ Pittsburgh, 57; Damon Runyon Mem Found res fel, 58-61; Health Res & Serv Found grant, 60-61, Leukemia Found, 62, Health Res Found Western NY, 63, Nat Cancer Inst, 64-67 & Am Heart Asn, 69-70; res assoc, Nat Cancer Inst, 61-62; res asst prof, State Univ NY Buffalo, 62-67 & Xavier Univ, Ohio, 67- *Honors & Awards:* Knight of the Order of Merit, Italian Repub. *Mem:* Biophys Soc; Am Inst Biol Sci; Am Soc Zool. *Res:* Physiochemical and immunological properties of deoxyribonucleoproteins from normal and abnormal sources; aging. *Mailing Add:* Dept of Biol Cleveland State Univ Cleveland OH 44115

MESSING, FREDRIC, b Brooklyn, NY, June 8, 48; m 70; c 1. PHYSICS. *Educ:* Carnegie-Mellon Univ, BS, 70; Univ Pa, PhD(physics), 75. *Prof Exp:* Res assoc, Lab Nuclear Studies, Cornell Univ, 74-77; asst prof, 77-81, ASSOC PROF PHYSICS, DEPT PHYSICS, CARNEGIE-MELLON UNIV, 81- *Concurrent Pos:* Consult, Deutsches Elektronen Synchrotron, 80. *Res:* Lepton beams; weak interactions; quark models; resonance production and decay. *Mailing Add:* Dept Physics Carnegie-Mellon Univ Schenley Park Pittsburgh PA 15213

MESSING, RALPH ALLAN, b Newark, NJ, Jan 16, 27; m 55; c 3. ENZYMOLOGY. *Educ:* City Col New York, BS, 49; Purdue Univ, MS, 51. *Prof Exp:* Res assoc neurol, Sch Med, Univ Ark, 52-54; assoc res biochemist, Ethicon, Inc, Div Johnson & Johnson, 55-61; chief enzymologist, Schwarz Labs, Inc, 61-63; SR RES ASSOC, CORNING GLASS WORKS, 63- *Mem:* AAAS; Am Inst Chem; Am Chem Soc; NY Acad Sci. *Res:* Immobilization, preparation, purification and characterization of enzymes; reactions of proteins on inorganic surfaces; metabolism; industrial and clinical microbiology. *Mailing Add:* Sullivan Park Corning Glass Works Corning NY 14830

MESSING, RITA BAILEY, b Brooklyn, NY, July 7, 45; m 65; c 1. NEUROPHARMACOLOGY, PSYCHOPHARMACOLOGY. *Educ:* Brooklyn Col, BA, 66; Princeton Univ, PhD(psychol), 70. *Prof Exp:* Asst prof psychol, Rutgers Univ, 69-72; res assoc, Mass Inst Technol, 73-74, Med Found fel neuropharmacol, 74-75; assoc researcher psychobiol & neuropharmacol, Univ Calif, Irvine, 76-81; RES ASSOC, DEPT PHARMACOL, UNIV MINN, 81- *Concurrent Pos:* Co-prin investr, USPHS grants, Univ Calif, Irvine, 76-81. *Mem:* Am Soc Pharmacol & Exp Therapeut; Soc Neurosci; Am Psychol Asn; AAAS. *Res:* Neurochemical mechanisms of learning and memory and opiate analgesia and addiction; functions of endogenous opioid systems; effects of malnutrition on neurochemical and behavioral development. *Mailing Add:* Dept Pharmacol Univ Minn Minneapolis MN 55455

MESSING, SHELDON HAROLD, b Apr 6, 47; US citizen; m 67; c 2. ORGANIC CHEMISTRY, POLYMER CHEMISTRY. *Educ:* Brooklyn Col, BS, 67; Polytech Inst Brooklyn, PhD(org chem), 72. *Prof Exp:* SR RES CHEMIST, DOW CHEM CO, 72-, RES LEADER, 81- *Mem:* Am Chem Soc; Sigma Xi. *Res:* Physical organic chemistry applied to the synthesis and development of processes for compounds applicable in the agricultural field; pharmaceutical compounds and ion-exchange resins. *Mailing Add:* 2801 Whitewood Dr Midland MI 48640

MESSING, SIMON D, b Frankfurt-am-Main, Ger, July 13, 22; US citizen; m 67; c 1. CULTURAL ANTHROPOLOGY, MEDICAL ANTHROPOLOGY. *Educ:* City Col New York, BSS, 49; Univ Pa, PhD(anthrop), 57. *Prof Exp:* Interdisciplinary res, Behav Inst, Univ Pa, 52-53; asst prof soc sci, Paine Col, 56-58; assoc prof anthrop, Hiram Col, 58-60; assoc prof, Univ SFla, 60-64; researcher & field consult, US AID-Ethiopia, 61-67; PROF ANTHROP, SOUTHERN CONN STATE COL, 68- *Mem:* Fel AAAS; Am Anthrop Asn; fel Soc Appl Anthrop; fel Am Pub Health Asn; fel Am Sociol Asn. *Res:* Applied anthropology of Africa, especially in public health attitudes and practices. *Mailing Add:* Dept of Anthrop Southern Conn State Col New Haven CT 06515

MESSINGER, HENRY PETER, b Vienna, Austria, July 1, 21; US citizen; m 56; c 2. ELECTRICAL ENGINEERING. *Educ:* Okla State Univ, BS, 43; Ill Inst Technol, MS, 46; Univ Ill, PhD(elec eng), 51. *Prof Exp:* Eng physicist, Capehart Farnsworth Corp, Int Tel & Tel Corp, 50-52; elec engr, Inst Air Weapons Res, Univ Chicago, 52-56; asst prof elec eng, 56-63, ASSOC PROF ELEC ENG, ILL INST TECHNOL, 63- *Concurrent Pos:* Consult, ITT Kellogg, 58-63, Argonne Nat Lab, 63-64, Amphenol Corp, 66-67, Amtron Inc, 68-70 & Teletype Co, 70-71. *Mem:* Inst Elec & Electronics Engrs. *Res:* Computer logic and fault diagnostics; operations research in connection with evaluations of air weapons effectiveness. *Mailing Add:* Dept Elec Eng 3301 S Dearborn St Chicago IL 60616

MESSMER, DENNIS A, b Wessington Springs, SDak, Dec 22, 37; m 65; c 1. MICROBIOLOGY, BIOCHEMISTRY. *Educ:* SDak State Univ, BS, 63, MS, 64; Kans State Univ, PhD(bact), 68. *Prof Exp:* Asst prof, 68-72, ASSOC PROF MICROBIOL, SOUTHWESTERN STATE UNIV OKLA, 72- *Concurrent Pos:* Danforth fel, 71. *Mem:* AAAS; Am Soc Microbiol. *Res:* Metabolic interrelationships among bacteria in regard to substrate utilization. *Mailing Add:* Div Allied Health Southwestern State Univ Weatherford OK 73096

MESSMER, RICHARD PAUL, b Pittsburgh, Pa, Nov 24, 41; m 67. CHEMICAL PHYSICS. *Educ:* Carnegie Inst Technol, BS, 63; Univ Alta, PhD(theoret chem), 67. *Prof Exp:* Res assoc theoret chem, Mass Inst Technol, 67-68; lectr chem, Univ Alta, 68-69; STAFF MEM, RES & DEVELOP CTR, GEN ELEC CO, 69- *Concurrent Pos:* Vis scientist, Dept of Mat Sci & Eng, Mass Inst Technol, 73-; adj prof, Dept Physics, Univ Pa, 80- *Mem:* AAAS; Am Chem Soc; Am Phys Soc. *Res:* Quantum theory of solid state, especially chemically related problems; theoretical studies of chemisorption, surfaces, deep defect levels in semiconductors, transition metal complexes and anisotropic molecular crystals. *Mailing Add:* Res & Develop Ctr Gen Elec Co PO Box 8 Schenectady NY 12301

MESSMER, TRUDY OTTILIA, b Long Beach, Calif, Apr 1, 47. CELL PHYSIOLOGY, ANIMAL PHYSIOLOGY. *Educ:* Univ Calif, Irvine, BS, 69; Univ Calif, San Diego, PhD(biol), 73. *Prof Exp:* Damon Runyon fel cell biol, 73-75, res assoc cell biol, 75-77, SR RES ASSOC MOLECULAR BIOL, SALK INST BIOL STUDIES, 77- *Res:* The control of cell proliferation especially with respect to the cancerous state versus the noncancerous state, and factors controlling the commitment to and initiation of DNA synthesis and mitosis. *Mailing Add:* Salk Inst PO Box 85800 San Diego CA 92138

MESSNER, ROBERT LEE, experimental high energy physics, elementary particle physics, see previous edition

MESTECKY, JIRI, b Prague, Czech, June 3, 41; m; c 2. IMMUNOLOGY, IMMUNOCHEMISTRY. *Educ:* Charles Univ, Prague, MD, 64. *Prof Exp:* Asst, Inst Microbiol & Immunol, Fac Med, Charles Univ, Prague, 61-63; sr res asst immunol, Inst Microbiol, Czech Acad Sci, 63-65; instr, Inst Microbiol, Fac Med, Charles Univ, Prague, 65-66; vis res assoc, 67-68, from instr to asst prof, 68-72, assoc prof, 72-76, PROF MICROBIOL, UNIV ALA, BIRMINGHAM, 76-, SCIENTIST, INST DENT RES, 72-, CANCER RES INST, 73-, ARTHRITIS RES CTR, 79- & CYSTIC FIBROSIS RES CTR, 81- *Concurrent Pos:* Vis fel microbiol, Univ Ala, Birmingham, 67; WHO travel stipend. *Mem:* Am Asn Immunol; Soc Exp Biol & Med; Am Asn Pathologists; Am Soc Microbiol; NY Acad Sci. *Res:* Protein chemistry; secretory antibodies; innate immune factors. *Mailing Add:* 2244 Garland Dr Birmingham AL 35216

MESZLER, RICHARD M, b Peekskill, NY, Aug 30, 42; m 65; c 2. NEUROSCIENCE, ELECTRON MICROSCOPY. *Educ:* NY Univ, BA, 64; Univ Louisville, PhD(anat), 69. *Prof Exp:* NIH res fel anat, Albert Einstein Col Med, 69-71; instr, 71-72, asst prof, 72-76, ASSOC PROF ANAT, SCH DENT, UNIV MD, 76- *Mem:* Am Soc Cell Biol; Am Asn Anatomists; Soc Neurosci. *Res:* Structure-function relationships in nervous system; synaptology of trigeminal system; thermoreception; reptilian CNS; cell biology. *Mailing Add:* Dept of Anat Univ of Md Dent Sch Baltimore MD 21201

MESZOELY, CHARLES ALADAR MARIA, b Szekesfehervar, Hungary, Apr 24, 33; US citizen; m 61; c 2. PALEONTOLOGY, PARASITOLOGY. *Educ:* Northeastern Univ, BS, 61; Boston Univ, MA, 63, PhD(biol), 67. *Prof Exp:* Instr biol, Northeastern Univ, 66-68; res assoc biophys, Armed Forces Inst Path, 68-70; ASSOC PROF BIOL, NORTHEASTERN UNIV, 70- *Concurrent Pos:* Vis lectr dept life sci, Trent Polytech, Nottingham, Eng, 77. *Mem:* Soc Vert Paleont. *Res:* Paleontology, especially evolution and systematics of fossil and recent anguid lizards, and other Cenozoic lower vertebrates; parasitology, especially ultrastructure and ultrastructural changes in the malarial parasite. *Mailing Add:* Dept of Biol Northeastern Univ Boston MA 02115

METANOMSKI, WLADYSLAW VAL, b Vienna, Austria, Oct 3, 23; US citizen; m 66; c 1. POLYMER CHEMISTRY, INFORMATION SCIENCE. *Educ:* Univ London, BSc, 52; Univ Toronto, MASc, 60, PhD(chem eng), 64. *Prof Exp:* Chemist, Anal & Res Lab, Dearborn Chem Co Ltd, Ont, 52-56, chem engr, Tech Field Serv, 56-58; demonstr chem eng, Univ Toronto, 58-64; asst ed, 64-66, group leader, 66-71, asst to ed, 71-72, MGR DEVELOP, CHEM ABSTR SERV, AM CHEM SOC, 72- *Mem:* Am Chem Soc. *Res:* High polymers; electron exchangers; chemical information science; indexing chemical literature; chemical compound nomenclature; vocabulary control; development of computer-based information processing system. *Mailing Add:* Chem Abstr Serv PO Box 3012 Columbus OH 43210

METCALF, ARTIE LOU, b Dexter, Kans, July 5, 29. ZOOLOGY. *Educ:* Kans State Col, BS, 56; Univ Kans, MA, 57, PhD(zool), 64. *Prof Exp:* From instr to assoc prof, 62-68, PROF ZOOL, UNIV TEX, EL PASO, 69- *Mem:* AAAS; Am Malacol Union; Am Quaternary Asn; Conchol Soc Gt Brit & Ireland; Ger Malacozool Soc. *Res:* Systematics and paleoecology of terrestrial mollusks. *Mailing Add:* Dept of Biol Sci Univ of Tex El Paso TX 79968

METCALF, BRIAN WALTER, b Perth, Western Australia, July 13, 45; m 70. BIO-ORGANIC CHEMISTRY. *Educ:* Univ Western Australia, BSc Hons, 66, PhD(org chem), 70. *Prof Exp:* Fel org chem, Univ Col, Univ London, 70-71, Stanford Univ, 71-73; res scientist, Res Ctr, Merrell Int, 73-78; res scientist org chem, Merrell Res Ctr, 78-79, HEAD, ORGAN CHEM, MERRELL DOW PHARMACEUT, DOW CHEM CO, 79- *Mem:* Am Chem Soc. *Res:* Design synthesis and biochemistry of irreversible enzyme inhibitors. *Mailing Add:* Merrell Res Ctr 2100 E Galbraith Rd Cincinnati OH 65215

METCALF, FREDERIC THOMAS, b Oak Park, Ill, Dec 28, 35; m 57; c 2. APPLIED MATHEMATICS. *Educ:* Lake Forest Col, BA, 57; Univ Md, MA, 59, PhD(appl math), 61. *Prof Exp:* Asst engr, Electronics Div, Westinghouse Elec Co, 57-58; mathematician, Phys Chem Div, US Naval

Ord Lab, 60-62, res mathematician, Math Dept, 62-63; asst res prof appl math, Inst Fluid Dynamics & Appl Math, Univ Md, 63-66; assoc prof, 66-69, chmn dept, 68-70, PROF MATH, UNIV CALIF, RIVERSIDE, 69- *Concurrent Pos:* Consult, US Naval Ord Lab, 64-66. *Mem:* AAAS; Am Math Soc; Math Asn Am. *Res:* Dynamical systems with two degrees of freedom; finite difference schemes for partial differential equations; inequalities; second order ordinary differential equations; fluid flow about bodies of revolution. *Mailing Add:* Dept of Math Univ of Calif Riverside CA 92502

METCALF, HAROLD, b Boston, Mass, June 11, 40; m 63; c 3. PHYSICS, LASER SPECTROSCOPY. *Educ:* Mass Inst Technol, ScB, 62; Brown Univ, PhD(physics), 68. *Prof Exp:* Res assoc physics, Brown Univ, 67-68; res assoc, 68-70, asst prof, 70-74, ASSOC PROF PHYSICS, STATE UNIV NY STONY BROOK, 74- *Concurrent Pos:* Vis assoc prof, Mass Inst Technol, 77-78; consult, Nat Bureau Standards, 81. *Mem:* Am Phys Soc; Optical Soc Am. *Res:* Experimental atomic physics; precision measurements; experimental quantum electrodynamics; level crossing spectroscopy; laser spectroscopy; astrophysics; problems of human visual perception; simple atoms and molecules; quantum beat spectroscopy; Stark and Zeeman spectroscopy. *Mailing Add:* Dept of Physics State Univ of NY Stony Brook NY 11790

METCALF, HOMER NOBLE, b Ellington, Conn, Mar 9, 17. HORTICULTURE. *Educ:* Univ Conn, BS, 39; Cornell Univ, MS, 43. *Prof Exp:* Asst, Tree Fruit Br Exp Sta, Wenatchee, Wash, 44-45 & Agr Res Div, Gen Lab, Libby, McNeill & Libby, 45-47; from asst prof to assoc prof, 47-62, prof 62-79, EMER PROF HORT, MONT STATE UNIV, 79- *Mem:* Fel AAAS; Bot Soc Am; Torrey Bot Club; Int Asn Plant Taxon; Int Soc Hort Sci. *Res:* Pomology; ornamental horticulture; horticultural biosystematics. *Mailing Add:* Dept Plant & Soil Sci Mont State Univ Bozeman MT 59717

METCALF, ISAAC STEVENS HALSTEAD, b Cleveland, Ohio, Aug 17, 12; m 41; c 3. GROSS ANATOMY, COMPARATIVE ANATOMY. *Educ:* Oberlin Col, BA, 34; Columbia Univ, MA, 36; Case Western Reserve Univ, PhD(biol), 40. *Prof Exp:* From asst prof to assoc prof biol & chem, The Citadel, 37-57, prof biol, 57-66; prof anat, 66-80, EMER PROF ANAT, MED UNIV SC, 80- *Mem:* Nat Audubon Soc. *Res:* Neuroanatomy; sense organs of Elasmobranchs. *Mailing Add:* Dept of Anat Med Univ SC 171 Ashley Ave Charleston SC 29425

METCALF, ROBERT ALAN, population biology, see previous edition

METCALF, ROBERT HARKER, b Chicago, Ill, Aug 29, 43; m 68. MICROBIOLOGY. *Educ:* Earlham Col, AB, 65; Univ Wis-Madison, MS, 68, PhD(bact), 70. *Prof Exp:* Asst prof, 70-75, assoc prof, 75-81, PROF BIOL SCI, CALIF STATE UNIV, SACRAMENTO, 81- *Mem:* Am Soc Microbiol; AAAS; Soc Appl Bacteriology. *Res:* Food and water microbiology; solar energy applications for serious cooking and water disinfection. *Mailing Add:* Dept Biol Sci Calif State Univ Sacramento CA 95819

METCALF, ROBERT LEE, b Columbus, Ohio, Nov 13, 16; m 40; c 3. ENTOMOLOGY. *Educ:* Univ Ill, BA, 39, MA, 40; Cornell Univ, PhD(entom), 43. *Prof Exp:* From asst entomologist to assoc entomologist, Tenn Valley Authority, Ala, 43-46; from asst entomologist to assoc entomologist, Citrus Exp Sta, Univ Calif, Riverside, 46-53, prof entom & entomologist, 53-68; head dept zool, 69-73, PROF ENTOM, UNIV ILL, URBANA-CHAMPAIGN, 68- *Concurrent Pos:* Vchancellor, Univ Calif, Riverside, 62-67; consult, WHO; President's Sci Adv Comt. *Mem:* Nat Acad Sci; fel Am Acad Arts & Sci; Am Chem Soc; Entom Soc Am (pres, 58). *Res:* Insect physiology and toxicology; mosquito control. *Mailing Add:* Dept of Entomol 320 Morrill Hall Univ of Ill Urbana IL 61801

METCALF, THEODORE GORDON, b Rockville, Conn, Oct 9, 18; m 42; c 4. MICROBIOLOGY. *Educ:* Mass Col Pharm, BS, 40; Univ Kans, PhD(bact), 50. *Prof Exp:* Asst virus res, Parke, Davis & Co, 42-44; from instr to assoc prof bact, Univ Kans, 46-56; assoc prof, 59-61, PROF BACT, UNIV NH, 61-, PROF MICROBIOL, 81- *Concurrent Pos:* NSF fel, 59. *Mem:* Am Soc Microbiol; Am Acad Microbiol. *Res:* Respiratory and enteric viruses; rickettsiae; pathogenic bacteriology; immunology; environmental virology-viruses of vertebrates occurring in polluted surface waters, shellfish and estuarine waters. *Mailing Add:* Dept of Microbiol Spaulding Life Sci Bldg Univ NH Durham NH 03824

METCALF, WILLIAM, b Norwood, Mass, Dec 31, 07; m 50. SURGERY. *Educ:* Mass Inst Technol, BSc & MSc, 31; Johns Hopkins Univ, MD, 37. *Prof Exp:* Res fel surg, Johns Hopkins Univ, 38-39; Cushing fel, Sch Med, Yale Univ, 39-40, asst surg, 41-43; asst chief, Vet Admin Hosp, Hines, NY, 47-48; teaching fel, St Vincents Hosp, New York, 50-52; instr, Sch Med, NY Univ, 52-55; from asst prof to assoc prof, 54-62, prof, 62-76, EMER PROF SURG, ALBERT EINSTEIN COL MED, YESHIVA UNIV, 76- *Mem:* AAAS; Am Soc Surg of Hand; AMA; Am Col Surg. *Res:* General and hand surgery; surgical metabolism and shock; plasma and plasma expanders; nitrogen metabolism; anabolic steroids; mathematical (expoential) models for cancer survival. *Mailing Add:* Albert Einstein Col Med Yeshiva Univ New York NY 10461

METCALF, WILLIAM KENNETH, b Whitley Bay, Eng, Apr 30, 21; m 44; c 7. HUMAN ANATOMY. *Educ:* Univ Durham, MB & BS, 43; Bristol Univ, MD, 60. *Prof Exp:* From lectr to sr lectr anat, Bristol Univ, 48-64, reader, 64-68; prof, Univ Iowa, 68-73; PROF ANAT & CHMN DEPT, UNIV NEBR MED CTR, 73- *Concurrent Pos:* USPHS fel, 69-73. *Honors & Awards:* Media Fair 1st Prize, Health Educ Media Asn-Health Sci Communications Asn, 75. *Mem:* Am Asn Anat; Anat Soc Gt Brit & Ireland; Brit Soc Hemat; Brit Physiol Soc. *Res:* Hematology; cell kinetics; physical properties of cells; cellular immunology; education, especially effect of objectives and efficiency of programmed instruction. *Mailing Add:* Dept of Anat Univ Nebr Med Ctr Omaha NE 68105

METCALFE, DARREL SEYMOUR, b Arkansaw, Wis, Aug 28, 13; m 42; c 2. AGRONOMY. *Educ:* Univ Wis, BS, 41; Kans State Univ, MS, 42; Iowa State Univ, PhD(plant physiol, crop breeding), 50. *Prof Exp:* Asst, Kans State Univ, 40-42; prof agron, Iowa State Univ, 46-56, asst dir student affairs, 56-58; ASST DIR, AGR EXP STA, UNIV ARIZ, 58-, DIR, RESIDENT INSTR & ASSOC DEAN, COL AGR, 80- *Concurrent Pos:* Consult, AID, Brazil, 62-73 & Orgn Econ Coop & Develop, Europe, 63-65; mem comt agr educ & nat res, Nat Acad Sci-Nat Res Coun, 66-70; consult, Nat Acad Sci, Egypt, 80, Consortium Int Develop, NYemen & Inst Int Educ, Somalia & Kenya, 81. *Mem:* Fel Am Soc Agron. *Res:* Seed production of forage grasses and legumes. *Mailing Add:* Col Agr Univ Ariz Tucson AZ 85721

METCALFE, DAVID RICHARD, b Carroll, Man, Oct 14, 23; m 49; c 2. PLANT BREEDING, GENETICS. *Educ:* Univ Man, BSA, 50, PhD(genetics, plant breeding), 60; Univ Wis, MS, 53. *Prof Exp:* RES SCIENTIST GENETICS & PLANT BREEDING, RES BR, AGR CAN, 50- *Mem:* Agr Inst Can; Genetic Soc Can. *Res:* Breeding two-rowed barley varieites for the eastern prairie region of Canada. *Mailing Add:* Agr Can Res Sta Univ Man Campus 25 Dafoe Rd Winnipeg MB R3T 2M6 Can

METCALFE, JAMES, b New Bedford, Mass, Aug 16, 22; m 44; c 4. MEDICINE. *Educ:* Brown Univ, AB, 44; Harvard Univ, MD, 46; Am Bd Internal Med, dipl, 53. *Prof Exp:* Med house officer, Peter Bent Brigham Hosp, Boston, 46-47, asst, 50-51, sr asst, 51-52; ward med officer, US Naval Hosp, Newport, RI, 47-49; instr, Harvard Med Sch, 53-55, assoc med, 55-59, tutor, 57-58, asst prof, 59-61; assoc prof, 61-64, PROF MED, MED SCH, UNIV ORE, 64- *Concurrent Pos:* Res fel, Peter Bent Brigham Hosp, 50-51; res fel physiol, Harvard Med Sch, 49-50, 52-53; fel, Boston Lying-in Hosp, 52-53; assoc physician, Bosotn Lying-in Hosp, 52-59, vis physician, 59-61; Am Heart Asn estab investr, 53-59; jr assoc, Peter Bent Brigham Hos;, 53-56, assoc, 56-58, sr assoc, 58-61; chmn cardiovasc res, Ore Heart Asn, 61- *Mem:* Am Physiol Soc; Am Fedn Clin Res; Am Clin & Climat Asn; Am Soc Clin Invest. *Res:* Modifications of maternal physiology during pregnancy and their effects on the course of disease. *Mailing Add:* Heart Res Lab Univ of Ore Sch of Med Portland OR 97201

METCALFE, JOSEPH EDWARD, III, b Fallowfield Twp, Pa, May 27, 38; m 59; c 3. PHYSICAL CHEMISTRY, FUEL TECHNOLOGY. *Educ:* Pa State Univ, BS, 60, MS, 62, PhD(fuel technol), 65. *Prof Exp:* Res asst fuel technol, Pa State Univ, 60-62 & 63-65; sr res chemist, 65-74, res supvr electrokinetics, 68-71 & gasoline phys res, 71-74, supvr technol assessment, 74-76, SUPVR ALT ENERGY SOURCES, STAND OIL CO OHIO, 76- *Mem:* Am Chem Soc. *Res:* Fused salt batteries; carbon technology; molecular sieves; adsorption; physical properties of gasoline; coal technology; catalysts; coal technology energy research. *Mailing Add:* Res Dept Broadway Lab Stand Oil Co Ohio 3092 Broadway Cleveland OH 44115

METCALFE, LINCOLN DOUGLAS, b Melstone, Mont, Feb 11, 21; m 48; c 1. ANALYTICAL CHEMISTRY. *Educ:* Univ Chicago, BS, 47. *Prof Exp:* Head anal sect, Res Div, Armour & Co, 47-60, head anal res sect, Res Labs, Armour Indust Chem Co, 60-66, ASST RES DIR ANAL & PHYS CHEM & INSTRUMENTAL RES, RES LABS, ARMAK CO, 66- *Concurrent Pos:* Mem lipid anal comt, Nat Heart Inst, 58-59; mem adv bd, J Chromatographic Sci & Handbook Chromatography; mem bd dirs, Sugar Processing Res, Inc. *Honors & Awards:* Bond Award, Am Oil Chem Soc, 64; Nat Merit Award, Am Soc Testing & Mat, 66. *Mem:* Am Chem Soc; Am Soc Testing & Mat; Am Oil Chem Soc; Sugar Indust Technologists. *Res:* Nonaqueous titrations; gas and high pressure liquid chromatography; infrared and ultraviolet spectrophotometry as applied to lipid and protein chemistry, especially fatty acid derivatives. *Mailing Add:* Res Labs Armak Co 8401 W 47th St McCook IL 60525

METCALFE, TOM BROOKS, b Smithville, Tex, Feb 26, 20; m 44; c 4. CHEMICAL ENGINEERING, ENGINEERING EDUCATION. *Educ:* Univ Tex, BS, 41, MS, 47; Ga Inst Technol, PhD(chem eng), 53. *Prof Exp:* Chemist, Dow Chem Co, 41-44; res engr, Shell Oil Co, 52-62; head dept chem eng, WVa Inst Technol, 62-63; PROF CHEM ENG & HEAD DEPT, UNIV SOUTHWESTERN LA, 63- *Concurrent Pos:* Asst prof, Univ Houston, 53-57; consult, Off Saline Water, US Dept Interior, 65-69 & US Bur Pub Roads, 66-73; educ consult, NSF, 73-76 & Ciba-Geigy Corp, 75-78. *Mem:* Fel Am Inst Chem Engrs; Am Soc Eng Educ. *Res:* Corrosion; materials science; kinetics; petroleum refining; fluid dynamics. *Mailing Add:* 109 Juanita Dr Lafayette LA 70506

METCOFF, JACK, b Chicago, Ill, Feb 2, 17; m 43; c 2. PHYSIOLOGY, NUTRITION. *Educ:* Northwestern Univ, BS, 38, BM, 42, MD, 43, MS, 44; Harvard Univ, MPH, 44. *Prof Exp:* From asst to assoc pediat, Harvard Med Sch, 48-53, asst prof, 53-56; chmn dept, Michael Reese Hosp, 56-70; PROF PEDIAT BIOCHEM & MOLECULAR BIOL, UNIV OKLA HEALTH SCI CTR, 70-, GEORGE LYNN CROSS RES PROF PEDIAT BIOCHEM & MOLECULAR BIOL, 78- *Concurrent Pos:* Prof, Med Sch, Northwestern Univ, 56-63; prof & chmn dept, Chicago Med Sch, 63-68. *Mem:* Fel Am Acad Pediat; Am Physiol Soc; Am Soc Nephrology; Am Soc Clin Nutrit; Am Inst Nutrit. *Res:* Cell metabolism; electrolyte and renal physiology; relations between intracellular ions and intercellular metabolites during prematurity; normal growth and development of the human infant; severe chronic infantile malnutrition; Kwashiorkor; fetal malnutrition; metabolism of isolated kidneys; leukocyte metabolism; nutrition in pregnancy; renal disease in children; metabolism in uremia. *Mailing Add:* Dept Pediat Health Sci Ctr Univ Okla PO Box 26901 Oklahoma City OK 73190

METEER, JAMES WILLIAM, b Columbus, Ohio, Apr 7, 21; m 44; c 4. FORESTRY, COMPUTER SCIENCE. *Educ:* Univ Mich, BSF, 44, MF, 47. *Prof Exp:* Asst prof forestry, Agr Exp Sta, Ohio State Univ, 47-54, consult forester, 54-65; from asst prof to assoc prof, 64-73, PROF FORESTRY, SCH FORESTRY, MICH TECHNOL UNIV, 73- *Mem:* Soc Am Foresters; Forest Prod Res Soc. *Res:* Forest management and growth investigations; continuous forest inventory control with computer processing of data; computer applications development; forest economic analysis. *Mailing Add:* Sch Forestry Mich Technol Univ Houghton MI 49931

METER, DONALD M(ERVYN), b Omaha, Nebr, Aug 10, 31; m 61; c 2. CHEMICAL ENGINEERING. *Educ:* Univ Minn, BS, 53; Princeton Univ, MSE, 55; Univ Wis, PhD(chem eng), 64. *Prof Exp:* Res engr, Edison Labs, Thomas A Edison, Inc, 54-56; instr chem eng, Univ Wis, 57-58; sr res scientist, Squibb Inst Med Res, Olin Mathieson Chem Corp, 62-68, res fel, E R Squibb & Sons, 69-73; res engr, Armour Pharm Co, 73-77; MGR CHEM PROCESS DEVELOP, G D SEARLE & CO, 78- *Mem:* Am Inst Chem Engrs; Am Chem Soc. *Res:* Turbulent flow and viscoelastic properties of dilute non-Newtonian polymer solutions. *Mailing Add:* Searle Res & Develop PO Box 5110 Chicago IL 60680

METEYER, THOMAS EDWARD, synthetic organic chemistry, see previous edition

METH, IRVING MARVIN, b Brooklyn, NY, July 27, 29; m 55; c 4. ELECTRONICS, INSTRUMENTATION. *Educ:* City Col New York, BEE, 51; Polytech Inst Brooklyn, MEE, 56. *Prof Exp:* Engr, RCA Labs, 51-57; PROF ELEC ENG, CITY COL NEW YORK, 58- *Concurrent Pos:* Vis engr, Brookhaven Nat Lab, 58-; consult, USAEC, 60-65 & Port of NY Authority, 70-75; vis prof, Polytech Inst Brooklyn, 65-66; vis lectr, Bell Tel Labs, 69-70. *Mem:* Sr mem Inst Elec & Electronics Engrs. *Res:* Digital communications, control systems, electronics and electronic systems; bioengineering instrumentation and telemetering of information; electrical safety; applied cryogenics; super conducting power cables; microelectronics. *Mailing Add:* Dept of Elec Eng City Col of NY Convent Ave & 138th St New York NY 10031

METHERELL, ALEXANDER FRANZ, b Canton, China, Aug 21, 39; US citizen; m 64; c 3. RADIOLOGY, ULTRASONIC ENGINEERING. *Educ:* Kingston Polytech Inst, Dip Tech, 61; Bristol Univ, PhD(eng), 64; Univ Miami, MD, 76; Am Bd Radiol, dipl, 81. *Prof Exp:* Res assoc aeronaut, Univ Minn, 64-65; sr engr scientist, Douglas Aircraft Co, 65-66; res scientist acoust holography, Douglas Advan Res Labs, McDonnell Douglas Corp, 66-70, dir med imaging, 70-74; assoc prof radiol, Univ Calif, Irvine, 76-79; RADIOLOGIST, SOUTH BAY HOSP, REDONDO BEACH, CALIF, 79- *Concurrent Pos:* Assoc prof eng, Univ Calif, Los Angeles, 69-70; clin assoc prof radiol, Univ Calif, Irvine, 71-76, adj assoc prof eng, 73-76; assoc ed, Trans Sonics & Ultrasonics, 71-; mem cardiol adv comt, Nat Heart, Lung & Blood Inst, 78-81. *Mem:* Am Inst Ultrasound Med; Alliance Eng Med & Biol; Inst Elec & Electronics Engrs; Am Col Med Imaging. *Res:* Ultrasound imaging; medical imaging. *Mailing Add:* Radiol Dept South Bay Hosp 574 N Prospect Ave Redondo Beach CA 90277

METHOD, PETER FRANCIS, physical chemistry, see previous edition

METRIONE, ROBERT M, b Teaneck, NJ, Aug 22, 33; m 57; c 3. BIOCHEMISTRY. *Educ:* Bowling Green State Univ, BS, 55; Univ Nebr, MS, 60, PhD(biochem), 63. *Prof Exp:* Res assoc biochem, Yale Univ, 63-65, asst prof, 65-67; asst prof, 67-72, ASSOC PROF BIOCHEM, THOMAS JEFFERSON UNIV, 72- *Mem:* AAAS; Am Chem Soc; Am Soc Biol Chem. *Res:* Structure-function relationships of proteolytic enzymes; cathepsins; role DNA polymerases in polyploidy in the trophoblast. *Mailing Add:* Dept Biochem Thomas Jefferson Univ Philadelphia PA 19107

METROPOLIS, NICHOLAS CONSTANTINE, b Chicago, Ill, June 11, 15; m 55; c 3. APPLIED MATHEMATICS, THEORETICAL PHYSICS. *Educ:* Univ Chicago, BS, 36, PhD(physics), 41. *Prof Exp:* Res assoc, Univ Chicago, 41, res assoc, Metall Lab & instr physics, 42; res assoc, Columbia Univ, 42; res assoc & group leader, Los Alamos Sci Lab, 43-46, consult, 46-48, mem staff & group leader 48-57; prof physics, Univ Chicago & Enrico Fermi Inst Nuclear Studies, 57-65, dir inst comput res, 58-65; mem staff, 65-80, SR FEL, LOS ALAMOS NAT LAB, 81- *Concurrent Pos:* Asst prof, Univ Chicago & Inst Nuclear Studies, 46-48; consult, Argonne Nat Lab, Brookhaven Nat Lab & Lawrence Radiation Lab, Univ Calif; mem adv panel univ comput facilities, NSF, 59- & adv comt comput activities; chmn comput adv group, AEC, 59-62; mem, UN Tech Mission to India, 61; vis prof, Univ Colo, 64; mem adv comt res, NSF, 73-75; deleg, US-USSR Sci & Technol Exchange, Moscow, 76. *Mem:* Fel Am Phys Soc; Am Math Soc; Soc Indust & Appl Math. *Res:* Theoretical nuclear physics; electronic computing; logical design of general purpose computers; pure and applied mathematical analysis of inherent error propagation; studies of non-linear differential equations; theoretical investigations of nuclear cascades. *Mailing Add:* Los Alamos Nat Lab MS 210 Los Alamos NM 87544

METRY, AMIR ALFI, b Minia, Egypt, May 4, 42; US citizen; m 66; c 2. ENVIRONMENTAL ENGINEERING. *Educ:* Cairo Univ, BS, 63, MS, 67; Drexel Univ, MS, 69, PhD(environ eng), 73; Am Acad Environ Engrs, dipl, 73. *Prof Exp:* Proj mgr sanit eng, Naim Mahfouz Eng, Cairo, Egypt, 63-68; res assoc environ eng, Drexel Univ, 68-73; dir, MTL Industs, Md, 72-73; vpres waste mgt, Foy F Weston Inc, Pa, 73-78; vpres res & tech serv, IU Conversion Systs Inc, 78-81; VPRES RESIDUALS MGT, ROY F WESTON, INC, 81- *Concurrent Pos:* Adj instr, Cairo Univ, 64-67; adj prof, Drexel Univ, 74-77; adj assoc prof, Temple Univ, 76- *Mem:* Water Pollution Control Fedn; Am Soc Civil Engrs; Inst Environ Sci; Nat Soc Prof Engrs. *Res:* Investigation of the fate of contaminants in the environment; simulation contaminant migration; evaluation of waste treatment technologies; design of pollution control systems; detoxification and management of hazardous wastes; management of radioactive waste. *Mailing Add:* Roy F Weston Inc West Chester PA 19380

METS, LAURENS JAN, b Santa Barbara, Calif, Sept 14, 46; m 71; c 1. MOLECULAR BIOLOGY, GENETICS. *Educ:* Pomona Col, BA, 68; Harvard Univ, MA, 70, PhD(biochem & molecular biol), 73. *Prof Exp:* Staff fel phys biol, NIH, 72-75; asst prof biol, Case Western Reserve Univ, 75-80; MEM FAC, CARNEGIE INST, BALTIMORE, 80- *Mem:* AAAS; Am Soc Cell Biol; Am Soc Plant Physiologists; Genetics Soc Am. *Res:* Genetics and biogenesis of chloroplast ribosomes; chloroplast genetics; rhythm biology. *Mailing Add:* Carnegie Inst 115 W University Pkwy Baltimore MD 21210

METTE, HERBERT L, b Kassel, Ger, Oct 26, 25; US citizen; m 58; c 1. SOLID STATE PHYSICS. *Educ:* Univ Gottingen, dipl physics, 52. *Prof Exp:* Res asst solid state physics, Univ Gottingen, 52-53; scientist, Ger Nat Bur Standards, 53-56; physicist, Res & Develop Lab, 56-58, leader device physics sect, Solid State Devices Div, 58-65, chief integrated devices tech br, Integrated Electronics Div, 65-73, LEADER ADVAN IC TECHNOL TEAM, MICROELECTRONICS DIV, US ARMY ELECTRONICS TECHNOL & DEVICES LAB, FT MONMOUTH, 73- *Concurrent Pos:* Dep Army mem, Adv Group Electron Devices, Dept of Defense, 76- *Mem:* Fel Am Phys Soc; sr mem Inst Elec & Electronics Engrs. *Res:* Organic semiconductors; photomagneto and magnetothermal effects in semiconductors; integrated electronics; materials, devices and processes research. *Mailing Add:* 650 Valley Rd Brielle NJ 08730

METTEE, HOWARD DAWSON, b Boston, Mass, Aug 6, 39; m 63; c 3. SPECTROCHEMISTRY. *Educ:* Middlebury Col, BA, 61; Univ Calgary, PhD(phys chem), 64. *Prof Exp:* Fel spectros & photochem, Nat Res Coun Can, 64-66 & Univ Tex, Austin, 66-68; asst prof, 68-74, ASSOC PROF CHEM, YOUNGSTOWN STATE UNIV, 74- *Mem:* Royal Soc Chem; Am Chem Soc; Sigma Xi. *Res:* Energy transfer and relaxation; primary photochemical events and gas phase kinetics; chemical applications of spectroscopy; thermodynamics of gas phase complexes; photoelectrochemistry of solar energy. *Mailing Add:* Dept Chem Youngstown State Univ Youngstown OH 44555

METTEE, MAURICE FERDINAND, b Mobile, Ala, Apr 28, 43; m 68; c 2. AQUATIC BIOLOGY. *Educ:* Spring Hill Col, BS, 65; Univ Ala, MA, 67, MS, 70, PhD(biol), 74. *Prof Exp:* Res asst biol, Univ Ala, 74-75; environ biologists, 75-77, CHIEF, ENVIRON DIV, GEOL SURV ALA, 77- *Concurrent Pos:* US Forest Serv grant ichthyol, Univ Ala, 74; aquatic biologist, US Air Force Acad, 74; res grant, US Fish & Wildlife Serv, 75-78, consult, Okaloosa Darter in Fla, 75-78. *Mem:* Am Ichthyol & Herpet; Am Fisheries Soc; Sigma Xi. *Res:* Studies on the systematics, ecology, reproductive behavior, embryology and development of freshwater and marine fishes; endangered and threatened vertebrate life in the southeastern United States. *Mailing Add:* Ala Geol Surv Environ Div PO Box O University AL 35486

METTER, DEAN EDWARD, b Champaign, Ill, Aug 1, 32; m 54; c 3. HERPETOLOGY. *Educ:* Eastern Ill Univ, BS, 57; Wash State Univ, MS, 60; Univ Idaho, PhD(zool), 63. *Prof Exp:* Instr zool, Univ Idaho, 63-64; asst prof, 64-69, ASSOC PROF ZOOL, UNIV MO-COLUMBIA, 69- *Mem:* Am Soc Ichthyologists & Herpetologists. *Res:* Distribution and differentiation of amphibian populations. *Mailing Add:* 204 Russell Blvd Columbia MO 65201

METTER, GERALD EDWARD, b Los Angeles, Calif, Oct 15, 44. BIOSTATISTICS, ONCOLOGY. *Educ:* Univ Calif, Berkeley, AB, 66, PhD(biostatist), 72. *Prof Exp:* Statistician, Ctr Dis Control, USPHS, 67-69; asst prof biostatist, Tulane Univ, 72-73; asst prof statist & human oncol, Univ Wis-Madison, 73-77; biostatistician, Div Cancer Control & Rehab, Nat Cancer Inst, 77-79; DIR, DEPT BIOSTATIST, CITY OF HOPE MED CTR, 79- *Concurrent Pos:* Lectr biomath, Univ Calif, Los Angeles, 79- *Mem:* Am Soc Prev Oncol; Am Statist Asn; Biomet Soc; AAAS; Am Soc Clin Oncol. *Res:* Clinical trials methodology: design, conduct, analysis; applied stochastic models; statistical methods in epidemiology. *Mailing Add:* City of Hope Med Ctr 1500 E Duarte Rd Duarte CA 91010

METTER, RAYMOND EARL, b Champaign, Ill, Aug 25, 25; m 48; c 2. GEOLOGY. *Educ:* Ohio State Univ, MS, 52, PhD(geol), 55. *Prof Exp:* Instr math, Ohio State Univ, 48-50, asst geol, 50-52, res assoc physics, Res Found, 53-54; res geologist, Res Lab, Carter Oil Co Div, Stand Oil Co (NJ), 55-58, res geologist & group head, Jersey Prod Res Co, 58-65; res geologist, 65-66, RES ASSOC, EXXON PROD RES CO, 66- *Mem:* Am Asn Petrol Geol; Geol Soc Am. *Res:* Petroleum geology; applied organic geochemistry; geology of subsurface fluids. *Mailing Add:* Exxon Prod Res Co Box 2189 Houston TX 77001

METTLER, FREDERICK ALBERT, b New York, NY, June 13, 07; wid; c 3. NEUROLOGY, ANATOMY. *Educ:* Clark Univ, AB, 29; Cornell Univ, MA, 31, PhD(anat), 33; Univ Ga, MD, 37. *Hon Degrees:* ScD, Clark Univ, 51. *Prof Exp:* Asst anat, Med Col, Cornell Univ, 30-31, instr, 31-33; instr physiol, Med Col, St Louis Univ, 33-34; from asst prof to prof anat, Sch Med, Univ Ga, 34-42; assoc prof, 41-51, prof, 51-75, EMER PROF ANAT, COL PHYSICIANS & SURGEONS, COLUMBIA UNIV, 75-; DISTINGUISHED PROF ANAT, HEALTH SCI MED SCH, UNIFORMED SERV UNIV, 78- *Concurrent Pos:* Guest investr, Univ Ill, 31-38, Harvard Univ, 35 & Univ Rochester, 38-40; Commonwealth Fund vis prof, Long Island Med Col, 43-44; lectr, Univ Edinburgh, 45, Rutgers Univ, 48 & Univ PR, 53; mem, Div Med Sci, Nat Res Coun, 47-50 & Intersoc Comt, NSF, 47-50; res consult, NJ State Hosp, Greystone Park, 47-71; coordr res, State Dept Ment Hyg, NY, 48-49, dir, 49-50; chmn comt psychosurg, Div Ment Hyg, Nat Adv Ment Health Coun, USPHS, 49-52; mem, US Nat Conf Deleg, UNESCO, 52-54; adv, Yerkes Primate Ctr, Atlanta, Ga, 73-76; res consult, Res Ctr, Rockland State Hosp, Orangeburg, NY, 74-76. *Mem:* Soc Exp Biol & Med; Am Asn Anat; Am Neurol Asn; fel NY Acad Med; assoc NY Acad Sci. *Res:* Gross anatomy; physiology and pathology of the nervous system. *Mailing Add:* Pippin Hill Exp Area Blairstown NJ 07825

METTLER, JOHN D(ANIEL), JR, b Snydertown, Pa, Feb 5, 15; m 37; c 2. ELECTROLYTIC CHEMISTRY, METALLURGY. *Educ:* Lehigh Univ, BS, 41. *Prof Exp:* Technician, Socony-Vacuum Oil Co, NY, 41-42; asst chem engr, Electro Metall Co Div, Union Carbide Corp, 42-50, sr chem engr, 50-60, from mgr econ appraisals to asst mgr cent planning, Metals Div, 60-63, mem planning staff, Chem Div, 63-70, staff metallurgist, Metals Div, 70-78; RETIRED. *Mem:* Am Chem Soc. *Res:* Crude petroleum cracking; wet and dry metallurgy of chromium, cobalt, silicon, uranium, tungsten, titanium; electrodeposition of metals. *Mailing Add:* RD 2 Box 450 Schuylkill Haven PA 17972

METTLER, LAWRENCE EUGENE, biology, see previous edition

METTLER, RUBEN FREDERICK, b Shafter, Calif, Feb 23, 24; m 55; c 2. ELECTRICAL ENGINEERING. *Educ:* Calif Inst Technol, BS, 44, MS, 47, PhD(elec & aeronaut eng), 49. *Prof Exp:* From engr to assoc dir radar div, Hughes Aircraft Co, 49-54; spec consult, US Dept Defense, 54-55; from dir guided missile res div, Systs Eng Staff to asst gen mgr, Space Tech Labs, Ramo-Wooldridge Corp, 55-58, from exec vpres to pres & mem bd dirs, Space Tech Labs, Inc, 58-63, pres, TRW Systs & exec vpres & mem bd dirs, TRW Inc, 63-68, exec vpres & asst pres, 68-69, PRES, TRW INC, 69- *Concurrent Pos:* Aide to Asst Secy Defense Res & Develop, 54-55; mem, Defense Indust Adv Coun, 62-, indust vchmn, 64-; chmn, President's Sci Policy Task Force, 69-70. *Mem:* Nat Acad Eng; fel Inst Elec & Electronics Engrs; fel Am Inst Aeronaut & Astronaut. *Res:* Systems engineering; systems integration and test. *Mailing Add:* TRW Inc 1 Space Park Redondo Beach CA 90278

METTRICK, DAVID FRANCIS, b London, Eng, 1932; Can citizen. PARASITOLOGY, PATHOLOGICAL PHYSIOLOGY. *Educ:* Univ Wales, BSc, 54; Univ London, PhD(parasitol), 57, DSc(parasitol), 73. *Prof Exp:* Lectr zool, Univ Rhodesia & Nyasaland, 58-61; sr lectr zool, Univ WI, 62-67; assoc prof, 67-71, assoc chmn dept, 73-75, PROF ZOOL, UNIV TORONTO, 71-, CHMN DEPT, 75- *Concurrent Pos:* Prof parasitol, Fac Med, Univ Toronto, 71-; pres, Biol Coun Can, 74-79; Can rep to coun, World Fedn Parasitologists, 74-78; chmn, Can Coun Animal Care, 75-77; chmn, Animal Biol Grants Comt, Nat Res Coun Can, 75-76; chmn, Fifth Int Cong Parasitol, 82. *Honors & Awards:* Queen Elizabeth II Silver Jubilee Medal, 77. *Mem:* Am Soc Parasitologists; Can Soc Zoologists; Brit Soc Parasitol; fel Royal Soc Can; Can Pub Health Asn. *Res:* Ecology and physiology of intestinal parasites; pathophysiology; membrane transport; metabolism of intestinal parasites; symbiology. *Mailing Add:* Dept of Zool Univ of Toronto Toronto ON M5S 1A1 Can

METZ, CHARLES BAKER, b New York, NY, Dec 27, 16; m 40; c 2. DEVELOPMENTAL BIOLOGY. *Educ:* Johns Hopkins Univ, AB, 39; Calif Inst Technol, PhD(embryol), 42. *Prof Exp:* Instr biol, Wesleyan Univ, 42-46; instr zool, Yale Univ, 46-47, asst prof, 47-52; asst prof, Univ Calif, 52; assoc prof, Univ NC, 52-53; from assoc prof to prof, Fla State Univ, 53-64, assoc dir oceanog inst, 58-62, prof, Inst Space Biosci, 61-64; prof biol, 64-70, PROF MOLECULAR EVOLUTION & ZOOL, INST MOLECULAR EVOLUTION, UNIV MIAMI, 70- *Concurrent Pos:* Nat Res Coun fel, Ind Univ, 45-46; Gosney fel, Calif Inst Technol, 50; Lillie fel, Marine Biol Lab, Woods Hole, 53, instr, 47-52, mem, Corp Trustees, 56-65; ed, Biol Bull, 80- *Mem:* AAAS; Am Soc Nat; Soc Exp Biol & Med; Am Soc Zool (secy, 61-63); Soc Gen Physiol. *Res:* Echinoderm development; physiology of reproduction in protozoa and marine invertebrates; mammalian immuno-reproduction; electron microscopy of protozoa and gametes. *Mailing Add:* Inst Molecular Evolution Univ Miami 521 Anastasia Ave Coral Gables FL 33124

METZ, CHARLES EDGAR, b Bayshore, NY, Sept 11, 42; m 67; c 2. MEDICAL PHYSICS, DIAGNOSTIC PERFORMANCE ANALYSIS. *Educ:* Bowdoin Col, BA, 64; Univ Pa, MS, 66, PhD(radiol physics), 69. *Prof Exp:* Instr, 69-71, asst prof, 71-75, assoc prof, 76-80, PROF RADIOL, UNIV CHICAGO, 80- *Concurrent Pos:* Mem, Diag Res Adv Group, Nat Cancer Inst, 80- *Mem:* Sigma Xi. *Res:* Evaluation of diagnostic performance in terms of signal detection theory and decision analysis; theoretical analysis of medical imaging systems; medical image enhancement by computer. *Mailing Add:* Dept Radiol Box 420 Univ Chicago Chicago IL 60637

METZ, CLYDE, b Gary, Ind, May 3, 40; m 61; c 2. PHYSICAL CHEMISTRY. *Educ:* Rose-Hulman Inst Technol, BS, 62; Ind Univ, PhD(phys chem), 66. *Prof Exp:* Asst, Ind Univ, 62-66; asst prof, 66-70, ASSOC PROF CHEM, IND UNIV-PURDUE UNIV, INDIANAPOLIS, 70- *Honors & Awards:* Leiber Teaching Assoc Award, Ind Univ, 66. *Mem:* Am Chem Soc; Electrochem Soc. *Res:* Fused salt electrochemistry, phase equilibria, thermodynamics and x-ray crystallography. *Mailing Add:* 4217 Melbourne Rd Indianapolis IN 46208

METZ, DAVID A, b Cleveland, Ohio, Sept 10, 33; m 60; c 3. AUDIOLOGY, SPEECH PATHOLOGY. *Educ:* Western Reserve Univ, BA, 60, MA, 65, PhD(aural harmonics), 67. *Prof Exp:* Res asst speech path, Western Reserve Univ, 64-67; asst prof, 67-71, ASSOC PROF AUDIOL, CLEVELAND STATE UNIV, 77- DIR SPEECH PATH & AUDIOL PROG, 67-, CHMN DEPT SPEECH & HEARING, 74- *Mem:* Am Speech & Hearing Asn; Acoust Soc Am. *Res:* Aural harmonics; temporary threshold shift; speech discrimination. *Mailing Add:* Speech & Hearing Clin Cleveland State Univ Cleveland OH 44115

METZ, DONALD C(HARLES), b Kidder, Mo, Dec 22, 08; m 35; c 3. ELECTRICAL ENGINEERING, INDUSTRIAL ENGINEERING. *Educ:* Purdue Univ, BSEE, 30, MSIE, 49. *Hon Degrees:* Dr Sci, Capital Inst Technol, 74. *Prof Exp:* Engr, Frigidaire Div, Gen Motors Corp, 30-32 & 33-36; statist ed, Bus News Pub Co, 32-33; sales engr, Hughes Heating & Air Conditioning Co, 36-40; supvr elec progs, Purdue Univ, 46-47, supvr instr, 47-50, actg head tech inst, 50-51; dir tech inst, Univ Dayton, 51-63; prin, Tech Col, Ibadan, Nigeria, 63-65; asst dean sch appl arts & sci, Western Mich Univ, 65-67; assoc dean, 67-73, EMER DEAN ENG TECHNOL, SOUTHWEST MINN STATE UNIV, 74- *Concurrent Pos:* Consult, US Air Force Purchasing Surv Comt, 51-52; in-chg Nat Surv Eng Technol Enrollments & Grad, 53-63; mem working group on supporting tech personnel, President's Comt Scientists & Engrs, 56-57; chmn region VII, Nat Surv Tech Inst Ed, 57; comnr eng manpower comn, Engrs Joint Coun, 60-69; tech cols rep, Nigerian Tech & Com Exam Comt, 64-65. *Honors & Awards:* James H McGraw Award for Eng Technol Educ, 77. *Mem:* Am Soc Eng Educ; Nat Soc Prof Engrs; Newcomen Soc NAm. *Res:* Technical manpower as relates to supply and utilization of engineering technicians. *Mailing Add:* 908 Longwood Loop Mesa AZ 85208

METZ, DONALD J, b Brooklyn, NY, May 18, 24; m 47. PHYSICAL CHEMISTRY. *Educ:* St Francis Col, NY, BS, 47; Polytech Inst Brooklyn, MS, 49, PhD(phys chem), 55. *Prof Exp:* From assoc chemist to sr chemist, 54-74, HEAD DIV CHEM SCI, BROOKHAVEN NAT LAB, 74- *Concurrent Pos:* Instr chem & physics, St Francis Col, NY, 47-54, from asst prof to assoc prof, 56-63, prof, 63-76. *Mem:* AAAS; fel Am Inst Chem; Am Chem Soc; Sigma Xi. *Res:* Radiation polymerization and radiation chemistry of organic compounds; mechanisms of vinyl polymerizations; biomaterials. *Mailing Add:* Brookhaven Nat Lab Upton NY 11973

METZ, EDWARD, b Crown Point, Ind, June 3, 21; m 43; c 3. ENGINEERING, MATERIALS SCIENCE. *Educ:* Purdue Univ, BEE, 43. *Prof Exp:* Asst lab supvr, Bryant Elec Co, Westinghouse Elec Corp, 45-52; lab supvr, 52-57, dir res, 57-74, DIR ENG SERV, LEVITON MFG CO, INC, 74- *Mem:* Am Soc Testing & Mat; assoc Inst Elec & Electronics Engrs; Am Soc Metals; Soc Motion Picture & Television Engrs; Am Soc Training & Develop. *Res:* Electrical wiring devices and wire; engineering materials; testing; methods; equipment. *Mailing Add:* Leviton Mfg Co Inc 59-25 Little Neck Pkwy Little Neck NY 11362

METZ, FLORENCE IRENE, b Willard, Ohio, Sept 1, 29. PHYSICAL CHEMISTRY, INORGANIC CHEMISTRY. *Educ:* Case Western Reserve Univ, AB, 51, MS, 56; Iowa State Univ, PhD(phys chem), 60. *Prof Exp:* Res chemist, Lewis Lab, Nat Adv Comt Aeronaut, Ohio, 51-55; instr & res fel, Iowa State Univ, 56-60; sr chemist, 60-63, dir, Germanium Info Ctr, 62-67, prin chemist, 63-67, sr adv chem, 67-68, head, Phys & Anal Chem Sect, 68-72, asst dir phys sci, 72-76, dir chem sci, 76-78, VPRES CHEM & BIOSCI, MIDWEST RES INST, 78-; VPRES, CHEM & BIOSCI, 78- *Concurrent Pos:* Lectr, Univ Mo, Kansas City, 61-65. *Mem:* AAAS; Am Chem Soc; Sigma Xi; Am Asn Corrosion Eng; Am Soc Test & Mat. *Res:* Biochemistry, psychology and physiology related to disease, especially cancer; chemistry of materials; evaluation of effects of radiation on materials; vacuum evaporation of thin metallic films on inorganic oxidizers; analytical chemistry; behavioral sciences. *Mailing Add:* Midwest Res Inst 425 Volker Blvd Kansas City MO 64110

METZ, FRED L, b McComb, Ohio, Apr 23, 35; m 60; c 2. BIO-ORGANIC CHEMISTRY. *Educ:* Bowling Green State Univ, BA, 57; Ind Univ, PhD(org chem), 62. *Prof Exp:* Summer res chemist, Monsanto Chem Co, 57 & 59; sr res chemist, 62-69, RES ASSOC, T R EVANS RES CTR, DIAMOND SHAMROCK CORP, 69- *Mem:* Inst Food Technol; AAAS; Am Chem Soc; Am Leather Chem Asn; Am Dairy Sci Asn. *Res:* Organic synthesis; amino acids; organic fluorine chemicals; leather chemicals; arsenic chemicals; paper chemicals; immobilized enzymes; food and dairy technology. *Mailing Add:* PO Box 348 Diamond Shamrock Corp Concord OH 44077

METZ, JOHN THOMAS, b Springfield, Ill, Jan 21, 47. ELECTROPHYSIOLOGY, BIOPSYCHOLOGY. *Educ:* St Louis Univ, BA, 70; Univ Chicago, PhD(biopsychol), 78. *Prof Exp:* Res assoc, 77-79, ASST PROF, DEPT PSYCHIAT, UNIV CHICAGO, 79- *Concurrent Pos:* Instr, Dept Psychol, St Xavier Col, 75, Northeastern Ill Univ, 76 & 77; res scientist, Ill Dept Mental Health, 80- *Mem:* Asn Psychophysiol Study Sleep; Soc Neurosci. *Res:* Pharmacological studies of muscle reflexes, event-related potentials, sleep physiology and their relationships to psychiatric illness. *Mailing Add:* Lab Biol Psychiat Ill State Psychiat Inst 1601 W Taylor Chicago IL 60612

METZ, MICHAEL JOSEPH, b Keokuk, Iowa, Feb 5, 43; m 64; c 3. AUDIOLOGY. *Educ:* Univ Iowa, BS, 66; Colo State Univ, MS, 67; Univ Denver, PhD(speech & hearing sci), 72. *Prof Exp:* ASSOC PROF COMMUN DIS, CALIF STATE UNIV, FULLERTON, 72- *Concurrent Pos:* Audiol consult, Pac State Hosp, 76- *Mem:* Am Speech & Hearing Asn; Am Audiol Soc. *Res:* Electrical activity of the auditory/vestibular system. *Mailing Add:* Dept of Commun Dis Calif State Univ Fullerton CA 92634

METZ, PETER ROBERT, b Seattle, Wash, Nov 22, 34; m 59; c 3. ELECTRICAL ENGINEERING. *Educ:* Univ Wash, BS, 56, PhD(elec eng), 65; Mass Inst Technol, SM, 58. *Prof Exp:* Engr, Boeing Co, 58-61; asst prof elec eng, Univ Wash, 65-72; coordr post-grad progs, Polytech Sch, Fed Univ Paraiba, 72-76; ENGR, BOEING CO, SEATTLE, WASH, 76- *Mem:* Inst Elec & Electronics Engrs. *Res:* Selection of Huffman sequences with desired ambiguity function magnitudes; optical data processing applied to bioengineering. *Mailing Add:* Boeing Co PO Box 3707 Seattle WA 98124

METZ, ROBERT, b New York, NY, June 2, 38; m 61; c 2. STRATIGRAPHY. *Educ:* City Col New York, BS, 61; Univ Ariz, MS, 63; Rensselaer Polytech Inst, PhD(stratig), 67. *Prof Exp:* Asst prof geol, State Univ NY Col Potsdam, 66-67; asst prof, Newark State Col, 67-70, assoc prof, 70-80, PROF GEOL, KEAN COL NJ, 80- *Concurrent Pos:* Sigma Xi grant-in-aid res; NY State grad fel award. *Mem:* Geol Soc Am; Soc Econ Paleontologists & Mineralogists; Nat Asn Geol Teachers; Sigma Xi. *Res:* Structure and taconic stratigraphy of the Cambridge Quadrangle, New York; stratigraphy and petrography of the Raritan Formation of New Jersey; media for use in making fossil impressions; raindrop impressions. *Mailing Add:* Dept of Earth & Planetary Environ Kean Col of NJ Union NJ 07083

METZ, ROBERT JOHN SAMUEL, b Johannesburg, SAfrica, Jan 23, 29; m 53; c 4. INTERNAL MEDICINE, ENDOCRINOLOGY. *Educ:* Univ Witwatersrand, MB, BCh, 51; Northwestern Univ, MS, 59; Univ Toronto, PhD(physiol), 62. *Prof Exp:* Res fel med & physiol, Northwestern Univ, 57-59; res fel, Banting & Best Dept Med Res, Univ Toronto, 59-61; assoc med, Northwestern Univ, Chicago, 62-64, asst prof, 64-69; chief metab res, 69-71, PRES, VIRGINIA MASON RES CTR, 71- *Concurrent Pos:* Chief, Med Div, Northwestern Univ, Chicago, 62-65; chief, Diabetes & Metab Serv, Cook County Hosp, Chicago, 62-65; attend physician, Passavant Mem Hosp, Chicago, 65-69; clin asst prof med, Univ Wash, 69-77, clin assoc prof, 77-; attend physician, Virginia Mason Hosp, 69- *Mem:* Am Diabetes Asn; Am Fedn Clin Res; fel Am Col Physicians; Endocrine Soc. *Res:* Diabetes and allied diseases. *Mailing Add:* Mason Clin 1118 Ninth Ave Seattle WA 98101

METZ, ROBERT WINFIELD, plant pathology, entomology, see previous edition

METZ, ROGER N, b Bedford, Ohio, Dec 15, 38; m 58; c 1. THEORETICAL PHYSICS. *Educ:* Oberlin Col, BA, 60; Cornell Univ, PhD(physics), 68. *Prof Exp:* Res asst physics, Lab Atomic & Solid State Physics, Cornell Univ, 65-67; NSF intern physics & math, Antioch Col, 67-68; asst prof, 68-78, ASSOC PROF PHYSICS, COLBY COL, 78-, CHMN DEPT, 74- *Mem:* Am Phys Soc; Am Asn Physics Teachers. *Res:* Statistical mechanics of fluids. *Mailing Add:* Dept of Physics Colby Col Waterville ME 04901

METZE, GERNOT, b Mahrisch Schonberg, Czech, Nov 1, 30; m 62. ELECTRICAL ENGINEERING. *Educ:* Iowa State Univ, BS, 53; Univ Ill, MS, 55, PhD(digital comput), 58. *Prof Exp:* Res asst, Elec Eng Dept & Digital Comput Lab, 53-57, res assoc, Digital Comput Lab, 58-59, res asst prof, 59-64, res asst prof elec eng, Coord Sci Lab, 65-66, res assoc prof, 66-70, RES PROF ELEC ENG, COORD SCI LAB, UNIV ILL, URBANA, 70- *Concurrent Pos:* Consult, ITT Kellogg, Ill, 65, Scully Int, 65-66, Emerson Elec, 66 & Tex Instruments Inc, 67- *Mem:* Inst Elec & Electronics Engrs. *Res:* Digital systems design; fault-tolerant computing; sequential machine theory; computer arithmetic. *Mailing Add:* Coord Sci Lab Univ Ill Urbana IL 61801

METZENBERG, ROBERT LEE, JR, b Chicago, Ill, June 11, 30; m 54; c 2. BIOCHEMISTRY. *Educ:* Pomona Col, AB, 51; Calif Inst Technol, PhD(biochem), 56. *Prof Exp:* From instr to assoc prof, 55-68, PROF PHYSIOL CHEM, UNIV WIS-MADISON, 68- *Concurrent Pos:* Am Cancer Soc fel, 55-58; Markle investr, 58-; res fel, Univ Zurich, 59-60; USPHS career development awardee, 63-73; genetics study sect, NIH, 69-73; assoc ed, Genetics J, 75- *Mem:* AAAS; Am Soc Biol Chemists; Am Chem Soc; Genetics Soc Am; Am Soc Microbiol. *Res:* Mechanism of action of urea cycle enzymes; genetic control of metabolism in Neurospora; control of metabolism in eucaryotes. *Mailing Add:* Dept of Physiol Chem Univ of Wis Madison WI 53706

METZGAR, DON P, b Hastings, Nebr, June 7, 29; m 50; c 2. VIROLOGY, IMMUNOLOGY. *Educ:* Hastings Col, BA, 56; Purdur Univ, PhD(microbiol), 61. *Prof Exp:* NSF fel cell physiol, Purdue Univ, 61-62; res fel virol, Merck Inst Therapeut Res, 62-67; sr res virologist, Nat Drug Co, 67-71; sect head cell biol res, Merrell Nat Labs, 71-77; V PRES OPERS, CONNAUGHT LABS INC, 77- *Mem:* AAAS; NY Acad Sci. *Res:* Tissue culture; radiochemistry; electron microscopy; vaccine development and relationship to antigenic potentiation. *Mailing Add:* VPres Opers Connaught Labs Inc Swiftwater PA 18370

METZGAR, LEE HOLLIS, b Olean, NY, Jan 10, 41; m 61; c 1. POPULATION DYNAMICS, BEHAVIORAL ECOLOGY. *Educ:* State Univ NY Col Fredonia, AB, 62; Univ Mich, MS, 64, MA, 66, PhD(zool), 68. *Prof Exp:* Teacher jr high sch, NY, 62-63; asst prof, 68-74, assoc prof, 68-74, chmn dept, 75-79, FULL PROF ZOOL, UNIV MONT, 80- *Mem:* Am Soc Mammal; Ecol Soc Am; Wildlife Soc. *Res:* Relationships between social organization and population dynamics in small mammals; behavioral regulation of rodent numbers and analyses of big game population changes. *Mailing Add:* 400 N Ave E Missoula MT 59801

METZGAR, RICHARD STANLEY, b Erie, Pa, Feb 2, 30; m 52; c 2. IMMUNOLOGY. *Educ:* Univ Fla, BS, 51; Univ Buffalo, MA, 57, PhD(immunol), 59. *Prof Exp:* Sr cancer res scientist, Roswell Park Mem Inst, 59-62; assoc prof, 62-72, PROF IMMUNOL, SCH MED, DUKE UNIV, 72- *Concurrent Pos:* Mem staff, Yerkes Primate Res Ctr, Emory Univ. *Mem:* AAAS; Am Asn Immunol; Am Asn Cancer Res; NY Acad Sci. *Res:* Cancer immunity; transplantation biology; tumor virology. *Mailing Add:* Dept of Microbiol & Immunol Duke Univ Sch of Med Durham NC 27710

METZGER, A(RTHUR) J(OSEPH), b Chicago, Ill, Nov 6, 09; m 38; c 2. CERAMIC ENGINEERING. *Educ:* Ohio State Univ, BCerE, 32, PhD, 67. *Prof Exp:* Ceramic engr, Charles Taylor Sons Co, Ohio, 34-37; res dir, Elgin Butler Brick Co, Tex, 37; res engr, Battelle Mem Inst, 38; ceramic engr, Louisville Fire Brick Works, Ky, 38-45; gen mgr, Wahl Refractory Prod Co, Ohio, 45-48; asst prof ceramic eng, Va Polytech Inst, 48-51, from assoc res prof to res prof, 51-67; prof ceramic eng & dir Refractories Indust Res Ctr, Ohio State Univ, 67-74; RETIRED. *Honors & Awards:* Arthur-Fredrick Greaves-Walker Award, Nat Inst Ceramic Engrs, 79. *Mem:* Fel Am Ceramic Soc; Ceramic Educ Coun (secy-treas, 58-59, vpres, 59-60, pres, 60-62); Nat Inst Ceramic Engrs (secy-treas, 56-57, vpres, 57-58, pres elect, 58-59, pres, 59-60). *Res:* Mechanical properties of refractories; light weight ceramic materials; thermochemical mineralogy. *Mailing Add:* 1494 Presidential Dr Columbus OH 43212

METZGER, ALBERT E, b New York, NY, Sept 10, 28; m 58; c 2. PLANETARY SCIENCE, RADIATION PHYSICS. *Educ:* Cornell Univ, AB, 49; Columbia Univ, MA, 51, PhD(nuclear chem), 58. *Prof Exp:* Chemist, Sylvania Elec Corp, 51-53; asst, Columbia Univ, 53-54; from scientist to sr scientist, 59-61, RES GROUP SUPVR, SPACE SCI DIV, JET PROPULSION LAB, CALIF INST TECHNOL, 61- *Mem:* Fel AAAS; Am Astrom Soc; Am Phys Soc; Am Geophys Union. *Res:* Geochemistry; gamma ray astronomy; x-ray physics; radiation physics; space science instrumentation. *Mailing Add:* 380 Olive Tree Lane Sierra Madre CA 91024

METZGER, BOYD ERNEST, b Hills, Minn, June 13, 34; m 59; c 3. MEDICINE, ENDOCRINOLOGY. *Educ:* State Univ Iowa, MD, 59. *Prof Exp:* Intern internal med, Michael Reese Hosp & Med Ctr, 59-60, resident, 60-63; surgeon, USPHS, 63-65; from instr to assoc prof med, 67-77, PROF MED, MED SCH, NORTHWESTERN UNIV, 77- *Concurrent Pos:* Fel biochem, Wash Univ, 65-67. *Mem:* Am Fedn Clin Res; Am Diabetes Asn; Endocrine Soc; Sigma Xi. *Res:* Intermediary metabolism; metabolism and nutrition in pregnancy; metabolic and hormonal disturbances in diabetes. *Mailing Add:* Ctr for Endocrinol Metab & Nutrit 303 E Chicago Ave Chicago IL 60611

METZGER, CHARLES O, b Nuremberg, Ger, Oct 22, 23; nat US; m 58; c 4. CHEMICAL ENGINEERING. *Educ:* City Col New York, BS, 45; Columbia Univ, MS, 48. *Prof Exp:* Develop engr semi works, Rohm & Haas Co, Pa, 48-50, group leader propellant res, Ala, 50-53, process develop, Pa, 53-58 sect head chem eng, 58-62, asst gen mgr, Rhee Industs Div, RI, 62-66, prod supt, Fayetteville Fibers Plant, 66-71, prod mgr, Fibers Div, 71-75, bus mgr, Carpet Nylon, 75-78, BUS MGR, CARODEL & KEMOS SUBSIDIARIES, ROHM & HAAS CO, PHILADELPHIA, 78- *Mem:* Am Chem Soc; Am Inst Chem Engrs. *Res:* Plastics; fibers. *Mailing Add:* 3 Wexford Ct Cherry Hill NJ 08034

METZGER, DANIEL SCHAFFER, b Greenville, Mich, Sept 3, 36; div; c 2. PHYSICS. *Educ:* Kalamazoo Col, BA, 58; Ohio State Univ, MSc, 62, PhD(physics), 65. *Prof Exp:* Vis asst prof physics, Ohio State Univ, 65-66; alt group leader, 74-76, group leader, 76-79, STAFF MEM EXP PHYSICS, LOS ALAMOS NAT LAB, 66-, ASSOC DIV LEADER, PHYSICS DIV, 79- *Concurrent Pos:* Mem eval panel electronics & elec eng, Nat Res Coun-Nat Acad Sci. *Mem:* Am Phys Soc; Inst Elec & Electronics Engrs. *Res:* X-ray spectroscopy; nuclear magnetic resonance in solids; spectral and fast transient measurements of radiation associated with nuclear weapons testing; airborne measurements of infrared radiation in aurorae; fiber optics applications in fast analog systems; research and development management. *Mailing Add:* Los Alamos Nat Lab Box 1663 Los Alamos NM 87544

METZGER, DARRYL E, b Salinas, Calif, July 11, 37; m 56; c 4. MECHANICAL ENGINEERING. *Educ:* Stanford Univ, BS, 59, MS, 60, MechE, 62, PhD(mech eng), 64. *Prof Exp:* Instr mech eng, Stanford Univ, 60-61; from asst prof to assoc prof mech eng, 63-70, PROF MECH & ENERGY SYSTS ENG, ARIZ STATE UNIV, 70-, HEAD DEPT, 74- *Concurrent Pos:* NASA-Am Soc Eng Educ fac fels, 64 & 65; consult, Magneto-Plasmadyn Br, Ames Res Ctr, NASA, 64-65, Garrett Turbine Engine Co, 66-76, Pratt & Whitney Aircraft, 77- & Pratt & Whitney, Can, 79- *Mem:* Am Soc Mech Engrs; assoc fel Am Inst Aeronaut & Astronaut. *Res:* Heat transfer; fluid mechanics and thermodynamics, particularly convective heat transfer; gas turbine engine heat transfer. *Mailing Add:* Dept of Mech Eng Ariz State Univ Tempe AZ 85281

METZGER, G H(ERBERT), b Cleveland, Ohio, Feb 27, 18; m 42; c 3. CHEMICAL ENGINEERING. *Educ:* Case Inst Technol, BS, 38, MS, 39. *Prof Exp:* Res chemist, Plaskon Co, 39-42; chem engr, B F Goodrich Co, 42-43, tech supvr, B F Goodrich Chem Co, 43-45, develop supvr, 45-57, mgr proj eng, 57-63, mgr design petrochem, 63-65, mgr proj eng & construct, 65-70, TECH CONSULT, PROJ ENG, B F GOODRICH CHEM CO, 70- *Mem:* Am Inst Chem Engrs. *Res:* Chemical process design, development and construction. *Mailing Add:* 2871 N Jefferson Blvd Lorain OH 44052

METZGER, GERSHON, b New York, NY, June 25, 35; m. CHEMISTRY, RESEARCH ADMINISTRATION. *Educ:* Yeshiva Univ, BA, 55; Columbia Univ, MA, 56, PhD, 59. *Prof Exp:* Asst, Columbia Univ, 55-59, Sloan res assoc, 59-60; res chemist, Esso Res & Eng Co, NJ, 60-64; sr chemist, Chem & Phosphates Co, Ltd, Israel, 64-65; assessor of patents, 65-68, head patent exploitation div, 68-69, dir phys sci div, 69-74, dep dir planning, 74-76, dep dir res funds, Ministry of Energy Intrastructure, 76-81, DEP DIR NAT COUN RES & DEVELOP, 81- *Concurrent Pos:* Instr, Yeshiva Univ, 60-62; assoc prof chem, Jerusalem Col Technol, 73-77. *Mem:* AAAS; Am Chem Soc. *Mailing Add:* Ministry of Energy Intrastructure Bldg 3 Hakirya Jerusalem Israel

METZGER, H PETER, b New York, Ny, Feb 22, 31; m 56; c 4. BIOCHEMISTRY, SCIENCE WRITING. *Educ:* Brandeis Univ, BA, 53; Columbia Univ, PhD, 65. *Prof Exp:* Res scientist, NY State Psychiat Inst, 65-66; sr res scientist, NY State Inst Neurochem & Drug Addiction, 66; res assoc biochem, Univ Colo, 66-68; staff scientist, Ball Bros Res Corp, 68-69, mgr adv progs, Environ Instrumentation Dept, 69-70; dir & consult, Colspan Environ Systs, Inc, 70-73; syndicated columnist, NY Times, 72-74 & Newspaper Enterprise Asn, New York, 74-77; ADMINR ENVIRON AFFAIRS, YORK, PUB SERV CO, COLO, 74- *Concurrent Pos:* Prin investr, USPHS res grant, 67-68; sci ed, Rocky Mt News, Denver, 74-77. *Mem:* AAAS; Am Chem Soc. *Res:* Mechanisms of enzyme action; neurochemistry; biochemical basis of memory; protein hormone production. *Mailing Add:* 2595 Stanford Ave Boulder CO 80303

METZGER, HENRY, b Mainz, Ger, Mar 23, 32; US citizen; m 57; c 3. BIOCHEMISTRY. *Educ:* Univ Rochester, AB, 53; Columbia Univ, MD, 57. *Prof Exp:* Intern internal med, Presby Hosp, New York, 57-58, asst resident, 58-59; res assoc, NIH, 59-61; Helen Hay Whitney Found fel, 61-63; SR INVESTR, ARTHRITIS & RHEUMATISM BR, NAT INST ARTHRITIS, DIABETES, DIGESTIVE & KIDNEY DIS, 63-, CHIEF SECT CHEM IMMUNOL, 73- *Mem:* Am Asn Immunol (secy-treas); Am Soc Biol Chemists. *Res:* Immunochemistry; protein chemistry; structure of immunoglobulins. *Mailing Add:* Nat Inst Arthritis Diabetes Digestive & Kidney Dis Bethesda MD 20815

METZGER, JAMES DAVID, b Columbia, Pa, Aug 23, 52; m 74; c 1. PHYTOHORMONES, SEED DORMANCY. *Educ:* Millersville State Col, BA, 74; Mich State Univ, PhD(bot), 80. *Prof Exp:* STAFF SCIENTIST, AGR RES SERV, US DEPT AGR, 80- *Mem:* Am Soc Plant Physiologists; AAAS; Weed Sci Soc Am. *Res:* Physiological and biochemical basis of seed dormancy and the role of phytohormones in plant growth and development. *Mailing Add:* Metabolism & Radiation Res Lab State Univ Sta Agr Res Serv USDA Fargo ND 58105

METZGER, JAMES DOUGLAS, b Allentown, Pa, Feb 10, 42; m 64. ORGANIC CHEMISTRY, AGRICULTURAL CHEMISTRY. *Educ:* Univ Nev, Reno, BS, 64, PhD(org chem), 69. *Prof Exp:* RES CHEMIST, E I DU PONT DE NEMOURS & CO, INC, 68- *Mem:* Am Chem Soc; AAAS. *Res:* Organic synthesis; agricultural chemicals formulation. *Mailing Add:* E I du Pont de Nemours & Co Inc Wilmington DE 19898

METZGER, MARVIN, b New York, NY, Oct 9, 20; m 50; c 3. PHYSICAL METALLURGY. *Educ:* Columbia Univ, AB, 41, BS, 42, MS, 48, PhD(metall), 55. *Prof Exp:* Metallurgist, Crucible Steel Co Am, 42-45; mem sci staff, Columbia Univ, 51-54; from asst prof to assoc prof phys metall, 54-60, PROF PHYS METALL, UNIV ILL, URBANA, 60- *Mem:* Am Soc Metals; Am Inst Mining, Metall & Petrol Engrs; Electrochem Soc; Nat Asn Corrosion Engrs. *Res:* Deformation and dislocation structure of crystals and composites; corrosion versus microstructure; film growth, defects and breakdown. *Mailing Add:* 315 Metall & Mining Bldg Univ of Ill 1304 W Green St Urbana IL 61801

METZGER, ROBERT MELVILLE, b Yokohama, Japan, May 7, 40; US citizen; m 70. CHEMISTRY, CHEMICAL PHYSICS. *Educ:* Univ Calif, Los Angeles, BS, 62; Calif Inst Technol, PhD(chem), 68. *Prof Exp:* Jr res asst chem, Atomics Int Div, NAm Aviation Corp, Calif, 61; res assoc chem, Stanford Univ, 68-71, lectr Italian, 69-71, res assoc chem eng, asst prof, 71-77, ASSOC PROF CHEM, UNIV MISS, 77- *Mem:* Am Chem Soc; Am Crystallog Asn; Am Phys Soc. *Res:* Solid state chemistry; organic crystals and conductors; crystallography; quantum mechanics; Madelung energy calculations; tight binding Hartree-Fock calculations; combustion colorimetry; computers in chemistry; x-ray radial distribution function studies of platinum catalysts; polarizabilities of organic molecules and ions. *Mailing Add:* Dept Chem Univ Miss University MS 38677

METZGER, ROBERT P, b San Jose, Calif, Jan 28, 40; m 68; c 2. BIOCHEMISTRY. *Educ:* Univ Calif, Los Angeles, BS, 61; San Diego State Col, MS, 63, PhD(chem), 67; Univ Calif, San Diego, PhD(chem), 67. *Prof Exp:* Lectr chem, San Diego State Col, 63-68, from asst prof to assoc prof phys sci, 68-77, PROF NATURAL SCI, SAN DIEGO STATE UNIV, 77- *Concurrent Pos:* vis res prof, Univ Genova, Italy, 79-; vis sr res scientist, Johns Hopkins Univ, 80. *Mem:* Fel AAAS; Am Chem Soc; The Chem Soc; Sigma Xi. *Res:* Enzymology; carbohydrate metabolism; diabetes mellitus. *Mailing Add:* Dept Natural Sci San Diego State Univ San Diego CA 92182

METZGER, SIDNEY, b New York, NY, Feb 1, 17; m 44; c 3. COMMUNICATIONS ENGINEERING. *Educ:* NY Univ, BS, 37; Polytech Inst Brooklyn, MEE, 50. *Prof Exp:* Engr, US Signal Corps Lab, NJ, 39-45; head radio relay div, Fed Telecommun Labs, Int Tel & Tel Corp, 45-54; mgr commun eng, Astro Electronic Prod Div, Radio Corp Am, 54-63; mgr, Eng Div, Commun Satellite Corp, 63-67, chief engr, 67-69, asst vpres & chief scientist, 69-80, vpres & chief scientist, 80-82; CONSULT ENGR, 82- *Honors & Awards:* Aerospace Award, Aerospace & Electronics Systs Soc, 75; Int Commun Award, Inst Elec & Electronics Engrs, 76. *Mem:* Nat Acad Eng; fel Inst Elec & Electronics Engrs; assoc fel Am Inst Aeronaut & Astronaut; Sigma Xi. *Mailing Add:* Apt 1522 10500 Rockville Pike Rockville MD 20852

METZGER, SIDNEY HENRY, JR, b Atlanta, Ga, Mar 29, 29; m 52; c 3. APPLIED CHEMISTRY. *Educ:* Univ Ala, BS, 51; Texas A&M Univ, MS, 56; Univ Ill, PhD(org chem), 62. *Prof Exp:* Chemist, Monsanto Co, 51-54; res chemist, Jefferson Chem Co, 60-62; sr chemist, 62-67, group leader, 67-71, DIR, MOBAY CHEM CO, 71-, MGR ELASTOMERIC A/D, MOBAY CHEM CORP, 73- *Mem:* Am Chem Soc; Soc Automotive Engrs; Am Inst Chemists. *Res:* Organophosphorus chemistry; reactions of epoxides; synthesis and reactions of carbodiimides and isocyanates. *Mailing Add:* Mobay Chem Co Penn-Lincoln Pkwy W Pittsburgh PA 15205

METZGER, THOMAS ANDREW, b Paterson, NJ, July 14, 44; m 70; c 4. PURE MATHEMATICS. *Educ:* Seton Hall Univ, BS, 65; Creighton Univ, MS, 69; Purdue Univ, West Lafayette, PhD(math), 71. *Prof Exp:* Asst prof math, Tex A&M Univ, 71-73; asst prof, 73-79, ASSOC PROF MATH, UNIV PITTSBURGH, 80- *Concurrent Pos:* Vis asst prof, Univ Tenn, 79. *Mem:* Am Math Soc; Math Asn Am. *Res:* Automorphic forms, applications to Riemann surfaces; weighted areal approximation in the complex plane; function theory. *Mailing Add:* Dept Math Univ Pittsburgh Pittsburgh PA 15260

METZGER, WESLEY JAMES, physics, see previous edition

METZGER, WILLIAM HENRY, JR, b Richmond, Va, Feb 17, 22; m 49. ELECTROCHEMISTRY, PHYSICAL CHEMISTRY. *Educ:* Univ Richmond, BS, 43. *Prof Exp:* From chemist to supv chemist, Dept Commerce, Nat Bur Standards, 43-68; supv chemist, Gen Serv Admin Cent Lab, 68-76; CONSULT CHEMIST, 76- *Mem:* Am Chem Soc; Am Electroplaters Soc; Am Soc Testing & Mat. *Res:* Industrial electroplating and metal finishing; development of practices and processes in electroforming; measurement of physical properties and thickness of metal coatings; calorimetry in aqueous and fused salt media; test methodology for commodity evaluation. *Mailing Add:* Port Clyde Rd Tenants Harbor ME 20405

METZGER, WILLIAM IRWIN, b Peekskill, NY, Oct 29, 15; m 41; c 2. MICROBIOLOGY. *Educ:* Purdue Univ, BS, 37, MS, 39; Univ Ill, PhD(bact), 46; Am Bd Med Microbiol, Dipl. *Prof Exp:* Asst gen biol, Purdue Univ, 37; instr bact, SDak State Col, 39-42 & Univ Ill, 42-46; res bacteriologist, Lederle Labs, Am Cyanamid Co, 46-54; DIR MICROBIOL, HEKTOEN INST MED RES, COOK COUNTY HOSP, 54-; RES ASSOC PREV MED, COL MED, UNIV ILL, 60- *Concurrent Pos:* Teaching, Sch Med Technol, Cook County Hosp, 67- *Mem:* AAAS; Am Soc Microbiol; Am Pub Health Asn; Am Acad Microbiol; Sigma Xi. *Res:* Antibiotics and chemotherapeutics; diagnostic microbiology; taxonomy; microbial ecology and antagonisms. *Mailing Add:* Hektoen Inst for Med Res Cook County Hosp 629 S Wood St Chicago IL 60612

METZGER, WILLIAM JOHN, b Freeport, Ill, Nov 7, 35; m 57, 79; c 2. GEOLOGY. *Educ:* Beloit Col, BS, 57; Univ Ill, MS, 59, PhD(geol), 61. *Prof Exp:* Asst geol, Univ Ill, 57-61; from asst prof to assoc prof geol, State Univ NY Col Fredonia, 61-71, actg chmn dept, 63-65, prof geol, 71-81; SR STAFF GEOLOGIST, DENVER WEST EXPLOR, CONOCO, INC, GOLDEN, COLO, 81- *Mem:* AAAS; fel Geol Soc Am; Am Asn Petrol Geol; Soc Econ Paleont & Mineral; Clay Minerals Soc. *Res:* Stratigraphy and sedimentation; petroleum geology. *Mailing Add:* Conoco Inc Denver W Explor 13949 W Colfax Ave Golden CO 80401

METZLER, CARL MAUST, b Masontown, Pa, Dec 13, 31; m 53; c 3. PHARMACOKINETICS, MODELING. *Educ:* Goshen Col, BS, 55; NC State Univ, PhD(biomath), 65. *Prof Exp:* Asst prof math, Goshen Col, 60-62; res scientist, 65-70; head res, 70-78, SR STATISTICIAN, UPJOHN CO, 78- *Mem:* AAAS; fel Acad Pharmaceut Sci; Biomet Soc; fel Am Statist Asn; Am Soc Clin Pharmacol & Therapeut. *Res:* Application of mathematical and statistical methods to chemical biological and medical research; development of mathematical, statistical and computer memodology. *Mailing Add:* Biostatist Upjohn Co 301 Henrietta St Kalamazoo MI 49001

METZLER, CHARLES VIRGIL, b Louisville, Ky, Jan 11, 29; m 52; c 6. CHEMICAL ENGINEERING, ENVIRONMENTAL ENGINEERING. *Educ:* Univ Louisville, BChE, 52, MChE, 53, PhD(chem eng), 60. *Prof Exp:* Instr chem eng, Univ Louisville, 53-60; sr res engr, Rocketdyne Div, NAm Aviation, Inc, 58-60, res specialist, 59-60; from asst prof to assoc prof eng, 60-66, chmn dept eng, 65-67, chmn dept urban studies & assoc dean eng, 70-73, PROF ENG, CALIF STATE UNIV, NORTHRIDGE, 66-, PROF URBAN STUDIES, 73- *Concurrent Pos:* Consult, Atomics Int Div, NAm Aviation, Inc, 60, consult & res specialist, Rocketdyne Div, 60-64; consult, Naval Missile Ctr, 64; consult adv tech staff, Marquardt Corp, 65-66; educ consult, Pac Missile Test Ctr, 73- & Calif State Univs & Cols, 76- *Mem:* Am Soc Eng Educ; Am Inst Chem Engrs. *Res:* High speed gas flow and heat transfer; supersonic combustion; water resources; professional education. *Mailing Add:* Sch of Eng Calif State Univ Northridge CA 91330

METZLER, DAVID EVERETT, b Palo Alto, Calif, Aug 12, 24; m 48; c 5. BIOCHEMISTRY. *Educ:* Calif Inst Technol, BS, 48; Univ Wis, MS, 50, PhD(biochem), 52. *Prof Exp:* Res scientist, Univ Tex, 51-53; from asst prof to assoc prof, 53-61, PROF BIOCHEM, IOWA STATE UNIV, 61- *Mem:* Am Chem Soc; Am Soc Photobiol; Am Soc Biol Chem. *Res:* Mechanisms of coenzyme action; electronic absorption spectra of vitamins, coenzymes and proteins. *Mailing Add:* Dept of Biochem & Biophys Iowa State Univ Ames IA 50011

METZLER, DWIGHT F, b Carbondale, Kans, Mar 25, 16; m 41; c 4. ENVIRONMENTAL ENGINEERING, PUBLIC HEALTH. *Educ:* Univ Kans, BS, 40, CE, 47; Harvard Univ, SM, 48; Am Acad Environ Engrs, dipl. *Prof Exp:* Asst engr, Kans Bd Health, 40-41, sanit engr, 46-48; from assoc prof to prof civil eng, Univ Kans, 48-66; dep comnr, NY State Dept Health, 66-70 & NY State Dept Environ Conserv, 70-74; secy, 74-79, DIR WATER SUPPLY DEVELOPMENT, KANS DEPT HEALTH & ENVIRON, 79- *Concurrent Pos:* Consult, USPHS, 43-46 & 57-66; housing consult, Chicago-Cook County Health Surv, 46; chief engr, Kans Bd Health, 48-62, adv, Govt India, 60; exec secy, Kans Water Resources Bd, 62-66; adv, WHO, 64-, chmn expert panel solid waste, 71. *Honors & Awards:* Fuller Award, Am Water Works Asn, 54; Bedell Award, Water Pollution Control Fedn, 63; Centennial Award, Am Pub Health Asn, 72. *Mem:* Nat Acad Eng; fel Royal Soc Health; Sigma Xi; Am Pub Health Asn (pres, 64-65); Am Soc Civil Engrs. *Res:* Studies of histoplosmosis in humans and nitrate cyanosis and occurrance of nitrates inwater; author or coauthor of over 85 publications. *Mailing Add:* Kans Dept of Health & Environ Forbes Field Topeka KS 66620

METZLER, RICHARD CLYDE, b Cleveland, Ohio, Oct 19, 37; m 60; c 2. PURE MATHEMATICS. *Educ:* Univ Mich, BS, 59; Wayne State Univ, MA, 62, PhD(math), 66. *Prof Exp:* Asst prof, 65-71, ASSOC PROF MATH, UNIV N MEX, 71- *Mem:* Math Asn Am; Am Math Soc. *Res:* Ordered topological vector spaces. *Mailing Add:* Dept of Math Univ of NMex Albuquerque NM 87131

METZNER, ARTHUR B(ERTHOLD), b Sask, Can, Apr 13, 27; nat US; m 48; c 3. CHEMICAL ENGINEERING. *Educ:* Univ Alta, BSc, 48; Mass Inst Technol, ScD(chem eng), 51. *Hon Degrees:* DASc, Katholieke Univ, Belgium, 75. *Prof Exp:* Res engr, Defense Res Bd, Can, 48; instr chem eng, Mass Inst Technol, 50-51 & Polytech Inst Brooklyn, 51-53; from asst prof to prof, 53-62, chmn dept, 70-78, H FLETCHER BROWN PROF CHEM ENG, UNIV DEL, 62- *Concurrent Pos:* Res chem engr, Colgate-Palmolive Co, 51-53. *Honors & Awards:* Am Chem Soc Sect Award, 58; Colburn Award, Am Inst Chem Engrs, 58, Walker Award, 70, Lewis Award, 77; Bingham Medal, Soc Rheology, 77. *Mem:* Nat Acad Eng; Am Chem Soc; Am Inst Chem Engrs. *Res:* Transport processes; rheology; fluid mechanics. *Mailing Add:* Dept of Chem Eng Univ of Del Newark DE 19711

METZNER, ERNEST KURT, b Phoenix, Ariz, Apr 17, 49. ORGANIC CHEMISTRY. *Educ:* Ariz State Univ, BS, 71; Univ Calif, Berkeley, PhD(chem), 74. *Prof Exp:* Fel chem, Stanford Res Inst, 74-75; RES SCIENTIST CALBIOCHEM-BEHRING CORP, AM HOECHST CORP, 75- *Mem:* Am Chem Soc. *Res:* Synthesis of biologically active compounds. *Mailing Add:* Calbiochem-Behring Corp PO Box 12087 San Diego CA 92112

METZNER, JEROME, b New York, NY, Apr 14, 11; m 32; c 3. BOTANY, CYTOLOGY. *Educ:* City Col New York, BA, 32; Columbia Univ, MA, 33, PhD(bot), 44. *Prof Exp:* Teacher high schs, NY, 44-49; asst prof educ, City Col New York, 49-50; chmn dept biol & gen sci, Jamaica High Sch, 50-53, dept biol & introd sci, High Sch Sci, 53-60 & dept biol, Francis Lewis High Sch, 60-67; prof, 67-81, EMER PROF BIOL, JOHN JAY COL, CITY UNIV NEW YORK, 81- *Concurrent Pos:* Lectr, Hunter Col, 46-48 & City Col New York, 47-; admin officer, Education Mission, US Dept Army, Korea, 48; educ dir, Nature Ctrs Young Am, Inc, 59-; mem gifted student comt biol sci curric study, Am Inst Biol Sci. *Mem:* AAAS; Am Soc Protozoologists; Am Micros Soc. *Res:* Protozoology; phycology; cytology. *Mailing Add:* 16 Pinehurst St Lido Beach NY 11551

METZNER, JOHN J(ACOB), b Queens, NY, June 23, 32. ELECTRICAL ENGINEERING. *Educ:* NY Univ, BEE, 53, MEE, 54, ScD(elec eng), 58. *Prof Exp:* Sr res scientist, Electrosci Lab, Sch Eng & Sci, NY Univ, 58-67, asst prof, 65-66, assoc prof elec eng, 67-73; assoc prof, Polytech Inst NY, 73-74; assoc prof, Wayne State Univ, 74-80, prof, 80; PROF ENG, OAKLAND UNIV, 81- *Mem:* Inst Elec & Electronics Engrs. *Res:* Communication theory;

techniques for reliable data communication involving error correcting codes and retransmission strategies; efficient utilization of data communication networks; fault tolerant computing. *Mailing Add:* Dodge Hall Eng Oakland Univ Rochester MI 48063

METZNER, WENDELL PHILLIPS, chemistry, deceased

MEUDT, WERNER J, b Koblenz, Ger, Nov 22, 31; US citizen; m 57; c 2. PLANT PHYSIOLOGY. *Educ:* Okla State Univ, BS, 59; Yale Univ, MS, 62; Rutgers Univ, PhD(plant physiol), 64. *Prof Exp:* RES PLANT PHYSIOLOGIST, USDA, 64- *Mem:* AAAS; Am Soc Plant Physiol; Bot Soc Am; Japanese Soc Plant Physiol; Scandinavian Soc Plant Physiol. *Res:* Metabolism and mode of action of plant growth hormones in tobacco; enzymatic oxidation on indole-3-acetic acid in plants; flowering physiology; photoperiodism; vernalization. *Mailing Add:* Plant Hormone & Regulator Lab USDA Agr Res Ctr West Beltsville MD 20705

MEULENERS, R(OBERT) L(AMBERT), b Cologne, Minn, Sept 9, 21. CHEMICAL ENGINEERING. *Educ:* Univ Minn, BS, 44. *Prof Exp:* Asst dir design & econ, Res & Develop Dept, Am Oil Co Div, Standard Oil Co Ind, 53-55, dir refining tech serv, 56-58, sect head design, 59-61, chief engr process eng, Gen Eng Dept, 62-78; CONSULT, 78- *Mem:* Am Inst Chem Engrs. *Res:* Design, economics and operation of petroleum refining and chemical production units. *Mailing Add:* Rte 1 Box 456 Prairie Grove AR 72753

MEULY, WALTER C, b Langenthal, Switz, Nov 5, 98; nat US; m; c 1. ORGANIC CHEMISTRY. *Educ:* Swiss Fed Inst Technol, AB, 21, PhD(org chem), 23. *Prof Exp:* Res chemist, Newport Co, 24-30; area supt, Fine Chem Div, New Brunswick Works, E I du Pont de Nemours & Co, 30-41, prod mgr, 41-44, chem supt, 44-53, res assoc, Jackson Lab, 53-58; dir res, 58-63, vpres res & develop, 63-75, CONSULT, RHODIA, INC, 75- *Mem:* AAAS; Am Chem Soc; Am Inst Chemists; NY Acad Sci. *Res:* Synthetic dyestuffs; perfume chemicals; pharmaceuticals; organic fine chemicals. *Mailing Add:* 685 River Rd Piscataway NJ 08854

MEUSSNER, R(USSELL) A(LLEN), b Pittsburgh, Pa, July 23, 20. PHYSICAL METALLURGY. *Educ:* Carnegie Inst Technol, PhD(phys metall), 52. *Prof Exp:* Res assoc chem, Forrestal Res Ctr, Princeton, 52-55; METALLURGIST, US NAVAL RES LAB, 55- *Res:* Gas-metal reactions. *Mailing Add:* US Naval Res Lab Washington DC 20390

MEUTEN, DONALD JOHN, b Waterbury, Conn, Oct 4, 48; m 79. PATHOLOGY, ENDOCRINOLOGY. *Educ:* Univ Conn, BS, 70; Cornell Univ, DVM, 74; Ohio State Univ, PhD(vet pathol), 81. *Prof Exp:* Intern vet med, Univ Guelph, 75-76; resident vet pathol, Cornell Univ, 76-77; clin instr vet clin pathol, Ohio State Univ, 77-78, res fel, 78-81; ASST PROF VET PATHOL, TEX A&M UNIV, 81- *Mem:* Am Col Vet Pathologists; Am Vet Med Asn. *Res:* Pahtogenesis of hypercalcemia associated with neoplasms in dogs. *Mailing Add:* Rte 4 Box 490 College Station TX 77840

MEUX, JOHN WESLEY, b Little Rock, Ark, Apr 25, 28; m 53; c 2. MATHEMATICS. *Educ:* Henderson State Teachers Col, BS, 53; Univ Ark, MS, 57; Univ Fla, PhD(math), 60. *Prof Exp:* Instr math, Univ Fla, 59-60; asst prof, Kans State Univ, 60-64; from asst prof to assoc prof, 64-77, chmn dept, 64-68, PROF MATH, MIDWEST UNIV, 77- DEAN SCH SCI & MATH, 68- *Mem:* Math Asn Am. *Res:* Orthogonal functions; numerical analysis. *Mailing Add:* Sch of Sci & Math Midwestern Univ Wichita Falls TX 76308

MEVERS, GUS ESPER, electrical engineering, see previous edition

MEWALDT, LEONARD RICHARD, b La Crosse, Wis, May 31, 17; m 41; c 2. ORNITHOLOGY. *Educ:* Univ Iowa, BA, 39; Univ Mont, MA, 48; Wash State Univ, PhD, 53. *Prof Exp:* From instr to assoc prof, 53-63, PROF ZOOL, SAN JOSE STATE UNIV, 63- *Mem:* Fel Am Ornith Union; Cooper Ornith Soc. *Res:* Biology of Zonotrichia and Nucifraga ecology and behavior. *Mailing Add:* Avian Biol Lab San Jose State Univ San Jose CA 95192

MEWBORN, ANCEL CLYDE, b Greene Co, NC, Sept 22, 32; m 54; c 2. ALGEBRA. *Educ:* Univ NC, AB, 54, MA, 57, PhD(math), 59. *Prof Exp:* Instr math, Yale Univ, 59-61; from asst prof to assoc prof, 61-70, PROF MATH, UNIV NC, CHAPEL HILL, 70- *Mem:* Am Math Soc; Math Asn Am. *Res:* Structure of prime and semi-prime rings. *Mailing Add:* Dept of Math Univ of NC Chapel Hill NC 27514

MEWISSEN, DIEUDONNE JEAN, b Ans, Belg, Oct 25, 24; m 53; c 3. RADIOLOGY, RADIOBIOLOGY. *Educ:* Univ Liege, MD, 50, Agrege, 61; Am Bd Radiol, cert therapeut radiol, 71. *Prof Exp:* Head radiobiol lab, Univ Brussels, 61-, prof radiobiol, Univ, 69-; mem, Belg Adv Coun Cancer, 63- & Hosps, 64- *Honors & Awards:* Prize, Cong Radiol & Electrol Latin Cult, Lisbon, 57; Dag Hammarskjoeld Int Award, Brussels, 80. *Mem:* AAAS; Radiation Res Soc; Royal Soc Med; Belg Cancer Soc (secy-gen, 71); Am Asn Cancer Res. *Res:* Radiation carcinogenesis; long term effects of radiation; toxicity and carcinogenicity of tritium and tritiated compounds. *Mailing Add:* A J Carlson Lab Pritzker Sch Med Univ Chicago Chicago IL 60637

MEXAL, JOHN GREGORY, b San Antonio, Tex, Oct 14, 46; m 68; c 1. PLANT PHYSIOLOGY, FOREST ECOLOGY. *Educ:* Univ NMex, BS, 69, MS, 71; Colo State Univ, PhD(plant physiol), 74. *Prof Exp:* SCIENTIST, SOUTHERN FORESTRY RES CTR, WEYERHAEUSER CO, 74- *Mem:* Sigma Xi. *Res:* Tree physiology, soil-plant-water relations; mycorrhizal associations; seed germination; revegetation. *Mailing Add:* Southern Forestry Res Ctr Weyerhaeuser Co Hot Springs AR 71901

MEYBOOM, PETER, b Barneveld, Netherlands, Apr 26, 34; Can citizen; m 57; c 3. HYDROGEOLOGY. *Educ:* Univ Utrecht, BSc, 56, MSc, 58, PhD(hydrogeol), 60. *Prof Exp:* Res officer, Alta Res Coun, Can, 58-60; res scientist, Geol Surv Can, Can Fed Dept Energy, Mines & Resources, 60-66, sect head hydrogeol, Inland Waters Br, 66-67, head groundwater subdiv, 67-69, sci adv, Can Fed Dept Finance, 70-71; dir sci policy, Can Fed Dept Environ, 71-73, dir gen sci centre, Can Fed Dept Supply & Serv, 73-75; asst secy, Can Ministry State Sci & Technol, 75-77; DEP SECY ADMIN POLICY, TREAS BD CAN, 77- SERV, 73- *Concurrent Pos:* Distinguished lectr, Can Inst Mining & Metall, 62-63. *Honors & Awards:* Can Centennial Medal, 67. *Res:* Hydrology; science policy. *Mailing Add:* 4 Cedarcrest Ave Ottawa ON K2E 5P8 Can

MEYBURG, ARNIM HANS, b Bremerhaven, Ger, Aug 25, 39; m 67; c 1. TRANSPORTATION ENGINEERING, TRANSPORTATION PLANNING. *Educ:* Northwestern Univ, MS, 68, PhD(civil eng), 71. *Prof Exp:* Asst prof transp eng, Cornell Univ, 69-75; vis prof transp eng, Tech Univ Munich, Ger, 76; assoc prof, 75-78, actg dept chmn, Dept Environ Eng, 77-78, PROF TRANSP ENG, CORNELL UNIV, 78-, CHMN, DEPT ENVIRON ENG, 80- *Concurrent Pos:* Res assoc, Transp Ctr, Northwestern Univ, 68-69; consult, NY State Dept Ed, 74-75, Calif Dept Transp, 75-76, Social Sci Res Inst, Munich, 78-81; vis assoc res engr, transp eng, Univ Calif, Irvine, 75; res fel, Alexander von Humboldt Found, 78-79; mem, Transp Res Bd & Transp Res Forum. *Mem:* Am Soc Civil Engrs; Oper Res Soc; Sigma Xi. *Res:* Disaggregate travel demand modeling; urban transporation planning; microcomputer-based analysis and modeling of transit operations; transportation-communications interactions; urban goods movement; technology assessment. *Mailing Add:* Sch Civil & Environ Eng Hollister Hall Cornell Univ Ithaca NY 14853

MEYDRECH, EDWARD FRANK, b Oak Park, Ill, July 21, 43; m 65; c 2. BIOSTATISTICS, EPIDEMIOLOGY. *Educ:* Univ Fla, BS, 65, MS, 67; Univ NC, PhD(biostat), 72. *Prof Exp:* Health serv officer, USPHS, 67-69; asst prof, Va Commonwealth Univ, 72-76; asst prof, 77-80, ASSOC PROF BIOSTATISTIST, UNIV MISS MED CTR, 80- *Mem:* Am Statist Asn; Biomet Soc; Sigma Xi. *Res:* Response surface methodology; epidemiologic studies; nonparametric statistics. *Mailing Add:* Dept Prev Med 2500 N State St Jackson MS 39216

MEYER, ALBERT RONALD, b New York, NY, Nov 5, 41; m 81; c 2. COMPUTER SCIENCE, MATHEMATICAL LOGIC. *Educ:* Harvard Univ, AB, 63, MA, 65, PhD(appl math), 72. *Prof Exp:* Asst prof comput sci, Carnegie-Mellon Univ, 67-69; asst prof elec eng & comput sci, 69-72, assoc dir, Lab Comput Sci, 78-81, PROF COMPUT SCI, MASS INST TECHNOL, 75- *Concurrent Pos:* Prin investr, NSF res grant, 72-; vis prof, Harvard Univ, 78-79. *Mem:* Asn Comput Mach; Math Asn Am; Soc Indust & Appl Math. *Res:* Computational complexity; algorithms; logic of programming; automata theory. *Mailing Add:* Mass Inst of Technol NE43-806 Lab Comput Sci 545 Technology Sq Cambridge MA 02139

MEYER, ALBERT WILLIAM, b Schenectady, NY, Nov 29, 06; m 31; c 4. PHYSICAL CHEMISTRY. *Educ:* Univ Chicago, BS, 27, PhD(phys chem), 30. *Prof Exp:* Res chemist, E I du Pont de Nemours & Co, 30-31; group leader, A O Smith Corp, Wis, 31-34; dept head, US Rubber Co, 34-54; dir explor res, Diamond Alkali Co, 54-57; head atomic & radiation res, US Rubber Co, 57-59, dir tech personnel & univ rel, 59-63; asst dir res, Stevens Inst Technol, 63-67; exec secy, Plastics Inst Am, 67-71; mem coun, Eng & Sci Soc Execs; mgr, Chem Div, Ad-Tech Personnel, 77-80; MEM STAFF, KELLEY-PEPPER ASSOC, 80- *Concurrent Pos:* Assoc prof eve div, NY Univ, 46-48; mem Gordon Res Conf, chmn, 51; chmn subcomt continuing educ, Coun Comt Chem Educ, Am Chem Soc, 69-; consult, 72- *Mem:* Soc Plastics Eng; Am Chem Soc; Sigma Xi. *Res:* Liquid ammonia as a solvent; contact catalysis; polymerization, emulsion and oil phase; rubber technology; agricultural chemicals; radiation chemistry; nuclear processes; polymer science and technology. *Mailing Add:* 138 Alexander Ave Upper Montclair NJ 07043

MEYER, ALVIN F, JR, b Shreveport, La, Sept 3, 20; m 42; c 2. ENVIRONMENTAL HEALTH, OCCUPATIONAL HEALTH. *Educ:* Va Mil Inst, BS, 41; Am Acad Environ Eng, dipl, 56; Indust Col Armed Forces, dipl, 62. *Prof Exp:* Chief environ health eng, hq, Air Mat Command, US Air Force, 49-61, hq, Strategic Air Command, 61-65, chief bioenviron eng, Off Surgeon Gen, 62-65, chief biomed sci corps, 65-69; spec asst legis, Off Adminr, Consumer Protection & Environ Health Serv, Dept Health, Educ & Welfare, 69-75; dir off noise abatement & control, Environ Protection Agency, 71-75; PRES, A F MEYER & ASSOC, INC, 75- *Concurrent Pos:* Vis fac mem, Va Mil Inst, 55-; asst prof, Creighton Univ, 55-61; mem nat adv coun environ health, 63-69; chmn environ pollution control comt, Dept Defense, 64-69. *Mem:* Aerospace Med Asn; Am Indust Hyg Asn; Am Soc Civil Eng; Am Pub Health Asn. *Res:* Environmental pollution control from toxic aerospace propellants; engineering control of environmental stresses on man; bioacoustics and noise control; occupational health and safety in fossil energy and industrial processes. *Mailing Add:* 1600 Longfellow St McLean VA 22101

MEYER, ALVIN HAROLD, civil engineering, see previous edition

MEYER, ANDREW U, b Berlin, Ger, Apr 21, 27; US citizen; m 64; c 2. ELECTRICAL ENGINEERING, CONTROL SYSTEMS. *Educ:* Northwestern Univ, MS, 58, PhD(elec eng), 61. *Prof Exp:* Develop engr, Assoc Res, Inc, Ill, 50-53; proj engr, Sun Elec Corp, 53-55; assoc elec engr, Armour Res Found, Ill Inst Technol, 56-57; mem tech staff, Bell Tel Labs, NJ, 61-65; assoc prof elec eng, 65-68, PROF ELEC ENG, NEWARK COL ENG, NJ INST TECHNOL, NEWARK, 68- *Concurrent Pos:* Vis prof, Mid East Tech Univ, Ankara, 69-70. *Mem:* AAAS; Inst Elec & Electronics Engrs; Soc Indust & Appl Math; Am Soc Eng Educ; Sigma Xi. *Res:* Automatic control systems; large scale systems; stability theory; biomedical control systems; computer-aided medical diagnosis; modeling of physiological systems; biomedical system analysis and modeling. *Mailing Add:* 746 Ridgewood Rd Millburn NJ 07041

MEYER, AXEL, b Copenhagen, Denmark, Mar 3, 26; nat US; m 50; c 3. METAL PHYSICS. *Educ:* City Col New York, BS, 48 & 50; Ga Inst Technol, MS, 52; Ill Inst Technol, PhD(physics), 56. *Prof Exp:* Res fel nuclear physics, Armour Res Found, Ill Inst Technol, 52-54; from asst prof to assoc prof physics, Univ Fla, 55-59; solid state physicist, Neutron Physics Div, Oak Ridge Nat Lab, 59-62, Solid State Div, 61-67; assoc prof, 67-69, PROF PHYSICS, NORTHERN ILL UNIV, 69- *Concurrent Pos:* Res Corp grant, 58. *Mem:* Am Phys Soc; fel Brit Inst Physics. *Res:* Theoretical solid state and metal physics, especially electronic structure; structure factors of liquid metals; transport properties and thermodynamics of metals and alloys in both liquid and solid state. *Mailing Add:* Dept of Physics Northern Ill Univ DeKalb IL 60115

MEYER, BERNARD HENRY, b Cincinnati, Ohio, June 3, 41; m 70; c 1. CHEMICAL ENGINEERING, POLYMER SCIENCE. *Educ:* Univ Cincinnati, BSChE, 64; Univ Akron, MS & PhD(polymer sci), 71. *Prof Exp:* Chem engr, Emery Industs, 64; SCIENTIST, PLASTICS GROUP, KOPPERS CO, 71- *Mem:* Am Chem Soc. *Res:* Impact resistant plastic resins; polymerization kinetics; reverse osmosis; composite resin morphologies and properties. *Mailing Add:* Plastics Group Koppers Co 440 College Park Dr Monroeville PA 15146

MEYER, BERNARD SANDLER, b Nantucket, Mass, July 20, 01; m 31, 48. BOTANY. *Educ:* Ohio State Univ, BA, 21, MA, 23, PhD(bot), 26. *Prof Exp:* Instr bot, Ohio State Univ, 23-27; assoc forest ecologist, Cent States Forest Exp Sta, US Forest Serv, 27-28; from asst prof to prof bot, Ohio State Univ, 28-71, chmn dept, 46-67, chmn dept bot & plant path, Agr Exp Sta, 48-66, EMER PROF BOT, OHIO STATE UNIV, 71- *Concurrent Pos:* Ed-in-chief J Bot, Bot Soc Am, 46-51; vis prof, Univ Cincinnati, 76. *Mem:* AAAS; Am Soc Plant Physiologists (pres, 43); Am Inst Biol Sci (vpres, 61); Bot Soc Am (vpres, 52). *Res:* Plant physiology; water relations; photosynthesis; mineral nutrition; photoperiodism. *Mailing Add:* Dept of Bot Ohio State Univ 1735 Neil Ave Columbus OH 43210

MEYER, BETTY MICHELSON, b Jersey City, NJ. BIOSTATISTICS. *Educ:* Brown Univ, AB, 45, ScM, 46; Univ Mich, MPH, 66, PhD(biostatist), 69. *Prof Exp:* From asst prof to assoc prof biostatist, Sch Pub Health, Univ Mich, 69-76, assoc dir, Ctr Res Dis of Heart, 72-76; dir epidemiol div, Inst Aerobics Res, 76-77, dir res, 77-79; PROF, COL NURSING, TEX WOMAN'S UNIV, 81- *Concurrent Pos:* Mem, Clin Applns & Prev Adv Comt, Div Heart & Vascular Dis, Nat Heart & Lung Inst, 75-76; fel, Epidemiol Coun, Am Heart Asn. *Mem:* Am Statist Asn; Am Women Sci; Biomet Soc; Soc Epidemiol Res; Sigma Xi. *Res:* Epidemiological studies related to heart disease, nutrition and occupational health; longitudinal studies. *Mailing Add:* Col Nursing Tex Woman's Univ 1810 Inwood Rd Dallas TX 75235

MEYER, BURNETT CHANDLER, b Denver, Colo, Mar 24, 21. MATHEMATICS. *Educ:* Pomona Col, BA, 43; Brown Univ, ScM, 45; Stanford Univ, PhD(math), 49. *Prof Exp:* Asst, Stanford Univ, 46-49; from asst prof to assoc prof math, Univ Ariz, 49-57; from asst prof to assoc prof, 57-68, PROF MATH, UNIV COLO, BOULDER, 68- *Mem:* Am Math Soc; Math Asn Am. *Res:* Complex analysis; real analysis; potential theory and history of mathematics. *Mailing Add:* Dept of Math Univ of Colo Boulder CO 80309

MEYER, CARL BEAT, b Zurich, Switz, May 5, 34; m 61; c 1. PHYSICAL INORGANIC CHEMISTRY. *Educ:* Univ Zurich, PhD(inorg chem), 60. *Prof Exp:* res chemist & fel Lawrence Radiation Lab, Univ Calif, 61-64; from asst prof to assoc prof, 64-75, PROF CHEM, UNIV WASH, 75- *Concurrent Pos:* Consult, Lawrence Berkeley Lab, Univ Calif, Berkeley, 64-; NSF grants, 64; consult, US Consumer Prod Safety Comn, 79-, Environ Protection Agency, 80-, US Dept Housing & Urban Develop, 81-; investr, Lawrence Berkeley Lab, Univ Calif, 79-; dir indust res, Sulphur Inst, Wash, DC, 65-69. *Honors & Awards:* Gold medal, Ger Cellular Plastics Soc, 80. *Mem:* AAAS; Am Phys Soc; Am Chem Soc; NY Acad Sci. *Res:* Inorganic physical chemistry of, high temperature molecules and sulphur-containing compounds; optical and raman spectroscopy of gaseous and aqueous systems; cryochemistry; formaldehyde resius; air chemistry. *Mailing Add:* Dept of Chem BG-10 Univ of Wash Seattle WA 98195

MEYER, CARL DEAN, JR, b Greeley, Colo, Nov 22, 42; c 2. MATHEMATICS, COMPUTER SCIENCE. *Educ:* Univ NC, BA, 64; Colo State Univ, MS, 66, PhD(math), 68. *Prof Exp:* PROF MATH, NC STATE UNIV, 68- *Mem:* Am Math Soc; Math Asn Am; Soc Indust & Appl Math. *Res:* Matrix theory; applied linear algebra; numerical analysis. *Mailing Add:* Dept of Math NC State Univ Raleigh NC 27650

MEYER, CAROL DIANE, organometallic chemistry, see previous edition

MEYER, CHARLES FREDERICK, b Gloucester, NJ, Apr 15, 13; m 38; c 3. MATHEMATICS, STATISTICS. *Educ:* Pa State Col, BS, 35; George Wash Univ, MA, 37, PhD(physics), 42. *Prof Exp:* From instr to asst prof physics, Wayne State Univ, 38-44; physicist, 44-46, group supvr, Appl Physics Lab, 47-57, div supvr, Appl Physics Lab, 57-81, PRIN STAFF PHYSICIST, JOHNS HOPKINS UNIV, 51-, ASST DIR, 81- *Concurrent Pos:* Consult, Joint Res & Develop Bd, Wash, DC, 48-51 & Weapons Syst Eval Group, US Dept Defense, 50-51 & 56-; asst secy, Defense Res & Develop, 54- *Mem:* Am Phys Soc; Opers Res Soc Am. *Res:* Military operations research. *Mailing Add:* Appl Physics Lab Johns Hopkins Univ Laurel MD 20810

MEYER, CHRISTIAN, b Magdeburg, Ger, Mar 26, 43; US citizen; m 66; c 2. STRUCTURAL ENGINEERING, STRUCTURAL MECHANICS. *Educ:* Univ Calif, Berkeley, MS, 66, PhD(civil eng), 70. *Prof Exp:* Sr systs engr, Albert C Martin & Assocs, 71-73; structure engr & consult, Stone & Webster Eng Corp, 73-78; ASSOC PROF CIVIL ENG, COLUMBIA UNIV, 78- *Mem:* Am Soc Civil Engrs; Am Concrete Inst; Sigma Xi; Int Asn Bridge & Structural Engrs. *Res:* Computer analysis of structures; earthquake engineering; structural design. *Mailing Add:* Dept Civil Eng Columbia Univ New York NY 10027

MEYER, CONRAD FREDERICK, b Santa Monica, Calif, Apr 23, 20; m 54; c 4. DEVELOPMENTAL PLANT ANATOMY. *Educ:* Syracuse Univ, BS, 49, MS, 50; Cornell Univ, PhD(plant anat), 54. *Prof Exp:* Asst bot, Syracuse Univ, 49-50; asst Cornell Univ, 51-53, instr, 53-54; asst prof biol, Tex Western Col, 54-56; from instr to asst prof, 56-60, ASSOC PROF BOT, RUTGERS UNIV, 60- *Mem:* AAAS; Bot Soc Am; Am Inst Biol Sci; Sigma Xi; Int Soc Plant Morphol. *Res:* Plant embryogeny; morphogenesis; developmental anatomy; histochemistry. *Mailing Add:* Dept of Bot Rutgers Univ 195 Univ Ave Newark NJ 07102

MEYER, DAVID BERNARD, b Rochester, NY, Jan 20, 23; m 52; c 3. ANATOMY. *Educ:* Wayne State Univ, BA, 48, PhD, 57; Univ Mich, MS, 50. *Prof Exp:* Instr biol, Wayne State Univ, 51-52, asst, 56-57, USPHS res fel, 57-58; NIH fel, 58-59; USPHS fel, 59-60, from instr to assoc prof, 60-70, PROF ANAT, SCH MED, WAYNE STATE UNIV, 70- *Concurrent Pos:* Vis prof, Graz Univ, 62-63; vis res anatomist, Carnegie Lab Embryol, Davis, Calif, 75-76. *Mem:* AAAS; Asn Res Vision & Ophthal; Am Asn Anat; Histochem Soc; Pan-Am Asn Anat. *Res:* Ocular development and histochemistry; prenatal ossification of the human skeleton; embryological histochemistry; origin, ultrastructure and chemistry of avian visual cells. *Mailing Add:* Dept of Anat Wayne State Univ Sch Med Detroit MI 48201

MEYER, DAVID LACHLAN, b East Orange, NJ, Dec 26, 43; m 70. INVERTEBRATE PALEONTOLOGY. *Educ:* Univ Mich, BS, 66; Yale Univ, Mphil, 69, PhD(geol), 71. *Prof Exp:* Fel, Smithsonian Inst, 70- 71, biologist, Smithsonian Trop Res Inst, 71-75; asst prof, 75-79, ASSOC PROF GEOL, UNIV CINCINNATI, 79- *Mem:* Paleont Soc; Soc Econ Paleontologists & Mineralogists; Geol Soc Am; Sigma Xi. *Res:* Ecology and functional morphology of recent and ancient crinoids (Echinodermata); coral reef ecology. *Mailing Add:* Dept of Geol Univ of Cincinnati Cincinnati OH 45221

MEYER, DELBERT HENRY, b Maynard, Iowa, Aug 28, 26; m 49; c 5. ORGANIC CHEMISTRY. *Educ:* Wartburg Col, BA, 49; Univ Iowa, PhD(chem), 53. *Prof Exp:* Chemist, Standard Oil Co, Ind, 53-61; chemist, Amoco Chem Corp, 61-67, res supvr, Res & Develop Dept, 67-77, DIR RES, AMOCO CHEM CORP, 77- *Mem:* Am Chem Soc. *Res:* Esterification and oxidation reactions; polymerization; synthetic fibers; flame retardant polymers. *Mailing Add:* Res & Develop Dept Amoco Chem Corp PO Box 400 Naperville IL 60540

MEYER, DIANE HUTCHINS, b Springfield, Mass, Feb 3, 37; m 67; c 4. CELL BIOLOGY. *Educ:* Russell Sage Col, BA, 58; Univ Vt, PhD(zool), 72. *Prof Exp:* Res asst pharmacol res, Sterling-Winthrop Res Inst, 58-59; res technician, Burroughs Wellcome Co, 60-62; res technician med res, Med Col, Univ Vt, 64-68; res officer, Med Col, Univ Western Australia, 73; RES ASSOC BASIC RES, MED COL, UNIV VT, 74- *Res:* Investigation of the role of ribonucleases, esterases and proteases in the turnover of RNA and protein in normal, developing, denervated and dystrophic muscle and in dystrophic human muscle; in vivo and in vitro studies concerning the role of RNase II in cellular defense and its relationship to interferon. *Mailing Add:* Dept Biochem Given Bldg Med Col Univ Vt Burlington VT 05401

MEYER, DONALD IRWIN, b St Louis, Mo, Feb 13, 26; m 50; c 2. PHYSICS. *Educ:* Mo Sch Mines, BS, 46; Univ Wash, PhD(physics), 53. *Prof Exp:* Mem staff, Los Alamos Sci Lab, 46-48; asst prof physics, Univ Okla, 52-54; with Brookhaven Nat Lab, 54-56; asst prof, 56, PROF PHYSICS, UNIV MICH, ANN ARBOR, 56- *Mem:* Am Phys Soc. *Res:* High energy nuclear physics. *Mailing Add:* Dept of Physics Univ of Mich Ann Arbor MI 48109

MEYER, DWAIN WILBER, b Fremont, Nebr, Jan 11, 44; m 66. AGRONOMY. *Educ:* Univ Nebr, Lincoln, BS, 66; Iowa State Univ, PhD(crop prod & physiol), 70. *Prof Exp:* Asst prof, 70-76, ASSOC PROF AGRON, NDAK STATE UNIV, 76- *Mem:* AAAS; Am Soc Agron; Crop Sci Soc Am; Am Forage & Grassland Coun. *Res:* Forage management, production and physiology; irrigated forage problems and systems; Sudangrass and crested wheatgrass digestibility; techniques of sodseeding in semi-arid grasslands; nutritive value of small grain straws; winter injury in irrigated alfalfa; hay preservation methods; high moisture hay preservatives. *Mailing Add:* Dept of Agron NDak State Univ Fargo ND 58102

MEYER, EDGAR F, b El Campo, Tex, July 19, 35; m 65; c 3. STRUCTURAL CHEMISTRY. *Educ:* NTex State Univ, BS, 59; Univ Tex, PhD(chem), 63. *Prof Exp:* Fel lab org chem, Swiss Fed Inst Technol, 63-65; fel dept biol, Mass Inst Technol, 65-67; asst prof, 65-74, ASSOC PROF BIOPHYS, TEX A&M UNIV, 74- *Concurrent Pos:* Res collabr chem, Brookhaven Nat Lab, 68-77; acad guest, Swiss Fed Inst Technol, 75-76. *Mem:* AAAS; Sigma Xi; Am Crystallog Asn; Am Chem Soc. *Res:* Crystallographic structure determinations with the assistance of digital computers; x-ray crystallography of biologically related substances; chemical information processing and the application of computational methods to chemical problems; modelling the interaction of small molecules with macromolecular receptors; protein crystallography. *Mailing Add:* Dept of Biochem & Biophys Tex A&M Univ College Station TX 77843

MEYER, EDMOND GERALD, b Albuquerque, NMex, Nov 2, 19; m 41; c 3. PHYSICAL CHEMISTRY. *Educ:* Carnegie Inst Technol, BS, 40, MS, 42; Univ NMex, PhD(chem), 50. *Prof Exp:* Jr chemist, Harbison Walker Refractories Co, 40-41; instr, Carnegie Inst Technol, 41-42; asst phys chem, US Bur Mines, 42-44; chemist, US Naval Res Lab, 44-46; res div, NMex Inst Mining & Technol, 46-48; head dept sci, Univ Albuquerque, 50-52; prof chem, NMex Highlands, 52-63, head dept, 52-58, dir inst sci res, 58-63, grad dean, 60-63; dean, Col Arts & Sci, 63-75, prof chem, 63-80, vpres res, 75-80, PROF ENERGY & NAT RESOURCES, UNIV WYO, 81- *Concurrent Pos:* Grants, Res Corp, AEC, NSF, USPHS, US Dept Energy, US Dept Interior & Am Heart Asn; Fulbright prof, Chile, 59; state sci adv, Wyo, 72-; consult, Los Alamos Sci Lab, NSF & US Dept Health, Social Serv Gen Acct Off; dir, Nat Gov Coun Sci & Technol, 74-, First Wyo Bank, Laramie, 76-, chmn, 81-,

Western Solar Utilization Network, 78-80, Consortium Univs Res Energy, 78-80 & Am Res & Design Scientist, Inc, 80-; exec consult, Diamond Shamrock, 80; pres, Coal Technol Corp, 81- *Mem:* Fel AAAS; Am Chem Soc; Biophys Soc; fel Am Inst Chem. *Res:* Energy systems; energy policy; thermodynamics; science education. *Mailing Add:* Univ Wyo Laramie WY 82071

MEYER, EDWARD DELL, b Buffalo, NY, Mar 27, 41; m 64; c 4. MICROBIOLOGY, BIOCHEMISTRY. *Educ:* Univ Ariz, BS, 63, MS, 72, PhD(microbiol), 75. *Prof Exp:* Res asst geosci/chem eng, Univ Ariz, 73-75; asst prof, 75-79, dir allied health, 77-79, chmn, Div Nat Sci, 78-79, asst to pres col, 79-81, ASSOC PROF BIOL, MADONNA COL, 79-, DEAN ADMIN SERV, 81- *Mem:* AAAS; Sigma Xi; Am Soc Microbiol; Am Inst Biol Sci. *Res:* Basic biology of psychophilic pseudomonads and psychrophilic yeasts; temperature related adaptations. *Mailing Add:* Madonna Col 36600 Schoolcraft Rd Livonia MI 48150

MEYER, EDWARD RAYMOND, environmental sciences, see previous edition

MEYER, EDWIN F, b Chicago, Ill, July 30, 37; m 59; c 6. PHYSICAL CHEMISTRY. *Educ:* DePaul Univ, BS, 59; Northwestern Univ, PhD(phys chem), 62. *Prof Exp:* NATO fel, Queen's Univ, Belfast, 62-63; res assoc phys adsorption, Naval Res Lab, 65-67; from asst prof to assoc prof, 67-78, PROF CHEM, DEPAUL UNIV, 78- *Mem:* Am Chem Soc. *Res:* Vapor pressure measurement; intermolecular interactions; thermodynamics; gas chromatography. *Mailing Add:* 1022 Dobson St Evanston IL 60202

MEYER, ERNEST ALAN, microbiology, see previous edition

MEYER, EUGENE, psychiatry, deceased

MEYER, EUGENE FRANK, JR, physical chemistry, see previous edition

MEYER, FERDINAND CLARK, b Dorchester, Ill, Jan 1, 19; m 40; c 5. ORGANIC CHEMISTRY, TECHNICAL MANAGEMENT. *Educ:* Shurtleff Col, AB, 38; Univ Ill, MS, 40; Univ Wis, PhD(org chem), 43. *Prof Exp:* Res chemist, Monsanto Chem Co, 43-49, group leader, 49-53, asst dir res, 54-57, assoc dir, 57-63, mgr & dir tech eval & control, 64-67, tech mgr, 68-71, dir tech opers, 72-73, dir biomed technol, New Enterprise Div, 74-77, dir spec proj, Med Dept, 78-80; RETIRED. *Mem:* Am Chem Soc. *Res:* Organic synthesis and processes; aromatic intermediates; fine chemicals and biologicals; biomedical product development. *Mailing Add:* 18 Roclare Lane Town & Country St Louis MO 63131

MEYER, FRANK HENRY, b Brooklyn, NY, July 11, 15; m 46; c 2. SOLID STATE PHYSICS, PHILOSOPHY OF SCIENCE. *Educ:* City Col New York, BS, 36; Polytech Inst Brooklyn, MS, 51; Univ Minn, MA, 68. *Prof Exp:* X-ray crystallogr, Textile Res Inst, NJ, 51-53; res physicist, Continental Oil Co, 54-60; res engr, Kaiser Aluminum & Chem Corp, 60-63; sr develop engr, Univac Div, Sperry Rand Corp, 63-65; teacher pub sch, Wis, 65-66; from asst prof to prof, 66-81, EMER PROF PHYSICS & PHILOS, UNIV WIS-SUPERIOR, 81- *Concurrent Pos:* Ed, Reciprocity, 71-; dir, New Sci Advocates, Inc, pres, 80- *Mem:* Am Phys Soc; Am Crystallog Asn; Am Asn Physics Teachers; Fedn Am Sci; Philos Sci Asn. *Res:* Solid state defect physics; solid surface chemistry; philosophy and history of science and education; solid and liquid cohesion theory; three-dimensional time; space time progression. *Mailing Add:* 1103 15th Ave SE Minneapolis MN 55414

MEYER, FRANKLIN VINCENT, b Perth Amboy, NJ, Feb 25, 48; m 68; c 2. NUMBER THEORY. *Educ:* Hamline Univ, BA, 69; Univ Minn, Minneapolis, MS, 71, PhD(math), 75. *Prof Exp:* ASST PROF MATH, BETHEL COL, MINN, 75- *Res:* Transcendence measures for transcendental numbers related to the exponential function; problems in foundations of mathematics; applications of the liar paradox; problems in the theory of diophantine approximation. *Mailing Add:* Dept of Math Bethel Col 3900 Bethel Dr St Paul MN 55112

MEYER, FRANZ, b Berlin, Ger, July 3, 23; nat US; m 60. BIOCHEMISTRY. *Educ:* Univ Heidelberg, MD, 53. *Prof Exp:* Res assoc, Univ Chicago, 54-60; res fel, Harvard Univ, 60-63; assoc prof, 63-74, PROF MICROBIOL, STATE UNIV NY UPSTATE MED CTR, 74- *Concurrent Pos:* NIH spec res fel, 60-62. *Res:* Lipid metabolism in microorganisms and lower invertebrates. *Mailing Add:* Dept of Microbiol State Univ NY Upstate Med Ctr Syracuse NY 13210

MEYER, FRED PAUL, b Holstein, Iowa, Aug 15, 31. PARASITOLOGY, FISH DISEASES. *Educ:* Univ Northern Iowa, BA, 53; Iowa State Univ, MS, 57, PhD(parasitol), 60. *Prof Exp:* Teacher high sch, Iowa, 53-56; asst, Iowa State Univ, 56-59; parasitologist & asst dir, Fish Farming Exp Sta, 60-73, dir fish control lab, 73-78, DIR, NAT FISH RES LAB, US FISH & WILDLIFE SERV, 78- *Concurrent Pos:* Instr, Miss State, 68- & Univ Wis-LaCrosse, 73-; mem fac, Nat Fisheries Acad, 78- *Mem:* Am Soc Parasitol; Am Fisheries Soc; Am Inst Fish Res Biol. *Res:* Fish parasitology and pathology with reference to diseases of fish; toxicology; chemical and drug registration, environmental stress and fish health; 85 publications. *Mailing Add:* PO Box 818 US Fish & Wildlife Serv LaCrosse WI 54601

MEYER, FRED WOLFGANG, b Heidenheim, W Ger, May 30, 47; US citizen; m 77. ATOMIC & MOLECULAR PHYSICS. *Educ:* Lawrence Univ, BA, 70; Univ Wis-Madison, MA, 73, PhD(physics), 76. *Prof Exp:* RES ASSOC PHYSICS, OAK RIDGE NAT LAB, 76- *Mem:* Am Phys Soc. *Res:* Electron-transfer between singly and multiply charged ions and atomic hydrogen and alkali metal atoms; crossed beam study of electron loss by hydrogen in collisions with multicharged ions; Rydberg atoms. *Mailing Add:* PO Box X Bldg 6003 Oak Ridge Nat Lab Oak Ridge TN 37830

MEYER, FREDERICK GUSTAV, b Olympia, Wash, Dec 7, 17; m 46. BOTANY. *Educ:* Wash State Univ, BSc, 39, MSc, 41; Wash Univ, PhD(bot), 49. *Prof Exp:* Lab asst bot, Wash State Univ, 39-51; dendrologist, Mo Bot Garden, 51-56; botanist, New Crops Res Br, Agr Res Serv, USDA, 57-63, RES BOTANIST CHG HERBARIUM, US NAT ARBORETUM, USDA, 63- *Concurrent Pos:* Mo Bot Garden grant, Univ Col & Univ London, 49-51; NSF fel, 55- *Honors & Awards:* Gold Seal, Nat Coun State Garden Clubs; Frank N Meyer Medal, Am Genetic Asn. *Mem:* Linnaean Soc London; Am Soc Plant Taxon; Am Hort Soc; Soc Study Evolution; Int Soc Plant Taxon. *Res:* Taxonomic botany of the flowering plants; studies in Coffea; evolution and taxonomy of cultivated plants; ethnobotany of archeological sites, especially Pompeii, Herculaneum and villas destroyed by Vesuvius; Valeriana; cultivated plants of southeastern United States; taxonomy of cultivated plants. *Mailing Add:* US Nat Arboretum Washington DC 20002

MEYER, FREDERICK RICHARD, b Brooklyn, NY, May 26, 38; m 62; c 2. MAMMALIAN PHYSIOLOGY. *Educ:* Valparaiso Univ, BS, 60; Ind Univ, MA, 62, PhD(physiol), 66. *Prof Exp:* Asst prof biol, Wilson Col, 65-67; PROF BIOL, VALPARAISO UNIV, 67- *Mem:* Am Physiol Soc; Sigma Xi; AAAS. *Res:* Temperature regulation in the laboratory rat and man. *Mailing Add:* Niels Sci Ctr Rm 243 Valparaiso Univ Valparaiso IN 46383

MEYER, GARSON, b Rochester, NY, Nov 22, 96; m 20; c 2. INDUSTRIAL CHEMISTRY. *Educ:* Univ Rochester, BS, 19. *Hon Degrees:* DCS, Pace Col, 72; DHL, Ithaca Col, 73. *Prof Exp:* Chemist, Res Labs, Eastman Kodak Co, 19-20, chief chemist, Camera Works, 20-45, dir chem, Metall & Plastics Lab, Apparatus & Optical Div, 45-62, spec tech adv, 62-65. *Mem:* Mem: AAAS; Am Chem Soc; Am Soc Testing & Mat; Soc Plastics Indust; Soc Plastics Eng. *Res:* Chemical induction and photographic development; industrial chemical development. *Mailing Add:* 1600 East Ave Rochester NY 14610

MEYER, GEORGE G, b Frankfurt, Ger, Nov 13, 31; nat US; m 53; c 3. PSYCHIATRY, SOCIAL PSYCHIATRY. *Educ:* Johns Hopkins Univ, BA, 51; Univ Chicago, MD, 55; Am Bd Psychiat & Neurol, cert psychiat, 64. *Prof Exp:* Resident, Univ Chicago, 58-61, chief resident psychiat, 60-61, from instr to assoc prof, 61-69; assoc prof, 69-71, PROF PSYCHIST, DENT SCH, UNIV TEX HEALTH SCI CTR, SAN ANTONIO, 71- *Concurrent Pos:* Nat Inst Ment Health career teacher grant, 61-63; consult to many orgn, 61-; assoc chief, Psychiat Inpatient Serv, Univ Chicago, 61-65, chief, 66-69; consult, Indian Health Serv, USPHS, 68- & NIH, 70- dir, Northwest San Antonio Ment Health Ctr, 69-74; vis lectr, Univ Edinburgh, 66; mem consult staff, Santa Rosa Med Ctr, San Antonio, 71-; mem bd, Econ Develop Corp, Mex-Am Unity Coun, 71-; mem exec bd, Crisis Ctr, San Antonio, 71-74; psychiat consult, Ecumenical Ctr Bexar County, 72-; vis prof, Univ Man, 77. *Mem:* Fel Am Psychiat Asn; fel Am Orthopsychiat Asn; Am Group Psychother Asn; Am Asn Med Cols; World Psychiat Asn. *Res:* Over 50 publications. *Mailing Add:* Dept Psychiat Univ Tex Health Sci Ctr San Antonio TX 78284

MEYER, GERALD, b Newport News, Va, Dec 31, 22; m 47; c 2. GEOLOGY. *Educ:* Univ NC, BS, 48. *Prof Exp:* Lab instr geol & geog, Univ NC, 47-48; geologist, Md, 48-57, dist geologist, WVa, 57-64, asst chief, 64-73, chief, 73-80, SR STAFF HYDROLOGIST, GROUNDWATER BR, US GEOL SURV, DC, 80- *Mem:* Geol Soc Am; Am Geophys Union; Am Water Resources Asn; Nat Water Well Asn; Am Water Works Asn. *Res:* Groundwater geology and hydrology. *Mailing Add:* Water Resources Div US Geol Surv Washington DC 20242

MEYER, GERARD G L, b La Tronche, France, May 13, 41; m 67; c 2. ELECTRICAL ENGINEERING. *Educ:* Univ Calif, Berkeley, MS, 69, PhD(elec eng), 70. *Prof Exp:* Res assoc elec eng, Univ Southern Calif, 70-71, asst prof, 71-72; asst prof, 72-76, assoc prof, 76-81, PROF ELEC ENG, JOHNS HOPKINS UNIV, 81- *Mem:* Inst Elec & Electronics Engrs; Asn Comput Mach; Math Programming Soc; Operations Res Soc. *Mailing Add:* Elec Eng & Comput Sci Dept Johns Hopkins Univ Baltimore MD 21218

MEYER, GERHARDT EUGENE, b Wis, Jan 31, 23; m 48; c 2. ENGINEERING, INSTRUMENTATION. *Educ:* Univ Wis, BSEE, 51. *Prof Exp:* Electrician, Kimberly Clark Corp, 41-42 & 46-48; res engr, Co, 51-57, res supvr, 57-64, res sect mgr, 64-66, develop sect mgr, Eng Res Div, Eng Develop Lab, 66-68, DIR ENG DEVELOP, ENG RES DIV, ENG DEVELOP LAB, E I DU PONT DE NEMOURS & CO, INC, 68- *Mem:* Assoc Inst Elec & Electronics Engrs. *Res:* Engineering research and development to provide the automated manufacturing systems required by industry. *Mailing Add:* 101 Beech St-EDL E I Du Pont de Nemours & Co Inc Wilmington DE 19898

MEYER, GLENN ARTHUR, b Baraboo, Wis, Mar 8, 34; m 61; c 3. NEUROSURGERY. *Educ:* Univ Wis, Madison, BS, 57, MD, 60. *Prof Exp:* Surg extern, Univ Wis Hosps, 59-60, res asst neurophysiol, Med Sch, Univ, 63-64, instr neurosurg & staff physician, Univ Hosps, 66; neurosurg consult, St Elizabeth's Hosp, 67-68; assoc prof, Univ Tex Med Br Galveston, 69-72; ASSOC PROF NEUROSURG, MED COL WIS, 72- *Concurrent Pos:* Staff physician, Mendota State Psychiat Hosp, 62-65; med adv, Social Security Admin, 70-72. *Mem:* AAAS; Cong Neurol Surg; Soc Neurosci; Am Col Surg; Am Asn Neurol Surg. *Res:* Spinal autonomic mechanisms in spinal shock; reconstruction of craniofacial anomalies; pain control with electrical stimulation; chronic monitoring of intracranial pressure with a fully implantable device; intravertricular hemorrhage in premature infants. *Mailing Add:* Dept of Neurosurg Med Col of Wis Milwaukee WI 53226

MEYER, GREGORY CARL, b Willmar, Minn, Feb 10, 18; m 42, 68; c 4. ORGANIC CHEMISTRY. *Educ:* Southwestern Univ, AB, 38; Univ Nebr, MA, 40, PhD(chem), 43. *Prof Exp:* Res chemist, 42-57, tech ed, 57-63, patent chemist, 63-78, LIT CHEMIST, E I DU PONT DE NEMOURS & CO, INC, 78- *Mem:* Am Chem Soc. *Res:* Additives for petroleum products. *Mailing Add:* Jackson Lab E I du Pont de Nemours & Co, Inc Wilmington DE 19898

MEYER, GUNTER HUBERT, b Stettin, Ger, Aug 19, 39; US citizen; m 66; c 3. NUMERICAL ANALYSIS, APPLIED MATHEMATICS. *Educ:* Univ Utah, BA, 61; Univ Md, MA, 63, PhD(math), 67. *Prof Exp:* PROF MATH, GA INST TECHNOL, 71- *Concurrent Pos:* Res mathematician, Mobil Res & Develop Corp, 67-71; consult, UNESCO-Univ Simon Bolivar, Caracas, Venezuela, 74; sr vis fel, Brunel Univ, Uxbridge, Eng, 75 & 78-79. *Mem:* Soc Indust & Appl Math; Math Asn Am; Am Soc Lubrication Engrs. *Res:* Numerical solution of boundary value problems, especially of free boundary problems. *Mailing Add:* Sch of Math Ga Inst of Technol Atlanta GA 30332

MEYER, HANS-OTTO, b Basel, Switz, Oct 29, 43; m 66; c 2. NUCLEAR PHYSICS. *Educ:* Univ Basel, PhD(exp nuclear physics), 70, Privatdozent, 77. *Prof Exp:* Res assoc nuclear physics, Univ Basel, 66-71, Univ Wis-Madison, 71-73, Los Alamos Sci Lab, NMex, 73-74; asst, Univ Wash, 74, Univ Basel, 74-78; ASSOC PROF NUCLEAR PHYSICS, IND UNIV, BLOOMINGTON, 78- *Mem:* Swiss Phys Soc; Am Phys Soc. *Res:* Reactions and scattering with polarized particles; nuclear structure; medium energy physics. *Mailing Add:* Dept of Physics Ind Univ Bloomington IN 47401

MEYER, HAROLD DAVID, b Indianapolis, Ind, Oct 17, 39; m 68; c 2. NUMERICAL ANALYSIS. *Educ:* Mass Inst Technol, SB & SM, 62; Univ Chicago, MS, 68, PhD(math), 69. *Prof Exp:* Sci & math analyst, Foreign Sci & Technol Ctr, US Army, 69-70, br chief & opers res analyst, Mil Assistance Command, Vietnam, 70-71; asst prof, 71-76, ASSOC PROF MATH, TEX TECH UNIV, 76- *Mem:* Am Math Soc. *Res:* Numerical solution of partial differential equations, finite element approaches, ill-posed problems and representations of solutions to be used numerically in conjunction with such problems. *Mailing Add:* Dept of Math Tex Tech Univ PO Box 4319 Lubbock TX 79409

MEYER, HARRY MARTIN, JR, b Palestine, Tex, Nov 25, 28; m 49; c 3. VIROLOGY, PEDIATRICS. *Educ:* Hendrix Col, BS, 49; Univ Ark, MD, 53. *Prof Exp:* Chief diag sect, Dept Virus & Rickettsial Dis, Walter Reed Army Inst Res, DC, 54-57; asst resident pediat, Sch Med, Univ NC, 57-59; chief sect gen virol, 59-64, chief lab viral immunol, 64-72, DIR BUR BIOLOGICS, FOOD & DRUG ADMIN, 72- *Honors & Awards:* Chevalier de l'Ordre Nat, Repub of Upper Volta, Africa, 63; Lett of Commendation from Pres, 66; Meritorious Serv Medal, Dept Health, Educ & Welfare, 66, Distinguished Serv Medal, 69; Mead Johnson Award for Pediat Res, 67; Max Weinstein Award for Med Res, United Cerebral Palsy Asns, 69; Int Award for Distinguished Sci Res, Joseph P Kennedy, Jr Found, 71. *Mem:* Am Asn Immunol; Am Pediat Soc; Am Acad Pediat; Am Epidemiol Soc; Am Soc Microbiol. *Res:* Virus vaccine; virus and rickettsial diseases. *Mailing Add:* Bur of Biologics Food & Drug Admin Bethesda MD 20014

MEYER, HARUKO, b Tokyo, Japan, Jan 17, 29; US citizen; m 60. BIOCHEMISTRY, MICROBIOLOGY. *Educ:* Toho Women's Col Sci, Japan, BS, 49; Tokyo Col Sci, MS, 51; State Univ NY Upstate Med Ctr, PhD(microbiol), 66. *Prof Exp:* RES ASSOC MICROBIOL, STATE UNIV NY UPSTATE MED CTR, 67- *Mem:* Am Soc Microbiol. *Res:* Lipid metabolism of parasitic organisms. *Mailing Add:* Dept of Microbiol State Univ of NY Upstate Med Ctr Syracuse NY 13210

MEYER, HARVEY JOHN, b St Paul, Minn, July 16, 35; m 62; c 2. GEOLOGY, COMPUTER SCIENCE. *Educ:* Univ Minn, BA, 57; Calif Inst Technol, MS, 59; Pa State Univ, PhD(sedimentary petrol), 64. *Prof Exp:* Res fel, Antarctica Proj, Univ Minn, 62-63; sr res scientist statist geol, Pan Am Petrol Corp, 63-66; mgr data processing, Can Stratig Serv Ltd, 66-71; lectr geol, Univ Calif, Davis, 71-72; EXPLOR SYSTS ANALYST, AMOCO PROD CO, 72- *Mem:* Geol Soc Am; Am Asn Petrol Geol; Int Asn Math Geol; Soc Econ Paleont & Mineral. *Res:* Digital computer and statistical methods applied to geological problems; hydrocarbon exploration; sedimentary petrology of clastic rocks and Antartica geology. *Mailing Add:* Amoco Prod Co 1670 Broadway Denver CO 80202

MEYER, HEINZ FRIEDRICH, b Suedmoslesfehn, Ger, Jan 4, 32; div; c 4. CHEMISTRY. *Educ:* Univ Frankfurt, Dr phil nat(org chem), 59. *Prof Exp:* Res asst, Ohio State Univ, 60-61 & C H Boehringer, Ger, 61-63; CHEMIST, UPJOHN CO, 63- *Mem:* Am Chem Soc; Soc Ger Chem. *Res:* Alkaloids; antibiotics; steroids. *Mailing Add:* Upjohn Co Kalamazoo MI 49002

MEYER, HENRY, zoology, deceased

MEYER, HENRY OOSTENWALD ALBERTIJN, b Warwickshire, Eng, Jan 18, 37; m 59; c 5. MINERALOGY, GEOCHEMISTRY. *Educ:* Univ London, BSc, 59, PhD(geol), 62. *Prof Exp:* Res asst mineral, Univ Col, Univ London, 61-66; sr fel mineral & exp petrol, Geophys Lab, Carnegie Inst Technol, 66-69; sr res assoc, Nat Res Coun, Goddard Space Flight Ctr, NASA, 69-71; assoc prof, 71-74, PROF PETROL, PURDUE UNIV, LAFAYETTE, 74- *Concurrent Pos:* NSF & NASA grants, Purdue Univ, 71- *Mem:* Mineral Soc Gt Brit & Ireland; Mineral Soc Am; Am Geophys Union. *Res:* Mineralogy and petrology of ultra basic igneous rocks, including lunar samples; high pressure phase equilibria studies pertinent to ultra basic igneous rocks; origin of diamond and kimberlite rock; electron microprobe and x-ray diffraction studies. *Mailing Add:* Dept of Geosci Purdue Univ Lafayette IN 47907

MEYER, HERIBERT, b Eisenstein, Ger, Nov 14, 13; m 45; c 2. FLUID MECHANICS. *Educ:* Munich Tech, Dipl Ing, 42. *Prof Exp:* Asst prof hydraul, Munich Tech, 41-43; design engr, J M Voith Ltd, Ger, 43-45, group leader heat recovery, 45-58; sr scientist, Mead Corp, Ohio, 58-63; res assoc hydrodyn of papermaking, Inst Paper Chem, 63-69, sr res assoc fluid mech, 63-72, prof chem eng & sr res assoc, 69-78; CONSULT ENG SCI, 78- *Mem:* AAAS; Am Asn Univ Professors. *Res:* Inhibited deflection of wall jets; aeromechanics; ordinary and partial differential equations; stress-strain behavior of random assemblages of deformable rods; flow through assemblages of elliptical cylinders; low and high re-number retention dynamics of small particles in fibrous porous media; ideal free jets from nozzels formed by three plates in non-symmetrical configurations; flow between two non-linear boundries moving paralled in opposite directions. *Mailing Add:* 1230 E Pershing St Appleton WI 54911

MEYER, HERMANN, b Frauenfeld, Switz, Mar 29, 27; nat US; m 52; c 3. VETERINARY ANATOMY. *Educ:* Univ Zurich, DVM, 50, Dr med vet(anat), 52; Cornell Univ, PhD(anat), 57. *Prof Exp:* Asst vet anat, Univ Zurich, 51-52; instr, Cornell Univ, 53-56, actg asst prof, 56-57; from asst prof to prof anat, Colo State Univ, 57-72; head vet anat dept, Univ Zurich, 72-73; pub rels dir, Poudre Valley Hosp, 73-75; prof vet anat & physiol, Univ Mo-Columbia, 75-79; PROF VET ANAT, OHIO STATE UNIV, 79- *Concurrent Pos:* Guest auditor, Univ Basel, 51-52; guest lectr, Univ Zurich, 63; consult, Nat Defense Educ Act Title IV grad fel prog, 66-68; vis prof, Cornell Univ, 67-68. *Mem:* Am Vet Med Asn; Am Asn Vet Anat (pres, 80-81); Am Asn Anat; World Asn Vet Anat; Ger Anat Soc. *Res:* Veterinary anatomy; functional neuromorphology; history of morphology. *Mailing Add:* Vet Anat Ohio State Univ 1900 Coffey Rd Columbus OH 43210

MEYER, IRVING, b Springfield, Mass, Mar 19, 20; m 53; c 3. ORAL SURGERY, ORAL PATHOLOGY. *Educ:* Univ Mass, BS, 41; Tufts Univ, DMD, 44; Univ Pa, MSc, 50, DSc, 58; Am Bd Oral Surg, dipl, 54. *Prof Exp:* Resident oral surg, Metrop Hosp, New York, 48-49; resident, Philadelphia Gen Hosp, Pa, 49-50; dir dept oral surg, Springfield Hosp Med Ctr, 74-76; instr oral surg & path, 50-60, assoc res prof, 60-65, assoc prof oral path, 65-66, res prof, 66-75, PROF ORAL PATH, SCH DENT MED, TUFTS UNIV, 75- *Concurrent Pos:* Instr grad sch med, Univ Pa, 49-51; chief oral surgeon, Wesson Mem Hosp, Springfield, Mass, 51-, secy-treas med staff, 72-74; oral surgeon, Mercy Hosp, 55-; oral surgeon, Springfield Hosp, 56-, pathologist, 57-; ed, Ann Conf Oral Cancer, 60 & 63; lectr, Grad Sch, Boston Univ, 62- & Harvard Univ, 67-; assoc ed & sect ed oral path, J Oral Surg, 65-; consult ed Oral Surg, Oral Med & Oral Path; pres, New Eng Soc Oral Surg, 63-64; mem, Adv Comt & examr, Am Bd Oral & Maxillofacial Surg, 70-, mem, Bd Dirs, 73-80; oral surgeon, Cancer Div, Western Mass Hosp; consult to var hosps, Mass; chief maxillofacial surg, Baystate Med Ctr, 76-; physician pvt pract. *Honors & Awards:* William J Gies Mem Award, Am Asn Oral & Maxillofacial Surgeons, 81. *Mem:* Am Asn Oral & Maxillofacial Surg (vpres, 78-79, pres 79-80); fel Am Acad Oral Path; NY Acad Sci. *Res:* Cancer of oral cavity and adnexia, especially in clinical aspects, etiology, therapy and pathology. *Mailing Add:* 50 Maple St Springfield MA 01103

MEYER, JAMES HENRY, b Lewiston, Idaho, Apr 13, 22; m 80; c 5. NUTRITION. *Educ:* Univ Idaho, BS, 47; Univ Wis, MS, 49, PhD(nutrit), 51. *Prof Exp:* Asst nutrit, Univ Wis, 47-51; from asst prof to prof animal husb & chmn dept, Univ Calif, Davis, 50-63, dean col agr, 63-69, CHANCELLOR, UNIV CALIF, DAVIS, 69- *Concurrent Pos:* Mem comt animal nutrit, Nat Acad Sci-Nat Res Coun, 65-67 & comn undergrad educ in biol. *Mem:* AAAS; Am Soc Animal Sci; Am Inst Nutrit. *Res:* Pasture and fiber nutrition; nutrient requirements; undernutrition. *Mailing Add:* Chancellor's Off Univ of Calif Davis CA 95616

MEYER, JAMES HENRY, b St Marys, Pa, July 20, 28; m 60; c 3. METEOROLOGY. *Educ:* Pa State Univ, BS, 53, MS, 55. *Prof Exp:* Meteorologist, Res & Develop Ctr, Intel & Reconnaissance Lab, Griffiss Air Force Base, NY, 54-55; atmospheric physicist, Lincoln Lab, Mass Inst Technol, 55-63; proj meteorologist, Tech Oper Inc, Mass, 63-64; proj mgr, Electromagnetic Res Corp, Md, 64-67; SR STAFF METEOROLOGIST, APPL PHYSICS LAB, JOHNS HOPKINS UNIV, 67- *Concurrent Pos:* Consult meteorologist, 73- *Mem:* Am Meteorol Soc; Am Geophys Union; Am Soc Testing & Mat. *Res:* Radar and radio meteorology; meteorological instrumentation; atmospheric and cloud physics; power plant siting and atmospheric pollution meteorology. *Mailing Add:* 12926 Allerton Lane Silver Spring MD 20904

MEYER, JAMES MELVIN, b West Palm Beach, Fla, Jan 18, 43; m 69; c 2. POLYMER CHEMISTRY. *Educ:* Ind Univ, BS, 64; Northwestern Univ, PhD(inorg chem), 68. *Prof Exp:* Asst prof chem, Univ Ill, 67-69; res chemist, 69-74, div head chem, 74-77, mfg mgr, 78, DIV SUPT, PROCESS, BEAUMONT WORKS, E I DU PONT DE NEMOURS & CO, INC, 78- *Res:* Development of uses for elastomeric polymers. *Mailing Add:* 5765 Longwood Beaumont TX 77707

MEYER, JAMES WAGNER, b Rhineland, Mo, May 22, 20; m 49; c 4. ENERGY CONVERSION. *Educ:* Univ Wis, PhB, 48, PhD(physics), 56; Dartmouth Col, MA, 50. *Prof Exp:* Asst physics, Dartmouth Col, 48-49, Univ Calif, 49-50 & Univ Wis, 50-52; mem staff, Lincoln Lab, Mass Inst Technol, 52-57, group leader, 57-59, assoc head radar div, 59-62, assoc head solid state div, 62-63, head radio physics div, 63-65; sr scientist, Educ Serv, Inc, 65-67; mem tech staff, Lincoln Lab, Mass Inst Technol, 67-70, prog mgr, Ctr Space Res, 70-73, prog dir, Energy Lab, Mass Inst Technol, 73-76; asst dir, Plasma Fusion Ctr, 76-80; CONSULT PHYSICIST,80- *Mem:* AAAS; Am Phys Soc; Am Asn Physics Teachers. *Res:* Microwave spectroscopy of solid state; cryogenics, electronics; radio physics; education; energy conservation; alternative energy sources; fusion energy; solar energy. *Mailing Add:* Box 696 Middleton Rd New Durham NH 03855

MEYER, JEAN-PIERRE, b Lyon, France, Aug 5, 29; US citizen; m 58; c 6. MATHEMATICS, TOPOLOGY. *Educ:* Cornell Univ, BA, 50, MA, 51, PhD(math), 54. *Prof Exp:* Asst prof math, Syracuse Univ, 56; res assoc, Brown Univ, 56-57; from vis asst prof to asst prof, 57-65, assoc prof, 65-79, PROF MATH, JOHNS HOPKINS UNIV, 79- *Mem:* Am Math Soc. *Res:* Algebraic topology. *Mailing Add:* Dept Math Johns Hopkins Univ Baltimore MD 21218

MEYER, JOHANNES HORST MAX, b Berlin, Ger, Mar 1, 26; m 53; c 2. PHYSICS. *Educ:* Univ Geneva, Lic es sc, 49; Univ Zurich, PhD(physics), 52. *Prof Exp:* Swiss Soc res fel math & physics, Clarendon Lab, Oxford Univ, 53-55, Nuffield fel, 55-57; lectr appl physics, Harvard Univ, 57-59; from asst prof to assoc prof, 59-64, PROF PHYSICS, DUKE UNIV, 64- *Concurrent Pos:* Sloan fel, 60-63; vis prof, Munich Tech Univ, 65; vis fel, Japanese Soc Sci, 71; consult, NSF, 72-; vis sci, Inst Laue-Langevin, Grenoble, France, 74; mem, vis comt, Mat Sci Lab, Cornell Univ, 78- *Mem:* Fel Am Phys Soc; Swiss Soc Natural Sci. *Res:* Phenomena at low temperatures; magnetism; properties of clathrate compounds; liquid and solid helium and hydrogen; critical phenomena. *Mailing Add:* 2716 Montgomery St Durham NC 27705

MEYER, JOHN AUSTIN, b St Mary's, Pa, Sept 18, 19; m 55. NUCLEAR CHEMISTRY, RADIATION CHEMISTRY. *Educ:* Pa State Univ, BS, 49, MS, 50; State Univ NY Col Environ Sci & Forestry, PhD(org chem), 58. *Prof Exp:* Asst chemist, Anal Lab, Speer Carbon Co, Pa, 45-47; chemist, Gulf Res & Develop Co, 50-52; asst head anal dept, Verona Res Ctr, Koppers Co, 52-54; PROF NUCLEAR & RADIATION CHEM & RADIOL SAFETY OFF STATE UNIV NY COL ENVIRON SCI & FORESTRY, 58-, DIR, ANAL & TECH SERV, 72- *Concurrent Pos:* Fel, Oak Ridge Inst Nuclear Studies, 57 & 66; consult various US & foreign industs; vis scientist, Pa State Univ, 80; chmn, Niagara-Finger Lakes Sect, Am Nuclear Soc, 81-82; Borden Chem Award, Forest Prod Res Soc, 79. *Honors & Awards:* Chancellor's Award for Excellence in Prof Serv, State Univ NY, 78. *Mem:* AAAS; Am Chem Soc; Am Nuclear Soc; Forest Prod Res Soc; NY Acad Sci. *Res:* Development of wood-polymer materials by the heat-catalyst method; neutron activation analysis; trace analytical methods; radiation chemistry. *Mailing Add:* Dept of Chem State Univ of NY Col of Environ Sci & Forestry Syracuse NY 13210

MEYER, JOHN RICHARD, b St Louis, Mo, Feb 25, 48; m 74; c 1. ENTOMOLOGY. *Educ:* Univ Ill, Urbana, BS, 69; Cornell Univ, MS, 73, PhD(entom), 74. *Prof Exp:* Fel biol, Cornell Univ, 70-74; teacher gen sci, Ithaca Pub Schs, 74-75; asst prof biol, Indiana Univ Pa, 75-76; ASST PROF ENTOM, NC STATE UNIV, 76- *Mem:* AAAS; Entom Soc Am; Am Soc Zoologists. *Res:* Host plant recognition by insects of economic importance; development of integrated pest management programs on fruit crops in the southeast. *Mailing Add:* 2718 Everett Ave Raleigh NC 27607

MEYER, JOHN ROGER, physiology, zoology, see previous edition

MEYER, JOHN SIGMUND, b Princeton, Ill, May 12, 37; m 63; c 3. MICRO-COMPUTERS, STATISTICS. *Educ:* Wartburg Col, BA, 59; Northwestern Univ, MS, 61; Iowa State Univ, PhD(statist), 73. *Prof Exp:* Instr math, Wartburg Col, 61-67; asst prof, 67-74, assoc prof, 74-80, chmn dept, 75-78, PROF MATH, CORNELL COL, 80- *Concurrent Pos:* Lectr micro-computers, Am Inst Prof Educ, 79-; vis assoc prof comput sci, Iowa State Univ, 78-79. *Res:* Confidence intervals for quantiles of finite populations. *Mailing Add:* Dept of Math Cornell Col Mt Vernon IA 52314

MEYER, JOHN STIRLING, b London, Eng, Feb 24, 24; nat US; m 47; c 5. NEUROLOGY. *Educ:* McGill Univ, MD, CM, 48, MSc, 49; Am Bd Psychiat & Neurol, dipl. *Prof Exp:* Demonstr histol, McGill Univ, 45-46, demonstr clin micros, 46-47, fel, 48-49; asst med, Sch Med, Yale Univ, 49-50; demonstr neuropath & teaching fel neurol, Harvard Med Sch, 50-52; USPHS sr res fel, 52-54; instr med, Harvard Med Sch, 54-56; assoc vis physician neurol, Boston City Hosp, 56-57; consult & lectr neurol, US Naval Hosp, Chelsea, Mass, 57; prof neurol & chmn dept, Sch Med, Wayne State Univ, 57-69; chmn dept, 69-76, PROF NEUROL BAYLOR COL MED, 76- *Concurrent Pos:* Asst, Montreal Neurol Inst, McGill Univ, 45-46; from jr intern to sr intern, New Haven Hosp, Conn, 49-50, vis neurologist & supvr EEG lab, 54-56; head dept neurol, Detroit Gen Hosp, 57-69; consult, Grace, Children's Sinai, Detroit Mem & Dearborn Vet Hosps, 57-69; chief neurol dept, Harper Hosp, Detroit, 63-69; chief neurol serv, Methodist & Ben Taub Gen Hosps, Houston, 69-76; consult, Vet Admin & Hermann Hosps, 69-; mem, President's Comn Heart Dis, Cancer & Stroke, 64-65, Nat Adv Comt Neurol Dis & Blindness, 65-69 & Subcomt Cerebrovasc Dis, Nat Heart Inst-Nat Inst Neurol Dis & Blindness Joint Coun, 65-71; chmn res subcomt, Nat Inst Neurol Dis & Blindness, 66; cheif cerebrovascular res, Vet Admin Med Ctr & Baylor Col Med, 76- *Honors & Awards:* Harold G Wolff Award, 77, 78 & 79. *Mem:* Am Neurol Asn; NY Acad Sci; Am Heart Asn; AMA. *Res:* Cerebral blood flow and metabolism studies in migraine and stroke patients. *Mailing Add:* Dept of Neurol Baylor Col of Med Houston TX 77030

MEYER, JUDY LYNN, b Milwaukee, Wis, May 22, 46; m 73; c 1. STREAM ECOLOGY, ECOSYSTEM ECOLOGY. *Educ:* Univ Mich, BS, 68; Univ Hawaii, MS, 71; Cornell Univ, PhD(ecol & evolution biol), 78. *Prof Exp:* Res assoc, Oceanog Dept, Univ Hawaii, 70-72; ASST PROF LIMNOL & ECOL, ZOOL DEPT, UNIV GA, 77- *Mem:* Am Soc Limnol & Oceanog; Ecol Soc Am; North Am Benthol Soc; AAAS. *Res:* Nutrient dynamics in stream ecosystems with emphasis on dissolved organic carbon and phosphorus; ecosystem analysis of a blackwater river; effects of watershed disturbance on aquatic ecosystems; role of fishes in nutrient cycling on coral reefs. *Mailing Add:* Zool Dept & Inst Ecol Univ Ga Athens GA 30602

MEYER, KARL, b Kerpen, Ger, Sept 4, 99; nat US; m 30; c 2. BIOCHEMISTRY. *Educ:* Univ Cologne, MD, 24; Univ Berlin, PhD(chem), 28. *Prof Exp:* Asst, Univ Berlin, 27-28; Int Educ Bd fel, Univ Zurich, 28-29; asst prof exp biol, Univ Calif, 31-33; from asst prof to prof, 33-67, EMER PROF BIOCHEM & SPEC LECTR & CONSULT, DEPT MED, COL PHYSICIANS & SURGEONS, COLUMBIA UNIV, 67- *Concurrent Pos:* Chemist, Presby Hosp, New York, 33-; prof biochem, Belfer Grad Sch Sci, Yeshiva Univ, 67-78. *Honors & Awards:* Lasker Award, 56; Duckett-Jones Mem & Gairdner Award, 59. *Mem:* Nat Acad Sci; fel Am Acad Arts & Sci; AAAS; Soc Exp Biol & Med; Am Chem Soc. *Res:* Mucopolysaccharides; glycoproteins; connective tissues; mucopolysaccharides and mycolytic enzymes. *Mailing Add:* Eye Res Div Columbia Univ 630 W 168th St New York NY 10032

MEYER, KENNETH A, b New York, NY, Feb 5, 32; m 55; c 3. MECHANICAL ENGINEERING. *Educ:* Cornell Univ, BME, 54; Stanford Univ, MSc, 60, Engr, 61, PhD(mech eng), 66. *Prof Exp:* STAFF MEM FLUID MECH, LOS ALAMOS SCI LAB, 61- *Res:* Incompressible fluid mechanics, especially numerical treatment of hydrodynamic instability of viscous shear flows and Lagrangian treatment of compressible flows with shocks. *Mailing Add:* Los Alamos Sci Lab Los Alamos NM 87544

MEYER, LAWRENCE DONALD, b Concordia, Mo, Apr 14, 33; m 54; c 3. AGRICULTURAL ENGINEERING, SOILS. *Educ:* Univ Mo, BS, 54, MS, 55; Purdue Univ, PhD(agr eng), 64. *Prof Exp:* Asst soil & water eng, Univ Mo, 54-55; agr engr, USDA, Purdue Univ, 55-73, from asst prof to assoc prof agr eng, 65-73, AGR ENGR, SEDIMENTATION LAB, USDA, 73- *Concurrent Pos:* Adj prof agr & biol eng, Miss State Univ, 75- *Mem:* Am Soc Agr Eng; Soil Conserv Soc Am; Soil Sci Soc Am. *Res:* Soil and water conservation engineering; mechanics of the soil erosion process; rainfall simulation; erosion research techniques; erosion control on construction sites. *Mailing Add:* Sedimentation Lab USDA PO Box 1157 Oxford MS 38655

MEYER, LEO FRANCIS, b Pittsburgh, Pa, July 19, 29; m 54; c 4. ORGANIC POLYMER CHEMISTRY. *Educ:* Duquesne Univ, BS, 56; Univ Richmond, MS, 66. *Prof Exp:* Res chemist, Gulf Res & Develop Ctr, 56-61; assoc chemist, 61-63, res chemist, 63-69, mgr res ctr, 69-80, DIR RES CTR, PHILIP MORRIS INC, 80- *Mem:* Am Chem Soc. *Res:* Polymers; catalysis; aromatic alkylations; aerosol filtration; gas adsorbants; tobacco processing; cigarette making; plastics extrusion; paper coating. *Mailing Add:* 8526 Hanford Dr Richmond VA 23229

MEYER, LEO MARTIN, b New York, NY, Jan 14, 06; m 28; c 1. HEMATOLOGY. *Educ:* City Col New York, BS, 26; Cornell Univ, AM, 27; Univ Md, MD, 31. *Prof Exp:* Assoc vis physician, Kings County Hosp, 33-51; dir labs, South Nassau Communities Hosp, 41-64; hematologist in chg, Queen's Hosp Ctr, Jamaica, NY, 64-71; chief hemat & oncol res, 71-74, COORDR SICKLE CELL PROGS, VET ADMIN CENT OFF, WASHINGTON, DC, 74- *Concurrent Pos:* Attend hematologist, Vet Admin Hosp, Bronx, 46-52; consult hematologist, Goldwater Mem Hosp, 47-; asst prof clin med, Sch Med, NY Univ, 50-; attend hematologist, Meadowbrook Hosp, 53-55; res collarbr, Brookhaven Nat Lab, 55-; mem med serv teams to Marshall Islands, AEC, 57-; Fulbright-Hays res scholar, Turku Univ, 67; NSF exchange scientist to India, 68-69; chief hemat sect, Vet Admin Hosp, Brooklyn, 70-79. *Mem:* Am Fedn Clin Res; Am Asn Path & Bact; Soc Exp Biol & Med; Am Asn Cancer Res; Am Soc Hemat. *Res:* Macrocytic anemia; leukemia; applications of radioisotopes in hematology. *Mailing Add:* Hemat Sect Vet Admin Hosp St Albans NY 11425

MEYER, LEON HERBERT, b Navasota, Tex, Sept 4, 26; m 58; c 2. PHYSICAL CHEMISTRY, CHEMICAL ENGINEERING. *Educ:* Ga Inst Technol, BChE, 49, MS, 51; Univ Ill, PhD(chem), 53. *Prof Exp:* Asst, Univ Ill, 52-53; res chemist & engr, Atomic Energy Div, Explosives Dept, 53-64, res mgr, Separations Chem Div, Savannah River Lab, 64-67, dir separations chem & Eng Sect, 67-69, asst dir, Savannah River Lab, 69-76, prog mgr, AED Tech Div, 76-79, MGR, SPECIAL PROGRAMS, SAVANNAH RIVER PLANT, E I DU PONT DE NEMOURS & CO, INC, 79- *Mem:* Am Chem Soc; Am Inst Chem Eng. *Res:* Vapor-liquid equilibrium; nuclear magnetic resonance; fused salt electrolysis; cryogenics; radiochemical separations; nuclear fuel cycle; quality assurance; environmental control; energy conservation. *Mailing Add:* 2219 Dartmouth Rd Augusta GA 30904

MEYER, MARTIN MARINUS, JR, b Wichita, Kans, Dec 24, 36; m 61; c 2. ORNAMENTAL HORTICULTURE, PLANT PHYSIOLOGY. *Educ:* Kans State Univ, BS, 58; Cornell Univ, MS, 61, PhD(hort), 65. *Prof Exp:* Asst nursery mgr, M Meyer & Son Nursery, Kans, 58-59; asst ornamental hort, Cornell Univ, 59-64; asst prof, 65-71, ASSOC PROF NURSERY MGT, UNIV ILL, URBANA, 71- *Mem:* AAAS; Am Soc Hort Sci; Tissue Cult Asn; Sigma Xi. *Res:* Physiology of propagation; growth and development of woody plants; tissue culture propagation. *Mailing Add:* 1107 Dorner Dr Dept Hort Univ Ill Urbana IL 61801

MEYER, MARVIN CHRIS, b Detroit, Mich, Sept 19, 41; m 66; c 2. BIOPHARMACEUTICS, PHARMACOKINETICS. *Educ:* Wayne State Univ, BS, 63, MS, 65; State Univ NY Buffalo, PhD(pharmaceut), 69. *Prof Exp:* Teaching asst pharmaceut, Wayne State Univ, 64-65 & State univ NY Buffalo, 66-68; asst prof, 69-75, PROF PHARMACEUT, UNIV TENN CTR HEALTH SCI, & DIR DIV DRUG METAB & BIOPHARMACEUT, 76-, ASST DEAN GRAD & RES PROG, 81- *Concurrent Pos:* Expert, US Food & Drug Admin, 73-76; consult, Berlex Labs, 75-, Cord Labs, 80-, Pfizer Pharmaceut, 81- & Glaxo, Inc, 80- *Honors & Awards:* Mead Johnson Undergrad Res Award, Am Asn Cols Pharm, 70. *Mem:* Am Pharmaceut Asn; Acad Pharmaceut Sci; Am Asn Cols Pharm. *Res:* Study and quantitation of the time course of drugs in humans and animals, especially studies of drug absorption, metabolism, distribution and elimination. *Mailing Add:* Dept Col Pharmaceut Univ of Tenn Ctr Health Sci Memphis TN 38163

MEYER, MARVIN CLINTON, b Jackson, Mo, Dec 20, 07; m 46; c 3. ANIMAL PARASITOLOGY. *Educ:* SE Mo State Univ, BS, 32; Ohio State Univ, AM, 36; Univ Ill, PhD(parasitol), 39. *Prof Exp:* Asst biol, SE Mo State Univ, 30-32; prin high sch, Mo, 32-36; asst zool, Univ Ill, 36-39; instr, Univ Ky, 39-41; adj prof & actg head dept, Douglass Col, Rutgers Univ, 41-42, adj prof, 46; from instr to prof, 46-73, EMER PROF ZOOL, UNIV MAINE, ORONO, 73- *Concurrent Pos:* Fulbright res scholar, NZ, 55-56; mem adv comt, Smithsonian Oceanog Sorting Ctr, 65-; sr vis res assoc, Smithsonian Inst, US Nat Mus, 67-68; mem nat screening comt, Inst Int Educ, 67- *Mem:* Am Micros Soc; Am Soc Parasitol; Am Soc Zool; Soc Syst Zool. *Res:* Parasitology; morphology and taxonomy of Hirudinea; parasites of fish and wildlife; invertebrate morphology; faunistic zoology. *Mailing Add:* Dept of Zool Univ of Maine Orono ME 04473

MEYER, MAURICE WESLEY, b Long Prairie, Minn, Feb 13, 25; m 46; c 2. PHYSIOLOGY, DENTISTRY. *Educ:* Univ Minn, BS, 53, DDS, 57, MS, 59, PhD(physiol), 60. *Prof Exp:* Res fel, 57-60, from instr to asst prof, 60-64, lectr, 61-73, assoc prof, 64-78, PROF DENT PHYSIOL & NEUROL, UNIV MINN, MINNEAPOLIS, 78- *Concurrent Pos:* Res career develop award, 63-69. *Mem:* AAAS; Am Physiol Soc; Sigma Xi; Soc Exp Biol & Med; Int Asn Dent Res. *Res:* Circulation; blood flow in teeth and supporting structures; cerebral blood flow. *Mailing Add:* Dept of Physiol 424 Millard Hall Univ of Minn Minneapolis MN 55455

MEYER, MERLE P, b Eldridge, Iowa, Feb 11, 20; m 56; c 2. FORESTRY. *Educ:* Univ Minn, BS, 49, PhD(forestry), 56; Univ Calif, MF, 50. *Prof Exp:* Instr, 52, PROF FORESTRY & FOREST RESOURCES, UNIV MINN, ST PAUL, 52- *Concurrent Pos:* Consult, Okla Res Inst, 52-54, US Forest Serv, 56 & Geotechnics & Resources, Inc, 59-62; Fulbright lectr, Norway, 61-62; guest lectr, Finland & Poland, 62; consult, UN Arg, 64-67; NSF vis scientist lectr, 65; consult, Bur Land Mgt, 70- *Mem:* Soc Am Foresters; Am Soc Photogram; Soc Range Mgt; Wildlife Soc. *Res:* Application of aerial photography to forest and rangeland resource inventory and management. *Mailing Add:* Univ of Minn Col of Forestry St Paul MN 55101

MEYER, NORMAN JAMES, b Wolsey, SDak, Feb 17, 26; m 52; c 2. PHYSICAL CHEMISTRY. *Educ:* Univ SDak, BA, 49; Univ Kans, PhD(chem), 56. *Prof Exp:* Res engr, Continental Oil Co, 54-56; res chemist, Monsanto Chem Co, 56-58; res assoc inorg & nuclear chem, Mass Inst Technol, 58-59; from asst prof to assoc prof, 59-74, PROF CHEM, BOWLING GREEN STATE UNIV, 74- *Concurrent Pos:* Vis prof, Middle East Tech, Ankara, 65-66. *Mem:* Am Chem Soc. *Res:* Hydrolysis of metal ions; ion exchange; thermodynamics of electrolytic solutions. *Mailing Add:* 36 Ranch Ct Bowling Green OH 43402

MEYER, NORMAN JOSEPH, b Wilkes-Barre, Pa, Aug 5, 30. ACOUSTICS. *Educ:* Pa State Univ, BS, 51, MS, 53; Univ Calif, Los Angeles, PhD(physics), 59. *Prof Exp:* Sr engr, HRB-Singer, 51-52; res engr, Lockheed Aircraft Corp, 55-56; res physicist, Ford Aerospace & Com, Aeronutronic Div, 59-61; staff physicist, Marshall Labs, 61-62; sr scientist, West Div, Ling-Temco-Vought Res Ctr, 62-67, dir, 68-70; pres & prin scientist, OAS-Western, 70-72; DIR, WYLE RES-WYLE LABS, 73-; CLIN PROF COMMUNITY & ENVIRON MED, UNIV CALIF COL MED, IRVINE, 78- *Concurrent Pos:* Mem comt hearing & bioacoust, Nat Acad Sci-Nat Res Coun, 68- *Mem:* Acoust Soc Am. *Res:* Experimental acoustics, primarily gases, transducers and instrumentation; noise control technology. *Mailing Add:* Wyle Labs 128 Maryland St El Segundo CA 90245

MEYER, ORVILLE R, b Cornelius, Ore, Mar 4, 26; m 52; c 3. NUCLEAR ENGINEERING, ELECTRICAL ENGINEERING. *Educ:* Univ Wash, BS, 46; Calif Inst Technol, MS, 49. *Prof Exp:* Engr, Bettis Atomic Power Lab, Westinghouse Elec Corp, 50-53, supvry engr, 53-57, chief test engr, 57-60, mgr reactor control, 60-66; sr staff scientist, Idaho Nuclear Corp, 66-70; mgr protection & control systs, Loft Proj, 70-79, MGR ADVANCED CONTROL TECH OFF, EG&G-IDAHO, 80- *Mem:* Am Nuclear Soc; Inst Elec & Electronics Engrs. *Res:* Control; instrumentation; protection and safety of nuclear reactors for electric power generation or propulsion. *Mailing Add:* RR 3 Box 213 Idaho Falls ID 83401

MEYER, PAUL, b Bern, Switz, July 6, 25; US citizen. NUCLEAR PHYSICS, NUCLEAR MEDICINE. *Educ:* Univ Wash, BS, 58, MS, 60. *Prof Exp:* Physicist reactor physics, Vallecitos Nuclear Ctr, Gen Elec, 60-66; PHYSICIST NUCLEAR PHYSICS & NUCLEAR MED, LAWRENCE LIVERMORE LAB, 66- *Mem:* Am Phys Soc. *Res:* Photonuclear reactions; nuclear medical diagnostics. *Mailing Add:* Lawrence Livermore Lab PO Box 808 (L280) Livermore CA 94550

MEYER, PAUL RICHARD, b New York, NY, Feb 2, 30; div; c 4. PURE MATHEMATICS, TOPOLOGY. *Educ:* Dartmouth Col, AB, 51, MS, 52; Columbia Univ, MA, 60, PhD(math), 64. *Prof Exp:* Engr, Eastman Kodak Co, NY, 54-55; from lectr to instr math, Columbia Univ, 56-61; asst prof, St John's Univ, 62-64 & Hunter Col, 64-67; assoc prof, 68-71, chmn dept, 71-76 & 77-80, PROF MATH, LEHMAN COL, 72- *Concurrent Pos:* NSF res grant, 66-68; vis assoc prof, Univ Tex, 68-69; sr vis fel, Westfield Col, Univ London, 71-72; chmn math sect, NY Acad Sci, 76-78; vis res grant, Univ Padna, Italy, 81. *Mem:* Am Math Soc; Math Asn Am; London Math Soc; fel NY Acad Sci, 74. *Res:* Spaces of real-valued functions; general topology. *Mailing Add:* Dept of Math Herbert H Lehman Col Bronx NY 10468

MEYER, PETER, b Berlin, Ger, Jan 6, 20; nat US; m 46; c 2. COSMIC RAY PHYSICS. *Educ:* Tech Univ, Berlin, dipl, 42; Univ Gottingen, PhD(physics), 48. *Prof Exp:* Mem staff physics, Univ Gottingen, 46-49; fel, Cambridge Univ, 49-50; mem res staff, Max Planck Inst Physics, Ger, 50-52; res assoc, 53-56, from asst prof to assoc prof, 56-78, PROF ENRICO FERMI INST, UNIV CHICAGO, 78-, DIR, 78- *Concurrent Pos:* Consult, NASA; mem cosmic ray comn, Int Union Pure & Appl Physics, 66-72 & space sci bd, Nat Acad Sci, 75-78; chmn cosmic physics div, Am Phys Soc, 72-73; foreign mem, Max Planck Inst Physics & astrophys, 73- *Mem:* Fel Am Phys Soc; fel AAAS; Am Geophys Union; Am Astron Soc. *Res:* Origin of cosmic radiation; astrophysics. *Mailing Add:* Enrico Fermi Inst Univ Chicago 933 E 56th St Chicago IL 60637

MEYER, R PETER, b Buffalo, NY, Dec 7, 43. NEUROANATOMY, GROSS ANATOMY. *Educ:* Heidelberg Col, BS, 70; Temple Univ, PhD(anat), 77. *Prof Exp:* SR INSTR ANAT, HAHNEMANN MED COL, 77- *Mem:* NY Acad Sci; Sigma Xi; Cajal Club; Southern Soc Anatomists. *Res:* Neural connections of mammalian forebrain; cytology and connections of autonomic nervous system; experimental neuropathology utilizing various light microscopic and electron microscopic methods. *Mailing Add:* Dept Anat MS 408 Hahnemann Med Col 230 N Broad St Philadelphia PA 19102

MEYER, RALPH A, JR, b Washington, DC, July 3, 43; m 69. PHYSIOLOGY, ENDOCRINOLOGY. *Educ:* Univ Md, College Park, BS, 65, PhD(zool), 69. *Prof Exp:* Nat Inst Dent Res fel biol, Rice Univ, 69-71; asst prof physiol & pharmacol, Col Dent, NY Univ, 71-73; asst prof & head div, 73-77, ASSOC PROF PHYSIOL, DENT, MARQUETTE UNIV, 77-, HEAD DIV, 80- *Mem:* AAAS; Am Physiol Soc; Am Soc Zool; Endocrine Soc; Am Soc Bone & Mineral Res. *Res:* Actions of hormones in promoting mineral and bone homeostasis and metabolic bone disease. *Mailing Add:* Dept Basic Sci Sch Dent Marquette Univ 604 N 16 St Milwaukee WI 53233

MEYER, RALPH O, b Covington, Ky, May 28, 38; m 59; c 2. SOLID STATE PHYSICS, FUEL TECHNOLOGY. *Educ:* Univ Ky, BS, 60; Univ NC, PhD(physics), 66. *Prof Exp:* Res assoc physics, Univ Ariz, 65-68; asst metallurgist, Mat Sci Div, Argonne Nat Lab, 68-73; reactor engr, 73-76, SECT LEADER, US NUCLEAR REGULATORY COMN, 76- *Mem:* Am Nuclear Soc. *Res:* Diffusion in solids; reactor fuel analysis. *Mailing Add:* US Nuclear Regulatory Comn Washington DC 20555

MEYER, RALPH ROGER, b Milwaukee, Wis, Feb 18, 40; m; c 4. CELL BIOLOGY, BIOCHEMISTRY. *Educ:* Univ Wis-Milwaukee, BS, 61, Madison, MS, 63 & PhD(zool), 66. *Prof Exp:* Res assoc Yale Univ, 66-67; NIH fel, State Univ NY Stony Brook, 67-69; asst prof, 69-75, assoc prof, 75-79, PROF BIOL SCI, UNIV CINCINNATI, 79- *Concurrent Pos:* NSF grant, Univ Cincinnati, 69-71, Am Cancer Soc grants, 69-73, 79-82; NIH res grant, 75-83. *Mem:* Am Soc Biol Chemists; AAAS; Am Soc Cell Biol; Am Soc Microbiol. *Res:* regulation and mechanism of DNA replication and repair in normal and neoplastic tissues; role of single-stranded DNA-binding protein in E coli and mammalian cells; molecular biology. *Mailing Add:* Dept of Biol Sci Univ of Cincinnati Cincinnati OH 45221

MEYER, RICH BAKKE, JR, b Houston, Tex, Nov 6, 43; m 69. MEDICINAL CHEMISTRY, ORGANIC CHEMISTRY. *Educ:* Rice Univ, BA, 65; Univ Calif, Santa Barbara, PhD(org chem), 68. *Prof Exp:* Res scientist, ICN Pharmaceut, Inc, 70-73, head dept bio-org chem, 73-75; asst prof pharmaceut chem, Univ Calif, San Francisco, 75-80; ASSOC PROF MED CHEM, COL PHARM, WASH STATE UNIV, PULLMAN, 80- *Mem:* Am Chem Soc. *Res:* Design and synthesis of cancer chemotherapeutic agents, enzyme inhibitors and analogs of cyclic adenosine monophosphate; enzyme mechanisms. *Mailing Add:* Col Pharm Wash State Univ Pullman WA 99164

MEYER, RICHARD ADLIN, b Norwood, Mass, Dec 12, 33; m 56; c 3. NUCLEAR CHEMISTRY & PHYSICS. *Educ:* Northeastern Univ, BS, 56, MS, 58; Univ Ill, Urbana, PhD, 63. *Prof Exp:* Asst chemist, Bird & Son, Inc, Mass, 52-56; res asst chem, Northeastern Univ, 56-58; nuclear physics, Univ Ill, Champaign-Urbana, 59-63, NATO fel nuclear chem, Danish AEC Res Estab, Roskilde, Denmark, 65-66; res scientist nuclear struct, 66-75, GROUP LEADER & PROG LEADER, LAWRENCE LIVERMORE LAB, UNIV CALIF, 75- *Concurrent Pos:* Lectr, Northeastern Univ, 60. *Mem:* Am Chem Soc; Am Phys Soc. *Res:* Nuclear structure; rapid automated chemical separations and spectroscopy measurements; nuclear radiation standards; radiation preservation of foods; electron dosimetry; high energy photonuclear reactions in complex nuclei. *Mailing Add:* Lawrence Livermore Lab PO Box 808 Livermore CA 94550

MEYER, RICHARD CHARLES, b Cleveland, Ohio, May 2, 30; m 63; c 2. VETERINARY MICROBIOLOGY, INFECTIOUS DISEASES. *Educ:* Baldwin-Wallace Col, BSc, 52; Ohio State Univ, MSc, 57, PhD(cellulose digestion), 61. *Prof Exp:* Asst microbiol, Ohio State Univ, 56-61, res assoc virol & germ free res, Ohio State Univ Res Found, 61-62; microbiologist, Virol Res Resources Br, Nat Cancer Inst, 62-64; asst prof swine dis & germ free res, Col Vet Med, Univ Ill, Urbana-Champaign, 65-68, assoc prof, 68-73, PROF VET PATH & HYG, COL VET MED & MICROBIOL, SCH LIFE SCI, 73- *Concurrent Pos:* Mem spec review comt, Extramural Activ, Cancer Ther Eval Br, Nat Cancer Inst, 66. *Mem:* AAAS; Am Inst Biol Sci; Am Soc Microbiol; Soc Cryobiol; fel Am Acad Microbiol. *Res:* Porcine and bovine viruses; tissue culture; enteric and respiratory tract infections; diseases of baby pigs; development of germ free techniques to study mixed synergistic infections and host-parasite relationships. *Mailing Add:* Dept Vet Pathobiol Col Vet Med Univ of Ill at Urbana-Champaign Urbana IL 61801

MEYER, RICHARD DAVID, b Allentown, Pa, Apr 26, 43. INFECTIOUS DISEASES. *Educ:* Univ Pittsburgh, BS, 63, MD, 67. *Prof Exp:* Intern med, Bellevue Hosp, NY Univ, 67-68, jr asst resident, 68-69; sr asst resident med, Albert Einstein Col Med-Bronx Munic Hosp, 69-70; clin res trainee infectious dis, Mem Hosp, Cornell Univ Med Col, 70-72; Lt Comdr microbiol, US Naval Med Res Inst, 72-74; asst prof med, 74-79, ASSOC PROF MED, SCH MED, UNIV CALIF, LOS ANGELES, 79-; ASST CHIEF, INFECTIOUS DIS SECT, WADSWORTH VET ADMIN HOSP, LOS ANGELES, 74- *Mem:* Am Soc Microbiol; fel Infectious Dis Soc Am; Am Fedn Clin Res; fel Am Col Physicians. *Res:* Clinical evaluation of antibiotics; Legionnaires' disease; fungal infections. *Mailing Add:* Infectious Dis Sect 691/111F Wadsworth Hosp Ctr Los Angeles CA 90073

MEYER, RICHARD ERNST, b 19. MATHEMATICS, GEOPHYSICS. *Educ:* Swiss Fed Inst Technol, Dipl Mech Eng, 42, Dr Sc Techn, 46; Brown Univ, MA, 62. *Prof Exp:* Jr sci officer math, Brit Ministry Aircraft Prod, 45-46; asst lectr, Univ Manchester, 46-47, Imp Chem Industs res fel, 47-52; sr lectr aeronaut, Univ Sydney, 53-56, reader, 56-57; assoc prof appl math, Brown Univ, 57-59, prof, 59-64; PROF MATH, UNIV WIS-MADISON, 64- *Concurrent Pos:* Vis mem, Courant Inst Math Sci, NY Univ, 63-64; consult, Aeronaut Res Labs, Australian Dept Supply, 55-57 & Rand Corp, 61-62; mem, NSF Postdoctoral Panel, Nat Res Coun, 68-69, chmn panel for math, 70; sr fel, Fluid Mech Res Inst, Univ Essex, 71-72. *Mem:* Fel Australian Acad Sci; Am Geophys Union; Soc Indust & Appl Math. *Res:* Asymptotic analysis; partial differential equations; plasma physics; water waves; meteorology; gas dynamics. *Mailing Add:* Dept of Math Univ of Wis Madison WI 53706

MEYER, RICHARD FASTABEND, b Covington, Ky, Sept 13, 21. ECONOMIC GEOLOGY. *Educ:* Dartmouth Col, AB, 47; Harvard Univ, MA, 50; Univ Kans, PhD(geol), 68. *Prof Exp:* Sr geologist, Humble Oil & Ref Co, 51-61; geologist, US Geol Surv, 64-66; petrol specialist, Off Oil & Gas, US Dept Interior, 66-72; GEOLOGIST, US GEOL SURV, 72-, CHIEF, OFF RESOURCE ANAL, 78- *Mem:* AAAS; Am Asn Petrol Geol; Soc Petrol Eng. *Res:* Petroleum origin and occurrence; stratigraphy. *Mailing Add:* PO Box 227 Warrenton VA 22186

MEYER, RICHARD IRWIN, b Chicago, Ill, Jan 30, 23; m 49; c 3. FOOD SCIENCE, FOOD TECHNOLOGY. *Educ:* Univ Ill, BS, 48, MS, 49. *Prof Exp:* Food technologist, Armed Forces Qm Food & Container Inst, 49-56, head dairy, oil & fat prods function, Applns Eng Br, 56-58, chief, Dairy, Oil & Fat Prods Br, 58-61; sr specialist dairy, oil & fat foods, Div Food Technol, 61-80, FOOD TECHNOLOGIST & GOV REGULATIONS CONSULT, FOOD & DRUG ADMIN, 80- *Mem:* Am Oil Chem Soc; Am Dairy Sci Asn; Inst Food Technol. *Res:* Development of processes for production of specialized food products, cheeses, butterlike foods, eggs; standards of identity for food products within specialty; extensive knowledge of dairy and oil food; US government regulations. *Mailing Add:* 1707 Wilmart St Rockville MD 20852

MEYER, RICHARD LEE, b Independence, Mo, June 5, 31; m 60; c 1. PHYCOLOGY. *Educ:* Mo Valley Col, BS, 54; Univ Minn, PhD(bot), 65. *Prof Exp:* Instr bot & biol, Univ Minn, 58-59; staff scientist, NSF-Int Indian Ocean Exped, 61-62; asst prof phycol & biol, Calif State Univ Chico, 65-68; PROF BOT & BACT, UNIV ARK, FAYETTEVILLE, 68- *Concurrent Pos:* Water Resources Res Off res grant, 68-; Nat Park Serv, 71-, Corps of Engrs, 72-; consult, Reserve Mining Co, Silver Bay, Minn, 72-76, Minn Pollution Control Agency, 74-76 & Limnetics, Inc, 75. *Mem:* AAAS; Bot Soc Am; Int Phycol Soc; Phycol Soc Am; Am Inst Biol Sci. *Res:* Morphology, cytology, life-history and systematics of the algal class Chrysophyceae and other flagellated algae; algal ecology. *Mailing Add:* Dept of Bot & Bact Univ of Ark Fayetteville AR 72701

MEYER, RICHARD LEE, b Red Wing, Minn, Aug 23, 37; m 61; c 2. AGRICULTURAL ECONOMICS. *Educ:* Univ Minn, BS, 59; Cornell Univ, MS, 67, PhD(agr econ), 70. *Prof Exp:* Peace Corps vol, Chile, 62-64, vol liaison officer, Peace Corps, Washington, DC, 64-65; chief party agr econ res, 70-72, res adv, 72-73, asst prof, 73-74, PROF AGR ECON, OHIO STATE UNIV, 74-, DIR INT PROGS, 81- *Mem:* Am Agr Econ Asn; Am Econ Asn. *Res:* Agricultural development in developing countries; allocation and productivity of agricultural credit; part-time farming and off-farm income. *Mailing Add:* Ohio State Univ 136 Derby Hall Columbus OH 43210

MEYER, ROBERT BRUCE, b St Louis, Mo, Oct 13, 43; m 66, 80; c 1. SOLID STATE PHYSICS, MATERIALS SCIENCE. *Educ:* Harvard Univ, BS, 65, PhD(appl physics), 70. *Prof Exp:* Res fel & lectr, 70-71, asst prof, 71-74, assoc prof appl physics, Harvard Univ, 74-78; ASSOC PROF PHYSICS, BRANDEIS UNIV, 78- *Concurrent Pos:* Sloan Found fel, Harvard Univ, 71-73; NORDITA fel and vis prof, Chalmers Univ, Gotebors, Sweden, 77. *Honors & Awards:* Joliot Curie Professorship & Medal, City of Paris, France, 78. *Mem:* Am Optical Soc; Am Phys Soc. *Res:* Liquid crystals; polymers; condensed molecular systems. *Mailing Add:* Physics Dept Brandeis Univ Waltham MA 02154

MEYER, ROBERT EARL, b Chicago, Ill, May 18, 32; m 62. PLANT PHYSIOLOGY. *Educ:* Purdue Univ, BS, 54, MS, 56; Univ Wis, PhD(agron), 61. *Prof Exp:* PLANT PHYSIOLOGIST, AGR RES SERV, USDA, 61- *Mem:* Weed Sci Soc Am; Soc Range Mgt. *Res:* Development of more efficient methods of brush control on rangeland of the Southwest using good conservation and management practices; evaluation of chemicals; developmental anatomy of woody plants. *Mailing Add:* USDA Dept of Range Sci Tex A&M Univ College Station TX 77843

MEYER, ROBERT F, b Switz, Mar 7, 25; nat US; m 52; c 4. PHARMACEUTICAL CHEMISTRY. *Educ:* Swiss Fed Inst Technol, PhD(chem), 50. *Prof Exp:* With pharmaceut chem, Univ Kans, 50-51; res chemist, 52-58, SR RES CHEMIST, PARKE, DAVIS & CO, 58- *Mem:* Am Chem Soc. *Res:* Chemistry of chloromycetin and analogs; hydroxyl aminderivatives; heterocycles; cardiovascular drugs; diuretics; antianginals; angiotensin converting enzyme inhibitors; hypolipidemics. *Mailing Add:* Res Dept Warner Lambert Parke Davis & Co Ann Arbor MI 48106

MEYER, ROBERT JAY, b Ithaca, NY, Oct 24, 49; m 71; c 1. GEOPHYSICS. *Educ:* Cornell Univ, BA, 71; Univ Ill, Urbana, MS, 73, PhD(physics), 77. *Prof Exp:* Assoc scientist, Xerox Corp, 77-80; RES GEOPHYSICIST, GULF RES & DEVELOP CO, 80- *Mem:* Am Phys Soc; Sigma Xi. *Res:* Investigating the physical mechanisms responsible for attenuoction of seismic waves in porous rocks. *Mailing Add:* PO Drawer 2038 Pittsburgh PA 15230

MEYER, ROBERT PAUL, b Milwaukee, Wis, Dec 14, 24; m 51; c 5. SEISMOLOGY, GEOPHYSICAL INSTRUMENTATION. *Educ:* Univ Wis-Madison, BS, 48, MS, 50, PhD(geol & geophysics), 57. *Prof Exp:* Asst prof, 59-63, assoc prof, 63-68, PROF GEOPHYSICS, UNIV WIS-MADISON, 68- *Concurrent Pos:* Exec comt mem, Consortium Continential Reflection Profiling, 71-; mem, Comt Seismol, Nat Res Coun, Nat Acad Sci, 75-78 & Comt Seismol, Panel Seismol Studies Continental Lithosphere, 80-83; chmn, Oceanog & Limnol Grad Prog, Univ Wis, 75-78, dir, Seismol Lab & Geophysics Comput Fac, 59- *Mem:* Soc Explor Geophysicists; Seismol Soc Am; Am Geophys Union. *Res:* Plate tectonics, seismic properties of convergent margins; crust-mantle parameters from reflection and refraction studies; digital field instrumentation; chirped seismic sources; parameterization of earthquake source properties using digital data. *Mailing Add:* Dept Geol & Geophysics Univ Wis-Madison 1215 W Dayton St Madison WI 53706

MEYER, ROGER J, b Olympia, Wash, May 14, 28; m 59; c 6. PEDIATRICS. *Educ:* Univ Wash, BS, 51; Wash Univ, MD, 55; Harvard Univ, MPH, 59. *Prof Exp:* Instr pediat, Med Sch, Harvard Univ, 59-62; asst prof, Col Med, Univ Vt, 62-65; assoc prof, Sch Med, Univ Va, 65-68; assoc prof, Sch Med, Northwestern Univ, Evanston, 68-74; assoc prof pub health, Sch Pub Health, Univ Ill, & asst dean continuing educ, 74-76; PROF HEALTH CARE, SCH PUB HEALTH, PEDIAT SCH MED, UNIV WASH, 76- *Concurrent Pos:* Dir, Infant Welfare Soc, Chicago, 68-70; regional med coordr, Social & Rehab Serv, Dept Health, Educ & Welfare, Chicago, 70-74; mem exec bd, Nat Comt Prev Child Abuse; mem child safety comt, Nat Safety Coun; lectr, Northwestern Univ & Chicago Med Sch; health adv, Mayor's Comt Senior Citizens, Chicago, admin dir, Div Health, Tacoma Pub Schs, 76-; sr proj dir, Dept Pediat, Madlian Army Med Ctr, Tacoma, Wash, 80- *Mem:* Am Cong Rehab Med; Am Acad Pediat; fel Am Pub Health Asn; Am Pediat Asn; NPac Pediat Soc Child & Family Health Care Found. *Res:* Epidemiology and control of childhood injury; diagnosis and management of child and family disorders; community health systems. *Mailing Add:* 709 N Yakima Ave Tacoma WA 98403

MEYER, RONALD HARMON, b Walsh, Ill, Dec 30, 29; m 51; c 4. ECONOMIC ENTOMOLOGY. *Educ:* Univ Ill, BS, 51, MS, 56, PhD(econ entom), 63. *Prof Exp:* Asst entomologist, 56-65, assoc entomologist, 65-76, ENTOMOLOGIST, ILL STATE NATURAL HIST SURV, 76- *Mem:* Entom Soc Am. *Res:* Integrated control of insects and mites on fruit crops. *Mailing Add:* Ill Natural Hist Surv 172 Natural Resources Bldg 607 E Peabody Champaign IL 60820

MEYER, RONALD WARREN, b Battle Creek, Iowa, July 10, 29; m 52. PLANT PATHOLOGY. *Educ:* Univ Mo, BS, 56, MA, 57; Univ Calif, Berkeley, PhD(plant path), 65. *Prof Exp:* Asst prof plant path, Everglades Exp Sta, Fla, 65-66; bot, 66-70, PROF BOT, CALIF STATE UNIV, FRESNO, 70- *Mem:* Mycol Soc Am; Am Phytopath Soc; AAAS; Am Inst Biol Sci; Bot Soc Am. *Res:* Heterokaryosis; soil and root inhabiting fungi; lichenology. *Mailing Add:* Dept of Biol Calif State Univ Fresno CA 93710

MEYER, STEPHEN FREDERICK, b Berkeley, Calif, Aug 9, 47. SOLID STATE PHYSICS, THIN FILM TECHNOLOGY. *Educ:* Whitman Col, BA, 69; Stanford Univ, MS, 70, PhD(appl physics), 74. *Prof Exp:* Res assoc physics, Univ Ill, Urbana-Champaign, 73-76; mem staff, Lawrence Livermore Nat Lab, Univ Calif, 76-80; DIR THIN FILM RES, SOUTHWALL CORP, PALO ALTO, CALIF, 80- *Mem:* Am Phys Soc; Am Vacuum Soc. *Res:* Properties of transition metal compounds; applications of thin film technology to materials. *Mailing Add:* Southwall Corp 3961 E Bayshore Rd Palo Alto CA 94303

MEYER, STUART LLOYD, b New York, NY, May 28, 37; c 3. PHYSICS, EDUCATION. *Educ:* Columbia Univ, AB, 57; Princeton Univ, PhD(physics), 62. *Prof Exp:* Res physicist, Nevis Cyclotron Labs, Columbia Univ, 61-63; asst prof physics, Rutgers Univ, 63-67, Rutgers fac fel, Rutherford High Energy Lab, Eng, 66-67; assoc prof physics, 67-77, assoc chmn dept, 68-70, assoc prof decision sci, Grad Sch Mgt, 75-76, assoc prof finance, 76-77, PROF POLICY & ENVIRON & TRANSP, GRAD SCH MGT, NORTHWESTERN UNIV, 77- *Concurrent Pos:* Consult, Nat Accelerator Lab, 70-71, NSF, 74-75, Lib Cong, 76, Nat Oceanic & Atmospheric Admin, 76-77, Pace Inst, 78-80, Northwest Reg Educ Lab, Walter Reed Army Med Ctr, Alaska Dept Educ, 78- & Res Med Ctr, 79-80; chmn gen fac comt, Northwestern Univ, 71-72; vis staff mem, Los Alamos Sci Lab, 72-80; prog dir intermediate energy physics, NSF, 74-75; fel, Ctr for Teaching Professions, 74-75. *Mem:* AAAS; Am Phys Soc; NY Acad Sci; Am Asn Physicists Med. *Res:* High energy interactions; muon physics; weak interactions; counter and spark-chamber techniques; data analysis; probability and statistics; philosophy of science; radiation shielding; neutrino physics; telecommunications; teleconferencing; medical electronics; telemedicine; information science; electronics. *Mailing Add:* Leverone Hall Northwestern Univ Evanston IL 60201

MEYER, THOMAS J, b Dennison, Ohio, Dec 3, 41; m 63; c 2. INORGANIC CHEMISTRY. *Educ:* Ohio Univ, BS, 63; Stanford Univ, PhD(chem), 66. *Prof Exp:* NATO fel, Univ Col, Univ London, 66-67; asst prof, 68-75, PROF CHEM, UNIV NC, CHAPEL HILL, 75- *Concurrent Pos:* Alfred P Sloan Found fel, 75. *Mem:* Am Chem Soc; Am Soc Univ Professors; fel AAAS. *Res:* Kinetics and mechanisms of inorganic and organo-metallic reactions; photochemistry; electrochemistry; catalysis. *Mailing Add:* Dept of Chem Univ of NC Chapel Hill NC 27514

MEYER, THOMAS NOLAN, mechanical engineering, plasma chemistry, see previous edition

MEYER, VERNON M(ILO), b New Prague, Minn, Dec 20, 24; m 51; c 4. AGRICULTURAL ENGINEERING. *Educ:* Univ Minn, BAgrEng, 51, MS, 55, PhD(agr eng), 78. *Prof Exp:* Engr trainee, Fed Land Bank, Minn, 51-52; agr engr, Minn Farm Bur Serv Co, 52-53; asst agr eng, Univ Minn, 53-54, instr, 54-56, res assoc, 56-58; from asst prof to assoc prof, 58-76, PROF AGR ENG, IOWA STATE UNIV, 76-, EXTEN AGR ENGR, 58- *Mem:* Am Soc Agr Engrs; Water Pollution Control Fedn. *Res:* Rural electrication and farmstead mechanization. *Mailing Add:* 200 Davidson Hall Iowa State Univ Ames IA 50011

MEYER, VICTOR BERNARD, b New York, NY, Dec 17, 20; m 47; c 2. ORGANIC POLYMER CHEMISTRY. *Educ:* City Col New York, BS, 42; Columbia Univ, AM, 49, PhD(org chem), 53. *Prof Exp:* Chemist, Montrose Chem Co, 42 & 46-47; asst, Columbia Univ, 48-50; group leader textile chem, United Merchants Labs, Inc, 53-57; res chemist, W R Grace & Co, 57; sr chemist, Air Reduction Co, Inc, 58-60; chemist & dir, Viburnum Assocs, 60-74, pres & tech dir, Viburnum Resins, Inc, 62-74; res assoc, J P Stevens & Co, Inc, 74-77; group leader, Weyerhaeuser Co, 77-78; mgr latex polymers, Cellomer Corp, 78-80; CONSULT, 80- *Concurrent Pos:* Consult chemist, 62-74. *Mem:* Am Chem Soc; Fedn Soc Coatings Technol; Am Asn Textile Chemists & Colorists. *Res:* Synthetic latex and resin development; emulsion polymers in paints, textiles, nonwoven fabrics and paper; aqueous coatings and adhesives; paint testing and evaluation. *Mailing Add:* 83 Briarwood Dr E Berkeley Heights NJ 07922

MEYER, VINCENT D, b McKees Rocks, Pa, Nov 7, 32; m 62; c 3. PHYSICAL CHEMISTRY, CHEMICAL PHYSICS. *Educ:* Duquesne Univ, BS, 54; Ohio State Univ, PhD(phys chem), 62. *Prof Exp:* Fel electron-impact spectros, Mellon Inst, 62-65; mem tech staff, Gen Tel & Electronics Labs Inc, NY, 65-72 & GTE Sylvania, Inc, Pa, 72-74, SR ENG SPECIALIST, GTE

SYLVANIA LIGHTING CTR, 74- *Mem:* Am Chem Soc; Am Phys Soc. *Res:* Electron scattering; molecular structure; energy transfer; high vacuum technique; quantum chemistry; cathodoluminescence; electro-optic phenomena; spectroscopy; mass spectrometry. *Mailing Add:* GTE Sylvania 100 Endicott St Danvers MA 01923

MEYER, W(ILLIAM) KEITH, b Souv Falls, SDak, Dec 21, 29; m 52; c 2. PHYSICAL CHEMSITRY. *Educ:* Morningside Col, BS, 51; Univ Ky, MS, 55; Mich State Univ, PhD(phys chem), 58. *Prof Exp:* Prof chemist, 58-67, sect supvr, 67-68, RES ASSOC, GULF SCI & TECHNOL CO, 68- *Concurrent Pos:* Union Carbide fel, Mich State Univ, 57-58. *Mem:* Am Chem Soc; Soc Petrol Eng; Am Soc Testing Mat; AAAS. *Res:* Secondary oil recovery; drilling fluids; marine transportation; tanker safety. *Mailing Add:* Gulf Sci & Technol Co PO Box 2038 Pittsburgh PA 15230

MEYER, WALTER, b Chicago, Ill, Jan 19, 32; m 53; c 5. NUCLEAR & CHEMICAL ENGINEERING. *Educ:* Syracuse Univ, BChE, 56, MChE, 57; Ore State Univ, PhD(chem eng), 64. *Prof Exp:* Res asst chem eng, Syracuse Univ, 57; prin chem engr, Battelle Mem Inst, 57-58; instr chem eng, Ore State Univ, 58-64, asst prof, 64; from asst prof to assoc prof nuclear eng, Kans State Univ, 64-72; PROF NUCLEAR ENG & CHMN, UNIV MO, 72-, CO-DIR, ENERGY SYSTS & RESOURCES PROG, 74-, CO-DIR, ENERGY & PUB POLICY CTR, 81- *Concurrent Pos:* Summer res engr, Hanford Atomic Labs, Wash, 59 & 60; consult, GA Pac Co, 64, Kerr McGee Co, 66-67, Gen Physics Corp, 67, Boeing Co, 70, Northeast Utilities Co, Univ Affairs Div, Argonne Nat Lab, 70-71, Wis Elec Power Co, Fed Trade Comn, 76-80 & EG&G Idaho Inc, 78; mem, Governor Kans Nuclear Energy Coun, 70; Dir, Dept Energy Summer Inst, 73-78 & NSF Summer Inst, 78. *Mem:* Am Inst Chem Engrs; Am Chem Soc; fel Am Nuclear Soc; Am Soc Eng Educ. *Mailing Add:* Dept Nuclear Eng Univ Mo Columbia MO 65211

MEYER, WALTER DAVIDSON, dynamic meteorology, see previous edition

MEYER, WALTER EDWARD, b Hackensack, NJ, Sept 15, 29; m 48; c 2. PHARMACEUTICAL CHEMISTRY. *Educ:* Rutgers Univ, BS, 51; NY Univ, MS & PhD(org chem), 64. *Prof Exp:* Biochemist, 51-53, RES CHEMIST, LEDERLE LABS DIV, AM CYANAMID CO, 53- *Mem:* Am Chem Soc. *Res:* Structure determination on compounds having pharmaceutical interest; synthesis of compounds related to physiologically active materials. *Mailing Add:* 40 Van Arden Ave Suffern NY 10901

MEYER, WALTER H, b Cincinnati, Ohio, Aug 19, 22; m 44; c 3. NUTRITION. *Educ:* Mich State Univ, BS, 48. *Prof Exp:* Proj engr, Procter & Gamble Co, 48-51, supvr qual control, Procter & Gamble Defense Corp, 51-54, sect head toilet goods prod, Procter & Gamble Co, 54-57 & food prod, 57-66, mgr prof & regulatory rels, 66-68, ASSOC DIR FOOD PROD, PROD DEVELOP DEPT, PROCTER & GAMBLE CO, 68- *Concurrent Pos:* Am Med Asn Food Indust Liaison Adv Panel. *Res:* Food safety and regulations. *Mailing Add:* Procter & Gamble Co 6071 Center Hill Rd Cincinnati OH 45224

MEYER, WALTER JOSEPH, b New York, NY, Jan 12, 43; m 67; c 1. MATHEMATICS. *Educ:* Queen's Col, BA, 64; Univ Wis, MS, 66, PhD(math), 70. *Prof Exp:* Asst prof, 69-74, ASSOC PROF MATH, ADELPHI UNIV, 74- *Res:* Graph theory; convex sets. *Mailing Add:* Dept of Math Adelphi Univ Garden City NY 11530

MEYER, WALTER LESLIE, b Toledo, Ohio, Feb 28, 31; m 54; c 3. ORGANIC CHEMISTRY. *Educ:* Univ Mich, BS, 53, MS, 55, PhD(chem), 57. *Prof Exp:* Instr & res assoc chem, Univ Mich, 57; NSF fel, Univ Wis, 57-58; from instr to asst prof chem, Univ Ind, 58-65; assoc prof, 65-68, chmn dept, 67-73, PROF CHEM, UNIV ARK, FAYETTEVILLE, 68- *Mem:* Am Chem Soc; Royal Soc Chem; AAAS. *Res:* Chemistry of natural products; stereochemistry; nuclear magnetic resonance; organic synthesis. *Mailing Add:* Dept of Chem Univ of Ark Fayetteville AR 72701

MEYER, WILLIAM A(UGUST) P(ETER), b Rheydt, Ger, June 20, 23; US citizen; m 46; c 2. MECHANICAL & AUTOMOTIVE ENGINEERING. *Educ:* Yale Univ, BE, 44, ME, 47, DEng, 59. *Prof Exp:* Engr, Standard Oil Co Ind, 47-50; asst instr mech eng, Yale Univ, 50-51; engr, Gulf Res & Develop Co, 53-56, group leader, 56-61, sect supvr, 61-69, sr scientist, 69-70, dir tech serv, US Mkt Dept, 70-72, mgr lube oils mkt, Gulf Oil Refining & Mkt Co, 73-75, coordr res & tech serv, 75-76, TECH CONSULT, GULF SCI & TECHNOL CO, GULF OIL CORP, 76- *Mem:* Soc Automotive Engrs; Am Petrol Inst. *Res:* Fuels and lubricants for internal combustion engines including fuel combustion, air pollution and low temperature lubricant performance; alternate fuels. *Mailing Add:* Gulf Sci & Technol Co PO Drawer 2038 Pittsburgh PA 15230

MEYER, WILLIAM ELLIS, b Bonne Terre, Mo, July 22, 36; m 62; c 2. ANIMAL SCIENCE. *Educ:* Univ Mo, BS, 60, MS, 62, PhD(agr), 65. *Prof Exp:* PROF AGR, SOUTHEAST MO STATE UNIV, 65-, CHMN DEPT, 70- *Mem:* Am Soc Animal Sci. *Res:* Meat technology. *Mailing Add:* 2221 Brookwood Cape Girardeau MO 63701

MEYER, WILLIAM LAROS, b Keyser, WVa, May 27, 36; m 67; c 5. ENZYMOLOGY, BIOCHEMICAL REGULATION. *Educ:* Yale Univ, BS, 56; Univ Wash, PhD(biochem), 62. *Prof Exp:* From instr to assoc prof, 62-81, PROF BIOCHEM, UNIV VT, 81-, CHMN CELL BIOL PROG, 81- *Concurrent Pos:* Res group, World Fedn Neurol, 72-; vis assoc prof & NIH spec res fel, Univ Western Australia, 73. *Mem:* AAAS; Am Chem Soc; Am Soc Biol Chemists; NY Acad Sci. *Res:* Physiological control of enzyme activity and turnover in muscle, cartilage and other tissues; proteases and ribonucleases and their relationship to neuromuscular diseases and interferon action; enzyme mechanisms; fructose metabolism; calcium metabolism; insect biochemistry. *Mailing Add:* Dept of Biochem Univ of Vt Col of Med Burlington VT 05405

MEYER, WILLIAM PAUL, organic chemistry, see previous edition

MEYER, WOLFGANG E(BERHARD), b Berlin, Ger, Aug 2, 10; nat US; m 46; c 1. MECHANICAL ENGINEERING. *Educ:* Stuttgart Tech, BSME, 33; Hannover Tech, dipl, 35. *Prof Exp:* Res engr, Daimler-Benz Co, Ger, 35-37; asst, Pa State Col, 37-38; eng lab supvr, Am Bosch Corp, Mass, 38-40; res engr, Yale Univ, 41-43; proj engr, Fuel Injection Div, Bulova Watch Co, NY, 44-45; chief engr, Res Eng Corp, Conn, 45-47; assoc prof, 47-51, prof eng res, 51-57, prof mech eng, 57-76, EMER PROF MECH ENG, PA STATE UNIV, 76- *Concurrent Pos:* Consult, Texaco, Inc, 50-55, Borg-Warner Corp, 55-, USPHS, 61-67, Fairchild-Hiller Corp, 65-66 & Fed Aviation Agency, 66-67; dir automotive res prog, Transp Inst, Pa State Univ, 68-77; chmn coun tech adv, Pa Air Pollution Comn, 62-63; mem adv group diesel smoke & odor, Calif Motor Vehicle Control Bd, 63-66; chmn comt surface properties-vehicle interaction, Transp Res Bd, 70-78. *Honors & Awards:* Metrop Life Award of Merit, 68. *Mem:* Fel Soc Automotive Engrs; hon mem Am Soc Testing & Mat. *Res:* Engine combustion; fuel systems; emissions; automotive brakes; braking systems; tire and road friction. *Mailing Add:* WEM Res Bldg B University Park PA 16802

MEYERAND, RUSSELL GILBERT, JR, b St Louis, Mo, Dec 2, 33; m 56; c 1. PLASMA PHYSICS. *Educ:* Mass Inst Technol, SB, 55, SM, 56, ScD(plasma physics), 59. *Prof Exp:* Mem staff, res lab electronics, Mass Inst Technol, 56-57; prin scientist, United Aircraft Res Labs, 58-64, chief res scientist, 64-67, DIR RES, UNITED TECHNOLOGIES RES CTR, 67- *Concurrent Pos:* Consult, Atomic Power Equip Dept, Gen Elec Co, 55-56 & Army Sci Adv Panel, 70-74; mem adv comt, Sch Arts & Sci, Univ Hartford, 65; mem eng adv comt, Hartford Grad Ctr, Rensselaer Polytech Inst, 65-, educ coun, Mass Inst Technol, 69-, mem vis comt, Dept Physics, 77-; adv comt on corp assocs, Am Inst Physics, 71-73; NASA Space Prog Adv Coun, 74-; chmn eval panel, Quantum Elec Div, Inst Basic Standards, Nat Bur Standards, 70-72; mem ad hoc laser adv panel, NASA Res & Tech Coun, 71-; panel on productivity enhancement, Off Sci & Technol, Exec Off of the President, 71- *Mem:* Nat Acad Eng; Am Phys Soc; fel Am Inst Aeronaut & Astronaut; sr mem Inst Elec & Electronics Engrs; Sigma Xi. *Res:* Plasma and laser physics; electronics. *Mailing Add:* United Technol Res Ctr Silver Lane East Hartford CT 06108

MEYERHOF, WALTER ERNST, b Kiel, Ger, Apr 29, 22; nat US; m 47; c 2. EXPERIMENTAL PHYSICS, NUCLEAR PHYSICS. *Educ:* Univ Pa, MA, 44, PhD(physics), 46. *Prof Exp:* Asst instr physics, Univ Pa, 43, res physicist, 44-46; asst prof physics, Univ Ill, 46-49; from asst prof to assoc prof, 49-59, chmn dept, 70-77, PROF PHYSICS, STANFORD UNIV, 59- *Concurrent Pos:* Sloan Found sr res fel, 55-59; Lilly Found tenured fac develop award, 77-78. *Mem:* Fel Am Phys Soc. *Mailing Add:* Dept Physics Stanford Univ Stanford CA 94305

MEYERHOF, WALTER ERNST, b Kiel, Ger, Apr 29, 22; nat US; m 47; c 2. EXPERIMENTAL PHYSICS, ATOMIC & MOLECULAR PHYSICS. *Educ:* Univ Pa, MA, 44, PhD(physics), 46. *Prof Exp:* Asst instr physics, Univ Pa, 43, res physicist, 44-46; asst prof physics, Univ Ill, 46-49; from asst prof to assoc prof, 49-59, chmn dept, 70-77, PROF PHYSICS, STANFORD UNIV, 59- *Concurrent Pos:* Sloan Found sr res fel, 55-59; Lilly Found tenured fac develop award, 77-78; Alexander von Humboldt US Sr Scientist Award, 80-81. *Mem:* Fel Am Phys Soc; fel AAAS. *Mailing Add:* Dept Physics Stanford Univ Stanford CA 94305

MEYERHOFER, DIETRICH, b Zurich, Switz, Sept 19, 31; nat US; m 54; c 2. SOLID STATE PHYSICS. *Educ:* Cornell Univ, BEng Phys, 54; Mass Inst Technol, PhD(physics), 58. *Prof Exp:* Asst solid state physics, Mass Inst Technol, 54-56; MEM TECH STAFF, RES LABS, RCA CORP, 58- *Mem:* Inst Elec & Electronics Eng; Am Phys Soc; Sigma Xi. *Res:* Galvanomagnetic and optical measurements in semiconductors and insulators; molecular lasers; holography; physical properties of photosensitive polymers; electrical and optical properties of liquid crystals; micolithography. *Mailing Add:* David Sarnoff Res Ctr RCA Corp Princeton NJ 08540

MEYERHOFF, A(LAN) A, mathematics, electrical engineering, see previous edition

MEYERHOFF, ARTHUR AUGUSTUS, b Northampton, Mass, Sept 9, 28; m 51; c 3. GEOLOGY. *Educ:* Yale Univ, BA, 47; Stanford Univ, MS, 50, PhD(geol), 52. *Prof Exp:* Geologist, US Geol Surv, 48-52; geologist, Calif Explor Co, Standard Oil Co Calif, 52-56, sr geologist, Cuba Calif Oil Co, 56-59, geophysicist, Chevron Oil Co, 59-60, res geologist, Calif Co, 60-65; pub mgr, Am Asn Petrol Geol, 65-75; prof geol, Okla State Univ, 75-77; PARTNER, MEYERHOFF & COX, INC, 75-; PARTNER & CO-OWNER, ASSOC RESOURCE CONSULTS, 75- *Concurrent Pos:* Dir, Tulsa Sci Found, 66-72; pres northeast div, Frontiers Sci Found Okla, Inc, 71-72, mem exec comt, 71-72; vis prof, Univ Calgary, 78; dir, Warren Explor, Ltd, 80- *Honors & Awards:* George C Mattson Award, Am Assoc Petrol Geologists. *Mem:* Fel AAAS; fel Geol Soc Am; Soc Econ Paleont & Mineral; Am Asn Petrol Geologists; Asn Earth Sci Educ (pres, 69-70). *Res:* Structural geology; geotectonics; stratigraphy; carbonate rock; paleobotany; plate tectonics, continental drift; Caribbean geology; petroleum resources worldwide, with specialty in USSR and People's Repub China. *Mailing Add:* PO Box 4602 Tulsa OK 74104

MEYERHOFF, MARK ELLIOT, b New York, NY, Apr 10, 53. ELECTROANALYTICAL CHEMISTRY, CLINICAL CHEMISTRY. *Educ:* Herbert H Leman Col, BA, 74; State Univ NY, Buffalo, PhD(anal chem), 79. *Prof Exp:* Teaching asst gen chem, State Univ NY, Buffalo, 74-75, res asst anal chem, 75-79; ASST PROF CHEM & ANAL CHEM, UNIV MICH, 79- *Concurrent Pos:* Fel anal chem, Univ Del, 79. *Mem:* Am Chem Soc; AAAS; Am Asn Clin Chemists. *Res:* Development of new ion-selective electrodes, particularly gas sensors and their application as detectors in novel biochemical assay arrangements, including enzyme-labelled competitive binding techniques. *Mailing Add:* Dept Chem Univ Mich Ann Arbor MI 48109

MEYEROTT, ROLAND EDWARD, b Baldwin, Ill, Nov 20, 16; m 44; c 6. ASTROPHYSICS, ATOMIC PHYSICS. *Educ:* Univ Nebr, BA, 38, MA, 40; Yale Univ, PhD(physics), 43. *Prof Exp:* Asst physics, Univ Nebr, 38-40; asst, Yale Univ, 40-41, phys asst, Med Sch, 41, instr physics, 42-47, res assoc, 47-49; sr physicist, Argonne Nat Lab, 49-53 & Rand Corp, 53-56; mgr physics, Missiles & Space Div, Lockheed Aircraft Corp, 56-62, mgr phys sci lab, Lockheed Missiles & Space Co, 62-66, dir sci, res & develop div, 66-69, asst to vpres res & develop div, 69-71, dir sci, res & develop div, 71-73; SCI CONSULT, 73- *Mem:* Fel Am Phys Soc. *Res:* Theoretical molecular physics; spectroscopy; atomic wave function calculations; opacity and equation of state of matter at higher temperatures; effects of minor species on atmosphere. *Mailing Add:* 27100 Elena Rd Los Altos Hills CA 94022

MEYERS, ALBERT IRVING, b New York, NY, Nov 22, 32; m 57; c 3. ORGANIC CHEMISTRY. *Educ:* NY Univ, AB, 54, PhD(chem), 57. *Prof Exp:* Res chemist, Cities Serv Res & Develop Co, 57-58; from asst prof to prof chem, La State Univ, 58-69, Boyd prof, 69-70; prof, Wayne State Univ, 70-72; PROF CHEM, COLO STATE UNIV, 72- *Concurrent Pos:* Res grants, NIH, 58-85, Res Corp, 58-59, New Orleans Cancer Soc, 59-60, Eli Lilly, 65-66, US Army, 66-69, G D Searle, 75-81, Hoffmann-La Roche, 70-75 & Petrol Res Fund, 69-75; vis res fel, Harvard Univ, 65-66; res grants, NSF, 69-82, US Army, 75-82, Petrol Res Fund, 75-78, G D Searle, 78 & Hoffmann-La Roche, 78; adj Boyd prof, La State Univ, 70-73; consult, G D Searle, 72- & Midwest Res Inst, 75-79; exec comt orgn div, Am Chem Soc, 75-77, chmn, 80-; chmn, Gordon Conf Heterocycles, 73 & Sterochem, 82. *Honors & Awards:* Distinguished Fac Award, La State Univ, 64; A G Clark Res Award, Colo State Univ, 80; Sigma Xi Award, 81. *Mem:* Am Chem Soc; fel Japan Chem Soc; The Chem Soc; Sigma Xi; Int Soc Heterocyclic Chem (vpres). *Res:* Synthetic organic chemistry; chemistry of heterocyclis compounds; asymmetric syntheses, total synthesis of natural products. *Mailing Add:* Dept of Chem Colo State Univ Ft Collins CO 80521

MEYERS, BERNARD LEONARD, b New York, NY, Apr 16, 37; m 58; c 2. STRUCTURAL MECHANICS, MATERIALS SCIENCE. *Educ:* Polytech Inst Brooklyn, BSCE, 58; Univ Mo, MS, 60; Cornell Univ, PhD(struct eng), 67. *Prof Exp:* Asst prof civil eng, Univ Mo, 60-64; prof, Univ Iowa, 67-73; PROJ MGR, BECHTEL CORP, ROCKVILLE, MD, 73- *Concurrent Pos:* Consult, Taylor Woodrow, Ltd, London, 71. *Mem:* Am Concrete Inst; Am Soc Civil Engrs; Am Soc Eng Educ. *Res:* Material behavior in civil engineering materials; behavior of structural concrete. *Mailing Add:* Bechtel Corp 6606 Sulky Lane Rockville MD 20852

MEYERS, CAL YALE, b Utica, NY, Nov 14, 27. ORGANIC CHEMISTRY. *Educ:* Cornell Univ, AB, 48; Univ Ill, PhD(org chem), 51. *Prof Exp:* Res fel, Princeton Univ, 51-53; res chemist, Union Carbide Plastics Co, 53-60; vis res prof, Bologna, 60-63; sr res assoc, Univ Southern Calif, 63; vis scholar, Univ Calif, Los Angeles, 63-64; assoc prof, 64-68, PROF CHEM, SOUTHERN ILL UNIV, CARBONDALE, 68- *Concurrent Pos:* Consult, Heliodyne Corp, 64 & Scripps Clin & Res Found, Calif, 64-; NSF res grant, 73; exchange scientist, Nat Acad Sci-Acad Sci, Ger Dem Repub, 82; Swedish Natural Sci Res Coun Award, 82; vis res lectr, Uppsala Univ, 82. *Honors & Awards:* Res Award, Union Carbide Corp, 57; Int Travel Award, NSF, 61, 70 & 71; Res Award, Am Chem Soc-Petrol Res Fund, 62; Res Award, Intra-Sci Res Found, 64; vis lectr, Polish Acad Sci, 78. *Mem:* Am Chem Soc; Italian Chem Soc; Sigma Xi. *Res:* Organosulfur bonding; reactions of carbon tetrahalides with alcohols, ketones and sulfones; isomerizations and eliminations of allylic ethers, sulfides, sulfoxides and sulfones; comparison of nucleophilic and one-electron-transfer reactivities of anions; aromatic-substitution reactions via one-electron transfers; radical/anion-radical pair mechanisms. *Mailing Add:* Dept of Chem Southern Ill Univ Carbondale IL 62901

MEYERS, DONALD BATES, b Cedar Rapids, Iowa, Jan 30, 22; m 50; c 4. PHARMACOLOGY. *Educ:* Univ Iowa, BS, 44, MS, 48, PhD(pharmaceut chem, pharmacol), 49. *Prof Exp:* Asst pharmaceut chem, Univ Iowa, 47-49; from asst prof to prof pharmacol, Butler Univ, 49-62, Baxter distinguished prof, 58; prof, Univ Tex, 62-63; sr pharmacologist, 63-68, res scientist, 68-72, RES ASSOC, TOXICOL DIV, ELI LILLY & CO, 72- *Concurrent Pos:* Lectr, Sch Nursing, Ind Methodist Hosp, 52-60; lectr, Butler Univ, 65- *Mem:* AAAS; Acad Pharmaceut Sci; Soc Toxicol. *Res:* Toxicology; neuropharmacology; drug metabolism. *Mailing Add:* Toxicol Div Eli Lilly & Co Box 708 Greenfield IN 46140

MEYERS, EARL LAWRENCE, b Victor, Iowa, Nov 1, 07; m 41; c 2. PHYSICAL CHEMISTRY. *Educ:* Coe Col, BS, 30; Univ Ill, PhD(chem), 34. *Prof Exp:* Res fel, 34; chem consult, 37-38; inspector, US Food & Drug Admin, 39-41, resident inspector, 46-51, new drug off, new drug br, 52-58, chief chemist div new drugs, 58-63, chief controls eval br, 63-66, dir div oncol & radiopharmaceut, 67-74; RETIRED. *Mem:* Fel AAAS; Am Chem Soc; NY Acad Sci; fel Am Inst Chem; Soc Nuclear Med. *Res:* X-rays; spectroscopy; rare earths; radiopharmaceuticals; stability of drugs; quality control of drugs. *Mailing Add:* 5225 S Seventh Rd Arlington VA 22204

MEYERS, EDWARD, b New York, NY, Aug 17, 27; m 62; c 1. MICROBIOLOGY. *Educ:* City Col New York, BS, 49; Univ Ky, MS, 51; PhD(bact), Univ Wis, 58. *Prof Exp:* Microbiologist, Nepera Chem Co, NY, 52; med bacteriologist, Ft Detrick, Md, 52-54; RES GROUP LEADER, SQUIBB INST MED RES, 58- *Mem:* Am Soc Microbiol; Sigma Xi; fel Am Acad Microbiol; Japanese Antibiotics Res Asn. *Res:* Area of microbial biochemistry dealing with fermentation, isolation and characterization of antibiotics and other microbial products; full or partial biosynthesis of new compounds; fermentation and analytical techniques. *Mailing Add:* Squibb Inst Med Res Box 4000 Princeton NJ 08540

MEYERS, ELWOOD WILLIAM, b Dallastown, Pa, June 6, 08; m 33; c 3. CHEMISTRY. *Educ:* Lebanon Valley Col, BS, 30. *Prof Exp:* Chemist, Hershey Foods Res Labs, Hershey Chocolate Corp, 30-47, chief chemist & dir res, 47-66, dir res, 66-80; RETIRED. *Mem:* Fel Am Chem Soc; Inst Food Technol; Am Dairy Sci Asn; Am Asn Candy Technol. *Res:* New products and process development for the manufacture of chocolate and chocolate products. *Mailing Add:* 1062 Fishburn Rd Hershey PA 17033

MEYERS, FREDERICK HENRY, b Ft Wayne, Ind, June 16, 18; m 47; c 3. PHARMACOLOGY. *Educ:* Univ Calif, MD, 49. *Prof Exp:* Intern, Univ Calif Hosp, 49-50; from instr to asst prof pharmacol, Univ Tenn, 50-53; from asst prof to assoc prof, 53-64, PROF PHARMACOL, SCH MED, UNIV CALIF, SAN FRANCISCO, 64- *Res:* Cardiovascular and autonomic physiology and pharmacology; problems of drug abuse. *Mailing Add:* Dept of Pharmacol Univ of Calif Sch of Med San Francisco CA 94143

MEYERS, GENE HOWARD, b Chicago, Ill, Dec 6, 42; m 71. PHYSICAL CHEMISTRY, COMPUTER SCIENCES. *Educ:* Univ Ill, Urbana, BS, 64; Univ Calif, Berkeley, PhD(phys chem), 69. *Prof Exp:* Sr systs analyst, 69-80, STAFF SCIENTIFIC ANALYST, KAISER ALUMINUM & CHEM CORP, PLEASANTON, 80- *Mem:* Am Chem Soc; Asn Comput Mach. *Res:* Laboratory automation; computer operating systems; data communications; microwave spectroscopy. *Mailing Add:* Kaiser Aluminum & Chem Corp 6177 Sunol Blvd Pleasanton CA 94566

MEYERS, HARVEY I, radiology, deceased

MEYERS, HERBERT, b New York, NY, Nov 15, 31; m 67; c 4. GEOPHYSICS. *Educ:* City Col New York, BS, 58. *Prof Exp:* Geophysicist geomagnetism, Coast & Geod Surv, 58-66; DIR CHIEF GEOPHYS, NAT OCEANIC & ATMOSPHERIC ADMIN, 66- *Concurrent Pos:* Mem, Geothermal Resource Coun, 74- *Mem:* Am Geophys Union; Soc Explor Geophysicists; AAAS; Sigma Xi. *Res:* Geophysical data management, including seismology, geomagnetism, marine geology. *Mailing Add:* Geophys & Solar-Terrest Data Ctr Solid Earth Data Serv EDIS-NOAA Boulder CO 80302

MEYERS, JAMES HARLAN, b Fountain Springs, Pa, Sept 5, 45; m 66; c 2. GEOLOGY. *Educ:* Franklin & Marshall Col, AB, 67; Ind Univ, Bloomington, MA, 69, PhD(geol), 71. *Prof Exp:* Lectr geol, Ind Univ, Bloomington, 71; asst prof geol, Muskingum Col, 71-80; MEM FAC, DEPT GEOL & EARTH SCI, WINONA STATE UNIV, 80- *Mem:* Geol Soc Am; Am Asn Petrol Geologists; Soc Econ Paleontologists & Mineralogists; Clay Minerals Soc. *Res:* Sedimentary petrology, paleoenvironments of sedimentary rocks; clay mineralogy, relating to provenance and environment of deposition of sedimentary rocks; sedimentology and recent analogs of ancient depositional environments. *Mailing Add:* Dept Geol & Earth Sci Winona State Univ Winona MN 55987

MEYERS, KENNETH PURCELL, b Jamaica, NY; m 57; c 2. CELL BIOLOGY, ENDOCRINOLOGY. *Educ:* NY Univ, AB, 53; Rutgers Univ, New Brunswick, MS, 65, PhD(endocrinol), 67. *Prof Exp:* Sr scientist, Worcester Found Exp Biol, Mass, 67-69; sr pharmacologist, Dept Pharmacol, 69-74, SR SCIENTIST, DEPT CELL BIOL, HOFFMAN-LA ROCHE INC, 74- *Mem:* Brit Soc Endocrinol; Soc Study Reprod; Sigma Xi. *Res:* Physiology and pharmacology of prostaglandin synthesis. *Mailing Add:* Res Div Hoffmann-La Roche Inc Nutley NJ 07110

MEYERS, LEROY FREDERICK, b New York, NY, June 30, 27. MATHEMATICS. *Educ:* Queens Col, NY, BS, 48; Syracuse Univ, MA, 50, PhD(math), 53. *Prof Exp:* Actg asst prof math, Univ Va, 53-54; from instr to asst prof, 54-62, ASSOC PROF MATH, OHIO STATE UNIV, 62- *Concurrent Pos:* Partic, numerical anal training prog, NSF-Nat Bur Standards, 59. *Mem:* Am Math Soc; Asn Comput Mach; Math Asn Am; Asn Symbolic Logic. *Res:* Mechanical translation; Hilbert space. *Mailing Add:* Dept of Math Ohio State Univ 231 W 18th Ave Columbus OH 43210

MEYERS, M DOUGLAS, b Mt Sterling, Ill, Jan 30, 33; m 61; c 2. INORGANIC CHEMISTRY. *Educ:* Univ Ill, BS, 55; Mass Inst Technol, PhD, 59. *Prof Exp:* From res chemist to sr res chemist, Am Cyanamid Co, 59-71; group leader, Kennecott Copper Co, 71-75; tech dir, Kocide Chem Corp, 75-78; DEVELOP CHEMIST, MARATHON-MORCO CO, 78- *Mem:* Am Chem Soc. *Res:* Transition metal complexes; copper chemistry; fungicides; aquatic chemicals; sulfonation; thixotropic materials; white mineral oil refining. *Mailing Add:* Marathon-Morco Co Drawer C Dickinson TX 77539

MEYERS, MARIAN BENNETT, b New York City, NY, Feb 22, 38; m 63; c 2. GENETICS, DRUG RESISTANCE. *Educ:* Barnard Col, AB, 59; Univ Md, MS, 62; Cornell Univ, PhD(biochem), 77. *Prof Exp:* Res chemist, Merck & Co, 62-63; lectr org chem, Barnard Col, 63-64 & Queens Col, 65-72; fel genetics, Albert Einstein Col Med, 77-79; fel, 79-81, RES ASSOC, SLOAN-KETTERING INST, 81- *Mem:* Am Chem Soc; Am Soc Cell Biol; NY Acad Sci; Am Women Sci; AAAS. *Res:* Mechanisms of resistance to vincristine; role of gene amplification in the development of resistance to vincristine; gene amplification in human neuroblastoma cells. *Mailing Add:* Century Trail Harrison NY 10528

MEYERS, MARTIN BERNARD, b Newark, NJ, Sept 12, 33; m 62. ORGANIC CHEMISTRY. *Educ:* Polytech Inst Brooklyn, BS, 54; Yale Univ, MS, 56, PhD(chem), 58. *Prof Exp:* NIH fel, Queen's Univ Belfast, 58-59; proj leader steroid res, Gen Mills, Inc, 59-61; Imp Chem Industs fel, Glasgow Univ, 61-64; sr lectr org chem, Col Technol, Belfast, 61-71; SR LECTR ORG CHEM, ULSTER POLYTECH, 71- *Mem:* Royal Soc Chem; fel Royal Inst Chem. *Res:* Plant biochemistry and biosynthesis; fungicides and chemistry of color photography. *Mailing Add:* Sch Phys Sci Ulster Polytech Jordanstown Northern Ireland Northern Ireland

MEYERS, NORMAN GEORGE, b Buffalo, NY, June 29, 30; m 58; c 4. MATHEMATICS. *Educ:* Univ Buffalo, BA, 52; Ind Univ, MA, 54, PhD(math), 57. *Prof Exp:* From instr to assoc prof, 57-68, PROF MATH, INST TECHNOL, UNIV MINN, MINNEAPOLIS, 68- *Mem:* Am Math Soc. *Res:* Partial differential equations; calculus of variations. *Mailing Add:* Dept of Math Univ of Minn Minneapolis MN 55455

MEYERS, PAUL, b Philadelphia, Pa, Sept 23, 39; div; c 2. MICROBIOLOGY, VIROLOGY. *Educ:* Temple Univ, BA, 61; State Univ NY Upstate Med Ctr, PhD(microbiol), 70. *Prof Exp:* Res assoc, Med Sch, Univ Miami, 70-71, from instr to asst prof microbiol, 72-73; consult, Mayo Clin, 73-80, from asst prof to assoc prof microbiol, Mayo Med Sch, 73-80. *Mem:* Am Asn Cancer Res; Transplantation Soc; Soc Gen Microbiol; Am Asn Immunologists; Am Soc Microbiol. *Res:* Viral oncology; immunology. *Mailing Add:* Dept Microbiol Mayo Clin & Med Sch Rochester MN 55901

MEYERS, PHILIP ALAN, b Hackensack, NJ, Mar 3, 41; m 65; c 3. ORGANIC GEOCHEMISTRY, OCEANOGRAPHY. *Educ:* Carnegie-Mellon Univ, BS, 64; Univ RI, PhD(oceanog), 72. *Prof Exp:* Chemist, Interchem Corp, 67-68; asst prof, 72-77, ASSOC PROF OCEANOG, UNIV MICH, ANN ARBOR, 77- *Concurrent Pos:* Vis scientist, Ind Univ, 79-80; assoc ed, Geophys Res Letters, 79-81. *Mem:* AAAS; Am Soc Limnol Oceanog; Geochem Soc; Sigma Xi; fel Geol Soc Am. *Res:* Organic geochemistry of water and sediments; distribution of fatty acids, alcohols and hydrocarbons in natural waters, sediments and organisms. *Mailing Add:* 2233 Space Res Bldg Univ of Mich Ann Arbor MI 48109

MEYERS, PHILIP HENRY, b Chicago, Ill, Feb 24, 33; m; c 3. RADIOLOGY. *Educ:* Univ Minn, BA, 52, BS, 53, MD, 55; Am Bd Radiol, dipl. *Prof Exp:* Intern, Kings County Hosp, Brooklyn, 55-56; resident radiol, Bellevue Hosp, New York, 56-57; asst prof, 62-64, assoc prof, 64-77, CLIN ASSOC PROF RADIOL, SCH MED, TULANE UNIV, 77- *Concurrent Pos:* Fel diag radiol, New York Hosp, 59-60; Nat Cancer Inst fel radiation ther & radioisotopes, NY Univ-Bellevue Med Ctr, 60-61; vis radiologist, Charity Hosp, New Orleans, La, 62-; consult radiologist, St Barnabas Hosp Chronic Dis, New York, 62-; consult assoc scientist, Biomed Comput Ctr, Tulane Univ, 64-65. *Mem:* Am Col Radiol; Soc Nuclear Med; Radiol Soc NAm. *Mailing Add:* 401 Emerald St New Orleans LA 70124

MEYERS, ROBERT ALLEN, b Los Angeles, Calif, May 15, 36; m 61; c 2. FUEL SCIENCE, ORGANIC CHEMISTRY. *Educ:* San Diego State Col, BA, 59; Univ Calif, Los Angeles, PhD(chem), 63. *Prof Exp:* Fel, Calif Inst Technol, 63-64; sr res chemist, Bell & Howell Res Ctr, 64-66; head org chem sect, Chem & Chem Eng Dept, 66-73, MGR ENERGY & NATURAL RESOURCES, SYSTS & ENERGY DIV, TRW SYSTS,73- *Concurrent Pos:* Mem, US-USSR working group on air pollution control, 74- *Mem:* Am Chem Soc; Am Inst Chem Engrs. *Res:* Organic synthesis chemistry; hydrometallury of sulfur; organic synthesis; aromatic nucleophilic substitution; oxidative mechanisms; polymer synthesis; desulfurization of fossil fuels through chemical reaction; design and construction of pilot test units for fuel processing. *Mailing Add:* TRW Systs One Space Park Redondo Beach CA 90278

MEYERS, SAMUEL PHILIP, b Asbury Park, NJ, Feb 21, 25; m 52; c 3. MARINE MICROBIOLOGY. *Educ:* Univ Fla, BS, 50; Univ Miami, MS, 52; Columbia Univ, PhD(bot), 57. *Prof Exp:* Res aide marine microbiol, Marine Lab, Univ Miami, 52-54, asst prof, 57-61, assoc prof, Inst Marine Sci, 61-68; PROF FOOD SCI & TECHNOL, LA STATE UNIV, BATON ROUGE, 68- *Mem:* AAAS; Mycol Soc; Am Soc Indust Microbiol; Am Soc Microbiol; Brit Soc Gen Microbiol. *Res:* Biology of marine fungi; microbial ecology; bionomics of marine yeasts; ecology of marine nematodes. *Mailing Add:* Dept of Food Sci & Technol La State Univ Baton Rouge LA 70803

MEYERS, VERA KOLB, b Belgrade, Yugoslavia, Feb 5, 48; m 76. ORGANIC CHEMISTRY, MEDICINAL CHEMISTRY. *Educ:* Univ Belgrade, BS, 71, MS, 73; Southern Ill Univ, Carbondale, PhD(org chem), 76. *Prof Exp:* Fel, Univ Res Found, La Jolla, Calif, 77-78; res assoc & instr chem, Southern Ill Univ, Carbondale, 78-81. *Concurrent Pos:* Fulbright travel grant, 73-76; tour speaker, Am Chem Soc, 80; adj asst prof chem, Southern Ill Univ, Carbondale, 81- *Mem:* Am Chem Soc; Sigma Xi; Serbian Chem Soc. *Res:* Reaction mechanisms; steroid chemistry; carbanion chemistry; electron transfer reactions; conformational analysis; mechanism of action of morphine agonists and antagonists. *Mailing Add:* Dept of Chem & Biochem Southern Ill Univ Carbondale IL 62901

MEYERS, VERNON J, b Pierre, SDak, Feb 6, 33; m 55; c 2. STRUCTURAL ENGINEERING. *Educ:* SDak Sch Mines & Technol, BS, 55; Purdue Univ, MS, 60, PhD(struct eng), 62. *Prof Exp:* Eng trainee, Gary Sheet & Tin Mill, US Steel Corp, 55-57, engr, 57-59; asst prof civil eng, 62-67, ASSOC PROF CIVIL ENG, PURDUE UNIV, WEST LAFAYETTE, 67- *Mem:* Am Soc Civil Engrs; Am Soc Eng Educ; Am Soc Testing & Mat. *Res:* Numerical computer analysis of structures; new methods of forming shell structures; use of new materials in construction. *Mailing Add:* Civil Eng Bldg Purdue Univ West Lafayette IN 47907

MEYERS, WAYNE MARVIN, b Aitch, Pa, Aug 28, 24; m 53; c 4. MEDICAL MICROBIOLOGY. *Educ:* Juniata Col, BS, 47; Univ Wis, MS, 53, PhD(microbiol), 55; Baylor Univ, MD, 59. *Prof Exp:* Res assoc, Univ Wis, 51-54; from asst to instr microbiol, Col Med, Baylor Univ, 54-59; intern med, Conemaugh Valley Mem Hosp, Johnstown, Pa, 59-60; staff physician, Berrien County Hosp, Berrien Ctr, Mich, 60-61; dir, Nyankanda Leprosarium, Burundi, 61-62; staff physician, Oicha Leprosarium, Repub Zaïre, 62-64, med dir, Kivuvu Leprosarium, 65-73; prof path, Univ Hawaii Sch Med, 73-75; CHIEF DIV MICROBIOL, ARMED FORCES INST PATH, 75- *Mem:* Sigma Xi; Int Acad Path; Int Leprosy Asn; Int Soc Trop Dermat; Am Soc Trop Med & Hyg. *Res:* Leprosy; filariasis; Mycobacterium Ulcerans infections; tropical and parasitic diseases. *Mailing Add:* Div of Microbiol Dept of Armed Forces Inst of Path Washington DC 20306

MEYERS, WILLIAM C, b Vicksburg, Miss, Apr 3, 31; m 54; c 3. PALYNOLOGY, GEOLOGY. *Educ:* Southern Ill Univ, BA, 56; Univ Tulsa, MS, 63, PhD(earth sci), 77. *Prof Exp:* Res geologist, Sinclair Res Labs, 56-68; SR RES SCIENTIST, EXPLOR & PROD RES, CITIES SERV OIL CO, 70- *Mem:* Am Asn Stratig Palynologists; Int Comt Coal Petrol; Comt Paleozoic Palynology. *Res:* Stratigraphic palynology and sedimentary environmental analysis; thermal alteration of kerogen and its organic geochemical products. *Mailing Add:* Explor & Prod Res Lab PO Box 50408 Tulsa OK 74150

MEYER-SCHUTZMEISTER, LUISE, nuclear physics, deceased

MEYERS-ELLIOTT, ROBERTA HART, b New York, NY, July 5, 37; m 78; c 2. IMMUNOLOGY. *Educ:* San Diego State Col, BS, 59; Univ Calif, Los Angeles, MS, 62, PhD(med microbiol, immunol), 64. *Prof Exp:* Immunologist, Sch Med, Univ Calif, Los Angeles, 60-62, immunochemist, 62-64; immunochemist, Calif Inst Technol, 64-67; asst prof ophthal, 73-75, assoc prof ophthal, 75-81, PROF OPHTHAL & JULES STEIN EYE INST, SCH MED, UNIV CALIF, LOS ANGELES, 81- *Concurrent Pos:* Nat Inst Allergy & Infectious Dis fel, 64-67; Nat Eye Inst res career develop award, 75- *Mem:* NY Acad Sci; Am Asn Immunol; Asn Res Vision & Ophthal; Reticuloendothelial Soc; Am Soc Microbiol. *Res:* Viral immunology and immunopathology; ocular immunology and inflammation; cellular immunity; autoimmune phenomena and ocular disorders. *Mailing Add:* Jules Stein Eye Inst Univ of Calif Ctr Health Sci Los Angeles CA 90024

MEYERSON, ARTHUR LEE, b East Orange, NJ, June 30, 38; m 61; c 1. MARINE GEOLOGY, MARINE GEOCHEMISTRY. *Educ:* Univ Pa, BA, 59; Lehigh Univ, MS, 61, PhD(geol), 71. *Prof Exp:* Instr geol, Upsala Col, 61-62; from instr to assoc prof, 62-75, chmn dept, 73-79, PROF EARTH & PLANETARY ENVIRON, KEAN COL NJ, 75- *Mem:* Atlantic Estuarine Res Soc; AAAS; Geol Soc Am; Soc Econ Paleontologists & Mineralogists. *Res:* Holocene stratigraphy; estuarine geochemistry. *Mailing Add:* Dept Earth & Planetary Environ Kean Col of NJ Union NJ 07083

MEYERSON, BERNARD STEELE, b NY, June 2, 54. SOLID STATE PHYSICS. *Educ:* City Univ New York, PhD(physics), 81. *Prof Exp:* Fel, 80-81, RES STAFF MEM, IBM CORP, 81- *Concurrent Pos:* Adj lectr, physics, City Col New York, 76-80. *Mem:* Am Phys Soc. *Res:* Preparation and analysis of novel semiconducting materials, with emphasis on correlating preparation techniques with resulting transport phenomenon in such films. *Mailing Add:* IBM T Watson Res Ctr PO Box 218 Yorktown NY 10598

MEYERSON, MARK DANIEL, b Alexandria, Va, Feb 14, 49; m 69. TOPOLOGY. *Educ:* Univ Md, BS, 71; Stanford Univ, MS, 73, PhD(math), 75. *Prof Exp:* vis lectr math, Univ Ill, Urbana, 75-78; ASST PROF MATH, US NAVAL ACAD, 78- *Mem:* Am Math Soc; Math Asn Am. *Res:* Geometric topology. *Mailing Add:* Dept of Math US Naval Acad Annapolis MD 21402

MEYERSON, SEYMOUR, b Chicago, Ill, Dec 4, 16; m 43; c 2. CHEMISTRY, MASS SPECTROMETRY. *Educ:* Univ Chicago, SB, 38. *Prof Exp:* Chemist, Res Dept, 46-61, chemist, Res & Develop Dept, Am Oil Co, 61-62, res assoc, 62-72, sr res assoc, 72-80, RES CONSULT, STANDARD OIL CO IND, 80- *Mem:* Am Chem Soc; Am Soc Mass Spectrometry; Am Soc Testing & Mat. *Res:* Mass spectrometry of organic compounds and applications thereof to study of molecular structures and reaction mechanisms. *Mailing Add:* Standard Oil Co (Ind) Res Dept PO Box 400 Naperville IL 60566

MEYLAN, MAURICE ANDRE, b Cortland, NY, Mar 16, 42. SEISMIC STRATIGRAPHY. *Educ:* State Univ NY Buffalo, BA, 64; Fla State Univ, MS, 68; Univ Hawaii, PhD(oceanog), 78. *Prof Exp:* Geologist, Offshore Explor, Shell Oil Co, 67-72; lectr, Dept Geol Sci, Univ Wis, Milwaukee, 78-79; ASST PROF, DEPT GEOL, UNIV SOUTHERN MISS, 80-, CHMN DEPT, 81- *Concurrent Pos:* Consult, Mining Ventures Div, Shell Oil Co, 76-77; co-investr, Dept Planning & Econ Develop, State Hawaii, 77-78; prin investr & mem bd dir, Miss Mineral Resources Inst, 81- *Mem:* AAAS; Am Asn Petrol Geologists; Am Geophys Union; Clay Mineral Soc; Geol Soc Am. *Res:* Determination of sediment depositional geometries indicative of certain types of mineral deposits can be delineated in Mississippi sound. *Mailing Add:* Dept Geol Southern Sta Box 9247 Hattiesburg MS 39401

MEYN, RAYMOND EVERETT, JR, b Mobile, Ala, Aug 29, 42; m 68; c 2. BIOPHYSICS, RADIATION BIOLOGY. *Educ:* Univ Kans, BS, 65, MS, 67, PhD(radiation biophys), 69. *Prof Exp:* USPHS fel, 69-70, asst physicist, 71-75, ASSOC PHYSICIST & ASSOC PROF BIOPHYS, UNIV TEX, M D ANDERSON HOSP & TUMOR INST, HOUSTON, 75- *Concurrent Pos:* Assoc mem, Univ Tex Grad Sch Biomed Sci, Houston, 71-74, mem, Grad Fac, 74- *Mem:* Biophys Soc; Radiation Res Soc; Am Asn Cancer Res. *Res:* Replication and repair of DNA in mammalian cells; regulation of growth and division; radiobiology of fast neutrons. *Mailing Add:* Dept of Physics Univ Tex MD Anderson Hosp & Tumor Inst Houston TX 77030

MEZEI, CATHERINE, b Budapest, Hungary, July 27, 31; Can citizen; m 54; c 1. BIOCHEMISTRY, PHARMACY. *Educ:* Univ Budapest, BS, 54; Univ BC, MS, 60, PhD(biochem), 64. *Prof Exp:* Fel, Ore State Univ, 64-67; asst prof, 67-73, ASSOC PROF BIOCHEM, DALHOUSIE UNIV, 73- *Concurrent Pos:* Med Res Coun Can res scholar, Dalhousie Univ, 67-73. *Mem:* Can Biochem Soc; Int Soc Neurochem; Am Soc Neurochem. *Res:* Biochemistry of nerve development. *Mailing Add:* Dept of Biochem Dalhousie Univ Halifax NS B3H 3J5 Can

MEZEI, MICHAEL, b Mezokovesd, Hungary, Oct 7, 27; Can citizen; m 54; c 1. PHARMACEUTICS. *Educ:* Med Univ Budapest, Dipl pharm, 54; Ore State Univ, PhD(pharm), 67. *Prof Exp:* Instr pharm, Univ BC, 57-64 & Ore State Univ, 65-67; asst prof, 67-71, assoc prof, 71-79, PROF PHARM, DALHOUSIE UNIV, 79- *Mem:* Am Pharmaceut Asn; Acad Pharmaceut Sci; Can Pharmaceut Asn; Ny Acad Sci. *Res:* Liposomes; formulation of dermatological preparations; biopharmaceutics; new drug delivery systems. *Mailing Add:* Dept Pharm Dalhousie Univ Col Pharm Halifax NS B3H 3J5 Can

MEZEI, MIHALY, b Budapest, Hungary, June 17, 44; US citizen; m 70. PHYSICAL CHEMISTRY. *Educ:* Eotvos Lorand Univ, Budapest, dipl chem, 67, PhD(chem), 72. *Prof Exp:* Res chemist, Hungarian Chem Ind Comput Ctr, 67-72; systs programmer, Young & Rubicam Int, Inc, 73-74; assoc res scientist, NY Univ, 74-76; adj assoc prof, 77-78, SR RES ASSOC STATIST MECH, HUNTER COL, 76- *Concurrent Pos:* Adj assoc prof, Manhattan Community Col, 78- & Seton Hall Univ, 80-81. *Mem:* Sigma Xi; Am Chem Soc; NY Acad Sci. *Res:* Statistical thermodynamics of molecular liquids; developments in Monte Carlo simulation methodology; computer simulation of aqueous solutions; free-energy calculation by Monte Carlo methods; quantum chemistry, especially development of methods applicable to not one-particle trial functions. *Mailing Add:* Dept Chem 695 Park Ave New York NY 10021

MEZEY, EUGENE JULIUS, b Cleveland, Ohio, Apr 9, 26; m 56; c 2. INORGANIC CHEMISTRY. *Educ:* Ohio Univ, BS, 50; Ohio State Univ, MS, 54, PhD(chem), 57. *Prof Exp:* Asst, Res Found, Ohio State Univ, 52-54, assoc, 54-55, res fel, 55-57; sr res chemist, Pittsburgh Plate Glass Co, 57-60, supvr explor inorganic group, 60-63; SR RES CHEMIST, COLUMBUS DIV, BATTELLE MEM INST, 63- *Concurrent Pos:* Instr, Univ Akron, 59-63; lectr, Ohio State Univ, 64-65, assoc, 65-66. *Mem:* Fel AAAS; Am Chem Soc; Am Ceramic Soc; Am Inst Chem; Int Microwave Power Inst. *Res:* Effluent control; minerals and metallurgical processes; fuels and fuel contaminants; technology assessment; hazardous materials disposal; process metallurgy of manganese nodules; plasmas and excited states; chemical process development; carbides; oxides; high energy processes; reactions induced with microwave energy and the use of microwaves in chemical processing. *Mailing Add:* Columbus Labs Battelle Mem Inst 505 King Ave Columbus OH 43201

MEZEY, KALMAN C, b Nagyvarad, Hungary, Sept 18, 09; US citizen; m 35; c 3. MEDICINE, PHARMACOLOGY. *Educ:* Univ Basel, MD, 33. *Hon Degrees:* Dr, Univ Javeriana Bogota, 75. *Prof Exp:* Asst internal med, Univ Hosp, Univ Basel, 33-36; asst, Univ Clin, Univ Vienna, 36-37; prof pharmacol, Pontifical Univ Javeriana, Colombia, 42-58; VPRES MED SCI, MERCK SHARP & DOHME INT, 59-; vis prof, Med Sch, Univ Vienna, 72; clin prof med, NJ Med Sch, 74- *Concurrent Pos:* Vis prof, Med Sch, Univ Vienna, 72; clin prof med, NJ Med Sch, 74-; attend physician, Vet Admin Med Ctr, East Orange, NJ, 74-; Biol Sci Bogota Award, 52-57. *Honors & Awards:* Cross of Boyaca Award, 57; Kalman C Mezey Chair of Pharmacol, Univ Javeriana Bogota, 75. *Mem:* Am Soc Pharmacol & Exp Therapeut; fel Am Col Clin Pharmacol & Chemother; Am Soc Trop Med & Hyg; AMA. *Res:* Pharmacology of drugs acting on the cardiovascular system; medicinal plants; arrow poisons; clinical pharmacology. *Mailing Add:* Merck Sharp & Dohme Int Rahway NJ 07065

MEZEY, PAUL G, b Nagyvarad, Hungary, Apr 28, 43; Can citizen. QUANTUM CHEMISTRY, THEORETICAL ORGANIC CHEMISTRY. *Educ:* Univ Budapest, MSc, 67, PhD(chem), 70, MSc, 72. *Prof Exp:* Res assoc chem, Hungarian Acad Sci, 67-73; res scientist & lectr, Univ Toronto, 73-77; asst prof, 77-79, ASSOC PROF CHEM, UNIV SASK, 79- *Concurrent Pos:* Lectr chem, Univ Budapest, 70-73. *Mem:* Int-Am Photochem Soc. *Res:* Reaction topology; quantum chemistry of molecular conformational changes and reactions; convergence properties of approximate molecular wave functions; quantum biochemistry. *Mailing Add:* Dept of Chem & Chem Engrs Univ of Sask Saskatoon SK S7N 0W0 Can

MEZGER, FRITZ WALTER WILLIAM, b Bryn Mawr, Oct 19, 28. THEORETICAL PHYSICS. *Educ:* Harvard Col, AB, 48; Univ Cincinnati, PhD(physics), 57. *Prof Exp:* Reactor physicist nuclear energy propulsion aircraft proj, Fairchild Co, 48-51; leader reactor physics subunit, Aircraft Nuclear Propulsion Dept, 51-54, supvr nuclear anal unit, 54-56, mgr appl math subsect, 56-59, controls & instrumentation develop subsect, 59-60 & physics & math subsect, 60-61, consult physicist space sci lab & proj scientist, Adv Space Proj Dept, 61-64, mgr space power & propulsion res, 64-68, mgr advan studies, 68-74, MGR RESOURCE PLANNING & MGT, ADVAN STUDIES, SPACE DIV, GEN ELEC CO, 74- *Mem:* Am Phys Soc; Am Nuclear Soc; Asn Comput Mach; Inst Elec & Electronics Eng; Am Inst Aeronaut & Astronaut. *Res:* Plasma propulsion; magneto-hydrodynamic power generation; laser applications; reactor physics; nuclear engineering; electrodynamics; control engineering; digital computer applications. *Mailing Add:* Gen Elec Co Space Div PO Box 8555 Philadelphia PA 19101

MEZGER-FREED, LISELOTTE, b Berlin, Ger, Feb 6, 26; US citizen; m 51; c 4. GENETICS, EMBRYOLOGY. *Educ:* Bryn Mawr Col, AB, 46; Wash Univ, MA, 48; Columbia Univ, PhD(zool), 52. *Prof Exp:* Instr biol, Brooklyn Col, 52-53; USPHS fel embryol, Inst Cancer Res, 54-57; instr, Temple Univ, 59-60; res assoc, Bryn Mawr Col, 61-66; res assoc, Inst Cancer Res, 66-70, asst mem, 70-77; prof dir cell biol, NSF, 78-79; RETIRED. *Mem:* Am Soc Cell Biol; Am Asn Cancer Res; Genetics Soc Am; AAAS; Soc Develop Biol. *Res:* Gene expression in vertebrate haploid cell lines. *Mailing Add:* 716 Andorra Rd Lafayette Hill PA 19444

MEZICK, JAMES ANDREW, b Scranton, Pa, July 4, 39; m 70; c 3. DERMATOLOGY, SKIN BIOLOGY. *Educ:* Univ Scranton, BS, 61; Ohio State Univ, PhD(biochem), 69. *Prof Exp:* Fel biochem, St Louis Univ, 69-71; sr res scientist, Pharmaceut Res, Johnson & Johnson, 71-77, asst mgr, New Prod Develop, 77-78, Dermat Biol, 78, Drug Disposition & Metab, 78-79; group leader skin biol, 79-80, group leader dermat, 80-82, RES FEL DERMAT PHAMACOL, ORTHO PHARMACEUT CORP, 82- *Honors & Awards:* Johnson Medal, 80. *Mem:* Soc Investigative Dermat; Am Acad Dermat; Am Soc Photobiol; AAAS. *Res:* Design and development of model systems to evaluate compounds for topical and systemic dermatological activity for anti-acne, anti-inflammatory applications; percutaneous absorption; development of sun protection sunscreen preparations. *Mailing Add:* 43 Valley Forge Dr New Brunswick NJ 08816

MEZZINO, MICHAEL JOSEPH, JR, b Galveston, Tex, Sept 5, 40; m 65; c 1. MATHEMATICS. *Educ:* Austin Col, BA, 62; Kans State Col Pittsburg, MA, 63; Univ Tex, Austin, PhD(math), 70. *Prof Exp:* Res mathematician, Tracor Inc, Tex, 65-66; instr math, Univ Tex, Austin, 70; asst prof, Southwestern Univ Tex, 70-74; ASSOC PROF MATH, UNIV HOUSTON, CLEAR LAKE CITY, 74- *Concurrent Pos:* Consult, Tracor Inc, Tex, 66- & J & J Marine Diving Co, 74- *Mem:* AAAS; Am Math Soc. *Res:* Mathematical modeling; computer graphics. *Mailing Add:* Sch of Sci & Technol Univ Houston Clear Lake City Houston TX 77058

MI, MING-PI, b Shanghai, China, May 24, 33; m 65. GENETICS. *Educ:* Taiwan Univ, BS, 54; Univ Wis, MS, 59, PhD(genetics), 63. *Prof Exp:* NSF fel genetics, 63-64, asst geneticist, 64-65, from asst prof to assoc prof, 65-71, PROF GENETICS, UNIV HAWAII, 71- *Concurrent Pos:* NIH res grant, 64-67 & 81-83. *Mem:* Am Soc Human Genetics; Biometric Soc; Genetics Soc Am; Am Genetic Asn. *Res:* Statistical and population genetics. *Mailing Add:* Dept of Genetics Univ of Hawaii Honolulu HI 96822

MIALE, JOSEPH NICOLAS, b Johnston, RI, May 9, 19; m 55; c 3. PETROLEUM CHEMISTRY. *Educ:* Providence Col, BS, 40; Tex A&M Univ, MS, 47. *Prof Exp:* Instr chem, Agr & Mech Col, Tex, 47; res chemist, Res Dept, 47-62, SR RES CHEMIST, CENT RES DIV, MOBIL RES & DEVELOP CORP, 62- *Mem:* Am Chem Soc; Int Cong Catalysis. *Res:* Exploratory research on processes and catalysts for hydrocarbon conversions. *Mailing Add:* 25 Merrit Dr Lawrenceville NJ 08648

MIATECH, GERALD JAMES, b Stambaugh, Mich, Dec 31, 22; m 45; c 3. GEOPHYSICS, SPACE SCIENCES. *Educ:* Mich Technol Univ, BS, 49; St Louis Univ, MS, 56; Univ Wis, PhD(geophys), 61. *Prof Exp:* Geophysicist, M A Hanna Co, Mich, 49-50; geophysicist & aerospace engr, US Air Force, 50-65; res scientist, Ames Res Ctr, NASA, Moffett Field, Calif, 66-72; geophysicist & aerospace engr, 72-74, SR MEM TECH STAFF & ENG SPECIALIST, ESL, INC, SUNNYVALE, CALIF, 74- *Mem:* AAAS; Am Geophys Union; Soc Explor Geophysicists; Sigma Xi. *Res:* Space systems; geophysical investigations for earth resources (vector aeromagnetometry). *Mailing Add:* 19300 Chablis Ct Saratoga CA 95070

MICALE, FORTUNATO JOSEPH, b Niagara Falls, NY, Aug 11, 32. PHYSICAL CHEMISTRY, COLLOID CHEMISTRY. *Educ:* St Bonaventure Univ, BA, 56; Niagara Univ, BS, 59; Purdue Univ, MS, 61; Lehigh Univ, PhD(phys chem), 65. *Prof Exp:* Res asst prof, 66-70, ASSOC PROF PHYS CHEM, LEHIGH UNIV, 70- *Mem:* Am Chem Soc. *Res:* Colloid and surface properties of inorganic oxides, polmer latexes and carbon; dispersion stability; solution adsorption. *Mailing Add:* Ctr Surface & Coatings Res Sinclair Lab Lehigh Univ Bethlehem PA 18015

MICELI, ANGELO SYLVESTRO, b New York, NY, Dec 24, 13; m 38; c 6. PHYSICAL CHEMISTRY. *Educ:* Wayne Univ, BS, 34, MS, 36; Univ Mich, PhD(chem), 42. *Prof Exp:* From asst to instr chem, Wayne Univ, 34-42; sr scientist, US Rubber Co, 42-48, head chem res & develop, Uniroyal Int, 48-51, from asst mgr res & develop to mgr res & develop, 51-60, sect mgr tires, 60-62, dept mgr, 62-65, dir develop int div, 65-67, dir res & develop, 67-75, dir res & develop, 75-78, MGT CONSULT, UNIROYAL TIRE CO, 78- *Res:* Adhesion of rubber to metal; general industrial adhesives; electrodeposition of alloys, especially brass; resinoid and rubber-bonded grinding wheels; development of gum plastics; kinetics of isotopic exchange reaction; organizational planning; tire technology and product development. *Mailing Add:* PO Box F Norris TN 37828

MICELI, MICHAEL VINCENT, b Chicago, Ill, Aug 23, 51; m 74; c 2. CARDIOLOGY, NUCLEAR MAGNETIC RESONANCE. *Educ:* Univ Ill, Champagne, BS, 73; Univ Ill Med Ctr, PhD(biochem), 79. *Prof Exp:* Food technologist, Quaker Oats Co, 73; res asst, Northwestern Univ Med Ctr, 74-75; teaching asst biochem, Univ Ill Med Ctr, 75-79, res assoc, 79-80; FEL, JOHNS HOPKINS UNIV, 80- *Res:* Heart metabolism and biochemistry studies by nuclear magnetic resonance techniques; projects include calcium loading in the intact heart, preservation of ischemia nyocardium and kinetics of creative kinase. *Mailing Add:* Div Cardiol Johns Hopkins Hosp 600 N Wolfe St Baltimore MD 21205

MICETICH, RONALD GEORGE, b Madras, India, May 28, 31; Can citizen; m 58; c 4. ORGANIC CHEMISTRY, MEDICINAL CHEMISTRY. *Educ:* Loyola Col, Madras, India, BSc, 52; Univ Madras, MA, 55; Univ Sask, PhD(org chem), 62. *Prof Exp:* Nat Res Coun Can fel, Prairie Regional Lab, Sask, Can, 62-63; res chemist, R&L Molecular Res Ltd, Alta, 63-69; from asst res dir to assoc res dir org & med chem, Raylo Chem Ltd, 69-71, res mgr, 71-75, actg res dir org & med chem, 75-78, res dir pharm chem, 78-81; PROF MED CHEM, UNIV ALTA, 81- *Mem:* Royal Soc Chem; Chem Inst Can; Int Soc Heterocyclic Chem; Am Chem Soc. *Res:* Heterocyclic chemistry; synthetic organic chemistry; organometallic chemistry; chemical modification of B-lactam antibiotics; anti-inflammatory agents; analgesics; immunoregulants; central nervous system active compounds; affinity drugs. *Mailing Add:* Fac Pharm Univ Alta Edmonton AB T6G 2N8 Can

MICH, THOMAS FREDERICK, b Milwaukee, Wis, May 26, 39; m 66. ORGANIC CHEMISTRY. *Educ:* Marquette Univ, BS, 61; Northwestern Univ, MS, 64; State Univ NY Buffalo, PhD(chem), 68. *Prof Exp:* Res assoc, Dartmouth Col, 67-68; sr res chemist, Monsanto Co, 68-69; res chemist, chem dept, 69-73, sr scientist, 73-79, res assoc, 79-81, SR RES ASSOC, PHARMACEUT RES DIV, WARNER LAMBERT/PARKE DAVIS & CO, 81- *Mem:* Am Chem Soc; Royal Soc Chem. *Res:* Synthetic organic and medicinal chemistry; antibacterials. *Mailing Add:* Chem Dept Ann Arbor Res Labs Parke Davis & Co 2800 Plymouth Ann Arbor MI 48106

MICHA, DAVID ALLAN, b Villa Mercedes, Argentina, Sept 12, 39; US citizen; m 65; c 2. CHEMICAL PHYSICS. *Educ:* Nat Univ Cuyo, Arg, Lic Physics, 62; Univ Uppsala, Sweden, Fil Lic, 65, Fil Doctor, 66. *Prof Exp:* Res assoc, Theoret Chem Inst, Univ Wis-Madison, 66-67; asst res physicist, Inst Pure & Appl Phys Sci, Univ Calif, San Diego, 67-69; assoc prof, 69-74, PROF CHEM & PHYSICS, UNIV FLA, 74- *Concurrent Pos:* Res grants, Am Chem Soc-Petrol Res Fund, 69-72, NSF, 71-73, 76-77, 78-80 & 81-83, Nat Res Coun, 71 & 75, Alfred P Sloan fel, 71-73, NATO, 76-78, Nat Resource Comput in Chem, 78 & NASA, 81; vis prof, Harvard Univ, 72, Univ Calif, San Diego, 73, Max Planck Inst fur Stromungsforsch, Gottingen, 76, Uppsala Univ, 77 & Imp Col, Univ London, 77; US sr scientist award, A von Humboldt Found, 76. docent, Univ Uppsala, 68; vis Lamberg Prof, Univ Gothenburg, 70. *Mem:* Fel Am Phys Soc; Am Chem Soc. *Res:* Molecular dynamics; electronic structure of matter; intermolecular forces; computational methods in theoretical chemistry. *Mailing Add:* Williamson Hall Univ Fla Gainesville FL 32611

MICHAEL, ALFRED FREDERICK, JR, b Philadelphia, Pa, Aug 10, 28; m 52; c 3. PEDIATRICS, NEPHROLOGY. *Educ:* Temple Univ, MD, 53. *Prof Exp:* Intern, Philadelphia Gen Hosp, 53-54; resident pediat, St Christopher's Hosp Children, Sch Med, Temple Univ, 54-55; from jr resident to sr resident, Children's Hosp & Col Med, Univ Cincinnati, 57-59, chief resident & instr, 59-60; USPHS fel, 60-63, Am Heart Asn estab investr, 63-68, assoc prof, 65-68, PROF PEDIAT, LAB MED & PATH, MED SCH, UNIV MINN, MINNEAPOLIS, 68- *Concurrent Pos:* Vis investr & Guggenheim fel, Copenhagen, Denmark, 66-67; mem sci adv bd, Nat Kidney Found, 77-; mem & pres, subspecialty bd pediat nephrol, Am Bd Pediat, 73-79. *Mem:* Soc Pediat Res; Am Asn Path; Am Asn Immunol; Am Soc Nephrology; Am Soc Pediat Nephrology. *Res:* Renal disease; immunopathology and mechanisms of glomerulonephritis. *Mailing Add:* Dept of Pediat Univ Of Minn Hosps Minneapolis MN 55455

MICHAEL, ARTHUR B, b Chilton, Wis, Nov 24, 23. PHYSICAL METALLURGY. *Educ:* Univ Wis, BS, 44; Univ Minn, MS, 47; Mass Inst Technol, ScD, 52. *Prof Exp:* Res engr, Allis Chalmers Mfg Co, 52-55; sr metallurgist, Fansteel Metall Corp, Ill, 55-57, asst dir res, 57-59, dir res, 59-63; mgr metals res, Glidden Co, SCM Corp, 63-68; PROF MECH & MAT ENG & CHMN DEPT MECH ENG, MILWAUKEE SCH ENG, 68- *Res:* Refractory metals; powder metallurgy; electronic materials; materials science. *Mailing Add:* 1707 N Prospect Ave Milwaukee WI 53202

MICHAEL, CHARLES REID, b Bucyrus, Ohio, June 30, 39; m 64; c 2. NEUROPHYSIOLOGY. *Educ:* Harvard Col, BA, 61; Harvard Univ, PhD(biol), 65. *Prof Exp:* Fel biophys, Johns Hopkins Univ, 65-68; asst prof, 68-71, PROF PHYSIOL, SCH MED, YALE UNIV, 71- *Mem:* AAAS; Soc Neurosci; Asn Res Vision & Ophthal. *Res:* Vision physiology of the mammalian central nervous system. *Mailing Add:* Dept of Physiol Yale Univ Sch of Med New Haven CT 06510

MICHAEL, EDWIN DARYL, b Mannington, WVa, Jan 22, 38; m 60; c 2. WILDLIFE MANAGEMENT. *Educ:* Marietta Col, BS, 59; Tex A&M Univ, MS, 63, PhD(wildlife ecol), 66. *Prof Exp:* From asst prof to assoc prof biol, Stephen F Austin State Col, 64-70; assoc prof, 70-74, PROF WILDLIFE MGT, WVA UNIV, 74-, ASSOC WILDLIFE BIOLOGIST, 77- *Mem:* Am Soc Mammal; Wildlife Soc; Copper Ornith Soc. *Res:* Ecology and management of forest wildlife. *Mailing Add:* Div of Forestry WVa Univ Morgantown WV 26506

MICHAEL, ERNEST ARTHUR, b Zurich, Switz, Aug 26, 25; nat US; div; c 3; m 66; c 2. TOPOLOGY. *Educ:* Cornell Univ, BA, 47; Harvard Univ, MA, 48; Univ Chicago, PhD(math), 51. *Prof Exp:* Fel, AEC, Inst Advan Study, 51-52 & Univ Chicago, 52-53; from asst prof to assoc prof, 53-60, PROF MATH, UNIV WASH, 60- *Concurrent Pos:* Mem, Inst Advan Study, 56-57, 60-61 & 68; ed, Proc, Am Math Soc, 68-71 & Gen Topology & Applns, 72-; vis, Math Res Inst, Swiss Fed Inst Technol, 73-74; Alexander von Humboldt Found sr Am scientist grant, Univ Stuttgart, 78-79. *Mem:* Am Math Soc; Math Asn Am. *Res:* General topology. *Mailing Add:* Dept Math Univ Wash Seattle WA 98105

MICHAEL, ERNEST DENZIL, JR, b Lewiston, Maine, Jan 18, 22; m 45; c 3. PHYSIOLOGY, ERGONOMICS. *Educ:* Purdue Univ, BPE, 47; Univ Ill, MS, 49, PhD, 52. *Prof Exp:* Dir athletics high sch, 47-48; instr phys ed, Univ Ill, 49-50 & 51-52; asst, USPHS, 50-51; from instr to assoc prof phys educ & physiol, 52-67, chmn dept ergonomics & phys educ, 73-76, PROF PHYS EDUC, UNIV CALIF, SANTA BARBARA, 67-, RES ASSOC, INST ENVIRON STRESS, 64- *Concurrent Pos:* Am Physiol Soc res fel, Lankenau Hosp, Philadelphia, Pa, 59; res fel, Valley Forge Heart Hosp, 59-60; consult, Water Safety Prog, YMCA, 59-; res prof, Inst Physiol, Univ Glasgow, Scotland, 67-68; Am Acad Phys Educ fel, res prof, Inst Sport, Warsaw, Poland, 78. *Mem:* Am Physiol Soc; Sigma Xi (pres, 78-79); fel Am Col Sports Med; Am Asn Health, Phys Educ & Recreation; NY Acad Sci. *Res:* Effects of training on the cardiovascular system; perception of levels of exertion; body composition and performance. *Mailing Add:* Dept Ergonomics & Phys Educ Univ of Calif Santa Barbara CA 93106

MICHAEL, HAROLD LOUIS, b Columbus, Ind, July 24, 20; m 54; c 5. CIVIL ENGINEERING. *Educ:* Purdue Univ, BS, 50, MS, 51. *Prof Exp:* Asst eng transp, 50-51, from instr to assoc prof, 52-62, from asst dir to assoc dir, Joint Hwy Res Proj, 54-77, PROF CIVIL ENG, PURDUE UNIV, WEST LAFAYETTE, 62-, HEAD TRANSP & URBAN ENG, 66-, DIR JOINT HWY RES PROJ & IN CHARGE URBAN RES PROJ, 77- *Concurrent Pos:* Mem comt vehicle characteristics & comt origin-destination surv, Hwy Res Bd, Nat Acad Sci-Nat Res Coun, 54-63, chmn comt characteristics traffic flow, 57-63, chmn dept traffic & opers, 64-69, chmn group 3 coun, Oper & Maintenance Transp Facil, 70-; chmn, West Lafayette Traffic Comn, 56-; consult, Ind Bd Regist Prof Engrs, 56-, Indianapolis Motor Speedway, 58-60 & USPHS, 65-; vpres, Ind Hwy for Survival, Inc, 60-64, pres, 65-; chmn, Lafayette Hwy Tech Comt, 65- & Nat Comt Uniform Traffic Control Devices; mem, Nat Comt Uniform Laws & Ord. *Mem:* Nat Soc Prof Engrs; Am Soc Civil Engrs; Inst Traffic Eng (secy-treas); Am Rwy Eng Asn; Am Soc Eng Educ. *Res:* Traffic engineering; transportation planning and economics; urban transportation planning, traffic safety and urban planning. *Mailing Add:* Civil Eng Bldg Purdue Univ West Lafayette IN 47907

MICHAEL, IRVING, b Pittsburgh, Pa, June 28, 29. SPACE PHYSICS, NUCLEAR PHYSICS. *Educ:* George Washington Univ, BSc, 50; Univ Wis, MSc, 51, PhD(physics), 58. *Prof Exp:* Res asst phys chem, Geophys Lab, Carnegie Inst Washington, 50; res asst nuclear physics, Univ Wis, 51-58, res assoc, 58-60: res fel, Univ Notre Dame, 60-62; sr scientist, Northrop Space Labs, Calif, 62-63; res physicist space physics br, Air Force Weapons Lab, NMex, 64; RES PHYSICIST SPACE PHYSICS LAB, AIR FORCE GEOPHYSICS LAB, 64- *Concurrent Pos:* Consult, Radiation Dynamics Corp, NY, 60. *Mem:* Am Phys Soc; Am Geophys Union; Am Vacuum Soc; Int Orgn Vacuum Sci & Technol; Am Soc Mass Spectrometry. *Res:* Satellite and deep-space probe measurements of the solar wind; low-energy nuclear physics; electrostatic accelerator development; high-voltage breakdown in vacuum; techniques and measurements in extreme-high vacuum; measurements of electric fields in space. *Mailing Add:* Plasma Particles & Fields Br Space Physics Div Air Force Geophysics Lab Hanscom AFB MA 01731

MICHAEL, JACOB GABRIEL, b Rimavska Sobota, Czech, July 2, 31; US citizen; m 58; c 4. IMMUNOLOGY. *Educ:* Hebrew Univ, Israel, BA, 55, MSc, 56; Rutgers Univ, PhD(microbiol), 59. *Prof Exp:* Res assoc & vis scientist, Nat Cancer Inst, 59-61; res assoc, Harvard Med Sch, 61-66; assoc prof, 66-73, PROF MICROBIOL & IMMUNOL, MED CTR, UNIV CINCINNATI, 73- *Concurrent Pos:* Am Soc Microbiol pres fel, 62; USPHS career develop award, 65- *Mem:* AAAS; Am Soc Microbiol; Am Asn Immunol. *Res:* Microbial immunity; regulation of immune response; immediate hypersensitivity. *Mailing Add:* Dept of Microbiol Univ of Cincinnati Med Ctr Cincinnati OH 45267

MICHAEL, JAMES RICHARD, b Peoria, Ill, Dec 6, 32; m 56; c 2. ORGANIC CHEMISTRY. *Educ:* Univ Ill, BS, 53; Cornell Univ, MS, 55, PhD(org chem), 57. *Prof Exp:* Res chemist, Esso Res & Eng Co, 57-62, tech serv coordr, Esso Chem Co, 62-63, supply coordr, 63-65, planning coordr, Gen Chem Div, NY, 65-66, mkt mgr indust chem, Esso Chem SA, Belg, 66-69; mgr int contracts, 69-70, mgr indust chem, coatings, planning & tech dept, Esso Stand Sekiyu K K, Akasaka, Japan, 70-71, dir mgr chem & opers, Esso Kagaku K K, Akasaka, Japan, 71-73, prod exec, Exxon Chem Co, 73-74, MGR, SOLVENTS TECHNOL DIV, EXXON CHEM CO, 74- *Mem:* AAAS; Am Chem Soc; fel Am Inst Chem; NY Acad Sci. *Res:* Chemical marketing in the international market; chemistry of organic nitrogen compounds; chemistry and synthesis of solid rocket propellants and ferrocene related compounds; mechanism and synthesis of new polymers; surface coating chemistry; oxgenated and hydrocarbon solvents. *Mailing Add:* Exxon Chem Co PO Box 536 Linden NJ 07036

MICHAEL, JOE VICTOR, b South Whitley, Ind, Oct 2, 35; m 60; c 3. PHYSICAL CHEMISTRY. *Educ:* Wabash Col, BA, 57; Univ Rochester, PhD(chem), 63. *Prof Exp:* Res assoc, Harvard Univ, 62-64 & Brookhaven Nat Lab, 64-65; asst prof, Carnegie-Mellon Univ, 65-70, assoc prof chem, 70-75; NAT ACAD SCI/NAT RES COUN SR RESIDENT RES ASSOC, GODDARD SPACE FLIGHT CTR, NASA, 75- *Concurrent Pos:* Vis prof, Cath Univ Am, 77-81 & Brookhaven Nat Lab, 81- *Mem:* NY Acad Sci; Am Chem Soc; Sigma Xi; Combustion Inst; AAAS. *Res:* Photochemistry; chemical kinetics; time-of-flight mass spectroscopy; shock tubes; flow reactors; resonance photometry. *Mailing Add:* Code 691 Astrochem Br Goddard Space Flight Ctr NASA Greenbelt MD 20771

MICHAEL, JOEL ALLEN, b Chicago, Ill, Mar 8, 40; m 65; c 2. NEUROPHYSIOLOGY. *Educ:* Calif Inst Technol, BS, 61; McGill Univ, MSc, 64; Mass Inst Technol, PhD(physiol), 65. *Prof Exp:* Carnegie fel neurophysiol, Nat Phys Lab, Teddington, Eng, 65-66; res fel psychiat, Mass Gen Hosp & Harvard Med Sch, Boston, 66-67; asst prof bioeng, Univ Ill, Chicago, 67-70, asst prof physiol, Col Med, 68-70; assoc prof biomed eng & neurol sci, 70-74, actg chmn dept, 74-76, ASSOC PROF PHYSIOL, RUSH MED COL, 74- *Concurrent Pos:* Asst attend bioengr, Presby-St Luke's Hosp, Chicago, 67-70. *Mem:* Am Physiol Soc; Inst Elec & Electronics Eng; Soc Neurosci. *Res:* Visual data processing; invertebrate neurobiology; physical bases of behavioral plasticity, learning and memory. *Mailing Add:* Dept of Physiol Rush Med Col Rush-Presby St Luke's Med Ctr Chicago IL 60612

MICHAEL, LESLIE WILLIAM, b San Francisco, Calif, Jan 26, 33; m 54. CHEMISTRY. *Educ:* Univ Calif, Berkeley, BA, 58; Fresno State Col, MS, 62; Univ Cincinnati, PhD(chem), 69. *Prof Exp:* Technician, Ortho Div, Chevron Chem Co, 58-60; AMA Educ Res Fund grant environ health, 68-69, res assoc chem, Col Med, Univ Cincinnati, 69-70, from asst prof to assoc prof environ health, 70-77; supvr, 77-80, AREA DIR OCCUPATIONAL SAFETY & HEALTH ADMIN, DEPT LABOR, 80- *Mem:* Am Chem Soc; Am Indust Hyg Asn. *Res:* Origin and chemistry of environmental materials with biological interactions; qualitative and quantitative chemical analysis; industrial hygiene; structure and physical chemical constants particularly with regard to essential and toxic metal compounds. *Mailing Add:* Occupational Safety & Health Admin 1240 E Ninth St Room 899 Cleveland OH 44199

MICHAEL, LLOYD HAL, b Susquehanna, Pa, Nov 14, 42; m 64; c 1. CARDIOVASCULAR PHYSIOLOGY, BIOCHEMISTRY. *Educ:* Moravian Col, BS, 64; Kent State Univ, MS, 66; Univ Ottawa, PhD(med physiol), 73. *Prof Exp:* Instr biol, St Lawrence Univ, 66-67, asst prof, 67-69; sr lectr physiol, Fac of Med, Univ Dar es Salaam, 73-75; instr med, 77-78, ASST PROF MED, SECT CARDIOVASC SCI, BAYLOR COL MED, 78- *Concurrent Pos:* Fel clin immunol, Col Physicians & Surgeons, Columbia Univ, 75; fel myocardial biol, Baylor Col Med, 76-77. *Mem:* Sigma Xi; Int Soc Heart Res; Am Heart Asn. *Res:* Investigation of processes causing faster and shorter duration of heart atrial contraction compared to ventricular contraction; studies to characterize mechanism of sodium-potassium-adenosine triphosphate function and specifically its unique interaction with glycoside. *Mailing Add:* Dept of Med Baylor Col of Med Houston TX 77030

MICHAEL, MAX, JR, b Athens, Ga, Feb 14, 16; m 44; c 5. INTERNAL MEDICINE. *Educ:* Univ Ga, BS, 35; Harvard Univ, MD, 39. *Prof Exp:* Asst med, Sch Med, Johns Hopkins Univ, 41-42; asst, Emory Univ, 45-47, assoc, 47-50, from asst prof to assoc prof, 52-54; prof, Col Med, State Univ NY, 54-58; exec dir, 58-67, prof med, Col Med, 58-77, asst dean educ prog, Jacksonville Hosps, 67-77, ASST DEAN JACKSONVILLE PROG, JACKSONVILLE HOSPS, UNIV FLA, 77- *Concurrent Pos:* Chief med serv, Vet Admin Hosp, Atlanta, 47-54; dir med serv, Maimonides Hosp, Brooklyn, 54-58; mem bd regents, Nat Libr Med, 68-72. *Mem:* Inst of Med of Nat Acad Sci; Am Tuberc Soc; Am Soc Clin Invest; Am Clin & Climat Asn; assoc Am Col Physicians. *Res:* Infectious diseases. *Mailing Add:* Col of Med Univ of Fla Jacksonville FL 32601

MICHAEL, NORMAN, b New York, NY, Dec 12, 31; m 63; c 1. INORGANIC CHEMISTRY, MECHANIC ENGINEERING. *Educ:* Columbia Univ, AB, 55. *Prof Exp:* Radiol chemist, US Navy Mat Lab, 54-56; nuclear chemist, Alco Prod Inc, 56-57; scientist, Atomic Power Div, Westinghouse Elec Corp, 57-62; sr res chemist, Astropower Lab, Douglas Aircraft Co, 62-63; chemist, Vallecitos Atomic Lab, Gen Elec Co, 63-66; SR ENGR, RES LABS, WESTINGHOUSE ELEC CORP, 66- *Mem:* Am Chem Soc. *Res:* Oxidation, corrosion and radioactive contamination of metals and alloys; alternate energy systems; fuel cell electrolytes and battery separators; inorganic ion exchangers for water purification. *Mailing Add:* Mats & Conversion Systs Dept Res & Develop Ctr Westinghouse Elec Corp Pittsburgh PA 15235

MICHAEL, PAUL ANDREW, b New York, NY, July 6, 28; m 53; c 2. PHYSICS. *Educ:* NY Univ, AB, 49, PhD, 59; Univ Chicago, BS, 53, MS, 55. *Prof Exp:* Jr test engr, Curtiss-Wright Corp, 53, physicist, Res Div, 55-56; physicist, 58-72, leader meteorol group, 72-75, HEAD ATMOSPHERIC SCI DIV, BROOKHAVEN NAT LAB, 75- *Concurrent Pos:* Instr, NY Univ, 56-58, adj asst prof, 58-59. *Mem:* Am Phys Soc; Am Nuclear Soc; Am Meteorol Soc. *Res:* Reactor and neutron physics; fluid dynamics; atmospheric diffusion. *Mailing Add:* Dept of Energy & Environ Brookhaven Nat Lab Upton NY 11973

MICHAEL, PAUL LEE, b Fairmont, WVa, June 7, 25; m 46; c 4. PHYSICS, ENVIRONMENTAL HEALTH. *Educ:* Fairmont State Col, BS, 48; Univ WVa, MS, 49; Univ Pittsburgh, PhD(occupational health), 55. *Prof Exp:* Instr physics, Univ WVa, 49-51; physicist, Nat Bur Stand, 51-52; sr physicist, Mine Safety Appliances Co, Pa, 52-54, supvr acoustics sect, 54-56, chief physicist, 56-59; assoc prof eng res, 59-69, PROF ENVIRON ACOUST & DIR ENVIRON ACOUST LAB, PA STATE UNIV, 70- *Concurrent Pos:* Indust consult, 59-; mem bioacoust comt & writing group, Am Nat Stand Inst. *Mem:* Acoust Soc Am; Am Conf Govt Indust Hyg; Audio Eng Soc; Am Speech & Hearing Asn; Am Indust Hyg Asn. *Res:* Hearing conservation; noise measurement and control; instrumentation and calibration; development of clinical test procedures for determining. *Mailing Add:* Pa State Univ Environ Acoust Lab 110 Moore Bldg University Park PA 16802

MICHAEL, RICHARD PHILLIP, b London, Eng, June 9, 24; US citizen; m 58; c 4. PSYCHIATRY, NEUROENDOCRINOLOGY. *Educ:* Univ London, MD, 51, PhD(neuroendocrinol), 60, DSc, 71; FRCPsych, 74. *Prof Exp:* Dir, Primate Behav Res Labs, 67-72; DIR, BIOL PSYCHIAT RES LABS, GA MENTAL HEALTH INST, 72-, PROF ANAT & PSYCHIAT, SCH MED, EMORY UNIV, 71- *Concurrent Pos:* Vis scientist, Clin Neuropharmacol Res Ctr, St Elizabeth's Hosp, Washington, DC, 59-, vis prof, Regional Primate Res Ctr, Univ Wis-Madison, 62-, consult physician psychiat, Bethlehem Royal & Maudsley Hosps, 63-72; reader, Inst Psychiat, Univ London, 68-72; rapporteur, WHO Sci Group Neuroendocrinol & Human Reproduction, Geneva, 64; consult, Brain & Behav Monograph, Sci Policy Studies, Orgn for Econ Coop & Develop, Paris, 72-; mem comn neuroendocrinol, Int Union Physiol Sci, 75-81. *Honors & Awards:* Distinction Award, Ministry Health, UK, 66; Manfred Sakel Award, Soc Biol Psychiat, 72. *Mem:* Primate Soc Gt Brit (pres, 70-73); Int Soc Psychoneuroendocrinol (pres, 75-78); Int Psychoanal Asn; Endocrine Soc; Am Psychoanal Asn. *Res:* Effects of hormones on the brain; biological aspects of psychiatry; ethological studies on the basis of motivation in higher primates; neuroendocrine and behavioral interrelationships. *Mailing Add:* Dept of Psychiat Emory Univ Sch Med Atlanta GA 30322

MICHAEL, THOMAS HUGH GLYNN, b Toronto, Ont, May 20, 18; m 42; c 3. CHEMISTRY, SCIENCE ADMINISTRATION. *Educ:* Univ Toronto, BA, 40. *Prof Exp:* Chemist, Ont Res Found, 40-41 & Protective Coatings Lab, Nat Res Coun Can, 41-46; chief chemist, Woburn Chems, Ltd, 46-53; dir res, Howards & Sons Can, Ltd, 53-58; EXEC DIR & SECY, CHEM INST CAN, 58- *Concurrent Pos:* Treas, Youth Sci Found, 61-71. *Honors & Awards:* Can Centennial Medal, 67; Can Silver Jubilee Medal, 78. *Mem:* Fel Royal Soc Chem; Am Chem Soc; fel Chem Inst Can (treas, 53-56); Coun Eng & Sci Soc Exec (pres, 69-70); Inst Asn Execs (pres, 71-72). *Res:* Chemistry of synthetic resins, particularly alkyds and plasticizers; chemistry of protective coatings; management of scientific societies and publications. *Mailing Add:* The Chem Inst of Can 151 Slater St Ottawa ON K1P 5H3 Can

MICHAEL, WILLIAM ALEXANDER, b Peoria, Ill, Mar 20, 25; m 55; c 2. MATHEMATICS. *Educ:* Univ Ill, AB, 48, MS, 49, PhD(math), 54. *Prof Exp:* Asst math, Univ Ill, 51-54; instr, Northwestern Univ, 54-55; staff mathematician, Res Lab, Int Bus Mach Corp, 55-65; mem res staff, Ampex Corp, 65-67 & Systs Develop Div, IBM Corp, 67-68; asst prof, 59 & 68-73, ASSOC PROF MATH, SAN JOSE STATE UNIV, 73- *Mem:* Am Math Soc. *Res:* Numerical and functional analysis. *Mailing Add:* Dept of Math San Jose State Univ San Jose CA 95192

MICHAEL, WILLIAM HERBERT, JR, b Richmond, Va, Dec 10, 26; m 52; c 2. SPACE SCIENCES. *Educ:* Princeton Univ, BS, 48, MS, 64, PhD(aerospace sci), 67; Univ Va, MS, 51; Col William & Mary, MA, 62. *Prof Exp:* Res scientist, Nat Adv Comn Aeronaut-NASA, Langley Res Ctr, 48-58, head trajectory anal group, 58-60, head mission anal sect, 60-69, head lunar & planetary sci br, 69-70, chief environ & space div, 70-76, sci/eng consult, 76-80; ASSOC DIR, VA ASSOC RES CAMPUS, NEWPORT NEWS, VA, 80- *Concurrent Pos:* Prin investr, Lunar Orbiter Selenodesy Exp, Langley Res Ctr, NASA, 65-69, team leader, Viking Mars Missions Radio Sci Team, 69-; mem work groups figure & motion of moon & laser tracking & appl, Comn 17, Int Astron Union & tracking & dynamics of satellites, Comt on Space Res; adj prof physics, Col William & Mary, 80- *Honors & Awards:* NASA Spec Serv Award, 67, Lunar Orbiter Proj Achievement Award, 68, Apollo Prog Spec Achievement Award, 69; NASA Medal for Except Sci Achievement, 77. *Mem:* Am Inst Aeronaut & Astronaut; Am Geophys Union; Int Astron Union. *Res:* Lunar and planetary exploration; space flight experiments in gravitational fields, geophysics, atmospheric properties and radio science; research administration. *Mailing Add:* 29 Haughton Lane Newport News VA 23606

MICHAEL, WILLIAM R, b Peoria, Ill, May 23, 30; m 53; c 4. TOXICOLOGY, PHARMACOLOGY. *Educ:* Univ Ill, BS, 52; Bradley Univ, MS, 57; St Louis Univ, PhD(biochem), 61. *Prof Exp:* Chemist, Northern Utilization Res Lab, USDA, 54-56; res biochemist, Miami Valley Lab, 61-74, mem staff, Sharon Woods Tech Ctr, 74-79, SECT HEAD, PACKAGE SOAP & DETERGENT PROD DEVELOP DIV, PROCTER & GAMBLE CO, 79- *Mem:* AAAS; Am Chem Soc; Soc Toxicol; Sigma Xi. *Res:* Drug metabolism; calcium and phosphate metabolism; pharmacokinetics; toxicology; product development. *Mailing Add:* 1 Vorydale Tech Ct Procter & Gamble Co Cincinnati OH 45217

MICHAELI, DOV, b Tel Aviv, Israel, May 28, 35; US citizen; m 62; c 2. IMMUNOCHEMISTRY, BIOCHEMISTRY. *Educ:* Hebrew Univ, Israel, BS, 60; Univ Calif, Berkeley, PhD(toxicol), 62. *Prof E :p:* Asst res scientist, Lab Med Entom, Kaiser Found Res Inst, 62-67, assoc res scientist, 67-71; ASSOC PROF BIOCHEM & SURG, SCH MED, UNIV CALIF, SAN FRANCISCO, 71- *Concurrent Pos:* NIH res career develop award. *Mem:* Am Asn Immunol; NY Acad Sci; Am Chem Soc. *Res:* Hematology; interaction of platelets with macromolecules; immunochemistry of collagen biochemistry and biology of wound healing from various sources; biochemistry and immunology of connective tissue. *Mailing Add:* 839 HSE Univ of Calif Sch of Med San Francisco CA 94143

MICHAELIDES, GEORGE J, b Cyprus; US citizen; c 2. TOPOLOGY. *Educ:* Va Polytech Inst, BS, 52, MS, 54; Univ Ga, PhD(math), 74. *Prof Exp:* Asst prof math & eng, Lamar Univ, 55-60; asst prof, 61-75, ASSOC PROF MATH, UNIV SFLA, 75- *Mem:* Math Asn Am; Am Math Soc. *Res:* Topology; analysis and numerical analysis. *Mailing Add:* Dept Math Univ SFla Tampa FL 33620

MICHAELIS, ARTHUR FREDERICK, b Bronx, NY, July 24, 41; m 64; c 2. PHARMACEUTICS, PHYSICAL PHARMACY. *Educ:* Bucknell Univ, BS, 63; Univ Wis, MS, 65, PhD(pharm), 67; Fairleigh Dickinson Univ, MBA, 75. *Prof Exp:* Sr chemist, Hoffmann-La Roche, Inc, Nutley, 67-70; dir qual control, Sandoz Pharmaceut, 70-71, dir pharmaceut & anal res, Sandoz, Inc, East Hanover, 71-77, dir pharmaceut develop, 77-79; PRES, APPL TECHNOL DIV, KV PHARMACEUT CORP, ST LOUIS, 79- *Concurrent Pos:* Lectr, Sch Pharm, Univ Md, 69. *Mem:* AAAS; Am Pharmaceut Asn; Acad Pharmaceut Sci; fel Am Inst chem; NY Acad Sci. *Res:* Physical chemistry of the ion pair extraction of pharmaceutical amines; physical pharmacy of drugs used in the prophylaxis and treatment of nerve gas casualties; new methods of optimizing drug delivery; high speed liquid chromatography. *Mailing Add:* 1425 Chesterfield Lakes Dr Chesterfield MO 63017

MICHAELIS, CARL I, b Paxico, Kans, May 11, 18. ORGANIC CHEMISTRY. *Educ:* Univ Kans, AB, 45, AM, 47; Univ Fla, PhD(org chem), 53. *Prof Exp:* Asst chem, Univ Kans, 45-47; instr, Fla State Univ, 47-50; from instr to asst prof, Univ Fla, 50-54; assoc prof, 54-62, PROF CHEM, UNIV DAYTON, 62-, PREMED ADV, 60- *Mem:* Sigma Xi; Am Chem Soc. *Res:* Quaternary ammonium compounds and their derivatives; epoxides; amines. *Mailing Add:* Dept of Chem Univ of Dayton Dayton OH 45469

MICHAELIS, ELIAS K, b Wad-Medani, Sudan, Oct 3, 44; m 67; c 1. NEUROCHEMISTRY, PSYCHOBIOLOGY. *Educ:* Fairleigh Dickinson Univ, BS, 66; St Louis Univ Med Sch, MD, 69; Univ Ky, PhD(physiol & biophys), 73. *Prof Exp:* Spec fel res, Dept Physiol & Biophys, Univ Ky, 72-73; asst prof, 73-77, assoc prof, 77-82, PROF, DEPT HUMAN DEVELOP, UNIV KANS, 82- *Mem:* Am Soc Neurochem; Soc Neurosci; NY Acad Sci; AAAS; Int Soc Biomed Res Alcoholism. *Res:* Characterization of L-glutamate receptors in neuronal membranes; membrane protein isolation and chemical analysis; characterization of membrane transport systems for amino acids, sodium, potassium, and calcium; neuronal membrane biophysics. *Mailing Add:* Dept Human Develop 130 Haworth Univ Kans Lawrence KS 66045

MICHAELIS, MARY LOUISE, b Denver, Colo, March 30, 43. MEMBRANE BIOCHEMISTRY, ADENOSINE NEUROMODULATION. *Educ:* Webster Col, St Louis, BA, 66; Univ Kans, Lawrence, MA, 68, PhD(neurosci), 78. *Prof Exp:* Asst prof psychol, Webster Col, St Louis, 67-68; consult, US Govt Follow Through Prog, 69-70; lab technician physiol & biophysics, Univ Ky, 70-72; RES SCIENTIST & PRIN INVESTR, CTR BIOMED RES, UNIV KANS, 78- *Concurrent Pos:* Courtesy asst prof, Dept Human Develop, Univ Kans, 78- *Mem:* Soc Neurosci; AAAS; Am Fedn Aging Res; Asn Women Sci. *Res:* Mechanisms of neurotransmitter release, particularly as they are affected by agents which modulate release processes; the influence of adenosine on calcium and potassium fluxes in synaptic membranes. *Mailing Add:* Ctr Biomed Res Univ Kans West Campus Lawrence KS 66045

MICHAELIS, PAUL CHARLES, b Bronx, NY, June 18, 35; m 58; c 1. SOLID STATE PHYSICS, ELECTRICAL ENGINEERING. *Educ:* Newark Col Eng, BS, 64, MS, 67. *Prof Exp:* Technician electronics mech, 59-63, assoc mem tech staff, 63-67, MEM TECH STAFF MAGNETICS RES & DEVELOP, BELL LABS, 67- *Honors & Awards:* Morris N Liebmann Award, Inst Elec & Electronics Engrs, 75. *Mem:* Inst Elec & Electronics Engrs; Am Phys Soc; AAAS. *Res:* Magnetic memory devices; magnetoresistance phenomena. *Mailing Add:* Bell Labs 600 Mountain Ave Murray Hill NJ 07974

MICHAELIS, ROBERT E(RNEST), JR, b Denver, Colo, Feb 24, 21; m 48; c 3. METALLURGY. *Educ:* Colo Sch Mines, EngMet, 47. *Prof Exp:* Technologist, Res Lab, US Steel Corp, 47-52; physicist in chg spectrog standard samples, Nat Bur Standards, 52-64, chief metal standards, Off Standard Ref Mat, 64-70, CHIEF METAL & INORG STANDARDS, NAT BUR STANDARDS, OFF STANDARD REF MAT, 70- *Mem:* Am Soc Testing & Mat. *Res:* Planning, preparation, testing and certification of metal and inorganic materials with respect to full characterization of physical and chemical peoperties; National Bureau of Standards standard reference materials for use in calibrating measurement systems or in producing scientific data that can be referred to a common base. *Mailing Add:* Off of Standard Ref Mat Nat Bur of Standards Washington DC 20234

MICHAELS, ADLAI ELDON, b Alma, Wis, Nov 22, 13; m 40; c 2. PHYSICAL CHEMISTRY. *Educ:* Univ Wis, BS, 35; Ohio State Univ, PhD, 40. *Prof Exp:* Asst, Ohio State Univ, 35-39; instr chem, Univ Tenn, 40-43; res chemist, Esso Res & Eng Co, 43-59; from asst prof to assoc prof, 59-67, PROF CHEM, WASHINGTON & JEFFERSON COL, 67-, SECY FAC, 65- *Mem:* Am Chem Soc. *Res:* Corrosion; electrochemistry; motor fuels; lubricants; fuel and lubricant additives; air pollution. *Mailing Add:* 73 Crest Vue Rd Washington PA 15301

MICHAELS, ALAN S(HERMAN), b Boston, Mass, Oct 29, 22; m 51; c 2. CHEMICAL ENGINEERING. *Educ:* Mass Inst Technol, SB, 46, SM, 47, ScD(chem eng), 48. *Prof Exp:* From asst prof to prof chem eng, Mass Inst Technol, 48-66, assoc dir, Soil Stabilization Lab, 50-61; pres, Amicon Corp, Mass, 62-70 & Pharmetrics Inc, 70-72; pres, Alza Res Corp & sr vpres & tech dir, Alza Corp, 72-75; PROF CHEM ENG & MED, STANFORD UNIV, 76- *Concurrent Pos:* Indust consult, 48-; asst tech dir, Seco Venture, 50-51; vis prof, Univ Col, Univ London, 59; consult, President's Adv Sci Comn, 61-62; partic conf hemodialysis, NIH, 64-; vis prof, Tech Univ Berlin, 65; consult, Off Saline Water, US Dept Interior, 65- *Mem:* AAAS; Am Chem Soc; Am Soc Eng Educ; Am Inst Chem Engrs; Am Inst Chem. *Res:* Surface, colloid and polymer chemistry and physics; membrane physics and separations technology. *Mailing Add:* 1800 Gough St San Francisco CA 94109

MICHAELS, DAVID D, b Cologne, Ger, July 16, 25; nat US; m 53; c 4. OPHTHALMOLOGY. *Educ:* Northern Ill Col Optom, OD, 47; Ill Inst Technol, BS, 51; Chicago Col Optom, MS, 52, DOS, 53; Roosevelt Univ, BS, 56; Univ Ill, MD, 57; Am Bd Ophthal, dipl, 64. *Prof Exp:* Instr neurol, Northern Ill Col Optom, 47-48, asst prof physiol optics, 48-49; asst physiol optics & ocular anat, Ill Col Optom, 49-51, chmn dept biol, 51-55, assoc prof path, 55-56; resident surgeon, Dept Ophthal, Cook County Hosp, Ill, 58-60; instr, 60-71, asst prof, 71-80, ASSOC PROF SURG, UNIV CALIF, LOS ANGELES, 80-; CHMN DEPT OPHTHAL, SAN PEDRO COMMUNITY HOSP, 60- *Concurrent Pos:* Lectr, Loyola Univ, Ill, 54-55; mem attend staff, Los Angeles County Hosp. *Mem:* Fel Optical Soc Am; fel Am Phys Soc; fel Am Acad Optom; fel Am Acad Ophthal & Otolarnygol; fel Int Col Surgeons. *Res:* Visual adaptation; chemistry; electrical responses of the eye; neuroanatomy; ocular anatomy and surgery; color vision; clinical diagnosis; physiologic optics; biochemistry. *Mailing Add:* 1350 W Seventh St San Pedro CA 90732

MICHAELS, IRA A L, chemical physics, see previous edition

MICHAELS, JOHN EDWARD, b Boston, Mass, Feb 2, 39; m 65; c 2. CELL BIOLOGY. *Educ:* Harvard Univ, AB, 64; Boston Univ, PhD(biol), 70. *Prof Exp:* Fel anat, McGill Univ, 71-74; asst prof, 74-81, ASSOC PROF ANAT, COL MED, UNIV CINCINNATI, 81- *Mem:* Am Asn Anatomists; Am Soc Cell Biol; AAAS. *Res:* Formation of cell coat glycoproteins and their transport from the Golgi apparatus to the cell surface studied by electron microscopy and related techniques. *Mailing Add:* Dept of Anat Col of Med Univ of Cincinnati Cincinnati OH 45267

MICHAELSON, I ARTHUR, b New York, NY, Mar 15, 25; m 58; c 3. PHARMACOLOGY. *Educ:* NY Univ, BA, 50; George Washington Univ, PhD(pharmacol), 59. *Prof Exp:* Fel, Lab Chem Pharmacol, Nat Heart Inst, 59-61; USPHS fel, Agr Res Coun Inst Animal Physiol, Cambridge Univ, 61-63; fel, Lab Chem Pharmacol, Nat Heart Inst, 63-65; asst prof, 65-67, assoc prof pharmacol, 67-77, PROF ENVIRON HEALTH, COL MED, UNIV CINCINNATI, 77- *Concurrent Pos:* USPHS res career develop award, 67-72; vis scientist, Toxicol Unit, Med Res Coun, Carshalton, Surrey, Eng, 71-72. *Mem:* Am Soc Pharmacol & Exp Therapeut. *Res:* Intermediary metabolism of drugs and biochemical pharmacology; subcellular localization of biogenic amines and the effect of drugs on synthesis, storage and release; toxicology; effect of metals on brain development and neurochemistry. *Mailing Add:* Dept of Environ Health Univ Cincinnati Col Med Cincinnati OH 45267

MICHAELSON, JERRY DEAN, b Monterey, Calif, Nov 26, 43; m 66; c 2. COHERENT OPTICS, MICROWAVE INTEGRATED CIRCUITS. *Educ:* Univ Southern Calif, BSEE, 66, MSEE, 71, PhD(elec eng), 79. *Prof Exp:* Mem assoc staff, 64-66, mem tech staff, 66-82, SECT MGR, THE AEROSPACE CORP, 82- *Mem:* Soc Photo Optical Instrumentation Engrs. *Res:* Nonlinear optical processing; high speed gas digital circuits; low noise microwave frequency synthesizers. *Mailing Add:* The Aerospace Corp PO Box 92957 Los Angeles CA 90009

MICHAELSON, MERLE EDWARD, b Hudson, Wis, Feb 14, 21; m 44; c 3. PLANT PATHOLOGY. *Educ:* Wis State Col, River Falls, BS, 43; Colo State Univ, MS, 48; Univ Minn, PhD(plant path, bot), 53. *Prof Exp:* Asst prof bot, Colo State Univ, 46-49; res asst plant path, Univ Minn, St Paul, 49-52; asst prof bot, Univ Mo, 52-54; plant pathologist crops res div, Agr Res Serv, SDak Agr Exp Sta, USDA, 54-59; prof biol, St Cloud State Col, 59-67, actg dean grad sch, 66-67; PROF BIOL, UNIV WIS-RIVER FALLS, 67-, ASST DEAN COL ARTS & SCI, 75- *Concurrent Pos:* Chmn dept biol, Univ Wis-River Falls, 67-72. *Mem:* AAAS; Am Phytopath Soc; Mycol Soc Am; Nat Asn Biol Teachers. *Res:* Mycology; diseases of corn and flax. *Mailing Add:* Dept of Biol Univ of Wis River Falls WI 54022

MICHAELSON, S(TANLEY) D(AY), b New York, NY, Sept 4, 13; m 39; c 2. MINING & METALLURGICAL ENGINEERING. *Educ:* Lehigh Univ, BS, 34. *Hon Degrees:* EM, Univ Mont, 60. *Prof Exp:* Engr in chg mining lab, Allis-Chalmers Mfg Co, Wis, 35-37, metall engr mining dept, 37-39, field engr, 39-41, dir basic industs res lab, 46-47; from spec engr to chief engr raw mat, US Steel Corp, Ala, 47-54; chief engr western mining divs, Kennecott Copper Corp, 54-68, chief engr, Metal Mining Div & dir, Eng Ctr, 68-75; CONSULT MINING & METALL ENGR, 75- *Concurrent Pos:* Mem sci adv comn, Selective Serv Syst, 57-, adv coun, Col Mines & Mineral Indust, Univ Utah, 58- & adv panel mining, Nat Acad Sci-Nat Res Coun, 67; adj prof mining eng, Univ Utah, 75-; chmn panel explor, solution mining & underground mining, Comn on Surface Mining & Reclamation, Nat Res Coun, 78-80. *Honors & Awards:* Richards Award, Am Inst Mining, Metall & Petrol Engrs, 62. *Mem:* Col Mining & Metall Soc Am; hon mem Am Inst Mining, Metall & Petrol Engrs (vpres, 60); distinguished mem Soc Mining Engrs (pres, 59). *Res:* Open pit and underground mining engineering; mineral beneficiation; pyrometallurgy; mines plant design and mine design; economic evaluations for mineral projects and mines. *Mailing Add:* 304 First Security Bldg 405 S Main St Salt Lake City UT 84111

MICHAELSON, SOLOMON M, b New York, NY, Apr 23, 22; m 50; c 2. RADIATION BIOLOGY, PHYSIOLOGY. *Educ:* City Col New York, BS, 42; Middlesex Univ, DVM, 46; Am Col Lab Animal Med, dipl. *Prof Exp:* Asst prof immunol, Univ Ark, 47-48; sr pharmacologist, Eaton Labs, Norwich Pharmacal Co, 48-53; from asst prof to assoc prof radiation biol, 58-72, CHIEF RADIATION PHYSIOL & THER, ATOMIC ENERGY PROJ, UNIV ROCHESTER, 53-, ASSOC PROF MED, 67- ASSOC PROF LAB ANIMAL MED, SCH MED & DENT, 68-, PROF RADIATION BIOL & BIOPHYS, 72- *Concurrent Pos:* Consult, UNRRA, 46-47, Armed Forces Radiobiol Res Inst, 63-70, Walter Reed Army Inst Res, 65-70, Vet Admin, 66-, Nat Acad Sci-Nat Res Coun, 72-, Elec Power Res Inst, 75- & Nat Coun Radiation Protection & Measurement, 79-; vis lectr, Am Inst Biol Sci; assoc ed, J Microwave Power, 74-; ed, Radiation & Environ Biophysics; consult, Elec Power Res Inst, 75; lect series dir, NATO /AGARD, 75; co-dir fourth course, Int Sch Radiation Damage & Protection, Erice, Sicily, 80. *Mem:* Am Col Vet Toxicologists; Am Physiol Soc; Radiation Res Soc; Health Physics Soc; Sigma Xi. *Res:* Mechanisms of injury and recovery from electromagnetic radiations, especially neuroendocrine physiology. *Mailing Add:* Dept Radiation Biol & Biophys Univ Rochester Sch Med & Dent Rochester NY 14642

MICHAL, EDWIN KEITH, b Independence, Kans, Sept 17, 32; m 56; c 4. NEUROPHYSIOLOGY. *Educ:* Kans Wesleyan Univ, BA, 54; Univ Ill, MS, 62, PhD(physiol), 65. *Prof Exp:* Asst prof, 65-72, ASSOC PROF PHYSIOL, OHIO STATE UNIV, 72- *Mem:* Am Physiol Soc; Soc Neurosci. *Res:* Neural mechanisms in behavior; neuroendocrinology; neural control of respiration. *Mailing Add:* Dept of Physiol Ohio State Univ Col Med Columbus OH 43210

MICHAL, EUGENE J(OSEPH), b Reno, Nev, Oct 23, 22; m 51; c 4. METALLURGY. *Educ:* Univ Nev, BS, 43; Mass Inst Technol, MS, 47, ScD, 51. *Prof Exp:* Physicist, Mare Island Navy Yard, 43-44; instr metall, Mass Inst Technol, 49-51; res metallurgist, AEC, Watertown Arsenal, 48-49; supvr metall res, Nat Lead Co, 51-68; asst to vpres, INCO Inc, NY, 68-70; dir res & develop, Climax Molybdenum Co, 70-76, vpres, 76-77; PRES, AMAX EXTRACTIVE RES & DEVELOP INC, 77- *Mem:* Am Inst Mining, Metall & Petrol Engrs; Combustion Inst; fel Brit Inst Mining & Metall; Am Inst Chem Engrs; Am Mgt Asn. *Res:* Process metallurgy; metallurgical slags; hydrometallurgy; electric steelmaking. *Mailing Add:* AMAX Inc 1707 Cole Blvd Golden CO 80401

MICHALAK, JOSEPH T(HOMAS), b Philadelphia, Pa, July 1, 32; m 56; c 3. PHYSICAL METALLURGY OF LOW-CARBON STEEL. *Educ:* Drexel Inst, BS, 55; Carnegie Inst Technol, MS, 58, PhD(metall eng), 60. *Prof Exp:* Scientist, 59-68, sr scientist, 68-76, ASSOC RES CONSULT PHYS METALL, BASIC RES DIV, RES LAB, US STEEL CORP, 76- *Mem:* Am Inst Mining, Metall & Petrol Engrs. *Res:* Physical and mechanical metallurgy of low-carbon steel, especially recovery, recrystallization and texture development; quench aging; strain aging; internal friction; formability. *Mailing Add:* US Steel Corp Res Lab MS-59 125 Jamison Lane Monroeville PA 15146

MICHALEK, JOEL EDMUND, b Detroit, Mich, Aug 30, 44. STATISTICS. *Educ:* Wayne State Univ, BS, 66, MA, 68, PhD(math statist), 73. *Prof Exp:* Instr math, RI Col, 70-71; asst prof statist, Syracuse Univ, 73-76; MATH STATISTICIAN, US AIR FORCE SCH AEROSPACE MED, 76- *Mem:* Am Statist Asn; Inst Math Statist. *Res:* Survival analysis. *Mailing Add:* USAFSAM/BRM Brooks AFB TX 78235

MICHALIK, EDMUND RICHARD, b Munhall, Pa, Aug 5, 15; m 46; c 1. APPLIED MATHEMATICS, STATISTICS. *Educ:* Univ Pittsburgh, BA, 37, MA, 40. *Prof Exp:* Instr math, Univ Pittsburgh, 40-42, asst prof math statist, 46-52; sr analyst rev planning, US Dept Army, 52-53; consult appl math & statist, Atlantic Res Co, 53-54; head dept appl math, Mellon Inst, 54-57; sr staff engr, Glass Res Ctr, PPG Indust, Inc, 57-80. *Mem:* Math Asn Am; Brit Soc Glass Technol. *Res:* Use of electronic digital machines in mathematic, statistics, industrial problems; glass strength and glass strengthening. *Mailing Add:* 3711 Spring St West Mifflin PA 15122

MICHALOWICZ, JOSEPH C(ASIMIR), b Washington, DC, Mar 4, 16; m 40; c 5. ELECTRICAL ENGINEERING. *Educ:* Cath Univ Am, BEE, 40, MEE, 51. *Prof Exp:* Asst engr, Rural Electrification Admin, USDA, 40-42; from instr to asst prof elec eng, 42-44, 46-51, head dept, 52-59, asst dean, Sch Eng & Archit, 69-71, dean admis, financial aid & records & registrar, 73-78, ASSOC PROF ELEC ENG, CATH UNIV AM, 51- *Concurrent Pos:* Cottrell grant, Res Corp, NY, 50-52. *Mem:* Fel Inst Elec & Electronics Engrs; Sigma Xi. *Res:* Electronic instrumentation; electronic automotive fuelmeter. *Mailing Add:* 7409 Wyndale Rd Chevy Chase MD 20015

MICHALOWICZ, JOSEPH VICTOR, b Oct 23, 41; m 63; c 2. MATHEMATICS, SYSTEMS ANALYSIS. *Educ:* Catholic Univ Am, BA, 63, PhD(math), 67. *Prof Exp:* Mathematician, Res Anal Corp, 66-67; asst prof math, Catholic Univ Am, 67-73; MATHEMATICIAN, HARRY DIAMOND LABS, 73- *Concurrent Pos:* Lectr elec eng, Catholic Univ Am, 66-67; NSF fel category theory, Bowdoin Col, 69; consult, Res Anal Corp, 67-70 & Harry Diamond Labs, 70-73. *Mem:* Am Math Soc; Mil Opers Res Soc; Math Asn Am. *Res:* Systems analysis and cost effectiveness studies; analyses of laser-guided missiles; research in category theory. *Mailing Add:* 5855 Glen Forest Dr Falls Church VA 22041

MICHALOWSKI, JOSEPH THOMAS, b Newburgh, NY, Dec 17, 43. GEOCHEMISTRY. *Educ:* Marist Col, BA, 68; Univ Calif, Santa Barbara, PhD(chem), 72. *Prof Exp:* Res assoc chem, Univ Calif, Santa Barbara, 72-73, lectr, 73; res assoc biochem, St Louis Univ, 73-74; RES SCIENTIST GEOCHEM, PHILLIPS PETROL CO, 74- *Mem:* Am Geophys Union; Am Chem Soc; AAAS; Geol Soc Am; Sigma Xi. *Res:* Electrochemistry and mechanics of migration of multi-phase fluids through porous rocks; problems of petroleum migration. *Mailing Add:* Res & Develop Rm 244 GB Phillips Petrol Co Bartlesville OK 74004

MICHALSKE, TERRY ARTHUR, b Dunkirk, NY, Jan 19, 53. FRACTURE SURFACE ANALYSIS, FRACTURE MECHANICS. *Educ:* Alfred Univ, BS, 75, PhD(ceramic sci), 79. *Prof Exp:* Fel, Nat Bur Standards, 79-81; MEM TECH STAFF, SANDIA NAT LABS, 81- *Mem:* Am Ceramic Soc. *Res:* Fracture properties of brittle materials; stress corrosion effects in brittle materials; effect of ceramic microstructure on fracture properties. *Mailing Add:* Div 5845 Sandia Nat Labs Albuquerque NM 87115

MICHALSKI, CHESTER JAMES, b Detroit, Mich, June 7, 42; m. MOLECULAR BIOLOGY. *Educ:* Mich State Univ, BS, 65, MS, 67; Univ NC, PhD(biochem), 71. *Prof Exp:* Fel biochem, St Judes Children's Res Hosp, Memphis, 71-72; fel, 72-75, asst prof, 75-79, ASSOC PROF MOLECULAR BIOL & DIR MULTIDISCIPLINE LABS, FAC MED, MEM UNIV NFLD, 79- *Mem:* Am Soc Microbiol; Can Soc Microbiol; Asn Multidiscipline Educ Health Sci; Can Biochem Soc; NY Acad Sci. *Res:* Structure and function of the macromolecular components involved in the protein synthesizing system of E coli cells and the molecular events involved in hormone regulation of the fungi. *Mailing Add:* Fac Med Mem Univ Nfld St John's NF A1B 3V6 Can

MICHALSKI, RAYMOND J, b Harvey, Ill, Oct 30, 28; m 57; c 3. ENVIRONMENTAL CHEMISTRY. *Educ:* Univ Ill, BS, 52. *Prof Exp:* Microbiologist, Nat Dairy Co, 52-56; microbiologist, 56-65, group leader antifoam, 65-68, weed control-antifoam, 68-71 & surface active chem, 71-73, sr group leader mineral processing & flotation aids, 73-75, sr group leader pollution control emulsion breaking & spray bood chem, 75-78, TECH DIR, PULP & PAPER RES, NALCO CHEM CO, 79- *Mem:* Am Soc Microbiol; Soc Indust Microbiol; Sigma Xi; Tech Asn Pulp & Paper Indust; Paper Indust Mgt Asn. *Res:* Additives in paper processing areas, especially slime control, dispersants, wire life improvers, mold proofing agents and antifoams for varied industrial applications; pollution control and mineral process aids. *Mailing Add:* Nalco Chem Co 1801 Diehl Rd Naperville IL 60540

MICHALSKI, RYSZARD SPENCER, b Kalusz, Poland, May 7, 37. COMPUTER SCIENCES. *Educ:* Warsaw Tech Univ, BS, 59; Leningrad Polytech Inst, MS, 61; Silesia Tech Univ, Poland, PhD(comput sci), 69. *Prof Exp:* Logical designer comput sci, Inst Math Mach, Polish Acad Sci, Warsaw, 61-62, res scientist, Inst Automatic Control, 62-70; vis asst prof, 70-72, ASSOC PROF COMPUT SCI, UNIV ILL, URBANA, 72- *Concurrent Pos:* Lectr comput sci & electronics, State Tech Col, Warsaw, Poland, 64-68; Fulbright fel, US State Dept, 70; NSF res award, 75, 77 & 79; sr fel, British Sci Res Coun, 77. *Mem:* Asn Comput Mach; Pattern Recognition Soc; Sigma Xi; Polish Inst Arts & Sci in Am. *Res:* Computer induction and plausible reasoning; data bases; pattern recognition and artificial intelligence; applications to agriculture and medicine; expert systems, multiple-valued logic, intelligent systems. *Mailing Add:* Dept Comput Sci 1304 W Springfield Ave Univ of Ill Urbana IL 61801

MICHALSKY, JOSEPH JAN, JR, b Dayton, Tex, Oct 8, 47; m 74; c 1. ASTRONOMY, ATMOSPHERIC SCIENCE. *Educ:* Lamar Univ, BS, 69; Univ Ky, MS, 71, PhD(physics), 74. *Prof Exp:* Fel astron, Battelle Inst, Ger, 74-76; res scientist, 76-80, SR RES SCIENTIST ASTRON & ATMOSPHERIC SCI, NORTHWEST LABS, BATTELLE MEM INST, 80- *Mem:* Am Astron Soc. *Res:* Astronomical polarimetry of planetary systems and binary stars associated with x-ray sources; spatial and spectral measurements of both direct and diffuse insolation and their interpretation. *Mailing Add:* Battelle Northwest Labs Box 999 Richland WA 99352

MICHAUD, GEORGES JOSEPH, b Quebec, Que, Apr 30, 40; m 66; c 2. ASTROPHYSICS. *Educ:* Univ Laval, BA, 61, BSc, 65; Calif Inst Technol, PhD(astron), 69. *Prof Exp:* Asst prof, 69-73, assoc prof, 73-79, PROF PHYSICS, UNIV MONTREAL, 79- *Honors & Awards:* Steacie Prize, 80. *Mem:* Am Astron Soc; Can Astron Soc; Int Astron Union. *Res:* The chemical abundance of the elements; nucleosynthesis and diffusion in stellar envelopes and atmospheres. *Mailing Add:* Dept of Physics Univ of Montreal Box 6128 Montreal PQ H3C 3J7 Can

MICHAUD, HOWARD H, b Berne, Ind, Oct 12, 02; m 28; c 1. ENVIRONMENTAL MANAGEMENT. *Educ:* Bluffton Col, AB, 25; Ind Univ, MA, 30. *Prof Exp:* Teacher pub schs, Ind, 25-45; prof, 45-71, EMER PROF CONSERV, PURDUE UNIV, 71- *Concurrent Pos:* Del, Int Union Conserv Nature & Natural Resources, 48 & 66. *Honors & Awards:* Osborn Wildlife Conserv Award, 59. *Mem:* Conserv Educ Asn (pres, 56-57); Am Asn Biol Teachers (pres, 48); hon mem Soil Conserv Soc Am; Wildlife Soc. *Res:* Science and conservation education. *Mailing Add:* 301 E Stadium Ave West Lafayette IN 47906

MICHAUD, LAURENT, b Montreal, Que, May 25, 15; nat US; m 49; c 3. NUTRITION, VETERINARY MEDICINE. *Educ:* Univ Montreal, DVM, 36; Univ Wis, PhD(biochem), 48. *Prof Exp:* Pvt pract, Que, Can, 36-39; dir, Que Exp Fur Farm, 39-41, Biochem & Vet Res Labs, Que, 48-49 & Biochem Diag Lab, Waterbury Hosp, Conn, 49-50; mgr vet nutrit & dir, Prog Planning & Control, Merck Sharp & Dohme Res Labs, 50-80; RETIRED. *Mem:* Am Soc Animal Sci; Am Asn Vet Nutrit; Am Vet Med Asn; Am Dairy Sci Asn; Animal Nutrit Res Coun. *Res:* Animal physiology and nutrition. *Mailing Add:* Merck Sharp & Dohme Res Labs Rahway NJ 07065

MICHAUD, RONALD NORMAND, b Madawaska, Maine, July 7, 37; m 58; c 2. MICROBIOLOGICAL CONTROL. *Educ:* Univ Maine, BS, 63; Cornell Univ, MS, 66, PhD(microbiol), 68. *Prof Exp:* Assoc res microbiologist, 68-71, group leader, 71-74, res microbiologist, 74-75, head bact sect, 75-80, HEAD MICROBIOL CONTROL SECT, STERLING-WINTHROP RES INST DIV, STERLING DRUG INC, 80- *Mem:* Am Soc Microbiol; Soc Indust Microbiol. *Res:* Microbiological control aspects of the pharmaceutical product development of dosage types. *Mailing Add:* Microbiol Control Sect Sterling Winthrop Res Inst Rensselaer NY 12144

MICHAUD, TED C, b Ft Wayne, Ind, Oct 5, 29; m 55; c 3. ZOOLOGY. *Educ:* Purdue Univ, BS, 51; Univ Mich, MS, 54; Univ Tex, PhD(zool), 59. *Prof Exp:* From asst prof to assoc prof, 59-70, PROF BIOL, CARROLL COL, WIS, 70- *Concurrent Pos:* Mem, Demog Inst, Cornell Univ, 71; mem steering comt, Cent States Col Asn Environ Studies Comt; second vpres, Asn Midwestern Col Biol Teachers, 80-81. *Mem:* AAAS; Soc Study Evolution; Am Soc Ichthyol & Herpet; Ecol Soc Am; Nat Biol Soc. *Res:* Amphibian behavior and evolution. *Mailing Add:* Dept of Biol Carroll Col 100 N East Ave Waukesha WI 53186

MICHEJDA, CHRISTOPHER JAN, b Kielce, Poland, Dec 19, 37; US citizen; m 64; c 1. PHYSICAL ORGANIC CHEMISTRY, BIO-ORGANIC CHEMISTRY. *Educ:* Univ Ill, BS, 59; Univ Rochester, PhD(org chem), 64. *Prof Exp:* NSF fel, Harvard Univ, 63-64; from asst prof to prof org chem, Univ Nebr, Lincoln, 75-78; HEAD CHEM CARCINOGENS, FREDERICK CANCER RES CTR, 78-; ADJ PROF CHEM, UNIV MD, COLLEGE PARK, 78- *Concurrent Pos:* NIH spec fel, Swiss Fed Inst Technol, 72-73; assoc prog dir for chem dynamics, NSF, 75-77. *Mem:* Am Chem Soc. *Res:* Free radical chemistry; chemical carcinogenesis. *Mailing Add:* Frederick Cancer Res Ctr Frederick MD 21701

MICHEJDA, OSKAR, b Trzyniec, Czech, May 19, 22; m 48; c 1. CIVIL ENGINEERING. *Educ:* Wroclaw Polytech Univ, MScEng, 50, DSc(exp stress anal), 61. *Prof Exp:* Asst prof appl mech & strength of mat, Czestochowa Polytech Univ, 54-65; sr lectr, Univ Khartoum, 65-66; assoc prof, Cooper Union Inst Technol, 66-68; prof civil eng, Ind Inst Technol, 68-74; eng specialist, 74-80, PRIN ENGR, BURNS & ROE, 80- *Res:* Theory of structures; experimental stress analysis. *Mailing Add:* Burns & Roe 670 Winters Ave Paramus NJ 07652

MICHEL, ANTHONY NIKOLAUS, b Rekasch, Romania, Nov 17, 35; US citizen; m 57; c 5. ELECTRICAL ENGINEERING, MATHEMATICS. *Educ:* Marquette Univ, BSEE, 58, MS, 64, PhD(elec eng), 68; Tech Univ Graz, Austria, DSc(math), 73. *Prof Exp:* Sr res engr, AC Electronics Div, Gen Motors Corp, Wis, 58-65; from asst prof to assoc prof elec eng, 68-74, Off Naval Res grant, Eng Res Inst, 68-72, PROF ELEC ENG, IOWA STATE UNIV, 74- *Concurrent Pos:* NSF grants, Eng Res Inst, 72-; assoc ed, Inst Elec & Electronics Engrs Trans on Circuits & Systs, 77-79. *Mem:* Inst Elec & Electronics Engrs. *Res:* Automatic control theory; differential equations; large scale systems. *Mailing Add:* Dept of Elec Eng Iowa State Univ Ames IA 50011

MICHEL, BURLYN EVERETT, b Ladoga, Ind, Mar 7, 23; m 46; c 3. PLANT PHYSIOLOGY. *Educ:* Univ Chicago, SB, 48, PhD(bot), 50. *Prof Exp:* Asst prof bot, Univ Iowa, 51-58; assoc prof, 58-64, PROF BOT, UNIV GA, 64- *Concurrent Pos:* Plant physiologist, Agr Res Serv, USDA, 59-62. *Mem:* Am Inst Biol Sci; Bot Soc Am; Am Soc Plant Physiol. *Res:* Plant-water relations and mineral absorption. *Mailing Add:* Dept of Bot Univ of Ga Athens GA 30602

MICHEL, DAVID JOHN, b Denison, Tex, July 24, 42. METALLURGY, CRYSTALLOGRAPHY. *Educ:* Univ Mo-Rolla, BSMetE, 64; Pa State Univ, MSMet, 66, PhD(metall), 68. *Prof Exp:* Asst metallurgist, Homer Res Lab, Bethlehem Steel Co, 64; res asst metall, Pa State Univ, 64-68, fel, 68-69; metallurgist, Div Res, US AEC, 69-71; res asst prof mat sci, Univ Cincinnati, 71-72; res metallurgist, 72-73, HEAD HIGH TEMPERATURE METALS SECT, US NAVAL RES LAB, 73- *Honors & Awards:* Nat Capital Award for Prof Achievement Eng, Washington, DC Coun Eng & Architectural Soc, 78. *Mem:* AAAS; Am Soc Metals; Am Inst Mining, Metall & Petrol Engrs; Am

Crystallog Asn; Am Nuclear Soc. *Res:* Radiation effects in materials; mechanical behavior of materials; intermetallic compounds; x-ray crystallography; alloy theory; phase equilibria; phase transformations in solids; electron microscopy. *Mailing Add:* Thermostruct Mat Br US Naval Res Lab Code 6396 Washington DC 20375

MICHEL, F CURTIS, b La Crosse, Wis, June 5, 34; m 58; c 2. ASTROPHYSICS, SPACE PHYSICS. *Educ:* Calif Inst Technol, BS, 55, PhD(physics), 62. *Prof Exp:* Res fel astrophys, Calif Inst Technol, 62-63; from asst prof to assoc prof space sci, 63-70, prof physics, space physics & astron, 70-74, chmn dept space physics & astron, 74-79, BUCHANAN PROF ASTROPHYS, RICE UNIV, 74- *Concurrent Pos:* Scientist-astronaut, NASA, 65-69; mem lunar atmosphere working group, planetary atmospheres subcomt, Space Sci Steering Comt, 66-67; mem sch natural sci, Inst Advan Study, 71-72; trustee, Univs Space Res Asn, 75-; Guggenheim fel, Paris France, 79-80. *Mem:* AAAS; Am Phys Soc; Am Astron Soc; Am Geophys Union. *Res:* Gravitational collapse; particle acceleration; pulsars; magnetospheric tail structure; solar wind interaction with moon and planets; elementary particles; weak magnetism; nuclear parity violation; symmetries; gravitationally induced electric fields. *Mailing Add:* Dept of Space Physics & Astron Rice Univ Houston TX 77001

MICHEL, GERD WILHELM, b Darmstadt, Ger, July 4, 30; m 59. NATURAL PRODUCTS CHEMISTRY. *Educ:* Darmstadt Tech Univ, Dipl chem, 56, Dr rer nat, 59. *Prof Exp:* Res assoc chem, Urbana, Ill, 59-62; res chemist res div, Photo Prod Dept, E I du Pont de Nemours & Co, 62-64, tech serv specialist, 64-65; asst to dir sales indust chem, E Merck A G, Darmstadt, 66-67; res fel, 67, SR RES FEL, SQUIBB INST MED RES, 67- *Mem:* Am Chem Soc; Soc Ger Chem; NY Acad Sci. *Res:* Chemistry of Mannich-bases, nitrones, alkaloids, steroids; antibiotics; photo polymerization; chemical process development. *Mailing Add:* 5 Oak Pl Province Hill Princeton NJ 08540

MICHEL, HARDING B, b Louisville, Ky, Aug 17, 24; m 48, 70; c 1. MARINE ZOOLOGY. *Educ:* Duke Univ, AB, 46; Univ Miami, MS, 49; Univ Mich, PhD, 57. *Prof Exp:* Asst zool, 46-48, asst instr, 48-50, instr, Marine Lab, 54-57, asst prof, 57-67, assoc prof, Inst Marine Sci, 67-70, PROF BIOL OCEANOG, ROSENSTIEL SCH MARINE & ATMOSPHERIC SCI, UNIV MIAMI, 70- *Concurrent Pos:* Asst ed, Bull Marine Sci of the Gulf & Caribbean, 52-53. *Mem:* AAAS; Soc Syst Zool; Soc Study Evolution; Marine Biol Asn UK; Sigma Xi. *Res:* Invertebrate embryology; marine zooplankton; distribution of oceanic zooplankton in Caribbean Sea; ecology of estuaries in South Vietnam; zooplankton of the Arabian Gulf. *Mailing Add:* Rosenstiel Sch Marine & Atms Sci 4600 Rickenbacker Causeway Miami FL 33149

MICHEL, KARL HEINZ, b Marklissa, Ger, Nov 9, 29; m 59. BIO-ORGANIC CHEMISTRY. *Educ:* Weihenstephan Univ, Ger, BS, 56, dipl, 64; Landau Univ, BS, 58. *Prof Exp:* Chem engr, Cent Lab, Swedish Pharmaceut Soc, 59-60; res asst org chem, Royal Inst Pharm, Stockholm, 60-65; res assoc org chem, Iowa State Univ, Ames, 65-66; res assoc, Royal Inst Pharm, Stockholm, 66-67; proj leader, Fleischmann Lab, Stamford, Conn, 67-69; sr biochemist, 69-75, RES SCIENTIST, ELI LILLY & CO, INDIANAPOLIS, IND, 75- *Res:* Isolation, characterization, structure determination and biological evaluation of new antibiotics and other biological active compounds; designer of chromatography instrumentation, patentee and consultant in fields. *Mailing Add:* Eli Lilly & Co MC-539 Indianapolis IN 46206

MICHEL, KENNETH EARL, b Chicago, Ill, May 22, 30; m 58; c 2. CYTOGENETICS. *Educ:* Northern Ill Univ, BS, 51, MS, 52; Univ Minn, PhD(genetics), 66. *Prof Exp:* Instr sci, Gavin Sch, 54-57; instr biol, Waldorf Col, 57-62; assoc prof, 66-68, prof genetics, 68-77, PROF BIOL, SLIPPERY ROCK STATE COL, 77- *Concurrent Pos:* Chmn dept genetics, Slippery Rock State Col, 66-74; mem, Maize Genetics Coop. *Mem:* Genetics Soc Am; Am Genetics Asn. *Res:* Interrelated behavior of non-homologous chromosomes in maize; chromosome pairing and disjunction. *Mailing Add:* Dept of Biol Slippery Rock State Col Slippery Rock PA 16057

MICHEL, LESTER ALLEN, b Mexico, Ind, Mar 5, 19; m 42; c 5. CHEMISTRY. *Educ:* Taylor Univ, AB, 41; Purdue Univ, MS, 44; Univ Colo, PhD(phys chem), 47. *Prof Exp:* Asst chem, Purdue Univ, 41-44; tech adv, Manhattan Proj, Linde Air Prod Co, NY, 44-45; asst chem, Univ Colo, 45-46; from instr to prof, 47-70, chmn dept chem, 59-70, VERNER Z REED PROF CHEM, COLO COL, 70- *Concurrent Pos:* Res Corp grant, 48. *Mem:* AAAS; Am Chem Soc. *Res:* Calorimetry; crystal growth; vapor pressures; isothermal flow calorimeter for vapor phase reactions; surface chemistry. *Mailing Add:* Dept of Chem Colo Col Colorado Springs CO 80903

MICHEL, RICHARD EDWIN, b Saginaw, Mich, Oct 31, 28; m 51; c 3. SOLID STATE PHYSICS. *Educ:* Mich State Univ, BS, 50, MS, 53, PhD(physics), 56. *Prof Exp:* Mem tech staff, RCA Labs, 56-62; sr res physicist, Gen Motors Res Labs, 62-73; instr, 71-73, DEAN, LAWRENCE INST TECHNOL, 73- *Res:* Magnetic resonance; magnetic materials; polymers; semiconductors. *Mailing Add:* Lawrence Inst of Technol 21000 W Ten Mile Rd Southfield MI 48075

MICHEL, ROBERT GEORGE, b Sheffield, Eng, Jan 21, 49; m 72; c 2. ATOMIC SPECTROMETRY, ANALYTICAL INSTRUMENTATION. *Educ:* Sheffield Polytech, BSc, 71, PhD(anal chem), 74. *Prof Exp:* Fel, Univ Fla, 74-76, Univ Strathclyde, 76-78; ASST PROF ANAL CHEM, UNIV CONN, 79- *Concurrent Pos:* Mem staff, Inst Mat Sci, Univ Conn, 79-, asst prof, Sch Allied Health, 81-82; Sr Fulbright-Hays Award for Travel, 74. *Mem:* Royal Soc Chem; Am Chem Soc; Soc Appl Spectroscopy; Sigma Xi. *Res:* Atomic and molecular emission; absorption and fluorescence in plasmas; flames and electrothermal atomizers; development of instrumentation and of sensitive, selective and accurate methods for trace analysis of components in materials based on the above spectroscopic techniques. *Mailing Add:* Dept Chem U 60 Univ Conn Storrs CT 06268

MICHEL, RUDOLPH HENRY, organic chemistry, see previous edition

MICHELAKIS, ANDREW M, b Greece, Aug 12, 27; US citizen; m 64; c 2. MEDICINE. *Educ:* Athens Col Agr, BS, 52; Univ Kans, MS, 56; Ohio State Univ, PhD(chem), 59; Western Reserve Univ, MD, 64. *Prof Exp:* Asst chem, Univ Kans, 54-55; asst, Ohio State Univ, 55-59; intern, Mt Sinai Hosp, Cleveland, 64-65; resident, Vet Admin Hosp, 65-66; from instr to assoc prof med, Sch Med, Vanderbilt Univ, 66-74, from asst prof to assoc prof pharmacol, 68-74; dir clin pharmacol, 74-77, PROF MED & PHARMACOL, MICH STATE UNIV, 74- *Concurrent Pos:* Fel endocrinol, Vanderbilt Univ, 66-68. *Mem:* Am Fedn Clin Res; Endocrine Soc; Soc Exp Biol & Med; Am Soc Pharmacol & Exp Therapeut. *Res:* Endocrinology; hypertension and cardiovascular diseases; clinical pharmacology. *Mailing Add:* Dept of Pharmacol Mich State Univ Col Human Med East Lansing MI 48824

MICHELI, PAUL LOTHAR, chemical engineering, see previous edition

MICHELI, ROBERT ANGELO, b San Francisco, Calif, Dec 31, 22; m 77. ORGANIC CHEMISTRY. *Educ:* Univ Calif, BS, 51; Duke Univ, PhD(org chem), 54. *Prof Exp:* Asst, Duke Univ, 51-53; Nat Cancer Inst res fel, Harvard Univ, 54-56; res chemist, Dow Chem Co, 56-58, Western Regional Res Lab, USDA, Calif, 58-62 & Univ Basel, 62-64; res chemist, 64-75, RES FEL, HOFFMANN-LA ROCHE, INC, 75- *Mem:* Am Chem Soc. *Res:* Steroid and medicinal chemistry. *Mailing Add:* Chem Res Dept Hoffmann-La Roche Inc Nutley NJ 07110

MICHELMAN, JOHN S, b Portsmouth, Ohio, Apr 19, 38; m 64; c 3. ORGANIC & EMULSION CHEMISTRY. *Educ:* Univ Cincinnati, BS, 60; Harvard Univ, MA, 62, PhD(chem), 65. *Prof Exp:* Asst prof chem, Univ Cincinnati, 66-67; VPRES CHEM, MICHELMAN CHEM, INC, 65- *Mem:* Am Chem Soc. *Res:* Water based coatings; emulsion technology. *Mailing Add:* Michelman Chem Inc 9089 Shell Rd Cincinnati OH 45236

MICHELS, CORINNE ANTHONY, b New York, NY, Jan 2, 43; m 64; c 2. GENE EXPRESSION, YEAST GENETICS. *Educ:* Queens Col, BS, 63; Columbia Univ, MS, 65, PhD(genetics), 69. *Prof Exp:* Res assoc, Columbia Univ, 69-70; res fel, Albert Einstein Col Med, 70-72; asst prof, 72-79, ASSOC PROF BIOL, QUEENS COL, 79- *Mem:* Genetics Soc Am; Am Soc Microbiol; AAAS. *Res:* Regulation of gene expression, specifically, in glucose repression in yeast using genetics and gene splicing to study this phenonemon. *Mailing Add:* Dept Biol Queens Col Flushing NY 11367

MICHELS, DONALD JOSEPH, b Brooklyn, NY, Apr 17, 32; m 61; c 6. PHYSICS. *Educ:* St Peter's Col NJ, BS, 54; Fordham Univ, MS, 56; Cath Univ Am, PhD(physics), 70. *Prof Exp:* RES PHYSICIST, NAVAL RES LAB, 61- *Mem:* Optical Soc Am; Am Geophys Union. *Res:* Extreme ultraviolet spectroscopy; solar radiation and solar-terrestrial effects; space physics and spacecraft instrumentation. *Mailing Add:* E O Hulburt Ctr Space Res Code 4173 Naval Res Lab Washington DC 20375

MICHELS, H(ORACE) HARVEY, b Philadelphia, Pa, Dec 9, 32; m 58, 75; c 2. CHEMICAL PHYSICS. *Educ:* Drexel Inst Technol, BSChE, 55; Univ Del, MChE, 57, PhD, 60. *Prof Exp:* Res engr, G & W H Corson Co, Inc, Pa, 51-53; sr anal engr, 59-62, sr res scientist, 62-68, SR THEORET PHYSICIST, UNITED TECHNOLOGIES CORP, 68- *Concurrent Pos:* Adj asst prof, Rensselaer Polytech, Hartford Grad Ctr, 60-65, adj assoc prof, 65-69, adj prof, 69-72; Nat Bur Stand vis fel, Joint Inst for Lab Astrophys, Univ Colo, 70; vis scholar, Quantum Inst, Univ Calif, Santa Barbara, 71; adj prof, Univ Hartford, 75- *Mem:* Am Chem Soc; fel Am Phys Soc; Sigma Xi. *Res:* Quantum mechanics of the electronic structure of atoms and molecules; thermochemistry and kinetics of reacting gaseous systems at high temperatures; atomic recombination and transport processes. *Mailing Add:* Physics Dept United Technologies Res Ctr East Hartford CT 06108

MICHELS, JULIAN GETZ, b Savannah, Ga, July 30, 20; m 46; c 5. ORGANIC CHEMISTRY. *Educ:* Univ Ga, BS, 41; Univ Tenn, MS, 43; Lehigh Univ, PhD(org chem), 49. *Prof Exp:* Res chemist explosives, Trojan Powder Co, 43-44 & Atlas Powder Co, 49-51; res chemist, 51-59, chief sect phys & anal chem, 59-70, res assoc, 70-79, SR RES ASSOC, NORWICH-EATON PHARMACEUT, 79- *Mem:* NY Acad Sci; Sigma Xi. *Res:* Heterocyclic chemistry. *Mailing Add:* Star Rte Norwich NY 13815

MICHELS, LESTER DAVID, b Chicago, Ill, Feb 5, 48; m 69. RENAL PHYSIOLOGY. *Educ:* Univ Minn, BS ChE, 70, PhD(physiol), 75. *Prof Exp:* Process res engr, Dow Chem Co, 70-71; res specialist renal transplant, Dept Surg, Univ Minn, 75-76; LECTR, DEPT PHYSIOL, UNIV MINN & RES PHYSIOLOGIST, MINNEAPOLIS MED RES FOUND, 76- *Mem:* Am Physiol Soc; Am Soc Nephrol; Int Soc Nephrol. *Res:* Glomerular filtration dynamics and permeability in normal and disease states. *Mailing Add:* Minneapolis Med Res Found Minneapolis MN 55415

MICHELS, LLOYD R, b San Francisco, Calif, Aug 2, 16; m 43; c 2. CHEMICAL & NUCLEAR ENGINEERING. *Educ:* Univ Calif, BS, 38; Univ Ill, MS, 40, PhD(chem eng), 41. *Prof Exp:* Asst chem, Univ Ill, 39-41; res chem engr & metallurgist, Permanente Metals Corp, Calif, 41-42; asst chem engr, US Bur Mines, Wash, 42-43, assoc chem engr, Utah, 43-45; develop engr, Titanium Div, Nat Lead Co, 45-51; lead engr, Calif Res & Develop Co, 51-53; tech expert, Magnesium Prod Dept, Dow Chem Co, 53-54; sr engr, Gen Elec Co, 54-63, mgr separations process design eng, 63-66; mgr eng & res, Isochem, Inc, 66-67; prin design engr, Atomic Prod Equip Dept, Gen Elec Co, 67-76; mgr spec projs, Gen Elec Uranium Mgt Corp, 76-80; CONSULT, NUCLEAR & CHEM PROCESSES & SYSTS, 80- *Mem:* Am Chem Soc; Am Inst Chem Engrs; Am Nuclear Soc. *Res:* Magnesium; titanium metal, pigments and tetrachloride; chemical separations related to atomic power reactors; process design and economic evaluation. *Mailing Add:* 1713 Husted Ave San Jose CA 95124

MICHELS, ROBERT, b Chicago, Ill, Jan 21, 36; c 2. PSYCHIATRY, PSYCHOANALYSIS. *Educ:* Univ Chicago, BA, 53; Northwestern Univ, MD, 58; Am Bd Psychiat & Neurol, dipl, 64; Columbia Univ, cert psychoanal med, 67. *Prof Exp:* Res fel, Lab Clin Sci, NIMH, 62-64; from instr to assoc prof psychiat, Col Physicians & Surgeons, Columbia Univ, 64-74; PROF PSYCHIAT & PSYCHIATRIST IN CHIEF, NY HOSP-CORNELL MED CTR, 74- *Concurrent Pos:* Spec lectr & instr psychiat, Columbia Univ, 60-74, attend psychiatrist, Student Health Serv, 66-74, mem fac & supv & training analyst, Psychoanal Ctr Training & Res, 67-; assoc fel, Inst Policy Studies, Washington, DC, 63-64; NIMH career teacher award, Columbia Univ, 64-66; from asst to attend psychiatrist, Vanderbilt Clin & Presby Hosp, 64-74; from asst to attend psychiatrist, St Lukes Hosp Ctr, New York, 66-; from asst examr to dir, Am Bd Psychiat & Neurol, 67-82; secy, Inst Soc, Ethics & Life Sci, 71-77. *Mem:* Fel Am Psychiat Asn; Royal Medico-Psychol Asn; Asn Res Nerv & Ment Dis; Am Psychoanal Asn; Group Advan Psychiat. *Res:* Psychiatric education. *Mailing Add:* Dept of Psychiat NY Hosp-Cornell Med Ctr New York NY 10021

MICHELSEN, ARVE (NMI), b Hamar, Norway, Oct 25, 23; US citizen; m 51; c 2. RADIOBIOLOGY. *Educ:* Univ Ariz, BS, 50; Stanford Univ, MS, 51; Johns Hopkins Univ, PhD(biomed eng), 70. *Prof Exp:* Res engr, Aerojet Gen Corp, 56-58; proj engr, 58-68, DIV & DEPT STAFF ENGR, APPL PHYSICS LAB, JOHNS HOPKINS UNIV, 68-, MEM PRIN PROF STAFF, 78- *Mem:* Radiation Res Soc. *Res:* Electromagnetic radiating and receiving systems; ordnance devices; flash x-ray systems and radiography; biomedical engineering; radiobiology; systems engineering, integration and analysis. *Mailing Add:* Appl Physics Lab Johns Hopkins Univ Laurel MD 20707

MICHELSOHN, MARIE-LOUISE, topology, see previous edition

MICHELSON, EDWARD HARLAN, b St Louis, Mo, June 6, 26; m 52 & 68; c 6. MALACOLOGY, PUBLIC HEALTH. *Educ:* Univ Fla, BS, 49, MS, 51; Harvard Univ, PhD(biol), 56. *Prof Exp:* Instr biol, Cambridge Jr Col, 51-53; asst, 53-55, res assoc, 55-57, from instr to asst prof, 57-69, assoc mollusks, Mus Comp Zool, 57-77, ASSOC PROF TROP PUB HEALTH, SCH PUB HEALTH, HARVARD UNIV, 69- *Concurrent Pos:* La State Univ-China Med Bd fel, 59; advisor Schistosomiasis, Pan Am Health Orgn, Orgn Am States, WHO, 70. *Mem:* Am Soc Trop Med & Hyg; Am Soc Parasitol; Am Malacol Union; NY Acad Sci; Netherlands Malacol Soc. *Res:* Ecology of the terrestrial mollusca of Florida; taxonomy of West Indian land and fresh water mollusca; biological control of the intermediate snails host of Schistosomiasis. *Mailing Add:* Harvard Sch of Pub Health 665 Huntington Ave Boston MA 02115

MICHELSON, ERIC LEE, b Philadelphia, Pa, Sept 18, 47; m 77. CARDIAC ELECTROPHYSIOLOGY, CARDIOLOGY. *Educ:* Univ Pa, BA, 69, MS, 69; Columbia Univ Col Physicians & Surgeons, MD, 73. *Prof Exp:* Intern, Hosp Univ Pa, 73-74, resident, 74-76, fel, 76-78, res fel, 78-79; asst prof med, 79-82, ASSOC PROF MED, THOMAS JEFFERSON UNIV, JEFFERSON MED COL, 82-; ASSOC INVESTR, LANKENAU MED RES CTR, 79- *Concurrent Pos:* Adj asst prof physiol, Univ Pa Sch Vet Med, 79-; chief, Clin Res Unit, Lankenau Med Res Ctr, 79-; prin investr, Clin Investigatorship Award, Nat Heart, Lung & Blood Inst, NIH, 80- & grant-in-aid award, Am Heart Asn; course co-dir & fac, Am Col Cardiol, 79- *Mem:* Am Fedn Clin Res; fel Am Physiol Soc; fel Am Col Physicians; fel Am Col Cardiol. *Res:* Studies to determine the electrophysiologic mechanisms responsible for the lethal disorders of cardiac rhythm afflicting patients with chronic ischemic heart disease; electropharmacology of potential new antiarrhythmic drugs. *Mailing Add:* Lankenau Hosp West of City Line Ave Philadelphia PA 19151

MICHELSON, IRVING, b NJ, Jan 4, 22; m 54; c 7. FLUID DYNAMICS, PHYSICAL OCEANOGRAPHY. *Educ:* Ga Inst Technol, BS, 43; Calif Inst Technol, MS, 47, PhD(aeronaut, math), 51. *Prof Exp:* Lectr, Univ Calif, Los Angeles, 51-54; res engr, Odin Assocs, 54-57; prof aeronaut eng & head dept, Pa State Univ, 57-60; PROF AEROSPACE ENG, ILL INST TECHNOL, 60-, PROF MECH ENG, 81- *Concurrent Pos:* Consult, US Naval Ord Test Sta, 50-, Rand Corp, 51-52, IIT Res Inst, 60-, US Air Force, Argonne Nat Lab, US Naval Observ, C-E-I-R, Inc & Smithsonian Astrophys Observ; vis prof, Univ Nancy, 61-; mem, Adv Comt Pan-Am Policy, 70- *Mem:* Am Astron Soc. *Res:* Astrodynamics; orbital and celestial mechanics; aerodynamics; tides. *Mailing Add:* Dept of Mech & Aerospace Eng Ill Inst of Technol Chicago IL 60616

MICHELSON, LESLIE PAUL, b New York, NY, June 23, 43; m 70; c 3. HARDWARE SYSTEMS. *Educ:* Adelphi Univ, BA, 66, MS, 68, PhD(exp physics), 75. *Prof Exp:* Lectr physics, Adelphi Univ, 68-74; res collabr, Brookhaven Nat Lab, 70-74, Dept Nuclear Med, Mt Sinai Hosp, 74-75; MGR, BIOL MED ENG LAB COMPUT SERV, UNIV MED & DENT NJ, 75- *Mem:* Am Phys Soc. *Res:* Application of digital computer technology to data acquisition; control and analysis problems in a medical research environment. *Mailing Add:* 29 Norfolk Ave Maplewood NJ 07040

MICHELSON, LOUIS, b Lynn, Mass, Mar 24, 19; m 41; c 1. PHYSICS. *Educ:* Mass Inst Technol, BS, 40. *Prof Exp:* Physicist, Corning Glass Works, 40-41; electronic engr, Sanborn Instruments Co, 45-46; gen mgr, Allied Cement & Chem Co, 46-47; tech dir electromagnetics, US Army Ord Submarine Mine Lab, 47-50; chief, Mine Div, US Naval Ord Lab, 50-51; tech dir torpedo hydrodynamics & acoust, US Naval Underwater Ord Sta, 51-55; mgr rocket engines, Flight Propulsion Lab, Gen Elec Co, 55-60, space environ simulator fac, Missile & Space Vehicle Dept, 60-61, Nimbus Proj, Spacecraft Dept, 61-64, NASA progs, 64-65 & adv requirements, 65-66; pres, Spacerays, 66-67; PRES, LION PRECISION CORP, 67- *Concurrent Pos:* Mem acoust & ord panels, Res & Develop Bd, 47-50 & planning coun & torpedo planning adv comt, Bur Ord, 51-55. *Mem:* Am Mgt Asn; Am Ord Asn; Am Inst Aeronaut & Astronaut; Inst Elec & Electronics Eng. *Res:* Underwater sound and electric phenomena; electromagnetic fields; electronic control systems; rocket propulsion; high vacuum techniques. *Mailing Add:* 25 Beechcroft Rd Newton MA 02158

MICHELSON, MALVIN J, organic chemistry, see previous edition

MICHELSON, PAUL ELLIOTT, b Albany, NY, Aug 11, 42; m 67; c 2. OPHTHALMOLOGY, RETINAL DISEASES. *Educ:* Johns Hopkins Univ, BA, 64, Sch Med, MD, 67. *Prof Exp:* Asst chief, Gorgas Hosp, US Army Med Corps, 71-73; clin asst ophthalmol, Mass Eye & Ear Infimary, 74-77; HEAD, DIV OPHTHALMOL, SCRIPPS CLIN & RES INST, 78-; CLIN ASST PROF, UNIV CALIF, SAN DIEGO, 78- *Concurrent Pos:* Clin instr opthalmol, Harvard Med Sch, 74-77; adj mem, Res Inst Scripps Clin, 81-; mem, Int Educ Comt, Am Acad Ophthalmol, 81- *Mem:* Am Acad Ophthalmol; Pan Am Asn Ophthalmol; Am Col Surgeons; Am Uveitis Soc. *Res:* Uveitis, ocular tumor, diseases of retina and vitreous cataract. *Mailing Add:* 10666 N Torrey Pines LaJolla CA 92037

MICHENER, AUBREY W(ESTLAKE), JR, chemical engineering, see previous edition

MICHENER, CHARLES DUNCAN, b Pasadena, Calif, Sept 22, 18; m 40; c 4. ENTOMOLOGY. *Educ:* Univ Calif, BS, 39, PhD(entom), 41. *Prof Exp:* Tech asst entom, Univ Calif, 39-42; from asst cur to assoc cur Lepidoptera & Hymenoptera, Am Mus Natural Hist, 42-48; from assoc prof to prof, 48-59, chmn dept entom, 49-61 & 72-75, actg chmn, Dept Systematics & Ecology, 68-69, ELIZABETH M WATKINS PROF ENTOM, UNIV KANS, 59, WATKINS PROF SYSTS & ECOL, 69-; DIR SNOW ENTOM MUS, 74- *Concurrent Pos:* State entomologist, Southern Div, Kans, 49-61; Am ed, Insectes Sociaux, 54-55 & 62-; Guggenheim fel & res prof, Univ Parana, 55-56; pres, Am sect, Int Union Study Soc Insects, 57-60, vpres, Western Hemisphere Sect, 79-80, pres, 77-82; Fulbright scholar, Univ Queensland, 58-59; ed, Evolution, Soc Study Evolution, 62-64; Guggenheim fel, Africa, 66-67; assoc ed, Annual Review Ecology & Systematics, 70-; res assoc, Am Mus Natural Hist, 49- *Honors & Awards:* A Cressey Morrison Prize, NY Acad Sci, 43. *Mem:* Nat Acad Sci; Entom Soc Am; Soc Study Evolution (pres, 67); Soc Syst Zoologists (pres, 68); hon fel Am Entom Soc. *Res:* Biology and taxonomy of bees; behavior of social insects; principles of systematics; bee systematics and behavior. *Mailing Add:* Dept of Entom Univ of Kans Lawrence KS 66045

MICHENER, CHARLES EDWARD, b Red Deer, Alta, Can, Jan 4, 07; m 36; c 3. GEOLOGY. *Educ:* Univ Toronto, BA, 31; Cornell Univ, MS, 32; Univ Toronto, PhD, 40. *Prof Exp:* Explor geologist, 32-35; geologist, Int Nickel Co, Ltd, 35-39, res geologist, 39-44, chief explor geologist, 44-45, vpres, 55-69; consult geologist, C E Michener & Assoc, Ltd, 69-70; CONSULT GEOLOGIST, DERRY, MICHENER & BOOTH, 70- *Mem:* Soc Econ Geologists; Am Inst Mining, Metall & Petrol Eng; Can Inst Mining & Metall. *Res:* Mining geology. *Mailing Add:* Derry Michener & Booth 2302-401 Bay St Toronto ON M5H 2Y4 Can

MICHENER, HAROLD DAVID, b Pasadena, Calif, Dec 21, 12; m 39; c 4. MICROBIOLOGY. *Educ:* Calif Inst Technol, BS, 34, PhD(plant physiol), 37. *Prof Exp:* Asst, Scripps Inst, Calif, 37-38; jr pomologist, Exp Sta, Univ Hawaii, 38-40; asst, Calif Inst Technol, 40-42; from jr chemist to assoc chemist, USDA, 42-55, from chemist to sr chemist, Western Mkt & Nutrit Res Ctr, 55-65, prin chemist, 65-80, EMER PRIN CHEMIST, WESTERN REGIONAL RES CTR, SCI & EDUC ADMIN-AGR RES, USDA, 80- *Mem:* AAAS; Inst Food Technol; Am Soc Microbiol; Am Inst Biol Sci. *Res:* Heat resistance of bacterial spores; heat resistant fungi; food poisoning and spoilage of microbial origin; microbiological standards for foods; psychrophils; growth and survival of microorganisms at low temperatures; microbiology of frozen and chilled foods. *Mailing Add:* Western Regional Res Ctr USDA Berkeley CA 94710

MICHENER, JOHN WILLIAM, b Wilkinsburg, Pa, May 14, 24; m 53; c 2. PHYSICS. *Educ:* Carnegie Inst Technol, BS, 46, MS & PhD(physics), 53. *Prof Exp:* Asst physics, Carnegie Inst Technol, 42-50; physicist, Owens-Corning Fiberglas Corp, 51-59; head, Dept Physics, 59-73, mgr, Textile Testing Dept, 75-80, MGR, RES SERV DIV, MILLIKEN RES CORP, 80- *Mem:* Am Phys Soc; AAAS; Am Soc Testing & Mat. *Res:* Glass structure; mechanical properties of glass; radiation damage in glass; structure and properties of textile fibers; physics of textiles; static electricity in textile materials. *Mailing Add:* Milliken Res Corp Res Serv Div Spartanburg SC 29304

MICHIE, DAVID DOSS, b Aniston, Ala, Feb 23, 36; m 66. CARDIOVASCULAR PHYSIOLOGY. *Educ:* Trinity Univ, Tex, BS, 58, MSc, 59; Univ Tex, PhD(physiol), 66. *Prof Exp:* Sr res physiologist, Technol Inc, 65-67; asst prof physiol, Med Sch, Creighton Univ, 67-70; asst prof surg, Sch Med, Univ Miami, 70-73; prof physiol & bioeng & chmn dept, Eastern Va Med Sch, 73-78; PRES, CLIN PHYSIOL ASSOCS, 78- *Mem:* Fel Am Col Cardiol; Am Physiol Soc; Soc Exp Biol & Med; fel Am Col Angiol. *Res:* Clinincal trials of pharmaceuticals; noninvasive vascular diagnostics; cardiodynamics; non-invasive vascular diagnostic procedures. *Mailing Add:* 1377 Wainwright Way Ft Myers FL 33907

MICHIE, JARVIS D, US citizen. CIVIL ENGINEERING. *Educ:* Univ Tex, BS, 55; La State Univ, MS, 61. *Prof Exp:* Res asst, Hydraul Group, Dept Civil Eng, Univ Tex, 54-55; design engr, Struct Design Group, Ethyl Corp, 57-61; design engr, Ezra Meir & Assocs, 62; assoc res engr, Dept Struct Res, 62-63, sr res engr, 63-69, group leader, 69-71, sect mgr, 71-76, dir Struct Systs & Fire Technol Dept, 76-80, DIR STRUCT ENG DEPT, SOUTHWEST RES INST, 80- *Concurrent Pos:* Chmn, Comt Roadside Safety Appurtenances, Transp Res Bd. *Mem:* Am Soc Civil Engrs; Nat Soc Prof Engrs. *Mailing Add:* Dept Struct Eng Southwest Res Inst PO Drawer 28510 San Antonio TX 78284

MICHL, JOSEF, b Prague, Czech, Mar 12, 39; m 69. CHEMISTRY. *Educ:* Charles Univ, Prague, MS, 61; Czech Acad Sci, PhD(chem), 65. *Prof Exp:* Fel, Univ Houston, 65-66 & Univ Tex, Austin, 66-67; res chemist, Inst Phys Chem, Czech Acad Sci, 67-68; asst prof, Aarhus Univ, 68-69; fel chem, 69-70, res assoc prof, 70-71, assoc prof, 71-75, PROF CHEM, UNIV UTAH, 75-, CHMN DEPT, 79- *Concurrent Pos:* A P Sloan Found fel, 71-75. *Honors &*

Awards: Alexander Von Humboldt US sr scientist award, 80. *Mem:* Am Chem Soc; Interam Photochem Soc; The Chem Soc; Europ Photochem Asn. *Res:* Quantum organic chemistry; electronic spectroscopy of organic molecules; low temperature chemistry, especially preparation of new species and photochemical mechanisms. *Mailing Add:* Dept of Chem Univ of Utah Salt Lake City UT 84112

MICHLMAYR, MANFRED, b Thorn, Poland, Aug 14, 43; Austrian citizen; m 68; c 2. INORGANIC CHEMISTRY, CATALYSIS. *Educ:* Vienna Tech Univ, BSc, 63, MSc, 66, PhD(inorg chem), 67. *Prof Exp:* Asst prof inorg chem, Vienna Tech Univ, 66-67; res assoc electrochem, Czech Acad Sci, 67; NSF fel electrochem, Univ Calif, Riverside, 67-68; res chemist, Shell Develop Co, 68-72; sr res chemist, 72-80, SR RES ASSOC, CHEVRON RES CO, STANDARD OIL CO CALIF, 80- *Concurrent Pos:* Session chmn, Gordon Res Conf, 75. *Honors & Awards:* Karoline Krafft Medal, Austrian Govt, 68. *Mem:* Am Chem Soc; Catalysis Soc; Electrochem Soc. *Res:* Catalysis in petroleum and synthetic fuel processing, including search for novel catalysts and new processes; mechanistic studies of heterogeneous catalytic systems; extractive metallurgy. *Mailing Add:* Chevron Res Co 576 Standard Ave Richmond CA 94801

MICKAL, ABE, b Talia, Lebanon, June 15, 13; US citizen; m 42; c 4. OBSTETRICS & GYNECOLOGY. *Educ:* La State Univ, BS, 36, MD, 40; Am Bd Obstet & Gynec, dipl, 51. *Prof Exp:* Instr anat, 45-46, from clin instr to clin assoc prof, 49-59, chmn dept, 59-80, PROF OBSTET & GYNEC, UNIV NEW ORLEANS MED CTR, 59-, EMER CHMN DEPT, 80- *Mem:* Fel Am Col Surgeons; AMA; Am Col Obstetricians & Gynecologists; Asn Univ Profs (pres, 76-77); Soc Gynec Oncol. *Mailing Add:* Dept Obstet & Gynec Univ New Orleans Sch Med New Orleans LA 70112

MICKEL, HUBERT SHELDON, b Bridgeton, NJ, Aug 27, 37; m 79; c 3. NEUROLOGY, NEUROCHEMISTRY. *Educ:* Eastern Nazarene Col, BS, 58; Harvard Med Sch, MD, 62; Am Bd Neurol & Psychiat, dipl, 71. *Prof Exp:* Intern, Mary Fletcher Hosp, Burlington, Vt, 62-63; resident internal med, Royal Victoria Hosp, Montreal, Que, 63-64; resident neurol, Boston City Hosp, 64-67; consult neurol, Travis State Sch, Austin, Tex, 68-70; instr, 70-71, asst prof, 71-77, ASST CLIN PROF NEUROL, HARVARD MED SCH, 77-; ASSOC NEUROL, CHILDREN'S HOSP MED CTR, 76-; DIR EMERGENCY MED, CARNEY HOSP, 81- *Concurrent Pos:* Res fel neurol, Harvard Med Sch, 64-67, NIH spec fel chem, Harvard Univ, 67-68; consult, Boston State Hosp, 70-71; asst neurol, Children's Hosp Med Ctr, 70-76; instr, Sch Med, Boston Univ, 70-; pre-med adv, Leverett House, Harvard Col, 71-; asst neurol, Beth Israel Hosp, Boston, 71-79; mem consult staff, Emerson Hosp, Concord, 71-75; dir med & res, Wrentham State Sch, Mass, 73-76, dir dept neurol, Wrentham State Sch Div, Children's Hosp Med Ctr, 74-76; hon res assoc, Dept Chem, Harvard Univ, 76-78; fel shock-trauma, Washington Hosp Ctr, Washington, DC, 81. *Mem:* AAAS; Am Acad Neurol; NY Acad Sci; Am Chem Soc; Am Oil Chemists Soc. *Res:* Lipid neurochemistry; peroxidation of unsaturated lipids; neurology and neurochemistry of mental retardation; biological effects of lipid peroxidation; neurological emergencies; neurology of music. *Mailing Add:* Dir Emergency Med Carney Hosp Boston MA 02124

MICKEL, JOHN THOMAS, b Cleveland, Ohio, Sept 9, 34; m 59; c 4. PLANT TAXONOMY, PLANT MORPHOLOGY. *Educ:* Oberlin Col, BA, 56; Univ Mich, MA, 58, PhD(fern taxon), 61. *Prof Exp:* From asst prof to assoc prof bot, Iowa State Univ, 61-69; CUR FERNS, NY BOT GARDEN, 69- *Concurrent Pos:* Sigma Xi res grant, 62-63; Iowa State Alumni Asn res grant, 62-63; NSF grant, 63-66 & 69-; Nat Acad Sci-Nat Res Coun sr vis res assoc, Smithsonian Inst, 67-68; adj prof, City Univ New York, 69-; ed, Fiddlehead Forum, Am Fern Soc, 74- & Brittonia, 76-78. *Mem:* Am Fern Soc (vpres, 70-71, pres, 72-73); Bot Soc Am; Am Soc Plant Taxon; Int Asn Plant Taxon; Brit Pteridological Soc. *Res:* Monographic studies in the fern genus Anemia; taxonomic work on the ferns of southern Mexico; phylogeny of the ferns. *Mailing Add:* NY Bot Garden Bronx NY 10458

MICKELBERRY, WILLIAM CHARLES, b Seattle, Wash, May 26, 33; m 58; c 4. FOOD SCIENCE. *Educ:* Wash State Univ, BS, 55; Purdue Univ, MS, 60, PhD(food sci), 63. *Prof Exp:* From asst prof to assoc prof food sci & biochem, Clemson Univ, 62-68; mgr prod develop, Western Farmers Asn, 68-73; prod develop mgr, 73-78, RES & DEVELOP MGR, ORE FREEZE DRY FOODS, INC, 78- *Concurrent Pos:* Mem, Res & Develop Assocs, Food & Container Inst, 63-68; mem poultry & egg inst, Am Res Coun, 68-74. *Mem:* Inst Food Technol. *Res:* Influence of dietary and environmental factors upon the food quality attributes of poultry meats; poultry meat tenderness; freeze dried foods, processes of freeze dried compressed foods research and development. *Mailing Add:* Ore Freeze Dry Foods Inc PO Box 1048 Albany OR 97321

MICKELSEN, JOHN RAYMOND, b Portland, Ore, June 1, 28; m 50; c 4. PHYSICAL CHEMISTRY. *Educ:* Linfield Col, BA, 50; Ore State Col, MA, 53, PhD(phys chem), 56. *Prof Exp:* Instr chem, Ore State Col, 54-55; from instr to asst prof, 55-61, ASSOC PROF CHEM, PORTLAND STATE UNIV, 61- *Concurrent Pos:* Rask-Orsted fel, Copenhagen Univ, 66-67. *Mem:* Am Chem Soc; Am Electroplaters Soc. *Res:* Ionic equilibria in nonaqueous solvents; equilbria of complex ions. *Mailing Add:* Dept Chem 1620 SW Park Ave Portland OR 97207

MICKELSEN, W DUANE, b Coulee City, Wash, June 27, 36; m 56; c 4. VETERINARY MEDICINE. *Educ:* Wash State Univ, DVM, 70. *Prof Exp:* Practr, Weiser Vet Clin, Idaho, 70-71 & Isenhart Vet Clin, Wenatchee, Wash, 71-72; ASST PROF LARGE ANIMAL MED, WASH STATE UNIV, 72- *Concurrent Pos:* Embryo transplant consult, Embryonics, Inc, Tenn, 74-75. *Mem:* Am Vet Med Asn; Am Asn Bovine Practrs; Soc Theriogenology. *Res:* Long term preservation of the bovine embryo; superovulation and embryo transplant in the mare and in the cow. *Mailing Add:* Dept of Vet Clin Med & Surg Wash State Univ Pullman WA 99163

MICKELSON, JOHN CHESTER, b Winter, Wis, Nov 16, 20; m 47; c 4. GEOLOGY. *Educ:* Augustana Col, AB, 41; Univ Iowa, MS, 48, PhD(geol), 49. *Prof Exp:* Asst geol, Univ Iowa, 47-49; asst prof, Wash State Univ, 49-54; staff geologist, Sohio Petrol Co, 54-60; sr geologist, DX Sunray Oil Co, 61; assoc prof, 61-66, PROF GEOL & GEOL ENG, SDAK SCH MINES & TECHNOL, 66-, CHMN DEPT, 68-, HEAD GEOL & GEOL ENG, 77- *Mem:* Geol Soc Am; Am Asn Petrol Geol. *Res:* Cretaceous stratigraphy and sedimentation of the Rocky Mountains; geomorphology and Pleistocene geology of Iowa and eastern Washington, particularly loesses. *Mailing Add:* Dept Geol & Geol Eng SDak Sch Mines & Technol Rapid City SD 57701

MICKELSON, JOHN CLAIR, b Canton, SDak, Aug 4, 29; m 52; c 2. MICROBIOLOGY. *Educ:* SDak State Col, BS, 51, MS, 57; Iowa State Univ, PhD(dairy bact), 60. *Prof Exp:* From asst prof to assoc prof, 60-71, PROF MICROBIOL, MISS STATE UNIV, 71- *Mem:* AAAS; Am Soc Microbiol; Am Inst Biol Sci. *Res:* Dairy microbiology; microbial lipases active on butter oil; electrolytic decomposition of human wastes; electrolytic demineralization of algae. *Mailing Add:* Dept of Microbiol Miss State Univ Mississippi State MS 39762

MICKELSON, KENNETH EUGENE, biochemistry, see previous edition

MICKELSON, MICHAEL EUGENE, b Columbus, Ohio, May 3, 40; m 66; c 2. MOLECULAR SPECTROSCOPY, PLANETARY ATMOSPHERES. *Educ:* Ohio State Univ, BSc, 62, PhD(physics), 69. *Prof Exp:* PROF PHYSICS, DENISON UNIV, 69- *Concurrent Pos:* Physicist, Electromagnetic Metrol Div, Laser & Infrared Standards Lab, Aerospace Guidance & Metrol Ctr, 80-81 & 81-82. *Mem:* Optical Soc Am; Am Astron Soc; Am Asn Physics Teachers; Sigma Xi. *Res:* Spectroscopic studies under high resolution of both laboratory and telescopic spectra of molecules of astrophysical interest. *Mailing Add:* Dept of Physics & Astron Denison Univ Granville OH 43023

MICKELSON, MILO NORVAL, b Iowa Co, Wis, Feb 27, 11; m 41; c 4. PHYSIOLOGICAL BACTERIOLOGY. *Educ:* Univ Wis, BS, 35; Iowa State Univ, PhD(physiol bact), 39. *Prof Exp:* Res bacteriologist, Com Solvents Corp, Ind, 39-40; instr bact, Univ Mich, 40-45; sr res bacteriologist, Midwest Res Inst, 45-61; MEM STAFF, NAT ANIMAL DIS LAB, 61- *Concurrent Pos:* Assoc, Med Ctr, Kans, 52-61. *Mem:* AAAS; Am Chem Soc; Am Soc Microbiol; Am Acad Microbiol. *Res:* Industrial fermentations; growth requirements of microorganisms; intermediary metabolism of microorganisms. *Mailing Add:* 1803 Meadow Lane Ames IA 50010

MICKELSON, RICHARD W, b Detroit, Mich, Nov 14, 30. CHEMICAL ENGINEERING. *Educ:* Wayne State Univ, BS, 53, MS, 62, PhD(chem eng), 64. *Prof Exp:* Process engr, Naugatuck Chem Div, US Rubber Co, 53-56, process control supvr, 56-58; asst prof chem eng, 62-66, ASSOC PROF CHEM ENG, WAYNE STATE UNIV, 66- *Mem:* Am Inst Chem Engrs; Am Chem Soc; N Am Thermal Anal Soc. *Res:* kinetics of thermal decomposition; combustion of chars. *Mailing Add:* Dept of Chem Eng Wayne State Univ Detroit MI 48202

MICKELSON, ROME H, b Twin Valley, Minn, Feb 16, 31; m 69. AGRICULTURAL ENGINEERING. *Educ:* NDak State Univ, BS, 55. *Prof Exp:* Asst engr, NDak State Univ, 55; agr engr, Northern Great Plains Res Ctr, Soil & Water Conserv Res Div, 55-61, agr engr, Southwestern Great Plains Res Ctr, Tex, 61, agr engr, Cent Great Plains Res Sta, Colo, 61-66, acting supt, 66-72, location leader, 72-79, AGR ENGR, CENT GREAT PLAINS RES STA, AGR RES SERV, USDA, 79- *Mem:* Am Soc Agr Engrs; Am Geophys Union; Am Soc Agron; fel Soil Conserv Soc Am; Soil Sci Soc Am. *Res:* Land forming practices and runoff management for moisture conservation on dryland areas; ground water drainage and salinity investigations; water harvest techniques; sprinkler irrigation scheduling and management; deep and reduced tillage for irrigated and dryland systems. *Mailing Add:* US Cent Great Plains Res Sta PO Box K Akron CO 80720

MICKENS, RONALD ELBERT, b Petersburg, Va, Feb 7, 43; m 77. PHYSICS. *Educ:* Fisk Univ, BA, 64; Vanderbilt Univ, PhD(physics), 68. *Prof Exp:* Lab instr physics, Fisk Univ, 61-64, lectr, 66-67, lectr math, 67-68; NSF res fel physics, Mass Inst Technol, 68-70; asst prof, 70-72, assoc prof, 72-79, PROF PHYSICS, FISK UNIV, 79- *Concurrent Pos:* Vis prof, Howard Univ, 70-71, Mass Inst Technol, 73-74, Atlanta Univ, 78-79, Vanderbilt Univ, 80-81 & Joint Inst for Lab Astrophys, 81-82; res grants, NSF, 71-73 & NASA, 75-78. *Mem:* AAAS; Am Phys Soc. Sigma Xi. *Res:* Complex angular momentum; Regge theory; analytic properties of collision amplitudes; asymptotic bounds on the behavior of scattering amplitudes. *Mailing Add:* Dept of Physics Fisk Univ Nashville TN 37203

MICKEY, DONALD LEE, b Fairfield, Iowa, Mar 28, 43; m 62; c 2. ASTROPHYSICS. *Educ:* Harvard Univ, AB, 64; Princeton Univ, PhD(astrophys sci), 68. *Prof Exp:* Res assoc astrophys, Princeton Univ, 68-69; res fel physics, Calif Inst Technol, 69-70; asst astronr, 70-77, ASSOC ASTRONR ASTROPHYS, INST ASTRON, UNIV HAWAII, 77- *Res:* Solar physics; spectroscopy. *Mailing Add:* Inst for Astron Univ of Hawaii Kula Maui HI 96790

MICKEY, GEORGE HENRY, b Claude, Tex, Jan 26, 10; m 32; c 2. CYTOGENETICS. *Educ:* Baylor Univ, AB, 31; Univ Okla, MS, 34; Univ Tex, PhD(genetics), 38. *Prof Exp:* Asst zool, Univ Okla, 32-34; asst genetics, Univ Tex, 34-35, instr zool, 35-38; from instr to assoc prof, La State Univ, 38-48; assoc prof, Northwestern Univ, Ill, 49-56; prof & chmn dept, La State Univ, 56-59, dean grad sch, 59-60; cytogeneticist, 60-66, prof biol, 66-69, assoc dean grad sch, 69-70, actg dean, 70-71, dean Grad Sch, New eng inst, 71-75; CLIN ASSOC CYTOGENETICS, DUKE UNIV MED CTR, 75- *Concurrent Pos:* Guggenheim fel, 48; res fel, Calif Inst Technol & Univ Tex, 48; prin biologist, Oak Ridge Nat Lab, 53; vis prof, Univ Bridgeport, 71. *Mem:* AAAS; Am Soc Nat; Genetics Soc Am; Soc Study Evolution; Am Soc Zool. *Res:* Genetics and cytology of Drosophila; cytology of Romalea; radiation genetics; mutation studies; cytogenetic effects of radio frequency waves; human cytogenetics; tissue culture. *Mailing Add:* Cytogenetics Box 3062 Duke Univ Med Ctr Durham NC 27710

MICKEY, MAX RAY, JR, b Pagosa Springs, Colo, Mar 24, 23; m 48; c 2. STATISTICS. *Educ:* Va Polytech Inst, BS, 47; Iowa State Col, PhD(statist), 52. *Prof Exp:* Asst prof statist, Iowa State Col, 52-55; assoc mathematician, Rand Corp, 55-58; statistician, Gen Anal Corp, 58-60 & CEIR, Inc, 60-63; RES STATISTICIAN, DEPT BIOMATH, UNIV CALIF, LOS ANGELES, 63- *Mem:* Economet Soc; Inst Math Statist; fel Am Statist Asn; Inst Statist Inst. *Res:* Application of statistical concepts and methods to applied problems of research, particularly in medicine. *Mailing Add:* Dept of Biomath Univ of Calif Los Angeles CA 90024

MICKLE, ANN MARIE, b Columbus, Ohio, Sept 12, 45. PLANT PHYSIOLOGY, AQUATIC BIOLOGY. *Educ:* Ohio State Univ, BSc, 67; Univ Wis, PhD(bot), 75. *Prof Exp:* Res assoc bot, Kellogg Biol Sta, Mich State Univ, 76-77; asst prof, 77-81, ASSOC PROF BIOL, LASALLE COL, 81- *Mem:* AAAS; Am Soc Plant Physiologists; Am Soc Limnol & Oceanog; Bot Soc Am; Am Inst Biol Sci. *Res:* Aquatic macrophyte physiology; inorganic nutrient uptake rates, use in evaluating environmental nutrient availability and modification of lake inlet waters by littoral flora. *Mailing Add:* Dept Biol LaSalle Col Philadelphia PA 19141

MICKLE, MARLIN HOMER, b Windber, Pa, July 5, 36. ELECTRICAL ENGINEERING. *Educ:* Univ Pittsburgh, BS, 61, MS, 63, PhD(elec eng), 67. *Prof Exp:* Jr engr, IBM Corp, 62; from asst prof to assoc prof elec eng, 67-75, PROF ELEC ENG, UNIV PITTSBURGH, 75-, DIR, COMPUT ENG PROG, 81- *Concurrent Pos:* Prog dir, Syst Theory & Appln Prog, NSF, Washington, DC, 74-75; consult, Westinghouse, Contraves Goerz Corp, Pittsburgh, & Anal Sci Corp, Reading, Mass, 78-; vpres, Power Resources, Inc & pres, Mickle Comput Technologies, Inc. *Mem:* Inst Elec & Electronics Engrs; Am Platform Asn; Am Asn Univ Professors. *Res:* Computer systems; socio-economic systems; optimization; electric power systems. *Mailing Add:* 348 Benedum Eng Hall Univ Pittsburgh Pittsburgh PA 15261

MICKLES, JAMES, b Rochester, NY, May 17, 23; m 46; c 2. MEDICINAL CHEMISTRY. *Educ:* Brigham Young Univ, BS, 44; Purdue Univ, MS, 49. *Prof Exp:* Chemist Qm Corps Proj, Columbia Univ, 45-47; from asst prof to assoc prof, 50-67, dean students & dir admis, 74-77, PROF CHEM, MASS COL PHARM, 67-, VPRES OPER, 77-, DEAN ADMIN, 81- *Mem:* Am Chem Soc; Am Pharmacuet Asn; fel Am Inst Chem. *Res:* Chelates of pharmacologically active compounds; synthesis of anti-radiation compounds. *Mailing Add:* Dept of Chem 179 Longwood Ave Boston MA 02115

MICKLEY, HAROLD S(OMERS), b Seneca Falls, NY, Oct 14, 18; m 41; c 2. CHEMICAL ENGINEERING. *Educ:* Calif Inst Technol, BS, 40, MS, 41; Mass Inst Technol, ScD(chem eng), 46. *Prof Exp:* Chem engr, Union Oil Co, Calif, 41-42; proj engr, Mass Inst Technol, 43-45, from asst prof to prof chem eng, 46-61, Ford prof eng, 61-70, dir ctr advan eng, 63-70; vpres technol, 71, exec vpres, 72-81, DIR, STAUFFER CHEM CO, 67-, VCHMN, 81- *Concurrent Pos:* Chem engr, Artisan Metals Co, Mass, 42-44, Godfrey L Cabot Corp, 44-45, Am Aviation Co, Calif, 46 & Ranger Aircraft Engines Co, NY, 46; consult, Fairchild Engine & Airplane Corp, 46-57 & E I du Pont de Nemours & Co, Inc, 57- *Mem:* Nat Acad Eng; Am Chem Soc; fel Am Inst Chem Engrs; Am Acad Arts & Sci; fel AAAS. *Res:* Momentum, heat and mass transfer; heterogeneous catalysts; automatic process control; viscoelastic behavior of high polymers; applied mathematics; transport processes in fluids; kinetics and catalysis; industrial chemistry. *Mailing Add:* 11 Pequot Trail Westport CT 06880

MICKLICH, JOHN R, b Pueblo, Colo, Aug 14, 25; m 47 & 56; c 3. MATHEMATICS. *Educ:* Baker Univ, AB, 48; Eastern NMex Univ, MS, 56; Univ NMex, EdD(math educ), 69. *Prof Exp:* Storekeeper, Kans Power & Light Co, 48-52; instr math, NMex Mil Inst, 52-63; asst prof, 63-68, ASSOC PROF MATH, NORTHERN ARIZ UNIV, 68- *Concurrent Pos:* Dir stud sci training prog, NSF, 69- *Mem:* Math Asn Am. *Res:* Mathematics education; effect of homework on student performance. *Mailing Add:* Dept of Math Northern Ariz Univ Flagstaff AZ 86011

MICKO, MICHAEL M, b Trebisov, Czechoslvakia, Nov 9, 35; Can citizen; m 61; c 2. WOOD SCIENCE, ENGINEERING. *Educ:* Slovak Tech Univ, Bratislava, BEng, 59, PhD(polymer chem), 66; Univ BC, PhD(wood sci & technol), 73. *Prof Exp:* Asst engr polymers, Slovak Acad Sci, 59-61; asst prof fiber technol, Slovak Tech Univ, Bratislava, 66-69; res assoc bioresource eng, Univ BC, 73-77; asst prof, 77-80, ASSOC PROF WOOD SCI, UNIV ALTA, 80- *Mem:* Soc Prof Engrs; Forest Prod Res Soc; Soc Wood Sci & Technol; Tech Asn Pulp & Paper Indust; Can Pulp & Paper Asn. *Res:* Chemical and engineering aspects of wood products; wood quality tree improvement; wood energy; energy from forest chemical composition of wood; engineering properties of wood products. *Mailing Add:* Fac of Forestry & Agr Univ of Alta Edmonton AB T6G 2G7 Can

MICKS, DON WILFRED, b Mt Vernon, NY, Nov 23, 18; m 44; c 4. PREVENTIVE MEDICINE, COMMUNITY HEALTH. *Educ:* NTex State Univ, BS, 40, MS, 42; Johns Hopkins Univ, ScD(parasitol), 49. *Prof Exp:* Instr zool, NTex State Univ, 40-42; asst, Univ Mich, 42; asst med entom, Sch Hyg & Pub Health, Johns Hopkins Univ, 46-48; from asst prof to assoc prof, 49-59, PROF PREV MED & COMMUNITY HEALTH, UNIV TEX MED BR GALVESTON, 59-, CHMN DEPT, 66- *Concurrent Pos:* Fulbright scholar, Italy, 53-54; scientist-biologist, Div Environ Health, WHO, Switz, 58-59, consult, Pakistan, 69; mem, Med Resources Adv Panel, Tex Air Control Bd. *Mem:* Fel AAAS; fel Royal Soc Trop Med & Hygiene; fel Am Pub Health Asn; Entom Soc Am; Am Soc Trop Med & Hyg. *Res:* Insect transmission of disease; arthropod venoms; control of mosquito-borne diseases. *Mailing Add:* Dept Prev Med & Commun Health Univ of Tex Med Br Galveston TX 77550

MICZEK, KLAUS A, b Burghausen, Ger, Sept 28, 44; m 70; c 1. PSYCHOPHARMACOLOGY, ETHOLOGY. *Educ:* Paedagogische Hochsch, Berlin, teaching cert, 66; Univ Chicago, PhD(biopsychol), 72. *Prof Exp:* Asst prof psychol, Carnegie-Mellon Univ, 72-76, assoc prof, 76-79; ASSOC PROF PSYCHOL, TUFTS UNIV, 79- *Concurrent Pos:* Prin investr, Nat Inst Drug Abuse & Pittsburgh Found res grants, 74-; res grant, Nat Inst Alcohol Abuse & Alcoholism, 79- *Mem:* AAAS; Soc Neurosci; Am Psychol Asn; Behav Pharmacol Soc; Int Soc Res Aggression. *Res:* Drugs, primate behavior and aggression. *Mailing Add:* Dept Psychol Tufts Univ Medford MA 02155

MIDDAUGH, PAUL RICHARD, b Fargo, NDak, Feb 11, 20; m 43; c 2. FUEL ALCOHOLS, FOOD PROTEINS. *Educ:* NDak Agr Col, BS, 42; Univ Wis, MS, 48, PhD(bact, biochem), 51. *Prof Exp:* Asst bact, Univ Wis, 46-48, exten div, 48-51; med bacteriologist chem corps, US Dept Army, Utah, 51-52, Ft Detrick, Md, 52-53, supvry bacteriologist, 53-59; dir, Pilot Plant, Grain Processing Corp, Iowa, 59-64; assoc prof microbiol, SDak State Univ, 64-67, prof, 67-80; DIR RES & DEVELOP, NORTHWEST PAC ENERGY CO, 80- *Concurrent Pos:* Consult fuel alcohol, Nat Acad Sci & Indonesia. *Mem:* Soc Indust Microbiol; Am Soc Microbiol; Sigma Xi; Inst Food Technol; Am Chem Soc. *Res:* Enzymatic cellulose conversion to fuel alcohols; commercial fermentation plants to produce fuel alcohols and food and feed proteins. *Mailing Add:* Northwest Pac Energy Co 1721-132 Ave NE Bellevue WA 98005

MIDDAUGH, RICHARD LOWE, b Salamanca, NY, Oct 2, 38. INORGANIC ELECTROCHEMISTRY. *Educ:* Harvard Univ, AB, 60; Univ Ill, MS, 62, PhD(chem), 65. *Prof Exp:* From asst prof to assoc prof chem, Univ Kans, 64-75; vis assoc prof chem, Northeastern Univ, 76-77, staff scientist, Inst Chem Anal, Appl & Forensic Sci, 77-78; sr electrochemist, 78-81, PROJ MGR, BATTERY PROD DIV, UNION CARBIDE CORP, 81- *Mem:* Am Chem Soc. *Res:* Chemistry of battery systems. *Mailing Add:* Union Carbide Corp PO Box 6116 Cleveland OH 44101

MIDDELKAMP, JOHN NEAL, b Kansas City, Mo, Sept 29, 25; m 49, 74; c 4. PEDIATRICS. *Educ:* Univ Mo, BS, 46; Wash Univ, MD, 48. *Prof Exp:* Med intern, Gallinger Munic Hosp, 48-49; asst resident pediat, St Louis Children's Hosp, 49-50 & 52-53, co-chief resident, 53; from instr to assoc prof, 54-70, PROF PEDIAT, SCH MED, WASH UNIV, 70- *Concurrent Pos:* Consult, Homer G Phillips Hosp, St Louis, Mo, 54-, Barnes & Allied Hosp, 54-, Crippled Children's Servs, Univ Ill, 55- & Univ Mo, 66-; fel internal med, Wash Univ, 60-61, USPHS fel anat, 61-62. *Mem:* Sigma Xi; Am Acad Pediat; Am Soc Microbiol; Am Pediat Soc; Infectious Dis Soc Am. *Res:* Infectious diseases; ambulatory pediatrics. *Mailing Add:* Dept of Pediat PO Box 14871 St Louis MO 63178

MIDDENDORF, DONALD FLOYD, b Templeton, Iowa, Feb 26, 31; m 62; c 1. POULTRY NUTRITION, BIOCHEMISTRY. *Educ:* Iowa State Univ, BS, 54; Univ Md, MS, 58, PhD(poultry nutrit), 59. *Prof Exp:* Poultry res specialist, Cent Soya Co, Inc, 59-65; res specialist, Upjohn Co, Inc, Mich, 65-67; nutrit specialist, 67-68, POULTRY FEEDS DIR, CENT SOYA CO, INC, 68- *Concurrent Pos:* Mem, Alfalfa Res Coun, 64-72. *Mem:* Poultry Sci Asn; NY Acad Sci; Am Inst Chem. *Res:* General poultry nutrition, especially amino acids; protein and energy areas; effect of environment upon performance of growing and laying chickens and turkeys. *Mailing Add:* Cent Soya Co Inc 1200 N Second St Decatur IN 46733

MIDDENDORF, WILLIAM H, b Cincinnati, Ohio, Mar 23, 21; m 46; c 5. PRODUCT LIABILITY, ELECTRICAL INSULATION. *Educ:* Univ Va, BEE, 46; Univ Cincinnati, MS, 48; Ohio State Uinv, PhD(elec eng), 60. *Prof Exp:* PROF ELEC ENG, UNIV CINCINNATI, 48- *Concurrent Pos:* Dir eng & res, Waskworth Elec Mfg Co, Inc, 66-; dir, Nat Elec Mfr Assoc, Univ Cincinnati, Elec Insulation Lab, 77-; consult, Cincinnati Develop & Mfg Co, 60-66, Allis Chalmers Mfg co, 56-58. *Mem:* Fel Inst Elec & Electronics Engrs; Am Soc Eng Educ. *Res:* Accelerated life tests of electrical insulation to improve consistency of test data; circuit analysis and product design monograms on product diability and invention. *Mailing Add:* Univ Cincinnati Loc 30 Cincinnati OH 45221

MIDDLEBROOK, JOHN LESLIE, b Salem, Ore, Dec 16, 46; m 66; c 3. BIOCHEMISTRY, PHARMACOLOGY. *Educ:* Pac Univ, BS, 68; Duke Univ, PhD(chem), 72. *Prof Exp:* Fel pharmacol, Med Sch, Stanford Univ, 72-74, RES SCIENTIST BIOCHEM & PHARMACOL, US ARMY MED RES INST INFECTIOUS DIS, 75- *Concurrent Pos:* NIH fel, Med Sch, Stanford Univ, 73-74; Arthritis Found fel, 74-75; instr pharmacol, Hood Col, 76- *Mem:* Am Chem Soc; Sigma Xi; Am Soc Biol Chemists. *Res:* Steroid, hormone and toxin receptors; cell biology; protein transport. *Mailing Add:* US Army Med Res Ft Detrick Frederick MD 21701

MIDDLEBROOK, R(OBERT) D(AVID), b Eng, May 16, 29; nat US; m; c 2. ELECTRONICS. *Educ:* Cambridge Univ, BA, 52, MA, 56; Stanford Univ, MS, 53, PhD(elec eng), 55. *Prof Exp:* Sr tech instr electronics, Royal Air Force, Eng, 48-49; asst, Stanford Univ, 53-55; from asst prof to assoc prof, 55-65, PROF ELECTRONICS, CALIF INST TECHNOL, 65- *Concurrent Pos:* Consult, 59- *Honors & Awards:* Award, Nat Prof Group on Indust Engrs, 58. *Mem:* Fel Inst Elec & Electronics Engrs. *Res:* New solid-state devices, their development, representation and application; electronics education; power conversion and control. *Mailing Add:* Dept of Elec Eng Calif Inst of Technol Pasadena CA 91125

MIDDLEDITCH, BRIAN STANLEY, b Bury St Edmunds, Eng, July 15, 45; m 70; c 1. BIOCHEMICAL ECOLOGY, ANALYTICAL BIOCHEMISTRY. *Educ:* Univ London, BSc, 66; Univ Essex, MSc, 67; Glasgow Univ, PhD(chem), 71. *Prof Exp:* Res asst chem, Glasgow Univ,

67-71; vis asst prof lipid res, Baylor Col Med, 71-73, res instr, 74-75; asst prof biophys sci, 75-80, ASSOC PROF BIOCHEM & BIOPHYS SCI, UNIV HOUSTON, 80- *Mem:* Am Chem Soc; Am Soc Mass Spectrom; Phys Soc; Inst Physics. *Res:* Environmental effects of offshore oil production; shrimp farming; steroids; prostaglandins and other lipids. *Mailing Add:* Dept Biochem & Biophys Sci Univ Houston Houston TX 77004

MIDDLEHURST, BARBARA MARY, b Penarth, Wales, Sept 10, 15. ASTRONOMY. *Educ:* Cambridge Univ, BA, 36, MA, 47. *Prof Exp:* Observer astron, Univ Observ, St Andrews Univ, 51-54, lectr, Univ, 54-59; res assoc, Yerkes Observ, Chicago, 59-60; res assoc, Lunar & Planetary Lab, Univ Ariz, 60-68; astron ed, Encycl Britannica, 68-72; MEM STAFF, LUNAR SCI INST, NASA BAY, 72- *Concurrent Pos:* Goethe Link fel, Ind Univ, 53, Fulbright travel grant & res assoc, 53-54; Carnegie Trust Scottish Univs res grant, 54; prin investr, Off Naval Res Proj Grant, 63; mem comn, Int Astron Union, 64; NSF proj grant, 66; consult, Lockheed Electronics, 69; consult, Chicago Sch Dist 97, 69-70. *Mem:* Hon fel Am Geophys Union; Am Astron Soc; Royal Astron Soc; Brit Astron Asn. *Res:* Stellar, lunar and planetary research; discovery of the Middlehurst effect, that is, tidally related periodicity in reported shortlived lunar phenomena, substantiated in a similar periodicity in seismic signals recorded by instruments landed on the moon. *Mailing Add:* Lunar Sci Inst NASA Bay Houston TX 77058

MIDDLEMAN, STANLEY, chemical engineering, see previous edition

MIDDLESWORTH, EDWARD MILLARD, JR, physics, computer engineering, see previous edition

MIDDLETON, ALEX LEWIS AITKEN, b Banchory, Scotland, May 20, 38; Can citizen; m 62; c 3. ZOOLOGY, ECOLOGY. *Educ:* Univ Western Ont, BSc, 61, MSc, 62; Monash Univ, Australia, PhD(zool), 66. *Prof Exp:* Asst prof, 66-70, ASSOC PROF ZOOL, UNIV GUELPH, 70- *Mem:* Am Ornith Union; Can Soc Zoologists; Royal Australasian Union Ornithologists; Cooper Ornith Soc. *Res:* Ecology of birds, particularly histology and physiology of breeding cycles. *Mailing Add:* Dept of Zool Univ of Guelph Guelph ON N1G 2W1 Can

MIDDLETON, ARTHUR EVERTS, b Erie, Pa, June 10, 19; m 41; c 2. SOLID STATE PHYSICS, ELECTRONICS. *Educ:* Westminster Col, BS, 40; Purdue Univ, MS, 42, PhD(physics), 44. *Prof Exp:* Asst physics, Purdue Univ, 40-43, instr, 43-45; res engr, Fed Tel & Radio Co, NJ, 45; res engr, Battelle Mem Inst, 45-47, asst supvr res, 47-51, supvr, 51-53; dir physics & phys chem labs, P R Mallory & Co, Inc, 53-57; tech counr & group leader, Large Lamp Eng Dept, Gen Elec Co, 58-59; mgr & dir solid state div, Harshaw Chem Co, 59-62; chief scientist, Ohio Semiconductors Div, Tecumseh Prod, Inc, 62-64; vpres & dir, 64-75, EXEC VPRES, SECY & DIR, OHIO SEMITRONICS INC, 75-; PROF ELEC ENG, OHIO STATE UNIV, 65- *Concurrent Pos:* Consult, Adv Group Electronic Parts, 55-57; mem adv panel dielectrics, Nat Adv Bd, 56; dir, N Pittsburgh Tel Co, 56-; mem adv panel passive components, Wright Air Develop Ctr, 57; dir, Ohio Semiconductors, Inc, 58-60; lectr, Univ Mich, 65. *Mem:* Electrochem Soc; Am Phys Soc; Inst Elec & Electronics Engrs. *Res:* Nuclear reactions in photographic emulsions; galvanomagnetic properties of semiconductors; thermoelectric materials and devices; Hall effect and electroluminescent devices; integrated circuit technology; solid state radiation detection; solar energy convertors; electrophotographic plates; new semiconductors and other electronic components. *Mailing Add:* Dept of Elec Eng Ohio State Univ Columbus OH 43210

MIDDLETON, CHARLES CHEAVENS, b Pilot Point, Tex, Apr 12, 30; m; c 2. EXPERIMENTAL PATHOLOGY. *Educ:* Univ Mo-Columbia, BS & DVM, 58; Mich State Univ, MS, 61; Am Col Lab Animal Med, dipl, 66. *Prof Exp:* Instr vet surg, Univ Pa, 58-59; instr physiol & pharmacol, Mich State Univ, 60-62; fel cardiovasc res, Bowman Gray Sch Med, 62-63, from instr to asst prof lab animal med, 63-66; from asst prof community health & med practices to assoc prof, 66-77, assoc prof vet path, 66-75, PROF MED PATH, UNIV MO-COLUMBIA, 77-, PROF VET PATH, 75-, DIR SINCLAIR RES FARM, 66- *Concurrent Pos:* Co-investr, Dept Health, Educ & WElfare grants, 67-68, 68-70 & 68-72; post doctoral thesis adv, Sch Med & Sch Vet Med, Univ Mo-Columbia, 67-; mem coun arterosclerosis Am Heart Asn. *Mem:* Am Inst Biol Sci; Int Primatol Soc; Am Col Lab Animal Med; Am Vet Med Asn; NY Acad Sci. *Res:* Atherosclerosis; pathology of laboratory animals. *Mailing Add:* Sinclair Res Farm R R 3 Columbia MO 65201

MIDDLETON, DAVID, b New York, NY, Apr 19, 20; m 45, 71; c 4. PHYSICS, STATISTICAL COMMUNICATION THEORY. *Educ:* Harvard Univ, AB, 42, AM, 45, PhD(physics), 47. *Prof Exp:* Res assoc, Off Sci Res & Develop proj, Harvard Univ, 42-45, res fel electronics, 47-49, asst prof appl physics, 49-54; CONSULT PHYSICIST, 54- *Concurrent Pos:* Consult, Govt & Industs, 49-; adj prof, Columbia Univ, 60-61, Rensselaer Polytech Inst, 61-70 & Univ RI, 66- & Rice Univ, 80-; mem, Naval Res Adv Comt, 70-77, Navy Lab Adv Bd Undersea Warfare, 70-77, Navy Lab Adv Bd Res, 71-77 & US study group 1A, Int Radio Consult Comt, 71-; contractor, Off Naval Res, Dept Defense, Inst Telecommun Sci, Off Telecommun & Nat Telecommun & Info Admin, 78-, Dept Commerce, NASA & Nat Oceanic & Atmospheric Admin; consult, Off Telecommun Policy-Exec Off of Pres, 74-78. *Honors & Awards:* Award, Nat Electronic Conf, 56; Wisdom Award of Honor, 70. *Mem:* Fel AAAS; fel Am Phys Soc; Am Math Soc; fel Inst Elec & Electronics Eng; NY Acad Sci. *Res:* Communication theory in radar, radio, underwater sound, seismology, optics, mechanics, electronics, space sciences; applied mathematics; scattering theory; wave surface oceanography; man-made and natural EM environments; electromagnetic compatability. *Mailing Add:* 127 E 91st St New York NY 10028

MIDDLETON, EDWARD JAMES, toxicology, see previous edition

MIDDLETON, ELLIOTT, JR, b Glen Ridge, NJ, Dec 15, 25; m 48; c 4. INTERNAL MEDICINE. *Educ:* Princeton Univ, AB, 47; Columbia Univ, MD, 50; Am Bd Internal Med, dipl, 58; Am Bd Allergy, dipl, 62. *Prof Exp:* Intern, Presby Hosp, New York, 50-51, asst resident, 51-53; asst med, Col Physicians & Surgeons, Columbia Univ, 56-57, instr, 57-60, assoc, 60-69; dir, Clin Serv & researcher, Children's Asthma Res Inst & Hosp, Nat Asthma Ctr, 69-77; PROF MED & PEDIAT & DIR ALLERGY DIV, STATE UNIV NY, 77- *Concurrent Pos:* Nat Heart Inst clin fel, Presby Hosp, New York, 51-53; clin fel, NIH, 53-54; clin & res fel, Inst Allergy, Roosevelt Hosp, 55; asst, Immunochem Lab, Col Physicians & Surgeons, Columbia Univ, 52; physician pvt pract, 56-69; asst attend physician, Mountainside Hosp, Montclair, NJ, 58-62, assoc attend, 62-; asst physician, Presby Hosp, NY, 60. *Mem:* AAAS; Am Fedn Clin Res; Am Asn Immunologists; Am Acad Allergy (pres, 72-73); Harvey Soc. *Res:* Allergy; immunology; biochemical mechanisms of human allergic reactions by in vitro techniques; chemical mediators of allergic reactions. *Mailing Add:* Sch of Med State Univ of NY Buffalo NY 20414

MIDDLETON, FOSTER H(UGH), b Detroit, Mich, Dec 4, 22; m 48; c 4. ELECTRICAL ENGINEERING. *Educ:* Univ Mich, BS, 47; Johns Hopkins Univ, DrEng, 59. *Prof Exp:* Test engr, Ford Motor Co, Mich, 48-50; group leader instrumentation, Sperry Gyroscope Co, 50-52; res staff asst acoust, Johns Hopkins Univ, 52-54, instr elec eng, 54-59; from assoc prof to prof, 59-66, PROF OCEAN ENG & CHMN DEPT, UNIV RI, 66- *Concurrent Pos:* Vis prof, Glasgow Univ, 71-72; panel mem, Marine Bd Panels, Nat Acad Eng, 72- *Res:* Underwater acoustics, ocean instrumentation. *Mailing Add:* Dept of Ocean Eng Univ of RI Kingston RI 02881

MIDDLETON, GERARD VINER, b Capetown, SAfrica, May 13, 31; m 59; c 3. GEOLOGY. *Educ:* Imp Col, Univ London, BSc, 52, dipl & PhD(geol), 54. *Prof Exp:* Geologist, Standard Oil Co Calif, 54-55; lectr, 55-61, assoc prof, 61-67, chmn dept, 59-62, PROF GEOL, McMASTER UNIV, 67-, CHMN DEPT, 78- *Concurrent Pos:* Consult, Shell Oil Co, 56-57 & 59. *Honors & Awards:* Logan Medal, Geol Asn Am, 80. *Mem:* Soc Econ Paleontologists & Mineralogists; Am Asn Petrol Geol; Geol Asn Can; fel Royal Soc Can; Int Asn Sedimentol (vpres, 78-). *Res:* Sedimentary petrography; sedimentology. *Mailing Add:* Dept Geol McMaster Univ Hamilton ON L8S 4M1 Can

MIDDLETON, JOHN T(YLOR), b Chicago, Ill, Sept 15, 12; m; c 4. AIR POLLUTION. *Educ:* Univ Calif, BS, 35; Univ Mo, PhD(bot, plant path), 40. *Prof Exp:* Asst botanist, Univ Mo, 36-39; jr plant pathologist, Exp Sta, Univ Calif, 39-43, asst plant pathologist, 43-48, assoc plant pathologist, 48-54, plant pathologist, 54-57, prof path & chmn dept, Los Angeles & Riverside, 57-63, dir, Statewide Air Pollution Res Ctr, Riverside, 62-67; dir, Nat Ctr Air Pollution Control, Dept Health Educ & Welfare, 67-68, comnr, Nat Air Pollution Control Admin, 68-71, dept asst adminr, US Environ Protection Agency, 71-73; prof mgr, UN PROF EMER, UNIV CALIF, 67-; CONSULT, US SENATE COMT ENVIRON & PUB WORKS, 73-; ENVIRON MGT, WHO, 77- *Concurrent Pos:* Consult, govt & various indust orgns, 49-; mem & past chmn, Calif Motor Vehicle Pollution Control Bd, 60-66; mem, Nat Adv Comn Air Pollution to US Surgeon Gen, 63-66; adv, WHO, 63-, dir, Int Reference Ctr on Air Pollution Control, 71-73, mem, Expert Panel on Air Pollution, 72-; mem exec comt, Hwy Res Bd, Nat Acad Sci-Nat Res Coun, 70- *Honors & Awards:* Richard Beatty Mellon, Air Pollution Control Asn, 72; Environ Qual, Nat Acad Sci, 76. *Mem:* Air Pollution Control Asn. *Res:* Air pollution control. *Mailing Add:* 2811 Albemarle St NW Washington DC 20008

MIDDLETON, PAULETTE BAUER, b Beeville, Tex, Dec 8, 46; m 70; c 1. ATMOSPHERIC CHEMISTRY, CHEMICAL PHYSICS. *Educ:* Univ Tex, Austin, BA, 68, MA, 71, PhD(chem), 73. *Prof Exp:* Instr chem, Univ Tex, 73-74, res assoc aerosol physics, Dept Chem Eng, 73-75; res fel, Nat Ctr for Atmospheric Res, 75-76; res assoc, Atmospheric Sci Res Ctr, State Univ NY Albany, 76-77; vis scientist, 77-79, SPC STAFF SCIENTIST, NAT CTR ATMOSPHERIC RES, 79- *Concurrent Pos:* Mem, Nat Acad Sci Climatol Effects Resource Group, Risk/Impact Panel Comt Nuclear & Alt Energy Systs, 76-77; prin investr, Acid Precipitation Exp, 78-79; mem, Physics & Chem Rev Panel, Environ Protection Agency, 80- & proj dir, Urban Visual Air Qual Study, 81- *Mem:* AAAS; Air Pollution Control Asn. *Res:* Gas and aerosol transport and transformation in the troposphere and stratosphere; assessing impacts of visibility degradation, acid rain and climate change. *Mailing Add:* Nat Ctr for Atmospheric Res Boulder CO 80307

MIDDLETON, PETER JAMES, b Leeston, NZ, Sept 29, 32; m 59. MEDICAL VIROLOGY. *Educ:* Univ NZ, MB & ChB, 57; Univ Otago, NZ, MD, 63; FRCPath(A), 65; CRCP(C), 70. *Prof Exp:* Asst lectr path, Med Sch, Univ Otago, NZ, 60-62; trainee clin virol, Regional Virus Lab, Ruchill, Glasgow, Scotland, 63-64; from lectr to sr lectr microbiol, Med Sch, Univ Otago, NZ, 64-68; CHIEF VIROL, HOSP SICK CHILDREN, TORONTO, 68- *Concurrent Pos:* Prof med microbiol, Fac Med & asst prof microbiol & parasitol, Univ Toronto, 68- *Mem:* Can Pub Health Asn; Can Soc Microbiol; Australian Col Path; Am Soc Microbiol; Infectious Dis Soc Am. *Res:* Gastro-enteritis viral; evaluation of viral diagnostic techniques; multiple sclerosis. *Mailing Add:* Dept Virol Hosp Sick Children 555 Univ Ave Toronto ON M5G 1X8 Can

MIDDLETON, RICHARD B, b Rockford, Ill, Nov 24, 36; div; c 2. MICROBIAL GENETICS, MEDICAL LAW. *Educ:* Harvard Univ, AB, 58, Am, 60, PhD(biol), 63. *Prof Exp:* Res fel bact genetics, Brookhaven Nat Lab, 62-64; asst prof biol, Am Univ Beirut, 64-65; asst prof genetics, McGill Univ, 65-71; assoc prof, 71-75, prof microbiol & genetics, Mem Univ Nfld, 75-77; PROF MICROBIOL & ASSOC DEAN BASIC SCI, COL MED & DENT NJ, 77- *Concurrent Pos:* Res grants, Rockefeller Found, 64-65, Med Res Coun Can, 66-68 & 72-76, Res Corp, 66-68, Nat Res Coun Can, 66-77, Int Cell Res Orgn, Int Lab Genetics & Biophys, Naples, 67, Food & Drug Directorate, Dept Nat Health & Welfare Can, 69-71, World Health Orgn, Ctr Immunol, State Univ NY Buffalo, 71, Tissue Cult Asn, Jones Cell Sci Ctr, Lake Placid, NY, 72, Europ Molecular Biol Orgn, Biozentrum, Univ Basel, Switz, 72, March Dimes, Nat Found, Jackson Lab, Bar Harbor, Maine, 74,

Dept Secy State Can, 75, Dept Nat Health & Welfare Can, 75-78 & NIH, 78-81; vis prof genetics, State Univ NY, Plattsburg, 74; prof microbiol, Rutgers Univ, 78- *Mem:* AAAS; Am Soc Microbiol; Can Soc Cell Biol; Genetics Soc Am; NY Acad Sci. *Res:* Genetic homology of Salmonella typhimurium and Escherichia Coli; fertility of intergeneric crosses of enteric bacteria; legal reform for donation of human tissues for scientific uses. *Mailing Add:* Col Med & Dent NJ PO Box 55 Piscataway NJ 08854

MIDDLETON, ROY, b Atherton, Eng, Oct 3, 27; m 50; c 2. NUCLEAR PHYSICS. *Educ:* Univ London, BSc, 48; Univ Liverpool, PhD(nuclear physics), 51. *Hon Degrees:* MA, Univ Pa, 71. *Prof Exp:* Fel nuclear physics, Univ Liverpool, 51-54, teaching asst, 54-55; prin sci officer, Atomic Weapons Res Estab, Aldermaston, Eng, 55-64; vis prof, 64-65, PROF NUCLEAR PHYSICS, UNIV PA, 65- *Concurrent Pos:* Co-prin investr, NSF tandem accelerator grant; mem physics div rev comt, Oak Ridge Nat Labs, 70-74 & Argonne Nat Lab, 75- *Honors & Awards:* Tom W Bonner Prize, Am Phys Soc, 79. *Mem:* Brit Inst Physics; fel Am Phys Soc. *Res:* Nuclear experimental research; negative ion source development; accelerator development. *Mailing Add:* Univ of Pa Dept of Physics 209 S 33rd St Philadelphia PA 19174

MIDDLETON, WILLIAM JOSEPH, b Amarillo, Tex, Apr 9, 27; m 48; c 2. ORGANIC CHEMISTRY. *Educ:* NTex State Col, BS, 48, MS, 49; Univ Ill, PhD(chem), 52. *Prof Exp:* RES CHEMIST, E I DU PONT DE NEMOURS & CO, INC, 52- *Honors & Awards:* Award, Am Chem Soc. *Mem:* Am Chem Soc; Sigma Xi. *Res:* Cyanocarbon, organic fluorine, heterocyclic and medicinal chemistry. *Mailing Add:* RR 2 Box 95 Ridge Rd Chadds Ford PA 19317

MIDGLEY, A REES, JR, b Burlington, Vt, Nov 9, 33; m 55; c 3. ENDOCRINOLOGY, DEVELOPMENT BIOLOGY. *Educ:* Univ Vt, BS, 55, MD, 58. *Prof Exp:* Sarah Mellon Scaife fel path, Univ Pittsburgh, 58-61; Sarah Mellon Scaife fel, 61-62, res assoc, 62-63, from instr to assoc prof, 63-70, PROF PATH, UNIV MICH, ANN ARBOR, 70-, DIR, CTR HUMAN GROWTH & DEVELOP, 80- *Concurrent Pos:* Nat Inst Child Health & Human Develop career develop award, 66-76. *Honors & Awards:* Parke Davis Award, Am Soc Exp Path, 70; Ayerst Award, Endocrine Soc, 77. *Mem:* Am Asn Path; Soc Study Reproduction; Endocrine Soc; Am Soc Cell Biol; Am Physiol Soc. *Res:* Reproductive endocrinology; immunoendocrinology; development biology. *Mailing Add:* Ctr Human Growth & Develop Univ Mich 300 North Ingalls Bldg Ann Arbor MI 48104

MIDGLEY, JAMES EARDLEY, b Kansas City, Mo, Sept 18, 34; m 61; c 6. SYSTEMS THEORY. *Educ:* Univ Mich, BS(eng phys), BS(eng math) & BS (eng mech), 56; Calif Inst Technol, PhD(physics), 63. *Prof Exp:* Res assoc magnetosphere, Univ Tex, Dallas, 63-64, asst prof gravity waves, 64-67, ASSOC PROF PHYSICS, UNIV TEX, DALLAS, 67- *Concurrent Pos:* NSF fel, Calif Inst Technol, 58-61. *Res:* Computer operating systems; data structures; computer graphics. *Mailing Add:* Univ Tex Dallas Dept Physics Box 688 Richardson TX 75080

MIDLAND, MICHAEL MARK, b Ft Dodge, Iowa, Jan 1, 46; m 72. ORGANIC CHEMISTRY, ORGANOMETALLIC CHEMISTRY. *Educ:* Iowa State Univ, BS, 68; Purdue Univ, PhD(org chem), 72. *Prof Exp:* Assoc chem, Purdue Univ, 72-75; lectr, 75-76, asst prof, 76-80, ASSOC PROF CHEM, UNIV CALIF, RIVERSIDE, 80- *Concurrent Pos:* Alfred P Sloan fel, 78-82. *Mem:* Am Chem Soc; AAAS. *Res:* New chemistry of organoboranes and organolithiums; new synthetic reactions; investigation of reaction mechanisms; asymmetric synthesis. *Mailing Add:* Dept Chem Univ Calif Riverside CA 92521

MIDLER, MICHAEL, JR, b New York, NY, Aug 15, 36; m 60; c 3. CHEMICAL & BIOCHEMICAL ENGINEERING. *Educ:* Cornell Univ, BChE, 59, PhD(biochem eng), 64. *Prof Exp:* Res assoc, 62-72, res fel, 72-78, SR RES FEL, MERCK SHARP & DOHME RES LABS, 78- *Mem:* Am Inst Chem Engrs; Am Chem Soc. *Res:* Crystallization; resolution of stereoisomers; ultrasonic processing; mixing; liquid-liquid extraction; chemical reaction engineering. *Mailing Add:* Chem Eng Res & Develop PO Box 2000 Rahway NJ 07065

MIDLIGE, FREDERICK HORSTMANN, JR, b Hoboken, NJ, June 13, 35; m 61; c 2. VIROLOGY, MICROBIOLOGY. *Educ:* Muhlenberg Col, BS, 57; Lehigh Univ, MS, 59, PhD(biol), 68. *Prof Exp:* From instr to asst prof, 63-72, assoc prof, 72-76, PROF BIOL, FAIRLEIGH DICKINSON UNIV, 76- *Mem:* AAAS; Am Soc Microbiol. *Res:* Virus diseases of fish; morphology and maturation of lymphocystis virus. *Mailing Add:* Dept of Biol Fairleigh Dickinson Univ Madison NJ 07940

MIDURA, THADDEUS, b Chicopee, Mass, Dec 2, 31; m 65; c 2. FOOD TECHNOLOGY. *Educ:* Univ Mass, BS, 57, MS, 59; Univ Mich, MPH, 61, PhD(environ health), 64. *Prof Exp:* Sanitarian, Food & Milk Lab, Springfield Health Dept, Mass, 56; sanitarian, Environ Health, Philadelphia Health Dept, Pa, 57; instr food technol, Univ Mass, 58-60; fel, 64-66, res microbiologist, Div Labs, 66-80, CHIEF, MICROBIOL DIS LAB, DEPT HEALTH SERV, CALIF STATE DEPT PUB HEALTH, 80- *Mem:* Am Soc Microbiol; Am Pub Health Asn; Inst Food Technol. *Res:* Public health microbiology; anaerobic bacteriology and microorganisms significant in food-borne diseases; laboratory aspects of environmental associated disease outbreaks. *Mailing Add:* 2151 Berkeley Way Berkeley CA 94704

MIECH, RALPH PATRICK, b South Milwaukee, Wis, Aug 17, 33; m 57; c 5. BIOCHEMISTRY, PHARMACOLOGY. *Educ:* Marquette Univ, BS, 55, MD, 59; Univ Wis, PhD(pharmacol), 63. *Prof Exp:* Intern med, St Mary's Hosp, Duluth, Minn, 59-60; Nat Cancer Inst fel, Univ Wis, 61-63; asst prof, 63-69, ASSOC PROF MED SCI, BROWN UNIV, 69- *Concurrent Pos:* Nat Inst Neurol Dis & Blindness grant, 69-72; NSF fel, 69-72. *Mem:* Am Soc Pharmacol & Exp Therapeut; Am Col Emergency Physicians. *Res:* Enzymes of nucleotide synthesis; theophylline metabolism; nucleotide metabolism in parasitic organisms; nucleotide metabolism in the brain; purine transport via the blood; inhibitor of bronchial camp phosphodiesterase. *Mailing Add:* Dept of Med Sci Brown Univ Providence RI 02912

MIECH, RONALD JOSEPH, b Milwaukee, Wis, Feb 23, 35; m 60; c 2. MATHEMATICS. *Educ:* Univ Ill, Urbana, BS, 59, PhD(math), 63. *Prof Exp:* Res fel math, Nat Bur Standards, Washington, DC, 63-64; from asst prof to assoc prof, 64-74, PROF MATH, UNIV CALIF, LOS ANGELES, 74- *Res:* Number theory; group theory. *Mailing Add:* Dept Math Univ Calif Los Angeles CA 90024

MIED, RICHARD PAUL, b Baltimore, Md, Dec 5, 46; m 70; c 2. PHYSICAL OCEANOGRAPHY, FLUID MECHANICS. *Educ:* Johns Hopkins Univ, BES, 68, PhD(fluid mech), 72. *Prof Exp:* Pres intern oceanog, 72-73, RES SCIENTIST OCEANOG, NAVAL RES LAB, 73- *Mem:* Am Geophys Union; Res Soc NAm; Sigma Xi. *Res:* Modeling and simulation of ocean features with horizontal extents of tens to hundreds of kilometers, and time scales of days to months. *Mailing Add:* Naval Res Lab Code 4310 Overlook Ave Washington DC 20375

MIEDEMA, EDDY, biochemistry, organic chemistry, see previous edition

MIEDERHOFF, PATRICK ANDREW, b Sikeston, Mo, Aug 17, 40. BEHAVIORAL MEDICINE & PHARMACY. *Educ:* St Louis Col Pharm, BS, 63; Univ Louisville, MA, 71; Univ Ky, PharmD, 74. *Prof Exp:* Asst prof, 74-77, ASSOC PROF PHARM, XAVIER UNIV LA, 77- *Concurrent Pos:* Consult, New Orleans Vet Admin Hosp, 75-79 & NIH, 80-82. *Mem:* Am Soc Hosp Pharmacists; Soc Behav Med; Biofeedback Soc Am. *Res:* Behavioral aspects of drug use, drug misuse, drug abuse, compliance, prescribing patterns, and patient education. *Mailing Add:* Col Pharm Xavier Univ Pine & Palmetto St New Orleans LA 70125

MIEHLE, WILLIAM, b Ulm, Ger, Mar 31, 15; nat US; m 48; c 2. MATHEMATICS. *Educ:* Mass Inst Technol, SB, 38; Univ Pa, MS, 59. *Prof Exp:* Engr, Radio Corp Am, 40-46; res engr, Philco Corp, 46-49; designer & comput analyst, Res Ctr, Burroughs Corp, 49-56; mem staff, Inst Coop Res, Pa, 56-58; asst prof math, Pa Mil Col, 58-60; asst prof math, Villanova Univ, 60-80. *Concurrent Pos:* Consult, Auerbach Electronics Corp, 60 & Appl Psychol Serv, 61- *Res:* Operations research; information retrieval; numerical analysis. *Mailing Add:* 1240 Steel Rd Havertown PA 19083

MIEKKA, RICHARD G(EORGE), b Pontiac, Mich, Oct 18, 33; m 58; c 3. CHEMICAL ENGINEERING. *Educ:* Univ Mich, BS(chem) & BS(chem eng), 56; Mass Inst Technol, SM, 58, ScD(chem eng), 61. *Prof Exp:* Chem engr, WVa Pulp & Paper Co, 61-62; mgr chem res, Amicon Corp, Mass, 62-63, electrochem, Deco Div, 63-64; res chemist, 64-69, res sect head, 69-73, mgr chem res div, 73-81, GROUP MGR TECH DEVELOP, DENNISON MFG CO, FRAMINGHAM, 81- *Mem:* Soc Photog Scientists & Engrs; Am Chem Soc; Am Vacuum Soc; NY Acad Sci. *Res:* Nonwoven fabrics; polyelectrolyte structures; fuel cells and related electrochemical devices; electrostatic copying systems; pressure sensitive adhesives, tags, labels, metallized paper and inks. *Mailing Add:* 199 Goodman's Hill Rd Sudbury MA 01776

MIELCZAREK, EUGENIE V, b New York, NY, Apr 22, 31; m 54; c 2. SOLID STATE PHYSICS, BIOLOGICAL PHYSICS. *Educ:* Queens Col NY, BS, 53; Catholic Univ, MS, 57, PhD(physics), 63. *Prof Exp:* Physicist, Nat Bur Standards, 53-57; from res asst to res assoc physics, Catholic Univ, 57-62, asst res prof, 62-65; PROF PHYSICS, GEORGE MASON UNIV, 65- *Concurrent Pos:* Vis scientist, NIH, 77-78; mem vis scientist prog, Am Inst Physics, 64-; vis prof, Hebrew Univ Jerusalem, 81. *Mem:* Am Phys Soc; Biophysical Soc; Sigma Xi; Am Asn Physics Teachers; Asn Women Sci. *Res:* Solid state low temperature physics; semiconductors; Mossbauer spectroscopy of metal and biological compounds; biophysics; Fermi surfaces of metals. *Mailing Add:* Dept Physics George Mason Univ Fairfax VA 22030

MIELE, ANGELO, b Formia, Italy, Aug 21, 22; m. AEROSPACE ENGINEERING. *Educ:* Univ Rome, DrCE, 44, DrAeE, 46. *Prof Exp:* Aerodyn engr, Inst Aircraft Technol, Argentina, 47-50; prof mech, Sch Mil Aviation, 50-52; asst prof aeronaut eng, Polytech Inst Brooklyn, 52-55; prof, Purdue Univ, 55-59; dir astrodyn & flight mech, Sci Res Labs, Boeing Co, 59-64; PROF ASTRONAUT & MATH SCI, RICE UNIV, 64- *Concurrent Pos:* Consult, Allison Div, Gen Motors Corp, Inc, 55-58 & Guided Missiles Div, Douglas Aircraft Co, Calif, 55-58; ed-in-chief, J Optimization Theory & Appln, 67-; assoc ed, J Astronaut Sci, 65-, Appl Math &Comput, 75- & Optimal Control Appln & Methods, 79-; ed, Math Concepts & Methods Sci & Eng, 74- *Honors & Awards:* Knight Commander, Order of Merit, Italian Repub, 72; Levy Medal, Franklin Inst, 74; Brouweer Award, Am Astronaut Soc, 80; Pendray Award, Am Inst Aeronaut & Astronaut, 82. *Mem:* Fel Am Astronaut Soc; assoc fel Am Inst Aeronaut & Astronaut; cor mem Int Acad Astronaut; Italian Aerotech Asn; corresp mem Acad Sci Turin. *Res:* Dynamics of extraterrestrial, interplanetary and terrestrial flight; flight performance; calculus of variations; astronautical engineering; high speed aerodynamics; computing methods; numerical optimization techniques; numerical analysis. *Mailing Add:* Dept of Mech Eng 230 Ryon Bldg Rice Univ Houston TX 77001

MIELENZ, JONATHAN RICHARD, b Denver, Colo, Mar 25, 48; m 74; c 2. MOLECULAR BIOLOGY, BIOCHEMISTRY. *Educ:* Wittenberg Univ, AB, 70; Univ Ill, MS, 73, PhD(microbiol), 76. *Prof Exp:* NSF fel agron, Plant Growth Lab, Univ Calif, Davis, 76-78; res scientist microbial genetics, 79-80, SR RESEARCHER AND TEAM LEADER, GENETIC ENG, MOFFETT TECH CTR, CORN PROD CORP INT, 80- *Mem:* Sigma Xi; Am Soc Microbiol. *Res:* Improvement of microbial strains used in corn processing through the use of both conventional genetics and recombinant DNA technology. *Mailing Add:* Dept Biotechnology Box 345 Argo IL 60501

MIELENZ, KLAUS DIETER, b Berlin, Ger, May 8, 29; c 2. OPTICS, SPECTROSCOPY. *Educ:* Univ Berlin, BSc, 49; Free Univ Berlin, MSc, 52, PhD(physics), 55. *Prof Exp:* Asst physics, Free Univ Berlin, 49-52; physicist, R Fuess Optical Co, Ger, 52-58 & Nat Bur Standards, 58-60; tech mgr, R Fuess Optical Co, 60-63; proj leader optical masers, Nat Bur Standards, 63-

71, proj leader spectrophotom & luminescence spectrometry, 72-79; sci & technol fel & sr policy specialist, US Dept Com, 79-80; CHIEF, RADIOMETRIC PHYSICS DIV, NAT BUR STANDARDS, 81- *Concurrent Pos:* Guest res worker, Inst Appl Spectros, Dortmund, Ger, 57; adj prof, George Washington Univ, 68-72; chmn comt, Int Comn Illum, 73-79, secy & chmn, 81- *Honors & Awards:* Silver Medal, US Dept Commerce, 66; Superior Accomplishment Award, US Dept Commerce, 72 & Sustained Super Performance Award, 75. *Mem:* Fel Optical Soc Am; German Soc Appl Optics. *Res:* Physical optics; spectrochemistry; spectroscopic instruments; spectrophotometry, luminescence spectrometry; radiometry; metrology; thin films; optical masers; vacuum techniques. *Mailing Add:* 6 Waycross Ct Kensington MD 20795

MIELKE, EUGENE ALBERT, b Visalia, Calif, Mar 1, 46; m 68; c 1. POMOLOGY, PLANT PHYSIOLOGY. *Educ:* Calif State Polytech Col, San Luis Obispo, BS, 69; Mich State Univ, MS, 70, PhD(hort, pomol), 74. *Prof Exp:* Lectr crop prod, Calif State Polytech Col, San Luis Obispo, 68-69; asst prof hort & pomol, Mich State Univ, 74-75; ASST PROF POMOL, VITICULTURE & ENOL, UNIV ARIZ, 75- *Concurrent Pos:* Ariz rep, Western Region Coord Comt, Flowering & Fruit Set, 75- & Western Regional Proj, 77-; regional ed, Pecan Quart, 75- *Mem:* Am Soc Hort Sci; Am Soc Plant Physiologists; Japanese Soc Plant Physiologists; Am Soc Enologists; Scand Soc Plant Physiol. *Res:* Flowering, fruit-set, and fruit growth and development of pecans and pistachios; extraction, purification, identification and measurement of plant growth substances; identification of physiological factors limiting yield; table, juice and wine grape feasibility and production in the four corners region; hormonal metabolism. *Mailing Add:* Dept of Plant Sci Bldg 36 Univ of Ariz Col of Agr Tucson AZ 85721

MIELKE, JAMES EDWARD, b Toledo, Ohio, Oct 6, 40; m 66; c 2. GEOCHEMISTRY. *Educ:* Mass Inst Technol, BS, 62; Univ Ariz, MS, 65; George Washington Univ, PhD(geochem), 74. *Prof Exp:* Geologist, Universal Eng Corp, 63-64; geologist, Radiation Biol Lab, Smithsonian Inst, 64-73; SCI POLICY ANALYST, CONG RES SERV, LIBR CONG, 73- *Mem:* AAAS; Am Geophys Union. *Res:* Science policy in the earth and marine sciences with regard to matters of current and future interest to Congress. *Mailing Add:* 2803 Washington Ave Chevy Chase MD 20815

MIELKE, MARVIN V, b Marshfield, Wis, May 2, 39; m 69. TOPOLOGY. *Educ:* Univ Wis, BS, 60, MS, 61; Ind Univ, PhD(math), 65. *Prof Exp:* Teaching assoc math, Ind Univ, 61-65; mem, Inst Advan Studies, 65-66; res assoc, 66-77, RES PROF MATH, UNIV MIAMI, 77- *Mem:* Am Math Soc; Math Asn Am. *Res:* Differential and algebraic topology. *Mailing Add:* Dept Math Univ Miami Coral Gables FL 33124

MIELKE, PAUL THEODORE, b Racine, Wis, Sept 28, 20; m 46; c 3. MATHEMATICS. *Educ:* Wabash Col, AB, 42; Brown Univ, ScM, 46; Purdue Univ, PhD(math), 51. *Prof Exp:* Instr math, Brown Univ, 43-44; from instr to asst prof, Wabash Col, 46-51; sr group engr digital comput, Dynamics Staff, Boeing Airplane Co, 52-57; assoc prof math, Wabash Col, 57-63, prof & chmn dept, 63-69; assoc dir, Comt Undergrad Prog Math, 69-70, exec dir, 70-71; chmn dept, 71-78, PROF MATH, WABASH COL, 71- *Concurrent Pos:* Mem bd gov, Math Asn Am, 72-75; assoc ed math educ, Am Math Monthly, 74-78. *Mem:* Math Asn Am; Am Math Soc. *Res:* Digital computing; linear algebra. *Mailing Add:* Dept of Math Wabash Col Crawfordsville IN 47933

MIELKE, PAUL W, JR, b St Paul, Minn, Feb 18, 31; m 60; c 3. STATISTICS, METEOROLOGY. *Educ:* Univ Minn, BA, 53, PhD(biostatist), 63; Univ Ariz, MA, 58. *Prof Exp:* Asst math, Univ Ariz, 57-58; asst biostatist, Univ Minn, 58-62, lectr, 62-63; from asst prof to assoc prof, 63-73, PROF STATIST, COLO STATE UNIV, 73- *Mem:* AAAS; fel Am Statist Asn; Biomet Soc; Am Meteorol Soc; Am Geophys Union. *Res:* Permutation inference procedures; nonparametric techniques; parametric approximations; simulation investigations; quantal assay methods; weather modification studies. *Mailing Add:* Dept of Statist Colo State Univ Ft Collins CO 80523

MIENTKA, WALTER EUGENE, b Amherst, Mass, Oct 1, 25; m 54; c 4. MATHEMATICS. *Educ:* Univ Mass, BS, 48; Columbia Univ, MA, 49; Univ Colo, PhD, 55. *Prof Exp:* Instr math, Univ Mass, 49-52; instr & asst, Univ Colo, 52-55; instr, Univ Mass, 55-56; asst prof, Univ Nev, 56-57; from asst prof to assoc prof, 57-70, vchmn dept, 70-75, PROF MATH, UNIV NEBR, LINCOLN, 70-; EXEC DIR, MATH ASN AM, 76- *Concurrent Pos:* Fac fel, Univ Nebr, Lincoln, 60 & 64-65; res scholar, Univ Calif, Berkeley, 64-65. *Mem:* Am Math Soc; Math Asn Am; Indian Math Soc. *Res:* Theory of numbers. *Mailing Add:* Dept Math 915 Oldfather Hall Univ of Nebr Lincoln NE 68588

MIER, MILLARD GEORGE, b Glendale, Calif, Nov 26, 35; m 60; c 2. SOLID STATE PHYSICS. *Educ:* Occidental Col, AB, 57; Bryn Mawr Col, PhD(physics, math), 67. *Prof Exp:* Instr physics, Mt Holyoke Col, 62-64; res physicist, Owens-Corning Fiberglas Tech Ctr, 64-68; RES PHYSICIST, AIR FORCE AVIONICS LAB, WRIGHT-PATTERSON AFB, 68- *Concurrent Pos:* Adj prof elec eng, Air Force Inst Technol, 68- *Mem:* Am Asn Physics Teachers; Am Phys Soc; Am Asn Univ Prof; Inst Elec & Electronics Engrs; Electrochem Soc. *Res:* Computer memory technology, especially magnetic bubble, electron beam and ion-implant memories; thin film electronic properties, especially compound semiconductor, metallic and insulating films; optical properties of solids and thin films. *Mailing Add:* Electronic Res Br Air Force Avionics Lab Wright-Patterson AFB OH 45433

MIES, FREDERICK HENRY, b New York, NY, Oct 3, 32; m 53; c 3. QUANTUM CHEMISTRY. *Educ:* City Col New York, BS, 56; Brown Univ, PhD(phys chem), 61. *Prof Exp:* Nat Bur Standards-Nat Res Coun fel phys chem, 61-62, PHYS CHEMIST, NAT BUR STANDARDS, 62- *Mem:* Am Phys Soc. *Res:* Scattering theory; chemical kinetics and energy transfer; pressure broadening and continuum spectroscopy; autoionization and predissociation. *Mailing Add:* 268 Phys Bldg Nat Bur Standards Washington DC 20234

MIESCH, ALFRED THOMAS, b Hammond, Ind, May 10, 27; m 50; c 2. GEOLOGY. *Educ:* St Joseph's Col Ind, BS, 50; Ind Univ, MA, 54; Northwestern Univ, PhD, 61. *Prof Exp:* Geol technician, NMex Bur Mines & Mineral Resources, 51-52; asst, Ind Univ, 52-53; RES GEOLOGIST, REGIONAL GEOCHEM BR, US GEOL SURV, 53- *Concurrent Pos:* Asst, Northwestern Univ, 56-57. *Mem:* Geol Soc Am; Geochem Soc; Int Asn Math Geol; Soc Environ Geochem & Health. *Res:* Distribution of minor elements in rocks and ores; Colorado Plateau uranium deposits; statistical methods in geologic and geochemical research; geochemical prospecting; environmental geochemistry. *Mailing Add:* US Geol Surv Fed Ctr Box 25046 Denver CO 80225

MIESCHER, GUIDO, b Zurich, Switz, Dec 13, 21; nat US; m 54; c 1. MICROBIOLOGY. *Educ:* Swiss Fed Inst Technol, dipl, 47, PhD(microbiol, plant path), 49. *Prof Exp:* RES MICROBIOLOGIST, IMC CORP, 49- *Mem:* Am Chem Soc. *Res:* Nutrition and metabolism of plants and microorganisms; development of industrial fermentations. *Mailing Add:* IMC Corp Terre Haute IN 47808

MIESEL, JOHN LOUIS, b Erie, Pa, Nov 26, 41; m 64; c 3. ORGANIC CHEMISTRY. *Educ:* Univ Notre Dame, BS, 62; Univ Ill, PhD(org chem), 66. *Prof Exp:* Sr org chemist, 66-74, RES SCIENTIST, ELI LILLY & CO, 74- *Mem:* Am Chem Soc. *Res:* Synthesis of heterocyclic compounds; structure-activity relationships in insecticides; photochemistry as a synthetic tool. *Mailing Add:* Eli Lilly & Co Indianapolis IN 46206

MIESSLER, GARY LEE, b Independence, Kans, Jan 5, 49. PHOTOCHEMISTRY. *Educ:* Univ Tulsa, BChem, 70; Univ Minn, PhD(inorg chem), 78. *Prof Exp:* Instr, 78-79, ASST PROF CHEM, ST OLAF COL, 79- *Concurrent Pos:* Prin investr, Res Corp, 81- & Petrol Res Grant, Am Chem Soc, 81-; teacher & scholar, Camille & Henry Dreyfus Found, 81- *Mem:* Am Chem Soc. *Res:* Synthesis and photochemistry of transition metal complexes with sulfur ligands; organometallic chemistry and homogeneous catalysis. *Mailing Add:* Northfield MN 55057

MIETLOWSKI, WILLIAM LEONARD, b Buffalo, NY, Sept 25, 47. BIOSTATISTICS. *Educ:* Canisius Col, BS, 69; Univ Rochester, MA, 71, PhD(statist), 74. *Prof Exp:* Teaching asst statist, Univ Rochester, 69-73, tech assoc biostatist, Heart Res Follow-up Study, 73-74; res asst prof statist sci, Statist Lab, State Univ NY Buffalo, 74-77; statistician, Sidney Farber Cancer Inst, 78-80; MEM STAFF, SANDOZ INC, 80- *Concurrent Pos:* Coord statistician, Lung Cancer Group, Vet Admin, 74-; asst prof biostatist, Harvard Univ Sch Pub Health, 78- *Mem:* Am Statist Asn; Biomet Soc; AAAS; Inst Math Statist. *Res:* Application of biometric methods to lung cancer clinical trials; multivariate descriptive statistics; discriminant analysis with mixed data; comparison of correlated covariance matrices. *Mailing Add:* Sandoz Inc Rte 10 East Hanover NJ 07936

MIEURE, JAMES PHILIP, b McLeansboro, Ill, July 5, 41; m 66; c 2. CHEMISTRY. *Educ:* Kenyon Col, AB, 63; Purdue Univ, MS, 66; Tex A&M Univ, PhD(chem), 68. *Prof Exp:* Sr res chemist, 68-73, res specialist, 73-74, res group leader, 74-77, mgr environ sci, 77-80, MGR PROD ACCEPTABILITY, MONSANTO CO, 80- *Mem:* Am Chem Soc; Am Soc Testing Mat; Chem Mfrs Asn. *Res:* Environmental analytical chemistry; environmental fate and aquatic toxicity of chemicals; safety assessment of chemicals. *Mailing Add:* Monsanto Co 800 N Lindberg St Louis MO 63166

MIEYAL, JOHN JOSEPH, b Cleveland, Ohio, Feb 17, 44; m 66; c 4. BIOCHEMISTRY, PHARMACOLOGY. *Educ:* John Carroll Univ, BS, 65; Case Western Reserve Univ, PhD(biochem), 69. *Prof Exp:* NIH fel, Brandeis Univ, 69-71; asst prof pharmacol & biochem, Med Sch, Northwestern Univ, Chicago, 71-76; ASSOC PROF PHARMACOL, MED SCH, CASE WESTERN RESERVE UNIV, 76-, ASSOC PROF CHEM, 81- *Concurrent Pos:* Grants, Res Corp Am, 71-75, Chicago Heart Asn, 74-76, Nat Inst Gen Med Sci, 74-81, Am Heart Asn, 76-79 & Nat Cancer Inst, 77-81. *Mem:* Am Soc Pharmacol & Exp Therapeut; Am Soc Biol Chem; AAAS; Am Chem Soc; Sigma Xi. *Res:* Physicochemical studies of molecular interactions; mechanisms of enzymic reactions; drug metabolism and toxicity; chemistry. *Mailing Add:* Dept Pharmacol Med Sch Case Western Reserve Univ Cleveland OH 44106

MIFFITT, DONALD CHARLES, b Holyoke, Mass, Mar 10, 44; m 67; c 2. ELECTRONIC ENGINEERING. *Educ:* Lowell Technol Inst, BS, 66. *Prof Exp:* Proj engr, US Air Force, Electronic Systs Div, 66-70; sr engr, Bowmar/Ali, Inc, 70-74; prin engr, Gillette Adv Tech Lab, Gillette Co, 74-79; DIR ELEC ENG, PARKER BROS, 79- *Mem:* Inst Elec & Electronics Engrs. *Res:* Application of electronics technology to new comsumer products; microcomputers for timing and control; speech recognition/synthesis; temperature measurement; high density memories; video techniques. *Mailing Add:* Parker Bros 50 Dunham Rd Beverly MA 01915

MIFFLIN, MARTIN DAVID, b Olympia, Wash, Mar 29, 37; m 59; c 4. HYDROGEOLOGY. *Educ:* Univ Wash, Seattle, BS, 60; Mont State Univ, MS, 63; Univ Nev, PhD(hydrogeol), 68. *Prof Exp:* Geologist, Pan Am Petrol Corp, 59, US Geol Surv, 62; res assoc, Water Resouces Ctr, Desert Res Inst, 63-69; assoc prof geol, Univ Fla, 69-75; assoc dir, 75-77, RES PROF, WATER RESOURCES CTR, DESERT RES INST, 77- *Concurrent Pos:* Resident consult, World Bank & chief, Groundwater Planning, Nat Water Plan, Mex, 73-75; chief resident adminr & sr hydrogeologist, UN Develop Prog Proj, Chile, 78-79; consult, Govt Tunisia, USAID, 80. *Mem:* Nat Water Well Asn. *Res:* Groundwater resource assessment: exploration development, management flow system delineation and subsidence; arid and carbonate rock terrains; quaternary lakes and isostatic rebound in the Great Basin. *Mailing Add:* 1500 E Tropicana Suite 201 Las Vegas NV 89109

MIGAKI, GEORGE, b Troy, Mont, Apr 26, 25; m 52; c 2. VETERINARY PATHOLOGY, COMPARATIVE PATHOLOGY. *Educ:* Wash State Univ, BS & DVM, 52; Am Col Vet Path, dipl, 62. *Prof Exp:* Pvt pract, 52-54; vet meat inspector, Meat Inspection Div, USDA, 54-57, vet pathologist, 57-62, head vet pathologist, 62-68; VET PATHOLOGIST, REGISTRY COMP PATH, ARMED FORCES INST PATH, 68- *Concurrent Pos:* Clin prof path, Uniformed Serv Univ Sch Med. *Mem:* Am Asn Avian Pathologists; Int Acad Path; Int Asn Aquatic Animal Med; Am Vet Med Asn; US Animal Health Asn. *Res:* Comparative pathology of diseases in a wide variety of animals in which a similar disease exists in humans, including the documentation and classification of animal models of human disease. *Mailing Add:* Registry Compar Path Armed Forces Inst Path Washington DC 20306

MIGDALOF, BRUCE HOWARD, b Brooklyn, NY, July 19, 41; m 67; c 4. XENOBIOLOGY, DRUG METABOLISM. *Educ:* Cornell Univ, BA, 62; Purdue Univ, MS, 65; Univ Pittsburgh, PhD(org chem), 69. *Prof Exp:* Sr scientist drug metab, Sandoz Pharmaceuts, Sandoz-Wander Inc, 69-72; sr scientist, 72-74, group leader drug disposition, McNeil Labs Inc, 74-77; DIR DRUG METAB, SQUIBB INST MED RES, 77- *Mem:* Am Soc Pharmacol & Exp Therapuet; Am Chem Soc; NY Acad Sci; Int Soc Study Xenobiotics; Am Pharaceut Asn. *Res:* Drug metabolism and disposition; bioavailability; pharmacokinetics; clinical pharmacology; drug biotransformation pathways; pharmacodynamic-pharmacokinetic correlations. *Mailing Add:* Squibb Inst for Med Res PO Box 191 New Brunswick NJ 08903

MIGEON, BARBARA RUBEN, b Rochester, NY, July 31, 31; m 60; c 3. MEDICAL GENETICS. *Educ:* Smith Col, BA, 52; Univ Buffalo, MD, 56. *Prof Exp:* Intern pediat, Johns Hopkins Hosp, 56-57, asst resident, 57-59; fel endocrinol, Med Sch, Harvard Univ, 59-60; fel genetics, 60-62, from instr to assoc prof pediat, 62-79, PROF PEDIAT, SCH MED, JOHNS HOPKINS UNIV, 79- *Concurrent Pos:* Pediatrician, Johns Hopkins Hosp, 62-; mem genetics study sect, NIH, 75- *Honors & Awards:* Citation, Nat Bd Med Col Pa, 71. *Mem:* Am Soc Human Genetics; Am Soc Pediat Res. *Res:* Somatic cell genetics; regulation of expression of X-linked genes; X chromosome inactivation; complementation analysis of human inborn errors. *Mailing Add:* Dept of Pediat Johns Hopkins Hosp Baltimore MD 21205

MIGEON, CLAUDE JEAN, b Lievin, France, Dec 22, 23; m 60; c 3. PEDIATRICS, ENDOCRINOLOGY. *Educ:* Lycee de Reims, France, BA, 42; Univ Paris, MD, 50. *Prof Exp:* Asst med biochem, Univ Paris, 47-50; Am Field Serv fel, 50-51; res fel pediat, Johns Hopkins Univ, 51-52; res instr biochem, Univ Utah, 52-54; from asst prof to assoc prof, 54-71, PROF PEDIAT, JOHNS HOPKINS UNIV, 71- & DIR, PEDIAT ENDOCRINE CLIN & LABS, 73- *Concurrent Pos:* Fulbright traveling fel, 50; Mayer fel, 51-52; NIH res career award, 64. *Mem:* Endocrine Soc; Soc Pediat Res; Am Soc Clin Invest; Am Physiol Soc; Am Pediat Soc. *Res:* Pediatric endocrinology, particularly steroids biochemistry; abnormalities of human sex differentiation; adrenal function; transplacental passage of stesteroids from mother to fetus. *Mailing Add:* Dept of Pediat Johns Hopkins Hosp Baltimore MD 21205

MIGET, RUSSELL JOHN, b Long Beach, Calif, Oct 22, 42; m 63; c 2. MARINE MICROBIOLOGY. *Educ:* Univ Fla, BS, 64; Fla State Univ, PhD(oceanog), 71. *Prof Exp:* Res assoc marine microbiol, Inst Marine Sci, Univ Tex, 71-75; PRES, TURTLE COVE LAB, INC, 75- *Res:* Marine microbial ecology. *Mailing Add:* Turtle Cove Lab Inc No 10 Tarpon St Box 219 Port Arkansas TX 78373

MIGHTON, CHARLES JOSEPH, b Saskatoon, Sask, Oct 13, 13; nat US; m 37; c 2. ORGANIC CHEMISTRY. *Educ:* Univ Sask, BSc, 33, MSc, 35; Univ Chicago, PhD(org chem), 37. *Prof Exp:* Res chemist, Inst Am Meat Packers, 36; res chemist, Exp Sta, E I du Pont de Nemours & Co, Del, 37-42, res supvr, 42-46, mgr, Rubber Chem Div, Akron Lab, Ohio, 46-50, asst to lab mgr, 51-60, res assoc govt & patent liaison, Pharmaceut Div, Biochem Dept, 61-75; RETIRED. *Mem:* AAAS; Am Chem Soc; fel Am Inst Chem. *Res:* Raman spectroscopy; plastics; coating compositions and adhesives; synthetic rubbers and derivatives; inorganic colloids; pharmaceuticals. *Mailing Add:* 10 Madelyn Ave Wilmington DE 19803

MIGHTON, HAROLD RUSSELL, b Saskatoon, Sask, Can, Jan 6, 19; nat US; m 43; c 2. CHEMISTRY. *Educ:* Univ Sask, BA, 39, MA, 41; Columbia Univ, PhD(org chem), 45. *Prof Exp:* Res chemist comt med res, Off Sci Res & Develop Proj, Columbia Univ & Rockefeller Inst, 44-45 & Goodyear Tire & Rubber Co, Ohio, 45-48; res chemist rayon dept, E I du Pont de Nemours & Co, Inc, 48-50 & film dept, 50-52, res assoc, 52-53, res supvr, 53-57, res mgr, 57-68, mgr tech liaison, 68-72, planning mgr, Cent Res & Develop Dept, 72-80; RETIRED. *Mem:* Am Chem Soc; Sigma Xi; Chem Inst. *Res:* Surface chemistry; antimalarials; high polymers; thermodynamics of crystallization in high polymers. *Mailing Add:* 711 Ambleside Dr Wilmington DE 19808

MIGLIORE, HERMAN JAMES, b Detroit, Mich, July 13, 46. MECHANICAL ENGINEERING, APPLIED MECHANICS. *Educ:* Univ Detroit, BS, 68, MS, 69, PhD(mech eng), 75. *Prof Exp:* Intern, Chrysler Corp, 73-75; res engr, Naval Civil Eng Lab, 75-77; asst prof, 77-80, ASSOC PROF, PORTLAND STATE UNIV, 80- *Concurrent Pos:* Design consult, numerical methods & comput aided design. *Mem:* Am Soc Mech Engrs; Am Soc Eng Educ; Sigma Xi. *Res:* Numerical analysis of nonlinear systems in cable dynamics, structure-fluid interaction and plastic deformation manufacturing processes; investigation of prediction and relief of residual stress; computer aided design procedures. *Mailing Add:* Div Eng PO Box 751 Portland State Univ Portland OR 97207

MIGLIORE, PHILIP JOSEPH, b Pittsburgh, Pa, Dec 18, 31; m 57; c 3. MEDICINE. *Educ:* Univ Pittsburgh, BS, 54, MD, 56. *Prof Exp:* Asst pathologist, Univ Tex M D Anderson Hosp & Tumor Inst, 64-69; ASST PROF PATH, BAYLOR COL MED, 69- *Concurrent Pos:* Asst pathologist, Methodist Hosp, Houston, 69-78, assoc pathologist, 78- *Mem:* AAAS; AMA; Am Soc Clin Path. *Res:* Gamma globulins; myeloma proteins. *Mailing Add:* Dept of Path Methodist Hosp Houston TX 77025

MIGNAULT, JEAN DE L, b Sherbrooke, Que, Feb 3, 24; m 53; c 3. MEDICINE, CARDIOLOGY. *Educ:* Univ Montreal, BA, 45, MD, 51; FRCP(C). *Prof Exp:* Clin monitor cardiol, Maisonneuve Hosp, 56-58; asst prof, Univ Montreal & Inst Cardiol Montreal, 58-61, from asst prof to assoc prof, Univ Montreal & Hotel-Dieu Hosp, 62-69, dir cardiac lab, Hosp, 62-69, head dept cardiol, 65-69; chmn dept med, 69-73, dean sch med, 70-73, PROF MED, MED SCH, UNIV SHERBROOKE, 69- *Mem:* Fel Am Col Cardiol; fel Am Col Chest Physicians; Can Med Asn; Can Cardiovasc Soc; fel Am Col Physicians. *Res:* Development of the new cardiac catheterization unit, the Saturn. *Mailing Add:* Fac of Med Univ of Sherbrooke Sherbrooke PQ J1H 5N4 Can

MIGNEREY, ALICE COX, Brooklyn, NY, Nov 6, 49; m 70. HEAVY-ION REACTION MECHANISMS. *Educ:* Univ Rochester, BS, 71, MS, 73, PhD(nuclear chem), 75. *Prof Exp:* Fel nuclear chem, Univ Rochester, 75-76; res assoc, Chem Div, Argonne Nat Lab, 76-79; ASST PROF GEN CHEM & NUCLEAR CHEM, UNIV MD, 79- *Mem:* Am Phys Soc; Am Chem Soc. *Res:* Nuclear reaction mechanisms in heavy-ion induced reactions; mechanisms including preequilibium emission of light particles, the deep-inelastic reaction and projectile fragmentation ateneries of million-electron-volt particles. *Mailing Add:* Dept Chem Univ Md College Park MD 20742

MIGNERY, ARNOLD LOUIS, b West Unity, Ohio, Apr 18, 18; m 42; c 4. FORESTRY. *Educ:* Univ Mich, BS, 40, MF, 49. *Prof Exp:* Res forester, Southern Forest Exp Sta, US Forest Serv, 46-56, res ctr leader, 56-64, prin silviculturist & proj leader, 64-75; RETIRED. *Res:* Silviculture and forest management techniques; southern tree species. *Mailing Add:* R R Box 120 Sewanee TN 37375

MIGNONE, ROBERT JOSEPH, b Philadelphia, Pa, Apr 21, 45. SET THEORY. *Educ:* Pa State Univ, PhD(math), 79. *Prof Exp:* Vis asst prof math, Univ Tex, Dallas, 79-81; ASST PROF MATH, COL CHARLESTON, 81- *Mem:* Am Math Soc; Asn Symbolic Logic. *Res:* Consequences of the axiom of determinateness on the smallest uncountable cardinals; characterizations of huge cardinals. *Mailing Add:* Math Dept Col Charleston Charleston SC 29424

MIHAILOFF, GREGORY A, b Mansfield, Ohio, Aug 17, 45; m 67; c 3. NEUROANATOMY, NEUROBIOLOGY. *Educ:* Ashland Col, BS, 68; Ohio State Univ, MS, 73, PhD(anat), 74. *Prof Exp:* asst prof, 74-80, ASSOC PROF CELL BIOL, UNIV TEX HEALTH SCI CTR, 80- *Concurrent Pos:* Prin investr, NSF res grant, Neurobiology Prog, 80-83 & Nat Inst Neurol Commun Disorders Stroke, NIH, 81-84. *Mem:* Soc Neurosci; Am Asn Anatomists; Cajal Club. *Res:* Neurobiology of cerebro-cerebellar interaction; electron microscopy; neurophysiology. *Mailing Add:* Dept Cell Biol 5323 Harry Hines Blvd Dallas TX 75235

MIHAILOVSKI, ALEXANDER, b Sofia, Bulgaria, Nov 8, 37; US citizen; m 69. ORGANIC CHEMISTRY. *Educ:* Pa State Univ, BS, 60; Univ Calif, Los Angeles, PhD(org chem), 67. *Prof Exp:* Asst gen & org chem, Univ Calif, Los Angeles, 63-66 & org chem, 66-67; from res chemist to sr res chemist, 67-72, SECT SUPVR, WESTERN RES CTR, STAUFFER CHEM CO, 72- *Mem:* AAAS; Am Chem Soc; Royal Soc Chem. *Res:* Acetylene-allene chemistry; organic reaction mechanisms; synthetic organic chemistry in agricultural pest control. *Mailing Add:* Western Res Ctr Stauffer Chem Co 1200 S 47th St Richmond CA 94804

MIHAJLOV, VSEVOLOD S, b Kladanj, Yugoslavia, Feb 12, 25; nat US; m 51; c 3. PHYSICAL CHEMISTRY, ORGANIC CHEMISTRY. *Educ:* Univ Munich, BS, 49; Clark Univ, AM, 54, PhD, 56. *Prof Exp:* Sr scientist, 56-68, mgr process & mat develop, 68-69, mgr color technol area, 69-74, prin scientist & mgr copy qual technol, 74-81, PRIN SCIENTIST & MGR COLOR STRATEGY, XEROX CORP, 81- *Concurrent Pos:* Abstractor, Chem Abstr, 53-70. *Mem:* Am Chem Soc; Soc Photog Sci & Eng; Int-Soc Color Coun. *Res:* Photographic science; graphic arts; photosensitive systems; imaging; xerography; color; color vision. *Mailing Add:* Xerox Corp Xerox Sq PO Box 1540 Rochester NY 14603

MIHALAKIS, NICHOLAS JOHN, clinical microbiology, immunochemistry, see previous edition

MIHALAS, BARBARA R WEIBEL, b Berkeley, Calif, Oct 18, 39; m 61, 75; c 3. SOLAR PHYSICS, RADIATION HYDRODYNAMICS. *Educ:* Univ Colo, BA, 61, MS, 77, PhD(astrophysics), 79. *Prof Exp:* Fel, Advan Study Prog, Nat Ctr Atmospheric Res, 79-81; asst astronomer, Sacramento Peak Observ, 81-82; VIS SCIENTIST, HIGH ALTITUDE OBSERV, NAT CTR ATMOSPHERIC RES, 82- *Mem:* Am Astron Soc; AAAS. *Res:* Theory and observation of acoustic-gravity waves in the solar atmosphere; theory of spectral line formation in the presence of small-scale fluctuations in velocity and thermodynamic variables. *Mailing Add:* High Altitude Observ Nat Ctr Atmospheric Res Boulder CO 80307

MIHALAS, DIMITRI, b Los Angeles, Calif, Mar 20, 39; m 63, 75; c 2. ASTROPHYSICS. *Educ:* Univ Calif, Los Angeles, AB, 59; Calif Inst Technol, MS, 60, PhD(astron, physics), 64. *Prof Exp:* Mem tech staff, TRW Space Tech Labs, 59; Higgins vis fel astron, Princeton Univ, 63-64, asst prof, 64-67; asst prof physics & astrophys & mem joint inst lab astrophys, Univ Colo, 67-68; from assoc prof to prof astron, Univ Chicago, 68-71; sr scientist, High Altitude Observ, 71-79; astronomer, Sacramento Peak Observ, 79-82; SR SCIENTIST, HIGH ALTITUDE OBSERV, 82- *Concurrent Pos:* Alfred P Sloan res fel, 69-71; mem comn 12 & 36, Int Astron Union; mem astron adv panel, NSF, 72-75; assoc ed, Astrophys J, 70- & J Comput Physics, 81-; adjoint prof depts astrogeophysics & dept physics & astrophysics, Univ Colo, 72-; vis prof dept astrophysics, Oxford Univ, 77-78; sr vis fel, Univ Col London, 78; consult, Los Alamos Nat Lab, 81- *Honors & Awards:* Helen B Warner Prize, Am Astron Soc, 74. *Mem:* Nat Acad Sci; Am Astron Soc; Int Astron Union; Explorers Club. *Res:* Physics of stellar atmospheres and abundances of elements in the stars; theory of radiative transfer; radiation hydrodynamics; solar physics. *Mailing Add:* High Altitude Observ Box 3000 Boulder CO 80307

MIHALCZO, JOHN THOMAS, b Yonkers, NY, May 30, 31; m 52; c 6. NUCLEAR ENGINEERING, PHYSICS. *Educ:* NY Univ, BA, 53, MS, 56; Univ Tenn, Knoxville, PhD(nuclear eng), 70. *Prof Exp:* Physicist, Res Div, Curtiss Wright Corp, 53-58 & Oak Ridge Nat Lab, 58-68; mem res staff physics & nuclear eng, Y-12 Plant, Nuclear Div, Union Carbide Corp, 68-73; MEM STAFF, INSTRUMENTATION & CONTROLS DIV, OAK RIDGE NAT LAB, UNION CARBIDE CORP, 73- *Concurrent Pos:* Ford Found prof nuclear eng, Univ Tenn, 71- *Mem:* Am Phys Soc; Am Nuclear Soc. *Res:* Critical and subcritical assemblies; pulse reactors; prompt neutron decay by the pulsed neutron and the Rossi methods; reactor physics; radiation shielding; fusion energy research. *Mailing Add:* Fusion Energy Div Oak Ridge Nat Lab Oak Ridge TN 37830

MIHALISIN, JOHN R(AYMOND), b Passaic, NJ, Dec 18, 24. METALLURGY. *Educ:* Yale Univ, BE, 49; Mass Inst Technol, ScD, 53. *Prof Exp:* Supvr metall eng, Curtiss-Wright Corp, 53-55; sr metallurgist, Int Nickel Co, Inc, 55-72; TECH MGR, ALLOY DIV, HOWMET GAS TURBINE COMPONENTS CORP, 72- *Mem:* Am Soc Metals; Electron Micros Soc Am; Sigma Xi; Am Inst Mining, Metall & Petrol Engrs; Ger Soc Electron Micros. *Res:* Physical metallurgy, especially electron and x-ray diffraction, electron microscopy, electron probe microanalysis and x-ray flourescence; design and development of new high temperature alloys; corrosion resistant alloys and evaluation of their performance in service. *Mailing Add:* Alloy Div Roy St Dover NJ 07801

MIHALISIN, TED WARREN, b Houston, Tex, Feb 11, 40; m 61; c 3. LOW TEMPERATURE PHYSICS. *Educ:* Cornell Univ, BA, 61; Univ Rochester, PhD(physics), 67. *Prof Exp:* assoc prof, 69-75, PROF PYSICS, TEMPLE UNIV, 75- *Concurrent Pos:* Assoc scientist dept physics, Gulf Gen Atomic Inc, Calif, 67-69. *Mem:* Am Phys Soc. *Res:* Study of valence fluctuations, Kondo lattice phenomena, magnetic ordering and superconductivity in rare earth intermetallic compounds. *Mailing Add:* Dept of Physics Temple Univ Philadelphia PA 19122

MIHALOV, JOHN DONALD, b Los Angeles, Calif, Dec 28, 37. SOLAR-TERRESTRIAL RELATIONS. *Educ:* Calif Inst Technol, BS, 59, MS, 61. *Prof Exp:* Mem tech staff, Space Tech Lab, Inc, 59-60; res asst, Ctr Radiophysics & Space Res, Cornell Univ, 60-61; scientist, Jet Propulsion Lab, NASA, 61; mem tech staff, Aerospace Corp, 61-66; RES SCIENTIST, AMES RES CTR, NASA, 66- *Mem:* Am Phys Soc; Am Geophys Union; AAAS. *Res:* Author or co-author of over 59 publications dealing with experimental data on the earths radiation belts, the interplanetary medium, the magnetospheres of Jupiter and Saturn, and the solar wind interaction with the moon and with Venus. *Mailing Add:* 761 Garland Dr Palo Alto CA 94303

MIHALYI, ELEMER, b Deva, Roumania, Jan 11, 19; nat US; m 48; c 2. BIOCHEMISTRY. *Educ:* Univ Kolozsvar, Hungary, MD, 43; Cambridge Univ, PhD, 63. *Prof Exp:* Instr med chem, Univ Kolozsvar, 41-44 & biochem, Univ Budapest, 46-48; guest investr, Nobel Inst Med, Stockholm, 48-49; res assoc, Inst Muscle Res, Woods Hole, 49-51; res fel, Harrison Dept Surg Res, Pa, 51-55; chemist, Lab Cell Biol, Nat Heart, Lung & Blood Inst, 55-78; CHEMIST, CLIN PATH DEPT, HEMATOL SERV, NIH, 78- *Mem:* Am Soc Biol Chemists; Am Chem Soc; Int Soc Hemat. *Res:* Protein chemistry; proteins involved in blood coagulation; heavy intermediates in proteolytic breakdown of proteins; physicochemical and chemical studies of the transformation of fibrinogen into fibrin. *Mailing Add:* Nat Inst Health Lab Cell Biol Bldg 3Rm B1-17 Bethesda MD 20014

MIHELICH, JOHN WILLIAM, b Colorado Springs, Colo, Jan 2, 22; m 46; c 3. NUCLEAR PHYSICS. *Educ:* Colo Col, AB, 42; Univ Ill, PhD(physics), 50. *Prof Exp:* Assoc physicist, Brookhaven Nat Lab, 50-54; from asst prof to assoc prof, 54-61, PROF PHYSICS, UNIV NOTRE DAME, 61- *Mem:* Fel Am Phys Soc. *Res:* Radioactivity; decay schemes; internal conversion of gamma ray transitions; gamma ray spectra. *Mailing Add:* Dept of Physics Univ of Notre Dame South Bend IN 46556

MIHICH, ENRICO, b Fiume, Italy, Jan 4, 28; m 54; c 1. PHARMACOLOGY. *Educ:* Univ Milan, MD, 51. *Prof Exp:* Instr, Inst Pharmacol, Univ Milan, 51, asst prof, 52 & 54-56; from sr cancer res scientist to prin cancer res scientist, Roswell Park Mem Inst, 57-71; assoc prof, 62-68, PROF BIOCHEM PHARMACOL, ROSWELL PARK DIV GRAD SCH, STATE UNIV NY BUFFALO, 68-, CHMN PROG PHARMACOL, 69-; DIR DEPT EXP THERAPEUT, ROSWELL PARK MEM INST, 71- *Concurrent Pos:* Vis res fel, Sloan-Kettering Inst Cancer Res, 52-54; dir lab pharmacol, Valeas Pharmaceut Indust, Italy, 54-56; docent pharmacol, Univ Milan, 62. *Mem:* AAAS; Am Soc Pharmacol & Exp Therapeut; Soc Exp Biol & Med; Am Asn Cancer Res; NY Acad Sci. Res; General and pre-clinical pharmacology; cancer biology and experimental therapy. *Mailing Add:* Dept of Exp Therapeut Roswell Park Mem Inst Buffalo NY 14263

MIHINA, JOSEPH STEPHEN, b New York, NY, May 4, 18; m 49; c 2. ORGANIC CHEMISTRY. *Educ:* NY Univ, BS, 38; Mich State Col, MS, 48, PhD(chem), 50. *Prof Exp:* Asst foreman, Oil Tempering, Washburn Wire Co, 38-41; field inspector, Chem Warfare Serv, 41-43; fel, Northwestern Univ, 50-51; res chemist, 51-66, mgr chem mfg, 66-77, MGR CHEM PROC OPTIMIZATION, G D SEARLE & CO, 77- *Mem:* Am Chem Soc. *Res:* Emulsion polymerization; tetrazoles steroids. *Mailing Add:* 8959 N Lockwood Ave Skokie IL 60077

MIHM, MARTIN C, JR, b Pittsburgh, Pa. DERMATOLOGY, PATHOLOGY. *Educ:* Duquesne Univ, BA, 55; Univ Pittsburgh, MD, 61; Am Bd Dermat, dipl, 69; Am Bd Path, dipl, 74, cert dermatopath, 75. *Prof Exp:* Clin & res fel dermat, Mass Gen Hosp, 64-67, clin fel path, 69-72, asst pathologist & asst dermatologist, 72-75; res fel dermat, 69-72, asst prof path, 72-75, ASSOC PROF PATH, HARVARD MED SCH, 75-; ASST DERMATOLOGIST, MASS GEN HOSP, 72-, ASSOC PATHOLOGIST, 75- *Concurrent Pos:* Assoc staff, Brigham & Women's Hosp, 75-; consult path, Cambridge City Hosp & Children's Hosp Med Ctr, 75-; consult dermatopath, Addison Gilbert Hosp, 75-; chief dermatopath residence training prog, Mass Gen Hosp, Brigham & Women's Hosp & Children's Hosp Med Ctr, Boston, 77-; consult path, Beth Israel Hosp, Boston, Mass, 78- & Boston Vet Admin Med Ctr, 79- *Mem:* Am Acad Dermat; Am Dermat Asn; Am Soc Dermatopath; Am Soc Clin Oncol; fel Am Col Physicians. *Res:* Biology of malignant melanoma, host response to this tumor and its histology; morphology of delayed hypersensitivity reactions in man; other aspects of cutaneous inflammation. *Mailing Add:* Dept Dermatopath Warren Bldg Mass Gen Hosp Fruit St Boston MA 02114

MIHOLITS, ERNEST M(ARTIN), water chemistry, environmental engineering, see previous edition

MIHRAM, GEORGE ARTHUR, b Norman, Okla, Sept 21, 39; m 65. MATHEMATICAL STATISTICS, SYSTEMIC SCIENCES. *Educ:* Univ Okla, BS, 60; Okla State Univ, MS & PhD(statist), 65. *Prof Exp:* Mathematician, Opers Res Inc, 65-66; systs analyst, Orgn Joint Chiefs of Staff, 66-68; asst prof statist, Univ Pa, 68-74. *Concurrent Pos:* Consult, Hq US Air Force, 68-69, Acad Natural Sci, 70-71, Opers Res Inc, 72-73 & IBM Corp, 73; NSF int travel grant, 75 & NATO travel grant, 77; instr, Southern Calif Univ, 78-79. *Honors & Awards:* Joint Serv Commendation Medal, Joint Chiefs of Staff. *Mem:* Fel AAAS; Asn Comput Mach; Inst Math Statist; Oper Res Soc Am; Sigma Xi. *Res:* The scientific method is a six-stage modelling process which mimes isomorphically the modelling process (genetic, then neural models) by which all life on earth has to date been assured; tele-cybernetics. *Mailing Add:* PO Box 1188 Princeton NJ 08540

MIHRAN, THEODORE GREGORY, b Detroit, Mich, June 28, 24; m 53; c 3. MICROWAVE ELECTRONICS. *Educ:* Stanford Univ, AB, 44, MS, 47, PhD(elec eng), 50. *Prof Exp:* PHYSICIST, CORP RES & DEVELOP, GEN ELEC CO, 50- *Concurrent Pos:* Lectr, Union Col, NY, 52-53 & 60-61; vis assoc prof, Cornell Univ, 63-64; assoc ed, Inst Elec & Electronics Engrs Trans on Electron Devices, 70-73. *Mem:* Inst Elec & Electronics Eng; Am Phys Soc; Int Microwave Power Inst. *Res:* Electron physics; microwave tubes and electronics; kylstrons; space charge wave amplification; plasmas; MOSFET modeling; microwave ovens. *Mailing Add:* Res & Develop Ctr Gen Elec Co PO Box 8 Schenectady NY 12301

MIHURSKY, JOSEPH ANTHONY, b Alpha, NJ, May 4, 33; m 55; c 1. ECOLOGY. *Educ:* Lafayette Col, BA, 54; Lehigh Univ, MS, 57, PhD(ecol), 62. *Prof Exp:* Res assoc, 62-67, res asst prof, 67-68, chmn & assoc prof, Dept Environ Res, 68-74, chmn & prof, 74-75, lab head & prof, 75-76, PROF MARINE ECOL, CHESAPEAKE BIOL LAB, UNIV MD, 77- *Concurrent Pos:* Res asst, Moyer-Trembley Consult, 56-62; chmn water working group, Comn Power Plant Siting, Nat Acad Eng, 69-70; panel mem, US Nat Water Comn, 71-72; adv comt mem, Cong Ad-Hoc Comt Environ Matters, US Govt, 68-69; planning comt mem, Inst del a Vie & Acad Sci, France, 73-74; consult adv, US Army Corp Engrs, 73-74 & Calif Marine Rev Comt, 75- *Mem:* Sigma Xi; Estuarine Res Fedn; AAAS; Fedn Am Scientists. *Res:* Determining factors that regulate abundance of estuarine populations and communities; environmental effects of coastal nuclear and fossil fueled power plants; pollution ecology; estuarine fish population dynamics and regional planning. *Mailing Add:* Ctr Environ & Estuarine Studies Univ Md Box 38 Solomons MD 20688

MIJAL, CHESTER FRANCIS, physical chemistry, organic chemistry, see previous edition

MIJOVIC, JOVAN, b Belgrade, Yugoslavia, Sept 4, 48. ENGINEERING. *Educ:* Univ Belgrade, BS, 72; Univ Wis-Madison, MS, 74, PhD(chem eng), 78. *Prof Exp:* ASST PROF CHEM ENG, POLYTECH INST NY, 78- *Concurrent Pos:* Prin investr res grants, various insts, 79- *Mem:* Am Inst Chem Engrs: Soc Plastics Engrs. *Res:* Processing structure property durability correlations in advanced composite materials composed of a thermosetting resin matrix (epoxy, polyimide or polyester) and fibrous reinforcement (glass, carbon, boron). *Mailing Add:* Polytech Inst NY 333 Jay St Brooklyn NY 11201

MIKA, EDWARD STANLEY, b Whiting, Ind, Aug 16, 20; m 64. PHARMACOGNOSY. *Educ:* Univ Chicago, BS, 42, PhD(bot), 54; Wash State Univ, MS, 50. *Prof Exp:* Jr radiobiologist, Argonne Nat Lab, 46-49; res assoc bot & pharmacol, Univ Chicago, 53-60; from asst prof to assoc prof, 61-69, PROF PHARMACOG, COL PHARM, UNIV ILL, CHICAGO, 69- *Honors & Awards:* Newcomb Award Pharmacog. *Mem:* Soc Econ Bot; Am Soc Pharmacog; Am Asn Col Pharm; Acad Pharmaceut Sci; Soc Econ Bot (treas, 76-81). *Res:* Medicinal plants; chemical composition, growth and development. *Mailing Add:* Col of Pharm 833 S Wood St Chicago IL 60612

MIKA, LEONARD ALOYSIUS, b Bay City, Mich, Apr 17, 17; m 43; c 2. MICROBIOLOGY. *Educ:* Univ Mich, BS, 47, MS, 49; George Wash Univ, PhD, 55; Am Bd Microbiol, Dipl, 63. *Prof Exp:* Asst bact, Univ Mich, 47-49, sr investr, US Army For Sci & Technol Ctr, Ft Detrick, 49-62, staff microbiologist, 62-68, phys sci admin, 68-73, dir, 73-77; res assoc, Sch Med, Univ Va, 77-80; RETIRED. *Mem:* Am Soc Microbiol; Soc Exp Biol & Med; Am Asn Immunol; fel Am Acad Microbiol; NY Acad Sci. *Res:* Research administration. *Mailing Add:* 102 Melissa Pl Charlottesville VA 22901

MIKA, THOMAS STEPHEN, b Chicago, Ill, July 16, 41. MINERAL ENGINEERING, CHEMICAL ENGINEERING. *Educ:* Stanford Univ, BS, 62; Columbia Univ, MS, 63; Univ Calif, Berkeley, DEng, 71. *Prof Exp:* Asst prof mat sci & eng, Univ Calif, Berkeley, 70-75; scientist & proj leader, 75-79, MGR, DEVELOPER PROCESSING AREA, XEROX CORP, 79- *Honors & Awards:* Arthur Claudet Prize, Brit Inst Mining & Metall, 76. *Mem:* Am Inst Mining, Metall & Petrol Engrs; Am Inst Chem Engrs; Brit Inst Mining & Metall; Sigma Xi. *Res:* Comminution; mathematical modeling of particulate processing unit operations; flotation; applied colloid chemistry; particulate technology; emulsification; dispersion; polymer processing. *Mailing Add:* Xerox Corp Develop Process Area Xerox Sq W-143 Rochester NY 14644

MIKAMI, HARRY M, b Seward, Alaska, Dec 28, 15; m 55. MINERALOGY, CERAMICS. *Educ:* Univ Alaska, BS, 37; Yale Univ, MS, 42, PhD(petrol), 45. *Prof Exp:* Engr, US Smelting, Ref & Mining Co, Alaska, 37 & Am Creek Operating Co, Alaska, 38-39; geologist, Conn Geol Surv, 43-45; instr mineral, Yale Univ, 45; res scientist, E J Lavino & Co, 45-60, res mgr, 60-65, dir res, 65-67, dir res & develop, Lavino Div, Int Minerals & Chem, Corp, 67-74; RES MGR, BASIC REFRACTORIES, KAISER ALUMINUM & CHEM CORP, 74- *Concurrent Pos:* Instr, Pa State Univ, 48-49; consult, Villanova Univ, 57-58. *Mem:* Fel Am Ceramic Soc; fel Mineral Soc Am; Am Soc Testing & Mat; fel Geol Soc Am; Am Chem Soc. *Res:* Ceramic mineralogy and microstructure; phase equilibria of periclase-chromite-orthosilicate systems; high temperature materials; basic oxygen and electric arc furnace refractories; industrial minerals. *Mailing Add:* Ctr for Technol PO Box 877 Pleasanton CA 94566

MIKE, VALERIE, b Budapest, Hungary, Aug 20, 34; US citizen. STATISTICS, BIOSTATISTICS. *Educ:* Manhattanville Col, BA, 56; NY Univ, MS, 59, PhD(math), 67. *Prof Exp:* From tech asst to mem tech staff, Bell Tel Labs, Inc, 56-67; res assoc, Sloan-Kettering Inst Cancer Res, 67-68, assoc, 68-70; asst prof, Med Col, Cornell Univ, 70-74; assoc mem, Sloan-Kettering Inst Cancer Res, 73-78; assoc prof, Med Col, Cornell Univ & Grad Sch Med Sci, 74-78; HEAD, BIOSTATIST LAB, SLOAN-KETTERING INST CANCER RES, 73-, MEM, 78-; PROF BIOSTATIST, MED COL, CORNELL UNIV & GRAD SCH MED SCI, 79- *Concurrent Pos:* Consult, Nat Cancer Inst, 76-; mem oncol drugs adv comt, Food & Drug Admin, 78-81. *Mem:* AAAS; Inst Math Statist; Am Statist Asn; Biomet Soc; Am Asn Cancer Res. *Res:* Statistical theory and methodology, with application in the biomedical sciences. *Mailing Add:* Biostatist Lab 1275 York Ave New York NY 10021

MIKELL, WILLIAM GAILLARD, b Columbia, SC, Sept 13, 23; m 53; c 2. ENVIRONMENTAL CONTROL, OCCUPATIONAL HEALTH LABORATORIES. *Educ:* Univ SC, BS, 44; Univ Va, MS, 47, PhD(physics), 52. *Prof Exp:* Engr, Westinghouse Elec Corp, 44-45; physicist, Inst Textile Tech, 47-49; instr, Univ Va, 50-51; res physicist, 52-56, res supvr, 56-57, res mgr, Spunbonded Prod Div, Textile Fibers Dept, 57-66, res mgr indust mkt, Indust Fibers Div, 66-71, asst to tech dir, Textile Fibers Dept, Indust Fibers Div, 71-78, ENVIRON CONTROL MGR, DUPONT EXP STA, E I DU PONT DE NEMOURS & CO, INC, 78- *Mem:* Am Phys Soc. *Res:* Industrial fiber technology; environmental technology for laboratories; industrial hygiene; chemical laboratory safety and occupational health. *Mailing Add:* Cent Res & Develop Dept E I du Pont de Nemours & Co Inc Wilmington DE 19898

MIKES, JOHN ANDREW, b Budapest, Hungary, Jan 20, 22; m 48; c 1. CHEMISTRY. *Educ:* Pazmany Peter Univ, Budapest, dipl, 45, PhD(org chem), 48; Eotvos Lorand Univ, Budapest, DSc, 68. *Prof Exp:* Asst prof polymer chem, Budapest Tech Univ, 45-48; tech mgr, Hutter & Lever, Co, Budapest, 48-49; dir res & consult serv plastics inst, Nat Polymer Res Ctr, Budapest, 50-69; dir res & develop, Water Treatment Develop Co, Tatabanya, 69-70; consult, Treadwell Corp, New York, 70 & Mocatta Metals Corp, 71; mgr res, Lundy Electronics, Inc, Glen Head, NY, 71-73; mgr develop, Buckman Labs, Inc, Memphis, Tenn, 73-74; mgr res & develop, Ionac Chem Co, Birmingham, NJ, 74-76; SR RES FEL, CIBA-GEIGY CO, ARDSLEY, 76- *Concurrent Pos:* Ed, Ion Exchange & Membranes, 71-76. *Mem:* Am Chem Soc; fel Am Inst Chem. *Res:* Polymer synthesis; water treatment process development; polymer structure research; ion exchangers; membranes; porosity; cross linking; author of over 100 publications. *Mailing Add:* 16 Dixwell Rd New City NY 10956

MIKES, PETER, b Prague, Czech, Oct 28, 38; m 69; c 3. POLYMER PHYSICS, INK JET PRINTING. *Educ:* Czech Tech Univ, ing Phys, 61; Charles Univ, Prague, CSc, 65. *Prof Exp:* Scientist polymers, Inst Macromolecular Chem, Czech, 65-69; fel spectroscopy, Dept Polymer Sci, Case Western Reserve Univ, 69-71; sr scientist syst sci, Res Ctr, Rockland State Hosp, NY, 71-73; SCIENTIST RHEOLOGY, XEROX CORP, 73- *Concurrent Pos:* Imp Chem Indust fel textiles, Univ Leeds, 66-67. *Mem:* Am Phys Soc; Inst Elec & Electronics Engrs; Comput Soc. *Res:* Mechanical properties of polymers; rheology of elastomers; printing physics; digital control. *Mailing Add:* 16641 Cowell St San Leandro CA 94578

MIKESELL, JAN ERWIN, b Macomb, Ill, Feb 19, 43; m 65. PLANT ANATOMY. *Educ:* Western Ill Univ, BSc, 65, MSc, 66; Ohio State Univ, PhD(bot), 73. *Prof Exp:* Researcher virol & immunol, Viral & Immunol Lab, Sixth US Army Med Labs, 67-69; asst prof, 73-80, ASSOC PROF BOT, GETTYSBURG COL, 80- *Mem:* Bot Soc Am; AAAS; Sigma Xi; Can Soc Plant Physiologists. *Res:* Investigations of anomalous secondary thickening in vascular plants; especially patterns of development and directions of differentiation of anomalous types of cambia in dicotyledonous plants; investigation of flower and fruit development. *Mailing Add:* Dept of Biol Gettysburg Col Gettysburg PA 17325

MIKESELL, SHARELL LEE, b Coshocton, Ohio, Nov 24, 43; m 65. POLYMER CHEMISTRY. *Educ:* Olivet Nazarene Col, AB, 65; Ohio State Univ, MS, 68; Univ Akron, PhD(polymer chem), 71. *Prof Exp:* Prod develop engr polymer chem, Gen Elec Co, 71-72, proj mgr, 72-74, mgr indust mkt develop tech mkt, 74-75, mgr indust prod develop polymer chem, Laminated & Insulating Mat Bus Dept, 75-76; MGR TEXTILE SYSTS LAB, OWENS-CORNING FIBERGLAS TECH CTR, 76- *Mem:* Am Chem Soc. *Res:* Development of high performance thermosetting epoxy and phenolic resins used in high pressure copper clad and multilayer laminates for printed wiring applications; development of fiber glass textile products. *Mailing Add:* Tech Ctr Owens-Corning Fiberglas Granville OH 43023

MIKESKA, EMORY EUGENE, b Abbott, Tex, Aug 24, 27; m 48; c 2. PHYSICS. *Educ:* Univ Tex, BS, 47, MA, 50. *Prof Exp:* Jr seismic observer, Magnolia Petrol Co, 47-49; res physicist, Defense Res Lab, Univ Tex, Austin, 50-61; sr physicist &proj dir, Tracor, Inc, 61-67; RES SCIENTIST ASSOC, APPL RES LAB, UNIV TEX, AUSTIN, 67- *Concurrent Pos:* Consult, Boner & Lane, 54-59; consult & partner, Lane & Mikesa, 60-61. *Mem:* Fel Acoust Soc Am; Audio Eng Soc. *Res:* Noise control; architectural acoustics; underwater sound. *Mailing Add:* 7613 Rustling Rd Austin TX 78731

MIKHAIL, ADEL AYAD, b Cairo, Egypt, Nov 8, 34; US citizen; m 58; c 2. MEDICINAL CHEMISTRY, BIOMEDICAL ENGINEERING. *Educ:* Univ Alexandria, BPharm, 55, MPharmaceut Chem, 60; Univ Minn, Minneapolis, PhD(med chem), 66. *Prof Exp:* NIH fel & assoc scientist, Cancer Res Lab, Vet Admin Hosp, Minneapolis, Minn, 66; asst prof, Col Pharm, Univ Alexandria, 66-70; USDA Forest Serv fel & res assoc pharm, Ohio State Univ, 70-72; res mgr, 73-78, VPRES TECH MED, INC, 78- *Mem:* Am Chem Soc. *Res:* Drug design; synthesis; structure elucidation of natural products; biocompatability of polymers; cardiovascular prosthesis and hemodialysis devices; quality control and res and development of medical devices. *Mailing Add:* 2332 W 111th St Bloomington MN 55431

MIKHAIL, WADIE F, b Egypt, Apr 16, 29; US citizen; m 63; c 2. STATISTICS. *Educ:* Cairo Univ, BSc, 49; Univ NC, PhD(math statist), 60. *Prof Exp:* Lectr math, Teachers Col, Cairo, 49-57; assoc statistician, 60-62, staff statistician, 62-66, adv statistician, 66-69, SR STATISTICIAN, IBM CORP, 69- *Mem:* Inst Math Statist; Am Statist Asn. *Res:* Probabilistic modeling of wiring space requirements for large scale integration technology. *Mailing Add:* 75 Pleasant Ridge Dr Poughkeepsie NY 12603

MIKIC, BORA, b Loznica, Yugoslavia, Mar 1, 32; m 57; c 2. HEAT TRANSFER, BIOENGINEERING. *Educ:* Univ Belgrade, Dipl eng, 57; Mass Inst Technol, ScD(mech eng), 66. *Prof Exp:* Res engr, Aero-Tech Inst, Univ Belgrade, 57-60; asst fluid mech, Univ Belgrade, 60-61; lectr fluid mech & heat transfer, Khartoum Tech Univ, 61-64; res asst heat transfer, 64-66, from asst prof to assoc prof mech eng, 66-73, PROF MECH ENG, MASS INST TECHNOL, 73- *Concurrent Pos:* Nat Res Coun sr fel, Oxford Univ, 75-76. *Mem:* Am Soc Mech Engrs; Sigma Xi. *Res:* Contact resistance, dropwise condensation, nucleate boiling; mass transfer; boiling; condensation; fusion nuclear reactor; utilization of geothermal energy. *Mailing Add:* Dept of Mech Eng Mass Inst Technol Cambridge MA 02139

MIKITEN, TERRY MICHAEL, b New York, NY, June 1, 37; m 60; c 3. NEUROPHYSIOLOGY. *Educ:* NY Univ, BA, 60; Albert Einstein Col Med, PhD(pharmacol), 67. *Prof Exp:* Res asst neurosurg, Mt Sinai Hosp, NY, 59-60; asst pharmacologist, Schering Corp, NJ, 60-61; USPHS fel, Med Sch, Columbia Univ, 67-69; asst prof physiol, 69-75, ASSOC PROF PHYSIOL, UNIV TEX MED SCH SAN ANTONIO, 75- *Concurrent Pos:* Consult, Bexar County Hosp, 69-; regional chmn, Osteogenesis Imperfecta Found, 71-76; chmn, San Antonio Neurosci Group, 76-77. *Mem:* AAAS; Soc Neurosci; NY Acad Sci. *Res:* Neurophysiology and pharmacology of synaptic transmission; desensitization of cholinergic receptors; electrophysiology of excitable and non-excitable membranes. *Mailing Add:* Dept of Physiol & Med Univ of Tex Med Sch San Antonio TX 78284

MIKKELSEN, DAVID ROBERT, b Ames, Iowa, May 10, 49; m 72; c 2. COMPUTATIONAL PHYSICS. *Educ:* Calif Inst Technol, BS, 71; Univ Wash, PhD(physics), 75. *Prof Exp:* Res fel, Calif State Polytech Univ, 75-77; res assoc physics, 77-80, RES STAFF PHYSICIST, PLASMA PHYSICS LAB, PRINCETON, 80- *Mem:* Am Phys Soc. *Res:* Numerical simulation of magnetically confined plasma experiments. *Mailing Add:* C-Site Forrestal Campus PO Box 451 Princeton NJ 08544

MIKKELSEN, DUANE SOREN, b Payson, Utah, Nov 1, 21; m 43; c 4. SOIL FERTILITY, AGRONOMY. *Educ:* Brigham Young Univ, BS, 46; Rutgers Univ, PhD, 49. *Prof Exp:* From asst prof to assoc prof, 49-63, PROF AGRON, UNIV CALIF, DAVIS, 63- *Concurrent Pos:* Consult, Rockefeller Found, Colombia, 62; IRI Res Inst, Brazil, 62, 68-71, Chile-Calif Proj, 63, Int Rice Comn, Manila, Philippines, 64 & 66, Int Atomic Energy Agency, Hong Kong, 66, & Peace Corp Training Progs, 67; vis scientist & Rockefeller Found grant, Int Rice Res Inst, Manila, Philippines, 67-68; chmn, US Rice Tech Working Group, 67-68; mem rice fertilizer adv comt, Tenn Valley Auth, 68-71; consult, Amazon Basin Develop, 70-74 & Malaysian Agr Res Develop, 74; consult agr develop, Govt of Venezuela, 69, Australia, 76, Thailand, 76 & Oman, 77; vis scientist micronutrient proj, Int Atomic Energy Agency, 74; vis scientist, Int Rice Res Inst, 77-78. *Mem:* Fel Soil Sci Soc Am; Crop Sci Soc Am; fel Am Soc Agron; Am Soc Plant Physiol. *Res:* Plant-soil interrelations; mineral nutrition of plants; mineral nutrition of rice; chemistry of flooded soils. *Mailing Add:* 617 Oeste Dr Davis CA 95616

MIKKELSEN, WILLIAM MITCHELL, b Minneapolis, Minn, May 25, 23; m 48; c 6. INTERNAL MEDICINE. *Educ:* Univ Mich, MD, 49. *Prof Exp:* From asst prof to assoc prof, 57-69, asst dir health prog, 59-62, actg dir, 62-66, dir, Periodic Health Appraisal Unit, 66-77, PROF INTERNAL MED, MED SCH, UNIV MICH, ANN ARBOR, 69- *Concurrent Pos:* Assoc physician, Rackham Arthritis Res Unit, Univ Mich, Ann Arbor, 55-; attend physician, Vet Admin Hosp, 55- *Mem:* Soc Advan Med Syst; Am Soc Clin Pharmacol & Therapeut; Am Col Physicians; Am Fedn Clin Res; Am Geriatrics Soc. *Res:* Rheumatic diseases; evaluation and application of periodic health appraisal techniques. *Mailing Add:* Univ of Mich Med Ctr Ann Arbor MI 48108

MIKKELSON, RAYMOND CHARLES, b Blue Earth, Minn, Mar 22, 37; m 60; c 1. SOLID STATE PHYSICS, COMPUTER APPLICATIONS IN SCIENCES. *Educ:* St Olaf Col, BA, 59; Univ Ill, MS, 61, PhD(physics), 65. *Prof Exp:* From asst prof to assoc prof, 65-75, head, Dept Physics & Astron, 76-79, PROF PHYSICS, MACALESTER COL, 75-, DIR MACALESTER NSF CAUSE PROJ LAB COMPUTING & GRAPHICS, 80- *Concurrent Pos:* Assoc Cols Midwest physics fac mem, Argonne Nat Lab, 71, vis scientist, Physics Div, 71-72; vis scholar, Univ Minn, 79. *Mem:* Am Asn Physics Teachers; Am Phys Soc; Am Asn Univ Professors. *Res:* Interactions of radiation with solids; channeling; environmental radiation levels; teaching of university-college physics; real-time computer instrumentation. *Mailing Add:* Dept of Physics Macalester Col St Paul MN 55105

MIKKOLA, DONALD E(MIL), b Champion, Mich, July 30, 38; m 60; c 2. METALLURGICAL ENGINEERING, MATERIALS SCIENCE. *Educ:* Mich Technol Univ, BS, 59; Northwestern Univ, MS, 61, PhD(mat sci), 64. *Prof Exp:* From asst prof to assoc prof, 64-72, PROF METALL ENG, MICH TECHNOL UNIV, 72- *Concurrent Pos:* Fulbright-Hays res scholar, Helsinki Univ Technol, Finland, 73-74; mem, Eng Accreditation Comn, Accreditation Bd Eng & Technol, 81- *Mem:* Am Soc Metals; Am Inst Mining, Metall & Petrol Engrs; Am Crystallog Asn. *Res:* Applications of x-ray and electron techniques; structure-property relationships; shock hardening; erosion; order-disorder phenomena. *Mailing Add:* Dept of Metall Eng Mich Technol Univ Houghton MI 49931

MIKLOFSKY, HAAREN A(LBERT), b Rochester, NY, Nov 25, 20; m 49; c 2. CIVIL ENGINEERING. *Educ:* George Washington Univ, BCE, 46; Yale Univ, ME, 47, DrEng, 50. *Prof Exp:* Asst instr civil eng, George Washington Univ, 47-48, from asst prof to assoc prof & exec officer dept, 49-55; assoc prof, Rensselaer Polytech Inst, 55-62; prof, Univ SC, 62-66; PROF CIVIL ENG, UNIV ARIZ, 66-, PROF ENG MECH, 81- *Concurrent Pos:* Asst in instr, Yale Univ, 48-49; gen engr, Nat Bur Standards, 50-53. *Mem:* Am Soc Civil Engrs; Am Soc Eng Educ. *Res:* Suspension bridges and arches; finite element analysis. *Mailing Add:* 7442 E 18th St Tucson AZ 85710

MIKLOWITZ, JULIUS, b Schenectady, NY, May 22, 19; m 48; c 2. MECHANICS, MECHANICAL ENGINEERING. *Educ:* Univ Mich, BS, 43, MS, 48, PhD(appl mech), 49. *Prof Exp:* Res engr plasticity, Res Labs, Westinghouse Elec Corp, 43-46 & 49; asst prof eng & head dept, NMex Inst Mining & Technol, 49-51; res engr solid mech, US Naval Ord Test Sta, 51-56; assoc prof appl mech, 56-62, PROF APPL MECH, CALIF INST TECHNOL, 62- *Concurrent Pos:* Consult, Space Technol Labs, Ramo-Wooldridge Corp, 56-60, Nat Eng Sci Co, 60-64 & Aerospace Corp, 68-; NSF sr fel, 64-65; mem, US Nat Comn Theoret & Appl Mech, Nat Acad Sci, 76-80. *Mem:* AAAS; fel Am Soc Mech Engrs; Int Soc Interaction, Mech & Math. *Res:* Propagation of waves in elastic and inelastic media; yield phenomena in steel and polymers; fracture of steel. *Mailing Add:* 5255 Vista Miguel Dr La Canada CA 91011

MIKNIS, FRANCIS PAUL, b DuBois, Pa, Jan 31, 40; m 60; c 3. NUCLEAR MAGNETIC RESONANCE. *Educ:* Univ Wyo, BS, 61, PhD(chem), 66. *Prof Exp:* Sr scientist, Aeronutronic Div, Philco-Ford Corp, 66-67; RES CHEMIST, LARAMIE ENERGY RES CTR, ENERGY RES & DEVELOP ADMIN, 67-, PROJ LEADER, 75- *Mem:* Am Chem Soc; Am Asn Physics Teachers; Sigma Xi. *Res:* Nuclear magnetic resonance of solids, particularly oil shales; elemental analysis of fossil fuels. *Mailing Add:* 1819 W Hill Rd Laramie WY 82070

MIKOLAJ, PAUL G(EORGE), b Cleveland, Ohio, Jan 6, 36. CHEMICAL ENGINEERING, ENVIRONMENTAL SCIENCES. *Educ:* Cleveland State Univ, BS, 58; Univ Rochester, MS, 60; Calif Inst Technol, PhD(chem eng), 65. *Prof Exp:* Fel, Calif Inst Technol, 65; res engr, Chevron Res Co, 66-67; asst prof chem eng, Univ Calif, Santa Barbara, 67-73; sr engr, Oceanog Serv, Inc, 73-74 & Dames & Moore, 74-76; DIR REFINING REGULATION, TOSCO CORP, 76- *Concurrent Pos:* Adv Coun, S Coast Air Qual Mgt Dist, 77- *Mem:* AAAS; Am Inst Chem Engrs; Am Chem Soc; Air Pollution Control Asn. *Res:* Environmental policy and regulation; air and water pollution control; toxic and hazardous substances. *Mailing Add:* 10100 Santa Monica Blvd Los Angeles CA 90067

MIKOLAJCIK, EMIL MICHAEL, b Colchester, Conn, Jan 14, 26; m 53; c 2. DAIRY MICROBIOLOGY. *Educ:* Univ Conn, BS, 50; Ohio State Univ, MS, 51, PhD(dairy microbiol), 59. *Prof Exp:* Prof dairy mfg, Univ PR, 51-61; from asst prof to assoc prof, 61-74, PROF FOOD SCI, OHIO STATE UNIV, 74- *Concurrent Pos:* NIH grants, 61- *Honors & Awards:* Pfizer Award in Cheese Res, 74. *Mem:* Sigma Xi; Am Dairy Sci Asn; Am Soc Microbiol; Int Asn Milk, Food & Environ Sanit; Inst Food Technol. *Res:* Mechanisms of bacteriophage action on lactic organisms; bacterial metabolism of organisms associated with the dairy industry, particularly on lactic streptococci and spore formers; immunoglobulins of bovine milk and colostrum; flat-sour sporeformers in canned thermally processed foods; processing and storage of human milk. *Mailing Add:* Dept of Food Sci & Nutrit Ohio State Univ Columbus OH 43210

MIKOLAJCZAK, ALOJZY ANTONI, b Czestochowa, Poland, Jan 14, 35; m 61; c 3. THERMODYNAMICS, AERODYNAMICS. *Educ:* Cambridge Univ, BA, 57, MA, 61, PhD(magneto-hydrodynamics), 65. *Prof Exp:* Tech asst rocket performance, Rolls-Royce Ltd, 57-60, sect leader jet engines, 60-61; asst prof jet engine & rocket propulsion, Mass Inst Technol, 65-66; consult aerodynamicist, Pratt & Whitney Aircraft, 66-67, head compressor res, 67-72, asst chief engr aerocomponents, 72-77, mgr aerodyn, Thermodyn & Control Systs, 77-79; CORP DIR TECH PLANNING, UNITED TECHNOLOGIES CORP, 79- *Honors & Awards:* Gas Turbine Power Award, Am Soc Mech Engrs, 71 & 72. *Mem:* Am Inst Aeronaut & Astronaut; Am Soc Mech Engrs. *Res:* Turbomachinery, including axial and centrifugal compressors and turbines, combustion, inlets and nozzles, ducts and diffusers, noise and emissions, structures and aeroelasticity, controls and fuel systems for gas turbines. *Mailing Add:* United Technologies Corp One Financial Plaza Hartford CT 06101

MIKOLAJCZAK, KENNETH LEE, b Elcho, Wis, Oct 23, 32; c 2. NATURAL PRODUCTS CHEMISTRY. *Educ:* Wis State Col, Stevens Point, BS, 58. *Prof Exp:* From asst chemist to chemist, 58-68, RES CHEMIST, NORTHERN REGIONAL RES LAB, USDA, 68- *Mem:* Am Chem Soc; Phytochem Soc NAm. *Res:* Gas-liquid chromatographic analysis of fatty acid methyl esters; isolation and characterization of unknown and unusual fatty acids from plant seed oils; identification and synthesis of other natural compounds found in plant extracts; antitumor compounds. *Mailing Add:* Northern Regional Res Ctr 1815 N University St Peoria IL 61604

MIKOLASEK, DOUGLAS GENE, b Menominee, Mich, Aug 23, 30; m 59; c 3. MEDICINAL CHEMISTRY. *Educ:* Univ Mich, BS, 52, PhD(med chem), 62. *Prof Exp:* Control chemist, Marinette Paper Co, Scott Paper Co, 54; develop chemist, Abbott Labs, 55-56, res chemist, 56-58; sr scientist, 62-68, group leader chem develop, 68-71, prin investr, 71-75, PRIN RES ASSOC, MEAD JOHNSON RES CTR, 75- *Concurrent Pos:* Parke-Davis fel, Univ Kans, 58-60. *Mem:* AAAS; Am Chem Soc. *Res:* Quinoline chemistry and antimalarial research. *Mailing Add:* Mead Johnson Res Ctr 2404 Pennsylvania Ave Evansville IN 47721

MIKSAD, RICHARD WALTER, b Trenton, NJ, Aug 24, 40; m 70; c 3. OCEANOGRAPHY, METEOROLOGY. *Educ:* Bradley Univ, BSME, 63; Cornell Univ, MSc, 64; Mass Inst Technol, ScD(oceanog), 70. *Prof Exp:* Res staff pollution, Ctr Study Responsive Law, 70; res scientist fluid dynamics, Imperial Col, 70-72; asst res prof atmospheric sci, Univ Miami, 72-74; asst prof, 74-77, ASSOC PROF ENG, UNIV TEX, AUSTIN, 77- *Concurrent Pos:* Nat Res Coun fel, Imperial Col, 70-72. *Mem:* Am Phys Soc; Am Geophys Union; Am Meteorol Soc; Am Soc Mech Engrs; Am Soc Civil Engrs. *Res:* Fluid dynamics; non-linear hydrodynamic stability; wave-structure interaction. *Mailing Add:* Environ Health Eng Group Bldg ECJ 8. 214 Univ Tex Austin TX 78712

MIKSCH, EDMOND STEWART, energy conversion, see previous edition

MIKSCHE, JEROME PHILLIP, plant morphology, see previous edition

MIKULA, BERNARD C, b Johnstown, Pa, Aug 29, 24; m 51; c 2. GENETICS, TAXONOMY. *Educ:* Col William & Mary, BS, 51; Univ Wash, St Louis, PhD(bot), 56. *Prof Exp:* Asst, Mo Bot Garden, 51-56; proj assoc genetics, Univ Wis, 56-60; from asst prof to assoc prof, 60-67, PROF GENETICS, DEFIANCE COL, 67- *Concurrent Pos:* Vis fel ctr biol of natural syst, Wash Univ, 66-67. *Mem:* AAAS; Genetics Soc Am; Am Inst Biol Sci. *Res:* Mechanisms of allelic variation. *Mailing Add:* Dept of Genetics Defiance Col Defiance OH 43512

MIKULA, JAMES J, physical chemistry, see previous edition

MIKULCIK, E(DWIN) C(HARLES), b Glenside, Sask, Dec 10, 36; m 66; c 1. MECHANICAL ENGINEERING. *Educ:* Univ Sask, BE, 60, MSc, 61; Cornell Univ, PhD(mech eng), 68. *Prof Exp:* Instrumentation engr, Du Pont Can, Ltd, 62-63; systs engr, RCA Victor Co, Ltd, 63-65; asst prof mech eng, 68-71, ASSOC PROF MECH ENG, UNIV CALGARY, 71- *Mem:* Eng Inst Can. *Res:* Dynamics, stability and control of ground vehicles; adaptive and optimum control systems; identification and optimal design of dynamic mechanical systems. *Mailing Add:* Dept of Mech Eng Univ of Calgary Calgary AB T2N 1N4 Can

MIKULCIK, JOHN D, b Ilasco, Mo, July 30, 36; m 61; c 3. AGRONOMY. *Educ:* Univ Mo, BS, 58, MS, 59, PhD(soils), 64. *Prof Exp:* From asst prof to assoc prof, 63-73, PROF AGRON, MURRAY STATE UNIV, 73- *Mem:* AAAS; Am Soc Agron; Soil Sci Soc Am. *Res:* Soil testing; levels of nitrate and phosphate in runoff from rural watersheds; levels of nitrate in soils under barn lot conditions. *Mailing Add:* Dept of Agr Murray State Univ Murray KY 42072

MIKULEC, RICHARD ANDREW, b New Brighton, Pa, Feb 26, 28; m 63; c 1. ORGANIC CHEMISTRY. *Educ:* Wayne State Univ, BS, 51; Wash State Univ, MS, 53, PhD(chem), 56. *Prof Exp:* Res fel chem, Univ Minn, 56-57; res investr, 57-77, RES ANAL CHEMIST, G D SEARLE & CO, 77- *Mem:* Am Chem Soc. *Res:* Separation and analytical techniques applied to pharmaceutical products. *Mailing Add:* G D Searle & Co PO Box 5110 Chicago IL 60680

MIKULSKI, CHESTER MARK, b Philadelphia, Pa, Nov 26, 46; m 70; c 2. INORGANIC CHEMISTRY. *Educ:* Drexel Univ, BS, 69, PhD(inorg chem), 72. *Prof Exp:* Fel, Dept Chem, Univ Pa, 72-76; ASST PROF INORG CHEM, BEAVER COL, 76- *Mem:* Am Chem Soc; Am Inst Chemists. *Res:* The synthesis and characterization of metal complexes with organo-phosphoryl, nitryl and -sulfuryl ligands; decomposition of phosphoryl and thiophosphoryl esters in the presence of metal salts; paramagnetic non-metal silicon and phosphorus compounds; synthesis of polymeric metallic conductors. *Mailing Add:* Dept of Chem & Physics Beaver Col Glenside PA 19038

MIKULSKI, JAMES J(OSEPH), b Chicago, Ill, Feb 18, 34; m 59; c 3. ELECTRICAL ENGINEERING. *Educ:* Fournier Inst Technol, BS, 55; Calif Inst Technol, MS, 56; Univ Ill, Urbana, PhD(elec eng), 59. *Prof Exp:* Mem staff, Lincoln Lab, Mass Inst Technol, 59-65; sr staff engr, Mil Electronics Div, 65-68, sect mgr, Commun Res Lab, Commun Div, 68-76, MGR RES, MOTOROLA, INC, 76- *Mem:* Inst Elec & Electronics Engrs. *Res:* Communication theory; signal processing; radar; system and network theory; electromagnetic theory. *Mailing Add:* Dept Res 1301 E Algonquin Schaumburg IL 60196

MIKULSKI, PIOTR W, b Warsaw, Poland, July 20, 25; m 60; c 1. MATHEMATICAL STATISTICS. *Educ:* Sch Planning & Statist, Warsaw Tech Univ, Dipl, 50, MS, 51; Univ Calif, Berkeley, PhD(statist), 61. *Prof Exp:* Adj statist, Sch Planning & Statist, Warsaw Tech Univ, 50-57, Inst Math, Polish Acad Sci, 52-57; asst prof, Univ Ill, Urbana, 61-62; from asst prof to assoc prof, 62-70, PROF STATIST, UNIV MD, COLLEGE PARK, 70- *Mem:* Inst Math Statist. *Res:* Nonparametric methods in statistics; asymptotic optimal properties of statistical procedures. *Mailing Add:* Dept of Math Univ of Md College Park MD 20742

MILAKOFSKY, LOUIS, b Philadelphia, Pa, Feb 21, 41; m 63; c 1. ANALYTICAL PHARMACOLOGY, CHEMICAL EDUCATION. *Educ:* Temple Univ, BA, 62; Univ Wash, PhD(org chem), 67. *Prof Exp:* Chemist, Dupont Co, 62; asst chem, Univ Wash, 62-67; fel & instr, Ind Univ, 67-68; asst prof, Pa State Univ, Scranton, 68-71, ASST PROF CHEM, PA STATE

UNIV, BERKS CAMPUS, 71- *Mem:* Am Chem Soc; Piaget Soc; Nat Sci Teachers Asn; Soc Col Sci Teaching. *Res:* Chemical education and Piaget: a new paper-pencil inventory to assess cognitive functioning; amino acids as stress chemicals. *Mailing Add:* Dept Chem Pa State Univ Berks Campus RD 5 Tulpehocken Rd Reading PA 19608

MILAM, DENVER FRANKLIN, b Charleston, WVa, Aug 23, 19; m 53; c 1. MEDICINE. *Educ:* WVa Univ, AB, 42, BS, 43; Univ Pa, MD, 44; Am Bd Urol, dipl, 54. *Prof Exp:* Asst instr urol, Univ Pa, 45-46 & 48-49, instr, 49-50; instr, Sch Med, Creighton Univ, 50-54; assoc prof, 60-63, PROF UROL, SCH MED, WVA UNIV, 63-, CHMN DEPT, 60- *Mem:* AAAS; Am Urol Asn; fel Am Col Surgeons; Int Soc Urol. *Res:* Genito-urinary surgery; urodynamics; physiology of sex; accessory organs. *Mailing Add:* Dept Urol WVa Univ Med Ctr Morgantown WV 26506

MILAN, FREDERICK ARTHUR, b Waltham, Mass, Mar 10, 24; m 59; c 3. PHYSICAL ANTHROPOLOGY. *Educ:* Univ Alaska, BA, 52; Univ Wis, MS, 59, PhD(anthrop), 62. *Prof Exp:* Observer meteorol, Mt Wash Observ, NH, 43-44, 46-47; observer meteorol, Arctic Sect, US Weather Bur, 47-48; res physiologist, US Air Force Arctic Aeromed Lab, 53-54, 56-57, 59-61; res physiologist, Oper Deepfreeze, Little Am V, Antarctica, 57-58; chief environ protection br, US Air Force Arctic Aeromed Lab, 62-67; assoc scientist-lectr anthrop, Univ Wis-Madison, 67-71; chief behav sci br, Arctic Health Res Ctr, USPHS, 71-73; prof anthrop, 71-73, chem dept, 75-77, PROF HUMAN ECOL & ANTHROP, INST ARCTIC BIOL, UNIV ALASKA, 73- *Concurrent Pos:* Dir, Int Study of Eskimos, US Nat Comt Int Biol Prog, US Nat Acad Sci, DC, 67-; mem, US Man & Biosphere Nat Comt, 77-81, consult panel, Health Prog, Labrador, 79- *Res:* Comparative physiology and human biology of aboriginal populations in polar regions; general anthropology of polar regions; human ecology of arctic populations. *Mailing Add:* Inst Arctic Biol Univ Alaska Fairbanks AK 99701

MILANI, SALVATORE, b Akron, Ohio, Feb 1, 27; m 55; c 2. NUCLEAR PHYSICS. *Educ:* Univ Akron, BS, 50; Ohio State Univ, PhD(physics), 56. *Prof Exp:* Scientist reactor physics, Gen Elec Co, 56; sr scientist reactor exp physics, 57-58, supvr, 58-60, mgr, 60-72, MGR NUCLEAR DESIGN & ANAL, BETTIS ATOMIC POWER LAB, 72- *Mem:* Am Nuclear Soc. *Res:* Reactor experiments, design and analysis. *Mailing Add:* 415 Sequoia Dr Pleasant Hills PA 15236

MILANI, VICTOR JOHN, b Mt Vernon, NY, Sept 26, 45; m 73. MICROBIOLOGY. *Educ:* City Univ New York, BS, 67; NY Univ, MS, 71, PhD(microbiol), 73. *Prof Exp:* Teaching assoc biol, NY Univ, 67-71; asst prof biol, Manhattan Community Col, 71-74; PROF SCI & CHMN DEPT, BAY PATH JR COL, 74- *Concurrent Pos:* Res assoc, Lab Plant Morphogenesis, Manhattan Col, 73-74. *Mem:* AAAS; Am Inst Biol Sci; Am Soc Microbiol; NY Acad Sci; Sigma Xi. *Res:* The effects of concanavalin A on growth and tumor inducing ability of Agrobacterium tumefaciens. *Mailing Add:* Dept of Sci Bay Path Jr Col Longmeadow St Longmeadow MA 01106

MILANO, MICHAEL JOHN, analytical chemistry, see previous edition

MILANOVICH, FRED PAUL, b Rochester, Pa, Nov 22, 44; m 68; c 2. LASER SPECTROSCOPY. *Educ:* US Air Force Acad, BS, 67; Univ Calif, Davis, MS, 68, PhD(appl sci), 74. *Prof Exp:* Proj officer, Air Force Weapons Lab, 68-71; PHYSICIST, LAWRENCE LIVERMORE NAT LAB, 74- *Mem:* Am Chem Soc. *Res:* Application of lasers to biological systems; Raman spectroscopic investigations of macromolecular and membrane structure; macro and micro laser raman spectroscopy with applications in atomic and molecular analysis. *Mailing Add:* PO Box 808 L-524 Livermore CA 94550

MILAZZO, FRANCIS HENRY, b Syracuse, NY, Aug 7, 28; m 56; c 2. MICROBIOLOGY, PHYSIOLOGY. *Educ:* WVa Wesleyan Col, BS; Syracuse Univ, MSc, 53, PhD(microbiol), 60. *Prof Exp:* Res asst bact, microbiol & biochem, Res Inst, Syracuse Univ, 54-60; from asst prof to assoc prof, 60-70, PROF MICROBIOL, QUEEN'S UNIV, ONT, 70- *Mem:* Am Soc Microbiol; Can Soc Microbiol. *Res:* Sulfur metabolism of gram negative bacteria with particular reference to synthesis and control of aryl and alkylsulfatases; study of the chemical structure and biological properties of pseudomonas aeruginosa lipopolysaccharides. *Mailing Add:* Dept of Microbiol & Immunol Queen's Univ Kingston ON K7L 3N6 Can

MILBERG, MORTON EDWIN, b New York, NY, July 21, 26; m 62; c 3. SOLID STATE CHEMISTRY. *Educ:* Rutgers Univ, BS, 46; Cornell Univ, PhD(phys chem), 49. *Prof Exp:* Asst chem, Cornell Univ, 46-48; fel, Univ Minn, 49-50; instr, Univ NDak, 50-52; res chemist, 52-59, supvr phys & inorg chem sect, Chem Dept, 59-61, staff scientist, 61-69, PRIN RES SCIENTIST, SCI LAB, FORD MOTOR CO, 69- *Concurrent Pos:* Chmn, Gordon Res Conf Glassy State, 71; prog chmn, Glass Div, Am Ceramic Soc, 74-75. *Mem:* Am Chem Soc; Am Crystallog Asn; Am Ceramics Soc. *Res:* Structure and properties of noncrystalline solids; diffusion in glass; high temperature ceramic materials. *Mailing Add:* Res Staff Ford Motor Co Box 2053 Dearborn MI 48121

MILBERGER, ERNEST CARL, b Galatia, Kans, Apr 2, 21; m 45; c 2. CHEMISTRY. *Educ:* Univ Mo, AB, 41, MA, 43; Case Western Reserve Univ, PhD(org chem), 57. *Prof Exp:* Chemist, Tex Co, NY, 42-46; sr chemist, 46-60, sect leader, 60-63, SR RES ASSOC, STANDARD OIL CO, 63- *Mem:* Am Chem Soc. *Res:* Petrochemical process research; heterogeneous catalysis. *Mailing Add:* Standard Oil Co 4440 Warrensville Center Rd Cleveland OH 44128

MILBERT, ALFRED NICHOLAS, b Great Lakes, Ill, Aug 28, 46; m 67; c 2. MEDICINAL CHEMISTRY, TOXICOLOGY. *Educ:* Seattle Univ, BS, 71; Univ Kans, MS, 74, PhD(med chem), 76. *Prof Exp:* Proj officer, Pub Health Serv, Nat Inst Occup Safety & Health, 75-81; TOXICOLOGIST, BUR FOODS, FOOD & DRUG ADMIN, 81- *Mem:* AAAS; Am Chem Soc. *Res:* Design and synthesis of biologically active compounds; mechanisms of drug action at the molecular level; product safety evaluation; environmental and occupational health as related to chemical agents. *Mailing Add:* Div Toxicol HFF-159 200 C St SW Washington DC 20204

MILBOCKER, DANIEL CLEMENT, b Gaylord, Mich, May 25, 31; m 59; c 3. HORTICULTURE. *Educ:* Mich State Univ, BS, 65, MS, 66; Pa State Univ, PhD(hort), 69. *Prof Exp:* Asst prof ornamental hort, Univ Ky, 69-74; PLANT PHYSIOLOGIST, VA TRUCK & ORNAMENTALS RES STA, 74- *Mem:* Am Soc Hort Sci; Weed Sci Soc Am. *Res:* Herbicide evaluation for nursery crops; propagation and container culture of ornamental plants; improvement of ornamental species through genetic and cytological research. *Mailing Add:* Va Truck & Ornamentals Res Sta 1444 Diamond Springs Rd Virginia Beach VA 23455

MILBRATH, GENE MCCOY, b Corvallis, Ore, Feb 15, 41; m 64; c 2. PLANT PATHOLOGY. *Educ:* Ore State Univ, BS, 63; Univ Ariz, MS, 66, PhD(plant path), 70. *Prof Exp:* Asst prof plant path, Univ Hawaii, 70-71; asst plant path, Univ Ill, Urbana, 71-77; plant pathologist, Univ Calif, Salinas, 77-78; PLANT PATHOLOGIST, DEPT AGR, SALEM, ORE, 78- *Mem:* Am Phytopath Soc; Int Soc Plant Path. *Res:* Epidemiology of plant viruses; characterization of plant viruses of economic plants; detection of viruses in shade and fruit trees; virus certification of ornamental and fruit trees; diseases of ornamental plants. *Mailing Add:* Plant Div Agr Bldg Dept of Agr Salem OR 97310

MILBURN, NANCY STAFFORD, b Syracuse, NY, Sept 7, 27; m 51; c 2. PHYSIOLOGY, ELECTRON MICROSCOPY. *Educ:* Radcliff Col, AB, 49, PhD, 58; Tufts Univ, MS, 50. *Prof Exp:* Asst, Tufts Univ, 49-52; asst, Harvard Univ, 56-58; from instr to assoc prof, 58-71, actg chmn dept, 67-68, dean, Jackson Col, 72-80, PROF PHYSIOL, TUFTS UNIV, 71-, RES ASSOC NEUROPHYSIOL, 58-, DEAN, LIBERAL ARTS & JACKSON COL, 80- *Concurrent Pos:* Mem, Nat Res Coun; chmn, Coun Int Exchange of Scholars, 78-81; trustee, Radcliffe Col, 77- & Corp Woods Hole Oceanog Inst, 81-; coordr, New Eng Region, Am Coun Educ Nat Identification Proj for Women Adminr, 77-80. *Mem:* Am Soc Zool; Am Physiol Soc; fel AAAS; Am Soc Cell Biol; Entom Soc Am. *Res:* Neurophysiology, especially synaptic transmission, neurohormones and synaptic transmitters; electron microscopy of insect nervous system, receptor organs and effectors. *Mailing Add:* Dept Biol Tufts Univ Medford MA 02155

MILBURN, RICHARD HENRY, b Newark, NJ, June 3, 28; m 51; c 2. ELEMENTARY PARTICLE PHYSICS. *Educ:* Harvard Univ, AB, 48, AM, 51, PH PhD(physics), 54. *Prof Exp:* Instr physics, Harvard Univ, 54 & 56-57, asst prof, 57-61; assoc prof, 61-65, PROF PHYSICS, TUFTS UNIV, 65- *Concurrent Pos:* Guggenheim fel, Orgn Europ Res Nucleaire, Geneva, 60; prin investr, 78- *Mem:* AAAS; Am Phys Soc; Am Asn Physics Teachers. *Res:* Physics of elementary particles; lasers. *Mailing Add:* Dept of Physics Tufts Univ Medford MA 02155

MILBURN, RONALD MCRAE, b Wellington, NZ, May 29, 28; m 55. INORGANIC CHEMISTRY. *Educ:* Victoria Univ, BSc, 49, MSc, 51; Duke Univ, PhD(chem), 54. *Prof Exp:* Demonstr chem, Victoria Univ, NZ, 51-52; asst, Duke Univ, 52-54; lectr, Victoria Univ, NZ, 55; res assoc, Univ Chicago, 56-57; from asst prof to assoc prof, 57-68, PROF CHEM, BOSTON UNIV, 68- *Concurrent Pos:* Fulbright grant, 52; instr & res assoc, Duke Univ, 54 & 56; NIH fel, Oxford Univ, 65-66; vis fel, Australian Nat Univ, 74-75. *Mem:* Am Chem Soc. *Res:* Reactions and stabilities of complex ions; mechanisms of inorganic reactions; reactions of phosphate esters and polyphosphates. *Mailing Add:* Dept of Chem Boston Univ Boston MA 02215

MILBY, THOMAS HUTCHINSON, b South Bend, Ind, Feb 7, 31; m 53; c 3. OCCUPATIONAL MEDICINE, TOXICOLOGY. *Educ:* Purdue Univ, BS, 53; Univ Cincinnati, MD, 57, MS, 65; Univ Calif, Berkeley, MPH, 66; Am Bd Prev Med, dipl & cert occup med, 66. *Prof Exp:* Intern med, Ohio State Univ Hosp, 58; med officer, Div Occup Health, USPHS, 59-62; med officer, Bur Occup Health, Calif State Dept Pub Health, 62-66, chief, 66-73; CONSULT OCCUP MED, TOXICOL & EPIDEMIOL, 73- *Concurrent Pos:* Mem comn pesticides & environ health, Secy Health, Educ & Welfare, 69; mem study sect, Nat Inst Occup Safety & Health, 69-72; spec consult, WHO, 70; assoc prof, Sch Pub Health, Univ Calif, Berkeley, 70-; chmn task group on occup exposure to pesticides, Fed Working Group on Pest Mgt, Nat Inst Occup Safety & Health, 72-74. *Mem:* Fel Am Occup Med Asn; fel Am Acad Occup Med. *Res:* Toxicology and epidemiology and chemical-related diseases. *Mailing Add:* 524 Woodmont Ave Berkeley CA 94708

MILCH, LAWRENCE JACQUES, b New York, NY, Sept 5, 18; m 42; c 4. PHARMACOLOGY, BIOCHEMISTRY. *Educ:* Univ Iowa, AB, 40; Rutgers Univ, PhD(physiol, biochem), 50. *Prof Exp:* Biophysicist, US Air Force Sch Aviation Med, 50-55, chief dept pharmacol & biochem, 55-59, dep comdr, 6102 Air Base Wing, Yakota Air Base, 59-61, head space biophys task group, Univ Calif, Berkeley, 61-62; staff res dir, Miles Labs, 62-66; asst res dir, Human Health Res & Develop Div, Dow Chem, USA, 66-71, dir develop, Zionsville, Ind, 72-73; instr physiol & biochem, Butler Univ, 73-76; INSTR PHARMACOL, YAVAPAI COL, CLARKDALE, 77- *Mem:* Am Soc Pharmacol & Exp Therapeut. *Res:* Coronary artery disease; traumatic injury; biophysical instrumentation; drug mechanisms; toxicology. *Mailing Add:* M J Lawrence Mem Hosp PO Box 548 Cottonwood AZ 86326

MILCH, PAUL R, b Budapest, Hungary, May 1, 34; US citizen; m 62; c 2. OPERATIONS RESEARCH, STATISTICS. *Educ:* Brown Univ, BS, 57; Stanford Univ, PhD(statist), 66. *Prof Exp:* ASSOC PROF OPERS RES DEPT, NAVAL POSTGRAD SCH, 63- *Concurrent Pos:* Statistician, Data Dynamics Inc, Calif, 65-66; opers analyst, Mellonics Inc, Litton Industs, 68-70 & BDM, Calif, 71-75. *Mem:* Am Statist Asn; Int Studies Asn; Opers Res Soc Am. *Res:* Probability theory; queueing theory; stochastic processes; reliability; birth and death processes; manpower problems; quantitative political science. *Mailing Add:* Dept of Opers Res Naval Postgrad Sch Monterey CA 93950

MILDER, JACK WALTER, b Chicago, Ill, May, 21, 25; m 52; c 2. INTERNAL MEDICINE. *Educ:* Univ Notre Dame, BS, 48; Northwestern Univ, BS, 50, MD, 51. *Prof Exp:* Resident internal med, Hines Vet Admin Hosp, Ill, 51-54; pvt pract, Ill, 54-57; exec secy surg study sect, Div Res Grants, NIH, 57-58; RES ADMINR, AM CANCER SOC, 58- *Concurrent Pos:* Consutl, St Mary's Hosp, Kankakee, Ill, 54-57. *Mem:* AAAS; NY Acad Sci. *Res:* Therapy and diagnosis of cancer; biochemical approach to mechanisms of action and metabolism of chemotherapeutic agents; immunologic approach to cancer. *Mailing Add:* American Cancer Soc 777 Third Ave New York NY 10017

MILDVAN, ALBERT S, b Philadelphia, Pa, Mar 3, 32; m 57; c 3. BIOPHYSICS, ENZYMOLOGY. *Educ:* Univ Pa, AB, 53; Johns Hopkins Univ, MD, 57. *Prof Exp:* Intern med, Baltimore City Hosps, Md, 57-58; res assoc cell physiol, Geront Br, NIH, 58-60; NIH res fel biochem, Inst Animal Physiol, Cambridge, Eng, 60-62; NIH res fel biophys, 62-64, assoc, 64-65, from asst prof to assoc prof phys biochem, 65-74, assoc mem, Inst, 68-73, mem, Inst Cancer Res, 73-81, PROF PHYS BIOCHEM, JOHNSON FOUND, SCH MED, UNIV PA, 74-, MEM, INST CANCER RES, 73-; JPROF PHYSIOL CHEM & CHEM, SCH MED, JOHNS HOPKINS UNIV, 81- *Concurrent Pos:* Advan fel, Am Heart Asn, 63-65, estab investr, 65-70, mem coun basic sci, 71-; NIH res grant, 65-; NSF res grant, 65; mem adv panel molecular biol, NSF, 71-74. *Mem:* Am Soc Biol Chemists; Brit Biochem Soc. *Res:* mechanisms of enzymes action and metal activation of enzymes. *Mailing Add:* Inst for Cancer Res 7701 Burholme Ave Philadelphia PA 19111

MILES, CHARLES BURKE, b Salt Lake City, Utah, Jan 2, 15; m 36; c 2. CHEMISTRY. *Educ:* Univ Utah, BA, 35; Purdue Univ, PhD(phys chem), 40. *Prof Exp:* Anal chemist, Kalunite, Inc, Utah, 35-36; asst, Purdue Univ, 37-40; res chemist, US Rubber Co, Mich, 40-41; group leader, Pa Salt Mfg Co, 41-43; group leader, Magnolia Petrol Co, Tex, 43-46; dir res & develop, Newark Sect, Westvaco Chem Div, Food Mach & Chem Corp, 46-54, res dir, Westvaco Mineral Prods Div, 54-58, asst res dir, Inorg Chem Dept, 58-60; tech dir, Chem Res Div, Socony Mobil Oil Co, 60, mgr res & develop dept, Mobil Chem Co Div, 60-63; tech adv to pres, Kaiser Aluminum & Chem Corp, 63-64, corp tech dir, 64-68, tech adv, Patent Dept, 68-71, sr res assoc, 71-80; RETIRED. *Mem:* Am Chem Soc. *Res:* Inorganic chemicals; fluorides; phosphorus; magnesia; barium; thermochemistry; research and development administration and planning. *Mailing Add:* 42 Diamond Dr Danville CA 94526

MILES, CHARLES DAVID, b Kansas City, Mo, Aug 11, 26; m 53; c 2. INVERTEBRATE ZOOLOGY. *Educ:* Univ Kans, AB, 50, MA, 56; Univ Ariz, PhD(zool), 61. *Prof Exp:* Asst prof biol, Eureka Col, 61-64; from asst prof to assoc prof, 64-72, PROF ZOOL, UNIV MO-KANSAS CITY, 72- *Mem:* Am Malacol union; Sigma Xi. *Res:* Land snail taxonomy and distribution; anatomy; physiology. *Mailing Add:* Dept of Biol Univ of Mo 5100 Rockhill Rd Kansas City MO 64110

MILES, CHARLES DONALD, b Franklin, Ind, Dec 17, 38; m 66; c 1. PLANT PHYSIOLOGY. *Educ:* Franklin Col, AB, 63; Indiana Univ, PhD(bot), 67. *Prof Exp:* NIH fel plant biochem, Cornell Univ, 67-69; asst prof, 69-75, assoc prof bot, 75-80, PROF BIOL SCI, UNIV MO-COLUMBIA, 80- *Mem:* AAAS; Am Soc Plant Physiol; Bot Soc Am; Am Inst Biol Sci; Phytochem Soc NAm. *Res:* Development and control of pigmentation in higher plants; mechanism of photosynthetic phosphorylation and electron transport; chloroplast fluorescence and luminescence; analysis of photosynthesis with genetic mutants of maize; genetics of photosynthesis and chloroplasts. *Mailing Add:* Div of Biol Univ of Mo Columbia MO 65211

MILES, CHARLES P, b Chicago, Ill, June 19, 22; m 54; c 3. PATHOLOGY, CYTOLOGY. *Educ:* Univ Calif, Berkeley, BA, 47; Univ Calif, San Francisco, MD, 53; Am Bd Path, dipl, 59. *Prof Exp:* Bank Am-Giannini Found fel, 55-56; Nat Cancer Inst fel, 57-58; asst prof in residence nuclear med & radiation biol, Univ Calif, Los Angeles, 58-59; from instr to asst prof path, Stanford Univ, 59-62; assoc, Sloan-Kettering Inst, 62-66; assoc prof, Univ Utah, 66-69; assoc prof, Univ Calif, San Francisco, 69-70; PROF PATH, UNIV UTAH, 70- *Concurrent Pos:* Asst attend pathologist, Mem Hosp, NY, 62-66. *Mem:* Am Soc Exp Path; Am Asn Path & Bact; Am Asn Cancer Res; Soc Human Genetics. *Res:* Cytology analysis in cancer and in tissue culture strains. *Mailing Add:* Dept of Path Univ of Utah Salt Lake City UT 84132

MILES, CORBIN I, b Detroit, Mich, Feb 5, 40; m 60; c 4. ANALYTICAL CHEMISTRY. *Educ:* Northwestern Mo State Col, Bs, 62; Wayne State Univ, MS, 69, PhD(chem), 71. *Prof Exp:* Chemist method develop res & qual control, Detroit, Minneapolis & Kansas City dist labs, 62-72, consumer safety officer, 72-75, CHIEF GENERALLY RECOGNIZED AS SAFE REV BR, BUR FOOD, FOOD & DRUG ADMIN, 75- *Concurrent Pos:* Instr chem, Wayne County Community Col, 71-72; prin investr safety re-eval food ingredients classified as generally recognized as safe, Food & Drug Admin, 75- *Mem:* Am Chem Soc; Asn Off Anal Chemists. *Res:* Technical safety of ingredients used in human foods in the United States. *Mailing Add:* Food & Drug Admin Bur Foods 200 C St SW Washington DC 20204

MILES, DAVID H, b Price, Utah, Apr 19, 28; m 52; c 11. ORGANIC CHEMISTRY, COMPUTER SCIENCE. *Educ:* Brigham Young Univ, BS, 53; Iowa State Univ, PhD(org chem), 57. *Prof Exp:* Fel dairy chem & gas chromatography, Iowa State Univ, 57-58; res chemist, PPG Ind, Inc, Chem Div, 58-60; from asst prof to prof chem, Brigham Young Univ, Hawaii Campus, 60-73; special instr comput sci, Brigham Young Univ, 73-76; comput analyst, Utah County, Utah, 76-77; PROF CHEM, BRIGHAM YOUNG UNIV, HAWAII CAMPUS, 77- *Concurrent Pos:* NSF fac fel, 66-67. *Mem:* Am Chem Soc; Asn Develop of Computer-Based Instrnl Systs. *Res:* Reaction of epoxides and organometallic compounds and computers in chemistry. *Mailing Add:* Brigham Young Univ PO Box 132 Laie HI 96762

MILES, DELBERT HOWARD, b Warrior, Ala, Jan 4, 43; m 63; c 2. SYNTHETIC ORGANIC CHEMISTRY. *Educ:* Birmingham-Southern Col, BS, 65; Ga Inst Technol, PhD(org chem), 70. *Prof Exp:* NIH res fel org chem, Stanford Univ, 69-70; asst prof, 70-74, assoc prof, 74-78, coordr chem sci grad prog, 76-81, PROF CHEM, MISS STATE UNIV, 78- *Mem:* Am Soc Pharmacog; Phytochem Soc NAm; Am Pharmaceut Asn; Am Chem Soc; Sigma Xi. *Res:* Isolation, structure elucidation and synthesis of natural products which exhibit biological activity of some type or which possess some biosynthetic significance. *Mailing Add:* Dept of Chem Miss State Univ State College MS 39762

MILES, DONALD ORVAL, b Callaway, Nebr, May 29, 39; m 60; c 1. MEDICAL MICROBIOLOGY. *Educ:* Hastings Col, BA, 64; Univ Nebr, Lincoln, MS, 67, PhD(microbiol), 72. *Prof Exp:* Asst lectr biol, Univ Nebr, Lincoln, 70-71, instr med bact, 72; asst prof microbiol, Sch Health Sci, Grand Valley State Cols, 73-76; clin microbiologist & chief sect microbiol & immunoserol, Dept Path, St Mary's Hosp, 76-81; CLIN MICROBIOLOGIST, ST FRANCIS MED CTR, 81- *Concurrent Pos:* Res assoc, Dept Microbiol, Univ Nebr, Lincoln, 71 & Dept Oral Biol, Col Dent, 73; clin microbiologist & microbiol consult, Dept Path, Microbiol Lab, St Mary's Hosp, Grand Rapids, 74-76, mem infection control comt & assoc mem med & dent staff, 75-81. *Mem:* Am Soc Microbiol; Sigma Xi. *Res:* Amino acid metabolism of gram negative non-spore forming anaerobes; periplasmic enzymes of gram negative bacilli; microbiology of infection control in hospitals. *Mailing Add:* Lab Div St Francis Med Ctr Cape Girardean MO 63701

MILES, ERNEST PERCY, JR, b Birmingham, Ala, Mar 16, 19; m 45; c 2. MATHEMATICS. *Educ:* Birmingham-Southern Col, BA, 37; Duke Univ, MA, 39, PhD(math), 49. *Prof Exp:* Teacher high sch, Ala, 38-39; instr math, NC State Col, 40-41; assoc prof, Ala Polytech Inst, 49-58; mem staff, Nat Sci Found, 58; assoc prof math, 58-61, dir comput ctr, 61-71, PROF MATH, FLA STATE UNIV, 61- *Concurrent Pos:* Vis assoc prof & Air Force Off Sci Res contract, Inst Fluid Dynamics & Appl Math, Univ Md, 57-58; participant, Nat Sci Found Training Prog Numerical Anal, Nat Bur Standards, 59; res grants, Air Force Off Sci Res, 60-61, Nat Sci Found, 62-72; consult, Nat Sci Found, 59-63, 65-70 & US Off Educ, 65-71; coun mem, Conf Bd Math Socs, 74- *Mem:* Fel AAAS; Am Math Soc; Math Asn Am; Asn Comput Mach; Soc Indust & Appl Math. *Res:* Partial differential equations; numerical methods; information retrieval; computer uses in education. *Mailing Add:* Dept of Math Fla State Univ Tallahassee FL 32306

MILES, FRANK BELSLEY, b Champaign, Ill, May 15, 40; m 66; c 2. MATHEMATICS. *Educ:* Univ Ill, BS, 61; Univ Calif, Berkeley, PhD(chem), 65; Univ Wash, MS, 70, PhD(math), 72. *Prof Exp:* NIH fel, Univ Calif, Los Angeles, 64-65; asst prof chem, Univ Calif, Santa Barbara, 65-68; NSF fel, Univ Wash, 69-71, instr math, 71, res asst, 71-72; asst prof, 72-76, assoc prof, 76-81, PROF MATH, CALIF STATE UNIV, DOMINGUEZ HILLS, 81- *Mem:* Am Math Soc; Math Asn Am. *Res:* Harmonic analysis. *Mailing Add:* Dept Math Calif State Univ Dominguez Hills CA 90747

MILES, GEORGE BENJAMIN, b Erin, Tenn, May 14, 26; m 56; c 1. ORGANIC CHEMISTRY. *Educ:* Univ Tenn, BS, 50, PhD(chem), 58. *Prof Exp:* Chemist, US Naval Ord Lab, 53-54; instr chem, Univ Tenn, 57-58; res chemist, Dacron Res Lab, Textile Fibers Dept, E I du Pont de Nemours & Co, 58-61; from asst prof to assoc prof, 61-69, chmn dept chem, 69-77, PROF CHEM, APPALACHIAN STATE UNIV, 77- *Mem:* Am Chem Soc. *Res:* Polymer and steroid chemistry; organic mechanisms. *Mailing Add:* Dept of Chem Appalachian State Univ Boone NC 28608

MILES, HARRY V(ICTOR), b Columbus, Ohio, Nov 8, 14; m 50; c 2. CHEMICAL ENGINEERING. *Educ:* Ohio State Univ, BChE, 36. *Prof Exp:* Appl engr, Airtemp Div, Chrysler Corp, Ohio, 36-39; sales engr, Infilco, Inc, Ill, 39-44; staff engr, Garfield Div, Houdaille-Hershey Corp, Ill, 44-46, mgr res & develop, Honan-Crane Div, Ind, 46-50; mgr res & develop, US Hoffman Mach Corp, NY, 50-53; asst dir res & develop, Oliver United Filters Inc, 53-56, asst dir res, 56-59, filtration develop engr, 59-62, mgr pulp & paper technol, 62-71; dir tech admin, Dorr-Oliver Inc, 71-80; RETIRED. *Mem:* Am Inst Chem Engrs. *Res:* Pulp and paper technology; filtration; equipment design; research and development administration; air and water conditioning. *Mailing Add:* 7579 Estrella Circle Boca Raton FL 33433

MILES, HENRY HARCOURT WATERS, b Burnside, La, Sept 18, 15; m 39; c 2. PSYCHIATRY, PSYCHOANALYSIS. *Educ:* Tulane Univ, BS, 36, MD, 39. *Prof Exp:* Res fel psychiat, Harvard Med Sch, 46-48; asst, Harvard Univ & Mass Gen Hosp, 49-52; from asst prof to assoc prof clin psychiat, 52-66, PROF PSYCHIAT, SCH MED, TULANE UNIV, 66- *Concurrent Pos:* Training & supv analyst, New Orleans Psychoanal Inst, 56-; consult, Family Serv Soc New Orleans, 57-64. *Mem:* Am Psychosom Soc; AMA; fel Am Psychiat Asn; Am Psychoanal Asn. *Res:* Evaluation of psychotherapy; personality factors in cardiovascular diseases. *Mailing Add:* 1446 Arabella St New Orleans LA 70115

MILES, JAMES LOWELL, b Buckhannon, WVa, Aug 15, 37; m 68. CHEMISTRY, BIOCHEMISTRY. *Educ:* WVa Univ, BS, 59, MS, 61, PhD(biochem), 64. *Prof Exp:* Trainee clin chem, Hosp Univ Pa, 64-65; RES BIOCHEMIST, E I DU PONT DE NEMOURS & CO, INC, WILMINGTON, 66- *Mem:* Am Chem Soc; Am Asn Clin Chemists. *Res:* Alpha-chymotrypsin; clinical and analytical chemistry; enzyme assay systems; lipoprotein electrophoresis. *Mailing Add:* 44 Quartz Mill Rd Newark DE 19711

MILES, JAMES S, b Baltimore, Md, Apr 16, 21; m 44; c 4. MEDICINE. *Educ:* Grinnell Col, AB, 42; Univ Chicago, MD, 45; Am Bd Orthop Surg, dipl, 54. *Prof Exp:* Intern, Univ Clins, Sch Med, Univ Chicago, 45-46, resident, 48-51, instr orthop, 51-52; from instr to assoc prof orthop surg, 52-65, chmn div, 58-73, actg chmn dept orthop, 73-74, PROF ORTHOP SURG, SCH MED, UNIV COLO, DENVER, 65-, CHMN DEPT ORTHOP, 74- *Concurrent*

Pos: Am Orthop Asn traveling fel, 59; consult, Vet Admin Hosp, Denver, Colo & Fitzsimons Army Hosp, Denver. *Mem:* Orthop Res Soc; fel Am Col Surgeons; Am Acad Orthop Surg; Am Orthop Asn; Clin Orthop Soc. *Res:* Histochemistry of articular cartilage; vascular supply of femoral head. *Mailing Add:* Dept of Orthop Univ of Colo Sch of Med Denver CO 80262

MILES, JAMES WILLIAM, b Henderson, Ky, Sept 19, 18; m 51; c 1. PESTICIDE CHEMISTRY. *Educ:* Western Ky Univ, BS, 40; Univ Ill, MS, 47, PhD(anal chem), 53. *Prof Exp:* Instr chem, Louisville Col Pharm, 41-42; from asst prof to assoc prof, Univ Ky, 47-55, prof pharmaceut chem & head dept, 55-58; asst chief, Chem Sect, Tech Develop Lab, 58-64, chief chem sect, Tech Develop labs, Commun Dis Ctr, 64-74, CHIEF PESTICIDES BR, BUR OF TROP DIS, CTR FOR DIS CONTROL, USPHS, 74- *Concurrent Pos:* Mem expert adv panel on insecticides, WHO, 71-, mem sci & tech adv comt, WHO Onchocerciasis Control Prog, 74- *Honors & Awards:* Superior Serv Award, USPHS, 78. *Mem:* Am Chem Soc; Sigma Xi. *Res:* development of methods of analysis of pesticide residues in the environment; research on pesticide formulations and analysis of formulations. *Mailing Add:* Bur of Trop Dis Ctr for Dis Control USPHS Atlanta GA 30333

MILES, JOHN B(RUCE), b St Louis, Mo, Feb 2, 33; m 58; c 2. MECHANICAL ENGINEERING, FLUID DYNAMICS. *Educ:* Mo Sch Mines, BS, 55, MS, 57; Univ Ill, PhD(mech eng, fluid flow), 63. *Prof Exp:* Instr eng mech, Univ Mo-Rolla, 55-58; from instr to asst prof appl sci, Univ Southern Ill, 58-63; assoc prof mech eng, 63-68, PROF MECH ENG, UNIV MO-COLUMBIA, 68- *Concurrent Pos:* NSF, NASA & US Air Force res grants, 65-; Ford Found eng residency, Gen Elec Co, 65-66; Nat Res Coun sr res assoc, Ames Res Ctr, NASA, 71; vis prof, Dept Aeronaut & Astronaut, Stanford Univ, 71; sabbatical leave, Solar Energy Res Inst, 81. *Mem:* Am Soc Mech Engrs; Am Soc Eng Educ; Am Inst Aeronaut & Astronaut; Sigma Xi. *Res:* Fluid flow and heat transfer, especially separated flow, jet mixing and turbulence; bio-heat transfer as applied to temperature control in liquid cooled garments; jet mixing studies using a laser velocimeter. *Mailing Add:* Dept Mech & Aerospace Eng Univ Mo Columbia MO 65201

MILES, JOHN WILDER, b Cincinnati, Ohio, Dec 1, 20; m 43; c 3. GEOPHYSICS. *Educ:* Calif Inst Technol, BS, 42, MS, 43, PhD(elec eng), 44. *Prof Exp:* Staff mem radiation lab, Mass Inst Technol, 44; res eng, Lockheed Aircraft Corp, Calif, 44-45; from asst prof to prof eng, Univ Calif, Los Angeles, 45-55, prof eng & geophys, 55-61; prof appl math, Inst Adv Studies, Australian Nat Univ, 62-64; chmn appl mech & eng sci, 68-74, chmn, Acad Senate, 77-78, PROF APPL MECH & GEOPHYS, UNIV CALIF, SAN DIEGO, 65-, VCHANCELLOR ACAD AFFAIRS, 80- *Concurrent Pos:* Fulbright lectr, Univ NZ, 51; vis lectr, Univ London, 52; Guggenheim fel, 58-59 & 68-69; Fulbright res fel, Cambridge Univ, 69. *Mem:* Nat Acad Sci; fel Am Inst Aeronaut & Astronaut; Fedn Am Sci; AAAS; Am Geophys Union. *Res:* Wave propagation and generation; hydrodynamic stability; geophysical fluid mechanics. *Mailing Add:* Inst Geophys & Planetary Physics Univ of Calif at San Diego La Jolla CA 92093

MILES, JOSEPH BELSLEY, b Champaign, Ill, June 17, 42; m 70. MATHEMATICS. *Educ:* Univ Ill, BS, 63; Univ Wis, MS, 64, PhD(math), 68. *Prof Exp:* Res assoc, Cornell Univ, 68-69; from asst prof to assoc prof, 69-79, PROF MATH, UNIV ILL, URBANA, 79- *Concurrent Pos:* Off Naval Res fel, Cornell Univ, 68-69; res assoc, Univ Md, 75-76. *Mem:* Am Math Soc. *Res:* Functions of a complex variable. *Mailing Add:* Dept of Math Univ of Ill Urbana IL 61801

MILES, MARION LAWRENCE, b Columbus, Ga, Sept 5, 29; m 56; c 3. ORGANIC CHEMISTRY. *Educ:* Univ Ga, BS, 57, MS, 59; Univ Fla, PhD(org chem), 63. *Prof Exp:* Fel, Duke Univ, 63-64; asst prof, 65-69, ASSOC PROF ORG CHEM, NC STATE UNIV, 69- & DIR ORG LABS, 77- *Mem:* Am Chem Soc. *Res:* Physical properties of multiple carbanions; mechanisms of condensation reactions. *Mailing Add:* Dept of Chem NC State Univ Raleigh NC 27650

MILES, MAURICE HOWARD, b St George, Utah, Nov 20, 33; m 60; c 2. SOLID STATE PHYSICS. *Educ:* Univ Utah, BS, 55, PhD(physics), 63. *Prof Exp:* Res assoc metall, Univ Ill, 63-65; ASST PROF PHYSICS, WASH STATE UNIV, 65- *Mem:* Am Phys Soc. *Res:* Internal friction in metals; electronic properties of dislocations in semiconductors. *Mailing Add:* Dept of Physics Wash State Univ Pullman WA 99163

MILES, MAURICE JARVIS, b St George, Utah, Nov 24, 07; m 31; c 11. ANALYTICAL CHEMISTRY, ENVIRONMENTAL CHEMISTRY. *Educ:* Brigham Young Univ, AB, 30; Univ Utah, MA, 33. *Prof Exp:* Dir phys sci, Dixie Jr Col, 33-53; chief chemist, Titanium Metals Corp Am, 53-70; res assoc, Desert Res Inst, Univ Nev Syst, 70-80; CONSULT, TITANIUM METALS CORP AM, 80- *Concurrent Pos:* Consult, US Bur Mines, Boulder City, 74-80. *Mem:* AAAS; Am Chem Soc; Am Soc Test & Mat. *Res:* Corrosion rate of selected metals and alloys in Lake Mead water; rapid x-ray ion-exchange analyses of titanium alloys; water pollution analyses related to Lake Mead; trace metals in geothermal waters; trace metals in soils; atmospheric dusts; state of the art in industrial ponding of effluents. *Mailing Add:* 135 Elm St Henderson NV 89015

MILES, MELVIN HENRY, b St George, Utah, Jan 18, 37; m 62; c 3. ELECTROCHEMISTRY, PHYSICAL CHEMISTRY. *Educ:* Brigham Young Univ, BA, 62; Univ Utah, PhD(phys chem), 66. *Prof Exp:* NATO res fel electrochem, Munich Tech, 65-66; res chemist, Naval Weapons Ctr, 67-69; asst prof, 69-72, ASSOC PROF CHEM, MID TENN STATE UNIV, 72- *Mem:* Electrochem Soc; Am Inst Chem; Sigma Xi. *Res:* Fast reaction kinetics; electrode kinetics; electrochemical energy conversion; electrode catalysis; fuel cells; viscosity; specific conductivity; water electrolysis; properties of mixed solvents; hydrogen production; oxygen electrode reaction. *Mailing Add:* Mid Tenn State Univ Box 323 Murfreesboro TN 37130

MILES, NEIL WAYNE, b River Falls, Wis, June 22, 37; m 59; c 2. HORTICULTURE, PLANT PHYSIOLOGY. *Educ:* Univ Minn, BS, 59, MS, 64, PhD(hort), 65. *Prof Exp:* Exten horticulturist, Univ Minn, St Paul, 65-66; POMOLOGIST, KANS STATE UNIV, 66- *Mem:* Am Soc Hort Sci; Am Pomol Soc. *Res:* Physiological studies on fruit crops. *Mailing Add:* Dept of Hort & Forestry Kans State Univ Waters Hall Manhattan KS 66506

MILES, PHILIP GILTNER, b Olean, NY, Aug 10, 22; m 49; c 3. BOTANY. *Educ:* Yale Univ, BA, 48; Indiana Univ, PhD(bot), 53. *Prof Exp:* Res assoc bot, Univ Chicago, 53-54; res fel, Harvard Univ, 54-56; from asst prof to assoc prof, 56-70, PROF BIOL, STATE UNIV NY BUFFALO, 70- *Concurrent Pos:* Fulbright res scholar, Japan, 63-64; vis scientist, US-China Coop Sci Prog, 70-71; vis prof, Nat Taiwan Univ, 70-71 & 77-78. *Mem:* AAAS; Bot Soc Am; Genetics Soc Am; Mycol Soc Am; Soc Study Evolution. *Res:* Genetics and physiology of sexual mechanisms in fungi. *Mailing Add:* Dept of Biol State Univ NY Buffalo NY 14214

MILES, RALPH FRALEY, JR, b Philadelphia, Pa, May 15, 33. PHYSICS, SYSTEMS DESIGNS. *Educ:* Calif Inst Technol, BS, 55, MS, 60, PhD(physics), 63. *Prof Exp:* Sr engr, Jet Propulsion Lab, 63-65, supvr syst eng, 65-69; vis fel econ systs, Stanford Univ, 69-70; vis asst prof aeronaut & environ eng sci, Calif Inst Technol, 70-71; mgr, Mission Anal & Eng, Outer Planets Missions, 71-75, supvr oper res, 75-82, MEM TECH STAFF, JET PROPULSION LAB, 82- *Mem:* AAAS; Opers Res Soc Soc Am. *Res:* Density of cosmic ray neutrons in the atmosphere; systems analysis; design analysis. *Mailing Add:* 3608 Canon Blvd Altadena CA 91001

MILES, RANDALL JAY, b Crawfordsville, Ind, Oct 27, 52; m 75. SOIL MANAGEMENT. *Educ:* Purdue Univ, BS, 74, MS, 76; Tex A&M Univ, PhD(soils), 81. *Prof Exp:* Instr, Tex A&M Univ, 76-81; ASST PROF SOILS TEACHING, UNIV TENN, 81- *Mem:* Am Soc Agron; Soil Conservation Soc Am; Sigma Xi; Nat Asn Col Teachers Agr. *Res:* Use of soil survey for soil management applications with special emphasis on production agriculture; soil erosion; soil varicability; soil genesis. *Mailing Add:* Box 1071 Plant & Soil Sci Dept Univ Tenn Knoxville TN 37996

MILES, RICHARD DAVID, b Bunkie, La, Oct 29, 47; m 76. EGG SHELL QUALITY, AMINO ACID METABOLISM. *Educ:* Univ Ark, BS, 71, MS, 72; Purdue Univ, PhD(poultry nutrit), 76. *Prof Exp:* Asst prof, 76-81, ASSOC PROF POULTRY NUTRIT, POLUTRY SCI DEPT, UNIV FLA, 81- *Mem:* Poultry Sci Asn; Sigma Xi. *Res:* Dietary mineral interrelattionships in laying hens; egg shell quality; influence of antibiotics and probiotics in laying hens, broilers, quail and turkeys; amino acid and nitrogen metabolism in poultry. *Mailing Add:* Poultry Sci Dept Univ Fla Archer Rd Gainesville FL 32611

MILES, ROBERT D(OUGLAS), b Bloomfield, Ind, Dec 23, 24; m 46; c 1. CIVIL ENGINEERING. *Educ:* Purdue Univ, BS, 49, MS, 51. *Prof Exp:* Asst, 49-50, from instr airphoto interpretation to assoc prof civil eng & airphoto interpretation, 50-68, PROF CIVIL ENG & AIRPHOTO INTERPRETATION, PURDUE UNIV, 68- *Mem:* Am Soc Eng Educ; Am Soc Photogram; Nat Soc Prof Engrs; Am Soc Civil Engrs. *Res:* Airphoto interpretation and site selection; aerial surveys for planning civil engineering projects and regional planning programs to include natural resources inventories. *Mailing Add:* Joint Hwy Res Proj Sch of Civil Eng Purdue Univ West Lafayette IN 47907

MILES, WYNDHAM DAVIES, b Wilkes-Barre, Pa, Nov 21, 16; m 52; c 4. HISTORY OF CHEMISTRY. *Educ:* Philadelphia Col Pharm, BS, 42; Pa State Univ, MS, 44; Harvard Univ, PhD(hist of sci), 55. *Prof Exp:* Instr chem, Pa State Univ, 44-50, asst prof, 52-53; historian, US Army Chem Corps, 53-60; specialist in sci, Nat Arch, 60-61; historian, Polaris Proj, 61-62; HISTORIAN, NIH, 62- *Honors & Awards:* Dexter Award in Hist of Chem, 71. *Mem:* Am Chem Soc. *Res:* History of American chemistry. *Mailing Add:* 24 Walker Ave Gaithersburg MD 20877

MILEWICH, LEON, b Buenos Aires, Arg, Mar 26, 27; US citizen; m 59; c 3. ORGANIC CHEMISTRY. *Educ:* Univ Buenos Aires, BS, 56, MS, 58, PhD(org chem), 59. *Prof Exp:* Chemist, Res Inst Armed Forces, Arg, 55-58, res chemist, 60-61; fel, Sch Pharm, Univ Md, 61-64; fel, Sch Med, Johns Hopkins Univ, 64-66, instr gynec & obstet, 66-67; res assoc, Southwest Found Res & Educ, 67-72; asst prof, 72-77, ASSOC PROF, DEPT OBSTET & GYNEC, UNIV TEX SOUTHWESTERN MED SCH DALLAS, 77- *Concurrent Pos:* NIH fel, 63-64. *Mem:* AAAS; Am Chem Soc; Royal Soc Chem; Arg Chem Asn; NY Acad Sci. *Res:* Steroids. *Mailing Add:* Dept Obstet & Gynec Univ Tex Southwestern Med Sch Dallas TX 75235

MILEWSKI, JOHN VINCENT, b Suffern, NY, Nov 4, 28; m 52; c 3. CERAMICS ENGINEERING, MATERIALS SCIENCE. *Educ:* Univ Notre Dame, BSChE, 51; Stevens Inst Technol, MS, 59; Rutgers Univ, PhD(ceramic eng), 72. *Prof Exp:* Sr mat engr, Thiokol Chem Corp, 51-61; proj engr, Curtiss-Wright Corp, 61-62; vpres, Thermokinetic Fibers, 63-68; res assoc mat res, Exxon Res & Eng Co, 68-77; STAFF ENGR, LOS ALAMOS SCI LAB, 77- *Mem:* Am Ceramic Soc; Am Soc Testing & Mat; Soc Plastics Indust. *Res:* High strength materials; growth of single crystal whiskers; development of production processes for whiskers; theory of application of whiskers; short fibers; fiber packing concepts; fillers for plastics. *Mailing Add:* Los Alamos Sci Lab MS-528 Los Alamos NM 87544

MILEY, G(EORGE) H(UNTER), b Shreveport, La, Aug 6, 33; m 58; c 2. NUCLEAR & FUSION ENGINEERING. *Educ:* Carnegie Inst Technol, BS, 55; Univ Mich, MS, 56, PhD(chem eng), 59. *Prof Exp:* Instr metall, Univ Mich, 57; analyst reactor critical exp, Knolls Atomic Power Lab, 58-61; asst prof nuclear eng & physics, 61-64, assoc prof nuclear eng, 65-67, PROF NUCLEAR ENG & CHAIRPERSON DEPT, UNIV ILL, URBANA, 67- *Concurrent Pos:* Vis prof, Cornell Univ, 69-70; NATO sr fel, 75; ed, Univ Fusion Asn Newsletter, 80- & J Nuclear Technol-Fusion, 81- *Honors & Awards:* Western Elec Award, Am Soc Eng Educ, 77. *Mem:* Fel Am Nuclear Soc; Am Phys Soc; Am Soc Eng Educ. *Res:* Fusion plasma engineering; nuclear reactor physics and kinetics; direct energy conversion; fusion technology. *Mailing Add:* 221 Nuclear Eng Lab Univ of Ill Urbana IL 61801

MILFORD, FREDERICK JOHN, b Cleveland, Ohio, July 1, 26; m 51; c 1. PHYSICS. *Educ:* Case Inst Technol, BS, 49; Mass Inst Technol, PhD(physics), 52. *Prof Exp:* Asst physics, Mass Inst Technol, 49-51; instr, Case Western Reserve Univ, 49-51, 52-56, asst prof, 56-59; div consult, 59-64, sr fel & chief theoret physics div, 64-66, dir, Inst Res Phys Sci, 65-73, inst scientist, 73, mgr physics & electronics dept, 73-74, mgr physics electronics & nuclear technol, 74-76, ASSOC DIR, BATTELLE MEM INST, 76- *Mem:* Fel Am Phys Soc; Am Math Soc; Am Nuclear Soc; AAAS; Int Glaciological Soc. *Res:* Meson field theory; theoretical nuclear physics; cosmic ray primaries; nuclear magnetic resonance; nuclear moments; electronic structure of solids; magnetism; helium films at low temperature. *Mailing Add:* Battelle Mem Inst 505 King Ave Columbus OH 43201

MILFORD, GEORGE NOEL, b Victoria, PEI, Can, May 4, 24; nat US; m 48; c 3. POLYMER CHEMISTRY. *Educ:* Mt Allison Univ, BSc, 44; Dalhousie Univ, MSc, 48; McGill Univ, PhD(chem), 53. *Prof Exp:* Asst chemist, Best Yeast Co, 45-46; res chemist, Dom Steel & Coal Corp, 48-50; res chemist, 53-60, SR RES CHEMIST, E I DU PONT DE NEMOURS & CO, 60- *Mem:* Am Chem Soc. *Res:* Preparation of monomers and polymers; synthetic fibers, Orlon, Lycra, hollow fibers, Nomex. *Mailing Add:* Textile Fibers Dept Benger Lab E I du Pont de Nemours & Co Waynesboro VA 22980

MILFORD, MURRAY HUDSON, b Honey Grove, Tex, Sept 29, 34; m 61; c 2. SOIL SCIENCE, SOIL MINERALOGY. *Educ:* Tex A&M Univ, BS, 55, MS, 59; Univ Wis, PhD(soil sci), 62. *Prof Exp:* Fel soil chem & res specialist, Cornell Univ, 62-63, from asst prof to assoc prof soil sci, 63-68; assoc prof, 68-74, PROF SOIL SCI, TEX A&M UNIV, 74- *Mem:* Fel AAAS; fel Am Soc Agron; fel Soil Sci Soc Am; Clay Minerals Soc; Soil Conserv Soc Am. *Res:* Compacted layers in soils; potassium and magnesium chemistry of soils; movement and degradation of clay minerals in soils in relation to drainage; clay-organic interactions; soil micromorphology. *Mailing Add:* Dept of Soil & Crop Sci Tex A&M Univ College Station TX 77840

MILGRAM, MICHAEL STEPHEN, applied mathematics, theoretical physics, see previous edition

MILGRAM, RICHARD JAMES, b South Bend, Ind, Dec 5, 39; m 64; c 2. MATHEMATICS. *Educ:* Univ Chicago, BSc & MSc, 61; Univ Minn, PhD(math), 64. *Prof Exp:* Instr math, Univ Minn, 63-64; instr, Princeton Univ, 64-66; from asst prof to assoc prof, Univ Ill, Chicago, 66-69; PROF MATH, STANFORD UNIV, 69- *Concurrent Pos:* Assoc mem inst advan study, Univ Ill, 67-68; vis prof, Princeton Univ, 69-70; ed, Duke J of Math & Pac J of Math. *Mem:* Am Math Soc. *Res:* Algebraic and differential topology; theory of H-spaces; construction of classifying spaces; structure and classification of manifolds and Poincare duality spaces; structure of the Steenrod algebras. *Mailing Add:* Dept of Math Stanford Univ Stanford CA 94305

MILGROM, FELIX, b Rohatyn, Poland, Oct 12, 19; nat; m 41; c 2. MEDICAL BACTERIOLOGY, IMMUNOLOGY. *Educ:* Wroclaw Univ, MD, 47. *Hon Degrees:* Dr med, Univ Vienna, Austria, 76, Univ Lund, Sweden, 79, Univ Heidelberg, Ger, 79, Univ Bergen, Norway, 80. *Prof Exp:* From asst prof to assoc prof microbiol, Sch Med, Wroclaw Univ, 46-53, prof & dir in charge, 54; dir in charge, Inst Immunol & Exp Ther, Polish Acad Sci, 54; prof microbiol & head dept, Silesian Med Sch, 54-57; from res assoc to res assoc prof bact & immunol, 58-62, assoc prof, 62-67, prof & chmn, Dept Microbiol, 67-81, DISTINGUISHED PROF, DEPT MICROBIOL, SCH MED, STATE UNIV NY BUFFALO, 81- *Concurrent Pos:* Ed-in-chief, Int Archives Allergy & Appl Immunol. *Mem:* Am Asn Immunol; Soc Exp Biol & Med; Am Acad Microbiol; Col Int Allergologicum; Transplantation Soc. *Res:* Serology of syphilis and rheumatoid arthritis; natural antibodies; autoimmune processes; transplantation; tissue antigens; tumor immunology. *Mailing Add:* Dept of Microbiol Sch of Med State Univ of NY Buffalo NY 14214

MILGROM, JACK, b Chicago, Ill, May 21, 27; m 48; c 3. POLYMER CHEMISTRY. *Educ:* Univ Chicago, AB, 50, MS, 51, PhD(org chem), 59. *Prof Exp:* Sr chemist, Ninol Labs, Chicago, Ill, 51-56; proj chemist, Standard Oil Co Ind, 56-60; group leader polymerization catalysis, Gen Tire & Rubber Co, 60-66; mgr polymerization & process res, Foster Grant Co, Inc, 66-68; sr staff mem, Arthur D Little Inc, 68-81; SR CONSULT, SRI INT, 81- *Concurrent Pos:* Adv, Acad Sci, 74-75. *Mem:* Am Chem Soc; NY Acad Sci; Am Soc Test & Mat. *Res:* Free-radical and coordination chemistry; organometallics; catalysis; environmental studies; radiation chemistry; polymer technology; impact of technology on society; packaging; solid waste management. *Mailing Add:* SRI Int 360 Lexington Ave New York NY 10017

MILHAM, ROBERT CARR, b Grand Haven, Mich, June 20, 22; m 79. ENVIRONMENTAL CHEMISTRY. *Educ:* Alma Col, BSc, 44; Univ Wis, PhD(inorg chem), 51. *Prof Exp:* Tester, Petrol Lab, Leonard Refining, Mich, 40-42; calculator, Sugar Lab, Hawaiian Sugar Planters Asn, 45-46; asst radiochem, Univ Wis, 46-52; chemist, 52-64, engr, Reactor Eng Div, 64-70, chemist, Radiol Sci Div, 70-78, CHEMIST, ENVIRON EFFECTS DIV, SAVANNAH RIVER LAB, E I DU PONT DE NEMOURS & CO, INC, 73- *Res:* Radiochemistry; radiological physics; trace element analysis in environmental samples; activation analysis; determination of radionuclides in environmental water and air samples; bioassay; plutonium in urine. *Mailing Add:* Savannah River Lab Bldg 735-A E I du Pont de Nemours & Co Inc Aiken SC 29801

MILHAM, SAMUEL, JR, b Albany, NY, May 12, 32; c 3. HUMAN GENETICS, EPIDEMIOLOGY. *Educ:* Union Col, NY, BS, 54; Albany Med Col, MD, 58; Johns Hopkins Univ, MPH, 61. *Prof Exp:* Develop consult, NY State Dept Health, 62-67; assoc prof pub health, Univ Hawaii, 67-68; supvr pop studies, 68-80, HEAD, EPIDEMIOL SECT, WASH STATE DEPT SOCIAL & HEALTH SERV, 80- *Res:* Chronic disease epidemiology; occupational and environmental carcinogenesis; congenital defects. *Mailing Add:* Wash State Dept Social & Health Serv LB-15 Olympia WA 98504

MILIAN, ALWIN S, JR, b Tampa, Fla, May 29, 32. FLUORINE CHEMISTRY. *Educ:* Mass Inst Technol, BS, 54; Univ Calif, PhD(chem), 58. *Prof Exp:* Org chemist, 58-67, SR RES CHEMIST, PLASTICS DEPT, DU PONT EXP STA, 67- *Mem:* Am Chem Soc. *Res:* Fluorocarbon chemistry; synthetic organic chemistry; analytical chemistry; industrial hygiene. *Mailing Add:* Plastics Dept Du Pont Exp Sta Wilmington DE 19898

MILIC-EMILI, JOSEPH, b Sesana, Yugoslavia, May 27, 31; m 57; c 4. PHYSIOLOGY. *Educ:* Univ Milan, MD, 55. *Prof Exp:* Asst prof physiol, Univ Milan, 55-58; asst prof, Univ Liege, 59-60; NIH res fel, Sch Pub Health, Harvard Univ, 60-63; from asst prof to assoc prof, 64-70, PROF PHYSIOL, MCGILL UNIV, 70-, CHMN DEPT, 73- *Concurrent Pos:* Med Res Coun Can fel, McGill Univ, 63-; prof, Univ Clin, Royal Victoria Hosp, Montreal, 64- *Mem:* Am Physiol Soc; Can Physiol Soc; Can Soc Clin Invest; Can Thoracic Soc. *Res:* Physiology of respiration. *Mailing Add:* Dept of Physiol McGill Univ Montreal PQ H3A 2B4 Can

MILICI, ROBERT CALVIN, b New Haven, Conn, Aug 8, 31; m 58; c 2. GEOLOGY. *Educ:* Cornell Univ, AB, 54; Univ Tenn, MS, 55, PhD(geol), 60. *Prof Exp:* Instr geol, Univ Tenn, 55-58; geologist, Tenn Div Geol, 58-62; geologist, Va Div Mineral Resources, 62-63; chief geologist res, Tenn Div Geol, 63-79; VA COMNR MINERAL RESOURCES & STATE GEOLOGIST, 79- *Concurrent Pos:* US Geol Surv grant, 75-77; US Dept Energy contract & Eastern Gas Shales Proj, 76-79; US Bur Mines grant & res assoc, Univ Tenn, Chattanooga, 77-78. *Mem:* AAAS; Geol Soc Am; Am Asn Petrol Geol; Soc Econ Paleont & Mineral; Am Inst Mining Metall & Petrol Engrs. *Res:* Geologic mapping; stratigraphy, structural geology, mineral resources and coal reserve studies in Tennessee; evaluation of oil and gas resources in southern Appalachians; coal mine roof fall study, southwestern Virginia; development and management of geologic and mineral resource programs for Commonwealth of Virginia. *Mailing Add:* 2091 Whippoorwill Rd Charlottesville VA 22901

MILIONIS, JERRY PETER, b New York, NY, Mar 6, 26; m 48; c 3. ORGANIC CHEMISTRY. *Educ:* Brooklyn Col, BS, 47; Purdue Univ, PhD(chem), 51. *Prof Exp:* Asst, Purdue Univ, 47-49 & 50-51; res chemist, 51-54 & new prod develop dept, 54-57, group leader res, 57-63, dir org pigments res, 63-70, mgr agr res & develop, 70-74, SR RES CHEMIST AGR RES & DEVELOP, AM CYANAMID CO, 74-, COORDR INT AGR RES & DEVELOP, 77- *Mem:* Am Chem Soc. *Res:* Sulfur and heterocyclic chemistry; polymer degradation; pigments. *Mailing Add:* 58 Marcy St Somerset NJ 08873

MILKEY, ROBERT WILLIAM, b Washington, DC, Jan 21, 44; m 65. ASTRONOMY. *Educ:* Amherst Col, BA, 65; Ind Univ, Bloomington, MA, 67, PhD(astrophys), 70. *Prof Exp:* Res assoc, Los Alamos Sci Lab, 70-71; asst astronr, Kitt Peak Nat Observ, 71-75, mgr comput serv, 75-79, asst dir admin serv, 79-80; ASST DIR, INST ASTRON, UNIV HAWAII, 80- *Mem:* Int Astron Union; Am Astron Soc; Royal Astron Soc. *Res:* Solar physics; structure of the solar chromosphere; hydromagnetics of the solar atmosphere; radiative transfer and spectral line formation; research administration. *Mailing Add:* Inst Aston Univ Hawaii 2680 Woodlawn Dr Honolulu HI 96822

MILKIE, TERENCE H, b Port Arthur, Can, Oct 3, 53; m 75. POLYMER CHEMISTRY. *Educ:* Lakehead Univ, HBSc, 76, MSc, 77. *Prof Exp:* Assoc mem res staff, 78-80, MEM RES STAFF, XEROX RES CTR, CAN, 80- *Mem:* Am Chem Soc. *Res:* Polymer photochemistry related specifically to the short and long wave photolysis of p-substituted styrenes; rheological characterization of materials for xerographic processes. *Mailing Add:* 2480 Dunwin Dr Mississauga ON L5L 1J9 Can

MILKMAN, ROGER DAWSON, b New York, NY, Oct 15, 30; m 58; c 4. POPULATION GENETICS, EVOLUTIONARY GENETICS. *Educ:* Harvard Univ, AB, 51, AM, 54, PhD(biol), 56. *Prof Exp:* Asst marine embryol, Marine Biol Lab, 54-55; Nat Sci Found res fel genetics, lab genetics & physiol, Nat Ctr Sci Res, France, 56-57; instr zool, Univ Mich, 57-59, asst prof, 59-60; assoc prof, Syracuse Univ, 60-67, prof, 67-68; PROF ZOOL, UNIV IOWA, 68- *Concurrent Pos:* Instr, Marine Biol Lab, 62-64, investr, 61, 65-72; USPHS res fel, Biol Labs, Harvard Univ, 66-67; assoc ed, Evolution, 74- *Mem:* Fel AAAS; Genetics Soc Am; Soc Study Evolution; Am Soc Zool; Am Soc Naturalists (secy, 80-82). *Res:* Nucleotide sequence polymorphism in E coli; selection theory; genetic structure of species; electrophoretic analysis; Drosophila; genetic basis of natural variation; polygenes; temperature effects. *Mailing Add:* Dept of Zool Univ of Iowa Iowa City IA 52242

MILKOVIC, MIRAN, b Mar 29, 28; US citizen; m 67; c 1. ELECTRONICS, INSTRUMENTATION. *Educ:* Univ Ljubljana, MSc, 56; Swiss Fed Inst Technol, PhD(electronics), 65. *Prof Exp:* Develop engr, Grundig, Develop Ctr, 56-57; prog mgr, Landis & Gyr Cent Res Lab, 57-69; consult engr, 69-71, RES ENGR, GEN ELEC CO RES & DEVELOP CTR, 71- *Mem:* Inst Elec & Electronics Engrs. *Res:* Electron devices and circuits; instrumentation; sensors; data conversion; data acquisition; analog microelectronic circuits design. *Mailing Add:* Gen Elec Co Corp Res & Develop Schenectady NY 12305

MILKOVICH, RALPH, b Clairton, Pa, Apr 7, 29; m 53; c 5. POLYMER CHEMISTRY. *Educ:* Duquesne Univ, BS, 51; State Univ NY, MS, 57; Akron Univ, PhD, 59. *Prof Exp:* Cadet chemist, Koppers Co, Inc, 51-55; res chemist, Shell Chem Co, Calif, 59-63; group leader plastics polymerization res, Gen Tire & Rubber Co, 63-66, sect head explor polymers, 66-69; asst dir org & polymer res, Moffett Tech Ctr, CPC Int, Inc, 69-74; mgr explor polymers, 74-79, mgr new prod develop, Arco Polymers, 79-81, MGR NEW PROD DEVELOP, ARCO CHEM, INC, 81- *Concurrent Pos:* Chmn, Gordon Res Conf Polymers, 63, discussion leader, 71; chmn meeting arrangements, Polymer Div, Joint Polymer-Rubber Div Meeting, 73. *Honors & Awards:* Orr Award, Soc Plastics Engrs, 58. *Mem:* Am Chem Soc; AMA; Soc Petrol Engrs. *Res:* Anionic mechanisms; block polymerization; chemically joined phase separated systems; polymer alloys. *Mailing Add:* 3801 Westchester Pike Newtown Square PA 19073

MILKOWSKI, JOHN DAVID, medicinal chemistry, see previous edition

MILL, THEODORE, b Hamilton, Ont, Apr 17, 31; nat US; m 57; c 2. ORGANIC CHEMISTRY. *Educ:* Wayne State Univ, BS, 53; Univ Wash, PhD(chem), 57. *Prof Exp:* Res fel chem, Hickrill Res Found, NY, 56-57; res chemist, Org Chem Dept, E I du Pont de Nemours & Co, 57-60; SR ORGANIC CHEMIST, STANFORD RES INST, 60-, CHMN PHYS ORG CHEM DEPT, 64- *Mem:* Am Chem Soc; Sigma Xi. *Res:* Physical organic chemistry; photochemistry; oxidation and free radical chemistry; environmental chemistry. *Mailing Add:* Dept of Phys Org Chem Stanford Res Inst Menlo Park CA 94025

MILLAR, C KAY, b Syracuse, NY, Oct 28, 34. INTERNAL MEDICINE, CARDIOLOGY. *Educ:* Syracuse Univ, AB, 56; State Univ NY Upstate Med Ctr, MD, 60. *Prof Exp:* Resident internal med, State Univ NY Upstate Med Ctr, 61-64; NIH trainee cardiol, 64-67; asst prof internal med, State Univ NY Upstate Med Ctr, 67-68; asst prof, 68-73, ASSOC PROF INTERNAL MED, MED CTR, UNIV UTAH, 73- *Mem:* Am Heart Asn. *Res:* Electrocardiography; relation of electrical to mechanical activity in the intact heart; body surface potentials of cardiac origin. *Mailing Add:* Cardiol Div Bldg 100 Univ of Utah Med Ctr Salt Lake City UT 84112

MILLAR, CHARLES HOWARD, reactor physics, see previous edition

MILLAR, DAVID BOSIE-SEURS, III, b New York, NY, Sept 19, 31; m 54. PHYSICAL BIOCHEMISTRY. *Educ:* City Col New York, BS, 54; Duke Univ, PhD(biochem), 61. *Prof Exp:* Res assoc biochem, Med Ctr, Univ Ky, 59-60, res fel, 60-62; Nat Cancer Inst fel, 62-63; Nat Acad Sci-Nat Res Coun res assoc, 63-65; res biochemist, 65-70, head, Biochem Div, 70-79, HEAD, BIOCHEM TOXICOL BR, NAVAL MED RES INST, 79- *Honors & Awards:* Outstanding Young Scientist Award, Wash Acad Sci, 66. *Mem:* AAAS; Am Soc Biol Chem; fel NY Acad Sci. *Res:* fluorescent conjugates of biopolymers; protein self association; structure-function relationship of acetylcholinesterase; drug binding studies; nerve regeneration; effects of microwave radiation on neural membranes. *Mailing Add:* Naval Med Res Inst Nat Naval Med Ctr Bethesda MD 20014

MILLAR, DOUGLAS ARTHUR JOHN, b London, Eng, Dec 4, 23; Can citizen; m 45; c 6. MECHANICAL ENGINEERING. *Educ:* Univ BC, BASc, 49; Mass Inst Technol, ME, 51, ScD, 52. *Prof Exp:* Asst res officer mech eng div, Nat Res Coun Can, 52-56; turbine aerodynamicist, Can Pratt & Whitney Aircraft Div, United Aircraft Corp, 57-59, head aerodyn sect, 59-61; assoc prof, 61-65, chmn div aerothermodyn, 68-70, PROF ENG, CARLETON UNIV, 65- *Concurrent Pos:* Consult, Orenda Ltd, Nat Res Coun & Comput Devices Can; sr engr, Davis, Eryou & Assocs, 77- *Mem:* Am Soc Mech Engrs; fel Can Aeronaut & Space Inst; Soc Automotive Engrs. *Res:* Thermal and fluids engineering; thermodynamics and fluid dynamics, particularly of gas turbines and components. *Mailing Add:* Dept of Mech & Aero Eng Carleton Univ Ottawa ON K1S 5B6 Can

MILLAR, GORDON HALSTEAD, b Newark, NJ, Nov 28, 23; m 57; c 5. THERMODYNAMICS, SPECTROSCOPY. *Educ:* Univ Detroit, BME, 49; Univ Wis, PhD(mech eng), 52. *Hon Degrees:* DSc, Univ Detroit, 77. *Prof Exp:* Supvr mech eng dept, Ford Motor Co, 53-57; eng mgr, Meriam Instrument Co, 57-59; dir new prod, McCulloch Corp, 59-63; dir res, Deere & Co, 63-69, asst gen mgr, John Deere Waterloo Tractor Works, 69-71, spec assignment, 71-72, VPRES ENG, DEERE & CO, 72- *Mem:* Nat Acad Eng; NY Acad Sci; Soc Automotive Engrs; Am Soc Mech Engrs; Am Soc Agr Engrs. *Res:* Combustion thermodynamics; high speed photoelectric electro-optical circuits; engineering; fuels and lubricants. *Mailing Add:* Deere & Co John Deere Rd Moline IL 61265

MILLAR, J(ULIAN) Z(IMMERMAN), b Mattoon, Ill, July 3, 01; m 23; c 2. ELECTRONICS. *Educ:* Univ Ill, BSEE, 23. *Prof Exp:* Eng apprentice, Traffic Dept, Western Union Tel Co, DC, 23-25, asst chief operator, 25-26, asst to oper pract engr, NY, 26, eng asst, Electronics Div, Res & Eng Dept, Water Mill Lab, 26-40, engr, 40-41, radio res engr, 45-49, res dir, 49-53, asst vpres, 53-65; sr scientist, Commun Systs Inc, Paramus, 65-67; TELECOMMUN-ELECTRONICS CONSULT, 67-; ASSOC, TELECONSULT, INC, WASHINGTON, DC, 69- *Concurrent Pos:* Dir & consult, Hazeltine Corp, Commack, NY. *Mem:* Fel Inst Elec & Electronics Engrs; Soc Motion Picture & TV Engrs; fel Radio Club Am; fel AAAS. *Res:* General digital transmission development and engineering. *Mailing Add:* Hazeltine Corp Commack NY 11725

MILLAR, JACK WILLIAM, b Ogden, Utah, July 11, 22; m 46; c 4. MEDICINE. *Educ:* Stanford Univ, AB, 45; George Washington Univ, MD, 47; Harvard Univ, MPH, 51, MS, 52; Am Bd Prev Med, dipl, 56. *Prof Exp:* Intern, Naval Hosp, Bethesda, Md, 47-48; med officer in chg, Tinian Leprosarium, Tinian Island, 48-50; med dir & epidemiologist, Am Leprosy Found, Far East, 50-53; instr epidemiol, Naval Med Sch, Md, 54-55, cmndg officer, Naval Med Res Unit 1, Berkeley, Calif, 55-60, dir prev med div, Bur Med & Surg, Navy Dept, 60-67; VIVIAN GILL PROF EPIDEMIOL & ENVIRON HEALTH, SCH MED & HEALTH SCI, GEORGE WASHINGTON UNIV, 67- *Concurrent Pos:* Pres, Gorgas Mem Inst Trop Med; consult epidemiol & trop med, Vet Admin Hosp, Wilmington, Del; sabbatical leave, dir, Pho Tem Gorgas Mem Lab, Panama, 81-82. *Mem:* Am Soc Trop Med & Hyg; Am Pub Health Asn; AMA; fel Am Col Prev Med. *Res:* Epidemiology; infectious diseases; leprosy; tropical diseases. *Mailing Add:* Dept of Allied Health George Washington Univ Washington DC 20037

MILLAR, JOHN DAVID, b Dallas Co, Tex, May 24, 21; m 47; c 1. ANALYTICAL CHEMISTRY. *Educ:* Trinity Univ, BA, 47. *Prof Exp:* Chemist, Found Appl Res, 47-49; chemist, Southwest Res Inst, 49-52; org chemist, Celanese Corp Am, 52-53; assoc chemist, 53-62, sr res chemist, 62-80, STAFF SCIENTIST, SOUTHWEST RES INST, 80- *Concurrent Pos:* Lab instr, Evening Div, San Antonio Col, 57-59. *Mem:* Am Chem Soc; Sigma Xi. *Res:* Process development; gas chromatography and trace analysis; technical literature and reports; determination of chlorinated pesticides and polychlorinated biphenyls in water. *Mailing Add:* Southwest Res Inst 6220 Culebra Rd San Antonio TX 78284

MILLAR, JOHN DONALD, b Newport News, Va, Feb 27, 34; m 57; c 3. PREVENTIVE MEDICINE, EPIDEMIOLOGY. *Educ:* Univ Richmond, BS, 56; Med Col Va, MD, 59; London Sch Hyg & Trop Med, dipl trop pub health, 66. *Prof Exp:* Intern, Univ Utah Hosps, 59-60, asst resident med, 60-61; asst chief EIS, Epidemiol Br, 61-62, chief, 62-63, dep chief surveillance sect, 63-64, chief smallpox unit, 63-65, chief invests unit, Smallpox Eradication Prog, 66, chief prog, 66-70, dir, Bur State Serv, 70-78, asst dir, Ctr Dis Control, 78-80, dir, Ctr Environ Health, 80-81, DIR, NAT INST OCCUPATIONAL SAFETY & HEALTH, USPHS, 81- *Concurrent Pos:* Mem sci group smallpox eradication, WHO, 67-, mem comn eval smallpox eradication in SAm, 73, consult expanded immunization prog, 74; assoc mem comn immunization, Armed forces Epidemiol Bd, 68-71; mem rural health coord comt, USPHS, 75-, mem comt maternal & child health, 75-; chmn, Prog & Policies Adv Comt, Ctr Dis Control, 78; clin assoc, Dept Community Med, Sch Med, Emory Univ; mem exec comt, Nat Toxicol Prog, 81. *Honors & Awards:* Surgeon General's Commendation Medal, USPHS, 65; Pres Citation for Mgt Improvement, 72; Award of Excellence, 77. *Mem:* AMA; Am Pub Health Asn; Royal Soc Trop Med & Hyg; Asn Pub Health Physicians. *Res:* Epidemiology of acute viral illness; mass immunization against infectious disease; infectious disease eradication and control techniques. *Mailing Add:* Nat Inst Occupational Safety & Health Ctr for Dis Control Atlanta GA 30333

MILLAR, JOHN ROBERT, b Edinburgh, Scotland, June 3, 27; m 55; c 3. ORGANIC POLYMER CHEMISTRY. *Educ:* Univ Cambridge, BA, 48, ARIC, 49, MA, 52; FRIC, 59. *Prof Exp:* Res chemist, Howards of Ilford Ltd, 48-50; sr res chemist, Permutit Co Ltd, UK, 50-73; group leader res & develop, Functional Polymers Div, Diamond Shamrock Corp, 73-80; SR RES SCIENTIST, DUOLITE INT, 80- *Concurrent Pos:* Chmn, Gordon Res Conf Ion Exchange, 75-77 & 77-79. *Mem:* Soc Chem Indust; Royal Soc Chem; Royal Inst Chem; Am Chem Soc. *Res:* Preparation, characterization and properties of functional polymers as a function of their chemical and physical structures, including the effect of macroporosity on ion-exchangers and sorbents. *Mailing Add:* 1743 Edgewood Rd Redwood City CA 94062

MILLAR, ROBERT FYFE, b Guelph, Ont, Jan 23, 28. APPLIED MATHEMATICS. *Educ:* Univ Toronto, BA, 51, MA, 52; Cambridge Univ, PhD, 57. *Prof Exp:* Jr res officer, Microwave Sect, Radio & Elec Div, Nat Res Coun Can, 52-53, asst res officer, 57-60; visitor, Courant Inst Math Sci, NY Univ, 60-61; assoc prof math, Royal Mil Col, Ont, 61-63; sci asst electromagnetic theory lab, Tech Univ Denmark, 63-66; sr res officer, Antenna Eng Sect, Radio & Elec Eng Div, Nat Res Coun Can, 66-73; PROF MATH, UNIV ALTA, 73- *Mem:* Am Math Soc; Soc Indust & Appl Math; Can Math Asn; Can Appl Math Soc. *Res:* Diffraction and scattering of waves; scattering by periodic structures; complex variable methods in partial differential equations. *Mailing Add:* Dept of Math Univ of Alta Edmonton AB T6G 2G1 Can

MILLAR, WAYNE NORVAL, b Beverly, Mass, Oct 10, 42; m 65; c 2. MICROBIOLOGY. *Educ:* Bucknell Univ, BS, 64; Pa State Univ, MS, 66, PhD(microbiol), 69. *Prof Exp:* From asst prof to assoc prof bact, WVa Univ, 69-73; sr scientist, 73-77, head microbiol & fermentation prod res, 77-81, MGR ANTIBIOTIC FERMENTATION TECHNOL, ELI LILLY & CO, 81- *Mem:* Am Soc Microbiol; Sigma Xi. *Res:* Soil and water microbiology; isolation of antibiotic producing microorganisms; microbial ecology; fermentation technology. *Mailing Add:* 315 Restin Rd Greenwood IN 46142

MILLARD, BEN, b Painswick, Eng, Dec 5, 20; m 43; c 6. PHYSICAL CHEMISTRY. *Educ:* Bristol Univ, BSc, 42, PhD(chem), 47. *Prof Exp:* Res assoc surface chem, Amherst Col, 49-50; asst prof chem, Univ NH, 50-55, assoc prof, 55-57; asst dir res, 57-67, vpres & res dir, 79, TECH DIR RES, RES DEPT, S D WARREN CO DIV, SCOTT PAPER CO, 67- *Concurrent Pos:* Exp officer, Brit Ministry of Supply, 42-45. *Res:* Mass spectrometry; physical adsorption; surface chemistry; photochemistry. *Mailing Add:* Res Dept S D Warren Co Westbrook ME 04092

MILLARD, FREDERICK WILLIAM, b Johnson City, NY, Feb 10, 31; m 53; c 2. PHOTOGRAPHIC CHEMISTRY. *Educ:* Pa State Univ, BS, 53; Mich State Univ, PhD(org chem), 58. *Prof Exp:* Sr chemist, Tex US Chem Co, 57-60; res specialist, Gen Aniline & Film Corp, 60-63, tech assoc silver halide photochemistry, 63-74, MGR GRAPHIC FILMS RES & DEVELOPMENT, GAF CORP, 74- *Mem:* Am Chem Soc; Soc Photog Sci & Eng; Tech Asn Graphic Arts. *Res:* Photopolymerization theory and adaptation to a photographic system; elucidation of free radical reactions in solution; silver halide technology, particularly in graphic arts; non silver imaging systems; photographic processing solution formulation. *Mailing Add:* Hinds St Box 151 Montrose PA 18801

MILLARD, GEORGE BUENTE, b Kansas City, Kans, Feb 13, 17; m 43; c 4. INORGANIC CHEMISTRY. *Educ:* Wash State Univ, BS, 42, MS, 55. *Prof Exp:* Tech sales agr chem, Sherwin-Williams Co, 46-47, asst to vpres & gen mgr, Calif, 47-49; vpres, Mid-State Chem Co, 49-54; PROF CHEM, YAKIMA VALLEY COL, 51- *Concurrent Pos:* Mem bd, Northwest Col & Univ Asn Sci, 71- *Mem:* Sigma Xi. *Res:* Investigation of some complex ions of zinc by polarographic methods. *Mailing Add:* 201 N 27th Ave Yakima WA 98902

MILLARD, HERBERT DEAN, b Grayling, Mich, May 22, 24; m 48; c 4. DENTISTRY. *Educ:* Univ Mich, DDS, 52, MS, 56. *Prof Exp:* From instr to assoc prof, 52-64, PROF ORAL DIAG, SCH DENT, UNIV MICH, ANN ARBOR, 64-, CHMN DEPT, 56- *Mem:* Am Acad Oral Med; Am Dent Asn; Am Asn Dent Sch; Orgn Teachers Oral Diag. *Res:* Relationships of oral disease to systemic disease; procedures in oral diagnosis. *Mailing Add:* Dept of Oral Diag & Radiol Univ of Mich Sch of Dent Ann Arbor MI 48109

MILLARD, HUGH THOMPSON, JR, radiochemistry, geochemistry, see previous edition

MILLARD, RICHARD JAMES, b Peabody, Mass, Oct 3, 18; m 49; c 1. ELECTROCHEMISTRY. *Educ:* Boston Col, BS, 49, MS, 50. *Prof Exp:* Res engr, 50-65, MGR ENG DEPT, SPRAGUE ELEC CO, 65- *Mem:* Am Chem Soc; Electrochem Soc; Inst Elec & Electronic Engrs. *Res:* Thin films on metals; dielectric breakdown; electrolytic oxidation; identification of phenols; electrolytic capacitor development and engineering. *Mailing Add:* Sprague Elec Co North Adams MA 01247

MILLBURN, GEORGE P, b Cleveland, Ohio, Aug 10, 25; m 46, 81; c 2. NUCLEAR PHYSICS. *Educ:* Case Western Reserve Univ, BS, 50; Univ Calif, Berkeley, PhD(physics), 56. *Prof Exp:* Res physicist, Lawrence Radiation Lab, Univ Calif, 50-56, nuclear weapons, 56-59; dept mgr re-entry systs, Aeronutronic Div, Ford Motor Co, 59-62; assoc gen mgr & gen mgr reentry systs div, Aerospace Corp, 62-68, corp dir technol, 68, gen mgr off develop planning, 68-71, gen mgr technol div, 71-78; TECH ASST TO DEP UNDER SECY, DEFENSE RES & ADVAN TECHNOL, 78- *Res:* Reentry physics; weapon system analysis; nuclear weapon design; high energy particle physics; neutron production; military space technology. *Mailing Add:* Apt 1007 5300 Columbia Pike Arlington VA 22204

MILLEA, MICHAEL FRANCIS, b Chicago, Ill, May 31, 29; m 53; c 8. MATHEMATICAL STATISTICS. *Educ:* Univ Ill, BS, 52, PhD(physics), 57. *Prof Exp:* Mem tech staff, Pac Semiconductors Inc, 57-63; mem tech staff, 63-76, SR SCIENTIST RES & DEVELOP, THE AEROSPACE CORP, 76- *Res:* Solid state diffusion; semiconductor device physics; device reliability; superconducting devices; cosmic background measurements; statistical decision theory. *Mailing Add:* The Aerospace Corp PO Box 92957 Los Angeles CA 90009

MILLEMANN, RAYMOND EAGAN, b New York, NY, Jan 18, 28; m 55; c 3. ZOOLOGY. *Educ:* Dartmouth Col, AB, 48; Univ Calif, Los Angeles, MA, 51, PhD(zool), 54. *Prof Exp:* Teaching asst zool, Univ Calif, Los Angeles, 49-53; from instr to asst prof bact & parasitol, Sch Med, Univ Rochester, 55-63; assoc prof fisheries, Ore State Univ, 63-69, prof, 69-75; RES BIOLOGIST, OAK RIDGE NAT LAB, 77- *Mem:* Am Soc Parasitol; Soc Protozool; Am Soc Trop Med & Hyg; Am Micros Soc; Wildlife Dis Asn. *Res:* Taxonomy and life cycles of helminths; fish diseases and parasites; marine biology; aquatic toxicology. *Mailing Add:* Environ Sci Div PO Box X Oak Ridge TN 37830

MILLENER, DAVID JOHN, b Auckland, NZ, May 2, 44. THEORETICAL NUCLEAR PHYSICS. *Educ:* Univ Auckland, NZ, BSc, 66, MSc, 68; Oxford Univ, Eng, DPhil(nuclear physics), 72. *Prof Exp:* Int Bus Mach res fel nuclear physics, Oxford Univ, Eng, 72-74, res fel, 74-75; from asst physicist to assoc physicist, 76-80, PHYSICIST NUCLEAR PHYSICS, BROOKHAVEN NAT LAB, 80- *Res:* Calculations of the structure and properties of light nuclei. *Mailing Add:* Physics Dept Brookhaven Nat Lab Upton NY 11973

MILLER (GILBERT), CAROL ANN, b Greenville, Ohio, June 27, 43; m 66; c 1. MICROBIOLOGY, IMMUNOLOGY. *Educ:* Defiance Col, BA, 65; Ariz State Univ, MS, 69; Ore State Univ, PhD(microbiol), 70. *Prof Exp:* Clin immunologist, Wilson Mem Hosp, Johnston City, NY, 70-73; res scientist, 73-78, sr res scientist micro-immunol, Ames Res Lab, 78-79, MGR, PROJ MGT, AMES DIV OF MILES LABS, INC, 79- *Mem:* Am Soc Microbiol. *Res:* Development of immunological and chemical test systems which will be used to detect pathognomonic levels of hormones and microbial products in human biological fluids. *Mailing Add:* Ames Div Miles Labs Inc 1127 Myrtle St Elkhart IN 46515

MILLER, A EUGENE, b Philadelphia, Pa, Apr 27, 29; m 57; c 2. MATHEMATICS, RESEARCH ADMINISTRATION. *Educ:* Univ Pa, BA, 51, MA, 53. *Prof Exp:* Asst res engr, Burroughs Corp, 51-55, develop engr, 55-58; mem tech staff, Auerbach Corp, Va, 58-62, prog mgr info systs eng, 62-70, dir prog develop, Auerbach Assocs, 70-72; vpres opers, 72-80, VPRES TECH SUPPORT, INS INST HWY SAFETY, 80- *Mem:* AAAS; Inst Elec & Electronics Engrs; Sigma Xi; Asn Comput Mach. *Res:* Reducing losses, human and economic, resulting from or associated with the highway transportation system. *Mailing Add:* Ins Inst of Hwy Safety 600 New Hampshire Ave Washington DC 20037

MILLER, A(NNA) KATHRINE, b East Orange, NJ, June 8, 13. BACTERIOLOGY. *Educ:* Moravian Col Women, BA, 34; Columbia Univ, MS, 36; Cornell Univ, PhD(bact), 42; Am Bd Med Microbiol, dipl. *Prof Exp:* Asst dir phys educ, Moravian Col Women, 34-35, asst prof biol, 36-41; substitute, Wells Col, 42-43; res fel, Merck Inst, Merck & Co, Inc, 43-74, sr res fel, 74-76, sr investr, 76-78, consult, 79; RETIRED. *Mem:* Fel AAAS; Am Soc Microbiol; fel Am Acad Microbiol; fel NY Acad Sci; Sigma Xi. *Res:* Experimental antibacterial chemotherapy, particularly the development of mouse tests for evaluating new antibiotic agents. *Mailing Add:* 104 B Duncan Hill Westfield NJ 07090

MILLER, AARON, medicine, see previous edition

MILLER, ADOLPHUS JAMES, b Patterson, Ark, Mar 8, 12; m 37; c 1. AGRICULTURAL ENGINEERING. *Educ:* Hampton Inst, BS, 37; Mich State Univ, MS, 46, EdD(voc educ, farm mech), 56. *Prof Exp:* Instr, jr high sch, Del, 37-40; rural eng, Prairie View State Col, 40-42; from instr to assoc prof agr eng & mech, 42-67, prof, 67-77, EMER PROF AGR MECH EDUC, VA STATE UNIV, 77- *Mem:* Am Voc Educ Res Asn; Am Soc Agr Engrs. *Res:* Agricultural mechanics; fire hazards and fire survival education in Virginia. *Mailing Add:* Dept Agr Mech Va State Univ Petersburg VA 23803

MILLER, AKELEY, b Phoenix, Ariz, Mar 12, 26; m 49; c 2. MATHEMATICAL PHYSICS, GENERAL PHYSICS. *Educ:* Univ SDak, BA, 50, MA, 52; Univ Mo, Columbia, PhD, 60. *Prof Exp:* Instr physics, Univ SDak, 52-55; asst prof, 60-65, ASSOC PROF PHYSICS, UTAH STATE UNIV, 65- *Concurrent Pos:* Sabbatical leave, Univ NC, Chapel Hill, 78-79. *Mem:* AAAS; Sigma Xi. *Res:* Physics of light sources. *Mailing Add:* Dept of Physics Utah State Univ UMC 41 Logan UT 84322

MILLER, ALAN CHARLES, b Trona, Calif, June 9, 45. MARINE ECOLOGY. *Educ:* Stanford Univ, BA, 67; Univ Ore, MA, 68, PhD(biol), 74. *Prof Exp:* Marine ecologist, Southern Calif Coastal Water Res Proj, 74; ASST PROF ECOL, CALIF STATE UNIV, LONG BEACH, 74- *Mem:* AAAS; Ecol Soc Am; Am Soc Naturalists. *Res:* Species diversity and trophic structure of marine communities. *Mailing Add:* Dept of Biol Calif State Univ Long Beach CA 90840

MILLER, ALAN DALE, b Everett, Wash, May 29, 31; m 56; c 4. CERAMIC ENGINEERING. *Educ:* Univ Wash, BS, 57, PhD(ceramic eng), 67. *Prof Exp:* Proj metallurgist, Pratt & Whitney Aircraft Div, United Aircraft Corp, 58-64; asst prof ceramic eng, 67-75, ASSOC PROF CERAMIC ENG, UNIV WASH, 75- *Mem:* Am Ceramic Soc; Nat Inst Ceramic Engrs; Am Soc Eng Educ. *Res:* High temperature thermochemistry; nature of refractory compounds; processing of electronic ceramics; analysis of brittle fracture processes. *Mailing Add:* Div of Ceramic Eng Univ of Wash 307 Roberts Hall Seattle WA 98195

MILLER, ALAN R(OBERT), b Alameda, Calif, Feb 4, 32; m 57; c 2. MATERIALS SCIENCE, SOFTWARE SYSTEMS. *Educ:* Univ Calif, Berkeley, BS, 53 & 58, MS, 61, PhD(eng), 64. *Prof Exp:* Res asst, Gen Atomic Div, Gen Dynamics Corp, 56-58; phys chemist, Aerojet-Gen Nucleonics Div, Gen Tire & Rubber Co, 58-67; assoc prof, 67-80, PROF METALL & MAT ENG, NMEX INST MINING & TECHNOL, 80- *Concurrent Pos:* Software ed, Interface Age, 78- *Mem:* AAAS; Am Chem Soc; Am Soc Metals; Sigma Xi. *Res:* Thermodynamics and high temperature chemistry; vapor-pressure determinations. *Mailing Add:* Dept of Metall & Mat Eng Campus Sta Jones Hall Socorro NM 87801

MILLER, ALBERT, b Brooklyn, NY, Mar 18, 11; m 50; c 1. MEDICAL ENTOMOLOGY. *Educ:* Cornell Univ, BS, 33, MS, 34, PhD(insect embryol), 38. *Prof Exp:* Asst entom & parasitol, Cornell Univ, 34-35, instr, 35-38; instr entom & plant path, Univ Ark, 38-40; guest genetics, Carnegie Inst Washington, 40-41; from instr to asst prof, Sch Med, Tulane Univ, 41-48, assoc prof med entom, 48-76; scientist, Int Ctr Med Res, Cali, Colombia, 77-78; RETIRED. *Mem:* AAAS; Entom Soc Am; Am Soc Trop Med & Hyg; Soc Syst Zool; Am Mosquito Control Asn. *Res:* Insect morphology, embryology and taxonomy; biology of medically important arthropods; coprophilic fauna. *Mailing Add:* 1600 Green Acres Rd Metairie LA 70003

MILLER, ALBERT EUGENE, b Albion, Nebr, June 22, 38. PHYSICAL METALLURGY. *Educ:* Colo Sch Mines, Engr, 60; Iowa State Univ, PhD(metall), 64. *Prof Exp:* Atomic Energy Comn assoc metall, Ames Lab, 64-66; assoc prof, Univ Alta, 66-67; assoc prof metall, 67-81, PROF METALL ENG & MAT SCI, UNIV NOTRE DAME, 81- *Mem:* Am Soc Metals. *Res:* Alloy theory; magnetism in solids; metallurgical aspects of superconductivity. *Mailing Add:* Dept of Metall Box E Univ of Notre Dame Notre Dame IN 46556

MILLER, ALBERT THOMAS, b New York, NY, May 7, 39; m 61; c 4. COLLAGEN, PROTEIN CHEMISTRY. *Educ:* Univ Ga, BSA, 62; Univ Mass, MS, 63; Rutgers Univ, PhD, 81. *Prof Exp:* Res technician fats & oils, Lever Brothers Co, 61-62; res asst microbiol, Univ Mass Exp Sta, 62-63; food chemist proteins, Colgate Palmolive Co, 63-66; assoc scientist proteins, 66-73, sr scientist prod develop, 75-76, mgr prod develop, 76-77, assoc dir res, Devro Div, 77-81, DIR RES, DEVRO INC/JOHNSON & JOHNSON, 81- *Mem:* Inst Food Technol; Sigma Xi; Am Leather Chemists Asn. *Res:* Chemistry of proteins; collagen; meat science; natural polymers; edible packaging materials. *Mailing Add:* Devro Inc/Johnson & Johnson PO Box 858 Loeser Ave Somerville NJ 08876

MILLER, ALEX, b Paterson, NJ, Aug 19, 25; m 51; c 2. BIOSTATISTICS, STATISTICS. *Educ:* Purdue Univ, BS, 48; Columbia Univ, MS, 66; Univ Calif, Berkeley, MPH, 70. *Prof Exp:* Sr biostatician, New York Med Col, Flower-Fifth Ave Hosps, 66-69; statistician, Warner-Lambert Co Res Inst, 71-74; RES STATISTICIAN, NABISCO, INC, RES & DEVELOP CTR, 75- *Mem:* Am Statist Asn; Am Pub Health Asn. *Res:* Experimental design; data analysis. *Mailing Add:* Nabisco Res Ctr 2111 Rte 208 Fair Lawn NJ 07410

MILLER, ALFRED CHARLES, b Amsterdam, NY, Sept 10, 47; m 67; c 2. SURFACE PHYSICS, SURFACE CHEMISTRY. *Educ:* Clarkson Col Technol, BS, 68, MS, 70, PhD(physics), 77. *Prof Exp:* Asst prof physics, Hartwick Col, 76-77; adj asst prof, Clarkson Col Technol, 77-78; SR SCIENTIST, ALCOA TECH CTR, 78- *Mem:* Am Phys Soc; Am Vacuum Soc; Sigma Xi; Am Soc Testing & Mat. *Res:* Surface science; reactions at surfaces; properties of metal and metal oxide thin films; ion-surface interaction; ion scattering spectroscopy; sputtering phenomena; surface properties of light metal alloys. *Mailing Add:* Process Chem & Physics Alcoa Tech Ctr Alcoa Center PA 15069

MILLER, ALISTAIR IAN, b Edinburgh, Scotland, July 6, 40; m 64; c 4. CHEMICAL ENGINEERING. *Educ:* Univ Glasgow, BSc, 62; Univ London, DIC & PhD(chem eng), 66. *Prof Exp:* Chem engr, 66-80, HEAD CHEM ENG BR, CHALK RIVER NUCLEAR LABS, ATOMIC ENERGY CAN LTD, 80- *Mem:* Chem Inst Can. *Res:* Research and development of new and established heavy water production processes and other separations of protium, deuterium and tritium. *Mailing Add:* Chem Eng Br Chalk River Nuclear Labs Chalk River ON K0J 1J0 Can

MILLER, ALLAN STEPHEN, b Arlington Heights, Ill, Feb 21, 28; m 50; c 3. SOLID STATE PHYSICS. *Educ:* Univ Notre Dame, BS, 49, MS, 50; Univ Ill, PhD(physics), 57. *Prof Exp:* Assoc physicist, Res Lab, Int Bus Mach Corp, 57-59, staff physicist, 59-61, develop physicist, IBM Components Div, 61-64; res assoc, Nat Res Corp, 64-66; asst dir res, Norton Res Corp, 66-70; consult solid state physics, Light Emitting Diodes, 71-72; mgr process develop, multigraphics develop ctr, Addressograph Multigraph Corp, 72-77; explor planning specialist, 77-78, MGR PHYSICS SECT, BABCOCK & WILCOX, ALLIANCE RES CTR, 78- *Mem:* Am Phys Soc. *Res:* Photoconductivity in semiconductors and insulators; light emitting diodes; transistors; solid state oxygen sensors. *Mailing Add:* 86 S Hayden Pkwy Hudson OH 44236

MILLER, ALLEN H, b Brooklyn, NY, June 23, 32; m 75. PHYSICS. *Educ:* Brooklyn Col, AB, 53; Rutgers Univ, MS, 55, PhD(physics), 60. *Prof Exp:* Physicist, Electronics Corp Am, 55-56; res assoc physics, Univ Ill, 60-62; asst prof, 62-65, ASSOC PROF PHYSICS, SYRACUSE UNIV, 65- *Mem:* Am Phys Soc; Sigma Xi. *Res:* Solid state theory; many-particle problem; thermal physics. *Mailing Add:* Dept of Physics Syracuse Univ Syracuse NY 13210

MILLER, ALVIN LEON, b Bowling Green, Ky, Mar 8, 38. OCCUPATIONAL HEALTH. *Educ:* Western Ky Univ, BS, 60; Univ Cincinnati, MS, 62; Northwestern Univ, PhD(environ health eng), 72. *Prof Exp:* Res asst cancer res, Kettering Lab, Univ Cincinnati, 61-62; health serv officer, R A Taft Sanit Eng Ctr, USPHS, 62-65; health physicist, Sargent & Lundy Engrs, 72; asst prof indust hyg & occup health, 72-76, ASSOC PROF INDUST HYG & OCCUP HEALTH, SCH PUB HEALTH, UNIV ILL MED CTR, 76- *Concurrent Pos:* Consult, Occup Safety & Health Admin, 74-77; Environ Health Resources Ctr, Ill Inst Environ Qual, 74 & State of Ill, 74-75; Nat Safety Coun, 75- *Mem:* Am Indust Hyg Asn; Health Physics Soc; Soc Occup & Environ Health; Am Pub Health Asn. *Res:* Occupational and environmental health, with particular emphasis on industrial hygiene and health physics; voluntary accreditation of occupational health programs in industry; bio-effects of physical and chemical agents; radiation dosimetry; health impact of aircraft noise upon human health. *Mailing Add:* Univ of Ill Med Ctr Sch Pub Health PO Box 6998 Chicago IL 60680

MILLER, ANTHONY BERNARD, b Woodford, Eng, Apr 17, 31; m 52; c 5. EPIDEMIOLOGY. *Educ:* Univ Cambridge, BA, 52, MB & BChir, 55; FRCP(C), 72. *Prof Exp:* House officer, Oldchurch Hosp, Romford, Eng, 55-57; med officer, Royal Air Force, Netheravon, Eng, 57-59; med registr, Luton & Dunstable Hosp, Eng, 59-61; mem sci staff, Med Res Coun Tuberc & Chest Dis Unit, London, 61-71; assoc prof prev med & statist, 72-76, DIR EPIDEMIOL UNIT, NAT CANCER INST CAN, 71-; PROF PREV MED & BIOSTATIST, UNIV TORONTO, 76- *Concurrent Pos:* Mem working cadre, Bladder Cancer Proj, US, 73-75; mem epidemiol comt, Breast Cancer Task Force, US, 73-77, chmn, 75-77; mem, Fed Task Force Cervical Cytol Screening, Can, 74-76 & 80-81, Union Int Contre le Cancer comt, controlled therapeut trials, 78-82 & Multidisciplinary Proj, breast cancer, 78-82, bd sci counr, div resources, Centres & Comn Activities, US Nat Cancer Inst, 80-82, US Nat Acad Sci Comt, diet, nutrit & cancer, 80-82, Sci Coun, Int Agency Res Cancer, Lyon, 81- *Mem:* Can Oncol Soc (secy-treas, 75-79, pres, 80-81); Soc Epidemiol Res; Int Epidemiol Asn; Int Asn Study Lung Cancer; Am Soc Prev Oncol (pres-elect, 81). *Res:* Epidemiology of breast, bladder, larynx, lung, gastric colo-rectal cancer and cerebral tumors; radiation, occupation and cancer; monitoring for environmental carcinogenesis; evaluation of screening for cervix and breast cancer; controlled clinical trials in cancer. *Mailing Add:* NCIC Epidemiol Unit Fac Med McMurrich Bldg Univ Toronto Toronto ON M5S 2R8 Can

MILLER, ARCHIE PAUL, solid state physics, see previous edition

MILLER, ARILD JUSTESEN, b Pine City, Minn, May 16, 18; m 43; c 3. PHYSICAL CHEMISTRY. *Educ:* Carleton Col, BA, 39; Purdue Univ, PhD(phys chem), 43. *Prof Exp:* Asst, Carleton Col, 39-41, prof chem & chmn dept, 49-60; asst, Purdue Univ, 41-42; res chemist, Metall Lab, Univ Chicago, 43-45; chemist, Clinton Labs, Tenn, 45-46; asst prof chem, Antioch Col, 46-49; DIR ADMIS & ASSOC DEAN, INST PAPER CHEM, 60- *Concurrent Pos:* Res chemist, Kettering Found, 46-49. *Mem:* Am Chem Soc. *Res:* Photosynthesis; photochemistry; radiation chemistry; radiochemistry; heats of combustion; solubilities of organic compounds; heats of combustion of some polynitroparaffins. *Mailing Add:* Inst of Paper Chem PO Box 1039 Appleton WI 54912

MILLER, ARNOLD, b New York, NY, May 8, 28; m 50; c 3. PHYSICAL CHEMISTRY. *Educ:* Univ Calif, Los Angeles, BS, 48, PhD(chem), 51. *Prof Exp:* Asst, Univ Calif, Los Angeles, 48-49; res phys chemist, William Wrigley Res Lab, 51; res phys chemist, Armour Res Found, Ill Inst Technol, 52-54, supvr phys chem, 55-56; mgr chem, Borg Warner Res Ctr, 56-59; chief mat res, Autonetics Div, NAm Aviation, Inc, 59-62, dir phys res, 62-66, dir cent microelectronics, NAm Rockwell Corp, 66-68; gen mgr res & develop div, Whittaker Corp, 68-69, gen mgr, 69-71; pres, Theta Sensors, Inc, 71-73; dir eng sci, 73-78, dir res & adv develop, 78-81, VPRES, XEROX CORP, 81- *Concurrent Pos:* Pres, Space Sci, Inc, 68-71. *Honors & Awards:* Armour Res Found Award, 53; Award, Bur Ord, US Navy, 53; Indust Res 100 Awards, 64, 69. *Mem:* Am Chem Soc; Am Phys Soc; Am Vacuum Soc. *Res:* Surface physics and chemistry; photochemistry; epitaxial growth; chemical vapor deposition. *Mailing Add:* 505 Westchester Place Fullerton CA 92635

MILLER, ARTHUR, b Cambridge, Mass, July 25, 12; m 42; c 3. ELECTRICAL ENGINEERING. *Educ:* Mass Inst Technol, SB, 34, ScD(elec eng), 38. *Prof Exp:* Radio serv, 27-36; res & develop engr, Sanborn Co, 36-50, from chief elec engr to dir res, 50-67, dir res, Sanborn Div, Hewlett-Packard Co, 67-69; OWNER, ARTHUR MILLER ELECTRONICS INSTRUMENTATION, 69- *Concurrent Pos:* Physicist, Dept Terrestrial Magnetism, Carnegie Inst Technol, 41; res assoc, Mass Inst Technol, 41-42. *Mem:* AAAS; fel Inst Elec & Electronics Engrs; sr mem Instrument Soc Am. *Res:* Electrocardiographs; electronic instruments. *Mailing Add:* Arthur Miller Elec Instrumen 91 Walnut Hill Rd Chestnut Hill MA 02167

MILLER, ARTHUR, b New York, NY, Apr 3, 30; m 61; c 3. SOLAR ENERGY. *Educ:* Polytech Inst Brooklyn, BS, 51; Calif Inst Technol, PhD(chem), 57. *Prof Exp:* Asst chem, Brookhaven Nat Lab, 50-51; asst, Los Alamos Sci Lab, 52; MEM TECH STAFF, RCA LABS, 56- *Mem:* Am Crystallog Asn; Am Phys Soc. *Res:* Magnetic materials; crystal chemistry of spinels; x-ray and neutron diffraction crystallography; crystal optics; radiochemistry; ferroelectrics; nonlinear optics; electro-optic materials; integrated optics; properties of glasses; finite-element analysis. *Mailing Add:* David Sarnoff Res Ctr RCA Labs Princeton NJ 08540

MILLER, ARTHUR I, b New York, NY, Feb 6, 40; m 62; c 2. HISTORY OF SCIENCE, THEORETICAL PHYSICS. *Educ:* City Col New York, BS, 61; Mass Inst Technol, PhD(physics), 65. *Prof Exp:* Asst prof physics, 65-70, assoc prof, 70-76, prof, 76-80, PROF PHILOS & HIST & AFFIL, PHYSICS DEPT, UNIV LOWELL, 80- *Concurrent Pos:* Nat Endowment for Humanities fel, Harvard Univ, 72-73, assoc, Physics Dept, 73-, Guggenheim fel, 79-80. *Mem:* Am Phys Soc; Hist Sci Soc Am; Am Asn Physics Teachers; AAAS. *Res:* Interdisciplinary research in the history of 19th and 20th century science and technology. *Mailing Add:* Dept Philos Univ Lowell North Campus Lowell MA 01854

MILLER, ARTHUR JOSEPH, b San Francisco, Calif, Jan 18, 43; m 65; c 3. NEUROPHYSIOLOGY, PHYSIOLOGY. *Educ:* Univ Calif, Los Angeles, PhD(physiol), 70. *Prof Exp:* Trainee, Brain Res Inst, Univ Calif, Los Angeles, 70; asst prof physiol, Univ Ill Med Ctr, 70-75, adj asst prof otolaryngol, 74-75; asst prof, 75-78, ASSOC PROF PHYSIOL, DEPT GROWTH & DEVELOP & CTR FOR CRANIOFACIAL ANOMALIES, UNIV CALIF, SAN FRANCISCO, 78- *Concurrent Pos:* NIH grants, Univ Ill Med Ctr, 71-75. *Mem:* Neurosci Soc; Am Physiol Soc; Int Asn Dent Res; Am Dent Asn. *Res:* Neuromuscular control; cranial reflexes and respiration in developing and adult animals; sudden infant death syndrome; motor control of cranial musculature; swallowing. *Mailing Add:* Ctr for Craniofacial Anomalies Univ Calif San Francisco CA 94143

MILLER, ARTHUR R, b Boston, Mass, Aug 6, 15; m 41; c 2. PHYSICAL OCEANOGRAPHY. *Prof Exp:* assoc scientist, Woods Hole Oceanog Inst, 46-80; RETIRED. *Concurrent Pos:* Grant from Woods Hole Oceanog Inst, Scripps Inst, Univ Calif, 50; consult, US Weather Bur, 55; mem, Int Comn Bibliog Phys Oceanog, 60-; mem working panel, Int Indian Ocean Exped, 61-63, lectr, US Biol Prog, Bermuda Biol Sta, 62; UN consult, 78; pres, Assoc Scientist, Woods Hole, Inc. *Mem:* AAAS; Am Geophys Union; Am Soc Limnol & Oceanog; Explorers Club. *Res:* Tide and storm surge research; cooperative investigations of the Mediterranean; general ocean research, ocean thermal energy. *Mailing Add:* Assoc Scientists Woods Hole Inc PO Box 721 Woods Hole MA 02543

MILLER, ARTHUR SIMARD, b Sidney, Mont, Mar 4, 35; m 66. ORAL PATHOLOGY. *Educ:* Mont State Univ, BS, 57; Wash Univ, DDS, 59; Ind Univ, MSD, 63. *Prof Exp:* Instr oral path, Sch Dent, Ind Univ, 63-66; from asst prof to assoc prof, 66-72, prof path, 72-81, PROF ORAL BIOL & PATH, SCH DENT, TEMPLE UNIV, 81-, CHMN DEPT, 68- *Concurrent Pos:* Consult, Cent Am Registry Oral Path, 66-; consult dent aptitude testing, Am Dent Asn, 71- *Mem:* Am Dent Asn; Am Acad Oral Path; Int Asn Dent Res. *Res:* Oral diseases and neoplasms; use of the computer in oral pathology; teaching improvements and innovations. *Mailing Add:* Dept of Path Temple Univ Sch of Dent Philadelphia PA 19140

MILLER, AUDREY, b Danville, Pa, Nov 15, 37; m. ORGANIC CHEMISTRY. *Educ:* Univ Rochester, BS, 59; Univ Ill, MS, 60; Columbia Univ, PhD(org chem), 62. *Prof Exp:* Res assoc org chem, NMex Highlands Univ, 63-64; asst prof, 64-70, assoc prof, 70-81, PROF CHEM, UNIV CONN, 81- *Concurrent Pos:* NSF fel, 63-64, sci fac fel, 71-72. *Mem:* Am Chem Soc. *Res:* Models of biological oxidations and reductions; sulfur and nitrogen compounds. *Mailing Add:* Dept Chem Univ Conn Storrs CT 06268

MILLER, AUGUST, b Isola, Miss, Nov 28, 33; m 63. ATMOSPHERIC PHYSICS. *Educ:* NMex State Univ, BS, 55, PhD(physics), 61; Univ Md, MS, 58. *Prof Exp:* Eng specialist, Ariz Div, Goodyear Aircraft Corp, 61-62; mem res staff, Northrop Space Labs, 62-64; PROF PHYSICS, NMEX STATE UNIV, 64-, HEAD DEPT, 79- *Mem:* Am Phys Soc; Am Asn Physics Teachers. *Res:* Scanning electro-optical image sensors; very low pressure radio frequency gaseous discharges; radio frequency plasmoids; atmospheric optics; satellite meteorology. *Mailing Add:* Dept of Physics NMex State Univ Las Cruces NM 88003

MILLER, AUGUSTUS TAYLOR, JR, b Arlington, Tex, Apr 14, 10; m 38; c 1. PHYSIOLOGY. *Educ:* Emory Univ, BS, 31, MS, 33; Univ Mich, PhD(physiol), 39; Duke Univ, MD, 53. *Prof Exp:* Res assoc, W H Maybury Sanatorium, Mich, 36-39; from instr to assoc prof, 39-50, PROF PHYSIOL, SCH MED, UNIV NC, CHAPEL HILL, 50- *Mem:* Am Physiol Soc. *Res:* Aging. *Mailing Add:* Dept of Physiol Univ of NC Sch of Med Chapel Hill NC 27514

MILLER, BARRY, b Passaic, NJ, Jan 22, 33; m 65; c 2. ELECTROCHEMISTRY. *Educ:* Princeton Univ, AB, 55; Mass Inst Technol, PhD(chem), 59. *Prof Exp:* Instr chem, Harvard Univ, 59-62; MEM TECH STAFF, CHEM RES DEPT, BELL TEL LABS, 62- *Mem:* Am Chem Soc; Electrochem Soc. *Res:* Electrochemical kinetics; photoelectrochemistry. *Mailing Add:* Bell Labs Murray Hill NJ 07974

MILLER, BENNETT, plasma physics, science administration, see previous edition

MILLER, BERNARD, b Monticello, NY, Sept 1, 30; m 65. ORGANIC CHEMISTRY. *Educ:* City Col New York, BS, 51; Columbia Univ, MA, 53, PhD(org chem), 55. *Prof Exp:* NIH fel, Univ Wis, 55-56, NSF, 56-57; res chemist, Am Cyanamid Co, 57-60, sr res scientist, 60-67; assoc prof, 67-72, PROF CHEM, UNIV MASS, AMHERST, 72- *Mem:* Am Chem Soc. *Res:* Organic reaction mechanisms; molecular rearrangements; organic phosphorus chemistry. *Mailing Add:* Dept Chem Univ Mass Amherst MA 01002

MILLER, BERNARD, b New York, NY, Apr 9, 27; m 58; c 2. POLYMER SCIENCE, TEXTILES. *Educ:* Va Polytech Inst, BS, 48, MS, 49; McGill Univ, PhD(chem), 55. *Prof Exp:* Jr chemist, Hoffman-La Roche Inc, 49-52; res chemist, Celanese Corp Am, 55-56; asst prof polymer chem, Lowell Technol Inst, 56-58; Du Pont fel, Textile Res Inst, 58-59; res chemist, E I du Pont de Nemours & Co, 59; asst prof phys chem, Am Univ, 59-61, assoc prof,

61-66; sr scientist, 66-67, assoc dir chem res, 67-69, ASSOC DIR RES, TEXTILE RES INST, 69- *Concurrent Pos:* NASA res grant, 62-64; USPHS res grant, 62-66; consult, NIH, 63-64; Fiber Soc nat lectr, 73-74. *Honors & Awards:* Harold Dewitt Smith Medal, Am Soc Testing & Mat, 77. *Mem:* AAAS; Am Chem Soc; Fiber Soc; Info Coun on Fabric Flammability; NAm Thermal Anal Soc. *Res:* Fiber science; flammability; fiber surface properties; thermal analysis; calorimetry; cellulose chemistry; thermal properties of polymers. *Mailing Add:* Textile Res Inst Princeton NJ 08540

MILLER, BERTRAND JOHN, physics, deceased

MILLER, BETTY M (TINKLEPAUGH), b Corunna, Mich, Apr 23, 30; m 64. PETROLEUM GEOLOGY, RESOURCE ASSESSMENT. *Educ:* Cent Mich Univ, AB, 52; Mich State Univ, MS, 55, PhD(geol), 57. *Prof Exp:* Cartographer & geologist, McClure Oil Co, 54-55; asst natural sci, Mich State Univ, 56-57, instr, 57-58; res geologist, Pure Oil Co, 58-65; sr res geologist & geostatistician, Sun Oil Co, 66-73; geologist, 73-74, prog cheif resource appraisal group, Oil & Gas Resources Br, 74-80, ASST DIR, EASTERN REGION, US GEOL SURV, 80- *Concurrent Pos:* Asst, Mich State Univ, 54-55. *Mem:* AAAS; Geol Soc Am; Am Asn Petrol Geol. *Res:* Geostatistical and computer applications as related to petroleum geology, including information theory and operations research; carbonate petrography and geochemistry; basin analysis petroleum occurrence; oil and gas resource appraisal methodology and appraisals and assessments of the national and worldwide petroleum resources. *Mailing Add:* US Geol Surv Nat Ctr MS 109 12201 Sunrise Valley Dr Reston VA 22092

MILLER, BILLIE LYNN, b Harrodsburg, Ky, Nov 19, 34; m 59; c 2. MEDICINE. *Educ:* Eastern Ky Univ, BS, 54; Univ Chicago, MD, 57; Am Bd Pediat, dipl, 68, cert cardiol, 70. *Prof Exp:* Intern, Hosp, Univ Mich, Ann Arbor, 57-58; resident cardiol, Hammersmith Hosp, London, Eng, 58-59; fel, St Thomas Hosp, 59-61; fel, Nat Heart Hosp, 61-62; res assoc, London Hosp, 62; asst med investr, Nat Inst Cardiol Mex, 62-65; resident pediat, 66-68, spec clin fel pediat cardiol, 68-69, instr pediat, 69-70, ASST PROF PEDIAT, COL MED, UNIV FLA, 70- *Concurrent Pos:* Consult, Fla Bur Crippled Children, 68- *Mem:* Fel Am Acad Pediat; fel Am Col Cardiol; Am Heart Asn. *Res:* Analysis of disorders of cardiac rhythm in infants and children; application of computer techniques to the interpretation of the body surface manifestations of the electrical activity of the heart in infants and children. *Mailing Add:* Dept of Pediat Univ of Fla Col of Med Gainesville FL 32605

MILLER, BOBBY JOE, b Bakersfield, Mo, Feb 7, 34; m 61; c 3. SOIL GENESIS. *Educ:* Univ Tenn, PhD(soils), 72. *Prof Exp:* Instr soils, Univ Mo, 65-69; ASSOC PROF SOILS, LA STATE UNIV & A&M COL, 73- *Mem:* Am Soc Agron; Soil Sci Soc Am; Clay Minerals Soc. *Res:* Morphology and classification; soil mineralogy; soil chemistry. *Mailing Add:* Dept of Agron La State Univ Baton Rouge LA 70803

MILLER, BRINTON MARSHALL, b Delaware Co, Pa, Dec 30, 26; m 48; c 3. MICROBIOLOGY, PROTOZOOLOGY. *Educ:* Univ Va, BA, 50, MS, 51; Purdue Univ, PhD(plant sci), 56. *Prof Exp:* Teacher high sch, Va, 51-53; sr microbiologist, 56-66, sect head, 66-73, asst dir basic animal sci, 73-75, DIR ANIMAL INFECTIONS, BASIC ANIMAL SCI, MERCK SHARP & DOHME RES LABS, 75- *Concurrent Pos:* Asst ed, Am Biol Teacher, 53-56, Appl Microbiol, 57-61; vis biologist, Am Inst Biol Sci, 70-73; chmn coun, Proj Biotech, Am Inst Biol Sci-Nat Sci Found, 71-75; ed-in-chief, Manual Lab Safety, Am Soc Microbiol; int mem, Mex Prog Dairy Prod in Tropics & mem steering comt biosafety guidelines, Ctr Disease Control, NIH. *Honors & Awards:* Merit Award, Soc Indust Microbiol, 70. *Mem:* AAAS; Soc Indust Microbiol (secy, 58-61, pres, 63); Wildlife Soc; Am Soc Microbiol (treas, 75-); fel Am Acad Microbiol. *Res:* Pathology of mycoplasma; parasitic Protozoa of man and animals, especially trypanosomes and Coccidia; water microbiology; biotechnology training. *Mailing Add:* Merck Sharp & Dohme Res Labs Rahway NJ 07065

MILLER, BRUCE LINN, b Grove City, Pa, Sept 8, 23; m 48; c 2. PHYSICS, MATHEMATICS. *Educ:* SDak State Univ, BS, 47; Univ Kans, MS, 51, PhD(physics), 53. *Prof Exp:* Jr physicist, Univ Iowa, 43-44; res physicist, Sandia Corp, NMex, 53-55; from asst prof to assoc prof, 55-70, PROF PHYSICS, GRAD FAC, S DAK STATE UNIV, 70- *Mem:* Am Inst Physics; Am Asn Physics Teachers. *Res:* Geometrical and physical optics; biological effects of nuclear radiation. *Mailing Add:* 1326 LeGeros Dr Brookings SD 57006

MILLER, BRUCE NEIL, b New York, NY, Dec 12, 41; m 66. THEORETICAL PHYSICS. *Educ:* Columbia Univ, BA, 63; Univ Chicago, MSc, 65; Rice Univ, PhD(physics), 69. *Prof Exp:* Asst physicist, IIT Res Inst, 65; post doctoral fel, Rice Univ, 69-70; post doctoral fel, State Univ NY Albany, 70-71; ASST PROF PHYSICS, TEX CHRISTIAN UNIV, 71- *Mem:* Am Phys Soc; Am Asn Physics Teachers. *Res:* Statistical physics; transport theory; electromagnetic theory; light scattering; critical phenomena; information theory; nonlinear dynamics. *Mailing Add:* Dept Physics Tex Christian Univ Ft Worth TX 76129

MILLER, BYRON F, b Robinson, Kans, Aug 20, 31; m 52; c 5. POULTRY NUTRITION. *Educ:* Kans State Univ, BS, 53, MS, 60, PhD(animal nutrit), 60. *Prof Exp:* From instr to asst prof, 60-66, ASSOC PROF POULTRY PRODS, COLO STATE UNIV, 66- *Mem:* Poultry Sci Asn; Inst Food Technol. *Res:* Poultry products and food technology. *Mailing Add:* Dept of Animal Sci Colo State Univ Ft Collins CO 80521

MILLER, C ARDEN, b Shelby, Ohio, Sept 19, 24; m 48; c 4. PEDIATRICS, PUBLIC HEALTH. *Educ:* Yale Univ, MD, 48. *Prof Exp:* From instr to assoc prof pediat, Med Ctr, Univ Kans, 51-57, from asst dean to dean, Sch Med, 57-66, provost, 65-66, dir med ctr, 60-66; vchancellor health sci, 66-71, PROF MATERNAL & CHILD HEALTH, SCH PUB HEALTH, UNIV NC, CHAPEL HILL, 66- *Concurrent Pos:* Markle scholar med sci, 55-60; chmn exec comt, Citizens Bd Inquiry, Health Serv for Americans, 68-74; trustee, Appalachian Regional Hosps & Alan Guttmacher Inst, 74-, chmn bd, 79- *Mem:* Inst Med-Nat Acad Sci; Am Pub Health Asn (pres, 74-75); Asn Teachers Maternal & Child Health (pres, 79); Am Soc Pediat Res. *Res:* Health policy; handicapped children; child health. *Mailing Add:* Rosenau Hall Univ of NC Chapel Hill NC 27514

MILLER, C DAVID, b Baltimore, Md, Apr 7, 31; m 61; c 2. ANALYTICAL CHEMISTRY. *Educ:* Columbia Univ, AB, 52; Univ Md, MS, 59; Univ Fla, PhD(anal chem), 64. *Prof Exp:* Anal res chemist, E I du Pont de Nemours & Co, 52-53; DIR, RES & DEVELOP & ENG, AM INSTRUMENT CO, 60-61 & 64- *Mem:* Am Chem Soc; Soc Appl Spectroscopy; Electron Micros Soc Am. *Res:* Development of clinical and analytical instrumentation; atomic and molecular spectroscopy, luminescence, electrochemical, neutron activation and enthalpimetric analysis. *Mailing Add:* Am Instrument Co 8030 Georgia Ave Silver Spring MD 20910

MILLER, C EUGENE, b Buffalo, NY, Sept 25, 28; m 69. ENGINEERING MECHANICS, CIVIL ENGINEERING. *Educ:* Manhattan Col, BA, 53; Fordham Univ, MS, 56; Rensselaer Polytech Inst, MS, 60, PhD(mech), 63. *Prof Exp:* Instr physics & math, De La Salle Inst, 50-55, Christian Bros Acad, 55-57, La Salle Inst, 57-58 & Hillside Hall Jr Col, 58-63; asst prof mech, Manhattan Col, 63-69, res dir rheol, 64-69; dir air pollution res, NY State Dept Health, 69-70; PROF ENVIRON & BIOMED ENG, UNIV LOUISVILLE, 70- *Concurrent Pos:* Consult rheol, Montefiore Hosp, 63-64; consult air pollution, Chem Construct Co, 65-70; NY State Dept Health res grant & res assoc, Roswell Park Mem Inst, 68-70; NIH & Hearst Found res grants, 78- *Mem:* Am Soc Civil Engrs; Soc Rheol; Am Soc Eng Educ; Air Pollution Control Asn; Am Soc Mech Engrs. *Res:* Rheology; vibrations; bionics; biorheology; plates and shells; fetal membranes; mechanics in pregnancy. *Mailing Add:* Dept of Civil Eng Univ of Louisville Louisville KY 40208

MILLER, C SAMUEL, b Trinidad, Colo, July 5, 31; m 56; c 3. PHYSICAL METALLURGY. *Educ:* Colo Sch Mines, MetE, 59; Univ Denver, MS, 62, PhD, 70. *Prof Exp:* Asst, Univ Denver Res Inst, 59-62, assoc, 62-66; assoc prof physics, 66-78, ASSOC PROF BASIC ENG, COLO SCH MINES, 78- *Mem:* Am Soc Metals; Am Soc Testing & Mat; Am Ceramic Soc. *Res:* Mechanical properties of refractory metals; thermophysical properties of refractory metals, particularly intermediate phase materials in molybdenum-tungsten-rare earth elements binary systems. *Mailing Add:* Dept of Physics Colo Sch of Mines Golden CO 80401

MILLER, CARL ELMER, b Flint, Mich, Apr 28, 37; m 65. MOLECULAR PHYSICS. *Educ:* Univ Mich, BA, 59, MS, 61, PhD(physics), 67. *Prof Exp:* Instr physics, Flint Jr Community Col, 61-63; from asst prof to assoc prof physics, Mankato State Col, 67-76; sr scientist, 76-79, develop engr, 78-80, SUPVR MATS & APPLN, AC SPARK PLUG CO, 80- *Mem:* Am Phys Soc; Soc Automotive Engrs; Hist Sci Soc. *Res:* Organic materials science and engineering, including organic coatings, plastics and theoretical modeling for automotive applications. *Mailing Add:* Mat Appln AC Spark Plug 1300 N Dort Ave Flint MI 48506

MILLER, CARL HENRY, JR, b Cleveland, Ohio, Sept 18, 20; m 51. PHYSIOLOGICAL CHEMISTRY, ELECTRON MICROSCOPY. *Educ:* Ohio State Univ, BSc, 42, PhD(physiol chem), 67. *Prof Exp:* Asst physics, Case Inst Technol, 45-46, sr technician biochem, 48-56; res asst, Ohio State Univ, 59-67; Nat Inst Ment Health traineeship & assoc res scientist, Med Sch, NY Univ, 67-69; ASSOC PROF BIOL, JERSEY CITY STATE COL, 69- *Mem:* AAAS; Electron Micros Soc Am. *Res:* Biochemistry of mental illness; metabolism of catecholamines. *Mailing Add:* Dept of Biol 2039 Kennedy Blvd Jersey City NJ 07305

MILLER, CARL STINSON, b Edmonton, Alta, July 23, 12; nat US; m 44; c 2. PHYSICAL CHEMISTRY. *Educ:* Univ Alta, BSc, 35, MSc, 36; Univ Minn, PhD, 40. *Prof Exp:* RES CHEMIST GRAPHIC ARTS, MINN MINING & MFG CO, 40- *Mem:* Am Chem Soc. *Res:* Photographic thermal and electric processes of graphic reproduction. *Mailing Add:* 44 Miller Crest Ln St Paul MN 55106

MILLER, CARLOS OAKLEY, b Jackson, Ohio, Feb 19, 23. PLANT PHYSIOLOGY. *Educ:* Ohio State Univ, BSc, 48, MA, 49, PhD, 51. *Prof Exp:* Proj assoc bot, Univ Wis, 51-55, asst prof, 55-57; from asst prof to assoc prof, 57-60, PROF PLANT SCI, IND UNIV, BLOOMINGTON, 63- *Mem:* Bot Soc Am; Am Soc Plant Physiol (secy, 60-61, vpres, 62). *Res:* Plant growth substances, particularly those of kinetin type; chemical control of plant development; control of plant growth by light; plant growth and development. *Mailing Add:* Dept of Biol Indiana Univ Bloomington IN 47405

MILLER, CAROL RAYMOND, b Asheville, NC, Sept 10, 38; m 59; c 2. PLANT BREEDING, PLANT PATHOLOGY. *Educ:* West Carolina Col, BS, 60; Clemson Univ, MS, 62, PhD(plant path), 65. *Prof Exp:* Res asst, Clemson Univ, 63-64; asst prof plant path, Univ Fla, 64-71; asst dir tobacco res & prod, 71-72, DIR TOBACCO RES & PROD, COKER'S PEDIGREED SEED CO, 72- *Mem:* Am Phytopath Soc. *Res:* Tobacco diseases and breeding. *Mailing Add:* Club Colony Box 578 Hartsville SC 29550

MILLER, CECIL R, b Morrow Co, Ohio, Oct 17, 33; m 54; c 4. VETERINARY MEDICINE. *Educ:* Ohio State Univ, DVM, 58. *Prof Exp:* Large animal pract, Leipsic Vet Serv, 58-67; res vet, Dow Chem Co, 67-68; FIELD DEVELOP INVESTR, SMITH KLINE LABS, 68-, MGR TECH/REGULATORY SERV, 80- *Mem:* Indust Vet Asn; Am Asn Bovine Practitioners; Am Asn Swine Practitioners; Am Asn Avian Pathologists; Am Vet Med Asn. *Res:* Swine diseases, poultry, bovine nutrition; applied aspects of disease and management conditions. *Mailing Add:* Smith Kline Animal Health Prods 1600 Paoli Pike West Chester PA 19380

MILLER, CHARLES BENEDICT, b Minneapolis, Minn, Apr 28, 40; m 63; c 2. BIOLOGICAL OCEANOGRAPHY. *Educ:* Carleton Col, BA, 63; Scripps Inst Oceanog, PhD(biol oceanog), 69. *Prof Exp:* NSF fel, Univ Auckland, 69-70; asst prof, 70-75, assoc prof, 75-80, PROF BIOL OCEANOG, SCH OCEANOG, ORE STATE UNIV, 80- *Mem:* Am Soc Limnol & Oceanog. *Res:* Zooplankton ecology; biological oceanography of the subarctic pacific ocean. *Mailing Add:* Sch Oceanog Ore State Univ Corvallis OR 97331

MILLER, CHARLES DOUGLAS F, b Alabama, NY, Mar 20, 25; Can citizen; m 49; c 5. ENTOMOLOGY. *Educ:* Univ Guelph, BSA, 48; Univ BC, MSA, 51; McGill Univ, PhD, 67. *Prof Exp:* Scientist, Biosyst Res Inst, 51-68, head entom sect, 68-73, res coordr biosyst, res br, Agr Can, 73-78; PROG MGR, PROTECTION, PAC FOREST RES CTR, ENVIRON, CAN, 78- *Mem:* Entom Soc Can. *Res:* Environmental management and taxonomy of Hymenoptera, especially Vespoidea and Chalcioloidea. *Mailing Add:* 842 Coles St Victoria BC V9A 4N6 Can

MILLER, CHARLES EDWARD, b Baltimore, Md, June 19, 18; m 42; c 2. ORGANIC CHEMISTRY. *Educ:* Wash Col, Md, BS, 40. *Prof Exp:* Chemist, Madison Glue Corp, Ind, 40-41; org chemist, Tech Command, Army Chem Ctr, 45-50, asst chief, Test Div, Chem & Radiol Labs, 50-56, chief, Test Div, Chem Res & Develop Labs, 56-62, dep dir, Develop Support Directorate, Edgewood Arsenal, 62-63; chief tech adv for Chem, Biol & Radiol, Hq, US Army Test & Eval Command, Aberdeen Proving Ground, 63-73; RETIRED. *Honors & Awards:* Meritorious Civilian Serv Award, Dept of Army, 73. *Mem:* Am Ord Asn. *Res:* Chemical warfare; materials testing; esterification; process laboratory design, erection and operation. *Mailing Add:* 27 Lake Dr Bel Air MD 21014

MILLER, CHARLES EDWARD, b Philadelphia, Pa, Feb 16, 25; m 44; c 1. MYCOLOGY. *Educ:* Furman Univ, BS, 51; Univ NC, MA, 54, PhD(bot), 57. *Prof Exp:* Asst bot, Univ NC, Chapel Hill, 51-57, Am Bact Soc fel, 57-58; instr biol, Emory Univ, 58-59; asst prof bot, Tex A&M Univ, 59-62; assoc prof, Univ Maine, 62-65; assoc prof, 65-70, PROF & CHMN DEPT BOT, OHIO UNIV, 70- *Mem:* Bot Soc Am; Mycol Soc Am; Brit Mycol Soc. *Res:* Taxonomy; morphology; ecology; physiology; ultrastructure of zoosphoric fungi (aquatic Phycomycetes). *Mailing Add:* Dept Bot Ohio Univ Athens OH 45701

MILLER, CHARLES ELLSWORTH, bionucleonics, see previous edition

MILLER, CHARLES FREDERICK, III, b Springfield, Ill, Feb 12, 41; m 66; c 2. MATHEMATICS. *Educ:* Lehigh Univ, BA, 62; NY Univ, MS, 64; Univ Ill, PhD(math), 69. *Prof Exp:* Instr math, Univ Ill, 68-69; mem, Inst Advan Study, Princeton, NJ, 69-70; NSF fel, Oxford Univ, 70-71; asst prof math, Princeton Univ, 71-76; PROF MATH, MELBOURNE UNIV, 76- *Mem:* Am Math Soc; Math Asn Am; Australian Math Soc; Asn Symbolic Logic. *Res:* Mathematical logic; combinatorial group theory; decision problems in algebra; geometric methods to group theory. *Mailing Add:* Dept of Math Melbourne Univ Parkville Victoria 3052 Australia

MILLER, CHARLES G(ARDNER), b Chicago, Ill, Nov 18, 13; m 37; c 5. PHYSICS, RADIOCHEMISTRY. *Educ:* Univ Calif, Berkeley, AB, 40, PhD(physics), 49. *Prof Exp:* Assoc prof physics, Univ Calif, Santa Barbara, 48-59; dir res, Isotopes Specialties Co, 59-60, US Nuclear Corp, 60-64; physicist, Appl Nucleonics Corp, Calif, 64-67; MEM TECH STAFF, JET PROPULSION LAB, CALIF INST TECHNOL, 67- *Concurrent Pos:* Res assoc, Clarendon Lab, Oxford & Milan Polytech Inst, 56-57; res fel, Israel Atomic Energy Comn, 65-66; physicist, US Off Sci, Res & Develop, 43-46. *Mem:* Fel AAAS; fel Am Inst Aeronaut & Astronaut; Am Asn Physics Teachers; Am Phys Soc; Inst of Environ Sci. *Res:* Radiation chemistry; radioisotope technology; electrical plasma; infrared and ultraviolet effects; optical physics and imaging; photochemistry and energy conversion. *Mailing Add:* Jet Propulsion Lab Calif Inst Technol Pasadena CA 91109

MILLER, CHARLES G, b Greensburg, Ind, Feb 9, 40; m 65; c 3. MICROBIOLOGY, BIOCHEMISTRY. *Educ:* Ind Univ, Bloomington, AB, 63; Northwestern Univ, PhD(biochem), 68. *Prof Exp:* USPHS fel, Univ Calif, Berkeley, 68-70; asst prof, 70-76, ASSOC PROF MICROBIOL, SCH MED, CASE WESTERN RESERVE UNIV, 76- *Mem:* Am Chem Soc; Am Soc Microbiol. *Res:* Biochemical genetics. *Mailing Add:* Dept of Microbiol Sch of Med Case Western Reserve Univ Cleveland OH 44106

MILLER, CHARLES LESLIE, b Tampa, Fla, June 5, 29; m 49; c 4. CIVIL ENGINEERING. *Educ:* Mass Inst Technol, BS, 51, MS, 58. *Prof Exp:* Proj engr, Michael Baker, Jr Inc, 51-52, asst to vpres, 52-54, exec engr, 54-55; from asst prof to assoc prof surv, Mass Inst Technol, 55-61, prof civil eng, 61-78, dir photogram lab, 55-60, civil eng systs lab, 60-64 & Inter-Am Prog, 61-65, head dept civil eng, 61-69, dir, Urban Systs Lab, 68-76; PRES, CLM SYSTS INC & C L MILLER CO, INC, 68- *Concurrent Pos:* Chmn, President Elect's Task Force on Transp, 68; consult, Govt Puerto Rico; dir, Spaulding & Slye, Inc; mem adv bd, Ford Found & Latin Am Sci Bd, Nat Acad Sci; chmn bd, CLM/Systs, Inc & Community Assistance Corp; dir, Geo-Transport Found. *Honors & Awards:* George Westinghouse Award, Am Soc Eng Educ. *Mem:* Fel Am Soc Civil Engrs; Am Soc Photogram; Asn Comput Mach; Am Soc Eng Educ; fel Am Acad Arts & Sci. *Res:* Civil engineering systems; information systems and computer methods in civil engineering; man-machine communications and programming systems; surveying and transportation problems. *Mailing Add:* 234 E Davis Tampa FL 33606

MILLER, CHARLES PHILLIP, b Oak Park, Ill, Aug 29, 1894; m 31; c 2. CLINICAL MEDICINE. *Educ:* Univ Chicago, BS, 16; Rush Univ, Chicago, MD, 19; Univ Mich, MS, 20. *Prof Exp:* Intern, Presby Hosp, Chicago, Ill, 18-19; asst path, Univ Mich, 19-20, asst prof, 20; asst res, Rockefeller Inst Hosp, New York City, 20-24, asst path & bact, 24-25; from asst prof to prof med, 25-60, EMER PROF MED, UNIV CHICAGO, 60- *Concurrent Pos:* Vol asst, Prussian Inst Infectious Dis, Berlin, 26; consult, Argonne Nat Lab; consult Secy War, 41-49; sr sci officer, Off Sci & Technol, Am Embassy, London, Eng, 48; mem div, Comt Biol & Med Sci, NSF, 55-60; vchmn, Farm Found, 58- *Mem:* Nat Acad Sci; AAAS; Am Soc Clin Invest (vpres, 38); Am Soc Exp Path (secy-treas, 30-34, vpres, 36, pres, 37); Radiation Res Soc. *Res:* Experimental meningococcal and gonococcal infection; biology of meningococcus and gonococcus; action of antibiotics on bacteria; bacterial antagonism; effect of ionizing radiation on susceptibility to infection. *Mailing Add:* 5757 Kimbark Ave Chicago IL 60637

MILLER, CHARLES STANDISH, b Independence Kans, Jan 24, 27; m 52; c 4. PLANT PHYSIOLOGY. *Educ:* Tex A&M Univ, PhD(plant physiol), 59. *Prof Exp:* Sci aide agr res, Bur Plant Indust, Soils & Agr Eng, USDA, 51-52; asst agronomist, Tex Agr Exp Sta, 52-53; asst prof, 58-65, ASSOC PROF PLANT PHYSIOL, TEX A&M UNIV, 65- *Mem:* Am Soc Plant Physiol; Weed Sci Soc Am. *Res:* Abscission physiology of cotton. *Mailing Add:* Dept of Plant Sci Tex A&M Univ College Station TX 77843

MILLER, CHARLES WILLIAM, b Quantico, Va, June 7, 42; m 66. BIOLOGY. *Educ:* Purdue Univ, BS, 64; Colo State Univ, MS, 66, PhD(physiol), 69. *Prof Exp:* Res fel, Univ Wash, 68-70; asst prof radiol & radiation biol, 71-75, ASSOC PROF PHYSIOL & BIOPHYSICS, COLO STATE UNIV, 75- *Mem:* Am Physiol Soc; Am Inst Ultrasound in Med. *Res:* Blood flow characteristics at bends and branch points; arterial wall mechanical properties; pulse wave velocity variations with age and blood pressure; noninvasive studies of blood flow in man; investigations of renal function as affected by age and low doses of ionizing radiation; echocardiography; veterinary applications of ultrasound. *Mailing Add:* Dept of Physiol & Biophys Colo State Univ Ft Collins CO 80523

MILLER, CHRIS H, b Indianapolis, Ind, Feb 28, 42; m 63; c 3. ORAL MICROBIOLOGY. *Educ:* Butler Univ, BA, 64; Univ NDak, MS, 66, PhD(microbiol), 69. *Prof Exp:* Nat Inst Gen Med Sci res fel, Purdue Univ, 69-70; asst prof med & dent microbiol, Med Ctr, Ind Univ-Purdue Univ, Indianapolis, 70-75; assoc prof, 76-81, PROF & CHMN, DEPT ORAL MICROBIOL, IND UNIV, SCH DENT, INDIANAPOLIS, 81- *Mem:* Am Soc Microbiol; Int Asn Dent Res; Am Asn Dent Sch. *Res:* Ecology of oral bacteria; mechanisms of bacterial dental-plaque formation; bacterial extra-cellular polysaccharides; pathogenicity of actinomycetes. *Mailing Add:* Dept Oral Microbiol Ind Univ Sch Dent Indianapolis IN 46202

MILLER, CLARENCE A(LPHONSO), b Houston, Tex, Sept 1, 38; m 65; c 1. CHEMICAL ENGINEERING. *Educ:* Rice Univ, BA & BS, 61; Univ Minn, PhD(chem eng), 69. *Prof Exp:* Engr, Div Naval Reactors, US Atomic Energy Comn, Washington, DC, 61-65; asst prof chem eng, Carnegie-Mellon Univ, 69-78, prof, 78-81; PROF CHEM ENG, RICE UNIV, 81- *Mem:* Am Inst Chem Engrs; Am Chem Soc; Am Inst Mining, Metall & Petrol Engrs. *Res:* Interfacial phenomena; enhanced oil recovery. *Mailing Add:* Dept of Chem Eng Rice Univ Houston TX 77001

MILLER, CLIFFORD DANIEL, b Salem, Ore, Nov 30, 41; m 75. QUATERNARY GEOLOGY, VOLCANOLOGY. *Educ:* Univ Wash, BS, 65, MS, 67; Univ Colo, PhD(geol), 71. *Prof Exp:* Teaching asst geol, Univ Wash, 65-67 & Univ Colo, 67-70; explor geologist, Standard Oil Co Calif, 70-71; prof geol, Colgate Univ, 71-74; RES SCIENTIST GEOL, US GEOL SURV, 74- *Concurrent Pos:* Penrose grant, Geol Soc Am, 72; NSF grant, 72-73; consult, Cossitt Concrete Co, NY, 73-74. *Mem:* Geol Soc Am; Glaciol Soc; Am Quaternary Asn. *Res:* Stratigraphic study of Quaternary glacial and eruptive products from North American volcanoes; appraisal of future volcanic hazards at Mount Shasta, California. *Mailing Add:* Eng Geol Br MS 903 KCG Box 25046 Denver CO 80225

MILLER, CLIFFORD H, b Chicago, Ill, Dec 9, 32. DENTISTRY. *Educ:* Northwestern Univ, DDS, 57. *Prof Exp:* Instr oper dent, 59-61, from asst prof to assoc prof, 61-66, chmn dept oper dent, 69-72, PROF DENT HISTOL & OPER DENT, NORTHWESTERN UNIV, CHICAGO, 66-, ASSOC DEAN, 72- *Mem:* Fel Am Col Dent; Am Dent Asn. *Res:* Bio-mechanics relating to restorative dentistry; operative dentistry; dental histology. *Mailing Add:* 300 N State Chicago IL 60610

MILLER, CONRAD HENRY, b Lowell, WVa, July 28, 26; m 47; c 2. PLANT PHYSIOLOGY. *Educ:* Va Polytech Inst, BS, 54, MS, 55; Mich State Univ, PhD(hort), 57. *Prof Exp:* Asst prof bot & plant path, Mich State Univ, 57; from asst prof to assoc prof, 57-69, PROF HORT, NC STATE UNIV, 69- *Concurrent Pos:* Mem working group, Plant Growth Regulator. *Mem:* Am Soc Hort Sci. *Res:* Vegetable production research, especially plant nutrition and growth regulators. *Mailing Add:* Dept of Hort Sci NC State Univ Raleigh NC 27650

MILLER, CONSTANCE WARREN, fluid dynamics, see previous edition

MILLER, CURTIS C, b Shamokin, Pa, Nov 26, 35; m 58; c 2. GENETICS, ANIMAL BREEDING. *Educ:* Iowa State Univ, BS, 61; Mich State Univ, MS, 65, PhD(dairy sci), 68. *Prof Exp:* Exten dairyman, Mich State Univ, 61-64; statistician, 68-71, mgr animal regulatory affairs & statist serv, 71-73, RES MGR ANIMAL REGULATORY AFFAIRS, STATIST SERV & THERAPEUT, ANIMAL HEALTH RES & DEVELOP, 73- *Mem:* Am Dairy Sci Asn; Am Genetic Asn; Crop Sci Soc Am; Am Statist Asn; Biomet Soc. *Res:* Animal breeding, especially response to selection; population genetics, especially effects of selection, linkage, and dominance on genetic parameters. *Mailing Add:* Upjohn Co Kalamazoo MI 49001

MILLER, DANIEL NEWTON, JR, b St Louis, Mo, Aug 22, 24; m 50; c 2. GEOLOGY. *Educ:* Mo Sch Mines, MS, 51; Univ Tex, PhD(geol), 55. *Prof Exp:* Jr geologist, Stanolind Oil & Gas Co, 51-52, geologist, 55-57; sr geologist, Pan Am Petrol Corp, 57-59 & Lion Oil Div, Monsanto Chem Co, 59-60; consult geologist, Barlow & Haun, Inc, 60-63; prof geol & chmn dept, Southern Ill Univ, 63-69; state geologist & exec dir, Wyo Geol Surv, 69-81. *Concurrent Pos:* Comnr, Wyo Oil & Gas Conserv Comn; Wyo rep, Dept Interior-Oil Shale Environ Adv Comt, 75-76; Wyo rep, Fed Power Comt-Supply Tech Adv Task Force-Prospective Expor & Develop; chmn, fed liason comt, Asn Am State Geologists, 77-78. *Mem:* Am Asn Petrol Geol; Am Inst Prof Geologists; Asn Am States Geologists (secy-treas, 75-76, pres, 78-79). *Res:* Sedimentation; sedimentary petrology and stratigraphic interpretation of sedimentary rocks and the diagenetic alteration that they have undergone; effect of tectonism on late diagenetic alteration in sedimentary rocks related to petroleum accumulation. *Mailing Add:* 1301 20th St NW #314 Washington DC 20036

MILLER, DANIEL WEBER, b Omaha, Nebr, Jan 24, 26; m 47; c 2. EXPERIMENTAL NUCLEAR PHYSICS. *Educ:* Univ Mo, BS, 47; Univ Wis, PhD(physics), 51. *Prof Exp:* Res assoc, 51-52, from asst prof to assoc prof, 52-62, assoc dean, Col Arts & Sci, 62-64, actg chmn dept physics, 64-65, assoc dean res & advan studies, 72-73, PROF PHYSICS, IND UNIV, BLOOMINGTON, 62- *Concurrent Pos:* Consult, Los Alamos Nat Lab, 59-64 & 82-; co-prin investr, Nuclear Reactions Res & 200 MeV Cyclotron Facil, Ind Univ, 63-, co-dir, 79-; mem bd dirs, Midwest Univs Res Asn, 64-71; del, Argonne Univ Asn, 66-; chmn, Publ Comt Div Nuclear Physics, Am Phys Soc, 75-77. *Mem:* Fel Am Phys Soc; Sigma Xi; AAAS. *Res:* Nuclear reaction mechanisms and nuclear structure investigations utilizing light-ion charged particle beams at intermediate energies; polarization in nuclear reactions; total cross sections of nuclei for fast neutrons. *Mailing Add:* Physics Dept Ind Univ Bloomington IN 47405

MILLER, DARRELL ALVIN, b Lincoln, Ill, Sept 27; 32; m 53; c 4. GENETICS, PLANT BREEDING. *Educ:* Univ Ill, BS, 58, MS, 60; Purdue Univ, PhD(genetics, plant breeding), 62. *Prof Exp:* Asst prof plant breeding & genetics, NC State Univ, 62-64, asst prof in charge crop sci teaching, 64-65, asst dir of instr, Sch Agr & Life Sci, 65-67; assoc prof, 67-71, PROF PLANT BREEDING & GENETICS IN ALFALFA, UNIV ILL, URBANA, 71- AGRON TEACHING COORD, 69- *Concurrent Pos:* Mem, Crop Sci Writing Conf, 65-74; agron coord for jr cols, 68- *Mem:* Fel Am Soc Agron; Crop Sci Soc Am; Nat Sci Teacher Asn; Sigma Xi; fel Am Soc Agronomists. *Res:* Inheritance of cytoplasmic male sterility and its interaction in sorghum and alfalfa; alfalfa protein investigations, weevil resistance and physical genetics; allelophathic investigations with alfalfa. *Mailing Add:* Dept of Agron Turner Hall Univ of Ill Urbana IL 61801

MILLER, DAVID, b Chicago, Ill, Dec 31, 28; m 62. CHEMICAL ENGINEERING. *Educ:* Ill Inst Technol, BS, 50, MS, 51, PhD(chem eng), 55. *Prof Exp:* Asst purification lard, Ill Inst Technol, 51, asst chem eng, 51-52; res engr, Inst Gas Technol, 52, instr chem eng, 53-55; asst chem engr, Chem Eng Div, Argonne Nat Lab, 54-56, assoc chem engr, Int Inst Nuclear Soc & Eng, 56-64 & Reactor Physics Div, 64-71; TECH DIR, TOTAL SYSTS, 71- *Concurrent Pos:* Lectr, Northwestern Univ, 56; chmn, Nat Heat Transfer Conf, 64, co-chmn, 71; reporter, Int Heat Transfer Confs, 66 & 70; vis prof, Univ Ill, Chicago & Univ Ill, Urbana, 70-71; assoc prof, City Col Chicago, 73- *Mem:* Am Inst Chem Engrs; Am Soc Mech Engrs; Am Soc Eng Educ. *Res:* Thermal and mechanical design problems; physical properties of materials at extreme conditions; air and water pollution control; coal gasification and coal derived chemicals. *Mailing Add:* Total Systs 5522 Main St Downers Grove IL 60515

MILLER, DAVID ARTHUR, b Marion, Ohio, Jan 7, 42; m 72; c 1. MEDICAL PHYSIOLOGY. *Educ:* Ohio Northern Univ, BSEE, 64; Ohio Univ, MSEE, 66; Ohio State Univ, PhD(physiol), 72. *Prof Exp:* Lectr physiol, Ohio State Univ, 72-73; ASST PROF PHYSIOL, MED COL GA, 73- *Res:* Respiratory mechanics and control. *Mailing Add:* Dept of Physiol Med Col of Ga Augusta GA 30902

MILLER, DAVID CLAIR, b Worcester, Mass, Apr 17, 34. SYSTEMATIC ENTOMOLOGY, INVERTEBRATE ZOOLOGY. *Educ:* Univ Calif, Riverside, BA, 57; Univ Wash, PhD(zool), 62. *Prof Exp:* Asst zool, Univ Wash, 57-61; lectr biol, 61-62, instr, 62-64, asst prof, 64-71, assoc prof, 72-81, PROF BIOL, CITY COL NEW YORK, 81- *Mem:* Am Soc Zool; Entom Soc Am; Soc Syst Zool; Soc Study Evolution; Coleopterists' Soc. *Res:* Systematics; biology and evolution of the beetle family Hydrophilidae. *Mailing Add:* Dept of Biol City Col of New York New York NY 10031

MILLER, DAVID HARRY, b Callington Cornwall, Eng, Mar 3, 39; m 61; c 2. EXPERIMENTAL HIGH ENERGY PHYSICS. *Educ:* Imp Col Univ London, BSc, 60, PhD(high energy physics), 63. *Prof Exp:* Res assoc, 63-65, asst prof, 65-68, assoc prof, 68-76, PROF HIGH ENERGY PHYSICS, PURDUE UNIV, 76- *Concurrent Pos:* Guggenheim fel, 72; vis scientist, Europ Orgn Nuclear Res, Geneva, 72-73; res grantee & prin investr, US Dept Energy. *Mem:* Fel Am Phys Soc. *Res:* Study of elementary particles using experimental techniques; electron positron annihilations at high energy. *Mailing Add:* Dept of Physics Purdue Univ West Lafayette IN 47907

MILLER, DAVID HEWITT, b Russell, Kans, 1918; m 62; c 1. CLIMATOLOGY. *Educ:* Univ Calif, Los Angeles, AB, 39, MA, 44, PhD(geog), Berkeley, 53. *Hon Degrees:* DLitt, Univ Newcastle, 79. *Prof Exp:* Meteorologist, Corps Engrs, US Army, 41-43, forecaster, Transcontinental & Western Air Lines, 43-44; climatologist, Off Qm Gen, 44-46; meteorologist-hydrologist, snow invests, 46-50, asst dir, 50-53; chief environ anal br, Qm Res & Eng Lab, Mass, 53-58; meteorologist, US Forest Serv, Calif, 59-64; prof geog, 64-75, PROF ATMOSPHERIC SCI, DEPT GEOL SCI, UNIV WIS-MILWAUKEE, 75- *Concurrent Pos:* NSF res fel, 52-53; vis lectr, Clark Univ, 57-58, Univ Ga, 58, Univ Calif, Berkeley, 61 & 63 & Univ Wis, 62; Fulbright lectr, Univ Newcastle, Australia, 66; Nat Acad Sci exchange scientist, USSR Acad Sci, 69; Fulbright sr scholar, Univs Newcastle & Macquarie, 71. *Mem:* Am Meteorol Soc; Asn Am Geog; Ecol Soc Am; Foresters; Am Geophys Union. *Res:* Snow hydrology; climatology; radiation earth's surface; energy/mass analysis of environmental impact; energy and mass budget at earth's surface; especially snow cover, forests, and cities; hydrology. *Mailing Add:* Dept of Geol Sci Univ of Wis-Milwaukee Milwaukee WI 53201

MILLER, DAVID LEE, b Seattle, Wash, May, 44; m; c 1. SOLID STATE PHYSICS. *Educ:* Whitman Col, AB, 66; Univ Ill, Urbana, MS, 67, PhD(physics), 73. *Prof Exp:* Fel, Coord Sci Lab, Univ Ill, Urbana, 73-74; assoc & asst scientist, Brookhaven Res Labs, 74-77; MEM TECH STAFF, ROCKWELL INT CORP SCI CTR, 77- *Mem:* Am Phys Soc; Am Vacuum Soc. *Res:* Molecular beam epitaxy of III-V compounds; solar cell research; superconductivity; surface physics. *Mailing Add:* Rockwell Int Sci Ctr 1049 Camino dos Rios Thousand Oaks CA 91360

MILLER, DAVID LEE, b Knoxville, Tenn, Aug 15, 38; m 61; c 2. PHYSICAL ORGANIC CHEMISTRY, MOLECULAR BIOLOGY. *Educ:* Oberlin Col, BA, 60; Harvard Univ, PhD(chem), 66. *Prof Exp:* NIH fel, 65-66; asst prof chem, Oberlin Col, 66-68; staff fel, Nat Heart Inst, 68-69; res assoc, 69-71, asst mem, Roche Inst Molecular Biol, 71-81; HEAD, MOLECULAR BIOL DEPT, NY STATE BASIC RES DEVELOP ABILITIES, 81- *Mem:* Am Chem Soc; Fedn Am Soc of Exp Biol. *Res:* Reactions of organic polyphosphates; mechanism of protein biosynthesis; control of plasma protein synthesis. *Mailing Add:* Molecular Biol NY State Inst Basic Res 1050 Forest Hill Rd Nutley NJ 07110

MILLER, DAVID MILROY, physical chemistry, see previous edition

MILLER, DAVID R(ADFORD), b St Louis, Mo, Sept 29, 23; m 50; c 4. CHEMICAL ENGINEERING. *Educ:* Washington Univ, BS, 44; Mass Inst Technol, SM, 48; Purdue Univ, PhD(chem eng), 57. *Prof Exp:* Asst supvr prod, 47-50, proj engr plant develop, 50-52, SR GROUP LEADER RES, MONSANTO CO, 55- *Res:* Fluid dynamics; lubrication; hydraulics; thermodynamics. *Mailing Add:* 1646 Rathford Dr St Louis MO 63141

MILLER, DAVID S, b Brooklyn, NY, July 24, 45; m 78. MEMBRANE BIOCHEMISTRY, ENVIRONMENTAL TOXICOLOGY. *Educ:* Brooklyn Col, BS, 66; Univ Maine, PhD(biochem), 73. *Prof Exp:* Assoc res scientist, 73-78, RES SCIENTIST, MT DESERT ISLAND BIOL LAB, 78- *Concurrent Pos:* Prin investr, US Pub Health Serv & lectr biochem dept, Univ Maine, 78- *Mem:* AAAS; Am Physiol Soc; Sigma Xi. *Res:* Biochemistry and physiology of epithelial membrane transport; effects of chemicals, especially environmental pollutants and drugs on membrane function. *Mailing Add:* Mt Desert Island Biol Lab Salisbury Cove ME 04672

MILLER, DENNIS DEAN, b Webster, SDak, Feb 26, 45; m 75. FOOD SCIENCE, NUTRITION. *Educ:* Augsburg Col, BA, 67; Univ Wash, MS, 69; Cornell Univ, PhD(nutrit), 78. *Prof Exp:* Instr chem, NDak State Sch Sci, 68-70; asst prof chem, Univ Minn Tech Col, 70-74; NSF fac fel, Univ Wis, 74-75; ASST PROF FOOD SCI, CORNELL UNIV, 78- *Mem:* Inst Food Technologists; AAAS. *Res:* In vitro methodology for assessment of food iron and zinc bioavailabilities; methods development for using iron stable isotopes as biological tracers; study of factors and mechanisms that influence the bioavailability of iron and zinc in human foods. *Mailing Add:* Dept of Food Sci Stocking Hall Cornell Univ Ithaca NY 14853

MILLER, DEREK HARRY, b Hull, Eng, Jan 18, 24; m 47; c 3. PSYCHIATRY, PSYCHOANALYSIS. *Educ:* Univ Leeds, MB, ChB, 47, MD, 55. *Prof Exp:* Psychiatrist, Menninger Found, Topeka, Kans, 55-59; dir adolescent unit, Tavistock Clin, London, 59-69; dir adolescent psychiat prog, Med Sch, Univ Mich, Ann Arbor, 69-75, prof psychiat & assoc chmn, 75-76, PROF PSYCHIAT, NORTHWESTERN UNIV, CHICAGO & CHIEF ADOLESCENT PROG, NORTHWESTERN MEM HOSP, 76- *Concurrent Pos:* Assoc mem, Inst Psychoanal, London, 64-68; lectr, Inst Sociol, Bedford Col, 65-69, Inst Archit, Univ Cambridge, 65-69 & WHO, 67-69; training grant adolescent psychiat, Univ Mich, 72-75; consult, W S Hall Psychiat Inst, Columbia, SC, 72-79. *Mem:* Brit Psychoanal Soc; Am Psychiat Asn; AMA; Am Soc Adolescent Psychiat; Royal Col Psychiatrists. *Res:* Adolescent psychiatry, drug abuse, prediction of homicidal behavior and relationship between physical maturation and psychological development. *Mailing Add:* 320 E Huron Chicago IL 60611

MILLER, DON CURTIS, b Oakland, Calif, Apr, 29, 35; m 60; c 2. MARINE ENVIRONMENTAL BIOLOGY. *Educ:* Univ Del, BA, 57; Duke Univ, MA, 62, PhD(zool), 65. *Prof Exp:* Lectr, Queens Col, City Univ New York, 62-65, instr, 65-67; asst prof, Union Col, 67-71; res aquatic biol, 71-73, RES GROUP LEADER, ENVIRON PROTECTION AGENCY, 73- *Concurrent Pos:* Interim dir, I C Darling Marine Ctr, Univ Maine, 65; res assoc, Baruch Coastal Res Inst, Univ SC, 73-; adj prof zool, Univ RI, 75-; US Rep, Int Hydrol Prog, UN Educ Sci & Cult Orgn, 76-79. *Mem:* Am Soc Zoologists; AAAS; Am Soc Limnol & Oceanog; Ecol Soc Am; New Eng Estuarine Soc. *Res:* Physiological ecology of estuarine animals; crustacean morphometrics; thermal biology; power plant impact assessment; aquatic toxicology; sublethal pollutant effects (development, physiological, behavioral); ocean disposal hazard assessment. *Mailing Add:* Environ Res Lab Environ Protection Agency S Ferry Rd Narragansett RI 02882

MILLER, DON DALZELL, b Menomonie, Wis, Apr 8, 13. ALGEBRA. *Educ:* Wayne State Univ, AB, 34, MA, 36; Univ Mich, PhD(math), 41. *Prof Exp:* Instr math, Lawrence Inst Technol, 35-36 & Univ Ohio, 38-42; from assoc prof to prof, 46-78, EMER PROF MATH, UNIV TENN, KNOXVILLE, 78- *Concurrent Pos:* Fulbright lectr, Univ Besancon, 64-65. *Mem:* Am Math Soc; Math Asn Am. *Res:* Semigroups, semirings, binary relations. *Mailing Add:* Lucina 5913 Shell Point Village Fort Myers FL 33908

MILLER, DON HAROLD, statistics, operations research, see previous edition

MILLER, DON WILSON, b Westerville, Ohio, Mar 16, 42; m 66; c 3. NUCLEAR ENGINEERING, PHYSICS. *Educ:* Miami Univ, BSc, 64, MSc, 66; Ohio State Univ, PhD(nuclear eng), 71. *Prof Exp:* Res engr, NAm Aviation, 63-64; from asst prof to assoc prof, 71-80, PROF NUCLEAR ENG, OHIO STATE UNIV, CHMN DEPT & DIR, NUCLEAR REACTOR LAB, 77- *Mem:* Am Nuclear Soc; Am Soc Eng Educ; Inst Elec & Electronics Engrs. *Res:* Nuclear reactor instrumentation and control; nuclear medical instrumentation; energy policy analysis. *Mailing Add:* Dept Nuclear Eng Ohio State Univ 206 W 18th Ave Columbus OH 43210

MILLER, DONALD ELBERT, b Germano, Ohio, Apr 6, 06; m 31; c 1. BIOLOGY. *Educ:* Thiel Col, AB, 25 & 28; Univ Mich, MS, 29, PhD(zool), 35. *Prof Exp:* Teacher high schs, Pa, 25-28, 30-31; asst zool, Univ Mich, 29-30; instr biol Gustavus Adolphus Col, 31-33; zool, Univ Idaho, 35-36; asst prof sci, 36-39, from assoc prof to prof, 39-72, EMER PROF BIOL, BALL STATE UNIV, 72- *Res:* Limnology. *Mailing Add:* 5949 Shagway Rd RR 2 Ludington MI 49431

MILLER, DONALD GABRIEL, b Oakland, Calif, Oct 29, 27; m 49; c 2. PHYSICAL CHEMISTRY. *Educ:* Univ Calif, BS, 49; Univ Ill, PhD(phys chem), 53. *Prof Exp:* Asst chem, Univ Ill, 49-52; asst prof, Univ Louisville, 52-54; res assoc, Brookhaven Nat Lab, NY, 54-56; CHEMIST, LAWRENCE LIVERMORE LAB, UNIV CALIF, 56- *Concurrent Pos:* Fulbright prof, Univ Lille & Cath Univ Lille, 60-61; vis fel, Australian Nat Univ, 79 & 81. *Mem:* Am Chem Soc; Math Asn Am; Asn Symbolic Logic. *Res:* Thermodynamics of irreversible processes; electrolyte solutions; history of science. *Mailing Add:* Lawrence Livermore Lab Univ of Calif Livermore CA 94550

MILLER, DONALD MORTON, b Chicago, Ill, July 24, 30; m 63; c 1. COMPARATIVE PHYSIOLOGY. *Educ:* Univ Ill, AB, 60, MA, 62, PhD(physiol), 65. *Prof Exp:* Sci asst org chem, Polymer Res Lab, Univ Ill, 60, asst physiol & biophys, 60-63, 63-64, comp physiol trainee, 63, 65; from asst prof to assoc prof, 66-75, PROF PHYSIOL, SOUTHERN ILL UNIV, CARBONDALE, 76- *Concurrent Pos:* USPHS fel protozool & parasitol, Univ Calif, Los Angeles, 55-66. *Mem:* AAAS; Am Soc Zool; Am Micros Soc; Bot Soc Am; Am Physiol Soc. *Res:* Primitive motile systems, parasite nervous systems and halotolerent organisms. *Mailing Add:* Dept of Physiol Southern Ill Univ Carbondale IL 62901

MILLER, DONALD NELSON, b St Louis, Mo, Aug 25, 23; m 57; c 3. CHEMICAL ENGINEERING. *Educ:* Washington Univ, BSChE, 43, MS, 57; Univ Wis, PhD(chem eng), 55. *Prof Exp:* Consult, 55-70, sr consult chem eng, 70-79, PRIN CONSULT, KINETICS & REACTOR DESIGN, E I DU PONT DE NEMOURS & CO, INC, 80- *Mem:* Am Inst Chem Engrs; Am Chem Soc. *Res:* Chemical kinetics; mass transfer; reactor scaleup. *Mailing Add:* E I Du Pont de Nemours & Co Inc 1007 Market St Wilmington DE 19898

MILLER, DONALD PIGUET, b New Orleans, La, Oct 11, 27; m 51; c 3. CHEMICAL PHYSICS, CRYSTALLOGRAPHY. *Educ:* Agr & Mech Col, Tex, BS, 48; Tulane Univ, MS, 52; Polytech Inst Brooklyn, PhD, 62. *Prof Exp:* Asst biophys, Tulane Univ, 51; fel physics, Polytech Inst Brooklyn, 53-54, instr, 54-57; mem tech staff, Cent Res Lab, Tex Instruments, Inc, 57-63; assoc prof, 63-77, PROF CHEM PHYSICS, CLEMSON UNIV, 77- *Mem:* Am Crystallog Asn; Am Inst Chemists. *Res:* X-ray crystallography; electron diffraction; solid state physical chemistry and chemical physics. *Mailing Add:* Dept of Physics Clemson Univ Clemson SC 29631

MILLER, DONALD RICHARD, b Hamilton, Ont, July 4, 36; m 69. MATHEMATICAL BIOLOGY. *Educ:* Univ Toronto, BA, 60, MA, 61, PhD(appl math), 64. *Prof Exp:* Instr math, Univ Toronto, 61-63; asst prof, Univ Western Ont, 63-65, assoc prof appl math, 65-68, res assoc cancer res lab, 68-69; assoc prof indust & systs eng, Univ Fla, Cape Canaveral, 69-71; assoc prof & grad coord, Univ Fla, Gainesville, 71-73; GROUP LEADER, BIOMATH & ECOTOXICOL, DIV OF BIOL SCI, NAT RES COUN CAN 73- *Concurrent Pos:* Mem, Can Comt Man & the Biosphere, MAB Secretariat, Environ Can, Ottawa. *Mem:* Am Col Toxicol; Soc Toxicol Can. *Res:* Environmental studies; pollutant transport; toxic effects and mechanisms of environmental pollutants in agnatic systems; risk assessment. *Mailing Add:* Biol Sci Group Leader Ecotoxicol Nat Res Coun Ottawa ON K1A 0R6 Can

MILLER, DONALD SPENCER, b Ventura, Calif, June 12, 32; m 54; c 3. GEOCHEMISTRY. *Educ:* Occidental Col, AB, 54; Columbia Univ, AM, 56, PhD, 60. *Prof Exp:* Asst, Lamont Geol Observ, Columbia Univ, 54-59; res scientist, 59-60; from asst prof to assoc prof, 60-69, chmn dept, 69-76, PROF GEOCHEM, RENSSELAER POLYTECH INST, 69-, CHMN DEPT, 80- *Concurrent Pos:* NSF sci fac fel & guest prof, Univ Berne, 66-67; guest res prof, Max-Planck-Inst Nuclear Physics, Heidelberg, 77-78. *Mem:* Geol Soc Am; Nat Asn Geol Teachers; Geochem Soc. *Res:* Geochronology; Colorado Plateau uranium-lead ages; fission track techniques in geology. *Mailing Add:* Dept of Geol Rensselaer Polytech Inst Troy NY 12181

MILLER, DONALD WRIGHT, b Columbus, Wis, May 28, 27; m 52; c 6. MATHEMATICS. *Educ:* Univ Wis, BS, 50, MS, 51, PhD(math), 57. *Prof Exp:* From instr to assoc prof, 55-69, PROF MATH, UNIV NEBR, LINCOLN, 69- *Mem:* Am Math Soc; Math Asn Am; London Math Soc. *Res:* Algebra, especially the structure of semigroups. *Mailing Add:* Dept of Math Univ of Nebr Lincoln NE 68508

MILLER, DOROTHEA STARBUCK, b Iowa City, Iowa, Nov 12, 08; m 31. ZOOLOGY. *Educ:* Univ Iowa, BA, 28, MS, 35, PhD(zool), 38. *Prof Exp:* Asst zool, Univ Iowa, 33-38; asst prof, Conn Col, 39-43; instr, Univ Wis, 44-45; res asst, Toxicity Lab, Univ Chicago, 45-46, from instr to asst prof biol sci, 46-63, res assoc zool & asst dean students, Biol Sci Div, 54-63; asst prog dir, NSF, Washington, DC, 63-64; PROG ADMINSTR, GENETICS TRAINING & ANAT SCI TRAINING COMTS, NAT INST GEN MED SCI, 64- *Concurrent Pos:* USPHS res grants, 48-50, 54-63. *Mem:* AAAS; Am Soc Zool; Radiation Res Soc; Genetics Soc Am. *Res:* Audiogenic seizures in mice; mammalian genetics; influence of low-level radiation on audiogenic seizures. *Mailing Add:* Nat Inst Gen Med Sci Bethesda MD 20205

MILLER, DOROTHY ANNE SMITH, b New York, NY; m 54; c 3. GENETICS, CYTOGENETICS. *Educ:* Wilson Col, BA, 52; Yale Univ, PhD(biochem), 57. *Prof Exp:* From res asst to res assoc, 63-73, ASST PROF HUMAN GENETICS, COL PHYSICIANS & SURGEONS, COLUMBIA UNIV, 73- *Res:* Chromosome analysis of human, mouse and interspecific somatic cell hybrids. *Mailing Add:* Dept Human Genetics & Develop Columbia Univ Col of Phys & Surg New York NY 10032

MILLER, DOUGLAS GORDON, b Cortland, NY, July 13, 29; m 57. PHYSICS. *Educ:* Yale Univ, AB, 51; Univ Rochester, PhD, 58. *Prof Exp:* From instr to asst prof physics, Harvard Univ, 57-65; ASSOC PROF PHYSICS, HAVERFORD COL, 65- *Res:* Scattering theory and experimental nuclear physics, particularly strong interactions. *Mailing Add:* Dept of Physics Haverford Col Haverford PA 19041

MILLER, DOUGLAS KENNETH, b Devils Lake, NDak, Dec 8, 47; m 78. BIOCHEMISTRY, CELL PHYSIOLOGY. *Educ:* Univ NDak, BS, 70; Harvard Univ, MA, 71, PhD(biochem), 76. *Prof Exp:* Res fel path, Med Sch, Tufts Univ, 75-78; ADJ ASST PROF PHYSIOL, COL MED & DENT NJ-RUTGERS MED SCH, 78- *Concurrent Pos:* Teaching fel biochem, Harvard Univ, 71-75. *Mem:* AAAS; Soc Complex Carbohydrates. *Res:* Glycoprotein biosynthesis and turnover; tumor cell growth and metastasis; cell virus interactions; lysosomes. *Mailing Add:* Dept of Physiol Rutgers Med Sch Piscataway NJ 08854

MILLER, DOUGLASS ROSS, b Monterey Park, Calif, Feb 15, 42; m 64; c 2. ENTOMOLOGY. *Educ:* Univ Calif, Davis, BS, 64, MS, 65, PhD(entom), 69. *Prof Exp:* RES ENTOMOLOGIST, SYST ENTOM LAB, AGR RES SERV, USDA, 69- *Concurrent Pos:* Adj assoc prof entom, Univ Md, 73-; res assoc, Dept Entom, Smithsonian Inst, 78- *Mem:* Pan-Pac Entom Soc; Entom Soc Am; Soc Syst Zool; Sigma Xi. *Res:* Systematics of scale insects with emphasis on the families Pseudococcidae and Eriococcidae. *Mailing Add:* 511 Hexton Hill Rd Silver Spring MD 20904

MILLER, DUANE DOUGLAS, b Great Bend, Kans, July 15, 43; m 62; c 3. MEDICINAL CHEMISTRY. *Educ:* Univ Kans, BS Pharm, 66; Univ Wash, PhD(med chem), 69. *Prof Exp:* Asst prof, 69-74, assoc prof, 74-80, PROF MED CHEM, COL PHARM, OHIO STATE UNIV, 80- *Mem:* Am Chem Soc; AAAS. *Res:* Drugs used to treat asthma; mechanism of adrenergic and dopaminergic drugs; inhibitors of platelet aggregation. *Mailing Add:* Dept of Med Chem Col of Pharm Ohio State Univ Columbus OH 43210

MILLER, DUDLEY GRANT, b Santa Barbara, Calif, Sept 17, 23; m 47; c 3. NUCLEAR CHEMISTRY, CORROSION CHEMISTRY. *Educ:* Univ Calif, Los Angeles, BS, 48. *Prof Exp:* Res chemist radiochem, Gen Elec Co, 48-56; sr engr, Aerophys Develop Corp, 56-58; radio chemist, 58-67, CONSULT NUCLEAR CHEMIST, KNOLLS ATOMIC POWER LAB, GEN ELEC CO, 67- *Mem:* AAAS. *Res:* Radiochemistry; nuclear reactor technology; radiation chemistry; radiation induced corrosion effects; hydrogen diffusion. *Mailing Add:* Knolls Atomic Power Lab Gen Elec Co Schenectady NY 12301

MILLER, DWANE GENE, b Cheyenne, Wyo, May 15, 34; m 59; c 2. AGRONOMY. *Educ:* Univ Wyo, BS, 60, MS, 64, PhD(crop sci), 66; Iowa State Univ, PhD, 65. *Prof Exp:* Instr pub sch, Wyo, 60-62; asst prof biol, Southern Ore Col, 66-67; from asst prof to assoc prof agron, Wash State Univ, 67-77; PROF PLANT & SOIL SCI & CHMN DEPT, TEX TECH UNIV, 77- *Mem:* Crop Sci Soc; Nat Asn Cols & Teachers Agr; Am Soc Agron. *Res:* Hybrid wheat, especially artificial induction of male sterility; histological and physiological studies on gametocides and their action; simulated hail studies in wheat and peas; minimum tillage practices in peas; water use studies in sorghum; teaching of agronomy. *Mailing Add:* Dept of Plant & Soil Sci Tex Tech Univ Lubbock TX 79409

MILLER, E(UGENE), b New York, NY, Feb 2, 22; m 47; c 2. CHEMICAL ENGINEERING. *Educ:* City Col New York, BChE, 44; Polytech Inst Brooklyn, MChE, 47; Univ Del, PhD(chem eng), 49. *Prof Exp:* Test engr, Soconv-Vacuum Oil Co, 44; develop engr, MW Kellogg Co Div, Pullman Inc, 44-47, res engr, 49-52; chief res, Army Rocket & Guided Missile Agency, Redstone Arsenal, 52-57; dir res & develop, Olin Mathieson Chem Corp, 57-59; consult, 59-60; asst tech dir, Lockheed Propulsion Co, 60-65, asst to dir res, Lockheed Palo Alto Res Lab, 65-67, mgr propulsion eng, Lockheed Missiles & Space Co, 67-69; pres, Browning Arms Co Inc, 69-73; PROF & CHMN, DEPT CHEM & METAL ENG, MACKAY SCH MINES, UNIV NEV, 73- *Mem:* Am Chem Soc; Am Inst Chem Engrs. *Res:* Combustion; smoke; thermodynamics. *Mailing Add:* Dept Chem & Metal Eng Univ Nev Reno NV 89507

MILLER, EDMUND K(ENNETH), b Milwaukee, Wis, Dec 24, 35; m 58; c 2. COMPUTER MODELING, SIGNAL PROCESSING. *Educ:* Mich Technol Univ, BS, 57; Univ Mich, MS, 58 & 61, PhD(elec eng), 65. *Prof Exp:* Asst res engr, Radiation Lab, Univ Mich, 58-65, assoc res engr, High Altitude Eng Lab, 66-68; sr staff scientist, MB Assocs, Calif, 68-71; sr staff scientist electronics eng, 71-80, DIV LEADER, ENG RES DIV, LAWRENCE LIVERMORE NAT LAB, 80- *Concurrent Pos:* Instr physics, Mich Technol Univ, 58-59. *Mem:* Inst Elec & Electronics Engrs; Am Phys Soc; Sigma Xi; Int Sci Radio Union. *Res:* Computer modeling applications in electromagnetics, and the development of associated numerical methods; time-domain analysis; signal processing and inverse problems. *Mailing Add:* 140 Berwick Pl San Ramon CA 94583

MILLER, EDSEL LEO, organic chemistry, see previous edition

MILLER, EDWARD, b Newark, NJ, Mar 10, 22; m 47. MECHANICAL ENGINEERING. *Educ:* Newark Col Eng, BS, 48; Univ Del, MME, 49; Columbia Univ, MA, 51; Stevens Inst Technol, MS, 52; NY Univ, MAeroE, 59. *Prof Exp:* Mech designer, Crucible Steel Corp Am, 41-44; assoc prof mech eng, 48-60, asst exec assoc, 48-63, assoc chmn, 63-70, PROF MECH ENG, NJ INST TECHNOL, 60-, ACTG DEAN ENG, 80- *Concurrent Pos:* Consult, Savoy Trunk Co, 52-57, Burt Kaplan Asn, 57-58 & Mohawk Refining Co, 58-59; vis lectr, Rutgers Univ, 54-57; adj assoc prof, NY Univ, 59. *Honors & Awards:* Cert of Award, Am Soc Mech Engrs, 58 & 59. *Mem:* Am Soc Mech Engrs; Am Soc Eng Educ. *Res:* Experimental stress analysis; dynamic and vibration analysis. *Mailing Add:* NJ Inst of Technol 323 High St Newark NJ 07102

MILLER, EDWARD, b Monticello, NY, July 30, 32; m 61. MATERIALS SCIENCE. *Educ:* City Col New York, BChE, 53; NY Univ, MS, 55, DEngSc(metall), 59. *Prof Exp:* Asst eng sci, NY Univ, 53-59, assoc, 59-61, from asst prof to assoc prof, 61-68; assoc prof mech eng, 68-73, PROF MECH ENG, CALIF STATE UNIV, LONG BEACH, 73- *Honors & Awards:* Ralph R Teetor Award, Am Soc Automotive Engrs, 75; Linback Award, 75. *Mem:* Am Inst Mining, Metall & Petrol Engrs; Am Soc Eng Educ; Soc Plastics Engrs. *Res:* Phase relationships and thermodynamic properties of solids and liquids; mechanical properties of polymers. *Mailing Add:* Dept Mech Eng Calif State Univ Long Beach CA 90801

MILLER, EDWARD FREDERICK, petroleum chemistry, see previous edition

MILLER, EDWARD GEORGE, b Columbiana, Ohio, Mar 29, 34; m 57; c 2. ORGANIC CHEMISTRY. *Educ:* Manchester Col, AB, 56; Cornell Univ, PhD(org chem), 61. *Prof Exp:* From instr to assoc prof, 60-74, PROF CHEM & CHMN DEPT, MANCHESTER COL, 74- *Concurrent Pos:* USPHS fel, Princeton Univ, 65-66; vis prof, Silliman Univ, Philippines, 71-72. *Mem:* AAAS; Am Chem Soc. *Res:* Reaction mechanisms and stereochemistry. *Mailing Add:* Dept of Chem Manchester Col North Manchester IN 46962

MILLER, EDWARD GODFREY, JR, b Pittsburgh, Pa, Feb 16, 41; m 64; c 1. BIOCHEMISTRY, ONCOLOGY. *Educ:* Univ Tex, BS, 63, PhD(chem), 69. *Prof Exp:* Fel, McArdle Labs, Univ Wis, 69-72; asst prof, 72-75, assoc prof biochem, 75-81, ASST PROF BIOCHEM & MICROBIOL, BAYLOR UNIV, 81- *Res:* Ribosomal RNA synthesis; modification of nuclear proteins; synthesis of poly ADP-ribose; DNA repair. *Mailing Add:* Dept of Biochem Baylor Col of Dent Dallas TX 75246

MILLER, EDWARD JOSEPH, b Akron, Ohio, Oct 27, 35; m 64; c 3. BIOCHEMISTRY, RADIOBIOLOGY. *Educ:* Spring Hill Col, BS, 60; Univ Rochester, PhD(radiation biol), 64. *Prof Exp:* Res assoc biochem, Nat Inst Dent Res, 63-71; PROF BIOCHEM & SR INVESTR, INST DENT RES, UNIV ALA, BIRMINGHAM, 71- *Honors & Awards:* Award for Basic Res Oral Sci, Int Asn Dent Res, 71; Carol Nachman Prize Rheumatol, 78. *Mem:* AAAS; Am Chem Soc; Am Rheumatol Asn; Am Soc Biol Chemists. *Res:* chemistry and bioloy of the genetically-distinct collagens. *Mailing Add:* Univ of Ala Med Ctr Univ Sta Birmingham AL 35294

MILLER, EDWARD TITUS, b Englewood, NJ, Apr 15, 27; m 50; c 3. GEOPHYSICS. *Educ:* Mass Inst Technol, BS, 49; Columbia Univ, MA, 52, PhD(geophys), 55. *Prof Exp:* Res assoc geophys, Lamont Geol Observ, Columbia Univ, 49-56; sr res geophysicist, Humble Oil & Ref Co, 56-65; dir data processing, Alpine Geophys Assocs, Inc, 65-68; sr explor geophysicist, Exxon Co, USA, 68-80; SR SYSTS ENGR, GEN ELEC CO, 80- *Mem:* AAAS; Soc Explor Geophys; Seismol Soc Am; Acoust Soc Am; Inst Elec & Electronics Engrs. Eng. *Res:* Seismology; applied mathematics; oceanography; data processing; underwater acoustics; computer science. *Mailing Add:* Gen Elec Co PO Box 2500 Daytona Beach FL 32015

MILLER, ELEANOR MARIE, b Philadelphia, Pa, Aug 5, 00. MEDICAL RESEARCH. *Educ:* Univ Penn, BS, 32; Catholic Univ, MS, 38. *Prof Exp:* Teacher high sch, Pa, 26-35; from instr to prof chem, 35-72, chmn div natural sci, 54-72, EMER PROF CHEM, CHESTNUT HILL COL, 72-; DIR, ST JOSEPH VILLA-MED TECHNOL LAB, 72- *Mem:* Am Chem Soc; Nat Sci Teachers Asn. *Res:* Column chromatographic analysis of metal ions; spectrophotometric studies of complex salts. *Mailing Add:* Dept of Chem Chestnut Hill Col Philadelphia PA 19118

MILLER, ELIZABETH CAVERT, b Minneapolis, Minn, May 2, 20; m 42; c 2. ONCOLOGY. *Educ:* Univ Minn, BS, 41; Univ Wis, MS, 43, PhD(biochem), 45. *Prof Exp:* Finney-Howell Found med res fel oncol, 45-47, from instr to assoc prof, 47-69, PROF ONCOL, MED CTR, UNIV WIS-MADISON, 69-; PROF ONCOL, WIS ALUMNI RES FOUND, 80- *Honors & Awards:* Co-recipient, Teplitz-Langer Award, Ann Langer Cancer Res Found, 63, Papanicolaou Res Award, Papanicolaou Cancer Res Inst, 75, Lewis S Rosenstiel Award, Brandeis Univ, 76, Nat Award Basic Sci, Am Cancer Soc, 77; Lucy Wortham James Award, James Ewing Soc, 65; Bertner Award Cancer Res, M D Anderson Hosp & Tumor Inst, 71; Wis Nat Div Award, Am Cancer Soc, 73; Founders Award, Chem Indust Inst Toxicol, 78; Bristol-Myers Award Cancer Res, 78; Int Annual Award, Gairdner Found, 78; Prix Griffuel, Asn Develop Res Cancer, France, 79; 3M Life Sci Award, Fedn Am Soc Exp Biol, 79; Mott Award, Gen Motors Cancer Res Found, 80. *Mem:* Nat Acad Sci; Am Soc Biol Chemists; Am Asn Cancer Res; Am Acad Arts Sci; hon mem Japanese Cancer Asn. *Res:* Experimental chemical carcinogenesis. *Mailing Add:* McArdle Lab Univ Wis Med Ctr Madison WI 53706

MILLER, ELIZABETH ESHELMAN, b Waxahachie, Tex, Aug 6, 19; c 44. BIOCHEMISTRY, IMMUNOLOGY. *Educ:* Univ Colo, BS, 43; Univ Pa, MS, 54, PhD(med microbiol), 55. *Prof Exp:* Technician plant path, Rockefeller Inst, 43-45; asst chem, Biochem Res Found, 45-46; asst gen biochem, Inst Cancer Res, 46-52; asst med microbiol, Henry Phipps Inst, Univ Pa, 52-55; res assoc, Cancer Res Unit & Dept Biochem, Sch Med, Tufts Univ, 56-57; res assoc protein chem & immunol, Bio-Res Inst, 57-61, res assoc, Univ Pittsburgh, 61-62; ASSOC SURG RES, UNIV PA, 62-, ASST PROF SURG RES, 73- *Res:* Chemistry and immunology of cancer. *Mailing Add:* 1333 Prospect Hill Rd Villanova PA 19085

MILLER, ELWOOD MORTON, b Barnesville, Ohio, July 15, 07; m 31; c 1. ZOOLOGY. *Educ:* Bethany Col, BS, 29, DSc, 62; Univ Chicago, MS, 30, PhD(zool), 41. *Prof Exp:* From instr to prof, 30-74, EMER PROF ZOOL, UNIV MIAMI, 74- *Concurrent Pos:* Asst to dir biol Century Prog Expos, Chicago, 33; chmn dept zool, Univ Miami, 46-53, dean arts & sci, 53-66; mem, State Bd Exam Basic Sci, Fla, 46-67. *Mem:* Am Soc Zool. *Res:* Termite biology; social insects. *Mailing Add:* 730 Maybank Dr Hendersonville NC 28739

MILLER, ELWYN RITTER, b Edon, Ohio, Dec 10, 23; m 51; c 5. ANIMAL NUTRITION. *Educ:* Mich State Univ, BS, 48, PhD(animal nutrit), 56. *Prof Exp:* Instr educ, 51-52, from asst to assoc prof, 52-66, PROF NUTRIT, MICH STATE UNIV, 66- *Honors & Awards:* Am Feed Mfg Nutrit Award, Am Soc Animal Sci, 65, Gustav Bohstedt Trace Mineral Res Award, 69; Calcium Carbonate Mineral Res Award, Nat Feed Ingredients Asn, 66. *Mem:* AAAS; Am Soc Animal Sci; Soc Exp Biol & Med; Am Inst Nutrit. *Res:* Hematology, immunology and nutritional requirements of baby pig; mineral nutrition of swine; normal growth and physiological development of swine fetus. *Mailing Add:* Dept Animal Sci Mich State Univ East Lansing MI 48823

MILLER, EMERY B, b Bloomington, Ill, Aug 11, 25; m 48; c 4. ORGANIC CHEMISTRY. *Educ:* Univ Ill, BS, 47; Rice Univ, MS, 49, PhD(org & phys chem), 51. *Prof Exp:* Res chemist, Org Div, Monsanto Chem Co, Mo, 51-53; chem res dir, Maumee Chem Co, Ohio, 53-64; pres, Peninsular Chem Res, Fla, 64-65; mgr res & develop, Houston Res Inst, 65-67; res dir, Tenneco Hydrocarbon Chem Div, 67-69; PRES, EMCHEM CORP, 69- *Mem:* Am Chem Soc; Royal Soc Chem. *Mailing Add:* Emchem Corp Box 876 Pearland TX 77581

MILLER, EMIL C, b Litchfield, Nebr, Nov 21, 07; m 40; c 1. PHYSICS. *Educ:* St Olaf Col, AB, 31; Univ Iowa, MS, 35, PhD, 51. *Prof Exp:* Asst math, St Olaf Col, 30-31; teacher high sch, Minn, 31-36, 37-39; mathematician, Corps Engrs, US Army, 36-37; prof physics & chmn dept, 39-42 & 47-73, EMER PROF PHYSICS & CHMN DEPT, LUTHER COL, IOWA, 74- *Mem:* Am Asn Physics Teachers; Sigma Xi. *Res:* Astronomy; science education. *Mailing Add:* 107 Western Ave Decorah IA 52101

MILLER, EUGENE D, b Wilkes Barre, Pa, June 18, 31; m; c 3. PHYSICAL CHEMISTRY. *Educ:* King's Col, Pa, BS, 55; Catholic Univ, PhD(phys chem), 61. *Prof Exp:* Res chemist, Atlantic Ref Co, 60-64; assoc prof phys & anal chem, Cheyney State Col, 64-67; PROF CHEM, LUZERNE COUNTY COMMUNITY COL, 67- *Mem:* Am Chem Soc. *Res:* Free radical reactions and heterogeneous catalysis. *Mailing Add:* Luzerne County Community Col Nanticoke PA 18634

MILLER, FLOYD GLENN, b Chicago, Ill, May 25, 35; m 62; c 2. INDUSTRIAL & SYSTEMS ENGINEERING. *Educ:* Univ Ill, Urbana, BS, 57, PhD(mech eng), 61. *Prof Exp:* Advan mfg engr, Bell & Howell Co, 60-62; tech develop mgr, 3M Co, 62-66; asst mgr systs & planning, Northern Trust Co, 66-69, mgr, 69-70; ASST TO DIR PHYS PLANT & ASST PROF INDUST ENG, UNIV ILL, CHICAGO CIRCLE, 71-, ACTG DEPT HEAD, 81- *Concurrent Pos:* Mem mgt fac, DePaul Univ, 70- *Mem:* Asn Systs Mgt; Am Inst Indust Engrs. *Res:* Work measurement; work simplification; clerical systems design; standard data techniques; physical plant systems design; automated reporting systems; manual systems analysis. *Mailing Add:* 626 Wellington Chicago IL 60657

MILLER, FLOYD LAVERNE, b Arbela, Mich, Apr 12, 05; m 26; c 3. PHYSICAL CHEMISTRY. *Educ:* Eastern Mich Univ, BA, 26; Univ Mich, MS, 27, PhD(phys chem), 29. *Prof Exp:* Instr chem, Eastern Mich Univ, 26-27; res chemist, Esso Res & Eng Co, 30-31, head, Chem Res Group, 31-33, lubricating sect, 33-37, asst dir, Res Div, 37-45, from assoc dir to dir, 45-53, mgr, Contract, Legal & Patent Dept, 53-55, from dep coordr to coordr, Legal, Patent & Info Dept, 55-65; CONSULT, 65- *Concurrent Pos:* Chem Found res grant, 29-30; chmn cmt chem, Elec Insulation Conf, Nat Res Coun, 38-40; vchmn, Res & Develop Bd, US Dept Defense, 52. *Mem:* Am Chem Soc; Soc Automotive Eng. *Res:* Surface and colloid chemistry; petroleum fuels and lubricants, petroleum processes. *Mailing Add:* Van Beuren Rd Morristown NJ 07960

MILLER, FOIL ALLAN, b Aurora, Ill, Jan 18, 16; m 41; c 2. PHYSICAL CHEMISTRY, STRUCTURAL CHEMISTRY. *Educ:* Hamline Univ, BS, 37; Johns Hopkins Univ, PhD(chem), 42. *Prof Exp:* Nat Res Coun fel, Univ Minn, 42-44; asst prof chem, Univ Ill, 44-48; head spectros div, Mellon Inst, 48-58, sr fel fundamental res, 58-67; prof & dir, Spectros Lab, 67-81, EMER PROF CHEM, UNIV PITTSBURGH, 81- *Concurrent Pos:* Lectr, Univ Pittsburgh, 52-63, adj prof, 63-67; Guggenheim fel, 57-58; ed, Spectrochimica Acta, 57-63; Reilly lectr, Univ Notre Dame, 67; adj sr fel, Mellon Inst, 67-74, mem comn molecular spectros, Int Union Pure & Appl Chem, 67-75, secy, 69-75; vis prof, Tohoku Univ, Sendai, Japan, 77. *Honors & Awards:* Pittsburgh Spectros Award, 64; Pittsburgh Award, Am Chem Soc, 65; Hasler Award, Soc for Appl Spectros, 73. *Mem:* Am Chem Soc; Optical Soc Am; Coblentz Soc (pres, 59-60); hon mem Soc Appl Spectros. *Res:* Infrared, Raman and electronic spectra. *Mailing Add:* Dept of Chem Univ of Pittsburgh Pittsburgh PA 15260

MILLER, FOREST LEONARD, JR, b Cincinnati, Ohio, June 18, 36; m 61; c 3. EXPERIMENTAL STATISTICS. *Educ:* Purdue Univ, BS, 58, MS, 59; NC State Univ, PhD(statist), 75. *Prof Exp:* Consult statistician, Nuclear Div, Union Carbide Corp, 59-79; SR STATISTICIAN & RES PROF, DESSERT RES INST, 79- *Mem:* Am Statist Asn; Biomet Soc; Inst Math Statist; Royal

Statist Soc; Health Physics Soc. *Res:* Development of conditional probability integral transformations and their application; development of tests for extreme value distributions. *Mailing Add:* Desert Res Inst 1500 E Tropicana Suite 201 Las Vegas NV 89109

MILLER, FRANCIS JOSEPH, b Montgomery, Ala, Aug 6, 17; m 45; c 2. ANALYTICAL CHEMISTRY. *Educ:* Univ Ala, AB, 39. *Prof Exp:* Anal chemist, Oak Ridge Nat Lab, 46-67, tech ed & writer, Isotopes Div, 67-68; ASST PROF RES & ADMIN ASST TO DIR RES, UNIV TENN, MEM RES CTR & HOSP, KNOXVILLE, 68- *Mem:* Am Chem Soc; Sigma Xi. *Res:* Instrumental methods of analysis; research administration; technical editing and writing. *Mailing Add:* Univ of Tenn Mem Res Ctr & Hosp 1924 Alcoa Hwy Knoxville TN 37920

MILLER, FRANCIS MARION, b Central City, Ky, Dec 28, 25; m 47; c 3. ORGANIC CHEMISTRY. *Educ:* Western Ky State Col, BS, 46; Northwestern Univ, PhD(chem), 49. *Prof Exp:* Res assoc org chem, Harvard Univ, 48-49; asst prof sch pharm, Univ Md, 49-51, assoc prof, 51-61, prof & chmn dept, 61-68; head dept, 68-77, PROF CHEM, NORTHERN ILL UNIV, 68- *Concurrent Pos:* Consult, Chem Corps, US Army, 55-69; guest prof, Univ Heidelberg, 58-59. *Mem:* Am Chem Soc. *Res:* Alkaloids; heterocyclics; mechanisms of organic reactions; medicinal chemistry. *Mailing Add:* Dept Chem Northern Ill Univ De Kalb IL 60115

MILLER, FRANK L, b Kansas City, Mo, Aug 31, 30; m 58; c 3. ATOMIC PHYSICS, COSMIC RAY PHYSICS. *Educ:* Univ Okla, BS, 51, MS, 57, PhD(physics), 64. *Prof Exp:* Asst prof physics, Ft Lewis Col, 63-66; assoc prof, 66-73; PROF PHYSICS, US NAVAL ACAD, 73- *Mem:* Am Phys Soc; Am Asn Physics Teachers; AAAS; Sigma Xi. *Res:* Atomic excitation by electron bombardment. *Mailing Add:* Dept of Physics US Naval Acad Annapolis MD 21402

MILLER, FRANK NELSON, JR, b Alexandria, Va, Apr 15, 19; m 54; c 2. PATHOLOGY. *Educ:* George Washington Univ, BS, 43, MD, 48. *Prof Exp:* Asst scientist chem, Allegheny Ballistics Lab, 43-44; asst resident path, Univ Hosp, 49-50, from asst prof to assoc prof, 51-63, assoc dean, 66-73, PROF PATH, GEORGE WASHINGTON UNIV, 63- *Concurrent Pos:* Teaching fel, George Washington Univ, 50-51; attend, Mont Alto Vet Admin Hosp, 56-58; consult, US Air Force Hosp, Washington, DC, 55-58, Baker Vet Admin Hosp, Martinsburg, WVa, 60-68 & Vet Admin Hosp, Washington, DC, 68- *Mem:* AAAS; Int Acad Path; AMA; fel Col Am Path; fel Am Soc Clin Pathologists. *Res:* Neoplasms of the breast and female genital tract. *Mailing Add:* 2300 I St NW Washington DC 20037

MILLER, FRANKLIN, JR, b St Louis, Mo, Sept 8, 12; m 37; c 1. PHYSICS, SCIENCE EDUCATION. *Educ:* Swarthmore Col, AB, 33; Univ Chicago, PhD(physics), 39. *Prof Exp:* Asst physics, Univ Chicago, 35-37; from instr to asst prof, Rutgers Univ, 37-48; assoc prof, Kenyon Col, 48-58, chmn dept, 55-66, 69-73, prof physics, 59-81; RETIRED. *Honors & Awards:* Millikan Lectr Award, Am Asn Physics Teachers, 70. *Mem:* AAAS; Am Phys Soc; Am Asn Physics Teachers; Fedn Am Sci; Soc for Social Responsibility in Sci (pres, 53-55). *Res:* Musical acoustics; educational science films. *Mailing Add:* PO Box 313 Gambier OH 43022

MILLER, FRANKLIN STUART, b Columbus, Ohio, June 3, 06; m 39; c 1. ECONOMIC GEOLOGY. *Educ:* Williams Col, AB, 28; Harvard Univ, AM, 31, PhD(geol), 34. *Prof Exp:* Geologist, Western Mining Corp, Australia, 34-36; instr geol, Univ Ill, 36-37; consult geologist, Can & Calif, 37-38; instr mineral, Univ Calif, 38-39; field supt, Roseville & Roaring River Gold Dredging Cos, 39-40; consult geologist, Univ Toronto, 40-41; asst dir, Mining Div, War Prod Bd, 41-45; consult geologist, Univ Ohio, 46-47; asst mgr, Pac Tin Consol Corp, Malaya, 48-50, vpres, NY, 50-66, pres, 66-72, chmn, 72-75; vpres, Feldspar Corp, 55-66, pres, 66-72, dir, 55-78; dir, Pac Tin Consol Corp, 50-77; RETIRED. Partner, Guggenheim Bros, 73-; dir, Co-Co Del, Inc, 73- *Mem:* Fel AAAS; fel Geol Soc Am; Soc Econ Geol; Am Inst Mining, Metall & Petrol Eng; Can Inst Mining & Metall. *Res:* Petrology of the intrusive rocks; geologic structure of ore deposits; graphs for geologic calculations; production and resources of tin. *Mailing Add:* PO Box 266 Salisbury CT 06068

MILLER, FRANKLYN DAVID, b Hazleton, Pa, Feb 6, 21; m 44; c 1. PHYSICAL CHEMISTRY, ORGANIC CHEMISTRY. *Educ:* Ursinus Col, BS, 42; Univ Pa, MS, 44, PhD(chem), 50. *Prof Exp:* Asst, Kind & Knox Gelatin Co, 42-43; asst instr chem, Univ Pa, 42-44, 46-49; MGR ANAL RES, US INDUST CHEM CO DIV, NAT DISTILLERS & CHEM CORP, 49-, RES SCIENTIST, 74- *Mem:* AAAS; Am Chem Soc; Am Mgt Asn. *Res:* Instrumental analysis; process development; analytical chemistry; technical planning and evaluation; long range research planning; biochemistry. *Mailing Add:* 8871 Falmouth Dr Cincinnati OH 45231

MILLER, FRED KEY, b Alhambra, Calif, Dec 1, 37; m 61. GEOLOGY. *Educ:* Univ Calif, Riverside, BA, 61; Stanford Univ, PhD(geol), 66. *Prof Exp:* GEOLOGIST, US GEOL SURV, 65- *Mem:* Geol Soc Am. *Res:* Regional geologic problems in southwest Arizona and southeastern California; regional geologic problems in northeastern Washington, especially Precambrian structure and stratigraphy. *Mailing Add:* US Geol Surv 345 Middlefield Rd Menlo Park CA 94025

MILLER, FREDERICK ARNOLD, b La Crosse, Wis, Dec 1, 26; m 51; c 4. PHYSICAL CHEMISTRY. *Educ:* Luther Col, Iowa, BA, 49; Iowa State Univ, PhD(chem), 53. *Prof Exp:* ASSOC SCIENTIST, DOW CHEM USA, 53- *Mem:* Am Chem Soc. *Res:* Synthetic latex; colloid chemistry; organic coatings; emulsion polymerization technology; latex based formulations. *Mailing Add:* Dow Chem Co 1603 Bldg Midland MI 48640

MILLER, FREDERICK POWELL, b Springfield, Ohio, Oct 17, 36; m 65. SOIL SCIENCE, AGRONOMY. *Educ:* Ohio State Univ, BSc, 58, MSc, 61, PhD(agron, soil classification), 65. *Prof Exp:* Res asst soil chem, Ohio State Univ, 59-62, soil classification, 62-63; soil scientist, Ohio Dept Natural Resources, 63-64; res asst soil classification, Ohio State Univ, 64-65; soil & water resource specialist, 65-69, from asst prof to assoc prof, 65-74, PROF SOILS, UNIV MD, COLLEGE PARK, 74- *Mem:* Am Soc Agron; Soil Sci Soc Am; Soil Conserv Soc Am; Int Soc Soil Sci. *Res:* Physical, chemical and mineralogical characterization of soil Fragipans; electrophoretic separation of soil clay minerals; soil survey interpretation. *Mailing Add:* Dept of Agron Univ of Md College Park MD 20742

MILLER, FREDERICK WARREN, chemical engineering, see previous edition

MILLER, FREDRIC N, b Chicago, Ill, May 26, 41; m 62; c 2. PAPER CHEMISTRY. *Educ:* Ill Inst Technol, BSc, 62, PhD(org chem), 67. *Prof Exp:* Res chemist, WVa Pulp & Paper Co, 66-69; sr scientist, Am Can Co, 69-72, supvr converting group, 72-74, mgr prod develop, Tissue & Towel, 74-77; dir, Tech Asn Pulp & Paper Indust, 77-78; GEN MGR RES & ENG, TEEPAK INC, 78- *Mem:* Am Chem Soc; Tech Asn Pulp & Paper Indust. *Res:* Cellulose chemistry; collagen chemistry; specialty papers; consumer paper products; paperboard; non-wovens; flame retardancy of cellulosics and cellulosic blends; dry forming of paper; embossing; synthetic and natural binders; injection molding and thermoforming; converting of paper and paperboard. *Mailing Add:* Teepak Inc 915 N Michigan Ave Danville IL 61832

MILLER, FREEMAN DEVOLD, b Somerville, Mass, Jan 4, 09; m 33. ASTRONOMY. *Educ:* Harvard Univ, SB, 30, MA, 32, PhD(astron), 34. *Prof Exp:* Dir Swasey Observ, Denison Univ, 34-40; assoc prof astron, Univ Mich, Ann Arbor, 46-55; assoc dean Horace H Rackham Sch Grad Studies, 59-66, actg chmn dept astron, 60-61; prof, 55-77, EMER PROF ASTRON, UNIV MICH, ANN ARBOR, 77- *Mem:* Am Astron Soc; Int Astron Union. *Res:* Comets. *Mailing Add:* Dept Astron Dennison Bldg Univ of Mich Ann Arbor MI 48109

MILLER, G(ERSON) H(ARRY), b Philadelphia, Pa, Mar 2, 24; m 61; c 2. MATHEMATICS, MEDICAL STATISTICS. *Educ:* Pomona Col, BA, 49; Temple Univ, MEd, 51; Univ Southern Calif, PhD(ed psychol, math), 57; Univ Ill, ABD, 65. *Prof Exp:* Instr math, Los Angeles Sch Dist, 53-57; assoc prof math & ed, Western Ill Univ, 57-60; prof, Towson State Col, 60-61; prof math, Parsons Col, 61-65; assoc prof, Wis State Univ, Whitewater, 65-66; prof & dir math educ res, Tenn Technol Univ, 66-68; prof math & systs analyst, Comput Ctr, Edinboro State Col, 68-72, asst dir, Off Instnl Res, 73-80. *Concurrent Pos:* Dir, Nat Study Math Requirements for Scientists & Engrs, 65-; dir, Studies on Smoking & Stop Smoking Clin, 73-; bd mem, Nat Interagency Coun on Smoking & Health. *Mem:* AAAS; Math Asn Am; Am Chem Soc; Am Soc Eng Educ; NY Acad Sci. *Res:* History of mathematics; comparative mathematics education; retention and deficencies in mathematics; analysis; set theory; curricular improvements in science and engineering; smoking and health research. *Mailing Add:* 104 Valley View Dr Edinboro PA 16412

MILLER, GABRIEL LORIMER, b New York, NY, Jan 18, 28. PHYSICS. *Educ:* Univ London, BSc, 49, MSc, 52, PhD(physics), 57. *Prof Exp:* Physicist, Instrumentation Div, Brookhaven Nat Lab, 57-63; MEM TECH STAFF, BELL TEL LABS, 63- *Mem:* Am Phys Soc; fel Inst Elec & Electronics Eng. *Res:* Nuclear instrumentation; satellite experiments; solid state; electronics. *Mailing Add:* Bell Tel Labs Murray Hill NJ 07974

MILLER, GARY A, b Newark, NJ, Dec 5, 45. NUTRITION, FOOD SCIENCE. *Educ:* Rutgers Univ, BS, 68, PhD(food sci), 74. *Prof Exp:* Asst prof food & nutrit, Univ Nebr, Lincoln, 74-76; res scientist, 76-78, group leader, Food Sci Group, 78-80, MGR PHARMACEUT PROD DEVELOP, MCGAW LABS, CALIF, 81- *Mem:* Sigma Xi; Inst Food Technologists; NY Acad Sci; AAAS. *Res:* Development and evaluation of biological assays and rapid chemical indices to measure protein nutritive value; product development of medical foods and parenteral solutions. *Mailing Add:* PO Box 11887 McGaw Labs Santa Ana CA 92711

MILLER, GARY GLENN, topology, theoretical physics, see previous edition

MILLER, GARY L, b Columbia, Pa, July 26, 40; m 62; c 2. ECOLOGY, BOTANY. *Educ:* Millersville State Col, BS, 62; Univ NC, Chapel Hill, MA, 65, PhD(bot), 68. *Prof Exp:* Instr bot, Univ NC, Chapel Hill, 68-69; asst prof, 69-72, assoc prof, 72-76, PROF BIOL, EISENHOWER COL, 76- *Concurrent Pos:* Vis prof ecol, Mt Lake Biol Sta, Univ Va, 71-79; adj prof, Univ NH, 78-80. *Mem:* Am Inst Biol Sci; AAAS. *Res:* Radiation effects on plant communities; terrestrial succession; aquatic vegetation of the Finger Lakes; ecological impact of 2,4-diclorophenoxyacetic acid on aquatic vegetation communities; aquatic botany; wetlands botany. *Mailing Add:* Dept Environ Studies Eisenhower Col Seneca Falls NY 13148

MILLER, GARY WILLIAM, immunobiology, see previous edition

MILLER, GENE WALKER, b Utah, Dec 21, 25; m 53; c 5. PLANT BIOCHEMISTRY. *Educ:* Utah State Univ, BS, 50, MS, 54; NC State Univ, PhD(bot), 57. *Prof Exp:* Plant biochemist, Utah State Univ, 57-69, actg dean col sci, 67; dean, Col Environ Sci, Huxley Col, Western Wash Univ, 69-74; HEAD DEPT BIOL, UTAH STATE UNIV, 74- *Concurrent Pos:* USPHS spec fel, Univ Münster, 61 & 66; mem staff, Univ Melbourne, Australia, 81. *Mem:* AAAS; Biochem Soc; Am Soc Plant Physiol; Japanese Soc Plant Physiol; Am Asn Univ Professors. *Res:* Mineral nutrition of plants, especially the role of metals and nutrients, electron transport system, oxidative phosphorylation and plant metabolism; effects of air pollutants on biochemical reactions; environmental study programs. *Mailing Add:* Dept Biol UMC 53 Utah State Univ Logan UT 84322

MILLER, GEORGE, b Chicago, Ill, Jan 15, 20; m 44; c 2. ENGINEERING PHYSICS. *Educ:* Univ Western Ky, BS, 42. *Prof Exp:* Develop engr, Librascope Inc, 54-55; proj engr, Barton Instrument Corp, 55-56, asst chief engr, 56-58; dept mgr reliability, Torpedo Div, Aerojet Gen, 58-61, dept mgr reliability & qual assurance, Reon Div, 61-63, asst div mgr prod assurance, 63-64; supvr reliability, Rockwell Space Div, NAm Aviation Inc, 64-67; model engr, Douglas Aircraft Div, McDonnell-Douglas Corp, 67; CHIEF RELIABILITY ENGR, RALPH M PARSONS CO, 67- *Honors & Awards:* Appreciation Awards, US Off Res & Develop & War Dept, Army Serv Forces, Corps Engrs, Manhattan Dist, 44; Commemorative Medal, Atomic Energy Comn, 62. *Mem:* Am Soc Qual Control. *Res:* Application of system and cost effectiveness analysis techniques to military and commercial systems development; math model derivation relating system parameters to mission objectives and effectiveness criteria providing management insight into system requirements. *Mailing Add:* 100 W Walnut St Pasadena CA 91124

MILLER, GEORGE ALFORD, b Madison, Wis, Dec 24, 25; m 63. PHYSICAL CHEMISTRY. *Educ:* Univ Wis, BS, 50; Univ Mich, PhD(chem), 55. *Prof Exp:* Res assoc, Univ Mich, 55-56; instr, Am Cols Istanbul, 56-57; res assoc, Univ Mich, 57-58; from asst prof to assoc prof, 58-70, PROF CHEM, GA INST TECHNOL, 70- *Mem:* Am Chem Soc. *Res:* Thermodynamics, kinetic theory of gases and light scattering. *Mailing Add:* Sch of Chem Georgia Inst of Technol Atlanta GA 30332

MILLER, GEORGE C, b Portland, Ore, June 8, 25; m 59; c 2. ICHTHYOLOGY. *Educ:* Univ Wash, BS, 51; Ore State Col, BS, 56, MS, 60. *Prof Exp:* Aquatic biologist, Ore Fish Comn, 51-52, 56, 57-58; fisheries adv to Liberia, US For Opers Admin, 52-54; aquatic biologist, Wash State Dept Fisheries, 54-55 & Ore State Col, 58-59; fisheries biologist, Biol Lab, Bur Com Fisheries, US Fish & Wildlife Serv, Ga, 60-65 & Miami Lab, Southeast Fisheries Ctr, Nat Marine Fisheries Serv, Fla, 65-80; CONSULT, 81- *Concurrent Pos:* Adj asst prof marine biol, Fla Atlantic Univ. *Mem:* Am Soc Ichthyol & Herpet; Gulf & Caribbean Fisheries Inst; Nat Shellfisheries Asn. *Res:* Invertebrate biology; marine ecology; systematic zoology; and zoogeography; biology of marine organisms in relation to technological development. *Mailing Add:* 16140 SW 108 Ct Miami FL 33157

MILLER, GEORGE E, b Banbury, Eng, May 12, 37; m 64; c 2. PHYSICAL CHEMISTRY, RADIOCHEMISTRY. *Educ:* Oxford Univ, BA, 59, DPhil (chem), 63. *Prof Exp:* Res assoc chem, Univ Kans, 63-65; res assoc, 65-68, LECTR CHEM & REACTOR SUPVR, UNIV CALIF, IRVINE, 68- *Mem:* Am Chem Soc; Am Nuclear Soc. *Res:* Reactor utilization in chemistry; activation analysis applications in geochemistry, archeology and medicine; synthesis of labelled molecules and particles. *Mailing Add:* Dept Chem Univ Calif Irvine CA 92715

MILLER, GEORGE EARL, b Buffalo, NY, Dec 5, 28; m 54; c 4. UNDERWATER ACOUSTICS. *Educ:* St Lawrence Univ, BS, 51, MS, 53. *Prof Exp:* Assoc res staff mem, Res Div, Raytheon Co, 53-58, sr engr, Submarine Signal Div, 58-60; proj engr, Harris Anti-Submarine Warfare Div, Gen Instrument Corp, 60-61; physicist, Arthur D Little, Inc, 61-78; SR ENG SCIENTIST, RCA GOVT SYSTS DIV, 78- *Mem:* Acoust Soc Am. *Res:* Industrial and medical applications of ultrasonics; ultrasonic and sonar transducer design; anti-submarine warfare systems analysis. *Mailing Add:* RCA Govt Systs Div Automated Systs PO Box 588 Burlington MA 01803

MILLER, GEORGE EDWARD, b Swarthmore, Pa, June 15, 19; m 49; c 3. MEDICINE. *Educ:* Univ Penn, AB, 40, MD, 43. *Hon Degrees:* MD, Univ Uppsala, Sweden, 77. *Prof Exp:* Intern, asst res & res med, Buffalo Gen Hosp, 43-45; mem staff, Niagara Sanatorium, Lockport, NY, 47-48; asst prof med, Univ Buffalo, 52-56, assoc prof, 56-59; assoc prof med, Univ Ill Med Ctr, 59-60, prof, 60-71, dir res med educ, 59-76, prof med educ, 71-79, coordr int activ, 76-79; DIR, RUDD HEALTH CTR, HAMILTON COL, CLINTON, NY, 79- *Concurrent Pos:* Res fel, Buffalo Gen Hosp, 48-50, mem res div, 50-59, dir house staff educ, 54-59. *Mem:* Asn Am Med Cols. *Res:* Medical education. *Mailing Add:* Ctr Educ Develop 808 S Wood St Chicago IL 60612

MILLER, GEORGE H, JR, b Iowa City, Iowa, Dec 16, 24; m 45; c 4. UROLOGY. *Educ:* Princeton Univ, AB, 47; Univ Pa, MD, 48. *Prof Exp:* Intern, Univ Chicago, 49, resident, 54, from instr to assoc prof urol, 54-58; assoc prof, 58-62, chief div urol, 58-70, prof urol, Col Med, Univ Fla, 62-77 & asst dean Vet Admin Hosp Rels, 70-77; STAFF, VET ADMIN HOSP, 78- *Concurrent Pos:* Chief staff & urol sect, Vet Admin Hosp, Gainesville, 70- *Mem:* Am Urol Asn; AMA; Am Col Surgeons. *Res:* Urinary tract infection and urinary stone disease. *Mailing Add:* Vet Admin Hosp Togus ME 04330

MILLER, GERALD R, b McClure, Ill, Dec 4, 34; m 58; c 2. WEED SCIENCE. *Educ:* Univ Ill, BS, 56, MS, 57; Mich State Univ, PhD(weed control, physiol), 63. *Prof Exp:* Exten agronomist, Purdue Univ, 63-64; EXTEN AGRONOMIST, UNIV MINN, ST PAUL, 64- *Mem:* Weed Sci Soc Am (secy, 75-76); Crop Sci Soc Am; Am Soc Agron. *Res:* Weed control; crop-weed competition; herbicide development. *Mailing Add:* 1428 Arden Pl St Paul MN 55112

MILLER, GERALD R, b Wellsville, NY, Dec 6, 39; m 61; c 2. MATERIALS SCIENCE, PHYSICS. *Educ:* Cornell Univ, BMetE, 62, MS, 63, PhD, 65. *Prof Exp:* Assoc prof mat sci, 65-76, PROF MAT SCI & ENG, UNIV UTAH, 76-, ADJ ASSOC PROF PHYSICS, 68- *Concurrent Pos:* Sci Res Coun fel, Univ Edinburgh, 71-72. *Mem:* Am Phys Soc. *Res:* Amorphous semiconducting devices; point defects in solids; transport theory. *Mailing Add:* Dept of Physics Univ of Utah Salt Lake City UT 84112

MILLER, GERALD RAY, b Milwaukee, Wis, Nov 13, 36; m 58; c 2. PHYSICAL CHEMISTRY. *Educ:* Univ Wis, BS, 58; Univ Ill, MS, 60, PhD(chem), 62. *Prof Exp:* NSF fel phys chem, Oxford Univ, 61-63; asst prof, 65-71, assoc chmn, 77-79, ASSOC PROF PHYS CHEM, UNIV MD, COLLEGE PARK, 71- *Concurrent Pos:* Assoc dir fels, Nat Acad Sci-Nat Res Coun, 74-76. *Mem:* Am Chem Soc; The Chem Soc; Am Phys Soc; AAAS. *Res:* Nuclear magnetic resonance and electron spin resonance spectroscopy; molecular and solid state structure. *Mailing Add:* Dept Chem Univ Md College Park MD 20742

MILLER, GERTRUDE NEVADA, b Dover, Del, July 6, 19. PLANT TAXONOMY. *Educ:* Univ WVa, BS, 41, MA, 43; Cornell Univ, PhD(plant taxon), 53. *Prof Exp:* Asst bot & plant taxon, Cornell Univ, 44-47; instr biol, Wells Col, 47-50 & Hollins Col, 53-54; from asst prof, Northern State Col to assoc prof, 54-57, prof biol & chmn dept math, Natural Sci & Health Professions, 60-80; RETIRED. *Mem:* Nat Asn Biol Teachers; Nat Sci Teachers Asn; Am Nature Study Soc; Am Inst Biol Sci. *Res:* Taxonomic revision of the genus Fraximus. *Mailing Add:* PO Box 56 Piney Flats TN 37686

MILLER, GLENDON RICHARD, b Columbus, Ohio, Oct 28, 38; m 66; c 2. MICROBIOLOGY, BIOCHEMISTRY. *Educ:* Southern Ill Univ, BA, 60, MA, 62; Univ Mo-Columbia, PhD(microbiol), 66. *Prof Exp:* Res microbiologist, Colgate Palmolive Res Ctr, 66-68; asst prof bact & physiol, 68-73, grad coordr dept, 75-80, ASSOC PROF BIOL, WICHITA STATE UNIV, 73- *Concurrent Pos:* Consult, Koch Eng, 71-, Dolo Foods, 79- & Great Plains, 81- *Mem:* AAAS; Am Soc Microbiol. *Res:* Radiation repair enzymes of yeasts; antibiotics; antibiotic combination; resistance and cross-resistance to antibiotics; effects of antibiotics on the ribosome. *Mailing Add:* Dept of Biol Sci Wichita State Univ Wichita KS 67208

MILLER, GLENN HARRY, b Pittsburgh, Pa, Feb 10, 22; m 51; c 3. CHEMISTRY. *Educ:* Geneva Col, BS, 43; Brown Univ, PhD(chem), 48. *Prof Exp:* Chemist, Oak Ridge Nat Lab, 44; sr chemist, Butadiene Div, Koppers Co, Inc, 44-45; chemist, Tex Co, 48-49; from instr to assoc prof, 49-63, chmn dept, 60-64, PROF CHEM, UNIV CALIF, SANTA BARBARA, 63- *Concurrent Pos:* Nat Res Coun Can fel, 56-57; Fulbright-Hays lectr, Univ Malaya, 67-68 & Univ Liberia, 74-75. *Mem:* Am Chem Soc. *Res:* Popcorn polymerization; polymers; photolysis. *Mailing Add:* Dept of Chem Univ of Calif Santa Barbara CA 93106

MILLER, GLENN HOUSTON, b Washington, DC, June 15, 20; m 45; c 3. PHYSICS. *Educ:* Wake Forest Col, BS, 42; Cornell Univ, PhD(appl physics), 47. *Prof Exp:* Asst eng physics, Cornell Univ, 42-44; res engr, Stromberg-Carlson Co, NY, 44-46; asst eng physics, Cornell Univ, 46-47; asst prof physics, Iowa State Univ, 47-55; prof elec eng & asst dir ord res lab, Univ Va, 55-59; sr physicist & assoc head physics div, Denver Res Inst, 59-61; staff mem, Sandia Corp, 61-64, supvr atomic physics, 65-71, supvr radiation source diagnostics, 71-75, supvr, Laser Appln Div, 76-79, SUPVR EXP PLANNING DIV, SANDIA NAT LABS, 79- *Mem:* Fel Am Phys Soc. *Res:* Ionization yields for atomic particles in gases; production of high velocity molecular beams; condensation of atoms on surfaces; interaction of energetic ions with gases; electron physics. *Mailing Add:* Div 1112 Sandia Nat Labs PO Box 5800 Albuquerque NM 87185

MILLER, GLENN JOSEPH, b Crete, Nebr, June 28, 25; m 50; c 3. BIOCHEMISTRY. *Educ:* Doane Col, BA, 51; Purdue Univ, MS, 53, PhD(biochem), 56. *Prof Exp:* Asst, Purdue Univ, 51-56; from asst prof to prof biochem, 56-76, head div, 72-76, PROF FOOD BIOCHEM, DIV ANIMAL SCI, UNIV WYO, 76- *Mem:* AAAS; Am Oil Chem Soc; NY Acad Sci; Am Meat Sci Asn; Inst Food Technol. *Res:* Implication of fats in foods with emphasis upon animal products. *Mailing Add:* Div of Animal Sci Univ Sta Box 3354 Laramie WY 82071

MILLER, GORDON LEE, b Milwaukee, Wis, Sept 27, 38. MATHEMATICS. *Educ:* Moorhead State Col, BS, 64; NDak State Univ, MS, 65; Univ Northern Colo, EdD(math), 70. *Prof Exp:* From instr to asst prof, 65-72, assoc prof, 72-80, PROF MATH, UNIV WIS-STEVENS POINT, 80- *Mem:* Math Asn Am; Nat Coun Teachers Math. *Res:* Analysis. *Mailing Add:* Dept of Math Univ of Wis-Stevens Point Stevens Point WI 54481

MILLER, GROVER CLEVELAND, b Jackson, Ky, Jan 23, 27; m 51; c 4. ZOOLOGY. *Educ:* Berea Col, AB, 50; Univ Ky, MS, 52; La State Univ, PhD(zool), 57. *Prof Exp:* Asst parasitologist, La State Univ, 56-57; from instr to assoc prof, 57-69, PROF ZOOL, NC STATE UNIV, 69- *Mem:* Am Soc Parasitol. *Res:* Invertebrate zoology; parasitology; trematodes of freshwater fishes; helminth parasites in wild animals. *Mailing Add:* Dept of Zool NC State Univ Raleigh NC 27650

MILLER, GUTHRIE, b Greensburg, Ind, Oct 16, 42. PLASMA PHYSICS. *Educ:* Calif Inst Technol, BS, 64; Stanford Univ, PhD(physics), 70. *Prof Exp:* Res asst high energy physics, Stanford Linear Accelerator Ctr, 67-71; res assoc, Univ Wash, 71-74; STAFF MEM CONTROLLED THERMONUCLEAR RES DIV, LOS ALAMOS NAT LAB, 74- *Mem:* Am Phys Soc. *Res:* Confinement of high temperature plasmas, experimental and theoretical magnetohydrodynamics. *Mailing Add:* Mail Stop 650 Los Alamos Nat Lab Los Alamos NM 87545

MILLER, HALSEY WILKINSON, JR, b Camden, NJ, July 1, 30; m 81; c 3. GEOLOGY, PALEONTOLOGY. *Educ:* Temple Univ, AB, 54; Yale Univ, MS, 54; Univ Kans, PhD(geol), 58. *Prof Exp:* Geologist, State Geol Surv, Kans, 55-57; asst prof invert paleont, Univ Ariz, 57-63; assoc prof geol, High Point Col, 63-67; asst prof, Ft Hays Kans State Col, 67-69; PROF GEOL, SOUTHERN ILL UNIV, 69- *Honors & Awards:* Res Award, Southern Ill Univ, 71. *Mem:* Paleont Soc; Soc Vert Paleont; Am Asn Petrol Geol. *Res:* Cretaceous stratigraphy and paleontology; Cretaceous-Tertiary boundary line; fossil molluscs; lower vertebrates paleoecology. *Mailing Add:* Fac of Earth Sci Southern Ill Univ Edwardsville IL 62025

MILLER, HAROLD A, b St Paul, Minn, Mar 14, 21; m 46. PHYSICAL CHEMISTRY. *Educ:* Univ Minn, BS, 42; NY Univ, PhD(phys chem), 51. *Prof Exp:* Asst agr biochem, Univ Minn, 41-42; asst chem, NY Univ, 49-50; res chemist, 50-62, asst dir res, 62-72, DIR RES, MEARL CORP, 72- *Mem:* Am Phys Soc; Am Chem Soc; Soc Cosmetic Chemists; Electron Micros Soc Am; NY Acad Sci. *Res:* Crystal growth; surface chemistry; nacreous pigments; structure of crystals and molecules; infrared spectroscopy. *Mailing Add:* Mearl Corp 217 N Highland Ave Ossining NY 10562

MILLER, HAROLD CHARLES, b Canton, Ohio, Nov 28, 41; m 63; c 3. MICROBIOLOGY, IMMUNOLOGY. *Educ:* Hiram Col, AB, 64; Mich State Univ, MS, 66, PhD(microbiol), 68. *Prof Exp:* Instr microbiol, Mich State Univ, 68; res assoc immunol, Roswell Park Mem Inst, 68-70; res assoc, State Univ NY Buffalo, 70-71, asst prof path & immunol, 71; asst prof, 71-74, assoc prof, 74-78, PROF MICROBIOL, MICH STATE UNIV, 78- *Concurrent Pos:* Am Cancer Soc fel, Roswell Park Mem Inst, 68-71; Nat Cancer Inst fel, Univ Buffalo, 68-71; Am Cancer Soc Fac Res Award, 76-81. *Mem:* Am Asn Immunologists; Am Soc Microbiol. *Res:* Cellular immunology including differentiation of primitive marrow stem cells into B and T lymphocytes and development of immunological memory; lymphocyte surface markers, phenotypes and membrane changes that influence function. *Mailing Add:* Dept of Microbiol & Pub Health Mich State Univ East Lansing MI 48824

MILLER, HARRY, b Detroit, Mich, July 11, 15; m 44; c 2. MECHANICAL ENGINEERING. *Educ:* City Col New York, BME, 37. *Prof Exp:* Jr engr, Master Wire & Die Co, 37-38; marine engr, Brooklyn Navy Yard, 38-44; engr, Fed Tel Co, 44-45 & Shirgun Corp, 45-47; head, Dept Eng Transp Flight Controls, 48-67, head, Dept Eng Flight Control Systs, 67-69, mgr, Dept Eng Flight Guid Systs & Instrumentation, 69-80, ENG DIR COMMUN SYSTS, SPEERY FLIGHT SYSTS DIV, SPERRY CORP, 80- *Concurrent Pos:* Lectr, City Col New York, 47-50. *Mem:* Am Soc Mech Engrs. *Res:* Automatic flight control systems; pressure sensitive devices. *Mailing Add:* 5136 N 68th Pl Scottsdale AZ 85253

MILLER, HARRY BROWN, b Cumberland, Md, May 25, 13; m 41. ORGANIC CHEMISTRY. *Educ:* Univ NC, BS, 36, PhD(chem), 46. *Prof Exp:* With Standard Oil Co (NJ), 36-42; instr chem, Armstrong Jr Col, Ga, 45-47; from asst prof to assoc prof, 47-61, PROF CHEM, WAKE FOREST UNIV, 61- *Mem:* AAAS; Am Chem Soc. *Res:* Reactions of organic halogen compounds; fluorine chemistry. *Mailing Add:* Box 7241 Reynolda Sta Winston-Salem NC 27109

MILLER, HARRY GALEN, b Annapolis, Md, May 17, 37; m 57; c 2. PHYSICS. *Educ:* Defiance Col, BS, 59; Ohio State Univ, PhD(nuclear physics), 63. *Prof Exp:* Teacher high sch, 58-59; admissions counsr, 59-60, from asst prof to assoc prof, 63-73, PROF PHYSICS, DEFIANCE COL, 73- *Concurrent Pos:* Resident assoc, Argonne Nat Lab, Ill, 69-70, consult, 70-72. *Res:* Nuclear energy levels; gamma-ray spectroscopy. *Mailing Add:* Dept of Physics Defiance Col Defiance OH 43512

MILLER, HARVEY ALFRED, b Sturgis, Mich, Oct 19, 28; m 52; c 2. BRYOLOGY, PLANT PATENTS. *Educ:* Univ Mich, BS, 50; Univ Hawaii, MS, 52; Stanford Univ, PhD(biol), 57. *Prof Exp:* Asst bot, Univ Hawaii, 50-53; asst herbarium, Stanford Univ, 53-55; instr bot, Univ Mass, 55-56; from instr to asst prof bot, Univ Miami, Ohio, 56-61, assoc prof & curator herbarium, 61-67; prof biol & bot, chmn div biol sci & chmn prog gen biol, Wash State Univ, 67-69; vis prof bot, Univ Ill, Urbana, 69-70; chmn dept biol sci, 70-75, PROF BOT, UNIV CENT FLA, 70- *Concurrent Pos:* Asst, herbarium, Univ Mich, 51; grant-in-aid, Sigma Xi, 54; Guggenheim fel, 58-59; prin investr bryophytes, NSF res grant, Pac Islands; hon mem staff, Hattori Bot Lab, Japan; prin investr bryophytes of Micronesia; NSF US-Japan Coop Sci prog grant; vis lectr, Col Guam, 65; prin investr, Miami Univ-NSF exped, Micronesia & Philippines, 65; ed, Fla Scientist, 73-78; res assoc, John Young Sci Ctr, Orlando's Museum of Sci & Technol, 75-; consult plant patents. *Mem:* Am Bryol & Lichenological Soc (vpres Am Bryol Soc, 62-63, pres, 64-65); Asn Trop Biol; Am Soc Plant Taxon; fel AAAS; Int Asn Plant Taxon. *Res:* Biochemical taxonomy of bryophytes; taxonomy and distribution of Pacific Island bryophytes; world phytogeography; geobotany of bryophytes. *Mailing Add:* Dept of Biol Sci Univ Cent Fla Orlando FL 32816

MILLER, HARVEY I, b Brooklyn, NY, May 25, 32; m 54; c 1. PHYSIOLOGY. *Educ:* City Col New York, BS, 55; Hahnemann Med Col, MS, 58, PhD(physiol), 61. *Prof Exp:* Biochemist, Lab & Res Div, State Dept Health, NY, 55-57; asst lipid physiol, Hahnemann Med Col, 58-61; res assoc, Lankenau Hosp, Philadelphia, 61-73; assoc prof, Cardiol Div, Hahnemann Med Col, 72-73; assoc prof, 73-76, PROF PHYSIOL, UNIV NEW ORLEANS MED CTR, 76- *Concurrent Pos:* Assoc prof, Jefferson Med Col, 66-74; estab investr, Am Heart Asn, 69-74. *Mem:* Am Physiol Soc; Am Heart Asn; Am Col Sports Med. *Res:* Myocardial metabolism; shock; exercise. *Mailing Add:* Dept of Physiol La State Univ Med Ctr New Orleans LA 70112

MILLER, HELEN CARTER, b Indianapolis, Ind, Dec 7, 25; m 57; c 3. VERTEBRATE ZOOLOGY, ETHOLOGY. *Educ:* Butler Univ, AB, 48; Cornell Univ, MA, 52, PhD(vert zool), 62. *Prof Exp:* Instr biol, Miami Univ, Ohio, 53-56; instr, 63-74, asst prof, 74-80, ASSOC PROF BIOL, OKLA STATE UNIV, 80- *Res:* Ethological and ecological research on fishes and birds. *Mailing Add:* Dept Biol Okla State Univ Stillwater OK 74074

MILLER, HELENA AGNES, b Rudolph, Ohio, Apr 25, 13. BOTANY. *Educ:* Ohio State Univ, BA & BSc, 35, MS, 38; Radcliffe Col, PhD(biol), 45. *Prof Exp:* Teacher high sch, Ohio, 35-37; asst bot, Ohio State Univ, 38-39; lectr biol, Hiram Col, 39; teacher, Milton Acad, 39-41; instr bot, Conn Col, 44-45 & Wellesley Col, 45-48; from assoc prof to prof, Duquesne Univ, 48-66, asst dean arts & sci, 66-78, prof biol, 75-78. *Mem:* Bot Soc Am; Soc Develop Biol. *Res:* Developmental anatomy of certain angiosperms; study of growth by culturing embryos of certain angiosperms in vitro. *Mailing Add:* Off of the Dean of Arts & Sci Duquesne Univ Pittsburgh PA 15219

MILLER, HERBERT CHAUNCEY, b East Orange, NJ, Nov 2, 07; m 34; c 3. PEDIATRICS. *Educ:* Yale Univ, AB, 30, MD, 34. *Prof Exp:* Asst pediat, Sch Med, Yale Univ, 34-37, from instr to assoc prof, 37-45; chmn dept, 45-72, prof, 45-78, EMER PROF PEDIAT, MED CTR, UNIV KANS, 78- *Honors & Awards:* Abraham Jacobi Award, Am Acad Pediat, 81. *Mem:* Am Pediat Soc; Soc Pediat Res; fel Am Acad Pediat. *Res:* Diseases of children; fetology; neonatology. *Mailing Add:* PO Box 176 Northford CT 06472

MILLER, HERBERT CRAWFORD, b Lenoir, NC, Mar 30, 44; m 67; c 2. ANALYTICAL CHEMISTRY. *Educ:* Univ Ala, BS, 66, PhD(anal chem), 73. *Prof Exp:* Res chemist, 72-76, head, Anal Chem Sect, 76-80, HEAD, ANAL & PHYS CHEM DIV, SOUTHERN RES INST, 80- *Mem:* Am Chem Soc; Am Soc Testing & Mat. *Res:* Environmental chemistry; pollution abatement; chemical analyses for trace constituents. *Mailing Add:* Southern Res Inst 2000 Ninth Ave S Birmingham AL 35205

MILLER, HERBERT KENNETH, b New York, NY, Apr 5, 21; m 43; c 2. BIOCHEMISTRY. *Educ:* City Col New York, BS, 40; Univ Ill, MS, 47; Columbia Univ, PhD(biochem), 51. *Prof Exp:* Res assoc infectious diseases, Pub Health Res Inst City New York, Inc, 51-53, assoc, 53-56; biochemist, VA Hosp, Bronx, NY, 56-62; from adj asst prof to assoc prof, 62-72, PROF CHEM, MANHATTAN COL, 72- *Concurrent Pos:* Assoc scientist, Div Cell Biol, Sloan-Kettering Inst Cancer Res, NY, 62-74. *Mem:* Am Chem Soc; Am Soc Microbiol. *Res:* Glutamine peptides; influenza virus nucleic acids; adenovirus infected cells; macromolecular methylation; control of DNA synthesis in chick fibroblasts; purine metabolism. *Mailing Add:* Dept Chem Manhattan Col Bronx NY 10471

MILLER, HERMAN LUNDEN, b Detroit, Mich, Apr 23, 24; m 51. NUCLEONICS, OPTICS. *Educ:* Univ Mich, BS, 48, MS, 51. *Prof Exp:* Physicist, Res Labs, Ethyl Corp, 48-49; prof physicist, Rocky Flats Plant, Dow Chem Co, 50-55; mem res staff, Proj Matterhorn, Princeton Univ, 55-65; staff engr, Aerospace Systs Div, Bendix Corp, 65-72; sr nuclear engr, Commonwealth Assocs, Inc, 73-80; RETIRED. *Mem:* Am Phys Soc; Inst Elec & Electronics Engrs; Am Nuclear Soc. *Res:* Nuclear radiation instrumentation; optical instrumentation. *Mailing Add:* 1924 Dunmore Rd Ann Arbor MI 48103

MILLER, HERMAN T, b Syracuse, Mo, Feb 28, 31; m 56. BIOCHEMISTRY, IMMUNOCHEMISTRY. *Educ:* Lincoln Univ, Mo, BS, 53; Kans State Univ, MS, 58; Univ Mo, PhD(biochem), 62. *Prof Exp:* Asst biochem, Kans State Univ, 55-58; from asst to instr, Univ Mo, 58-62; NIH fels, Univ Calif, Davis, 62-64, asst protein biochem, 64-65, res biochemist, 65-66; PROF CHEM, LINCOLN UNIV, MO, 66- *Res:* Immunochemistry as a tool in studying structure and function relationships of protein molecules. *Mailing Add:* Dept of Chem Lincoln Univ Jefferson City MO 65102

MILLER, HILLARD CRAIG, b Northampton, Pa, Dec 15, 32; m 56; c 4. APPLIED PHYSICS. *Educ:* Lehigh Univ, BA, 54, MS, 55; Pa State Univ, PhD(physics), 60. *Prof Exp:* Physicist, Gen Elec Res Labs, 60-67, PHYSICIST, GEN ELEC CO, 67- *Mem:* AAAS; Am Phys Soc; Inst Elec & Electronics Eng; Am Vacuum Soc; Royal Astron Soc Can. *Res:* Electrical discharges in gases and vacua. *Mailing Add:* Gen Elec Co PO Box 11508 St Petersburg FL 33733

MILLER, HOWARD CHARLES, b Syracuse, NY, Feb 6, 17; m 53; c 2. ENTOMOLOGY. *Educ:* State Univ NY, BS, 41; Cornell Univ, PhD(entom), 51. *Prof Exp:* Entomologist, Forest Insect Div, USDA, 46; asst, Cornell Univ, 47-50; from asst prof to assoc prof biol sci, 54-69, exten entomologist & pathologist, 50-71, PROF BIOL SCI, STATE UNIV NY COL ENVIRON SCI & FORESTRY, PUB SERV & CONTINUING EDUC, 73-, EXTEN SPECIALIST BIOL SCI & ASSOC PUB SERV OFFICER, TREE PEST SERV, 71- *Mem:* AAAS; Entom Soc Am; Soc Am Foresters; Lepidop Soc. *Res:* Insect ecology; forest insect and disease problems; wildlife parasites; medical entomology; biology; urban forestry. *Mailing Add:* Dept Environ & Forest Biol Col Environ Sci & Forestry State Univ NY Syracuse NY 13210

MILLER, HUGH HUNT, b Griffin, Ga, Feb 11, 25; m 47; c 5. CHEMISTRY, REACTOR TECHNOLOGY. *Educ:* Univ NC, Chapel Hill, BS, 46. *Prof Exp:* Res chemist, Oak Ridge Nat Lab, 46-55; chief anal chem, Nuclear Power Dept, Curtiss Wright Corp, 55-58; res adminr, US Atomic Energy Comn, 58-61; vpres, Numec Instruments & Controls Corp, 61-65, pres, 65-67; vpres, Waters Assocs Inc, 67-70; dir mkt res & process instrumentation, Esterline Corp, 70-71; EXEC DIR, OFF FOREIGN SECY, NAT ACAD ENG, 71- *Concurrent Pos:* Assoc fac mem, Duquesne Univ, 66-67; mem adv bd, int prog, Ga Inst Technol, 76-78, Inst Res & Interactions Technol & Soc, Univ Pittsburgh, 77-79 & Asn Media-Based Continuing Educ for Engrs, Inc, 78-; consult, NSF, 78-80, Congressional Res Serv, 79, USAID, 81, NATO, 81-, State Dept, 81- *Mem:* Am Chem Soc; Am Nuclear Soc; Am Soc Testing & Mat; Am Ceramic Soc; AAAS. *Res:* Instrumental methods of chemical analysis; polarography; coulometry; liquid chromatography; radioisotope technology. *Mailing Add:* Off of the Foreign Secy Nat Acad Eng 2101 Constitution Ave Washington DC 20418

MILLER, I GEORGE, JR, b Chicago, Ill, Apr 18, 37; m 62; c 3. MICROBIOLOGY. *Educ:* Harvard Univ, AB, 58, MD, 62; Yale Univ, MA, 76. *Prof Exp:* Asst prof pediat & epidemiol, 69-74, from assoc prof to prof, 74-79, JOHN F ENDERS PROF PEDIAT & EPIDEMIOL, YALE UNIV, 79- *Res:* Medical virology, especially the onocogenic herpes virus; Epstein-Barr virus. *Mailing Add:* Dept Pediat & Inf Dis Yale Univ New Haven CT 06520

MILLER, IAN MCKENZIE, microbiology, see previous edition

MILLER, INGLIS J, JR, b Columbus, Ohio, Mar 17, 43; m 63; c 2. PHYSIOLOGY, ANATOMY. *Educ:* Ohio State Univ, BS, 65; Fla State Univ, PhD(sensory physiol), 68. *Prof Exp:* USPHS trainee, Univ Pa, 68-71; asst prof anat, 71-77, ASSOC PROF ANAT, BOWMAN GRAY SCH MED, WAKE FOREST UNIV, 77- *Mem:* Am Asn Anat; Soc Neurosci; Am Chem Senses Soc. *Res:* Gustatory neurophysiology; neuroanatomy of peripheral gustatory system. *Mailing Add:* Dept Anat Bowman Gray Sch Med Winston-Salem NC 27103

MILLER, IRVIN ALEXANDER, b Schellsburg, Pa, Nov 29, 32; m 56; c 3. THEORETICAL PHYSICS. *Educ:* Drexel Inst Technol, BS, 55; Univ Pa, MS, 59; Temple Univ, PhD, 68. *Prof Exp:* From instr to asst prof, 55-70, asst vpres acad affairs, 70-77, ASSOC PROF PHYSICS & ATMOS SCI, DREXEL UNIV, 70-, ASSOC VPRES ACAD AFFAIRS, 77- *Concurrent Pos:* Actg dean sci, Drexel Univ, 69-70. *Mem:* Am Soc Eng Educ; Am Asn Physics Teachers. *Res:* Electron paramagnetic resonance. *Mailing Add:* 415 W Allens Lane Philadelphia PA 19119

MILLER, IRVING F(RANKLIN), b New York, NY, Sept 27, 34; m 62; c 2. BIOENGINEERING, CHEMICAL ENGINEERING. *Educ:* NY Univ, BChE, 55; Purdue Univ, MSChE, 56; Univ Mich, PhD(chem eng), 60. *Prof Exp:* Res assoc fluid dynamics, Res Inst, Univ Mich, 59; res scientist, Res Labs, United Aircraft Corp, 59-61; from asst prof to prof chem eng, Polytech Inst Brooklyn, 61-72, chmn bioeng prog, 66-72, head dept chem eng, 70-72; prof bioeng & head dept & prof physiol, Med Ctr, 73-79, actg head dept systs eng, 78-79, DEAN, GRAD COL & ASSOC VICE CHANCELLOR RESEARCH, UNIV ILL, CHICAGO CIRCLE, 79- *Concurrent Pos:* Consult to various indust, 63- *Mem:* AAAS; Am Chem Soc; Biomed Eng Soc; NY Acad Sci; Am Inst Chem Engrs. *Res:* Transport processes; membrane phenomena; biological processes; thermodynamics and irreversible thermodynamics; ion exchange; chemical kinetics; fluid dynamics; propulsion. *Mailing Add:* Grad Col Box 4348 Univ Ill Chicago Circle Chicago IL 60680

MILLER, IRWIN, b New York City, NY, July 3, 28; m 52; c 3. SURVEY, RESEARCH ADMINISTRATION. *Educ:* Alfred Univ, BA, 50; Purdue Univ, MS, 52; Va Polytech Inst, PhD, 56. *Prof Exp:* Mathematician, Appl Res Lab, US Steel Corp, 56-58; prof statist, Ariz State Univ, 58-65; mem prof staff, 65-73, VPRES, ARTHUR D LITTLE, INC, 73-; CHMN, OPINION RES CORP, 75-, CHIEF EXEC OFFICER, 80- *Concurrent Pos:* Adj prof math & dir comput ctr, Wesleyan Univ, 69-71. *Mem:* AAAS; Am Statist Asn; Inst Math Statist; Biomet Soc. *Res:* Mathematical statistics; continuous stochastic processes; inference. *Mailing Add:* Opinion Res Corp N Harrison St Princeton NJ 08540

MILLER, IVAN KEITH, b Rapid City, SDak, July 28, 21; m 45. POLYMER CHEMISTRY. *Educ:* SDak State Col, BS, 43; Univ Minn, PhD, 50. *Prof Exp:* Asst, SDak State Col, 42, instr chem, 43; civilian with Off Rubber Res, Univ Minn, 45-50; res chemist, Rayon Dept, 50-58, res assoc, 58-67, RES FEL, TEXTILE FIBERS DEPT, E I DU PONT DE NEMOURS & CO, INC, 67- *Mem:* AAAS; Am Chem Soc. *Res:* Reaction mechanisms concerning polymerization reactions; rubber; synthetic resins; viscose rayon; nylon. *Mailing Add:* Textile Fibers Dept E I du Pont de Nemours & Co Inc Wilmington DE 19803

MILLER, JACK CULBERTSON, b Pomona, Calif, Sept 29, 25; m 54; c 2. THEORETICAL PHYSICS. *Educ:* Pomona Col, BA, 47; Univ Calif, MA, 49; Oxford Univ, DPhil, 55. *Prof Exp:* Mathematician, Radiation Lab, Univ Calif, 48-49; from instr to assoc prof, 52-66, PROF PHYSICS, POMONA COL, 66- *Concurrent Pos:* NSF fac fel, 61-62 & 68-69. *Mem:* Am Phys Soc; Am Geophys Union. *Res:* Mathematical physics; physical oceanography. *Mailing Add:* Dept of Physics Pomona Col Claremont CA 91711

MILLER, JACK MARTIN, b Cornwall, Ont, Feb 20, 40. INORGANIC CHEMISTRY. *Educ:* McGill Univ, BSc, 61, PhD(chem), 64; Cambridge Univ, PhD(chem), 66. *Prof Exp:* From asst prof to assoc prof, 66-75, chmn dept, 75-79, PROF CHEM, BROCK UNIV, 75- *Concurrent Pos:* Nat Res Coun Can overseas fel, Cambridge Univ, 64-66. *Mem:* Fel Chem Inst Can; Am Chem Soc; fel Royal Soc Chem; Am Soc Mass Spectrometry; Spectros Soc Can. *Res:* Nuclear magnetic resonance and mass spectra of donor-acceptor complexes; mass spectra of organometallic and coordination compounds; strong hydrogen bonding. *Mailing Add:* Dept of Chem Brock Univ St Catharines ON L2S 3A1 Can

MILLER, JACK W, b Knoxville, Tenn, Sept 26, 25; m 52; c 1. PHARMACOLOGY. *Educ:* San Diego State Col, AB, 49; Univ Calif, MS, 52, PhD(pharmacol), 54. *Prof Exp:* Asst pharmacol, Univ Calif, 52-53, lectr, 53-54; from instr to assoc prof, Univ Wis, 54-62; assoc prof, 62-67, PROF PHARMACOL, UNIV MINN, MINNEAPOLIS, 67- *Concurrent Pos:* Mem pharmacol-toxicol comt, Nat Inst Gen Med Sci; Med Curric Course Coordr, Univ Minn, Minneapolis, 76- *Mem:* Am Soc Pharmacol & Exp Therapeut; Soc Exp Biol & Med; NY Acad Sci. *Res:* Pharmacology of morphine-type drugs; uterine drugs; adrenergic receptors; catecholamines; drug receptor theory; posterior pituitary hormones. *Mailing Add:* Dept Pharmacol Univ Minn Minneapolis MN 55455

MILLER, JAMES ALBERT, JR, b Peitaiho, China, June 21, 07; US citizen; m 78; c 2. ANATOMY. *Educ:* Col Wooster, AB, 28, DSc, 61; Univ Chicago, PhD(zool), 37. *Prof Exp:* Instr biol, Assiut Col, Egypt, 28-31; instr, Univ Ohio, 35-37; instr anat, Med Sch, Univ Mich, 37-42; asst prof, Univ Tenn, 42-46; from assoc prof to prof, Sch Dent, Emory Univ, 46-54, prof div basic health sci, Univ, 54-60; prof anat & chmn dept, 60-72, asst dean basic med sci, 72-73, EMER PROF ANAT, SCH MED, TULANE UNIV, 73- *Concurrent Pos:* NSF sr fel, 57-58; Fulbright fels, Finland, 62 & Ger, 72; Alexander von Humboldt sr res award, 73-74; vis prof anat, Sch Med, Tufts Univ, 77 & 79; vis prof & actg chmn, Univ SFla, Tampa, 78-79. *Honors & Awards:* Res Prize, Asn Southeast Biol, 59; Res Citation, Sigma Xi, 59. *Mem:* Am Soc Zool; Soc Cryobiol; Soc Develop Biol; Am Physiol Soc; Am Asn Anat. *Res:* Hypothermia in the resuscitation of asphyxiated neonates, effects on heart and brain of hypothermia and metabolic depressants; cooling and resuscitating animals from zero degrees centigrade; hyperbaric oxygen and blockage of differentiation; physiology and histochemistry of development in coelenterates. *Mailing Add:* 307 Shorewood Dr East Falmouth MA 02536

MILLER, JAMES ALEXANDER, b Dormont, Pa, May 27, 15; m 42; c 2. ONCOLOGY. *Educ:* Univ Pittsburgh, BS, 39; Univ Wis, MS, 41, PhD(biochem), 43. *Prof Exp:* From instr to assoc prof, 44-52, PROF ONCOL, MED CTR, UNIV WIS-MADISON, 52-; PROF ONCOL, WIS ALUMNI RES FOUND, 80- *Concurrent Pos:* Finney-Howell Found Med res fel, Med Ctr, Univ Wis-Madison, 43-44. *Honors & Awards:* Co-recipient, Teplitz-Langer Award, Ann Langer Cancer Res Found, 63 & Lucy Wortham James Award, James Ewing Soc, 65; G H A Clowes Award, Am Asn Cancer Res, 69; co-recipient, Bertner Award, M D Anderson Hosp & Tumor Inst, 71, Wis Nat Div Award, Am Cancer Soc, 73, Papanicolaou Res Award, Papanicolaou Cancer Res Inst, 75, Lewis S Rosenstiel Award, Brandeis Univ, 76, Nat Award Basic Sci, Am Cancer Soc, 77, Founders' Award, Chem Indust Inst Toxicol, 78, Bristol-Myers Award in Cancer Res, 78 & Int Ann Award, Gairdner Found, 78; Freedman Found Award, NY Acad Sci, 79; 3M Life Sci Award, Fed Am Soc Exp Biol, 79; Mott Award, Gen Motors Cancer Res Found, 80. *Mem:* Nat Acad Sci; Am Soc Biol Chemists; Am Acad Arts & Sci; Am Asn Cancer Res; hon mem Japanese Cancer Asn. *Res:* Experimental chemical carcinogenesis. *Mailing Add:* McArdle Lab Univ of Wis Med Ctr Madison WI 53706

MILLER, JAMES ANGUS, b Huntington, WVa, Aug 16, 46; m 71. THEORETICAL CHEMICAL PHYSICS, FLUID DYNAMICS. *Educ:* Univ Cincinnati, BS, 69; Cornell Univ, MEng, 70, PhD, 74. *Prof Exp:* MEM TECH STAFF, SANDIA NAT LABS, AM TEL & TEL CO, CALIF, 74- *Mem:* Am Phys Soc; Am Chem Soc; Am Inst Aeronaut & Astronaut; Combustion Inst; Sigma Xi. *Res:* Chemical kinetics and reactive collision dynamics; non-equilibrium statistical; mechanics and thermodynamics; molecular quantum theory; theory of flame, detonation and explosion phenomena in gases; physical gas dynamics; applied mathematics. *Mailing Add:* Combustion Sci Dept Sandia Labs Livermore CA 94550

MILLER, JAMES AVERY, b Los Angeles, Calif, Sept 12, 32; m 54; c 4. AERONAUTICS. *Educ:* Stanford Univ, BSME, 55, MSME, 56; Ill Inst Technol, PhD(mech eng), 63. *Prof Exp:* Consult heat transfer & fluid mech, Stanford Res Inst, 56-57; instr mech eng, Ill Inst Technol, 57-63, consult IIT Res Inst, 60-63; ASSOC PROF AERONAUT, NAVAL POSTGRAD SCH, 63- *Concurrent Pos:* Prin investr, NSF grant, 62-63; consult, Anderson Co, 62-63; chmn, Heat Transfer & Fluid Mech Inst, 65-66. *Mem:* AAAS; Am Soc Mech Engrs; Am Inst Aeronaut & Astronaut. *Res:* Free and forced convection heat and mass transfer; nonsteady boundary layer flows. *Mailing Add:* Dept of Aeronaut Naval Postgrad Sch Monterey CA 93940

MILLER, JAMES C, b Tulsa, Okla, Dec 27, 31; m 53; c 2. ELECTRICAL ENGINEERING. *Educ:* Rensselaer Polytech Inst, BEE, 53; Yale Univ, MEng, 58, PhD(elec eng), 62. *Prof Exp:* Mem tech staff comput, David Sarnoff Res Ctr, RCA Labs, Inc, 58-69, mgr design automation & test technol, 69-71, mgr mgt info systs, Solid State Div, 71-76; MGR TECH PROJS, RCA CORP, LANCASTER, PA, 76- *Honors & Awards:* Honeywell Award & Yale & David Sarnoff Award, 62. *Mem:* Inst Elec & Electronics Engrs; Asn Comput Mach. *Res:* Computer research; memories; high speed logic; design automation; management information systems. *Mailing Add:* RCA Corp New Holland Pike Lancaster PA 17601

MILLER, JAMES EDWARD, b Hanover, Pa, Apr 28, 42; c 2. BIOCHEMISTRY. *Educ:* Shippensburg State Col, BS, 63; Univ NDak, MS, 65, PhD(biochem), 68. *Prof Exp:* USPHS grant, Sch Med, Temple Univ, 68-70; res investr, 70-78, RES SCIENTIST BIOCHEM, G D SEARLE & CO, 78- *Mem:* AAAS; Am Chem Soc. *Res:* Enzyme chemistry; protein purification; assay development; lipid metabolism; nutrition; hormonal control of metabolism. *Mailing Add:* Dept Biol Res G D Searle & Co PO Box 5110 Chicago IL 60680

MILLER, JAMES EUGENE, b Loudonville, Ohio, Aug 12, 38; m 63; c 2. BIOCHEMISTRY, MICROBIOLOGY. *Educ:* Denison Univ, BA, 60; Harvard Univ, MA, 63; Amherst Col, PhD(biochem), 65. *Prof Exp:* Fel bact, Univ Calif, Los Angeles, 65-66; res assoc, NASA, 66-69; res biochemist, Corp Res Lab, Allied Chem Corp, 69-71; asst prof, 71-80, ASSOC PROF BIOL & CHMN DEPT, DEL VALLEY COL, 80- *Res:* Bacterial physiology. *Mailing Add:* Dept Biol Del Valley Col Doylestown PA 18901

MILLER, JAMES FRANKLIN, b Lancaster, Pa, July 18, 12; m 38; c 1. ANALYTICAL CHEMISTRY. *Educ:* Franklin & Marshall Col, BS, 35; Pa State Univ, MS, 37, PhD(anal chem), 39. *Prof Exp:* Asst, Pa State Univ, 35-39, instr chem, Altoona Undergrad Ctr, 39-42; asst prof chem, The Citadel, 42; res fel, Res Found, Purdue Univ, 43-44; fel rubber res, Mellon Inst, 44-46, sr fel insecticides, 46-48, coal tar constituents, 48-49, arsenic, 49-51, head anal chem sect, 51-59; lab dir gen chem cent res & eng, Div, Continental Can Co, 59-64, mgr appl res, Corp Res & Develop Dept, 64-68; *Concurrent Pos:* Civilian with AEC; Off Sci Res & Develop; US Rubber Reserve Corp. *Mem:* Am Chem Soc; Am Inst Chem Eng. *Res:* Inorganic non-ferrous analysis; analysis of organic halogen compounds and alcohol; butadiene coverter products; physical properties and behavior of emulsions; air elutriation of particular matter; behavior of fractionated particulate matter on falling utilization of arsenic; organic micro-analysis; polarography; spectrophotometry. *Mailing Add:* Alpha Chi Sigma Fraternity S Kitley Ave Bldg 1 Indianapolis IN 46219

MILLER, JAMES FREDERICK, b Lancaster, Ohio, June 14, 19; m 56; c 1. FUEL SCIENCE. *Educ:* Ohio State Univ, BS, 51. *Prof Exp:* Res chemist, Titanium Div, Nat Lead Co, 51-53; res chemist, 53-58, res proj leader, 58-60, asst chief phys chem div, 60-69, assoc chief phys & inorg chem div, 69-72, sr res chemist, 72-74, SR RES CHEMIST, PROCESS DEVELOP SECT, COLUMBUS LABS, BATTELLE, 74- *Res:* Inorganic chemical process development; synthesis and process reactions and studies of phase equilibria in aqueous, molten salt, and other inorganic systems; coal processing and conversion chemistry; solid state materials synthesis and crystal growth. *Mailing Add:* Columbus Labs Battelle 505 King Ave Columbus OH 43201

MILLER, JAMES FREDERICK, b Davenport, Iowa, Feb 18, 43; m 67. MICROPALEONTOLOGY, INVERTEBRATE PALEONTOLOGY. *Educ:* Augustana Col, Ill, AB, 65; Univ Wis-Madison, MA, 68, PhD(geol), 71. *Prof Exp:* Assoc prof geol, Univ Utah, 70-74; ASST PROF GEOL, SOUTHWEST MO STATE UNIV, 74- *Mem:* AAAS; Geol Soc Am; Paleont Soc; Int Paleont Asn; Paleont Asn. *Res:* Taxonomy, evolution, and biostratigraphy of Cambrian and Lower Ordovician conodonts; stratigraphic position of Cambrian-Ordovician boundary; Paleozoic crinoids. *Mailing Add:* Dept Geog & Geol Southwest Mo State Univ Springfield MO 65802

MILLER, JAMES GEGAN, b St Louis Mo, Nov 11, 42; m 66. ULTRASOUND, MEDICAL BIOPHYSICS. *Educ:* St Louis Univ, AB, 64; Washington Univ, MA, 66, PhD(physics), 69. *Prof Exp:* Res assoc physics, 69-70, asst prof, 70-72, assoc prof, 72-77, res asst prof med, 76-81, PROF PHYSICS, WASHINGTON UNIV, 77-, ASSOC DIR BIOMED PHYSICS, LAB FOR ULTRASONICS, 74-, RES ASSOC PROF MED, 81- *Concurrent Pos:* Sigma Xi nat lectr, 81-82. *Mem:* Inst Elec & Electronic Engrs; Am Phys Soc; Am Inst Ultrasound Med. *Res:* Ultrasonics, biomedical physics, ultrasonic tissue characterization; acoustic magnetic resonance; ultrasonic resonators and transducers; phonon-charge carrier interactions; ultrasonic materials characterization. *Mailing Add:* Dept of Physics Washington Univ St Louis MO 63130

MILLER, JAMES GILBERT, b El Dorado, Ark, Aug 2, 46; m 69; c 2. GENERAL RELATIVITY. *Educ:* Univ Calif, Berkeley, BA, 68; Princeton Univ, PhD(appl math), 72. *Prof Exp:* Asst prof math, Univ Calif, Los Angeles, 72-74 & asst prof physics, Univ Utah, 74-76; ASST PROF MATH, TEX A&M UNIV, 76- *Mem:* Am Math Soc. *Res:* Global properties of solutions of Einstein's field equations in general relativity, including symmetries, horizons and singularities. *Mailing Add:* Dept Math Tex A&M Univ College Station TX 77843

MILLER, JAMES KINCHELOE, b Elkton, Md, June 16, 32; m 60; c 2. ANIMAL NUTRITION, PHYSIOLOGY. *Educ:* Berry Col, BS, 53; Univ Ga, MS, 59, PhD(animal nutrit), 62. *Prof Exp:* Tech asst dairy nutrit, Univ Ga, 57-58, asst, 58-60; asst prof, 61-67, ASSOC PROF DAIRY PHYSIOL, AGR RES LAB, UNIV TENN, 67-, ASSOC PROF, COMPARATIVE ANIMAL RES LAB, UNIV TENN-DEPT ENERGY, 73- *Honors & Awards:* Gustav Bohstedt Mineral & Trace Mineral Award, Am Soc of Animal Sci, 74. *Mem:* Am Dairy Sci Asn; Am Inst Nutrit; Am Soc Animal Sci. *Res:* Nutrition and physiology of the dairy cow; mineral metabolism; effects of soil ingestion; hypomagnesemia (grass tetany) in cattle. *Mailing Add:* UT-DOE Comparative Animal Res Lab 1299 Bethel Valley Rd Oak Ridge TN 37830

MILLER, JAMES L, b Chicago, Ill, May 10, 35; m 58; c 3. ORGANIC CHEMISTRY. *Educ:* Eastern Ill Univ, BS, 57; Univ Iowa, MS, 62, PhD(chem), 63. *Prof Exp:* From asst prof to assoc prof, 63-74, PROF CHEM, EAST TENN STATE UNIV, 74- *Mem:* Am Chem Soc. *Res:* Mechanisms concerning the bromination of stilbene and tolan; cycloaddition reactions which involve benzyne intermediates. *Mailing Add:* Dept of Chem East Tenn State Univ Johnson City TN 37601

MILLER, JAMES MILTON, b Austin, Tex, Sept 22, 25. COMPUTER SCIENCE, STATISTICS. *Educ:* Univ Tex, BS, 52, MA, 54, PhD(chem), 57. *Prof Exp:* Res scientist chem, Univ Tex, 56-57; engr, Esso Res & Eng Co, 58-60; RES STAFF MEM, THOMAS J WATSON RES CTR, IBM CORP, NEW YORK, 60- *Mem:* Am Statist Asn. *Res:* Probability and statistics; medical research data analysis. *Mailing Add:* Thomas J Watson Res Ctr PO Box 218 Yorktown Heights NY 10598

MILLER, JAMES MONROE, b Lancaster, Pa, Aug 7, 33; m 55; c 2. ANALYTICAL CHEMISTRY. *Educ:* Elizabethtown Col, BS, 55; Purdue Univ, MS, 58, PhD(anal chem), 60. *Prof Exp:* From asst prof to assoc prof, 59-69, PROF ANAL CHEM, DREW UNIV, 69-, CHMN DEPT CHEM, 71- *Concurrent Pos:* Vis lectr, Univ Ill, Urbana, 64-65; indust consult, 63-; dir, NSF Col Sci Improv Prog, 67-70; vis prof, Univ Amsterdam, 71. *Mem:* AAAS; Am Asn Clin Chemists; Am Chem Soc. *Res:* Gas chromatography; applications in teaching; studies of thermal conductivity detector response; liquid chromatography; detectors; clinical applications; determination of non-ionic detergents by column liquid chromatography. *Mailing Add:* Dept of Chem Drew Univ Madison NJ 07940

MILLER, JAMES NATHANIEL, b Detroit, Mich, Mar 16, 26; m 51; c 2. INFECTIOUS DISEASES. *Educ:* Univ Calif, Los Angeles, BA, 50, MA, 51, PhD(infectious dis), 56. *Prof Exp:* Jr res microbiologist, 56-58, asst prof infectious dis, 58-64, from asst prof to assoc prof microbiol & immunol, 66-72, PROF MICROBIOL & IMMUNOL, SCH MED, UNIV CALIF, LOS ANGELES, 72- *Mem:* Am Soc Microbiol; Am Asn Immunologists; Am Veneral Dis Asn. *Res:* Venereal diseases; immunobiology of syphilis. *Mailing Add:* Dept Microbiol & Immunol Univ Calif Sch of Med Los Angeles CA 90024

MILLER, JAMES P, JR, b Bellevue, Pa, July 12, 21; m 45; c 4. CIVIL ENGINEERING. *Educ:* Univ Pittsburgh, BS, 43, MS, 51, PhD(econ), 63. *Prof Exp:* Oper engr, Kopper Co, Pa, 43-44; res assoc, Mellon Inst Indust Res, 45-47; ASSOC PROF CIVIL ENG & DIR PROG WATER RESOURCE ENG, UNIV PITTSBURGH, 47-, GRAD PROG COORDR, CIVIL ENG DEPT, 77- *Mem:* AAAS; Am Soc Testing & Mat; Am Water Works Asn; Water Pollution Control Fedn; Am Soc Eng Educ. *Res:* Water resource engineering material sciences. *Mailing Add:* Dept of Civil Eng Sch of Eng Univ of Pittsburgh Pittsburgh PA 15260

MILLER, JAMES Q, b Lakewood, Ohio, July 6, 26; m 50; c 4. NEUROLOGY, CYTOGENETICS. *Educ:* Haverford Col, BA, 49; Columbia Univ, MD, 53. *Prof Exp:* Nat Inst Neurol Dis & Blindness spec fel neuropath, Harvard Univ, 60-62; asst prof, 62-67, asst dean sch med, 62-70, assoc prof, 67-72, PROF NEUROL, SCH MED, UNIV VA, 72-, NEUROLOGIST, UNIV HOSP, 62- *Mem:* Am Acad Neurol; Am Epilepsy Soc; AMA. *Res:* Chromosome disorders and anomalies of the central nervous system. *Mailing Add:* Dept of Neurol Univ of Va Hosp Charlottesville VA 22901

MILLER, JAMES R(USSEL), b Cincinnati, Ohio, Mar 23, 31; div; c 3. CHEMICAL & NUCLEAR ENGINEERING. *Educ:* Univ Cincinnati, ChemE, 54. *Prof Exp:* Chem engr, Standard Oil Co Ind, 54-55; tech engr nuclear propulsion dept, Gen Elec Co, 57-61 & nuclear mat & propulsion opers, 61-62; sr res engr, Atomics Int Div, N Am Aviation, Inc, 62-67, supvr large radioisotope heat source develop, Atomics Int Div, N Am Rockwell Corp, 67-69, supvr systs nuclear auxiliary power fuels, 69-71, MEM TECH STAFF, ENERGY SYSTS GROUP, ROCKWELL INT CORP, 71- *Res:* Radiation effects on materials; reactor fuel and control materials development. *Mailing Add:* Rockwell Int Corp 8900 Desoto Ave Canoga Park CA 91304

MILLER, JAMES RAY, b Lancaster, Pa, Feb 2, 48; m 70; c 2. BIOLOGY, AGRICULTURE. *Educ:* Millersville State Col, BA, 70; Penn State Univ, PhD(entom), 75. *Prof Exp:* Res assoc entom, NY State Agr Exp Sta, 74-77; asst prof, 77-81, PROF ENTOM, MICH STATE UNIV, 81- *Honors & Awards:* Grad Student Recognition Award, Eastern Br Entom Soc Am, 73. *Mem:* AAAS; Entom Soc Am. *Res:* Chemical interactions between plants and insects. *Mailing Add:* Pesticide Res Lab Mich State Univ East Lansing MI 48824

MILLER, JAMES REGINALD, b Mimico, Ont, Nov 6, 28; m 54; c 5. GENETICS. *Educ:* Univ Toronto, BA, 51, MA, 53; McGill Univ, PhD, 59. *Prof Exp:* Asst develop physiol, Jackson Mem Lab, Maine, 54-56; res assoc genetics, Dept Neurol Res, 58-60, from asst prof to prof pediat, 60-73, head div med genetics, 67-78, PROF MED GENETICS, UNIV BC, 73- *Mem:* Genetics Soc Am; Teratology Soc; Can Col Med Geneticists; Am Soc Human Genetics; Genetics Soc Can. *Res:* Developmental and population genetics of human beings and other mammals. *Mailing Add:* Dept of Med Genetics Univ of BC Vancouver BC V6T 1W5 Can

MILLER, JAMES RICHARD, b St Louis, Mo, June 11, 22; m 45; c 2. APPLIED INDUSTRIAL HYGIENE. *Educ:* Mo Sch Mines, BS, 44; Wash Univ, PhD(chem), 51. *Prof Exp:* Asst chem, Mo Sch Mines, 43; chemist, Ralston-Purina Co, 46-47; asst chem, Washington Univ, 47-50; res chemist, Shell Oil Co, 51-58, sr res chemist, Wood River Res Lab, 58-69; sr res scientist, Shell Res Ltd, Thorton Res Ctr, Chester, Eng, 69-70; MEM STAFF, SUPV HEALTH & ENVIRON, SHELL DEVELOP CO, WESTHOLLOW RES CTR, HOUSTON, 75-, CHMN RADIATION SAFETY COMT, 80- *Mem:* Am Chem Soc; AAAS; Sigma Xi; fel Am Inst Chem; NY Acad Sci. *Res:* Oxidation and free radical chemistry; electron spin resonance; application of radiochemical techniques to problems in manufacture and use of petroleum; chemistry of porphyrins; corrosion chemistry; interaction of elastomers with organic solutions. *Mailing Add:* Westhollow Res Ctr Shell Develop Co Box 1380 Houston TX 77001

MILLER, JAMES ROBERT, b Milford, Nebr, July 2, 22; m 45; c 5. ORGANIC CHEMISTRY, ZOOLOGY. *Educ:* Iowa State Univ, BS, 43; Syracuse Univ, PhD(chem), 50. *Prof Exp:* Res asst & jr res chemist, Parke, Davis & Co, 43-47; from asst prof to assoc prof, 50-53, dept head, 52-65, PROF CHEM, HARTWICK COL, 54- *Concurrent Pos:* Consult lab, Fox Hosp, 58-61. *Mem:* AAAS; Am Chem Soc; Ecol Soc Am; Am Soc Naturalists; Am Ornith Union. *Res:* Synthetic organic medicinals and heterocyclic compounds; avian ecology and biogeography. *Mailing Add:* Dept of Chem Hartwick Col Oneonta NY 13820

MILLER, JAMES ROBERT, b Holcomb, Mo, Jan 7, 41; m 59; c 3. SOLID STATE PHYSICS. *Educ:* Mo Sch Mines, BS, 62; Tex Christian Univ, MS, 64, PhD(physics), 66. *Prof Exp:* Assoc prof, 66-70, PROF PHYSICS, EAST TENN STATE UNIV, 70- *Res:* Electron spin resonance and nuclear magnetic resonance. *Mailing Add:* Dept of Physics East Tenn State Univ Johnson City TN 37601

MILLER, JAMES ROLAND, b Millington, Md, May 19, 29; m 54; c 2. SOIL CHEMISTRY, AGRONOMY. *Educ:* Univ Md, BS, 51, MS, 53, PhD(soil chem), 56. *Hon Degrees:* State Farmer Degree, FFA, 60. *Prof Exp:* Asst, Univ Md, 51-56; soil scientist chem, Soils & Plant Relationship Sect, Agr Res Serv, USDA, 56-58; from asst prof to assoc prof soils, 58-63, PROF & HEAD DEPT AGRON, UNIV MD, COLLEGE PARK, 63- *Concurrent Pos:* Consult, NASA, 65-; mem, Potash & Phosphate Inst Adv Coun (vchmn, 77, chmn, 78). *Mem:* Soil Conserv Soc Am; fel Soil Sci Soc Am; fel Am Soc Agron. *Res:* Soil test methods for determining available nutrients in soils; fission products; reactions in soils and uptake by plants. *Mailing Add:* Dept of Agron Univ of Md College Park MD 20742

MILLER, JAMES TAGGERT, JR, b Sunbury, Pa, Apr 21, 43. THEORETICAL PHYSICS. *Educ:* Pa State Univ, BS, 65, PhD(physics), 70. *Prof Exp:* Intern radar syst anal, 72-73, mem fac, 73-74, sect supvr, 74-77, sect supvr sensor syst, Appl Physics Lab, 77-79, mem staff, 79-80, PRIN MEM STAFF, COMBAT SYST INTEGRATIONS GROUP, JOHNS HOPKINS HOSP, 80- *Mem:* Am Phys Soc. *Res:* Automated sensor system design, interfacing and data utilization in multisensor environments. *Mailing Add:* Johns Hopkins Univ/Appl Physics Lab Johns Hopkins Rd Laurel MD 20707

MILLER, JANE ALSOBROOK, b New Orleans, La, Feb 21, 28; c 2. CHEMISTRY. *Educ:* Agnes Scott Col, AB, 48; Tulane Univ, MS, 50, PhD(hist of chem), 60. *Prof Exp:* Instr chem, Tulane Univ, 50-52; res asst pharmacol, Washington Univ, 53-54, orthop surg, 63-65, res instr, 65; instr, 65-67, ASST PROF CHEM, UNIV MO-ST LOUIS, 67- *Mem:* Am Chem Soc; Hist Sci Soc; AAAS. *Res:* History of chemistry; chemical education. *Mailing Add:* Dept of Chem Univ of Mo-St Louis St Louis MO 63121

MILLER, JANICE MARGARET, b McPherson, Kans, Nov 11, 38; m 62; c 2. VETERINARY PATHOLOGY. *Educ:* Kans State Univ, BS, 60, DVM, 62, MS, 63; Univ Wis-Madison, PhD(vet sci), 69. *Prof Exp:* Res assoc animal nutrit, Mass Inst Technol, 64-65; Leukemia Soc Am spec fel, Univ Wis-Madison, 70-72; RES VET PATH, NAT ANIMAL DIS LAB, 72- *Mem:* Am Vet Med Asn; Am Col Vet Path. *Res:* Viral oncogenesis; leukemia of cattle. *Mailing Add:* Dept of Path Nat Animal Dis Lab Ames IA 50010

MILLER, JARRELL E, b San Antonio, Tex, Nov 14, 13; m 39; c 4. MEDICINE. *Educ:* Baylor Univ, MD, 38; Am Bd Radiol, dipl, 42. *Prof Exp:* Intern, Robert B Green Mem Hosp, San Antonio, Tex, 38-39; resident radiol, Cleveland City Hosp, Ohio, 39-42; assoc prof, 47-56, clin prof, 56-66, PROF RADIOL, UNIV TEX HEALTH SCI CTR, DALLAS, 66- *Concurrent Pos:* Radiologist, Parkland Hosp, Dallas, 46-49, Children's Med Ctr, 47-65 & St Paul Hosp, Dallas, 67-; consult, Vet Hosps, Lisbon & McKinney, Tex, 46-57; dir dept radiol, Med Ctr, Baylor Univ, 49-66; lectr, Univ Tex Med Br, Galveston, 59-; deleg, AMA, 71- *Honors & Awards:* Distinguished Serv Award, Tex Med Asn, 71. *Mem:* Fel Am Col Radiol (pres, 67-); Radiol Soc NAm; Am Roentgen Ray Soc (vpres, 63); Nat Tuberc & Respiratory Dis Asn; Am Cancer Soc. *Res:* Hypertrophic phyloric stenosis; angiocardiography; anatomy of the heart and great vessels; childhood malignancies. *Mailing Add:* 6115D Averill Way Dallas TX 75225

MILLER, JERRY K, b Valley City, NDak, Sept 4, 34. ANALYTICAL CHEMISTRY. *Educ:* Univ Minn, BChem, 57, PhD(anal chem), 66; Univ Mo, MA, 63. *Prof Exp:* RES CHEMIST, AM CYANAMID CO, 66- *Mem:* Am Chem Soc. *Res:* Light scattering; polymer characterization. *Mailing Add:* Am Cyanamid Co 1937 W Main St Stamford CT 06904

MILLER, JERRY ROLAND, medicine, see previous edition

MILLER, JOEL STEVEN, b Detroit, Mich, Oct 14, 44; m 70; c 3. INORGANIC CHEMISTRY. *Educ:* Wayne State Univ, BS, 67; Univ Calif, Los Angeles, PhD(inorg chem), 71. *Prof Exp:* Res assoc inorg chem, Stanford Univ, 71-72; assoc scientist, 72-73, scientist, Webster Res Ctr, Xerox Corp, 73-78; mem tech staff & proj mgr, Sci Ctr, Rockwell Int Corp, 78-79; PRIN SCIENTIST & GROUP LEADER, OCCIDENTAL RES CORP, 79- *Concurrent Pos:* Vis prof chem, Univ Calif, Irvine, 81. *Mem:* AAAS; Am Phys Soc; Am Chem Soc; fel Royal Soc Chem. *Res:* Synthetic and physical inorganic chemistry; anisotropic inorganic and organic complexes; synthetic metals; homogeneous catalysis; inorganic/organometallic synthesis; structure-function relationships. *Mailing Add:* Occidental Res Corp PO Box 19601 Irvine CA 92713

MILLER, JOHN ALLEN, b Elton, La, Jan 4, 42; m 64; c 2. AGRICULTURAL ENGINEERING, ENTOMOLOGY. *Educ:* Univ Southwestern La, BS, 64; Tex A&M Univ, MS, 65, PhD(agr eng), 77. *Prof Exp:* Agr engr, USDA Agr Res Serv, 65-78, AGR ENGR, SCI & EDUC ADMIN-AGR RES, USDA, 78- *Concurrent Pos:* Eng consult, Food & Agr Orgn, UN Develop Proj, 74-75. *Mem:* Am Soc Agr Engrs; Entom Soc Am; Controlled Release Soc. *Res:* Improving effectiveness, efficiency and safety of livestock pest management; controlled release of pesticides; computer simulation of pest populations and control strategies. *Mailing Add:* USDA Agr Res Serv PO Box 232 Kerrville TX 78028

MILLER, JOHN CLARK, physical chemistry, see previous edition

MILLER, JOHN DAVID, b Todd, NC, Aug 9, 23; m 46:; c 3. PLANT BREEDING, PLANT GENETICS. *Educ:* NC State Col, BS, 48, MS, 50; Univ Minn, PhD(plant breeding), 53. *Prof Exp:* Res fel, seedstocks prod, Univ Minn, 53; asst prof cereal breeding, Kans State Univ, 53-57; assoc prof, 57-61, adj prof agron, Agr Exp Sta, Va Polytech Inst & State Univ, 61-78; SR AGRONOMIST, AGR RES SERV, USDA, 75-, ADJ RES ASSOC, GA AGR EXP STA, 78- *Concurrent Pos:* Res agronomist, Agr Res Serv, USDA, 57-72, res leader, 72-78. *Mem:* Am Soc Agron; Am Genetics Asn. *Res:* Forage breeding; statistical techniques in crops research; improved breeding methods for forages; improved small plot machinery; breeding for tolerance to acid soils. *Mailing Add:* Dept of Agron Ga Coastal Plain Exp Sta Tifton GA 31794

MILLER, JOHN FREDERICK, b Los Angeles, Calif, Mar 24, 28; m 54; c 4. METEOROLOGY. *Educ:* Univ Calif, Los Angeles, AB, 51. *Prof Exp:* Meteorologist, Coop Studies Sect, Hydrologic Serv Div, US Weather Bur, 53-59 & Dept Navy, 59-62; asst chief coop studies, Off Hydrol, Weather Bur, 62-64, chief spec studies br, 64-71, CHIEF WATER MGT INFO DIV, OFF HYDROL, NAT WEATHER SERV, NAT OCEANIC & ATMOSPHERIC ADMIN, 71- *Mem:* Am Meteorol Soc; Am Geophys Union. *Res:* Investigation of rainfall with respect to cause, frequency, magnitude and estimating the limiting amounts. *Mailing Add:* 13420 Oriental St Rockville MD 20853

MILLER, JOHN GEORGE, b Philadelphia, Pa, Oct 18, 08; m 40; c 2. PHYSICAL CHEMISTRY. *Educ:* Univ Pa, AB, 29, MSc, 30, PhD(chem), 32. *Prof Exp:* Res chemist, Dermat Res Labs, Pa, 29-30; asst, 30-31, from asst instr to prof, 31-79, EMER PROF CHEM, UNIV PA, 79- *Concurrent Pos:* Proj leader, Thermodyn Res Lab, Univ Pa, 45-51; vis examr, Swarthmore Col, 50-52; consult, Englehard Minerals & Chems Corp, NJ, 44-, Smith, Kline & French Labs, 46-49, Pennwalt Corp, 49-71 & Eastern Regional Res Labs, USDA, 53-57. *Mem:* Fel AAAS; Am Phys Soc; Clay Minerals Soc; Am Chem Soc; Am Inst Chemists. *Res:* Molecular structure; dielectric constant measurements; homogeneous catalysis; reaction mechanisms; surface chemistry; gas properties; calorimetry. *Mailing Add:* Dept of Chem Univ of Pa Philadelphia PA 19104

MILLER, JOHN GRIER, b Boston, Mass, Feb 5, 43. MATHEMATICS. *Educ:* Univ Chicago, SB, 63, SM, 64; Rice Univ, PhD(math), 67. *Prof Exp:* Asst prof math, Univ Calif, Los Angeles, 67-69; asst prof, Columbia Univ, 69-72; asst prof math, Ill State Univ, 72-76; asst prof, Southern Ill Univ, 76-78; ASST PROF MATH, IND UNIV-PURDUE UNIV INDIANAPOLIS, COLUMBUS, IND, 78- *Mem:* Am Math Soc. *Res:* Topology. *Mailing Add:* Dept of Math Ind Univ-Purdue Univ Columbus IN 47201

MILLER, JOHN H, III, b Drexel Hill, Pa, Aug 28, 29. ELECTRONIC PHYSICS. *Educ:* Univ Pa, BA, 51; Princeton Univ, MA, 54, PhD(nuclear physics), 61. *Prof Exp:* Instr physics, Princeton Univ, 55-58; asst prof, 58-66, ASSOC PROF PHYSICS, UNIV DEL, 66-, ASSOC CHMN DEPT, 68- *Mem:* Am Phys Soc; Am Asn Physics Teachers. *Res:* Applications of electronic systems, especially integrated circuits and microcomputer, to undergraduate and graduate laboratories and lecture demonstrations. *Mailing Add:* Dept of Physics Univ of Del Newark DE 19711

MILLER, JOHN HENRY, b Washington, DC, Mar 16, 33; m 54. PLANT PHYSIOLOGY. *Educ:* Yale Univ, BS, 54, MS, 57, PhD(bot), 59. *Prof Exp:* Nat Cancer Inst fel bot, Yale Univ, 59-60, instr, 60-62; from asst prof to assoc prof, 62-70, PROF BOT, SYRACUSE UNIV, 70- *Mem:* Am Soc Plant Physiol; Bot Soc Am; Scand Soc Plant Physiol. *Res:* Photophysiology; developmental physiology; cell differentiation. *Mailing Add:* Dept of Biol Syracuse Univ Syracuse NY 13210

MILLER, JOHN HOWARD, b Columbus, Ohio, Oct 13, 43; m 65; c 1. RADIATION PHYSICS. *Educ:* Davidson Col, BS, 66; Univ Va, PhD(physics), 71. *Prof Exp:* Res assoc physics, Univ Fla, 72-74 & Los Alamos Sci Lab, 74-75; STAFF SCIENTIST PHYSICS, PAC NORTHWEST LAB, BATTELLE MEM INST, 75- *Mem:* Am Phys Soc; Radiation Res Soc. *Res:* Theory of physical and chemical events resulting from energy deposition by ionizing radiation and the relationship of these events to biological effects of the radiation. *Mailing Add:* Pac Northwest Lab Battelle Mem Inst Richland WA 99352

MILLER, JOHN JAMES, b Schreiber, Ont, Oct 13, 18; m 51. MICROBIOLOGY. *Educ:* Univ Toronto, BA, 41, PhD(bot), 44. *Prof Exp:* Agr asst, Can Dept Agr, 44-46, asst plant pathologist, 46-47; from asst prof to assoc bot, 47-60, PROF BIOL, MCMASTER UNIV, 60- *Mem:* Can Soc Microbiol; Can Bot Asn. *Res:* Mycology; yeast sporulation and spore germination. *Mailing Add:* Dept of Biol McMaster Univ Hamilton PQ L8S 4K1 Can

MILLER, JOHN JOHNSTON, III, b San Francisco, Calif, Apr 9, 34; m 58; c 4. PEDIATRICS, IMMUNOBIOLOGY. *Educ:* Wesleyan Univ, BA, 55; Univ Rochester, MD, 60; Univ Melbourne, PhD(immunol), 65. *Prof Exp:* Intern pediat, Univ Calif, San Francisco, 60-61, resident, 61-62; resident, 65, clin teaching asst, 65-67, asst prof pediat, 67-73, sr attend physician, 73-77, assoc prof clin pediat, 77-79, DIR RHEUMATIC DIS SERV, CHILDREN'S HOSP, MED CTR, STANFORD UNIV, 67-, PROF CLIN PEDIAT, 79- *Concurrent Pos:* Consult, US Naval Radiol Defense Lab, 67-69. *Mem:* Fel Am Acad Pediat; Am Rheumatism Asn; Am Asn Immunol; Soc Pediat Res; Am Fedn Clin Res. *Res:* Pediatric rheumatology; drug-induced systemic lupus; immunologic abnormalities in juvenile rheumatoid arthritis. *Mailing Add:* Children's Hosp Stanford Univ Med Ctr Stanford CA 94305

MILLER, JOHN JOSEPH, organic chemistry, see previous edition

MILLER, JOHN MICHAEL, evolutionary botany, population botany, see previous edition

MILLER, JOHN ROBERT, b Berwyn, Ill, June 22, 44; m 67; c 1. PHYSICAL CHEMISTRY, RADIATION CHEMISTRY. *Educ:* Ore State Univ, BS, 66, Univ Wis, PhD(phys chem), 71. *Prof Exp:* Appointee phys & radiation chem, 71-74, asst chemist, 74-76, CHEMIST, ARGONNE NAT LAB, 76- *Mem:* Am Chem Soc. *Res:* Electron transfer over long distances by quantum mechanical tunneling; picosecond pulse radiolysis. *Mailing Add:* Chem 200 Argonne Nat Lab Argonne IL 60439

MILLER, JOHN WALCOTT, b Royal Oak, Mich, Nov 10, 30; m 72; c 2. ANALYTICAL CHEMISTRY, INDUSTRIAL HYGIENE. *Educ:* Wesleyan Univ, BA, 53; Northwestern Univ, PhD(anal chem), 56. *Prof Exp:* Methods develop chemist, 56-60, mgr, Chem Methods Sect, 60-75, supvr, Chromatogr Sect, 75-77, MGR, ENVIRON SAFETY BR, PHILLIPS PETROL CO, 77- *Concurrent Pos:* Nat Acad Sci exchange fel, Prague, 68; chmn, Gordon Res Conf Anal Chem, 75 & Anal Chem Div, Am Chem Soc, 76-77. *Res:* Coulometric analysis; photometric titrations; organic sulfur functional groups analysis; ultraviolet spectroscopy; redox reactions; polarography of coordination compounds; crude oil source identification; water pollution analysis. *Mailing Add:* 1734 S Osage Bartlesville OK 74003

MILLER, JOHN WESLEY, plant pathology, see previous edition

MILLER, JOHN WESLEY, JR, b Philadelphia, Pa, Aug 30, 35; m 58; c 2. MARINE ZOOLOGY, ENTOMOLOGY. *Educ:* Dickinson Col, BS, 57; Pa State Univ, MS, 60, PhD(entom), 62. *Prof Exp:* Fel entom & parasitol, Univ Calif, Berkeley, 62-63; from asst prof to assoc prof, 63-74, PROF BIOL, BALDWIN-WALLACE COL, 74- *Concurrent Pos:* Mem, Comt Marine Invertebrates, Nat Res Coun, 76-81. *Mem:* AAAS; Sigma Xi; Am Inst Biol Sci. *Res:* Laboratory culture and use of marine organisms in the undergraduate curriculum; insects as vectors of plant diseases, specifically the relationship of certain plant viruses to their aphid vectors. *Mailing Add:* Dept Biol Baldwin-Wallace Col Berea OH 44017

MILLER, JON PHILIP, b Moline, Ill, Mar 30, 44; m 65; c 2. BIOCHEMISTRY, MOLECULAR PHARMACOLOGY. *Educ:* Augustana Col, Ill, AB, 66; St Louis Univ, PhD(biochem), 70. *Prof Exp:* Fel biophys chem, ICN Nucleic Acid Res Inst, 70-71, biochemist, 72, head molecular pharm, 72-73, head drug metab, 73-74, head biol div, Nucleic Acid Res Inst, 74-76; head, SRI/NCI Liaison Group, 76-78, sr bioorg chemist, 78-80, DIR, MED BIOCHEM PROG, SRI INT, 80-, ASSOC DIR, BIOMED RES LAB, 81- *Res:* Structure-activity relationships and pharmacological activities of c-adenosine monophosphate analogs; development and mechanism of action and metabolism of drugs; control of cellular growth and differentiation. *Mailing Add:* SRI Int 333 Ravenswood Ave Menlo Park CA 94025

MILLER, JOSEF MAYER, b Philadelphia, Pa, Nov 29, 37; m 60; c 1. PHYSIOLOGY, PSYCHOLOGY. *Educ:* Univ Calif, Berkeley, BA, 61; Univ Wash, PhD(physiol), 65. *Prof Exp:* Asst prof psychol, Univ Mich, 67-68; from asst prof to assoc prof physiol & otolaryngol, 68-77, PROF OTOLARYNGOL, PHYSIOL & BIOPHYS, PHYSIOL & OTOLARYNGOL, UNIV WASH, 77- *Concurrent Pos:* USPHS fel, Univ Mich, 65-67; Deafness Res Found grant, Univ Wash, 69-71, NIH res grant, 69-73. *Mem:* AAAS; Am Physiol Soc; Acoust Soc Am; Soc Neurosci; Psychonomic Soc. *Res:* Physiological and behavioral acoustics; animal psychophysics; sensory neurophysiology. *Mailing Add:* Dept of Otolaryngol Univ of Wash Seattle WA 98195

MILLER, JOSEPH, b San Francisco, Calif, Apr 3, 37; m 59; c 3. CHEMICAL & NUCLEAR ENGINEERING. *Educ:* Univ Calif, Los Angeles, BS, 57, MS, 58, PhD(eng), 61. *Prof Exp:* Assoc eng, Univ Calif, Los Angeles, 59-61, lectr, 61-69; supvr nuclear reactor eng, Atomics Int Div, N Am Aviation Inc, 61-65; asst mgr, Combustion Systs Lab, TRW Systs Group, 65-74; mgr, Power Systs Technol Lab, 74-79, mgr, High Energy Laser Off, TRW Defense & Space Systs Group, 76-81, MGR, RES & TECHNOL OPER, TRW SPACE & TECHNOL GROUP, REDONDA BEACH, 81- *Mem:* Am Nuclear Soc; Am Inst Aeronaut & Astronaut. *Res:* High energy laser research and development; combustion systems and chemical process development; rocket engine and propulsion system development; nuclear reactor physics; heat and mass transfer; thermodynamics. *Mailing Add:* 19855 Greenbriar Dr Tarzana CA 91356

MILLER, JOSEPH EDWIN, b Carrollton, Mo, Nov 4, 42; m 62; c 2. PLANT BIOCHEMISTRY, PLANT PHYSIOLOGY. *Educ:* Colo State Univ, BS, 64, MS, 66; Utah State Univ, PhD(plant biochem), 69. *Prof Exp:* Asst prof plant physiol, Univ Colo, Denver, 69-73; res assoc, Univ Ill, 73-75; res assoc, 75-80, RES SCIENTIST, ARGONNE NAT LAB, 80- *Mem:* Am Soc Plant Physiologists. *Res:* Plant growth and development, especially physiology of flowering; air pollutant effects on plant growth and physiology. *Mailing Add:* Argonne Nat Lab 9700 S Cass Ave Argonne IL 60439

MILLER, JOSEPH HENRY, b Yonkers, NY, May 27, 24; m 48; c 2. MEDICAL PARASITOLOGY. *Educ:* Univ Mich, BS, 48, MS, 49; NY Univ, PhD(biol), 53. *Prof Exp:* Asst biol, NY Univ, 51-53; instr, 53-55, from asst prof to assoc prof, 55-70, PROF MED PARASITOL, SCH MED, LA STATE UNIV, NEW ORLEANS, 70- *Concurrent Pos:* Fel, China Med Bd, Cent Am, 56; scientist, vis staff, Charity Hosp, New Orleans, 53-; vis prof, Fac Med, Nat Univ Mex, 66, Col Med, Univ Ariz, 75-76; consult, Family Med Proj, Abha Col Med Sci, Univ Riyadh, Saudi Arabia, 81. *Mem:* Am Soc Trop Med & Hyg; Am Soc Parasitol; fel Royal Soc Trop Med & Hyg; Electron Micros Soc Am (treas, 70-71); Soc Protozool. *Res:* Medical parasitology, especially electron microscopy of parasites. *Mailing Add:* Dept of Trop Med & Med Parasitol La State Univ Sch of Med New Orleans LA 70112

MILLER, JOSEPH MORTON, b Boston, Mass, Nov 9, 21; m 48; c 3. CLINICAL MEDICINE, PREVENTIVE MEDICINE. *Educ:* Harvard Univ, AB, 42, MD, 45, MPH, 60. *Prof Exp:* Intern med, Mt Sinai Hosp, New York, 45-46; res fel biochem, Trudeau Found, 48; NIH fel, Med Sch, Harvard Univ, 48-50; instr, 50-64, RES ASSOC MED, SCH PUB HEALTH, HARVARD UNIV, 65-; PROG DIR, PROJ HOPE, GUATEMALA. *Mem:* Fel Am Col Physicians. *Res:* Rheumatic fever; streptococcal disease; epidemiology of coronary artery disease. *Mailing Add:* One Boylston Plaza Prudential Ctr Boston MA 02199

MILLER, JOYCE MARY, b Belton, Tex, Mar 12, 45; m 72. BIOCHEMISTRY. *Educ:* Southwest Tex State Univ, BS, 67, MA, 68; Tex A&M Univ, PhD(biochem), 72. *Prof Exp:* Fel lipoprotein chem, Sch Med, Univ Southern Calif, 72-74; res assoc, Sch Med, Wash Univ, 74-75; asst prof, 75-81, PROF BIOL SCI, MARYVILLE COL, MO, 81- *Concurrent Pos:* NIH fel, 73. *Mem:* AAAS; Sigma Xi. *Res:* Determination of qualitative and/or quantitative variations in the peptide composition of various serum lipoprotein classes with increasing age of an individual by protein characterization and immunological techniques. *Mailing Add:* Maryville Col 13550 Conway Rd St Louis MO 63141

MILLER, JUDITH EVELYN, b Rahway, NJ, Dec 30, 51. MICROBIAL GENETICS. *Educ:* Cornell Univ, BSc, 73; Case Western Reserve Univ, PhD(microbiol), 78. *Prof Exp:* Teaching specialist microbiol, Cornell Univ, 73; ASST PROF LIFE SCI, WORCESTER POLYTECH INST, 78- *Mem:* Am Soc Microbiol; AAAS; Sigma Xi. *Res:* Ethanol production from apple pomace; microbial lignin degradation; viability and genetic recombination in Escherichia coli. *Mailing Add:* Dept Life Sci Worcester Polytech Inst Worcester MA 01609

MILLER, JULIAN CREIGHTON, JR, b Baton Rouge, La, Mar 6, 40; m 65; c 2. PLANT BREEDING, PLANT GENETICS. *Educ:* La State Univ, BS, 65, MS, 67; Mich State Univ, PhD(hort), 72. *Prof Exp:* Res asst hort, La State Univ, 66-67, Univ Wis-Madison, 67-68, Mich State Univ, 68-72; asst prof, Tex Agr Exp Sta, Lubbock, 72-75; assoc prof, 75-82, PROF HORT, TEX A&M UNIV, 82-, INTERIM DEPT HEAD HORT SCI, 80- *Concurrent Pos:* Prin investr, Coop State Res Serv grants, US Agency for Int Develop, 77-80, 78-79 & 79-82. *Mem:* AAAS; Am Soc Hort Sci; Am Genetic Asn; Am Soc Agron; Am Inst Biol Sci. *Res:* Potato variety development; vegetable legume improvement; breeding for enhanced biological nitrogen fixation. *Mailing Add:* Dept of Hort Sci Tex A&M Univ College Station TX 77843

MILLER, JULIUS SUMNER, b Billerica, Mass, May 17, 09; m 34. PHYSICS. *Educ:* Boston Univ, BS, 32, MA, 33; Univ Idaho, MS, 40. *Prof Exp:* Master math, Cheshire Acad, 36-37; instr physics, Dillard Univ, 37-38, prof, 41-51; PROF PHYSICS, EL CAMINO COL, 53- *Concurrent Pos:* Chmn dept physics, Mich Col Mining & Technol, 48-49; Carnegie grant, Inst Advan Studies, 50-51; physics ed, Sch Sci & Math, 50-; assoc res physicist, Univ Calif, Los Angeles, 56-; lectr, Uppsala Univ, Sweden, Oslo Univ, Norway & Univ Milan, Italy, 64; Isaac Newton mem lectr, Brit Broadcasting Co, 65; consult, Walt Disney Prods, 60-, Orgn Econ Coop & Develop, Paris, France, 62 & TV progs, Norway & NZ, 63 & Australia, 64-65; lectr physics, TV progs, Australia, 62-74, South Africa, 75; vis prof, Villanova Col Brisbane, Australia, 79 & Pulteney Grammer Sch, Adelaide, Australia, 81. *Mem:* Am Asn Physics Teachers. *Res:* Electron configuration in the elements; analytical mechanics; demonstration experiments in physics; physics of toys; history of science. *Mailing Add:* 16711 Cranbrook Ave Torrance CA 90504

MILLER, KEITH WYATT, b Chard, UK, March 37, 41; m 70; c 2. PHARMACOLOGY. *Educ:* Oxford Univ, BA, 63, DPhil, 67. *Prof Exp:* NSF fel chem, Univ Calif, Berkeley, 67-69; res fel pharmacol, Oxford Univ, UK, 69-71; instr, 71-73, asst prof, 73-76, ASSOC PROF PHARMACOL, HARVARD MED SCH, 76- *Mem:* Am Soc Pharmacol & Exp Therapeut; Biophys Soc; Undersea Med Soc; Brit Pharmacol Soc; Brit Biophys Soc. *Res:* Mechanism of action of general anesthetics and their reversal by pressure; thermodynamics of small moleculer-membrane interactions; lipid modulation of protein function. *Mailing Add:* Dept Pharmacol Harvard Med Sch 25 Shattuck St Boston MA 02115

MILLER, KENNETH JAY, b New York, NY, Oct 12, 24; m 48; c 5. PHYSICAL CHEMISTRY. *Educ:* Eastern Nazarene Col, BS, 49; Johns Hopkins Univ, MA, 50, PhD(phys chem), 52. *Prof Exp:* Develop engr semiconductors, Westinghouse Elec Corp, Pa, 52-55; asst prof chem, Mt Union Col, 55-58; sr scientist phys chem, Res & Advan Develop Div, Avco Corp, 58-59; mem tech staff semiconductors, Bell Tel Labs, 59-68; PROF CHEM, NORTHEAST LA UNIV, 68- *Mem:* Am Chem Soc. *Res:* Thermodynamics and electrochemistry; semiconductors. *Mailing Add:* Dept Chem Northeast La Univ Monroe LA 71209

MILLER, KENNETH JOHN, b Chicago, Ill, Mar 24, 39; m 63, 75; c 2. THEORETICAL CHEMISTRY. *Educ:* Ill Inst Technol, BS, 60; Johns Hopkins Univ, MA, 64; Iowa State Univ, PhD(chem), 66. *Prof Exp:* Nat Acad Sci-Nat Res Coun resident res assoc, Nat Bur Standards, 66-67; asst prof, 67-72, assoc prof, 72-81, PROF THEORET CHEM, RENSSELAER POLYTECH INST, 81- *Mem:* Am Chem Soc. *Res:* Theoretical biochemistry; interaction of molecules with nucleic acids; design of antitumor agents; characterization of binding sites for intercalating agents and proteins on nucleic acids; molecular polarizabilities; chemical reactivities of heterocyclic systems. *Mailing Add:* Dept of Chem Rensselaer Polytech Inst Troy NY 12181

MILLER, KENNETH L, b Lock Haven, Pa, Aug 14, 43; m 61; c 2. HEALTH PHYSICS, MEDICAL HEALTH PHYSICS. *Educ:* Lock Haven State Col, BS, 65; Univ Pittsburgh, MS, 70; Am Bd Health Physics, cert, 76. *Prof Exp:* Teacher math & sci, Pa High Sch, 65-66; health physics asst, Pa State Univ, Pittsburgh, 66-69; fel radiation safety, Univ Pittsburgh, 69-70; assoc health physicist, Pa State Univ, 70-71; res assoc, 71-78, asst prof, 78-81, ASSOC PROF RADIOL, MILTON S HERSHEY MED CTR, PA STATE UNIV, 81-, DIR, DIV HEALTH PHYSICS, 71- *Concurrent Pos:* Consult, various Pa Hosps, clins & physicians, 70- *Mem:* Health Physics Soc; Am Asn Physicists Med; Am Pub Health Asn; Am Nuclear Soc; AAAS. *Res:* Radioisotope /radiation utilization in research and medicine; equipment design; problem solving. *Mailing Add:* Health Physics Off 500 University Dr Hershey PA 17033

MILLER, KENNETH LERON, b Magrath, Alta, Sept 6, 24. POLYMER CHEMISTRY. *Educ:* Brigham Young Univ, BA, 48; Ore State Univ, PhD, 52. *Prof Exp:* RES & DEVELOP CHEMIST, E I DU PONT DE NEMOURS & CO, INC, 52- *Mem:* Am Chem Soc. *Mailing Add:* 113 Wood Rd Louisville KY 40222

MILLER, KENNETH M, SR, b Chicago, Ill, Nov 20, 21; m 43, 70; c 4. ELECTRONICS. *Educ:* Ill Inst Technol, 40-41; Univ Calif, Los Angeles, 61. *Prof Exp:* Electronics engr, Rauland Corp, 41-48; gen mgr, Learcal Div, Lear, Inc, 48-59; vpres & gen mgr, Motorola Aviation Electronics, Inc, 59-60 & Instrument Div, Daystrom, Inc, 61; gen mgr, Singer Co, 62-65; vpres & gen mgr, Lear Jet Corp, 65-66; pres & dir, Infonics, Inc, Calif, 67-68; vpres & gen mgr, Comput Industs, Inc, Calif, 68-69; vpres & dir, Am Standard Corp, 69-71; pres, Wilcox Elec, Inc & dir, World Wide Wilcox, Inc, 71-73; PRES, CHIEF EXEC OFFICER & DIR, PENRIL CORP, 74- *Concurrent Pos:* Trustee, Park City Hosp, Bridgeport, Conn, 62-64; mem bd assocs, Univ Bridgeport, 62-64. *Mem:* Sr mem Inst Elec & Electronics Engrs; sr mem Instrument Soc Am; Am Soc Nondestructive Testing; Armed Forces Commun Electronics Asn; AAAS. *Res:* Business administration; automatic flight controls; communication and navigation systems; video, audio and radio frequency consumer electronic devices; electromechanical components; precision instruments. *Mailing Add:* Penril Corp 5520 Randolph Rd Rockville MD 20852

MILLER, KENNETH MELVIN, b Indianapolis, Ind, Aug 17, 43; m 69; c 1. FRESH WATER ECOLOGY, FOOD SCIENCE. *Educ:* Ind Univ, AB, 65, AM, 67, PhD(zool), 75. *Prof Exp:* Instr biol, Purdue Univ, NCent Campus, 70-74; lab mgr, 75-76, qual control mgr, 76-81, TECHNICAL DIR, AM HOME FOODS, 81- *Concurrent Pos:* Guest lectr, Purdue NCent, 81. *Mem:* Am Soc Qual Control; Am Inst Biol Sci. *Res:* Species association and diversity in aquatic coleoptera and odonata; heat processing parameters in food canning. *Mailing Add:* Am Home Foods 352 Fail Rd PO Box 5004 LaPorte IN 46350

MILLER, KENNETH PHILIP, b Northfield, Minn, Sept 17, 15; m 41; c 4. ANIMAL BREEDING. *Educ:* Univ Minn, BS, 39, MS, 40; Ohio State Univ, PhD(dairy husb), 56. *Prof Exp:* From instr to assoc prof, 41-79, PROF ANIMAL BREEDING, SOUTHERN EXP STA, UNIV MINN, WASECA, 79- *Mem:* AAAS; Am Soc Animal Sci; Am Dairy Sci Asn. *Res:* Animal nutrition. *Mailing Add:* 808 Fifth Ave SE Waseca MN 56093

MILLER, KENNETH RAYMOND, b Rahway, NJ, July 14, 48; m 72. CELL BIOLOGY. *Educ:* Brown Univ, ScB, 70; Univ Colo, PhD(biol), 74. *Prof Exp:* Lectr biol, Harvard Univ, 74-76, asst prof, 76-80; ASSOC PROF, BROWN UNIV, 80- *Mem:* AAAS; Am Soc Cell Biol; Am Soc Photobiol. *Res:* Structure, biochemistry, and function of biological membranes; most importantly, the photosynthetic membrane. *Mailing Add:* Div Biol & Med Brown Univ Providence RI 02912

MILLER, KENNETH SIELKE, b New York, NY, June 4, 22; m 53; c 2. MATHEMATICS. *Educ:* Columbia Univ, BS, 43, AM, 47, PhD(math), 50. *Prof Exp:* Lectr, Columbia Univ, 49; from inst to prof math, NY Univ, 50-64; SR STAFF SCIENTIST, ELECTRONICS RES LABS, COLUMBIA UNIV, 64-; ADJ PROF MATH, FORDHAM UNIV, 64- *Concurrent Pos:* Mem staff, Inst Advan Study, 50 & 58-59; consult, Army Res Off, Systs Res Labs & Fed Sci Corp. *Mem:* Am Math Soc. *Res:* Differential operators; multivariate distributions; complex stochastic processes. *Mailing Add:* 25 Bonwit Rd Town of Rye Port Chester NY 10573

MILLER, KENNETH WAYNE, pharmacology, biopharmaceutics, see previous edition

MILLER, KENT D, b Detroit, Mich, May 9, 25; m 50; c 3. BIOCHEMISTRY. *Educ:* Oberlin Col, AB, 49; Wayne State Univ, MS, 51, PhD, 54; Albany Med Col, MD, 62. *Prof Exp:* Res scientist, Div Labs & Res, NY State Dept Health, 54-57, sr res scientist, 57-62, asst dir, 62-69; PROF MED, SCH MED, UNIV MIAMI, 69-, PROF MICROBIOL, 76- *Mem:* Am Chem Soc; Am Soc Biol Chemists; Am Soc Hemat; Soc Exp Biol & Med. *Res:* Blood proteins; coagulation; bacterial enzymes; immunology. *Mailing Add:* Univ Miami Dept of Med Biscayne Annex Miami FL 33152

MILLER, KIM IRVING, b Boone, NC, July 26, 36; m 73. PLANT TAXONOMY. *Educ:* Appalachian State Teachers Col, BS, 58; Purdue Univ, MS, 61, PhD(bot), 64. *Prof Exp:* Vis asst prof biol, Purdue Univ, 64-65, res assoc & cur herbarium, 65-66; asst prof biol, Eastern Ky Univ, 66-67 & Appalachian State Univ, 67-68; asst prof, 68-71, chmn dept, 73-78, assoc prof, 72-78, PROF BIOL & CHMN DIV SCI & MATH & DIR, ENVIRON CTR, JACKSONVILLE UNIV, 78- *Mem:* Bot Soc Am; Am Soc Plant Taxon. *Res:* Evolution and systematics of Euphorbiaceae and related families. *Mailing Add:* Dept of Biol Jacksonville Univ Jacksonville FL 32211

MILLER, KIRK, b New York, NY, June 25, 49; m 72; c 2. PHYSIOLOGICAL ECOLOGY, COMPARATIVE PHYSIOLOGY. *Educ:* Antioch Col, BA, 72; Colo State Univ, MS, 74; Univ Okla, PhD(zool), 78. *Prof Exp:* ASST PROF BIOL, FRANKLIN & MARSHALL COL, 78- *Mem:* AAAS; Am Soc Zoologists. *Res:* Respiration and metabolism of amphibians; locomotion of amphibians. *Mailing Add:* Dept of Biol Franklin & Marshall Col Lancaster PA 17604

MILLER, KNUDT JOHN, horticulture, plant physiology, see previous edition

MILLER, LARRY GENE, b Corsicana, Tex, Dec 30, 46; m 69; c 3. PHARMACEUTICS. *Educ:* Univ Miss, BS, 69, PhD(pharmaceut), 72. *Prof Exp:* Sr scientist prod develop, Mead Johnson & Co, 72-73; sr pharmacist pharmaceut res, 73-76, mgr pharm res prod develop, 76-78, DIR PROD DEVELOP, A H ROBINS CO, INC, 78- *Concurrent Pos:* Preceptor indust clerkship, Sch Pharm, Med Col Va. *Mem:* Am Pharmaceut Asn; Acad Pharmaceut Sci; Controlled Release Soc. *Res:* Design of dosage forms for pharmaceutical compounds so as to meet the necessary requirements of stability, delivery and bioavailability; new product formula implementation to commercial manufacturing. *Mailing Add:* A H Robins Co Inc 1211 Sherwood Ave Richmond VA 23220

MILLER, LARRY LEE, organic chemistry, see previous edition

MILLER, LARRY O'DELL, b Los Angeles, Calif, Feb 26, 39; m 72. DEVELOPMENTAL BIOLOGY, NEUROPHYSIOLOGY. *Educ:* Univ Calif, Santa Barbara, BA, 61, MA, 64, PhD(biol), 67. *Prof Exp:* Res biologist, Firestone Tire & Rubber Co, 67-69; lectr biol, Univ Calif, Santa Barbara, 69-71; INSTR BIOL, MOORPARK COL, 71-, HEAD DEPT, 76- *Mem:* AAAS. *Res:* Biochemical control of eukaryotic cellular differentiation. *Mailing Add:* Dept of Biol Moorpark Col Ventura CA 93021

MILLER, LAURENCE HERBERT, b Newark, NJ, Oct 11, 34; m 59; c 2. DERMATOLOGY. *Educ:* Muhlenberg Col, BS, 56; Univ Lausanne, MD, 61. *Prof Exp:* Intern, Newark Beth Israel Hosp, 62-63; house physician, East Orange Gen Hosp, 63; resident, NY Univ Med Ctr, 63-66; DERMAT PROG DIR, NAT INST ARTHRITIS, DIABETES, DIGESTIVE & KIDNEY DIS, 66- *Concurrent Pos:* Mem, Dermat Found, 68; asst prof, Sch Med, Johns Hopkins Univ, 69-; mem, Sci Adv Bd, Nat Psoriasis Found, 71-; tech consult, Skin & Allergy News, 73- *Mem:* Fel Am Acad Dermat; Soc Invest Dermat; Am Dermat Asn. *Res:* Varicella-Zoster virus; cell controls in psoriasis. *Mailing Add:* 10902 Old Coach Rd Potomac MD 20854

MILLER, LAWRENCE INGRAM, b Jackson Center, Ohio, May 12, 14; m 39; c 2. PHYTOPATHOLOGY. *Educ:* Oberlin Col, AB, 36; Va Polytech Inst, MS, 38; Univ Minn, PhD(plant path), 53. *Prof Exp:* Freeport Sulphur Co fel plant path, 38-40, asst plant pathologist, Agr Exp Sta, 40-42, assoc prof, 49-55, prof plant path, 55-80, ASSOC PLANT PATHOLOGIST, AGR EXP STA, VA POLYTECH INST & STATE UNIV, 49-, EMER PROF PLANT PATH, 80- *Concurrent Pos:* Mem comt biol control of soilborne plant pathogens, Nat Acad Sci-Nat Res Coun, 57-65; NATO res grant plant nematol, 73-74; mem exec coun, Intersoc Consortium for Plant Protection, 76-78. *Honors & Awards:* J Shelton Horsley Res Award, Va Acad Sci, 60; Golden Peanut Res Award, Nat Peanut Coun, 63. *Mem:* Int Soc Plant Path; Soc Europ Nematol; Brit Asn Appl Biol; Am Phytopath Soc; Am Soc Nematol. *Res:* Plant nematology, particularly Heterodera and Globodera species; diseases of the peanut. *Mailing Add:* Dept Plant Path & Physiol Va Polytech Inst & State Univ Blacksburg VA 24061

MILLER, LEE STEPHEN, b Jacksonville, Fla, June 5, 30; m 50; c 2. ELECTRONICS. *Educ:* Ind Inst Technol, BS, 52; Clemson Univ, PhD(eng physics), 67. *Prof Exp:* Engr, Microwave Lab, Int Tel & Tel Co, 52-54; head antenna dept, Radiation Inc, 54-57; vpres, Melbourne Eng Corp, 57-58; sr staff engr, Sperry Rand Corp, 58-62; mem tech staff, Thompson-Ramo-Wooldridge Corp, 62-64; sr div scientist, Res Triangle Inst, 68-80; MEM STAFF, APPL SCI ASSOCS, INC, 80- *Concurrent Pos:* Mem countermeasures group, Electronics Warfare Coun, 55-57; NASA grant, Res Triangle Inst, 68-69. *Mem:* AAAS; Inst Elec & Electronics Engrs. *Res:* Radar; electromagnetic scattering; stochastic system theory; information theory; remote sensor systems; biomedical engineering. *Mailing Add:* Appl Sci Assocs Inc 105 E Chamtham Apex NC 27502

MILLER, LEON LEE, b Rochester, NY, Dec 7, 12; m 35, 58; c 6. BIOCHEMISTRY. *Educ:* Cornell Univ, BA & MA, 34, PhD(org chem), 37; Univ Rochester, MD, 45. *Prof Exp:* Res org chemist, Calco Chem Co, NJ, 37-38; instr path & pharmacol, Sch Med & Dent, Univ Rochester, 45-46; asst prof biochem, Jefferson Med Col, 46-48; assoc prof radiation biol & biochem, 48-59, prof, 59-78, EMER PROF RADIATION BIOL, BIOPHYS & BIOCHEM, UNIV ROCHESTER, 78- *Mem:* AAAS; Am Chem Soc; Am Soc Biol Chem; NY Acad Sci. *Res:* Organic synthesis; blood and liver proteins and their functions; liver injury; enzyme, protein and amino acid metabolism; isolated liver perfusion. *Mailing Add:* Dept of Radiation Biol & Biophys Univ of Rochester Sch of Med Rochester NY 14642

MILLER, LEONARD DAVID, b Jersey City, NJ, July 8, 30; m 67; c 2. SURGERY. *Educ:* Yale Univ, AB, 51; Univ Pa, MD, 55. *Prof Exp:* Asst instr surg, 56-57 & 59-64, assoc in surg, 64-66, from asst prof to prof surg, 66-78, vchmn dept, 72-78, JOHN RHEA PROF SURG & CHMN DEPT, UNIV PA, 78-, J WILLIAM WHITE PROF SURG RES, 70-, DIR HARRISON DEPT SURG RES, 72- *Concurrent Pos:* NIH sr clin trainee, Univ Pa, 64-65, NIH grants, 65-, John A Hartford Found, Inc grant, 66-; intern, Hosp Univ Pa, 55-56, resident surg, 56-57 & 59-64, dir, Shock & Trauma Clin Res Unit, 67-72; exec officer, Harrison Dept Surg Res, Univ Pa, 67-68, dir NIH training grant, 67-72; vis surgeon, Vet Admin Hosp, 71-; consult, Children's Hosp Philadelphia, 73-; chmn comt surg educ, Soc Univ Surg, 68-71; actg chmn dept surg, Am Surg Asn. *Honors & Awards:* Distinguished Teaching Award, Lindback Found, 70. *Mem:* AAAS; Soc Univ Surg; Soc Surg Alimentary Tract; Am Soc Surg Trauma; Am Surg Asn. *Mailing Add:* Dept of Surg 1000 Ravdin Hosp of the Univ of Pa Philadelphia PA 19104

MILLER, LEONARD EDWARD, b New York, NY, Aug 24, 19; m 46; c 4. ORGANIC CHEMISTRY. *Educ:* Univ Mich, BS, 40, MS, 42, PhD(org chem), 43. *Prof Exp:* H H Rackham asst, Univ Mich, 43-44; instr chem, Univ Ill, 46-48, instr & admin asst to head dept, 48-51; prof & head dept, Univ NDak, 51-52; assoc prof & dir labs, Univ Ill, 52-56; sr res chemist & sr staff asst, Calif Res Corp, Standard Oil Co Calif, 56-59, res assoc, 59-64; dir explor res, 64-72, HEAD, CHEM PROD RES DEPT, LUBRIZOL CORP, 72- *Concurrent Pos:* Instr exten, Univ Calif, 58-64. *Mem:* AAAS; Am Chem Soc. *Res:* New monomers and polymers; synthesis and applications. *Mailing Add:* Chem Prod Res Dept Lubrizol Corp 29400 Lakeland Blvd Wickliffe OH 44092

MILLER, LEONARD ROBERT, b New York, NY, Oct 31, 33; m 57; c 3. PATHOLOGY, CELL BIOLOGY. *Educ:* Bethany Col, BS, 54; Univ Pittsburgh, MS, 55; Albany Med Col, MD, 59; Am Bd Path, dipl, 65. *Prof Exp:* Intern, Beverly Hosp, 59-60; resident path, Sch Med, Yale Univ, 61-64, instr, 64-67; asst prof path, Sch Med, Univ Ariz, 67-68; assoc prof, Med Ctr, Univ Okla, 68-70, vis assoc prof physiol & biophys, 70-72; CLIN ASSOC PROF PATH, UNIV CALIF, LOS ANGELES & SCH MED, UNIV UTAH, 73- *Concurrent Pos:* Res fel, 60-61; USPHS trainee path, 61-63, spec fel, 63-64; Off Naval Res grant, 68-; consult, Tissue Bank, Naval Med Res Inst, 64-67; sect chief histopath, Armed Forces Radiobiol Res Inst, 64-67; pvt pract path, Sargent, Miller & Morrison Prof Corp, 72- *Mem:* AAAS; Am Asn Pathologists & Bacteriologists; Int Acad Path; Soc Cryobiol. *Res:* In vivo, in vitro mammalian and bacterial cell function; cellular control mechanisms; phage induction; mammalian cell transformation; adaptation; immunology; cryobiology; ultrastructure of immune response; inhibition and enhancement of cell repair. *Mailing Add:* Sargent Miller & Morrison Prof Corp 890 Cherry St Tulare CA 93274

MILLER, LEROY JESSE, b Lebanon, Pa, Aug 12, 33; m 54; c 3. POLYMER CHEMISTRY, PHOTOCHEMISTRY. *Educ:* Elizabethtown Col, BS, 54; Univ Del, MS, 57, PhD(chem), 59. *Prof Exp:* Sr res engr, Atomics Int Div, NAm Aviation Inc, 58-60; sr res chemist, Sundstrand Corp, 60-62; mem tech staff, 62-71, group head, 71-78, staff engr, 71-78, SECT HEAD, HUGHES AIRCRAFT CO, 78- *Mem:* AAAS; Am Chem Soc; Soc Photog Sci & Eng; Electrochem Soc; Sigma Xi. *Res:* radiation resists; thermally stable aromatic polymers; photopolymerization; liquid crystals; photogalvanic effects; radiation damage; reaction mechanisms. *Mailing Add:* 8313 Hillary Dr Canoga Park CA 91304

MILLER, LESTON WAYNE, b Seattle, Wash, Apr 10, 28; m 56; c 2. ELECTRODYNAMICS. *Educ:* Univ Wash, BS, 51, PhD(physics), 59. *Prof Exp:* MEM STAFF, LOS ALAMOS SCI LAB, UNIV CALIF, 59- *Mem:* Am Geophys Union; Am Phys Soc. *Res:* Radio frequency electromagnetic radiations from nuclear explosions; magnetospheric physics; ionospheric physics; weapon testing. *Mailing Add:* Los Alamos Sci Lab Univ of Calif Los Alamos NM 87545

MILLER, LEWIS F, polymer chemistry, colloid chemistry, see previous edition

MILLER, LLOYD GEORGE, b Brighton, Colo, Dec 15, 34. NUTRITION, BIOCHEMISTRY. *Educ:* Colo State Univ, BS, 62, PhD(nutrit), 67; Univ Nebr, MS, 64. *Prof Exp:* Mgr nutrit, Theracon Co, 71-72; mgr, 67-71, dir prod develop, 72-82, ASST GEN MGR, CARNATION CO, 82- *Mem:* Am Soc Animal Sci. *Res:* Small animal nutrition; product development of foods for the dog and cat. *Mailing Add:* Carnation Res Labs 8015 Van Nuys Blvd Van Nuys CA 91412

MILLER, LOIS KATHRYN, b Lebanon, Pa, Oct 8, 45; m 74. BIOCHEMISTRY, VIROLOGY. *Educ:* Upsala Col, BS, 67; Univ Wis-Madison, PhD(biochem), 72. *Prof Exp:* Fel, Calif Inst Technol, 71-74, Imperial Cancer Res Fund, London, 74-76; asst prof, 76-79, ASSOC PROF BIOCHEM, UNIV IDAHO, 79- *Concurrent Pos:* Adj prof, Wash State Univ, 78-; NIH grant, 77- *Mem:* AAAS; Am Soc Microbiol. *Res:* Nucleic acid biochemistry; molecular biology; insect virology; viral genetics; recombinant DNA technology and biological insect pest control. *Mailing Add:* Dept of Bacteriol & Biochem Univ of Idaho Moscow ID 83843

MILLER, LORRAINE THERESA, b Dane, Wis, Mar 12, 31. NUTRITION, BIOCHEMISTRY. *Educ:* Univ Wis, BS, 53, MS, 58, PhD(nutrit, biochem), 67. *Prof Exp:* Dietitian, Med Ctr, Univ Mich, 54-56; instr foods & nutrit, Mich State Univ, 58-63; asst prof, 66-69, ASSOC PROF FOODS & NUTRIT, ORE STATE UNIV, 69- *Mem:* Am Dietetic Asn; AAAS. *Res:* Metabolism of tryptophan in vitamin B6 deficiency; metabolism of vitamin B6. *Mailing Add:* Dept of Foods & Nutrit Ore State Univ Corvallis OR 97331

MILLER, LOUIS HOWARD, b Baltimore, Md, Feb 4, 35; m 59; c 1. TROPICAL MEDICINE, PARASITOLOGY. *Educ:* Haverford Col, BA, 56; Wash Univ, MD, 60; Columbia Univ, MS, 64. *Prof Exp:* Intern, Mt Sinai Hosp, New York, 60-61; resident med, Montefiore Hosp, Bronx, 61-62 & Mt Sinai Hosp, 62-63; res physician, SEATO Med Res Lab, Bangkok, Thailand, 65-67; asst prof trop med, Col Physicians & Surgeons, Columbia Univ, 67-71, assoc prof, 71; HEAD SECT MALARIA, LAB PARASITIC DIS, NAT INST ALLERGY & INFECTIOUS DIS, 71- *Concurrent Pos:* NIH fel, Cedar-Sinai Med Ctr, 64-65. *Mem:* AAAS; fel Am Col Physicians; Am Soc Trop Med & Hyg; Infectious Dis Soc Am; Royal Soc Trop Med & Hyg. *Res:* Malaria; ultrastructure; immunology; physiology. *Mailing Add:* Lab of Parasitic Dis Bldg 5 Nat Inst Allergy & Infect Dis Bethesda MD 20014

MILLER, LOWELL D, b Chicago, Ill, Jan 20, 33; m 59; c 2. BIOCHEMISTRY, PHARMACOLOGY. *Educ:* Univ Mo, BS, 57, MS, 58, PhD(biochem), 60. *Prof Exp:* Res asst biochem, Univ Mo, 57-60; res biochemist, Neisler Labs, Inc, 60-61, sr res biochemist, 61-64, dir biol res, 64-66, dir toxicol & biochem, Union Carbide Develop Dept, Ill, 66-69; assoc dir biomed res, Warren-Teed Pharmaceut, 69-71; tech dir clin labs & pres, Lab Exp Biol, 71-73; mem staff, 73-76, VPRES CORP RES & DEVELOP, MARION LABS, INC, 76- *Concurrent Pos:* Mem fac, Millikin Univ, 63-68. *Mem:* Am Chem Soc; NY Acad Sci; Am Asn Clin Chem; Soc Toxicol. *Res:* Pharmaceutical research; development of screening tests for biological activity; drug metabolism and toxicology. *Mailing Add:* Marion Labs Inc 10236 Bunker Ridge Rd Kansas City MO 64137

MILLER, LYLE DEVON, b Lebanon, Ind, Dec 8, 38; m 62; c 2. VETERINARY PATHOLOGY. *Educ:* Kans State Univ, BS, 61, DVM, 63; Univ Wis-Madison, MS, 68, PhD, 71. *Prof Exp:* pathologist, Vet Serv, Nat Animal Dis Ctr, USDA, 71-81; PROF COL VET MED, IOWA STATE UNIV, 81- *Mem:* Am Vet Med Asn; Am Asn Vet Lab Diagnosticians; Am Col Vet Pathologists; US Animal Health Asn; Nat Asn Fed Vets. *Mailing Add:* Dept Vet Path Col Vet Med Iowa State Univ Ames IA 50011

MILLER, LYLE HERBERT, neuropsychology, psychophysiology, see previous edition

MILLER, LYNN, b McCook, Nebr, Nov 6, 32; m 57; c 2. MICROBIAL GENETICS. *Educ:* San Francisco State Col, BS, 57; Stanford Univ, PhD(biol), 62. *Prof Exp:* NIH fel microbiol, Hopkins Marine Sta, Stanford Univ, 62-64; NIH fel genetics, Univ Wash, 64-65; asst prof biol, Am Univ, Beirut, 65-68 & Adelphi Univ, 68-70; assoc prof, 70-74, dean, Sch Natural Sci, 77-78, PROF BIOL, HAMPSHIRE COL, 74- *Concurrent Pos:* Vis scholar, Univ Wash, 75. *Mem:* AAAS; Genetics Soc Am; Am Inst Biol Sci; Am Soc Microbiol. *Res:* Sterol metabolism and genetics in Saccharomyces; human population genetics. *Mailing Add:* Sch of Natural Sci Hampshire Col Amherst MA 01002

MILLER, LYSTER KEITH, b Tonapah, Nev, Aug 8, 32; m 60; c 3. PHYSIOLOGY. *Educ:* Univ Nev, BS, 55, MS, 57; Univ Alaska, PhD(zoophysiol), 66. *Prof Exp:* Res physiologist, Arctic Health Res Ctr, USPHS, Alaska, 60-62; instr, 62-66, asst prof, 66-69, ASSOC PROF PHYSIOL, INST ARCTIC BIOL, UNIV ALASKA, 69- *Mem:* AAAS; Am Soc Zoologists; Am Physiol Soc; Entom Soc Am; Soc Cryobiol. *Res:* Comparative neurophysiology insect freezing tolerance and physiology of marine mammals; temperature adaptation in peripheral nerve; mechanisms of freezing tolerance in insects and other invertebrates; temperature regulation and gross energetics in northern mammals, especially aquatic species; biometeorology of cold regions. *Mailing Add:* Inst Arctic Biol Univ Alaska Fairbanks AK 99701

MILLER, M(URRAY) H(ENRI), b Brooklyn, NY, Oct 1, 28; m 58. ELECTRICAL ENGINEERING. *Educ:* Univ Mich, BSE, 50, MSE, 51, PhD, 59. *Prof Exp:* Res assoc, Eng Res Inst, Univ Mich, Ann Arbor, 51-59, lectr, 52, from asst prof to assoc prof elec eng, 59-69; assoc prof, 69-76, PROF ELEC ENG, UNIV MICH, DEARBORN, 76-, CHMN DEPT, 75- *Concurrent Pos:* Sr scientist, KMS Indust, Mich, 67. *Mem:* Inst Elec & Electronics Engrs; Am Soc Eng Educ; AAAS. *Res:* Electron tubes; physical electronics. *Mailing Add:* Elec Eng Dept Univ Mich 4901 Evergreen Rd Dearborn MI 48128

MILLER, MARCIA MADSEN, b Santa Monica, Calif, May 31, 44; m 66; c 1. BIOLOGY. *Educ:* Univ Calif, Davis, BS, 65, MA, 66; Univ Calif, Los Angeles, PhD(bot), 72. *Prof Exp:* Fel biol, Calif Inst Technol, 72-75; res scientist, City Hope Nat Med Ctr, 75-78; fel, Biozentrum, Univ Basel, 78-79; RES SCIENTIST, CITY HOPE NAT MED CTR, 79- *Concurrent Pos:* NSF fel, 65-66; NIH fel, 73-75; Swiss NSF Int fel, 78-79. *Mem:* AAAS; Am Soc Cell Biologists; Sigma Xi. *Res:* Role of cell surface determinants of developmental and tumorgenic systems. *Mailing Add:* City Hope Nat Med Ctr 1500 E Duarte Rd Duarte CA 91010

MILLER, MARTIN WESLEY, b Belden, Nebr, Jan 8, 25; m 48; c 3. MICROBIOLOGY. *Educ:* Univ Calif, AB, 50, MS, 52, PhD(microbiol), 58. *Prof Exp:* Res food technologist, 57-59, from asst prof to assoc prof, 59-70, PROF FOOD TECHNOL, UNIV CALIF, DAVIS, 70- *Concurrent Pos:* Fulbright sr res scientist award, Australia, 64-65. *Mem:* Am Soc Microbiol; fel Inst Food Technologists; fel Am Acad Microbiol; Nutrit Today Soc; Japanese Mycol Soc. *Res:* Ecology and taxonomy of yeasts; dehydration and drying of fruits; food science and technology educational curricula; food fermentations and microbial (fungal and yeast) food spoilage. *Mailing Add:* Dept of Food Sci Technol Univ of Calif Davis CA 95616

MILLER, MARVIN FRED, b Chicago, Ill, Sept 16, 24; m 44; c 4. PSYCHIATRY. *Educ:* State Univ Iowa, MD, 49. *Prof Exp:* Resident psychiat, USPHS, 50-53, staff psychiatrist, 53-57; from asst prof to assoc prof, 57-69, prof psychiat, 69-81, PROF PSYCHIAT & BEHAV SCI, SCH MED, LA STATE UNIV, NEW ORLEANS, 81- *Mem:* Am Psychiat Asn. *Mailing Add:* Dept of Psychiat La State Univ Sch of Med New Orleans LA 70112

MILLER, MARY H, b Cascade, Mo, Nov 5, 26; m 52; c 1. GEOLOGY. *Educ:* Univ Mo, AB, 47, MA, 55. *Prof Exp:* Instr geol, Univ Mo, 51-52; asst commodity geologist, US Geol Surv, 52-55; ed asst, Geol Soc Am, 55-56; asst commodity geologist, 56-63, GEOLOGIST, US GEOL SURV, 63-, GEOLOGIST, MINERAL RESOURCCES, 80- *Mem:* Geol Soc Am. *Res:* Economic geology of antimony and bismuth deposits; plains base-metal mineralization; wilderness studies; Rolla Missouri quadrangle. *Mailing Add:* US Geol Surv Fed Ctr Bldg 25 Box 25046 MS 905 Lakewood CO 80225

MILLER, MATTHEW WILLIAM, b Columbus, Mont, Mar 14, 15. PHOTOGRAPHIC CHEMISTRY. *Educ:* Mont State Col, BS, 36; Univ Ill, PhD(org chem), 40. *Prof Exp:* Asst chemist, Univ Ill, 36-39; sr chemist, Resinous Prods & Chem Co, Pa, 40-42; chief, Sci Br, Field Info Agencies Technol, 3M Co, Ger, 46-47, sr chemist, Org Sect & Cent Res Dept, 47-49, group leader, Cent Res Dept, 49-51, assoc dir, 51-53, bus mgr, 53-54, tech dir, Abrasives Div, 54-62, dir sci & tech commun, 62-66, chmn, Minn 3M Res, Ltd, 66-80, group tech dir, Photog Prod, 71-80; RETIRED. *Concurrent Pos:* Tech dir, 3M Co, Ferrania Spa, Ferrania, Italy, 67-70, Photo Prod Lab, 70-71; liason officer, Off Sci Res & Develop. *Mem:* AAAS; Am Chem Soc; Soc Chem Indust; Soc Photosci Engrs. *Mailing Add:* 4000 E Country Line Rd White Bear Lake MN 55110

MILLER, MAURICE MAX, b New Albany, Ind, Feb 18, 29. NUCLEAR PHYSICS. *Educ:* Ind Univ, AB, 48, MS, 50, PhD(nuclear physics), 52. *Prof Exp:* Asst, Off Naval Res, Ind, 48-52; sr nuclear engr, Convair Div, Gen Dynamics Corp, 52-53; mem staff physics, Los Alamos Sci Lab, 53, instr nuclear weapons, Armed Forces Spec Weapons Proj, 53-55; mgr, Nuclear Lab Div, Lockheed Aircraft Corp, 55-62, mgr, Nuclear Aerospace Div, Lockheed, Ga Co, 62-72, consult engr, 72-80, MGR SYSTS ENG DIV, LOCKHEED MISSILES & SPACE CO, 80- *Mem:* Am Phys Soc; Am Nuclear Soc. *Res:* Effects of nuclear radiation on organic and metallic materials; scintillation spectroscopy and measurement of nuclear decay schemes; experimental analysis of beta decay matrix elements; theory of strong interactions. *Mailing Add:* 632 W Garland Terrace Sunnyvale CA 94086

MILLER, MAX K, b Cleburne, Tex, Oct 25, 34; m 58; c 2. MATHEMATICS, GEOPHYSICS. *Educ:* Univ Tex, Austin, BS & BA, 57, MA, 63, PhD(math), 66. *Prof Exp:* Res scientist, Defense Res Lab, Univ Tex, Austin, 60-65; res geophysicist, Tex Instruments, Inc, 65-75; res scientist assoc, Appl Res Lab, Univ Tex, Austin, 75-80; MGR, PETROL SUPPORT GROUP, CRAY RES, INC, 80- *Concurrent Pos:* Teaching asst math, Univ Tex, Austin, 63-65. *Mem:* Inst Elec & Electronic Engrs; Acoust Soc Am; Soc Petrol Engrs; Soc Explor Geophys. *Res:* Numerical inversion of Laplace transforms; acoustic and seismic wave propagation; numerical analysis; signal processing; vector computers. *Mailing Add:* 7407 Valburn Dr Austin TX 78731

MILLER, MAYNARD MALCOLM, b Seattle, Wash, Jan 23, 21; m 51; c 2. GEOLOGY. *Educ:* Harvard Univ, SB, 43; Columbia Univ, MA, 48; Cambridge Univ, PhD(geol), 57. *Prof Exp:* Asst prof navig, Princeton Univ, 46; geologist, Gulf Oil Corp, Cuba, 47; geologist, Off Naval Res, 49-51; vis staff mem, Fed Inst Snow & Avalanche Res, Switz, 52; demonstr phys geog, Cambridge Univ, 54; res assoc geol, Lamont Geol Observ, NY, 55-57; sr scientist, Columbia Univ, 58-59; from asst prof to prof geol, Mich State Univ, 59-75, dir glaciol arctic sci inst, 60-75; DEAN, COL MINES & DIR GLACIOL & ARCTIC SCI INST, UNIV IDAHO, 75-; CHIEF, IDAHO BUR MINES & GEOL, 75- *Concurrent Pos:* Mem var geol & geophys expeds, 40-72; dir & geologist, Juneau Icefield Res Prog, Alaska, 46-; exec dir, Found Glacier & Environ Res, Wash, 55-, pres, 75-; consult, Boeing Co & US Air Force, 59-60, State of Alaska, 61-63 & US Forest Serv, 63-; res grants from numerous founds and corps, 60-; dir, Alaskan Commemorative Glacier Proj, Nat Geog Soc, 64-74; dir, Lemon Glacier Proj, Int Hydrol Decade Prog, Alaska, 65-72; dir, Sea Ice Proj, US Navy Oceanog Off, 67-68; chmn, World Explor Ctr Found, 68-71; mem tech & mineral educ mission, People's Repub China, 81. *Honors & Awards:* Co-recipient, Hubbard Medal, Nat Geog Soc, 63; Karo Award, Soc Am Mil Engrs, 65; Franklin L Burr Award, Nat Geog Soc, 67. *Mem:* Fel Geol Soc Am; Am Inst Prof Geologists; fel Arctic Inst NAm; Am Asn State Geologists; Am Inst Mining, Metall & Petrol Engrs. *Res:* Glaciology and hydrology applications; geomorphology; mining and environmental geology; volcanology; photogrammetry; inter-disciplinary factors in variation of existing glaciers and sea ice, and related problems in Pleistocene and Holocene geology, climatology and actic periglacial geology. *Mailing Add:* Off of the Dean Univ of Idaho Moscow ID 83843

MILLER, MELTON M, JR, b Burlington, Vt, Nov 15, 33; m 54; c 4. CIVIL ENGINEERING. *Educ:* Univ Vt, BSCE, 55; Purdue Univ, MSCE, 58, PhD(civil eng), 64. *Prof Exp:* Instr civil eng, Purdue Univ, 57-63; asst prof, 63-68, ASSOC PROF CIVIL ENG, UNIV MASS, AMHERST, 68- *Mem:* Am Soc Eng Educ; Am Soc Civil Engrs. *Res:* Model studies for civil engineering structures; analysis and design of structures; computer applications to civil engineering structures. *Mailing Add:* Marston Hall Univ of Mass Amherst MA 01003

MILLER, MELVIN J, b St Anthony, Idaho, Sept 11, 40; m 60; c 5. CHEMICAL ENGINEERING, PHYSICS. *Educ:* Univ Utah, BS, 64, PhD(chem eng), 68. *Prof Exp:* Sr res chemist, 68-73, res assoc, 74-77, LAB HEAD, EASTMAN KODAK CO, 77- *Mem:* Am Inst Chem Engrs. *Res:* Surface and bulk rheology; photographic systems; control process equipment; computer stimulation of physical processes; hydrodynamics; transport phenomena. *Mailing Add:* Eastman Kodak Co Res Labs Bldg 59 Kodak Park Rochester NY 14650

MILLER, MELVIN P, b Baltimore, Md, May 17, 35; m 64; c 1. PHYSICAL CHEMISTRY. *Educ:* Loyola Col, Md, BS, 57; Princeton Univ, PhD(molten salts), 62. *Prof Exp:* From instr to assoc prof, 60-69, PROF CHEM, LOYOLA COL, MD, 69- *Concurrent Pos:* NSF grant, Conf Surface Colloid & Macromolecular Chem, Lehigh Univ, 65; res partic for col teachers, Boston Univ, 69; sci fac fel, Johns Hopkins Univ & NSF, 71-72, courtesy fel, 72-78, prof eve col, 75; res chemist, Chem Systs Lab, Aberdeen Proving Ground, 80-; consult infrared analysis of polymers. *Mem:* Am Chem Soc; Sigma Xi. *Res:* Transport properties of molten salts; heterogeneous catalysis; electroanalytical techniques; surface chemistry; infrared studies of carbon monoxide on metal catalysts. *Mailing Add:* Dept Chem Loyola Col Baltimore MD 21210

MILLER, MEREDITH, b Murfreesboro, Tenn, Jan 2, 22; m 46; c 3. PHYSICAL CHEMISTRY. *Educ:* Vanderbilt Univ, BA, 43, MS, 44; Univ Wis, PhD(chem), 50. *Prof Exp:* Instr chem & physics, Middle Tenn State Col, 46-47; res chemist, Film Dept, E I du Pont de Nemours & Co, NY, 50-54, Va, 54-59, staff scientist, 59-63; prin chemist, 63-67, prog mgr, Huntsville Div, 67-76, PRIN PROPOSAL MGR, THIOKOL CORP, 76- *Res:* Mechanical and physical properties of elastomers; solid propellant rocket motors. *Mailing Add:* Hunstville Div Thiokol Corp Huntsville AL 35807

MILLER, MICHAEL CHARLES, b Brooklyn, NY, Aug 9, 42; m 68. AQUATIC ECOLOGY, BIOLOGICAL LIMNOLOGY. *Educ:* Ind Univ, AB, 64, MS, 66; Mich State Univ, PhD(bot), 72. *Prof Exp:* Asst prof, 70-76, ASSOC PROF BIOL SCI, UNIV CINCINNATI, 76- *Concurrent Pos:* Consult & prin investr, NSF grant, Tundra Biome, Aquatic Prog, 71-74; prin investr, NSF grants, Res Arctic Tundra Environ, 75-77 & Arctic Lake Process Studies, 77-; consult, Dayton Power & Light Co, 71-78. *Mem:* Am Soc Limnol & Oceanog; Int Soc Theoret & Appl Limnol; Phycol Soc Am; Sigma Xi. *Res:* Phytoplankton ecology, especially algal-zooplankton interrelationships; large river and arctic limnology; thermal effects and oil pollution effects on phytoplankton. *Mailing Add:* Dept of Biol Sci Univ of Cincinnati Cincinnati OH 45221

MILLER, MICHAEL E, b New York, NY, Apr 12, 37; m 59; c 4. IMMUNOLOGY, CELL BIOLOGY. *Educ:* Mass Inst Technol, SB, 58; Downstate Med Ctr, State Univ NY, MD, 62. *Prof Exp:* Asst prof pediat, Sch Med, Univ Pa, 67-71; assoc prof pediat, Drew Postgrad Med Sch, M L King, Jr Hosp Sch Med/Univ Calif, Los Angeles, 71-75; RES PROF PEDIAT & CHIEF PEDIAT IMMUNOL & HEMAT/ONCOL, SCH MED, UNIV CALIF, LOS ANGELES, HARBOR GEN HOSP CAMPUS, 76- *Concurrent Pos:* Fel immunol, Children's Hosp Philadelphia & Univ Pa, 65-67; dir clin immunol lab, Children's Hosp Pa, 66-71; dir res prog, Drew Postgrad Med Sch, 73-74, assoc dean, 74-75. *Honors & Awards:* Res Career Develop Award, USPHS, 69; Ross Young Investr Award, Western Soc Pediat Res, 77; E Mead Johnson Award Pediat Res, 77. *Mem:* Am Acad Pediat; Soc Pediat Res; Am Asn Immunologists; Am Acad Allergy; Am Soc Clin Invest. *Res:* Mechanisms of movement of human granulocytes, especially cell deformability and studies of fine structure by high-speed cinemicrography; studies of opsonization by the fifth component of complement. *Mailing Add:* Harbor-Univ Calif Los Angeles Med Ctr 1000 W Carson St Torrance CA 90509

MILLER, MILLAGE CLINTON, III, b Enid, Okla, Aug 28, 32; m 65. BIOSTATISTICS. *Educ:* Univ Okla, BS, 54, MA, 60, PhD(biostatist), 61. *Prof Exp:* NIH trainee, Med Ctr, Univ Okla, 59-61; grant, Okla State Univ, 61-62; assoc prof prev med, Univ Okla, 62-67; assoc prof biostatist, Tulane Univ, 67-69; PROF BIOMET & CHMN DEPT, MED UNIV SC, 69- *Concurrent Pos:* Consult, Fed & State Govts & various acad & res insts, 59-; joint appointment, Biostatist Unit & Med Res Comput Ctr, Univ Okla Med Ctr, 62-66, assoc prof prev med & pub health, Sch Med, 66-67. *Mem:* Biomet Soc; fel Am Statist Asn; Inst Math Statist; Asn Comput Mach; Am Pub Health Asn. *Res:* Experimental design; multivariate analysis; medical application of statistics; biomedical applications of computers. *Mailing Add:* Dept Biomet Med Univ SC Charleston SC 29401

MILLER, MILTON H, b Indianapolis, Ind, Sept 1, 27; m; c 3. PSYCHIATRY. *Educ:* Ind Univ, BS, 46, MD, 50. *Prof Exp:* Intern, Indianapolis Gen Hosp, 51; resident, Menninger Sch Psychiat, 53; from instr to prof, Univ Wis, 55-72; prof psychiat & head dept, Univ BC, 72-78; PROF & CHMN DEPT PSYCHIAT, LOS ANGELES COUNTRY HARBOR/UNIV CALIF MED CTR, LOS ANGELES, 78-, PROF & VCHMN DEPT PSYCHIAT, UNIV CALIF, LOS ANGELES, 78- *Concurrent Pos:* Examr, Royal Col Psychiat, Can; mem exec bd, World Fedn Ment Health; dep dir, Ment Health Serv, Coastal Region, Los Angeles County, 78- *Mem:* Fel Royal Col Psychiat; fel Am Psychiat Asn; Can Psychiat Asn. *Mailing Add:* Harbor-Univ Calif Med Ctr 1000 W Carson St Torrance CA 90509

MILLER, MILTON LEONARD, b McKeesport, Pa, Feb 12, 04; m 38; c 1. PSYCHIATRY. *Educ:* Harvard Univ, AB, 25, Harvard Med Sch, MD, 29. *Prof Exp:* Asst, Dept Psychiat & Neurol, Cornell Med Sch-New York Hosp, 35-36; staff mem, Chicago Inst Psychoanal, 39-41; pres, Southern Calif Psychoanal Inst, 50-59; prof, 59-76, EMER PROF PSYCHIAT, SCH MED, UNIV NC, CHAPEL HILL, 76- *Concurrent Pos:* Rockefeller fel neurol, Nat Hosp, Queens Sq, London, 34-35 & psychiat, Payne-Whitney Psychiat Clin, New York Hosp, 35-36; assoc, Dept Criminol & Jurisp, Univ Ill Med Sch, 39-40; training analyst, Los Angeles Psychoanal Inst, 46-50; collab ed, Int J Psychoanal, 50-51; pres & training analyst, Inst Psychoanal Med Southern Calif, 50-59; assoc clin prof psychiat, Med Sch, Univ Southern Calif, 53-59; sr attend psychiatrist, Los Angeles County Gen Hosp, 53-59; mem & training analyst, Washington Psychoanal Inst, 60-65; dir & training analyst, Ilniv NC-Duke Univ Psychoanal Training Prog, 60-; mem, Bd Dirs, Am Fund Psychiat, 61-69; consult, Bur Hearings & Appeals, Dept Health, Educ & Welfare, 66- *Mem:* AAAS; Am Psychosom Soc; Int Psychoanal Asn; fel Am Psychiat Asn; fel Am Psychoanal Asn. *Res:* Psychosomatic research; psychobiography; psychoanalysis. *Mailing Add:* Dept of Psychiat Univ of NC Sch of Med Chapel Hill NC 27514

MILLER, MITCHEL CHARLES, entomology, serology, see previous edition

MILLER, MORTON W, b Neptune, NJ, Aug 4, 36; m 68. RADIOBIOLOGY, CYTOGENETICS. *Educ:* Drew Univ, BA, 58; Univ Chicago, MS, 60, PhD(bot), 62. *Prof Exp:* Res assoc radiobiol, Brookhaven Nat Lab, 63-65; second officer, Int Atomic Energy Agency, 65-67; mem staff, Dept Radiation Biol & Biophys, 67-75, asst dir atomic energy proj, 69-77, ASSOC PROF RADIATION BIOL & BIOPHYS, SCH MED & DENT, UNIV ROCHESTER, 75- *Concurrent Pos:* NATO fel, Oxford Univ, 62-63; planetary quarantine adv panel, Am Inst Biol Sci, 71-73; mem comt, Nat Acad Sci-Nat Res Coun, 75-77, ultrasound comt, Nat Coun Radiation Protection & Measurements, 80-, Bioeffects comt, Am Inst Ultrasound Med, 81-; chief ed, Environ & Exp Bot, 77- *Mem:* AAAS; Radiation Res Soc; Am Inst Biol Sci; Environ Mutagen Soc; NY Acad Sci. *Res:* Effects/mechanisms of action of electric fields & ultrasound. *Mailing Add:* Dept of Radiation Biol & Biophys Univ Rochester Sch of Med & Dent Rochester NY 14642

MILLER, MURRAY HENRY, b Ont, Can, July 10, 31; m 54; c 3. SOIL FERTILITY. *Educ:* Ont Agr Col, BSA, 53; Purdue Univ, MS, 55, PhD(agr), 57. *Prof Exp:* From asst prof to assoc prof, 57-66, PROF SOIL SCI, ONT AGR COL, UNIV GUELPH, 66- *Concurrent Pos:* Head dept soil sci, Univ Guelph, 66-71. *Mem:* Am Soc Agron; Agr Inst Can; Can Soc Soil Sci; Int Soc Soil Sci; Soil Conserv Soc Am. *Res:* Soil fertility, especially chemistry of nutrient elements in soils and their absorption by plants; plant nutrients, environmental quality and land productivity; soil physical factors and crop yield. *Mailing Add:* Dept Land Resource Sci Ont Agr Col Univ Guelph Guelph ON N1G 2W1 Can

MILLER, MYRON, b Rochester, NY, Mar 31, 33; m 56; c 3. INTERNAL MEDICINE, ENDOCRINOLOGY. *Educ:* Univ Ill, Urbana, BS, 55; State Univ NY Upstate Med Ctr, MD, 59. *Prof Exp:* Intern & resident internal med, Univ Wis-Madison, 59-63; instr med, 65-67, asst prof med & clin investr endocrinol, 67-71, assoc prof med, 71-75, PROF MED, STATE UNIV NY UPSTATE MED CTR, 75- *Concurrent Pos:* NIH fel endocrinol, Univ Wis-Madison, 62-63; res assoc, Vet Admin Hosp, Syracuse, NY, 65-67, clin investr, 67-71, chief med serv, 72- *Mem:* Int Soc Neuroendocrinol; Endocrine Soc; Am Col Physicians; Am Fedn Clin Res; Am Physiol Soc. *Res:* Hypothalamic-pituitary regulation with special interest in the regulation of posterior pituitary function and the role of altered posterior pituitary function in disease states associated with abnormal water regulation. *Mailing Add:* Dept of Med State Univ of NY Upstate Med Ctr Syracuse NY 13210

MILLER, NANCY E, b Long Beach, NY, Aug 20, 47; Div. PSYCHOPATHOLOGY, GERIATRICS. *Educ:* NY Univ, BA, 69; Harvard Univ, MA, 70; Univ Chicago, PhD(adult develop & aging), 78. *Prof Exp:* Res assoc geriatric psychiat, Sch Med, Univ Chicago, 72-77; clin psychologist, Div Public Health, City Chicago, 72-77; INSTR GERIATRIC PSYCHIAT, SCH MED, GEORGETOWN UNIV, 78-; CLIN PSYCHOLOGIST, MOBILE MED CARE, 78- *Concurrent Pos:* Exec secy, Aging & Mental Health, Initial Review Group, 77-79, chief, Clin Res Prog Aging, Nat Inst Mental Health, Alcohol Drug Abuse & Mental Health Admin, 77-, rep aging, Int Prog Diagnosis, World Health Prog, 80-, res rep, White House Conf Aging, 81; mem, Task Force Nonenclature & Statist, Am Psychiat Asn, 78-81. *Mem:* AAAS; Am Psychol Asn; Gerontol Soc Am; Int Neuropsychol Soc; Soc Neurosci. *Res:* Assessment, cause and treatment of psychopathology in middle and late life, with special emphasis on states of altered brain funciton; Alzheimers Disease, depression and the interaction of medical and psychiatric disease. *Mailing Add:* Ctr Studies Mental Health Aging NIMH 5600 Fishers Lane Rm 11A16 Rockville MD 20852

MILLER, NATHAN C, b Winnfield, La, Dec 13, 37; m 67. ORGANIC CHEMISTRY. *Educ:* Emory Univ, BA, 59; Fla State Univ, PhD(org chem), 64. *Prof Exp:* Res assoc, Univ Vt, 64-65; asst prof, Winthrop Col, 65-66; asst prof, 66-74, ASSOC PROF CHEM, UNIV SOUTH ALA, 74- *Mem:* Am Chem Soc. *Res:* Synthesis of small, bicyclic ring systems and study of decarboxylation of bridgehead B-keto acids; synthesis of alkaloids; stereoselective reactions. *Mailing Add:* Dept of Chem Univ of SAla Mobile AL 36688

MILLER, NEAL ELGAR, b Milwaukee, Wis, Aug 3, 09; m 48; c 2. PSYCHOPHYSIOLOGY. *Educ:* Univ Wash, BS, 31; Stanford Univ, MA, 32; Yale Univ, PhD(psychol), 35. *Hon Degrees:* DSc, Univ Mich, 65, Univ Pa, 68, St Lawrence Univ, 73, Univ Uppsala, 77 & La Salle Col, 79. *Prof Exp:* Fel, Vienna Psychoanal Inst, Austria, 35-36; asst psychol, Inst Human Rels, Yale Univ, 36-41, res assoc, 41-42 & 46-50, prof, 50-52, James Rowland Angell prof, 52-66; prof & head lab, 66-80, EMER PROF PHYSIOL PSYCHOL & HEAD LAB, 80- *Concurrent Pos:* Mem fel comt, Found Fund Res Psychiat, 56-61; bd sci counrs, NIMH, 57-61; chmn div anthrop & psychol, Nat Res Coun, 58-60, chmn comt brain sci, 69-71; mem bd sci overseers, Jackson Mem Lab, 50-79, chmn, 62-76; Langfield lectr & Sigma Xi lectr, 68; bd sci counrs, Nat Inst Child Health & Human Develop, 69-72; mem clin prog proj res comt, NIMH, 74-78, mem, Bd Mental Health & Behavior Med, NIH, 80- *Honors & Awards:* Warren Medal, Soc Exp Psychol, 54; Cleveland Prize, AAAS, 57; Am Psychol Asn Award, 59; Nat Medal of Sci, 65; Gold Medal, Am Psychol Found, 75. *Mem:* Nat Acad Sci; Soc Neurosci (pres, 71-72); AAAS; Acad Behav Med Res (pres, 78-79); Am Psychol Asn (pres, 60-61 & 80-81). *Res:* Learning and behavior theory; conflict, fear and stress;

mechanisms of psychosomatic effects; physiological and behavioral studies of motivation; electrical and chemical stimulation of the brain; instrumental learning of visceral responses; behavioral medicine; conflict, fear and stress. *Mailing Add:* 1230 York Ave Rockefeller Univ New York NY 10021

MILLER, NEIL AUSTIN, b Grand Rapids, Mich, Apr 9, 32; m 61; c 2. FOREST ECOLOGY. *Educ:* Mich State Univ, BSF, 58; Memphis State Univ, MS, 64; Southern Ill Univ, PhD(bot), 68; Oak Ridge Radiation Inst, grad, 71. *Prof Exp:* Teacher high sch & chmn dept biol & physics, Grand Rapids, Mich, 59-62; teacher high sch, Memphis, Tenn, 62-64; instr bot & forestry, Western Ky Univ, 64-65; res asst bot, Southern Ill Univ, 65-66, fel, 66-68; assoc prof bot, 68-77, ASSOC PROF BIOL, MEMPHIS STATE UNIV, 77- *Concurrent Pos:* Ill Acad Sci grant, 67-68; consult forestry. *Mem:* Soc Am Foresters; Am Soc Plant Physiol; Ecol Soc Am; Am Inst Biol Sci. *Res:* Plant-water balance research dealing with transpiration retardants and soil water conditions related to soil textures and structure characteristics; microclimatic investigations. *Mailing Add:* Dept of Biol Memphis State Univ Memphis TN 38152

MILLER, NICHOLAS CARL, b Mason City, Iowa, Aug 9, 42; m 71. CHEMICAL ENGINEERING, BIOMEDICAL ENGINEERING. *Educ:* Iowa State Univ, BS, 64, MS, 67, PhD(chem eng), 72. *Prof Exp:* Propellant develop engr, Olin Chem Group, Olin Corp, 64-65; res physiologist, Med Sch, Univ Calif, Davis, 72-73; chem engr, Cent Res Lab, 73-81, SUPVR, PHARMACEUT RES & DEVELOP, RIKER LABS, 3M CO, 81- *Mem:* Am Inst Chem Engrs; Am Chem Soc; Fine Particle Soc. *Res:* Fine particle size distribution and characterization methods development; generation and processing of fine particulates for medical applications; evaluation of dispersions; pharmaceutical aerosol preparation. *Mailing Add:* Riker Labs 3M Ctr 270-4S St Paul MN 55101

MILLER, NORMAN E, b Tinley Park, Ill, Aug 14, 31; m 52; c 7. INORGANIC CHEMISTRY. *Educ:* Northern Ill State Teachers Col, BS, 53; Univ Nebr, MS, 55, PhD, 58. *Prof Exp:* Chemist, Cent Res Dept, E I du Pont de Nemours & Co, 58-63; assoc prof, 63-66, PROF CHEM, UNIV S DAK, 66- *Concurrent Pos:* Mem fac, Assoc Western Univs, Los Alamos Sci Lab, 72. *Mem:* Am Chem Soc; Sigma Xi. *Res:* Lewis acid-base phenomena; inorganic synthesis; boronhydride synthesis and reactivity studies; glid chemistry. *Mailing Add:* Dept of Chem Univ of SDak Vermillion SD 57069

MILLER, NORMAN GUSTAV, b Thermopolis, Wyo, Mar 20, 25; m 54; c 2. MICROBIOLOGY. *Educ:* Western Reserve Univ, BS, 48; Wash State Univ, MS, 50, PhD(bact), 53; Am Bd Microbiol, Dipl. *Prof Exp:* From instr to assoc prof, 55-67, PROF MICROBIOL, COL MED, UNIV NEBR, OMAHA, 67- *Concurrent Pos:* Secy, West-Northcent Interprof Seminar Dis Common to Animals & Man. *Mem:* AAAS; Am Soc Microbiol; Wildlife Dis Asn; Med Mycol Soc Am; Int Soc Human & Animal Mycol. *Res:* Infectious diseases of animals transmissible to man; medical mycology. *Mailing Add:* 4625 N 81 Omaha NE 68105

MILLER, NORTON GEORGE, b Buffalo, NY, Feb 4, 42; m 64. BOTANY. *Educ:* State Univ NY Buffalo, BA, 63; Mich State Univ, PhD(bot), 69. *Prof Exp:* Asst cur, Arnold Arboretum, Harvard Univ, 69-70; vis asst prof bot, Univ NC, Chapel Hill, 70-71, asst prof, 71-74; ASSOC PROF BIOL, HARVARD UNIV, 75-; assoc cur, 75-80, botanist, 80-81, SR RES BOTANIST, ARNOLD ARBORETUM & GRAY HERBARIUM, 81- *Mem:* AAAS; Am Bryol & Lichenol Soc; Bot Soc Am; Am Quaternary Asn; Am Soc Plant Taxon. *Res:* Plant systematics and floristics, especially of bryophytes and seed plants; quaternary paleoecology and polynology; pollen and plant macrofossil analysis; tertiary and quaternary history of the bryophyta. *Mailing Add:* Harvard Univ Herbaria 22 Divinity Ave Cambridge MA 02138

MILLER, ORLANDO JACK, b Oklahoma City, Okla, May 11, 27; m 54; c 3. HUMAN GENETICS, OBSTETRICS & GYNECOLOGY. *Educ:* Yale Univ, BS, 46, MD, 50. *Prof Exp:* Intern, St Anthony Hosp, Oklahoma City, Okla, 50-51; asst resident obstet & gynec, Grace-New Haven Community Hosp, 54-57, resident & instr, 57-58; res asst human genetics, Univ Col, Univ London, 58-60; from instr to assoc prof obstet & gynec, 60-70, PROF HUMAN GENETICS & DEVELOP, OBSTET & GYNEC, COL PHYSICIANS & SURGEONS, COLUMBIA UNIV, 70- *Concurrent Pos:* Nat Res Coun fel anat, Yale Univ, 53-54; Pop Coun fel human genetics, Galton Lab, Univ Col, Univ London, 58-60; Josiah Macy, Jr fel obstet & gynec, Columbia Univ, 60-61; NSF sr fel, Oxford Univ, 68-69; career scientist, Health Res Coun, New York, 61-71; ed, Cytogenetics, 71-72; assoc ed, Cytogenetics & Cell Genetics, 72 & Birth Defects Compendium, 73; consult, J Med Primatol, 78- *Mem:* AAAS; Am Soc Human Genetics; Am Soc Cell Biol; Genetics Soc Am; Soc Gynec Invest. *Res:* Cytogenetics. *Mailing Add:* Dept of Human Genetics & Develop Columbia Univ New York NY 10032

MILLER, ORSON K, JR, b Cambridge, Mass, Dec 19, 30; m 54; c 3. MYCOLOGY. *Educ:* Univ Mass, BS, 52; Univ Mich, MF, 57, PhD(bot), 63. *Prof Exp:* Res forester, Northeastern Forest Exp Sta, USDA, 56-57; asst bot, Univ Mich, 58-59, fel, 60-61; plant pathologist, Intermt Forest & Range Exp Sta, USDA, 61-65 & Forest Dis Lab, 65-70; assoc prof, 70-73, PROF BOT, VA POLYTECH INST & STATE UNIV, 73-, CUR FUNGI, 74- *Mem:* AAAS; Mycol Soc Am; Bot Soc Am; Am Soc Plant Taxon; Arctic Inst NAm. *Res:* Taxonomy, ecology and physiology of Homobasidiomycetes; arctic and northern fungi. *Mailing Add:* Dept of Biol Va Polytech Inst & State Univ Blacksburg VA 24061

MILLER, OSCAR L, JR, b Gastonia, NC, Apr 12, 25; m 48; c 2. CELL BIOLOGY. *Educ:* NC State Univ, BS, 48, MS, 50; Univ Minn, Minneapolis, PhD, 60. *Prof Exp:* Nat Inst Cancer fel, 60-61; res assoc, Biol Div, Oak Ridge Nat Lab, 61-63, res staff mem, 63-73; prof biol, 73-79, LEWIS & CLARK PROF BIOL, UNIV VA, 78-, CHMN DEPT, 73- *Concurrent Pos:* Prof, Univ Tenn-Oak Ridge Grad Sch Biomed Sci, 67-73; Alexander von Humboldt sr scientist fel, 80. *Mem:* Nat Acad Sci; Am Soc Cell Biol; fel AAAS; Soc Develop Biol. *Res:* Correlation of fine structure and genetic activity in chromosomes of prokaryotic and eukaryotic cells; identification of specific genes in action. *Mailing Add:* Dept of Biol Univ of Va Charlottesville VA 22901

MILLER, OSCAR NEAL, b Canton, Mo, Feb 5, 19; m 47; c 2. PHARMACOLOGY, IMMUNOLOGY. *Educ:* Univ Mo, BS, 41, MA, 42; Harvard Univ, PhD(biol chem), 50; Am Bd Nutrit, Dipl. *Prof Exp:* Asst state chemist, Mo Dept Agr, 42-43; res assoc, Children's Fund Mich, 46-47; instr biochem & nutrit, Med Br, Univ Tex, 50-51; from asst prof to prof biochem & med, Sch Med, Tulane Univ, 53-68; assoc dir biol res, 70-76, DIR DEPT BIOCHEM NUTRIT, HOFFMANN-LA ROCHE INC, 68-, DIR EXP BIOL, 76- *Mem:* Am Soc Clin Nutrit; Am Soc Biol Chemists; Am Soc Clin Pharacol & Therapeut; Am Asn Univ Professors; fel NY Acad Sci. *Res:* Enzymology; pharmacology. *Mailing Add:* Div Exp Biol Hoffmann-La Roche Inc Nutley NJ 07110

MILLER, OTTO N, b Harlan, Iowa, Jan 20, 09; m 35; c 2. CHEMICAL ENGINEERING. *Educ:* Iowa State Univ, BS, 30; Univ Mich, MS, 33, PhD(chem eng), 34. *Prof Exp:* Res chemist, El Segundo Refinery, Standard Oil Co, Calif, 34-40, chief process engr, Arabian Am Oil Co, NY, 41-43, asst to gen mgr mfg dept & supt cracking div, El Segundo Refinery, Standard Oil Co, Calif, 44-46, asst to vpres & gen mgr, Mfg Dept, 46-54, vpres, 54-57, vpres natural gas utilization, crude pricing & East Coast opers, 57-59, dir & vpres, 59-61, pres, 61-66, chmn bd dirs & chief exec off, 66-74. *Concurrent Pos:* Dir, Am Petrol Inst, 61, chmn bd dirs, 69-71, mem bus coun, 67. *Mem:* Nat Acad Eng. *Mailing Add:* 555 Market St 1624 San Francisco CA 94105

MILLER, OWEN WINSTON, b St Louis, Mo, Feb 17, 22; m 50; c 3. INDUSTRIAL ENGINEERING. *Educ:* Washington Univ, St Louis, BS, 50, MS, 58, ScD(indust eng), 66. *Prof Exp:* Asst chief indust eng, Am Steel Foundries, Ill, 50-54; instr, Washington Univ, St Louis, 54-58, asst prof, 59-62, lectr, Spec Bell Tel Prog, 62-63; asst prof, 64-65, assoc prof, 65-78, PROF INDUST ENG & DIR, BUS & INDUST PRODUCTIVITY CTR, UNIV MO-COLUMBIA, 78-, DIR, INDUST ENG GRAD PROG, KANSAS CITY, 77- *Concurrent Pos:* Consult indust, 55-61, indust & fed govt, 63-; consult to Dr Galen Cook, Ellis Fischel State Cancer Hosp, Columbia, Mo, 66-67; co-prin investr, automated patient hist acquisition syst proj, Mo Regional Med Prof, 67-70, consult, stroke intensive care proj, 68-71, co-investr, advan technol proj, 70-71, co-dir, automated physicians' asst proj, 71-72; co-prin investr water pollution models, Mo Water Resources Res Ctr, US Dept Interior, 70-71; mem bd dirs, Community Rehab Ctr, Columbia, 79- *Mem:* Am Inst Indust Engrs; Am Statist Asn; fel Am Soc Qual Control; NY Acad Sci; Sigma Xi. *Res:* Quality control and reliability fields; economics of industrial sampling; industrial engineering techniques applied to hospitals and medical activities; industrial engineering analysis methods in surgical operations; measuring direct cost of government regulations on small business; rural and small business productivity improvement. *Mailing Add:* Dept of Indust Eng Univ of Mo Columbia MO 65211

MILLER, PARK HAYS, JR, b Philadelphia, Pa, Jan 22, 16; m 76; c 3. PHYSICS. *Educ:* Haverford Col, BS, 36; Calif Inst Technol, PhD(physics), 40. *Prof Exp:* Asst physics, Calif Inst Technol, 36-39; from instr to prof, Univ Pa, 39-56; chmn exp physics dept, Gen Atomic Div, Gen Dynamics Corp, 56-62, asst dir lab, 60-69; prof physics & chmn dept, US Int Univ, Calif Western Campus, 69-74; sr tech adv, Gen Atomic Co, 74-81; PRES, EXTRAGALACTIC ENTERPRISES INC, 81- *Concurrent Pos:* Chmn dept physics, Univ Pa, 45-46; consult, US Naval Ord Lab, 51-65, US Dept Defense, 52-55 & 60-62, NASA, 58-60 & Mat Adv Bd, Nat Acad Sci, 56 & 60-61; actg ed, Rev Sci Instruments, Am Inst Physics, 53-55. *Mem:* Fel Am Phys Soc; Soc Explor Geophys; Am Geophys Union; Am Nuclear Soc; Am Asn Physics Teachers. *Res:* Electrical properties of solids; semiconductor devices; radiation effects; x-ray diffraction; optical instruments; energy conversion; design of fusion power reactors. *Mailing Add:* Extragalactic Enterprises Inc 7723 Fay Ave Suite 2 La Jolla CA 92037

MILLER, PATRICK MARTIN, plant pathology, see previous edition

MILLER, PAUL, b Philadelphia, Pa, Jan 15, 22. SOLID STATE PHYSICS. *Educ:* George Washington Univ, BS, 43; Univ Pa, MS, 49, PhD(physics), 55. *Prof Exp:* MEM TECH STAFF, BELL LABS, INC, 54- *Mem:* Am Phys Soc. *Res:* Surface and transistor physics; microelectronics; semiconductors; integrated-circuit reliability physics. *Mailing Add:* Bell Labs 555 Union Blvd Allentown PA 18103

MILLER, PAUL DEAN, b Cedar Falls, Iowa, Apr 4, 41; m 65; c 2. ANIMAL BREEDING. *Educ:* Iowa State Univ, BS, 63; Cornell Univ, MS, 66, PhD(animal genetics), 68. *Prof Exp:* Asst prof animal breeding, Cornell Univ, 67-71; DIR BREEDING PROGS, AM BREEDERS SERV, 71- *Concurrent Pos:* Chmn, Beef Sire Eval Comt, Am Asn Animal Breeders. *Mem:* Biomet Soc; Am Soc Animal Sci; Am Dairy Sci Asn; Am Asn Animal Breeders. *Res:* Population genetics; statistical estimation and linear models; computer simulation. *Mailing Add:* Am Breeders Serv De Forest WI 53532

MILLER, PAUL LEROY, JR, b Guthrie, Okla, June 27, 34; m 55; c 3. MECHANICAL ENGINEERING. *Educ:* Kans State Univ, BS, 57, MS, 61; Okla State Univ, PhD(mech eng), 66. *Prof Exp:* From instr to assoc prof, 57-72, PROF MECH ENG, KANS STATE UNIV, 72-, HEAD DEPT, 75- *Concurrent Pos:* Consult, Radio Corp Am & Whirlpool Corp, 61-64, Wright-Patterson AFB, 67-69, Air Duffusion Coun, Chicago, 69-, Gen Serv Admin, Washington, DC, 77- & US Dept Energy, Washington, DC, 79-81. *Mem:* Am Soc Eng Educ; Am Soc Heat, Refrig & Air Conditioning Engrs; Am Soc Mech Engrs. *Res:* Heat transfer; fluid flow; instrumentation; air distribution. *Mailing Add:* Dept of Mech Eng Col of Eng Kans State Univ Manhattan KS 66506

MILLER, PAUL SCOTT, b Brooklyn, NY, Oct 12, 43; m 71. BIO-ORGANIC CHEMISTRY. *Educ:* State Univ NY Buffalo, BA, 65; Northwestern Univ, Ill, PhD(chem), 69. *Prof Exp:* Am Cancer Soc fel nucleic acid chem, 69-73, asst prof biochem & biophys sci, 73-80, ASSOC PROF BIOCHEM, BIOPHYS DIV, JOHNS HOPKINS UNIV, 80- *Mem:* AAAS; Am Chem Soc. *Res:* Chemical and enzymatic synthesis of nucleic acids and nucleic acid derivatives; interaction of nucleic acids with proteins and nucleic acids; chemical modification of nucleic acids. *Mailing Add:* Div Biophys Johns Hopkins Univ Baltimore MD 21205

MILLER, PAUL THOMAS, b Atlanta, Ga, May 12, 44; m 77. INORGANIC CHEMISTRY, EDUCATIONAL ADMINISTRATION. *Educ:* Birmingham-Southern Col, BS, 66; Vanderbilt Univ, MA & PhD(chem), 71. *Prof Exp:* Instr, 71-72, asst prof, 72-75, assoc prof chem & phys sci, 75-81, PROF CHEM & CHMN, DIV MATH & SCI, VOL STATE COMMUNITY COL, 81-, COORDR CHMN, 80- *Concurrent Pos:* NSF res grant, 66; res grant, Tulane Univ Scholars & Fels Prog, 66; grad teaching fel, Vanderbilt Univ, 66-69 & 70-71. *Mem:* AAAS; Am Chem Soc; Sigma Xi. *Res:* Structure and properties of coordination compounds; chemical education in the two year college; analytical methods for environmental pollution studies; water pollution by heavy metals. *Mailing Add:* Dept of Chem Volunteer State Community Col Gallatin TN 37066

MILLER, PAUL WILLIAM, b Mt Vernon, Ind, May 2, 01; m 28. PLANT PATHOLOGY. *Educ:* Univ Ky, BS, 23, MS, 24; Univ Wis, PhD(plant path), 29. *Prof Exp:* Instr plant path, Univ Wis, 27-29; agent, 29-30, assoc plant pathologist, 30-44, plant pathologist, 44-70, EMER RES PLANT PATHOLOGIST, USDA, ORE STATE UNIV, 70- *Res:* Fire blight disease of apples; prune russet; vegetable seed diseases; walnut blight; filbert blight; strawberry root rot; strawberry virus diseases; control of rose mildew and rose rust. *Mailing Add:* 703 NW 30th St Corvallis OR 97330

MILLER, PAULINE MONZ, b Harrisburg, Pa, Apr 2, 31; div. BOTANY, INFORMATION SCIENCE. *Educ:* Pa State Univ, BS, 52; Univ Pa, PhD(bot), 56; Syracuse Univ, MSLS, 76. *Prof Exp:* Instr bot, Wheaton Col, 56-57; instr, Conn Col, 57-59, res assoc, 59-61; res assoc, Yale Univ, 61-62; res assoc, Syracuse Univ, 62-71, ADJ PROF BOT, UNIV COL, SYRACUSE UNIV, 71-, HEAD SCI & TECHNOL LIBR, 78- *Mem:* Am Libr Asn. *Res:* Light effects on plant development; organization and dissemination of science information; economic botany. *Mailing Add:* 117 Euclid Terr Syracuse NY 13210

MILLER, PERCY HUGH, b Yazoo Co, Miss, June 18, 22; m; c 4. AERODYNAMICS. *Educ:* Miss State Univ, BS, 50; Univ Colo, MS, 51; Univ Tex, PhD(aerospace eng), 62. *Prof Exp:* Instr eng, Univ Colo, 50-51; design specialist, Gen Dynamics/Pomona, 51-58; asst prof aerospace eng, Univ Tex, 58-65; assoc prof mech eng, Univ Mo, 65-67; PROF MECH ENG, LA STATE UNIV, BATON ROUGE, 67- *Concurrent Pos:* Consult, Tracor, Inc, 60- & Monsanto Co, 62-; sr assoc, Hanneman Assocs, Inc, 61- *Mem:* Assoc fel Am Inst Aeronaut & Astronaut; Am Soc Eng Educ. *Res:* Aerodynamics and dynamics of aerospace vehicles including analysis, synthesis and preliminary design; safety engineering and design. *Mailing Add:* Dept of Mech Eng 2513B CEBA Bldg La State Univ Baton Rouge LA 70803

MILLER, PHILIP, b New Haven, Conn, Nov 4, 12; m 52; c 2. CHEMICAL ENGINEERING, NUCLEAR ENGINEERING. *Educ:* Yale Univ, BS, 34, DEng, 38. *Prof Exp:* Chem engr, Tenn Valley Authority, Ala, 37-47; sr eng specialist, H K Ferguson Co, 47-52; POWER CONSULT, NY OFF, STONE & WEBSTER ENG CORP, 52- *Honors & Awards:* Walker Award, Am Inst Chem Engrs, 46. *Mem:* Fel AAAS; Am Chem Soc; Am Nuclear Soc; Am Inst Chem Engrs. *Res:* Crystallization of ammonium nitrate; production and purification of res phosphorus, alumina from clay, calcium metaphosphate and copper arsenite; industrial applications of fission products; atomized magnesium; pulp and paper; petrochemicals; nuclear power. *Mailing Add:* Stone & Webster Eng Corp NY PO Box 2703 New York NY 10116

MILLER, PHILIP, organic chemistry, pesticide chemistry, see previous edition

MILLER, PHILIP ARTHUR, b Hastings, Nebr, Feb 1, 23; m 45; c 2. PLANT BREEDING. *Educ:* Univ Nebr, BSc, 43, MSc, 47; Iowa State Col, PhD(plant breeding), 50. *Prof Exp:* Res assoc agron, Iowa State Col, 49-50, asst prof, 50-52; from assoc prof to prof agron, NC State Univ, 59-77; MEM STAFF, BELTSVILLE AGR RES CTR-WEST, SCI & EDUC ADMIN, NPS, USDA, 77- *Concurrent Pos:* Dir, NC State Univ Agr Mission, Peru, 59-61. *Mem:* Fel Am Soc Agron; Sigma Xi. *Res:* Genetics; corn; cotton; soybeans; quantitative inheritance. *Mailing Add:* Beltsville Agr Res Ctr-West NPS Agri Res Serv USDA Beltsville MD 20705

MILLER, PHILIP CLEMENT, b Chicago, Ill, Mar 23, 33; m 58; c 2. ECOLOGY. *Educ:* Oberlin Col, BA, 54; Iowa State Univ, MS, 59; Univ Colo, PhD(plant ecol), 64. *Prof Exp:* Res asst ecol, Inst Arctic-Alpine Res, 60-64, res assoc, 64; asst prof ecol & biostatist, Univ Notre Dame, 64-65; asst prof ecol, 65-71, PROF BIOL, SAN DIEGO STATE UNIV, 71- *Mem:* AAAS; Ecol Soc Am; Am Inst Biol Sci; Am Meteorol Soc. *Res:* Mathematical models of ecological systems. *Mailing Add:* Dept of Biol San Diego State Univ San Diego CA 92115

MILLER, PHILIP DIXON, b Albuquerque, NMex, June 7, 32; m 64; c 4. ACCELERATOR BASED ATOMIC PHYSICS. *Educ:* Calif Inst Technol, BS, 54; Rice Inst, MA, 56, PhD(physics), 58. *Prof Exp:* PHYSICIST, OAK RIDGE NAT LAB, 58-, DIR, VAN DE GRAAFF LAB, 74- *Mem:* Fel Am Phys Soc. *Res:* Atomic collisions physics; low energy physics using Van de Graaff accelerator, including charged particle scattering and reactions and neutron cross sections; measurement of electric and magnetic dipole moments of neutron; properties of the neutron. *Mailing Add:* 5500 Bldg Oak Ridge Nat Lab PO Box X Oak Ridge TN 37830

MILLER, PHILIP JOSEPH, b Camden, SC, Mar 20, 41; m 62; c 3. PHYSICAL CHEMISTRY. *Educ:* Johns Hopkins Univ, ScB, 67; Univ Md, PhD(phys chem), 71. *Prof Exp:* Res assoc phys chem, Univ Md, 71-72; instr & res assoc, Brown Univ, 72-74; res scientist, Block Eng, Inc, 74-76; ASST PROF PHYS & ANAL CHEM, UNIV DETROIT, 76- *Mem:* Am Chem Soc; Am Phys Soc; Soc Appl Spectros; Sigma Xi. *Res:* Molecular spectroscopy; hydrogen bonding in solids; structure and dynamics of disordered materials; laser applications in chemistry. *Mailing Add:* Dept of Chem Univ of Detroit Detroit MI 48221

MILLER, R(AYMOND) E(DWARD), b Bay City, Mich, Oct 9, 28; m 55; c 4. COMPUTER SCIENCE, ELECTRICAL ENGINEERING. *Educ:* Univ Wis, BS, 50; Univ Ill, BS, 54, MS, 55, PhD(elec eng), 57. *Prof Exp:* Asst, Digital Comput Lab, Univ Ill, 53-56, res assoc, 57; res staff mem, Res Ctr, IBM Corp, 57-81; PROF & DIR, SCH INFO & COMPUT SCI, GA INST TECHNOL, 80- *Concurrent Pos:* Vis asst prof, Digital Comput Lab, Univ Ill, 60-61; sr res fel elec eng, Calif Inst Technol, 62-63; lectr, Univ Conn, 65-69; Mackay lectr, Univ Calif, Berkeley, 69-70; adj prof, NY Univ, 69-73; ed-in-chief, Asn Comput Mach Jour, 72-76; vis lectr, Yale Univ, 73-; adj prof, Polytech Inst NY, 73-80. *Mem:* Fel Inst Elec & Electronics Engrs; Asn Comput Mach; Sigma Xi. *Res:* Theory of computation; switching and automata theory. *Mailing Add:* Sch Info & Comput Sci Georgia Inst Technol 225 N Ave Atlanta GA 30332

MILLER, RALPH ENGLISH, b Hanover, NH, Sept 23, 33; m 62; c 3. PHARMACOLOGY. *Educ:* Dartmouth Col, AB, 58; Harvard Univ, MD, 61, MS, 66, DSc, 70. *Prof Exp:* Intern, Mary Hitchcock Mem Hosp, Hanover, NH, 61-62; NIMH fel, Walter Reed Army Inst Res, 62-64; NASA res & spec fel, Dept Physiol, Harvard Sch Pub Health, 65-69; spec fel physiol, Stanford Univ, 69-70; asst prof, 70-75, assoc prof pharmacol, 75-81, RESIDENT MED, UNIV KY, 81- *Concurrent Pos:* Chief physiol sect, Dept Neuroendocrinol, Walter Reed Army Inst Res, 64-65. *Mem:* Am Diabetes Asn; Am Physiol Soc; Soc Neurosci; Endocrine Soc. *Res:* Neuro-endocrinol; autonomic neuroendocrinol; role of autonomic nervous system in regulation of hormone secretion from the pancreas and kidney. *Mailing Add:* Dept Pharmacol Col Med Univ Ky Lexington KY 40506

MILLER, RALPH LEROY, b Fountain Hill, Pa, Jan 28, 09; m 39; c 2. ECONOMIC GEOLOGY, STRATIGRAPHY. *Educ:* Haverford Col, BS, 29; Columbia Univ, PhD(geol), 37. *Prof Exp:* Lab asst geol, Columbia Univ, 32-34, lectr, 34-37, instr, 37-46; assoc geologist, US Geol Surv, 42-43, geologist, 44-47, sr geologist, 47-49, chief, Navy Oil Unit, 48-51, Fuels Br, 51-57, staff geologist, 58, tech adv, Foreign Geol Br, Afghanistan, 58, Mex, 59-61, Columbia, 62, Cent Am, 63-70, SKorea, 79, Mexico, 80, Costa Rica, 81, sr res geologist, Off Int Geol, 70-79; RETIRED. *Mem:* Fel Geol Soc Am; Am Asn Petrol Geol; Am Inst Mining, Metall & Petrol Engrs. *Res:* Areal geology and stratigraphy of southeast Utah; areal geology, stratigraphy and structure of Appalachian Mountains from southern New York to Tennessee; manganese deposits of Appalachians; oil geology of southern Appalachians; geology and oil resources of the Arctic slope of Alaska; geology of Central America; energy resources, Latin America; geology of northwestern New Mexico. *Mailing Add:* 5215 Abingdon Rd Bethesda MD 20816

MILLER, RAYMOND EDWIN, b Cincinnati, Ohio, July 6, 37; m 61; c 5. PHYSICS. *Educ:* Xavier Univ, Ohio, BS, 59; Johns Hopkins Univ, PhD(physics), 65. *Prof Exp:* Instr physics, Johns Hopkins Univ, 62-65, NASA fel, 65-66; from asst prof to assoc prof, 66-71, PROF PHYSICS & CHMN DEPT, XAVIER UNIV, OHIO, 71- *Concurrent Pos:* NASA grant, Johns Hopkins Univ, 68-71. *Mem:* AAAS; Am Asn Physics Teachers; Optical Soc Am. *Res:* Atmospheric physics; atomic and molecular physics; biophysics. *Mailing Add:* Dept of Physics Xavier Univ Cincinnati OH 45207

MILLER, RAYMOND JARVIS, b Claresholm, Alta, Mar 19, 34; m 56; c 3. SOIL CHEMISTRY, PHYSICAL CHEMISTRY. *Educ:* Univ Alta, BS, 57; Washington State Univ, MS, 60; Purdue Univ, PhD(soil chem), 62. *Prof Exp:* From asst prof to assoc prof soil & phys chem, NC State Univ, 62-65; from assoc prof to prof, Univ Ill, Urbana, 65-73; assoc dean, Col Agr, 73-80, DEAN, COL AGR, UNIV IDAHO, 80-, DIR, IDAHO AGR EXP STA, 73- *Concurrent Pos:* Asst dir, Agr Exp Sta, Univ Ill, Urbana, 69, assoc dir, 70, coordr, Col Agr Coun Environ Qual, 70; chmn exp sta sect, Nat Asn State Univ & Land Grants Col, 76-77; mem, US-USSR Joint Comn Coop Agr, 77-79. *Mem:* Soil Sci Soc Am; Clay Minerals Soc; Am Soc Plant Physiol; Am Soc Agron; AAAS. *Res:* Clay-water interactions; structure of water in porous media and the effects of water structure on biological activity; membrane transport; agricultural research. *Mailing Add:* Col of Agr Univ of Idaho Moscow ID 83843

MILLER, RAYMOND MICHAEL, b Chicago, Ill, July 16, 45. MICROBIAL ECOLOGY, ECOLOGICAL ENGINEERING. *Educ:* Colo State Univ, BS, 69; Ill State Univ, MS, 71, PhD(mycol), 75. *Prof Exp:* Fel microbial ecol, Land Reclamation Prog, 75-76, asst biologist, 76-79, SCIENTIST MICROBIAL ECOL, DIV ENVIRON IMPACT STUDIES, ARGONNE NAT LAB, 80- *Mem:* AAAS; Am Soc Microbiol; Mycol Soc Am; Soil Sci Soc Am; Sigma Xi. *Res:* Reestablishment of below-ground ecosystems in relation to surface-mined lands; carbon and nitrogen flow in disturbed ecosystems; application of ecological principles to mining techniques; ecology of mycorrhiza. *Mailing Add:* Land Reclamation Prog EIS-8 Argonne Nat Lab Argonne IL 60439

MILLER, RAYMOND SUMNER, b Rochester, NY, Oct 15, 19; m 45; c 2. ANALYTICAL CHEMISTRY. *Educ:* McMaster Univ, BA, 41. *Prof Exp:* Asst still operator, Eastman Kodak Co, 41-42; chemist, Manhattan Proj, Los Alamos, NMex, 44-45, asst to area engr, Oak Ridge, Tenn, 45-46; sr res chemist, Eastman Kodak Co, 46-81; RETIRED. *Mem:* Am Chem Soc; Am Nuclear Soc. *Res:* Photo theory; micro analytical technology; radio tracer technology. *Mailing Add:* 3 Woodview Dr Rochester NY 14624

MILLER, RAYMOND WOODRUFF, b St David, Ariz, Jan 13, 28; m 51; c 5. SOIL FERTILITY, ENVIRONMENTAL SCIENCE. *Educ:* Univ Ariz, BS, 52, MS, 53; Wash State Univ, PhD(agron, soil chem), 56. *Prof Exp:* From asst prof to assoc prof, 56-69, PROF SOILS, UTAH STATE UNIV, 69- *Concurrent Pos:* Consult, Centro Interamericano de Desarollo Integral de Aguas y Tierras, Venezuela, 69-71, USAID, Gambia, Africa, 77, Honduras, 78 & Bolivia, 79. *Mem:* Am Soc Agron; Soil Conserv Soc Am; Soil Sci Soc Am; Int Soil Sci Soc. *Res:* Soil mineralogy; soil genesis; solid waste management; soil fertility. *Mailing Add:* Dept of Soil Sci & Biometeorol Utah State Univ Logan UT 84322

MILLER, REGIS BOLDEN, b Meyesdale, Pa, Aug 29, 43; div; c 2. PLANT ANATOMY. *Educ:* WVa Univ, BS, 66; Univ Wis, MS, 68; Univ Md, PhD(bot), 73. *Prof Exp:* RES BOTANIST, FOREST PROD LAB, US FOREST SERV, USDA, 70- *Mem:* Int Asn Wood Anatomists; Int Asn Plant Taxon; Bot Soc Am; Asn Trop Biol; Int Soc Trop Foresters. *Res:* Systematic wood anatomy of Flacourtiaceae, Juglandaceae and Leguminosae; potassium calcium sulfate crystals in wood of Capparis; aluminum detection in wood using chrome azarol-s; vestured pits; computer assisted hardwood identification. *Mailing Add:* US Forest Prod Lab Box 5130 Madison WI 53705

MILLER, REID C, US citizen. CHEMICAL ENGINEERING. *Educ:* Univ Tulsa, BS, 62; Univ Calif, Berkeley, MS, 64, PhD(chem eng), 68. *Prof Exp:* From asst prof to prof chem eng & chem, 68-79, ASSOC DEAN ENG, UNIV WYO, 79- *Concurrent Pos:* NSF, AGA & Exxon res grants, Univ Wyo, 69- *Mem:* Am Inst Chem Engrs; Am Chem Soc; Am Soc Eng Educ. *Res:* Equilibrium and nonequilibrium properties of mixtures of dense fluids; interpretation of the properties of dense fluid mixtures based on the intermolecular potential between unlike species and the resulting fluid structure. *Mailing Add:* Dept of Chem Eng Univ of Wyo Laramie WY 82071

MILLER, RENE H(ARCOURT), b Tenafly, NJ, May 19, 16; div; c 2. AEROSPACE ENGINEERING. *Educ:* Univ Cambridge, BA, 37, MA, 54. *Prof Exp:* Aeronaut engr, G L Martin Co, Md, 37-39; chief aeronaut & develop, McDonnell Aircraft Corp, Mo, 39-44; assoc prof aeronaut eng, 44-57, prof flight vehicle eng, 57-61, head dept aeronaut & astronaut, 68-78, SLATER PROF FLIGHT TRANSP, MASS INST TECHNOL, 61- *Concurrent Pos:* Vpres eng, Kaman Aircraft Corp, Conn, 52-54; consult, Vertol Div, Boeing Co; mem, US Air Force Sci Adv Bd, 59-70; mem comn aircraft aerodynamics, NASA, 60-70; mem tech adv bd, Fed Aviation Agency, 64-66; mem, Army Sci Adv Panel, 66-70; chmn aviation sci adv group; mem aircraft panel, President's Sci Adv Comn. *Honors & Awards:* US Army Decoration for Meritorious Civilian Serv, 67; Sylvanus Albert Reed Award, Inst Aeronaut & Astronaut, 69; Klemin Award, Helicopter Soc. *Mem:* Nat Acad Eng; hon fel Helicopter Soc; hon fel Inst Aeronaut & Astronaut; fel Royal Aeronaut Soc; Fr Asn Aeronaut & Space Eng Technicians. *Res:* Helicopter and airplane design; jet propulsion; vertical take-off and landing aircraft; space systems engineering. *Mailing Add:* Dept of Aeronaut & Astronaut Mass Inst Technol Cambridge MA 02139

MILLER, RICHARD ALBERT, b Heber Springs, Ark, Mar 8, 12; m 42; c 2. MATHEMATICS. *Educ:* Univ Miss, AB, 33, MA, 34. *Prof Exp:* Asst prof math, Univ Miss, 34-35; asst, Univ Iowa, 35-38 & Univ Ill, 38-41; asst prof, Univ Miss, 46-56; proj nuclear physicist, Ft Worth Div, Gen Dynamics Corp, 56-67, proj opers res analyst, 67-70; MATHEMATICIAN, FREESE & NICHOLS, CONSULT ENGRS, 70- *Concurrent Pos:* Adj prof, Eve Col, Tex Christian Univ, 57- *Mem:* Math Asn Am; Soc Indust & Appl Math. *Res:* Algebraic and differential geometry; games; mathematical programming; hydrological studies; water resource studies. *Mailing Add:* 4071 W Seventh St Ft Worth TX 76107

MILLER, RICHARD ALLEN, b Union, NY, May 15, 44; m 66. SYSTEMS ENGINEERING. *Educ:* Union Col, BS, 66; Mass Inst Technol, MS, 67; Case Western Reserve Univ, PhD(systs eng), 71. *Prof Exp:* Asst prof, 71-76, assoc prof, 76-80, PROF INDUST, SYSTS ENG & POLIT SCI, OHIO STATE UNIV, 80- *Mem:* Inst Elec & Electronics Engrs; Human Factors Soc; Am Inst Indust Engrs; Am Polit Sci Asn. *Res:* Systems theory; theory of mathematical modeling; human-machine systems modeling and design; computer applications. *Mailing Add:* Dept of Indust & Systs Eng 1971 Neil Ave Columbus OH 43210

MILLER, RICHARD AVERY, b Erie, Pa, June 23, 11. ENDOCRINOLOGY. *Educ:* Univ Pittsburgh, BS, 32; Univ Iowa, MS, 34, PhD(endocrinol), 37. *Prof Exp:* Res cytologist, Dept Genetics, Carnegie Inst, 37-46; asst prof anat, Univ Minn, 46-48; from asst prof to assoc prof, 48-56, prof, 56-76, EMER PROF ANAT, ALBANY MED COL, 76- *Concurrent Pos:* Vis scientist, NIH, 59-60. *Mem:* Am Soc Zool; Am Asn Anat. *Res:* Pituitary adrenal relations; secretory phenomena in cells; neural pathways in brain stem and thalamus. *Mailing Add:* Dept of Anat Albany Med Col Albany NY 12208

MILLER, RICHARD EDWARD, b Hollis, NY, May 31, 37; m 58. PHYSICAL CHEMISTRY, CHEMICAL PHYSICS. *Educ:* Stevens Inst Technol, BE, 59; Univ Wash, PhD(phys chem), 66. *Prof Exp:* Design engr, Boeing Co, 59-62; asst phys chem, Univ Wash, 62-66; res fel, Princeton Univ, 66-67; res fel, Mich State Univ, 67-68, asst prof, 68-69, lab mgr, mem fac, Ohio State Univ, 74-75; SAFETY OFFICER, ERLING RIIS RES LAB, 75- *Concurrent Pos:* Consult, Spectra Physics, Inc, 68-71. *Res:* Molecular and crystal structure using infrared and Raman spectroscopic techniques. *Mailing Add:* Erling Riis Res Lab PO Box 2328 Mobile AL 36601

MILLER, RICHARD GRAHAM, b St Catharines, Ont, Oct 2, 38; m 63; c 2. BIOPHYSICS, IMMUNOBIOLOGY. *Educ:* Univ Alta, BS, 60, MS, 61; Calif Inst Technol, PhD(physics & biol), 66. *Prof Exp:* Res asst physics, Calif Inst Technol, 61-66, fel, 66; fel, 66-67, SR SCIENTIST BIOPHYS, ONT CANCER INST, 67- *Concurrent Pos:* Vis scientist, Walter & Eliza Hall Inst, Melbourne, Australia, 72-73; asst prof med biophys, Univ Toronto, 67-71, assoc prof, 71-76, prof, 76-, mem, Inst Med Sci, 70- & Inst Immunol, 73- *Mem:* Am Asn Immunologists; Can Soc Cell Biol; Can Soc Immunol. *Res:* Development of procedures for the analysis and sorting of viable mammalian cells; study of initiation of and cellular mechanisms in cell mediated immune responses; self, non-self discrimination. *Mailing Add:* Ont Cancer Inst 500 Sherbourne St Toronto ON M4X 1K9 Can

MILLER, RICHARD HENRY, b Aurora, Ill, Aug 31, 26; m 52. ASTROPHYSICS. *Educ:* Iowa State Col, BS, 46; Univ Chicago, PhD(physics), 57. *Prof Exp:* Engr construct cyclotron, Univ Chicago, 47-51, Calif Res & Develop Co div, Standard Oil Co Calif, 52 & Brazilian Nat Res Coun, 52-54; asst physics, 54-57, res assoc, 57-59, asst prof, 59-62, ASSOC PROF ASTROPHYSICS, UNIV CHICAGO, 63- *Concurrent Pos:* Assoc dir, Inst Comput Res, Univ Chicago, 62-63, dir, 63-66, actg chmn, Comt Info Sci, 65-66; mem summer study group, Stanford Linear Accelerator Ctr, 64; Nat Res Coun-NASA sr resident res assoc, Goddard Inst Space Studies, 67 & 68; consult astronr, Kitt Peak Nat Observ, 70 & 71; sr resident res assoc, NASA-Ames Res Ctr, 75-77. *Mem:* Am Phys Soc; Am Astron Soc; Asn Comput Mach. *Res:* Structure, formation, and dynamics of extragalactic nebulae; computers on-line for experiments; stellar dynamics; astronomical instrumentation. *Mailing Add:* Inst for Comput Res 5640 Ellis Ave Chicago IL 60637

MILLER, RICHARD J, b Schenectady, NY, Aug 20, 37. PHYSICAL CHEMISTRY. *Educ:* Union Col, NY, BS, 59; Lehigh Univ, PhD(phys chem), 64. *Prof Exp:* Asst chem Lehigh Univ, 59-60 & 63-64; from asst prof to assoc prof, 64-72, PROF CHEM, STATE UNIV NY COL CORTLAND, 72- *Concurrent Pos:* Vis assoc prof, Tufts Univ, 70-71; res collabr, Brookhaven Nat Lab, 78-79. *Mem:* Am Chem Soc; AAAS. *Res:* Thermodynamics. *Mailing Add:* Dept of Chem State Univ of NY Col Cortland NY 13045

MILLER, RICHARD KEITH, b Fresno, Calif, June 12, 49; m 71; c 1. APPLIED MECHANICS, CIVIL ENGINEERING. *Educ:* Univ Calif, Davis, BS, 71; Mass Inst Technol, MS, 72; Calif Inst Technol, PhD(appl mech), 75. *Prof Exp:* asst prof mech eng, Univ Calif, Santa Barabara, 75-79; ASSOC PROF CIVIL ENG, UNIV SOUTHERN CALIF, LOS ANGELES, 79- *Concurrent Pos:* Eng consult, Astro Res Corp & Jet Propulsion Lab. *Mem:* Am Soc Mech Engrs; Am Soc Civil Engrs; Am Acad Mech. *Res:* Structural dynamics; nonlinear mechanics. *Mailing Add:* Dept Civil Eng Univ Southern Calif Los Angeles CA 90007

MILLER, RICHARD KEITH, b Clarinda, Iowa, Apr 19, 39; m 63; c 2. MATHEMATICS. *Educ:* Iowa State Univ, BS, 61; Univ Wis, MS, 62, PhD(math), 64. *Prof Exp:* Asst prof math, Univ Minn, Minneapolis, 64-66; from asst prof to assoc prof appl math, Brown Univ, 66-71; assoc prof math, 72-74, PROF MATH, IOWA STATE UNIV, 74- *Concurrent Pos:* With Collins Radio Co, 61 & 62; Fulbright res fel, Ger, 76. *Mem:* Am Math Soc; Soc Indust & Appl Math. *Res:* Asymptotic behavior of ordinary differential equations and Volterra integral equations. *Mailing Add:* Dept of Math Iowa State Univ Ames IA 50010

MILLER, RICHARD KERMIT, b Scranton, Pa, Oct 17, 46. DEVELOPMENTAL PHARMACOLOGY, TOXICOLOGY. *Educ:* Dartmouth Col, AB, 68; Dartmouth Med Sch, PhD(pharmacol & toxicol), 73. *Prof Exp:* Fel develop biol, Jefferson Med Col, 72-74; Asst prof obstet & gynec, 74-80 & pharmacol & toxicol, DIR, DIV RES, DEPT OBSTET & GYNEC, SCH MED & DENT, UNIV ROCHESTER, 78-, ASSOC PROF OBSTET & GYNEC, PHARMACOL & TOXICOL, 80- *Concurrent Pos:* Prin investr, Nat Cancer Inst & Nat Inst Environ Health Sci grants, 77- *Mem:* Teratology Soc; Soc Gynec Invest; Am Soc Pharmacol & Exp Therapeuts; Sigma Xi. *Res:* Transplacental carcinogenicity; teratogenicity; drug metabolism; placental function and the biochemical mechanisms underlying abnormal mammalian development especially in relationship to environmental exposures. *Mailing Add:* Dept Obstet-Gynec Sch Med & Dent Univ Rochester Rochester NY 14642

MILLER, RICHARD LEE, b Glendale, Calif, May 30, 42; m 64; c 2. BIOCHEMISTRY. *Educ:* San Jose State Col, BS, 64; Ariz State Univ, PhD(biochem), 69. *Prof Exp:* Res biochemist, 69-72, SR RES BIOCHEMIST, BURROUGHS WELLCOME & CO, 72- *Mem:* Am Chem Soc; Am Soc Biol Chemists. *Res:* Purine metabolism; nucleotide interconversion; enzymology. *Mailing Add:* Wellcome Res Labs Burroughs Wellcome & Co Research Triangle Park NC 27709

MILLER, RICHARD LEE, b Boston, Mass, Apr 9, 40. INVERTEBRATE ZOOLOGY, DEVELOPMENTAL BIOLOGY. *Educ:* Univ Chicago, BS, 62, PhD(zool), 65. *Prof Exp:* NIH res fel, Calif Inst Technol & Univ Calif, Berkeley, 65-66; asst prof zool, Ore State Univ, 66-68; asst prof, 68-74, ASSOC PROF BIOL, TEMPLE UNIV, 74- *Concurrent Pos:* NIH career develop award, 71-75. *Mem:* Am Soc Cell Biol; AAAS; Am Soc Zoologists. *Res:* Chemical mediation of fertilization in the invertebrates, especially sperm attraction; chemical nature of the attractants and their mode of action. *Mailing Add:* Dept of Biol Temple Univ Philadelphia PA 19122

MILLER, RICHARD LINN, b Portland, Ore, Sept 7, 33; m 59; c 3. CHEMICAL ENGINEERING. *Educ:* Ore State Univ, BS, 55, MS, 59; Univ Minn, PhD(chem eng), 62. *Prof Exp:* Res engr, Rocketdyne Div, NAm Rockwell Corp, Calif, 55-57; res engr, Chevron Res Corp, 62-64; res engr, 64-67, chief biol systs br, Environ Systs Div, 67-71, CHIEF CREW ENVIRON BR, CREW TECHNOL DIV, US AIR FORCE SCH AEROSPACE MED, 71- *Mem:* AAAS; Am Inst Chem Engrs; Aerospace Med Asn; Air Pollution Control Asn; SAFE Asn. *Res:* Research and development on life support apparatus for advanced aerospace systems. *Mailing Add:* Crew Technol Div (VNL) USAF Sch Aerospace Med Brooks AFB TX 78235

MILLER, RICHARD LLOYD, b Mishawaka, Ind, Jan 30, 31; m 52; c 7. ENTOMOLOGY, HORTICULTURE. *Educ:* Purdue Univ, BS, 57; Iowa State Univ, MS, 59, PhD(entom), 62. *Prof Exp:* Exten entomologist, Univ Ky, 62-67; assoc prof entom, 70-74, PROF ENTOM, OHIO STATE UNIV, 74-, EXTEN ENTOMOLOGIST, 67- *Mem:* Entom Soc Am. *Res:* Insect and mite control on fruits, vegetables, ornamentals, turf, yard and garden. *Mailing Add:* Ohio Coop Exten Serv Ohio State Univ Columbus OH 43210

MILLER, RICHARD LLOYD, b Mesa, Ariz, Aug 22, 31; m 52; c 6. EXTRACTIVE CHEMICAL METALLURGY. *Educ:* Ariz State Univ, BA, 57, MS, 60; Univ Utah, PhD(metall), 68. *Prof Exp:* Chemist, Motorola Inc, Phoenix, 59-61; asst prof chem, Univ Tex, El Paso, 61-65; chemist, Univ Utah, 65-66, res asst metall, 66-68; asst prof metall, Univ Wash, 68-69; SCI SPECIALIST METALL, EG&G INC, IDAHO, 69- *Concurrent Pos:* Affil prof metall, Univ Idaho, 70- *Mem:* Metall Soc Am; Inst Mining, Metall & Petrol Engrs. *Mailing Add:* 2285 Curlew Dr Idaho Falls ID 83401

MILLER, RICHARD LYNN, b Stevens Point, Wis, Sept 27, 45; m 73; c 3. ANTIVIRAL DRUG RESEARCH, MOLECULAR BIOLOGY. *Educ:* Univ Wis, BS, 68; Univ Minn, PhD(microbiol), 74. *Prof Exp:* Fel, Pa State Med Sch, 75-77; sr microbiologist, 77-79, RES SPECIALIST, RIKER LABS, 3M CO, 79- *Concurrent Pos:* Asst prof, Univ Minn, 77-80. *Mem:* Am Soc Microbiol; AAAS; NY Acad Sci. *Res:* Antiviral drug research and virus biochemistry, including herpes virus, DNA polymerases and picornavirus structure and replication. *Mailing Add:* Riker Labs Bldg 270-25 3M Co St Paul MN 55144

MILLER, RICHARD PRESSLY, b Troy, Ohio, Feb 18, 22; m 44; c 3. BIOCHEMISTRY. *Educ:* Miami Univ, BA, 47, MA, 48; Univ Ill, PhD(chem), 51. *Prof Exp:* RES SCIENTIST, ELI LILLY & CO, 51- *Mem:* AAAS; Am Chem Soc. *Res:* Biochemistry of hypertension; separation methods and analytical biochemistry; biochemistry of end-stage renal disease. *Mailing Add:* Eli Lilly & Co Indianapolis IN 46285

MILLER, RICHARD ROY, b Salt Lake City, Utah, Aug 3, 41. MATHEMATICS, CHEMISTRY. *Educ:* Univ Utah, BS, 63, PhD(math), 69. *Prof Exp:* From asst prof to assoc prof, 69-77, PROF MATH, WEBER STATE COL, 77- *Mem:* Am Math Soc; Math Asn Am. *Res:* Functional analysis. *Mailing Add:* Dept of Math Weber State Col Ogden UT 84408

MILLER, RICHARD SAMUEL, b Cleveland, Ohio, July 4, 22; m 46; c 2. ANIMAL ECOLOGY. *Educ:* Univ Colo, BA, 49; Oxford Univ, DPhil(animal ecol), 51. *Prof Exp:* Instr biol, Harvard Univ, 52-55; assoc biologist, Colo State Univ, 55-58; from asst prof to assoc prof, Univ Sask, 59-67; prof, 67-68, OASTLER PROF ECOL, SCH FORESTRY, YALE UNIV, 68- *Mem:* Am Soc Mammal; Ecol Soc Am; Am Soc Naturalists; Brit Ecol Soc. *Res:* Population ecology. *Mailing Add:* Sch Forestry & Environ Studies Yale Univ New Haven CT 06511

MILLER, RICHARD WILLIAM, b Moline, Ill, July 24, 47; m 68; c 1. ECOLOGY, LIMNOLOGY. *Educ:* Col William & Mary, BS, 69; Univ Ga, PhD(zool), 75. *Prof Exp:* asst prof, 75-80, PROF ZOOL, BUTLER UNIV, 80- *Concurrent Pos:* Res scientist, The Inst Ecol, 79-81. *Mem:* AAAS; Am Soc Limnol & Oceanog; Ecol Soc Am. *Res:* Community structure and nutrient cycling in freshwater ecosystems, including the impact of man. *Mailing Add:* Dept of Zool Butler Univ Indianapolis IN 46208

MILLER, RICHARD WILSON, b Miami, Fla, May 14, 34; m 57; c 2. BIOCHEMISTRY, BIOPHYSICS. *Educ:* Mass Inst Technol, SB, 56, PhD(biochem), 61. *Prof Exp:* Res assoc enzymol, Mass Inst Technol, 61; res assoc, Sheffield Sci Sch, 62-63 & Univ Mich, 63-64; biochemist, New Eng Inst Med Res, 64-68; SR RES SCIENTIST, CHEM & BIOL RES INST, RES BR, CAN AGR, 68- *Concurrent Pos:* NIH fel, 62-64; USPHS grant, 65-68; vis scientist, ARC unit nitrogen fixation, Univ Sussex, 78-79. *Mem:* AAAS; Am Soc Biol Chemists; Fedn Am Socs Exp Biol. *Res:* Respiratory control over pyrimidine biosynthesis; role of free radicals and superoxide anion in biosynthesis, biodegradation and toxicity mechanisms in microorganisms and plants; mechanism of metalloprotein catalysis; membrane-bound enzymes; membrane composition and physical structure; spin labels in biological membranes; membrane factors in microbiol nitrogen fixation. *Mailing Add:* Chem & Biol Res Inst Res Br Can Agr Ottawa ON K1A 0C6 Can

MILLER, ROBERT ALAN, b Montclair, NJ, Jan 30, 43; m 71; c 2. PHYSICS, COMPUTER SCIENCE. *Educ:* Univ Ill, BS, 65, MS, 66, PhD(physics), 70. *Prof Exp:* Res assoc physics, Col William & Mary, 70-72; res assoc, Rutgers Univ, 72-74; physicist, Fusion Energy Corp, 74-77; physicist, Princeton Gamma-tech, 77-81; VPRES SCI & TECHNOL, SCI TRANSFER ASSOCS, 81- *Concurrent Pos:* Consult, Fusion Energy Corp, 77- *Mem:* Am Phys Soc; Inst Elec & Electronics Engrs; Sigma Xi. *Res:* Low, medium and high energy nuclear physics; solar energy; energy economics; x-ray fluorescence; materials analysis; fusion; transfer of science and technology to developing countries. *Mailing Add:* 17 Ryan Rd Cranbury NJ 08512

MILLER, ROBERT BURNHAM, b Dallas, Tex, Dec 14, 42; m 66; c 3. APPLIED STATISTICS. *Educ:* Univ Iowa, BA, 64, MS, 65, PhD(statist), 68. *Prof Exp:* Asst prof, 68-73, ASSOC PROF STATIST & BUS, UNIV WIS-MADISON, 73- *Honors & Awards:* Halmstad Prize, Actuarial Educ & Res Fund, 79. *Mem:* AAAS; Am Statist Asn; Am Inst Decision Sci. *Res:* Statistical problems in risk theory; time series analysis applied to business and economic problems. *Mailing Add:* 339 W Commerce Bldg Univ of Wis Madison WI 53706

MILLER, ROBERT CARL, b Chicago, Ill, Oct 26, 38; m 69. EXPERIMENTAL HIGH ENERGY PHYSICS, CRYOGENICS. *Educ:* Ill Inst Technol, BS, 61; Northern Ill Univ, MS, 65, CAS, 72. *Prof Exp:* RESEARCHER, ARGONNE NAT LAB, 61- *Mem:* Am Phys Soc; Am Nuclear Soc; Inst Elec & Electronics Engrs; Am Asn Physics Teachers; Instrument Soc Am. *Res:* Spin dependence in proton-proton scattering; phenomenology of pion-proton, proton-proton and proton-neutron scattering including amplitude analysis; polarized proton and deuteron targets. *Mailing Add:* Bldg 362 Rm E-293 Argonne Nat Lab Argonne IL 60439

MILLER, ROBERT CHARLES, b State College, Pa, Feb 2, 25; m 52; c 3. OPTICAL PHYSICS, SOLID STATE PHYSICS. *Educ:* Columbia Univ, AB, 48, MA, 52, PhD(physics), 56. *Prof Exp:* Asst physics, Columbia Univ, 49-51, lectr, 51-53; mem tech staff, Bell Tel Labs, 54-67; mem, Inst Defense Anal, 67-68; head optical electronics res dept, 68-77, MEM TECH STAFF, BELL LABS, 77- *Mem:* Fel Am Phys Soc; NY Acad Sci. *Res:* Ferroelectricity; nonlinear optics; optical spectroscopy of semiconductor heterostructures. *Mailing Add:* Dept 11150 Rm 1C-325 Bell Labs Murray Hill NJ 07974

MILLER, ROBERT CHRISTOPHER, b Washington, DC, Dec 31, 35; m 65; c 3. CYTOGENETICS, CELL BIOLOGY. *Educ:* Univ Nebr-Lincoln, BSc, 62; Ohio State Univ, MSc, 68, PhD(genetics), 71. *Prof Exp:* Lab technician, King County Cent Blood Bank, Inc, Seattle, 62-63 & Cleveland Clin Found Hosp, 63-65; res asst cytogenetics, Ohio State Univ Hosp, 65-66; grad sch genetics, Ohio State Univ, 66-71; staff scientist, Inst Med Res, Camden, NJ, 72-81; DIR, CYTOGENETICS LAB, PA HOSP, PHILADELPHIA, 81-; ASST PROF OBSTET & GYNEC, MED COL, UNIV PA, 81- *Concurrent Pos:* Prin investr, Nat Inst Environ Health Sci grant, 75-78; coadjutant asst prof, Rutgers Univ, Camden Col, 77. *Res:* Genetics of sex; role of chromosome aberrations in embryo mortality; mutagenesis; chemically induced heritable chromosome defects. *Mailing Add:* Dept Obstet Gynec Pa Hosp 8th & Spruce Sts Philadelphia PA 19107

MILLER, ROBERT CLAY, b Quincy, Mass, Feb 26, 23; m 49; c 2. ORGANIC CHEMISTRY. *Educ:* Northeastern Univ, BS, 47; Columbia Univ, AM, 48; Temple Univ, PhD(org chem), 56. *Prof Exp:* Res chemist, Socony Mobil Oil Co, Inc, 48-56 & exp sta, E I du Pont de Nemours & Co, 56-58; asst prof chem, St Vincent Col, 58-59; from asst prof to assoc prof, DePaul Univ, 59-68; chmn dept, 68-79, chmn sci div, 70-74, PROF CHEM, ADRIAN COL, 68- *Mem:* Am Chem Soc; Royal Soc Chem. *Res:* Synthesis of organophosphorus compounds; new polymerization systems; reaction mechanisms; correlation of structure of compounds with infrared spectra; polymer chemistry. *Mailing Add:* Dept of Chem Adrian Col Adrian MI 49221

MILLER, ROBERT DEMOREST, b Omaha, Nebr, Sept 25, 19; m 41; c 3. SOIL PHYSICS. *Educ:* Univ Mo, BS, 40; Univ Nebr, MS, 42; Cornell Univ, PhD(soil physics), 48. *Prof Exp:* Asst soil physicist, Univ Calif, 48-52; assoc prof, 52-59, PROF SOIL PHYSICS, CORNELL UNIV, 59- *Concurrent Pos:* Fulbright res fel, Norway, 65-66; Royal Norweg Coun Sci & Indust Res fel, 65-66; dean fac, Cornell Univ, 67-71. *Mem:* Soil Sci Soc Am; fel Am Soc Agron; Am Geophys Union. *Res:* Soil-water interactions; freezing and heaving of soil; freezing of water in porous media. *Mailing Add:* Dept of Agron Cornell Univ Ithaca NY 14853

MILLER, ROBERT DENNIS, b Philadelphia, Pa, Sept 23, 41; m 63; c 3. ORGANIC CHEMISTRY. *Educ:* Lafayette Col, BS, 63; Cornell Univ, PhD(org chem), 68. *Prof Exp:* RES SCIENTIST, IBM CORP, 68- *Mem:* AAAS; Am Chem Soc. *Res:* Organic photochemistry dealing with the production of highly strained, theoretically interesting molecules; high temperature thermal fragmentation reactions; synthetic methods. *Mailing Add:* IBM Res 5600 Cottle Rd San Jose CA 95193

MILLER, ROBERT DUWAYNE, b Galesburg, Ill, Nov 27, 12; m 37; c 3. PHYSICS. *Educ:* Knox Col, AB, 34; Univ Ill, MS, 35; Washington Univ, PhD(physics), 37. *Prof Exp:* Res geophysicist, Subterrex, Tex, 37-38; geophysicist, Shell Oil Co, 38-58, mgr tech info, Shell Develop Co, 58-69, CONSULT, SHELL DEVELOP CO, 69- *Concurrent Pos:* Physicist, Carnegie Inst Dept Terrestrial Magnetism, 42-43; physicist, Appl Physics Lab, Johns Hopkins Univ, 43-45. *Mem:* Am Phys Soc; Soc Explor Geophysicists; Am Geophys Union. *Res:* Diffuse scattering of x-rays; electrical methods of oil exploration. *Mailing Add:* 6150 Cedar Creek Houston TX 77027

MILLER, ROBERT E(DWIN), b Jackson, Mich, Feb 3, 23; m 46; c 4. ELECTRONICS. *Educ:* Univ Mich, BSE, 44, MSE, 47. *Prof Exp:* Res engr, Willow Run Res Ctr, Univ Mich, 47-48, engr, 48-49, res engr, 49-58; vpres, Strand Eng Co, 58-62; tech adv, Burroughs Ann Arbor Lab, 62-64; res engr, Inst Sci & Technol, Univ Mich, Ann Arbor, 64-71; PRES & GEN MGR, LASER SYSTS CORP, 71- *Mem:* Inst Elec & Electronics Engrs. *Res:* Automation; data handling; computing; radar systems; electro-optics. *Mailing Add:* Laser Systs Corp 117 N First St Ann Arbor MI 48104

MILLER, ROBERT EARL, b Rockford, Ill, Oct 4, 32. MECHANICS. *Educ:* Univ Ill, BS, 54, MS, 55, PhD(theoret & appl mech), 59. *Prof Exp:* From instr to assoc prof, 55-68, PROF THEORET & APPL MECH, UNIV ILL, URBANA, 68- *Mem:* Am Acad Mech; Am Soc Eng Educ; Am Inst Aeronaut & Astronaut. *Res:* Theoretical and applied mechanics. *Mailing Add:* 217 Talbot Lab Univ of Ill Urbana IL 61801

MILLER, ROBERT ERNEST, b Des Moines, Iowa, July 31, 36; m 57; c 3. PLANT PATHOLOGY, SOIL MICROBIOLOGY. *Educ:* Simpson Col, BA, 58; Cornell Univ, MS, 62, PhD(plant path), 63. *Prof Exp:* Res assoc, 63-70, RES SCIENTIST, CAMPBELL INST AGR RES, 70- *Concurrent Pos:* Res grant plant path, Univ Calif, Berkeley, 65-66. *Mem:* Am Phytopath Soc; Am Soc Microbiol. *Res:* Ecology and physiology of soil-borne plant pathogens; biological control of soil-borne plant pathogens; genetics of fungi. *Mailing Add:* Campbell Inst for Agr Res Campbell Soup Co Napoleon OH 43545

MILLER, ROBERT FREDERICK, b Fredonia, NY, July 26, 21; m 46; c 1. ANIMAL NUTRITION. *Educ:* Cornell Univ, BS, 48, MNS, 49, PhD(animal nutrit), 51. *Prof Exp:* Asst dir res, Kasco Mills, 51-54; dir res, Park & Pollard, 55-56; ASSOC DIR TECH AFFAIRS, USA OPERS, AGVET DIV, MERCK, SHARP & DOHME RES LABS, MERCK & CO, INC, 56- *Mem:* Poultry Sci Asn; Am Soc Animal Sci; Animal Nutrit Res Coun; Am Inst Biol Sci. *Res:* Animal health; physiology; parasitology. *Mailing Add:* MSD-Agvet Div Merck & Co, Inc Rahway NJ 07065

MILLER, ROBERT GERARD, b Orange, NJ, Jan 30, 25; m 50; c 4. OPERATIONS RESEARCH, METEOROLOGY. *Educ:* Rutgers Univ, BA, 51; NY Univ, MS, 52; Harvard Univ, PhD(statist), 61. *Prof Exp:* Res staff, Mass Inst Technol, 52-55; dir, Math Statist Div, Travelers Res Ctr, 55-64; mem tech staff, Bell Telephone Labs, 64-65; res fel, Travelers Res Ctr, Inc, 65-71; sr scientist, Life Ins Marketing & Res Asn, 71-76; chief scientist, Air Weather Serv, US Air Force, 76-77; SR SCIENTIST, TECH DEVELOP LAB, NAT WEATHER SERV, 77- *Concurrent Pos:* Consult, Air Force Geophysics Lab, 58-62; expert lectr, World Meterol Orgn, UN, 61; instr, Univ Conn, 62-65; adj prof, St Louis Univ, 77. *Mem:* fel Am Meterol Soc; Am Statist Asn; Sigma Xi. *Res:* Techniques development in statistical meteorology; discriminant; analysis in weather prodiction; statistical forecasting. *Mailing Add:* 5701 DunHorse Lane Derwood MD 20855

MILLER, ROBERT GERRY, b Northampton, Mass, Mar 23, 44; c 1. MECHANICAL ENGINEERING, HEAT TRANSFER. *Educ:* Norwich Univ, BS, 65; Univ Mass, MS, 68; Rutgers Univ, PhD(mech eng), 73. *Prof Exp:* Thermal res engr, Chicago Bridge & Iron Co, 73-75; sr res engr, 75-78, RES ASSOC, JIM WALTER RES CORP, 78- *Concurrent Pos:* Adj instr, Mech Eng Dept, Univ SFla, 81- *Honors & Awards:* Centennial Medallion, Am Soc Mech Engrs, 80. *Mem:* Am Soc Mech Engrs; Am Soc Testing & Mat. *Res:* Thermal resistance measurements of thermal insulation materials; guarded calibrated hot box testing; thermal contact resistance. *Mailing Add:* Jim Walter Res Corp 10301 Ninth St N St Petersburg FL 33702

MILLER, ROBERT H, b Glenside, Pa, Nov 28, 25; m 48; c 3. ELECTRICAL ENGINEERING, INSTRUMENTATION. *Educ:* Va Polytech Inst, BS, 48; Mass Inst Technol, PhD(instrumentation), 64. *Prof Exp:* Engr, Western Union Res Labs, 48-49, Kearfott Co, Inc, 49-50 & Grumman Aircraft Eng Corp, 50-53; chief elec eng, Poly-Sci Corp, 54, chief engr, 55-56, vpres eng, 55-59, vpres res & develop, 60-63; ASSOC PROF ELEC ENG, VA POLYTECH INST & STATE UNIV, 64- *Concurrent Pos:* Consult, Poly-Sci Corp, 64- *Mem:* Inst Elec & Electronics Engrs. *Res:* Electromechanical transducers, especially electromagnetic bearings, differential transformers, motors and sliding contact devices. *Mailing Add:* Dept of Elec Eng Va Polytech Inst & State Univ Blacksburg VA 24060

MILLER, ROBERT H(ENRY), b Vassar, Mich, Feb 20, 30; m 53; c 2. CHEMICAL ENGINEERING. *Educ:* Univ Mich, BSE, 52, MSE, 56, PhD(mass transfer), 59. *Prof Exp:* Res engr, 58-61, res supvr, 61-68, supvr res planning & eval, 68-72, mgr res econ, 72-79, dir planning & admin, 79-80, MGR PROG ANAL, CORP TECHNOL, CORP RES, ALLIED CORP, 80- *Mem:* AAAS; Am Chem Soc; Sigma Xi. *Res:* Economic evaluation of research projects; research planning. *Mailing Add:* Allied Corp PO Box 1021-R Morristown NJ 07960

MILLER, ROBERT HAROLD, b Philadelphia, Pa, Feb 10, 19; m 42; c 2. BOTANY. *Educ:* Univ Calif, Berkeley, AB, 50; Ore State Univ, PhD(bot), 54. *Prof Exp:* Asst prof biol, Univ Nev, Reno, 53-59 & Univ Wichita, 59-60; assoc prof bot, Univ Ky, 60-63; plant scientist & remote sensing specialist, Washington DC, 67-77, nat prog staff scientist, 72-77, PLANT SCIENTIST, PLANT INDUST STA, AGR RES SERV, USDA, 63-, PLANT SCIENTIST, FRUIT LAB, BELTSVILLE, 77- *Concurrent Pos:* Sigma Xi res grant, Univ Nev, Reno, 55-56; AID assoc prof, Inst Technol, Univ Indonesia, 60-63. *Mem:* AAAS; Bot Soc Am; Int Soc Plant Morphol; Soc Econ Bot; Asn Trop Biologists. *Res:* Plant anatomy and morphology; systematic botany; remote sensing technology; analytical and morphological studies of tropical vegetation; fruit anatomy and morphology; root anatomy. *Mailing Add:* 10104 Phoebe Lane Adelphi MD 20783

MILLER, ROBERT HAROLD, b Fremont, Wis, Sept 19, 33; m 57; c 3. SOIL SCIENCE, MICROBIOLOGY. *Educ:* Wis State Univ, River Falls, BS, 58; Univ Minn, MS, 61, PhD(soil microbiol), 64. *Prof Exp:* From asst prof to assoc prof agron, Ohio State Univ, 64-70, prof, 70-81; HEAD & PROF DEPT SOIL SCI, NC STATE UNIV, 82- *Concurrent Pos:* Fulbright lectr, 74-75; bd dir, Am Soc Agron & Soil Sci Soc Am, 78-81. *Mem:* fel Am Soc Agron; fel Soil Sci Soc Am; Sigma Xi; Am Soc Microbiol. *Res:* Plant rhizosphere microorganisms and their interactions with plants; ecology and physiology of Rhizobium japonicum; chemistry of soil organic matter; recycling of organic wastes in soil. *Mailing Add:* Dept Soil Sci NC State Univ Raleigh NC 27650

MILLER, ROBERT HOOVER, genetics, biometry, see previous edition

MILLER, ROBERT JAMES, b Dennison, Ohio, June 27, 44; m 68. CERAMICS ENGINEERING, CHEMISTRY. *Educ:* Ohio State Univ, BCerE & MS, 67, PhD(ceramic eng), 70. *Prof Exp:* SR RES ENGR, AC SPARK PLUG DIV, GEN MOTORS CORP, FLINT, 69- *Mem:* Soc Automotive Engrs; Am Ceramic Soc; Nat Inst Ceramic Engrs. *Res:* Automotive emissions catalysts for removal of hydrocarbons, carbon monoxide and oxides of nitrogen; catalyst support materials. *Mailing Add:* 300 South St Davison MI 48423

MILLER, ROBERT JAMES, II, b Dunn, NC, Jan 14, 33; m 59; c 3. PLANT PHYSIOLOGY, ECOLOGY. *Educ:* NC State Univ, BS, 56; Yale Univ, MF, 62, MS, 65, PhD(biol), 67. *Prof Exp:* From assoc prof to prof biol, Radford Col, 65-72; PROF BIOL & DEAN, ST MARY'S COL, 73- *Concurrent Pos:* Chmn dept biol, Radford Col, 67-68, dean sch natural sci, 68-71, vpres acad affairs, 71-72. *Mem:* Sigma Xi; Am Soc Plant Physiol; Ecol Soc Am; Soc Am Foresters. *Res:* Nitrogen relations of higher plants; ecology of wetlands. *Mailing Add:* 4008 Brownstone Circle Raleigh NC 27609

MILLER, ROBERT JOSEPH, b Ironton, Ohio, June 10, 41; m 73; c 1. EXPERIMENTAL HIGH ENERGY PHYSICS. *Educ:* Univ Detroit, BS, 63; Purdue Univ, MS, 66, PhD(physics), 69. *Prof Exp:* Fel exp high energy physics, Rutherford Lab, Sch Res Coun UK, 68-72; res assoc, Argonne Nat Lab, 72-75, asst physicist, 75-78; ASST PROF, DEPT PHYSICS, MICH STATE UNIV, EAST LANSING, 78- *Mem:* Am Phys Soc. *Res:* Form factors of K meson; anti-neutrino interaction with protons; search for fluctuations in the pi meson-proton interaction; anti-proton, proton interaction. *Mailing Add:* Dept of Physics Mich State Univ East Lansing MI 48824

MILLER, ROBERT JOSEPH, b Keokuk, Iowa, Nov 17, 39; m 65; c 2. MARINE ECOLOGY. *Educ:* William Jewell Col, AB, 61; Col William & Mary, MA, 64; NC State Univ, PhD(zool), 70. *Prof Exp:* Nat Res Coun Can fel, Marine Ecol Lab, Fisheries Res Bd Can, 69-71, res scientist, St John's Biol Sta, 71-79; RES SCIENTIST, HALIFAX LAB, FISHERIES & OCEANS CAN, 79- *Mem:* Am Soc Limnol & Oceanog; AAAS. *Res:* Energy flow in marine populations; marine fisheries management; efficiency of baited traps. *Mailing Add:* PO Box 550 Halifax NS B3J 2S7 Can

MILLER, ROBERT L, b Chicago, Ill, Jan 26, 26; m 47; c 4. PHYSICAL CHEMISTRY, ACADEMIC ADMINISTRATION. *Educ:* Univ Chicago, PhB, 48, BS, 50, MS, 51; Ill Inst Technol, PhD(chem), 63. *Prof Exp:* From instr to assoc prof chem & assoc dean, Univ Ill, Chicago, 51-68; PROF CHEM & DEAN COL ARTS & SCI, UNIV NC, GREENSBORO, 68- *Concurrent Pos:* Asst dean, Univ Ill, Chicago, 62-65. *Mem:* AAAS; Sigma Xi. *Res:* Applications of quantum mechanics to desription of chemical compounds of biological interest. *Mailing Add:* Col Arts & Sci Univ NC Greensboro NC 27412

MILLER, ROBERT LLEWELLYN, b Chicago, Ill, Jan 19, 29; m 53; c 1. POLYMER SCIENCE. *Educ:* Mass Inst Technol, BS, 50; Brown Univ, PhD(chem), 54. *Prof Exp:* Res chemist, Monsanto Chem Co, 53-59, res specialist, 59-62, group leader, Chemstrand Res Ctr, Inc, Monsanto Co, 62-64, scientist, NC, 64-69, Mo, 69-71; SR RES SCIENTIST, MIDLAND MACROMOLECULAR INST, 72-, ASSOC PROF, 80- *Concurrent Pos:* Sr vis scholar, Univ Manchester, 68-69; adj prof, Case Western Reserve Univ, 78-; adj prof, Cent Mich Univ, 81- *Mem:* AAAS; Am Chem Soc; Am Phys Soc; Am Crystallog Asn. *Res:* Solid state physics as applied to polymers, particularly semicrystalline polymers. *Mailing Add:* Midland Macromolecular Inst 1910 W St Andrews Dr Midland MI 48640

MILLER, ROBERT RUSH, b Colorado Springs, Colo, Apr 23, 16; m 40; c 5. ICHTHYOLOGY. *Educ:* Univ Calif, AB, 38; Univ Mich, MA, 43, PhD(zool), 44. *Prof Exp:* Asst ichthyol surv, Nev, Univ Mich, 38 & Div Fishes, Mus Zool, 39-44; assoc cur fishes, US Nat Mus, Smithsonian Inst, 44-48; from asst prof to prof zool, 48-80, PROF BIOL SCI, UNIV MICH, ANN ARBOR, 80-, CUR FISHES, MUS ZOOL, 56- *Concurrent Pos:* Mem, Univ Mich expeds, 38-42, 50 & 59-, Mex, 39, 50 & 55-82, Ichthyol Surv, Guatemala, US Dept State, Smithsonian Inst & Govt Guatemala, 46-47, Biol Surv, Arnhem Land, Govt Australia, Nat Geol Soc & Smithsonian Inst, 48; assoc cur, Mus Zool, Univ Mich, 48-56; ichthyol ed, Copeia, Am Soc Ichthyol & Herpet, 50-55; collabr, US Nat Park Serv, 60-; Guggenheim fel, 73-74. *Honors & Awards:* Award Excellence, Am Fisheries Soc, 75. *Mem:* AAAS; Am Soc Ichthyol & Herpet (vpres, 61, pres, 65); Soc Syst Zool; Soc Study Evolution; Soc Vert Paleont. *Res:* Taxonomy, distribution, variation, hybridization, ecology, life history and evolution of fishes; paleoichthyology. *Mailing Add:* Univ Mus Bldg Univ of Mich Ann Arbor MI 48109

MILLER, ROBERT STEPHEN, b Perth Amboy, NJ, Jan 6, 34; m 55; c 3. POLYMER CHEMISTRY, POLYMER ENGINEERING. *Educ:* Rutgers Univ, BSChem, 58. *Prof Exp:* Polymer chemist, Tex-US Chem Co, 58-62; proj leader plastics & polymers, Atlantic Refining Co, 62-65; sr chemist & engr, 65-69, proj leader acrylics, 69-70, group leader polymers, 70-72, supvr polymer res & develop, 72-75, mgr polymer res & develop, 75-77, DIR POLYMERS & PLASTICS RES & DEVELOP, TENNECO CHEM INC, 77- *Mem:* Soc Plastics Engrs. *Res:* Polymer science and technology especially polymerization process engineering; polymer structure and properties; plastic processing properties; polymerization process productivity. *Mailing Add:* Tenneco Chem Inc Turner Pl Piscataway NJ 08854

MILLER, ROBERT VANCE, b Enid, Okla, Nov 30, 25; m 55; c 3. APPLIED PHYSICS. *Educ:* Univ Okla, BS, 46; Univ Calif, Berkeley, MA, 50; Univ Tenn, PhD(physics), 62. *Prof Exp:* Physicist, Radioisotope Unit, Vet Admin Med Teaching Group Hosp, Memphis, Tenn, 53-56; assoc res engr, Boeing Airplane Co, 56-57; res assoc physics, Oak Ridge Inst Nuclear Studies, 57-59; asst, Univ Tenn, 59-61; tech specialist physics res, Rocketdyne Div, NAm Aviation, Inc, Calif, 62-66; sr systs analyst, Comput & Software, Inc, Calif, 66-70; res engr, Sierracin Corp, 71-76; FORENSIC ENGR, VON HAENEL & ASSOC, 78- *Mem:* AAAS; Am Phys Soc; Inst Elec & Electronics Engrs. *Res:* Theory and calculation of spectral absorption coefficients; nuclear radiation detectors; mathematical analysis; thin films for applied optics; thin film solar cells. *Mailing Add:* 23203 Via Calisero Valencia CA 91355

MILLER, ROBERT VERNE, b Modesto, Calif, Dec 27, 45; m 68. MICROBIAL GENETICS, MOLECULAR GENETICS. *Educ:* Univ Calif, Davis, BA, 67; Univ Ill, Urbana, MS, 69, PhD(microbiol), 72. *Prof Exp:* Res assoc molecular genetics, Univ Calif, Berkeley, 72-74; asst prof microbiol, Univ Tenn, Knoxville, 74-78, assoc prof, 78-80; ASSOC PROF BIOCHEM, CHICAGO MED SCH, LOYOLA UNIV, 80- *Concurrent Pos:* Dernham fel, Am Cancer Soc, Calif, 72-74. *Mem:* AAAS; Sigma Xi; Am Soc Microbiol; Genetics Soc Am; Am Soc Biol Chemists. *Res:* Genetic and biochemical mechanisms of host-viral interactions in Pseudomonas aeruginosa, particularly the host's contribution to vegetive-temperate response of phage and phage conversion of the host. *Mailing Add:* Dept Biochem & Biophys Med Ctr Loyola Univ 2160 S First Ave Maywood IL 60153

MILLER, ROBERT VICTOR, systematic icthyology, research administration, see previous edition

MILLER, ROBERT W, b Warrensville, NC, Aug 7, 31; m 53; c 2. AGRONOMY. *Educ:* Berea Col, BS, 53; Ohio State Univ, MSc, 60, PhD(agron), 63. *Prof Exp:* Asst county agent, NC State Univ, 55-57; asst prof plant breeding, Cornell Univ, 62-63; from asst prof to assoc prof turfgrass mgt, 63-71, PROF AGRON & TURFGRASS MGT, OHIO STATE UNIV, 71- *Mem:* Am Soc Agron; Crop Sci Soc Am. *Res:* Crop physiology; turfgrass management. *Mailing Add:* Dept of Agron Ohio State Univ 1827 Neil Ave Columbus OH 43210

MILLER, ROBERT WALKER, JR, b Philadelphia, Pa, Nov 3, 41; m 66; c 1. PLANT PATHOLOGY. *Educ:* Univ Del, BS, 64, PhD(plant path & ecol), 71; Univ Ariz, MS, 70. *Prof Exp:* Exten specialist, 71-72, asst prof, 72-77, assoc prof, 77-81, PROF PLANT PATH, CLEMSON UNIV, 81- *Mem:* Am Phytopath Soc; Soc Nematologists. *Res:* Epidemiology, cultural and chemical controls of the foliar diseases of pecans. *Mailing Add:* Dept Plant Path & Physiol Clemson Univ Clemson SC 29631

MILLER, ROBERT WARWICK, b Brooklyn, NY, Sept 29, 21; m 55. PEDIATRICS, EPIDEMIOLOGY. *Educ:* Univ Pa, AB, 42, MD, 46; Univ Mich, MPH, 58, DrPH, 61. *Prof Exp:* Mem atomic energy proj, Univ Rochester, 51-53; chief pediat, Atomic Bomb Casualty Comn, Hiroshima, Japan, 53-55, chief child health surv, Hiroshima & Nagasaki, 58-60; prof assoc, Nat Acad Sci, 55-57; chief epidemiol br, 61-75, CHIEF CLIN EPIDEMIOL BR, NAT CANCER INST, 76- *Mem:* Soc Pediat Res; Am Pediat Soc. *Res:* Epidemiology of cancer; congenital malformations and radiation effects. *Mailing Add:* Clin Epidemiol Br A-521 Landow Bldg Nat Cancer Inst Bethesda MD 20205

MILLER, ROBERT WITHERSPOON, b Chester, SC, Oct 29, 18; m 43; c 4. ORGANIC CHEMISTRY. *Educ:* Erskine Col, AB, 39; Univ NC, PhD(org chem), 48. *Prof Exp:* Asst instr chem, Clemson Univ, 39-40; chemist, Tenn Eastman Corp, 48-52, sr chemist, Eastman Chem Prod Inc, 52-53, sales rep, 53-56, prod mgr, 56-57, dist sales mgr, 57-58, chief sales develop rep, 58-65, mgr new prod sales, 65-73, res assoc, 73-77, STAFF ASST, LAB INDUST MED, TENN EASTMAN CO, EASTMAN KODAK CO, 77- *Mem:* Am Chem Soc; Sigma Xi. *Mailing Add:* Eastman Kodak Co Tennessee Eastman Co PO Box 511 Kingsport TN 37664

MILLER, ROGER HEERING, b Dayton, Ohio, June 8, 31; m 57; c 4. PHYSICS, ACCELERATOR PHYSICS. *Educ:* Princeton Univ, AB, 53; Stanford Univ, PhD(physics), 64. *Prof Exp:* GROUP LEADER, STANFORD LINEAR ACCELERATOR CTR, STANFORD UNIV, 61-, ADJ PROF PHYSICS, 78- *Concurrent Pos:* Electron optics consult, Haimson Res Corp, 75- *Res:* Accelerator physics; injection and positron production; electron beam optics. *Mailing Add:* Stanford Linear Accelerator Ctr Stanford Univ Stanford CA 94305

MILLER, RONALD ELDON, b Spokane, Wash, May 13, 41; m 62; c 2. CHEMICAL METALLURGY. *Educ:* Wash State Univ, BS, 64, PhD(metall), 70; Univ Ill, MS, 65. *Prof Exp:* Asst prof metall eng, Univ Wis-Madison, 69-73; sect head, 73-80, MGR, ALCOA LABS, 80- *Concurrent Pos:* NSF res initiation grant, 71-72. *Mem:* Am Inst Mining, Metall & Petrol Engrs; Am Soc Metals; Am Soc Testing & Mat. *Res:* Desulfurization of coal; thermodynamics and kinetics of reactions; alloy development; phase transformations; aluminum metal quality; melting technology; energy conservation; recycling. *Mailing Add:* Alcoa Labs Alcoa Center PA 15069

MILLER, RONALD KENT, immunobiology, allergy, see previous edition

MILLER, RONALD LEE, b Magnolia, Ky, Feb 2, 36; m 59; c 3. BIOCHEMISTRY. *Educ:* Western Ky State Col, BS, 58; Univ Ky, PhD(biochem), 67. *Prof Exp:* Instr biol sci, Cornell Univ, 67-68; fel, Roche Inst Molecular Biol, 68-70, sr investr, 70-72; asst prof, 72-79, ASSOC PROF BIOCHEM, MED UNIV SC, 79- *Mem:* AAAS; Am Chem Soc; Am Soc Biol Chem. *Res:* Connective tissue metabolism; protein synthesis, particularly isolation of protein initiation factors from rabbit reticulocytes; purification and properties of lectins. *Mailing Add:* Dept of Biochem Med Univ of SC Charleston SC 29401

MILLER, ROSCOE EARL, b Shelby Co, Ind, Jan 6, 18; m 52; c 3. MEDICINE. *Educ:* Ind Univ, BS, 48, MD, 51; Am Bd Radiol, dipl, 55. *Prof Exp:* Intern, Univ Chicago Hosp, 52, resident radiol, 55, instr, Univ, 55-56; from asst prof to assoc prof, 56-66, prof, 66-76, DISTINGUISHED PROF RADIOL, MED CTR, IND UNIV, INDIANAPOLIS, 76- *Concurrent Pos:* USPHS fel, Univ Lund, 64-65; mem adv panel radiologic contrast media, US Pharmacopeia; consult, Sta Hosp, Ft Benjamin Harrison, Cent State Hosp & Vet Admin Hosp; mem ed adv bd, J Radiol; assoc ed, J Gastrointestinal Radiol; mem comt cancer detection, Am Col Radiol; mem coun cancer, Am Gastroenterol Asn, 75-78; mem adv panel radiologic contrast media, US Pharmacopeia, 70-80. *Honors & Awards:* Walter B Cannnon Medal, Soc Gastrointestinal Radiologists, 80. *Mem:* Radiol Soc NAm; Am Col Radiol; Am Gastroenterol Asn; Am Roentgen Ray Soc; Soc Gastrointestinal Radiol. *Res:* Radiology of the abdomen and gastrointestinal diseases; design and development of radiological equipment; radiological contrast media. *Mailing Add:* Dept of Radiol Ind Univ Med Ctr Indianapolis IN 46202

MILLER, ROSWELL KENFIELD, b Glen Cove, NY, Aug 4, 32; m 55; c 3. FOREST MANAGEMENT. *Educ:* State Univ NY Col Forestry, Syracuse Univ, BS, 58, MF, 59; Univ Mich, Ann Arbor, PhD(forest mgt), 72. *Prof Exp:* Forester, US Forest Serv, Ore, 59-60; forest engr, Crown Zellerbach Corp, Ore, 60-64; logging engr, Navajo Forest Prod Industs, NMex, 64; chief of surv, NMex State Hwy Dept, Gallup, 64-65; asst prof, 65-67 & 69-72, ASSOC PROF FORESTRY, MICH TECHNOL UNIV, 72- *Mem:* Soc Am Foresters; Am Soc Photogram; Am Congress Surv & Mapping. *Res:* Cost control; planning natural resource use; small business management; land surveying. *Mailing Add:* Forestry Dept Mich Technol Univ Houghton MI 49931

MILLER, ROY G, JR, b Columbus, Ohio, Dec 23, 33; m 55; c 4. ORGANIC CHEMISTRY. *Educ:* Ohio Wesleyan Univ, BA, 55; Univ Mich, MS, 60, PhD(chem), 63. *Prof Exp:* Res chemist, Elastomer Chem Dept, Exp Sta, E I du Pont de Nemours & Co, 63-65; from asst prof to assoc prof, 65-72, PROF CHEM, UNIV NDAK, 72- *Concurrent Pos:* Vis prof, Dartmouth Col, 77-78. *Mem:* Am Chem Soc; Sigma Xi. *Res:* Organic reaction mechanisms; organometallic chemistry and homogeneous catalysis. *Mailing Add:* Dept of Chem Univ of NDak Grand Forks ND 58202

MILLER, ROY RICHARD, b Dayton, Ohio, Dec 17, 36; m 58; c 2. PHYSICAL CHEMISTRY, AERONAUTICAL & ASTRONOMICAL ENGINEERING. *Educ:* Mass Inst Technol, BS, 58; Univ Chicago, PhD(chem), 63. *Prof Exp:* Chemist, Cent Res Labs, Am Cyanamid Co, 58-59; sr res chemist, 62-67, staff chemist, 67-71, dept head, 71-78, SR CHEMIST, ALLEGANY BALLISTICS LAB, HERCULES INC, 78- *Concurrent Pos:* Vis scientist, Air Force Propulsion Lab, 81-82. *Mem:* Am Inst Phys; Soc Rheol. *Res:* Influence of fillers on properties of filled plastics; kinetics of polymerization reactions; combustion processes. *Mailing Add:* Allegany Ballistics Lab Hercules Inc Box 210 Cumberland MD 21502

MILLER, RUDOLPH J, b Gbely, Czech, Sept 25, 34; US citizen; m 57; c 3. ETHOLOGY, ICHTHYOLOGY. *Educ:* Cornell Univ, BS, 56, PhD(vert zool), 61; Tulane Univ, MS, 58. *Prof Exp:* NIH fel, Univ Groningen, 61-62; from asst prof to assoc prof, 62-69, chmn dept gen & evolutionary biol, 77-79, PROF ZOOL, OKLA STATE UNIV, 69- *Concurrent Pos:* Vis investr, Univ Hawaii, 71-72; vis prof, Cornell Univ, 80 & Univ Wash, 81. *Mem:* AAAS; Am Soc Ichthyol & Herpet; Animal Behav Soc. *Res:* Fish behavior; comparative aspects and motivation analysis, primarily on anabantid, centrarchid and cyprinid fishes; fish feeding ecology; correlative studies of brain, sense organs and behavior; streamfish ecology. *Mailing Add:* Dept Zool Okla State Univ Stillwater OK 74075

MILLER, RUPERT GRIEL, b Lancaster, Pa, Jan 31, 33; m 59; c 2. STATISTICS. *Educ:* Princeton Univ, AB, 54; Stanford Univ, PhD(statist), 58. *Prof Exp:* Assoc prof, Univ Calif, 58-59, Stanford Univ, 59-63 & Johns Hopkins Univ, 63-64; assoc prof, 64-71, PROF STATIST, STANFORD UNIV, 71- *Res:* Biostatistics and stochastic processes. *Mailing Add:* Dept of Statist Stanford Univ Stanford CA 94305

MILLER, RUSSEL BRYAN, b Tyler, Tex, May 31, 40; m 69; c 2. ORGANIC CHEMISTRY. *Educ:* Washington & Lee Univ, BS, 62; Rice Univ, PhD(chem), 67. *Prof Exp:* Res fel, Columbia Univ, 66-68; asst prof, 68-75, assoc prof, 75-80, PROF CHEM, UNIV CALIF, DAVIS, 75- *Mem:* AAAS; Am Chem Soc; Sigma Xi. *Res:* Synthetic natural product chemistry; new synthetic methods; conformational analysis. *Mailing Add:* Dept Chem Univ Calif Davis CA 95616

MILLER, RUSSELL BENSLEY, b Lake Wales, Fla, Aug 20, 46; m 71. POLLINATION ECOLOGY. *Educ:* Carleton Col, BA, 68; Yale Univ, PhD(biol), 74. *Prof Exp:* Asst prof, 74-80, assoc prof, 80-81, RES ASSOC, DEPT BIOL SCI, MT HOLYOKE COL, 81- *Concurrent Pos:* Fac, Rocky Mountain Biol Lab, 74- & Ctr Europ Studies, Tufts Univ, 81-; sr investr, Rocky Mountain Biol Lab, 76- *Mem:* Bot Soc Am; Ecol Soc Am; Soc Study Evolution. *Res:* Field studies on the pollination ecology of Angiosperms. *Mailing Add:* Dept Biol Sci Mt Holyoke Col South Hadley MA 01075

MILLER, RUSSELL LEE, b Cairo, Ga, Dec 23, 22; m 53; c 4. CROP SCIENCE. *Educ:* Univ Ga, BSA, 50, MS, 52; La State Univ, PhD, 58. *Prof Exp:* Instr agron, Univ Ga, 51-52; from instr to assoc prof, 52-68, PROF AGRON, LA STATE UNIV, BATON ROUGE, 68- *Mem:* Am Soc Agron; fel Nat Asn Cols & Teachers Agr (vpres, 80 & pres, 81); Crop Sci Soc Am. *Res:* Agronomic education; teaching improvement. *Mailing Add:* Dept of Agron La State Univ Baton Rouge LA 70803

MILLER, RUSSELL LOYD, JR, b Harvey, WVa, June 30, 39; m 63; c 2. IMMUNOPHARMACOLOGY. *Educ:* Howard Univ, Col Liberal Arts, BS, 61, Col Med, MD, 65. *Prof Exp:* Med internship, Med Ctr, Univ Mich, Ann Arbor, 65-66, resident internal med, 66-68; res fel, Dept Internal Med, Div Clin Pharm, Univ Calif, San Francisco, 68-73; vis scientist, Roche Inst Molecular Biol, 73-74; assoc prof, Dept Med & Pharmacol, 74-79, PROF CLIN PHARMACOL & DEAN, COL MED, HOWARD UNIV, 79- *Concurrent Pos:* Fel, Cardiovasc Res Inst, Univ Calif, San Francisco, 68-73; dir, Div Clin Pharmacol, Col Med, Howard Univ, 74-79; vis prof, Dist Columbia Gen Hosp, 74-79; consult, Dept Pharmacol, Univ Miami, 74-79, Med Letter Drugs & Therapeut, 74-; scholar clin pharmacol, Burroughs Wellcome Found, 77. *Mem:* Am Fedn Clin Res; Am Soc Clin Pharmacol & Therapeut; Am Soc Pharmacol & Exp Therapeut; Am Col Physicians; Nat Med Asn. *Res:* Study of neurotransmitters, neuromodulators, vasoactive peptides, and their relation to clinical conditions; application of techniques of immunopharmacology to improve the understanding of drug actions. *Mailing Add:* Office Dean Col Med Howard Univ 520 W St NW Washington DC 20059

MILLER, SANDRA CAROL, b Montreal, Que, Feb 18, 46. IMMUNOLOGY, HEMATOLOGY. *Educ:* Sir George Williams Univ, BSc, 68; McGill Univ, MSc, 71, PhD(hemat), 75. *Prof Exp:* Lectr anat, McGill Univ, 75-76; fel immuno-hemat, Baylor Col Med, 76-78; ASST PROF ANAT, MCGILL UNIV, 78- *Mem:* Am Asn Anatomists; Int Soc Exp Hemat; Can Soc Immunol; Can Asn Anatomists. *Res:* Regulation of cells involved in spontaneous killing of tumor cells in vitro; cells mediating resistance to foreign bone marrow grafts in vivo. *Mailing Add:* Dept Anat 3640 University St Montreal PQ H3A 2B2 Can

MILLER, SANFORD ARTHUR, b Brookly, NY, May 12, 31; m 58; c 2. BIOCHEMISTRY, NUTRITION. *Educ:* City Col New York, BS, 52; Rutgers Univ, MS, 56, PhD(physiol, biochem), 57. *Prof Exp:* Chemist, Appl Res Br, Army Chem Ctr, Md, 52; asst, Bur Biol Res, Rutgers Univ, 54-55, Dept Physiol & Biochem, 55-57; res assoc & supvr animal labs, Dept Food Technol, 57-59, from asst prof to assoc prof, 59-70, dir training prog oral sci, 70-78, PROF NUTRIT BIOCHEM, MASS INST TECHNOL, 70-; DIR, BUR FOODS, FDA, 78- *Concurrent Pos:* Mem, Expert Comt Generally Regarded as Safe Substances, Fedn Am Socs Exp Biol, Food & Drug Admin, 72-78 & Comt Maternal & Child Health & Comt Contraceptive Steroids, Nat Inst Child Health Develop, 73- *Honors & Awards:* Conrad Elvehsem Award, Am Inst Nutrit, 81. *Mem:* AAAS; Perinatal Res Soc; Am Soc Pediat Res; Inst Food Technologists; Am Inst Nutrit. *Res:* Nutrition and development; infant nutrition; synthetic dietary energy sources; oral biology. *Mailing Add:* Dept Nutrit & Food Sci Mass Inst Technol Cambridge MA 02139

MILLER, SANFORD STUART, b Paterson, NJ, June 1, 38; m 67; c 2. MATHEMATICAL ANALYSIS. *Educ:* Mass Inst Technol, BS, 60; Wash Univ, MA, 66; Univ Ky, PhD(math), 71. *Prof Exp:* Asst prof math, Ball State Univ, 66-68; from asst prof to assoc prof, 71-76, PROF MATH, STATE UNIV NY COL BROCKPORT, 76- *Concurrent Pos:* Fel, Int Res Exchange Bd, Poland & Romania, 73-74; Nat Acad Sci exchange scientist, Romania, 74; Fulbright Advan Res Award, Romania, 76; Sigma Xi fac award, 76; exchange scientist, Romania, 77 & 79; fel, Int Res Exchange Bd, Poland, 78, Romania, 80 & Nat Acad Sci, Bulgaria, 81. *Mem:* Am Math Soc; Math Asn Am. *Res:* Theory of functions of a complex variable, univalent function theory and differential inequalities in the complex plane. *Mailing Add:* Dept Math State Univ NY Col Brockport NY 14420

MILLER, SCOTT CANNON, b Salt Lake City, Utah, July 3, 47; m 71; c 1. CELL BIOLOGY, ANATOMY. *Educ:* Univ Utah, BS, 67, PhD(anat), 70. *Prof Exp:* RES ASST PROF RADIOBIOL, UNIV UTAH, 77- *Concurrent Pos:* Res fel, Harvard Univ, 74-77. *Mem:* Am Soc Bone & Mineral Res. *Res:* Mineral metabolism and endocrine effects on bone; cell surface properties of cancer cells. *Mailing Add:* Div Radiobiol Univ Utah Salt Lake City UT 84112

MILLER, SHELBY A(LEXANDER), b Louisville, Ky, July 9, 14; m 52; c 1. CHEMICAL ENGINEERING. *Educ:* Univ Louisville, BS, 35; Univ Minn, PhD(chem eng), 44. *Prof Exp:* Asst chemist, Corhart Refractories Co, Ky, 35; asst chem eng, Univ Minn, 35-39; chem engr, Eng Dept, E I du Pont de Nemours & Co, 40-46; assoc prof chem eng, Univ Kans, 46-50, prof, 50-55; prof, Univ Rochester, 55-69, chmn dept, 55-68; assoc lab dir, 69-74, dir, Ctr Educ Affairs, 69-79, SR CHEM ENGR, CHEM ENG DIV, ARGONNE NAT LAB, 79- *Concurrent Pos:* Fulbright lectr, King's Col, Durham, 52-53; vis prof, Univ Calif, Berkeley, 67-68. *Mem:* AAAS; Am Chem Soc; Am Soc Eng Educ; Am Inst Chem Engrs; NY Acad Sci. *Res:* Agitation; gas dispersion; filtration; fluidized-bed combustion. *Mailing Add:* Argonne Nat Lab 9700 S Cass Ave Argonne IL 60439

MILLER, SHERWOOD ROBERT, b Lamont, Alta, Apr 16, 32; m 55; c 4. POMOLOGY. *Educ:* Univ Alta, BSc, 54, MSc, 56; Cornell Univ, PhD(pomol), 65. *Prof Exp:* RES SCIENTIST HORT, CAN DEPT AGR, 56- *Concurrent Pos:* Supt, Smithfield Exp Farm, Agr Can. *Mem:* Am Soc Hort Sci; Can Soc Hort. *Res:* Use of synthetic and endogenous growth regulators in apple production; spacing trials with emphasis on tree walls and high density plantings. *Mailing Add:* Can Dept Agr PO Box 340 Trenton ON K8V 5R5 Can

MILLER, SIDNEY ISRAEL, b Saskatoon, Sask, Can, May 22, 23; nat US; m 50; c 3. PHYSICAL ORGANIC CHEMISTRY. *Educ:* Univ Man, BSc, 45, MSc, 46; Columbia Univ, PhD(chem), 51. *Prof Exp:* Instr chem, Univ Man, 46 & Univ Mich, 50-51; from instr to assoc prof, 51-64, PROF CHEM, ILL INST TECHNOL, 64- *Concurrent Pos:* NSF sr fel, Univ Col, Univ London, 63-64; vis scientist, Argonne Nat Lab, 71-72 & Japan Soc Prom Sci, 73; vis fel, Latrobe Univ, Australia, 77-78. *Mem:* Am Chem Soc; Am Asn Univ Profs. *Res:* Solution kinetics; mechanisms; stereochemistry; acetylene chemistry; heterocyclics; coal. *Mailing Add:* Dept of Chem Ill Inst of Technol Chicago IL 60616

MILLER, STANLEY CUSTER, JR, b Kansas City, Mo, July 30, 26; m 57; c 3. THEORETICAL PHYSICS. *Educ:* Univ Colo, BS, 48; Univ Calif, PhD(physics), 53. *Prof Exp:* From asst prof to assoc prof, 53-61, PROF PHYSICS, UNIV COLO, BOULDER, 61- *Mem:* Am Phys Soc. *Res:* Theoretical work in quantum mechanics, optics, electrical noise and solid state semiconductors. *Mailing Add:* Dept of Physics & Astrophys Univ of Colo Boulder CO 80309

MILLER, STANLEY LLOYD, b Oakland, Calif, Mar 7, 30. CHEMISTRY. *Educ:* Univ Calif, BS, 51; Univ Chicago, PhD(chem), 54. *Prof Exp:* Jewett fel chem, Calif Inst Technol, 54-55; instr biochem, Col Physicians & Surgeons, Columbia Univ, 55-58, asst prof, 58-60; from asst prof to assoc prof, 60-68, PROF CHEM, UNIV CALIF, SAN DIEGO, 68- *Mem:* AAAS; Am Chem Soc; Am Soc Biol Chem; Nat Acad Sci. *Res:* Origin of life; natural occurrence of clathrate hydrates; general anesthesia mechanisms. *Mailing Add:* Dept of Chem Univ of Calif at San Diego La Jolla CA 92093

MILLER, STEPHEN DOUGLAS, b Greeley, Colo, Mar 27, 46; m 69; c 1. WEED SCIENCE. *Educ:* Colo State Univ, BS, 68; NDak State Univ, MS, 70, PhD(agron), 73. *Prof Exp:* Asst agron, 73-75, asst prof, 75-80, ASSOC PROF AGRON, NDAK STATE UNIV, 80- *Mem:* Weed Sci Soc Am; Agron Soc Am; Crop Sci Soc Am. *Res:* Biology and control of wild oats in field crops; effect of reduced tillage systems on crop yield and crop pests. *Mailing Add:* Dept of Agron NDak State Univ Fargo ND 58102

MILLER, STEVEN J, b Ft Eustis, Va, July 13, 55. PHARMACEUTICAL CHEMISTRY. *Educ:* Univ Toledo, BS, 76; Univ Calif, Los Angeles, PhD(chem), 81. *Prof Exp:* RES CHEMIST, E I DU PONT DU NEMOURS & CO, INC, 81- *Mem:* Am Chem Soc. *Res:* Synthesis of natural products or other biologically interesting molecules as well as the rational design of potential pharmaceuticals. *Mailing Add:* E I Du Pont de Nemours & Co Inc Exp Sta Bldg 335 Wilmington DE 19898

MILLER, STEVEN RALPH, b Cleveland, Ohio, Feb 26, 36; m 58; c 2. PHYSICAL CHEMISTRY. *Educ:* Case Western Reserve Univ, BS, 58; Mass Inst Technol, PhD(phys chem), 62. *Prof Exp:* Res assoc, Mass Inst Technol, 62; asst prof chem, 62-68, ASSOC PROF CHEM, OAKLAND UNIV, 68- *Mem:* AAAS; Am Chem Soc. *Res:* Nuclear magnetic resonance relaxation phenomena in ferroelectric solids; gas phase reaction kinetics; oxidation of sulfur dioxide; aerosol formation. *Mailing Add:* Dept of Chem Oakland Univ Rochester MI 48063

MILLER, STEWART E(DWARD), b Milwaukee, Wis, Sept 1, 18; m 40; c 3. COMMUNICATIONS. *Educ:* Mass Inst Technol, SB & SM, 41. *Prof Exp:* Engr, 49-54, asst dir radio res, 54-58, DIR GUIDED WAVE RES, BELL TEL LABS, INC, 58- *Concurrent Pos:* Mem, Intel Systs Panel, Sci Adv Bd, 53-56. *Honors & Awards:* Award, Naval Ord Develop, 45; Morris N Liebmann Award, Inst Elec & Electronics Engrs, 72, Baker Award, 75; Stuart Ballentine Medal, Franklin Inst, 77. *Mem:* Nat Acad Sci; fel Optical Soc Am; fel Inst Elec & Electronics Engrs. *Res:* Microwave radio research; communications systems; wave guide transmission lines; optical communications; fiber optical transmission for communication. *Mailing Add:* 67 Wigwam Rd Locust NJ 07760

MILLER, TERRY ALAN, b Girard, Kans, Dec 18, 43; m 66; c 2. CHEMICAL PHYSICS. *Educ:* Univ Kans, BA, 65; Cambridge Univ, PhD(chem), 68. *Prof Exp:* SUPVR, BELL LABS, INC, 68- *Concurrent Pos:* Asst prof, Princeton Univ, 68-71 & Stanford Univ, 72. *Mem:* Am Phys Soc. *Res:* Microwave and laser spectroscopy of transient molecular species, free radicals, ions and excited states; chemical reactions and kinetics of atoms and simple molecules. *Mailing Add:* Bell Labs Inc 600 Mountain Ave Murray Hill NJ 07974

MILLER, TERRY LEE, b Aberdeen, SDak, Dec 14, 40; m 64. BIOCHEMISTRY. *Educ:* San Diego State Col, AB, 64, MS, 65; Ore State Univ, PhD(biochem), 69. *Prof Exp:* NIH fel, Univ Colo, 68-70; asst prof biochem, 70-72, res assoc, Environ Health Sci Ctr, 73-75, ASST PROF, DEPT AGR CHEM, ORE STATE UNIV, 75- *Concurrent Pos:* Consult, Salem Mem Hosp, 71-72. *Mem:* Am Chem Soc. *Res:* Protein chemistry; membrane chemistry; mechanisms of action of membrane active compounds; effects of selected environmental toxicants on biological and artificial membranes. *Mailing Add:* Dept of Agr Chem Ore State Univ Corvallis OR 97331

MILLER, TERRY LYNN, b Fulton, Ky, July 9, 45. MICROBIOLOGY. *Educ:* Univ Ky, BS, 67; NC State Univ, MS, 69; Univ Ill, Urbana, PhD(microbiol), 73. *Prof Exp:* Res assoc, Univ Ill, Urbana, 73-74; res scientist I, 74-76, res scientist II, 76-81, RES SCIENTIST III ENVIRON MICROBIOL, DIV LABS & RES, NY STATE DEPT HEALTH, 82- *Mem:* Am Soc Microbiol; AAAS; NY Acad Sci; Sigma Xi. *Res:* Physiology, biochemistry and ecology of microorganisms emphasizing anaerobic ecosystems (intestinal tract, waste digestion) including studies of methanogenesis. *Mailing Add:* NY State Dept Health Ctr Labs & Res Albany NY 12201

MILLER, THEODORE CHARLES, b Troy, NY, July 23, 33; m 59; c 3. PHARMACEUTICAL CHEMISTRY, PATENT LAW. *Educ:* Princeton Univ, AB, 55; Univ Ill, PhD(chem), 59. *Prof Exp:* Res chemist, 59-69, patent agent trainee, 69-70, PATENT AGENT, STERLING-WINTHROP RES INST, 70- *Mem:* Am Chem Soc. *Res:* Free radical rearrangements; synthesis of steroid hormones and heterocyclic compounds. *Mailing Add:* Sterling-Winthrop Res Inst Rensselaer NY 12144

MILLER, THEODORE LEE, b Crab Orchard, WVa, May 25, 40; m 70; c 2. PHYSICAL CHEMISTRY. *Educ:* Concord Col, BS, 66; Marshall Univ, MS, 70; Univ Cincinnati, PhD(chem), 74. *Prof Exp:* Instr chem, Univ Va, 74-75; asst prof chem, King's Col, Pa, 75-77; ASST PROF CHEM, OHIO WESLEYAN UNIV, 77- *Mem:* AAAS; Am Chem Soc; Sigma Xi. *Res:* Luminescence spectroscopy; metal ions in biological systems; crocetin chemistry (an atherosclerosis drug); on-line computerized instrumentation. *Mailing Add:* Dept Chem Ohio Wesleyan Univ Delaware OH 43015

MILLER, THOMAS, b Asheville, NC, Apr 17, 32; m 54; c 1. PLANT PATHOLOGY. *Educ:* NC State Univ, BS, 62, MS, 64, PhD(plant path), 72. *Prof Exp:* PLANT PATHOLOGIST, SOUTHEASTERN FOREST EXP STA, US FOREST SERV, 64- *Concurrent Pos:* Adj prof forest pathol, Univ Fla. *Mem:* Am Phytopath Soc; Soc Am Foresters. *Res:* Mechanisms of resistance in southern pines to Cronartium fusiforme; fungus diseases of pine strobili, cones and seed; mycology-rust fungi; control of tree diseases through silviculture; integrated forest; pest management. *Mailing Add:* SE Forest Exp Sta Sch Forest Resources & Conserv Univ Fla Gainesville FL 32611

MILLER, THOMAS ALBERT, b Sharon, Pa, Jan 5, 40; m 65; c 2. ENTOMOLOGY. *Educ:* Univ Calif, Riverside, BA, 62, PhD(entom), 67. *Prof Exp:* USPHS fel & res assoc insect physiol, Univ Ill, Urbana, 67-68; NATO fel insect physiol, Glasgow Univ, 68-69; from asst prof & asst entomologist to assoc prof & assoc entomologist, 69-76, PROF ENTOM & ENTOMOLOGIST, UNIV CALIF, RIVERSIDE, 76- *Mem:* Am Chem Soc; Am Soc Zoologists; Brit Soc Exp Biol. *Res:* Insect neurophysiology; insect toxicology; mode of action of insecticides; insect cardiac physiology. *Mailing Add:* Dept of Entom Univ of Calif Riverside CA 92521

MILLER, THOMAS EDWARD, b Minneapolis, Minn, Apr 3, 39; m 62; c 2. IMMUNOCHEMISTRY. *Educ:* Univ Minn, BA, 62, MS, 64, PhD(microbiol), 67. *Prof Exp:* Res assoc biomed res, Trudeau Res Inst, Inc, 67-76; head, Diag Immunol Sect, Squibb Inst Med Res, 76-80; MEM STAFF, DEPT IMMUNOGDIAGNOSTICS, WAMPOLE LABS, 80- *Mem:* AAAS; Am Asn Immunol; Am Soc Microbiol. *Res:* Modulation of immune response; allergenicity studies; radiometric assays; diagnostic assay development. *Mailing Add:* Dept Immunodiagnostics Wampole Labs Half-Acre Rd Cranbury NJ 08512

MILLER, THOMAS GORE, b Greenfield, Ohio, Nov 3, 24; m 53; c 3. ORGANIC CHEMISTRY. *Educ:* Miami Univ, AB, 48; Univ Ill, MS, 49, PhD(chem), 51. *Prof Exp:* Res chemist, E I du Pont de Nemours & Co, 51-57; from asst prof to assoc prof, 57-69, head dept, 69-79, PROF CHEM, LAFAYETTE COL, 69- *Concurrent Pos:* NSF sci fac fel & vis res fel, Princeton Univ, 70-71. *Mem:* Am Chem Soc; Sigma Xi. *Res:* Molecular rearrangements; clathrate compounds; general organic chemistry. *Mailing Add:* Dept of Chem Lafayette Col Easton PA 18042

MILLER, THOMAS LEE, b Elkhart, Ind, Nov 24, 35; m 62; c 3. BIOCHEMISTRY, MICROBIOLOGY. *Educ:* Ind State Univ, AB, 61; Univ Wis, MS, 64, PhD(biochem), 66. *Prof Exp:* Res asst biochem, Univ Wis, 61-66; res assoc microbiol, 66-67, head microbiol sect, 67-70, RES MGR FERMENTATION MICROBIOL, UPJOHN CO, 70- *Mem:* Am Chem Soc; Am Soc Microbiol. *Res:* Hydrocarbon fermentations; steroid bioconversions; microbiological processes; measurement and control of fermentation variables; antibiotic fermentations. *Mailing Add:* 7599 Orchard Hill Ave Kalamazoo MI 49001

MILLER, THOMAS MARSHALL, b Ft Worth, Tex, Aug 20, 40; m 71. ATOMIC PHYSICS. *Educ:* Ga Inst Technol, BS, 62, MS, 64, PhD(physics), 68. *Prof Exp:* Asst prof physics, NY Univ, 68-74; physicist, Stanford Res Inst, 74-78; ASSOC PROF, UNIV OKLA, 78- *Mem:* Am Phys Soc. *Res:* Transport properties of low energy ions and electrons in gases; ion-molecule reactions; interactions of low energy electrons with thermal atom beams; low-energy atom-atom collisions; atomic polarizabilities; photodissociation. *Mailing Add:* Dept of Physics & Astron Univ Okla Norman OK 73019

MILLER, THOMAS PATRICK, b Minneapolis, Minn, Aug 30, 36; m 59; c 2. GEOLOGY. *Educ:* Univ Minn, Duluth, BA, 58; Univ Minn, MS, 61; Stanford Univ, PhD(geol), 71. *Prof Exp:* GEOLOGIST, US GEOL SURV, 61- *Concurrent Pos:* Chief, Br Alaskan Geol. *Mem:* AAAS; fel Geol Soc Am. *Res:* Volcanology; geothermal energy; hydrothermal uranium deposits; igneous petrology. *Mailing Add:* Gould Hall Alaska Pacific Univ Anchorage AK 99504

MILLER, THOMAS WILLIAM, b Providence, RI, June 12, 29; m 52; c 3. NATURAL PRODUCTS CHEMISTRY. *Educ:* Univ RI, BS, 50. *Prof Exp:* Res chemist, 51-61, sr res chemist, 61-69, res fel, 69-70, asst dir, 70-74, sr res fel, 74-81, SR INVESTR, MERCK SHARP & DOHME RES LABS, 81- *Mem:* Am Soc Microbiol; Am Chem Soc. *Res:* Natural products; isolation of antibiotics, vitamins and other fermentation products. *Mailing Add:* Merck Sharp & Dohme Res Labs PO Box 2000 Rahway NJ 07065

MILLER, TRACY BERTRAM, b Syracuse, NY, Oct 19, 27; m 54; c 3. PHARMACOLOGY. *Educ:* Cornell Univ, AB, 48; Univ Buffalo, MA, 53, PhD, 59. *Prof Exp:* Instr pharmacol, Univ Buffalo, 53-54; res assoc physiol, Harvard Med Sch, 64-66; assoc prof pharmacol & surg res, State Univ NY Upstate Med Ctr, 66-71; PROF PHARMACOL & PHYSIOL, MED SCH, UNIV MASS, 71- *Concurrent Pos:* Am Heart Asn res fel, Col Med, State Univ NY Upstate Med Ctr, 59-64, Am Heart Asn estab investr, 62-67. *Res:* Renal pharmacology; cerebro-spinal fluid physiology. *Mailing Add:* Dept of Pharmacol Univ of Mass Med Sch Worcester MA 01605

MILLER, VICTOR CHARLES, b Stamford, Conn, Mar 17, 22; c 2. GEOMORPHOLOGY. *Educ:* Columbia Univ, BA, 43, MA, 48, PhD(geomorphol), 53. *Prof Exp:* Photogeologist, Sinclair Wyo Oil & Gas Co, 47-49; lectr, Dept Geol, Columbia Univ, 49-51; photogeologist, Geophoto Serv, 51-52; partner, Miller-McCulloch, Alta, 52-54; pres, Miller-McCulloch, Ltd, 54-56, V C Miller & Assocs, Photogeologists, Ltd, Can, 56-57 & Miller & Assocs, Inc, Colo, 57-62; prof geol & chmn dept, Univ Libya, 62-64 & C W Post Col, Long Island Univ, 64-67; PROF GEOL, IND STATE UNIV, TERRE HAUTE, 67- *Concurrent Pos:* Geol panel mem, Comt Remote Sensing for Earth Resource Surv, Nat Res Coun, 73- *Mem:* AAAS; Geol Soc Am; Am Soc Photogram; Am Asn Petrol Geologists. *Res:* Photogeology; photogeomorphology; remote sensing, air photos, radar, infra-red, Skylab and Earth Resources Technol Satellite imagery. *Mailing Add:* Dept of Geog & Geol Ind State Univ Terre Haute IN 47809

MILLER, VICTOR JAY, b Geff, Ill, Jan 12, 21; m 45; c 3. HORTICULTURE. *Educ:* Univ Ill, BS, 42, MS, 47, PhD(hort), 49. *Prof Exp:* Asst bot, Univ Ill, 45-47, asst hort, 47-49; from asst prof to assoc prof & chmn dept, Univ Nebr, 49-58; PROF HORT, ARIZ STATE UNIV, 58- *Mem:* Am Soc Hort Sci. *Res:* Fruits and woody ornamentals; turf. *Mailing Add:* Div of Agr Ariz State Univ Tempe AZ 85281

MILLER, W(ENDELL) E(ARL), b Cissna Park, Ill, June 23, 13; m 41; c 2. ELECTRICAL ENGINEERING. *Educ:* Univ Ill, BS, 36, MS, 46. *Prof Exp:* Trial installation engr, Bell Tel Labs, Inc, NY, 36-39; power sales engr, Northern Ind Pub Serv Co, 39-41; from instr to prof elec eng, 41-70, asst dean eng, 50-55, from asst head dept to assoc head dept, 55-70, EMER PROF ELEC ENG, UNIV ILL, URBANA, 71- *Concurrent Pos:* Dir environ affairs, Ill Power Co, 70-78. *Mem:* Am Soc Eng Educ; Nat Soc Prof Engrs. *Res:* Industrial research and development. *Mailing Add:* 311 Floral Park Savoy IL 61874

MILLER, WADE ELLIOTT, II, b Los Angeles, Calif, Oct 20, 32; m 60; c 3. VERTEBRATE PALEONTOLOGY, GEOLOGY. *Educ:* Brigham Young Univ, BS, 60; Univ Ariz, MS, 63; Univ Calif, Berkeley, PhD(paleont), 68. *Prof Exp:* Instr geol & phys sci, Santa Ana Col, 61-64; instr geol, Fullerton Jr Col, 68-71; ASSOC PROF GEOL, BRIGHAM YOUNG UNIV, 71- *Concurrent Pos:* Geologist & paleontologist, Los Angeles County Mus, 69- *Mem:* Soc Vert Paleont; Paleont Soc; Soc Mammal. *Res:* Pleistocene mammals of Southern California; fossil vertebrates of Utah, especially mammals, late Cenozoic vertebrates of Mexico. *Mailing Add:* Dept of Zool Brigham Young Univ Provo UT 84601

MILLER, WALLACE E, b Winona, Minn, Oct 24, 19; m; c 2. ORTHOPEDIC SURGERY. *Educ:* Wabash Col, AB, 41; Harvard Med Sch, MD, 44; Am Bd Orthop Surg, dipl, 54. *Prof Exp:* Chmn dept orthop, Jackson Mem Hosp, 57-71; PROF ORTHOP & REHAB, SCH MED, UNIV MIAMI, 57- *Concurrent Pos:* Prof orthop & chief orthop sect, Miami Vet Hosp, 72-79; examr, Am Bd Orthop Surg, 55-79. *Mem:* AMA; Am Acad Orthop Surg. *Res:* Orthopedics. *Mailing Add:* Univ of Miami Sch of Med PO Box 016960 Miami FL 33101

MILLER, WALTER BERNARD, III, b Pensacola, Fla, Mar 10, 42; m 64. PHYSICAL CHEMISTRY. *Educ:* Univ Calif, Los Angeles, BS, 63; Harvard Univ, PhD(phys chem), 69. *Prof Exp:* Asst prof, 68-73, LECTR CHEM, UNIV ARIZ, 73- *Res:* Chemical kinetics in crossed molecular beams. *Mailing Add:* Dept of Chem Univ of Ariz Tucson AZ 85721

MILLER, WALTER CHARLES, b Philadelphia, Pa, Dec 9, 18; m 44; c 7. EXPERIMENTAL NUCLEAR PHYSICS. *Educ:* St Joseph's Col, Pa, BS, 40; Univ Notre Dame, MS, 42, PhD(physics), 48. *Prof Exp:* Asst physics, Univ Notre Dame, 40-43, instr & asst, Manhattan Proj, 43-44; res assoc, Los Alamos Sci Lab, 44-45; from instr to assoc prof, 45-64, PROF PHYSICS, UNIV NOTRE DAME, 64-, CHMN DEPT, 75- *Mem:* Am Phys Soc. *Res:* Electrostatic accelerators; electronics; energy levels; x-rays; nuclear excitation. *Mailing Add:* Dept of Physics Univ of Notre Dame Notre Dame IN 46556

MILLER, WALTER E, b New York, NY, Jan 28, 14; m 43; c 3. PHYSICAL CHEMISTRY. *Educ:* City Col New York, BS, 35, ChE, 36; NY Univ, PhD(chem), 41. *Prof Exp:* Instr, 41-42 & 46-49, from asst prof to assoc prof, 49-66, PROF CHEM, CITY COL NEW YORK, 66- *Concurrent Pos:* Asst instr, NY Univ, 41-42; mem, US Army Chem Corps Adv Coun, 64-69. *Mem:* AAAS; Am Chem Soc; NY Acad Sci. *Res:* Cryogenics; rocket fuels; photo-sensitization; atomic physics; design of radio transmitters and receivers; high polymers; ion exchange; water demineralization; electrolytic treatment of water. *Mailing Add:* Dept of Chem City Col of New York New York NY 10031

MILLER, WALTER PETER, b Dickinson, NDak, Jan 7, 32; m 60; c 7. ORGANIC POLYMER CHEMISTRY. *Educ:* Univ Minn, BA, 53, PhD, 57. *Prof Exp:* Fel, Max Planck Inst Coal Res, Ger, 57-58; proj chemist, Union Carbide Chem Co, 58-64, group leader, 65-75, develop assoc, 76-77, ASSOC DIR, CHEM DIV, UNION CARBIDE CORP, 77- *Concurrent Pos:* Fulbright travel grant, 57-58. *Mem:* Am Chem Soc. *Res:* Emulsion polymerization; organic chemistry. *Mailing Add:* 1207 Shady Way South Charleston WV 25309

MILLER, WARREN FLETCHER, JR, b Chicago, Ill, Mar 17, 43; m 69; c 2. NUCLEAR ENGINEERING. *Educ:* US Mil Acad, BS, 64; Northwestern Univ, MS, 70, PhD(nuclear eng), 73. *Prof Exp:* Asst prof, Northwestern Univ, 72-74; staff mem, Los Alamos Sci Lab, 74-75, sect leader, 75, group leader nuclear eng, 75-78, dep assoc dir, 80-81, assoc dir, 81-82. *Concurrent Pos:* Consult, Sargent & Lundy Engrs & Argonne Nat Lab, 73-74; NSF res grant, 73-74; vis prof, Howard Univ, 79-80; mem tech adv comt, NMex Energy Res & Develop Inst. *Mem:* Nat Tech Asn; Am Nuclear Soc. *Res:* Neutral and charged particle transport theory; numerical analysis; radioactive waste management; radiation shielding. *Mailing Add:* Los Alamos Sci Lab MS 269 Los Alamos NM 87545

MILLER, WARREN JAMES, b New Kensington, Pa, Oct 12, 31; m 58; c 3. PHYSICAL CHEMISTRY. *Educ:* Pa State Univ, BS, 57; Fla State Univ, PhD(chem), 62. *Prof Exp:* Res chemist, 62-64, sr res chemist, 64-69, RES ASSOC, RES LABS, EASTMAN KODAK CO, 69- *Mem:* Am Chem Soc. *Res:* Photographic theory; colloid and surface chemistry. *Mailing Add:* Eastman Kodak Co Res Labs 343 State St Rochester NY 14650

MILLER, WARREN VICTOR, b Rochester, NY, Oct 4, 44; m 67; c 3. INORGANIC CHEMISTRY, ANALYTICAL CHEMISTRY. *Educ:* Clarkson Col Technol, BS, 66; State Univ NY Binghamton, PhD(chem), 70. *Prof Exp:* Res assoc inorg chem, Clarkson Col Technol, 70-72; chief chemist, Alpha Anal Labs, 72-74; VPRES, SPEX INDUSTS INC, 74- *Mem:* Am Chem Soc. *Res:* Inorganic synthesis; purification of elements and their compounds; platinum group metal chemistry. *Mailing Add:* Spex Industs Inc 3880 Park Ave Metuchen NJ 08840

MILLER, WATKINS WILFORD, b Hawthorne, Calif, Feb 21, 47; m 69; c 2. SOIL FERTILITY, WATER POLLUTION. *Educ:* Calif Polytech State Univ, BS, 68; Univ Calif, PhD, 73. *Prof Exp:* Agr chemist, Soil Testing Serv, Nelson Labs, Stockton, Calif, 69-70; res asst soil water repellency, Univ Calif, Riverside, 70-73; exten specialist natural resource develop, 73-75, asst prof, 75-78, asst soil & water scientist, 77-81, ASSOC PLANT, SOIL & WATER SCIENTIST, UNIV NEV, RENO, 81- *Mem:* Am Soc Agron; Soil Sci Soc Am; AAAS. *Res:* Soil fertility analysis and calibration; water quality of irrigation return flows; rural development resource inventories; soil and water testing service for Nevada residents; water management, especially Humbolt River system. *Mailing Add:* Div of Plant Soil & Water Sci Univ of Nev Col of Agr Reno NV 89557

MILLER, WAYNE L(EROY), b Salem, Ore, Dec 6, 24. NUCLEAR & CHEMICAL ENGINEERING. *Educ:* Ore State Univ, BS, 50; Univ Tulsa, MS, 54. *Prof Exp:* Chem engr, US Bur Mines, Ore, 50-52; instr & asst prof chem & petrol refinery eng, Univ Tulsa, 54-57; chem engr, Esso Res & Eng Co, NJ, 57-58; asst prof nuclear eng, 61-75, ASST PROF CHEM ENG, UNIV NEV, RENO, 75- *Mem:* Am Chem Soc; Am Inst Chem Engrs; Am Soc Eng Educ. *Res:* Radiation effects on chemical systems. *Mailing Add:* Dept of Chem Eng Univ of Nev Reno NV 89557

MILLER, WILBUR HOBART, b Boston, Mass, Feb 15, 15; m 41; c 3. ORGANIC CHEMISTRY, BIOCHEMISTRY. *Educ:* Univ NH, BS, 36, MS, 38; Columbia Univ, PhD(chem), 42. *Prof Exp:* From asst to instr chem, Univ NH, 36-38; asst, Columbia Univ, 38-39, statutory asst, 39-40; res chemist, Stamford Res Lab, Am Cyanamid Co, 41-49, tech rep, Washington, DC, 49-53, dir custom sales, Lederle Labs, 53-54, dir indust appln, Fine Chem Div, 54-55, dir food indust develop, Farm & Home Div, 55-57; tech dir prod for agr, Cyanamid Int, 57-60; sr scientist, Dunlap & Assocs, Inc, Conn, 60-66; coordr new prod develop, 66-67, mgr commercial res, 67-69, DIR DIVERSIFICATION DEVELOP, CELANESE CORP, NEW YORK, 69- *Honors & Awards:* Am Design Award, 48. *Mem:* Fel AAAS; fel Am Inst Chemists; Am Chem Soc; Inst Food Technologists; Soc Chem Indust Am (treas, 80-). *Res:* Agricultural chemicals; animal health and food industry products; chemotherapy; enzyme, organic and general industrial chemistry. *Mailing Add:* 19 Crestview Ave Stamford CT 06907

MILLER, WILLARD, JR, b Ft Wayne, Ind, Sept 17, 37; m 65; c 2. APPLIED MATHEMATICS, MATHEMATICAL PHYSICS. *Educ:* Univ Chicago, SB, 58; Univ Calif, Berkeley, PhD(appl math), 63. *Prof Exp:* NSF fel, Courant Inst, NY Univ, 63-64, vis mem, 64-65; from asst prof to assoc prof, 65-72, PROF MATH, UNIV MINN, MINNEAPOLIS, 72-, HEAD, SCH MATH, 78- *Concurrent Pos:* Vis mem, Ctr Math Res, Univ Montreal, 73-74; assoc ed, J Math Physics, 73-75 & Applicable Anal, 78-; managing ed, J Math Anal, 75-81. *Mem:* Am Math Soc; Soc Indust & Appl Math. *Res:* Applications of group theory to special functions; separation of variables. *Mailing Add:* Sch of Math Univ of Minn Minneapolis MN 55455

MILLER, WILLIAM, b New York, NY, Sept 1, 22; m 57; c 3. EXPERIMENTAL SOLID STATE PHYSICS. *Educ:* City Col New York, BBA, 43; Univ Pa, PhD(physics), 48. *Prof Exp:* Physicist, Nat Bur Standards, 48-56; from asst prof to assoc prof, 57-67, PROF PHYSICS, CITY COL NEW YORK, 67- *Concurrent Pos:* Opers analyst, Opers Res Off, Johns Hopkins Univ, 52-53; sr physicist & consult, Am Mach & Foundry Co, 56- *Mem:* AAAS; Am Phys Soc; Am Asn Physics Teachers. *Res:* Noise theory; electromagnetic waves; x-rays; solid state. *Mailing Add:* Dept of Physics City Col of New York New York NY 10031

MILLER, WILLIAM ALFONSO, b Portland, Ore, Mar 16, 12; m 38; c 6. PHYSICS. *Educ:* Ore State Col, BS, 32, MS, 36; Purdue Univ, PhD(physics), 41. *Prof Exp:* Instr physics, Univ Ore, 36-37; asst, Purdue Univ, 37-39; res assoc, Radiation Lab, Mass Inst Technol, 41-42; res & design engr, RCA Labs, 42-61; sr staff scientist, Elec Syst Div, Fairchild-Hiller Corp, 61-65 & Radiometrics Div, Polarad Electronics Corp, 65-67; consult, Sanders Assocs, 67-68; staff scientist, Loral Electronic Systs, 68-69, chief scientist, 69-74; DISPLAY CONSULT, 74- *Mem:* Am Phys Soc; Am Astron Soc; Am Geophys Union; Soc Photo-Optical Instrument Engrs; sr mem Inst Elec & Electronics Engrs. *Res:* New semiconducting materials; radio transmitter and antenna design; improvement of frequency stability of radio transmitters; special electron tubes; uranium and thorium fission; radio propagation; solar physics; communication systems design; satellite systems, precision radar and optical systems engineering; special CRT display design. *Mailing Add:* 9 Dogwood Lane Miller Place NY 11764

MILLER, WILLIAM ALFRED, physical metallurgy, see previous edition

MILLER, WILLIAM ANTON, b Cedar, Mich, Apr 16, 35; m 60; c 4. MATHEMATICS EDUCATION. *Educ:* Mich State Univ, BS, 56, MAT, 61; Univ Ill, Urbana, MA, 63; Univ Wis, Madison, PhD(math educ), 68. *Prof Exp:* Teacher, Sunfield Community Schs, 56-60, Oak Park Schs, 60-61 & Waverly Schs, 61-62; asst prof math educ, Wis State Univ, Whitewater, 65-67, assoc prof math, 67-68; assoc prof, 68-71, PROF MATH, CENT MICH UNIV, 71- *Mem:* Math Asn Am. *Res:* Learning theory as it relates to mathematics. *Mailing Add:* 407 E Grand Ave Mt Pleasant MI 48858

MILLER, WILLIAM B, b Tipp City, Ohio, Mar 6, 17; m 39; c 3. MECHANICAL & AERONAUTICAL ENGINEERING. *Educ:* Purdue Univ, BSME, 39. *Prof Exp:* Jr engr, Bendix Aviation Corp, 39-40; jr engr, USAF, 40-42, asst engr, 42-43, assoc engr, 43-44, aeronaut engr, 44-46, sr engr, 46-48, chief test unit struct, Wright Air Develop Ctr, 48-55, asst chief struct, Systs Command, 55-60, chief struct div, Systs Eng Group, 60-76, tech dir airframe subsysts eng, Aeronaut Systs Div, 67-76; CONSULT ENG, 76- *Concurrent Pos:* Mem, NASA Res Adv Comt Aircraft Struct, 52-; mem struct & mat panel, Adv Group Aerospace Res & Develop, NATO, 55-, dept chmn, 65- *Mem:* Assoc fel Am Inst Aeronaut & Astronaut. *Res:* Aerospace structures and their testing, design, requirements, loads and dynamics. *Mailing Add:* 521 Earnshaw Dr Dayton OH 45429

MILLER, WILLIAM BRUNNER, b Bethlehem, Pa, July 27, 23; m 48; c 4. MATHEMATICS. *Educ:* Lehigh Univ, BS, 47, MA, 55, PhD(math), 62. *Prof Exp:* Elec engr, Western Elec Co, Inc, 47-49; engr, Laros Textiles Co, 50-53; prof math, Moravian Col, 53-62; assoc prof, 63-80, PROF MATH, WORCESTER POLYTECH INST, 80- *Concurrent Pos:* Instr, Lehigh Univ, 59-60. *Mem:* Math Asn Am; Soc Indust & Appl Math. *Res:* Separation and oscillation theorems of linear differential equations. *Mailing Add:* Dept of Math Worcester Polytech Inst Worcester MA 01609

MILLER, WILLIAM ELDON, b McAllen, Tex, July 13, 30; m 78; c 4. FOREST ENTOMOLOGY. *Educ:* La State Univ, BS, 50; Ohio State Univ, MS, 51, PhD(entom), 55; Mich State Univ, MS, 61. *Prof Exp:* WGer Govt fel, Univ Gottingen, 56-57; entomologist, 56-64, prin insect ecologist, 64-80, CHIEF INSECT ECOLOGIST, US FOREST SERV, 80- *Concurrent Pos:* Ed, Forest Sci, 75; adj prof entom, Univ Minn, Twin Cities, 76- *Mem:* Entom Soc Am; Soc Am Foresters; Lepidop Soc. *Res:* Population dynamics; insect control techniques; taxonomy of Microlepidoptera; energetics of forest ecosystems; causes of insect outbreak. *Mailing Add:* NCent Forest Exp Sta 1992 Fowell Ave St Paul MN 55108

MILLER, WILLIAM EUGENE, b Longmont, Colo, Mar 3, 16; m 46; c 3. AUDIOLOGY. *Educ:* Univ Wichita, BS, 40, MA, 47; Northwestern Univ, PhD(audiol), 50. *Prof Exp:* Audiologist & asst dir, Inst Logopedics, Wichita, 49-65; actg dept chmn, 65-68, ASSOC PROF, DEPT COMMUNICATIVE DIS & SCI, WICHITA STATE UNIV, 49- *Mem:* Am Speech & Hearing Asn; Acad Rehab Audiol; Am Audiol Soc. *Res:* Procedures to improve aural rehabilitation and communication among aging adults. *Mailing Add:* Dept Communicative Dis & Sci Wichita State Univ Wichita KS 67208

MILLER, WILLIAM FRANKLIN, b Stone Creek, Ohio, Jan 16, 20; m 42, 58; c 5. MEDICINE. *Educ:* Wittenberg Univ, BA, 42; Case Western Reserve Univ, MD, 45; Am Bd Internal Med, dipl, 56. *Prof Exp:* Intern, City Hosp, Cleveland, Ohio, 45-46; resident med, neurol & radiol, Dayton Vet Admin Hosp, 46-48; resident med, Dallas Vet Admin Hosp, Tex, 48-51; clin instr, 51-53, from asst prof to assoc prof, 53-67, PROF MED, UNIV TEX HEALTH SCI CTR DALLAS, 67- *Concurrent Pos:* Dir cardio-respiratory lab, McKinney Vet Admin Hosp, Tex, 51-53; dir pulmonary div, Parkland Mem Hosp & Woodlawn Hosps, 53-67; dir, Pulmonary Div, Methodist Hosp, 67-; consult, Surgeon Gen, Lackland Air Force Hosp, 59-72, & Brooke Army Hosp, San Antonio, 61-71; consult, US Surgeon Gen, Comt Health Aspects Tobacco, 64-65; Parkland Mem, Vet Admin, St Paul, Baylor, Methodist & Presby Hosps, Dallas; consult chronic pulmonary dis sect, NIH, 65-67, task force respiratory dis, Nat Heart & Lung Inst, 71 & comt clin training physicians assts, Sch Allied Health Professions, Univ Tex, 72; chmn med adv bd, Am Asn Inhalation Ther; mem med adv bd, Cystic Fibrosis Found; med ed, Respiratory Care, 66- *Honors & Awards:* Med Movie Award, Am Col Chest Physicians, 67. *Mem:* AAAS; Am Thoracic Soc; fel Am Col Chest Physicians; Am Fedn Clin Res; Soc Critical Care Med. *Res:* Clinical pulmonary asthma; chronic bronchitis and emphysema. *Mailing Add:* Pulmonary Div Methodist Hosp Dallas Box 225999 Dallas TX 75265

MILLER, WILLIAM FREDERICK, b Vincennes, Ind, Nov 19, 25; m 49; c 1. COMPUTER SCIENCE, ACADEMIC ADMINISTRATION. *Educ:* Purdue Univ, BS, 49, MS, 51, PhD(physics, math), 56. *Hon Degrees:* DSc, Purdue Univ, 72. *Prof Exp:* Assoc physicist, Argonne Nat Lab, 56-59, dir appl math div, 59-64; vpres & provost, 71-78, PROF COMPUT SCI, STANFORD UNIV, 65-, HERBERT HOOVER PROF PUB & PVT MGT, GRAD SCH BUS, 79- *Concurrent Pos:* Vis prof, Purdue Univ, 62-63; prof lectr, Univ Chicago, 62-64; mem math & comput sci res adv comt, AEC & US deleg study group digital technol, Europ Nuclear Energy technol, Europ Nuclear Energy Agency, 62-; consult, Argonne Nat Lab, 65-68 & Comput Usage Corp, 69-72; mem comput sci & eng bd, Nat Acad Sci, 68-71; mem sci info coun, NSF, 71-72; dir, Boothe Invest Corp, 72-, Varian Assocs Inc, 73-, Fireman's Fund Ins Co, 77-, Annual Reviews Inc, 77- & Resolve Ctr Environ Conflict Resolution, 78-; mem educ adv bd, John Simon Guggenheim Mem Found, 76- *Mem:* AAAS; Am Phys Soc; Am Math Soc; Asn Comput Mach; Inst Elec & Electronics Engrs. *Res:* Computer science and applications; computational physics; nuclear scattering; computing machinery; university administration; computers in management; socio-economic models for planning; policy and planning for science and technology; international science and technology. *Mailing Add:* Stanford Univ Stanford CA 94305

MILLER, WILLIAM HENRY, b Baltimore, Md, Aug 7, 26; m 57; c 3. BIOLOGY. *Educ:* Haverford Col, BA, 49; Johns Hopkins Univ, MD, 54. *Prof Exp:* Intern med, Baltimore City Hosps, 54-55; res assoc, Rockefeller Inst, 55-58, asst prof, 58-64; assoc prof physiol & ophthalmol, 64-69, PROF OPHTHALMOL, PHYSIOL & VISUAL SCI, SCH MED, YALE UNIV, 69- *Res:* Anatomy and physiology of invertebrate eyes. *Mailing Add:* Dept of Ophthal & Vis Sci Yale Univ Sch of Med New Haven CT 06510

MILLER, WILLIAM HUGHES, b Kosciusko, Miss, Mar 16, 41; m 66; c 2. CHEMICAL PHYSICS. *Educ:* Ga Inst Technol, BS, 63; Harvard Univ, AM, 64, PhD(chem physics), 67. *Prof Exp:* NATO fel, Univ Freiburg, 67-68; Soc Fels jr fel, Harvard Univ, 68-69; from asst prof to assoc prof, 69-74, PROF CHEM, UNIV CALIF, BERKELEY, 74-, PRIN INVESTR, INORG MAT RES DIV, LAWRENCE BERKELEY LAB, 69- *Concurrent Pos:* Sloan Found fel, 70; Guggenheim Mem fel, 75-76; fel, Churchill Col, Cambridge Univ, 75-76; Miller prof, Miller Inst Sci, Univ Calif, Berkeley. *Honors & Awards:* Int Acad Quantum Molecular Sci Ann Prize, Paris, 74. *Res:* Quantum theory of atomic and molecular collisions; semiclassical theories and quantum effects in inelastic and reactive scattering of atoms and molecules; collisional transfer of electronic energy. *Mailing Add:* Dept of Chem Univ of Calif Berkeley CA 94720

MILLER, WILLIAM JACK, b Nathans Creek, NC, Feb 7, 27; m 50; c 4. ANIMAL NUTRITION. *Educ:* NC State Col, BS, 48, MS, 50; Univ Wis, PhD(animal nutrit), 52. *Prof Exp:* Wis Alumni Res Found asst, Univ Wis, 50-52; res assoc dairy physiol, Univ Ill, 52-53; from asst prof to prof, 53-64, ALUMNI FOUND DISTINGUISHED PROF DAIRY SCI, UNIV GA, 73- *Honors & Awards:* Nutrit Res Award, Am Feed Mfrs Asn, 63; Excellence in Res Award, Sigma Xi, 69; Borden Award, Am Dairy Sci Asn, 71; Gustav Bohstedt Mineral Res Award, Am Soc Animal Sci, 71; Morrison Award, Am Soc Animal Sci, 80. *Mem:* AAAS; Soc Environ Geochem & Health; Am Inst Nutrit; Am Dairy Sci Asn; Am Soc Animal Sci. *Res:* Zinc, manganese, cadmium, nickel and mercury nutrition and metabolism; mineral nutrition of animals; ruminant nutrition; forage evaluation and utilization. *Mailing Add:* Dept of Animal & Dairy Sci Univ of Ga Athens GA 30602

MILLER, WILLIAM JOHN, physical chemistry, see previous edition

MILLER, WILLIAM KNIGHT, b Salisbury, NC, Nov 14, 18; m 46; c 2. ANALYTICAL CHEMISTRY. *Educ:* Catawba Col, AB, 40; Univ NC, PhD(anal chem), 50. *Prof Exp:* Chemist, Carbide & Carbon Chem Co, Oak Ridge Nat Lab, 50-52; anal supvr, S C Johnson & Son, Inc, 52-80; RETIRED. *Mem:* Am Chem Soc; Soc Appl Spectros. *Res:* Infrared spectrophotometry; gas chromatography. *Mailing Add:* 567 A Fairways Circle Ocala FL 32672

MILLER, WILLIAM LAUBACH, b Charlottesville, Va, Apr 9, 43; m 68; c 2. BIOCHEMISTRY, REPRODUCTIVE ENDOCRINOLOGY. *Educ:* Bucknell Univ, BS, 65; Cornell Univ, M Nut Sci, 67, PhD(biochem), 70. *Prof Exp:* Res biochemist, Walter Reed Army Inst Res, 70-73; Rockefeller fel, Univ Wis-Madison, 73-76; asst prof, 76-80, ASSOC PROF BIOCHEM, NC STATE UNIV, 80- *Concurrent Pos:* Prin investr, NIH grant, 77-86. *Mem:* AAAS; Am Chem Soc; Endocrine Soc. *Res:* Control of gonadotropin synthesis and release; steroid (especially estrogen) hormone action; peptide hormone action, pituitary culture, protein synthesis and RNA characterization. *Mailing Add:* Dept Biochem NC State Univ Raleigh NC 27650

MILLER, WILLIAM LAWRENCE, b Medford, Ore, May 12, 37; m 61; c 2. MINERAL RESEARCH. *Educ:* Univ Calif, Davis, BS, 63, MS, 67. *Prof Exp:* Assoc chemist nitroplasticizers develop, Aerojet Gen Corp, Gen Tire & Rubber Co, 63-64; chemist minerals res, Bur Mines, 66-70, prog analyst minerals progs, US Dept Interior, 70-71, staff phys scientist metall res, Bur Mines, 71-77, chief, Div Metall, 77-79, CHIEF, RES DIRECTORATE

STAFF, BUR MINES, US DEPT INTERIOR, 79- *Concurrent Pos:* Alt mem coord comt mat res & develop, Fed Coun Sci & Technol, 69. *Mem:* Am Chem Soc. *Res:* Development of new and improved technologies that will result in more efficient production and processing of minerals, more healthful and safer working conditions for workers in the mineral industries and that are more compatible with a quality environment. *Mailing Add:* US Dept Interior Bur Mines 2401 E St NW Washington DC 20241

MILLER, WILLIAM LLOYD, b Waterman, Ill, Mar 22, 35; m 57; c 4. AGRICULTURAL ECONOMICS. *Educ:* Univ Ill, Urbana, BS, 57, MS, 60; Mich State Univ, PhD(agr econ), 65. *Prof Exp:* from asst prof to assoc prof, Agr Econ, Purdue Univ, 65-76, prof, 76-81; DEPT HEAD, AGR ECON, UNIV NEBR, LINCOLN, 82- *Mem:* Am Agr Econ Asn; Am Econ Asn; Am Water Resources Asn. *Res:* Resource economics. *Mailing Add:* Dept Agr Econ Univ Nebr Lincoln NE 68588

MILLER, WILLIAM LOUIS, b Springville, Utah, June 28, 25; m 52; c 3. BIOCHEMISTRY. *Educ:* Brigham Young Univ, BS, 48; Univ Wis, MS, 50, PhD(biochem), 52. *Prof Exp:* Asst biochem, Univ Wis, 48-52; res scientist pharmacol, 52-59, res assoc endocrinol, 59-68, sr res scientist, dept metab dis res, 68-77, RES ASSOC, DEPT FERTILITY RES, UPJOHN CO, 77- *Mem:* Am Soc Pharmacol & Exp Therapeut; Soc Exp Biol & Med. *Res:* Fate studies on drugs, especially metabolic detoxification of drugs by mammals; skin sterols and azo-dye carcinogenesis; diabetes; hypoglycemic agents; biochemistry of hormone action; lipid metabolism; reproductive physiology; biotelemetry techniques. *Mailing Add:* Upjohn Co 301 Henrietta Kalamazoo MI 49001

MILLER, WILLIAM MARTIN, organic chemistry, see previous edition

MILLER, WILLIAM RALPH, b Seneca, Pa, Nov 5, 17; m 45. MECHANICAL ENGINEERING. *Educ:* Cleveland State Univ, BME, 49; Case Inst Technol, MSME, 55; Pa State Univ, PhD(eng mech), 65. *Prof Exp:* Instr eng, Evansville Col, 49-50; engr, Trabon Eng Corp, Ohio, 51-54; asst prof mech eng, Case Inst Technol, 56-60; sr eng specialist, TRW, Inc, Ohio, 62-63; chmn dept mech eng, 64-70, PROF MECH ENG, UNIV TOLEDO, 64- *Concurrent Pos:* Res engr, Thompson Prod, Inc, Ohio, 54-56. *Mem:* Am Soc Mech Engrs; Soc Exp Stress Anal. *Res:* Metal fatigue. *Mailing Add:* Dept Mech Eng Univ Toledo Toledo OH 43606

MILLER, WILLIAM REYNOLDS, JR, b Philadelphia, Pa, Dec 29, 39. POLYMER CHEMISTRY, PHYSICAL CHEMISTRY. *Educ:* Princeton Univ, AB, 61; Columbia Univ, MA, 62, PhD(chem), 65. *Prof Exp:* Fel, Wash Univ, 65-66; proj scientist plastics, Koppers Co, Inc, 68-74, proj scientist plastics, Arco/Polymers, Inc, 74-78; res asst prof, Dept Metall & Mat Eng, Univ Pa, 78-79; lectr chem, Chatham Col, 79-80; SR CHEMIST, TREMCO, INC, 80- *Mem:* Am Chem Soc; Soc Rheol; Soc Plastics Eng. *Res:* Rheology, especially plastics solids and melts; polymer evaluation; dielectric properties of plastics; electron spin resonance spectroscopy of organic free radicals in solution. *Mailing Add:* Tremco Inc 10701 Shaker Blvd Cleveland OH 44104

MILLER, WILLIAM RIEDEL, organic chemistry, see previous edition

MILLER, WILLIAM ROBERT, b Norwalk, Ohio, Mar 11, 43; m 64; c 3. GEOCHEMISTRY. *Educ:* Ohio State Univ, BCE, 68; Univ Wyo, MS, 72, PhD(geol), 74. *Prof Exp:* Prod engr, Mobil Oil Corp, 68-69; teaching asst geochem, Univ Wyo, 69-72; GEOLOGIST, BR EXPLOR RES, US GEOL SURV, 74- *Mem:* Asn Explor Geochemists; Sigma Xi. *Res:* Low temperature geochemistry, particularly reactions involving natural waters and solid phases; weathering and controls on the partitioning of trace elements between natural waters and solid phases; hydrogeochemical exploration; geochemical exploration. *Mailing Add:* US Geol Surv Mail Stop 973 Fed Ctr Bldg 25 Lakewood CO 80225

MILLER, WILLIAM ROBERT, JR, b Baltimore, Md, June 17, 34; m 58; c 3. ELECTRON PHYSICS, SOLID STATE PHYSICS. *Educ:* Gettysburg Col, BA, 56; Univ Del, MA, 61, PhD(physics), 65. *Prof Exp:* Engr, Westinghouse Elec Corp, 58-59, sr engr, 65-67; teaching asst, Univ Del, 59-61; engr, RCA Corp, 67-68; instr, 68, asst prof, 68-76, ASSOC PROF PHYSICS, PA STATE UNIV, 76- *Concurrent Pos:* Instr physics, York Col Pa, 69- *Mem:* Inst Elec & Electronics Engrs; Am Phys Soc; Am Asn Physics Teachers. *Res:* Solid state and semiconductor devices; plasmonexcitation in solids. *Mailing Add:* 1029 Preston Rd Lancaster PA 17601

MILLER, WILLIAM TAYLOR, b Winston-Salem, NC, Aug 24, 11; m 51. ORGANIC CHEMISTRY, FLUORINE CHEMISTRY. *Educ:* Duke Univ, AB, 32, PhD(org chem), 35. *Prof Exp:* Postdoctoral appt, Stanford Univ, 35-36; from instr to assoc prof, 36-47, prof, 47-77, EMER PROF CHEM, CORNELL UNIV, 77- *Concurrent Pos:* Off investr & consult, Nat Defense Res Comt, 41-43; mem fluorocarbon adv comt, Manhattan Proj, 43-45; head fluorocarbon res, SAM Labs, Manhattan Proj, Columbia Univ & Carbide & Carbon Chem Corp, 43-46; consult var govt & indust labs, 47-; consult, M W Kellogg Co, 47-57, E I du Pont de Nemours & Co, Inc, 57-77. *Honors & Awards:* Award for Creative Work in Fluorine Chem, Am Chem Soc, 74. *Mem:* Fel AAAS; Am Chem Soc; Royal Soc Chem. *Res:* Chemistry of carbon-fluorine and related highly halogenated compounds; chemistry of haloorgano-metallic compounds. *Mailing Add:* Baker Lab Dept of Chem Cornell Univ Ithaca NY 14853

MILLER, WILLIAM THEODORE, b Belleville, Ill, Feb 8, 25. ORGANIC CHEMISTRY, BIOLOGICAL CHEMISTRY. *Educ:* St Louis Univ, AB, 47, BS, 51; St Mary's Col, Kans, STL, 56; Univ Calif, Berkeley, PhD(chem), 61. *Prof Exp:* Teacher, Marquette Univ High Sch, 51-52; asst prof, 61-66, assoc prof chem, 66-75, chmn dept, 69-75, dir div natural sci & math, 75-77, PROF CHEM, REGIS COL, COLO, 75- *Concurrent Pos:* Res grants, NIH, 62-, Am Chem Soc Petrol Res Fund, 63- & NSF, 64; res fel, Lab Nuclear Med & Radiation Biol, Univ Calif, Los Angeles, 67-69; vis prof, Sogang Univ, Korea, 78-79. *Mem:* AAAS; Am Chem Soc; Sigma Xi. *Res:* Comparative study of lipids isolated from in vitro and in vivo grown tubercle bacillus; synthetic organic chemistry; polynuclear aromatic hydrocarbons. *Mailing Add:* Dept Chem Regis Col W 50th & Lowell Blvd Denver CO 80221

MILLER, WILLIAM WADD, III, b Starkville, Miss, Oct 4, 32; m 57; c 2. REPRODUCTIVE PHYSIOLOGY. *Educ:* Miss State Univ, BS, 54, MS, 58; Auburn Univ, PhD(reprod physiol), 62. *Prof Exp:* Assoc prof biol, Howard Col, 62-67; assoc prof, 67-81, PROF BIOL, NORTHEAST LA UNIV, 81- *Concurrent Pos:* Sigma Xi grant, 65-66. *Mem:* AAAS; Soc Study Reproduction; Am Soc Zoologists. *Res:* Physiology of reproduction; endocrinology. *Mailing Add:* Dept of Biol Northeast La Univ Monroe LA 71201

MILLER, WILLIAM WALTER, b Oakland, Calif, Sept 17, 41; m 63; c 2. BIOCHEMISTRY. *Educ:* Univ Calif, Berkeley, BS, 63; Calif Inst Technol, PhD(biochem), 67. *Prof Exp:* Res chemist, E I du Pont de Nemours & Co, 67-73; appln chemist, 73-76, MGR ADVAN DEVELOP, BECKMAN INSTRUMENTS, INC, 76- *Mem:* AAAS; Am Chem Soc; Am Asn Clin Chemists; NY Acad Sci. *Res:* Clinical chemistry methods development. *Mailing Add:* 5046 Lupine St Yorba Linda CA 92686

MILLER, WILLIAM WEAVER, b Winchester, Va, Sept 1, 33; m 58; c 2. PEDIATRICS, CARDIOLOGY. *Educ:* Va Mil Inst, BA, 54; Univ Pa, MD, 58; Am Bd Pediat, dipl, 66, cert pediat cardiol, 70. *Prof Exp:* Intern, Univ Pa Hosp, 59; intern, Children's Hosp Philadelphia, 62-63; instr pediat, Med Sch, Univ Pa, 63-65; instr, Harvard Med Sch, 65-66; assoc, Med Sch, Univ Pa, 66-69, asst prof, 69; assoc prof pediat, Univ Tex Health Sci Ctr, Dallas, & dir pediat cardiol div, Children's Med Ctr, 69-76; MEM FAC, MED COL VA, 76- *Concurrent Pos:* Fel pediat cardiol, Children's Hosp, Philadelphia, 64-65, res fel, 66-67; assoc cardiologist & assoc dir cardiovasc labs, 67-69; res fel pediat cardiol, Children's Hosp Med Ctr, Boston, 65-66. *Honors & Awards:* Am Acad Pediat Award, 69. *Mem:* Am Acad Pediat; Am Heart Asn. *Res:* Oxygen transport; myocardial chemistry; congenital heart disease. *Mailing Add:* Med Col Va MCV Sta Box 291 Richmond VA 23298

MILLER, WILLIE, b Bolivar, Tenn, Aug 24, 42; m 61; c 1. PLANT SCIENCE, SOIL SCIENCE. *Educ:* Tenn State Univ, BS, 71, MS, 72; Univ Tenn, PhD(plant & soil sci), 76. *Prof Exp:* RES REP AGR CHEM, ELI LILLY & CO, 76- *Mem:* Soil Sci Soc Am; Weed Sci Soc Am. *Res:* Research and development of new agricultural chemicals; registered agricultural chemicals. *Mailing Add:* Eli Lilly & Co PO Box 3008 Omaha NE 68103

MILLER, WILLWAM ROBERT, b Arlington, Ala, Sept 1, 24; m 47; c 2. VIROLOGY, MICROBIOLOGY. *Educ:* Auburn Univ, DVM, 50, MS, 63; Purdue Univ, PhD(virol), 68; Am Bd Vet Pub Health, dipl, 73. *Prof Exp:* From instr to asst prof, 60-68, assoc prof microbiol, 68-71, ASSOC PROF PATHOL, SCH VET MED, AUBURN UNIV, 71- *Concurrent Pos:* Collabr, USDA, 61-65; Nat Inst Neurol Dis & Blindness spec fel, 65-67; consult virol, Kans State Univ-AID, India, 71. *Mem:* Am Vet Med Asn; Sigma Xi; Asn Am Vet Cols; Am Asn Food Hyg Vet; Am Soc Microbiol. *Res:* Pathogenesis of animal virus diseases, specifically respiratory and neurological diseases. *Mailing Add:* Dept Path & Parasitol Sch Vet Med Auburn Univ Auburn AL 36849

MILLER, WILMER GLENN, b Mt Orab, Ohio, Aug 28, 32. POLYMER CHEMISTRY. *Educ:* Capital Univ, BS, 54; Univ Wis, PhD(chem), 58. *Prof Exp:* Res fel chem, Harvard Univ, 58-59 & Univ Minn, 59-60; from asst prof to assoc prof, Univ Iowa, 60-67; assoc prof, 67-70, PROF CHEM, UNIV MINN, MINNEAPOLIS, 70- *Concurrent Pos:* Guggenheim fel, 64. *Mem:* Am Chem Soc. *Res:* Physical chemical studies of synthetic and biological polymers and suntactants; thermodynamics and dynamics of polymer liquid crystals; motion of polymers at or near an interface; suntactant microstructures. *Mailing Add:* Dept of Chem Univ of Minn Minneapolis MN 55455

MILLER, WILMER JAY, b Lawton, Okla, July 15, 25; m 52; c 2. IMMUNOLOGY, GENETICS. *Educ:* Univ Okla, BA, 48; Univ Wis, PhD(genetics, zool), 54. *Prof Exp:* Proj assoc immunogenetics, Univ Wis, 53-55; assoc specialist, Sch Vet Med, Univ Calif, 55-62, lectr, 56-57; ASSOC PROF GENETICS, IOWA STATE UNIV, 62- *Mem:* Fel AAAS; Am Inst Biol Sci; Genetics Soc Am; Am Genetic Asn; NY Acad Sci. *Res:* Immunogenetics of birds and bovines. *Mailing Add:* Dept of Genetics Iowa State Univ Ames IA 50011

MILLERO, FRANK JOSEPH, JR, b Greenville, Pa, Mar 16, 39; m 65; c 3. PHYSICAL CHEMISTRY. *Educ:* Ohio State Univ, BS, 61; Carnegie-Mellon Univ, 64, PhD(phys chem), 65. *Prof Exp:* Asst chem, Carnegie-Mellon Univ, 61-63, asst thermochem, 63-65, fel, 65; phys chemist, Esso Res & Eng Co, 65-66; res scientist, 66-68, from asst prof to assoc prof, 68-73, PROF CHEM, OCEANOG & PHYS CHEM, ROSENSTIEL SCH OF MARINE & ATMOSPHERIC SCI, UNIV MIAMI, 73- *Concurrent Pos:* Mem oceanog panel, NSF, 73-75; mem, SCOR Panel on Oceanog Standards, UNESCO, 75; vis prof, Inst di Ricerca sulle Acque, Rome, 79-80; mem ocean sci bd, Nat Acad Sci, 81- *Mem:* AAAS; Am Chem Soc; Am Geophys Union; Geochem Soc. *Res:* Solution thermodynamics; electrolyte solutions; thermochemistry; chemical oceanography; physical chemistry of aqueous solutions including seawater. *Mailing Add:* Rosenstiel Sch of Marine & Atmospheric Sci Univ of Miami Miami FL 33149

MILLER-STEVENS, LOUISE TERESA, biology, see previous edition

MILLET, MARION PAUL, human anatomy, see previous edition

MILLET, PETER J, b New York, NY, June 28, 40. NUCLEAR MAGNETIC RESONANCE. *Educ:* Rensselaer Polytech Inst, BS, 61; Syracuse Univ, MS, 63, PhD(physics), 69. *Prof Exp:* Asst prof, 68-74, assoc prof, 74-80, PROF PHYSICS, HAMILTON COL, 80- *Concurrent Pos:* Vis assoc prof, Cornell Univ, 80-81, fel, 81. *Mem:* Am Phys Soc; Am Asn Physics Teachers. *Res:* Theoretical physics including quantum mechanics of three body problem in Heisenberg model of a ferromagnet; experimental studies of luminescence in cadmium sulfide; nuclear magnetic resonance studies of magnetic coupling between liquid helium and susbstrate at low temperature. *Mailing Add:* Dept Physics Hamilton Col Clinton NY 13323

MILLETT, FRANCIS SPENCER, b Madison, Wis, Aug 2, 43; m 68. BIOCHEMISTRY. *Educ:* Univ Wis, BS, 65; Columbia Univ, PhD(chem physics), 70. *Prof Exp:* NIH fel biochem, Calif Inst Technol, 70-72; asst prof, 72-76, assoc prof, 76-80, PROF CHEM, UNIV ARK, FAYETTEVILLE, 80- *Mem:* Am Chem Soc (secy-treas, 73-75); Am Soc Biol Chem. *Res:* Interaction of proteins with biological membranes utilizing nuclear magnetic resonance methods; function of cytochrome C in mitochondria utilizing F-19 nuclear magnetic resonance methods. *Mailing Add:* Dept of Chem Univ of Ark Fayetteville AR 72701

MILLETT, KENNETH CARY, b Hustiford, Wis, Nov 16, 41. MATHEMATICS. *Educ:* Mass Inst Technol, BS, 63; Univ Wis-Madison, MS, 64, PhD(math), 67. *Prof Exp:* Instr math, Mass Inst Technol, 67-69; from asst prof to assoc prof, 69-78, PROF MATH, UNIV CALIF, SANTA BARBARA, 78- *Mem:* Am Math Soc; Math Asn Am. *Res:* Geometric and algebraic topology. *Mailing Add:* Dept of Math Univ of Calif Santa Barbara CA 93106

MILLETT, MERRILL ALBERT, b Lake Mills, Wis, Nov 17, 15; m 42; c 3. WOOD CHEMISTRY. *Educ:* Univ Wis, BA, 38, MA, 39, PhD(phys chem), 43. *Prof Exp:* Asst chemist, US Forest Prod Lab, 42-43, chemist, 43-77; RETIRED. *Res:* Modified woods; cellulose and wood chemistry; molecular properties of celluloses; chromatographic analysis of woods and pulps; cellulose and cellulose esters; characterization and chemical utilization of wood residues; kinetics of aging of wood and cellulose; wood and pulping residues as animal feedstuffs. *Mailing Add:* 322 N Hillside Terr Madison WI 53705

MILLETT, WALTER ELMER, b Hampton, Ill, July 26, 17; m 44. PHYSICS. *Educ:* Univ Fla, BS, 40, MS, 42; Harvard Univ, PhD(physics), 49. *Prof Exp:* Res assoc, Radiation Lab, Mass Inst Technol, 42-45; AEC fel, Calif Inst Technol, 49-50; from instr to asst prof, Univ Fla, 50-52; from asst prof to assoc prof, 52-61, PROF PHYSICS, UNIV TEX, AUSTIN, 61- *Mem:* Fel Am Phys Soc. *Res:* Positron decay; electron and ion optics; scintillation spectrometry. *Mailing Add:* Dept of Physics Univ of Tex Austin TX 78712

MILLETTE, CLARKE FRANCIS, b Bridgeport, Conn, Oct 22, 47. REPRODUCTIVE BIOLOGY, IMMUNOLOGY. *Educ:* Johns Hopkins Univ, BS, 69; Rockefeller Univ, PhD(biochem), 75. *Prof Exp:* Fel physiol, 75-77, ASST PROF ANAT, HARVARD MED SCH, 77- *Mem:* Am Soc Cell Biol; Soc Develop Biol. *Res:* Biochemistry and immunology of gametes and gametogenesis. *Mailing Add:* Lab Human Reprod & Reprod Biol Harvard Med Sch Boston MA 02115

MILLETTE, GERARD J F, b Montreal, Que, Feb 17, 21; m 45; c 5. SOIL CHEMISTRY. *Educ:* McGill Univ, BSc, 45, MSc, 48; Pa State Univ, PhD(agron), 55. *Prof Exp:* Jr pedologist, Can Dept Agr, Que, 45-49; sr pedologist, Ont, 49-53, officer-in-chg soil surv, NB, 53-61; proj mgr land & water surv, UN Spec Fund, Togo, Africa, 61-64; ASSOC PROF SOIL SCI, MacDONALD COL, McGILL UNIV, 64- *Concurrent Pos:* Mem, Nat Soil Surv Comt Can, 53-; indust consult. *Mem:* Agr Inst Can; Can Soil Sci Soc; Brit Soc Soil Sci; Int Soc Soil Sci. *Res:* Soil mapping and classification; interpretive surveys, land use, integrated area planning, land assessment; soil genesis, study of soil-plant-climate ecosystem. *Mailing Add:* Dept of Renewable Resources MacDonald Col of McGill Univ Ste Anne de Bellevue PQ H9X 1C0 Can

MILLETTE, ROBERT LOOMIS, b Rockville Centre, NY, May 17, 33; m 57; c 2. BIOCHEMISTRY, VIROLOGY. *Educ:* Ore State Col, BS, 54; Calif Inst Technol, PhD(biochem), 65. *Prof Exp:* USPHS res fel, Max Planck Inst Biochem, Ger, 64-67; asst prof path, Med Ctr, Univ Colo, Denver, 67-80; vis asst prof, Dept Microbiol & Biophys, Univ Chicago, 74-75; ASSOC PROF, DEPT IMMUNOL & MICROBIOL, SCH MED, WAYNE STATE UNIV, 75- *Mem:* Am Soc Microbiol. *Res:* Herpes virus transcription and gene expression; in vitro transcription of viral eukaryotic genes by RNA polymerase II; eukayotic gene transfer in vitro. *Mailing Add:* Sch Med Wayne State Univ 540 E Canfield Detroit MI 48201

MILLHONE, RALPH STANLEY, b Des Moines, Iowa, Aug 7, 32. CHEMICAL ENGINEERING. *Educ:* Iowa State Univ, BS, 54, MS, 59. *Prof Exp:* Res engr, E I du Pont de Nemours & Co, Inc, 54-55; SR ENGR ASSOC, CHEVRON OIL FIELD RES CO, STANDARD OIL CO CALIF, 59- *Concurrent Pos:* Instr well completions, Univ Southern Calif, 77-80. *Mem:* Soc Petrol Engrs; Am Inst Mining, Metall & Petrol Engrs. *Res:* Oil and gas production including drilling, well completions, sand control, formation damage, corrosion, natural gas processing, assisted recovery (thermal) and production logging. *Mailing Add:* Chevron Oil Field Res Co PO Box 446 La Habra CA 90631

MILLHOUSE, EDWARD W, JR, b West Hartford, Conn, Oct 28, 22. ELECTRON MICROSCOPY, CYTOCHEMISTRY. *Educ:* Univ Ill, BS, 49, MS, 54, PhD(cytol, anat), 60. *Prof Exp:* NIH fel anat, Sch Med, Ind Univ, 60-61; from instr to asst prof, 61-71, ASSOC PROF ANAT, CHICAGO MED SCH, 71- *Mem:* Electron Micros Soc Am; Am Asn Anatomists. *Res:* Electron microscopy and cyto- and histochemistry of the endocrine organs. *Mailing Add:* Dept of Anat Chicago Med Sch 2020 W Ogden Ave Chicago IL 60612

MILLHOUSE, OLIVER EUGENE, b Westerville, Ohio, Aug 21, 41. NEUROLOGY, ANATOMY. *Educ:* Ohio State Univ, BS, 63; Univ Calif, Los Angeles, PhD(anat), 67. *Prof Exp:* From instr to asst prof, 69-75, ASSOC PROF NEUROL & ANAT, COL MED, UNIV UTAH, 75- *Concurrent Pos:* Res fel, Dept Anat, Harvard Med Sch, 67-69. *Mem:* Am Asn Anat; Pan-Am Asn Anat. *Res:* Structural organization of the mammalian hypothalamus by light and electron microscopy, especially intrinsic connections and relations with other areas of the central nervous system. *Mailing Add:* Dept of Neurol Univ of Utah Salt Lake City UT 84132

MILLIAN, STEPHEN JERRY, b Okeechobee, Fla, Feb 15, 27; m 56; c 4. VIROLOGY. *Educ:* Brooklyn Col, BS, 49; Ohio State Univ, MS, 50, PhD(bact), 53; Am Bd Microbiol, dipl pub health & med lab virol, 63; Columbia Univ, MDPE, 75. *Prof Exp:* Asst, Ohio State Univ, 50-51; bacteriologist-virologist, Res Div, Armour Pharmaceut Co, 53-57; virologist biol res, Charles Pfizer & Co, Inc, 57-59; assoc cancer res scientist, Roswell Park Mem Inst, 60-61; chief virus unit, 61-72, asst dir virol & immunol; MEM STAFF, BUR LABS, NEW YORK CITY DEPT HEALTH, 72-; ASSOC PROF CLIN PEDIAT, MED SCH NY UNIV, 73- *Concurrent Pos:* WHO travel-study award, 72; assoc mem, Pub Health Res Inst New York, 61-68; lectr pub health, Hunter Col, 76-; lab consult, First Army Med Lab, 66-67; res assoc, Mt Sinai Hosp, 66-76; consult, Prof Exam Serv, 66-71. *Mem:* Harvey Soc; fel Am Soc Microbiol; fel Am Pub Health Asn; fel NY Acad Sci; fel NY Acad Med. *Res:* Laboratory diagnosis of viral and rickettsial infections; human and veterinary biologics. *Mailing Add:* Bur Labs New York City Dept Health 445 First Ave New York NY 10016

MILLICH, FRANK, b New York, NY, Jan 31, 28; m 60; c 2. POLYMER CHEMISTRY, PHOTOCHEMISTRY. *Educ:* City Col New York, BS, 49; Polytech Inst Brooklyn, 56, PhD(polymer chem), 59. *Prof Exp:* Chemist, Norda Essential Oils & Chem Co, 50-55; Am Cancer Soc res fel, Cambridge Univ, 58-59 & Univ Calif, Berkeley, 59-60; from asst prof to assoc prof, 60-64, res assoc, Syst Space Sci Res Ctr, 66-71, PROF POLYMER CHEM, UNIV MO-KANSAS CITY, 67- *Concurrent Pos:* Consult, Missiles & Space Div, Lockheed Aircraft Corp, Calif, 59-60, Gulf Oil Corp, Kans, 70- & Midwest Res Inst, Mo, 70- *Mem:* AAAS; Am Chem Soc; Royal Soc Chem. *Res:* New polymer synthesis and characterization; chemical evolution; kinetics of nonenzymatic synthesis of polypeptides and nucleic acids; kinetics of dye-sensitive photochemical reactions; synthesis of new chemotherapeutic drugs; interfacial synthesis; luminescence; polyisocyanides. *Mailing Add:* Dept of Chem Univ of Mo 5100 Rockhill Rd Kansas City MO 64110

MILLICHAP, JOSEPH GORDON, b Wellington, Eng, Dec 18, 18; US citizen; m 46, 70; c 4. NEUROLOGY, PEDIATRICS. *Educ:* Univ London, MB, 46, MD, 50; Am Bd Pediat, dipl, 58; Am Bd Psychiat & Neurol, dipl, 60, cert child neurol, 68; FRCP, 71; Am Bd EEG, dipl, 75. *Prof Exp:* House physician med & pediat units, St Bartholomew's Hosp, London, 46-47, demonstr physiol, 47-48, chief asst pediat, 51-53; house physician, Great Ormond St Hosp, 50-51; assoc res prof pharmacol, Univ Utah, 54-55; asst prof neurol, George Washington Univ, 55-56; asst prof pediat & pharmacol, Albert Einstein Col Med, 56-58, assoc prof, 58-59; assoc prof pediat neurol & pharmacol, Mayo Grad Sch Med, Univ Minn, 61-63, pediat neurologist, Mayo Clin, 60-63; PROF NEUROL & PEDIAT, NORTHWESTERN UNIV, CHICAGO, 63- *Concurrent Pos:* Traveling fel, Brit Med Res Coun, 53-54; fel pediat, Harvard Univ, 53-54, Nat Inst Neurol Dis spec fel neurol, 58-60; pediat neurologist, Children's Mem Hosp, Wesley Hosp & Passavant Hosp; vis physician, DC Gen Hosp, 55-56; vis scientist, Clin Ctr, Nat Inst Neurol Dis, 55-56; vis pediatrician, Bronx Munic Hosp Ctr, NY, 56-58; resident, Mass Gen Hosp, 58-60; mem, Gov Adv Coun Develop Disabilities, 71- *Mem:* AAAS; Soc Pediat Res; Am Soc Pharmacol & Exp Therapeut; Soc Exp Biol & Med; Am Epilepsy Soc. *Res:* Pediatric neurology; neuropharmacology of anticonvulsant drugs; biochemistry of developing nervous system; etiology of neurological disorders of children; behavior and learning disabilities epilepsy; electroencephalography. *Mailing Add:* 700 N Michigan Ave Chicago IL 60611

MILLIER, WILLIAM F(REDERICK), b Skaneateles, NY, Aug 31, 21; m 47; c 4. AGRICULTURAL ENGINEERING. *Educ:* Cornell Univ, BS, 45, PhD, 50. *Prof Exp:* Dist agr engr, State Univ NY Col Agr, Cornell Univ, 42-44, 45-47; res assoc agr eng, Univ Minn, 49-52; assoc prof, 52-64, PROF AGR ENG, CORNELL UNIV, 64- *Mem:* Am Soc Agr Engrs. *Res:* Farm power and machinery; tree fruit harvesting and post harvest handling; seed coating. *Mailing Add:* Dept of Agr Eng Riley-Robb Hall Cornell Univ Ithaca NY 14853

MILLIGAN, BARTON, b Cincinnati, Ohio, Oct 22, 29; m 54; c 1. ORGANIC CHEMISTRY. *Educ:* Haverford Col, AB, 51; Univ NC, MA, 53, PhD(chem), 55. *Prof Exp:* Lectr org chem, Univ Sydney, 55; Fulbright fel chem, Univ Adelaide, 56; assoc prof, Univ Miss, 56-64; from assoc prof to prof, Fla Atlantic Univ, 64-67; res chemist, 67-75, mgr res nitration prod, 75-77, mgr explor res, Indust Chem Res & Develop, 77-81, RES ASSOC, INDUST CHEM TECHNOL, AIR PROD & CHEM INC, 81- *Concurrent Pos:* NSF fac fel, 63-64. *Mem:* AAAS; Am Chem Soc. *Res:* Free radical reactions; process research. *Mailing Add:* Air Prod & Chem Inc PO Box 538 Allentown PA 18037

MILLIGAN, GEORGE CLINTON, b PEI, Can, Sept 6, 19; m 42; c 3. ECONOMIC GEOLOGY, STRUCTURAL GEOLOGY. *Educ:* Dalhousie Univ, MSc, 48; Harvard Univ, AM, 50, PhD(struct geol), 60. *Prof Exp:* Geologist, Man Dept Mines, 50-57; assoc prof, 57-66, PROF GEOL, DALHOUSIE UNIV, 66- *Concurrent Pos:* Nat Res Coun Can fel & guest prof, Swiss Fed Inst Technol, 64-65; Nat Res Coun Can exchange lectr, Univ Fed Pernambuco, Brazil, 74. *Mem:* Can Inst Mining & Metall; Mineral Asn Can; Geol Asn Can; Geol Soc Am. *Mailing Add:* Dept of Geol Dalhousie Univ Halifax NS B3H 3J5 Can

MILLIGAN, JOHN H, b Gary, Ind, Apr 21, 33; m 59; c 1. THERMAL PHYSICS, TECHNOLOGY PLANNING. *Educ:* Purdue Univ, BSME, 59, MSME, 63, PhD, 65. *Prof Exp:* Engr, Lockheed Aircraft Corp, 59-61; phys scientist, 65-76, PHYS SCIENTIST RES & DEVELOP PLANNING, CENT INTEL AGENCY, 77- *Mem:* Sigma Xi; NY Acad Sci. *Res:* Intermolecular potential constants for various gases as determined from their viscosity over wide range of temperature; calculation of thermodynamic properties of dissociating and ionizing alkali-metal vapors; reentry physics and orbital mechanics problems. *Mailing Add:* 3358 Annandale Rd Falls Church VA 22042

MILLIGAN, JOHN VORLEY, b Edmonton, Alta, Feb 21, 36; m 58; c 3. MEDICAL PHYSIOLOGY. *Educ:* Univ Alta, BSc, 58, MSc, 60; Univ Minn, PhD(physiol), 64. *Prof Exp:* Lectr physiol, McGill Univ, 64-66; asst prof, 66-70, ASSOC PROF PHYSIOL, QUEEN'S UNIV, ONT, 70- *Concurrent Pos:* Assoc ed, Can J Physiol & Pharmacol, 73-; fel, Int Brain Res Orgn/UNESCO, 74. *Mem:* Soc Neurosci; Am Physiol Soc; Int Soc Neuroendocrinol; Can Physiol Soc. *Res:* Mechanisms of excitation-contraction coupling in muscle; computer analysis; ion and fluorescent dye interactions with plasma membrane; stimulus-secretion coupling in pituitary. *Mailing Add:* Dept of Physiol Queen's Univ Kingston ON K7L 3N6 Can

MILLIGAN, LARRY PATRICK, b Innisfail, Alta, Dec 12, 40; m 62; c 3. BIOCHEMISTRY, NUTRITION. *Educ:* Univ Alta, BSc, 61, MSc, 63; Univ Calif, Davis, PhD(nutrit), 66. *Prof Exp:* From asst prof to assoc prof, 66-74, PROF ANIMAL SCIENCE, UNIV ALTA, 74- *Concurrent Pos:* Consult, UN, 81. *Mem:* Nutrit Soc; Agr Inst Can; Can Soc Animal Sci. *Res:* Nitrogen metabolism in animals, particularly ruminants; energy metabolism in animals. *Mailing Add:* Dept of Animal Sci Univ of Alta Edmonton AB T6G 2G7 Can

MILLIGAN, MANCIL W(OOD), b Shiloh, Tenn, Nov 21, 34; m 56; c 2. MECHANICAL & AEROSPACE ENGINEERING. *Educ:* Univ Tenn, BSME, 56, MS, 58, PhD(eng sci), 63. *Prof Exp:* Res engr, Boeing Co, 56-57, 58-59; instr mech eng, 57-58, from asst prof to assoc prof aerospace eng, 63-73, PROF & HEAD MECH & AEROSPACE ENG, UNIV TENN, KNOXVILLE, 73- *Concurrent Pos:* Consult, Oak Ridge Nat Lab, 59-; pres, Xcel Eng, Knoxville. *Mem:* Am Soc Mech Engrs; Am Inst Aeronaut & Astronaut; Am Soc Eng Educ. *Res:* Low-density gas dynamics; numerical methods in gas dynamics and heat transfer; industrial noise control. *Mailing Add:* Dept of Mech & Aerospace Eng Univ of Tenn Knoxville TN 37916

MILLIGAN, MERLE WALLACE, b Des Moines, Iowa, Mar 7, 22; m 48; c 3. MATHEMATICS. *Educ:* Monmouth Col, BS, 47; Univ Ill, MA, 49; Okla State Univ, EdD(higher educ, math), 60. *Prof Exp:* Asst math, Univ Ill, 47-52; from asst prof to assoc prof, Adams State Col, 53-62; prof, Albion Col, 62-66; dean arts & sci, 66-72, PROF MATH, METROP STATE COL, 66- *Concurrent Pos:* NSF grant, 57, 63, 73. *Mem:* Am Asn Univ Prof; Math Asn Am. *Res:* Analog computation; higher education. *Mailing Add:* Metrop State Col 1006 11th St Denver CO 80204

MILLIGAN, ROBERT T(HOMAS), b Taylorville, Ill, Dec 22, 19; m 48; c 4. CHEMICAL ENGINEERING, CHEMISTRY. *Educ:* Univ Ill, BS, 41; Ohio State Univ, PhD(chem eng), 45. *Prof Exp:* Asst instr, Ohio State Univ, 41-44; process engr, Shell Develop Co Div, Shell Oil Co, 44-59, supvr licensing & design eng, 59-70, asst mgr tech dept, Res & Develop, Polymers Div, Shell Chem Co, 70-73; mgr pollution control technol, Bechtel Corp, 73-76, PRIN ENGR RES & ENG, BECHTEL GROUP INC, 73-, MGR ORG CHEM PROCESS DEVELOP, 76- *Mem:* Am Chem Soc; fel Am Inst Chem Engrs. *Res:* Process design of petrochemical plants; plastics and resins research; advanced chemical technology; alternative energy processes; advanced methods of pollution control. *Mailing Add:* 2 Vista del Mar Orinda CA 94563

MILLIGAN, TERRY WILSON, b Hackensack, NJ, Aug 29, 35; m 57; c 3. ORGANIC CHEMISTRY, PHOTOGRAPHIC CHEMISTRY. *Educ:* Marietta Col, BS, 56; Univ Ill, PhD(org chem), 59. *Prof Exp:* Res scientist, 59-64, asst proj mgr 64-66, mgr color photog res, 66-72, asst to pres, 72-73, mgr, 74-76, sr tech mgr int technol, 76-80, DIR APPLN DEVELOPS, POLAROID CORP, CAMBRIDGE, 80- *Mem:* AAAS; Am Chem Soc. *Res:* Organic synthesis of dyes, hetero-cyclics, photographic developers; spectroscopic interactions between functional groups; reduction-oxidation reactions; coating technology; diffusion transfer photography; polyester films, polymer coatings, paper and plastic laminations; sensitometry and color analysis. *Mailing Add:* Polaroid Corp 549 Technology Square Cambridge MA 02139

MILLIGAN, WILBERT HARVEY, III, b Pittsburgh, Pa, Jan 17, 45; m 71; c 1. VIROLOGY. *Educ:* Washington & Jefferson Col, BA, 66; Univ Pittsburgh, PhD(microbiol), 72; Sch Dent Med, Southern Ill Univ, DMD, 79. *Prof Exp:* Lab instr microbiol & physiol, Washington & Jefferson Col, 65-66, lab instr gen biol, 66; teaching asst microbiol, Univ Pittsburgh, 66-67; lab instr, Allegheny Community Col, 67-69; vis assoc prof micrbiol, Sch Dent Med, Southern Ill Univ, Edwardsville, 72-79. *Concurrent Pos:* Abstractor, Am Dent Asn, 75-; consult gastroenterol, Sch Med, Washington Univ, 75-79. *Mem:* Sigma Xi; Am Soc Microbiol; AAAS; Int Asn Dent Res; Am Asn Dent Schs. *Res:* Hepatitis transmission in dentistry; methods for sterilization in dentistry; herpes-simplex latency; immunization against dental caries; immunopathology; viral-mycoplasma interactions; dental caries and peridontal disease; self-instructional learning modules. *Mailing Add:* 3823 Old William Penn Highway Murrysville PA 15668

MILLIGAN, WINFRED OLIVER, b Coulterville, Ill, Nov 5, 08; m 36, 60. PHYSICAL INORGANIC CHEMISTRY. *Educ:* Ill Col, AB, 30; Rice Univ, MA, 32, PhD(chem), 34. *Hon Degrees:* ScD, Ill Col, 46; DSc, Tex Christian Univ, 60. *Prof Exp:* From res chemist to prof chem, Rice Univ, 34-63; vchancellor res, mem bd dirs & pres, Res Found, Tex Christian Univ, 63-65; DISTINGUISHED RES PROF CHEM, BAYLOR UNIV, 65-; DIR RES, ROBERT A WELCH FOUND, 55- *Concurrent Pos:* Res chemist, Harshaw Chem Co, Ohio, 34; Nat Acad Sci-Nat Res Coun fels, 54-59; consult, Houdry Process Corp, 36-45, Humble Oil & Ref Co, 45-62 & Oak Ridge Nat Lab, 50-; mem comt appln x-ray & electron diffraction, Nat Acad Sci-Nat Res Coun, 38-41, mem panel permanent magnetic mat, 52, mem comt clay mineral, 53-; mem Am Chem Soc adv comt, US Army Chem Corps, 54-62, chmn, 58-62; mem, Tex Adv Comt Atomic Energy, 55-; ed, Res Bull, Robert A Welch Found, 53-, Proc Conf Chem Res, 57- & Clay Minerals, Nat Acad Sci-Nat Res Coun, 55; pres, Southwest Sci Forum, 77-78. *Mem:* Fel Am Inst Chem; fel Am Phys Soc; Am Crystallog Asn; Faraday Soc; Am Chem Soc. *Res:* X-ray and electron diffraction; electron microscopy; adsorption of gases in solids; magnetic susceptibility; oxides; hydroxides; colloids; general catalysis studies; heavy metal cyano-complexes; inorganic catalysts. *Mailing Add:* Robert A Welch Found 2010 Bank of Southwest Bldg Houston TX 77002

MILLIKAN, ALLAN G, b Charleston, WVa, July 31, 27; m 77; c 4. PHOTOGRAPHY, ASTRONOMY. *Educ:* Oberlin Col, AB, 49; Purdue Univ, MS, 51. *Prof Exp:* Photog engr, Color Technol, Eastman Kodak Co, 51-57, res assoc, Res Labs, 58-71; vis scientist astron, Kitt Peak Nat Observ, 71-72; SR RES ASSOC SCI PHOTOG, EASTMAN KODAK RES LABS, 72- *Concurrent Pos:* Mem working group photog mat, Am Astron Soc, 66-; mem organizing comt, Int Astron Union Working Group on photog problems. *Mem:* Am Astron Soc; Int Astron Union. *Res:* Photographic emulsion as a scientific data recorder; improvement of plates and films used in scientific photography; photographic detection of faint objects. *Mailing Add:* Eastman Kodak Co Res Labs B-59 1669 Lake Ave Rochester NY 14650

MILLIKAN, CLARK HAROLD, b Freeport, Ill, Mar 2, 15; m 66; c 3. MEDICINE, NEUROLOGY. *Educ:* Univ Kans, MD, 39; Am Bd Psychiat & Neurol, dipl, 46. *Prof Exp:* Intern, St Luke's Hosp, Cleveland, 39-40, from asst resident to resident med, 40-41; resident neurol, Univ Iowa, 41-44, from instr to asst prof, 44-49; from assoc prof to prof, Mayo Found, Univ Minn, 49-65, prof neurol, Mayo Grad Sch Med, Univ Minn, 65-76; consult, 49-76, head neurol sect, Mayo Clin, 55-65; PROF NEUROL, SCH MED, UNIV UTAH, 76- *Concurrent Pos:* Chmn comt cerebrovascular dis, USPHS & mem adv coun, Nat Inst Neurol Dis & Blindness, 61-65; chmn, Joint Coun Subcomt Cerebrovascular Dis, Nat Inst Neurol Dis & Blindness & Nat Heart Inst, mem nat adv comt regional med progs, NIH; past chmn, Coun Cerebrovascular Dis, Am Heart Asn, ed, Stroke; ed, J Cerebral Circulation, 70- *Honors & Awards:* William O Thompson Gold Medal Award, Am Geratrics Soc, 71. *Mem:* AMA; Asn Res Nerv & Ment Dis (pres, 61); Am Neurol Asn (pres, 74); fel Am Col Physicians; fel Am Acad Neurol. *Res:* Cerebrovascular disease; author or coauthor of over 150 publications. *Mailing Add:* Dept of Neurol Sch Med Univ Utah Salt Lake City UT 84132

MILLIKAN, DANIEL FRANKLIN, JR, b Lyndon, Ill, May 31, 18. BOTANY. *Educ:* Iowa State Univ, BS, 47; Univ Mo, PhD, 54. *Prof Exp:* Asst bot, 47-52, instr, 52-54, asst prof hort, 54-58, assoc prof, 58-68, PROF PLANT PATH, UNIV MO-COLUMBIA, 68- *Concurrent Pos:* USDA assignment, Poland, 66; Polish Minister Agr grant, 70 & 72; Nat Acad Sci-Polish Acad Sci grants, 74-77 & 81. *Mem:* Fel AAAS; Am Phytopath Soc; Am Soc Hort Sci; Bot Soc Am; foreign mem Polish Acad Sci. *Res:* Pathology of fruit, vegetable and woody ornamental crops; virology; virus diseases of stone and pome fruit crops. *Mailing Add:* Dept of Plant Path Rm 108 Waters Hall Univ of Mo Columbia MO 65201

MILLIKAN, LARRY EDWARD, b Sterlin, Ill, May 12, 36; m 62; c 2. DERMATOLOGY, IMMUNOLOGY. *Educ:* Monmouth Col, AB, 58; Univ Mo, MD, 62. *Prof Exp:* Physician intern & med officer, Great Lakes Naval Training Ctr, US Navy, 62, med officer aviation med, Naval Air Sta, Pensacola, Fla, 62-64, flight surgeon, Quonset Point, McGuire AFB, 64-67; resident dermat, Univ Hosp, Ann Arbor, Mich, 67-70; asst prof, 70-73, ASSOC PROF DERMAT, MED CTR, UNIV MO-COLUMBIA, 73- *Concurrent Pos:* Consult physiciant, Student Health Serv, 70-, Vet Admin Hosp, 72- & Ellis Fischell State Cancer Hosp, 72-; mem, Eczema Task Force, Nat Prog Dermat, 73; contrib ed, Int J Dermat, 75- *Mem:* Sigma Xi; Soc Invest Dermat; AAAS; Am Acad Dermat. *Res:* Cellular immunity; immunity in neoplasms; melanoma; immune surveillance. *Mailing Add:* Dept Dermat M752 Med Ctr Univ Mo Columbia MO 65201

MILLIKAN, ROGER CONANT, b Tiffin, Ohio, Jan 27, 31; m 53; c 5. CHEMICAL PHYSICS. *Educ:* Oberlin Col, BS, 53; Univ Calif, PhD, 57. *Prof Exp:* Phys chemist, Res Lab, Gen Elec Co, 56-67; PROF CHEM, UNIV CALIF, SANTA BARBARA, 67- *Mem:* Am Chem Soc; fel Am Phys Soc; fel Optical Soc Am. *Res:* Infrared spectroscopy; combustion; high temperature reactions; vibrational relaxation; fluorescence; shock tubes; lasers. *Mailing Add:* Dept of Chem Univ of Calif Santa Barbara CA 93106

MILLIKEN, JOHN ANDREW, b Saskatoon, Sask, May 15, 23; m 46; c 7. INTERNAL MEDICINE. *Educ:* Queen's Univ, Ont, MD, CM, 46; FRCP(C), 54; Am Bd Internal Med, dipl, 60. *Prof Exp:* From asst prof to assoc prof, 56-71, PROF MED QUEEN'S UNIV, ONT, 71-; HEAD DEPT MED, HOTEL DIEU HOSP, 56- *Mem:* Am Col Physicians; NY Acad Med; fel Am Col Chest Physicians; fel Am Col Cardiol; Can Med Asn. *Res:* Cardiology. *Mailing Add:* Dept of Med Queen's Univ Kingston ON K7L 3N6 Can

MILLIKEN, SPENCER RANKIN, b Dallas, Tex, Dec 5, 24; m 45; c 4. PHYSICAL CHEMISTRY. *Educ:* Ga Inst Technol, BS, 50; Emory Univ, MS, 51; Pa State Univ, PhD, 54. *Prof Exp:* Asst fuel tech, Pa State Univ, 50-53; res engr lubricants, Aluminum Co Am, 53-57, asst chief, 57-58; res & sales coordr, Foote Mineral Co, 58-60, mgr metall res, 60; dir res, Northern Ill Gas Co, 60-65; mgr appl physics, Roy C Ingersoll Res Ctr, Borg-Warner Corp, 65-66; vpres res & develop, Welco Industs Div, Electronic Assistance Corp, 66-72, vpres, Corp, 72-75; vpres eng, Fuel & Energy Consults, 75-79; VPRES, SR MILLIKEN & ASSOCS, 79- *Mem:* Am Chem Soc; Am Inst Chem; Am Inst Mining, Metall & Petrol Eng; NY Acad Sci. *Res:* Chemical constitution of coal; nature and structure of carbons; mineral preparation; lubricants; high purity metal preparation; nonferrous metals fabrication; metal films. *Mailing Add:* 97 W River Rd Rumson NJ 07760

MILLIKEN, W(ILLIAM) F(RANKLIN), JR, b Old Town, Maine, Apr 18, 11; m 53; c 3. AERONAUTICAL ENGINEERING. *Educ:* Mass Inst Technol, BS, 34. *Prof Exp:* Mem staff, Chance-Vought Aircraft Co, 36-38, Vought-Sikorsky Aircraft, 38-39; asst chief flight test, Boeing Aircraft Co, Wash, 39-43; flight & aerodyn test, Avion, Inc, 43-44; asst head flight res, Cornell Aeronaut Lab, Inc, 44-47, head, 48-56, actg head vehicle dynamics dept, 56-69, dir, Full-Scale Div, 56-77; WITH MILLIKEN RES ASSOCS, INC, WILLIAMSVILLE, NY, 77- *Concurrent Pos:* Consult transp res comt, Bur Pub Rds, 64-; mem panel naval vehicles, Nat Acad Sci, 60-61, comt future concepts, Hwy Res Bd, Nat Acad Sci-Nat Res Coun, 64-; adv comt res & develop, Maritime Comn. *Honors & Awards:* Laura Taber Barbour Air Safety Award, 67. *Mem:* Soc Automotive Engrs. *Res:* Flight test organization; crew training and procedures; dynamic stability and control. *Mailing Add:* With Milliken Res Assocs Inc 245 Brompton Rd Williamsville NY 14221

MILLIMAN, GEORGE ELMER, b New York, NY, Nov 15, 37; m 62; c 2. ANALYTICAL CHEMISTRY. *Educ:* Univ Rochester, BS, 59; Carnegie Inst Technol, PhD(chem), 64. *Prof Exp:* Res chemist, Jersey Prod Res Co, 64 & Esso Prod Res Co, Tex, 64-69; SR RES CHEMIST, EXXON RES & ENG CO, 69- *Mem:* Am Chem Soc. *Res:* Synthesis; spectroscopy; trace analysis. *Mailing Add:* Exxon Res & Eng Co PO Box 121 Linden NJ 07036

MILLIMAN, JOHN D, b Rochester, NY, May 5, 38; m 63; c 2. OCEANOGRAPHY, GEOLOGY. *Educ:* Univ Rochester, BS, 60; Univ Wash, MS, 63; Univ Miami, PhD(oceanog), 66. *Prof Exp:* Res asst radiation biol lab, Univ Wash, 61; res asst, Inst Marine Sci, Univ Miami, 63-66, res fel, 66; asst scientist, 66-71, ASSOC SCIENTIST, WOODS HOLE OCEANOG INST, 71- *Concurrent Pos:* Alexander von Humboldt Found scholar, Lab Sedimentology, Univ Heidelberg, 69-70. *Mem:* AAAS; Geol Soc Am; Soc Econ Paleontologists & Mineralogists. *Res:* Deposition and diagenesis of marine sediments; continental shelf sedimentation; Holocene history and shallow structure; submarine precipitation and lithification of marine carbonates. *Mailing Add:* Woods Hole Oceanog Inst Woods Hole MA 02543

MILLINER, ERIC KILLMON, b Wilmington, Del, June 3, 45; m 73. PSYCHOTHERAPY, INFANT PSYCHIATRY. *Educ:* Wheaton Col, BS, 66; Hahnemann Med Col, MD, 73. *Prof Exp:* Resident adult psychiat, Mayo Grad Sch Med, 73-74, Hahnemann Med Col, 74-76; STAFF CONSULT ADULT PSYCHIAT, MAYO CLINIC, 77- *Concurrent Pos:* Mayo Found scholar infant psychiat, Irvine Med Ctr, Univ Calif, 81- *Mem:* Am Psychiat Asn. *Res:* Longitudinal studies of infancy and childhood development to elucidate predictors of adult personality organization and psychopathology; clarifying precursors of adult self and object representations through direct observation of children during separation-individualization (ages 18 through 36 months). *Mailing Add:* Apt 312 1520 Rodney Dr Los Angeles CA 90027

MILLING, MARCUS EUGENE, b Galveston, Tex, Oct 8, 38; m 59; c 1. PETROLEUM GEOLOGY; SEDIMENTOLOGY. *Educ:* Lamar Univ, BS, 61; Univ Iowa, MS, 64, PhD(geol), 68. *Prof Exp:* Res specialist, sr res specialist & sr res geologist, Exxon Prod Res Co, 68-77; sr supvry geologist, Exxon Co USA, 77-79, dist geologist, 79-80; MGR GEOL RES, ARCO OIL & GAS CO, 80- *Mem:* Fel Geol Soc Am; Am Asn Petrol Geol; Soc Econ Paleontologists & Mineralogists; Int Asn Sedimentol. *Res:* Geomorphology; environmental facies analysis of Pleistocene and recent sediments; seismic stratigraphy deep-sea fans. *Mailing Add:* ARCO Oil & Gas Co PO Box 2819 Dallas TX 75221

MILLINGTON, JAMES E, b New York, NY, Mar 13, 30; m 65. ORGANIC CHEMISTRY. *Educ:* Lincoln Univ, Pa, AB, 51; Univ Western Ont, MSc, 53, PhD(chem), 56. *Prof Exp:* Asst, Defence Res Bd Can, Univ Western Ont, 53-55; res chemist, Allis-Chalmers Mfg Co, 56-61, proj leader, 61-63, sect head, 63-67, mgr org chem, 67-69; sect head, 69-80, MGR, AM HOECHST CORP, 80- *Mem:* Am Chem Soc. *Res:* Polymers; structure-properties relationships; polymer characterization. *Mailing Add:* Res & Develop 289 N Main St Leominster MA 01453

MILLINGTON, WILLIAM FRANK, b Ridgewood, NJ, June 16, 22; m 47; c 2. PLANT MORPHOGENESIS. *Educ:* Rutgers Univ, BSc, 47, MSc, 49; Univ Wis, PhD(bot hort), 52. *Prof Exp:* Res assoc, Roscoe B Jackson Mem Lab, Maine, 51-53; from instr to asst prof bot, Univ Wis, 53-59; from asst prof to assoc prof, 59-68, PROF BOT, MARQUETTE UNIV, 68- *Mem:* Am Soc Plant Physiol; Am Inst Biol Sci; Bot Soc Am; Phycol Soc Am. *Res:* Plant development; regulation of form and pattern. *Mailing Add:* Dept Biol Marquette Univ Milwaukee WI 53233

MILLION, RODNEY REIFF, b Idaville, Ind, Apr 3, 29; m 55; c 4. RADIOTHERAPY. *Educ:* Ind Univ, BS, 51, MD, 54; Am Bd Radiol, dipl, 63. *Prof Exp:* Intern, Harbor Gen Hosp, Torrance, Calif, 54-55; resident radiol, Ind Univ, 58-60; resident, Univ Tex M D Anderson Hosp & Tumor Inst, 60-62; assoc prof radiol & chief radiother sect, Ind Univ, 62-64; from assoc prof to prof radiol, 64-74, AM CANCER SOC PROF CLIN ONCOL, UNIV FLA, 74- *Res:* Radiation therapy. *Mailing Add:* Div of Radiother Univ of Fla Gainesville FL 32610

MILLIS, ALBERT JASON TAYLOR, b Philadelphia, Pa, Oct 4, 41; m 65; c 2. CELL BIOLOGY. *Educ:* Univ Pa, PhD(biol), 71. *Prof Exp:* Instr biol, Univ Pa, 67-69; res assoc pediat, Sch Med, Univ Wash, 71-72, res instr, 73, res asst prof, 74; asst prof, 74-77, MEM FAC BIOL, STATE UNIV NY ALBANY, 77- *Concurrent Pos:* Res asst prof, Dept Pediat, Albany Med Col, 76- *Mem:* Am Soc Cell Biol. *Res:* Regulation of the mammalian cell cycle and cellular proliferation; effects of growth promoting polypeptides on the mammalian tissue culture cell surface; somatic cell genetics. *Mailing Add:* 226 Biol Bldg Dept of Biol State Univ of NY Albany NY 12222

MILLIS, JOHN SCHOFF, b Palo Alto, Calif, Nov 22, 03; m 29; c 3. MEDICAL EDUCATION. *Educ:* Univ Chicago, BS, 24, MS, 27, PhD(physics), 31. *Hon Degrees:* Fifteen from var US cols & univs. *Prof Exp:* Master, Howe Sch, Ind, 24-26; from instr to prof physics, Lawrence Col, 27-41, dir, Underwood Astron Observ, 27-37, res assoc inst paper chem, 31-37, dean col, 36-41, dean admin, 38-41; pres, Univ Vt, 41-49; pres, Western Reserve Univ, 49-67; pres, Nat Fund Med Educ, 71-75; chancellor, 67-69, EMER CHANCELLOR, CASE WESTERN RESERVE UNIV, 69-; CHMN, NAT FUND MED EDUC, 75- *Concurrent Pos:* Consult sci info coun, NSF, 58-61; chmn citizens comn grad med educ, AMA, 62-66; mem nat adv coun med, dent, optom & podiatric educ, USPHS, 66-68; ad hoc consult, Group Continuing Med, Nat Libr Med, 66; mem, Nat Adv Coun Dent Res, 69-73; vpres, Nat Fund Med Educ, 69-71; mem, Comn Foreign Med Grads, 70-; chmn study comn dietetics, Am Dietetic Asn, 70-72; chmn, Nat Bd Med Examr, 75-79, mem, 71-; past trustee, Carnegie Found Advan Teaching; vpres, Nat League Nursing, Inc; chmn, President's Adv Panel Heart Dis, 72; chmn study comn pharm, Am Asn Cols Pharm, 73-76; trustee, Am Nurses' Found, 73-76. *Honors & Awards:* Lahey Award; Russell Award; Welch Medal. *Mem:* Sr mem Inst Med-Nat Acad Sci; fel AAAS; Am Acad Orthopaedic Surgeons; Am Acad Family Physicians; hon mem Am Hosp Asn. *Res:* Atomic and molecular spectroscopy; physical properties of paper; higher education. *Mailing Add:* Rm 341 Baker Case Western Reserve Univ Cleveland OH 44106

MILLIS, ROBERT LOWELL, b Martinsville, Ill, Sept 12, 41; m 65; c 2. ASTRONOMY, PLANETARY SCIENCE. *Educ:* Eastern Ill Univ, BA, 63; Univ Wis, PhD(astron), 68. *Prof Exp:* ASTRONR, LOWELL OBSERV, 67- *Mem:* Astron Soc Pacific; Div Planetary Sci; Am Astron Soc; Int Astron Union. *Res:* Planetary satellites and ring systems; occultation studies of solar system objects; comets. *Mailing Add:* Lowell Observ PO Box 1269 Flagstaff AZ 86001

MILLMAN, BARRY MACKENZIE, b Toronto, Ont, Oct 17, 34; m 59, 77; c 5. CONTRACTION MECHANISMS. *Educ:* Carleton Univ, BSc, 57; King's Col, Univ London, PhD(biophys), 63. *Prof Exp:* Mem sci staff, Brit Med Res Coun, Biophys Res Unit, King's Col, Univ London, 61-66; from asst prof to prof biol sci, Brock Univ, 67-74, chmn dept, 66-71; chmn biophys interdept group, 75-80, PROF PHYSICS, UNIV GUELPH, 74- *Concurrent Pos:* Res grants, Can Med Res Coun, 66-68, Can Nat Res Coun, 68-, Muscular Dystrophy Asn, 67-69 & 75-79 & Ont Heart Found, 75-77. *Mem:* Biophys Soc; Brit Biophys Soc; Brit Physiol Soc; Can Soc Cell Biologists (treas, 68-71); force balance in biological gels. *Res:* Muscle structure as determined by x-ray diffraction; contraction mechanisms and muscle physiology, especially invertebrate muscles; intermolecular and inter particle forces in aqueous gel system of biological interest; tobacco mosaic virus and the muscle filament lattice. *Mailing Add:* Dept of Physics Univ of Guelph Guelph ON N1G 2W1 Can

MILLMAN, GEORGE HAROLD, b Boston, Mass, June 2, 19; m 43; c 1. IONOSPHERIC PHYSICS. *Educ:* Univ Mass, BS, 47; Pa State Univ, MS, 49, PhD(physics), 52. *Prof Exp:* Asst physics, Pa State Univ, 47-50, instr eng res, 50-52; engr, 52-54, res liaison scientist, 54-55, consult physicist, 62-70, SPECIALIST ELECTROMAGNETIC PROPAGATION, GEN ELEC CO, 55-, SR CONSULT PHYSICIST, 70-; ADJ PROF, DEPT ELEC & COMP ENG, SYRACUSE UNIV, 76- *Concurrent Pos:* Mem, Comn F, wave phenomena in non-ionized media & Comn G, ionospheric radio, 58; mem, US Study Group 6, ionospheric propagation, Int Radio Consultative Comt; assoc ed, Radio Sci, 81- *Mem:* Am Phys Soc; fel Inst Elec & Electronics Engrs; Am Geophys Union; NY Acad Sci. *Res:* Electromagnetic-atmospheric propagation; ionospheric and space physics; radar and radio astronomy; atmospheric effects on radio wave propagation. *Mailing Add:* 504 Hillsboro Pkwy Syracuse NY 13214

MILLMAN, IRVING, b New York, NY, May 12, 23; m 49; c 2. IMMUNOLOGY, MEDICAL MICROBIOLOGY. *Educ:* City Col New York, BS, 48; Univ Ky, MS, 51; Northwestern Univ, PhD, 54. *Prof Exp:* Res bacteriologist, Armour & Co, 49-52; instr bact, Northwestern Univ, 54-55, asst prof, 55-58; asst, Pub Health Res Inst New York, 58-61; res fel, Merck Inst Therapeut Res, 61-67; assoc mem, Inst, 67-78, assoc prof, 71-81, PROF, HAHNEMAN MED COL, 81-, MEM, CLIN RES UNIT, INST CANCER RES, 78- *Mem:* NY Acad Sci; Soc Exp Biol & Med; Am Soc Microbiol; Reticuloendothelial Soc; Am Asn Cancer Res. *Res:* Immunology, hepatitis and cancer research. *Mailing Add:* Clin Res Unit Inst Cancer Res Philadelphia PA 19111

MILLMAN, JACOB, b Russia, May 17, 11; nat US; m 36; c 2. ELECTRONICS. *Educ:* Mass Inst Technol, BS, 32, PhD, 35. *Prof Exp:* Asst physics, Mass Inst Technol, 35-36; from instr to assoc prof elec eng, City Col New York, 36-51; prof, 51-76, EMER PROF ELEC ENG, COLUMBIA UNIV, 76- *Concurrent Pos:* Mem staff, Radiation Lab, Mass Inst Technol, 42-46; consult, 46-74; Fulbright lectr, Univ Rome, 59-60 & Univ of the Repub, Montevideo, Uruguay, 68. *Honors & Awards:* Educ Medal, Inst Elec & Electronics Engrs, 70. *Mem:* AAAS; fel Am Phys Soc; Am Soc Eng Educ; fel Inst Elec & Electronics Engrs. *Res:* Physical electronics; electronic circuits; pulse and digital circuits. *Mailing Add:* Dept of Elec Eng Columbia Univ New York NY 10027

MILLMAN, PETER MACKENZIE, b Toronto, Ont, Aug 10, 06; m 31; c 2. ASTROPHYSICS, PLANETARY SCIENCES. *Educ:* Univ Toronto, BA, 29; Harvard Univ, AM, 31, PhD(astron), 32. *Prof Exp:* Agassiz scholar, Harvard Col Observ, 32-33; astronr & lectr, Dunlap Observ, Univ Toronto, 33-45; navig oper res, Royal Can Air Force, 41-46; chief stellar physics div, Dominion Observ, Ottawa, 46-55; head upper atmosphere res, 55-71, GUEST SCIENTIST, HERZBERG INST ASTROPHYS, NAT RES COUN CAN, OTTAWA, 71- *Concurrent Pos:* Consult, Air Force Staff Col, Toronto, 45-60, Avco-Everett Res Labs, Mass, 62-67, NASA Marshall Space Flight Ctr, 72-; assoc, Harvard Col Observ, 55-75; nat reporter for Aurora & Meteors, Int Geophys Year, Can, 56-58; counr, Smithsonian Inst, 66-72; res assoc, Dudley Observ, 74- *Honors & Awards:* J Lawrence Smith Medal, Nat Acad Sci, 54; Gold Med, Acad Sci Czech, 80. *Mem:* Fel Royal Soc Can; Royal Astron Soc Can (pres, 60-62, hon pres, 81-85); fel Can Aeronaut & Space Inst; fel Meteoritical Soc (pres, 62-66); Am Astron Soc. *Res:* Stellar spectroscopy, especially radial velocities; radio meteor studies and meteor spectroscopy; chemistry of interplanetary particles; topographical features on planetary bodies of solar system, in particular impact cratering and its chronology. *Mailing Add:* Herzberg Inst of Astrophys Nat Res Coun Can Ottawa ON K1A 0R6 Can

MILLMAN, RICHARD STEVEN, b Boston, Mass, Apr 15, 45; c 2. GEOMETRY. *Educ:* Mass Inst Technol, BS, 66; Cornell Univ, MS, 69, PhD(math), 71. *Prof Exp:* Asst prof math, Ithaca Col, 70-71; asst prof, 71-74, ASSOC PROF MATH & ASST TO PRES, SOUTHERN ILL UNIV, CARBONDALE, 74- *Mem:* Math Asn Am; Am Math Soc. *Res:* Eigenvalues of Laplace operator on Riemannian manifolds; holomorphic connections on fiber bundles. *Mailing Add:* Dept of Math Southern Ill Univ Carbondale IL 62901

MILLMAN, ROBERT BARNET, b New York, NY, Aug 25, 39. PUBLIC HEALTH, PSYCHIATRY. *Educ:* Cornell Univ, BA, 61; State Univ NY, MD, 65. *Prof Exp:* Intern, Bellevue Hosp, NY, 65-66; asst physician, New York Hosp, 68-70; asst prof, Rockefeller Univ, 70-72; asst prof pub health, 70-76, DIR, ADOLESCENT DEVELOP PROG, MED CTR, MED COL, CORNELL UNIV, 70-, CLIN PROF PUB HEALTH, 79- CLIN ASST PROF PSYCHIAT, 77- *Concurrent Pos:* Consult, NY Dept Corrections, 71-72, Manhattan Borough Presidents' Comt Drug Abuse, 71-74; adj asst prof, Rockefeller Univ, 72-; assoc ed, Millbank Mem Fund Quart, 72-; mem comnr adv comt, NY Addiction Serv Agency, 74-; mem adv comt drug abuse, NY Comnr Health, 75-; mem task force ment health aspects of use & misuse of psychoactive drugs, President's Comn Ment Health, 77; mem adv comt, Gen Pediat Acad Develop Prog, Robert Wood Johnson Found, 78; dir Alcohol & Drug Abuse Prog, Payne Whitney Psychiat Clin, 78; fel, WHO, 79; ed bd, Hosp & Community Psychiat, 80- *Mem:* Am Pub Health Asn; Am Med Soc Alcoholism. *Res:* Pathogenesis and patterns of drug and alcohol abuse; characterization of the addictive process, with particular respect to abstinence syndromes. *Mailing Add:* Med Col Cornell Univ 411 E 69th St New York NY 10021

MILLNER, ELAINE STONE, b Staten Island, NY; c 2. CANCER EPIDEMIOLOGY, HUMAN DEVELOPMENT & BEHAVIOR. *Educ:* Cornell Univ, BS, 53; Kean Col, MA, 69, Prof dipl, 71; Columbia Univ, DrPh(epidemiol), 75. *Prof Exp:* Microbiologist, Res Lab, Wallerstein Labs; chemist, Organon Res Labs, 65; asst prof psychol, Kean Col, 70; psychologist, Cladwell Bd Educ, West Caldwell, NJ, 71-72, consult child develop, 71-73; epidemiologist, Dept Pediat, Col Physicians & Surgeons, Roosevelt Hosp, 75-76, proj dir & co-prin investr, 76-77; sr res scientist & dir, Hepatitis Eval Unit, NY City Dept Health, Bur Preventable Dis, 78-80; ACTG PROG DIR EPIDEMIOL, DIV CANCER CAUSE & PREV, SPEC PROGS BR, NAT CANCER INST, 80- *Concurrent Pos:* Vis scientist, Lab Epidemiol, NY Blood Ctr, 78; lectr, Sch Public Health, Columbia Univ, 78-80. *Mem:* Soc Epidemiol Res; Am Public Health Asn; NY Acad Sci; Am Pyschol Asn; Sigma Xi. *Mailing Add:* #910 10500 Rockville Pike Rockville MD 20852

MILLS, ALFRED PRESTON, b Fallon, Nev, Jan 8, 22; m 46; c 2. PHYSICAL CHEMISTRY. *Educ:* Univ Nev, BS, 43; Tulane Univ, PhD(phys chem), 49. *Prof Exp:* From instr to asst prof, 49-56, chmn div natural sci & math, 60-61, actg asst dean grad sch, 64-65, ASSOC PROF PHYS CHEM, 56- & ADJ ASST DEAN GRAD SCH FOR CURRIC, UNIV MIAMI, 73- *Mem:* AAAS; Am Chem Soc; Am Phys Soc; Am Inst Chemists; Sigma Xi. *Res:* Thermodynamics of solutions; prediction of physical properties of liquid solutions; dielectric constant and dipole moment, viscosity; physical properties of silicon compounds and nitro compounds. *Mailing Add:* Dept of Chem Univ of Miami Coral Gables FL 33124

MILLS, ALLEN PAINE, JR, b Apr 21, 40; US citizen. ATOMIC PHYSICS. *Educ:* Princeton Univ, BA, 62; Brandeis Univ, MA, 64, PhD(physics), 67. *Prof Exp:* From instr to assoc prof physics, Brandeis Univ, 67-75; MEM TECH STAFF, BELL LABS, 75- *Mem:* Am Phys Soc. *Res:* Atomic physics of positronium. *Mailing Add:* Bell Labs Murray Hill NJ 07974

MILLS, ANTHONY FRANCIS, b Cape Town, SAfrica, Jan 21, 38. MECHANICAL ENGINEERING. *Educ:* Univ Cape Town, BSc, 57 & 59, MSc, 60; Imp Col, Univ London, Dipl, 62; Univ Calif, Berkeley, PhD(eng), 66. *Prof Exp:* Lectr eng, Univ Cape Town, 58-61; asst prof, 66-76, assoc prof, 76-80, PROF ENG & APPL SCI, UNIV CALIF, LOS ANGELES, 80- *Concurrent Pos:* Consult, TRW Systs Group, 67- *Mem:* Am Soc Mech Engrs; Am Inst Aeronaut & Astronaut. *Res:* Heat and mass transfer; condensation phenomena. *Mailing Add:* Dept of Energy & Kinetics Univ of Calif Los Angeles CA 90024

MILLS, B(LAKE) D(AVID), JR, b Seattle, Wash, Apr 8, 12; m 45; c 3. MECHANICAL ENGINEERING. *Educ:* Univ Wash, BS, 34, ME, 47; Mass Inst Technol, SM, 35. *Prof Exp:* Test engr, Gen Elec Co, 35-36; instr appl mech & eng mat, Mass Inst Technol, 36-41; from assoc prof to prof mech eng, 46-77, EMER PROF MECH ENG, UNIV WASH, 77- *Mem:* Am Soc Mech Engrs; Am Soc Metals. *Res:* Properties of engineering materials; vibration; applied mechanics. *Mailing Add:* Dept of Mech Eng Univ of Wash Seattle WA 98195

MILLS, DALLICE IVAN, b Endeavor, Wis, July 27, 39; m 61; c 1. BOTANY, GENETICS. *Educ:* Wis State Univ, Stevens Point, BS, 61; Syracuse Univ, MS, 64; Mich State Univ, PhD(bot, plant path), 69. *Prof Exp:* Teacher high schs, Wis & Ariz, 61-65; spec res asst bot & plant path, Mich State Univ, 65-69; NIH res fel genetics, Univ Wash, 69-72; asst prof biol sci, Univ Ill Chicago Circle, 72-76; asst prof, 76-80, ASSOC PROF BOT, ORE STATE UNIV, 80- *Mem:* Genetics Soc Am; Am Soc Microbiol; AAAS; Am Phytopath Soc. *Res:* Fungal and microbial genetics; genetics and physiology of host-parasite interactions. *Mailing Add:* Dept of Bot Ore State Univ Corvallis OR 97331

MILLS, DON HARPER, b Peking, China, July 29, 27; US citizen; m 49; c 2. FORENSIC MEDICINE. *Educ:* Univ Cincinnati, BS, 50, MD, 53; Univ Southern Calif, JD, 58. *Prof Exp:* CONSULT FORENSIC MED, 58- *Concurrent Pos:* Fel path, Univ Southern Calif, 54-55, instr path, 58-62, from asst clin prof to assoc clin prof path, 62-69, clin prof, 69-; instr humanities, Loma Linda Univ, 60-66, assoc clin prof, 66-; exec ed, Trauma, 64-; mem ed bd, J Forensic Sci, 65-; dep med examr, Off Los Angeles County Coroner, 57-61; mem attend staff, Los Angeles County Hosp, 59-; affil staff, Hosp Good Samaritan, Los Angeles, 67-; res consult, Secy Comn Med Malpract, Dept Health, Educ & Welfare, 72-73; mem adv coun, Assembly Comt Med Malpract, State Calif, 73-75; expert consult, Off Secy, Dept Health, Educ & Welfare, 75-76; consult, Armed Forces Inst Path, Dept Defense, 74-; Health Resources Admin, Dept Health, Educ & Welfare, 75-76; adminr & prin investr med insurance feasibility study, Calif Med Asn, 76-77; mem adv comt, Joint Legis Comt Tort Reform, State Calif, 77- & mem sci adv bd, Armed Forces Inst Path, Dept Defense, 78-80. *Mem:* AAAS; fel Am Acad Forensic Sci; AMA; Am Bar Asn; fel Am Col Legal Med (pres, 74-76). *Res:* Forensic medicine, primarily sub-field of legal rights and responsibilities of physicians and hospitals. *Mailing Add:* 1141 Los Altos Ave Long Beach CA 90815

MILLS, DOUGLAS LEON, b Berkeley, Calif, Apr 2, 40; m 61. SOLID STATE PHYSICS. *Educ:* Univ Calif, Berkeley, BS, 61, PhD(physics), 65. *Prof Exp:* NSF fel physics, Paris, 65-66; from asst prof to assoc prof, 66-74, PROF PHYSICS, UNIV CALIF, IRVINE, 74- *Mem:* Am Phys Soc. *Res:* Theoretical investigations of magnetic materials, lattice vibrations, surface effects, light scattering from solids and properties of alloys. *Mailing Add:* Dept of Physics Univ of Calif Irvine CA 92664

MILLS, EARL RONALD, b Los Angeles, Calif, Mar 28, 43; m 69; c 2. ECOLOGY, ENVIRONMENTAL MANAGEMENT. *Educ:* La State Univ, Baton Rouge, BS, 68, MS, 70; Tex A&M Univ, PhD(biol), 74. *Prof Exp:* Teaching asst bot, La State Univ, 68-69; res asst, Tex A&M Univ, 70-74; biologist, US Army Corp Engrs, 74-78; ENVIRON SPECIALIST, STRATEGIC PETROL RESERVE, US DEPT ENERGY, 78- *Concurrent Pos:* Instr environ mgt & policy, Univ Houston, Clear Lake City, 76. *Mem:* AAAS; Gulf Estuarine Res Soc; Estuarine Res Fedn. *Mailing Add:* 4615 Orleans Blvd New Orleans LA 70121

MILLS, ELLIOTT, b New York, NY, July 17, 35; m 60; c 2. PHARMACOLOGY, PHYSIOLOGY. *Educ:* City Col New York, BS, 57; Columbia Univ, PhD(pharmacol), 64. *Prof Exp:* Nat Inst Neurol Dis & Blindness trainee, Col Physicians & Surgeons, Columbia Univ, 64-65; Nat Heart Inst fel physiol, Middlesex Hosp Med Sch, London, Eng, 65-67; spec fel cardiovasc res inst, Med Ctr, Univ Calif, San Francisco, 67-68; asst prof, 68-74, assoc prof physiol & pharmacol, 74-77, ASSOC PROF PHARMACOL & PHYSIOL, MED CTR, DUKE UNIV, 77- *Concurrent Pos:* Estab investr, Am Heart Asn, 74- *Mem:* Am Phys Soc. *Res:* Chemoreceptor mechanisms; brainstem and reflex control of cardiovascular function; cardiovascular pharmacology. *Mailing Add:* Dept of Pharmacol Duke Univ Med Ctr Durham NC 27701

MILLS, ERIC LEONARD, b Toronto, Ont, July 7, 36; m 62; c 2. BIOLOGICAL OCEANOGRAPHY. *Educ:* Carleton Univ, Can, BSc, 59; Yale Univ, MS, 62, PhD(marine biol), 64. *Prof Exp:* Asst prof biol, Queen's Univ, Ont, 63-67; assoc prof, 67-71, PROF OCEANOG & BIOL, DALHOUSIE UNIV, 71- *Concurrent Pos:* Sessional lectr, Carleton Univ, Can, 60; instr, Marine Biol Lab, Woods Hole, Mass, 64-67, mem corp, 65-; instr, Huntsman Marine Lab, NB, 71-73; vis scholar, Corpus Christi Col, Cambridge Univ, 74-75. *Mem:* AAAS; Am Ornithologists Union; Am Soc Limnol & Oceanog; Can Soc Zoologists; Marine Biol Asn UK. *Res:* Taxonomy and ecology of amphipod crustaceans; marine ecology; deep-sea biology; history of oceanography. *Mailing Add:* Dept of Oceanog Dalhousie Univ Halifax NS O3H 4S1 Can

MILLS, FRANK D, b Cleveland, Ohio, July 29, 37; m 61; c 3. ORGANIC CHEMISTRY. *Educ:* Western Reserve Univ, BA, 60, MS, 61, PhD, 66. *Prof Exp:* Res chemist cereal carbohydrates, Northern Regional Res Ctr, 66-80, RES CHEMIST PESTICIDES, BELTSVILLE AGR RES CTR E, USDA, 80- *Honors & Awards:* Citation, USDA, 70. *Mem:* Sigma Xi; Am Chem Soc. *Res:* Carbohydrates, structure and synthesis; pesticide chemistry. *Mailing Add:* Beltsville Agr Res Ctr E Agr Envrion Qual Inst USDA Beltsville MD 20705

MILLS, FREDERICK EUGENE, b Streator, Ill, Nov 12, 28; m 50; c 3. PHYSICS. *Educ:* Univ Ill, BS, 49, MS, 50, PhD(physics), 55. *Prof Exp:* Res assoc physics, Cornell Univ, 54-56; scientist, Midwestern Univs Res Asn, 56-64, assoc dir sci, 64-65, dir, 65-66; prof physics, Univ Wis Phys Sci Lab, 66-70, dir, 67-70; chmn accelerator dept, Brookhaven Nat Lab, 70-73; SCIENTIST, FERMI NAT ACCELERATOR LAB, 73- *Concurrent Pos:* Physicist, Saclay Nuclear Res Ctr, France, 61-62; adj prof, Nuclear Eng Dept, Univ Wis, 74- *Mem:* Fel Am Phys Soc. *Res:* Accelerators; high energy and plasma physics; energy loss of fast particles in motion; photoproduction of pi mesons; advanced accelerators. *Mailing Add:* Fermi Nat Lab PO Box 500 Batavia IL 60510

MILLS, G(EORGE) J(ACOB), b Philadelphia, Pa, Aug 23, 24; m 48; c 2. METALLURGICAL ENGINEERING, PHYSICS. *Educ:* Pa State Univ, BS, 45, MS, 47; Univ Pa, PhD(metall), 51. *Prof Exp:* Chief res br, Metall Lab, Frankford Arsenal, US Dept of Army, 51-56; res specialist, Chem & Mat Sect, Jet Propulsion Lab, Calif Inst Technol, 56-58; mgr mat dept, Aeronutronic Div, Ford Motor Co, 58-64; prog mgr, Res Anal Corp, 64-68; prin engr plans & progs, 68-70, dir mat sci lab, 70-75, ASST TECH PLANNING, NORTHROP CORP LABS, 75- *Mem:* Am Soc Metals; Am Inst Mining, Metall & Petrol Engrs; Am Inst Aeronaut & Astronaut; Am Defense Preparedness Asn. *Res:* Physical metallurgy; solid state physics; materials science; composites; electronic materials; thin film devices. *Mailing Add:* 12142 Sky Lane Santa Ana CA 92705

MILLS, GEORGE ALEXANDER, b Saskatoon, Sask, Mar 20, 14; nat US; m 40; c 4. PHYSICAL CHEMISTRY, FUEL SCIENCE. *Educ:* Univ Sask, BSc, 34, MSc, 36; Columbia Univ, PhD(chem), 40. *Prof Exp:* Asst chem, Columbia Univ, 36-39; instr, Dartmouth Col, 39-40; res chemist, Houdry Process & Chem Co, 40-47, asst dir res, 47-52, dir, 52-67; dir res, Houdry Lab, Air Prod & Chem Inc, 67-68; asst dir coal res, US Bur Mines, Washington, DC, 68-70, chief div coal, 70-74, asst dir, Off Coal Res, 74-75; dir fossil energy res, Energy Res & Develop Admin, 75-77, SR SCIENTIST, FOSSIL FUEL, DEPT ENERGY, 77- *Honors & Awards:* Storch Award, Am Chem Soc, 75. *Mem:* AAAS; Am Chem Soc; Am Inst Chem Engrs; Am Inst Mining, Metall & Petrol Engrs; Catalysis Soc (pres). *Res:* Active hydrogen; separation of isotopes; exchange reactions with oxygen isotopes; reaction kinetics; petroleum refining; clay minerals; mechanism of catalytic reactions; high polymers; organic nitrogen chemicals; polyurethanes; synthetic fuels from coal; materials research; combustion and power. *Mailing Add:* Dept of Energy 20 Massachusetts Ave NW Washington DC 20545

MILLS, GEORGE HIILANI, b Pepeekeo, Hawaii, June 10, 21; m 44; c 4. MEDICINE. *Educ:* Colo Col, BA, 44, MA, 45; Boston Univ, MD, 50. *Prof Exp:* Intern, Queens Med Ctr, Honolulu, 50-51, resident internal med, 51-54; partner, Alsup Clin, Honolulu, 54-70; med dir, Kamehameha Sch, 62-78; MEM FAC, SCH MED, UNIV HAWAII, 78- *Concurrent Pos:* Med dir, Manalani Hosp, 60-78; mem nat adv comt, Juv Justice & Delinq Prev, 75-77. *Mem:* Inst of Med of Nat Acad Sci. *Mailing Add:* Kamehameha Schs Kapalama Heights Honolulu HI 96817

MILLS, GEORGE SCOTT, applied physics, see previous edition

MILLS, GORDON CANDEE, b Fallon, Nev, Feb 13, 24; m 47; c 3. BIOCHEMISTRY. *Educ:* Univ Nev, BS, 46; Univ Mich, MS, 48, PhD(biochem), 51. *Prof Exp:* Res assoc biochem, Col Med, Univ Tenn, 50-55; PROF BIOCHEM, UNIV TEX MED BR GALVESTON, 55- *Mem:* Am Chem Soc; Am Soc Biol Chem; Sigma Xi; Am Asn Univ Prof. *Res:* Erythrcyte metabolism; genetic disorders of erythrocytes; metabolic control mechanisms. *Mailing Add:* Div Biochem Univ Tex Med Br Galveston TX 77550

MILLS, HARRY ARVIN, b Paintsville, Ky, Dec 11, 46; m 68; c 2. VEGETABLE CROPS. *Educ:* Univ Ky, BS, 69; Univ Mass, MS, 72, PhD(plant sci, soil sci), 75. *Prof Exp:* Asst prof, 74-76, MEM FAC HORT, UNIV GA, 76- *Mem:* AAAS; Sigma Xi; Am Soc Hort Sci; Am Soc Agron. *Res:* Soil fertility and plant nutrition of vegetable crops; nitrogen utilization. *Mailing Add:* Plant & Soil Sci Dept of Hort Univ of Ga Athens GA 30601

MILLS, HOWARD LEONARD, b Huntington, WVa, May 8, 20. PLANT PHYSIOLOGY, PLANT MORPHOLOGY. *Educ:* Marshall Col, BS, 44, MS, 49; Univ Iowa, PhD(plant physiol), 51. *Prof Exp:* Instr bot, Univ Iowa, 49-51; from asst prof to assoc prof bot, 51-61, PROF BIOL SCI, MARSHALL COL, 61- *Concurrent Pos:* NSF fel, Univ Wyo, 55; NSF-AEC fel, Univ Mich, 59; res assoc, NMex Highlands Univ, 59-60; consult, Div Radiol Health, USPHS, 65-; res consult, Environ Protection Agency, 72- *Mem:* Bot Soc Am; Am Soc Plant Physiol. *Res:* Physiology of growth and floral initiation; anthocyanin production and localization; algal nutrition; bactericides; radiobotany; fission product uptake by plant roots; physiognomic analyses of vegetation. *Mailing Add:* 1234 Ninth St Huntington WV 25701

MILLS, IRA KELLY, b Richmond, Kans, Oct 31, 21; m 43; c 2. PLANT PHYSIOLOGY. *Educ:* Univ Southern Calif, AB, 52, MS, 53; Ore State Col, PhD(bot), 56. *Prof Exp:* From asst prof to assoc prof bot, 56-68, asst plant pathologist, 56-62, PROF BOT, MONT STATE UNIV, 68- *Concurrent Pos:* Fulbright-Hays lectr, Chung Hsing Univ, Taiwan, 66-67; consult, Gen Biol & Genetics Rev Panel, NIH, 68-70. *Mem:* AAAS; Am Soc Plant Physiol. *Res:* Effects of virus infection on host plant physiology; metabolism of aquatic plants and systems. *Mailing Add:* Dept of Biol Mont State Univ Bozeman MT 59715

MILLS, JACK F, b Galesburg, Ill, Feb 3, 28; m 53; c 5. ORGANIC CHEMISTRY. *Educ:* Knox Col, BA, 50; Univ Iowa, PhD(chem), 53. *Prof Exp:* Fel, Univ Ill, 53-54; res chemist, 56-62, sr res chemist, 62-74, sr res specialist, 74-77, RES ASSOC, DOW CHEM USA, 77- *Concurrent Pos:* Instr, Delta Col. *Res:* Halogen and polyhalogen compounds and their reactions; study of basic complexes; disinfection and pollution studies; spectrometric studies; synthesis of biological active compounds. *Mailing Add:* 4524Andre St Midland MI 48640

MILLS, JAMES HERBERT LAWRENCE, b Guelph, Ont, Jan 14, 33; m 59; c 4. VETERINARY PATHOLOGY. *Educ:* Univ Toronto, BSA, 55, DVM, 61; Univ Conn, MS, 64, PhD(virol), 66; Am Col Vet Path, dipl, 66. *Prof Exp:* Vet practitioner, Ont, 61-62; instr animal dis, Univ Conn, 62-66, assoc prof vet path, 66-67; assoc prof, 67-71, PROF VET PATH, UNIV SASK, 71-, HEAD DEPT, 77- *Mem:* Am Vet Med Asn; US Animal Health Asn; NY Acad Sci; Can Vet Med Asn; Int Acad Path. *Res:* Veterinary virology and pathology, particularly bovine mucosal disease; veterinary parasitology, especially lungworms. *Mailing Add:* Dept Vet Path Col Vet Med Univ of Sask Saskatoon SK S7H 0W0 Can

MILLS, JAMES IGNATIUS, b Morganfield, Ky, Nov 11, 44; m 66; c 2. SOLAR PHYSICS, ENERGY POLICY. *Educ:* Univ Okla, BS, 66, PhD(physics), 71. *Prof Exp:* Assoc scientist nuclear physics, Aerojet Nuclear Co, 72-75; vis asst prof & fel teaching & res, Miami Univ, 75-76; SCIENTIST SOLAR PHYSICS, EG&G IDAHO, INC, 76- *Concurrent Pos:* Consult, Nuclear Reactor Safety Anal Consult, EG&G Idaho, Inc & Nuclear Regulatory Comn, 75-76, Alternative Energy Syst Utilization & Develop, 77- *Mem:* Sigma Xi; Int Solar Energy Soc; Am Phys Soc; Am Nuclear Soc. *Res:* Solar energy research and development including total solar energy concepts; alternative energy systems research and development on bio-mass low-head hydropower wind; energy use forecasting and energy policy development. *Mailing Add:* EG&G Idaho Inc PO Box 1625 Idaho Falls ID 83401

MILLS, JAMES WILSON, b Dayton, Ohio, June 7, 42; m 64; c 1. PHYSICAL CHEMISTRY. *Educ:* Earlham Col, AB, 63; Brown Univ, PhD(chem), 68. *Prof Exp:* Res assoc, Joint Inst Lab Astrophys & Univ Colo, 68-69; asst prof chem, Drew Univ, 69-73; asst prof chem, 73-76, ASSOC PROF CHEM, 76- & CHMN DEPT, FT LEWIS COL, 77- *Concurrent Pos:* Cotrrell Res Corp grant, Drew Univ, 70-71 & Petrol Res Fund grant, 72-73; consult, Four Corners Environ Res Inst, 74- *Mem:* Am Chem Soc; Am Phys Soc. *Res:* Molecular spectroscopy; quantum mechanics of small molecules; instrumentation. *Mailing Add:* Dept of Chem Ft Lewis Col Durango CO 81301

MILLS, JANET E (AULT), b Bremerton, Wash, Jan 20, 43. ALGEBRA. *Educ:* Western Wash State Col, BA, 65; Pa State Univ, PhD(math), 70. *Prof Exp:* Asst prof math, Univ Fla, 70-71; asst prof, 74-78, ASSOC PROF MATH, JAMES MADISON UNIV, 78- *Mem:* Am Math Soc; Math Asn Am. *Res:* Algebraic semigroups, particularly in constructions and classifications of inverse and regular semigroups. *Mailing Add:* Dept Math & Comput Sci James Madison Univ Harrisonburg VA 22807

MILLS, JERRY LEE, b Midland, Tex, Mar 6, 43. INORGANIC CHEMISTRY. *Educ:* Univ Tex, Austin, BS, 65, PhD(inorg chem), 69. *Prof Exp:* Fel, Ohio State Univ, 69-70; asst prof, 70-76, assoc prof, 76-80, PROF CHEM, TEX TECH UNIV, 80- *Mem:* Am Chem Soc; Royal Soc Chem. *Res:* Preparation, reactivity, and structure of non-transition metal compounds. *Mailing Add:* Dept Chem Tex Tech Univ Lubbock TX 79409

MILLS, JOHN BLAKELY, III, b Griffin, Ga, June 15, 39; m 64; c 2. BIOCHEMISTRY. *Educ:* Ga Inst Technol, BS, 61; Emory Univ, PhD(biochem), 65. *Prof Exp:* NSF fel, Cambridge Univ, 65-66; Whitehead fel, 66-67, from instr to asst prof, 67-74, ASSOC PROF BIOCHEM, EMORY UNIV, 74- *Res:* Chemistry of protein hormones. *Mailing Add:* Dept of Biochem Emory Univ Atlanta GA 30322

MILLS, JOHN JAMES, b Motherwell, Scotland, May 12, 39; m 71; c 4. MATERIALS SCIENCE, PHYSICS. *Educ:* Glasgow Univ, BSc, 61; Univ Durham, PhD(appl physics), 65. *Prof Exp:* Res fel, Imp Col, Univ London, 64-66; sr scientist, Ill Inst Technol, 66-71; Humbolt res fel, Inst Silicate Res, Ger, 71-73; sect leader, Rosenthal Joint Stock Co, Ger, 73-75; sr scientist, 75-79, MGR, FABRIC RES & DEVELOP, MARTIN MARIETTA LABS, MD, 79- *Concurrent Pos:* Lectr, Ill Inst Technol, 67-69. *Mem:* Am Phys Soc; Brit Inst Physics; Am Ceramic Soc; Soc Rheology; Soc Glass Technol, Ger. *Res:* Influences of environment on mechanical properties of glasses, ceramics, adhesives, composites and metals; rheology of organic and inorganic glasses: mechanical metallurgy processess. *Mailing Add:* Martin Marietta Labs 1450 S Rolling Rd Baltimore MD 21227

MILLS, JOHN NORMAN, b Neenah, Wis, Sept 29, 32; m 76; c 4. BIOCHEMISTRY. *Educ:* Wis State Col, BA, 54; Okla State Univ, MS, 56; Univ Okla, PhD, 65. *Prof Exp:* Asst chem, Okla State Univ, 54-58; from instr to asst prof, Okla Baptist Univ, 58-65; sr investr, Okla Med Res Found, 65-67; assoc prof, 67-71, PROF CHEM, OKLA BAPTIST UNIV, 71- *Concurrent Pos:* NIH res grant, 68- *Mem:* Am Chem Soc. *Res:* Human gastric proteolytic enzymes and zymogens; protein structure; enzyme activity. *Mailing Add:* Dept of Chem Okla Baptist Univ Shawnee OK 74801

MILLS, JOHN T, b Redhill, Eng, July 31, 37; m 65; c 2. PLANT PATHOLOGY. *Educ:* Univ Sheffield, BSc, 59; Univ London, PhD(plant path), dipl, Imp Col, 62. *Prof Exp:* Plant pathologist, Tate & Lyle Cent Agr Res Sta, Trinidad, WI, 63-67; RES SCIENTIST, RES STA, CAN DEPT AGR, 67- *Mem:* Can Phytopath Soc; Am Phytopath Soc. *Res:* Ecology of fungi occurring in stored cereals and oil seeds; fluorescence microscopy of seeds invaded by fungi. *Mailing Add:* Can Dept Agr Res Sta 195 Dafoe Rd Winnipeg MB R3T 2M9 Can

MILLS, KING LOUIS, JR, b Leslie, Ark, Nov 14, 16; m 42, 58; c 1. PETROLEUM CHEMISTRY. *Educ:* Ark State Teachers Col, BS, 38; Univ Ark, MS, 42. *Prof Exp:* Res chemist, 43-54, group leader, 54-65, SECT MGR, RES & DEVELOP DEPT, PHILLIPS PETROL CO, 65- *Mem:* Am Chem Soc; Am Inst Chem Engrs. *Res:* Petroleum refining processes; hydrocarbon conversions; heterogeneous catalysis; petrochemicals; carbon black technology. *Mailing Add:* Res & Develop Dept 101G PRC Phillips Petrol Co Bartlesville OK 74004

MILLS, LEWIS CRAIG, JR, b Chicago, Ill, May 19, 23; m 47; c 4. INTERNAL MEDICINE. *Educ:* Baylor Univ, MD, 46; Am Bd Internal Med, dipl, 57; Endocrinol & Metab Bd, dipl, 75. *Prof Exp:* Intern, John Sealey Hosp, Galveston, Tex, 46-47; resident, Jefferson Davis Hosp, Houston, 49-51 & Methodist Hosp, Houston, 52; from instr to asst prof internal med, Baylor Col Med, 53-57; from asst prof to assoc prof, 57-61, clin prof, 61-64, dir endocrinol & metab dis, Hosp, 69-74, assoc dean affil, 74-77, PROF MED, HAHNEMANN MED COL, 64-, V PRES FOR HEALTH AFFAIRS, 77- *Concurrent Pos:* Fel cardiol, Jefferson Davis Hosp, Houston, 51; res fel endocrinol, Peter Bent Brigham Hosp, Boston, 52-53; sr attend physician, Hahnemann Hosp, 58-, assoc vpres med affairs. *Honors & Awards:* Lindback Found Award, 64. *Mem:* Am Soc Pharmacol & Exp Therapeut; Soc Exp Biol & Med; Am Diabetes Asn; Am Fedn Clin Res; fel Am Col Physicians. *Res:* Endocrinology; metabolism; diabetes; vasopressor drugs; shock. *Mailing Add:* Dept of Med Hahnemann Med Col & Hosp 230 N Broad St Philadelphia PA 19102

MILLS, NORMAN THOMAS, b Hammond, Ind, Jan 16, 32; m 58; c 6. CHEMICAL ENGINEERING. *Educ:* Purdue Univ, BS, 59; Univ Del, MS, 61. *Prof Exp:* Res engr, Standard Oil Co, Whiting, Ind, 58-59, Linde Div, Union Carbide, Speedway, Ind, 60-64, Allison Div, Gen Motors Corp, Indianapolis, Ind, 64-66; SR ENGR, SUPV RES ENGR & ASSOC DIR, INLAND STEEL CO, EAST CHICAGO, IND, 66- *Concurrent Pos:* Prog chmn, Int Iron & Steel Congress, 75-78. *Mem:* Sigma Xi; Iron & Steel Soc; Am Inst Mining, Metall & Petrol Engrs (pres, 80-83). *Res:* Cokemaking; ironmaking; steelmaking; casting (static and continuous); hot and cold working of steel; steel coating processes; thermal processing of steel. *Mailing Add:* Inland Steel Res Labs 3001 E Columbus Dr East Chicago IN 46312

MILLS, ROBERT BARNEY, b Lane, Kans, Feb 10, 22; m 45; c 1. ENTOMOLOGY. *Educ:* Kans State Univ, BS, 49, PhD(entom), 64; Univ Colo, MEd, 53. *Prof Exp:* High sch teacher, Kans, 49-61; from asst prof to assoc prof, 63-76, PROF ENTOM, KANS STATE UNIV, 76- *Mem:* Entom Soc Am. *Res:* Stored product entomology. *Mailing Add:* Dept of Entom Kans State Univ Manhattan KS 66506

MILLS, ROBERT GAIL, b Effingham, Ill, Jan 20, 24; m 46; c 2. NUCLEAR PHYSICS. *Educ:* Princeton Univ, BSE, 44; Univ Mich, MA, 47; Univ Calif, Berkeley, PhD(nuclear physics), 52. *Prof Exp:* Instr elec eng, Princeton Univ, 43-44, res assoc elec eng & physics, 45-46; res assoc, Univ Mich, 46-47; Nat Res Coun res fel physics, Univ Zurich, 52-53, instr, 53-54; MEM SR TECH STAFF, PRINCETON UNIV, 54-, PROF, 73- *Mem:* Am Nuclear Soc; Am Phys Soc; fel Inst Elec & Electronics Engrs. *Res:* Controlled thermonuclear research; research machines. *Mailing Add:* 150 Prospect Ave Princeton NJ 08540

MILLS, ROBERT LAURENCE, b Englewood, NJ, Apr 15, 27; m 48; c 5. THEORETICAL PHYSICS. *Educ:* Columbia Univ, AB, 48, PhD(physics), 55; Cambridge Univ, BA, 50, MA, 54. *Prof Exp:* Res assoc physics, Brookhaven Nat Lab, 53-55; mem sch math, Inst Advan Study, 55-56; from asst prof to assoc prof, 56-62, PROF PHYSICS, OHIO STATE UNIV, 62- *Honors & Awards:* Rumford Premium Award, AAAS, 80. *Mem:* Am Phys Soc; Am Asn Univ Professors; Fedn Am Scientists; Arms Control Asn. *Res:* Quantum field theory; many-body theory; theory of alloys. *Mailing Add:* Dept of Physics Ohio State Univ Columbus OH 43210

MILLS, ROBERT LEROY, b Canton, Ohio, June 6, 22; m 45; c 4. SOLID STATE CHEMISTRY. *Educ:* Washington & Jefferson Col, BS, 43; Calif Inst Technol, MS, 48; Stanford Univ, PhD(chem), 50. *Prof Exp:* Asst chem, Calif Inst Technol, 43-48 & Stanford Univ, 48-49; mem staff, 50-75, ASST GROUP LEADER, LOS ALAMOS NAT LAB, UNIV CALIF, 75- *Mem:* Fel AAAS; fel Am Inst Chemists. *Res:* High pressure physics; equation of state; low temperature physics; studies of light molecules to 200 kbar; high pressure solid state chemistry. *Mailing Add:* Los Alamos Nat Lab Univ Calif PO Box 1663 Los Alamos NM 87545

MILLS, ROGER EDWARD, b Cleveland, Ohio, Nov 19, 30; m 58; c 2. PHYSICS. *Educ:* Ohio State Univ, BSc & MSc, 52, PhD(physics), 63. *Prof Exp:* Physicist, Battelle Mem Inst, 60-63, sr physicist, 63-67, assoc div chief, 67-69; assoc prof, 69-75, asst vpres acad affairs, 74-81, PROF PHYSICS, UNIV LOUISVILLE, 75- *Mem:* Am Phys Soc. *Res:* Ferrimagnetism; critical phenomena. *Mailing Add:* Dept Physics Univ Louisville Louisville KY 40292

MILLS, RUSSELL CLARENCE, b Milwaukee, Wis, Nov 13, 18; m 40; c 5. MEDICAL EDUCATION. *Educ:* Univ Wis, BS, 40, MS, 42, PhD(biochem), 44. *Prof Exp:* Asst biochem, Univ Wis, 40-44; from asst prof to assoc prof, 46-51, assoc dean grad sch, 63-70 & sch med, 63-72, assoc vchancellor, 72-75, asst to chancellor, 75-76, univ dir support & serv, 76-79, PROF BIOCHEM, UNIV KANS, 51-, DIR GERONT & ASSOC TO CHANCELLOR, 79- *Concurrent Pos:* Alan Gregg traveling scholar med educ, Far East, 70-71; consult, Asn Am Med Cols, 75-77. *Mem:* AAAS; Am Soc Biol Chemists; Geront Soc Am. *Res:* Health and social services for the frail elderly. *Mailing Add:* 2203 W 70th Terr Shawnee Mission KS 66208

MILLS, THOMAS K, b Hartford, Conn, Nov 8, 42; m 70; c 1. ELECTRONICS ENGINEERING. *Educ:* Johns Hopkins Univ, BS, 64; NC State Univ, MEE, 66, PhD(elec eng), 70. *Prof Exp:* Electronics engr, US Army, 70-72; ELECTRONICS ENGR, HARRY DIAMOND LABS, US ARMY ELECTRONICS RES & DEVELOP COMMAND, 72- *Mem:* Inst Elec & Electronics Engrs. *Mailing Add:* Harry Diamond Labs 2800 Powder Mill Rd Adelphi MD 20783

MILLS, THOMAS MARSHALL, b Des Moines, Iowa, Nov 2, 38; m 60; c 2. REPRODUCTIVE ENDOCRINOLOGY. *Educ:* Univ Iowa, BA, 61, MS, 64, PhD(zool), 67. *Prof Exp:* Trainee steroid biochem, Ohio State Univ, 67-68; res assoc, Endocrine Lab, Univ Miami, 68-71; asst prof, 71-76, ASSOC PROF ENDOCRINOL, MED COL GA, 76- *Mem:* Endocrine Soc; Soc Study Reproduction. *Res:* Control of ovulation; ovarian steroid synthesis; metabolism of ovarian tissues. *Mailing Add:* Dept of Endocrinol Med Col of Ga Augusta GA 30902

MILLS, WENDELL HOLMES, JR, b Detroit, Mich, July 31, 45; m 69. NUMERICAL ANALYSIS, DIFFERENTIAL EQUATIONS. *Educ:* Univ Mich, BSE, 68, PhD(math), 76; Univ Fla, MS, 72. *Prof Exp:* Mem tech staff, Rockwell Int, 68-72; ASST PROF MATH, PA STATE UNIV, 76- *Concurrent Pos:* Co prin investr, NSF, 81- *Mem:* Am Math Soc; Soc Indust & Appl Math. *Res:* Numerical solution and analysis of and scientific programming for dynamical problems in engineering. *Mailing Add:* Dept Math Pa State Univ 413 McAllister Bldg University Park PA 16802

MILLS, WILLIAM CLEARON, JR, b Wake Co, NC, Oct 24, 25; m; c 1. POULTRY SCIENCE, MARKETING. *Educ:* NC State Univ, BS, 50; Mich State Univ, 60, PhD(poultry mkt), 63. *Prof Exp:* Sales & serv work, Siler City Mills, NC, 50-52; exten turkey specialist, 52-63, assoc prof poultry sci & proj leader, Poultry Sci Exten, 63-66, PROF POULTRY SCI & CHG POULTRY SCI EXTEN, AGR EXTEN SERV, NC STATE UNIV, 66- *Concurrent Pos:* Consult mkt mgt. *Mem:* Poultry Sci Asn. *Res:* Market research in turkey grades and pricing. *Mailing Add:* 208 Scott Hall NC State Univ Raleigh NC 27607

MILLS, WILLIAM HAROLD, b New York, NY, Nov 9, 21; m 49; c 3. MATHEMATICS. *Educ:* Swarthmore Col, AB, 43; Princeton Univ, MA, 47, PhD(math), 49. *Prof Exp:* Physicist, Aberdeen Proving Ground, 43-44; asst in instr, math, Princeton Univ, 48-49; from instr to assoc prof, Yale Univ, 49-64; MATHEMATICIAN, INST DEFENSE ANAL, 63- *Mem:* Am Math Soc. *Res:* Combinatorics; number theory; algebra. *Mailing Add:* Inst Defense Anal Thanet Rd Princeton NJ 08540

MILLS, WILLIAM RAYMOND, JR, b Dallas, Tex, Feb 14, 30; m 52; c 3. NUCLEAR SCIENCE. *Educ:* Rice Inst, BA, 51; Calif Inst Technol, PhD(physics), 55. *Prof Exp:* Res asst, Knolls Atomic Power Lab, Gen Elec Co, 55-56; sr res technologist, Socony Mobil Oil Co, Inc, 56-63; RES ASSOC, FIELD RES LAB, MOBIL RES & DEVELOP CORP, 63- *Concurrent Pos:* Adj prof, Southern Methodist Univ, 69- *Mem:* Am Phys Soc; Sigma Xi; Am Nuclear Soc. *Res:* Gamma-ray spectroscopy, especially of common earth elements; neutron physics; pulsed neutron phenomena. *Mailing Add:* Mobil Res & Develop Corp PO Box 900 Dallas TX 75221

MILLS, WILLIAM RONALD, b Clarksville, Tenn, June, 30, 47; m 69; c 1. PLANT BIOCHEMISTRY, PHOTOSYNTHESIS. *Educ:* Austin Peay State Univ, BS, 69, MS, 73; Miami Univ, PhD(bot), 77. *Prof Exp:* Teacher biol, Christian Coun High Sch, 69-71; teaching asst, Austin Peay State Univ, 71-73; res asst bot, Miami Univ, 73-77; fel biochem, Rothamsted Exp Sta, Eng, 77-78; res assoc, Carleton Univ, Can, 78-79; ASST PROF BIOL, UNIV HOUSTON, CLEAR LAKE, 79- *Mem:* AAAS; Am Soc Plant Physiologists; Am Inst Biol Sci. *Res:* Biosynthesis of essential amino acids and proteins in leaves of crop plants and the regulation of these processes; isolation and purification of physiologically active organelles from plants. *Mailing Add:* Univ Houston at Clear Lake City 2700 Bay Area Blvd Houston TX 77058

MILLS, WILLIAM T(ERRELL), b Ga, Dec 1, 28; m 51; c 4. AGRICULTURAL ENGINEERING. *Educ:* Univ Ga, BS, 49; NC State Col, MS, 55. *Prof Exp:* Irrig engr, Schroer Implement Co, Ga, 49-51; res asst agr eng, NC State Col, 53-55, res instr, 55-58, res asst prof, 58-61; res analyst, 61-77, MKT RES MGR, LILLISTON IMPLEMENT CO, 77- *Mem:* Am Soc Agr Engrs. *Res:* Development and marketing of farm machinery. *Mailing Add:* Lilliston Corp Box 3930 Albany GA 31708

MILLSAPS, KNOX, b Birmingham, Ala, Sept 10, 21; div; c 4. APPLIED FLUIDS MATHEMATICS, ENGINEERING MECHANICS. *Educ:* Auburn Univ, BS, 40; Calif Inst Technol, PhD, 43. *Prof Exp:* Assoc prof aeronaut eng, Ohio State Univ, 47-48; mathematician, Off Air Res, US Dept Air Force, 48-49 & 50-51, chief mathematician, Wright Air Develop Ctr, 52-55, chief scientist, Missile Develop Ctr, 56-60, chief scientist, Off Aerospace Res & exec dir, Off Sci Res, 60-63; res prof aerospace eng, Univ Fla, 63-68; head prof mech eng, Colo State Univ, 68-73; PROF ENG SCI & CHMN DEPT, UNIV FLA, 73- *Concurrent Pos:* Prof, Auburn Univ, 49-52 & Mass Inst Technol, 55-56. *Mem:* Am Inst Aeronaut & Astronaut; Soc Eng Sci; Am Math Soc; Math Asn Am; Am Phys Soc. *Res:* Fluid mechanics; heat transfer. *Mailing Add:* PO Box 13857 Gainesville FL 32604

MILLSTEIN, LLOYD GILBERT, b Brooklyn, NY, Jan 2, 32; m 53; c 2. MEDICAL PHYSIOLOGY, INFORMATION SCIENCE. *Educ:* NY Univ, BA, 53; Rutgers Univ, MS, 60, PhD(physiol, biochem), 64. *Prof Exp:* Microbiologist, Univ Hosp, Bellevue Med Ctr, 53; med writer pharmaceut, Squibb Inst Med Res Div, 55-57, toxicologist, 57-64; sr scientist, Smith Kline & French Labs, 64-67; dir sci info & commun, NcNeil Labs, 67-77; dir, Prescription Drug Labeling Staff, 77-81, DEP DIR, DIV DRUG ADVERTISING & LABELING, BUR DRUGS, 81- *Concurrent Pos:* Fed Drug Admin liaison, Nat Inst Aging, NIH, 77- *Mem:* Sigma Xi; AAAS; Am Heart Asn; NY Acad Sci. *Res:* Drug regulatory affairs; gerontology; pharmacology and drug evaluation. *Mailing Add:* Bur of Drugs HFD-171 5600 Fishers Lane Rockville MD 20857

MILMAN, DORIS H, b New York, NY, Nov 17, 17; m 41; c 1. MEDICINE, PSYCHIATRY. *Educ:* Barnard Col, BA, 38; NY Univ, MD, 42; Am Bd Pediat, dipl. *Prof Exp:* From asst prof to assoc prof pediat psychiat, 64-73, actg chmn dept, 73-75, chief-of-serv pediat, State Univ Hosp, 73-75, PROF PEDIAT, STATE UNIV NY DOWNSTATE MED CTR, 73-, ACTG CHMN DEPT, 82-, CHIEF-OF-SERV, 82- *Concurrent Pos:* Chief-of-serv, Kings County Hosp Ctr, 73-75 & 82. *Mem:* AMA; Am Pediat Soc; Am Psychiat Asn; Am Acad Pediat. *Res:* Minimal brain impairment; group work with parents of handicapped children; school phobia; adolescent phenomena; drug abuse. *Mailing Add:* 126 Westminster Rd Brooklyn NY 11218

MILMAN, HARRY ABRAHAM, b Cairo, Egypt, May 16, 43; US citizen; m 68; c 2. BIOCHEMICAL PHARMACOLOGY. *Educ:* Columbia Univ, BS, 66; St John's Univ, NY, MS, 68; George Washington Univ, PhD(pharmacol), 78. *Prof Exp:* scientist toxicol, Nat Cancer Inst, 70-80; SR TOXICOLOGIST, US ENVIRON PROTECTION AGENCY, 80- *Mem:* Am Soc Pharmacol & Exp Therapeut; Soc Toxicol; Int Asn Comparative Res Leukemia & Related Dis. *Res:* Assessment of the carcinogenecity of chemical compounds and the study of tumor markers; metabolism and homeostasis of asparagine. *Mailing Add:* 14317 Bauer Dr Rockville MD 20853

MILMORE, JOHN EDWARD, b Brooklyn, NY, Oct 31, 43; m 66; c 2. NEUROENDOCRINOLOGY, PHARMACOLOGY. *Educ:* Fordham Univ, BS, 65; Long Island Univ, MS, 68; Rutgers Univ, PhD(physiol), 74. *Prof Exp:* Res asst pharmacol, US Vitamin Inc, 65-66; res asst endocrinol, Hoffmann-La Roche Inc, 66-68; res assoc pharmacol, Squibb Inst Med Res, 68-75; res assoc nutrit, Am Health Found, 75-78; ASST PROF PHARMACOL, NY MED COL, 78- *Mem:* AAAS; Endocrine Soc; NY Acad Sci. *Res:* Endocrine and central nervous system pharmacology; hypothalamic peptides; prolactin; hormones and mammary cancer; endogenous opioids. *Mailing Add:* 5 Oriole Lane Peekskill NY 10566

MILNE, DAVID BAYARD, b Evanston, Ill, Oct 24, 40; m 66; c 2. NUTRITIONAL BIOCHEMISTRY, BIOINORGANIC CHEMISTRY. *Educ:* Wash State Univ, BS, 62; Ore State Univ, MS, 65, PhD(biochem), 68. *Prof Exp:* Res assoc biochem, NC State Univ, 67-69; res chemist, Vet Admin Hosp, Long Beach, Calif, 69-77; res chemist, Letterman Army Inst Res, 74-79; RES CHEMIST, HUMAN NUTRIT RES CTR, SCI & EDUC ADMIN, USDA, 79- *Mem:* Am Inst Nutrit; Soc Environ Geochem & Health; Am Chem Soc. *Res:* Copper metabolism; metabolism and function of new essential trace elements; methods for assessment of nutritional status; clinical chemistry. *Mailing Add:* Human Nutrit Res Ctr Sci & Educ Admin USDA Grand Forks ND 58202

MILNE, DAVID HALL, b Highland Park, Mich, Dec 15, 39; m 64. ENTOMOLOGY. *Educ:* Dartmouth Col, BA, 61; Purdue Univ, PhD(entom), 68. *Prof Exp:* Asst prof gen sci, Ore State Univ, 67-71; MEM FAC, EVERGREEN STATE COL, 71- *Concurrent Pos:* NASA fel, 80-81. *Mem:* AAAS; Pac Estuarine Res Soc; Fel Am Soc Elec Eng. *Res:* Computer simulation of predation, competition processes; computer simulation of ecosystem dynamics; crab population biology. processes; computer simulation of ecosystem dynamics. *Mailing Add:* Dept of Biol Evergreen State Col Olympia WA 98505

MILNE, EDMUND ALEXANDER, b Eugene, Ore, Mar 3, 27; m 54; c 2. NUCLEAR PHYSICS. *Educ:* Ore State Col, BA, 49; Calif Inst Technol, MS, 50, PhD(nuclear physics), 53. *Prof Exp:* Asst, Calif Inst Technol, 52-53, res fel, 53-54; asst prof, 54-58, ASSOC PROF PHYSICS, NAVY POSTGRAD SCH, 58- *Mem:* Am Phys Soc. *Res:* Energy levels of light nuclei. *Mailing Add:* Dept of Physics Naval Postgrad Sch Monterey CA 93940

MILNE, ERIC CAMPBELL, b Perth, Scotland, Feb 8, 29; Can citizen; m 55; c 5. RADIOLOGY. *Educ:* Univ Edinburgh, MB, ChB, 56, DMRD, 60; Royal Col Radiologists, Eng, FRCR, 62. *Prof Exp:* Intern med surg, Monmouth Med Ctr, NJ, 56-57; resident chest dis, Tulare-Kings Counties Hosp, Calif, 57-58; sr house officer radiol, Royal Infirmary, Univ Edinburgh, 58-60; radiologist, McKellar Gen Hosp, Ft William, Ont, 61-65; asst prof radiol, Univ Western Ont, 65-66 & Peter Bent Brigham Hosp, Harvard Med Sch, 66-68; prof & dir exp radiol, Radiol Res Labs, Univ Toronto, 68-75, consult, Dept Lab Animal Serv, 69-75; chmn dept, 75-80, PROF RADIOL SCI, COL MED, UNIV CALIF, IRVINE, 75- *Concurrent Pos:* UK Med Res Found fel, Depts Radiol & Med, Royal Infirmary, Univ Edinburgh, Edinburgh, 60-61; Ont Cancer Found Gordon Richards fel, Cardiovasc Res Inst, Univ Calif, San Francisco, 65-66; chmn, Nat Adv Comt, Mayo Clinic Biotechnol Resource, 78-81; Fogarty sr int fel, 81. *Mem:* Am Col Radiologists; Soc Photo-Optical Instrument Engrs; Fleischner Soc (pres, 79-80); Asn Univ Radiologists. *Res:* Tumor circulation; radiologic diagnosis of early pulmonary diseases; analysis of x-ray image formation; radiologic magnification techniques; lung water pulmonary microcirculation; x-ray tube construction; three dimensional image presentation; image analysis. *Mailing Add:* Dept of Radiol Sci Univ of Calif Col of Med Irvine CA 92664

MILNE, FRANK JAMES, b Aberdeen, Scotland, Mar 30, 19; Can citizen; m 44; c 3. VETERINARY MEDICINE. *Educ:* Royal (Dick) Vet Col, MRCVS, 41; Colo Agr & Mech Col, DVM, 52; Univ Zurich, Dr Med Vet, 62; Am Col Vet Surg, dipl, 66. *Prof Exp:* Lectr surg, Royal Vet Col, London, 48-49; asst prof, Colo Agr & Mech Col, 50-53; prof obstet, 53-71, PROF SURG, ONT VET COL, UNIV GUELPH, 53- *Concurrent Pos:* Ed, Am Asn Equine Practitioners, 56-; vis prof, Univ Ibadan, Nigeria, 72-73. *Mem:* Am Vet Med Asn; Am Asn Equine Practitioners (vpres, 69, pres, 71); Can Vet Med Asn; Brit Vet Asn; Brit Equine Vet Asn. *Res:* Equine surgery. *Mailing Add:* Dept of Clin Studies Ont Vet Col Univ Guelph Guelph ON N1G 2W1 Can

MILNE, GEORGE MCLEAN, JR, b Port Chester, NY, Dec 29, 43; m 65; c 2. MEDICINAL CHEMISTRY, PHARMACOLOGY. *Educ:* Yale Univ, BSc, 65; Mass Inst Technol, PhD(org chem), 69. *Prof Exp:* NIH fel chem, Stanford Univ, 69-70; mgr, Dept Pharmacol, 70-78, proj leader, Med Chem Res, 73, DIR, DEPT IMMUNOL & INFECTIOUS DISEASES RES, PFIZER CENT RES, PFIZER INC, 81- *Mem:* Am Chem Soc; Sigma Xi. *Res:* Design and pharmacological evaluation of central nervous system drugs; antiemetic and analgesic pharmacology; biologic response modifiers for infectious, chronic degenerative and inflammatory diseases. *Mailing Add:* Dept Immunol & Infectious Diseases Pfizer Cent Res Pfizer Inc Groton CT 06340

MILNE, GEORGE WILLIAM ANTHONY, b Stockport, Eng, May, 1937; US citizen. CHEMISTRY. *Educ:* Univ Manchester, BSc, 57, MS, 58, PhD, 60. *Prof Exp:* Res fel, Univ Wis, 60-61; vis fel, Lab Chem, Nat Inst Arthritis & Metab Dis, 62-63, vis assoc, 63-64; chemist, Lab Chem, Nat Heart, Lung & Blood Inst, 65-81; CHIEF INFO TECHNOL BR, DIV CANCER TREATMENT, NAT CANCER INST, 81- *Concurrent Pos:* Adj prof chem, Georgetown Univ, 67-; NIH mgr, NIH/Environ Protection Agency Chem Info Syst, 72-81. *Mem:* AAAS; Am Chem Soc; The Chem Soc. *Res:* Chemistry of steroids, terpenes, alkaloids, amino acids, nucleosides, nucleotides, carbohydrates, and application of nuclear magnetic resonance spectroscopy and mass spectrometry to studies in these fields, particularly biological function of various members of these classes; use of computers to handle data associated with chemicals; use of physical properties data to identify compounds; problems of information retrieval in chemistry and biology. *Mailing Add:* Nat Cancer Inst Div Cancer Treatment 8300 Colesville Rd Rm 416 Silver Spring MD 20910

MILNE, GORDON GLADSTONE, b Deland, Fla, July 13, 16; m 44; c 3. OPTICS. *Educ:* Univ Sask, BA, 38, MA, 39; Univ Rochester, PhD(optics, physics), 50. *Prof Exp:* Res physicist, Inst Optics, Univ Rochester, 42-45, res assoc optics, 45-60, sr res assoc, 60-66; PHYSICIST, TROPEL, INC, 66- *Mem:* AAAS; Optical Soc Am; Soc Photog Scientists & Engrs. *Res:* Optical instrumentation; manufacture of precision optics. *Mailing Add:* Tropel Inc 60 O'Connor Rd Fairport NY 14450

MILNE, JOHN B, inorganic chemistry, see previous edition

MILNE, LORUS JOHNSON, b Toronto, Ont, Sept 12; nat US. BIOLOGY. *Educ:* Univ Toronto, BA, 33; Harvard Univ, MA, 34, PhD(biol), 36. *Prof Exp:* Asst zool, Harvard Univ, 34-36; prof biol, Southwestern Univ, 36-37; adj prof, Randolph-Macon Woman's Col, 37-39, assoc prof, 39-42; war res, Aviation Med, Johnson Found, Univ Pa, 42-47; assoc prof zool, Univ Vt, 47-48; assoc prof, 48-51, PROF ZOOL, UNIV NH, 51- *Concurrent Pos:* Res grants, Carnegie Corp, Sigma Xi, Am Acad Arts & Sci, Am Philos Soc, Cranbrook Inst Sci & Explorers Club; Fund Advan Educ fac fel, 53-54; exchange lectr, Univs, US-SAfrica Leader Exchange Prog, 59; vis prof environ technol, Fla Int Univ, 74; mem, Marine Biol Lab, Woods Hole. Consult-writer, Biol Sci Curriculum Study, 60-61; Univ NH-Explorers Club deleg, Nairobi Meetings, Int Union Conserv Nature, 63; UNESCO biol consult, NZ, 66. Mem exped, Panama, 51, Cent Am, 53-54, BWI & SAm, 56-57 & 77-78, Equatorial Africa, 59 & 63, NAfrica, Near East, Southeast Africa & Australia, 66. *Honors & Awards:* Nash Award, 54. *Mem:* Fel AAAS; Am Soc Zoologists; Animal Behav Soc. *Res:* Behavioral ecology; natural history. *Mailing Add:* 1 Garden Lane Durham NH 03824

MILNE, MARGERY (JOAN) (GREENE), b New York, NY, Jan 18, 15. BIOLOGY. *Educ:* Hunter Col, BA, 33; Columbia Univ, MA, 34; Radcliffe Col, MA, 37, PhD(zool), 39. *Prof Exp:* Instr zool, Univ Maine, 36-37; instr biol, Randolph-Macon Woman's Col, 39-40; asst prof biol & bact, Richmond Prof Inst, Col William & Mary, 40-42 & Beaver Col, 42-47; asst prof bot, Univ Vt, 47-48; asst prof zool, Univ NH, 48-50; assoc prof biol, Mass State Teachers Col, Fitchburg, 56; vis prof, Northeastern Univ, 58; consult biologist, Biol Sci Curric Study, Am Inst Biol Sci, Univ Colo, 60; res assoc, Univ NH, 65-74; LECTR, PARKS & RECREATION, UNIV, NH, 75- *Concurrent Pos:* Grantee, Am Acad Arts & Sci, Sigma Xi & Am Philos Soc; mem exped, Panama, 51, Cent Am, 53-54, BWI & SAm, 56-57 & 77-78, Equatorial Africa, 63 & NAfrica, Near East, Southeast Asia, Australia & New Zealand, 66; exchangee, US-SAfrica Leader Exchange Prog, 59; UNESCO biol consult, NZ, 66; vis prof environ technol, Fla Int Univ, 74- *Honors & Awards:* George Westinghouse Award, 47; Nash Conserv Award, 54; Saxton Mem Award, 54. *Mem:* AAAS; Nat Audubon Soc; Wilderness Soc. *Res:* Animal behavior; ecology; science writing. *Mailing Add:* 1 Garden Lane Durham NH 03824

MILNE, THOMAS ANDERSON, b Winfield, Kans, Dec 29, 27; m 54; c 3. PHYSICAL CHEMISTRY. *Educ:* Univ Kans, AB, 50, PhD(chem), 55. *Prof Exp:* Res engr high temperature chem, Atomics Int Div, NAm Aviation, Inc, 54-57; sr chemist, Stanford Res Inst, 57-60; sr physicist, Midwest Res Inst, 60-63, prin physicist, 63-68, sr adv chem, 68-77, actg br chief, Biol & Chem Conversion Br, 77-78; Prin chemist, 78-80, BR CHIEF, THEROCHEM & ELECTROCHEM RES BR, SOLAR ENG RES INST, 80- *Mem:* AAAS; Am Soc Mass Spectros; Am Combustion Inst; Am Chem Soc; Int Solar Energy Soc. *Res:* Molecular beam formation and sampling at high pressures; combustion processes; thermodynamic behavior of systems at high temperature; mass spectroscopic study of high temperature reactions; homogeneous nucleation; biomass conversion; coal combustion; inhibition chemistry; pyrolysis chemistry. *Mailing Add:* Solar Energy Res Inst 1536 Cole Blvd Golden CO 80401

MILNER, ALICE N, b Bay City, Tex, Sept 5, 25. BIOCHEMISTRY. *Educ:* Tex Woman's Univ, BS, 46, MA, 47; Baylor Univ, PhD(biochem), 59. *Prof Exp:* Instr chem, Centenary Col La, 47-50; head clin chem, Baylor Hosp, Dallas, Tex, 50-52; phys scientist, Vet Admin Hosp, Dallas, 52-53; Nat Cancer Inst fel biochem & oncol, Univ Tex M D Anderson Hosp & Tumor Inst, 59-62, res assoc biochem, 62-65; dir biochem, Moody Clin Res Lab, Col Med, Baylor Univ, 65-67; assoc prof nutrit, 67-80, prog dir coord undergrad progs in dietetics, 74-77, prof & actg chmn, 78-80, CHMN, DEPT NUTRIT, TEX WOMAN'S UNIV, 80- *Mem:* AAAS; Am Chem Soc; Am Asn Cancer Res; Am Dietetic Asn. *Res:* Bionutritional interrelationships; bionutritional aspects of mental retardation and obesity. *Mailing Add:* TWU Res Inst Tex Woman's Univ Denton TX 76204

MILNER, BRENDA (ATKINSON), b Manchester, Eng, July 15, 18; m 44. NEUROPSYCHOLOGY. *Educ:* Cambridge Univ, BA, 39, MA, 46, ScD, 72; McGill Univ, PhD(psychol), 52. *Hon Degrees:* LLD, Queen's Univ, 80. *Prof Exp:* Exp officer, Ministry of Supply, UK, 41-44; asst prof psychol, Univ Montreal, 45-52; res assoc, Univ, 52-53, from lectr neurol & neurosurg & psychologist, Montreal Neurol Inst to assoc prof psychol, Univ, 53-69, PROF NEUROL & NEUROSURG, MCGILL UNIV, 69-, HON PROF PSYCHOL, 77- *Honors & Awards:* Distinguished Sci Contrib Award, Am Psychol Asn, 73 & Can Psychol Asn, 81; Karl Spencer Lashely Award, Am Philos Asn, 79. *Mem:* Am Psychol Asn; Am Acad Neurol; Brit Exp Psychol Soc; fel Royal Soc London; Royal Soc Can. *Res:* Brain function; perception and learning in human patients undergoing brain operation for focal cortical epilepsy. *Mailing Add:* Montreal Neurol Inst McGill Univ 3801 University St Montreal PQ H3A 2B4 Can

MILNER, CLIFFORD E, b Concord, NH, Aug 10, 28; m 51; c 5. PHYSICAL CHEMISTRY. *Educ:* Wesleyan Univ, BA, 50, MA, 52; Yale Univ, PhD(phys chem), 55. *Prof Exp:* Res chemist, 55-71, sr res chemist, 71-77, RES ASSOC, E I DU PONT DE NEMOURS & CO, INC, 77- *Mem:* Am Chem Soc; Soc Photog Scientists & Engrs. *Res:* Pressure dependence of the dielectric constant of water; photographic emulsions and processing solutions; diffusion transfer processes. *Mailing Add:* 1763 Winton Rd N Rochester NY 14609

MILNER, DAVID, b Birkenhead, Eng, July 23, 38; US citizen; m 61; c 2. ANALYTICAL CHEMISTRY. *Educ:* LRIC, 75Univ Santa Clara, MBA, 80. *Prof Exp:* Tech asst chem, Distiller Co Ltd, Eng, 56-61; tech asst, Eli Lilly Ltd, Eng, 61-62, control chemist, 62-64; sect head pharmaceut anal, Syntex Corp, 64-81; TECH MGR, CHEM INDUST, NZ, 81- *Mem:* Royal Inst Chem; fel Royal Soc Chem. *Res:* Development of analytical methods for pharmaceutical dosage forms. *Mailing Add:* Chem Indust 46 Ben Lomond Crescent Pakuranga 94304 New Zealand

MILNER, ERIC CHARLES, b London, Eng, May 17, 28; m 54; c 4. MATHEMATICS. *Educ:* Univ London, BSc, 49, MSc, 50, PhD(math), 63. *Prof Exp:* Lectr math, Univ Malaya, 52-61 & Univ Reading, 61-67; PROF MATH, UNIV CALGARY, 67-, CHMN DIV PURE MATH, DEPT MATH, STATIST & COMPUT SCI, 74- *Mem:* Am Math Soc; Math Asn Am; Can Math Cong; London Math Soc. *Res:* Set theory; combinatorics; graph theory. *Mailing Add:* Dept Math Statist & Comput Sci Univ of Calgary Calgary AB T2N 1N4 Can

MILNER, JOHN AUSTIN, b Pine Bluff, Ark, June 11, 47. NUTRITION. *Educ:* Okla State Univ, BS, 69; Cornell Univ, PhD(nutrit), 74. *Prof Exp:* Res assoc animal sci, Cornell Univ, 74-75; asst prof, 75-79, ASSOC PROF NUTRIT, UNIV ILL, URBANA-CHAMPAIGN, 79- *Concurrent Pos:* Young Investr Award, Nutrit Found, 77-78. *Mem:* Sigma Xi; Nutrit Today Soc; Inst Food Technol; Am Asn Animal Sci; Am Inst Nutrit. *Res:* Relationship of dietary factors effecting ammonia detoxification and the synthesis of arginine, carbohydrates, pyrimidines or polyamines in normal and diseased states; relationship of diet to cancer with special emphasis on selenium and arginine. *Mailing Add:* Dept of Food Sci Univ of Ill Urbana IL 61801

MILNER, MAX, b Edmonton, Alta, Jan 24, 14; nat US; m 42; c 2. FOOD SCIENCE, NUTRITION. *Educ:* Univ Sask, BSc, 38; Univ Minn, MS 41, PhD(biochem), 45. *Hon Degrees:* LLD, Univ Sask, 79. *Prof Exp:* Res chemist, Pillsbury Mills, Inc, Minn, 41-42; res assoc, Univ Minn, 45-46; prof cereal chem, Kans State Univ, 47-59; sr food technologist, UNICEF, 59-71; dir secretariat, Protein-Calorie Adv Group UN Syst, 71-75; coordr, NSF-Mass Inst Technol Protein Resources Study, 75; nutrit coordr, Off Technol

Assessment, US Cong, 76; assoc dir int nutrit prog, Mass Inst Technol, 76-78; EXEC OFFICER, AM INST NUTRIT, 78- *Concurrent Pos:* Consult, Food & Agr Orgn, UN, 54-58; adj prof, Columbia Univ, 64-; sr lectr, Mass Inst Technol, 75-; mem panel world food supply, President's Sci Adv Comt, 68-; chmn, Gordon Res Conf Food & Nutrit, 68. *Honors & Awards:* Inst Food Technologists Int Award. *Mem:* Fel AAAS; Am Chem Soc; Am Inst Nutrit; Am Asn Cereal Chem; Inst Food Technologists. *Res:* Cereal chemistry; nutrition, protein technology and development. *Mailing Add:* Am Inst of Nutrit 9650 Rockville Pike Bethesda MD 20014

MILNER, PAUL CHAMBERS, b Washington, DC, Aug 23, 31. PHYSICAL CHEMISTRY. *Educ:* Haverford Col, BS, 52; Princeton Univ, MA, 54, PhD(chem), 56. *Prof Exp:* Mem tech staff, 57-69, HEAD, ELECTROCHEM & CONTAMINATION RES DEPT, BELL LABS, 69- *Mem:* Am Chem Soc; Electrochem Soc. *Res:* Electrochemistry; kinetics; thermodynamics. *Mailing Add:* Bell Labs Murray Hill NJ 07974

MILNER, REID THOMPSON, b Carbondale, Ill, Aug 13, 03; m 28, 39; c 1. *Educ:* Univ Ill, BS, 24, MS, 25; Univ Calif, PhD(phys chem), 28. *Prof Exp:* From asst to assoc chemist, US Bur Mines, 29-30; assoc chemist, USDA, 30-36, sr chemist, Regional Soybean Indust Prod Lab, Bur Agr Chem & Eng, 36-39, dir, 39-41, head anal & phys chem div, Northern Regional Res Lab, 41-48, dir, 48-54; prof food sci & head dept, 54-71, EMER PROF FOOD SCI, UNIV ILL, URBANA, 71- *Mem:* AAAS; Am Chem Soc; Am Oil Chem Soc (vpres, 46, pres, 47); Inst Food Technologists (pres, 74). *Res:* Low temperature specific heats; microanalysis; gas analysis; agricultural and food chemistry. *Mailing Add:* 614 W Florida Ave Urbana IL 61801

MILNES, ARTHUR G(EORGE), b Heswall, Eng, July 30, 22; nat US; m 55; c 3. ELECTRICAL ENGINEERING. *Educ:* Bristol Univ, BSc, 43, MSc, 47, DSc(elec eng), 56. *Prof Exp:* Engr, Royal Aircraft Estab, Eng, 43-54; vis assoc prof elec eng, Carnegie Inst Technol, 54-55; engr, Royal Aircraft Estab, Eng, 56-57; assoc prof, 57-59, assoc head dept, 66-69, PROF ELEC ENG, CARNEGIE-MELLON UNIV, 60- *Concurrent Pos:* Bd mem, Sensormatic Electronics Corp, 68- *Mem:* Fel Inst Elec & Electronics Engrs; fel Am Phys Soc; Electrochem Soc; fel Brit Inst Elec Engrs. *Res:* Semiconductor device studies; heterojunctions; deep impurities; solar cells. *Mailing Add:* Dept of Elec Eng Carnegie-Mellon Univ Pittsburgh PA 15213

MILNOR, JOHN WILLARD, b Orange, NJ, Feb 20, 31; m 54 & 68; c 3. MATHEMATICS. *Educ:* Princeton Univ, AB, 51, PhD(math), 54. *Hon Degrees:* ScD, Syracuse Univ, 65; DSc, Univ Chicago, 67. *Prof Exp:* Higgins res asst math, Princeton Univ, 53-54, Higgins lectr, 54-55, from asst prof to prof, 55-62, Henry Putnam Univ prof, 62-67, chmn dept, 63-66; prof, Mass Inst Technol, 68-70; PROF MATH, INST ADVAN STUDY, 70- *Concurrent Pos:* Alfred P Sloan fel, 55-59; vis prof, Univ Calif, Berkeley, 59-60; mem, Inst Advan Study, 63-; vis prof, Univ Calif, Los Angeles, 67-68. *Honors & Awards:* Fields Medal, Univ Stockholm, 62; Nat Medal Sci, 66. Mem: Nat Acad Sci; Am Math Soc; Am Acad Arts & Sci; Am Philos Soc. *Mem:* Int Cong Math. *Res:* Topology of manifolds. *Mailing Add:* Inst for Advan Study Princeton NJ 08540

MILNOR, TILLA SAVANUCK KLOTZ, b New York, NY, Sept 29, 34; div; c 2. MATHEMATICS. *Educ:* NY Univ, BA, 55, MS, 56, PhD(math), 59. *Prof Exp:* NSF fel, 58-59; instr math, Univ Calif, Los Angeles, 59-60, lectr, 60-61, from asst prof to assoc prof, 61-69; assoc prof, Boston Col, 69-70; chmn dept, 70-73, PROF MATH, DOUGLASS COL, RUTGERS UNIV, 70-, CHMN DEPT, 78- *Concurrent Pos:* Vis mem, Courant Inst Math Sci, NY Univ, 64-65 & 77. *Mem:* Math Asn Am; Am Math Soc. *Res:* Differential geometry of immersed surfaces, especially questions involving ordinary or nonstandard conformal structures on surfaces; geometric application of methods form Riemann surface theory. *Mailing Add:* Dept of Math Douglass Col Rutgers Univ New Brunswick NJ 08903

MILNOR, WILLIAM ROBERT, b Wilmington, Del, May 4, 20; m 44; c 2. MEDICAL PHYSIOLOGY. *Educ:* Princeton Univ, AB, 41; Johns Hopkins Univ, MD, 44. *Prof Exp:* From instr to assoc prof med, 51-69, PROF PHYSIOL, SCH MED, JOHNS HOPKINS UNIV, 69- *Concurrent Pos:* Nat Heart Inst res fel, 49-51; physician, Johns Hopkins Hosp, 52-, physician-in-chg heart sta, 51-60. *Mem:* Fel Am Col Physicians; Am Physiol Soc; Am Fedn Clin Res. *Res:* Cardiovascular physiology; hemodynamics; vascular and cardiac mechanics; control of pulsatile blood flow. *Mailing Add:* Dept of Physiol Johns Hopkins Univ Sch of Med Baltimore MD 21205

MILO, GEORGE EDWARD, b Montpelier, Vt, Nov 6, 32; m 56; c 4. CARCINOGENESIS, BIOCHEMISTRY. *Educ:* Univ Vt, BA, 58, MS, 61; State Univ NY Buffalo, PhD(virol), 68. *Prof Exp:* Instr biol, Rosary Hill Col, 63-65; NIH fel, Roswell Park Mem Inst, 67-69; sr res virologist, Battelle Mem Inst, 69; asst prof vet pathobiol, 69-75, assoc prof, 75-80, PROF PHYSIOL CHEM, COL MED, OHIO STATE UNIV, 80-, SR RES ASSOC, CAMPUS CANCER CTR, 79- *Mem:* Tissue Cult Asn; Am Asn Cancer Res; Am Soc Biol Chemists. *Res:* Chemical toxicology and in vitro chemical carcinogenesis; carcinogen, carcinogen and steroid administration to human cell systems in vitro. *Mailing Add:* Dept of Physiol Chem Ohio State Univ Col of Med Columbus OH 43210

MILO, HENRY L(OUIS), JR, b Lynn, Mass, May 11, 20; m 44; c 1. AERONAUTICAL & MECHANICAL ENGINEERING. *Educ:* Northeastern Univ, BS, 43. *Prof Exp:* Design engr, Foxboro Co, Foxboro, 46-51, div engr, 51-56, mgr spec prod eng, 56-59, mgr prod design eng, 56-62, mgr eng, 62-63, mgr eng & gen mgr, Neponset Plant, 63-65, vpres US mfg, 65, vpres & corp dir res eng & develop, 65-67; vpres & gen mgr, 67-69, EXEC VPRES, LYTRON INC, 69-, TREAS, 71- *Concurrent Pos:* Mem bd dirs, Lytron Inc & Davidson Fan Co, Woburn, Mass, Nutmeg Steel Castings, Branford, Conn, Fed Street Capital Corp, Boston & Auburn Int, Danvers, Mass. *Mem:* NY Acad Sci; AAAS; Nat Soc Prof Engrs; Am Soc Mech Engrs. *Res:* Pneumatic circuitry and control devices; heat exchangers. *Mailing Add:* 5 Country Club Dr Walpole MA 02081

MILONE, CHARLES ROBERT, b Uhrichsville, Ohio, Feb 13, 13; m 40; c 2. ORGANIC POLYMER CHEMISTRY. *Educ:* Mass Inst Technol, BS, 36, PhD(org chem), 39. *Prof Exp:* Res chemist, Goodyear Tire & Rubber Co, 39-45, sect head, 45-52; supt develop lab, Goodyear Atomic Corp, 52-57, mgr tech div, 57-60, dep gen mgr, 60-67; dir gen prod develop, Goodyear Tire & Rubber Co, 67-68, dir res & gen prod develop, 68-70, vpres, 70-77; RETIRED. *Mem:* AAAS; Am Chem Soc. Res. *Res:* Synthetic rubber; polymerization; new plastics and their applications; gaseous diffusion; atomic energy. *Mailing Add:* 4451 Deauville Ave Stow OH 44224

MILONE, EUGENE FRANK, b New York, NY, June 26, 39; m 59; c 2. ASTRONOMY, ASTRO PHYSICS. *Educ:* Columbia Univ, AB, 61; Yale Univ, MS, 63, PhD(astron), 67. *Prof Exp:* From instr to asst prof physics, Gettysburg Col, 66-71; dir, Hatter Planetarium, 66-71; astronr, US Naval Res Lab, 67-79; asst prof, 71-75, assoc prof, 75-81, PROF PHYSICS, UNIV CALGARY, 81-; CO-SUPVR, ROTHNEY ASTROPHYS OBSERV, 75- *Concurrent Pos:* Lutheran Church Am & Gettysburg Col res & creativity grant, 67-68, Gettysburg Col fac fel, 68-69 & 71-72; Can Nat Res Coun grants, 71-; NATO res grant, 79-81; Can Nat Sci Eng Res Coun major equip grant, 81-82. *Mem:* AAAS; Am Astron Soc; Sigma Xi; NY Acad Sci; Can Astron Soc. *Res:* Optical and infrared photometry and spectroscopy of variable stars, especially interactiong binaries; eclipsing binaries; ultraviolet solar and stellar limb darkening; rapid alternate detection system for differential variable starphotometry. *Mailing Add:* Dept of Physics Univ of Calgary Calgary AB T2N 1N4 Can

MILONE, NICHOLAS ARTHUR, b Italy, Nov 20, 03; nat US; m 34; c 1. PUBLIC HEALTH. *Educ:* Cornell Univ, BS, 29, MS, 51. *Prof Exp:* Instr bact, Cornell Univ, 29-30; state bacteriologist & sanitarian, State Dept Health, NY, 30-49; res bacteriologist, 49-51, res lectr, 51-59, from assoc prof to prof, 60-74, EMER PROF ENVIRON HEALTH, SCH PUB HEALTH, UNIV MICH, ANN ARBOR, 74- *Concurrent Pos:* Consult, Nat Sanit Found, 51-58; proj dir microbiol study foods, Comn Environ Hyg, Armed Forces Epidemiol Bd, Washington, DC, 59-, assoc mem comn, 62-; consult, Panama CZ Health Bur, 61, WHO, 62 & NY State Dept, 67- *Mem:* Fel AAAS; Am Soc Microbiol; Inst Food Technologists; fel Am Pub Health Asn; NY Acad Sci. *Res:* Environmental health; food sanitation and technology; toxic properties of plastic pipe for potable water supplies; bacteriological studies of automatic clothes washing; bacterial toxins; photography; thermometry; microbicides; blood; milk; water; automatic food vending. *Mailing Add:* 2329 Yorkshire Rd Ann Arbor MI 48104

MILSTEIN, FREDERICK, b New York, NY, May 14, 39; m 60; c 3. ENGINEERING, MATERIALS SCIENCE. *Educ:* Univ Calif, Los Angeles, BSc, 62, MS, 63, PhD(eng & appl sci), 66. *Prof Exp:* Nat Ctr Sci Res grant, Electrostatic & Solid State Physics Lab, France, 66-67; res scientist mat sci, Rand Corp, Calif, 67-69; actg asst prof energy & kinetics, Sch Eng & Appl Sci, Univ Calif, Los Angeles, 69-70; from asst prof to assoc prof mat sci, 70-78, assoc dean, Col Eng, 73-75, PROF MAT SCI, UNIV CALIF, SANTA BARBARA, 78-, CHMN, DEPT MECH ENG, 81- *Concurrent Pos:* Lectr, Univ Calif, Los Angeles, 67-69; consult, Rand Corp, Calif, 69-71 & Civil Eng Lab, US Navy, Calif, 78-; vis fel, Clare Hall, Univ Cambridge, 75; sr fel electronics, Weizmann Inst Sci, Israel, 75-76; prin investr grants, NSF & EG&G, Inc, 78- *Res:* Crystal elasticity; magnetism in solids; thermodynamics and statistical mechanics; mechanical behavior and phase transformations in solids; physical metallurgy; solid state physics; theoretical elasticity; electrostatics. *Mailing Add:* Dept of Mech Eng Univ of Calif Santa Barbara CA 93106

MILSTEIN, JAIME, b Argentina, Feb 20, 46; Israel citizen; m 75; c 2. MATHEMATICS. *Educ:* Univ Calif, Berkeley, BA, 70, MA, 73, PhD(math), 75. *Prof Exp:* Asst prof math, Univ Calif, Los Angeles, 75-77; ASST PROF MATH, UNIV SOUTHERN CALIF, 77- *Concurrent Pos:* Vis fel math, Univ Calif, Berkeley, 76; prin investr, NSF & Air Force Off Sci Res, 79-83; assoc prof math, Israel Inst Technol, 82. *Mem:* Am Math Soc; Sigma Xi. *Res:* Inverse problem of large non-linear differential systems; parameter identification of dynamical system described by non-linear ordinary differential equations; mathematical biology; mathematical modelling in biology; pharmaco-kinetics; algorithms non-linear optimization. *Mailing Add:* Dept Math Univ Southern Calif University Park Los Angeles CA 90007

MILSTEIN, STANLEY RICHARD, b Brooklyn, NY, Nov 27, 44. ORGANIC CHEMISTRY, MEDICINAL CHEMISTRY. *Educ:* Rensselaer Polytech Inst, BS, 66; Adelphi Univ, PhD(chem), 74. *Prof Exp:* Res assoc, Dept Chem, Pomona Col, 72-73; asst prof, Dept Chem, Adelphi Univ, 73-74; res assoc, Col Pharm, Univ Cincinnati, 74-78, vis asst prof org chem, 78-79; MGR, TECH SERV, ANDREW JERGENS CO, 80-; ADJ ASST PROF ORGANIC CHEM, UNIV CINCINNATI, 80- *Concurrent Pos:* Soc Cosmetics Chemists grant, 78-79. *Mem:* AAAS; Am Chem Soc; Am Inst Chemists; Royal Soc Chem; Sigma Xi. *Res:* Organic synthesis of biologically active compounds; computer-assisted development of quantitative structure-activity relationships between biological activity and chemical structure; Hansch approach; synthesis of new cosmetic raw materials; claim substantiation. *Mailing Add:* Andrew Jergens Co 2535 Spring Grove Ave Cincinnati OH 45214

MILSTIEN, JULIE BLOCK, b Waynesboro, Va, Oct 11, 42; m 66; c 2. MOLECULAR BIOLOGY. *Educ:* Randolph-Macon Woman's Col, AB, 64; Univ Southern Calif, PhD(biochem), 68. *Prof Exp:* Res biochemist, Viral Leukemia & Lymphoma Br, Nat Cancer Inst, 72; consult, Litton Biomet, Inc, 73; RES CHEMIST, BUR BIOLOGICS, FOOD & DRUG ADMIN, 74- *Concurrent Pos:* Staff fel biophys, Lab Phys Biol, Nat Inst Arthritis & Metab Dis, 68-70, sr staff fel, 70-72; spec fel, Nat Cancer Inst, 72-73; vis grant, Netherlands Soc Pure & Appl Physics. *Mem:* Biophys Soc; Am Soc Microbiol; NY Acad Sci; fel Am Acad Microbiol; Asn Women Sci. *Res:* Molecular biology of measles and polio viruses. *Mailing Add:* Bldg 29A Rm B-05 8800 Rockville Pike Bethesda MD 20014

MILSTOC, MAYER, b Iasy, Rumania, Dec 14, 20; US citizen; m 45. MEDICINE, PATHOLOGY. *Educ:* Univ Bucharest, MD, 52; State Univ NY, MD, 65; Am Bd Path, cert anat & clin path, 69. *Prof Exp:* Asst in res, Inst Res Antibiotics, Bucharest, 51-55, chief lab, 55-57; chief lab clin path, Colentina Hosp, 57-61; asst path, Montefiore-Morrisania Hosp, New York, 66; asst prof path, 67-73, ASSOC PROF CLIN PATH, MED CTR, NY UNIV, 73-; DIR LABS, GOLDWATER MEM HOSP, 69- *Concurrent Pos:* Asst prof microbiol, Inst Medico Pharmaceut, Sch Med, Bucharest. *Mem:* Col Am Path; Am Soc Clin Path. *Res:* Biology of microorganisms, especially antibiotic problems; enzymes, especially cholinesterase in the normal and the diseased. *Mailing Add:* 370 E 76th St New York NY 10021

MILSUM, JOHN H, b Sussex, Eng, Aug 15, 25; Can citizen; m 55; c 2. HEALTH & HEALTH CARE SYSTEM. *Educ:* Univ London, BSc, 45; Mass Inst Technol, SM, 55, ME, 56, ScD(control eng), 57. *Prof Exp:* Proj engr, Nat Res Coun Can, 50-54, head anal sect, 57-61; Abitibi prof control eng, McGill Univ, 61-72, dir biomed eng unit, 66-72; Imp Oil prof gen systs, 72-77, PROF HEALTH CARE & EPIDEMIOL, UNIV BC, 72-, DIR HEALTH SYSTS, COORDR'S OFF HEALTH SCI CTR, 72- *Concurrent Pos:* Consult health care systs, Sci Coun Can, 72; assoc ed, Automatica, Behav Sci, Kubernetes, Methods Info & Med & J Gen Systs; adv ed ser biomed eng & health systs, John Wiley & Sons, Inc. *Mem:* Fel AAAS; sr mem Inst Elec & Electronics Engrs; Sigma Xi; Soc Prospective Med; Soc Gen Systs Res. *Res:* Health dynamics and promotion; general systems theory; control; homeostasis; hierarchy; optimization; health and spirituality. *Mailing Add:* Health Sci Ctr Univ of BC Vancouver BC V6T 1W5 Can

MILTON, ALBERT FENNER, b New York, NY, Oct 16, 40; m 76. SOLID STATE PHYSICS. *Educ:* Williams Col, BA, 62; Harvard Univ, MA, 63, PhD(appl physics), 68. *Prof Exp:* Staff mem, Inst Defense Anal, 68-71; res physicist, 71-77, head optical warfare br, 77-80, HEAD ELECTRO OPTICAL TECHNOL BR, NAVAL RES LAB, 80- *Mem:* Am Phys Soc. *Res:* Integrated optics; fiber optics; IR focal plane arrays; photoconductivity; infrared detection; photoemission. *Mailing Add:* 2939 28th St NW Washington DC 20008

MILTON, CHARLES, b New York, NY, Apr 25, 96; m 33; c 2. GEOLOGY. *Educ:* Univ Iowa, BA, 23; Johns Hopkins Univ, PhD(geol), 29. *Prof Exp:* Geologist, Gulf Oil Co, 25-26, Sinclair Explor Co, 27-28 & US Geol Surv, 31-65; adj prof, 65-66, res prof, 66-74, QUONDAM RES PROF GEOL, GEORGE WASHINGTON UNIV, 74-; GEOLOGIST, US GEOL SURV, 70- *Concurrent Pos:* Consult, US Dept Interior, 67-69; vis res geologist, Univ Calif, Berkeley, 75-78. *Mem:* AAAS; fel Geol Soc Am; fel Mineral Soc Am; Soc Econ Geologists; Can Mineral Soc. *Res:* Petrology; mineralogy; economic geology. *Mailing Add:* Beechbank Rd Forest Glen Silver Spring MD 20910

MILTON, DANIEL JEREMY, b Washington, DC, July 28, 34; div. GEOLOGY. *Educ:* Harvard Univ, AB, 54, PhD(geol), 61; Calif Inst Technol, MS, 56. *Prof Exp:* Geologist geochem & petrol br, 54, fuels br, 56 & regional geophys br, 59-61, geologist, Br Astrogeol, 61-77, GEOLOGIST, BR EASTERN REGION GEOL, US GEOL SURV, 77- *Mem:* Geol Soc Am; Mineral Soc Am; Meteoritical Soc. *Res:* Astrogeology; terrestrial impact structures; appalachian geology. *Mailing Add:* 928 US Geol Surv Reston VA 22092

MILTON, JAMES E(DMUND), b Florala, Ala, May 12, 34; m 56; c 2. ENGINEERING SCIENCES, APPLIED PHYSICS. *Educ:* Univ Fla, BANE, 60, PhD(physics), 66. *Prof Exp:* Asst prof aerospace eng, Univ Fla, 66-73, resident dir & assoc engr, Grad Ctr, 73-77, RESIDENT DIR & ENGR, GRAD CTR, UNIV FLA, 77- *Concurrent Pos:* Consult, US Air Force Armament Lab, 71-72 & 79-81. *Mem:* Am Inst Aeronaut & Astronaut; Am Soc Eng Educ. *Res:* Flight dynamics; aerodynamics; terradynamics. *Mailing Add:* Univ Fla Grad Ctr PO Box 1918 Eglin AFB FL 32542

MILTON, JOHN CHARLES DOUGLAS, b Regina, Sask, June 1, 24; m 53; c 4. NUCLEAR PHYSICS. *Educ:* Univ Man, BSc, 47; Princeton Univ, MA, 49, PhD(physics), 51. *Prof Exp:* From asst res officer to sr res officer physics, 51-67, HEAD NUCLEAR PHYSICS, CHALK RIVER NUCLEAR LABS, ATOMIC ENERGY CAN, LTD, 67- *Concurrent Pos:* Vis physicist, Lawrence Radiation Lab, Univ Calif, 60-62; dir res, Ctr Nuclear Res, Strasbourg, 75; vis physicist, Ctr Study, Bruyeres-le-Chatel, France, 75-76; chmn, Nuclear Physics Grants Selection Comt, Nat Sci & Eng Res Coun Can, 77- *Mem:* Royal Soc Can; Am Phys Soc; Can Asn Physicists. *Res:* Fission physics; directional correlation of radiations in radioactive decay; production of very high thermal neutron fluxes; intermediate energy physics; high voltage electrostatic accelerators. *Mailing Add:* Box 459 Deep River ON K0J 1P0 Can

MILTON, KIRBY MITCHELL, b St Joseph, Mich, May 4, 23; m 45, 68; c 8. CHEMISTRY. *Educ:* Harvard Univ, SB, 43; Univ Mich, MS, 48, PhD(org chem), 51. *Prof Exp:* Res chemist, Am Cyanamid Co, Conn, 43-44 & Manhattan Dist, 44-46; res & develop chemist, 50-59, RES ASSOC, EASTMAN KODAK CO, 59- *Mem:* AAAS; Am Chem Soc; Am Inst Chemists; Soc Photog Scientists & Engrs. *Res:* Photographic emulsions and supports; gelatin; plasticizers; polymers. *Mailing Add:* Eastman Kodak Co Bldg 9 343 State Rd Rochester NY 14650

MILTON, NANCY MELISSA, b Salem, Ore, July 17, 42; c 1. GEOBOTANY, REMOTE SENSING. *Educ:* Howard Univ, BS, 73; Johns Hopkins Univ, PhD(geog), 81. *Prof Exp:* Botanist, Johns Hopkins Univ, 73-75; BOTANIST, US GEOL SURV, RESTON, VA, 75- *Concurrent Pos:* Adv & tutor, Wash Int Col, 74-77. *Mem:* AAAS. *Res:* Analysis of the geographic distribution and spectral reflectance characteristics of plant species with respect to lithology and mineralization for the purpose of interpreting remotely sensed imagery from aircraft and satellite platforms for mineral appraisal. *Mailing Add:* MS 927 Nat Ctr US Geol Surv Reston VA 22092

MILTON, OSBORNE, b Denver, Colo, Oct 10, 20; m 45; c 4. ELECTRICAL & METALLURGICAL ENGINEERING. *Educ:* Univ Mo, BSEE, 45, MetEng, 56. *Prof Exp:* Trainee, Westinghouse Elec Corp, 45-46; researcher, Labs, Denver & Rio Grande Western RR Co, 47; mem staff, Los Alamos Sci Lab, 47-49; mem staff, 49-56, sect supvr, 56-65, MEM TECH STAFF, SANDIA NAT LAB, 65- *Mem:* AAAS; sr mem Inst Elec & Electronics Engrs. *Res:* Electrostatic fields; dielectrics; x-ray diffraction; materials science. *Mailing Add:* 9024 Los Arboles Ave NE Albuquerque NM 87112

MILTON, ROY CHARLES, b St Paul, Minn, Mar 10, 34; m 55; c 2. STATISTICAL COMPUTING, OPHTHALMOLOGY. *Educ:* Univ Minn, BA, 55, MA, 63, PhD(statist), 65. *Prof Exp:* Statistician, Atomic Bomb Casualty Comn, 64-66; sr scientist, Comput Ctr, Univ Wis-Madison, 66-70; statistician, Atomic Bomb Casualty Comn, 70-71; RES MATH STATISTICIAN, NAT EYE INST, 72- *Mem:* Asn Comput Mach; Int Asn Statist Comput; Am Statist Asn; Biomet Soc. *Res:* Application of digital computers to applied and theoretical statistical research; biostatistical applications in ophthalmology. *Mailing Add:* Off of Biomet & Epidemiol Nat Eye Inst Bldg 31/6A18 Bethesda MD 20205

MILZ, WENDELL COLLINS, b Bedford, Ohio, Feb 21, 18; m 42; c 3. PHYSICAL CHEMISTRY. *Educ:* Hiram Col, BA, 40. *Prof Exp:* Asst chief chemist, Cleveland Plant, Aluminum Co Am, 40-48, res engr, Alcoa Res Labs, 48-57, asst chief lubricants div, 57-67; sci assoc, Alcoa Tech Ctr, 67-79; RETIRED. *Mem:* Am Chem Soc; Sigma Xi; Am Soc Testing & Mat. *Res:* Lubricants; friction; wear; forging. *Mailing Add:* 1725 Pleasant Ave New Kensington PA 15068

MILZOFF, JOEL ROBERT, b New York, NY, Mar 23, 44; m 71. TOXICOLOGY, PHARMACOLOGY. *Educ:* Columbia Univ, BS, 66; Ind Univ Sch Med, MS, 69, PhD(toxicol), 72; Am Bd Forensic Toxicol, dipl. *Prof Exp:* TOXICOLOGIST, TOXICOL SECT, DEPT HEALTH LABS, CONN, 72- *Concurrent Pos:* Clin assoc, Dept Lab Med, Univ Conn Sch Med, 77- *Mem:* Fel Acad Forensic Sci; Soc Forensic Toxicologists; Sigma Xi. *Res:* Forensic toxicology. *Mailing Add:* Conn Dept Health Labs 10 Clinton St Hartford CT 06101

MIMEAULT, VICTOR JOSEPH, plastics chemistry, color science, see previous edition

MIMMACK, WILLIAM EDWARD, b Eaton, Colo, Aug 22, 26. OPTICS. *Educ:* Univ Colo, BA, 56; Univ Rochester, PhD(optics), 73. *Prof Exp:* Res physicist, White Sands Missile Range, Dept of Army, 51-73; STAFF OPTICAL ENGR, KEUFFEL & ESSER CO, 74- *Honors & Awards:* Karl Fairbanks Award, Soc Photo-Optical Instrumentation Engrs, 61. *Mem:* Optical Soc Am; Am Phys Soc; Soc Photo-Optical Instrumentation Engrs. *Res:* Geometrical optics; lens design; lens design methods; optimization. *Mailing Add:* Keuffel & Esser Co 20 Whippany Rd Morristown NJ 07960

MIMS, CHARLES WAYNE, b Waukegan, Ill, May 3, 44; m 68; c 1. MYCOLOGY. *Educ:* McNeese State Col, BS, 66; Univ Tex, Austin, PhD(bot), 69. *Prof Exp:* Asst prof, 69-77, ASSOC PROF BIOL, STEPHEN F AUSTIN STATE UNIV, 77- *Mem:* Bot Soc Am; Mycol Soc Am. *Res:* Morphogenesis in fungi, ultrastructure. *Mailing Add:* Dept of Biol Stephen F Austin State Univ Nacogdoches TX 75961

MIMS, WILLIAM B, b Mansfield, Eng, Feb 13, 22. PHYSICS, BIOPHYSICS. *Educ:* Oxford Univ, Eng, MA, 52, PhD(nuclear physics), 52. *Prof Exp:* Sr sci officer nuclear physics, UK Atomic Energy Authority, 55-56; MEM TECH STAFF SOLID STATE PHYSICS, BELL LABS, MURRAY HILL, NJ, 56- *Concurrent Pos:* Prof physics, Univ Calif, Los Angeles, 67-68; vis prof physics, Univ Konstanz, WGer, 72. *Mem:* Fel Am Phys Soc. *Res:* Solid state physics; biophysics. *Mailing Add:* RD 2 Box 31 Glen Gardner NJ 08826

MIN, DAVID BYONG, food chemistry, see previous edition

MIN, KONGKI, b Seoul, Korea, May 24, 31; m 58; c 1. NUCLEAR PHYSICS. *Educ:* Amherst Col, BA, 57; Univ Ill, PhD(physics), 63. *Prof Exp:* Res assoc physics, Univ Va, 62-63, asst prof, 63-68; assoc prof, 68-77, PROF PHYSICS, RENSSELAER POLYTECH INST, 77- *Mem:* Am Phys Soc. *Res:* Photonuclear reactions; nuclear spectroscopy. *Mailing Add:* Dept of Physics Rensselaer Polytech Inst Troy NY 12181

MIN, KWANG-SHIK, b Seoul, Korea, Sept 25, 27; m 56; c 2. MATHEMATICAL PHYSICS, NUCLEAR SCIENCE. *Educ:* Seoul Nat Univ, BS, 51; Univ Minn, MS, 59, PhD(physics), 61. *Prof Exp:* Instr physics, Seoul Nat Univ, 55-57; res assoc reactor physics, Argonne Nat Lab, 61-62; asst prof physics, Seoul Nat Univ, 62-64; assoc prof, 64-71, UNIV FAC RES GRANT, ETEX STATE UNIV, 65-, PROF PHYSICS, 71- *Mem:* Am Phys Soc; Korean Phys Soc. *Res:* Neutron transport theory; reactor theory; thermal neutron scattering; application of stochastic processes in physics. *Mailing Add:* 2802 Rix Commerce TX 75428

MIN, TONY C(HARLES), b Shanghai, China, Jan 5, 23; nat US; m 68. ENGINEERING MECHANICS, MECHANICAL ENGINEERING. *Educ:* Chiao Tung Univ, BS, 47; Univ Tenn, MS, 53, PhD(eng sci), 69. *Prof Exp:* Instr mech eng, Univ Tenn, 50-51; mech engr, Div Design, Tenn Valley Authority, 51-54; res engr, Res Lab, Am Soc Heating, Refrig & Air-Conditioning Engrs, 54-57; assoc prof mech eng, Auburn Univ, 57-64; instr eng mech, Univ Tenn, 64-68; prof eng mech, Mich Technol Univ, 68-78; prog mgr, Res & Develop Br, Off Asst Secy Conserv & Solar Appln, Dept Energy, 78-80; PROF ENG MECH, MICH TECHNOL UNIV, 80- *Concurrent Pos:* NSF sci fac fel, Univ Minn, 61-63; consult, Oak Ridge Nat Lab, 63-68. *Mem:* Am Soc Mech Engrs; Am Soc Eng Educ; Am Phys Soc; Am Acad Mech; NY Acad Sci. *Res:* Fluid mechanics; heat transfer; applied mathematics; solar energy; environmental conditioning. *Mailing Add:* Dept Eng Mech Mich Technol Univ Houghton MI 49931

MINAH, GLENN ERNEST, b Providence, RI, Mar 15, 39; m 67; c 4. ORAL MICROBIOLOGY. *Educ:* Duke Univ, AB, 61; Univ NC, DDS, 66; Univ Mich, MS, 70, PhD(microbiol), 76. *Prof Exp:* Asst prof, 76-81, ASSOC PROF ORAL MICROBIOL & PEDIAT DENT, DENT SCH, UNIV MD, 81- *Concurrent Pos:* Consult, Children's Oral Health Prog, & Nat Caries Prog, Nat Inst Dent Res, NIH, 76- *Mem:* Am Soc Microbiol; Int Asn Dent Res; Acad Oral Med. *Res:* Microbial etiology; pathogenesis, diagnosis and treatment of oral diseases; dental caries; peridontal diseases; oral infections of immunosuppressed cancer patients. *Mailing Add:* Dept Microbiol Dent Sch Univ Md Baltimore MD 21201

MINARD, FREDERICK NELSON, b Iowa, July 2, 22; m 44; c 2. NEUROCHEMISTRY. *Educ:* Iowa State Univ, BS, 43, PhD(biochem), 49. *Prof Exp:* Res chemist, 49-59, res assoc, 59-65, RES FEL, ABBOTT LABS, 65- *Mem:* Am Soc Neurochem; Int Soc Neurochem; Am Soc Biol Chemists. *Res:* Neurochemistry. *Mailing Add:* Abbott Labs North Chicago IL 60064

MINARD, ROBERT DAVID, b Buffalo, NY, Mar 21, 41; m 66; c 2. MASS SPECTROMETRY. *Educ:* St Olaf Col, BA, 63; Univ Wis, PhD, 68. *Prof Exp:* Asst prof chem, Col of the Virgin Islands, 68-69; fel, Univ Ill, Chicago Circle, 69-70, asst prof, 70-73; LECTR CHEM, PA STATE UNIV, 73- *Mem:* AAAS; Am Chem Soc; Am Soc Mass Spectrometry. *Res:* Mass spectrometry; pesticide degradation; chemistry of hydrogen cyanide in chemical evolution; coal structure. *Mailing Add:* Dept Chem Pa State Univ University Park PA 16802

MINARIK, CHARLES EDWIN, b Westfield, Mass, Nov 20, 11; m 35; c 2. PLANT PHYSIOLOGY. *Educ:* Univ Mass, BS, 33, MS, 35; Rutgers Univ, PhD(plant physiol), 39. *Prof Exp:* Asst plant physiol, Rutgers Univ, 35-39; plant physiologist, Exp Sta, Agr & Mech Col Tex, 39-46; chief, Chem Br, Chem Corps, US Army, 46-52, crops div, 52-67, dir plant sci lab, Ft Detrick, 67-71, chief vegetation control div, 71-72; RETIRED. *Concurrent Pos:* Ed, Weeds, Weed Sci Soc Am, 53-54. *Honors & Awards:* Amos A Fries Gold Medal, Am Ord Asn, 67; Meritorious Civilian Serv Award, US Dept Army, 72. *Mem:* AAAS; Bot Soc Am; Am Soc Plant Physiol; Weed Sci Soc Am; Am Inst Biol Sci. *Res:* Plant growth regulators; weed control; radioactive tracers in plant physiology; nutrition. *Mailing Add:* PO Box 682 West Harwich MA 02671

MINASSIAN, DONALD PAUL, b New York, NY, Dec 8, 35; m 64; c 2. MATHEMATICS. *Educ:* Fresno State Col, BA, 57; Brown Univ, MA, 64; Univ Mich, Ann Arbor, MS, 65, EdD(math), 67. *Prof Exp:* Assoc prof, 67-73, PROF MATH, BUTLER UNIV, 73- *Mem:* Assoc Soc Acturies; Math Asn Am; Soc Indust & Appl Math; Asn Study Grants Econ. *Res:* Ordered algebraic structures, particularly ordered groups of modern algebra; foreign aid; industrial concentration. *Mailing Add:* 410 Blue Ridge Rd Indianapolis IN 46208

MINATOYA, HIROAKI, b Japan, Nov 8, 11; US citizen; m 45; c 2. PHARMACOLOGY, PHYSIOLOGY. *Educ:* Univ Ore, BA, 38; Univ Ill, MS, 42; Nara Med Col, Japan, PhD(pharmacol), 64. *Prof Exp:* Res asst physiol, Col Med, Univ Ill, 41-42 & 44-48; pharmacologist, Sterling-Winthrop Res Inst, 48-71, sr res pharmacologist, 71-76; RETIRED. *Mem:* Am Soc Pharmacol & Exp Therapeut; Am Chem Soc; Sigma Xi. *Res:* Conditioned reflex and insulin hypoglycemia; experimental hypertension in dogs; diuretics; antihypertensive compounds in the renal hypertensive rat; catecholamines, especially absorption, metabolism and elimination; bronchodilators in dogs. *Mailing Add:* 10 Van Buren Ave East Greenbush NY 12061

MINC, HENRYK, b Lodz, Poland, Nov 12, 19; m 43; c 3. ALGEBRA. *Educ:* Univ Edinburgh, MA, 55, PhD(math), 59. *Prof Exp:* Lectr math, Dundee Tech Col, Scotland, 56-58; lectr, Univ BC, 58-59, asst prof, 59-60; assoc prof, Univ Fla, 60-63; PROF MATH, UNIV CALIF, SANTA BARBARA, 63- *Concurrent Pos:* Vis prof, Israel Inst Technician, 69- *Honors & Awards:* Ford Award, Math Asn Am, 66. *Mem:* Am Math Soc; Edinburgh Math Soc; Israel Math Union. *Res:* Linear and multilinear algebra; matrix theory; combinatorial analysis. *Mailing Add:* Dept of Math Univ of Calif Santa Barbara CA 93106

MINCEY, BEVERLY JEAN, b Gainesville, Ga. INORGANIC CHEMISTRY. *Educ:* Bethany Nazarene Col, BS, 61; Univ Tenn, Chattanooga, MAT, 63; Univ Ga, PhD(inorg chem), 74. *Prof Exp:* Asst prof chem, Trevecca Nazarene Col, 67-71; chemist, Neutron Devices Dept, 74-79, PROG MGR, PROCESS DEVELOP, GEN ELEC CO, 79- *Mem:* Am Chem Soc. *Res:* Synthesis and characterization of thermal battery related materials; scale-up of synthesis processes from laboratory to pilot plant operation. *Mailing Add:* PO Box 11508 St Petersburg FL 33733

MINCH, EDWIN WILTON, b Warren, Ohio, Apr 6, 51. AGRONOMY, ENTOMOLOGY. *Educ:* Cornell Univ, BS, 73; Ariz State Univ, PhD(zool), 77. *Prof Exp:* Asst prof anat & physiol, Ariz State Univ, 77, asst prof biol, 78-81; BIOLOGIST, WESTERN SOD CO, 81- *Concurrent Pos:* Consult, Western Sod Co, 78-81; Writing fac, Phoenix Col, 79- *Mem:* Asn Study Animal Behav; Am Soc Zoologists; Am Arachnological Soc; Brit Arachnological Soc. *Res:* Annual and daily activity patterns of arthropods, especially Araneae and Coccoidea; general turfgrass culture. *Mailing Add:* 2207 W Main St Mesa AZ 85201

MINCH, MICHAEL JOSEPH, b Klamath Falls, Ore, Apr 7, 43. PHYSICAL ORGANIC CHEMISTRY. *Educ:* Ore State Univ, BS, 65; Univ Wash, PhD(chem), 70. *Prof Exp:* NIH fel chem, Univ Calif, Santa Barbara, 70-72; asst prof chem, Tulane Univ, 72-74; asst prof, 74-78, ASSOC PROF CHEM, UNIV PAC, 78- *Mem:* Am Chem Soc. *Res:* Synthesis and characterization of surfactants; micellar catalysis; nuclear magnetic resonance spectroscopy of biochemically significant complexes; methyl transfer reactions in biochemistry. *Mailing Add:* Dept of Chem Univ of the Pac Stockton CA 95211

MINCK, ROBERT W, b Defiance, Ohio, Sept, 26, 34; m 58; c 4. ELECTRICAL ENGINEERING. *Educ:* Univ Notre Dame, BS, 56; Univ Wis-Madison, MS, 58, PhD(elec eng), 60. *Prof Exp:* Res scientist, Sci Lab, Ford Motor Co, 60-76, staff scientist, Sci Res Lab, 76-80; TECH SPECIALIST, ADVANCED DEVELOP OPER, FORD AEROSPACE & COMMUN CORP, 80- *Mem:* Inst Elec & Electronics Engrs. *Res:* Nonlinear optics; battery development; laser development; energy conversion. *Mailing Add:* Rm 21 Bldg 11 Aeronutronic Div Ford Aerospace & Comm Corp Ford Rd Newport Beach CA 92660

MINCKLER, JEFF, b Knox, NDak, June 4, 12; m 33; c 6. PATHOLOGY. *Educ:* Univ Mont, AB, 37; Univ Minn, MA & PhD(neuroanat), 39; St Louis Univ, MD, 44. *Prof Exp:* Asst anat, Univ Minn, 37-39; from instr to asst prof, Creighton Univ, 39-41; instr, St Louis Univ, 41-43, instr path, 43-45; asst prof, Med Sch, Univ Ore, 45-46, prof gen path & actg head dept, Sch Dent, 49-59; assoc clin prof path, Med Sch, Univ Colo, 60-71; dir labs, Century City Hosp, 73-75; ASSOC RES PROF NEUROSURG, MED CTR, LOMA LINDA UNIV, 71-; DIR LABS, MAD RIVER COMMUNITY HOSP, ARCATA, CALIF, 75- *Concurrent Pos:* Dir labs, Gen Rose Mem Hosp, 60-71 & Eisenhower Med Ctr, 71-73; lectr radiol, Univ Calif, Los Angeles; adj prof, Univ Denver, 65-71 & speech & hearing, Humboldt State Univ, Arcata, Calif, 76- *Mem:* AAAS; Am Asn Anat; Am Asn Neuropath; Am Soc Clin Path; Int Acad Path. *Res:* General and speech pathology; neuropathology; neuroanatomy. *Mailing Add:* Labs 3800 Janes Rd Mad River Community Hosp Arcata CA 95521

MINCKLER, LEON SHERWOOD, JR, b Lockport, NY, Apr 4, 30; m 51; c 2. ORGANIC CHEMISTRY, POLYMER CHEMISTRY. *Educ:* Univ Southern Ill, BA, 51; Northwestern Univ, PhD(org chem), 55. *Prof Exp:* Asst org chem, Northwestern Univ, 51-53; sr chemist, Esso Res & Eng Co, 55-67, res assoc, 67-74, RES ASSOC, EXXON CHEM CO, 74- *Mem:* Am Chem Soc; Am Inst Chemists. *Res:* Polymers; butyl rubber; cationic polymerization; stereochemistry; polymer modification; oil additives. *Mailing Add:* 78 Crestwood Dr Watchung NJ 07060

MINCKLER, TATE MULDOWN, b Kalispell, Mont, Apr 1, 34; m 56; c 5. PATHOLOGY. *Educ:* Reed Col, BA, 55; Univ Ore, MD, 59. *Prof Exp:* Pathologist, Nat Cancer Inst, Washington, DC, 63-65, head tissue path unit, 64-65; asst pathologist & med systs analyst, Univ Tex M D Anderson Hosp & Tumor Inst, Houston, 65-69, chief sect med info mgt systs, Dept Biomath, 67-69; head dept med automation, Presby Med Ctr, 69-71; assoc prof lab med & dir comput div, Sch Med, Univ Wash, 71-75; assoc pathologist & adminr, 75-76, PATHOLOGIST, MAD RIVER COMMUNITY HOSP, ARCATA, CALIF, 76- *Mem:* AAAS; Soc Cryobiol; Am Soc Clin Path; fel Col Am Path; Soc Comput Med. *Res:* Development of medical information systems, especially pathology data automation, application of computers to medical problems; utilization of human tissues for research and patient care; clinical and anatomical pathology; cryobiology; medical records. *Mailing Add:* Mad River Community Hosp 3800 Janes Rd Arcata CA 95521

MINCKLEY, WENDELL LEE, b Ottawa, Kans, Nov 13, 35; m 56; c 4. ICHTHYOLOGY, AQUATIC ECOLOGY. *Educ:* Kans State Univ, BS, 57; Univ Kans, MA, 59; Univ Louisville, PhD, 62. *Prof Exp:* Asst prof zool, Western Mich Univ, 62-63; from asst prof to assoc prof, 63-77, PROF ZOOL, ARIZ STATE UNIV, 77-, DIR LOWER COLO RIVER BASIN RES LAB, 72- *Concurrent Pos:* Fac res grant, Western Mich, 62-63; NSF grant, 63-65; Fac Res Comt awards, Ariz State Univ, 63-65; Sport Fishery Inst res grant, 65-66. *Mem:* Am Soc Ichthyologists & Herpetologists; Am Fisheries Soc; Wildlife Soc; Am Soc Limnol & Oceanog; Am Inst Biol Sci. *Res:* Systematic and ecological ichthyology; radiation, stream, crustacean and algal ecology; crustacean taxonomy. *Mailing Add:* Dept of Zool Ariz State Univ Tempe AZ 85281

MINDA, CARL DAVID, b Cincinnati, Ohio, Nov 5, 43; m 73. MATHEMATICAL ANALYSIS. *Educ:* Univ Cincinnati, BS, 65, MS, 66; Univ Calif, San Diego, PhD(math), 70. *Prof Exp:* Asst prof math, Univ Minn, 70-71; from asst prof to assoc prof, 71-80, PROF MATH, UNIV CINCINNATI, 80- *Concurrent Pos:* Vis assoc prof, Univ Calif, San Diego, 80-81. *Mem:* Am Math Soc; Math Asn Am. *Res:* Complex analysis; Riemann surfaces. *Mailing Add:* Dept of Math Sci Univ of Cincinnati Cincinnati OH 45221

MINDAK, ROBERT JOSEPH, b Chicago, Ill, Mar 1, 25; m 53; c 6. MECHANICAL ENGINEERING. *Educ:* Northwestern Univ, US, 46, MS, 48. *Prof Exp:* Lectr mech eng, Northwestern Univ, 46-48; asst res engr, Standard Oil Co, Ind, 48-52; assoc res engr, Armour Res Found, Ill Inst Technol, 52-55; phys sci adminr, Off Naval Res, 55-68, staff asst to asst chief res, 68-74, mech engr, 74-80. *Concurrent Pos:* Lectr, Ill Inst Technol, 50-56. *Mem:* Am Soc Mech Engrs. *Res:* Heat transfer; magnetohydrodynamics; gas dynamics; air conditioning; refrigeration; temperature measurement; thermodynamics; scientific and technical information; mechanized information systems; research and development management. *Mailing Add:* 3714 Forest Grove Dr Annandale VA 22003

MINDE, KARL KLAUS, b Leipzig, Ger, Dec 27, 33; Can citizen; c 3. PSYCHIATRY. *Educ:* Columbia Univ, MA, 60; Munich Univ, MD, 57. *Prof Exp:* Staff physician, Queen Elizabeth Hosp, 65-71; WHO sr lectr psychiat, Makerere Univ, Uganda, 71-73; staff physician, 73, assoc prof, 73-78, DIR PSYCHIAT RES, HOSP SICK CHILDREN, 73-; ASST PROF PEDIAT, UNIV TORONTO, 75-, PROF PSYCHIAT, 78-, PROF PEDIAT, 80- *Concurrent Pos:* Staff physician, Montreal Childrens Hosp, 65-73; asst prof psychiat, McGill Univ, 66-73; consult psychiat, Baird Residential Treatment Ctr, Burlington, Vt, 65-67. *Mem:* Can Psychiat Asn; Am Psychiat Asn; Am Acad Child Psychiat; Can Med Asn; Soc Res Child Develop. *Res:* Bonding between premature babies and their mothers, and a follow-up study of kindergarten children to determine whether the screening instrument was effective in picking up children at risk for behavior disorders. *Mailing Add:* Hosp for Sick Children 555 University Ave Toronto ON M5G 1X8 Can

MINDEL, JOSEPH, b New York, NY, May 3, 12; m 34, 75; c 1. HISTORY OF SCIENCE, SCIENCE EDUCATION. *Educ:* City Col New York, BS, 32; Columbia Univ, MA, 37; NY Univ, PhD(chem), 43. *Prof Exp:* Instr high sch, NY, 32-46, head dept sci, 46-60; secy to pres, Bd Ed, NY, 60-61; staff mem, 61-69, Secy steering comt, 69-75, educ dir, Lincoln Lab, Mass Inst Technol, 71-75, CONSULT, LINCOLN LAB, MASS INST TECHNOL, 75-; CONSULT, DEFENSE COMMUN AGENCY, US DEPT DEFENSE, 76- *Concurrent Pos:* Consult, Beth Israel Hosp, Boston, 75-76; consult & mem teaching staff, Washington Sch Psychiat, Washington, DC, 80-81. *Mem:* AAAS; NY Acad Sci. *Mailing Add:* 527 Grant Pl Frederick MD 21701

MINDELL, EUGENE R, b Chicago, Ill, Feb 24, 22; m 45; c 4. ORTHOPEDIC SURGERY. *Educ:* Univ Chicago, BS, 43, MD, 45. *Prof Exp:* PROF ORTHOP SURG & HEAD DEPT, SCH MED, STATE UNIV NY BUFFALO, 64- *Concurrent Pos:* Nat Res Coun fel orthop surg, Univ Chicago Clin, 48-49; Orthop Res & Educ Found res grant, 58-61; NIH res grant, 63-; examr bone path, Am Bd Orthop Surg, 57-, mem, 78- *Mem:* Am Orthop Asn; Am Soc Surg Trauma; Orthop Res Soc (pres elect, 71); Am Acad Orthop Surg; fel Am Col Surg. *Res:* Mechanisms by which chondrogenesis occurs; bone pathology; structure and function of cartilage; chemotherapy in bone sarcoma; experimental studies on strength of remodeled bone. *Mailing Add:* Dept of Orthop Surg State Univ of NY Sch of Med Buffalo NY 14214

MINDEN, HENRY THOMAS, b New York, NY, Aug 23, 23; m 53; c 3. CHEMICAL PHYSICS. *Educ:* Johns Hopkins Univ, BA, 43; Columbia Univ, PhD(chem), 52. *Prof Exp:* Mem tech staff, Bell Tel Labs, Inc, 48 & RCA Labs, 50-52; sr physicist, Midway Labs, Chicago, 52-56; eng specialist, Res Labs, Sylvania Elec Prod, Inc, 56-60; physicist, Semiconductor Prod Dept, Gen Elec Co, 60-62; TECH STAFF MEM, SPERRY RAND RES CTR, 62- *Mem:* Am Phys Soc; Inst Elec & Electronic Engrs; Optical Soc Am. *Res:* Semiconductor materials and devices; laser optics. *Mailing Add:* Sperry Rand Res Ctr Sudbury MA 01776

MINDICH, LEONARD EUGENE, b New York, NY, May 24, 36; m 59; c 3. MICROBIAL PHYSIOLOGY. *Educ:* Cornell Univ, BS, 57; Rockefeller Univ, PhD, 62. *Prof Exp:* Asst virol, 62-64, assoc, 64-70, ASSOC MEM MICROBIOL, PUB HEALTH RES INST OF CITY OF NEW YORK, INC, 70- *Concurrent Pos:* Mem microbial chem study sect, NIH, 72-76. *Mem:* AAAS; Am Soc Microbiol. *Res:* Genetics of bacteriocin production, fractionation of desoxyribonucleic acid and the synthesis of bacterial membranes. *Mailing Add:* 180 Riverside Dr New York NY 10024

MINDLIN, HAROLD, b Bethlehem, Pa, Nov 23, 30; m 58; c 2. MATERIALS SCIENCE. *Educ:* Lehigh Univ, BS, 56, MS, 60. *Prof Exp:* Assoc stress analyst, Lockheed Aircraft Corp, 56-57; asst struct & fatigue testing, Fritz Eng Lab, Lehigh Univ, 57-60; engr, Metall Res Div, Reynolds Metals Co, 60-63, supvr mech testing sect, 63-65; res engr, 65-77, assoc div chief, Struct Mat Eng, 67-69, sect mgr, 69-77, PROG MGR, STRUCT MAT ENG & MGR, METALS & CERAMICS INFO CTR, COLUMBUS DIV, BATTELLE MEM INST, 77- *Mem:* Am Soc Testing & Mat; Soc Exp Stress Anal; Am Soc Civil Engrs. *Res:* Fatigue, crack propagation and fracture behavior of materials and structures; materials information. *Mailing Add:* Metals & Ceramics Info Ctr Battelle-Columbus 505 King Ave Columbus OH 43201

MINDLIN, RAYMOND D(AVID), b New York, NY, Sept 17, 06; wid. APPLIED MECHANICS & MATHEMATICS. *Educ:* Columbia Univ, BA, 28, BS, 31, CE, 32, PhD(elasticity), 36. *Hon Degrees:* DSc, Northwestern Univ, 75. *Prof Exp:* Asst civil eng, 32-38, from instr to prof, 38-67, James Kip Finch prof appl sci, 67-75, EMER PROF APPL SCI, COLUMBIA UNIV, 75- *Concurrent Pos:* Mem exec comt, Eastern Photoelasticity Conf, 38-41; consult physicist, Dept Terrestrial Magnetism, Carnegie Inst, 40-42; consult, Nat Defense Res Comt, 41-42 & Off Sci Res & Develop; consult, Appl Physics Lab, Johns Hopkins Univ, 42-45 & Bell Tel Labs, Inc, 43-51; secy adv bd, Appl Mech Revs, 48-56; mem, US Nat Comt Theoret & Appl Mech, 48-56; mem gen assembly, Int Union Theoret & Appl Mech, 49-56. *Honors & Awards:* Presidential Medal for Merit, 46; Res Prize, Am Soc Civil Engrs, 58, von Karman Medal, 61; Timoshenko Medal, Am Soc Mech Engrs, 64; C B Sawyer Award, US Army Electronics Command, 67; Trent-Crede Award, Acoust Soc Am, 71; Frocht Award, Soc Exp Stress Anal, 74; Medal, Am Soc Mech Engrs, 76; Nat Medal Sci, 79. *Mem:* Nat Acad Sci; Nat Acad Engrs; fel & hon mem Am Soc Mech Engrs; fel Acoust Soc Am; fel Am Acad Arts & Sci. *Res:* Theory of elasticity; photoelasticity; vibrations; applied mechanics; Piezoelectric crystal resonators. *Mailing Add:* 89 Deer Hill Dr Ridgefield CT 06877

MINDLIN, ROWLAND L, b New York, NY, Jan 30, 12; m 40, 76; c 2. PEDIATRICS, COMMUNITY HEALTH. *Educ:* Harvard Univ, BS, 33, MD, 37, MPH, 62. *Prof Exp:* Dir maternal & child health, Boston Dept Health & Hosps, 71-74; dir ambulatory care, St Mary's Hosp, Brooklyn, 74-78; V PRES & MED DIR, MILE SQ HEALTH CTR, CHICAGO, 78- *Concurrent Pos:* Chmn coun child & adolescent health, Am Acad Pediat; mem comt med in soc, NY Acad Med. *Mem:* Am Acad Pediat; NY Acad Med; Am Pub Health Asn. *Res:* Medical care in maternal and child health. *Mailing Add:* Mile Square Health Ctr 2045 W Washington Blvd Chicago IL 60612

MINEAR, JOHN W, b Odessa, Tex, Dec 30, 37; m 64; c 2. GEOPHYSICS. *Educ:* Rice Univ, BA, 60, PhD(geophys), 64. *Prof Exp:* Res geophysicist, Res Triangle Inst, 65-71, mgr geosci dept, 71-74; PLANETARY SCIENTIST, NASA-JOHNSON SPACE CTR, 74- *Concurrent Pos:* Adj prof, Univ NC, 65-74; fel, Dept Earth & Planetary Sci, Mass Inst Technol, 68-69. *Mem:* Seismol Soc Am; Am Geophys Union. *Res:* Thermal evolution of the terrestrial planets and the moon; physical environment of crustal evolution, magma migration and chemical differentiation of planetary objects; comparative planetology of solid solar system objects. *Mailing Add:* Johnson Space Ctr SN6 Houston TX 77058

MINEHART, RALPH CONRAD, b Mitchell, SDak, Jan 25, 35; m 59; c 3. EXPERIMENTAL NUCLEAR PHYSICS. *Educ:* Yale Univ, BS, 56; Harvard Univ, MA, 57, PhD(physics), 62. *Prof Exp:* Res assoc & lectr physics, Yale Univ, 62-66; asst prof, 66-68, assoc prof, 68-81, PROF, UNIV VA, 81- *Concurrent Pos:* Vis staff mem, Swiss Inst Nuclear Res, 75-76. *Mem:* Am Phys Soc. *Res:* High energy experimental physics; polarized nucleon-nucleon scattering with bubble chamber analysis; high energy photoproduction of charged particles; medium energy nuclear physics; interactions of pi mesons with nucleons and nuclei; meson decay and neutrino mass. *Mailing Add:* Dept of Physics Univ of Va Charlottesville VA 22901

MINER, BRYANT ALBERT, b Moroni, Utah, Aug 9, 34; m 60; c 7. PHYSICAL CHEMISTRY. *Educ:* Univ Utah, BA, 61, PhD(phys chem), 65. *Prof Exp:* From asst prof to assoc prof, 64-73, PROF CHEM, WEBER STATE COL, 73- *Mem:* Am Chem Soc. *Res:* Significant structure theory of liquids and electrochemistry; reactions and kinetics. *Mailing Add:* 4260 Jefferson Ave Ogden UT 84403

MINER, FREND JOHN, b Loveland, Colo, Dec 8, 28; m 58; c 2. ANALYTICAL CHEMISTRY. *Educ:* Univ Colo, BA, 50; Ore State Univ, MS, 52, PhD(chem), 55. *Prof Exp:* Asst chem, Ore State Univ, 50-54; sr res chemist, 54-68, assoc scientist, 68-77, MGR CHEM RES & DEVELOP, ROCKY FLATS PLANT, ROCKWELL INT, 77- *Mem:* Am Chem Soc; Am Soc Test & Mat; Sigma Xi. *Res:* Ion exchange separations; complex ions; chemistry of plutonium. *Mailing Add:* 2445 Dartmouth Ave Boulder CO 80303

MINER, GARY DAVID, b Waseca, Minn, Dec 17, 42; m 69; c 1. BEHAVIORAL GENETICS, NEUROSCIENCE. *Educ:* Hamline Univ, BS, 64; Univ Wyo, MS, 66; Univ Kans, PhD(genetics), 70. *Prof Exp:* Res assoc psychiat genetics, Univ Minn, 70-72, asst prof, 72-77; prof biol & behav genetics, Northwest Nazarene Col, 77-82, actg chmn, Dept Biol, 78-82; PROF BIOL, EASTERN NAZARENE COL, 82- *Concurrent Pos:* Prin investr, Nichiman Res Found grant, 77-78, Res Corp grant, 78-80; fel psychiat epidemiol, Univ Iowa, 80-82. *Mem:* AAAS; Soc Neurosci; Behav Genetics Asn; Int Soc Neurochem. *Res:* Brain proteins in schizophrenia, dementia and old age; Alzheimer's disease; brain proteins and aluminum; genetics of behavior. *Mailing Add:* Eastern Nazarene Col Quincy MA 02170

MINER, GEORGE KENNETH, b Asheville, NC, Dec 16, 36; m 62; c 3. MAGNETIC RESONANCE. *Educ:* Thomas More Col, AB, 58; Univ Notre Dame, MS, 60; Univ Cincinnati, PhD(physics), 65. *Prof Exp:* From instr to assoc prof, Thomas More Col, 64-74, prof physics, 74-76, chmn dept, 66-76; ASSOC PROF PHYSICS, UNIV DAYTON, 76- *Concurrent Pos:* NSF sci fac fel, Univ Dayton, 71; dir, Univ Dayton, NSF Chantanqua Field Ctr, 80-84. *Mem:* Am Phys Soc; Am Asn Physics Teachers; AAAS. *Res:* Radiation damage; electron paramagnetic resonance of rare earths in fluorites. *Mailing Add:* Dept of Physics Univ of Dayton Dayton OH 45469

MINER, GORDON STANLEY, b Howell, Mich, Apr 25, 40; m 64; c 2. SOIL FERTILITY, AGRONOMY. *Educ:* Mich State Univ, BS, 62, MS, 64; NC State Univ, PhD(soil sci), 69. *Prof Exp:* Res agronomist, Rockefeller Found, 69-71; regional dir, Int Soil Fertil Eval & Improv Proj, Costa Rica & Nicaragua, 71-74; asst prof, 74-79, ASSOC PROF SOIL SCI, NC STATE UNIV, 79- *Mem:* Sigma Xi; Am Soc Agron. *Res:* Plant bed and field management of tobacco for mechanized production. *Mailing Add:* Dept of Soil Sci NC State Univ Raleigh NC 27607

MINER, J RONALD, b Scottsburg, Ind, July 4, 38; m 63; c 3. LIVESTOCK WASTE MANAGEMENT, ODOR CONTROL. *Educ:* Univ Kans, BSE, 59; Univ Mich, MSE, 60; Kans State Univ, PhD(chem eng), 67. *Prof Exp:* Sanitary engr, Kans State Dept Health, 59-64; asst prof agr eng, Iowa State Univ, 67-71, assoc prof, 71-72; assoc prof, 72-76, PROF & HEAD AGR ENG, ORE STATE UNIV, 76- *Concurrent Pos:* Environ engr, UN Develop Prog, Singapore, 80-81; expert witness, Various law firms & livestock enterprises faced with pollution complaints; consult, Am Nat Cattlemen's Asn, 77- *Mem:* Am Soc Agr Engrs; Water Pollution Control Fedn; Am Soc Engrs Educ; Sigma Xi. *Res:* Minimize or eliminate adverse environmental impacts of livestock and poultry production, particular emphasis on animal waste management and odor control; author or co-author of over 80 technical publications. *Mailing Add:* Dept Agr Eng Ore State Univ Corvallis OR 97331

MINER, JAMES JOSHUA, b Waldo, Ark, June 11, 28; m 57; c 4. NUTRITION, BIOCHEMISTRY. *Educ:* Univ Ark, Fayetteville, BS, 53, MS, 54; La State Univ, Baton Rouge, PhD(nutrit), 62. *Prof Exp:* Poultry husbandman, Poultry Res Br, Agr Res Serv, USDA, 56-58; dir res, Ala Flour Mills, Nebr, 60-62; nutritionist, Loret Mills, Seed Feed Supply Co, 62-65; exten serv poultry man, Univ Ark, 65-66; VPRES FARM PROD, PILGRIM INDUSTS, INC, 66- *Mem:* Am Soc Animal Sci; Poultry Sci Asn. *Res:* Biological evaluation of protein supplements for non-ruminants. *Mailing Add:* Pilgrim Industs Inc 110 S Texas St Pittsburgh TX 75686

MINER, MERTHYR LEILANI, b Honolulu, Hawaii, Apr 13, 12; m 37; c 4. VETERINARY PATHOLOGY. *Educ:* Utah State Univ, BS, 37; Iowa State Univ, DVM, 41. *Prof Exp:* Asst vet bact, Mich State Univ, 41-43; from asst prof to assoc prof, 43-54, head dept, 54-73, prof, 54-77, EMER PROF VET SCI, UTAH STATE UNIV, 77- *Concurrent Pos:* Fel, Ralston Purina Co, Univ Minn, 53-54. *Mem:* Am Vet Med Asn; US Animal Health Asn; Am Asn Avian Path. *Res:* Microbiology; staphylococci; salmonellae; avian skeletal diseases; bovine coccidia. *Mailing Add:* 996 Sumac Dr Logan UT 84321

MINER, NORMAN ALLEN, molecular biology, virology, see previous edition

MINER, NORMAN H(ARTLEY), b Saltsburg, Pa, Dec 1, 32; m 60; c 2. ENVIRONMENTAL SCIENCES, WATER RESOURCES. *Educ:* State Univ NY Col Forestry, Syracuse, BS, 53, MS, 57. *Prof Exp:* Res forester watershed mgt, Pac Northwest Forest & Range Exp Sta, US Forest Serv, 57-

66, assoc hydrologist, Southeastern Exp Sta, 66-68; forestry officer, Food & Agr Orgn, UN, 68-70; res assoc forestry & hydrol, 71-78, SR RES ASSOC, NEW ENG RES, INC, 78- *Concurrent Pos:* Consult, forester, 79- *Mem:* Am Water Resources Asn; Am Geophys Union; Soc Am Foresters. *Res:* Environmental impacts of land and water resources development; forest hydrology; water quality studies. *Mailing Add:* Meetinghouse Hill Rd Sterling MA 01564

MINER, ROBERT SCOTT, JR, b Chicago, Ill, June 16, 18; m 42; c 3. ORGANIC CHEMISTRY. *Educ:* Univ Chicago, SB, 40; Polytech Inst Brooklyn, MS, 53; Princeton Univ, MA, 55, PhD(org chem), 56. *Prof Exp:* Develop chemist, Merck & Co, Inc, NJ, 40-44; chief res chemist, Tung-Sol Lamp Works, Inc, 45-47; asst mfg chemist, Ciba Pharmaceut Co, 47-49, mfg chemist, 49-58, mgr chem mfg div, 58-59, dir, 59-69; asst to chmn dept physics, Princeton Univ, 70-74, res assoc fac chem, 74-75, mem prof res staff, 75-81; CONSULT CHEMIST ENGR, 70- *Concurrent Pos:* Fel & eve instr, Union Jr Col, 56-58, guest lectr, 60; guest lectr, Westfield High Sch, 60-; mem, Westfield Bd Educ, 62-65, pres, 64-65; guest lectr, MacMurray Col, 63, trustee, 65-70; chem consult, Haemodialysis Team, Overlook Hosp, 64-; NSF fel chem catalysis, USSR, 75, 76, & 78; consult chemist engr, United Nations, 77-; lectr chem safety, 79- *Honors & Awards:* Honor Scroll Award, Am Inst Chem, 71. *Mem:* AAAS; Am Chem Soc; Royal Soc Chem; fel Am Inst Chem (treas, 70-75); Am Inst Chem Eng. *Res:* Synthesis of carbohydrates; vitamins; sulfonamides; steroid hormones; pharmaceuticals; chemical education; catalysis and electrode phenomena involving precious metals; large scale pharmaceutical and intermediate synthesis. *Mailing Add:* 1139 Lawrence Ave Westfield NJ 07090

MINERBO, GERALD N, b Alexandria, UAR, Nov 21, 39; US citizen; m 66; c 2. THEORETICAL PHYSICS. *Educ:* Polytech Inst Brooklyn, 60; Cambridge Univ, PhD(theoret physics), 65. *Prof Exp:* Res assoc theoret physics, Atomic Energy Res Estab, Harwell, Eng, 64-65; proj physicist, Vitro Lab, Vitro Corp Am, 65-66; asst prof physics, Adelphi Univ, 66-71; STAFF MEM, LOS ALAMOS SCI LAB, 71- *Concurrent Pos:* Consult, Vitro Corp Am, 66-68; vis prof, Univ Buenos Aires, 68-69. *Mem:* Am Phys Soc. *Res:* Theory of elementary particles; formal theory of scattering; atomic physics; radiation transfer; laser theory. *Mailing Add:* Los Alamos Sci Lab Mail Stop 232 Los Alamos NM 87545

MINES, ALLAN HOWARD, b New York, NY, Apr 11, 36; m 59; c 2. PHYSIOLOGY. *Educ:* Univ Ill, Urbana, BS, 61, MS, 62; Univ Calif, San Francisco, PhD(physiol), 68. *Prof Exp:* From lectr to asst prof, 68-74, ASSOC PROF PHYSIOL, MED CTR, UNIV CALIF, SAN FRANCISCO, 74- *Mem:* Am Physiol Soc. *Res:* Comparative physiology; regulation of respiration, particularly the mechanism responsible for ventilatory acclimatization to altitude. *Mailing Add:* Dept of Physiol Univ of Calif Med Ctr San Francisco CA 94143

MINET, RONALD G(EORGE), b New York, NY, Aug 13, 22; m 77; c 1. CHEMICAL ENGINEERING. *Educ:* City Col New York, BChE, 43; Stevens Inst Technol, MS, 50; NY Univ, DSc(chem eng), 59. *Prof Exp:* Res engr, Foster Wheeler Corp, 47-50, group leader, 50-52; chief process engr, United Engrs & Constructors, Inc, 52-61; mgr carbon dept, FMC Corp, 61-63; vpres process eng, Comp Tecnica Ind Petroli, 65-69; managing dir, Chem Projs Int, 69-72; pres, 72-78, CHMN BD, KINETICS TECHNOL INT CORP, 78-; CHMN BD, PYROTEC, 81- *Mem:* Am Chem Soc; Am Inst Chem Engrs; Am Inst Mining, Metall & Petrol Engrs. *Res:* Coal processing; catalytic processes; fluidized bed processes; petroleum and petrochemical processing; methanol. *Mailing Add:* Kinetics Technol Int Corp 221 E Walnut Ave Pasadena CA 91101

MINFORD, JAMES DEAN, b Clairton, Pa, Feb 27, 23; m 44; c 2. METALLURGICAL CHEMISTRY. *Educ:* Carnegie Inst Technol, BS, 43; Univ Pittsburgh, MLitt, 48, PhD(chem), 51. *Prof Exp:* Res chemist org chem, Goodyear Tire & Rubber Co, 44; asst chem, Univ Pittsburgh, 46-50, res assoc biochem, Sch Pub Health, 50-52, instr biochem & nutrit, 52-53; sect head, 53-72, group leader, Chem Metall Div, 72-76, sci assoc alloy technol, 76-78, SCI ASSOC, JOINING DIV, ALCOA LABS, 78- *Mem:* AAAS; Sigma Xi; Adhesion Soc; Am Soc Testing & Mat; fel Am Inst Chemists. *Res:* Porphyrin synthesis in microorganisms; cancer in experimental animals; nutritional factors in disease; corrosive action of cooling waters on metals; reactions of aluminum and halogenated hydrocarbons; adhesives; high polymers; surface cleaning aluminum; metal joint durability; joining dissimilar materials. *Mailing Add:* Joining Div Alcoa Labs Alcoa Center PA 15069

MING, LI CHUNG, b Shantung, China, July 19, 45; m 72. CRYSTAL CHEMISTRY, X-RAY DIFFRACTION. *Educ:* Nat Taiwan Univ, BS, 67; Univ Rochester, MS, 71, PhD(geol), 74. *Prof Exp:* Teaching asst, Nat Taiwan Univ, 68-69; teaching asst, Univ Rochester, 70-73, res asst, 73-74, res assoc, 74-75; asst geophysicist, 76-80, ASSOC GEOPHYSICIST, UNIV HAWAII, 80- *Mem:* Am Geophys Union; Sigma Xi. *Res:* Laboratory simulation of the physical conditions, temperature and pressure, of the earth's deep interior and postulation of the most likely chemical constituents and the stable mineral assemblages. *Mailing Add:* Hawaii Inst Geophysics 2525 Correa Rd Honolulu HI 96822

MING, SI-CHUN, b Shanghai, China, Nov 10, 22; US citizen; m 57; c 6. PATHOLOGY. *Educ:* Nat Cent Univ, China, MD, 47. *Prof Exp:* Resident path, Mass Gen Hosp, Boston, 52-56; from instr to asst prof, Harvard Med Sch, 56-67; assoc prof, Med Sch, Univ Md, 67-71; PROF PATH, MED SCH, TEMPLE UNIV, 71- *Concurrent Pos:* Assoc pathologist, Beth Israel Hosp, Boston, 56-67; Nat Cancer Inst sr fel, Dept Tumor Biol, Karolinska Inst, Sweden, 64-65. *Mem:* Int Acad Path; Am Asn Pathologists; NY Acad Sci; AAAS. *Res:* Digestive tract disease, gastrointestinal oncology, carcinogenesis and tumor-host relationship. *Mailing Add:* Dept of Path Temple Univ Med Sch Philadelphia PA 19110

MINGES, MERRILL LOREN, b Denver, Colo, Sept 25, 37; m 60; c 4. MATERIALS SCIENCE, CHEMICAL ENGINEERING. *Educ:* Mass Inst Technol, BSc, 59, MSc, 60; Ohio State Univ, PhD(chem eng), 68. *Prof Exp:* Proj engr, 60-63, group leader thermophys res, 64-65, tech mgr thermal protection systs, 66-71, br chief, Elastomers & Coatings Br, 73-75, asst div chief, Electromagnetic Mats Div, 75-77, asst chief, Systs Div, 77-79, CHIEF, ELECTROMAGNETICS DIV, US AIR FORCE MATS LAB, 79- *Concurrent Pos:* Consult, Adv group Aerospace Res & Develop, NATO, 66-; consult, Adv Res Projs Agency, 67-; consult math adv bd, Nat Acad Sci, 68-; Sloan exec fel, Stanford Univ, 71-72; mem adv bd, Int J High Temperatures-High Pressures; task group chmn, Comt Data Sci & Technol, Int Council Sci Union, 78- *Honors & Awards:* US Air Force Sci Achievement, 68, 69. *Mem:* Assoc fel Am Inst Aeronaut & Astronaut; Sigma Xi. *Res:* High temperature thermophysical properties; high temperature heat transfer; materials applications for advanced reentry vehicles, space and propulsion systems; thermo-optical properties. *Mailing Add:* 3216 Suburban Dr Dayton OH 45433

MINGLE, JOHN O(RVILLE), b Oakley, Kans, May 6, 31; m 57; c 2. NUCLEAR ENGINEERING, CHEMICAL ENGINEERING. *Educ:* Kans State Univ, BS, 53, MS, 58; Northwestern Univ, PhD(chem eng), 60; Washburn Univ, JD, 80. *Prof Exp:* Training engr, Gen Elec Co, 53-54; instr chem eng, 56-58, from asst prof to assoc prof nuclear eng, 60-65, Black & Veatch distinguished prof, 73-77, PROF NUCLEAR ENG, KANS STATE UNIV, 65-, DIR INST COMPUTATIONAL RES ENG, 69- *Concurrent Pos:* Res grants, NSF, 62-65, 65-67, Petrol Res Fund, 63-66, Dept Defense, 68-71 & AEC, 69-71; vis prof, Univ Southern Calif, 67-68; consult, Gulf-Gen Atomic, 68 & Wilson & Co, Engrs, 72-81; resident res assoc, Argonne Nat Lab, 76-77. *Mem:* Am Nuclear Soc; Am Inst Chem Engrs; Am Soc Eng Educ; Nat Soc Prof Engrs; Sigma Xi. *Res:* Nuclear heat transfer; applied mathematics; numerical analysis; nuclear transport theory; engineering law. *Mailing Add:* Dept of Nuclear Eng Kans State Univ Manhattan KS 66506

MINGORI, DIAMOND LEWIS, b Jersey City, NJ, June 7, 38; m 60. DYNAMICS, CONTROL SYSTEMS. *Educ:* Univ Calif, Berkeley, BS, 60, Los Angeles, MS, 62; Stanford Univ, PhD(aeronaut, astronaut), 66. *Prof Exp:* Mem tech staff, Aerospace Corp, 66-68; asst prof appl mech, 68-73, ASSOC PROF APPL MECH, UNIV CALIF, LOS ANGELES, 73- *Concurrent Pos:* Consult, Aerospace Corp, Calif, 68-70, 77-; consult, Comsat Corp, Md, 69-70, Jet Propulsion Lab, Calif Inst Technol, 76-, Aerojet Elec Optical Systs, 77, TRW Systs, 78-, Acurex Corp, 78 & NASA Adv Comn, 78- *Mem:* Am Inst Aeronaut & Astronaut; Am Acad Mech. *Res:* Applied mechanics with applications in space vehicle attitude control and ground vehicle dynamics; attitude dynamics and control of gravity dual-spin and large flexible craft. *Mailing Add:* Dept of Mech & Struct Sch Eng & Appl Sci Los Angeles CA 90024

MINGRONE, LOUIS V, b Pittsburgh, Pa, Jan 27, 40; m 64; c 3. BOTANY. *Educ:* Slippery Rock State Col, BS, 62; Ohio Univ, MS, 64; Wash State Univ, PhD(bot, taxon), 68. *Prof Exp:* Assoc prof, 68-73, PROF BIOL & BOT, BLOOMSBURG STATE COL, 73- & ASST CHMN, 78- *Mem:* Bot Soc Am; Am Soc Plant Taxon; Am Inst Biol Sci. *Res:* Plant systematics; cytotaxonomy and phytochemistry of the secondary plant constituents; floristic studies. *Mailing Add:* Dept Biol Allied Health Bloomsburg State Col Bloomsburg PA 17815

MINIATS, OLGERTS PAULS, b Besagola, Lithuania, Sept 13, 23; Can citizen; m 47; c 3. VETERINARY MEDICINE. *Educ:* Univ Toronto, DVM, 55; Univ Guelph, MSc, 66. *Prof Exp:* Clinician, High River Vet Clin, 55-64; asst prof, 66-72, assoc prof clin res, 72-81, PROF, DEPT CLIN STUDIES, ONT VET COL, UNIV GUELPH, 81- *Mem:* Can Vet Med Asn; Asn Gnotobiotics; Asn Advan Baltic Studies; Am Asn Swine Practitioners; Latvian Am Asn Univ Teachers & Professors. *Res:* Development of techniques for procurement and rearing of gnotobiotic research animals; investigation of the characteristics of gnotobiotic swine; application of gnotobiotic animals for the investigation of infectious diseases. *Mailing Add:* Dept of Clin Studies Ont Vet Col Univ of Guelph Guelph ON N1G 2W1 Can

MINICH, MARLIN, b Orange, Calif, Aug 13, 38; m 60; c 5. CIVIL ENGINEERING, ENGINEERING MECHANICS. *Educ:* Fenn Col, BCE, 61; Case Western Reserve Univ, MSEM, 64, PhD(civil eng), 68. *Prof Exp:* Asst eng mech, Case Inst Technol, 61-67; assoc prof civil eng & eng mech, Cleveland State Univ, 67-79; PROF CIVIL ENG, OHIO NORTHERN UNIV, 79- *Mem:* Am Soc Civil Eng; Am Soc Eng Educ. *Res:* Design and analysis of structures and their related behavior. *Mailing Add:* Dept Civil Eng Ohio Northern Univ Ada OH 45810

MINICK, CHARLES RICHARD, b Sheridan, Wyo, Feb 28, 36; m 57; c 3. PATHOLOGY. *Educ:* Univ Wyo, BS, 57; Cornell Univ, MD, 60. *Prof Exp:* Intern path, New York Hosp, 60-61; from asst to asst prof, 65-70, assoc prof, 70-76, PROF PATH, MED COL, CORNELL UNIV, 76- *Concurrent Pos:* USPHS trainee, Cornell Univ, New York Hosp Med Ctr, 61-65, asst res path, 62-63, chief resident, 63-64, asst attend pathologist, 64-70, assoc attend pathologist, 70-76; A Hending pathologist, 76- mem coun arteriosclerosis, Am Heart Asn. *Mem:* AAAS; Harvey Soc; Am Asn Path & Bact; Am Soc Exp Path; Am Heart Asn. *Res:* Pathology of arteriosclerosis and hypertension; immunology; culture of cells derived from blood vessels; scanning and transmission electron microscopy. *Mailing Add:* Dept of Path Cornell Univ Med Col New York NY 10021

MINK, GAYLORD IRA, b Lafayette, Ind, Sept 23, 31; m 54; c 4. PLANT VIROLOGY. *Educ:* Purdue Univ, BS, 56, MS, 59, PhD(plant path), 62. *Prof Exp:* Asst prof plant path, Purdue Univ, 62; from asst to assoc plant pathologist, 62-72, PROF, IRRIGATED AGR RES & EXTEN CTR, WASH STATE UNIV, 73-, PLANT PATHOLOGIST, 73- *Mem:* Am Phytopath Soc. *Res:* Identification, purification and serology of plant viruses; nature of inactivation of plant virus. *Mailing Add:* Irrigated Agr Res & Exten Ctr Wash State Univ Prosser WA 99350

MINK, IRVING BERNARD, b New York, NY, Sept 23, 27; m 50; c 4. HEMATOLOGY. *Educ:* Univ Buffalo, BA, 48; State Univ NY Buffalo, MS, 69. *Prof Exp:* Asst cancer res scientist pharmacol, 61-62, cancer res scientist hematol, 62-69, SR CANCER RES SCIENTIST HEMATOL & HEMOSTASIS, ROSWELL PARK MEM INST, 69- *Concurrent Pos:* Instr pharmacol, Sch Pharm, Univ Buffalo, 56-62; mem bd, Oper Comt & 2nd vpres, Western NY Br, Nat Hemophilia Ctr, 69-76, mem bd, 76-; asst res prof, Roswell Park Div, Grad Sch, State Univ NY Buffalo, 72-; clin instr dept path, Med Sch, State Univ NY, Buffalo; res prof, Niagara Univ. *Mem:* AAAS; Int Soc Thrombosis & Hemostasis. *Res:* Hemostatic mechanism; cancer chemotherapy; bleeding and clotting disorders associated with malignancy; platelet function; development of hemostatic mechanism methodological procedures. *Mailing Add:* 665 N Forest Rd Amherst NY 14221

MINK, JAMES WALTER, b Elgin, Ill, Apr 23, 35; m 59; c 1. MILLIMETER WAVES, CONFORMAL ANTENNAS. *Educ:* Univ Wis-Madison, BS, 61, MS, 62, PhD(elec eng), 64. *Prof Exp:* Res assoc elec eng, Univ Wis-Madison, 61-64; res physical scientist electromagnetic res, Inst Explor Res, 64-71, Commu-Automatic Data Processing Lab, 71-76; ELEC ENGR, US ARMY RES OFF, 76- *Concurrent Pos:* Bd dir & secy, Raleigh Acad, 78-; adj assoc prof, NC State Univ, 79- *Mem:* Inst Elec & Electronics Engrs; Int Sci Radio Union; Soc Photo-Optical Instrumentation Engrs. *Res:* Areas of conformal micro and millimeter wave antennas; millimeter wave integrated circuits and devices for high speed optical communications. *Mailing Add:* US Army Res Off Box 12211 Research Triangle Park NC 27709

MINK, JOHN F, b Nesquehoning, Pa, June 3, 24; m 51; c 1. HYDROLOGY, GEOLOGY. *Educ:* Pa State Univ, BS, 49; Univ Chicago, MS, 51. *Prof Exp:* Res engr, US Steel Co, Ill, 51-52 & Crane Co, 52; asst geologist, Hawaiian Sugar Planters Asn, 52-53; chem supt, Pac Chem & Fertilizer Co, Hawaii, 53-56; geologist, US Geol Surv, 56-60; hydrologist-geologist, Honolulu Bd Water Supply, 60-68; sr analyst, CONSAD Res Corp & Res Anal Corp, 68-69; vpres, Earth Sci Group, Inc, 69-72; CONSULT WATER RESOURCES & EARTH SCI, 72- *Concurrent Pos:* Consult, Govt Guam, 64-; res affil, Water Resources Ctr, Univ Hawaii, 64-; USPHS grant, Johns Hopkins Univ, 65-67; consult, Honolulu Bd Water Supply & State of Hawaii mem state water comn, Hawaii; affil, Univ Guam, 75- *Mem:* AAAS; Am Geophys Union; Am Water Resources Asn; Geol Soc Am. *Res:* Applications of operations research to water supply; water development and supply, particularly development of ground water in islands and along coasts; groundwater flow; contamination of groundwater; stochastic hydrology of streams on tropical islands. *Mailing Add:* PO Box 4452 Honolulu HI 96813

MINK, JOHN R, b Peru, Ill, Sept 8, 27; m 52; c 6. DENTISTRY. *Educ:* Ind Univ, AB, 51, DDS, 56, MSD, 61. *Prof Exp:* Asst prof pedodont, Ind Univ, 57-62; assoc prof, 62-65, PROF PEDODONT, UNIV KY, 65- *Mem:* Am Acad Pedodont; Int Asn Dent Res. *Res:* Pedodontics; replanting teeth; pulp of the tooth root resorption. *Mailing Add:* Dept Pediat Dent Univ Ky Lexington KY 40536

MINK, LAWRENCE ALBRIGHT, b Birmingham, Ala, Nov 10, 36; m 60; c 1. EXPERIMENTAL PHYSICS, PROGRAMMING. *Educ:* NC State Univ, BE, 58, MS, 61, PhD(nuclear physics), 66. *Prof Exp:* Instr physics, NC State Univ, 65-66; asst prof, 66-69, ASSOC PROF PHYSICS, ARK STATE UNIV, 69- *Mem:* AAAS; Am Phys Soc; Sigma Xi. *Res:* Thin liquid films; solar energy conversion. *Mailing Add:* Div Math & Physics Ark State Univ State University AR 72467

MINKER, JACK, b Brooklyn, NY, July 4, 27; m 51; c 2. MATHEMATICS. *Educ:* Brooklyn Col, BA, 49; Univ Wis, MS, 50; Univ Pa, PhD(math), 59. *Prof Exp:* Dynamics engr, Bell Aircraft Corp, 51-52; engr, Radio Corp Am, 52-57, mgr info tech, Data Systs Ctr, 57-63; tech dir & acting off mgr, 63-67; chmn dept, 74-79, PROF COMPUT SCI, UNIV MD, 67- *Concurrent Pos:* Invited lectr, Gordon Res Conf Info Storage & Retrieval, 60; co-chmn Nat Conf Info Storage & Retrieval Asn Comput Mach, 60; mem Nat Acad Sci-US Nat Comt Fedn Info Documentationalists, 69-72; mem adv comt, Annual Rev Info Sci & Technol, 70-; vchmn, Jerusalem Conf Info Technol, 71; co-chmn conf & prog, Nat Info Storage & Retrieval Conf, 71; mem adv comt, Encycl Comput Sci, 71-; mem staff grad sch, NIH; mem, NASA Study Group Mach Intel & Robotics, 78-81; mem adv comt computing, NSF, 79-, chmn, 80- *Mem:* Asn Comput Mach; AAAS; Inst Elec & Electronics Engrs; Soc Indust & Appl Math. *Res:* Computer application; information storage and retrieval; data base systs; operations research; artificial intelligence. *Mailing Add:* Dept of Comput Sci Univ of Md College Park MD 20742

MINKIEWICZ, VINCENT JOSEPH, b Shenandoah, Pa, Oct 24, 38; m 65; c 2. SOLID STATE PHYSICS. *Educ:* Villanova Univ, BS, 60; Univ Calif, Berkeley, PhD(physics), 65. *Prof Exp:* Assoc scientist solid state physics, Brookhaven Nat Lab, 65-72; assoc prof, Univ Md, College Park, 72-74; RES STAFF MEM, IBM CORP, 75- *Mem:* Am Phys Soc. *Res:* Magnetic materials; magnetic bubbles. *Mailing Add:* IBM Res Lab San Jose CA 95193

MINKIN, JEAN ALBERT, b Philadelphia, Pa, Nov 17, 25; m 47; c 2. COAL PETROLOGY, COAL PETROCHEMISTRY. *Educ:* Bryn Mawr Col, BA, 47. *Prof Exp:* Res engr, Franklin Inst Lab, 47-51; physicist, Nat Bur Standards, 51-52; res assoc, Inst Cancer Res, 60-68; RES PHYSICIST, US GEOL SURV, 68- *Mem:* Am Crystallog Asn; Mineral Soc Am; Am Asn Petrol Geologists. *Res:* Development of methodology for rapid quantitative evaluation of petrographic and chemical properties of coal constituents; application of data obtain to interpretation of genetic and diagenetic factors influencing vertical and lateral variations in coal quality and thickness. *Mailing Add:* 3440 Round Table Ct Annandale VA 22003

MINKOFF, ELI COOPERMAN, b New York, NY, Sept 5, 43; m 68; c 2. EVOLUTIONARY BIOLOGY, COMPARATIVE ANATOMY. *Educ:* Columbia Univ, AB, 63; Harvard Univ, AM, 67, PhD(biol), 69. *Prof Exp:* Res asst primate anat, New Eng Regional Primate Res Ctr, Southboro, Mass, 67-68; asst prof, 68-75, actg chmn dept, 76-77, ASSOC PROF BIOL, BATES COL, 76-, ACTG CHMN DEPT, 81- *Mem:* Soc Study Evolution; Am Soc Zoologists; Soc Vert Paleont; Soc Syst Zool; Am Soc Mammalogists. *Res:* Anatomy and evolutionary biology of primates and other mammals; neuromuscular anatomy, especially of facial nerve and facial muscles, vertebrate paleontology; evolutionary theory. *Mailing Add:* Dept of Biol Bates Col Lewiston ME 04240

MINKOWITZ, STANLEY, b Brooklyn, NY, July 1, 28; m 57; c 3. PATHOLOGY, DERMATOLOGICAL PATHOLOGY. *Educ:* City Col New York, BS, 48; Univ Colo, MS, 50; Univ Geneva, MD, 56. *Prof Exp:* Chief surg path, Kings County Hosp Med Ctr, 62-71; CLIN ASSOC PROF PATH, STATE UNIV NY DOWNSTATE MED CTR, 71-; DIR LABS, MAIMONIDES MED CTR, 71- *Concurrent Pos:* Fel pediat med, Jewish Chronic Dis Hosp, 57; asst prof path, State Univ NY Downstate Med Ctr, 63-67, assoc prof, 67-71, consult vet pathologist, 64-; consult pathologist, Brooklyn Women's Hosp, 63- & Unity Hosp, Brooklyn, 65-; consult, Brooklyn State Hosp, 67- *Res:* Organic chemistry, especially amino acids synthesis; experimental study of the use of gold leaf in skin graft; heterotopic liver transplantation; coxsackie B-virus infection in adult mice; research in aging; homologous lung transplantation. *Mailing Add:* Maimonides Med Ctr 4802 Tenth Ave Brooklyn NY 11219

MINKOWSKI, JAN MICHAEL, b Zurich, Switz, Mar 7, 16; nat US; m 51; c 4. SOLID STATE PHYSICS. *Educ:* Swiss Fed Inst Technol, Dipl Physicist, 49; Johns Hopkins Univ, PhD(physics), 63. *Prof Exp:* Res physicist, Inst Tehoret Physics, Switz, 49-50; res physicist solid state physics, Erie Resistor Corp, 50-52; head phys res, Carlyle Barton Lab, 52-63, assoc prof, 63-80, PROF ELEC ENG, JOHNS HOPKINS UNIV, 80- *Mem:* Am Phys Soc. *Res:* Quantum electronics. *Mailing Add:* Dept of Elec Eng 308 Barton Hall Johns Hopkins Univ Baltimore MD 21218

MINKOWYCZ, WOLODYMYR J, b Libokhora, Ukraine, Oct 21, 37; US citizen. MECHANICAL ENGINEERING, HEAT TRANSFER. *Educ:* Univ Minn, BS, 58, MS, 61, PhD(mech eng), 65. *Prof Exp:* From asst prof to assoc prof, 66-79, PROF HEAT TRANSFER, UNIV ILL, CHICAGO CIRCLE, 79- *Concurrent Pos:* Assoc ed, Int J Heat & Mass Transfer, 67-; coord ed, Lettin Heat & Mass Transfer, 74-; ed, Numerical Heat Transfer J, 78- *Mem:* Am Soc Mech Engrs. *Res:* Heat transfer; two-phase flows; non-similar boundary layers; geothermal heat transfer; numerical methods. *Mailing Add:* Dept Energy Eng Box 4348 Univ Ill Chicago Circle Chicago IL 60680

MINN, FREDRICK LOUIS, b Waukegan, Ill, Aug 9, 35. MEDICINE, PHYSICAL CHEMISTRY. *Educ:* Univ Ill, AB, 57, PhD(chem), 64; Univ Miami, MD, 73. *Prof Exp:* Asst prof chem, Columbia Univ, 63-65; assoc prof, George Washington Univ, 65-74, asst med, 73-74; asst dir clin pharmacol, Squibb Inst Med Res, 74-76; asst dir clin invest, 76-80, CLIN RES FEL, MCNEIL PHARMACEUT, JOHNSON & JOHNSON, 80- *Concurrent Pos:* Consult engr, Lockheed Electronics Co, Lockheed Aircraft Corp & Taag Designs, Inc, 67-70. *Mem:* Am Chem Soc; AMA; Am Col Clin Pharmacol; Am Soc Clin Pharmacol & Therapeut. *Res:* Clinical pharmacology; theoretical chemistry. *Mailing Add:* McNeil Pharmaceut McKean Road Spring House PA 19477

MINNE, RONN N, b Menominee, Mich, Oct 3, 24. INORGANIC CHEMISTRY. *Educ:* Northwestern Univ, BS, 50, AM, 51; Harvard Univ, PhD(chem), 60. *Prof Exp:* Teacher high sch, Ill & NMex, 51-54; teacher chem, Culver Mil Acad, 54-56, chmn dept, 60-65; chmn, Sci Div, 72-80, INSTR CHEM, PHILLIPS ACAD, 65- *Concurrent Pos:* Off Naval Res grant, 62-65; vis scholar, Cambridge Univ, 71-72; instr chem, Martha Cochran Found, 80- *Mem:* AAAS; Am Chem Soc; Am Inst Chem; NY Acad Sci. *Res:* Inorganic polymers; silicon chemistry. *Mailing Add:* Dept of Chem Phillips Acad Andover MA 01810

MINNEAR, WILLIAM PAUL, b Pittsburgh, Pa, July 17, 46; m 70; c 2. METALLURGY, CERAMIC SCIENCE. *Educ:* Pa State Univ, BS, 68, MS, 69 & 76, PhD(metall), 75. *Prof Exp:* MEM STAFF, CUTTING & WEAR RESISTANT MAT PROG, CORP RES & DEVELOP, GEN ELEC CO, 75- *Mem:* Am Ceramic Soc; Sigma Xi. *Res:* Reactions between solids, notably carbon and refractory metals and liquid metals; grain growth and ripening phenomena in liquid metal solutions; novel refractory composites. *Mailing Add:* Gen Elec Co PO Box 8 Schenectady NY 12301

MINNEMAN, KENNETH PAUL, b Sacramento, Calif, Sept 1, 52; m 81. NEUROPHARMACOLOGY, NEUROCHEMISTRY. *Educ:* Mass Inst Technol, BS, 74; Univ Cambridge, Eng, PhD(pharmacol), 77. *Prof Exp:* Fel, Med Ctr, Univ Colo, 77-80; ASST PROF PHARMACOL, EMORY UNIV, 80- *Res:* Biochemical studies of neurotransmitter receptors. *Mailing Add:* Dept Pharmacol Emory Univ Atlanta GA 30324

MINNEMAN, MILTON J(AY), b Brooklyn, NY, July 31, 23; m 55; c 1. ELECTRONICS ENGINEERING. *Educ:* Cooper Union, BEE, 43, EE, 52; Univ Pa, MSEE, 49; Polytech Inst New York, PhD(elec eng), 66. *Prof Exp:* Elec develop engr, Radio Corp Am, NJ, 43-47; sect head, Martin Co, Md, 47-52; chief engr, Utility Electronics Corp, NJ, 52; chief fuel gage engr, Avien, Inc, NY, 52-54; chief electronics engr, Bulova Res & Develop Labs, Inc, 54-56; chief electrophys res, Repub Aviation Corp, 56-64; prog mgr space systs, Fairchild Hiller Corp, 64-65; tech dir systs & instruments div, Bulova Watch Co, Inc, 65-67; eng consult to group vpres, Airborne Instruments Lab Div, Cutler-Hammer, Inc, 67-68, tech asst to exec vpres, 68-69; dir eng electronic systs div, Gen Instrument Corp, 69-73; spec asst, 73-81, DIR, MOBILITY & SPEC PROJ, OFF OF DEFENSE, 81- *Concurrent Pos:* Adj inst, Polytech Inst New York, 66-72. *Mem:* Sr mem Inst Elec & Electronics Engrs. *Res:* Inertial navigation and guidance systems; fuel gages; magnetics; nuclear magnetic resonance; space craft systems; communications; radar; data processing; nuclear systems. *Mailing Add:* 8815 Hidden Hill Lane Potomac MD 20854

MINNEMEYER, HARRY JOSEPH, b Buffalo, NY, July 12, 32; c 3. ORGANIC CHEMISTRY. *Educ:* Univ Buffalo, BA, 58, PhD(chem), 62. *Prof Exp:* Res assoc chem, State Univ NY Buffalo, 61-66, lectr, Millard Fillmore Col, 63-64; chemist, Starks Assocs, Inc, 66-67, supvr, 67-68, sect mgr, 68-69; sr res chemist, Lorillard Res Ctr, 70, supvr org chem, 70-75, mgr res, 75-80, DIR RESEARCH, LORILLARD, DIV LOEWS THEATERS, INC, 80- *Mem:* Am Chem Soc. *Res:* Organic synthesis; heterocyclic and medicinal chemistry; reaction mechanisms; tobacco science. *Mailing Add:* Lorillard Res Ctr 420 English St Greensboro NC 27420

MINNERS, HOWARD ALYN, b Rockville Centre, NY, Sept 1, 31; m 58; c 2. MEDICINE. *Educ:* Princeton Univ, AB, 53; Yale Univ, MD, 57; Harvard Univ, MPH, 60; Am Bd Prev Med, cert aerospace med, 65. *Prof Exp:* Intern, Wilford Hall US Air Force Hosp, 57-58, flight surgeon, Langley Air Force Base, Va, 61-62; head flight med br, Manned Spacecraft Ctr, NASA, 62-66; spec asst to chief, Off Int Res, NIH, 66-68; from asst chief to chief, Geog Med Br, 68-72, assoc dir collab res, 72-76, assoc dir int res, Nat Inst Allergy & Infectious Dis, NIH, 76-77; RESPONSIBLE OFFICER OFF RES PROM & DEVELOP, WHO, GENEVA, SWITZ, 77- *Concurrent Pos:* Am Bd Prev Med fel, 66. *Mem:* AAAS; AMA; Aerospace Med Asn; Am Pub Health Asn; Am Soc Trop Med & Hyg. *Res:* Ecology, distribution and determinants of disease prevalence in man; career motivation for international biomedical research; tropical medicine. *Mailing Add:* Res Prom & Develop World Health Orgn 1211 Geneva 27 Switzerland

MINNICH, JOHN EDWIN, b Long Beach, CAlif, Oct 23, 42; m 68; c 2. ENVIRONMENTAL PHYSIOLOGY, VERTEBRATE ZOOLOGY. *Educ:* Univ Calif, Riverside, AB, 64; Univ Mich, Ann Arbor, PhD(zool), 68. *Prof Exp:* Asst prof, 68-72, ASSOC PROF ZOOL, UNIV WIS-MILWAUKEE, 72- *Concurrent Pos:* Wis Alumni Res Found fel physiol, 69-71; environ consult, Environ Analysts, Inc, 74-; textbook consult physiol, MacMillan & Co, Inc, 74- & Wadsworth Pub Co, 75-; reviewer, Reg Biol Div, NSF, 78-; reviewer, Am J Physiol & J Morphol, 79- *Mem:* Sigma Xi; Am Soc Ichthyol & Herpet; Am Soc Zool; Ecol Soc Am; Soc Study Amphibians & Reptiles. *Res:* Environmental physiology of animals; water, electrolyte, energy and nitrogen metabolism of terrestrial vertebrates; excretion and osmoregulation of vertebrates; ecological changes, as seen through rephotography. *Mailing Add:* Dept Zool Univ Wis PO Box 413 Milwaukee WI 53201

MINNICH, VIRGINIA, b Zanesville, Ohio, Jan 24, 10. HEMATOLOGY, NUTRITION. *Educ:* Ohio State Univ, BSc, 37; Iowa State Col, MS, 38. *Hon Degrees:* DSc, William Woods Col, 72. *Prof Exp:* From res asst to res assoc, 39-58, from asst res prof to assoc res prof, 68-74, prof, 74-78, EMER PROF MED, SCH MED, WASH UNIV, 78-; DIR, CLIN HEMATOL LAB, BARNES HOSP, 75- *Concurrent Pos:* Fulbright award, Turkey, 64-65; hon mem Turkish Soc Hematol. *Mem:* Am Fedn Clin Res; Am Soc Hemat; Int Soc Hemat. *Res:* Iron metabolism; platelet agglutinins; abnormal hemoglobins; thalassemia. *Mailing Add:* Div of Hemat Wash Univ Sch of Med St Louis MO 63110

MINNICK, DANNY RICHARD, b Export, Pa, July 17, 37; m 71. ENTOMOLOGY. *Educ:* Southern Missionary Col, BA, 61; Univ Fla, MS, 67, PhD(entom), 70. *Prof Exp:* Asst entom, Univ Fla, 65-70; asst prof biol, Fla Keys Community Col, 70-71; asst prof, 71-76, ASSOC PROF ENTOM, UNIV FLA, 76- *Concurrent Pos:* Danforth assoc. *Honors & Awards:* Outstanding Grad Studies Entom Soc Am, 70; Serv Award, Am Beekeeping Fedn. *Mem:* Entom Soc Am; Nat Asn Col Teachers Agr; Am Beekeeping Fedn; Sigma Xi. *Res:* Insect behavior and ecology; pest management of forage and pasture. *Mailing Add:* Dept of Entom McCarty Hall Univ of Fla Gainesville FL 32611

MINNICK, ROBERT C, b Houston, Tex, Feb 7, 26. ELECTRICAL ENGINEERING, PHYSICS. *Educ:* Johns Hopkins Univ, BA, 50; Harvard Univ, AM, 51, PhD(appl math), 53. *Prof Exp:* From instr to asst prof appl math, Harvard Univ, 53-57; sr physicist, Burroughs Corp, 57-60; sr res engr, Stanford Res Inst, 60-65; prof elec eng, Mont State Univ, 66-70; prof elec eng & comput sci & dir lab comput sci & eng, Rice Univ, 71-73; PRES, MINNICK ENG CO, 73-; PRES & CHIEF EXEC OFFICER, MACK FIVE SYSTS INC, 79- *Mem:* Sr mem Inst Elec & Electronics Engrs; Asn Comput Mach. *Res:* Switching theory; design of digital computer subsystems and systems; cellular logic components. *Mailing Add:* Minnick Eng Co PO Box 306 Ouray CO 81427

MINNIX, RICHARD BRYANT, b Salem, Va, June 20, 33; m 55; c 3. PHYSICS. *Educ:* Roanoke Col, BS, 54; Univ Va, MS, 57; Univ NC, Chapel Hill, PhD(physics), 65. *Prof Exp:* From instr to assoc prof, 56-69, PROF PHYSICS, VA MIL INST, 69-, HEAD DEPT, 74- *Mem:* Am Phys Soc; Am Asn Physics Teachers. *Res:* Defects in solids, particularly by radiation damage; lecture demonstrations as method of instruction and/or stimulation of public interest in science. *Mailing Add:* Dept of Physics Va Mil Inst Lexington VA 24450

MINOCHA, HARISH C, b Aug 31, 32; m 55; c 4. MICROBIOLOGY. *Educ:* Punjab Univ, India, BVSc, 55; Kans State Univ, MS, 63, PhD(bact), 67. *Prof Exp:* Res asst microbiol, Indian Vet Res Inst, 55-61; res asst, Kans State Univ, 61-66, res assoc, 66-67; asst prof, NC State Univ, 67-69; assoc prof microbiol, 69-77, PROF VIROL, KANS STATE UNIV, 77-, MEM, BASIC CANCER CTR, 80- *Concurrent Pos:* Nat Cancer Soc res grant, 69-72; res grant, USDA, 72- & animal health res grant, 80-81; sr scientist, Mid Am Cancer Ctr, 75- *Mem:* Am Soc Microbiol; Asn Am Vet Med Cols. *Res:* Biochemical studies on polyoma and shope fibroma virus infected tissue cultures; immunological studies on swine and equine influenza viruses; antigenic analysis of influenza viruses; bovine respiratory disease. *Mailing Add:* Dept Infectious Dis Kans State Univ Manhattan KS 66502

MINOCK, MICHAEL EDWARD, b Los Angeles, Calif, Dec 6, 37. VERTEBRATE ECOLOGY. *Educ:* Stanford Univ, AB, 60; Calif State Univ, Northridge, MA, 65; Univ Nebr, Omaha, MS, 66; Utah State Univ, PhD(zool), 70. *Prof Exp:* Teacher biol, Los Angeles City Schs, 62-65; instr, State Univ NY Col, Brockport, 69-70; NIH fel behav biol & ecol, Univ Minn, 70-71; asst prof, 71-77, ASSOC PROF BIOL, UNIV WIS CTR-FOX VALLEY, 77- *Mem:* Sigma Xi; Am Ornithologists Union; Wilson Ornith Soc; Ecol Soc Am; Cooper Ornith Soc. *Res:* Bird social organizations and their ecological significance. *Mailing Add:* Univ Wis Ctr-Fox Valley Midway Rd Menasha WI 54952

MINOGUE, ROBERT BROPHY, b Covington, Ky, Jan 31, 28; m 54; c 4. NUCLEAR ENGINEERING. *Educ:* Thomas More Col, Ky, BS, 49; Univ Cincinnati, MS, 51; Oak Ridge Sch Reactor Technol, cert nuclear eng, 52. *Prof Exp:* Chief, Nuclear Technol Br, Bur Ships, US Navy, 52-56; head, Triga Design Sect, Gen Atomic Div, Gen Dynamics Corp, 57-60, head, Nuclear Plant Eng Sect, 60-67; dep dir standards, US Atomic Energy Comn, 67-74; dir standards develop, 75-80, DIR RES, US NUCLEAR REGULATORY COMN, 80- *Concurrent Pos:* Mem, Sr Adv Group Safety Standards, Int Atomic Energy Agency, 75-; lectr, Sch Nuclear Eng, Ga Inst Technol, 76-79. *Mem:* Am Soc Testing & Mat. *Res:* Radiation shielding and radiological safety; reactor coolant technology; research reactor and nuclear power plant development and safety; power plant siting. *Mailing Add:* 14007 Castaway Dr Rockville MD 20853

MINOR, CHARLES OSCAR, b Churdan, Iowa, June 22, 20; m 43; c 3. FORESTRY. *Educ:* Iowa State Col, BS, 41; Duke Univ, MF, 42, DF, 58. *Prof Exp:* Asst prof forestry, La State Univ, 46-54; admin forester, Kirby Lumber Corp, 54-56; assoc prof forestry, Clemson Col, 58; dean, Sch Forestry, 58-79, PROF FORESTRY, NORTHERN ARIZ UNIV, 58- *Concurrent Pos:* Consult forester, 79- *Mem:* Soc Am Foresters; Am Forestry Asn; Am Soc Photogrammetry. *Res:* Forest management and mensuration, including aerial photo interpretation. *Mailing Add:* PO Box 966 Flagstaff AZ 86001

MINOR, JAMES E(RNEST), b Davenport, Wash, Apr 10, 19; m 50; c 3. PHYSICAL CHEMISTRY, METALLURGY. *Educ:* Wash State Univ, BS, 41; Univ Wash, PhD(phys chem), 50. *Prof Exp:* Phys chemist, Procter & Gamble Co, 50-52; mgr fuel design & fuel fabrication, Hanford Labs, Gen Elec Co, 52-65; mgr metal fabrication develop, 65-68, sr res assoc, 68-72, MGR MAJOR PROJ DEVELOP, PAC NORTHWEST LABS, BATTELLE MEM INST, 72- *Mem:* Am Chem Soc; Am Soc Metals; Am Inst Chem Engrs. *Res:* Physical and fabrication metallurgy of fissionable metals, high strength alloys and refractory metals; defense programs; nuclear fuel development; nuclear waste vitrification; seasonal thermal energy storage. *Mailing Add:* 2105 Symons St Richland WA 99352

MINOR, JOHN THREECIVELOUS, b Marshall, Mo, Feb 11, 21; m 46; c 4. ORGANIC CHEMISTRY, INFORMATION SCIENCE. *Educ:* Mo Valley Col, AB, 42; Univ Pittsburgh, MS, 46; Univ Kans, PhD(chem), 50. *Prof Exp:* Res assoc, Univ Rochester, 44-46; asst prof, Westminster Col, 49-51; res chemist, Commercial Solvents Corp, 51-54; group leader, John Deere Chem Co, 54-61; group leader, 61-70, SR INFO SPECIALIST, CONTINENTAL OIL CO, 70- *Mem:* Am Chem Soc; fel Am Inst Chem. *Res:* Aromatic fluorides; nitroaliphatics; ammonia and urea chemistry. *Mailing Add:* Continental Oil Co PO Box 1267 Library Ponca City OK 74601

MINOR, RONALD R, b Donora, Pa, Sept 13, 36; m 58; c 4. DEVELOPMENTAL ANATOMY, EXPERIMENTAL PATHOLOGY. *Educ:* Univ Pa, VMD, 66, PhD(path), 71. *Prof Exp:* Assoc, Univ Pa, 71-72, asst prof anat, med, path & vet med, 72-76; ASSOC PROF DEPT PATH, CORNELL UNIV, 76- *Mem:* Am Vet Med Asn; Soc Develop Biol; Soc Cell Biol; AAAS. *Res:* Regulation of mesodermal differentiation and connective tissue development; basement membrane-laminin and procollagen; inheritable diseases of connective tissue; toxicity of intracellular helium 3, carbon 14 and sulfer 35. *Mailing Add:* Dept of Path Cornell Univ Ithaca NY 14853

MINOR, W(ILBERT) R(AYMOND), b Hopewell, Va, May 24, 31; m 54; c 4. MECHANICAL ENGINEERING. *Educ:* Va Polytech Inst, BS, 53, MS, 58. *Prof Exp:* Proj engr, E I du Pont de Nemours & Co, 55-56, area engr, 56; asst prof, Va Polytech Inst, 56-58; mech engr, 58-63, develop engr, 63-65, appln engr, 65-68, mkt develop engr, 68-70, tech serv supvr, 70-76, STAFF ENGR, TRANSP & DISTRIBUTION DEPT, E I DU PONT DE NEMOURS & CO, INC, 76- *Res:* Combustion; new fuel additives; transportation equipment; heat transfer; teflon heat exchanger; design and rating of heat exchangers for industrial applications; development, design and servicing of reverse osmosis devices; design and construction of solar greenhouse and water desalination system. *Mailing Add:* 844 Crossan Rd Newark DE 19711

MINORE, DON, b Chicago, Ill, Oct 31, 31; m 63; c 2. ECOLOGY. *Educ:* Univ Minn, BS, 53; Univ Calif, Berkeley, PhD(bot), 66. *Prof Exp:* Res forester, Pac Northwest Forest & Range Exp Sta, US Forest Serv, 55, 57-60; asst bot, Univ Calif, Berkeley, 61-63, teaching fel, 63-65; PLANT ECOLOGIST, FORESTRY SCI LAB, US FOREST SERV, 65- *Mem:* Ecol Soc Am; Soc Am Foresters; Northwest Sci Asn. *Res:* Species-site relationships in the mixed conifer forests of Oregon and Washington; vaccinium ecology and physiology; hardwood autecology. *Mailing Add:* Forestry Sci Lab 3200 Jefferson Way Corvallis OR 97331

MINOT, MICHAEL JAY, b Apr 4, 46; m 73; c 2. CHEMICAL ENGINEERING. *Educ:* New York Univ, BA, 68; Johns Hopkins Univ, PhD(chem), 73. *Prof Exp:* Sr chemist elec mat tech, 74-76, sr scientist surface chem res, 76-78, PLANT MFG ENGR, CANTON PLANT, CORNING GLASS WORKS, 78- *Concurrent Pos:* Adj prof modern glass technol, Clarkson Col, 80. *Mem:* Am Chem Soc. *Res:* Surface properties of glass; physical-inorganic chemistry. *Mailing Add:* Corning Glass Works Canton NY 13617

MINOTTI, PETER LEE, b Burlington, Vt, Aug 20, 35; m 62; c 2. WEED SCIENCE. *Educ:* Univ Vt, BS, 57, MS, 62; NC State Univ, PhD(soil sci, plant physiol), 65. *Prof Exp:* Crop physiologist, Int Minerals & Chem Corp, 65-66; ASSOC PROF VEG CROPS, CORNELL UNIV, 66- *Mem:* Weed Sci Soc Am; Am Soc Hort Sci. *Res:* Vegetable weed control; weed-crop competition. *Mailing Add:* Dept of Veg Crops Cornell Univ Ithaca NY 14850

MINOWADA, JUN, b Kyoto, Japan, Nov 5, 27; m 59; c 3. PATHOLOGY, IMMUNOLOGY. *Educ:* Mie Med Col, Japan, BS, 48; Kyoto Univ, MD, 52, DMedSci, 59. *Prof Exp:* Sr res assoc, 61-64, sr res scientist, 66-67, assoc res scientist, 68-72, prin res scientist, 73-74, ASSOC CHIEF SCIENTIST, ROSWELL PARK MEM INST, 75-; RES PROF, ROSWELL PARK DIV, GRAD SCH, STATE UNIV NY BUFFALO, 69- *Concurrent Pos:* Int Atomic Energy Agency res fel, Roswell Park Mem Inst, 60; vis fel, Karolinska Inst, Sweden, 64-66. *Mem:* Am Asn Cancer Res; Am Soc Microbiol; Am Soc Clin Oncol. *Res:* Leukemia-lymphoma; immunology. *Mailing Add:* 376 Countryside Lane Williamsville NY 14221

MINSAVAGE, EDWARD JOSEPH, b Nanticoke, Pa, June 1, 18; m 51. MEDICAL MICROBIOLOGY. *Educ:* Univ Scranton, BS, 49; Univ Pa, MS, 51, PhD(microbiol), 55. *Prof Exp:* Ed asst, Biol Abstracts, 50-51; res bacteriologist, Eaton Labs, Inc, 51-52; instr, Med Sch, Univ Pa, 54-55, res assoc, 55-57; from asst prof to assoc prof biol, 57-67, PROF BIOL, KING'S COL, PA, 67- *Concurrent Pos:* USPHS res grant bact physiol, 63-66. *Mem:* AAAS; Am Soc Microbiol. *Res:* Cytology and cytochemistry; bacterial respiration and oxygen transport systems; analysis and biochemistry of nucleic acids and their derivatives; electrophoresis and chromatographic analysis; microphotography; organ deficiency in experimental animals; loss of essential biochemical intermediates by normal cells. *Mailing Add:* 221 S Hanover St Nanticoke PA 18634

MINSHALL, GERRY WAYNE, b Billings, Mont, Aug 30, 38; m 63; c 3. AQUATIC ECOLOGY. *Educ:* Mont State Univ, BS, 61; Univ Louisville, PhD(zool), 65. *Prof Exp:* NATO fel, Freshwater Biol Asn, Eng, 65-66; from asst prof to assoc prof, 66-74, PROF ZOOL, IDAHO STATE UNIV, 74- *Concurrent Pos:* Fac res grants, Idaho State Univ, 66, 68, 70, 73 & 75; US Dept Health, Educ & Welfare res grant, 68-69; NSF-Int Biol Prog grant, 70-74, Anal Ecosyst Prog grant, 74-78; US Forest Serv grants, 75 & 77; US Corps Eng grants, 72 & 77; US Soil Conserv Serv grant, 76-78. *Mem:* Am Soc Limnol & Oceanog; Inst Asn Theoret & Appl Limnol; Ecol Soc Am. *Res:* Ecology of flowing waters, benthic invertebrates; productivity; detritus; invertebrate drift; pollution. *Mailing Add:* Dept of Biol Idaho State Univ Pocatello ID 83209

MINSHALL, WILLIAM HAROLD, b Brantford, Ont, Dec 6, 11; m 39; c 2. PLANT PHYSIOLOGY. *Educ:* Ont Agr Col, BSA, 33; McGill Univ, MSc, 38, PhD(plant physiol), 41. *Prof Exp:* Asst bot, 33-41, from jr botanist to botanist, 41-51, sr plant physiologist, 51-75, HON RES ASSOC, CAN DEPT AGR RES INST, LONDON, ONT, 75- *Concurrent Pos:* Hon lectr, Univ Western Ont, 52-76. *Mem:* Fel AAAS; Am Soc Plant Physiol; Bot Soc Am; fel Weed Sci Soc Am; Can Soc Plant Physiol. *Res:* Physiology of herbicidal action; metabolic root pressure and uptake of solutes; plant phenology. *Mailing Add:* 91 Huron St London ON N6A 2H9 Can

MINSKER, DAVID HARRY, b Huntingdon, Pa, Jan 17, 38; m 65; c 1. PHYSIOLOGY, PHARMACOLOGY. *Educ:* Juniata Col, BS, 63; Univ Wis, PhD(physiol), 67. *Prof Exp:* Res pharmacologist thrombosis, 67-69, res pharmacologist hypertension, 69-71, res fel thrombosis & teratology, 71-77, RES FEL TERATOLOGY, MERCK SHARP & DOHME RES LABS, 77- *Mem:* Am Heart Asn; Int Soc Thrombosis & Hemostasis. *Res:* Development of anti-thrombotic drugs; teratology; toxicology; embryology. *Mailing Add:* Merck Sharp & Dohme Res Labs West Point PA 19486

MINSKY, MARVIN LEE, b New York, NY, Aug 9, 27; m 52; c 3. MATHEMATICS. *Educ:* Harvard Univ, BA, 50; Princeton Univ, PhD(math), 54. *Prof Exp:* Asst math, Princeton Univ, 50-53; res assoc, Tufts Univ, 53-54; jr fel, Soc Fels, Harvard Univ, 54-57; mem staff, Lincoln Lab, 57-58, from asst prof to prof math, 58-64, PROF ELEC ENG, MASS INST TECHNOL, 64- *Mem:* Nat Acad Sci; fel Am Acad Arts & Sci; fel Inst Elec & Electronics Eng; fel NY Acad Sci. *Res:* Artificial intelligence; theory of computation; psychology; engineering. *Mailing Add:* Dept of Elec Eng Mass Inst of Technol Cambridge MA 02139

MINSTER, JOSEPH, b New York, NY, Oct 5, 30; m 58; c 1. HYDROLOGY. *Educ:* Inst Geol, Moscow, USSR, MS, 53. *Prof Exp:* Chief technologist constuct dewaterius, grouting & sturry walls, Trust Hydrospetzstroy, Moscow, USSR, 53-73; assoc chief engr, Moretrench Am Corp, Rockaway, NJ, 75-78; SR HYDROGEOLOGIST, DAMES & MOORE, 79- *Mem:* Am Soc Civil Engrs; Nat Water Well Asn. *Mailing Add:* 555 N Ave Apt 7C Ft Lee NJ 07024

MINTA, JOE ODURO, b Fomena, Ghana, Mar 16, 42; m 70; c 1. IMMUNOLOGY. *Educ:* Univ Ghana, BSc, 66; Univ Guelph, MSc, 68; Univ Toronto, PhD(biochem), 71. *Prof Exp:* Res asst chem, Univ Guelph, 66-68; res asst biochem, Univ Toronto, 68-71; fel immunol, Med Res Coun Can, 71-73; asst prof, 73-78, ASSOC PROF PATH, UNIV TORONTO, 78-, MEM INST IMMUNOL, 74-, ASSOC PROF MED, 79- *Concurrent Pos:* Res scholar, Can Heart Found, 73-77; clin immunopathologist, Toronto Western Hosp, 77-79; res assoc, Can Arthritis & Rheumatism Soc, 79- *Mem:* AAAS; NY Acad Sci; Can Soc Immunol; Am Asn Exp Path; Am Asn Immunologists. *Res:* Immunochemistry, immunogenetics and immunopathology of the complement system. *Mailing Add:* Med Sci Bldg Rm 6308 Univ Toronto Dept Path Toronto ON M5S 1A8 Can

MINTHORN, MARTIN LLOYD, JR, b Grand Rapids, Mich, Aug 8, 22; m 55, 64; c 4. ENVIRONMENTAL HEALTH, RESEARCH ADMINISTRATION. *Educ:* Univ Nebr, BS, 44, MS, 49; Univ Ill, PhD(biochem), 53. *Prof Exp:* Jr chemist, Nat Bur Stand, 44-46; from res assoc to instr biochem, Univ Ill, 52-55; instr, Wash Univ, 53-54; res assoc, Univ Tenn, 55-56, asst prof, 57-64; BIOCHEMIST, ASST BR CHIEF, DEP PROG MGR & DIV DIR, HEALTH & ENVIRON RES, AEC, US ENERGY RES & DEVELOP ADMIN, US DEPT ENERGY, 64-; PROF LECTR, GEORGE WASHINGTON UNIV, 75- *Concurrent Pos:* USPHS sr res fel, 57-61. *Mem:* AAAS; Sigma Xi; Am Chem Soc; fel Am Inst Chem; Biolectromagnetics Soc. *Res:* Biochemistry of amino acids; stereochemistry; isotopic tracers; health impacts of energy technologies. *Mailing Add:* Off Health & Environ Res ER-72 US Dept Energy Washington DC 20545

MINTON, ALLEN PAUL, b Takoma Park, Md, July 5, 43; m 70; c 2. BIOPHYSICAL CHEMISTRY. *Educ:* Univ Calif, Los Angeles, BS, 64, PhD(phys chem), 68. *Prof Exp:* Guest scientist, Polymer Dept, Weizmann Inst Sci, 68-70, staff fel, 70-74, sr staff fel, 74-75; res chemist, Lab Biophys Chem, 75-78, RES CHEMIST, LAB BIOCHEM PHARMACOL, NAT INST ARTHRITIS, DIABETES, DIGESTIVE & KIDNEY DIS, 78- *Concurrent Pos:* Guest scientist, Polymer & Biophysics Depts, Weizmann Inst Sci, 78-79. *Res:* Intermolecular interactions in biochemistry; aggregation of biological macromolecules in solution; biochemical equilibria and kinetics in concentrated protein solutions; gelation of sickle-cell hemoglobin; non-ideality in concentrated protein solutions. *Mailing Add:* 3019 Kramer Wheaton MD 20902

MINTON, NORMAN A, b Spring Garden, Ala, Oct 12, 24; m 44; c 1. PLANT NEMATOLOGY. *Educ:* Auburn Univ, BS, 50, MS, 51, PhD(zool), 60. *Prof Exp:* Asst county agr agent, Coop Exten Serv, Ala, 51-53; horticulturist, Berry Col, 53-55; nematologist, Auburn Univ, 55-64, NEMATOLOGIST, COASTAL PLAIN EXP STA, US DEPT AGR, 64- *Concurrent Pos:* Assoc ed, Nematropica, 77- *Mem:* Am Phytopath Soc; Soc Nematol; Orgn Trop Am Nematologists; Am Peanut Res & Educ Soc, Inc. *Res:* Host-parasite relationship of nematodes to plants; nematode-fungus relationship to plant diseases; nematode population dynamics as influenced by crops, cultural practices, and chemicals; development of nematode resistant varieties; economic nematode control. *Mailing Add:* Coastal Plain Exp Sta US Dept Agr Tifton GA 31773

MINTON, PAUL DIXON, b Dallas, Tex, Aug 4, 18; m 43; c 2. STATISTICS. *Educ:* Southern Methodist Univ, BSc, 41, MSc, 48; NC State Col, PhD(exp statist), 57. *Prof Exp:* Instr math, Univ NC, 48, asst, Inst Statist, 49-52, statist asst, Inst Res Social Sci, 51-52; asst prof math, Southern Methodist Univ, 52-55; assoc prof statist, Va Polytech Inst, 55-56; assoc prof math & dir comput lab, Southern Methodist Univ, 57-61, prof statist & chmn dept, 61-72; dean, Sch Arts & Sci, 72-79, DIR, INST STATIST, VA COMMONWEALTH UNIV, 79- *Concurrent Pos:* Consult statist, indust & med res groups. *Mem:* Biomet Soc; Inst Math Statist; fel Am Statist Asn; fel Am Soc Qual Control; Math Asn Am. *Res:* Distribution theory; experimental statistics. *Mailing Add:* Va Commonwealth Univ 901 W Franklin Richmond VA 23284

MINTON, SHERMAN ANTHONY, b New Albany, Ind, Feb 24, 19; m 43; c 3. HERPETOLOGY, MICROBIOLOGY. *Educ:* Ind Univ, AB, 39, MD, 42. *Prof Exp:* From asst prof to assoc prof microbiol, Sch Med, Ind Univ, Indianapolis, 47-48; vis prof, Postgrad Med Ctr, Karachi, Pakistan, 58-62; assoc prof, 62-67, PROF MICROBIOL, SCH MED, IND UNIV, INDIANAPOLIS, 67- *Concurrent Pos:* Res assoc, Am Mus Natural Hist, 57-64. *Mem:* Am Soc Trop Med & Hyg; Am Soc Ichthyol & Herpet; Int Soc Toxinology (pres, 66-68); Soc Study Amphibians & Reptiles. *Res:* Venomous animals and the injuries they cause; geographic distribution and taxonomy of amphibians and reptiles; serological techniques in taxonomy; arthropods as human parasites and disease vectors. *Mailing Add:* Dept of Microbiol Ind Univ Med Ctr Indianapolis IN 46202

MINTURN, ROBERT EDWARD, physical chemistry, see previous edition

MINTY, GEORGE JAMES, JR, b Detroit, Mich, Sept 16, 29; m 59; c 1. MATHEMATICS. *Educ:* Wayne State Univ, BS, 49, MA, 51; Univ Mich, PhD(math), 59. *Prof Exp:* Res assoc math, Res Ctr, Univ Mich, 57-58, asst prof 60-64, assoc prof, 64-65; res instr, Duke Univ, 58-59; instr, Univ Wash, Seattle, 59-60; PROF, IND UNIV, BLOOMINGTON, 65- *Concurrent Pos:* Vis mem, Courant Inst Math Sci, NY Univ, 64-65; Sloan fel, 65-67; vis prof, Univ Calif, Berkeley, 71; US sr scientist awardee, Alexander von Humboldt, 73- 74; vis prof, Inst Appli Math, Univ Hamburg, 73-74. *Mem:* AAAS; Am Math Soc; Math Asn Am; Soc Indust & Appl Math. *Res:* Functional analysis; convexity theory; mathematical physics; graph and network theory; mathematical programming. *Mailing Add:* Dept of Math Ind Univ Bloomington IN 47401

MINTZ, A AARON, b Houston, Tex, July 29, 22; m 47; c 3. MEDICINE. *Educ:* Rice Inst, BA, 48; Univ Tex, MD, 48. *Prof Exp:* From instr to assoc prof pediat, 52-73, PROF PEDIAT & COMMUNITY MED, BAYLOR COL MED, 73- *Res:* Pediatrics. *Mailing Add:* Dept of Pediat Baylor Col of Med Houston TX 77030

MINTZ, BEATRICE, b New York, NY, Jan 24, 21. BIOLOGY. *Educ:* Hunter Col, AB, 41; Univ Iowa, MS, 44, PhD(zool), 46. *Prof Exp:* Res asst zool, Univ Iowa, 42-46, instr, 46; from instr to assoc prof biol sci, Univ Chicago, 46-60; assoc mem, Inst Cancer Res, 60-65; prof med genetics, Univ Pa, 65-75; SR MEM, INST CANCER RES, 65- *Concurrent Pos:* Fulbright res scholar, Univ Paris, 51 & Univ Strasbourg, 51; Harvey Soc lectr, 76; mem bd adv, Jane Coffin Children's Mem Fund, 77-; NIH lectr, 78. *Mem:* Nat Acad Sci; fel AAAS; Am Soc Zoologists; Genetics Soc Am; Soc Develop Biol. *Res:* Gene control of differentiation and disease in mammals; embryo-maternal relationships. *Mailing Add:* Inst for Cancer Res 7701 Burholme Ave Philadelphia PA 19111

MINTZ, ESTHER URESS, b New York, NY, May 18, 07; m 29; c 1. PHYSICS. *Educ:* Hunter Col, BA, 28; Columbia Univ, MA, 31; NY Univ, PhD, 36. *Prof Exp:* Instr physics, Hunter Col, 28-33; res asst biophys, Columbia Univ, 36-39; instr physics, Hunter Col, 39-42; physicist, Signal Corps Labs, US Dept Army, NJ, 42-44; instr math, Fieldston Sch, 54-57; from asst prof to prof, 57-73, EMER PROF PHYSICS & ASTRON, BARUCH COL, CITY UNIV NEW YORK, 73- *Mem:* Am Phys Soc. *Res:* Optics; spectroscopy; astronomy for non-science student. *Mailing Add:* 301 E 79th St New York NY 10021

MINTZ, FRED, b New York, NY, June 30, 18; m 42, 76; c 2. MECHANICAL ENGINEERING, ACOUSTICS. *Educ:* George Washington Univ, BS, 40, MechEng, 46; Univ Calif, Los Angeles, ME, 65. *Prof Exp:* Physicist, David Taylor Model Basin, US Dept Navy, 40-46 & Bur Ships, 46-49; asst supvr acoust res sect, Armour Res Found, Ill Inst Technol, 49-51, supvr mech instrumentation & vibrations sect, 51-55; group engr, Eng Lab, Lockheed-Calif Co, 55-57, mgr physics res dept, 57-60, Phys & Chem Sci Dept, 60-64 & Vehicle Systs Lab, 64-70, sr res & develop engr, 70-73; prog mgr, Off Noise Abatement, US Environ Protection Agency, 73-82; SR SCIENTIST, NOISE CONTROL TECHNOL DIV, UNDERWATER SYSTS, INC, 82- *Concurrent Pos:* Mem subpanel acoust noise reduction, Panel Acoust, Res & Develop Bd, Dept Defense, 47-51; mem comt hearing & bioacoust, Nat Acad Sci-Nat Res Coun, 62-70. *Mem:* AAAS; fel Acoust Soc Am; Inst Elec & Electronics Engrs. *Res:* Shock and vibration engineering, especially measurement and control; acoustical engineering, especially noise control. *Mailing Add:* 4601 N Park Ave Chevy Chase MD 20815

MINTZ, LEIGH WAYNE, b Cleveland, Ohio, June 12, 39; m 62; c 2. PALEONTOLOGY, STRATIGRAPHY. *Educ:* Univ Mich, BS, 61, MS, 62; Univ Calif, Berkeley, PhD(paleont), 66. *Prof Exp:* From asst prof to assoc prof, 65-75, assoc dean instr, 69-70, assoc dean sci, 71-72, actg dean instr, 72-73, dean undergrad studies, 73-79, PROF GEOL SCI, CALIF STATE UNIV, HAYWARD, 75-, ASSOC VPRES ACAD PROG, 79- *Mem:* Paleont Soc; Geol Soc Am; Sigma Xi. *Res:* Paleozoic crinozoan and Mesozoic echinozoan echinoderms; fossil and recent irregular echinoids; Cenozoic biostratigraphy; historical geology, particularly the significance of plate tectonics in earth history. *Mailing Add:* Asst Vpres Acad Prog Calif State Univ Hayward CA 94542

MINTZ, SHELDON, medical research, see previous edition

MINTZ, YALE, b New York, NY, Mar 30, 16; m 42; c 3. METEOROLOGY. *Educ:* Dartmouth Col, AB, 37; Columbia Univ, MA, 42; Univ Calif, Los Angeles, PhD(meteorol), 49. *Prof Exp:* Instr meteorol, NY Univ, 43-44; from instr to assoc prof, 44-54, prof, 54-81, EMER PROF METEOROL, UNIV CALIF, LOS ANGELES, 81- *Concurrent Pos:* Vis prof, Hebrew Univ, Jerusalem, 46-48 & 70- *Honors & Awards:* Meisinger Award, Am Meteorol Soc, 67. *Mem:* Fel Am Meteorol Soc. *Res:* Numerical calculation of global climates. *Mailing Add:* Dept of Meteorol Univ of Calif Los Angeles CA 90024

MINTZER, DAVID, b New York, NY, May 4, 26; m 49; c 2. GAS DYNAMICS, UNDERWATER ACOUSTICS. *Educ:* Mass Inst Technol, BS, 45, PhD(physics), 49. *Prof Exp:* Res assoc, US Navy Opers Eval Group, Mass Inst Technol, 46-48, res assoc, Acoust Lab, 48-49, mem staff, 49; asst prof physics, Brown Univ, 49-55; res assoc, Yale Univ, 55-56, assoc prof & dir lab marine physics, 56-62; assoc dean, 70-73, actg dean, 71-72, PROF MECH ENG & ASTRONAUT SCI, NORTHWESTERN UNIV, 62-, PROF ASTROPHYS, 68-, VPRES RES & DEAN SCI, 73- *Concurrent Pos:* Mem mine adv comt, Nat Acad Sci-Nat Res Coun, 63-73; mem bd trustees, Educ Commun, 75-, chmn, 78-81; mem, Appl Res Lab Adv Bd, Pa State Univ, 76-, chmn, 80-; mem bd trustees, Adler Planetarium, Chicago, Ill, 76- *Mem:* Fel Am Phys Soc; fel Acoust Soc Am; Am Soc Mech Eng; Am Soc Eng Educ; Am Astron Soc. *Res:* Kinetic theory; plasma physics; wave propagation. *Mailing Add:* Northwestern Univ Rebecca Crown Ctr 633 Clark St Evanston IL 60201

MINTZER, OLIN WESLEY, III, b Spokane, Wash, June 6, 16; m 40; c 3. TERRAIN ANALYSIS, REMOTE SENSING. *Educ:* Univ Tenn, BSCE, 42; Purdue Univ, MS, 49. *Prof Exp:* Asst prof highway eng, Sch Civil Eng, Purdue Univ, 49-52; asst prof civil eng, Case Inst Technol, 52-56; prof int coop, Punjab Eng, Chandigarh, India, 56-58; assoc prof civil eng, Ohio State Univ, 58-74, prof, 74-80; vis prof res, Eng Topo Lab, US Army, Ft Belvoir, Va, 80-81; PROF CIVIL ENG, OHIO STATE UNIV, 81- *Mem:* Am Soc Photogrammetry; Am Soc Civil Engrs; Nat Soc Prof Engrs. *Res:* Professional, theoretical, and practical knowledge of principles and techniques of photointerpretation; terrain analysis; remote sensing applications in engineering practice; acquisition; analysis and integration of data from radar and thermal infrared scanners; aerial photography and multispectral scanners for soils, landcover vegetation, hydrological and geological purposes. *Mailing Add:* 2027 Indianola Ave Columbus OH 43201

MINYARD, JAMES PATRICK, b Greenwood, Miss, May 11, 29; m 56; c 5. ORGANIC CHEMISTRY. *Educ:* Miss State Univ, BS, 51, PhD(org chem, 67. *Prof Exp:* From asst chemist to chemist, Miss State Chem Labs, 58-64; res chemist, Boll Weevil Res Lab, Agr Res Serv, US Dept Agr, 64-67; PROF CHEM, MISS STATE UNIV, 67-; STATE CHEMIST, MISS STATE CHEM LABS, 67- *Concurrent Pos:* Instr, Miss State Univ, 59-64. *Mem:* AAAS; fel Am Chem Soc; fel Asn Off Anal Chemists (pres, 82); Asn Am Feed Control Off (pres, 76); Asn Am Plant Food Control Off. *Res:* Instrumental analysis; pesticide residues; natural products; organic reaction mechanisms; pesticide photochemistry; insect pheremones; environmental analytical chemistry and toxicology of agricultural chemicals to humans, plants and animals. *Mailing Add:* Box CR Miss State Univ Mississippi State MS 39762

MINZNER, RAYMOND ARTHUR, b Lawrence, Mass, June 9, 15; m 40; c 4. AERONOMY, METEOROLOGY. *Educ:* Mass State Col, BS, 37, MS, 40. *Prof Exp:* Lab instr physics, Mass State Col, 38-41; instr, Univ Ariz, 41-42; res assoc electronics, Mass Inst Technol, 42-45; electronic engr, Air Force Cambridge Res Ctr, 46-50, physicist & unit chief, 50-53, sect chief atmospheric standards, 53-56, chief compos sect, 56-58; staff physicist, Geophys Corp Am, 59-64, prin scientist, GCA Tech Div, GCA Corp, Mass, 65-67; aerospace technologist, Electronic Res Ctr, NASA, 67-70, aerospace technologist, Goddard Space Flight Ctr, 70-76, sr res scientist, 76-80; environ scientist, Space Div, Gen Elec Co, 80-81; CONSULT, 81- *Concurrent Pos:* Mem comt for exten, US Standard Atmosphere, 53-, co-ed, 75. *Mem:* Am Meteorol Soc; Am Geophys Union; Sigma Xi. *Res:* Statistical studies and uncertainty of inferred meteorological parameters; stratospheric climatology; cloud motion vs wind relationships; cloud height from aircraft photos and satellite imagery; standard and model atmospheres. *Mailing Add:* 3263 Windmill Village Punta Gorda FL 33950

MIONE, ANTHONY J, b Brooklyn, NY, Mar 8, 27; m 49; c 4. NUCLEAR ENGINEERING, PHYSICS. *Educ:* US Mil Acad, BS, 49; NC State Univ, MS, 53, PhD(nuclear eng), 63. *Prof Exp:* Adminr plans & opers, Mat Lab, Wright Field, US Air Force, Ohio, 53-56, dep br chief mat physics, 56-58, res & develop adminr nuclear powered aircraft, Hq, Air Res & Develop Command, Andrews AFB, Md, 58-60, instr, 63-64, from assoc prof to permanent prof physics, US Air Force Acad, 64-74, head dept, 66-74; mgr energy resources, Ctr for Energy Systs, Washington, DC, 74-78; sr engr develop, 78-80, MGR, LAB OPERS, NEUTRON DEVICES DEPT, GEN ELEC CO, ST PETERRSBURG, FLA, 80- *Concurrent Pos:* Chief scientist, Europ Off Aerospace Res, 69-71; consult, Americans for Energy Independence, 76-77. *Mem:* Am Phys Soc; Sigma Xi. *Res:* Materials for nuclear reactor fuels, principally uranium carbide; solid state bonding. *Mailing Add:* 12906 Mia Circle Largo FL 33540

MIOVIC, MARGARET LANCEFIELD, b Salem, Ore, Apr 15, 43; m 64; c 3. MICROBIOLOGY. *Educ:* Radcliffe Col, BA, 65; Univ Pa, PhD(microbiol), 70. *Prof Exp:* Instr microbiol, Cornell Univ, 70-72 & biochem, 73-74; asst prof, 75-81, ASSOC PROF BIOL, SWARTHMORE COL, 81- *Mem:* Am Soc Microbiol. *Res:* Metabolic regulation in photosynthetic bacteria. *Mailing Add:* Martin Biol Bldg Swarthmore Col Swarthmore PA 19081

MIQUEL, JAIME, b Agres, Spain, Jan 7, 29; US citizen; m 55; c 2. GERONTOLOGY. *Educ:* Univ Granada, MSc, 50, PhD(pharmacol), 52. *Prof Exp:* NIH res assoc, Nat Inst Neurol Dis & Blindness, 58-61; res scientist, 61-65, CHIEF BR EXP PATH, AMES RES CTR, NASA, 65- *Concurrent Pos:* Span Inst Pharmacol fel, Span Ministry of Educ, Madrid, 52-54; Cajal Inst fel, Span Ministry of Educ, Valencia, 55-58. *Mem:* Geront Soc; Am Asn Neuropath; Span Soc Geront; Soc Invert Path. *Res:* Experimental gerontology; experimental neuropathology; radiobiology. *Mailing Add:* NASA Ames Res Ctr Moffett Field CA 94035

MIR, GHULAM NABI, b Srinagar, Kashmir, June 26, 39; US citizen; m 68; c 2. PHARMACOLOGY, PHYSIOLOGY. *Educ:* Univ Jammu & Kashmir, BSc, 58; Punjab Univ, India, B Pharm, 63, M Pharm, 65; Univ Miss, PhD(pharmacol), 71. *Prof Exp:* Anal chemist, Drug Res Labs, Kashmir, 58-59; res pharmacologist, Inst Hist Med & Med Res, New Delhi, India, 65-66; group leader toxicol, 72-73 & gastrointestinal pharmacol, 73-75, sect head, 75-81, HEAD DEPT PHARMACOL, WILLIAM H RORER, INC, PA, 82- *Mem:* Soc Toxicol; Am Pharmaceut Asn; Sigma Xi; Am Soc Pharmacol & Exp Therapeut. *Res:* Drug effects on gastric secretion; peptic and duodenal ulcers; intestinal motility; intestinal absorption and secretion; uterine contraction and general toxicity of drugs; experimental therapy. *Mailing Add:* Div of Res William H Rorer Inc Ft Washington PA 19034

MIR, LEON, b Krystynopol, Poland, July 13, 38; US citizen; m 66; c 1. CHEMICAL ENGINEERING. *Educ:* Columbia Univ, AB, 58, BS, 59; Mass Inst Technol, MS, 61, ScD(chem eng), 63. *Prof Exp:* Engr, Esso Res & Eng Co, NJ, 63-65; proj leader & actg prog mgr large scale gas chromatog, Abcor, Inc, 65-71; sr consult scientist, Avco Systs Div, Avco Corp, 71-77; SR CONSULT SCI, ABCOR, INC, NEWTON, MASS, 77- *Mem:* Am Chem Soc; Am Inst Chem Engrs. *Res:* Physical chemistry of polyelectrolytes; chromatographic processes; applied mathematics. *Mailing Add:* Abcor Inc 15 Hobart Rd Newton MA 02159

MIRABELLA, FRANCIS MICHAEL, JR, b Dec 27, 43; m 67. POLYMER CHEMISTRY. *Educ:* Univ Bridgeport, BA, 66; Univ Conn, MS, 74, PhD(polymer chem), 75. *Prof Exp:* Res chemist, Technichem Co, 66-69; analyst, Olin Corp, 69-72; teaching asst anal chem, Univ Conn, 72-75; res scientist polymer eval, Arco/Polymers Inc, Atlantic Richfield Co, 75-77; RES SCIENTIST POLYMER EVAL, NORTHERN PETROCHEM CO, 77- *Mem:* Am Chem Soc. *Res:* Theory of composition of copolymers and relationship of copolymer composition to molecular weight. *Mailing Add:* Northern Petrochem Co PO Box 459 Morris IL 60450

MIRABILE, CHARLES SAMUEL, JR, b Hartford, Conn, Jan 10, 37; m 60; c 3. PSYCHIATRY. *Educ:* Yale Univ, BA, 59; McGill Univ, MDCM, 63. *Prof Exp:* PSYCHIATRIST PVT PRACT, SHARON CLIN, 69-, RES PSYCHIATRIST, INST LIVING, 67- *Concurrent Pos:* Mem med staff, Hotchkiss Sch, 70-, Indian Mountain Sch, 78, Berkshire Sch, 79 & Salisbury Sch, 81- *Mem:* AAAS; Am Psychiat Asn. *Res:* Orienting mechanisms; sensory function and perception; neurophysiology of individual difference; neurophysiologic correlates of mental illness. *Mailing Add:* Inst of Living 400 Washington St Hartford CT 06106

MIRABITO, JOHN A, b Somerville, Mass, May 16, 17; m 39. METEOROLOGY. *Educ:* Wake Forest Col, BS, 41; Mass Inst Technol, cert, 43. *Prof Exp:* Meteorologist, Pac Fleet & Naval Air Reserve Training Prog, US Navy, 42-52, personnel & training officer meteorol, Off Chief Naval Oper, 52-54, staff meteorologist & oceanographer, Naval Support Forces, Antarctica, 54-59, exec officer, Fleet Weather Cent, DC, 59-61, staff meteorologist & oceanographer, 6th Fleet, 61-63; marine serv coordr, Environ Sci Serv Admin, 63-70; res prog mgr, Nat Marine Fisheries Serv, Nat Oceanic & Atmospheric Admin, 71-72, prog analyst, 72-81; RETIRED. *Concurrent Pos:* Exec secy working group VIII, US-USSR Bilateral on Protection of Environ, 75. *Mem:* AAAS; Am Meteorol Soc; Am Geophys Union. *Res:* Polar meteorology in Antarctica; oceanographic forecasts; marine science, air-sea interaction; fisheries research management. *Mailing Add:* 4713 Jasmine Dr Rockville MD 20853

MIRACLE, CHESTER LEE, b Barbourville, Ky, Apr 30, 34; m 57; c 3. MATHEMATICS. *Educ:* Berea Col, 54, BA; Auburn Univ, MS, 56; Univ Ky, PhD(math), 59. *Prof Exp:* From instr to asst prof, 59-63, ASSOC PROF MATH, UNIV MINN, MINNEAPOLIS, 63- *Mem:* Am Math Soc; Math Asn. *Res:* Analytical continuation and summability of series. *Mailing Add:* Dept of Math Univ of Minn Minneapolis MN 55455

MIRAGLIA, GENNARO J, b Italy, Jan 18, 29; US citizen; m 54; c 3. MEDICAL MICROBIOLOGY, PHYSIOLOGY. *Educ:* St Bonaventure Univ, BS, 51; Univ NH, MS, 57; Univ Tenn, PhD(bact), 60. *Prof Exp:* Fel bact, Bryn Mawr Col, 61-62; asst prof bact, Seton Hall Col Med & Dent, 62-63; RES FEL, SQUIBB INST MED RES, 63- *Mem:* AAAS; Am Soc Microbiol; NY Acad Sci. *Res:* Host-bacteria interrelationships; gram-negative infections; effect of low ambient temperature on infections; chemotherapy of a number of bacterial infections. *Mailing Add:* Squibb Inst for Med Res Princeton NJ 08540

MIRALDI, FLORO D, b Lorain, Ohio, Mar 21, 31; m 57; c 1. BIOENGINEERING, NUCLEAR MEDICINE. *Educ:* Col Wooster, AB, 53; Mass Inst Technol, SB, 53, SM, 55, ScD(nuclear eng), 59; Case Western Reserve Univ, MD, 70. *Prof Exp:* Engr, Atomic Power Div, Westinghouse Elec Corp, 55; asst prof elec eng, Purdue Univ, 58-59; from asst prof to assoc prof nuclear eng, 59-69, assoc prof biomed eng, Schs Eng & Med, 69-72, PROF BIOMED ENG, SCHS ENG & MED, CASE WESTERN RESERVE UNIV, 72-, ASSOC PROF RADIOLOGY, NUCLEAR SCANNERS & RADIATION DIAG, 81- *Concurrent Pos:* Asst radiologist, Univ Hosps of Cleveland, 71-72, radiologist, 72-; chief nuclear med, Cleveland Metrop Gen Hosp, 73-; mem adv comt biotechnol & human resources, NASA, 63-65; pres, Am Radiation Res Corp, 63-; mem res adv bd, Euclid Clin Found, 66-69. *Mem:* AAAS; Am Nuclear Soc; Soc Nuclear Med. *Res:* Radiological health; applications of radiation and radioisotopes; nuclear reactor physics; nuclear medical instrumentation. *Mailing Add:* Dept of Radiol Univ Hosps Cleveland OH 44106

MIRAND, EDWIN ALBERT, b Buffalo, NY, July 18, 26. BIOLOGY. *Educ:* Univ Buffalo, BA, 47, MA, 49; Syracuse Univ, PhD, 51. *Hon Degrees:* DSc, Niagara Univ, 70; DSc, D'Youville Col, 74. *Prof Exp:* Asst, Univ Buffalo, 47, instr biol, 48; instr, Utica Col, Syracuse, 50; assoc cancer res scientist, 51-60, asst to Inst Dir, 60-67, PRIN CANCER RES SCIENTIST, DIR CANCER RES, ROSWELL PARK MEM INST, 67-, ASSOC DIR, INST, 67- *Concurrent Pos:* Res prof, Grad Sch, State Univ NY Buffalo, 54-, prof & dir grad studies, 67-, dean, Roswell Park Grad Div, Grad Sch, 67-; prof & dean, Roswell Park Grad Div, Niagara Univ, 68-, coun mem, 71-; prof, Canisius Col, 68-; mem comt tech guid, Nat Acad Sci-Nat Res Coun, Human Cancer Virus Task Force, NIH, 63-; consult, Cornell Aeronaut Labs, 62-; prof clin cancer comt mem, Nat Cancer Inst, 74-; chmn, USA Nat Comt, Int Union Against Cancer, 80-; secy-gen, 13th Int Cancer Cong, 78-82. *Honors & Awards:* Billings Silver Medal, AMA, 60. *Mem:* Fel AAAS; Radiation Res Soc; Am Soc Zool; Soc Exp Biol & Med; Am Asn Cancer Res (secy-treas, 67-). *Res:* Abnormality of iron metabolism in iron deficiency anemias; erythropoietin; relationships of viruses to cancer; gnotobiology. *Mailing Add:* Roswell Park Mem Inst 666 Elm St Buffalo NY 14263

MIRANDA, CONSTANCIO F, b Raia-Goa, India, Dec 4, 26; m 57; c 4. STRUCTURAL & CIVIL ENGINEERING. *Educ:* Univ Bombay, BE, 49; Univ Notre Dame, MS, 62; Ohio State Univ, PhD(struct eng), 64. *Prof Exp:* Asst lectr civil eng, Col Eng, Poona, 50; asst engr & exec engr, Govt Bombay, India, 50-60; from teaching asst to instr, Univ Notre Dame, 60-62; instr & res assoc, Ohio State Univ, 62-64; assoc res engr, Air Force Shock Tube Facility, Univ NMex, 64-65; chmn dept, 65-80, PROF CIVIL ENG, UNIV DETROIT, 65-, DIR, PROF ADV SERV CTR, 76- *Concurrent Pos:* Indust engr, Messrs Ibcon Ltd, India, 50; instr nuclear defense design, Off Civil Defense, 65-; res grant & tech proj dir, Army Tank Automotive Ctr, 66-; prin, Miranda, Baker & Assocs, Consult Engrs, Mich, 67. *Mem:* Am Soc Civil Engrs; Am Soc Eng Educ; assoc mem Indian Inst Eng. *Res:* Structural engineering in general, particularly stability; design in the inelastic range; matrix formulation of structural problems; soil mechanics; nuclear defense and hydraulic engineering. *Mailing Add:* Dept of Civil Eng Univ of Detroit Detroit MI 48221

MIRANDA, GILBERT A, b Los Angeles, Calif, Oct 21, 43; div; c 4. DETONATION PHYSICS, CRYOGENICS. *Educ:* Calif State Col, Los Angeles, BS, 65; Univ Calif, Los Angeles, MS, 66, PhD(solid state physics), 72. *Prof Exp:* APPL PHYSICIST, LOS ALAMOS SCI LAB, UNIV CALIF, 72- *Res:* Critical current measurements of 10-50 kiloampere superconducting cables, braids and monolithic wires; measurements of the effects of colliding detonation waves on metals; nuclear magnetic resonance; initiation of insensitive high explosives and generation of shaped detonation waves. *Mailing Add:* Los Alamos Sci Labs MS-960 Los Alamos NM 87545

MIRANDA, HENRY A, JR, b New York, NY, Sept 20, 24; m 50; c 2. GEOENVIRONMENTAL SCIENCE. *Educ:* Iona Col, BS, 52; Fordham Univ, MS, 53, PhD(physics), 56. *Prof Exp:* Sr scientist, Hudson Labs, Columbia Univ, 56-60; sr consult engr, Braddock, Dunn & McDonald, Inc, Tex, 60-62; sr scientist & group leader radiation physics, Lowell Tech Inst Res Found, 62-65; sr scientist & dept mgr atmospheric sci, GCA Technol Div, 65-67, dir space sci lab, 67-72; VPRES & DIR RES, EPSILON LABS, INC, 72- *Mem:* Am Geophys Union; Am Phys Soc; Inst Elec & Electronics Eng. *Res:* Earth and atmospheric radiation; turbulent oceanic diffusion; scintillation counting; optical and infrared tracking systems; nuclear effects; spectroscopy; densitometry; optical instrumentation; laser development; aeronomy; upper-atmospheric winds and diffusion; stratospheric aerosols; aerosol physics; imaging systems; photogrammetry. *Mailing Add:* Epsilon Labs, Inc 4 Preston Ct Bedford MA 01730

MIRANDA, QUIRINUS RONNIE, b Bombay, India, June 4, 39; US citizen; m 76. VIROLOGY, MICROBIOLOGY. *Educ:* Univ Bombay, BSc, 61, MSc, 66; Univ Manchester, PhD(virol), 71. *Prof Exp:* Sr scientist & virologist, Schering-Plough Corp, 71-74; asst res microbiol, Univ Calif, Los Angeles, 74-75; sr proj leader, Organon Diag, Akzona, Inc, 75-78; MGR RES & DEVELOP, INT DIAG TECHNOL, INC, 78- *Concurrent Pos:* Adj asst prof, Univ Southern Calif, 77- *Mem:* AAAS; Am Soc Microbiol; Soc Gen Microbiol; Tissue Culture Asn; NY Acad Sci. *Res:* Rapid diagnosis of pathogens using IFA and EIA; interfernon; viral chemotherapy and viral vaccines. *Mailing Add:* Int Diag Technol 2551 Walsh Ave Santa Clara CA 95050

MIRANDA, THOMAS JOSEPH, b Ewa Mill, Hawaii, Nov 18, 27; m 53; c 5. ORGANIC POLYMER CHEMISTRY. *Educ:* San Jose State Col, AB, 51, MA, 53; Univ Notre Dame, PhD(org chem), 59; Ind Univ, MBA, 80. *Prof Exp:* Instr chem, San Jose State Col, 52-53; chemist, Eitel-McCullough Inc, 53; dir res chem, O'Brien Corp, 59-69; sr res mat scientist, 69-71, STAFF SCIENTIST, WHIRLPOOL CORP, 71- *Concurrent Pos:* Tech ed, J Coatings Technol. *Honors & Awards:* Ernest T Trigg Award, Fedn Socs Coatings Technol, 67; George Baugh Heckel Award, Fedn Socs Coatings Technol, 80. *Mem:* AAAS; Am Chem Soc; Am Oil Chem Soc; fel Am Inst Chemists; Sigma Xi. *Res:* Stereospecific polymerization of olefins; radiation polymerization of olefins; rocket fuels; emulsion polymerization; thermosetting acrylics; epoxy resins; water soluble polymers; thermal analysis; polymer stabilization; coatings technology. *Mailing Add:* Elisha Gray II Res & Eng Ctr Whirlpool Corp Monte Rd Benton Harbor MI 49022

MIRANKER, WILLARD LEE, b Brooklyn, NY, Mar 8, 32; m 52; c 3. MATHEMATICS. *Educ:* NY Univ, BA, 52, MS, 53, PhD(math), 57. *Prof Exp:* Asst math, NY Univ, 53-56; mem staff, Bell Tel Labs, Inc, 56-58; staff mathematician, Res Ctr, Int Bus Mach Corp, 59-63; sr res fel, Calif Inst Technol, 63-64; asst to dir res, 65, STAFF MATHEMATICIAN, RES CTR, IBM CORP, 65-, ASST DIR, MATH SCI DEPT, 72- *Concurrent Pos:* Adj prof, City Univ New York, 66-67; vis prof dept math, Hebrew Univ, Israel, 68-69; adj prof, Dept Math, NY Univ, 70-73; vis prof, Univ Paris, 74-75; vis lectr, Yale Univ, 73-74; adj prof, State Univ NY, Purchase, 77. *Mem:* Fel AAAS; Am Math Soc; Soc Indust & Appl Math. *Res:* Applied mathematics; numerical analysis. *Mailing Add:* IBM Corp PO Box 218 Yorktown Heights NY 10598

MIRARCHI, RALPH EDWARD, b Mt Carmel, Pa, Jan 30, 50; m 77. WILDLIFE BIOLOGY. *Educ:* Muhlenberg Col, BS, 71; Va Polytech Inst & State Univ, MS, 75, PhD(wildlife biol), 78. *Prof Exp:* ASST PROF WILDLIFE, DEPT ZOOL-ENTOM, AUBURN UNIV, 78- *Mem:* Wildlife Soc; Wilson Ornith Soc; Am Ornith Union; Wildlife Management Inst. *Res:* Effects of biotic and abiotic factors upon reproductive physiology of wildlife species. *Mailing Add:* Dept Zool-Entom Auburn Univ Auburn AL 36830

MIRCETICH, SRECKO M, b Skela, Yugoslavia, Sept 2, 26; US citizen; m 56; c 2. PLANT PATHOLOGY. *Educ:* Univ Sarajevo, BS, 52; Univ Belgrade, MS, 54; Univ Calif, Riverside, PhD(plant path), 66. *Prof Exp:* Teaching asst plant path, Sch Agr, Univ Sarajevo, 49-52; asst plant pathologist, Exp Sta Subtrop Agr, Bar, Yugoslavia, 52-54, head plant protection dept, 54-57; res assoc plant path, Univ Calif, Riverside, 58-66; res plant pathologist, Plant Sci Res Div, 66-73, PLANT PATHOLOGIST, AGR RES SERV, US DEPT AGR, WESTERN REGION, 73- *Honors & Awards:* CIBA-Geigy Award, Am Phytopath Soc. *Mem:* Am Phytopath Soc; Int Soc Plant Path. *Res:* Soilborne pathogens and diseases; soil ecology of Phytophthora and Pythium; soil populations; diseases of fruit and nut trees; Phytophthora root and crown rot of deciduous fruit and nut trees. *Mailing Add:* Dept of Plant Path Univ of Calif Davis CA 95616

MIRELS, HAROLD, b New York, NY, July 29, 24; m 53; c 3. AERONAUTICAL ENGINEERING. *Educ:* Cooper Union, BME, 44; Case Inst Technol, MS, 49; Cornell Univ, PhD(aeronaut eng), 53. *Prof Exp:* Aeronaut res engr, NASA, 44-61, chief plasma physics br, 60-61; head adv propulsion & fluid mech dept, 61-64, head aerodyn & heat transfer dept, 64-76, asst dir, 77-80, ASSOC DIR, AEROPHYSICS LAB, AEROSPACE CORP, 80- *Concurrent Pos:* Spec lectr, Case Inst Technol, 50, Fenn Col, 54-61 & Univ Calif, Los Angeles, 72-77; mem fluid mech comt, NASA, 60-61, mem adv subcomt fluid dynamics, 67-70. *Mem:* Fel Am Inst Aeronaut & Astronaut; fel Am Phys Soc. *Res:* Aerodynamics; gas dynamics; heat transfer; chemical lasers. *Mailing Add:* 3 Seahurst Rd Rolling Hills CA 90274

MIRES, RAYMOND WILLIAM, b Mansfield, Tex, Mar 16, 33; div; c 3. PHYSICS. *Educ:* Tex Tech Univ, BS, 55, MS, 60; Univ Okla, PhD(physics), 64. *Prof Exp:* Mathematician, Holloman Air Develop Ctr, Holloman AFB, NMex, 55-56; engr, Martin Co, 56-57; instr physics, Tex Tech Univ, 57-60; asst, Univ Okla, 60-64; from asst prof to assoc prof, 64-71, PROF PHYSICS, TEX TECH UNIV, 71- *Concurrent Pos:* Physicist, LTV Electrosysts, Inc, Tex, 66-67; Advan Res Projs Agency res grant, Tex Tech Univ, 67-72; consult forensic physicist, 67- *Mem:* AAAS; Am Phys Soc; Am Asn Physics Teachers. *Res:* Optical and magnetic properties of solids; atomic structure; forensic applications of engineering physics. *Mailing Add:* Dept of Physics Tex Tech Univ Lubbock TX 79409

MIRHEJ, MICHAEL EDWARD, b Dhour-Shweir, Lebanon, Dec 25, 31; US citizen; div; c 2. TEXTILE TECHNOLOGY. *Educ:* McGill Univ, BSc, 58; Univ Western Ont, MSc, 59; Univ BC, PhD(chem oceanog, chem physics), 62. *Prof Exp:* Fel physics, Univ BC, 62-63; sr res chemist, Polymer Corp Ltd, Ont, 63-66; res chemist, 66-75, sr res chemist, 75-81, RES ASSOC, CHATTANOOGA NYLON PLANT, E I DU PONT DE NEMOURS &

CO INC, 81- *Res:* Nuclear magnetic resonance spin echo technique to study influence of paramagnetic oxygen on proton relaxation; polymer synthesis and characterization; auto regenerating dehydrogenation catalysts; development of new textile products. *Mailing Add:* Forest Park Dr Signal Mountain TN 37377

MIRKES, PHILIP EDMUND, b Oshkosh, Wis, May 8, 43; m 68; c 2. DEVELOPMENTAL BIOLOGY, DEVELOPMENTAL BIOCHEMISTRY. *Educ:* St Norbert Col, BS, 65; Univ Mich, MS, 67, PhD(zool), 70. *Prof Exp:* Trainee zool, Univ Wash, 70-71, fel genetics, 71-73; asst prof biol, Univ SC, 73-79; RES ASST PROF, UNIV WASH, 79- *Concurrent Pos:* Prin investr, Res Corp grant, 75-78 & NSF grant, 78-81; mid career develop award-toxicol, Nat Inst Environ Health Sci, 79-81. *Mem:* AAAS; Soc Teratology; Soc Develop Biol. *Res:* Molecular mechanisms of teratogenesis. *Mailing Add:* Univ Wash Seattle WA 98195

MIRKIN, BERNARD LEO, b New York, NY, Mar 31, 28; m 54; c 2. PEDIATRICS, CLINICAL PHARMACOLOGY. *Educ:* NY Univ, AB, 49; Yale Univ, PhD(pharmacol), 53; Univ Minn, MD, 64. *Prof Exp:* Instr physiol & pharmacol, State Univ NY Downstate Med Ctr, 52-54, 56-57, asst prof pharmacol, 57-58, res assoc, 58-60; from asst prof to assoc prof, 66-72, PROF PEDIAT & PHARMACOL, MED SCH, UNIV MINN, MINNEAPOLIS, 72-, DIR DIV CLIN PHARMACOL, 66- *Concurrent Pos:* Consult, NIH & Nat Res Coun-Nat Acad Sci; fel, Jesus Col, Oxford Univ & Ford Found. *Mem:* Am Soc Pharmacol & Exp Therapeut; Am Soc Clin Pharmacol & Therapeut; Soc Pediat Res. *Res:* Pharmacology of neurohumoral mediators; developmental pharmacology. *Mailing Add:* Dept Pediat & Pharmacol Med Sch Univ Minn Minneapolis MN 55455

MIROCHA, CHESTER JOSEPH, b Cudahy, Wis, Feb 7, 30; m 52; c 6. PLANT PATHOLOGY. *Educ:* Marquette Univ, BS, 55; Univ Calif, PhD(plant path), 60. *Prof Exp:* Lab technologist, Univ Calif, 57-60; res plant pathologist, Union Carbide Chem Co, 60-63; from asst prof to assoc prof plant path & physiol, 63-66, PROF PLANT PATH, UNIV MINN, ST PAUL, 72- *Concurrent Pos:* Chmn comt mycotoxicol, Int Soc Plant Path. *Mem:* AAAS; Am Phytopath Soc. Mycotoxicology; physiology of fungi; mass spectroscopy; analytical chemistry. *Mailing Add:* Dept of Plant Path Univ of Minn St Paul MN 55101

MIRONESCU, STEFAN GHEORGHE DAN, b Bucharest, Romania, Dec 26, 32; m 65; c 1. CELL BIOLOGY. *Educ:* Acad Med Sci, Bucharest, Romania, MD, 57, Inst Virol, PhD(chem & viral oncol), 71. *Prof Exp:* Asst prof anat, Fac Med, Acad Med Sci, Bucharest, Romania, 58, from sci investr to sr sci investr exp oncol, Inst Oncol, 61-67, sr sci investr chem carcinogenesis, Inst Endocrinol, 68-72; vis prof cell biol, Thomas Jefferson Univ, 72-74; sci investr cell biol, Blood Res Lab, Am Nat Red Cross, 74-77; PROF PATH, SCH MED, BOOKER T WASHINGTON CTR, UNIV SC, 77- *Concurrent Pos:* Vis sr scientist, NSF, 72. *Honors & Awards:* Stefan Nicolau Medal Sci Merit, Inst Virol, Acad Med Sci, Bucharest, Romania, 71. *Mem:* Am Asn Cancer Res; Sigma Xi; Biophys Soc. *Res:* Control of cell replication in normal, carcinogen-treated and tumor cells; factors controlling iniation of DNA synthesis, chemical carcinogenesis and cell cycle; preservation of cells by freezing. *Mailing Add:* Dept of Path Booker T Washington Ctr Columbia SC 29208

MIROWITZ, L(EO) I(SAAK), b Mannheim, Ger, Dec 11, 23; nat US; m 47; c 3. STRUCTURAL DYNAMICS. *Educ:* Wash Univ, BS, 44, MS, 57. *Prof Exp:* From asst res engr to sr res engr flutter & vibrations, McDonnell Aircraft Corp, 46-51, from design engr to sr design engr, 51-54, proj dynamics engr, 54-57, chief dynamics engr, 57-58, chief struct dynamics engr, 58-64, eng mgr, Space & Missile Systs, 64-66, Voyager prog mgr, 66-69; dir advan technol, McDonnell Douglas Astronaut Co, 69-75; VPRES DIVERSIFICATION, MCDONNELL DOUGLAS CORP, 75-; PRES, VITEK SYSTS, INC, 79- *Concurrent Pos:* Mem subcomt vibration & flutter, NASA, 56-58; dir, Microdata, Inc, 79- & Coaliquid, Inc, 81- *Mem:* Assoc fel Am Inst Aeronaut & Astronaut; Am Soc Microbiol. *Res:* Applied mechanics; influence of dynamics, flutter and vibrations on design; reliability and performance of aircraft, missiles and control systems; design of space and missile systems. *Mailing Add:* McDonnell Douglas Corp Box 516 St Louis MO 63166

MIRSHAK, SAMUEL, b Jacksonville, Fla, Oct 20, 29; m 53; c 5. CHEMICAL ENGINEERING. *Educ:* Northwestern Univ, BS, 52, MS, 53. *Prof Exp:* Res supvr, 53-68, res mgr, 68-69, dir nuclear eng & mat, 69-75, gen supt works tech, 75-77, gen supt prod, Savannah River Plant, 77-78, DIR RES, SAVANNAH RIVER LAB, E I DU PONT DE NEMOURS & CO, INC, 79- *Mem:* Am Nuclear Soc; Sigma Xi. *Res:* Reactor engineering, advanced operational planning and manufacturing. *Mailing Add:* Savannah River Lab E I du Pont de Nemours Co Inc Aiken SC 29808

MIRSKY, ALLAN FRANKLIN, b New York, NY, Feb 2, 29; m 51; c 2. NEUROPSYCHOLOGY, CLINICAL PSYCHOLOGY. *Educ:* City Col NY, BS, 50; Yale Univ, MS, 52, PhD(psychol), 54. *Prof Exp:* Res psychologist, Lab Psychol, Nat Inst Mental Health, 54-61; prof neuropsychol, Sch Med, Boston Univ, 61-80; CHIEF, LAB OF PSYCHOL & PSYCHOPATH, NAT INST MENTAL HEALTH, 80- *Concurrent Pos:* Consult, Nat Inst Mental Health, Nat Sci Found & Nat Inst Neurological & Communicative Disorders & Stroke, 55-80. *Mem:* Am Psychol Asn; Am EEG Soc; Soc Neurosci; Int Neuropsychol Soc; Am Col Neuropsychopharm. *Res:* Neuropsychology and neurophysiology of attention and attention impairment. *Mailing Add:* Lab Psychol & Psychopath Nat Inst Mental Health Bethesda MD 20205

MIRSKY, ARTHUR, b Philadelphia, Pa, Feb 8, 27; m 61; c 1. ENVIRONMENTAL GEOLOGY, URBAN GEOLOGY. *Educ:* Univ Calif, Los Angeles, BA, 50; Univ Ariz, MS, 55; Ohio State Univ, PhD(stratig geol), 60. *Prof Exp:* Field geologist, Atomic Energy Comn, 51-53; consult uranium geologist, 55-56; asst dir Inst Polar Studies, Ohio State Univ, 60-67, asst prof geol, 64-67; from asst to assoc prof, 67-72, PROF GEOL, IND UNIV-PURDUE UNIV, INDIANAPOLIS, 73-, CHMN DEPT, 69- *Concurrent Pos:* NSF res grant, 62-63. *Mem:* Geol Soc Am; Soc Econ Paleont & Mineral; Nat Asn Geol Teachers; Am Inst Prof Geologists; AAAS. *Res:* Environmental and urban geology; geologic factors in urban planning; history of Man's use of geologic resources; medical geology; archaeological geology; stratigraphy-sedimentation and geologic hazards in urbanization. *Mailing Add:* Dept of Geol Ind Univ-Purdue Univ Indianapolis IN 46202

MIRSKY, JOSEPH HERBERT, pharmacology, see previous edition

MIRSKY, W(ILLIAM), b Poland, July 10, 22; nat US; m 50; c 2. MECHANICAL ENGINEERING. *Educ:* Univ Conn, BS, 44; Univ Mich, MS, 51, PhD(mech eng), 56. *Prof Exp:* Assoc eng ballistic comput, Westinghouse Elec Corp, 46-50; from instr to assoc prof mech eng, 55-70, PROF MECH ENG, UNIV MICH, ANN ARBOR, 70- *Mem:* Am Soc Mech Engrs. *Res:* Combustion of fuel drops and sprays; effect of ultrasonic energy on combustion; internal combustion engines; air pollution. *Mailing Add:* Dept of Mech Eng Univ of Mich Ann Arbor MI 48109

MIRVISH, SIDNEY SOLOMON, b Cape Town, SAfrica, Mar 12, 29; m 60; c 2. CANCER. *Educ:* Univ Cape Town, BSc, 48, MSc, 50; Cambridge Univ, PhD(org chem), 55. *Prof Exp:* Lectr physiol, Univ Witwatersrand, 55-60; res assoc chem carcinogenesis, Weizmann Inst Sci, 61-69; assoc prof, 69-72, PROF CHEM CARCINOGENESIS, EPPLEY INST RES CANCER, UNIV NEBR MED CTR, OMAHA, 72- *Concurrent Pos:* Res fel med, Hadassah Med Sch, Hebrew Univ, Israel, 60-61; Eleanor Roosevelt Inst Cancer fel, McArdle Labs, Med Sch, Univ Wis-Madison, 65-66, res fel, Univ, 65-67. *Mem:* Am Chem Soc; Am Asn Cancer Res. *Res:* Chemical carcinogenesis; metabolism, formation and carcinogenic action of urethane and N-nitroso compounds; biochemistry of carcinogenesis in esophagus and stomach. *Mailing Add:* Eppley Inst for Res in Cancer Univ of Nebr Med Ctr Omaha NE 68105

MIRVISS, STANLEY BURTON, b Minneapolis, Minn, Sept 15, 22; m 49; c 2. SYNTHETIC ORGANIC CHEMISTRY. *Educ:* Univ Wis, BS, 44, PhD(org chem), 50. *Prof Exp:* Asst org chem, Univ Wis, 46-49; from res chemist to proj leader, Chems Res Div, Esso Res & Eng Co, 50-60, res assoc, 60-63; SUPVR ORG CHEM RES, EASTERN RES CTR, STAUFFER CHEM CO, 63- *Mem:* AAAS; Am Chem Soc; NY Acad Sci; Am Inst Chem. *Res:* Organometallic chemistry; polymerization; catalysis; high pressure reactions; organic synthesis; organophorus chemistry; phosphorus. *Mailing Add:* Eastern Res Ctr Stauffer Chem Co Dobbs Ferry NY 10522

MIRZA, JOHN, b Baghdad, Iraq, Dec 1, 22; m 45; c 2. ORGANIC CHEMISTRY. *Educ:* DePauw Univ, AB, 44; Univ Ill, PhD(org chem, biochem & physiol), 49. *Prof Exp:* Res chemist, Rohm & Haas Co, 49-51; RES CHEMIST, MILES LABS, INC, 51-, VPRES, 70- *Mem:* Am Chem Soc. *Res:* Syntheses from 2-vinylpyridine; applications of dialdehyde polysaccharides. *Mailing Add:* 1077 Greenleaf Apt 308 Elkhart IN 46514

MISAQI, FAZLOLLAH LEO, b Kushka, Russia, Oct 16, 26; m 54; c 3. MINING ENGINEERING, HEALTH PHYSICS. *Educ:* Univ Tehran, BS, 51; Mining & Metall Col Austria, DrEngSc, 59; Univ Okla, MS, 70. *Prof Exp:* Mining engr, Sherkate San'ati Va Maadani, Iran, 52-54 & Sherkate Maaden Loot, 54-62; mining engr & asst prof mining eng, NMex Inst Mining & Technol, 62-69; mining engr, Pittsburgh Safety & Mining Res Ctr, 70-71; ming engr, Denver Mining Res Ctr, US Bur Mines, 71-72 & Denver Tech Support Ctr, 72-75; staff engr, Div Health Metal/Non-Metal Mine Health & Safety, Mine Enforcement & Safety Admin, Arlington, Va, 75-76; CHMN, RESIDENT EDUC DEPT, NAT MINE HEALTH & SAFETY ACAD, 76- *Mem:* Am Inst Mining Metall & Petrol Engrs; Austrian Sci & Technol Soc Mining. *Mailing Add:* 25 Marie Ct Daniels WV 25832

MISCH, DONALD WILLIAM, b Providence, RI, Jan 1, 29; m 59; c 3. CELL BIOLOGY. *Educ:* Northeastern Univ, BS, 53; Univ Mich, MS, 58, PhD(zool), 63. *Prof Exp:* Trainee electron micros, Biol Labs, Harvard Univ, 62-63; asst prof, 63-68, ASSOC PROF ZOOL, UNIV NC, CHAPEL HILL, 68-, DIR, ELECTRON MICROS LAB, 80- *Concurrent Pos:* Vis scholar, Dept Zool, Duke Univ, 75. *Mem:* AAAS; Am Soc Cell Biol; Sigma Xi. *Res:* Intestinal structure and function (insects); exocrine gland secretion; mucociliiary clearance. *Mailing Add:* Dept Zool Univ NC Chapel Hill NC 27514

MISCH, HERBERT LOUIS, b Sandusky, Ohio, Dec 7, 17; m 39; c 2. AUTOMOTIVE ENGINEERING. *Educ:* Univ Mich, BS, 41. *Prof Exp:* Chief engr, Packard Motor Car Co, 41-56; dir advan planning, Cadillac Div, Gen Motors Corp, 56-57; mem staff, 57-70, vpres eng & mfg, 70-72, V PRES ENVIRON SAFETY ENG, FORD MOTOR CO, 72- *Mem:* Nat Acad Eng; Soc Automotive Engrs; Coord Res Coun; Am Soc Body Engrs. *Mailing Add:* Ford Motor Co American Rd Dearborn MI 48121

MISCH, PETER, b Berlin, Ger, Aug 30, 09; nat US; m 47; c 3. GEOLOGY. *Educ:* Univ Gottingen, PhD(geol), 32. *Prof Exp:* Asst geol, Univ Gottingen, 32-33; geologist, Himalayan Exped to Nanga Parbat, 34-35; prof geol, Sun Yat-Sen Univ, 36-40 & SW Assoc Univ, Hunming, China, 40-46; from asst prof to assoc prof, 47-50, PROF GEOL, UNIV WASH, 50- *Concurrent Pos:* Guggenheim fel, 54; vis prof, Univ Bonn & Univ Gottingen, 59. *Mem:* Geol Soc Am; Mineral Soc Am; Geochem Soc; Am Asn Petrol Geol; Am Geophys Union. *Res:* Structural geology; metamorphic petrology. *Mailing Add:* Dept Geol Sci Univ Wash Seattle WA 98195

MISCHKE, CHARLES R(USSELL), b Queens, NY, Mar 2, 27; m 51; c 2. MECHANICAL ENGINEERING. *Educ:* Cornell Univ, BSME, 47, MME, 50; Univ Wis, PhD(mech eng), 53. *Prof Exp:* From asst prof to assoc prof mech eng, Univ Kans, 53-57; prof & chmn dept, Pratt Inst, 57-64; PROF MECH ENG, IOWA STATE UNIV, 64- *Concurrent Pos:* Consult, John Deere Ankeny Works, Ia & Deere & Co, Ill & FMS Corp, Iowa. *Honors &*

Awards: Ralph R Teetor Award, Soc Automotive Engrs, 77. *Mem:* Am Soc Mech Engrs; Am Soc Eng Educ; Soc Automotive Engrs. *Res:* Engineering analysis; computer aided design; mechanical engineering design; originator of Iowa Cadet algorithm for computer aided design. *Mailing Add:* Dept Mech Eng Iowa State Univ Ames IA 50010

MISCHKE, RICHARD E, b Bristol, VAa, Aug 19, 40; m 62; c 2. PARTICLE PHYSICS, NUCLEAR PHYSICS. *Educ:* Univ Tenn, BS, 61; Univ Ill, MS, 62, PhD(physics), 66. *Prof Exp:* From instr to asst prof physics, Princeton Univ, 66-71; staff mem, 71-75, assoc group leader, 75-78, DEP GROUP LEADER, MP DIV, LOS ALAMOS NAT LAB, 78- *Concurrent Pos:* Mem bd dirs users group, Los Alamos Meson Physics Facil, 77-79. *Mem:* Fel Am Phys Soc. *Res:* Experimental high energy physics; experimental research in particle and nuclear physics at medium energies. *Mailing Add:* Los Alamos Nat Lab MP4 M5846 Los Alamos NM 87545

MISCHKE, ROLAND A(LAN), b New York, NY, May 28, 30; m 61; c 2. CHEMICAL ENGINEERING. *Educ:* Pratt Inst, BChE, 50; Northwestern Univ, PhD(chem eng), 61. *Prof Exp:* Jr chem engr, Chem Construct Corp, 50-53; chem eng asst, Army Chem Ctr, Md, 53-55; process engr, Chem Construct Corp, 55-58; ASSOC PROF CHEM ENG, VA POLYTECH INST & STATE UNIV, 61- *Concurrent Pos:* Consult, Mfg Res Lab, IBM Corp, 69-70. *Mem:* Am Inst Chem Engrs; Am Soc Eng Educ. *Res:* Heat transfer; reaction kinetics; educational methods. *Mailing Add:* Dept of Chem Eng Va Polytech Inst & State Univ Blacksburg VA 24061

MISCHLER, TERRENCE WYNN, endocrinology, clinical pharmacology, see previous edition

MISCONI, NEBIL YOUSIF, b Baghdad, Iraq, Dec 8, 39; m 72; c 1. ASTRONOMY. *Educ:* Istanbul Univ, BS, 65; State Univ NY Albany, PhD(astron & space sci), 75. *Prof Exp:* Lab instr physics, Univ Baghdad, 66-70; res asst astron, Dudley Observ, NY, 70-75; res assoc astron, Space Astron Lab, State Univ NY Albany, 75-80; MEM STAFF, SPACE ASTRON LAB, UNIV FLA, GAINESVILLE, 80- *Concurrent Pos:* Co-prin investr, Laser Levitation Exp, Goddard Space Flight Ctr, 78-79; co-investr, Joint NASA/Eng Study Authorization Div Solar Polar Mission, 79-81; scientific collabr, Study Interplanetary Dust, NASA, 75-82. *Mem:* Am Astron Soc; Sigma Xi. *Res:* Interplanetary medium; zodiacal light; dynamics of cosmic dust; cometary physics; background starlight. *Mailing Add:* Space Astron Lab Exec Park E Albany NY 12203

MISEK, BERNARD, b New York, NY, Mar 29, 30; m 56; c 4. PHARMACEUTICAL CHEMISTRY, COSMETIC CHEMISTRY. *Educ:* Columbia Univ, BS, 51; Univ Md, MS, 53; Univ Conn, PhD(pharm), 56. *Prof Exp:* Pharmaceut chemist, Nepera Chem Co, 53-54; asst prof pharm, Univ Houston, 56-57; head pharm res & develop, Lloyd Brothers Inc, 57-59; dir med prod develop, Nopco Chem Co, 59-60; sr scientist explor res, Richardson-Merrell Inc, 60-64, asst dir, 64-66, dir, 66-72; mgr res & develop, 72-80, RES MGR, BEECHAM PROD, 80- *Mem:* Am Pharmaceut Asn; Soc Cosmetic Chem. *Res:* Pharmaceutical, toiletry and cosmetic product development; dermatological products; dentifrices; proprietary drugs; feminine hygiene; hair care; personal products. *Mailing Add:* Tara Dr Pomona NY 10970

MISELIS, RICHARD ROBERT, b Boston, Mass, Mar 13, 45; m 65; c 2. NEUROBIOLOGY. *Educ:* Tufts Univ, BS, 67; Univ Pa, VMD, 73 & PhD(biol), 73. *Prof Exp:* Fel, Dept Neurophysiol, Col France, 73-75; asst prof, 75-80, ASSOC PROF ANIMAL BIOL, SCH VET MED, UNIV PA, 80- *Mem:* AAAS; Soc Neurosci; Am Asn Anatomists; Sigma Xi. *Res:* Neurological and physiological basis of feeding and drinking behavior. *Mailing Add:* Lab Anat Sch Vet Med Univ Pa Philadelphia PA 19104

MISENER, GERALD CARMAN, b Welland, Ont, Aug 30, 45; m 68; c 2. AGRICULTURAL ENGINEERING. *Educ:* Univ Guelph, BSc, 68, MSc, 69; Univ Ill, PhD(eng), 73. *Prof Exp:* RES SCIENTIST, RES BR AGR CAN, 69- *Concurrent Pos:* Harry G & Harriett A Wright fel, Univ Ill, 72-73; adj instr, Mich State Univ, 73-74. *Mem:* Am Soc Agr Engrs; Can Soc Agr Engrs. *Res:* Development and testing of agricultural machinery and techniques which can be applied to the potato crop and the application of systems engineering to agricultural sector. *Mailing Add:* 45 Mayland Ct Fredericton NB A0G 2C0 Can

MISENHIMER, HAROLD ROBERT, b Pocatello, Idaho, Feb 13, 31; m 53; c 4. OBSTETRICS & GYNECOLOGY. *Educ:* George Washington Univ, MD, 56. *Prof Exp:* Intern, LDS Hosp, Salt Lake City, Utah, 56-57, resident obstet & gynec, 57-60; staff physician, US Air Force Med Corps, Bergstrom AFB, Tex, 60-62, mem teaching staff, Wilford Hall Hosp, Lackland AFB, Tex, 62-64; asst prof, Sch Med, Univ Md, Baltimore, 64-70; from assoc prof to prof obstet & gynec & dir perinatal biol, Rush Med Col, 70-75; PROF OBSTET & GYNEC, SCH MED, TEX TECH UNIV, 75- *Concurrent Pos:* From asst chief to assoc chief obstet & gynec, Baltimore City Hosps, 64-70; instr, Sch Med, Johns Hopkins Univ, 67-70; fel placental physiol, Carnegie Inst Washington, 67-70. *Mem:* Am Bd Obstet & Gynec; Am Col Obstetricians & Gynecologists. *Res:* Placental structure and function in subhuman primates and human beings; studies of high risk pregnancy in general and the specific causes. *Mailing Add:* Regional Acad Health Ctr 4815 Alameda Ave El Paso TX 79905

MISER, HUGH J(ORDAN), b Fayetteville, Ark, May 23, 17. OPERATIONS RESEARCH. *Educ:* Vanderbilt Univ, BA, 38; Armour Inst Technol, MS, 40; Ohio State Univ, PhD(math), 46. *Prof Exp:* Asst math, Armour Inst Technol, 38-40 & Ohio State Univ, 40-42, 45-46; instr, Ill Inst Technol, 42-44; lectr, Lawrence Col, 44; opers analyst, US Air Force, 45, 49-52, dep asst for oper sci lab, Res Triangle Inst, 59-60; dir appl sci div, Opers Eval Group, Mass Inst Technol, 60-62; asst to dir systs planning, Mitre Corp, Mass, 62-65; vpres & dir environ systs mgt studies dept, Travelers Res Ctr, Inc, Conn, 65-69; prof indust eng & opers res, Univ Mass, Amherst, 69-78, head dept, 76-78; RES HEAD, INT INST APPL SYSTS ANAL, AUSTRIA, 79- *Concurrent Pos:* Mem, Nat Res Coun, 67-73; mem, Nat Acad Sci Adv Panel to Tech Anal Div, Nat Bur Standards, 67-69, chmn, 69-72; ed, Opers Res, 68-74; consult, NSF, 69-74; consult & mem syst & prog anal panel, US Gen Acctg Off, 72-77. *Mem:* Fel AAAS; Am Math Soc; Am Statist Asn; Opers Res Soc Am (secy, 58-61, vpres, 61-62, pres, 62-63); Can Oper Res Soc. *Mailing Add:* Int Inst Appl Systs Anal A-2361 Laxenburg Austria

MISFELDT, MICHAEL LEE, b Davenport, Iowa, June 15, 50; m 73; c 1. IMMUNOREGULATION. *Educ:* Univ Ill, Urbana, BS, 72; Univ Iowa, PhD(microbiol), 77. *Prof Exp:* Staff fel, res, Lab Molecular Genetics, Nat Inst Child Health Develop, NIH, 77-81; ASST PROF IMMUNOL, DEPT MICROBIOL, UNIV MO-COLUMBIA, 81- *Mem:* Am Soc Microbiol; AAAS; NY Acad Sci; Am Asn Immunologists. *Res:* Regulatory processes occurring within the immune system; mechanisms by which thymus-derived lymphocyes regulate antibody formation and secretion. *Mailing Add:* Dept Microbiol M-264 Med Sci Bldg Univ Mo Columbia MO 65212

MISH, LAWRENCE BRONISLAW, b Stamford, Conn, Feb 27, 23; m 50; c 4. BOTANY. *Educ:* Univ Conn, AB, 50; Harvard Univ, AM, 50, PhD(bot), 53. *Prof Exp:* From instr to asst prof biol, Wheaton Col, 53-59; PROF BOT, BRIDGEWATER STATE COL, 59- *Concurrent Pos:* Res asst, United Fruit Co, 60-63; ecol consult, 71-; mem, SShore Nature Ctr. *Mem:* AAAS; Bot Soc Am. *Res:* Biology of lichens, their algae and fungi; marine and fresh water plankton; taxonomy of flowering plants. *Mailing Add:* Dept of Biol Bridgewater State Col Bridgewater MA 02324

MISHELEVICH, DAVID JACOB, b Pittsburgh, Pa, Jan 26, 42; m 81; c 1. COMPUTER SCIENCES, BIOMEDICAL ENGINEERING. *Educ:* Univ Pittsburgh, BS, 62; Johns Hopkins Univ, MD, 66, PhD(biomed eng), 70. *Prof Exp:* Intern med, Baltimore City Hosps, 66-67; staff assoc neurophysiol, Nat Inst Neurol Dis & Stroke, 67-69; exec vpres, Nat Educ Consults, 71-72; asst prof med comput sci, Southwestern Med Sch, Univ Tex Health Sci Ctr, Dallas, 72-74, dir, PhD Grad Prog Math Sci, 73-76 & 81-, dir, MS/PhD Grad Prog Biomed Eng, 74-75; actg dir, Info Systs, Dallas County Hosp Dist, 75; dir, Med Comput Res Ctr, 72-80, assoc prof, 74-79, PROF MED COMPUT SCI, SOUTHWESTERN MED SCH, UNIV TEX HEALTH SCI CTR DALLAS, 79-, ASST PROF INTERNAL MED, 72-, CHMN DEPT, 73- *Concurrent Pos:* NIH spec fel, Johns Hopkins Univ, 69-71, fel med & biomed eng, Sch Med, 69-71; attending physician, Dallas County Hosp Dist, 73-; adj assoc prof math sci, Univ Tex, Dallas, 74-79, adj prof, 79-; adj assoc prof math, Univ Tex, Arlington, 74-, adj assoc prof biomed eng, 75-79, adj prof, 79-; mem NIH study sect, Biomed Libr Review Comt, 78-; tech adv info systs, Dallas County Hosp Dist, 75-, dir, 78-79; mem spec adv group, Nat Ctr Health Serv Res, 79-81; pres, Mishelevich Assocs Inc, 81-; consult numerous orgns. *Mem:* Am Hosp Asn; AAAS; Asn Comput Mach; Inst Elec & Electronics Eng. *Res:* Computer applications in medicine specializing in clinical information and laboratory automation systems; clinical decision making; computer-based text processing and publication; health evaluation; iconic communication and computer graphics. *Mailing Add:* Dept Med Comput Sci Univ Tex Health Sci Ctr Dallas TX 75235

MISHELOFF, MICHAEL NORMAN, b Brooklyn, NY, Feb 15, 44; m 71. SEMICONDUCTOR DEVICE PHYSICS. *Educ:* Calif Inst Technol, BS, 65; Univ Calif, Berkeley, PhD(physics), 70. *Prof Exp:* Instr physics, Princeton Univ, 70-73; res assoc, Univ Nebr, Lincoln, 73-76; exp physicist, Lawrence Livermore Lab, 76-80; MEM RES STAFF, FAIRCHILD CAMERA & INSTRUMENT ADVAN RES & DEVELOP LAB, 80- *Res:* Semiconductor device physics. *Mailing Add:* 7465 Limerick Ave Dublin CA 94566

MISHKIN, ELI ABSALOM, b Poland, Apr 25, 17; m 47; c 2. APPLIED PHYSICS. *Educ:* Israel Inst Technol, Ingenieur, 42, ScD, 52. *Prof Exp:* Lectr elec eng, Israel Inst Technol, 48-53; asst prof, Mass Inst Technol, 53-55; assoc prof, 55-60, PROF APPL PHYSICS, POLYTECH INST NEW YORK, 60- *Concurrent Pos:* Res fel physics, Harvard Univ, 68; consult, Lawrence Livermore Lab, 73-76. *Mem:* Am Phys Soc; NY Acad Sci. *Res:* Electromagnetic theory; automatic control systems; quantum and nonlinear optics; laser induced fusion. *Mailing Add:* Dept of Elec Eng & Appl Physics Polytech Inst of New York Brooklyn NY 11201

MISHKIN, MORTIMER, b Fitchburg, Mass, Dec 13, 26. NEUROPSYCHOLOGY. *Educ:* Dartmouth Col, AB, 46; McGill Univ, MA, 49, PhD(psychol), 51. *Prof Exp:* Res psychologist, Inst Living, 51-55; RES PHYSIOLOGIST, NIMH, 55- *Concurrent Pos:* Consult ed, J Comp & Physiol Psychol, 63-73, Neuropsych- ologia, 63-, Exp Brain Res, 65- & Brain Res, 74-78; mem, Psychol Servs Panel, NIH, 59-61, Exp Psychol Sect, 65-69; mem neural prosthesis tech adv comt, Nat Inst Neurol & Commun Dis & Stroke, 70-75. *Honors & Awards:* Superior Serv Award, USPHS, 70. *Mem:* Am Psychol Asn; AAAS; Int Brain Res Orgn; Soc Neurosci; Int Neuropsychol Soc. *Res:* Forebrain mechanisms underlying basic mental processes (perception, memory, affect, volition) in primates. *Mailing Add:* 6404 Highland Dr Chevy Chase MD 20015

MISHLER, JOHN MILTON, IV, b Cairo, Ill, Sept 25, 46; m 81; c 1. HEMATOLOGY. *Educ:* Univ Calif, San Diego, AB, 70, ScM, 71, Univ Oxford, DPhil, 78. *Prof Exp:* Assoc clin coordr biol, McGaw Labs, 72-74, clin coordr, 74-75; res fel hematol, Radcliffe Infirmary, Oxford, 75-78, Med Res Coun Leukemia Unit, Royal Postgrad Med Sch, 77-78; sr res fel, Lab Tumorimmunol, Med Clin, Cologne, 78-80; CHIEF, BLOOD RES BR, NAT HEART, LUNG & BLOOD INST, NIH, 80- *Concurrent Pos:* Co-chmn, Interagency Tech Comt, Nat Heart, Lung & Blood Inst, NIH, 81-; referee, NSF. *Mem:* Am Soc Hemat; NY Acad Sci; Int Soc Hemat; Am Asn Blood Banks; Int Soc Blood Transfusion. *Res:* Pharmacology of the hydroxyethyl starches, and the various aspects surrounding the use of leukapheresis and plateletpheresis in medical applications. *Mailing Add:* 4400 East-West Hwy (1114) Bethesda MD 20814

MISHMASH, HAROLD EDWARD, b Richmond, Calif, Nov 8, 42; m 64; c 3. ANALYTICAL CHEMISTRY. *Educ:* Iowa State Univ, BS, 64; Kans State Univ, PhD(anal chem), 68. *Prof Exp:* RES SPECIALIST, CENT RES LABS, 3M CO, 68-, MGR INORG ANAL RES, 81- *Mem:* Microbeam Anal Soc; Am Vacuum Soc. *Res:* Electron microprobe analysis; scanning electron microscopy; emission spectroscopy; ion beam surface studies using ion scattering and secondary ion mass spectroscopy; x-ray photoelectron spectroscopy (ESCA) investigations of surface defects and modifications. *Mailing Add:* Cent Res Labs 3M Co PO Box 33221 St Paul MN 55133

MISHOE, LUNA I, b Bucksport, SC, Jan 5, 17; m 44; c 4. MATHEMATICS, MATHEMATICAL PHYSICS. *Educ:* Allen Univ, BSc, 38; Univ Mich, MSc, 42; NY Univ, PhD(math), 53. *Prof Exp:* Prof math & physics & head dept, Kittrell Col, 39-42 & Del State Col, 46-48; from assoc prof to prof physics, Morgan State Col, 48-60, chmn div natural sci, 57-60; PRES, DEL STATE COL, 60- *Concurrent Pos:* Consult, Ballistics Res Lab, Aberdeen Proving Ground, 57-60; mem bd dirs, Univ City Sci Ctr, Pa; mem bd trustees, Univ Del, 69-; mem adv bd, US Coast Guard Acad, New London, Conn, 72-; mem bd dirs, Nat Asn Equal Opportunity Higher Educ, 72-, WHYY TV, 74- & Am Coun Educ, 78-; chmn, Del Postsec Educ Comn, 74-; mem, Gov Task Force Cost-of-Living Pay Increase Formulas, 74- *Mem:* Am Math Soc; Soc Indust & Appl Math; Math Asn Am. *Res:* Ordinary differential equations; eigenfunction expansions; boundary value problems; ballistics; physics of upper atmosphere. *Mailing Add:* Off the President Delaware State Col Dover DE 19901

MISHUCK, ELI, b Buenos Aires, Arg, July 27, 23; nat US; m 44; c 2. PHYSICAL CHEMISTRY. *Educ:* Brooklyn Col, BA, 44; Polytech Inst Brooklyn, MS, 46, PhD(chem), 50. *Prof Exp:* Res assoc chem, Manhattan Proj, SAM Labs, Columbia Univ, 44-46; chief chemist, Bingham Bros Co, NJ, 46-48; res chemist polymers, Polytech Inst Brooklyn, 48-50; head dept solid propellant res, Aerojet-Gen Corp, Gen Tire & Rubber Co, 50-63, sr mgr chem & biol opers, Space-Gen Corp, 63-66, dir chem & biol systs, 66-70, pres, Aerojet Med & Biol Systs, 70-74; gen mgr, Organon Diagnostics, Inc, 74-77; ASST V PRES, SCI APPLN, INC, 77- *Concurrent Pos:* Mem tech adv bd to pres, Gen Tire & Rubber Co. *Res:* Biological and chemical detection; medical diagnostic equipment; life sciences; environmental sciences; oceanography; biomedical instrumentation; cultural resources managements. *Mailing Add:* Sci Appln Inc 1200 Prospect St La Jolla CA 92038

MISIASZEK, EDWARD T, b Utica, NY, May 23, 28; m 52; c 2. SOIL MECHANICS, ENGINEERING GEOLOGY. *Educ:* Clarkson Col Technol, BCE, 52, MCE, 54; Univ Ill, PhD(soil mech), 60. *Prof Exp:* Instr mech, Lehigh Univ, 54-55; instr mech, Univ Ill, 55-60, asst prof civil eng, 60-62; assoc prof, 62-66, asst dean eng, 66-68, ASSOC DEAN ENG, CLARKSON COL TECHNOL, 68- *Concurrent Pos:* Chmn, NY State 4 year-2 year Eng Col Curric Study Comt, 69-; mem, NY State Bd Eng & Land Surv, 71. *Mem:* Am Soc Civil Engrs; Am Soc Eng Educ; Nat Soc Prof Engrs. *Res:* Soil foundations, compaction and consolidation; physical properties of soils. *Mailing Add:* Clarkson Col Technol Potsdam NY 13676

MISIEK, MARTIN, b Buffalo, NY, Sept 6, 19; m 45; c 2. MICROBIOLOGY. *Educ:* Univ Buffalo, BA, 43; Syracuse Univ, MS, 49, PhD(microbiol), 55. *Prof Exp:* ASST DIR MICROBIOL DEPT, BRISTOL LABS, SYRACUSE, 43- *Mem:* Am Soc Microbiol. *Res:* In vitro evaluation of antibacterial agents. *Mailing Add:* Bristol Labs Syracuse NY 13201

MISKEL, JOHN ALBERT, b San Francisco, Calif, Aug 21, 19; m 49. CHEMISTRY. *Educ:* Univ Calif, BS, 43; Washington Univ, PhD(chem), 49. *Prof Exp:* Jr scientist, Manhattan Proj, Univ Calif, 43-46; asst phys chem, Washington Univ, 46-48, AEC fel phys sci, 48-49; from res assoc to chemist, Brookhaven Nat Lab, 49-55; CHEMIST, LAWRENCE LIVERMORE LAB, UNIV CALIF, 55- *Concurrent Pos:* mem comt disarmament, US Deleg, 81-82. *Mem:* Am Phys Soc. *Res:* Chemistry of heavy elements; fission fragments; ranges of fission fragments; neutron cross sections; absolute beta counting; nuclear excitation functions; radiochemistry. *Mailing Add:* Lawrence Livermore Lab Univ Calif PO Box 808 Livermore CA 94550

MISKEL, JOHN JOSEPH, JR, b Brooklyn, NY, Aug 2, 33; m 55; c 7. POLYMER CHEMISTRY, ORGANIC CHEMISTRY. *Educ:* Univ Notre Dame, BS, 55; Univ Pa, PhD(org chem), 60. *Prof Exp:* Polymer chemist, Atlantic Ref Co, 59-60; supvr polymer develop, Rexall Chem Co, 60-68; MGR RES & DEVELOP, PROCESS CHEM DIV, DIAMOND SHAMROCK CORP, 68- *Mem:* Am Chem Soc; Soc Chem Indust; Am Oil Chem Soc. *Res:* Polyolefin process and product research; specialty polymers and surfactants. *Mailing Add:* Process Chem Div Diamond Shamrock Corp Box 2386R Morristown NJ 07960

MISKIMEN, CARMEN RIVERA, b Mayaguez, PR, Mar 15, 33; m 63; c 4. PLANT PATHOLOGY, VIROLOGY. *Educ:* Univ PR, Mayaguez, BS, 53; Univ Wis-Madison, PhD(plant path), 62. *Prof Exp:* Instr sci, Commonwealth of PR Dept Educ, 53-55; technician III, US Dept Agr, PR, 55-58, res plant pathologist, Crops Res Div, 62-63; from asst prof to assoc prof, 63-73, PROF BIOL, UNIV PR, MAYAGUEZ, 73-, COORDR MED TECHNOL, 73- *Concurrent Pos:* Sugarcane grant & NIH res grant, 73- *Mem:* Am Phytopath Soc. *Res:* Mosaic and other viruses of economically important crops; morphology and histology of insect visual structures. *Mailing Add:* Dept Biol Univ PR Mayaguez PR 00708

MISKIMEN, GEORGE WILLIAM, b Appleton, Wis, May 21, 30; m 63; c 4. NEUROPHYSIOLOGY, POPULATION ECOLOGY. *Educ:* Ohio Univ, BS, 53, MS, 55; Univ Fla, PhD(biol, entom), 66. *Prof Exp:* Entomologist, VI Agr Prog, US Dept Agr, 58-61, invests leader, Grain & Forage Insects, Agr Res Serv, PR, 62-66; dir entomol pioneering res lab, 66-72, PROF BIOL, UNIV PR, 66- *Concurrent Pos:* USDA Hatch grant, Univ PR, 64-67; USDA res grant, 72-; NIH res grant, 73- & NSF grants, 74 & 76-78; adj prof ophthal, Sch Med, Univ Fla, 81- *Mem:* Entom Soc Am; Asn Trop Biol; Soc Syst Zool; Int Soc Sugarcane Technol; Coleopterists Soc. *Res:* Electrophysiology and anatomy of vertebrate lenses; electrophysiology and anatomy of insect visual receptors; ecology of insects; population dynamics; relationships between agriculturally important pests, climate, and biological control organisms. *Mailing Add:* Dept Biol Univ PR Mayaguez PR 00708

MISKOVSKY, NICHOLAS MATTHEW, b Passaic, NJ, Oct 4, 40; m 71; c 1. PHYSICS. *Educ:* Rutgers Univ, New Brunswick, AB, 62; Pa State Univ, PhD(physics), 70. *Prof Exp:* ASST PROF PHYSICS, PA STATE UNIV, 70- *Res:* Theoretical solid state physics; optical properties and band structure of solids; calculation of phonon spectra. *Mailing Add:* 104 Davey Lab Pa State Univ University Park PA 16802

MISLEVY, PAUL, b Scranton, Pa, May 5, 41; m 64; c 1. AGRONOMY. *Educ:* Pa State Univ, BS, 66, MS, 69, PhD(agron), 71. *Prof Exp:* Asst prof, 71-77, ASSOC PROF AGRON, UNIV FLA, 77- *Mem:* Am Soc Agron; Am Forage & Grassland Coun; Weed Sci Soc Am. *Res:* Forage management; crop physiology; herbicides; multicropping; phosphate spoil bark reclamation. extension. *Mailing Add:* Agr Res Ctr Univ of Fla Ona FL 33865

MISLIVEC, PHILIP BRIAN, b Danville, Ill, Feb 12, 39. MYCOLOGY, PLANT PATHOLOGY. *Educ:* St Meinrad Col, BS, 61; Ind State Univ, Terre Haute, MA, 65; Purdue Univ, PhD(plant path), 68. *Prof Exp:* Asst prof bot, Ind State Univ, Terre Haute, 68-69; RES MYCOLOGIST, US FOOD & DRUG ADMIN, 69- *Concurrent Pos:* Prof, US Dept Agr Grad Sch, DC, 70- *Mem:* Mycol Soc Am; Inst Food Technologists; Am Soc Microbiol. *Res:* Effects of environment and microbial competition on growth and toxin production by mycotoxin-producing mold species; mold systematist. *Mailing Add:* Food & Drug Admin 200 C St SW Washington DC 20204

MISLOVE, MICHAEL WILLIAM, b Washington, DC, Feb 8, 44. MATHEMATICS. *Educ:* Univ of the South, BA, 65; Univ Tenn, Knoxville, PhD(math), 69. *Prof Exp:* Asst prof math, Univ Fla, 70; asst prof, 70-75, assoc prof, 75-79, PROF MATH, TULANE UNIV, LA, 79- *Concurrent Pos:* NSF res grant, Tulane Univ, La, 71-80; Humboldt Found res fel, 76, 78 & 82. *Mem:* AAAS; Am Math Soc; Sigma Xi. *Res:* Topological algebra, abstract harmonic analysis on groups and semigroups. *Mailing Add:* Dept of Math Tulane Univ New Orleans LA 70118

MISLOW, KURT MARTIN, b Berlin, Ger, June 5, 23; nat US; m 48; c 2. CHEMISTRY. *Educ:* Tulane Univ, BS, 44; Calif Inst Technol, PhD(org chem), 47. *Hon Degrees:* Dr, Free Univ Brussels, 74 & Univ Uppsala, 77; DSc, Tulane Univ, 75. *Prof Exp:* From instr to prof chem, NY Univ, 47-64; chmn dept, 68-74, H S TAYLOR PROF CHEM, PRINCETON UNIV, 64- *Concurrent Pos:* Guggenheim fel, 56, 75; Sloan fel, 59; FMC lectr, Princeton, 63; mem adv panel, NSF, 63-66; mem med and org chem panel, NIH, 63-66; univ lectr, Univ London, 65; J A McRae mem lectr, Queen's Univ, 67; H A Iddles lectr, Univ NH, 72; E C Lee lectr, Univ Chicago, 73; lectr, Nobel Inst, Royal Swed Acad Sci, 74; Churchill fel, Univ Cambridge, 75; A A Vernon lectr, Northeastern Univ, 76; PPG Indust lectr, Ohio Univ, 77; J Musher Mem lectr, Hebrew Univ Jerusalem, 78; distinguished vis speaker, Univ Calgary, 78; indust-sci lectr, Ramapo Col, 80; hon lectr, Ariz State Univ, 81. *Honors & Awards:* James Flack Norris Award, Am Chem Soc, 75. *Mem:* Nat Acad Sci; fel AAAS; Am Chem Soc; Royal Soc Chem. *Res:* Stereochemistry. *Mailing Add:* Dept of Chem Princeton Univ Princeton NJ 08540

MISNER, CHARLES WILLIAM, b Jackson, Mich, June 13, 32; m 59; c 4. THEORETICAL PHYSICS, COSMOLOGY. *Educ:* Univ Notre Dame, BS, 52; Princeton Univ, MA, 54, PhD(physics), 57. *Prof Exp:* Instr, Princeton Univ, 56-59, asst prof, 59-63; assoc prof physics & astron, 63-66, prof physics & astron, 66-76, PROF PHYSICS, UNIV MD, COLLEGE PARK, 76- *Concurrent Pos:* Sloan res fel, 58-62; lectr, Les Houches, Univ Grenoble, 63; NSF sr fel, Univ Cambridge, 66-67 & Niels Bohr Inst, Copenhagen, 67; vis prof, Princeton Univ, 69-70 & Calif Inst Technol, 72; Guggenheim fel, 72; vis fel, All Souls Col, Oxford, 73; mem, NSF Adv Comt Res, 73- *Honors & Awards:* Notre Dame Sci Centennial Award, 65. *Mem:* AAAS; Am Phys Soc; Am Math Soc; Royal Astron Soc; Philos Sci Asn. *Res:* General relativity; relativistic astrophysics; philosophy of physics. *Mailing Add:* Dept of Physics & Astron Univ of Md College Park MD 20742

MISNER, ROBERT DAVID, b Waynesville, Ill, May 1, 20; m 49; c 2. PHYSICS. *Educ:* George Washington Univ, BS, 46. *Prof Exp:* Physicist, 42-44, electronic engr, 45-54, sect head data processing, 54-66, BR HEAD SIGNAL EXPLOITATION, US NAVAL RES LAB, 66- *Honors & Awards:* Silver Technol Medal, Asn Old Crows, 70. *Mem:* Sigma Xi; Asn Old Crows; Inst Elec & Electronics Engrs. *Res:* Radio frequency intercept and data handling, especially data storage and processing techniques; magnetic tape storage. *Mailing Add:* 5815 Blackhawk Dr Washington DC 20745

MISNER, ROBERT E, b Yonkers, NY, May 25, 41; m 68. ORGANIC CHEMISTRY. *Educ:* Manhattan Col, BS, 63; Fordham Univ, PhD(org chem), 68. *Prof Exp:* Teaching asst org chem, Fordham Univ, 63-65, res asst, 65-67; SR RES CHEMIST, AM CYANAMID CO, 67- *Mem:* Am Chem Soc. *Res:* Organic Synthesis of basic organic chemicals; heterocyclic synthesis; research and development of dyes and organic intermediates. *Mailing Add:* 40 Winding Way RD 3 Flemington NJ 08822

MISRA, DWARIKA NATH, b Sarai-Miran, India, Mar 17, 33; m 54; c 3. PHYSICAL CHEMISTRY, SURFACE CHEMISTRY. *Educ:* Univ Lucknow, BS, 51, MSc, 53; Howard Univ, PhD(phys chem), 63. *Prof Exp:* Res asst phys chem, Regional Res Lab, Hyderabad, India, 54-58; NSF fel, Pa State Univ, 63-66; sr scientist, Itek Corp, Mass, 66-68; lectr, Howard Univ, 70-72; RES ASSOC, AM DENT ASN HEALTH FOUND, 72- *Mem:* Am Chem Soc; Sigma Xi. *Res:* Adsorption and catalysis on heterogeneous surfaces; surface chemistry of semiconducting oxides and hydroxyapatite, behavior and kinetics of adsorbed organic molecules; chemical bond between bone material and resins. *Mailing Add:* Am Dent Asn Health Found Res Unit Nat Bur of Standards Washington DC 20234

MISRA, HARA PRASAD, b Khallikote, Orissa, India, June 1, 40; m 62; c 3. BIOCHEMISTRY, VETERINARY MEDICINE. *Educ:* Utkal Univ, BVSc & AH, 62; Va Polytech Inst & State Univ, MS, 68, PhD(biochem), 70. *Prof Exp:* Vet asst surgeon, Orissa Govt, India, 62-64; instr biochem, Orissa Univ Agr & Technol, 64-66; res asst poultry sci, Va Polytech Inst & State Univ, 66-68, res asst biochem, 68-70; res assoc, Duke Univ, 70-73 & 75-78; asst prof microbiol, Univ Ala, Birmingham, 73-75; asst res biochemist & lectr physiol sci, Univ Calif, Davis, 78-80. *Concurrent Pos:* Assoc scientist, Cancer Res Ctr, Univ Ala, Birmingham, 73-75; asst adj prof, Univ Calif, Davis, 80- *Mem:* Am Soc Biol Chemists; Tissue Cult Asn; NY Acad Sci. *Res:* Superoxide and superoxide dismutase; radiation biology; environmental toxicology; oxidative damage and cell dysfunction. *Mailing Add:* Physiol Sci Univ of Calif Davis CA 95616

MISRA, RAJENDRA KUMAR, statistics, see previous edition

MISRA, SUSHIL, b Budaun, India, Sept 5, 40. NUCLEAR PHYSICS, SOLID STATE PHYSICS. *Educ:* Agra Univ, BSc, 58; Gorakhpur Univ, MSc, 60; Univ St Louis, PhD(physics), 64. *Prof Exp:* Jr res scholar physics, Indian Asn Cultivation Sci, Calcutta, 60-61; fel, Univ Toronto, 64-67; asst prof, 67-70, assoc prof, 70-77, PROF PHYSICS, CONCORDIA UNIV, 77- *Concurrent Pos:* Consult, Electronics & Equip Div, McDonnell Aircraft Corp, Mo, 64. *Mem:* Am Phys Soc. *Res:* Electron paramagnetic resonance; nuclear quadrupole resonance; reorientation of oriented nuclei; Mossbauer detection of dynamically oriented nuclei; low-temperature magnetic ordering; spin-diffusion; nuclear rotational spectrum. *Mailing Add:* Dept Physics Concordia Univ Montreal PQ H3G 1M8 Can

MISSEN, R(ONALD) W(ILLIAM), b St Catharines, Ont, Feb 26, 28; m 51; c 4. CHEMICAL ENGINEERING. *Educ:* Queen's Univ, Ont, BSc, 50, MSc, 51; Univ Cambridge, PhD(phys chem), 56. *Prof Exp:* Chem engr, Polysar Corp, Ont, 51-53; from asst prof to assoc prof chem eng, 56-68, assoc dean grad studies, 76-77, PROF CHEM ENG, UNIV TORONTO, 68-, V PROVOST PROF FACILITIES, 77- *Concurrent Pos:* Dir, Chem Eng Res Consult, Ltd. *Honors & Awards:* Plummer Medal, 62. *Mem:* Faraday Soc; fel Chem Inst Can; Can Soc Chem Engrs. *Res:* Process kinetics and thermodynamics; equilibrium and non-equilibrium properties of solutions. *Mailing Add:* Dept of Chem Eng Univ of Toronto Toronto ON M5S 1A4 Can

MISSIMER, JOHN HERTEL, particle physics, nuclear physics, see previous edition

MISTLER, RICHARD EDWARD, b New York, NY, Mar 17, 35; m 59; c 2. CERAMIC ENGINEERING. *Educ:* Alfred Univ, BS, 59; Rensselaer Polytech Inst, MMetallEng, 61; Mass Inst Technol, ScD(ceramics), 67. *Prof Exp:* Ceramic engr, Knolls Atomic Power Lab, Gen Elec Co, 59-63; sr res engr, 67-69, mem res staff & res leader ceramics processing, 69-78, dir res & develop, Plessey, Frenchtown Div, 78-81, VPRES, FRENCHTOWN AM CORP, MATLIN CO, INC, 81- . *Mem:* AAAS; fel Am Ceramic Soc; Int Soc Hybrid Microelectronics. *Res:* Research and development of ceramic materials and processes. *Mailing Add:* Frenchtown Am Corp 8th & Harrison Frenchtown NJ 08825

MISTREE, FARROKH, b Ponna, India. COMPUTER AIDED DESIGN, OCEAN ENGINEERING. *Educ:* Indian Inst Technol, BTech, 68; Univ Calif, Berkeley, MS, 70, PhD(eng), 74. *Prof Exp:* Res fel, Univ New South Wales, Australia, 74-76, lectr appl mech, 76-80, sr lectr, 80-81; ASSOC PROF MECH ENG, UNIV HOUSTON, 81- *Honors & Awards:* Walter Atkinson Mem Award, Royal Inst Naval Architects, Sydney, 77. *Mem:* Royal Inst Naval Architects; Soc Naval Architects & Marine Engrs; Am Soc Mech Engrs; Am Soc Eng Educ; Oper Res Soc Am. *Res:* Developing design methods and the necessary decision support software for enhancing the effectiveness of designers operating in a computer assisted design environment; design of damage tolerant systems. *Mailing Add:* Dept Mech Eng Cent Campus Univ Houston Houston TX 77004

MISTRETTA, CHARLOTTE MAE, b Washington, DC, Feb 16, 44; m 68. NEUROPHYSIOLOGY, DEVELOPMENTAL PHYSIOLOGY. *Educ:* Trinity Col, Washington, DC, BA, 66; Fla State Univ, MS, 68, PhD(sensory physiol), 70. *Prof Exp:* Am Asn Univ Women fel, Nuffield Inst Med Res, Oxford Univ, 70-72; sr res assoc, 72-74, asst res scientist, 74-76, ASSOC RES SCIENTIST, DEPT ORAL BIOL, SCH DENT, UNIV MICH, ANN ARBOR, 76-, ASSOC RES SCIENTIST, CTR HUMAN GROWTH & DEVELOP, 75-, ASSOC PROF RES, SCH NURSING, GRAD STUDIES, 75- *Concurrent Pos:* Lectr, Ctr Human Growth & Develop, Univ Mich, Ann Arbor, 73-75; mem int comn olfaction & taste, Int Union Physiol Sci, 74-; Res Career Develop Award, Nat Inst Dent Res, 78-83. *Mem:* AAAS; Am Physiol Soc; Europ Chemoreception Res Orgn; Asn Chemoreception Sci; Soc Neurosci. *Res:* Investigation of the development of the sense of taste using anatomical, behavioral and electrophysiological techniques, including study of fetal swallowing activity; study of nerve-epithelium tissue interactions in development. *Mailing Add:* Dept of Oral Biol Univ of Mich Sch of Dent Ann Arbor MI 48109

MISTRIC, WALTER J, JR, b Opelousas, La, Dec 3, 24; m 46; c 2. ENTOMOLOGY. *Educ:* La State Univ, BS, 49; Tex A&M Univ, MS, 50, PhD(entom), 54. *Prof Exp:* Agr inspector, State Dept Agr, La, 46; asst plant path, La State Univ, 48-49; field aide, Bur Entom & Plant Quarantine, US Dept Agr, 49-50, agent, 50; from instr to asst prof entom, Tex A&M Univ, 50-55; from asst prof to prof, 55-81, EMER PROF ENTOM, NC STATE UNIV, 81- *Mem:* Entom Soc Am. *Res:* Insect control. *Mailing Add:* Dept of Entom NC State Univ Box 5215 Raleigh NC 27650

MISTRY, NARIMAN BURJOR, b Bombay, India, Oct 21, 37; US citizen; m 64; c 2. PHYSICS. *Educ:* Univ Bombay, BS, 56; Columbia Univ, MA, 60, PhD(neutrino physics), 63. *Prof Exp:* Res asst high-energy physics, Columbia Univ, 63-64; instr & res assoc, 64-67, SR RES ASSOC HIGH-ENERGY PHYSICS, CORNELL UNIV, 67- *Concurrent Pos:* vis prof, Phys Inst, Aachen, WGer, 73-74. *Mem:* Am Phys Soc. *Res:* High energy particle physics; cosmic rays; spark chambers; high energy neutrino interactions; weak interaction physics; high energy photon and electron physics; electron-positron storage ring design and colliding beam experiments. *Mailing Add:* Dept Physics Cornell Univ Ithaca NY 14853

MISTRY, SORAB PIROZSHAH, b Bombay, India, Dec 18, 20; nat US; m 53; c 2. BIOCHEMISTRY, NUTRITION. *Educ:* Univ Bombay, BSc, 42; Indian Inst Sci, Bangalore, MSc, 46; Cambridge Univ, PhD(biochem), 51. *Prof Exp:* Sr res asst, Indian Inst Sci, Bangalore, 45-47; instr, Dunn Nutrit Lab, Cambridge Univ, 48-50, Med Res Coun fel, 50-52; fel, 52-54, res assoc, 54, from asst prof to assoc prof animal nutrit, 54-62, assoc prof, 62-66, PROF BIOCHEM, UNIV ILL, URBANA, 66- *Concurrent Pos:* Sreenivasaya res award, 45-46; vis prof, Univ Amsterdam, 56 & Univ Zurich, 56-57, 63-64; NIH spec fel, 63-64; vis prof, Ind Inst Sci, Bangalore, 70 & Univ Madrid, 71; prof, Autonoma Univ, Madrid, 79 & Swiss Fed Inst Technol, Zurich, 79 & 81. *Mem:* Am Soc Biol Chemists; Am Inst Nutrit; Brit Biochem Soc. *Res:* Nutritional and comparative biochemistry; regulation of metabolic processes. *Mailing Add:* Dept of Animal Sci Univ of Ill Urbana IL 61801

MITACEK, EUGENE JAROSLAV, b Hluk, Moravia, Czech, Apr 22, 35; US citizen; m 64; c 1. BIOCHEMISTRY. *Educ:* Palacky Univ, Czech, MA, 58; Charles Univ, Prague, PhD(chem & chem educ), 66. *Prof Exp:* Instr chem, State Lyceum, Veseli na Morave, 58-60, asst prof chem & res assoc chem educ, Inst Educ, Charles Univ, Prague, 60-66, sr res assoc prof chem & chem educ, 66-67; head dept earth sci, UN Int Sch, NY, 67-70; asst prof chem, 70-74, ASSOC PROF CHEM, DEPT LIFE SCI, NY INST TECHNOL, 74-; ASSOC PROF BIOCHEM, DEPT BASIC HEALTH SCI, NY INST CHIROPRACTIC, 75- *Concurrent Pos:* Lectr, Inst Educ, Univ Warsaw, 61 & 64, Univ Sofia, 63 & Univ Zagreb, 65; consult, Prague Br, UNESCO, Paris, 64-67; Nuffield Found fel, Univ London, 67; res fel, Inst Environ Med, NY Univ Med Sch, 74-75. *Honors & Awards:* Hon Prof, San Marcos Univ, Lima, Univ Buenos Aires & Univ Rio de Janeiro, 78 & Med Sch Univ Haiti, 79-81. *Mem:* AAAS; Am Chem Soc; Nat Sci Teachers Asn; NY Acad Sci. *Res:* Geochemistry; polarographic analysis; structural chemistry; comparative chemical education; effectiveness of teaching methods in chemistry; motivation and learning in chemistry; biochemistry of cancer; clinical chemistry; environmental chemistry; nutrition. *Mailing Add:* Dept Life Sci NY Inst Technol Old Westbury NY 11568

MITACEK, PAUL, JR, b Johnson City, NY, Jan 1, 32; m 67. PHYSICAL CHEMISTRY. *Educ:* Oberlin Col, AB, 54; Pa State Univ, PhD(chem), 62. *Prof Exp:* Res asst chem, Cryogenic Lab, Pa State Univ, 61-62; instr, Bucknell Univ, 62-63; resident res assoc radiation physics, Argonne Nat Lab, 63-67; from asst prof to assoc prof, 67-77, PROF CHEM, ST JOHN FISHER COL, 77-, CHMN DEPT, 70- *Mem:* Am Chem Soc. *Res:* Cryogenics; radiation dosimetry of mixed radiations of neutrons and gamma rays; mini and microprocessor computers; interfacing of laboratory equipment. *Mailing Add:* 164 Willowbend Rd Rochester NY 14618

MITALA, JOSEPH JERROLD, b Trenton, NJ, June 21, 47; m 70; c 1. PHARMACOLOGY, TERATOLOGY. *Educ:* Temple Univ Sch Pharm, BS, 70, MS, 73, PhD(pharmacol), 77. *Prof Exp:* Asst prof pharmacotherapeut, Ferris State Col Sch Pharm, 76-79, assoc prof pharm/pharmacol, 79-81; RES SCIENTIST REPROD TOXICOL, ADRIA LABS, INC, 81- *Concurrent Pos:* Pharmacol instr, Temple Univ Sch Dent Hyg, 72-76, Camden County Col, 73-76, Community Col Philadelphia, 75-76; teaching asst, Temple Univ Sch Pharm, 71-76; asst examr, Pa State Bd Pharm, 72-76. *Honors & Awards:* Pharm Res Award, Lunsford-Richardson, 70. *Mem:* Teratol Soc; Sigma Xi. *Res:* General pharmacology; reproductive toxicology; pharmacy. *Mailing Add:* Adria Labs Inc PO Box 16529 Columbus OH 43216

MITALAS, ROMAS, b Kaunas, Lithuania, Feb 28, 33; nat Can. THEORETICAL PHYSICS, ASTROPHYSICS. *Educ:* Univ Toronto, BA, 57, MA, 58; Cornell Univ, PhD(physics), 64. *Prof Exp:* Asst prof physics, 64-68, asst prof astron, 68-72, ASSOC PROF ASTRON, UNIV WESTERN ONT, 73- *Mem:* Am Phys Soc; Am Astron Soc; Can Astron Soc. *Res:* Stellar structure and evolution. *Mailing Add:* Dept of Astron Univ of Western Ont London ON N6A 5B8 Can

MITCH, FRANK ALLAN, b State College, Pa, Apr 21, 20; m 67. ORGANIC CHEMISTRY. *Educ:* Pa State Col, AB, 41, MS, 48. *Prof Exp:* Researcher, Photo Prod, E I du Pont de Nemours & Co, Inc, 41-45; control, Floridin Co, 49-51, researcher, 51-58; mem staff res & develop, Ariz Chem Co, 58-61; MGR TECH SERV, GLIDDEN ORGANICS, 61- *Mem:* AAAS; Am Chem Soc; Soc Soft Drink Technol. *Res:* Soft drinks; tall oil; terpenes; essential oils. *Mailing Add:* 4134 Rogero Rd Jacksonville FL 32211

MITCH, WILLIAM EVANS, b Birmingham, Ala, July 22, 41; m 65; c 2. NEPHROLOGY. *Educ:* Harvard Univ, BA, 63, MD, 67. *Prof Exp:* Intern med, Peter Bent Brigham Hosp, 67-68, asst resident, 68-69; clin assoc oncol, Nat Cancer Inst, 69-71; fel med, Johns Hopkins Univ, 71-73; chief resident, Peter Bent Brigham Hosp, 73-74; asst prof med & pharmacol, Johns Hopkins Univ, 74-78, assoc prof, 78-79; ASSOC PROF MED, HARVARD MED SCH, 79- *Mem:* Am Soc Nephrology; Am Inst Nutrit; Am Soc Clin Nutrit; Am Fedn Clin Res; Am Soc Clin Invest. *Res:* Nutritional therapy of chronic renal insufficiency. *Mailing Add:* 45 Francis St Brigham & Womens Hosp Boston MA 02115

MITCHAM, DONALD, b Hazlehurst, Miss, Nov 15, 21. PHYSICS. *Educ:* Tulane Univ, BS, 48. *Prof Exp:* Physicist, 48-68, RES PHYSICIST, SOUTHERN REGIONAL RES LAB, US DEPT AGR, 68- *Mem:* Am Crystallog Asn; Am Asn Textile Chem & Colorists; Soc Appl Spectros; Am Oil Chem Soc; Sigma Xi. *Res:* X-ray diffraction of cotton cellulose; physical properties of textiles; structure of fatty acids by x-ray diffraction. *Mailing Add:* 3326 Marigny New Orleans LA 70122

MITCHEL, RONALD EDWARD JOHN, biochemistry, see previous edition

MITCHELL, A RICHARD, b Pine Bluff, Ark, Feb 27, 39; m 59; c 2. APPLIED MATHEMATICS. *Educ:* Southern Methodist Univ, BS, 60; NMex State Univ, MS, 62, PhD(math), 64. *Prof Exp:* Assoc prof math, Hendrix Col, 64-65; asst prof, 65-67, assoc prof, 67-77, PROF MATH, UNIV TEX, ARLINGTON, 77- *Mem:* Am Math Soc; Math Asn Am. *Res:* Differential equations. *Mailing Add:* Dept of Math Univ of Tex Arlington TX 76019

MITCHELL, ALEXANDER REBAR, b San Pedro, Calif, June 13, 38; m 63; c 1. BIOCHEMISTRY. *Educ:* Univ Calif, Berkeley, BA, 61; Ind Univ, PhD(biochem), 69. *Prof Exp:* Asst biochem, Edgewood Arsenal, US Army, 62-63; res assoc, Rockefeller Univ, 69-75, asst prof biochem, 75-77; CHEMIST, LAWRENCE LIVERMORE LAB, UNIV CALIF, 77- *Mem:* Am Chem Soc; AAAS; NY Acad Sci. *Res:* Chemical synthesis of peptides; solid phase peptide synthesis; enzyme models; peptide antibiotics and hormones; development of peptide substrates for the determination of proteinase activities in neoplastic cells. *Mailing Add:* Lawrence Livermore Lab L-324 PO Box 808 Livermore CA 94550

MITCHELL, ALVA DOYLE, b Cainsville, Mo, Jan 23, 42; m 73; c 2. AGRICULTURE & FOOD CHEMISTRY. *Educ:* Colo State Univ, BS, 63, MS, 69; Univ Wis, PhD(nutrit sci), 76. *Prof Exp:* Fel, Dept Path, Med Sch, Univ Wis, 76-78; res physiologist, Metab & Radiation Res Lab, US Dept Agr, 78-81; RES ASSOC, DEPT ANIMAL SCI, NDAK STATE UNIV, 81- *Mem:* Sigma Xi; AAAS; Int Soc Study Xenobiotics. *Res:* Animal metabolism; amino acid metabolism; regulation of cholesterol synthesis; metabolism of zenobiotics. *Mailing Add:* 2205 N 10th St Fargo ND 58102

MITCHELL, ANN DENMAN, cell biology, biochemical genetics, see previous edition

MITCHELL, BARRY MILLER, b Toronto, Ont, June 25, 34. MATHEMATICS. *Educ:* Univ Toronto, BA, 55, MA, 56; Brown Univ, PhD(math), 60. *Prof Exp:* Instr math, Columbia Univ, 60-64; asst prof, Bowdoin Col, 65-68; acad guest, Swiss Fed Inst Technol, 68-69; sr res fel, Dalhousie Univ, 69-71; assoc prof, 71-73, PROF MATH, RUTGERS UNIV, NEW BRUNSWICK, 73- *Mem:* Am Math Soc; Math Asn Am. *Res:* Homological algebra. *Mailing Add:* Dept of Math Rutgers Univ New Brunswick NJ 08903

MITCHELL, BENJAMIN EVANS, b Delhi, La, Feb 15, 20; m 48; c 3. MATHEMATICS. *Educ:* La State Univ, AB, 41, AM, 48; Univ Wis, PhD(math), 51. *Prof Exp:* Asst prof math, Ala Polytech Inst, 51-52; from asst prof to assoc prof, 52-64, PROF MATH, LA STATE UNIV, BATON ROUGE, 64- *Mem:* Am Math Soc; Math Asn Am. *Res:* Matric theory; algebra. *Mailing Add:* Dept of Math La State Univ Baton Rouge LA 70803

MITCHELL, BRIAN JAMES, b Minneapolis, Minn, July 25, 36; m 60; c 2. GEOPHYSICS. *Educ:* Univ Minn, BA, 62, MS, 65; Southern Methodist Univ, PhD(geophys), 70. *Prof Exp:* Physicist rock properties, US Bur Mines Res Ctr, 62-65; res fel seismol, Calif Inst Technol, 71-72; geophysicist mining res, Newmont Explor Ltd, 72-73; asst prof, 74-76, assoc prof, 76-80, PROF GEOPHYS & CHMN, DEPT EARTH & ATMOSPHERIC SCI, ST LOUIS UNIV, 80- *Mem:* Am Geophys Union; Seismol Soc Am; Soc Explor Geophysicists; Royal Astron Soc. *Res:* Crust and upper mantle structure; seismic surface wave propagation; arctic research. *Mailing Add:* Dept of Earth & Atmospheric Sci St Louis Univ St Louis MO 63156

MITCHELL, CARY ARTHUR, b Woodstock, Ill, May 28, 43; m 68; c 3. PLANT STRESS PHYSIOLOGY. *Educ:* Univ Ill, BS, 65; Cornell Univ, MS, 68; Univ Calif, Davis, PhD(plant physiol), 72. *Prof Exp:* Asst prof, 72-78, ASSOC PROF PLANT PHYSIOL, DEPT HORT, PURDUE UNIV, 78- *Concurrent Pos:* Consult, Am Elec Power Co, 75-; prin investr, Controlled Ecol Life Support Syst & Space Shuttle Prog, grants from Nat Aeronaut & Space Admin, NASA Space Biol Prog, 76- *Mem:* Am Soc Plant Physiologists; Am Soc Hort Sci; Am Inst Biol Sci; AAAS; Am Soc Photobiol. *Res:* Mechanical stress regulation of plant growth-effects of wind, shaking, and touching on plant hormones and metabolism; physiology of flood tolerance in woody plants; mechanisms of seed dormancy; controlled environment agriculture; physiology of plant stress hardening. *Mailing Add:* Dept Hort Purdue Univ West Lafayette IN 47907

MITCHELL, CHARLES ELLIOTT, b Newark, NJ, Apr 14, 41; c 2. MECHANICAL ENGINEERING. *Educ:* Princeton Univ, BSE, 63, MA, 65, PhD(aerospace & mech sci), 67. *Prof Exp:* Res asst combustion physics, Princeton Univ, 63-67; asst prof, 67-71, assoc prof, 71-80, PROF MECH ENG, COLO STATE UNIV, 80- *Concurrent Pos:* Consult, RDA, Inc, 77-79; fac fel, Laramie Energy Tech Ctr, 79-80. *Mem:* Combustion Inst; Am Inst Aeronaut & Astronaut. *Res:* Combustion instability; nonlinear wave oscillations; combustion of fossil fuels; acoustics; gas dynamics. *Mailing Add:* Dept of Mech Eng Colo State Univ Ft Collins CO 80521

MITCHELL, CLIFFORD L, b Ottumwa, Iowa, Dec 7, 30; m 54; c 4. PHARMACOLOGY. *Educ:* Univ Iowa, BA, 52, BS, 54, MS, 58, PhD(pharmacol), 59. *Prof Exp:* Asst prof, Col Med, Univ Iowa, 59-60 & 62-66, from assoc prof to prof pharmacol, 66-73; sr res scientist, Riker Labs, 73-74, mgr cent nerv syst & cardiopulmonary pharmacol, 74-76; head behav toxicol prog, 76-77, CHIEF LAB BEHAV & NEUROL TOXICOL, NAT INST ENVIRON HEALTH SCI, 77- *Concurrent Pos:* Res fel, Stanford Univ, 60-62; adj prof pharmacol, Univ NC, 77- *Mem:* AAAS; Am Soc Pharmacol & Exp Therapeut; Soc Neurosci; Soc Exp Biol & Med. *Res:* Neuropharmacology; neurotoxicology; primarily analgesic fields and neurobehavioral toxicology. *Mailing Add:* Nat Inst of Environ Health Sci Box 12233 Research Triangle Park NC 27709

MITCHELL, DAVID FARRAR, b Arkansas City, Kans, Dec 15, 18; m 43; c 3. DENTISTRY. *Educ:* Univ Ill, BS, 40, DDS, 42; Univ Rochester, PhD(path), 48; Am Bd Oral Path, dipl, 69. *Prof Exp:* Instr dent, Univ Rochester, 48; assoc prof dent & chmn div oral histol & path, Sch Dent, Univ Minn, 48-55, actg chmn div periodontia, 49-51, chmn div oral diag, 49-54; PROF & CHMN DEPT ORAL DIAG, SCH DENT, IND UNIV, INDIANAPOLIS, 55- *Concurrent Pos:* Pres, Am Bd Oral Path, 69. *Mem:* AAAS; Am Acad Oral Path (pres, 61); Am Asn Dent Res (pres, 75); Int Asn Dent Res; Am Dent Asn. *Res:* Aviation chemistry; production and prevention of experimental dental caries and periodontal disease; tissue reactions to dental materials; oral pathology. *Mailing Add:* 8808 Caplock Lane Indianapolis IN 46206

MITCHELL, DAVID HILLARD, b Philadelphia, Pa, May 17, 45. GERONTOLOGY, GENETICS. *Educ:* Stanford Univ, BA, 67; Harvard Univ, MA, 70, PhD(biochem), 75. *Prof Exp:* Res fel geront, 75-78, STAFF SCIENTIST GERONT, BOSTON BIOMED RES INST, 78- *Concurrent Pos:* Prin investr, Nat Inst Aging res grant, 78-81. *Mem:* Geront Soc. *Res:* Genetics and biochemistry of aging. *Mailing Add:* 78 Gilman Boston MA 02145

MITCHELL, DAVID WESLEY, b Columbia, SC, Jan 28, 13; m 43; c 2. METALLURGY, PHYSICAL CHEMISTRY. *Educ:* Univ Calif, Berkeley, BS, 38; Univ Utah, MS, 40; Univ Calif, PhD(metall), 47. *Prof Exp:* From instr to assoc prof metall, Dept Mineral Technol, Univ Calif, Berkeley, 42-57; mgr dir res develop minerals, chem, metall & ceramics, Foote Mineral Co, 57-62; prof metall, NMex Inst Mining & Technol, 62-73; vpres & tech dir elec & magnetic separation solids, Carpco Inc, 74-80; CONSULT, 80- *Concurrent Pos:* Vpres & tech dir, Oil Shale Corp, 55-57; expert in metall, UNESCO, 70-72. *Mem:* Am Inst Mining, Metall & Petrol Engrs. *Res:* Electrostatic and magnetic separation of minerals and waste products. *Mailing Add:* 7000 Arroyo Del Oso Northeast Albuquerque NM 87109

MITCHELL, DEAN LEWIS, b Montour Falls, NY, Apr 9, 29; m 51; c 4. SOLID STATE PHYSICS. *Educ:* Syracuse Univ, BS, 52, PhD(physics), 59. *Prof Exp:* Asst prof physics, Utica Col, Syracuse Univ, 58-61; res physicist, Naval Res Lab, 61-70, head solid state appln br, 70-74; prog dir solid state physics, 74-81, SECT HEAD CONDENSED MATTER SCI, NSF, 81- *Concurrent Pos:* Nat Acad Sci-Acad Sci USSR exchange prog fel, A F Ioffe Phys Tech Inst, Leningrad, 67-68. *Mem:* AAAS; Am Phys Soc. *Res:* Optical and magneto-optical properties; electronic band structure of solids; semiconductors; infrared sources and detectors. *Mailing Add:* Div of Mat Res NSF 1800 G St NW Washington DC 20550

MITCHELL, DENNIS KEITH, b Hollywood, Calif, Apr 17, 46. INORGANIC CHEMISTRY. *Educ:* Univ Calif, Los Angeles, BS, 68; Univ Calif, Santa Barbara, PhD(chem), 72. *Prof Exp:* Asst prof chem, Univ Andes, Venezuela, 73-76; res asst chem, Univ Calif, Berkeley, 76-77; lectr chem, Calif State Univ, Hayward, 77-80; ASST PROF, LOS ANGELES CITY COL, 80- *Concurrent Pos:* Res grant, Nat Coun Sci & Tech Res, Venezuela, 75-76. *Mem:* Am Chem Soc. *Res:* Organometallic synthesis and catalysis. *Mailing Add:* Dept Chem LA City Col 855 N Vermont Ave Los Angeles CA 90029

MITCHELL, DONALD GILMAN, b Somerville, Mass, Sept 17, 17; m 42; c 2. FOOD TECHNOLOGY. *Educ:* Mass Inst Technol, SB, 38. *Prof Exp:* Chemist, Walter Baker & Co, Inc, 38-41, res chemist, 46-50, asst to res dir, 50-54, qual control mgr, 54-59, mgr chocolate develop, 59-62, MGR TECH SERV, BAKER'S CHOCOLATE & COCONUT DIV, GEN FOODS CORP, DOVER, 62- *Honors & Awards:* Stroud Jordan Award, Am Asn Candy Technologists, 80; Res & Educ Award, Nat Confectioners Asn, 80. *Mem:* Am Chem Soc; Inst Food Technologists; Am Asn Candy Technologists; Am Soc Bakery Engrs. *Res:* Quality control and research and development on chocolate products and their processing. *Mailing Add:* 706 North Shore Dr Milford DE 19963

MITCHELL, DONALD J, b New Castle, Pa, May 12, 38; m 68. PHYSICAL CHEMISTRY, CRYSTALLOGRAPHY. *Educ:* Westminster Col, Pa, BS, 60; Vanderbilt Univ, PhD(phys chem), 64. *Prof Exp:* Res chemist with Dr Jerome Karle, Naval Res Labs, US Govt, DC, 64-67; ASST PROF CHEM, JUNIATA COL, 67-, CHMN DEPT, 77- *Concurrent Pos:* NSF fel, 75. *Mem:* Am Chem Soc; Am Crystallog Asn. *Res:* Crystal structure analysis by x-ray diffraction, particularly gas bearing shales, coals and polymers. *Mailing Add:* Dept of Chem Juniata Col Huntingdon PA 16652

MITCHELL, DONALD JOHN, b Saskatoon, Sask, May 20, 39; m 61. PLANT PHYSIOLOGY. *Educ:* Univ Sask, BA, 60, MA, 64; Case Western Reserve Univ, PhD(plant physiol), 68. *Prof Exp:* Lab technician plant physiol, Univ Sask, 60-61; fel, McMaster Univ, 68-69; chmn dept environ sci, 73-78, LECTR II BIOL, SELKIRK COL, 69-; CHMN ACAD STUDIES & PERFORMING ARTS, DAVID THOMPSON UNIV CTR, 80- *Mem:* Can Soc Plant Physiol; Am Soc Plant Physiol; Can Bot Asn. *Res:* Amino and organic acid metabolism and compartmentation in germinating seedlings; cellulase activity in growing seedlings. *Mailing Add:* David Thompson Univ Ctr 820 10th St Nelson BC V1L 3C7 Can

MITCHELL, DONALD W(ILLIAM), b New York, NY, May 24, 23; m 51; c 6. MINING ENGINEERING, COMBUSTION. *Educ:* Pa State Univ, BS, 48; Columbia Univ, MS, 51. *Prof Exp:* Engr, H C Frick Coke Co, Pa, 41-42; mining engr, Hudson Coal Co, 46-50; mining engr, US Bur Mines, 51-59, chief mine exp sect, 59-74, projxcoordrxengxappln,x65-74,xstaffxengr, xPitasst chief, Br Dust Explosions, 61-65, proj coordr eng appln, 65-74, staff engr, Pittsburgh Mining & Safety Res Ctr, 71-74; prin mining engr, Mining Safety & Health Admin, 74-78; CHIEF ENGR, GATES ENG CO, 78- *Concurrent Pos:* Chmn eng comt, Coal Mining Sect, Nat Safety Coun, 63-; chmn task force underground storage of oil, gas & nuclear waste, 76-78. *Honors & Awards:* Secy Labor Spec Recognition Award, US Dept of Labor, 78. *Res:* Dust explosions and fires; strata control. *Mailing Add:* Gates Eng Co Suite 630 Parkway Ctr Inn Pittsburgh PA 15220

MITCHELL, EARL BRUCE, b Louisville, Miss, Sept 1, 27; m 50; c 3. ENTOMOLOGY. *Educ:* Miss State Univ, BS, 50, MS, 51, PhD(entom), 71. *Prof Exp:* Entomologist, La State Univ, 51-52 & Food Mach Corp, 53-54; farmer, 54-62; ENTOMOLOGIST, BOLL WEEVIL RES LAB, AGR RES SERV, USDA, MISSISSIPPI STATE, 63- *Mem:* Entom Soc Am. *Res:* Use of pheromones, traps, insecticides, sterile males, and combinations of these for the purpose of suppressing or eradicating the boll weevil. *Mailing Add:* USDA-ARS-SR PO Box 5367 Mississippi State MS 39762

MITCHELL, EARL DOUGLASS, JR, b New Orleans, La, May 16, 38; m 59; c 3. BIOCHEMISTRY. *Educ:* Xavier Univ La, BS, 60; Mich State Univ, MS, 63, PhD(biochem), 66. *Prof Exp:* Res assoc, 67-69, asst prof, 69-74, ASSOC PROF BIOCHEM, OKLA STATE UNIV, 74- *Mem:* Am Chem Soc. *Res:* Chemical and physical studies of barley and amylase; plant glycosidases; cell-free biosynthesis of monoterpenoid compounds. *Mailing Add:* Dept of Biochem Okla State Univ Stillwater OK 74074

MITCHELL, EARL NELSON, b Centerville, Iowa, Aug 30, 26; m 55. PHYSICS. *Educ:* Univ Iowa, BA, 49, MS, 51; Univ Minn, PhD(physics), 55. *Prof Exp:* Res physicist, Univac Div, Sperry Rand Corp, 55-58; from asst prof to assoc prof physics, Univ NDak, 58-62; vis assoc prof, 62-65, assoc prof, 65-69, asst chmn dept, 68-76, PROF PHYSICS, UNIV NC, CHAPEL HILL, 69- *Mem:* Am Phys Soc; Am Soc Enologists; Am Asn Physics Teachers. *Res:* Solid state physics; structure, electric and magnetic properties of thin films. *Mailing Add:* Dept Physics Univ NC Chapel Hill NC 27514

MITCHELL, EDGAR DEAN, b Hereford, Tex, Sept 17, 30; m 51; c 2. AERONAUTICS. *Educ:* Carnegie Inst Technol, BS, 52; US Naval Postgrad Sch, BS, 61; Mass Inst Technol, ScD(aeronaut, astronaut), 64. *Hon Degrees:* ScD, NMex State Univ, 71; DrEng, Carnegie Mellon Univ, 71. *Prof Exp:* US Navy, 52-, res proj pilot, Air Develop Squadron Five, 58-59, chief proj mgt div, Navy Field Off, Manned Orbiting Lab, Los Angeles, 64-65, mem staff, Aerospace Res Pilot Sch, Edwards AFB, 65-66, astronaut, Manned Spacecraft Ctr, NASA, 66-75; PRES, EDGAR D MITCHELL CORP, 75- *Concurrent Pos:* Mem backup crew, Apollo X Lunar Circumnavig, 69, prime crew, Apollo XIV Lunar Explor, 70, back up crew, Apollo XVI Lunar Explor, 72; chmn bd, Inst Noetic Sci, 73-; mem bd dirs, Info Sci Inc, 77- *Honors & Awards:* Naval Aviator Award, Daughters Am Revolution; US Navy Distinguished Serv Medal; NASA Distinguished Serv Medal; Presidential Medal of Freedom; Gold Medal, City of New York. *Mem:* Soc Exp Test Pilots; Am Inst Aeronaut & Astronaut; Parapsychol Asn. *Mailing Add:* 6155 Palm Beach Lakes Blvd No 616 West Palm Beach FL 33401

MITCHELL, EVERETT ROYAL, b Itasca, Tex, Sept 17, 36; m 57; c 1. ENTOMOLOGY. *Educ:* Tex Tech Univ, BS, 59; NC State Univ, MS, 61, PhD(entom, bot), 63. *Prof Exp:* Res entomologist, Cotton Insects Br, USDA, Florence, SC, 63-65; asst prof entom & head dept, Coastal Plain Exp Sta, Univ Ga, Tifton, 65-67; prof biol sci & chmn div sci & math, Tarrant County Community Col, Ft Worth, Tex, 67-69; sr res biologist, Monsanto Co, St Louis, 69-70; res entomologist, 71, actg dir lab, 71-72, RES LEADER ECOL GROUP, INSECT ATTRACTANTS LAB, 72- *Concurrent Pos:* Assoc prof entom & nematol, Univ Fla, 71-77, prof, 77- *Mem:* Entom Soc Am. *Res:* Biology, ecology, behavior and control of economic pests of field and vegetable crops, particularly chemical messengers produced by insects. *Mailing Add:* Insect Attractants Lab USDA PO Box 14565 Gainesville FL 32604

MITCHELL, GARY EARL, b Louisville, Ky, July 5, 35; m 57; c 2. PHYSICS. *Educ:* Univ Louisville, BS, 56; Duke Univ, MA, 58; Fla State Univ, PhD(physics), 62. *Prof Exp:* Res assoc physics, Columbia Univ, 62-64, asst prof, 64-68; assoc prof, 68-74, PROF PHYSICS, NC STATE UNIV, 74- *Concurrent Pos:* Humboldt sr scientist award, 75-76. *Mem:* Fel AAAS; Am Phys Soc. *Res:* Nuclear structure physics, including electromagnetic transitions; high resolution proton scattering; fine structure of analog states. *Mailing Add:* Dept of Physics NC State Univ Raleigh NC 27650

MITCHELL, GARY F, b Chicago, Ill, Apr 16, 40; m 65. PHOTOGRAPHIC CHEMISTRY. *Educ:* Calif Inst Technol, BS, 62; Mass Inst Technol, PhD(org chem), 67. *Prof Exp:* Sr res chemist, 67-75, RES ASSOC, EASTMAN KODAK CO, 75- *Res:* Photographic film design. *Mailing Add:* 343 State Rochester NY 14608

MITCHELL, GEORGE ERNEST, JR, b Duoro, NMex, June 7, 30; m 52; c 3. ANIMAL SCIENCE. *Educ:* Univ Mo, BS, 51, MS, 54; Univ Ill, PhD(animal sci), 56. *Prof Exp:* Asst animal sci, Univ Ill, 54-56, asst prof, 56-60; assoc prof animal husb, 60-67, PROF ANIMAL SCI, UNIV KY, 67- *Concurrent Pos:* Sr Fulbright Res Scholar, NZ, 73-74; mem subcomt beef cattle nutrit, Nat Res Coun. *Mem:* AAAS; Am Registry Cert Animal Scientists; Am Soc Animal Sci; Am Dairy Sci Asn; Am Inst Nutrit. *Res:* Vitamin A metabolism; digestive physiology; carbohydrate utilization; rumen function; ruminant-nonruminant comparisons; effect of hormones on nutritive requirements; beef cattle feeding and management. *Mailing Add:* Dept of Animal Sci Univ of Ky Lexington KY 40506

MITCHELL, GEORGE JOSEPH, b Vancouver, BC, Nov 21, 25; m 56; c 4. WINTER ECOLOGY. *Educ:* Univ BC, BA, 50, MA, 52; Wash State Univ, PhD(zool), 65. *Prof Exp:* Sr wildlife biologist, Govt Can, Alta, 52-62, chief wildlife biologist, 62-66; assoc prof, 66-73, PROF BIOL, UNIV REGINA, CAN, 73- *Concurrent Pos:* exec bd, Wildlife Soc Can, 81- *Mem:* Wildlife Soc; Can Soc Zoologists; Wildlife Soc Can; Am Soc Mammalogists. *Res:* Ecology, behavior, reproductive biology and parasites and diseases of wild ungulates, canids, small mammals and anseriform and galliform birds. *Mailing Add:* Biol Dept Univ Regina Regina SK S4S OA2 Can

MITCHELL, GEORGE REDMOND, JR, b Cleveland, Ohio, Mar 3, 17; m 53; c 2. ORGANIC POLYMER CHEMISTRY. *Educ:* Mass Inst Technol, BS, 39, MS, 40; Case Inst Technol, PhD(org chem), 53. *Prof Exp:* Shift foreman, Synthetic Rubber Plant, B F Goodrich Chem Co, 41-42, process engr, 42-43, plant chem engr, 43-44, group leader, 44-49; group leader dispersion coating, film res & develop dept, Olin Mathieson Chem Corp, 51-55, asst sect chief, 55-58, chem develop mgr, 58-59; SECT LEADER MAT RES & DEVELOP, GLASTIC CORP, 59- *Mem:* Am Chem Soc; fel Am Inst Chemists; Am Soc Testing & Mat; Am Inst Chem Engrs; Inst Elec & Electronics Engrs. *Res:* Thermosetting reinforced polyester laminates and molding compounds; power and electronic electrical properties of reinforced thermosetting plastics; film forming thermoplastics; oxidation of hydrocarbons; synthetic rubber; chemical engineering process development; pilot plant design and operation. *Mailing Add:* Gates Rd Gates Mills OH 44040

MITCHELL, GERALDINE VAUGHN, nutritional sciences, biochemistry, see previous edition

MITCHELL, H REES, b New London, Conn, Oct 13, 08; m 37; c 4. PHYSICS. *Educ:* Trinity Col, Conn, BS, 31; Johns Hopkins Univ, PhD(physics), 38. *Prof Exp:* Instr math, Gettysburg Col, 37-38; asst prof physics, The Citadel, 38-44; physicist, Appl Physics Lab, Johns Hopkins Univ, 44-48; asst prof, Georgetown Univ, 48-51; assoc prof, 51-58, prof 58-76, EMER PROF PHYSICS, MICH TECHNOL UNIV, 76- *Mem:* AAAS; Am Phys Soc; Am Asn Physics Teachers. *Res:* Thin metallic films servomechanisms; computing mechanism of gun fire control and guided missiles. *Mailing Add:* PO Box 215 Manset ME 04656

MITCHELL, HAROLD HUGH, b New York, NY, Apr 10, 16. MEDICINE. *Educ:* Univ Ariz, BS, 36; Univ Southern Calif, MS, 38; Wash Univ, MD, 45. *Prof Exp:* Lectr bact, Univ Southern Calif, 38-41; asst med dir, Calif Physicians Serv, 48-52; from assoc scientist to sr scientist, Physics Div, Rand Corp, 52-71; SR SCIENTIST, R&D ASSOCS, 71- *Concurrent Pos:* Chmn, Gov's Adv Comt Radiol Defense, Calif, 62-68. *Mem:* AAAS; AMA. *Res:* Biological and environmental consequences of nuclear war radiation effects and radiobiology; mass casualty; civil defense. *Mailing Add:* R&D Assocs 4640 Admiralty Way Marina del Ray CA 90291

MITCHELL, HENRY ANDREW, b Joplin, Mo, Oct 6, 36; m 61; c 3. MAMMALIAN PHYSIOLOGY. *Educ:* Southwest Mo State Col, BS, 58; Univ Ariz, MS, 60, PhD(zool), 63. *Prof Exp:* Asst zool, Univ Ariz, 58-63; asst prof biol, 63-68, asst dean, Sch Grad Studies, 69, assoc prof biol & assoc dean, Col Arts & Sci, 68-73, lectr med & assoc dean, Sch Med, 72-73, actg dean, Col Arts & Sci, 74-75, assoc provost health sci, 73-80, asst vchancellor, 80-81, PROF BIOL, MED & PHARM, UNIV MO-KANSAS CITY, 73-, ASSOC VCHANCELLOR ACAD AFFAIRS, 81- *Concurrent Pos:* Mem, Am Conf Acad Deans; field ctr coordr, NSF Chautauqua-Type Short Courses Prog for Col Teachers, 71-80; proj adminr, Western Mo Area Health Educ Ctr, 75-77. *Mem:* Fel AAAS; Am Soc Mammal; Am Inst Biol Sci; Mex Natural Hist Soc. *Res:* Hematological studies of bats. *Mailing Add:* Off Acad Affairs Univ Mo 5100 Rockhill Rd Kansas City MO 64110

MITCHELL, HENRY COOPER, entomology, see previous edition

MITCHELL, HERSCHEL KENWORTHY, b Los Nietos, Calif, Nov 27, 13; m 34; c 4. BIOCHEMISTRY. *Educ:* Pomona Col, AB, 36; Ore State Col, MS, 38; Univ Tex, PhD(org chem, biochem), 41. *Prof Exp:* Res assoc chem, Ore State Col, 38-39; res biochemist, Univ Tex, 41-43; res assoc biochem, Stanford Univ, 43-46; sr res fel, 46-48, assoc prof biol, 48-53, PROF BIOL, CALIF INST TECHNOL, 53- *Concurrent Pos:* NSF sr fel zool, Univ Zurich, 59-60. *Mem:* Am Soc Biol Chemists; Soc Gen Physiol; Am Chem Soc; Genetics Soc Am; Am Soc Naturalists. *Res:* Growth factors for microorganisms; microchemical methods; biochemical genetics in neurospora; synthesis of compounds of biological significance; biochemistry of Drosophila; moleculr basis of differentiation. *Mailing Add:* Dept of Biol Calif Inst of Technol Pasadena CA 91125

MITCHELL, HUGH BERTRON, b Bolton, Miss, Dec 8, 23; m 45; c 4. RADIOBIOLOGY, AEROSPACE MEDICINE. *Educ:* La State Univ, MD, 47; Univ Calif, Berkeley, MBioradiol, 65. *Prof Exp:* Physician, Tulsa Clin, Okla, 48-49; pvt pract, Richton, Miss, 49-50; med corps, US Navy, 50-52; physician, Baton Rouge Clin, La, 52-57; med corps, US Air Force, 57-75, med officer, Barksdale Air Force Base Hosp, 57-58, med officer, Sch Aviation Med, Randolph Air Force Base, 58, med officer spec weapons prog & radiobiol, Off Surgeon, Strategic Air Command Hq, 59-62, from dep dir to dir, Armed Forces Radiobiol Res Inst, Nat Naval Med Ctr, Md, 65-71, surgeon, 314th Air Div & comdr, Osan Air Force Base Hosp, Korea, 71-72, staff, Radiobiol Div, US Air Force Sch Aerospace Med, 72-73, comdr, US Air Force Hosp, Plattsburgh Air Force Base, NY, 73-75; AREA MED DIR, SPRINGS MILLS, INC, FT MILL, SC, 75- *Mem:* AMA; Asn Mil Surg US; Am Occup Med Asn. *Res:* General medicine and surgery; occupational medicine; medical aspects of special weapons and of disaster operations; combined effects of radiation plus other stresses. *Mailing Add:* Springs Mills Inc Ft Mill SC 29715

MITCHELL, J ANDREW, b Dallas, Tex, May 8, 41; m 71. REPRODUCTIVE PHYSIOLOGY, NEUROENDOCRINOLOGY. *Educ:* Southern Methodist Univ, BS, 63; Univ Kans, PhD(physiol), 69. *Prof Exp:* Asst prof, 72-77, ASSOC PROF ANAT, SCH MED, WAYNE STATE UNIV, 77- *Concurrent Pos:* NIH fel, Dept Anat, Baylor Col Med, 69-72. *Mem:* AAAS; Am Asn Anat; Soc Study Reproduction; Am Asn Hist Med. *Mailing Add:* Dept of Anat Wayne State Univ Sch of Med Detroit MI 48201

MITCHELL, JACK HARRIS, JR, b Auburn, Ala, Sept 15, 11; m 44; c 4. BIOCHEMISTRY. *Educ:* Clemson Col, BS, 33; Purdue Univ, PhD(biochem), 41. *Prof Exp:* Asst chemist, State Chem Lab, SC, 33-36; asst, Columbia Univ, 36-37; asst, Purdue Univ, 37-40, asst chemist, 40-41; res chemist, Am Meat Inst Found, Univ Chicago, 41-42 & Petrol Chem Co, Md, 46-47; head biochem sect, Southern Res Inst, Ala, 47-50; asst chief, Stability Div, Qm Food & Container Inst, Univ Ill, 50-55, chief chem & microbiol div, 55-57; head dept food tech & human nutrit, 57-64, prof food sci, 64-77, EMER

PROF FOOD SCI, CLEMSON UNIV, 77- *Concurrent Pos:* Mem bd dirs, Res & Develop Assocs for Military Food & Packaging Systs, Inc, 64-67; captain, Edgewood Arsenal, Chem Warfare Res. *Mem:* Inst Food Technol; fel Inst Food Technologists. *Res:* Research administration; food biochemistry; lipids; food processing and product development. *Mailing Add:* 101 Bradley St Clemson SC 29631

MITCHELL, JAMES EMMETT, b Triadelphia, WVa, July 18, 39; m 62; c 2. CHEMICAL ENGINEERING. *Educ:* WVa Univ, BSChE, 61; Univ Ill, Urbana, MS, 63, PhD(chem eng), 65. *Prof Exp:* From res engr to sr res engr, Esso Res & Eng Co, 65-73, sect head, 73-75, lab dir, 75-78; VPRES RES & DEVELOP, ALBANY INT CORP, 79- *Mem:* Am Chem Soc; Am Inst Chem Engrs; Am Phys Soc; AAAS. *Res:* Fluid mixing and mechanics; electrical aspects of combustion; adsorption and other separation processes. *Mailing Add:* Albany Int Corp PO Box 1907 Albany NY 12201

MITCHELL, JAMES GEORGE, b Kitchener, Ont, Apr 25, 43; c 3. COMPUTER SCIENCE. *Educ:* Univ Waterloo, BSc, 66; Carnegie-Mellon Univ, PhD(comput sci), 70. *Prof Exp:* Programmer, Berkeley Comput Corp, 70-71; mem res staff comput sci, 71-79, PRIN SCIENTIST, PALO ALTO RES CTR, XEROX CORP, 79- *Concurrent Pos:* Sr vis fel, Comput Lab, Cambridge Univ, 80-81. *Mem:* Asn Comput Mach; Inst Elec & Electronics Engrs; Brit Comput Soc. *Res:* Programming systems and methodologies; reliable software; programming languages; personal computer systems; computer networks; computer architecture; distributed computing. *Mailing Add:* Xerox Palo Alto Res Ctr 3333 Coyote Hill Rd Palo Alto CA 94304

MITCHELL, JAMES K(ENNETH), b Manchester, NH, Apr, 19, 30; m 51; c 5. GEOTECHNICAL ENGINEERING. *Educ:* Rensselaer Polytech Inst, BCE, 51; Mass Inst Technol, SM, 53, ScD(civil eng), 56. *Prof Exp:* Asst soil mech, Mass Inst Technol, 51-55; asst prof civil eng & asst res engr, 58-63; assoc prof & assoc res engr, 63-68, PROF CIVIL ENG & RES ENG, UNIV CALIF, BERKELEY, 68-, CHMN DEPT, 79- *Concurrent Pos:* Mem, Transp Res Bd, Nat Res Coun; mem, US Nat Coun, IntSoc Soil Mech & Found Engrs; prin investr, Soil Mech Exp, Apollo 14-17; geotech consult, 60- *Honors & Awards:* Thomas A Middlebrooks Award, Am Soc Civil Engrs, 62, 70 & 73; Walter L Huber Prize, Am Soc Civil Engrs, 65, Norman Medal, 72. *Mem:* Nat Acad Eng; fel Am Soc Civil engrs; Clay Minerals Soc; Am Soc Eng Educ. *Res:* Soil behavior; soil and site improvement; in-situ measurement of soil properties. *Mailing Add:* Dept Civil Eng 440 Davis Hall Univ Calif Berkeley CA 94720

MITCHELL, JAMES WINFIELD, b Durham, NC, Nov 16, 43; m 65; c 2. ANALYTICAL CHEMISTRY. *Educ:* NC A&T State Univ, BS, 65; Iowa State Univ, PhD(anal chem), 70. *Prof Exp:* SUPVR ANAL CHEM, BELL LABS, 70-, HEAD, ANAL CHEM DEPT, 75- *Concurrent Pos:* Pharmacia Prize, Percy L Julian Res Award. *Mem:* Am Chem Soc; Am Nuclear Soc; Am Inst Chem; NY Acad Sci. *Res:* Quantitative analysis of submicrogram amounts of inorganic species by radiochemical methods; ultrapurification of reagents for trace analysis. *Mailing Add:* MH 1D 239 Bell Labs Mountain Ave Murray Hill NJ 07974

MITCHELL, JERE HOLLOWAY, b Longview, Tex, Oct 17, 28; m 60; c 3. CARDIOVASCULAR PHYSIOLOGY. *Educ:* Va Mil Inst, BS, 50; Univ Tex Southwestern Med Sch, MD, 54. *Prof Exp:* From intern to resident med, Parkland Mem Hosp, Dallas, 54-56; from sr asst surgeon to surgeon, Lab Cardiovasc Physiol, Nat Heart Inst, 58-62; from asst prof to assoc prof med & physiol, 62-69, PROF MED & PHYSIOL, SOUTHWESTERN MED SCH, UNIV TEX HEALTH SCI CTR, DALLAS, 69- *Concurrent Pos:* Nat Heart Inst cardiac trainee, Univ Tex Southwestern Med Sch, Dallas, 56-57, res fel, 57-58, USPHS career develop award, 68-73; estab investr, Am Heart Asn, 62-67, chmn coun basic sci, 69-71, fel, Coun Clin Cardiol & Coun Circulation; vis sr scientist, Lab Physiol, Oxford Univ, 70-71; dir, Pauline & Adolph Weinberger Lab Cardiopulmonary Res, 66-; dir, Harry S Moss Heart Ctr, 76-; vis sr scientist, August Krogh Inst, Univ Copenhagen, 76, 81; consult, Appl Physiol & Orthop Study Sect, Nat Heart Lung Blood Inst, 79-81 & Respiration & Appl Physiol Study Sect, 81- *Honors & Awards:* Young Investr Award, Am Col Cardiol, 61. *Mem:* Am Physiol Soc; Am Soc Clin Invest; fel Am Col Cardiol; Am Asn Physicians. *Res:* Cardiovascular and exercise physiology. *Mailing Add:* Southwestern Med Sch Univ of Tex Health Sci Ctr Dallas TX 75235

MITCHELL, JOAN LAVERNE, b Palo Alto, Calif, May 24, 47. DATA COMPRESSION, PHYSICS. *Educ:* Stanford Univ, BS, 69; Univ Ill, Urbana, MS, 71, PhD(physics), 74. *Prof Exp:* RES STAFF APPL RES, T J WATSON RES CTR, IBM CORP, 74-, MGR, 79- *Mem:* Am Phys Soc. *Res:* Data compression algorithm development including hardware design; display of images; image processing; ultrasonic printing. *Mailing Add:* T J Watson Res Ctr PO Box 218 Yorktown Heights NY 10598

MITCHELL, JOHN, JR, b Catonsville, Md, Oct 5, 13; m 35; c 2. ANALYTICAL CHEMISTRY. *Educ:* Johns Hopkins Univ, BE, 35; Univ Del, MS, 45. *Prof Exp:* Control chemist, Consol Edison Co, NY, 35; chem engr, E I du Pont de Nemours & Co, Inc, 35-36, chemist, 36-37, anal chemist, 37-45, res supvr, 45-51, sr supvr, 51-66, res mgr, 66-78; RETIRED. *Concurrent Pos:* Consult, analytical chem & polymer sci, 79- *Honors & Awards:* Fisher Award Anal Chem, 64; Anachem Award, Asn Anal Chemists, 74. *Mem:* Am Chem Soc. *Res:* Organic and physical chemistry; chemical engineering. *Mailing Add:* 3 Meadows Lane The Meadows Wilmington DE 19807

MITCHELL, JOHN ALEXANDER, b Providence, RI, Aug 5, 45; m 67; c 2. PARASITOLOGY, MICROBIOLOGY. *Educ:* Okla State Univ, BS, 67; Univ Mont, PhD(zool), 75. *Prof Exp:* Vector control officer, Tulsa City-County Health Dept, 69-70; lab coordr physiol, Univ Mont, 72-73; res asst statist anal, Mont Coop Wildlife Res Unit, 73-75; asst prof & chmn dept biol, Pac Univ, 75-80; ASST DIR, WILDLIFE-WILDLANDS INST, 80- *Mem:* AAAS; Am Soc Parasitologists; Soc Protozoologists; Sigma Xi. *Res:* Disease causation and epidemiology/epizootiology; protozoan parasites; medical mycology. *Mailing Add:* Wildlife-Wildlands Inst 5200 Upper Miller Creek Rd Missoula MT 59803

MITCHELL, JOHN CAMPBELL, b Redditch, Eng, Mar 19, 23; Can citizen; m 45, 71; c 4. DERMATOLOGY, MEDICINE. *Educ:* Univ London, MB & BS, 48, MD, 50; FRCP(C), 61; FRCP, 72. *Prof Exp:* Asst prof, 57-72, ASSOC PROF DERMAT, UNIV BC, 72- *Concurrent Pos:* Med Res Coun Can fel, Univ BC, 65-72; consult, Shaughnessy Hosp, BC Cancer Inst & Vancouver Gen Hosp, 55- *Mem:* Can Dermat Asn; Am Acad Dermat. *Res:* Investigation of allergic contact dermatitis, especially from plants. *Mailing Add:* 691 W 28th Vancouver BC V7V 4L7 Can

MITCHELL, JOHN CHARLES, b Jourdanton, Tex, April 23, 32; m 53; c 2. RADIATION PHYSICS. *Educ:* St Marys Univ, Tex, BS, 58. *Prof Exp:* Radiation proj eng, Ling Temco Vought, 58-64; MGR & RES PROG DIR & CHIEF RADIATION PHYSICS, US AIR FORCE AEROSPACE MED, 64- *Concurrent Pos:* Chmn, Tri-Service Electromagnetic Radiation Panel, 78-82 & Panel VIII Res Study Group 2, NATO, 79-82. *Mem:* Inst Elec & Electronics Engrs; Aerospace Med Asn; Am Conf Govt Indust Hygienists; Bioelectromagnetic Soc. *Res:* Biological effects of radio frequency electromagnetic radiation; electromagnetic interference; electromagnetic compatibility. *Mailing Add:* USAFSAM/RZP Brooks AFB San Antonio TX 78235

MITCHELL, JOHN DOUGLAS, b Bennington, Vt, Dec 16, 44; m 66; c 2. INSTRUMENTATION, ELECTROMAGNETICS. *Educ:* Pa State Univ, BS, 66, MS, 68, PhD(elec eng), 73. *Prof Exp:* From asst prof to assoc prof elec eng, Univ Tex, El Paso, 73-80; ASSOC PROF ELEC ENG, PA STATE UNIV, 80- *Mem:* Inst Elec & Electronics Engrs; Am Geophys Union; AAAS. *Res:* Electrical properties of the middle atmosphere; designing probes for measuring atmospheric electrical parameters, planning and conducting field experiments to obtain data, and analyzing and interpretinng the measurement results. *Mailing Add:* Elec Eng Dept Pa State Univ 332 Elec Eng East University Park PA 16802

MITCHELL, JOHN EDWARDS, b San Francisco, Calif, Mar 27, 17; m 42; c 3. PLANT PATHOLOGY. *Educ:* Univ Minn, BS, 39; Univ Wis, PhD(biochem), 48. *Prof Exp:* Asst plant path, Univ Minn, 39-40 & 41-42; asst plant path, Univ Wis, 46-48; plant pathologist, Camp Detrick, Md, 48-51, chief biol br, C Div, 51-56; assoc prof plant path, 56-63, PROF PLANT PATH, UNIV WIS-MADISON, 63-, CHMN DEPT, 75- *Mem:* Am Phytopath Soc; Am Soc Plant Physiol; Sigma Xi. *Res:* Ecology and control of soil borne plant pathogens; resistance of roots to disease; soil environment and plant disease. *Mailing Add:* Dept of Plant Path Univ of Wis 1630 Linden Dr Madison WI 53706

MITCHELL, JOHN JACOB, b Schenectady, NY, Mar 4, 17; m 42; c 3. PHYSICAL CHEMISTRY. *Educ:* Johns Hopkins Univ, PhD(chem), 41. *Prof Exp:* Asst chem, Johns Hopkins Univ, 40-41; phys chemist, Tex Co, 41-53, staff chemist, Texaco Inc, 53-57, res assoc, 57-60, sr res technologist, 60-82; RETIRED. *Concurrent Pos:* Supvr lab, Manhattan Eng Dist, Fercleve Corp, Oak Ridge, Tenn, 44-45. *Mem:* AAAS; Am Chem Soc; Am Phys Soc; Health Physics Soc. *Res:* Mass spectroscopy; use of radioactive tracers; radiation chemistry; use of isotope tracers in studying reaction mechanisms; research planning. *Mailing Add:* 226 Main St Fishkill NY 12524

MITCHELL, JOHN LAURIN AMOS, b Lincoln, Nebr, July 18, 44; m 68; c 2. CELL PHYSIOLOGY, BIOLOGICAL RHYTHMS. *Educ:* Oberlin Col, BA, 66; Princeton Univ, PhD(biol), 70. *Prof Exp:* Fel cancer res, McArdle Labs Cancer Res, Univ Wis-Madison, 70-73; asst prof, 73-78, ASSOC PROF BIOL, NORTHERN ILL UNIV, 78- *Mem:* Am Soc Cell Biol; Am Soc Biol Chemists; Sigma Xi. *Res:* Regulation of polyamine synthesis in Physarum polycephalum as well as in normal, cancer and cystic fibrosis tissues; post-translational enzyme modifications; biochemistry of cell cycle. *Mailing Add:* Dept of Biol Sci Northern Ill Univ De Kalb IL 60115

MITCHELL, JOHN MURRAY, JR, b New York, NY, Sept 17, 28; m 56; c 4. METEOROLOGY. *Educ:* Mass Inst Technol, BS, 51, MS, 52; Pa State Univ, PhD(meteorol), 60. *Prof Exp:* Weather observer, Blue Hill Meteorol Observ, Harvard Univ, 46-52; mem staff, Div Indust Coop Meteorol Res, Mass Inst Technol, 52; weather officer, Air Weather Serv, US Air Force, 52-55; meteorologist, US Weather Bur, 55-65; proj scientist, 65-74, sr res climatologist, 74-79, SCI ADV, NAT OCEANIC & ATMOSPHERIC ADMIN, 80- *Concurrent Pos:* Ed, Meteorol Monogr, Am Meteorol Soc, 65-73, Weatherwise, 79-; lectr, Univ Calif, Berkeley, 65; vis assoc prof, Univ Wash, 69; vis scientist, Nat Ctr Atmospheric Res, 77; chmn, US Nat Comt for Int Union Quaternary Res, 70-75; mem, Comt on Atmospheric Sci, Nat Acad Sci, 74-77, Comt on Impacts Stratospheric Change, 75-80 & Polar Res Bd, 78- *Honors & Awards:* 2nd Half Century Award, Am Meteorol Soc, 79. *Mem:* Fel Am Meteorol Soc; fel AAAS; Am Geophys Union; Glaciol Soc; Royal Meteorol Soc. *Res:* Climatic change; climate modification; time series analysis; paleoclimatology. *Mailing Add:* Nat Oceanic & Atmospheric Admin Rm 625 Gramax Bldg 8060 13th St Silver Spring MD 20910

MITCHELL, JOHN PETER, b Toronto, Ont, June 28, 32; m 56; c 2. PHYSICS. *Educ:* Univ Toronto, BA, 55, MA, 57, PhD(physics), 60. *Prof Exp:* Engr, Bell Tel Co, Can, 55-56; teacher math & physics, York Mem Col Inst, Toronto, 60-63; MEM TECH STAFF, BELL LABS, INC, 63- *Mem:* Am Phys Soc; Inst Elec & Electronics Eng. *Res:* Surface effects of radiation on semiconductor devices; resistivity of dilute alloys of lead at low temperatures; thin insulating films for cryogenic use; materials used for printed circuits. *Mailing Add:* Bell Labs Inc Room 5E-125 Whippany NJ 07981

MITCHELL, JOHN RICHARD, b Marysville, Ohio, Sept 18, 27; m 49; c 3. MICROBIOLOGY, PUBLIC HEALTH. *Educ:* Ohio State Univ, DVM, 53; Univ Mich, Ann Arbor, MPH, 60, DrPH, 63. *Prof Exp:* Pvt pract vet med, 53-56; pub health vet, Dept Health, City of Columbus, Ohio, 55-60; sr vet officer, USPHS, 63-65; PUB HEALTH LAB SCIENTIST, DEPT PUB HEALTH, STATE OF MICH, 65- *Mem:* Am Vet Med Asn. *Res:* Virology, especially development of viral vaccines. *Mailing Add:* Bur of Dis Control & Lab Ser Mich Dept of Pub Health Lansing MI 48909

MITCHELL, JOHN TAYLOR, b Buffalo, NY, Aug 16, 31; m 62; c 3. DEVELOPMENTAL BIOLOGY, EXPERIMENTAL EMBRYOLOGY. *Educ:* Amherst Col, BA, 53; NY Univ, MS, 64, PhD(biol), 66. *Prof Exp:* Asst cancer res scientist, Roswell Park Mem Inst, 56-60; res asst biol, NY Univ, 60-62, NIH fel, Dept Biol, 62-66; NIH staff fel, Nat Cancer Inst, Md, 66-68; asst prof anat, State Univ NY Upstate Med Ctr, 68-75; ASSOC PROF BIOL, COLGATE UNIV, 75- *Concurrent Pos:* State Univ NY Res Found grant, 68-70. *Mem:* AAAS; Soc Develop Biol; Am Soc Cell Biol; Am Asn Anat; Am Soc Zoologists. *Res:* Developmental biology, especially cytogenetic, cytological and in vitro approaches; effect of chemical compounds on early developing mammalian, avian and reptilian embryos; neoplastic conversion of cells in vitro; teratology. *Mailing Add:* Dept of Biol Colgate Univ Hamilton NY 13346

MITCHELL, JOHN WESLEY, b Christchurch, NZ, Dec 3, 13; m 76. PHYSICS. *Educ:* Univ NZ, BSc, 33, MSc, 34; Oxford Univ, DrPhil, 38, DSc, 60. *Prof Exp:* Res physicist, Brit Ministry Supply, 39-45; reader exp physics, Bristol Univ, 45-59; prof, 59-65, William Barton Rogers prof, 65-79, EMER PROF PHYSICS & SR RES FEL, UNIV VA, 79- *Honors & Awards:* Boys Prize, Brit Inst Physics & Phys Soc, 55; Renwick Mem Medal, Royal Photog Soc, 56. *Mem:* Hon mem Soc Photog Sci & Eng; fel Am Phys Soc; fel Royal Soc; fel Royal Inst Chem; fel Royal Photog Soc. *Res:* Physics of crystals; surface properties of crystalline materials; dislocations and plastic deformation of ionic crystals and metals; theory of photographic sensitivity. *Mailing Add:* Dept of Physics Univ of Va Charlottesville VA 22901

MITCHELL, JOHN WRIGHT, b Palo Alto, Calif, Mar 17, 35; m 55; c 3. MECHANICAL ENGINEERING. *Educ:* Stanford Univ, BS, 56, MS, 57, Engr, 59, PhD(mech eng), 63. *Prof Exp:* From asst prof to assoc prof, 62-71, PROF MECH ENG, UNIV WIS-MADISON, 71- *Concurrent Pos:* Consult, Oscar Mayer, Westinghouse, New Zealand; vis assoc prof, Yale Univ, 70. *Mem:* Am Soc Mech Engrs; Am Soc Eng Educ. *Res:* Heat transfer and natural conversion; solar cooling systems; desiccant air conditioning systems. *Mailing Add:* Col of Eng Univ of Wis Madison WI 53705

MITCHELL, JOSEPH CHRISTOPHER, b Albany, Ga, Oct 8, 22; m 45; c 3. PARASITOLOGY, ENTOMOLOGY. *Educ:* Ft Valley State Col, BS, 43; Atlanta Univ, MS, 49. *Hon Degrees:* DSc, London Inst Appl Res, 72. *Prof Exp:* Chmn dept sci high schs, Ga, 43-44, 44-45, 47 & 48-49; scholar, Atlanta Col Mortuary Sci, 45-46, instr physiol, 47-48; asst prof biol, Ft Valley State Col, 49-52; chmn dept phys sci & zool, Ala State Jr Col, 52-54; interim pres, S D Bishop State Col, 81; ASSOC PROF BIOL & CHMN DIV NATURAL SCI & MATH, S D BISHOP STATE COL, 70- *Concurrent Pos:* Carnegie res grant-in-aid & sci fac grant, 50-52; res technician, Cornell Univ, 70; Elem & Sec Educ Act title III field reader, US Off Educ; consult sec sci pub schs, Southwest Ga; proj dir sci improv, NSF, NSF fel, Cornell Univ, 61-62, Ford Found fel, 69-70, res assoc Entom & Med Entom, 70. *Mem:* AAAS; Am Soc Microbiol; Nat Sci Teachers Asn; Nat Asn Biol Teachers; Nat Inst Sci. *Res:* Mammalian physiology. *Mailing Add:* S D Bishop State Col 351 N Broad St Mobile AL 36603

MITCHELL, JOSEPHINE MARGARET, b Edmonton, Alta; nat US; m 53. MATHEMATICS. *Educ:* Univ Alta, BS, 34; Bryn Mawr Col, MA, 41, PhD(math), 42. *Prof Exp:* Teacher pub sch, Alta, 35-38; instr math, Hollins Col, 42-44; instr, Conn Col, 44-45; assoc prof, Winthrop Col, 45-46; assoc prof, Tex State Col Women, 46-47; asst prof, Okla State Univ, 47-48; asst prof, Univ Ill, 48-54; with adv electronics lab, Gen Elec Co, 55-56; with res lab, Westinghouse Elec Corp, 56-57; assoc prof math, Univ Pittsburgh, 57-58; assoc prof, Pa State Univ, 58-61, prof, 61-69; PROF MATH, STATE UNIV NY BUFFALO, 69- *Concurrent Pos:* Grantee, Am Philos Soc, 48; NSF grant, 52-53; sr fel, 64-65; mem, Inst Adv Study & Am Asn Univ Women fel, 54-55; Air Force contract, 60-63; mem, US Army Math Res Ctr, Univ Wis, 64-65; Math Asn Am Lectr, 65-72; NSF contract, 68-71; sabbatical leave, Univ Mich & Calif, Berkeley, 74 & vis fel, Australian Nat Univ, 81. *Mem:* AAAS; Am Math Soc; Math Asn Am. *Res:* Multiple Fourier and orthogonal series; bounded symmetric domains in space of several complex variables; solutions of partial differential equations. *Mailing Add:* Dept Math State Univ NY Ctr at Buffalo Diefendorf Hall Buffalo NY 14214

MITCHELL, KENNETH FRANK, b Hornchurch, Eng, Apr 18, 40; m 61; c 2. IMMUNOBIOLOGY. *Educ:* Heriot Watt Univ, BSc, 69; Univ Pa, PhD(immunol), 75. *Prof Exp:* Technician biochem, Animal Health Trust, Eng, 56-59; May & Baker, Eng, 59-62 & Brit Vitamin Prod Ltd, 62-66; instr, Univ Pa, 69-72, res specialist immunol, 72-75, fel immunol, 75-77, asst prof path, 77-81; asst prof, Wistar Inst, 78-82; STAFF SCIENTIST, E I DU PONT DE NEMOURS & CO, INC,, 82- *Mem:* Fel Royal Soc Arts; Brit Inst Biol. *Res:* Structure of human, normal & tumor cell antigens; structure of guinea pig normal and tumor antigens; immunobiology and immunogenetics of the laboratory rat; immunochemistry of receptors on T and B cells. *Mailing Add:* E I du Pont de Nemours & Co Inc 1007 Market St Wilmington DE 19898

MITCHELL, KENNETH JOHN, b Bralorne, BC, Sept 8, 38; m 68; c 2. FOREST MENSURATION. *Educ:* Univ BC, BSF, 61; Yale Univ, MF, 64, PhD(forest mensuration), 67. *Prof Exp:* Res officer forest mensuration, Can Forestry Serv, Govt of Can, 61-67, res scientist, 67-70; asst prof forest mgt, Yale Univ, 70-75; vis prof forestry, Univ BC, 75-76; assoc prof forest resources, Univ Idaho, 76-80; TECH ADV BIOMET, RES BR, BC MINISTRY OF FORESTS, 80- *Mem:* Soc Am Foresters; Can Inst Forestry. *Res:* Dynamics and simulated yield of Douglas Fir and lodge pole pine. *Mailing Add:* Res Br BC Ministry of Forests 1450 Government St Victoria BC V8W 3E7

MITCHELL, LANE, b Atlanta, Ga, July 14, 07; m 36; c 1. CERAMIC ENGINEERING. *Educ:* Ga Inst Technol, BS, 29; Univ Ill, MS, 31; Pa State Univ, PhD(ceramics), 41. *Prof Exp:* Asst clay prod, Univ Ill, 29-31 & Rutgers Univ, 31-32; teacher high sch, Ga, 32-34; asst geologist, State Geol Surv, 34-36; from asst prof to prof ceramic eng, 36-73, dir sch, 41-73, EMER DIR, GA INST TECHNOL, 73- *Honors & Awards:* Wilson Award, Am Ceramic Soc, 56. *Mem:* Fel Am Ceramic Soc; Nat Inst Ceramic Engrs. *Res:* Nature of clay; structure of hydroxylaptite; Georgia kaolins; electronics. *Mailing Add:* Sch of Ceramic Eng Ga Inst Technol Atlanta GA 30332

MITCHELL, LAWRENCE GUSTAVE, b West Chester, Pa, Oct 15, 42; div; c 2. ANIMAL PARASITOLOGY, PROTOZOOLOGY. *Educ:* Pa State Univ, BS, 64; Univ Mont, PhD(zool), 70. *Prof Exp:* NIH fel, Stella Duncan Mem Res Inst, Univ Mont, 70, asst prof zool, 70-71; asst prof zool & biol, 71-78, ASSOC PROF ZOOL, IOWA STATE UNIV, 78- *Concurrent Pos:* Instrnl sci equip prog grant, NSF, 74; coinvestr, NSF Comprehensive Assistance to Undergrad Sci Educ Prog grant, 76-79. *Mem:* Soc Protozoologists; AAAS; Am Soc Parasitologists; Wildlife Disease Asn; Am Inst Biol Sci. *Res:* Host-parasite relations and ecology of Myxozoa; pathology of parasitic infections in fishes. *Mailing Add:* Dept Zool Iowa State Univ Ames IA 50011

MITCHELL, MADELEINE ENID, b Jamaica, WI, Dec 14, 41. NUTRITION. *Educ:* McGill Univ, BSc, 63; Cornell Univ, MS, 65, PhD(nutrit), 68. *Prof Exp:* ASSOC PROF NUTRIT, WASH STATE UNIV, 69- *Mem:* Am Dietetic Asn; Nutrit Today Soc. *Res:* Protein and amino acid nutrition; carnitine; nutritional status of human subjects. *Mailing Add:* White Hall 308 Home Econ Res Ctr Wash State Univ Pullman WA 99164

MITCHELL, MALCOLM STUART, b New York, NY, May 6, 37; m 59, 76; c 3. ONCOLOGY, TUMOR IMMUNOLOGY. *Educ:* Harvard Univ, AB, 57; Yale Univ, MD, 62. *Prof Exp:* From instr to assoc prof med & pharmacol, Sch Med, Yale Univ, 68-78; PROF MED & MICROBIOL, SCH MED, UNIV SOUTHERN CALIF & DIR CLIN INVESTS & CHIEF MED ONCOL, UNIV SOUTHERN CALIF CANCER CTR, 78- *Concurrent Pos:* Ed, Int Encyclopedia Pharmacol & Therapeut, 75-, Yale J Biol & Med, 76-78 & J Immunol, 77-; assoc ed, J Immunopharmacol, 78-, Cancer Res, 80- & Cancer Invest, 81- *Mem:* Am Asn Immunologists; Am Soc Clin Invest; Am Asn Cancer Res; Am Soc Clin Oncol; Am Fedn Clin Res. *Res:* Modulation of immunity; cytophilic antibodies; macrophage-mediated immunity; cancer chemotherapy; clinical pharmacology of antineoplastic agents. *Mailing Add:* Univ Southern Calif Cancer Ctr 2025 Zonal Ave Los Angeles CA 90033

MITCHELL, MAURICE MCCLELLAN, JR, b Lansdowne, Pa, Nov 27, 29; m 52. PHYSICAL CHEMISTRY. *Educ:* Carnegie Inst Technol, BS, 51, MS, 57, PhD(phys chem), 60. *Prof Exp:* Group leader process chem group, Coal Coke & Coal Chem Div, Appl Res Lab, US Steel Corp, 51-56; asst, Carnegie Inst Technol, 56-58; sr technologist & group leader phys chem group, Coal Chem Div, Appl Res Lab, US Steel Corp, 60-61, actg head process chem sect, 61; supvr phys chem br, Res Div, Melpar, Inc, 61-64; group leader, Res & Develop Dept, Atlantic-Richfield Co, 64-73; dir res & develop, Houdry Div, 73-81, DIR RES & PLANNING ENG & SR RES SCIENTIST, ASHLAND OIL INC, 81- *Concurrent Pos:* Instr eve sch, Carnegie Inst Technol, 60-61; consult, Blaw-Knox Co, 52-53 & Melpar, Inc, 64-66; ed newsletter, Catalysis Soc, 70-77. *Mem:* AAAS; Am Chem Soc; Sigma Xi. *Res:* Chemical kinetics; heterogeneous and homogeneous catalysis; catalytic processes; preparation of catalysts; transition metal chemistry; coal chemistry. *Mailing Add:* Petrol Res & Develop Ashland Oil Inc PO Box 391 Ashland KY 41101

MITCHELL, MERLE, b Dallas, Tex, Apr 1, 21. MATHEMATICS. *Educ:* Southern Methodist Univ, BA, 42; Univ NMex, MA, 43; Peabody Col, PhD, 58. *Prof Exp:* Instr math, Univ NMex, 44-46; asst, Univ Wis, 46-48; instr, Arlington State Col, 48-49; instr, 49-58, from asst prof to assoc prof, 58-71, PROF MATH, UNIV NMEX, 71- *Mem:* Nat Coun Teachers Math. *Mailing Add:* Dept of Math Univ of NMex Albuquerque NM 87131

MITCHELL, MICHAEL A, b Austin, Tex, Dec 23, 41; m 65. PHYSICS. *Educ:* Univ Calif, Riverside, BA, 64; Univ Conn, MS, 66, PhD(physics), 70. *Prof Exp:* Res physicist, US Naval Ord Lab, 70-74, RES PHYSICIST, NAVAL SURFACE WEAPONS CTR, WHITE OAK LAB, 74- *Concurrent Pos:* Air Force Off Sci Res-Nat Res Coun fel, 70-72. *Mem:* AAAS; Am Phys Soc. *Res:* Transport and magnetic properties of metal alloys; transport properties and structure of metallic materials; amorphous metals. *Mailing Add:* Naval Surface Weapons Ctr White Oak Lab Code R32 Silver Spring MD 20910

MITCHELL, MICHAEL ROGER, b Detroit, Mich, Jan 24, 41; m 63; c 2. PHYSICAL METALLURGY. *Educ:* Lawrence Inst Technol, BS, 63; Wayne State Univ, MS, 69; Univ Ill, Urbana, PhD(theoret & appl mech), 76. *Prof Exp:* Design engr, Eng & Foundry Div, Ford Motor Co, Mich, 63-65, staff mem sci res, Metall Dept, 65-71; res & teaching asst, Univ Ill, Urbana, 71-76, vis asst prof metall eng, 76-77; mem tech staff, 77-79, MGR PHYS METALL, ROCKWELL INT SCI CTR, 79- *Concurrent Pos:* Consult, Deere & Co, Ill & Structural Dynamics Res Corp, Ohio, 76-77. *Honors & Awards:* Colwell Award, Soc Automotive Engrs, 75. *Mem:* Am Soc Testing & Mat; Sigma Xi. *Res:* Cyclic deformation and fracture behavior of materials; casting technology; laser surface alloying, slip mode changes cumulative fatigue damage analysis; hydrogen assisted fatigue crack initiation and propagation; threshold stress intensity leads; statistics of fatigue; environmental effects. *Mailing Add:* Rockwell Int Sci Ctr 1049 Camino Dos Rios Thousand Oaks CA 91360

MITCHELL, MYRON JAMES, b Denver, Colo, Apr 11, 47; m 73; c 1. ECOLOGY. *Educ:* Lake Forest Col, BA, 69; Univ Calgary, PhD(soil ecol), 74. *Prof Exp:* Res asst soil ecol, Cornell Univ, 69-70 & Univ Calgary, 70-74; Nat Res Coun Can fel math modelling, Univ BC, 74-75; asst prof invert zool & ecol energetics, 75-80, PROF INVERT ZOOL & POP BIOL, STATE UNIV NY COL ENVIRON SCI & FORESTRY, 80- *Mem:* Ecol Soc Am; AAAS; Acarological Soc Am; Brit Ecol Soc; Sigma Xi. *Res:* Study of floral-faunal interactions and how these interactions affect decomposition, mineral cycling, and energy transformation in terrestrial and aquatic ecosystems; sulfur dynamics. *Mailing Add:* Dept Environ & Forest Biol State Univ of NY Col of Environ Sci & Forestry Syracuse NY 13210

MITCHELL, NORMAN L, b Jamaica, WI, Nov 21, 28; m 68. PLANT PATHOLOGY. *Educ:* Univ London, BSc, 62; Univ Western Ont, PhD(bot), 67. *Prof Exp:* Instr biol, WI Col, Jamaica, 62-64; asst prof, 67-69, assoc prof, 69-81, PROF BIOL, LOMA LINDA UNIV, 81- *Mem:* AAAS; Bot Soc Am; Am Soc Microbiol. *Res:* Electron microscopic studies on powdery mildews mainly Sphaerotheca macularis of strawberry. *Mailing Add:* Dept of Biol Loma Linda Univ Riverside CA 92350

MITCHELL, OLGA MARY MRACEK, b Montreal, Que, Aug 5, 33; m 56; c 2. TELECOMMUNICATIONS. *Educ:* Univ Toronto, BA, 55, MA, 58, PhD(physics), 62; Pace Univ, MS, 82. *Prof Exp:* Res asst textile & metal physics, Ont Res Found, 55-57, res assoc metal physics, 62-63; mem tech staff & supvr, Bell Labs, 63-77; asst eng mgr, 77-80, DIST MGR, AM TEL & TEL CO, 80- *Mem:* Am Phys Soc; Acoust Soc Am. *Res:* Digital transmission systems; acoustics and signal processing; interaction of ultrasonic waves in crystals with dislocations, phonons, electrons; nuclear photodisintegration. *Mailing Add:* Am Tel & Tel Co Rm 3258C2 295 N Maple Ave Basking Ridge NJ 07920

MITCHELL, ORMOND GLENN, b Long Beach, Calif, Sept 17, 27. HUMAN ANATOMY, HISTOLOGY. *Educ:* San Diego State Univ, AB, 49; Univ Southern Calif, MS, 53, PhD(zool), 57. *Prof Exp:* Instr zool, Univ Southern Calif, 57; asst prof biol, Calif State Polytech Col, 57-62; res assoc, Univ Southern Calif, 62-63; from asst prof to assoc prof anat, Col Dent, NY Univ, 63-69; prof biol, Adelphi Univ, 69-71; assoc prof, 71-75, PROF ANAT, COL DENT, NY UNIV, 75- & CHMN DEPT, 71- *Mem:* AAAS; Am Soc Mammal; Int Asn Dent Res; NY Acad Sci; Harvey Soc. *Res:* Growth and development of skin and hair, glands and control of secretion. *Mailing Add:* Dept of Anat NY Univ Col Dent 421 First Ave New York NY 10010

MITCHELL, OWEN ROBERT, b Beaumont, Tex, July 4, 45; m 68; c 3. IMAGE PROCESSING, PATTERN RECOGNITION. *Educ:* Lamar Univ, BSEE, 67; Mass Inst Technol, SMEE, 68, PhD(elec eng), 72. *Prof Exp:* Asst prof, 72-78, ASSOC PROF ELEC ENG, PURDUE UNIV, 78- *Concurrent Pos:* Expert engr, White Sands Missle Range, 77 & 79; prin investr, Army Res Off, 81-82. *Mem:* Inst Elec & Electronics Engrs. *Res:* Digital image processing for bandwidth compression and information extraction; shape and texture analysis for computer vision systems used in inspection, cartography, and guidance. *Mailing Add:* Elec Eng Bldg Purdue Univ West Lafayette IN 47907

MITCHELL, RALPH, b Dublin, Ireland, Nov 26, 34; m 57; c 3. MICROBIOLOGY. *Educ:* Trinity Col, Dublin, BA, 56; Cornell Univ, MS, 59, PhD, 61. *Prof Exp:* Res assoc, Cornell Univ, 61-62; sr scientist, Weizmann Inst, 62-65; from asst prof to assoc prof appl microbiol, 65-70, GORDON McKAY PROF APPL BIOL, HARVARD UNIV, 70- *Mem:* Am Soc Microbiol; Brit Soc Gen Microbiol. *Res:* Microbial ecology; applied microbiology; microbial predator-prey systems; chemoreception in microorganisms; marine fouling, biological control of disease; microbial corrosion; water pollution; energy production. *Mailing Add:* Div of Appl Sci Harvard Univ Cambridge MA 02138

MITCHELL, RALPH GERALD, b Waltham, Mass, Sept 9, 25; m 52; c 4. DAIRY HUSBANDRY, GENETICS. *Educ:* Univ Mass, BS, 50; Univ Wis, MS, 54, PhD(dairy sci), 58. *Prof Exp:* Asst farm mgr, Univ Mass, 50-51, instr animal husb, 51-53; asst, Univ Wis, 53-57; from asst prof to assoc prof dairy sci, Univ WVa, 57-64; assoc prof, 64-69, PROF ANIMAL GENETICS, RUTGERS UNIV, NEW BRUNSWICK, 69- *Mem:* AAAS; Am Soc Animal Sci; Am Genetics Asn; Am Dairy Sci Asn. *Res:* Population genetics and animal breeding; dairy cattle; farm management. *Mailing Add:* Dept of Animal Sci Cook Col Rutgers Univ New Brunswick NJ 08903

MITCHELL, RALPH I, b Ashland, Ky, June 16, 25; m 45; c 3. CHEMICAL ENGINEERING. *Educ:* Ohio State Univ, BChE, 49, MS, 50, PhD(biomed eng), 71. *Prof Exp:* Chief chemist, Sheldrick Mfg Co, 50-52; assoc fel, 52-65, res adv, 65-72, sr scientist, 72-80, PROG MGR, COLUMBUS DIV, BATTELLE MEM INST, 80- *Mem:* Am Inst Chem Engrs; Am Soc Testing & Mat; Am Indust Hyg Asn. *Res:* Aerosol filtration; development of therapeutic aerosols; thermal deposition; lung retention of aerosols; inhalation toxicology; industrial hygiene; epidemiology. *Mailing Add:* Columbus Div Battelle Mem Inst 505 King Ave Columbus OH 43201

MITCHELL, REGINALD HARRY, b Woking, Eng, Sept 1, 43; Can citizen; m 65; c 2. ORGANIC CHEMISTRY, ENVIRONMENTAL CHEMISTRY. *Educ:* Univ Cambridge, BA, 65, PhD(chem), 68, MA, 69. *Prof Exp:* Res fel org chem, Fitzwilliam Col, Univ Cambridge, 67-68; res assoc, Univ Ore, 68-70; sr scientist, Formica Res Div, Eng, 70-71, mgr res & develop, 71-72; asst prof, 72-75, ASSOC PROF ORG CHEM, UNIV VICTORIA, BC, 75- *Concurrent Pos:* Fel, Univ Ore, 68-70; course tutor technol, Open Univ, Eng, 72; actg chmn, Dept Chem, Univ Victoria, 81-82. *Mem:* Am Chem Soc; Royal Soc Chem; Chem Inst Can. *Res:* Synthesis of novel aromatic hydrocarbons; new synthetic reactions; hydrocarbons and pesticides in the environment; synthesis and transformations. *Mailing Add:* Dept Chem Univ Victoria Victoria BC V8W 2Y2 Can

MITCHELL, RICHARD LEE, b Cleveland, Ohio, Sept 23, 38; m 63; c 3. ELECTRICAL ENGINEERING. *Educ:* Purdue Univ, BS, 60, MS, 61, PhD(elec eng), 64. *Prof Exp:* Sect head elec eng, Aerospace Corp, 64-68; sr scientist, Technol Serv Corp, 68-74; VPRES, MARK RESOURCES INC, 74- *Mem:* Inst Elec & Electronics Engrs. *Res:* Radar system analysis and simulation; signal processing. *Mailing Add:* Mark Resources Inc 4676 Admiralty Way Suite 303 Marina del Rey CA 90291

MITCHELL, RICHARD SCOTT, b Longmont, Colo, Jan 28, 29. MINERALOGY, CRYSTALLOGRAPHY. *Educ:* Univ Mich, BS, 50, MS, 51, PhD(mineral), 56. *Prof Exp:* From asst prof to assoc prof geol, 53-63, prof, 63-69, chmn dept, 64-69, PROF ENVIRON SCI, UNIV VA, 69- *Concurrent Pos:* Exec ed, Rocks & Minerals mag, 76- *Mem:* AAAS; fel Mineral Soc Am; fel Geol Soc Am; Sigma Xi; Mineral Asn Can. *Res:* Morphology and crystal structures of inorganic compounds; structural polytypism; metamict state; mineralogy of coal ash. *Mailing Add:* Dept of Environ Sci Clark Hall Univ of Va Charlottesville VA 22903

MITCHELL, RICHARD SIBLEY, b Barnsdall, Okla, Sept 19, 32; m 59; c 4. ANALYTICAL CHEMISTRY. *Educ:* Austin Col, AB, 58; Univ Okla, MS, 63, PhD(chem), 64. *Prof Exp:* Res chemist, Lion Oil Co Div, Monsanto Chem Co, 57 & 59-61; from asst prof to assoc prof chem, 64-71, PROF CHEM, ARK STATE UNIV, 71- *Mem:* Am Chem Soc. *Res:* Gas chromatography and electroanalytical methods. *Mailing Add:* Box 700 Dept Chem Ark State Univ State University AR 72467

MITCHELL, RICHARD WARREN, b Lynchburg, Va, Aug 15, 23; m 45 & 62; c 3. PHYSICS. *Educ:* Lynchburg Col, BS, 44; Agr & Mech Col, Tex, MS, 53, PhD(physics), 60. *Prof Exp:* Instr math & physics, Lynchburg Col, 45-47; from instr to asst prof physics, Agr & Mech Col, Tex, 47-62, res assoc, Res Found, 54-60; ASSOC PROF PHYSICS, UNIV S FLA, 62- *Mem:* Am Asn Physics Teachers. *Res:* Raman and infrared spectroscopy; nuclear magnetic resonance studies relating relaxation times of protons to physical properties of solutions. *Mailing Add:* Dept of Physics Univ of S Fla Tampa FL 33620

MITCHELL, ROBERT A, b Oakland, Calif, Sept 11, 22; m 51; c 4. PHYSIOLOGY. *Educ:* Univ Calif, Berkeley, BS, 47; Creighton Univ, MS, 52, MD, 53. *Prof Exp:* Intern Hosp, Univ Nebr, 53-54, resident internal med, 54-55; resident, Hosp, 55-57, asst res physician, Univ, 59-61, from instr to assoc prof med, 60-74, PROF PHYSIOL & MED, UNIV CALIF, SAN FRANCISCO, 74-, ASSOC STAFF MEM, UNIV CALIF HOSP, 60- *Concurrent Pos:* Bank of Am Giannini fel pulmonary physiol, Cardiovasc Res Inst, Univ Calif, San Francisco, 57-59; USPHS res career develop award, 63- *Mem:* Am Physiol Soc. *Res:* Regulation of respiration; chemoreceptors. *Mailing Add:* 338 Marietta Dr San Francisco CA 94127

MITCHELL, ROBERT ALEXANDER, b Belfast, Northern Ireland, Apr 3, 35. BIOCHEMISTRY. *Educ:* Queen's Univ Belfast, BSc, 55, PhD(chem), 60. *Prof Exp:* Teacher chem, Col Technol, Belfast, 57-60; asst prof, 65-72, ASSOC PROF BIOCHEM, WAYNE STATE UNIV, 72- *Concurrent Pos:* Fel biochem, Okla State Univ, 60-62, Univ Minn, 63 & Univ Calif, Los Angeles, 63-65. *Mem:* Am Chem Soc; Biophys Soc; Am Soc Biol Chem. *Res:* Mitochondrial energy metabolism; enzyme kinetics; use of substrate analogs to study enzyme catalysis and regulation; metabolic alterations in Reye's Syndrome. *Mailing Add:* Dept of Biochem Wayne State Univ Sch of Med Detroit MI 48201

MITCHELL, ROBERT BRUCE, b Rochester, Pa, Sept 24, 42; m 65; c 1. PHYSIOLOGY. *Educ:* Denison Univ, BS, 64; Ohio Univ, MS, 66; Pa State Univ, PhD(physiol), 69. *Prof Exp:* ASSOC PROF BIOL, PA STATE UNIV, 69- *Mem:* AAAS; Geront Soc. *Res:* Quantitative histochemistry; cytophotometric and interferometric analyses of nucleic acids and protein in aging cells biology of aging. *Mailing Add:* 208 Mueller Lab Pa State Univ University Park PA 16802

MITCHELL, ROBERT CURTIS, b Ft Dodge, Iowa, Mar 29, 28; m 49; c 3. ASTROPHYSICS. *Educ:* NMex State Univ, BS, 49, PhD(physics), 66; Univ Wash, MS, 52. *Prof Exp:* Physicist ultrasonics, Anderson Labs, West Hartford, Conn, 52-53; physicist atmosphere, Univ Conn, 53; solar observer, Harvard Col Observ, 53-54; teacher math & sci, Colo Rocky Mountain Sch, 54-56 & Gadsden High Sch, Anthony, NMex, 56-62; INSTR PHYSICS, CENT WASH UNIV, 66-, CHMN DEPT GEOL & PHYSICS, 78- *Mem:* Am Asn Physics Teachers; Am Asn Variable Star Observers. *Res:* Photometry and photography of variable stars. *Mailing Add:* Dept of Geol & Physics Cent Wash Univ Ellensburg WA 98926

MITCHELL, ROBERT DALTON, b Bellingham, Wash, June 2, 23; m 45; c 3. MEDICINE. *Educ:* La Sierra Col, BS, 44; Col Med Evangelists, MD, 47, MSc, 60; Am Bd Internal Med, dipl & cert gastroenterol. *Prof Exp:* Asst clin prof, 56-64, asst prof, 64-66, ASSOC PROF MED, SCH MED, LOMA LINDA UNIV, 66- *Mem:* AMA; fel Am Col Physicians; Am Gastroenterol Asn. *Res:* Gastroenterology. *Mailing Add:* Loma Linda Univ Med Ctr Loma Linda CA 92354

MITCHELL, ROBERT L(YNNE), b Floresville, Tex, Oct, 25, 23; m 52; c 3. CHEMICAL ENGINEERING. *Educ:* Tex Col Arts & Industs, BS, 43; Mass Inst Technol, SM, 47. *Prof Exp:* Pilot plant engr, Celanese Corp Am, 47-49, group leader, 49-52, chief chem engr, 52-55, dir eng res, 55-57, dir tech & econ eval dept, 57-60; vpres planning, 60-64, vpres com develop & int, 64-66, vpres tech & mfg, 66-67, vpres & mgr, 67-69, exec vpres, 67-71, pres, 71-76, exec vpres, 76-80, VCHMN, CELANESE CORP, 80- *Mem:* Am Chem Soc; Am Inst Chem Eng. *Res:* Hydrocarbon oxidation; petrochemicals. *Mailing Add:* Celanese Corp 1211 Ave of the Americas New York NY 10036

MITCHELL, ROBERT W, b Wellington, Tex, Apr 25, 33; m 54; c 3. BIOSPELEOLOGY, ECOLOGY. *Educ:* Tex Tech Col, BS, 54, MS, 55; Univ Tex, PhD(zool), 65. *Prof Exp:* From instr to asst prof biol, Lamar State Col, 57-61; from asst prof to assoc prof, 65-74, PROF BIOL SCI, TEX TECH

UNIV, 74- *Mem:* Soc Study Evolution; Nat Speleol Soc; Ecol Soc Am. *Res:* Distributional, ecological and evolutionary study of cave dwelling animals, particularly invertebrates. *Mailing Add:* Dept of Biol Sci Tex Tech Univ Lubbock TX 79409

MITCHELL, RODGER (DAVID), b Wheaton, Ill, July 22, 26. POPULATION BIOLOGY. *Educ:* Univ Mich, PhD(zool), 54. *Prof Exp:* Instr zool, Univ Vt, 54-57; asst prof biol, Univ Fla, 57-61, assoc prof zool, 61-69; PROF ZOOL, OHIO STATE UNIV, 69- *Concurrent Pos:* NSF fac fel, Univ Calif, Berkeley, 59-60; Fulbright res fel, Ibaraki Univ, Japan, 65-66; Fulbright prof, Univ Agr Sci, Bangalore, India, 76-77. *Mem:* AAAS; Am Micros Soc; Ecol Soc Am; Soc Study Evolution; Am Soc Naturalists. *Res:* Morphology and biology of water mites; population biology; analysis of agro-ecosystems. *Mailing Add:* Fac of Zool Ohio State Univ Columbus OH 43210

MITCHELL, ROGER HAROLD, b Englewood, NJ, Nov 27, 46; m 71; c 2. EXPERIMENTAL PATHOLOGY, IMMUNOPATHOLOGY. *Educ:* Lafayette Col, AB, 68; Med Col Va, PhD(exp path), 76. *Prof Exp:* Res staff mem, Dept Microbiol & Immunol, Bowman Gray Sch Med, Wake Forest Univ, 76-78; RES ASSOC, TUMOR-HOST SECT, BIOMED DIV, SAMUEL ROBERTS NOBLE FOUND, 78- *Concurrent Pos:* Res grant, Dept Microbiol & Immunol, Bowman Gray Sch Med, Wake Forest Univ, 77-78. *Mem:* Reticuloendothelial Soc; Soc Exp Biol & Med; Sigma Xi. *Res:* Immunological and pathological mechanisms involved in host defenses against carcinogenesis; immunopathology of infectious diseases; leukocytic endogenous mediator; endogenous pyrogen. *Mailing Add:* Tumor-Host Sect Biomed Div Noble Foundation Rte 1 Ardmore OK 73401

MITCHELL, ROGER L, b Grinnell, Iowa, Sept 13, 32; m 55; c 4. AGRONOMY, CROP PHYSIOLOGY. *Educ:* Iowa State Univ, BS, 54, PhD(agron), 61; Cornell Univ, MS, 58. *Prof Exp:* From asst prof to prof agron, Iowa State Univ, 61-69; chmn dept agron, Univ Mo-Columbia, 69-72, dean exten div, 72-75; vpres agr, Kans State Univ, 75-80; CHMN, DEPT AGRON, UNIV MO-COLUMBIA, 81- *Concurrent Pos:* Prof in chg farm oper curriculum, 62-66; Am Coun Educ acad admin intern, Univ Calif, Irvine, 66-67. *Mem:* Fel AAAS; fel Am Soc Agron (pres-elect, 78-79, pres, 79-80, past pres, 80-81); Crop Sci Soc Am (pres, 75-76). *Res:* Soybean physiology; rooting patterns under field conditions; sorghum physiology. *Mailing Add:* 135 Mumford Hall Univ Mo Columbia MO 65211

MITCHELL, ROGER W, b Ft Worth, Tex, Oct 20, 37; m 59; c 2. MATHEMATICS. *Educ:* Hendrix Col, AB, 59; Southern Methodist Univ, MS, 61; NMex State Univ, PhD(math), 64. *Prof Exp:* From asst prof to assoc prof, 64-77, PROF MATH, UNIV TEX, ARLINGTON, 77- *Mem:* Am Math Soc; Math Asn Am; Soc Indust & Appl Math; Nat Coun Teachers Math. *Res:* Infinite Abelian groups; algebra. *Mailing Add:* Dept Math Univ Tex Arlington TX 76019

MITCHELL, ROY ERNEST, b Ft Worth, Tex, Aug 27, 36; m 58; c 1. INORGANIC CHEMISTRY, ENOLOGY. *Educ:* Tex A&M Univ, BS, 58; Purdue Univ, PhD(inorg chem), 64. *Prof Exp:* Fel, Tex A&M Univ, 64-65; asst prof chem, Purdue Univ, 65-66; asst prof, 66-79, ASSOC PROF CHEM, TEX TECH UNIV, 79- *Mem:* Am Chem Soc; Am Soc Enologists. *Res:* Vinification procedures for Texas grapes; buffer nature of wine; wine analysis. *Mailing Add:* Dept of Chem Tex Tech Univ Lubbock TX 79409

MITCHELL, STEPHEN AMES, b New York City, NY, Aug 17, 51; m 77. ALGEBRAIC TOPOLOGY. *Educ:* Univ Wash, PhD(math), 81. *Prof Exp:* MOORE INSTR MATH, MASS INST TECHNOL, 81- *Mem:* Am Math Soc. *Mailing Add:* Math Dept Mass Inst Technol Cambridge MA 02139

MITCHELL, STEPHEN KEITH, b Houston, Tex, Aug 15, 42; m 75; c 1. UNDERWATER ACOUSTICS. *Educ:* Univ Tex, BS, 64, MA, 66, PhD(physics), 76. *Prof Exp:* RES SCIENTIST ASSOC, APPL RES LABS, UNIV TEX, 64- *Mem:* Acoust Soc Am; Sigma Xi. *Res:* Ocean acoustics, particularly measurement and analysis of ocean acoustic parameters and signal propagation modeling and measurements. *Mailing Add:* Appl Res Labs Univ Tex Box 8029 Austin TX 78712

MITCHELL, T(HOMAS) A(LVA), JR, b Copperhill, Tenn, Oct 16, 20; div; c 3. MECHANICAL ENGINEERING. *Educ:* Mass Inst Technol, BSME, 43. *Prof Exp:* Tech supvr, Clinton Eng Works, 43-45; engr, 46-52, sr res mech engr, 53-62, supt res eng & maintenance, 63-66, supt mech eng res, 66, SR RES ASSOC, RES LABS, EASTMAN CHEM DIV, EASTMAN KODAK CO, 67- *Mem:* Am Soc Mech Engrs; NY Acad Sci; AAAS. *Res:* Mechanical engineering research for development and product of fibers, plastics and chemicals. *Mailing Add:* Res Labs Eastman Chem Div Kingsport TN 37662

MITCHELL, TERENCE E, b Haywards Heath, Eng, May 18, 37; m 61; c 2. PHYSICAL METALLURGY, CERAMICS. *Educ:* Univ Cambridge, BA, 58, MA & PhD(physics), 62. *Prof Exp:* Fel physics, Cavendish Lab, Univ Cambridge, 61-63; from asst prof to assoc prof metall, 63-75, PROF METALL, CASE WESTERN RESERVE UNIV, 75-, DIR, HIGH VOLTAGE ELECTRON MICROSCOPE, 69- *Concurrent Pos:* Vis scientist, Stanford Univ & Ames Lab, NASA, 75-76; chmn, High-Voltage Electron Micros-Tandem Steering Comt, Argonne Nat Lab, 80-; grantee, US Air Force Off Sci Res, 65-70, 74-, NSF, 66-, Dept Energy, 70-, US Army Res Off, 70-75, 79- & NASA, 74-77, 81- *Mem:* Am Inst Mech Engrs; Am Ceramics Soc; Am Soc Testing & Mat; Electron Micros Soc Am. *Res:* Mechanical properties of metals and alloys; work-hardening; dislocation theory; elasticity; electron microscopy; internal friction; deformation and phase transformation in ceramics; radiation damage and nuclear materials; oxidation and passivation of metals. *Mailing Add:* Dept of Metall & Mat Sci University Circle Cleveland OH 44106

MITCHELL, THEODORE, b Chicago, Ill, Apr 30, 26; m 57; c 2. ABSRACT HARMONIC ANALYSIS. *Educ:* Ill Inst Technol, BS, 51, MS, 57, PhD(math), 64. *Prof Exp:* Jr mathematician inst air weapons res, Univ Chicago, 52-54, mathematician, 54-58, sr staff mem labs appl sci, 59-62; staff mathematician, Weapons Systs Eval Group, Inst Defense Anal, 58-59; sr mathematician, Acad Intersci Methodology, 63-64; lectr math, State Univ NY Buffalo, 64-65, assoc prof, 65-67; assoc prof, 67-69, PROF MATH, TEMPLE UNIV, 69- *Mem:* AAAS; Am Math Soc; Opers Res Soc Am; Math Asn Am. *Res:* Functional analysis; invariant means; fixed point theorems; game theory; probability theory. *Mailing Add:* Dept Math TU-038-16 Temple Univ Philadelphia PA 19122

MITCHELL, THOMAS F, SR, b Milwaukee, Wis, July 27, 23; m 46; c 6. PROTEIN CHEMISTRY. *Educ:* Marquette Univ, BS, 49. *Prof Exp:* Chemist, Bio-Process Co, 50-55; sr res chemist, Lakeside Labs, 55-62; consult protein synthesis, Toni Co, 62-63, res chemist, 63-64; res chemist, 64-67, asst dir res, 67-68, DIR RES, GLUE DIV, DARLING & CO, 68- *Mem:* Am Chem Soc; Am Inst Chem; Tech Asn Pulp & Paper Indust; Forest Prod Res Soc; Am Soc Testing & Mat. *Res:* Collagen-proteins and aliphatic amines and their reaction products; vegetable proteins; natural polymer extractions. *Mailing Add:* Darling & Co 4650 S Racine Chicago IL 60609

MITCHELL, THOMAS GEORGE, b Philadelphia, Pa, Feb 27, 27; m 46; c 6. PHYSIOLOGY, NUCLEAR MEDICINE. *Educ:* St Joseph's Col, Pa, BS, 50; Univ Rochester, MS, 56; Georgetown Univ, PhD(physiol), 63; Am Bd Radiol, dipl, 58. *Prof Exp:* Med Serv Corpsman, US Navy, 50-69, asst supvr radioisotope lab, Naval Hosp, St Albans, NY, 51-55, med nuclear physicist, Bethesda Naval Hosp, Md, 56-60, physiologist & med nuclear physicist, Naval Med Res Unit 2, Taipei, Taiwan, 63-65, med nuclear physicist, Radiation Exposure Eval Lab, Naval Hosp, 65-69; assoc prof radiol sci, Sch Hyg & Pub Health, Johns Hopkins Univ, 69-74; DIR RADIATION CONTROL, ASSOC PROF PHYSIOL & BIOPHYS & ASSOC PROF RADIOL, MED CTR, GEORGETOWN UNIV, 74- *Concurrent Pos:* Lectr, Naval Med Sch, Bethesda, 56-63 & 65-; adj acad staff, Children's Hosp, DC, 59-63; lectr, Sch Hyg & Pub Health, Johns Hopkins Univ, 65-70; instr, Sch Med & Dent, Georgetown Univ, 65-69; consult, Naval Med Res Inst, 65-70. *Mem:* Am Col Radiol; Soc Nuclear Med; Health Physics Soc; Am Asn Physicists in Med. *Res:* Medical nuclear physics; clinical applications of radioisotopes; regional blood flow. *Mailing Add:* 3605 Dustin Rd Burtonsville MD 20730

MITCHELL, THOMAS GREENFIELD, b New York, NY, Mar 30, 41; div; c 2. MICROBIOLOGY, IMMUNOLOGY. *Educ:* NTex State Univ, BA, 63; Tulane Univ, PhD(microbiol & immunol), 71. *Prof Exp:* Res assoc, Microbiol Dept, La State Univ Med Ctr, La State Univ, 71-72; res specialist pediat, Univ Minn, 72-74; asst prof, 74-80, ASSOC PROF MED MYCOL, DUKE UNIV MED CTR, 80-, DIR CLIN MYCOL LAB & SEROL LAB, HOSP, 74- *Concurrent Pos:* Prin investr, Minn Med Found res grant, 72-73 & Nat Inst Allergy & Infectious Dis res grant, 76-; co-investr, Univ Minn res grant, 73-74 & Nat Inst Allergy & Infectious Dis res grant, 74-77; prin investr, res grants, Nat Inst Allergy & Infectious Dis, 76-79. *Mem:* Am Soc Microbiol; Med Mycol Soc Am; Sigma Xi; Int Soc Animal Human Mycol. *Res:* Host defense mechanisms against mycotic infections; fungal morphogenesis; serodiagnosis of fungal disease. *Mailing Add:* Dept of Microbiol & Immunol Box 3803 Duke Univ Med Ctr Durham NC 27710

MITCHELL, THOMAS OWEN, b New York, NY, Oct 18, 44; m 77. ORGANIC CHEMISTRY, PETROLEUM CHEMISTRY. *Educ:* Trinity Col, Conn, BS, 66; Northwestern Univ, Ill, PhD(org chem), 70. *Prof Exp:* Res chemist, 70-73, SR RES CHEMIST, MOBIL RES & DEVELOP CORP, 73- *Mem:* Am Chem Soc. *Res:* Catalysis in petrochemistry; catalytic chemistry; organosilicon chemistry; coal chemistry and conversion. *Mailing Add:* Mobil Res & Develop Corp PO Box 1025 Princeton NJ 08540

MITCHELL, TOM M, US citizen. EXPERT SYSTEMS, MACHINE LEARNING. *Educ:* Mass Inst Technol, BS, 73; Stanford Univ, MS, 75, PhD(elec eng & comput sci), 78. *Prof Exp:* asst prof, 78-82, ASSOC PROF COMPUT SCI, RUTGERS UNIV, 80- *Concurrent Pos:* Consult, Defense Res Estab Atlantic, Halifax, Nova Scotia, 80-81; prin investr, Improving Problem Solving Strategies by Exp, NSF, 80- & Automating Expertise Digital Syst Design. *Mem:* Inst Elec & Electronic Engrs; Asn Comput Mach. *Res:* Applications of artificial intelligence and expert systems; artificial intelligence approaches to problems in curcuit design and medicine; automated improvement of problem-solving strategies through practice. *Mailing Add:* Comput Sci Dept Hill Ctr Rutgers Univ New Brunswick NJ 08903

MITCHELL, VAL LEONARD, b Salt Lake City, Utah, Sept 9, 38; m 61; c 4. CLIMATOLOGY. *Educ:* Univ Utah, BS, 64; Univ Wis-Madison, MS, 67, PhD(meteorol), 69. *Prof Exp:* Res asst meteorol, Univ Wis-Madison, 64-69; from asst prof to assoc prof earth sci, Mont State Univ, 69-74; asst prof meteorol, Univ Wis-Madison, 74-78; STATE CLIMATOLOGIST, WIS GEOL & NATURAL HIST SURV, UNIV WIS-EXTEN, 74-, ASSOC PROF METEOROL, UNIV WIS-MADISON, 78- *Mem:* Am Meteorol Soc; Asn Am Geogr. *Res:* Applied climatology; interaction between the atmosphere and the biosphere; climatology of mountainous regions. *Mailing Add:* Dept of Meteorol Univ of Wis Madison WI 53706

MITCHELL, WALLACE CLARK, b Ames, Iowa, Nov 12, 20; m 58; c 3. ENTOMOLOGY. *Educ:* Iowa State Col, BS, 47, PhD(zool, entom), 55. *Prof Exp:* Sr engr aide & entomologist malaria control in war areas, USPHS, Fla, 42-43; asst to state entomologist, Nursery Inspection, State Dept Agr, Iowa, 47-49; instr zool & entom & asst entom, Agr Exp Sta, Univ Hawaii, 49-53; field entomologist midwestern area, Geigy Agr Chem Inc, 53-54; asst prof zool & entom, SDak State Col, 55-56; entomologist fruit insect sect, Agr Res Serv, USDA, 56-62; assoc prof entom & assoc entomologist, 62-69, actg dir, Hawaii Agr Exp Sta, 69-70, prof entom, chmn dept & entomologist, 68-77, actg dean, Col Trop Agr, 75-76, actg assoc dean, Col Trop Agr & Human Resources, 80-82, PROF ENTOM, UNIV HAWAII, 78- *Mem:* Entom Soc

Am; Am Registry Cert Entomologists. *Res:* Economic entomology; field evaluation of fruit fly lures, attractants, insecticide sprays, sterilization and eradication procedures for control of fruit and vegetable insects; tropical economic entomology; insect behavior, pest management; insect ecology. *Mailing Add:* Dept Entomol Col Trop Agr Univ Hawaii Honolulu HI 96822

MITCHELL, WALTER EDMUND, JR, b Franklin, Mass, Nov 16, 25. ASTRONOMY. *Educ:* Tufts Univ, BS, 49; Univ Va, MS, 51; Univ Mich, PhD, 58. *Prof Exp:* Asst astron, Univ Mich, 51-52, observer infrared proj, Mt Wilson Observ, 53-55; vis asst prof astron, Brown Univ, 56-57; from instr to assoc prof, 57-69, PROF ASTRON, OHIO STATE UNIV, 69- *Mem:* Am Astron Soc; Royal Astron Soc. *Res:* Solar spectroscopy. *Mailing Add:* Dept Astron Ohio State Univ Columbus OH 43210

MITCHELL, WILLIAM ALEXANDER, b Raymond, Minn, Oct 21, 11; m 38; c 7. FOOD SCIENCE, CARBOHYDRATE CHEMISTRY. *Educ:* Nebr Wesleyan Univ, BA, 35; Univ Nebr, MS, 38. *Hon Degrees:* DrSci, Nebr Wesleyan Univ, 80. *Prof Exp:* Teacher high sch, Nebr, 35-36; asst chem, Univ Nebr, 37-38; org res chemist, Eastman Kodak Co, NY, 38-41; head biochem sect, Gen Foods Corp, 41-53, head biocolloids sect, 53-56, sect head chem res, 56-62, res specialist, 62-68, sr res specialist, 68-76; FOOD CONSULT, 76- *Mem:* Am Chem Soc. *Res:* Synthetic organic biochemistry; wheat flour; starch; proteins; fats and oils; emulsifiers; gas reactions; enzymes; gelatin; food processing and products; sugars; pectins; gums; colloid chemistry; coffee; food flavors; cake mixes; eggs; carbonation systems; Kodachrome couplers. *Mailing Add:* 175 Jacksonville Rd Lincoln Park NJ 07035

MITCHELL, WILLIAM COBBEY, b Rochester, NY, Aug 2, 39; m 62; c 4. SOLID STATE PHYSICS, ENERGY CONVERSION. *Educ:* Oberlin Col, AB, 61; Wash Univ, PhD(physics), 67. *Prof Exp:* Sr res physicist, 3M Co, 67-69; Nat Bur Standards-Nat Res Coun fel, Nat Bur Standards, 69-71; consult, Thermoelec Syst Sect, 71-72, sr res physicist, 72-75, res specialist, 75-76, mat res supvr, 76-78, MGR, 3M CO, 79- *Mem:* Am Phys Soc. *Res:* Non-equilibrium statistical mechanics; solid state transport theory; thermoelectric materials; energy storage. *Mailing Add:* Elec Prod Group Bldg 260-5B 3M Ctr St Paul MN 55144

MITCHELL, WILLIAM H, b Acworth, NH, Dec 12, 21; m 46; c 2. AGRONOMY, BOTANY. *Educ:* Univ NH, BS, 46, MS, 49; Pa State Univ, PhD(agron, bot), 60. *Prof Exp:* Headmaster & teacher high sch, NH, 45-47; from asst res prof to assoc res prof agron, 49-71, PROF PLANT SCI, UNIV DEL, 71- *Concurrent Pos:* Dir, Int Coop Improv Asn, 53-66; chmn collabrs regional pasture res lab, Pa State Univ, 60-66; tech comt, Northeastern Regional Res Group, 66-68; mem, Am Grassland Coun. *Mem:* Soil Sci Soc Am; Am Soc Agron; Crop Sci Soc Am. *Res:* Management of forage crops and turf; soil fertility. *Mailing Add:* Dept of Plant Sci Univ of Del Newark DE 19711

MITCHELL, WILLIAM JOHN, b Minneapolis, Minn. SET THEORY. *Educ:* Univ Wis, BA, 65; Berkeley Sch, PhD(math), 70. *Prof Exp:* Instr math, Univ Chicago, 70-72; asst prof math, Rockefeller Univ, 72-77; mem staff math, Inst Advan Studies in Humanities, New York, 77-78; ASSOC PROF MATH, PA STATE UNIV, 79- *Res:* Inner models for large cardinals. *Mailing Add:* Dept Math Pa State Univ State College PA 16802

MITCHELL, WILLIAM MARVIN, b Atlanta, Ga, Mar 3, 35; m 59; c 3. PATHOLOGY, ONCOLOGY. *Educ:* Vanderbilt Univ, BA, 57, MD, 60; Johns Hopkins Univ, PhD(biol, biochem), 66. *Prof Exp:* Mem house staff med, Johns Hopkins Hosp, 60-61; from asst prof to assoc prof microbiol, 66-74, asst prof med, 69-77, assoc prof, 74-78, PROF PATH, VANDERBILT UNIV, 78- *Concurrent Pos:* USPHS fel biol, McCullom-Pratt Inst, Johns Hopkins Univ, 61-66; USPHS grant & Vanderbilt Inst award, 66-67; planning dir, Vanderbilt Cancer Ctr, 71-73; Nat Inst Arthritis & Metab Dis grant, 66-81; Nat Cancer Inst grant, 71-73; staff physician, Vet Admin Hosp, 66-67; consult, NIH, 71-; vis prof, Inst Anat Path, Univ Lausanne, 76-77; Eleanor Roosevelt Int Cancer fel, 76-77. *Mem:* AAAS; Am Asn Pathologists; Int Acad Path; Am Asn Cancer Res; AMA. *Res:* Structure and function of proteins, including cell collagen, proteolytic enzymes and bacterial exotoxins; oncology, including cell control mechanisms and oncogenic virology; macromolecular chemistry; protein structure-function; molecular pathology. *Mailing Add:* Vanderbilt Hosp 1211 22nd Ave S Nashville TN 37212

MITCHELL, WILLIAM WARREN, b Butte, Mont, Mar 10, 23; m 55; c 2. AGRONOMY, BOTANY. *Educ:* Univ Mont, BA, 57, MA, 58; Iowa State Univ, PhD(bot), 62. *Prof Exp:* Instr biol sci, Western Mont Col, 58-59; asst prof, Chadron State Col, 62-63; PROF AGRON & HEAD DEPT, INST AGR SCI, UNIV ALASKA, 63- *Mem:* Am Soc Plant Taxon; Sigma Xi; Soc Range Mgt; Am Agron Soc; Am Forage & Grassland Coun. *Res:* Applications of introduced and indigenous grass taxa; varietal selection and development of grasses; revegetation; biosystematics of grasses. *Mailing Add:* Agr Exp Sta Box AE Palmer AK 99645

MITCHEM, JOHN ALAN, b Sterling, Colo, July 28, 40; m 62; c 2. MATHEMATICS. *Educ:* Univ Nebr, Lincoln, BS, 62; Western Mich Univ, MA, 67, PhD(math), 70. *Prof Exp:* Asst prof math, 70-72, assoc prof, 72-77, PROF & CHMN MATH, SAN JOSE STATE UNIV, 77- *Mem:* Math Asn Am; Am Math Soc. *Res:* Graph theory, especially partioning problems. *Mailing Add:* Dept of Math San Jose State Univ San Jose CA 95192

MITCHEN, JOEL RAMON, immunology, cancer, see previous edition

MITCHNER, HYMAN, b Vancouver, BC, Nov 23, 30; m 53; c 4. PHARMACEUTICAL CHEMISTRY. *Educ:* Univ BC, BA, 51, MSc, 53; Univ Wis, Madison, PhD(pharmaceut chem), 56. *Prof Exp:* Asst prof pharmaceut chem, Sch Pharm, Univ Wis, Madison, 56-59; group leader anal res, Miles Lab, 59-61, sect head, 61-63; dir qual control, Barnes-Hind Labs, 63-66; dir, 66-69, vpres qual control, 69-78, VPRES QUAL ASSURANCE & TECH SERV, SYNTEX LABS INC, 78- *Mem:* Am Pharmaceut Asn; Am Chem Soc; Am Soc Qual Control; fel Acad Pharmaceut Sci. *Res:* Analytical research on drug products; physical chemical studies in drug systems. *Mailing Add:* Qual Assurance & Tech Serv Div Syntex Corp 3401 Hillview St Palo Alto CA 94302

MITCHNER, MORTON, b Vancouver, BC, Jan 17, 26; US citizen; m 60; c 2. MAGNETOHYDRODYNAMICS. *Educ:* Univ BC, BA, 47, MA, 48; Harvard Univ, PhD(physics), 52. *Prof Exp:* Sheldon traveling fel, Harvard Univ, 52-53, res fel appl sci, 53-54; staff mem opers res, Arthur D Little, Inc, 54-58; staff scientist, Lockheed Missiles & Space Co, 58-63; vis lectr mech eng, 63-64, assoc prof, 64-69, PROF MECH ENG, STANFORD UNIV, 69- *Concurrent Pos:* Vis prof eng sci, Columbia Univ, 61-62; consult, United Tech Ctr, United Aircraft Corp, 65-68; mem & chmn steering comt, Eng Appln Magnetohydrodynamics, 67-; consult, Nat Comt Nuclear Energy, Italy, 70-71. *Mem:* Am Phys Soc; Am Inst Aeronaut & Astronaut; Opers Res Soc Am. *Res:* High temperature gas dynamics; plasma physics; magnetohydrodynamics; kinetic theory; turbulence; combustion aerodynamics; energy conversion; operations research; electrostatic precipitation. *Mailing Add:* Dept of Mech Eng Stanford Univ Stanford CA 94305

MITCHUM, RONALD KEM, b Elk City, Okla, Dec 2, 46; m 65; c 2. MASS SPECTROMETRY. *Educ:* Southwestern Okla State Univ, BS, 68; Okla State Univ, PhD(chem), 73. *Prof Exp:* Fel mass spectrometry, Univ Houston, 72-74 & Univ Warwick, 74-75; fel mass spectrometry, Univ Nebr-Lincoln, 75-76; RES CHEMIST, NAT CTR TOXICOL RES, HEW/FOOD & DRUG ADMIN, 76- *Mem:* Am Chem Soc; AAAS; Am Soc Mass Spectrometry. *Res:* Atmospheric pressure, field desorption and development of analytical methodology for the analysis of toxicants in environmental media. *Mailing Add:* Dept of Chem Nat Ctr for Toxicol Res Jefferson AR 72079

MITESCU, CATALIN DAN, b Bucharest, Romania, May 2, 38; Can citizen; m 72; c 3. PHYSICS. *Educ:* McGill Univ, BEng, 58; Calif Inst Technol, PhD(physics), 66. *Prof Exp:* From instr to assoc prof, 65-77, PROF PHYSICS, POMONA COL, 77- *Concurrent Pos:* Vis prof, Univ Paris Sud, 71-72, Univ Provence, Aix-Marseille I, 76, Univ Provence, 77, Ecole Super Phys Chim Indust, Paris & Univ Provence, 79. *Mem:* Am Phys Soc. *Res:* Low temperature physics-superconductivity, thin films; liquid helium; phase transitions; liquid crystals; percolation. *Mailing Add:* Dept of Physics Pomona Col Claremont CA 91711

MITHOEFER, JOHN CALDWELL, b Cincinnati, Ohio, Feb 12, 20; m 42; c 3. MEDICINE. *Educ:* Brown Univ, BA, 41; Harvard Univ, MD, 44. *Prof Exp:* From instr to asst clin prof med, Col Physicians & Surgeons, Columbia Univ, 52-68; prof med & chief cardiopulmonary div, Dartmouth Med Sch, 68-72; PROF MED & DIR PULMONARY DIV, MED UNIV SC, 72- *Concurrent Pos:* Assoc physician & dir cardiopulmonary lab, Mary Imogene Bassett Hosp; mem staff, Fac Med, Paris, 54 & postgrad sch med, Hammersmith Hosp, London, Eng, 62; mem pulmonary training comt & chmn rev comt nat res & demonstration ctrs, Nat Heart & Lung Inst; fel coun clin cardiol, Am Heart Asn. *Mem:* Am Soc Clin Invest; Am Fedn Clin Res; fel Am Col Cardiol; fel Am Col Chest Physicians; Asn Univ Cardiol. *Res:* Cardiopulmonary physiology. *Mailing Add:* Dept of Med Med Univ of SC Charleston SC 29401

MITLER, HENRI EMMANUEL, b Paris, France, Oct 26, 30; US citizen; div; c 2. ASTROPHYSICS, NUCLEAR PHYSICS. *Educ:* City Col New York, BS, 53; Princeton Univ, PhD(nuclear structure), 60. *Prof Exp:* Jr physicist, Nuclear Develop Assocs, 53; instr physics, Princeton Univ, 57-58; res assoc physics & adj lectr, Brandeis Univ, 59-60; sr staff physicist, Smithsonian Astrophys Observ, 61-75; res assoc, Harvard Col Observ, 62-75, lectr astron, 63-75, RES ASSOC DIV APPL SCI, HARVARD UNIV, 75- *Concurrent Pos:* Lectr, Brandeis Univ, 67-68 & 71-72. *Mem:* Am Phys Soc; Am Astron Soc. *Res:* Quantum theory; nuclear structure and reactions; origin of the elements; radiochemical production in meteoroids; nucleosynthesis by cosmic rays; electron-ion screening in dense plasmas; origin of the moon; fire, such as evolution of fires in compartments. *Mailing Add:* Eng Sci Lab Harvard Univ 40 Oxford St Cambridge MA 02138

MITOFF, S(TEPHAN) P(AUL), b San Francisco, Calif, May 17, 24; m 48; c 3. CERAMICS, SYSTEMS ENGINEERING. *Educ:* Univ Calif, BS, 50, PhD(eng sci), 56. *Prof Exp:* Asst, Univ Calif, 50-55; res assoc & ceramist, Res Labs, 55-73, prin investr high temperature battery proj, Res & Develop Ctr, 73-79, PROJ TECH LEADER, GEN ELEC CO, 79- *Mem:* Fel Am Ceramic Soc; Am Phys Soc. *Res:* Electrical conductivity; defect structure; thermodynamics of oxides and salts; fuel cells; solid electrolytes; batteries; battery system design; ceramic engineering. *Mailing Add:* Res & Develop Ctr Gen Elec Co PO Box 8 Schenectady NY 12301

MITOMA, CHOZO, b San Francisco, Calif, July 21, 22; m 50; c 4. BIOCHEMICAL PHARMACOLOGY. *Educ:* Univ Calif, BA, 48, PhD(biochem), 51. *Prof Exp:* Asst, Univ Calif, 48-51; biochemist, NIH, 52-59; sr biochemist, 59-69, DIR BIOMED RES LAB, SRI INT, 69- *Concurrent Pos:* Hite fel, Univ Tex, 51-52. *Mem:* Am Soc Biol Chem; Am Soc Pharmacol & Exp Therapeut; Soc Exp Biol & Med. *Res:* Intermediary metabolism of amino acids; mechanism of action of drugs; drug metabolism; neurochemistry. *Mailing Add:* Biomed Res Lab SRI Int Menlo Park CA 94025

MITRA, GRIHAPATI, b Oct 29, 27; m 58; c 1. INORGANIC CHEMISTRY. *Educ:* Univ Calcutta, BSc, 47, MSc, 49, DSc, 54. *Prof Exp:* Fel chem, Univ Wash, Seattle, 55-57; res officer, AEC, India, 58; lectr chem, Dum Dum Col, 59-60; fel physics, Pa State Univ, 60-61; asst prof chem, 61-64, chmn dept, 64-67, PROF CHEM, KING'S COL, PA, 67- *Concurrent Pos:* Vis lectr, Sylvania Elec Prods, Inc, Pa, 62; dir rocket fuel res, Adv Res Projs Agency, 63-67; res dir, Beryllium Corp, 67. *Mem:* AAAS; Am Chem Soc; Indian Chem Soc. *Res:* Preparation and properties of compounds containing halogens. *Mailing Add:* Dept Chem King's Col Wilkes-Barre PA 18702

MITRA, SANKAR, b Calcutta, India, July 7, 37; m 66; c 2. MOLECULAR BIOLOGY, BIOCHEMISTRY. *Educ:* Univ Calcutta, BSc, 57, MSc, 59; Univ Wis-Madison, PhD(biochem), 64. *Prof Exp:* Res asst biochem, Univ Calcutta, 59-60; res asst, Univ Wis-Madison, 60-62, res fel, 62-63; res assoc, Stanford Univ, 64-65; Indian Govt Coun Sci & Indust Res sci officer, Bose Inst, India, 66-67, sr res fel, 67-70, reader, 71; BIOCHEMIST, BIOL DIV, OAK RIDGE NAT LAB, 71- *Concurrent Pos:* Mem panel V, Int Cell Res Orgn, 69-73; lectr sch biomed sci, Univ Tenn, 72- *Mem:* Indian Soc Biol Chem; Am Soc Biol Chemists. *Res:* Molecular biology of viruses and nucleic acids; synthesis of nucleic acids in vivo and in vitro; repair and miscoding properties of simple alkylated bases in DNA. *Mailing Add:* Biol Div Oak Ridge Nat Lab Oak Ridge TN 37830

MITRA, SHASHANKA S, b Calcutta, India, May 20, 32; m 63; c 2. PROBABILITY. *Educ:* Univ Calcutta, BS, 52, MS, 54; Univ Wash, PhD(math), 61. *Prof Exp:* Teaching asst math, Univ Wash, 56-61; asst prof, Univ Idaho, 61-62, Univ Ariz, 62-64, Clarkson Col Technol, 64-67, Western Wash State, 67-69 & Wilkes Col, 69-72; ASST PROF MATH, PA STATE UNIV, 72- *Mailing Add:* 16 Alberts Ct Dubois PA 15801

MITRA, SUNANDA, b Bengal, Feb 5, 36; m 60; c 2. VISUAL CONTRAST SENSITIVITY, CONTRAST DETECTION PERIMETERY. *Educ:* Calcutta Univ, BS, 55, MS, 57; Phillipps Univ, WGer, PhD(physics), 66. *Prof Exp:* Res assoc nuclear physics, Saha Inst Nuclear Physics, India, 58-59; lectr physics, Lady Brabourne Col, India, 59-64; res asst, Phillipps Univ, WGer, 64-66; res assoc, plasma physics, 69-73, biomed inst, 74-75, RES ASSOC VISUAL SCI, DEPT OPTHALMOL, SCH MED, TEX TECH UNIV, 77- *Mem:* Optical Soc Am; Asn Res Vision & Opthalmol. *Res:* Development of a method of determining spatial contrast sensitivity function loss in maculopathy with an aim to detect and classify macular disorders at an early stage. *Mailing Add:* Dept Opthalmol & Visual Sci Health Sci Ctr Tex Tech Univ Lubbock TX 79430

MITROVIC, MILAN, b Yugoslavia, Sept 11, 20; nat US; m 51; c 4. VETERINARY MEDICINE. *Educ:* Univ Perugia, DVM, 45; Univ Bologna, dipl, 47. *Prof Exp:* Asst prof clin path, Univ Perugia, 45-46, asst dir animal exp sta, 46-51; head vet lab, State Livestock Sanit Bd, Ark, 52-54; asst mgr vet path, Res Div, Salsbury Labs, 54-56, res assoc & proj leader, 56-57, head microbiol dept, 57-61; asst prof vet sci, Pa State Univ, 61-62; mgr biol lab, Agr Res Dept, 62-67, res group chief, Animal Health Res Dept, 68-73, res sect head, 74-78, sr res fel, Res Planning & Develop Dept, 78-81, ASST DIR, CORP LICENSING DEPT, HOFFMAN-LA ROCHE INC, 81- *Mem:* Am Soc Microbiol; Am Asn Avian Path; Am Vet Med Asn; Indust Vet Asn; NY Acad Sci. *Res:* Bacteriology; virology; pathology; diagnosis; product development; biological production; experimental chemotherapy. *Mailing Add:* Corp Licensing Dept Hoffmann-La Roche Inc Nutley NJ 07110

MITRUKA, BRIJ MOHAN, b Hanuman Garh Town, Rajasthan, India, May 12, 37; US citizen; wid; c 3. MICROBIOLOGY, VETERINARY MEDICINE. *Educ:* Rajasthan Vet Col, BVSc & AH, 59; Mich State Univ, MS, 62, PhD(microbiol, pub health), 65. *Prof Exp:* Vet asst surg, Vet Hosp, Hanamangarh County, Rajasthan, 59-60; USPHS fel & res assoc microbiol, Mich State Univ, 65-66; res assoc, Cornell Univ, 66-68; clin pathologist, Sch Med, Yale Univ, 68-69, asst prof lab animal sci & lab med, 69-74; assoc prof, Sch Med, Univ Pa, 74-78; DIR CLIN LABS & RES & DEVELOP, BHP INC, WEST CHESTER, PA, 78- *Concurrent Pos:* USPHS grants, Yale Univ, 69-73; prof microbiol & head dept, Punjab Agr Univ, 74-78; dir qual control, BHP Inc; res prof microbiol, Temple Univ, 78- *Mem:* AAAS; Am Soc Microbiol; Am Asn Clin Chem; Am Vet Med Asn. *Res:* Bases of microbial pathogenicity; microbial metabolites detection and identification in tissues and body fluids; microbial metabolism in vitro and in vivo; study of pathogenic mechanisms involved in infectious diseases of man and animals; rapid, automated diagnosis in infectious and non-infectious diseases; manufacturing and development of in vitro diagnostic products. *Mailing Add:* 7104 Sellers Ave Upper Darby PA 19082

MITSCH, WILLIAM JOSEPH, b Wheeling, WVa, Mar 29, 47; m 70; c 1. AQUATIC ECOLOGY. *Educ:* Univ Notre Dame, BS, 69; Univ Fla, ME, 72, PhD(environ eng sci), 75. *Prof Exp:*Asst prof ecol, Ill Inst Technol, 75-79; ASSOC PROF SYSTS ECOL, UNIV LOUISVILLE, 79- *Concurrent Pos:* Consult var pub & pvt clients, 75-; res grant & consult, Argonne Nat Lab, 76-78; var grants, 76-83; chmn & ed, Energy Ecol Modelling Int Conf, 81. *Mem:* Ecol Soc Am; Sigma Xi; Am Soc Limnol & Oceanog; Inst Ecol; Inst Soc Ecol Modelling. *Res:* Energy flow in ecological systems, ecological modelling, environmmental impact of energy development; wetland and freshwater ecology. *Mailing Add:* Systems Sci Inst Univ Louisville Louisville KY 40292

MITSCHER, LESTER ALLEN, b Detroit, Mich, Aug 20, 31; m 53; c 3. BIO-ORGANIC CHEMISTRY. *Educ:* Wayne State Univ, BS, 53, PhD(chem), 59. *Prof Exp:* Spec instr pharm, Wayne State Univ, 56-58; res scientist bio-org chem, Lederle Labs, Am Cyanamid Co, 58-61, group leader fermentation biochem, 61-67; prof pharmacog & natural prod, Col Pharm, Ohio State Univ, 67-75; UNIV DISTINGUISHED PROF MEDICINAL CHEM & CHMN DEPT, UNIV KANS, 75- *Concurrent Pos:* Intersearch prof, Victorian Col Pharm, Melbourne, Australia. *Mem:* Am Chem Soc; Am Soc Pharmacog; The Chem Soc; Am Soc Microbiol; Japanese Antibiotics Asn. *Res:* Chemistry of organic compounds of natural origin, especially alkaloids, terpenes, steroids and antibiotics. *Mailing Add:* Col of Pharm Univ of Kans Malott Hall Lawrence KS 66044

MITSUI, AKIRA, b Japan, Jan 25, 29; m 64; c 3. BIOLOGICAL OCEANOGRAPHY. *Educ:* Univ Tokyo, BS, 51, MA, 55, PhD(plant physiol), 58. *Prof Exp:* PROF BIOL OCEANOG, SCH MARINE & ATMOSPHERIC SCI, UNIV MIAMI, 72- *Mem:* Am Soc Microbiol; Am Soc Plant Physiologists; Int Asn Hydrogen Energy. *Res:* Marine biochemistry; bioenergetics; bioconversion of solar energy; hydrogen energy. *Mailing Add:* Univ Miami 4600 Rickenbacker Causeway Miami FL 33149

MITSUTOMI, T(AKASHI), b Honolulu, Hawaii, Dec 20, 23; m 48. SYSTEMS ENGINEERING. *Educ:* Mass Inst Technol, 52, MS, 53. *Prof Exp:* Machinist-draftsman, Am Can Co, Hawaii, 42-45, 48-49; res engr, Autonetics Div, NAm Aviation, Inc, 53-55, eng supvr, 55-59, group leader, 59-62, res mgr adv tech, 62-64, staff sci adv to vpres, 64-65, res mgr appl res, 65-67, dir adv tech, NAm Rockwell Corp, 67-71; vpres, Datapet Corp, 71-72; PRES, HYCON, INC, 72- *Concurrent Pos:* Instr, Univ Calif, Los Angeles, 57-58, lectr, 61- *Mem:* Inst Elec & Electronics Engrs. *Res:* Research and advanced development of microelectronics, solid state devices and space system controls; velocity meters and platform dynamic analysis and synthesis; microelectronics-large scale integration; data communication systems; microcomputer developments. *Mailing Add:* 515 Peralta Hills Dr Anaheim CA 92807

MITTAG, THOMAS WALDEMAR, b Pecs, Hungary, Mar 14, 37; m 59; c 2. PHARMACOLOGY, BIOCHEMISTRY. *Educ:* Univ Cape Town, BS, 59, Hons, 61, PhD(org chem), 64. *Prof Exp:* Jr lectr chem, Univ Cape Town, 63-65; staff scientist, Worcester Found Exp Biol, 66-67; instr pharmacol, New York Med Col, Flower & Fifth Ave Hosps, 68-69, asst prof, 69-71; assoc prof, 71-78, PROF PHARMACOL, MT SINAI SCH MED, 78-, ASSOC PROF OPHTHAL, 77- *Concurrent Pos:* Res fel biochem, Purdue Univ, 65-66; res fel pharmacol, Georgetown Univ, 67-69; NIH grants, 69-81. *Mem:* AAAS; Asn Res Vision Opthal; NY Acad Sci; Am Soc Pharmacol & Exp Therapeut. *Res:* Molecular pharmacology of neurohormone receptors; active site directed ligands for enzymes and receptors. *Mailing Add:* Dept Pharmacol Mt Sinai Sch Med New York NY 10029

MITTAL, KAMAL KANT, b Pihani, India, July 1, 35; c 2. IMMUNOGENETICS, TRANSPLANTATION IMMUNOLOGY. *Educ:* Agra Univ, BS, 54, DVM, 58; Univ Ill, Urbana, MS, 62, PhD(immunogenetics), 65. *Prof Exp:* Res assoc animal sci, Univ Ill, Urbana, 65-66; res fel biol, Calif Inst Technol, 66-67; res geneticist II, Dept Surg, Univ Calif, Los Angeles, 67-69; asst prof microbiol, Baylor Col Med, Houston, 69-70; asst prof immunogenetics, Univ Calif, Los Angeles, 70-72; asst prof surg & physiol, Northwestern Univ, Chicago, 72-75; RES MICROBIOLOGIST, BUR BIOLOGICS, FOOD & DRUG ADMIN, DEPT HEALTH & HUMAN SERV, 75- *Mem:* AAAS; Transplantation Soc; Am Asn Immunol; Am Soc Hemat. *Res:* Human histocompatibility systems--genetics, immunology, serology and immunoreproduction. *Mailing Add:* Bur Biologics FDA/HHS Bldg 29 Rm 232 8800 Rockville Pike Bethesda MD 20205

MITTAL, KASHMIRI LAL, b Kilrodh, India, Oct 15, 45; m 70; c 4. PHYSICAL CHEMISTRY. *Educ:* Panjab Univ, Chandigarh, BSc, 64; Indian Inst Technol, New Delhi, MSc, 66; Univ Southern Calif, PhD(phys chem), 70. *Prof Exp:* Res assoc, Pa State Univ, 70-71; fel chem, Univ Pa, 71-72; fel, IBM Corp, San Jose, Calif, 72-74, staff engr, Poughkeepsie, 74-77, STAFF ENGR, IBM CORP, HOPEWELL JUNCTION, 77- *Mem:* Am Chem Soc; Electrochem Soc; Am Vacuum Soc; Adhesion Soc; fel Am Inst Chemists. *Res:* Surface, colloid, polymer and electrochemistry; surface properties of materials; adhesion and corrosion. *Mailing Add:* Dept 49F Bldg 300-40E IBM Corp Hopewell Junction NY 12533

MITTAL, YASHASWINI DEVAL, b Poona, India, Oct 1, 41. STATISTICS. *Educ:* Poona Univ, BSc, 61; Univ Ill, Urbana, MS, 66; Univ Calif, Los Angeles, PhD(math), 72. *Prof Exp:* Teaching asst math, Univ Ill, Urbana, 64-66 & Univ Calif, Los Angeles, 66-71; asst prof, Northwestern Univ, Evanston, 72-73; vis mem, Inst Advan Study, Princeton, 73-74; asst prof statist, Stanford Univ, 74-80; ASSOC PROF STATIST, VA POLYTECH INST, 80- *Mem:* Am Math Soc; Inst Math Statist. *Res:* Convergence properties of maxima of stationary Gaussian processes. *Mailing Add:* Dept of Statist Va Tech Blacksburgh VA 24060

MITTELMAN, ARNOLD, b New York, NY, Dec 21, 24; m 56; c 2. SURGERY, MEDICINE. *Educ:* Columbia Univ, AB, 49, MD, 54; Am Bd Surg, dipl, 66. *Prof Exp:* Instr surg, Columbia-Presby Med Ctr, 59-61; assoc cancer res surgeon, 61-65, ASSOC CHIEF RES SURGEON & DIR SURG DEVELOP ONCOL, ROSWELL PARK MEM INST, 65-, ASSOC RES PROF BIOCHEM, 69- *Concurrent Pos:* Asst attend & asst vis surgeon, Presby Hosp, NY, 61. *Mem:* AAAS; Am Inst Chem; Am Asn Cancer Res. *Res:* Nucleic acid and steroid biochemistry; acid base physiology. *Mailing Add:* Surg Develop Oncol Roswell Park Mem Inst Buffalo NY 14263

MITTELMANN, EUGENE, industrial electronics, deceased

MITTELSTAEDT, STANLEY GEORGE, b Connell, Wash, Oct 15, 09; m 40; c 4. PHARMACEUTICAL CHEMISTRY, PHARMACY. *Educ:* Northwest Nazarene Col, 34; State Univ Wash, BS & MS, 38; Purdue Univ, PhD(pharm, pharmaceut chem), 48. *Prof Exp:* Asst, State Univ Wash, 37-38; asst, Purdue Univ, 38-40; actg head dept chem, Boise Jr Col, 40-42; assoc prof, Univ Tex, 48-51; asst dean, Sch Pharm, 51-53, prof pharm & pharmaceut chem, 51-77, dean, 53-77, EMER PROF PHARM & PHARMACEUT CHEM, SCH PHARM, UNIV ARK, & EMER DEAN, 77- *Concurrent Pos:* Co-ed, Vet Drug Encyclop; mem nat adv coun health educ, Dept Health, Educ & Welfare, Washington, DC, 72-76; exec vpres, Sounds of Music Found, Inc, 77-; consult Health Sci & Serv. *Mem:* AAAS; Am Chem Soc; Am Pharmaceut Asn. *Res:* Iodo-radio opaques. *Mailing Add:* 317 N Ridge Rd Little Rock AR 72207

MITTEN, LORING G(OODWIN), b Danville, Ill, Dec 29, 20; m 42; c 3. INDUSTRIAL ENGINEERING. *Educ:* Drexel Inst, BS, 42; Mass Inst Technol, SM, 47; Ohio State Univ, PhD(indust eng), 52. *Prof Exp:* Prof indust eng, Ohio State Univ, 48-57; prof indust eng & mgt sci, Northwestern Univ, 57-70, chmn dept, 63-65; PROF MGT SCI & CHMN DIV, UNIV BC, 70- *Mem:* Fel AAAS; fel Am Soc Qual Control; Inst Mgt Sci; Am Inst Indust Engrs; Soc Indust & Appl Math. *Res:* Operations research and management science with emphasis on mathematical models of sequencing problems, optimal design and operation of industrial processes, dynamic programming and sequential decision processes. *Mailing Add:* Fac of Com & Bus Admin Univ of BC Vancouver BC V6T 1W5 Can

MITTENTHAL, JAY EDWARD, b Boston, Mass, July 28, 41; m 68; c 2. NEUROBIOLOGY. *Educ:* Amherst Col, BA, 62; Johns Hopkins Univ, PhD(biophys), 70. *Prof Exp:* Fel neurobiol, Stanford Univ, 70-72; asst prof biol, Purdue Univ, 73-79; res assoc, Univ Ore, 79-81; ASST PROF ANAT SCI, UNIV ILL, 81- *Mem:* Sigma Xi; Am Soc Zool; Soc Neurosci; Soc Develop Biol. *Res:* Developmental processes generating external form and patterns of neural connectivity. *Mailing Add:* Dept Anat Sci Univ Ill 506 S Mathews Ave Urbana IL 61801

MITTERER, RICHARD MAX, b Lancaster, Pa, Sept 8, 38; m; c 4. GEOCHEMISTRY. *Educ:* Franklin & Marshall Col, BS, 60; Fla State Univ, PhD(geol), 66. *Prof Exp:* Fel geophys lab, Carnegie Inst, 66-67; asst prof geosci, Southwest Ctr Advan Studies, 67-69; from asst prof to assoc prof, 69-80, PROF GEOSCI, UNIV TEX, DALLAS, 80-, HEAD DEPT, 75- *Concurrent Pos:* Mem bd dir, Geol Info Library, Dallas. *Mem:* AAAS; Geol Soc Am; Soc Econ Paleont & Mineral; Geochem Soc. *Res:* Amino acid diagenesis; carbonate geochemistry; sedimentary geochemistry. *Mailing Add:* Progs for Geosci Univ of Tex at Dallas Box 688 Richardson TX 75080

MITTIER, JAMES CARLTON, physiology, endocrinology, see previous edition

MITTLEMAN, JOHN, b Roslyn Heights, NY. UNDERWATER NONDESTRUCTIVE TESTING. *Educ:* Cornell Univ, BS, 69; Mass Inst Technol, MS, 70. *Prof Exp:* Task leader, 74-76, MEM DIVING & SALVAGE DEPT, DIVER TOOLS DIV, NAVAL COASTAL SYSTS CTR, 76- *Concurrent Pos:* Navy weapons control systs fel, Mass Inst Technol, 73-74. *Honors & Awards:* Solbery Award, Am Soc Naval Eng, 81. *Mem:* Am Soc Photogrammetry; Marine Technol Soc; Am Soc Testing & Mat; Sigma Xi. *Res:* Underwater stereophotographic ultrasonic and magnetic particle inspection systems. *Mailing Add:* 400 S MacArthur Ave Panama City FL 32401

MITTLEMAN, MARVIN HAROLD, b New York, NY, Mar 13, 28; m 55; c 3. PHYSICS. *Educ:* Polytech Inst Brooklyn, BS, 49; Mass Inst Technol, PhD(physics), 53. *Prof Exp:* Instr physics, Columbia Univ, 52-55; staff scientist, Lawrence Radiation Lab, Livermore, Calif, 55-65; staff scientist space sci lab, Univ Calif, Berkeley, 65-68; assoc prof physics, 68-69, exec officer PhD prog, 70-74, PROF PHYSICS, CITY COL NEW YORK, 69- *Concurrent Pos:* Div Sci & Indust Res, Brit Govt fel, Univ Col, Univ London, 62-63; NASA grant, Univ Calif, Berkeley, 69-70; consult, Lockheed Aircraft Corp, Calif, Convair, Inst Defense Anal, DC & Goddard Space Flight Ctr, NASA. *Mem:* Fel Am Phys Soc. *Res:* Atomic scattering and structure; quantum optics. *Mailing Add:* Dept of Physics City Col of New York New York NY 10031

MITTLER, ARTHUR, b Paterson, NJ, July 15, 43; m 66. PHYSICS. *Educ:* Drew Univ, BA, 65; Univ Ky, MS, 67, PhD(physics), 70. *Prof Exp:* Asst prof, 69-77, ASSOC PROF PHYSICS, UNIV LOWELL, 77- *Mem:* AAAS; Am Phys Soc; Am Nuclear Soc. *Res:* Low energy nuclear physics; neutron cross section measurements. *Mailing Add:* Dept of Physics & Appl Physics Univ of Lowell Lowell MA 01854

MITTLER, SIDNEY, b Detroit, Mich, Aug 2, 17; m 42, 69; c 3. GENETICS, ZOOLOGY. *Educ:* Wayne Univ, BS, 38, MS, 39; Univ Mich, PhD(zool), 44. *Prof Exp:* Asst, Wayne State Univ, 38-39; asst, Univ Mich, 39-42; instr biol, Bowling Green State Univ, 45-46; from instr to asst prof zool, genetics & physiol, Ill Inst Technol, 46-52, res biologist, IIT Res Found, 52-60; PROF BIOL SCI, NORTHERN ILL UNIV, 60- *Concurrent Pos:* IIT Res Found Award, 55. *Mem:* Fel AAAS; Genetics Soc Am; Radiation Res Soc; Environ Mutagen Soc. *Res:* Genetics, radiation and chemical mutagenesis. *Mailing Add:* Dept of Biol Sci Northern Ill Univ DeKalb IL 60115

MITTMAN, BENJAMIN, b Chicago, Ill, Dec 24, 28; m 50; c 2. COMPUTER SCIENCE. *Educ:* Ill Inst Technol, BS, 50; Univ Calif, Los Angeles, MA, 51. *Prof Exp:* Mathematician, Boeing Airplane Co, 51-53; sci rep, Remington Rand Univac Div, Sperry Rand Corp, 56-58; mathematician, Armour Res Found, Ill Inst Technol, 58-65, mgr comput appln, Ill Inst Technol Res Inst, 65-66; PROF COMPUT SCI, NORTHWESTERN UNIV, 66-, DIR VOGELBACK COMPUT CTR, 66- *Concurrent Pos:* Mem panel comput applns in res, NSF. *Mem:* AAAS; Asn Comput Mach; Am Soc Info Sci; Inst Elec & Electronics Engrs; Int Comput Chess Asn. *Res:* Information retrieval; computing center management; computer graphics; computer chess. *Mailing Add:* Vogelback Comput Ctr Northwestern Univ Evanston IL 60201

MITTON, JEFFRY BOND, b Glen Ridge, NJ, Mar 16, 47; m 69. POPULATION GENETICS. *Educ:* Univ Conn, BA, 69; State Univ NY Stony Brook, PhD(ecol, evolution), 73. *Prof Exp:* NIH fel genetics, Univ Calif, Davis, 73-74; asst prof, 74-79, ASSOC PROF BIOL, DEPT ENVIRON POP & ORGANISMIC BIOL, UNIV COLO, BOULDER, 79-, RES ASSOC, INST BEHAV GENETICS, 75-, RES ASSOC, INST ARCTIC ALPINE RES, 80- *Concurrent Pos:* Vis res scientist, Marine Biol Lab, Woods Hole, Mass. *Mem:* Genetics Soc Am; Soc Study Evolution (secy, 82-84); AAAS; Sigma Xi; Soc Syst Zool. *Res:* Processes of natural selection resulting in population structuring and geographic variation of gene frequencies; protein polymorphisms; multi locus systems. *Mailing Add:* Dept of Environ Pop & Org Biol Univ of Colo Boulder CO 80309

MITUS, WLADYSLAW J, b Zywiec, Poland, May 14, 20; US citizen; m 52; c 2. PATHOLOGY, HEMATOLOGY. *Educ:* Univ Edinburgh, MB, ChB, 46. *Prof Exp:* Intern med, Weymouth & Dist Hosp, Eng, 48-49; registr, Kilton Hosp Workshop, 49-52; res pathologist, Children's Hosp, Sheffield, 52-53; res assoc, New Eng Ctr Hosp, Boston, 57-69; CHIEF HEMAT & DIR RES, CARNEY HOSP, 69-; ASSOC PROF MED, TUFTS UNIV, 65- *Concurrent Pos:* Fel path, City Hosp, Cleveland, Ohio, 54-55; fel hemat, Blood Res Lab, New Eng Ctr Hosp, Boston, 55-57; USPHS grant, 57-58; asst prof, Tufts Univ, 60-65; consult, Med Found, Boston, 61-63. *Mem:* Am Soc Exp Path; Am Soc Hemat; sr mem Am Fedn Clin Res. *Mailing Add:* Carney Hosp 2100 Dorchester Ave Boston MA 02124

MITZ, MILTON AARON, biochemistry, deceased

MIURA, CAROLE K MASUTANI, b Hilo, Hawaii, June 8, 38; m 62; c 2. MATHEMATICAL STATISTICS. *Educ:* Cornell Univ, BA, 60; Univ Hawaii, MA, 62; Boston Univ, PhD(math), 73. *Prof Exp:* Teaching asst, Dept Math, 61-62, instr, 62-65, ASST PROF MATH DISCIPLINE, UNIV HAWAII, HILO, 73- *Mem:* Am Statist Asn. *Res:* Theoretical studies of inverse gaussian distribution; statistical studies of remedial education. *Mailing Add:* Dept Math Univ Hawaii Hilo HI 96720

MIURA, GEORGE AKIO, b Honolulu, Hawaii, Aug 6, 42. PLANT ENZYMES, PHYTOHORMONES. *Educ:* Univ Hawaii, BS, 64; Ind Univ, PhD(plant physiol), 68. *Prof Exp:* Res biologist, Univ Calif, San Diego, 68-70; ref fel, McMaster Univ, Hamilton, Ont, 70-72; BIOL SCI ASST, MED RES INST CHEM DEFENSE, US ARMY, 79- *Res:* Plant enzymes especially cholinesterase; plant hormones especially cytokinins; plant tissue culture. *Mailing Add:* Hq & Hq DetachmentMed Res Inst Chem Defense US Army Aberdeen Proving Ground MD 21010

MIURA, ROBERT MITSURU, b Selma, Calif, Sept 12, 38; m 61; c 2. BIOMATHEMATICS, NONLINEAR WAVE PROPAGATION. *Educ:* Univ Calif, Berkeley, BS, 60, MS, 62; Princeton Univ, MA, 64, PhD(aerospace eng), 66. *Prof Exp:* Res assoc nonlinear wave propagation, Plasma Physics Lab, Princeton Univ, 65-67; asst prof math, NY Univ, 68-71; assoc prof, Vanderbilt Univ, 71-75; vis assoc prof, 75-76, assoc prof, 76-78, PROF MATH, UNIV BC, 78- *Concurrent Pos:* Assoc res scientist, Courant Inst Math, NY Univ, 67-69; John Simon Guggenheim fel, 80-81; sr Killam Lon fel, Univ BC, 80-81; vis prof, Kyoto Univ, 81; assoc ed, Can J Math, 81- *Mem:* AAAS; Am Math Soc; Soc Indust & Appl Math; NY Acad Sci; Can Appl Math Soc. *Res:* Nonlinear partial differential equations; nonlinear wave propagation; fluid mechanics; asymptotic methods; kinetic theory; Mathematical neurophysiology; reaction-diffusion problems; singular perturbation boundary-value problems of differential-difference equations. *Mailing Add:* Dept of Math Univ of BC Vancouver BC V6T 1Y4 Can

MIURA, TAKESHI, b Fukuoka, Japan, Apr 10, 25. MEDICAL ENTOMOLOGY. *Educ:* Utah State Univ, BSc, 55, MSc, 56; NC State Univ, PhD(entom), 67. *Prof Exp:* Assoc vector control specialist mosquito res, Calif State Pub Health Dept, 61, 62 & 63-64; asst specialist, Sch Pub Health, 64-65, lab technician, 66-67, assoc specialist, 67-75, SPECIALIST, MOSQUITO CONTROL RES LAB, UNIV CALIF, 75- *Mem:* AAAS; Soc Vector Ecologists; Entom Soc Am; Am Mosquito Control Asn; Am Inst Biol Sci. *Res:* Biology and ethology of mosquitoes. *Mailing Add:* Mosquito Control Res Lab Univ Calif 5544 Air Terminal Dr Fresno CA 93727

MIWA, THOMAS KANJI, b Honolulu, Hawaii, Apr 14, 27; m 60; c 3. ORGANIC CHEMISTRY, BIOCHEMISTRY. *Educ:* Univ Hawaii, BA, 52, MS, 54; Univ Wis, PhD(biochem), 58. *Prof Exp:* asst chem, Univ Hawaii, 52-54; asst biochem, Univ Wis, 54-58; chemist, Sci & Educ Admin-Agr Res, USDA, 58-79; DIR, MIWA JOJOBA LABS, 79- *Concurrent Pos:* Chmn, Int Comt Jojoba Res & Develop, 73-; co-dir, Consejo Int Jojoba, 75-79. *Mem:* Am Chem Soc; Am Oil Chem Soc; Jojoba Soc (pres, 79-). *Res:* Biological and chemical synthesis of proteins, polypeptides, amino and fatty acids; waxes; plasticization of vinyl polymers; borohydride reactions; gas chromatography; conservation of electron spin; lubricants; allylic plastics; jojoba. *Mailing Add:* Miwa Jojoba Labs 505 S Rockford Dr Tempe AZ 85281

MIX, DWIGHT FRANKLIN, b Fayetteville, Ark, Feb 18, 32; m 54; c 2. ELECTRICAL ENGINEERING. *Educ:* Univ Ark, BS, 56, MS, 61; Purdue Univ, PhD(elec eng), 66. *Prof Exp:* Design engr, Gen Dynamics/Convair, Tex, 56-59 & Tex Instruments, Inc, 59; instr elec eng, Univ Ark, 59-61 & Purdue Univ, 61-65; asst prof, 65-70, ASSOC PROF ELEC ENG, UNIV ARK, FAYETTEVILLE, 70- *Mem:* Inst Elec & Electronic Engrs; Am Soc Eng Educ. *Res:* Statistical communication theory. *Mailing Add:* Dept Elec Eng Univ Ark Fayetteville AR 72701

MIX, MICHAEL CARY, b Deer Park, Wash, June 27, 41; m 62; c 2. INVERTEBRATE PATHOLOGY, ENVIRONMENTAL CARCINOGENS. *Educ:* Wash State Univ, BS, 63; Univ Wash, PhD(fisheries), 70. *Prof Exp:* Asst prof biol, 70-74, ASSOC PROF BIOL, ORE STATE UNIV, 74- *Concurrent Pos:* Consult, Shapiro & Assoc, Nalco Environ, Inc. *Mem:* AAAS; Nat Shellfisheries Asn; Soc Invert Path; NY Acad Sci; Sigma Xi. *Res:* Chemical carcinogens in the marine environment; histopathological effects of irradiation on higher invertebrates; experimental invertebrate pathobiology; diseases of invertebrates; cell renewal systems of mollusks; invertebrate oncology. *Mailing Add:* Dept of Gen Sci Ore State Univ Corvallis OR 97331

MIXAN, CRAIG EDWARD, b Berwyn, Ill, July 21, 46; m 69; c 2. ORGANIC CHEMISTRY. *Educ:* Holy Cross Col, BA, 68; Northwestern Univ, PhD(org chem), 72. *Prof Exp:* RES LEADER ORG CHEM, DOW CHEM CO, 72- *Mem:* Am Chem Soc; Sigma Xi. *Res:* Synthesis of bioactive compounds; agricultural products; process research and development. *Mailing Add:* Dow Chem Co 1710 Bldg Midland MI 48640

MIXON, AUBREY CLIFTON, b Tifton, Ga, Sept 20, 24; m 43. AGRONOMY, PLANT BREEDING. *Educ:* Univ Ga, BSA, 49; NC State Univ, MSA, 53; Auburn Univ, PhD(plant path), 66. *Prof Exp:* Asst agronomist, Fla Agr Exten Serv, 53-57; res agronomist, Coop Ala Agr Exp Sta & USDA, 57-73, res agronomist, Col Agr, Coop Univ Ga Coastal Plain Sta & USDA, 73-81. *Concurrent Pos:* Res agronomist, Auburn Agr Exp Sta, 57-73; coordr, USDA Nat Winter Peanut Nursery, Mayaguez, PR, 72-; adj res assoc, Col Agr, Univ Ga, 73-81; recorder, Nat Peanut Prod Workshop, 74. *Honors & Awards:* Twenty-Five Year Serv Award, USDA, 77. *Mem:* Am Peanut Res & Educ Asn; Am Soc Agron; AAAS; Am Inst Biol Sci. *Res:* Breeding, agronomic, physiological, ecological and pathological investigations associated with developing peanut varieties that are resistant to toxin-producing fungi. *Mailing Add:* Coastal Plain Exp Sta Tifton GA 31794

MIXON, FOREST ORION, b Anderson, SC, Dec 4, 31; m 57; c 2. CHEMICAL ENGINEERING, MATHEMATICS. *Educ:* NC State Univ, BS, 52, MS, 54; Univ Del, PhD(chem eng), 58. *Prof Exp:* Res engr, E I du Pont de Nemours & Co, Inc, 58-62; MGR PROCESS ENG DEPT, RES TRIANGLE INST, 62- *Concurrent Pos:* Adj prof, Univ NC, Chapel Hill, 72- & NC State Univ, 76-; chem eng consult to statist analysts. *Mem:* Sigma Xi; Am Inst Chem Engrs. *Res:* Water and air pollution control; enivronmental control of coal gasification processes; process research and analysis in hydrodynamics and heat transfer. *Mailing Add:* Res Triangle Inst PO Box 12194 Research Triangle Park NC 27709

MIXTER, RUSSELL LOWELL, b Williamston, Mich, Aug 7, 06; m 31; c 4. ANATOMY. *Educ:* Wheaton Col, Ill, AB, 28; Mich State Col, MS, 30; Univ Ill, PhD(anat), 39. *Prof Exp:* From instr to prof zool, Wheaton Col, Ill, 28-79. *Concurrent Pos:* Instr, Univ Ill, 35-36; ed jour, Am Sci Affil, 64-68. *Mem:* Am Sci Affil (pres, 51-54). *Res:* Macrophages of connective tissue; flexed tail in mice; evolution; spiders of Black Hills. *Mailing Add:* 1006 N President St Wheaton IL 60187

MIYA, TOM SABURO, b Hanford, Calif, Apr 6, 23; m 48; c 1. PHARMACOLOGY. *Educ:* Univ Nebr, BSc, 47, MSc, 48; Purdue Univ, PhD(pharmacol), 52. *Prof Exp:* Asst, Univ Nebr, 47-48; from instr to asst prof pharmacol, Purdue Univ, 48-56; chmn dept, Univ Nebr, 56-57; prof, Purdue Univ, West Lafayette, 58-76, head dept, 64-76; PROF PHARMACOL, SCH MED & DEAN SCH PHARM, UNIV NC, CHAPEL HILL, 77- *Concurrent Pos:* Mem rev comt, US Pharmacopoeia, 70-80 & pharmacol-toxicol prog comt, Nat Inst Gen Med Sci; assoc ed, Toxicol & Appl Pharmacol; chmn chem & biol info handling panel, Res Resources Div, HEW, NIH, 75-76. *Honors & Awards:* Award, Am Pharmaceut Asn, 64. *Mem:* AAAS; Am Soc Pharmacol & Exp Therapeut; Soc Exp Biol & Med; Am Chem Soc; Am Asn Cols Pharm (pres, 75-76). *Res:* Hormonal determinants of drug metabolism; factors modifying the normal disposition of drugs. *Mailing Add:* Sch of Pharm Univ of NC Chapel Hill NC 27514

MIYADA, DON SHUSO, b Oceanside, Calif, May 21, 25; m 60; c 4. BIOCHEMISTRY. *Educ:* Univ Calif, Los Angeles, BS, 49; Mich State Univ, PhD, 53. *Prof Exp:* Res assoc dept food tech, Univ Calif, 53-55; res assoc dept chem, Ohio State Univ, 55-56; res assoc, McArdle Mem Lab, Univ Wis, 56-57; asst res biochemist dept med, Univ Calif, Los Angeles, 57-61; biochemist, Long Beach Vet Admin Hosp, 61-67; biochemist, Biochem Procedures, Inc, 67-69; BIOCHEMIST, ORANGE COUNTY MED CTR, ORANGE, 69- *Concurrent Pos:* Adj asst prof depts path & biochem, Univ Calif, Irvine, adj assoc prof. *Mem:* AAAS; Am Chem Soc; Am Asn Clin Chem; NY Acad Sci. *Res:* Clinical chemistry. *Mailing Add:* Univ Calif Irvine Med Ctr 101 City Dr S Orange CA 92668

MIYAGAWA, ICHIRO, b Hiratsuka, Japan, Mar 5, 22; m 49; c 3. CHEMICAL PHYSICS. *Educ:* Nagoya Univ, BS, 45; Univ Tokyo, DrS(chem physics), 54. *Prof Exp:* Res assoc chem, Nagoya Univ, 48-49; res assoc chem, Univ Tokyo, 50-55, asst prof, Inst Solid State Physics, 60-62; res assoc, Duke Univ, 56-59, vis asst prof, 63-64; from asst prof to assoc prof, 65-71, PROF PHYSICS, UNIV ALA, 71- *Mem:* Am Phys Soc. *Res:* Dielectric constant of liquids; electron spin resonance of irradiated molecular crystals. *Mailing Add:* Dept of Physics Univ of Ala University AL 35486

MIYAI, KATSUMI, pathology, see previous edition

MIYAKODA, KIKURO, b Yonago City, Japan, Nov 7, 27; m 54; c 1. METEOROLOGY, GEOPHYSICS. *Educ:* Tokyo Univ, BS, 56, PhD(geophys), 61. *Prof Exp:* GROUP LEADER & RES METEOROLOGIST, GEOPHYS FLUID DYNAMICS LAB, PRINCETON UNIV, 65-, VIS PROF METEOROL, 68- *Mem:* Am Geophys Union; fel Am Meteorol Soc; Japan Meteorol Soc; Royal Meteorol Soc; Sigma Xi. *Res:* Numerical weather prediction; long-range weather forecast; meteorological dynamics. *Mailing Add:* Geophys Fluid Dynamics Lab Princeton Univ Princeton NJ 08540

MIYAMOTO, MICHAEL DWIGHT, b Honolulu, Hawaii, Apr 22, 45; m 73. NEUROPHARMACOLOGY. *Educ:* Northwestern Univ, Evanston, BA, 66, PhD(biol), 71. *Prof Exp:* Instr pharmacol, Rutgers Med Sch, Col Med & Dent, NJ, 70-72; asst prof, Health Ctr, Univ Conn, 72-78; ASSOC PROF PHARMACOL, COL MED, E TENN STATE UNIV, 78- *Concurrent Pos:* Pharm Mfrs Asn Found grant, 75; USPHS grant neurol dis & stroke, 75-79; Epilepsy Found Am award, 76. *Mem:* Am Soc Pharmacol & Exp Therapeut; Soc Neurosci. *Res:* Neuromuscular transmitter release; receptor mechanisms. *Mailing Add:* Dept of Pharmacol ETenn State Univ Col of Med Johnson City TN 37601

MIYAMOTO, SEIICHI, b Nagasaki, Japan, Oct 1, 44; US citizen; c 1. SOIL PHYSICS, SOIL CHEMISTRY. *Educ:* Gifu Univ, BS, 67; Kyushu Univ, MS, 69; Univ Calif, Riverside, PhD(soil sci), 71. *Prof Exp:* Res assoc soil sci, Univ Ariz, 71-75; res assoc & asst prof soil sci, NMex State Univ, 75-77; ASST PROF SOILS WATER ENG, EL PASO RES CTR, TEX A&M UNIV, 77- *Mem:* Am Soc Agr Engrs; Soil Sci Soc Am; Am Soc Agron. *Res:* Irrigation and drainage; water quality; mine-spoil reclamation. *Mailing Add:* Tex A&M Univ Res Ctr 1380 A&M Circle El Paso TX 79927

MIYANO, KENJIRO, b Okayama, Japan, May 25, 47; m 75; c 1. LIQUID INTERFACES, MONOMOLECULAR FILMS. *Educ:* Univ Tokyo, BS, 70; Northwestern Univ, PhD(physics), 75. *Prof Exp:* Res assoc physics, Lawrence Berkeley Lab, 75-76; res assoc, 76-78, asst physicist, 78-81, PHYSICIST, ARGONNE NAT LAB, 81- *Mem:* Am Phys Soc; Phys Soc Japan; Am Chem Soc. *Res:* Ultrasonics and light scattering in liquid crystals; surface acoustic waves; liquid interfaces and monomolecular films. *Mailing Add:* Argonne Nat Lab 9700 S Cass Ave Argonne IL 60439

MIYASHIRO, AKIHO, b Okayama, Japan, Oct 30, 20. PETROLOGY. *Educ:* Univ Tokyo, BSc, 43, PhD(petrol), 53. *Prof Exp:* Asst instr petrol, Univ Tokyo, 46-58, assoc prof, 58-67; vis prof, Lamont-Doherty Geol Observ, Columbia Univ, 67-70; PROF GEOL, STATE UNIV NY ALBANY, 70-, NSF RES GRANT, 71- *Concurrent Pos:* Vis int scientist, Am Geol Inst, 65. *Honors & Awards:* Prize, Geol Soc Japan, 58; A L Day Medal, Geol Soc Am, 77. *Mem:* Mineral Soc Am; Geol Soc London; Geol Soc France. *Res:* Metamorphic and igneous petrology; earth science, especially geology. *Mailing Add:* Dept of Geol Sci State Univ of NY 1400 Washington Ave Albany NY 12222

MIZE, CHARLES EDWARD, b Smithville, Tex, Mar 3, 34; m 62; c 1. PEDIATRICS, BIOCHEMISTRY. *Educ:* Rice Inst, BA, 55; Johns Hopkins Univ, PhD(biochem), 61, MD, 62. *Prof Exp:* From intern pediat to resident, Johns Hopkins Hosp, 62-64; staff assoc metab, Nat Heart Inst, 64-67; asst prof, 67-73, ASSOC PROF PEDIAT & BIOCHEM, UNIV TEX HEALTH SCI CTR DALLAS, 74- *Mem:* Soc Pediat Res; Am Soc Neurochem; Am Soc Human Genetics; Am Fedn Clin Res; NY Acad Sci. *Res:* Biochemistry of nutrition in growth and development; metabolic disorders of childhood. *Mailing Add:* Univ of Tex Health Sci Ctr 5323 Harry Hines Blvd Dallas TX 75235

MIZE, JACK PITTS, b Kansas City, Mo, July 27, 23; m 49; c 3. NUCLEAR PHYSICS. *Educ:* Duke Univ, BS, 47; Univ Rochester, MS, 49; Iowa State Col, PhD(physics), 53. *Prof Exp:* Res assoc physics, Inst Atomic Res, Iowa State Col, 53; mem staff, Los Alamos Sci Lab, 53-60; TECH STAFF MEM PHYSICS, TEX INSTRUMENTS, INC, DALLAS, 60- *Mem:* Fel Am Phys Soc. *Res:* Nuclear spectroscopy; plasma and solid state physics. *Mailing Add:* 918 Beechwood Richardson TX 75080

MIZE, JOE H(ENRY), b Colorado City, Tex, June 14, 34; m 66; c 1. COMPUTER SIMULATION MODELING, PRODUCTION CONTROL. *Educ:* Tex Tech Col, BS, 58; Purdue Univ, MS, 63, PhD(indust eng), 64. *Prof Exp:* Indust engr, White Sands Missile Range, NMex, 58-61; assoc prof eng, Auburn Univ, 64-65, assoc prof indust eng, 66-69, dir comput ctr, 65-69; prof, indust eng, Ariz State Univ, 69-72; prof & head, dept indust eng & mgt, 72-80, REGENTS PROF, INDUST ING, OKLA STATE UNIV, 80-, DIR, INST ENERGY ANALYSIS, 80- *Concurrent Pos:* Chmn, Tech Adv Coun, Southern Growth Policies Bd, 76-78; consult, various orgns, 64-; prin investr, several res projs, NSF, Dept Energy; ed indust eng, Prentice Hall Int Series, 72- *Honors & Awards:* H B Maynard Innovative Achievement Award, Am Inst Indust Engrs, 77. *Mem:* Am Inst Indust Engrs (exec vpres, 78-80, pres, 81-82); Am Soc Eng Educ; Nat Soc Prof Engrs. *Res:* Development of new operations research techniques based upon sound mathematical and statistical foundations; modeling and analysis of socio-economic systems, such as energy systems, state econometric models. *Mailing Add:* 1511 N Glenwood Stillwater OK 74074

MIZEJEWSKI, GERALD JUDE, b Pittsburgh, Pa, Aug 1, 39; m 65; c 5. DEVELOPMENTAL PHYSIOLOGY, IMMUNOLOGY. *Educ:* Duquesne Univ, BS, 61; Univ Md, MS, 65, PhD(zool), 68. *Prof Exp:* From asst zool to res asst immunol, Univ Md, 61-68; from res assoc to lectr, Med Sch, Univ Mich, 68-71; asst prof physiol & immunol, Univ SC, 71-74; sr res scientist-III, Div Labs & Res, 74-78, SR RES SCIENTIST-IV, BIRTH DEFECTS INST, DIV LABS & RES, NY STATE DEPT HEALTH, 78- *Concurrent Pos:* Am Cancer Soc grant, Univ Mich, 69-70; Upjohn res grant, 69-70; Abbott radio-pharmaceut res gift, 69-71 & Cal-Biochem res gift, 78-80; res asst prof, Dept Pediat, Albany Med Col, 78-, adj asst prof, Dept Obstet & Gynec, 80- *Mem:* AAAS; Am Soc Zool; Am Inst Biol Sci; Reticuloendothelial Soc; NY Acad Sci. *Res:* Alpha-fetoprotein bioassay and perinatal and neonatal biology; breast carcinoma; carcinoembryonic antigen, tumor transplantation; radiolabeled antibodies and antigens; hepatoma and lymphoma cell culture; cytotoxic antibodies; pregnancy interruption; estradiol binding assays; sexual differentiation of gonads; study onset of puberty, immunoadsorbants; affinity chromatography; immunochemistry. *Mailing Add:* Div Labs & Res NY State Dept Health Albany NY 12201

MIZELL, LOUIS RICHARD, b Gettysburg, Pa, Jan 25, 18; m 43; c 4. TEXTILE CHEMISTRY. *Educ:* Gettysburg Col, AB, 38; Georgetown Univ, MS, 42. *Prof Exp:* Res assoc, Textile Found, Inc, 39-42; mem staff, Harris Res Labs, Inc, 46-58, asst dir, 58-67; wool mgr new mkt outlets, 67-80, WOOL DIR NEW MKT OUTLETS, INT SECRETARIAT, WOODBURY, 80- *Mem:* Am Chem Soc; Fiber Soc; Am Asn Textile Chem & Colorists; Am Inst Chem; World Future Soc. *Res:* Chemical and engineering research on fibrous materials; conception and development of new products and processes and taking them to commercial fruition on a world-wide scale. *Mailing Add:* 108 Sharon Lane Greenlawn NY 11740

MIZELL, MERLE, b Chicago, Ill, Apr 25, 27; m 58; c 2. DEVELOPMENTAL GENETICS, ONCOLOGY. *Educ:* Univ Ill, Urbana, BS, 50, MS, 52, PhD(zool), 57. *Prof Exp:* Asst, Univ Ill, Urbana, 54-57; instr zool, 57-60, from asst prof to assoc prof biol, 60-70, assoc prof anat, Med Sch, 69-70, PROF ANAT, MED SCH & PROF BIOL, TULANE UNIV, 70-, DIR CHAPMAN H HYAMS III LAB TUMOR CELL BIOL, 69- *Concurrent Pos:* Am Cancer Soc & Cancer Asn Greater New Orleans grant, Tulane Univ; NSF grant; Damon Runyon Mem Fund grant; NIH grant; consult, Spec Virus Cancer Prog, Nat Cancer Inst & proj site visitor, Cancer Res Ctrs, 69-; corp mem, Marine Biol Lab. *Mem:* AAAS; Am Soc Zool; Am Inst Biol Sci; Soc Exp Biol & Med (secy, 69-71); Soc Develop Biol. *Res:* Cellular differentiation; mechanism of limb regeneration in spontaneous regeneration and induced regeneration; role of viruses as agents of normal and neoplastic differentiation; effects of the regeneration environment on neoplastic growths; amphibian tumor biology; genetic engineering; oncogenic herpesviruses. *Mailing Add:* Lab Tumor Cell Biol Tulane Univ New Orleans LA 70118

MIZELL, SHERWIN, b Chicago, Ill, Apr 27, 31; m 57; c 3. GROSS ANATOMY. *Educ:* Univ Ill, BS, 52, MS, 54, PhD(physiol), 58. *Prof Exp:* Res fel, Med Col SC, 58-59, from instr to asst prof anat, 59-64; assoc prof physiol sch med, Creighton Univ, 64-65; assoc prof anat & physiol, 65-75, PROF ANAT, MED SCI PROG, IND UNIV, BLOOMINGTON, 75-, HEAD SECT, 76- *Mem:* AAAS; Am Asn Anat; Am Soc Zool; Am Physiol Soc; Am Soc Photobiol. *Res:* Biological rhythms; synchronization and mechanisms responsible for changes in physiology and behavior; physiology and endocrinology of amphibians. *Mailing Add:* Med Sci Prog Ind Univ Bloomington IN 47401

MIZERES, NICHOLAS JAMES, b Pittsburgh, Pa, Nov 13, 24; m 52; c 1. ANATOMY. *Educ:* Kent State Univ, BS, 48; Mich State Univ, MS, 51; Univ Mich, PhD(anat), 54. *Prof Exp:* From instr to assoc prof, 54-66, PROF ANAT, SCH MED, WAYNE STATE UNIV, 66- *Honors & Awards:* Lamp Award, 59. *Mem:* AAAS; Asn Am Med Cols; Am Asn Anat. *Res:* Human anatomy; cardiovascular research, especially heart coronary circulation and the autonomic nervous system; descriptive anatomy related to surgery. *Mailing Add:* Dept of Anat Wayne State Univ Sch Med Detroit MI 48201

MIZIANTY, MICHAEL FRANCIS, b Carbondale, Pa, July 8, 32; m 55; c 5. ORGANIC CHEMISTRY, PHOTOGRAPHY. *Educ:* Univ Scranton, BS, 54; Lehigh Univ, PhD(org chem), 63. *Prof Exp:* Chemist, GAF Corp, 56-59, res specialist, 62-70; res mgr, Memorex Corp, 70-72; RES DIR, XIDEX CORP, 72- *Mem:* Am Chem Soc; Soc Photographic Scientists & Engrs. *Res:* Organic chemistry as applied to various aspects of photographic systems; chemistry of aromatic diazonium salts as photosensitive agents in high resolution microphotography. *Mailing Add:* Xidex Corp 305 Soquel Way Sunnyvale CA 94086

MIZIOLEK, ANDRZEJ WLADYSLAW, b Hannover, Ger, Feb 17, 50; US citizen; m 74; c 1. PHYSICAL CHEMISTRY. *Educ:* Wayne State Univ, BS, 71; Univ Calif, Berkeley, PhD(chem), 76. *Prof Exp:* Fel chem, Univ Calif, Irvine, 76-77; asst res chemist, Scripps Inst Oceanog, Univ Calif, San Diego, 77-81; RES PHYSICIST, US ARMY BALLISTIC RES LAB, 81- *Mem:* Am Chem Soc; Sigma Xi; Optical Soc Am; AAAS. *Res:* Application of laser spectroscopy to combustion and chemical analysis problems. *Mailing Add:* Ignition & Combustion Br US Army Ballistic Res Br Aberdeen Proving Grounds MD 21005

MIZIORKO, HENRY MICHAEL, b Philadelphia, Pa, Oct 11, 47; m 71; c 2. ENZYMOLOGY. *Educ:* St Joseph's Col, Pa, BS, 69; Univ Pa, PhD(biochem), 74. *Prof Exp:* Fel physiol chem, Sch Med, Johns Hopkins Univ, 74-77; asst prof, 77-80, ASSOC PROF BIOCHEM, MED COL WIS, 81- *Concurrent Pos:* Mellon Found fel, Sch Med, Johns Hopkins Univ, 76-77; NIH res career develop award, 79-84. *Mem:* Am Chem Soc; Am Soc Biol Chemists; Biophys Soc. *Res:* Mechanism of enzyme action; regulation in biological systems; ketogenesis; photosynthetic carbon assimilation; cholesterogenesis. *Mailing Add:* Dept of Biochem 8701 Watertown Plank Rd Milwaukee WI 53226

MIZMA, EDWARD JOHN, b Rochester, NY, Mar 29, 34; m 60; c 3. CLINICAL CHEMISTRY, CHEMICAL ENGINEERING. *Educ:* Bucknell Univ, ScB, 55; Cornell Univ, PhD(chem eng), 59. *Prof Exp:* Tech assoc, Mfg Exp Div, 58-71, supvr eng div, 71-72, supvr mfg exp div, 72-76, asst dir mfg tech div, 76-80, ASST DIR HEALTH SAFETY & HUMAN FAC LAB, DIR CLIN CHEM TECH CTR, EASTMAN KODAK CO, 80- *Mem:* AAAS. *Res:* Biochemical engineering; continuous electrophoresis equipment; rheology of viscous fluids especially polymer solutions; direction of pilot plant and semi-plant coating machines; technical supervision. *Mailing Add:* 311 North Ave Hilton NY 14468

MIZRAHI, SADI, chemical engineering, see previous edition

MIZUBA, SETH SETSUO, mycology, bacteriology, see previous edition

MIZUKAMI, HIROSHI, b Otaru-Shi, Japan, Oct 11, 32; m 59. BIOPHYSICS, HEMATOLOGY. *Educ:* Int Christian Univ, Tokyo, BA, 57; Univ Ill, PhD(biophys), 63. *Prof Exp:* Res fel phys chem, Univ Minn, 62-65, res fel med, Univ Hosps, 64-65; from asst prof to assoc prof biol, 65-74, PROF BIOL, WAYNE STATE UNIV, 74- *Concurrent Pos:* Vis res prof, Tokyo Med & Dent Univ, 73-74. *Mem:* AAAS; Biophys Soc; Am Chem Soc. *Res:* Structure and function of proteins, gas transport and membranes of erythrocytes; sickle cells, muscle proteins. *Mailing Add:* Dept of Biol Wayne State Univ Detroit MI 48202

MIZUNO, ELMER T, electrical engineering, mathematics, see previous edition

MIZUNO, WILLIAM GEORGE, b Ocean Falls, BC; nat US; m 48; c 3. BACTERIOLOGY. *Educ:* Univ Minn, BA, 48, MS, 50, PhD, 56. *Prof Exp:* Bacteriologist, 43-47, res bacteriologist, 48-65, sr res scientist, 65-71, mgr corp tech serv, 71-77, ASSOC DIR CORP SCI & TECHNOL, ECON LAB, INC, 77- *Concurrent Pos:* Hon fel, Univ Minn, 58. *Mem:* Am Soc Microbiol; Am Pub Health Asn; Sigma Xi. *Res:* Endamoeba histolytica; biocidal agents; cysticides; bactericides; fungicides; sanitation; bacterial metabolism; radioactive tracers; surface active agents; detergents; enzymes. *Mailing Add:* 1541 E Sixth St St Paul MN 55106

MIZUSHIMA, MASATAKA, b Tokyo, Japan, Mar 30, 23; US citizen; m 55; c 5. MOLECULAR PHYSICS. *Educ:* Univ Tokyo, BA, 46, DrSc(physics), 51. *Prof Exp:* Res assoc physics, Duke Univ, 52-55; from asst prof to assoc prof, 55-60, PROF PHYSICS, UNIV COLO, BOULDER, 60- *Concurrent Pos:* Mem staff, Nat Bur Standards, 55-69; vis prof univ & inst solid state physics, Univ Tokyo, 62-63, fac sci, Univ Rennes, 64, inst atomic physics, Univ Bucharest, 69-70, Cath Univ Nijmegen, 72 & Univ Electro-Comm, Tokyo, 80-81. *Mem:* Am Phys Soc. *Res:* Theory of microwave and laser spectroscopy; molecular structure, particularly hyperfine structure and Zeeman effect; theory of radiation processes; propagation of radiation through earth's atmosphere. *Mailing Add:* Dept of Physics & Astrophys Univ of Colo Boulder CO 80309

MIZUTANI, SATOSHI, b Yokohama, Japan, Nov 19, 37; m 66. VIROLOGY. *Educ:* Tokyo Univ Agr & Tech, BS, 62; Univ Kans, PhD(microbiol), 69. *Prof Exp:* Res scientist antibiotics, Nippon Kayaku Co, Ltd, 62-65; instr tumor virol, McArdle Lab Cancer Res, Univ Wis-Madison, 71-72, asst scientist, 72-75, assoc scientist, 75-80; sr scientist, Abbott Lab, North Chicago, 80-81; DIR, CELL & MOLECULAR BIOL GENETICS DIV, BETHESDA RES LAB, INC, 81- *Concurrent Pos:* Scholar, Leukemia Soc Am, Inc, 73-78. *Mem:* Am Soc Microbiol. *Res:* Molecular mechanism of replication of RNA tumor viruses and their relatives; mechanism of tumor formation by RNA tumor viruses; gene structure and expression in eukaryotes; manipulation of genes of eukaryotes. *Mailing Add:* Bethesda Res Labs Inc 8717 Grovemont Circle Gaithersburg MD 20877

MJOLSNESS, RAYMOND C, b Chicago, Ill, Apr 22, 33; m 58; c 3. FLUID DYNAMICS, ATOMIC PHYSICS. *Educ:* Reed Col, BA, 53; Oxford Univ, BA, 55; Princeton Univ, PhD(math physics), 63. *Prof Exp:* Asst physics, Los Alamos Sci Lab, 58-61; asst prof math, Reed Col, 61-62; theoret physicist space sci lab, Gen Elec Co, 62-64, consult, 64; staff mem, Los Alamos Sci Lab, 64-67; assoc prof astron, Pa State Univ, 67-69; STAFF MEM, LOS ALAMOS SCI LAB, 69- *Concurrent Pos:* State secy, Rhodes Scholar Trust, 74-76. *Mem:* Am Phys Soc; Math Asn Am. *Res:* Plasma stability; collisional relaxation of plasmas; scattering of electrons on atoms and molecules; cosmology and galaxy formation; laser energy absorption; fluid dynamics and hydrodynamic turbulence theory. *Mailing Add:* Los Alamos Sci Lab Los Alamos NM 87544

MJOSUND, ARNE, b Fana, Norway, Nov 13, 21. INDUSTRIAL ENGINEERING. *Educ:* Norweg Sch Econ & Bus Admin, dipl, 51; Johns Hopkins Univ, PhD(indust eng), 65. *Prof Exp:* Secy planning, Norweg Off Fisheries, 46-48; secy shipping, Jansen's Shipowner Co, 51-52; res assoc, Soc Indust Res, N Norway, 52-55; dir statist, Norweg Naval Hq, 55-66; assoc prof indust eng, 66-71, PROF INDUST ENG, UNIV ALA, 71- *Concurrent Pos:* Sr instr & res asst, Johns Hopkins Univ, 61-63; consult, US Army Missile Command, 66- *Mem:* AAAS; Opers Res Soc Am; Am Statist Asn; Am Soc Eng Educ. *Res:* Operations research; organization theory. *Mailing Add:* Dept of Comput Sci & Opers Res Univ of Ala PO Box 6316 University AL 35486

MLODOZENIEC, ARTHUR ROMAN, b Buffalo, NY, Mar 29, 37. PHYSICAL CHEMISTRY, PHARMACY. *Educ:* Fordham Univ, BS, 59; Univ Wis, PhD, 64. *Prof Exp:* Res assoc prod develop, Upjohn Co, 64-68; sr phys chemist, Solid Surfaces Lab, Hoffmann-La Roche, Inc, 68-74, group leader appl sci, 74-76, mgr qual control, 77-78, dir res & diag prod, 78-80; EXEC DIR INT RES, MERCK, SHARP & DOHME RES LAB, 81- *Concurrent Pos:* Nat chmn, Indust Pharmaceut Technol, 74-78; adj prof, Sch Pharm, Univ Ky, 77- & pharmaceut chem, Univ Kans, 81-; mem exec comt, Acad Pharmaceut Sci, 78-81 & Nat Nominating Comt, 79-82. *Honors & Awards:* Cosmetic Soc Award, Soc Cosmetic Chem, 79. *Mem:* AAAS; Soc Cosmetic Chem; Am Chem Soc; Sigma Xi; fel Acad Pharmaceut Sci. *Res:* Thermal analysis; molecular organic solid physics; scanning electron microscopy and surface analysis; small particle technology; particle flow and cohesion; phase transitions; liquid crystal behavior; microencapsulation of drugs; drug specifications; dosage form design. *Mailing Add:* Qual Control Dept Hoffmann-La Roche Inc Nutley NJ 07110

MO, CHARLES TSE C, b China; US citizen. PLASMA PHYSICS, PROBABILITY THEORY. *Educ:* Calif Inst Technol, MS, 66, PhD(elec eng & physics), 69. *Prof Exp:* Res asst elec eng, Calif Inst Technol, 65-69, Sloan res fel, 69-70, res fel, 70-72, sr res fel, 72-73; MEM SR TECH STAFF & PROF MGR, RES & DEVELOP ASSOCS, MARINA DEL REY, CALIF, 73- *Concurrent Pos:* Anthony fel, Calif Inst Technol, 66. *Mem:* Am Phys Soc; Int Union Radio Sci; Sigma Xi. *Res:* Electrodynamics; relativity; probability and mathematical statistics; waves in plasma. *Mailing Add:* 782 Radcliffe Ave Pacific Palisades CA 90272

MO, LUKE WEI, b Shantung, China, June 3, 34; m 60; c 2. PHYSICS. *Educ:* Nat Taiwan Univ, BS, 56; Tsing Hua Univ, Taiwan, MS, 59; Columbia Univ, PhD(physics), 63. *Prof Exp:* Res assoc physics, Columbia Univ, 63-64; res physicist linear accelerator ctr, Stanford Univ, 65-69; asst prof physics, Univ Chicago, 69-76; assoc prof, 76-78, PROF PHYSICS, VA POLYTECH INST & STATE UNIV, 78- *Concurrent Pos:* Guggenheim fel, 81. *Mem:* Fel Am Phys Soc. *Res:* Electromagnetic and weak interactions in high energy physics; experiments on conserved-vector current theorem; electron scatterings; time-reversal invariance; muon-nucleon and neutrino-electron scatterings at Fermilab; search for axion-like particles. *Mailing Add:* Dept of Physics Va Polytech Inst & State Univ Blacksburg VA 24061

MOAD, M(OHAMED) F(ARES), b Damascus, Syria, Sept 23, 28; m 58; c 2. ELECTRICAL ENGINEERING. *Educ:* Ga Inst Technol, BS & MS, 57, PhD(elec eng), 61. *Prof Exp:* Instr elec eng, Ga Inst Technol, 57-61; dir dept of studies, Syrian Broadcasting Serv, 61-63; asst prof elec eng, 63-68, ASSOC PROF ELEC ENG, GA INST TECHNOL, 68- *Res:* Network theory; communication; systems. *Mailing Add:* Dept of Elec Eng Ga Inst of Technol Atlanta GA 30332

MOAK, CHARLES DEXTER, b Marshall, Tex, Feb 24, 22; m 43; c 2. PHYSICS. *Educ:* Univ Tenn, BS, 43, PhD(physics), 54. *Prof Exp:* Asst, Univ Chicago, 44; PHYSICIST, OAK RIDGE NAT LAB, 44- *Mem:* Am Phys Soc. *Res:* Alpha particles accompanying fission; slow neutron cross-sections;

neutron capture gamma-ray studies; high-voltage accelerator research on light element charged-particle reactions; interactions of heavy particles with matter. *Mailing Add:* Oak Ridge Nat Lab Oak Ridge TN 37830

MOAK, JAMES EMANUEL, b Norfield, Miss, Oct 26, 16; m 43; c 3. FOREST ECONOMICS. *Educ:* Univ Fla, BSF, 52; Ala Polytech Inst, MSF, 53; State Univ NY Col Forestry, Syracuse, PhD(forestry econ), 65. *Prof Exp:* Instr forestry, 53-54, from asst prof to assoc prof, 54-66, PROF FORESTRY, MISS STATE UNIV, 66- *Concurrent Pos:* Sci fac fel, 59. *Mem:* Soc Am Foresters. *Mailing Add:* Dept of Forestry Miss State Univ Mississippi State MS 39762

MOAT, ALBERT GROOMBRIDGE, b Nyack, NY, Apr 23, 26; m 49; c 3. MICROBIOLOGY. *Educ:* Cornell Univ, BS, 49, MS, 50; Univ Minn, PhD(bact), 53; Am Bd Microbiol, dipl. *Prof Exp:* From asst prof to prof bact, microbiol & immunol, Hahnemann Med Col, 52-78; PROF MICROBIOL & CHMN DEPT, SCH MED, MARSHALL UNIV, 78- USPHS spec res fel & vis prof, Cornell Univ, 71-72. *Mem:* AAAS; Am Soc Microbiol; Am Chem Soc; Am Soc Biol Chem; fel Am Acad Microbiol. *Res:* Nutrition, metabolism and genetics of microorganisms. *Mailing Add:* Dept of Microbiol Marshall Univ Sch of Med Huntington WV 25701

MOATES, ROBERT FRANKLIN, b Birmingham, Ala, May 16, 38; m 62; c 2. TOBACCO CHEMISTRY, TECHNOLOGY. *Educ:* Duke Univ, BS, 60; Univ SC, PhD(org chem), 66. *Prof Exp:* RES CHEMIST, R J REYNOLDS TOBACCO CO, 65- *Mem:* Am Chem Soc; The Chem Soc. *Res:* Alkaloid isolation; synthesis of alkaloid systems; synthetic organic chemistry; synthesis of natural products; isolation and identification of natural products. *Mailing Add:* Res Dept R J Reynolds Tobacco Co Winston-Salem NC 27102

MOATS, ROBERT R(YDER), electronics, see previous edition

MOATS, WILLIAM ALDEN, b Des Moines, Iowa, Nov 30, 28; m 58; c 2. FOOD BIOCHEMISTRY. *Educ:* Iowa State Univ, BS, 50; Univ Md, PhD(chem), 57. *Prof Exp:* Asst chem, Univ Md, 50-55; res chemist, Field Crops & Animal Prod Br, Mkt Qual Res Div, 57-72, res chemist, Agr Mkt Res Inst, Sci & Educ Admin-Agr Res, 72-80, RES CHEMIST, MEAT SCI RES LAB, ANIMAL SCI INST, AGR RES SERV, USDA, 80- *Mem:* Am Chem Soc; Am Soc Microbiol; Poultry Sci Asn; Am Dairy Sci Asn. *Res:* Quality tests for dairy products; staining of bacteria for microscopic examination; determination of pesticide residues in foods; heat resistance of bacteria; improved media for salmonella detection; egg washing and sanitizing procedures; physicochemical methods for detecting antibiotic residues. *Mailing Add:* Agr Res Ctr USDA Bldg 201-East Beltsville MD 20705

MOAVENZADEH, FRED, b Rasht, Iran, Oct 14, 35; m 61; c 2. CIVIL ENGINEERING, MATERIALS SCIENCE. *Educ:* Univ Tehran, BS, 58; Cornell Univ, MS, 60; Purdue Univ, PhD(civil eng), 62. *Prof Exp:* Field engr, Kampsax Overseas, Inc, 56; res asst civil eng, Purdue Univ, 60-62; asst prof, Ohio State Univ, 62-65; assoc prof, 65-72, PROF CIVIL ENG, MASS INST TECHNOL, 72-, DIR TECHNOL ADAPTATION PROG, 75- *Concurrent Pos:* Comt mem, Hwy Res Bd, Nat Acad Sci-Nat Res Coun; vis prof civil eng, Grad Sch Design, Harvard Univ, 70- *Honors & Awards:* Sanford E Thompson Award, Am Soc Testing & Mat. *Mem:* Bldg Res Inst-Nat Acad Eng; Am Concrete Inst; Am Soc Civil Engrs; AAAS; Sigma Xi. *Res:* Mechanics of materials; viscoelasticity; highway engineering and construction. *Mailing Add:* Mass Inst of Technol Rm 1-171 77 Massachusetts Ave Cambridge MA 02139

MOAWAD, ATEF H, b Dec 2, 35; Can citizen; m 66; c 2. OBSTETRICS & GYNECOLOGY, PHARMACOLOGY. *Educ:* Cairo Univ, MD, 58; Jefferson Med Col, MS, 63; Am Bd Obstet & Gynec, dipl, 68; FRCS(C), 69. *Prof Exp:* Fel obstet & gynec, Case Western Reserve Univ, 64-65; vis investr, Univ Lund, 65-66; from lectr pharmacol to assoc prof obstet & gynec & pharmacol, Univ Alta, 66-72; prof obstet & gynec & pharmacol, 72-75, PROF OBSTET & GYNEC, DIV BIOL SCI & PRITZKER SCH MED, UNIV CHICAGO, 75-, PROF PEDIAT, 76- *Concurrent Pos:* Brush Found scholar, 66-67. *Mem:* Fel Am Col Obstet & Gynec; Soc Gynec Invest; Pharmacol Soc Can; NY Acad Sci; Can Med Asn. *Res:* Reproductive physiology and pharmacology, chiefly of the structure and function of uterine and fallopian tube smooth muscle. *Mailing Add:* Chicago Lying-In Hosp 5841 S Maryland Ave Chicago IL 60637

MOAZED, CYRUS, physics, see previous edition

MOAZED, K(HOSROW) L(OUIS), b Meshed, Iran, Sept 14, 30; nat US; m 53; c 4. PHYSICAL METALLURGY. *Educ:* Rensselaer Polytech Inst, BS, 53, MMetEng, 56; Carnegie Inst Technol, MS, 58, PhD(metall), 59. *Prof Exp:* Res assoc metall res, Rensselaer Polytech Inst, 53-56; proj engr, Carnegie Inst Technol, 56-59; from asst prof to assoc prof metall, Ohio State Univ, 59-68; PROF MAT ENG, NC STATE UNIV, 68- *Mem:* AAAS; Am Phys Soc; Am Soc Metals; Am Inst Mining, Metall & Petrol Engrs; fel Am Inst Chemists. *Res:* Structure and properties of metallic surfaces; thermodynamics and kinetics of surface reactions; transformations in solids; field emission microscopy. *Mailing Add:* 207 Page Hall NC State Univ Raleigh NC 27607

MOBERG, GARY PHILIP, b Monmouth, Ill, Feb 14, 41; m 67; c 2. PHYSIOLOGY, NEUROENDOCRINOLOGY. *Educ:* Monmouth Col, Ill, BA, 63; Univ Ill, Urbana, MS, 65, PhD(physiol), 68. *Prof Exp:* NIH fel med ctr, Univ Calif, San Francisco, 68-70; asst prof animal sci & animal physiol, 70-76, ASSOC PROF ANIMAL SCI & ANIMAL PHYSIOL, UNIV CALIF, DAVIS, 76-, RES PHYSIOLOGIST, CALIF PRIMATE RES CTR, 79- *Concurrent Pos:* NIH res grants, Univ Calif, Davis, 71-76 & 79-; vis prof, Utrecht Med Sch, Neth & NATO sr scientist fel, 77; affil, Calif Primate Res Ctr, 77-79. *Mem:* AAAS; Am Physiol Soc; Endocrine Soc; Am Soc Animal Sci; Soc Neurosci. *Res:* Neural control of the anterior pituitary; effects of stress on endocrine system regulation and behavior; stress physiology. *Mailing Add:* Dept of Animal Sci Univ of Calif Davis CA 95606

MOBERLY, LAWRENCE ALLAN, low temperature physics, see previous edition

MOBLEY, CARROLL EDWARD, b Baltimore, Md, Oct 22, 41; m 64; c 2. MATERIALS SCIENCE. *Educ:* Johns Hopkins Univ, BA, 63, PhD(mech), 68. *Prof Exp:* Sr researcher metall, Battelle Columbus Labs, 67-78; assoc prof, 78-81, PROF METALL, OHIO STATE UNIV, 81- *Concurrent Pos:* Vis prof mech & mat sci, Johns Hopkins Univ, 76-77. *Honors & Awards:* IR-100 Award, Indust Res Mag, 75. *Mem:* Am Soc Metals; Am Inst Mining, Metall & Petrol Engrs; Sigma Xi; Am Foundrymen's Soc. *Res:* Solidification of metals; structure and properties of rapidly solidified materials; process metallurgy of iron and steel production; high velocity deformation of metals. *Mailing Add:* Dept Metall Eng 116 W 19th Ave Columbus OH 43210

MOBLEY, CURTIS DALE, b Canyon, Tex, June 15, 47; m 79. HYDROLOGIC OPTICS, CLIMATE FORECASTING. *Educ:* Univ Tex, Austin, BS, 69; Univ Md, College Park, PhD(meteorol), 77. *Prof Exp:* Nat Res Coun res assoc, Pac Marine Environ Lab, 77-79, INST SCIENTIST, JOINT INST, STUDY OF ATMOSPHERE & OCEAN, UNIV WASH & PAC MARINE ENIVRON LAB, NAT OCEANIC & ATMOSPHERIC ADMIN, SEATTLE, 79- *Mem:* Am Meteorol Soc. *Res:* Computational fluid dynamics, especially free-surface fluid flows; numerical studies of light in the ocean (hydrologic optics); fundamental numerical research in statistical-dynamical climate forecasting. *Mailing Add:* Pac Marine Environ Lab 3711 15th Ave NE Seattle WA 98105

MOBERG, WILLIAM KARL, b Fargo, NDak, July 1, 48; m 70; c 2. ORGANIC CHEMISTRY, AGRICULTURAL & FOOD CHEMISTRY. *Educ:* Bowdoin Col, AB, 69; Harvard Univ, AM, 71, PhD(chem), 74. *Prof Exp:* Fel chem, Mass Inst Technol, 74-77; mem staff chem, Cent Res Dept, 77-80, MEM STAFF, BIOCHEM DEPT, E I DU PONT DE NEMOURS & CO INC, 80- *Concurrent Pos:* NIH fel, 75-77. *Mem:* Am Chem Soc. *Res:* Organic synthesis. *Mailing Add:* Biochem Dept E324-304 E I du Pont de Nemours & Co Inc Wilmington DE 19898

MOBLEY, HAROLD MORTON, b Houston, Tex, Jan 5, 18; m 47; c 4. PLANT PHYSIOLOGY. *Educ:* Univ Houston, BS, 46, MS, 48; Univ Tex, PhD(bot), 62. *Prof Exp:* Instr photog, physics & Math, Univ Houston, 46-52; teacher, Sr High Sch, Tex, 52-55; asst prof eng drawing, Univ Tex, 55-60, bot & zool, 61-67; prof biol, McMurry Col, 67-68; assoc prof biol, 69-74, PROF BOT, WESTERN STATE COL, 74- *Mem:* AAAS; Bot Soc Am. *Res:* Circadian rhythms. *Mailing Add:* Div of Natural Sci & Math Western State Col Gunnison CO 81230

MOBLEY, J GRAHAM, electrical engineering, see previous edition

MOBLEY, JACK ERVIN, b Little Rock, Ark, Nov 12, 25; m 47; c 4. UROLOGY. *Educ:* Univ Ark, BS, 46; Vanderbilt Univ, MD, 48; Mayo Grad Sch Med, Univ Minn, MS, 56; FRCS(C). *Prof Exp:* Asst prof urol, Sch Med, Tulane Univ, 66-67; from assoc prof to prof, Sch Med, Univ Ark, Little Rock, 66-72, head dept, 66-72; prof urol & chmn dept, Rush-Presby-St Luke's Med Ctr, 72-74; prof urol & assoc dean clin sci, Sch Med, Univ SDak, 74-76; PROF UROL & DEAN, COL MED, E TENN STATE UNIV, 76- *Mem:* Am Col Surgeons; AMA; NY Acad Sci. *Res:* Renal physiology, lymphatics and transplantation. *Mailing Add:* Off of the Dean ETenn State Univ Col of Med Johnson City TN 37601

MOBLEY, JEAN BELLINGRATH, b Norfolk, Va, Mar 13, 27; m 49; c 2. MATHEMATICS, MATHEMATICS EDUCATION. *Educ:* Duke Univ, AB, 48; Univ NC, MA, 54, PhD, 70. *Prof Exp:* Teacher, Pub Schs, NC, 48-56; asst prof math, Flora MacDonald Col, 56-59, assoc prof & head dept, 59-61; assoc prof, St Andrews Presby Col, 61-63; prof educ & head dept sec educ, 63-80, PROF MATH, PFEIFFER COL, 63- *Mem:* Nat Coun Teachers Math; Nat Educ Asn; Math Asn Am. *Res:* Geometry; mathematics education. *Mailing Add:* Dept Math Pfeiffer Col Misenheimer NC 28109

MOBLEY, RALPH CLAUDE, b Buffalo, NY; m. NUCLEAR PHYSICS. *Educ:* Univ Wis, PhD(physics), 50. *Prof Exp:* Res assoc physics, Univ Wis, 50-51; res assoc, Duke Univ, 51-53; from asst prof to assoc prof, La State Univ, 53-61; chmn dept, 61-72, PROF PHYSICS, OAKLAND UNIV, 61- *Concurrent Pos:* Indust consult, 63- *Mem:* Fel Am Phys Soc; Inst Elec & Electronics Engrs. *Res:* Photoneutron thresholds; charged particle scattering; neutron scattering; ion buncher and accelerator development and neutron scattering by time-of-flight method; mass spectrometry; monopole and macromolecule mass spectrometer development. *Mailing Add:* Dept of Physics Oakland Univ Rochester MI 48063

MOBLEY, RICHARD MORRIS, b Atlanta, Ga, Oct 12, 38; div; c 1. ACCELERATOR & PARTICLE PHYSICS. *Educ:* Dartmouth Col, BA, 60; Yale Univ, PhD(physics), 67. *Prof Exp:* Physicist accelerator & particle, Fermilab, 68-72; physicist accelerator & plasma, Lawrence Berkeley Lab, 72-76; PHYSICIST ACCELERATOR, BROOKHAVEN NAT LAB, 77- *Res:* Ion sources; high energy beam manipulation and transport. *Mailing Add:* Accelerator Dept Bldg 911B Brookhaven Nat Lab Upton NY 11973

MOBRAATEN, LARRY EDWARD, b Fergus Falls, Minn, Sept 6, 38; m 67; c 2. GERMPLASM PRESERVATION, CRYOBIOLOGY. *Educ:* Univ Calif, Berkeley, AB, 62; Univ Maine, Orono, PhD(zool), 72. *Prof Exp:* Curie Found fel immunogenetics, 72-74; assoc staff scientist immunogenetics, 74-79, ASSOC STAFF SCIENTIST GENETICS, JACKSON LAB, 80- *Concurrent Pos:* Lectr zool, Univ Maine, Orono, 75- *Mem:* Assoc Sigma Xi; Am Asn Tissue Banks; Genetics Soc Am; Soc Cryobiol. *Res:* Cryopresevation of mouse embryos; analysis of histocompatibility mutations in mice. *Mailing Add:* Jackson Lab Bar Harbor ME 04609

MOCELLA, MICHAEL THOMAS, b Chicago, Ill, Aug 24, 48; m 70; c 2. CATALYSIS, ORGANOMETALLIC CHEMISTRY. *Educ:* Mich State Univ, BS, 70; Univ Ill, PhD(inorg chem), 74. *Prof Exp:* Res assoc chem, Cornell Univ, 74-76; res chemist, Air Prod & Chem, Inc, 76-78; sr res chemist, Oxirane Int, 78-81; GROUP LEADER & SR RES CHEMIST, ARCO CHEM CO, 81- *Mem:* Am Chem Soc; Catalysis Soc. *Res:* Inorganic chemistry; small molecule activation. *Mailing Add:* ARCO Chem Co 3801 W Chester Pike Newtown Square PA 19073

MOCH, IRVING, JR, b New York, NY, Jan 28, 27; m 51. CHEMICAL ENGINEERING. *Educ:* Columbia Univ, AB, 47, BS, 49, MS, 50, PhD(chem eng), 56. *Prof Exp:* Res engr, E I du Pont de Nemours & Co, Inc, La Porte, Tex, 54-63, supt pilot plant, 63-68, tech supt, Electrochem Dept, 68-72, res supt, Polymer Prod Dept, 72-78, DEVELOP & TECH SERV MGR, POLYMER PROD DEPT, E I DU PONT DE NEMOURS & CO, INC, 78- *Mem:* AAAS; Am Inst Chem Engrs; Am Chem Soc; Sigma Xi. *Res:* Process and products development. *Mailing Add:* Polymer Prod Dept Permasep Bldg E I du Pont de Nemours & Co Inc Wilmington DE 19898

MOCHEL, JACK MCKINNEY, b Boston, Mass, Jan 27, 39; m 62; c 3. PHYSICS. *Educ:* Cornell Univ, BA, 61; Univ Rochester, PhD(physics), 65. *Prof Exp:* Fel physics, Univ Rochester, 65-66; from asst prof to assoc prof, 66-77, PROF PHYSICS, UNIV ILL, 77- *Concurrent Pos:* A P Sloan fel, 68-74; assoc, Ctr Advan Study, 73-74. *Mem:* Am Phys Soc; Sigma Xi. *Res:* Low temperature physics; properties of helium in two and three dimension; superconductivity and phase transitions. *Mailing Add:* Dept of Physics Univ of Ill Urbana IL 61801

MOCHEL, MYRON GEORGE, b Fremont, Ohio, Oct 9, 05; m 30; c 3. MECHANICAL ENGINEERING. *Educ:* Case Inst Technol, BS, 29; Yale Univ, MS, 30. *Prof Exp:* Develop engr, Socony Mobil Oil Co, Inc, 31-37; mech design & develop engr, Gearing Eng Div, Westinghouse Elec Corp, 37-43; mech design engr, Underwater Sound Lab, Harvard Univ, 43-45; supvr training, Steam Turbine Div, Worthington Corp, 45-49; assoc prof eng graphics, 49-55, prof mech eng, 55-71, EMER PROF MECH ENG, CLARKSON COL TECHNOL, 71- *Concurrent Pos:* Lectr, Eve Div, Univ Pittsburgh, 38-43 & NY State Adult Educ Prog, 46-49; partic, Conf Eng Graphics Sci Eng, NSF, 60; adv mgr, J Eng Graphics, 63-66. *Mem:* Am Soc Mech Engrs; Nat Soc Prof Engrs; Am Soc Eng Educ. *Res:* Fundamentals of engineering graphics. *Mailing Add:* 3 Castle Dr Potsdam NY 13676

MOCHEL, VIRGIL DALE, b Woodland, Ind, Oct 29, 30; m 51; c 3. PHYSICAL CHEMISTRY, PHYSICS. *Educ:* Purdue Univ, BS, 52, MS, 54; Univ Ill, PhD(nuclear magnetic resonance), 60. *Prof Exp:* Chief chemist, Globe Am Corp, 53-54; res chemist, US Army Chem Ctr, 54-56; sr chemist, Corning Glass Works, 59-64; res chemist, 64-66, sr res chemist, 66-67, RES ASSOC POLYMER NUCLEAR MAGNETIC RESONANCE, FIRESTONE TIRE & RUBBER CO, AKRON, 67- *Mem:* Am Chem Soc; Am Phys Soc. *Res:* High resolution nuclear magnetic resonance; kinetics; polymer structure studies; electroluminescence; photoluminescence; semiconduction; photoconduction; glass composition. *Mailing Add:* 1804 Wall Rd Wadsworth OH 44281

MOCHRIE, RICHARD DOUGLAS, b Lowell, Mass, Feb 17, 28; m 50; c 3. DAIRY SCIENCE. *Educ:* Univ Conn, BS, 50, MS, 53; NC State Col, PhD(rumen nutrit), 58. *Prof Exp:* Res technician, Univ Conn, 50-53; asst animal sci, 53-54, res instr, 54-58, from asst prof to assoc prof, 58-72, fac senate vchmn, 80-81, chmn, 81-82, PROF ANIMAL SCI, NC STATE UNIV, 72- *Concurrent Pos:* Mem comt abnormal milk control & adv to Coun I, Nat Conf Interstate Milk Shipments, 71- *Mem:* Am Dairy Sci Asn; Nat Mastitis Coun (vpres, 75-76, pres, 76-); Int Asn Milk, Food & Environ Sanitarians, Inc; Asn Off Analytical Chemists. *Res:* Dairy cattle nutrition, physiology of lactation and forage utilization. *Mailing Add:* Dept of Animal Sci NC State Univ Raleigh NC 27650

MOCK, DAVID CLINTON, JR, b Redlands, Calif, May 6, 22; m 52. INTERNAL MEDICINE. *Educ:* Univ Southern Calif, AB, 44; Hahnemann Med Col, MD, 48; Am Bd Internal Med, dipl, 58. *Prof Exp:* Intern, Hahnemann Hosp, Philadelphia, 48-49; resident, Community Hosp of San Mateo County, Calif, 49-50, resident med, 50-51 & 54; chief med serv, Navajo Base Hosp, Ft Defiance, Ariz, 51-53, med officer in chg, 52-53; resident med, Vet Admin Hosp, Oklahoma City, Okla, 54-55; pvt pract, Calif, 55-56; from clin asst to assoc prof, 56-72, assoc dean med student affairs, 69-76, PROF MED, COL MED, UNIV OKLA, 72-, ASSOC DEAN POSTDOCTORAL EDUC, 76-, DIR, CONTINUING MED EDUC, 80- *Concurrent Pos:* Res fel exp therapeut, Col Med, Univ Okla, 56-57; Upjohn fel, 57-59; attend physician, Vet Admin Hosp, Oklahoma City, 56- & Univ Okla Hosp, 59-; dir therapeut, Univ Okla, 58-60, asst dean student affairs, 66-69. *Mem:* Am Fedn Clin Res; fel Am Col Physicians; NY Acad Sci. *Res:* Clinical drug investigation. *Mailing Add:* Univ of Okla Col of Med PO Box 26901 Oklahoma City OK 73190

MOCK, DOUGLAS WAYNE, b New York, NY, July 4, 47; m 69. ANIMAL BEHAVIOR, ECOLOGY. *Educ:* Cornell Univ, BS, 69; Univ Minn, MS, 72, PhD(ecol), 76. *Prof Exp:* Fel ethol, Smithsonian Inst, 76-77; vis scientist, Percy Fitzpatrick Inst African Ornith, Univ Cape Town, 77; ASST PROF ZOOL, UNIV OKLA, 78- *Honors & Awards:* Alexander P Wilson Prize, Wilson Ornith Soc, 75; A Brazier Howell Prize, Cooper Ornith Soc, 76. *Mem:* Animal Behav Soc; Ecol Soc Am; Wilson Ornith Soc; Cooper Ornith Soc; Am Ornithologists Union. *Res:* Evolutionary biology, especially theoretical and field studies of ecology and behavior of vertebrates; evolution of social organization, mating systems and communication in birds. *Mailing Add:* Dept of Zool Univ of Okla Norman OK 73019

MOCK, GORDON DUANE, b Bloomington, Ill, Oct 21, 27; m 54; c 2. MATHEMATICS. *Educ:* Univ Ill, BS, 50, MS, 51; Univ Wis, PhD(educ), 59. *Prof Exp:* Teacher high sch, Ill, 51-53; teacher lab sch, Univ Wis-Madison, 54-55; teacher lab sch, Univ Southern Ill-Carbondale, 55-56; teacher lab sch, Univ Wis-Madison, 56-58; teacher math, State Univ NY Col Oswego, 58-60; assoc prof, 60-67, PROF MATH, WESTERN ILL UNIV, 67- *Concurrent Pos:* NSF sci fac fel, 63-64. *Mem:* Am Math Soc; Math Asn Am. *Res:* Mathematics education. *Mailing Add:* Dept of Math Western Ill Univ Macomb IL 61455

MOCK, JAMES JOSEPH, b Geneseo, Ill, Feb 15, 43; m 66; c 3. AGRONOMY, PLANT BREEDING. *Educ:* Monmouth Col, Ill, BA, 65; Iowa State Univ, PhD(agron), 70. *Prof Exp:* From asst prof to prof plant breeding, Iowa State Univ, 70-78; DIR CORN RES, NORTHRUP KING CO, 78- *Mem:* Am Soc Agron; Crop Sci Soc Am. *Res:* Physiological corn breeding; breeding maize genotypes that will efficiently intercept and convert solar energy into grain. *Mailing Add:* Res Ctr Northrup King Co Stanton MN 55081

MOCK, JOHN E(DWIN), b Altoona, Pa, Sept 29, 25; m 47; c 2. NUCLEAR ENGINEERING. *Educ:* US Mil Acad, BS, 47; Purdue Univ, BS & MS, 50, PhD(nuclear eng), 60; Ohio State Univ, MS, 53; George Washington Univ, MS, 65, MBA, 68. *Prof Exp:* US Air Force, 47-68, proj scientist, Wright Air Develop Ctr, Ohio, 49-54, staff scientist, Hq Ger, 55-58, sci dir, Defense Atomic Support Agency, Washington, DC, 60-64, staff scientist, Nuclear Res Assocs, NY, 64-66, sci dir, Advan Res Projs Agency, Washington, DC, 66-68; dir, Ga Sci & Technol Comn, 68-76, Ga Ctr Technol Forecasting & Technol Assessment, 69-76 & Ga Inst Biotechnol, 69-76; SR TECHNOL ADV, US ENERGY RES & DEVELOP ADMIN, WASHINGTON, DC, 76- *Concurrent Pos:* Assoc prof, George Washington Univ, 60-64; consult, Kaman Nuclear Div, 64-65; assoc prof US Air Force Acad, 64-65; consult, Off Secy Defense, 68-71; adv, Gulf Univs Res Corp, 68-71; Southern Interstate Nuclear Bd, 68-; dir, Coastal State Orgn, 69-70; mem coun, State Govts Comt Sci & Technol, 69-; chmn, Nat Gov Coun Sci & Technol, 70-71; consult comt cities of future, Nat Acad Eng, 70- *Honors & Awards:* Mark Mills Award, Am Nuclear Soc, 60. *Mem:* AAAS; Am Chem Soc; Am Phys Soc; Opers Res Soc Am; Am Soc Eng Educ. *Res:* Nuclear effects; space physics; electromagnetic propagation; heat transfer; reentry physics; reaction rates; clathrate formation; theoretical analysis; game theory; civil defense; military strategy; oceanography; science policy. *Mailing Add:* US Energy Res & Develop Admin Washington DC 20545

MOCK, ORIN BAILEY, b Elmer, Mo, Oct 22, 38; m 67; c 3. REPRODUCTIVE PHYSIOLOGY, MAMMALOGY. *Educ:* Northeast Mo State Col, BS, 60, MA, 65; Univ Mo-Columbia, PhD(zool), 70. *Prof Exp:* Teacher high schs, Mo, 59-60 & 61-62; vol, Peace Corps, Philippines, 62-64; from asst prof to assoc prof, Northeast Mo State Univ, 69-76; ANAT, KIRKSVILLE COL OSTEOP MED, 76- *Mem:* AAAS; Am Soc Mammalogists. *Res:* Reproduction in the least shrew, Cryptotis parva; taxonomy of North American shrews. *Mailing Add:* Dept Anat Kirksville Col Osteo Med Kirksville MO 63501

MOCK, STEVEN JAMES, b Philadelphia, Pa, July 3, 34; m 60; c 5. GEOLOGY, GLACIOLOGY. *Educ:* Antioch Col, BA, 57; Dartmouth Col, MA, 65; Northwestern Univ, PhD(geol), 75. *Prof Exp:* Geologist glaciol, Snow, Ice & Permafrost Res Estab, 59-61, res geologist, Cold Regions Res & Eng Lab, 61-77, CHIEF TERRESTRIAL SCI BR, US ARMY RES OFF, 77- *Mem:* Am Geophys Union; AAAS; Int Glaciol Soc. *Res:* Glacier-climate interactions; quantitative geomorphology; climatic trends. *Mailing Add:* Army Res Off PO Box 12211 Research Triangle Park NC 27709

MOCK, WILLIAM L, b Los Angeles, Calif, Aug 5, 38. ORGANIC CHEMISTRY. *Educ:* Calif Inst Technol, BS, 60; Harvard Univ, PhD(org chem), 65. *Prof Exp:* ASSOC PROF CHEM, UNIV ILL, CHICAGO CIRCLE, 72- *Concurrent Pos:* Fel, A P Sloan Found, 72. *Mem:* Am Chem Soc. *Res:* Synthetic methods; reaction mechanisms; pericyclic reactions; organosulfur chemistry; bioorganic chemistry. *Mailing Add:* Dept of Chem Univ of Ill Box 4348 Chicago IL 60680

MOCKETT, PAUL M, b San Francisco, Calif, Apr 9, 36; m 65; c 3. EXPERIMENTAL HIGH ENERGY PHYSICS, PARTICLE PHYSICS. *Educ:* Reed Col, BA, 59; Mass Inst Technol, PhD(physics), 65. *Prof Exp:* Res assoc physics, Mass Inst Technol, 65-67; asst physicist, Brookhaven Nat Lab, 67-70, assoc physicist, Div Particles & Fields, 70-72; sr res assoc, 72-75, res assoc prof, 75-81, RES PROF PHYSICS, UNIV WASH, 81- *Mem:* Am Phys Soc. *Res:* Experimental particle physics. *Mailing Add:* 4209 55th Ave NE Seattle WA 98105

MOCKFORD, EDWARD LEE, b Indianapolis, Ind, June 16, 30. TAXONOMY, ENTOMOLOGY. *Educ:* Ind Univ, AB, 52; Univ Fla, MS, 54; Univ Ill, PhD, 60. *Prof Exp:* Asst limnol, Lake & Stream Surv, Ind, 48-52; asst biol, Univ Fla, 52-54; tech asst entom, Nat Hist Surv, Ill, 56-60; from asst prof to assoc prof biol sci, 60-66, PROF BIOL SCI, ILL STATE UNIV, 66- *Mem:* Soc Syst Zool; Wilson Ornith Soc; Entom Soc Am; Asn Trop Biol. *Res:* Taxonomic entomology; taxonomy and evolution of insects, especially order Psocoptera. *Mailing Add:* Dept of Biol Sci Ill State Univ Normal IL 61761

MOCKLE, JERRY AUGUSTE, b Doucet, Que, Sept 16, 26; m 51; c 1. PHARMACOGNOSY, PHARMACOLOGY. *Educ:* Univ Montreal, BScPharm, 52; Univ Paris, PharmD, 55. *Prof Exp:* From asst prof to prof pharmacog, Univ Montreal, 55-71, secy fac, 61-65, vdean, 65-69; dir, Opers Br-Drugs, 71-73, dir, Opers Br-Prof Servs, 73-75, DIR GEN ADJ, OPERS BR, QUE HEALTH INS BD, 75- *Mem:* AAAS; Am Soc Pharmacog; Soc Econ Bot; Am Chem Soc; Pharmacol Soc Can. *Res:* Chemistry and pharmacology of medicinal plants of various origin, particularly those used in popular medicine in Canada. *Mailing Add:* Opers Br Que Health Ins Bd PO Box 6600 Quebec PQ G1K 7T3 Can

MOCKROS, LYLE F(RED), b Chicago, Ill, July 19, 33; m 60; c 3. FLUID MECHANICS, BIOMECHANICS. *Educ:* Northwestern Univ, BS, 56, MS, 57; Univ Calif, Berkeley, PhD(fluid mech), 62. *Prof Exp:* Asst res engr, Inst Eng Res, Univ Calif, Berkeley, 59-62; asst prof civil eng, 62-66, assoc prof civil eng & eng sci, 66-70, PROF CIVIL ENG & ENG SCI, TECHNOL INST, NORTHWESTERN UNIV, 70- *Mem:* Biomed Eng Soc; Am Soc Eng Educ; Am Soc Civil Engrs; Am Soc Artificial Internal Organs. *Res:* Biological fluid mechanics; artificial lungs; transport processes; blood coagulation. *Mailing Add:* Dept of Civil Eng Technol Inst Northwestern Univ Evanston IL 60201

MOCZYGEMBA, GEORGE A, b Panna Maria, Tex, Jan 7, 39; m 66; c 3. POLYMER CHEMISTRY, INORGANIC CHEMISTRY. *Educ:* Univ Tex, Austin, BS, 62, PhD(chem), 69. *Prof Exp:* Instr chem, St Edward's Univ, 65-67; SR CHEMIST, PHILLIPS PETROL CO, 68- *Mem:* Am Chem Soc; Sigma Xi. *Res:* Polymerization mechanisms, kinetics and catalysis; polymer research for rubber and plastic applications. *Mailing Add:* 824 SE Crestland Bartlesville OK 74003

MODAK, ARVIND T, b Bombay, India; US citizen; m 65; c 2. NEUROCHEMISTRY, TOXICOLOGY. *Educ:* Univ Bombay, BSc, 61, BSc, 63, MSc, 65; Univ Tex, Austin, MS, 68, PhD(pharmacol), 70. *Prof Exp:* Demonstr pharmacol, Univ Bombay, 63-64, lectr, 64-65; teaching asst pharm, Univ Tex, Austin, 65-70; fel pharmacol, Health Sci Ctr, Univ Tex, San Antonio, 70-72; pharmacologist & toxicologist, Pharma Corp, 72-74; res coordr, 73-75, ASST PROF PHARMACOL, HEALTH SCI CTR, UNIV TEX, 75- *Concurrent Pos:* Adj instr pharmacol, Health Sci Ctr, Univ Tex, 72-74. *Mem:* Am Soc Neurochem. *Res:* Study of labile metabolites in the central nervous system--acetylcholine, cyclic nucleotides, indoleamines and catecholamines through the use of microwave irradiation technique; modification of these metabolites by drugs and heavy metals. *Mailing Add:* Dept Pharmacol Health Sci Ctr Univ Tex San Antonio TX 78284

MODAK, ASHOK TRIMBAK, b Pune, India, Apr 11, 46; m 71. MECHANICAL ENGINEERING, PHYSICAL CHEMISTRY. *Educ:* Indian Inst Technol, BTech, 68; Univ Calif, Berkeley, MS, 69, PhD(mech eng), 73. *Prof Exp:* Prod design engr air pollution control, Ford Motor Co, 69-71; res specialist combustion, Factory Mutual Res Corp, 73-80; SR PROJ MGR, COMBUSTION RES & DEVELOP, NORTHERN RES & ENG CORP, 80- *Concurrent Pos:* Consult fire safety & combustion in gas turbine engines. *Mem:* Am Soc Mech Engrs; Combustion Inst; Sigma Xi; NY Acad Sci. *Res:* Combustion problems; heat and mass transfer in flames and fires; gaseous radiation; diffusion flame structure and chemical kinetics; soot formation and burnout in flames; flammability of plastics; combustion in gas turbine engines and in fluidized beds. *Mailing Add:* 51 Bates Rd Watertown MA 02172

MODDERMAN, JOHN PHILIP, b Grand Rapids, Mich, Dec 4, 44; m 79; c 1. FOOD ADDITIVE CHEMISTRY. *Educ:* Calvin Col, AB, 67; Wayne State Univ, PhD(anal chem), 71. *Prof Exp:* Fel chemiluminescence res, Univ Ga, 71-73; CHEMIST, DIV CHEM & PHYSICS, FOOD & DRUG ADMIN, 73- *Concurrent Pos:* Consult, Joint Food & Agr Orgn/WHO Expert Comt Food Additives; mem deleg, Codex Alimentanus Comt Food Additives. *Mem:* Am Chem Soc; AAAS. *Res:* Analytical chemistry of additives and contaminants in food. *Mailing Add:* Div Chem & Physics HFF-458 FDA 200 C St SW Washington DC 20204

MODE, CHARLES J, b Bismarck, NDak, Dec 29, 27; m 60; c 1. MATHEMATICS, POPULATION STUDIES. *Educ:* NDak State Univ, BS, 52; Kans State Univ, MS, 53; Univ Calif, Davis, PhD(genetics), 56. *Prof Exp:* Res fel statist, NC State Univ, 56-57; prof math, Mont State Univ, 57-66; assoc prof statist, State Univ NY Buffalo, 66-70; PROF MATH, DREXEL UNIV, 70- *Concurrent Pos:* Mem, Inst Pop Studies, Drexel Univ. *Mem:* Biomet Soc; Inst Math Statist; Am Math Soc; Pop Asn Am; Int Union Sci Study Pop. *Res:* Probability theory; application of mathematics and statistics to biology and medicine, particularly in family planning evaluation; stochastic processes; branching processes, models of population growth; mathematical demography; computer simulation. *Mailing Add:* Dept of Math Drexel Univ 32nd & Chestnut Sts Philadelphia PA 19104

MODE, VINCENT ALAN, b Gilroy, Calif, May 25, 40; m 76; c 1. APPLIED RESEARCH MANAGEMENT, SYSTEM DYNAMICS. *Educ:* Whitman Col, AB, 62; Univ Ill, Urbana, PhD(inorg chem), 65; Golden Gate Univ, MBA, 80. *Prof Exp:* Res chemist, Lawrence Livermore Lab, Univ Calif, 65-71, group leader, 71-75, sect leader, 75-77, assoc div leader, 77-80; EXEC DIR, BC RES, 80- *Concurrent Pos:* Pres, Techwest Enterprises, Ltd, 81- *Mem:* Sigma Xi. *Res:* Fluorescence of rare earth chelates; high pressure liquid chromatography of inorganic species; development of interactive computer programs and large data base analysis; computer simulation of management problems. *Mailing Add:* BC Res 3650 Wesbrook Mall Vancouver BC V6S 2L2 Can

MODEL, FRANK STEVEN, b New York, NY, May 5, 42; m 65; c 2. CHEMISTRY, POLYMER SCIENCE. *Educ:* Mass Inst Technol, BS, 63; Harvard Univ, MA, 65, PhD(chem), 68. *Prof Exp:* Res chemist, Celanese Res Co, Summit, 67-72, proj leader, 72-75, sr res chemist, 72-76; dir res, Gelman Sci Inc, Ann Arbor, 76, vpres res & develop, 76-79; sr res assoc, 79-80, LAB MGR, PALL CORP, GLEN COVE, 80- *Mem:* AAAS; Am Chem Soc; Sigma Xi. *Res:* Physical chemistry of formed polymers; polymer processing; membrane science and technology; microfiltration processes and devices; ultrafiltration; reverse osmosis; hemodialysis; polymer characterization; biomedical applications of polymers; electrophoresis and immunodiffusion; inorganic photochromism. *Mailing Add:* 28 Buttonwood Dix Hills NY 11746

MODEL, PETER, b Frankfurt, Ger, May 17, 33; US citizen; m 81; c 1. MOLECULAR BIOLOGY, GENETICS. *Educ:* Stanford Univ, AB, 53; Columbia Univ, PhD(biochem), 65. *Prof Exp:* Res assoc biochem, Columbia Univ, 65-67; NSF fel, 67-69, asst prof, 69-75, ASSOC PROF BIOCHEM, ROCKEFELLER UNIV, 75- *Mem:* Am Soc Microbiol. *Res:* Genetics and physiology of prokaryotic membrane protein biosynthesis; in vitro protein synthesis; bacteriophage genetics and physiology. *Mailing Add:* Rockefeller Univ New York NY 10021

MODELL, JEROME HERBERT, b St Paul, Minn, Sept 9, 32; m 52; c 3. ANESTHIOSOLOGY. *Educ:* Univ Minn, BA, 54, BS & MD, 57; Am Bd Anesthesiol, dipl, 64. *Prof Exp:* Jr scientist internal med, Sch Med, Univ Minn, 57-59; from instr to assoc prof anesthesiol, Sch Med, Univ Miami, 63-69; PROF ANESTHESIOL & CHMN DEPT, COL MED, UNIV FLA, 69- *Concurrent Pos:* NIH res career develop award, 67-69. *Mem:* AAAS; Am Soc Anesthesiol; Asn Univ Anesthetists. *Res:* Pathophysiology and treatment of near-drowning; physiologic applications of liquid breathing; intensive pulmonary therapy. *Mailing Add:* Dept of Anesthesiol Univ of Fla Col of Med Gainesville FL 32601

MODELL, MICHAEL, b Brooklyn, NY, Mar 31, 39; m 59; c 2. CHEMICAL ENGINEERING. *Educ:* Mass Inst Technol, BS, 60, MS, 61, ScD(chem eng), 64. *Prof Exp:* Asst prof, 64-70, ASSOC PROF CHEM ENG, MASS INST TECHNOL, 70- *Mem:* AAAS; Am Chem Soc; Am Inst Chem Engrs. *Res:* Thermodynamics; heterogeneous catalysis; pollution control. *Mailing Add:* Dept of Chem Eng Mass Inst of Technol Cambridge MA 02139

MODELL, WALTER, b Waterbury, Conn, July 18, 07; m 33; c 1. PHARMACOLOGY. *Educ:* City Col New York, BS, 28; Cornell Univ, MD, 32. *Prof Exp:* From instr clin pharmacol to prof pharmacol, 32-73, dir clin pharmacol, 56-73, EMER PROF PHARMACOL, MED COL, CORNELL UNIV, 73- *Concurrent Pos:* Ed-in-chief, Clin Pharmacol & Therapeut, 60-; mem bd dirs, US Pharmacopoeia. *Mem:* Am Soc Pharmacol & Exp Therapeut; Am Soc Clin Pharmacol & Therapeut; fel AMA; fel Am Col Physicians; NY Acad Sci. *Res:* Clinical pharmacology. *Mailing Add:* PO Box 119 Larchmont NY 10538

MODER, JOSEPH J(OHN), b St Louis, Mo, Dec 12, 24; m 51; c 6. OPERATIONS RESEARCH, STATISTICS. *Educ:* Washington Univ, BS, 47; Northwestern Univ, MS, 49, PhD(chem eng), 50. *Prof Exp:* Chem engr, Petrolite Corp, 47; asst, Northwestern Univ, 47-50; assoc prof indust eng, Ga Inst Technol, 50-59, prof, 59-64, res assoc, Exp Sta, 50-57; chmn dept, 66-78, PROF MGT SCI, UNIV MIAMI, 64- *Concurrent Pos:* NSF fel, Iowa State Univ, 60-61 & Stanford Univ, 61-62; Joseph Lucas vis prof eng prod, Univ Birmingham, 73-74. *Mem:* Am Inst Indust Engrs; Am Statist Asn; Opers Res Soc Am; Inst Mgt Sci; Proj Mgt Inst. *Res:* Project management methodology and network techniques; work sampling; operations research and systems analysis in health services. *Mailing Add:* Dept of Mgt Sci Univ of Miami Coral Gables FL 33124

MODESITT, DONALD ERNEST, b Richmond, Ind, Oct 14, 36; m 59; c 3. ENVIRONMENTAL & SANITARY ENGINEERING. *Educ:* Mo Sch Mines, BS, 58; Univ Mo-Rolla, MS, 66; Okla State Univ, PhD(bioenviron eng), 70. *Prof Exp:* Civil engr, State of Ill Div Hwy, 58-60; from instr to asst prof, 60-73, ASSOC PROF CIVIL ENG, UNIV MO-ROLLA, 73- *Mem:* Water Pollution Control Fedn; Am Water Works Asn; Am Soc Civil Engrs; Nat Soc Prof Engrs; Am Acad Environ Engrs. *Res:* Bioenvironmental engineering; water quality, waste water treatment, disinfection of water and wastewater. *Mailing Add:* Dept Civil Eng Univ Mo-Rolla Rolla MO 65401

MODI, V J, b Bhavnagar, India, Dec 15, 30; m 59; c 1. AERONAUTICAL ENGINEERING. *Educ:* Univ Bombay, BE, 53; Indian Inst Sci, Bangalore, dipl, 55; Univ Wash, MS, 56; Purdue Univ, PhD(aeronaut eng), 59. *Prof Exp:* Bombay Govt fel, 53-55; res asst, Univ Wash, 55-56 & Purdue Univ, 56-57; res specialist dynamics, Cessna Aircraft Co, 59-61; from asst prof to assoc prof mech eng, 61-67, PROF MECH ENG, UNIV BC, 67- *Mem:* Sr mem Am Astronaut Soc; assoc fel Can Aeronaut & Space Inst; Am Soc Mech Engrs; Am Inst Aeronaut & Astronaut. *Res:* Aeroelasticity; separated flows; industrial aerodynamics; dynamics of offshore structures; bioengineering;

satellite dynamics. *Mailing Add:* Dept of Mech Eng Univ of BC Vancouver BC V6T 1W5 Can

MODIC, FRANK JOSEPH, b Cleveland, Ohio, Sept 20, 22; m 56; c 4. PHYSICAL CHEMISTRY, ORGANIC CHEMISTRY. *Educ:* Case Western Reserve Univ, BS, 43; Iowa State Col, PhD(phys org chem), 51. *Prof Exp:* Jr chem engr, Kellex Corp, 43-45; prod supvr, Carbide & Carbon Chem Co, 45-46; instr chem, Iowa State Col, 46-48; CHEMIST, SILICONE PROD DEPT, GEN ELEC CO, 51- *Mem:* Am Chem Soc; Royal Soc Chem. *Res:* Physical-organic research in organosilicon chemistry; reaction mechanisms and synthesis of silicones and silicone copolymers. *Mailing Add:* Silicone Prod Dept Gen Elec Co Waterford NY 12188

MODINE, FRANKLIN ARTHUR, b Sault Ste Marie, Mich, Feb 8, 36; m 63; c 2. PHYSICS. *Educ:* Mich State Univ, BS, 60; Univ Southern Calif, MA, 66; Univ Ore, PhD(physics), 71. *Prof Exp:* Engr, NAm Aviation, 61-66; physicist, Aerojet Gen, 66-67; PHYSICIST, OAK RIDGE NAT LAB, 71- *Mem:* Am Phys Soc. *Res:* Optical and magnetic properties of solids. *Mailing Add:* Solid State Div Oak Ridge Nat Lab Oak Ridge TN 37830

MODISETTE, JERRY LEE, applied physics, see previous edition

MODLER, H WAYNE, b Kingston, Ont, Oct 20, 43; m 68; c 2. PROTEIN CHEMISTRY, DIARY TECHNOLOGY. *Educ:* Univ Guelph, BSA, 67; Mich State Univ, MS, 69, PhD(food sci), 73. *Prof Exp:* RES SCIENTIST DAIRY, FOOD RES INST, CAN DEPT AGR, 73- *Mem:* Am Dairy Sci Asn; Can Inst Food Sci & Technol; Sigma Xi. *Res:* Whey utilization; milk quality; dairy processing; food processing; polyurethane foam from oilseed by-products; blood utilization; feeding whey to livestock; enzymology of blue cheese. *Mailing Add:* Food Res Inst Can Dept Agr Res Br Ottawa ON K1A 0C5 Can

MODLIN, HERBERT CHARLES, b Chicago, Ill, Jan 12, 13; m 33; c 1. PSYCHIATRY. *Educ:* Univ Nebr, BSc, 35, MD, 38, MA, 40. *Prof Exp:* Intern, Univ Nebr Hosp, 38-39; resident neuropsychiat, Clarkson Hosp, 39-40; fel psychiat, Pa Hosp, Philadelphia, 40-41 & Adams House, Boston, 41-42; resident neurol, Montreal Neurol Inst, 42-43; chief neuropsychiat serv, Winter Vet Admin Hosp, 46-49; SR PSYCHIATRIST, MENNINGER FOUND, 49-; ASSOC PROF PSYCHIAT, SCH MED, UNIV KANS, 60-, PROF COMMUNITY & FORENSIC PSYCHIAT, 76- *Concurrent Pos:* Lectr, Sch Law, Univ Kans, 47- *Honors & Awards:* Golden Apple Award, Am Acad Phychiat & Law. *Mem:* Am Psychiat Asn; Sigma Xi. *Res:* Community and social psychiatry; psychiatric education. *Mailing Add:* Menninger Found Topeka KS 66601

MODLIN, RICHARD FRANK, b Toledo, Ohio, Nov 16, 37; m 76. LIMNOLOGY, ZOOLOGY. *Educ:* Univ Wis-Milwaukee, BS, 67, MS, 69; Univ Conn, PhD(marine ecol), 76. *Prof Exp:* Teaching asst zool, Univ Wis-Milwaukee, 65-67; aquatic biologist, Wis Dept Nat Resources, 68; res asst limnol, Ctr Great Lakes Studies, 68-69, res assoc, 69-70; fisheries supvr, Conn Dept Environ Protection, 70-72; teaching asst biol, Univ Conn, 72-76; ASST PROF BIOL, UNIV ALA, HUNTSVILLE, 76- *Concurrent Pos:* Prin investr, Proj-77-14, Univ Ala, Huntsville, 76-77 & Proj-78-16, 77-78; vis prof marine sci, Dauphin Island Sea Lab, 79-; res grant, Tenn Valley Authority, 79-81. *Mem:* Am Soc Limnol & Oceanog; Int Asn Theoret & Appl Limnol; NAm Benthological Soc; Estuarine Res Fedn; Sigma Xi. *Res:* Limnology of estuaries, reservoirs and temporary waters; ecology, physiology and taxonomy of benthic invertebrates, crustacea; fisheries biology; southern estuaries and Gulf of Mexico. *Mailing Add:* Dept Biol Univ Ala Huntsville AL 35899

MODRAK, JOHN BRUCE, pharmacology, see previous edition

MODRESKI, PETER JOHN, b New Brunswick, NJ, Dec 22, 46; m 68; c 1. EXPERIMENTAL PETROLOGY, MINERAL CHEMISTRY. *Educ:* Rutgers Univ, BA, 68; Pa State Univ, MS, 71, PhD(geochem), 72. *Prof Exp:* Res chemist laser chem, Air Force Weapons Lab, Kirtland AFB, 72-75; mem tech staff geochem, Sandia Labs, 75-79; GEOCHEMIST, US GEOL SURV, 79- *Mem:* Geol Soc Am; Mineral Soc Am. *Res:* Chemistry and phase relations of minerals and hydrothermal solutions, relating to the genesis of ore deposits; chemistry of magnetite; geochemistry of cobalt; luminescence of minerals. *Mailing Add:* US Geol Surv Box 25046 Fed MS 922 Denver CO 80225

MODREY, JOSEPH, b New York, NY, Jan 29, 16; m 43; c 2. MECHANICAL ENGINEERING. *Educ:* Columbia Univ, BS, 37, MME, 38; Rensselaer Polytech Inst, DEng, 63. *Prof Exp:* Res engr gas turbine design, Wright Aeronaut Corp, 38-47; prof mach design, Polytech Inst Brooklyn, 47-55; prof mech eng & head dept, Union Col, 55-65; PROF MECH ENG, PURDUE UNIV, 65- *Concurrent Pos:* Sr scientist, Midwest Appl Sci Corp. *Mem:* Am Soc Mech Engrs; Soc Automotive Engrs; Am Soc Eng Educ. *Res:* Very high speed machinery, vibration and lubrication. *Mailing Add:* Sch of Mech Eng Purdue Univ West Lafayette IN 47907

MODRZAKOWSKI, MALCOLM CHARLES, b Enid, Okla, Mar 12, 52; m 73; c 2. MICROBIOLOGY. *Educ:* Univ Mass, Amherst, BS, 74; Univ Ga, PhD(microbiol), 77. *Prof Exp:* Fel, Univ NC, Chapel Hill, 77-79; ASST PROF MICROBIOL, DEPT ZOOL & MICROBIOL, OHIO UNIV, 79-, ASST PROF BIOMED SCI, COL OSTEOPATRIC MED, 79- *Concurrent Pos:* Prin investr, Pub Health Serv grants, 80- *Mem:* Am Soc Microbiol. *Res:* Inter-relationships that exist between intrusive gram-negative bacteria and host non-specific leukocyte defense mechanisms. *Mailing Add:* Ohio Univ Col Osteopatric Med 353 Irvine Hall Athens OH 45701

MOE, CHESNEY RUDOLPH, b Rainy River, Ont, Oct 6, 08; US citizen; m 35, 51; c 2. PHYSICS. *Educ:* Stanford Univ, AB, 29, AM, 31; Univ Southern Calif, PhD(physics), 41. *Prof Exp:* Asst, 29-30, instr, 31-35, from asst prof to prof, 35-73, assoc chmn div phys sci, 56-62, chmn dept physics, 62-65, EMER PROF PHYSICS, SAN DIEGO STATE UNIV, 73- *Concurrent Pos:* Mem bd rev, Marine Phys Lab, Univ Calif, 46-51; consult, US Navy Electronics Lab, 53-56, Tracor Corp, Tex & Calif, 67-69 & Jet Propulsion Lab, 69 & 70. *Mem:* Fel Acoust Soc Am. *Res:* Acoustics. *Mailing Add:* 4669 E Talmadge Dr San Diego CA 92116

MOE, DENNIS L, b SDak, Apr 1, 17; m 43; c 4. AGRICULTURAL ENGINEERING. *Educ:* SDak State Univ, BS, 48, MS, 49; Augustana Col, PhD, 71. *Prof Exp:* Field supvr, Mutual Benefit Life Ins Co, 40; asst chemist, Am Chem & Potash Corp, 41; from instr to assoc prof, 46-56, from asst agr engr to assoc agr engr, 46-56, PROF AGR ENG & HEAD DEPT & AGR ENGR, AGR EXP STA, SDAK STATE UNIV, 56-, DIR, INST IRRIGATION TECHNOL, 68- *Concurrent Pos:* Consult, State Eng Bd Dirs & indust firms; NSF nat grant panel, mem, Review Comn, Eng Coun Prof Develop; Am consult, foreign univs, Western Europe & Scandinavia; consult struct eng; mem, Eng Accreditation Teams. *Mem:* Fel Am Soc Agr Eng; Am Soc Eng Educ; Soil Conserv Soc Am. *Res:* Farm structures, power and machinery; development of lightweight aggregate from native shales and clays; low pressure gas in farm tractors; silage and structures; world food production and energy used in food chain production; review of research institutes and universities. *Mailing Add:* Dept of Agr Eng SDak State Univ Brookings SD 57006

MOE, GEORGE, b Portland, Ore, Dec 31, 25; m 52; c 2. PHYSICAL CHEMISTRY, INORGANIC CHEMISTRY. *Educ:* Reed Col, BA, 47; Univ Rochester, PhD(chem), 50. *Prof Exp:* Asst chem, Univ Rochester, 47-49; instr, Univ Buffalo, 50-51; from res chemist to head astronaut dept, Aerojet-Gen Corp Div, Gen Tire & Rubber Co, 51-60; vpres res, Astropower, Inc, Douglas Aircraft Corp, 60-64, dir, Astropower Lab, Missiles & Space Syst Div, 64-70, dep dir res & develop, 70-72, dir res & develop, 72-76, DIR, ENERGY SYSTS, MCDONNELL-DOUGLAS ASTRONAUT CO, 76- *Mem:* Am Chem Soc; Am Phys Soc; Am Inst Aeronaut & Astronaut. *Res:* Aerospace technology; electrochemical systems; advanced computers and advanced materials; synthesis and evaluation of high-energy propellants; photochemistry and radiation chemistry of free radicals; solid state reactions. *Mailing Add:* 12231 Afton Lane Santa Ana CA 92705

MOE, GEORGE WYLBUR, b Opportunity, Wash, Apr 24, 42. ENGINEERING PHYSICS. *Educ:* Gonzaga Univ, BS, 66; Univ Wash, PhD(physics), 74. *Prof Exp:* res assoc physics, Columbia Radiation, Columbia Univ, 73-78; PRIN MEM RES STAFF, RIVERSIDE RES INST, 78- *Mem:* Inst Elec & Electronics Engrs; Am Phys Soc; Am Inst Physics; Soc Photo-Optical Instrumentation Engrs. *Res:* Electro-optical data acquisition systems; image to signal processing; real-time computer applications; experimental atomic physics. *Mailing Add:* Riverside Res Inst 330 W 42nd St New York NY 10018

MOE, GORDON KENNETH, b Fairchild, Wis, May 30, 15; m 38; c 6. PHYSIOLOGY. *Educ:* Univ Minn, BS, 37, MS, 39, PhD(physiol), 40; Harvard Univ, MD, 43. *Prof Exp:* From asst to instr physiol, Univ Minn, 36-40; Porter fel, Western Reserve Univ, 40-41; instr pharmacol, Harvard Med Sch, 41-44, assoc, 44; from asst prof to assoc prof, Med Sch, Univ Mich, 44-50; prof & chmn dept, 50-60, res prof physiol, 60-80, EMER PROF, COL MED, STATE UNIV NY UPSTATE MED CTR, 80-; DIR RES, MASONIC MED RES LAB, 60- *Concurrent Pos:* Consult, Walter Reed Army Med Ctr, 46-53; Am Physiol Soc traveling fel, Int Physiol Cong, Oxford, 47; USPHS spec fel, Nat Inst Cardiol, Mex, 48; mem teaching mission, WHO, UN, Israel & Iran, 51; chmn basic sci coun, Am Heart Asn, 60-62, chmn res comt, 60-61; mem nat heart & lung adv coun, NIH, 70-74. *Mem:* AAAS (secy sect med, 49-53, chmn, 58); Am Physiol Soc; hon mem Mex Nat Acad Med; hon mem Mex Soc Cardiol; hon fel Am Col Cardiol. *Res:* Physiology and pharmacology of the cardiovascular system. *Mailing Add:* Masonic Med Res Lab Utica NY 13503

MOE, JAMES BURTON, b Hayfield, Minn, Oct 4, 40. VETERINARY PATHOLOGY, MICROBIOLOGY. *Educ:* Univ Minn, BS, 62, DVM, 64; Univ Calif, PhD(comp path), 78. *Prof Exp:* Staff pathologist, 69-75, MICROBIOLOGIST INFECTIOUS DIS, US ARMY MED RES INST, 78- *Concurrent Pos:* Vis consult, Armed Forces Inst Path, 73-75; consult, Physicians Clin Lab, 76-78; Calif Lung Asn grant, 77-78. *Mem:* Am Col Vet Pathologists; Int Acad Path. *Res:* Immunological, pathological and virological studies of infectious diseases affecting animals and man; pathological studies of neoplastic diseases of various animal species. *Mailing Add:* 7627 Shookstown Rd Frederick MD 21701

MOE, MAYNARD L, b Lake Mills, Iowa, Jan 5, 35; m 57; c 3. ELECTRICAL ENGINEERING. *Educ:* Iowa State Univ, BS, 57; Northwestern Univ, MS, 59, PhD(elec eng), 61. *Prof Exp:* From asst prof to prof elec eng, Univ Denver, 61-75; PRES, DENCOR, INC, 74- *Concurrent Pos:* Res engr, Denver Res Inst, 61-75. *Mem:* Inst Elec & Electronics Engrs. *Res:* Feedback control system design; application of artificial intelligence to control systems; biomedical control systems; energy control systems. *Mailing Add:* Dencor Inc 2750 S Shoshone Englewood CO 80110

MOE, MICHAEL K, b Milwaukee, Wis, Nov 17, 37; m 61; c 1. ELEMENTARY PARTICLE PHYSICS. *Educ:* Stanford Univ, BS, 59; Case Western Reserve Univ, MS, 61, PhD(physics), 65. *Prof Exp:* Res fel cosmic ray physics, Calif Inst Technol, 65-66; asst res physicist, 66-68, asst prof physics, 68-73, asst res physicist, 73-75, assoc res physicist, 75-80, RES PHYSICIST, UNIV CALIF, IRVINE, 80- *Res:* Low level scintillation spectrometry; cosmic rays; experimental search for double beta decay. *Mailing Add:* Sch of Phys Sci Univ of Calif Irvine CA 92717

MOE, MILDRED MINASIAN, b Philadelphia, Pa, Nov 18, 29; m 51; c 2. ATMOSPHERIC PHYSICS, MECHANICS OF SATELLITE MOTIONS. *Educ:* Univ Calif, Los Angeles, BA, 51, MA, 53, PhD(physics), 57. *Prof Exp:* Mem tech staff, Ramo-Wooldridge Corp, Calif, 56-60; asst prof physics, Loyola Univ Los Angeles, 67-70, res assoc, 70-72; asst res physicist, Physics Dept, Univ Calif, Irvine, 73-78; CONSULT, 79- *Mem:* Am Phys Soc; Am Asn Physics Teachers. *Res:* Quantum mechanical scattering theory; supersonic jet flows; satellite orbital and attitude motions; gas-surface interactions; measurement of upper-atmospheric properties; atmospheric modeling. *Mailing Add:* 1520 Sandcastle Dr Corona del Mar CA 92625

MOE, OSBORNE KENNETH, b Los Angeles, Calif, Dec 29, 25; m 51; c 2. PHYSICS. *Educ:* Univ Calif, Los Angeles, BA, 51, MA, 53, PhD(planetary & space sci), 66. *Prof Exp:* Analyst airborne radar facil, Radio Corp Am, 54-55; mem tech staff, Ramo-Wooldridge Corp, 56-59, consult satellite orbits & model atmospheres, Space Tech Labs, 60-63, consult orbital predictions & model atmospheres, TRW, Inc, 63-67; sr res scientist, McDonnell Douglas Astronaut Co, 67-75; CONSULT, 75- *Concurrent Pos:* Asst res geophysicist, Univ Calif, Los Angeles, 66-67; consult, Aerospace Corp, 65-67 & Northrop Corp, 67. *Mem:* Am Geophys Union; Am Meteorol Soc; Am Inst Aeronaut & Astronaut. *Res:* Theoretical analysis of the various types of density and composition measurements in the thermosphere; adsorption and energy accommodation at artificial satellite surfaces; thermospheric models; solar-terrestrial relationships; improvement of ozone measurements. *Mailing Add:* 1520 Sandcastle Dr Corona del Mar CA 92625

MOE, PAUL G, b Rochester, Minn, Apr 6, 31; m 55; c 2. BACTERIOLOGY. *Educ:* Univ Ill, BS, 53, MS, 54; Rutgers Univ, PhD(soil chem), 59. *Prof Exp:* Agronomist, Found Agr Res, 54-55; chemist, Chem Process Co, 55-56; asst prof, Purdue Univ, 59-67; vis asst prof, Ore State Univ, 67-68; assoc prof bacteriol, 68-72, PROF BACTERIOL & BACTERIOLOGIST, WVA UNIV, 72- *Concurrent Pos:* Sr lectr, WVa Univ-AID contract, Makerere Univ Col, Uganda, 68-72; vis sr lectr, Univ Nairobi, 72. *Mem:* Am Soc Agron; Soil Sci Soc Am; Am Chem Soc; Am Soc Microbiol. *Res:* Waste disposal; environmental microbiology; biodegradation of environmental pollutants. *Mailing Add:* Div Plant Sci WVa Univ Morgantown WV 26506

MOE, ROBERT ANTHONY, b Jersey City, NJ, Mar 26, 23; m 49; c 3. PHYSIOLOGY. *Educ:* Seton Hall Univ, BS, 48; Fordham Univ, MS, 49, PhD(physiol), 51. *Prof Exp:* Asst biol, Grad Sch, Fordham Univ, 48-51; head physiol testing sect, Toxicol Res Div, Inst Med Res, E R Squibb & Sons, 51-59; head cardiovasc sect, Pharmacol Dept, Hoffmann-La Roche, Inc, 59-65, from asst dir pharmacol dept to asst dir biol res div, 65-70; dir biol res, Searle Labs, 70-72, vpres res & develop, 72-73, sr vpres sci affairs, 73-76, exec vpres, 76-79; CONSULT SCI AFFAIRS & VPRES RES & DEVELOP, AYERST LABS, 79- *Mem:* AAAS; Am Soc Pharmacol & Exp Therapeut; assoc fel Am Soc Clin Pharmacol & Therapeut. *Res:* Toxicology and physiology of biological preparations; cardiovascular and autonomic systems. *Mailing Add:* Ayerst Labs 685 Third Ave New York NY 10017

MOECKEL, W(OLFGANG) E(RNST), b Ger, Feb 11, 22; nat US; m 50; c 1. AEROSPACE ENGINEERING. *Educ:* Univ Mich, BS, 44. *Prof Exp:* Aeronaut res scientist, Nat Adv Comt Aeronaut, Lewis Res Ctr, NASA, 44-47, sect head, Spec Projs Br, 47-50, chief, 50-55, asst chief, Propulsion Aerodyn Div, 55-58, chief, Electromagnetic P. pulsion Div, 58-71, chief, Phys Sci Div, 71-77, chief scientist, 77-80; CONSULT, 80- *Honors & Awards:* Arthur S Flemming Award, 60; NASA Exceptional Sci Achievement Award, 69. *Mem:* AAAS; assoc fel Am Inst Aeronaut & Astronaut; Am Phys Soc. *Res:* Supersonic and hypersonic aerodynamics and propulsion; fluid mechanics; astronautics; space propulsion systems. *Mailing Add:* 29033 Lincoln Rd Bay Village OH 44140

MOEDRITZER, KURT, b Prague, Czech, June 20, 29; nat US; m 57; c 3. ORGANOMETALLIC CHEMISTRY, ORGANIC CHEMISTRY. *Educ:* Univ Munich, dipl, 53, PhD(inorg chem), 55. *Prof Exp:* Asst inorg chem, Univ Munich, 53-56, asst & instr, 57-59; Fulbright fel, Univ Southern Calif, 56-57; instr, Munich Br, Univ Md, 58-59; sci fel, 59-77, SR SCI FEL, MONSANTO CO, 77- *Concurrent Pos:* Ed, Synthesis & Reactivity in Inorg & Metal-org Chem. *Mem:* Am Chem Soc. *Res:* Inorganic and organic phosphorus compounds; inorganic polymers; organometallics; metal hydrides; nuclear magnetic resonance; agricultural chemistry. *Mailing Add:* Monsanto Co St Louis MO 63167

MOEHLMAN, PATRICIA DES ROSES, b Washington, DC, Oct 5, 43. BEHAVIORAL ECOLOGY. *Educ:* Wellesley Col, BA, 65; Univ Tex, Austin, MA, 68, Univ Wis-Madison, PhD(zool), 74. *Prof Exp:* Instr biol, State Univ Calif, Chico, 73-74; fel zool, Univ Wis-Madison, 75-80; vis scientist animal behav, Univ Cambridge, 80-81; ASST PROF ANIMAL ECOL, YALE UNIV, 81- *Concurrent Pos:* Scientist behav ecol, Serengeti Res Inst, 76-82. *Mem:* Sigma Xi; Animal Behav Soc; Am Soc Mammalogists; Royal Geog Soc. *Res:* Behavioral ecology of feral asses (Equus asinus) in Death Valley National Monument and siverbacked (Canis mesomelas) and golden jackals (Canis aureus) in the Serengeti, Tanzania. *Mailing Add:* Sch Forstry & Environ Studies Yale Univ New Haven CT 06511

MOEHLMAN, ROBERT STEVENS, b Rochester, NY, Feb 23, 10; m 34; c 2. GEOLOGY. *Educ:* Univ Rochester, AB, 31; Harvard Univ, AM, 32, PhD, 35. *Prof Exp:* Teaching asst & instr, Harvard Univ, 32-35; field asst, US Geol Surv, 35; mine geologist, Anaconda Copper Mining Co, Mont, 36-38; explor geologist, Ariz, 38-40, Nev & Calif, 40-44; field geologist, SAm Mines Co, NY, 45-46, chief geologist, 47-50; vpres, Austral Oil Co, 51-53, exec vpres, 54-62; pres, Newmont Oil Co, 62-78; OIL & GAS CONSULT, 78- *Concurrent Pos:* Chmn of bd, Can Export Gas & Oil Ltd, 74- *Mem:* Soc Econ Geol; fel Geol Soc Am; Am Asn Petrol Geol; Soc Petrol Eng; Nat Petrol Coun. *Res:* Policy for energy supplies; economics of production of minerals and hydrocarbons. *Mailing Add:* Suite 917 600 Jefferson Ave Houston TX 77002

MOEHRING, DAVID MARION, forest soils, forest ecology, see previous edition

MOEHRING, JOAN MARQUART, b Orchard Park, NY, Sept 23, 35; m 74. CELL BIOLOGY. *Educ:* Syracuse Univ, BS, 61; Rutgers Univ, MS, 63, PhD(microbiol), 65. *Prof Exp:* Fel microbiol, Stanford Univ, 65-68; res assoc cell & tissue cult, Dept Med Microbiol, 68-70, res assoc, Dept Med, 70-71, res assoc, Dept Path, 71-73, res assoc & asst prof cell & tissue cult & consult & res assoc spec ctr res pulmonary fibrosis, Col Med, 73-77, res assoc prof, 77-80, RES PROF CELL & TISSUE CULT, DEPT MED MICROBIOL, UNIV VT, 80- *Mem:* Am Soc Microbiol; Tissue Cult Asn; Sigma Xi. *Res:* Application of cell and tissue culture to biomedical research; use of cultured mammalian cells to study the molecular action of bacterial toxins and the genetics of resistance to toxins. *Mailing Add:* Dept of Med Microbiol Univ of Vt Burlington VT 05401

MOEHRING, THOMAS JOHN, b New York, NY, Aug 15, 36; m 64. MEDICAL MICROBIOLOGY. *Educ:* Fairleigh Dickinson Univ, BS, 61; Rutgers Univ, MS, 63, PhD(microbiol), 66. *Prof Exp:* Fel, Stanford Univ, 65-68; asst prof, 68-72, assoc prof, 72-76, PROF MED MICROBIOL, UNIV VT, 76- *Mem:* Sigma Xi; Am Soc Microbiol; Tissue Cult Asn; AAAS. *Res:* Cell culture in biomedical research; mechanisms of pathogenesis; in vitro action of microbial toxins; biochemical genetics of cultured cells; protein synthesis. *Mailing Add:* Dept of Med Microbiol Univ of Vt Col of Med Burlington VT 05401

MOEHS, PETER JOHN, b Yonkers, NY, Apr 4, 40; m 65; c 2. CHEMISTRY. *Educ:* Norwich Univ, BS, 62; Univ NH, PhD(inorg chem), 67. *Prof Exp:* Asst prof chem, 69-74, chmn div sci, 71-72, ASSOC PROF CHEM, SAGINAW VALLEY COL, 74- *Mem:* Am Chem Soc; NY Acad Sci. *Res:* Chemistry of Group IV organometallics. *Mailing Add:* Dept Chem Saginaw Valley Col 2250 Pierce Rd University Center MI 48710

MOELLER, ARTHUR CHARLES, b Cleveland, Ohio, Dec 14, 19. ELECTRICAL ENGINEERING, MATHEMATICS. *Educ:* Western Reserve Univ, BS, 41; Mich State Univ, MS, 48; Marquette Univ, BEE, 51; Univ Wis, PhD(elec eng), 65. *Prof Exp:* Asst math, Mich State Univ, 41-43; instr, Denison Univ, 43-44; instr, Marquette Univ, 44-51, elec eng, 51-52, asst prof, 52-58; res asst, Univ Wis, 58-60; asst prof, 60-65, chmn dept, 61-63, actg dean col, 63-64, dean, 64-65, assoc prof, 65-70, V PRES ACAD AFFAIRS, MARQUETTE UNIV, 65-, PROF ELEC ENG, 70- *Mem:* AAAS; Am Math Soc; Asn Comput Mach; Math Asn Am; Inst Elec & Electronics Engrs. *Res:* Calculation of propagation constants in waveguides loaded with dielectric slabs; numerical solution of elliptic boundary value problems. *Mailing Add:* 6999 N Crestwood Dr Glendale WI 53209

MOELLER, CARL WILLIAM, JR, b Carroll, Iowa, Mar 2, 24; m 52; c 2. INORGANIC CHEMISTRY. *Educ:* Harvard Univ, BS, 49; Univ Southern Calif, PhD(chem), 54. *Prof Exp:* Asst chem, Univ Southern Calif, 49-53; Fulbright fel, Univ Tübingen, 54-55; dep dept head br, 54-80, from instr to assoc prof inorg chem, 55-78, PROF INORG CHEM, UNIV CONN, 78-, ACTG DEPT HEAD, 80- *Mem:* AAAS; Am Chem Soc. *Res:* Magnetochemical studies of free radicals and solid ternary oxides; photochemistry of coordination compounds; organoboron chemistry; chemical bonding. *Mailing Add:* Dept Chem Univ Conn Storrs CT 06268

MOELLER, D(ADE) W(ILLIAM), b Grant, Fla, Feb 27, 27; m 49; c 5. ENVIRONMENTAL ENGINEERING, RADIATION PROTECTION. *Educ:* Ga Inst Technol, BCE & MS, 48; NC State Col, PhD, 57; Harvard Univ, AM, 69. *Prof Exp:* Asst radioactive waste, Johns Hopkins Univ, 48-49; res engr, Los Alamos Sci Lab, 49-52; staff asst, Radiol Health Br, USPHS, 52-54; res assoc reactor cooling systs, Oak Ridge Nat Lab, 56-57; chief radiol training, Robert A Taft Sanit Eng Ctr, USPHS, 57-61, officer in chg, Northeastern Radiol Health Lab, 61-66; ASSOC DIR, KRESGE CTR ENVIRON HEALTH, SCH PUB HEALTH, HARVARD UNIV, 66-, PROF & HEAD DEPT ENVIRON HEALTH SCI, 68- *Concurrent Pos:* Chmn, Am Bd Health Physics, 67-70; mem, Nat Coun Radiation Protection & Measurements, 67-; mem, Adv Comt Reactor Safeguards, US Nuclear Regulator Comn, 73-, chmn, 76; mem, Comt 4, Int Comn Radiol Protection, 78- *Mem:* Nat Acad Eng; AAAS; fel Am Nuclear Soc; Am Pub Health Asn; Health Physics Soc (pres, 71-72). *Res:* Sources and disposition of radioactive wastes and general environmental health. *Mailing Add:* 27 Wildwood Dr Bedford MA 01730

MOELLER, HENRY WILLIAM, b Woodbury, NJ, Aug 4, 37; c 2. MARINE BIOLOGY. *Educ:* Drew Univ, AB, 59; Rutgers Univ, MS, 65, PhD(bot), 69. *Prof Exp:* Physiologist, Wallace Pharmaceut Corp, NJ, 61-62; from instr to asst prof marine sci, Southampton Col, 65-69; asst prof, 69-72, coordr marine sci, 69-77, assoc prof marine sci, 72-80, PROF BIOL, DOWLING COL, 81- *Concurrent Pos:* Pres, Hydro Bot Co, Shelter Island, NY, 81. *Mem:* Am Phycol Soc; Int Phycol Soc; Am Soc Limnol & Oceanog; NY Acad Sci. *Res:* Marine botany; mass culture of marine algae in a water charged atmosphere for energy, food and biochemicals. *Mailing Add:* Dept of Biol Dowling Col Oakdale NY 11769

MOELLER, THEODORE WILLIAM, b Cincinnati, Ohio, Jan 26, 43; m 66; c 2. FOOD SCIENCE. *Educ:* Ohio State Univ, BS, 65; Mich State Univ, MS, 67, PhD(food sci), 71. *Prof Exp:* Group leader food res, 71, MGR PET FOODS RES, JOHN STUART RES LAB, QUAKER OATS CO, 71- *Concurrent Pos:* Mgr/dir qual assurance, Int Foods Res & Develop, 76-81, dir, 81- *Mem:* Inst Food Technologists. *Mailing Add:* Quaker Oats Co 617 W Main St Barrington IL 60010

MOELLMANN, GISELA E BIELITZ, b Dessau, Ger, Feb 15, 29; US citizen; m; c 1. CELL BIOLOGY, CYTOCHEMISTRY. *Educ:* Univ Dayton, BS, 53; Yale Univ, PhD(anat), 67. *Prof Exp:* Am Cancer Soc fel, 66-68, res assoc anat, 68-69, res assoc dermat & lectr anat, 69-73, asst prof, 73-78, ASSOC PROF DERMAT & LECTR CELL BIOL, SCH MED, YALE UNIV, 78- *Mem:* AAAS; Am Soc Cell Biol; Soc Invest Dermat; Sigma Xi. *Res:* Cell biology, especially the fine structure and cytochemistry of mammalian and amphibian pigment cells; intracellular transport of particles; topography of peptide hormone receptor sites; fine-structural changes in vitiligo. *Mailing Add:* LCI 500 Dept Dermat Yale Univ Sch of Med New Haven CT 06510

MOELTER, GREGORY MARTIN, b Dover, NJ, Aug 14, 19; m 42; c 2. CHEMICAL ENGINEERING. *Educ:* Newark Col Eng, BS, 41; NY Univ, MS, 44. *Prof Exp:* Anal chemist, Barrett Chem Co, 40; from sr res engr to sect head fiber spinning res, Celanese Corp Am, 41-63; develop mgr, 63-65, tech mgr, 65-72, tech adminr, 72-75, PROJ MGR, CELANESE FIBERS CO, 75- *Mem:* AAAS; Am Chem Soc; Am Inst Chem Engrs; Am Soc Eng Educ. *Res:* Technology of synthetic fibers productions. *Mailing Add:* 3637 Henshaw Rd Charlotte NC 28209

MOEN, ALLEN LEROY, b Badger, Minn, June 15, 33; m 59; c 3. SURFACE PHYSICS. *Educ:* Pac Lutheran Univ, BA, 55; Wash State Univ, MS, 61, PhD(physics), 68. *Prof Exp:* Asst physics, 55-57, 59-60 & 61-63; asst prof, 63-68, ASSOC PROF PHYSICS & CHMN DEPT, CENT COL IOWA, 68- *Concurrent Pos:* Res asst, Wash State Univ, 66-68. *Mem:* Am Asn Physics Teachers; Am Vacuum Soc. *Res:* Ion bombardment of metals; sputtering; surface physics; ultra-high vacuum physics. *Mailing Add:* Dept of Physics Cent Col Pella IA 50219

MOEN, WALTER B(ONIFACE), b Rockville Centre, NY, Feb 13, 20; m 46; c 2. MECHANICAL ENGINEERING. *Educ:* Pratt Inst, BME, 40; Columbia Univ, MS, 46. *Prof Exp:* Jr engr, Combustion Eng Co, NY, 40-41; instr mech eng, Pratt Inst, 41-47; asst engr, Thatcher Furnace Co, NJ, 47-48; res engr, Res Lab, Air Reduction Co, Inc, 48-52, head metall res sect, 52-56, asst dir, 56-59, eng mgr, Spec Prod Dept, 59-60, mgr, Cryogenics Eng Dept, 60-62, asst chief engr, Cent Eng Dept, 63-67, asst to group vpres, 67-69; dir res & develop, Am Sterilizer Co, 69-71; mgr auto arc div, Nat Standard Co, 71-73; dir eng, Consol Energy Prod, Inc, 73-75; MANAGING DIR TECH PROGS, AM SOC MECH ENGRS, 75- *Mem:* Am Soc Mech Engrs; Am Soc Eng Educ; Am Welding Soc. *Res:* Industrial combustion processes; arc and gas welding; propellant evaluation; propulsion; inorganic chemical manufacture; ocean engineering. *Mailing Add:* Am Soc of Mech Engrs 345 E 47th St New York NY 10017

MOENCH, ROBERT HADLEY, b Boston, Mass, Oct 23, 26; m 55; c 3. GEOLOGY. *Educ:* Boston Univ, AB, 50, AM, 51, PhD(geol), 54. *Prof Exp:* GEOLOGIST, US GEOL SURV, 52- *Mem:* AAAS; Geol Soc Am; Soc Econ Geol. *Res:* Stratigraphy, structure and tectonics of metamorphic rocks, mineral resources and environmental geology, especially in New England. *Mailing Add:* US Geol Surv Fed Ctr Box 25046 MS-930 Lakewood CO 80225

MOENS, PETER B, b Neth, May 15, 31; Can citizen; m 53; c 5. CELL BIOLOGY, CYTOGENETICS. *Educ:* Univ Toronto, BScF, 59, MA, 61, PhD(biol), 63. *Prof Exp:* Assoc prof, 64-72, chmn dept natural sci, Atkinson Col, 74-77, PROF BIOL, YORK UNIV, 72- *Concurrent Pos:* Assoc ed, Genetic Soc Can, 70. *Mem:* Fel Royal Soc Can; Genetics Soc Am (pres, 78-); Genetics Soc Can; Can Soc Cell Biol; Am Cell Biol Soc. *Res:* Electron microscopy; meiosis; development of germ cells in fungi, plants and animals with emphasis on genetically significant aspects; specifically electron microscopy of the synaptonemal complex. *Mailing Add:* Dept Biol York Univ Downsview ON M3J 2R3 Can

MOERMOND, TIMOTHY CREIGHTON, b Sioux City, Iowa, Apr 4, 47; m 68; c 1. ECOLOGY. *Educ:* Univ Ill, Urbana-Champaign, BS, 69; Harvard Univ, PhD(biol), 74. *Prof Exp:* Asst prof, 73-81, ASSOC PROF ZOOL, UNIV WIS-MADISON, 81- *Mem:* Ecol Soc Am; Am Ornithologists Union; Soc Study Evolution; Am Soc Ichthyologists & Herpetologists; Wilson Ornith Soc. *Res:* Field and theoretical studies of foraging strategies and habitat use patterns. *Mailing Add:* Dept of Zool Univ of Wis Madison WI 53706

MOERTEL, CHARLES GEORGE, b Milwaukee, Wis, Oct 17, 27; c 4. MEDICINE, ONCOLOGY. *Educ:* Univ Ill, BS, 52, MD, 53; Univ Minn, MS, 58. *Prof Exp:* From instr to assoc prof, Mayo Grad Sch Med, Univ Minn, 60-71, PROF MED & CHMN DEPT ONCOL, MAYO MED SCH, 71-; CONSULT ONCOL, MAYO CLIN, 58- *Concurrent Pos:* Adv comt oncol drugs, Fed Drug Admin, 74-80; dir, Mayo Comprehensive Cancer Ctr, 75- *Honors & Awards:* Walter Hubert lectureship, British Asn Cancer Res; Ejnar Perman Mem lectureship, Swedish Surg Asn. *Mem:* Am Col Physicians; Am Asn Cancer Res; Am Soc Clin Oncol; Am Gastroenterol Asn; Soc Surg Onocol. *Res:* Gastrointestinal cancer. *Mailing Add:* Mayo Clin Rochester MN 55901

MOESCHBERGER, MELVIN LEE, b Berne, Ind, June 26, 40; m 62; c 3. APPLIED STATISTICS, PUBLIC HEALTH. *Educ:* Taylor Univ, BS, 62; Ohio Univ, MS, 65; NC State Univ, PhD(statist), 70. *Prof Exp:* Instr math, Taylor Univ, 62-63; res assoc biostatist, Univ NC, Chapel Hill, 65-70; asst prof, Univ Mo-Columbia, 70-76; assoc prof statist, Ohio State Univ, 76-80; ASSOC PROF PREV MED, OHIO STATE UNIV, 80- *Concurrent Pos:* NIH res grant, 74; math statistician, Nat Ctr Toxicol Res, 76-78. *Mem:* Am Statist Asn; Biomet Soc. *Res:* Survival analyses and competing risk theory. *Mailing Add:* Dept Prev Med Ohio State Univ Columbus OH 43210

MOFFA, DAVID JOSEPH, b Fairmont, WVa, Dec 6, 42; m 64; c 2. BIOCHEMISTRY, CLINICAL CHEMISTRY. *Educ:* WVa Univ, AB, 64, MS, 66, PhD(biochem), 68. *Prof Exp:* Res asst biochem, 64-68, instr, Sch Med, 68-70, ASST PROF BIOCHEM, SCH MED, WVA UNIV, 70-; DIR, BIOPREPS LABS, 69- *Concurrent Pos:* NIH res fel, WVa Univ, 68-70. *Mem:* Am Asn Clin Chem; Am Soc Clin Pathologists; Am Med Technologists. *Res:* Metabolism of vitamin A; lipid metabolism; enzymology; clinical methodology. *Mailing Add:* BioPreps Labs Box 888 Fairmont WV 26554

MOFFAT, JAMES, b Turtle Creek, Pa, Feb 24, 21; m 46; c 1. CHEMISTRY. *Educ:* Allegheny Col, BS, 42; Northwestern Univ, PhD(org chem), 48. *Prof Exp:* Asst prof chem, Univ Miami Fla, 47-49; res fel, Calif Inst Technol, 49-50; sr res chemist, Nepera Chem Co, 51; res assoc, Northwestern Univ, 51-53; res asst prof chem, Univ Louisville, 53-58; asst prof, 58-62, ASSOC PROF CHEM, UNIV MO-KANSAS CITY, 62- *Mem:* AAAS; Am Chem Soc. *Res:* Heterocyclic compounds; organic isocyanides; hydrogen bonding; tautomerism. *Mailing Add:* 2709 Rochester Ave Kansas City MO 64120

MOFFAT, JOHN BLAIN, b Owen Sound, Ont, Aug 7, 30; m 56; c 3. PHYSICAL CHEMISTRY, QUANTUM CHEMISTRY. *Educ:* Univ Toronto, BA, 53, PhD(phys chem), 56. *Prof Exp:* Res chemist, Res & Develop Lab, Du Pont Can Ltd, 56-61; from asst prof to assoc prof, 61-74, PROF CHEM, UNIV WATERLOO, 74- *Mem:* Am Chem Soc; The Royal Soc Chem; Am Phys Soc; fel Chem Inst Can. *Res:* Molecular orbital theory; molecular structure and chemical bonding; surface chemistry and catalysis; adsorption, reaction kinetics and spectroscopic studies; surface chemistry; heterogeneous catalysis. *Mailing Add:* 226 Lincoln Rd Waterloo ON N2J 2P3 Can

MOFFAT, JOHN KEITH, b Edinburgh, Scotland, Apr 3, 43. BIOPHYSICS. *Educ:* Univ Edinburgh, BSc, 65; Cambridge Univ, PhD(protein crystallog), 70. *Prof Exp:* Sci staff mem protein crystallog, Med Res Coun Lab Molecular Biol, 68-69; res assoc reaction kinetics, 69-70, asst prof biochem & molecular biol, 70-76, ASSOC PROF BIOCHEM & MOLECULAR BIOL, CORNELL UNIV, 77- *Concurrent Pos:* Merck, Sharp & Dohme fac develop award, Cornell Univ, 70. *Honors & Awards:* Res Career Develop Award, NIH, 78. *Mem:* Am Crystallog Asn; Biophys Soc. *Res:* Protein structure determination by physico-chemical techniques; relation between structure and function in hemoglobin, calcium binding proteins and polypeptide hormones; protein crystallography; synchroton radiation. *Mailing Add:* Sect Biochem Molecular & Cell Biol Cornell Univ Ithaca NY 14853

MOFFAT, ROBERT J, b Grosse Pointe, Mich, Nov 29, 27; m 49; c 1. MECHANICAL ENGINEERING. *Educ:* Univ Mich, BS, 52; Wayne State Univ, MS, 61; Stanford Univ, MS, 66, PhD(heat transfer), 67. *Prof Exp:* Sr res engr, Res Labs, Gen Motors Corp, 52-62; assoc prof, 66-71, PROF MECH ENG & CHMN, THERMOSCI DIV, STANFORD UNIV, 71- *Mem:* Am Soc Mech Engrs; Instrument Soc Am. *Res:* Heat transfer, mass transfer, temperature measurement and systems or devices related to these fields. *Mailing Add:* Dept of Mech Eng Stanford Univ Stanford CA 94305

MOFFATT, CHARLES ALLEN, mechanical & biomedical engineering, see previous edition

MOFFATT, DAVID JOHN, b Staffordshire, Eng, July 23, 39; m 64; c 2. ANATOMY, MEDICAL EDUCATION. *Educ:* Bristol Univ, Eng, BSc, 61, MB & ChB, 64. *Prof Exp:* Demonstr anat, Bristol Univ, 65-67, res assoc, 67-68; from asst prof to assoc prof anat, Univ Iowa, 68-79; PROF & CHMN, DEPT ANAT, UNIV MO-KANSAS CITY, 79- *Concurrent Pos:* Vis prof anat, Univ Geissen, Ger, 75; consult, Asn Med Schs Mid East, 75- & 4th Saudi Med Conf, 79; vis prof anat, Cairo Univ, 76; mem learning mat panel, Nat Libr Med, 76-; ed, Health Sci News, 76-78; vis prof, El Minya Univ, Egypt & King Faisal Univ, Saudi Arabia, 79 & King Abdulaziz Univ, 80; external examr anat, King Abdulaziz Univ, Saudi Arabia, 80 & 81. *Mem:* Am Asn Anatomists; Nat Soc Performance & Instr; Anat Soc Gt Brit & Ireland; Int Exp Hemat Soc; Soc Exp Biol Med. *Res:* Use of mediated learning systems in medical education; programmed learning; experimental hematology; kinetics of stem cell proliferation; medical education systems. *Mailing Add:* Dept Anat Univ Mo 2411 Holmes St Kansas City MO 64108

MOFFATT, DAVID LLOYD, b Wheeling, WVa; m 50; c 2. ELECTRICAL ENGINEERING, ELECTROMAGNETISM. *Educ:* Ohio State Univ, BS, 58, MSc, 61, PhD(elec eng), 67. *Prof Exp:* Res assoc, 58-67, asst prof, 69-78, ASSOC PROF ELEC ENG, OHIO STATE UNIV, 78-, ASSOC SUPVR, ELECTRO-SCI LAB, 67- *Mem:* Sigma Xi; Int Union Radio Sci. *Res:* Radar target identification; time domain electromagnetics; radar cross section. *Mailing Add:* Dept of Elec Eng 1320 Kinnear Rd Columbus OH 43212

MOFFATT, JOHN GILBERT, b Victoria, BC, Sept 19, 30; m 53; c 4. ORGANIC CHEMISTRY. *Educ:* Univ BC, BA, 52, MSc, 53, PhD(org chem), 56. *Prof Exp:* Tech officer, Defence Res Bd Can, 53-54; res assoc, BC Res Coun, 56-60; group leader, Calif Corp Biochem Res, 60-61; head org chem, 61-65, assoc dir, 65-67, dir, Inst Molecular Biol, 67-77, dir synthetic chem, Inst Organic Chem, 77-81, DIR, INST BIO-ORG CHEM, SYNTEX RES, 81- *Mem:* Am Chem Soc; The Chem Soc; Am Soc Biol Chemists. *Res:* Chemistry of nucleosides, nucleotides, nucleoside polyphosphates, sugar phosphates, carbohydrates and nucleic acids. *Mailing Add:* Inst Bio-org Chem Syntex Res 3401 Hillview Ave Palo Alto CA 94304

MOFFATT, WILLIAM CRAIG, b Owen Sound, Ont, Apr 19, 33; m 56; c 2. FLUID MECHANICS, AERODYNAMICS. *Educ:* Queen's Univ, Ont, BSc, 56, MSc, 58; Mass Inst Technol, ScD(mech eng), 61. *Prof Exp:* Lectr mech eng, Royal Mil Col, Ont, 56; asst prof, Mass Inst Technol, 61-65; proj engr, Northern Res & Eng Corp, 65-66; assoc prof mech eng, 66-67, head dept, 69-78, PROF MECH ENG, ROYAL MIL COL CAN, 67- *Concurrent Pos:* Consult, Northern Res & Eng Corp, 61-65 & 66-; vis prof, Van Karman Inst, Brussels, 78-79. *Mem:* Am Soc Mech Engrs; Am Inst Aeronaut & Astronaut; assoc fel Can Aeronaut & Space Inst. *Res:* Magnetohydrodynamics; gas turbine propulsion; turbomachinery; plasma synamics; combustion. *Mailing Add:* Dept Mech Eng Can Serv Col Royal Mil Col Can Kingston ON K7L 2W3 Can

MOFFA-WHITE, ANDREA MARIE, b Marlboro, Mass, May 19, 49; m 78; c 1. POPULATION GENETICS. *Educ:* Fordham Univ, BS, 71; Univ RI, MS, 73, PhD(biol), 76. *Prof Exp:* Asst prof biol, Wheeling Col, 76-77; asst prof biol, WVa Univ, 77-81; ASST PEDIAT, UNIV FLA, GAINSVILLE, 81- *Mem:* AAAS; Sigma Xi; Am Soc Zoologists; Genetics Soc Am. *Res:* Etiology of neural tube defects in animal models; demographic and genetic changes in laboratory populations. *Mailing Add:* Dept Pediat Div Genetics Univ Fla Box J-296 Gainsville FL 32610

MOFFEIT, KENNETH CHARLES, b Vinson, Okla, Dec 24, 39; c 2. PHYSICS. *Educ:* Univ Calif, Riverside, BA, 65; Univ Calif, Berkeley, PhD(physics), 70. *Prof Exp:* Res assoc physics, Stanford Linear Accelerator Ctr, Stanford Univ, 70-74; staff physicist, Deutches, 74-76; STAFF PHYSICIST PHYSICS, STANFORD LINEAR ACCELERATOR CTR, STANFORD UNIV, 76- *Res:* High energy physics. *Mailing Add:* 845 Esplanada Way Stanford CA 94305

MOFFET, ALAN THEODORE, b St Paul, Minn, Mar 24, 36. RADIO ASTRONOMY. *Educ:* Wesleyan Univ, BA, 57; Calif Inst Technol, PhD(physics, astron), 61. *Prof Exp:* Fulbright scholar, Univ Bonn, 61-62; res fel radio astron, 62-66, Sloan fel, 63-67, from asst prof to assoc prof, 66-71, dir, Owens Valley Radio Observ, 75-80, PROF RADIO ASTRON, CALIF INST TECHNOL, 71- *Concurrent Pos:* Mem US Nat Comn J, Int Sci Radio Union (chmn, 78-81); vis prof, Nanjing Univ, China, 80; mem comt on radio frequencies, US Nat Res Coun, 79- *Mem:* Int Astron Union; Am Astron Soc; Am Phys Soc; Inst Elec & Electronics Eng; Int Sci Radio Union. *Res:* Structure and physical properties of extragalactic radio sources; design of radio telescopes and astronomical instruments. *Mailing Add:* Owens Valley Radio Observ Calif Inst of Technol Pasadena CA 91125

MOFFET, HUGH L, b Monmouth, Ill, Jan 6, 32; m 54; c 3. PEDIATRICS, INFECTIOUS DISEASES. *Educ:* Harvard Univ, AB, 53; Yale Univ, MD, 57. *Prof Exp:* Instr pediat, Bowman Gray Sch Med, 62-63; from asst prof to assoc prof, Med Sch, Northwestern Univ, Chicago, 63-71; assoc prof, 71-74, PROF PEDIAT, MED SCH, UNIV WIS-MADISON, 74- *Concurrent Pos:* Nat Inst Allergy & Infectious Dis fel, 60-63. *Res:* Diagnostic microbiology; epidemiology of pediatric infections. *Mailing Add:* 202 S Park St Madison WI 53715

MOFFETT, BENJAMIN CHARLES, JR, b Spring Lake, NJ, Oct 28, 23; m 49, 78; c 3. DENTAL RESEARCH. *Educ:* Syracuse Univ, BA, 48; NY Univ, PhD(anat), 52. *Prof Exp:* From asst prof to assoc prof anat, Med Col, Univ Ala, 52-63; assoc prof, Col Med, Wayne State Univ, 63-64; assoc prof, 64-67, PROF ORTHOD, SCH DENT, UNIV WASH, 67- *Concurrent Pos:* Res fel anat, Med Sch, Gothenburg Univ, 59-60; res fel anat, Armed Forces Inst Path, 60-61; vis prof, Sch Dent, Cath Univ Nijmegen, 71-72. *Honors & Awards:* Jerome Schweitzer Res Award, NY Acad Prosthodont, 69. *Mem:* Am Asn Anat; Int Asn Dent Res; hon mem Am Acad Craniomandible Disorders. *Res:* Arthrology; history of anatomy; cranio-facial morphogenesis. *Mailing Add:* Dept of Orthod Univ of Wash Sch of Dent Seattle WA 98195

MOFFETT, DAVID READ, accelerator physics, high energy physics, see previous edition

MOFFETT, JOSEPH ORR, b Peabody, Kans, Jan 9, 26; m 44; c 7. ENTOMOLOGY. *Educ:* Kans State Univ, BS, 49, MS, 50; Univ Wyo, PhD(entom), 74. *Prof Exp:* From instr to asst prof apicult, Colo State Univ, 49-59; ed & secy-treas, Am Beekeeping Fedn, 59-64; entomologist, Bee Res Lab, Agr Res Serv, Tucson, Ariz, 67-78, ENTOMOLOGIST, SCI & EDUC ADMIN, USDA, 78-; ENTOMOLOGIST, OKLA STATE UNIV, 80- *Mem:* Entom Soc Am; Sigma Xi. *Res:* Pollination of citrus and hybrid cotton; greenhouse pollination by bees; effect of herbicides on honeybees. *Mailing Add:* 501 Life Sci W Okla State Univ Stillwater OK 74074

MOFFETT, ROBERT BRUCE, b Madison, Ind, June 8, 14; c 2. ORGANIC CHEMISTRY, MEDICINAL CHEMISTRY. *Educ:* Hanover Col, AB, 37, Univ Ill, AM, 39, PhD(org chem), 41. *Hon Degrees:* DSc, Hanover Col, 59. *Prof Exp:* Asst, Univ Ill, 37-39; Abbott, Upjohn & Glidden fel, Northwestern Univ, 41-43; sr res chemist, George A Breon & Co, Mo, 43-44, asst dir labs, 44-47; res chemist, Upjohn Co, 47-77; RETIRED. *Mem:* Am Chem Soc; AAAS. *Res:* Chemiluminescence; benzopyrylium salts; steroids; analgesics; antispasmodics; drugs for mental diseases. *Mailing Add:* 2895 Bronson Blvd Kalamazoo MI 49008

MOFFITT, EMERSON AMOS, b McAdam, NB, Sept 9, 24; US citizen; m 51; c 3. ANESTHESIOLOGY. *Educ:* Dalhousie Univ, MD, CM, 51; Univ Minn, MS, 58; FRCP(C), 58; Am Bd Anesthesiol, dipl, 60. *Prof Exp:* Pvt pract, 51-54; resident anesthesiol, Mayo Grad Sch Med, Univ Minn, 54-57, from instr to assoc prof, 59-72; prof anesthesia & head dept, 73-80, ASSOC DEAN, CLIN AFFAIRS, DALHOUSIE UNIV, 80- *Concurrent Pos:* Consult, Mayo Clin, 57-72, sect head anesthesiol, 66-72, NIH grant gen med sci, Mayo Found, 67-72. *Mem:* Am Soc Anesthesiol; Int Anesthesia Res Soc; Can Anaesthetists Soc; Can Cardiovasc Soc; Sigma Xi. *Res:* Cardiovascular and metabolic effects of anesthetic state and cardiac surgery with whole body perfusion; metabolism in acute stress and shock. *Mailing Add:* Off Dean Fac Med Dalhousie Univ Sir Charles Tupper Med Bldg Halifax NS B37 4H7 Can

MOFFITT, HAROLD ROGER, b Ukiah, Calif, Aug 8, 34; m 54; c 3. AGRICULTURAL ENTOMOLOGY. *Educ:* Univ Calif, Davis, BS, 57, Univ Calif, Riverside, MS, 63, PhD(entom), 67. *Prof Exp:* Lab technician entom, Univ Calif, Riverside, 57-63, res asst, 63-67; res leader, 72-80, RES ENTOMOLOGIST, AGR RES SERV, USDA, 67- *Concurrent Pos:* Vis scientist, Entomology Div, Dept Sci & Indust Res, New Zealand, 80-81. *Mem:* AAAS; Entom Soc Am; Entom Soc Can; Int Orgn Biol Control. *Res:* Biology and control of insects and mites of agricultural importance; integrated control and applied ecology; biological and genetic control. *Mailing Add:* Yakima Agr Res Lab USDA 3706 Nob Hill Blvd Yakima WA 98902

MOFFITT, ROBERT ALLAN, b Gillette, Wyo, June 17, 18; m 44; c 4. CHEMISTRY, BIOCHEMISTRY. *Educ:* Univ Calif, Los Angeles, BA, 40; Univ Southern Calif, MS, 54. *Prof Exp:* Lab mgr, Fernando Valley Milling & Supply Co, 40-44 & Ralston Purina Co, 46-60; head anal lab, Res Labs, 60-67, MGR ANAL SERV, CARNATION CO, 67- *Mem:* Am Chem Soc; Am Asn Cereal Chem; Inst Food Technol. *Res:* Accurate analysis of chemical components of food products; contamination of foods; analytical chemistry; instrumentation. *Mailing Add:* 1960 Escarpa Dr Los Angeles CA 90041

MOFJELD, HAROLD OSWALD, b San Francisco, Calif, Nov 2, 40. PHYSICAL OCEANOGRAPHY. *Educ:* Univ Wash, BS, 63, MS, 65, PhD(geophys), 70. *Prof Exp:* Fel oceanog, Univ Wash, 70-71; res oceanogr, Atlantic Oceanog & Meteorol Labs, 71-76, OCEANOGR, PAC MARINE ENVIRON LAB, NAT OCEANIC & ATMOSPHERIC ADMIN, 76- *Concurrent Pos:* Adj prof oceanog, Univ Miami, 72-78; affil asst prof, Univ Wash, 76- *Mem:* Sigma Xi; Am Geophys Union. *Res:* Tides and tidal currents both on the continental shelves and in the open oceans; theoretical studies of time-dependent currents. *Mailing Add:* 3711 15th Ave NE Seattle WA 98105

MOG, DAVID MICHAEL, b Cleveland, Ohio, Oct 21, 42; m 68; c 2. BIOCHEMISTRY. *Educ:* Case Inst Technol, BS, 64; Calif Inst Technol, PhD(chem), 70. *Prof Exp:* Asst prof chem, Muskingum Col, 68-69; res fel Brazil, Nat Acad Sci, 70-73; asst prof chem, Oberlin Col, 73-78; admin officer, Chem Dept, Princeton Univ, 78-81; PROF ASSOC, BD SCI & TECHNOL INT, NAT ACAD SCI, 81- *Concurrent Pos:* Mem, Peace Corps Rev Comt, Nat Acad Sci, 73-74. *Mem:* Am Chem Soc; AAAS; Sigma Xi. *Res:* Renewable energy sources, especially liquid fuels from biomass; chemistry in agriculture including plant biochemistry and nutrition, tropical soil chemistry, tissue culture and genetic engineering; computer conferencing for development. *Mailing Add:* Nat Acad Sci 2101 Const Ave Northwest Washington DC 20418

MOGAB, CYRIL JOSEPH, b Philadelphia, Pa, Feb 12, 41; m 67. MATERIALS SCIENCE. *Educ:* Rutgers Univ, BS, 63; Mass Inst Technol, ScD(ceramics), 67. *Prof Exp:* Res asst ceramics, Mass Inst Technol, 63-64, asst prof, 66-70; MEM TECH STAFF, BELL TEL LABS, 70- *Concurrent Pos:* Ford Found fel eng, 67- *Mem:* Am Vacuum Soc. *Res:* Thin films; electronic materials; plasma etching and deposition. *Mailing Add:* Bell Tel Labs Rm 7B-414 Murray Hill NJ 07974

MOGABGAB, WILLIAM JOSEPH, b Durant, Okla, Nov 2, 21; m 48; c 5. INTERNAL MEDICINE, INFECTIOUS DISEASES. *Educ:* Tulane Univ, BS, 42, MD, 44; Am Bd Internal Med, dipl, 51; Am Bd Microbiol, dipl. *Prof Exp:* Intern, Charity Hosp La, New Orleans, 44-45; from asst to instr med, Sch Med, Tulane Univ, 46-49, instr, Div Infectious Dis, 49-51; Nat Found Infantile Paralysis fel, 51-52; asst prof, Baylor Col Med, 52-53; head virol div, Naval Med Res Unit 4, Great Lakes, Ill, 53-55; assoc prof, 56-62, PROF MED, SCH MED, TULANE UNIV, 62- *Concurrent Pos:* From resident to chief resident, Tulane Serv, Charity Hosp, La, 46-49, vis physician, 49-51 & sr vis physician, 61-75, consult, 76-; vis investr & asst physician, Hosp, Rockefeller Inst, 51-52; chief infectious dis, Vet Admin Hosp, Houston, 52-53; consult, Vet Admin Hosp, New Orleans, 56- *Mem:* Am Fedn Clin Res; AAAS; Am Pub Health Asn; Am Soc Clin Invest; Am Soc Cell Biol. *Res:* Virology; tissue culture; bacteriology. *Mailing Add:* Sect of Infect Dis Tulane Univ Sch of Med New Orleans LA 70112

MOGENSEN, HANS LLOYD, b Price, Utah, Dec 16, 38; m 58; c 2. PLANT ANATOMY, PLANT MORPHOLOGY. *Educ:* Utah State Univ, BS, 61; Iowa State Univ, MS, 63, PhD(plant anat), 65. *Prof Exp:* Assoc prof, 65-74, PROF BOT, NORTHERN ARIZ UNIV, 74- *Concurrent Pos:* Vis prof, Carlsberg Res Lab, Copenhagen, Denmark, 76-77. *Mem:* Bot Soc Am; Int Soc Plant Morphologists. *Res:* Ultrastructure of fertilization in flowering plants; plant development. *Mailing Add:* Dept of Biol Northern Ariz Univ Flagstaff AZ 86001

MOGENSON, GORDON JAMES, b Delisle, Sask, Jan 24, 31; m 54; c 2. PSYCHOPHYSIOLOGY. *Educ:* Univ Sask, BA, 55, MA, 56; McGill Univ, PhD(physiol psychol), 59. *Prof Exp:* From asst prof to assoc prof psychol, Univ Sask, 58-65; assoc prof psychol & physiol, 65-68, prof psychol, 68-77, EMER PROF PSYCHOL, UNIV WESTERN ONT, 77-, PROF PHYSIOL, 68-, CHMN DEPT, 77- *Concurrent Pos:* Ed, Can J Psychol, 69-74 & Newsletter, Int Comn Physiol Food & Fluid Intake, 74- *Mem:* AAAS; Am Psychol Asn; Animal Behav Soc; Can Psychol Asn; Can Physiol Soc. *Res:* Physiology of behavior; control systems for water and food intake, temperature regulation and self-stimulation; neural mechanisms for reinforcement and learning. *Mailing Add:* Dept of Physiol Univ of Western Ont London ON N6A 5B8 Can

MOGFORD, JAMES A, b McCamey, Tex, Dec 6, 30; m 53; c 4. PHYSICS. *Educ:* Tex Tech Col, BS, 56; Univ Wis, MS, 59. *Prof Exp:* Physicist, Midwestern Univs Res Asn, 59-61; staff mem, Sandia Labs, NMex, 61-67, supvr, Anal Div, Sandia Labs, Livermore, 67-74, supvr, Inductive Energy Storage Div, 74-75, MEM MGT STAFF, SANDIA NAT LABS, ALBUQUERQUE, 75- *Res:* Theoretical studies of orbit dynamics in particle accelerators; effects of radiation energy deposition; effects of photon-electron irradiation of materials and systems; design and development of pulsed-power systems. *Mailing Add:* Sandia Nat Labs Albuquerque NM 87185

MOGGIO, MARY VIRGINIA, b Baton Rouge, La, Mar 10, 47; div. ENVIRONMENTAL EPIDEMIOLOGY, ENVIRONMENTAL SCIENCES. *Educ:* Univ Pittsburgh, BS, 68; Univ NC, Chapel Hill, MSPH, 72. *Prof Exp:* Environ epidemiologist, 71-79, EPIDEMIOLOGIST, PEDIAT INFECTIOUS DIS, MED CTR, DUKE UNIV, 79- *Mem:* Am Pub Health Asn; Nat Environ Health Asn; Asn Practitioners Infection Control; Sigma Xi. *Res:* Environmental and nosocomial infection epidemiology in health care institutions; preventative disease epidemiology in pediatric population; risk for defined bacterial complication of previous underlying disease states; participation in preventative vaccine trials for pediatric populations. *Mailing Add:* Duke Univ Med Ctr PO Box 2951 Durham NC 27710

MOGHISSI, KAMRAN S, b Tehran, Iran, Sept 11, 25; US citizen; m 52; c 2. OBSTETRICS & GYNECOLOGY. *Educ:* Univ Tehran, BS, 47; Univ Geneva, MB & ChB, 51, MD, 52; Am Bd Obstet & Gynec, dipl, 67, cert, 80, dipl reprod endocrinol, 75. *Prof Exp:* Intern & resident obstet & gynec var hosps, Eng, 52-56; assoc prof, Med Sch & Nemazee Hosp, Univ Shiraz, 56-59; res assoc biochem, Sch Med, Wayne State Univ, 59-61; sr resident obstet & gynec, Detroit Gen Hosp, 61; from asst to assoc prof, 62-71, PROF OBSTET & GYNEC & CHIEF DIV REPROD BIOL & ENDOCRINOL, SCH MED, WAYNE STATE UNIV, 71- *Concurrent Pos:* Attend obstetrician & gynecologist, Detroit Gen Hosp, 62; sr attend, Hutzel Hosp, 62; surgeon, Harper Hosp, 63; gynecologist, Childrens Hosp Mich; examr, Am Bd Obstet & Gynec; consult, NIH & WHO. *Mem:* Fel Am Col Obstet & Gynec; fel Am Col Surg; Asn Planned Parenthood Physicians; Am Gynec Soc; Am Soc Androl. *Res:* Human reproduction and reproductive endocrinology; infertility and conception control. *Mailing Add:* Dept of Gynec & Obstet Wayne State Univ Sch of Med Detroit MI 48201

MOGREN, EDWIN WALFRED, b Minn, Sept 16, 21; m 44; c 2. FORESTRY. *Educ:* Univ Minn, BSF, 47, MF, 48; Univ Mich, PhD(forest ecol), 55. *Prof Exp:* Asst, Lake States Forest Exp Sta, US Forest Serv, 41; asst, Univ Minn, 47-48; from instr to asst prof forestry, 48-55, assoc prof forest mgt, 55-61, PROF FOREST MGT, COLO STATE UNIV, 61- *Concurrent Pos:* Collabr, Rocky Mt Forest & Range Exp Sta, 52-60. *Mem:* Fel AAAS; Soc Am Foresters; Ecol Soc Am. *Res:* Forest management; ecology; siliviculture. *Mailing Add:* Colo State Univ Col Forest & Natural Resources Ft Collins CO 80523

MOGRO-CAMPERO, ANTONIO, b Liverpool, Eng, Aug 25, 40; Bolivian citizen; m 66; c 3. SPACE PHYSICS, GEOPHYSICS. *Educ:* Columbia Univ, BS, 63; Univ Chicago, MS, 67, PhD(physics), 71. *Prof Exp:* Res engr, Lab Cosmic Physics, Univ San Andres, Bolivia, 63-65; res assoc physics, Enrico Fermi Inst, Univ Chicago, 70-74; res physicist & lectr, Univ Calif, San Diego, 74-75; PHYSICIST, GEN ELEC RES & DEVELOP CTR, 75- *Mem:* Am Phys Soc; Am Geophys Union. *Res:* Amorphous metals; gas flow in the Earth; earthquake prediction; Jupiter's and Earth's radiation belts; solar and galactic cosmic rays; lifetime control in semiconductor devices; metallization in microelectronic chips and devices. *Mailing Add:* Gen Elec Res & Develop Ctr PO Box 8 Schenectady NY 12301

MOGUS, MARY ANN, b Greensburg, Pa. BIOPHYSICS, APPLIED PHYSICS. *Educ:* Seton Hill Col, BA, 65; Pa State Univ, MS, 67, PhD(biophys), 70. *Prof Exp:* Res assoc bioacoust lab, Eye & Ear Hosp, Univ Pittsburgh, 70-71, NIH res fel, 71-72; res fel biophys lab, Carnegie-Mellon Univ, 72-74; asst prof, 74-78, ASSOC PROF PHYSICS, EAST STROUDSBURG STATE COL, 78- *Concurrent Pos:* Res fel, Carnegie-Mellon Univ, 81. *Mem:* Am Soc Photobiol; NY Acad Sci; Sigma Xi; Soc Archaeol Sci; AAAS. *Res:* Biophysics of sensory systems, vision and auditory; brain organization and information processing; physics applied to archaeology, infrared analysis of sites and artifacts; artifact composition studies; developing vision device for the low-visioned; microcomputers and education. *Mailing Add:* Dept Physics East Stroudsburg State Col East Stroudsburg PA 18301

MOHACSI, ERNO, b Zalaegerszeg, Hungary, Jan 26, 29; US citizen. ORGANIC CHEMISTRY, PHYSICAL CHEMISTRY. *Educ:* Eotvos Lorand Univ, Budapest, dipl org chem, 56; Columbia Univ MA, 60, PhD(org chem), 62. *Prof Exp:* Fel, Columbia Univ, 62-64 & Harvard, Univ 64-66; SR RES CHEMIST, HOFFMANN-LA ROCHE, INC, 66- *Mem:* Am Chem Soc. *Res:* Synthetic organic chemistry, especially structure elucidation and synthesis of alkaloids and other natural products. *Mailing Add:* 85 Hillcrest Ave Summit NJ 07901

MOHAMED, ALY HAMED, b Cairo, Egypt, Aug 29, 24; m 43; c 2. GENETICS. *Educ:* Univ Alexandria, BS, 46; Univ Minn, MS, 53, PhD(genetics), 54. *Prof Exp:* Asst genetics, Univ Alexandria, 46-48, lectr, 54-60, assoc prof, 60-63; res assoc range sci, Tex A&M Univ, 63-64, res fel genetics & air pollution trainee, 64-66; assoc prof, 66-69, PROF BIOL, UNIV MO-KANSAS CITY, 69- *Concurrent Pos:* Dept Health, Educ & Welfare res grant, 67-71. *Mem:* AAAS; Bot Soc Am; Genetics Soc Am; Am Genetic Asn; Int Soc Fluoride Res (vpres). *Res:* Plant cytogenetics and the inheritance of quantitative characters; studying the effect of some air pollutants on chromosomes. *Mailing Add:* Dept of Biol Univ of Mo Kansas City MO 64110

MOHAMMED, AUYUAB, b Trinidad, WI, Jan 11, 28; m 55; c 4. APPLIED MATHEMATICS. *Educ:* Univ Man, BSc, 54, MSc, 56; Univ BC, PhD(appl math), 65. *Prof Exp:* Sci officer, 54-60, HEAD APPL MATH SECT, DEFENCE RES ESTAB ATLANTIC, DEFENCE RES BD CAN, 61- *Mem:* Fel Acoust Soc Am; Asn Comput Mach; Inst Elec & Electronics Engrs; Brit Comput Soc. *Res:* Underwater acoustics; scientific applications of computers; non-linear and linear control theory; communication theory. *Mailing Add:* Defence Res Estab Atlantic PO Box 1012 9 Grove St Dartmouth NS B4Z 3Z7 Can

MOHAMMED, KASHEED, b Trinidad, WI, Apr 27, 30; m 64; c 2. NUTRITIONAL BIOCHEMISTRY, HUMAN PHYSIOLOGY. *Educ:* Univ Ariz, BS, 62, MS, 63, PhD(biochem), 67. *Prof Exp:* Scientist, Angostura Bitters, Trinidad, 52-56; NIH fel, Univ Ill Med Ctr, 67-69, res fel, 69; nutrit biochemist, Pharmaceut Div, Johnson & Johnson Res Ctr, 69-80; GROUP LEADER, ROSS LABS, CLEVELAND, OHIO, 80- *Concurrent Pos:* Sci adv, State Univ NY Agr & Tech Col, Canton, 70- *Mem:* AAAS; Am Chem Soc. *Res:* Research and development of enteral and parenteral products for therapeutic usages. *Mailing Add:* Ross Labs 625 Cleveland Ave Columbus OH 43216

MOHAMMED, M HAMDI A, b Minia, Egypt, May 10, 40; m 64; c 2. DENTAL MATERIALS, PROSTHODONTICS. *Educ:* Univ Alexandria, DDS, 63, MSD, 65; Northwestern Univ, MScD, 67; Univ Mich, PhD(dent mat), 71. *Prof Exp:* Res asst dent mat, Northwestern Univ, 66-67; res assoc, Marquette Univ, 67-68; lectr dent, Washtenaw Community Col, 68-69; res assoc dent mat, Univ Mich, 69-71, scholar, 70-71; from asst prof to assoc prof dent, Sch Dent Med, Univ Conn, 71-74; PROF DENT MAT & CHMN DEPT, COL DENT, UNIV FLA, 74- *Concurrent Pos:* Consult, Vet Admin Hosp, Gainesville, 74- & Williams Gold Refining Co, Inc, 74- *Honors & Awards:* Medal Sci Achievement, Repub Egypt, 63. *Mem:* Am Dent Asn; Am Soc Metals; Int Asn Dent Res; Am Asn Dent Sch. *Res:* Alloy systems for medical applications; structural design for dental appliances; development of implant materials; adaptation of laser beam holography to dental research. *Mailing Add:* Col of Dent Dept Dent Mat Univ of Fla Health Ctr Gainesville FL 32611

MOHAN, ARTHUR G, b Trenton, NJ, Mar 26, 35; m 59; c 4. ORGANIC CHEMISTRY. *Educ:* St Bonaventure Univ, BS, 57, MS, 59; Seton Hall Univ, PhD(org chem), 66. *Prof Exp:* Chemist, Nopco Chem Co, NJ, 59-65; res chemist, 66-73, sr res chemist, 73-75, PRIN RES SCIENTIST, CHEM RES DIV, AM CYANAMID CO, BOUND BROOK, 75- *Concurrent Pos:* Adj assoc prof chem, Seton Hall Univ, 72-80, adj prof, 80- *Mem:* Am Chem Soc. *Res:* Organic reaction mechanisms; catalysis and organic process research; photochemistry and chemiluminescence. *Mailing Add:* 34 Windy Willow Way Somerville NJ 08876

MOHAN, J(OSEPH) C(HARLES), JR, b Philadelphia, Pa, Nov 2, 21; m 47; c 2. CHEMICAL ENGINEERING. *Educ:* Pa State Univ, BS, 46. *Prof Exp:* Jr chem engr, Sinclair Oil Co, 46-48; sr chem engr, Pennsalt Chem Co, 48-57; sect leader res & develop, film opers, Am Viscose Div, FMC Corp, 57-66, mfg mgr, Indust Packaging Dept, 66-69; SECT LEADER POLYMER & PLASTICS RES & DEVELOP, AMOCO CHEM CORP, 69- *Mem:* Am Inst Chem Engrs. *Res:* Industrial chemicals; elemental fluorine development; benzene hexochloride; chlorofluorohydrocarbons; cellophane; polyethylene; polypropylene; polyvinyl-chloride and other plastic films; polymer stabilization; rheology applications. *Mailing Add:* Amoco Chem Corp PO Box 400 Naperville IL 60540

MOHAN, KSHITIJ, b Aligarh, India, Jan 26, 45; nat US; m 68; c 2. APPLIED OPTICS, SOLID STATE PHYSICS. *Educ:* Patna Univ, BSc, 63; Univ Colo, Boulder, MS, 67; Georgetown Univ, PhD(physics), 76. *Prof Exp:* Indust res assoc physics, Nat Bur Standards, 67-74; vis scientist, Bur Radiol Health, Food & Drug Admin, HEW, 75-76, sr staff fel, 76-77, dep br chief, Electro-Optics Br, 77-80; ANALYST, EXEC OFF OF THE PRESIDENT OF THE UNITED STATES, 80- *Concurrent Pos:* Mem, Coun Optical Radiation Measurements & mem comt Z-311, Am Nat Standards Inst. *Honors & Awards:* Citation Award, Nat Bur Standards, 75. *Mem:* Health Physics Soc. *Mailing Add:* Rm 8001 New Exec Off Bldg Exec Off of the President Washington DC 20503

MOHAN, NARENDRA, b India, Oct 5, 46; m 73. ELECTRICAL ENGINEERING, NUCLEAR ENGINEERING. *Educ:* Indian Inst Technol, India, BS, 67; Univ NB, MS, 69; Univ Wis-Madison, MS, 72, PhD(elec eng), 73. *Prof Exp:* Proj assoc elec eng, Univ Wis, 73-75; asst prof elec eng, 75-80, ASSOC PROF ELEC ENG, UNIV MINN, MINNEAPOLIS, 80- *Mem:* Inst Elec & Electronics Engrs. *Res:* High voltage direct current transmission; transients in power systems; power conditioning; solar and wind energy conversion systems. *Mailing Add:* Dept of Elec Eng 123 Church SE Minneapolis MN 55455

MOHAN, RAAM RAMANUJA, microbiology, see previous edition

MOHANDAS, THULUVANCHERI, b Guruvayur, India, Feb 26, 46; Can citizen. HUMAN GENETICS, CYTOGENETICS. *Educ:* Univ Kerala, India, BS, 66; Ind Agr Res Inst, MS, 69; McGill Univ, PhD(genetics), 72. *Prof Exp:* Fel human cytogenetics, Dept Pediat, Univ Man, 72-75; asst prof human cytogentics, 75-80, ASSOC PROF PEDIAT, HARBOR-UNIV CALIF LOS ANGELES MED CTR, 80- *Mem:* Genetics Soc Am; Genetics Soc Can; Am Soc Human Genetics. *Res:* Human cytogenetics; human gene mapping using somatic cell hybrids; mechanism of x chronosome inactivation. *Mailing Add:* Div of Med Genetics (E-4) Harbor Gen Hosp Torrance CA 90509

MOHANTY, GANESH PRASAD, b Cuttack, India, Mar 11, 34; m 69; c 1. MATERIALS SCIENCE. *Educ:* Utkal Univ, India, BS, 54; Mich Col Mining & Technol, MS, 58; Ill Inst Technol, PhD(metall), 61. *Prof Exp:* Res scientist, Res Div, A O Smith Corp, Wis, 60-63; from asst prof mat sci to prof eng sci, 63-76; mem staff, 76-81, PROF ENG SCI, UNIV NC, CHARLOTTE, 81- *Concurrent Pos:* NSF res grant, 64-70; partic fac, Chem Physics Prog, Fla State Univ, 70- *Mem:* Am Inst Mining, Metall & Petrol Engrs. *Res:* X-ray diffraction; imperfections in crystals; phase equilibria; structures of deformed intermetallics and amorphous substances; temperature diffusion and short range order scattering; diffusion in metallic systems; x-ray and electron optics and crystallography. *Mailing Add:* Dept of Eng Univ of NC Charlotte NC 28213

MOHANTY, SASHI B, b India, Sept 4, 32; m 57; c 2. MICROBIOLOGY, VIROLOGY. *Educ:* Univ Bihar, BVSc & AH, 56; Univ Md, MS, 61, PhD(microbiol), 63. *Prof Exp:* Vet asst surgeon, Civil Vet Dept, Govt Orissa, India, 56-60; asst microbiol, 60-63, asst prof vet sci & microbiol, 63-69, assoc prof vet sci, 69-74, PROF VET SCI, UNIV MD, 74- *Concurrent Pos:* NIH grant, 63-65; mem, Md State Proj Bovine Respiratory viruses, 63-; head working team on bovine, equine and porcine picorna viruses, WHO, Food & Agr Orgn, UN, 73- *Mem:* Am Soc Microbiol; Electron micros Soc Am; Soc Exp Biol & Med; Am Vet Med Asn. *Res:* Animal virus diseases; experimental infection of cattle with viruses; viral growth; electron microscopy; interferon induction; cellular immunity, prevention and control of animal diseases. *Mailing Add:* 4306 Kenny St Beltsville MD 20705

MOHANTY, SRI GOPAL, b Soro, India, Feb 11, 33; m 63; c 2. MATHEMATICS, STATISTICS. *Educ:* Utkal Univ, India, BA, 51; Indian Coun Agr Res, dipl agr & animal husb statist, 57; Punjab Univ, MA, 57; Univ Alta, PhD(math statist), 61. *Prof Exp:* Tech asst, Ministry Food & Agr, Govt of India, 54-56; asst statistician, Indian Coun Agr Res, 58-59; teaching asst math, Univ Alta, 59-61, sessional lectr, 61-62; from asst prof to assoc prof, State Univ NY Buffalo, 62-64; assoc prof, 64-72, PROF MATH, MCMASTER UNIV, 72- *Concurrent Pos:* Asst prof, Indian Inst Technol, New Delhi, 66-68. *Mem:* Am Statist Asn; Can Math Cong; Math Asn Am; Statist Soc Can; Int Statist Inst. *Res:* Combinatorial probability; random walk; discrete probability distributions; nonparametric methods in inferences; theory of queues; fluctuation theory; enumeration of trees and certain finite structures. *Mailing Add:* Dept of Math McMaster Univ Hamilton ON L8S 4L8 Can

MOHAPATRA, RABINDRA NATH, b Musagadia, India, Sept 1, 44; m 69; c 2. HIGH ENERGY PHYSICS. *Educ:* Utkal Univ, India, BSc, 64; Delhi Univ, MSc, 66; Univ Rochester, PhD(physics), 69. *Prof Exp:* Res assoc physics, Inst Theoret Physics, State Univ NY Stony Brook, 69-71 & Univ Md, College Park, 71-74; asst prof, 74-80, PROF PHYSICS, CITY COL NEW YORK, 80- *Concurrent Pos:* Alexander von Humboldt Found fel, 80-81.

Mem: Fel Am Phys Soc. *Res:* Gauge theories of weak, electromagnetic and strong interactions; approximate hadronic symmetries; quark models; neutrino interactions; selection rules in weak and strong interactions; field theories; radiative corrections to weak transitions; mass differences among elementary particles. *Mailing Add:* Dept of Physics 138th St & Convent Ave New York NY 10031

MOHAT, JOHN THEODORE, b El Paso, Tex, Apr 8, 24; m 45; c 2. MATHEMATICS. *Educ:* Tex Western Col, BA, Univ Tex, PhD (math), 55. *Prof Exp:* Instr math, Univ Tex, 51-55 & Duke Univ, 55-57; chief math br, Math Sci Div, Off Ord Res, US Dept Army, 57-59; from asst prof to assoc prof, 59-64, dir dept, 65-69, actg chmn dept, 75-77, PROF MATH, N TEX STATE UNIV, 64- *Concurrent Pos:* Vis asst prof, Duke Univ, 58-59. *Mem:* Am Math Soc; Math Asn Am. *Res:* General topology; points sets and transformations. *Mailing Add:* Dept of Math North Tex State Univ Denton TX 76203

MOHBERG, NOEL ROSS, b Britton, SDak, Dec 16, 39; m 63; c 2. BIOSTATISTICS. *Educ:* NDak State Univ, BS, 61; Va Polytech Inst, MS, 62; Univ NC, PhD(biostatist), 72. *Prof Exp:* Statistician, NIH, 63-65 & Sandia Corp, 65-68; biostatistician, 72-78, RES HEAD, BIOSTATISTICS, UPJOHN CO, 78- *Mem:* Biomet Soc; Am Statist Asn. *Res:* Methods of analysis of categorized data; design and analysis of clinical trials. *Mailing Add:* Upjohn Co 301 Henrietta St Kalamazoo MI 49001

MOHILNER, DAVID MORRIS, b Wichita, Kans, Jan 3, 30; m 58. ELECTROCHEMISTRY, PHYSICAL CHEMISTRY. *Educ:* Univ Kans, BS, 55, PhD(chem), 61. *Prof Exp:* Fel chem, La State Univ, 61-62; asst prof, Univ Pittsburgh, 62-64; fel, Univ Tex, Austin, 64-65; from asst prof to assoc prof, 65-71, PROF CHEM, COLO STATE UNIV, 71- *Concurrent Pos:* Mem electrochem comn, Int Union Pure & Appl Chem, 71-75; nat secy US, Int Soc Electrochem, 72-76. *Mem:* Am Chem Soc; Electrochem Soc. *Res:* Electrochemical thermodynamics and kinetics, especially theory of electrical double layer and its influence on kinetics of electrode reactions; application of digital computers to electrochemistry; mechanisms and electrode reactions; chemical thermodynamics; bioelectrochemistry. *Mailing Add:* Dept of Chem Colo State Univ Ft Collins CO 80521

MOHIUDDIN, SYED M, b Hyderabad, India, Nov 14, 34; m 61; c 3. CARDIOLOGY, INTERNAL MEDICINE. *Educ:* Osmania Univ, MD, 60; Creighton Univ, MS, 67; Laval Univ, DSc(med), 70. *Prof Exp:* Fel cardiol, Sch Med, Creighton Univ, 65-67; fel res cardiol, Laval Univ, 68-70, adj prof med, 69-70; asst prof, 70-74, assoc prof, 74-78, PROF MED, SCH MED, CREIGHTON UNIV, 78-, DIR CARDIAC GRAPHIC LAB, 73- *Concurrent Pos:* Fel, Coun Clin Cardiol. *Mem:* Can Cardiovasc Soc; Am Fedn Clin Res; fel Am Col Cardiol; fel Am Col Physicians. *Res:* Clinical cardiology; coronary flow and cardiac metabolism; cardiomyopathies; graphic methods in cardiology; cardiac pharmacology. *Mailing Add:* 601 N 30th St Omaha NE 68131

MOHLENBROCK, ROBERT H, JR, b Murphysboro, Ill, Sept 26, 31; m 57; c 3. SYSTEMATIC BOTANY. *Educ:* Southern Ill Univ, BS, 53, MA, 54; Wash Univ, PhD(bot), 57. *Prof Exp:* From asst prof to assoc prof, 57-66, chmn dept, 66-79, PROF BOT, SOUTHERN ILL UNIV, 66- *Mem:* Explorers Club; Nature Conservancy. *Res:* Flora of Midwest and Illinois; tropical legumes; national forests. *Mailing Add:* Dept of Bot Southern Ill Univ Carbondale IL 62901

MOHLENKAMP, MARVIN JOSEPH, JR, b Louisville, Ky, Apr 22, 40; m 63; c 4. FOOD CHEMISTRY. *Educ:* Univ Notre Dame, BS, 62; Univ Wis, MS, 65, PhD(biochem), 68. *Prof Exp:* CHEMIST, PROCTER & GAMBLE CO, 68- *Mem:* Am Chem Soc; Inst Food Technologists; Am Oil Chemists Soc. *Res:* Chemical and organoleptic aspects of food flavors with emphasis on thermally induced flavors. *Mailing Add:* Procter & Gamble Co Miami Valley Labs Box 39175 Cincinnati OH 45239

MOHLER, IRVIN C, JR, b Lancaster, Pa, Nov 4, 25; m 56; c 2. BACTERIOLOGY. *Educ:* Franklin & Marshall Col, BS, 49; Pa State Univ, MS, 52. *Prof Exp:* With US govt, 52-55; asst exec dir biol, Am Inst Biol Sci, 55-59; exec off, McCollum Pratt Inst, Johns Hopkins Univ, 59-61; asst to dir, Am Type Cult Collection, 61-67; asst dir biol sci commun proj, 67-75, ASST RES PROF, DEPT MED & PUB AFFAIRS, GEORGE WASHINGTON UNIV MED CTR, 75-, DIR, OFF SPONSORED RES, 78- *Concurrent Pos:* Managing ed, Environ Biol & Med. *Mem:* Am Soc Microbiol; Am Inst Biol Sci; Am Soc Info Sci. *Res:* Science administration. *Mailing Add:* 6 Stratton Ct Potomac MD 20854

MOHLER, JAMES DAWSON, b Liberal, Mo, June 2, 26; m 51; c 3. ZOOLOGY. *Educ:* Univ Mo, AB, 49, AM, 50; Univ Calif, PhD(zool), 55. *Prof Exp:* Instr zool, Univ Mo, 50-51; asst, Univ Calif, 51-53; from asst prof to assoc prof, Ore State Univ, 55-66; assoc prof, 66-69, PROF ZOOL, UNIV IOWA, 69- *Concurrent Pos:* USPHS trainee, Syracuse Univ, 63-64; vis scholar, Univ Ariz, 75; vis prof zool, Ariz State Univ, 75-76. *Mem:* Genetics Soc Am. *Mailing Add:* Dept of Zool Univ of Iowa Iowa City IA 52240

MOHLER, JOHN GEORGE, b Los Angeles, Calif, May 25, 32; m 58; c 3. MEDICINE, PULMONARY PHYSIOLOGY. *Educ:* Col Osteop Physicians & Surgeons, DO, 60; Univ Calif, MD, 62. *Prof Exp:* Instr med, Calif Col Med, 60-62; from instr to asst prof, 62-69, ASSOC PROF MED, UNIV SOUTHERN CALIF, 69-, MED DIR PULMONARY PHYSIOL LABS, LOS ANGELES COUNTY-UNIV SOUTHERN CALIF MED CTR, 69- *Concurrent Pos:* Fel pulmonary med, Los Angeles County-Univ Southern Calif Med Ctr, 64-66, assoc med dir pulmonary lab, 68-70; spec fel physiol, Sch Med, Univ Southern Calif, 66-67; instr med & spec fel physiol, Univ Colo, 68-69; co-dir, Univ Southern Calif air pollution res fel, 68-70; med dir pulmonary serv, Alhambra Community Hosp, 68-, chief med, 70-76, chief staff, 78-79, bd trustees, 81- *Mem:* Fel Am Col Med; fel Am Col Chest Med; Am Physiol Soc; Am Thoracic Soc; Am Fedn Clin Res. *Res:* Air pollution effects on human health, lung reactions specifically; study of exercise physiology generally, transients from rest to exercise to rest specifically; distribution of ventilation as measured by nitrogen clearance; dyspnea, cause and quantitation. *Mailing Add:* Pulmonary Physiol Labs 1200 N State St Los Angeles CA 90033

MOHLER, ORREN (CUTHBERT), b Indianapolis, Ind, July 28, 08; m 35; c 2. ASTRONOMY. *Educ:* Eastern Mich Univ, AB, 29; Univ Mich, AM, 30, PhD, 33. *Prof Exp:* Observer, McMath-Hulbert Observ, Univ Mich, 33; astronomer & instr astron, Swarthmore Col, 33-40; asst astronomer, 40-46, asst dir, 46-56, from asst prof to assoc prof, 45-56, chmn dept & dir univ observ, 62-70, dir, McMath-Hulbert Observ, 61-80, prof astron, 56-78, EMER PROF ASTRON, UNIV MICH, ANN ARBOR, 78- *Concurrent Pos:* Bd Gov, Cranbrook Inst Sci, 60-81, emer gov, Bd Gov, 81-; Fulbright res scholar, Inst Astrophys, Univ Liege, 60-61; dir, McMath-Hulbert Observ, Energy Conversion Devices, Inc, Mich, 80-; adj prof physics, Oakland Univ, Rochester, 80-; consult, Inst Amorphous Mats, ECD, Inc, Mich, 81- *Honors & Awards:* Naval Ord Develop Award, 46. *Mem:* Am Astron Soc. *Res:* Astronomical spectroscopy and cinematography; solar astronomy; solar astronomical instruments. *Mailing Add:* 405 Awixa Rd Ann Arbor MI 48104

MOHLER, RONALD RUTT, b Ephrata, Pa, Apr 11, 31; m 50; c 8. ELECTRICAL & SYSTEMS ENGINEERING. *Educ:* Pa State Univ, BS, 56; Univ Southern Calif, MS, 58; Univ Mich, PhD(systs), 65. *Prof Exp:* Designer, Textile Mach Works, Pa, 49-56; staff mem systs, Hughes Aircraft Co, Calif, 56-58; Los Alamos Sci Lab, Univ Calif, 58-65; assoc prof elec eng, Univ NMex, 65-69; vis assoc prof eng, Univ Calif, Los Angeles, 68-69; prof elec & nuclear eng & dir systs res ctr, Univ Okla, 69-70, prof info & comput sci & chmn dept, 70-71; head dept, 72-79, PROF ELEC & COMPUT ENG, ORE STATE UNIV, 72- *Concurrent Pos:* Prof, Univ NMex, 59-65; consult, Sandia Corp, 65-69, Aerojet Gen Corp, 66-69, Bonnevile Power Admin, 73-78 & Optimization Software, 69-; sr scientist award, NATO, 73-78; scientific visitor, Nat Acad Sci, USSR & China, People's Repub, 80. *Mem:* Am Soc Eng Educ; Inst Elec & Electronics Engrs. *Res:* Systems; computer control theory; optimization; nuclear systems; biological engineering; immune process; random processes. *Mailing Add:* Dept Elec & Comput Eng Ore State Univ Corvallis OR 97331

MOHLER, STANLEY ROSS, b Amarillo, Tex, Sept 30, 27; m 53; c 1. AEROSPACE MEDICINE. *Educ:* Univ Tex, BA & MA, 53, MD, 56. *Prof Exp:* Chem analyst, Longhorn Tin Smelter, Tex, 49-50; intern, USPHS, 56-57, med officer, Div Gen Med Sci, Ctr Aging Res, NIH, 57-61; dir, Civil Aeromed Res Inst, Oklahoma City, Okla, 61-65; chief, Aeromed Appln Div, Fed Aviation Admin, 65-78; PROF COMMUN MED, V CHMN DEPT & DIR AEROSPACE MED, SCH MED, WRIGHT STATE UNIV, 78- *Concurrent Pos:* Assoc prof prev med & pub health, Univ Okla, 61-65. *Honors & Awards:* Meritorious Serv Award, Fed Aviation Admin, 71. *Mem:* AAAS; Geront Soc; AMA. *Res:* Gerontology; general medicine; blood clotting; aviation medicine; aircraft accident research. *Mailing Add:* Dept of Commun Med PO Box 927 Dayton OH 45401

MOHLER, WILLIAM C, b Bridgeton, NJ, Nov 16, 27; m 56; c 3. COMPUTER SCIENCE, MEDICINE. *Educ:* Yale Univ, BA, 49; Columbia Univ, MD, 53. *Prof Exp:* Intern & resident, Presby Hosp, New York, 54-55; investr, Nat Cancer Inst, 56-65, asst dir labs & clins, 65-67, ASSOC DIR, DIV COMPUT RES & TECHNOL, NIH, 67- *Mem:* AAAS. *Res:* Computing in support of biomedical research and clinical medicine. *Mailing Add:* Comput Res & Technol Nat Inst of Health Bethesda MD 20205

MOHLING, FRANZ, b Jersey City, NJ, July 22, 30; m 62; c 2. THEORETICAL PHYSICS. *Educ:* Rensselaer Polytech Inst, BS, 51; Univ Wash, PhD(physics), 58. *Prof Exp:* Fel physics, Columbia Univ, 58-59, res assoc, 59-60; res assoc, Cornell Univ, 60-61; from asst prof to assoc prof, 61-69, PROF PHYSICS, UNIV COLO, BOULDER, 69- *Concurrent Pos:* US Govt Fulbright scholar, India, 63-64. *Mem:* Am Phys Soc. *Res:* Quantum statistics; many body problem; low-temperature physics, especially liquid helium. *Mailing Add:* Dept of Physics & Astrophys Univ of Colo Boulder CO 80309

MOHLKE, BYRON HENRY, b Valparaiso, Ind, Mar 4, 38; m 62; c 2. SPACE SCIENCE, COMPUTER SCIENCE. *Educ:* Purdue Univ, BSME, 59; Univ Wis, MS, 61. *Prof Exp:* PRIN PHYSICIST, ARVIN CO, CALSPAN CORP, 61- *Res:* Radar data analysis techniques; space object identification; system analysis and testing. *Mailing Add:* Systs Technol Dept 4455 Genesee St Buffalo NY 14225

MOHN, JAMES FREDERIC, b Buffalo, NY, Apr 11, 22; m 45; c 4. IMMUNOLOGY, MEDICAL BACTERIOLOGY. *Educ:* Univ Buffalo, MD, 44. *Prof Exp:* From instr to assoc prof, 45-55, prof bact & immunol, 55-76, PROF MICROBIOL & DIR, CTR IMMUNOL, SCH MED, STATE UNIV NY BUFFALO, 76- *Concurrent Pos:* Buswell fel, 59-; asst bacteriologist & serologist, Niagara Sanitorium, NY, 46-48, bacteriologist & dir lab, 48-53; asst bacteriologist, serologist & asst dir blood bank, Buffalo Gen Hosp, 47-58, assoc bacteriologist, serologist & assoc dir blood bank, 58-; consult, Blood Bank, Deaconess Hosp, Buffalo, 57- & Walter Reed Army Inst Res, 58-; mem, Subcomt Transfusion Probs, Nat Acad Sci-Nat Res Coun, 58- *Mem:* AAAS; Soc Exp Biol & Med; Am Soc Hemat; fel Inst Soc Hemat; Am Asn Immunologists. *Res:* Investigation of Rh substances and antibodies; blood group specific substances; characterization of blood group isoagglutins; immunologic aspects of hemolytic agents anemia; immunohematologic blood transfusion studies. *Mailing Add:* Dept of Microbiol State Univ of NY Sch of Med Buffalo NY 14214

MOHN, MELVIN P, b Cleveland, Ohio, June 19, 26; m 52; c 2. ANATOMY, HISTOLOGY. *Educ:* Marietta Col, AB, 50; Brown Univ, ScM, 52, PhD(biol), 55. *Prof Exp:* From instr to asst prof anat, State Univ NY Downstate Med Ctr, 55-63; from asst prof to assoc prof, 63-71, PROF ANAT, UNIV KANS MED CTR, KANSAS CITY, 71- *Concurrent Pos:* Vis prof,

Nat Med AV Ctr, 72. *Mem:* Fel AAAS; Am Asn Anat; Am Soc Zool; Am Inst Biol Sci; Electron Micros Soc Am. *Res:* Structure, function and embryology of skin and its appendages, particularly hair, nail and ceruminous glands; histochemistry; electron microscopy; comparative anatomy; effects of nutritional deficiencies; endocrine imbalances; irradiations; transplantations; wound healing and circulatory changes. *Mailing Add:* Dept Anat Univ Kans Med Ctr Kansas City KS 66103

MOHNEN, VOLKER A, b Stuttgart, WGer, Mar 11, 37; m 63; c 2. ATMOSPHERIC SCIENCES, PHYSICS. *Educ:* Univ Karlsruhe, BS, 59; Univ Munich, MS, 63, PhD(physics, meteorol astrophys), 66. *Prof Exp:* Res assoc, Univ Munich, 62-67; sr res assoc, Atmospheric Sci Res Ctr, 67-75, assoc dir, 72-75, assoc prof, 67-77, RES PROF ATMOSPHERIC SCI, STATE UNIV NY ALBANY, 77-, DIR, ATMOSPHERIC SCI RES CTR, 75- *Mem:* Fel AAAS; Am Chem Soc; fel NY Acad Sci; Deutsche Physikalische Gesellschaft; Am Inst Aeronaut & Astronaut. *Res:* Air pollution; aerosol physics; solar energy. *Mailing Add:* Atmospheric Sci Res Ctr State Univ NY E S 324 Albany NY 12222

MOHOS, STEVEN CHARLES, b Sopron, Hungary, Jan 20, 18; div; c 2. PATHOLOGY, IMMUNOLOGY. *Educ:* Pazmany Peter Univ, Budapest, MD, 41; Am Bd Path, dipl, 56. *Prof Exp:* Res fel exp path, Med Sch, Pazmany Peter Univ, 41-43, asst prof path, 42-43; med staff chief serv, Hosp of Int Red Cross, Ger, 46-50; resident path, Polyclin Hosp, Harrisburg, Pa, 51-52, 53-54, intern, 52-53; instr & res assoc, Med Col, Cornell Univ, 54-56; asst prof path, State Univ NY Downstate Med Ctr, 56-63; ASSOC PROF PATH, NEW YORK MED COL, 63- *Concurrent Pos:* Asst attend pathologist, New York Hosp, 54-56; Life Ins Res Fund, Off Naval Res & NIH res grants. *Honors & Awards:* Chinoin Award, 42. *Mem:* AMA; Col Am Path; Am Soc Exp Path; NY Acad Sci; Int Acad Path. *Res:* Tissue immunology; filtration membrane; immunological aspects of cancer research; transplantation immunity; experimental nephritis; in vivo effects of complement and application of electron microscopy to these problems. *Mailing Add:* Dept of Path New York Med Col Valhalla NY 10595

MOHR, C(HARLES) MICHAEL, chemical engineering, see previous edition

MOHR, JAY PRESTON, b Philadelphia, Pa, Mar 5, 37; m 62; c 2. NEUROLOGY. *Educ:* Haverford Col, AB, 58; Univ Va, MS & MD, 63. *Prof Exp:* USPHS fel pharmacol, Univ Va, 60-63; from intern to asst resident internal med, Mary Imogene Bassett Hosp, Cooperstown, NY, 63-65; asst resident neurol, NY Neurol Inst, Columbia-Presby Med Ctr, New York, 65-66; fel neurol, Mass Gen Hosp, Boston, 66-68, Nat Inst Neurol Dis & Stroke fel, 67-69; instr, Univ Md Hosp, Baltimore, 69-71; asst prof neurol, Harvard Med Sch, 72-78; PROF NEUROL & CHMN DEPT, UNIV S ALA, 78- *Concurrent Pos:* Asst neurologist, Johns Hopkins Hosp, 69-71 & Mass Gen Hosp, 72-75; assoc neurologist, Mass Gen Hosp, 75-78. *Mem:* Acad Aphasia; Am Acad Neurol. *Res:* Behavioral neurology; cerebrovascular disease; aphasiology. *Mailing Add:* Dept of Neurol 2451 Fillingim St Mobile AL 36617

MOHR, JOHN LUTHER, b Reading, Pa, Dec 1, 11; m 39; c 2. MARINE BIOLOGY, PROTOZOOLOGY. *Educ:* Bucknell Univ, AB, 33; Univ Calif, PhD(zool), 39. *Prof Exp:* Asst zool, Univ Calif, 34-38, technician, 38-42; res assoc, Pac Islands, Stanford Univ, 42-44; asst prof & res assoc, Allan Hancock Found, 44-47, vis asst prof zool, 47-48, asst prof, 48-54, assoc prof biol, 54-57, head dept, 59-62, prof, 57-77, EMER PROF BIOL, UNIV SOUTHERN CALIF, 77- *Concurrent Pos:* Vis prof, Univ Wash Friday Harbor Labs, 56-57; Guggenheim fel, Plymouth Lab, Marine Biol Asn UK; 57-58; chief marine zool group, Antarctic Ship Eltanin, 62 & 65; mem gen invert comt, Smithsonian Oceanog Sorting Ctr, 63-66; emer trustee, Biol Stain Comn, 72-, vpres, 76-; mem bd dirs, Calif Natural Areas Coord Coun. *Mem:* Am Soc Parasitologists; Am Soc Zoologists; Ecol Soc Am; Soc Protozoologists; Marine Biol Asn UK. *Res:* Protozoology and parasitology, especially opalinida, chonotrichs and ciliates of elephants; effects of drilling slurries on marine populations; irrationalities in marine bioassays; biology of polar seas; philosophy and folkways of biologists; biological stains. *Mailing Add:* Dept Biol Sci Univ Southern Calif Los Angeles CA 90007

MOHR, MILTON ERNST, b Milwaukee, Wis, Apr 9, 15; m 38; c 2. ELECTRICAL ENGINEERING. *Educ:* Univ Nebr, BS, 38. *Hon Degrees:* DrEng, Univ Nebr, 59. *Prof Exp:* Mem tech staff, Bell Tel Labs, 38-50; dept head, Radar Lab, Hughes Aircraft Co, Calif, 50-54; vpres & gen mgr, TRW Comput Div, Thompson-Ramo-Wooldridge, Inc, 54-64; vpres, Bunker-Ramo Corp, 64-66, pres, 66-70; PRES & CHIEF EXEC OFFICER, QUOTRON SYSTS INC, 70- *Mem:* Am Inst Aeronaut & Astronaut; fel Inst Elec & Electronics Engrs. *Mailing Add:* Quotron Systs Inc 5454 Beethoven St Los Angeles CA 90066

MOHR, RICHARD ARNOLD, b Bethlehem, Pa, Feb 23, 30; m 55; c 3. CHEMICAL ENGINEERING. *Educ:* Lehigh Univ, BS, 52; Rutgers Univ, MBA, 62. *Prof Exp:* Process engr, Union Carbide Corp, 52-73; PRIN RES ENGR, FMC CORP, 73- *Mem:* Asn Inst Chem Engrs. *Res:* Design new chemical processes by application of engineering principles to research concepts; development of new chemical processes; equipment design for chemical processes; economic evaluation of novel processes. *Mailing Add:* FMC Corp PO Box 8 Princeton NJ 08540

MOHR, SCOTT CHALMERS, b Jamestown, NY, Aug 30, 40; m 64; c 2. BIOCHEMISTRY. *Educ:* Williams Col, BA, 62; Harvard Univ, MA, 66, PhD(chem), 68. *Prof Exp:* NIH fel, Cornell Univ, 68-69; asst prof, 69-75, ASSOC PROF CHEM, BOSTON UNIV, 75- *Mem:* AAAS; Am Chem Soc. *Res:* Fast kinetics in biochemical systems; allosteric proteins; transfer RNA; nucleic acid-protein interactions; protein synthesis elongation factor I (Tu); compact states of nucleic acids; carcinogen-nucleic acid interactions. *Mailing Add:* Dept of Chem Boston Univ 675 Commwealth Ave Boston MA 02215

MOHR, WILLARD PHILLIP, food science, see previous edition

MOHRAZ, BIJAN, b Tehran, Iran, May 3, 37. CIVIL ENGINEERING. *Educ:* Univ Ill, BS, 61, MS, 62, PhD(civil eng), 66. *Prof Exp:* Asst civil eng, Univ Ill, Urbana, 62-66; proj engr, Agbabian-Jacobsen Assocs, 66-67; asst prof civil eng, Univ Ill, Urbana, 67-74; assoc prof, 74-81, PROF CIVIL ENG, SOUTHERN METHODIST UNIV, 81- *Concurrent Pos:* Consult, govt agencies & private indust; NSF grant, 80-82. *Mem:* Am Soc Civil Engrs; Seismol Soc Am; Sigma Xi; Earthquake Eng Res Inst. *Res:* Structural analysis and design; earthquake engineering. *Mailing Add:* Dept of Civil Eng Southern Methodist Univ Dallas TX 75275

MOHRENWEISER, HARVEY WALTER, b Mora, Minn, Oct 12, 40; m 61; c 2. BIOCHEMISTRY. *Educ:* Univ Minn, BS, 62, MS, 66; Mich State Univ, PhD(biochem), 70. *Prof Exp:* NIH fel, McArdle Lab, Univ Wis, 70-73; res chemist mutagenesis, Nat Ctr Toxicol Res, Food & Drug Admin, HEW, 73-76; ASST PROF HUMAN GENETICS, SCH MED, UNIV MICH, ANN ARBOR, 76- *Concurrent Pos:* Asst prof biochem, Univ Ark, 73- *Res:* Biochemical mechanisms of mutagenesis; structure, function and metabolic significance of variant enzymes; biochemical genetics. *Mailing Add:* Dept of Human Genetics Univ of Mich Med Sch Ann Arbor MI 48109

MOHRER, HENRY Z, b Frankfurt, Ger, Apr 23, 24; nat US; m 53; c 3. CHEMICAL ENGINEERING. *Educ:* State Univ NY, BS, 45. *Prof Exp:* Res chemist, US Gypsum Co, 45-48; chief chemist, Fed Paper Bd Co, Inc, 48-56; tech dir res, Old Town Corp, 56-57; plant mgr, Fed Paper Bd Co, Inc, 57-68; partner, Nicholson & Mohrer Assoc, 68-70; DIR PURCHASING, PHELPS DODGE CORP, 70- *Mem:* Tech Asn Pulp & Paper Indust. *Res:* Commercial utilization of secondary fibrous materials and their by-products; industrial processes for the manufacture of paper, board and allied materials. *Mailing Add:* 348 Ridge Rd Orange CT 06477

MOHRIG, JERRY R, b Grand Rapids, Mich, Feb 24, 36; m 60; c 3. BIOCHEMISTRY. *Educ:* Univ Mich, BS, 57; Univ Colo, PhD(chem), 63. *Prof Exp:* Asst prof, Hope Col, 64-67; from asst prof to assoc prof, 67-75, PROF CHEM, CARLETON COL, 75- *Res:* Organic reaction mechanisms; reactions of alkanediazonium ions; elimination reactions; enzymic catalysis. *Mailing Add:* Dept Chem Carleton Col Northfield MN 55057

MOHRMAN, HAROLD W, b Quincy, Ill, Oct 1, 17; m 39; c 4. CHEMISTRY. *Educ:* Univ Ill, BS, 39. *Prof Exp:* Res chemist, Monsanto Co, 39, group leader, 40-46, asst res dir, 46-50, dir res, Plastics Div, 50-59, assoc interests, 59-60 & overseas div, 60-63, dir polymer sect & overseas res, 63-68, sect dir, Corp Res Dept, 68-79; INDEPENDENT CONSULT, 79- *Mem:* AAAS; Am Chem Soc; NY Acad Sci; Soc Am Archeol. *Res:* Condensation resin and vinyl polymers; manufacture of phenolic and melaminealdehyde condensation products; polyelectrolytes and research administration. *Mailing Add:* 46 Ballas Ct St Louis MO 63131

MOHS, FREDERIC EDWARD, b Burlington, Wis, Mar 1, 10; m 34; c 3. SURGERY. *Educ:* Univ Wis, BS, 32, MD, 34. *Prof Exp:* Bowman cancer res fel, 35-38, assoc cancer res & instr surg, 39-42, from asst prof to assoc prof, 42-67, clin prof chemosurg, 67-80, CLIN PROF SURG, MED SCH, UNIV WIS-MADISON, 80-, DIR CHEMOSURG CLIN, UNIV HOSPS, 48- *Mem:* AAAS; AMA; Am Asn Cancer Res. *Res:* Chemosurgery for the microscopically controlled excision of cancer of the skin, lip, parotid gland and other external structures. *Mailing Add:* 600 Highland Ave Madison WI 53706

MOHSENIN, NURI N, b Tehran, Iran, Sept 15, 23; m 52; c 6. FOOD MATERIALS. *Educ:* Univ Tehran, BS, 47; Okla State Univ, BS, 51; Mich State Univ, MS, 53, PhD(agr eng), 56. *Prof Exp:* Prof agr eng, Pa State Univ, 60-79; CONSULT FOOD PHYSICS, 79- *Concurrent Pos:* Alexander von Humbolt US sr scientist award, 80. *Mem:* Am Soc Agr Engrs; Soc Rheol; Inst Food Technol. *Res:* Physical properties of food and agricultural materials; mechanical, thermal and electromagnetic radiation properties of foods and agricultural products. *Mailing Add:* Food Physics Info Systs 120 Meadow Lane State College PA 16801

MOHTADI, FARHANG, b Tehran, Iran, Jan 6, 26; m 52; c 3. CHEMICAL ENGINEERING, THERMODYNAMICS. *Educ:* Univ Tehran, BEng, 45; Univ Birmingham, BSc, 48, PhD(chem eng), 51. *Prof Exp:* Imp Chem Indust fel chem eng, Univ Birmingham, 52-55, lectr, 55-64; Bwisa prof & head dept, Univ WI, 64-67; head dept, 68-71, PROF CHEM ENG, UNIV CALGARY, 67- *Concurrent Pos:* Royal Norweg Coun fel, 62-63; mem, Royal Comn Sugar Indust Trinidad-WI, 66-67. *Mem:* Brit Inst Chem Engrs; fel Brit Inst Petrol; Am Inst Chem Engrs; Eng Inst Can; Chem Inst Can. *Res:* Electrokinetic phenomena in non-aqueous dispersions; flow and mass transfer from drops; physical behavior of particulate systems; degradation of oil in soil; combustion in a flowing stream of water. *Mailing Add:* Dept of Chem Eng Univ of Calgary Calgary AB T2N 1N4 Can

MOIOLA, RICHARD JAMES, b Reno, Nev, Oct 5, 37; m 70; c 2. SEDIMENTOLOGY. *Educ:* Univ Calif, Berkeley, AB, 59, PhD(geol), 69. *Prof Exp:* Geologist, Shell Oil Co, 60; res asst geol, Univ Calif, Berkeley, 61-63; res geologist, Field Res Lab, Mobil Oil Corp, Tex, 63-66, sr res geologist, Mobil Res & Develop Corp, 67-74, res assoc, 74-81, GEOL CONSULT, MOBIL RES & DEVELOP CORP, 81- *Concurrent Pos:* Lectr, Univ Tex, Dallas, 75, Continuing Educ Prog, Am Asn Petrol Geologists, 77-; assoc ed, Bull Am Asn Petrol Geologists, 77- *Mem:* Fel Geol Soc Am; Soc Econ Paleontologists & Mineralogists; Am Asn Petrol Geologists. *Res:* Sedimentology of modern and ancient siliciclastic deposits; physical stratigraphy; zeolitic diagenesis. *Mailing Add:* Mobil Res & Develop Corp Res Dept PO Box 900 Dallas TX 75221

MOIR, DAVID CHANDLER, b Globe, Ariz, Dec 9, 47; m 74; c 2. MATERIAL SCIENCE, RADIOGRAPHY. *Educ:* NMex State Univ, BS, 69; Ariz State Univ, MS, 70, PhD(physics), 75. *Prof Exp:* Res assoc fel nuclear & particle physics, 75-77, STAFF MEM MAT SCI & RADIOGRAPHY, LOS ALAMOS SCI LAB, 77- *Mem:* Am Phys Soc; Am Asn Physics Teachers. *Res:* Material response at high strain rates; quantitative flash radiography of explosive systems. *Mailing Add:* MS 942 M-2 PO Box 1663 Los Alamos NM 87545

MOIR, ROBERT YOUNG, b Estevan, Sask, Oct 30, 20; m 46; c 3. ORGANIC CHEMISTRY. *Educ:* Queen's Univ, Ont, BA, 41, MA, 42; McGill Univ, PhD(org chem), 46. *Prof Exp:* Jr chemist, Inspection Bd, Can, 41; res chemist, Indust, Org Chem, Res Labs, Dom Rubber Co, Ltd, 43-44, 46-49; from asst prof to assoc prof, 49-64, PROF CHEM, QUEEN'S UNIV, ONT, 64- *Mem:* Am Chem Soc; Chem Inst Can. *Res:* Steric effects in cyclohexanes and in diphenyl ethers; general synthesis. *Mailing Add:* 223 Victoria Kingston ON K7L 3Y9 Can

MOISE, EDWIN EVARISTE, b New Orleans, La, Dec 22, 18; div; c 2. MATHEMATICS. *Educ:* Tulane Univ La, BA, 40; Univ Tex, PhD(math), 47. *Hon Degrees:* MA, Harvard Univ, 60. *Prof Exp:* Instr math, Univ Tex, 46-47; from instr to prof, Univ Mich, 47-60; prof math & educ, Harvard Univ, 60-71; DISTINGUISHED PROF MATH, QUEENS COL NY, 71- *Concurrent Pos:* Nat Res Coun fel, Inst Advan Study, 49-50, asst, 50-51, Guggenheim fel, 56-57; vis prof, Res Ctr, Nat Polytech Inst, Mex, 70-71; Hudson prof, Auburn Univ, 80-81. *Mem:* Fel Am Acad Arts & Sci; Math Asn Am (pres, 67-68); Am Math Soc (vpres, 73-74). *Res:* Topology. *Mailing Add:* 118-17 Union Turnpike Apt 16-B Forest Hills NY 11375

MOISEYEV, ALEXIS N, b Paris, France, June 27, 32; US citizen. GEOCHEMISTRY, GEOLOGY. *Educ:* Sorbonne, Lic es Sci, 55, Univ Paris, Dr, 59; Stanford Univ, PhD(geochem), 66. *Prof Exp:* Mining geologist, Compagnie Royale Asturienne des Mines, 56-58 & 60-61; lectr geol, Univ Calif, Davis, 66-67; asst prof, San Jose State Col, 67-68; asst prof, 68-71, ASSOC PROF GEOL, CALIF STATE COL, HAYWARD, 71- *Mem:* Am Geophys Union; Geol Soc Am. *Res:* Geochemistry of hydrothermal processes and low temperature sedimentary deposits; plate tectonics. *Mailing Add:* Dept of Earth Sci Calif State Col Hayward CA 94542

MOISON, ROBERT LEON, b Fitchburg, Mass, Mar 15, 29; m 55; c 2. CHEMICAL ENGINEERING. *Educ:* Worcester Polytech Inst, BS, 50, MS, 51. *Prof Exp:* Res engr, Eng Res Lab, E I du Pont de Nemours & Co, 51-53 & 55-58, sr res eng, 58-61, res supvr, 61-63; proj leader, T L Daniels Res Ctr, Archer Daniels Midland Co, Minn, 63-64, group leader, 64-67; sect mgr, Ashland Oil & Refining Co, 67-70; consult engr, David R Conkey & Assocs, 70-71; CONSULT ENGR, ROBERT L MOISON & ASSOCS, 71- *Mem:* Am Chem Soc; Am Inst Chem Engrs; Am Sci Affiliation; Am Oil Chemists Soc; Consult Engrs Coun Am. *Res:* Chemical & food processing; process development and design; mass transfer; reactor design; pollution abatement. *Mailing Add:* 112 S Surrey Trail Apple Valley MN 55124

MOISSIDES-HINES, LYDIA ELIZABETH, b Newton, Mass, Mar 11, 48; m 74. MEDICINAL CHEMISTRY, INDUSTRIAL CHEMISTRY. *Educ:* Aurora Col, BS, 67; Univ Ill, Urbana-Champaign, MS, 69, PhD(org chem), 71. *Prof Exp:* Sr scientist med chem, Mead Johnson & Co, 71-75; mem staff, Patent Liaison Dept, 75-78, MEM SR STAFF, TECH INTEL DEPT, UPJOHN CO, 78- *Mem:* AAAS; Am Chem Soc; Metric Asn; Sigma Xi. *Mailing Add:* Corp Tech Libr 7284 Upjohn Co Kalamazoo MI 49001

MOJICA-A, TOBIAS, b Soata, Colombia, Mar 1, 43; m 74; c 1. MICROBIAL GENETICS, MOLECULAR BIOLOGY. *Educ:* Brandeis Univ, BA, 68; McGill Univ, MSc, 72; Polish Acad Sci, PhD(biochem), 74. *Prof Exp:* Res assoc radiobiol, Atomic Ctr, Belg, 74-76; res assoc biochem, Hunter Col, 76-77; ASST PROF MICROBIOL, COL MED & DENT NJ-NJ SCH OSTEOPATH MED, 77- *Concurrent Pos:* Mem, Grad Prog Microbiol, Rutgers Univ, 78- *Mem:* Sigma Xi; Am Soc Microbiol; Genetics Soc Am; Belg Biochem Soc; Colombian Soc Genetics. *Res:* Genetics and molecular biology of DNA processing systems in gram positive bacteria, membrane and cell wall in gram negative bacteria, phage DNA injection. *Mailing Add:* Dept of Microbiol NJ Sch Osteopath Med PO Box 55 Piscataway NJ 08854

MOKADAM, RAGHUNATH G(ANPATRAO), b Akola, India, Oct 13, 23; m 53; c 4. THERMODYNAMICS, FLUID MECHANICS. *Educ:* Benares Hindu Univ, BSc, 46; Univ Louisville, MME, 49; Univ Minn, PhD(mech eng), 53. *Prof Exp:* Jr engr, Govt Elec Dept, Univ Nagpur, 46-48; asst prof mech eng, Indian Inst Technol, Khragpur, 55-61, prof, 61-67; sr mech engr, Inst Gas Technol, Ill, 68-71; consult, Chicago, Ill, 71-72; PRIN ENGR, RES DEPT, SUNSTRAND CORP, 76- *Concurrent Pos:* Vis assoc prof, Ill Inst Technol, 66-68, adj assoc prof, 68-69, adj prof, 69-71. *Mem:* Am Soc Mech Engrs; Int Solar Energy Soc. *Res:* Nonreversible thermodynamics applied to fluid flow in porous media; turbulent steady-state flow of coal and gas mixtures in long transmission lines; energy; heat transfer; fluid flow and power; fluidics; refrigeration and airconditioning; properties of binary mixtures of fluids. *Mailing Add:* Res Dept 4747 Harrison Ave Rockford IL 61101

MOKLER, BRIAN VICTOR, b Los Angeles, Calif, May 1, 36; m 68; c 2. AEROSOL SCIENCE, INHALATION TOXICOLOGY. *Educ:* Pomona Col, BA, 58; Mass Inst Technol, SM, 60; Harvard Univ, SM, 68, ScD(environ health sci), 73; Am Bd Indust Hyg, dipl & cert air pollution, 75. *Prof Exp:* Chem engr, Arthur D Little Inc, 60-67; teaching asst environ health sci, Sch Pub Health, Harvard Univ, 69-70, teaching fel, 70-71; consult environ sci & air pollution, 73; MEM SR STAFF AEROSOL SCI, LOVELACE BIOMED & ENVIRON RES INST, 74- *Mem:* Am Chem Soc; Am Indust Hyg Asn; Sigma Xi; Am Acad Indust Hyg. *Res:* Chemistry and physics of disperse systems; aerosol generation and characterization methodology; condensation aerosols; aerosolized consumer products; toxicology of inhaled materials; use of simulation models in pharmacokinetics; industrial hygiene; characteristics of aerosols emitted from energy production and transportation sources. *Mailing Add:* Lovelace Biomed & Environ Res Inst Box 5890 Albuquerque NM 87185

MOKLER, CORWIN MORRIS, b Forsythe, Ill, Dec 10, 25; m 50; c 2. CARDIOVASCULAR PHYSIOLOGY, PHARMACOLOGY. *Educ:* Colo Col, BA, 50; Univ Nev, MS, 52; Univ Ill, PhD(physiol), 58. *Prof Exp:* Technician virol, Harvard Med Sch, 52-54; biologist, NIH, 54; asst anat, Univ Ill, 54-58; investr cardiac pharmacol & physiol, G D Searle & Co, Ill, 58-61; asst prof pharmacol, Univ Fla, 61-67; ASSOC PROF PHARMACOL, SCH PHARM, UNIV GA, 67- *Mem:* Am Soc Pharmacol & Exp Therapeut; Sigma Xi. *Res:* Cardiovascular physiology and pharmacology; cardiac excitability; anti-arrhythmic drugs. *Mailing Add:* Dept of Pharmacol Univ of Ga Sch of Pharm Athens GA 30602

MOKMA, DELBERT LEWIS, b Holland, Mich, Sept 21, 42; m 77. SOIL SCIENCE. *Educ:* Mich State Univ, BS, 64, MS, 66; Univ Wis-Madison, PhD(soil PhD(soil sci), 71. *Prof Exp:* From res asst to res assoc soil sci, 71-75, asst prof, 75-80, ASSOC PROF CROP & SOIL SCI, MICH STATE UNIV, 80- *Mem:* Soil Sci Soc Am; Am Soc Agron; Soil Conserve Soc Am; Int Soc Soil Sci. *Res:* Soil classification and mapping; use of remote sensing and soil surveys in land use planning; soil mineralogy. *Mailing Add:* Dept Crop & Soil Sci Mich State Univ East Lansing MI 48824

MOKOTOFF, MICHAEL, b Brooklyn, NY, Jan 23, 39; m 67; c 3. ORGANIC CHEMISTRY, MEDICINAL CHEMISTRY. *Educ:* Columbia Univ, BS, 60; Univ Wis, MS, 63, PhD(med chem), 66. *Prof Exp:* NIH staff fel med chem, Lab Chem, Nat Inst Arthritis & Metab Dis, 66-68; asst prof, 68-72, ASSOC PROF MED CHEM, SCH PHARM, UNIV PITTSBURGH, 72- *Concurrent Pos:* Health Res Serv Found grant, 69-70; Nat Cancer Inst grant, 70-73; res grant, Am Cancer Soc, 73-75; NIH grant, 76-79, contract, 80-83; Black Athletes Found grant, 77; Am Cancer Soc Inst grant, 79. *Mem:* Am Chem Soc; Am Asn Col Pharm. *Res:* Azabicyclo chemistry; potential inhibitors of asparagine biosynthesis; potential anti-sickling agents; thymus-active peptide analogs. *Mailing Add:* Sch Pharm 727-Salk Hall Univ of Pittsburgh Pittsburgh PA 15261

MOKRASCH, LEWIS CARL, b St Paul, Minn, May 9, 30. BIOCHEMISTRY. *Educ:* Col St Thomas, BS, 52; Univ Wis, PhD(physiol chem), 55; Am Bd Clin Chem, cert. *Prof Exp:* Res assoc psychiat & neurochem, Sch Med, La State Univ, 56-57; sr res assoc biochem & instr med, Univ Kans Med Ctr, Kansas City, 57-62, dir neurochem lab & assoc med, 59-62; from assoc to asst prof biol chem, Harvard Med Sch, 60-71; assoc prof, 71-76, actg head dept biochem, 78-79, PROF BIOCHEM, LA STATE UNIV MED CTR, NEW ORLEANS, 76- *Concurrent Pos:* Nat Inst Neurol Dis & Blindness spec fel, 60-62; assoc biochemist, McLean Hosp, Mass, 60-71; resident scientist, Neurosci Res Prog, Mass Inst Technol, 70-71; vis prof, Div Neurol, Duke Med Ctr, Durham, 81-82. *Mem:* Am Chem Soc; Am Asn Biol Chem; Am Soc Neurochem; Int Soc Neurochem; Am Asn Univ Professors. *Res:* Neurochemistry; clinical chemistry; metabolism and chemistry of brain proteins in relation to development; neurochemistry of aging; biochemical methods of analysis. *Mailing Add:* Dept of Biochem La State Univ Med Ctr New Orleans LA 70112

MOKRZYCKL, ANDREW GUSTAV, b Lwow, Poland, Oct 1, 99; nat US; m 56; c 2. AERONAUTICS, ENGINEERING. *Educ:* Inst Technol, Lwow, MME, 18, PhD, 25; Nat Sch Advan Aeronaut Studies, Paris, MAE, 20. *Prof Exp:* Dir, Samolot Aircraft Co, Poznan, Poland, 22-27; prof aeronaut, Inst Technol, Warsaw, 27-39 & Univ Montreal, 42-44; sr scientist, Gen Dynamics Corp, San Diego, 44-46; chief aerodyn, Ryan Aircraft Co, 46-50; dir flight res dept, US Air Force Flight Test Ctr, Edwards AFB, 50-52; sr scientist missile div, NAm Aviation Co, Los Angeles, 52-62; sr res specialist aircraft div, Northrop Corp, Hawthorne, 62-75; PRES, SCI RES FOUND, 75- *Mem:* Fel Am Inst Aeronaut & Astronaut; Royal Aeronaut Soc; Polish Inst Arts & Sci Am. *Res:* Studies in nuclear fusion. *Mailing Add:* 931 N Yale Ave Fullerton CA 92631

MOLAISON, HENRI J(EAN), b Opelousas, La, Dec 12, 11. ENGINEERING. *Educ:* Tulane Univ, BE, 32. *Prof Exp:* In chg routine lab, Jefferson Lake Sulphur Co, Inc, 32-36; asst off engr, H N Moody, 36-37; asst in chg, Asphalt Lab, Shell Oil Co, 37-39; mem staff, Indust Chem Sales, Indust Chem & Processing Co, Inc, 39-40; asst eng aide, Corps Engrs, US War Dept, 40; from jr chem engr to design eng, Eng & Develop Div, Southern Regional Res Lab, Bur Agr & Indust Chem, USDA, 40-57; design electrical engr, Joseph E Leininger & Assocs, Consult Engrs, 57-64; design elec engr, 64-76, CONSULT, J RAY MCDERMOTT & CO, INC, 77- *Concurrent Pos:* Instr elec eng, Tulane Univ, 43-46. *Mem:* Am Soc Mech Engrs; Am Inst Chem Engrs; Nat Soc Prof Engrs; Centre Genealogigue der l'Quest France; Soc Hist Acad Can. *Res:* Electrical engineering design in marine installations serving petroleum operations; genealogical research. *Mailing Add:* 5531 Marshal Foch St New Orleans LA 70124

MOLAU, GUNTHER ERICH, b Leipzig, Ger, Oct 15, 32; m 58; c 3. POLYMER CHEMISTRY. *Educ:* Carolo-Wilhelmina Inst Technol, BS, 56, MS, 59, PhD(chem), 61. *Prof Exp:* Chemist, Dow Chem Co, 61-63, res chemist, 63-65, sr res chemist, 65-72, ASSOC SCIENTIST, DOW CHEM USA, 69- *Mem:* Am Chem Soc. *Res:* Polymer chemistry; membranes; colloidal and heterogeneous polymers. *Mailing Add:* Dow Chem Co 2800 Mitchell Dr Walnut Creek CA 94598

MOLD, JAMES DAVIS, b Carlton, Minn, Sept 26, 20; m 46; c 3. BIO-ORGANIC CHEMISTRY. *Educ:* Univ Minn, BCh, 42; Northwestern Univ, MS, 44, PhD(org chem), 47. *Prof Exp:* Asst, Northwestern Univ, 42-44, asst chem, 44-46, res assoc, 46-47; biochemist, Parke, Davis & Co, 47-49; org chemist, Allied Sci Div, Biol Lab, US Army Chem Corps, 49-55; chief org chem res, Liggett & Myers Tobacco Co, 55-64, asst dir res, 64-79, CONSULT, LIGGETT GROUP, INC, 79- *Res:* Isolation of natural organic substances; synthesis of organic chemicals; degradation and structure proof of natural organic products; chemistry of tobacco and smoke. *Mailing Add:* Rte 7 Box 208A Durham NC 27707

MOLDAUER, PETER ARNOLD, b Vienna, Austria, June 18, 23; US citizen; div; c 3. NUCLEAR PHYSICS, QUANTUM MECHANICS. *Educ:* Northeastern Univ, BS, 44; Harvard Univ, MA, 47; Univ Mich, PhD(physics), 56. *Prof Exp:* Mem res staff, Gordon McKay Lab, Harvard Univ, 47-48 & Instrumentation Lab, Mass Inst Technol, 48-50; instr physics, Univ Conn, 55-57; assoc physicist, 57-67, SR PHYSICIST, ARGONNE

NAT LAB, 67- *Concurrent Pos:* Res assoc, Lab Nuclear Sci, Mass Inst Technol, 64-65. *Mem:* Fel Am Phys Soc. *Res:* Relativistic wave equations; theory of measurement; nuclear structure theory; nuclear reaction theory; neutron physics. *Mailing Add:* Argonne Nat Lab 9700 S Cass Ave Argonne IL 60439

MOLDAVE, KIVIE, b Kiev, Russia, Oct 22, 23; nat US; m 49; c 2. BIOCHEMISTRY. *Educ:* Univ Calif, AB, 47; Univ Southern Calif, MS, 50, PhD(biochem), 52. *Prof Exp:* USPHS res fels, Univ Wis, 52-53 & Fac Sci, Univ Paris, 53-54; from asst prof to prof biochem, Sch Med, Tufts Univ, 54-66; prof & chmn dept, Sch Med, Univ Pittsburgh, 66-70; chmn dept biol, 70-80, PROF BIOCHEM, COL MED, UNIV CALIF, IRVINE, 70- *Concurrent Pos:* Mem physiol chem study sect, NIH, 67-71 & res serv merit rev bd basic sci, Vet Admin, 72-76; mem adv coun res & clin invest awards, Am Cancer Soc, 76-81, Aging Review Comt, NIH, 77-81; ed, Methods Enzymol, Nucleic Acids & Protein Synthesis, 67-, co ed, Progress Nucleic Acids & Molecular Biol, 81- *Mem:* Am Soc Biol Chem; Am Chem Soc. *Res:* Nucleic acid and protein biosynthesis. *Mailing Add:* Dept of Biol Chem Univ of Calif-Calif Col of Med Irvine CA 92664

MOLDAWER, MARC, b Philadelphia, Pa, June 4, 22; m 63; c 3. MEDICINE, ENDOCRINOLOGY. *Educ:* Univ Pa, 39-42; Harvard Univ, MD, 50. *Prof Exp:* Intern med, Presby Hosp, Columbia Univ, 50-51, resident, 51-52; clin res fel endocrinol, Mass Gen Hosp, 52-55; res fel biochem, Cambridge Univ, 55-56; res fel endocrinol, Harvard Med Sch, 56-57; asst prof, 57-63, ASSOC PROF MED, BAYLOR COL MED, 63-; DIR MED ENDOCRINE SECT, METHODIST HOSP, HOUSTON, 63- *Concurrent Pos:* Consult, Tex Inst Rehab & Res, Ben Taub Gen, Methodist & Vet Admin Hosps, Houston, 58- *Mem:* AAAS; Endocrine Soc; Am Fedn Clin Res. *Res:* Gynecomastia and estrogen metabolism in the male; human growth hormone; immunology and physiology. *Mailing Add:* 110 Banks Houston TX 77006

MOLDAY, ROBERT S, b New York, NY, Oct 27, 43; m 72; c 2. BIOCHEMISTRY, CELL BIOLOGY. *Educ:* Univ Pa, BSc, 65, PhD(biochem), 71; Georgetown Univ, MSc, 67. *Prof Exp:* Res assoc biochem & fel, Calif Inst Technol, 72-75; asst prof, 75-80, ASSOC PROF BIOCHEM, UNIV BC, 80- *Concurrent Pos:* Am Cancer Soc fel, 72-74. *Mem:* Can Biochem Soc. *Res:* Protein and membrane biochemistry; electron microscopy; cell surface receptors; biochemistry of vision. *Mailing Add:* Dept Biochem Univ BC Vancouver BC V6T 1W5 Can

MOLDENHAUER, RALPH ROY, b Detroit, Mich, Apr 8, 35; m 59; c 2. PHYSIOLOGY, ECOLOGY. *Educ:* Mich State Univ, BS, 60; Ore State Univ, MS, 65, PhD(zool), 69. *Prof Exp:* ASSOC PROF BIOL, SAM HOUSTON STATE UNIV, 68- *Concurrent Pos:* Soc Sigma Xi res grant-in-aid, Sam Houston State Univ, 69-71, Am Mus Natural Hist Frank M Chapman Mem Fund grant, 70-72 & Am Philos Soc res grant, 71-72. *Mem:* Am Inst Biol Sci; Am Ornith Union; Cooper Ornith Soc; Ecol Soc Am. *Res:* Physiology and ecology of birds; salt and water balance; thermoregulation; behavioral adjustments in stressful environments. *Mailing Add:* Dept of Biol Sam Houston State Univ Huntsville TX 77340

MOLDENHAUER, WILLIAM CALVIN, b New Underwood, SDak, Oct 27, 23; m 47; c 5. SOIL SCIENCE, SOIL CONSERVATION. *Educ:* SDak State Univ, BS, 49; Univ Wis-Madison, MS, 51, PhD(soil sci), 56. *Prof Exp:* Asst agronomist, SDak State Univ, 49-54; soil scientist, Agr Res Serv, Tex, 54-57 & Iowa, 57-72, soil scientist & res leader, Minn, 72-75, SOIL SCIENTIST & DIR, NAT SOIL EROSION LAB, AGR RES SERV, USDA, WEST LAFAYETTE, 75- *Mem:* Fel Soil Conserv Soc (2nd vpres, 76, 1st vpres, 77, pres elect, 78, pres, 79); fel Am Soc Agron; fel Soil Sci Soc Am; Am Soc Agr Engrs. *Res:* Soil erosion research; soil management research. *Mailing Add:* Dept of Agron Life Sci Bldg Purdue Univ West Lafayette IN 47907

MÖLDER, S(ANNU), b Tallin, Estonia, Sept 1, 35; Can citizen; c 2. AERONAUTICAL ENGINEERING. *Educ:* Univ Toronto, BASc, 58, MASc, 61, MEng, 78. *Prof Exp:* Res asst aerophys, Inst Aerophys, Univ Toronto, 58-61; res assoc propulsion, McGill Univ, 63-64, from asst prof to assoc prof gas dynamics, 64-70, chmn mech eng dept, 69-70; chmn mech technol dept, 71-77, PROF MECH TECHNOL, RYERSON POLYTECH INST, 77- *Concurrent Pos:* Defense Res Bd Can grant propulsion, 63; consult, Appl Physics Lab, Johns Hopkins Univ, 64; mem assoc comt aerodyn, Nat Res Coun Can, 64; vis assoc prof, Univ Sydney, 70-71; consult, CANADAIR, Ltd, 81. *Mem:* Can Soc Mech Engrs; assoc fel Am Inst Aeronaut & Astronaut; fel Can Aeronaut & Space Inst. *Res:* Hypersonic propulsion; supersonic combustion ramjets; hypersonic air inlets; supersonic aerodynamics of wings; aerodynamics of curved shockwaves and their interactions. *Mailing Add:* 46 Brucedale Cres Willowdale ON M2K 2C7 Can

MOLDOVER, MICHAEL ROBERT, b New York, NY, July 19, 40. PHYSICS. *Educ:* Rensselaer Polytech Inst, BS, 61; Stanford Univ, MS, 62, PhD(physics), 66. *Prof Exp:* Res assoc physics, Stanford Univ, 66; asst prof, Univ Minn, Minneapolis, 67-72; physicist, 72-81, SR PHYSICIST, NAT BUR STANDARDS, 81- *Res:* Thermodynamic properties of liquids and solids, especially near phase transitions; low temperature physics; phase equilibria in fluid mixtures; physical acoustics; dynamics of phase changes in fluids; fluid-fluid and fluid-solid interface properties. *Mailing Add:* Thermophysics Div Nat Bur of Standards Washington DC 20234

MOLE, JOHN EDWIN, b Macon, Ga, May 14, 44; m 72. IMMUNOCHEMISTRY, BIOCHEMISTRY. *Educ:* Berry Col, BA, 66; NC State Univ, PhD(biochem), 72. *Prof Exp:* Fel immunol, 72-74, asst prof comp med, 74-75, ASST PROF MICROBIOL, UNIV ALA, BIRMINGHAM, 75-, ASSOC SCIENTIST COMPREHENSIVE CANCER CTR, 76- *Concurrent Pos:* NIH fel, 75-76, grants, 75-76 & 78-81; Nat Cancer grant, 76-79; Am Heart Asn grant, 78-80, prin investr, 79-84. *Mem:* Sigma Xi; Am Chem Soc; NY Acad Sci; Am Asn Immunologists. *Res:* Structure-function of biologically-active macromolecules. *Mailing Add:* 2243 Avanti Lane Birmingham AL 35226

MOLE, PAUL ANGELO, b Jamestown, NY, Mar 13, 38; m 57; c3. MUSCULAR PHYSIOLOGY, EXERCISE PHYSIOLOGY. *Educ:* Univ Ill, Urbana, BS, 60, MS, 62, PhD(physiol), 69. *Prof Exp:* NIH trainee nutrit, Sch Med, Wash Univ, 69-71; asst prof phys educ, Temple Univ, 71-74; asst prof physiol, La State Univ Med Ctr, 74-77; ASSOC PROF PHYS EDUC & FAC GRAD PHYSIOL, UNIV CALIF, DAVIS, 77- *Mem:* AAAS; NY Acad Sci; fel Am col Sports Med. *Res:* Biochemical adaptations to exercise and nutrition; biochemical and contractile properties of skeletal and heart muscle. *Mailing Add:* Muscle Lab Univ of Calif Davis CA 95616

MOLECKE, MARTIN A, b Cleveland, Ohio, Sept 14, 45; m 68; c 2. NUCLEAR CHEMISTRY. *Educ:* Bowling Green State Univ, BS, 67; Carnegie-Mellon Univ, MS, 70, PhD(nuclear chem), 72. *Prof Exp:* Fel, Carnegie-Mellon Univ, 72-73; sr scientist radiochem, Bettis Atomic Power Lab, Westinghouse Elec Co, 73-75; MEM TECH STAFF NUCLEAR SCI, SANDIA LABS, WESTERN ELEC CO, 76- *Mem:* Am Chem Soc; Am Nuclear Soc; Mat Res Soc. *Res:* Nuclear waste technology; high-level waste laboratory and in situ experimentation; waste package materials performance research; transuranic waste experimental characterization. *Mailing Add:* Sandia Nat Labs Div 4512 Albuquerque NM 87185

MOLENKAMP, CHARLES RICHARD, b San Francisco, Calif, Aug 26, 41; m 67; c 2. ATMOSPHERIC PHYSICS, POLLUTANT TRANSPORT & DEPOSITION. *Educ:* Calvin Col, BS, 63; Univ Ariz, MS, 68, PhD(atmospheric physics), 72. *Prof Exp:* PHYSICIST ATMOSPHERIC SCI, LAWRENCE LIVERMORE LAB, UNIV CALIF, 72- *Mem:* Am Meteorol Soc; Geothermal Resources Coun. *Res:* Cloud physics; numerical modeling; air quality associated with geothermal resource development, mesoseale atmospheric transport and diffusion; precipitation scavenging. *Mailing Add:* Lawrence Livermore Lab L-262 PO Box 808 Livermore CA 94550

MOLER, CLEVE B, b Salt Lake City, Utah, Aug 17, 39; m 60; c 3. NUMERICAL ANALYSIS, MATHEMATICAL SOFTWARE. *Educ:* Calif Inst Technol, BS, 61; Stanford Univ, PhD(math), 65. *Prof Exp:* Instr comput sci, Stanford Univ, 65; from asst prof to assoc prof math, Univ Mich, Ann Arbor, 66-72; assoc prof math, 72-74, prof, 74-80, CHMN, DEPT COMPUT SCI, UNIV NMEX, 80- *Concurrent Pos:* Off Naval Res assoc, Swiss Fed Inst Technol, 65-66; vis assoc prof, Stanford Univ, 70-71 & 78-79. *Mem:* Am Math Soc; Asn Comput Mach; Soc Indust & Appl Math. *Res:* Numerical analysis; computer science; linear algebra; partial differential equations. *Mailing Add:* Dept Comput Sci Univ NMex Albuquerque NM 87131

MOLES, OLIVER WALTON, b Aztec, NMex, Mar 24, 20; m 45; c 4. EXTRACTIVE METALLURGY, HIGH TEMPERATURE CHEMISTRY. *Educ:* La State Univ, BE, 44; Mass Inst Technol, SB, 47, ScD(metall), 50. *Prof Exp:* Res metallurgist, Res Lab, Am Smelting & Refining Co, 50-51 & Titanium Div, Nat Lead Co, 51-65; GROUP LEADER EXTRACTIVE METALL, OXIDATION & PIGMENT RES, WHITTIER RES LABS, KERR MCGEE CORP, 69-, SR PROCESS ENGR, 77- *Mem:* Am Inst Mining, Metall & Petrol Engrs. *Res:* Molten salt electrolysis to produce titanium, zirconium and other metals; high temperature oxidation processes for Tio2 pigment manufacture; conversion of vanadium oxides to carbides; conversion of Oklahoma coal to coke. *Mailing Add:* Kerr McGee Chem Corp PO Box 629 Theodore AL 36582

MOLGAARD, JOHANNES, b Kunming, China, Apr 23, 36; m 65; c 3. MATERIALS ENGINEERING, TRIBOLOGY. *Educ:* Queen's Univ Belfast, BS, 57; Univ Leeds, PhD(textiles), 66. *Prof Exp:* Tech officer, Brit Nylon Spinners Ltd, 57-63; Nat Res Coun Can fel, McMaster Univ, 66-68; from asst prof to assoc prof eng, 68-78, PROF ENG, MEM UNIV NFLD, 78- *Concurrent Pos:* Mem assoc comt on lubrication, Nat Res Coun Can, 71-; Alexander von Humboldt Found fel, Ger, 75-76. *Mem:* Can Soc Mech Engrs; Brit Inst Physics. *Res:* Wear of metals; friction of ice; system theory. *Mailing Add:* Fac Eng Mem Univ Nfld St John's NF A1C 5S7 Can

MOLINA, JOHN FRANCIS, b Jamaica, NY, Jan 4, 50; m 73; c 2. ANALYTICAL & PHYSICAL CHEMISTRY. *Educ:* Northeastern Univ, BS, 73; Univ New Orleans, PhD(chem), 77. *Prof Exp:* Chemist qual control drug anal, Fougera, Inc, 73; sr res chemist, Bristol-Myers Co, 77-78; res chemist & group leader spectrochem, Celanese Res Co, 78-81; INST ANAL GROUP LEADER, APOLLO TECNOLOGIES, INC, 81- *Mem:* Am Chem Soc; Soc Appl Spectros; Asn Am Univ Prof. *Res:* Trace analysis of both inorganic and organic substances via spectroscopic techniques, especially atomic absorption, atomic emission and x-ray fluorescence; wet chemical analysis and separation techniques, especially gas chromatography and high pressure liquid chromatography. *Mailing Add:* Apollo Technologies Inc 1 Apollo Dr Whippany NJ 07981

MOLINA, MARIO JOSE, CHEMICAL KINETICS, PHOTOCHEMISTRY. *Educ:* Univ Nat Autonoma De Mex, BS, 65; Univ Calif, Berkeley, PhD(phys chem), 72. *Prof Exp:* Asst prof chem eng, Univ Nat Autonoma De Mex, 67-68; res assoc phys chem, Univ Calif, Berkeley, 72-73; res assoc, 73-75, asst prof, 75-79, ASSOC PROF PHYS CHEM, UNIV CALIF, IRVINE, 79- *Concurrent Pos:* Fel, Alfred P Sloan Found, 76-78; teacher & scholar, Camille & Henry Dreyfus Found, 78-82; Mem, Panel Chem Kinetic & Photochem Data Eval, NASA, 78-, Comn Human Resources, Nat Res Coun, Nat Acad Sci, 78-81. *Mem:* Am Chem Soc; Am Phys Soc; Am Geophys Union; Sigma Xi; Photochem Soc. *Res:* Chemistry of the stratosphere particularly as it can be affected by man-made perturbations such as the release of chlorofluorocarbons; various aspects of the theory of stratospheric ozone depletion by chlorofluorocarbons. *Mailing Add:* Dept Chem Univ Calif Irvine CA 92717

MOLINA, RANDOLPH JOHN, b Los Angeles, Calif, May 13, 51; m 71; c 2. MYCOLOGY. *Educ:* Univ Calif, Santa Barbara, BA, 73; Ore State Univ, PhD(bot), 81. *Prof Exp:* Botanist, 73-80, RES BOTANIST, PAC NORTHWEST FOREST & RANGE EXP STA, FOREST SERV, USDA,

81- *Concurrent Pos:* Assoc prof, Dept Forest Sci, Ore State Univ, 81- *Mem:* Sigma Xi. *Res:* Specificity and compatibility between ectomycorrhizal fungus and host symbionts, with special emphasis on practical application of beneficial mycorrhizal relationships in forestry. *Mailing Add:* Foresty Sci Lab 3200 Jefferson Way Corvallis OR 97331

MOLINARI, PIETRO FILIPPO, b Mestre-Venice, Italy, Sept 9, 23; US citizen; m 56; c 2. ENDOCRINOLOGY, HEMATOLOGY. *Educ:* Univ Milan, DVM, 52, PhD(clin path), 60. *Prof Exp:* From asst prof clin vet med to assoc prof clin methodology, Univ Milan, 52-61, dir res lab, 61-64; endocrinologist, Mason Res Inst, 64-67, sr investr endocrinol, 67-71; asst dir hemat, St Vincent Hosp, 71-79; ASSOC PROF, DEPT MED, VET SCH, TUFTS UNIV, 79- *Concurrent Pos:* Ital Res Coun fel physiol, Vet Sch, Cornell Univ, 61; asst prof med, Med Sch, Univ Mass. *Mem:* Int Soc Exp Hemat; NY Acad Sci; Endocrine Soc. *Res:* Study of erythropoietic activity of hormones, particularly steroid hormones in laboratory animals and human cells in vitro. *Mailing Add:* Dept Med Vet Sch Tufts Univ 350 S Huntington Ave Jamaica Plains MA 02130

MOLINARI, ROBERT JAMES, b Peckville, Pa, May 30, 52. PHYSICAL POLYMER CHEMISTRY, CORROSION SCIENCE. *Educ:* Dartmouth Col, AB, 74, MBA, 79; Brown Univ, PhD(chem), 77. *Prof Exp:* Prof intern bus & chem res, Photopolymer Dept, Res Div, W R Grace & Co, 78; staff scientist, 79, group leader, 80, MKT DEVELOP MGR, RES DIV, RAYCHEM CORP, 81- *Concurrent Pos:* Consult, Schlumberger Corp, Ridgefield, Conn & Houston, Tex, 80. *Mem:* NY Acad Sci. *Res:* Electrical and dielectric properties of polymers, particularly industrial and biological macromolecules; polymer radiation chemistry and physics. *Mailing Add:* 150 W Edith #3 Los Altos CA 94022

MOLINARY, SAMUEL VICTOR, b Dante, Va, Jan 15, 39; m 59; c 3. BIOCHEMISTRY, GENETICS. *Educ:* Univ Va, BA, 61; Med Col Va, PhD(biochem genetics), 68. *Prof Exp:* Teacher high sch, Va, 61-62; res assoc biochem, Med Units, Univ Tenn Health Sci Ctr, Memphis, 68-69, asst prof biochem & sr staff biochemist, Child Develop Ctr, 69-72, assoc prof biochem & child develop & chief clin biochem, 72-76; sr res scientist-in-chg genetic toxicol, Searle Labs, 76-80, DIR SCI AFFAIRS, SEARLE FOOD RESOURCES, INC, 80- *Mem:* Am Asn Clin Chemists; Sigma Xi; NY Acad Sci; Environ Mutagens Soc; Am Asn Univ Prof. *Res:* Biochemical and genetics regulation of metabolism in bacteria and tissue culture cells; genetic toxicology; amino acid metabolism; food toxicology. *Mailing Add:* Searle Food Resources Inc Box 1045 Skokie IL 60076

MOLINE, HAROLD EMIL, b Frederic, Wis, Nov 13, 39; m 65; c 2. PHYTOPATHOLOGY, PLANT VIROLOGY. *Educ:* Univ Wis-River Falls, BSc, 67, MS, 69; Iowa State Univ, PhD(plant path), 72. *Prof Exp:* Plant pathologist, Northern Grain Insect Res Lab, Brookings, SDak, 72-73, RES PLANT PATHOLOGIST, HORT CROPS QUAL LAB, HORT SCI INST, AGR RES SERV, USDA, BELTSVILLE, MD, 74- *Concurrent Pos:* Asst prof, Bot Dept, Howard Univ, Washington, DC. *Mem:* Am Phytopath Soc; Bot Soc Am; Sigma Xi; Am Soc Plant Physiologists; Electron Micros Soc Am. *Res:* Epidemiology of post harvest diseases of fresh market fruits and vegetables; ultrastructural and histochemical modifications of host cells invaded by bacteria, fungi or viruses; physiological disorders. *Mailing Add:* Hort Sci Inst Hort Crops Qual Lab Beltsville Agr Res Ctr-W Beltsville MD 20705

MOLINE, SHELDON WALTER, b Chicago, Ill, Feb 15, 31; m 52; c 4. BIOCHEMISTRY, IMMUNOLOGY. *Educ:* Roosevelt Univ, BS, 52; Univ Chicago, PhD, 58; State Univ NY Buffalo, MBA, 69. *Prof Exp:* Res technician, Argonne Nat Lab, 52-56; res chemist, Linde Div, Union Carbide Corp, 58-63, sr staff biochemist, 64-67, proj scientist chem & plastics, 67-68, tech mgr fermentation, Chem Div, 68-71, dir res, Creative Agr Systs, 71-74, sr group leader, Corp Res Dept, 74-79; MGR MED DIAGNOSTICS, STAUFFER CHEM CO, 79- *Mem:* AAAS; Am Chem Soc; Inst Food Technol; Sigma Xi; NY Acad Sci. *Res:* Thermal properties and metabolic processes of biological systems at low temperatures; cryosurgery; cell culture; preservation of foods at low temperatures; shipment of produce and meats; seed and plant physiology; medical and health sciences. *Mailing Add:* 101 Greenridge Ave White Plains NY 10605

MOLINE, WALDEMAR JOHN, b Fredric, Wis, Oct 29, 34; m 57; c 3. AGRONOMY. *Educ:* Wis State Univ, Riverfalls, BS, 59; Univ Minn, MS, 61; Iowa State Univ, PhD(agron), 65. *Prof Exp:* Res asst agron, Univ Minn, 59-61; res assoc, Iowa State Univ, 61-65; asst prof, Univ Md, 65-66; from assoc prof to prof agron, Univ Nebr, Lincoln, 66-76; PROF AGRON & HEAD DEPT, UNIV ARK, 76- *Concurrent Pos:* Chmn mem comt & mem exec comt, Am Forage & Grassland Coun, 60-70; chmn pub rels & info comt, Am Soc Agron, Crop Sci Soc Am & Soil Sci Soc Am, 75. *Mem:* Am Soc Agron; Soc Range Mgt; Am Forage & Grassland Coun (pres, 75). *Res:* Forage crops management, production and utilization. *Mailing Add:* Dept of Agron Plant Sci 115 Univ of Ark Fayetteville AR 72701

MOLINI, ALBERTO E, b Yauco, PR, Oct 25, 24; m 53; c 4. CHEMICAL ENGINEERING. *Educ:* Univ Mich, BS & MS, 52, PhD(chem eng), 67. *Prof Exp:* Res asst, Eng Res Inst, Univ Mich, 52-55; res engr, Dacron Res Lab, E I du Pont de Nemours & Co, Inc, 56-63, res assoc, 66-68; chmn chmn eng dept, 68-70, assoc prof, 68-77, PROF CHEM ENG, UNIV PR, MAYAGUEZ, 77- *Concurrent Pos:* Dir, Rum Pilot Plant, Univ PR, 72-78; consult, Destileria Serralles, Inc, 78; vis prof, Carnegie-Mellon Univ, 78-79. *Mem:* AAAS; Am Inst Chem Engrs; Am Soc Eng Educ; Am Chem Soc; PR Inst Chem Engrs. *Mailing Add:* Dept Chem Eng Univ PR Mayaguez PR 00708

MOLINO, DONALD F(RANK), b Paterson, NJ, Oct 12, 28; m 54; c 3. CHEMICAL ENGINEERING. *Educ:* Mass Inst Technol, SB, 48; Rensselaer Polytech Inst, MChE, 50, PhD(chem eng), 59. *Prof Exp:* Instr chem eng, Rensselaer Polytech Inst, 49-53; NUCLEAR ENGR, KNOLLS ATOMIC POWER LAB, 56- *Mem:* Am Nuclear Soc. *Res:* Analytical and experimental nuclear engineering. *Mailing Add:* 878 Cunningham Ct Schenectady NY 12309

MOLINOFF, PERRY BROWN, b Smithtown, NY, June 3, 40; m 63; c 2. NEUROPHARMACOLOGY. *Educ:* Harvard Univ, BS, 62, MD, 67. *Prof Exp:* Intern med, Univ Chicago Hosps & Clins, 67-68; res assoc, NIMH, 68-70; vis fel biophys, Univ Col, London, 70-72; from asst prof to prof, 72-81, A N RICHARDS PROF PHARMACOL & CHMN, PHARMACOL DEPT, MED SCH, UNIV PENN, 81- *Concurrent Pos:* Guggenheim fel & Grass lectr neurosci; estab investr, Am Heart Asn. *Mem:* Am Soc Pharmacol & Exp Therapeut; Soc Neurosci; Am Soc Neurochem; Am Heart Asn; AAAS. *Res:* Regulation of norepinephrine synthesis; isolation and characterization of receptors. *Mailing Add:* Dept of Pharmacol Univ Colo Pa Philadelphia PA 19104

MOLINSKI, VICTOR JOSEPH, b Ticonderoga, NY, Nov 16, 23. NUCLEAR CHEMISTRY. *Educ:* Seton Hall Univ, BS, 52. *Prof Exp:* Chemist, Allen B Dumont Labs, 49-51, F W Berk & Co, 51-57 & Union Carbide Nuclear Co, 57-62, res chemist, Develop Dept, Union Carbide Corp, 62-73, DEVELOP MGR NUCLEONICS, UNION CARBIDE CORP, 73- *Mem:* Am Chem Soc; Soc Nuclear Med. *Res:* Analytical chemistry, both wet chemistry and instrumental analysis; radiochemistry, particularly neutron activation analysis; development of radiochemicals and radiodiagnostic agents and instruments for use in nuclear medicine. *Mailing Add:* Union Carbide Res Ctr Box 324 Tuxedo NY 10987

MOLKO, PATRICIA MICHELE, b Joliet, Ill, Nov 26, 46; m 71. SOFTWARE ENGINEERING, MATHEMATICS. *Educ:* Purdue Univ, BS, 68, MA, 69. *Prof Exp:* Engr math & comput sci, 69-73, tech group leader, 73-77, software syst engr navig software, 77-78, ground software syst engr, Galileo Proj, 78-81, SOFTWARE SYST MGR, GALILEO PROJ, JET PROPULSION LAB, CALIF INST TECHNOL, 81- *Res:* Ways to reduce the cost of software development by control and management of the software development process and application of effective tools and techniques. *Mailing Add:* Jet Propulsion Lab 4800 Oak Grove Dr Pasadena CA 91103

MOLL, ALBERT JAMES, b Vergennes, Ill, Feb 2, 37; m 64; c 2. CHEMICAL ENGINEERING. *Educ:* Univ Ill, BS, 59, Univ Wash, Seattle, MS, 61, PhD(chem eng), 66. *Prof Exp:* Chem engr res & develop, Union Carbide Corp, WVa, 66-70; sr staff engr, Chem Systs Inc, 70-72; sr engr & economist, 72-74, DIR, ENERGY TECHNOL DEPT, SRI INT, 74- *Mem:* Am Chem Soc; Am Inst Chem Engrs. *Res:* Synthetic fuels technology and economics; underground coal gasification; liquefied natural gas. *Mailing Add:* SRI Int Menlo Park CA 94025

MOLL, EDWARD OWEN, b Peoria, Ill, Nov 30, 39; m 60; c 2. ECOLOGY, HERPETOLOGY. *Educ:* Univ Ill, BS, 61, MS, 63; Univ Utah, PhD(zool), 68. *Prof Exp:* From asst prof to assoc prof, 68-78, PROF ZOOL, EASTERN ILL UNIV, 78- *Concurrent Pos:* Environ consult, Westinghouse Elec Corp, 73-74; consult turtle conserv, W Malaysian Game Dept, 75-76; res grants, NY Zool Soc, 75-78 & 81, World Wildlife Fund, 75-76 & 81, Am Philos Soc, 75-76 & Fauna Preserv Soc, 75-76 & 78; chmn, Freshwater Chelonian Specialist Group Species Survival Comn; mem, Marine Turtle Specialist Group, Int Union Conserv Nature. *Mem:* AAAS; Am Soc Ichthyologists & Herpetologists; Soc Study Amphibians & Reptiles; Herpetologists League. *Res:* Reptilian ecology; taxonomy; distribution and management of river turtles. *Mailing Add:* Dept Zool Eastern Ill Univ Charleston IL 61920

MOLL, HAROLD WESTBROOK, b Detroit, Mich, Apr 2, 14; m 38; c 3. ORGANIC CHEMISTRY, CHEMICAL ENGINEERING. *Educ:* Andrews Univ, BS, 37. *Prof Exp:* Res chemist, Dow Chem, USA, 37-48, supt latex pilot plant, 48-58, supvr, Instrument Lab, 59-63, tech expert, E C Britton Res Lab, 63-71, tech expert, Phys Res Lab, 72-77. *Concurrent Pos:* Adj prof chem, Andrew's Univ, Berrien Springs, Mich, 78- *Mem:* AAAS; Am Chem Soc; Instrument Soc Am. *Res:* Organic synthesis; polymers; latexes; chemical engineering; instrumentation science. *Mailing Add:* 1755 E Isabella Rd RFD 12 Midland MI 48640

MOLL, JOHN L, b Ohio, Dec 21, 21; m 44; c 3. ELECTRICAL ENGINEERING. *Educ:* Ohio State Univ, BSc, 43, PhD(elec eng), 52. *Prof Exp:* Develop engr magnetrons, Radio Corp Am, 44-45; asst math, Ohio State Univ, 46-49, instr & res assoc, 50-52; mem tech staff transistor develop, Bell Tel Labs, Inc, 53-56 & solid state electronics res, 56-58; from assoc prof to prof elec eng, Stanford Univ, 58-69; tech dir eng, Fairchild Microwave & Opto-electronics Div, Fairchild Camera & Instrument Corp, 69-74; tech dir, 74-81, DIR, INTEGRATED CIRCUITS LAB, HEWLETT-PACKARD CO, INC, 81- *Concurrent Pos:* NSF sr fel, Tech Univ Denmark, 64-65; consult, HP Assocs, Hewlett-Packard Co. *Mem:* Nat Acad Eng; Am Phys Soc; fel Inst Elec & Electronics Engrs. *Res:* Semiconductor electronics; high frequency oscilators; transistors. *Mailing Add:* 4111 Old Trace Rd Palo Alto CA 94306

MOLL, KENNETH LEON, b Jackson, Mo, Oct 16, 32; m 57; c 2. SPEECH PATHOLOGY. *Educ:* Southeast Mo State Col, BS, 54; Univ Iowa, MA, 59, PhD(speech path), 60. *Prof Exp:* Res assoc speech sci, 59-61, res asst prof, 61-64, assoc prof, 64-68, chmn, Dept Speech Path & Audiol, 68-76, assoc dean fac, 76-81, PROF SPEECH SCI, UNIV IOWA, 68-, ACTG VPRES ACAD AFFAIRS, 81- *Concurrent Pos:* Nat Inst Neurol Dis & Blindness spec fel, Univ Mich, 65-66. *Mem:* AAAS; Am Speech & Hearing Asn; Acoust Soc Am. *Res:* Physiological aspects of human speech production through use of x-ray techniques, electromyography and air pressure and air flow recordings. *Mailing Add:* Off of Acad Affairs Univ of Iowa Iowa City IA 52242

MOLL, MAGNUS, b East Orange, NJ, July 23, 28; m 58. ELECTRICAL & SYSTEMS ENGINEERING. *Educ:* Purdue Univ, BS, 53; Univ Ill, MS, 56; Ohio State Univ, PhD(elec eng), 62. *Prof Exp:* Prin elec engr, Battelle Mem Inst, 56-57, sr elec engr, 57-62, group consult, 62; mem prof staff, Arthur D Little Inc, Mass, 63-71; SR SCIENTIST, BOLT BERANEK & NEWMAN INC, 72- *Mem:* Inst Elec & Electronics Engrs. *Res:* Systems engineering and analysis; stochastic processes; sonar systems; signal processing. *Mailing Add:* Bolt Beranek & Newman Inc 1701 N Ft Myer Dr Arlington VA 22209

MOLL, PATRICIA PEYSER, b New Rochelle, NY, Oct 29, 46; m 69. HUMAN & POPULATION GENETICS. *Educ:* Univ Vt, BA, 68; State Univ NY, Stony Brook, PhD(biol), 75. *Prof Exp:* Systs analyst, Int Bus Mach, 68-69; math assoc, Brookhaven Nat Lab, 69-70; res asst ecol & evolution, State Univ NY, Stony Brook, 71-75; scholar, 75-78, ASST PROF EPIDEMIOL & ASST RES SCIENTIST, HUMAN GENEICS, UNIV MICH, ANN ARBOR, 79- *Concurrent Pos:* NIH fel, 76-78. *Mem:* Genetics Soc Am; Am Soc Human Genetics; Biomet Soc; Soc Epidemiol Res. *Res:* Genetic epidemiology. *Mailing Add:* Dept of Human Genetics 1137 E Catherine St Ann Arbor MI 48109

MOLL, RICHARD A, b Chicago, Ill, Sept 2, 35; m 55; c 6. METALLURGICAL & MECHANICAL ENGINEERING. *Educ:* Ill Inst Technol, BS, 62; Lehigh Univ, MS, 64, PhD(metall, mat sci), 66. *Prof Exp:* Asst experimentalist metall, IIT Res Inst, 55-62; instr, Lehigh Univ, 62-66; asst prof metall & mech eng, 66-74, assoc prof metall eng, 74-80, PROF METALL ENG, UNIV WIS-MADISON, 80- *Honors & Awards:* F L Plummer lectr, Am Welding Soc, 81. *Mem:* Am Soc Metals; Soc Mfg Engrs. *Res:* Product safety and liability prevention, especially as this relates to design manufacturing and warnings with current legal-engineering aspects of products. *Mailing Add:* Dept of Eng 432 N Lake St Madison WI 53706

MOLL, ROBERT HARRY, b Lackawanna, NY, July 17, 27; m 50; c 3. GENETICS. *Educ:* Cornell Univ, BS, 51; Univ Idaho, MS, 53; NC State Col, PhD(plant breeding), 57. *Prof Exp:* From asst prof to assoc prof, 57-65, PROF GENETICS, NC STATE UNIV, 65- *Mem:* AAAS; Am Soc Agron; Genetics Soc Am; Am Soc Naturalists. *Res:* Quantitative genetics; statistics; plant breeding; horticulture. *Mailing Add:* Dept of Genetics NC State Univ Raleigh NC 27650

MOLL, RUSSELL ADDISON, b Bound Brook, NJ, Aug 12, 46; m 69. LIMNOLOGY. *Educ:* Univ Vt, BA, 68; Long Island Univ, MS, 71; State Univ NY Stony Brook, PhD(biol), 74. *Prof Exp:* Jr res assoc, Dept Biol, Brookhaven Nat Lab, 72-73; res innvestr limnol, 74-76, asst res scientist, 76-81, ASSOC RES SCIENTIST, GREAT LAKES RES DIV, UNIV MICH, 81- *Mem:* Am Soc Limnol & Oceanog; AAAS; Phycol Soc Am; Ecol Soc Am; Int Asn Great Lakes Res. *Res:* Ecology and community structure of aquatic ecosystems; phytoplankton and bacterial distribution and productivity; data analysis and biostatistics applied to ecosystems. *Mailing Add:* Great Lakes Res Div IST Bldg Univ of Mich Ann Arbor MI 48109

MOLL, TORBJORN, b Norway, June 25, 19; m 48; c 2. MICROBIOLOGY. *Educ:* Vet Col Norway, DVM, 45; Univ Wis, MS, 50, PhD(microbiol), 52. *Prof Exp:* Asst prof obstet, Vet Col Norway, 47-48; asst & instr, Univ Wis, 48-52; assoc prof, 52-59, PROF VET MICROBIOL & PATH, WASH STATE UNIV, 59- *Concurrent Pos:* Fulbright res fel, Vet Col Norway, 61-62. *Res:* Diabetes mellitus-in vitro studies of Langeuhans islet cells. *Mailing Add:* Vet Col Wash State Univ Pullman WA 99163

MOLL, WILLIAM FRANCIS, JR, b Jacksonville Fla, Feb 20, 31; m 60; c 1. GEOCHEMISTRY, MINERALOGY. *Educ:* Univ Fla, BS, 54; Ind Univ, Bloomington, MA, 58; Wash Univ, PhD(geol), 63. *Prof Exp:* Instr mineral, Wash Univ, 59-60; technician, Emerson Elec Mfg Co, 61-62; fel mat res, Pa State Univ, 63-65; technologist, Baroid Div, Nat Lead Co, 65-67; mineralogist, Collodial Minerals Lab, Georgia Kaolin Co, Elizabeth, 67-74, head, 74-79; MGR TECH SERV & COM DEVELOP, CAB-O-SIL DIV, CABOT CORP, 79- *Mem:* Am Chem Soc; Mineral Soc Am; Mineral Soc Gt Brit & Ireland; Clay Minerals Soc; Soc Cosmetic Chemists. *Res:* Characterization and application of fine-particle inorganic materials, including surface chemistry and rheology; paragenesis and chemistry of layer silicates; surface modification of fine-particle materials; industrial mineralogy. *Mailing Add:* CAB O SIL Div Cabot Corp Tuscola IL 61953

MOLLARD, JOHN D A, b Regina, Sask, Jan 4, 24; m 52; c 3. CIVIL ENGINEERING, ENGINEERING GEOLOGY. *Educ:* Univ Sask, BE, 45; Purdue Univ, MSCE, 47; Cornell Univ, PhD(eng geol), 52. *Prof Exp:* Res asst civil eng, Purdue Univ, 45-47; res assoc, Cornell Univ, 50-51, res engr, 51-52; chief air surv engr, Geol Div, Prairie Farm Rehab Admin, Govt of Can, 52-56; PRES, CONSULT CIVIL ENGR & ENG GEOLOGIST, J D MOLLARD & ASSOCS, LTD, 56- *Concurrent Pos:* Air surv engr, Prairie Farm Rehab Admin, Fed Govt of Can, 47-49; tech adv aerial resources surv, Govt of Pakistan & Ceylon, 54-55; guest lectr & vis prof, Harvard Univ, 57, Univs Alta, Guelph & Man, 59-69, Univ Calif, Berkeley, 65 & Univ Hawaii, 67; lectr, Nat Res Coun Can Distinguished Lect Ser at Six Eastern Can Univs, 69; mem subcomt geotech res, Nat Res Coun Can, 70. *Mem:* Fel Am Soc Civil Engrs; fel Geol Soc Am; fel Geol Asn Can; Am Soc Photogram; Eng Inst Can. *Res:* Remote sensing of environments; photo interpretation for civil engineering and geological studies; hydrogeology; over 60 technical and scientific papers published. *Mailing Add:* 815 McCallum Hill Bldg Regina SK S4P 2G6 Can

MOLLENAUER, JAMES FREDERICK, nuclear physics, computer science, see previous edition

MOLLENAUER, LINN F, b Washington, Pa, Jan 6, 37; m 62; c 2. PHYSICS. *Educ:* Cornell Univ, BEngPhys, 59; Stanford Univ, PhD(physics), 65. *Prof Exp:* Asst prof physics, Univ Calif, Berkeley, 65-72; RES STAFF MEM, BELL LABS, 72- *Honors & Awards:* R W Wood Prize, Optical Soc Am, 82. *Mem:* Am Phys Soc; Inst Elec & Electronics Engrs; fel Optical Soc Am; fel AAAS. *Res:* Optical spectroscopy of solids; lasers; light scattering; infrared tunable lasers; color centers. *Mailing Add:* Bell Labs Rm 4C-306 Holmdel NJ 07733

MOLLER, KARLIND THEODORE, b Chisago City, Minn, May 25, 42; m 65; c 1. SPEECH PATHOLOGY. *Educ:* Univ Minn, Minneapolis, BS, 64, MA, 67, PhD(speech path), 70. *Prof Exp:* Nat Inst Dent Res spec res fel, 70-72, ASSOC PROF SPEECH PATH, SCH DENT UNIV MINN, MINNEAPOLIS, 70-, DIR CLEFT PALATE MAXILLOFACIAL CLIN, 77- *Mem:* Am Speech & Hearing Asn; Am Cleft Palate Asn. *Res:* Oral physiology; speech production; speech in persons with orofacial anomalies; modification of speech and oral structures. *Mailing Add:* 686 Arbogast Rd St Paul MN 55112

MOLLER, PETER, b Hamburg, Ger, Nov 19, 41; m 67; c 1. ETHOLOGY. *Educ:* Free Univ Berlin, dipl biol, 64, PhD(zool), 67. *Prof Exp:* Asst prof, 70-75, assoc prof, 75-81, PROF PSYCHOL, HUNTER COL, 82-; RES ASSOC, AM MUS NATURAL HIST, 72- *Concurrent Pos:* NATO res fel, Nat Ctr Sci Res, Paris, 68-69, Dr Carl Duisberg fel, 69-70; City Univ New York fac res grant, Hunter Col, 72-73, 78-79, NIMH, 80 & Nat Geog Soc, 76, 77. *Mem:* AAAS; Am Soc Zoologists; NY Acad Sci; Ger Zool Soc. *Res:* Sensory and behaviroal physiology; ethology and ecology of electric fish; arthropod orientation. *Mailing Add:* Dept of Psychol Hunter Col 695 Park Ave New York NY 10021

MOLLER, RAYMOND WILLIAM, b Brooklyn, NY, Jan 28, 20; m 48; c 8. MATHEMATICS. *Educ:* Manhattan Col, BS, 41; Cath Univ, PhD(math), 51. *Prof Exp:* Instr math, Trinity Col, 43-45; from instr to asst prof, 46-57, head dept, 57-70, ASSOC PROF MATH, CATH UNIV AM, 57- *Mem:* Am Math Soc; Math Asn Am. *Res:* Congruences; primitive roots; cyclotomic polynomials. *Mailing Add:* Dept of Math Cath Univ of Am Box 105 Washington DC 20017

MOLLERE, PHILLIP DAVID, b New Orleans, La, Dec 18, 44; m 68; c 2. SOLVENT EXTRACTION, HYDROMETALLURGY. *Educ:* Washington & Lee Univ, BS, 66; La State Univ, PhD(chem), 71. *Prof Exp:* Res assoc chem, Inst Inorg Chem II, Goethe Univ, Frankfurt, 71-72, Cornell Univ, 72-73; vis asst prof, Univ Mo, Kansas City, 73-74; res assoc, La State Univ, 74-75; res chemist prod develop, 75-78, supt chem res & develop, 79-82, MGR CHEM PROCESS DEVELOP, FREEPORT MINERALS RES & DEVELOP, 82- *Mem:* Am Chem Soc. *Res:* Chemical process development related to the recovery and/or grade improvement of mineral values (uranium, phosphate, gold, nickel, cobalt, sulfur, silver), from natural resources. *Mailing Add:* Freeport Minerals Res & Develop PO Box 26 Belle Chasse LA 70037

MOLLES, MANUEL CARL, JR, b Gustine, Calif, July 30, 48; m 77; c 1. STREAM ECOLOGY, REEF FISH ECOLOGY. *Educ:* Humboldt State Univ, BS, 70; Univ Ariz, PhD(zool), 76. *Prof Exp:* ASST PROF ECOL & CUR FISHES, UNIV NMEX, 75- *Mem:* AAAS; Ecol Soc Am; Am Soc Ichthyologists & Herpetologists. *Res:* Reef fish ecology; stream ecology. *Mailing Add:* Dept of Biol Univ of NMex Albuquerque NM 87131

MOLLICA, JOSEPH ANTHONY, b Providence, RI, Oct 24, 40; m 64; c 3. PHARMACEUTICAL CHEMISTRY, ANALYTICAL CHEMISTRY. *Educ:* Univ RI, BS, 62; Univ Wis, MS, 65, PhD, 66. *Prof Exp:* Sr chemist, Ciba Pharmaceut Co, 66-68, mgr phys chem, 68-70, asst dir anal res & develop, 70-75, dir, 75-78, sr dir anal res & develop & advan drug delivery systs, 78-80, EXEC DIR RES & DEVELOP, CIBA-GEIGY CORP, 80- *Mem:* NY Acad Sci; Am Chem Soc; Am Pharmaceut Asn; Acad Pharmaceut Sci. *Res:* Developmeht of analytical methods for pharmaceuticals; investigation of rates and mechanisms of organic reactions; pharmaceutical product development. *Mailing Add:* Pharmaceut Div Ciba-Geigy Corp Summit NJ 07901

MOLLO-CHRISTENSEN, ERIK LEONARD, b Bergen, Norway, Jan 10, 23; nat US; m 48; c 3. FLUID DYNAMICS, OCEANOGRAPHY. *Educ:* Mass Inst Technol, SB, 48, SM, 49, ScD, 54. *Prof Exp:* Fel, Norweg Defense Res Estab, 48-49, sci officer, 49-51; res assoc, Mass Inst Technol, 54-55, asst prof aeronaut eng, 54-57; sr res fel, Calif Inst Technol, 57-58; from assoc prof to prof aeronaut, 58-64, prof meteorol, 64-76, PROF OCEANOG, MASS INST TECHNOL, 76- *Honors & Awards:* Von Karman Award, Am Inst Aeronaut & Astronaut, 70. *Mem:* Am Inst Aeronaut & Astronaut; Am Meteorol Soc; Am Phys Soc; Am Acad Arts & Sci; Am Geophys Union. *Res:* Fluid mechanics. *Mailing Add:* Dept Meteorol Mass Inst Technol Cambridge MA 02139

MOLLOW, BENJAMIN R, b Trenton, NJ, Nov 26, 38; m 67. THEORETICAL PHYSICS. *Educ:* Cornell Univ, AB, 60; Harvard Univ, PhD(physics), 66. *Prof Exp:* NSF fel physics, Brandeis Univ, 66-68, asst prof, 68-69; asst prof, physics, 69-73, ASSOC PROF PHYSICS, UNIV MASS, BOSTON, 73- *Res:* Quantum optics; light scattering; parametric processes. *Mailing Add:* Dept of Physics Univ of Mass Boston MA 02125

MOLLOY, ANDREW A, b New York, NY, Mar 19, 30; m 66; c 4. CHEMISTRY. *Educ:* Marist Col, BA, 51; Cath Univ, PhD(chem), 61. *Prof Exp:* Teacher parochial schs, 51-56; asst prof chem & chmn dept, Marist Col, 60-66; dir career serv, Elmira Col, 74-77, assoc prof chem, 66-80, dean grad & advan studies, 77-80; VPRES & PROF CHEM, MARIST COL, 80- *Mem:* Am Chem Soc. *Res:* Organotin chemistry; mechanism of paper chromatographic separation of lower fatty acids. *Mailing Add:* Academic VPres Marist College Poughkeepsie NY 12601

MOLLOY, CHARLES THOMAS, b New York, NY, Nov 22, 14; m 36; c 2. PHYSICS. *Educ:* Cooper Union, BS, 35; NY Univ, MS, 38, PhD(physics), 48. *Prof Exp:* Res chemist, Muralo Co, NY, 35-38; res engr, Johns Manville Co, NJ, 38-42; physicist, Brooklyn Navy Yard, 42-45 & Bell Tel Labs, Inc, 45-50; head, Physics Res Dept, Labs Div, Vitro Corp Am, 50-54; staff engr sound & vibration, Lockheed Aircraft Corp, 54-59; sr staff engr, TRW Systs Group, Calif, 59-70, SR STAFF ENGR, WASH OPERS, TRW SYSTS CORP, 70- *Concurrent Pos:* Instr, Long Island Univ, 42-45 & Brooklyn Col, 39-42; adj prof, Polytech Inst Brooklyn, 50-53, Univ Southern Calif, 57-70 & Univ Calif, Los Angeles, 59- *Honors & Awards:* Cert Appreciation, Soc Automotive Eng, 61; Spec Merit Award, Inst Environ Sci, 62, Irwin Vigness Award, 71. *Mem:* Fel Acoust Soc Am; Am Math Soc; Math Asn Am; Audio Eng Soc; sr mem Inst Elec & Electronics Eng. *Res:* Underwater acoustics; applied mathematics; propagation of sound in lined tubes; radiation theory; loud speaker design; hearing; sound absorbing materials; transients; sound and vibration problems associated with aircraft and missiles. *Mailing Add:* 2400 Claremont Dr Falls Church VA 22043

MOLLOY, MARILYN, b Caney, Kans, Apr 24, 31. MATHEMATICS. *Educ:* Our Lady of the Lake Col, BS, 55; Univ Tex, MA, 62, PhD(math) 66. *Prof Exp:* From instr to asst prof, 59-70, ASSOC PROF MATH, OUR LADY OF THE LAKE COL, 70-, ASSOC ACAD DEAN, 72-, PLANNING OFFICER, 77- *Mem:* Math Asn Am; Am Math Soc. *Res:* Mathematical analysis; Stieltjes integral. *Mailing Add:* Dept of Math Our Lady of the Lake Col San Antonio TX 78205

MOLLUZZO, JOHN CHARLES, mathematics, computer science, see previous edition

MOLMUD, PAUL, b Brooklyn, NY, May 29, 23; m 57; c 2. PHYSICS. *Educ:* Brooklyn Col, AB, 43; Ohio State Univ, PhD(physics), 51. *Prof Exp:* Jr engr, Nat Union Radio Corp, NJ, 43-45; asst prof physics, Clarkson Col Technol, 51-53; sr res scientist, 54-68, mgr, Theoret Physics Dept, 68-74, SR RES SCIENTIST, TRW SYSTS INC, 74- *Mem:* Sr mem Inst Elec & Electronics Eng; Am Phys Soc. *Res:* Gaseous electronics; ionospheric disturbances; plasma physics; electromagnetic properties of rocket exhausts; electromagnetic fields from nuclear explosions; rarefied gas dynamics. *Mailing Add:* Theoret Physics Dept TRW Systs Inc Bldg R1/1086 1 Space Park Redondo Beach CA 90278

MOLNAR, CHARLES EDWIN, b Newark, NJ, Mar 14, 35; m 57; c 2. NEUROPHYSIOLOGY, COMPUTER SCIENCE. *Educ:* Rutgers Univ, BS, 56, MS, 57; Mass Inst Technol, ScD(elec eng), 66. *Prof Exp:* Staff assoc, Lincoln Lab, Mass Inst Technol, 57-61; res electronics engr, Air Force Cambridge Res Labs, 64-65; assoc prof physiol & biophys, 65-71, assoc prof elec eng, 67-71, assoc dir comput systs lab, 67-72, PROF PHYSIOL & BIOPHYS & ELEC ENG, WASH UNIV, 71-, DIR COMPUT SYSTS LAB, 72- *Concurrent Pos:* Vis prof, Int Brain Res Orgn Vis Sem, Univ Chile, 67; mem comput & biomath study sect, NIH, 71-74, chmn, 74-75. *Res:* Experimental studies of auditory system; models for activity of single neurons and neural networks; design of computer systems for biological research; macromodular computer systems. *Mailing Add:* 471 Toft Lane St Louis MO 63119

MOLNAR, GEORGE D, b Szekesfehervar, Hungary, July 30, 22; Can citizen; m 47; c 2. ENDOCRINOLOGY, INTERNAL MEDICINE. *Educ:* Univ Alta, BSc, 49, MD, 51; Univ Minn, PhD(med), 56; Am Bd Internal Med, dipl, 59. *Prof Exp:* From instr to prof, Mayo Grad Sch Med, 56-73, prof med, Mayo Med Sch, Univ Minn, 73-75; PROF MED & CHMN DEPT, UNIV ALTA, 75- *Mem:* AMA; Am Diabetes Asn; fel Royal Col Physicians & Surgeons; Endocrine Soc; fel Am Col Physicians. *Res:* Unstable diabetes; endocrine correlates of the diabetic state; insulin resistance and diabetes mellitus, applied physiologic, biochemical and clinical aspects; hepatic metabolism of insulin; pancreatic islet transplantation. *Mailing Add:* Dept Med 8-121 Clin Sci Bldg Univ Alta Edmonton AB T6G 2G7 Can

MOLNAR, GEORGE WILLIAM, b Detroit, Mich, Feb 14, 14; m 37; c 2. PHYSIOLOGY. *Educ:* Oberlin Col, AB, 36; Yale Univ, PhD(zool), 40. *Prof Exp:* Asst biol, Yale Univ, 36-39; instr zool, Miami Univ, 40-42; asst prof, RI State Col, 42-44; instr physiol, Sch Med & Dent, Univ Rochester, 44-46; physiologist, Army Med Res Lab, Ft Knox, Ky, 46-62; physiologist, Res Lab, Kerrville, Tex, 62-66, coord prof serv, Southern Res Support Ctr, Little Rock, 66-68, res physiologist, Vet Admin Hosp, Little Rock, 68-80; RETIRED. *Mem:* Am Physiol Soc; NY Acad Sci. *Res:* Thermal physiology of man. *Mailing Add:* Vet Admin Hosp Little Rock AR 72206

MOLNAR, IMRE, b Budapest, Hungary, Oct 25, 06; nat US; TELECOMMUNICATIONS ENGINEERING. *Educ:* Univ Berlin, Dipl, 30; Northwestern Univ, PhD, 50. *Prof Exp:* Installer, Int Tel & Tel Corp, 21-24; engr, Automatic Elec Co, Gen Tel & Electronics Corp, 30-56, dir develop labs, 56-59, tech dir, Automatic Elec Int, Inc, 59-63; sr res engr, Stanford Res Inst, 63-66; CONSULT, STANDDARD OIL CO CALIF, BECHTEL, & TRW, 66- *Concurrent Pos:* Lectr, Univ Ill, San Jose State Col, Mich State Univ & Univ Santa Clara; exchange grant, Nat Acad Sci; US deleg, Int Telecommunication Union, 60-67. *Mem:* Inst Elec & Electronics Engrs; Am Numis Soc. *Res:* Wire and radio communications; control and electronics; probability and mathematical statistics; chemistry; numismatics. *Mailing Add:* 1040 Rilma Ln Los Altos CA 94022

MOLNAR, JANOS, b Budapest, Hungary, Nov 28, 27; US citizen; m 55; c 2. BIOCHEMISTRY. *Educ:* Eotvos Lorand Univ, Budapest, dipl, 53; Northwestern Univ, PhD(biochem), 60. *Prof Exp:* Instr chem, Med Univ Budapest, 53-56; res asst biochem, Northwestern Univ, 60-62; res asst, 62-65, from asst prof to assoc prof, 65-74, PROF BIOCHEM, UNIV ILL COL MED, 74- *Mem:* AAAS; Am Soc Biol Chemists; Reticuloendothelial Soc; Am Chem Soc. *Res:* Metabolism of glycoproteins; mechanism of photocytosis; cell membranes topography and surface antigens as related to cancer cells. *Mailing Add:* Dept Biochem Univ Ill Col Med Chicago IL 60612

MOLNAR, MICHAEL ROBERT, b Passaic, NJ, Sept 15, 45; m 76. ASTROPHYSICS, SPACE PHYSICS. *Educ:* Bucknell Univ, BS, 67; Univ Wis-Madison, PhD(astron), 70. *Prof Exp:* Univ Wis proj assoc satellite opers, OAO Prog, Goddard Space Flight Ctr, 70-71; res assoc satellite data anal, Lab Atmospheric & Space Physics, Univ Colo, 71-73; asst prof astron, Univ Toledo, 73-77, assoc prof, 77-70; MEM STAFF, HYCEL, INC, 80- *Concurrent Pos:* Guest investr & researcher grants, NASA, 73- *Mem:* Am Astron Soc; Int Astron Union. *Res:* Ultraviolet satellite observations of magnetic and chemically peculiar stars; development of astronomical instrumentation, especially echelle spectrographs, image tubes and solid state devices with computer interfacing and software development. *Mailing Add:* Hycel Inc PO Box 36329 Houston TX 77036

MOLNAR, PETER HALE, b Pittsburgh, Pa, Aug 25, 43; c 1. SEISMOLOGY, TECTONOPHYSICS. *Educ:* Oberlin Col, AB, 65; Columbia Univ, PhD(geol & seismol), 70. *Prof Exp:* Res scientist seismol, Lamont-Doherty Geol Observ, Columbia Univ, 70-71; asst res scientist, Scripps Inst Oceanog, Univ Calif, San Diego, 71-73; exchange scientist, Acad Sci, USSR, 73; asst prof, 74-76, ASSOC PROF EARTH SCI, MASS INST TECHNOL, 78- *Mem:* Am Geophys Union; Seismol Soc Am Geol; Royal Astron Soc; Am Asn Petrol Geologists. *Res:* Plate tectonics; earthquake source mechanism; structure of the earth; evolution of the ocean floor; geophysics; large scale continental tectonics. *Mailing Add:* Dept Earth & Planetary Sci Mass Inst Technol Cambridge MA 02139

MOLNAR, STEPHEN JAMES, somatic cell genetics, see previous edition

MOLNAR, STEPHEN P, b Toledo, Ohio, July 8, 35; m 64; c 2. ORGANIC CHEMISTRY, INORGANIC CHEMISTRY. *Educ:* Univ Toledo, BS, 57; Purdue Univ, MS, 63; Univ Cincinnati, PhD(chem), 67. *Prof Exp:* Res chemist, Owens Ill Glass Co, 59-60; teaching asst chem, Purdue Univ, 60-63; res fel, Univ Cincinnati, 63-65, teaching asst, 65-67; asst prof, Miami Univ, 67-75; res chemist, 75-78, SR RES CHEMIST, ARMCO INC, 78- *Mem:* AAAS; Am Chem Soc. *Res:* Chemical kinetics; complexes of Group VIII elements; electronic and chemical spectroscopy; polymer chemistry; thermal analysis of polymers. *Mailing Add:* Research & Technology Armco Inc Middletown OH 45043

MOLNAR, ZELMA VILLANYI, b Komotau, Czech, Jan 29, 31; US citizen; div; c 2. PATHOLOGY. *Educ:* Med Univ Budapest, MD, 56; Univ Chicago, PhD(path), 73. *Prof Exp:* Res asst, Dept Surg, Univ Chicago, 57-58 & Dept Anat, 58, from res asst to res assoc, Depts Anat & Physiol, 58-61, resident trainee, Dept Path, 61-65, from instr to asst prof path, 65-73; assoc prof, 73-79, PROF PATH, LOYOLA UNIV, 79- *Concurrent Pos:* Lectr, Cook County Grad Sch Med, 74- *Honors & Awards:* Hektoen Award, Chicago Path Soc, 65. *Mem:* AAAS; Col Am Path; Sigma Xi; Am Soc Hemat. *Mailing Add:* Vet Admin Hosp Box 1216 Hines IL 60141

MOLNIA, BRUCE FRANKLIN, b Bronx, NY, Oct 17, 45. MARINE GEOLOGY. *Educ:* State Univ NY Binghamton, BA, 67; Duke Univ, MA, 69; Univ SC, PhD(geol), 72. *Prof Exp:* Geophys res asst, Lamont Geol Observ, 65-67; res fel geol, Duke Univ, 67-69 & Univ SC, 70-72; teaching fel, Cornell Univ, 69-70; asst prof, Amherst Col & Mt Holyoke Col, 72-73; geol oceanogr, US Bur Land Mgt, 73-74, MARINE GEOLOGIST, US GEOL SURV, US DEPT INTERIOR, 74- *Concurrent Pos:* Sci ed, SC Educ TV Network, 71-73; consult, Environ Defense Fund, 73. *Mem:* Geol Soc Am; Am Geophys Union; Soc Econ Paleontologists & Mineralogists. *Res:* Environmental hazards in the marine continental shelf system; marine pleistocene and modern sedimentation; ice rafting; glacial, shoreline and fluvial systems. *Mailing Add:* US Geol Surv 345 Middlefield Rd Menlo Park CA 94025

MOLOF, ALAN H(ARTLEY), b Vineland, NJ, Dec 18, 28; m 52; c 4. ENVIRONMENTAL & SANITARY ENGINEERING. *Educ:* Bucknell Univ, BS, 49; Univ Mich, MSE, 51, MSE, 53, PhD(sanit & civil eng), 61. *Prof Exp:* Res & develop engr, Dorr-Oliver, Inc, Conn, 57-58; sanit engr, Lederle Labs Div, Am Cyanamid Co, NY, 58-62; assoc prof civil eng, NY Univ, 62-80; MEM FAC, POLYTECH INST, NY, 80- *Mem:* Water Pollution Control Fedn; Am Water Works Asn; Am Soc Civil Engrs; Am Chem Soc; Air Pollution Control Asn. *Res:* Wastewater treatment; stream and estuarine pollution; effluent and river monitoring; water supply; industrial waste treatment; air pollution. *Mailing Add:* Polytech Inst 333 Jay St Brooklyn NY 11201

MOLOMUT, NORMAN, b Newark, NJ, Jan 21, 13; m 38; c 3. ONCOLOGY. *Educ:* Brooklyn Col, AB, 34; Univ Mich, MA, 35; Columbia Univ, PhD(bact), 39. *Prof Exp:* Asst virus res, Pasteur Inst, Mich, 34-35; from asst bacteriologist to assoc bacteriologist, Dept Med, Col Physicians & Surgeons, Columbia Univ, 39-46; dir, Biol Labs, Inc, NY, 46-54; dir res, 47-77, SCI DIR, WALDEMAR MED RES FOUND, INC, 77- *Mem:* Am Soc Microbiol; Am Asn Immunol; Am Soc Cell Biol; NY Acad Sci. *Res:* Cell growth; wound healing stimulation with immune sera; cancer biotherapy; effect of immune factors and extracts of living organisms; physiological factors and mechanism of response in resistance to infectious disease agents; cancer immunology. *Mailing Add:* Waldmar Med Res Found Woodbury NY 11797

MOLONEY, JOHN BROMLEY, b Lowell, Mass, Jan 18, 24; m 49; c 2. BIOLOGY. *Educ:* Tufts Col, BS, 47; George Washington Univ, MS, 53, PhD, 59. *Prof Exp:* Biologist, Nat Cancer Inst, 47-60, supvry res biologist, 60-64, head viral leukemia sect, 64-66, assoc chief viral biol br, 66-67, chief, Viral Leukemia & Lymphoma Br, 67-70, assoc sci dir viral oncol & chmn, Spec Virus Cancer Prog, 70-77, asst dir, 77-80; CONSULT BIOMED RES, 80- *Mem:* AAAS; Am Asn Cancer Res; Soc Exp Biol & Med; Am Soc Microbiol. *Res:* Biological and biochemical properties of tumor viruses, especially the leukemia agents, a murine sarcoma virus and the Rous virus. *Mailing Add:* 6814 Greyswood Rd Bethesda MD 20817

MOLONEY, MICHAEL J, b Albany, NY, Nov 16, 36; m 64; c 3. MICROWAVE PHYSICS. *Educ:* Ill Inst Technol, BS, 58; Univ Md, PhD(physics), 66. *Prof Exp:* Asst prof physics, Rose-Hulman Inst Technol, 66-68 & Lafayette Col, 68-70; assoc prof physics, 70-76, chmn dept, 70-72, PROF PHYSICS, ROSE-HULMAN INST TECHNOL, 76- *Concurrent Pos:* NSF res partic, Univ Md, 68; electronics engr, Naval Weapons Support Ctr, Crane, Ind, 72- *Mem:* Am Asn Physics Teachers. *Res:* Computer assisted analysis of microwave spectra involving quadropole or centrifugal distortion effects. *Mailing Add:* Dept of Physics Rose-Hulman Inst of Technol Terre Haute IN 47803

MOLONEY, WILLIAM CURRY, b Boston, Mass, Dec 19, 07; m; c 4. HEMATOLOGY. *Educ:* Tufts Col, MD, 32. *Hon Degrees:* DSc, Col of the Holy Cross, 61. *Prof Exp:* From asst to clin prof med, Med Sch, Tufts Univ, 34-67; clin prof, 67-71, prof, 71-74, EMER PROF MED, HARVARD MED SCH, 74-; EMER PHYSICIAN & CHIEF HEMAT DIV, PETER BENT BRIGHAM HOSP, 67- *Concurrent Pos:* Consult, Boston Hosps, 38-; consult, Boston City Hosp, 48-, dir clin labs; dir res, Atomic Bomb Casualty Comn, Hiroshima, Japan, 52-54. *Mem:* AAAS; fel Am Fedn Clin Res; fel AMA; fel Am Col Physicians; Asn Am Physicians. *Res:* Leukemia. *Mailing Add:* Brigham & Women's Hosp 75 Francis St Boston MA 02115

MOLOTSKY, HYMAN MAX, b Russia, Nov 1, 19; nat US; m 52; c 3. CARBOHYDRATE CHEMISTRY. *Educ:* Univ Man, BSc, 43; Univ Mo, AM, 49, PhD(chem), 53. *Prof Exp:* Asst chem, McGill Univ, 45-46 & Univ Mo, 47-52; sr res chemist, Velsicol Corp, 52-55, proj leader, 55-57; res chemist, Richardson Co, 57-58, proj leader, 58-59; res chemist, Corn Prod Co, 59-64, sect leader basic & appl res, Moffett Tech Ctr, 64-66, patent liaison & tech coordr, Moffett Res, 66-74, asst to exec dir res & develop, Indust Div, 74-78, ASST TO V PRES RES & DEVELOP, CORN PRODS, MOFFETT TECH CTR, CPC INT INC, 78- *Mem:* Am Chem Soc; Sigma Xi; AAAS. *Res:* Derivatives of sugars and starch for industrial applications; intermediates for urethane foams; synthetic organic intermediates; intermediates for resins and plasticisers. *Mailing Add:* Moffett Tech Ctr CPC INT INC Box 345 Argo IL 60501

MOLT, JAMES TEUNIS, b Plainfield, NJ, Mar 31, 47; m 75; c 2. NEUROSCIENCES, NEUROPHYSIOLOGY. *Educ:* Colgate Univ, AB, 69; Cornell Univ, PhD(physiol), 74. *Prof Exp:* Instr physiol, Albany Med Col, 74-76, asst prof, 76-80; ASST PROF PHYSIOL, HAHNEMANN MED COL, PHILADELPHIA, 80- *Concurrent Pos:* Fel, Albany Med Col, 74-76; Nat Inst Neurol & Commun Dis & Stroke grant, 76-79. *Mem:* Soc Neurosci; AAAS; Am Physiol Soc. *Res:* Sensory processing in the mammalian nervous system; experimental spinal cord trauma. *Mailing Add:* Dept Physiol & Biophys Hahnemann Med Col 230 N Broad St Philadelphia PA 19102

MOLTENI, AGOSTINO, b Como, Italy, Nov 12, 33; US citizen; m; c 2. EXPERIMENTAL PATHOLOGY. *Educ:* Univ Milan, MD, 57; Ital Bd Internal Med, cert, 63; State Univ NY Buffalo, PhD(path), 70. *Prof Exp:* Asst prof med, Univ Milano, 58-62; sr investr med res, Farmitalia, Milan, Italy, 63-65; Henry C & Bertha Buswell fel & res asst prof path, State Univ NY Buffalo, 70-72; assoc prof path, Univ Kans Med Ctr, Kansas City, 73-76; PROF PATH, NORTHWESTERN UNIV SCH MED, CHICAGO, 76- *Concurrent Pos:* NIH res career develop award, 72; consult path, Vet Admin Hosp, Kansas City, 73- *Honors & Awards:* Sharer, Albert E Lasker Award, 80. *Mem:* AMA; Am Soc Exp Path; Endocrine Soc; Am Soc Exp Biol & Med; Reticuloendothelial Soc. *Res:* Cardiovascular diseases, especially systemic and pulmonary hypertension. *Mailing Add:* Dept of Path Northwestern Univ Med Sch Chicago IL 60611

MOLTZAN, HERBERT JOHN, b Chicago, Ill, May 26, 33; m 55, 76; c 5. PROCESS CHEMISTRY. *Educ:* Ill Inst Technol, BS, 56; St Louis Univ, MS, 60. *Prof Exp:* Res chemist, Monsanto Co, 56-61, Vulcan Mat Corp, 61-65; sr engr, 65-66, mgr, EPI Eng, 66-68, mem tech staff, 68-76, SUPVR, PLASTICS LAB, TEX INSTRUMENTS, 76- *Mem:* Am Chem Soc; Electrochem Soc. *Res:* Electronic grade silicon; circuit boards; quartz; chloromethylations; plasticizer synthesis; catalytic hydrogenations; use and characterization of polymers for electronics. *Mailing Add:* 6935 Northaven Dallas TX 75230

MOLVIK, ARTHUR WARREN, b L'Anse, Mich, Mar 19, 43; m 68; c 3. PHYSICS. *Educ:* Concordia Col, Moorhead, Minn, BA, 64; Univ Wis-Madison, MA, 66, PhD(physics), 71. *Prof Exp:* PHYSICIST, LAWRENCE LIVERMORE LAB, 72- *Mem:* Am Phys Soc. *Res:* Magnetic confinement of thermonuclear plasmas; neutral beam and radio frequency heating of plasmas; minimum hamming distance stability. *Mailing Add:* 666 Hayes Ave Livermore CA 94550

MOLYNEUX, JOHN ECOB, b Philadelphia, Pa, May 19, 35; m 62; c 2. APPLIED MATHEMATICS, MECHANICAL ENGINEERING. *Educ:* Univ Pa, BS, 57, MS, 61, PhD(mech eng), 64. *Prof Exp:* Res scientist, Courant Inst Math Sci, NY Univ, 64-65; asst prof, 65-68, ASSOC PROF MECH & AEROSPACE SCI, UNIV ROCHESTER, 68- *Mem:* Soc Indust & Appl Math. *Res:* Statistical continuum theory; wave propagation in random media; effective material properties of random media; stochastic heat and mass transport. *Mailing Add:* Dept of Mech & Aerospace Sci River Campus Sta Rochester NY 14627

MOLYNEUX, RUSSELL JOHN, b Luton, Eng, Aug 3, 38; m 63; c 2. ORGANIC CHEMISTRY. *Educ:* Univ Nottingham, BSc, 60, PhD(org chem), 63. *Prof Exp:* NSF fel org chem, Univ Ore, 63-65; asst prof forest prod chem, Ore State Univ, 65-67; res assoc, 67-74, RES CHEMIST, WESTERN REGIONAL RES CTR, AGR RES SERV, USDA, 74- *Concurrent Pos:* Consult, US Brewers Asn, 68-74. *Mem:* Am Chem Soc; Royal Soc Chem; Phytochem Soc. *Res:* Naturally occurring quinones; naturally occurring phenolic compounds; constituents of toxic range plants; pyrrolizidine alkaloids; indolizidine alkaloids. *Mailing Add:* Western Regional Res Ctr Agr Res Serv 800 Buchanan St Albany CA 94710

MOLZ, FRED JOHN, b Mays Landing, NJ, Aug 13, 43; m 66; c 2. HYDROLOGY, SOIL PHYSICS. *Educ:* Drexel Univ, BS, 66, MSCE, 68; Stanford Univ, PhD(hydrol), 70. *Prof Exp:* From asst prof to alumni assoc prof, 70-80, DIR ENG EXP STA, ASST DEAN RES & PROF CIVIL ENG, AUBURN UNIV, 80- *Concurrent Pos:* Off Water Resources res grants Auburn Univ, 71-77; consult various private & govt agencies, 72-; Fed Hwy Admin res grant, 74-76; US Geol Survey res grant, 75-77; Dept Energy res grant, 77-79; vis prof, Univ Ill, 77; Battelle Aquifer Storage res grant, 80- *Mem:* Am Geophys Union; Am Soc Agron; Soil Sci Soc Am; Nat Water Well Asn; Am Soc Plant Physiol. *Res:* Transport process in the groundwater-soil-plant-atmosphere system including physical, mathematical, biological and engineering aspects. *Mailing Add:* Eng Exp Sta Auburn Univ Auburn AL 36849

MOMBERG, HAROLD LESLIE, b Sedalia, Mo, Mar 24, 29. ZOOLOGY, HISTOLOGY. *Educ:* Cent Mo State Col, BS, 51; Univ Mo, MA, 55, PhD(zool), 61. *Prof Exp:* Head dept biol, Hannibal-LaGrange Col, 55-57; instr zool, Univ Mo, 57-58; from assoc prof to prof biol, histol & embryol, William Jewell Col, 60-67, NSF res grant, 64-66; assoc prof biol, Cent Mo State Col, 67-69; assoc prof biol, 70-75, PROF BIOL, CENT METHODIST COL, 75-, HEAD, DEPT BIOL & GEOL, 74- *Mem:* AAAS; Am Soc Zoologists. *Res:* Mammalian implantation patterns and cycles; histochemistry and physiology of reproductive tract. *Mailing Add:* Dept of Biol Cent Methodist Col Fayette MO 65248

MOMENT, GAIRDNER BOSTWICK, b Brooklyn, NY, May 4, 05; m 37; c 5. DEVELOPMENTAL BIOLOGY. *Educ:* Princeton Univ, AB, 28; Yale Univ, PhD(zool), 32. *Prof Exp:* From instr to prof biol, 32-70, chmn dept, 45-58, EMER PROF BIOL SCI, GOUCHER COL, 70- *Concurrent Pos:* Lectr, Mt Desert Biol Lab, 38-39; vis assoc prof, Johns Hopkins Univ, 44-45; assoc prog dir inst sect, NSF, 60-61, chmn exec comt, Comn Undergrad Educ in Biol Sci, 63-66; prog coordr biol series, Voice of Am, 60-61; secy-gen, XVI Int Cong Zool, DC, 60-63; NIH guest scientist, Geront Res Ctr, Nat Inst Aging, Baltimore, Md, 70-; ed-in-chief, Growth, 72-; grants, Am Philos Soc, Am Cancer Soc, NIH & NSF; investr, Woods Hole Biol Lab& Beauford Biol Lab; investr & mem corp, Bermuda Biol Lab; mem, Gov Sci Adv Coun, 74- *Mem:* Fel AAAS; Am Soc Zoologists (secy, 57-60); Soc Develop Biol; Soc Gen Physiol; Am Inst Biol Sci. *Res:* Animal development and behavior; biochemical, electrical and anatomical study of animal growth; general biology; annelids; protein electrophoresis; regeneration; tissue culture. *Mailing Add:* Dept of Biosci Goucher Col Baltimore MD 21204

MOMMAERTS, WILFRIED, b Broechem, Belg, Mar 4, 17; nat US; m 44; c 3. PHYSIOLOGY. *Educ:* State Univ Leiden, BA, 37, MA, 39; Kolozsvar Univ, Hungary, PhD(biol, phys chem), 43. *Prof Exp:* Vis assoc prof biochem, Am Univ Beirut, 45-46, adj prof biochem & lectr phys chem, 46-47, assoc prof physiol, 47-48; res assoc biochem, Duke Univ, 48-53; assoc prof, Case Western Reserve Univ, 53-56; PROF MED & PHYSIOL, SCH MED, UNIV CALIF, LOS ANGELES, 56-, CHMN DEPT PHYSIOL, 66- *Concurrent Pos:* Estab investr, Am Heart Asn, 49-59; dir res lab, Los Angeles Heart Asn, 55-; conseiller exceptionel, Nat Inst Health & Med Res, France. *Honors & Awards:* DHc, Dijon Med Sch, France, 76. *Mem:* Biophys Soc; Am Physiol Soc; Am Heart Asn; fel Am Acad Arts & Sci. *Res:* Molecular physiology and biochemistry of contractile tissues; physical chemistry of tissue proteins and cellular processes; functional influences upon differential gene expression. *Mailing Add:* Dept of Physiol Univ of Calif Sch of Med Los Angeles CA 90024

MOMOT, WALTER THOMAS, b Hamtramck, Mich, Oct 12, 38; m 66; c 1. FISH BIOLOGY. *Educ:* Wayne State Univ, BS, 60; Univ Mich, MS, 61, PhD(fisheries), 64. *Prof Exp:* Asst prof zool, Univ Okla, 64; from instr to assoc prof, Ohio State Univ, 64-75; PROF ZOOL, LAKEHEAD UNIV, 75- *Mem:* AAAS; Am Fisheries Soc; Am Soc Limnol & Oceanog; Ecol Soc Am; Am Inst Fishery Res Biol. *Res:* Production, population dynamics, trophic ecology of fish and crayfish populations. *Mailing Add:* Dept of Biol Lakehead Univ Thunder Bay ON P7B 5E1 Can

MOMPARLER, RICHARD LEWIS, b New York, NY, Jan 6, 35; m 66. PHARMACOLOGY, BIOCHEMISTRY. *Educ:* Mich State Univ, BS, 57; Univ Vt, PhD(pharmacol), 66. *Prof Exp:* USPHS fel, Yale Univ, 64-65 & Int Lab Genetics, Italy, 66; asst prof biochem, McGill Univ, 67-74; assoc prof pharmacol, Sch Med, Univ Southern Calif, 74-77; PROF PHARMACOL, SCH MED, UNIV MONTREAL, 77- *Mem:* AAAS. *Res:* Cancer chemotherapy; enzymes; cell cycle; DNA replication. *Mailing Add:* Ctr Pediat Res Hosp Ste-Justine Montreal PQ H3T 1C5 Can

MONACELLA, VINCENT JOSEPH, b Erie, Pa, May 2, 26; m 61; c 4. HYDRODYNAMICS. *Educ:* Gannon Col, BS, 48. *Prof Exp:* Mathematician, David Taylor Model Basin, 53-54, physicist, 54-67, physicist, Naval Ship Res & Develop Ctr, 67-70, head, Submarine Dynamics Br, 70-71, asst res, David W Taylor Naval Ship Res & Develop Ctr, 71-74, asst res & develop, 74-81, ASST DESIGN SUPPORT & RES, DAVID W TAYLOR NAVAL SHIP RES & DEVELOP CTR, BETHESDA, MD, 81- *Mem:* Soc Naval Archit & Marine Eng. *Res:* Ship hydrodynamics; water waves; analysis of motions, forces and moments of arbitrary bodies in proximity of a fluid surface. *Mailing Add:* 2908 Hideaway Rd Fairfax VA 22031

MONACK, A(LBERT) J(AMES), b Charleroi, Pa, Dec 30, 04; m 26. MECHANICS. *Educ:* WVa Univ, BS, 27; Univ Ill, MS, 29; NY Univ, PhD(eng ed), 62. *Prof Exp:* Asst, Univ Ill, 29-32; consult engr, Pa, 32-35; develop engr, Western Elec Co, NY, 35-39; with Radio Corp Am, NJ, 39-42; vpres & dir eng, Mycalex Corp Am, 42-46; asst prof physics & chmn dept, Fairleigh Dickinson Col, 47-50, asst prof sci & eng, 50-54; asst prof physics, Newark Col Eng, 54-60, assoc prof, 60-66, prof, 66-70, EMER PROF APPL MECH, NJ INST TECHNOL, 70- *Concurrent Pos:* Instr, Cooper Union, 39-42; consult engr, 46- *Res:* Inorganic electrical insulations; glass-metal seals; machinable ceramic composition of high dielectric constant; engineering materials; applied mechanics; properties of materials. *Mailing Add:* 287 Mortimer Ave Rutherford NJ 07070

MONACO, ANTHONY PETER, b Philadelphia, Pa, Mar 12, 32; m 60; c 4. SURGERY, IMMUNOLOGY. *Educ:* Univ Pa, BA, 52; Harvard Med Sch, MD, 56. *Prof Exp:* From intern to resident surg, Mass Gen Hosp, 56-63; Am Cancer Soc fel, 63-67, from instr to assoc prof, 63-76, PROF SURG & CHIEF TRANSPLANTATION DIV, HARVARD MED SCH, 76- *Concurrent Pos:* Lederly fac award, 67-70; ed, Transplantation, 69-; chief transplantation unit, Harvard Surg Serv, New Eng Deaconess Hosp; pres, Interhosp Organ Bank New Eng, 73- *Mem:* Am Asn Immunol; Transplantation Soc (treas, 70, secy, 74-78, vpres, 78-). *Res:* Transplantation immunology and immunobiology; experimental and clinical transplantation. *Mailing Add:* Dept of Surg Harvard Med Sch Boston MA 02115

MONACO, LAWRENCE HENRY, b Philadelphia, Pa, Mar 31, 25; m 54; c 5. ZOOLOGY. *Educ:* LaSalle Col, BA, 49; Univ Notre Dame, MS, 52, PhD(parasitol), 54. *Prof Exp:* Instr biol sci, Del Mar Col, 54-57 & Villa Madonna Col, 57-58; from instr to assoc prof, 58-61, head dept, 61-66, dean, 66-82, PROF BIOL SCI, DUTCHESS COMMUNITY COL, 61- *Concurrent Pos:* Consult, Culinary Inst Am, 82- *Mem:* Am Inst Biol Sci; Sigma Xi. *Res:* Gill parasites of fish. *Mailing Add:* 6 Thorndale Ave Poughkeepsie NY 12603

MONAGHAN, PATRICK HENRY, b Memphis, Tenn, July 25, 22; m 43; c 2. GEOCHEMISTRY, PETROLEUM ENGINEERING. *Educ:* La Polytech Inst, BS, 43; La State Univ, MS, 49, PhD(chem), 50. *Prof Exp:* Field engr, Sperry Gyroscope Co, 46-47; instr chem, La State Univ, 49-50; asst res engr, Prod Res Div, Humble Oil & Ref Co, 50-51, from res engr to sr res engr, 51-59, from res specialist to sr res specialist, 59-65; res assoc, 65-73, res adv, 73-81, SR RES ADV, EXXON PROD RES CO, 81- *Mem:* AAAS; Am Asn Petrol Geologists; Am Chem Soc; Soc Econ Paleontologists & Mineralogists; Am Inst Mining, Metall & Petrol Eng. *Res:* Oil well drilling and completion techniques; geochemistry; instrumental analysis; organic geochemistry; petroleum geology; environmental management. *Mailing Add:* Exxon Prod Res Co Box 2189 Houston TX 77001

MONAGLE, DANIEL J, b Eddystone, Pa, Oct 14, 36; m 61; c 6. ORGANIC POLYMER CHEMISTRY. *Educ:* Mt St Mary's Col Md, BS, 58; Duquesne Univ, MS, 60; Univ Del, PhD(org polymer chem), 67. *Prof Exp:* Chemist, Hercules Res Ctr, Del, 60-65; lectr anal & gen chem, Univ Del, 65-66; res chemist, 66-70, res supvr coatings & spec prod, 70-77, mgr mat sci, 77-78, DIR TECHNOL WATER SOLUBLE POLYMERS, HERCULES RES CTR, 78- *Mem:* Am Chem Soc; Sigma Xi. *Res:* Synthesis process development, characterization and applications of synthetic water-soluble polymers, particularly polyelectrolytes; coatings; pigments; magnetic materials; cellulose and water soluble cellulose derivatives. *Mailing Add:* 605 Halstead Rd Sharpley Wilmington DE 19803

MONAGLE, JOHN JOSEPH, JR, b Chester, Pa, Feb 2, 29; m 54; c 5. ORGANIC CHEMISTRY. *Educ:* Villanova Univ, BS, 50; Polytech Inst Brooklyn, PhD(chem), 54. *Prof Exp:* Res chemist, Sinclair Res Labs, Inc, 54-56 & Jackson Lab, E I du Pont de Nemours & Co, 56-61; from asst prof to assoc prof chem, NMex State Univ, 61-63, prof & head dept, 63-67; prof, Univ Ala, Tuscaloosa, 67-68; dean col arts & sci, 68-70, assoc dir res ctr arts & sci, 70-71, PROF CHEM, NMEX STATE UNIV, 68-, ASSOC DEAN ARTS & SCI & DIR, ARTS RES CTR, 75- *Concurrent Pos:* Consult, Melpar Corp, 64. *Mem:* Am Chem Soc; Nat Coun Univ Res Adminrs; Soc Res Adminrs; AAAS. *Res:* Synthetic and physical organic chemistry; polymer chemistry; synthesis and properties of organophosphorus compounds; organic chemistry of polymers. *Mailing Add:* Col of Art & Sci NMex State Univ Box RC Las Cruces NM 88003

MONAHAN, ALAN RICHARD, b Schenectady, NY, June 17, 39; m 62; c 6. PHYSICAL CHEMISTRY, POLYMER CHEMISTRY. *Educ:* Rensselaer Polytech Inst, BChE, 61, PhD(phys chem), 64. *Prof Exp:* Sr chemist gaseous electronics res br, 64-66, scientist chem physics res br, 66-69, sr scientist org solid state physics res br, 69-71, prin scientist, Corp Physics Lab, 71-72, mgr org solid state physics area, 72-75, mgr-developer, Mat Technol Ctr, 75-78, MGR EXPLOR MAT AREA, XEROX CORP, 78- *Mem:* Am Chem Soc. *Res:* Thermal and photochemical conversions in polymers; photochromics; organic photoconductors; analytical chemistry; molecular spectroscopy; physical properties of dyes and pigments; research and development of of xerographic developer materials (toners and carriers); coating technology; small particle processing. *Mailing Add:* Xerox Corp 800 Phillips Rd Webster NY 14580

MONAHAN, AUDREY SMALL, see Miller, Audrey

MONAHAN, EDWARD CHARLES, b Bayonne, NJ, July 25, 36; m 60; c 3. OCEANOGRAPHY. *Educ:* Cornell Univ, BEP, 59; Univ Tex, Austin, MA, 61; Mass Inst Technol, PhD(oceanog), 66. *Prof Exp:* Res asst, Woods Hole Oceanog Inst, 64-65; asst prof physics, Northern Mich Univ, 65-68; asst prof oceanog, Hobart & William Smith Cols, 68-69; from asst prof to assoc prof oceanog, Univ Mich, Ann Arbor, 69-75; dir educ & res, Sea Educ Asn, Woods Hole, 75-76; STATUTORY LECTR PHYS OCEANOG, DEPT OCEANOG, UNIV COL, GALWAY, IRELAND, 76- *Concurrent Pos:* Adj assoc prof, Boston Univ, 75-76; Haltiner res chair prof, Naval Postgrad Sch, 81-82. *Mem:* Royal Meteorol Soc; Int Asn Theoret & Appl Limnol; Am Meteorol Soc; Am Geophys Union; Am Soc Limnol & Oceanog. *Res:* Air-sea interaction; marine aerosols; physical limnology; teaching of oceanography and meteorology; oceanographic instrumentation; design of drogues and drifters. *Mailing Add:* Dept Oceanog Univ Col Galway Ireland

MONAHAN, HUBERT HARVEY, b Oshkosh, Wis, Jan 14, 22; m 53. RESEARCH METEOROLOGY, OPERATIONAL WEATHER FORECASTING. *Educ:* Wis State Col, Oshkosh, BS, 47; Univ Wis-Madison, BBA, 59. *Prof Exp:* Weather officer forecasting, US Air Force, Dept Defense, 50-57; meteorologist, Atmospheric Sci Off, US Army Electronics Command, 59-61; staff weather officer, US Air Force, Dept Defense, 62-65; supvr meteorologist, US Weather Bur, Nat Oceanic & Atmospheric Admin, 66-67; meteorologist res, Atmospheric Sci Lab, US Army Electronics Command, 67-77; meteorologist climat, Atmospheric Sci Lab, US Army Electronics Res & Develop Command, NMex, 77-80; RETIRED. *Res:* Mesoscale time and space variability of low level meteorological phenomena and short term weather predictions for application of effects to Army tactical weapons systems. *Mailing Add:* 4723 Larkspur Ct El Paso TX 79924

MONAHAN, JAMES EMMETT, b Kansas City, Mo, Jan 10, 25; m 48. THEORETICAL PHYSICS. *Educ:* Rockhurst Col, BS, 48; St Louis Univ, MS, 50, PhD(physics, math), 53. *Prof Exp:* SR PHYSICIST, ARGONNE NAT LAB, 51- *Concurrent Pos:* Weizmann fel, 66-67; prof lectr, St Louis Univ, 66-; vis scientist, Univ Ohio, 71- *Mem:* Am Phys Soc. *Res:* Theoretical nuclear physics. *Mailing Add:* Physics Div-203 Argonne Nat Lab 9700 S Cass Ave Argonne IL 60439

MONAHAN, JOHN JAMES, b Dublin, Ireland, Oct 26, 46; m 77; c 1. MOLECULAR BIOLOGY, CELL BIOLOGY. *Educ:* Univ Dublin, BSc, 69; McMaster Univ, PhD(biochem), 73. *Prof Exp:* Fel biochem, McMaster Univ, 73-74; res assoc cell biol, Baylor Col Med, 74-75, instr, 75-77; ASST MEM CELL BIOL, ROCHE INST MOLECULAR BIOL, 77-; ASST PROF CELL BIOL, NY UNIV, 80- *Concurrent Pos:* Med Res Coun Can fel, 74-75; NIH fel, 76-77. *Res:* Gene regulation in eucaryotic cell; genetic engineering. *Mailing Add:* Dept of Cell Biol Roche Inst of Molecular Biol Nutley NJ 07110

MONARD, JOYCE ANNE, nuclear physics, nuclear engineering, see previous edition

MONARO, SERGIO, b Padua, Italy, Apr 29, 32; m 66. NUCLEAR PHYSICS. *Educ:* Univ Milan, Doctorate, 59; Univ Rome, Libera Docenza, 67. *Prof Exp:* Fel, Nat Inst Nuclear Physics, Naples, 60-61, Inst Nuclear Physics Res, Amsterdam, 61, Nat Inst Nuclear Physics, Naples, 61-62 & Brookhaven Nat Lab, 62-63; physicist, Euratom, Ispra-Varese, Italy, 64-65; PROF PHYSICS, UNIV MONTREAL, 65- *Mem:* Am Phys Soc. *Res:* Nuclear spectroscopy; nuclear reactions at low energy. *Mailing Add:* Dept of Physics Univ of Montreal Montreal PQ H3C 3J7 Can

MONCHAMP, ROCH ROBERT, b Manchester, NH, Sept 27, 31; m 69; c 3. SOLID STATE CHEMISTRY, CRYSTAL GROWTH. *Educ:* St Anselms Col, AB, 53; Mass Inst Technol, PhD(chem), 59. *Prof Exp:* Sr res chemist, Res Lab, Merck & Co, 59-63; mgr crystal growth res & develop, Airtron Div, Litton Precision Prod, Inc, NJ, 64-67 & Raytheon Co, 67-73; chief engr, Saphikon Div, Tyco Labs, Inc, 73-75; MGR CRYSTAL GROWTH DEPT, ADOLF MELLER CO, 75- *Mem:* AAAS; Am Asn Crystal Growth; fel Am Inst Chemists. *Res:* Semiconductors; lasers and acoustic crystals; crystal growth; hydrothermal synthesis. *Mailing Add:* Adolf Meller Co PO Box 6001 Providence RI 02904

MONCHICK, LOUIS, b Brooklyn, NY, Dec 27, 27; m 66. CHEMICAL PHYSICS. *Educ:* Boston Univ, AB, 48, MA, 51, PhD(chem), 54. *Prof Exp:* Cloud physicist, Air Force Cambridge Res Ctr, 53-54; fel radiation chem, Univ Notre Dame, 54-56; res assoc fused salts, Knolls Atomic Power Lab, Gen Elec Co, 56-57; CHEMIST, APPL PHYSICS LAB, JOHNS HOPKINS UNIV, 57-, LECTR DEPT CHEM ENG, 80- *Concurrent Pos:* Assoc prof chem, Johns Hopkins Univ, 68-69, vis prof chem, 75-76. *Mem:* Am Chem Soc; Am Phys Soc. *Res:* Diffusion controlled reactions; kinetic theory of gases; intermolecular forces; molecular collisions. *Mailing Add:* Johns Hopkins Univ Appl Phys Lab Johns Hopkins Rd Laurel MD 20810

MONCRIEF, EUGENE CHARLES, b Washington, DC, July 7, 32; m 55; c 1. ENGINEERING MANAGEMENT. *Educ:* Va Polytech Inst, BS, 54, MS, 55, PhD(chem eng), 57. *Prof Exp:* Res assoc chem eng, Sterling Forest Lab, Union Carbide Nuclear Co, 57-58; develop specialist, Oak Ridge Nat Lab, 58-63; tech adv, Res & Develop Div, Nuclear Develop Ctr, Babcock & Wilcox Co, 63-64, sect chief, 64-69, mgr process develop commercial nuclear fuel, 69-71, mgr fuel contract, Fuel Dept, 61, mgr qual & tech serv, NUMEC, 71-73, mgr mfg, 73-76, gen mgr, indust & marine div, 76-77, vpres, Indust & Marine Div, 77-81, SR VPRES, FOSSIL POWER & CONSTRUCT GROUP, BABCOCK & WILCOX CO, 81- *Concurrent Pos:* Vis lectr, Darden Grad Sch Bus Admin, Univ Va, 78- *Mem:* Am Nuclear Soc; Am Inst Chem Engrs; Soc Naval Architects & Marine Engrs; Am Mgt Soc; Tech Asn Pulp & Paper Indust. *Res:* Uranium and tungsten separation technology; nuclear fuel reprocessing and cycle development; nuclear chemical engineering; utility and industrial boiler manufacture and development. *Mailing Add:* 300 Sand Run Rd Akron OH 44313

MONCRIEF, JOHN WILLIAM, b Brunswick, Ga, Jan 23, 41; m 63; c 3. CHEMISTRY. *Educ:* Emory Univ, BS, 63; Harvard Univ, PhD(phys chem), 66. *Prof Exp:* Asst prof chem, Amherst Col, 66-68; from asst prof to assoc prof, Emory Univ, Atlanta, 68-76, PROF CHEM, DEAN & DIV EXEC, OXFORD COL EMORY UNIV, 76- *Concurrent Pos:* Res grants, NIH, 66-70, Eli Lilly, 68-69, NSF, 71-74, & Sloan fel, Emory Univ, 68-70. *Mem:* Am Chem Soc; Am Crystallog Asn; Sigma Xi. *Res:* X-ray crystallography; structures of organic and inorganic molecules; relation of mechanism to structures. *Mailing Add:* Off of the Dean Oxford Col of Emory Univ Oxford GA 30267

MONCRIEFF-YEATES, ALEXANDER JOHN, b Dublin, Ireland, Aug 1, 26; US citizen; m 50; c 4. EXPERIMENTAL PHYSICS, COMPUTER ENGINEERING. *Educ:* Trinity Col, Dublin, BA, 48; Univ Dublin, BS, 48, MS, 50. *Prof Exp:* Researcher photoconductivity, RCA Res Labs, 50-55; chief physicist aircraft instruments, Aeronaut Div, Robertshaw-Fulton, 55-56; res dir aerospace, Res Labs Div, Conrac Corp, 56-62; res dir, Marine Acoust Serv, 62-66; pres, Consult Serv, 66-74; PRES, AEROHEATOR CORP, 75- *Concurrent Pos:* NASA res grant, 52; res contracts, US Air Force Wright-Patterson Ctr, 54; consult, Dade Reagents Div, Am Hosp Supply, 66-69; radiol officer, Amecom Div, Litton Indust Inc, 69-74; res dir comput technol, Eng Systs Corp, 74-76. *Mem:* Fel Royal Phys Soc Gt Brit. *Res:* Energy research; aerodynamic heat exchangers; plasma physics; computer research; microprocessors; medical instrumentation. *Mailing Add:* Aeroheator Corp Box 1461 Springfield VA 22151

MONCTON, DAVID EUGENE, b New York, NY, Oct 7, 48; m 75. SOLID STATE PHYSICS. *Educ:* Cornell Univ, BS, 70; Mass Inst Technol, MS, 73, PhD(physics), 75. *Prof Exp:* MEM TECH STAFF PHYSICS RES, BELL LABS, 75- *Mem:* Am Phys Soc. *Res:* X-ray and neutron scattering studies of condensed matter systems. *Mailing Add:* Bell Labs 600 Mountain Ave Murray Hill NJ 07974

MONCUR, NORMAN KENT, b Lovell, Wyo, Mar 26, 39; m 63; c 2. PHYSICS. *Educ:* San Jose State Col, BS, 62; Mich State Univ, MS, 64, PhD(physics), 67. *Prof Exp:* Staff assoc laser physics, Gulf Gen Atomic, 67-68; sr res scientist laser physics, 68-80, MGR, LASER DIV, KMS FUSION INC, 80- *Res:* Laser fusion. *Mailing Add:* KMS Fusion Inc PO Box 1567 Ann Arbor MI 48106

MONCURE, HENRY, JR, b Stafford, Va, Feb 16, 30; m 55; c 4. ORGANIC POLYMER CHEMISTRY. *Educ:* Univ Va, BS, 51, PhD(org chem), 58. *Prof Exp:* Instr, US Naval Acad, 53-55; NIH fel, Cambridge Univ, 58-59; from chemist to sr res chemist, 59-68, from res supvr to sr supvr, 68-74, res mgr, Plastics Prod & Resins Dept, 74-80, TECH MGR, POLYMER PROD DEPT, E I DU PONT DE NEMOURS & CO, INC, 80- *Mem:* Am Chem Soc. *Res:* Ring chain tautomerism; aromatic polymides; polymer stability; composite polymers; fluorocarbon polymers, plastics for use in harsh environments; engineering plastics. *Mailing Add:* 1601 Woodsdale Rd Bellvue Manor Wilmington DE 19809

MOND, BERTRAM, b New York, NY, Aug 24, 31; m 57; c 3. MATHEMATICS. *Educ:* Yeshiva Univ, BA, 51; Bucknell Univ, MA, 59; Univ Cincinnati, PhD(math), 63. *Prof Exp:* Mech comput analyst, Gen Elec Co, 59-60; res assoc biomet, Col Med & instr math, Univ Cincinnati, 62-63; res mathematician, Aerospace Res Labs, Wright-Patterson AFB, Ohio, 63-69; dean, Sch Phys Sci, 76-78, PROF MATH, LA TROBE UNIV, 69-, CHMN DEPT, 70- *Concurrent Pos:* Lectr eve col, Univ Cincinnati, 61-64; ed, J Australian Math Soc, 69-74, mem coun, 69-74. *Mem:* Am Math Soc; Australian Math Soc. *Res:* Operations research; linear and nonlinear programming; approximation theory. *Mailing Add:* Dept of Math La Trobe Univ Bundoora 3083 Melbourne Australia

MONDER, CARL, b US, Aug 24, 28; m 59; c 2. BIOCHEMISTRY. *Educ:* City Col New York, BS, 50; Cornell Univ, MS, 52; Univ Wis, PhD(biochem), 56. *Prof Exp:* Assoc technologist, Res Lab, Gen Foods Corp, 52-54; USPHS fel, Sch Med, Tufts Univ, 56-57; from instr to asst prof biochem, Albert Einstein Col Med, 58-69; res assoc prof, 69-78, prof biochem & sci, Mt Sinai Sch Med, 78-81; head, Sect Steroid Studies, Res Inst Skeletomuscular Dis, Hosp for Joint Dis, 64-81; SR SCIENTIST, POPULATION COUN, NY, 81- *Concurrent Pos:* Vis prof chem, Stevens Inst Technol, 63-69; USPHS career develop award, 69-74; adj prof biochem & adj prof pediat, Cornell Med Sch, 81- *Mem:* AAAS; Am Soc Biol Chem; Am Chem Soc; Endocrine Soc; NY Acad Sci. *Res:* steroid chemistry and metabolism; hormone action; perinatal metabolism and development; tumor metabolism. *Mailing Add:* Population Coun 1230 York Ave New York NY 10021

MONDOLFO, L(UCIO) F(AUSTO), b Senigallia, Italy, Aug 20, 10; nat US; m 35; c 2. METALLURGY, MATERIALS SCIENCE. *Educ:* Univ Bologna, BS, 29; Milan Polytech Inst, Dr Sc(indust eng), 33. *Prof Exp:* Metallurgist, Isotta Fraschini, Italy, 35-38; metallurgist, US Reduction Co, Ill, 39; chemist, R Lavin Sons, 39-40; res metallurgist, Reynolds Metals Co, Ky, 40-41, asst chief res metallurgist, NY, 43-45; chief metallurgist, Howard Foundry, Ill, 42-43; assoc prof metall, Ill Inst Technol, 46-59, prof, 51-65, head dept, 55-65; sr res metallurgist, Revere Copper & Brass, Inc, 66-76; CONSULT, 76- *Concurrent Pos:* Adj prof, Rensselaer Polytech Inst, 78. *Mem:* AAAS; Am Soc Metals; Am Inst Mining, Metall & Petrol Engrs; Am Inst Chem; Brit Metals Soc. *Res:* Aluminum alloys; crystallization. *Mailing Add:* RD 1 Clinton NY 13323

MONDY, NELL IRENE, b Pocahontas, Ark, Oct 27, 21. AGRICULTURAL BIOCHEMISTRY. *Educ:* Ouachita Univ, BS & BA, 43; Univ Tex, MA, 45; Cornell Univ, PhD(biochem), 53. *Prof Exp:* Asst prof chem, Ouachita Univ, 43-44; asst biochem, Univ Tex, 44-45; res assoc, Cornell Univ, 45-46; from instr to asst prof chem, Sampson Col, 46-48; instr, 48-51, asst prof, 53-57, assoc prof, 57-81, PROF FOOD & NUTRIT, CORNELL UNIV, 81- *Concurrent Pos:* Prof food chem, Fla State Univ, 51-71; consult, Environ Protection Agency, 79-80. *Mem:* AAAS; Am Chem Soc; fel Am Inst chem; Inst Food Technol; NY Acad Sci. *Res:* Vitamin B-6 group; choline and betaine aldehyde dehydrogenase in rats; enzymes; phenols; ascorbic acid; alkaloids and lipids in potatoes. *Mailing Add:* Div Nutrit Sci N-204A Van Rnslr Cornell Univ Ithaca NY 14850

MONER, JOHN GEORGE, b Bayonne, NJ, Sept 4, 28; m 55; c 3. CELL PHYSIOLOGY, BIOCHEMISTRY. *Educ:* Johns Hopkins Univ, AB, 49; Princeton Univ, MA, 51, PhD(biol), 53. *Prof Exp:* From instr to assoc prof physiol, 55-73, PROF ZOOL, UNIV MASS, AMHERST, 73- *Concurrent Pos:* NSF sci fac fel, Biol Inst, Carlsberg Found, Copenhagen, 61-62; pub health spec fel biol, Univ Calif, San Diego; actg ed, J Protozool, 73-74. *Mem:* Soc Protozool; Am Soc Cell Biol. *Res:* Physiology and biochemistry of cell division, with emphasis on synchronized tetrahymena; nutrient uptake in tetrahymena. *Mailing Add:* Dept of Zool Univ of Mass Amherst MA 01003

MONET, MARION C(RENSHALL), b Los Angeles, Calif, Apr 23, 19; m 43; c 2. INFORMATION SCIENCE. *Educ:* Univ Kans, BA, 41; Mass Inst Technol, MS, 43; Drexel Inst, MS, 59; Univ Del, MEd, 60. *Prof Exp:* Jr engr, E I du Pont de Nemours & Co, 43-44 & Manhattan Proj, 44-46; res engr, Tech Info Serv, Sun Oil Co, 60-77; chem mkt analyst, Sun Petrol Prod Co, 77-81, SR PLANNING ANALYST, SUN REFINING & MKT CO, 81- *Mem:* Am Chem Soc; Am Inst Chem Engrs; Soc Women Engrs. *Res:* Long-range trends and predictions for energy, fuels, and petrochemicals; retrieval of scientific information, especially engineering information. *Mailing Add:* Sun Refining & Mkt Co 1801 Market St Philadelphia PA 19103

MONETI, GIANCARLO, b Rome, Italy, Nov 2, 31; m 55; c 5. ELEMENTARY PARTICLE PHYSICS. *Educ:* Univ Rome, Dr, 54, Libero Docente, 63. *Prof Exp:* Asst prof physics, Univ Rome, 54-62, Nat Res Coun Italy fel, 54-55; physicist nat comt nuclear energy, Frascati Labs, Italy, 57-60; vis assoc physicist, Brookhaven Nat Lab, 61-62; assoc prof physics, Univ Rome, 62-64 & hist of physics, 64-68; PROF PHYSICS, SYRACUSE UNIV, 68- *Concurrent Pos:* Mem bd dirs, Nat Agency Nuclear Physics, Italy, 66-68; vis scientist, Europ Orgn Nuclear Res, 74-75. *Honors & Awards:* Montecatini Prize, Ital Phys Soc, 63. *Mem:* Ital Phys Soc; Europ Phys Soc; fel Am Phys Soc. *Res:* History of physics; experimental elementary particle physics; meson and baryon resonances; antiproton annihilation. *Mailing Add:* Dept Physics 323 Physics Bldg Syracuse Univ Syracuse NY 13210

MONETTE, FRANCIS C, b Lowell Mass, Aug 9, 41; m 68; c 1. HEMATOLOGY, CELL PHYSIOLOGY. *Educ:* St Anselm's Col, BA, 62; NY Univ, MS, 65, PhD(biol), 68. *Prof Exp:* Teaching fel biol, NY Univ, 62-63, res asst, 63-65, asst res scientist, 65-68; NIH trainee hemat, St Elizabeth's Hosp-Tufts Med Sch, 68-71; asst prof biol, 71-77, asst prof health sci, 74-77, ASSOC PROF BIOL & HEALTH SCI, BOSTON UNIV, 77- *Concurrent Pos:* Lectr, Iona Col, 66-67; NIH res career develop award, 77-82. *Mem:* AAAS; Am Soc Hemat; Am Soc Cell Biol; Int Soc Exp Hemat; Am Phys Soc. *Res:* Experimental hematology; kinetics of cellular proliferation; regulation of cell production and differentiation; erythropoietic physiology and biochemistry; aging processes in mammals. *Mailing Add:* Dept Biol Sci Boston Univ 2 Cummington St Boston MA 02215

MONEY, JOHN WILLIAM, b Morrinsville, NZ, July 8, 21, US citizen. GENETICS, PEDIATRICS. *Educ:* Univ NZ, MA, 42, dipl, 44; Harvard Univ, PhD, 52. *Prof Exp:* Instr psychiat, 51-55, from asst prof to assoc prof med psychol, 55-72, ASSOC PROF PEDIAT, JOHNS HOPKINS UNIV, 59-, PROF MED PSYCHOL, 72-, PSYCHOLOGIST, JOHNS HOPKINS HOSP, 55-, DIR PSYCHOHORMONAL RES UNIT, 51- *Concurrent Pos:* NIH res career award, 62-72; mem bd dirs, Sex Info & Educ Coun US, 65-68; mem task force homosexuality, NIMH, 67-69; mem bd dirs, Neighborhood Family Planning Ctr, Inc, 70; mem develop & behav sci study sect, NIH, 70-74; Grant Found grant, 72- *Honors & Awards:* Co-recipient, Hofheimer Prize, Am Psychiat Asn, 56; Gold Medal Award, Children's Hosp Philadelphia, 66; Award, Soc Sci Study Sex, 72; Medal Honor, Erickson Educ Found, 76. *Mem:* Soc Sci Study Sex (pres, 75-76); Am Found Gender & Genetal Med & Sci (pres, 78-). *Res:* Medical psychology; sexology; behavioral endocrinology and genetics; gender identity; paraphilias; abuse dwarfism. *Mailing Add:* Dept Psychiat & Behav Sci Phipps 400 Johns Hopkins Univ Hosp Baltimore MD 21205

MONEY, KENNETH ERIC, b Toronto, Ont, Jan 4, 35; m 58; c 1. PHYSIOLOGY, BIOLOGY. *Educ:* Univ Toronto, BA, 58, MA, 59, PhD(physiol), 61. *Prof Exp:* Res scientist, Defence Res Med Labs, 61-66, sect head vestibular physiol, 66-76, dir biosci, 76-79, SR SCIENTIST, DEFENCE & CIVIL INST ENVIRON MED, 79-; ASSOC PROF PHYSIOL, UNIV TORONTO, 72- *Concurrent Pos:* Res assoc, Univ Toronto, 61-62, lectr, 62-68, asst prof, 69-72. *Mem:* Can Physiol Soc; fel Royal Soc Health; Aerospace Med Asn. *Res:* Vestibular physiology; motion sickness; histology of the inner ear; eye movements; alcohol. *Mailing Add:* Defence & Civil Inst of Environ Med PO Box 2000 Downsview ON M3M 3B9 Can

MONEY, LLOYD J(EAN), b Lawton, Okla, Sept 14, 20; m 44; c 3. ELECTRICAL ENGINEERING. *Educ:* Rice Univ, BS, 42; Purdue Univ, MS, 50, PhD(elec eng), 52. *Prof Exp:* Instr elec eng, Rice Univ, 42-43, 47-49, Tulane Univ, 46-47 & Purdue Univ, 49-52; mgr, Interceptor Systs Dept, Systs Anal Lab, Hughes Aircraft Co, 52-60, assoc mgr, Tactical Systs Lab, 60-62, mgr, Europ Opers Aeronaut Systs Div, 62-64, assoc mgr, Advan Projs Labs, Calif, 64-68; staff mgr advan progs, TRW, Inc, 68-71; asst dir, Off Systs Eng, Off of the Secy, Dept Transp, 71-77, actg dir, Off Univ Res, 72-74, actg assoc adminr res & develop, Urban Mass Transp Admin, 74, actg asst secy systs develop & tech, 77-78, dir, Transp Progs Bur, Res & Special Progs Admin, 78-79, DIR OFF UNIV RES, DEPT TRANSP, 81- *Concurrent Pos:* Vis scholar, Univ Calif, 80-81. *Mem:* Inst Elec & Electronics Engrs; NY Acad Sci. *Res:* Airborne weapons design; automatic control systems; system planning, analysis and coordination, including radar computers, navigation, missiles and automatic controls; transportation engineering; research and development administration. *Mailing Add:* Res & Special Progs Admin 400 Seventh St SW Rm 9201 Washington DC 20590

MONFORE, GERVAISE EDWIN, b Waverly, Kans, Feb 26, 10; m 36; c 1. INSTRUMENTATION. *Educ:* Col of Emporia, AB, 32; Univ Denver, MS, 50. *Prof Exp:* Jr physicist, Nat Bur Stand, 36-41; res physicist, B F Goodrich Co, 42-45; res engr, US Bur Reclamation, 4S-55; res physicist, Portland Cement Asn, 55-60, from sr res physicist to prin res physicist, 67-73; mem fac, Physics Dept, Southwest Mo State Univ, 79-80; RETIRED. *Mem:* Sigma Xi. *Res:* Properties and behavior of portland cement and concrete, including strength, stress, elasticity, creep, shrinkage, electrical and thermal conductivity, heat of hydration and corrosion of embedded metals, fiber reinforcement; ice pressure. *Mailing Add:* 4083 S Eaton Ave Springfield MO 65807

MONFORTON, GERARD ROLAND, b Windsor, Ont, July 21, 38; m 60; c 4. CIVIL ENGINEERING. *Educ:* Assumption Univ, BASc, 61, MASc, 62; Case Western Reserve Univ, PhD(civil eng), 70. *Prof Exp:* Lectr civil eng, Univ Windsor, 62-64; res asst solid mech, Case Western Reserve Univ, 64-68; from asst prof to assoc prof civil eng, 68-76, PROF CIVIL ENG, UNIV WINDSOR, 76- *Mem:* Eng Inst Can; Am Soc Civil Engrs. *Res:* Solid mechanics; structural design. *Mailing Add:* Dept of Civil Eng Univ of Windsor Windsor ON N9B 3P4 Can

MONGAN, EDWIN LAWRENCE, JR, b Cincinnati, Ohio, June 27, 19; m 49; c 8. CHEMICAL ENGINEERING, THERMODYNAMICS. *Educ:* Univ Cincinnati, ChE, 42. *Prof Exp:* Chemist soap mfg, DuBois Co, 46; instr chem eng, Univ Cincinnati, 47-51; ENGR & PRIN CONSULT ECON CHEM THERMODYN, E I DU PONT DE NEMOURS & CO, INC, 51- *Concurrent Pos:* Adj prof, Univ Louisville, 51-53; mem adv bd coal res, City Univ New York, 72-; adj prof, Univ Del, 73-76. *Res:* Commercial applications of research; chemical process conception and development; chemical thermodynamics; economics. *Mailing Add:* 6 Calgary Rd Newark DE 19711

MONGEAU, J DENIS, b St Hyacinthe, Que, Dec 1, 30; m 56; c 2. VETERINARY MEDICINE, BACTERIOLOGY. *Educ:* Univ Montreal, BA, 52, DVM, 56; Univ Toronto, MSc, 58. *Prof Exp:* Lectr poultry path, Ont Vet Col, 58-59; prof bact, Sch Vet Med, Univ Montreal, 59-67; SCI ADV, BUR VET MED, DRUG DIRECTORATE, HEALTH PROTECTION BR, DEPT HEALTH & WELFARE, CAN, 67- *Mem:* Am Soc Microbiol; US Animal Health Asn; Can Soc Microbiol. *Res:* Pathology; infectious diseases. *Mailing Add:* 96 Desjardins Hull ON K1N 5N9 Can

MONGEAU, MAURICE, b Montreal, Que, Oct 17, 20; m 49; c 6. PHYSICAL MEDICINE. *Educ:* Univ Montreal, BA, 42, MD, 48; Am Bd Phys Med & Rehab, dipl, 55. *Prof Exp:* Asst med dir, Rehab Inst Montreal, 53-62; asst dir, Sch Rehab, 55-70, ASSOC PROF MED, FAC MED, UNIV MONTREAL, 62-; CHIEF SERV PHYS MED & REHAB, REHAB INST MONTREAL, 62- *Concurrent Pos:* Consult, Dept Vet Affairs, St Anne's Hosp, 54-60 & Pasteur Hosp, 54-; secy, Can Asn Univ Schs Phys Med & Rehab, 59-65. *Mem:* Can Med Asn; Can Asn Phys Med & Rehab (secy-treas, 56-61, pres, 65-66). *Res:* Medico-psycho-social aspects in rehabilitation of hemiplegia, cerebral palsy, poliomyelitis, paraplegia and amputee; bioengineering in prosthetics for upper extremity amputee and lower extremity amputee; congenital malformations of the extremities. *Mailing Add:* Rehab Inst of Montreal 6300 Darlington Ave Montreal PQ H3S 2J4 Can

MONGINI, PATRICIA KATHERINE ANN, b Cottonwood, Ariz, Dec 13, 50. IMMUNOLOGY. *Educ:* Northern Ariz Univ, BS, 72; Stanford Univ, PhD(med microbiol), 76. *Prof Exp:* Fel immunol, Sch Med, Tufts Univ, 76-78; fel immunol, lab immunol, Nat Inst Allergy & Infectious Dis, 78-81; ASST PROF HOSP JOITN DIS, MT SINAI SCH MED, NEW YORK, NY, 82- *Mem:* AAAS; Am Asn Immunologists. *Res:* The role of lymphocyte trapping in the induction of immune responses to antigens; regulation of B lymphocyte activation. *Mailing Add:* Dept Rheumatic Dis 301 E 17th St Hosp Joint Dis New York NY 10003

MONIE, IAN WHITELAW, b Paisley, Scotland, May 24, 18; nat US; m 42; c 4. ANATOMY. *Educ:* Glasgow Univ, MB, ChB, 40, MD, 72. *Prof Exp:* From demonstr to lectr anat, Glasgow Univ, 42-47; from asst prof to assoc prof, Univ Man, 47-52; from asst prof to prof anat, 52-70, vchmn dept, 58-63, chmn dept, 63-70, PROF ANAT & EMBRYOL, UNIV CALIF, SAN FRANCISCO, 70- *Concurrent Pos:* Cur of unclaimed dead, Northern Calif, 60-66; mem study sect human develop, NIH, 65-69; Guggenheim fel, 67-68. *Mem:* AAAS; Am Asn Anat; Anat Soc Gt Brit & Ireland; Teratology Soc (pres, 64-65). *Res:* Mammalian embryology and teratology; human gross anatomy; comparative embryology. *Mailing Add:* Dept of Anat Univ of of Calif San Francisco CA 94143

MONIOT, ROBERT KEITH, b Butler, Pa, Nov 26, 50. METEORITICS. *Educ:* State Univ NY, Fredonia, BS, 72; Univ Calif, Berkeley, PhD(physics), 79. *Prof Exp:* RES FEL, DEPT PHYSICS, RUTGERS UNIV, 79- *Mem:* Am Phys Soc; Am Vacuum Soc; AAAS. *Res:* Measurement of beryllium-10 in meteorites and terrestrial materials by technique of accelerator-based mass spectrometry; mass-spectrometric analysis of noble gases in meteorites. *Mailing Add:* Dept Physics Rutgers Univ Piscataway NJ 08854

MONISMITH, CARL L(EROY), b Harrisburg, Pa, Oct 23, 26; m 49; c 2. CIVIL ENGINEERING. *Educ:* Univ Calif, BS, 50, MS, 54. *Prof Exp:* From instr to asst prof civil eng & chmn dept, 52-61 & 74-79, assoc prof, 61-66, asst res engr, 55-61, assoc res engr, 61-66, PROF CIVIL ENG & RES ENGR, INST TRANSP STUDIES, UNIV CALIF, BERKELEY, 66- *Concurrent Pos:* Consult, Chevron Res Co, Standard Oil Co Calif, Woodward Clyde Consults & Corps Eng, US Army; assoc, Transp Res Bd, Nat Acad Sci-Nat Res Coun, chmn sect B, Group 2, Div A, 73-79. *Honors & Awards:* Emmons Award, Asn Asphalt Paving Technologists, 61 & 65; K B Woods Award, 72. *Mem:* Nat Acad Eng; Am Soc Civil Engrs; Am Soc Testing & Mat; Am Soc Eng Educ; Asn Asphalt Paving Technologists. *Res:* Physical behavior of asphalts and asphalt paving mixtures; behavior and design and rehabilitation of pavements for highways and airports; highway engineering. *Mailing Add:* Dept Civil Eng 760 Davis Hall Univ Calif Berkeley CA 94720

MONIZ, WILLIAM BETTENCOURT, b New Bedford, Mass, Feb 12, 32; m 55; c 6. PHYSICAL CHEMISTRY. *Educ:* Brown Univ, BS, 53; Pa State Univ, PhD(org chem), 60. *Prof Exp:* Petrol Res Fund fel, Pa State Univ, 60-61; NIH vis scientist, Univ Ill, 61-62; head nuclear magnetic resonance spectros sect, Chem Div, 62-74, HEAD POLYMER DIAG SECT, CHEM DIV, NAVAL RES LAB, 74- *Concurrent Pos:* Mem admis comt, Am Chem Soc, 65-66. *Mem:* Am Chem Soc; Sigma Xi. *Res:* Magnetic resonance; materials degradation; polymer characterization. *Mailing Add:* Code 6120 Naval Res Lab Washington DC 20375

MONJAN, ANDREW ARTHUR, b New York, NY, Feb 9, 38; m 69; c 2. NEUROSCIENCES, IMMUNOPATHOLOGY. *Educ:* Rensselaer Polytech Inst, BS, 60; Univ Rochester, PhD(psychol), 65; Johns Hopkins Univ, MPH, 71. *Prof Exp:* USPHS res fel, Univ Rochester, 64-66; asst prof psychol & physiol, Univ Western Ont, 66-69; USPHS community health trainee, 69-70, asst prof, 71-75, ASSOC PROF EPIDEMIOL, SCH HYG & PUB HEALTH, JOHNS HOPKINS UNIV, 75- *Mem:* Asn Res Vision & Ophthal; NY Acad Sci; Teratol Soc; Sigma Xi; Am Asn Immunologists. *Res:* Effects of viruses upon the nervous system; developmental pathogenesis, mechanisms of immunopathology and long term psychological sequela; stress and the immune systems. *Mailing Add:* Dept of Epidemiol Sch of Hyg & Pub Health Johns Hopkins Univ Baltimore MD 21205

MONK, CARL DOUGLAS, b Hurdles Mill, NC, July 28, 33; m 57; c 2. PLANT ECOLOGY. *Educ:* Duke Univ, AB, 55; Rutgers Univ, MS, 58, PhD(bot), 59. *Prof Exp:* Asst prof bot, Univ Fla, 59-64; from asst prof to assoc prof, 64-71, PROF BOT, UNIV GA, 71- *Mem:* Bot Soc Am; Ecol Soc Am; Torrey Bot Club; Am Soc Naturalists; Brit Ecol Soc. *Res:* Vegetation analysis; mineral cycling. *Mailing Add:* Dept of Bot Univ of Ga Athens GA 30602

MONK, CLAYBORNE MORRIS, b Atlantic City, NJ, Dec 4, 38; m 65; c 2. BIOPHARMACEUTICS, PHARMACOKINETICS. *Educ:* Howard Univ, BS, 60; Univ Calif, San Francisco, PhD(pharmaceut chem), 75. *Prof Exp:* Asst prof pharm, Sch Pharm, Univ Southern Calif, 72-75; asst prof, 76-80, ASSOC PROF PHARM, SCH PHARM, TEX SOUTHERN UNIV, 80- *Mem:* AAAS; Am Pharmaceut Asn; Nat Pharmaceut Asn; Am Asn Col Pharm; Am Inst Hist Pharm. *Res:* Biopharmaceutics and pharmacokinetics with special interest in drug disposition within the maternal-placental-fetal system. *Mailing Add:* Sch Pharm Tex Southern Univ 3201 Wheeler Ave Houston TX 77004

MONK, JAMES DONALD, b Childress, Tex, Sept 27, 30; m 53; c 2. MATHEMATICS. *Educ:* Univ Chicago, AB, 51; Univ NMex, BS, 56; Univ Calif, Berkeley, MA, 59, PhD(math), 61. *Prof Exp:* Math analyst, Los Alamos Sci Labs, 51-53; instr math, Univ Calif, Berkeley, 61-62, asst res mathematician, 63-64; asst prof, 62-63 & 64-65, assoc prof, 65-67, PROF MATH, UNIV COLO, BOULDER, 67- *Concurrent Pos:* NSF res grants, 63-; vis prof, Univ Calif, Berkeley, 67-68. *Mem:* Am Math Soc; Asn Symbolic Logic. *Res:* Algebraic logic; general algebra; model theory; foundations of set theory. *Mailing Add:* Dept of Math Univ of Colo Boulder CO 80302

MONK, MARY ALICE, b Racine, Wis, May 23, 26; m 67. EPIDEMIOLOGY, PUBLIC HEALTH. *Educ:* Oberlin Col, AB, 48; Univ Mich, MA, 51, PhD(psychol), 54. *Prof Exp:* Instr prev med, Univ Buffalo, 53-58; asst prof epidemiol, Med Sch, Tulane Univ, 58-60; from asst prof to assoc prof chronic dis, Sch Hyg & Pub Health, Johns Hopkins Univ, 60-69; assoc prof environ med, State Univ NY Downstate Med Sch, 69-70; prof community & prev med, New York Med Col, 70-80; MEM FAC, DEPT EPIDERMIOL, JOHNS HOPKINS UNIV, 80- *Concurrent Pos:* Mem epidemiol & dis control study sect, NIH, 72-75. *Mem:* AAAS; Am Pub Health Asn; Am Psychol Asn; Am Statist Asn. *Res:* Epidemiology of chronic diseases such as mental illness, gastrointestinal disease and cancer; medical education and medical careers. *Mailing Add:* Dept Epidermiol Johns Hopkins Univ Public Health 615 N Wolfe St Baltimore MD 21205

MONKE, EDWIN J, b Ill, June 7, 25; m 63; c 3. AGRICULTURAL ENGINEERING. *Educ:* Univ Ill, BS, 50, MS, 53, PhD(civil eng), 59. *Prof Exp:* Instr, Univ Ill, 51-58; from asst prof to assoc prof, 58-67, PROF AGR ENG, PURDUE UNIV, 67- *Mem:* Am Geophys Union; fel Am Soc Agr Engrs; Nat Soc Prof Engrs; Am Soc Eng Educ; Soil Conserv Soc Am. *Res:* Groundwater hydraulics; watershed hydrology; erosion and sedimentation control; water quality. *Mailing Add:* Dept Agr Eng Purdue Univ West Lafayette IN 47907

MONLUX, ANDREW W, b Algona, Iowa, Jan 29, 20; m 50; c 2. VETERINARY PATHOLOGY. *Educ:* Iowa State Univ, DVM, 42, MS, 47; George Washington Univ, PhD(comp path), 51. *Prof Exp:* Pvt pract, Iowa, 42; asst, Iowa State Univ, 46-47; vet, USDA, Colo & DC, 51-56; head dept, 56-72, PROF VET PATH, OKLA STATE UNIV, 56-, REGENTS PROF, 72- *Mem:* Am Vet Med Asn; US Animal Health Asn; Conf Res Workers Animal Dis; Vet Cancer Soc; Vet Urol Soc. *Res:* Pathology of neoplastic and kidney diseases; lead and photosensitivity syndromes of animals. *Mailing Add:* Dept of Vet Path Okla State Univ Stillwater OK 74074

MONLUX, WILLIAM S, b Algona, Iowa, Jan 8, 15; m 56. PATHOLOGY, MICROBIOLOGY. *Educ:* Iowa State Univ, DVM, 37; Cornell Univ, PhD, 48. *Prof Exp:* Instr path, Cornell Univ, 37-41; fel, Royal Vet Col Sweden, 48; pathologist, Bur Animal Indust, Washington, DC, 49; fel path, Univ Pretoria, 49-50; prof, Tex A&M Univ, 50-53 & Iowa State Univ, 53-62; leader path invest, Nat Animal Dis Lab, Iowa, 62-63, asst dir res, 63-72; staff mem res, Food & Drug Admin, 72-76, assoc dir path, 74-76; CONSULT PATH, 76- *Mem:* Am Vet Med Asn; Conf Res Workers Animal Dis; Am Col Vet Path; US Animal Health Asn; Am Asn Vet Lab Diagnosticians. *Res:* Canine leptospirosis; toxoplasmosis; oncology, especially pulmonary neoplasms; porcine and bovine nutrition; pulmonary adenomatosis; erysipelas. *Mailing Add:* 1213 S Second St Ames IA 50010

MONMONIER, MARK STEPHEN, b Baltimore, Md, Feb 2, 43; m 65. CARTOGRAPHY, INFORMATION SYSTEMS. *Educ:* Johns Hopkins Univ, BA, 64; Pa State Univ, MS, 67, PhD(geog), 69. *Prof Exp:* Asst prof geog, Univ RI, 69-70 & State Univ NY, Albany, 70-73; assoc prof, 73-79, PROF GEOG, SYRACUSE UNIV, 79- *Concurrent Pos:* Consult, Syracuse Police Dept, 76-79; mem, US Nat Comt, Int Cartog Asn, 77-81, assoc ed, Am Cartogr, 77-; res geographer, US Geol Surv, 79- *Mem:* Am Cong Surv & Mapping; Asn Am Geogrs; Am Soc Photogram; Can Cartog Soc; Sigma Xi. *Res:* Automated mapping; especially computer-assisted map design and pattern recognition; cartographic communication; information policy and geographic data bases. *Mailing Add:* Dept of Geog Syracuse Univ Syracuse NY 13210

MONN, DONALD EDGAR, b Chambersburg, Pa, June 21, 38; m 63; c 1. DATA PROCESSING SYSTEMS, ANALYTICAL CHEMISTRY. *Educ:* Elizabethtown Col, BS, 59; Univ Del, PhD(anal chem), 64. *Prof Exp:* Anal chemist & group leader, Data Mgt Group & tech asst, 64-80, MGR, RES SERV DIV, CONTINENTAL OIL CO, 80- *Mem:* Am Chem Soc. *Res:* Interfacing analytical instruments to computers and data acquisition equipment; writing computer programs to perform analytical calculations; techniques of data evaluation; evaluation of data base systems; coordination of office automation planning and implementation. *Mailing Add:* Continental Oil Co PO Drawer 1267 Ponca City OK 74601

MONNIER, DWIGHT CHAPIN, academic administration, deceased

MONOPOLI, RICHARD V(ITO), b Providence, RI, Nov 22, 30; m 56; c 2. ELECTRICAL ENGINEERING. *Educ:* US Naval Acad, BSc, 52; Brown Univ, MSc, 60; Univ Conn, PhD(elec eng), 65. *Prof Exp:* Design engr, Int Bus Mach Corp, NY, 56-57; proj engr, Indust Div, Speidel Corp, 57-62; asst automatic control, Univ Conn, 62-65; assoc prof elec eng, 65-69, PROF ELEC ENG, UNIV MASS, AMHERST, 69- *Mem:* Inst Elec & Electronics Engrs; Am Soc Eng Educ. *Res:* Automatic control; application of magnetohydrodynamic principles to gyroscope design; development of tape recorders for missile use; application of Liapunov's direct method to control system design. *Mailing Add:* Dept of Elec Eng Univ of Mass Amherst MA 01003

MONOSON, HERBERT L, b Chicago, Ill, Dec 23, 36; m 65; c 2. MYCOLOGY. *Educ:* Western Ill Univ, BS, 58, MS, 60; Univ Ill, Urbana, PhD(bot), 67. *Prof Exp:* From asst prof to assoc prof, 66-77, PROF BIOL, BRADLEY UNIV, 77- *Concurrent Pos:* Res Corp grant, Bradley Univ, 71-72. *Mem:* Mycol Soc Am. *Res:* Phycology; nematology; hormonal regulation of fungi; rust fungi taxonomy. *Mailing Add:* Dept of Biol Bradley Univ Peoria IL 61625

MONOSTORI, BENEDICT JOSEPH, b Kovagoors, Hungary, July 4, 19; US citizen. PHYSICS. *Educ:* Pazmany Peter Univ, Budapest, BS, 45; Pontifical Univ, St Anselm, Rome, MA, 51; Fordham Univ, PhD(physics), 64. *Prof Exp:* Instr math & physics, St Stephen's Acad, Hungary, 45-48; prof philos, St Bernard's Col, Hungary, 48-50; instr math, Acad Mary Immaculate, Wichita Falls, Tex, 55-56; instr math & philos, 56-60, asst prof physics, 60-64,

ASSOC PROF PHYSICS, UNIV DALLAS, 64-, CHMN DEPT, 71- *Mem:* Am Phys Soc; Am Asn Physics Teachers. *Res:* Molecular spectra and structure; Raman spectroscopy; philosophy of science. *Mailing Add:* Dept Physics Univ Dallas Irving TX 75061

MONRAD, DITLEV, b Copenhagen, Denmark, Aug 2, 49; m 72; c 1. MATHEMATICS, STATISTICS. *Educ:* Copenhagen Univ, BA, 72; Univ Calif, Berkeley, PhD(math), 76. *Prof Exp:* Asst prof math, Univ Southern Calif, 76-78; ASST PROF MATH, UNIV ILL, URBANA, 78- *Res:* Probability theory. *Mailing Add:* Dept of Math Univ of Ill Urbana IL 61801

MONROE, A(LFRED) J(AMES), electrical engineering, see previous edition

MONROE, BARBARA SAMSON GRANGER, b New York, NY, Aug 23, 13; m 51; c 1. ANATOMY. *Educ:* Mt Holyoke Col, AB, 35, AM, 37; Cornell Univ, PhD(zool), 43. *Prof Exp:* Instr zool, Wilson Col, 40-41; instr, Univ Ariz, 43-45; from instr to assoc prof, 45-66, prof, 66-79, RES PROF ANAT, SCH MED, UNIV SOUTHERN CALIF, 79- *Mem:* Am Soc Zool; Am Asn Anat; Electron Micros Soc Am. *Res:* Endocrinology; histology; electron microscopy of the intestine, thyroid, neurohypophysis and hypothalamus; freeze fracture of median eminence and ependyma of third nentride. *Mailing Add:* Dept of Anat Sch of Med Univ of Southern Calif Los Angeles CA 90033

MONROE, BRUCE MALCOLM, b Indianapolis, Ind, July 7, 40; m 68. ORGANIC CHEMISTRY, ANALYTICAL CHEMISTRY. *Educ:* Wabash Col, AB, 62; Univ Ill, Urbana, MS, 64, PhD(org chem), 67. *Prof Exp:* NIH fels, Calif Inst Technol, 67-69; res chemist, Explosives Dept, 69-71, res chemist, Cent Res & Develop Dept, Exp Sta, 71-81, SECT SUPVR, HASKELL LAB TOXICOL & INDUST MED, E I DU PONT DE NEMOURS & CO, INC, 81- *Mem:* Am Chem Soc; Royal Soc Chem; Sigma Xi. *Res:* Organic photochemistry; industrial hygiene analyses. *Mailing Add:* 3030 Maple Shade Lane Wilmington DE 19810

MONROE, BURT LEAVELLE, JR, b Louisville, Ky, Aug 25, 30; m 60. ORNITHOLOGY. *Educ:* Univ Louisville, BS, 53; La State Univ, PhD(zool), 65. *Prof Exp:* Vis instr zool, La State Univ, 65; from asst prof to assoc prof, 65-74, PROF VERT ZOOL, UNIV LOUISVILLE, 74-, CHMN DEPT BIOL, 71- *Mem:* Soc Syst Zool; Am Soc Ichthyologists & Herpetologists; Am Ornith Union; Wilson Ornith Soc; Cooper Ornith Soc. *Res:* Distribution and systematics of birds, especially Neotropical; entomology, especially Lepidoptera and Coleoptera; herpetology; zoogeography. *Mailing Add:* Dept of Biol Univ of Louisville Louisville KY 40292

MONROE, ELIZABETH MCLEISTER, b Pittsburgh, Pa, Dec 11, 40; m 68. ORGANIC CHEMISTRY. *Educ:* Bucknell Univ, BS, 62; Univ Ill, Urbana, MS, 64, PhD(org chem), 68. *Prof Exp:* Info chemist, 69-71, SR INFO CHEMIST, E I DU PONT DE NEMOURS & CO, INC, 71- *Mem:* Am Chem Soc. *Res:* Chemical information. *Mailing Add:* 3030 Maple Shade Lane Wilmington DE 19810

MONROE, EUGENE ALAN, b Kansas City, Kans, May 31, 34; m 54; c 3. MINERALOGY, CRYSTALLOGRAPHY. *Educ:* Univ Wis, BS, 55; Univ Ill, MS, 59, PhD(geol-mineral), 61; Columbia Univ, DDS(dent), 73. *Prof Exp:* Asst prof, 61-73, ASSOC PROF CRYSTALLOG, STATE UNIV NY COL CERAMICS, ALFRED UNIV, 73- *Mem:* Soc Biomat; Sigma Xi; NY Acad Sci; Am Dental Asn; Calcified Tissue Group. *Res:* Electron microscopy and crystallography of materials; biomedical material development; mineralogical studies; dental research. *Mailing Add:* State Univ of NY Col of Ceramics Alfred Univ Alfred NY 14802

MONROE, GORDON EUGENE, b Feb 25, 34; US citizen; m 60; c 2. AGRICULTURAL ENGINEERING. *Educ:* Mich State Univ, BS, 61; Univ Hawaii, MS, 69. *Prof Exp:* Agr engr, Agr Eng Res Div, Agr Res Serv, East Lansing, Mich, 61-64, proj agr engr, Honolulu, Hawaii, 64-71, res leader, Eng Unit, Byron, Ga, 71-79, RES LEADER, HARVEST & PROD UNIT, AGR RES-SCI ADMIN, USDA, TIFTON, GA, 79- *Concurrent Pos:* Consult, Res Corp, Univ Hawaii, 76-77. *Honors & Awards:* Super Serv Award, USDA, 66. *Mem:* Am Soc Agr Engrs. *Res:* Harvesting, handling and processing crops for energy in agriculture; systems and mechanization of harvesting, handling and other related operations in the production of fruit and tree-nut crops. *Mailing Add:* Agr Res SEA USDA PO Box 87 Byron GA 31008

MONROE, PAUL S(EELY), b Youngstown, Ohio, Dec 10, 16; m 45; c 2. ENGINEERING. *Educ:* Rutgers Univ, BS, 40. *Prof Exp:* Draftsman, DeLaval Steam Turbine Co, NJ, 35-36; designer, Merck & Co, 40, sr engr, 41-44; supv engr, Kellex Corp, NY, 44-45; oper engr, Oak Ridge Nat Lab, 45; asst chief engr, Pfaudler Co, 45-46, chief engr, 46-50; chief proj engr, Vitro Corp Am, 50-53; dir eng, Sci Design Co, Inc, 53-63, vpres, 57-63, vpres, SD Plants, Inc, 58-63; exec vpres, Halcon Int, Inc, 63-77, vpres, 77-81; RETIRED. *Concurrent Pos:* Consult, US Corps Engrs, 56-57. *Res:* Pressure vessel design; plant designs; filters, pumps, drives, heat exchangers; chemical, dairy and food equipment; instruments and valves; chemical and industrial plant construction. *Mailing Add:* 27 Lenape Trail Chatham NJ 07928

MONROE, PEARLE ARVEL, b Bowdoin, Mont, Jan 6, 21; m 46; c 2. ORGANIC CHEMISTRY, BIOCHEMISTRY. *Educ:* Univ Idaho, BS, 47, MS, 49; Ind Univ, PhD(org chem), 52. *Prof Exp:* Asst chem, Univ Idaho, 47-48, actg instr, 48-49; res chemist, Goodyear-Sumatra Plantations Co, 52-58; prof org chem & biochem, 58-77, PROF CHEM, STATE UNIV NY COL OSWEGO, 77- *Concurrent Pos:* NIH spec fac fel, Univ Calif, San Francisco, 64. *Mem:* Am Chem Soc. *Res:* Synthesis and properties of amino-thiophenes and their derivatives; natural rubber; thiophene derivatives of biological interest. *Mailing Add:* Dept of Chem State Univ of NY Col at Oswego Oswego NY 13126

MONROE, ROBERT JAMES, b Dysart, Iowa, Dec 28, 18; m 42. STATISTICS. *Educ:* Iowa State Univ, BS, 39; NC State Col, PhD, 49. *Prof Exp:* Res collabr & supvr, Statist Lab, USDA, Iowa State Univ, 39-41; instr mach comput, NC State Col, 41-42, instr statist, 46-49, asst prof statist & plant sci statistician, 48-52, assoc prof exp statist, 52-53; chief, Oper Anal Off, Air Force Missile Test Ctr, 53-54; PROF EXP STATIST, SCH PHYS & MATH SCI, NC STATE UNIV, 54- *Concurrent Pos:* Agent, USDA, 41-42; vis prof, Med Col Va, 61-62. *Mem:* Biomet Soc; fel Am Statist Asn. *Res:* Estimation of nutrition requirements; statistical methodology; biometry; operations research. *Mailing Add:* Dept of Statist NC State Univ Box 5457 Raleigh NC 27650

MONROE, RONALD EUGENE, b Porterville, Calif, Jan 17, 33; m 58; c 1. ENTOMOLOGY. *Educ:* Fresno State Col, BA, 56; Ore State Col, MS, 58; Kans State Univ, PhD(entom), 64. *Prof Exp:* Jr vector control officer, Bur Vector Control, State Dept Pub Health, Calif, 55-56; med entomologist insects affecting man & animals, Agr Res Serv, USDA, Ore, 57-58, gen entomologist, Insect Physiol Lab, 58-61, from asst prof to prof entom, Mich State Univ, 64-73; PROF ZOOL, SAN DIEGO STATE UNIV, 73- *Mem:* Entom Soc Am. *Res:* Biochemistry and physiology of insects, chiefly lipid, carbohydrate and amino acid metabolism and insect nutrition and reproduction. *Mailing Add:* Dept of Zool San Diego State Univ San Diego CA 92182

MONROE, RUSSELL RONALD, b Des Moines, Iowa, June 7, 20; m 45; c 3. MEDICINE. *Educ:* Yale Univ, BS, 42, MD, 44. *Prof Exp:* Asst med, Yale Univ, 45-46; from asst prof to assoc prof psychiat, Sch Med, Tulane Univ, 50-60; PROF PSYCHIAT, SCH MED, UNIV MD, BALTIMORE, 60-, CHMN DEPT PSYCHIAT & DIR INST PSYCHIAT & HUMAN BEHAV, 76- *Mem:* Am Psychiat Asn; Am Acad Psychoanal. *Res:* Episodic behavioral disorders. *Mailing Add:* Inst of Psychiat & Human Behav Univ of Md Sch of Med Baltimore MD 21201

MONROE, STUART BENTON, b Manassas, Va, Oct 26, 34; m 60; c 3. ORGANIC CHEMISTRY, POLYMER CHEMISTRY. *Educ:* Randolph-Macon Col, BS, 56; Univ Fla, PhD(org chem), 62. *Prof Exp:* Res chemist, Hercules Res Ctr, Del, 61-65; assoc prof, 65-67, chmn dept chem, 75-78, chmn area sci & math, 78-81, PROF ORG CHEM, RANDOLPH-MACON COL, 67- *Mem:* Am Chem Soc. *Mailing Add:* Dept of Chem Randolph-Macon Col Ashland VA 23005

MONROE, WATSON HINER, b Parkersburg, WVa, Dec 1, 07; m 33; c 1. GEOLOGY. *Prof Exp:* From jr geologist to geologist, US Geol Surv, 30-49, chief, Eastern Field Invests Sect, Fuels Br, 49-53, staff geologist, 53-55, chief, P R Coop Invest, Gen Geol Br, 55-66, res geologist, Atlantic Environ Br, 66-72, consult geologist, 72-81; RETIRED. *Concurrent Pos:* Lectr, Univ PR, 60-65 & 68-69. *Mem:* Fel Geol Soc Am; Am Asn Petrol Geol. *Res:* Stratigraphy of Cretaceous and Tertiary rocks of the Gulf Coast Plain; karst geology; stratigraphy, structure, economic geology and geomorphology of Puerto Rico. *Mailing Add:* 126 E North St Leesburg VA 22075

MONSAROFF, ADOLPH, b USSR, Feb 21, 12; m 37. CHEMICAL ENGINEERING. *Educ:* Univ Toronto, BASc, 34. *Prof Exp:* Plant supt, Mallinckrodt Chem Works, Can, 38-44; plant mgr, Monsanto Can, Ltd, 45-50, vpres, 51-58, exec vpres, 59-62; vpres mkt & develop, Domtar Chem Ltd, 63-64, vpres & managing dir, 64-68, pres, 68-77; DIR, OFF INDUST RES, McGILL UNIV, 77- *Mem:* Soc Plastics Indust; Am Inst Chem Engrs; fel Chem Inst Can. *Res:* Unit operations; manufacturing techniques; fine organic chemicals; plastics and resins. *Mailing Add:* Off of Indust Res 408 Dawson Hall 853 Sherbrooke St W Montreal PQ H3A 2T6 Can

MONSAY, EVELYN HOPE, elementary particle physics, theoretical physics, see previous edition

MONSE, ERNST ULRICH, b Bautzen, Ger, Jan 10, 27; m 70; c 2. PHYSICAL CHEMISTRY. *Educ:* Univ Mainz, MS, 53, PhD(phys chem), 57. *Prof Exp:* Res assoc phys chem, Columbia Univ, 57-59; res assoc, 59-64, assoc prof, 64-74, PROF PHYS CHEM, RUTGERS UNIV, NEWARK, 74- *Mem:* Sigma Xi. *Res:* Isotope effects and their correlation with molecular structures and force fields. *Mailing Add:* Dept Chem Rutgers Univ 73 Warren St Newark NJ 07102

MONSEN, HARRY, b Trondheim, Norway, Aug 24, 24; nat US; m 50; c 2. ANATOMY. *Educ:* Univ Minn, MS, 51; Univ Ill, PhD(anat), 54. *Prof Exp:* Asst anat, Univ Minn, 49-51; asst cancer biol, 51-54, from instr to assoc prof, 54-70, PROF ANAT, UNIV ILL COL MED, 70- *Res:* Cancer biology; carcinogenesis; pituitary-adrenal-gonadal interrelationships. *Mailing Add:* Dept of Anat Univ of Ill Col of Med Chicago IL 60680

MONSIMER, HAROLD GENE, b Las Vegas, NMex, Feb 5, 28; m 63; c 2. ORGANIC CHEMISTRY. *Educ:* Univ Calif, BS, 52; Wayne State Univ, MS, 54, PhD(chem), 57. *Prof Exp:* Sr res chemist, Nat Drug Co, 56-65; head org chem, MacAndrews & Forbes Co, 65-66; sr res chemist, 66-73, PROJ LEADER, PENNWALT CORP, 73- *Mem:* NY Acad Sci; Am Chem Soc; Royal Soc Chem. *Res:* Medicinal chemistry; organic synthesis. *Mailing Add:* Penwalt Corp 900 1st Ave Norristown PA 19406

MONSON, ARVID MONROE, b Pequot Lakes, Minn, Feb 9, 38; m 64; c 1. MICROBIOLOGY, GENETICS. *Educ:* Univ Minn, BS, 59, MS, 64, PhD(genetics), 68. *Prof Exp:* Asst prof biol, Allegheny Col, 67-76, assoc prof, 76-81. *Concurrent Pos:* Fel, Univ NC-Chapel Hill, 72-73. *Mem:* AAAS; Sigma Xi. *Res:* Translocation in fungi mutagenesis in microorganisms. *Mailing Add:* 2513 E 88th St Apt 216 Tulsa OK 74136

MONSON, FREDERICK CARLTON, b Philadelphia, Pa, Aug 3, 39; m 65; c 3. REPRODUCTIVE PHYSIOLOGY, LIGHT/ELECTRON MICROSCOPY. *Educ:* Lehigh Univ, BA, 65, MS, 67, PhD(biol), 71. *Prof Exp:* ASST PROF BIOL, ST JOSEPH'S COL, PA, 71- *Concurrent Pos:*

Consult, microscopy, 77. *Mem:* Soc Study Reproduction; Soc Develop Biol; Electron Microscope Soc Am; Sigma Xi. *Res:* Physiology of contractility; metabolism and histochemistry of the seminiferons tubule; development of the Sertoli cell population in rat and mouse testes; electron and light microscopy of Myoiol and Sertoli cells in the testes. *Mailing Add:* Dept of Biol St Joseph's Col Philadelphia PA 19131

MONSON, JAMES EDWARD, b Oakland, Calif, June 20, 32; m 54; c 3. ELECTRICAL ENGINEERING. *Educ:* Stanford Univ, BS, 54, MS, 55, PhD(elec eng), 61. *Prof Exp:* Mem tech staff, Bell Tel Labs, 55-56; develop engr, Hewlett-Packard Co, 56-61; ROBERT C SABINI PROF ENG, HARVEY MUDD COL, 61- *Concurrent Pos:* Consult, Bell & Howell Res Labs, 61-73 & Spin Physics, Inc, 74-; Ford Found residency in eng practice, Western Elec Co, 65-66; dir, Pac Measurements, Inc, 66-76; vis prof, Trinity Col, Dublin, 71-72; Fulbright res grant & sr lectr, Tehnichki Fakultet, Titograd, Yugoslavia, 75-76 & 80. *Mem:* Inst Elec & Electronics Engrs; Am Soc Eng Educ. *Res:* Magnetic recording and modulation techniques. *Mailing Add:* Dept of Eng Harvey Mudd Col Claremont CA 91711

MONSON, LEON A, metallurgy, see previous edition

MONSON, PAUL HERMAN, b Fargo, NDak, Sept 29, 25; m 50; c 3. PLANT TAXONOMY. *Educ:* Luther Col, BA, 50; Iowa State Univ, MS, 52, PhD(plant taxon), 59. *Prof Exp:* Instr biol, Luther Col, 52-55; instr bot, Iowa State Univ, 57-58; from asst prof to assoc prof, 58-68, PROF BIOL, UNIV MINN, DULUTH, 68-, CUR, OLGA LEKELA HERBARIUM, 74- *Concurrent Pos:* Partic, NSF Acad Year Inst, Brown Univ, 65-66. *Mem:* Am Soc Plant Taxon; Nat Asn Biol Teachers. *Res:* Flora of the midwest and aquatic plants; Nymphaea. *Mailing Add:* Dept of Biol Univ of Minn Duluth MN 55812

MONSON, RICHARD STANLEY, b Los Angeles, Calif, May 28, 37; m 66; c 2. CHEMISTRY. *Educ:* Univ Calif, Los Angeles, BS, 59; Univ Calif, Berkeley, PhD(chem), 64. *Prof Exp:* From asst prof to assoc prof, 63-72, PROF CHEM, CALIF STATE UNIV, HAYWARD, 72- *Concurrent Pos:* Fulbright-Hays fel & lectr, Univ Sarajevo, Yugoslavia, 72-73. *Mem:* Am Chem Soc. *Res:* Organic reaction mechanisms; novel methods of organic synthesis; reactions of organophosphorus intermediates. *Mailing Add:* Dept of Chem Calif State Univ Hayward CA 94542

MONSON, WARREN GLENN, b Clay Center, Nebr, Dec 24, 26; m 58; c 2. AGRONOMY. *Educ:* Univ Nebr, BSc, 51, MSc, 55, PhD, 58. *Prof Exp:* Asst agron, Univ Nebr, 57-58; res agronomist, NY, 58-66, RES AGRONOMIST, SCI & EDUC ADMIN-AGR RES, 66- *Mem:* Am Soc Agron; Crop Sci Soc Am; Am Forage & Grassland Coun. *Res:* Management and quality of pasture and forage crops. *Mailing Add:* Sci & Educ Admin USDA Tifton GA 31794

MONSON, WILLIAM JOYE, poultry nutrition, animal nutrition, see previous edition

MONSON, WILLIAM L(AMON), chemical engineering, see previous edition

MONSOUR, VICTOR, b Shreveport, La, Aug 28, 22; m 50; c 2. MICROBIOLOGY. *Educ:* La State Univ, Baton Rouge, BS, 48, MS, 50; Univ Tex, Austin, PhD(microbiol), 54. *Prof Exp:* Bacteriologist, Shreveport, Charity Hosp, La, 50-51; microbiologist, Confederate Med Ctr, Shreveport, La, 54-57; asst dir bur of lab, Div Health Mo, 57-59; PROF MICROBIOL & HEAD DEPT, MCNEESE STATE UNIV, 59- *Concurrent Pos:* Consult, Ark-La-Tex area hosps & clins, 54-56; on loan from Div Health Mo to sch Med, Wash Univ, 58-59; consult, area industs, La, 68- *Mem:* Air Pollution Control Asn; AAAS; Sigma Xi; Am Pub Health Asn; Nat Environ Health Asn. *Res:* Microbial metabolism; environmental science; chemical andand/or biological pollution. *Mailing Add:* Dept of Microbiol McNeese State Univ Lake Charles LA 70601

MONT, GEORGE EDWARD, b New Bedford, Mass, Aug 6, 35; m 57; c 4. POLYMER CHEMISTRY. *Educ:* Brown Univ, BS, 57; Clark Univ, MA, 59, PhD(chem), 64. *Prof Exp:* Res chemist, Shawiningan Resins Corp, 61-63; res specialist chem, 63-76, GROUP LEADER, MONSANTO CO, 76- *Res:* Polymer structure-property relationships, poly(vinyl butyral) chemistry. *Mailing Add:* Monsanto Co 190 Grochmal Ave Indian Orchard MA 01151

MONTAGNA, WILLIAM, b Roccacasale, Italy, July 6, 13; nat US; m 39, 80; c 4. BIOLOGY. *Educ:* Bethany Col, WVa, AB, 36; Cornell Univ, PhD(histol, embryol), 44. *Hon Degrees:* DSc, Bethany Col, WVa, 60; DBiolSci, Univ Sardinia, 64. *Prof Exp:* Instr zool, Cornell Univ, 44-45; from instr to asst prof anat, Long Island Col Med, 45-47; from asst prof to Herbert L Ballou prof biol, Brown Univ, 48-63; dir, Ore Regional Primate Res Ctr & prof exp biol & head div, Med Sch, Univ Ore, 63-82; PROF DERMAT, ORE HEALTH SCI UNIV, 82- *Concurrent Pos:* Spec lectr, Univ London, 53; vis prof, Univ Cincinnati, 58; mem sci comt, Int Cong Dermat, 62; consult, Nat Inst Child Health & Human Develop, 65-; counr, Japan Monkey Ctr, Aichi, 65-; mem adv comt, Washington County Child Develop Prog, Ore, 65-; mem comn natural sci, Nat Bd Fels, Bethany Col, 66-; sci consult, Inst Clin Dermat, Univ Cattolica Sacro Cuore, Rome, Italy, 81-; Harold Cummins Memorial lectr, Sch Med, Tulane Univ, New Orleans, 80; Louis A Duhring lectr, Pa Acad Dermat, Hershey, 81; William Montagna annual lectr, State Univ NY Downstate Med Ctr, 81; Frederick G Novy lectr, Univ Calif, Davis, 81. *Honors & Awards:* Soc Cosmetic Chemists Award, 57; Gold Award, Am Acad Dermat, 58; Gold Medal, Decorated Cavaliere Order of Merit, Ital Repub, 63; Cavaliere Ufficiale, Italian Repub, 69, Commendatore, 75; Stephen Rothman Award in Dermat, 72; Aubrey R Watzek Award, Lewis & Clark Col, 77; Hans Schwarzkopf Res Award, German Dermat Soc, 81. *Mem:* Soc Investigative Dermat; Am Acad Dermat; Geront Soc; NY Acad Sci; Sigma Xi (vpres, 57, pres, 60). *Res:* Cytophysiology; histophysiology and comparative anatomy of the skin; skin of primates; prosimians; primate reproduction. *Mailing Add:* Ore Regional Primate Res Ctr 505 NW 185th Ave Beaverton OR 97005

MONTAGNE, JOHN M, b White Plains, NY, Apr 17, 20; m 42; c 2. PHYSICAL GEOLOGY, ENVIRONMENTAL GEOLOGY. *Educ:* Dartmouth Col, BA, 42; Univ Wyo, MA, 51, PhD(geol), 55. *Prof Exp:* From instr to asst prof geol, Colo Sch Mines, 53-57; asst prof, 57-62, PROF GEOL, MONT STATE UNIV, 62- *Concurrent Pos:* Supply instr, Univ Wyo, 53-54; mem, Int Field Inst Geol, Italy, 64; mem curric panel, Am Geol Inst. *Mem:* Geol Soc Am; Am Inst Prof Geol; Glaciol Soc; Am Quarternary Asn (treas, 70-76); Am Asn Petrol Geol. *Res:* Cenozoic history of the Rocky Mountain region, particularly structural, stratigraphic and geomorphologic aspects; Pleistocene glacial geology and geomorphology; field geology in undergraduate geological education; snow dynamics; geology applied to land use planning. *Mailing Add:* Dept Earth Sci Mont State Univ Bozeman MT 59715

MONTAGUE, BARBARA ANN, b Hagerstown, Md, Aug 29, 29. INFORMATION SCIENCE. *Educ:* Randolph-Macon Woman's Col, AB, 51. *Prof Exp:* Anal chemist, Res Div, Plastics Dept, 51-60, info chemist, 60-61, head plastic dept info syst, 61-64, develop coord, Cent Report Index, Info Syst Dept, 64-67, supvr tech opers, 67-74, mgr info serv photo prods, Int Opers Div, 74-76, mgr info systs develop, 76-77, compensation supvr, 77-80, COMPENSATION CONSULT, CORP EMPLOYEE RELS DEPT, E I DU PONT DE NEMOURS & CO, INC, 80- *Concurrent Pos:* Mem adv bd, J Chem Info & Comput Sci, Am Chem Soc, 75-79. *Mem:* Am Chem Soc (chmn, Div Chem Info). *Res:* Quantitative organic analysis; spectra-structure correlations qualitative and quantitative using infrared spectroscopy; designing, installation, operation and testing of coordinate indexing systems for storage and retrieval of scientific and technical information. *Mailing Add:* RD 2 Box 26A Friends Meeting House Rd Hockessin DE 19707

MONTAGUE, DANIEL GROVER, b Yakima, Wash, July 7, 37; m 57; c 4. PHYSICS. *Educ:* Ore State Col, BS, 59; Univ Wash, MS, 63; Univ Southern Calif, PhD(physics), 66. *Prof Exp:* Reactor physicist, Gen Elec Co, Wash, 59-61; sr sci officer, Rutherford High Energy Lab, Sci Res Coun, Chilton, Eng, 66-69; asst prof, 69-74, ASSOC PROF PHYSICS, WILLAMETTE UNIV, 74- *Mem:* AAAS; Am Phys Soc; Am Asn Physics Teachers. *Res:* Charged particle scattering and induced reactions for projectiles in the 10 to 50 million electron volts range. *Mailing Add:* Dept of Physics Willamette Univ Salem OR 97301

MONTAGUE, ELEANOR D, b Genoa, Italy, Feb 11, 26; US citizen; m 53; c 4. RADIOTHERAPY. *Educ:* Univ Ala, BA, 47; Med Col Pa, MD, 50. *Prof Exp:* Resident path, Kings County Hosp, Brooklyn, 52-53; resident radiol, Columbia-Presby Med Ctr, 53-55; radiologist, 6160th US Air Force Hosp, Japan, 55-56; staff physician, Am Tel & Tel Co, NY, 56-57; Am Cancer Soc fel radiother, Univ Tex M D Anderson Hosp & Tumor Inst, 59-61, from asst radiotherapist to radiotherapist, 61-69, assoc prof radiother, 66-69; assoc clin prof radiol, Baylor Col Med, 69-72; PROF RADIATION THER, UNIV TEX M D ANDERSON HOSP & TUMOR INST, 73- *Mem:* Am Col Radiol; Am Radium Soc; Radiol Soc NAm; Am Soc Therapeut Radiol; AMA. *Res:* Clinical use of radiation therapy for treatment of neoplasia. *Mailing Add:* Dept of Radiation Ther M D Anderson Hosp & Tumor Inst Houston TX 77030

MONTAGUE, FREDRICK HOWARD, JR, b Lafayette, Ind, May 31, 45; m 68; c 1. WILDLIFE ECOLOGY. *Educ:* Purdue Univ, BS, 67, PhD(vert ecol), 75. *Prof Exp:* From res asst wildlife ecol to teaching asst, 70-75, ASST PROF WILDLIFE ECOL & DIR OFF STUDENT SERV, PURDUE UNIV, 75- *Mem:* Wildlife Soc; Am Soc Mammalogists. *Res:* Ecology of wild canids in Midwest; urban wildlife and disease; farm game management; farm habitat improvement projects. *Mailing Add:* Dept Forestry & Natural Resources Purdue Univ West Lafayette IN 47907

MONTAGUE, HARRIET FRANCES, b Buffalo, NY, June 9, 05. MATHEMATICS. *Educ:* Univ Buffalo, BS, 27, MA, 29; Cornell Univ, PhD(math), 35. *Prof Exp:* Asst, 27-29, from instr to prof, 29-73, dir, NSF Inst Math, 57-70, actg chmn dept math, 61-64, dir undergrad studies, Dept Math, 70-73, EMER PROF MATH, STATE UNIV NY BUFFALO, 73- *Mem:* Am Math Soc; Math Asn Am. *Res:* Mathematics education. *Mailing Add:* 236 Fayette Ave Kenmore NY 14223

MONTAGUE, JOHN H, b Man, July 16, 25; m 55; c 2. NUCLEAR PHYSICS. *Educ:* Univ Man, BSc, 46; Univ Chicago, SM, 48, PhD(physics), 50. *Prof Exp:* Fel nuclear physics, Nat Res Coun Can, Chalk River, Ont, 50-52; physicist, Assoc Elec Industs, Eng, 52-54; lectr physics, Queen's Univ, Ont, 54-55; sr Harwell fel nuclear physics, Atomic Energy Res Estab, Eng, 55-58, prin scientist, 58-66; prof physics, Queen's Univ, Ont, 66-73; PRIN SCIENTIST, ATOMIC ENERGY RES ESTAB, HARWELL, ENG, 74- *Concurrent Pos:* Prin res fel, Atomic Energy Res Estab, Harwell, Eng, 71-73. *Mem:* Am Phys Soc; Sigma Xi; Royal Soc Arts; Can Asn Physicists. *Res:* Nuclear physics, mainly at low energies with electrostatic generators; research and development management and planning. *Mailing Add:* Bus Develop Group Harwell Lab Harwell OX11ORA England

MONTAGUE, MICHAEL JAMES, b Flint, Mich, Dec 25, 47. PLANT PHYSIOLOGY, CELL BIOLOGY. *Educ:* Univ Mich-Flint, AB, 70, Univ Mich, Ann Arbor, MS, 72, PhD(cell & molecular biol), 74. *Prof Exp:* Res assoc plant physiol, Stanford Univ, 74-75; RES GROUP LEADER, MONSANTO AGR PROD CO, 75- *Mem:* Am Soc Plant Physiologists. *Res:* Investigate biochemical events involved in plant development, including the biochemical action of plant hormones and other processes which lead to differentiation. *Mailing Add:* Monsanto Agr Prod Co 800 N Lindbergh Blvd St Louis MO 63166

MONTAGUE, PATRICIA TUCKER, b Emporia, Kans, Nov 4, 37; m 65; c 2. MATHEMATICS, COMPUTER SCIENCE. *Educ:* Kans State Univ, BS, 57; Univ Wis-Madison, MS, 58, PhD(math), 61. *Prof Exp:* From instr to asst prof math, Univ Ill, Urbana, 61-67; assoc prof, Univ Tenn, Knoxville, 67-75; ASSOC PROF, UNIV NEBR, OMAHA, 77- *Mem:* Am Math Soc; Math Asn Am. *Res:* Algebra; representations of finite groups. *Mailing Add:* 304 S 50th Ave Omaha NE 68132

MONTAGUE, STEPHEN, b Los Angeles, Calif, July 17, 40; m 65; c 2. MATHEMATICS. *Educ:* Pomona Col, BS, 62; Univ Ill, Urbana, PhD(math), 67; Univ Tenn, Knoxville, MS, 75. *Prof Exp:* Asst prof math, Univ Tenn, Knoxville, 67-74; asst prof math, Univ Nebr, Omaha, 75-80; TECH ANALYST, TRW CORP, 80- *Mem:* Asn Comput Mach; Math Asn Am; Oper Res Soc Am. *Res:* Algebra; transitive extentions of finite permutation groups; operations research; optimization techniques; non-linear programming. *Mailing Add:* TRW Corp 1103 Galvia Rd S Bellevue NE 68123

MONTALBETTI, RAYMON, b Cranbrook, BC, Can, Feb 7, 24; m 49; c 3. PHYSICS. *Educ:* Univ Alta, BSc, 46; Univ Sask, PhD(nuclear physics), 52. *Prof Exp:* Res officer physics, Nat Res Coun Can, 46-49; sci officer upper atmospheric physics, Defense Res Bd, 52-64, officer in charge, Defense Res North Lab, 58-60; from asst prof to assoc prof, 60-68, PROF PHYSICS, UNIV SASK, 68-, HEAD PHYSICS DEPT, 76- *Mem:* Can Asn Physicists. *Res:* Photonuclear reactions; auroral and upper atmospheric physics. *Mailing Add:* Dept of Physics Univ of Sask Saskatoon SK S7H 0W0 Can

MONTALVO, JOSE MIGUEL, b Cali, Colombia, June 30, 28; m 51; c 5. MEDICINE, PEDIATRICS. *Educ:* Univ Tenn, BS, 51, MD, 57; Am Bd Pediat & Am Bd Pediat Endocrinol, dipl. *Prof Exp:* From intern pediat to chief resident, Frank T Toby Children's Hosp, Univ Tenn, 57-59, Rockefeller Found fel, 58-59; asst prof, Univ Valle, Colombia, 59-60; chief resident, Frank T Toby Children's Hosp, Univ Tenn, 60-61; from instr to assoc prof, 62-74, PROF PEDIAT, MED CTR, UNIV MISS, 74-, CHIEF DIV PEDIAT ENDOCRINOL, 80- *Concurrent Pos:* Consult, Miss State Ment Hosp, Whitfield & USPHS Indian Hosp, Philadelphia, 61- *Mem:* Endocrine Soc; Am Soc Pediat Nephrology; Am Fedn Clin Res; Int Soc Nephrology; fel Am Acad Pediat. *Res:* Pediatric endocrine and metabolic disorders. *Mailing Add:* Dept Pediat Univ Miss Med Ctr Jackson MS 39216

MONTALVO, JOSEPH G, b Cottonport, La, Oct 30, 37; m 61; c 1. ANALYTICAL CHEMISTRY. *Educ:* Univ Southwestern La, BS, 59, MS, 61; La State Univ, New Orleans, PhD(anal chem), 68. *Prof Exp:* Anal chemist, Shell Oil Co, 61-64; NSF res fel, La State Univ, New Orleans, 65-68, res fel, 68-69; mgr, Dept Anal Chem, 71-77, ANAL CHEMIST, GULF SOUTH RES INST, 69-, STAFF SCIENTIST, 77- *Mem:* Am Chem Soc; Am Soc Testing & Mat. *Res:* Ion-selective electrodes; dipsticks; personnel badges; dioxin methods development; total organic chlorine instrumentation. *Mailing Add:* Gulf South Res Inst PO Box 26518 New Orleans LA 70186

MONTALVO, RAMIRO A, b Monterrey, Mex, Dec 18, 37; US citizen; m 67; c 2. SOLID STATE PHYSICS. *Educ:* Ill Inst Technol, BS, 60; Northwestern Univ, PhD(physics), 67. *Prof Exp:* Asst physics, Northwestern Univ, 60-66; physicist, Aerospace Res Labs, Off Aerospace Res, US Air Force, 66-69; res scientist, Geomet Inc, 69-73; prin staff mem, Opers Res Inc, 73-76; ELECTRONIC ENGR, US NAVY, 76- *Mem:* Am Phys Soc. *Res:* Magnetic properties of metals at low temperatures; operations research; test and evaluation; data and voice communications; underwater acoustics; computer modeling. *Mailing Add:* 3 Simms Court Kensington MD 20895

MONTANA, ANDREW FREDERICK, b Oil City, Pa, Jan 15, 30; m 67. ORGANIC CHEMISTRY. *Educ:* Seattle Pac Col, BS, 51; Univ Wash, PhD(org chem), 57. *Prof Exp:* Asst prof chem, Seattle Pac Col, 55-61 & Univ Hawaii, 61-63; assoc prof & dept chmn, 63-70, PROF CHEM, CALIF STATE UNIV, FULLERTON, 70- *Mem:* AAAS; Am Chem Soc; NY Acad Sci. *Res:* Pseudoaromatics. *Mailing Add:* Dept of Chem Calif State Univ 800 N State College Blvd Fullerton CA 92634

MONTANO, PEDRO ANTONIO, b Havana, Cuba, Feb 26, 40; m 62; c 2. SOLID STATE PHYSICS, PHYSICAL CHEMISTRY. *Educ:* Israel Inst Technol, BSc, 67, MSc, 68, PhD(physics), 72. *Prof Exp:* Res assoc, Univ Calif, Santa Barbara, 72-75; asst prof, 75-77, assoc prof solid state physics, 78-80, PROF PHYSICS, WVA UNIV, 80- *Concurrent Pos:* NSF grant, 78. *Mem:* Am Phys Soc; Mat Res Soc. *Res:* Matrix isolation techniques; characterization of metal clusters; mineral matter in coal; synthetic fuels; catalysis. *Mailing Add:* Dept of Physics WVa Univ Morgantown WV 26506

MONTEITH, LARRY KING, b Bryson City, NC, Aug 17, 33; m 52; c 3. ELECTRICAL ENGINEERING, SOLID STATE ELECTRONICS. *Educ:* NC State Univ, BS, 60; Duke Univ, MS, 62, PhD(elec eng), 65. *Prof Exp:* Mem tech staff, Bell Tel Labs, 60-62; res engr, Res Triangle Inst, 62-66, sr scientist, 66-67, group leader mat & devices, 67-68; assoc prof solid state electronics, 68-72, prof, 72-74, prof elec eng & head dept, 74-78, DEAN ENG, NC STATE UNIV, 78- *Concurrent Pos:* Consult, Res Triangle Inst, 68- *Mem:* AAAS; Inst Elec & Electronics Engrs; Am Soc Elec Engrs. *Res:* Charge transport in organic polymers; metal-organic compounds and silicon oxides; electronic properties and device applications of silicon; electronic materials. *Mailing Add:* Dept of Elec Eng NC State Univ Daniels 232 Raleigh NC 27607

MONTELARO, JAMES, b Melville, La, Mar 3, 21; m 55; c 1. HORTICULTURE. *Educ:* Southwest La Inst, BS, 41; La State Univ, MS, 50; Univ Fla, PhD(hort), 52. *Prof Exp:* Asst hort, Univ Fla, 52-55; horticulturist, Minute Maid Corp, 55-57; assoc veg specialist, 58-65, VEG CROPS SPECIALIST, UNIV FLA, 65-, PROF, INST FOOD & AGR SCI, 74- *Mem:* Am Soc Hort Sci. *Res:* Nutrition and physiology of vegetable crops. *Mailing Add:* Inst Food Sci Univ of Fla Gainesville FL 32611

MONTEMURRO, DONALD GILBERT, b North Bay, Ont, May 27, 30; m 54; c 2. NEUROANATOMY, NEUROENDOCRINOLOGY. *Educ:* Univ Western Ont, BA, 51, MSc, 54, PhD(physiol), 57. *Prof Exp:* Sr res asst, Med Sch, Univ Western Ont, 57-58; Brit Empire Cancer Campaign exchange fel, Chester Beatty Res Inst, Royal Cancer Hosp, London, 58-60; Cancer Inst Can res fel, Sch Med, Yale Univ, 60-61; assoc prof physiol, 61-68, anat, Health Sci Centre, 68-72, chmn dept anat, 73-78, PROF ANAT, HEALTH SCI CENTRE, UNIV WESTERN ONT, 72- *Mem:* Fel Royal Soc Med; Can Neurol Soc; Am Asn Anatomists; Can Asn Anat. *Res:* Endocrinology; histology and physiology of the adeno- and neurohypophysis; role of the hypothalamus in water and energy metabolism; scanning and transmission electron microscopy; neuroanatomy and neuroendocrine function of the hypothalamus. *Mailing Add:* Dept of Anat Univ Western Ont Health Sci Ctr London ON N6A 5C1 Can

MONTENYOHL, VICTOR IRL, b Akron, Ohio, Mar 18, 21; m 46; c 3. CHEMISTRY. *Educ:* Stanford Univ, AB, 42; Princeton Univ, MA, 47, PhD(chem), 50. *Prof Exp:* Res assoc, Princeton Univ, 42-46; res chemist, Budget & Planning Div, E I du Pont de Nemours, Co, Inc, 47-53, res supvr, 53-63, chief supvr, 74-79; RETIRED. *Mem:* AAAS; Am Chem Soc; Am Soc Metals. *Res:* Surface chemistry; corrosion; non-destructive testing; metallurgy; research planning and funding. *Mailing Add:* 1050 Two Notch Rd Aiken SC 29801

MONTES, LEOPOLDO F, b Buenos Aires, Arg, Nov 22, 29; m 61; c 6. DERMATOLOGY, MYCOLOGY. *Educ:* Univ Buenos Aires, MD, 54; Univ Mich, MS, 59; FRCPS(C). *Prof Exp:* Resident dermat, Pirovano Hosp, Buenos Aires, 55; resident, Pa Hosp, Philadelphia, 55-56; resident, Med Ctr, Univ Mich, 56-57, from jr clin instr to sr clin instr, 57-60, res assoc anat, Med Sch, 59, NSF grant & res assoc zool, 60-61, USPHS grant & res assoc anat & dermat, 62; asst prof dermat, Baylor Col Med, 63-66; assoc prof, 66-70, PROF DERMAT, MED CTR, UNIV ALA, BIRMINGHAM, 70-, ASSOC PROF MICROBIOL, 69- *Concurrent Pos:* USPHS res career develop award, 65-71; ed, J Cutaneous Path. *Mem:* Int Soc Trop Dermat; Am Acad Dermat; Soc Invest Dermat; fel Am Acad Microbiol; Am Dermat Asn. *Res:* Cutaneous manifestations of systemic diseases; histochemistry, mainly oxidative enzymes; cutaneous infections caused by yeast; electron microscopy; fine structure of psoriatic skin; acne vulgaris; cytochemistry of the axillary sweat glands. *Mailing Add:* Dept of Dermat Univ of Ala Med Ctr Birmingham AL 35294

MONTET, GEORGE LOUIS, b Ventress, La, Dec 10, 19; m 46; c 2. CHEMICAL PHYSICS. *Educ:* La State Univ, BS, 40; Univ Chicago, MS, 49, PhD(chem), 51. *Prof Exp:* Plant engr, Bird & Son, Inc, 40-42 & 46; shift supt, Huntsville Arsenal, 42; assoc chemist, 51-74, proj leader, 72-78, CHEMIST, ARGONNE NAT LAB, 74-, PROG MGR, ENVIRONMENTAL IMPACT STUDIES, 78- *Concurrent Pos:* Fulbright lectr, Univ Ankara, 62-63; adj prof, Northern Ill Univ, 68-71. *Mem:* AAAS; Am Phys Soc; Sigma Xi. *Res:* Solid state physics; quantum chemistry; statistical mechanics; environmental assessment. *Mailing Add:* 424 Bunning Dr Downers Grove IL 60515

MONTGOMERIE, ROBERT DENNIS, b Toronto, Ont, Jan 22, 47. ECOLOGY, EVOLUTIONARY BIOLOGY. *Educ:* Univ Guelph, BSc, 72; McGill Univ, PhD(biol), 79. *Prof Exp:* Lectr ecol, Univ Victoria, 78-79; fel, McGill Univ, 79-80; RES FEL & ASST PROF, QUEEN'S UNIV, 80- *Mem:* Ecol Soc Am; Am Soc Naturalists; Soc Study Evolution; Am Ornithologists Union; Can Soc Zoologists. *Res:* Evolutionary ecology; competition; behavioral ecology; community structure; energetics; foraging; arctic and tropical ecology; nectar-feeding animals; pollination ecology. *Mailing Add:* Dept Biol Queen's Univ Kingston ON K7L 3N6 Can

MONTGOMERY, ANTHONY JOHN, b Lincoln, Eng, July 13, 37; m 60; c 4. OPTICS. *Educ:* Univ London, BSc, 58, PhD(optics), 61, DIC, 61. *Prof Exp:* Sr scientist optics, IIT Res Inst, 61-69; mgr imaging systs, Xerox Corp, NY, 69-73, dept mgr, Xerox Res, Eng, 73-75, mgr advan develop, Conn, 75-80, MGR FUJI-XEROX RELATIONS, XEROX CORP, 80- *Mem:* Optical Soc Am; Soc Photog Sci & Eng; fel Brit Inst Physics. *Res:* Optical instrumentation; image evaluation; analysis of imaging systems; psychophysics of images. *Mailing Add:* Xerox Corp Stamford CT 06904

MONTGOMERY, ARTHUR VERNON, b Sinton, Tex, Nov 17, 22; m 56; c 4. PHYSIOLOGY. *Educ:* Univ Ariz, BS, 46; Univ Colo, PhD(physiol), 53, MD, 57. *Prof Exp:* Instr physiol, Univ Tex Med Br Galveston, 49-50; res assoc, Med Sch, Univ Colo, 50-52, instr, 52-54, instr surg, 54-57, dir, Halsted Lab Exp Surg, 57-59; chief exp toxicol, US Air Force Sch Aerospace Med, 59-60, chief physiol & biophys, 60-61; mgr life sci depts, McDonnell Aircraft Corp, 61-70, DIR LIFE SCI SUBDIV, McDONNELL DOUGLAS ASTRONAUT CO, 70- *Concurrent Pos:* Am Heart Asn fel, 57-59. *Honors & Awards:* Hektoen Gold Medal, AMA, 55. *Mem:* Am Physiol Soc. *Res:* Physiology of intrarenal pressure; satiation of thirst; applications of general hypothermia to cardiac surgery; environmental physiology. *Mailing Add:* McDonnell Douglas Astronaut Co PO Box 516 St Louis MO 63166

MONTGOMERY, CHARLES GRAY, b Philadelphia, Pa, Apr 9, 37; m 66; c 2. THEORETICAL PHYSICS. *Educ:* Yale Univ, BA, 59; Calif Inst Technol, MS, 61, PhD(physics), 65. *Prof Exp:* Vis lectr physics, Hollins Col, 65; from asst prof to assoc prof, 65-75, PROF PHYSICS, UNIV TOLEDO, 75- *Concurrent Pos:* Consult, Owens-Ill, Inc, 65-70 & GTE Labs, Inc, 75-76. *Mem:* Am Phys Soc; Am Asn physics Teachers. *Res:* Statistical and solid state physics. *Mailing Add:* Dept Physics Univ Toledo Toledo OH 43606

MONTGOMERY, DANIEL MICHAEL, b Indianapolis, Ind, Nov 2, 43; m 66; c 1. RADIATION ECOLOGY, RADIOCHEMISTRY. *Educ:* St Martin's Col, BS, 65; Purdue Univ, Lafayette, PhD(nuclear chem), 69. *Prof Exp:* Res assoc nuclear chem, Univ Marburg; NSF res assoc, Carnegie-Mellon Univ, 70-71; res chemist, Nat Environ Res Ctr, Environ Protection Agency, 71-74, head radioecol sect, 74-78; RADIATIONS SPECIALIST ENVIRON & SPEC PROJ SECT, US NUCLEAR REGULATORY COMN, 78- *Concurrent Pos:* Vis scientist, Europ Orgn Nuclear Res, Geneva, Switz, 69-70. *Res:* Radiochemical analysis of environmental samples; radioecology; neutron activation analysis; radiological surveillance at nuclear facilities. *Mailing Add:* US Nuclear Regulatory Comn 101 Marietta St Atlanta GA 30303

MONTGOMERY, DAVID CAMPBELL, b Milan, Mo, Mar 5, 36; m 57; c 2. PLASMA PHYSICS, STATISTICAL MECHANICS. *Educ:* Univ Wis, BS, 56; Princeton Univ, MA, 58, PhD(physics), 59. *Prof Exp:* Assoc, Proj Matterhorn, Princeton Univ, 59-60; res assoc physics, Univ Wis, 61, instr, 61-62; res asst prof, Univ Md, 62-64; vis researcher, State Univ Utrecht, 64-65; from assoc prof to prof physics, Univ Iowa, 65-77; PROF PHYSICS, COL WILLIAM & MARY, 77- *Concurrent Pos:* Consult, Oak Ridge Nat Lab, 62-70, Goddard Space Flight Ctr, NASA, 63-64 & Los Alamos Sci Lab, 69-71; vis assoc prof, Univ Calif, Berkeley, 69-70; assoc ed, Physics of Fluids, 71, 72 & 73; assoc ed, Int J Eng Sci, 71-; vis prof, Hunter Col, 73-74, adj prof, 74-75; consult, NASA, 77-; vis res prof, Univ Md, College Park, 77-; consult, NASA Hq, 77-; vis staff mem, Los Alamos Nat Lab, 77- *Mem:* Fel Am Phys Soc; Sigma Xi; Am Geophys Union. *Res:* Theoretical plasma physics; kinetic theory; strongly magnetized plasmas; turbulence theory; non-equilibrium statistical mechanics and transport theory. *Mailing Add:* Dept Physics Col William & Mary Williamsburg VA 23185

MONTGOMERY, DAVID CAREY, b Elmhurst, Ill, Aug 21, 38; m 68. PHYSICS, INSTITUTIONAL RESEARCH. *Educ:* Mass Inst Technol, BS, 60; Univ Ill, MS, 61, PhD(physics), 67. *Prof Exp:* From instr to asst prof physics, Oberlin Col, 66-71, registrar & asst provost, 71-73, dir, Inst Res & Planning, 73-74; coordr, State Univ Syst Fla, 75-76, dir planning & anal, 77-82; SR RES SCIENTIST, CTR NUCLEAR STUDIES, MEMPHIS STATE UNIV, 82- *Mem:* Am Phys Soc; Am Asn Higher Educ; Asn Instit Res. *Res:* Evaluation of educational programs. *Mailing Add:* Ctr Nuclear Studies Memphis State Univ Memphis TN 38152

MONTGOMERY, DEANE, b Weaver, Minn, Sept 2, 09; m 33; c 2. TOPOLOGY. *Educ:* Hamline Univ, BA, 29; Univ Iowa, MS, 30, PhD(math), 33. *Prof Exp:* Nat Res Coun fel, Harvard Univ, 33-34 & Inst Adv Study, 34-35; from asst prof to prof math, Smith Col, 35-46; assoc prof, Yale Univ, 46-48; Guggenheim fel, 41-42, mem, Nat Defense Res Comt Proj, 45-46, mem, Inst Advan Study, 48-51, PROF MATH, INST ADVAN STUDY, 51- *Concurrent Pos:* Vis assoc prof, Princeton Univ, 43-45. *Mem:* Nat Acad Sci; Int Math Union (pres, 75-78); Am Philos Soc. *Res:* Topology; topological groups. *Mailing Add:* Inst Advan Study Princeton NJ 08540

MONTGOMERY, DONALD BRUCE, b Hartford, Conn, July 1, 33; m 57; c 2. PHYSICS, ELECTRICAL ENGINEERING. *Educ:* Williams Col, BA, 57; Mass Inst Technol, BS & MS, 57; Univ Lausanne, DSc, 68. *Prof Exp:* Mem staff eng, Arthur D Little, Inc, 57-59; mem staff magnet develop, Lincoln Lab, 59-61, group leader magnet develop, 61-78, ASSOC DIR TECHNOL, PLASMA FUSION CTR, MASS INST TECHNOL, 78- *Res:* High field magnet design; cryogenics and superconductivity. *Mailing Add:* Nat Magnet Lab Mass Inst of Technol Cambridge MA 02139

MONTGOMERY, DONALD JOSEPH, b Cincinnati, Ohio, June 11, 17; m 42; c 4. SOLID STATE PHYSICS. *Educ:* Univ Cincinnati, ChE, 39, PhD(theoret physics), 45. *Prof Exp:* Instr, Univ Cincinnati, 42-44; res assoc, Princeton Univ, 45-46, asst prof, 46-47; physicist, London Br, Off Naval Res, 47-48, Ballistic Res Labs, 48-50 & Textile Res Inst, 50-53; assoc prof physics, 53-56, prof, 56-60, res prof, 60-65, prof metall, mech & mat sci & chmn dept, 66-71, PROF PHYSICS, MICH STATE UNIV, 66-, RES PROF ENG, 71- *Concurrent Pos:* Fulbright lectr, Univ Grenoble, 59-60, Guggenheim fel, 60; spec asst to dir, Off Grants & Res Contracts, NASA, Washington, DC, 64-65; vis res physicist, Space Sci Lab, Univ Calif, Berkeley, 65-66; mem, Int Inst for Empirical Socioecon, Augsburg-Leiterhofen, 74-75; Fulbright sr researcher & vis prof, Dept Macroecon, Univ Augsburg, Ger; mem, Textile Res Inst. *Mem:* AAAS; Am Phys Soc; Soc Social Studies Sci; Policy Studies Orgn; Acad Polit Sci. *Res:* Materials science, solid state, chemical physics; technology and public policy; sociotechnical assessment. *Mailing Add:* Col Eng Mich State Univ East Lansing MI 48824

MONTGOMERY, DOUGLAS C(ARTER), b Roanoke, Va, June 5, 43; m 65. INDUSTRIAL ENGINEERING. *Educ:* Va Polytech Inst, BS, 65, MS, 67, PhD(indust eng), 69. *Prof Exp:* Instr indust eng, Va Polytech Inst, 65-69; from asst prof to assoc prof, 69-78, PROF INDUST & SYSTS ENG, GA INST TECHNOL, 78- *Mem:* Am Inst Indust Engrs; Am Statist Asn; Opers Res Soc Am; Inst Mgt Sci; Am Soc Qual Control. *Res:* Engineering statistics, including experimental design; operations research; inventory theory; forecasting and time series analysis. *Mailing Add:* Sch of Indust & Systs Eng Ga Inst of Technol Atlanta GA 30303

MONTGOMERY, EDWARD BENJAMIN, b Louisville, Ky, June 15, 15; m 42; c 4. PHYSICS. *Educ:* Univ Louisville, BA, 42. *Prof Exp:* Ballistic physicist, Okla Ord Works, 42-43; asst, Metall Lab, Univ Chicago, 43-44; physicist, Hanford Works, Gen Elec Co, 44-50, group head exp physics, 49-51, sect chief pile applns, 51-52, physicist adv tech, 52-54, data processing specialist, 54-56, mgr systs anal, Comput Dept, 56-57, consult prod planning, 57-59, consult physicist comput applns, 59-61, proj engr educ tech proj, 61-63; res consult, Syracuse Univ, 63-65, dean sch libr sci, 65-68; PROF MED COMPUT SCI, UNIV TX HEALTH SCI CTR, DALLAS, 68- *Mem:* AAAS; Am Phys Soc; Inst Elec & Electronics Engrs. *Res:* Information systems; mass data handling; automation of research process; higher education analyst. *Mailing Add:* 6720 Greenwich Lane Dallas TX 75230

MONTGOMERY, EDWARD HARRY, b Houston, Tex, July 8, 39; m 63; c 3. PHARMACOLOGY, PHYSIOLOGY. *Educ:* Univ Houston, BS, 61, MS, 63; Univ Tex, PhD(pharmacol), 67. *Prof Exp:* Teaching fel, Univ Houston, 61-63, Nat Inst Dent Res training grant, 63-67; from asst prof to assoc prof pharmacol, Dent Sch, Univ Ore, 67-72; ASSOC PROF PHARMACOL, UNIV TEX DENT BR HOUSTON, 72- *Concurrent Pos:* USPHS gen res serv fund grant, Univ Ore, 67-69, Nat Inst Dent Res grant, 69- *Honors & Awards:* Lehn & Fink Award, 61. *Mem:* AAAS; Sigma Xi; Int Asn Dent Res. *Res:* Role of vasoactive polypeptides as inflammatory mediators; mechanism of action of anti-inflammatory drugs; release of catecholamines by bradykinin and other vasoactive polypeptides; studies of the mediator systems involved in gingival inflammation. *Mailing Add:* Dept of Pharmacol Univ of Tex Dent Br Houston TX 77025

MONTGOMERY, EDWIN HANSEN, b San Fernando, Calif, Dec 17, 26; m 50; c 5. MINING ENGINEERING. *Educ:* Colo Sch Mines, Engr Mines, 51. *Prof Exp:* Cartog engr, US Geol Surv Calif, 51-52; mining engr, Miami Copper Co, Ariz, 52-54; multiplex operator, Ryall Engr Co, Colo, 54; valuation engr, Colo State Off, US Bur Land Mgt, US Dept Interior, 54-60, valuation engr, Div Minerals, DC, 60-61, staff asst, Off Secy Resource Prog Staff, US Dept Interior, 61-65, chief mining staff, US Bur Land Mgt, 65-67, chief br energy & mineral resources, 67-69, leader, Energy & Minerals Staff, 69-80; CONSULT ENGR, 80- *Mem:* Am Inst Mining, Metall & Petrol Engrs. *Res:* Geology; mineral economics; effects and reclamation of surface-mined land; public land and mining law administration; oil shale development and policy; ecology and environment, especially as related to mineral development. *Mailing Add:* 7716 S Newland St Littleton CO 80123

MONTGOMERY, ERROL LEE, b Roseburg, Ore, May 1, 39; m 60; c 2. HYDROGEOLOGY. *Educ:* Ore State Univ, BS, 62; Univ Ariz, MS, 63, PhD(hydrogeol), 71. *Prof Exp:* Groundwater geologist, Wyo State Engrs Off, 63-65; geohydrologist, Wright Water Engrs, Colo, 65-67; asst prof geol, Northern Ariz Univ, 70-77; PRIN, HARGIS & MONTGOMERY, INC, 79- *Concurrent Pos:* Hydrogeologist, Harshbarger & Assocs, 68-79; Fulbright-Hays scholar, Lisbon, Portugal, 78. *Mem:* Am Geophys Union; Am Water Resources Asn; Asn Eng Geol. *Res:* Hydrogeology; applications of geophysics to hydrogeology; aquifer and aquifer systems analysis; engineering geology. *Mailing Add:* 447 E Canyon View Place Tucson AZ 85704

MONTGOMERY, G(EORGE) FRANKLIN, b Oakmont, Pa, May 1, 21; m 67; c 1. ELECTRICAL ENGINEERING. *Educ:* Purdue Univ, BS, 41. *Prof Exp:* Radio engr, Naval Res Lab, Washington, 41-44; electronic scientist, Nat Bur Standards, 46-58, chief, Electronic Instrumentation Div, 58-60, Instrumentation Div, 60-64 & Measurement Eng Div, 64-75, sr eng adv, 75-78; CONSULT ENGR, 78- *Mem:* Fel Inst Elec & Electronics Engrs; Audio Eng Soc. *Res:* Instrumentation and communication circuit design; modulation theory; product performance. *Mailing Add:* 2806 Kanawha St NW Washington DC 20015

MONTGOMERY, GEORGE PAUL, JR, b Atlanta, Ga, Jan 5, 43; m 68; c 1. LASERS. *Educ:* Loyola Col, Md, BS, 64; Univ Ill, Urbana, MS, 66, PhD(physics), 71. *Prof Exp:* Nat Acad Sci-Nat Res Coun resident res assoc, US Naval Res Lab, 70-72; ASSOC SR RES PHYSICIST, GEN MOTORS RES LABS, 72- *Mem:* Optical Soc Am; Sigma Xi; Am Phys Soc. *Res:* Coherent optical data processing. *Mailing Add:* Gen Motors Res Labs GM Tech Ctr Warren MI 48090

MONTGOMERY, HUGH, b Austin, Tex, Apr 17, 04; m 30; c 3. MEDICINE. *Educ:* Haverford Col, BS, 25; Harvard Univ, MD, 30. *Prof Exp:* Res, Harvard Med Sch & Marine Biol Lab, Woods Hole, 27-28; intern, Mass Gen Hosp, 31-32; res fel pharmacol, 32-35, instr clin med, 35-41, Heckscher fel, 37-38, Thompson fel, 38-39, assoc med, 41-47, asst prof clin med, 47-52, from assoc prof to prof med, 52-60, EMER PROF MED, SCH MED, UNIV PA, 72- *Mem:* AAAS; Am Soc Clin Invest; Am Med Asn; Asn Am Physicians; fel Am Col Physicians. *Res:* Peripheral circulation; metabolism and oxygen tension of tissue; chemical constitution of glomerular and tubular fluids. *Mailing Add:* 932 Merion Square Rd Gladwyne PA 19035

MONTGOMERY, HUGH LOWELL, b Muncie, Ind, Aug 26, 44; div; c 2. MATHEMATICS. *Educ:* Univ Ill, BS, 66; Cambridge Univ, PhD(math), 72. *Prof Exp:* From asst prof to assoc prof, 72-75, PROF MATH, UNIV MICH, ANN ARBOR, 75- *Concurrent Pos:* Fel math, Trinity Col, Cambridge Univ, 69-73; Sloan Found fel, 74-77. *Honors & Awards:* Salem Prize, Fr Math Soc, 74. *Mem:* Am Math Soc; Math Asn Am. *Res:* Number theory; analytic number theory. *Mailing Add:* Dept of Math Univ of Mich Ann Arbor MI 48109

MONTGOMERY, ILENE NOWICKI, b Detroit, Mich, Aug 20, 42; m 68; c 2. NEUROGENETICS, NEUROIMMUNOLOGY. *Educ:* Univ Detroit, BS, 64; Univ Mo, MS, 67; Univ Ill, Urbana, PhD(genetics), 73. *Prof Exp:* Fel molecular biol, Univ, 73-75, fel immunol, 75-77, RES ASSOC IMMUNOL, SCH MED, WAYNE STATE UNIV, 77- *Mem:* Sigma Xi; Genetics Soc Am; Am Genetic Asn. *Res:* Genetics of neuroimmunolgy, with particular emphasis on the genetics of neurologic disorders of immunologic etiology. *Mailing Add:* Dept Immunol & Microbiol Sch Med Wayne State Univ 540 E Canfield Detroit MI 48201

MONTGOMERY, JAMES DOUGLAS, b Morristown, NJ, July 28, 37. BOTANY, TAXONOMY. *Educ:* Bucknell Univ, BS, 59; Rutgers Univ, MS, 61, PhD(bot), 64. *Prof Exp:* From instr to assoc prof biol, Upsala Col, 64-74; RES BIOLOGIST, ICHTHYOL ASSOCS, 74- *Mem:* Am Soc Plant Taxonomists; Am Fern Soc; Ecol Soc Am; Torrey Bot Club. *Res:* Ecology and effects of power plants; floristics; hybridization and distribution of ferns; biosystematics. *Mailing Add:* Ichthyol Assocs Rd 1 Berwick PA 18603

MONTGOMERY, JOHN ATTERBURY, b Greenville, Miss, Mar 29, 24; m 47; c 4. ORGANIC CHEMISTRY, MEDICINAL CHEMISTRY. *Educ:* Vanderbilt Univ, BA, 46, MS, 47; Univ NC, PhD(chem), 51. *Prof Exp:* Fel, Univ NC, 51-52; chemist, 52-56, head org div, 56-62, dir org chem res, 61-74, vpres, 74-80, SR VPRES & DIR KETTERING MEYER LAB, SOUTHERN RES INST, 81- *Concurrent Pos:* Adj prof, Birmingham Southern Col, 57-62; mem chem adv panel, Cancer Chemother Nat Serv Ctr, Nat Cancer Inst, 60-61, consult, 62-70; consult, Health Res Facilities Br, NIH, 62-63, mem med chem study sect, 64-68 & 71, mem exp therapeut study sect, 75-79, mem biol org & natural prod chem study sect, 81-83; mem bd sci adv, Sloan Kettering Inst; adj sr scientist, Comprehensive Cancer Ctr, Univ Ala. *Honors & Awards:* Herty Award, Am Chem Soc, 74; T O Soine Award, Unif Minn, 79; Southern Chemist Award, Am Chem Soc, 80. *Mem:* AAAS; Am Chem Soc; Sigma Xi; Am Soc Pharmacol & Exp Therapeut; fel NY Acad Sci. *Res:* Organic syntheses; biochemistry; chemotherapy; pharmacology. *Mailing Add:* Southern Res Inst 2000 Ninth Ave S Birmingham AL 35205

MONTGOMERY, LAWRENCE KERNAN, b Denver, Colo, May 6, 35; m 58; c 2. ORGANIC CHEMISTRY, PHYSICAL CHEMISTRY. *Educ:* Colo State Univ, BS, 57; Calif Inst Technol, PhD(chem), 61. *Prof Exp:* Fel, Harvard Univ, 60-62; from instr to asst prof, 62-67, ASSOC PROF CHEM, IND UNIV, BLOOMINGTON, 67- *Concurrent Pos:* Consult ed org chem, Holt, Reinhart & Winston, 67- *Mem:* Am Chem Soc. *Res:* Reaction mechanisms; deuteron nuclear magnetic resonance; electron diffraction studies on short-lived molecular species. *Mailing Add:* Dept of Chem Ind Univ Bloomington IN 47401

MONTGOMERY, MABEL D, b Delevan, NY, Aug 18, 19. MATHEMATICS. *Educ:* Houghton Col, AB, 39; Univ Buffalo, MA, 49, PhD(math), 53. *Prof Exp:* Teacher pub schs, NY, 39-46; instr math, Univ Buffalo, 46-54, supvr credentials, 54-58; assoc prof, 58-62, prof, 62-81, EMER PROF MATH, STATE UNIV NY COL BUFFALO, 81- *Mem:* Math Asn Am; Am Math Soc; Nat Coun Teachers Math. *Res:* Topology; mathematics education. *Mailing Add:* 236 Fayette Ave Kenmore NY 14223

MONTGOMERY, MAX MALCOLM, b Williamsburg, Iowa, June 14, 04; m 29; MEDICINE. *Educ:* Univ Iowa, BS, 27; Univ Ill, MD, 31, MS, 40; Am Bd Internal Med, dipl, 41. *Prof Exp:* Res fel path, Cook County Hosp, 37-39; from asst prof to prof med, 46-71, EMER PROF MED, UNIV ILL MED CTR, 71- *Mem:* Am Rheumatism Asn; Am Fedn Clin Res. *Res:* Rheumatic diseases. *Mailing Add:* 2052 N Lincoln Pkwy Chicago IL 60614

MONTGOMERY, MICHAEL DAVIS, b San Luis Obispo, Calif, June 4, 36; m 58; c 4. PHYSICS. *Educ:* Stanford Univ, BS, 58, MS, 59; Univ NMex, PhD(physics), 67. *Prof Exp:* Staff physicist, Los Alamos Sci Lab, 62-75; mem staff, Max Planck Inst Extraterrestrial Physics, 75-77; STAFF PHYSICIST, LOS ALAMOS SCI LAB, 77- *Concurrent Pos:* Assoc ed, J Geophys Res, Am Geophys Union, 72-74. *Mem:* Am Phys Soc; Am Geophys Union; NY Acad Sci; Sigma Xi. *Res:* Space plasma physics; laser fusion; electron beam plasma heating. *Mailing Add:* Los Alamos Sci Lab Los Alamos NM 87545

MONTGOMERY, MONTY J, b Longview, Miss, Dec 26, 39; m 61; c 3. DAIRY SCIENCE. *Educ:* Miss State Univ, BS, 61; Univ Wis, MS, 63, PhD(dairy sci), 65. *Prof Exp:* From asst prof to assoc prof, 65-76, PROF ANIMAL SCI, UNIV TENN, KNOXVILLE, 76- *Mem:* Am Dairy Sci Asn. *Res:* Dairy cattle nutrition especially feed intake regulation and forage evaluation; applied dairy cattle feeding. *Mailing Add:* Dept of Animal Sci Univ of Tenn Knoxville TN 37916

MONTGOMERY, MORRIS WILLIAM, b Fargo, NDak, Mar 24, 29; m 50; c 4. FOOD SCIENCE, BIOCHEMISTRY. *Educ:* NDak State Univ, BS, 51, MS, 57; Wash State Univ, PhD(dairy sci, biochem), 61. *Prof Exp:* Qual control supvr dairy tech, Nat Dairy Prod Corp, Wis, 53-54, asst prod mgr, 54-55, prod mgr, 55-57; res assoc food sci, 61-63, asst prof, 63-69, ASSOC PROF FOOD SCI, ORE STATE UNIV, 69- *Concurrent Pos:* US Dept Health, Educ & Welfare grant, 65-67; vis prof, State Univ Campinas, Brazil, 73-74. *Mem:* Inst Food Technologists; Am Chem Soc. *Res:* Enzymic browning of fruits; polyphenol oxidase; fish muscle enzymes. *Mailing Add:* Dept of Food Sci & Technol Ore State Univ Corvallis OR 97331

MONTGOMERY, PAUL CHARLES, b Philadelphia, Pa, Jan 29, 44; m 64; c 3. IMMUNOLOGY, MICROBIOLOGY. *Educ:* Dickinson Col, BSc, 65; Univ Pa, PhD(microbiol), 69. *Prof Exp:* Smith Kline & French traveling fel, Nat Inst Med Res, London, 69-70; asst prof, 70-73, assoc prof, 74-81, PROF MICROBIOL, SCH DENT MED, UNIV PA, 81-, CHMN IMMUNOL GRAD GROUP, 81- *Concurrent Pos:* Fogarty sr int fel, Int Inst of Cellular & Molecular Path, Cath Univ Louvain, 78-79. *Mem:* Am Soc Microbiol; Brit Soc Immunol; Am Asn Immunol. *Res:* Localized immunity, induction and structural characterization of secretory antibody; immune response, homogeneous antibody, relationship of antigenic structure to antibody combining site structure. *Mailing Add:* Dept of Microbiol Sch Dent Med Univ of Pa 4001 Spruce St Philadelphia PA 19104

MONTGOMERY, PETER WILLIAMS, b Denver, Colo, May 27, 35; m 60; c 3. PHYSICAL CHEMISTRY. *Educ:* Univ Colo, BA, 57; Univ Calif, Berkeley, PhD(phys chem), 61. *Prof Exp:* Sr res chemist, Cent Res Labs, Minn Mining & Mfg Co, 61-67 & Isotope Power Lab, 67-69; asst prof chem, St Cloud State Col, 69-71; consult & itinerant lectr, 71-74; dir, HMO feasibility study, 74, dir resource develop, Ramsey Action Progs, 74-76; CONSULT HUMAN SERV, HEALTH & SOCIAL SERV PLANNING, 76- *Mem:* AAAS. *Res:* High pressure physics and chemistry; thermodynamics. *Mailing Add:* 1477 Goodrich Ave St Paul MN 55105

MONTGOMERY, PHILIP O'BRYAN, JR, b Dallas, Tex, Aug 16, 21; m 53; c 4. PATHOLOGY. *Educ:* Southern Methodist Univ, BS, 42; Columbia Univ, MD, 45; Am Bd Path, dipl. *Prof Exp:* Intern, Mary Imogene Bassett Hosp, 46; fel path, Univ Tex Southwest Med Sch Dallas, 50-51; asst path & cancer, Cancer Res Inst, New Eng Deaconess Hosp, 51-52; from asst prof to assoc prof, 52-61, NIH career develop award, 62-68, assoc dean, 68-70, PROF PATH, UNIV TEX HEALTH SCI CTR DALLAS, 61- *Concurrent Pos:* Consult path var hosps, 52-; mem sci adv comt, Damon Runyan Mem Fund Cancer Res, 66-72, mem bd dir, 74-; pres bd dirs, Damon Runyon-Walter Winchell Cancer Fund, 74-; spec asst to chancellor, Univ Tex Syst, 71-75; mem bd regents, Uniformed Serv Univ of Health Sci, 74-; pres, Biol Humanics Found, Dallas, 74- *Honors & Awards:* Astronauts' Silver Snoopy Award for Prof Excellence, 70. *Mem:* Fel Am Soc Clin Path; AMA; fel Col Am Path; fel NY Acad Sci; fel Royal Micros Soc. *Res:* Pathological aspects of medicolegal cases; ultraviolet irradiation and microscopy; time-lapse photography; cell ultrastructure; carcinogenesis and nucleolar structure and function. *Mailing Add:* 6343 Kalani Pl Dallas TX 75240

MONTGOMERY, RAYMOND BRAISLIN, b Philadelphia, Pa, May 5, 10; m 44; c 4. PHYSICAL OCEANOGRAPHY. *Educ:* Harvard Univ, AB, 32; Mass Inst Technol, SM, 34, ScD(oceanog), 38. *Prof Exp:* Asst meteorol, Mass Inst Technol, 35-36, mem staff, 44-45; jr meteorol statistician, Bur Agr Econ, USDA, 36-37; jr oceanogr, Woods Hole Oceanog Inst, 38-40, phys oceanogr, 40-42 & 45-49; assoc prof meteorol, NY Univ, 43-44; vis prof oceanog, Brown Univ, 49-54; from assoc prof to prof, 54-75, EMER PROF OCEANOG, JOHNS HOPKINS UNIV, 75- *Concurrent Pos:* Nat Res Coun fel, Univ Berlin, Ger & Helsinki, Finland, 38-39; vis prof, Scripps Inst, Univ Calif, San Diego, 48; Fulbright res scholar, Commonwealth Sci & Indust Res Orgn, Australia, 58; mem corp, Woods Hole Oceanog Inst, 70-80; vis prof, Univ Hawaii, 71; prof, State Univ NY, Stony Brook, 78. *Honors & Awards:* Sverdrup Gold Medal Award, Am Meteorol Soc, 77. *Mem:* Oceanog Soc Japan. *Res:* Analysis of water characteristics and oceanic flow patterns; oceanic leveling. *Mailing Add:* 44 Whitman Rd Woods Hole MA 02543

MONTGOMERY, REX, b Birmingham, Eng, Sept 4, 23; nat US; m 48; c 4. BIOCHEMISTRY. *Educ:* Univ Birmingham, BSc, 43, PhD(chem), 46, DSc(chem), 63. *Prof Exp:* Res chemist, Colonial Prod Res Coun, Eng, 43-46 & Dunlop Rubber Co, 46-47; sci off, Ministry of Supply, Brit Govt, 47-48; fel, Ohio State Univ, 48-49; Sugar Res Found fel, USDA, 49-51; res assoc, Univ Minn, 51-55; from asst prof to assoc prof, 55-64, PROF BIOCHEM, UNIV IOWA, 64-, ASSOC DEAN, COL MED, 74- *Concurrent Pos:* Mem staff, Physiol Chem Study Sect, NIH, 68-72, Drug Develop Contract Rev Comt, Nat Cancer Inst, 75-77, Develop Therapeut Comt, Nat Cancer Inst, 77-; USPHS sr fel, Australian Nat Univ, 69-70; prog dir, Physician's Asst Prog, Col Med, Univ Iowa, 73-76. *Mem:* Am Chem Soc; Biochem Soc; Am Soc Biol Chem; Royal Soc Chem. *Res:* Carbohydrates; protein-carbohydrate complexes; natural products; glycoproteins; carbohydrases; metal complexes of biological import; carbohydrate synthesis; membrane biochemistry; polypeptide antitumor agents. *Mailing Add:* Dept of Biochem Univ of Iowa Iowa City IA 52240

MONTGOMERY, RICHARD A(LAN), b Vancouver, BC, Jan 11, 19; nat US; m 44; c 6. ELECTRICAL ENGINEERING. *Educ:* Univ BC, BA, 40; Calif Inst Technol, MS, 46, PhD(elec eng), 48. *Prof Exp:* Jr res physicist, Nat Res Coun Can, 41-43; asst, Calif Inst Technol, 46-48; develop engr, Gen Elec Co, 48-51, Boeing Airplane Co, 51-62, Off Secy Defense, 62-64 & Boeing Co, 64-74; MEM STAFF, R&D ASSOCS, 74- *Concurrent Pos:* Consult, Off Secy Defense, 64-& Ballistic Syst Div, US Air Force, 66-69; mem, Army Sci Adv Panel & Army Sci Bd, 68- *Mem:* Inst Elec & Electronics Engrs. *Res:* Guided missiles; under-water ordnance. *Mailing Add:* R&D Assocs PO Box 9695 Marina Del Rey CA 90291

MONTGOMERY, RICHARD C, b Stark, Kans, Jan 21, 22; m 52; c 2. GEOLOGY. *Educ:* Univ Idaho, BS, 49; Univ Nebr, MA, 51, PhD(geog, geol), 62. *Prof Exp:* Intel analyst geog, Eng Strategic Intel Div, Army Map Serv, 51-53; prof earth sci, Willamette Univ, 53-66; PROF GEOG, CALIF STATE UNIV, FRESNO, 66- *Mem:* Asn Am Geog; Am Geol Inst. *Res:* Arid land morphology; volcanic landforms; late Pleistocene paleoclimatology. *Mailing Add:* Dept of Geog Calif State Univ Fresno CA 93726

MONTGOMERY, RICHARD GLEE, b Grayslake, Ill, Feb 9, 38; m 61; c 3. MATHEMATICS. *Educ:* San Francisco State Col, AB, 60; Brown Univ, MAT, 65; Clark Univ, MA, 68, PhD(math), 69. *Prof Exp:* Asst prof math, Humboldt State Col, 69-70; assoc prof, 70-81, PROF MATH, SOUTHERN ORE STATE COL, 81- *Mem:* Math Asn Am. *Res:* Algebraic, topological and categorical structures of rings of continuous functions. *Mailing Add:* Dept Math Southern Ore State Col Ashland OR 97520

MONTGOMERY, ROBERT S(TUART), b Glen Ellyn, Ill, Feb 11, 24; m 46; c 6. TRIBOLOGY. *Educ:* Northwestern Univ, BChE, 45, AM, 50; Columbia Univ, AM, 48; Princeton Univ, PhD(org chem), 51. *Prof Exp:* Res engr, Res Ctr, Johns-Manville Corp, 46-47; asst, Princeton Univ, 48-50; assoc res scientist, Dow Chem Co, 51-64; mat scientist, Res Ctr, Ingersoll-Rand Co, 64-69; RES CHEMIST, BENET RES & ENG LABS, WATERVLIET ARSENAL, 69- *Mem:* Am Chem Soc; Am Soc Lubrication Engrs; Am Soc Mech Engrs; Soc Rheol; Soc Eng Sci. *Res:* Friction, wear and lubrication; materials science. *Mailing Add:* Benet Res & Eng Labs Watervliet Arsenal Watervliet NY 12189

MONTGOMERY, RONALD EUGENE, b Rural Valley, Pa, Feb 17, 37; m 61; c 4. ORGANIC CHEMISTRY, PESTICIDE CHEMISTRY. *Educ:* Waynesburg Col, BS, 59; Duke Univ, MA, 62, PhD(org chem), 64. *Prof Exp:* Res assoc, Duke Univ, 63-64; res chemist, 64-69, sr res chemist, 69, mgr org synthesis, Agr Chem Div, 69-76, mgr insecticide/nematicide res, 76-80, mgr process res, 80-81, DIR PROCESS RES & ENG, FMC CORP, 81- *Mem:* Am Chem Soc. *Res:* Biological laboratory evaluation, field testing, process research and manufacturing of pesticides. *Mailing Add:* Agr Chem Group FMC Corp Box 8 Princeton NJ 08540

MONTGOMERY, ROYCE LEE, b Hartsville, Tenn, Nov 8, 33; m 67; c 1. GROSS ANATOMY, NEUROANATOMY. *Educ:* Univ Va, BA, 55; WVa Univ, MS, 60, PhD(gross anat), 63. *Prof Exp:* Instr gross anat & neuroanat, Med Sch, WVa Univ, 63-65; from instr to asst prof, 68-72, ASSOC PROF GROSS ANAT & NEUROANAT, SCH MED, UNIV NC, CHAPEL HILL, 72- *Mem:* Am Asn Anat. *Res:* Functional and morphological studies related to the temporomandibular joint. *Mailing Add:* Dept Anat Univ NC Sch Med Chapel Hill NC 27514

MONTGOMERY, STEWART ROBERT, b Pottsville, Pa, July 16, 24; m 60. INDUSTRIAL CHEMISTRY, ORGANIC CHEMISTRY. *Educ:* Pa State Univ, BS, 49; Univ Rochester, PhD(org chem), 55. *Prof Exp:* Res chemist org synthesis, Cent Res Lab, Allied Chem Corp, 49-51; res chemist petrochem, Res Dept, Lion Oil Co, Monsanto Co, 55-61; sr res chemist, Indust Catalysts Res Dept, 61-73, Indust Chem Dept, 73-78, SR RES CHEMIST, CATALYST RES GROUP, DEPT RES, DAVISON DIV, W R GRACE & CO, 78- *Mem:* Am Chem Soc; Catalysis Soc NAm; Sigma Xi. *Res:* Synthesis of amino acids, organosilicon compounds and aromatic hydrocarbons; heterogeneous, vaporphase catalysis; synthetic resins; chemistry of asphalt and bitumens; oxidation of hydrocarbons; raney nickel; preparation and evaluation of industrial catalysts. *Mailing Add:* Dept Res Davison Chem Div 7379 Rt 32 Columbia MD 21044

MONTGOMERY, SUSAN, b Tampa, Fla, Apr 2, 43. ALGEBRA. *Educ:* Univ Mich, Ann Arbor, BA, 65; Univ Chicago, MS, 66, PhD(math), 69. *Prof Exp:* Asst prof math, DePaul Univ, 69-70; asst prof, 70-75, assoc prof, 75-82, PROF MATH, UNIV SOUTHERN CALIF, 82- *Concurrent Pos:* Vis asst prof, Hebrew Univ Jerusalem, 73; vis assoc prof, Univ Chicago, 78; vis res assoc, Univ Leeds, 81. *Mem:* Am Math Soc; Asn Women Math; Math Asn Am; London Math Soc. *Res:* Automorphisms and involutions of associative rings. *Mailing Add:* Dept of Math Univ of Southern Calif Los Angeles CA 90007

MONTGOMERY, THEODORE ASHTON, b Los Angeles, Calif, Oct 27, 23. PUBLIC HEALTH, PEDIATRICS. *Educ:* Univ Southern Calif, MD, 46; Harvard Univ, MPH, 52; Am Bd Pediat & Am Bd Prev Med, dipl. *Prof Exp:* Consult pediat, Calif Dept Pub Health, 52-53; pvt pract, 52-54; consult child health, 54-58, chief maternal & perinatal health, 58-61 & bur maternal & child health, 61-62, from asst chief to chief div prev med serv, 62-72, dep dir, Calif Dept Pub Health, 69-72, chief div prev med, Alameda County Health Agency, 73-74, MED CONSULT, CALIF DEPT HEALTH, BERKELEY, 74- *Concurrent Pos:* Mem, Surg Gen Adv Comt Immunization Practices, 64-68, President's Adv Comt Ment Retarded, 65 & Ment Retarded Proj Rev Comt, USPHS, 65-66; chmn, Calif Interdept Coun on Food & Nutrit, 77- *Mem:* Fel Am Acad Pediat; fel Am Pub Health Asn. *Res:* Maternal and child health morbidity and mortality causation and procedures for reducing these factors, including designing and implementing approaches to preventive measures. *Mailing Add:* 85 Wildwood Gardens Piedmont CA 94611

MONTGOMERY, WILLIAM WAYNE, b Proctor, Vt, Aug 20, 23. OTOLARYNGOLOGY. *Educ:* Middlebury Col, AB, 44; Univ Vt, MD, 47; Am Bd Otolaryngol, dipl, 56. *Prof Exp:* Intern, Mary Fletcher Hosp, Burlington, Vt, 47-48; physician pvt pract, Vt, 48-50; resident otolaryngol, Mass Eye & Ear Infirmary, 52-55, asst, 55-56; asst otol, 56-58, from instr to assoc prof, 59-70, PROF OTOLARYNGOL, HARVARD MED SCH, 70-; SR SURGEON, DEPT OTOLARYNGOL, MASS EYE & EAR INFIRMARY, 69- *Concurrent Pos:* Asst surgeon, Mass Eye & Ear Infirmary, 58-60, assoc surgeon, 60-69. *Honors & Awards:* Harris P Mosher Award, 63. *Mem:* Fel Am Col Surgeons; AMA; Am Acad Ophthal & Otolaryngol; Am Broncho-Esophagol Asn; Am Laryngol Asn. *Res:* Dysfunctions of the human larynx; reconstruction of the cervical respiratory areas; carcinoma of the head and neck; radical surgery of the nose and sinuses; surgery of the upper respiratory system. *Mailing Add:* Mass Eye & Ear Infirmary 243 Charles St Boston MA 02114

MONTGOMERY, WILLSON LINN, b Detroit, Mich, May 8, 46; m 73. BEHAVIORAL ECOLOGY, ICHTHYOLOGY. *Educ:* Univ Calif, Berkeley, BA, 68; Univ Calif, Los Angeles, MA, 73; Ariz State Univ, PhD(zool), 78. *Prof Exp:* ACTG ASST PROF ZOOL, ARIZ STATE UNIV, 79- *Mem:* Am Soc Ichthyologists & Herpetologists; Sigma Xi; Am Soc Zoologists. *Res:* Physiological and behavioral bases of ecological patterns in fishes; impact of herbivorous fishes on marine algal communities; interspecific feeding associations of fishes. *Mailing Add:* Dept of Zool Ariz State Univ Tempe AZ 85281

MONTH, MELVIN, b Montreal, Que, June 20, 36; m 57; c 2. ACCELERATOR PHYSICS. *Educ:* McGill Univ, BSc, 57, MSc, 61, PhD(physics), 64; Hofstra Univ, MBA, 73. *Prof Exp:* Res assoc physics, Univ Ill, Urbana, 64-66; PHYSICIST ACCELERATOR PHYSICS, BROOKHAVEN NAT LAB, 66- *Concurrent Pos:* Consult, High Energy Physics Off, Dept of Energy, 79- *Mem:* AAAS; Am Phys Soc. *Res:* Particle beams in accelerators; analysis of beam stability at high currents; limitations in colliding beam performance; analysis of facility development. *Mailing Add:* Accelerator Dept Brookhaven Nat Lab Upton NY 11973

MONTI, JOHN ANTHONY, b Birmingham, Ala, Aug 7, 49; m 72; c 2. PHYSIOLOGY, BIOPHYSICS. *Educ:* Birmingham-Southern Col, BS, 71; Univ Ala, Birmingham, PhD(physiol, biophys), 75. *Prof Exp:* res assoc, 76-79, RES ASST PROF NEUROBIOL, NEUROSCI PROG, UNIV ALA, BIRMINGHAM, 79- *Mem:* Soc Neurosci; Biophys Soc. *Res:* Membrane biochemistry and biophysics; central nervous system metabolism; fluorescence spectroscopy, theory and applications. *Mailing Add:* Neurosci Prog Univ Sta Birmingham AL 35294

MONTI, STEPHEN ARION, b Ross, Calif, Nov 23, 39; m 81. ORGANIC CHEMISTRY. *Educ:* Univ Calif, Berkeley, BS, 61; Mass Inst Technol, PhD(org chem), 64. *Prof Exp:* Asst prof chem, Mich State Univ, 64-66; NSF fel, Harvard Univ, 66-67; asst prof, 67-71, assoc prof, 71-79, asst to the pres, 74-81, PROF CHEM, UNIV TEX, AUSTIN, 79-, ASSOC VPRES ACADEMIC PLANNING, 81- *Res:* Synthetic organic chemistry; natural products and related areas. *Mailing Add:* Dept of Chem Univ of Tex Austin TX 78712

MONTIE, THOMAS C, b Cleveland, Ohio, Oct 8, 34; m 56; c 2. BIOCHEMISTRY, MICROBIOLOGY. *Educ:* Oberlin Col, AB, 56; Univ Md, MS, 58, PhD(microbial physiol), 60. *Prof Exp:* Asst bot, Univ Md, 56-58, fungus physiol, 59-60; res assoc, Inst Cancer Res, 60-62; asst mem, Albert Einstein Med Ctr, 62-67, assoc mem, 67-69; assoc prof, 69-78, PROF MICROBIOL, UNIV TENN, KNOXVILLE, 78- *Concurrent Pos:* Prin investr, Cystic Fibrosis Grant, 80-81. *Mem:* AAAS; Am Soc Microbiol; Am Chem Soc; fel Am Inst Chem; Am Inst Biol Sci. *Res:* Location, synthesis, regulation, mode of action and chemistry of toxic proteins from bacteria; microbial physiology; amino acid transport and metabolism; Pseudomenas pathogenicity; vaccines. *Mailing Add:* Dept Microbiol Univ Tenn Knoxville TN 37916

MONTIERTH, MAX ROMNEY, b Phoenix, Ariz, Dec 12, 38; m 59; c 5. CERAMIC ENGINEERING, CHEMICAL ENGINEERING. *Educ:* Brigham Young Univ, BES, 63; Univ Utah, PhD(ceramic eng), 67; Harvard Sch Bus, PMD, 72. *Prof Exp:* Sr ceramic engr, Tech Staffs, Corning Glass Works, 66-70, mgr glass-ceramic prod develop, 70-72, mgr mkt & prod develop, Electronic Mat, TV Div, 72-74, mgr special prod develop, 74-75, mgr prod develop, Optical Waveguide Technol, 75-79, tech leader, Indust Heat Exchanges, 79-80, TECH LEADER, DIESEL PARTICULATE FILTER TECH STAFFS DIV, CORNING GLASS WORKS, 80- *Concurrent Pos:* Mem staff, Elmira Col, 68-70. *Mem:* Am Ceramic Soc. *Res:* Effects of crystal morphology and composition on physical properties of glass-ceramics; glass, glass-ceramic and ceramic materials for electronic applications; glass composition and fiber forming optical waveguides; polymer coatings for OWG fibers; high temperature low-expansion ceramics, heat exchange materials and mechanisms. *Mailing Add:* Corning Glass Works DB-2 Sullivan Park Corning NY 14831

MONTIETH, RICHARD VOORHEES, b Indianapolis, Ind, Aug 13, 13; m 41; c 4. CHEMISTRY. *Educ:* Butler Univ, AB, 35. *Prof Exp:* Chemist, Allison Div, 40-44, supvr bearing chem lab, 44-54, gen supvr prod metall lab, 54-58, supvr prod metall sect, 58-64, sr exp metallurgist foundry technol, 64-66, sr exp metallurgist, Detroit Diesel Allison Div, Gen Motors Corp, 66-74; CONSULT, 74- *Mem:* Am Soc Metals. *Res:* Metallurgical, nonferrous and ferrous and high temperature alloys, selection and properties. *Mailing Add:* 2350 W 65th St Indianapolis IN 46260

MONTJAR, MONTY JACK, b Latrobe, Pa, Aug 12, 24. PHYSICAL CHEMISTRY. *Educ:* St Vincent Col, BS, 49; Univ Notre Dame, MS, 50; Carnegie Inst Technol, PhD(phys chem), 55. *Prof Exp:* Chemist, Callery Chem Co, 54-57; asst prof chem, Pa State Univ, 57-60; from asst prof to assoc prof, St Vincent Col, 60-65; assoc scientist, Brookhaven Nat Lab, 66-68; assoc prof chem, Mt Sinai Sch Med, 68-70; ASSOC PROF CHEM, PA STATE UNIV, HAZLETON, 70- *Res:* RNA; protein biosynthesis; tissue transplantation; fractionation; peptide synthesis. *Mailing Add:* Dept of Chem Pa State Univ Hazleton PA 18201

MONTO, ARNOLD SIMON, b Brooklyn, NY, Mar 22, 33; m 58; c 4. EPIDEMIOLOGY, INFECTIOUS DISEASES. *Educ:* Cornell Univ, BA, 54, MD, 58. *Prof Exp:* Intern & asst resident med, Vanderbilt Univ Hosp, 58-60; USPHS fel, Med Sch, Stanford Univ, 60-62; mem virus dis sect, Nat Inst Allergy & Infectious Dis, 62-65; from res assoc to assoc prof, 65-75, PROF EPIDEMIOL, SCH PUB HEALTH, UNIV MICH, ANN ARBOR, 75- *Concurrent Pos:* NIH career develop award, 68; consult, NIH. *Mem:* Am Epidemiol Soc; Soc Exp Biol & Med; Am Asn Immunologists; Infectious Dis Soc Am; Soc Epidemiol Res. *Res:* Epidemiology of respiratory and enteric disease in the community; viral diseases and diagnosis; evaluations of vaccines. *Mailing Add:* Dept of Epidemiol Univ of Mich Sch Pub Health Ann Arbor MI 48109

MONTOURE, JOHN ERNEST, b Shawano, Wis, May 10, 27; m 48; c 4. DAIRY SCIENCE, AGRICULTURAL BIOCHEMISTRY. *Educ:* Univ Wis, BS, 54, MS, 55; Wash State Univ, PhD(dairy sci), 61. *Prof Exp:* Asst prof dairy sci, 61-70, head dept food sci, 70-75, ASSOC PROF FOOD SCI, UNIV IDAHO, 70-, FOOD SCIENTIST, 73- *Mem:* Am Dairy Sci Asn; Inst Food Technol. *Res:* Pesticide detection and analytical methods; fate of pesticides in dairy products; enzyme isolation; bacteriology. *Mailing Add:* Dept of Food Sci Univ of Idaho Moscow ID 83843

MONTROLL, ELLIOTT WATERS, b Pittsburgh, Pa, May 4, 16; m 43; c 10. MATHEMATICS, PHYSICS. *Educ:* Univ Pittsburgh, BS, 37, PhD(math), 40. *Prof Exp:* Asst math, Univ Pittsburgh, 37-39; res asst chem, Columbia Univ, 39-40; Sterling res fel, Yale Univ, 40-41; res assoc, Cornell Univ, 41-42; instr physics, Princeton Univ, 42-43; head math res group, Kellex Corp, NY, 43-45; adj prof chem, Polytech Inst Brooklyn, 44-46; from asst prof to assoc prof physics & math, Univ Pittsburgh, 46-48; vis prof, NY Univ, 50; res prof, Inst Fluid Dynamics & Appl Math, Univ Md, 51-61; Lorentz prof, Univ Leiden, 61; dir gen sci, IBM Tech Ctr, 61-63; vpres, Inst Defense Anal, 63-66; Einstein prof physics & chem & dir, Inst Fundamental Studies, Univ Rochester, 66-81; PROF, INST PHYS SCI & TECHNOL, UNIV MD, 81- *Concurrent Pos:* Head physics br, Off Naval Res, Wash, DC, 48-50, dir phys sci div, 52-54; Guggenheim Mem fel, Univ Brussels, 58-59; Fulbright lectr, Univ Grenoble, 59; ed, J Math Physics, 59-70; chmn, Comn Sociotechnical Systs, Nat Res Coun. *Honors & Awards:* Lancaster Prize, Opers Res Soc Am, 61; J Willard Gibbs lectr, Am Math Soc, 82. *Mem:* Nat Acad Sci; fel Am Acad Arts & Sci; fel Am Phys Soc; hon mem NY Acad Sci. *Res:* Statistical mechanics; theory of probability; mathematical physics; mathematical modeling of biological and sociological phenomenon. *Mailing Add:* Inst Phys Sci & Technol Univ Md College Park MD 20742

MONTROSE, CHARLES JOSEPH, JR, b Pittsburgh, Pa, Jan 3, 42; m 63; c 3. PHYSICS. *Educ:* John Carroll Univ, BS, 62, MS, 64; Cath Univ Am, PhD(physics), 67. *Prof Exp:* Asst prof, 67-70, ASSOC PROF PHYSICS, CATH UNIV AM, 70- *Mem:* Am Phys Soc; Acoust Soc Am. *Res:* Study of the structure and dynamics of the liquid state using ultrasonic and optical techniques; laser spectroscopy. *Mailing Add:* Dept of Physics Cath Univ Am Washington DC 20064

MONTROSS, C(HARLES) F(RANK), b Paris, France, June 13, 11; nat US; m 35; c 2. CHEMICAL ENGINEERING, COMPUTER SCIENCE. *Educ:* NY Univ, AB, 37; Cooper Union, BChE, 41; Polytech Inst Brooklyn, MChE, 46. *Prof Exp:* Night supvr, Westvaco Chlor-Alkali Div, Food Mach Chem Corp, NJ, 41-42; process engr, Lummus Co, NY, 42-48; mgr econ eval, Gen Aniline & Film Corp, 49-61; sr bus analyst, Am Cyanamid Co, 61-64; mgr planning, Nat Aniline Div, Allied Chem Corp, 64-66; chmn eng sci, 68-75, PROF ENG, MIDDLESEX COUNTY COL, 66- *Concurrent Pos:* Adj prof, Polytech Inst Brooklyn, 44-64. *Mem:* AAAS; Am Inst Chem Engrs; Am Chem Soc; NY Acad Sci; Am Soc Eng Educ. *Res:* Economic and project evaluations; distillation; pilot plants; acquisitions; planning. *Mailing Add:* Dept of Comput Sci Middlesex County Col Edison NJ 08817

MONTROY, LEO DENNIS, fresh water ecology, see previous edition

MONTS, DAVID LEE, b Taylorville, Ill, Apr 14, 51. CHEMISTRY. *Educ:* Univ Ill, Urbana, BS, 73; Columbia Univ, MA, 74, PhD(chem), 78. *Prof Exp:* Fel chem, William Marsh Rice Univ, 77-79; lectr, Princeton Univ, 79-81; ASST PROF CHEM, UNIV ARK, FAYETTEVILLE, 81- *Concurrent Pos:* Prin investr, Univ Ark, Fayetteville, 81- *Mem:* Am Chem Soc; Am Phys Soc; Sigma Xi. *Res:* Laser spectroscopy is used to probe intramolecular energy transfer and also state-to-state photochemistry of supersonically cooled molecules. *Mailing Add:* Dept Chem Univ Ark Fayetteville AR 72701

MONTY, KENNETH JAMES, b Sanford, Maine, Sept 11, 30; m 52; c 2. BIOCHEMISTRY, CELL BIOLOGY. *Educ:* Bowdoin Col, BA, 51; Univ Rochester, PhD(biochem), 56. *Prof Exp:* Fel biochem, McCollum-Pratt Inst, Johns Hopkins Univ, 55-57, asst prof biol, 57-63; head dept, 63-75, 77-79, PROF BIOCHEM, UNIV TENN, KNOXVILLE, 63-, COORDR BIOL SCI, 73- *Mem:* AAAS; Am Chem Soc; Am Soc Biol Chem; NY Acad Sci. *Res:* Cellular physiology; sulfur metabolism; microbial genetics and metabolic control; biological adaptation. *Mailing Add:* Biol Coord Univ of Tenn Knoxville TN 37916

MONTZINGO, LLOYD J, JR, b Chicago, Ill, Nov 29, 27; m 48; c 6. MATHEMATICS. *Educ:* Houghton Col, AB, 49; Univ Buffalo, MA, 51, PhD, 61. *Prof Exp:* From instr to asst prof math, Roberts Wesleyan Col, 51-56; from instr to asst prof, Univ Buffalo, 56-62; assoc prof, 62-66, chmn dept, 62-73, dir, Sch Sci, 73-78, PROF MATH, SEATTLE PAC UNIV, 66- *Concurrent Pos:* NSF sci fac fel, Univ Wash, 70-71. *Mem:* Math Asn Am (assoc secy, 58-62). *Res:* Mathematical statistics. *Mailing Add:* Sch Sci Seattle Pac Univ Seattle WA 98119

MONZEL, FRED JACOB, b Grand Rapids, Mich, Jan 13, 31. MECHANICAL ENGINEERING, ENGINEERING MECHANICS. *Educ:* Purdue Univ, BSME, 55; Univ Fla, MSE, 64, PhD(eng mech), 67. *Prof Exp:* Engr, Allison Div, Gen Motors Corp, 55-56; engr, Flight Propulsion Div, Gen Elec Co, 56-62; sr engr, Astronuclear Lab, Westinghouse Elec Corp, 62-63; MGR AIRCRAFT ENGINE GROUP, GEN ELEC CO, 67- *Res:* Preliminary design of turbomachinery for advanced jet engines. *Mailing Add:* Gen Elec Co Aircraft Engine Eng Div Neuman Way Cincinnati OH 45215

MOOBERRY, JARED BEN, b Pekin, Ill, Mar 6, 42; m 75. SYNTHETIC ORGANIC CHEMISTRY. *Educ:* Univ Ill, BS, 64; Cornell Univ, PhD(chem), 69. *Prof Exp:* Fel chem, Swiss Fed Inst Technol, 69-70; res assoc, Cornell Univ, 70-71; RES CHEMIST, EASTMAN KODAK RES LABS, 71- *Mem:* Am Chem Soc. *Res:* Synthesis of organic chemicals of photographic utility. *Mailing Add:* Eastman Kodak Res Labs Rochester NY 14650

MOOD, ALEXANDER MCFARLANE, b Amarillo, Tex, May 31, 13; m 36; c 3. APPLIED MATHEMATICS, PUBLIC POLICY. *Educ:* Univ Tex, BA, 34; Princeton Univ, PhD(math statist), 40. *Prof Exp:* Instr appl math, Univ Tex, 40-42; statistician, Bur Labor Statist, 42-44; res assoc, Princeton Univ, 45; prof math statist, Iowa State Col, 45-48; dep chief, Math Div, Rand Corp, 48-55; pres, Gen Anal Corp, 55-60; vpres in charge, Los Angeles Res Ctr, C-E-I-R, Inc, 60-64; asst commissioner ed, US Off Ed, 64-67; dir, Pub Policy Res Orgn, 67-73, prof, 73-77, EMER PROF ADMIN & POLICY ANALYST, UNIV CALIF, IRVINE, 73- *Concurrent Pos:* Guest lectr, Army War Col & Air War Col; consult, US Dept Defense; del, NATO Opers Res Conf, Paris, 58, Int Opers Res Conf, Aix-en-Provence, 60 & Oslo, 63. *Mem:* Am Math Soc; Opers Res Soc Am (pres, 63); Soc Indust & Appl Math; fel Inst Math Statist (pres, 56). *Res:* Mathematical statistics; operations research; game theory; administration; policy analysis. *Mailing Add:* 4705 Royce Rd Irvine CA 92715

MOODERA, JAGADEESH SUBBAIAH, b Bangalore, India, Dec 3, 10. SOLID STATE PHYSICS. *Educ:* Mysore Univ, India, BSc, 71, MSc, 73; Indian Inst Technol, Madras, India, PhD(solid state physics), 78. *Prof Exp:* Fel, physics, Indian Inst Technol, India, 78; res assoc, magnetism, Physics Dept, WVa Univ, 79-81; MEM RES STAFF, SUPERCONDUCTIVITY & TUNNELING, NAT MAGNET LAB, MASS INST TECHNOL, 81- *Mem:* Astron Soc Pac. *Res:* Electrical properties of thin film; magnetic properties of antiferromagnets and semiconductors; electron spin polarized tunneling into ferromagnets from superconductors; dreaming. *Mailing Add:* NW14-2114 Mass Inst Technol 170 Albany St Cambridge MA 02139

MOODY, ARNOLD RALPH, b Augusta, Maine, Oct 8, 41; m 65. PLANT PATHOLOGY. *Educ:* Univ Maine, BS, 63; Univ NH, MS, 65; Univ Calif, Berkeley, PhD(plant path), 71. *Prof Exp:* Asst res plant pathologist, Univ Calif, Berkeley, 71-72; res plant pathologist, Changins Fed Agr Exp Sta, Nyon, Switz, 72-74; ASSOC PROF PLANT PATH, VA STATE UNIV, 74- *Mem:* Am Phytopath Soc. *Res:* Plant diseases; control of plant disease through natural resistance mechanisms; physiology of disease resistance. *Mailing Add:* Va State Univ Box 501 Petersburg VA 23803

MOODY, DAVID BURRITT, b Rochester, NY, June 20, 40; m 64; c 2. PSYCHOACOUSTICS. *Educ:* Hamilton Col, BA, 62; Columbia Univ, MA, 64, PhD(psychol), 67. *Prof Exp:* Dept HEW res fel, Kresge Hearing Res Inst, Med Sch, 67-68, res assoc psychoacoustics, 68-71, asst prof otorhinolaryngol, 71-79, asst prof psychol, Univ, 69-80, ASSOC RES SCIENTIST OTORHINILARYNGOL, KRESGE HEARING INST, MED SCH, UNIV MICH, ANN ARBOR, 79-, ASSOC PROF PSYCHOL, UNIV, 80- *Mem:* AAAS; Acoust Soc Am; Asn Res Otorhinolaryngol. *Res:* Psychoacoustics; hearing in non-human primates; experimentally produced hearing loss; computers in psychology. *Mailing Add:* Kresge Hearing Res Inst Univ of Mich Ann Arbor MI 48109

MOODY, DAVID COIT, III, b Florence, SC, Dec 21, 48; m 68. INORGANIC CHEMISTRY. *Educ:* Univ SC, BS, 67; Ind Univ, PhD(chem), 75. *Prof Exp:* Res asst chem, Ind Univ, 72-75; fel chem, 75-77, MEM STAFF, LOS ALAMOS NAT LAB, 77- *Mem:* Am Chem Soc; Sigma Xi. *Res:* Synthetic and structural inorganic chemistry as related to the binding of small molecule noxious gases such as sulfur dioxide, nitric oxide, and carbon monoxide, by transition metals; organometallic actinide chemistry. *Mailing Add:* Los Alamos Nat Lab Los Alamos NM 87545

MOODY, DAVID WRIGHT, b Boston, Mass, Nov 23, 37; m 63; c 1. HYDROLOGY. *Educ:* Harvard Univ, AB, 60; Johns Hopkins Univ, PhD(geog), 64. *Prof Exp:* Hydrologist, Water Resources Div, 64-74, prog analyst, Off of Dir, 74-77, STAFF SCIENTIST, WATER RESOURCES DIV, US GEOL SURV, 77- *Concurrent Pos:* Am Polit Sci Asn Cong Fel, 76-77; mem geophysics study comt, Panel Geophysics Data & Pub Policy, Nat Res Coun, 81-83. *Mem:* AAAS; Geol Soc Am; Am Geophys Union; Am Water Resources Asn; World Future Soc. *Res:* Information systems; long-range planning; water resources assessment; water policy analysis. *Mailing Add:* Nat Ctr Stop 409 US Geol Surv Reston VA 22092

MOODY, EDWARD GRANT, b Thatcher, Ariz, Dec 23, 19; m 43; c 7. ANIMAL NUTRITION. *Educ:* Univ Ariz, BS, 41; Kans State Col, MS, 47; Purdue Univ, PhD(nutrit), 51. *Prof Exp:* Asst dairy husb, Kans State Col, 46-47; asst, Purdue Univ, 47-49, instr, 49-51; from asst prof to assoc prof, 51-63, PROF ANIMAL SCI, ARIZ STATE UNIV, 63- *Mem:* Am Soc Animal Sci; Am Dairy Sci Asn; Soc Nutrit Educ. *Res:* Fat metabolism in ruminants; dairy herd management and production. *Mailing Add:* Div of Agr Ariz State Univ Tempe AZ 85281

MOODY, ERIC EDWARD MARSHALL, b Neath, Gt Brit, Dec 15, 38; m 67; c 2. MOLECULAR GENETICS, VENEREAL DISEASES. *Educ:* Univ London, BSc, 64; Univ Edinburgh, PhD(molecular biol), 71. *Prof Exp:* Res scientist molecular genetics, Southwest Ctr Advan Studies, 65-68; tech officer, Med Res Coun Gt Brit, 68-71; asst prof, 72-77, ASSOC PROF MOLECULAR GENETICS, UNIV TEX HEALTH SCI CTR, 77- *Concurrent Pos:* Fel, Col Med, Univ Ariz, 71-72. *Mem:* Soc Gen Microbiol; Am Venereal Dis Asn. *Res:* Molecular genetics of plasmids; genetics of virulence and antibiotic resistance in Candida albicans. *Mailing Add:* Dept of Microbiol Univ of Tex Health Sci Ctr San Antonio TX 78284

MOODY, FRANK GORDON, b Franklin, NH, May 3, 28; m 64; c 3. SURGERY. *Educ:* Dartmouth Col, BA, 52; Cornell Univ, MD, 56. *Prof Exp:* Surg intern, NY Hosp-Cornell Med Ctr, 56-57, surg residency, 57-63; clin instr surg, Med Ctr, Univ Calif, San Francisco, 63-65, asst prof, 65-66; assoc prof, Univ Ala, 66-69, prof, 69-71; PROF SURG & CHMN DEPT, UNIV UTAH, 71- *Concurrent Pos:* Cardiovasc Res Inst fel, 63-65; Am Heart Asn advan res fel, 63-65; consult, Vet Admin Hosp, Birmingham, Ala, 66-; mem surg training comt, Nat Inst Gen Med Sci, 68-72; mem med sect A, NIH, 72-75 & surg sect B, 75-80. *Mem:* Biophys Soc; Am Col Surg; Am Gastroenterol Asn; Am Surg Asn; Soc Surg Alimentary Tract. *Res:* Gastric acid secretion; pancreatic function; portal hypertension. *Mailing Add:* Dept of Surg Univ of Utah Med Ctr Salt Lake City UT 84132

MOODY, HARRY JOHN, b Birsay, Sask, May 8, 26; m 52; c 3. MICROWAVE PHYSICS, COMMUNICATIONS ENGINEERING. *Educ:* Univ Sask, BEng, 48, MS, 50; McGill Univ, PhD(physics), 55. *Prof Exp:* Asst, Univ Ill, 50-51; res asst, Nat Res Coun Can, 51-55; sr physicist, Can Marconi Co, 55-61; sr mem sci staff, RCA Ltd, Montreal, 61-73, res fel, 73-77; STAFF SCIENTIST, SPAR AEROSPACE LTD, 77- *Mem:* Can Asn Physicists. *Res:* Microwave; millimeter wave; infrared; characterizing and optimizing a space system for SCPC communications. *Mailing Add:* 4470 Coronation Montreal PQ H4B 2C4 Can

MOODY, HERBERT R(UDOLPH), b Boston, Mass, Feb 12, 19; m 48; c 2. CHEMICAL ENGINEERING. *Educ:* Mass Inst Technol, BS, 41. *Prof Exp:* Chem engr, Chas Lennig Co, 41; chem engr, Micromedic Syst, Inc, Rohm & Haas Co, 46-48, supvr plant develop eng, 48-55, res supvr, 55-61, asst dir res, 61-65, asst plant mgr, 65-70, pres & gen mgr, 71-77; CONSULT, 80- *Mem:* Am Chem Soc; Am Inst Chem Engrs. *Res:* Development of processes for the manufacture of organic chemicals; pilot plant activity; petrochemical manufacturing; corporate management of biomedical instrument and reagents manufacturing; process hazard control. *Mailing Add:* 5 Blackwell Pl Philadelphia PA 19147

MOODY, JOHN ROBERT, b Richmond, Va, Feb 6, 42. ANALYTICAL CHEMISTRY. *Educ:* Univ Richmond, BS, 64; Univ Md, College Park, MS, 67, PhD(anal chem), 70. *Prof Exp:* Asst anal chem, Univ Md, 70; RES CHEMIST, US NAT BUR STANDARDS, WASHINGTON, DC, 71- *Mem:* Am Chem Soc; Am Soc Testing & Mat; Soc Appl Spectros. *Res:* General analytical procedures, including wet, electroanalytical, spectrophotometric, radiochemical and chromatographic procedures as applied to isotope dilution mass spectrometry; high accuracy trace analysis; investigation of stoichiometry and separations. *Mailing Add:* 2846 E Weyburn Rd Richmond VA 23235

MOODY, JOSEPH E, JR, b Pleasantville, NJ, Sept, 22, 23; m 51; c 3. PHARMACEUTICAL CHEMISTRY. *Educ:* Univ Conn, BS, 50, MS, 55, PhD(pharmaceut chem), 60. *Prof Exp:* From asst prof to assoc prof pharm, Fla Agr & Mech Univ, 54-57; chemist, Div Pharmaceut Chem, US Food & Drug Admin, 59-62, res chemist, 62-67; group leader anal res, White Labs, Schering Corp, NJ, 67-70; mgr, USV Pharmaceut Corp, 70-72, dir anal res & develop, 72-78, ASSOC DIR, ANAL CHEM DEPT, REVLON HEALTH CARE GROUP, REVLON INC, 78- *Mem:* Am Chem Soc; Am Pharmaceut Asn; Asn Off Anal Chemists; Acad Pharmaceut Sci. *Res:* Development of new analytical procedure for official amphetamine preparations; chemical assay for thyroid powder and tablets; analytical profile of chlorthalidone. *Mailing Add:* Revlon Health Care Group One Scarsdale Rd Tuckahoe NY 10707

MOODY, JUDITH BARBARA, b Detroit, Mich, Oct 14, 42. GEOCHEMISTRY, MINERALOGY. *Educ:* Univ Mich, Ann Arbor, BS, 64, MS, 67; McGill Univ, PhD(geochem), 74. *Prof Exp:* Geochemist, Anaconda Am Brass Ltd, Bathurst, NB, 67; vis scientist geochem, Univ Liege, 68-70; asst prof geochem, Univ NC, Chapel Hill, 74-80; PROJ MGR, OFF NUCLEAR WASTE ISOLATION, BATTELLE MEM INST, COLUMBUS, OHIO, 80- *Concurrent Pos:* Mem women geoscientist comt, Am Geol Inst, 72-77; NSF grant, 75-80; consult, Pedco Environ, 77 & Vulcan

Mat Co, 78. *Mem:* Am Geol Inst; Am Geophys Union; Geochem Soc; Mineral Soc Am; Can Mineral Soc. *Res:* Mineral stability as a function of temperature, pressure and composition; mechanisms of geochemical processes at low temperatures and pressures; mineralogic applications to materials science. *Mailing Add:* Off Nuclear Waste Isolation Battelle Mem Inst 505 King Ave Columbus OH 43201

MOODY, LEROY STEPHEN, b Elyria, Ohio, Nov 18, 18; m 45; c 3. PHYSICAL CHEMISTRY. *Educ:* Wesleyan Univ, BA, 41; Univ Wis, PhD(phys chem), 44. *Prof Exp:* Res chemist, Mass Inst Technol, 44-45; res chemist, 45-51, supvr prod eval, 51-52, specialist mkt res & prod planning, 52-54 & proj eval, 55-57, mgr, New Prod Develop Lab, 57-59 & polycarbonate eng, 59-64, managing dir, N V Polychemie, AKU-GE, Netherlands, 64-67, gen mgr irradiation processing oper, Vallecitos Nuclear Ctr, Calif, 67-69 & reactor fuels & reprocessing dept, 69-71, mgr strategy planning oper, 71-74, res & develop mgr mat sci & eng, 74-78, RES & DEVELOP MGR MAT SCI & ENG, CORP RES & DEVELOP CTR, GEN ELEC CO, 78- *Mem:* AAAS; Am Chem Soc; Am Nuclear Soc. *Res:* General management; administration of scientific programs; technology transfer; international technical programs. *Mailing Add:* Corp Res & Develop Ctr Gen Elec Co PO Box 8 Schenectady NY 12309

MOODY, MARTIN L(UTHER), b Corpus Christi, Tex, Apr 14, 25; m 50; c 4. CIVIL & STRUCTURAL ENGINEERING. *Educ:* Univ Mo, BS, 49; Univ Colo, MS, 57; Stanford Univ, PhD(civil eng), 65. *Prof Exp:* Inspector construct, Pa Dept Hwy, 49-50; eng aide, Tex Hwy Dept, 50; civil engr, Brown & Root, 50-51; field engr, Denver Water Bd, Colo, 51-55; from instr to assoc prof civil eng, Univ Colo, Boulder, 55-69; assoc chmn dept, 68-72, assoc dean eng, 72-73, vchancellor for admin, 74-79, PROF CIVIL ENG, UNIV COLO, DENVER, 69-, CHMN DEPT, 81- *Mem:* Am Soc Civil Engrs; Seismol Soc Am. *Res:* Mechanical properties of materials; dynamic response of structures. *Mailing Add:* Dept of Civil & Environ Eng 1100 14th St Denver CO 80210

MOODY, MAX DALE, b Onaga, Kans, Sept 29, 24; m 50. MEDICAL BACTERIOLOGY. *Educ:* Univ Kans, AB, 48, MA, 49, PhD(bact), 53; Am Bd Med Microbiol, dipl. *Prof Exp:* Asst med bact, Univ Kans, 46-53; in chg spec projs lab, Nat Commun Dis Ctr, USPHS, 53-62, chief staphylococcus & streptococcus unit, 62-67, dir, Nat Streptococcal Dis Ctr, 67-70, chief reagents eval unit, Ctr Dis Control, 70-71; TECH DIR, WELLCOME REAGENTS DIV, BURROUGHS WELLCOME CO, 71- *Concurrent Pos:* Mem expert adv panel coccal infections, WHO, 67-; secy subcomt streptococci & pneumococci, Int Cong Microbiol; mem comt on rheumatic fever, Am Heart Asn; assoc mem, Comn on Staphylococcal & Streptococcal Dis, Armed Forces Epidemiol Bd; area chmn microbiol, Nat Comt Clin Lab Standards, 78-; chmn, Conf Pub Health Lab Dirs, 80-81. *Honors & Awards:* Kimble Methodology Res Award, 67; USPHS Commendation Medal, 68. *Mem:* Am Soc Microbiol; Sigma Xi; fel Am Acad Med Microbiol; NY Acad Sci; Am Pub Health Asn. *Res:* Pathogenesis and immunity of Tularemia; rapid detection and identification of pathogenic microorganisms; fluorescent antibody identification of bacterial pathogens. *Mailing Add:* Wellcome Reagents Div Burroughs Wellcome Co Research Triangle Park NC 27709

MOODY, PAUL AMOS, b Randolph Center, Vt, Jan 13, 03; m 27; c 2. ZOOLOGY. *Educ:* Morningside Col, AB, 24; Univ Mich, PhD(zool), 27. *Prof Exp:* Asst zool, Univ Mich, 25-26; from asst prof to prof, 27-45, dir grad study, 42-49, Howard Prof Natural Hist & prof zool, 45-68, EMER PROF NATURAL HIST & ZOOL, UNIV VT, 68- *Mem:* Am Philos Soc grant-in-aid, 41. Mem: AAAS; Am Soc Mammal; Am Soc Human Genetics; Am Soc Zool. *Res:* Evolution; serological investigations of mammalian relationships; human genetics. *Mailing Add:* 197 Howard St Burlington VT 05401

MOODY, ROBERT ADAMS, b Swampscott, Mass, Oct 1, 34; m; c 5. NEUROSURGERY. *Educ:* Univ Chicago, BA, 55 & 56, MD, 60. *Prof Exp:* Intern, Royal Victoria Hosp, Mon, 60-61; resident surg, Univ Vt, 61-62 & resident neurosurg, 62-66; asst prof neurosurg, Univ Chicago, 66-71; asst prof, Sch Med, Tufts Univ, 71-74; chmn div neurosurg, Cook County Hosp, 74-81, assoc chmn, dept surg, 76-81; prof neurosurg, Abraham Lincoln Sch Med, Univ Ill Med Ctr, 74-81; CHIEF NEUROSURG, GUTHRIE CLINIC, SAYRE, PA, 81- *Concurrent Pos:* Fel neurosurg, Lahey Clin, 63-64. *Mem:* Am Asn Neurol Surg; Am Col Surgeons; AMA. *Res:* Head injury; blood brain barrier; brain scanning; microvascular surgery. *Mailing Add:* Guthrie Clinic Guthrie Square Sayre PA 18840

MOODY, WILLIS E, JR, b Raleigh, NC, Mar 30, 24; m 47; c 5. CERAMIC ENGINEERING. *Educ:* NC State Col, BS, 48, MS, 49, PhD(ceramic eng), 56. *Prof Exp:* Ceramic engr, Elec Auto-Lite Co, Ohio, 49-50; ceramic engr, Lab Equip Corp, Mich, 50-51; instr ceramics & metall, NC State Col, 51-56; PROF CERAMIC ENG & RES ASSOC, ENG EXP STA, GA INST TECHNOL, 56- *Mem:* AAAS; fel Am Ceramic Soc; Nat Inst Ceramic Engrs (vpres, 78, pres, 80); Ceramic Educ Coun (pres, 63); Am Soc Eng Educ. *Res:* High temperature ceramics and metals; dental materials; clays; application of materials to nuclear reactors; electrical ceramics; solar energy. *Mailing Add:* Sch Ceramic Eng Ga Inst Technol Atlanta GA 30332

MOOERS, CALVIN NORTHRUP, b Minneapolis, Minn, Oct 24, 19; m 45; c 2. MATHEMATICS, SOFTWARE SYSTEMS. *Educ:* Univ Minn, AB, 41; Mass Inst Technol, MS, 48. *Prof Exp:* Physicist, Naval Ord Lab, Md, 41-46; PROPRIETOR & DIR RES, ZATOR CO, 47-; PRES & DIR RES, ROCKFORD RES, INC, 61- *Mem:* Int Fedn Doc; Asn Comput Mach; Am Soc Info Sci; Inst Elec & Electronics Eng. *Res:* Programming languages; information retrieval and processing, including theory, systems and machines; reactive typewriter. *Mailing Add:* 13 Bowdoin St Cambridge MA 02138

MOOERS, CHRISTOPHER NORTHRUP KENNARD, b Hagerstown, Md, Nov 11, 35; m 60; c 2. PHYSICAL OCEANOGRAPHY, FLUID DYNAMICS. *Educ:* US Naval Acad, BS, 57; Univ Conn, MS, 64; Ore State Univ, PhD(phys oceanog), 69. *Prof Exp:* NATO fel, Univ Liverpool, 69-70; from asst prof to assoc prof phys oceanog, Sch Marine & Atmospheric Sci, Univ Miami, 70-76; assoc prof, 76-78, PROF PHYS OCEANOG, COL MARINE STUDIES, UNIV DEL, 78- *Mem:* Challenger Soc; Am Soc Limnol & Oceanog; Oceanog Soc Japan; Am Meteorol Soc; Sigma Xi. *Res:* Fluid dynamics of continental margins; oceanic fronts, coastal upwelling, transient circulations due to storms, tidal and other long waves and wave-mean current interactions; analysis of observations; geophysical fluid dynamics. *Mailing Add:* Col Marine Studies Univ of Del PO Box 286 Lewes DE 19958

MOOERS, HOWARD T(HEODORE), b Minneapolis, Minn, May 19, 21; m 47; c 4. SYSTEMS ANALYSIS, INFLUENCE FUZING. *Educ:* Univ Minn, BEE, 43, MS, 49. *Prof Exp:* Design engr, Zator Co, Mass, 47-48; chief elec res engr, Minneapolis-Honeywell Regulator Co, 50-52, proj engr, Solid State Res, 52-54, chief appln engr transistor circuitry, 54-56, asst dir eng transistor design, 56-57, staff asst transistor sales, 57-59; mgr, Appl Res Am Electronics Co, 59-61; mgr mil elec dept, Rosemount Eng Co, 61-62; proj supvr, Govt & Aeronaut Prod Div, 63-66, STAFF ENGR, DEFENSE SYSTEMS DIV, HONEYWELL, INC, 66- *Mem:* Sr mem Inst Elec & Electronics Engrs. *Res:* Semiconductor devices; circuitry; power conditioning and influence fuzing; specifically magnetic influence fuzing for scatterable mines; variation of magnetic signatures of military vehicles and their charges with compass heading and geomagnetic latitudes; detection and localizing algorithms, countermeasures and counter counter measures. *Mailing Add:* 3983 Heathcote Rd Wayzata MN 55391

MOOG, FLORENCE, b Brooklyn, NY, Jan 24, 15. DEVELOPMENTAL BIOLOGY. *Educ:* NY Univ, AB, 36; Columbia Univ, AM, 38, PhD(zool), 44. *Hon Degrees:* ScD, La Salle Col, 74. *Prof Exp:* Med records clerk, US Dept Labor, 37-38; instr, Univ Del, 40; res assoc, 42-45, from instr to prof zool, 45-74, REBSTOCK PROF BIOL, WASH UNIV, 74- *Concurrent Pos:* Merck fel, Cambridge Univ, 54-55; mem study sect human embryol & develop, NIH, 66-70; Walker-Ames prof, Univ Wash, 73. *Honors & Awards:* AAAS-Westinghouse Award, 48. *Mem:* Am Soc Zool; Soc Develop Biol; Am Soc Cell Biol. *Res:* Functional development of digestive tract; enzymogenesis in vertebrate development; developmental endocrinology of vertebrates. *Mailing Add:* Dept Biol Wash Univ St Louis MO 63130

MOOK, DEAN TRITSCHLER, b Ridgeway, Pa, Aug 3, 35; m 54; c 4. ENGINEERING MECHANICS. *Educ:* Va Polytech Inst & State Univ, BS, 58, MS, 61; Univ Mich, Ann Arbor, PhD(eng mech), 66. *Prof Exp:* Instr, 58-60, ASST PROF ENG MECH, VA POLYTECH INST & STATE UNIV, 66- *Concurrent Pos:* Instr, Univ Mich, Ann Arbor, 60. *Mem:* Am Inst Aeronaut & Astronaut; Am Soc Mech Engrs; Am Soc Civil Engrs. *Res:* Aerodynamics; viscous flows; nonlinear oscillations. *Mailing Add:* Dept of Eng Mech Va Polytech Inst & State Univ Blacksburg VA 24061

MOOK, DELO EMERSON, II, b Cleveland, Ohio, Apr 28, 42; m 65. ASTRONOMY. *Educ:* Case Inst Technol, BS, 64; Univ Mich, PhD(astron), 69. *Prof Exp:* Instr, Lawrence Univ, 67; res assoc astron, Univ Chicago, 69-70; asst prof astron, 70-76, ASSOC PROF PHYSICS & ASTRON, DARTMOUTH COL, 76- *Mem:* Am Astron Soc; Royal Astron Soc; Int Astron Union; Astron Soc Pac. *Res:* Astronomical photometry; polarimetry; celestial x-ray sources. *Mailing Add:* Dept of Physics & Astron Dartmouth Col Hanover NH 03755

MOOK, HERBERT ARTHUR, JR, b Meadville, Pa, Apr 17, 39; m 65; c 1. APPLIED PHYSICS, SOLID STATE PHYSICS. *Educ:* Williams Col, BA, 60; Harvard Univ, MA, 61, PhD(physics), 65. *Prof Exp:* PHYSICIST, OAK RIDGE NAT LAB, 65- *Mem:* Fel Am Phys Soc. *Res:* Neutron diffraction studies of solid state physics, especially magnetic materials; polarized and inelastic neutron scattering investigations of the spin density and magnetic excitations in the rare earths and transition metals. *Mailing Add:* Solid State Div PO Box X Oak Ridge TN 37830

MOOKERJEA, SAILEN, b Jamalpur, India, Sept 1, 30; m 56; c 2. BIOCHEMISTRY, PHYSIOLOGY. *Educ:* Univ Calcutta, BSc, 49, MSc, 51, PhD(physiol), 56. *Prof Exp:* Lectr biochem, Univ Nagpur, India, 53-61; lectr physiol, Univ Calcutta, 61-62; res assoc, Banting & Best Dept Med Res, Univ Toronto, 62-65, from asst prof to assoc prof med, 65-76; PROF BIOCHEM, MEM UNIV NFLD, 76-, CHMN DEPT, 78- *Concurrent Pos:* Nat Res Coun Can fel, 56-57; res fel, Banting & Best Dept Med Res, Univ Toronto, 57-58; Med Res Coun scholar, 65-70; mem grants comt, Nat Res Coun Can, 78-79. *Mem:* Can Biochem Soc; US Soc Biol Chemists; Brit Biochem Soc; Am Inst Nutrit. *Res:* Lipoprotein biosynthesis; role of soluble and membrane glycosyltransferases; membrane metabolism; role of choline in membrane function and lipoprotein biogenesis; control of glycoprotein biosynthesis. *Mailing Add:* Dept of Biochem Mem Univ of Nfld St Johns NF A1B 3X9 Can

MOOKHERJI, TRIPTY KUMAR, b Calcutta, India, Sept 15, 38; m 65; c 1. SOLID STATE PHYSICS. *Educ:* Agra Univ, BSc, 57, MSc, 59; Univ Burdwan, DPhil(physics), 66. *Prof Exp:* Res assoc, Marshall Space Flight Ctr, NASA, 66-68; sr physicist solid state, 68-79, SR SYSTS ANALYST, TELEDYNE-BROWN ENG, 80- *Concurrent Pos:* Mem, Indian Asn Cultivation of Sci. *Honors & Awards:* New Technol Utilization Award, NASA, 72. *Mem:* Am Phys Soc; Optical Soc Am. *Res:* Electronic excitation; color center; optical band structure; surface physics; growing and characterization of metallic and nonmetallic crystals; manufacturing in space; photovoltaic solar energy conversion; amniotic fluid study. *Mailing Add:* Teledyne-Brown Eng Cummings Res Park Huntersville AL 35807

MOOLENAAR, ROBERT JOHN, b DeMotte, Ind, Nov 30, 31; m 55; c 3. PHYSICAL CHEMISTRY, ENVIRONMENTAL SCIENCES. *Educ:* Hope Col, BA, 53; Univ Ill, PhD, 57. *Prof Exp:* Instr phys chem, Univ Ill, 56-57; chemist, 57-65, sr res chemist, 65-69, assoc scientist, 69-74, DIR ENVIRON SCI RES, DOW CHEM CO, 74- *Mem:* Am Chem Soc; Soc Environ Toxicol & Chem. *Res:* Inorganic chemistry; biodegradation; photodegradation; toxicology. *Mailing Add:* Dow Chem Co 1702 Bldg Midland MI 48640

MOOLGAVKAR, SURESH HIRAJI, b Bombay, India, Jan 3, 43; m 68; c 2. MATHEMATICAL BIOLOGY, EPIDEMIOLOGY. *Educ:* Univ Bombay, MB & BS, 65; Johns Hopkins Univ, PhD(math), 73. *Prof Exp:* Instr math, Johns Hopkins Univ, 72-73; asst prof math, Ind Univ, Bloomington, 73-77; asst prof, 77-80, ASSOC PROF RES MED, UNIV PA, 80-; EPIDEMIOLOGIST & RES PHYSICIAN, FOX CHASE CANCER CTR, 77- *Concurrent Pos:* Sr fel, Univ Wash, 76-77. *Honors & Awards:* Lester R Ford Award, Math Asn Am, 77. *Res:* Application of mathematical and statistical techniques in the biological sciences especially epidemiology. *Mailing Add:* Fox Chase Cancer Ctr 7701 Burholme Ave Philadelphia PA 19111

MOOLTEN, FREDERICK LONDON, b New York, NY, Oct 11, 32; m 60; c 4. CANCER. *Educ:* Harvard Col, BA, 53; Harvard Med Sch, MD, 63. *Prof Exp:* Internship med, Mass Gen Hosp, Boston, 63-64, residency, 64-65 & 67-68, res fel, 65-67, 68-69; res assoc, 69-71, asst prof, 71-74, ASSOC PROF MICROBIOL, SCH MED, BOSTON UNIV, 74- *Concurrent Pos:* Fel, Am Cancer Soc, 65-67 & NIH, 69-71. *Honors & Awards:* Cancer Res Scholar Award, Am Cancer Soc, 71. *Mem:* Am Asn Cancer Res. *Res:* Tumor immunotherapy studies aimed at eradicating tumor cells selectively with antitumor antibodies conjugated to potent cytotoxins; immunization against carcinogens. *Mailing Add:* Sch of Med Boston Univ 80 E Concord St Boston MA 02118

MOOLTEN, SYLVAN E, b New York, NY, Sept 1, 04; m 28; c 2. INTERNAL MEDICINE, PATHOLOGY. *Educ:* Columbia Univ, AB, 24, MD, 28; Am Bd Path, dipl, 38; Am Bd Internal Med, dipl, 41. *Prof Exp:* Atten physician, Mt Sinai Hosp, New York, 34-42; dir lab, Middlesex Gen Hosp, 46-70, dir lab res, 56-70; DIR LAB, ROOSEVELT HOSP, 50-; assoc prof, Col Physicians & Surgeons, Columbia Univ, 63-67. *Concurrent Pos:* Consult, St Peter's Gen Hosp, 41-, dir lab, 46-56; res grants, USPHS, 50-55 & 61-66, NJ Heart Asn, 56-58 & Wesson Fund for Med Res, 61; consult, Middlesex Gen Hosp, 56-; clin prof, Rutgers Med Sch, Col Med & Dent NJ, 63- *Mem:* AAAS; Col Am Path; Am Col Physicians; Am Soc Clin Oncol; Asn Hosp Med Educ. *Res:* Lung pathology; blood platelets and thrombosis; Hodgkin's disease; pulmonary lymphatics; adsorption of virus-like agents to erythrocytes; systemic lupus erythematous. *Mailing Add:* 103 N 4th Pl Highland Park NJ 08904

MOOMAW, JAMES CURTIS, agronomy, see previous edition

MOOMAW, WILLIAM RENKEN, b Kansas City, Mo, Feb 18, 38; m 64; c 2. MOLECULAR SPECTROSCOPY, ENVIRONMENTAL SCIENCES. *Educ:* Williams Col, BA, 59; Mass Inst Technol, PhD(phys chem), 65. *Prof Exp:* Asst prof chem, Williams Col, 64-65; researcher, Univ Calif, Los Angeles, 65-66; asst prof, 66-71, ASSOC PROF CHEM, WILLIAMS COL, 72- *Concurrent Pos:* Froman distinguished prof, Russell Sage Col, 71; vis scholar, Univ Calif, Los Angeles, 71-72; AAAS Cong Sci fel, 75-76. *Mem:* AAAS; Am Phys Soc; Am Chem Soc. *Res:* Electronic spectra of small organic molecules; nature of the triplet states of these molecules; excited states and structure of molecular complexes; application of physical science to environmental problems. *Mailing Add:* Dept of Chem Williams Col Williamstown MA 02167

MOON, BYONG HOON, b Seoul, Korea, Jan 15, 26; US citizen; m 57; c 4. PHARMACOLOGY, MEDICINAL CHEMISTRY. *Educ:* Seoul Nat Univ, BSc, 51; Univ Nebr, BPharm, 60, MS, 64; Wash State Univ, PhD(pharmacol), 69. *Prof Exp:* Res assoc pharmacol, Univ Ill Col Med, 69-72; instr pharmacol, 72-73, asst prof & asst scientist, 73-80, ASSOC PROF PHARMACOL & ASSOC SCIENTIST INTERNAL MED, RUSH MED COL, 81-, COURSE DIR MED PHARMACOL, 74-, NURSING PHARMACOL, COL NURSING, 75- *Mem:* Am Soc Pharmacol & Exp Therapeut. *Res:* The synthesis of 3-aminopiperidone derivatives to provide a basis for study of structure versus potential anticonvulsant activity relationshop; norepinephrine-adenosine triphosphate complex formation, spectroscopical proof of a complex in vitro and in adrenal medulary granules; role of dopaminergic mechanisms in noloxone-induced inhibition of apomorphine-induced sterotyped behavior; pharmacological analysis of electric foot-shock-induced antinociception and role of pituitary opioid peptides in physostigmine-induced antinociception. *Mailing Add:* Rush-Presby-St Luke's Med Ctr 1725 W Harrison Chicago IL 61612

MOON, DEUG WOON, b Korea; US citizen. MATERIALS SCIENCE ENGINEERING. *Educ:* Seoul Nat Univ, BS, 61; State Univ NY, 70; Rensselaer Polytech Inst, PhD(mat sci eng), 75. *Prof Exp:* Fel mat, Rensselaer Polytech Inst, 75-77; MEM STAFF MAT SCI, NAVAL RES LAB, 77- *Mem:* Am Soc Metals; Am Welding Soc. *Res:* High energy laser applications in materials processing, particularly in the area of welding; solidification; interaction between heat source and solids; structure, property and process parameters relationships. *Mailing Add:* Code 6324 Naval Res Lab Washington DC 20375

MOON, DONALD W(AYNE), b Herrick, Ill, Apr 1, 34; c 2. MATERIALS SCIENCE, MECHANICAL ENGINEERING. *Educ:* Univ Ill, BS, 56, MS, 57; Calif Inst Technol, PhD(mat sci), 66. *Prof Exp:* Proj engr eng staff, Gen Motors Corp, 58-61 & defense systs, 61; asst prof mech eng, Univ Calif, Davis, 65-72, group leader, 72-74, assoc div leader, 75-77, dep div leader, 77-78, div leader, 78-81, ASSOC PROG LEADER, PRECISION ENG PROG, LAWRENCE LIVERMORE NAT LAB, UNIV CALIF, 81- *Concurrent Pos:* NSF fes initiation grant, 67-69. *Mem:* AAAS; Am Soc Metals; Nat Soc Prof Engrs; Am Inst Mining, Metall & Petrol Engrs. *Res:* Dislocation theory; observation and application to the deformation of crystalline solids; mechanical deformation of biological materials. *Mailing Add:* Lawrence Livermore Lab Univ of Calif PO Box 808 L-144 Livermore CA 94551

MOON, FRANCIS C, b Brooklyn, NY, May 1, 39; m 62; c 3. SOLID MECHANICS. *Educ:* Pratt Inst, BSME, 62; Cornell Univ, MS, 64, PhD(theoret & appl mech), 67. *Prof Exp:* Asst prof mech & aerospace eng, Univ Del, 66-67; asst prof aerospace & mech sci, Princeton Univ, 67-74; assoc prof, 75-81, PROF & CHMN, DEPT THEORET & APPL MECH, CORNELL UNIV, 81- *Concurrent Pos:* Consult, Rand Corp, Calif, 67-69, Boeing Vertol, 71-72, Int Tel & Tel Corp, 78, SCM Corp, 79-80 & Argonne Nat Lab, 80- *Mem:* AAAS; Am Soc Mech Engrs; Am Acad Mech. *Res:* Wave propagation in solids; composite materials; magneto-elasticity; magnetic levitation of trains; superconducting magnets. *Mailing Add:* Dept of Theoret & Appl Mech Thurston Hall Cornell Univ Ithaca NY 14850

MOON, GEORGE D(ONALD), JR, b Dayton, Ohio, Apr 15, 27; m 53; c 4. CHEMICAL ENGINEERING. *Educ:* Univ Dayton, BChE, 49. *Prof Exp:* Asst chem eng, Univ Cincinnati, 49-51, from instr to assoc prof, 51-73; partner & sr process engr, 73-80, VPRES, RAPHAEL KATZEN ASSOCS INT, INC, 80- *Concurrent Pos:* Consult, Raphael Katzen Assocs, 57-73; adj assoc prof chem eng, Univ Cincinnati, 73- *Honors & Awards:* Chem Engr of Year Award, Am Inst Chem Engrs, 78. *Mem:* Am Soc Eng Educ; Am Inst Chem Engrs; Am Chem Soc. *Res:* Distillation-perforated tray contractors; computers in engineering design. *Mailing Add:* Raphael Katzen Assocs 1050 Delta Ave Cincinnati OH 45208

MOON, HARLEY W, b Tracy, Minn, Mar 1, 36; m 56; c 4. VETERINARY PATHOLOGY. *Educ:* Univ Minn, BS, 58, DVM, 60, PhD(vet path), 65. *Prof Exp:* Instr vet path, Univ Minn, 60-62, NIH res fel, 62-65; asst scientist, Brookhaven Nat Lab, 65-66; assoc prof vet path, Univ Sask, 66-68; res veterinarian, Nat Animal Dis Lab, Agr Res Serv, USDA, 68-73; PROF VET PATH, IOWA STATE UNIV, 74- *Concurrent Pos:* Res collabr, Brookhaven Nat Lab, 66- *Mem:* Am Vet Med Asn; Am Col Vet Path. *Res:* Infectious diseases of the intestinal tract of animals; role of the lymphocyte in the immune response. *Mailing Add:* Dept of Vet Path Iowa State Univ Ames IA 50010

MOON, JOHN WESLEY, b Hornell, NY. MATHEMATICS. *Educ:* Bethany Nazarene Col, BA, 59; Mich State Univ, MS, 60; Univ Alta, PhD(math), 62. *Prof Exp:* Nat Res Coun Can fel, Univ Col, Univ London, 62-64; from asst prof to assoc prof, 64-69, PROF MATH, UNIV ALTA, 69- *Concurrent Pos:* Vis prof, Univ Cape Town, 70-71; vis, Math Inst, Oxford Univ, 71 & Univ Witwatersrand, 77-78. *Mem:* Am Math Soc; Can Math Soc. *Res:* Graph theory; combinatorial analysis. *Mailing Add:* Dept Math Univ Alta Edmonton AB T6G 2G1 Can

MOON, MILTON LEWIS, b New Providence, Iowa, Dec 16, 22; m 47; c 4. PHYSICS, ENVIRONMENTAL SCIENCES. *Educ:* Iowa State Teachers Col, BA, 43; Univ Iowa, MS, 48, PhD(physics), 51. *Prof Exp:* Physicist, 51-72, POWER PLANT SITE EVAL PROG MGR, APPL PHYSICS LAB, JOHNS HOPKINS UNIV, 72- *Concurrent Pos:* Mem, Environ Res Guid Comt, 72-75. *Res:* Communications and navigation systems; environmental effects; cooling systems; air pollution; impact modelling. *Mailing Add:* 10510 Greenacres Dr Silver Spring MD 20903

MOON, PETER CLAYTON, b St Louis, Mo, May 17, 40. DENTAL MATERIALS. *Educ:* Univ Toledo, BS, 64; Univ Va, MS, 67, PhD(mat sci), 71. *Prof Exp:* Mat scientist, Texaco Exp, Inc, 66-68; ASSOC PROF DENT MAT, SCH DENT, MED COL VA, VA COMMONWEALTH UNIV, 71- *Mem:* Int Asn Dent Res; Am Asn Dent Res; Am Chem Soc. *Res:* Mechanical properties; fracture; mineralization of bone and teeth; metallurgy; polymers; interfacial bonding. *Mailing Add:* Dept of Restorative Dent Med Col Va Sch of Dent Richmond VA 23298

MOON, RALPH MARKS, JR, b Bombay, India, Oct 11, 29; US citizen; m 50; c 4. PHYSICS. *Educ:* Univ Kans, BA, 50, MA, 52; Mass Inst Technol, PhD(physics), 63. *Prof Exp:* Physicist, Naval Ord Test Sta, Calif, 52-54; PHYSICIST, OAK RIDGE NAT LAB, 63- *Mem:* Am Phys Soc. *Res:* Neutron diffraction; magnetism. *Mailing Add:* Solid State Div Oak Ridge Nat Lab Oak Ridge TN 37830

MOON, RICHARD C, b Beech Grove, Ind, July 25, 26; m 48; c 3. ENDOCRINOLOGY. *Educ:* Butler Univ, BS, 50; Univ Cincinnati, MS, 52, PhD(zool), 55. *Prof Exp:* Instr physiol, Col Pharm, Univ Cincinnati, 53-54, instr zool, 54-55; asst prof biol, Duquesne Univ, 55-58; asst prof physiol, Med Units, Univ Tenn, Memphis, 59-63, from assoc prof to prof physiol & biophys, 63-73; head endocrinol res, 73-74, sr sci adv, 74-77, HEAD PATHOPHYSIOL, RES INST, ILL INST TECHNOL, 77- *Concurrent Pos:* Nat Cancer Inst res fel endocrinol, Univ Mo, 58-59; Lederle med fac award, 63-66; Nat Cancer Inst spec res fel, Imp Cancer Res Fund, London, Eng, 65-66; guest investr, Ben May Lab Cancer Res, Univ Chicago, 61. *Mem:* AAAS; Am Physiol Soc; Endocrine Soc; Soc Exp Biol & Med; Am Asn Cancer Res; Soc Study Reproduction. *Res:* Hormonal control of mammary gland growth and hormonal influence upon mammary tumor formation; chemical carcinogenesis. *Mailing Add:* Ill Inst of Technol Res Inst 10 W 35 St Chicago IL 60616

MOON, ROBERT JOHN, b Carbondale, Pa, Aug 6, 42; m 66; c 1. MICROBIOLOGY. *Educ:* Eastern Col, AB, 64; Bryn Mawr Col, PhD(biol), 69. *Prof Exp:* From instr to asst prof, 68-75, ASSOC PROF MICROBIOL, MICH STATE UNIV, 75- *Concurrent Pos:* NIH fel, Harvard Univ, 72-73. *Mem:* AAAS; Am Soc Microbiol. *Res:* Medical microbiology and immunology; host responses to infectious agents. *Mailing Add:* Dept of Microbiol & Pub Health Mich State Univ East Lansing MI 48824

MOON, SUNG, b Seoul, Korea, Oct 6, 28; US citizen; m 61; c 2. ORGANIC CHEMISTRY. *Educ:* Univ Ill, BS, 56; Mass Inst Technol, PhD(org chem), 59. *Prof Exp:* Res assoc org chem, Mass Inst Technol, 59-62; from asst prof to assoc prof, 62-71, PROF ORG CHEM, ADELPHI UNIV, 71- *Concurrent Pos:* Am Chem Soc Petrol Res Fund grant, 65-68. *Mem:* Am Chem Soc; Royal Soc Chemists. *Res:* Organic synthesis and reaction mechanisms. *Mailing Add:* Dept of Chem Adelphi Univ Garden City NY 11530

MOON, TAG YOUNG, b Seoul, Korea, May 11, 31; US citizen; m 59; c 4. PHYSICAL CHEMISTRY, STATISTICAL MECHANICS. *Educ:* Seoul Nat Univ, BS, 59; Yale Univ, PhD(chem), 65. *Prof Exp:* Lectr & NSF grants, Yale Univ, 65-66; RES CHEMIST, DOW CHEM USA, 66- *Mem:* Am Chem Soc; Am Soc Testing & Mat; Nat Asn Corrosion Engrs; Electrochem Soc; NY Acad Sci. *Res:* Statistical thermodynamics of surfaces; interaction of colloidal particles; physics and chemistry of concrete; corrosion of steel; decontamination of nuclear power plants; solidification of radioactive waste. *Mailing Add:* 4109 Moorland Dr Midland MI 48640

MOON, THOMAS CHARLES, b Detroit, Mich, Apr 1, 40; m 63; c 2. SCIENCE EDUCATION, ECOLOGY. *Educ:* Kalamazoo Col, BA, 62; Oberlin Col, MAT, 63; Mich State Univ, PhD(sci educ, biol), 69. *Prof Exp:* Teacher, Detroit Country Day Sch, 63-64 & Farmington High Sch, 64-66; sr lectr sci educ, Mich State Univ, 66-69; dir environ studies, 74-77, PROF SCI EDUC & BIOL, CALIF STATE COL, PA, 69- *Concurrent Pos:* Sci consult, Rand McNally & Co, Ill, 68-72. *Mem:* AAAS. *Res:* Interdisciplinary environmental science and its effects on science education endeavors; stress factors in aquatic ecosystems. *Mailing Add:* Dept Biol Calif State Col California PA 15419

MOON, THOMAS EDWARD, b Pontiac, Mich, Aug 16, 43; m 64; c 1. BIOMETRICS. *Educ:* Northern Ill Univ, BS, 65; Univ Chicago, MS, 67; Univ Calif, Berkeley, PhD(biostatist), 73. *Prof Exp:* Mathematician, US Army Aberdeen Proving Grounds, 67; statistician, NIH, 67-70; biostatistician, Gorgas Mem Inst, Mid Am Res Unit, 73-74; asst biometrician, M D Anderson Hosp & Tumor Inst, 74-77; assoc prof, Dept Family & Community Med, 77-81, HEAD, BIOSTATIST, BIOMATH, CANCER EPIDEMIOL & PROCESSING INFO UNIV, CANCER CTR DIV, UNIV ARIZ, 77-, ASST DIR, CANCER CTR DIV, 77-, ADJ ASSOC PROF DEPT FAMILY & COMMUNITY MED, 81- *Concurrent Pos:* Asst biometrician, Southwest Oncol Group, 74-77; asst prof biomet, Grad Sch Biomed Sci, Univ Tex, 74-77. *Mem:* Am Statist Asn; Sigma Xi; Am Soc Clin Oncol; Biomet Soc. *Res:* Applications of statistical methods to biomedical research. *Mailing Add:* Cancer Ctr Div Univ of Ariz Tucson AZ 85724

MOON, THOMAS WILLIAM, b Portland, Ore, June 10, 44; m 65; c 2. COMPARATIVE PHYSIOLOGY, BIOCHEMISTRY. *Educ:* Ore State Univ, BSc, 66, MA, 68; Univ BC, PhD(zool), 71. *Prof Exp:* Fel, Marine Sci Res Lab, Mem Univ, 71-72; asst prof, 72-76, ASSOC PROF BIOL, UNIV OTTAWA, 76- *Concurrent Pos:* Partic exped, Galapagos Island, 70, Kona Coast, Hawaii, 73 & Amazon, 76; vis prof zool, Univ Toronto, 75, Odense Univ, Denmark, 79, St Andrews Univ, Scotland, 79 & Nat Marine Fisheries, Honolulu, 81; mem fac fisheries, Kagoshima Univ & fel, Japen Soc Prom Sci, 82. *Mem:* Am Phys Soc; Am Soc Zoologists; Can Soc Zoologists; Can Soc Physiologists. *Res:* Organism-environment interactions using the tools of biochemistry to probe molecular strategies associated with the adaptation process; nutritive strategies during fasting in vertebrates. *Mailing Add:* 1913 Dauphin Rd Ottawa ON K1N 6N5 Can

MOON, WILCHOR DAVID, b Rose Bud, Ark, June 2, 33; m 53; c 2. MATHEMATICS. *Educ:* State Col Ark, BS, 58; Univ Tenn, Knoxville, MA, 62; Okla State Univ, PhD(math), 67. *Prof Exp:* Instr math, Univ Tenn, Knoxville, 60-62; asst prof, Southern State Col, Ark, 62-63; assoc prof, Ark Col, 63-65, prof math & chmn, Sci Div, 66-68; PROF MATH, UNIV CENT ARK, 68-, DEAN UNDERGRAD STUDIES, 72- *Concurrent Pos:* Consult, Health Physics Div, Union Carbide Nuclear, Oak Ridge Nuclear Co, Tenn, 60-62; vis lectr, Ark Acad Sci, 66-68. *Mem:* Math Asn Am (1st vpres, 71-72); Am Math Soc. *Res:* Topology; geometry. *Mailing Add:* Off of Dean Undergrad Studies Univ of Cent Ark Conway AR 72032

MOONAN, WILLIAM JEANE, b Austin, Minn, Oct 29, 23; m 52; c 2. STATISTICS. *Educ:* Univ Minn, BS, 48, MS, 50, PhD(statist), 52. *Prof Exp:* Asst prof statist, Univ Minn, 53-54; dir statist dept, US Naval Personnel Res Activity, 54-68; vpres prog develop, Nat Comput Systs, 68-71; MEM STAFF, NAVAL PERSONNEL RES & TRAINING LAB, 71- *Mem:* Am Statist Asn; Asn Comput Mach; Inst Math Statist; Opers Res Soc Am. *Res:* Design of experiments; multivariate analysis. *Mailing Add:* Naval Personnel Res & Training Lab San Diego CA 92152

MOONEY, CHARLES FRANK, b Baltimore, Md, June 15, 21; m 46, 64. PHYSICS. *Educ:* Drew Univ, AB, 42; Johns Hopkins Univ, PhD(physics), 52. *Prof Exp:* Physicist, Bausch & Lomb, Inc, 51-64, res scientist, 64-67, sect head grating res, 62-67; ASSOC PROF PHYSICS, COMMUNITY COL FINGER LAKES, 68- *Mem:* Am Asn Physics Teachers. *Res:* Classical and optical physics; polarization; infrared filters; aspheric surfaces; glass making; extended range and surface contour interferometry; diffraction grating profile measurement; ellipsoid for exciting lasers. *Mailing Add:* Dept of Physics Community Col of the Finger Lakes Canandaigua NY 14424

MOONEY, DAVID SAMUEL, b Albany, NY, Oct 13, 28; m 60; c 2. ORGANIC CHEMISTRY. *Educ:* State Univ NY Albany, BA, 50, MA, 51; Rensselaer Polytech Inst, PhD(org chem), 55. *Prof Exp:* Asst org chem, Rensselaer Polytech Inst, 51-55; from asst prof to assoc prof, 55-65, PROF ORG CHEM, WASHINGTON & JEFFERSON COL, 65- *Mem:* Am Chem Soc. *Res:* Organo lithium compounds; organic reaction mechanisms. *Mailing Add:* Dept of Chem Washington & Jefferson Col Washington PA 15301

MOONEY, EDWARD, JR, b New Castle, Pa, Aug 11, 42; m 70. NUCLEAR SCIENCE, GEOPHYSICS. *Educ:* Youngstown State Univ, BS, 64; Cornell Univ, MS, 66; Va Polytech Inst, PhD(nuclear sci), 71. *Prof Exp:* ASSOC PROF PHYSICS, YOUNGSTOWN STATE UNIV, 66- *Concurrent Pos:* Assoc prof res physics, Col Med, Northeastern Ohio Univs, 76- *Mem:* Am Inst Physics; Sigma Xi. *Res:* Neutron activation analysis studies of environmental pollutants; coronary monitoring during exercise stress testing using micro and mini computers. *Mailing Add:* Dept of Physics 410 Wick Ave Youngstown OH 44555

MOONEY, HAROLD MORTON, b Northfield, Mass, Dec 15, 22; m 46; c 2. GEOPHYSICS. *Educ:* Harvard Univ, BS, 43; Calif Inst Technol, MS, 48, PhD(geophys), 50. *Prof Exp:* Engr, Gen Elec Co, 43-44, Manhattan Proj, 44-46 & Geophys Explors, Ltd, 46; from asst prof to assoc prof, 50-65, PROF GEOPHYS, UNIV MINN, MINNEAPOLIS, 65-, GEOL, 74- *Concurrent Pos:* Vis lectr, Fed Inst Tech & Inst for Geophys, Zurich, 59 & Victoria Univ, Wellington, 68; consult, US Army, US AEC & oil & mining indust. *Mem:* Soc Explor Geophys; Seismol Soc Am; Acoust Soc Am; Am Geophys Union; Europ Asn Explor Geophys. *Res:* Geophysical instrumentation; electrical exploration; magnetic properties of rocks; theory of seismic wave propagation. *Mailing Add:* Dept of Geol & Geophys Univ Minn Minneapolis MN 55455

MOONEY, JOHN BERNARD, b Coalinga, Calif, June 9, 26; m 49; c 2. ANALYTICAL CHEMISTRY, MATERIALS RESEARCH. *Educ:* Univ Santa Clara, BS, 50; Stanford Univ, MS, 53. *Prof Exp:* Jr develop chemist, Int Minerals & Chem Corp, 51-54; instr chem, Univ Santa Clara, 54-57; res chemist, Kaiser Aluminum & Chem Corp, 57-59; chief chemist, Thermatest Labs, Inc, 59-60; sr engr chem, Varian Assocs, 60-69; mgr mat technol & corp vpres, Photophys, Inc, 69-75; SR RES CHEMIST, SRI INT, 76- *Concurrent Pos:* Vis assoc, Calif Inst Technol, 75-76. *Mem:* Electrochem Soc. *Res:* Emission spectroscopy; gas chromatography; materials research; chemical vapor deposition. *Mailing Add:* Stanford Res Inst Menlo Park CA 94025

MOONEY, LARRY ALBERT, b Idaho Falls, Idaho, Jan 28, 36; m 58; c 7. CLINICAL CHEMISTRY. *Educ:* Willamette Univ, BS, 58; Univ Wash, PhD(biochem), 64; Am Bd Clin Chem, dipl. *Prof Exp:* Fel lipid biochem, Va Mason Res Ctr, 64-66; res fel, 66-68; clin biochemist, Mason Clin, 68-69; ASSOC DIR CHEM LAB, SACRED HEART HOSP, 69- *Concurrent Pos:* Biomed consult, Athletics W Running Club, 78- *Mem:* AAAS; assoc Am Soc Clin Path; Am Asn Clin Chem; NY Acad Sci; Am Chem Soc. *Res:* Biosynthesis of essential fatty acids and biological elongation of fatty acids; development of analytical methods for clinical chemistry; application of biochemical knowledge to problems in medicine; applications of microprocessors in the clinical laboratory. *Mailing Add:* Chem Lab Sacred Heart Hosp 1200 Adler St Eugene OR 97401

MOONEY, MARGARET L, b Stinnett, Tex, July 29, 29. METEOROLOGY. *Educ:* Univ Calif, Los Angeles, BA, 62. *Prof Exp:* Meteorologist, Dept Army, Dugway Proving Ground, 62-66; meteorologist, 66-71, supv meteorologist, 71-81, DIR METEOROL SERV, PAC GAS & ELEC CO, 81- *Mem:* Am Meteorol Soc; Air Pollution Control Asn; Weather Modification Asn; Am Soc Testing & Mat; Am Wind Energy Asn. *Res:* Techniques for prediction of dispersion of airborne materials; structure of low level atmospheric turbulence and diffusion processes; micrometeorological studies. *Mailing Add:* Pac Gas & Elec Co Rm 328 San Francisco CA 94106

MOONEY, PATRICIA MAY, b Bryn Mawr, Pa, July 12, 45. SOLID STATE PHYSICS. *Educ:* Wilson Col, AB, 67; Bryn Mawr Col, MA, 69, PhD(physics), 72. *Prof Exp:* Asst prof physics, Hiram Col, 72-74; asst prof physics, Vassar Col, 74-80; RES MEM STAFF, WATSON RES CTR, IBM CORP, 80- *Concurrent Pos:* Res assoc, Physics Dept, State Univ NY Albany, 77-78; res, Group Physique Solides, l'Ecole Normale Superieure, Univ Paris VII, 79-80. *Mem:* Am Phys Soc; Am Asn Physics Teachers; Sigma Xi. *Res:* Point defects in semiconductors; transport properties of semiconductors; semiconductor devices for opto-electronics. *Mailing Add:* IBM Watson Res Ctr PO Box 218 Yorktown Heights NY 10598

MOONEY, PAUL DAVID, b Stroud, Okla, Aug 10, 43; m 66; c 4. MEDICINAL CHEMISTRY, BIOCHEMISTRY. *Educ:* Okla State Univ, BS, 66, MS, 69, PhD(chem), 71. *Prof Exp:* Res staff, Dept Pharmacol, Sch Med, Yale Univ, 71-74; asst prof, 74-80, ASSOC PROF BIOCHEM, OKLA COL OSTEOP MED & SURG, 80- *Concurrent Pos:* Adj asst prof chem, Quinnipiac Col, 72-74 & Univ Tulsa, 79-81. *Mem:* Am Chem Soc. *Res:* Development of ribonucleoside diphosphate reductase inhibitors that are potential antineoplastic agents; also the chemistry, reactions and biological activity of pyridine, quinoline, isoquinoline and indole derivatives. *Mailing Add:* 1111 W 17th Tulsa OK 74101

MOONEY, RICHARD T, b New York, NY, Jan 12, 25; m 50; c 2. RADIOLOGICAL HEALTH. *Educ:* Pratt Inst, BS, 44; NY Univ, MS, 52; Am Bd Radiol, dipl. *Prof Exp:* Jr physicist, Physics Lab, New York, City Dept Hosps, 50-51; SR PHYSICIST, FRANCIS DELAFIELD HOSP, 51-; DIR PHYSICS SERV, NEW YORK CITY HEALTH & HOSPS CORP, 67-; STAFF PHYSICIST, LENOX HILL HOSP & ST CLARE'S HOSP, 70- *Concurrent Pos:* Staff scientist, AEC contracts, Columbia Univ; staff physicist, Westchester County Med Ctr, 69-; clin assoc, NY Med Col; consult, Vet Admin, hosps & indust; mem, Sci Comt Number 7 & 9, mem task group M-2 & consult subcomt M-2, Nat Coun Radiation Protection. *Mem:* Assoc fel Am Col Radiol; Radiol Soc NAm; Am Asn Physicists in Med; Am Phys Soc; Health Physics Soc. *Res:* Radiation protection and dose distribution in patients. *Mailing Add:* 4 Edgemont Circle Scarsdale NY 10583

MOONEY, RICHARD WARREN, b Lynn, Mass, Aug 2, 23; m 44; c 3. PHYSICAL CHEMISTRY, INORGANIC CHEMISTRY. *Educ:* Tufts Univ, BS, 44; Cornell Univ, PhD(phys chem), 51. *Prof Exp:* Engr, Bakelite Corp, NJ, 46-47; sr engr, Lighting Div, Sylvania Elec Prod Inc, Gen Tel & Electronics Corp, Mass, 53-56, engr-in-chg, Chem & Metall Div, 56-58, sect head, 58-59, eng mgr, 59-64, mgr res & develop, 65-66, chief engr, 66-69, vpres & gen mgr, 69-73, pres, Wilbur B Driver Div, 73-79, VPRES PROD IMPROV, GEN TEL & ELECTRONICS CORP, 79- *Concurrent Pos:* Ed, J Electrochem Soc, 63-64; Fulbright-Hays res scholar, Tech Univ Norway, 64-65. *Mem:* Am Chem Soc; fel Am Inst Chemists. *Res:* Phosphors; phosphates; tungsten and molybdenum; x-ray crystallography; theoretical spectroscopy. *Mailing Add:* Gen Tel & Electronics Inc Stamford Forum Stamford CT 06904

MOONEY, ROBERT ARTHUR, b Rochester, NY, May 29, 33; m 58; c 5. APPLIED CHEMISTRY. *Educ:* Univ Rochester, BS, 55; Univ Ill, PhD(org chem), 59. *Prof Exp:* RES CHEMIST PHOTOG SCI, EASTMAN KODAK CO, 58- *Mem:* Soc Photog Sci & Eng. *Res:* Silver and non-silver photography; photographic support manufacture. *Mailing Add:* Chem Mfg Div Eastman Kodak Co 343 State St Rochester NY 14650

MOONEY, THOMAS FAULKNER, JR, analytical chemistry, industrial hygiene, see previous edition

MOOR, WILLIAM C(HATTLE), b St Louis, Mo, Jan 17, 41; m 64. INDUSTRIAL ENGINEERING, ORGANIZATION THEORY. *Educ:* Washington Univ, BS, 63, MS, 65; Northwestern Univ, PhD(indust eng), 69. *Prof Exp:* Asst prof, 68-73, ASSOC PROF INDUST ENG, ARIZ STATE UNIV, 73- *Mem:* Am Inst Indust Engrs; Sigma Xi. *Res:* Study of information-related behavior in research and development; study of organizational structure and process; application of industrial engineering techniques to the analysis of complex human and man/machine systems. *Mailing Add:* Dept of Indust Eng Ariz State Univ Tempe AZ 85281

MOORCROFT, DONALD ROSS, b Toronto, Ont, June 2, 35; m 64; c 3. PHYSICS. *Educ:* Univ Toronto, BASc, 57; Univ Sask, MSc, 60, PhD(physics), 62. *Prof Exp:* NATO sci fel & Rutherford fel, Radiophysics Lab, Stanford Univ, 62-63; from asst prof to assoc prof, 63-74, PROF PHYSICS, UNIV WESTERN ONT, 74- *Mem:* Can Asn Physicists; Am Asn Physics Teachers; Am Geophys Union. *Res:* Physics of the upper atmosphere; propagation and scattering of radio waves in ionized media; small-scale ionospheric structure. *Mailing Add:* Dept of Physics Univ of Western Ont London ON N6B 2A3 Can

MOORCROFT, WILLIAM HERBERT, b Detroit, Mich, Feb 1, 44; m 71; c 3. PSYCHOBIOLOGY, SLEEP. *Educ:* Augustana Col, BA, 66; Princeton Univ, PhD(psychol), 70. *Prof Exp:* USPHS fel ment retardation, Nebr Psychiat Inst & instr psychol, Col Med, Univ Nebr, 70-71; ASSOC PROF PSYCHOL, LUTHER COL, IOWA, 71- *Concurrent Pos:* Vis res psychologist, Ment Retardation Ctr, Univ Calif, Los Angeles, 72; fel, Sleep Disorders Serv, Rush-St Lukes-Presby Med Ctr, Chicago, Ill, 80. *Mem:* Asn Psychophysiol Study Sleep. *Res:* Developmental psychobiology; ontogeny of anatomical, pharmacological and electrophysiological correlates of behavior; sleep and dream changes during pregnancy. *Mailing Add:* Dept of Psychol Luther Col Decorah IA 52101

MOORE, A(RTHUR) DONALD, b Assiniboia, Sask, Apr 28, 23; m 53; c 2. ELECTRICAL ENGINEERING, COMMUNICATIONS. *Educ:* Queen's Univ, Ont, BSc, 45, MSc, 50; Stanford Univ, PhD(elec eng), 53. *Prof Exp:* Jr engr, Turbo Res, Ltd, Ont & Power Jets, Ltd, Eng, 45-46; jr design engr, Gas Turbine Div, Avro Can, 46-47; instr elec eng, Queen's Univ, Ont, 47-49; instr, Univ BC, 49-50; asst, Electronics Res Lab, Stanford Univ, 50-52; from asst prof to assoc prof elec eng, 52-61, PROF ELEC ENG, UNIV BC, 61-, HEAD DEPT, 70- *Concurrent Pos:* Nat Res Coun Can sr res fel, 64-65. *Mem:* Am Soc Eng Educ; Inst Elec & Electronics Engrs. *Res:* Network theory; communication theory; electronic instrumentation; computer-aided design. *Mailing Add:* Dept of Elec Eng Univ of BC Vancouver BC V6T 1W5 Can

MOORE, AIMEE N, b Conway, SC, Nov 8, 18. NUTRITION. *Educ:* Univ NC, BS, 39; Columbia Univ, MA, 47; Mich State Univ, PhD(higher educ), 59. *Prof Exp:* Intern hosp dietetics, Univ Mich, 40; hosp dietitian, Miss State Sanatorium & Stuart Circle Hosp, Richmond, Va, 40-43; teacher inst mgt, Col Human Ecol, Cornell Univ, 47-61; dir dept nutrit & dietetics, 61-80, PROF FOOD SYSTS MGT, MED CTR, UNIV MO-COLUMBIA, 61-, DIR DIETETIC EDUC, HEALTH SCI CTR, 80- *Concurrent Pos:* Rose fel, Am Dietetic Asn, 56 & 58; consult, Vet Admin Dietetic Adv Coun, 61-63; NIH educ grant, 71-77. *Mem:* Am Dietetic Asn; Am Home Econ Asn; Am Inst Decision Sci; Asn Schs Allied Health Prof. *Res:* Applications of computer technology in hospital departments of nutrition and dietetics; labor productivity in hospital food service. *Mailing Add:* Dept Nutrit & Dietetics Univ Mo-Columbia Med Ctr W128 Columbia MO 65201

MOORE, ALEXANDER MAZYCK, b Charleston, SC, Nov 6, 17; m 45; c 4. ORGANIC CHEMISTRY, INFORMATION SCIENCE. *Educ:* Col Charleston, BS, 38; Johns Hopkins Univ, PhD(org chem), 42. *Prof Exp:* Lab asst biol, Col Charleston, 36-38; lab asst chem, Johns Hopkins Univ, 38-42; res chemist, Socony-Vacuum Oil Co, Inc, NJ, 42-44 & Surv Antimalarial Drugs, Md, 44-46; res chemist, Parke, Davis & Co, 46-52, lab dir org chem, 52; admin fel, Mellon Inst, 52-56; asst to vpres, Parke, Davis & Co, 56-66, dir res info, 66-78; RETIRED. *Mem:* Am Chem Soc; NY Acad Sci. *Res:* Chemicals from petroleum; classification and nomenclature of organic compounds; chemotherapy; pharmaceuticals; science information. *Mailing Add:* 805 Heatherway Ann Arbor MI 48104

MOORE, ALLEN MURDOCH, b Ithaca, NY, Mar 15, 40; m 69; c 2. ECOLOGY, ZOOLOGY. *Educ:* Cornell Univ, AB, 61; Univ Tex, Austin, PhD(zool), 68. *Prof Exp:* Fel, Univ NC, 68-69; asst prof, 68-76, ASSOC PROF BIOL, WESTERN CAROLINA UNIV, 76- *Concurrent Pos:* Cooperator, Southeastern Forest Exp Sta, US Forest Serv, 73- *Mem:* AAAS; Ecol Soc Am; Fedn Am Scientists. *Res:* Systems ecology, especially ecological modelling; energy flow in ecosystems; human impact on ecosystems. *Mailing Add:* Dept of Biol Western Carolina Univ Cullowhee NC 28723

MOORE, ALTON WALLACE, b Lewiston, Idaho, Sept 16, 16; m 45; c 3. DENTISTRY. *Educ:* Univ Calif, DDS, 41; Univ Ill, MS, 48; Am Bd Orthod, dipl, 55. *Prof Exp:* Intern dent, Univ Chicago, 41-42; instr oral path & diag, Univ Louisville, 42-43, asst prof, 43-44; from instr to asst prof, Univ Ill, 45-48; assoc prof, 48-50, head dept orthod, 48-66, dir grad dent educ, 51-58, actg asst dean, Sch Dent, 55-56, head dept dent sci & lit, 66-70, assoc dean sch dent, 66-77, prof orthod, 50-80, dean, 77-80, EMER PROF ORTHOD & EMER DEAN SCH DENT, UNIV WASH, 80- *Concurrent Pos:* Grieve Mem lectr, 56; dir, Am Bd Orthod, 59-60, secy, 60-65, pres, 65-66; Wylie Mem lectr, 67; mem dent study sec, Nat Inst Dent Res, 70-74, chmn, 71-74; Fogarty Int sr fel, Roman Cath Univ Nijmegen, 76-77. *Honors & Awards:* Award, Am Asn Orthod, 49; Albert H Ketcham Mem Award, Am Bd Orthod, 73. *Mem:* Am Asn Orthod; Am Dent Asn; fel Am Col Dent; Int Asn Dent Res. *Res:* Orthodontics; human facial growth and cephalometric appraisal of orthodontic treatment. *Mailing Add:* Dept Orthod Univ Wash Sch Dent SM-46 Seattle WA 98195

MOORE, ANDREW BROOKS, b Walton County, Ga, June 27, 52. PIGMENT CHEMISTRY, RISK ANALYSIS. *Educ:* Univ Ga, BS, 73, MS, 76; Univ Mass, PhD(food sci), 80. *Prof Exp:* SCI ASSOC FOOD SCI, GROCERY MFRS AM, 80- *Mem:* Inst Food Technologists; Can Inst Food Sci & Technol; Asn Off Anal Chemists; Int Asn Milk, Food & Environ Sanitarians; NY Acad Sci. *Res:* Food safety, technology, sanitation and processing. *Mailing Add:* Grocery Mfrs Am 1010 Wisconsin Ave NW Washington DC 20007

MOORE, ARNOLD ROBERT, b New York, NY, Jan 14, 23; m 46; c 2. SOLID STATE PHYSICS. *Educ:* Polytech Inst Brooklyn, BS, 42; Cornell Univ, PhD(physics), 49. *Prof Exp:* Res engr, Victor Div, Radio Corp Am, Pa, 42-45, RES PHYSICIST, RCA LABS, DAVID SARNOFF RES CTR, 49- *Concurrent Pos:* Vis prof, Brown Univ, 70-71. *Mem:* Fel Am Phys Soc; NY Acad Sci. *Res:* Electrical, optical and magnetic properties of semi-conducting and insulating crystals; photoelectricity; acoustoelectric interactions; semi-conducting devices. *Mailing Add:* RCA Labs David Sarnoff Res Ctr Princeton NJ 08540

MOORE, ARTHUR WILLIAM, b Windsor, Ont, July 22, 37; m 60; c 4. CHEMICAL ENGINEERING. *Educ:* Mem Univ, BSc, 57; Mass Inst Technol, SM, 59; Univ London, PhD(chem eng), 63. *Prof Exp:* Res engr, Textile Fibres Div, Can Indust Ltd, 59-60; res scientist, Res Labs, Philips' Gloeilampenfabrieken, Neth, 63-66; SR RES SCIENTIST, CARBON PROD DIV, UNION CARBIDE CORP, 66- *Mem:* Am Inst Chem Engrs. *Res:* Carbon and graphite; pyrolytic refractories; induction heating; semiconductors; textile fibers. *Mailing Add:* Parma Tech Ctr Carbon Prods Div Union Carbide Corp 12900 Snow Rd Parma OH 44130

MOORE, BARRY NEWTON, b San Antonio, Tex, Jan 27, 41. PLASMA PHYSICS. *Educ:* Univ Tex, Austin, BS, 62, MA, 69, PhD(physics), 72. *Prof Exp:* Engr, Missiles & Space Div, LTV Aerospace Corp, 62-67; res assoc plasma physics, Fusion Res Ctr, Univ Tex, Austin, 73-76; PHYSICIST, AUSTIN RES ASSOCS, 76- *Mem:* Sigma Xi; Am Phys Soc; Inst Elec & Electronic Engrs. *Res:* Feasibility studies of fuel cycles for advanced fusion reactors; applications of radio-frequency heating to plasmas; plasma simulation; plasma waves. *Mailing Add:* Austin Res Assocs 1901 Rutland Dr Austin TX 78758

MOORE, BENJAMIN LABREE, b Louisville, Ky, Feb 10, 15; m 43; c 2. NUCLEAR PHYSICS. *Educ:* Davidson Col, AB, 34; Vanderbilt Univ, MA, 35; Cornell Univ, PhD(physics), 40. *Prof Exp:* Asst, Cornell Univ, 35-40; physicist, Bur Ord, Navy Dept, 40-42 & Naval Mine Warfare Sch, 42-44; sr physicist, Tenn Eastman Corp, 44-46; res fel, Harvard Univ, 46-49, asst dir comput lab, 49-50; mem staff, Los Alamos Sci Lab, Univ Calif, 50-51, asst div leader, 51-60, assoc div leader, 60-73; SCI CONSULT, 73- *Concurrent Pos:* Extra-mural prof, Washington Univ, 57-59; consult, Los Alamos Sci Lab, 73- *Mem:* Fel AAAS; Am Phys Soc. *Res:* Nuclear physics; isotope separation by electromagnetic means; design of large scale digital computing machines; atomic weapons. *Mailing Add:* 15802 Lake Forest Dr Sun City AZ 85351

MOORE, BERRIEN, III, b Atlanta, Ga, Nov 12, 41; m 67. MATHEMATICS. *Educ:* Univ NC, BS, 63; Univ Va, PhD(math), 69. *Prof Exp:* Asst prof, 69-75, ASSOC PROF MATH, UNIV NH, 75- *Mem:* Am Math Soc. *Res:* Hilbert space; operator theory. *Mailing Add:* 30 Silver Dover NH 03820

MOORE, BETTY CLARK, b Dedham, Mass, Jan 1, 15; m 38; c 1. EMBRYOLOGY. *Educ:* Radcliff Col, AB, 36; Columbia Univ, MA, 37, PhD(zool), 49. *Prof Exp:* Asst zool, Manhattanville Col, 37-40; res assoc embryol, Columbia Univ, 49-50; instr biol, Queens Col, 51-52; res assoc cytochem, Columbia Univ, 54-69, lectr, 64-69; RES ASSOC BIOL, UNIV CALIF, RIVERSIDE, 69- *Mem:* Am Soc Zool; Am Soc Cell Biol; Am Soc Nat. *Res:* Biological sciences; population genetics of drosophila. *Mailing Add:* Dept of Biol Univ of Calif Riverside CA 92521

MOORE, BILL C, b Kansas City, Mo, Sept 12, 07; m 42; c 2. MATHEMATICS, OPERATIONS RESEARCH. *Educ:* Univ Kans, AB, 29; Princeton Univ, AM, 37. *Prof Exp:* Assoc prof math, Tex A&M Univ, 48-74; RETIRED. *Concurrent Pos:* Consult, Humble Oil Co, 54 & 55 & Dow Chem Co, 56; guest worker, Nat Bur Standards, 59. *Mem:* AAAS; Math Asn Am. *Res:* Optimization; digital computers. *Mailing Add:* Dept of Math Tex A&M Univ 1000 Munson College Station TX 77840

MOORE, BLAKE WILLIAM, b Ohio, Sept 18, 26; m 55. BIOCHEMISTRY. *Educ:* Univ Akron, BS, 48; Northwestern Univ, PhD(biochem), 52. *Prof Exp:* Asst biochem, Northwestern Univ, 48-52; asst prof, Sch Dent, 52-57, instr cancer res, 57-58, asst prof biochem in cancer res, 58-59, from asst prof to assoc prof, 59-70, PROF BIOCHEM IN PSYCHIAT, SCH MED, WASHINGTON UNIV, 70- *Mem:* AAAS; Am Soc Biol Chemists. *Res:* Neurochemistry; proteins; biochemistry of cancer; protein chromatography; enzymes. *Mailing Add:* 4633 Pershing St Louis MO 63108

MOORE, BOBBY GRAHAM, b Fulton, Miss, June 22, 40; m 60; c 2. CELL BIOLOGY. *Educ:* Miss State Univ, BS, 62, MS, 64; Auburn Univ, PhD(biochem), 68. *Prof Exp:* Res technologist microbiol, Oak Ridge Nat Lab, 64-65; instr, Auburn Univ, 65-68; asst prof, 68-72, ASSOC PROF BIOL, UNIV ALA, TUSCALOOSA, 72- *Concurrent Pos:* Grant-in-aid, Univ Ala, 69-71. *Mem:* AAAS. *Res:* Biochemistry of nucleic acid methylation in diverse organisms and environmental toxicology of naturally occurring chemical substances. *Mailing Add:* Dept of Biol Univ of Ala University AL 35486

MOORE, CALVIN C, b New York, NY, Nov 2, 36; m 74. MATHEMATICS. *Educ:* Harvard Univ, AB, 58, MA, 59, PhD(math), 60. *Prof Exp:* From asst prof to assoc prof, 61-66, dean phys sci, 71-76, dir, Ctr Pure & Appl Math, 77-80, Miller res prof, 78-79, PROF MATH, UNIV CALIF, BERKELEY, 66-, DIR, MATH SCI RES INST, 81- *Concurrent Pos:* Mem, Inst Adv Study, 64-65; Alfred P Sloan Found fel, 65-67; mem bd trustees, Am Math Soc, 71-79; assoc ed, Pac J Math, 77-; mem, Pres Comt Nat Medal Sci, 79-81. *Mem:* Am Math Soc; fel Am Acad Arts & Sci. *Res:* Group representations. *Mailing Add:* Dept Math Univ Calif Berkeley CA 94720

MOORE, CARL, b Cleveland, Ohio, Aug 28, 19; m 56; c 2. POLYMER CHEMISTRY, COLLOID CHEMISTRY. *Educ:* Ohio State Univ, BA, 41; Oberlin Col, MA, 43; Case Inst, PhD(phys chem), 51. *Prof Exp:* Chemist, Standard Oil Co Ohio, 41; asst gen chem, Oberlin Col, 41-43; res assoc colloid sci, Govt Synthetic Rubber Prog, Case Inst, 43-52; chemist, 52-62, sr res chemist, 62-73, RES SPECIALIST, DOW CHEM CO, 73- *Mem:* Am Chem Soc; Sigma Xi. *Res:* Physical chemistry of latexes; emulsion polymerization; colloid science; radiation grafting of polymers; organic basic research; complexing resins; plastics and latex foam; rheology of polymer solutions; latex paints; adhesion of coatings; organic coatings. *Mailing Add:* 1105 Evamar Dr Midland MI 48640

MOORE, CARL EDWARD, b Frankfort, Ky, Sept 25, 15; m 40; c 4. ANALYTICAL CHEMISTRY. *Educ:* Eastern Ky State Col, BS, 39; Univ Louisville, MS, 47; Ohio State Univ, PhD(anal chem), 52. *Prof Exp:* Chemist, Nat Distillers Prod Corp, 39-41 & E I du Pont de Nemours & Co, 41-45; instr, Univ Louisville, 47-50; PROF CHEM, LOYOLA UNIV CHICAGO, 52- *Mem:* Am Chem Soc; Soc Appl Spectros. *Res:* Organic reagents for inorganic analysis; analytical methods for detection and determination of atmospheric contaminants. *Mailing Add:* Dept of Chem Loyola Univ Chicago IL 60626

MOORE, CARLETON BRYANT, b New York, NY, Sept 1, 32; m 59; c 2. GEOCHEMISTRY, METEORITES. *Educ:* Alfred Univ, BS, 54; Calif Inst Technol, PhD(chem, geol), 60. *Hon Degrees:* DSc, Alfred Univ, 77. *Prof Exp:* Asst prof geol, Wesleyan Univ, 59-61; asst prof geol, 61-66, assoc prof chem & geol, 66-70, PROF CHEM & GEOL, ARIZ STATE UNIV, 70-, DIR CTR METEORITE STUDIES, 61- *Concurrent Pos:* Prin investr, Apollo 11-17, mem preliminary exam team, Apollo 12-17; ed, Meteoritics. *Mem:* Geochem Soc; Geol Soc Am; Am Chem Soc; Am Geophys Union; Mineral Soc Am; Meteoritical Soc (pres, 66). *Res:* Chemistry and mineralogy of meteorites; analytical geochemistry. *Mailing Add:* Ctr Meteorite Studies Ariz State Univ Tempe AZ 85281

MOORE, CAROL WOOD, b Columbus, Ohio, Sept 23, 43; m 66; c 1. GENETICS. *Educ:* Ohio State Univ, BS, 65; Pa State Univ, MS, 69, PhD(genetics), 70. *Prof Exp:* Teacher pub schs, NY, 65-67; asst human genetics, 70-71, res assoc, 71-74, asst prof biol, 74-77, ASSOC PROF RADIATION BIOL & BIOPHYS, SCH MED & DENT, UNIV ROCHESTER, 77- *Mem:* Genetics Soc Am; AAAS. *Res:* Recombination and mutation in yeast cells. *Mailing Add:* Dept Univ of Rochester Sch Med & Dent Rochester NY 14627

MOORE, CECILIA LOUISE, physical organic chemistry, see previous edition

MOORE, CHARLEEN MORIZOT, b Shreveport, La, July 29, 44; div. CYTOGENETICS. *Educ:* Northeast La Univ, BS, 66; Ind Univ, Bloomington, MA, 67; Univ Tenn, Knoxville, PhD(zool), 71. *Prof Exp:* Fel med cytogenetics, John F Kennedy Inst, Sch Med, Johns Hopkins Univ, 71-73; ASST PROF PEDIAT & DIR MED CYTOGENETICS LAB, UNIV TEX HEALTH SCI CTR HOUSTON, 74- *Mem:* Am Soc Human Genetics; Genetics Soc Am; Tissue Cult Asn. *Res:* Chromosome behavior. *Mailing Add:* 6431 Fannin Houston TX 77030

MOORE, CHARLES B(ERNARD), b Cincinnati, Ohio, May 1, 27; m 49; c 3. ELECTRICAL ENGINEERING, PHYSICS. *Educ:* Univ Cincinnati, EE, 51; Univ Pa, MS, 60. *Prof Exp:* Jr engr, Cincinnati Gas & Elec Co, 50-51; res engr, Eng Res Lab, 51-60, field engr, Wash Works, 60-62, sr res engr, 62-65, res supvr, 65-70, res mgr, 70-77, eng mgr, Instrument Prod, Sci & Process Div, 77-79, MGR APPL PHYSICS, ENG DEPT, E I DU PONT DE NEMOURS & CO, INC, 79- *Mem:* Inst Elec & Electronics Engrs; Sigma Xi. *Res:* Laboratory and process instruments; mass spectrometers; liquid chromatographs; process photometer systems; use of computing techniques in process control; automatic inspection systems. *Mailing Add:* Eng Dept Louviers Bldg E I Du Pont de Nemours & Co Inc Wilmington DE 19898

MOORE, CHARLES GODAT, b Linn, Mo, July 13, 27; m 57; c 3. MATHEMATICS. *Educ:* Cent Mo State Col, BS, 51, MS, 54; Univ Mich, MA, 60, PhD, 67. *Prof Exp:* Teacher high schs, Mo, 51-53, 54-59 & Kemper Mil Sch, 53-54; from asst prof to assoc prof, 60-74, PROF MATH, NORTHERN ARIZ UNIV, 74- *Res:* Mathematics education; continued fractions. *Mailing Add:* Dept of Math Fac Box 4015 Northern Ariz Univ Flagstaff AZ 86011

MOORE, CLARENCE L, b Britton, SDak, Dec 6, 31; m 55; c 3. DAIRY SCIENCE. *Educ:* SDak State Univ, BS, 53, MS, 57, PhD(dairy sci), 59. *Prof Exp:* Area livestock specialist, Univ Hawaii, 59-61; assoc prof, 61-67, PROF DAIRY SCI, ILL STATE UNIV, 67- *Concurrent Pos:* Sabbatical, Ruakura Animal Res Sta, Hamilton, NZ, 72. *Mem:* Am Dairy Sci Asn. *Res:* Calf nutrition; physiology of milk secretion; dairy cattle management; animal behavior. *Mailing Add:* Dept of Agr Ill State Univ Normal IL 61761

MOORE, CLAUDE HENRY, b Greensboro, Ala, May 8, 23; m 56; c 5. POULTRY GENETICS. *Educ:* Auburn Univ, BS, 47; Kans State Col, MS, 48; Purdue Univ, PhD(poultry genetics), 52. *Prof Exp:* Asst, Kans State Col, 46-48 & Purdue Univ, 48-50; asst nat coordr, Poultry Div, Agr Res Serv, USDA, 50-56; assoc prof, 56-59, PROF POULTRY SCI & HEAD DEPT, AUBURN UNIV, 59- *Mem:* AAAS; Poultry Sci Asn. *Res:* Poultry breeding and physiology. *Mailing Add:* Dept of Poultry Sci Auburn Univ Auburn AL 36830

MOORE, CLYDE H, JR, b Jacksonville, Fla, June 10, 33; m 53; c 3. GEOLOGY. *Educ:* La State Univ, BS, 55; Univ Tex, MS, 59, PhD(geol), 61. *Prof Exp:* Res geologist, Shell Develop Co, 61-66; from asst prof to assoc prof, 66-73, PROF GEOL & DIR APPL CARBONATE RES PROG, LA STATE UNIV, BATON ROUGE, 77- *Mem:* Am Asn Petrol Geol; Soc Econ Paleont & Mineral. *Res:* Carbonate petrology; recent carbonate sedimentation and stratigraphy in Caribbean and Gulf Coastal plain. *Mailing Add:* Dept of Geol La State Univ Baton Rouge LA 70803

MOORE, CONDICT, b Essex Fells, NJ, Apr 29, 16; m 43; c 2. SURGERY. *Educ:* Princeton Univ, BA, 38; Columbia Univ, MD, 42. *Prof Exp:* Resident path, St Luke's Hosp, 46-47; resident surg, Methodist Hosp, Brooklyn, 47-49; resident, Mem Hosp, New York, 49-52; from instr to asst prof, 52-62, clin assoc prof, 62-65, assoc prof, 65-69, PROF SURG, SCH MED, UNIV LOUISVILLE, 69- *Concurrent Pos:* Fel surg, Mem Hosp, New York, 49-51. *Mem:* Fel Am Col Surgeons; James Ewing Soc; Am Radium Soc. *Res:* Cancer research; carcinogenesis; tobacco and oral cancer. *Mailing Add:* Cancer Ctr Univ of Louisville Sch of Med Louisville KY 40292

MOORE, CORNELIUS FRED, b Louisville, Ky, Mar 18, 36; m 61; c 5. NUCLEAR PHYSICS, ATOMIC PHYSICS. *Educ:* Univ Notre Dame, BS, 59; Univ Louisville, MS, 61; Fla State Univ, PhD(physics), 64. *Prof Exp:* Asst, Univ Louisville, 60-61; asst, Fla State Univ, 61-63, instr, 63-64, res assoc, 64-65; res scientist, Univ Tex, Austin, 65, asst prof physics, 65-68; vis prof, Univ Heidelberg, 68-69; assoc prof, 69-71, PROF PHYSICS, UNIV TEX, AUSTIN, 71- *Mem:* Am Phys Soc. *Res:* Isobaric analogue states as compound nuclear resonances; fission studies; low energy electron scattering on ions; atoms and molecules; meson-nuclear physics. *Mailing Add:* Dept of Physics Univ of Tex Austin TX 78712

MOORE, CRAIG DAMON, b Youngstown, Ohio, July 13, 42; div. ACCELERATOR PHYSICS, EXPERIMENTAL HIGH ENERGY PHYSICS. *Educ:* Ohio Univ, BS, 64; Univ Wis, PhD(physics), 70. *Prof Exp:* Res assoc physics, State Univ NY Stony Brook, 70-73; PHYSICIST, FERMI NAT LAB, 73- *Mem:* Am Phys Soc. *Res:* Radiation shielding experiments; high energy muon scattering. *Mailing Add:* Fermi Nat Lab PO Box 500 Batavia IL 60510

MOORE, CYRIL L, biochemistry, biophysics, see previous edition

MOORE, DAN HOUSTON, b Elk Creek, Va, Apr 7, 09; m 41, 75; c 2. BIOPHYSICS. *Educ:* Duke Univ, AB, 32, MA, 33; Univ Va, PhD(physics), 36. *Hon Degrees:* DS, Emory & Henry Col, 74. *Prof Exp:* Instr physics, Univ Columbia Univ, 36-38; assoc anat, Col Physicians & Surgeons, Columbia Univ, 39-43, from asst prof to assoc prof, 43-53, assoc prof microbiol, 53-58; assoc mem & prof biophys, Rockefeller Inst, 58-66; mem & head dept biophys cytol, Inst Med Res, Camden, NJ, 66-77; AM CANCER SOC PROF, DEPT MICROBIOL & IMMUNOL, HAHNEMANN MED COL & HOSP, 77- *Concurrent Pos:* Mem div war res, Off Sci Res & Develop, 40-45; sci liaison officer, Off Naval Res, London, 49-51; mem virol & rickettsiology study sect, USPHS, 59-63; assoc ed, Cancer Res, 70-74; Am Cancer Soc res prof, 73. *Mem:* Soc Exp Biol & Med; Am Physiol Soc; Harvey Soc; Electron Micros Soc. *Res:* Tumor viruses; electron microscopy; characterization of proteins by electrophoresis and ultracentrifugation. *Mailing Add:* Dept Microbiol & Immunol Hahnemann Med Col 230 N Broad St Philadelphia PA 19102

MOORE, DAN HOUSTON, II, b New York, NY, Sept 24, 41; m 66; c 1. BIOSTATISTICS. *Educ:* Univ Calif, Santa Barbara, BA, 63; Univ Calif, Berkeley, PhD(biostatist), 70. *Prof Exp:* Biostatistician, Univ Pa, 70-73; BIOSTATISTICIAN, LAWRENCE LIVERMORE LAB, UNIV CALIF, 73- *Mem:* Biomet Soc; Sigma Xi; Am Statist Asn. *Res:* Application of statistical methods to mutation research; mixture decomposition; non-linear curve fitting; discriminant analysis. *Mailing Add:* Biomed Div L-452 Livermore Lab Univ of Calif Livermore CA 94550

MOORE, DANIEL CHARLES, b Cincinnati, Ohio, Sept 9, 18; m 45; c 4. ANESTHESIOLOGY. *Educ:* Amherst Col, BA, 40; Northwestern Univ, BM & MD, 44. *Prof Exp:* Clin assoc prof, 56-64, CLIN PROF ANESTHESIOL, SCH MED, UNIV WASH, 65- *Concurrent Pos:* Mem consult staff, Children's Orthop Hosp, 62-; dir anesthesiol, Mason Clin & chmn dept, Virginia Mason Hosp, 47-72, sr consult, 72-; NIH grant anesthesiol, 67-71. *Honors & Awards:* Distinguished Serv Award, Am Soc Anesthesiologists, Inc, 76; Labat Award, Am Soc Regional Anesthesia, 77. *Mem:* AMA; Am Soc Anesthesiol (1st vpres, 53-54, 2nd vpres, 54-55, pres-elect, 57-58, pres, 58-59); Acad Anesthesiol; Pan-Am Med Asn. *Res:* Local anesthetic agents and their distribution and fate in man. *Mailing Add:* Virginia Mason Res Ctr 1000 Seneca St Seattle WA 98101

MOORE, DAVID GILLIS, b Long Beach, Calif, July 11, 25; m 45; c 5. MARINE GEOLOGY, MARINE GEOPHYSICS. *Educ:* Univ Southern Calif, AB, 50, MS, 52; State Univ Groningen, PhD, 66. *Prof Exp:* Jr res geologist, Scripps Inst, Univ Calif, San Diego, 52-55; oceanographer, Electronics Lab, US Navy, 55-69, oceanog, Naval Undersea Ctr, 69-75; chief scientist, Deep Sea Drilling Proj, 76-79, CONSULT, MARINE GEOL & GEOPHYS, SCRIPPS INST OCEANOG, UNIV CALIF, SAN DIEGO, 80- *Concurrent Pos:* Consult, Nekton, Inc; res assoc, Scripps Inst Oceanog, Univ Calif, San Diego. *Honors & Awards:* Francis P Shepard Medal, Soc Econ Paleont & Mineral, 67. *Mem:* Geol Soc Am; fel AAAS; Am Geophys Union. *Res:* Continental margin tectonics, structure and sedimentation; marine geology; sedimentology. *Mailing Add:* Scripps Inst of Oceanog Univ Calif San Diego La Jolla CA 92093

MOORE, DAVID JAY, b Cecil, Pa, Sept 8, 36; m 58; c 2. ANIMAL ECOLOGY. *Educ:* Clarion State Col, BS, 59; Ohio Univ, MS, 61; NC State Univ, PhD(animal ecol), 69. *Prof Exp:* Asst prof biol, SMacomb Community Col, Mich, 62-63; from asst prof to assoc prof, 63-73, dean, Sch Natural Sci, 71-72, PROF BIOL, RADFORD UNIV, 73-, VPRES ACAD AFFAIRS, 72- *Concurrent Pos:* Teacher pub schs, Mich, 61-63. *Res:* Water pollution, especially effects of fluoride pollution on the blue crab. *Mailing Add:* Off VPres Acad Affairs Radford Univ Radford VA 24141

MOORE, DAVID LEE, b Springfield, Mo, June 25, 40; m 66; c 2. ORAL & MAXILLOFACIAL SURGERY. *Educ:* Drury Col, AB, 62; Wash Univ, DDS, 66; Univ Mo-Kansas City, MD, 75. *Prof Exp:* Resident oral surg, Geisinger Med Ctr, Danville, Pa, 66-68; asst dent surgeon, Barnes Hosp, St Louis, Mo, 69-70; asst prof oral surg, 74-81, PROF CHEM, SCH MED & DENT, UNIV MO-KANSAS CITY, 81- *Mem:* Am Asn Oral & Maxillofacial Surgeons; Am Dent Asn; AMA. *Res:* Surgical correction of mandibular retrusion with mandibular alveolar protrusion and extrusion; use of silastic chin implants; contraindications and complications of silastic chin implants. *Mailing Add:* 4400 Broadway Suite 400 Kansas City MO 64111

MOORE, DAVID SHELDON, b Plattsburg, NY, Jan 28, 40; m 64; c 2. STATISTICS. *Educ:* Princeton Univ, AB, 62; Cornell Univ, PhD(math), 67. *Prof Exp:* Asst prof math & statist, 67-71, assoc prof, 71-76, PROF STATIST, PURDUE UNIV, 77- *Concurrent Pos:* Assoc ed, J Am Statist Asn, 74-77; asst dean, Grad Sch, Purdue Univ, 77-80; prog dir, NSF, 80-81. *Mem:* Inst Math Statist; Math Asn Am; Am Statist Asn. *Res:* Mathematical statistics, especially tests of fit, large sample theory and nonparametric statistics. *Mailing Add:* Dept of Statist Purdue Univ Lafayette IN 47907

MOORE, DAVID WARREN, b Bennettsville, SC, July 7, 1939. GEOMORPHOLOGY, GLACIOLOGY. *Educ:* Col Wooster, BA, 61; Univ NC, Chapel Hill, MS, 72; Univ Ill, Urbana, PhD(geol), 81. *Prof Exp:* Consult geologist, Am Dredging Co, Philadelphia, 68; explor geologist, United Nuclear Corp, New York, 69; planning consult, Laz, Edwards & Dankert Architects, Champaign, Ill, 73-74; GEOLOGIST, US GEOL SURV, 75- *Mem:* Geol Soc Am; Am Quaternary Asn; Sigma Xi. *Res:* Bedrock mapping in the thrust belt at Idaho-Wyoming border determining bedrock structures for economic mineral appraisal; quaternary deposits of southern San Juan Mountains, Colorado; glacial deposits in central Illinois. *Mailing Add:* US Geol Surv Mail Stop 913 Box 25046 Fed Ctr Denver CO 80225

MOORE, DONALD A(RCHIE), b Minerva, Ohio, Feb 19, 20; m 44; c 1. CHEMICAL ENGINEERING. *Educ:* Carnegie Inst Technol, BS, 42; Univ Mich, MSE, 47, PhD(chem eng), 52. *Prof Exp:* Chem engr, Monsanto Chem Co, 41; shift supvr, E I du Pont de Nemours & Co, Inc, 42-44; develop engr, Univ Mich, 46-48; res engr, 52-58, res supvr, 58-65, lab serv mgr, 65-69, lab serv supvr, 69-71, staff engr, 71-79, SR RES ENGR, E I DU PONT DE NEMOURS & CO, INC, 79- *Mem:* Am Inst Chem Engrs. *Res:* Polymers; films. *Mailing Add:* E I Du Pont de Nemours & Co Inc PO Box 89 Circleville OH 43113

MOORE, DONALD BAKER, b Little Rock, Ark, Aug 14, 23; m 64; c 3. EXPERIMENTAL PHYSICS. *Educ:* Univ Calif, AB, 47. *Prof Exp:* Jr physicist, Naval Radiol Defense Lab, 50-51; physicist, Calif Res & Develop Co, 51-54, Missile Systs Div, Lockheed Aircraft Corp, 54-55 & Stanford Res Inst, 55-68; STAFF PHYSICIST, EXPLOSIVE TECHNOL, INC, 68- *Mem:* Soc Motion Picture & TV Eng; Am Phys Soc; Am Statist Asn. *Res:* Theory, application, and effects of explosives; electrical discharge phenomenology; ion optics; statistical analysis; computer applications to experiment and theory; ultra high speed optical and electronic instrumentation. *Mailing Add:* Explosive Technol Inc Box KK Fairfield CA 94533

MOORE, DONALD R, b Reading, Pa, Dec 29, 33; m 72; c 4. ORGANIC CHEMISTRY, POLYMER CHEMISTRY. *Educ:* Lafayette Col, BS, 54; Harvard Univ, AM, 55, PhD(org chem), 58, Harvard Bus Sch, AMP, 75. *Prof Exp:* Chemist, Trubek Labs, 58-62; group leader, Cent Res Lab, J P Stevens & Co, Inc, 62-63, sect leader, 63-68, mgr, 68-69; mgr org fiber chem, Burlington Industs Res Ctr, 70-72; mgr tech, Abrasive Technol Ctr, 72-74, dir, 75-77, GEN MGR, ACTIVATED CARBON DIV, CARBORUNDUM CO, 77- *Mem:* Am Chem Soc; Am Inst Chem; Am Asn Textile Chemists & Colorists. *Res:* Organic synthesis; reaction mechanisms. *Mailing Add:* 3108 E River Rd Grand Island NY 14072

MOORE, DONALD RICHARD, b West Palm Beach, Fla, Feb 16, 21; m 70; c 1. MALACOLOGY. *Educ:* Univ Miami, BS, 54, PhD, 64; Miss Southern Col, MS, 60. *Prof Exp:* Field biologist, Oyster Div, State Bd Conserv, Fla, 53 & Shell Develop Co, 54; res scientist marine invert, Inst Marine Sci, Univ Tex, 55; asst marine biologist, Gulf Coast Res Lab, Miss, 55-60; res instr, Inst Marine Sci, 60-64, asst prof, 64-73, ASSOC PROF MARINE INVERT, UNIV MIAMI, 73- *Concurrent Pos:* Consult, Shell Oil Co, Tex, 55-64 & Freeport Sulphur Co, La, 58-60. *Mem:* Am Malacol Union (pres, 74-75); Paleont Soc; Soc Syst Zool. *Res:* Ahermatypic corals; distribution of marine invertebrates, especially mollusks; systematics; ecology and zoogeography; marine geology; systematics, distribution and biology of marine micromollusca. *Mailing Add:* Sch of Marine Sci Univ of Miami Miami FL 33149

MOORE, DONALD VINCENT, b York, Nebr, Dec 29, 15; m 42; c 2. PARASITOLOGY. *Educ:* Hastings Col, BA, 37; Univ Nebr, MA, 39; Rice Inst, PhD(parasitol), 42. *Prof Exp:* Asst, Univ Nebr, 37-39; sr parasitologist, Bur Labs, State Health Dept, Texas, 42-46; asst prof prev med, Col Med, NY Univ, 46-52, assoc prof, 52-55; asst prof microbiol, 55-74, ASSOC PROF PATH, MICROBIOL & MED TECHNOL, SOUTHWESTERN MED SCH, UNIV TEX HEALTH SCI CTR, DALLAS, 74- *Concurrent Pos:* Lectr, Univ Tex, 43-46; asst parasitologist, Bellevue Hosp, 47-55; lectr, Shelton Col, 50; assoc attend microbiologist, Univ Hosp, Post-Grad Med Sch, NY Univ, 50-55; mem, Nat Res Coun-NSF biol sci fel panel, 61-63, Nat Res Coun res associateships panel, 72-74. *Honors & Awards:* Spec Award, Am Soc Parasitol, 77. *Mem:* Am Micros Soc; Am Soc Parasitol (secy-treas, 66-77); Am Soc Trop Med & Hyg; Sigma Xi. *Res:* Acanthocephala life histories; schistosomiasis; helminthology; trypanosomiasis medical parasitology; drug resistance in malaria; diagnostic medical parasitology. *Mailing Add:* Dept Path Univ Tex Health Sci Ctr Dallas TX 75235

MOORE, DOUGLAS HOUSTON, b Los Angeles, Calif, Apr 22, 20; m 47; c 2. APPLIED MATHEMATICS. *Educ:* Univ Calif, Berkeley, AB, 42; Univ Calif, Los Angeles, MA, 48, PhD(eng), 62. *Prof Exp:* Instr math, West Coast Univ, 49-53; res engr, NAm Aviation, Inc, 53-54 & Hughes Aircraft Co, 55-56; instr math, West Coast Univ, 56-58; from asst prof to prof, Calif State Polytech Col, 58-68; assoc prof, 68-70, actg dir concentration in environ control, 69-70, prof math, Univ Wis-Green Bay, 70-75; ASSOC PROF, NORTHROP UNIV, INGLEWOOD, CALIF, 78- *Mem:* Math Asn Am; Inst Elec & Electronics Engrs. *Res:* Heaviside operational calculus; operational calculus of sequences; scalar dimensional analysis. *Mailing Add:* 555 Seventh St Santa Monica CA 90402

MOORE, DUANE GREY, b Barron, Wis, Nov 18, 29; m 54; c 4. FOREST SOILS. *Educ:* Univ Wis, BS, 53, MS, 55, PhD(soils), 60. *Prof Exp:* Proj assoc bot & chem, Univ Wis, 59-62; asst prof soil sci, Univ Hawaii, 62-65; SOIL SCIENTIST, FORESTRY SCI LAB, PAC NORTHWEST FOREST & RANGE EXP STA, 65- *Concurrent Pos:* Soil-herbicide chemist, Hawaiian Sugar Planter's Asn Exp Sta, Honolulu, 63. *Mem:* AAAS; Am Soc Agron; Soil Sci Soc Am; Int Soc Soil Sci. *Res:* Forest fertilization and water quality; pesticide residues in the forest-soil ecosystem; micronutrient fertility of range forage and soil herbicide interactions as related to water quality. *Mailing Add:* 1065 SW Stamm Pl Corvallis OR 97330

MOORE, DUANE MILTON, b Rochelle, Ill, Apr 17, 33; m 53; c 3. MINERALOGY, GEOCHEMISTRY. *Educ:* Univ Ill, BA, 58, MS, 61, PhD(geol), 63. *Prof Exp:* Asst geologist, Ill State Geol Surv, 62-63; asst prof geol, Marshall Univ, 63-64; asst prof, 64-70, ASSOC PROF GEOL, KNOX COL, ILL, 70- *Mem:* Mineral Soc Am; Geochem Soc; Geol Soc Am. *Res:* Mineralogical and geochemical investigations of sedimentary rocks, especially distribution of trace metallic elements; man in geologic perspective. *Mailing Add:* Dept of Geol Knox Col Galesburg IL 61401

MOORE, DUNCAN THOMAS, b Biddeford, Maine, Dec 7, 46; m 69. OPTICS, OPTICAL ENGINEERING. *Educ:* Univ Maine, Orono, BA, 69; Univ Rochester, MS, 71, PhD(optics), 74. *Prof Exp:* Optical engr, Western Elec Co, Inc, Princeton, NJ, 69-71; asst prof, 74-78, ASSOC PROF OPTICS, INST OPTICS, UNIV ROCHESTER, 78- *Concurrent Pos:* Consult optical eng, 71- *Mem:* Optical Soc Am; Am Ceramic Soc; fel Soc Photog & Instrumentation Engrs. *Res:* Design of optical systems with gradient index materials; design of optical instruments for metrology; medical optical instrumentation. *Mailing Add:* Inst of Optics Univ of Rochester Rochester NY 14627

MOORE, EARL NEIL, b Warner, Ohio, June 8, 04; m 31; c 4. VETERINARY MEDICINE. *Educ:* Ohio State Univ, BSc, 27, DVM, 30. *Prof Exp:* Hatchery mgr, Portsmouth Accredited Hatchery, Ohio, 27; asst vet, WVa Dept Agr, 30-34, vet in chg, 34-37; asst prof animal path, WVa Univ, 37-44; assoc prof poultry path, Univ Del, 44-46; prof poultry dis, State Univ NY Vet Col, Cornell Univ, 46-51; prof poultry sci & assoc chmn dept, Ohio Exp Sta, 51-56; with Int Coop Admin-Kans State Univ Team, India, 56-62; consult poultry & livestock, Ford Found, India, 63-65; AID-Kans State Univ adv to dean, Vet Cols, Andhra Pradesh Agr Univ, Hyderabad & Tirupathi, India, 66-67; prof microbiol & poultry sci, Ahmadu Bello Univ, Nigeria, 67-70; mem staff, Int Exec Serv Corps, 70-76; RETIRED. *Honors & Awards:* Int Vet Cong Prize, Am Vet Med Asn, 73. *Mem:* Am Vet Med Asn; Am Asn Avian Path. *Res:* Animal and poultry diseases; mastitis; fowl typhoid; coccidiosis; pullorum; artificial insemination of turkeys. *Mailing Add:* 636 Beall Ave Wooster OH 44691

MOORE, EARL NEIL, b Morgantown, WVa, Dec 19, 32; m 59; c 2. PHYSIOLOGY, CARDIOLOGY. *Educ:* Cornell Univ, DVM, 56; State Univ NY, PhD, 62; Univ Pa, MA, 71. *Prof Exp:* Pvt pract, 56; from asst prof to assoc prof physiol animal biol, 62-70, PROF PHYSIOL, SCH VET MED & GRAD SCH ARTS & SCI, UNIV PA, 70-, PROF PHYSIOL IN MED, HOSP, 71- *Concurrent Pos:* William Stroud Estab investr, Am Heart Asn, 66-71; fel, Am Col Cardiol, 72. *Mem:* Am Physiol Soc; Am Heart Asn; Cardiac Muscle Soc; Soc Gen Physiol. *Res:* Cardiac arrhythmias; cardiac electrophysiology; His' bundle electrocardiology; electrocardiology of congenital heart disease; Wolf-Parkinson-White syndrome; cardiac pharmacology. *Mailing Add:* Comp Cardiovasc Studies Unit Univ of Pa Sch of Vet Med Philadelphia PA 19104

MOORE, EARL PHILLIP, b Jan 16, 27; US citizen; m 53; c 3. INDUSTRIAL CHEMISTRY. *Educ:* Univ Miami, BS, 50, MS, 52; Ohio State Univ, PhD(org chem), 57. *Prof Exp:* Res chemist, Plastics Dept, 57-63, sales res chemist, Indust Chem Dept, Tech Serv Labs, 63-67, sr sales res chemist, 67-73, staff chemist, Indust Chem Dept, 73-77, RES ASSOC, CHEM & PIGMENTS DEPT, EXP STA, E I DU PONT DE NEMOURS & CO, INC, 77- *Res:* Industrial inorganic and organic chemical research and development. *Mailing Add:* Chem & Pigments Dept Exp Sta E I du Pont de Nemours & Co Inc Wilmington DE 19898

MOORE, EDGAR TILDEN, JR, b Middlesboro, Ky, Jan 18, 37; m 58; c 3. APPLIED PHYSICS. *Educ:* Univ Ky, BS, 58. *Prof Exp:* Physicist, Lawrence Radiation Lab, 59-62; physicist, 63-67, mgr shock dynamics dept, 67-70, dep dir appl sci div, 70-72, dir appl sci div, 72-75, vpres, 75-81, SR VPRES, BUS OPERS, PHYSICS INT CO, SAN LEANDRO, 81- *Mem:* Soc Petrol Engrs; Soc Explosive Engrs. *Res:* Design and development of new methods to enhance the recovery of oil, gas and other natural resources using chemical explosives; use of one and two dimensional, finite-differencing computer programs. *Mailing Add:* Rockcor Inc Physics Int Co 2700 Merced St Piedmont CA 94611

MOORE, EDWARD FORREST, b Baltimore, Md, Nov 23, 25; m 50; c 3. COMPUTER SCIENCE. *Educ:* Va Polytech Inst, BS, 47; Brown Univ, MS, 49, PhD(math), 50. *Prof Exp:* Asst prof math, Electronic Digital Comput Proj, Univ Ill, 50-51; mem tech staff, Bell Tel Labs, Inc, 51-66; PROF COMPUT SCI & MATH, UNIV WIS-MADISON, 66- *Concurrent Pos:* Vis lectr,

Harvard Univ, 61-62; vis prof, Mass Inst Technol, 61-62 & Stevens Inst Technol, 65-66. *Mem:* AAAS; Am Math Soc; Inst Elec & Electronic Engrs; Soc Indust & Appl Math; Math Asn Am. *Res:* Logical design of switching circuits; automata theory; data base management; binary codes; graph theory; diagnostic identification problems. *Mailing Add:* Univ Wisconsin Madison WI 53706

MOORE, EDWARD LEE, b Springfield, Mo, Dec 12, 29; m 55; c 3. INORGANIC CHEMISTRY. *Educ:* Drury Col, BS, 51; Washington Univ, MS, 56. *Prof Exp:* Res chemist, Monsanto Co, 56-61, sr res chemist, 61-64, res group leader nitrogen chem, 64-67, mgr mfg technol, Inorg Div, 67-69, mgr mfg, Spec Chem Systs, 69-71; mgr mfg technol, 71-77, MGR MFG SERV SPECIALISTS, CHEM DIV, MONSANTO INDUST CHEM CO, 77- *Mem:* Am Chem Soc. *Res:* Chlorinated cyanurates; inorganic phosphates; sulfuric acid and sulfuric acid catalyst. *Mailing Add:* Inorg Div Monsanto Co 800 N Lindbergh St Louis MO 63166

MOORE, EDWARD T(OWSON), b Wytheville, Va, Feb 26, 37; m 65. ELECTRICAL ENGINEERING. *Educ:* Va Polytech Inst, BS, 58; Duke Univ, PhD(elec eng), 63. *Prof Exp:* Engr, Sperry Farragut Co Div, Sperry Rand Corp, 58-59; res assoc elec eng, Duke Univ, 61-64; PRES, WILMORE ELECTRONICS CO, INC, 64- *Concurrent Pos:* Consult, Duke Power Co & Disston Div, H K Porter Co, Va, 63 & NC Res Triangle Inst, 63-; res fel, Duke Univ, 63- *Mem:* Inst Elec & Electronics Engrs. *Res:* Energy conversion; power conditioning; feedback control systems; nonlinear circuits. *Mailing Add:* 4416 Sunny Ct Durham NC 27705

MOORE, EDWARD WELDON, b Madisonville, Ky, July 6, 30; m 63; c 5. GASTROENTEROLOGY, ELECTROCHEMISTRY. *Educ:* Vanderbilt Univ, BA, 52, MD, 55. *Prof Exp:* Intern med, Harvard Med Serv, Boston City Hosp, 55-56; resident, Lemuel Shattuck Hosp, 56-57; clin assoc cancer, Nat Cancer Inst, 57-59; resident med, Harvard Med Serv, Boston City Hosp, 59-60; from asst prof to assoc prof, Med Sch, Tufts Univ, 64-70, instr physiol, 66-70; PROF MED, MED COL VA, VA COMMONWEALTH UNIV, 70-, PROF PATH, 76- *Concurrent Pos:* USPHS res fel, Harvard Med Sch, 60-62; Med Found Boston fel, Med Sch, Tufts Univ, 62-65 & NIH res career develop award, 65-70; consult, Gen Med Study Sect, NIH, 70-; informal consult, Electrochem Sect, Nat Bur Stand, 70-; consult, NASA, 71-; consult, Rev Panel Over-the-counter Antacids, Food & Drug Admin, 72- *Mem:* AAAS; Am Fedn Clin Res; Am Gastroenterol Asn; NY Acad Sci; Am Soc Clin Invest. *Res:* Gastrointestinal physiology; ion-exchange electrodes in biomedical research. *Mailing Add:* Health Sci Ctr Med Col of Va Richmond VA 23298

MOORE, EDWIN FORREST, b Dallas, Tex, Nov 16, 12; wid. ECONOMIC STATISTICS. *Educ:* Howard Payne Col, AB, 38; Univ Tex, MA, 41; Univ Mo, PhD(statist), 50. *Prof Exp:* Instr math, Howard Payne Col, 39-41; prof, Hannibal-LaGrange Col, 41-42; civilian instr aerial navig, Bur Aeronaut, US Dept Navy, 42-44; dean, Hannibal-LaGrange Col, 45-48; instr statist, Univ Mo, 48-50; chmn dept statist & dir div res, Sch Bus, Baylor Univ, 50-54; chief statist qual control, Rocket Fuels Div, Phillips Petrol Co, 54-58; chief statist design exp, Astrodyne, Inc, 58-59; chief qual assurance dept, Rocketdyne Solid Rocket Div, NAm Aviation, Inc, 59-62, res specialist, 62-67; mem tech staff, Autonetics Div, NAm Rockwell Corp, 67-72; chmn dept bus, East Tex Baptist Col, 72-78; CONSULT QUALITY CONTROL, INTERTEK SERV CORP, 81- *Mem:* Am Statist Asn; sr mem Am Soc Qual Control; Math Asn Am; Am Inst Aeronaut & Astronaut. *Res:* Reliability analysis; probability inference; statistical experiment design; statistical quality control; business and economic indices. *Mailing Add:* 3001 E Travis Marshall TX 75670

MOORE, EDWIN GRANVILLE, b Joliet, Ill, Apr 12, 50; m 70; c 2. PHYSICAL BIOCHEMISTRY, ENZYMOLOGY. *Educ:* Univ Ill, BS, 72; Cornell Univ, PhD(biochem), 76. *Prof Exp:* Scholar biochem, Univ Mich, 76-78; RES SCIENTIST BIOCHEM, DIAG DIV, ABBOTT LABS, 78- *Concurrent Pos:* NIH fel, 76. *Mem:* AAAS; Biophys Soc; NY Acad Sci. *Res:* Physical chemical characterization of hemoglobin and flavoenzyme, lipoamide dehydrogenase; rapid kinetic and thermodynamic investigations of ligand binding and details of enzyme mechanisms. *Mailing Add:* Dept 90P AP9 Abbott Labs North Chicago IL 60064

MOORE, EDWIN LEWIS, b Springfield, Mass, May 26, 16; m. FOOD SCIENCE. *Educ:* Mass State Col, BS, 38, MS, 40, PhD(food tech), 42. *Prof Exp:* Fel, Fla Citrus Comn & collabr, Bur Agr & Indust Chem, USDA, 42-48; Fla Citrus Comn fel, Citrus Exp Sta, 47-67, res chemist, 67-77, RES SCIENTIST III & ADJ PROF, FLA DEPT CITRUS, UNIV FLA, 77- *Honors & Awards:* Award, USDA, 52. *Mem:* Am Chem Soc; Inst Food Technol. *Res:* Nutrition; citrus by-products and processing. *Mailing Add:* Agr Res & Educ Ctr Univ Fla 700 Exp Sta Rd Lake Alfred FL 33850

MOORE, EDWIN NEAL, b Dallas, Tex, Aug 14, 34; m 62; c 2. ATOMIC PHYSICS. *Educ:* Southern Methodist Univ, BS, 57; Yale Univ, MS, 58, PhD(physics), 62. *Prof Exp:* Lectr physics, Univ Calif, Santa Barbara, 61-62; asst prof, 62-67, NASA res grant, 65-71, chmn dept, 69-73, ASSOC PROF PHYSICS, UNIV NEV, RENO, 67- *Mem:* Am Phys Soc; Am Asn Physics Teachers. *Res:* Theoretical calculations of accurate atomic wave functions and photoionization cross-sections and other continuum problems. *Mailing Add:* Dept of Physics Univ of Nev Reno NV 89507

MOORE, ELLIOTT PAUL, b Ninnekah, Okla, May 24, 36. ASTROPHYSICS. *Educ:* Univ Chicago, BA, 56, BS, 57; Univ Ariz, PhD(astron), 68. *Prof Exp:* actg chmn, Dept Physics, 77-78, ASSOC PROF ASTROPHYS, NMEX INST MINING & TECHNOL, 68- *Concurrent Pos:* Co-dir, Joint Observ Cometary Res, 74- *Mem:* Int Astron Union; Am Astron Soc; Astron Soc Pac. *Res:* Co-dir, Joint Observ Cometary Res, 74- Mem: Int Astron Union; Am Astron Soc; Astron Soc Pac. Res: Comets; plasma taildynamics; stellar content of galaxies; instrumentation. *Mailing Add:* Dept of Physics Campus Sta Socorro NM 87801

MOORE, EMMETT BURRIS, JR, b Bozeman, Mont, June 14, 29; m 60; c 2. CHEMICAL PHYSICS. *Educ:* Wash State Univ, BS, 51; Univ Minn, PhD(phys chem), 56. *Prof Exp:* Asst prof physics, Univ Minn, Duluth, 57-59; staff mem solid state physics, Boeing Sci Res Labs, 59-73; lectr phys chem, Seattle Univ, 73; dir power plant siting, Minn Environ Qual Bd, 73-76; gen mgr, Richland Div, Olympic Eng Corp, 76-78; SR SCIENTIST ENERGY SYSTS, PAC NORTHWEST LABS, BATTELLE MEM INST, 78- *Mem:* AAAS; Am Phys Soc; Am Chem Soc. *Res:* Energy and environmental policy; molecular and crystal structure; electron paramagnetic resonance in biological systems; decommissioning of nuclear facilities. *Mailing Add:* Battelle Northwest Box 999 Richland WA 99352

MOORE, ERIN COLLEEN, b Arlington, Tex, Nov 16, 24. BIOCHEMISTRY, ONCOLOGY. *Educ:* Univ Tex, BA, 45, MA, 50; Univ Wis, PhD(oncol), 58. *Prof Exp:* Anal chemist, Univ Tex, 45-50; asst biochem, Dept Genetics, Carnegie Inst, 50-52; jr res chemist, Int Minerals & Chem Corp, 52-54; asst biochem & oncol, Univ Wis, 55-58; sr fel biochem, 58-59, asst, 59-66, ASSOC BIOCHEMIST, UNIV TEX M D ANDERSON HOSP & TUMOR INST HOUSTON, 66-; ASSOC PROF BIOCHEM, UNIV TEX GRAD SCH BIOMED SCI HOUSTON, 66- *Concurrent Pos:* USPHS fel, Univ Uppsala, 61-63. *Mem:* AAAS; Am Chem Soc; Am Asn Cancer Res; Am Soc Biol Chem. *Res:* Biosynthesis of deoxyribonucleotides; intermediary metabolism of nucleotides; biochemical effects of antitumor agents. *Mailing Add:* Dept of Biochem Univ of Tex M D Anderson Hosp & Tumor Inst Houston TX 77030

MOORE, ERNEST J(ULIUS), b Stuttgart, Ger, Oct 15, 19; nat US; m 42; c 3. ELECTRICAL ENGINEERING. *Educ:* Calif, MS, 43, PhD(elec eng), 50. *Prof Exp:* Asst elec eng, Univ Calif, 41; electronics engr antenna develop, US Naval Electronics Lab, Calif, res engr systs studies, Stanford Res Inst, 50-56, mgr systs eval dept, 56-68, exec dir, Eng Systs Div, 68-74, vpres off res opers, 74-77, vpres progs & admin, 77-80, VPRES HEALTH & SOCIAL SYSTS, SRI INT, 80- *Mem:* Sigma Xi; sr mem Inst Elec & Electronics. *Res:* Electromagnetic boundary value problems; requirements for and evaluation of large systems and system complexes, especially communication nets, air defense weapons and environmental systems. *Mailing Add:* SRI Int 333 Ravenswood Ave Menlo Park CA 94025

MOORE, EUGENE ROGER, b Saginaw, Mich, Oct 20, 33; m 58; c 4. POLYMER CHEMISTRY, PROCESS DEVELOPMENT. *Educ:* Mich Tech Univ, BS(chem) & BS(chem eng), 56; Case Inst, PhD(chem eng), 62. *Prof Exp:* Chem engr, Dow Chem Co, 56-58; asst, Case Inst, 58-59; proj leader, Nuclear & Basic Res Lab, 61-67, group leader, 67-70, sr res engr phys res, 70-72, res specialist styrene molding polymers res & develop, 72-74, mfg rep process develop, 74-81, RES ASSOC STYRENE MOLDING POLYMERS, DOW CHEM CO, 81- *Honors & Awards:* Union Carbide Corp Award, Am Chem Soc, 61. *Mem:* Am Chem Soc; Sigma Xi. *Res:* Chemistry and physics of alkyd resins; exploration of the chemistry of reactive copolymers; process design and development. *Mailing Add:* 5600 Woodview Pass Midland MI 48640

MOORE, FENTON DANIEL, b Cleveland, Ohio, Nov 4, 38; m 61; c 5. ANATOMY, CELL BIOLOGY. *Educ:* John Carroll Univ, BS, 64, MS, 66; Case Western Reserve Univ, PhD(anat), 71. *Prof Exp:* NSF fel, 71-72, asst prof, 72-77, ASSOC PROF BIOL, JOHN CARROLL UNIV, 77- *Mem:* Am Soc Cell Biol; AAAS; Int Fedn Cell Biol; Int Res Group Acetabularia. *Res:* Chloroplast biogenesis and intraplastidal biosynthesis; biochemical correlates of fish distribution. *Mailing Add:* Dept of Biol John Carroll Univ Cleveland OH 44118

MOORE, FLETCHER BROOKS, b Heiberger, Ala, June 15, 26; m 54; c 2. ELECTRICAL & ELECTRONIC ENGINEERING. *Educ:* Ala Polytech Inst, BS, 48; Ga Inst Technol, 49. *Prof Exp:* Physicist, Navy Exp Sta, Panama City, Fla, 49-50, electronic scientist, 50-52, elec engr, Mixing Comput Unit, 52-53, chief, Simulator Unit, 53-54, dep chief, Analog Comput Sect, 54-56, chief control sect, Army Ballastic Missile Agency, Redstone, Ala, 56-58, chief, Navig Br, Redstone Arsenal, Ala, 59-62; chief guid & control br, 62-63, chief guid & control div, 63-69, dir astrionics lab, 69-74, DIR ELECTRONICS & CONTROL LAB, SCI & ENG, MARSHALL SPACE FLIGHT CTR, 74- *Mem:* Assoc fel Am Inst Aeronaut & Astronaut; Inst Navig. *Res:* Guidance and control; instrumentation; power systems; solar energy; optical systems; communications; automated systems. *Mailing Add:* Electronics & Control Lab Marshall Space Flight Ctr Marshall Space Flight Center AL 35812

MOORE, FRANCIS BERTRAM, b Des Moines, Iowa, July 31, 05; m. PHYSICAL CHEMISTRY. *Educ:* Des Moines Univ, BA, 26; Iowa State Col, PhD(phys chem), 40. *Prof Exp:* Instr & asst coach high sch, Iowa, 26-27, 29-32, prin & coach, 27-29; instr chem, Iowa State Col, 33-40; assoc prof & head dept, Phillips Univ, 40-43; prof, Southeast Mo State Col, 43-52; assoc prof, 52-61, prof, 61-74, head dept, 54-72, EMER PROF CHEM, UNIV MINN, DULUTH, 74- *Mem:* Am Chem Soc. *Res:* Electron sharing ability of organic radicals; qualitative separation of copper and cadmium; condensation of mercaptans with chloral in the gaseous phase; chemical composition of western Lake Superior waters; extension of studies of the bathophanthroline determination of iron. *Mailing Add:* Dept Chem Univ Minn Duluth MN 55812

MOORE, FRANCIS DANIELS, b Evanston, Ill, Aug 17, 13; m 35; c 5. SURGERY. *Educ:* Harvard Univ, AB, 35, MD, 39. *Hon Degrees:* MCh, Nat Univ Ireland, 61; LLD, Glasgow Univ, 65; DSc, Suffolk Univ, 66; FRCS, 67, FRCS(E), 68, FRCS(C), 70 & FRCS(I), 72; MD, Univ Goteberg, Sweden, 75, Univ Edinburgh, 76, Univ Paris, 76. *Prof Exp:* Nat Res Coun fel med, Harvard Univ, 41-42; instr, 43-46, assoc, 46-47, asst prof & tutor, 47-48, Moseley prof surg, 48-76, Elliott Carr Cutler prof surg, 76-80, EMER MOSELEY PROF SURG, HARVARD MED SCH, 80-; EMER SURGEON-IN-CHIEF, PETER BENT BRIGHAM HOSP, 80- *Concurrent Pos:* Asst resident surgeon, Mass Gen Hosp, Boston, 42-43, resident surgeon, 43, asst surg, 43-

46, asst surgeon, 46; surgeon-in-chief, Peter Bent Brigham Hosp, 48-76, surgeon, 76- consult, Surgeon Gen, Korea, 51; vis prof, Univ Edinburgh, 52 & Univ London, 55; chmn surg study sect, USPHS, 56-59; vis prof, Univ Colo, 58 & Univ Otago, NZ, 67; mem, Exec Comt, Nat Res Coun; chmn, Adv Comt Metab Trauma, Off Surgeon Gen; consult, Surgeon Sidney Farber Cancer Inst, 76- & Health Resources Admin, HEW, 76; mem bd regents, Uniformed Serv Univ Health Sci, 76; pres, Mass Health Data Consortium, Inc, 81- *Honors & Awards:* Lister Medal, Royal Col Surgeon, 78; Gross Medal, Am Surgeon Asn, 78. *Mem:* Nat Acad Sci; Soc Univ Surgeons (pres, 58-); hon mem Polish Acad Sci; Am Surg Asn (pres, 71-; AMA. *Res:* Clinical surgery as related to gastrointestinal tracts; biochemistry of cellular changes in surgical as revealed by radioactive and stable isotopes; metabolic care in trauma; transplantation of tissues and organs; cancer of the breast; surgical manpower and health care delivery. *Mailing Add:* Countway Libr 10 Shattuck St Boston MA 02115

MOORE, FRANK ARCHER, b Tribune, Kans, Mar 30, 20; m 48; c 3. BIOCHEMISTRY. *Educ:* Ft Hays Kans State Col, BS, 42; Kans State Univ, MS, 52, PhD(chem), 60. *Prof Exp:* Jr inspector powder & explosives, Weldon Spring Ord Works, 42-43; chemist & analyst, Phillips Petrol Co, 47-49; asst chem, Univ Calif, 51-52, lab technician food technol, 52; asst chem, Kans State Univ, 52-56; instr, NMex State Univ, 56-59; from asst prof to assoc prof, 59-67, PROF CHEM, ADAMS STATE COL, 67- *Mem:* Am Chem Soc; AAAS; Sigma Xi. *Res:* Interaction of proteins with small molecules; organic chemistry; blood lipids; history of chemistry. *Mailing Add:* Dept of Chem Adams State Col Alamosa CO 81102

MOORE, FRANK DEVITT, III, b Philadelphia, Pa, June 16, 31; m 59; c 2. HORTICULTURE. *Educ:* Pa State Univ, BS, 58; Univ Del, MS, 60; Univ Md, PhD(hort), 64. *Prof Exp:* Asst hort, Univ Del, 58-60 & Univ Md, 60-64; asst horticulturist, 64-70, ASSOC PROF HORT, COLO STATE UNIV, 70- *Concurrent Pos:* Sr res horticulturist, 3M Co, 69; mem, Inst Soc Hort Sci. *Mem:* AAAS; Am Soc Hort Sci; Am Inst Biol Sci. *Res:* Effect of environment and nutrition on plant growth and physiology; vegetable crops. *Mailing Add:* Dept of Hort Plant Sci Bldg Colo State Univ Ft Collins CO 80521

MOORE, FRANK LESLIE, JR, b Brooklyn, NY, Mar 14, 17; m 42; c 3. PHYSICS. *Educ:* Union Univ, NY, BS, 39; Lafayette Col, MS, 41; Princeton Univ, MA, 47, PhD(spectros), 49. *Prof Exp:* assoc physicist, Div War Res, Univ Calif, Los Angeles, 44-45; instr physics, Princeton Univ, 42-44 & 46-48; from instr to asst prof, Dartmouth Col, 48-51; asst prof, Cornell Univ, 51-55; from asst prof to assoc prof physics, Clarkson Col Technol, 55-63, prof, 63-82; RETIRED. *Mem:* Am Phys Soc; Am Asn Physics Teachers; Optical Soc Am. *Res:* Ionic and molecular spectra; plasma physics. *Mailing Add:* Dept of Physics Clarkson Col of Technol Potsdam NY 13676

MOORE, FRANK LUDWIG, b Fremont, Ohio, Mar 22, 45; m 68; c 1. ENDOCRINOLOGY. *Educ:* Col Wooster, BA, 67; Univ Colo, MA & PhD(biol), 74. *Prof Exp:* Teacher biol, Pub Schs, Lakewood, Ohio & Denver, Colo, 67-71; instr, Univ Colo, 71-72; ASST PROF BIOL, ORE STATE UNIV, 73- *Mem:* Am Soc Zoologists; Sigma Xi; Am Inst Biol Sci. *Res:* Reproductive endocrinology of amphibia. *Mailing Add:* Dept Zool Ore State Univ Corvallis OR 97331

MOORE, FRANKLIN K(INGSTON), b Milton, Mass, Aug 24, 22; m 46; c 6. FLUID MECHANICS, MECHANICAL ENGINEERING. *Educ:* Cornell Univ, BS, 44, PhD(aeronaut eng), 49. *Prof Exp:* Aeronaut res scientist, Nat Adv Comt Aeronaut, 49-55; dir aerodyn div, Cornell Aeronaut Lab, Inc, 55-65; head dept thermal eng, 65-73, JOSEPH C FORD PROF MECH ENG, CORNELL UNIV, 65- *Concurrent Pos:* Consult, Brookhaven Nat Lab & CE-Lummus. *Mem:* Am Soc Mech Engrs; Am Inst Aeronaut & Astronaut; Am Phys Soc. *Res:* Thermal engineering; boundary layer theory; power systems heat rejection; thermal pollution. *Mailing Add:* 294 Grumman Hall Cornell Univ Ithaca NY 14850

MOORE, FRED EDWARD, b Lafayette, Colo, Mar 16, 23. GEOLOGY. *Educ:* Univ Colo, BA, 48; St Louis Univ, MS, 50; Univ Wyo, PhD(geol), 59. *Prof Exp:* Oceanogr, Hydrographic Off, US Navy, 50; photogeologist, Geophoto Serv, Colo, 51-54; instr, 55-59, from asst prof to assoc prof, 59-71, PROF GEOL, COLO SCH MINES, 71- *Mem:* Geol Soc Am; Soc Econ Paleont & Mineral; Am Asn Petrol Geol; Am Geophys Union. *Res:* Geomorphology, particularly Pleistocene history of the Front Range. *Mailing Add:* Dept of Geol Colo Sch of Mines Golden CO 80401

MOORE, GARRY EDGAR, b Washington, DC, Aug 29, 48; m 76. NUCLEAR PHYSICS, SPACE SCIENCES. *Educ:* Va Polytech Inst & State Univ, BS, 70; Fla State Univ, MS, 73, PhD(physics), 75. *Prof Exp:* Res assoc nuclear physics & fel, Univ Pa, 75-77; ANALYST SPACE SCI, ANAL SERV, INC, 77- *Concurrent Pos:* Fulbright fel, W Ger. *Mem:* Am Phys Soc; Am Inst Aeronaut & Astronaut. *Res:* Advanced space systems concepts and technology planning, utility of crews in space, comprehensive study of tritium induced nuclear reactions, nuclear structure of light nuclei and lithium induced transfer reactions. *Mailing Add:* 3203 Holly Hill Dr Falls Church VA 22042

MOORE, GARY THOMAS, b Dallas, Tex, Apr 6, 42; m 61; c 3. VETERINARY MEDICINE, LABORATORY ANIMAL SCIENCE. *Educ:* Tex A&M Univ, BS, 65, DVM, 66. *Prof Exp:* Res veterinarian, Div Microbiol, US Army, Vet Corps, 66-68; veterinarian, Yerkes Regional Primate Ctr, Emory Univ, 68-69; chief res support br, 69-72, DIR, DEPT ANIMAL RESOURCES & FACIL, SOUTHWEST FOUND RES & EDUC, 72- *Concurrent Pos:* Mem, Nat Comt Conserv Nonhuman Primates, Inst of Lab Animal Resources, 73-75; prin investr, NIH contract, 74-78, grant, 78-83. *Mem:* Am Asn Lab Animal Sci. *Res:* Management of laboratory and animal medicine colonies; experimental surgery; reproductive physiology and domestic breeding of nonhuman primates. *Mailing Add:* Southwest Found for Res & Educ PO Box 28147 San Antonio TX 78284

MOORE, GEORGE A(NDREW), b New York, NY, Feb 14, 13; m 39; c 5. MICROSCOPY, METALLURGY. *Educ:* Union Col, BS, 34; Harvard Univ, MA, 35; Princeton Univ, PhD(chem), 39. *Prof Exp:* Asst instr chem & metall, Princeton Univ, 35-39, instr, 39-40; res engr, Battelle Mem Inst, 40-47; asst prof metall eng, Univ Pa, 48-51; metallurgist, Nat Bur Standards, 51-78; RETIRED. *Concurrent Pos:* Lectr, Univ Md, 54-62; chmn organizing comt, Fourth Int Cong Stereology, 75; consult, var indust & govt, 78- *Honors & Awards:* Award, Electrochem Soc, 39; Award of Merit, Am Soc Testing & Mat, 77. *Mem:* Am Soc Metals; Electrochem Soc; fel Am Soc Testing & Mat; Am Inst Mining, Metall & Petrol Engrs; Int Soc Stereology. *Res:* Hydrogen in metals; absorption and evolution; analysis; effect on microstructure and properties; hydrogen in steel brittle failures; low temperature properties; high purity metals; superconducting alloys; quantitative microscopy; computer analysis of micrographs; automated image analysis. *Mailing Add:* 1108 Agnew Dr Rockville MD 20851

MOORE, GEORGE EDWARD, b Evanston, Ill, Sept 28, 22; m 49; c 2. CONTINUING EDUCATION, PERSONNEL DEVELOPMENT. *Educ:* Northwestern Univ, BS, 43; Univ Tenn, PhD(chem), 61. *Prof Exp:* Asst chem, Univ Minn, 43-44 & Univ Chicago, 44; res chemist, Clinton Labs, Oak Ridge Nat Lab, 44-48 & Union Carbide Nuclear Co, 48-71; res chemist, Chem Div, 71-74, res staff dir admin, 74-78, HEAD, UNIV RELS & PERSONNEL DEVELOP, OAK RIDGE NAT LAB, 78- *Concurrent Pos:* Chemist, Metall Lab, Manhattan Eng Dist, 44. *Mem:* AAAS; Am Chem Soc; Sigma Xi; Am Soc Eng Educ. *Res:* Heterogeneous catalysis; radiation chemistry; ion exchange; corrosion; chemistry of actinide elements; molecular beams; gas-surface interactions; water pollution research; radiological protection. *Mailing Add:* Oak Ridge Nat Lab PO Box X Oak Ridge TN 37830

MOORE, GEORGE EDWARD, b Pittsburgh, Pa, Oct 28, 03; m 31; c 3. PHYSICS. *Educ:* Calif Inst Technol, BS, 27; Columbia Univ, MA, 32. *Prof Exp:* Develop engr, Bell Tel Labs, Inc, 27-36, res physics, 37-40, develop, 40-45, mem res staff, 46-66; prof, 66-74, EMER PROF PHYSICS, STATE UNIV NY BINGHAMTON, 74- *Mem:* Fel Am Phys Soc; Inst Elec & Electronics Eng. *Res:* Thermionics; gas discharges; chemical reactions; recombination in mercury; catalysis; surface physics. *Mailing Add:* Dept of Physics State Univ of NY Binghamton NY 13901

MOORE, GEORGE EMERSON, JR, b Lebanon, Mo, Jan 2, 14; m 39; c 3. GEOLOGY. *Educ:* Univ Mo, AB, 36, MA, 38; Harvard Univ, MA, 41, PhD(geol), 47. *Prof Exp:* Instr geol, Univ Mo, 38-39; rodman, US Geol Surv, Washington, DC, 39; asst, Harvard Univ, 40-42; geologist, A P Green Fire Brick Co, Mo, 42-46; asst, Harvard Univ, 46-47; from instr to assoc prof, 47-64, PROF GEOL, OHIO STATE UNIV, 64- *Mem:* Geol Soc Am. *Res:* Structure and metamorphism of southwestern New Hampshire, bedrock geology of southeastern New England. *Mailing Add:* Dept of Geol Ohio State Univ Columbus OH 43210

MOORE, GEORGE EUGENE, b Minneapolis, Minn, Feb 22, 20; m 44; c 5. SURGERY, ONCOLOGY. *Educ:* Univ Minn, BA, 42, MA, 43, BS, 44, BM, 46, MD, 47, PhD, 50; Am Bd Surg, dipl. *Prof Exp:* Lab asst physiol, Univ Minn, 41-42, asst histol & zool, 42-43, intern surg, Univ Hosps, 46-47, clin instr, Med Sch, 48-50, asst prof & cancer coordr, 51, assoc prof, 51-52; res prof biol & dir, Roswell Park Div, Grad Sch, State Univ NY Buffalo, 53-69, clin prof surg, Sch Med, 62-73; PROF SURG, UNIV COLO, DENVER, 73-; CHIEF DIV SURG ONCOL, DENVER GEN HOSP, 73- *Concurrent Pos:* Markle Fund scholar, 48-53; dir & chief surg, Roswell Park Mem Inst, 53-69; consult, Nat Cancer Chemother Ctr, NIH, 56; dir pub health res, NY State Dept Health, 69- *Honors & Awards:* Gross Award, 50; Chilean Iodine Educ Bur Award, Am Pharmaceut Asn, 51. *Mem:* Soc Exp Biol & Med; Soc Univ Surgeons; Am Surg Asn; NY Acad Sci. *Res:* Localization of brain tumors; carcinogenesis; experimental biology and oncology; cell culture chemotherapy; cancer surgery. *Mailing Add:* Dept of Surg Denver Gen Hosp W Eighth Ave & Cherokee St Denver CO 80204

MOORE, GEORGE THOMAS, b Chicago, Ill, Oct 15, 29; m 57; c 1. MARINE GEOLOGY, STRATIGRAPHY. *Educ:* Univ Notre Dame, BS, 52; Ind Univ, MA, 54, PhD(geol), 56. *Prof Exp:* Geologist, Chevron Oil Co, 56-67; assoc prof, Northeastern Ill Univ, 67-69; SR RES GEOLOGIST, CHEVRON OIL FIELD RES CO, 69- *Concurrent Pos:* Indust observer adv bd, Nat Oceanog Data Ctr. *Mem:* Geol Soc Am; Am Asn Petrol Geologists. *Res:* Deltaic and deep sea sedimentary accumulations along continental margins associated with major river systems of the world; relationship of petroleum accumulation to this environment of sedimentation. *Mailing Add:* Chevron Oil Field Res Co PO Box 446 La Habra CA 90631

MOORE, GEORGE WILLIAM, b Palo Alto, Calif, June 7, 28; m 60; c 2. GEOLOGY. *Educ:* Stanford Univ, BS, 50, MS, 51; Yale Univ, PhD(geol), 60. *Prof Exp:* Geologist, US Geol Surv, 51-66; geologist-in-chg, La Jolla Marine Geol Lab, 66-75; GEOLOGIST, US GEOL SURV, 75- *Concurrent Pos:* Res assoc, Scripps Inst Oceanog, 70-75; partic, Deep Sea Drilling Proj, Leg 57, 77. *Mem:* AAAS; fel Geol Soc Am; Nat Speleol Soc (pres, 63); Am Asn Petrol Geologists. *Res:* Stratigraphy and geochemistry of sedimentary rocks; structural geology; cave mineralogy; marine geophysics. *Mailing Add:* US Geol Surv MS-99 345 Middlefield Rd Menlo Park CA 94025

MOORE, GERALD L, b Cincinnati, Ohio, Apr 24, 39. BIOCHEMISTRY, ANALYTICAL CHEMISTRY. *Educ:* Univ Cincinnati, BS, 61, PhD(biochem), 67; Xavier Univ, Ohio, MS, 63. *Prof Exp:* Res biochemist blood, US Army Med Res Lab, Ft Knox, Ky, 67-74, RES BIOCHEMIST BLOOD, LETTERMAN ARMY INST RES, 74- *Concurrent Pos:* Asst prof chem, Univ Ky, Ft Knox Exten, 71-74 & Bowling Green State Univ, Ft Knox Exten, 73-74. *Mem:* Am Chem Soc; Am Asn Blood Banks; AAAS; Sigma Xi; Soc Armed Forces Med Lab Scientists. *Res:* Metabolism and membrane structure and function of red blood cells; improved methods of blood storage and blood banking techniques; hemoglobin biochemistry. *Mailing Add:* Blood Res Div Letterman Army Inst of Res Presidio of San Francisco CA 94129

MOORE, GLENN D, b Barron, Wis, Apr 9, 23; m 47; c 3. ENTOMOLOGY, PLANT BREEDING. *Educ:* Univ Wis, BS, 50, MS, 51; Univ Minn, PhD, 68. *Prof Exp:* res agronomist & asst to mgr, Res Serv Dept, 52-80, SR ENTOMOLOGIST & DIR ENTOMOLOGY, NORTHRUP KING CO, 80- *Mem:* AAAS; Entom Soc Am; Weed Sci Soc Am; Am Seed Trade Asn; Plant Resistance to Insects Asn. *Res:* Insect resistance in crop plants; alfalfa pollination for seed production; fungicide and fungicide-insecticide seed treatments; herbicides and their application in field crops and vegetables; forage crop management studies. *Mailing Add:* Northrup King Co 13410 Research Rd Eden Prairie MN 55344

MOORE, GORDON EARLE, b San Francisco, Calif, Jan 3, 29; m 50. PHYSICAL CHEMISTRY. *Educ:* Univ Calif, BS, 50; Calif Inst Technol, PhD(chem), 54. *Prof Exp:* Asst chem, Calif Inst Technol, 50-52; res chemist phys chem, Johns Hopkins Univ, 53-56; mem tech staff, Shockley Semiconductor Labs, Beckman Instruments Corp, 56-57; head eng, Fairchild Semiconductor Corp, 57-58, dir res & develop, 58-68; exec vpres, 68-75, pres, 75-79, CHMN BD, INTEL CORP, 79- *Mem:* Electrochem Soc; Am Phys Soc; Inst Elec & Electronics Engrs. *Res:* Molecular spectroscopy and structure; semiconductors; transistors; microcircuits. *Mailing Add:* Intel Corp 3065 Bowers Ave Santa Clara CA 95051

MOORE, GORDON GEORGE, b Des Moines, Iowa, Mar 18, 35; m 56; c 3. ORGANIC CHEMISTRY. *Educ:* Iowa State Univ, BS, 56; Yale Univ, MS, 58, PhD(org chem), 62. *Prof Exp:* Res assoc, Brookhaven Nat Lab, 60-62; asst prof org chem, Marshall Univ, 62-65; from asst prof to assoc prof, 65-77, PROF ORG CHEM, PA STATE UNIV, OGONTZ CAMPUS, 77- *Concurrent Pos:* Res chemist, USDA, Pa, 68- *Mem:* Am Chem Soc. *Res:* Organic mechanisms; organic synthesis; compounds of biochemical interest. *Mailing Add:* Dept of Chem Pa State Univ Ogontz Campus Abington PA 19001

MOORE, GRAHAM JOHN, b Bristol, Eng, Feb 13, 46; Can citizen; m 78; c 2. PEPTIDE SYNTHESIS, PROTEIN CHEMISTRY. *Educ:* Univ Exeter, UK, BSc, 67, MSc, 69; Univ Ottawa, PhD(biochem), 72. *Prof Exp:* Fel, Max Planck Inst Molecular Genetics, 72-73; fel, 73-76, ASST PROF PHARMACOL & BIOCHEM, UNIV CALGARY, CAN, 76- *Mem:* Soc Endocrinol; Can Biochem Soc; Pharmacol Soc Can; Western Pharmacol Soc. *Res:* Synthesis and evaluation of peptide hormones and analogues; biosynthesis of neurohypophysial hormones. *Mailing Add:* Dept Pharmacol & Therapeut Fac Med Univ Calgary Calgary AB T2N 1N4 Can

MOORE, GREGORY FRANK, b Bismarck, NDak, Sept 25, 51; m 74. GEOLOGY. *Educ:* Univ Calif, Santa Barbara, BA, 73; Johns Hopkins Univ, MA, 74; Cornell Univ, PhD(geol), 77. *Prof Exp:* Res asst, Cornell Univ, 74-77, fel, 77; asst res geologist structural geol, Scripps Inst Oceanog, Univ Calif, 78-82; RES GEOLOGIST, RES LAB, CITIES SERV OIL CO, 82- *Concurrent Pos:* Lectr, Univ Calif, San Diego, 80-82. *Mem:* Geol Soc Am; Am Geophys Union; Soc Explor Geophysicists; Soc Econ Paleontologists & Mineralogists; Int Asn Sedimentologists. *Res:* Structural geology; sedimentology and marine geophysics applied to the study of convergent plate margins in an attempt to understand subduction and collision and the interplay between tectonics and sedimentation. *Mailing Add:* Explor Prod Res Cities Serv Co Box 3908 Tulsa OK 74102

MOORE, GREGORY H, b Salt Lake City, Utah, Sept 8, 44. HISTORY OF MATHEMATICS. *Educ:* Univ Calif, Berkeley, AB, 66; Univ Toronto, MA, 73, MSc, 75, PhD(hist math), 79. *Prof Exp:* Lectr math, 75-81, UNIV RES FEL, UNIV TORONTO, 81- *Concurrent Pos:* Res assoc, Russell Ed Proj, McMaster Univ, 80-81; vis prof, Dept Math, Stanford Univ, 82. *Mem:* Can Soc Hist & Philos Math. *Res:* History of the foundations of mathematics (logic and set theory), especially the axiom of choice; continuum hypothesis; independence proofs in set theory. *Mailing Add:* Dept Math Univ Toronto Toronto ON M5S 1A1 Can

MOORE, H(ERBERT) CARLTON, b Milford, Mass, Apr 3, 03; m 28; c 2. ENGINEERING. *Educ:* Mass Inst Technol, SB, 24, SM, 33, ScD(mech eng), 41. *Prof Exp:* Asst, Mass Inst Technol, 24-26, from asst instr to asst prof, 26-41; asst engr, Shreve, Lamb, Harmon, Fay, Spofford & Thorndike, 41-43; sr mech engr, Metcalf & Eddy, Boston, 43-50, chief mech dept, 50-61, mech consult, 61-71; CONSULT SOLID WASTE MGT, 71- *Mem:* Am Soc Mech Engrs; Am Soc Heating, Refrigerating & Air Conditioning Engrs; Air Pollution Control Asn. *Res:* Engineering thermodynamics of mixtures; combustion and incineration of solid and liquid wastes and attendant problems with air and water pollution. *Mailing Add:* 145 Beaumont Ave Newtonville MA 02160

MOORE, HAL G, b Vernal, Utah, Aug 14, 29; m 56; c 3. MATHEMATICS. *Educ:* Univ Utah, BS, 52, MS, 57; Univ Calif, Santa Barbara, PhD(math), 67. *Prof Exp:* Jr high sch teacher, Utah, 52-53; instr math, Carbon Jr Col & Carbon High Sch, 53-55; instr, Purdue Univ, 57-61, admin asst to chmn dept, 60-61; exec asst to chmn dept, 61-64, from asst prof to assoc prof, 61-71, PROF MATH, BRIGHAM YOUNG UNIV, 71- *Mem:* Sigma Xi; Am Math Soc; Math Asn Am. *Res:* Structure of rings and universal algebras. *Mailing Add:* Dept of Math Brigham Young Univ Provo UT 84602

MOORE, HAROLD ARTHUR, b Brackettville, Tex, Feb 4, 25. NUCLEAR PHYSICS. *Educ:* St Mary's Univ, Tex, BS, 44; Wash Univ, MS, 48; Univ Fla, PhD, 56. *Prof Exp:* Asst, Wash Univ, 46-48; physicist, Mo Res Labs, Inc, 48-51; asst, Univ Fla, 51-52, 55-56, instr phys sci, 52-55; from asst prof to assoc prof, 56-62, PROF PHYSICS, BRADLEY UNIV, 62- *Concurrent Pos:* Consult, Metric Photo Br, US Naval Ord Test Sta, Calif, 57-58. *Mem:* Am Phys Soc; Am Asn Physics Teachers. *Res:* Fast resolving time coincidence circuits; deuteron stripping reactions on carbon and oxygen; unified field theory. *Mailing Add:* Dept of Physics Bradley Univ Peoria IL 61625

MOORE, HAROLD BEVERIDGE, b Alix, Ark, Sept 11, 28; m 50; c 2. MEDICAL BACTERIOLOGY. *Educ:* San Diego State Col, AB, 51; Univ Calif, Los Angeles, MA, 55, PhD(microbiol), 57; Am Bd Med Microbiol, dipl pub health & med, 65. *Prof Exp:* Chief microbiologist, Donald N Sharp Mem Community Hosp, San Diego, 57-60; from asst prof to assoc prof, 60-67, PROF MICROBIOL, SAN DIEGO STATE UNIV, 67- *Concurrent Pos:* Consult, Donald N Sharp Mem Community Hosp, San Diego, 60- & Palomar Hosp, Escondido, 64- *Mem:* AAAS; Am Soc Microbiol. *Res:* Isolation, identification, taxonomy and clinical significance of poorly defined gram negative rods; clincally significant anaerobic bacteria. *Mailing Add:* Dept of Microbiol San Diego State Univ San Diego CA 92182

MOORE, HAROLD EMERY, JR, botany, deceased

MOORE, HAROLD W, b Ft Collins, Colo, May 21, 36; m 59; c 2. ORGANIC CHEMISTRY. *Educ:* Colo State Univ, BS, 59; Univ Ill, PhD(chem), 63. *Prof Exp:* Asst prof, 65-69, assoc prof, 69-74, chmn dept, 70-74, PROF CHEM, UNIV CALIF, IRVINE, 74- *Mem:* Am Chem Soc. *Res:* Organic chemistry, especially synthesis and mechanistic studies. *Mailing Add:* Dept of Chem Univ of Calif Irvine CA 92650

MOORE, HARRY BALLARD, JR, b Rocky Mount, NC, Sept 28, 28; m 55; c 5. WOOD PRODUCTS INSECTS. *Educ:* E Carolina Col, AB, 51; Purdue Univ, MS, 55; NC State Univ, PhD(entom), 64. *Prof Exp:* Chief inspector, NC Struct Pest Control Comn, 58-60; from instr to assoc prof, 60-76, PROF ENTOM, NC STATE UNIV, 76-, PROF WOOD & PAPER SCI, 77- *Mem:* Entom Soc Am; Sigma Xi. *Res:* Wood-destroying insects. *Mailing Add:* Dept of Entom NC State Univ Raleigh NC 27650

MOORE, HENRY J, II, b Albuquerque, NMex, Sept 2, 28; m 59; c 2. GEOLOGY. *Educ:* Univ Utah, BS, 51; Stanford Univ, MS, 59, PhD(geol), 65. *Prof Exp:* Prospector-geologist, 54-55; geologist, US Geol Surv, 55-57; asst geol, Stanford Univ, 57-59; GEOLOGIST ASTROGEOL, US GEOL SURV, 60- *Concurrent Pos:* Team leader, Phys Properties Viking Mars. *Honors & Awards:* Spec Commendation for Astronaut Training, Geol Soc Am, 73; Exceptional Serv Viking, NASA, 77. *Mem:* AAAS; Sigma Xi; Geol Soc Am; Am Inst Mining, Metall & Petrol Engrs; Am Geophys Union. *Res:* Application of the principles of geology to lunar and Martian problems; investigation of experimental craters produced by projectile impacts with rocks; application of remote sensing data to lunar problems. *Mailing Add:* 528 Jackson Dr Palo Alto CA 94303

MOORE, J STROTHER, b Seminole, Okla, Sept 11, 47; m 68; c 1. COMPUTER SCIENCE. *Educ:* Mass Inst Technol, BS, 70; Univ Edinburgh, PhD(comput logic), 73. *Prof Exp:* Mem res staff comput sci, Xerox Palo Alto Res Ctr, 73-76; RES MATHEMATICIAN COMPUT SCI, STANFORD RES INST, 76- *Res:* Automatic computer program verification and advanced debugging aids. *Mailing Add:* Stanford Res Inst 7017 Elmsdale Dr PO Box 20324 San Jose CA 95120

MOORE, JAMES ALEXANDER, b Johnstown, Pa, Nov 8, 23; m 51; c 3. ORGANIC CHEMISTRY. *Educ:* Washington & Jefferson Col, BS, 43; Purdue Univ, MS, 44; Pa State Col, PhD(chem), 49. *Prof Exp:* Res chemist, Parke, Davis & Co, 49-55; from asst prof to assoc prof, 55-63, PROF CHEM, UNIV DEL, 63- *Concurrent Pos:* Asst, Univ Basel, 52-53; sr ed, J Org Chem, 63-; NIH spec fel, 64-65. *Mem:* Am Chem Soc. *Res:* Novel heterocyclic systems; new forms of chemical publications. *Mailing Add:* Dept Chem Univ Del Newark DE 19711

MOORE, JAMES ALFRED, b Brooklyn, NY, Aug 30, 39; m 66; c 2. ORGANIC CHEMISTRY, POLYMER CHEMISTRY. *Educ:* St John's Univ, NY, BS, 61; Polytech Inst Brooklyn, PhD(chem), 67. *Prof Exp:* NIH fel, Univ Mainz, 67-68; res assoc, Univ Mich, Ann Arbor, 68-69; asst prof, 69-75, coordr polymer sci & eng, 73-77, ASSOC PROF CHEM, RENSSELAER POLYTECH INST, 75- *Concurrent Pos:* Assoc ed, Org Preparations & Procedures Int, 73- *Mem:* Am Chem Soc. *Res:* Synthesis, characterization and reactions of novel polymers; structure-property relationships; polymer reagents. *Mailing Add:* Rensselaer Polytech Inst Troy NY 12181

MOORE, JAMES CARLTON, b Harrodsburg, Ky, May 31, 23; m 46; c 3. PHYSIOLOGY. *Educ:* Univ Ky, BS, 44; Univ Louisville, MD, 46. *Prof Exp:* Commonwealth Fund fel, Mass Inst Technol, 49-50; from asst prof to assoc prof physiol, 53-70, asst dean student affairs, 73-74, PROF PHYSIOL & BIOPHYS, SCH MED, UNIV LOUISVILLE, 70-, ASSOC DEAN ADMIS, 74- *Mem:* AAAS; Biophys Soc; Am Physiol Soc; Soc Exp Biol & Med. *Res:* Blood volume measurement; mechanics of respiration; pulmonary edema; pulmonary circulation; microcirculation. *Mailing Add:* Health Sci Ctr Louisville KY 40202

MOORE, JAMES ELTON, chemical physics, see previous edition

MOORE, JAMES FREDERICK, JR, b Barbourville, Ky, July 19, 38; m 65; c 2. PLANT PATHOLOGY. *Educ:* Western Ky Univ, BS, 65; Clemson Univ, MS, 68; Univ Ariz, PhD(plant path), 76. *Prof Exp:* Res asst plant path, Clemson Univ, 65-69; plant pathologist, Dept Agr, Guam, 69-72; res assoc, Univ Ariz, 72-75; res plant pathologist, 75-80, ASSOC RES PROF & ASSOC DIR RES, STATE FRUIT EXP STA, SOUTHWEST MO STATE UNIV, 80- *Mem:* Am Phytopath Soc; Am Hort Sci. *Res:* Disease of fruit and nut crops; ecology of soil-borne plant pathogens and soil microorganisms; antibiosis; chemical, cultural and biological control; epiphytology. *Mailing Add:* Rte 2 Box 246 Mountain Grove MO 65711

MOORE, JAMES GEORGE, b Buffalo, NY, Oct 31, 19; m 46; c 3. EVAPORATION, DISTILLATION & DEHYDRATION. *Educ:* Univ Buffalo, BS, 41; Cornell Univ, MS, 44; Univ Calif, Berkley, BS, 60; Northwestern Col, PhD(chem eng), 80. *Prof Exp:* Process engr, 45-54, dir res, 54-57, dir res & develop, 57-69, mgr, 69-79, MGR RES & DEVELOP PILOT

PLANT, FIELD SERV, PROCESS ENG, BLAW-KNOX FOOD & CHEM EQUIP, CO, 79- *Concurrent Pos:* Lectr, Govt Manpower Sci Utilization Prog, 41-44, Ctr Prof Advan, 56-82, Grad Sch, State Univ NY, Buffalo, 81-; mem adv comts, Cornell Univ & Erie County Community Col, 60-; approved delegate, US Foreign Trade Mission Appointment, 62- *Mem:* Am Inst Chem Engrs; fel Am Chem Soc; Inst Food Technologists; Am Soc Agr Engrs; Can Inst Food Sci & Technol. *Res:* Design and manufacture of process equipment for food, chemical, pharmaceutical and allied industries; chemical process research; heat transfer. *Mailing Add:* 4125 Clardon Dr Williamsville NY 14221

MOORE, JAMES GREGORY, b Palo Alto, Calif, Apr 30, 30; m 52; c 2. GEOLOGY. *Educ:* Stanford Univ, BS, 51; Univ Wash, MS, 52; Johns Hopkins Univ, PhD(geol), 54. *Prof Exp:* Instr geol, Johns Hopkins Univ, 52-53; GEOLOGIST, US GEOL SURV, 56- *Concurrent Pos:* Scientist-in-charge, Hawaiian Volcano Observ, US Geol Surv, 62-64 & chief br field geochem & petrol, 70-74. *Mem:* Geol Soc Am; Geochem Soc. *Res:* Petrology and geochemistry of igneous rocks; structural geology; volcanology; submarine geology. *Mailing Add:* US Geol Surv 345 Middlefield Rd Menlo Park CA 94025

MOORE, JAMES MENDON, b Winchester, Mass, Apr 25, 25; m 50; c 4. INDUSTRIAL ENGINEERING. *Educ:* Rensselaer Polytech Inst, BME, 50; Cornell Univ, MS, 56; Stanford Univ, PhD(indust eng), 65. *Prof Exp:* Prod control supvr, Stanley Tools, 50-52; instr indust eng, Cornell Univ, 52-56; asst prof mech eng, Clarkson Tech Col, 56-60; prof indust eng & chmn dept, Northeastern Univ, 61-73; PROF INDUST ENG & OPERS RES, VA POLYTECH INST & STATE UNIV, 73- *Concurrent Pos:* Fulbright lectr, Tech Univ Helsinki, 68-69; vis Lucas prof eng prod, Univ Birmingham, Eng, 75-76; indust consult, 60- *Mem:* Am Inst Indust Engrs; Am Soc Eng Educ; Opers Res Soc Am; Inst Mgt Sci. *Res:* Application of computers to solve problems involving the location of economic activities in an optimal manner. *Mailing Add:* Dept Indust Eng & Opers Res Va Polytech Inst & State Univ Blacksburg VA 24061

MOORE, JAMES NORMAN, b Vilonia, Ark, June 10, 31; m 53; c 2. HORTICULTURE. *Educ:* Univ Ark, BSA, 56, MS, 57; Rutgers Univ, PhD(hort), 61. *Prof Exp:* Instr hort, Univ Ark, 57; res assoc pomol, Rutgers Univ, 57-61; res horticulturist, USDA, 61-64; assoc prof, 64-69, PROF HORT, UNIV ARK, FAYETTEVILLE, 69- *Concurrent Pos:* Hon asst prof, Rutgers Univ, 61-64; assoc ed, Am Soc Hort Sci, 80-84. *Honors & Awards:* Woodbury Award, Am Soc Hort Sci, 58, Gourley Award, 63 & Ware Res Award, 72. *Mem:* Am Soc Hort Sci (vpres-elect, 81-82); Am Genetic Asn; Am Pomol Soc; Int Soc Hort Sci; NY Acad Sci. *Res:* Fruit breeding and genetics; physiology of fruit crops. *Mailing Add:* 316 Plant Sci Bldg Univ Ark Fayetteville AR 72701

MOORE, JAMES THOMAS, b Mineola, NY, Feb 9, 52; m 78. ATMOSPHERIC SCIENCES. *Educ:* New York Univ, BS, 74; Cornell Univ, MS, 76, PhD(atmospheric sci), 79. *Prof Exp:* Teaching res asst meteorol, Dept Agron, Cornell Univ, 74-78; asst prof meteorol, Earth Sci Dept, State Univ NY, Oneonta, 78-80; ASST PROF METEOROL, DEPT EARTH SCI & ATMOSPHERIC SCI, ST LOUIS UNIV, 80- *Concurrent Pos:* Fac fel, NASA, 79 & Am Soc Eng Educ, 80. *Mem:* Am Meteorol Soc; Nat Weather Asn. *Res:* Dynamics of jet stream propagation, especially with respect to the diagnosis and forecasting of severe local storms including thunderstorms, hailstorms, strong surface winds and tornadoes. *Mailing Add:* Dept Earth & Atmospheric Sci St Louis Univ PO Box 8099 St Louis MO 63156

MOORE, JAMES W(ALLACE) I, b Birmingham, Ala, Feb 19, 23; m 48; c 3. MECHANICAL ENGINEERING. *Educ:* Tenn Polytech Inst, BS, 51; Univ Ky, MS, 52; Purdue Univ, PhD(mech eng), 62. *Prof Exp:* Proj engr, Carbide & Carbon Chem Co, 52-55; proj engr, Allison Div, Gen Motors Corp, 55-56, sr proj engr, 56-58; res asst mech eng, Purdue Univ, 59-62; assoc prof, 62-67, sesquicentennial fel to Barcelona, Spain, 71-72, PROF MECH ENG, UNIV VA, 67- *Concurrent Pos:* NASA res grants, 64-71; Dept of Defense res grant, 67-72. *Mem:* Am Soc Mech Engrs. *Res:* Automatic control; algebraic techniques in control design; automatic control in aerodynamic drag instrumentation and in a wind tunnel force balance system; automatic control systems. *Mailing Add:* Dept of Mech Eng Univ of Va Charlottesville VA 22901

MOORE, JAY WINSTON, b Madison, Wis, Apr 20, 42; m 65. DEVELOPMENTAL GENETICS, POULTRY GENETICS. *Educ:* Cedarville Col, BS, 64; Univ Nebr, MS, 67; Univ Mass, PhD(genetics), 70. *Prof Exp:* From asst prof to assoc prof, 70-77, PROF BIOL, EASTERN COL, 77- *Mem:* AAAS; Genetics Soc Am; Sigma Xi; Am Soc Affil; Am Inst Biol Sci. *Res:* Plumage color inheritance; genetic factors controlling pigment and keratin development. *Mailing Add:* Dept of Biol Eastern Col St Davids PA 19087

MOORE, JERRY LAMAR, b Anderson, SC, Feb 28, 42; m 66; c 2. NUTRITION. *Educ:* Clemson Univ, BS, 63; Univ Wis, MS, 65, PhD(food sci, biochem), 68. *Prof Exp:* Clin lab officer, Wilford Hall US Air Force Med Ctr, 68-69, biomed lab officer, Nutrit Br, US Air Force Sch Aerospace Med, 69-72; assoc dir nutrit, Pillsbury Co, 72-74, assoc dir corp res & develop, 74-77; V PRES RES & DEVELOP, MEAD JOHNSON NUTRIT DIV, 78- *Concurrent Pos:* Mem, Food & Nutrit Bd, Nat Res Coun, Nat Acad Sci, 82-84. *Mem:* Am Dietetic Asn; Sigma Xi; Inst Food Technol; Soc Nutrit Educ (secy, 74-77 & pres, 82-83). *Res:* Management of applied human nutrition and product development leading to new or nutritionally improved foods and special dietary products, new health related services and more effective informational and educational materials. *Mailing Add:* Mead Johnson & Co 2404 Pennsylvania Ave Evansville IN 47721

MOORE, JEWEL ELIZABETH, b Hot Springs, Ark, June 5, 18. BOTANY. *Educ:* Henderson State Univ, AB, 40; Univ Ark, MS, 48; Univ Tenn, PhD(bot), 58. *Prof Exp:* Teacher high sch, Ark, 40-42; instr sci, Beebe Br, Ark State Univ, 42-47; PROF BIOL, UNIV CENT ARK, 47- *Mem:* Am Inst Biol Sci; Bot Soc Am; Am Fern Soc; Am Bryol & Lichenological Soc; Nat Audobon Soc. *Res:* Arkansas plants; bryophytes; ecology. *Mailing Add:* Dept of Biol Univ Cent Ark Conway AR 72032

MOORE, JOANNE IWEITA, b Greenville, Ohio, July 23, 28. PHARMACOLOGY. *Educ:* Univ Cincinnati, AB, 50; Univ Mich, PhD(pharmacol), 59. *Prof Exp:* Asst, Christ Hosp Inst Med Res, Cincinnati, 50-55; asst pharmacol, Univ Mich, 55-57; fel cardiovasc pharmacol, Basic Sci Div, Emory Univ, 59-61; asst prof, 61-66, assoc prof, 66-71, actg chmn dept, 69-70, interim chmn dept, 71-73, PROF PHARMACOL, COL MED, UNIV OKLA, 71-, CHMN DEPT, 73- *Concurrent Pos:* Mem, Special Study Sect, NIH, Div Res Grants; Fogarty Sr Int fels. *Mem:* Am Soc Pharmacol & Exp Therapeut; Soc Exp Biol & Med; Am Soc Clin Res; Asn Med Sch Pharmacol; NY Acad Sci. *Res:* Cardiovascular pharmacology; mechanism of action of drugs upon the contractile and/or conduction system of the heart. *Mailing Add:* Dept of Pharmacol Univ of Okla Col of Med Oklahoma City OK 73190

MOORE, JOHN (NEWTON), b Columbus, Ohio, Apr 2, 20; m 41; c 2. PLANT PATHOLOGY. *Educ:* Denison Univ, AB, 41; Mich State Univ, MS, 43, EdD, 52. *Prof Exp:* Instr math, 43-44, instr biol sci, 46-53, from asst prof to assoc prof natural sci, 53-70, prof, 70-82, EMER PROF NATURAL SCI, MICH STATE UNIV, 82- *Mem:* Nat Asn Biol Teachers; Nat Sci Teachers Asn; Creation Res Soc; Nat Asn Geol Teachers; Soc Study Evolution. *Res:* Study of philosophy of science, especially teaching of organic evolution, natural selection and related topics. *Mailing Add:* Dept Natural Sci Mich State Univ East Lansing MI 48824

MOORE, JOHN ALEXANDER, b Charles Town, WVa, June 27, 15; m 38; c 1. EVOLUTIONARY BIOLOGY. *Educ:* Columbia Univ, AB, 36, MS, 39, PhD(zool), 40. *Prof Exp:* Asst zool, Columbia Univ, 36-39; tutor biol, Brooklyn Col, 39-41; instr, Queens Col, NY, 41-43; from asst prof to prof zool, Barnard Col & Columbia Univ, 43-69, chmn dept, Col, 48-52, 53-54 & 60-66, chmn dept, Univ, 49-52; PROF BIOL, UNIV CALIF, RIVERSIDE, 69- *Concurrent Pos:* Res assoc, Am Mus Natural Hist, 42-, Fulbright res scholar, Australia, 52-53; managing ed, J Morphol, 55-60; Guggenheim fel, 59-60; partic, Biol Sci Curric Study, 59-76; mem, US Nat Comn, Int Union Biol Sci, 76-; mem, Comn Human Resources, Nat Res Coun, 80- *Mem:* Nat Acad Sci; Am Acad Arts & Sci; Am Soc Zoologists (pres, 74); Am Soc Naturalists (pres, 72); hon mem Australian Soc Herpet. *Res:* Evolution of amphibians and Drosophila. *Mailing Add:* Dept of Biol Univ of Calif Riverside CA 92521

MOORE, JOHN ARTHUR, b Salem, Mass, Feb 9, 39; m 62; c 3. TOXICOLOGY. *Educ:* Mich State Univ, BS, 61, DVM, 63, MS, 67; Am Col Lab Animal Med, dipl, 68; Am Bd Toxicol, dipl, 80. *Prof Exp:* Asst dir lab animal med, Sch Med, Western Reserve Univ, 63-65; asst prof vet med, Mich State Univ, 65-69; chief animal sci, 69-71, assoc dir res resources, 75-80, CHIEF ENVIRON BIOL CHEM, NAT INST ENVIRON HEALTH SCI, 71- *Concurrent Pos:* Exec secy comt coord toxicol & related progs, HEW, 74-76, chmn subcomt health effects polybrominated biphenyl, 77; consult, Am Asn Accreditation Lab Animal Care, 74-; chmn comt health effects dibenzodioxins & dibenzofurans, Int Agency Res Cancer, 78. *Honors & Awards:* Super Serv Award, HEW, 75. *Mem:* Soc Toxicol; Teratology Soc; Am Vet Med Asn. *Res:* Chemical toxicology research and methods development; functional teratogenic defects; effects of chemicals on immune response; development and use of experimental animals for research. *Mailing Add:* Nat Inst of Environ Health Sci NIH PO Box 12233 Research Triangle Park NC 27709

MOORE, JOHN BAILY, JR, b Hattiesburg, Miss, Apr 26, 44; m 67; c 2. BIOCHEMISTRY. *Educ:* Wake Forest Univ, BS, 66; Purdue Univ, MS, 68; Johns Hopkins Univ, PhD(biochem), 71. *Prof Exp:* NIH fel biochem, Stanford Univ, 71-73; res scientist, Lederle Labs, Am Cyanamid Co, 73-75; ASST PROF BIOCHEM, TEX A&M UNIV, 75- *Mem:* Am Chem Soc. *Res:* Protein chemistry and enzymology; experimental growth factor, nerve growth factor and cyclic nucleotide phosphodiesterases from human lung tissue. *Mailing Add:* Dept of Biochem & Biophys Tex A&M Univ College Station TX 77843

MOORE, JOHN CARMAN GAILEY, b Belleville, Ont, Aug 15, 16; m 52; c 3. ECONOMIC GEOLOGY. *Educ:* Univ Toronto, BA, 38; Cornell Univ, MS, 40; Harvard Univ, PhD, 55. *Prof Exp:* Field asst, Ont Dept Mines, 37-39; geologist, Int Petrol Co, Ecuador, 40-41, Labrador Mining & Explor Co, 46 & Oliver Iron Mining Co, Venezuela, 47; tech officer, Geol Surv Can, 48-51; geologist, Photog Surv Corp, Ltd, 51-52, Am Metal Co, Ltd, 52-54 & Dom Gulf Co, 54-56; div supvr, McIntyre Porcupine Mines, Ltd, 56-61; vis lectr geol, Univ NB, 61-62; from asst prof to assoc prof, 62-68, head dept, 66-73, PROF GEOL, MT ALLISON UNIV, 68- *Mem:* Geol Soc Am; Geol Asn Can; Can Inst Mining & Metall; Asn Explor Geochemists; Soc Econ Geologists. *Res:* Dispersion haloes around ore deposits. *Mailing Add:* 1 Bennett St PO Box 471 Sackville NB E0A 3C0 Can

MOORE, JOHN COLEMAN, b Staten Island, NY, May 27, 23. MATHEMATICS. *Educ:* Mass Inst Technol, BS, 48; Brown Univ, PhD(math), 52. *Prof Exp:* Fine instr, 53, NSF fel, 53-55, from asst prof to assoc prof, 55-60, PROF MATH, PRINCETON UNIV, 60- *Mem:* Am Math Soc; Math Asn Am; London Math Soc. *Res:* Algebraic topology; homological algebra. *Mailing Add:* Fine Hall Dept of Math Box 37 Princeton Univ Princeton NJ 08540

MOORE, JOHN CRISWELL, chemistry, deceased

MOORE, JOHN DAVID, animal physiology, parasitology, see previous edition

MOORE, JOHN DOUGLAS, b Austin, Tex, Oct 5, 39; m 63. MATHEMATICS. *Educ:* Idaho State Univ, BS, 61, MS, 63; Syracuse Univ, PhD(math), 69. *Prof Exp:* Asst prof math, State Univ NY Col Oswego, 67-69; asst prof, 69-77, ASSOC PROF MATH, ARIZ STATE UNIV, 77- *Mem:* Am Math Soc; Math Asn Am. *Res:* Theory of Abelian groups. *Mailing Add:* Dept of Math Ariz State Univ Tempe AZ 85281

MOORE, JOHN DOUGLAS, b Chicago, Ill, July 11, 43; m 65; c 1. MATHEMATICS. *Educ:* Univ Calif, Berkeley, BA, 65, PhD(math), 69. *Prof Exp:* Asst prof, 69-75, ASSOC PROF MATH, UNIV CALIF, SANTA BARBARA, 75- *Mem:* Am Math Soc; Math Asn Am. *Res:* Isometric immersions of Riemannian manifolds. *Mailing Add:* Dept of Math Univ of Calif Santa Barbara CA 93106

MOORE, JOHN DUAIN, b Lancaster, Pa, Dec 11, 13; m 40; c 2. PLANT PATHOLOGY. *Educ:* Pa State Univ, BS, 39; Univ Wis, PhD(plant path), 45. *Prof Exp:* From asst prof to assoc prof, 45-54, prof, 54-80, EMER PROF PLANT PATH & EMER DIR UNIV EXP FARMS, UNIV WIS-MADISON, 80- *Concurrent Pos:* Plant pathologist, USDA, 56-65; prof plant sci & head dept, Fac Agr, Univ Ife, Nigeria, 68-70, dean grad studies, 69, dean agr, 69-70; consult, Univ Calabar, Nigeria & Inst Pertanian Bogor, Indonesia, 81- *Mem:* AAAS; Am Phytopath Soc; Bot Soc Am; Am Inst Biol Sci. *Res:* Fungus, bacterial and virus diseases of sour cherries and apples; effects of fungicides on quality of cherries and apples; greenhouse energy conservation. *Mailing Add:* Dept Plant Path Univ Wis-Madison Madison WI 53706

MOORE, JOHN EDWARD, b Kirkersville, Ohio, Mar 7, 35; m 57; c 1. RUMINANT NUTRITION. *Educ:* Ohio State Univ, BS, 57, MS, 58, PhD(animal sci), 61. *Prof Exp:* PROF ANIMAL SCI, UNIV FLA, 61- *Concurrent Pos:* Chmn, S Pasture & Forage Crop Improv Conf, 79. *Mem:* Am Dairy Sci Asn; Am Soc Animal Sci; Nutrit Today Soc; Am Forage & Grassland Coun. *Res:* Forage evaluation and utilization. *Mailing Add:* Nutrit Lab Univ of Fla Gainesville FL 32611

MOORE, JOHN EZRA, b Columbus, Ohio, Jan 25, 31; m 56. HYDROLOGY, GROUNDWATER GEOLOGY. *Educ:* Ohio Wesleyan Univ, BA, 53; Univ Ill, MS, 58, PhD(geol), 60. *Prof Exp:* Geologist, Am Zinc Co, Mo, 53-54; teaching asst geol, Univ Ill, 57-60; geologist, Nev Test Site, Nev & Colo, 60-63, proj chief, Groundwater Br, Water Resources Div, 63-67, supvry hydrologist, Colo Dist, 67-71, staff hydrologist, Rocky Mt Region, 71-75, chief, Southwest Fla Subdist Tampa, 75-78; staff hydrologist, Water Resources Div, 78-79, DEP ASST CHIEF HYDROLOGIST SCIENTIFIC PUB & DATA MGT, US GEOL SURV, 79- *Mem:* Soc Econ Paleont & Mineral; fel Geol Soc Am; Am Water Res Asn; Asn Earth Sci Ed. *Res:* Clay mineralogy; sedimentation; groundwater hydrology; application of electrical analog and digital models to the study of groundwater and surfacewater systems; evaluations of water resources for planning and management. *Mailing Add:* US Geol Surv Water Resources Div MS440 Reston VA 22092

MOORE, JOHN GEORGE, JR, b Berkeley, Calif, Sept 17, 17; m 46; c 4. OBSTETRICS & GYNECOLOGY. *Educ:* Univ Calif, AB, 39, MD, 42. *Prof Exp:* From intern to resident obstet & gynec, Univ Calif, 42-49; from instr to asst prof, Univ Iowa, 50-51; from asst prof to prof, Univ Calif, Los Angeles, 51-65; prof & chmn dept, Col Physicians & Surgeons, Columbia Univ, 65-69; PROF OBSTET & GYNEC & CHMN DEPT, SCH MED, UNIV CALIF, LOS ANGELES, 69- *Concurrent Pos:* Dir, Am Bd Obstet & Gynec, 67-73, pres, 74-78. *Mem:* Soc Gynec Invest (pres, 66); Asn Profs Gynec & Obstet (pres, 73); Soc Gynec Oncol; Am Asn Obstet & Gynec; Am Gynec Soc. *Res:* Carcinoma of the uterine cervix; tissue culture growth of genital tissues. *Mailing Add:* Dept of Obstet & Gynec Univ of Calif Sch of Med Los Angeles CA 90024

MOORE, JOHN HAYS, b Pittsburgh, Pa, Nov 6, 41; m 63; c 2. PHYSICAL CHEMISTRY, MOLECULAR PHYSICS. *Educ:* Carnegie Inst Technol, BS, 63; Johns Hopkins Univ, MA, 65, PhD(chem), 67. *Prof Exp:* Res assoc chem, Johns Hopkins Univ, 67-69; from asst prof to assoc prof, 69-78, PROF CHEM, UNIV MD, COLLEGE PARK, 78- *Concurrent Pos:* Vis fel, Joint Inst Lab Astrophys, Colo, 75-76; prog officer, Nat Sci Found, 80-81. *Mem:* Am Phys Soc. *Res:* Valence electronic structure of molecules; electron transmission spectroscopy; (e,ze) spectroscopy; atomic physics; ionospheric physics. *Mailing Add:* Dept of Chem Univ of Md College Park MD 20742

MOORE, JOHN MARSHALL, JR, b Winnipeg, Man, Aug 14, 35; m 58; c 3. GEOLOGY, PETROLOGY. *Educ:* Univ Man, BSc, 56; Mass Inst Technol, PhD(petrol), 60. *Prof Exp:* Queen Elizabeth II fel, 60-62, from asst prof to assoc prof, 62-75, chmn dept, 75-78, PROF GEOL, CARLETON UNIV, 75- *Concurrent Pos:* Guest prof, Inst Mineral, Univ Geneva, 68-69; adv, Can Int Develop Agency, Ethiopia, 72-74; consult regional planning & resource develop, Y Bojard Assocs, Vancouver, 78- *Mem:* Geol Asn Can; Soc Int Develop; Mineral Asn Can; Mineral Soc Am. *Res:* Precambrian geology; metamorphic petrology; resources and development. *Mailing Add:* Dept of Geol Carleton Univ Ottawa ON K1S 5B6 Can

MOORE, JOHN R(OBERT), b St Louis, Mo, July 5, 16; m 41; c 3. MECHANICAL ENGINEERING. *Educ:* Washington Univ, BS, 37. *Prof Exp:* Asst chief engr, Mech Sect, Aeronaut & Marine Eng, Gen Elec Co, 40-45 & Chief Theoret Sect, Proj Hermes, 45-46; assoc prof mech & dir, Dynamical Control Lab, Washington Univ, 46-48; group leader, Electromech Eng Dept, NAm Aviation, Inc, 48-53, dir dept, 53-55, gen mgr, Autonetics Div, 55-57, pres, 60-66, vpres, NAM Aviation, 57-66, exec vpres & mem bd, NAm Rockwell Corp, 66-76; ENG MGR, ITT CANNON ELEC, 76- *Concurrent Pos:* Vis assoc prof, Univ Calif, Los Angeles, 48-56; mem space technol panel, Air Force Sci Adv Bd, 59-60; adv bd, Joint Task Force Two, Dept Defense, 60- *Mem:* Am Inst Aeronaut & Astronaut; Am Inst Navig; fel Inst Elec & Electronics Engrs. *Res:* Airborne controls; computers; missile guidance systems. *Mailing Add:* ITT Cannon Elec 666 Dyer Rd Santa Ana CA 92705

MOORE, JOHN ROBERT, b Bridgeville, Pa, Mar 3, 34; m 55; c 2. PLANT ECOLOGY. *Educ:* Clarion State Col, BS, 57; Univ Pittsburgh, 62, PhD(biol), 65. *Prof Exp:* Pub sch teacher, Pa, 57-62; asst biol, Univ Pittsburgh, 62-65; assoc prof, 65-67, PROF BIOL, CLARION STATE COL, 67- *Mem:* Ecol Soc Am. *Res:* Primary production of vascular aquatic plants. *Mailing Add:* Dept Biol Clarion State Col Clarion PA 16214

MOORE, JOHN THOMAS, mathematics, deceased

MOORE, JOHN V, animal breeding, see previous edition

MOORE, JOHN WARD, b Lancaster, Pa, July 17, 39; m 61. COMPUTERS & CHEMISTRY, CHEMISTRY EDUCATION. *Educ:* Franklin & Marshall Col, AB, 61; Northwestern Univ, PhD(phys chem), 65. *Prof Exp:* NSF fel phys chem, Univ Copenhagen, 64-65; asst prof inorg chem, Ind Univ, Bloomington, 65-71; assoc prof, 71-75, PROF CHEM, EASTERN MICH UNIV, 76- *Concurrent Pos:* Fel, Ctr Study Contemp Issues, Eastern Mich Univ, 74-75. *Mem:* AAAS; Nat Sci Teachers Asn; Sigma Xi; Am Chem Soc. *Res:* Coordination chemistry; molecular orbital theory; chemical education; environmental chemistry; computer/instrument interfacing; computer graphics; computer aided instruction. *Mailing Add:* Dept of Chem Eastern Mich Univ Ypsilanti MI 48197

MOORE, JOHN WILLIAMSON, b Houston, Tex, Jan 16, 21; m 43; c 2. PHYSICAL CHEMISTRY. *Educ:* Univ Tex, BS, 41, AM, 42. *Prof Exp:* Tutor phys chem, Univ Tex, 41-42; jr chem engr, Tenn Valley Authority, 42-43, asst chem engr, 43-44; chem engr, Nat Cotton Coun, 44-45; chem engr, Southern Alkali Corp, 45-48, supvr res labs, PPG Industs, Inc, 48-55, dir res, 55-70, dir develop, 67-70, mgr chem div tech ctr, Barberton, Ohio, 70-78, mgr res & develop planning & admin, 78-79; CONSULT, 79- *Mem:* Am Chem Soc. *Res:* Kinetics; industrial process development. *Mailing Add:* 2701 E Franklin St Richmond VA 23223

MOORE, JOHN WILSON, b Winston-Salem, NC, Nov 1, 20; m 44, 78; c 3. NEUROPHYSIOLOGY. *Educ:* Davidson Col, BS, 41; Univ Va, MA, 42, PhD(physics), 45. *Prof Exp:* Researcher, RCA Labs, 45-46; asst prof physics, Med Col Va, 46-50; biophysicist, Naval Med Res Inst, 50-54; biophysicist, Nat Inst Neurol Dis & Blindness, 54-56, assoc chief lab biophys, 56-61; assoc prof physiol, 61-65, PROF PHYSIOL, DUKE UNIV, 65- *Concurrent Pos:* Nat Neurol Res Found fel, 61-66; trustee, Marine Biol Lab, Woods Hole, 71-79, 81-85, exec comn, 78-79; Dupont fel, Nat Neurol Res Found Scientist. *Honors & Awards:* K S Cole Award, Biophys Soc, 81. *Mem:* AAAS; Am Physiol Soc; Biophys Soc; Inst Elec & Electronic Engrs; Soc Neurosci. *Res:* Neurophysiological experiments, computation and instrumentation. *Mailing Add:* Dept of Physiol Duke Univ Med Ctr Durham NC 27710

MOORE, JOHNES KITTELLE, b Washington, DC, Apr 20, 31; div; c 3. MARINE ECOLOGY, MARINE EDUCATION. *Educ:* Bowdoin Col, AB, 53; Univ RI, PhD(oceanog), 67. *Prof Exp:* Asst acct exec, Batton, Barton, Durstine & Osborn, Inc, 55-60; res asst oceanog, Narragansett Marine Lab, Univ RI, 61-66; from asst prof to assoc prof, 66-74, PROF BIOL, SALEM STATE COL, 74- *Concurrent Pos:* Consult, NSF, 67-69; Woods Hole Oceanog Inst sr fel marine policy, 78-79. *Mem:* New Eng Estuarine Res Soc; Nat Marine Educ Asn. *Res:* Estuarine ecology; marine science education. *Mailing Add:* Dept of Biol Salem State Col Salem MA 01970

MOORE, JOHNNIE NATHAN, b San Fernando, Calif, Mar 25, 47. STRATIGRAPHY, TECTONICS. *Educ:* San Fernando Valley Col, BS, 70; Univ Calif, Los Angeles, MS, 73, PhD(geol), 76. *Prof Exp:* Lectr geol, Calif State Univ, Fresno, 76-77; ASST PROF GEOL, UNIV MONT, 77- *Concurrent Pos:* Mgr uranium eval contract, Bendix Field Eng, 78-79. *Mem:* Geol Soc Am; Soc Econ Paleontologists & Mineralogists. *Res:* Precambrian-Cambrian depositional environments; controls of sedimentation on stable margins; lacustrine delta sedimentation. *Mailing Add:* Dept of Geol Univ of Mont Missoula MT 59801

MOORE, JON THOMAS, b Kingsport, Tenn, Nov 25, 43. POLYMER PHYSICS. *Educ:* Ga Inst Technol, BEE, 65; Univ Tenn, MS, 66; Univ Va, PhD(physics), 70. *Prof Exp:* Res physicist, 70-79, RES ASSOC, TENN EASTMAN CO, EASTMAN KODAK CO, 79- *Mailing Add:* Tenn Eastman Co PO Box 511 Kingsport TN 37662

MOORE, JOSEPH B, b Potchefstroom, SAfrica, Dec 17, 10; m 37; c 1. ECONOMIC ENTOMOLOGY. *Educ:* Cornell Univ, BS, 33, MS, 35, PhD(entom), 37. *Prof Exp:* Asst res entom, NY Exp Sta, Geneva, 35-39; entomologist, State Col Wash, 39; entomologist, McLaughlin Gormley King Co, 39-71, vpres & dir res & develop, 54-71, sr staff vpres, 71-77, dir res & develop, 74-77, bd dir, 77-80; RETIRED. *Concurrent Pos:* Dir, Hardwicke Chem Co. *Mem:* Am Chem Soc; Entom Soc Am. *Res:* New insecticides and their use in the field. *Mailing Add:* McLaughlin Gormley King Co 8810 10th Ave N Minneapolis MN 55427

MOORE, JOSEPH CURTIS, b Washington, DC, June 5, 14; m 40; c 3. MAMMALOGY. *Educ:* Univ Ky, BS, 39; Univ Fla, MS, 42, PhD(biol), 53. *Prof Exp:* Asst bot, Univ Ky, 37-39; asst biol, Univ Fla, 39-41; park biologist, Everglades Nat Park, 49-55; res fel, Dept Mammals, Am Mus Natural Hist, 55-61; cur mammals, Field Mus Natural Hist, 62-71, res assoc, 71-73; mem staff, Ecol & Systematics, Fla Southern Col, 72-80; RETIRED. *Concurrent Pos:* Hon lectr, Dept Anat, Univ Chicago, 65-71. *Mem:* AAAS; Am Soc Mammal; Zool Soc London. *Res:* Systematics and zoogeography of mammals, world-wide in Cetacea and Sciuridae; ecology of vertebrates, especially Sciuridae and Sirenia in Florida; local mid-peninsular Florida ecology, especially vertebrate, terrestrial and volant, emphasizing animal and plant relationships to each other, the seasons, temperature, and rainfall. *Mailing Add:* 4210 Mossy Oak Dr Lakeland FL 33805

MOORE, JOSEPH HERBERT, b Spartanburg, SC, May 13, 22; m 43; c 2. CIVIL ENGINEERING. *Educ:* The Citadel, BS, 43; Pa State Univ, MS, 49; Purdue Univ, PhD, 61. *Prof Exp:* Civil engr, The Citadel, 46-48, asst prof, 49-50; asst prof, Pa State Univ, Capitol Campus, 48-55, assoc prof civil eng, 56-62, prof eng, 67-72; head progs eng & technol, 67-70, head div eng & technol, 70-72, dir div eng technol, 72-78, PROF CIVIL ENG, VA POLYTECH INST, 72- *Concurrent Pos:* Consult, Gannett, Fleming, Corddry & Carpenter, Inc, 53-55, Hwy Res Bd, 72-, Van Note-Harvey Asn, 76- & Olver Inc, 75-; mem, Eng Manpower Comn, Eng Joint Coun, 77-80; prof bridge engr, Joseph K Knoerle & Assocs, 55-56; prof & head dept, Clemson Univ, 62-67. *Mem:* Am Soc Civil Engrs; Am Soc Eng Educ. *Res:* Structures and transportation. *Mailing Add:* Dept of Civil Eng Va Polytech Inst & State Univ Blacksburg VA 24061

MOORE, JOSEPH NEAL, b New York, NY, Jan 21, 48. GEOLOGY. *Educ:* City Col NY, BS, 69; Pa State Univ, MS, 72, PhD(geol), 75. *Prof Exp:* Staff geologist, Anaconda Co, 75-77; GEOLOGIST, EARTH SCI LAB, UNIV UTAH RES INST, 77- *Mem:* Geol Soc Am. *Mailing Add:* Earth Sci Lab 391-A Chipeta Way Salt Lake City UT 84108

MOORE, JOSEPHINE CARROLL, b Ann Arbor, Mich, Sept 20, 25. NEUROANATOMY, ELECTROMYOGRAPHY. *Educ:* Univ Mich, BA, 47, MS, 59, PhD(anat), 64; Eastern Mich Univ, BS, 54. *Prof Exp:* From instr to asst prof occup ther, Eastern Mich Univ, 55-60; instr anat, Med Sch, Univ Mich, 64-66; from asst prof to assoc prof, 66-74, PROF ANAT, MED SCH, UNIV S DAK, 74-, VCHM DEPT ANAT, 78- *Mem:* AAAS; Am Asn Anat; World Fedn Occup Ther; Am Occup Ther Asn. *Res:* Rehabilitation of handicapped individuals, especially dealing with neuroanatomical and neurophysiological concepts; neurobehavioral sciences and rehabilitation. *Mailing Add:* Dept of Anat Univ of SDak Med Sch Vermillion SD 57069

MOORE, KEITH LEON, b Brantford, Ont, Oct 5, 25; m 49; c 5. ANATOMY. *Educ:* Univ Western Ont, 49, MSc, 51, PhD(micros anat), 54. *Prof Exp:* Lectr anat, Univ Western Ont, 54-56; from asst prof to prof, Univ Man, 56-76; PROF ANAT & CHMN, UNIV TORONTO, 76- *Concurrent Pos:* Consult, Children's Hosp, Winnipeg, Man, 59-76. *Mem:* Am Asn Anat; Anat Soc Gt Brit & Ireland; Can Asn Anat (secy, 62-65, pres, 66-68); Can Fedn Biol Socs; Can Cytol Coun. *Res:* Embryology and teratology. *Mailing Add:* Dept of Anat Univ of Toronto Med Sci Bldg Toronto ON M5S 1A8 Can

MOORE, KENNETH BOYD, b Pratt, Kans, Jan 31, 17; c 2. PSYCHIATRY. *Educ:* Univ Kans, AB, 38, MA, 40, PhD(psychol), 43, MD, 47; Am Bd Psychiat & Neurol, dipl psychiat, 54. *Prof Exp:* Clin dir, Ypsilanti State Hosp, Mich, 58-60, asst med supt, 60-61; assoc chief staff, 61-72, CHIEF MENT HYG CLIN, VET ADMIN HOSP, 72- *Concurrent Pos:* Mem, Ment Health Res Inst, Univ Mich, 59-60; asst prof clin psychiat, Sch Med, Univ Ky, 61- *Mem:* Fel Am Psychiat Asn; Am Psychol Asn. *Res:* Treatment of schizophrenia; out-patient psychiatric treatment methods. *Mailing Add:* Vet Admin Hosp Ment Hyg Clin Lexington KY 40507

MOORE, KENNETH EDWIN, b Edmonton, Alta, Aug 8, 33; m 53; c 3. BIOCHEMICAL PSYCHOPHARMACOLOGY, NEUROENDOCRINOLOGY. *Educ:* Univ Alta, BS, 55, MS, 57; Univ Mich, PhD(pharmacol), 60. *Prof Exp:* Instr pharmacol, Dartmouth Med Sch, 60-61, asst prof, 62-65; assoc prof, 66-69, PROF PHARMACOL, MICH STATE UNIV, 70- *Concurrent Pos:* Mem rev comt pharmacol & endocrinol, NIH, 68-70, mem pharmacol study sect, 75-79; vis scholar, Cambridge Univ, Eng, 74. *Mem:* Am Soc Pharmacol & Exp Therapeut; Pharmacol Soc Can; Soc Exp Biol & Med; Soc Neurosci; Am Col Neuropsychopharmacol. *Res:* Biochemical pharmacology, neuropharmacology and toxicology related to the role of endocrine and nervous systems; central nervous system transmitters; catecholamines. *Mailing Add:* Dept of Pharmacol Mich State Univ East Lansing MI 48823

MOORE, KENNETH HOWARD, b Leek, Eng, June 20, 07; nat US; m 41; c 2. PHYSICS. *Educ:* Rensselaer Polytech Inst, BS, 30, MS, 33, PhD(physics), 45. *Prof Exp:* Instr physics & elec eng, 30-36, from instr to prof physics, 36-73, EMER PROF PHYSICS, RENSSELAER POLYTECH INST, 73- *Mem:* Am Phys Soc; Am Soc Eng Educ; Am Asn Physics Teachers. *Res:* X-ray and electron diffraction studies, particularly of treated surfaces and of epitaxy propagated through overlayers; development of demonstration, teaching and grading techniques. *Mailing Add:* RD 1 Box 37 Johnsonville NY 12094

MOORE, KENNETH VIRGIL, b Emporia, Kans, May 16, 33; m 52; c 2. NUCLEAR SCIENCE. *Educ:* Kans State Teachers Col, BA, 54; Stanford Univ, MS, 64. *Prof Exp:* Jr geophysicist, Gulf Oil Corp, 56; nuclear analyst, Phillips Petrol Co, Atomic Energy Div, 57-63, group leader nuclear res, 64-69; group leader thermal hydraulics, Idaho Nuclear Corp, 69-71, Aerojet Nuclear Corp, 71-74; vpres anal, 74-81, SR VPRES, ENERGY INC, 81- *Mem:* Am Soc Mech Engrs; Soc Automotive Engrs. *Res:* Major director and author of thermal hydraulic (transient, two-phase water) computer codes used by the governments and the nuclear reactor industry for safety analysis and experimental predictions. *Mailing Add:* Energy Inc PO Box 736 Idaho Falls ID 83401

MOORE, KRIS, b Frost, Tex, Apr 11, 41; m 64; c 4. STATISTICS, COMPUTER SCIENCE. *Educ:* Univ Tex, Austin, BA, 64, MA, 66; Tex A&M Univ, PhD(statist), 74. *Prof Exp:* Engr scientist res, Tracor Inc, 64-67; instr math, Tex Tech Univ, 67-69; ASSOC PROF STATIST, BAYLOR UNIV, 70- *Concurrent Pos:* Consult, Tex Educ Res Corp, 76-78, Word Inc, 77-78, Joe L Ward's, 78- & Cherry Law Firm, 81- *Mem:* Am Statist Asn; Decision Sci. *Res:* Nonparametric multivariate statistics. *Mailing Add:* Baylor Univ Hankamer Sch of Bus Waco TX 76703

MOORE, LARRY WALLACE, b Menan, Idaho, Aug 24, 37; m 61; c 4. PLANT PATHOLOGY. *Educ:* Univ Idaho, BS, 62, MS, 64; Univ Calif, Berkeley, PhD(plant path), 70. *Prof Exp:* ASSOC PROF PLANT PATH, ORE STATE UNIV, 69- *Mem:* Am Phytopath Soc; Am Soc Microbiol. *Res:* Biological disease control; biology of phytopathogenic bacteria; bacterial biology. *Mailing Add:* Dept of Bot & Plant Path Ore State Univ Corvallis OR 97331

MOORE, LAURENCE DALE, b Danville, Ill, July 12, 37; m 58; c 4. PLANT PATHOLOGY. *Educ:* Univ Ill, BS, 59; Pa State Univ, MS, 61, PhD(plant path), 65. *Prof Exp:* Asst, Pa State Univ, 59-65; asst prof, 65-70, ASSOC PROF PLANT PATH, VA POLYTECH INST & STATE UNIV, 70- *Mem:* Am Phytopath Soc; Am Soc Plant Path; Int Soc Plant Path. *Res:* Physiology of disease; role of enzymes and plant nutrition in disease development; air pollution effects on the physiology and biochemistry of plants. *Mailing Add:* Dept Plant Path & Physiol Va Polytech Inst & State Univ Blacksburg VA 24061

MOORE, LAWRENCE EDWARD, b Conway, SC, May 28, 38; m 64; c 2. INORGANIC CHEMISTRY. *Educ:* Davidson Col, BS, 60; Univ Tenn, PhD(chem), 64. *Prof Exp:* Asst prof chem, Wofford Col, 66-70; from asst prof to assoc prof, 70-77, PROF CHEM, UNIV SC, SPARTANBURG, 77- *Mem:* Am Chem Soc; AAAS; Sigma Xi. *Res:* Coordination compounds of nickel in which the perchlorate ion is a ligand; aromatic substituent effects in coordination compounds of nickel with substituted pyridines. *Mailing Add:* Dept Chem Univ SC Spartanburg SC 29303

MOORE, LEE E, b Chelsea, Okla, Mar 6, 38; m 64; c 2. NEUROPHYSIOLOGY, BIOPHYSICS. *Educ:* Univ Okla, BS, 60; Duke Univ, PhD(physiol), 66. *Prof Exp:* Asst prof physiol, Ohio Univ, 66-68; from asst prof to assoc prof physiol, Med Sch, Case Western Reserve Univ, 68-76; PROF PHYSIOL & BIOPHYS, MED BR, UNIV TEX, 76- *Concurrent Pos:* Nat Inst Neurol Dis & Stroke res grant, 67-75. *Mem:* Neurosci Soc; Biophys Soc; Soc Gen Physiol; Am Physiol Soc. *Res:* Cellular neurophysiology; biophysics of membrane transport; effect of low temperature on the ionic conductance of myelinated nerve; ion permeability of skeletal muscle; ion conduitance fluituation analysis of nerve; optical fluituation spectroscopy of nerve and muscle. *Mailing Add:* Dept of Physiol & Biophys Med Br Univ of Tex Galveston TX 77550

MOORE, LEON, b Waldron, Ark, Oct 2, 31; m 51; c 4. ENTOMOLOGY. *Educ:* Univ Ark, BSA, 57, MS, 59; Kans State Univ, PhD, 72. *Prof Exp:* Surv entomologist, Agr Exp Sta, 59-62, assoc prof entom & assoc entomologist, 74-77, PROF ENTOM, UNIV ARIZ, 77-, EXTEN ENTOMOLOGIST, AGR EXP STA, 62- *Mem:* Entom Soc Am. *Res:* Extension entomology with emphasis on educational programs on cotton and vegetable insects, cereal and forage crop insects and pesticides. *Mailing Add:* Dept of Entom Univ of Ariz Tucson AZ 85721

MOORE, LEONARD ORO, b Payson, Utah, Sept 20, 31; m 54; c 2. RESEARCH ADMINISTRATION, ORGANIC CHEMISTRY. *Educ:* Brigham Young Univ, BS, 53; Iowa State Univ, PhD(chem), 57. *Prof Exp:* Europ Res Assocs fel, Swiss Fed Inst Technol, 57-58; res chemist, Union Carbide Chem Co, 58-64 & Olefins Div, Union Carbide Corp, 64-71; mgr res, 71-76, MGR RES & DEVELOP, ANSUL CO, 76- *Concurrent Pos:* Chmn adv comt, Kanawha Valley Grad Ctr. *Mem:* Am Chem Soc; fel Am Inst Chemists; Sigma Xi; AAAS. *Res:* Halogen chemicals; fluorocarbons; pesticides; free radicals; kinetics; environmental chemistry; organometallics; glycol derivatives. *Mailing Add:* Ansul Res Ctr PO Drawer 1165 Weslaco TX 78596

MOORE, LOUIS DOYLE, JR, b Royston, Ga, Sept 16, 26; m 48; c 2. POLYMER CHEMISTRY. *Educ:* Duke Univ, BS, 47; Mass Inst Technol, PhD(phys chem), 51. *Prof Exp:* Res chemist, 51-57, sr res chemist, 57-67, res assoc, 67-71, SR RES ASSOC, TENN EASTMAN CO, 71- *Mem:* Am Chem Soc; Sigma Xi. *Res:* Molecular characterization of polymers; polymer rheology; polymer morphology. *Mailing Add:* Tennessee Eastman Co Eastman Rd PO Box 511 Kingsport TN 37662

MOORE, MARION E, b Boise City, Okla, May 22, 34; m 53; c 1. MATHEMATICS. *Educ:* W Tex State Univ, BS, 57; Tex Tech Col, MS, 60; Univ NMex, PhD(math), 68. *Prof Exp:* Instr math, W Tex State Univ, 58-61 & Univ NMex, 61-66; asst prof, 66-70, ASSOC PROF MATH, UNIV TEX, ARLINGTON, 70- *Concurrent Pos:* vis prof, Tex Tech Univ, 81. *Mem:* Math Asn Am; Am Math Soc; Sigma Xi. *Res:* Ring theory. *Mailing Add:* Dept of Math Univ of Tex Arlington TX 76010

MOORE, MARVIN G, b Harrison, Ark, Dec 8, 08; m 35; c 1. MATHEMATICS. *Educ:* Univ Ark, AB, 31; Univ Ill, MA, 32, PhD(math), 38. *Prof Exp:* Instr math, Ala Polytech Inst, 36-37 & Ind Univ, 37-40; prof, Tri-State Col, 40-43; from asst prof to prof & chmn dept, 43-74, EMER PROF MATH, BRADLEY UNIV, 74- *Mem:* Am Math Soc; Math Asn Am; Soc Indust & Appl Math. *Res:* Generalizations of Fourier series in complex plane; relativity; expansions in series of exponential functions; residual stresses. *Mailing Add:* 708 Henryetta Springdale AR 72764

MOORE, MARY ELIZABETH, b New London, Conn, Dec 7, 30; m 74. RHEUMATOLOGY. *Educ:* Douglass Col, AB, 52; Rutgers Univ, MS, 58, PhD(psychol), 60; Temple Univ, MD, 67. *Prof Exp:* Res assoc sociol, Rutgers Univ, 52-60; assoc psychol & psychiat, Univ Pa, 60-63; asst prof, 72-75, assoc prof, 76-81, PROF MED, SCH MED, TEMPLE UNIV, 81- *Concurrent Pos:* Attend staff, Temple Univ Hosp, 70-, Fel, Philadelphia Found, 72-; assoc dir, Pain Control Ctr, Temple Univ Hosp, 78- *Mem:* Fel Am Col Physicians; Am Rheumatologic Asn. *Res:* Rheumatic diseases, methods of pain relief. *Mailing Add:* Temple Univ Hosp 3401 N Broad St Philadelphia PA 19140

MOORE, MARYALICE CONLEY, b Stoneham, Mass, June 1, 18; m 42; c 2. ORGANIC CHEMISTRY. *Educ:* Simmons Col, BS, 39; Mass Inst Technol, PhD(org chem), 43. *Prof Exp:* Chemist, E I du Pont de Nemours & Co, 43-47; res assoc civil eng, Mass Inst Technol, 47-48; from lectr to assoc prof, 56-66, PROF ORG CHEM, STONEHILL COL, 66- *Concurrent Pos:* NSF col teachers res participation grant, 64-65. *Mem:* Am Chem Soc. *Res:* Organic synthesis of compounds of biochemical interest. *Mailing Add:* PO Box 447 Brewster MA 02631

MOORE, MAURICE LEE, b Laurel Hill, Fla, Sept 11, 09; m 33; c 3. MEDICINAL CHEMISTRY. *Educ:* Univ Fla, BS, 30, MS, 31; Northwestern Univ, PhD(org chem), 34. *Prof Exp:* Asst chem, Univ Fla, 27-31; asst instr gen chem, Dental Sch, Northwestern Univ, 31-34; Smith fel org chem, Yale Univ, 34-36; res chemist, Sharp & Dohme, Inc, Pa, 36-43; dir org res, Frederick Stearns & Co, Mich, 43-45, asst dir res, 45-47; dir, Smith, Kline & French Labs, Pa, 47-51; vpres, Vick Chem Co, 51-59; dir new prod develop, Sterling Drug Inc, 59-65, exec vpres, Winthrop Labs Div, 59-70, corp sci officer, 70-74; RETIRED. *Mem:* AAAS; Am Chem Soc; Soc Chem Indust; Am Pharmaceut Asn; fel Am Inst Chemists. *Res:* Research and development of new therapeutic agents. *Mailing Add:* 7 Brookside Circle Bronxville NY 10708

MOORE, MELITA HOLLY, b Joplin, Mo. STATISTICS. *Educ:* Wellesley Col, BA, 32; Univ Mich, MA, 34. *Prof Exp:* Instr math, Pvt sch & Wellesley Col, 34-41; admin asst math & physics, Naval Ord Lab, 41-45; chief statist serv, C/L Br, Bur Labor Statist, 45-46; chief res sect, UN Statist Off, 46-55, statist consult, 57-76; STATIST CONSULT, NAT BUR ECON RES, 77- *Mem:* Am Statist Asn. *Mailing Add:* 1171 Valley Rd New Canaan CT 06840

MOORE, MICHAEL LEE, b Dallas, Tex, July 12, 46. PHYSICAL CHEMISTRY. *Educ:* Gallaudet Col, BA, 68; Southern Methodist Univ, MS, 70; N Tex State Univ, PhD(chem), 76. *Prof Exp:* Eng aide chem, Ling Temco Vought Inc, 65-69; res technician, N Tex State Univ, 71-75; chemist, Shirco Inc, 76-77; prog specialist, Tex Comn for the Deaf, 77-81; MEM STAFF, SOUTHWEST JR COL FOR THE DEAF, 81- *Mem:* Am Chem Soc; AAAS. *Res:* Organometallics; NMR spectroscopy; adsorption and desorption of carbons. *Mailing Add:* Southwest Jr Col for the Deaf Ave C Big Spring TX 79720

MOORE, MICHAEL STANLEY, b Grass Creek, Wyo, Oct 24, 30; m 54; c 4. NUCLEAR PHYSICS. *Educ:* Rice Univ, BA, 52, MA, 53, PhD(physics), 56. *Prof Exp:* Physicist, Atomic Energy Div, Phillips Petrol Co, 56-66 & Idaho Nuclear Corp, 66-68; STAFF MEM, LOS ALAMOS SCI LAB, 68- *Mem:* Fel Am Phys Soc; fel Am Nuclear Soc. *Res:* Neutron cross sections by time of flight; fission physics. *Mailing Add:* 104 Tesuque Los Alamos NM 87544

MOORE, MORTIMER NORMAN, b Los Angeles, Calif, Mar 16, 27; m 58; c 2. MATHEMATICAL PHYSICS. *Educ:* Univ Calif, Los Angeles, BA, 50; Univ London, PhD(math physics), 55. *Prof Exp:* Sr res scientist, Atomics Int, NAm Aviation, 55-57; lectr theoret physics, Birkbeck Col, London, 57-61; assoc prof physics, 61-66, PROF PHYSICS, CALIF STATE UNIV, NORTHRIDGE, 66-, PROF ASTRON, 74- *Concurrent Pos:* Consult, Inst Nuclear Res, Stuttgart, Ger, 58, Atomics Int, 59-64 & Fr AEC fast reactor prog, 64-65; vis prof, Univ Ariz, 69. *Mem:* Am Phys Soc; Am Nuclear Soc; Brit Inst Physics. *Res:* Stochastic processes; transport processes; partial coherence theory; low energy neutron physics; non-equilibrium processes; laser physics. *Mailing Add:* Dept Physics Calif State Univ 18111 Nordoff St Northridge CA 91330

MOORE, NADINE HANSON, b Idaho Falls, Idaho, Feb 10, 41; m 63. MATHEMATICS. *Educ:* Idaho State Univ, BS, 63; Syracuse Univ, MA, 65, PhD(math), 69. *Prof Exp:* Instr math, State Univ NY Col Oswego, 68-69; asst prof math, Ariz State Univ, 69-75. *Mem:* Am Math Soc. *Res:* Homological algebra; structure of projective modules. *Mailing Add:* 5223 E Tamblo Dr Phoenix AZ 85044

MOORE, NELSON JAY, b Greenville, Ohio, Aug 29, 41; m 64; c 2. ETHOLOGY, ORNITHOLOGY. *Educ:* Manchester Col, BA, 63; Ohio State Univ, MS, 68; Univ Ariz, PhD(zool), 72. *Prof Exp:* ASSOC PROF BIOL, OHIO NORTHERN UNIV, 72-, CHMN BIOL DEPT, 80- *Mem:* Am Ornithologists Union; Cooper Ornith Soc; Inland Bird Banding Asn. *Res:* Description and analysis of the behaviors of the Yellow-eyed Junco; wintering bird ecology of northwestern Ohio. *Mailing Add:* Dept of Biol Ohio Northern Univ Ada OH 45810

MOORE, NOEL E(DWARD), b Ft Wayne, Ind, Dec 23, 34; m 57; c 3. CHEMICAL ENGINEERING. *Educ:* Purdue Univ, West Lafayette, BSChE, 56, PhD(chem eng), 67; Mass Inst Technol, MS, 58. *Prof Exp:* Asst prof chem eng, Univ Ky, 64-68; assoc prof, 68-72, PROF CHEM ENG, ROSE-HULMAN INST TECHNOL, 72- *Concurrent Pos:* Consult, Humble Oil & Refining Co, 67, Dow Chem Co, 68 & Eli Lilly & Co, 73-75; dir div air pollution control, Vigo County Health Dept, 69-71. *Mem:* Am Soc Eng Educ; Am Inst Chem Engrs; Air Pollution Control Asn. *Res:* Process control; air pollution. *Mailing Add:* Dept of Chem Eng Rose-Hulman Inst of Technol Terre Haute IN 47803

MOORE, PAUL BRIAN, b Stamford, Conn, Nov 24, 40. MINERALOGY, CRYSTALLOGRAPHY. *Educ:* Mich Technol Univ, BS, 62; Univ Chicago, SM, 63, PhD(geophys), 65. *Prof Exp:* NSF fel, Swed Natural Hist Mus, Stockholm, 65-66; from instr to assoc prof, 66-71, PROF MINERAL & CRYSTALLOG, UNIV CHICAGO, 72- *Honors & Awards:* Dreyfus Found Award, 71; Mineral Soc Am Award, 73; Alexander von Humboldt Sr Sci Award, 76. *Mem:* Am Crystallog Asn; Mineral Soc Am; Mineral Asn Can; Am Geophys Union; Explorers Club. *Res:* Descriptive, paragenetic and taxonomic mineralogy; crystal structure analysis of silicates, phosphates and arsenates; crystallochemical classifications; dense-packed structures; polyhedra theory. *Mailing Add:* Dept of Geophys Sci Univ of Chicago Chicago IL 60637

MOORE, PAUL HARRIS, b Trenton, Mo, Apr 6, 38; m 65; c 2. PLANT PHYSIOLOGY, AGRONOMY. *Educ:* Calif State Univ, Long Beach, BS, 61; Univ Calif, Los Angeles, MA, 65, PhD(plant physiol), 66. *Prof Exp:* PLANT PHYSIOLOGIST, USDA AGR RES EXP STA, HAWAIIAN SUGAR PLANTERS ASN, 67- *Concurrent Pos:* Fel Univ Calif, Los Angeles, 66-67. *Mem:* Am Soc Plant Physiologists; AAAS; Crop Sci Soc Am; Int Soc Sugar Cane Technologists; Plant Growth Regulator Working Group. *Res:* Developmental biology; regulatory role of phytohormones in growth and development; cellular differentiation; growth regulation; gibberellins; plant cell and tissue culture; flowering; photoperiodism; stress physiology. *Mailing Add:* 99-193 Aiea Heights Dr Aiea HI 96701

MOORE, PETER BARTLETT, b Boston, Mass, Oct 15, 39; m 66; c 2. BIOCHEMISTRY. *Educ:* Yale Univ, BS, 61; Harvard Univ, PhD(biophys), 66. *Prof Exp:* NSF fel, Univ Geneva, 66-67; US Air Force Off Sci Res fel, Med Res Coun Lab, Cambridge, Eng, 67-69; from asst prof to assoc prof molecular biophysics & biochem, 69-76, assoc prof, 76-79, PROF CHEM & MOLECULAR BIOPHYSICS & BIOCHEM, YALE UNIV, 76-, NIH & NSF RES GRANTS, 79- *Concurrent Pos:* NIH & NSF res grants, 69-; Guggenheim fel, Univ Oxford, 79-80. *Mem:* AAAS; Sigma Xi; Am Chem Soc; Am Soc Biol Chem; Biophys Soc. *Res:* Structure and function of ribosomes; application of neutron scattering to study of quaternary structure; macromolecular structure. *Mailing Add:* PO Box 6666 Dept Chem Yale Univ New Haven CT 06511

MOORE, PETER FRANCIS, b New York, NY, July 24, 36; m 60; c 5. PHARMACOLOGY. *Educ:* Fordham Univ, BS, 56; Purdue Univ, MS, 59, PhD(pharmacol), 61. *Prof Exp:* Mem staff, 61-73, SR RES INVESTR, PHARMACOL DEPT, PFIZER, INC, 73- *Mem:* AAAS; Am Heart Asn. *Res:* Pulmonary-asthma, allergy, immediate hypersensitivity, bronchodilators, leukotrienes, inflammation, mucolytics; cyclic mononucleotides; hypolipemics; diuretics. *Mailing Add:* Pharmacol Dept Eastern Point Rd Groton CT 06340

MOORE, RALPH BISHOP, b Carbonear, Nfld, Mar 23, 41; m 65; c 2. INDUSTRIAL CHEMISTRY, ANALYTICAL CHEMISTRY. *Educ:* Mem Univ Nfld, BSc, 62; Univ Alta, PhD(phys org chem), 67. *Prof Exp:* Res chemist, 67-69, process chemist, 69-74, sr process chemist, 74-79, sr supervisor, 79-81, SUPT, DEPT ORG CHEM, E I DU PONT DE NEMOURS & CO INC, 81- *Res:* Organolead chemistry; photochemistry; reaction kinetics, sodium borohydride chemistry; trace metal analysis; organofluorine chem. *Mailing Add:* 8 Candlewick Ct New Castle DE 19720

MOORE, RAMON EDGAR, b Sacramento, Calif, Dec 27, 29. MATHEMATICS, COMPUTER SCIENCE. *Educ:* Univ Calif, AB, 50; Stanford Univ, PhD(math), 63. *Prof Exp:* PROF COMPUT SCI, UNIV WIS-MADISON, 68- *Concurrent Pos:* Alexander von Humboldt Found sr scientist award, 75. *Mem:* Soc Neurosci. *Res:* Interval analysis; neural modeling; celestial mechanics; computing methods. *Mailing Add:* Dept of Comput Sci Univ of Wis Madison WI 53706

MOORE, RAYMOND A, b Britton, SDak, Nov 16, 27; m 51: c 4. AGRONOMY, PLANT PHYSIOLOGY. *Educ:* SDak State Univ, BS, 51, MS, 56; Purdue Univ, PhD(agron), 63. *Prof Exp:* High sch voc agr instr, SDak, 51-56; instr agron, 56-58, asst agronomist field crops, 58-62, assoc prof, 63-67, head dept plant sci, 69-73, PROF FIELD CROPS, S DAK STATE UNIV, 67-, DIR S DAK EXP STA, 73- *Mem:* Am Soc Agron; Soc Range Mgt. *Res:* Administration; university teaching; pasture crops. *Mailing Add:* 207 17th Ave Brookings SD 57006

MOORE, RAYMOND F, JR, b Fishersville, Va, Dec 17, 27; m 51; c 3. ENTOMOLOGY. *Educ:* Bridgewater Col, BS, 51; Univ Richmond, MA, 56; Rutgers Univ, PhD(entom), 59. *Prof Exp:* Entomologist, USDA, 59-65; asst prof biol, Univ SC, 65-66; ENTOMOLOGIST, USDA, 66- *Mem:* AAAS; Entom Soc Am; Am Chem Soc. *Res:* Insect physiology and nutrition. *Mailing Add:* PO Box 2131 Florence SC 29501

MOORE, RAYMOND H, b Spokane, Wash, May 29, 18; m 41; c 2. INORGANIC CHEMISTRY, CHEMICAL ENGINEERING. *Educ:* Gonzaga Univ, BS, 40. *Prof Exp:* Asst anal chem, Gonzaga Univ, 40-41; asst org chem, Univ Pittsburgh, 41-42; asst chemist, Explosives Div, US Bur Mines, 42-44, anal chemist, Electrometall Sta, 44-47; sr scientist, Hanford Atomic Prods Dept, Gen Elec Co, 47-65, STAFF SCIENTIST, PAC NORTHWEST LAB DIV, BATTELLE MEM INST, 65- *Mem:* Am Chem Soc; Am Inst Mining Engrs. *Res:* Instrumental methods of analysis; infrared spectroscopy; inorganic and physical chemistry; fused salt chemistry; radiochemical separations process development; kinetics of diffusion in metals; chemical process design-development; molten salt chemistry; coal liquefaction and gasification; hot fuelgas cleaning. *Mailing Add:* 2041 Greenbrook Blvd Richland WA 99352

MOORE, RAYMOND KENWORTHY, b Meriden, Conn, Jan 9, 42; m 61; c 4. GEOCHEMISTRY, MINERALOGY. *Educ:* Univ Fla, BS, 63, MS, 65; Pa State Univ, PhD(geochem), 69. *Prof Exp:* Res assoc, Mat Res Labs, Pa State Univ, 69-70; ASSOC PROF GEOL, RADFORD COL, 70-, CHMN DEPT, 81- *Mem:* Mineral Asn Can. *Res:* Petrology; spectroscopic studies of minerals; geomorphological processes; spectroscopic properties of naturally occurring solids; landform development. *Mailing Add:* Dept of Geol Radford Col Radford VA 24142

MOORE, RAYMOND KNOX, b Orlando, Fla, Apr 15, 44. GEOTECHNICAL ENGINEERING. *Educ:* Okla State Univ, BSCE, 66, MS, 68; Univ Tex, Austin, PhD(civil eng), 71. *Prof Exp:* Asst prof, 71-78, ASSOC PROF CIVIL ENG, DEPT CIVIL ENG, AUBURN UNIV, 78- *Concurrent Pos:* Mem, Transp Res Bd, Nat Acad Sci. *Mem:* Am Soc Civil Engrs. *Res:* Physical and engineering properties of soils; soil stabilization; geotechnical engineering soil testing. *Mailing Add:* Dept Civil Eng Auburn Univ Auburn AL 36849

MOORE, REGINALD GEORGE, b Brantford, Ont, Mar 16, 32; m 57; c 3. INVERTEBRATE PALEONTOLOGY. *Educ:* Univ Western Ont, BSc, 54; Univ Mich, MS, 55, PhD(geol), 60. *Prof Exp:* Instr geol, Oberlin Col, 57-58; assoc prof, 60-71, PROF GEOL, ACADIA UNIV, 71- *Res:* Non-marine invertebrate paleontology and paleoecology; malacology. *Mailing Add:* Dept of Geol Acadia Univ Wolfville NS B0P 1X0 Can

MOORE, RICHARD, b Los Angeles, Calif, Jan 19, 27; m 57, 69; c 2. MEDICAL PHYSICS, BIOMEDICAL ENGINEERING. *Educ:* Univ Mo, BS, 49; Univ Rochester, PhD(biophys), 56; George Washington Univ, DSc(bioeng), 70; Am Bd Health Physics, cert; Am Bd Radiol, cert diag radiol physics, 75. *Prof Exp:* Asst biophys, Univ Rochester, 52-53, res assoc, 53-56; biophysicist, Metab Dis Br, Nat Inst Arthritis & Metab Dis, 57-60; res biophysicist, Blood Prog Res Lab, Am Nat Red Cross, 60-69; ASSOC PROF RADIOL, SCH MED, UNIV MINN, MINNEAPOLIS, 69- *Concurrent Pos:* Sr asst engr, Div Sanit Eng Serv, USPHS, 55-57, lectr, R A Taft Sanit Eng Ctr, 56-57; vis prof, Howard Univ, 58-; consult, Comt Data Logging Systs, NIH, 59-60 & Dept Biophys, Div Nuclear Med, Walter Reed Army Inst Res, 61-65; from vis asst prof to vis prof, Sch Med, George Washington Univ, 64-69; assoc ed, Pattern Recognition, 68- & Comput in Biol & Med, 69-; contrib ed, Med Electronics & Data, 70-; consult ed, Measurements & Data, 71-; mem coun cardiovasc radiol, Am Heart Asn. *Mem:* Fel AAAS; fel Soc Advan Med Systs; Am Col Radiol; Am Asn Physicists in Med; Radiol Soc NAm. *Res:* Radioisotopic tracing; compartmental analysis; radiological physics; ultracentrifugation; radiation biology; diagnostic radiologic sciences; membrane permeability; mathematical modeling; computer simulation. *Mailing Add:* Dept of Radiol Univ of Minn Sch of Med Minneapolis MN 55455

MOORE, RICHARD ALLAN, b Mansfield, Ohio, Jan 11, 24; m 49; c 3. MATHEMATICS. *Educ:* Washington Univ, AB, 48, AM, 50, PhD, 53. *Prof Exp:* Instr math, Univ Nebr, 53-54 & Yale Univ, 54-56; from asst prof to assoc prof, 56-67, assoc head dept, 65-71, chmn dept, 71-75, PROF MATH, CARNEGIE-MELLON UNIV, 67-, ASSOC HEAD DEPT, 75- *Mem:* Am Math Soc; Math Asn Am. *Res:* Ordinary differential equations, especially second order equations. *Mailing Add:* Dept of Math Carnegie-Mellon Univ Pittsburgh PA 15213

MOORE, RICHARD ANTHONY, b Pittsburgh, Pa, Oct 29, 28; m 55; c 8. ORGANIC CHEMISTRY. *Educ:* Duquesne Univ, BS, 51; Purdue Univ, MS, 56; Univ Pittsburgh, PhD(org chem), 62. *Prof Exp:* Proj officer, Wright Air Develop Ctr, Ohio, 51-53; teaching asst chem, Purdue Univ, 53-56; res chemist, Develop Dept, Koppers Co, Inc, Pa, 56-57; teaching asst chem, Univ Pittsburgh, 57-58; res chemist, Wyandotte Chem Corp, 61-72, SR RES CHEMIST, BASF WYANDOTTE CORP, 72- *Mem:* Am Chem Soc; fel Am Inst Chem; Sigma Xi. *Res:* Heterocyclic and organic fluorine chemistry; polyethers research. *Mailing Add:* Res Dept BASF Wyandotte Corp Wyandotte MI 48192

MOORE, RICHARD ARTHUR, b Pratt, Kans, Jan 20, 30; m 55; c 2. *Educ:* Univ Kans, BS, 51, MS, 54, PhD(physics), 63. *Prof Exp:* Sr nuclear engr, Convair/Gen Dynamics/Ft Worth, 56-59; staff mem reactor critical exp, 63-74, sr staff engr, 74-78, MGR REACTOR PROG DEVELOP, GEN ATOMIC CO, 78- *Mem:* Atomic Indust Forum; Am Nuclear Soc. *Res:* Fast reactor physics; integral tests of basic fast neutron cross sections; gas-cooled nuclear reactor design. *Mailing Add:* Gen Atomic Co Box 81608 San Diego CA 92138

MOORE, RICHARD BYRON, microbiology, marine ecology, see previous edition

MOORE, RICHARD DANA, b Battle Creek, Mich, Feb 11, 26. ANATOMY. *Educ:* Olivet Col, BS, 48; Mich State Univ, MS, 52, PhD(anat), 56. *Prof Exp:* Asst biol, Olivet Col, 48-49; asst anat, Mich State Univ, 51-55; from asst prof to prof & actg head dept biol, Hardin-Simmons Univ, 55-66; assoc prof, Albright Col, 66-67; assoc prof, 67-70, chmn dept, 68-70, PROF BIOL, McMURRY COL, 70- *Concurrent Pos:* Am Physiol Asn fels, N Tex State Col, 59- *Mem:* NY Acad Sci. *Res:* Histology of urinary system of domestic animals; human histology. *Mailing Add:* Dept of Biol McMurry Col Abilene TX 79605

MOORE, RICHARD DAVIS, b Salina, Kans, Mar 17, 32. BIOPHYSICS. *Educ:* Purdue Univ, PhD(oxytocin action), 63; Ind Univ, MD, 57. *Prof Exp:* NIH fel biophys, Sch Med, Univ Md, 63-64, res asst prof, 64; assoc prof, 64-67, PROF BIOPHYSICS, STATE UNIV NY COL PLATTSBURGH, 67- *Mem:* AAAS; Biophys Soc. *Res:* Cellular control mechanisms, especially ionic regulation; role of ions in hormone action and gene activation; electrical interactions between hormones and receptor sites; active transport. *Mailing Add:* Div of Sci & Math State Univ of NY Col Plattsburgh NY 12901

MOORE, RICHARD DONALD, b Spokane, Wash, Mar 7, 24; m 46; c 4. PATHOLOGY. *Educ:* Western Reserve Univ, MD, 47; Am Bd Path, dipl, 55. *Prof Exp:* Resident path, Univ Hosps, Western Reserve Univ, 49-52, from instr to sr instr, Sch Med, 52-55, asst prof, 55-56; asst prof, Sch Med, Univ Rochester, 56-57; assoc prof, Sch Med, Western Reserve Univ, 57-67, prof, 67-69; PROF PATH & CHMN DEPT, MED SCH, UNIV ORE, 69- *Mem:* Am Soc Exp Path; Reticuloendothelial Soc; Am Asn Path & Bact. *Res:* Structure and function of connective tissue and the reticuloendothelial system. *Mailing Add:* Dept of Path Univ of Ore Med Sch Portland OR 97201

MOORE, RICHARD E, b San Francisco, Calif, July 30, 33; m 60; c 4. ORGANIC CHEMISTRY. *Educ:* Univ San Francisco, BS, 57, MS, 59; Univ Calif, Berkeley, PhD(org chem), 62. *Prof Exp:* Res assoc, 63-66, from asst prof to assoc prof org chem, 66-75, PROF CHEM, UNIV HAWAII, HONOLULU, 75- *Mem:* Am Chem Soc. *Res:* Structure determination, chemistry and synthesis of natural products from marine animals and plants. *Mailing Add:* Dept Chem Univ Hawaii Honolulu HI 96822

MOORE, RICHARD K(ERR), b St Louis, Mo, Nov 13, 23; m 44; c 2. MICROWAVE REMOTE SENSING, RADIO WAVE PROPAGATION. *Educ:* Washington Univ, BSEE, 43; Cornell Univ, PhD(elec eng), 51. *Prof Exp:* Test equip engr, Victor Div, Radio Corp Am, 43-44; instr elec eng & res engr, Washington Univ, 47-49; res assoc, Cornell Univ, 49-51; res engr & sect supvr, Sandia Corp, 51-55; assoc prof elec eng, Univ NMex, 55-56, prof, 56-72, chmn dept, 55-62; dir, Remote Sensing Lab, 64-74, BLACK & VEATCH PROF ELEC ENG, UNIV KANS, 62- *Concurrent Pos:* Mem, Int Sci Radio Union; pres, Cadre Corp, 68- *Honors & Awards:* Tech Achievement Award, Coun Oceanic Eng, Inst Elec & Electronics Engrs, 78. *Mem:* Am Soc Eng Educ; Am Soc Photogram; fel Inst Elec & Electronics Engrs. *Res:* Submarine, tropospheric and ionospheric wave propagation; radar scattering; submarine communication; traveling wave analogies; application of radar and radio propagation to earth sciences. *Mailing Add:* Remote Sensing Labs Univ Kans 2291 Irving Hill Rd Lawrence KS 66045

MOORE, RICHARD LEE, b Philadelphia, Pa, June 20, 18; m 42; c 3. PLASMA PHYSICS, THEORETICAL PHYSICS. *Educ:* Univ Calif, Los Angeles, AB, 41, MA, 42; Ohio State Univ, PhD(physics), 53. *Prof Exp:* Meteorologist & res physicist, US Army & US Air Force, 41-51; res asst physics, Los Alamos Sci Lab, 51-53; mem staff, 54, staff asst, Weapon Systs Anal Dept, Northrop Aircraft, Inc, Calif, 54-56; sr assoc, Planning Res Corp, Calif, 56-57; consult physicist, R L Moore Consults, 57-62; head appl & theoret physics, Douglas Aircraft Co, Inc, Calif, 62-66, mgr phys sci & math res, 66-70; phys scientist, US Army Weapons Command, 71-73, phys scientist, US Army Armament Command, 73-78, OPERS RES ANALYST, US ARMY ARMAMENT RES & DEVELOP COMMAND, 78- *Mem:* Am Phys Soc; assoc fel Am Inst Aeronaut & Astronaut. *Res:* Operations analysis; Gauss-Hertz principle in continuum theory; data reduction principles; clear air turbulence; tropical cyclone theory. *Mailing Add:* 358 W Shore Tr Sparta NJ 07871

MOORE, RICHARD NEWTON, b Bernice, La, Mar 4, 26; m 60; c 3. ORGANIC CHEMISTRY. *Educ:* Miss Col, BS, 49. *Prof Exp:* Chemist, Southern Regional Res Lab, USDA, 49-57; res chemist, 57-59, sr res chemist, 59-67, res specialist, 67-68, res group leader, 68-70, sr res specialist, Hydrocarbons & Polymers Div, 70-76, FEL PETROCHEM RES, MONSANTO CO, 76- *Mem:* Am Chem Soc; Sigma Xi. *Res:* Chemistry of hydrocarbons, free radical reactions and process research. *Mailing Add:* Monsanto Co 800 N Lindbergh Blvd St Louis MO 63166

MOORE, RICHARD OWEN, b Zanesville, Ohio, Apr 30, 20; m 49. BIOCHEMISTRY. *Educ:* DePauw Univ, AB, 42; Cornell Univ, PhD(biochem), 51. *Prof Exp:* Res assoc biochem, Sch Med, Ind Univ, 46-48; PROF BIOCHEM, OHIO STATE UNIV, 51-, ASSOC DEAN BIOL SCI, 71- *Concurrent Pos:* Vis prof, Harvard Med Sch, 59-60. *Mem:* AAAS; Am Chem Soc. *Res:* Lipogenesis; mammary gland metabolism; hormone action; isoenzymes. *Mailing Add:* Col of Biol Sci Ohio State Univ Columbus OH 43210

MOORE, RICHARD WAYNE, veterinary microbiology, see previous edition

MOORE, ROBERT ALONZO, b Indianapolis, Ind, June 15, 31; m 58; c 3. MATHEMATICS. *Educ:* Hanover Col, BA, 53; Ind Univ, Bloomington, PhD(math), 60. *Prof Exp:* Asst prof math, Pa State Univ, 61-64; ASSOC PROF MATH, SOUTHERN ILL UNIV, CARBONDALE, 64- *Mem:* Am Math Soc; Math Asn Am. *Res:* Class field theory. *Mailing Add:* Dept of Math Southern Ill Univ Carbondale IL 62901

MOORE, ROBERT AVERY, b Cullman, Ala, Aug 12, 32; m 56; c 3. ELECTRICAL ENGINEERING. *Educ:* Univ Ala, BS, 54; Northwestern Univ, MS, 56, PhD(elec eng), 60. *Prof Exp:* Sr engr, Appl Physics Group, 58-68, MGR SOLID STATE MICROWAVES, WESTINGHOUSE DEFENSE & ELECTRONICS SYSTS CTR, BALTIMORE, 68- *Mem:* Inst Elec & Electronics Engrs. *Res:* Research and development on antennas; solid state microwaves, and ultrasonic technology. *Mailing Add:* 1243 Balfour Dr Arnold MD 21012

MOORE, ROBERT B, b Windsor, Nfld, June 28, 35; m 58. NUCLEAR PHYSICS. *Educ:* McGill Univ, BEngPhys, 57, MSc, 59, PhD(physics), 61. *Prof Exp:* Lectr, 61-63, from asst prof to assoc prof, 63-77, PROF PHYSICS, McGILL UNIV, 77- *Mem:* Am Phys Soc; Can Asn Physicists; Eng Inst Can. *Res:* Nuclear reactions; nuclear spectroscopy; fission and short-lived isomeric states; heavy ion accelerators; proton and heavy ion irradiations. *Mailing Add:* Dept Physics McGill Univ Montreal PQ H3A 2T6 Can

MOORE, ROBERT BYRON, b Bangkok, Siam, Nov 11, 29; US citizen; m 55; c 2. CHEMICAL ENGINEERING. *Educ:* Univ Mich, BS, 52. *Prof Exp:* Process engr, Phillips Petrol Co, 52-59; eng supvr, 59-61, opers supt, 61-63, proj engr, 63-67, proj mgr, 67-71, ECON EVALUATOR, AIR PROD & CHEM, INC, 71- *Res:* Optimization of cryogenic separation processes; development of gas separation techniques; production and utilazation of hydrogen 2 and cobalt synthesis gases. *Mailing Add:* 2951 Edgemont Ct Allentown PA 18103

MOORE, ROBERT CONLEY, b Rock Hill, SC, Nov 24, 41; m 73; c 2. PHARMACY ADMINISTRATION, PUBLIC HEALTH ADMINISTRATION. *Educ:* Univ SC, AB, 66; Univ Ga, BS, 70; Univ Tenn, Memphis, PharmD, 71. *Prof Exp:* Asst prof pharm, Col Pharm, Univ Fla, 71-72; asst prof pharm admin, Inst Community & Area Develop, Sch Pharm, Univ Ga, 72-77; SR CLIN RES ASSOC, ABBOTT LABS, 77- *Concurrent Pos:* Consult pharm, Ga Dept Human Resources & Ga Medicaid Prog, 75- *Mem:* AAAS; Sigma Xi. *Res:* Applied research for development and implementation of demonstration projects directed toward community health, especially rural health delivery; thromboembolic disease therapy. *Mailing Add:* D420-APGC Abbott Labs N Chicago IL 60064

MOORE, ROBERT E(DWARD), b Winsted, Conn, July 29, 23; m 46; c 3. MECHANICAL ENGINEERING. *Educ:* Univ Wis, BSME, 48. *Prof Exp:* Mech engr, Wis Axle Div, Rockwell Standard Corp, 48-51, chief inspector, Ohio Axle & Gear Div, 51-53; mech engr, John I Thompson & Co, 53-57, vpres, 57-65; PRES, POTOMAC RES, INC, 65- *Mem:* Am Soc Mech Engrs. *Res:* Engineering and research management in the field of military hardware development; system planning of technical, scientific or socio-economic efforts. *Mailing Add:* 3610 Bent Branch Court Falls Church VA 22041

MOORE, ROBERT EARL, b South Bend, Ind, Dec 26, 23; m 47, 56; c 3. ATMOSPHERIC CHEMISTRY & PHYSICS, ENVIRONMENTAL SCIENCES. *Educ:* Purdue Univ, BS, 45; Univ Chicago, SM, 48, PhD(chem), 50. *Prof Exp:* Chemist, Navy Inorg Chem Res Proj, Chicago, 47-50; chemist, Oak Ridge Nat Lab, 50-80; MEM STAFF, LOCKHEED MISSILES & SPACE CO, OAK RIDGE, TENN, 80- *Mem:* AAAS; Am Chem Soc. *Res:* Physical chemistry; chemical processes; computer-implemented modeling of atmospheric dispersion and deposition of air pollutants and radionuclides; environmental radiation dose calculations; radiation damage; solvent extraction processes; high-temperature phase equilibria. *Mailing Add:* 107 E Irving Lane Oak Ridge TN 37830

MOORE, ROBERT EMMETT, b Wichita Falls, Tex, Nov 17, 31; m 53; c 3. VERTEBRATE ECOLOGY. *Educ:* N Tex State Univ, BA, 52; Ore State Univ, MS, 59; Univ Tex, PhD(mammalian speciation), 62. *Prof Exp:* From asst prof to assoc prof, 62-72, PROF ZOOL, MONT STATE UNIV, 72- *Mem:* Am Soc Naturalists; Ecol Soc Am; Am Soc Mammal; Sigma Xi. *Res:* Isolating mechanisms in the speciation of small mammals; population biology of small mammals. *Mailing Add:* Dept of Biol Mont State Univ Bozeman MT 59715

MOORE, ROBERT H, b Baltimore, Md, Dec 19, 30; m 58; c 4. MATHEMATICS. *Educ:* Univ Md, BS, 53, MA, 55; Univ Mich, PhD(math), 59. *Prof Exp:* NSF fel, Munich Tech Univ, 59-60; res mathematician, Math Res Ctr, US Army, Univ Wis, 60-63; asst prof, 63-68, ASSOC PROF MATH, UNIV WIS-MILWAUKEE, 68- *Mem:* Am Math Soc; Math Asn Am. *Res:* Functional analytic study of certain approximation methods in numerical analysis, especially collectively compact operators and Newton's method, generalized inverses of linear operators; numerical solution of hyperbolic partial differential equations. *Mailing Add:* Dept of Math Univ of Wis Milwaukee WI 53201

MOORE, ROBERT HALDANE, b Brownsville, Tenn, Dec 10, 46; m 79; c 3. NEUROPHARMACOLOGY, NEUROPHYSIOLOGY. *Educ:* Univ Tenn, BS, 69, PhD(pharmacol), 73. *Prof Exp:* Res assoc, Lafayette Neuropsychiatric Clin, 73-75; asst prof physiol, 75-81, ASST PROF PHARMACOL, KIRKSVILLE COL OSTEOP MED, 81- *Concurrent Pos:* Adj asst prof pharmacol, Kirksville Col Osteop Med, 77- *Mem:* Sigma Xi; Soc Neurosci; Nat Soc Med Res; Am Asn Lab Animal Sci. *Res:* Central nervous system regulation of the cardiovascular system; limbic modulation of behavioral and cardiovascular parameters; central action of hallucinogens; cardiovascular effects of enclogenous opioids. *Mailing Add:* Dept Pharmacol Kirksville Col Osteop Med Kirksville MO 63501

MOORE, ROBERT J(AMES), b Aberdeen, Wash, May 31, 17; m 41; c 2. PHYSICAL CHEMISTRY. *Educ:* Univ Wash, BS, 37, MS, 40. *Prof Exp:* Asst chief chem, Fibreboard Prod, Inc, 37-38; res chemist, Shell Develop Co Div, 41-55; group leader phys chem, Shell Oil Co Inc, 55-57; spec assignment, Shell Res Ltd Eng, 57-58; asst chief res chemist, Shell Oil Co, 59-60, chief res chemist, 61-63; asst dept mgr, Shell Develop Co, 64; dept mgr, Shell Chem Co, 64-70; SR ENGR, PETRO-CHEM DIV, SHELL CHEM CO, 70- *Mem:* Am Chem Soc; Soc Automotive Engrs; NY Acad Sci. *Res:* Engine lubricants and fuels; waxes; resins and polymers applications; liquid viscosity. *Mailing Add:* Shell Chem Co Box 2463 Houston TX 77001

MOORE, ROBERT LEE, b Gainesville, Tex, Dec 28, 20; m 53. PHYSICAL CHEMISTRY. *Educ:* N Tex State Univ, BA, 42; Univ Tex, MA, 44, PhD(phys chem), 47. *Prof Exp:* Instr math, N Tex State Univ, 41-42; instr chem, Univ Tex, 42-45; chemist, Hanford Atomic Prod Oper, Gen Elec Co, 47-56, mgr fission prod chem, 56-65; mgr, Pac Northwest Lab, Battelle Mem Inst, 65-70; MGR APPL CHEM & ANAL, WESTINGHOUSE HANFORD CORP, 70- *Mem:* Am Chem Soc; Am Nuclear Soc; fel Am Inst Chemists. *Res:* Nuclear fuel processing; separations chemistry; waste treatment; analytical chemistry. *Mailing Add:* Rte 1 Box 5238 Richland WA 99352

MOORE, ROBERT STEPHENS, b Dubuque, Iowa, Sept 12, 33; m 56; c 3. POLYMER SCIENCE, POLYMER CHEMISTRY. *Educ:* Univ Wis, BS, 55, PhD(phys chem), 62. *Prof Exp:* Mem tech staff, Bell Tel Labs, Inc, 62-69; res assoc, 69-71, head, Polymer Phys Chem Lab, 71-81, HEAD, CHEMIPHOTOGRAPHIC SYSTS LAB, EASTMAN KODAK CO, 81- *Mem:* Am Chem Soc; fel Am Phys Soc; Soc Rheol; Sigma Xi. *Res:* Viscoelastic properties of polymers; dilute solution properties of polymers; rheological and rheo-optical properties of polymers; spectroscopy of polymers; light scattering from polymeric systems; light sensitive polymers for lithographic and microresist applications; physical chemistry; technical management. *Mailing Add:* Polymer Phys Chem Lab Eastman Kodak Co Rochester NY 14650

MOORE, ROBERT VERNON, b Columbus, Ga, Nov 17, 20; m 44; c 3. RADIOCHEMISTRY. *Educ:* Col Charleston, BS, 42; Columbia Univ, MA, 49; Univ NC, PhD(chem), 53. *Prof Exp:* From instr to assoc prof chem, The Citadel, 46-57; res assoc, Med Col SC, 57-59, asst prof, 59-63; chief chemist, Ecol Field & Training Sta, USPHS, 63-70; RES CHEMIST, ENVIRON RES LAB, ENVIRON PROTECTION AGENCY, 70- *Concurrent Pos:* Mem coun arteriosclerosis, Am Heart Asn. *Mem:* Am Chem Soc; Am Nuclear Soc. *Res:* Elemental concentrations in water and sediments. *Mailing Add:* 3325 N Embry Cresent Chamblee GA 30341

MOORE, ROBERT YATES, b Harvey, Ill, Dec 5, 31; m 69; c 4. NEUROLOGY, PEDIATRIC NEUROLOGY. *Educ:* Lawrence Univ, BA, 53; Univ Chicago, MD, 57, PhD(psychol), 62; Am Bd Psychiat & Neurol, dipl & cert neurol, 66. *Hon Degrees:* MD, Univ Lund, 74. *Prof Exp:* Intern, Univ Mich Hosp, 58-59; instr anat & res neurol, Sch Med, Univ Chicago, 59-64, from asst prof to prof pediat, neurol & anat, 64-74; PROF NEUROSCI, UNIV CALIF, SAN DIEGO, 74- *Concurrent Pos:* Markle scholar, 65-70; consult, NIH, 71-75 & Food & Drug Admin, 72-; assoc, Neurosci Res Prog, 74- *Mem:* Am Acad Neurol; Am Neurol Asn; Child Neurol Soc; Am Soc Clin Invest; Soc Pediat Res. *Res:* Organization and function of monoamine neuron systems in the mammalian brain; central neural regulation of diurnal rhythms. *Mailing Add:* Dept of Neurosci Univ of Calif at San Diego La Jolla CA 92037

MOORE, ROBIN G(ALE), b Chicago, Ill, Sept 24, 38; m 57; c 4. ENGINEERING. *Educ:* Univ Ark, BS, 60, MS, 62, PhD(chem eng), 65. *Prof Exp:* Asst chem eng, Univ Ark, 60-64; engr, Esso Res Labs, Humble Oil Co, 64, SR RES ENGR, EXXON RES & DEVELOP LABS, 64- *Mem:* Am Chem Soc; Am Inst Chem Engrs; Instrument Soc Am. *Res:* Electrokinetics; fuels research. *Mailing Add:* Exxon Res & Develop Labs Box 2226 Baton Rouge LA 70821

MOORE, RONALD LEE, b Ft Wayne, Ind, Mar 30, 42; m 72; c 2. SOLAR PHYSICS, ASTROPHYSICS. *Educ:* Purdue Univ, BS, 64; Stanford Univ, MS, 65, PhD(aeronaut & astronaut sci), 72. *Prof Exp:* Res fel, 72-75, SR RES FEL SOLAR PHYSICS, CALIF INST TECHNOL, 75- *Concurrent Pos:* Consult, Solar XUV Spectral Irradiance Monitor Study, NASA, 76, leader thermal phase team, Skylab Solar Workshop Solar Flares, 76-79, chmn solar physics panel, NASA Space Sci Platform Study, 78- *Mem:* Am Astron Soc; Int Astron Union. *Res:* Physics of solar flares; fine-scale structure and dynamics of quiet solar atmosphere, especially oscillations, spicules, macrospicules, and ephemeral active regions; energy balance of solar corona; solar magnetic cycle. *Mailing Add:* Solar Astron 264-33 Calif Inst Technol Pasadena CA 91125

MOORE, ROSCOE MICHAEL, JR, b Richmond, Va, Dec 2, 44; m 69; c 2. EPIDEMIOLOGY. *Educ:* Tuskegee Inst, BS, 68, DVM, 69; Univ Mich, MPH, 70. *Prof Exp:* Researcher gnotobiotics, NIH, 70-71; epidemiologist, Ctr Dis Control, 71-73 & Food & Drug Admin, 73-74; sr epidemiologist, Nat Inst Occup Safety & Health, 74-81; SR EPIDEMIOLOGIST, BUR RADIOL HEALTH, FOOD & DRUG ADMIN, 81- *Concurrent Pos:* Consult, Dade County, Fla Health Dept & Ala State Health Dept, 72-73; adv, Washington Tech Inst, 74-77; assoc dir epidemiol & biostatist, Cancer Ctr, Col Med, Howard Univ, 80-81. *Mem:* Am Pub Health Asn; Soc Occup & Environ Health; fel Am Col Vet Toxicologist; Soc Epidemiol Res; AAAS. *Res:* Epidemiology of chemical carcinogenesis in man and animals; growth and development among human fetuses during different stages of gestation. *Mailing Add:* Bur Radiol Health Food & Drug Admin 12709 Twinbrook Pkwy Rockville MD 20857

MOORE, RUFUS ADOLPHUS, b Brackettville, Tex, Feb 8, 23. PHYSICS. *Educ:* St Mary's Univ, Tex, BS, 43; Univ Tex, MA, 49, PhD(physics), 58. *Prof Exp:* Asst math & physics, Univ Tex, 48-50, res scientist physics, Defense Res Lab, 51-52, asst math & physics, Univ, 53; mathematician, Sch Aviation Med, 54-56; asst math & physics, Univ Tex, 56-58; mathematician, Personnel Lab, Wright Air Develop Ctr, 58-59; asst prof physics, St Mary's Univ, Tex, 59-62; assoc prof, 62-66, PROF PHYSICS, STATE UNIV NY COL OSWEGO, 66- *Mem:* AAAS; Am Math Soc; Inst Elec & Electronics Engrs; Am Phys Soc; Am Asn Physics Teachers. *Res:* Molecular theory; electronic communications. *Mailing Add:* Dept of Physics State Univ of NY Oswego NY 13126

MOORE, RUSSELL THOMAS, b Las Animas, Colo, Dec 30, 43; m 64; c 2. PLANT ECOLOGY. *Educ:* Univ Idaho, BS, 66; Utah State Univ, PhD(plant ecol), 72. *Prof Exp:* Fel plant ecophysiol, San Diego State Univ, 71-73; proj mgr plant ecol, 73-75, sect mgr Mining & Reclamation, 75-79, PROJ MGR MULTIDISCIPLINARY MINING PROJS, ECOL CONSULTS, INC, 79- *Mem:* Ecol Soc Am; Soc Range Mgt. *Res:* Environmental impact studies associated with large scale development of oil shale, coal, and hard rock minerals throughout the western states. *Mailing Add:* 966 Wagonwheel Dr Ft Collins CO 80526

MOORE, STANFORD, b Chicago, Ill, Sept 4, 13. BIOCHEMISTRY. *Educ:* Vanderbilt Univ, AB, 35; Univ Wis, PhD(org chem), 38. *Hon Degrees:* MD, Free Univ Brussels, 54; Dr, Univ Paris, 64; DSc, Univ Wis, 74. *Prof Exp:* Asst, 39-42, assoc, 42 & 45-49, assoc mem, 49-52, PROF BIOCHEM & MEM, ROCKEFELLER UNIV, 52- *Concurrent Pos:* Chmn, Panel on Proteins, Comt on Growth, Nat Res Coun, 47-49; vis Franqui prof, Free Univ Brussels, 50-51; vis investr, Cambridge Univ, 51; trustee, Vanderbilt Univ, 74- *Honors & Awards:* Co-recipient Nobel Prize in Chem, 72; Linderstrom-Lang Medal, 72; Richards Medal, Am Chem Soc, 72. *Mem:* Nat Acad Sci; AAAS; Am Chem Soc; Am Soc Biol Chem (treas, 57-59, pres, 66); Am Acad Arts & Sci. *Res:* Chromatography; chemistry of carbohydrates, proteins and amino acids. *Mailing Add:* Rockefeller Univ York Ave & 66th St New York NY 10021

MOORE, STEVENSON, III, b Chicopee, Mass, May 13, 28; m 48; c 4. ENTOMOLOGY. *Educ:* Am Int Col, AB, 49; Univ Mass, MS, 51; Cornell Univ, PhD(entom), 53. *Prof Exp:* Asst entom, Cornell Univ, 51-53; from asst prof to assoc prof entom, 53-72, PROF AGR ENTOM & ENTOMOLOGIST, UNIV ILL, URBANA, 72- *Concurrent Pos:* Proj leader exten entom & pesticide coordr, Univ Ill, 73. *Mem:* AAAS; Entom Soc Am. *Res:* Livestock, field crop and household insect control. *Mailing Add:* 169 Natural Resources Bldg Univ of Ill Urbana IL 61801

MOORE, THEODORE CARLTON, JR, b Kinston, NC, Feb 16, 38; m 60; c 2. OCEANOGRAPHY, MARINE GEOLOGY. *Educ:* Univ NC, BS, 60; Univ Calif, San Diego, PhD(oceanog), 68. *Prof Exp:* Res assoc oceanog, Ore State Univ, 68-69, asst prof, 69-75; assoc prof, 75-78, PROF OCEANOG, UNIV RI, 78- *Mem:* AAAS; Am Geophys Union. *Res:* Stratigraphy and sedimentation in the deep-sea; micropaleontological studies of Radiolaria and calcareous nanoplankton. *Mailing Add:* Grad Sch of Oceanog Univ of RI Kingston RI 02881

MOORE, THERAL ORVIS, b Emerson, Ark, Oct 16, 27; m 62; c 2. MATHEMATICS. *Educ:* Univ Ark, BA, 49, MA, 51; Univ Mo, PhD(math), 55. *Prof Exp:* Asst math, Univ Mo, 51-55; asst prof, 55-66, ASSOC PROF MATH, UNIV FLA, 66- *Mem:* Am Math Soc; Math Asn Am. *Res:* Topology; lattice theory; abstract algebra. *Mailing Add:* Dept of Math Univ of Fla Gainesville FL 32611

MOORE, THERON LANGFORD, b Mayo, Va, Nov 24, 34; m 59; c 3. ORGANIC CHEMISTRY. *Educ:* Yale Univ, BS, 56; Univ Calif, Los Angeles, PhD(org chem), 61. *Prof Exp:* Chemist, Procter & Gamble Co, 61-66; assoc prof, 66-68, PROF CHEM, NORFOLK STATE UNIV, 68- *Mem:* AAAS; Am Chem Soc. *Mailing Add:* Dept of Chem Norfolk State Univ Norfolk VA 23504

MOORE, THOMAS ANDREW, b Pensacola, Fla, June 3, 44; m 68; c 2. BIOCHEMISTRY, BIOPHYSICS. *Educ:* Tex Tech Univ, BA, 68, PhD(chem), 75. *Prof Exp:* Res assoc chem, Univ Wash, 73-76; asst prof, 76-81, ASSOC PROF CHEM, ARIZ STATE UNIV, 81- *Mem:* Am Chem Soc; Am Soc Photobiol. *Res:* Biochemistry; photobiology; molecular spectroscopy. *Mailing Add:* Dept Chem Ariz State Univ Tempe AZ 85281

MOORE, THOMAS CARROL, b Sanger, Tex, Sept 22, 36; m 56; c 3. PLANT PHYSIOLOGY. *Educ:* N Tex State Univ, BA, 56; Univ Colo, MA, 58, PhD(bot), 61. *Prof Exp:* Instr biol, Univ Colo, 58-59; asst prof bot, Ariz State Col, 61-63; from asst prof to assoc prof, 63-71, PROF BOT, ORE STATE UNIV, 71-, CHMN DEPT BOT & PLANT PATH, 73- *Concurrent Pos:* Ed-in-chief, J Plant Growth Regulation, 81-85. *Mem:* Am Soc Plant Physiologists; Bot Soc Am; Int Plant Growth Substances Asn; Sigma Xi. *Res:* Hormonal regulation of growth and flowering in angiosperms, including metabolic control mechanisms; modes of action of plant growth-regulating chemicals; physiological ecology of seed plants. *Mailing Add:* Dept of Bot & Plant Path Ore State Univ Corvallis OR 97331

MOORE, THOMAS D, bacteriology, see previous edition

MOORE, THOMAS D, b Cleveland, Okla, Sept 7, 30; m 50; c 5. MEDICINE. *Educ:* Okla State Univ, BS, 51; Univ Okla, MD, 54; Am Bd Pediat, dipl, 60. *Prof Exp:* Intern, Letterman Gen Hosp, 54-55; pediat resident, New York Hosp-Cornell Med Ctr, 55-57; chief pediat serv, Ramey AFB, PR, 57-60 & Hamilton AFB, Calif, 60-61; dir clin res, Ross Labs, Ohio, 62-65, med dir, 65-67, vpres sci affairs, 67-69; assoc prof, 69-75, PROF PEDIAT, UNIV TEX HEALTH SCI CTR DALLAS, 75- *Mem:* AAAS; Am Acad Pediat; AMA. *Mailing Add:* Suite 802 Stemmons Tower North 2710 Stemmons Freeway Dallas TX 75207

MOORE, THOMAS EDWIN, b Amarillo, Tex, Jan 15, 18; m 42; c 4. INORGANIC CHEMISTRY. *Educ:* Univ Tex, BA, 40, MS, 42, PhD(chem), 46. *Prof Exp:* Res assoc, Radio Res Lab, Harvard Univ, 43-45; US Signal Corps fel, Northwestern Univ, 46-47; from asst prof to assoc prof, 47-57, prof, 57-82, EMER PROF CHEM, OKLA STATE UNIV, 82- *Mem:* Am Chem Soc. *Res:* Solvent extraction of inorganic salts; nonaqueous solutions; thermodynamics of electrolyte mixtures. *Mailing Add:* Dept of Chem Okla State Univ Stillwater OK 74074

MOORE, THOMAS EDWIN, b Champaign, Ill, Mar 10, 30; m 51; c 2. ZOOLOGY, ENTOMOLOGY. *Educ:* Univ Ill, BS, 51, MS, 52, PhD, 56. *Prof Exp:* Asst, Ill Natural Hist Surv, 52-56; from instr to assoc prof, 56-67, chmn Comt Trop Studies, 74-79, chmn dept ecol & evolutionary biol, 77-78, 81-82, PROF ZOOL, UNIV MICH, ANN ARBOR, 67-, CUR INSECTS, MUS ZOOL, 59- *Concurrent Pos:* Mem, Orgn Trop Studies, vis prof, 70 & 72; mem, Nat Acad Sci-Nat Res Coun panel on NSF grad fels, 71-73. *Mem:* AAAS; Entom Soc Am; Soc Study Evolution; Royal Entom Soc London; Asn Trop Biol. *Res:* Acoustical behavior of insects; evolution and systematics of cicadas; forensic entomology. *Mailing Add:* Mus of Zool Univ of Mich Ann Arbor MI 48109

MOORE, THOMAS FRANCIS, b Camden, NJ, Oct 1, 22; m 48; c 2. GEOCHEMISTRY. *Educ:* Southern Methodist Univ, BS, 44; Johns Hopkins Univ, MS & PhD(chem), 50. *Prof Exp:* From group leader petrol recovery res to sr res engr, Atlantic Refining Co, 42-67; prin res engr, 67-76, DIR, RES & DEVELOP DEPT, ATLANTIC RICHFIELD CO, DALLAS, 76- *Concurrent Pos:* Res chemist, Tenn Eastman Div, Oak Ridge. *Mem:* AAAS; Soc Petrol Engrs. *Res:* Petroleum reservoir engineering and numerical simulation; uranium purification and extraction; surface chemistry of silica; petroleum production and exploration research; economic feasibility analysis; thermal oil recovery methods; in-situ solution mining of uranium. *Mailing Add:* 100 West Shore Pl Richardson TX 75080

MOORE, THOMAS WARNER, b New Haven, Conn, Mar 22, 28; m 51; c 3. SOLID STATE PHYSICS. *Educ:* Calif Inst Technol, BS, 50; Univ Calif, Berkeley, PhD(physics), 61. *Prof Exp:* Staff mem, Gen Elec Res & Develop Ctr, 61-67; assoc prof physics, 67-75, chmn dept, 76-80, PROF PHYSICS, MT HOLYOKE COL, 75- *Mem:* Am Phys Soc. *Res:* Metal physics; transport phenomena in metals at cryogenic temperatures. *Mailing Add:* Dept Physics Mt Holyoke Col South Hadley MA 01075

MOORE, VAUGHN CLAYTON, b Osawatomie, Kans, May 16, 34; m 56; c 3. RADIOLOGICAL PHYSICS, BIOPHYSICS. *Educ:* Univ Kans, BS, 56, MS, 57; Univ Minn, PhD(biophys), 68; Am Bd Radiol, dipl, 64. *Prof Exp:* Health physicist, Univ Chicago, 57-58, asst dir health physics, 58-59; asst prof radiol, Health Sci Ctr, Univ Minn, 68-70, asst prof therapeut radiol, 70-75; DIR RADIATION PHYSICS, NEUROPSYCHIAT INST, FARGO, 75- *Concurrent Pos:* Attend, Vet Admin Hosp, Minneapolis, 68-75; consult, St Joseph's Hosp, St Paul, 69-75; adj prof physics & bionucleonics, NDak State Univ, 75- *Mem:* Am Asn Physicists in Med. *Res:* Applications of electron linear accelerators and computers to radiation therapy. *Mailing Add:* 3601 Evergreen Rd Fargo ND 58102

MOORE, VERNON LEON, b Albion, Okla, Oct 21, 36; m 70; c 1. IMMUNOLOGY, PATHOLOGY. *Educ:* Okla State Univ, BS, 63; Tripler Army Med Ctr Sch Med, MT, 64; Bowman Gray Sch Med, MS, 70, PhD(microbiol), 72. *Prof Exp:* From instr to asst prof, 72-77, ASSOC PROF MED, MED COL WIS, 77-, ASST PROF PATH, 76- *Concurrent Pos:* Res assoc, Vet Admin Ctr, 72-75, res health scientist, 75-; Nat Heart Lung & Blood Inst fel, 77-80; NC Tuberc & Respiratory Dis Asn, 71-72. *Mem:* Am Asn Immunologists; Reticuloendothelial Soc; Fedn Am Soc Exp Biol; Am Soc Clin Pathologists; Sigma Xi. *Res:* Cellular immunology; immunology of the respiratory tract; immunogenetics of chronic granulomatous inflammation. *Mailing Add:* Vet Admin Hosp Res Serv 5000 W National Ave Milwaukee WI 53193

MOORE, W CALVIN, b Oklahoma City, Okla, Oct 21, 10; m 31; c 3. CHEMICAL ENGINEERING. *Prof Exp:* Develop engr, Oak Ridge Gaseous Diffusion Plant, Union Carbide Corp, 44-45, eng dept head, 45-51, asst chief engr, 51-54, proj engr, Oak Ridge Nat Lab, 54, asst plant supt, Oak Ridge Y-12 Plant, 54-58, proj mgr plastics appln packaging, Union Carbide Corp, NY, 58-59; nuclear reactor develop, Gen Atomic Div, Gen Dynamics Corp, Calif, 59-62; vpres eng & res, York Div, Borg-Warner Corp, 62-76; RETIRED. *Concurrent Pos:* Consult mgt & res, 76- *Mem:* Am Inst Chem Engrs; Am Soc Heating, Refrig & Air-Conditioning Engrs; Am Nuclear Soc; Int Solar Energy Soc. *Res:* Chemical and metallurgical processes and related process equipment; air conditioning, refrigeration and ice making equipment. *Mailing Add:* 360 Tri-Hill Dr York PA 17403

MOORE, WALTER EDWARD CLADEK, b Rahway, NJ, Oct 12, 27; m 49; c 3. MEDICAL MICROBIOLOGY, BACTERIOLOGY. *Educ:* Univ NH, BS, 51; Univ Wis, MS, 52, PhD(dairy husb, bact), 55. *Prof Exp:* Asst, Alumni Res Found, Univ Wis, 51-52; assoc prof, 54-61, PROF BACT, VA POLYTECH INST & STATE UNIV, 61-, DEPT HEAD, ANAEROBE LAB, 71- *Concurrent Pos:* Vchmn judicial comn, Int Comn Bact Nomenclature, 75- *Honors & Awards:* Kimble Methodology Res Award, Conf Pub Health Lab Dirs, 73. *Mem:* AAAS; Am Soc Microbiol; Am Acad Microbiol. *Res:* Intestinal and anaerobic microbiology. *Mailing Add:* Anaerobe Lab Va Polytech Inst & State Univ Blacksburg VA 24061

MOORE, WALTER GUY, b Detroit, Mich, June 21, 13; m 39; c 6. AQUATIC BIOLOGY, ECOLOGY. *Educ:* Wayne State Univ, BA, 34; Univ Minn, MA, 38, PhD(zool), 40. *Prof Exp:* Instr, Wayne State Univ, 34-35; asst, Univ Minn, 35-40; from instr to assoc prof, 40-51, actg chmn depts biol & med technol, 42-44, prof, 51-79, EMER PROF BIOL, LOYOLA UNIV, LA, 79- *Mem:* AAAS; Ecol Soc Am; Am Micros Soc; Am Soc Limnol & Oceanog. *Res:* Limnology; ecology of Anostraca; temporary ponds. *Mailing Add:* Dept of Biol Sci Loyola Univ New Orleans LA 70118

MOORE, WALTER JOHN, b New York, NY, Mar 25, 18; m 43; c 3. PHYSICAL CHEMISTRY. *Educ:* NY Univ, BS, 37; Princeton Univ, PhD(phys chem), 40. *Prof Exp:* Nat Res Coun fel, Calif Inst Technol, 40-41; from instr to assoc prof chem, Cath Univ Am, 41-51; Guggenheim & Fulbright fels, Bristol Univ, 51-52; prof chem, Ind Univ, Bloomington, 52-63, res prof, 63-74; PROF CHEM, UNIV SYDNEY, 74- *Concurrent Pos:* Manhattan proj engr, US Army, 42-46; NSF sr fel, Paris, 58-59; vis prof, Harvard Univ, 60 & Univ Brasil, 62 & 63; chmn comn phys chem, Nat Acad Sci-Nat Res Coun, 64-66; Austalian Am Educ Found prof, Univ Queensland, 66, vis prof, 68- *Honors & Awards:* James F Norris Award, Am Chem Soc, 65. *Mem:* Am Chem Soc; Biophys Soc; Am Soc Biol Chemists; Am Soc Neurochem; Int Soc Neurochem. *Res:* Solid state chemistry; neurochemistry; biophysical chemistry of brain function. *Mailing Add:* Sch of Chem Univ of Sydney Sydney NSW 2006 Australia

MOORE, WALTER L(EON), b Estrella, Calif, Mar 12, 16; m 42; c 4. WATER RESOURCES ENGINEERING, HYDRAULICS. *Educ:* Calif Inst Technol, BS, 37, MS, 38; Univ Iowa, PhD(mech, hydraul), 51. *Prof Exp:* Asst, Soil Conserv Serv Coop Lab, Calif Inst Technol, 39-40; res engr & analyst, Lockheed Aircraft Corp, 40-47; assoc prof, 47-53, chmn dept, 58-65, PROF CIVIL ENG, UNIV TEX, AUSTIN, 53- *Concurrent Pos:* US deleg, Working Group Educ & Training, Int Hydraul Decade, UNESCO, 65-75; coordr water resources, Hydraul Div, Am Soc Civil Engrs, 72-74. *Honors & Awards:* Collingwood Prize, Am Soc Civil Engrs, 44. *Mem:* AAAS; Am Soc Civil Engrs; Am Soc Eng Educ; Am Geophys Union; Am Water Resources Asn. *Res:* Stilling basins; diffusion; fluid mechanics; hydrology; hydraulic structures. *Mailing Add:* Dept Civil Eng Univ Tex Austin TX 78712

MOORE, WALTER LEROY, b Omaha, Nebr, Oct 24, 25; m 46; c 2. GEOLOGY. *Educ:* Utah State Univ, BS, 50; Univ Wis, MS, 54, PhD(geol), 59. *Prof Exp:* Mem staff geol, Gulf Oil Corp, 54-60; assoc prof, 60-66, PROF GEOL, UNIV NDAK, 66- *Concurrent Pos:* In-serv inst dir, NSF, 63-66. *Mem:* Am Asn Petrol Geol; Soc Econ Paleont & Mineral. *Res:* Stratigraphy; paleontology; sedimentary petrology. *Mailing Add:* Dept of Geol Univ of NDak Grand Forks ND 58201

MOORE, WARD WILFRED, b Cowden, Ill, Feb 12, 24; m 49; c 4. PHYSIOLOGY. *Educ:* Univ Ill, AB, 48, MS, 51, PhD(physiol), 52. *Prof Exp:* Asst animal physiol, Univ Ill, 50-52, res assoc, 52-54; asst prof physiol, Okla State Univ, 54-55; from asst prof to assoc prof physiol, 55-66, actg chmn dept anat, 71-73, assoc dean basic med sci, 71-76, PROF PHYSIOL, IND UNIV, INDIANAPOLIS, 66-, ASSOC DEAN & DIR MED SCI PROG, 76- *Concurrent Pos:* Vis prof, Jinnah Postgrad Med Ctr, Karachi, 63-64; mem staff, Rockefeller Found & vis prof & chmn dept physiol, Fac Sci, Mahidol Univ, Thailand, 68-71. *Mem:* AAAS; Am Physiol Soc; Am Asn Anat; Endocrine Soc; Am Soc Nephrology. *Res:* Neuroendocrinology; stress; regulation of antidiuretic hormone secretion. *Mailing Add:* Med Sci Prog Meyers Hall 203 Ind Univ Sch of Med Bloomington IN 47401

MOORE, WARREN KEITH, b Wellington, Kans, Feb 11, 23; m 44; c 5. MATHEMATICS. *Educ:* Southwestern Col, Kans, AB, 47; Univ Kans, MA, 48, PhD(math), 51. *Prof Exp:* Cottrell asst, Univ Kans, 48-49, instr math, 51-52; from asst prof to assoc prof, 52-63, chmn dept, 61-79, PROF MATH, ALBION COL, 63- *Mem:* Am Math Soc; Math Asn Am. *Res:* Mathematical analysis. *Mailing Add:* Dept Math Albion Col Albion MI 49224

MOORE, WAYNE ELDEN, b McLeansboro, Ill, Sept 2, 19; m 44; c 4. PETROLEUM GEOLOGY. *Educ:* Univ Ill, BS, 46; Cornell Univ, MS, 48, PhD(geol), 50. *Prof Exp:* Assoc prof geol, Va Polytech Inst, 50-56; paleontologist, Chevron Oil Co, Stand Oil Co, Calif, 56-70; chmn dept, 72-81, PROF GEOL, CENT MICH UNIV, 71- *Mem:* Am Asn Petrol Geologists; Geol Soc Am; Paleont Soc; Am Asn Stratig Palynologists; AAAS. *Res:* Origin, maturation and migration of Paleozoic petroleum and subsurface brines, especially in Michigan; micropaleontology of the source beds. *Mailing Add:* Dept of Geol Cent Mich Univ Mt Pleasant MI 48859

MOORE, WESLEY SANFORD, b San Bernardino, Calif, Aug 1, 35; m 60; c 2. SURGERY. *Educ:* Univ Southern Calif, BS, 55; Univ Calif, San Francisco, MD, 59. *Prof Exp:* Intern surg, Univ Calif Hosps, San Francisco, 59-60; asst resident surg, Vet Admin Hosp, San Francisco, 60-63, chief resident, 63-64; from clin instr to assoc prof surg, Sch Med, Univ Calif, San Francisco, 66-77; chief vascular surg sect, Vet Admin Hosp, 66-77; PROF SURG & CHIEF VASCULAR SURG SECT, UNIV ARIZ COL MED, 77-; chief vascular surg serv, Vet Admin Hosp, Tucson, 77-80; CHIEF SECT VASCULAR SURG, CTR HEALTH SCI, UNIV CALIF, LOS ANGELES, 80- *Concurrent Pos:* NIH fel cerebrovascular insufficiency, 66-67; mem comt prosthetics & orthotics, Nat Acad Sci. *Mem:* Soc Vascular Surg; Int Cardiovascular Soc; Am Heart Asn; fel Am Col Surg; Soc Univ Surgeons. *Res:* Vascular surgery; circulation research; stroke prevention; amputation surgery and rehabilitation. *Mailing Add:* Ctr Health Sci Univ Calif, Los Angeles Los Angeles CA 90024

MOORE, WILLARD S, b Jackson, Miss, Sept 27, 41. MARINE GEOCHEMISTRY. *Educ:* Millsaps Col, BS, 62; Columbia Univ, MA, 65; State Univ NY Stony Brook, PhD(earth & space sci), 69. *Prof Exp:* Oceanogr, Ocean Floor Anal Div, US Naval Oceanog Off, 69-76; assoc prof, 76-81, PROF GEOL & MARINE SCI & CHMN DEPT GEOL, UNIV SC, 81- *Concurrent Pos:* Vis asst prof, State Univ NY Stony Brook, 70; vis res fel, Tata Inst Fundamental Res, India, 71; vis adj prof, Univ SC, 70 & 71. *Mem:* AAAS; Am Chem Soc; Sigma Xi; Am Geophys Union. *Res:* Radioisotopes in the ocean; manganese nodules; radium in groundwaters; paleo sea levels; ocean mixing. *Mailing Add:* Dept of Geol Univ of SC Columbia SC 29208

MOORE, WILLIAM EARL, b Tuscaloosa, Ala, Nov 10, 41; m 63; c 2. PROTEIN CHEMISTRY. *Educ:* Southern Univ, BS, 63; Purdue Univ, PhD(protein chem), 67. *Prof Exp:* From assoc prof to prof chem, Southern Univ, 67-77; dir, Inst Serv Educ, 75-77; MEM FAC, NORFOLK STATE COL, 77- *Concurrent Pos:* Charles Pfizer res fel med, La State Univ, 68; consult, Oxford Univ Press, 71; NIH res fel biomed, Naperville Tech Ctr, Standard Oil Co, 72; guest lectr, Purdue Univ, 73; prog assoc, Inst Serv Educ, 74-75; consult interdisciplinary sci, Clark Col, 75. *Mem:* AAAS; Sigma Xi; Am Chem Soc; Inst Food Technologists; Nat Sci Teachers Asn. *Res:* Physicochemical studies of protein stability by examining denaturation in various media. *Mailing Add:* Dept of Chem Box 2849 Norfolk VA 23504

MOORE, WILLIAM MARSHALL, b Lincoln, Nebr, Dec 25, 30; m 58, 68; c 4. PHYSICAL CHEMISTRY. *Educ:* Colo Col, BA, 52; Iowa State Univ, PhD(phys chem), 59. *Prof Exp:* Res chemist, Monsanto Chem Co, 52-53; NIH fel, Cambridge Univ, 59-60; from asst prof to assoc prof, 60-69, PROF CHEM, UTAH STATE UNIV, 69- *Mem:* Am Chem Soc; Am Soc Photobiol. *Res:* Mechanisms for photochemical reactions; atmospheric chemistry and photochemistry; emission spectroscopy. *Mailing Add:* Dept of Chem Utah State Univ Logan UT 84321

MOORE, WILLIAM ROBERT, b Minneapolis, Minn, July 18, 28; m 56; c 3. ORGANIC CHEMISTRY. *Educ:* Univ Calif, Los Angeles, BS; Univ Minn, PhD, 54. *Prof Exp:* Res assoc org chem, Mass Inst Technol, 54-55, from instr to assoc prof, 55-72; PROF CHEM & CHMN DEPT, WVA UNIV, 72- *Mem:* AAAS; Am Chem Soc. *Res:* Mechanisms of organic reactions; unsaturated cyclic hydrocarbons; highly-strained compounds; carbenes. *Mailing Add:* Dept of Chem WVa Univ Morgantown WV 26506

MOORE, WILLIAM SAMUEL, b Manhatten, Kans, June 8, 42; m 63; c 2. POPULATION BIOLOGY. *Educ:* Mich State Univ, BS, 66; Univ Conn, PhD(biol), 71. *Prof Exp:* Asst prof, 71-75, ASSOC PROF BIOL, WAYNE STATE UNIV, 75- *Mem:* Soc Study Evolution; Ecol Soc Am; Genetics Soc Am. *Res:* Evolution and adaptive strategies of various genetic systems. *Mailing Add:* Dept of Biol Wayne State Univ Detroit MI 48202

MOORE, WILLIAM T(HOMAS), b Birmingham, Ala, June 12, 03; m 28; c 3. ENGINEERING. *Educ:* US Naval Acad, BS, 24. *Prof Exp:* Mem test dept, Coke Works, Tenn Coal Iron & RR Co, Ala, 24-26; mem res, develop & eng design dept, Babcock & Wilcox Co, NY, 26-37, mem refractories res, Ga, 38-39, supvr, Refractories Develop Lab, 40-41, appln engr, NY, 45-46; mech engr, Power Pile Div, Oak Ridge Nat Lab, 46-48; group supvr, Argonne Nat Lab, 48-51; appln engr, Babcock & Wilcox Co, 51-53, exec asst, Atomic Energy Div, 53-55, mgr, 55-62, chief tech adv, 62-68; CONSULT, 69- *Mem:* Am Soc Mech Engrs; Am Nuclear Soc. *Res:* Design of nuclear reactors, boilers and heat transfer equipment; development of firebrick and refractory products; steam generation; nuclear development and technical editing. *Mailing Add:* 2224 Indian Hill Rd Lynchburg VA 24503

MOORE, WILLIS EUGENE, b Plain City, Ohio, Dec 28, 24; m 45; c 4. PHARMACY. *Educ:* Ohio State Univ, BSc, 49, PhD(pharmaceut chem), 53. *Prof Exp:* Asst prof pharmaceut chem, George Washington Univ, 53-56; res assoc, Sterling Winthrop Res Inst, 56-59, assoc mem, 59-60, mem & sect head, 60-63, asst dir pharm div, 64-68; assoc prof, 68-73, asst dean col pharm, 71-72, actg dean col pharm, 73-74, assoc dean col pharm & allied health prof, 74-76, PROF PHARMACEUT, COL PHARM, WAYNE STATE UNIV, 73-, DIR, CONTINUING EDUC PROGS, 76- *Mem:* Am Pharmaceut Asn. *Res:* Biopharmaceutics; research management; product development. *Mailing Add:* Col of Pharm Wayne State Univ Detroit MI 48202

MOORE-EDE, MARTIN C, b London, Eng, Nov 22, 45; m 79; c 1. CIRCADIAN PHYSIOLOGY, AEROSPACE PHYSIOLOGY. *Educ:* Univ London, BSc, 67; Guy's Hosp Med Sch, MB, BS, 70; Harvard Univ, PhD(physiol), 74. *Prof Exp:* Instr, physiol, Guy's Hosp Med Sch, 70; intern, Toronto East Gen Hosp, 70-71; res fel, Peter Bent Brigham Hosp, 71-74; assoc in surg, 74-75, asst prof, 75-81, ASSOC PROF PHYSIOL, HARVARD MED SCH, 81- *Concurrent Pos:* Consult surg, Peter Bent Brigham Hosp, 74- & comt biosphere effects of extremely low frequency radiation, Nat Res Coun, 77; mem, NASA Sci Working Group, primate res, 80- & Nat Acad Sci Subcomt, space biol & med, 82-; chmn, Int Sci Adv Bd, Work & Sleep Schedules, 81- & Int Comn on Circadian Rhythm & Sleep Physiol, 82-; guest ed, Photochem & Photobiol, 81. *Mem:* Am Physiol Soc; Aerospace Med Soc; Asn Psychophysiol Study of Sleep; Soc Neurosci; Endocrine Soc. *Res:* Anatomy and physiology of the circadian timing system; regulation of sleep-wake, thermoregulatory and fluid and electrolyte rhythms; applications of circadian theory to clinical medicine and occupational schedules. *Mailing Add:* Dept Physiol & Biophysics Harvard Med Sch 25 Shattuck St Boston MA 02115

MOOREFIELD, HERBERT HUGHES, b Baltimore, Md, July 25, 18; m 53; c 1. TOXICOLOGY. *Educ:* Univ Md, BS, 51; Univ Ill, MS, 52, PhD, 53. *Prof Exp:* Res assoc, Univ Ill, 53-54; entomologist, Boyce Thompson Inst, 54-60; dir agr res, Res Sta, Union Carbide Chem Co, 60-64; asst dir res & develop, NC, 64-67, mgr agr prod mkt develop, Calif, 67-72, technol mgr agr prod, 72-77, CORP RES FEL, RES & DEVELOP DEPT, TECH CTR, UNION CARBIDE CORP, 77- *Res:* Pesticides; insect physiology-toxicology. *Mailing Add:* Union Carbide Agr Prod Co PO Box 12014 Alexander Dr Research Park Triangle NC 27709

MOOREHEAD, THOMAS J, b Jersey City, NJ, Nov 1, 47. METABOLISM, ORGANIC CHEMISTRY. *Educ:* St Peter's Col, NJ, BS, 69; Univ Notre Dame, PhD(chem), 75. *Prof Exp:* Res asst bio-org chem, Pa State Univ, University Park, 74-77; RES SCIENTIST BIOCHEM, NORWICH-EATON PHARMACEUT, NORWICH, 77- *Mem:* Am Chem Soc. *Res:* Metabolism of developmental drugs for antibiotic, anti-hypertensive or muscle relaxant use. *Mailing Add:* Norwich-Eaton Pharmaceut PO Box 191 Norwich NY 13815

MOOREHEAD, WELLS RUFUS, b Hickory Flat, Miss, July 20, 31; m 62; c 1. CLINICAL CHEMISTRY, BIOCHEMISTRY. *Educ:* Miss State Univ, BS, 53, MS, 60; Univ Tenn, PhD(biochem), 65. *Prof Exp:* Assoc prof, 70-76, PROF CLIN PATH, MED CTR, IND UNIV, INDIANAPOLIS, 76-, ASSOC DIR CLIN CHEM, 70- *Mem:* AAAS; Am Asn Clin Chemists; NY Acad Sci; Sigma Xi. *Res:* Serum enzyme activity levels in different disease conditions. *Mailing Add:* Dept Path Univ Hosp N-440 Ind Univ Med Ctr Indianapolis IN 46223

MOORES, ELDRIDGE MORTON, b Phoenix, Ariz, Oct 13, 38; m 65; c 2. PETROLOGY, STRUCTURAL GEOLOGY. *Educ:* Calif Inst Technol, BS, 59; Princeton Univ, MA, 61, PhD(geol), 63. *Prof Exp:* Teaching asst geol, Princeton Univ, 62-63, NSF vis res fel, 63-65, res assoc, 65-66; lectr, 66-67, from asst prof to assoc prof, 67-75, chmn dept, 71-72 & 73-76, PROF GEOL, UNIV CALIF, DAVIS, 75- *Mem:* Geol Soc Am; Mineral Soc Am; Am Geophys Union. *Res:* Ophiolites and plate tectonics; plate tectonics of deformed belts; history of plate interactions. *Mailing Add:* Dept of Geol Univ of Calif Davis CA 95616

MOORES, MEAD STEPHEN, b Pittsburgh, Pa, Jan 4, 27; m 48; c 4. ORGANIC CHEMISTRY. *Educ:* Carnegie Inst Technol, BS, 52, MS, 57, PhD(org chem), 59. *Prof Exp:* Res chemist resins & adhesives, Koppers Co, Inc, Pa, 52-55, res chemist organometallics, 58-62; res chemist dyes, NJ, 62-69, sr supvr, 69-71, chief supvr, 71-73, tech mgr, PR, 73-75, chief supvr, 75-77, res assoc spec chem, 77-78, TECH SERV CONSULT, E I DU PONT DE NEMOURS & CO, INC, 78- *Res:* Organic synthesis; dye chemistry. *Mailing Add:* Tech Lab Chambers Works E I du Pont de Nemours & Co Inc Deepwater NJ 08023

MOORES, RUSSELL R, b St Louis, Mo, Feb 25, 35; m 57; c 7. MEDICINE. *Educ:* Ark State Univ, BS, 55; Univ Ark, MD, 58; Am Bd Internal Med, dipl, 65. *Prof Exp:* From intern to resident med, Strong Mem Hosp, Rochester, NY, 58-60; resident, Barnes Hosp, St Louis, Mo, 60-61; NIH fel hemat, 61-63; staff hematologist, US Naval Hosp, Oakland, Calif, 63-65; from asst prof to assoc prof med, 65-71, assoc dean curric, 72-74, ASSOC DEAN SPEC PROGS, MED COL GA, 74-, PROF HUMANITIES & MED, 71- *Mem:* Am Soc Hemat; AMA; fel Am Col Physicians; Am Fedn Clin Res; fel Int Soc Hemat. *Res:* Erythropoiesis. *Mailing Add:* Off Humanities Med Col Ga Augusta GA 30904

MOORHEAD, EDWARD DARRELL, b Massillon, Ohio, May 9, 30; m 54; c 2. ELECTROCHEMISTRY, CHEMICAL INSTRUMENTATION. *Educ:* Ohio State Univ, BSc, 54, PhD(chem), 59. *Prof Exp:* Fel chem, Princeton Univ, 59-60; instr chem, Harvard Univ, 60-63; asst prof chem, Rutgers Univ, 63-69; ASSOC PROF CHEM ENG, UNIV KY, 69- *Concurrent Pos:* Consult author, D Van Nosrand Pub, 59-62; prin investr, Res Corp, 64-65, Alfred P Sloan Found, 65-66, Nat Sci Found, 67-69 & 78-81, IBM, 64-65, NIH, 74-77, Am Cancer Soc, UK, 74 & 77. *Mem:* Sigma Xi; Am Chem Soc. *Res:* Various aspects of electrochemical charge transfer processes and electroanalytical measurements, particularly as these topics are related to electrode hydrodynamics, catalyzed charge transfer, ionic equilibria and computer data acqusition and control. *Mailing Add:* Dept Chem Eng Univ Ky Lexington KY 40506

MOORHEAD, JAMES BENNETT, physics, computer science, see previous edition

MOORHEAD, JOHN WILBUR, b Neodesha, Kans, Aug 7, 42; m 70; c 3. CELLULAR IMMUNOLOGY. *Educ:* Univ Kans, BA, 64; Mich State Univ, MS, 66; State Univ NY, Buffalo, PhD(immunol), 70. *Prof Exp:* Fel immunol, 70-73, instr, 73-75, asst prof, 75-80, ASSOC PROF IMMUNOL, UNIV COLO MED SCH, 80- *Concurrent Pos:* Spec fel, Leukemia Soc Am, 73-75; NIH grant, 76-79; NIH res grant, 76-81. *Mem:* Am Asn Immunol. *Res:* Immunoregulation of the immune response. *Mailing Add:* Dept of Med Univ of Colo Med Sch Denver CO 80262

MOORHEAD, PAUL SIDNEY, b El Dorado, Ark, Apr 18, 24; m 49; c 3. CYTOGENETICS. *Educ:* Univ NC, AB, 48, MA, 50; Univ Tex, PhD(zool), 54. *Prof Exp:* Res assoc cytol, Med Br, Univ Tex, 54-56, Runyan Mem fel, 55; res assoc, Sch Med, Univ Pittsburgh, 56-58; assoc mem, Wistar Inst Anat & Biol, 59-69; ASSOC PROF HUMAN GENETICS, SCH MED, UNIV PA, 69- *Mem:* Genetics Soc Am; Am Soc Human Genetics; Environ Mutagen Soc; Am Asn Cancer Res; Tissue Cult Asn. *Res:* Mammalian chromosomes. *Mailing Add:* Dept of Human Genetics Univ of Pa Sch of Med Philadelphia PA 19104

MOORHEAD, PHILIP DARWIN, b Pratt, Kans, Nov 21, 33; m 56; c 3. VETERINARY PATHOLOGY. *Educ:* Kans State Univ, BS & DVM, 57; Purdue Univ, MS, 64, PhD(vet path), 66. *Prof Exp:* Vet, gen pract, 57-62; instr vet path, Col Vet Med, Purdue Univ, 63-66; ASSOC PROF VET PATH, OHIO AGR RES & DEVELOP CTR, 66- *Concurrent Pos:* Secy, NC-65 Comt Poultry Respiratory Dis, Coop Res Serv, USDA, 69- *Mem:* Am Vet Med Asn; Am Asn Avian Path; Conf Res Workers Animal Dis. *Res:* Sporadic toxocologic environmental infections and non-specific problems in chickens and turkeys. *Mailing Add:* 816 Quinby Ohio Agr Res & Develop Ctr Wooster OH 44691

MOORHEAD, WILLIAM DEAN, b Youngstown, Ohio, Nov 2, 36; m 65; c 1. THEORETICAL PHYSICS. *Educ:* Ohio Wesleyan Univ, BA, 58; Ohio State Univ, PhD(physics), 68. *Prof Exp:* Asst prof physics & astron, Youngstown State Univ, 68-72, assoc prof, 68-78; SR RES PHYSICIST, SHELL DEVELOP CO, 78- *Mem:* Am Phys Soc. *Res:* Theories of angular momentum, magnetism, and the many body problem; statistical physics. *Mailing Add:* Physics & Comput Sci Dept Shell Develop Co Box 481 Houston TX 77001

MOORHOUSE, JOHN A, b Winnipeg, Man, Oct 4, 26; m 80. MEDICINE, ENDOCRINOLOGY. *Educ:* Univ Man, MD, 50, MSc, 55; FRCP(C), FACP. *Prof Exp:* Fel path, Winnipeg Gen Hosp, Man, 50-51, asst resident med, 51-53, chief resident, 53-54; res fel metab, Res & Educ Hosp & Presby Hosp, Univ Ill, 54-56; res fel & clin asst endocrinol & metab, Univ Mich Hosp, 56-58; res assoc, Clin Invest Unit, Winnipeg Gen Hosp, 58-61; from asst prof to assoc prof, 60-72, PROF PHYSIOL, UNIV MAN, 72-, ASSOC PROF MED, 70-; ASST PHYSICIAN, HEALTH SCI CTR, 63- *Concurrent Pos:* Dir endocrine & metab lab, Health Sci Ctr, 61-77. *Mem:* Fel Am Col Physicians; Endocrine Soc; Am Diabetes Asn; Can Soc Clin Invest. *Res:* Carbohydrate and fat metabolism, particularly as related to diabetes mellitus. *Mailing Add:* Health Sci Ctr NA511-700 McDermot Ave Winnipeg MB R3E 0T2 Can

MOORING, FRANCIS PAUL, b Stokes, NC, Feb 6, 21; m 48; c 3. NUCLEAR PHYSICS. *Educ:* Duke Univ, BA, 44; Univ Wis, PhD(physics), 51. *Prof Exp:* Instr physics, Duke Univ, 44-46; assoc physicist, 51-75, PHYSICIST, ARGONNE NAT LAB, 75- *Concurrent Pos:* Fulbright res fel, Univ Helsinki, Finland, 62-63; adj prof, St Louis Univ, 66- *Mem:* Am Phys Soc; AAAS. *Res:* Particle accelerators; nuclear physics-nuclear cross sections from 0.1-3.0 MeV. *Mailing Add:* 295 Abbotsford Ct Glen Ellyn IL 60137

MOORING, JOHN STUART, b Long Beach, Calif, July 14, 26; m 55; c 4. BOTANY. *Educ:* Univ Calif, Santa Barbara, AB, 50; Univ Calif, Los Angeles, PhD, 56. *Prof Exp:* Instr biol, Occidental Col, 55; from instr to asst prof bot, Wash State Univ, 55-61; vis asst prof, Univ Calif, Riverside, 61-62, lectr, 62-63; from asst prof to assoc prof, 63-69, PROF BOT, UNIV SANTA CLARA, 69- *Concurrent Pos:* NSF res grants, 60-63, 65-66 & 66-69. *Mem:* Bot Soc Am; Soc Study Evolution. *Res:* Biosystematics. *Mailing Add:* Dept of Biol Univ of Santa Clara Santa Clara CA 95053

MOORING, PAUL K, b Houston, Tex, Sept 16, 23; m 62; c 2. PEDIATRIC CARDIOLOGY, PEDIATRICS. *Educ:* NY Univ, BS, 55; Columbia Univ, MD, 57. *Prof Exp:* Intern med, Bellevue Hosp, NY, 57-58; res pediat, Presby Med Ctr-Babies Hosp, 58-60; NIH vis fel pediat cardiol, Presby Med Ctr, NY, 60-62; from asst prof to assoc prof pediat, 62, 71, dir pediat cardiol & cardiovasc labs, 64, 71, PROF PEDIAT & MED, SCH MED, UNIV NEBR, OMAHA, 71- *Mem:* Am Acad Pediat; AMA; fel Am Col Cardiol; Am Heart Asn. *Res:* Radiotelemetry electrocardiology at maximum stress; educational television as a technique for postgraduate physician education; heart disease in the retarded; teenage heart disease. *Mailing Add:* Dept Pediat Univ Nebr Omaha NE 68105

MOOR-JANKOWSKI, JAN K, b Czestochowa, Poland, Feb 5, 24; US citizen. IMMUNOGENETICS, PRIMATOLOGY. *Educ:* Univ Bern, MD, 54. *Prof Exp:* Prin investr, Alpine Isolates Genetic Res Prog, Swiss Nat Fund Sci Res, 53-57; res asst, Inst Human Genetics, Univ Geneva, 55-57; res assoc, Inst Study Human Variation, Columbia Univ, 57-58; NIH spec res fel, Blood Group Res Unit, Lister Inst Prev Med, London & Dept Path, Cambridge Univ, 59-62; vis scientist, Human Genetics Br, NIH, 62-64; chief div exp immunogenetics oncol, Yerkes Primate Ctr, Emory Univ, 64-65; res assoc prof forensic med, 65-69, dir, Lab Exp Med & Surg Primates, 69-76, RES PROF FORENSIC MED, MED SCH, NY UNIV, 69- *Concurrent Pos:* Ed-in-chief, Primates in Med & J Med Primatol. *Mem:* AAAS; Am Soc Human Genetics; Am Soc Immunol; Tissue Cult Asn; Soc Cryobiol. *Res:* Immunological specificity of tissue cells in culture; primate immunogenetics; experimental medicine in nonhuman primates. *Mailing Add:* Dept Forensic Med Sch of Med NY Univ New York NY 10016

MOORMAN, ROBERT BRUCE, b Chadron, Nebr, Oct 21, 16; m 43; c 3. FISHERIES. *Educ:* Iowa State Col, BS, 39, MS, 42, PhD(fisheries mgt), 53. *Prof Exp:* Asst, Iowa State Univ, 39-42, exten wildlife conservationist, 48-53; asst prof zool, Kans State Univ, 53-56; from asst prof to assoc prof, 56-69, PROF ZOOL & ENTOM, IOWA STATE UNIV, 69-, EXTEN WILDLIFE CONSERVATIONIST, 56- *Concurrent Pos:* With Iowa Conserv Comn, 46-48. *Mem:* Am Fisheries Soc; Wildlife Soc. *Res:* Fisheries management in farm ponds; bobwhite quail. *Mailing Add:* Dept of Animal Ecol Iowa State Univ Ames IA 50011

MOORREES, COENRAAD FRANS AUGUST, b Hague, Neth, Oct 23, 16; nat US; m 39; c 2. ORTHODONTICS. *Educ:* State Univ Utrecht, dipl, 39; Univ Pa, DDS, 41. *Hon Degrees:* AM, Harvard Univ, 59; Dr Med, Univ Utrecht, 71. *Prof Exp:* Intern, Eastman Dent Dispensary, 41; sr fel orthod, 47-48, actg chief dept orthod, 48-56, assoc prof, 59-64, PROF ORTHOD, FORSYTH DENT CTR, HARVARD UNIV, 64-, CHIEF DEPT, 56- *Concurrent Pos:* Mem sci exped, Aleutian Islands, 48; res fel ondontol, Peabody Mus, 51-66, res assoc odontol, 66-68, hon assoc, 68- *Mem:* Am Asn Orthod; Am Asn Phys Anthrop; Int Asn Dent Res; Neth Soc Study Orthod; Neth Dent Soc. *Res:* Child growth and development, especially face and dentition; dental anthropology; evolutionary and racial aspects of the dentition. *Mailing Add:* Forsyth Dent Ctr 140 The Fenway Boston MA 02115

MOOS, ANTHONY MANUEL, b Madrid, Spain, June 14, 13; m 39; c 2. PHYSICAL CHEMISTRY. *Educ:* Univ Geneva, Chem Eng, 33; Univ Paris, ScD(phys chem), 37. *Prof Exp:* Chief chemist, Lederle Labs, Am Cyanamid Co, NY, 37-44 & R H Macy & Co, 44-46; dir chem res, Eversharp, Inc, 46-48; vpres, Patterson, Moos & Co, Inc, 48-53, pres, 54; gen mgr, Patterson, Moos Div, Universal Winding Co, 54-59; VPRES, LEESONA CORP, WARWICK, 59- *Mem:* AAAS; Am Chem Soc; NY Acad Sci; Inst Elec & Electronics Engrs; Am Phys Soc. *Res:* Industrial and organic physical chemistry; nucleonics; ordnance engineering; electronic instrumentation. *Mailing Add:* 14 Cindy Lane Portsmouth RI 02871

MOOS, CARL, b New York, NY, Mar 3, 30; m 51; c 3. BIOCHEMISTRY, CELL PHYSIOLOGY. *Educ:* Mass Inst Technol, SB, 50; Columbia Univ, PhD(biophys), 57. *Prof Exp:* Res assoc chem, Northwestern Univ, 55-57; res assoc physiol, Col Med, Univ Ill, 57-58, instr, 58-59; assoc biophys, Sch Med, State Univ NY Buffalo, 59-61, asst prof, 61-66; assoc prof biol sci, 66-69, ASSOC PROF BIOCHEM, STATE UNIV NY STONY BROOK, 69- *Concurrent Pos:* Vis scientist, King's Col, Univ London, 70-71 & 77-78. *Mem:* Fel AAAS; Biophys Soc; Soc Gen Physiologists; Am Soc Biol Chemists. *Res:* Muscle contraction; molecular mechanisms of contraction and relaxation; role of muscle proteins. *Mailing Add:* Dept of Biochem State Univ of NY Stony Brook NY 11794

MOOS, GILBERT ELLSWORTH, b Hasbrouck Heights, NJ, May 1, 15; m 44; c 2. ORGANIC CHEMISTRY, BIOCHEMISTRY. *Educ:* St Lawrence Univ, BS, 36; Mass Inst Technol, SM, 37, PhD(org chem), 39, Am Inst Chem, cert. *Prof Exp:* Instr chem, Rollins Col, 39-40; res assoc vitamins, Mass Inst Technol, 40; res chemist, Am Oak Leather Co, Ohio, 41-42; res chemist, Celanese Corp Am, NJ & Md, 42-49, head spinning res, 49-52; from asst prof to assoc prof chem, St Lawrence Univ, 52-63; PROF CHEM, STATE UNIV NY COL FREDONIA, 63- *Concurrent Pos:* Chmn dept chem, State Univ NY Col Fredonia, 63-68, sabbatical leaves, 69-70 & 78; consult, Howard Smith Paper Mills, Ltd; dir, Allegheny Mountain Sci Fair, 75-77. *Mem:* Fel AAAS; Am Chem Soc; fel Am Inst Chemists; assoc NY Acad Sci. *Res:* Syntheses of proteins and lipoproteins; cancer chemotherapy. *Mailing Add:* 34 Middlesex Rd Fredonia NY 14063

MOOS, HENRY WARREN, b New York, NY, Mar 26, 36; m 57; c 4. PHYSICS. *Educ:* Brown Univ, BA, 57; Univ Mich, MA, 59, PhD(physics), 61. *Prof Exp:* Res assoc physics, Stanford Univ, 61-63, actg asst prof, 63-64; from asst prof to assoc prof, 64-71, PROF PHYSICS, JOHNS HOPKINS UNIV, 71- *Concurrent Pos:* Sloan Found fel, 65-67; vis fel, Joint Inst Lab Astrophys & Lab Atmospheric & Space Physics, Univ Colo, 72-73 & 80-81; mem, NASA & Dept Energy Comts; consult indust. *Mem:* Fel Am Phys Soc; Am Astron Soc. *Res:* Astrophysics; atomic spectroscopy; ultraviolet astronomy; ultraviolet spectroscopy of fusion plasmas. *Mailing Add:* Dept of Physics Johns Hopkins Univ Baltimore MD 21218

MOOSMAN, DARVAN ALBERT, b Toledo, Ohio. ANATOMY, SURGERY. *Educ:* Bowling Green Univ, AB, 34; Univ Mich, MD, 37, MS, 47; Am Bd Surg, dipl, 52. *Prof Exp:* Intern & asst resident surg, Univ Mich Hosp, Ann Arbor, 37-40; resident, St Joseph Mercy Hosp, Pontiac, 40-42; clin instr surg, Hosp, 50-52, PROF CLIN ANAT, MED CTR, UNIV MICH, ANN ARBOR, 52- *Concurrent Pos:* Vis prof clin anat, Med Sch, Univ Hawaii, 70 & Med Ctr, Univ Ala, Birmingham, 73. *Mem:* Am Soc Abdominal Surg. *Res:* Biliary duct system; blood supply liver; thyroid gland. *Mailing Add:* Dept of Anat Univ of Mich Med Ctr Ann Arbor MI 48104

MOOSSY, JOHN, b Shreveport, La, Aug 24, 25; m 51; c 2. NEUROPATHOLOGY, NEUROLOGY. *Educ:* Tulane Univ, MD, 50. *Prof Exp:* USPHS fel neuropath, Columbia Univ, 53-54; lectr, Sch Med, Tulane Univ, 54-60; from asst prof to prof neurol & path, Sch Med, La State Univ, 57-65; PROF PATH, SCH MED, UNIV PITTSBURGH, 65- *Concurrent Pos:* Ed-in-chief, J Neuropath Exp Neurol, 81- *Mem:* Am Asn Neuropath (pres, 74-75); Am Neurol Asn (vpres, 77-78); Am Acad Neurol (secy-treas, 63-65); Coun Biol Ed; Asn Res Nervous & Mental Dis. *Res:* Neuropathology and neurology, especially vascular disease in the nervous system. *Mailing Add:* Dept Path Univ Pittsburgh Sch Med Pittsburgh PA 15261

MOOZ, ELIZABETH DODD, b Middletown, Conn, Nov 22, 39; m 64; c 2. BIOCHEMISTRY. *Educ:* Hollins Col, BA, 61; Tufts Univ, PhD(biochem), 67. *Prof Exp:* Instr res surg, Univ Pa Grad Hosp, 67-68; fel biochem, Univ Del, 68-71, asst prof health sci, 71-73; res assoc chem, Bowdoin Col, 73-76; asst prof biochem, 77-78, res fel, Med Col VA, 78-79; RES SCIENTIST, PHILIP

MORRIS, USA, 79- *Concurrent Pos:* Mem, New Eng Bd Higher Educ, 74-75. *Mem:* AAAS; Sigma Xi; Am Chem Soc. *Res:* Biosynthesis of gluthathione; amino acid transport, enzyme purification, substrate specificity, multifunctional enzymes; biochemical modification of tobacco; tobacco process development. *Mailing Add:* Philip Morris USA Res Ctr PO Box 26583 Richmond VA 23261

MOOZ, WILLIAM ERNST, b Staten Island, NY, Feb 28, 29. RESOURCE ANALYSIS, METALLURGICAL ENGINEERING. *Educ:* Mass Inst Technol, SB, 50. *Prof Exp:* Res engr/develop engr/asst to plant mgr, Titanium Metals Corp Am, 50-60; econ analyst, US Borax & Chem Co, 60-62; exec vpres, G B Smith Chem Works Inc, 62-64; SR STAFF MEM RESOURCE ANALYST, RAND CORP, 64- *Concurrent Pos:* Chmn bd dir, Met-L-Chek Corp, 64-, NDT Europa BV, 66-68; mem, Calif Gov Energy Seminar, 73; Southern Gov Energy Comt, 74. *Mem:* Am Inst Mining, Metall & Petrol Engrs; Am Inst Non-Destructive Testing. *Res:* Capital costs of light water reactor and breeder reactor power plants; sectoral demand for electrical energy; transportation model energy intensiveness; peacetime military aircraft attrition. *Mailing Add:* Box 1714 Santa Monica CA 90406

MOPPER, KENNETH, b Philadelphia, Pa, Jan 4, 47; m 77; c 2. MARINE ORGANIC CHEMISTRY. *Educ:* Queens Col, City Univ New York, BA, 68; Mass Inst Technol, MS, 71, Woods Hole Oceanog Inst, PhD(oceanog), 73. *Prof Exp:* Fel, Dept Eng Chem, Univ Gothenburg, Swed, 73-74; staff researcher, Geol Inst, Univ Hamburg, WGer, 75-77; guest researcher, Dept Anal & Marine Chem, Univ Gothenburg, Swed, 77-80; ASST PROF MARINE CHEM, MARINE STUDIES, UNIV DEL, 80- *Mem:* AAAS; Sigma Xi. *Res:* Cycling of organic compounds in marine environments with emphasis on the formation of humics; trace analysis of carbohydrates; amino and carboxylic acids; phenols, thiols and volatile halocarbons. *Mailing Add:* Col Marine Studies Univ Del 700 Pilottown Rd Lewes DE 19958

MOPPETT, CHARLES EDWARD, b London, Eng, Sept 23, 41; m 65; c 2. ORGANIC CHEMISTRY. *Educ:* Univ London, BSc & ARCS, 63, PhD(org chem) & dipl, Imp Col, 66. *Prof Exp:* Res grant org chem, Res Inst Med & Chem, Cambridge, Mass, 66-67 & Harvard Univ, 67-69; res chemist, Dow Chem USA, 69-73; RES CHEMIST, PFIZER, USA, 73- *Mem:* The Chem Soc; Am Chem Soc. *Res:* Organic chemistry, especially structure determination of natural products and their synthesis; general synthetic chemistry; new synthetic methods; discovery isolation; physico-chemical characterization; chemistry and biology of microbial metabolites. *Mailing Add:* Cent Res Pfizer Inc Groton CT 06340

MOPSIK, FREDERICK ISRAEL, b New York, NY, May 20, 38; m 65; c 1. PHYSICAL CHEMISTRY. *Educ:* Queen's Col, NY, BS, 59; Brown Univ, PhD(chem), 64. *Prof Exp:* PHYS CHEMIST, POLYMERS DIV, NAT BUR STANDARDS, 63- *Mem:* Am Phys Soc. *Res:* Dielectrics research; equations of state; polymer research. *Mailing Add:* Dielectrics Sect Nat Bur of Standards Washington DC 20234

MOQUIN, JOSEPH CHARLES, b Middleboro, Mass, July 7, 24; m 48; c 8. INDUSTRIAL ENGINEERING. *Educ:* Wash Univ, BSIE, 49. *Prof Exp:* Indust engr, Beltex Corp, Mo, 49-50 & Rice-Stix Co, 50-52; prog dir, US Army Ord Mgt Eng Training Prog, Rock Island, Ill, 52-56, chief mgt engr, Army Ord Missile Command, 58-59; exec vpres, Brown Eng Co, Inc, 59-66, PRES, TELEDYNE BROWN ENG, 66- *Concurrent Pos:* Indust engr, United Wood Heel Co, Mo, 50-52. *Mem:* Am Ord Asn; Am Inst Aeronaut & Astronaut. *Mailing Add:* Teledyne Brown Eng Res Park Huntsville AL 35807

MORA, EMILIO CHAVEZ, b Valedon, NMex, Aug 14, 28; m 52; c 4. BACTERIOLOGY. *Educ:* Univ NMex, BS, 51; NMex State Univ, MS, 54; Kans State Univ, PhD(bact), 59. *Prof Exp:* Assoc prof, 58-70, PROF POULTRY SCI, AUBURN UNIV, 70- *Mem:* Am Soc Microbiol. *Res:* Chemistry of virus-host cell relationships; virus vaccines; electron microscopy. *Mailing Add:* Dept of Poultry Sci Auburn Univ Auburn AL 36830

MORABITO, JOSEPH MICHAEL, b Asbury Park, NJ, Feb 26, 41; m 68; c 4. ELECTRONIC SPECTROSCOPY. *Educ:* Univ Notre Dame, BSMet, 63; Univ Pa, PhD(mat sci), 67. *Prof Exp:* Fel low energy electron diffraction, Univ Calif, Berkeley, 68-69; vis scientist thin film res & develop, Phillips Res, Neth, 69-70; mem tech staff, 70-74, SUPVR THIN FILM RES & DEVELOP, BELL LABS, AM TEL & TEL CO, 75- *Concurrent Pos:* Consult, NSF, Dept Energy, Elec Power Res Inst, 74- *Mem:* Am Vacuum Soc. *Res:* Thin film research and development using auger electron spectroscopy and secondary ion mass spectrometry; bonding techniques; interdiffusion studies; solar cells. *Mailing Add:* 1236 Moffit Ave Bethleham PA 18018

MORACK, JOHN LUDWIG, b Schenectady, NY. PHYSICS. *Educ:* Union Col, NY, BS, 61; Ore State Univ, PhD(physics), 67. *Prof Exp:* From asst prof to assoc prof, 67-78, PROF PHYSICS, UNIV ALASKA, 78- *Mem:* Am Phys Soc; Am Asn Physics Teachers. *Res:* Acoustics; geophysics. *Mailing Add:* Dept of Physics Univ of Alaska Fairbanks AK 99701

MORAHAN, PAGE SMITH, b Newport News, Va, Jan 7, 40. VIROLOGY, IMMUNOLOGY. *Educ:* Agnes Scott Col, BA, 61; Hunter Col, MA, 64; Marquette Univ, PhD(microbiol), 69. *Prof Exp:* Res technician, Rockefeller Univ, 61-65; NIH trainee, Med Col Va, 69-70, A D Williams Jr acad fel, 70, from asst prof to prof microbiol, 71-82; PROF & CHMN MICROBIOL, MED COL PA, 82- *Concurrent Pos:* NIH res career development award, 74; mem, Nat Cancer Inst manpower rev comt, 77-81; vis researcher, Harvard Med Sch, 78-79. *Mem:* AAAS; Am Asn Immunologists; Reticuloendothelial Soc; Am Chem Soc; Sigma Xi. *Res:* Host resistance to viruses and tumors; interferon inducers and antitumor drugs; interferon and immunity in age-related resistance to viruses; immunomodulators. *Mailing Add:* Dept Microbiol Med Col Pa Philadelphia PA 19129

MORAIS, REJEAN, b Montreal, Que, Oct 26, 38; m 63; c 2. BIOCHEMISTRY. *Educ:* Univ Montreal, BSc, 60, MSc, 62, PhD(biochem), 65. *Prof Exp:* Res fel med, Harvard Med Sch, 65-67; asst prof, 67-73, assoc prof, 73-79, PROF BIOCHEM, UNIV MONTREAL, 79-; RES ASST CANCER BIOCHEM, INST CANCER MONTREAL, NOTRE-DAME HOSP, 67- *Mem:* Am Asn Cancer Res; AAAS. *Res:* Role of mitochondrial genes on cell phenotype; carcinogenic effect of alpha particles on human bronchial epithelium. *Mailing Add:* Inst of Cancer of Montreal Notre-Dame Hosp Montreal PQ H2L 4M1 Can

MORALES, DANIEL RICHARD, b San Francisco, Calif, Jan 1, 29; m 57. CLINICAL BIOCHEMISTRY. *Educ:* Univ San Francisco, BS, 55; Calif Inst Technol, MS, 56; Univ Calif, PhD(biochem), 62. *Prof Exp:* Fel pharmacol, Yale Univ, 62-65, res assoc, 65-66; asst prof, Sch Med, Univ Kans, 66-68; res clin chemist, 68-72, CHIEF CLIN CHEM LAB SECT, CALIF DEPT HEALTH SERV, 72- *Res:* Forensic alcohol analysis; drug analysis; nutritional surveys; laboratory tests for pesticide toxicity; genetic disease testing; newborn screening tests. *Mailing Add:* 7141 Mound Ave El Cerrito CA 94530

MORALES, GEORGE JOHN, b Havana, Cuba, Nov 24, 45; US citizen; m 68. PLASMA PHYSICS. *Educ:* Fairleigh-Dickinson Univ, BS, 67; Univ Calif, San Diego, MS, 71, PhD(physics), 73. *Prof Exp:* Asst res physicist & adj asst prof physics, 73-78, assoc res physicist & adj assoc prof physics, 78-82, ASSOC PROF PHYSICS, UNIV CALIF, LOS ANGELES, 82- *Mem:* Am Phys Soc. *Res:* Nonlinear phenomena in plasmas theory experiment and computer simulation; heating of fusion plasmas; ionosphere modification. *Mailing Add:* Dept of Physics Univ of Calif Los Angeles CA 90024

MORALES, GUSTAVO ADOLFO, geology, micropaleontology, see previous edition

MORALES, MANUEL FRANK, b San Pedro, Honduras, July 23, 19; US citizen. BIOPHYSICS. *Educ:* Univ Calif, AB, 39, PhD(physiol), 42; Harvard Univ, AM, 41. *Prof Exp:* Teaching fel physiol, Univ Calif, 41-42; instr physics, Western Reserve Univ, 42-43; instr math biophys & asst prof physiol, Univ Chicago, 46-48; head phys biochem div, Naval Med Res Inst, 48-57; prof biochem & chmn dept, Dartmouth Med Sch, 57-60; prof biochem, 60, PROF BIOPHYS, DEPT BIOCHEM & BIOPHYS & CARDIOVASC RES INST, SCH MED, UNIV CALIF, SAN FRANCISCO, 60- *Concurrent Pos:* Mem panel physiol, Comt Undersea Warfare, Nat Res Coun, 49; mem US cultural mission, Honduras, 51 & physiol study sect, USPHS, 52-; mem, Nat Adv Res Resources Coun, 67-, mem sr fel selection comt; mem molecular biol panel, NSF, bd sci coun, Nutrit Inst Am; career investr, Am Heart Asn, 60-; ed, Ann Rev Biophys & Bioeng. *Honors & Awards:* Flemming Award, US Fed Serv. *Mem:* Nat Acad Sci; Am Soc Biol Chem; Soc Gen Physiol; Biophys Soc (pres, 68). *Res:* Biochemical thermodynamics and kinetics; physical chemistry of muscle contraction. *Mailing Add:* HWS-841 Univ of Calif San Francisco CA 94143

MORALES, RAUL, b San Pedro Sula, Honduras, Sept 27, 35; US citizen; m 59; c 4. ANALYTICAL CHEMISTRY. *Educ:* Univ Southwestern La, BS, 61; La State Univ, PhD(anal chem), 66. *Prof Exp:* Asst prof chem, Nicholls State Col, 65-66; res chemist, Indust & Biochem Dept, E I du Pont de Nemours & Co, 66-75; MEM STAFF, LOS ALAMOS NAT LAB, 75- *Mem:* Am Chem Soc. *Res:* Precipitations from homogeneous solution; titrations in non-aqueous solvents; metabolism and analytical chemistry of agricultural chemicals; sampling and trace analytical methods for carcinogenic substances in the occupational environment. *Mailing Add:* 116 La Senda Rd Los Alamos NM 87544

MORAN, DANIEL AUSTIN, b Chicago, Ill, Feb 17, 36; m 68; c 2. TOPOLOGY. *Educ:* St Mary's Univ, Tex, BS, 57; Univ Ill, MS, 58, PhD(math), 62. *Prof Exp:* Res instr math, Univ Chicago, 62-64; from asst prof to assoc prof, 64-76, assoc chmn dept, 69-70, PROF MATH, MICH STATE UNIV, 76- *Concurrent Pos:* Vis scholar, Cambridge Univ, 70-71 & Univ Col NWales, 78. *Mem:* Am Math Soc; Math Asn Am. *Res:* Theory of topological manifolds. *Mailing Add:* Dept of Math Mich State Univ East Lansing MI 48823

MORAN, DAVID TAYLOR, b New York, NY, June 30, 40; m 63; c 2. NEUROBIOLOGY, CELL BIOLOGY. *Educ:* Princeton Univ, AB, 62; Brown Univ, PhD(biol), 69. *Prof Exp:* NIH fel, Harvard Univ, 69-70; NIH fel, 70-71, ASST PROF ANAT, MED SCH, UNIV COLO, DENVER, 71- *Mem:* Am Soc Cell Biol; AAAS; Am Soc Zoologists; Sigma Xi. *Res:* Neurobiology of sensory transduction in mechanoreceptors. *Mailing Add:* 4200 E 9th Ave PO Box 62912 Denver CO 80262

MORAN, DENIS JOSEPH, b New York, NY, Aug 1, 42; m 70; c 1. DEVELOPMENTAL BIOLOGY. *Educ:* City Univ NY, BA, 67; NY Univ, PhD(biol), 72. *Prof Exp:* Asst prof biol, NY Univ, 71-72; res assoc develop biol, Columbia Col Physicians & Surgeons, 72-73; ASSOC PROF BIOL, STATE UNIV NY, 73- *Concurrent Pos:* Consult, Orthopedic Res Labs, Columbia Univ, 73-, vis scientist, 76 & 78; NSF grant, 74-75. *Mem:* Am Soc Cell Biologists; Sigma Xi; Bioelectrochem Soc; AAAS. *Res:* Roles of extracellular materials and of microfilaments and microtubules in morphogenesis. *Mailing Add:* Develop Biol Lab State Univ NY New Paltz NY 12562

MORAN, EDWARD FRANCIS, JR, b Lowell, Mass, July 1, 32; m 58; c 4. INORGANIC CHEMISTRY. *Educ:* Villanova Univ, BS, 54; Univ Pa, PhD(inorg chem), 61. *Prof Exp:* Asst, Yale Univ, 60-62; SR RES CHEMIST INORG RES, EXP STA, E I DU PONT DE NEMOURS & CO, 62- *Mem:* Am Chem Soc. *Res:* Synthesis and structure determination of inorganic polymers; low-temperature spectroscopy; hydrometallurgy of copper concentrates and ores; synthesis of zeolite catalysts. *Mailing Add:* Exp Sta E I du Pont de Nemours & Co Wilmington DE 19898

MORAN, JAMES MICHAEL, JR, b Plainfield, NJ, Jan 3, 43; m 74; c 2. ASTRONOMY, ELECTRICAL ENGINEERING. *Educ:* Univ Notre Dame, BS, 63; Mass Inst Technol, SM, 65, PhD(elec eng), 68. *Prof Exp:* Staff scientist radio physics, Mass Inst Technol, Lincoln Lab, 68-70; STAFF SCIENTIST ASTRON, SMITHSONIAN ASTROPHYS OBSERV, 70- *Concurrent Pos:* Prof pract astron, Harvard Univ, 79. *Honors & Awards:* Rumford Prize, Am Acad Arts & Sci, 71; Newton L Pierce Prize, Am Astron Soc, 78. *Mem:* Am Astron Soc; AAAS; Int Astron Union; Inst Elec & Electronics Engrs. *Res:* Very long baseline interferometry; early stellar evolution and molecular cosmic masers. *Mailing Add:* Smithsonian Astrophys Observ 60 Garden St Cambridge MA 02138

MORAN, JAMES PATRICK, b Cleveland, Ohio, Jan 1, 38; m 61; c 4. FLUID MECHANICS, PHYSICS OF FLUIDS. *Educ:* Mass Inst Technol, BS, 59, MS, 61, PhD(aeronaut, astronaut), 67. *Prof Exp:* Assoc prof aeronaut & astronaut, Mass Inst Technol, 67-72; mem staff, Aerodyne Res Inc, 72-78; MEM STAFF, AVCO EVERETT RES LAB, 78- *Res:* Hypersonic aerodynamics; rarefied gas dynamics; laser physics; laser aerodynamics; thermodynamics. *Mailing Add:* 41 Atlantic Winthrop MA 02152

MORAN, JOHN F, b Waterbury, Conn, Apr 27, 26; m 53; c 4. ELECTRONIC ENGINEERING, NUCLEAR MAGNETIC RESONANCE. *Educ:* Univ Calif, Berkeley, EE, 50; Stanford Univ, MS, 57. *Prof Exp:* Field engr, Int Bus Mach Corp, 50-52; design engr, 52-56, field engr, 56-57, European Serv mgr, Holland, 57-59, proj mgr, 59-61, mgr, Calif, 61-67, chief engr, Nippon Elec Varian Ltd, 68-70, MGR, VARIAN ASSOCS, 70- *Mem:* Sr mem Inst Elec & Electronics Engrs. *Res:* Development of nuclear magnetic resonance instrument systems; electronic design; computer instrumentation. *Mailing Add:* 1062 Los Robles Ave Palo Alto CA 94306

MORAN, JOHN J, b Scranton, Pa, Jan 11, 27; m 52; c 3. MEDICINE. *Educ:* Univ Scranton, BS, 48; Jefferson Med Col, MD, 52. *Prof Exp:* Assoc path, Univ Pa & assoc pathologist, Univ Hosp, 57-61; from asst prof to assoc prof path, Jefferson Med Col, 61-77, asst dir clin labs, Hosp, 61-77; CHMN & DIR DIV LAB MED, GEISINGER MED CTR, 77- *Concurrent Pos:* Consult, Philadelphia Vet Admin Hosp, 57-59. *Mem:* AMA; Col Am Path; Am Soc Clin Path; Int Acad Path. *Res:* Pathology. *Mailing Add:* Div of Lab Med Geisinger Med Ctr Danville PA 17821

MORAN, JOHN P, b Queens Village, NY, Apr 24, 34; m 55; c 4. AERODYNAMICS. *Educ:* Cornell Univ, BME, 59, MAeroE, 60, PhD(aerospace eng), 65. *Prof Exp:* Propulsion engr, Grumman Aircraft Eng Co, 56-58, consult, 58-59; staff scientist, Therm Adv Res Div, Inc, 60-65; asst prof theoret mech, Cornell Univ, 65-68; asst prof aerospace eng & mech, 68-69, ASSOC PROF AEROSPACE ENG & MECH, UNIV MINN, MINNEAPOLIS, 69- *Concurrent Pos:* Consult, United Technol Res Ctr, 78-80. *Mem:* Am Inst Aeronaut & Astronaut. *Res:* Numerical methods in fluid mechanics. *Mailing Add:* Dept of Aerospace Eng & Mech 126 Aerospace Bldg Univ of Minn Minneapolis MN 55455

MORAN, JOSEPH MICHAEL, b Boston, Mass, Feb 14, 44; div. CLIMATOLOGY, PALEOCLIMATOLOGY. *Educ:* Boston Col, BS, 65, MS, 67; Univ Wis-Madison, PhD(meteorol), 72. *Prof Exp:* From instr to assoc prof earth sci, Univ Wis-Green Bay, 69-75; vis assoc prof climat, Univ Ill, Urbana, 75-76; assoc prof, 76-80, PROF SCI & ENVIRON CHANGE, UNIV WIS-GREEN BAY, 80- *Mem:* Am Meteorol Soc; AAAS; Sigma Xi; Nat Asn Geol Teachers; Nat Sci Teachers Asn. *Res:* Pleistocene climatology; nature of climatic change; environmental science education; coauthor of textbooks on environmental science. *Mailing Add:* Col Environ Sci Univ Wis Green Bay WI 54302

MORAN, JULIETTE MAY, b New York, NY, June 12, 17. ORGANIC CHEMISTRY. *Educ:* Columbia Univ, BS, 39; NY Univ, MS, 48. *Prof Exp:* Asst chem, Columbia Univ, 41; jr engr, Signal Corps Lab, US Army, 42-43; jr chemist, Process Develop Dept, Gen Aniline & Film Corp, 43-44, tech asst, 44-48, tech asst to dir, Cent Res Lab, 49-52 & com develop, 52-55, supvr tech serv, Com Develop Dept, 55-59, sr develop specialist, Develop Dept, 59-60, mgr planning, 61, asst to pres, 62-67, vpres, GAF Corp, 67-71, sr vpres, 71-74, exec vpres, 74-80, VCHMN, GAF CORP, 80- *Mem:* Fel AAAS; Am Chem Soc; Com Develop Asn; fel Am Inst Chem. *Res:* Structure of hemocyanine; synthesis and application of dyestuffs, detergents and acetylene derivatives; technical information systems; commercial development; research administration. *Mailing Add:* GAF Corp 140 W 51st St New York NY 10020

MORAN, NEIL CLYMER, b Phoenix, Ariz, Oct 12, 24; Wid; c 3. PHARMACOLOGY. *Educ:* Stanford Univ, AB, 49, MD, 50. *Prof Exp:* Irving fel physiol, Stanford Univ, 50-51; med officer, USPHS Hop, Savannah, Ga, 51-52; Nat Heart Inst pharmacologist, Emory Univ, 52-54; head sect pharmacodynamics, Nat Heart Inst, Bethesda, Md, 54-56; assoc prof pharmacol, 56-62, prof & chmn dept, 62-80, CHARLES HOWARD CANDLER PROF PHARMACOL, EMORY UNIV, 80- *Concurrent Pos:* USPHS sr res fel, 57-60, res career develop award, 60-62; asst ed, J Pharmacol & Exp Therapeut, 58-60, ed, 61-65; vis scientist, Karolinska Inst, Sweden, 60-61; mem res career award comt, Nat Inst Gen Med Sci, 64-68; mem res comt, Am Heart Asn, 68-73, chmn, 72-73; mem res comt A, Nat Heart & Lung Inst, 75-78. *Honors & Awards:* Citation for Distinguished Serv to Res, Am Heart Asn, 74. *Mem:* AAAS; Am Soc Pharmacol & Exp Therapeut; Soc Exp Biol & Med; Am Heart Asn; Am Asn Univ Prof. *Res:* Cardiovascular and autonomic pharmacology and physiology; allergy. *Mailing Add:* Dept of Pharmacol Emory Univ Atlanta GA 30322

MORAN, PAUL RICHARD, b Buffalo, NY, June 1, 36; m 58; c 4. SOLID STATE PHYSICS. *Educ:* Univ Notre Dame, BS, 58; Cornell Univ, PhD(physics), 63. *Prof Exp:* Staff consult scientist, Kaman Nuclear Co, Colo, 63; NSF fel physics, Univ Ill, Urbana, 63-65; from asst prof to assoc prof, 65-73, PROF PHYSICS, UNIV WIS-MADISON, 73- *Mem:* AAAS; Am Phys Soc. *Res:* Magnetic resonance and optical studies of defect states in insulating solids. *Mailing Add:* Dept of Physics Sterling Hall Univ of Wis Madison WI 53706

MORAN, REID (VENABLE), b Los Angeles, Calif, June 30, 16. PLANT TAXONOMY. *Educ:* Stanford Univ, AB, 39; Cornell Univ, MS, 42; Univ Calif, PhD(bot), 51. *Prof Exp:* Botanist, Santa Barbara Bot Garden, 47-48; instr bot, Bailey Hortorium, Cornell Univ, 51-53; lectr Far East prog, Univ Calif, 53-56; CUR BOT, SAN DIEGO MUS NATURAL HIST, 57- *Concurrent Pos:* Ed, San Diego Mus Natural Hist, 57-62, actg dir, 65-66. *Mem:* Am Fern Soc; Am Soc Plant Taxon; Bot Soc Am; Int Asn Plant Taxon. Res; Taxonomy of Crassulaceae and Cactaceae; vascular flora of Baja California. *Mailing Add:* Natural Hist Mus Box 1390 San Diego CA 92112

MORAN, THOMAS FRANCIS, b Manchester, NH, Dec 11, 36; m 60; c 4. PHYSICAL CHEMISTRY. *Educ:* St Anselm's Col, BA, 58; Univ Notre Dame, PhD(chem), 62. *Prof Exp:* Asst instr chem, Univ Notre Dame, 58-59, res asst, 59-62; AEC fel, Brookhaven Nat Lab, 62-64, assoc scientist, 64-66; asst prof, 66-68, assoc prof, 68-72, PROF CHEM, GA INST TECHNOL, 72- *Concurrent Pos:* Danforth fel, 71- *Mem:* AAAS; Am Chem Soc; Am Phys Soc; Sigma Xi; Am Soc Mass Spectros. *Res:* Collisions of electrons and ions with molecules; mass spectrometry; energy transfer processes; kinetics of chemical reactions. *Mailing Add:* Sch Chem Ga Inst Technol Atlanta GA 30332

MORAN, THOMAS IRVING, b Amsterdam, NY, Nov 8, 30; m 53; c 4. PHYSICS. *Educ:* Union Univ, NY, BS, 53; Yale Univ, PhD, 57. *Prof Exp:* Res physicist, Gen Elec Co, 58-59; res assoc physics, Syracuse Univ, 59, asst prof, 60; res assoc, Brookhaven Nat Lab, 61-63; Fulbright sr scholar, Univ Heidelberg, 63-64; asst prof, 64-74, ASSOC PROF PHYSICS, UNIV CONN, 74- *Mem:* Am Phys Soc. *Res:* Thermal diffusion; atomic beams; atomic physics; optical biophysics. *Mailing Add:* Dept of Physics Univ of Conn Storrs CT 06268

MORAN, THOMAS J, b St Paul, Minn, Aug 19, 38; m 61; c 4. MECHANICS. *Educ:* Univ Notre Dame, BS, 60; Univ Minn, MS, 65, PhD(eng mech), 69. *Prof Exp:* From instr to asst prof mech, Ill Inst Technol, 68-73; MECH ENGR, ARGONNE NAT LAB, 73- *Mem:* Am Soc Mech Engrs; Sigma Xi; AAAS. *Res:* Stability theory in nonlinear dynamics and oscillations; dynamics, stability and vibrations of vehicles; seismic and structural analysis of nuclear reactor cores. *Mailing Add:* Argonne Nat Lab 9700 S Cass Ave Argonne IL 60439

MORAN, THOMAS JAMES, b Rennerdale, Pa, Oct 14, 12; m 41; c 4. PATHOLOGY, MEDICINE. *Educ:* Univ Pittsburgh, BS & MD, 36; Am Bd Path, dipl, 45. *Prof Exp:* Dir labs, City Hosp, Pittsburgh, Pa, 39-42; pathologist, Welborn Hosp, Ind, 46; mem staff, Hosp, Danville, Va, 46-50 & St Margaret Hosp, 50-54; from asst prof to prof path, Univ Pittsburgh, 54-62; DIR LABS, MEM HOSP, DANVILLE, 62- *Mem:* Am Soc Clin Path; Am Asn Pathologists; Int Acad Path; Col Am Path; Path Soc Gt Brit & Ireland. *Res:* Aspiration pneumonia; cortisone effects. *Mailing Add:* Creekside Danville VA 24541

MORAN, THOMAS PATRICK, b Detroit, Mich, Nov 6, 41; m 71; c 2. COMMUNICATION SCIENCE. *Educ:* Univ Detroit, BArch, 65; Carnegie-Mellon Univ, PhD(comput sci), 74. *Prof Exp:* SCIENTIST COMPUT SCI & PSYCHOL, PALO ALTO RES CTR, XEROX CORP, 74- *Mem:* Asn Comput Mach; Am Psychol Asn; Human Factors Soc. *Res:* Psychology of human-computer interaction; User-oriented system design; information processing analysis of human cognitive behavior. *Mailing Add:* Xerox Palo Alto Res Ctr 3333 Coyote Hill Rd Palo Alto CA 94304

MORAN, WALTER HARRISON, JR, b Grand Forks, NDak, Nov 16, 30; m 52; c 2. SURGERY, PHYSIOLOGY. *Educ:* Univ NDak, BA, 52, BS, 53; Harvard Univ, MD, 55; Am Bd Surg, dipl, 63. *Prof Exp:* Intern, Dept Surg, Univ Minn Hosps, 55-56; from instr to assoc prof surg, 60-70, dir surg res labs, 60-73, coordr div & actg dir emergency room, 73-81, PROF PHYSIOL, SURG & BIOPHYS, SCH MED, WVA UNIV, 70-, CHIEF EMERGENCY SERV, 81- *Concurrent Pos:* Med fel, Dept Surg, Univ Minn Hosps, 56-58, med fel specialist, 58-59, Nat Heart Inst fel, 59-60; USPHS fel, Sch Med, WVa Univ, 60-63; Nat Inst Arthritis & Metab Dis res career develop award, 62-67; co-dir metab unit, Univ Hosp, WVa Univ, 61-70. *Mem:* Endocrine Soc; AMA; Soc Univ Surgeons; Am Physiol Soc. *Res:* Biophysics; surgical endocrinology, especially vasopressin physiology; burn surgery. *Mailing Add:* Dept Surg WVa Univ Med Ctr Morgantown WV 26506

MORAN, WILLIAM RODES, b Los Angeles, Calif, July 29, 19. GEOLOGY. *Educ:* Stanford Univ, AB, 42. *Prof Exp:* Geologist, Union Oil Co, Calif, 43-46, Paraguay, 46-50, sr geologist, Nev, 50-51, Cia Petrol de Costa Rica, 51-52, mem spec explor staff, 52-59, actg mgr, Union Oil Develop Corp, Australia, 59-60, for opers, Los Angeles, 60-63, VPRES & MGR, MINERALS EXPLOR CO, UNION OIL CO, CALIF, 63-, VPRES, AUSTRALIA DIV, 68-, VPRES, EXPLOR MOLYCORP, 79- *Concurrent Pos:* Consult, Stanford Univ Archive Recorded Sound, hon cur, 70-; assoc ed, Bull, Am Asn Petrol Geologists, 56-; dir, Quebec Columbium Ltd & Geosat Inc, 80- *Mem:* Fel AAAS; fel Am Geog Soc; Am Inst Mining, Metall & Petrol Engrs; fel Geol Soc Am; fel Geol Soc London. *Res:* Historical sound recording; mining administration; mining and petroleum geology. *Mailing Add:* 1335 Olive Lane La Canada CA 91011

MORAND, JAMES M(CHURON), b Cincinnati, Ohio, Jan 27, 38; m 60; c 2. SANITARY ENGINEERING. *Educ:* Univ Cincinnati, CE, 60, MS, 61; Univ Wis, PhD(sanit eng), 64. *Prof Exp:* From asst prof to assoc prof, 64-75, PROF CIVIL ENG, UNIV CINCINNATI, 75- *Mem:* Am Water Works Asn; Water Pollution Control Fedn; Am Soc Civil Engrs; Sigma Xi; Am Soc Eng Educ. *Res:* Water and waste treatment; biological waste treatment. *Mailing Add:* Dept of Civil Eng Univ of Cincinnati Cincinnati OH 45221

MORAND, PETER, b Montreal, Can, Feb 11, 35; m 57; c 2. ORGANIC CHEMISTRY, BIOCHEMISTRY. *Educ:* Bishop's Univ, Can, BSc, 56; McGill Univ, PhD(org chem), 59. *Prof Exp:* NATO fel, Imp Col, Univ London, 59-61; sr chemist, Ayerst Labs, Can, 61-63; asst prof, 63-67, asst vrector acad, 68-71, assoc prof org chem, 67-81, dean fac sci & eng, 76-81, PROF CHEM, UNIV OTTAWA, 81- *Concurrent Pos:* Nat Res Coun Can grants, 63-; Ont Res Found grant, 64-65; Med Res Coun Can grants, 78-; res grants, Nat Sci Eng Res Coun Can, 77- *Mem:* Am Chem Soc; Royal Soc Chem; fel Chem Inst Can. *Res:* Chemistry of natural products; conformational transmission effects and reaction mechanisms; biosynthesis of estrogens; stereochemistry; regiospecific reactions. *Mailing Add:* Dept of Chem Univ of Ottawa Ottawa ON K1N 6N5 Can

MORARI, MANFRED, b Graz, Austria, May 13, 51. CHEMICAL ENGINEERING. *Educ:* Swiss Fed Inst Technol, dipl, 74; Univ Minn, PhD(chem eng), 77. *Prof Exp:* asst prof, 77-80, ASSOC PROF CHEM ENG, UNIV WIS-MADISON, 80- *Honors & Awards:* D P Eckman Award, Am Automatic Control Coun, 80. *Mem:* Am Inst Chem Engrs; Am Chem Soc. *Res:* Process design; process control. *Mailing Add:* Dept of Chem Eng Univ Wis Madison WI 53706

MORATH, RICHARD JOSEPH, b St Paul, Minn, July 13, 25; m 52; c 2. ORGANIC CHEMISTRY. *Educ:* Univ Minn, BChem, 49; Wash State Univ, MS, 51, PhD(chem), 54. *Prof Exp:* Res assoc, Univ NC, 53-54 & Univ Iowa, 54-55; asst prof org chem, Univ Dayton, 55-57; from asst prof to assoc prof, 57-70, PROF CHEM, COL ST THOMAS, 70- *Mem:* Am Chem Soc; The Chem Soc. *Res:* Organic syntheses; reaction mechanisms. *Mailing Add:* Dept of Chem Col of St Thomas St Paul MN 55105

MORAVCSIK, MICHAEL JULIUS, b Budapest, Hungary, June 25, 28; US citizen; m 56; c 2. HIGH ENERGY PHYSICS, SCIENCE POLICY. *Educ:* Harvard Col, AB, 51; Cornell Univ, PhD(theoret physics), 56. *Prof Exp:* Res assoc theoret physics, Brookhaven Nat Lab, 56-58; physicist & head elem particle & nuclear theory group, Lawrence Radiation Lab, Univ Calif, 58-67; dir inst, 69-72, RES ASSOC, INST THEORET SCI & PROF PHYSICS, UNIV ORE, 67- *Concurrent Pos:* Vis prof, Purdue Univ, 57, Int Atomic Energy Agency, Atomic Energy Ctr, Pakistan AEC, Lahore, 62-63, Osaka Univ, 72, Nat Lab High Energy Physics Japan, 72 & Physics Dept & Sci Policy Res Univ, Sussex Univ, 75-76; vis lectr, Harvard Univ, 66-67 & Univ Chile, 78; mem spec study group role sci & technol in develop in 70's, Nat Acad Sci, Woods Hole, Mass; Scientists & Engrs Econ Develop grant, Nigeria, 74; mem adv comt East Asia, Comt Int Exchange Persons, 71-74; SEED grant, Nigeria, 75; NATO sr fel sci, Sci Policy Res Unit, Brighton, Eng, 74; consult, Los Alamos Meson Physics Facil, NMex; mem, Grants Adv Panel, Fund Overseas Res Grants & Educ & Coun Sci & Technol Develop, 78- *Mem:* Sigma Xi; Am Asn Physics Teachers; fel Am Phys Soc. *Res:* Theoretical elementary particle physics, especially as it is related to experiments; photoproduction processes; nuclear forces; spin structure of particle reactions; assignments of intrinsic quantum numbers; problems of science policy, organization and management in developing countries; nuclear and elementary particle physics. *Mailing Add:* Inst of Theoret Sci Univ of Ore Eugene OR 97403

MORAWA, ARNOLD PETER, b Detroit, Mich, Feb 14, 40; m 65; c 3. PEDODONTICS, ORAL BIOLOGY. *Educ:* Univ Mich, DDS, 64, MS, 66 & 68, PhD(anat), 73. *Prof Exp:* Asst prof, 73-77, ASSOC PROF DENT & HOSP DENT, UNIV MICH, ANN ARBOR, 77- *Concurrent Pos:* Consult, Hawthorne Ctr, State Mich, 66-72, Plymouth State Home, 68-72 & Ctr Study Ment Retardation, Univ Mich, 75-; pedodontist, pvt pract, Ann Arbor, 66- *Mem:* Int Asn Dent Res. *Res:* Biochemical and ultrastructural evaluation of dilute formocresol upon dental pulp; concurrent studies of clinical application of this medicament; biochemical and ultrastructural effects of hypoxia upon protein secreting cells. *Mailing Add:* 3920 Waldenwood Ann Arbor MI 48105

MORAWETZ, CATHLEEN SYNGE, b Toronto, Ont, May 5, 23; nat US; m 45; c 4. APPLIED MATHEMATICS. *Educ:* Univ Toronto, BS, 44; Mass Inst Technol, MS, 46; NY Univ, PhD(math), 51. *Hon Degrees:* Dr, Eastern Mich Univ, 80. *Prof Exp:* Res assoc, 51-57, from asst prof to assoc prof, 57-66, PROF MATH, COURANT INST MATH SCI, NY UNIV, 66- *Concurrent Pos:* Guggenheim fels, 66-67 & 78-79; term trustee, Princeton Univ. *Honors & Awards:* Josiah Willard Gibbs lectr, Am Math Soc, 81. *Mem:* Am Math Soc; Soc Indust & Appl Math. *Res:* Applications of partial differential equations. *Mailing Add:* Courant Inst Math Sci NY Univ 251 Mercer St New York NY 10012

MORAWETZ, HERBERT, b Prague, Czech, Oct 16, 15; nat US; m 45; c 4. PHYSICAL CHEMISTRY. *Educ:* Univ Toronto, BASc, 43, MASc, 44; Polytech Inst Brooklyn, PhD(chem), 50. *Prof Exp:* Res chemist, Bakelite Co, 45-49; fel, NIH, 50-51; from asst prof to assoc prof, 51-58, PROF POLYMER CHEM, POLYTECH INST BROOKLYN, 58-, DIR, POLYMER RES INST, 76- *Concurrent Pos:* NIH fel, 67-68. *Mem:* AAAS; Am Chem Soc. *Res:* Molecular association of polymers; reaction kinetics in polymer solutions; polyelectrolyte chelates; solid state polymerization; enzyme models. *Mailing Add:* Dept of Chem Polytech Inst of Brooklyn Brooklyn NY 11201

MORAWITZ, HANS, b Neustadt, Austria, Feb 6, 35; m 63; c 1. THEORETICAL PHYSICS. *Educ:* Stanford Univ, BS, 56, PhD(physics), 63. *Prof Exp:* Staff physicist, IBM Res Lab, 63-65; Australian Dept Supply fel & sr lectr physics, Monash Univ, Australia, 65-66; Austrian Ministry Educ res assoc, Univ Vienna, 66-67; STAFF PHYSICIST, IBM RES LAB, 67- *Mem:* Am Phys Soc. *Res:* Theoretical atomic, molecular and solid state physics; surface physics; cooperative radiative processes; phase transition in organic solids and magnetic systems; macroscopic quantum states. *Mailing Add:* Dept K31 IBM Res Lab 5600 Cottle Rd San Jose CA 95193

MORBEY, GRAHAM KENNETH, b Birmingham, Eng, Apr 5, 35; m 60; c 2. TEXTILE CHEMISTRY, CHEMICAL ENGINEERING. *Educ:* Univ Birmingham, BSc, 56; Univ Toronto, MASc, 57; Princeton Univ, MA, 58, PhD(chem eng), 61. *Prof Exp:* Res scientist, Dunlop Res Ctr, Can, 60-61, asst tech dir, Dunlop Tyre Co, Eng, 61-63; group leader, Celanese Fibers Mkt Co, 63-64, develop mgr, 64-67, develop dir, 67-69; tech dir, Hoechst Fibers Inc, 69-72; dir appl res, Personal Prod Co, 72-77, dir develop, 77-79; VPRES RES & DEVELOP, TEXON INC, 79- *Mem:* Textile Res Inst; Tech Asn Pulp & Paper Indust; Soc Cosmetic Chemists; Fiber Soc; AAAS. *Res:* Polymer chemistry; statistics; fiber physics and textiles. *Mailing Add:* Texon Inc Canal St South Hadley MA 01075

MORCK, CHARLES W(ILLIAM), JR, b Philadelphia, Pa, Jan 3, 20; m 43; c 3. MECHANICAL ENGINEERING, COMBUSTION ENGINEERING. *Educ:* Temple Univ, JD, 51; Drexel Univ, BS, 56, MS, 63. *Prof Exp:* Assoc engr, 45-48, res engr, 48-54, sr res engr, 54-58, res group mgr, 58-67, RES SECT MGR, SELAS CORP AM, 67- *Mem:* Combustion Inst; Franklin Inst; Am Gas Asn; Am Soc Mech Engrs. *Res:* Industrial gas, oil and dual fuel burners and furnaces; gas-air mixing equipment and protective devices; combustion; heat transfer; fluid flow; glass melting and forming; high temperature applications; refinery heaters; furnace atmosphere controllers; noise suppressors for combustion equipment. *Mailing Add:* Res & Develop Selas Corp of Am Dresher PA 19025

MORCK, ROLAND ANTON, b Crookston, Minn, July 11, 13; m 39; c 4. BIOCHEMISTRY. *Educ:* St Olaf Col, BA, 35; Pa State Univ, MS, 37, PhD(biochem), 39. *Prof Exp:* Nutrit specialist, R B Davis Co, 39-41, chemist, 41-43, chief chemist, 44-55; res chemist, Nat Biscuit Co, 55-58, asst dir res, 58-72, dir res, Nabisco, Inc, 72-75, vpres res, 75-78; RETIRED. *Mem:* AAAS; Am Chem Soc; Am Oil Chem Soc; Am Asn Cereal Chem; Inst Food Technol. *Res:* Food research. *Mailing Add:* 32 Abbington Terr Glen Rock NJ 07452

MORCK, TIMOTHY ANTON, b Glenn Ridge, NJ, May 11, 49; m 72; c 2. NUTRITION. *Educ:* Pa State Univ, BS, 71; Cornell Univ, MS, 75, PhD(nutrit), 78. *Prof Exp:* Res assoc, State Univ NY Upstate Med Ctr, 78; instr med, Univ Kans Med Ctr, 78-81; CHIEF NUTRIT PHYSIOL SECT, VET ADMIN MED CTR, HAMPTON, VA, 81- *Concurrent Pos:* Asst prof biochem & instr med, Eastern Va Med Sch, 81- *Res:* Interaction of dietary components that affect the bioavailability of food ion in humans; assessment of nutritional status and repletion of malnourished elderly hospitalized patients using various protein to calorie ratios. *Mailing Add:* Nutrit Physiol Sect Med Serv 111 Vet Admin Med Ctr Hampton VA 23667

MORCOCK, ROBERT EDWARD, b Washington, DC, Aug 26, 38; m 67; c 2. PHYSIOLOGICAL ECOLOGY, ENVIRONMENTAL TOXICOLOGY. *Educ:* NC Wesleyan Col, BA, 66; Wake Forest Univ, MA, 70, PhD(physiol ecol), 74. *Prof Exp:* Res assoc parasitol, Univ Mass, Amherst, 74-76; asst prof biol, Hood Col, Frederick, Md, 76-80; MEM STAFF, US ENVIRON PROTECTION AGENCY, 80- *Mem:* AAAS; Sigma Xi; Soc Environ Toxicol & Chem; Am Soc Parasitologists. *Res:* Physiology and biochemistry of symbiotic helminths; carbon dioxide fixation by developing cestodes; effects of malnutrition on host-parasite relations; toxic effects of chemicals on biologic systems. *Mailing Add:* 1415 Taney Ave Frederick MD 21701

MORDESON, JOHN N, b Council Bluffs, Iowa, Apr 22, 34; m 60; c 5. MATHEMATICS. *Educ:* Iowa State Univ, BS, 59, MS, 61, PhD(math), 63. *Prof Exp:* PROF MATH, CREIGHTON UNIV, 63- *Mem:* Am Math Soc. *Res:* Field theory and ring theory. *Mailing Add:* Dept of Math Creighton Univ Omaha NE 68178

MORDFIN, LEONARD, b Brooklyn, NY, June 23, 29; m 54; c 3. NONDESTRUCTIVE EVALUATION, MATERIALS ENGINEERING. *Educ:* Cooper Union, BME, 50; Univ Md, MS, 54, PhD, 66. *Prof Exp:* Mech engr, 50-56, aeronaut res engr, 56-67, phys sci adminr, Off Aerospace Res, Va, 67-69; aerospace engr, Eng Mech Sect, US Air Force, 69-77; dep chief, 77-81, ACTG CHIEF, OFF NONDESTRUCTIVE EVAL, NAT BUR STANDARDS, 81- *Concurrent Pos:* Tech consult, Soc Automotive Engrs, 75-77. *Mem:* Am Soc Testing & Mat; Soc Exp Stress Anal; Am Soc Mech Engrs; Am Soc Nondestructive Testing. *Res:* Nondestructive testing; residual stresses; engineering mechanics; mechanical test methods; creep; standards and specifications. *Mailing Add:* Off Nondestructive Eval Nat Bur Standards Washington DC 20234

MORDUCHOW, MORRIS, b Rogachev, Russia, Sept 25, 21; US citizen; m 75. FLUID DYNAMICS, SOLID DYNAMICS. *Educ:* Brooklyn Col, BA, 42; Polytech Inst Brooklyn, BAEE, 44, MAEE, 45, PhD(aeronaut eng), 47. *Prof Exp:* Res assoc aero eng, Polytech Inst Brooklyn, 44-47, instr, 47-50, from asst prof to prof appl mech, 50-76, PROF MECH & AEROSPACE ENG, POLYTECH INST NEW YORK, 76- *Concurrent Pos:* Mem nat tech comt struct, Am Inst Aeronaut & Astronaut, 72-73; adj prof, Brooklyn Col, 70-72; res grants Nat Adv Comt Aeronaut, Off Naval Res, 45-57. *Honors & Awards:* I B Laskowitz Award, NY Acad Sci, 80- *Mem:* Assoc fel Am Inst Aeronaut & Astronaut; Am Math Soc; Math Asn Am; Soc Indust & Appl Math; AAAS. *Res:* Fluid dynamics; solid dynamics; numerical analysis. *Mailing Add:* Polytech Inst New York Brooklyn NY 11201

MORDUCHOWITZ, ABRAHAM, b New York, NY, Aug 17, 33; m 56; c 3. ORGANIC POLYMER CHEMISTRY. *Educ:* Yeshiva Col, BA, 54; Univ Chicago, MS, 58, PhD(org photochem), 62. *Prof Exp:* Chemist, 62-63, sr chemist, 63-68, res chemist, 68-75, SR RES CHEMIST, BEACON RES LAB, TEXACO INC, 75-, CAMPUS TECH RECRUITER, 75-, GROUP LEADER, 80- *Mem:* Am Chem Soc. *Res:* Synthesis and study of solution properties of macromolecules; solar energy conversion; enhanced oil recovery. *Mailing Add:* 3 Crown Rd Monsey NY 10952

MORDUE, DALE LEWIS, b Colchester, Ill, Apr 26, 33; m 60; c 3. PHYSICS, MATHEMATICS. *Educ:* Western Ill Univ, BS, 54; Univ Ill, Urbana, MS, 59; Tex A&M Univ, PhD(physics), 65. *Prof Exp:* Teacher high sch, Ill, 56-58; instr phys sci & chem, Evansville Col, 59-61; asst physics, Tex A&M Univ, 61-63; from asst prof to assoc prof, 65-71, PROF PHYSICS, MANKATO STATE UNIV, 71- *Concurrent Pos:* Dir, Energy Efficiency Sch Bldg Prog, Dept Energy, 78. *Res:* Biophysics using electrophysiological methods to determine spectral sensitivity of insects; conservation and solar energy. *Mailing Add:* Dept Physics Mankato State Univ Mankato MN 56001

MORE, KENNETH RIDDELL, b Vancouver, BC, Jan 9, 10; nat US; m 42; c 2. PHYSICS. *Educ:* Univ BC, BA, 29, MA, 31; Univ Calif, PhD(physics), 34. *Prof Exp:* Asst physics, Univ BC, 29-31; asst, Univ Calif, 31-34, fel, 34-35; Royal Soc Can fel, Mass Inst Technol, 35-36; Sterling fel, Yale Univ, 36-38; instr physics, Ohio State Univ, 38-44, asst prof, 44-45; res physicist, Phillips Petrol Co, Okla, 46-47; prof physics, Univ BC, 47-50; opers analyst, US Dept Air Force, 50-61; sr physicist, Stanford Res Inst, 61-63; opers res scientist, Ctr Naval Anal, 63-64, dir naval objectives anal group, 64-67, naval implications technol & tech group, Naval Res Lab, 67-68; sci & eng adv, US Bur Mines, 68-70, chief off opers res, 70-72, staff asst educ & training, 72-73; staff asst educ & training, Mining Enforecement & Safety Admin, Dept Interior, 73-75, coordr, Res & Planning Off, Nat Mine Health & Safety Acad, 75-80; RETIRED. *Concurrent Pos:* Mem staff, Radiation Lab, Mass Inst Technol, 42-45. *Mem:* AAAS; fel Am Phys Soc; Opers Res Soc Am. *Res:* Atomic and molecular spectroscopy; microwave magnetron design; nuclear physics; operations research. *Mailing Add:* 9901 E Bexhill Dr Kensington MD 20895

MORE, RICHARD MICHAEL, b Kenosha, Wis, July 27, 42; m 60; c 2. THEORETICAL PHYSICS. *Educ:* Univ Calif, Riverside, BA, 63; Univ Calif, San Diego, MS, 64, PhD(physics), 68. *Prof Exp:* Res assoc, Univ Pittsburgh, 68-69, asst prof physics, 69-76, assoc prof physics & astron, 76-77; MEM STAFF, LAWRENCE LIVERMORE LAB, UNIV CALIF, 77- *Mem:* Am Phys Soc. *Res:* Laser-produced plasmas; atomic physics of dense plasmas; laser and particle-beam effects; fast-ion energy deposition and ion implantation; statistical mechanics and large-scale computational physics. *Mailing Add:* Lawrence Livermore Lab PO Box 808 Livermore CA 94550

MORE, ROBERT HALL, b Kitchener, Ont, Dec 16, 12; m 43; c 3. PATHOLOGY. *Educ:* Univ Toronto, MD, 39; McGill Univ, MS, 42; FRCPS(C), 61. *Prof Exp:* Jr intern, Toronto Gen Hosp, 39-40, sr intern surg, 42-43; lectr path, McGill Univ, 43-46, Fraser asst prof comp path, 47-49, Fraser prof, 50-51; prof path & head dept, Queen's Univ, Ont, 51-67; Strathcona prof & chmn dept, Path Inst, McGill Univ, 67-77, prof path, 77-; RETIRED. *Concurrent Pos:* Fel, Univ Toronto, 42-43; prosector, Royal Victoria Hosp, Montreal, 43-46; pathologist, Women's Gen Hosp, 45-46; asst pathologist, NY Hosp, 46-47; res assoc, Med Col, Cornell Univ, 46-47; consult pathologist & pathologist, Kingston Gen Hosp, 51-; consult pathologist, Hotel Dieu Hosp, 51-; attend pathologist, Montreal Gen Hosp, 77- *Mem:* Am Asn Path & Bact; Can Soc Exp Path; Can Asn Path; Path Soc Gt Brit & Ireland. *Res:* Relation of hypersensitivity to cardiovascular renal diseases; arteriosclerosis. *Mailing Add:* RR 1 Martintown ON K0C 1S0 Can

MOREAU, JEAN RAYMOND, b Village des Aulnaies, Que, June 27, 24; m 50; c 4. FOOD SCIENCE. *Educ:* Laval Univ, BA, 44, BSc, 48; Mass Inst Technol, PhD(food sci & eng), 57. *Prof Exp:* Res asst biol, Dept Fisheries, Que, 48-49; supt fisheries plant, 49-51; sr res scientist, Can Packers Ltd, 57-64; prof food sci, Univ Toronto, 64-65; PROF FOOD SCI & BIOCHEM ENG, LAVAL UNIV, 65- *Concurrent Pos:* Sci consult to govt & indust, 67- *Honors & Awards:* United Inventors & Scientists Am Achievement Award, 73; Knight Mark Twain Outstanding Contrib Mod Educ. *Mem:* Sigma Xi; fel Brit Royal Soc Arts; Int Platform Asn; Can Inst Food Sci & Technol; Soc Am Inventors. *Res:* Food science and engineering; hygiene, quality and nutritive value of meat, meat products, vitamins and beverages. *Mailing Add:* Dept of Chem Eng Laval Univ Ste-Foy PQ G1K 7P4 Can

MOREHART, ALLEN L, b Williamsport, Pa, Apr 1, 33; m 57; c 5. PHYTOPATHOLOGY, MEDICAL MYCOLOGY. *Educ:* Lycoming Col, AB, 59; Univ Del, MS, 61, PhD(biol sci), 64. *Prof Exp:* Res asst plant path, Univ Del, 59-61, res assoc, 61-64; fel med mycol & res assoc microbiol, Univ Okla, 64-65; asst prof, WVa Univ, 65-68; assoc prof biol, Lycoming Col, 68-71, chmn dept, 69-71; actg chmn, Dept Plant Sci, 72-76, assoc prof, 71-81, PROF PLANT PATH, UNIV DEL, 81- *Concurrent Pos:* Danforth Assoc, 69. *Mem:* AAAS; Mycol Soc Am; Am Soc Microbiol; Int Soc Human & Animal Mycol; Am Phytopath Soc. *Res:* Mechanism of fungicidal action; fungal physiology; epidemiology of verticillium wilt on yellow-poplar trees, and pine-wood nematode infestations of Japanese black pines in Delaware's coastal zone. *Mailing Add:* Dept of Plant Sci Univ of Del Newark DE 19711

MOREHEAD, FREDERICK FERGUSON, JR, b Roanoke, Va, July 30, 29; m 54; c 5. PHYSICAL CHEMISTRY, EXPERIMENTAL SOLID STATE PHYSICS. *Educ:* Swarthmore Col, BA, 50; Univ Wis, MS, 51, PhD(phys chem), 53. *Prof Exp:* Asst prof chem, Union Col, NY, 53-54; mem staff, Lamp Develop Lab, Gen Elec Co, Ohio, 54-59; MEM STAFF, T J WATSON RES CTR, IBM CORP, 59- *Mem:* Am Phys Soc; Sigma Xi. *Res:* Luminescence and photoconductivity in II-IV compounds; electroluminescence; ion implantation; diffusion modeling. *Mailing Add:* IBM Watson Res Ctr Box 218 Yorktown Heights NY 10598

MOREHOUSE, ALPHA L, b Lafayette, Ind, Sept 27, 23; m 47; c 4. BIOCHEMISTRY. *Educ:* Purdue Univ, BS, 48; Pa State Univ, MS, 50, PhD(biochem), 52. *Prof Exp:* SR BIOCHEMIST, GRAIN PROCESSING CORP, 52-, MGR, SPEC PRODS RES, 80- *Mem:* Am Chem Soc; Am Asn Cereal Chemists. *Res:* Poultry nutrition; recovery of vitamins and antibiotics from fermentation liquors; chemical modification of corn starch; enzymatic hydrolysis of starch; biological value of proteins; extraction and purification of plant proteins. *Mailing Add:* Tech Dept Grain Processing Corp Muscatine IA 52761

MOREHOUSE, CLARENCE KOPPERL, b Boston, Mass, Apr 8, 17; m 42; c 2. ELECTROCHEMISTRY. *Educ:* Tufts Col, BS, 39; McGill Univ, MS, 40; Mass Inst Technol, PhD(chem), 47. *Prof Exp:* Res chemist, Naval Ord Lab, Washington, DC, 42-43 & Nat Bur Standards, 43-45; leader battery res & develop, Olin Industs, Inc, Ill, 47-49, asst dir res, Elec Div, Conn, 49-52, mgr, Res & Develop, 52-53; chemist, Res Labs, Radio Corp Am, 53-58, mgr battery & capacitor develop & eng, Semiconductor & Mat Div, 58-59, component develop, 59-60; vpres eng, Globe Battery Co Div, 60-67, vpres res & eng, 67-70, vpres & gen mgr, 70-77, VPRES TECHNOL, INT DIV, GLOBE-UNION INC, 77- *Honors & Awards:* Achievement Award, Labs, Radio Corp Am, 57. *Mem:* Am Chem Soc; Electrochem Soc. *Res:* Inorganic and physical chemistry, specifically batteries and capacitors; corrosion and chemistry of less familiar elements. *Mailing Add:* Conquistador Estates 1812 Camino Real Ave Stuart FL 33494

MOREHOUSE, LAURENCE ENGLEMOHR, b Danbury, Conn, July 13, 13; m 73; c 2. PHYSIOLOGY. *Educ:* Springfield Col, BS, 36, MEd, 37; Univ Iowa, PhD(phys ed), 41. *Prof Exp:* Asst, Univ Iowa, 37-40; head dept health & phys ed, Univ Wichita, 41-42; asst prof ed, Univ Kans, 42; fel, Harvard Univ, 45-46; assoc prof phys educ & assoc aviation med, Univ Southern Calif, 46-54; PROF KINESIOL, UNIV CALIF, LOS ANGELES, 54- *Concurrent Pos:* Mem exped, Nat Acad Sci, NH, 46; researcher, Off Naval Res, 47-49; chief performance physiol sect, Care of Flyer Dept, Randolph Air Force Sch Aviation Med, 49; mem port study comt, Nat Res Coun, 58-; specialist, US State Dept, 60-61, consult to minister sci res, UAR, 63; consult, Henry Dryfuss, 60-63, Douglas Aircraft Co, 63- & Mayor's Space Adv Comt, 65-; Nat Res Coun vis scientist, Manned Spacecraft Ctr, NASA, 68-69; adv, Fitness Systs Inc, 74-82, Los Robles Regional Med Ctr, 79-80. *Mem:* Am Physiol Soc; Ergonomics Res Soc; Human Factors Soc; Aerospace Med Asn; Am Asn Health, Phys Educ & Recreation. *Res:* Physiology of exercise; industrial physiology; sports medicine; aerospace medicine; kinesiology; fatigue. *Mailing Add:* Dept of Kinesiology Univ of Calif Los Angeles CA 90024

MOREHOUSE, LAWRENCE G, b Manchester, Kans, July 21, 25; c 2. VETERINARY PATHOLOGY, VETERINARY MICROBIOLOGY. *Educ:* Kans State Univ, BS & DVM, 52; Purdue Univ, MS, 56, PhD(animal path), 60. *Prof Exp:* Supvr brucellosis labs, USDA, Purdue Univ, 53-60, staff vet, Agr Res Serv, 60-61, discipline leader path & toxicol, Animal Health Div, Nat Animal Dis Lab, Iowa, 61-64; chmn dept, 64-71, PROF VET PATH, UNIV MO-COLUMBIA, 64-, DIR VET MED DIAG LAB, 71- *Concurrent Pos:* Consult, Agr Res Serv, USDA, 64-; mem, Comt Salmonellosis, NCent US Poultry Dis Conf, 62-, studies enteric dis in young swine, NCent State Tech Comt, 64- & Nat Conf Vet Lab Diagnosticians; chmn Accreditation Bd, Am Asn Vet Lab Diagnosticians. *Honors & Awards:* Cert Merit, USDA, 59, 63 & 64; E P Pope Mem Award for Outstanding Contributions to Diag Vet Med, 75. *Mem:* AAAS; Am Vet Med Asn; Am Asn Avian Path; Am Asn Vet Lab Diagnosticians (pres, 78-79); fel Royal Soc Health. *Res:* Virus-host cell relationships in tissue culture systems; respiratory diseases of poultry; brucellosis and tuberculosis in domestic animals; enteric diseases of young swine; rabies in swine; streptococcic lymphadenitis of swine. *Mailing Add:* Vet Med Diagn Lab Sch Vet Med Univ Mo-Columbia Columbia MO 65201

MOREHOUSE, MARGARET GULICK, b Champaign, Ill, Aug 22, 04; m 33. BIOCHEMISTRY. *Educ:* Univ Calif, AB, 27; Univ Southern Calif, PhD(biochem), 39. *Prof Exp:* Asst biochem, 29-33 & 36-40, instr, 40-46, asst prof, 46-54, assoc prof, 54-72, EMER ASSOC PROF BIOCHEM, SCH MED, UNIV SOUTHERN CALIF, 73- *Mem:* Am Soc Biol Chem; Soc Exp Biol & Med; Am Oil Chem Soc. *Res:* x-radiation effects upon absorption of a labeled dioleoylstearin; doubly labeled glyceride absorption and synthesis of intestinal mucosa; absorption of lipids linked to fatty acid composition and placement; dietary fat-level effects; rat heart lipids under normal and stress conditions together with changes in diet and age. *Mailing Add:* Dept Biol Sci Univ Southern Calif Los Angeles CA 90007

MOREHOUSE, NEAL FRANCIS, b Emmett, Idaho, Sept 7, 08; m 36; c 1. POULTRY SCIENCE. *Educ:* Kans State Col, BS, 33; Iowa State Col, MS, 35, PhD(parasitol), 42. *Prof Exp:* Instr zool, Univ Omaha, 36-37; scientist protozool, Salsbury Labs, 37-73, mgr, Poultry Res Farm, 44-60, appl res, 60-70; RES CONSULT, 71- *Mem:* AAAS; Am Soc Parasitol; Soc Protozool; Poultry Sci Asn; World Poultry Sci Asn. *Res:* Helminthology; protozoology; life cycle of Capillaria caudinflata; therapeutics of poultry parasites; growth stimulants, especially arsonic acids. *Mailing Add:* 1600 Stewart St Fayetteville AR 72701

MOREHOUSE, SHEILA MCENNESS, b Auburn, NY. INORGANIC CHEMISTRY. *Educ:* Salve Regina Col, BA, 59; Cornell Univ, MS, 62; Imp Col, Univ London, dipl, 63; Columbia Univ, PhD(inorg chem), 70. *Prof Exp:* Res asst inorg chem, Mass Inst Technol, 63-65; asst prof, 70-76, ASSOC PROF CHEM, MANHATTANVILLE COL, 76- *Mem:* AAAS; Am Chem Soc; NY Acad Sci. *Res:* Coordination chemistry; organometallic compounds. *Mailing Add:* Dept of Chem Manhattanville Col Purchase NY 10577

MOREJOHN, G VICTOR, zoology, genetics, see previous edition

MOREJON, CLARA BAEZ, b Matanzas, Cuba, Nov 30, 40; US citizen; m 65; c 2. CHEMISTRY. *Educ:* Univ Miami, BS, 64, MS, 67. *Prof Exp:* Scientist II spec chem, 66-70, supvr spec chem & chem res & develop, 70-72, SR RES SCIENTIST IMMUNOCHEM RES & DEVELOP, DADE DIV, AM HOSP SUPPLY CORP, 72-, RADIATION SAFETY OFFICER, 70- *Mem:* Am Chem Soc. *Res:* Radioimmunoassay and competitive protein binding procedures for compounds of clinical significance. *Mailing Add:* Dade Div Am Hosp Supply Corp 1851 Delaware Pkwy Miami FL 33152

MORELAND, ALVIN FRANKLIN, b Morven, Ga, Sept 5, 31; m 55; c 3. VETERINARY MEDICINE, COMPARATIVE MEDICINE. *Educ:* Ga Teachers Col, BS, 51; Univ Ga, MS, 52, DVM, 60; Am Col Lab Animal Med, Dipl. *Prof Exp:* NIH fel lab animal med, Bowman Gray Sch Med, 60-62; asst prof exp path, Univ Va, 62-63; from asst prof to assoc prof, 63-72, PROF COMP MED, COL MED, UNIV FLA, 72-, HEAD DIV, 63-, HEAD DIV LAB ANIMAL & WILDLIFE MED, COL VET MED, 76- *Concurrent Pos:* Vchmn, Coun Accreditation, Am Asn Accreditation of Lab Animal Care, 68-72, chmn, 72-74; consult field lab animal med. *Mem:* AAAS; Am Vet Med Asn; Am Asn Lab Animal Sci; NY Acad Sci. *Res:* Atherosclerosis; subhuman primate medicine. *Mailing Add:* Box J-6 JHMHC Univ of Fla Col of Med Gainesville FL 32601

MORELAND, CHARLES GLEN, b St Petersburg, Fla, Nov 24, 36; m 60; c 3. PHYSICAL CHEMISTRY. *Educ:* Univ Fla, BS, 60, MS, 62, PhD(phys chem), 64. *Prof Exp:* From asst prof to assoc prof, 64-76, PROF CHEM, NC STATE UNIV, 76- *Honors & Awards:* Sigma Xi Res Award. *Mem:* Am Chem Soc. *Res:* Nuclear magnetic resonance; thermodynamics and kinetics of redistribution reactions of organo-arsenic (V) and antimony (V) derivatives. *Mailing Add:* Dept of Chem NC State Univ Raleigh NC 27607

MORELAND, DONALD EDWIN, b Enfield, Conn, Oct 12, 19; m 54; c 3. PLANT PHYSIOLOGY, WEED SCIENCE. *Educ:* NC State Univ, BS, 49, MS, 50, PhD(plant physiol), 53. *Prof Exp:* Asst, 50, res asst prof field crops, 53-61, assoc prof crop sci, 61-65, PROF CROP SCI, BOT & FORESTRY, NC STATE UNIV, 65-; PLANT PHYSIOLOGIST, SOUTHERN REGION, AGR RES SERV, USDA, 53-, RES LEADER, 73- *Concurrent Pos:* Asst, State Univ NY Col Forestry, Syracuse, 52-53; mem toxicol study sect, NIH, 63-67. *Mem:* Fel AAAS; Am Soc Plant Physiol; Bot Soc Am; fel Weed Sci Soc Am. *Res:* Mechanism of action of herbicides and growth regulators; photosynthesis; respiration; enzymology; translocation. *Mailing Add:* Dept of Crop Sci NC State Univ Raleigh NC 27650

MORELAND, FERRIN BATES, b Portland, Ore, Aug 12, 09; m 37; c 2. FORENSIC TOXICOLOGY, CLINICAL CHEMISTRY. *Educ:* Ore State Univ, BS, 30; Rice Univ, MA, 32; Vanderbilt Univ, PhD(biochem), 36; Am Bd Clin Chem, Dipl, 51; Am Bd Toxicol Chem, Dipl, 72; Am Bd Forensic Toxicol, Dipl, 76. *Prof Exp:* Asst biochem, Vanderbilt Univ, 32-36; instr, Tulane Univ, 36; chemist-bacteriologist, Tenn Dept Pub Health, 36; instr biochem, Univ Iowa, 36-42; chief chemist, Kans Dept Pub Health Labs, 45-47; assoc prof biochem, Col Med, Baylor Univ, 47-65; biochemist & dir clin lab, Tex Inst Rehab & Res, 59-65; chief, Biomed Support Sect, Crew Systs Labs, Brown & Root-Northrop, Manned Spacecraft Ctr, Tex, 65-67, mgr, Bio-Med Support Labs, 67-68; dir clin chem & qual control, Metab Res Found, 68-70; chief toxicologist, 70-79, CONSULT TOXICOLOGIST, OFF HARRIS COUNTY MED EXAMR, 79- *Concurrent Pos:* Biochemist, Methodist Hosp, Houston, 47-52 & US Vet Admin Hosp, 49-65. *Mem:* Am Chem Soc; Am Asn Clin Chemists (vpres, 57-58, pres, 58-59); Am Acad Forensic Sci; Int Asn Forensic Toxicol; Forensi Sci Soc. *Res:* Biochemical effects of amonia; methods for clinical chemistry and analytical toxicology; gallbladder activity. *Mailing Add:* 3752 Jardin Houston TX 77005

MORELAND, G(EORGE) RICHARD, electrical engineering, see previous edition

MORELAND, PARKER ELBERT, JR, b Ft Worth, Tex, Nov 5, 31; m 55; c 3. APPLIED PHYSICS, ENGINEERING MANAGEMENT. *Educ:* Baylor Univ, BS, 54; Harvard Univ, AM, 55, PhD(physics), 62. *Prof Exp:* Asst physicist, Argonne Nat Lab, 62-70; sr physicist, Packard Instrument Co, Ill, 70-73; VPRES-TECH DIR, SPERRY DIV, AUTOMATION INDUSTS, INC, 73- *Mem:* Am Phys Soc; Acoust Soc Am; Am Soc Nondestructive Testing. *Res:* Mass spectroscopy; atomic masses; ion-molecule reactions; nuclear instrumentation; x-ray fluorescence spectrometry; ultrasonic transducers and instrumentation; materials evaluation. *Mailing Add:* Sperry Prod Div PO Box 3500 Danbury CT 06810

MORELAND, WALTER THOMAS, JR, b New London, NH, Apr 30, 26; m 48; c 4. MEDICINAL CHEMISTRY, PHARMACOLOGY. *Educ:* Univ NH, BS, 48, MS, 50; Mass Inst Technol, PhD(chem), 52. *Prof Exp:* Res chemist, Chas Pfizer & Co, Inc, Groton, 52-59, proj leader, 59-61, group supvr, 61-63, sect mgr, 63-65, asst dir med chem res, 65-68, dir, 68-72, exec dir med chem res, 72-76, exec dir med sci, 76-80, VPRES MED SCI, CENT RES, PFIZER, INC, 80- *Mem:* Am Chem Soc; AAAS; NY Acad Sci. *Res:* Cardiovascular drugs; adrenergic agents; medicinal products; antibiotics; central nervous system; cardiopulmonary and metabolic diseases. *Mailing Add:* Cent Res Pfizer Inc Eastern Pt Rd Groton CT 06340

MORELL, PIERRE, b Dominican Repub, Dec 10, 41; US citizen; m 65; c 2. BIOCHEMISTRY. *Educ:* Columbia Univ, AB, 63; Albert Einstein Col Med, PhD(biochem), 68. *Prof Exp:* Asst prof biochem in neurol, Albert Einstein Col Med, 69-72; assoc prof, 72-76, PROF BIOCHEM & NUTRIT, BIOL SCI RES CTR & DIR CURRICULLUM NEUROBIOL, UNIV NC, 77- *Concurrent Pos:* Nat Inst Ment Health fel, Ment Health Res Inst, Univ Mich, Ann Arbor, 68-69. *Mem:* Am Soc Neurochem; Int Soc Neurochem; Am Soc Biol Chemists. *Res:* Neurochemistry including metabolism of myelin, axonal transport and neurotoxicology; myelin proteins; cultured neuroblastoma cells. *Mailing Add:* Biol Sci Res Ctr 220H Univ NC Chapel Hill NC 27514

MORELL, SAMUEL ALLAN, b Worcester, Mass, Feb 5, 09; m 36; c 1. BIOCHEMISTRY. *Educ:* Univ Wis, BA, 30, MS, 31, PhD(biochem), 34. *Prof Exp:* Asst org chem, Calif Inst Technol, 38-39; assoc biochemist, Bur Plant Indust, USDA, 39-40, assoc chemist, Div Agr Residues, Northern Regional Res Lab, Bur Agr & Indust Chem, 41-42, chemist, 42-45; head fine chem dept, Pabst Brewing Co, Wis, 48-58; PROF BIOCHEM IN PATH, MED COL WIS, 58-; DIR BIOCHEM DEPT, MILWAUKEE BLOOD CTR, 58- *Concurrent Pos:* Fel biochem, Univ Wis, 34-36; Lilly fel, Mt Sinai Hosp, New York, 36-38. *Mem:* Am Chem Soc; Am Asn Clin Chem; Am Soc Biol Chem. *Res:* Enzymes and coenzymes; nucleotides; fine chemicals derived from yeast; erythrocyte metabolism; hemoglobin; thiol functions in erythrocytes. *Mailing Add:* Milwaukee Blood Ctr 1701 W Wisconsin Ave Milwaukee WI 53233

MORELLO, EDWIN FRANCIS, b Marseilles, Ill, Jan 12, 28. ORGANIC CHEMISTRY. *Educ:* Univ Ill, BS, 48; Univ Minn, PhD(org chem), 52. *Prof Exp:* Res chemist, Standard Oil Co, Ind, 52-57; group leader, 58-65, res chemist, 65-72, RES ASSOC, AMOCO CHEM CORP, 72- *Mem:* Am Chem Soc. *Res:* Engineering polymers; high-temperature polymers; organic chemicals; solid propellants; catalysis. *Mailing Add:* 19 Olympus Dr Apt 1A Naperville IL 60540

MORELLO, JOSEPHINE A, b Boston, Mass, May 2, 36; m 71. MEDICAL MICROBIOLOGY. *Educ:* Simmons Col, BS, 57; Boston Univ, AM, 60, PhD(microbiol), 62; Am Bd Microbiol, Cert med microbiol. *Prof Exp:* Instr microbiol, Boston Univ, 62-64; res assoc, Rockefeller Univ, 64-66; resident med microbiol, Col Physicians & Surgeons, Columbia Univ, 66-68, asst prof microbiol, 68-69; asst prof, 70-73, assoc prof path & med, 73-78, PROF PATH & MED, UNIV CHICAGO, 78-, DIR CLIN MICROBIOL, 70- *Concurrent Pos:* Dir microbiol, Harlem Hosp Ctr, 68-69. *Mem:* Acad Clin Lab Physicians & Scientists; Am Soc Microbiol; fel Am Acad Microbiol; Am Soc Clin Path; Sigma Xi. *Res:* Phagocytosis and cellular immunology; improved methods of clinical microbiology; epidemiology and characteristics of pathogenic neisseria. *Mailing Add:* Box 290 Univ of Chicago Chicago IL 60637

MORELOCK, JACK, b Houston, Tex, Nov 27, 28; m 58. OCEANOGRAPHY. *Educ:* Univ Houston, BS, 50 & 53; Tex A&M Univ, PhD(oceanog), 67. *Prof Exp:* Geologist, Magnolia Petrol Co, Tex, 53; teaching asst geol, Univ Kans, 53-55; explor geologist, Continental Oil Co, Wyo, 55-59 & Oasis Oil Co, Libya, 59-62; teaching asst oceanog, Tex A&M Univ, 62-66; prof & head dept, Fla Inst Technol, 66-69 & Inst Oceanog, Univ Oriente, Venezuela, 69-72; assoc prof, 71-80, PROF MARINE SCI, UNIV PR, MAYAGUEZ, 80- *Concurrent Pos:* Consult to secy natural resources, Dept Natural Resources, Book Study Asn, PR, 74-, US Geol Surv, 80. *Mem:* Soc Econ Paleont & Mineral; Explorers Club. *Res:* Geological oceanography in areas of marine sedimentation; beach and coastal processes; estuarine geology; coral reef studies. *Mailing Add:* Dept of Marine Sci Univ of PR Mayaguez PR 00708

MOREL-SEYTOUX, HUBERT JEAN, b Calais, France, Oct 6, 32; US citizen; m 60; c 4. HYDROLOGY, WATER RESOURCES. *Educ:* Nat Sch Civil Eng, Paris, MS, 56; Stanford Univ, PhD(eng), 62. *Prof Exp:* Res engr, Chevron Res Co, 62-66; assoc prof civil eng, 66-74, PROF CIVIL ENG, ENG RES CTR, COLO STATE UNIV, 74- *Concurrent Pos:* Charge de Rech, Centre Nat de la Rech Sci, Univ de Grenoble, France, 72-73. *Mem:* Am Soc Civil Engrs; Am Geophys Union; Soil Sci Soc Am; Am Inst Mining, Metall & Petrol Engrs; Int Asn Hydraul Res. *Res:* Floods; movement of water and air in soils; infiltration; recharge; drainage; groundwater models; stream-aquifer interaction models and management; oil reservoir behavior simulation on digital computers. *Mailing Add:* A305 Eng Res Ctr Colo State Univ Ft Collins CO 80523

MORENG, ROBERT EDWARD, poultry physiology, see previous edition

MORENO, CARLOS JULIO, b Sevilla, Colombia, July 30, 46; US citizen; m 72; c 1. MATHEMATICS. *Educ:* NY Univ, BA, 68, PhD(math), 71. *Prof Exp:* Asst prof, 71-80, ASSOC PROF MATH, UNIV ILL, URBANA-CHAMPAIGN, 80- *Concurrent Pos:* Assoc mem, Ctr Advan Study, Univ Ill, 75-76; vis mem, Inst Advan Study, Princeton, 75-76; vis mem, Inst Hautes Etudes Scientifique, Paris, 79-80; Fulbright sr visitor, Colombia, 80. *Mem:* Am Math Soc; Math Asn Am; NY Acad Sci. *Res:* Applications of group representations and automorphic forms to problems in number theory and algebraic geometry; analytic properties of Euler products. *Mailing Add:* 273 Altgeld Hall Univ Ill Dept Math Urbana IL 61801

MORENO, ESTEBAN, b San Juan, PR, Aug 3, 26; US citizen. MEDICINE, PATHOLOGY. *Educ:* Columbia Univ, BA, 48; Temple Univ, MD, 51. *Prof Exp:* Attend pathologist, Univ Hosp, PR, 57-63; assoc prof, 61-73, PROF PATH, SCH MED, UNIV PR, SAN JUAN, 73- *Concurrent Pos:* Attend path, Oncol Hosp, PR Med Ctr, 66-73. *Res:* Dermatopathology; training of physicians in pathology. *Mailing Add:* Dept of Path GPO Box 5067 Univ of Pr Sch of Med San Juan PR 00936

MORENO, HERNAN, b Medellin, Colombia, Sept 9, 39; m 64; c 3. PEDIATRICS, HEMATOLOGY. *Educ:* Berchmans Col, Colombia, BS, 56; Univ Valle, Colombia, MD, 63; Am Bd Pediat, dipl, 67; Educ Coun for Med Grad, cert. *Prof Exp:* Intern, Univ Hosp, Cali, Colombia, 61-62, jr pediat resident, Dept Pediat, 62-63, sr pediat resident, 63-64; pediat resident, Children's Hosp, Birmingham, Ala, 64-65; instr pediat, Col Med, Univ Cincinnati, 65-67; from instr to assoc prof pediat, Sch Med, Univ Ala, Birmingham, 67-76, dir pediat hemat & oncol div, 69-76; CHIEF PEDIAT CLIN & CHIEF PEDIAT, CARRAWAY METHODIST MED CTR, 78- *Concurrent Pos:* Fel pediat hemat, Children's Hosp Res Found, Cincinnati, Ohio, 65-67; consult, Children's Hosp, Birmingham, 67-; mem hosps & clins staff, Sch Med, Univ Ala, 68- *Mem:* Am Acad Pediat; Am Soc Hemat; NY Acad Sci. *Res:* Cancer chemotherapy. *Mailing Add:* Dept Pediat 1529 N 25th St Birmingham AL 35234

MORENO, OSCAR, b Camaguey, Cuba, Jan 5, 46. ALGEBRA, COMBINATORICS. *Educ:* Univ PR, BA, 67; Univ Calif, Berkeley, MA, 68, PhD(math), 73. *Prof Exp:* Instr gen studies, Univ PR, 68-69; teaching asst, Dept Math, Univ Calif, 69-72, teaching & res assoc, Dept Math & Electronics Lab, 72-73; asst prof, 74-78, ASSOC PROF MATH, UNIV PR, 78- *Concurrent Pos:* Consult, NSF Miss Proj, Univ PR, 77-78; Univ PR fel, 77-79; NSF grant, 78-80. *Mem:* NY Acad Sci; Am Math Soc; Inst Elec & Electronics Engrs. *Res:* Finite fields and combinatorial theory; its application to coding theory; goppa codes. *Mailing Add:* Dept of Math Univ PR Rio Piedras PR 00926

MORENO, THEODORE, b Palo Alto, Calif, Sept 2, 20; m 45; c 3. ELECTRICAL ENGINEERING. *Educ:* Stanford Univ, AB, 41, AM, 42; Mass Inst Technol, ScD, 49. *Prof Exp:* Proj engr, Sperry Gyroscope Co, NY, 42-46; res assoc, Mass Inst Technol, 46-49; res physicist, Hughes Aircraft Co, 49-51; mgr res & develop, Tube Div, 51-60, vpres, Tube Div, 60-66, vpres equip group, 66-68, vpres info systs group, 68-74, CORP V PRES, VARIAN ASSOCS, 74- *Mem:* Fel Inst Elec & Electronics Engrs. *Res:* Microwave techniques and components; microwave vacuum tubes. *Mailing Add:* Varian Assocs 611 Hansen Way Palo Alto CA 94303

MORENO-BLACK, GERALDINE S, b Brooklyn, NY, Aug 25, 46. PHYSICAL ANTHROPOLOGY. *Educ:* State Univ NY Buffalo, BA, 67; Univ Ariz, MA, 70; Univ Fla, PhD(anthrop), 74. *Prof Exp:* ASST PROF ANTHROP, UNIV ORE, 74- *Mem:* Am Asn Phys Anthropologists; Soc Med Anthrop; Am Anthrop Asn; AAAS. *Res:* Affect of disturbed habitat conditions on diet, behavior and social structure of non-human primates with emphasis on African Colobinae; natural diets of non-human primates; human ecology; human nutrition; growth and development. *Mailing Add:* Dept of Anthrop Univ of Ore Eugene OR 97403

MORENZONI, RICHARD ANTHONY, b Sonoma, Calif, Sept 30, 46; m 74. MICROBIOLOGY. *Educ:* Univ Calif, Davis, BS, 68, PhD(microbiol), 73. *Prof Exp:* RES & STAFF MICROBIOLOGIST, E & J GALLO WINERY, 73- *Mem:* Sigma Xi. *Res:* Industrial research related to microbiological practices or problems encountered in the production of wines and spirits. *Mailing Add:* Res Microbiol Dept E & J Gallo Winery PO Box 1130 Modesto CA 95353

MOREST, DONALD KENT, b Kansas City, Mo, Oct 4, 34; m 63; c 2. NEUROSCIENCE. *Educ:* Univ Chicago, BA, 55; Yale Univ, MD, 60. *Prof Exp:* Sr asst surgeon, NIH, 60-63; asst prof anat, Univ Chicago, 63-65; assoc, 65-67, from asst prof to assoc prof anat, Harvard Med Sch, 67-77; PROF ANAT, UNIV CONN HEALTH CTR, 77-, PROF COMMUN SCI, UNIV, 81- *Concurrent Pos:* Res assoc otolaryngol, Mass Eye & Ear Infirmary, 65-77. *Honors & Awards:* Herrick Award Comp Neurol, 66. *Mem:* AAAS; Am Asn Anatomists; Soc Neurosci; Asn Res Otolaryngol; Sigma Xi. *Res:* Neuroembryology; neuroanatomy; connections of central neural pathways and neurocytology; autonomic and sensory systems; auditory system; neurobiology. *Mailing Add:* Dept of Anat Univ of Conn Health Ctr Farmington CT 06032

MORETON, JULIAN EDWARD, b Mobile, Ala, July 5, 43; m 63; c 3. NEUROPHARMACOLOGY, BEHAVIORAL PHARMACOLOGY. *Educ:* Univ Miss Sch Pharm, BS, 66, PhD(pharmacol), 71. *Prof Exp:* NIMH fel, Psychiat Res Univ, Sch Med, Univ Minn, 71-73; res assoc, Sch Med, Univ Cincinnati, 73-74; asst prof, 74-77, ASSOC PROF PHARMACOL & TOXICOL, SCH PHARM, UNIV MD, 77- *Concurrent Pos:* Co-prin investr, res grants, Nat Inst Drug Abuse, 74-82. *Mem:* Am Soc Pharmacol & Exp Therapeut; Soc Neurosci; Am Asn Col Pharm; AAAS. *Res:* Neuropharmacology and behavioral pharmacology of drug abuse and drug dependence using EEG, behavioral and self-administration techniques in the rat and monkey. *Mailing Add:* Dept Pharmacol & Toxicol Sch Pharm Univ Md Baltimore MD 21201

MORETON, ROBERT DULANEY, b Brookhaven, Miss, Sept 24, 13; m 45. RADIOLOGY. *Educ:* Millsaps Col, BS, 34; Univ Miss, cert, 36; Univ Tenn, MD, 38; Am Bd Radiol, dipl, 43. *Prof Exp:* Intern, Lloyd Noland Mem Hosp, Fairfield, Ala, 38-39; instr, Sch Med, Univ Miss, 40; lectr, Univ Tex Med Br, Galveston, 45-50; from instr to assoc prof clin radiol, Univ Tex Southwestern Med Sch, Dallas, 51-65; PROF RADIOL, UNIV TEX M D ANDERSON HOSP & TUMOR INST, HOUSTON, 65-, VPRES PROF & PUB AFFAIRS, 69- *Concurrent Pos:* Fel radiol, Mayo Found, 40-42; staff radiologist, Scott & White Hosp & Clin & Santa Fe Hosp, Temple, Tex, 42-50; chmn & partner, Bond Radiol Group, Tex, 50-65; consult var hosps, companies & railroads, Tex, 52-65; chmn & dir dept radiol, Harris Hosp, Ft Worth & Ft Worth Childrens Hosp, 61-65; vpres, Univ Cancer Found, Tex, 65-; founding mem bd, Carter Blood Bank & Bd Radiation & Res Found Southwest; mem bd & exec comt, Radiation Ctr, Ft Worth; chmn, Tex Bd Health, 75-80. *Mem:* Am Col Radiol; AMA; Am Roentgen Ray Soc; Am Geriat Soc; Indust Med Asn. *Mailing Add:* Univ of Tex M D Anderson Hosp & Tumor Inst Houston TX 77030

MORETTI, G(INO), b Turin, Italy, Jan 2, 17; US citizen; m 41; c 5. APPLIED MATHEMATICS, FLUID DYNAMICS. *Educ:* Univ Turin, PhD(math), 39. *Prof Exp:* Asst prof mech, Turin Polytech Inst, 45-48; prof fluid mech, Univ Cordoba, 48-55; prof classical & fluid mech, Inst Physics, Bariloche, 55-58; sci supvr, Gen Appl Sci Labs, Inc, 58-67; PROF AEROSPACE ENG, POLYTECH INST NEW YORK, 67- *Concurrent Pos:* Adv, Aerotech Inst Cordoba, 48-55; res scientist, Atomic Energy Comn, Argentina, 55-58. *Mem:* Assoc fel Am Inst Aeronaut & Astronaut. *Res:* Numerical gas dynamics; time-dependent, three-dimensional, inviscid and viscous flows; real gas and chemical effects. *Mailing Add:* Polytech Inst of New York Brooklyn NY 11201

MORETTI, PETER M, b Zurich, Switz, Apr 13, 35; US citizen; m 77; c 4. MECHANICAL ENGINEERING. *Educ:* Calif Inst Technol, BS, 57, MS, 58; Stanford Univ, PhD(mech eng), 65. *Prof Exp:* Proj mgr nuclear eng, Interatom, Bensberg, Ger, 64-68; sr engr, Westinghouse ARD, 68-70; PROF MECH ENG, OKLA STATE UNIV, 70- *Concurrent Pos:* Fulbright grant, Technische Hochschule, Darmstadt, 58-59; prog mgr solar tech div wind syst br, US Dept Energy, 77-78; consult flow-induced vibrations; wind turbines; alternative energy systems; regional energy system modeling. *Mem:* Am Soc Mech Engrs. *Res:* Heat-exchanger vibrations; wind-power applications; stratified lakes. *Mailing Add:* Sch of Mech & Aerospace Eng Okla State Univ Stillwater OK 74078

MORETTI, RICHARD LEO, b Ft Collins, Colo, Feb 15, 29; m 54; c 3. CARDIOVASCULAR PHYSIOLOGY. *Educ:* Univ Calif, Riverside, AB, 57, Berkeley, MA, 60, PhD(zool), 64. *Prof Exp:* Lectr embryol, Univ Calif, Riverside, 64-65, asst prof embryol & asst res zoologist, Air Pollution Res Ctr, 65-73; res biologist, 73-80, RES PHYSIOLOGIST, BRUCE LYON MEM RES LAB, CHILDREN'S HOSP, OAKLAND, 80- *Concurrent Pos:* Consult, May, Ecker, Iverson & Young Cardiac & Thoracic Surgery Med Group. *Mem:* Am Physiol Soc; Soc Exp Biol Med. *Res:* Mechanisms regulating coronary blood flow; mechanisms controlling platelet aggregation; vascular and hemostatic factors in sickle cell disease. *Mailing Add:* Bruce Lyon Mem Res Lab Children's Hosp Oakland CA 94609

MORETTO, LUCIANO G, b Bisuschio, Italy, Feb 18, 40; m 65; c 2. NUCLEAR CHEMISTRY, NUCLEAR PHYSICS. *Educ:* Univ Pavia, Italy, Laurea, 64, Libera Docenza(nuclear chem), 70. *Prof Exp:* Teaching assoc, Univ Pavia, 64-65, asst prof chem, 68-71; fel nuclear chem, Lawrence Berkeley Lab, 65-68; from asst prof to assoc prof, 71-77, PROF CHEM, UNIV CALIF, BERKELEY, 77- *Concurrent Pos:* Sr scientist, Lawrence Berkeley Lab, 71-; assoc ed, Nuclear Physics, 76- *Res:* Transport properties in heavy ion induced reactions; fission-statistical properties of excited atomic nuclei. *Mailing Add:* Lawrence Berkeley Lab Nuclear Sci Div Berkeley CA 94720

MORETZ, WILLIAM HENRY, b Hickory, NC, Oct 23, 14; m 47; c 6. SURGERY. *Educ:* Lenoir-Rhyne Col, BS, 35; Harvard Univ, MD, 39. *Hon Degrees:* DSc, Lenoir-Rhyne Col, 61. *Prof Exp:* Instr surg, Sch Med, Univ Rochester, 44-47; from asst prof to assoc prof, Sch Med, Univ Utah, 47-55; prof & chmn dept, 55-72, PRES, MED COL GA, 72- *Concurrent Pos:* Attend surgeon, North Bench Vet Admin Hosp & assoc surgeon, Salt Lake Gen Hosp, Salt Lake City, Utah, 47-55; consult surgeon, Tooele Army Hosp, 51-55; chief surg, Eugene Talmadge Mem Hosp, Ga, 55-72; consult, US Vet Admin Hosp, 55- *Mem:* Soc Univ Surgeons; Am Surg Asn; Int Cardiovasc Soc; Int Soc Surgeons; Soc Surg Alimentary Tract. *Res:* Thrombo-embolism and arterial diseases. *Mailing Add:* Dept of Surg Med Col of Ga Augusta GA 30902

MOREWITZ, HARRY ALAN, b Newport News, Va, June 2, 23; m 48; c 2. NUCLEAR PHYSICS. *Educ:* Col William & Mary, BS, 43; Columbia Univ, AM, 49; NY Univ, PhD(physics), 53. *Prof Exp:* Res assoc cosmic rays, NY Univ, 49-53; supvr reactor physics, Westinghouse Elec Corp, 53-59; proj mgr, 59-80, SR STAFF ENGR, ATOMICS INT DIV, ROCKWELL INT CORP, 80- *Concurrent Pos:* Proj engr, Metavac, Inc, 52-53; lectr, Dept Radiol, Ctr Health Sci, Univ Calif, Los Angeles, 68-72; mem, Adv Comt Reactor Physics, US AEC, 69-73; consult. *Mem:* Am Phys Soc; Am Nuclear Soc; Sigma Xi; NY Acad Sci; Health Physics Soc. *Res:* Reactor physics; reactor safety; aerosol physics; transient liquid metal heat transfer; radiation dosimetry. *Mailing Add:* 5300 Bothwell Rd Tarzana CA 91356

MOREY, BOOKER WILLIAMS, b Rochester, NY, May 12, 41; m 69. MINERAL ENGINEERING. *Educ:* Pa State Univ, BS, 63, MS, 65; Stanford Univ, PhD(mineral processing), 69. *Prof Exp:* Sr res engr, Garrett Res & Develop Co, Inc, 69-72, group leader, Occidental Res Corp, 72-78; dir advan technol, Envirotech Corp, 78-81; CONSULT, 81- *Mem:* Am Inst Mining, Metall & Petrol Engrs; Filtration Soc; Can Inst Mining & Metall; Brit Inst Mining & Metall; Mining & Metall Soc Am. *Res:* Development of separation equipment for solid-solid, liquid-solid and gas-solid separations; equipment and process development for ores and coal processing and scrap and municipal refuse recycling; sulfide and antimony hydrometallurgy. *Mailing Add:* 164 Pecora Way Menlo Park CA 94025

MOREY, DARRELL DORR, b Manhattan, Kans, Dec 6, 14; m 40; c 6. AGRONOMY. *Educ:* Kans State Col, BS, 37; Tex Tech Col, MS, 38; Iowa State Col, PhD(agron), 47. *Prof Exp:* Asst, Tex Tech Col, 37-38, instr crops, 38-39; jr supvr grain inspection, Grain Br, USDA, Minn, 39-44; assoc, Exp Sta, Iowa State Col, 44-47; assoc prof agron, Univ Ga, 48-49; assoc agronomist, Fla Agr Exp Sta, 49-53; assoc plant breeder, 53-65, PLANT BREEDER RYE TRITICALE, WHEAT BREEDING INVESTS, GA COASTAL PLAIN EXP STA, CROP RES DIV, AGR RES SERV, USDA & PROF AGRON, UNIV GA, 65- *Concurrent Pos:* Mem, Nat Oat Conf Comt, 51-52 & Nat Wheat Improv Coun, 73-75; coordr, Uniform Southern Soft Wheat Exps, 73-76. *Mem:* Crop Sci Soc Am; Am Soc Agron. *Res:* Breeding disease resistance in small grains; genetics and cytology of cereals; rye breeding; triticale breeding; wheat breeding. *Mailing Add:* Ga Coastal Plain Exp Sta PO Box 748 Tifton GA 31794

MOREY, GLENN BERNHARDT, b Duluth, Minn, Oct 17, 35; m 67; c 2. GEOLOGY, STRATIGRAPHY & SEDIMENTATION. *Educ:* Univ Minn, Duluth, BA, 53, Minneapolis, MS, 62, PhD(geol), 65. *Prof Exp:* Instr geol, Univ Minn, Minneapolis, 64-6S, asst prof, Minn Geol Surv, 65-69, prin geologist Precambrian, Minn Geol Surv, 73-76, ASSOC PROF GEOL, UNIV MINN, ST PAUL, 69-, ASSOC DIR, MINN GEOL SURV, 76-, CHIEF GEOLOGIST, 79- *Concurrent Pos:* Group leader, Int Geol Correlation Prog & Int Union geol sci, 75-; co-leader, Int Union Geol Sci, 75- *Mem:* Fel Geol Soc Am; Soc Econ Geol. *Res:* Field and laboratory studies of Precambrian rocks, principally in Minnesota and the Lake Superior Region. *Mailing Add:* Minn Geol Surv Univ of Minn St Paul MN 55108

MOREY, PHILIP RICHARD, b Cleveland, Ohio, July 3, 40; m 67. PLANT ANATOMY, INDUSTRIAL HYGIENE. *Educ:* Univ Dayton, BS, 62; Yale Univ, MS, 64, PhD(biol), 67. *Prof Exp:* NIH fel, Univ Calif, Santa Barbara, 67; lectr biol, Harvard Univ, 68-70, forest botanist, 67-70; assoc prof biol, 70-77, PROF BIOL, TEX TECH UNIV, 77- *Concurrent Pos:* Sabbatical leave, Environ Invest Br, Nat Inst Occup Safety & Health, HHW, 81-83. *Mem:* Bot Soc Am; Am Indust Hyg Asn; Weed Sci Soc Am; Am Soc Agron; Sigma Xi. *Res:* Anatomy of agronomic plants; herbicide effects on plant growth; identification and analysis of vegetable dusts relative to industrial hygiene. *Mailing Add:* Dept of Biol Tex Tech Univ Lubbock TX 79409

MOREY, ROBERT VANCE, b Sturgis, Mich, Jan 19, 45; m 65; c 2. AGRICULTURAL ENGINEERING. *Educ:* Mich State Univ, BS, 67; Purdue Univ, PhD(agr eng), 71. *Prof Exp:* From asst prof to assoc prof, 70-81, PROF AGR ENG, UNIV MINN, 81- *Mem:* Am Soc Engrs; Soc Comput Simulation; Sigma Xi. *Res:* Grain drying; storage and handling; computer modeling and simulation. *Mailing Add:* Dept of Agr Eng Univ of Minn St Paul MN 55108

MOREY, W(OODRUFF) A(NDERSON), engineering, deceased

MOREY-HOLTON, EMILY RENE, b Kirksville, Mo, Dec 9, 36; m 67; c 1. PHARMACOLOGY, PHYSIOLOGY. *Educ:* W Va Univ, BA, 58, BS, 61, PhD(pharmacol), 64. *Prof Exp:* Technician surgical res, Peter Bent Brigham Hosp, 58-59; instr pharmacol, Sch Med, Univ Pittsburgh, 63-67; asst prof pharmacol, Med Sch, Ind Univ, 67-68; aerospace technologist biomed, NASA-Wallops Flight Ctr, 68-74; SR RES SCIENTIST BIOMED, NASA-AMES RES CTR, 74- *Mem:* Endocrine Soc; Am Soc Bone & Mineral Res. *Res:* Calcium homeostasis; disuse-type atrophy produced by space flight. *Mailing Add:* Biomed Res Div 239-14 Ames Res Ctr NASA Moffett Field CA 94035

MORFOPOULOS, VASSILIS C(ONSTANTINOS) P, b Athens, Greece, Oct 22, 37; US citizen; m 62. METALLURGICAL & MATERIALS ENGINEERING. *Educ:* Purdue Univ, BS, 58, MS, 61; Columbia Univ, EngScD(eng sci), 64. *Prof Exp:* Res assoc metall eng, Purdue Univ, 57-60 & Columbia Univ, 60-61; res engr, US Steel Corp, 61; instr chem, City Univ New York, 61-63; res engr, Argonne Nat Lab, AEC, 63; Am Iron & Steel res fel metall eng, Columbia Univ, 64-65; sr metall scientist, 65-66, TECH DIR RES & DEVELOP TESTING, AM STANDARDS TESTING BUR, 66- *Concurrent Pos:* Consult, govt & indust, 66-; mem, Int Comn Chem Thermodyn & Kinetics; mem, Transp Res Bd, Nat Res Coun. *Mem:* AAAS; Am Inst Mining, Metall & Petrol Engrs; Am Soc Eng Educ; Asn Consult Chemists & Chem Engrs; NY Acad Sci. *Res:* Research and consulting in fields of corrosion and oxidation phenomena; low and high temperature thermodynamics; liquid metals and compounds; surface phenomena; electrometallurgy and electrode phenomena; electrical and magnetic properties of matter; failure and stress analysis; metal finishing, joining and working. *Mailing Add:* Am Standards Testing Bur 40 Water St New York NY 10004

MORGAL, PAUL WALTER, b Council Bluffs, Iowa, Dec 10, 11; c 3. CHEMICAL ENGINEERING, INDUSTRIAL CHEMISTRY. *Educ:* Iowa State Univ, BS, 33, MS, 35, PhD(chem), 37. *Prof Exp:* Chemist rayon plant, Du Pont Rayon Co, 33-34; develop engr inorg salts, Gen Chem Co, 37-38; Rackham Found fel indust agr prod, Mich State Univ, 38-42; eng assoc hydrogenation coal, Ind Gas Assoc, Purdue Univ, 42-43; process engr petrol refining, Union Oil Calif, 43-47, proj mgr petrol refining construct, 48-77; CONSULT CHEM ENGR, RES DEPT, UNION OIL CO CALIF, BREA, 78- *Concurrent Pos:* Instr, Univ Calif, 48-63. *Mem:* Am Chem Soc; Am Inst Chem Engrs. *Res:* Industrial uses of agricultural products; hydrogenation of coal. *Mailing Add:* Union Oil Co Calif 376 S Valencia Ave Brea CA 92621

MORGALI, JAMES R, b Salem, Ore, Sept 7, 32; m 57; c 3. CIVIL ENGINEERING. *Educ:* Willamette Univ, BA, 56; Stanford Univ, BS, 56, MS, 57, PhD(civil eng), 64. *Prof Exp:* PROF CIVIL ENG, UNIV OF THE PAC, 61- *Mem:* Am Soc Civil Engrs; Am Soc Eng Educ. *Res:* Synthesis of runoff hydrographs from small drainage areas. *Mailing Add:* Dept Civil Eng Univ the Pac Stockton CA 95204

MORGAN, ADRIAN J(OHN), b Cincinnati, Ohio, Nov 12, 26; m 48; c 3. ELECTRICAL ENGINEERING. *Educ:* Purdue Univ, BS, 48; Univ Cincinnait, MS, 58. *Prof Exp:* Asst instr, 48-49, from instr to assoc prof, 49-67, PROF ELEC ENG, UNIV DAYTON, 67- *Mem:* Am Soc Eng Educ. *Res:* Electronic warfare; infrared; dielectrics; electromagnetics; dynamics; components; semiconductors; vacuum devices. *Mailing Add:* Dept of Elec Eng 300 College Park Dayton OH 45469

MORGAN, ALVIN H(ANSON), b Highmore, SDak, July 8, 08; m 37; c 4. RADIO ENGINEERING. *Educ:* Kans State Univ, BS, 37; Georgetown Univ, MS, 52. *Prof Exp:* Electronic engr, Shell Geophys Div, Okla, 37-41; asst chief field opers sect, Nat Bur Standards, 46-51, proj leader in charge frequency & time standards, High Frequency Standards Sect, 51-54, chief frequency & time dissemination, Boulder Lab, 54-63; chief frequency-time dissemination res, 63-68, sci consult, 68; prof electronics, 69-76, EMER PROF ELECTRONICS, METROP STATE COL, 76- *Concurrent Pos:* Lectr, George Washington Univ, 53-54; instr, Exten Ctr, Univ Colo, 63; supvr design & construct, radio stas WWVB & WWVL. *Mem:* AAAS; Inst Elec & Electronics Engrs; Sigma Xi; NY Acad Sci. *Res:* Design of radio equipment for radio propagation measurement; frequency measurements; oscillators; transistors. *Mailing Add:* Salina Star Rte Boulder CO 80302

MORGAN, ANTONY RICHARD, b Mombasa, Kenya, Jan 5, 40. MOLECULAR BIOLOGY. *Educ:* Cambridge Univ, BA, 61; Univ Alta, PhD(chem), 64. *Prof Exp:* Proj assoc DNA chem & enzymol, Enzyme Inst, Univ Wis-Madison, 65-67, asst prof, 67-69; asst prof DNA chem & enzymol, 69-77, PROF DNA CHEM & ENZYMOL, UNIV ALTA, 77- *Mem:* AAAS; Can Fedn Biol Socs. *Res:* Chemical mechanism of DNA replication in vitro; three-stranded complexes between DNA and RNA and their biological implications for transcription; multistranded nucleic acid complexes and DNA replication. *Mailing Add:* Dept Biochem Univ Alta Edmonton AB T6G 2H7 Can

MORGAN, ARTHUR I, JR, b Berkeley, Calif, May 21, 23; m 48; c 2. CHEMICAL ENGINEERING. *Educ:* Univ Calif, BS, 43, MS, 48; Swiss Fed Inst Technol, PhD(chem eng), 52. *Prof Exp:* Chem engr, 52-58, head unit opers invest, 58-62, chief eng & develop lab, 62-69, CTR DIR, WESTERN REGIONAL RES CTR, USDA, 69- *Concurrent Pos:* Adj prof nutritional sci & lectr chem eng, Univ Calif, Berkeley, 67-; Consult, ITT, 80. *Honors & Awards:* Babcock-Hart Award, Inst Food Technol, 68; Food & Bioeng Award, Am Inst Chem Engrs, 71. *Mem:* Am Chem Soc; Am Inst Chem Engrs; Inst Food Technol. *Res:* Heat transfer, drying, fluid flow and evaporation relative to agricultural products. *Mailing Add:* Western Regional Res Ctr USDA 800 Buchanan St Berkeley CA 94710

MORGAN, BERNARD S(TANLEY), JR, b Brooklyn, NY, June 30, 27; m 51; c 5. ENGINEERING. *Educ:* US Naval Acad, BS, 51; Univ Mich, MS(aeronaut eng) & MS(instrumentation eng), 57, PhD(instrumentation eng), 63. *Prof Exp:* US Air Force, 51-79, missile officer, 3499 mobil training wing, 51-55, asst aeronaut eng, US Air Force Inst Technol, 58-60, proj scientist, Air Force Off Sci Res, 60-65, dir, Aerospace Mech Div, F J Seiler Res Lab, Colo, 65-69, vcomdr aerospace res labs, Wright-Patterson AFB, 69-70, chief, Command Control & Reconnaissance Div & asst chief staff studies & anal, hq, 71-73, comdr, Air Force Cambridge Res Labs, 74-76, comdr, Air Force Geophyics Lab, 76-79; VPRES SYSTS TECHNOL & INTEGRATION, BDM CORP, 79- *Mem:* Fel Inst Elec & Electronics Engrs; Am Inst Aeronaut & Astronaut; Am Soc Mech Engrs; Am Automatic Control Coun (pres, 78-79). *Res:* Multivariable control systems; high speed aerodynamics; operations research; applied mathematics. *Mailing Add:* 2808 Bentley St Huntsville AL 35801

MORGAN, BEVERLY CARVER, b New York, NY, May 29, 27; m 54; c 3. PEDIATRIC CARDIOLOGY. *Educ:* Duke Univ, MD, 55; Am Bd Pediat, dipl, 60, cert cardiol, 61. *Prof Exp:* Intern & asst resident pediat, Stanford Univ, 55-56; trainee pediat cardiol, Babies Hosp, Columbia Univ, 57-60; dir cardiol, Heart Sta, Robert Green Hosp, San Antonio, Tex, 60-62; from instr to assoc prof pediat, Sch Med, Univ Wash, 62-73, prof & chmn dept, 73-80; PROF PEDIAT & CHMN DEPT, SCH MED, UNIV CALIF, IRVINE, 80- *Concurrent Pos:* Clin fel, Babies Hosp, Columbia Univ, 56-57, res fel, Cardiovasc Lab, Presby Hosp, 59-60; NIH res career prog award, 66-71; consult to Surgeon Gen, Brooke Army Med Ctr, Tex, 60-62; clin lectr, Sch Med, Univ Tex, 60-62; mem pulmonary training comt, Nat Heart & Lung Inst, 72, mem pulmonary acad award panel, 72-; mem comt NIH training & fel progs, Nat Res Coun, 72-74; mem, Grad Med Educ Nat Adv Comt, 76-80. *Mem:* Am Pediat Soc; Asn Med Sch Pediat Dept Chmn (secy-treas, 81-); Am Acad Pediat; Soc Pediat Res; Am Col Cardiol. *Res:* Clinical research; effects of respiration on circulation. *Mailing Add:* Dept Pediat Sch Med Univ Wash Seattle WA 98195

MORGAN, BRUCE HARRY, b Sharon, Pa, Sept 30, 31; m 58; c 2. PHYSICS. *Educ:* Harvard Univ, AB, 53; Calif Inst Technol, MS, 54; George Washington Univ, JD, 68. *Prof Exp:* Assoc engr systs anal, Westinghouse Elec Corp, 56-57; ASSOC PROF GEN PHYSICS, US NAVAL ACAD, 57- *Mem:* Am Asn Physics Teachers. *Res:* General physics. *Mailing Add:* Dept of Physics Michelson Hall US Naval Acad Annapolis MD 21402

MORGAN, BRUCE HENRY, b Chicago, Ill, Jan 21, 20; m 75; c 2. FOOD MICROBIOLOGY. *Educ:* Purdue Univ, BS, 41; Rutgers Univ, PhD(microbiol), 53. *Prof Exp:* Res bacteriologist, Continental Can Co, Inc, Ill, 41-42 & Baxter Labs, 43; bacteriologist, US Biol Warfare Res Labs, 47-49; res bacteriologist, Nat Canners Asn Res Labs, DC, 52-53; dep for radiation preservation, Off Sci Dir, Qm Food & Container Inst, Ill, 54-57; mgr packaging eng, Continental Can Co, Inc, 58-64, dir corp new prod res, 64-67; dir res & eng, Lamb Weston, Inc, 67-68, vpres res & eng, 68-73; sr vpres corp develop, 74-79, PRES AMFAC AQUATECH, AMFAC FOODS, INC, 80- *Concurrent Pos:* Asst ed, Food Res, 59-61; mem, Adv Bd, Food Res Inst, 59-63; instr, Ill Inst Technol, 63-64; mem, Bd Dirs, Qm Res & Develop Assocs, 64-67 & Bd Govs, Food Update, Food & Drug Law Inst, 70-77; mem, Food Industs Adv Comt, Nutrit Found, 66-67 & Indust Action Comt, Am Health Found, 71-73. *Mem:* Am Soc Microbiol; Inst Food Technologists (treas, 70-74); fel Royal Soc Health. *Res:* Radiation biology of microbiological population; radiation chemistry of foods; vegetable freezing and dehydration. *Mailing Add:* PO Box 23564 Portland OR 97223

MORGAN, BRYAN EDWARD, b Lamesa, Tex, Jan 15, 19; m 40. PETROLEUM ENGINEERING, CHEMISTRY. *Educ:* W Tex State Univ, BS, 40. *Prof Exp:* Chemist, Oil Refining Lab, Phillips Petrol Co, 41-42; plant chemist, J S Abercrombie Co, 43-44, lab supvr, 44-46; res engr, Humble Oil & Refining Co, 46-50, sr res engr, 50-60, sr res specialist, 60-64, res assoc, Esso Prod Res Co, 64-77; SR ENGR ASSOC, EXXON PROD RES CO, 77- *Concurrent Pos:* Vchmn nat comt standardization oil well cements, Am Petrol Inst, 62- *Mem:* Soc Petrol Engrs. *Res:* Drilling; logging; formation evaluation; formation stimulation for production of oil and gas. *Mailing Add:* Exxon Prod Res Co PO Box 2189 Houston TX 77001

MORGAN, CARL ROBERT, anatomy, see previous edition

MORGAN, CARL WILLIAM, b Long Island, Kans, Feb 16; m 40; c 2. CIVIL ENGINEERING. *Educ:* Kans State Univ, BS, 38; Univ Tex, MS, 51, PhD(civil eng, math), 58. *Prof Exp:* Instr surv, 46-47, from asst prof to assoc prof civil eng, 47-77, PROF CIVIL ENG & DIR ENG, CAREER ASST CTR & COOP ENG PROGS, UNIV TEX, AUSTIN, 77-, RES ENGR, STRUCT MECH RES LAB, 70- *Mem:* Am Soc Civil Engrs; Am Soc Eng Educ; Am Geophys Union; Int Asn Hydraul Res. *Res:* Fluid mechanics; hydrology. *Mailing Add:* Dept of Civil Eng Univ of Tex Col of Eng Austin TX 78712

MORGAN, CAROLYN B, b Winston-Salem, NC, Dec 3, 47. DATA ANALYSIS. *Educ:* Vanderbilt Univ, BA, 69; Wright State Univ, MS, 73; Union Univ, PhD(statist admin & eng systs), 82. *Prof Exp:* Programmer, Frigidaire Div, Gen Motors, Ohio, 69-70; teacher math, Dayton Bd Educ, 70-71; grad teaching asst, Wright State Univ, Ohio, 71-73; STATISTICIAN & COMPUT, GEN ELEC RES & DEVELOP, 73- *Mem:* Am Statist Asn. *Res:* Simple iterative least squares technique for estimating the parameters of a linear regression model when the dependent variable is from an extreme valve or its related weibull distribution and the data are censored. *Mailing Add:* 12 Huntwood Dr Clifton Park NY 12065

MORGAN, CHARLES D(AVID), b Spring Valley, NY, Nov 7, 34; m 56; c 4. MECHANICAL ENGINEERING. *Educ:* Stevens Inst Technol, ME, 56; Rensselaer Polytech Inst, MS, 60; Lehigh Univ, PhD(mech eng), 65. *Prof Exp:* Engr, Nuclear Div, Combustion Eng Co, 56-60; instr mech eng, Lehigh Univ, 60-64; prin engr, Atomic Energy Div, Babcock & Wilcox Co, 64-67, unit mgr thermal-hydraul methods, Nuclear Power Generation Dept, 67-73, mgr, tech staff, 73-80; TECH CONSULT, 80- *Mem:* Am Soc Mech Engrs. *Res:* Film boiling from vertical surfaces; two phase flow studies; effects of turbulent mixing on burnout; applications of thermal/hydraulics to nuclear reactor design and safety. *Mailing Add:* Babcock & Wilcox Co PO Box 1260 Lynchburg VA 24501

MORGAN, CHARLES O, b Fairfield, Iowa, Nov 28, 31; m 52; c 2. HYDROLOGY. *Educ:* Univ Iowa, BA, 54, MS, 56. *Prof Exp:* Geologist, US Geol Surv, Mich, 56, La, 56-63, Kans, 63-67, hydrologist, 67-70, Calif, 70-77, Va, 77-81; HYDROLOGIST, DEPT DEFENSE, 81- *Concurrent Pos:* US AID consult, Pakistan, 69 & 70; UN consult, Turkey, 79. *Honors & Awards:* Superior Performance Award, US Geol Surv, 65. *Mem:* Geol Soc Am; Int Asn Math Geol. *Res:* Salt-water encroachment and chemical facies changes in coastal aquifers; digital computer techniques as applied in the field of hydrology. *Mailing Add:* AFRCE-MX/DEEC Norton AFB Box 4408 San Bernadino CA 92409

MORGAN, CHARLES ROBERT, b Kingston, Pa, July 18, 34; m 68. PHYSICAL ORGANIC CHEMISTRY. *Educ:* Pa State Univ, BS, 56; Mass Inst Technol, PhD(org chem), 63. *Prof Exp:* Res assoc, Mass Inst Technol, 63-65; res chemist, Org Res Dept, 65-73, sr res chemist, Photopolymer Systs, 73-74, MGR PROD DEVELOP, W R GRACE & CO, 74- *Mem:* Am Chem Soc; Inter-Am Photochem Soc. *Res:* Kinetics and mechanisms of organic reactions; cyanide and sulfur chemistry; nucleophilicity and solvent isotope effects; organometallic reactions; polymer stabilization; photochemistry and photopolymers. *Mailing Add:* W R Grace & Co Columbia MD 21044

MORGAN, COUNCILMAN, b Boston, Mass, Sept 6, 20; m 45; c 4. MICROBIOLOGY, VIROLOGY. *Educ:* Harvard Univ, BS, 43; Columbia Univ, MD, 46. *Prof Exp:* From intern to resident med, Bellevue Hosp, New York, 46-53; from asst prof med to prof microbiol, Col Physicians & Surgeons, Columbia Univ, 54-78, assoc dean students & curric, 70-72, assoc dean curric affairs, 72-78; EXEC DIR, ASSEMBLY LIFE SCI, NAT RES COUN, 78- *Mem:* Am Soc Microbiol; Am Asn Clin Invest; Am Asn Immunol; Am Soc Cell Biol; hon mem Fr Soc Electron Microscope. *Res:* Structure and development of viruses; science administration. *Mailing Add:* Nat Acad Sci 2101 Constitution Ave NW Washington DC 20418

MORGAN, DAVID WILLIAM, b Nashville, Tenn, June 11, 44; div; c 1. BIOLOGICAL OCEANOGRAPHY, AQUATIC BIOLOGY. *Educ:* Univ Ga, BS, 66; Univ RI, PhD(biol oceanog), 73. *Prof Exp:*Asst prof biol, Univ Notre Dame, 72-80; ENVIRON CONSULT, 81- *Concurrent Pos:* Lectr, Ind Univ, 81. *Mem:* AAAS; Am Fisheries Soc; Animal Behav Soc. *Res:* Behavior of aquatic vertebrates, especially as affected by human environmental perturbation; wetland resource allocation and management; fisheries dynamics; systems for processing natural resources data. *Mailing Add:* Dept of Biol Univ of Notre Dame Notre Dame IN 46556

MORGAN, DAVID ZACKQUILL, b Fairmont, WVa, Mar 27, 25; m 48; c 2. INTERNAL MEDICINE. *Educ:* WVa Univ, AB, 48, BS, 50; Med Col Va, MD, 52; Am Bd Internal Med, dipl, 64. *Prof Exp:* From instr to assoc prof, 63-73, asst dean, 65-72, PROF MED, SCH MED, WVA UNIV, 73-, ASSOC DEAN, 72- *Mem:* Fel Am Col Physicians. *Res:* Cardiology. *Mailing Add:* Dept Med Sch Med WVa Univ Morgantown WV 26506

MORGAN, DONALD E(ARLE), b Regina, Sask, Sept 1, 17; US citizen; m 41; c 5. INDUSTRIAL ENGINEERING, APPLIED MATHEMATICS. *Educ:* Ore State Univ, BS, 40; Stanford Univ, MS, 62, PhD(indust eng), 64. *Prof Exp:* Mgr appln eng, Electronics Div, Westinghouse Elec Corp, 40-46; owner & gen mgr, Intermt Surg Supply Co, 46-60; prof indust eng, Stanford Univ, 63-65; owner & sr staff mem, Decision Studies Group, 65-68; HEAD DEPT INDUST ENG, CALIF STATE POLYTECH UNIV, SAN LUIS OBISPO, 68- *Concurrent Pos:* Prin investr, US Air Force Systs Command, 62-64, US Navy & Exec Br, US Govt, 64-66. *Mem:* Am Inst Indust Engrs; Inst Elec & Electronics Engrs; Am Soc Qual Control. *Res:* Management decision processes using applied mathematical, statistical, and decision theoretic aids implanted by electronic data processing equipment based on economic and human factors. *Mailing Add:* Dept of Indust Eng Calif State Polytech Univ San Luis Obispo CA 93407

MORGAN, DONALD O'QUINN, b Star, NC, Mar 24, 34; m 59; c 2. VETERINARY IMMUNOLOGY. *Educ:* NC State Univ, BS, 55, MS, 63; Univ Ga, DVM, 59; Univ Ill, PhD(physiol), 67. *Prof Exp:* Res asst microbiol, NC State Univ, 59-62, instr animal sci, 62-63; diagnostician, Dept Agr, NC, 63-64; NIH fel, Univ Ill, 64-67, asst prof vet physiol, 67; vet med officer, Plum Island Animal Dis Lab, Agr Res Serv, USDA, 67-69; from asst prof to assoc prof vet sci, Univ Ky, 69-74; assoc prof vet med, Col Vet Med, Univ Ill, Urbana, 74-76; MEM STAFF, PLUM ISLAND ANIMAL DIS CTR, SCI & EDUC ADMIN-AGR RES, USDA, 76- *Mem:* NY Acad Sci; Am Soc Vet Physiol & Pharmacol; Am Vet Med Asn; Am Soc Microbiol; Conf Res Workers Clin Dis. *Res:* Exotic viral diseases of food animals, research and development of foot and mouth diseases vaccines; participation in international vaccine field trials in South America. *Mailing Add:* 2930 Little Neck Rd Cutchogue NY 11935

MORGAN, DONALD PRYSE, b Indianapolis, Ind; m 52; c 3. PREVENTIVE MEDICINE. *Educ:* Ind Univ, MD, 47; Northwestern Univ, PhD(physiol), 53. *Prof Exp:* Asst prof physiol, Sch Med, Ind Univ, 53-54; asst prof, Med Sch, Northwestern Univ, 54-60; pvt pract, Ariz, 60-67; epidemiologist, Community Pesticide Proj, Univ Ariz, 67-73; asst prof prev med, 73-77, ASSOC PROF PREV MED, MED SCH, UNIV IOWA, 77- *Mem:* Soc Toxicol; Am Physiol Soc. *Res:* Pesticide toxicology; environmental toxicology. *Mailing Add:* Inst Agr Med Univ Iowa Med Sch Oakdale IA 52319

MORGAN, DONALD R, b Boston, Mass, May 26, 33; m 61; c 2. SOLID STATE PHYSICS. *Educ:* Boston Col, BS, 55, MS, 57; Univ Notre Dame, PhD(physics), 61. *Prof Exp:* Res engr, Melpar Inc, Mass, 56-57; instr physics, Univ Notre Dame, 60-61; from asst prof to assoc prof, 61-70, PROF PHYSICS, ST MARY'S COL, MINN, 70-, CHMN DIV NATURAL SCI & MATH, 62- *Mem:* Am Phys Soc; Am Asn Physics Teachers. *Res:* Physical electronics; thermionic and field emission with special emphasis on the effects of absorbed molecules on the work function. *Mailing Add:* Dept of Physics St Mary's Col Winona MN 55987

MORGAN, EVAN, b Spokane, Wash, Feb 26, 30; m 59; c 1. ANALYTICAL CHEMISTRY. *Educ:* Gonzaga Univ, BS, 52; Univ Wash, MS, 54, PhD(anal chem), 56. *Prof Exp:* Staff chemist, Int Bus Mach Corp, 56-60; group supvr, Olin Mathieson Chem Corp, 60-64; assoc prof chem, High Point Col, 64-65; sr chemist, Metall Res Dept, Reynolds Metals Co, Va, 65-72; group supvr, 72, sr res chemist, 72-81, SR RES SPECIALIST, BABCOCK & WILCOX, 81- *Mem:* Am Chem Soc; Am Soc Testing & Mat. *Res:* Electrochemistry; nuclear fuels; gas chromatography; evolved gas analysis; mass spectrometry. *Mailing Add:* PO Box 239 Lynchburg VA 24505

MORGAN, FRANK W, b Green Bay, Wis, Jan 9, 15; m 39; c 2. CHEMICAL ENGINEERING, MATHEMATICS. *Educ:* Purdue Univ, BSChE, 36; Union Univ, NY, MS, 70. *Prof Exp:* Chem engr, Texaco Res Ctr, Texaco, Inc, NY, 36-52, Tex, 52-55 & Beacon, 55-77; RETIRED. *Concurrent Pos:* Instr, Eve Div, Dutchess Community Col, 59-; mem comt info retrieval, Am Petrol Inst, 62-63; mkt assoc, Matt Jordan Realty, Inc, 77-; energy adv, NY State Energy Off, 81- *Mem:* Am Chem Soc; Am Statist Asn; Am Inst Chem Engrs; Am Soc Qual Control; Asn Comput Mach. *Res:* Gasoline middle distillate and lube oil processing; motor and diesel oil development; gasoline research; digital and analog computing; information retrieval. *Mailing Add:* Losee Rd Wappingers Falls NY 12590

MORGAN, GEORGE L, b Cleveland, Ohio, Aug 8, 37. INORGANIC CHEMISTRY. *Educ:* Case Inst, BS, 58; Univ Ill, MS, 60, PhD(inorg chem), 63. *Prof Exp:* From asst prof to assoc prof, 62-72, PROF INORG CHEM, UNIV WYO, 72- *Mem:* Am Chem Soc; Royal Soc Chem. *Res:* Electron-deficient bonding; structures of organometallic compounds; infrared and nuclear magnetic resonance spectroscopy. *Mailing Add:* Dept of Chem Univ of Wyo Laramie WY 82070

MORGAN, GEORGE WALLACE, b Shreveport, La, Aug 14, 41; m 62; c 4. POULTRY PHYSIOLOGY. *Educ:* Miss State Univ, BS, 64, MS, 66, PhD(animal physiol), 70. *Prof Exp:* Staff fel immunol, Div Biologics Standards, 70-73; physiologist, Bur Biologics, Food & Drug Admin, 73-74; ASST PROF IMMUNOL & PHYSIOLOGIST, DEPT POULTRY SCI, NC STATE UNIV, 74- *Mem:* Poultry Sci Asn; Sigma Xi. *Res:* Physiological regulation of immune responsiveness. *Mailing Add:* NC State Univ PO Box 5307 Raleigh NC 27650

MORGAN, H KEITH, b Indianapolis, Ind, June 6, 42. NUCLEAR PHARMACY. *Educ:* Purdue Univ, BS, 65, MS, 70, PhD(bionucleonics), 70. *Prof Exp:* Adv sr fel nuclear pharm, M D Anderson Hosp & Tumor Inst, 70-71; radiopharm instr, Univ Tex Med Br, 71-76; ASST PROF PHARMACEUT, UNIV HOUSTON COL PHARM, 76- *Mem:* Soc Nuclear Med; Am Pharmaceut Asn; Soc Health Physics; Am Soc Hosp Pharmacists; Am Asn Col Pharm. *Res:* Synthesis, development and evaluation of radiopharmaceuticals; use of radiation in pharmacy and biological rresearch, radiation health physics. *Mailing Add:* Col of Pharm Univ of Houston Houston TX 77027

MORGAN, HARRY CLARK, b Kalamazoo, Mich, Dec 17, 16; m; c 3. PHYSICS. *Educ:* Mich State Univ, BS, 38, MS, 39. *Prof Exp:* Physicist, Moraine Prod Div, Gen Motors Corp, 39-41; partner, Optron Labs, Ohio, 41-42; proj engr, Curtis Eng Co, 42-47; nuclear physicist, Mound Labs, Monsanto Chem Co, 47-49; owner, Morgan Instruments Co, 49-52; proj engr, Electronics Div, Century Metalcraft Corp, 52-54; lead engr instrumentation data handling, Rocketdyne Div, NAm Aviation Inc, 54-57; sr engr, Res Div, Cohu Electronics, Inc, 57-58; mem tech staff, Ramo Wooldridge Div, TRW, Inc, 58-60; mem tech staff, Autonetics Div, NAm Rockwell Corp, 60-70, space div, 70-71, sr staff assoc, Sci Ctr, 71-74; mem staff, Eon Instrumentation Inc, 74-77; consult & audio visual design, 79-81, sr engr, 2nd Found: Design Digital Scan Converters Med Ultrasonic Scanners, 79-81, ENG SPECIALIST, GUIDANCE & CONTROL SYSTS DIV, LITTON INDUST, INC, 81- *Mem:* Am Phys Soc; Inst Elec & Electronics Engrs; Am Inst Aeronaut & Astronaut. *Res:* Computers and digital data handling systems; optics and nuclear physics; analog electronic systems. *Mailing Add:* 9901 Lurline Apt 202 Chatsworth CA 91311

MORGAN, HORACE C, b Piedmont, Ala, July 3, 28; m 56; c 2. CLINICAL PATHOLOGY. *Educ:* Auburn Univ, DVM, 55, MS, 58. *Prof Exp:* Instr physiol, Auburn Univ, 55-58, asst prof, 58-59; asst prof clin path, Univ Ga, 60-61, from asst prof to assoc prof physiol, 61-65, assoc prof clin path, 65-70; prof & dir continuing educ & learning resources, 70-73, asst dean, 73-81, ASSOC DEAN, SCH VET MED, AUBURN UNIV, 81- *Concurrent Pos:* Consult, WHO, 73-81, Am Animal Hosp Asn, 80- *Mem:* Am Vet Med Asn; Am Soc Vet Physiol & Pharmacol; Am Soc Vet Clin Path (pres, 67); Am Physiol Soc; Biol Photog Asn. *Res:* Liver function; heartworm disease; renal function; medical photography; hematology of domestic animals; fetal electrocardiography. *Mailing Add:* Dept of Admin Sch of Vet Med Auburn Univ Auburn AL 36830

MORGAN, HOWARD E, b Bloomington, Ill, Oct 8, 27; m 47; c 3. PHYSIOLOGY, BIOCHEMISTRY. *Educ:* Johns Hopkins Univ, MD, 49. *Prof Exp:* Intern obstet & gynec, Vanderbilt Univ, 49-50, asst resident, 50-54, instr, 53-54, res assoc physiol, 54-55, from instr to prof, 57-67; prof, 67-80, EVAN PUGH PROF PHYSIOL, HERSHEY MED CTR, PA STATE UNIV, 80-, CHMN DEPT, 67- *Concurrent Pos:* Fel, Howard Hughes Med Inst, 54-55, investr, 57-; vis scientist, Cambridge Univ, 60-61; ed, Am J Physiol, 81; mem, Adv Coun, Nat Heart, Lung & Blood Inst, 79- *Mem:* Am Soc Biol Chemists; Am Physiol Soc; Int Soc Heart Res; Biophys Soc; Brit Biochem Soc. *Res:* Mechanism of hormone action; regulation of glucose and glycogen metabolism; membrane transport; regulation of protein and RNA turnover. *Mailing Add:* Dept of Physiol Pa State Univ Hershey Med Ctr Hershey PA 17033

MORGAN, IRA LON, b Ft Worth, Tex, Aug 3, 26; m 48; c 3. NUCLEAR PHYSICS. *Educ:* Tex Christian Univ, BA, 49, MA, 51; Univ Tex, PhD(physics), 54. *Prof Exp:* Instr physics, Tex Christian Univ, 48-51; res scientist, Univ Tex, 51-56; vpres nuclear physics, Tex Nuclear Corp, 56-60, exec vpres & dir res, 60-66, pres, 66-68; prof physics & dir ctr nuclear studies, Univ Tex, Austin, 68-73; pres, CSI Corp, 68-75; PRES, SCI MEASUREMENT SYSTS, INC, AUSTIN, TEX, 75- *Concurrent Pos:* AEC fel, 54-56; vpres, Nuclear-Chicago Corp, 65-78; consult, Los Alamos Sci Lab; mem, Bd Dirs, Capital Area Radiation & Res Found; chmn, Adv Comt Isotopes & Radiation Develop, AEC, 70-72; mem, Comn Nuclear Sci, Nat Res Coun & Tech Electronic Prod Radiation Safety Standards Comn, Food & Drug Admin, 74-77. *Mem:* Fel Am Phys Soc; fel Am Nuclear Soc; Am Inst Mgt. *Res:* Inelastic neutron scattering; activation analysis; radiation interaction in biological systems; photon tourography; nucleon-nucleon interactions. *Mailing Add:* 3800 Palomar Lane Austin TX 78759

MORGAN, JAMES FREDERICK, b Gretna, La, Oct 21, 15; m 43; c 6. INDUSTRIAL HYGIENE. *Educ:* George Washington Univ, BS, 39. *Prof Exp:* Asst chemist, US Food & Drug Admin, 39-42, biochemist, 46-47; head chem hygienist, Indust Hyg Found, Inc, 47-55; dir indust hyg, Pa RR Co, 55-61; asst to dir, Haskell Labs, 61-73, CONSULT INDUST HYG, E I DU PONT DE NEMOURS & CO, INC, 73- *Concurrent Pos:* Lectr, Grad Sch Pub Health, Univ Pittsburgh, 50-55; consult, Threshold Limit Values Comt, Am Cong Govt Indust Hyg, 72- *Mem:* Am Chem Soc; Am Indust Hyg Asn. *Res:* Physical and chemical environmental health factors; industrial toxicology; design of company operated industrial hygiene services; direction of company-wide industrial hygiene program; composition, analysis and health effects of diesel exhaust; scientific information storage and retrieval; industrial chemical carcinogenic agents. *Mailing Add:* 612 Merion Ave Havertown PA 19083

MORGAN, JAMES FREDERICK, b Minneapolis, Minn, June 20, 41; m 68; c 4. NUCLEAR PHYSICS. *Educ:* St Mary's Col, Minn, BA, 63; Univ Minn, MA, 66, PhD(physics), 68. *Prof Exp:* Res fel, Calif Inst Technol, 68-70; res assoc, Ohio State Univ, 70-74, asst prof nuclear physics, 74-77; MEM STAFF, LAWRENCE LIVERMORE LAB, UNIV CALIF, 77- *Mem:* Am Phys Soc. *Res:* Nuclear astrophysics; understanding of the origin and abundance of the elements, nuclear spectroscopy via analog resonances; understanding of extreme states of matter. *Mailing Add:* Lawrence Livermore Lab PO Box 808 L-43 Livermore CA 94550

MORGAN, JAMES JOHN, b New York, NY, June 23, 32; m 57; c 6. ENVIRONMENTAL SCIENCE, WATER CHEMISTRY. *Educ:* Manhattan Col, BCE, 54; Univ Mich, MSE, 56; Harvard Univ, AM, 62, PhD(water chem), 64. *Prof Exp:* Instr, Univ Ill, 56-60; assoc prof chem & eng, Univ Fla, 63-65; assoc prof eng, 65-69, dean students, 72-75, exec officer, 74-80, PROF ENVIRON ENG SCI, CALIF INST TECHNOL, 69-, VPRES STUDENTS AFFAIRS, 80- *Concurrent Pos:* Ed, Environ Sci & Technol, Am Chem Soc, 66-74. *Honors & Awards:* Water Purification Award, Am Water Works Asn, 63; Award, Am Chem Soc, 80. *Mem:* AAAS; Am Chem Soc; Am Water Works Asn; Am Soc Limnol & Oceanog. *Res:* Chemistry of natural water systems; coagulation processes in aqueous systems; water purification. *Mailing Add:* Div of Eng & Appl Sci Calif Inst of Technol Pasadena CA 91125

MORGAN, JAMES PHILIP, b Cincinnati, Ohio, Jan 13, 48; m 73. CLINICAL PHARMACOLOGY, CARDIOLOGY. *Educ:* Univ Cincinnati, BS, 70, MD, 76, PhD(pharmacol), 74. *Prof Exp:* Instr pharmacol, Univ Cincinnati, 76; clin fel internal med, Mayo Clin, 76-79, ASST PROF PHARMACOL & INSTR MED, MAYO MED SCH, 80-, FEL, CARDIOVASC DIS & INTERNAL MED & DIR, ADVAN CARDIAC LIFE SUPPORT PROG, MAYO CLIN, 79- *Concurrent Pos:*Dir, Advanced Cardiac Life Support Prog, Mayo Clin, 79-; affiliate fac, Minn Heart Asn, 80- *Mem:* Am Med Asn; Am Pharmaceut Asn; Am Col Physicians; Am Soc Internal Med. *Res:* Cardiovascular and autonomic pharmacology. *Mailing Add:* Mayo Clin First Ave SW Rochester MN 55901

MORGAN, JAMES RICHARD, b Tacoma, Wash, Oct 23, 53. EARTHQUAKE ENGINEERING. *Educ:* Univ Ill, BSCE, 75, MSCE, 77, PhD(civil eng), 79. *Prof Exp:* Res asst civil eng, Univ Ill, Urbana-Champaign, 75-79; asst prof, Univ Houston, 79-81; ASST PROF CIVIL ENG, TEX A&M UNIV, 81- *Concurrent Pos:* Teaching asst, Univ Ill, Urbana-Champaign, 77-78; prin investr, NSF, 80-82. *Mem:* Am Soc Civil Eng; Am Soc Eng Educ; Am Concrete Inst; Sigma Xi. *Res:* Structural mechanics and dynamics including earthquake ground motion effects on structures, foundation compliance and soil structure interaction; dynamic analysis of tension-leg offshore platforms; behavior and design of window glass. *Mailing Add:* Civil Eng Dept Tex A&M Univ College Station TX 77843

MORGAN, JOE PETER, b Olds, Iowa, July 30, 31; m 52; c 4. VETERINARY RADIOLOGY. *Educ:* Iowa State Teachers Col, BA, 52; Colo State Univ, DVM, 60, MS, 62; Royal Vet Col, Sweden, Vet med dr, 67. *Prof Exp:* Instr radiol, Colo State Univ, 60-63, asst prof, 63-64 & 67-68; chmn dept radiol sci, 74-77, PROF RADIOL, SCH VET MED, UNIV CALIF, DAVIS, 68- *Res:* Comparative orthopedics. *Mailing Add:* Dept of Radiol Sci Univ of Calif Sch of Vet Med Davis CA 95616

MORGAN, JOHN CLIFFORD, II, b Darby, Pa, Oct 29, 38; m 61; c 4. MATHEMATICAL STATISTICS, PURE MATHEMATICS. *Educ:* San Diego State Col, AB, 64; Univ Calif, Berkeley, MA, 68, PhD(statist), 71. *Prof Exp:* Asst prof math, Syracuse Univ, 72-76; asst prof, 76-78, ASSOC PROF MATH, CALIF STATE POLYTECH UNIV, POMONA, 78- *Mem:* Asn Symbolic Logis; Polish Math Soc; Am Statist Asn. *Res:* Methods of classifying point sets, including Baire category, measure theory and dimension theory; history of mathematics. *Mailing Add:* Dept of Math Calif State Polytech Univ Pomona CA 91768

MORGAN, JOHN D(AVIS), JR, b Newark, NJ, Feb 14, 21; m 53; c 2. MINERAL ENGINEERING, RESOURCE ECONOMICS. *Educ:* Pa State Col, BS, 42, MS, 47, PhD(mining eng), 48, EM, 50; Indust Col Armed Forces, dipl, 53. *Prof Exp:* Asst for mat & stockpile policies, Nat Security Resources Bd, 48-51; dir mat rev div, Defense Prod Admin, 51-53; strategic mat expert, Off Defense Mobilization, 53-56; head, Dept Sci & Math, Daytona Beach Community Col, 61-71; asst dir, 71-74, actg dir, 73-74 & 77-78, assoc dir, 74-78, CHIEF STAFF OFFICER, US BUR MINES, 79- *Concurrent Pos:* Rep, interdept stockpile comt, Munitions Bd, Dept Defense, 48-53; US Govt rep, UN Sci Conf Conserv & Utilization of Resources, 49; mem staff, President's Cabinet Mineral Policy Comt, 53-54; mem Nat Defense Exec Reserve, 56-; consult, Off Defense Mobilization, 56-61, mem spec stockpile adv comt to dir, 57-58; minerals indust consult, 56-71; mem comt scope & conduct of mat res, Nat Acad Sci, 59-60, mem comt mineral sci & technol & chmn panel on mineral econ & resources, 66-70; Dept Interior liaison, Coun Int Econ Policy staff, 73-77, Econ Policy Bd staff, 74-77, Fed Prepardeness Agency-Fed Emergency Mgt Agency stockpile activities, 76-, Dept Defense Mat Steering Group, 75- & Winter Energy Emergency Planning Group, Dept Energy, 77-; Dept Interior alt rep to Trade Policy Review Group, 75-81; chmn, Minerals Review Comt, Nonfuel Minerals Policy Study, 78. *Honors & Awards:* Nat Krumb lectr, 73. *Mem:* Fel Soc Am Mil Engrs; Sigma Xi; Am Defense Preparedness Asn; Am Inst Mining, Metall & Petrol Engrs; distinguished mem Soc Mining Engrs. *Res:* Geopolitics of strategic and critical materials; mineral economics and national mineral policy. *Mailing Add:* 5013 Worthington Dr Bethesda MD 20816

MORGAN, JOHN DERALD, b Hays, Kans, Mar 15, 39; m 62; c 4. ELECTRICAL ENGINEERING. *Educ:* La Polytech Inst, BSEE, 62; Univ Mo-Rolla, MSEE, 65; Ariz State Univ, PhD(eng), 68. *Prof Exp:* Elec engr, Tex Eastman Div, Eastman Kodak Co, 62-63; instr elec eng, Univ Mo-Rolla, 63-65 & Ariz State Univ, 65-68; assoc prof, 68-76, EMERSON ELEC PROF ELEC ENG, UNIV MO-ROLLA, 76-, CHMN DEPT, 78- *Concurrent Pos:* Consult, Ariz Pub Serv Co, 68, A B Chance Co, 69-, Westinghouse Corp, 70- & Emerson Elec, 76-; mem planning comt elec div, Am Power Conf, 68-; vis prof, Carnegie-Mellon Univ, 70 & Univ Pittsburgh, 70; Nat Acad Sci exchange prof, Romania, 71. *Mem:* Sr mem Inst Elec & Electronics Engrs; Am Soc Eng Educ; Am Soc Testing & Mat; Nat Soc Prof Engrs. *Res:* Power systems control, analysis, and design; power apparatus testing techniques; high voltage operation of power systems; dielectric materials analysis and design. *Mailing Add:* Dept of Elec Eng Univ Mo Rolla MO 65401

MORGAN, JOHN WALTER, b Walsall, Eng, Jan 27, 32; m 59; c 2. GEOCHEMISTRY, RADIOCHEMISTRY. *Educ:* Univ Birmingham, BSc, 55; Australian Nat Univ, PhD(geochem), 66. *Prof Exp:* Sci asst electronics, Atomic Energy Res Estab, UK, 48-51, asst exp off, 51-52, anal chem, 55-59; exp off, Australian Atomic Energy Comn Res Estab, 59-61, sr res scientist, 66-68; res asst geochem, Australian Nat Univ, 61-66, res fel, 66; res assoc, Univ Ky, 68-69, chem, 69-70; sr res assoc geochem, Enrico Fermi Inst, Univ Chicago, 70-76; assoc prof geochem, Univ Tex, San Antonio, 76-77; res chemist, 77-80, CHIEF CHEMIST, US GEOL SURV, RESTON, VA, 81- *Mem:* AAAS; Am Chem Soc; Inst Asn Geochem & Cosmochem; Am Geophys Union; Meteoritical Soc. *Res:* Application of analytical chemistry, particularly those aspects involving isotope and radiochemistry to the problems of earth and space science. *Mailing Add:* US Geol Surv MS-924 Nat Ctr Reston VA 22092

MORGAN, JOSEPH, b Kiev, Russia, Mar 4, 09; nat US; m 42; c 2. PHYSICS, X-RAY CRYSTALLOGRAPHY. *Educ:* Temple Univ, AB, 31, MA, 33; Mass Inst Technol, PhD(physics), 37. *Prof Exp:* Asst physics, Temple Univ, 29-31; supvr, Wave Length Proj, Mass Inst Technol, 37-38; from instr to asst prof physics, Tex Agr & Mech Col, 38-41; from asst prof to prof physics, 41-78, dir res coord, 69-76, EMER PROF PHYSICS, TEX CHRISTIAN UNIV, 78- *Concurrent Pos:* Dir eng, Tex Christian Univ, 52-69, chmn, Div Natural Sci, 53-55 & Dept Physics, 58-59, vpres, Univ Res Found, 66-73. *Mem:* Am Phys Soc; Am Asn Physics Teachers. *Res:* Optical spectroscopy and physical optics; x-ray diffraction; neutron diffraction; nuclear physics. *Mailing Add:* 9004 Windflower Lane Annandale VA 22003

MORGAN, JULIET, b Clacton-on-Sea, Eng, Jan 30, 37; m 59; c 2. CELL BIOLOGY, ZOOLOGY. *Educ:* Australian Nat Univ, BSc, 66; MacQuarie Univ, MS, 68; Univ Ky, PhD(cell biol), 70. *Prof Exp:* Asst zool, Australian Nat Univ, 64-66; exp officer, Australian AEC, 66-68; res asst cell biol, T H Morgan Sch Biol Sci, Univ Ky, 68-70; asst prof, 78-81, ASSOC PROF CELL BIOL, DEPT MED, UNIV CHICAGO, 81-, RES ASSOC, 78- *Concurrent Pos:* Proj dir & coprin investr, Multiple Risk Factor Intervention Trial, 78-82. *Mem:* Tissue Culture Asn; Soc Exp Biol & Med; Sigma Xi. *Res:* Basic research in muscle disease; cell structure and function; cell recognition, aggregation and adhesion; cell ultrastructure; preventive medicine; reduction of heart attacks in middle aged men. *Mailing Add:* Dept of Med Univ of Chicago Chicago IL 60637

MORGAN, KATHLEEN GREIVE, b Dayton, Ohio, Sept 22, 50; m 73; c 1. PHARMACOLOGY, BIOPHYSICS. *Educ:* Col Mt St Joseph, BS, 72; Univ Cincinnati, PhD(pharmacol), 76. *Prof Exp:* Grass fel, 75, fel, 76-79, ASST PROF PHYSIOL, MAYO FOUND, 79-, ASST PROF PHARMACOL, 81- *Concurrent Pos:* Minn Heart Asn fel, 77- *Mem:* AAAS; Am Physiol Soc; Sigma Xi; Biophys Soc. *Res:* Vascular and gastrontestinal smooth muscle; smooth muscle; pharmacology and electrophysiology of microcirculation; putative peptide neurotransmitters. *Mailing Add:* Dept Pharmacol Mayo Found Rochester MN 55905

MORGAN, KATHRYN A, b Riverside, Calif, Nov 18, 22. MATHEMATICS. *Educ:* Stanford Univ, AB, 42, AM, 43, PhD(math), 46. *Prof Exp:* From instr to asst prof, 46-57, ASSOC PROF MATH, SYRACUSE UNIV,.57- *Res:* Number theory. *Mailing Add:* Dept of Math Syracuse Univ Syracuse NY 13210

MORGAN, LEE ROY, JR, b New Orleans, La, Nov 5, 36; m 57; c 4. PHARMACOLOGY, CHEMOTHERAPY. *Educ:* Tulane Univ, BS, 58, MS, 59, PhD, 60; Imp Col, Univ London, DIC, 61; La State Univ, MD, 71. *Prof Exp:* Instr, 61-63, asst prof, 63-72, assoc prof, 72-73, PROF PHARMACOL, SCH MED, LA STATE UNIV, MED CTR, 73-, CHMN DEPT, 80- *Concurrent Pos:* Res assoc, Imp Col, Univ London, 60-61; asst prof, Loyola Univ, 61-63; vis prof pharmacol, Sch Med, Univ Costa Rica, 63; consult clin biochemist, Charity Hosp, New Orleans, 67- *Honors & Awards:* Sigma Xi Award, 58. *Mem:* AAAS; Am Chem Soc; Royal Soc Chem; Soc Exp Med & Biol; Am Asn Cancer Res. *Res:* Drug profiles; enzyme kinetics; immunology and chemotherapy of cancer. *Mailing Add:* Pharmacol Dept La State Univ Sch Med 1901 Perdido St New Orleans LA 70112

MORGAN, LEON OWEN, b Oklahoma City, Okla, Oct 25, 19; m 42; c 4. CHEMISTRY. *Educ:* Oklahoma City Univ, BA, 41; Univ Tex, MS, 43; Univ Calif, PhD(chem), 48. *Prof Exp:* Anal chemist, Okla Gas & Elec Co, 41; instr chem, Univ Tex, 41-44; res assoc, Metall Lab, Univ Chicago, 44-45; chemist, Radiation Labs, Univ Calif, 45-47; from asst prof to assoc prof, 47-61, PROF CHEM, UNIV TEX, AUSTIN, 62- *Concurrent Pos:* Consult, Los Alamos Nat Lab, 61- *Mem:* Am Chem Soc; Am Phys Soc. *Res:* Transuranium elements; nuclear and electron paramagnetic resonance and relaxation; fast reaction rate processes; radiation effects; inorganic biochemistry. *Mailing Add:* Dept Chem Univ Tex Austin TX 78712

MORGAN, LUCIAN L(LOYD), b Wichita Falls, Tex, Dec 22, 28. AEROSPACE ENGINEERING, CHEMICAL ENGINEERING. *Educ:* Tex A&M Univ, BS, 49; Southern Methodist Univ, MS, 59; Univ Southern Calif, MS, 75. *Prof Exp:* Process engr, US Gypsum Co, 49-50; process analyst, Gen Dynamics/Ft Worth, 50-52, sr chemist, 52-55, res chemist, 55-56, asst chief chemist, 56-58, sr eng chemist, 58-60, design specialist supvr, Gen Dynamics/Astronautics, 60-62; res specialist, 62-63, staff engr, 63-67, sr staff engr, 67-80, MGR SYST ENG, LOCKHEED MISSILES & SPACE CO, 80- *Mem:* Am Inst Aeronaut & Astronaut; Air Force Asn. *Res:* Laser systems; vehicle design; project engineering; high energy laser systems. *Mailing Add:* Lockheed Missiles & Space Co 3251 Hanover St Palo Alto CA 94304

MORGAN, M(ILLETT) GRANGER, b Hanover, NH, Mar 17, 41; m 63; c 2. SCIENCE POLICY, ENVIRONMENTAL MANAGEMENT. *Educ:* Harvard Univ, BA, 63; Cornell Univ, MS, 65; Univ Calif, San Diego, PhD(appl physics), 69. *Prof Exp:* Lectr appl physics & info sci, Univ Calif, San Diego, 70-71, actg asst prof info sci, 71-72, dir comput jobs through training proj, 69-72; prog dir, Comput Impact on Soc, NSF, 72-74; assoc res physicist, Biomed & Environ Assessment Group, Brookhaven Nat Lab, 74-75; asst prof elec eng & pub affairs & coordr elec eng & pub affairs grad prog, 75-77, PROF ELEC ENG, ENG & PUB POLICY & HEAD DEPT ENG & PUB POLICY, CARNEGIE-MELLON UNIV, 80- *Concurrent Pos:* Consult, NSF, 74- & Brookhaven Nat Lab, 75-; mem, Health Risk Assessment Sub Comt, Sci Adv Bd, Environ Protection Agency; mem review comt, Environ Impact Studies Div, Argonne Nat Lab. *Mem:* AAAS; Am Geophys Union; Inst Elec & Electronics Engrs; Air Pollution Control Asn. *Res:* Problems in technology and public policy in which technical issues play a central role; techniques for dealing with uncertainty in quantitative policy analysis; risk assessment; social impacts of eletrical technologies. *Mailing Add:* Eng & Pub Policy Carnegie-Mellon Univ Pittsburgh PA 15213

MORGAN, MARVIN THOMAS, b Nashville, Tenn, Jan 27, 21. NUCLEAR ENGINEERING. *Educ:* Tenn Technol Univ, BS, 50. *Prof Exp:* Jr physicist irradiation & post irradiation exp on high temperature gas-cooled reactor fuel, 51-53, assoc physicist, 53-56, physicist, 56-70, res assoc, 70-76, develop assoc nuclear waste disposal, 76-77, DEVELOP STAFF MEM NUCLEAR WASTE DISPOSAL, OAK RIDGE NAT LAB, 77- *Mem:* Sigma Xi. *Res:* High temperature gas-cooled reactor fuels; nuclear waste fixation in concrete; thermal properties of rocks and concrete; properties of concrete related to borehole plugging. *Mailing Add:* 109 N Purdue Ave Oak Ridge TN 37830

MORGAN, MEREDITH WALTER, b Kingman, Ariz, Mar 22, 12; m 37; c 1. OPTOMETRY, VISUAL PHYSIOLOGY. *Educ:* Univ Calif, AB, 34, MA, 39, PhD(physiol), 41. *Hon Degrees:* DOS, Ill Col Optom, 68; DOS, Southern Calif Col Optom, 75; DSc, Pa Col Optom, 76. *Prof Exp:* Clin asst optom, 36-42, from instr to assoc prof, 42-51, dean sch optom, 60-73, prof physiol optics & optom, 51-75, EMER PROF PHYSIOL OPTICS & OPTOM, UNIV CALIF, BERKELEY, 75- *Concurrent Pos:* Pvt pract, 34-60; mem ed coun, Am J Optom, 55-74; mem, Coun Optom Educ, 60-73; mem rev comt construct schs optom, USPHS, 64-65, nat adv coun med, dent, optom, podiatric & vet educ, 65-67; mem adv coun, Nat Eye Inst, 69-71; vis prof, Univ Waterloo, Can, 74 & Univ Ala, 77. *Honors & Awards:* Nelson Achievement Award, 59; Prentice Medal, Am Acad Optom, 67; Apollo Award, Am Optom Asn, 75. *Mem:* Am Optom Asn; AAAS; Geront Soc; Am Acad Optom (pres, 53-54). *Res:* Accommodation and convergence; binocular vision. *Mailing Add:* 1217 Skycrest 4 Walnut Creek CA 94595

MORGAN, MERLE L(OREN), b Whittier, Calif, May 28, 19; m 52; c 2. PRECISION ELECTRICAL MEASUREMENTS. *Educ:* Calif Inst Technol, BS, 49, MS, 50, PhD(elec eng), 54. *Prof Exp:* Res engr, McCullough Tool Co, Calif, 46-48; dir res & eng, Electro-Sci Industs, 54-78; CONSULT, 78- *Mem:* Inst Elec & Electronics Engrs. *Res:* Precision electrical measurements. *Mailing Add:* 1480 NW 138th Ave Portland OR 97229

MORGAN, MICHAEL ALLEN, b Los Angeles, Calif, July 8, 48; m 66. ELECTRICAL ENGINEERING, APPLIED MATHEMATICS. *Educ:* Calif State Polytech Univ, BS, 71; Univ Calif, Berkeley, MS, 73, PhD(elec eng, comput sci), 76. *Prof Exp:* Staff scientist, Sci Appl, Inc, 75; res asst, Univ Calif, Berkeley, 71-76; res eng in radar systs, Stanford Res Inst, 76-77; asst prof elec eng, Univ Miss, 77-80; MEM FAC, DEPT ELEC ENG, NAVAL POST GRAD SCH, 80- *Concurrent Pos:* Consult, Stanford Res Inst, 77-78 & Dept of Bioeng, Univ Utah, 78-; consult, Arnold Eng Develop Ctr, 78- *Mem:* Inst Elec & Electronics Engrs, 76- *Res:* Electromagnetics; antennas; microwave techniques; communications theory and signal processing; nxnumerical analysis; applied mathematics and statistics. *Mailing Add:* Dept of Elec Eng Naval Post Grad Sch Monterey CA 93940

MORGAN, MICHAEL DEAN, b Marion, Ind, Oct 27, 41; m 66; c 1. PLANT ECOLOGY. *Educ:* Butler Univ, BA, 63; Univ Ill, Urbana-Champaign, MS, 65, PhD(bot), 68. *Prof Exp:* Asst prof, 68-72, ASSOC PROF BIOL, UNIV WIS-GREEN BAY, 72- *Concurrent Pos:* Wis Alumni Res Fund grant, Univ Wis-Green Bay, 72. *Mem:* Ecol Soc Am; Am Inst Biol Sci; AAAS; Sigma Xi; Nat Sci Teachers Asn. *Res:* Relationships between climatic change and plant distribution and production; ecological relationships during late Pleistocene; plant phenology; science education for nonscience majors. *Mailing Add:* Col of Environ Sci Univ of Wis Green Bay WI 54302

MORGAN, MONROE TALTON, SR, b Mars Hill, NC, June 29, 33; m 60; c 2. ENVIRONMENTAL HEALTH, PUBLIC HEALTH. *Educ:* ETenn State Univ, BA & CPHS, 60; Univ NC, Chapel Hill, MSPH, 62; Tulane Univ, La, DrPh(environ & pub health), 69. *Prof Exp:* Sanitarian, Fairfax County Health Dept, Va, 60-61; training officer pub health, Va State Health Dept, 62-63; PROF ENVIRON HEALTH & CHMN DEPT, E TENN STATE UNIV, 63- *Concurrent Pos:* Consult ed, Nat J Environ Health, 69-; consult environ health educ, Nat Environ Health Asn, 70-; mem, Pub Health Rev Comt, 71-75. *Mem:* Am Pub Health Asn; Nat Environ Health Asn (2nd vpres, 71-). *Res:* Survival of aerobic sporeformers and mycobacterium tuberculosis vas hominis; human ecology as it relates to environmental stresses. *Mailing Add:* Dept of Environ Health ETenn State Univ Johnson City TN 37601

MORGAN, MORRIS HERBERT, b Atlanta, Ga, Feb 10, 50; m 69; c 1. CHEMICAL ENGINEERING. *Educ:* Vanderbilt Univ, BS, 69; Univ Dayton, BS, 73; Rensselaer Polytech Inst, PhD(chem eng), 78. *Prof Exp:* Develop engr chem eng, Inland Mfg Div Gen Motors Corp, 69-72; safety engr chem eng, Mound Labs Monsanto Co, 72-73; STAFF CHEM ENGR, GEN ELEC RES & DEVELOP CTR, 73- *Concurrent Pos:* Mem NY State comt, high technol, 78-79; mem comt Educ & Utilization Engrs, Nat Acad Engrs, 81. *Mem:* Am Inst Chem Engr. *Res:* Fluid and particle mechanics of spouted bed systems; fluid bed reactor modeling and hetagenous catalysis. *Mailing Add:* Rm 4B34 Bldg KY Gen Elec Corp Res & Develop Ctr Schenectady NY 12345

MORGAN, NEAL O, b Los Angeles, Calif, May 13, 28; m 52; c 3. MEDICAL ENTOMOLOGY, ECOLOGY. *Educ:* SDak State Col, BS, 56, MS, 57; Va Polytech Inst, PhD(entom), 62. *Prof Exp:* Entomologist, Entom Res Div, Tex, 61-65, invest leader fly control, Md, 65-72, res entomologist, Chem & Biophys Control Lab, Agr Environ Qual Inst, Entom Res Div, 72-76, chief, biol eval chem lab, 76-79, SUPVR, RES ENTOM LIVESTOCK INSPECTION LAB, AGR ENVIRON QUAL INST, AGR RES SERV, USDA, BELTSVILLE, 79- *Mem:* Entom Soc Am; Ecol Soc Am. *Res:* Insects and ticks affecting man and animals, their ecology, physiology and control methods; electromagnetic forces as insect attractants and repellants; insect fumigants. *Mailing Add:* Bldg 476 Beltsville Agr Res Ctr-E Beltsville MD 20705

MORGAN, OMAR DRENNAN, JR, b Shelbyville, Mo, Mar 5, 13; m 42; c 2. PLANT PATHOLOGY. *Educ:* Ill State Univ, BEd, 40; Univ Ill, PhD(plant path), 50. *Prof Exp:* Teacher high sch, 41-42; asst plant path, Univ Ill, 48-49; from asst prof to prof plant path, Univ Md, 49-81; RETIRED. *Mem:* Am Phytopath Soc. *Res:* Soil fumigation for control of soil borne diseases; developing tobacco resistance to major diseases. *Mailing Add:* 3108 Gumwood Dr Hyattsville MD 20783

MORGAN, ORA BILLY, JR, b Kershaw, SC, March 24, 30; m 53; c 2. NUCLEAR ENGINEERING, ENGINEERING PHYSICS. *Educ:* NC State Univ, BS, 56, MS, 58; Univ Wis, PhD(nuclear eng), 70. *Prof Exp:* Res staff mem fusion energy, Oak Ridge Nat Lab, 58-62, assoc group leader, 62-69, group leader, 69-74, assoc div dir, 74-77, DIV DIR FUSION ENERGY, OAK RIDGE NAT LAB, 77- *Concurrent Pos:* Oak Ridge Nat Lab fel, Univ Wis, 66-68. *Mem:* Fel Am Phys Soc; Am Nuclear Soc. *Res:* Developing fusion reactors as a long-term energy source with special emphasis on developing, applying and understanding ion sources and neutral injection plasma heating systems. *Mailing Add:* Oak Ridge Nat Lab PO Box Y Bldg 9201-2 Oak Ridge TN 37830

MORGAN, PAGE WESLEY, b Phoenix, Ariz, Apr 3, 33; m 55; c 3. PLANT PHYSIOLOGY, BIOCHEMISTRY. *Educ:* Tex A&M UNiv, BS, 55, MS, 58, PhD(plant physiol), 61. *Prof Exp:* Asst plant physiol & range mgt, 56-58, Anderson-Clayton fel plant physiol, 58-60, from asst prof to assoc prof, 60-69, PROF PLANT PHYSIOL, TEX A&M UNIV, 69- *Concurrent Pos:* Cotton Producers Inst grants, 62-73; NSF grants, 64-74; mem, Plant Growth Regulator Working Group, Am Soc Plant Physiol. *Mem:* Am Soc Plant Physiol; Japanese Soc Plant Physiol. *Res:* Plant regulatory mechanisms; phytohormones; enzymes; destruction of auxin; synthesis of ethylene; interaction of phytohormones; auxin transport; floral initiation; apical dominance in grain sorghum. *Mailing Add:* Dept of Plant Sci Tex A&M Univ College Station TX 77843

MORGAN, PAUL E(MERSON), b Hudson, Iowa, June 18, 23; m 45; c 3. CIVIL ENGINEERING. *Educ:* Iowa State Univ, BS, 44, MS, 56. *Prof Exp:* City engr, Algona, Iowa, 46-48; consult, Estherville, Iowa, 48-50; sanit engr, State Dept Health, Iowa, 50-53; from asst prof to assoc prof civil eng, 53-64, asst dean, Col Eng, 64-69, PROF CIVIL ENG, IOWA STATE UNIV, 64-, ASSOC DEAN, COL ENG, 69-, DIR ENG EXTEN, 81- *Mem:* Am Soc Civil Engrs; Nat Soc Prof Engrs; Am Waterworks Asn; Am Soc Eng Educ; Water Pollution Control Fedn. *Res:* Water. *Mailing Add:* 104 Marston Hall Iowa State Univ Ames IA 50011

MORGAN, PAUL HARPER, b Paris, Tenn, Aug 15, 40. BIOCHEMISTRY. *Educ:* Bethel Col, Tenn, BS, 63; Vanderbilt Univ, PhD(biochem), 70. *Prof Exp:* Instr chem, David Lipscomb High Sch, Nashville, Tenn, 63-65; NIH sr fel biochem, Univ Wash, 70-72; ASST PROF BIOCHEM, UNIV S ALA, 72- *Mem:* Am Chem Soc; Sigma Xi. *Res:* Mechanism of activation of the first component of complement; development of quantitative models for the interpretation of nutritional responses and animal growth curves. *Mailing Add:* Dept of Biochem Univ of SAla Col of Med Mobile AL 36688

MORGAN, PAUL NOLAN, b Konawa, Okla, Jan 15, 27; m 52; c 3. MICROBIOLOGY, IMMUNOLOGY. *Educ:* Univ Ark, BS, 52, MS, 56; Univ Okla, PhD(microbiol), 63. *Prof Exp:* Res microbiologist, Med Res Sect, 63-74, CLIN VIROLOGIST, LAB SERV, VET ADMIN HOSP, 74- *Concurrent Pos:* From asst to prof microbiol, Med Ctr, Univ Ark, Little Rock, 63-78. *Mem:* AAAS; Am Soc Microbiol; Am Soc Trop Med & Hyg; Int Soc Toxinology. *Res:* Viral replication in cell cultures; basic immunochemistry; spider venoms. *Mailing Add:* Vet Admin Hosp Med Res Sect 300 E Roosevelt Rd Little Rock AR 72206

MORGAN, PAUL WINTHROP, b West Chesterfield, NH, Aug 30, 11; m 39; c 2. TEXTILE FIBERS, POLYMER SYNTHESIS. *Educ:* Univ Maine, BS, 37; Ohio State Univ, PhD(org chem), 40. *Prof Exp:* Asst chem, Ohio State Univ, 37-40, Du Pont fel, 40-41; res chemist, E I du Pont de Nemours & Co, 41-46, res assoc, 46-50, Pioneering Res Labs, Textile Fibers Dept, Exp Sta, E I du Pont De Nemours & Co, 50-57, res fel, 57-73, sr res fel, 73-76; CONSULT, 76- *Concurrent Pos:* Mem, Polymer Nomenclature Comt, Am Chem Soc, 70-75; chmn, Gordon Conf Polymers, 74, Polymer Div Awards Comt, 75-76, alt coun, 76-77, coun, 78. *Honors & Awards:* Am Chem Soc Award, 60, Polymer Chem Award, 76; Howard N Potts Medal, Franklin Inst, 76; Swinburne Medal, Plastics & Rubber Inst, London, 78; Citation, Am Soc Metals, 78. *Mem:* Nat Acad Eng; Franklin Inst; Am Chem Soc. *Res:* Cellulose derivatives; moisture permeability of polymers; low temperature and interfacial polycondensations; condensation polymers; thermally stable polymers; extended chain polymers and their liquid crystalline solutions; high strength-high modulus fibers; tire cord and reinforcement fibers. *Mailing Add:* 822 Roslyn Ave West Chester PA 19380

MORGAN, R JOHN, b Fairfax, Okla, Nov 28, 23. BIOMEDICAL ENGINEERING. *Educ:* Colo Sch Mines, EM, 49; Colo State Univ, MS, 60; Iowa State Univ, PhD(biomed eng), 69. *Prof Exp:* Design engr, Aeronaut Electronics, Inc, 49-52 & Sandia Corp, 52-54; pres, Scintillonics, Inc, 54-62; from instr to asst prof elec eng, 60-67, asst prof bioeng, 67-80, ASSOC PROF BIOENG, COLO STATE UNIV, 80- *Concurrent Pos:* Consult instrumentation probs, TV stas & indust co, 58- *Mem:* AAAS; Inst Elec & Electronics Engrs; Instrument Soc Am. *Res:* Data processing of neuroelectric signals from animals and man. *Mailing Add:* Dept of Physiol & Biophys Colo State Univ Ft Collins CO 80523

MORGAN, RAYMOND P, b Frederick, Md, Nov 24, 43; div; c 2. ECOLOGY, PHYSIOLOGY. *Educ:* Frostburg State Col, BS, 66; Univ Md, PhD(zool), 71. *Prof Exp:* Res assoc, Univ Md, 71-74, res asst prof, 74-77; prin res scientist, Columbus Div, Battelle Mem Inst, 77-79; ASST PROF, UNIV MD, 79- *Mem:* Am Fisheries Soc; AAAS; Am Inst Fishery Res Biologist; Am Soc Zoologists; Estuarine Res Fedn. *Res:* Biochemical systematics; pollution ecology; physiological ecology; ecology of fishes. *Mailing Add:* Appalachian Environ Lab Frostburg State Col Gunter Hall Frostburg MD 21532

MORGAN, RAYMOND VICTOR, JR, b Brownwood, Tex, May 10, 42; m 67. MATHEMATICS. *Educ:* Howard Payne Col, BA, 64; Vanderbilt Univ, MA, 65; Univ Mo, PhD(math), 69. *Prof Exp:* Instr math, Univ Mo, 69; asst prof math, Southern Methodist Univ, 69-75; ASSOC PROF MATH & CHMN DEPT, SUL ROSS STATE UNIV, ALPINE, TEX, 75-, DIR, SCI DIV, 79- *Mem:* Nat Coun Teachers Math; Am Math Soc; Math Asn Am. *Res:* Non-associative algebra; generalizations of alternative algebras and their structures relative to Peirce decompositions and Wedderburn decompositions. *Mailing Add:* Dept of Math Sul Ross State Univ Alpine TX 79830

MORGAN, RELBUE MARVIN, b Oxford, Miss, May 7, 39; m 58. PHYSICS. *Educ:* Christian Bros Col, BS, 62; Iowa State Univ, PhD(physics), 67. *Prof Exp:* Asst prof, 67-69, ASSOC PROF PHYSICS, CHRISTIAN BROS COL, 69- *Mem:* Am Phys Soc; Am Asn Physics Teachers. *Res:* Electronic properties of metals and alloys; electrical and optical properties of thin metal films. *Mailing Add:* Dept of Physics Christian Bros Col Memphis TN 38104

MORGAN, RICHARD C, b Jamaica, NY, June 9, 38; m 61; c 3. APPLIED MATHEMATICS. *Educ:* Stevens Inst Technol, BE, 59; NY Univ, MS, 62, PhD(math), 65. *Prof Exp:* From instr to assoc prof math, St John's Univ, NY, 60-69, chmn dept, 65-70, prof, 69-80; MEM FAC, UNIV MD, COLLEGE PARK, 80- *Mem:* Am Math Soc; Math Asn Am; Inst Elec & Electronics Eng. *Res:* Electromagnetic diffraction theory; partial differential equations; fluid dynamics. *Mailing Add:* Univ Md College Park MD 20742

MORGAN, ROBERT LEE, b Clawson, Mich, Nov 26, 29; m 52; c 2. ORGANIC CHEMISTRY. *Educ:* Antioch Col, BS, 52; Univ Chicago, PhD(chem), 60. *Prof Exp:* Asst chemist, Univ Chicago, 52-53; org res chemist, Cent Res Dept, E I du Pont de Nemours & Co, 60-62, res chemist, Elastomers Dept, 62-67, prod develop chemist, 67-71, market develop rep, 71-72, supvr wire & cable indust develop & serv, 72-74, DIV HEAD, PROD DEVELOP, ELASTOMERS DEPT, E I DU PONT DE NEMOURS & CO, INC, 74- *Concurrent Pos:* Inst, Salem Col, 52. *Res:* Steroids; organo-inorganic chemistry; homogeneous catalysis; elastomers. *Mailing Add:* E I du Pont de Nemours & Brandywine Bldgs E I du Pont de Nemours & Co Inc Wilmington DE 19802

MORGAN, ROBERT P, b Brooklyn, NY, Feb 26, 34; m 58; c 2. TECHNOLOGY & HUMAN AFFAIRS. *Educ:* Cooper Union, BChE, 56; Mass Inst Technol, MS, 59, NuclE, 61; Rensselaer Polytech Inst, PhD(chem eng), 65. *Prof Exp:* Asst dir, Oak Ridge Eng Pract Sch, Mass Inst Technol, 58-59; instr chem eng, Rensselaer Polytech Inst, 60-64; asst prof nuclear & chem eng, Univ Mo-Columbia, 64-68; vis assoc prof eng & actg dir int develop technol prog, 68-69, assoc prof eng & dir ctr develop technol, 69-76, PROF ENG, WASH UNIV, 76-, CHMN DEPT TECHNOL & HUMAN AFFAIRS, 71- *Concurrent Pos:* Consult, Off Sci & Soc, NSF, 77-79 & NASA, 78-80; nat lectr, Sigma Xi, 80-82. *Honors & Awards:* Chester F Carlson Award, Am Soc Eng Educ, 78. *Mem:* AAAS; Fedn Am Sci; Am Soc Eng Educ. *Res:* Science, technology and international development; appropriate technology for renewable resource utilization. *Mailing Add:* Dept of Technol & Human Affairs Wash Univ St Louis MO 63130

MORGAN, RUSSELL HEDLEY, b London, Ont, Oct 9, 11; nat US; m 38; c 2. RADIOLOGY. *Educ:* Univ Western Ont, BA, 34, MD, 37. *Hon Degrees:* DSc, Univ Western Ont, 63, Univ Chicago, 69. *Prof Exp:* From instr to assoc prof roentgenol, Univ Chicago, 42-46; med officer-in-chg radiol sect, Tuberc Control Div, USPHS, 44-46; prof radiol, Sch Med, 46-77, radiologist-in-chief, Univ Hosp, 46-71, dean sch med, 71-75, vpres health divs, 73-75, univ prof med, 75-77, EMER PROF RADIOL, EMER PROF ENVIRON HEALTH SCI & EMER UNIV PROF MED, JOHNS HOPKINS UNIV, 77- *Concurrent Pos:* Sr consult radiation, Off Surgeon Gen, USPHS. *Mem:* Am Roentgen Ray Soc; Am Thoracic Soc; Radiol Soc NAm; Am Col Radiol. *Res:* Electronic image tubes; angiocardiographic methods for detection of gastric cancer; mass photofluorographic examinations of the chest for tuberculosis; design of x-ray automatic timers. *Mailing Add:* Off Dean Sch Med Johns Hopkins Univ Baltimore MD 21205

MORGAN, SAMUEL POPE, b San Diego, Calif, July 14, 23; m 48; c 4. MATHEMATICAL PHYSICS, COMPUTER SCIENCE. *Educ:* Calif Inst Technol, BS, 43, MS, 44, PhD(physics), 47. *Prof Exp:* Asst physics, Univ Calif, 43-44 & Calif Inst Technol, 44-47; mem tech staff, Bell Tel Labs, 47-59, head, Math Physics Dept, 59-67, dir comput technol, 69-70, DIR COMPUT SCI RES, BELL LABS, INC, NJ, 67- *Mem:* AAAS; Am Phys Soc; Soc Indust & Appl Math; Asn Comput Mach. *Res:* Electromagnetic theory; mechanics of continua; wave propagation; special mathematical functions; numerical methods; research administration. *Mailing Add:* Comput Sci Res Ctr Bell Labs Inc Murray Hill NJ 07974

MORGAN, STANLEY L, b Sandyville, Ohio, Jan 28, 18; m 41; c 3. PHARMACEUTICS, CHEMICAL ENGINEERING. *Educ:* Case Inst Technol, BSChE, 39. *Prof Exp:* Chem engr, 40-42, mgr blood plasma labs, 42-43, gen mgr, 43-63, vpres, 63-64, EXEC VPRES, BEN VENUE LABS, INC, 64- *Mem:* Am Inst Chem Engrs; Am Chem Soc; NY Acad Sci; Am Soc Testing & Mat; fel Am Inst Chem. *Res:* Pharmaceuticals under aseptic conditions; ethylene oxide sterilization; freeze drying; racing chemistry; preservation of viable organisms; cryobiology. *Mailing Add:* 270 Northfield Rd Bedford OH 44146

MORGAN, THOMAS ANTHONY, physics, see previous edition

MORGAN, THOMAS EDWARD, astrophysics, see previous edition

MORGAN, THOMAS EDWARD, JR, b Jacksonville, Fla, Nov 9, 29; m 54; c 3. INTERNAL MEDICINE, BIOCHEMISTRY. *Educ:* Duke Univ, BS, 50, MD, 54. *Prof Exp:* Intern & resident med, Hosps, Stanford & Columbia Univs, 54-57; asst physician, Presby Hosp, New York, 57-60; res assoc biochem, Sch Med, Univ Wash, 62-64, asst prof internal med, 64-68, assoc prof med, 68-73, assoc dean acad affairs, 68-74, prof med, 73-74; DIR DIV BIOMED RES & DEP DIR DEPT ACAD AFFAIRS, ASN AM MED COLS, 75- *Concurrent Pos:* Nat Found res fel, Columbia Univ, 57-60; NIH spec res fel, 62-64; USPHS res career award, 65-; asst physician, Francis Delafield Hosp, New York, 59-60; mem med scientist comt, Nat Inst Gen Med, 69-72, mem nat heart & lung adv coun, Nat Heart & Lung Inst, 72-75. *Mem:* Am Fedn Clin Res; Am Soc Clin Invest; Am Col Physicians; Am Thoracic Soc. *Res:* Transport mechanisms; pulmonary surface active lipids; lipid biosynthesis. *Mailing Add:* 11515 34th Ave NE Seattle WA 98125

MORGAN, THOMAS HARLOW, b Jacksonville, Fla, May 31, 45. ASTROPHYSICS, PLANETARY SCIENCES. *Educ:* Univ Fla, BS, 66, PhD(physics), 72. *Prof Exp:* Fel, Nat Res Coun, NASA Johnson Space Ctr, 73-74; ASST PROF PHYSICS ASTRON, HOUSTON BAPTIST UNIV, 75- *Mem:* Am Phys Soc; Astron Soc of Pac; Soc Photo Optical Instrumentation Engrs. *Res:* Ultraviolet observations of stars and planets; ground based observations in the infrared one to three microns of emission-line objects and planetary atmospheres; high spatial resolution planetary imagery. *Mailing Add:* Johnson Manned Spacecraft Ctr Astrophys Sect 23 Houston TX 77058

MORGAN, THOMAS JOSEPH, b Brooklyn, NY, Oct 20, 43; m 68; c 2. ATOMIC PHYSICS. *Educ:* Carroll Col, BA, 65; Mont State Univ, BSc, 66; Univ Calif, Berkeley, MSc, 68, PhD(eng physics), 71. *Prof Exp:* Univ fel pure & appl physics, Queen's Univ Belfast, 71-73; asst prof, 73-80, ASSOC PROF PHYSICS, WESLEYAN UNIV, 80- *Concurrent Pos:* Consult, Oak Ridge Nat Lab, 76-, mem, Atomic Data Ctr; mem, Nat Bur Standards; vis scientist, Lawrence Berkeley Lab, 74, Oak Ridge Nat Lab, 75 & Univ Mex, 79. *Mem:* Am Phys Soc. *Res:* Heavy particle collision phenomena; atomic beams; collisional properties of excited states. *Mailing Add:* Dept of Physics Wesleyan Univ Middletown CT 06457

MORGAN, THOMAS KENNETH, JR, b Upper Darby, Pa, Oct 25, 49; m 71; c 3. ORGANIC CHEMISTRY. *Educ:* Villanova Univ, BS, 71; Univ Del, PhD(chem), 75. *Prof Exp:* Res assoc org chem, State Univ NY Binghamton, 75-77; sr chemist org chem, Cooper Labs, Inc, 77-79; SR ORG CHEMIST, BERLEX LABS, 79- *Concurrent Pos:* NIH fel, 76-77. *Mem:* AAAS; Am Chem Soc. *Mailing Add:* Berlex Labs Inc 110 E Hanover Ave Cedar Knolls NJ 07927

MORGAN, WALTER CLIFFORD, b Ledyard, Conn, Dec 22, 21; m 48; c 3. ANIMAL GENETICS. *Educ:* Univ Conn, BSc, 46, PhD(genetics), 53; George Washington Univ, MSc, 49. *Prof Exp:* Animal geneticist, Nat Cancer Inst, 46-49; res assoc mammalian genetics, Columbia Univ, 50-53; asst prof poultry genetics, Univ Tenn, 53-54; assoc prof, 54-58, PROF GENETICS & PHYSIOL, SDAK STATE UNIV, 58- *Concurrent Pos:* Vis scientist, Radiobiol Dept, Nuclear Energy Ctr, Mol, Belg, 68-69. *Honors & Awards:* Outstanding Poultry Genetic Res Award, Czechoslovakian Govt, 79. *Mem:* Am Genetic Asn; World Poultry Sci Asn; Am Inst Biol Sci; Radiation Res Soc; NY Acad Sci. *Res:* Developmental genetics of poultry and mice; physiology of reproduction; new mutations; lethals; irradiation effects on chick embryos and on wheat. *Mailing Add:* 1610 First St Brookings SD 57006

MORGAN, WALTER L(EROY), b Passaic, NJ, Dec 20, 30. ENGINEERING MANAGEMENT, SYSTEMS ENGINEERING. *Educ:* Carnegie-Mellon Univ, BS, 54. *Prof Exp:* Res engr, David Sarnoff Res Labs, Radio Corp Am, 54-55, sr systs engr, Defense Prod Div, 55-59, Astro-Electronic Div, 59-70; mem tech staff long range planning, Comsat Labs, Commun Satellite Corp, 70-75, sr staff exec, 75-80; CONSULT & PRES, COMMUN CTR CLARKSBURG, 80- *Concurrent Pos:* Lectr, Univ Calif, Los Angeles, 78; consult ed, Satellite Commun Mag, 80- *Honors & Awards:* Aerospace Commun Award, Am Inst Aeronaut & Astronaut, 82. *Mem:* AAAS; sr mem Inst Elec & Electronics Engrs; fel Am Inst Aeronaut & Astronaut; Int Acad Astronaut. *Res:* Planning and management of telecommunications applications; operations analysis of communication via satellite; international and domestic telecommunication system analysis; marleat research. *Mailing Add:* Commun Ctr Clarksburg 2723 Green Valley Rd Clarksburg MD 20871

MORGAN, WILLIAM BRUCE, b Fairfield, Iowa, Dec 20, 26; m 50; c 2. HYDRODYNAMICS, NAVAL ARCHITECTURE. *Educ:* US Merchant Marine Acad, BS, 50; Univ Iowa, MS, 51; Univ Calif, Berkeley, DEng(naval archit), 61. *Prof Exp:* Hydraul engr, Propeller Br, David Taylor Model Basin, 51-52, naval architect, 52-58, supv naval architect propeller res & design, Supercavitating & Design Sect, 58-62, supv naval architect ship propulsion & head propeller br, 62-70, head Naval Hydromech Div, Naval Ship Res & Develop Ctr, 70-80, ASSOC TECH DIR SHIP PERFORMANCE, DAVID TAYLOR NAVAL SHIP RES & DEVELOP CTR, 80- *Mem:* Soc Naval Archit & Marine Engrs; Am Soc Mech Engrs; Ger Soc Naval Archit; Am Soc Naval Engrs; Sigma Xi. *Res:* Ship hydrodynamics, especially propeller design theories for conventional, contrarotating, supercavitating and ducted propellers; cavitation and propulsion in general. *Mailing Add:* 110 Upton Rockville MD 20850

MORGAN, WILLIAM JASON, b Savannah, Ga, Oct 10, 35; m 59; c 2. GEOPHYSICS. *Educ:* Ga Inst Technol, BS, 57; Princeton Univ, PhD(physics), 64. *Prof Exp:* Res assoc, 64-66, from asst prof to assoc prof, 66-77, PROF GEOPHYS, PRINCETON UNIV, 77- *Mem:* Am Geophys Union. *Res:* Mantle convection; heat flow; plate tectonics; marine geophysics. *Mailing Add:* Dept of Geol & Geophys Sci Princeton Univ Princeton NJ 08540

MORGAN, WILLIAM KEITH C, b July 1, 29; US citizen; m 53; c 3. INTERNAL MEDICINE. *Educ:* Univ Sheffield, MB, ChB, 53, MD, 61; MRCP(D), 58, FRCP(E), 71, FACP, 72, FRCP(C), 78. *Prof Exp:* From instr to assoc prof, Univ Md, 59-67; assoc prof, 67-70, prof med, Med Ctr, WVa Univ, 70-78, head div pulmonary dis, 74-78; PROF MED, UNIV WESTERN ONT, 78-, DIR CHEST DIS SERV, UNIV HOSP, 78- *Concurrent Pos:* Chief, Appalachian Lab Occup Respiratory Dis, Nat Inst Occup Safety & Health, 67-71, dir, 71-74. *Mem:* Am Thoracic Soc; Brit Med Asn; Am Col Chest Physicians. *Res:* Chest diseases and occupational medicine. *Mailing Add:* Univ Hosp Rm 6-0F6 Univ Western Ont Box 5339 Postal Sta A London ON N6A 5A5 Can

MORGAN, WILLIAM L, JR, b Honolulu, Hawaii, Nov 18, 27; m 54; c 2. INTERNAL MEDICINE, CARDIOVASCULAR DISEASES. *Educ:* Yale Univ, BA, 48; Harvard Med Sch, MD, 52; Am Bd Internal Med, dipl, 62. *Prof Exp:* Instr med, Harvard Univ, 56-58, tutor med sci, 57-58; assoc, Div Cardiovasc Dis, Henry Ford Hosp, 58-62; assoc prof, 62-66, PROF MED, SCH MED & DENT, UNIV ROCHESTER, 66-, ASSOC CHMN DEPT MED & DIR EDUC PROGS, 69- *Concurrent Pos:* Clin assoc, Nat Heart Inst; mem, Am Bd Internal Med, 73-, mem, Residency Rev Comt, 74- *Mem:* Fel Am Col Physicians. *Res:* Cardiovascular hemodynamics; cardiac arrhythmias; medical education; physical diagnosis. *Mailing Add:* Dept of Med Strong Mem Hosp Rochester NY 14642

MORGAN, WILLIAM R(ICHARD), b Cambridge, Ohio, Mar 27, 22; m 46; c 2. MECHANICAL ENGINEERING, TECHNICAL MANAGEMENT. *Educ:* Ohio State Univ, BS, 44; Purdue Univ, MS, 50, PhD, 51. *Prof Exp:* Asst mech, Ohio State Univ, 43-44; design engr, Curtiss-Wright Corp, 46-47; instr, Purdue Univ, 47-51; group leader heat transfer & thermodyn anal unit, Aircraft Nuclear Propulsion Dept, Gen Elec Co, 51-53, supvr exp mech eng unit, 53-55, supvr controls anal unit & mgr controls anal subsect, Flight Propulsion Lab Dept, 55-57, mgr controls develop design subsect, 57-59, mgr vertical take off & landing aircraft prog, 59-63, prog dir high bypass propulsion engines, 63-67, mgr acoustic eng, 67-69, mgr quiet engine prog, Advan Technol Prog Dept, 69-72; vpres & gen mgr, SDRC Int, Inc, 72-80; CONSULT ENG & MGT, 80- *Mem:* Am Soc Mech Engrs; Acoust Soc Am; Inst Noise Control Eng. *Res:* Heat transfer; thermodynamics; fluid dynamics. *Mailing Add:* 312 Ardon Lane Cincinnati OH 45215

MORGAN, WILLIAM WILSON, b Bethesda, Tenn, Jan 3, 06; m 28, 66; c 2. ASTRONOMY. *Educ:* Univ Chicago, BS, 27, PhD, 31. *Hon Degrees:* Dr, Nat Univ Cordoba; DSc, Yale Univ, 78. *Prof Exp:* Asst astron, Yerkes Observ, Univ Chicago, 26-32, from instr to prof, 32-66, chmn dept, 60-66, dir, Yerkes & McDonald Observs, 60-63, Bernard E & Ellen C Sunny distinguished serv prof, 66-74, EMER PROF, UNIV CHICAGO, 74- *Honors & Awards:* Bruce Gold Medal Award, Astron Soc Pac, 58; Henry Draper Medal, Nat Acad Sci, 80. *Mem:* Nat Acad Sci; Am Acad Arts & Sci; Royal Danish Acad; Royal Soc Sci Liege; cor mem Arg Nat Acad Sci. *Res:* Stellar spectroscopy; galaxies. *Mailing Add:* Yerkes Observ Williams Bay WI 53191

MORGAN, WINFIELD SCOTT, b Takoma Park, Md, Jan 9, 21; m 48; c 5. PATHOLOGY. *Educ:* Albright Col, BS, 42; Temple Univ, MD, 45. *Prof Exp:* Resident path, Mass Gen Hosp, 48-51, asst, 52-53, from asst pathologist to assoc pathologist, 53-62; dir path, Cleveland Metrop Gen Hosp, 62-67; dir labs, Aultman Hosp, Canton, Ohio, 67-74; PROF PATH & DIR SURG PATH, MED CTR, WVA UNIV, 74- *Concurrent Pos:* Fel med, Guthrie Clin, Sayre, Pa, 46; Am Cancer Soc-Brit Empire Cancer Campaign exchange fel, Oxford Univ, 51-52; Nat Cancer Inst spec res fel cellular physiol, Wenner-Gren Inst, Univ Stockholm, 58-60; consult, Health Res Facil Br, NIH, 65-67; instr, Med Sch, Tufts Univ, 52-60; Harvard Med Sch, 60-61, assoc, 61-62; prof, Sch Med, Case Western Reserve Univ, 62-67. *Mem:* Am Asn Path & Bact; Am Soc Exp Path; NY Acad Med; Int Acad Path. *Res:* Biochemical pathology. *Mailing Add:* Dept of Path WVa Univ Med Ctr Morgantown WV 26506

MORGAN, WYMAN, b Russellville, Ala, Jan 7, 41; m 59. INORGANIC CHEMISTRY. *Educ:* Florence State Col, BS, 62; Univ Fla, PhD(chem), 67. *Prof Exp:* Res chemist, Inorg Div, Monsanto Co, 67-71, sr res chemist, Monsanto Indust Chem Co, 71-75, sr res specialist, 75-77, mgr Manpower & Personnell Develop, Corp Res & Develop, 77-80, mgr Chem Res, Corp Res & Develop Biomed Prog, 80-81, MGR RES & DEVELOP, NUTRIT CHEM DIV, MONSANTO INDUST CHEM CO, 81- *Res:* Chemistry of metallic elements; exploratory process development. *Mailing Add:* Monsanto Co 800 N Lindbergh Blvd St Louis MO 63166

MORGANE, PETER J, b Atlanta, Ga, May 14, 31. NEUROPHYSIOLOGY, PSYCHOPHARMACOLOGY. *Educ:* Tulane Univ, BS, 48; Northwestern Univ, MS, 57, PhD(physiol), 59. *Prof Exp:* Resident res, Northwestern Univ, 56-59; instr physiol, Col Med, Univ Tenn, 59, asst prof, 59-61; sr physiologist, Life Sci Br, Goodyear Aircraft Corp, Ohio, 61-62; sr vis scientist, Brain Res Unit, Mex, 62-63; chmn div neurol sci, Commun Res Inst, 63-68; SR SCIENTIST, WORCESTER FOUND EXP BIOL, 68- *Concurrent Pos:* Affil prof, Worcester Polytech Inst, Clark Univ & Boston Univ, 69-; mem panel neurobiol, NSF, 71-74; mem study sect, Nat Inst Neurol Dis & Stroke, 74-78; dir post-doctoral training prog neurobiol, NIMH, 70-74; chmn, Neurol B Study Sect, NIH, 76-78. *Mem:* Am Physiol Soc; Am Asn Anatomists; fel Am Col Neuropsychopharmacol; Am Psychol Asn; NY Acad Sci. *Res:* Comparative morphology of the brains of mammals, especially whale brain anatomy; neural regulation of food and water intake; hypothalamic-limbic interactions in behavior; anatomical, physiological, pharmacological and neurobiochemical studies on the sleep states; quantitative electroencephalographic analysis following pharmacological manipulation of the biogenic amines; neurophysiological role of serotonin; effects of protein malnutrition on developing brain; electro-ontogenesis of the brain. *Mailing Add:* Worcester Found for Exp Biol 222 Maple Ave Shrewsbury MA 01545

MORGANROTH, JOEL, b Detroit, Mich, Oct 29, 45; m 72. CARDIOLOGY, INTERNAL MEDICINE. *Educ:* Univ Mich, BS, 68, MD, 70; Am Bd Internal Med, dipl, 73, Am Bd Cardiovasc Dis, dipl, 75. *Prof Exp:* From intern to resident, Beth Israel Hosp, Harvard Med Sch, 70-72; clin assoc cardiol, Nat Heart & Lung Inst, 72-74; clin instr med, Georgetown Univ, 74; clin fel, 74-75, asst prof med, Med Sch, Univ Pa, 75-78, dir, Ecg-Exercise Lab & assoc dir, Non-Invasive Lab, Univ Hosp, 75-78; ASSOC PROF MED, THOMAS JEFFERSON MED COL, PHILADELPHIA, 78-; ASSOC DIR CARDIOVASC SECT, LANKENAN HOSP, 78- *Concurrent Pos:* Fel, Coun on Clin Cardiol & Artherosclerosis. *Honors & Awards:* Physician Recognition Award, AMA, 73-76, 76-79 & 79-82. *Mem:* Am Fedn Clin Res; fel Am Col Physicians; fel Am Col Cardiol; Am Heart Asn; fel Am Col Chest Physicians. *Res:* Pathophysiology of clinical ischemic heart disease utilizing primarily non-invasive techniques; echocardiography and exercise testing with particular attention to computerized models; evaluation of pathogenesis and treatment of sudden cardiac death. *Mailing Add:* 2221 Med Sci Bldg City & Lancaster Ave Philadelphia PA 19151

MORGANS, LELAND FOSTER, b Stuttgart, Ark, June 30, 39; m 60; c 2. HISTOLOGY, ZOOLOGY. *Educ:* Tex Lutheran Col, BS, 61; Univ Ark, Fayetteville, MS, 65; Okla State Univ, PhD(zool), 68. *Prof Exp:* Asst prof biol, Phillips Univ, 68-69; asst prof, 69-77, ASSOC PROF BIOL, UNIV ARK, LITTLE ROCK, 77- *Mem:* AAAS; Sigma Xi; Am Asn Anatomists. *Res:* Comparative vertebrate physiology. *Mailing Add:* Dept of Biol Univ of Ark Little Rock AR 72204

MORGENSTERN, ALAN LAWRENCE, b Brooklyn, NY, Dec 21, 33; m 60; c 2. PSYCHIATRY. *Educ:* Cornell Univ, BA, 54; Duke Univ, MD, 59. *Prof Exp:* Intern internal med, Med Sch, Duke Univ, 59-60; resident psychiat, Med Sch, Univ Colo, 60-63; from instr to assoc prof, 65-81, PROF CLIN PSYCHIAT, MED SCH, UNIV ORE, 81- *Concurrent Pos:* WHO travel-study fel, Inst Psychiat, London, 72-73; consult, Training Br, NIMH & prog develop, Good Samaritan Hosp, Portland, 74-, chmn dept psychiat. *Mem:* Fel Am Psychiat Asn; AMA. *Res:* Tests of clinical competence for psychiatrists; psychotherapy of borderline states; marital psychotherapy. *Mailing Add:* 7929 SW Ruby Terr Portland OR 97219

MORGENSTERN, LEON, b Pittsburgh, Pa, July 14, 19. SURGERY. *Educ:* Brooklyn Col, BA, 40; NY Univ, MD, 43. *Prof Exp:* Pvt pract, 52-59; asst prof surg, Albert Einstein Col Med, 59-60; asst clin prof, 64-70, assoc clin prof, 70-74, CLIN PROF SURG, SCH MED, UNIV CALIF, LOS ANGELES, 74-; DIR SURG, CEDARS OF LEBANON HOSP, 60-; DIR SURG, CEDARSSINAI MED CTR, 73- *Mem:* Am Col Surgeons; Soc Surg Alimentary Tract; Am Gastroenterol Asn; Int Soc Surgeons. *Res:* Gastric physiology and cancer; carcinoma gastric stump; vagotomy and gastric carcinoma; partial splenectomy; splenic hemostasis; postoperative jaundice; inflammatory bowel disease; malignant diverticulitis; wound healing; carcinoma of breast. *Mailing Add:* Dept of Surg Cedars-Sinai Med Ctr Los Angeles CA 90048

MORGENSTERN, MATTHEW, b New York, NY. COMPUTER SCIENCE. *Educ:* Columbia Univ, BS, 68, MS, 70; Mass Inst Technol, SM, 75, PhD(comput sci), 76. *Prof Exp:* Tech staff comput sci, Bell Telephone Labs, 68-70; res asst, Mass Inst Technol, 70-76; ASST PROF COMPUT SCI, RUTGERS UNIV, 76- *Concurrent Pos:* Vis fac, Goddard Space Flight Ctr, NASA, 80-81. *Mem:* Asn Comput Mach; Inst Elec & Electronic Engrs; AAAS; Sigma Xi. *Res:* Database systems research, design, and development: schema design to support multiple data model views for users of distrubuted information systems; file and index structure implementation; intelligent systems and user interfaces; automatic programming: computer aided design of information systems. *Mailing Add:* Dept Comput Sci Hill Ctr Rutgers Univ New Brunswick NJ 08903

MORGENSTERN, N(ORBERT) R, b Toronto, Ont, May 25, 35; m 60; c 3. SOIL MECHANICS, ENGINEERING GEOLOGY. *Educ:* Univ Toronto, BASc, 56; Univ London, DIC & PhD(soil mech), 64. *Prof Exp:* Res asst soil mech, Imp Col, Univ London, 58-60, lectr civil eng, 60-68; PROF CIVIL ENG, UNIV ALTA, 68- *Concurrent Pos:* Consult to var eng firms & govt agencies, 60-; Nat Res Coun Trans Can lect tour, 67. *Honors & Awards:* Brit Geotech Soc Prizes, 61 & 66; Huber Res Prize, Am Soc Civil Engrs, 72; Can Geotech Soc Prize, 77, Legget Award, 79; Rankine lectr, Brit Geotech Soc, 81. *Mem:* Fel Royal Soc Can; Can Geotech Soc; Am Soc Civil Engrs; Asn Eng Geol; Brit Geotech Soc. *Res:* Mechanics of landslides and other geomorphological processes; properties of natural materials; design and construction of dams; relation between mechanics and geological structures; permafrost engineering; underground excavations; rock mechanics. *Mailing Add:* Dept Civil Eng Univ Alta Edmonton AB T6G 2G7 Can

MORGENTHALER, FREDERIC R(ICHARD), b Cleveland, Ohio, Mar 12, 33; m 58; c 2. ELECTRICAL ENGINEERING. *Educ:* Mass Inst Technol, SB & SM, 56, PhD(elec eng), 60. *Prof Exp:* From asst prof to assoc prof, 60-68, PROF ELEC ENG, MASS INST TECHNOL, 68- *Concurrent Pos:* Ford Found fel, Mass Inst Technol, 60-62; res fel appl physics, Harvard Univ, 60-61, vis lectr, 61. *Mem:* Fel Inst Elec & Electronics Engrs; Sigma Xi; Am Phys Soc. *Res:* Microwave magnetics; ultrasonics; electromagnetic theory. *Mailing Add:* Dept of Elec Eng Rm 13-3102 A Mass Inst of Technol Cambridge MA 02139

MORGENTHALER, GEORGE WILLIAM, b Chicago, Ill, Dec 16, 26; m 49; c 4. MATHEMATICS. *Educ:* Concordia Col, BS, 46; Univ Chicago, MS, 48, PhD, 53; Univ Denver, MS, 63; Mass Inst Technol, MS, 70. *Prof Exp:* Mathematician, Inst Air Weapons Res, Chicago, 51-55, group leader, 55-58; assoc prof math & head dept, Chicago Undergrad Div, Univ Ill, 58-60; mgr electronics & math res dept, Martin Co, 60-65, dir res & develop, Martin Marietta Corp, 66-69, corp dir res & develop, 70-74, vpres tech opers, 74-76, V PRES & GEN MGR, MARTIN MARIETTA AEROSPACE, BALTIMORE, 76- *Concurrent Pos:* Instr, Ill Inst Technol, 51-58; adj prof, Univ Colo, 60-65, vis prof, 70-76; bk rev ed, J Astronaut Sci, 63-78. *Mem:* Fel AAAS; Sigma Xi; Opers Res Soc Am; Inst Math Statist; fel Am Astronaut Soc (pres, 64-66). *Res:* Statistics; operations research; applied mathematics; astronautics. *Mailing Add:* 1264 Fenwick Garth Arnold MD 21012

MORGERA, SALVATORE DOMENIC, b Providence, RI, Aug 5, 46. DIGITAL SIGNAL PROCESSING, PATTERN RECOGNITION. *Educ:* Brown Univ, BSc, 68, MSc, 70, PhD(eng & appl math), 75. *Prof Exp:* Sr res scientist, advan technol, Submarine Signal Div, Raytheon Co, 68-78; PROF ELEC ENG, FAC ENG & COMPUT SCI, CONCORDIA UNIV, 78- *Concurrent Pos:* Scientist, Nat Security Indust Orgn, 70-78; sr consult & prin investr, Dept Fisheries & Oceans, Bedford Inst Oceanog, 78-; dir, Commun Circuits & Systs Group, Govt Que, Minister Educ, 78-; sr consult, Can Marconi Ltd, 81- *Mem:* Inst Elec & Electronics Engrs; Sigma Xi; Statist Soc Can; Am Statist Asn. *Res:* Detection and estimation theory; pattern recognition; algorithms for cyclic convolutions over finite fields and the use of these algorithms in the relation between systems of bilinear forms and linear error correcting codes. *Mailing Add:* Dept Elec Eng Concordia Univ 1455 de Maisonneuve Blvd W Montreal PQ H3G 1M8 Can

MORHARDT, J EMIL, b Bishop, Calif, Aug 19, 42; m 65. COMPARATIVE PHYSIOLOGY, ECOLOGY. *Educ:* Pomona Col, AB, 64; Rice Univ, PhD(vert physiol), 68. *Prof Exp:* Asst prof biol, Wash Univ, 67-75; dir biol serv & chief scientist, Henningson, Durham & Richardson, Ecosci Div, 75-78; dir environ progs, Western States, Ecol Analysts, Inc, 78-80; MEM STAFF, SCI DIV, HORT ECOL, 80- *Concurrent Pos:* Environ consult, Mo Bot Garden, 73-75 & Harland Bartholomew & Assocs, 74-75. *Mem:* AAAS; Am Soc Zoologists; Ecol Soc Am; Am Soc Naturalists; Am Soc Mammalogists. *Res:* Physiology and behavioral temperature regulation in the vertebrates; relationships between animals and environmental energy, food and water; environmental analyses. *Mailing Add:* Sci Div Hort Ecol 804 Anacopa Santa Barbara CA 93101

MORHARDT, SYLVIA STAEHLE, ecology, environmental management, see previous edition

MORI, KANAKA FRED, b Tokyo, Japan, Feb 4, 25; Can citizen; m 64; c 1. BIOCHEMISTRY, ENDOCRINOLOGY. *Educ:* Univ Tokyo, DVM, 48; Univ Montreal, PhD(exp med), 63. *Prof Exp:* Lectr biochem, Univ Tottori, 50-55, asst prof, 55-57; asst prof, Col Osteop Med & Surg, 59-61; fel, Cardiovasc Res Inst, Sch Med, Univ Calif, San Francisco, 61; res scientist, Animal Dis Res Inst, Can Dept Agr, 62-64; res scientist, 64-69, sect head, 69-73, SR SCIENTIST, DRUG RES LABS, CAN DEPT NAT HEALTH & WELFARE, 73- *Mem:* Am Chem Soc; Endocrine Soc. *Res:* Structure-activity relationship of protein hormones. *Mailing Add:* 30 Parkmount Circle Ottawa ON K2H 5T3 Can

MORI, KEN, b Tobata, Japan, July 14, 25; US citizen; m 62. PATHOLOGY. *Educ:* Univ Tokyo, 51. *Prof Exp:* Clin instr path, Col Med, State Univ NY Downstate Med Ctr, 63-66; assoc pathologist, 66-68, PATHOLOGIST, BETH ISRAEL HOSP, 68-; ASST PROF PATH, MT SINAI SCH MED, 67- *Concurrent Pos:* Asst pathologist, Maimonides Hosp, Brooklyn, NY, 63-66. *Mem:* Col Am Path. *Res:* Human pathology; electromicroscopy. *Mailing Add:* Dept of Path Mt Sinai Sch of Med New York NY 10029

MORI, PETER TAKETOSHI, b Montebello, Calif, Feb 16, 25; m 57; c 3. ORGANIC CHEMISTRY. *Educ:* Park Col, BS, 45; Okla State Univ, MS, 48; Purdue Univ, PhD, 54. *Prof Exp:* Res chemist, Dearborn Chem Co, 52-55, Am Potash & Chem Corp, 55-57, Turco Prod, Inc, 57 & Stuart Co, 58-62; RES CHEMIST, ICI UNITED STATES, INC, 62- *Mem:* AAAS; Am Chem Soc; Sigma Xi. *Res:* Medicinals, insecticides; detergents and corrosion inhibitors. *Mailing Add:* 1309 Quincy Dr Green Acres Wilmington DE 19803

MORI, RAYMOND I, b Hawaii, Oct 7, 26; m 51; c 4. ORGANIC CHEMISTRY. *Educ:* Univ Hawaii, BA, 49; Northwestern Univ, PhD(chem), 55. *Prof Exp:* Org chemist, Hawaiian Pineapple Co, Ltd, 54-61; asst dir qual assurance, Dole Co, 61-64, dir qual assurance, 64-69; CORP DIR QUAL ASSURANCE, CASTLE & COOKE FOODS, INC, 69- *Mem:* Am Chem Soc; Inst Food Technologists; Asn Offs Agr. *Res:* Quality control; enzymes. *Mailing Add:* Castle & Cooke Foods 50 California St San Francisco CA 94111

MORI, SCOTT ALAN, b Janesville, Wis, Oct 13, 41. PLANT TAXONOMY. *Educ:* Univ Wis-Stevens Point, BS, 64; Univ Wis-Madison, MS, 68, PhD(bot), 74. *Prof Exp:* Instr bot, Univ Wis-Marshfield, 69-74, taxonomist, Mo Bot Garden, 74-75; taxonomist, 75-77, ASSOC CUR, NY BOT GARDEN, 77- *Concurrent Pos:* taxonomist, Cocoa Res Ctr, Itabuna, Bahia, Brazil, 78-80. *Mem:* Org Trop Biol; Bot Soc Am; Brazilian Bot Soc. *Res:* Taxonomy of neotropical lecythidaceae (Brazil Nut Family); phenology and floral biology of tropical trees. *Mailing Add:* NY Bot Garden Bronx NY 10458

MORI, SHUJI, b Tokyo, Japan, April 22, 37; m 69; c 3. OIL & GAS TECHNOLOGY. *Educ:* Tokyo Inst Technol, BS, 61; Univ Utah, MS, 70, PhD(fuel eng), 73. *Prof Exp:* Engr, Japan Gas Chem Co, 61-65; educ officer chem eng, Tokyo Inst Technol, 65-68; Eng, Exxon Res & Eng, 73-74; mgr, S Mori & Assoc, 74-76; sr eng, Inst Mines & Minerals Res, 76-80; SR ENG, MIDWEST RES INST, 80- *Concurrent Pos:* Vis res assoc, WVa Univ, 68-69; assoc mem, H-Coal Tech Adv Comt, 76-80. *Mem:* Am Chem Soc; Am Inst Chem Engrs. *Res:* Petroleum refining and synthetic fuels; coal liquefaction, gasification and coal characterization; new catalysts for upgrading of synthetic oils; fuel technology based on earth science. *Mailing Add:* 8415 Broadmoor Overland Park KS 66212

MORIARTY, C MICHAEL, b Schenectady, NY, Apr 12, 41; m 66, 75; c 3. PHYSIOLOGY, BIOPHYSICS. *Educ:* Carnegie Inst Technol, BS, 62; Cornell Univ, MS, 65; Univ Rochester, PhD(biophys), 68. *Prof Exp:* Instr physiol & biophys, Sch Med, Univ Iowa, 68-70; asst prof, 70-73, ASSOC PROF PHYSIOL & BIOPHYS, UNIV NEBR MED CTR, OMAHA, 73- *Concurrent Pos:* USPHS fel, Sch Med, Univ Iowa, 68-70; NSF res grant, 71-74, NIH res grants, 74- & Am Cancer Soc grant, 75-77. *Mem:* Am Physiol Soc; Am Soc Cell Biol. *Res:* Cell physiology, membrane transport; calcium; hormone regulation. *Mailing Add:* Dept of Physiol & Biophys Univ of Nebr Med Ctr Omaha NE 68105

MORIARTY, DANIEL DELMAR, JR, b New Orleans, La, June 16, 46; m 69; c 1. ANIMAL BEHAVIOR. *Educ:* La State Univ, New Orleans, BA, 68; Tulane Univ, MS, 72, PhD(psychol), 73. *Prof Exp:*Asst prof, 73-77, ASSOC PROF EXP PSYCHOL, UNIV SAN DIEGO, 77- *Mem:* Animal Behav Soc; Am Psychol Asn. *Res:* Genetic analysis of the behavioral response of frustration in rats and mice; effects of food deprivation and partial reinforcement on estrus cycling in female rats; effects of irrelevant drive on aversively motivated instrumental responses; Hippocampal chemical stimulation and delay of reinforcement. *Mailing Add:* Dept of Psychol Univ of San Diego San Diego CA 92110

MORIARTY, DAVID JOHN, b Chicago, Ill, Feb 25, 48; m 74. ECOLOGY, BIOSTATISTICS. *Educ:* Univ Ill, Urbana, BS, 70, MS, 72, PhD(zool), 76. *Prof Exp:* asst prof, 76-80, ASSOC PROF BIOL SCI, CALIF STATE POLYTECH UNIV, 80- *Mem:* Ecol Soc Am; AAAS; Am Inst Biol Sci; Biomet Soc; Am Ornithologists Union. *Res:* Application of multivariate statistics to investigations of structure of vertebrate communities; adaptive value of flocking in birds. *Mailing Add:* Dept of Biol Sci Calif State Polytech Univ Pomona CA 91768

MORIARTY, JOHN ALAN, b Chicago, Ill, Jan 17, 44; m 69. THEORETICAL SOLID STATE PHYSICS. *Educ:* Univ Calif, Berkeley, AB, 65; Stanford Univ, PhD(appl physics), 71. *Prof Exp:* Res assoc, Los Alamos Sci Lab, NMex, 71-73; res assoc, Univ Cambridge, 73-74; res assoc physics, Col William & Mary, 74-79; ASST PROF, UNIV CINCINNATI, 79- *Concurrent Pos:* Contractor, NASA Langley Res Ctr, 74-79; prin investr, NASA grants, 79-; consult, Lawrence Livermore Nat Lab, 81- *Mem:* Am Phys Soc; Sigma Xi. *Res:* Electronic structure and properties of metals and semiconductors; pseudopotential, tight-binding, and resonance methods. *Mailing Add:* Dept Elec & Comput Eng Univ Cincinnati Cincinnati OH 45221

MORIARTY, JOHN LAWRENCE, JR, b Fayette, Iowa, Nov 26, 32. PHYSICAL CHEMISTRY, METALLURGY. *Educ:* St Ambrose Col, BA, 55; Univ Iowa, MS, 57, PhD(chem), 60. *Prof Exp:* Resident res assoc phys chem, Argonne Nat Lab, 60-61; dir chem & metall res, Lunex Co, 61-68; sr scientist, Instruments & Life Support Div, Bendix Corp, 68-70; independent consult, metallurgist & chemist, 71-73; PROF PHYSICS, BETTENDORF SCH, 73- *Mem:* Am Chem Soc; Am Soc Metals; Am Crystallog Asn. *Res:* Physical chemistry, metallurgy and crystallography of rare earths, their compounds and alloys, including intermetallic compounds of binary systems; metallurgical chemistry of nodular iron and steelmaking; superalloys. *Mailing Add:* 1917 Perry St Davenport IA 52803

MORIARTY, ROBERT M, b New York, NY, Oct 9, 33; m 57; c 3. ORGANIC CHEMISTRY. *Educ:* Fordham Univ, BS, 55; Princeton Univ, PhD(org chem), 59. *Prof Exp:* Res worker org chem, Merck, Sharpe & Dohme, 55-56; NSF, NATO, Fulbright & NIH fels, Harvard Univ & Univ Munich, 59-61; from assoc prof to prof org chem, Cath Univ Am, 61-68; PROF ORG CHEM, UNIV ILL, CHICAGO CIRCLE, 68- *Mem:* Am Chem Soc; Royal Soc Chem. *Res:* Biochemistry; physical methods. *Mailing Add:* Dept of Chem Univ of Ill at Chicago Circle Chicago IL 60680

MORIBER, LOUIS G, b New York, NY, July 12, 17; m 41; c 2. CELL BIOLOGY. *Educ:* Brooklyn Col, AB, 38; Columbia Univ, MA, 52, PhD(zool, cytol), 56. *Prof Exp:* Jr aquatic physiologist, US Fish & Wildlife Serv, 41-43; assoc prof, 50-67, PROF BIOL, BROOKLYN COL, 67-, CHMN DEPT, 81- *Concurrent Pos:* Exec officer, PhD prog biol, City Univ New York, 71-81. *Res:* Cytochemistry; cellular endocrinology. *Mailing Add:* Dept of Biol Brooklyn Col Brooklyn NY 11210

MORIE, GERALD PRESCOTT, b St Louis, Mo, Mar 20, 39; m 61; c 3. ANALYTICAL CHEMISTRY. *Educ:* Cent Mo State Col, BS, 61; Ohio State Univ, MS, 63, PhD(anal chem), 66. *Prof Exp:* Asst instr chem, Ohio State Univ, 65; res chemist, 66-67, sr res chemist, 68-74, RES ASSOC, TENN EASTMAN CO, EASTMAN KODAK CO, 74- *Honors & Awards:* Philip Morris Award in Tobacco Sci, 76. *Mem:* Am Chem Soc; Sigma Xi. *Res:* Solvent extraction of metal chelates; chemical separations especially liquid chromatography; selective ion electrodes; gas chromatography; analysis of tobacco smoke. *Mailing Add:* Tenn Eastman Co Cent Res Bldg Kingsport TN 37660

MORIGI, EUGENE MARIO EDMUND, bacteriology, immunology, see previous edition

MORIN, DORNIS CLINTON, b Detroit, Mich, Oct 9, 23; m 48; c 3. PLASMA PHYSICS, ELECTRICAL ENGINEERING. *Educ:* Wayne State Univ, BS, 48, MSE, 51; Univ Wis, PhD(physics), 62. *Prof Exp:* Instr elec eng, Wayne State Univ, 48-51; res assoc, Univ Mich, 50-52; test engr, Vickers, Inc, 52-54; res assoc, Univ Mich, 54-55; mgr res dept, Dynex, Inc, 55-58; engr, Midwestern Univs Res Asn, 59-62, physicist, 62-63; res assoc, Univ Wis, 63-64, asst prof physics, Univ Wis-Milwaukee, 64-68; assoc prof, Univ Wis-Whitewater, 68-71; proj assoc, Plasma Physics Group, Univ Wis-Madison, 71-76; comput specialist, Systs Group, 76-80, ENGR NEWS LOG INT, SYSTS BY GRABER, 80- *Concurrent Pos:* Consult, Dynex, Inc, 58-60. *Mem:* AAAS; Am Phys Soc; Inst Elec & Electronics Eng; Asn Comput Mach. *Res:* Mechanics; fluid mechanics; electromagnetic theory; electronics; automatic control systems; applied mathematics. *Mailing Add:* 622 Jacobson Ave Madison WI 53714

MORIN, FRANCIS JOSEPH, b Laconia, NH, Oct 10, 17; m 46; c 7. SOLID STATE PHYSICS. *Educ:* Univ NH, BS, 39, MS, 40. *Prof Exp:* Mem tech staff, Bell Tel Labs, Inc, 41-62; assoc dir, Sci Ctr, NAm Aviation, Inc, 62-67, dir, Space Sci, Space & Info Systs Div, 65-67, dir, Sci Ctr, NAm Rockwell Corp, 67-70, mem tech staff, Sci Ctr, 70-74, DISTINGUISHED FEL, SCI CTR, ROCKWELL INT CORP, 74- *Concurrent Pos:* Vis prof physics, Univ Mo, 75. *Mem:* Am Chem Soc; Am Phys Soc. *Res:* Semiconductors; low temperature; electronic transport and energy-band structure in solids; transition metal oxides; diffusion and dislocations in solids; transition metal superconductors; surface physics; mechanism of catalysis of d-band surface states. *Mailing Add:* 877 St Charles Dr Thousand Oaks CA 91360

MORIN, GEORGE CARDINAL ALBERT, b Natick, Mass, June 7, 43; m 72; c 1. ALTERNATE ENERGY, SOIL PHYSICS. *Educ:* Univ Ariz, Tuscon, BS, 65, MS, 68, PhD(soil physics), 77. *Prof Exp:* Geologist, Tex Water Develop Bd, 68-69; res assoc agr eng, Univ Ariz, 70-76; asst prof agr eng, Univ Nebr, Lincoln, 76-80; ASST PROF AGR ENG, NMEX STATE UNIV, 80- *Mem:* Soil Sci Soc Am; Am Soc Agr Engrs. *Res:* Alternate energy, including solar, wind and biomass fuel; soil and water management including irrigation scheduling and water harvesting. *Mailing Add:* Plains Br Sta Star Rte Box 77 Clovis NM 88101

MORIN, JAMES GUNNAR, b Minneapolis, Minn, Sept 13, 42. INVERTEBRATE ZOOLOGY, INVERTEBRATE PHYSIOLOGY. *Educ:* Univ Calif, Santa Barbara, BA, 65; Harvard Univ, MA, 67, PhD(biol), 69. *Prof Exp:* Asst prof, 69-77, ASSOC PROF ZOOL, UNIV CALIF, LOS ANGELES, 77- *Concurrent Pos:* Nat Inst Neurol Dis & Stroke fel, Univ Calif, Los Angeles, 69-72. *Mem:* AAAS; Am Soc Zoologists; Soc Exp Biol & Med. *Res:* Bioluminescence in marine invertebrate, especially cnidaria; physiology of primitive nervous systems; community structure of subtidal sand bottoms. *Mailing Add:* Dept of Zool Univ of Calif Los Angeles CA 90024

MORIN, LEO GREGORY, b Berlin, NH, May 9, 41; m 68; c 3. CLINICAL BIOCHEMISTRY. *Educ:* Spring Hill Col, BS, 65; Boston Col, PhD(molecular biol), 68. *Prof Exp:* Asst prof biol, Rollins Col, 68-70; res biochemist, Sunland Hosp, Orlando, Fla, 70-71 & Kiess Instruments, Inc, 71-73; CLIN BIOCHEMIST & DIR CLIN CHEM, VET ADMIN HOSP, ATLANTA, 73- *Concurrent Pos:* Assoc prof, Sch Med, Emory Univ, 76- *Mem:* AAAS; Am Chem Soc; Am Asn Clin Chem. *Res:* Metabolic regulation and disorders; analytical methodology; creatine kinase enzymology. *Mailing Add:* 4805 Banner Elk Dr Stone Mountain GA 30083

MORIN, MAURICE KENNETH, b Watertown, Mass, Sept 2, 33; m 55; c 4. COMPUTER SCIENCE. *Educ:* Boston Univ, BA, 55. *Prof Exp:* Systs programmer aerospace comput, 55-61, head systs sect, 62-66, head systs br, 66-71, mgr proj off, 72-75, asst chief, Comput Div, 76-81, CHIEF, CENT SCI COMPUT FACIL, LANGLEY RES CTR, NASA, 81- *Res:* Implementation and management of large scientific computing facilities supporting analytical computing, real time digital simulation and research data reduction. *Mailing Add:* 281 E Queens Dr Williamsburg VA 23185

MORIN, RICHARD DUDLEY, b Quincy, Ill, Oct 5, 18; m 42; c 4. MEDICINAL CHEMISTRY. *Educ:* Univ Mich, BS, 40, MS, 42, PhD(org chem), 43. *Prof Exp:* Res chemist, Battelle Mem Inst, 43-52, asst div chief, 52-62, res assoc, 62-63; assoc prof, 63-70, PROF MED CHEM, SCH MED, UNIV ALA, BIRMINGHAM, 70- *Mem:* AAAS; Am Chem Soc. *Res:* Alkaloid synthesis; synthesis and biochemical and psychopharmacological action of psychotomimetic agents related to mescaline and psilocybin; structure-activity relationships among excitant and depressant compounds. *Mailing Add:* Neurosci Prog Sch of Med Univ of Ala Birmingham AL 35294

MORIN, THOMAS LEE, b Rahway, NJ, Aug 27, 43; m 65; c 1. OPERATIONS RESEARCH. *Educ:* Rutgers Univ, BS, 65; Univ NMex, MS, 67; Case Western Reserve Univ, MS, 70, PhD(opers res), 71. *Prof Exp:* Spec lectr opers res, Case Western Reserve Univ, 69-70; opers res analyst, Univ Assocs, Inc, 70-71; asst prof opers res, Dept Indust Eng & Mgt Sci, Technol Inst, Northwestern Univ, Evanston, 71-77; ASSOC PROF OPERS RES, SCH INDUST ENG, PURDUE UNIV, 77- *Concurrent Pos:* NSF grant, Urban Systs Eng Ctr, Northwestern Univ, Evanston, 71-72. *Mem:* Opers Res Soc Am; Inst Mgt Sci; Am Soc Civil Engrs. *Res:* Dynamic programming; optimization of stochastic processes; application of operations research to urban and water resources systems. *Mailing Add:* Sch of Indust Eng Grissom Hall Purdue Univ West Lafayette IN 47907

MORIN, WALTER ARTHUR, b Salem, Mass, Oct 31, 33; m 57; c 7. NEUROPHYSIOLOGY. *Educ:* Merrimack Col, AB, 58; Boston Col, MS, 60; Clark Univ, PhD(physiol), 66. *Prof Exp:* Assoc prof, 61-74, PROF ZOOL, BRIDGEWATER STATE COL, 74- *Concurrent Pos:* NIH res grants, 66-67 & 69-71; Nat Res Coun Can Fel, Univ Toronto, 67-68; Sigma Xi res grant, 69-70. *Mem:* Am Soc Zool. *Res:* Excitatory and inhibitory synaptic vesicles in crustaceans. *Mailing Add:* Dept of Zool Bridgewater State Col Bridgewater MA 02324

MORINIGO, FERNANDO BERNARDINO, b Parana, Arg, June 1, 36; m 63. PHYSICS. *Educ:* Univ Southern Calif, BS, 57; Calif Inst Technol, PhD(physics), 63. *Prof Exp:* Asst prof physics, Calif State Col, Los Angeles, 63-64; vis prof, Univ Freiburg, 64-65; from asst prof to assoc prof, 65-70, PROF PHYSICS, CALIF STATE UNIV, LOS ANGELES, 71- *Concurrent Pos:* Res fel, Calif Inst Technol, 63-64, sr res fel, 65; res physicist, Lab Nuclear Spectrometry, Nat Ctr Sci Res, Strasbourg, France, 68-69; res fel, Niels Bohr Inst, Copenhagen, 73; vis prof, Calif Inst Technol, 77-78. *Mem:* Am Phys Soc. *Res:* Nuclear beta decay; experimental nuclear spectroscopy; theoretical nuclear physics; nuclear reaction theory. *Mailing Add:* Dept of Physics Calif State Univ 5151 State College Dr Los Angeles CA 90032

MORINO, LUIGI, b Rome, Italy, July 21, 38; m 65; c 2. AERODYNAMICS. *Educ:* Univ Rome, DrMechEng, 63, DrAeroEng, 66. *Prof Exp:* Asst prof aerospace eng, Univ Rome, 65-68; sr res engr, Mass Inst Technol, 68-69; assoc prof, 69-77, PROF AEROSPACE & MECH ENG & DIR, CTR COMPUT & APPL DYNAMICS, BOSTON UNIV, 77- *Concurrent Pos:* NATO fel, Mass Inst Technol, 67-68; adj assoc prof, Boston Univ, 68-69; consult, Mass Inst Technol, 69-72 & Aerospace Syst Inc, 72-77; prin investr, NASA grant, 72-, NSF, 75-77, 79-81, Dept Energy, 76-78, Army Res Off, 79-; pres, Anal & Comput Sci Inc, 77- *Mem:* Am Inst Aeronaut & Astronaut; AAAS. *Res:* Computational steady, oscillatory and unsteady subsonic and supersonic aerodynamics of complex aircraft configurations; extensions to helicopters, windmills and buildings; transonic flows; boundary layers and separated flows. *Mailing Add:* Boston Univ 110 Cummington St Boston MA 02215

MORISAWA, MARIE, b Toledo, Ohio, Nov 2, 19. GEOLOGY, GEOMORPHOLOGY. *Educ:* Hunter Col, AB, 41; Union Theol Sem, MA, 45; Univ Wyo, MA, 52; Columbia Univ, PhD(geol), 60. *Prof Exp:* Instr geol, Bryn Mawr Col, 55-59; asst prof, Mont State Univ, 59-61; assoc prof, Antioch Col, 63-69; assoc prof, 69-75, PROF GEOL, STATE UNIV NY BINGHAMTON, 75- *Mem:* Geol Soc Am; Am Quaternary Asn; Am Geophys Union. *Res:* Fluvial geomorphology; environmental geomorphology, geology and planning; geological aesthetics. *Mailing Add:* Dept of Geol State Univ of NY Binghamton NY 13901

MORISHIMA, AKIRA, b Tokyo, Japan, Apr 18, 30; US citizen; m 61; c 2. PEDIATRICS, CYTOGENETICS. *Educ:* Keio Univ, Japan, MD, 54, PhD(med), 61. *Prof Exp:* Fulbright travel grant, 55-57; fel pediat endocrinol, Col Physicians & Surgeons, Columbia Univ, 58-61; instr pediat, 61-63, assoc, 63-65, asst prof pediat endocrinol, 65-66; asst prof, Med Ctr, Univ Calif, San Francisco, 66-68; ASSOC PROF PEDIAT ENDOCRINOL, COL PHYSICIANS & SURGEONS, COLUMBIA UNIV, 68- *Concurrent Pos:* From asst attend to assoc attend pediatrician, Babies Hosp, New York, 63-; NIH res career develop award, 66-68. *Mem:* NY Acad Sci; Environ Mutagen Soc; Am Soc Human Genetics; Soc Pediat Res; Lowson Wilkins Pediat Endocrine Soc. *Res:* Human cytogenetics; endocrinology. *Mailing Add:* Babies Hosp 622 W 168th St New York NY 10032

MORISHIMA, HISAYO ODA, b Ito-shi, Japan, July 27, 29; m 61; c 2. MEDICINE. *Educ:* Toho Univ, MD, 51; Tokyo Univ, PhD(med), 60. *Prof Exp:* Resident anesthesiol, Sch Med, Tokyo Univ, 54-56; dir anesthesiol, Izu Teishin Hosp, Shizuoka-ken, Japan, 56-59; resident, DC Gen Hosp, 59-60 & Washington Hosp Ctr, DC, 60-61; res assoc, Col Physicians & Surgeons, Columbia Univ, 61-66; clin instr, Med Ctr, Univ Calif, San Francisco, 66-68; asst prof anesthesiol, 68-74, ASSOC PROF ANESTHESIOL, COL PHYSICIANS & SURGEONS, COLUMBIA UNIV, 74- *Mem:* Am Soc Anesthesiol; Soc Obstet Anesthesia & Perinatology. *Res:* Fetal and neonatal physiology and pharmacology; obstetric anesthesia. *Mailing Add:* Dept of Anesthesiol Columbia Univ New York NY 10032

MORISON, IAN GEORGE, b Perth, Australia, Jan 31, 28; m 72; c 4. FORESTRY. *Educ:* Univ Western Australia, BScFor, 51; Australian Forestry Sch, DipFor, 52; Univ Wash, PhD(forestry), 70. *Prof Exp:* Sr scientist soils, 69-72, ASSOC PROF FORESTRY, COL FOREST RESOURCES, UNIV WASH, DIR INST FOREST PROD & DIR DIV CONTINUING EDUC FOREST RESOURCES, 72- *Concurrent Pos:* Proj mgr regional forest nutrit res prog & land use res appl nat needs, NSF, 69-72. *Mem:* Am Soc Agron; AAAS; Soc Am Foresters; Am Soc Plant Physiologists; Int Soc Soil Sci. *Res:* Growth response of Douglas fir to application of nitrogenous fertilizers and the relationship of response to stand, soil and foliar characteristics. *Mailing Add:* Col of Forest Resources Univ of Wash Seattle WA 98195

MORISON, ROBERT SWAIN, b Milwaukee, Wis, Nov 25, 06; m 36; c 2. NEUROPHYSIOLOGY. *Educ:* Harvard Univ, AB, 30, MD, 35. *Hon Degrees:* DSc, Loyola Univ Ill, 70 & Univ Rochester, 73. *Prof Exp:* Res physician, Collis P Huntington Mem Hosp, Boston, 34-35; Austin teaching fel, Harvard Med Sch, 35-36, instr physiol, 36-38, assoc anat, 38-41, asst prof, 41-44; from asst dir to assoc dir med sci, Rockefeller Found, 44-51, med & pub health, 51-55, dir biol & med res, 55-59, med & natural sci, 59-64; prof biol & dir div biol sci, 64-70, Richard J Schwartz prof sci & soc, 70-75, EMER PROF SCI & SOC, CORNELL UNIV, 75- *Concurrent Pos:* Vis prof, Mass Inst Technol, 75- *Mem:* AAAS; Am Physiol Soc; Am Asn Anat; Am Acad Arts & Sci. *Res:* Electrophysiology; neuromuscular junction; thalamo-cortical relations; science policy; biomedical ethics. *Mailing Add:* Box 277 Peterborough NH 03458

MORISSET, PIERRE, b Quebec, Que, Nov 17, 38; m 70; c 2. PLANT TAXONOMY, PLANT ECOLOGY. *Educ:* Laval Univ, BA, 58, BScA, 62; Univ Cambridge, PhD(bot), 67. *Prof Exp:* Botanist plant taxon, Bot Garden Montreal, 67-68; res assoc, Smithsonian Inst, Washington, DC, 68. PROF BIOL, LAVAL UNIV, 68- *Concurrent Pos:* Univ Col N Wales, Bangor, UK, 76-77. *Mem:* Can Bot Asn; Genetics Soc Can; Inst Asn Plant Taxon; Soc Bibliog Natural Hist; Bot Soc Brit Isles. *Res:* Biosystematic studies of vascular plants; ecology and distribution of Arctic-Alpine species in eastern Canada; population biology of weedy plant species; flora of Northern Quebec. *Mailing Add:* Dept of Biol Laval Univ Quebec PQ G1K 7P4 Can

MORITA, EIICHI, b Waipahu, Hawaii, Oct 16, 16; m 25. RUBBER CHEMISTRY. *Educ:* WVa State Col, BS, 61; WVa Univ, MS, 64; Osaka Univ, PhD(chem), 68. *Prof Exp:* Anal res chemist, Dunlop Rubber Co Ltd, Japan, 40-55 & Honolulu Gas Co, Hawaii, 55-56; sr res chemist, Monsanto Co, 56-74, res specialist, Monsanto Indust Chem Co, 74-78, sr res specialist, 78-81; RETIRED. *Mem:* Am Chem Soc; Soc Rubber Indust Japan. *Res:* Bonding rubber to other materials; synthesis and application of chemicals in elastomers; vulcanization of various elastomers; mechanism of vulcanization. *Mailing Add:* 95-122 Kuahelani Ave Mililani Town HI 96789

MORITA, HIROKAZU, b Steveston, BC, July 17, 26; m 65. ORGANIC CHEMISTRY. *Educ:* Univ Man, BSc, 48, MSc, 49; Univ Notre Dame, PhD(org chem), 51. *Prof Exp:* US Off Naval Res fel, Northwestern Univ, 51-52; agr res off, Chem Div, Sci Serv, Can Dept Agr, 52-57, res off chem, Soil Res Inst, 67, RES SCIENTIST CHEM, SOIL RES INST, CAN DEPT AGR, 67- *Concurrent Pos:* Goodyear res fel, Princeton Univ, 56-57; Commonwealth Sci & Indust Res Orgn vis scientist, Univ Melbourne, 66-67. *Mem:* Fel AAAS; Phytochem Soc NAm; Am Chem Soc; fel Chem Inst Can; Can Soc Soil Sci. *Res:* Natural products in peat; organic mass spectrometry; gas and high pressure liquid chromatography; synthesis and properties of polyphenols; differential thermal analysis of organic polymers. *Mailing Add:* Dept of Chem & Biol Res Inst Agr Can Ottawa ON K1A 0C6 Can

MORITA, RICHARD YUKIO, b Pasadena, Calif, Mar 27, 23; m 53; c 3. MICROBIOLOGY, OCEANOGRAPHY. *Educ:* Univ Nebr, BS, 47; Univ Southern Calif, MS, 49; Univ Calif, PhD(microbiol, oceanog), 54. *Prof Exp:* Asst, Univ Southern Calif, 47-49; asst, Univ Calif, 49-54, res microbiologist, Scripps Inst Oceanog, 54-55; asst prof bact, Univ Houston, 55-58; assoc prof, Univ Nebr, 58-62; PROF MICROBIOL & OCEANOG, ORE STATE UNIV, 62- *Concurrent Pos:* Microbiologist, Mid-Pac Exped, 50 & Trans-Pac Exped, 53; vis investr, Danish Galathea Deep-Sea Exped, 52 & Dodo Exped, 64; prog dir biochem, NSF, 68-69, mem, Panel Molecular Biol, 69-70; consult, Nat Inst Gen Med Sci, 68-71; proj reviewer, Environ Protection Agency, 72; mem, Panel Biol Oceanog, NSF, 73; Queen Elizabeth II sr fel, Govt Australia, 73-74; Japan Soc Promotion Sci fel, 78. *Mem:* NY Acad Sci; Soc Gen Microbiol; Oceanog Soc Japan; Can Soc Microbiol; fel Am Acad Microbiol. *Res:* Effect of hydrostatic pressure on the physiology of microorganisms; study of Beggiatoa, marine psychophilic bacteria; eutrophication. *Mailing Add:* Dept Microbiol Ore State Univ Corvallis OR 97331

MORITA, TETSU, b Seattle, Wash, Feb 5, 23; m 53; c 4. ELECTRONICS. *Educ:* Univ Nebr, BS, 44; Harvard Univ, MS, 45, PhD, 49. *Prof Exp:* Head antenna group, Harvard Univ, 50-52; head radiation syst group, 52-65, mgr electromagnetic sci lab, 65-71, DIR, ELECTROMAGNETIC SCI LAB, SRI INT, 71- *Concurrent Pos:* Consult, Gen Tel & Electronics Corp, Mass, 52 & Trans Sonics, Inc, 50-52. *Mem:* Am Phys Soc; Sigma Xi; fel Inst Elec & Electronics Engrs. *Res:* Antenna system research; environmental studies; re-entry physics; plasma diagnostic studies. *Mailing Add:* Electromagnetic Sci Lab SRI Int 333 Ravenswood Ave Menlo Park CA 94025

MORITA, TOSHIKO N, b Los Angeles, Calif, May 29, 26; m 53; c 3. FOOD MICROBIOLOGY. *Educ:* Univ Calif, Los Angeles, BS, 48, MA, 50, PhD(zool), 52. *Prof Exp:* Res assoc chemother, Barlow Sanitarium, 51-52; serologist, Vet Admin, 52-53; res assoc biochem, Scripps Metab Clin, 53-55; asst prof biol, Univ Houston, 57-58; asst prof immunol, Ore State Univ, 65-67; res assoc biol, Georgetown Univ, 68-69; RES ASSOC FOOD & NUTRIT, ORE STATE UNIV, 70- *Res:* Staph toxins. *Mailing Add:* Dept Food & Nutrit Ore State Univ Corvallis OR 97330

MORITA, WILLIAM HIDEO, b Pasadena, Calif, Apr 28, 21; m 47; c 2. AERONAUTICAL & MECHANICAL ENGINEERING. *Educ:* Univ Nebr, BSME, 44; Univ Southern Calif, MSME, 54. *Prof Exp:* Stress analyst aircraft & missiles, Consol Vultee Aircraft Corp, 47-49; sr struct engr missiles & boosters, Space Div, NAm Aviation, Inc, Calif, 49-52, sr design engr, 52-56, missiles, 56-57, design specialist weapon systs, 57-60, launch vehicles, 60-61, proj engr lunar & planetary systs, 62-63, proj mgr, 63-66, proj engr launch vehicles, 66-68, engr space shuttle prog, 69-79, study mgr, adv systs, 79-81, PROJ MGR, COMPOSITE STRUCT ADV ENG, SPACE DIV, NORTH AM ROCKWELL CORP, DOWNEY, 81- *Mem:* Am Inst Aeronaut & Astronaut; Soc Advan Mat & Process Eng. *Res:* Advanced space vehicle concepts; launch vehicles, spacecraft and advanced tankage design and development; space shuttle program conceptual design and development; shuttle growth design, orbiter composite structures. *Mailing Add:* Space Div Rockwell Int Corp 12214 Lakewood Blvd Downey CA 90241

MORITSUGU, TOSHIO, b Honolulu, Hawaii, Apr 2, 25; m 59; c 2. SUGAR CHEMISTRY. *Educ:* Univ Louisville, BA, 49; Ohio State Univ, MS, 51, PhD(org chem), 54. *Prof Exp:* Res fel, Ohio State Univ, 54-55; assoc technologist sugar cane res, 55-68, SUGAR TECHNOLOGIST, EXP STA, HAWAIIAN SUGAR PLANTERS' ASN, 68- *Concurrent Pos:* Mem, US Nat Comt Sugar Anal & Int Comt Uniform Methods Sugar Anal. *Mem:* AAAS; fel Am Inst Chemists; Am Chem Soc; Int Soc Sugar Cane Technol; Sigma Xi. *Res:* Carbohydrate chemistry; crystallization, clarification and ion exchange in sugar cane processing; steric effects in organic chemistry; cane factory analysis, control and calculations. *Mailing Add:* Hawaiian Sugar Planters' Asn Exp Sta 99-193 Aiea Hts Dr Aiea HI 96701

MORITZ, BARRY KYLER, b Elizabeth, NJ, Apr 16, 41; m 65; c 2. PHYSICS, COMPUTER SCIENCE. *Educ:* Calif Inst Technol, BS, 63; Univ Md, PhD(physics), 69. *Prof Exp:* Asst physics, Univ Md, 63-69; NSF fel, E O Hulburt Ctr Space Res, US Naval Res Lab, Washington, DC, 69-71; sr assoc, PRC Info Sci Co, 71-75, prin, 75-81; PRES, MEASUREMENT CONCEPT CORP, 81- *Concurrent Pos:* Lectr, The Heights, Washington, DC, 69-70. *Mem:* Asn Comput Mach. *Res:* General relativity, astrophysics and cosmology; solar corona and streamers; digital image analysis and pattern recognition; distributed logic systems; associative and parallel techniques; computer information and science. *Mailing Add:* 201 W Pine St Rome NY 13440

MORITZ, CARL ALBERT, b Bellevue, Ky, Jan 27, 14; m 43; c 5. GEOLOGY. *Educ:* Univ Kans, AB, 40; Harvard Univ, MA, 48, PhD(geol), 50. *Prof Exp:* Jr geologist, St Louis Smelting & Refining, 41; topog engr, US Coast & Geod Surv, 42-43; jr geologist, Union Mines Develop Corp, 44; sr geologist, Phillips Petrol Co, 44-46; instr, Univ Tenn, 46; asst prof, Dartmouth Col, 48-53; CONSULT GEOLOGIST, ALEX W McCOY ASSOCS, INC, 53- *Mem:* Fel Geol Soc Am; Paleont Soc; Am Asn Petrol Geologists; Am Inst Mining, Metall & Petrol Engrs. *Res:* Stratigraphy; sedimentation and petroleum geology. *Mailing Add:* 5223 S Birmingham Pl Tulsa OK 74105

MORITZ, ROGER HOMER, b Cleveland, Ohio, Mar 11, 37; div; c 4. APPLIED MATHEMATICS, ENGINEERING STATISTICS. *Educ:* Valparaiso Univ, BS, 59; Univ Pittsburgh, MS, 61, PhD(math), 64. *Prof Exp:* Asst math, Univ Pittsburgh, 59-61; sr engr, Goodyear Atomic Corp, 62-64; res mathematician, Cornell Aeronaut Lab, Inc, Cornell Univ, 64-70; assoc prof, 70-80, PROF MATH, ALFRED UNIV, 80-, CHMN DEPT, 70- *Concurrent Pos:* Instr math, State Univ NY Buffalo, 65-69. *Mem:* Math Asn Am. *Res:* Summability and infinite series; number theory; applied mathematics; Egyptian fractions. *Mailing Add:* Dept of Math Alfred Univ Alfred NY 14802

MORIYAMA, IWAO MILTON, b San Francisco, Calif, Jan 26, 09; m 46; c 2. PUBLIC HEALTH. *Educ:* Univ Calif, BS, 31; Yale Univ, MPH, 34, PhD(pub health statist), 37. *Prof Exp:* Sanit engr, George Williams Hooper Found Med Res, Calif, 31-32; asst, Pierce Lab Hyg, Conn, 33-39; tech secy comt hyg housing, Am Pub Health Asn, 39-40; jr biometrician, US Bur Census, Washington, DC, 40-46; chief mortality anal sect, Nat Off Vital Statist, 47-61, dir off health statist anal, Nat Ctr Health Statist, 61-71, chief statist dept, Atomic Bomb Casualty Comn, 71-73, assoc dir int statist, Nat Ctr Health Statist, USPHS, 74-75, chief, dept epidemeol & statist, Radiation Effects Res Found, 75-78, DEP EXEC DIR, INT INST FOR VITAL REGISTRATION & STATISTICS, 78- *Concurrent Pos:* Mem, Int Union for Sci Study Pop; secy, US Nat Comt, Vital & Health Statist. *Mem:* Fel AAAS; fel Am Statist Asn; fel Am Pub Health Asn. *Res:* Vital and health statistics; demography. *Mailing Add:* 7120 Darby Rd Bethesda MD 20034

MORIYASU, KEIHACHIRO, b Tacoma, Wash, Jan 26, 40. EXPERIMENTAL HIGH ENERGY PHYSICS. *Educ:* Mass Inst Technol, BS, 62; Univ Calif, Berkeley, PhD(physics), 67. *Prof Exp:* NSF fel, 67-68; res assoc physics, Stanford Linear Accelerator Ctr, 68-71; sr res assoc, 71-73, ASST PROF PHYSICS, UNIV WASH, 71- *Concurrent Pos:* NSF foreign travel grant, 74. *Mem:* Am Inst Physics. *Res:* Experimental investigation of elementary particle interactions at high energy. *Mailing Add:* Dept of Physics Univ of Wash Seattle WA 98195

MORIZUMI, S JAMES, b San Francisco, Calif, Nov 13, 23; m 55; c 1. APPLIED SCIENCES, THERMODYNAMICS. *Educ:* Univ Calif, Berkeley, BS, 55; Calif Inst Technol, MS, 57; Univ Calif, Los Angeles, PhD(appl math), 70. *Hon Degrees:* Mech Eng, Kumamoto Univ. *Prof Exp:* Aerodynamicist aerodyn & performance group, Douglas Aircraft, 55-60; mem tech staff aerothermal dept, TRW Defense & Space Syst, 60-68; res engr IR radiation heat transfer, Univ Calif, Los Angeles, 68-69; mem tech staff, Electro-Optical Sensor Dept, TRW Defense & Space Syst Group, 69-71, Space Guid Software Design Dept, 71-73, Mission Design Dept, 73-76, HEL Optical Dept, 76-77, staff engr, Syst Survivability Dept, 77-78, staff scientist opers syst, 78-81; DIR GUID & CONTROL/SPACE APPLICATIONS, HYDRAULIC RES TEXTRON, 81- *Concurrent Pos:* Invited lectr, Univ Ariake, 75, Univ Kumamoto, 75 & 81 & Univ Kyushu, 81. *Mem:* Sigma Xi; Am Inst Aeronaut & Astronaut. *Res:* Molecular gas non grey thermal radiation, vibration rotation bands; applied mathematics, mathematical logic, methodology and optimization; laser, electro-optic sensing, guidance and control, trajectory analysis, detection/pointing/tracking. *Mailing Add:* TRW Defense & Space Syst Group Redondo Beach CA 90278

MORK, DAVID PETER SOGN, b Thief River Falls, Minn, Sept 25, 42; m 66. BIOLOGY. *Educ:* Moorhead State Col, BS, 64; Purdue Univ, MS, 66, PhD(bionucleonics), 69. *Prof Exp:* Asst prof, 68-75, assoc prof, 75-79, lectr, Sch Nursing, 73-79, PROF BIOL, ST CLOUD STATE COL, 79- *Mem:* AAAS; Am Soc Health Physics; Am Soc Zoologists. *Mailing Add:* Dept of Biol Sci St Cloud State Univ St Cloud MN 56301

MORKEN, DONALD A, b Crookston, Minn, Feb 2, 22; m 47; c 2. BIOPHYSICS. *Educ:* Cornell Univ, BEE, 49; Univ Rochester, PhD(biophys), 54. *Prof Exp:* From instr to asst prof, 54-61, ASSOC PROF RADIATION BIOL, SCH MED & DENT, UNIV ROCHESTER, 61-, ASSOC PROF BIOPHYS, 77- *Mem:* Radiation Res Soc; Inst Elec & Electronics Engrs; Biophys Soc; Health Physics Soc. *Res:* Effects of ionizing radiation on physiological functions of organisms. *Mailing Add:* Dept Radiation Biol & Biophys Sch Med & Dent Univ Rochester Rochester NY 14627

MORKOC, HADIS, b Erzurum, Turkey, Oct 2, 47; US citizen; m 76. SEMICONDUCTORS. *Educ:* Istanbul Tech Univ, BS, 68, MS, 69; Cornell Univ, PhD(elec eng), 76. *Prof Exp:* Instr elec eng, Istanbul Tech Univ, 69-71; fel, Cornell Univ, 76; mem tech staff, Varian Assoc, Inc, 76-78; ASST PROF ELEC ENG, UNIV ILL, 78- *Concurrent Pos:* Consult, Gen Dynamics, 80-81, Hughes, 81 & Int Bus Mach, 81- *Mem:* Sr mem Inst Elec & Electronics Engrs; Electrochem Soc; AAAS. *Res:* Compound semiconductor materials prepared by molecular beam epitaxy; high speed three terminal devices. *Mailing Add:* Coord Sci Lab 1101 W Springfield Ave Urbana IL 61801

MORKOVIN, MARK V(LADIMIR), b Prague, Czech, July 28, 27; nat US; m 40; c 2. FLUID DYNAMICS, AEROMECHANICAL ENGINEERING. *Educ:* Southern Calif Col, AB, 37; Syracuse Univ, MA, 38; Univ Wis, PhD(appl math), 42. *Prof Exp:* Instr, Mich State Col, 41-42; Rockefeller fel, Brown Univ, 42-43, instr civil eng, 43; res aerodynamicist, Bell Aircraft Corp, NY, 43-46 & Off Naval Res, Washington, DC, 46-47; asst & assoc prof aeronaut eng, Univ Mich, 47-51; res scientist, Johns Hopkins Univ, 51-58; prin staff scientist, Res Dept, Baltimore Div, Martin Co, 58-67; PROF MECH & MECH & AEROSPACE ENG, ILL INST TECHNOL, 67- *Concurrent Pos:* Lectr Johns Hopkins Univ, 51-67; consult in the field; mem subcomt high-speed aerodyn, Nat Adv Comt Aeronaut, 46-49; mem adv res comt fluid dynamics, NASA, 68-70; mem tech comt fluid dynamics, Am Inst Aeronaut & Astronaut, 73-74; assoc mem fluid mech comt, Am Soc Mech Engrs; Alexander von Humboldt sr award, 77-78; sr exchange scientist with USSR Acad Sci, Nat Acad Sci, 79. *Honors & Awards:* First Fluid & Plasmadynamics Award, Am Inst Aeronaut & Astronaut, 76. *Mem:* AAAS; Sigma Xi; fel Am Soc Mech Engrs; fel Am Inst Aeronaut & Astronaut; fel Am Phys Soc. *Res:* Experimental and theoretical fluid dynamics; transition and turbulent flow; stability and transition to turbulence; unsteady flows; separated flows; coupled fluid-elastic instabilities; turbulent heat transfer; simulation of wind effects in the atmospheric boundary layer. *Mailing Add:* 1104 Linden Ave Oak Park IL 60302

MORLANG, BARBARA LOUISE, b Conn. NUTRITION. *Educ:* Brigham Young Univ, BS, 60; Columbia Univ, MS, 64; Univ Mass, PhD(food & nutrit), 69. *Prof Exp:* Therapeut dietitian, Yale-New Haven Community Hosp, 61-62 & St Luke's Hosp, New York, 62-64; nutrit consult, Bur Nutrit, City New York, 64-65; dir & nutritionist, Springfield Dairy Coun, Mass, 65-66; STATE NUTRIT CONSULT, VA DEPT HEALTH, 70- *Mem:* Am Dietetic Asn; Am Home Econ Asn; Am Pub Health Asn. *Res:* Nutritional status of local populations. *Mailing Add:* Southwest Regional Off Suite 130 1314 Peters Creek Rd Roanoke VA 24017

MORLANG, CHARLES, JR, b Apr 21, 35; US citizen; m 64. PLANT MORPHOLOGY. *Educ:* City Col New York, BS, 56; Columbia Univ, PhD(bot), 65. *Prof Exp:* Lab instr gen bot, Columbia Univ, 56-59, Grad Morphol Lab, 59-60, lectr bot, 60-63, coordr, Biol Methods Sect, Univ High Sch Sci Honors Prog, 61-64; lectr biol, City Col New York, 64-65; asst prof, Mass State Col Westfield, 65-67; chmn dept, 78-81, ASSOC PROF BIOL, HOLLINS COL, 67- *Concurrent Pos:* Consult ecol curric, Am Inst Biol Sci, 73-75; consult, Blue Ridge Parkway Nat Park, Roanoke City Schs & Va State Dept Health. *Mem:* AAAS; Bot Soc Am; Torrey Bot Club; Am Inst Biol Sci; Sigma Xi. *Res:* Plant morphogenesis; neoplasms in ferns; ecological education; morphogenesis in ferns; electron microscopy; ecological problems. *Mailing Add:* Dept of Biol Hollins Col Hollins VA 24020

MORLEY, COLIN GODFREY DENNIS, b Sittingbourne, Eng, Nov 12, 41; div; c 2. BIOCHEMISTRY. *Educ:* Univ Nottingham, BSc, 63; Australian Nat Univ, PhD(biochem), 69. *Prof Exp:* Res scientist, Imp Chem Industs, 63-64; asst lectr chem, Woolwich Col Further Educ, London, 64-65; NIH fel, Nat Heart & Lung Inst, 68-70; asst prof, Dept Med, Univ Chicago, 70-76; asst prof, 76-81, ASSOC PROF DEPT BIOCHEM, RUSH PRESBYTERIAN ST LUKES MED CTR, CHICAGO, 81- *Concurrent Pos:* Guest lectr, Purdue Univ, Calumet Campus, 74-75, 77-78 & 80-81. *Mem:* AAAS; Royal Soc Chem; Tissue Culture Asn; Am Chem Soc. *Res:* Cell biology, particularly control of cell growth in mammalian systems, hormonal aspects of such control; relationship between normal and cancer cells for growth control. *Mailing Add:* 1640 W Greenleaf Apt 3B Chicago IL 60626

MORLEY, DOUROSSOFF EDMUND, b Edmonton, Alta, Nov 9, 11; nat US; m 59. SPEECH PATHOLOGY. *Educ:* Eastern Mich Univ, AB, 33; Univ Mich, MA, 38, PhD(speech path, hearing), 49. *Prof Exp:* Teacher pub sch, Mich, 34-39; instr Eng & speech, Univ Pa, 39-40; instr speech, Pa State Teachers Col, Calif, 40-44; supvr speech correction, Commonwealth of Pa, 44-45; from instr to prof speech path, 49-69, prof phys med & rehab & speech, 69-76, EMER PROF PHYS MED & REHAB & SPEECH, MED SCH, UNIV MICH, ANN ARBOR, 76- *Concurrent Pos:* Consult, United Cerebral Palsy Asn Mich, 55- & US Vet Admin Hosp, 55-; Fulbright lectr, Univ Oslo, 56-57; teacher, Am Acad, Am Community Schs, Athens, Greece, 64-65. *Mem:* Fel Am Speech & Hearing Asn. *Res:* Neurological disorders; audiology. *Mailing Add:* 701 Barton Dr Ann Arbor MI 48105

MORLEY, GAYLE L, b Moroni, Utah, Feb 29, 36; m 64; c 3. THEORETICAL SOLID STATE PHYSICS. *Educ:* Brigham Young Univ, BS, 58; Univ Calif, Los Angeles, MS, 60; Iowa State Univ, PhD(physics), 67. *Prof Exp:* Microwave engr, Hughes Aircraft Co, 58-60; fel, Tex A&M Univ, 67-68; assoc prof, Mankato State Univ, 68-77, prof physics & electronics eng technol, 77-79; ASSOC PROF MATH/PHYSICS, COL IDAHO, 79- *Res:* Theory of lattice vibrations in solids. *Mailing Add:* Dept Math/Physics Col Idaho Caldwell ID 83605

MORLEY, GEORGE W, b Toledo, Ohio, June 6, 23; m 46; c 3. MEDICINE. *Educ:* Univ Mich, BS, 44, MD, 49, MS, 55; Am Bd Obstet & Gynec, dipl, 53, cert gynec oncol, 74. *Prof Exp:* Intern, 49-50, from asst resident to resident, 50-54, from instr to assoc prof, 56-70, PROF OBSTET & GYNEC, MED CTR, UNIV MICH, ANN ARBOR, 70- *Concurrent Pos:* Consult, US Vet Admin Hosp, Ann Arbor, Mich, 56- & Wayne County Gen Hosp, Eloise, 60- *Mem:* Fel Am Col Surg; fel Am Col Obstet & Gynec; Soc Gynec Oncol; Soc Pelvic Surg; Int Soc Study Vulvar Dis. *Res:* Malignancy of the female genital tract. *Mailing Add:* Dept of Obstet & Gynec Univ of Mich Med Ctr Ann Arbor MI 48104

MORLEY, HAROLD VICTOR, b Buenos Aires, Arg, July 21, 27; m 53; c 1. PESTICIDE CHEMISTRY, ENVIRONMENTAL CHEMISTRY. *Educ:* Univ London, BSc, 48, PhD(org chem), 55. *Prof Exp:* Asst lectr chem, Royal Free Hosp, Sch Med, Univ London, 51-57; fel, Nat Res Coun Can, 57-59 & McMaster Univ, 59-60; res scientist, Anal Chem Res Serv, Can Dept Agr, 60-71, Chem Biol Res Inst, 71-72, res coordr, Environ & Resources, Res Br, Can Dept Agr, Ottawa, 72-78; DIR LONDON RES INST, 78- *Concurrent Pos:* Mem, Reference Group Land Use Activities, Int Joint Comn, 73-77. *Mem:* The Chem Soc; Chem Inst Can. *Res:* Determination and function of ergothioneine in biological fluids; goitrogenic compounds, especially imidazole-2-thiols; porphyrins, especially structure of chlorophylls; pesticide residue chemistry. *Mailing Add:* London Res Ctr Agr Can Univ Sub PO London ON N6A 5B7 Can

MORLEY, LLOYD ALBERT, b Provo, Utah, Oct 28, 40; m 75; c 1. MINING ENGINEERING, ELECTRICAL ENGINEERING. *Educ:* Univ Utah, BS, 68, PhD(mining eng), 72. *Prof Exp:* Technician & dept mgr elec, Strevell Paterson Co, 61-67; asst prof, 71-75, assoc prof, 75-80, PROF MINING ENG, PA STATE UNIV, 80- *Concurrent Pos:* Consult, Cumberland Coal Div, US Steel Corp, 75-78, Dept Mine Safety, Pa Dept Environ Resources, 77-, Skelley & Loy, 80- & IMC, 81; res grants Bur Mines, US Dept Interior, 72- *Mem:* Am Inst Mining Metall & Petrol Engrs; Soc Mining Engrs; sr mem Inst Elec & Electronics Engrs. *Res:* Mine electrical systems; protective relaying, transients, monitoring and simulation, power equipment design; coal mining. *Mailing Add:* Pa State Univ 119 Mineral Sci Bldg University Park PA 16802

MORLEY, MICHAEL DARWIN, b Youngstown, Ohio, Sept 29, 30; m 54. MATHEMATICAL LOGIC. *Educ:* Case Inst Technol, BS, 51; Univ Chicago, MS, 53, PhD, 62. *Prof Exp:* Sr mathematician, Labs Appl Math, Univ Chicago, 55-61; instr math, Univ Calif, Berkeley, 62-63; asst prof, Univ Wis-Madison, 63-66; assoc prof, 67-70, PROF MATH, CORNELL UNIV, 70- *Mem:* Am Math Soc; Asn Symbolic Logic. *Res:* Foundations of mathematics. *Mailing Add:* 325 Highland Rd Ithaca NY 14850

MORLEY, ROBERT EMMETT, JR, b St Louis, Mo, April 20, 51; m 72; c 1. COMMUNICATIONS SYSTEMS. *Educ:* Washington Univ, St Louis, BS, 73, MS, 75, DSc, 77. *Prof Exp:* Staff engr, Lincoln Lab, Mass Inst Technol, 75; vpres engr, Micro-Term Inc, 76-81; ASST PROF ELEC ENG, WASHINGTON UNIV, ST LOUIS, 81- *Honors & Awards:* Young Prof Award, Inst Elec & Electronics Engrs, 81. *Mem:* Inst Elec & Electronics Engrs. *Res:* Design of very large scale integration systems for digital signal processing. *Mailing Add:* Washington Univ Box 1127 St Louis MO 63130

MORLEY, THOMAS PATERSON, b Manchester, Eng, June 13, 20; Can citizen; m 43; c 3. NEUROSURGERY. *Educ:* Oxford Univ, BA, 41, BM, BCh, 43; FRCS, 49; FRCPS(C), 53. *Prof Exp:* Consult, Sunnybrook Hosp, Dept Vet Affairs, Govt of Can, 54-60; chmn, Div Neurosurg, Univ & Toronto Gen Hosp, 64-79, PROF SURG, UNIV TORONTO, 64- *Concurrent Pos:* Ont Cancer Treatment & Res Found res fel, 55-65; consult, Toronto E Gen Hosp, 62-69, Queen Elizabeth Hosp, Toronto, 63-, Princess Margaret Hosp, 63-, Ont Cancer Inst, 63- & Wellesley Hosp, Toronto, 64-69. *Mem:* Am Asn Neurol Surg; Soc Neurol Surg; Neurosurg Soc Am; Can Neurosurg Soc (secy, 60-64, pres, 71-72); Soc Brit Neurol Surg. *Res:* Diagnostic use of radioisotopes in neurosurgery; echoencephalography; recovery of tumor cells from blood in glioma cases; radiotherapy in gliomas. *Mailing Add:* Toronto Gen Hosp Toronto ON M5G 1L7 Can

MORLOCK, CARL G, b Crediton, Ont, Sept 11, 06; nat US; m 37; c 2. MEDICINE. *Educ:* Univ Western Ont, BA, 29, MD, 32; Univ Minn, MS, 37. *Prof Exp:* Intern, Victoria Hosp, London, Ont, 32-33, resident physician, 33-34; from instr to prof clin med, Mayo Grad Sch Med, 39-72, prof med, 72-75, EMER PROF MED, MAYO MED SCH, UNIV MINN, 75-, CONSULT, MAYO CLIN, 39- *Mem:* AMA; Am Gastroenterol Asn; fel Am Col Physicians. *Res:* Peptic ulcer and its complications; gastric carcinoma; anorexia nervosa; regional enteritis; arteriolar pathology of hypertension; blood pressure in renal tumors; liver disease; hemochromatosis; suprarenal insufficiency. *Mailing Add:* Mayo Clin 200 First St SW Rochester MN 55901

MORNEWECK, SAMUEL, b Meadville, Pa, Sept 3, 39; m 61. ORGANIC BIOCHEMISTRY. *Educ:* Allegheny Col, BS, 60; Case Inst Technol, PhD(org chem), 65. *Prof Exp:* Chemist, Agr Prod Labs, Esso Res & Eng Co, 65-67, res chemist, 67-70; asst prof, 70-75, ASSOC PROF CHEM, ST PETER'S COL, NJ, 75- *Res:* Determination of steric substituent constants. *Mailing Add:* Dept of Chem St Peter's Col Jersey City NJ 07306

MOROI, DAVID S, b Tokyo, Japan, Oct 15, 26; m 59; c 3. THEORETICAL PHYSICS. *Educ:* St Paul's Univ, Tokyo, BSc, 53; Johns Hopkins Univ, PhD(physics), 59. *Prof Exp:* Res assoc physics, Iowa State Univ, 59-61, instr, 60-61; res assoc, Univ Notre Dame, 61-63; asst prof, 63-68, assoc prof, 68-73, PROF PHYSICS, KENT STATE UNIV, 74- *Concurrent Pos:* US Air Force Off Sci Res grant, 64-69. *Mem:* Am Phys Soc. *Res:* Quantum electrodynamics; field theory; electromagnetic and other physical properties of liquid crystals; elementary particles in intense laser beams. *Mailing Add:* Dept of Physics Kent State Univ Kent OH 44242

MORONI, ENEO C, b Fiume, Italy, Feb 6, 23; US citizen; m 60; c 1. INDUSTRIAL ORGANIC CHEMISTRY. *Educ:* Univ Milan, PhD(phys org chem), 49. *Prof Exp:* Res chemist, Ledoga SpA, Italy, 49-55; prod chemist, Industria Saccarifera Parmense, 55-56; prod chemist, Pitt-Consol Chem Co Div, Consol Coal Co, 56-57, res chemist, 57-64; sr res chemist, Jones & Laughlin Steel Corp, 64-67; res chemist, Pittsburgh Energy Res Ctr, US Bur Mines, 67-75; prog mgr, Energy Res & Develop Admin, 75-78; PROG MGR, DEPT ENERGY, 78- *Mem:* Am Chem Soc. *Res:* Activated carbons; phenolic and cresylic acids resins; catalytic alkylation, dealkylation and isomerization of phenols and thiophenols; corrosion and coating surface phenomena; organometallics; coal desulfurization and liquefaction. *Mailing Add:* Apt 334N 1600 S Eads St Arlington VA 22202

MOROS, STEPHEN ANDREW, b New York, NY, July 29, 28; m 57; c 2. ANALYTICAL CHEMISTRY. *Educ:* Polytech Inst Brooklyn, BS, 48, PhD(electroanal chem), 61; Cornell Univ, MS, 50. *Prof Exp:* Proj group leader, Foster D Snell, Inc, NY, 50-53; res chemist, Am Cyanamid Co, NJ, 58-71; sr chemist, 71-73, group leader, 73-78, mgr, 78-81, ASST DIR,

HOFFMANN-LA ROCHE INC, 81- *Mem:* NAm Thermal Anal Soc; Am Chem Soc; Int Confederation for Thermal Anal; Am Pharmaceut Asn; Am Soc Testing & Mat. *Res:* Electroanalytical chemistry, including coulometry and potentiometry; organic electrosynthesis; instrumentation; thermal methods of analysis; spectroscopic methods; radiotracers; instrumental methods of analysis; spectrochemical analysis. *Mailing Add:* 144 Konner Ave Pine Brook NJ 07058

MOROSIN, BRUNO, b Klamath Falls, Ore, Feb 10, 34; m 58; c 4. PHYSICAL CHEMISTRY. *Educ:* Univ Ore, BA, 56; Univ Wash, PhD, 59. *Prof Exp:* Asst, Univ Wash, 56-59; mem tech staff, Hughes Aircraft Co, 60-61; staff mem, Sandia Labs, 61-67, supvr chem physics div, 67-73, supvr solid state mat, 73-80, SUPVR, SHOCK WAVE & EXPLOSIVE PHYSICS DIV, SANDIA NAT LABS, 80- *Mem:* Am Chem Soc; Am Phys Soc; Am Crystallog Asn. *Res:* Diffraction studies; structural properties related to magnetic and dielectric behavior. *Mailing Add:* 12317 Eastridge Dr NE Albuquerque NM 87112

MOROSOFF, NICHOLAS, b New York, NY, Jan 27, 37; m 67; c 2. PHYSICAL CHEMISTRY, POLYMER CHEMISTRY. *Educ:* Queens Col, NY, BS, 58; Polytech Inst Brooklyn, PhD(phys chem), 65. *Prof Exp:* NIH fel, 65-67; PHYS CHEMIST, CAMILLE DREYFUS LAB, RES TRIANGLE INST, 67- *Concurrent Pos:* Adj assoc prof, NC State Univ, 76- *Mem:* Am Chem Soc; Am Phys Soc; Am Crystallog Asn. *Res:* X-ray scattering from polymers; polymer morphology; solid state polymerization; plasma polymerization; surface chemistry. *Mailing Add:* 1806 Euclid Rd Durham NC 27713

MOROSON, HAROLD, b New York, NY, Aug 9, 27; m 52; c 2. RADIATION IMMUNOLOGY, RADIOBIOLOGY. *Educ:* Columbia Univ, BS, 50; Univ Del, MS, 55; Polytech Inst Brooklyn, PhD(phys chem), 58. *Prof Exp:* Res chemist, Reichhold Chem Inc, 52-56; asst prof chem, Newark Col Eng, 59-61; res assoc biophys, 61-63, assoc radiobiol & sect head, Sloan-Kettering Inst Cancer Res, 63-72, asst prof biophys, Sloan-Kettering Div, Cornell Univ, 63-72; assoc prof radiol & chief, Div Radiobiol, 72-77, PROF RADIOL & DIR, DIV RADIOBIOL, NY MED COL, 77- *Concurrent Pos:* NIH fel, Chester Beatty Res Inst, London, Eng, 58-59; Damon Runyon grant, 69-72; Nat Cancer Inst res grants, 72-80. *Mem:* Radiation Res Soc; Biophys Soc; Am Soc Exp Path; Am Asn Cancer Res; Am Cancer Soc. *Res:* Effects of ultraviolet and ionizing radiation on bacterial and mammalian cells; biophysical changes in DNA; radiation sensitization of tumors; radiation immunology; cancer research; experimental radiotherapy; radiation pathology. *Mailing Add:* Div of Radiobiol NY Med Col Flower & 5th Ave Hosp Valhalla NY 10595

MOROWITZ, HAROLD JOSEPH, b Poughkeepsie, NY, Dec 4, 27; m 49; c 5. BIOENERGETICS, ORIGIN OF LIFE. *Educ:* Yale Univ, BS, 47, MS, 50, PhD(biophys), 51. *Prof Exp:* Biophysicist, Nat Bur Standards, 51-53 & Nat Heart Inst, 53-55; from asst prof to assoc prof, 55-67, PROF BIOPHYS & BIOCHEM, YALE UNIV, 67- *Concurrent Pos:* Mem planetary biol subcomt, NASA, 66-72; assoc ed, J Biomed Computing, 69-; mem eval panel phys chem, Nat Bur Standards, 69-74; columnist, Hosp Pract, 74- *Mem:* AAAS; Explorer's Club; Biophys Soc; Am Inst Biol Scientists. *Res:* Energy transduction in biological systems; prebiotic chemistry; thermodynamic foundations of biology. *Mailing Add:* 56 Ox Bow Lane Woodbridge CT 06525

MOROZ, LEONARD ARTHUR, b Winnipeg, Man, Dec 9, 35; m; c 3. IMMUNOLOGY, BIOCHEMISTRY. *Educ:* Univ Man, MD, 59; FRCP(C), 64. *Prof Exp:* Res fel, Mass Gen Hosp & Harvard Med Sch, 61-63; guest investr, Rockefeller Univ, 64-67; asst prof, 67-73, ASSOC PROF, McGILL UNIV, 73- *Concurrent Pos:* Med res scholar, Med Res Coun Can, 67-72; Helen Hay Whitney Found fel, 64-67. *Mem:* Am Asn Immunologists; Am Fedn Clin. *Res:* Am Rheumatism Asn; Am Acad Allergy; Can Soc Clin Invest. Res: Proteolytic enzymes; fibrinolysis; inflammation; immunologically mediated lung disease; connective tissue diseases; immunochemistry. *Mailing Add:* Royal Victoria Hosp 687 Pine Ave W Montreal PQ H3A 1A1 Can

MOROZ, WILLIAM JAMES, b Toronto, Ont, Aug 29, 27; m 54; c 3. MECHANICAL ENGINEERING, METEOROLOGY. *Educ:* Univ Toronto, BASc, 49, MASc, 51; Univ Mich, MS, 62, PhD(meteorol), 64. *Prof Exp:* Combustion engr, Empire Hanna Coal Co, 50-57; lectr mech eng, Univ Toronto, 57-61, asst prof, 65-67, assoc prof, 67-68; prof mech eng & dir, Ctr Air Environ Studies, Pa State Univ, 68-76; vpres, Jas F MacLaren Consult Engrs, 77-80; SUPVR SCI & FIELD STUDIES, ENVIRON DEPT, ONT HYDRO, 80- *Concurrent Pos:* Consult, Air Pollution Control Serv, Ont, 65-68, actg head meteorol & air qual sect, 67-68; consult, James F McLaren, Ltd, 65-67; mem adv comt, Nat Air Pollution Control Tech, Environ Protection Agency, 73-76; adj prof mech eng, Univ Toronto, 79- *Honors & Awards:* Centennial Medal, Am Soc Mech Engrs, 79. *Mem:* fel Royal Meteorol Soc; Can Inst Combustion & Fuel Technol (pres, 67 & 68); Am Soc Mech Engrs; fel NY Acad Sci. *Res:* Air pollution control; atmospheric diffusion and dispersion; particle technology; combustion. *Mailing Add:* RR 2 Hastings ON K0L 1Y0 Can

MOROZOWICH, WALTER, b Irwin, Pa, Oct 27, 33; m 69; c 1. MEDICINAL CHEMISTRY. *Educ:* Duquesne Univ, BS, 55; Ohio State Univ, MS, 56, PhD(pharmaceut chem), 59. *Prof Exp:* SR RES SCIENTIST, UPJOHN CO, 59- *Mem:* Am Pharmaceut Asn; Am Chem Soc. *Res:* Analogs and prodrug derivatives of steroids, sulfonylureas, antibiotics and prostaglandins. *Mailing Add:* Upjohn Co 301 Henrietta St Kalamazoo MI 49001

MORR, CHARLES VERNON, b Ashland, Ohio, Oct 7, 27; m 51; c 2. FOOD CHEMISTRY. *Educ:* Ohio State Univ, BS, 52, MS, 55, PhD(dairy technol), 59. *Prof Exp:* Res assoc food, Carnation Res Lab, Calif, 59-61; asst prof milk protein res, Ohio State Univ, 61-64; from asst prof to prof, Univ Minn, St Paul, 64-73; dir protein res, Ralston Purina Co, 73-76; prof & chmn dept, Nutrit & Food Technol, Tex Tech Univ, 76-78; prof, 78-80, STENDER PROF, DEPT FOOD SCI, CLEMSON UNIV, 80- *Honors & Awards:* Dairy Res Award, Am Dairy Sci Asn, 73. *Mem:* Am Chem Soc; Am Dairy Sci Asn; Inst Food Technologists. *Res:* Chemistry and functional properties of plant proteins. *Mailing Add:* Dept Food Sci Clemson Univ Clemson SC 29631

MORRAL, F(ACUNDO) R(OLF), b Chemnitz, Ger, June 19, 07; nat US; m 34; c 5. METALLURGY, METALLURGICAL ENGINEERING. *Educ:* Mass Inst Technol, BS, 32; Purdue Univ, PhD(metall), 40. *Prof Exp:* Mgr, Textile Mill, Martin Morral, Sabadell, Spain, 34-36; res metallurgist, Continental Steel Corp, 38-41; asst prof metall, Pa State Univ, 41-43; indust fel, Mellon Inst Sci, 43-44; group leader, Metal Trades Lab, Am Cyanamid Co, 44-48; assoc prof mat eng, Syracuse Univ, 48-51; x-ray sect head, Dept Metall Res, Kaiser Aluminum & Chem Corp, 51-56; head, Cobalt Info Ctr Proj & consult, Battelle Mem Inst, 56-72; assoc dir Emilio Jimeno Inst Technol & Metall, Univ Barcelona, 72-73; CONSULT, 73- *Concurrent Pos:* Foreign affil, Royal Acad Exact Physical & Natural Sci. *Mem:* Fel AAAS; Am Inst Mining, Metall & Petrol Engrs; Am Soc Metals; hon mem Tech Soc Metall Spain. *Res:* Cobalt; metallurgy; engineering education. *Mailing Add:* 2075 Arlington Ave Columbus OH 43221

MORRAL, JOHN ERIC, b Kokomo, Ind, Aug 3, 39; c 2. PHYSICAL METALLURGY. *Educ:* Ohio State Univ, BMetE, 64, MS, 65; Mass Inst Technol, PhD, 69. *Prof Exp:* Asst prof metall, Univ Ill, Urbana, 68-71; ASSOC PROF METALL, UNIV CONN, 71- *Mem:* Am Inst Mining, Metall & Petrol Engrs; Am Soc Metals. *Res:* Kinetics and thermodynamics of phase transformations. *Mailing Add:* Dept of Metall Univ of Conn Storrs CT 06268

MORRE, D JAMES, b Drake, Mo, Oct 20, 35; m 56; c 3. BIOCHEMISTRY. *Educ:* Univ Mo, BS, 57; Purdue Univ, MS, 59; Calif Inst Technol, PhD(biochem), 63. *Prof Exp:* From asst prof to assoc prof, 63-71, PROF MED CHEM & DIR PURDUE CANCER CTR, PURDUE UNIV, LAFAYETTE, 71- *Honors & Awards:* Purdue Cancer Res Award, 78. *Mem:* Am Soc Cell Biol; Am Soc Biol Chem; Am Asn Cancer Res. *Res:* Cell growth; cancer; Golgi apparatus structure-function; membrane biogenesis; cell surfaces; secretion. *Mailing Add:* Dept of Med Chem Purdue Univ Lafayette IN 47906

MORRE, DOROTHY MARIE, b Bonnots Mill, Mo, Jan 18, 35; m 56; c 3. NUTRITION, NEUROANATOMY. *Educ:* Univ Mo, BS, 58; Purdue Univ, PhD(nutrit), 77. *Prof Exp:* Lab technician, Ger Cancer Res Ctr, 76; vis asst prof, 78, ASST PROF NUTRIT, DEPT FOODS & NUTRIT, PURDUE UNIV, 78- *Concurrent Pos:* Prin investr, Am Cancer Soc, 78-79; co-prin investr, NIH, 78-81. *Mem:* Sigma Xi; Am Dietetics Asn; assoc mem, Am Inst Nutrit; Am Soc Cell Biologists. *Res:* Chemopreventative effect of vitamin A on tumorigenesis and metastasis; hematological profile; cytotoxicity of megadoses, lysosomal stability and liability; ultrastructural changes. *Mailing Add:* Dept of Foods & Nutrit 109 Stone Hall West Lafayette IN 47907

MORRE, WILLIAM W(ALLACE), b Pasadena, Calif, Jan 24, 12; m 33; c 3. CIVIL ENGINEERING, FOUNDATION ENGINEERING. *Educ:* Calif Inst Technol, BS, 33, MS, 34. *Prof Exp:* Consult engr, 35-38; PARTNER, DAMES & MOORE, 38- *Mem:* Nat Acad Eng; Am Soc Civil Engrs; Am Soc Testing & Mat; Soc Am Mil Engrs. *Mailing Add:* Dames & Moore 500 Sansome St San Francisco CA 94111

MORREL, BERNARD BALDWIN, b Lynchburg, Va, Nov 28, 40; m 64; c 1. MATHEMATICS. *Educ:* Univ Va, BA, 62, MA, 66, PhD(math), 68. *Prof Exp:* Teaching asst math, Johns Hopkins Univ, 62-64; from teaching asst appl math to jr instr math, Univ Va, 65-68; asst prof math, Univ Ga, 68-75; vis asst prof, Ind Univ, Bloomington, 75-77; ASSOC PROF MATH SCI, IND UNIV-PURDUE UNIV, INDIANAPOLIS, 77- *Mem:* Am Math Soc; Math Asn Am; Soc Indust & Appl Math. *Res:* Functional analysis; theory of operators in Hilbert Space. *Mailing Add:* Dept of Math Sci 1201 E 38th St Indianapolis IN 46205

MORRELL, FRANK, b New York, NY, June 4, 26; c 4. NEUROLOGY, NEUROPHYSIOLOGY. *Educ:* Columbia Univ, AB, 48, MD, 51; McGill Univ, MSc, 55; Am Bd Psychiat & Neurol, dipl, 58. *Prof Exp:* Med intern, Montefiore Hosp, New York, 51-52, chief resident neurol, 53-54; from instr to assoc prof neurol, Med Sch, Univ Minn, 55-61; prof & chmn dept, Sch Med, Stanford Univ, 61-69; prof neurol & psychiat, New York Med Col, 69-72; PROF NEUROL SCI, MED COL, RUSH UNIV, 72- *Concurrent Pos:* Rosenthal fel, Nat Hosp, London, Eng, 52-53; fel neurophysiol, Montreal Neurol Inst, 54-55; consult, Epilepsy Found Am, 59-; consult, NIH & NSF, 61-; assoc neurosci res prog, Mass Inst Technol, 62-; mem brain sci comt, Nat Acad Sci, 66-70; Wall Mem lectr, Children's Hosp, DC, 67. *Mem:* Fel Royal Soc Health; Am Electroencephalog Soc; Am Epilepsy Soc; Am Acad Neurol; Soc Neurosci. *Res:* Pathophysiology of epilepsy and neural mechanisms of learning. *Mailing Add:* Dept of Neurol Sci Rush Univ Med Col Chicago IL 60612

MORRELL, GEORGE, b Trenton, NJ, Jan 10, 43. CLINICAL TOXICOLOGY, BIOCHEMISTRY. *Educ:* Univ Kansas City, Mo, BS, 68; St John's Univ, MS, 71. *Prof Exp:* Toxicol technician, Suffolk County Med Examr Off, NY, 70-71; supvr toxicol, Ctr Lab Med, Inc, NJ, 71-75, gen mgr & chief toxicologist lab opers, NJ, 75-77, tech dir & chief toxicologist, Pa, 77-78; CHIEF TOXICOLOGIST & BIOCHEMIST, H C PRIBOR & ASSOCS, INC & CHIEF TOXICOLOGIST & GEN MGR, MDS REF LAB, MDS HEALTH GROUP, INC, 78- *Concurrent Pos:* Instr toxicol, Med Lab Sci Symposia, C W Post Ctr, Long Island Univ, 78-79. *Mem:* AAAS; Am Asn Clin Chem; NY Acad Sci; Am Asn Drug Detection Labs; Am Chem Soc. *Res:* Industrial toxicology, especially biologic monitoring; clinical toxicology, especially therapeutical drug monitoring; analytical biochemistry, especially hormonal and enzyme assays. *Mailing Add:* Int Clin Labs Five Park Place PO Box 70 Nashville TN 37203

MORRELL, JOSEPH SALVADOR, mathematics, see previous edition

MORRELL, WILLIAM EGBERT, b Logan, Utah, July 30, 09; m 33; c 3. CHEMISTRY, SCIENCE EDUCATION. *Educ:* Utah State Univ, BS, 33; Univ Calif, PhD(phys chem), 38. *Hon Degrees:* LHD, Suffolk Univ, 73. *Prof Exp:* Instr phys sci, Chicago City Col, 38-42; from instr to prof phys sci, Univ Ill, 42-59; prog dir summer study, NSF, 59-76; RETIRED. *Concurrent Pos:* Asst prog dir summer study, NSF, 58-59. *Honors & Awards:* Meritorious Serv Award, NSF, 75. *Mem:* AAAS; Am Chem Soc. *Mailing Add:* 301 N Beauregard St #715 Alexandria VA 22312

MORREY, CHARLES BRADFIELD, JR, b Columbus, Ohio, July 23, 07; m 37; c 3. MATHEMATICS. *Educ:* Ohio State Univ, AB, 27, MA, 28; Harvard Univ, Phd(math), 31. *Prof Exp:* Asst, Ohio State Univ, 27-28; instr math, Harvard Univ, 29-31; Nat Res Coun fel, Princeton Univ, 31-32 & Rice Inst, 32-33; from instr to prof, 33-73, chmn dept, 49-54, EMER PROF MATH, UNIV CALIF, BERKELEY, 73- *Concurrent Pos:* Tutor, Harvard Univ, 30-31; vis prof, Univ Calif & Inst Advan Study, 37-38; mathematician, Aberdeen Proving Ground, Md, 42-45; mem math div, Nat Res Coun, 53- & Inst Advan Study, 54-55. *Mem:* Nat Acad Sci; Am Acad Arts & Sci; Am Math Soc (pres elect, 66, pres, 67 & 68); Math Asn Am. *Res:* Area of surfaces; calculus of variations; elliptic partial differential equations. *Mailing Add:* 210 Yale Ave Berkeley CA 94708

MORREY, JOHN ROLPH, b Joseph, Utah, May 30, 30; m 52; c 5. PHYSICAL CHEMISTRY, INORGANIC CHEMISTRY. *Educ:* Brigham Young Univ, BA, 53; Univ Utah, PhD(phys chem), 58. *Prof Exp:* Sr scientist, Gen Elec Co, 58-63, tech specialist, 63-64; res assoc chem, 65-77, STAFF SCIENTIST, PAC NORTHWEST LABS, BATTELLE MEM INST, 77- *Concurrent Pos:* Adj assoc prof, Wash State Univ, 67- *Mem:* AAAS; Am Chem Soc; NY Acad Sci. *Res:* Boron hydride fused salt and actinide element chemistry; chemical kinetics; molecular spectroscopy; computer applications to chemistry; laser chemistry; thermodynamics and materials; chemistry of coal. *Mailing Add:* Dept of Phys Sci 325 Bldg 300 Area Northwest Labs Battelle Mem Inst Richland WA 99352

MORRILL, BERNARD, b Boston, Mass, May 31, 10; m 40; c 1. MECHANICAL ENGINEERING. *Educ:* Mass Inst Technol, BSME, 47; Univ Del, MME, 49; Univ Mich, PhD, 59. *Prof Exp:* From instr to prof, 47-60, actg chmn dept, 59-60, chmn, 60-64, chmn engr dept, 72-73, Henry C & J Archer Turner prof, 67-75, EMER PROF MECH ENG, SWARTHMORE COL, 75- *Concurrent Pos:* NSF sci fac fel, Imp Col, Univ London, 64-65. *Mem:* Am Soc Mech Engrs; Am Soc Eng Educ; Soc Eng Sci; NY Acad Sci. *Res:* Mechanical vibration, linear and nonlinear. *Mailing Add:* 21 Oberlin Ave Swarthmore PA 19081

MORRILL, CALLIS GARY, b Tridell, Utah, Nov 6, 38; m 64; c 5. PHYSIOLOGY. *Educ:* Brigham Young Univ, BA, 64; Univ Calif, San Francisco, PhD(physiol), 70. *Prof Exp:* NIH res fel physiol, Univ Colo Med Ctr, 71-73; RES ASSOC PHYSIOL, NAT ASTHMA CTR, DENVER, 73- *Concurrent Pos:* Am Lung Asn fel, Nat Asthma Ctr, 74-75; NIH res grant, 75. *Mem:* Am Thoracic Soc. *Res:* Ventilatory control of asthmatic children; effects of low levels of carbon monoxide on exercise tolerance. *Mailing Add:* Dept of Clin Physiol Nat Asthma Ctr 1999 Julian St Denver CO 80204

MORRILL, CHARLES D(UNCKER), b St Louis, Mo, Oct 31, 19; m 42; c 5. ELECTRONICS. *Educ:* Univ Ill, BS, 41. *Prof Exp:* Engr, Am Tel & Tel Corp, 46-48; develop engr, 48-50, group leader electronic comput, 50-53, sect head, 53-56, dept mgr, 56-60, div mgr mil guid & data handling systs, 60-70, chief engr, Electronics Div, 70-80, ASST CHIEF ENGR, DEFENSE SYSTS DIV, GOODYEAR AEROSPACE CORP, 80- *Mem:* Fel Inst Elec & Electronics Engrs. *Res:* Military electronics; terminal guidance; trainers and simulators; intelligence and command control; associative array processor development; undersea weapons. *Mailing Add:* Goodyear Aerospace Corp Akron OH 44315

MORRILL, GENE A, b Bend, Ore, Aug 5, 31; m 60; c 2. BIOCHEMISTRY, DEVELOPMENTAL BIOLOGY. *Educ:* Univ Portland, BS, 54; Univ Utah, PhD(biochem), 59. *Prof Exp:* Res asst prof, 63-64, from asst prof to assoc prof, 65-76, PROF PHYSIOL, ALBERT EINSTEIN COL MED, 76- *Concurrent Pos:* Fel biochem, Albert Einstein Col Med, 58-60, sr fel physiol, 62; fel, Inst Training Res Behav & Neurol Sci, 60-61; City of New York Health Res Coun career scientist award, 69- *Mem:* Biophys Soc; Am Physiol Soc; Am Soc Biol Chemists; Soc Develop Biol. *Res:* Cell physiology; developmental biology; biophysics. *Mailing Add:* Albert Einstein Col of Med Yeshiva Univ New York NY 10461

MORRILL, JAMES LAWRENCE, JR, b Graves Co, Ky, Nov 23, 30; m 52; c 5. DAIRY SCIENCE. *Educ:* Murray State Col, BS, 58; Univ Ky, MS, 59; Iowa State Univ, PhD(dairy cattle nutrit), 63. *Prof Exp:* From instr to assoc prof, 62-78, PROF & DIARY CATTLE RES NUTRITIONIST, AGR EXP STA, KANS STATE UNIV, 78- *Mem:* Am Dairy Sci Asn; Am Soc Animal Sci. *Res:* Dairy cattle nutrition, especially nutrition of young. *Mailing Add:* Dept of Animal Sci Kans State Univ Manhattan KS 66506

MORRILL, JOHN BARSTOW, JR, b Chicago, Ill, Nov 20, 29; m 53; c 2. DEVELOPMENTAL BIOLOGY. *Educ:* Grinnell Col, BA, 51; Iowa State Col, MS, 53; Fla State Univ, PhD(zool), 58. *Prof Exp:* From instr to asst prof biol, Wesleyan Univ, 58-65; assoc prof, Col William & Mary, 65-67; assoc prof, 67-69, PROF BIOL, NEW COL, FLA, 69-, COORDR ENVIRON STUDIES PROG, 74- *Concurrent Pos:* NSF fel, 58; NIH special fel, 64; mem corp, Marine Biol Lab. *Mem:* Am Soc Zoologists; Soc Develop Biol. *Res:* Development of mollusk eggs; experimental analyses of molluscan development; effects of chemicals on mollusk eggs. *Mailing Add:* Div Natural Sci New Col-USF Sarasota FL 33580

MORRILL, JOHN ELLIOTT, b Oak Park, Ill, Nov 4, 35; m 58; c 3. MATHEMATICS. *Educ:* DePauw Univ, BA, 57; Univ Mich, MA, 60, PhD(math), 64. *Prof Exp:* From asst prof to assoc prof math, DePauw Univ, 64-70; vis assoc prof, Univ Mich, 70-71; assoc prof, 71-76, PROF MATH, DePAUW UNIV, 76- *Concurrent Pos:* Acad guest, Res Inst Math, ETH, Zurich, 72-73. *Mem:* Assoc Soc Actuaries; Am Math Soc; Math Asn Am. *Res:* Actuarial mathematics; mathematical economics. *Mailing Add:* Dept Math DePauw Univ Greencastle IN 46135

MORRILL, LAWRENCE GEORGE, b Tridell, Utah, July 21, 29; m 49; c 4. SOIL CHEMISTRY, FERTILITY. *Educ:* Utah State Univ, BS, 55, MS, 56; Cornell Univ, PhD(soil chem), 59. *Prof Exp:* From assoc chem to sr chemist, Thiokol Chem Corp, Utah, 59-66; res specialist, Cornell Univ, 60-61; assoc prof, 66-75, PROF SOIL CHEM & FERTIL, OKLA STATE UNIV, 75- *Mem:* Am Soc Agron; Soil Sci Soc Am. *Res:* Soil chemistry and fertility research and teaching. *Mailing Add:* Dept of Agron Okla State Univ Stillwater OK 74074

MORRILL, TERENCE CLARK, b Albany, NY, Mar 1, 40; m 65; c 2. ORGANIC CHEMISTRY, SPECTROMETRY. *Educ:* Syracuse Univ, BS, 61; San Jose State Col, MS, 64; Univ Colo, PhD(org chem), 66. *Prof Exp:* NSF fel org chem, Yale Univ, 66-67; from asst prof to assoc prof, 67-75, PROF ORG CHEM, ROCHESTER INST TECHNOL, 75- *Concurrent Pos:* Vis assoc prof, Univ Rochester, 75, vis prof, 81; NSF sci fac fel, 75-77; fel, Rochester Inst Technol, 76-78. *Mem:* Am Chem Soc; Sigma Xi; AAAS. *Res:* Stereochemistry of addition and solvolysis reactions; mechanisms of additions, solvolyses and oxidation reactions: alkylations; hydrazone chemistry; use of lanthanide shift reagents; reactions of organoboranes and organomercurials. *Mailing Add:* Dept of Chem Rochester Inst of Technol Rochester NY 14623

MORRILL, WENDELL LEE, b Madison, SDak, May 22, 41; m 65; c 2. ENTOMOLOGY, AGRICULTURE. *Educ:* SDak State Univ, BS, 67, MS, 68; Univ Fla, PhD(entom), 71. *Prof Exp:* Res assoc fire ants, Univ Fla, 71-73; asst prof grassland entom, Univ Ga, 73-78; ASSOC PROF CROPPING SYSTS ENTOM, MONT STATE UNIV, 78- *Mem:* Entom Soc Am. *Res:* Insect/plant relationships; effects of changing farming practices on insect populations. *Mailing Add:* Dept of Biol Mont State Univ Bozeman MT 59717

MORRIN, PETER ARTHUR FRANCIS, b Dublin, Ireland, Oct 8, 31; m 60; c 3. MEDICINE. *Educ:* Nat Univ Ireland, MB, BCh & BAO, 54, BSc, 55; FRCP(C), 61. *Prof Exp:* Instr med, Wash Univ, 60-61; lectr, 62-63, from asst to assoc prof, 63-76, PROF MED, QUEEN'S UNIV, ONT, 76- *Mem:* Am Fedn Clin Res; Can Med Asn; Can Soc Clin Invest; Am Soc Nephrol; Am Soc Artificial Internal Organs. *Res:* Nephrology. *Mailing Add:* Renal Unit Kingston Gen Hosp Kingston ON K7L 2V7 Can

MORRIS, ALAN DAVID, b Baltimore, Md, Jan 4, 31; m 51; c 3. ELECTRICAL ENGINEERING. *Educ:* Johns Hopkins Univ, BE, 51, DrEng, 55. *Prof Exp:* Res asst, Inst Coop Res, Johns Hopkins Univ, 51-55; res engr, Opers Res, Inc, Md, 58-61; assoc prof physics, Am Univ, 61-65, dir opers res, Ctr Technol & Admin, 65-69; SR PARTNER, MORRIS & WARD, CONSULT ENGRS, 69- *Concurrent Pos:* Consult, Children's Convalescent Hosp, Washington, DC, 60-67. *Mem:* Am Consult Engrs Coun; Nat Soc Prof Engrs. *Res:* Forensic science and engineering. *Mailing Add:* 5817 Plainview Rd Bethesda MD 20034

MORRIS, ALBERT GREGORY, b Philadelphia, Pa, Sept 28, 23; m 47; c 1. INORGANIC CHEMISTRY. *Educ:* Haverford Col, AB, 48; Univ Del, MS, 50, PhD(chem), 53. *Prof Exp:* Asst mech drawing & descriptive geometry, Univ Del, 48 & 50; res engr labs div, Radio Corp Am, 52-55; sr res chemist, Foote Mineral Co, Pa, 55-59, group leader semiconductor res, 59-60; dir res, United Mineral & Chem Corp, 60-62; asst prof chem, Villanova Univ, 64-67; ASSOC PROF CHEM, PA STATE UNIV, DELAWARE COUNTY CAMPUS, 67- *Concurrent Pos:* Consult, Technol Data, Pa, 62- *Mem:* AAAS; Am Chem Soc; Am Phys Soc; Am Soc Testing & Mat. *Res:* Inorganic fluoride chemistry; infrared photoconductivity of germanium; preparation of silicon, germanium, intermetallic semiconductor materials, chemical literature. *Mailing Add:* Dept Chem Pa State Univ Delaware County Media PA 19063

MORRIS, ALLAN J, b Linn Grove, Iowa, June 26, 26; m 56; c 2. BIOCHEMISTRY. *Educ:* Iowa State Univ, BA, 55; Univ Utah, MA, 57, PhD(biochem), 59. *Prof Exp:* From asst prof to assoc prof, 63-72, PROF BIOCHEM, MICH STATE UNIV, 72- *Concurrent Pos:* NIH fels, City of Hope Hosp, Duarte, Calif, 59-60, Med Sch, Univ Ky, 60-62 & Nat Inst Med Res, London, 62-63; mem staff, Dept of Human Genetics & Develop, Col Physicians & Surgeons, Columbia Univ, 70-71. *Mem:* AAAS; Am Soc Biol Chemists; Brit Biochem Soc. *Res:* Genetics and molecular biology of hemoglobin biosynthesis; metabolism of nucleotides in red blood cells. *Mailing Add:* Dept of Biochem Mich State Univ East Lansing MI 48824

MORRIS, ALVIN LEONARD, b Detroit, Mich, July 2, 27; wid; c 3. DENTISTRY. *Educ:* Univ Mich, DDS, 51; Univ Rochester, PhD(path), 57. *Prof Exp:* Asst prof oral med & actg head dept oral diag, Sch Dent, Univ Pa, 57-60, asst prof, Grad Sch Med, 58-61, assoc prof & head dept, 60-61; dean, Sch Dent, Univ Ky, 61-68, asst vpres, Med Ctr, 68-69, spec asst to pres admin, 69-70, prof oral diag & oral med, 61-75, vpres admin, 70-75; exec dir, Asn Acad Health Ctrs, 75-79; PROF DENT MED & ASSOC V PRES HEALTH AFFAIRS, UNIV PA, 79- *Concurrent Pos:* Consult, Vet Admin, Lexington, Ky, 62; consult, USPHS, Ky, 63, chmn dent study sect, Nat Inst Dent Res, 65-67; mem army med serv adv comt prev dent, Off Surgeon Gen, 67-74; mem nat adv coun educ health professions, NIH, 68-72; mem dent adv comt, Dept Defense, 70-73; pres, Am Fund Dent Educ, 70-74. *Mem:* Nat Inst Med; AAAS; Int Asn Dent Res. *Res:* Experimental oral cancer with emphasis on the histochemistry and biochemistry of carcinogenesis; normal and abnormal keratinization of oral mucosa. *Mailing Add:* Sch Dent Med 4001 Spruce St Philadelphia PA 19104

MORRIS, ARTHUR EDWARD, b Billings, Mont, Apr 26, 35; m 57; c 2. METALLURGY. *Educ:* Mont Col Mineral Sci & Technol, BS, 56; Purdue Univ, MS, 59; Pa State Univ, PhD(metall), 65. *Prof Exp:* Extractive metallurgist, Boulder City Sta, US Bur Mines, 59-61; from asst prof to assoc prof metall, 65-74, PROF METALL, UNIV MO-ROLLA, 74- *Concurrent Pos:* Metallurgist, Lawrence Livermore Lab, 73. *Mem:* Am Soc Metals; Am Inst Mining, Metall & Petrol Engrs. *Res:* Chemical metallurgy; phase equilibria, thermodynamics and kinetics of reactions in high temperature metallurgical systems. *Mailing Add:* 809 Bray Ave Rolla MO 65401

MORRIS, BROOKS T(HERON), b Pasadena, Calif, June 11, 13; m 39; c 5. AERONAUTICAL & CIVIL ENGINEERING. *Educ:* Stanford Univ, AB, 34, CE, 38. *Prof Exp:* Jr civil engr, US Bur Reclamation, Colo, 34-36; asst hydraul mach, Calif Inst Technol, 38-39; assoc hydraul engr, Co-op Lab, Soil Conserv Serv, USDA, Calif Inst Technol, 39-42; res engr, C F Braun & Co, 42-43; proj engr & asst dir res, Aerojet Eng Corp, Calif, 43-46; chief propulsion sect, Aircraft Res & Develop Div, Willys-Overland Motors, Inc, 46-47; chief res & develop div, Gen Tire & Rubber Co, Calif, 48-49; proj engr, pulse-jet & subsonic ramjet engines, Marquardt Corp, 49-50, admin engr, 51-52, chief proj engr, 53-54, exec engr, 54-59, dir propulsion div, 60-61; mgr, Qual Assurance & Reliability Off, Jet Propulsion Lab, Calif Inst Technol, 61-81; CONSULT ENGR, 81- *Mem:* Am Soc Civil Engrs; assoc fel Am Inst Aeronaut & Astronaut; Am Geophys Union; Earthquake Eng Res Inst. *Res:* Reliability of space exploration systems; development of pulsejet engines, ramjet engines and rocket motors. *Mailing Add:* 3745 Normandy Dr Flintridge CA 91011

MORRIS, BYRON FREDERICK, marine ecology, oceanography, see previous edition

MORRIS, CHARLES EDWARD, b Detroit, Mich, Feb 17, 41; m 68. SOLID STATE PHYSICS. *Educ:* Iowa State Univ, BS, 63, PhD(physics), 68. *Prof Exp:* MEM STAFF, LOS ALAMOS NAT LAB, 68- *Mem:* Am Phys Soc. *Res:* Shock wave physics; mechanical properties of solids and liquids; optical properties of solids. *Mailing Add:* Los Alamos Nat Lab PO Box 1663 Los Alamos NM 87544

MORRIS, CHARLES ELLIOT, b Denver, Colo, Mar 30, 29; m 51; c 2. NEUROLOGY. *Educ:* Univ Denver, BA, 50, MA, 51; Univ Colo, MD, 55. *Prof Exp:* Teaching fel neurol, Harvard Med Sch, 56-59; from asst prof to prof neurol & med, Sch Med, Univ NC, Chapel Hill, 61-76; PROF NEUROL & CHMN DEPT, UHS/CHICAGO MED SCH, 76-; ACTG CHIEF, NEUROL SERV, VET ADMIN MED CTR, NORTH CHICAGO, 76- *Concurrent Pos:* Consult coun drugs, AMA, 66; dir, Nat Insts Neurol Dis & Stroke Res Ctr, Agana, Guam, 70-71. *Mem:* Fel Am Acad Neurol; Asn Res Nerv & Ment Dis; AMA; Am Epilepsy Soc. *Res:* Neuroimmunology, especially investigations into the pathogenesis and diagnosis of autoimmune diseases of the central and peripheral nervous system; diseases of muscle; Parkinsonism and neurogenic amines; amyotropic lateral sclerosis; movement disorders. *Mailing Add:* Chicago Med Sch Bldg 50 Suite 233 North Chicago IL 60064

MORRIS, CLETUS EUGENE, b Alcorn County, Miss, Jan 30, 35; m 62; c 1. ORGANIC CHEMISTRY. *Educ:* Auburn Univ, BS, 59, PhD(org chem), 66. *Prof Exp:* RES CHEMIST, SOUTHERN REGIONAL RES CTR, AGR RES SERV, USDA, 65- *Mem:* Am Chem Soc; Am Asn Textile Chemists & Colorists. *Res:* Chemical modification of cotton; antimicrobial agents; heterocyclic compounds; identification of constituents important to flavor and quality of food products and development of instrumental methods for determining them. *Mailing Add:* Southern Regional Res Ctr USDA PO Box 19687 New Orleans LA 70179

MORRIS, DANIEL LUZON, b Newtown, Conn, July 29, 07; m 29, 61, 75. CHEMISTRY. *Educ:* Yale Univ, AB, 29, PhD(org chem), 34. *Prof Exp:* Field dir speed surv, State Hwy Dept, Conn, 33-34; fel physiol, Sch Med, Yale Univ, 34-35; teacher, Putney Sch, 35-44; res chemist, Mead Johnson & 44-48; lab supvr, Food, Chem & Res Labs, Inc, 48-51; head dept sci, 51-69, teacher math & sci Lakeside Sch, 51- *Concurrent Pos:* Fulbright exchange teacher, Eng, 58-59. *Mem:* AAAS; Am Chem Soc. *Res:* Descriptive geometry of four dimensions; lipids from animal sources; effects of colloids on crystallization; isolation, determination and physiological effects of carbohydrates; isolation of tryptophane; Christian theology. *Mailing Add:* Lakeside Sch 14050 First Ave NE Seattle WA 98125

MORRIS, DAVID, b Jackson, Miss, May 9, 33; m 59; c 2. CIVIL ENGINEERING. *Educ:* Clemson Col, BS, 55; NC State Univ, MS, 60; Rensselaer Polytech Inst, DrEngSc, 64. *Prof Exp:* Jr engr, Am Bridge Co, 55-56; asst engr, Southern Prestressed Concrete, 60-61; instr struct, Rensselaer Polytech Inst, 62-64; struct designer, Gorgwer & Kraas, Consults, 64-66; ASSOC PROF CIVIL ENG, UNIV VA, 66- *Mem:* Am Soc Civil Engrs. *Res:* Civil engineering systems and structural analysis and design. *Mailing Add:* Dept of Civil Eng Univ of Va Charlottesville VA 22901

MORRIS, DAVID ALBERT, b Marietta, Ohio, July 30, 36; m 58; c 2. GEOCHEMISTRY, EXPLORATION GEOLOGY. *Educ:* Marietta Col, BS, 58; Univ Kans, MS, 61, PhD(geol), 67. *Prof Exp:* From res geologist to sr res geologist, 67-69, mgr appl projs sect, 70-75, MGR GEOCHEM BR, EXPLOR PROD RES DIV, PHILLIPS PETROL CO, 75- *Mem:* AAAS; Am Asn Petrol Geologists; Soc Econ Paleontologists & Mineralogists; Geol Soc Am. *Res:* Stratigraphy, sedimentation and depositional environments of Pennsylvania rocks in North America and Europe; paleogeomorphology of coal swamps and formation of coal splits; origin and geology of petroliferous source rocks and migration of oil; diagenesis and compaction of rocks. *Mailing Add:* Res & Develop Div Phillips Petrol Co 142 RB 1 Bartlesville OK 74004

MORRIS, DAVID ALEXANDER NATHANIEL, b Jamaica, WI, May 13, 44; m; c 2. PHYSICAL CHEMISTRY, CLINICAL CHEMISTRY. *Educ:* Interam Univ Puerto Rico, BS, 66; Univ Wis-Milwaukee, MS, 71; Univ Notre Dame, PhD(phys chem), 77. *Prof Exp:* Asst res scientist, 70-73, assoc res scientist, 73-76, res scientist clin chem, 76-79, RES & DEVELOP SUPVR, MILES LABS INC, 79- *Concurrent Pos:* Spec assignment, Notre Dame Radiation Lab, 74-76. *Mem:* Am Chem Soc; Am Asn Clin Chemists. *Res:* Methods for clinical analysis of body fluids; chemical reactions in paper matrix; chemical reactions of material applied to solid surfaces; instrumental measurement of color. *Mailing Add:* Ames Miles Labs Div PO Box 70 Elkhart IN 46515

MORRIS, DAVID JULIAN, b Ramsgate, Eng, May 17, 39; m 65; c 2. ORGANIC CHEMISTRY, ENDOCRINOLOGY. *Educ:* Oxford Univ, BA, 60, MA & DPhil(org chem), 63. *Prof Exp:* Fel with Prof F W Barnes, Brown Univ, 63-66; sect leader med chem, Beecham Res Labs, 66-68; asst prof biochem pharmacol, 68-75, assoc prof, 75-80, PROF BIOCHEM PHARMACOL, BROWN UNIV, 80-; chief biochemist, Dept Med, 68-80, CHIEF BIOCHEMIST, DEPT LAB MED, MIRIAM HOSP, PROVIDENCE, 68- *Mem:* Endocrine Soc; Am Asn Clin Chem; Am Chem Soc. *Res:* Mechanism of action of aldosterone in kidney; primary receptors of steroid hormones in target tissues; characterization and physiological role of aldosterone metabolites in the kidney; steroid metabolism. *Mailing Add:* Dept of Lab Med Miriam Hosp Providence RI 02990

MORRIS, DAVID ROBERT, b Whittier, Calif, June 25, 39; m 61; c 2. BIOCHEMISTRY. *Educ:* Univ Calif, Los Angeles, BA, 61; Univ Ill, PhD(chem), 64. *Prof Exp:* NIH fel, 64-66; asst prof biochem, 66-70, assoc prof, 70-77, PROF BIOCHEM, UNIV WASH, 77- *Concurrent Pos:* John Simon Guggenheim fel, 71-72. *Mem:* AAAS; Am Chem Soc; Am Soc Biol Chem; Am Soc Microbiol. *Res:* Regulation of cell growth and division; biological function of polyamines. *Mailing Add:* Dept Biochem Univ Wash Seattle WA 98195

MORRIS, DAVID ROWLAND, b London, Eng, June 18, 30; m 56; c 3. CHEMICAL ENGINEERING & METALLURGY. *Educ:* Univ Birmingham, BSc, 51; Univ London, PhD(chem eng), 54. *Prof Exp:* Sci officer, Atomic Energy Res Estab, Eng, 54-57, sr officer, 57-59; lectr chem eng, Univ London, 59-66; assoc prof, 66-73, PROF CHEM ENG, UNIV NB, 73- *Honors & Awards:* Corecipient, Extractive Metall Technol Award, Am Inst Mining, Metall, & Petrol Engrs, 81. *Mem:* Electrochem Soc; Int Electrochem Soc; Can Inst Mining & Metall; assoc Brit Inst Chem Engrs. *Res:* Graphite technology; fluidization; thermodynamics of alloy systems; high temperature electrochemistry; metallurgical processes; corrosion. *Mailing Add:* Dept of Chem Eng Univ of NB Fredericton NB E3B 5A3 Can

MORRIS, DEREK, b Hove, Eng, May 6, 30; m 53; c 3. METROLOGY, QUANTUM PHYSICS. *Educ:* London Univ, BSc, 50, PhD(physics), 53. *Prof Exp:* Fel, Div Pure Physics, Nat Res Coun, Can, 53-55; sci officer, Guided Weapons Dept, Royal Aircraft Estab, Eng, 55-57; from asst res officer to assoc res officer div appl physics, 57-75, SR RES OFFICER, NAT RES COUN, CAN, 75- *Concurrent Pos:* Assoc ed, Transactions Instrumentation & Measurement, Inst Elec & Electronics Engrs, 80- *Mem:* Can Asn Physicists. *Res:* Atomic frequency standards. *Mailing Add:* Elec/Time Stnds Sect Div Physics Sect Nat Res Coun Montreal Rd Ottawa ON K1A 0R6 Can

MORRIS, DONALD E(DWARD), materials engineering, see previous edition

MORRIS, DONALD EUGENE, b Tulsa, Okla, July 9, 40; m 63; c 4. ORGANOMETALLIC CHEMISTRY, HOMOGENEOUS CATALYSIS. *Educ:* Univ Tulsa, BS, 63; Northwestern Univ, PhD(inorg chem), 67. *Prof Exp:* NSF res grant, Stanford Univ, 67-68; res chemist, 68-73, res specialist, 73-77, sr res specialist, 77-81, SR GROUP LEADER CORP RES LABS, MONSANTO CO, 81- *Mem:* Am Chem Soc. *Res:* Metal complexes and their application in homogeneous catalysis. *Mailing Add:* Corp Res Labs Monsanto Co 800 N Lindbergh Blvd St Louis MO 63166

MORRIS, EDWARD C, b West Branch, Iowa, Apr 4, 16; m 44; c 5. CHEMISTRY. *Educ:* William Penn Col, BS, 40; Friends Univ, AB, 49; Univ Iowa, MS, 57. *Prof Exp:* Prof physicist x-ray sect, Nat Bur Stand, Washington, DC, 42-43; assoc prof physics & chem, William Penn Col, 56-63; asst prof chem & phys sci, Asbury Col, 63-81; RETIRED. *Res:* Solubility of metal chlorides in nonaqueous acetic acid, especially metals that complex spectrophotometric studies of species. *Mailing Add:* Asbury Col Wilmore KY 40390

MORRIS, ELLIOT COBIA, b Ely, Nev, June 24, 26; m 50; c 3. ASTROGEOLOGY, MINERALOGY. *Educ:* Univ Utah, BS, 50, MS, 53; Stanford Univ, PhD(geol), 62. *Prof Exp:* Seismic comput, Seismic Explor, Inc, Wyo, 53-54; asst explor geologist, Phillips Petrol Co, Utah, 54-56; geologist & coordr Surveyor TV invests, Astrogeol Br, 61-69, Geologist, Viking Mars Lander Imaging Team, 69-78, GEOLOGIST, ASTROGEOL BR, US GEOL SURV, 69- *Concurrent Pos:* Staff scientist planetary progs, NASA hq, 70-71. *Mem:* AAAS; Geol Soc Am. *Res:* Structural and stratigraphic geology of Western Uinta and Wasatch Mountains, Utah and southern Alaskan areas; sedimentary mineralogy of central California; astrogeologic studies. *Mailing Add:* 515 N Bertrand Flagstaff AZ 86001

MORRIS, EUGENE RAY, b Albion, Nebr, Aug 26, 30; m 52; c 2. HUMAN NUTRITION, TRACE ELEMENTS. *Educ:* Univ Mo, BS, 52, MS, 56, PhD(agr chem), 62. *Prof Exp:* Assoc chemist, Midwest Res Inst, 62-64; instr agr chem, Univ Mo, 64-68; RES CHEMIST, HUMAN NUTRIT RES CTR, USDA, BELTSVILLE, 68- *Mem:* Am Chem Soc; Am Inst Nutrit; Am Asn Cereal Chemists; Soc Environ Biochem & Health. *Res:* Animal and human nutrition; physiological chemistry of magnesium; unidentified growth factors; iron and zinc bioavailability. *Mailing Add:* Agr Res Ctr Nutrit Inst Beltsville MD 20705

MORRIS, EVERETT FRANKLIN, b Bellmont, Ill, May 23, 24; m 46, 74; c 2. BOTANY. *Educ:* Eastern Ill Univ, BS, 50; Univ Wyo, MS, 52; Univ Iowa, PhD(bot), 55. *Prof Exp:* Asst prof biol, Millikin Univ, 55-57; assoc prof, Martin Br, Univ Tenn, 57-58; asst mycologist, Ill Natural Hist Surv, 58; from asst prof to assoc prof, 58-66, prof biol, Western Ill Univ, 66-78, co-adminr,

A L Kibbe Life Sci Sta, 65-70, chmn dept biol sci, 69-78; prof biol & dean, Sch Sci & Nursing, Purdue Univ, Calumet Campus, 78-80; PROF BIOL & DEAN ACAD AFFAIRS, LA STATE UNIV, ALEXANDRIA, 80- *Mem:* Mycol Soc Am. *Res:* Taxonomy of myxomycetes and Fungi Imperfecti. *Mailing Add:* Dean Acad Affairs Louisiana State Univ Alexandria LA 71301

MORRIS, FRED JOHN, b Chicago, Ill, Dec 6, 19; m 42; c 2. PHYSICS. *Educ:* Tex Col Arts & Indust, BS, 42; Univ Tex, MS, 44, PhD(physics), 51. *Prof Exp:* Instr physics, Univ Tex, 46-51; PRES & DIR RES, ELECTRO-MECH CO, 51- *Concurrent Pos:* Sci adv, Joint Spectrum Eval Group, Joint Chiefs of Staff, DC, 57-58; consult, Dept of Defense, 59- *Mem:* AAAS; Soc Am Mil Eng. *Res:* Electronics and magnetics, particularly development of measurement techniques. *Mailing Add:* 510 Dragon Lane Austin TX 78734

MORRIS, FRED(ERICK) W(ILLIAM), JR, b Los Angeles, Calif, Feb 28, 22; m 49. ELECTRONIC & COMMUNICATIONS ENGINEERING. *Educ:* Calif Inst Technol, BS, 44; Capitol Inst Technol, DSc, 75. *Prof Exp:* asst prof elec eng, Univ Southern Calif, 47-50; chief res studies, Eng Labs, Signal Corps, US Army, 50-53; Signal Corps resident engr, Electronic Defense Lab, 53-54; electronic eng & mgt consult, Fred W Morris, Jr & Assocs, 54-64; assoc dir telecommun mgt, Exec Off of the President, 64-66; vpres corp planning, Radiation Inc, 66-69; PRES, TELE-SCI ASSOCS, 69- *Concurrent Pos:* Nat Aeronaut & Space Coun, 64-65; vpres & dir, Electromagnetic Tech Corp & Satellite Kennedy & Co, Calif; dir, Astro Tech Corp; mem res & develop bd, Dept Defense, 50-53; mem, President Johnson's Task Force on Commun Policy, 67-68; consult, Stanford Res Inst, Mass Inst Technol & Inst Defense Anal. *Mem:* Sr mem Inst Elec & Electronics Engrs; fel Am Inst Aeronaut & Astronaut; Am Mgt Asn. *Res:* Electronic warfare; communications systems engineering, policy and management. *Mailing Add:* Tele-Sci Assocs 137 Ash Lane Portola Valley CA 94025

MORRIS, GENE FRANKLIN, b Cedar Rapids, Iowa, Nov 22, 34; m 59; c 4. ORGANIC CHEMISTRY. *Educ:* Iowa State Univ, BS, 55; Kans State Univ, PhD(org chem), 61. *Prof Exp:* USPHS fel, Duke Univ, 59-61, Iowa State Univ, 61-63, instr chem, 63-66; from asst prof to assoc prof, Wis State Univ, Eau Claire, 66-69; vis prof, Univ Calgary, 69; ASSOC PROF CHEM, WESTERN CAROLINA UNIV, 69- *Mem:* Am Chem Soc. *Res:* Physical organic chemistry; mechanisms of reactions, epoxidations, hydrogenations. *Mailing Add:* Dept of Chem Western Carolina Univ Cullowhee NC 28723

MORRIS, GEORGE COOPER, JR, b Evanston, Ill, Feb 15, 24; m 46; c 5. SURGERY. *Educ:* Univ Pa, MD, 48. *Prof Exp:* Instr surg, Sch Med, Univ Pa, 49-50; from instr to assoc prof, 50-68, PROF SURG, BAYLOR COL MED, 68- *Concurrent Pos:* Markle scholar. *Mem:* Soc Vascular Surg; Soc Thoracic Surgeons; Am Col Chest Physicians; Am Asn Surg Trauma; Am Surg Asn. *Res:* Cardiovascular research. *Mailing Add:* Tex Med Ctr Baylor Col of Med Houston TX 77030

MORRIS, GEORGE RONALD, b McLeausboro, Ill, June 11, 43; m 64; c 1. ATOMIC PHYSICS, MOLECULAR PHYSICS. *Educ:* Murray State Univ, BA, 68, MS, 67; Univ Ill, PhD(physics), 75. *Prof Exp:* Res assoc elem particle physics, Enrico Fermi Inst, Univ Chicago, 74-76; asst physicist elem particle physics, Brookhaven Nat Lab, 76-79; SR SCIENTIST PHYSICS, KAMAN SCI CORP, 79- *Mem:* Am Phys Soc. *Res:* Atomic and molecular collision phenomena; nuclear instrumentation for geophysical well logging; accelerator tube design; high voltage technology. *Mailing Add:* Kaman Sci Corp Box 7463 Colorado Springs CO 80933

MORRIS, GEORGE V, b Providence, RI, Nov 18, 30; m 59; c 2. PHYSICAL CHEMISTRY, ANALYTICAL CHEMISTRY. *Educ:* Providence Col, BS, 52; Univ RI, MS, 57, PhD(phys chem), 62. *Prof Exp:* Asst chem, Univ RI, 55-56; res chemist, Nat Res Corp, Mass, 56-57 & Eltex Res Corp, RI, 57-59; asst chem, Univ RI, 59-61; res chemist, US Naval Underwater Ord Sta, 62-65; from instr to assoc prof, 63-72, PROF PHYS CHEM, SALVE REGINA COL, 72- *Concurrent Pos:* Sr engr, Raytheon Co, RI, 66- *Mem:* Am Chem Soc. *Res:* Research and development of continuous total organic carbon analyzer; development of stable, long deployment life, dissolved oxygen probe; thermal decomposition of inorganic superoxides. *Mailing Add:* Dept of Physics & Chem Salve-Regina Col Newport RI 02840

MORRIS, GEORGE WILLIAM, b Granite, Okla, Apr 23, 21; m 59; c 2. MATHEMATICS, MATHEMATICAL PHYSICS. *Educ:* Southest Inst Technol, BA, 42; Univ Okla, MA, 48; Univ Calif, Los Angeles, PhD(math), 57. *Prof Exp:* Instr math, Univ Tulsa, 47-48; engr, Northrop Aircraft, Inc, 51-53; sr engr, NAm Aviation, Inc, 53-58; proj engr, Aerolab Develop Co, 58-60; mem tech staff, Land-Air, Inc, Point Mugu, 60-62 & Douglas Aircraft Co, 62-68; PROF MATH, NAVAL POSTGRAD SCH, 68- *Mem:* Soc Indust & Appl Math. *Res:* Numerical analysis; celestial mechanics; exterior ballistics; elasticity; aerodynamics; electromagnetic wave propagation; thermodynamics; operations research. *Mailing Add:* Dept Math Naval Postgrad Sch Monterey CA 93940

MORRIS, GERALD BROOKS, b Decatur, Tex, July 2, 33; m 59. GEOPHYSICS. *Educ:* Tex A&M Univ, 56, MS, 62; Univ Calif, San Diego, PhD(earth sci), 69. *Prof Exp:* Res engr, Res Lab, Carter Oil Co, 57-58 & Jersey Prod Res Co, 58-63; asst res geophysicist, Marine Phys Lab, Univ Calif, San Diego, 69-70; asst prof geophys, Univ Hawaii, 70-72; res geophysicist, Marine Phys Lab, Univ Calif, San Diego, 72-77; SUPVRY RES PHYSICIST, NAVAL OCEAN RES & DEVELOP ACTIV, 77- *Mem:* Soc Explor Geophysicists; Am Geophys Union; Acoust Soc Am. *Res:* Underwater acoustics and sound propagation; explosion seismology, particularly marine seismic refraction studies; elastic properties of earth materials. *Mailing Add:* Naval Ocean Res & Develop Activ Code 340 NSTL Station MS 39529

MORRIS, GERALD PATRICK, b Edmonton, Alta, June 13. 39; m 64; c 2. CELL BIOLOGY, GASTROENTEROLOGY. *Educ:* Univ BC, BSc, 64, MSc, 66; Queens Univ, Belfast, PhD(zool), 68. *Prof Exp:* Lectr zool, Univ BC, 65-66; NIH fel electron micros, Univ Kans, 68-69; asst prof biol, 69-74, ASSOC PROF BIOL, QUEENS UNIV, ONT, 74- *Mem:* Am Soc Cell Biol; Micros Soc Can. *Res:* Ultrastructure and biochemistry of insect neurosecretion and experimental gastric ulcers. *Mailing Add:* Dept Biol Queens Univ Kingston ON K7L 3N6 Can

MORRIS, GLENN KARL, b Toronto, Ont, Oct 26, 38; m 64; c 6. ENTOMOLOGY, ANIMAL BEHAVIOR. *Educ:* Ont Agr Col, Univ Guelph, BSA, 62; Cornell Univ, MS, 65, PhD(entom), 67. *Prof Exp:* Lectr, 67-68, asst prof, 68-74, ASSOC PROF ZOOL, UNIV TORONTO, 74- *Mem:* Animal Behav Soc; Entom Soc Can; Royal Can Inst. *Res:* Sound communication of long horned grasshoppers. *Mailing Add:* 4 St Clarens Toronto ON M6K 2S3 Can

MORRIS, HAL TRYON, b Salt Lake City, Utah, Oct 24, 20; m 42; c 3. GEOLOGY. *Educ:* Univ Utah, BS, 42, MS, 47. *Prof Exp:* Geologist, 46-69, RES GEOLOGIST, US GEOL SURV, 69- *Mem:* Fel AAAS; fel Geol Soc Am; Soc Econ Geologists. *Res:* Mineral deposits; structural geology; stratigraphy; geochemical pros- pecting; detection and discovery of concealed ore deposits. *Mailing Add:* 345 Middlefield Rd Menlo Park CA 94025

MORRIS, HALCYON ELLEN MCNEIL, b Delphos, Kans, May 24, 27; m 59. MATHEMATICS. *Educ:* Kans State Univ, BS, 51; Univ Tulsa, MS, 58. *Prof Exp:* Mathematician, Carter Oil Co, 51-58, Jersey Prod Res Co, 58-59, Pan Am Petrol Co, 60-63 & Naval Electronics Lab, 64-68; supvry mathematician, Naval Undersea Ctr, San Diego, Calif, 68-76, MEM STAFF, NAVAL OCEAN RES & DEVELOP ACTIV, NAT SPACE TECHNOL LAB STA, MS, 76- *Mem:* Seismol Soc Am; Acoust Soc Am. *Res:* Detection of submarines by surveillance systems; development of theory for new sonar systems; opportunities in science for women; underwater acoustics, especially sound propagation and botton reflection loss. *Mailing Add:* Code 230 Naval Ocean Res & Develop Activ Nat Space Technol Lab Sta MS 39529

MORRIS, HAROLD H, b Lincoln, Nebr, Mar 24, 43; m 61; c 3. NEUROLOGY. *Educ:* Baylor Col Med, MD, 68. *Prof Exp:* Intern med, Methodist Hosp, Houston, 68-69; med officer, USPHS, 69-71; resident, 71-74, ASST PROF NEUROL, UNIV TEX MED BR, 74- *Mem:* Am Acad Neurol; Am Epilepsy Soc; AMA. *Res:* Clinical neurophysiology and electroencephalography. *Mailing Add:* Dept of Neurol Univ of Tex Med Br Galveston TX 77550

MORRIS, HAROLD HOLLINGSWORTH, JR, b Shanghai, China, Sept 23, 17; US citizen; m 44; c 2. MEDICINE, PSYCHIATRY. *Educ:* Haverford Col, BS, 39; Tulane Univ, MD, 43. *Prof Exp:* ASSOC PROF PSYCHIAT, SCH MED, UNIV PA, 56- *Concurrent Pos:* Clin dir psychiat, Inst Pa Hosp, 48-56; consult, Episcopal Diocese Pa, 54-, Vet Admin Hosp, Coatesville, 56-, Am Friends Serv Comt, 62 & Peace Corps, 64; dir, Mercy-Douglass Hosp, Philadelphia, 56-63 & Misericordia Hosp, 66- *Mem:* Am Psychiat Asn. *Res:* Effect of phenothiazines on schizophrenia; long-term follow-up studies on 3, 000 patients, including 225 children; effect of psychological mileu on organic illness. *Mailing Add:* Fitzgerald-Mercy Hosp Darby PA 19023

MORRIS, HAROLD PAUL, b Salem, Ind, May 8, 00; m 28; c 3. NUTRITION, BIOCHEMISTRY. *Educ:* Univ Minn, BS, 25, PhD(biochem), 30; Kans State Col, MS, 26. *Prof Exp:* Asst animal genetics, Kans State Col, 25-26; asst animal nutrit, Exp Sta, Univ Ill, 26-28; asst biochem & dairy chem, Exp Sta, Univ Minn, 28-30; res assoc, Bur Fisheries, US Dept Commerce, 31-32; jr bacteriologist, Bur Home Econ, USDA, 33-34, assoc biochemist, Food & Drug Admin, 34-38; biochemist, Nat Cancer Inst, 38-41, sr nutrit chemist, 41-48, prin biochemist, 48-51, head nutrit & carcinogenesis sect, Lab Biochem, 51-68; PROF BIOCHEM, COL MED, HOWARD UNIV, 68- *Concurrent Pos:* Mem incentive awards bd, NIH, 57-61, chmn, 60-61; US organizer, US-Japanese Exchange Mission, Conf Biol & Biochem Eval Malignancy in Exp Hepatomas, Kyoto, Japan, 65. *Honors & Awards:* Superior Serv Award, Nat Cancer Inst, 56. *Mem:* Am Chem Soc; Am Soc Biol Chemists; Soc Exp Biol & Med; Am Asn Cancer Res; Am Inst Nutrit. *Res:* Mouse nutrition; radio and chemical isotopic tracers; hereditary factors influencing food utilization in the rat; development of a spectrum of transplantable rat hepatocellular carcinomas and kidney tumors, both of different growth rate and possessing many variable biological and biochemical characteristics. *Mailing Add:* Dept of Biochem Howard Univ Col of Med Washington DC 20059

MORRIS, HARRIS LEE, physical chemistry, chemical engineering, see previous edition

MORRIS, HENRY MADISON, JR, b Dallas, Tex, Oct 6, 18; m 40; c 6. HYDRAULIC ENGINEERING, HYDROGEOLOGY. *Educ:* Rice Inst, BS, 39; Univ Minn, MS, 48, PhD(civil eng), 50. *Hon Degrees:* LLD, Bob Jones Univ, 66. *Prof Exp:* Mem State Hwy Dept, Tex, 38-39; from jr engr to asst engr, Int Boundary Comn, 39-42; instr civil eng, Rice Inst, 42-46; from instr to asst prof & proj supvr, St Anthony Falls Hydraul Lab, Univ Minn, 46-51; prof civil eng & head dept, Southwestern La Inst, 51-56; prof appl sci, Univ Southern Ill, 57; prof civil eng & head dept, Va Polytech Inst & State Univ, 57-70; vpres acad affairs, Christian Heritage Col, 70-78, pres, 78-80; dir, 70-80, PRES, INST CREATION RES, SAN DIEGO, 80- *Mem:* Fel AAAS; fel Am Soc Civil Engrs; Am Geophys Union; Geol Soc Am; Am Asn Petrol Geol. *Res:* Conduit and engineering hydraulics; design of hydraulic structures; hydraulic studies; hydro-morphology. *Mailing Add:* Inst for Creation Res 2716 Madison Ave San Diego CA 92119

MORRIS, HERBERT ALLEN, b Okla, Sept 15, 19; m 45; c 3. MATHEMATICS. *Educ:* Southeastern State Col, BA, 46; Univ Tex, MA, 51. *Prof Exp:* Asst prof math, Lamar State Col, 51-S5 & Colo Sch Mines, 55-57; mathematician, Atomic Energy Div, Phillips Petrol Co, 57-59, sr mathematician, Comput Dept, 59-65; dir, Comput Ctr, 65-74, ASSOC PROF COMPUT SCI, BRADLEY UNIV, 74-, CHMN DEPT, 65- *Concurrent Pos:* Adj prof, Okla State Univ, 60-65. *Mem:* Soc Indust & Appl Math; Asn Comput Mach. *Res:* Numerical analysis; point set topology; operations research. *Mailing Add:* Comput Ctr Bradley Univ Peoria IL 61625

MORRIS, HERBERT COMSTOCK, b Dayton, Ohio, Apr 18, 17; m 43; c 5. CHEMICAL ENGINEERING, CHEMISTRY. *Educ:* Univ Dayton, BCE, 42. *Prof Exp:* Chem engr, Beacon Res Labs, Texaco, Inc, 42-49, asst to dir res, NY, 49-55, supvr, Port Arthur Res Labs, 55-67, dir res, Beacon Res Labs, 67-70, asst mgr petrol res, 70-77; mgr, Texaco, Inc, 77-79, BUS MGR, TEXACO CHEM CO, 79- *Mem:* Am Chem Soc; Am Inst Chem Engrs; Sci Res Soc Am. *Res:* Petroleum research; process and product development; research administration. *Mailing Add:* Texaco Chem Co 610 Santa Maria Sugar Land TX 77478

MORRIS, HORTON HAROLD, b Post, Tex, May 26, 22; m 45; c 3. CLAY MINERALOGY, PULP AND PAPER TECHNOLOGY. *Educ:* Tex Tech Col, BS, 49; Univ Maine, MS, 52. *Prof Exp:* From instr to assoc prof chem, Univ Maine, 52-57; res dir, South Clays, Inc, 57-63; vpres res & develop, Freeport Kaolin Co, 63-74; pres, SSI Consults, 74-79; VPRES RES & DEVELOP, FREEPORT KAOLIN CO, 79- *Mem:* AAAS; Am Chem Soc; Tech Asn Pulp & Paper Indust; Am Soc Test & Mat; NY Acad Sci. *Res:* Molecular rearrangements; Glycidic esters; 2, 3-dihydroxy esters and halohydrins; kaolin clay studies; mineral benefaction; delaminated clays; calcined clays. *Mailing Add:* Freeport Res Ctr Gordon GA 31031

MORRIS, HOWARD ARTHUR, b Draper, Utah, Feb 9, 19; m 41; c 4. FOOD SCIENCE. *Educ:* Univ Minn, MS, 49, PhD(dairy technol), 52. *Prof Exp:* Asst & instr, 46-51, asst prof dairy technol, 52-55, assoc prof dairy indust, 55-60, PROF FOOD SCI, UNIV MINN, ST PAUL, 60- *Honors & Awards:* Pfizer Award, Am Diary Sci Asn, 81. *Mem:* Am Soc Microbiol; Inst Food Technologists; Am Dairy Sci Asn. *Res:* Chemistry, bacteriology and enzymology applied to food processing. *Mailing Add:* Dept Food Sci & Nutrit Univ Minn St Paul MN 55101

MORRIS, HUGHLETT LEWIS, b Big Rock, Tenn, Mar 18, 31; m 50; c 3. SPEECH PATHOLOGY. *Educ:* Univ Iowa, BA, 52, MA, 57, PhD(speech path), 60. *Prof Exp:* Clinician speech & hearing, Pub Schs, Iowa, 54-56; res assoc otolaryngol & maxillofacial surg, 58-61, coordr cleft palate clin, 59-64, res asst prof otolaryngol & maxillofacial surg, 61-64, assoc prof otolaryngol, maxillofacial surg, speech path & audiol, 65-67, PROF OTOLARYNGOL & MAXILLOFACIAL SURG, SPEECH PATH & AUDIOL, UNIV IOWA, 68-, DIR DIV SPEECH & HEARING, DEPT OTOLARYNGOL & MAXILLOFACIAL SURG & DIR CLEFT PALATE RES PROG, 65-, CHMN DEPT SPEECH PATH & AUDIOL, 76- *Concurrent Pos:* Ed, Cleft Palate J, Am Cleft Palate Asn, 64-70; prin investr, Proj Res Grant, Nat Inst Dent Res Prog, 65-; mem, Am Bds Examrs Speech Path & Audiol, 73-76; vpres, Am Cleft Palate Educ Found, 74-75. *Mem:* AAAS; fel Am Speech & Hearing Asn; Am Cleft Palate Asn (pres, 73-74). *Res:* Cleft lip and palate; disorders of the voice. *Mailing Add:* Dept Otolaryng-Maxillofac Surg Univ of Iowa Hosps Iowa City IA 52242

MORRIS, J(AMES) WILLIAM, b Clarksville, Tex, June 25, 18; m 49; c 3. CHEMICAL ENGINEERING. *Educ:* Univ Tex, BS, 40, MS, 41, PhD(chem eng), 44. *Prof Exp:* Instr chem eng, Univ Tex, 40-44; chem engr, 44, 45-47, chem engr, Tenn, 44, supvr, Wash, 44-45, Del, 47 & Ohio, 47-49, process engr, Del, 50, from asst tech supt to tech supt, Ind, 50-53, SECT DIR, SAVANNAH RIVER LAB, E I DU PONT DE NEMOURS & CO, INC, 53- *Mem:* AAAS; Am Nuclear Soc; Am Chem Soc; Am Inst Chem Engrs; Am Soc Eng Educ. *Res:* Cooperative engineering education; cooperative education; technical personnel placement. *Mailing Add:* 3418 Meadow Dr Aiken SC 29801

MORRIS, JAMES ALBERT, b Crawfordsville, Ind, June 4, 42; div; c 2. ENZYMOLOGY, MICROBIAL BIOCHEMISTRY. *Educ:* Wabash Col, BA, 64; Purdue Univ, PhD(microbiol), 69. *Prof Exp:* Res assoc gustation, Monell Chem Senses Ctr, Univ Pa, 70-73; sr microbiologist, 73-80, PROJ BIOCHEMIST, INT FLAVORS & FRAGRANCES, INC, 80- *Mem:* Am Chem Soc. *Res:* Production or modification of flavors by microbial and/or enzymatic processes. *Mailing Add:* 1515 Hwy 36 Union Beach NJ 07735

MORRIS, JAMES ALLEN, b Vienna, Ga, Jan 18, 29; m 50; c 3. MECHANICAL ENGINEERING. *Educ:* Mass Inst Technol, BSME, 52. *Prof Exp:* Teacher, high sch, Ga, 49-50; gen engr, Warner Robins AFB, 50-51; test engr, US Naval Eng Exp Sta, Md, 52-55; proj engr, Ford Sci Lab, Mich, 55-57 & Arnold Eng Develop Ctr, Tenn, 57-68; proj mgr gen consult, Planning Res Corp, 68-73; mgr printer mechanisms, Sci Systs Inc, Ala, 73-80; SR STAFF SYSTS ENGR, SCI APPLN INC, 80- *Concurrent Pos:* Instr, Tenn State Univ, 62-68. *Mem:* Assoc fel Am Inst Aeronaut & Astronaut. *Res:* Ultra low pressure research; cryogenic studies; propulsion research and development; transportation; environmental simulation; heat transfer; design and development of high speed printers. *Mailing Add:* Rte 2 Box 271A Somerville AL 35670

MORRIS, JAMES F, b New York, NY, Mar 22, 22. MEDICINE. *Educ:* Ohio Wesleyan Univ, AB, 43; Univ Rochester, MD, 48. *Prof Exp:* Fel med bact, Sch Med, Univ Rochester, 50-51; instr med, Col Med, Univ Utah, 53-54; assoc prof, 57-71, PROF MED, UNIV ORE, 71- *Concurrent Pos:* Chief pulmonary & infectious dis, Vet Admin Med Ctr, Portland, 57- *Mem:* Am Thoracic Soc. *Res:* Clinical pulmonary physiology, primarily obstructive airway diseases. *Mailing Add:* Dept Med Vet Admin Med Ctr Portland OR 97201

MORRIS, JAMES G, b Parkersburg, WVa, Mar 20, 28; m 53; c 1. METALLURGICAL ENGINEERING, MATERIALS SCIENCE. *Educ:* Purdue Univ, BS, 51, PhD(metall eng), 56. *Prof Exp:* Instr metall, Purdue Univ, 53-56; res engr, Dow Chem Co, 56-57; proj engr, Kaiser Aluminum & Chem Corp, 57-58; sr res metallurgist, Olin Mathieson Chem Corp, 58-59; asst prof metall, 59-60, dir honors prog, 64-65, chmn dept, 65-67, dir grad studies, 67-68, ASSOC PROF METALL, UNIV KY, 60- *Concurrent Pos:* NSF fac partic res award, 75 & 76; sr res fel & consult, United Technol Corp, 76-; numerous res contracts with industs & govt orgn; res consult, Adv Technol Group & Continental Packaging Co, Inc, Stamford, Conn. *Honors & Awards:* Tarr Award, 51. *Mem:* AAAS; Am Inst Mining, Metall & Petrol Engrs; Am Soc Eng Educ; NY Acad Sci; Sigma Xi. *Res:* Thermomechanical processing; deformation dynamics; warm and hot working; softening kinetics; fracture toughness. *Mailing Add:* Col of Eng Anderson Hall Univ of Ky Lexington KY 40506

MORRIS, JAMES GRANT, b Brisbane, Australia, Aug 30, 30; m 59; c 3. ANIMAL NUTRITION. *Educ:* Univ Queensland, BAgrSc, 53, Hons, 55, BSc, 58, MAgrSci, 59; Utah State Univ, PhD(nutrit & biochem), 61. *Prof Exp:* Dir husb res, Animal Res Inst, Brisbane, Australia, 65-69; assoc prof ruminant nutrit & assoc nutritionist, 69-75, PROF ANIMAL SCI & PHYSIOL CHEM & NUTRITIONIST, EXP STA, UNIV CALIF, DAVIS, 75- *Mem:* Brit Nutrit Soc; Australian Soc Animal Prod; Am Inst Nutrit; Am Soc Animal Sci; Brit Soc Animal Prod. *Res:* Nutrition of ruminants, particularly grazing cattle and sheep; mineral nutrition; feline nutrition. *Mailing Add:* Dept of Animal Sci Univ of Calif Davis CA 95616

MORRIS, JAMES JOSEPH, JR, b Jersey City, NJ, Aug 16, 33; m 54; c 3. INTERNAL MEDICINE, CARDIOLOGY. *Educ:* Hofstra Univ, BA, 55; State Univ NY, MD, 59. *Prof Exp:* Intern, 59-60, instr, 60-61, resident, 61-62, instr, 62-63, chief resident, 63-64, assoc, 64-66, asst prof, 66-70, assoc prof med, 70-80, PROF MED CARDIOL, DUKE UNIV, 80- *Concurrent Pos:* USPHS fels, 60-61, 62-63 & spec fel, 64-67. *Mem:* Am Heart Asn; Am Col Physicians. *Res:* Electrocardiology; arrhythmia; cardiac catherization; hemodynamics. *Mailing Add:* Dept of Med Cardiovasc Lab Duke Univ Med Ctr Durham NC 27710

MORRIS, JAMES RUSSELL, b Turlock, Calif, Nov 21, 41; m 69. PHYSICS, OPTICS. *Educ:* Univ Calif, Berkeley, AB, 64, MA, 68, PhD(physics), 77. *Prof Exp:* Comput programmer, US Air Force, 65-67; math programmer, 68, COMPUTATIONAL PHYSICIST, LAWRENCE LIVERMORE NAT LAB, 73- *Mem:* Optical Soc Am; Am Phys Soc. *Res:* Computational modeling of non-linear optical propagation effects; thermal blooming, self-focusing, and coherent pulse propagation. *Mailing Add:* Lawrence Livermore Nat Lab PO Box 808 L-71 Livermore CA 94550

MORRIS, JAMES T, b Langdale, Ala, April 16, 50; c 1. COMPUTER MODELING. *Educ:* Univ Va, BA, 73; Yale Univ, MS, 75, PhD(environ sci), 79. *Prof Exp:* Fel, Ecosyst Ctr, Marine Biol Lab, Woods Hole, 79-81; ASST PROF, DEPT BIOL, UNIV SC, 81- *Mem:* Ecol Soc Am; AAAS; Am Soc Limnol & Oceanog. *Res:* Plant physiological ecology, plant nutrition and nutrient cycling within wetland ecosystems. *Mailing Add:* Dept Biol Univ SC Columbia SC 29208

MORRIS, JERRY LEE, JR, b Charlotte, NC, Feb 27, 52; m 72; c 2. ELECTROCHEMISTRY, INSTRUMENTATION. *Educ:* NC State Univ, BS, 74; Univ Ill, Urbana-Champaign, PhD(chem), 78. *Prof Exp:* Scientist assoc res electrochem, Lockheed Palo Alto Res Lab, 78-80; staff scientist, Energy Systs Lab, The Continental Group, Inc, 80-82; DIR PROGS, PINNACLE RES INST, 82- *Mem:* Am Chem Soc; Electrochem Soc; AAAS. *Res:* Electrochemistry of battery systems; electrochemical corrosion and passivation; electrochemistry of semiconductors; chemiluminescence; electrochemical kinetics; analytical methods development. *Mailing Add:* Pinnacle Res Inst 10432 N Tantau Ave Cupertino CA 95014

MORRIS, JOHN CARRELL, b Philadelphia, Pa, May 30, 14; m 40, 67 & 73; c 3. SANITARY CHEMISTRY. *Educ:* Rutgers Univ, BS, 34; Princeton Univ, AM, 35, PhD(phys chem), 38. *Hon Degrees:* AM, Harvard Univ, 49. *Prof Exp:* Instr chem, Harvard Univ, 38-41; asst prof, Bucknell Univ, 41-42 & Worcester Polytech Inst, 42-43; from instr to assoc prof sanit chem, 44-58, Allston Burr Sr Tutor, 59-64, GORDON MCKAY PROF SANIT CHEM, HARVARD UNIV, 58- *Concurrent Pos:* WHO expert consult, Univ Alexandria, 58-59; vis lectr, Int Courses Sanit Eng, Delft, Neth, 64-; mem safe drinking water comt, Nat Acad Sci, 75-76. *Honors & Awards:* Buswell-Porges Award, Inst Advan Sanit Res Int, 73. *Mem:* Am Water Works Asn; Int Water Supply Asn; Am Chem Soc; Water Pollution Control Fedn. *Res:* Kinetics and equilibria of reactions in water and sewage treatment; dynamics of water disinfection; reactions of aqueous chlorine with organic and nitrogenous compounds. *Mailing Add:* 127 Pierce Hall Harvard Univ Cambridge MA 02138

MORRIS, JOHN EDWARD, b Pasadena, Calif, July 9, 36; m 58; c 2. DEVELOPMENTAL BIOLOGY, CELL BIOLOGY. *Educ:* Stanford Univ, BA, 58; Univ Hawaii, MS, 60; Univ Calif, Los Angeles, PhD(zool), 66. *Prof Exp:* Investr, Wenner-Gren Inst, Sweden, 65-67 & Univ Chicago, 67-68; asst prof zool, 68-74, ASSOC PROF ZOOL, ORE STATE UNIV, 74- *Concurrent Pos:* Vis asst prof pediat, Univ Chicago, 74-75. *Mem:* AAAS; Am Inst Biol Sci; Am Soc Zoologists; Am Soc Cell Biol; Soc Develop Biol. *Res:* Tissue and cell interactions during embryonic differentiation and growth; control mechanisms in differentiation. *Mailing Add:* Dept Zool Ore State Univ Corvallis OR 97331

MORRIS, JOHN EMORY, b Takoma Park, Md, June 15, 37. BIOCHEMISTRY, ONCOLOGY. *Educ:* Cornell Univ, BA, 59; Univ Wis, MS, 62, PhD(oncol), 66. *Prof Exp:* Res asst clin oncol, Univ Wis-Madison, 61-65; Am Peace Corps vis asst prof biochem, Fac Med, Pahlavi Univ, Iran, 66-67; asst prof, 67-70, assoc prof, 70-76, PROF CHEM, STATE UNIV NY COL BROCKPORT, 76- *Concurrent Pos:* Vis scientist biol & med, Argonne Nat Lab, 73-74 & 81- *Mem:* Am Chem Soc. *Res:* Carcinogenesis in gerbils; nitrogen metabolism and its regulation in gerbils; carcinogenic activity of nitrofurans; synthesis of substituted furans; protein structure; mechanism of enzyme regulation. *Mailing Add:* Dept of Chem State Univ of NY Col Brockport NY 14420

MORRIS, JOHN LEONARD, b Des Moines, Iowa, Dec 12, 29; m 52; c 2. PLANT BREEDING, PLANT PATHOLOGY. *Educ:* Iowa State Univ, BS, 61; Utah State Univ, PhD(plant breeding & path), 67. *Prof Exp:* Fieldman, 61-63, res asst seed develop, 63-68, DIR PEA & BEAN RES, ROGERS BROS CO, 68- *Mem:* Am Soc Agron; Sci Res Soc Am. *Res:* Breeding, development and research of snap beans and garden peas; seed quality research. *Mailing Add:* Rogers Bros Co PO Box 104 Twin Falls ID 83301

MORRIS, JOHN LLEWELYN, numerical analysis, see previous edition

MORRIS, JOHN MCLEAN, b Kuling, China, Sept 1, 14; m 51; c 5. SURGERY, GYNECOLOGY. *Educ:* Princeton Univ, AB, 36; Harvard Univ, MD, 40; Yale Univ, MA, 62; Am Bd Surg, dipl, 50; Am Bd Obstet & Gynec, dipl, 58. *Prof Exp:* Asst surg, Mass Gen Hosp, Boston, 47-52; assoc prof, 52-61, prof, 61-69, JOHN SLADE ELY PROF GYNEC, SCH MED, YALE UNIV, 69- *Concurrent Pos:* Am Cancer Soc fel, Radiumhemmet, Stockholm, Sweden, 51-52; consult gynecologist, Hosps, Conn, 52-; chief obstet & gynec, Yale-New Haven Hosp, 65-66; vis prof gynec & obstet, Stanford Univ, 66-67; vis prof, Univ Tex M D Anderson Hosp & Tumor Inst, 70; consult, Walter Reed Hosp, Gorgas Hosp & Tripler Gen Hosp. *Mem:* Fel Am Col Surg; fel Am Col Obstet & Gynec; Am Gynec Soc (vpres, 81-82); Am Fertil Soc; Soc Pelvic Surg. *Res:* Gynecology; surgery; endocrinology; radiation biology; intersexuality; agents affecting ovum development. *Mailing Add:* Dept of Obstet & Gynec Yale Univ New Haven CT 06511

MORRIS, JOSEPH ANTHONY, b Prince Georges Co, Md, Sept 6, 18; m 42; c 4. BACTERIOLOGY. *Educ:* Cath Univ Am, BS, 40, MS, 42, PhD(bact), 47. *Prof Exp:* Bacteriologist, Josiah Macy Jr Found, NY, 43-44, US Dept Interior & USDA, 44-47, Walter Reed Army Inst Res, DC, 47-56 & US Army Med Command, Japan, 56-59; virologist, NIH, 59-72; dir, Slow, Latent & Temperate Virus Br, Bur Biologics, Food & Drug Admin, 72-76; VCHMN, BELL OF ATRI, INC, 76- *Concurrent Pos:* Instr, Am Univ, 43-46. *Mem:* Am Soc Microbiol; Am Soc Trop Med & Hyg; Soc Exp Biol & Med; Am Asn Immunol; NY Acad Sci. *Res:* Virus and rickettsial diseases. *Mailing Add:* Bell of Atri Inc PO Box 40 College Park MD 20740

MORRIS, JOSEPH BURTON, b Del, Jan 25, 25. ANALYTICAL CHEMISTRY. *Educ:* Howard Univ, BS, 49, MS, 51; Pa State Univ, PhD(anal chem), 56. *Prof Exp:* Instr chem, Howard Univ, 51-53; asst, Pa State Univ, 53-56; res & develop chemist, E I du Pont de Nemours & Co, 56-57; from asst prof to assoc prof, 57-70, PROF ANAL CHEM, HOWARD UNIV, 70-, CHMN DEPT CHEM, 75- *Concurrent Pos:* Fel, Univ Brussels, 67-68. *Mem:* AAAS; Am Chem Soc. *Res:* Polarography; chronopotentiometry; voltammetry at solid electrodes; coulometry; instrumental methods of analysis; solid electrode voltammetry; trace analysis by anodic stripping voltammetry; differential pulse polarography. *Mailing Add:* Dept of Chem Howard Univ Washington DC 20001

MORRIS, JOSEPH RICHARD, b Richmond, Va, Aug 3, 35; m 59; c 2. TOPOLOGY. *Educ:* Va Polytech Inst, BS, 57, MS, 60; Univ Ala, MA, 65, PhD(math), 69. *Prof Exp:* Asst prof math, Samford Univ, 59-64; asst prof, 69-78, ASSOC PROF MATH, VA COMMONWEALTH UNIV, 78- *Mem:* Am Math Soc; Math Asn Am. *Res:* The existence of invariant means of Banach spaces and the common fixed point property for a family of functions. *Mailing Add:* Dept of Math Sci Va Commonwealth Univ Richmond VA 23284

MORRIS, JUSTIN ROY, b Nashville, Ark, Feb 20, 37; m 56; c 2. HORTICULTURE, PLANT PHYSIOLOGY. *Educ:* Univ Ark, BSA, 57, MS, 61; Rutgers Univ, PhD(hort), 64. *Prof Exp:* Asst hort, Univ Ark, 57-61; instr pomol, Rutgers Univ, 61-64; exten horticulturist & assoc prof food sci, 64-75, PROF HORT & FOOD SCI, UNIV ARK, FAYETTEVILLE, 75- *Concurrent Pos:* Consult indust, Int Exten, Fed Exten Serv, USDA, 71-72 & US AID, 74. *Honors & Awards:* Gourley Award, Am Soc Hort Sci, 79. *Mem:* Am Soc Hort Sci; Inst Food Technol; Am Soc Enol. *Res:* Preharvest production and handling of mechanically harvested fruits; production of processing systems. *Mailing Add:* Hort Food Sci Rte 11 Fayetteville AR 72701

MORRIS, KELSO BRONSON, b Beaumont, Tex; m 61; c 4. PHYSICAL INORGANIC CHEMISTRY. *Educ:* Wiley Col, BSc, 30; Cornell Univ, MSc, 37, PhD(inorg chem), 40. *Prof Exp:* Instr chem & math, Wiley Col, 30-37, from assoc prof to prof chem & head dept, 37-46; assoc prof, 46-60, head dept, 65-69, PROF CHEM, HOWARD UNIV, 61- *Concurrent Pos:* From assoc prof to prof & head chem sect, Air Force Inst Technol, 59-61. *Mem:* Fel AAAS; Am Chem Soc; Nat Asn Res Sci Teaching; fel Am Inst Chem. *Res:* Electrochemistry; chemistry of hydroxylamine; complexing tendencies of metal ions; chemistry of fused salts. *Mailing Add:* Dept of Chem Howard Univ Washington DC 20059

MORRIS, LAWRENCE ROBERT, b Toronto, Ont, Apr 7, 42; m 65; c 1. COMMUNICATION, COMPUTER SCIENCE. *Educ:* Univ Toronto, BASc, 65; Univ London, DIC & PhD(speech commun), 70. *Prof Exp:* Vis res assoc elec eng, Univ Rochester, 69-70; asst prof eng, 70-77, ASSOC PROF ENG & COMPUT SCI, CARLETON UNIV, 77- *Concurrent Pos:* Ont Dept Univ Affairs res grant, Carleton Univ, 71-72. *Mem:* Inst Elec & Electronics Engrs; Acoust Soc Am; assoc mem Brit Inst Elec Engrs. *Res:* Speech analysis, synthesis and perception; digital signal processing; interactive computer graphics; computer aided instruction. *Mailing Add:* Fac of Eng Carleton Univ Ottawa ON K1S 5B6 Can

MORRIS, LEO RAYMOND, b South Whitley, Ind, June 19, 22; m 45; c 3. INDUSTRIAL ORGANIC CHEMISTRY. *Educ:* Manchester Col, BA, 47; Univ Wis, PhD(org chem), 52. *Prof Exp:* Asst chemist, Univ Wis, 47-50; from org chemist to sr res chemist, 51-71, res specialist, 71-77, SR RES SPECIALIST, DOW CHEM USA, 77- *Mem:* Am Chem Soc. *Res:* Dehydrohalogenation, synthesis of new monomers and bioactive compounds; free-radical additions; ag-chemical process development. *Mailing Add:* Dow Chem USA Midland MI 48640

MORRIS, LUCIEN ELLIS, b Mattoon, Ill, Nov 30, 14; m 42; c 5. ANESTHESIOLOGY. *Educ:* Oberlin Col, AB, 36; Case Western Reserve Univ, MD, 43; Am Bd Anesthesiol, dipl, 49. *Prof Exp:* Intern, Grasslands Hosp, Valhalla, NY, 43; resident anesthesia, Wis Gen Hosp, Madison, 46-48; instr anesthesiol, Univ Wis, 48-49; from asst prof to assoc prof, Univ Iowa, 49-54; prof, Univ Wash, 54-60, clin prof, 61-68; prof anaesthesia, Fac Med, Univ Toronto, 68-70; prof anesthesia & chmn dept, 70-80, PROF ANESTHESIOL, MED COL OHIO, 80- *Concurrent Pos:* Mem traveling med fac, WHO & Unitarian Serv Comt, Israel & Iran, 51; mem subcomt anesthesia, Nat Res Coun, 56-61; dir anesthesia res labs, Providence Hosp, Seattle, 60-68, dir med educ & res, 65-68; chief anaesthetist, St Michael's Hosp Unit, Toronto, 68-70; vis prof, Anaesthetics Unit, London Hosp Med Col, 80-81. *Mem:* Am Soc Anesthesiol; Am Soc Pharmacol & Exp Therapeut; Soc Exp Biol & Med; fel Royal Col Surgeons; Asn Anaesthetists Gt Brit & Northern Ireland. *Res:* Cardiac conduction; placental transmission of drugs; anesthetic apparatus; fundamental neurophysiologic mechanism in anesthesia; carbon dioxide homeostasis; cardiac output; acid-base status with cardiopulmonary bypass and hypothermia; liver function with various anesthetic agents; medical education. *Mailing Add:* 3425 Bentley Blvd Toledo OH 43606

MORRIS, MANFORD D, b Kamiah, Idaho, Apr 18, 26; m 51; c 3. BIOCHEMISTRY. *Educ:* Univ San Francisco, BS, 49, MS, 51; Univ Calif, PhD(biochem), 58. *Prof Exp:* Asst res biochemist, Sch Med, Univ Calif, 58-61; asst prof, 61-65, assoc prof, 65-72, PROF BIOCHEM, SCH MED, UNIV ARK, LITTLE ROCK, 72-, PROF PEDIAT, 77- *Concurrent Pos:* Asst res biochemist, Clin Invest Ctr, US Naval Hosp, Oakland, 58-61. *Res:* Cholesterol metabolism; sterol methodology; primate lipid and lipoprotein metabolism; heritable diplipoproteinemia. *Mailing Add:* Dept of Biochem Univ Ark Med Sci Little Rock AR 72205

MORRIS, MARION CLYDE, polymer chemistry, see previous edition

MORRIS, MARK ROOT, b Aberdeen, Wash, Sept 2, 47; m 76; c 1. RADIO ASTRONOMY. *Educ:* Univ Calif, Riverside, BA, 69; Univ Chicago, PhD(physics), 75. *Prof Exp:* Res fel radio astron, Owens Valley Radio Observ, Calif Inst Technol, 74-77; ASST PROF DEPT ASTRON, COLUMBIA UNIV, 77- *Concurrent Pos:* Vis prof, Group d'Astrophys, Univ Sci et Med de Grenoble, 81-82. *Mem:* Am Astron Soc; Int Astron Union; Int Sci Radio Union. *Res:* Spectral lines of molecular species in interstellar medium and surrounding young and old stars; spectral line radio astronomy. *Mailing Add:* Dept of Astron Columbia Univ New York NY 10027

MORRIS, MARLENE COOK, b Washington, DC, Dec 20, 33; m 61; c 3. CRYSTALLOGRAPHY, PHYSICAL CHEMISTRY. *Educ:* Howard Univ, BS(chem), 55. *Prof Exp:* Res assoc, Off Ord Res, US Army, Howard Univ, 53-55; res assoc, 55-75, DIR, RES ASSOCIATESHIP INT CTR DIFFRACTION DATA, NAT BUR STANDARDS, 75- *Mem:* Am Crystallog Asn; Am Chem Soc; AAAS; Am Inst Physics; Sigma Xi. *Res:* Crystallography; x-ray powder diffraction. *Mailing Add:* Nat Bur Standards A221 Mat Bldg Washington DC 20234

MORRIS, MARY ROSALIND, b Ruthin, Wales, May 8, 20; US citizen. PLANT CYTOGENETICS. *Educ:* Ont Agr Col, BSA, 42; Cornell Univ, PhD(plant breeding), 47. *Prof Exp:* Asst agron, 47-51, from asst prof to assoc prof, 51-58, PROF CYTOGENETICS, UNIV NEBR, LINCOLN, 58- *Concurrent Pos:* Univ Nebr Johnson fel, Calif Inst Technol, 49-50; Guggenheim fel Sweden & Eng, 56-57. *Mem:* Fel AAAS; Genetics Soc Am; Crop Sci Soc Am; Genetics Soc Can; fel Am Soc Agron. *Res:* Wheat cytogenetics; assignment of genes for important wheat characters to specific chromosomes by use of aneuploids and chromosome substitutions. *Mailing Add:* Dept Agron Univ Nebr Lincoln NE 68583

MORRIS, MELVIN L, b Cincinnati, Ohio, Mar 27, 29. INORGANIC CHEMISTRY. *Educ:* Ohio State Univ, BSc, 51, MSc, 55, PhD(chem), 58. *Prof Exp:* Fel, Northwestern Univ, 58-59 & Ohio State Univ, 59-60; asst prof chem, Tex Tech Col, 60-61; from asst prof to assoc prof, NDak State Univ, 63-68; educ sci adminr, NSF, 68-69; assoc prof chem, 69-74, PROF CHEM, N DAK STATE UNIV, 74- *Concurrent Pos:* Res chemist, Wright Patterson AFB, Ohio, 61. *Mem:* Am Chem Soc. *Res:* Mass spectrometry and synthesis of inorganic compounds; inorganic synthesis of beta- diketone complexes. *Mailing Add:* Dept of Chem NDak State Univ Fargo ND 58102

MORRIS, MELVIN LEWIS, b New York, NY, Nov 28, 14; m 43; c 3. DENTISTRY, PERIDONTICS. *Educ:* City Col New York, BS, 34; Columbia Univ, MA, 37, DDS, 41; Am Bd periodont, dipl, 51. *Prof Exp:* From instr to clin prof, 48-70, adj prof dent, 70-72, CLIN PROF DENT, SCH DENT & ORAL SURG, COLUMBIA UNIV, 70- *Concurrent Pos:* NIH res grant, 66-68; consult, Vet Admin Hosp, Castle Point, 53-56 & Franklin Delano Hosp, 53-59; assoc attend dentist, Presbyterian Hosp. *Honors & Awards:* Hirschfeld Mem Award, 80. *Mem:* Am Dent Asn; Int Asn Dent Res; Am Acad Periodont. *Res:* Experimental wound healing of periodontal tissues. *Mailing Add:* Columbia Univ Sch of 630 W 168th St New York NY 10032

MORRIS, MELVIN SOLOMON, b Denver, Colo; m 33; c 2. RANGE SCIENCE. *Educ:* Colo State Univ, BS, 30, MS, 32. *Hon Degrees:* DSc, Univ Mont, 78. *Prof Exp:* From instr to asst prof bot, Colo State Univ, 30-36; assoc prof range mgt, 36; from asst prof to prof, lectr, 36-72, EMER PROF FORESTRY, UNIV MONT, 72- *Concurrent Pos:* Spec State Univ NY Col Forestry, 49, 50; collabr, US Forest Serv, 50-58 & Fish & Wildlife Serv, 50-62; dir bison site, US Grassland Biome, Int Biol Prog, 70-72; consult, rangeland ecol & range mgt, 72; comn mem, Environ Protection Comn, The Navajo Nation, Window Rock, Ariz, 74-76. *Mem:* Fel AAAS; fel Soc Mgt (treas, 49, pres-elec, 65, pres, 66); Soil Conserv Soc Am; Am Soc Agron; Am Inst Biol Sci. *Res:* Range ecology; land classification; natural resources and ecology of big sagebrush in Montana; primary productivity; grazing land management; grassland ecology. *Mailing Add:* 211 Mary Ave Missoula MT 59801

MORRIS, MICHAEL D, b New York, NY, Mar 27, 39; m 61; c 4. ANALYTICAL CHEMISTRY. *Educ:* Reed Col, BA, 60; Harvard Univ, MA, 62, PhD(chem), 64. *Prof Exp:* Asst prof chem, Pa State Univ, 64-69; ASSOC PROF CHEM, UNIV MICH, ANN ARBOR, 69- *Concurrent Pos:* Res grants, USPHS, 76-79 & 80-83 & NSF, 78-79 & 79-82. *Mem:* Soc Appl Spectros; Am Chem Soc. *Res:* Applications of Raman spectroscopy and laser spectroscopy to analytical chemistry. *Mailing Add:* Dept of Chem Univ of Mich Ann Arbor MI 48109

MORRIS, N RONALD, b New York, NY, July 22, 33; m 57; c 2. CELL BIOLOGY. *Educ:* Yale Univ, BS, 55, MD, 59. *Prof Exp:* Asst prof pharmacol, Sch Med, Yale Univ, 63-67; asst prof, 67-68, assoc prof, 68-72, PROF PHARMACOL, RUTGERS MED SCH, COL MED & DENT NJ, 72- *Concurrent Pos:* Sabbatical molecular biol, Med Res Ctr Lab, Cambridge, Eng. *Mem:* Am Soc Pharmacol & Exp Therapeut; Am Soc Cell Biol; Genetics Soc Am. *Res:* Biochemical genetics of mitosis; molecular genetics of tubulin. *Mailing Add:* Dept Pharmacol Rutgers Med Sch Col Med & Dent NJ Piscataway NJ 08854

MORRIS, NANCY MITCHELL, b Griffin, Ga, Jan 9, 40; m 62; c 1. SPECTROSCOPY, ANALYTICAL CHEMISTRY. *Educ:* LaGrange Col, AB, 60; Auburn Univ, MS, 64. *Prof Exp:* Chemist textiles anal, Res Div, West Point-Pepperell Mfg Co, 64-65; chemist vesicular photog, Kalvar Corp, 66; chemist, 66-72, RES CHEMIST TEXTILES ANAL, SOUTHERN REGIONAL RES CTR, USDA, 72- *Mem:* Am Chem Soc; Am Asn Textile Chemists & Colorists; Coblentz Soc; Soc Appl Spectros; Sigma Xi. *Res:* Trace metals in foods and fibers; effect of chemical modification on structure of cellulose by infrared and Fourier transform infrared spectroscopy; determination of endotoxins in cotton dust. *Mailing Add:* Southern Regional Res Ctr PO Box 19687 New Orleans LA 70179

MORRIS, OWEN G, b Shawnee, Okla, Feb 3, 27; m 48; c 2. AERODYNAMICS, AEROSPACE TECHNOLOGY. *Educ:* Univ Okla, BS, 47, MS, 48. *Prof Exp:* Instr mech, Univ Okla, 47-48; aeronaut res scientist, Nat Adv Comt Aeronaut, NASA, 48-49, aerospace technologist, 57-61, asst chief test div, 61-63, chief, Reliability & Qual Assurance Div, Apollo Spacecraft Prog Off, 63-65, chief, Lunar Module Proj Eng Div, 65-69, mgr lunar module, 69-72, mgr Apollo Spacecraft Prog, 72-73, mgr systs integration space shuttle, 73-80; PRES, EAGLE ENG, INC, 80- *Concurrent Pos:* Mgt consult. *Honors & Awards:* Exceptional Serv Medal, NASA, 69, Distinguished Serv Medal, 72. *Mem:* Assoc fel Am Inst Aeronaut & Astronaut. *Res:* Design, development and operation of the lunar module, the first manned lunar landing spacecraft; supersonic aerodynamics. *Mailing Add:* Eagle Eng Inc 17629 E Camino Real Suite 125 Houston TX 77058

MORRIS, PETER ALAN, b Oakland, Calif, Oct 6, 45; m 69; c 1. OPERATIONS RESEARCH, SYSTEMS ANALYSIS. *Educ:* Univ Calif, Berkeley, BS, 68; Stanford Univ, MS, 70, PhD(eng-econ syst), 71. *Prof Exp:* Opers res analyst, Off Systs Anal, Dept Defense, 71-74, opers res mgr, Modeling & Anal Off, Manpower & Reserve Affairs, 74; res scientist anal res group, Palo Alto Res Ctr, Xerox Corp, 74-79; PRIN, APPL DECISION ANAL, INC, 79- *Concurrent Pos:* Assoc ed, Mgt Sci, 71-; consult assoc prof eng-econ syst, Stanford Univ, 75- *Mem:* Inst Mgt Sci; Opers Res Soc Am; Inst Elec & Electronics Engrs. *Res:* Decision analysis; systems modeling; probabilistic models; use of experts. *Mailing Add:* Appl Decision Anal Inc 3000 Sand Hill Rd Menlo Park CA 94025

MORRIS, PETER ANDREW, b Rochester, NY, Dec 27, 21; m 53; c 2. NUCLEAR ENGINEERING, NUCLEAR PHYSICS. *Educ:* Swarthmore Col, BA, 43; Univ Va, PhD(nuclear physics), 51. *Prof Exp:* Physicist, E I du Pont de Nemours & Co, 51-57; div inspection, Atomic Energy Comn, 57-61, div compliance, 61-63, sci rep Tokyo, 63-65, dir div oper safety, 65-66, dir div reactor licensing, 66-72, dir off opers evaluation, 72-74; exec vpres nuclear eng, Scandpower Inc, 74-81; ADMIN JUDGE TECH, ATOMIC SAFETY & LICENSING BD PANEL, NUCLEAR REGULATORY COMN, 81- *Mem:* Fel Am Nuclear Soc; AAAS. *Res:* Nuclear reactor safety and design. *Mailing Add:* 10825 S Glen Rd Potomac MD 20854

MORRIS, PETER CRAIG, b Kansas City, Mo, Sept 5, 37; m 60; c 3. MATHEMATICS. *Educ:* Southern Ill Univ, BA, 59; Univ Iowa, MS, 61; Okla State Univ, PhD(math), 67. *Prof Exp:* Asst prof math, State Col Iowa, 63-65; Belg-Am Educ Found fel, 67-68; asst prof math, Fla State Univ, 68-72; assoc prof, 72-79, PROF MATH, SHEPHERD COL, 79-, HEAD DEPT, 72- *Concurrent Pos:* Sabbatical leave, Southern Ill Univ, Carbondale, 80-81. *Mem:* Am Math Soc; Math Asn Am. *Mailing Add:* Dept of Math Shepherd Col Shepherdstown WV 25443

MORRIS, RALPH DENNIS, b Humboldt, Sask, Feb 13, 40; m 63; c 2. BEHAVIORAL ECOLOGY. *Educ:* Univ Sask, BSc, 63, PhD(ecol), 69; Univ Colo, Boulder, BEd, 63. *Prof Exp:* Nat Res Coun Can fel biol, McGill Univ, 69-70; asst prof, 70-73, ASSOC PROF BIOL, BROCK UNIV, 73- *Mem:* Am Orinthol Union; Can Soc Orinthol; Can Soc Wildlife & Fishery Biol; Am Soc Mammalogists; Am Soc Naturalists. *Res:* Mate choice criteria and parental care activities in colonial nesting seabirds; foraging and movement patterns in gulls and terns; overwintering ecology and behaviour in common terns. *Mailing Add:* Dept of Biosci Brock Univ St Catherines ON L2S 3A1 Can

MORRIS, RALPH WILLIAM, b Cleveland Heights, Ohio, July 30, 28; m 55; c 5. PHARMACOLOGY. *Educ:* Ohio Univ, BA, 50, MS, 53; Univ Iowa, PhD(pharmacol), 55. *Prof Exp:* Asst pharmacol, Univ Iowa, 52-53; instr, Col Med, 55-56, from asst prof to assoc prof, Col Pharm, 56-69, PROF PHARMACOL, COL PHARM, UNIV MED CTR, 69- *Concurrent Pos:* Adj prof educ, Col Educ, Univ Ill, Circle Campus, 75- *Mem:* AAAS; Drug Info Asn; Am Soc Pharmacol & Exp Therapeut; Am Pharmaceut Asn; Int Soc Chronobiol. *Res:* Chronopharmacology; chronopathology; drug abuse; drug interactions; drug screening. *Mailing Add:* Dept of Pharmacog & Pharmacol Univ of Ill Col of Pharm Chicago IL 60612

MORRIS, RANDAL EDWARD, b Shoemaker, Calif, Dec 10, 45; m 70; c 2. IMMMUNOLOGY, VIROLOGY. *Educ:* Aurora Col, BS, 69; Northern Ill Univ, MS, 71; Emory Univ, PhD(microbiol), 74. *Prof Exp:* Fel microbiol, Univ Mich, 74-76; ASST PROF MICROBIOL, UNIV CINCINNATI, 76- *Mem:* Am Soc Microbiol. *Res:* Demonstration and quantitation of cell associated antigens at the ultrastructural level. *Mailing Add:* Dept Microbiol Univ Cincinnati 231 Bethesda Ave Cincinnati OH 45267

MORRIS, RICHARD HERBERT, b Oakland, Calif, Nov 22, 28; m 56; c 2. ELECTROMAGNETICS. *Educ:* Univ Calif, Berkeley, AB, 50, PhD(nuclear physics), 57. *Prof Exp:* Asst physics, Univ Calif, Berkeley, 50-53, asst nuclear physics, Lawrence Radiation Lab, 53-55; instr physics, Sacramento State Col, 56-57; from asst prof to assoc prof, 57-66, PROF PHYSICS, SAN DIEGO STATE COL, 66- *Concurrent Pos:* Consult, Naval Electronics Lab, 62-63. *Mem:* Am Asn Physics Teachers. *Res:* Theoretical physics; modern optics; teaching of physics. *Mailing Add:* Dept of Physics San Diego State Col San Diego CA 92182

MORRIS, RICHARD MILTON, JR, b St Louis, Mo, Dec 8, 19; m 43; c 2. CHEMICAL ENGINEERING. *Educ:* Univ Mo, BS, 43. *Prof Exp:* Res engr, Doane Agr Serv Inc, 42-43; tech serv mgr, Container Corp Am, 43-57; gen mgr & vpres, Wrenn Paper Co, 57-59; mgr containerboard res & develop, 59-71, mgr packaging res & develop, 71-77, MGR SPECIAL PROJ RES & DEVELOP, WEYERHAEUSER CO, 77- *Concurrent Pos:* Res adv comt, Tech Asn Pulp & Paper Indust. *Honors & Awards:* Cert of Appreciation, Tech Asn Pulp & Paper Indust, 71; Outstanding Serv Award, Repub China & China Purchasing Inst, Taiwan, 71. *Mem:* Tech Asn Pulp & Paper Indust; Inst Paper Chem; Fiber Box Asn. *Res:* Containerboard-container production process and product performance; packaging systems and market application for corrugated shipping container industry. *Mailing Add:* Weyerhaeuser Co Tacoma WA 98477

MORRIS, ROBERT CARTER, b Richmond, Va, Oct 3, 43; m 63; c 1. EXPERIMENTAL SOLID STATE PHYSICS. *Educ:* Hampden-Sydney Col, BS, 66; Univ Va, PhD(physics), 70. *Prof Exp:* Res assoc physics, Univ Va, 70-71, asst prof, 71-73; asst prof, 73-77, ASSOC PROF PHYSICS, FLA STATE UNIV, 77- *Mem:* Am Phys Soc. *Res:* Experimental studies of the normal and superconducting state properties of layer-structure, transition-metal dichalcogenide compounds and tungsten bronze compounds, both pure and doped with impurity atoms. *Mailing Add:* Dept of Physics Fla State Univ Tallahassee FL 32306

MORRIS, ROBERT CLARENCE, b Electra, Tex, Feb 19, 28; m 54; c 4. GEOLOGY. *Educ:* Tex Technol Col, BS, 52; Univ Wis, MS, 62, PhD(geol), 65. *Prof Exp:* Subsurface geologist, Int Petrol Co, Ltd, 52-56, explor geologist, 56-61; asst prof, Northern Ill Univ, 64-67, assoc prof, 67-78, prof geol, 78-79; prof geol & chmn, Eastern Ky Univ, 79-80; PROF GEOL & CHMN DEPT, UNIV ARK, 80- *Concurrent Pos:* NSF fel, Northern Ill Univ, 67-69. *Mem:* Am Asn Petrol Geologists; Soc Econ Paleontologists & Mineralogists; Geol Soc Am; Int Asn Sedimentol. *Res:* Stratigraphy and sedimentology of Carboniferous, Ouachita Mountains, Arkansas; petrology of cabonate banks; modern evaporite deposition; classification of disturbed bedding; sedimentary and tectonic history of northwest Peru. *Mailing Add:* Dept of Geol Univ Ark Fayetteville AR 72701

MORRIS, ROBERT CRAIG, b Hemet, Calif, Jan 7, 44; m 79. SINGLE CRYSTAL GROWTH, SOLID STATE LASER MATERIALS. *Educ:* Rensselaer Polytech Inst, BS, 66, PhD(mat sci), 71. *Prof Exp:* STAFF SCIENTIST, CORP RES & DEVELOP, ALLIED CORP, 71- *Honors & Awards:* Indust Res 100 Award, Indust Res & Develop Mag, 76 & 80. *Mem:* Am Asn Crystal Growth; AAAS; Sigma Xi. *Res:* New single crystal solid state laser materials. *Mailing Add:* Mat Lab Allied Corp PO Box 1021R Morristown NJ 07960

MORRIS, ROBERT GEMMILL, b Des Moines, Iowa, July 20, 29; m 55; c 3. SOLID STATE PHYSICS. *Educ:* Iowa State Univ, BS, 51, PhD(physics), 57; Calif Inst Technol, MS, 54. *Prof Exp:* Am-Swiss Found Sci exchange fel, Swiss Fed Inst Technol, 57-58; from asst prof to prof physics & head dept, SDak Sch Mines & Technol, 58-68; physicist, Physics Prog, Off Naval Res, Va, 68-72, actg dir, Electronics Prog, 72-73, dir, Electronics Prog, 73-74; dep dir, Off Technol Policy & Space Affairs, Bur Oceans & Int Environ & Sci Affairs, 74-76, actg dir, 76-77, dir, Off Soviet & East Europ Sci & Technol Affairs, 77-78, COUNSR SCI & TECHNOL AFFAIRS, US MISSION TO ORGN ECON COOP & DEVELOP PARIS, US DEPT STATE, 78- *Concurrent Pos:* Vis prof, Swiss Fed Inst Technol, 63-64. *Mem:* Fel Am Phys Soc; Inst Elec & Electronics Engrs. *Res:* Electrical, thermal and magnetic properties of semiconductor elements and compounds; technology transfer. *Mailing Add:* US Mission Orgn Econ Coop & Develop American Embassy Paris France

MORRIS, ROBERT HAMILTON, b Lackawanna, NY, Aug 3, 21; m 48; c 3. GEOLOGY. *Educ:* Upsala Col, BA, 48; Rutgers Univ, MS, 53. *Prof Exp:* Instr geol, Upsala Col, 48-50; geologist, Navy Oil Unit, US Geol Surv, DC, 50-54, photogeol sect, Colo, 54-58; Int Coop Admin prof geomorphol & photogeol, Univ Rio Grande do Sul, Brazil, 58-60; geologist & photogeologist, Ky Br, 60-64, photgeologist, Spec Projs Br, 65-72, GEOLOGIST, NUCLEAR REACTOR SITE INVESTS, OFF REGIONAL GEOL, US GEOL SURV, 72- *Mem:* Geol Soc Am; Asn Eng Geol; Am Asn Petrol Geologists; Geol Soc Am. *Res:* Sedimentation and heavy minerals; photogeology. *Mailing Add:* US Geol Surv Box 25046 Mail Stop 908 KAE Reston VA 22092

MORRIS, ROBERT WHARTON, b Liberal, Mo, Aug 27, 20; m 45; c 2. ICHTHYOLOGY. *Educ:* Wichita State Univ, AB, 42; Ore State Col, MS, 48; Stanford Univ, PhD(biol), 54. *Prof Exp:* Biologist agr exp sta, Ore State Col, 48-49 & US Fish & Wildlife Serv, 51-55; from instr to assoc prof, 55-68, PROF BIOL, UNIV ORE, 68- *Concurrent Pos:* Guggenheim fel, 62-63. *Res:* Biology of fishes and lower vertebrates. *Mailing Add:* Dept of Biol Univ of Ore Eugene OR 97403

MORRIS, ROBERT WILLIAM, b Staten Island, NY, Sept 28, 41; m 68; c 2. GEOLOGY, INVERTEBRATE PALEONTOLOGY. *Educ:* Duke Univ, AB, 63; Columbia Univ, MA, 65, PhD(geol), 69. *Prof Exp:* Teaching asst geol, Columbia Univ, 63-66; asst instr, Rutgers Univ, 66-67; asst prof, 68-74, ASSOC PROF GEOL, WITTENBERG UNIV, 75- *Mem:* Sigma Xi; Paleont Soc; Int Palaeont Union; Nat Asn Geol Teachers. *Res:* Paleoecology; micropaleontology. *Mailing Add:* Dept of Geol Wittenberg Univ Springfield OH 45501

MORRIS, ROSEMARY SHULL, b Los Angeles, Calif, Aug 11, 29. SCIENCE ADMINISTRATION, NUTRITION. *Educ:* Univ Calif, Berkeley, 50; Univ Southern Calif, BS, 53, MS, 56, PhD(biochem, nutrit), 59. *Prof Exp:* Res assoc biochem, Univ Southern Calif, 59; jr res biochemist, Univ Calif, Los Angeles, 59-61; res biochemist, Eastern Utilization Res & Develop Div, Agr Res Serv, USDA, Washington, DC, 61-66; res chemist, Div Nutrit, US Food & Drug Admin, 66-67 & Human Nutrit Res Div, Agr Res Serv, USDA, Md, 67-72; health scientist adminr, Nat Heart & Lung Inst, NIH, 72-75, asst chief res, Referral Br, 75-77, EXEC SECY CARDIOVASC RENAL STUDY SECT, DIV RES GRANTS, DIV RES GRANTS, NIH, 77- *Mem:* Am Inst Nutrit. *Res:* Lipid and cholesterol metabolism; vitamin E; essential fatty acids. *Mailing Add:* Div of Res Grants Nat Inst Health Bethesda MD 20014

MORRIS, ROY OWEN, b Kingston-on-Thames, Eng, May 24, 34; m 63; c 2. BIOCHEMISTRY. *Educ:* Univ London, BSc, 55, PhD(chem), 59. *Prof Exp:* Asst lectr chem & biochem, St Thomas Hosp Med Sch, London, Eng, 59-61; res assoc biochem, Sci Res Inst, 61-64, asst prof agr chem, 64-70, ASSOC PROF AGR CHEM, ORE STATE UNIV, 70-, ASSOC PROF CHEM, 74- *Mem:* AAAS; Am Soc Plant Physiol. *Res:* Biochemistry of plant development; protein and nucleic acid biosynthesis. *Mailing Add:* Dept of Agr Chem Ore State Univ Corvallis OR 97331

MORRIS, SAMUEL CARY, III, b Summit, NJ, Dec 16, 42; m 66; c 3. ENVIRONMENTAL HEALTH, ENVIRONMENTAL ENGINEERING. *Educ:* Va Mil Inst, BS, 65; Rutgers Univ, MS, 67; Univ Pittsburgh, ScD, 73. *Prof Exp:* Environ health engr serv div, US Army Med Lab, 66-67, chief div, 67-68; asst prof environ health sci, Ill State Univ, 71-72; res assoc, Grad Sch Pub Health, Univ Pittsburgh, 72-73; from asst to assoc scientist, 73-77, SCIENTIST BIOMED & ENVIRON ASSESSMENT DIV, BROOKHAVEN NAT LAB, 77- *Concurrent Pos:* Asst prof dept appl math sci, State Univ NY, Stonybrook, 76-78; adj asst prof dept eng & pub policy, Carnegie Mellon Univ, 76-; consult, Power Authority State NY, 77-, Columbus Div, Battelle Mem Inst, 76-77 & US Army Construct Eng Res Lab, 73-75; mem adv group health effects reactor safety study, US Nuclear Regulatory Comn, 75; sanit engr mobilization design, US Army, 69-74; chmn task force energy, Am Pub Health Asn, 76-77; mem air resources task group environ div, Am Soc Civil Engrs. 76- *Mem:* Am Pub Health Asn; Am Soc Civil Engrs; Air Pollution Control Asn; NY Acad Sci; Am Statist Asn. *Res:* Health and environmental effects of energy systems, particularly occupational health and safety in coal and nuclear, air pollution effects. *Mailing Add:* Dept of Energy & Environ Brookhaven Nat Lab Upton NY 11973

MORRIS, SIDNEY MACHEN, JR, b Tyler, Tex, Mar 31, 46. BIOLOGICAL CHEMISTRY. *Educ:* Univ Tex, Austin, BS, 68; Univ Calif, Berkeley, PhD(biochem), 75. *Prof Exp:* NIH fel physiol chem, Univ Wis Med Ctr, 75-78; MEM STAFF DEPT PHARMACOL, CASE WESTERN RESERVE UNIV, 78- *Res:* Molecular processes involved in eucaryotic gene regulation and development; amphibian metamorphosis; hormone action. *Mailing Add:* Dept of Pharmacol Case Western Reserve Univ Cleveland OH 44106

MORRIS, STANLEY P, b Montreal, Que, Nov 23, 37; m 63; c 4. THEORETICAL SOLID STATE PHYSICS. *Educ:* McGill Univ, BSc, 58, PhD(physics), 64. *Prof Exp:* Lectr physics, Loyola Col, Can, 63-64; asst prof, Sir George Williams Univ, 64-69; chmn dept, 74-79, ASSOC PROF PHYSICS, CONCORDIA UNIV, 69- *Mem:* Am Phys Soc; Am Asn Physics Teachers; Can Asn Physicists. *Res:* Electron interactions in the presence of a uniform magnetic field; Bloch electrons in a magnetic field. *Mailing Add:* Dept of Physics Concordia Univ SGW Campus 1455 de Maisonneuve Montreal PQ H3G 1M8 Can

MORRIS, THOMAS JACK, b Montreal, Que, Apr 28, 47; m 69; c 2. PLANT VIROLOGY, PLANT PATHOLOGY. *Educ:* MacDonald Col McGill Univ, BSc, 68; McGill Univ, MSc, 70; Univ of Nebr-Lincoln, PhD(plant virol), 73. *Prof Exp:* Asst prof biol, Univ NB, 74-76; ASST PROF PLANT PATH, UNIV CALIF, BERKELEY, 76- *Concurrent Pos:* Nat Res Coun Can, fels, 70-74. *Mem:* Am Phytopathological Soc; Soc Gen Microbiol. *Res:* Role of viruses and viroids in plant disease; comparative virology of plant and invertebrate viruses. *Mailing Add:* Dept of Plant Path Univ Calif Berkeley CA 94720

MORRIS, THOMAS WENDELL, b Emory, Ga, Jan 31, 30; m 54; c 2. PHYSICS. *Educ:* Duke Univ, BS, 51; Yale Univ, MS, 53, PhD(physics), 55. *Prof Exp:* PHYSICIST, BROOKHAVEN NAT LAB, 55- *Concurrent Pos:* Vis physicist, Saclay Nuclear Res Ctr, France, 59-60. *Mem:* Am Phys Soc. *Res:* Particle physics; computer applications; nuclear instrumentation. *Mailing Add:* 20 Pennsylvania St Upton NY 11973

MORRIS, WILLIAM GUY, b Great Falls, Mont, Jan 4, 40. PHYSICAL METALLURGY. *Educ:* Univ Calif, BS, 61; Mass Inst Technol, SM, 63, ScD(metall), 65. *Prof Exp:* Scientist, Adv Metals Res Corp, 63-65; res scientist, 65-78, proj mgr, 78-80, UNIT MGR, GEN ELEC CO, 80- *Mem:* Am Inst Mining, Metall & Petrol Engrs; Am Soc Metals; Microbeam Anal Soc. *Res:* Electron beam microprobe; scanning electron microscopy; electrical properties of polycrystalline ceramics. *Mailing Add:* Riverview Rd Rexford NY 12148

MORRIS, WILLIAM JOSEPH, b Baltimore, Md, Oct 14, 23; m 45; c 2. GEOLOGY. *Educ:* Syracuse Univ, BA, 48; Princeton Univ, MA & PhD(geol), 51. *Prof Exp:* Prof geol, Agr & Mech Col, Tex, 51-55; PROF GEOL, OCCIDENTAL COL, 55-, CHMN DEPT, 71- *Concurrent Pos:* Res assoc, Mus Natural Hist, Los Angeles. *Honors & Awards:* Arnold Guyot Mem Award, Nat Geog Soc, 68. *Mem:* Fel Geol Soc Am; Soc Vert Paleont; Am Asn Petrol Geologists; Soc Study Evolution. *Res:* Vertebrate paleontology; sedimentary petrology; invertebrate paleontology. *Mailing Add:* Dept of Geol Occidental Col 1600 Campus Rd Los Angeles CA 90041

MORRISETT, JOEL DAVID, b Winston-Salem, NC, May 2, 42; m 67; c 2. BIOPHYSICS, BIOCHEMISTRY. *Educ:* Davidson Col, BS, 64; Univ NC, Chapel Hill, PhD(org chem), 68. *Prof Exp:* NIH fel biophys, Stanford Univ, 70-71; asst prof, 71-75, ASSOC, PROF EXP MED, BAYLOR COL MED, 76- *Concurrent Pos:* Estab investr, Am Heart Asn, 74-79. *Mem:* Am Heart Asn; Biophys Soc; AAAS; Fedn Am Soc Exp Biol; NY Acad Sci. *Res:* Correlation and determination of structure and function of proteins, particularly enzymes and lipoproteins. *Mailing Add:* Div Atherosci & Lipoprotein Res Baylor Col of Med Houston TX 77030

MORRISH, ALLAN HENRY, b Winnipeg, Man, Apr 18, 24; m 52; c 2. PHYSICS. *Educ:* Univ Manitoba, BSc, 43; Univ Toronto, MA, 46; Univ Chicago, PhD(physics), 49. *Prof Exp:* Asst physics, Univ Chicago, 48-49; lectr, Univ BC, 49-50, res assoc 51-52; physicist, McGill Univ, 52-53; from res assoc to prof elec eng, Univ Minn, Minneapolis, 53-64; PROF PHYSICS, UNIV MAN, 64-, HEAD DEPT, 66- *Concurrent Pos:* Nat Res Coun Can fel, 50-51; Guggenheim fel, 57-58; pres, Can Asn Physicists, 74-75. *Honors & Awards:* Gold Medal Achievement in Physics, Can Asn Physicists, 77. *Mem:* Fel Am Phys Soc; Royal Soc Can; fel Brit Inst Physics; Can Asn Physicists. *Res:* Particle accelerators; elementary and small magnetic particles; nuclear emulsions; ferromagnetism; magnetic resonance; low temperatures; Mossbauer effect in magnetic materials. *Mailing Add:* Dept Physics Univ Man Winnipeg MB R3T 2N2 Can

MORRISON, ADRIAN RUSSEL, b Philadelphia, Pa, Nov 5, 35; m 58; c 5. NEUROANATOMY, NEUROPHYSIOLOGY. *Educ:* Cornell Univ, DVM, 60, MS, 62; Univ Pa, PhD(anat), 64. *Prof Exp:* NIH spec fel neurophysiol, Univ Pisa, 64-65; asst prof, 66-70, ASSOC PROF ANAT, SCH VET MED, UNIV PA, 70- *Mem:* Am Vet Med Asn; Am Asn Vet Anat; Am Asn Anat; Asn Psychophysiol Study Sleep. *Res:* Neuroanatomical and neurophysiological bases of mammalian behavior. *Mailing Add:* Dept of Animal Biol Sch Vet Med Univ of Pa Philadelphia PA 19104

MORRISON, ASHTON BYROM, b Belfast, Ireland, Oct 13, 22; m 50; c 1. PATHOLOGY. *Educ:* Queens Univ Belfast, MD, 46, PhD, 50; Duke Univ, MD, 46. *Prof Exp:* Asst lectr biochem, Queens Univ Belfast, 47-50 & anat, 50-51; mem sci staff exp med, Univ Cambridge, 52-55; assoc path, Duke Univ, 55-58; asst prof, Sch Med, Univ Pa, 58-61; assoc prof, Sch Med, Univ Rochester, 61-65; PROF PATH & CHMN DEPT, RUTGERS MED SCH, 65- *Concurrent Pos:* Markle scholar, 56-61. *Mem:* Am Asn Path; Am Fedn Clin Res; Am Physiol Soc; Soc Exp Biol & Med; Anatomical Soc Gt Brit & Ireland. *Res:* Experimental chronic renal insufficiency; experimental nephropathies. *Mailing Add:* Dept of Path Rutgers Med Sch Piscataway NJ 08854

MORRISON, CHARLES FREEMAN, JR, b Yakima, Wash, Sept 24, 29; m 52; c 4. THIN FILM PROCESSES, SPUTTERING. *Educ:* Univ Puget Sound, BS, 53; Mass Inst Technol, PhD(anal chem), 57. *Prof Exp:* From instr to asst prof anal chem, Wash State Univ, 57-62; res scientist, Granville-Phillips Co, Colo, 62-70; sr scientist, Universal Instruments Corp, 70-71; eng-opers mgr, Valleylab, Inc, 71-75, chief res, 75-76; gen mgr, 76-80, TECH VPRES, VAC-TEC SYSTS, 80- *Concurrent Pos:* NSF fel, 61-63. *Mem:* Am Chem Soc; Am Vacuum Soc. *Res:* Magnetically trapped plasmas are applied to produce thin film coating; specific processes are developed and fundamentals are re-explored for more effective methods of sputter coating and cleaning; analytical instruments; vacuum instrumentation; low pressure measurement methods; calibration techniques; biomedical instrumentation; electrosurgical mechanisms and methods. *Mailing Add:* 4790 Sioux Dr Boulder CO 80303

MORRISON, CLYDE ARTHUR, physics, electrical engineering, see previous edition

MORRISON, DAVID CAMPBELL, b Stoneham, Mass, Sept 1, 41; m 66. IMMUNOLOGY. *Educ:* Univ Mass, BS, 63; Yale Univ, MS, 66, PhD(molecular biol), 69. *Prof Exp:* Fel, Lab Biochem Pharm, Nat Inst Allergy & Infectious Dis, NIH, 69-71; fel, Dept Exp Path, Scipps Clin & Res Found, 71-74, asst, 74-75, assoc, Dept Immunopath, 75-78, assoc mem, 78-80; assoc prof, 80-81, PROF, DEPT MICROBIOL & IMMUNOL, EMORY UNIV, ATLANTA, 81-, WILLIAM P TIMMIE CHAIR, 80- *Concurrent Pos:* Res career develop award, Nat Inst Allergy & Infectious Dis, NIH, 75-80. *Mem:* Am Asn Immunol; Am Soc Exp Path; Am Soc Microbiol; NY Acad Sci; Reticuloendo Melitis Soc. *Res:* Interaction of bacterial lipopolysaccharides with cellular and humoral mediation systems; mechanisms of activation of peritoneal mast cells by various stimuli. *Mailing Add:* Dept Microbiol & Immunol Sch Med Emory Univ Atlanta GA 30087

MORRISON, DAVID DOUGLAS, b Danville, Ill, June 26, 40; m 66. ASTRONOMY, PLANETARY SCIENCE. *Educ:* Univ Ill, Urbana, BA, 62; Harvard Univ, AM, 64, PhD(astron), 69. *Prof Exp:* Res assoc astron, Cornell Univ, 68-69; asst astronr, 69-74, assoc astronr, 74-76, ASSOC PROF, INST ASTRON, UNIV HAWAII, 78- *Concurrent Pos:* Co-investr, Mariner Venus/Mercury Mission, infrared radiometer, 71-75; vis assoc, Calif Inst Technol, 72; vis assoc prof, Lunar & Planetary Lab, Univ Ariz, 75-76; vis scientist, Kitt Peak Nat Observ, 76; asst dep dir & staff scientist, Planetary Div, NASA Off Space Sci, 76-78; scientist & vchmn, Galileo Proj Sci Group, 77-78; assoc ed, J Geophys Res, 78- *Mem:* Int Astron Union; Am Astron Soc (secy-treas, 71-77); AAAS. *Res:* Planetary surfaces and atmospheres especially dealing with satellites, asteroids and comets; exploration of the planets by spacecraft; infrared astronomy. *Mailing Add:* Inst for Astron Univ of Hawaii Honolulu HI 96822

MORRISON, DAVID LEE, b Butler, Pa, Jan 25, 33; m 54; c 2. NUCLEAR CHEMISTRY, PHYSICAL CHEMISTRY. *Educ:* Grove City Col, BS, 54; Carnegie Inst Technol, MS, 60, PhD(chem), 61. *Prof Exp:* Chemist, Callery Chem Co, 54; sr chemist, Battelle Mem Inst, 61-65, from assoc chief to chief chem physics div, 65-70, mgr environ systs & processes sect, 70-74, mgr energy & environ prog off, 74-75, dir prog develop & mgt, 75-77; exec vpres,

77-79, PRES, ITT RES INST, CHICAGO, 80- *Concurrent Pos:* Mem, Comt N-19, Am Nat Standards Inst, 73- *Mem:* AAAS; Sigma Xi; Am Chem Soc; Am Nuclear Soc. *Res:* Energy and environmental research; technology and environmental impact assessment; research and development planning; nuclear reactor safety analysis; radiochemistry; research management. *Mailing Add:* 10 W 35th St Chicago IL 60616

MORRISON, DENNIS ROBERT, space life sciences, cell biology, see previous edition

MORRISON, DONALD ALLEN, b Mt Forest, Ont, July 20, 36; US citizen; m 69; c 1. PETROLOGY, GEOLOGY. *Educ:* State Univ NY Buffalo, BS, 62; Univ Alaska, MS, 64; Univ Idaho, PhD(geol), 68. *Prof Exp:* AEROSPACE SCIENTIST, MANNED SPACECRAFT CTR, NASA, 68- *Mem:* AAAS; Am Geophys Union; Geol Soc Am. *Res:* Lunar geology; petrology of lunar rocks; meteorite and micrometeorite studies as related to lunar surface processes; Precambrian geology. *Mailing Add:* NASA Manned Spacecraft Ctr SNG Houston TX 77058

MORRISON, DONALD FRANKLIN, b Stoneham, Mass, Feb 10, 31. MATHEMATICAL STATISTICS. *Educ:* Boston Univ, BS, 53, AM, 54; Univ NC, MS, 57; Va Polytech Inst, PhD, 60. *Prof Exp:* Asst math, Boston Univ, 53-54 & Univ NC, 54-56; res math statistician, Biomet Br, NIMH, 56-63; PROF STATIST, WHARTON SCH, UNIV PA, 63-, CHMN DEPT, 77- *Concurrent Pos:* Instr, Found Advan Educ in Sci, 60-63; mem staff, Lincoln Lab, Mass Inst Technol, 56, consult, 56-57; div comput sci, NIH, 63-65; mem tech staff, Bell Tel Labs, NJ, 67; ed, Am Statistician, 72-75; assoc ed, Biometrics, 72-75. *Mem:* Fel Am Statist Asn; Fel Inst Math Statist; Biomet Soc; Psychomet Soc; Royal Statist Soc. *Res:* Statistical theory and methodology; multivariate analysis. *Mailing Add:* Dept of Statist Wharton Sch Univ of Pa Philadelphia PA 19104

MORRISON, DONALD ROSS, b Tacoma, Wash, May 3, 22; m 43; c 3. MATHEMATICS, COMPUTER SCIENCE. *Educ:* Northern Ill State Teachers Col, BE, 42; Univ Wis, PhM, 46, PhD(math), 50. *Prof Exp:* Instr math, Univ Wis, 50; asst prof, Tulane Univ, 50-55; from mem staff to mgr, Sandia Corp, 55-71; PROF MATH & COMPUT SCI, UNIV N MEX, 71- *Concurrent Pos:* Consult, Los Alamos Sci Lab, Univ Calif, 71-74 & Sandia Corp, 77- *Mem:* Am Math Soc; Math Asn Am; Asn Comput Mach. *Res:* Pattern recognition; information retrieval; graph theory; abstract algebra. *Mailing Add:* 712 Laguayra Dr NE Albuquerque NM 87108

MORRISON, DOUGLAS WILDES, b Schenectady, NY, Nov 8, 47; m 76; c 1. ZOOLOGY. *Educ:* Univ Rochester, AB, 69; Cornell Univ, PhD(behav & ecol), 75. *Prof Exp:* Asst prof, 75-80, ASSOC PROF ZOOL, RUTGERS UNIV, NEWARK, 80- *Mem:* Animal Behav Soc; Ecol Soc Am; Asn Trop Biol; Am Soc Naturalists. *Res:* Radio-tracking studies of social, foraging and roosting behavior of neotropical fruit bats and New Jersey black birds. *Mailing Add:* Dept Zool & Physiol Rutgers Univ Newark NJ 07102

MORRISON, EDWARD JOSEPH, teratology, anatomy, see previous edition

MORRISON, ESTON ODELL, b Sabinal, Tex, Sept 18, 32; m 58; c 3. ENTOMOLOGY, PARASITOLOGY. *Educ:* Tex Col Arts & Indust, BS, 57; Tex A&M Univ, MS, 60, PhD(entom), 63. *Prof Exp:* Instr biol, Tex Col Arts & Indust, 60-61; asst prof, Lamar State Col, 63-66; assoc prof, 66-68, PROF BIOL, TARLETON STATE COL, 68- *Concurrent Pos:* Lamar Res Ctr grant, 65-66. *Mem:* Am Soc Parasitol. *Res:* Lung flukes of salientia; helminthology. *Mailing Add:* Box 219 Tarleton Sta Stephenville TX 76401

MORRISON, FRANK ALBERT, JR, b Greensburg, Pa, Feb 6, 43; m 63; c 2. MECHANICAL ENGINEERING. *Educ:* Carnegie Inst Technol, BS, 63, MS, 64, PhD(mech eng), 66. *Prof Exp:* NSF fel, Cambridge Univ, 66-67; from asst prof to prof mech eng, Univ Ill, Urbana-Champaign, 66-78, asst dean eng, 70-71; head, Thermo Fluid Mech Group, 78-80, CONTAINMENT PROG MGR, LAWRENCE LIVERMORE NAT LAB, 80- *Concurrent Pos:* Consult, Lawrence Livermore Lab, Univ Calif, 71-77. *Mem:* Am Soc Mech Engrs; AAAS. *Res:* Dynamics of aerosols; physicochemical hydrodynamics; flow in porous media; heat, mass and momentum transfer; heat transfer in electric fields. *Mailing Add:* 874 Columbine Ct San Ramon CA 94583

MORRISON, GARRETT LOUIS, geochemistry, see previous edition

MORRISON, GEORGE HAROLD, b New York, NY, Aug 24, 21; m 52; c 3. ANALYTICAL CHEMISTRY. *Educ:* Brooklyn Col, BA, 42; Princeton Univ, MA & PhD, 48. *Prof Exp:* Instr chem, Rutgers Univ, 48-50; head inorg & anal chem, Gen Tel & Electronics Labs, 51-61; PROF CHEM, CORNELL UNIV, 61- *Concurrent Pos:* Res chemist, US AEC, 49-51; mem chem adv panel, NSF, 62-65; chmn comt anal chem, Nat Acad Sci, Nat Res Coun, 66-75; NSF sr fel, Univ Calif, San Diego, 67-68; Guggenheim fel, Univ Paris, Orsay, 74-75. *Honors & Awards:* Anal Chem Award, Am Chem Soc, 71; Medal Soc Appl Spectros, 75; Benedetti-Pichler Award, Am Microchem Soc, 77. *Mem:* Fel AAAS; Am Chem Soc; Soc Appl Spectros. *Res:* Ion microprobe; microscopy; mass spectroscopy; radiochemistry; atomic spectroscopy; trace and microanalysis. *Mailing Add:* Dept of Chem Cornell Univ Ithaca NY 14853

MORRISON, GLENN C, b New Haven, Conn, Mar 24, 33; m 55; c 4. ORGANIC CHEMISTRY. *Educ:* Brown Univ, ScB, 54; Univ Rochester, PhD(org chem), 58. *Prof Exp:* Res chemist org chem, Am Cyanamid Co, 57-60; sr scientist, 60-70, SR RES ASSOC ORG CHEM, WARNER-LAMBERT/PARKE-DAVIS PHARMACEUT RES DIV, 70- *Mem:* Am Chem Soc. *Res:* Synthetic organic medicinals. *Mailing Add:* Warner-Lambert/Parke-Davis Pharmaceut Res Div 2800 Plymouth Rd Ann Arbor MI 48106

MORRISON, HARRY, b New York, NY, Apr 25, 37; m 58; c 3. ORGANIC CHEMISTRY. *Educ:* Brandeis Univ, BS, 57; Harvard Univ, PhD(org chem), 61. *Prof Exp:* NSF-NATO fel, Swiss Fed Inst Technol, 61-62; res fel org chem, Univ Wis, 62-63; from asst prof to assoc prof, 63-76, PROF CHEM, PURDUE UNIV, 76- *Concurrent Pos:* Mem bd fels, Brandeis Univ, 65-; vis scientist, Weizman Inst, Rehovot, Israel, 72; consult, Sun Chem Corp, 72-77, Eli Lilly Co, 77- & Great Lakes Chem Co, 77- *Mem:* Interam Photochem Soc; Sigma Xi; Am Soc Photobiol; Am Chem Soc; Royal Soc Chem. *Res:* Organic photochemistry; organic reaction mechanisms. *Mailing Add:* Dept of Chem Purdue Univ West Lafayette IN 47907

MORRISON, HUGH MACGREGOR, b Liverpool, Eng, Aug 28, 36; m 63; c 3. PHYSICS. *Educ:* Univ Edinburgh, BSc, 59, PhD(physics), 65. *Prof Exp:* Asst lectr physics, Univ Edinburgh, 62-65; asst prof, 65-70, ASSOC PROF PHYSICS, UNIV WATERLOO, 70- *Mem:* Brit Inst Physics. *Res:* Dislocation enhanced diffusion at relatively low temperatures; diffusion in metals. *Mailing Add:* Dept of Physics Univ of Waterloo Waterloo ON N2L 3G1 Can

MORRISON, HUNTLY FRANK, b Montreal, Que, May 16, 38; m 70; c 2. GEOPHYSICS. *Educ:* McGill Univ, BSc, 59, MSc, 61; Univ Calif, Berkeley, PhD(eng geosci), 67. *Prof Exp:* From asst prof to assoc prof, 67-77, PROF GEOPHYS ENG, UNIV CALIF, BERKELEY, 77- *Mem:* Am Geophys Union; Soc Explor Geophys; Europ Asn Explor Geophys. *Res:* Applied geophysics; electromagnetic and electrical prospecting methods. *Mailing Add:* Dept of Mat Sci & Eng Univ of Calif Berkeley CA 94720

MORRISON, IAN KENNETH, b Barrie, Ont, Aug 5, 39; m 69; c 2. FOREST SOILS, FOREST ECOLOGY. *Educ:* Univ Toronto, BScF, 62, MScF, 64, PhD(forestry, bot), 69. *Prof Exp:* RES SCIENTIST FORESTRY, CAN FORESTRY SERV, GREAT LAKES FOREST RES CTR, 68- *Honors & Awards:* J A Bothwell Award, 80. *Mem:* Can Inst Forestry; Soil Sci Soc Am; Ont Forestry Asn; Ont Prof Foresters Asn. *Res:* Production ecology and biogeochemical cycling of elements, particularly in wild conifer forest, including effects of fertilizers on growth; effects of both timber harvesting and acid precipitation on site productivity. *Mailing Add:* Can Forestry Serv Box 490 Sault Ste Marie ON P6A 5M7 Can

MORRISON, JACK WILLIAM, b Alta, Can, Aug 8, 22; m 43; c 2. CYTOGENETICS. *Educ:* Univ Alta, BSc, 50, MSc, 51; Univ London, PhD(bot, cytol), 53. *Prof Exp:* Cytogeneticist, Cereal Crops Div, Cent Exp Farm, 53-60, supt exp farm, 60-65, RES COORDR, RES BR, CAN DEPT AGR, 65- *Mem:* Agr Inst Can. *Res:* Cytogenetics in cereals; research management. *Mailing Add:* 126-3325 Uplands Dr Ottawa ON K1V 9V3 Can

MORRISON, JAMES ALEXANDER, b Medicine Hat, Alta, June 11, 18:; m 43; c 5. PHYSICAL CHEMISTRY. *Educ:* Univ Alta, BSc, 40, MSc, 41; McGill Univ, PhD(phys chem), 43. *Prof Exp:* Chemist, Dept Nat Defense, 43-45; Nat Res Coun fel, Pa State Col, 45-46; from asst res chemist to prin res chemist, Nat Res Coun Can, 46-66, dir div pure chem, 66-69; PROF CHEM & DIR INST MAT RES MCMASTER UNIV, 69- *Mem:* Am Phys Soc; Am Chem Soc; The Chem Soc; Chem Inst Can; Can Asn Phys. *Res:* Phase equilibria; solutions of high polymers; surface chemistry; adsorption; low temperature calorimetry; imperfections in solids; thermodynamics; solid state; neutron scattering. *Mailing Add:* Inst Mat Res McMaster Univ Hamilton ON L8S 4M1 Can

MORRISON, JAMES DANIEL, b Bryn Mawr, Pa, Mar 28, 36; m 58; c 3. ORGANIC CHEMISTRY. *Educ:* Franklin & Marshall Col, BS, 58; Northwestern Univ, PhD(org chem), 63. *Prof Exp:* From teaching asst to teaching assoc gen chem, Northwestern Univ, 58-62; NSF fel, Stanford Univ, 62-63; asst prof org chem, Wake Forest Col, 63-65; from asst prof to assoc prof, 65-72, PROF ORG CHEM, UNIV NH, 72- *Concurrent Pos:* NSF sci fac fel, Univ NC, 71-72. *Res:* Asymmetric organic reactions; chiral organometallics; homogeneous hydrogenation; epoxides; Grignard reagents; novel peptides. *Mailing Add:* Dept of Chem Parsons Hall Univ of NH Durham NH 03824

MORRISON, JOHN AGNEW, b Ridgefield Park, NJ, Mar 13, 32; m 54; c 3. CHEMISTRY. *Educ:* Fairleigh Dickinson Univ, BS, 59; Rutgers Univ, PhD(org chem), 70. *Prof Exp:* From chemist to res chemist, 57-73, GROUP LEADER, LEDERLE LABS, AM CYANAMID CO, 73- *Concurrent Pos:* Lectr, Fairleigh Dickinson Univ, 60- *Mem:* AAAS; Am Chem Soc; Can Asn Res Toxicol. *Res:* Pharmacokinetics; drug metabolism. *Mailing Add:* Lederle Lab Am Cyanamid Co Middletown Rd Pearl River NY 10965

MORRISON, JOHN ALBERT, b Wichita, Kans, Dec 1, 24; m 50; c 3. WILDLIFE MANAGEMENT, ECOLOGY. *Educ:* Mont State Univ, BS, 55, MS, 57; Wash State Univ, PhD(zool), 65. *Prof Exp:* Wildlife biologist, Idaho Fish & Game Dept, 57-61; res asst zool, Wash State Univ, 61-65; res biologist, lab perinatal physiol & chief sect primate ecol, US Dept Health, Educ & Welfare, PR, 65-67; leader, Okla Coop Wildlife Res Unit, Okla State Univ, 67-75; terrestrial ecologist, Western Energy & Land Use Team, 75-78, TEAM LEADER REGIONAL INFO & TECHNOL TRANSFER, US FISH & WILDLIFE SERV, ANCHORAGE, ALASKA, 78- *Mem:* Wildlife Soc; Sigma Xi; Ecol Soc Am. *Res:* Behavior, reproductive and nutritional physiology and general ecology of birds and mammals; environmental protection and reclamation of disturbed energy development locations. *Mailing Add:* US Fish & Wildlife Serv 1011 E Tudor Rd Anchorage AK 99503

MORRISON, JOHN ALLAN, b Beckenham, Eng, June 10, 27; nat US; m 55. APPLIED MATHEMATICS. *Educ:* Univ London, BSc, 52; Brown Univ, ScM, 54, PhD(appl math), 56. *Prof Exp:* Asst appl math, Brown Univ, 52-56; MEM TECH STAFF, MATH, PHYSICS & NETWORKS DEPT, BELL LABS, 56- *Concurrent Pos:* Vis prof mechanics, Lehigh Univ, 68. *Mem:* Am Math Soc; Inst Elec & Electronic Engrs; Soc Indust & Appl Math. *Res:* Mathematical physics; nonlinear oscillations; methods of averaging; stochastic differential equations; queueing theory. *Mailing Add:* Math of Physics & Networks Dept Bell Labs 600 Mountain Ave Murray Hill NJ 07974

MORRISON, JOHN COULTER, b Hickman, Ky, Sept 11, 43; m 67; c 3. OBSTETRICS & GYNECOLOGY, BIOCHEMISTRY. *Educ:* Memphis State Univ, BS, 65, Univ Tenn, MD, 68. *Prof Exp:* Res asst biochem, Univ Tenn, Memphis, 65-66, res assoc, 67-68; intern, City of Memphis Hosps, 68-69, resident, 69-72; from instr to asst prof obstet & gynec, Univ Tenn, Memphis, 71-75, assoc prof, 75-80; MEM FAC, MED CTR, UNIV MISS, 80- *Concurrent Pos:* Chief resident, City of Memphis Hosps, 71-72, asst prof, 72- *Mem:* Am Chem Soc; Am Col Obstet & Gynec; AMA; Am Fertil Soc. *Res:* Clinical research in obstetrics and gynecology; basic research in carcinogenesis and protein biosynthesis. *Mailing Add:* Univ Miss Med Ctr 2500 N State St Jackson MS 39216

MORRISON, JOHN EDDY, JR, b Ionia, Mich, Aug 1, 39; m 62; c 3. ENGINEERING, AGRICULTURE. *Educ:* Mich State Univ, BS, 61; Univ Mich, MS, 68; Univ Ky, PhD(agr engr), 78. *Prof Exp:* Engr res, Massey-Ferguson Inc, 61-66 & Eaton Corp, 66-68; ENGR RES, SCI & EDUC ADMIN, AGR RES, USDA, 68- *Honors & Awards:* Young Designer Award, Am Soc Agr Engrs, 74. *Mem:* Am Soc Agr Eng; Sigma Xi. *Res:* Tillage; planting; microenvironment; seeding; seed germination; plant stress; system design; physical properties of agricultural materials. *Mailing Add:* 4517 Chestnut Temple TX 76501

MORRISON, JOHN JOSEPH, mathematics, see previous edition

MORRISON, KENNETH JESS, b Rudy, Ark, Feb 14, 21; m 46; c 2. AGRONOMY. *Educ:* Kans State Univ, BS, 48; Purdue Univ, Lafayette, MS, 50, PhD(agr), 67. *Prof Exp:* Assoc agronomist, 66-68, AGRONOMIST, WASH STATE UNIV, 68-, EXTEN AGRONOMIST, 52- *Mem:* Western Soc Crop Sci; Soc Agron; Soc Range Mgt; Crop Sci Soc Am. *Res:* Effect of environment on cultivars of wheat and barley; interrelation of emergence in dry soils and cold hardiness in common winter wheats. *Mailing Add:* 1300 Orion Dr Pullman WA 99163

MORRISON, KENNETH N, b Guelph, Ont, Nov 14, 17; US citizen; m 48; c 4. DENTISTRY. *Educ:* Univ Toronto, DDS, 43; Univ Wash, MSD, 52. *Prof Exp:* Instr oper dent, 48-52, asst prof, 52-57, assoc prof fixed partial dentures, 57-65, prof, 65-70, chmn dept, 57-70, PROF RESTORATIVE DENT & CHMN DEPT, SCH DENT, UNIV WASH, 70-, ASSOC DEAN, 77- *Mem:* Am Acad Crown & Bridge Prosthodont (pres, 73-74). *Res:* Restorative dentistry; recording mandibular movement. *Mailing Add:* Univ of Wash Sch of Dent Seattle WA 98195

MORRISON, MALCOLM CAMERON, b Pittsburgh, Pa, Apr 12, 42; m 74; c 2. CHEMICAL ENGINEERING. *Educ:* Calif Inst Technol, BS, 64, PhD(chem eng), 69. *Prof Exp:* Sr scientist, Havens Int, 69-70; group leader, Calgon Corp, 70-72; chief eng, Chem Systs Inc, 72-76, vpres, 76-79; VPRES, PUROPORE, 79- *Mem:* Am Inst Chem Engrs; Am Soc Qual Control; Am Soc Testing Mat; Sigma Xi; Filtration Soc. *Res:* Engineering development in membrane technology, primarily in manufacturing techniques for flat sheet phase inversion membranes. *Mailing Add:* 29002 Silverado Canyon Rd Silverado CA 92676

MORRISON, MARTIN, b Detroit, Mich, Dec 9, 21; m 47; c 4. BIOCHEMISTRY. *Educ:* Univ Mich, BS, 47; Wayne State Univ, PhD(biochem), 52. *Prof Exp:* From instr to asst prof biochem, Sch Med & Dent, Univ Rochester, 52-60; head sect respiratory enzym, Dept Biochem, City of Hope Med Ctr, Duarte, Calif, 61-67; PROF BIOCHEM, UNIV TENN, MEMPHIS, 67-; CHMN BIOCHEM DEPT, ST JUDE CHILDREN'S RES HOSP, 67- *Concurrent Pos:* USPHS career develop award, 56-61; res fel, Molteno Inst, Cambridge Univ, 60-61. *Mem:* Am Soc Biol Chemists; Am Chem Soc; Sigma Xi; Am Soc Hematol; Am Phys Soc. *Res:* Membrane structure and function; peroxidase-catalyzed halogenation reactions; mammalian peroxidases, thyroid peroxidase and lactoperoxidase. *Mailing Add:* PO Box 318 332 N Lauderdale Memphis TN 38101

MORRISON, MILTON EDWARD, b Sigourney, Iowa, July 18, 39; m 61; c 3. CHEMICAL ENGINEERING. *Educ:* Iowa State Univ, BS, 61; Calif Inst Technol, MS, 62, PhD(chem eng), 65. *Prof Exp:* Res engr, E I du Pont de Nemours & Co, Inc, 65-66; chem res engr, Chem Res Lab, Aerospace Res Labs, US Air Force, 66-69; sect head, Res Lab, Am Enka Corp, 69-70, mgr melt spinning res, 70-72, tech mgr, 72-74, plant mgr, 74-75; mgr new venture develop, Akzona, Inc, 75-77; GEN MGR CATALYST DIV, ARMAK CO, 77- *Concurrent Pos:* Adj asst prof, Univ Dayton, 66-69. *Res:* Refining and petrochemical catalysts; polymers and man-made fibers. *Mailing Add:* Armak Co 13000 Baypark Rd Pasadena TX 77507

MORRISON, NANCY DUNLAP, b Schenectady, NY, Dec 14, 46; m 66. ASTRONOMY. *Educ:* Radcliffe Col, BA, 67; Univ Hawaii, MS, 71, PhD(astron), 75. *Prof Exp:* Res assoc astron, Joint Inst Lab Astrophys, Univ Colo, Boulder, 75-78; ASST PROF ASTRON, DEPT PHYSICS & ASTRON, UNIV TOLEDO, 78- *Mem:* Am Astron Soc; AAAS. *Res:* Photometry and spectroscopy of O-type stars, utilizing these techniques to determine the masses of stars in binary systems. *Mailing Add:* Dept of Astron 2801 W Bancroft Ave Toledo OH 43606

MORRISON, NATHAN, b RI, Dec 4, 12; m; c 1. MATHEMATICAL STATISTICS. *Educ:* Brooklyn Col, AB, 32. *Prof Exp:* Prin actuary, State Dept Labor, NY, 44-61; exec assoc, Assoc Hosp Serv NY, 61-73; CONSULT, 74- *Concurrent Pos:* Consult, US War Dept, 43-46; exec secy, State Adv Coun Employ & Unemploy Ins, NY, 43-70; vis prof, Cornell Univ, 56-; lectr, Teachers Col, Columbia Univ, 59-61 & State Univ NY, Stoneybrook, 77-78; adj prof, Grad Div, Brooklyn Col, 65-67. *Mem:* Fel Am Statist Asn; Economet Soc; Am Math Soc; fel AAAS; Inst Math Statist. *Res:* Labor market analysis and unemployment insurance; mathematical physics; social insurance; hospital and medical care. *Mailing Add:* 196 Elm St New Rochelle NY 10805

MORRISON, PETER REED, b Washington, DC, Nov 11, 19; m 45; c 6. COMPARATIVE PHYSIOLOGY, ENVIRONMENTAL PHYSIOLOGY. *Educ:* Swarthmore Col, BA, 40; Harvard Univ, PhD(biol), 47. *Prof Exp:* Asst physiol, Harvard Univ, 42; asst phys chem, Harvard Med Sch, 42-46; from asst prof to prof zool & physiol, Univ Wis, 47-64; prof zoophysiol, Inst Arctic Biol, Univ Alaska, 63-80, dir inst, 66-74, adv sci dir inst, 74-80; RETIRED. *Concurrent Pos:* Guggenheim & Fulbright fel, Australia, 54-55; NSF sr fel, SAm, 59-60. *Honors & Awards:* Petersen Found Prize Contrib Animal Biometerol, 75. *Mem:* Am Soc Zoologists; Am Soc Biol Chemists; Am Physiol Soc; Am Soc Mammal; Int Soc Biometeorol. *Res:* Energy metabolism and temperature regulation in mammals; fibrinogen and blood coagulation; comparative cold and high altitude physiology; hibernation. *Mailing Add:* Inst of Arctic Biol Univ of Alaska Fairbanks AK 99701

MORRISON, PHILIP, b Somerville, NJ, Nov 7, 15; m 38. PHYSICS. *Educ:* Carnegie Inst Technol, BS, 36; Univ Calif, PhD(theoret physics), 40. *Hon Degrees:* DSc, Case Western Reserve Univ, Rutgers Univ & Denison Univ. *Prof Exp:* Instr physics, San Francisco State Col, Calif, 41 & Univ Ill, 41-42; physicist, Metall Lab, Univ Chicago, 43-44; physicist & group leader, Los Alamos Sci Lab, Univ Calif, 44-46; from assoc prof to prof physics, Cornell Univ, 46-65; PROF PHYSICS, MASS INST TECHNOL, 65- *Honors & Awards:* Pregel Prize, 55; Babson Prize, 57; Oerstad Medal, 65. *Mem:* Nat Acad Sci; Am Phys Soc; Am Astron Soc; Fedn Am Scientists (chmn, 72-76). *Res:* Applications of physics in astronomy. *Mailing Add:* Dept of Physics Mass Inst Technol Cambridge MA 02139

MORRISON, RALPH M, b Annapolis, Md, June 23, 32; m 60. PLANT PHYSIOLOGY, MICROBIOLOGY. *Educ:* Col William & Mary, BS, 55; Ind Univ, PhD(bot), 60. *Prof Exp:* From instr to asst prof biol, 60-66, ASSOC PROF BIOL, UNIV NC, GREENSBORO, 66- *Mem:* AAAS; Mycol Soc Am; Bot Soc Am; Am Soc Plant Physiologists. *Res:* Mathematical method for studying the rate of seed germination; botany; mycology. *Mailing Add:* Dept of Biol Univ NC Greensboro NC 27412

MORRISON, RICHARD CHARLES, b Lowell, Mass, Jan 24, 38; m 60; c 4. ENERGY CONVERSION. *Educ:* Princeton Univ, AB, 59; Yale Univ, MS, 61, PhD(physics), 65. *Prof Exp:* From instr to asst prof physics, New Haven Col, 63-67; asst prof, Iowa State Univ, 67-74; PROF PHYSICS, UNIV NEW HAVEN, 74- *Concurrent Pos:* Assoc physicist, Ames Lab, AEC, 67-74; sr partner, Enercon Assocs, 75-; vis prof, Bldg Res Sta, Watford, England, 77-78. *Mem:* Am Nuclear Soc; Am Phys Soc; Am Asn Physics Teachers. *Res:* Nuclear instrumentation applied to environmental research; energy production, conversion, and consumption; alternative energy systems. *Mailing Add:* Dept of Physics Univ of New Haven West Haven CT 06516

MORRISON, RICHARD DUANE, physical metallurgy, see previous edition

MORRISON, ROBERT DEAN, b Wetumka, Okla, Sept 27, 15; m 39; c 1. BIOSTATISTICS. *Educ:* Okla State Univ, BS, 38, MS, 42; NC State Col, PhD(exp statist), 57. *Prof Exp:* From asst prof to assoc prof math, 46-61, PROF STATIST, OKLA STATE UNIV, 61-. STATISTICIAN, AGR EXP STA, 57- *Mem:* Biomet Soc; Am Statist Asn. *Res:* Technometrics; experimental statistics; statistics for agricultural research. *Mailing Add:* Dept of Statist Okla State Univ Stillwater OK 74074

MORRISON, ROBERT W, JR, b Columbia, SC, Dec 5, 38; m 61; c 2. ORGANIC CHEMISTRY. *Educ:* Davidson Col, BS, 60; Princeton Univ, MA, 62, PhD(org chem), 64. *Prof Exp:* Res chemist, Chemstrand Res Ctr, Inc, Monsanto Co, 64-69; sr res chemist, 69-73, GROUP LEADER, BURROUGHS WELLCOME & CO, USA, 73- *Concurrent Pos:* From vis asst prof to adj assoc prof chem, NC State Univ, 68-71. *Mem:* Am Chem Soc. *Res:* Synthesis of nitrogen heterocyclic compounds; enzyme inhibitors. *Mailing Add:* 2718 Weldon Trail Research Triangle Park NC 27709

MORRISON, ROLLIN JOHN, b Akron, Ohio, Oct 8, 37; m 64; c 2. HIGH ENERGY PHYSICS. *Educ:* Ohio Wesleyan Univ, BA, 59; Univ Ill, MA, 61, PhD(physics), 64. *Prof Exp:* Volkswagen fel, Ger Electron Syncrotron, 64-66; res physicist, 67, from asst prof to assoc prof, 67-78, PROF PHYSICS, UNIV CALIF, SANTA BARBARA, 78- *Mem:* Am Phys Soc. *Res:* Nuclear physics using the Mössbauer effect; high energy experimental physics. *Mailing Add:* Dept of Physics Univ of Calif Santa Barbara CA 93106

MORRISON, SHERIE LEAVER, b New Eagle, Pa, July 5, 42; m 64; c 2. IMMUNOLOGY. *Educ:* Stanford Univ, BA, 63, PhD(biol), 66. *Prof Exp:* Res assoc, Dept Biol, Columbia Univ, 66-70, Cold Spring Harbor Lab Quant Biol, 70 & Dept Molecular Biol Virus Labs, Univ Calif, Berkeley, 70-71; res fel, Dept Cell Biol, Albert Einstein Col Med, 71-74; ASST PROF MICROBIOL, COL PHYSICIANS & SURGEONS, COLUMBIA UNIV, 74- *Concurrent Pos:* Mem, Allergy & Immunol Study Sect, 78-82; prin investr, Nat Cancer Inst grant, 75-82. *Honors & Awards:* Career Scientist Award, Irma T Hirschl Trust, 75. *Mem:* Am Asn Immunologists. *Res:* Genetic biochemistry of immunoglobulin production by isolating and characterizing mouse myeloma cells mutant in their production of immunoglobulin. *Mailing Add:* Columbia Univ Col Physicians & Surgeons 630 W 168th St New York NY 10032

MORRISON, SPENCER HORTON, b Madison, Wis, Apr 17, 19; m 46; c 6. VETERINARY MEDICINE, ANIMAL NUTRITION. *Educ:* Cornell Univ, BS, 39, MS, 46, PhD(animal nutrit & physiol, biochem), 49; Univ Ga, DVM, 54. *Prof Exp:* Asst animal husb, Cornell Univ, 46-48; assoc, Univ Calif, 48-49; assoc prof dairying, Univ Ga, 49-54; tech sales dir, Feed & Soy Div, Pillsbury Mills, Inc, 54-57, res dir, 57-58; dir, Agricon, 58-78; ed & mgr, Morrison Pub Co, 58-78, partner, 40-78; RETIRED. *Mem:* Fel AAAS; Am Soc Animal Sci; Poultry Sci Asn; Am Dairy Sci Asn; Am Vet Med Asn. *Res:* Animal physiology; biochemistry; feeding value of concentrates and roughages; antibiotics, vitamins; physiology of reproduction; protein synthesis in ruminants. *Mailing Add:* Box 729 Wiarton ON N0H 2T0 Can

MORRISON, STANLEY ROY, b Saskatoon, Sask, Sept 24, 26; m 49; c 3. SURFACE CHEMISTRY, SURFACE PHYSICS. *Educ:* Univ BC, BA, 48, MA, 49; Univ Pa, PhD(physics), 52. *Prof Exp:* Res assoc solid state physics, Univ Ill, 52-54; sr scientist, Sylvania Elec Prod Inc, 54-55; from staff scientist to asst dir res, Res Ctr, Minneapolis-Honeywell Regulator Co, 54-64; SR PHYSICIST, STANFORD RES INST, 64- *Concurrent Pos:* Guest prof, Inst Physics & Chem, Gottingen Univ, 71-72. *Honors & Awards:* Cert of Recognition, NASA, 73 & 74. *Mem:* Am Phys Soc. *Res:* Adsorption and catalysis; semiconductor electrochemistry; electrical and chemical properties of surfaces; influence of adsorbed gases and other surface imperfections on the electrical properties of solid state materials and devices. *Mailing Add:* Stanford Res Inst Ravenswood Ave Menlo Park CA 94025

MORRISON, SUMNER MARTIN, b Boston, Mass, Jan 23, 19; m 46; c 3. MICROBIOLOGY. *Educ:* Univ Mass, BS, 41; Purdue Univ, MS, 42; Ohio State Univ, PhD(bact), 50. *Prof Exp:* Bacteriologist, Upjohn Co, 43-46; from asst to prof microbiol, 50-70, PROF MICROBIOL & CIVIL ENG & DIR ENVIRON HEALTH SERV, COLO STATE UNIV, 70- *Concurrent Pos:* Consult, US Pub Health Serv, 65-, NIH, 69-, off water progs, Environ Protection Agency, 68- & industry. *Mem:* AAAS; Am Soc Microbiol; Int Asn Milk, Food & Environ Sanitarians; Sigma Xi; Water Pollution Control Fedn. *Res:* Enteric bacteria, epidemiology staphylococcus aureus; ice sanitation; surface and ground water; feed lot wastes; low temperature waste treatment; microbiology and geologic formations; drinking water. *Mailing Add:* Dept of Microbiol Colo State Univ Ft Collins CO 80523

MORRISON, THOMAS GOLDEN, b Chicago, Ill, Sept 28, 18; m 50; c 2. STRUCTURAL ENGINEERING, ENGINEERING PHYSICS. *Educ:* Univ Ill, BS, 49, CE, 58; NMex State Univ, ScD(appl mech), 75. *Prof Exp:* Asst resistance of mat, Univ Ill, 47-49; bridge designer, Alfred Benesch & Assocs, 49-52; pvt consult engr, 52-53; sr tech adv mech, Am Mach & Foundry Co, 53-63; sr engr, Cosmic Ray Observ, Univ Chicago, 63-68, mgr & sr engr, High Altitude Cosmic Ray Observ, 68-73; instr, NMex State Univ, 73-75; ASSOC PROF, CHRISTIAN BROTHERS COL, 75- *Concurrent Pos:* Consult, Dept Physics & Astron, Univ Md, 73- *Mem:* Fel Am Soc Civil Engrs. *Res:* Applied mechanics; mechanics of dynamically loaded shell structures; transient vibrations; buckling of structure. *Mailing Add:* Christian Brothers Col 650 E Parkway S Memphis TN 38104

MORRISON, WILEY HERBERT, III, organic chemistry, see previous edition

MORRISON, WILLIAM ALFRED, b Chicago, Ill, Mar 27, 48; m 71. INORGANIC CHEMISTRY. *Educ:* Ill Wesleyan Univ, BA, 70; Univ Kans, PhD(inorg chem), 74. *Prof Exp:* Asst prof chem, Monmouth Col, 74-75; vis asst prof, 75-76, asst prof, 76-81, ASSOC PROF CHEM, UNIV EVANSVILLE, 81- *Mem:* Am Chem Soc; AAAS. *Res:* Transition metal organometallics; carbenes; metal-metal bonds; nonaqueous solvents. *Mailing Add:* 2008 E Mulberry Evansville IN 47714

MORRISON, WILLIAM D, b Provost, Alta, Oct 16, 27; m 49; c 4. ANIMAL NUTRITION, ANIMAL PHYSIOLOGY. *Educ:* Ont Agr Col, Toronto, BSA, 49; Univ Ill, MSc, 54, PhD(animal nutrit), 55. *Prof Exp:* Territory mgr, Master Feeds Div, Maple Leaf Mills Ltd, 49-52, nutritionist, 55-57, dir nutrit & res, 57-71; CHMN DEPT ANIMAL & POULTRY SCI, UNIV GUELPH, 71-, PROF, 77- *Mem:* AAAS; Am Soc Animal Sci Asn; Poultry Sci Asn; Nutrit Soc Can; World Poultry Sci Asn. *Res:* Amino acid utilization by the chick, with special emphasis on the D isomer; protein and energy requirements of chickens and turkeys; control and prevention of certain diseases in poultry. *Mailing Add:* Dept Animal & Poultry Sci Univ Guelph Guelph ON N1G 2W1 Can

MORRISON, WILLIAM HARVEY, JR, inorganic chemistry, see previous edition

MORRISON, WILLIAM JOSEPH, b Plainfield, NJ, Feb 17, 42. GENETICS. *Educ:* Clemson Univ, BS, 65; Pa State Univ, PhD(genetics), 69. *Prof Exp:* NIH fel genetics, Hershey Med Ctr, Pa State Univ, 69-70; NIH fel, Cornell Univ, 70-73; ASSOC PROF BIOL, SHIPPENSBURG STATE COL, PA, 73- *Mem:* AAAS; Genetics Soc Am; Sigma Xi; Am Genetic Asn. *Res:* Biochemical and development genetics; Drosophila genetics. *Mailing Add:* Dept of Biol Shippensburg State Col Shippensburg PA 17257

MORRISSETTE, MAURICE CORLETTE, b Clyde, Kans, Aug 27, 21; m 45; c 3. PHYSIOLOGY, PHARMACOLOGY. *Educ:* Kans State Univ, BS & DVM, 54; Okla State Univ, MS, 56, PhD(reprod physiol), 64. *Prof Exp:* Instr physiol & pharmacol, Sch Vet Med, Okla State Univ, 54-56, asst prof, 56-57; asst prof physiol, Kans State Univ, 57-59; from asst prof to assoc prof physiol & pharmacol, Okla State Univ, 59-69; PROF & HEAD DEPT, SCH VET MED, LA STATE UNIV, BATON ROUGE, 69- *Mem:* Am Soc Vet Physiologists & Pharmacologists (pres, 72-73); Am Vet Med Asn; Am Fertil Soc; Soc Study Reproduction; Am Col Vet Pharmacologists & Therapeutics. *Res:* Reproductive physiology; veterinary medicine; female reproduction in swine and cattle; veterinary physiology, pharmacology and toxicology. *Mailing Add:* Dept of Physiol & Pharmacol Sch of Vet Med La State Univ Baton Rouge LA 70803

MORRISSEY, BRUCE WILLIAM, b Danbury, Conn, Apr 18, 42; m 67; c 1. PHYSICAL CHEMISTRY, BIOCHEMISTRY. *Educ:* Rensselaer Polytech Inst, BS, 64, PhD(theoret chem), 70; Yale Univ, MS, 66. *Prof Exp:* Nat Res Coun res assoc, Nat Bur Standards, 70-72, res chemist, Polymer Div, 72-76, prog anal, Dir Off, 76-78, prog mgr, Water Pollution Measurements, 78-81. *Mem:* Am Chem Soc; Am Soc Artificial Internal Organs. *Res:* Polymer surface chemistry; determination of the conformation and conformational changes of adsorbed proteins and their reactivity and function at surfaces. *Mailing Add:* Legal Dept E I Du Pont de Nemours & Co Inc Wilmington DE 19898

MORRISSEY, DAVID JOSEPH, b White Plains, NY, Dec 7, 53; m 75; c 1. NUCLEAR CHEMISTRY. *Educ:* Pa State Univ, BS, 75; Univ Calif, Berkeley, PhD(chem), 78. *Prof Exp:* Fel nuclear chem, Nuclear Sci Div, Lawrence Berkeley Lab, 78-81; ASST PROF CHEM, MICH STATE UNIV, 81- *Mem:* Am Chem Soc; Am Phys Soc; AAAS; Sigma Xi. *Res:* Reaction mechanisms operating in heavy-ion reactions; detection of reaction products, their kinematic properties and other characterists such as internal excitation and intrinsic spin. *Mailing Add:* Chem Dept Chem Bldg Mich State Univ East Lansing MI 48824

MORRISSEY, J EDWARD, b Grinnell, Iowa, Aug 7, 32; m 57; c 2. ZOOLOGY, PHYSIOLOGY. *Educ:* St Ambrose Col, BA, 56; Northwestern Univ, Ill, MS, 58; Univ Mo-Columbia, PhD(zool), 68. *Hon Degrees:* MHL, Ottawa Univ, 72. *Prof Exp:* Instr biol, Stevens Col, 60-65; asst prof, MacMurray Col, 68; from asst prof to assoc prof, 68-77, PROF BIOL, OTTAWA UNIV, 77- *Mem:* AAAS. *Res:* Immunological development; studies of immune responses in chickens. *Mailing Add:* Dept of Biol Ottawa Univ Ottawa KS 66067

MORRISSEY, JEREMIAH JOSEPH, biochemistry, molecular biology, see previous edition

MORRISSEY, JOHN F, b Brookline, Mass, June 16, 24; m 50; c 2. MEDICINE, GASTROENTEROLOGY. *Educ:* Dartmouth Col, AB, 46; Harvard Univ, MD, 49. *Prof Exp:* Asst prof med, Univ Wis, 56-60; asst prof, Univ Wash, 60-62; from asst prof to assoc prof, 62-71, PROF MED, UNIV WIS-MADISON, 71- *Mem:* Am Gastroenterol Asn; Am Col Physicians; Am Fedn Clin Res; Am Soc Gastrointestinal Endoscopy. *Res:* Evaluation of new instruments for digestive tract endoscopy; effects of drugs on gastrointestinal mucosa. *Mailing Add:* Univ of Wis Hosps 1300 University Ave Madison WI 53706

MORRITZ, FRED LEONARD, b Chicago, Ill, Aug 13, 22; m 49; c 4. ORGANIC CHEMISTRY. *Educ:* Univ Chicago, BS, 42; Ill Inst Technol, PhD, 53. *Prof Exp:* Res chemist, Sinclair Res Labs, Inc, 52-55; sr chemist, Armour Res Found, 55-62; chief thin films res, Autonetics Div, NAm Aviation, Inc, Calif, 62-69; VPRES PROG, INDUST & SCI CONF MGT, INC, 69- *Mem:* AAAS; Am Chem Soc. *Res:* Catalytic reactions; thin films; semiconductors. *Mailing Add:* Indust & Sci Conf Mgt Inc 222 W Adams Chicago IL 60606

MORRONE, TERRY, b New York, NY, May 30, 36; m 62; c 2. PLASMA PHYSICS. *Educ:* Columbia Univ, BS, 57, MS, 58; Polytech Inst Brooklyn, PhD(electrophys), 64. *Prof Exp:* From asst prof to assoc prof, 64-76, PROF PHYSICS, ADELPHI UNIV, 76- *Mem:* Am Phys Soc. *Mailing Add:* Dept of Physics Adelphi Univ Garden City NY 11530

MORROW, ANDREW GLENN, b Indianapolis, Ind, Nov 3, 22; m 45; c 2. SURGERY. *Educ:* Wabash Col, AB, 43; Johns Hopkins Univ, MD, 46. *Prof Exp:* Asst, 50-51, from instr to asst prof, 51-60, ASSOC PROF SURG, JOHNS HOPKINS UNIV, 60-; CHIEF CLIN SURG, NAT HEART & LUNG INST, 53- *Mem:* Soc Vascular Surg (pres, 71-72); Soc Univ Surg; Am Asn Thoracic Surg; fel Am Col Surg; Am Fedn Clin Res. *Res:* Cardiovascular surgery; diagnostic methods and allied physiology. *Mailing Add:* Johns Hopkins Univ Med Sch 34th & Charles St Baltimore MD 21218

MORROW, BARRY ALBERT, b Regina, Sask, Aug, 39. PHYSICAL CHEMISTRY, SURFACE CHEMISTRY. *Educ:* Univ BC, BSc, 61, MSc, 62; Cambridge Univ, PhD(chem), 65. *Prof Exp:* Nat Res Coun fel, 65-66; lectr chem, Univ West Indies, 66-67; ASSOC PROF CHEM, UNIV OTTAWA, 67- *Mem:* Am Chem Soc; Royal Soc Chem. *Res:* Spectroscopic studies of adsorption and catalysis; spectroscopic studies of small molecules. *Mailing Add:* 45 Birch Ottawa ON K1K 3G5 Can

MORROW, CHARLES MARTIN, b Des Moines, Iowa, Jan 28, 47; m 70; c 2. SILICONE CHEMISTRY. *Educ:* SDak Sch Mines & Technol, BS, 73. *Prof Exp:* Chemist, 74-75, adv chemist, 75-78, SR CHEMIST SILICONES, 3M CO, 78- *Mem:* Am Chem Soc. *Mailing Add:* 3M Co 3M Ctr St Paul MN 55101

MORROW, CHARLES T(ERRY), b Clarksburg, WVa, June 20, 41; c 2. AGRICULTURAL ENGINEERING, BIOENGINEERING. *Educ:* Univ WVa, BSAE, 63; Pa State Univ, MSAE, 65, PhD(eng mech), 69. *Prof Exp:* Physicist, Eastern Utilization Lab, USDA, 65; ASSOC PROF AGR ENG, PA STATE UNIV, 67- *Concurrent Pos:* NSF grant, Pa State Univ, 70-71. *Mem:* Am Soc Agr Engrs; Am Acad Mech; Am Soc Eng Educ; Soc Exp Stress Anal; Inst Food Technol. *Res:* Mechanical characterization of biological tissue; physical properties of biological materials; biological stress analysis; mechanical harvesting of fruit; bioinstrumentation. *Mailing Add:* Dept of Agr Eng 249 Agr Eng Bldg Col of Agr Pa State Univ University Park PA 16802

MORROW, CHARLES TABOR, b Gloucester, Mass, May 3, 17; m 49; c 2. ACOUSTICS. *Educ:* Harvard Univ, AB, 37, SM, 38, ScD, 46. *Prof Exp:* Engr, Harvard Univ, 37-40, res assoc physics, 40-41, spec res assoc underwater sound, 41, instr radio & radar officers training, 42-44; lectr indust electronics, Northeastern Univ, 44-45; sr proj engr, Sperry Gyroscopy Co, 46-51; res physicist, Hughes Aircraft Co, Inc, 51-55; mem sr staff, Space Technol Labs, Inc, 55-60 & Aerospace Corp, Calif, 60-67; from mem staff to staff scientist, Western Div, LTV Res Ctr, 67-69; staff scientist, Advan Technol Ctr, Inc, 69-76; CONSULT, 76- *Honors & Awards:* Vigness Award, Inst Environ Sci, 71. *Mem:* Inst Environ Sci; Acoust Soc Am; Am Inst Aeronaut & Astronaut; Inst Elec & Electronics Eng; Am Soc Eng Educ. *Res:* Vibratory gyroscopes; silencing of diving masks; study of speech in gas oxygen and diving masks and in helium atmospheres; development of microphone for divers; shock and vibration analysis; prediction of structural response to aerodynamic turbulence and rocket noise; vibration instrumentation. *Mailing Add:* 1345 Cherry Tree Ct Encinitas CA 92024

MORROW, DARRELL ROY, solid state physics, polymer physics, see previous edition

MORROW, DAVID AUSTIN, b Tyrone, Pa, Jan 14, 35; m 65; c 2. THERIOGENOLOGY. *Educ:* Pa State Univ, BS, 56; Cornell Univ, DVM, 60, PhD(theriogenol), 67. *Prof Exp:* Pvt pract vet med, 60-61; intern, Cornell Univ, 61-62, asst, 62-64, NIH fel, 64-67, res assoc, 67-68; ASSOC PROF VET MED, MICH STATE UNIV, 68- *Mem:* Soc Study Reprod; Am Col Theriogenologists. *Res:* Bovine reproductive physiology; bovine theriogenology. *Mailing Add:* Large Animal Surg & Med Mich State Univ Col of Vet Med East Lansing MI 48824

MORROW, DEAN HUSTON, b Indianapolis, Ind, June 11, 31; m 53; c 3. ANESTHESIOLOGY, CARDIOVASCULAR PHYSIOLOGY. *Educ:* Butler Univ, BS, 53; Ind Univ, MD, 56; Am Bd Anesthesiol, dipl, 63. *Prof Exp:* Staff anesthesiologist, Clin Ctr, NIH, Md, 59-61, res anesthesiologist, 62-64; assoc prof anesthesiol, Col Med, Univ Ky, 64-66, prof anesthesiol & dir dept res, 66-73, prof pharmacol, 71-73; assoc dir clin res, Travenol Labs, 73-75; PROF ANESTHESIOL & PHARMACOL, BAYLOR COL MED, 75-, V CHMN DEPT ANESTHESIOL, 78-; MED DIR, DEPT BIOMED INSTRUMENTATION, MONITORING DEPT, METHODIST HOSP, HOUSTON, 76- *Concurrent Pos:* Nat Inst Gen Med Sci res career award, 67-71; res affil, Nat Heart Inst, 61; mem comt anesthesia, Nat Res Coun-Nat Acad Sci, 63-65. *Mem:* Am Soc Anesthesiol; Int Anesthesia Res Soc; Asn Univ Anesthetists; fel Am Col Anesthesiol; Am Soc Pharmacol & Exp Therapeut. *Res:* Pharmacology. *Mailing Add:* Dept of Anesthesiol D 435 Baylor Col of Med Houston TX 77030

MORROW, DUANE FRANCIS, b Detroit, Mich, June 23, 33; m 58; c 3. PHARMACEUTICAL CHEMISTRY. *Educ:* Wayne State Univ, BS, 54; Univ Ill, PhD(chem), 57. *Prof Exp:* From assoc res chemist to sr res chemist, Parke, Davis, & Co, 57-69; from group leader to sr investr, 69-74, PRIN INVESTR, RES CTR, MEAD JOHNSON & CO, 74- *Mem:* Am Chem Soc. *Res:* Pharmaceutical chemistry; steroids; anti-fertility. *Mailing Add:* Mead Johnson Res Ctr Evansville IN 47721

MORROW, JACK I, b New York, NY, Jan 30, 33; m 58; c 1. PHYSICAL INORGANIC CHEMISTRY. *Educ:* NY Univ, BA, 54, PhD(surface chem), 59. *Prof Exp:* From asst prof to assoc prof chem, 57-73, PROF CHEM, CITY COL, NEW YORK, 73- *Mem:* Fel Am Inst Chemists; Am Chem Soc. *Res:* Inorganic reaction mechanisms and instrumentation for the study of fast reactions. *Mailing Add:* Dept of Chem City Col of New York Convent Ave & 139th St New York NY 10031

MORROW, JAMES ALLEN, JR, b Little Rock, Ark, Sept 14, 41; m 68; c 1. MATHEMATICS. *Educ:* Calif Inst Technol, BSc, 63; Stanford Univ, PhD(math), 67. *Prof Exp:* Teaching asst math, Stanford Univ, 63-67; instr, Univ Calif, 67-68, lectr, 68-69; from asst prof to assoc prof, 69-78, PROF MATH, UNIV WASH, 78- *Mem:* Am Math Soc; Math Asn Am. *Res:* Complex manifolds; singularities. *Mailing Add:* Dept of Math Univ of Wash Seattle WA 98105

MORROW, JODEAN, b Woodbine, Iowa, Oct 16, 29; m 50; c 4. ENGINEERING MECHANICS. *Educ:* Rose-Hulman Inst Technol, BS, 50; Univ Ill, MS, 54, PhD(theoret & Appl mech), 57. *Prof Exp:* Asst proj engr, State Hwy Dept, Ind, 50-51; asst theoret & appl mech, 53-54, res assoc, 54-57, from asst prof to assoc prof, 57-64, PROF THEORET & APPL MECH, UNIV ILL, URBANA, 64-, GRAD PROG COORDR, 80- *Concurrent Pos:* Vis prof, Kyoto Univ, 69. *Mem:* Am Soc Testing & Mat; Soc Mat Sci Japan. *Res:* Mechanics of materials; flow and fracture of metals; fatigue; residual stresses; cyclic stress-strain behavior; contact fatigue. *Mailing Add:* Dept of Theoret & Appl Mech Univ of Ill Urbana IL 61801

MORROW, JOHN CHARLES, III, b Hendersonville, NC, Sept 20, 24; m 50; c 3. PHYSICAL CHEMISTRY. *Educ:* Univ NC, BS, 44; Mass Inst Technol, PhD(phys chem), 49. *Prof Exp:* From asst prof to assoc prof, 49-59, PROF CHEM, UNIV NC, CHAPEL HILL, 59-, PROVOST, 68- *Concurrent Pos:* NSF fac fel, Univ Heidelberg, 62-63; dean, Col Arts & Sci & Gen Col, 66-68; NATO sr fel, Univ Hamburg, 71. *Mem:* Am Chem Soc; Am Phys Soc; Am Crystallog Asn. *Res:* X-ray crystallography. *Mailing Add:* 263 Venable Hall Univ of NC Chapel Hill NC 27514

MORROW, KENNETH JOHN, JR, b Wallace, Idaho, Nov 2, 38; m 60. GENETICS. *Educ:* Whitman Col, AB, 60; Univ Wash, MS, 62, PhD(genetics), 64. *Prof Exp:* Fulbright fel, 64; NIH fel, Inst Genetics, Univ Pavia, 64-66; res assoc biol, Inst Cancer Res, Philadelphia, 66-68; asst prof physiol & cell biol, Univ Kans, 68-73; ASSOC PROF BIOCHEM, SCH MED, TEX TECH UNIV, 73- *Mem:* Am Soc Cell Biol; Am Tissue Cult Asn. *Res:* Somatic cell genetics; genetics of mammalian somatic cell cultivated in vitro; isolation of variants and their characterization; cell culture hybridization. *Mailing Add:* Dept of Biochem Sch of Med Tex Tech Univ Lubbock TX 79409

MORROW, LARRY ALAN, b Boise, Idaho, Oct 3, 38; m 57; c 4. WEED SCIENCE. *Educ:* Utah State Univ, BS, 65; Univ Nebr, MS, 71, PhD(weed sci), 74. *Prof Exp:* Biologist, 66-74, res agronomist, Sci & Educ Admin-Agr Res, 74-80, RES AGRONOMIST, AGR RES SERV, USDA, 80- *Mem:* Am Soc Agron; Crop Sci Soc Am; Coun Agr Sci & Technol; Weed Sci Soc Am. *Res:* Annual grass weed research in small grains. *Mailing Add:* 161 Johnson Hall Wash State Univ Pullman WA 99164

MORROW, NORMAN LOUIS, b Brooklyn, NY, Feb 1, 42; m 64; c 2. PHYSICAL CHEMISTRY, ANALYTICAL CHEMISTRY. *Educ:* Stevens Inst Technol, BS, 63; Univ Conn, PhD(chem), 67. *Prof Exp:* Res chemist, Exxon Res & Eng Co, NJ, 67-70; group head anal chem, Exxon Chem Co, USA, 70-73, chief chemist, 73-75; STAFF CHEMIST, EXXON CHEM CO, 75- *Mem:* Am Chem Soc. *Res:* Process and analytical chemistry of resins, adhesives and hot melts. *Mailing Add:* Exxon Chem Co Chem Specialities Technol Div PO Box 241 Baton Rouge LA 70821

MORROW, NORMAN ROBERT, b Barking, Eng, Mar 16, 37; US citizen; m 59; c 4. CHEMICAL ENGINEERING, SURFACE CHEMISTRY. *Educ:* Univ Leeds, BSc, 59, PhD(mineral sci), 62. *Prof Exp:* Res asst mineral eng, Univ Leeds, 59-62; res assoc, Columbia Univ, 63-64; sr res scientist, Esso Prod Res Co, Standard Oil, NJ, 64-69 & Petrol Recovery Res Inst, Univ Calif, 69-77; SR RES SCIENTIST, PETROL RECOVERY RES CTR, NMEX INST, 77- *Concurrent Pos:* Consult, Sulphur Utilization & Develop, Can, 74-75. *Mem:* Petrol Soc Can Inst Mining, Metall & Petrol Engrs; Am Chem Soc; Soc Petrol Engrs; Am Inst Mining, Metall & Petrol Engrs; Can Well Logging Soc. *Res:* Hydrocarbon phase behavior; capillarity of porous materials; wettability; thermodynamics; structure of porous media; stability of interfaces; adsorption; enhanced oil recovery; low interfacial tension systems; residual oil. *Mailing Add:* Petrol Recovery Res Ctr NMex Inst Socorro NM 87801

MORROW, PAUL EDWARD, b Fairmont, WVa, Dec 27, 22; m 47; c 2. TOXICOLOGY, PHARMACOLOGY. *Educ:* Univ Ga, BS, 42, MS, 47; Univ Rochester, PhD(pharmacol), 51. *Prof Exp:* Indust hygienist, Holston Ord Works, Tenn Eastman Corp, 42-43; asst, Univ Ga, 46-47; res assoc, 47-52, from instr to prof radiation biol & pharmacol, 52-69, PROF RADIATION BIOL, PHARMACOL, TOXICOL & BIOPHYS, SCH MED & DENT, UNIV ROCHESTER, 69- *Concurrent Pos:* NIH spec res fel, Univ Göttingen, 59-60; mem, Int Comn Radiol Protection, 65-77 & Nat Coun Radiation Protection & Measurements, 69-; mem subcomt health effects fossil fuel combustion, Nat Res Coun-Nat Acad Sci. *Mem:* Health Physics Soc; Radiation Res Soc; Am Soc Pharmacol & Exp Therapeut; Am Indust Hyg Asn; Am Thoracic Soc. *Res:* Radiation toxicology; deposition and retention of inhaled dusts; dust clearance mechanisms in the lung; radioactive dust hazards; aerosols; lung models. *Mailing Add:* Sch of Med & Dent Univ of Rochester Rochester NY 14642

MORROW, RICHARD ALEXANDER, b Powassan, Ont, Apr 19, 37; m 64; c 2. PARTICLE PHYSICS. *Educ:* Queens Univ, Ont, BSc, 58; Univ BC, MSc, 59; Princeton Univ, PhD(physics), 63. *Prof Exp:* Instr physics, Princeton Univ, 63-64; asst prof, Dartmouth Col, 64-70; assoc prof, 70-78, PROF PHYSICS, UNIV MAINE, ORONO, 78- *Mem:* Am Phys Soc. *Res:* Theoretical high energy physics. *Mailing Add:* Dept of Physics Univ of Maine Orono ME 04469

MORROW, RICHARD JOSEPH, b Portland, Ore, Aug 28, 28; m 58; c 5. NUCLEAR CHEMISTRY, PHYSICAL CHEMISTRY. *Educ:* Reed Col, BA, 52; Univ Idaho, MS, 58. *Prof Exp:* Res chemist, Reed Inst, 52 & Gen Elec Co, Hanford, Wash, 53-55, opers chemist, 56-58; nuclear chemist, Lawrence Livermore Lab, Univ Calif, 58-71; staff scientist atmospheric res, Tech Appln Ctr, US Air Force, 71-80; PHYS SCI OFFICER, US ARMS CONTROL & DISARMAMENT AGENCY, 80- *Mem:* AAAS; Am Chem Soc. *Res:* Nuclear decay schemes, actinide and rare earth separation chemistry; Raman and infrared studies of metal oxide systems; fast neutron reactions; radioactivity in the environment. *Mailing Add:* 5115 Holden St Fairfax VA 22030

MORROW, ROY WAYNE, b Hopkinsville, Ky, Sept 28, 42; m 66; c 1. ANALYTICAL CHEMISTRY. *Educ:* Murray State Univ, BS, 64; Univ Tenn, MS, 67, PhD(chem), 70. *Prof Exp:* DEVELOP CHEMIST, OAK RIDGE Y-12 PLANT, NUCLEAR DIV, UNION CARBIDE CORP, 70- *Mem:* Am Chem Soc; Soc Appl Spectros; Sigma Xi. *Res:* Flame emission and atomic absorption spectroscopy; gas chromatography. *Mailing Add:* 102 E Morningside Dr Oak Ridge TN 37830

MORROW, SCOTT, b Oklahoma City, Okla, Sept 11, 20; m 45; c 3. MICROSCOPY, EXPLOSIVES. *Educ:* Case Western Reserve Univ, BS, 47, MS, 49, PhD(inorg chem), 51. *Prof Exp:* Res chemist, Mound Lab, Monsanto Chem Co, Ohio, 51-53, Mass, 53-54 & Socony Mobil Co, NJ, 54-56; proj chemist, Thiokol Chem Co, 56-66; RES CHEMIST ENERGETICS, LOGISTICS COMMAND WEAPONS LAB, US ARMY ARMAMENT RES & DEVELOP COMMAND, DOVER, 66- *Mem:* Am Chem Soc. *Res:* Solid state propellants and explosives; catalysis and combustion research; mixed crystals and solid solutions; microscopy of thin films; thermal analysis by microscopy; ignition and combustion of gun propellants; electric ignition of guns; microscopical characterization of nitrocellulose and explosives. *Mailing Add:* 36 East Shore Rd Denville NJ 07834

MORROW, TERRY ORAN, b Latrobe, Pa, May 24, 47; m 75; c 1. MICROBIAL GENETICS. *Educ:* Grove City Col, BS, 69; Bowling Green State Univ, MA, 71, PhD(microbial genetics), 73. *Prof Exp:* Asst prof biol, Univ Wis-River Falls, 73-75; ASST PROF BIOL, CLARION STATE STATE UNIV, 75- *Mem:* Am Soc Microbiol; Sigma Xi; Am Inst Biol Sci. *Res:* Genetics of Staphylococcus aureus. *Mailing Add:* Dept of Biol Clarion State Col Clarion PA 16214

MORROW, THOMAS JOHN, b Kew Gardens, NY, Mar 11, 46; m; c 3. NEUROPHYSIOLOGY, PHYSIOLOGY. *Educ:* Fordham Univ, BS, 67; Long Island Univ, MS, 69; Univ Mich, PhD(physiol), 76. *Prof Exp:* Sanitarian pub health, Nassau County Health Dept, NY, 68-69; RES ASSOC II NEUROPHYSIOL, DEPT PHYSIOL, UNIV MICH, 75- *Mem:* NY Acad Sci; Int Asn Study Pain; Am Pain Soc. *Res:* Neurophysiology of pain and somesthesis. *Mailing Add:* Dept of Physiol Univ of Mich Ann Arbor MI 48109

MORROW, WALTER E, JR, b Springfield, Mass, July 24, 28; m 51; c 3. ELECTRICAL ENGINEERING, SPACE PHYSICS. *Educ:* Mass Inst Technol, SB, 49, SM, 51. *Prof Exp:* Asst elec eng, 49-51, staff mem, 51-55, asst group leader, 55-56, group leader, 56-64, assoc div head, 64-66, div head, 66-68, from asst dir to assoc dir, 68-77, DIR, LINCOLN LAB, MASS INST TECHNOL, 77-, PROF ELEC ENG & COMPUT SCI, 78- *Concurrent Pos:* Mem comn VI, Int Union Radio Sci, 62-; consult, Dept Navy, 71-; mem, NASA Space Appln Comt, 72-; mem, Nat Res Coun, Assembly Eng Space Appln Bd Comt on Satellite Commun, 75-; mem, Defense Commun Agency

Sci Adv Group, 76-; mem, Air Force Sci Adv Bd, 78. *Honors & Awards:* Edwin Howard Armstrong Achievement Award, Inst Elec & Electronics Engrs, 76. *Mem:* Fel Nat Acad Eng; fel Inst Elec & Electronics Engrs. *Res:* Ionospheric and tropospheric radio communication and propagation; orbital scatter communication; orbital dipole experiment; communication satellites; lunar and planetary radar studies. *Mailing Add:* Lincoln Lab Mass Inst of Technol Lexington MA 02173

MORROW, WILLIAM SCOT, b New York, NY, Jan 26, 31; m 70; c 1. BIOCHEMISTRY, ANALYTICAL CHEMISTRY. *Educ:* Philadelphia Col Pharm & Sci, BS, 59; St Joseph's Col, MS, 64; Univ NC, Chapel Hill, PhD(biochem), 69. *Prof Exp:* Res technician high temperature res, Res Inst Temple Univ, 55-58; assoc res chemist electronics res, Int Resistance Co, 59-60; res biochemist ophthal res, Wills Eye Hosp, 60-63; asst prof biol, Concord Col, 68-70; ASST PROF CHEM, WOFFORD COL, 70- *Mem:* Am Chem Soc; AAAS. *Res:* Chromosomal proteins, insect biochemistry; abiogenesis: early cellular organization; development of techniques in analytical chemistry. *Mailing Add:* Dept of Chem Wofford Col Spartanburg SC 29301

MORS, WALTER B, b Sao Paulo, Brazil, Nov 23, 20; m 44; c 3. NATURAL PRODUCTS CHEMISTRY. *Educ:* Univ Sao Paulo, BS, 42; Univ Brazil, Dr(chem), 60. *Prof Exp:* Res chemist, N Inst Agr, 43-46 & Inst Agr Chem, 47-62; dir, 78-81, PROF PHYTOCHEM, NATURAL PROD RES CTR, FED UNIV RIO DE JANEIRO, 63- *Concurrent Pos:* Ed annals, Brazilian Chem Soc, 59-62 & 81; privat-docent, Nat Sch Chem, Fed Univ Rio de Janeiro, 60; res chemist, Div Agr Technol, Ministry Agr, 63-66, dir, 66-72. *Mem:* Brazilian Acad Sci (gen secy, 65-69 & 78-80); Brazilian Soc Advan Sci; Brazilian Chem Asn (secy, 52-54, pres, 80-81); Soc Econ Bot. *Res:* Chemistry of natural products. *Mailing Add:* Estrada de Jacarepagua 6784 22700 Rio de Janeiro Brazil

MORSE, BERNARD S, b New York, NY, Sept 11, 34; m 60; c 2. HEMATOLOGY, INTERNAL MEDICINE. *Educ:* NY Univ, BA, 55, BS, 56; Seton Hall Univ, MD, 60. *Prof Exp:* Asst prof med, Tufts Univ, 67-69; assoc prof, 69-77, PROF MED, COL MED & DENT, NJ, 77- *Mem:* Am Soc Hemat; Int Soc Hemat; Am Fedn Clin Res. *Res:* Erythropoiesis; ferrokinetics. *Mailing Add:* Dept of Med 100 Bergen St Newark NJ 07103

MORSE, BURT JULES, b New York, NY, June 17, 26. APPLIED MATHEMATICS. *Educ:* City Col New York, BS, 49; Columbia Univ, AM, 51; NY Univ, PhD(math), 63. *Prof Exp:* Mathematician, Vitro Corp Am, 52-54; mathematician, Int Bus Mach Corp, 54-58; res assoc electromagnetic theory, NY Univ, 58-63; asst prof math, St John's Univ, NY, 63 & Univ NMex, 63-66; res mathematician, Gen Elec Co, 66-67 & Philco-Ford Corp, Pa, 67-68; mathematician, Nat Hurricane Res Lab, 68-73, MATHEMATICIAN, METEOROGICAL SATELLITE LAB, NAT OCEANIC & ATMOSPHERIC ADMIN, 73- *Mem:* Am Math Soc; Soc Indust & Appl Math. *Res:* Geophysical fluid dynamics; numerical analysis; meteorology; wave propagation. *Mailing Add:* Nat Oceanic & Atmospheric Admin NESS MSL WWB S-314-G Washington DC 20233

MORSE, DENNIS ERVIN, b Loup City, Nebr, Mar 21, 47; m 67; c 3. HUMAN ANATOMY. *Educ:* Hastings Col, BA, 69; Univ NDak, MS, 71, PhD(anat), 73. *Prof Exp:* Asst prof anat, George Washington Univ, 73-76; ASST PROF ANAT, MED COL OHIO, 76- *Mem:* Am Asn Anatomists; Am Soc Cell Biol; Sigma Xi; Electron Micros Soc Am. *Res:* Scanning and transmission electron microscopy of cardiovascular embryology; extracellular connective tissue ultrastructure; meningeal ultrastructure. *Mailing Add:* Dept of Anat C S 10008 Toledo OH 43699

MORSE, DOUGLASS HATHAWAY, ecology, see previous edition

MORSE, EDWARD EVERETT, b Gardner, Mass, June 7, 32; m 54; c 4. MEDICINE, HEMATOLOGY. *Educ:* Harvard Univ, AB, 54, MD, 58; Am Bd Path, dipl hemat, 69, cert blood banking, 73. *Prof Exp:* Asst surgeon, Nat Cancer Inst, 60-62; USPHS spec fel hemat, Johns Hopkins Hosp, 62-63, from instr to asst prof med, Johns Hopkins Univ, 63-68; assoc prof, 68-74, PROF LAB MED, SCH MED, UNIV CONN, FARMINGTON, 74-, DIR HEMAT DIV, 68- *Concurrent Pos:* Med dir, Conn Red Cross Blood Prog, 68-74, consult, 74-; consult, Newington Vet Admin Hosp, Hartford & Bristol Hosps. *Mem:* Fel Am Col Physicians; fel Am Soc Clin Path; fel Asn Clin Scientists. *Res:* Laboratory medicine; cell preservation; transfusion therapy; platelet fibrinogen and physiology; granulocyte function. *Mailing Add:* Dept of Lab Med Univ of Conn Health Ctr Farmington CT 06032

MORSE, ERSKINE VANCE, b Peoria, Ill, June 25, 21; m 45; c 4. VETERINARY MICROBIOLOGY, VETERINARY PUBLIC HEALTH. *Educ:* Cornell Univ, DVM, 44, MS, 48, PhD(vet bact), 49; Am Col Vet Prev Med, dipl & cert vet pub health, 75. *Prof Exp:* Asst pathogenic bact, Cornell Univ, 47-48, Am Vet Med Asn fel, 48-49; from asst prof to assoc prof vet sci, Univ Wis, 49-55; from assoc prof to prof microbiol & pub health, Mich State Univ, 55-58; prof & assoc dir vet med res inst, Iowa State Univ, 58-60; prof vet sci, head dept & dean sch agr exp sta, 60-70, H W HANDLEY PROF VET MED & ENVIRON HEALTH & ASSOC DIR ENVIRON HEALTH INST, SCH VET MED, PURDUE UNIV, 70- *Concurrent Pos:* Consult, Nat Asn Stand Med Vocab, 62-, Vet Admin, 66-74, Surgeon Gen, US Air Force, 68-70, USPHS & AID; alt chmn US deleg, Conf Vet Med Educ, Food & Agr Orgn-WHO, Copenhagen, 65; judge, Int Sci Fair, 65, 68, 69, 74-79; mem, Nat Bd Vet Med Examr, 65-74; nat counr, Purdue Res Found, 65-; mem bd trustees, Am Asn Accreditation of Lab Animal Care, 68-75, vchmn bd, 72-73, chmn bd, 74-75; mem nat coun health prof educ assistance, Dept Health, Educ & Welfare, 69-72; chmn comt animal health, Nat Res Coun-Nat Acad Sci, 69-72; evaluator-consult, NCent Asn Cols & Schs-Comn Insts Higher Educ, 72-; Purdue Univ liaison rep for vet serv to Asst Surgeon Gen, US Army, 73-; reviewer, Jour, Am Vet Med Asn, 74- & Am J Vet Res, 75- *Mem:* Soc Exp Biol & Med; Conf Res Workers Animal Dis; Am Vet Med Asn (secy, 66-69); US Animal Health Asn; Am Asn Lab Animal Sci. *Res:* College administration; environmental health; pathogenic bacteriology; infectious diseases of animals; salmonellosis, leptospirosis, vibriosis, brucellosis and corynebacterial infections; laboratory animal medicine; epidemiology, microbiology and treatment of zoonotic diseases; monitoring environmental quality and water pollution. *Mailing Add:* Sch of Vet Med Purdue Univ West Lafayette IN 47907

MORSE, FRANCIS, b Pittsfield, Mass, Sept 8, 17; m 45; c 4. AEROSPACE ENGINEERING. *Educ:* Yale Univ, BE, 39; Calif Inst Technol, MS, 40. *Prof Exp:* Aeronaut engr, Lockheed Aircraft Corp, 40-42 & Goodyear Aircraft Corp, 42-45; ASSOC PROF AEROSPACE ENG, COL ENG, BOSTON UNIV, 62-, ASSOC PROF THERMODYN & ENG MECH, 63- *Concurrent Pos:* Consult eng, 46- *Mem:* Am Soc Eng Educ; Am Inst Aeronaut & Astronaut. *Res:* Lighter-than-air craft design; aircraft propulsion; engineering graphics. *Mailing Add:* Col of Eng Boston Univ Boston MA 02215

MORSE, FRED A, b Colorado Springs, Colo, Jan 11, 37; m 57; c 3. SPACE PHYSICS. *Educ:* Univ Idaho, BS, 58; Univ Mich, MS, 60, PhD(phys chem), 62. *Prof Exp:* Fel, Univ Mich, 62; instr phys chem, Univ Del, 63-64; mem tech staff, 64-68, staff scientist, 68-72, assoc dept head atmospheric physics, 72-75; head atmospheric sci dept, Space Physics Lab, Aerospace Corp, 75-80; GROUP LEADER, NEUTRON MEASUREMENT GROUP P-15, LOS ALAMOS NAT LABS, 80- *Mem:* AAAS; Am Geophys Union. *Res:* Molecular and ion beam collision; atomic spectroscopy; atmospheric and auroral physics; chemiluminescent reaction rate; aeronomy; ionospheric physics. *Mailing Add:* Neutron Measurement Group P-15 Los Alamos Nat Labs D-406 Los Alamos NM 87545

MORSE, GARTH EDWIN, b Dell Rapids, SDak, Dec 16, 21; m 48; c 2. PHYSICS. *Educ:* Pasadena Col, AB, 50; Univ Southern Calif, MS, 58; Univ Calif, Riverside, PhD(physics), 66. *Prof Exp:* Physicist, Naval Ord Test Sta, 51-52; from asst prof to prof physics, Pasadena Col, 52-73; PROF PHYSICS, POINT LOMA COL, 73-, CHMN DEPT, 77- *Concurrent Pos:* Consult, DeMornay-Bonardi, Inc, Calif, 66-67. *Mem:* Am Asn Physics Teachers. *Res:* Lattice dynamics, especially microwave frequencies. *Mailing Add:* Dept of Physics Point Loma Col San Diego CA 92106

MORSE, HERBERT CARPENTER, III, b Washington, DC, May 7, 43; m 69; c 2. IMMUNOLOGY. *Educ:* Oberlin Col, BA, 65; Harvard Univ, MD, 70. *Prof Exp:* From intern to resident, Peter Bent Brigham Hosp, 70-72; res assoc, 72-75, SR INVESTR IMMUNOL, NAT INST ALLERGY & INFECTIOUS DIS, 75- *Concurrent Pos:* Attend physician, Arthritis & Rheumatism Br, Nat Inst Arthritis, Metab & Digestive Dis, 76- *Mem:* Am Asn Immunologists. *Res:* Interactions of viruses and the immune response; regulation of antibody formation. *Mailing Add:* Lab of Microbial Immunity Nat Inst Allergy & Infectious Dis Bethesda MD 20014

MORSE, IVAN E, JR, b Fountain, Mich, Dec 9, 25; m 51; c 3. MECHANICAL ENGINEERING. *Educ:* Mich State Univ, BS, 50, MS, 54; Purdue Univ, PhD(mech eng), 61. *Prof Exp:* From instr to asst prof mech eng, Mich State Univ, 50-61; assoc prof, 61-64, prof-in-chg dept, 67-68, PROF MECH ENG, UNIV CINCINNATI, 64- *Concurrent Pos:* Mem sci adv bd & consult, KDI Corp, 66-70. *Mem:* Am Soc Eng Educ; Am Soc Mech Engrs. *Res:* Machine tool vibrations; signature analysis; seismic qualification testing and design of mechanical equipment. *Mailing Add:* Dept of Mech Eng Univ of Cincinnati Cincinnati OH 45221

MORSE, J(EROME) G(ILBERT), b New York, NY, Oct 22, 21; m 49; c 2. ENERGY TECHNOLOGY, NUCLEAR ENGINEERING. *Educ:* Univ Pa, MS, 47; Ill Inst Technol, PhD(chem), 52. *Prof Exp:* Res chemist, Gen Elec Co, 51-52; asst prof chem, Univ Miami, 52-55; dir small power systs depts, Martin Co, 55-64, tech dir, Hispano-Martin, Paris, 65-67; mem tech staff res & develop, Martin Marietta Corp, Colo, 67, mgr space sci, 67-74; dep dir, Colo Energy Res Inst, 74-77; PRES, MORSE ASSOCS, INC, 77- *Concurrent Pos:* Staff consult, Oak Ridge Inst Nuclear Studies, 58-64; lectr, Colo Sch Mines, adj assoc prof, Dept of Physics, 76-; consult, Colo Energy Res Inst, 77- & US Dept Energy, 78- *Mem:* Am Chem Soc; fel Am Nuclear Soc; Sigma Xi. *Res:* Uranium exploration; environmental radiation. *Mailing Add:* 2221 East St Golden CO 80401

MORSE, JANE H, b Grosse Pointe, Mich, Aug 27, 29; m 56; c 2. IMMUNOLOGY. *Educ:* Smith Col, BA, 51; Columbia Univ, MD, 55. *Prof Exp:* Res assoc immunol, Rockefeller Univ, 60-62; instr & asst prof med, 62-75, ASSOC PROF CLIN MED, COL PHYSICIANS & SURGEONS, COLUMBIA UNIV, 75- *Concurrent Pos:* Mem, Allergy & Immunol Study Sect, USPHS, 73-77. *Mem:* Am Asn Immunologists; Am Rheumatism Asn. *Res:* Immune complexes and complement in autoimmune diseases; the role of inhibitors in the immune response. *Mailing Add:* 630 W 168th St Dept of Med New York NY 10032

MORSE, JOHN THOMAS, b Oakland, Calif, Apr 30, 35; m 60; c 2. ENVIRONMENTAL PHYSIOLOGY. *Educ:* Ore State Univ, BS, 56; Univ Calif, Davis, PhD(physiol), 68. *Prof Exp:* Pvt indust res grant, 68-69, asst prof, 68-72, ASSOC PROF PHYSIOL, CALIF STATE UNIV, SACRAMENTO, 72- *Mem:* Am Physiol Soc; Am Inst Biol Sci. *Res:* Physiological adaptations favoring physical work performance in varying environments. *Mailing Add:* 8151 Excelsior Rd Sacramento CA 95823

MORSE, JOHN WILBUR, b Ft Dodge, Iowa, Nov 11, 46. GEOCHEMISTRY. *Educ:* Univ Minn, BS, 69; Yale Univ, MPhil, 71, PhD(geol), 73. *Prof Exp:* Asst prof oceanog, Fla State Univ, 73-76; ASSOC PROF MARINE & ATMOSPHERIC CHEM, UNIV MIAMI, 76- *Mem:* Am Geophys Union; Int Asn Geochemists & Cosmochemists; Am Chem Soc. *Res:* Application of chemical kinetics and surface chemistry to diagenetic reactions in marine sediment. *Mailing Add:* RSMAS-Univ Miami 4600 Rickenbacker Causeway Miami FL 33149

MORSE, JOSEPH GRANT, b Colorado Springs, Colo, Oct 16, 39; m 63; c 2. INORGANIC CHEMISTRY. *Educ:* SDak State Col, BS, 61; Univ Mich, MS, 63, PhD(inorg chem), 67. *Prof Exp:* Lectr, Univ Mich, 65-66; asst prof, 68-74, ASSOC PROF CHEM, UTAH STATE UNIV, 74- *Mem:* AAAS; Am Chem Soc. *Res:* Synthesis and properties of new ligands, especially of phosphorus group; chemistry of pi-acid chelates; photochemistry of fluorophosphines. *Mailing Add:* Dept of Chem & Biochem Utah State Univ Logan UT 84332

MORSE, JOSEPH GRANT, b Ithaca, NY, May 26, 53; m 79. ENTOMOLOGY. *Educ:* Cornell Univ, BS, 75; Mich State Univ, MS(systs sci), 77, MS,(entom), 78, PhD(entom), 81. *Prof Exp:* ASST PROF ENTOM, UNIV CALIF, RIVERSIDE, 81- *Mem:* Entom Soc Am. *Res:* Utilization of quantitative research techniques in integrated pest management research programs; pest management of citrus and subtropical fruit crops. *Mailing Add:* Dept Entom Univ Calif Riverside CA 92521

MORSE, KAREN W, b Monroe, Mich, May 8, 40; m 63; c 1. INORGANIC CHEMISTRY. *Educ:* Denison Univ, BSc, 62; Univ Mich, MSc, 64, PhD(chem), 67. *Prof Exp:* Res scientist, Ballistic Res Inst, 67-68; lectr, 68-69, asst prof, 69-76, ASSOC PROF CHEM, UTAH STATE UNIV, 76- *Mem:* Am Chem Soc. *Res:* Synthesis and behavior of fluorophosphine derivatives; synthesis and photochemical behavior of transition metal copper complexes of borohydrides and substituted borohydrides. *Mailing Add:* Dept of Chem & Biochem Utah State Univ Logan UT 84322

MORSE, LEWIS DAVID, b Brooklyn, NY, Oct 29, 24; m 46; c 1. BIOCHEMISTRY, SYNTHETIC POLYMER RESEARCH. *Educ:* NY Univ, BA, 48; Brooklyn Col, MA, 52. *Prof Exp:* Res chemist, Col Physicians & Surgeons, Columbia Univ, 50-51 & Stein Hall Corp, 51-55; chief chemist & prod supvr, Myer 1890 Beverages, Inc, 55-59; proj leader, Am Sugar Refining Co, Inc, 59-63 & Nat Cash Register Co, 63-64; mgr prod res, Ionac Chem Co, NJ, 64-67; prod develop fel, 67, group leader fine chem, Prod Develop, Rahway, 67-80, RES ASSOC, CALGON CORP, MERCK & CO, INC, PITTSBURGH, PA, 80- *Mem:* AAAS; Am Chem Soc; Inst Food Technologists. *Res:* Polymer chemistry and synthesis; microencapsulation; ion exchange; carbonated beverage technology; flavor compounding; enzyme, sugar, starch, adhesive and microbiological chemistry; statistical design and analysis of experiments; vitamin technology in foods and medicinals; nutrition; antiseptics. *Mailing Add:* 2464 Southvue Dr Pittsburgh PA 15241

MORSE, MARY PATRICIA, b Hyannis, Mass, Aug 29, 38. MALACOLOGY. *Educ:* Bates Col, BS, 60; Univ NH, MS, 62, PhD(zool), 66. *Prof Exp:* Instr biol, Suffolk Univ, 62-63; from instr to asst prof, 64-70, ASSOC PROF BIOL, MARINE SCI INST, NORTHEASTERN UNIV, 70- *Concurrent Pos:* Trustee, Bates Col & Charles River Acad; res assoc malacol, Harvard Univ, 74-; Brasilian grant to study interstitial mollusks, 75; Fulbright fel, Fiji Islands, 78-79. *Mem:* Am Soc Zoologists; Malacol Soc London; Sigma Xi. *Res:* Systematics and biology of interstitial molluscs; fine structural studies of molluscan epithelia. *Mailing Add:* Marine Sci Inst Northeastern Univ Nahant MA 01908

MORSE, MELVIN LAURANCE, b Hopkinton, Mass, Feb 23, 21; m 49; c 2. GENETICS. *Educ:* Univ NH, BS, 44; Univ Ky, MS, 47; Univ Wis, PhD(genetics), 55. *Prof Exp:* Jr biologist radiation res, Biol Div, Oak Ridge Nat Lab, 47-51; res assoc genetics, Univ Wis, 55-56; res microbiologist, Webb-Waring Lung Inst, 56-58, asst dir inst, 59-71, actg dir, 71-72, from asst prof to assoc prof, Med Ctr, 56-66, vchmn dept, 71-73, PROF BIOPHYS & GENETICS, MED CTR, UNIV COLO, 66-, HEAD DIV GENETICS, WEBB-WARING LUNG INST, 56-, JAMES J WARING CHAIR BIOL, 60-, ASSOC DEAN GRAD SCH, 76- *Concurrent Pos:* USPHS sr res fel, 61, career develop award, 62-; consult, Army Med Res & Nutrit Lab, Fitzsimons Gen Hosp, 60-70; foreign res, Inst Molecular Biol, Univ Geneva, 62-63. *Mem:* Am Soc Microbiol; Genetics Soc Am; Biophys Soc; Am Genetic Asn; Soc Human Genetics. *Res:* Biochemical genetics; biophysics; microbiology. *Mailing Add:* Webb-Waring Lung Inst Univ of Colo Med Ctr Denver CO 80262

MORSE, N(ORMAN) L(ESTER), b Bethlehem, Pa, Nov 25, 17; m 45; c 3. CHEMICAL ENGINEERING. *Educ:* Lehigh Univ, BS, 40; Univ Rochester, PhD(phys chem), 43. *Prof Exp:* Petrol technologist, Shell Oil Co, Inc, 43-60, asst chief res technologist, Houston Res Lab, Shell Oil Co Refinery, Wood River, Ill, 60-70, Tech Adv, 70-76; TECH ADV, SHELL DEVELOP CO, 76- *Mem:* AAAS; Am Chem Soc; Am Inst Chem Engrs. *Res:* Mechanism; kinetics of catalytic reactions of hydrocarbons. *Mailing Add:* Shell Develop Co PO Box 1380 Houston TX 77001

MORSE, PHILIP DEXTER, II, b Bakersfield, Calif, Oct 17, 44; m 66; c 2. MOLECULAR BIOLOGY. *Educ:* Univ Calif, Davis, BA, 67, PhD(zool), 72. *Prof Exp:* Res assoc pharmacol, Univ Berne, 71-73; res assoc biophys, Pa State Univ, 73-75; ASST PROF BIOL, WAYNE STATE UNIV, 75- *Mem:* AAAS; Biophys Soc. *Res:* Structure and function of biological membranes using electron spin resonance and freeze-fracture electron microscopy; interrelationships between intracellular water order and membrane structure. *Mailing Add:* Dept of Biol Wayne State Univ Detroit MI 48202

MORSE, PHILIP MCCORD, b Shreveport, La, Aug 6, 03; m; c 2. THEORETICAL PHYSICS, OPERATIONS RESEARCH. *Educ:* Case Inst Technol, BS, 26; Princeton Univ, AM, 27, PhD(physics), 29. *Hon Degrees:* ScD, Case Inst Technol, 40. *Prof Exp:* Instr physics, Princeton Univ, 29-30; Int Res fel, Univ Munich & Cambridge Univ, 30-31; from asst prof to prof physics, 31-69, dir underwater sound lab, 39-42, dir comput ctr, 56-67, chmn fac, 58-60, dir opers res ctr, 58-69, EMER LECTR PHYSICS, MASS INST TECHNOL, 69- *Concurrent Pos:* Supvr sound control lab, Harvard Univ, 39-45; dir opers res group, Off Sci Res & Develop, US Navy, 42-46 & Brookhaven Nat Lab, 46-48; dep dir weapons systs eval group, Off Secy Defense, Nat Mil Estab, 49-50; ed, Annals of Physics, 57-77; dir, Control Data Corp, 64-; mem bd trustees, New Eng Regional Comput Net, 68-76; trustee, Rand Corp, 48-62, Inst Defense Anal, 55-60, Adage Inc, 58-64, Anal Serv Inc, 62-72 & Coun Libr Resources, 64- Chmn comt revision math tables, Nat Res Coun, 54-64, mem comt uses comput, 60-65, comt natural resources, 62-65; chmn adv panel opers res, Sci Adv, NATO, 59-65; chmn adv panel opers res, Orgn Econ Coop & Develop, 62-68; mem telecommun sci panel, Dept Com, 65-66; chmn, Nat Acad Sci Panel Opers Res Developing Countries, 74- *Honors & Awards:* Presidential Medal for Merit, 46; Silver Medal, Brit Oper Res Soc, 65; Lanchester Prize, Opers Res Soc Am, 69, Gold Medal, 74. *Mem:* Fel Nat Acad Sci; AAAS; fel Am Acad Arts & Sci; fel Acoust Soc Am (vpres, 46, pres, 50); fel Am Phys Soc (vpres, 70-71, pres, 71-72). *Res:* Acoustics; search theory; library operation; computer networking. *Mailing Add:* 126 Wildwood St Winchester MA 01890

MORSE, R(ICHARD) A(RDEN), b Independence, Kans, Feb 18, 20; m 42; c 1. PETROLEUM ENGINEERING. *Educ:* Univ Okla, BS, 42; Pa State Univ, MS, 47. *Prof Exp:* Petrol Engr, Halliburton Oilwell Cementing Co, 42-43; staff engr, Superior Oil Co, 43-44 & West Edmond Eng Asn, 44-45; asst, Pa State Col, 45-47; res sect head, Stanolind Oil & Gas Co, 47-55; assoc dir res, Gulf Res & Develop Co, Pa, 55-64; mgr, Mene Grande Oil Co, Venezuela, 64-70; PROF PETROL ENG, TEX A&M UNIV, 70- *Mem:* Am Inst Mining, Metall & Petrol Engrs (vpres, 60-). *Res:* Methods of recovery of oil and gas from natural reservoirs; oil well drilling, completion and stimulation. *Mailing Add:* Dept of Petrol Eng Tex A&M Univ College Station TX 77840

MORSE, RICHARD KENNETH, developmental physiology, see previous edition

MORSE, RICHARD STETSON, b North Abington, Mass, Aug 19, 11; m 35; c 2. PHYSICS. *Educ:* Mass Inst Technol, SB, 33. *Hon Degrees:* DSc, Polytech Inst Brooklyn, 59; PhD(eng), Clark Univ, 60. *Prof Exp:* Mem staff, Mass Inst Technol, 35; physicist, Eastman Kodak Co & Distillation Prod, Inc, NY, 35-40; pres, Nat Res Corp, 40-59; dir res & Asst Secy Army, 59-61; sr lectr, Sloan Sch Mgt, Mass Inst Technol, 62-72; PRES, MASS INST TECHNOL DEVELOP FOUND, INC, 72- *Concurrent Pos:* Dir, Dresser Industs, Inc, Compugraphic Corp, ECO, Inc; trustee, Midwest Res Inst, Boston Mus Sci, Marine Biol Lab, Woods Hole Oceanog Inst & Aerospace Corp, 74-; chmn bd vis, Air Force Systs Command; chmn & dir, Sci Energy Systs Corp; former mem, Defense Sci Bd & tech adv, Panel Biol & Chem Warfare, US Dept Defense; US Dept Com; chmn, Army Sci Adv Panel; mem gen adv comt, Energy Res & Develop Admin, 75- *Honors & Awards:* Dept of Army Distinguished Civilian Serv Medal. *Mem:* Nat Acad Eng; Am Chem Soc. *Res:* High vacuum technology; vacuum metallurgy; dehydration; evaporation of metals; vacuum pumps and gauges; photo processes. *Mailing Add:* Mass Inst Technol Develop Found Inc 77 Massachusetts Ave Cambridge MA 02139

MORSE, ROBERT MALCOLM, b Haverhill, Mass, Dec 21, 38; m 61; c 2. HIGH ENERGY PHYSICS. *Educ:* San Jose State Col, BA, 63; Univ Wis-Madison, MA, 65, PhD(physics), 69. *Prof Exp:* Res assoc physics, Univ Wis, 69-70; res assoc physics, Univ Colo, Boulder, 70-76, asst prof physics & astrophys, 74-76; asst prof, Univ Pa, 76-77; ASSOC SCIENTIST, UNIV WIS, 77- *Mem:* Am Phys Soc. *Res:* Weak interactions of strange particles; electron-positron storage ring physics; hadron calorimetery. *Mailing Add:* 207 S Allen Madison WI 53705

MORSE, ROBERT WARREN, b Boston, Mass, May 25, 21; m 43; c 3. PHYSICS. *Educ:* Bowdoin Col, BS, 43; Brown Univ, ScM, 47, PhD(physics), 49. *Hon Degrees:* ScD, Bowdoin Col, 66. *Prof Exp:* From asst prof to prof physics & head dept, Brown Univ, 49-62, dean col, 62-64; Asst Secy Navy for Res & Develop, 64-66; pres, Case Inst Technol, 66-67; pres, Case Western Reserve Univ, 67-71; dir res, 71-73, assoc dir & dean, 73-79, SR SCIENTIST, WOODS HOLE OCEANOG INST, 79- *Concurrent Pos:* Howard Found fel, Cambridge Univ, 54-55; mem comt undersea warfare, Nat Acad Sci, 58-64, chmn, 62-64, chmn bd human resources, 70-74, chmn ocean affairs bd, 71-75, comt emergency mgt, 81-82; chmn interagency comt oceanog, Fed Coun Sci & Technol, 64-66; mem, Naval Res Adv Comt, 71-74. *Mem:* Acoust Soc Am (pres, 65-66); fel Am Phys Soc; fel Am Acad Arts & Sci. *Res:* Ultrasonics and underwater sound; superconductivity and properties of electrons in metals. *Mailing Add:* Box 574 N Falmouth MA 02556

MORSE, ROGER ALFRED, b Saugerties, NY, July 5, 27; m 51; c 3. ENTOMOLOGY, APICULTURE. *Educ:* Cornell Univ, BS, 50, MS, 53, PhD(entom), 55. *Prof Exp:* Entomologist, State Plant Bd, Fla, 55-57; asst prof hort, Univ Mass, 57; from asst prof to assoc prof, 57-72, PROF APICULT, CORNELL UNIV, 72- *Concurrent Pos:* Vis prof, Col Agr, Univ Philippines, 68. *Mem:* Fel AAAS; Entom Soc Am; Bee Res Asn. *Res:* Evolution of the Apoidea; toxicity of insecticides to honey bees, honey wine, honey production and handling; social structure of honey bee colony. *Mailing Add:* Dept of Entom Cornell Univ Ithaca NY 14850

MORSE, RONALD LOYD, b Kearney, Nebr, May 15, 40; m 63; c 2. INDUSTRIAL ORGANIC CHEMISTRY. *Educ:* Univ Nebr, BS, 63; Univ Wis, PhD(org chem), 68. *Prof Exp:* sr res chemist, 67-80, SR RES SPECIALIST, MONSANTO INDUST CHEM CO, 80- *Mem:* Am Chem Soc. *Mailing Add:* 876 Holly Ridge Rd Ballwin MO 63011

MORSE, ROY EARL, b Boston, Mass, Nov 3, 16. FOOD SCIENCE. *Educ:* Univ Mass, BS, 40, MS, 41, PhD(food technol), 48. *Prof Exp:* Control food technologist, Hills Bros Co, NY, 41; instr food technol, Ore State Col, 41-42; packaging researcher, Owens-Ill Co, Calif, 42-43; prod mgr, Featherweight Foods, Maine, 43-44; instr food technol, Univ Mass, 46-48; assoc prof, Univ Ga, 48-49; group leader, Food Lab, Monsanto Chem Co, 49-51; dir res, Kingan & Co, Ind, 51-53 & Wm J Stange Co, 53-55; chmn dept food sci, Rutgers Univ, 55-59; vpres tech res, Thomas J Lipton, Inc, 59-66; vpres res, Pepsi Co, Inc, NY, 66-69; prof food sci, Rutgers Univ, New Brunswick, 69-80; SR VPRES, RJ REYNOLDS TOBACCO CO, WINSTON-SALEM, 80- *Concurrent Pos:* Mem nutrit adv comt, Govt Tunisia; ed, Biol Abstracts; vis prof, Univ New South Wales, 75-76 & Univ Iceland, 76. *Mem:* Fel AAAS; Am Chem Soc; Inst Food Technologists; Am Mgt Soc. *Mailing Add:* RJ Reynolds Tobacco Co Reynolds Bldg Winston-Salem NC 27101

MORSE, STEARNS ANTHONY, b Hanover, NH, Jan 3, 31; m 60; c 3. PETROLOGY. *Educ:* Dartmouth Col, AB, 52; McGill Univ, MSc, 58, PhD(geol), 62. *Prof Exp:* Mem, Blue Dolphin Labrador Exped, 49, 51, 52 & 54; petrologist, Brit Nfld Explor Ltd, Can, 59-61; geologist, Cold Regions Res & Eng Lab, US Army, 62; from asst prof to assoc prof geol, Franklin & Marshall Col, 62-71; assoc prof, 71-74, PROF GEOL, UNIV MASS, AMHERST, 74- *Concurrent Pos:* Carnegie Corp fel, Carnegie Inst Geophys Lab, Washington, DC, 67-68. *Honors & Awards:* Peacock Mem Prize, 62. *Mem:* AAAS; Geol Soc Am; Mineral Soc Am; Am Geophys Union; Mineral Asn Can. *Res:* Geochemistry; igneous and metamorphic petrology; layered intrusions and magma evolution; feldspars; anorthosites. *Mailing Add:* Dept of Geol Univ of Mass Amherst MA 01003

MORSE, STEPHEN ALLEN, b Los Angeles, Calif, Apr 11, 42; m 74. MICROBIOLOGY. *Educ:* San Jose State Col, BA, 64; Univ NC, MSPH, 66, PhD(microbiol), 69. *Prof Exp:* NSF fel, Univ Ga, 69-70; asst prof biol, Southeastern Mass Univ, 70-71; res assoc microbiol, Sch Pub Health, Harvard Univ, 71-72, asst prof, 72-74; asst prof microbiol, 74-75, ASSOC PROF MICROBIOL, HEALTH SCI CTR, UNIV ORE, 75- *Concurrent Pos:* Vis lectr, Sch Pub Health, Univ Calif, Los Angeles, 72; sr instr clin bact, Harvard Med Sch, 72-74. *Honors & Awards:* Mary Poston Award, NC Br, Am Soc Microbiol, 65. *Mem:* AAAS; Am Soc Microbiol; Soc Gen Microbiol; Am Veneral Dis Asn; Soc Exp Biol Med. *Res:* Physiology and metabolism of infectious agents. *Mailing Add:* Dept of Microbiol & Immunol Univ of Ore Health Sci Ctr Portland OR 97201

MORSE, STEPHEN IVOR, microbiology, medicine, see previous edition

MORSE, STEPHEN SCOTT, b New York, NY, Nov 22, 51; m 81. PATHOGENIC MICROBIOLOGY. *Educ:* City Col, City Univ NY, BS, 71; Univ Wis, Madison, MS, 74, PhD(bacteriol & virol), 77. *Prof Exp:* NSF trainee, Dept Bacteriol, Univ Wis-Madison, 71-72, res asst, Dept Bacteriol, Virol & Slow Virus Lab, Dept Vet Sci, 72-77; res fel microbiol & infectious dis, Med Col, Va Commonwealth Univ, 77-79, Nat Cancer Inst fel, 79-80, instr microbiol, 80-81; ASST PROF MICROBIOL, RUTGERS UNIV, 81- *Concurrent Pos:* Reader, Marine Biol Lab, Woods Hole Mass, 81; fac mem, Bur Biol Res & fel, Rutgers Col, Rutgers Univ, 81. *Mem:* Am Soc Microbiol; Biophys Soc; AAAS; Sigma Xi; NY Acad Sci. *Res:* Pathogenesis of infectious disease; viral immunology; mechanisms of host resistance to infection; phagocytic cell function; virus-macrophage interactions especially herpesvirus; role of macrophages in host defense against infecton; macrophage, mononuclear phagocyte cell biology. *Mailing Add:* Dept Biol Sci Div Microbiol Nelson Biol Lab Rutgers Univ New Brunswick NJ 08903

MORSE, THEODORE FREDERICK, b New York, NY, Feb 28, 32; m 55; c 2. ENGINEERING. *Educ:* Duke Univ, BA, 53, MA, 54; Hartford Univ, BSc, 58; Rennselaer Polytech Inst, MSc, 59; Northwestern Univ, PhD(eng), 61. *Prof Exp:* Res engr, Pratt & Whitney Aircraft Div, United Aircraft Corp, 55-59; sr res engr, Aeronaut Res Assocs Princeton, Inc, 61-63; from asst prof to assoc prof eng, 64-67, PROF ENG, BROWN UNIV, 67- *Concurrent Pos:* Sr Fulbright res fel, Ger Exp Estab Air & Space Res, Porz-Wahn, Ger, 69-70. *Res:* Kinetic theory of gases; fluid mechanics; laser isotope separation; gas laser theory. *Mailing Add:* Div of Eng Brown Univ Providence RI 02912

MORSE, WILLIAM HERBERT, b Yorktown, Va, May 30, 28; m 58; c 4. PHARMACOLOGY. *Educ:* Univ Va, BA, 50, MA, 52; Harvard Univ, PhD(psychol), 55. *Prof Exp:* Res fels psychol, 55-58, from instr to assoc prof psychol, Med Sch, 58-76, PROF PSYCHOBIOL, MED SCH, HARVARD UNIV, 76- *Mem:* Am Soc Pharmacol & Exp Therapeut. *Res:* Behavioral pharmacology and physiology. *Mailing Add:* Lab of Psychobiol Harvard Med Sch Boston MA 02115

MORT, ANDREW JAMES, b Kent, Eng, Apr 28, 51; m 80. PLANT POLYSACCHARIDE, POLYSACCHARIDE CHEMISTRY. *Educ:* McGill Univ, Montreal, BSc, 71; Mich State Univ, PhD(biochem),78. *Prof Exp:* Res asst, C F Kettering Res Lab, 77-81; ASST PROF, DEPT BIOCHEM, OKLA STATE UNIV, 81- *Mem:* Am Chem Soc; Am Soc Plant Physiologists; Am Phytopathol Soc. *Res:* Characterization of polysaccharides important in legume-rhizobium interactions; development of new methods for the determination of polysaccharide structure; use of liquid hydrogen fluoride to convert cellulose wastes to glucose. *Mailing Add:* Dept Biochem Okla State Univ Stillwater OK 74078

MORT, JOSEPH, b Oldham, Eng, Sept 21, 36; m 64; c 2. SOLID STATE PHYSICS. *Educ:* Univ Leicester, BSc, 59, PhD(physics), 62. *Prof Exp:* Res assoc physics, Univ Wis, 65-66; RES MGR PHYS SCI, XEROX CORP, 66- *Concurrent Pos:* Fulbright fel, Univ Ill, Urbana, 62-64; mem solid state sci panel, Nat Acad Sci, 78- *Mem:* Am Phys Soc. *Res:* Amorphous solids including polymers with principal interests in photoelectronic and transport properties, electrography and electronic materials and devices; amorphous inorganic and organic solids. *Mailing Add:* Xerox Webster Res Ctr Xerox Corp Xerox Sq W114 Rochester NY 14644

MORTARA, LORNE B, b Chicago, Ill, Sept 29, 32; m 57; c 4. HIGH ENERGY PHYSICS. *Educ:* Purdue Univ, BS, 53, PhD(physics), 63. *Prof Exp:* Asst physics, Purdue Univ, 56-63; res assoc, Univ Ariz, 63-65; sr scientist physics instrumentation, Albuquerque Lab, Edgerton, Germeshausen & Grier, Inc, 65-68; SR ENG PHYSICIST, AURA, INC, 68- *Mem:* AAAS; Am Phys Soc. *Res:* Instrumentation design; application of computer systems. *Mailing Add:* Kitt Peak Nat Observ Box 26732 Tucson AZ 85726

MORTEL, RODRIGUE, b Saint-Marc, Haiti, Dec 3, 33; m 71. OBSTETRICS & GYNECOLOGY. *Educ:* Univ Haiti, MD, 60; Am Bd Obstet & Gynec, dipl, 70. *Prof Exp:* Asst clin instr obstet & gynec, Hahnemann Med Col & Hosp, 67-68, instr, 68-70, sr instr, 70-71, asst prof, 71-72; asst prof obstet & gynec, 72-74, ASSOC PROF OBSTET & GYNEC, HERSHEY MED CTR, PA STATE UNIV, 74-, CHIEF DIV GYNEC ONCOL, 74- *Concurrent Pos:* USPHS grant gynec oncol, Hahnemann Med Col & Hosp, 68-69; USPHS grant, Mem Hosp Cancer & Allied Dis, New York, 69-70. *Mem:* Fel Am Col Obstet & Gynec; fel Am Col Surgeons; James Ewing Soc; NY Acad Sci. *Res:* Clinical research in gynecologic oncology. *Mailing Add:* Dept of Obstet & Gynec Hershey Med Ctr Pa State Univ Hershey PA 17033

MORTENSEN, EARL MILLER, b Salt Lake City, Utah, June 25, 33; m 62; c 4. PHYSICAL CHEMISTRY. *Educ:* Univ Utah, BA, 55, PhD(chem), 59. *Prof Exp:* NSF fel chem, Univ Calif, Berkeley, 59-60, lectr, 60-61, chemist, Radiation Lab, 60-62; asst prof chem, Univ Mass, Amherst, 62-69; ASSOC PROF CHEM, CLEVELAND STATE UNIV, 69- *Concurrent Pos:* NSF grant, 64-66; NSF grant, Univ Mass, Amherst, 68-69. *Mem:* Am Phys Soc; Am Chem Soc. *Res:* Theoretical reaction kinetics; polarizabilities and anisotropies of molecules; computer applications to chemical education. *Mailing Add:* Dept of Chem Cleveland State Univ Cleveland OH 44115

MORTENSEN, GLEN ALBERT, b Moscow, Idaho, Dec 1, 33; m 59; c 4. NUCLEAR ENGINEERING. *Educ:* Univ Idaho, BS, 55; Oak Ridge Sch Reactor Technol, dipl, 56; Univ Calif, Berkeley, PhD(nuclear eng), 63. *Prof Exp:* Engr, USAEC, Washington, DC, 56-58, Phillips Petrol Co, Idaho, 63-69, Idaho Nuclear Corp, 69-70 & Aerojet Nuclear Corp, 70-75; engr, 75-80, MGR COMPUT SCI DIV, INTERMOUNTAIN TECHNOLOGIES INC, 80- *Concurrent Pos:* Affil prof, Nat Reactor Testing Sta Educ Prog, Univ Idaho, 63- *Mem:* Am Nuclear Soc; Asn Comput Mach. *Res:* Database management systems; numerical methods; fluid flow; reactor kinetics. *Mailing Add:* Intermountain Technologies Inc PO Box 1604 1400 Benton St Idaho Falls ID 83401

MORTENSEN, HARLEY EUGENE, b Albuquerque, NMex, Mar 1, 31; m 52; c 5. ORGANIC BIOCHEMISTRY. *Educ:* Regis Col, BS, 54; Kans State Univ, PhD(org chem), 61. *Prof Exp:* Res chemist, Benger Lab, E I du Pont de Nemours & Co, 61-67; from asst prof to assoc prof, 67-75, PROF CHEM, SOUTHWEST MO STATE UNIV, 75- *Concurrent Pos:* NSF res partic, Acad Year Exten, Southwest Mo State Univ, 70-72. *Mem:* Am Chem Soc. *Res:* Organic synthesis; enzymology. *Mailing Add:* Dept of Chem Southwest Mo State Univ Springfield MO 65802

MORTENSEN, JOHN ALAN, b San Antonio, Tex, May 11, 29; m 57; c 1. HORTICULTURE, GENETICS. *Educ:* Tex A&M Univ, BS, 50, MS, 51; Cornell Univ, PhD(plant breeding), 58. *Prof Exp:* Plant breeder, Birds Eye Div, Gen Foods Corp, 57-60; asst geneticist, Fla Agr Exp Sta, 60-68, assoc prof, 68-77, assoc geneticist, 68-73, PROF & GENETICIST, INST FOOD & AGR SCI, AGR RES CTR, UNIV FLA, 77- *Mem:* Am Genetic Asn; Am Soc Hort Sci; Am Pomol Soc. *Res:* Disease and insect resistance in grapes; development of improved varieties of scions and rootstocks in grapes through breeding and testing; nutritional and inheritance studies in grapes. *Mailing Add:* Agr Res Ctr Univ of Fla PO Box 388 Leesburg FL 32748

MORTENSEN, RICHARD E, b Denver, Colo, Sept 29, 35. ENGINEERING. *Educ:* Mass Inst Technol, BSEE & MSEE, 58; Univ Calif, Berkeley, PhD(stochastic optimal control), 66. *Prof Exp:* Coop engr, Gen Elec Co, 55-57; mem tech staff guid & control, Space Technol Labs, Inc, 58-61; teaching fel elec eng, Univ Calif, Berkeley, 61-65; asst prof eng, 65-70, ASSOC PROF ENG & APPL SCI, UNIV CALIF, LOS ANGELES, 70- *Concurrent Pos:* Vis asst prof, Univ Colo, 66-67; consult, TRW Systs, Inc, Calif, 66- *Mem:* AAAS; Inst Elec & Electronics Engrs. *Res:* Space vehicle guidance and control; stochastic processes; optimal control theory. *Mailing Add:* Dept of Syst Sci Univ of Calif Los Angeles CA 90024

MORTENSON, LEONARD EARL, b Melrose, Mass, June 24, 28; m 52; c 4. BIOCHEMISTRY. *Educ:* RI State Col, BS, 50; Univ Wis, MS, 52, PhD(bact, biochem), 54. *Prof Exp:* Asst bact, Univ Wis, 50-52, asst, Enzyme Inst, 52-53, NSF fel, 53-54; res biochemist, E I du Pont de Nemours & Co, 54-61; assoc prof biol, Purdue Univ, West Lafayette, 62-66, prof, 66-81; SR RES ASSOC, EXXON RES & ENG CO, LINDEN, NJ, 81- *Concurrent Pos:* Vis scientist, Chem Dept, Stanford Univ, 75-76 & CNRS, Marseille, France, 78; Lembert traveling fel, Australian Acad Sci, 80. *Honors & Awards:* Hoblitzelle Nat Award, 65. *Mem:* corresp mem French Acad Sci; Am Soc Microbiol; Am Soc Biol Chemists; Am Chem Soc. *Res:* Biological nitrogen fixation; electron transport; energy and carbohydrate metabolism; biosynthetic reactions; ferredoxin biochemistry; hydrogenase. *Mailing Add:* Exxon Res & Eng Co PO Box 45 Linden NJ 07036

MORTER, RAYMOND LIONE, b Arlington, Wis, Sept 7, 20; m 46; c 2. FOOD ANIMAL MEDICINE, IMMUNOPATHOLOGY. *Educ:* Iowa State Univ, BS, 54, DVM, 57; Mich State Univ, MS, 58, PhD(microbiol & path), 60. *Prof Exp:* Asst vet anat, Iowa State Univ, 55-57; NSF fel vet microbiol, Mich State Univ, 57-59; asst prof, Vet Med Res Inst, Iowa State Univ, 59-60; assoc prof vet microbiol, path & pub health, 60-64, prof vet microbiol, Sch Vet Sci & Med, 64-66, head dept vet sci & assoc dean res, 66-76, PROF VET MED, SCH VET MED, PURDUE UNIV, WEST LAFAYETTE, 76- *Concurrent Pos:* AID staff, Philippines, 66; consult, Food & Agr Orgn, UN; bd dirs, Lab Supply Co, 71-; pres, Swineng, Inc. *Mem:* AAAS; Am Asn Lab Animal Sci; Am Soc Microbiol; Am Vet Med Asn; Am Soc Exp Path. *Res:* Mechanism and course of infectious diseases and health management of feedlot cattle. *Mailing Add:* Rm LA9 Lynn Hall Purdue Univ Sch of Vet Med West Lafayette IN 47907

MORTIMER, CHARLES EDGAR, b Allentown, Pa, Nov 21, 21; m 60; c 1. ORGANIC CHEMISTRY, HISTORY OF SCIENCE. *Educ:* Muhlenberg Col, BS, 42; Purdue Univ, MS, 48, PhD(chem), 50. *Prof Exp:* Line shift supvr, Hercules Powder Co, Va & Kans, 42-44; res assoc, Carbide & Carbon Chem Co, NY, 44-46; from asst prof to assoc prof, 50-59, PROF CHEM, MUHLENBERG COL, 59-, HEAD DEPT, 80- *Mem:* Am Chem Soc. *Res:* Chemical education. *Mailing Add:* Dept of Chem Muhlenberg Col Allentown PA 18104

MORTIMER, DONALD CHARLES, b Didsbury, Alta, Mar 4, 24; m 47; c 7. PLANT PHYSIOLOGY. *Educ:* Univ Alta, BSc, 45; Univ Wis, MS, 47, PhD(biochem), 50. *Prof Exp:* From asst res officer to assoc res officer, 50-76, SR RES OFFICER APPL BIOL, RES LABS, NAT RES COUN CAN, 76- *Res:* Ecology and physiology of freshwater plants; photosynthesis; heavy metal toxicology; translocation. *Mailing Add:* 933 Falaise Ottawa ON K2C 0M2 Can

MORTIMER, EDWARD ALBERT, JR, b Chicago, Ill, Mar 22, 22; m 44; c 3. MEDICINE. *Educ:* Dartmouth Col, AB, 43; Dartmouth Med Sch, dipl, 44; Northwestern Univ, MD, 47. *Prof Exp:* Resident pediat, Boston Children's Hosp, 50-52; from sr instr to prof, Case Western Reserve Univ, 52-66; prof & chmn dept, Sch Med, Univ NMex, 66-75; PROF COMMUNITY HEALTH & PEDIAT & CHMN DEPT COMMUNITY HEALTH, SCH MED, CASE WESTERN RESERVE UNIV, 75- *Concurrent Pos:* Markle scholar, Case Western Reserve Univ, 61-66; asst dir dept pediat, Cleveland Metrop Gen Hosp, 52-66; chief pediat, Bernalillo County Med Ctr, 66-75; mem comn streptococcal & staphylococcal dis, Armed Forces Epidemiol Bd, 69-72; mem epidemiol & dis control study sect, NIH, 69-73; chmn, Joint Coun Nat Pediat Soc, 72-74; vis prof epidemiol, Sch Pub Health, Harvard Univ, 73. *Mem:* Soc Pediat Res; Am Pediat Soc; Am Epidemiol Soc. *Res:* Pediatrics; epidemiology; rheumatic fever; streptococcal and staphylococcal diseases and infections. *Mailing Add:* Dept of Community Health Case Western Reserve Univ Cleveland OH 44106

MORTIMER, J(OHN) THOMAS, b Las Vegas, NMex, Oct 12, 39; m 67; c 1. BIOMEDICAL ENGINEERING. *Educ:* Tex Technol Col, BSEE, 64; Case Western Reserve Univ, MS, 65, PhD(eng), 68. *Prof Exp:* Swed Bd Technol Develop grant, Chalmers Univ Technol, Sweden, 68-69; asst prof biomed eng, 69-74, ASSOC PROF BIOMED ENG, CASE WESTERN RESERVE UNIV, 74-, DIR, APPL NEURAL CONTROL LAB, 64- *Concurrent Pos:* Vis prof, Univ Karlsruhe, WGer, 77-78. *Honors & Awards:* Humboldt Award, Alexander von Humboldt Found, 77. *Mem:* Biomed Eng Soc; Neuroelec Soc; Soc Neurosci. *Res:* Clinical application of electrical stimulation to the neuro-muscular system; applied neural control (electrical excitation of the nervous system). *Mailing Add:* Appl Neural Control Lab Case Western Reserve Univ Cleveland OH 44106

MORTIMER, KENNETH, b Aberdeen, Scotland, Apr 22, 22; nat US; m 49; c 4. ENGINEERING MECHANICS. *Educ:* Ill Inst Technol, BS, 47, MS, 49. *Prof Exp:* Instr mech eng, Ill Inst Technol, 48-50; from asst prof to assoc prof civil eng, 50-62, PROF CIVIL ENG, VALPARAISO UNIV, 62- *Concurrent Pos:* Consult, Chicago South Shore & South Bend RR & US Army Corps Engrs. *Mem:* Am Soc Eng Educ. *Res:* Computers; transportation. *Mailing Add:* Dept of Civil Eng Valparaiso Univ Valparaiso IN 46383

MORTIMER, RICHARD W(ALTER), b Philadelphia, Pa, Dec 7, 36; m 57; c 4. SOLID MECHANICS. *Educ:* Drexel Univ, BS, 62, MS, 64, PhD(appl mech), 67. *Prof Exp:* From instr to assoc prof, 65-76, PROF MECH ENG & CHMN DEPT MECH ENG & MECH, DREXEL UNIV, 76- *Concurrent Pos:* Am Soc Mech Engrs-NASA fac fel, Drexel Univ, 67, NASA grant, 67- *Mem:* Am Soc Mech Engrs; Am Inst Aeronaut & Astronaut; Soc Exp Stress Anal; Am Ord Asn; Am Acad Mech. *Res:* Dynamic elasticity; stress analysis; fluid mechanics; response of structures to impact loadings; wave propagation. *Mailing Add:* Mech & Struct ASG Drexel Univ 32nd & Chestnut Sts Philadelphia PA 19104

MORTIMER, ROBERT GEORGE, b Provo, Utah, Aug 25, 33; m 60; c 5. PHYSICAL CHEMISTRY, THEORETICAL CHEMISTRY. *Educ:* Utah State Univ, BS, 58, MS, 59; Calif Inst Technol, PhD(chem), 63. *Prof Exp:* Res chemist, Univ Calif, San Diego, 62-64; asst prof chem, Ind Univ, Bloomington, 64-70; asst prof, 70-72, ASSOC PROF CHEM, SOUTHWESTERN AT MEMPHIS, 72- *Res:* Statistical mechanics; irreversible thermodynamics; experimental study of transport processes in liquids. *Mailing Add:* Dept of Chem Southwestern at Memphis Memphis TN 38112

MORTIMER, ROBERT KEITH, b Didsbury, Alta, Nov 1, 27; nat US; m 49; c 4. GENETICS, BIOPHYSICS. *Educ:* Univ Alta, BSc, 49; Univ Calif, Berkeley, PhD(biophys), 53. *Prof Exp:* From instr to assoc prof, 53-66, PROF MED PHYSICS, UNIV CALIF, BERKELEY, 66-, CHMN MED, 72- *Mem:* AAAS; Genetics Soc Am; Radiation Res Soc. *Res:* Genetics and radiation biology of microorganisms. *Mailing Add:* Dept of Med Physics Univ of Calif Berkeley CA 94720

MORTIMORE, GLENN EDWARD, b Portland, Ore, Apr 13, 25; m 59; c 2. PHYSIOLOGY, BIOCHEMISTRY. *Educ:* Ore State Col, BS, 49; Univ Ore, MD, 52. *Prof Exp:* NSF fel, 57-58; sr investr, Nat Inst Arthritis & Metab Dis, 58-67; assoc prof, 67-71, PROF PHYSIOL, MILTON S HERSHEY MED CTR, PA STATE UNIV, 71- *Mem:* AAAS; Endocrine Soc; Am Fedn Clin Res; Am Physiol Soc; Am Soc Biol Chemists. *Res:* Mechanism of hormone action; effect of insulin of liver metabolism; regulation of metabolism and protein turnover; lysosomes. *Mailing Add:* Dept of Physiol Hershey Med Ctr Pa State Univ Hershey PA 17033

MORTLAND, MAX MERLE, b Streator, Ill, Mar 30, 23; m 47; c 4. SOIL CHEMISTRY. *Educ:* Univ Ill, BS, 46, MS, 47 & 50, PhD(agron), 51. *Prof Exp:* Asst prof soils, Univ Wyo, 51-53; from asst prof to assoc prof, 53-69, PROF SOIL SCI, MICH STATE UNIV, 69-, CROP SCI, 74- *Concurrent Pos:* Fulbright sr res scholar, Cath Univ Louvain, 61-62. *Mem:* Am Soc Agron; Soil Sci Soc Am. *Res:* Physical chemical reactions of soils; reactions of ammonia in soils; rate controlling processes in potassium release from minerals; clay-organic complexes. *Mailing Add:* Dept of Crop & Soil Sci Mich State Univ East Lansing MI 48823

MORTLOCK, ROBERT PAUL, b Bronxville, NY, May 12, 31; m 54; c 3. MICROBIAL PHYSIOLOGY. *Educ:* Rensselaer Polytech Inst, BS, 53; Univ Ill, PhD(bact), 58. *Prof Exp:* Bacteriologist, US Army Chem Corps Res & Develop Labs, 59-61; res assoc biochem, Mich State Univ, 61-63; from asst prof to prof, Univ Mass, Amherst, 68-78, head dept, 72-78; PROF MICROBIOL & CHMN DEPT, CORNELL UNIV, 78- *Concurrent Pos:* USPHS fel, 61-63. *Mem:* AAAS; Am Soc Microbiol; Am Acad Microbiol. *Res:* Physiological bacteriology; microbial physiology and metabolism; cellular regulatory mechanisms; carbohydrate metabolism and enzyme regulation in microorganisms; the utilization of uncommon and unnatural carbohydrates by microorganisms. *Mailing Add:* Dept of Microbiol Cornell Univ Ithaca NY 14850

MORTON, BRUCE ELDINE, b Loma Linda, Calif, May 9, 38; m 60, 76; c 2. BIOCHEMISTRY, REPRODUCTIVE BIOLOGY. *Educ:* La Sierra Col, BS, 60; Univ Wis, MS, 63, PhD(biochem), 65. *Prof Exp:* Fel, Inst Enzyme Res, Univ Wis, 65-66; NIH fel, Mass Inst Technol, 66-67; Harvard Univ res fel med, Beth Israel Hosp, 67-69; asst prof, 69-74, ASSOC PROF BIOCHEM, UNIV HAWAII, MANOA, 74- *Concurrent Pos:* Consult, New Eng Mem Hosp, Stoneham, Mass, 67-69 & St Francis Hosp, Honolulu, 70-71. *Mem:* Soc Study Reproduction; Am Soc Biol Chemists; Am Soc Andrology. *Res:* Biochemical mechanisms of sperm maturation and egg penetration; energy metabolism and control of cell movement; peptides and brain function; structure, function and control of ribosomes. *Mailing Add:* Dept of Biochem & Biophys Univ of Hawaii Manoa Campus Honolulu HI 96822

MORTON, DONALD CHARLES, b Kapuskasing, Ont, June 12, 33; m 70; c 2. ASTROPHYSICS. *Educ:* Univ Toronto, BA, 56; Princeton Univ, PhD, 59. *Prof Exp:* Astronr, US Naval Res Lab, 59-61; res assoc, Princeton Univ, 61-63, res staff mem, 63-65, res astronr, 65-68, sr res astronr & lectr astrophys sci, 68-76; DIR, ANGLO-AUSTRALIAN OBSERV, 76- *Mem:* Int Astron Union; Am Astron Soc; Royal Astron Soc; Royal Astron Soc Can; Astron Soc Australia (pres, 81-83). *Res:* spectroscopy of stars, interstellar gas, galaxies, quasars; stellar mass loss; interstellar abundances; space instrumentation and observations; detectors for ground based telescopes. *Mailing Add:* Anglo Australian Observ PO Box 296 Epping NSW 2121 Australia

MORTON, DONALD JOHN, b Brooklyn, NY, Jan 11, 31; m 53; c 3. INFORMATION SCIENCE. *Educ:* Univ Del, BS, 52; La State Univ, MS, 54; Univ Calif, Berkeley, PhD(plant path), 57; Simmons Col, MLS, 69, DA(libr sci), 76. *Prof Exp:* Asst prof plant nematol, NMex State Univ, 57-58; asst plant path, NDak State Univ, 59-61; sr res plant pathologist, USDA, Ga, 61-65; assoc prof plant path, Univ Del, 65-68; dir sci libr, Northeastern Univ, 69-70; asst prof hist of med, 70-74, ASSOC PROF LIBR SCI, MED SCH, UNIV MASS, 74-, LIBR DIR, 70- *Concurrent Pos:* Prof libr sci, Worcester State Col, 74- *Mem:* Mycol Soc Am; Med Libr Asn; Am Soc Info Sci; Am Libr Asn; Spec Libr Asn. *Res:* Air pollution effects on plants; serological studies of plant pathogens; organization and retrieval of scientific information. *Mailing Add:* Libr Univ of Mass Med Sch Worcester MA 01605

MORTON, DONALD LEE, b Richwood, WVa, Sept 12, 34; m 57; c 4. SURGERY, ONCOLOGY. *Educ:* Univ Calif, BA, 55, MD, 58; Am Bd Surg, dipl, 67; Am Bd Thoracic Surg, dipl, 69. *Prof Exp:* Intern med, Med Ctr, Univ Calif, 58-59, resident surg, 59-60; clin assoc, Nat Cancer Inst, 60-62; resident surg, Med Ctr, Univ Calif, 62-66; sr surgeon, Nat Cancer Inst, 66-69, head tumor immunol sect, 69-71; assoc prof surg, Sch Med, Johns Hopkins Univ, 70-71; PROF SURG & CHIEF DIV ONCOL & GEN SURG, SCH MED, UNIV CALIF, LOS ANGELES, 71- *Concurrent Pos:* Fel, Cancer Res Inst, Med Ctr, Univ Calif, 62-66; immunol adv mem, Spec Virus Cancer Prog, Nat Cancer Inst, 69-71, mem bd sci counr, 74-; mem comt for objective 6, Nat Cancer Plan, 71-; chief surg, Sepulveda Vet Admin Hosp, Calif, 71-74, chief oncol sect, Surg Serv, 74-; mem sci adv coun, Cancer Res Inst, Inc, 74- *Honors & Awards:* US Dept Health, Educ & Welfare Superior Serv Award, 70; Cancer Res Inst Inc Award, 75; Langer Award, 78. *Mem:* Am Asn Cancer Res; Am Surg Asn; Am Soc Clin Oncol; Soc of Surg Oncol; Soc Univ Surgeons. *Res:* Immunologic and virologic aspects of neoplastic disease, including immunotherapy of melanoma, skeletal and soft tissue sarcoma and mammary carcinoma; surgical oncology; thoracic surgery. *Mailing Add:* Ctr of Health Sci Univ of Calif Los Angeles CA 90024

MORTON, HARRISON LEON, b St Paul, Minn, Oct 19, 38; m 62; c 4. FOREST PATHOLOGY, URBAN FORESTRY. *Educ:* Univ Minn, BS, 61, MS, 64, PhD(plant path), 67. *Prof Exp:* From asst prof to assoc prof forest path, 72-78, PROF FOREST PATH, FORESTRY & WILDLIFE PROG, SCH NATURAL RESOURCES, UNIV MICH, ANN ARBOR, 78-, CHMN FISHERIES, 72- *Mem:* Int Soc Agr; Am Phytopath Soc; Soc Am Foresters. *Res:* Diseases of forest and shade trees. *Mailing Add:* S T Dana Bldg Sch of Natural Resources Ann Arbor MI 48109

MORTON, HELEN JANET, biochemistry, cytology, see previous edition

MORTON, HOWARD LEROY, b Moscow, Idaho, Dec 13, 24; m 50; c 2. PLANT PHYSIOLOGY. *Educ:* Univ Idaho, BS, 50, MS, 52; Agr & Mech Col, Tex, PhD(plant physiol), 61. *Prof Exp:* Asst agronomist, Univ Idaho, 52-57; res agronomist, Tex, 57-66, plant physiologist, 66-68, PLANT PHYSIOLOGIST, CROPS RES DIV, AGR RES SERV, USDA, ARIZ, 68- *Mem:* Weed Sci Soc Am; Am Soc Plant Physiol; Soc Range Mgt. *Res:* Absorption, translocation and metabolism of herbicides; weed control on range lands; range revegetation; poisonous weeds; pesticide residues; plant growth and development; controlled environment systems; effects of herbicides on honey bees. *Mailing Add:* Agr Res Serv USDA 2000 E Allen Rd Tucson AZ 85719

MORTON, JEFFREY BRUCE, b Chicago, Ill, Apr 25, 41; m 63; c 3. FLUID DYNAMICS. *Educ:* Mass Inst Technol, BS, 63; Johns Hopkins Univ, PhD(fluid mech), 67. *Prof Exp:* Res scientist, 67-68, asst prof aerospace eng, 68-72, ASSOC PROF AEROSPACE ENG, UNIV VA, 72- *Mem:* AAAS; Am Inst Aeronaut & Astronaut; Am Phys Soc. *Res:* Turbulence; boundary layers; fluid mechanics. *Mailing Add:* Dept of Mech & Aerospace Eng Univ of Va Charlottesville VA 22901

MORTON, JOHN DUDLEY, b Southampton, Eng, July 25, 14; US citizen. ENVIRONMENTAL HEALTH. *Educ:* Cambridge Univ, BA, 36, MA, 40. *Prof Exp:* Sect leader appl chem, Exp Sta, Eng, 36-47; asst dir aerobiol, Microbiol Res Estab, Eng, 47-62; lab mgr meteorol, Melpar Inc, 63-70; PRIN SCIENTIST ENVIRON HEALTH, ENVIRO CONTROL INC, 70- *Concurrent Pos:* Consult, Nat Acad Eng, 69-70. *Honors & Awards:* Officer, Order of the Brit Empire, 56. *Res:* Studies of human health in relation to environmental and occupational exposure to toxic substances. *Mailing Add:* Enviro Control Inc 11300 Rockville Pike Rockville MD 20852

MORTON, JOHN HENDERSON, b New Haven, Conn, Jan 15, 23; m 49; c 4. SURGERY. *Educ:* Amherst Col, BA, 45; Yale Univ, MD, 46. *Prof Exp:* Intern surg, gynec & obstet, Strong Mem Hosp & Rochester Munic Hosp, 46-47, asst resident surg, 47 & 49-52, resident, 53; from instr to assoc prof surg, 53-69, from instr to asst prof surg anat, 55-67, PROF HEALTH SERV, SCH MED & DENT, UNIV ROCHESTER, 69-, PROF SURG & ASST PROF SURG ANAT, 77- *Concurrent Pos:* From asst surgeon to assoc surgeon, Med Ctr, Univ Rochester, 54-62, sr assoc surgeon, 62- *Mem:* AMA; fel Am Col Surg; Am Asn Surg of Trauma; Am Burn Asn. *Res:* Liver and gastrointestinal tract. *Mailing Add:* Dept of Health Serv Univ of Rochester Sch of Med Rochester NY 14627

MORTON, JOHN KENNETH, b Tamworth, Eng, Jan 3, 28; m 51; c 2. BOTANY. *Educ:* Univ Durham, BSc, 44, PhD(bot), 53. *Prof Exp:* Lectr bot, Univ Ghana, 51-60, sr lectr & cur, Ghana Herbarium, 60-61; lectr, Birkbeck Col, London, 61-63; prof & chmn dept, Fourah Bay Col, Sierra Leone, 63-67; PROF BIOL, UNIV WATERLOO, 68-, CHMN DEPT, 74- *Mem:* Can Bot Asn (pres, 74-75); Bot Soc Brit Isles; Linnean Soc London; Am Soc Plant Taxonomists; Int Asn Plant Taxon. *Res:* Experimental taxonomy and biogeography of North American and tropical African vascular plants; palynology; evolution. *Mailing Add:* Dept of Biol Univ of Waterloo Waterloo ON N2L 3G1 Can

MORTON, JOHN ROBERT, III, b Palestine, Tex, June 5, 29; m 53; c 2. NUCLEAR SCIENCE. *Educ:* Univ Ala, BS, 50; Univ Calif, Berkeley, PhD(chem), 61. *Prof Exp:* Tech grad, Hanford Atomic Prod Oper, Gen Elec Co, 50-51, supvr health physics, 51-56; PHYSICIST, LAWRENCE LIVERMORE LAB, UNIV CALIF, 61- *Mem:* AAAS; Am Phys Soc; Am Nuclear Soc. *Res:* Nuclear weapons test diagnostic techniques; pinhole imagery; reactor and critical assembly physics; seeking evidence for neutrino decay from fission explosions. *Mailing Add:* L Div Lawrence Livermore Lab Univ of Calif PO Box 808 Livermore CA 94550

MORTON, JOHN ROYLANCE, b London, UK, Jan 9, 31; m 60; c 2. PHYSICAL CHEMISTRY. *Educ:* Univ Col, London, BSc, 53, PhD(phys chem), 57; Univ London, DSc, 68. *Prof Exp:* Sci officer chem, Royal Naval Sci Serv, 56-57; fel physics, Nat Res Coun , Can, 57-59; sr res fel, Nat Phys Lab, 59-62; RES OFFICER CHEM, NAT RES COUN CAN, 62- *Mem:* Can Inst Chem. *Res:* Spectra and structure of free radicals as studied by electron spin resonance. *Mailing Add:* Div of Chem Nat Res Coun Ottawa ON K1A 0R9 Can

MORTON, JOHN WEST, JR, b Dallas, Tex, Mar 3, 25; m 50; c 2. ORGANIC CHEMISTRY. *Educ:* Southern Methodist Univ, BS, 46; Iowa State Univ, PhD(org chem), 52. *Prof Exp:* Res chemist, Procter & Gamble Co, Ohio, 52-54; from assoc prof to prof chem, La Polytech Inst, 54-62; assoc prof chem, 62-74, PROF CHEM, WESTERN NMEX UNIV, 74-, CHMN DEPT, 77- *Mem:* Am Chem Soc. *Res:* Organolithium compounds. *Mailing Add:* Dept of Phys Sci Western NMex Univ Silver City NM 88061

MORTON, JOSEPH JAMES PANDOZZI, b Hartford, Conn, May 9, 41; m 68; c 2. PHARMACOLOGY, TOXICOLOGY. *Educ:* Univ Hartford, BS, 63; Univ Conn, MS, 66, PhD(pharmacol), 68. *Prof Exp:* Actg dir pharmacol, Natural Prod Res, Amazon Natural Drug Co, 67-68, dir, 68-69; toxicologist, Med Eval Dept, Gillette Res Inst, 69-70, med rev officer, 70-73, CHIEF OFF MED REV, GILLETTE MED EVAL LABS, 74- *Mem:* Soc Toxicol; Soc Cosmetic Chemists; Europ Soc Toxicol; Am Chem Soc. *Res:* Medical safety/toxicity evaluation of drugs, cosmetics and household chemical and electrical products; screening of natural products for potential therapeutic activity. *Mailing Add:* Gillette Med Eval Labs 1413 Research Blvd Rockville MD 20850

MORTON, MARTIN LEWIS, b Tony, Wis, May 1, 34; m 53; c 4. ZOOLOGY, PHYSIOLOGY. *Educ:* San Jose State Col, BA, 59, MA, 61; Wash State Univ, PhD(zoophysiol), 66. *Prof Exp:* Res asst zool, Wash State Univ, 63-65; res assoc, Univ Wash, 65-66, asst prof, 66-67; from asst prof to assoc prof, 67-77, PROF BIOL, OCCIDENTAL COL, 77- *Mem:* Am Ornith Union; Am Soc Mammal; Am Soc Zoologists; Ecol Soc Am; Am Inst Biol Sci. *Res:* Bioenergetics, orientation, phenology, endocrinology, annual cycles and biological clocks of migratory birds. *Mailing Add:* Dept of Biol Occidental Col 1600 Campus Rd Los Angeles CA 90041

MORTON, NEWTON ENNIS, b Camden, NJ, Dec 21, 29; m 49; c 5. POPULATION GENETICS. *Educ:* Univ Hawaii, BA, 51; Univ Wis, MS, 52, PhD, 55. *Prof Exp:* Geneticist, Atomic Bomb Casualty Comn, Japan, 52-53; fel, Nat Cancer Inst, 55-56; asst prof med genetics, Univ Wis, 56-60, assoc prof, 60-61; dir genetics res proj, 58-59, prof genetics, 61-69, chmn dept, 62-65, DIR POP GENETICS LAB, UNIV HAWAII, HONOLULU, 69-, PROF, SCH PUB HEALTH, 75- *Concurrent Pos:* Consult, NIH, 59 & genetics training comt, 61-65; mem expert adv comt human genetics, WHO, 61-; dir med genetics proj, Immigrants Hosp, Sao Paulo, Brazil, 62-63. *Honors & Awards:* Lederle Award, 58; Allan Award, 63. *Mem:* AAAS; Genetics Soc Am; Am Soc Human Genetics; Am Soc Naturalists; Brazilian Acad Sci. *Res:* Human and population genetics. *Mailing Add:* Pop Genetics Lab Univ of Hawaii Honolulu HI 96822

MORTON, PERRY WILKES, JR, b Strong, Ark, Jan 19, 23; m 58; c 3. PHYSICS. *Educ:* Rice Univ, BS, 47; Miss State Univ, MS, 51; Duke Univ, PhD(physics), 57. *Prof Exp:* Asst math & instr physics, Miss State Univ, 52-53; asst, Duke Univ, 53-57; from assoc prof to prof, Miss State Univ, 57-63; prof physics & math & chmn div natural sci, Ky Southern Col, 63-69; CHMN DEPT PHYSICS, SAMFORD UNIV, 69- *Mem:* Am Phys Soc. *Res:* Nuclear and classical physics; beta-ray spectroscopy. *Mailing Add:* Dept of Physics Samford Univ Birmingham AL 35209

MORTON, RICHARD ALAN, b Chicago, Ill, Dec 14, 38; m 62; c 4. BIOPHYSICS. *Educ:* Univ Chicago, SB, 61, SM, 62, PhD(biophys), 65. *Prof Exp:* Res assoc biophys, Johns Hopkins Univ, 65-67; NSF res fel, Univ Calif, Santa Barbara, 68, res assoc, 69; asst prof, 69-73, ASSOC PROF BIOL, MCMASTER UNIV, 73- *Mem:* Sigma Xi. *Res:* Structure and function of proteins, especially c and acetylchotinesterase; evolution of proteins and population genetics. *Mailing Add:* 16 Dalewood Circle Hamilton ON L8S 4B5 Can

MORTON, ROBERT ALEX, b Cincinnati, Ohio, Oct 17, 42; m 68; c 2. SEDIMENTOLOGY. *Educ:* Univ Chattanooga, BA, 65; WVa Univ, MS, 66, PhD(geol), 72. *Prof Exp:* Petrol geologist, Chevron Oil Co, 66-69; assoc res scientist geol, 72-76, res scientist geol, 76-80, lectr dept marine studies, 78-80, ASSOC DIR, BUR ECON GEOL, UNIV TEX, AUSTIN, 80-, LECTR, DEPT GEOL SCI, 78- *Mem:* Am Asn Petrol Geologists; Am Inst Prof Geologists; Int Asn Sedimentologists; Geol Soc Am; Soc Econ Paleontologists & Mineralogists. *Res:* Coastal processes; ancient and modern clastic depositional systems; marine geology; environmental geology. *Mailing Add:* 7107 Sungate Austin TX 78731

MORTON, ROGER DAVID, b Nottingham, Eng, Oct 20, 35; m 61; c 2. MINERALOGY. *Educ:* Univ Nottingham, BSc, 56, PhD(geol), 59. *Prof Exp:* Sci asst, Univ Oslo, 59-61; lectr geol, Univ Nottingham, 61-66; assoc prof, 66-73, PROF GEOL, UNIV ALTA, 73- *Concurrent Pos:* G V Hobson Bequest Fund, Brit Inst Mining & Metall, 62; consult, Can Int Develop Agency, 75- *Mem:* Fel Geol Asn Can; Can Inst Mining & Metall; Soc Econ Geologists; Mineral Soc Am. *Res:* Investigation of uranium deposits in northwest Canada and mineral resources of Indonesia. *Mailing Add:* Rm 366 Dept of Geol Univ Alta Edmonton AB T6G 2E3 Can

MORTON, ROGER ROY ADAMS, b Melbourne, Australia, June 1, 41; m 65; c 2. ELECTRICAL ENGINEERING. *Educ:* Royal Melbourne Inst Technol, Assoc dipl elec eng, 61; Univ Melbourne, BEE, 63; Monash Univ, Australia, PhD(elec eng), 66. *Prof Exp:* Exp officer comput res, Commonwealth Sci & Indust Res Orgn, Australia, 63-64; sr scientist image anal develop, 67-73, DIR RES & DEVELOP, IMAGE ANAL SYSTS, ANAL SYST DIV, BAUSCH & LOMB INC, 73- *Concurrent Pos:* Vis prof, Rochester Inst Technol, 77-78. *Honors & Awards:* Indust Res 100 Award, 71. *Mem:* Inst Elec & Electronics Engrs; Am Soc Testing & Mat; Int Soc Stereol. *Res:* Image analysis; instrument development; research and applications. *Mailing Add:* Anal Systs Div Bausch & Lomb Inc 820 Linden Ave Rochester NY 14625

MORTON, STEPHEN DANA, b Madison, Wis, Sept 7, 32. WATER CHEMISTRY, PHYSICAL CHEMISTRY. *Educ:* Univ Wis, BS, 54, PhD(chem), 62. *Prof Exp:* Asst prof chem, Otterbein Col, 62-66; fel water chem, Univ Wis, 66-67; res chemist, Warf Inst, 67-73, head environ qual dept, 73-76; mgr qual assurance, Raltech Sci Serv, 77-82; PRES, SDM CONSULTS, INC, 82- *Mem:* Am Chem Soc; Am Soc Limnol & Oceanog; Am Water Works Asn; Water Pollution Control Fedn; Am Soc Qual Control. *Res:* Water pollution; lake and stream studies; waste treatment; toxicology. *Mailing Add:* SDM Consults Inc 979 Johnathan Dr Madison WI 53713

MORTON, THOMAS HELLMAN, b Los Angeles, Calif, Feb 10, 47; m 75. ORGANIC CHEMISTRY. *Educ:* Harvard Univ, AB, 68; Calif Inst Technol, PhD(chem), 73. *Prof Exp:* Asst prof chem, Brown Univ, 72-80; vis asst prof chem, Brandeis Univ, 80-81; ASST PROF CHEM, UNIV CALIF, RIVERSIDE, 81- *Concurrent Pos:* Vis scholar, Interdisciplinary Progs Health, Howard Univ, 78-79. *Mem:* Am Chem Soc; Am Soc Mass Spectrometry; Asn Chemorecept Sci; Soc Neurosci. *Res:* Molecular rearrangements and the interaction of radiation with matter; molecular mechanisms of the sense of smell. *Mailing Add:* Univ Calif Chem Dept Riverside CA 92521

MORTON, WILLIAM EDWARDS, b Boston, Mass, June 30, 29; m 56; c 3. EPIDEMIOLOGY. *Educ:* Univ Puget Sound, BS, 52; Univ Wash, MD, 55; Univ Mich, MPH, 60, DrPH, 62. *Prof Exp:* Intern med, Doctors Hosp, Seattle, Wash, 55-56; USPHS heart dis control officer, Colo Dept Pub Health, 56-58; sr resident med, San Mateo County Hosp, Calif, 58-59; trainee epidemiol, Sch Pub Health, Univ Mich, 59-62; res epidemiologist, Colo Heart Asn & asst clin prof prev med, Med Sch, Univ Colo, 62-67; assoc prof, 67-70, PROF PUB HEALTH & PREV MED, MED SCH, UNIV ORE, 70-, HEAD DIV ENVIRON MED, 72- *Concurrent Pos:* Med res consult, Selective Serv, Colo, 64-67 & Ore, 70-76; consult, Environ Health Sci Ctr, Ore State Univ, 72- *Mem:* Am Heart Asn; Am Pub Health Asn; Am Cancer Soc; Am Occup Med Asn; Asn Teachers Prev Med. *Res:* Cancer epidemiology; hypertension; other cardiovascular diseases; screening method evaluation; environmental and occupational health hazards. *Mailing Add:* Environ Med Div Univ of Ore Med Sch Portland OR 97201

MORTVEDT, JOHN JACOB, b Dell Rapids, SDak, Jan 25, 32; m 55; c 3. SOIL CHEMISTRY. *Educ:* SDak State Col, BS, 53, MS, 59; Univ Wis, PhD(chem), 62. *Prof Exp:* soil chemist, Soils & Fertil Res Br, 62-80, SOIL CHEMIST, AGR RES & BR, NAT FERTIL DEVELOP CTR, TENN VALLEY AUTHORITY, 80- *Mem:* Fel Am Soc Agron; fel Soil Sci Soc Am. *Res:* Chemistry of micronutrients and their soil-plant-fertilizer relationships; heavy metal contaminants added to soils. *Mailing Add:* 213 Forest Hills Dr Florence AL 35630

MOSAK, RICHARD DAVID, b Washington, DC, Oct 8, 45; m 67; c 3. MATHEMATICAL ANALYSIS. *Educ:* Columbia Univ, AB, 66, PhD(math), 70. *Prof Exp:* Instr math, Yale Univ, 70-72 & Univ Chicago, 72-73; asst prof, 73-77, ASSOC PROF MATH, UNIV ROCHESTER, 77- *Mem:* Am Math Soc. *Res:* Harmonic analysis and representations of topological groups. *Mailing Add:* Dept of Math Univ of Rochester Rochester NY 14627

MOSBACH, ERWIN HEINZ, b Ger, Feb 18, 20; nat US; m 44. BIOCHEMISTRY. *Educ:* Columbia Univ, BA, 43, MA, 48, PhD(chem), 50. *Prof Exp:* Tutor chem, Brooklyn Col, 42-46; asst, Columbia Univ, 46-50; biochemist, Biol Div, Oak Ridge Nat Lab, 50-51; res assoc biochem, Col Physicians & Surgeons, Columbia Univ, 51-54, from asst prof to assoc prof, 54-61; assoc mem & chief biochem sect, Dept Lab Diag, Pub Health Res Inst New York, 61-71, mem & chief dept lipid res, 72-78; DIR, SURG LIPID LAB, BETH ISRAEL MED CTR, 78- *Concurrent Pos:* Lectr, Hunter Col, 51-54; consult, NY Infirmary, 57-; consult, Metab Study Sect, NIH, 67-71, mem lipid metab adv comt, 74-78, chmn, 78; adj assoc prof med, Med Sch, NY Univ, 61-78; asst dir bur labs, Dept Health, New York, 61-68; assoc ed, J Lipid Res, 68-72, ed, 76-78; consult, Manhattan Vet Admin Hosp, 71-; fel coun arteriosclerosis, Am Heart Asn; chmn, Search Comt, Vet Admin Spec Alcoholism Res Prog, 78; res prof surg, Mount Sinai Sch Med, 78- *Mem:* Am Soc Biol Chemists; Soc Exp Biol & Med; Am Inst Nutrit; Am Asn Study Liver Dis; Am Gastroenterol Asn. *Res:* Metabolism of sterols and bile acids. *Mailing Add:* Beth Israel Med Ctr 10 Nathan D Perlman Pl New York NY 10003

MOSBERG, ARNOLD T, b Cleveland, Ohio, Mar 4, 46; m 67. BIOMEDICAL ENGINEERING, FLUID MECHANICS. *Educ:* Ohio State Univ, BAAE, 69, MS, 73, PhD(biomed eng), 78. *Prof Exp:* Aeronaut eng combustion, Gen Elec Co, 69-70, Aeronaut eng thermodyn diag, 70-71; RES SCIENTIST BIOMED ENG, COLUMBUS DIV, BATTELLE MEM INST, 77- *Mem:* Asn Advan Med Instrumentation; Aerospace Med Asn; Am Inst Aeronaut & Astronaut; Int Lung Sounds Asn. *Res:* Biomedical engineering; pulmonary function studies; cardiovascular physiology; biofluid mechanics; biomedical device development and design; medical instrumentation design and evaluation. *Mailing Add:* Columbus Div Battelle Mem Inst 505 King Ave Columbus OH 43201

MOSBO, JOHN ALVIN, b Davenport, Iowa, June 11, 47; m 68; c 1. INORGANIC CHEMISTRY. *Educ:* Univ Northern Colo, BA, 69; Iowa State Univ, PhD(inorg chem), 73. *Prof Exp:* ASST PROF CHEM, BALL STATE UNIV, 73- *Mem:* Am Chem Soc. *Res:* Reaction mechanisms of phosphorus and boron compounds; heteroatom configurations and ring conformations of cyclic organophosphorus and organoboron compounds; reactions and mechanisms of low valent transition metal complexes. *Mailing Add:* Dept of Chem Ball State Univ Muncie IN 47306

MOSBORG, ROBERT J(OHN), b Chicago, Ill, Dec 20, 24; m 51; c 2. STRUCTURAL ENGINEERING. *Educ:* Univ Ill, BS, 46, MS, 49. *Prof Exp:* Eng aide, Bridge Dept, Ill Cent RR, 46-47; asst civil eng, 47-49, res assoc, 49-52, from asst prof to assoc prof, 52-76, asst head dept, 65-67, PROF CIVIL ENG, UNIV ILL, URBANA, 76- *Concurrent Pos:* NSF fac fels, 59, 60-62. *Mem:* Am Soc Civil Engrs; Am Soc Eng Educ; Am Concrete Inst. *Res:* Structural mechanics; dynamics; material behavior. *Mailing Add:* 1104 Civil Eng Bldg Univ of Ill Urbana IL 61801

MOSBURG, EARL R, JR, b Frederick, Md, Jan 23, 28; m 58; c 1. ATOMIC PHYSICS. *Educ:* Yale Univ, BS, 52, PhD(physics), 56. *Prof Exp:* PHYSICIST, NAT BUR STANDARDS, 56- *Concurrent Pos:* Mem subcomt neutron standards & measurements, Comt Nuclear Sci, Nat Res Coun, 59-61. *Mem:* Am Phys Soc. *Res:* Plasma physics; gas discharges; gaseous electronics. *Mailing Add:* Nat Bur of Standards Boulder CO 80302

MOSBY, JAMES FRANCIS, b Owensville, Ind, Nov 8, 37. CHEMICAL ENGINEERING. *Educ:* Purdue Univ, BS, 59, PhD(chem eng), 64. *Prof Exp:* Chem engr, Am Oil Co, 64-68, PROJ MGR, RES & DEVELOP DEPT, AMOCO OIL CO, 68- *Mem:* Am Chem Soc; Am Inst Chem Engrs. *Res:* Reaction mechanisms and reaction kinetics in multiphase systems; petroleum technology, particularly hydrotreating of petroleum distillates. *Mailing Add:* Amoco Oil Co Res & Develop PO Box 400 Naperville IL 60540

MOSBY, WILLIAM LINDSAY, b Rockford, Ill, Nov 30, 21; m 49. ORGANIC CHEMISTRY. *Educ:* Harvard Univ, BSc, 43; Ohio State Univ, PhD(org chem), 49. *Prof Exp:* Res chemist, Gen Aniline & Film Corp, 49-52; res chemist, Res Dept, 52-54, group leader, 55-58, res assoc, 59-76, PRIN RES SCIENTIST, AM CYANAMID CO, 76- *Concurrent Pos:* Am Cyanamid fel, Univ Munich, 64-65. *Mem:* Am Chem Soc. *Res:* Synthetic and theoretical organic chemistry; intermediates for dyes and pharmaceuticals; light stabilizers; vat dyes; polyester dyes; antioxidants; aromatic and polycyclic compounds and heterocyclic system with bridgehead nitrogen atoms. *Mailing Add:* Am Cyanamid Co Bound Brook NJ 08805

MOSCARELLO, MARIO ANTONIO, medicine, biochemistry, see previous edition

MOSCATELLI, EZIO ANTHONY, b New York, NY, Nov 17, 26; c 1. BIOCHEMISTRY, NEUROCHEMISTRY. *Educ:* Columbia Univ, AB, 48; Univ Ill, MS, 49, PhD(biochem), 58. *Prof Exp:* Assoc chemist, Merck & Co, Inc, 49-55; chemist, Nat Heart Inst, 58-59; sr chemist, Merck, Sharp & Dohme Res Labs, 59-62; asst prof biochem, Univ Tex Southwest Med Sch, Dallas, 62-70; assoc prof psychiat & biochem, Mo Inst Psychiat, 70-74; ASSOC PROF BIOCHEM, SCH MED & INVESTR, DALTON RES CTR, UNIV MO-COLUMBIA, 74- *Mem:* Am Chem Soc; Am Oil Chem Soc; Am Soc Biol Chemists; Am Soc Neurochem; Int Soc Neurochem. *Res:* Biochemistry of brain membrane lipids in alcohol abuse and cold adaptation. *Mailing Add:* Dalton Res Ctr Research Park Columbia MO 65211

MOSCHEL, ROBERT CARL, b Cincinnati, Ohio. ORGANIC CHEMISTRY, BIOCHEMISTRY. *Educ:* Ohio State Univ, BSc, 68, PhD(biochem), 73. *Prof Exp:* Res assoc org chem, Univ Ill, 73-75; CHEMIST, CHEM CARCINOGENESIS, FREDERICK CANCER RES CTR, 76- *Mem:* Am Chem Soc. *Res:* Chemical carcinogenesis; reactivity of chemical carcinogens with nucleic acids. *Mailing Add:* Frederick Cancer Ctr PO Box B Bldg 538 Frederick MD 21701

MOSCHOPEDIS, SPEROS E, b Piraeus, Greece, June 1, 26; Can citizen; m 56; c 3. ORGANIC CHEMISTRY. *Educ:* Nat Univ Athens, BSc, 54, PhD(chem), 69. *Prof Exp:* Teacher chem, Archimides Inst Technol, Greece, 54-56; chemist, Sherritt Gordon Mines, Ltd, Alta, 56-57; RES OFFICER ORG CHEM, RES COUN ALTA, 57- *Mem:* Am Chem Soc; Greek Chem Asn. *Res:* Humic acids, lignites, coals and asphaltic type bituminous materials; water-soluble derivatives of humic acids; synthesis of polypeptides. *Mailing Add:* Org Chem Div Res Coun Alta 11315 87th Ave Edmonton AB T6G 2C2 Can

MOSCHOVAKIS, JOAN RAND, b Glendale, Calif, Dec 24, 37; m 63. MATHEMATICS. *Educ:* Univ Calif, Berkeley, AB, 59; Univ Wis, MS, 61, PhD(math), 65. *Prof Exp:* Instr math, Oberlin Col, 63-64; asst prof, 65-67, 69-74, ASSOC PROF MATH, OCCIDENTAL COL, 74- *Mem:* Asn Symbolic Logic; Am Math Soc; Math Asn Am. *Res:* Foundations of mathematics; formal and symbolic logic; intuitionism; point set-topology. *Mailing Add:* Dept of Math Occidental Col Los Angeles CA 90041

MOSCHOVAKIS, YIANNIS N, b Athens, Greece, Jan 18, 38; m 63. MATHEMATICS. *Educ:* Mass Inst Technol, SB & SM, 60; Univ Wis, PhD(math), 63. *Prof Exp:* Actg instr math, Univ Wis, 62-63; Benjamin Peirce instr, Harvard Univ, 63-64; from asst prof to assoc prof, 64-74, PROF MATH, UNIV CALIF, LOS ANGELES, 74- *Mem:* Am Math Soc; Asn Symbolic Logic. *Res:* Foundations of mathematics; recursive functions; hierarchy theory. *Mailing Add:* Dept of Math Univ of Calif Los Angeles CA 90024

MOSCONA, ARON ARTHUR, b Haifa, Israel, July 4, 22; m 49; c 1. DEVELOPMENTAL BIOLOGY. *Educ:* Hebrew Univ Jerusalem, MSc, 47, PhD(zool), 50. *Prof Exp:* Res fel embryol, Strangeways Res Lab, Cambridge Univ, 50-52; assoc prof physiol, Sch Med, Hebrew Univ Jerusalem, 53-55; vis investr develop biol, Rockefeller Inst, 55-57; from assoc prof to prof zool, 58-69, prof biol, 69-74, LOUIS BLOCK PROF BIOL SCI & MEM COMT DEVELOP BIOL & GENETICS, UNIV CHICAGO, 74-, DIR TRAINING PROG IN DEVELOP BIOL, 69- *Concurrent Pos:* Vis assoc prof, Stanford Univ, 59; Claude Bernard vis prof, Univ Montreal, 60; Lillie fel, Marine Biol Lab, Woods Hole, 60 & vis prof, Univ Palermo, 66; ed, Exp Cell Res, Current Topics Develop Biol & Univ Chicago Pubs Biol. *Mem:* Nat Acad Sci; Am Asn Anat; Int Inst Embryol; fel NY Acad Sci; Int Soc Cell Biol. *Res:* Mechanisms of embryonic differentiation; tissue culture; cell physiology; neoplasia. *Mailing Add:* Dept of Biol Univ of Chicago Chicago IL 60637

MOSCONY, JOHN JOSEPH, b Philadelphia, Pa, Aug 26, 29. CHEMISTRY. *Educ:* St Joseph's Col, Pa, BS, 51, MS, 58; Univ Pa, PhD(chem), 65. *Prof Exp:* Chemist, Elec Storage Battery Co, 51-54 & Waterman Prod Co, 54-57; ENG LEADER, RCA CORP, 57- *Concurrent Pos:* Lectr, RCA Corp Eng Serv, 71- *Mem:* Am Chem Soc; Am Vacuum Soc. *Res:* High pressure synthesis of silicon fluorides; thermoelectric and thermionic energy conversion; materials and processes related to vacuum and color television picture tubes. *Mailing Add:* 936 Martha Ave Lancaster PA 17601

MOSCOVICI, CARLO, b Cairo, Egypt, July 27, 25; US citizen; m 55; c 2. VIROLOGY. *Educ:* Univ Rome, PhD(microbiol), 52. *Prof Exp:* Asst prof pediat, Med Sch, Univ Colo, 57-67; assoc prof, 67-71, PROF IMMUNOL & MICROBIOL, MED SCH, UNIV FLA, 71-, RES CAREER SCIENTIST, 78-; CHIEF VIROL RES LAB, VET ADMIN HOSP, 67- *Honors & Awards:* USPHS-Carrier Award, 61. *Res:* Tumor virology; avian tumor viruses; RNA tumor viruses; cell differentiation. *Mailing Add:* Virus Res Lab Vet Admin Hosp Gainesville FL 32601

MOSCOVICI, MAURICIO, b Sao Paulo, Brazil, Apr 26, 25; m 48; c 3. ANATOMY, SURGERY. *Educ:* Univ Brazil, DDS, 47, PhD(anat), 65; Univ Fluminense, Brazil, PhD(anat), 54. *Prof Exp:* From asst prof to prof anat, Fac Odontol, State of Rio de Janeiro, 49-60; prof, Fac Odontol, 60-64, prof, Fac Pharm, 64-74, hon prof, 65, PROF TITULAR ANAT, FAC MED, FED UNIV FLUMINENSE, RIO DE JANEIRO, 74-, HEAD DEPT, 67- *Concurrent Pos:* Fel, Neurol Inst, Univ Brazil, 59-60; fel anat, Tech Coop Prog, US Dept State-Agency Int Develop, 60-61; dent surgeon Welfare Inst, Labor Ministry, Brazil, 51-66, head clin oral-facial surg, Ipanema Hosp, 66-; ed, J Brazilian Dent Asn, 60-61; partic teacher's training prog oral biol, Chicago Col Dent Surg, Loyola Univ, 61; vis prof & lectr, Med Sch, Northwestern Univ, 67; vis prof, Med Col Ohio, 72; prof anat & head dept fac, Med Campos, Rio de Janeiro; prof anat, Univ Fedn Rio de Janeiro. *Mem:* AAAS; Am Asn Anat; Int Asn Dent Res; Brazilian Soc Anat; Port-Brazilian Soc Anat (pres, 74-76). *Res:* Oral, head and neck surgery; human anatomy; oral anatomy; mandibular nerve; facial nerve; ear anatomy; gastric-esophagus junction; human embryology; temporo mandibular joint. *Mailing Add:* Av Atlantica 720 Apt 1002 Leme ZC-07 Rio de Janeiro Brazil

MOSCOVITZ, HOWARD, b New York, NY, Apr 6, 23; m 58; c 3. CARDIOVASCULAR PHYSIOLOGY. *Educ:* City Col New York, BS, 43; NY Univ, MD, 46. *Prof Exp:* Asst attend physician, 58-64, assoc physician, 64-70, ATTEND PHYSICIAN, MT SINAI HOSP, NEW YORK, 70-, SR MEM CARDIAC CATHETERIZATION TEAM, 58- *Concurrent Pos:* Exec med officer, Jewish Hosp for Aged, 60-; assoc clin prof, Mt Sinai Sch Med, 66-75, clin prof med, 75-; attend cardiologist, Kingsbridge Vet Admin Hosp, 70-; fel coun clin cardiol, Am Heart Asn. *Mem:* Sr mem Am Fedn Clin Res; fel Am Col Physicians; fel Am Col Cardiol; fel Am Col Chest Physicians. *Res:* Intracardiac phonocardiography; cardiac catheterization. *Mailing Add:* Mt Sinai Hosp Levy Plaza One Gustave Lane New York NY 10029

MOSCOWITZ, ALBERT, b Manchester, NH, Aug 20, 29. PHYSICAL CHEMISTRY. *Educ:* City Col New York, BS, 50; Harvard Univ, MA, 54, PhD, 57. *Prof Exp:* Nat Res Coun-Am Chem Soc fel petrol res, Harvard Univ, 57-58 & Wash Univ, 58-59; from asst prof to assoc prof, 59-65, PROF PHYS CHEM, UNIV MINN, MINNEAPOLIS, 65- *Concurrent Pos:* Fulbright lectr & vis prof, Copenhagen Univ, 61-62, vis prof, 67-68; Alfred P Sloan Found fel, 62-66; mem nat screening comt, Fulbright Awards to Scandinavia, 65, chmn, 66; Seydel-Woolley vis prof, Ga Inst Technol, 66; adv ed, Chem Physics Lett, 67-; vchmn, Gordon Conf Theoret Chem, 68, chmn, 70; assoc ed, J Chem Physics, 70-73. *Mem:* AAAS; Am Chem Soc; Royal Soc Chem; The Chem Soc; fel NY Acad Sci. *Res:* Electronic structure of molecules; optical activity; Faraday effect; stereochemistry. *Mailing Add:* Dept of Chem Univ of Minn Minneapolis MN 55455

MOSE, DOUGLAS GEORGE, b Chicago, Ill, July 18, 42; m 69. GEOCHEMISTRY, GEOCHRONOLOGY. *Educ:* Univ Ill, Urbana, BS, 65; Univ Kans, MS, 68, PhD(geol), 71. *Prof Exp:* Asst prof geol, Brooklyn Col, 71-75; ASSOC PROF GEOL, GEORGE MASON UNIV, 75- *Mem:* Geol Soc Am; Geol Soc Can; Nat Asn Geol Teachers; Sigma Xi. *Res:* Evolution of igneous and metamorphic rocks in North American Precambrian and Paleozoic terranes. *Mailing Add:* Dept of Chem George Mason Univ Fairfax VA 22030

MOSELEY, HARRISON MILLER, b Dundee, Tex, Dec 14, 21. PHYSICS. *Educ:* Tex Christian Univ, AB, 43; Univ NC, PhD(physics), 50. *Prof Exp:* From asst prof to assoc prof, 50-65, PROF PHYSICS, TEX CHRISTIAN UNIV, 65- *Mem:* Am Phys Soc; Am Asn Physics Teachers. *Res:* Thermal diffusion; fundamental particle theory. *Mailing Add:* Dept of Physics Tex Christian Univ Ft Worth TX 76129

MOSELEY, HARRY EDWARD, b New Iberia, La, Oct 18, 29; m 55; c 2. CHEMISTRY. *Educ:* La State Univ, BS, 51, MS, 52, PhD(chem), 69. *Prof Exp:* Res chemist, Monsanto Chem Co, 54-61; from instr to assoc prof, 61-75, PROF CHEM, LA TECH UNIV, 75- *Mem:* AAAS; Am Chem Soc; Sigma Xi. *Res:* Separation and determination of the platinum metals. *Mailing Add:* 2506 Cypress Springs Ave Ruston LA 71270

MOSELEY, JOHN TRAVIS, b New Orleans, La, Feb 26, 42; m 61; c 2. ATOMIC PHYSICS, MOLECULAR PHYSICS. *Educ:* Ga Inst Technol, BS, 64, MS, 66, PhD(physics), 69. *Prof Exp:* Asst res physicist, Eng Exp Sta, Ga Inst Technol, 64-65; asst prof physics, Univ West Fla, 68-69; physicist, SRI Int, 69-75, sr physicist, 75-77, prog mgr, 77-79; assoc prof, 79-82, PROF, DEPT PHYSICS, UNIV ORE, 82-, DIR, CHEM PHYSICS INST, 81- *Concurrent Pos:* Vis scientist, Univ Paris, 75-76, vis prof, 77, 78, 80 & 82; mem, Comt Atomic & Molecular Sci, Nat Res Coun. *Mem:* Am Phys Soc; fel Am Chem Soc; AAAS. *Res:* Laser techniques are used to study small molecules, principally ions, in the gas phase; spectroscopy, reactions, multiphoton ionization, and photodissociation; photodissociation and photodetachment of ions. *Mailing Add:* Dept Physics Univ Oregon Eugene OR 94703

MOSELEY, KENNETH P(EELE), b McDonough, Ga, Jan 16, 22; m 46; c 2. CHEMICAL ENGINEERING. *Educ:* Ga Inst Technol, BChE, 47. *Prof Exp:* Physicist, Carbide & Carbon Chem Corp, Tenn, 46-47, chem engr, 47-52; prod engr, 52-56, mgr prod eng, Edgewood Arsenal, 56-62, mgr facil eng, 62-66, mgr prod eng, 66-71, DEP DIR MFG TECHNOL, EDGEWOOD ARSENAL, US ARMY CHEM CORPS, 71- *Mem:* Am Ord Asn. *Res:* Chemical plant engineering; engineering of chemical warfare items of offense and defense; chemical engineering applications in nuclear field; construction engineering. *Mailing Add:* 16 Lake Dr Bel Air MD 21014

MOSELEY, MAYNARD FOWLE, JR, b Boston, Mass, July 15, 18; m 49; c 2. PLANT ANATOMY. *Educ:* Univ Mass, BS, 40; Univ Ill, MS, 42, PhD(bot), 47. *Prof Exp:* Instr bot, Cornell Univ, 47-49; from instr to assoc prof, 49-63, PROF BOT, UNIV CALIF, SANTA BARBARA, 63- *Mem:* Bot Soc Am; Int Soc Plant Morphol; Int Asn Wood Anat. *Mailing Add:* Dept of Biol Sci Univ of Calif Santa Barbara CA 93106

MOSELEY, PATTERSON B, b Holland, Mo, May 27, 18; m 42; c 3. CHROMATOGRAPHY. *Educ:* Ouachita Col, BS, 43; La State Univ, MS, 49, PhD, 51. *Prof Exp:* Res chemist, Hercules Powder Co, Del, 51-57, res supvr, 57-64; assoc prof, 64-69, PROF CHEM, LA TECH UNIV, 69-, DIR RES, COL ARTS & SCI & DIR DIV ALLIED HEALTH, 68-, ASSOC DEAN COL ARTS & SCI, 70- *Mem:* AAAS; Am Chem Soc. *Res:* Adsorption chromatography; naval stores chemistry; ion exchange. *Mailing Add:* Col of Arts & Sci La Tech Univ Ruston LA 71270

MOSELEY, ROBERT DAVID, JR, b Minden, La, Feb 29, 24; m 47; c 3. RADIOLOGY. *Educ:* La State Univ, MD, 47; Am Bd Radiol, dipl, 55. *Prof Exp:* Asst resident radiol, Univ Chicago, 49-50; spec res proj, Los Alamos Sci Lab, 50-51, staff mem, Univ Calif, 51-52; from instr to prof radiol & chmn dept, Sch Med, Univ Chicago, 54-71, dir radiation protection serv, 60-71; asst chmn dept, 71-78, PROF RADIOL & CHIEF DIAG RADIOL DIV, UNIV NMEX, 71-, CHMN DEPT RADIOL, 78- *Concurrent Pos:* Assoc chief of staff, Los Alamos Med Ctr, 51-52; Am Cancer Soc clin fel, 55-56; tech adv, US deleg, Int Conf Peaceful Uses of Atomic Energy, Geneva, 58; prof radiol, Argonne Cancer Res Hosp, Chicago, 58-71; vis prof & res scholar, Roentgen Diag Dept, Univ Lund, 62-63; chief of staff, Bernalillo County Med Ctr, NMex, 71-72; mem bd dirs, Nat Coun Radiation Protection; mem radiation study sect, Div Res Grants, NIH, 71-75. *Mem:* Asn Univ Radiol (pres, 61-62); Radiol Soc NAm (1st vpres, 75-76); Am Col Radiol (pres, 72-73); Int Soc Radiol; hon fel Royal Col Radiologists. *Res:* Radiation protection; tract; diagnostic radiologic and nuclear instrumentation. *Mailing Add:* Dept of Radiol Univ of NMex Sch of Med Albuquerque NM 87131

MOSELEY, SHERRARD THOMAS, b Roanoke, Va, May 16, 21; m 41; c 1. ELECTRICAL ENGINEERING. *Educ:* Va Polytech Inst, BSEE, 42; Syracuse Univ, MEE, 52. *Prof Exp:* Elec engr, Gen Elec Co, 46-48; instr & res assoc elec eng, Syracuse Univ, 48-54; assoc prof & actg head dept, Univ SC, 57-62; pres, Wytheville Community Col, 62-67; res dir, Fla Jr Col Syst, 67-69; mgr duplicating prod div, Caldwell-Sites Co, 69-74; TRAINING COORDR, ELECTRO-OPTICAL PROD DIV, ITT CORP, 74- *Mem:* Inst Elec & Electronics Engrs. *Res:* Microwave antennas and propagation; ionospheric propagation at low frequencies. *Mailing Add:* ITT Corp Electro-Optical Prod Div 7635 Planation Rd Roanoke VA 24019

MOSELEY, WILLIAM DAVID, JR, b Cleveland, Ohio, Nov 27, 36. PHYSICAL CHEMISTRY. *Educ:* Williams Col, BA, 58; Wash State Univ, PhD(chem), 63. *Prof Exp:* Jr scientist quantum chem, Univ Uppsala, 63-66; asst prof chem, Howard Univ, 66-69; asst prof, 69-78, ASSOC PROF CHEM, WASH STATE UNIV, 78- *Res:* Quantum theory; valence theory; collisions. *Mailing Add:* NE 405 Colorado Wash State Univ Pullman WA 99163

MOSELY, LYNN JOHNSON, b Washington, DC, July 7, 48; m 72. ANIMAL BEHAVIOR, ORNITHOLOGY. *Educ:* Col William & Mary, BS, 70; Univ NC, Chapel Hill, PhD(zool), 76. *Prof Exp:* Instr biol, Elon Col, 75-77; ASST PROF BIOL, GUILFORD COL, 77- *Mem:* AAAS; Animal Behav Soc; Am Ornithologists Union; Wilson Ornith Soc; Am Soc Zoologists. *Res:* Behavior and communication in vertebrates, specifically auditory communication in colonial birds. *Mailing Add:* Dept of Biol Guilford Col Greensboro NC 27410

MOSEMAN, JOHN GUSTAV, b Oakland, Nebr, Dec 7, 21; m 48; c 3. PLANT PATHOLOGY, AGRONOMY. *Educ:* Univ Nebr, BS, 43; Wash State Univ, MS, 48; Iowa State Univ, PhD(agron, plant path), 50. *Prof Exp:* Res plant pathologist, NC, 50-54, res plant pathologist,Cereal Crops Res Br, 54-69, leader barley invest, 69-72, chmn, Plant Genetics & Germplasm Inst, 72-81, RES PLANT PATHOLOGIST, NORTHEASTERN REGION, SCI & EDUC ADMIN-AGR RES SERV, USDA, 81- *Mem:* Am Phytopath Soc; Am Soc Agron. *Res:* Develop improved wheat, barley germplasm by studying host pathogen interactions, resistance biotic, abiotic stresses, such as rusts, powdery mildew, salts and drouth; coevolution, and genetics of host pathogens. *Mailing Add:* 1918 Blackbriar Silver Springs MD 20903

MOSEMAN, ROBERT FREDRICK, b Indianapolis, Ind, Dec 18, 41; m 65; c 3. PESTICIDE CHEMISTRY. *Educ:* Marian Col, BS, 63; Univ NC, MS, 65; Univ Mo, PhD(agr chem), 71. *Prof Exp:* Chemist, NC State Bd Health, 65-66; chemist, USPHS, 66-68; res chemist, US Environ Protection Agency, 71-79; DEPT HEAD, ANAL CHEM DIV, RADIAN CORP, 79- *Mem:* Sigma Xi; Am Chem Soc. *Res:* Development of analytical methodology for the determination of trace levels of pesticides and other toxic substances and their transformation products in various types of biological and environmental samples. *Mailing Add:* Radian Corp Anal Chem Div 8500 Shoal Creek Austin TX 78766

MOSEN, ARTHUR WALTER, b Bemidji, Minn, July 11, 22; m 46; c 2. ANALYTICAL CHEMISTRY. *Educ:* Ore State Col, BS, 49, MS, 51. *Prof Exp:* Instr chem, San Diego State Col, 50-51; res asst anal chem, Los Alamos Sci Lab, 51-53, staff mem, 53-55; chemist, Rohr Corp, 55-56; staff mem, John Jay Hopkins Lab Pure & Appl Sci, Gen Atomic Div, Gen Dynamics Corp, 56-59, group leader anal chem, 59-66, asst chmn chem dept, 66-70; mgr anal chem br & sr staff mem, Mat Sci Dept, Gulf Gen Atomic Co, 70-73; mgr anal chem dept, Gen Atomic Co, 73-78; chief chemist, Industrial Marine, 78-81, prin chemist, AVX Mat Div, 79-81; RETIRED. *Concurrent Pos:* Lectr, San Diego State Col, 55-57 & 59-60. *Mem:* AAAS; Am Chem Soc; Am Soc Testing & Mat. *Res:* Analytical chemistry methods development applied particularly to nuclear reactor materials; gases in metals; rare earth elements. *Mailing Add:* 323 Alpine Ave Chula Vista CA 92010

MOSER, ALMA P, b Auburn, Wyo, Aug 9, 35; m 57; c 4. MECHANICAL ENGINEERING, APPLIED MECHANICS. *Educ:* Utah State Univ, BS, 61, MS, 63; Univ Colo, PhD(civil eng), 67. *Prof Exp:* Assoc engr, Thiokol Chem Corp, 61; from instr to assoc prof mech eng, 61-76, PROF MECH ENG & HEAD DEPT & DIR, PIPING SYSTS INST, UTAH STATE UNIV, 76- *Concurrent Pos:* Res assoc, Johns-Manville Corp, 72-75. *Mem:* Am Soc Mech Engrs; Am Water Works Asn; Sigma Xi. *Res:* Engineering elasticity; viscoelasticity; crack propagation and fracture analysis; soil-structure interaction mechanics. *Mailing Add:* Dept of Mech Eng Utah State Univ Logan UT 84322

MOSER, BRUNO CARL, b Elmhurst, Ill, Mar 31, 40; m 62; c 3. HORTICULTURE. *Educ:* Mich State Univ, BS, 62, MS, 64; Rutgers Univ, PhD(hort), 69. *Prof Exp:* From asst prof to assoc prof hort, Rutgers Univ, New Brunswick, 69-75; PROF HORT & HEAD DEPT, PURDUE UNIV, WEST LAFAYETTE, 75- *Honors & Awards:* Kenneth Post Award, Am Soc Hort Sci, 69. *Mem:* Am Soc Hort Sci; Int Plant Propagation Soc. *Res:* Physiology of root regeneration; bud dormancy; tuberization. *Mailing Add:* Dept of Hort Purdue Univ West Lafayette IN 47907

MOSER, CHARLES R, b Woodland, Calif, Oct 8, 39; m 60; c 1. DEVELOPMENTAL BIOLOGY. *Educ:* Humboldt State Col, AB, 61; State Univ NY Buffalo, PhD(biol), 67. *Prof Exp:* Asst prof, 66-71, assoc prof, 72-77, PROF BIOL SCI, CALIF STATE UNIV, SACRAMENTO, 77- *Res:* DNA, RNA, protein synthesis and their interrelationships in developing frog embryos. *Mailing Add:* Dept Biol Sci Calif State Univ Sacramento CA 95813

MOSER, DONALD EUGENE, b Steubenville, Ohio, Jan 22, 25; m 46; c 3. MATHEMATICS. *Educ:* Amherst Col, AB, 47; Brown Univ, AM, 49; Univ Pittsburgh, PhD(math), 56. *Prof Exp:* From instr to asst prof math, Univ Mass, 49-60; assoc prof, 60-70, PROF MATH, UNIV VT, 70- *Mem:* Math Asn Am. *Res:* Algebra; analysis. *Mailing Add:* Dept of Math Univ of Vt Burlington VT 05401

MOSER, FRANK, b Winnipeg, Man, Sept 5, 27; US citizen. SOLID STATE PHYSICS. *Educ:* Univ Man, BSc hons, 49; Univ Minn, MSc, 52. *Prof Exp:* Res physicist, Res Labs, Eastman Kodak Co, 52-81; MEM FAC, PHYSICS DEPT, ISRAEL INST TECHNOL, 81- *Concurrent Pos:* Vis scientist, Oxford Univ, 65-66 & Israel Inst Technol, 73-74. *Mem:* Am Phys Soc. *Res:* Electronic properties of semiconductors; photoeffects and imaging phenomena in semiconductors and other solids and thin films. *Mailing Add:* Technion Haifa 32000 Israel

MOSER, FRANK HANS, b Chicago, Ill, Aug 4, 07; m 30, 69; c 2. POLLUTION CHEMISTRY, PIGMENTS. *Educ:* Hope Col, AB, 28; Univ Mich, MS, 29, PhD(chem), 31. *Prof Exp:* Asst, Univ Mich, 28-31, chief analyst, Eng Res Dept, 31-32; sr res chemist, Nat Aniline Co, NY, 32-38; supt, Intermediate Dept, Standard Ultramarine Co, 38-53; supt, Intermediate & Phthalocyanine Depts, Standard Ultramarine & Color Co, 53-59, res dir, 59-64; res dir, Holland Suco Color Co, 65-68; tech dir pigments div, Chemetron Corp, 68-72; CONSULT PHTHALOCYANINE COMPOUNDS, 72- *Mem:* Am Chem Soc; fel Am Inst Chemists; NY Acad Sci. *Res:* Phthalocyanine compounds; pigments; intermediates for pigments and dyes; pigments application; process, product and raw material safety. *Mailing Add:* 3373 Lakeshore Dr Holland MI 49423

MOSER, GLENN ALLEN, b West Reading, Pa, Sept 19, 43. ORGANOMETALLIC CHEMISTRY, INORGANIC CHEMISTRY. *Educ:* Lebanon Valley Col, BSchem, 65; Bucknell Univ, MS, 68; Univ Mass, MS, 69, PhD(inorg chem), 72. *Prof Exp:* Sci Res Coun fel inorg chem & organometallic chem, Inorg Chem Lab, Oxford Univ, Eng, 72-74; res assoc inorg chem, Univ Wis-Madison, 74-76; RES CHEMIST POLYMER CHEM, HERCULES INC, 76- *Mem:* Am Chem Soc; Sigma Xi. *Res:* Organometallic research; homogeneous and heterogeneous catalysis; metathesis; cationic polymerization; hydrogenation. *Mailing Add:* 2521 Eaton Rd Chalfonte Wilmington DE 19810

MOSER, HERBERT CHARLES, b Camp Verde, Ariz, Mar 5, 29; m 51; c 2. PHYSICAL CHEMISTRY. *Educ:* San Jose State Col, BS, 52; Iowa State Univ, PhD(chem), 57. *Prof Exp:* From asst prof to assoc prof, 57-69, PROF CHEM, KANS STATE UNIV, 69- *Mem:* Am Chem Soc. *Res:* Atomic and free radical reactions; radiation chemistry; use of radioisotopes as tracers. *Mailing Add:* Dept of Chem Kans State Univ Manhattan KS 66506

MOSER, JAMES HOWARD, b Santa Rosa, Calif, Apr 29, 28; m 50; c 4. CHEMISTRY, CHEMICAL ENGINEERING. *Educ:* Univ Calif, BS, 50; Ore State Col, MS, 52, PhD(chem), 54. *Prof Exp:* Asst food technol, Ore State Col, 50-51, asst chem, 51-52; res chemist & techologist, Shell Oil Co, Calif, 54-60, sr res chemist, Houston Res Lab, 60-68, STAFF RES ENGR, SHELL DEVELOP CO, HOUSTON, TEX, 68- *Mem:* Am Inst Chem Eng; Sigma Xi. *Res:* Chemical and petroleum process design and development; applied mathematics and statistics; mathematical simulation of chemical and petroleum processes; control systems, environmental engineering; operations research; analytical and physical chemistry; reaction kinetics. *Mailing Add:* Shell Develop Co PO Box 1380 Houston TX 77001

MOSER, JOHN WILLIAM, JR, b Hagerstown, Md, Oct 8, 36; m 64; c 3. FOREST BIOMETRY. *Educ:* WVa Univ, BS, 58; Pa State Univ, MS, 61; Purdue Univ, PhD(forest biomet), 67. *Prof Exp:* Forester, US Forest Serv, 61-63 & Coop Exten Serv, WVa Univ, 63-64; asst, 64-66, from instr to assoc prof forestry & conserv, 66-78, PROF FORESTRY, PURDUE UNIV, WEST LAFAYETTE, 78- *Mem:* Biomet Soc; Soc Am Foresters. *Res:* Modeling the dynamics of forest stands; computer applications to forest management. *Mailing Add:* Dept of Forestry & Natural Resources Purdue Univ West Lafayette IN 47907

MOSER, JOSEPH M, b Spring Hill, Minn, Apr 13, 30. MATHEMATICAL STATISTICS. *Educ:* St John's Univ, Minn, BA, 54; St Louis Univ, MA, 55, PhD(math statist), 59. *Prof Exp:* Statistician, Aberdeen Proving Ground, Md, 55-56; from asst prof to assoc prof, 59-69, PROF MATH STATIST, SAN DIEGO STATE UNIV, 69- *Concurrent Pos:* Consult, Navy Electronics Lab, Calif, 64-71. *Mem:* Inst Math Statist; Math Asn Am; Am Statist Asn. *Res:* Distribution-free statistics. *Mailing Add:* Dept of Math San Diego State Univ San Diego CA 92182

MOSER, JÜRGEN (KURT), b Königsberg, Ger, July 4, 28; nat US; m 55; c 3. MATHEMATICS. *Educ:* Univ Göttingen, Dr rer nat, 52. *Prof Exp:* Asst math, Univ Göttingen, 53; res assoc, NY Univ, 53-54; asst, Univ Göttingen, 54-55; res assoc, NY Univ, 55-56, asst prof, 56-57; from asst prof to assoc prof, Mass Inst Technol, 57-60; dir, Courant Inst Math Sci, 67-70, PROF MATH, NY UNIV, 60- *Concurrent Pos:* Sloan fel, 62 & 63; Am Acad Arts & Sci fel, 64; Guggenheim fel, 70. *Honors & Awards:* G B Birkhoff Prize, 68; J Craig Watson Medal, 69. *Mem:* Nat Acad Sci; Am Math Soc; corresp mem Int Astron Union. *Res:* Ordinary and partial differential equations; spectral theory; celestial mechanics. *Mailing Add:* Courant Inst of Math Sci NY Univ New York NY 10012

MOSER, KENNETH BRUCE, b Malverne, NY, Mar 27, 33; m 58; c 5. CARBOHYDRATE CHEMISTRY. *Educ:* Tusculum Col, BS, 54; Duke Univ, PhD(chem), 59. *Prof Exp:* Res chemist, 58-60, sr res chemist, 60-70, lab head, 70-73, GROUP LEADER, A E STALEY MFG CO, 73- *Mem:* Am Chem Soc; Sigma Xi. *Res:* Synthesis of polycyclic aromatic systems containing quarternary nitrogen at the bridgehead position; preparation of acrylic polymer emulsions; carbohydrates; nitrogen heterocyclics; starch modification. *Mailing Add:* 3045 Mac Arthur Rd Decatur IL 62526

MOSER, KENNETH MILES, b Baltimore, Md, Apr 12, 29; m 51; c 4. MEDICINE. *Educ:* Haverford Col, AB, 50; Johns Hopkins Univ, MD, 54. *Prof Exp:* From instr to assoc prof med, Georgetown Univ, 58-68, chief pulmonary div, Univ Hosp, 61-68; assoc prof, 68-73, PROF MED, UNIV CALIF, SAN DIEGO, 73-, DIR PULMONARY DIV, 68-, DIR PULMONARY SPEC CTR RES, 70- *Concurrent Pos:* Dir head, chest & contagious dis div, Nat Naval Med Ctr, Md, 59-61; chief pulmonary sect, Georgetown Clin Res Inst, Bur Aviation Med, Fed Aviation Agency, 61-66; consult, US Naval Hosp, Md, 61 & NIH, 65- *Mem:* Am Thoracic Soc; Am Heart Asn; Am Fedn Clin Res; fel Am Col Physicians; fel Am Col Chest Physicians. *Res:* Pulmonary and cardiac physiology; blood coagulation; pathogenesis and therapy of thromboembolism; clinical pulmonary disease. *Mailing Add:* Pulmonary Div Univ Hosp 225 W Dickinson St San Diego CA 92103

MOSER, LOUISE ELIZABETH, b Racine, Wis, July 24, 43. MATHEMATICS. *Educ:* Univ Wis-Madison, BS, 65, MS, 66, PhD(math), 70. *Prof Exp:* Asst prof, 70-74, assoc prof, 74-80, PROF MATH, CALIF STATE UNIV, HAYWARD, 80- *Mem:* Am Math Soc; Math Asn Am. *Res:* Topology of 3-manifolds; knot theory; group theory; ring theory. *Mailing Add:* Dept Math Calif State Univ 25800 Hillary St Hayward CA 94542

MOSER, LOWELL E, b Akron, Ohio, Mar 19, 40; m 64; c 2. AGRONOMY. *Educ:* Ohio State Univ, BS, 62, PhD(agron), 67; Kans State Univ, MS, 64. *Prof Exp:* Asst prof agron, Ohio State Univ, 67-70; assoc prof, 70-75, PROF AGRON, UNIV NEBR-LINCOLN, 75- *Honors & Awards:* Teaching Award of Merit, Gamma Sigma Delta, 73; Distinguished Teaching Award, Univ Nebr, 74. *Mem:* Am Soc Agron; Crop Sci Soc Am; Soc Range Mgt. *Res:* Forage physiology; physiological investigation into cool and warm season grasses in Nebraska. *Mailing Add:* Dept of Agron Univ of Nebr Lincoln NE 68583

MOSER, PAUL E, b Auburn, Wyo, Jan 18, 42; m 63; c 4. PLANT BREEDING, PLANT PATHOLOGY. *Educ:* Utah State Univ, MS, 68, PhD(plant path & breeding), 71. *Prof Exp:* Fel plant path, McGill Univ, 71-72; PATHOLOGIST & PLANT BREEDER, GALLATIN VALLEY SEED CO, 72- *Mem:* Am Phytopath Soc; Sigma Xi. *Res:* Breeding of new pea and bean varieties; indexing and screening for disease resistance of peas and beans. *Mailing Add:* Gallatin Valley Seed Co Box 167 Twin Falls ID 83301

MOSER, PHYLIS B, b Cincinnati, Ohio, June 23, 47; m 69; c 1. NUTRITION. *Educ:* Univ Md, BS, 69, MS, 73, PhD(nutrit sci), 76. *Prof Exp:* Res nutritionist, Dept Pediat, Georgetown Med Ctr, 77-78; biologist, Carbohydrate Lab, Nutrit Inst, Agr Res Serv, USDA, 69-72; teaching asst nutrit, 72-74, res asst, 75, asst prof, 75-77, ASST PROF NUTRIT, DEPT FOOD, NUTRIT & INST ADMIN, UNIV MD, 78- *Mem:* Sigma Xi; Am Dietetic Asn; Soc Nutrit Educ; AAAS; Am Women in Sci. *Res:* Nutritional status of women and children especially in regard to minerals. *Mailing Add:* Dept Food Nutrit & Instnl Admin Univ Md College Park MD 20742

MOSER, ROBERT E, b Defiance, Ohio, Feb 18, 39; m 61; c 2. BIO-ORGANIC CHEMISTRY. *Educ:* Bowling Green State Univ, BS, 61; Yale Univ, MS, 63, PhD(org chem), 65. *Prof Exp:* Res specialist, Cent Res Dept, Monsanto Co, Mo, 65-69, group leader, 69-71; sr res chemist, 71-73, res group leader, 73-76, RES MGR, T R EVANS RES CTR, DIAMOND SHAMROCK CORP, 76- *Mem:* AAAS; Am Chem Soc. *Res:* Oxidation-reduction polymers and charge transfer interactions; chemical evolution; protein food and nutrition; design and synthesis of pesticides and drug health products; biological molecular interactions; research organization and management. *Mailing Add:* 10028 Knollwood Dr Mentor OH 44060

MOSER, ROBERT HARLAN, b Trenton, NJ, June 16, 23; m 48; c 2. MEDICINE. *Educ:* Villanova Col, BS, 43; Georgetown Univ, MD, 48; Am Bd Internal Med, dipl, recert, 74. *Prof Exp:* Intern, Washington, DC Gen Hosp, 48-49, fel pulmonary dis, 49-50; surgeon, Korea, 50-51; asst resident, Georgetown Univ Hosp, 51-52, chief resident, 52-53; chief med serv, US Army Hosp, Salzburg, Austria, 53-55; chief med serv, Wurzburg, Ger, 55-56; resident cardiol, Brooke Gen Hosp, 56-57, asst chief dept med, 57-59; fel hemat, Col Med, Univ Utah, 59-60; asst chief, US Army Tripler Gen Hosp, 60-64; chief, William Beaumont Gen Hosp, 65-67, Brooke Gen Hosp, 67-68 & Walter Reed Gen Hosp, 68-69; chief staff, Maui Mem Hosp, 72-73; EXEC V PRES, AM COL PHYSICIANS, 77- *Concurrent Pos:* Assoc prof med, Col Med, Baylor Univ, 58-59; flight controller, Proj Mercury, 59-62; consult & mem med eval team, Proj Gemini, 62-66; ed, Med Opinion & Rev, 66-; chief dept med, Brooke Gen Hosp, 67-68; consult, Proj Apollo, 67-73; clin prof med, Col Med, Univ Hawaii, 69-, Col Med, Wash Univ, 70- & Abraham Lincoln Sch Med, 74-; ed, Jour AMA, 73-75. *Mem:* Inst of Med of Nat Acad Sci; fel Am Col Physicians; fel Am Col Cardiol; Am Therapeut Soc; AMA. *Mailing Add:* Am Col of Physicians 4200 Pine St Philadelphia PA 19104

MOSER, RONNY LEE, b Anadarko, Okla, Aug 19, 54; m 74; c 2. ANIMAL SCIENCE & NUTRITION. *Educ:* Okla State Univ, BS, 76; Univ Nebr, MS, 78, PhD(swine nutrit), 80. *Prof Exp:* ASST PROF SWINE NUTRIT, UNIV MINN, 80- *Mem:* Am Soc Animal Sci. *Res:* Effect of nutrition on reproduction efficiency in sows with particular interest on the primiparous sow. *Mailing Add:* Dept Animal Sci 127 Peters Hall Univ Minn St Paul MN 55108

MOSER, ROY EDGAR, b Steubenville, Ohio, Sept 30, 22; m 42; c 2. FOOD TECHNOLOGY. *Educ:* Univ Mass, Amherst, BS, 47, MS, 49. *Prof Exp:* Food technologist, USDA, DC, 48-50; exten food technologist, Va Polytech Inst, 50-57; assoc prof food technol, Ore State Univ, 58-67, Univ Hawaii, Manoa Campus, 67-68 & Ore State Univ, 68-69; chmn dept food sci & technol, 70-73, PROF FOOD TECHNOL, UNIV HAWAII, MANOA CAMPUS, 69-, CHMN DEPT FOOD SCI & TECHNOL, 78- *Mem:* Fel Inst Food Technol. *Res:* Food processing. *Mailing Add:* Dept of Food Sci & Technol Univ of Hawaii Manoa Campus Honolulu HI 96822

MOSER, STEPHEN ADCOCK, b Artesia, Calif, Mar 24, 46; m 69; c 3. MICROBIOLOGY, MEDICAL MYCOLOGY. *Educ:* Calif State Univ, Long Beach, BS, 69, MS, 72; Ohio State Univ, PhD(med microbiol), 76. *Prof Exp:* trainee med mycol, 77-81, ASST PROF MICROBIOL & IMMUNOL MYCOL, SCH MED, TULANE UNIV, 81- *Mem:* Am Soc Microbiol; Med Mycological Soc Am. *Res:* Host-parasite relationships; chemistry of fungal antigens; immune response in mycotic diseases. *Mailing Add:* Dept of Microbiol & Immunol Tulane Univ New Orleans LA 70112

MOSER, W(ILLIAM) C(HARLES), b Keota, Iowa, Oct 11, 22; m 45; c 3. CHEMICAL ENGINEERING, ORGANIC CHEMISTRY. *Educ:* Purdue Univ, BS, 47. *Prof Exp:* Res engr cellulosic fibers, 47-50, chem engr supvr, 51-52, res supvr, 53-55, tech supvr, Nylon Technol, 56-57, tech supt, Orlon Technol Div, 58-60, process supt & asst plant mgr Dacron, 60-61, from asst plant mgr to plant mgr Nylon, 62-64, Nylon prod mgr, 65-68, dir, Qiana, Textile Fibers Dept, 68, asst gen dir mfg, 68-70, dir, Indust Fibers Div, Textile Fibers Dept, 70-78, GEN DIR MFG, E I DU PONT DE NEMOURS & CO, INC, 79- *Mem:* Am Chem Soc; Am Inst Chem Engrs; AAAS. *Res:* Synthetic textile fibers. *Mailing Add:* 119 Quintyns Rd Greenville DE 19807

MOSER, WILLIAM O J, b Winnipeg, Man, Sept 5, 27; m 53; c 3. MATHEMATICS. *Educ:* Univ Man, BSc, 49; Univ Minn, MA, 51; Univ Toronto, PhD(math), 57. *Prof Exp:* Lectr math, Univ Sask, 55-57, asst prof, 57-59; assoc prof, Univ Man, 59-64; assoc prof, 64-66, PROF MATH, McGILL UNIV, 66- *Concurrent Pos:* Ed, Can Math Bull, 61-69. *Mem:* Am Math Soc; Math Asn Am; Can Math Cong (pres, 75-77); Soc Indust & Appl Math. *Res:* Finite groups; combinatorial mathematics. *Mailing Add:* Dept Math McGill Univ 805 Sherbrooke St W Montreal PQ H3A 2K6 Can

MOSER, WILLIAM RAY, b Old Hickory, Tenn, Aug 3, 35; m 60; c 3. CATALYTIC SCIENCES. *Educ:* Mid Tenn State Univ, BS, 59; Mass Inst Technol, PhD(org chem), 64. *Prof Exp:* Res chemist, Monsanto Res SA, Switz, 66-67, staff scientist, 67-69; sr res chemist, Corp Res Labs, Esso Res & Eng Co, NJ, 69-75; res assoc, Badger Co, 75-81; PROF CHEM ENG, WORCESTER POLYTECH INST, 81- *Mem:* Am Chem Soc; NY Acad Sci; NAm Catalysis Soc; Am Inst Chem Engrs. *Res:* Homogeneous and heterogeneous catalysis in areas of chemical and petrochemical processes; organometallic synthesis and reaction mechanisms. *Mailing Add:* Dept Chem Eng Worcester Polytech Inst Worcester MA 01609

MOSES, CAMPBELL, JR, b Pittsburgh, Pa, Feb 12, 17; m 40; c 4. MEDICINE. *Educ:* Univ Pittsburgh, BS, 39, MD, 41. *Prof Exp:* Instr physiol & pharmacol, Sch Med, Univ Pittsburgh, 41-46, from asst prof to assoc prof med, 46-48, dir, Addison H Gibson Lab, 48-68, dir postgrad educ, 60-68; med dir, Am Heart Asn, 68-73; VPRES MED AFFAIRS, MEDICUS COMN, 74- *Concurrent Pos:* Mem coun arteriosclerosis, Am Heart Asn. *Mem:* Am Physiol Soc; Soc Exp Biol & Med; fel AMA; fel Am Col Physicians; Am Diabetes Asn. *Res:* Thrombosis and embolism; anticoagulants; liver and kidney function tests; nutrition, liver and kidney function in arteriosclerosis. *Mailing Add:* Medicus Commun Inc 909 Third Ave New York NY 10022

MOSES, EDWARD JOEL, b Newark, NJ, Oct 9, 38; m 65; c 2. UNDERWATER ACOUSTICS, OPERATIONS RESEARCH. *Educ:* Rensselaer Polytech Inst, BS, 60; Johns Hopkins Univ, PhD(physics), 67. *Prof Exp:* Res assoc physics, Vanderbilt Univ, 67-68, instr, 68-71; res scientist, Raff Assocs, Inc, Md, 71-75; dept head, Ocean Systs Dept, Gen Res Co, 75; sr proj staff, Opers Res, Inc, 75-78, prog dir, 78-80, assoc div dir, 80-81, EXEC SCIENTIST, ORI, INC, 81- *Mem:* Am Phys Soc. *Res:* Sound propagation and noise background in the oceans; statistical character of oceanic noise; statistics of signal detection; tactical analysis and operations research for naval operations and systems. *Mailing Add:* 14506 Woodcrest Dr Rockville MD 20853

MOSES, FRANCIS GUY, b Baltimore, Md, Nov 15, 37. PHYSICAL ORGANIC CHEMISTRY. *Educ:* Univ Del, BA, 59; Calif Inst Technol, PhD(chem), 67. *Prof Exp:* Fel chem, Iowa State Univ, 64-65; SUPV CHEMIST, E I DU PONT DE NEMOURS & CO, INC, 66- *Mem:* Am Chem Soc. *Res:* High pressure chemistry; reaction mechanisms; organic photochemistry. *Mailing Add:* 3 E Kenmore Dr Hyde Park Wilmington DE 19808

MOSES, GERALD ROBERT, b Chicago, Ill, June 7, 38; m 61; c 2. SPEECH PATHOLOGY. *Educ:* Loyola Univ Chicago, BS, 61; Western MIch Univ, MA, 65; Ohio State Univ, PhD(speech sci), 69. *Prof Exp:* Instr speech path, Miami Univ, 65-67; ASSOC PROF SPEECH EDUC, EASTERN MICH UNIV, 69- *Concurrent Pos:* Clin dir, Preble County Speech & Hearing Clin, Ohio, 65-67; ed, J Commun Path, 75- *Mem:* Am Speech & Hearing Asn; Am Asn Higher Educ. *Res:* Stuttering; experimental phonetics; supervision of public school speech therapy. *Mailing Add:* Speech Clin Eastern Mich Univ Ypsilanti MI 48197

MOSES, HAL LYNWOOD, b Goldston, NC, Oct 12, 34. MECHANICAL ENGINEERING. *Educ:* Va Polytech Inst, BS, 60; Mass Inst Technol, MS, 61, PhD(mech eng), 64. *Prof Exp:* Apprentice design, Newport News Shipbuilding & Dry Dock Co, 52-59; fel & asst prof mech eng, Mass Inst Technol, 64-66; engr, Corning Glass Works, NC, 66-69; assoc prof mech eng, 69-75, PROF MECH ENG, VA POLYTECH INST & STATE UNIV, 75- *Concurrent Pos:* Consult, Foster-Miller Assocs, Mass, 65-66; adj asst prof, NC State Univ, 66-69. *Mem:* Am Soc Mech Engrs. *Res:* Turbulent boundary layer; fluidics and fluid mechanics; gas turbines. *Mailing Add:* Dept of Mech Eng Va Polytech Inst & State Univ Blacksburg VA 24061

MOSES, HARRY ELECKS, b Canton, Ohio, Aug 30, 22; m 58; c 1. THEORETICAL PHYSICS. *Educ:* Univ Mich, BS, 44, MS, 47; Columbia Univ, PhD(physics), 50. *Prof Exp:* Res scientist aerodyn, Nat Adv Comt Aeronaut, 44-46 & Univ Mich, 46-47; asst physics, Columbia Univ, 47-49; asst wave propagation, NY Univ, 49-50, res assoc upper atmosphere res, 50-60; assoc prof physics, Polytech Inst Brooklyn, 60-61; staff mem, Geophys Corp Am, Mass, 61-62 & Lincoln Lab, Mass Inst Technol, 62-69; staff mem, Air Force Cambridge Res Labs, 69-76; mem staff, 76-80, RES PROF PHYSICS, CTR ATMOSPHERIC RES, UNIV LOWELL, 80- *Mem:* Fel Am Phys Soc; NY Acad Sci. *Res:* Aerodynamics and fluid flow; electromagnetic, acoustic and quantum direct and inverse scattering; soliton theory and nonlinear equations; information theory; applications of ground theory to quantum theory; meteorology and atmospheric physics. *Mailing Add:* Ctr for Atmospheric Res 450 Aiken St Lowell MA 01851

MOSES, HENRY A, b Gastonia, NC, Sept 8, 39. BIOCHEMISTRY, PHYSIOLOGY. *Educ:* Livingstone Col, BS, 59; Purdue Univ, MS, 62, PhD(biochem), 64. *Prof Exp:* Asst prof, 64-70, ASSOC PROF BIOCHEM, MEHARRY MED COL, 70-, PROVOST FOR INTERNAL AFFAIRS, 78- *Concurrent Pos:* Tenn Heart Asn res grant, 65; vis lectr, Wheaton Col, Mass, 65; consult biochemist, Vet Admin Hosp, Tuskegee, Ala, 65; asst prof, Tenn State Univ, 65-66; consult, George W Hubbard Hosp, Nashville; vis prof biochem, Fisk Univ, 67-; Environ Protection Agency grant, 74-77. *Mem:* AAAS; Am Chem Soc. *Res:* Zinc metabolism; biochemical effects of oral contraceptives; cadmium and lead toxicity; anti-cariogenic effects of vanadium compounds; trace minerals in the post-myocardial infracted patient; toxic metals in the environment. *Mailing Add:* Dept of Biochem Meharry Med Col Nashville TN 37208

MOSES, HERBERT A, b Hartford, Conn, July 22, 29; m 54; c 3. ATOMIC PHYSICS. *Educ:* Mich State Univ, BS, 51, MS, 53; Univ Conn, PhD(physics), 63. *Prof Exp:* From asst to instr physics, Mich State Univ, 51-56; res asst, Univ Conn, 56-59; from asst prof to assoc prof, 59-66, PROF PHYSICS, TRENTON STATE COL, 66- *Mem:* Am Asn Physics Teachers. *Res:* Experimental work in nuclear magnetic resonance in liquid crystals total cross sections for multiple electron stripping in atomic collisions at one hundred kiloelectron volts and five billion electron volts c-muon interactions; theoretical calculations of atomic wave functions for cesium and electron distribution in a deuterium plasma; nuclear magnetic resonance signals in liquid crystals. *Mailing Add:* Dept of Physics Trenton State Col Trenton NJ 08625

MOSES, JOEL, b Petach Tikvah, Israel, Nov 25, 41; US citizen; m 70; c 2. COMPUTER SCIENCE. *Educ:* Columbia Univ, BA, 62, MA, 63; Mass Inst Technol, PhD(math), 67. *Prof Exp:* From asst prof to assoc prof comput sci, 67-76, assoc head dept, 78-80, PROF COMPUT SCI & ENG, MASS INST TECHNOL, 77-, ASSOC DIR LAB COMPUT SCI, 74-, HEAD DEPT ELEC ENG & COMP SCI, 80- *Mem:* Sigma Xi; Asn Comput Mach. *Res:* Symbolic formula manipulation; symbolic integration algorithms; artificial intelligence. *Mailing Add:* Lab for Comput Sci Mass Inst of Technol Cambridge MA 02139

MOSES, LINCOLN ELLSWORTH, b Kansas City, Mo, Dec 21, 21; m 42, 68; c 5. STATISTICS. *Educ:* Stanford Univ, AB, 41, PhD(statist), 50. *Prof Exp:* Asst prof educ, Teachers Col, Columbia Univ, 50-52; from asst prof to assoc prof, 52-59, exec head dept, 64-68, assoc dean humanities & sci, 65-68, dean grad div, 69-75, PROF STATIST & BIOSTATIST, UNIV & SCH MED, STANFORD UNIV, 59- *Concurrent Pos:* Guggenheim fel, 60-61; fel, Ctr Advan Study in Behav Sci, 75-76; adminr, Energy Info Admin, US Dept Energy, 78-80; mem comt, Nat Statist coun, 75-77 & Inst Med Nat Acad Sci, 82-84. *Mem:* Nat Inst Med; Biomet Soc; Am Statist Asn; Inst Math Statist; AAAS. *Res:* Experimental design; biological and psychological applications of statistical methods; data analysis. *Mailing Add:* Dept of Statist Sequoia Hall Stanford Univ Stanford CA 94305

MOSES, MONTROSE JAMES, b New York, NY, June 26, 19; m 49; c 2. CELL BIOLOGY, ELECTRON MICROSCOPY. *Educ:* Bates Col, BS, 41; Columbia Univ, AM, 42, PhD(zool), 49. *Prof Exp:* Assoc cytochemist, Brookhaven Nat Lab, 48-52, cytochemist, 52-55; assoc prof anat, 59-66, PROF ANAT, SCH MED, DUKE UNIV, 66- *Concurrent Pos:* Vis investr, Rockefeller Inst, 54-55, asst, 55-, assoc, 55-56, asst prof cytol, 56-59; mem, Nat Res Coun, 62-64 & 70-74; mem molecular biol study sect, NIH, 66-69; adv ed, Int Rev Cytol, 71-76. *Mem:* Am Soc Zoologists; Genetics Soc Am; Am Soc Naturalists; Am Asn Anatomists; Am Soc Cell Biol (secy, 61-67, pres, 68-69). *Res:* Cytology; fine structure and cytochemistry of nucleus and chromosomes; synaptonemal complex in meiosis; microtubules in motility and cell differentiation; light and electron microscopic techniques for investigating cell structure and function. *Mailing Add:* Dept of Anat Duke Univ Sch of Med Durham NC 27710

MOSES, RAY NAPOLEON, JR, b Clinton, NC, Jan 23, 36; m 62; c 1. ASTRONOMY. *Educ:* Ga Inst Technol, BS, 64; Ohio State Univ, PhD(astron), 74. *Prof Exp:* Astronaut engr, Boeing Co, 64-67 & Lockheed Missiles & Space Co, Inc, 67-68; systs analyst, US Air Force, Wright-Patterson AFB, Ohio, 69-70; ASST PROF PHYSICS, FURMAN UNIV, 74- *Mem:* Am Astron Soc. *Res:* Solar system studies, especially those related to interplanetary exploration. *Mailing Add:* Dept of Physics Furman Univ Greenville SC 29613

MOSES, RONALD ELLIOT, b Chelsea, Mass, Dec 29, 30; m 52; c 2. ORGANIC CHEMISTRY. *Educ:* Harvard Univ, AB, 52; Northeastern Univ, MS, 59. *Prof Exp:* From jr res chemist to sr res chemist, Atlantic Gelatin Div, Gen Foods Corp, Mass, 54-60; sr prof chemist, Gillette Safety Razor Co, 60-66; proj chemist, 66-71, sr mgr res, 71-72, dir prod develop, 72-75, dir tech & admin serv, Toiletries Div, 75-77, DIR PROD DEVELOP-SKIN CARE PROD, PERSONAL CARE DIV, GILLETTE CO, 77- *Mem:* Fel Am Inst Chemists; Am Chem Soc; Soc Cosmetic Chemists. *Res:* Gelatin, processing and properties; organic synthesis, particularly of heterocyclic compounds, especially pyridines, quinolines and pyrimidines. *Mailing Add:* 1039 Shirley St Winthrop MA 02152

MOSES, SAUL, b Pittsburgh, Pa, Dec 31, 21; m 49; c 3. CHEMICAL ENGINEERING. *Educ:* Carnegie Inst Technol, BS, 42; Johns Hopkins Univ, PhD(chem eng), 48. *Prof Exp:* Chem engr, Calvert Distilling Co, Md, 42, Lasting Prod Co, 42-43 & Westinghouse Elec & Mfg Co, 43-44; chem engr-physicist, Naval Res Lab, 47-50; chem engr, 50-59, PRES, DENTOCIDE CHEM CO, 59- *Concurrent Pos:* Consult chem engr. *Mem:* AAAS; Am Chem Soc; Am Inst Chem Engrs; NY Acad Sci; Am Soc Safety Engrs. *Res:* Protective coatings; ultrasonics; process operations-unit phase changes; surface chemistry and plastics; evaluation of adhesion of organic coatings by ultrasonic vibrations. *Mailing Add:* 3525 Barton Oaks Rd Baltimore MD 21208

MOSES, WILLIAM, b New York, NY, Dec 27, 10; m 46; c 3. COMPARATIVE BIOCHEMISTRY. *Educ:* City Col New York, BS, 41; Univ Calif, PhD(comp biochem), 52. *Prof Exp:* Lab asst, Wallerstein Labs, S B Penick, CPC Int, Inc, New York, 35-41, res chemist, 41-42, group leader, 46-49; sect head, 46-49, sect head, 55-62, dir microbiol res, 62-76, CONSULT, 76- *Res:* Biochemistry; microbiology; fermentation; antibiotics; enzymes; tissue culture research. *Mailing Add:* 375 Harland Ave Haworth NJ 07641

MOSESSON, MICHAEL W, b New York, NY, Dec 31, 34; m 67; c 2. BIOCHEMISTRY, INTERNAL MEDICINE. *Educ:* Brooklyn Col, BS, 55; State Univ NY, 59. *Prof Exp:* Intern, II & IV Med Serv, Boston City Hosp, Mass, 59-60; asst resident, Ward Med Serv, Barnes Hosp, St Louis, Mo, 63-64, instr, Dept Med, 65-67; from asst prof to assoc prof med, 67-75, PROF MED, COL MED, STATE UNIV NY DOWNSTATE MED CTR, 75- *Concurrent Pos:* NIH res career develop award, 67; mem exec coun thrombosis, Am Heart Asn, 71-, co-chmn path res comt, 76- *Mem:* Am Fedn Clin Res; Int Soc Hemat; Am Soc Clin Invest; Am Soc Biol Chemists; Int Soc Thrombosis & Haemostasis. *Res:* Structure of fibrinogen and related proteins; metabolism of coagulation proteins; hemostasis. *Mailing Add:* Dept of Med State Univ NY Downstate Med Ctr Brooklyn NY 11203

MOSEVICH, JACK WALTER, applied mathematics, see previous edition

MOSHER, CAROL WALKER, b Loveland, Colo, June 23, 21; m 44; c 3. BIO-ORGANIC CHEMISTRY. *Educ:* Colo State Col, BS, 42; Pa State Col, MS, 43, PhD(chem), 47. *Prof Exp:* RES CHEMIST, STANFORD RES INST, 47- *Mem:* Am Chem Soc. *Res:* Organic syntheses; drug-DNA interactions. *Mailing Add:* 713 Mayfield Stanford CA 94305

MOSHER, CLIFFORD COLEMAN, III, b Lima, Ohio, Aug 18, 27; m 54; c 2. ELECTRICAL ENGINEERING. *Educ:* Mich State Univ, BS, 53; Univ Tex, MS, 55; Stanford Univ, PhD(elec eng), 65. *Prof Exp:* Consult, Magnetohydrodyn Proj, Dept Mech Eng, Stanford Univ, 63-65; asst prof elec eng, Univ Mo, 65-66; consult, Alternating & Direct Current Transmission Proj, Edison Elec Inst, 66-67; assoc prof elec eng & dir energy systs div, Drexel Univ, 67-77; POWER PROF ELEC ENG, WASH STATE UNIV, 77- *Concurrent Pos:* Chmn, Western Protective Relay Conf, 74-; mem, Int Conf on Large High-Tension Elec Systs. *Mem:* Inst Elec & Electronics Engrs; Nat Soc Prof Engrs; Am Soc Eng Educ. *Res:* Electrical power systems; technical and economic analysis, direct current transmission. *Mailing Add:* Dept of Elec Eng Wash State Univ Pullman WA 99164

MOSHER, DON R(AYMOND), b Davenport, Iowa, Aug 7, 21; m 42; c 4. PHYSICAL METALLURGY. *Educ:* St Ambrose Col, BS, 42; Univ Denver, MS, 60, PhD, 69. *Prof Exp:* Res engr, Res Lab, Westinghouse Elec Corp, 42-48; res scientist, Nat Adv Comt Aeronaut, 48-53; from instr to asst prof, 54-60, assoc prof, 60-80, EMER PROF METALL, UNIV COLO, BOULDER, 80- *Mem:* Am Soc Metals; Am Inst Mining, Metall & Petrol Engrs. *Res:* Internal friction; refractory metals; mechanical behavior; failure analysis. *Mailing Add:* EC OT 4-7 Dept of Mech Eng Univ of Colo Boulder CO 80309

MOSHER, HAROLD ELWOOD, b Sterling, Mass, Aug 6, 20; m 46; c 3. HORTICULTURE. *Educ:* Mass State Col, BS, 42; Univ Mass, BLA, 47, MLA, 57. *Prof Exp:* Landscape architect & supt grounds, Lake Placid Club, NY, 47-50; from instr to asst prof hort, Univ Mo, 50-58; assoc exten prof, 58-66, assoc prof landscape archit, 66-72, PROF LANDSCAPE ARCHIT, UNIV MASS, AMHERST, 72- *Res:* Ornamental plants and their uses in landscape architecture; ecological determinants in land use and landscaping. *Mailing Add:* Clark Hall Univ of Mass Amherst MA 01002

MOSHER, HARRY STONE, b Salem, Ore, Aug 31, 15; m 44; c 3. ORGANIC CHEMISTRY. *Educ:* Willamette Univ, AB, 37; Ore State Col, MS, 39; Pa State Col, PhD(org chem), 42. *Prof Exp:* Asst prof chem, Willamette Univ, 39-40; from instr to asst prof, Pa State Col, 43-46; from asst prof to assoc prof, 47-56, PROF CHEM, STANFORD UNIV, 56- *Concurrent Pos:* US sr res fel, Univ London, 59-60; Am Chem Soc fel, Univ Zurich, 67-68; vis prof, Univ Amsterdam, 75. *Mem:* AAAS; Am Chem Soc. *Res:* Stereochemistry; synthetic drugs; mechanisms of organic reactions; chemistry of pyridine compounds; peroxides; animal toxins. *Mailing Add:* Dept of Chem Stanford Univ Stanford CA 94305

MOSHER, JAMES ARTHUR, b Green, NY, Oct 25, 42; m 68; c 1. PHYSIOLOGICAL ECOLOGY, ORNITHOLOGY. *Educ:* Utica Col, BS, 65; State Univ NY Col Environ Sci & Forestry, MS, 73; Brigham Young Univ, PhD(zool), 75. *Prof Exp:* Res assoc physiol ecol, Naval Arctic Res Lab, Univ Alaska, 75-76; fel, 76, ASST PROF, APPALACHIAN ENVIRON LAB, CEES, UNIV MD, 77- *Concurrent Pos:* Mem bd, Raptor Res Found. *Mem:* Ecol Soc Am; AAAS; Am Ornithologists Union; Cooper Ornith Soc. *Res:* Study of avian ecology, especially birds of prey; physiological ecology of birds; thermoregulatory and metabolic adaptations of vertebrates. *Mailing Add:* Appalachian Environ Lab Univ of Md Frostburg MD 21532

MOSHER, JOHN IVAN, b Waterloo, NY, Sept 26, 33; m 60; c 4. HUMAN ECOLOGY. *Educ:* Hobart Col, BA, 56; Western State Col Colo, MA, 61; Utah State Univ, PhD, 72. *Prof Exp:* Chem analyst, NY Agr Sta, Cornell Univ, 58-59; instr biol, Lyndon Inst, Vt, 59-60; asst & preparator, Univ Rochester, 60-61; assoc prof, 61-77, PROF BIOL SCI, STATE UNIV NY COL BROCKPORT, 77- *Mem:* Ecol Soc Am; Am Soc Zoologists; Zool Soc London; Bio-Dynamic Farming & Gardening Asn; Sigma Xi. *Res:* Human ecology, connected with understanding the practical applications of basic ecological principles to living a life style harmonious with the environment; experimentations with shelter, biodynamic food production, and human reactions to employing environmentally sound living practices. *Mailing Add:* Dept of Biol State Univ of NY Brockport NY 14420

MOSHER, LOREN CAMERON, b Phoenix, Ariz, June 20, 38; m 63; c 4. PETROLEUM GEOLOGY, PALEONTOLOGY. *Educ:* Calif Inst Technol, BS, 60; Univ Wis, MS, 64, PhD(micropaleont), 67. *Prof Exp:* Asst prof geol, Fla State Univ, 67-71; assoc prof geosci, Univ Ariz, 71-75; res geologist, Phillips Petrol Co, 75-77, sect supvr, 77-79; MEM STAFF, CAM MOSHER & ASSOCS, 79- *Concurrent Pos:* NSF grant, Fla State Univ, 68-71; adj prof & mfg rep, Brigham Young Univ, 79- *Mem:* Am Asn Petrol Geologists; fel Geol Soc Am. *Res:* Petroleum and alternate energy; stratigraphic and zoologic studies of conodonts. *Mailing Add:* Cam Mosher & Assocs 1035 East 1010 North Pleasant Grove UT 84062

MOSHER, LOREN RICHARD, b Monterey, Calif, Sept 3, 33; div; c 3. PSYCHIATRY. *Educ:* Stanford Univ, BA, 56; Harvard Med Sch, MD, 61. *Prof Exp:* Resident psychiat, Mass Ment Health Ctr, 62-64; clin assoc twin studies, NIMH, 64-66; USPHS ment health spec res fel, Tavistock Clin, London, 66-67; asst prof psychiat, Conn Ment Health Ctr, Sch Med, Yale Univ, 67-68; CHIEF, CTR STUDIES SCHIZOPHRENIA, NIMH, 68- *Concurrent Pos:* Consult, Nat Naval Med Ctr, Bethesda, Md, 72-, Arbours Assoc, London, Eng, 72-, Woodley House, Washington, DC, 73-, Green Door, 77- & Crossing Place, 77- *Mem:* Fel Am Psychiat Asn; Am Col Neuropsychopharmacol; AAAS; Soc Psychother Res. *Res:* Psychosocial treatment of mental illness, specifically, schizophrenia; twin studies, schizophrenia; labeling of mental patients; deinstitutionalism of mental patients and their proper care in the community. *Mailing Add:* Rm 10C-26 Parklawn Bldg 5600 Fishers Lane Rockville MD 20857

MOSHER, MELVILLE CALVIN, b Port Chester, NY, Aug 1, 45. APPLIED MATHEMATICS. *Educ:* Univ Calif, Berkeley, BA, 69, PhD(math), 79. *Prof Exp:* Asst prof math, Univ Miami, Coral Gables, 79-81; RES MATHEMATICIAN, NUMERICAL FLUID MECH DIV, D W TAYLOR NAVAL SHIP RES & DEVELOP CTR, 81- *Mem:* Computional and mathematical fluid mechanics. *Mailing Add:* Code 1843 D W Taylor Naval Ship Res & Develop Ctr Bethesda MD 20084

MOSHER, MELVYN WAYNE, b Palo Alto, Calif, June 10, 40; m 63; c 3. PHYSICAL ORGANIC CHEMISTRY. *Educ:* Univ Washington, BA, 62; Univ Idaho, MS, 64, PhD(org chem), 68. *Prof Exp:* Fel, Univ Alta, 67-69; asst prof chem, Marshall Univ, 69-74; ASST PROF CHEM & ASST DIR, REGIONAL CRIME LAB, MO SOUTHERN STATE COL, 74- *Mem:* Am Chem Soc. *Res:* Free radical reactions and mechanisms; polar effects in free radical reactions; free radical introduction of functional groups into alkanes. *Mailing Add:* Dept of Chem Mo Southern State Col Joplin MO 64801

MOSHER, ROBERT E, mathematics, see previous edition

MOSHER, ROBERT EUGENE, b Detroit, Mich, Sept 27, 20; m 43; c 6. ANALYTICAL CHEMISTRY. *Educ:* Wayne State Univ, BS, 42, MS, 49, PhD(anal chem), 50. *Prof Exp:* Chemist rubber develop, US Rubber Co, 42-45 & 46-47; instr, Wayne State Univ, 47-50; DIR DEPT PHYSIOL & RES, PROVIDENCE HOSP, 50-; ADJ ASSOC PROF GEOL, WAYNE STATE UNIV, 80- *Mem:* Fel AAAS; Am Chem Soc; Am Fedn Clin Res; Am Asn Clin Chemists; Am Asn Lab Animal Sci. *Res:* Application of analytical chemistry to research in clinical and geochemical research. *Mailing Add:* Dept of Res Providence Hosp Southfield MI 48075

MOSHER, SHARON, b Freeport, Ill, Jan 6, 51. STRUCTURAL GEOLOGY, METAMORPHIC PETROLOGY. *Educ:* Univ Ill, Urbana, BS, 73, PhD(geol), 78; Brown Univ, 75. *Prof Exp:* ASST PROF GEOL, UNIV TEX, AUSTIN, 78- *Mem:* Am Geophys Union. *Res:* Structural geology and metamorphic petrology with an emphasis on deformation mechanisms, especially pressure solution, strain analysis, and field mapping of highly deformed terrains. *Mailing Add:* Dept of Geol Sci Univ of Tex Austin TX 78712

MOSHIRI, GERALD ALEXANDER, b Teheran, Iran, June 1, 29; US citizen. LIMNOLOGY, PHYSIOLOGICAL ECOLOGY. *Educ:* Oberlin Col, BA, 52, MA, 54; Univ Pittsburgh, PhD(biol), 68. *Prof Exp:* Instr biol sci, Cent Fla Jr Col, 64-66; asst prof, 69-73, assoc prof, 73-80, PROF BIOL, UNIV WEST FLA, 80- *Concurrent Pos:* Fed Water Pollution Control Admin sr res fel, Inst Ecol, Univ Calif, Davis, 68-69; consult, NASA, 71-72, Environ Protection Agency, 71-73 & Escambia & Pensacola Tech Adv Comt, 76- *Mem:* AAAS; Brit Freshwater Biol Asn; Ecol Soc Am; Am Soc Limnol & Oceanog; Int Asn Theoret & Appl Limnol. *Res:* Aquatic ecology; energetics of aquatic ecosystems, including problems involving cycling of nutrients and eutrophication of inland waters and estuaries. *Mailing Add:* Fac of Biol Univ of W Fla Pensacola FL 32504

MOSHMAN, JACK, b Richmond Hill, NY, Aug 12, 24; m 47; c 4. STATISTICS, OPERATIONS RESEARCH. *Educ:* NY Univ, BA, 46; Columbia Univ, MA, 47; Univ Tenn, PhD(math), 53. *Prof Exp:* Tutor math, Queens Col, NY, 47; instr, Univ Tenn, 47-50; sr statistician, Oak Ridge Nat Lab, 50-54; mem tech staff, Bell Tel Labs, Inc, 54-57; mem tech staff statist, Serv Div, C-E-I-R, Inc, 57-60, vpres & dir tech sci, 60-65, vpres & gen mgr appl res & mgt sci div, 65-66; managing dir, EBS Mgt Consults, Inc, Washington, DC, 66-67; sr vpres, Leasco Systs & Res Corp, Md, 67-69; PRES, MOSHMAN ASSOCS, INC, 69- *Concurrent Pos:* Statistician, AEC, 48-50; mem div math, Nat Res Coun-Nat Acad Sci, 53-56; lectr & mem adv comt math & statist, USDA Grad Sch, 59-75; prof lectr, George Washington Univ, 60-61; vis prof, Eagleton Inst Polit, Rutgers Univ, adj prof, 72-74; exec secy, Comt to Evaluate Nat Ctr Health Statist, 71-73; mem, Comt Nat Info Syst in Math Sci; mem adv comt statist policy, Off Mgt & Budget, 74-77; chmn, Inst Safety Anal, 75-; exec secy, Comt Eval Nat Ctr Social Statist, 76-77 & Expert Panel Eval Coop Health Statist Systs, 78- *Mem:* Opers Res Soc Am; Inst Mgt Sci; Asn Comput Mach (secy, 56-60, vpres, 60-62); fel Am Statist Asn; Inst Math Statist. *Res:* High speed electronic digital computers; Monte Carlo methods; operations research; mathematical models of political behavior; information systems; statistical problems of compliance with safety and other regulatory requirements. *Mailing Add:* Moshman Assocs Inc Suite 304 6400 Goldsboro Rd Washington DC 20034

MOSHONAS, MANUEL GEORGE, b Weirton, WVa, Jan 20, 32; m 55; c 3. CITRUS CHEMISTRY, ANALYTICAL CHEMISTRY. *Educ:* Fla State Univ, BS, 55. *Prof Exp:* Res chemist org chem, Nat Bur Standards, 55-57; res chemist polymer chem, Univ Fla, 57-59; res chemist fluorine chem, Peninsular Chem Res, Inc, 59-63; RES CHEMIST CITRUS CHEM, USDA, 63- *Honors & Awards:* Cert of Merit, Nat Bur Standards, 57. *Mem:* Am Chem Soc; Int Citricult Soc. *Res:* Citrus essential and essence oil composition; citrus juice essence composition and flavor; composition and flavor effects of abscission chemicals on quality of citrus products. *Mailing Add:* PO Box 1909 Winter Haven FL 33880

MOSHY, RAYMOND JOSEPH, b Brooklyn, NY, Aug 12, 25; m 48; c 5. FOOD SCIENCE. *Educ:* St John's Univ, NY, BS, 48; Fordham Univ, MS, 49, PhD(chem), 53. *Prof Exp:* Chemist res & develop, Am Lecithin Co, 50-52; synthetic org chem, Heyden Chem Corp, 52-55; proj leader, Res Ctr, Gen Foods Corp, 55-59; group mgr chem lab, Am Mach & Foundry Co, 59-60, sect mgr, 60-65, mgr chem develop lab, Res & Develop Div, 65-66, staff vpres & dir res div, 66-70; vpres res & develop, 70-75, VPRES & GROUP EXEC, HUNT-WESSON FOODS, INC, 75- *Mem:* Am Chem Soc; Sigma Xi; Am Inst Chemists; Inst Food Technologists; Indust Res Inst. *Res:* Agricultural chemicals; proteins; starches; food processing; nutrition; agricultural research. *Mailing Add:* Hunt-Wesson Foods Inc 1645 W Valencia Dr Fullerton CA 92634

MOSIER, ARVIN RAY, b Olney Springs, Colo, June 11, 45; m 65; c 2. AGRICULTURAL CHEMISTRY. *Educ:* Colo State Univ, BS, 67, MS, 68, PhD(soil sci), 74. *Prof Exp:* RES CHEMIST, AGR RES SERV, USDA, 67- *Mem:* AAAS; Am Soc Agron; Soil Sci Soc Am; Int Soc Soil Sci; Sigma Xi. *Res:* Distribution of nitrogen and organic compounds emanating from agricultural sources and the effect of these chemicals on soil, water and plant systems; nitrogen metabolism and nutrition of algae and higher plants; assess importance of volatile nitrogen losses from native and fertilized soils and determine factors that control soil nitrification and denitrification. *Mailing Add:* Agr Res Serv PO Box E Ft Collins CO 80522

MOSIER, BENJAMIN, b Corsicana, Tex, July 15, 26; m 54; c 4. CHEMISTRY. *Educ:* Tex A&M Univ, BS, 49, MS, 52; Univ Ill, PhD(chem), 57. *Prof Exp:* Instr chem, Kilgore Col, 49-50; asst, Tex A&M Univ, 50-51; res chemist, Gen Dynamics Corp, 51-52; res scientist, Humble Oil & Refining Co, 57-60; owner & res dir, 60-69, PRES, INST RES, INC, 69-, DIR, 60- *Concurrent Pos:* Lectr, Univ Houston, Rice Univ, Baylor Col Med, Univ Tex M D Anderson Hosp & Tumor Inst & Tex Res Inst Ment Sci; mem, Am Coun Independent Labs; adj res asst prof path, Baylor Col Med, 74-, res asst prof, 75-; sr res assoc, Dept Chem, Rice Univ, 75-; adj prof, Dept Chem, Kans State Univ, Manhattan, 77. *Honors & Awards:* Apollo & Gemini-Apollo Awards & Two Certs of Recognition, NASA. *Mem:* Am Chem Soc; Nat Asn Corrosion Eng; Am Inst Mining, Metall & Petrol Engrs; fel Am Inst Chemists; Royal Soc Chem. *Res:* Electrochemistry; surface and colloidal phenomena; microencapsulation; instrumental methods including polarography, infrared, ultraviolet and visible spectrometry, gas chromatography, nuclear radiation methods, x-ray diffraction and fluorescence; microprobe analysis; electron microscopy; mass spectrometry; nuclear magnetic spectroscopy; differential thermal, thermogravimetry, emission spectrographic and neutron activation analysis. *Mailing Add:* Inst for Res Inc 8330 Westglen Dr Houston TX 77042

MOSIER, DONALD EDWARD, immunology, see previous edition

MOSIER, H DAVID, JR, b Topeka, Kans, May 22, 25. PEDIATRICS, ENDOCRINOLOGY. *Educ:* Notre Dame Univ, BS, 48; Johns Hopkins Univ, MD, 52; Am Bd Pediat, dipl, 57. *Prof Exp:* Intern pediat, Johns Hopkins Hosp, 52-53; asst path, Univ Southern Calif, 54-55; fel pediat endocrinol, Johns Hopkins Hosp, 55-57; from asst prof to assoc prof pediat, Sch Med, Univ Calif, Los Angeles, 57-63; assoc prof, Univ Ill Col Med, 63-67; PROF PEDIAT & HEAD DIV ENDOCRINOL & METAB, UNIV CALIF, IRVINE-CALIF COL MED, 67- *Concurrent Pos:* Asst resident, Los Angeles Children's Hosp, Calif, 53-54, resident pediat path, 54-55; consult, Pac State Hosp, Pomona, Calif, 57-; dir res, Ill State Pediat Inst, 63-67; mem staff, Childrens Hosp Med Ctr, Long Beach. *Mem:* Endocrine Soc; Soc Pediat Res; Soc Exp Biol & Med; Lawson Wilkins Pediat Endocrine Soc; Sigma Xi. *Res:* Somatic growth and development. *Mailing Add:* Dept of Pediat CCM Univ of Calif Irvine CA 92717

MOSIER, JACOB EUGENE, b Hoxie, Kans, Feb 5, 24; m 45; c 4. VETERINARY MEDICINE. *Educ:* Kans State Univ, DVM, 45, MS, 48; Am Col Vet Internal Med, dipl. *Prof Exp:* Instr anat, surg & med, Kans State Univ, 45-47, instr surg & med, 47-48, asst prof large animal med, 48-49; asst prof large animal surg, Univ Ill, 49-50; assoc prof surg & med, 50-54, prof small animal med, 54-61, PROF SURG & MED & HEAD DEPT, KANS STATE UNIV, 61- *Concurrent Pos:* Mem nat adv comt, Food & Drug Admin, 71-76, consult, Bur Vet Med, 74- *Honors & Awards:* Am Animal Hosp Asn Award, 73; Comrs Spec Citation, Food & Drug Admin, 77; Intermoutain Vet Med Asn Award, 77. *Mem:* Am Vet Med Asn; NY Acad Sci; Am Animal Hosp Asn. *Res:* Canine pediatrics; internal medicine of the dog and cat; cause and effect of perinatal disease in the cat and dog; canine and feline geratrics. *Mailing Add:* Vet Med Ctr Kans State Univ Manhattan KS 66502

MOSIER, STEPHEN R, b San Rafael, Calif, Nov 14, 42; m 64; c 2. INTERNATIONAL SCIENCE & TECHNOLOGY AFFAIRS. *Educ:* Col William & Mary, BS, 64; Univ Iowa, MS, 67, PhD(physics), 70. *Prof Exp:* Res assoc physics, Univ Iowa, 69-70; res assoc radio astron, NASA Goddard Space Flight Ctr, 70-71, space scientist physics & astron, 71-78; PROG DIR US-JAPAN COOP SCI PROG, DIV INT PROGS, NSF, 78- *Honors & Awards:* Spec Achievement Award, NASA, 76. *Mem:* Am Geophys Union. *Res:* Space physics; magnetispheric radio physics; solar radio physics; international science and technology policy; United States-Japan relations in science and technology. *Mailing Add:* US-Japan Coop Sci prog Nat Sci Found Washington DC 20550

MOSIG, GISELA, b Schmorkau, Ger, Nov 29, 30. GENETICS. *Educ:* Univ Cologne, Dr rer nat(bot), 59. *Prof Exp:* Res assoc phage genetics, Vanderbilt Univ, 59-62; NIH fel, Carnegie Inst Genetics Res Unit, 62-63, res assoc, 63-65; from asst prof to assoc prof, 65-71, PROF MOLECULAR BIOL, VANDERBILT UNIV, 71- *Mem:* AAAS; Genetics Soc Am; Am Soc Microbiol; NY Acad Sci. *Res:* Mechanism of genetic recombination and replication of DNA in bacteriophage. *Mailing Add:* Dept of Molecular Biol Vanderbilt Univ Nashville TN 37235

MOSIMANN, JAMES EMILE, b Charleston, SC, Oct 26, 30; m 53; c 8. BIOSTATISTICS. *Educ:* Univ Mich, BA, 52, MS, 53, PhD(zool), 56; Johns Hopkins Univ, MS, 61. *Prof Exp:* Res assoc, Willow Run Labs, Univ Mich, 55; asst prof biol, Univ Montreal, 55-61; NIH res fel, 61-62; res assoc, Univ Ariz, 62-63; math statistician, 63-75, CHIEF LAB STATIST & MATH METHODOLOGY, DIV COMPUT RES & TECHNOL, NIH, 75- *Concurrent Pos:* NIH res fel, 59-60. *Mem:* Am Statist Asn; Biomet Soc; Am Soc Ichthyologists & Herpetologists; Royal Statist Soc. *Res:* Discrete probability models in biology; statistical distribution theory; biometry; ecological and population statistics. *Mailing Add:* Div of Comput Res & Technol NIH Bethesda MD 20014

MOSKAL, JOSEPH RUSSELL, b Saginaw, Mich, June 10, 50; m 80. DEVELOPMENTAL NEUROBIOLOGY. *Educ:* Univ Notre Dame, BSc, 72, PhD(chem), 77. *Prof Exp:* Res assoc, Dept Biochem, Mich State Univ, 77-79; staff fel, 79-81, SR STAFF FEL, LAB BIOCHEM GENETICS, NAT HEART LUNG & BLOOD INST, NIH, 82- *Res:* Identification, purification and regulation of cell surface glycoconjugates involved in the formation of synapses. *Mailing Add:* Nat Heart Lung & Blood Inst NIH Rm 1C-14 Bldg 36 Lab Biochem Genetics Bethesda MD 20205

MOSKALYK, RICHARD EDWARD, b Hafford, Sask, Apr 17, 36; m 57; c 3. MEDICINAL CHEMISTRY. *Educ:* Univ Sask, BS, 56, MSc, 59; Univ Alta, PhD(pharmaceut chem), 65. *Prof Exp:* Control chemist, Merck, Sharp & Dohme Ltd, Can, 56-57; res chemist, Food & Drug Directorate, Dept Nat Health & Welfare, 58-61; from asst prof to prof, 63-68, asst dean, 79-80, PROF PHARMACEUT CHEM, FAC PHARM & PHARMACEUT SCI, UNIV ALTA, 75-, ASSOC DEAN, 81- *Concurrent Pos:* Invited prof, Univ Geneva, 71-72. *Mem:* Can Pharmaceut Asn; Am Chem Soc; Chem Inst Can; Asn Fac Pharm Can. *Res:* Development of methodology for the determination of the bioavailability of drugs and their metabolites in biological fluids. *Mailing Add:* Fac of Pharm & Pharmaceut Sci Univ of Alta Edmonton AB T6G 2N8 Can

MOSKOVITS, MARTIN, b Apr 13, 43; Can citizen. SPECTROCHEMISTRY, SURFACE CHEMISTRY. *Educ:* Univ Toronto, BSc, 65, PhD(chem), 70. *Prof Exp:* Res scientist chem, Alcan Int, 70-71; asst prof, 72-78, ASSOC PROF CHEM, UNIV TORONTO, 78- *Mem:* Am Inst Chemists; Optical Soc Am. *Res:* Chemistry and spectroscopy of metal surfaces and metal particles, both bulk and isolated in rare gas solids, raman spectroscopy, difference raman, differential raman scattering, circular and linear. *Mailing Add:* Dept of Chem Univ of Toronto Toronto ON M5S 1A1 Can

MOSKOWITZ, ARTHUR, b New York, NY, Sept 2, 28; m 56; c 2. PHYSICAL CHEMISTRY, METALLURGY. *Educ:* Cornell Univ, BA, 49; Univ Chicago, MS, 51. *Prof Exp:* Chemist, Inst Study Metals, Univ Chicago, 51-53, chemist & supvr anal lab, 53-54; res chemist, Army Chem Ctr, 54-56; res engr, 56-61, supvr stainless sect, 61-64, mgr stainless res & develop, 64-65, assoc dir res, 65-69, dir appl res, Colt Industs, 69-71, V PRES TECH SERV, CRUCIBLE STAINLESS STEEL DIV, CRUCIBLE STEEL CO, 71- *Concurrent Pos:* Mem high alloys comt, Welding Res Coun. *Mem:* Am Soc Metals; Am Soc Testing & Mat. *Res:* Physical metallurgy; stainless steel; product properties including corrosion, mechanical properties, machinability, formability and hot workability; new alloys and processes. *Mailing Add:* 202 Woodbine Dr Beaver PA 15009

MOSKOWITZ, GERARD JAY, b Yonkers, NY, June 17, 40; m 63; c 1. BIOCHEMISTRY, ENZYMOLOGY. *Educ:* Univ Buffalo, BA, 62; State Univ NY, Buffalo, PhD(biochem), 68. *Prof Exp:* Res assoc oncol, Med Sch, Baylor Univ, 67-69; asst mem biochem, Albert Einstein Med Ctr, 69-70; mgr res & develop, Wallerstein Co, Div Baxter, 70-76; sr res scientist, Baxter-Travenol Labs Inc, 76-77; TECH DIR, DAIRYLAND FOOD LABS INC, 77- *Mem:* Am Chem Soc; Inst Food Technologists; AAAS; Sigma Xi; NY Acad Sci. *Res:* Preparation, isolation, purification, characterization of enzymes and their application in commercial processes; microbiology; propagation of microorganisms and the study of their enzyme systems and metabolic pathways. *Mailing Add:* PO Box 406 620 Progress Ave Waukesha WI 53186

MOSKOWITZ, GORDON DAVID, b New York, NY, Dec 25, 34; m 60; c 2. BIOMECHANICS, MECHANICAL ENGINEERING. *Educ:* City Col New York, BME, 60; Princeton Univ, MSE, 62, MA, 63, PhD(mech eng), 64. *Prof Exp:* Res engr plastics, E I du Pont de Nemours & Co, Inc, 63-64; asst prof mech eng, Univ Maine, 65-67; from asst prof to assoc prof, 67-77, PROF MECH ENG, DREXEL UNIV, 77- *Concurrent Pos:* Assoc dir, Rehab Eng Ctr, Mass Hosp, 77- *Honors & Awards:* Bausch & Lomb Award, 63. *Mem:* AAAS; Inst Elec & Electronics Engrs; Am Soc Testing & Mat; Am Soc Eng Educ. *Res:* Biomechanics of pulmonary and cardiovascular function; bioengineering design of medical support equipment; basic mechanisms of locomotion, design and development of electromyographic control of prosthetic limbs. *Mailing Add:* Biomed Eng & Sci Prog 32nd & Chestnut Sts Philadelphia PA 19104

MOSKOWITZ, JULES WARREN, b Newark, NJ, June 11, 34; m 57; c 1. PHYSICAL CHEMISTRY. *Educ:* Princeton Univ, AB, 56; Mass Inst Technol, PhD(chem), 61. *Prof Exp:* From asst prof to assoc prof, 63-72, PROF CHEM, NY UNIV, 72- *Concurrent Pos:* Consult, Bell Tel Labs, NJ, 65- *Mem:* Am Phys Soc. *Res:* Quantum mechanics of solid state and molecular systems; application of digital computers to problems of chemical interest. *Mailing Add:* Dept of Chem NY Univ New York NY 10003

MOSKOWITZ, MARK LEWIS, b Brooklyn, NY, Dec 5, 25; m 49; c 2. REPRODUCTIVE CHEMISTRY. *Educ:* City Col New York, BS, 50; Syracuse Univ, PhD(org chem), 54. *Prof Exp:* Org chemist, 54-59, supvr, Prod Develop Lab, 59-65, mgr reproduction prod res & develop, 65-69, tech dir, Off Systs Div, 69-74, mgr adv reproduction mat res & develop, 74-80, MGR EXPLOR RES & DEVELOP, GAF CORP, 80- *Mem:* AAAS; Am Chem Soc; Soc Photog Sci & Eng; Am Soc Test & Mat. *Res:* Diazotype coatings chemistry and sensitometry; light sensitive coatings; electrophotography. *Mailing Add:* 20 Ashburn Rd Wayne NJ 07470

MOSKOWITZ, MARTIN A, b New York, NY, June 25, 35; m 58; c 2. MATHEMATICS. *Educ:* Brooklyn Col, BA, 57; Univ Calif, Berkeley, MA, 59, PhD(math), 64. *Prof Exp:* Instr math, Univ Chicago, 64-66; asst prof, Columbia Univ, 66-69; assoc prof, 69-76, PROF MATH, GRAD CTR, CITY UNIV NEW YORK, 76- *Concurrent Pos:* Prin investr, NSF contract, 74-; vis prof, Univ Paris, 76, NSF sr fel, Paris, 76. *Mem:* Am Math Soc. *Res:* Topological groups, lie groups and representation theory. *Mailing Add:* Dept of Math City Univ of NY Grad Ctr New York NY 10036

MOSKOWITZ, MERWIN, b New York, NY, May 26, 21; m 44; c 3. MICROBIOLOGY, CELL BIOLOGY. *Educ:* Univ Mich, BS, 44; Univ Calif, PhD(bact), 49. *Prof Exp:* Asst chem, Univ Calif, 46-49; fel, USPHS, 49-50; instr microbiol, Yale Univ, 50; from asst prof to assoc prof bact, 51-61, prof biol, 61-73, PROF BIOL SCI, PURDUE UNIV, 73- *Mem:* AAAS; Am Soc Microbiol; Am Soc Cell Biol; Am Asn Immunol. *Res:* Medical microbiology; cell biology. *Mailing Add:* Dept of biol Sci Purdue Univ West Lafayette IN 47907

MOSKOWITZ, MICHAEL ARTHUR, b New York, NY, May 26, 42; m 65; c 1. NEUROSCIENCE. *Educ:* Johns Hopkins Univ, AB, 64; Tufts Univ, MD, 68; Am Bd Internal Med, cert, Am Bd Psychiat & Neurosurg, cert. *Prof Exp:* Chief resident, Dept Neurol, 72-73, instr, 74-76, asst prof, 76-80, ASSOC PROF NEUROL, SCH MED, HARVARD UNIV, 80- *Concurrent Pos:* Res assoc, Mass Inst Technol, 73-, lectr neurosci, Dept Nutrit, 75-, asst prof neursci, 77-; res fel, Found Fund Res Psychiat, 73-75, Alfred P Sloan Found, 76; estab investr, Am Heart Asn. *Mem:* Neurosci Soc; Am Acad Neurol. *Res:* Biogenic amines and neurological diseases; the pineal gland and its pathological implications. *Mailing Add:* Dept Neurol & Neurosurg Mass Gen Hosp Boston MA 02114

MOSKOWITZ, NORMAN, b Trenton, NJ, Jan 25, 22. ANATOMY. *Educ:* Rutgers Univ, BS, 43; Univ Pa, MS, 47, PhD(zool), 51. *Prof Exp:* Asst instr zool, Univ Pa, 48-50; lectr biol, Rutgers Univ, 58-59; from asst prof to assoc prof, 62-74, PROF ANAT, JEFFERSON MED COL, 74- *Concurrent Pos:* Fel neuroanat, Col Physicians & Surgeons, Columbia Univ, 59-62. *Mem:* Am Asn Anat; Harvey Soc. *Res:* Neuroanatomy; central auditory system. *Mailing Add:* Jefferson Med Col Dept of Anat Thomas Jefferson Univ Philadelphia PA 19107

MOSKOWITZ, RONALD, b New York, NY, Feb 15, 39; m 57; c 4. ELECTRICAL ENGINEERING. *Educ:* City Col New York, BEE, 61; Rutgers Univ, MSc, 63, PhD(elec eng), 67. *Prof Exp:* Assoc engr, Norden-Ketay Div, United Aircraft Corp, 58-59; engr, Radio Corp Am, 61-65; instr elec eng, Rutgers Univ, 65-67; prof, Univ Miss, 67; sr consult engr, Space Systs Div, Avco Corp, 67-68; exec vpres, 68-72, PRES, FERROFLUIDICS CORP, 72- *Concurrent Pos:* Mem tech staff, RCA Labs, David Sarnoff Res Ctr, 66. *Honors & Awards:* Henry Mem Award, City Col New York, 61. *Mem:* Inst Elec & Electronics Engrs; Am Soc Lubrication Engrs; Am Soc Mech Engrs; Am Inst Physics. *Res:* Ferromagnetic fluids; magnetic fine particles; demagnetization and depolarization phenomena; magnetic recording and resonance; spacecraft magnetism, dynamics and control. *Mailing Add:* Ferrofluidics Corp 40 Simon Street Nashua NH 03061

MOSLEY, JAMES W, b Temple, Tex, Aug 8, 29; m 53; c 2. EPIDEMIOLOGY. *Educ:* Univ Tex, BA, 50; Cornell Univ, MD, 54. *Prof Exp:* Intern med, New York Hosp, 54-55; chief hepatitis unit, Commun Dis Ctr, USPHS, Ga, 55-58; resident med, Peter Bent Brigham Hosp, 58-59; fel virol, Harvard Med Sch, 59-61; resident, New Eng Ctr Hosp, 61-62; chief hepatitis unit, Commun Dis Ctr, 62-66, chief viral dis sect, 66-70; assoc prof med, 70-75, PROF MED, UNIV SOUTHERN CALIF, 75-; DIR, HEPATIC EPIDEMIOL LAB, RANCHO LOS AMIGOS HOSP, 73- *Res:* Infectious diseases; epidemiology of viral hepatitis. *Mailing Add:* Liver Univ Rancho Los Amigos Hosp 7601 E Imperial Hwy Downey CA 90039

MOSLEY, JOHN ROSS, b Wichita, Kans, Oct 18, 22; m 50; c 2. PHYSICAL CHEMISTRY. *Educ:* Stanford Univ, AB, 44, PhD(chem), 49. *Prof Exp:* Mem staff, 48-68, assoc group leader, 68-73, ALT GROUP LEADER, LOS ALAMOS NAT LAB, 73- *Mem:* Am Chem Soc; Am Phys Soc; fel Am Inst Chemists. *Res:* Materials science; chemical kinetics; high vacuum. *Mailing Add:* Los Alamos Nat Lab PO Box 1663 MS-G780 Los Alamos NM 87544

MOSLEY, RONALD BRUCE, b Hyden, Ky, Mar 10, 43; m 66; c 2. SOLID STATE PHYSICS. *Educ:* Berea Col, AB, 65; Auburn Univ, MS, 68, PhD(physics), 73. *Prof Exp:* Asst prof physics, Va Commonwealth Univ, 73-78; RES PHYSICIST, SOUTHERN RES INST, 78- *Honors & Awards:* Outstanding Res Award, Sigma Xi, 74. *Mem:* Sigma Xi. *Res:* Electrical transport properties of thin films of semiconducting materials. *Mailing Add:* 2000 Ninth Ave S Birmingham AL 35205

MOSLEY, WILBUR CLANTON, JR, b Birmingham, Ala, Oct 30, 38; m 60; c 2. SOLID STATE PHYSICS, MATERIALS SCIENCE. *Educ:* Auburn Univ, BEP, 60, MS, 62; Univ Ala, Tuscaloosa, PhD(physics), 65. *Prof Exp:* res physicist, 65-80, STAFF PHYSICIST, NUCLEAR MAT DIV, SAVANNAH RIVER LAB, E I DU PONT DE NEMOURS & CO, INC, 80- *Mem:* Am Nuclear Soc; Am Soc Metals; Microbeam Anal Soc. *Res:* Chemical and radiation stability of compounds of actinides. *Mailing Add:* 202 Fairway Dr New Ellenton SC 29809

MOSLEY, WILEY HENRY, b Tsingkiangpu, China, Oct 17, 33; US citizen; m 56; c 3. EPIDEMIOLOGY. *Educ:* Southwestern at Memphis, BA, 55; Univ Okla, MD, 59; Johns Hopkins Univ, MPH, 65. *Prof Exp:* Intern med, Johns Hopkins Hosp, 59-60, asst resident, 60-61, resident, 63-64; epidemiologist epidemic intel serv, Commun Dis Ctr, USPHS, 61-63; head epidemiol div, Pakistan-SEATO Cholera Res Lab, 65-71; prof pop & chmn dept pop dynamics, Sch Hyg & Pub Health, Johns Hopkins Univ, 71-77; dir, Int Ctr Diarrheal Dis Res, Bangladesh, 77-79; sr assoc, Pop Coun, NY, 79-81; vis prof, Pop Studies & Res Inst, Univ Nairobi, Kenya, 79-81; PROG OFFICER, FORD FOUND, INDONESIA, 82- *Mem:* AAAS; Pop Asn Am; Am Pub Health Asn; Int Union Sci Study Pop; Int Epidemiol Asn. *Res:* Population dynamics; infectious diseases. *Mailing Add:* Ford Found 320 E 43rd St New York NY 10017

MOSQUIN, THEODORE, botany, taxonomy, see previous edition

MOSS, ALFRED JEFFERSON, JR, b Little Rock, Ark, Nov 22, 40; m 65. BIOPHYSICS, PHYSIOLOGY. *Educ:* Univ Ark, Little Rock, BS, 62, MS, 64, PhD(biophys, physiol), 70. *Prof Exp:* Res chemist, Dow Chem Co, 65-68; asst prof, 70-77, ASSOC PROF RADIOL & PHYSIOL, MED CTR, UNIV ARK, LITTLE ROCK, 77- *Mem:* Biophys Soc; Radiation Res Soc. *Res:* Radiation biophysics; molecular biology. *Mailing Add:* Div Nuclear Med & Radiation Biol Univ of Ark Med Ctr Little Rock AR 72201

MOSS, BERNARD, b New York, NY, July 26, 37; m 60; c 3. BIOCHEMISTRY, VIROLOGY. *Educ:* NY Univ, BA, 57, MD, 61; Mass Inst Technol, PhD(biochem), 67. *Prof Exp:* Intern med, Children's Hosp Med Ctr, Boston, Mass, 61-62; USPHS basic sci training fel, 62-66; investr, lab biol viruses, 66-71, HEAD MACROMOLECULAR BIOL SECT, LAB BIOL VIRUSES, NIH, 71- *Mem:* Am Soc Microbiol; Am Soc Biol Chemists; AAAS; Fedn Am Scientists. *Res:* Animal viruses; proteins, enzymes; assembly of virus particles; anti-viral substances. *Mailing Add:* Lab of Biol of Viruses Nat Inst of Health Bethesda MD 20014

MOSS, BUELON REXFORD, b Columbia, Ky, Oct 24, 37; m 59; c 3. ANIMAL NUTRITION, DAIRY SCIENCE. *Educ:* Berea Col, BS, 60; Univ Tenn, Knoxville, PhD(animal sci), 68. *Prof Exp:* Instr high sch, Ky, 61-63; res technician, Univ Tenn-AEC Agr Res Lab, Oak Ridge, 67-68; res assoc animal sci, Univ Tenn, Knoxville, 68-69; asst prof, 69-74, ASSOC PROF ANIMAL SCI & DAIRY NUTRIT, MONT STATE UNIV, 74- *Mem:* Am Dairy Sci Asn; Am Inst Nutrit; Poultry Sci Asn. *Res:* Forage evaluation; barleys as feeds for dairy calves, lactating cows and poultry; enzyme supplements to poultry rations. *Mailing Add:* Dept of Animal & Range Sci Mont State Univ Bozeman MT 59717

MOSS, CALVIN E, b Richmond, Va, Nov 27, 39; m 61. EXPERIMENTAL NUCLEAR PHYSICS. *Educ:* Univ Va, BS, 61; Calif Inst Technol, MS, 63, PhD(physics), 68. *Prof Exp:* Res assoc nuclear physics, Duke Univ, 67-69 & Univ Colo, 69-71; res fel, Australian Nat Univ, 71-72; res assoc, Univ Colo, 72-73; STAFF MEM, LOS ALAMOS SCI LAB, 73- *Mem:* Am Phys Soc. *Res:* Nuclear spectroscopy of light nuclei and accelerator development. *Mailing Add:* P-9 MS 480 Los Alamos Sci Lab Los Alamos NM 87545

MOSS, CLAUDE WAYNE, b Rural Hall, NC, Mar 20, 35; m 58; c 4. MICROBIOLOGY, BIOCHEMISTRY. *Educ:* NC State Univ, BS, 57, MS, 62, PhD(microbiol), 65. *Prof Exp:* Res assoc microbiol, NC State Univ, 63-65; RES MICROBIOLOGIST, CTR DIS CONTROL, USPHS, 65- *Honors & Awards:* Superior Performance Award, USPHS, 66. *Mem:* Sci Res Soc Am; Am Soc Microbiol. *Res:* Physiology and metabolism of pathogenic bacteria; application of chromatographic techniques to diagnostic bacteriology and clinical chemistry; cryobiology of microorganisms and animal cells; biochemistry of drug metabolism. *Mailing Add:* 5160 Antelope Lane Stone Mountain GA 30087

MOSS, DALE NELSON, b Thornton, Idaho, Mar 27, 30; m 53; c 8. AGRONOMY, PLANT PHYSIOLOGY. *Educ:* Ricks Col, BS, 55; Cornell Univ, MS, 55, PhD(crop physiol), 59. *Prof Exp:* Asst prof chem, Ricks Col, 55-56; asst agr scientist, Conn Agr Exp Sta, 59-61, assoc agr scientist, 61-63, agr scientist, 63-67; prof crop physiol, Univ Minn, St Paul, 67-77; HEAD DEPT CROP SCI, ORE STATE UNIV, CORVALLIS, 77- *Mem:* Fel Am Soc Agron; Crop Sci Soc Am (pres-elect, 75-76, pres, 76-77, past pres, 77-78); Am Soc Plant Physiol. *Res:* Effects on photosynthesis, respiration and transpiration of higher plants of light intensity, temperature, carbon dioxide concentration, nutrition, removal of storage organs, air turbulence, planting patterns, and age of leaves. *Mailing Add:* Dept of Crop Sci Ore State Univ Corvallis OR 97331

MOSS, DONOVAN DEAN, b Bunker Hill, Ind, Feb 28, 26; m 48; c 2. FISH BIOLOGY. *Educ:* Auburn Univ, BS, 49, MS, 50; Univ Ga, PhD(zool), 62. *Prof Exp:* Fisheries biologist, Ala State Dept Conserv, 51-56, asst chief fisheries, 56-57; res asst zool, Univ Ga, 57-61; from assoc prof to prof, Univ Ky, 62-65; assoc prof biol, Tenn Technol Univ, 65-67; assoc prof, 67-72, PROF FISHERIES, AUBURN UNIV, 72-, ASST DIR INT CTR AQUACULT, 70- *Mem:* Am Fisheries Soc; Am Soc Limnol & Oceanog. *Res:* Fish management and biology of fishes including ecological requirements of fish species. *Mailing Add:* Fisheries Bldg Auburn Univ Auburn AL 36830

MOSS, ERNEST KENT, physical organic chemistry, polymer chemistry, see previous edition

MOSS, FRANK ANTHONY JAMES, b Sept 5, 24; US citizen; m 51; c 3. INORGANIC CHEMISTRY, PHYSICAL CHEMISTRY. *Educ:* Univ London, BSc, 45; Univ Ill, PhD(inorg & phys chem), 52. *Prof Exp:* Res chemist, Delanium Ltd, Eng, 45-46 & Thorium Ltd, Imp Chem Industs, Eng, 46-49; process engr, Esso Standard Oil Co, La, 52-56; asst dir res, Mallinckrodt Chem Co, Mo, 56-63; corp mgr inorg res, Glidden Co, Ohio, 63-65, dir res, Chem Group, Md, 65-69; dir, Eastern Res Ctr, 69-75, DIR, WESTERN RES CTRS, STAUFFER CHEM CO, 75- *Mem:* Indust Res Inst;

Am Chem Soc; Electrochem Soc; Am Mgt Asn. *Res:* Rare earths; solvent hydrofining; lube oils; ore processing; columbium-tantalum; uranium; semiconductor silicon; fungicides; fine organics; metal powders; ceramic coatings; inorganic pigments. *Mailing Add:* Western Res Ctr Stauffer Chem Co Richmond CA 94804

MOSS, FRANK EDWARD, b Paris, Ill, Feb 10, 34; m 62; c 1. LOW TEMPERATURE PHYSICS. *Educ:* Univ Va, BEE, 56, MNE, 61, PhD(physics), 64. *Prof Exp:* Res engr electronics, Univ Va, 56-61, sr scientist cryog eng, 67-71; assoc prof, 71-76, PROF PHYSICS, UNIV MO-ST LOUIS, 76- *Concurrent Pos:* NSF fel, Univ Rome, 65-66, vis researcher, 66-67. *Mem:* Sigma Xi; AAAS; Fed Am Scientists; Am Phys Soc. *Res:* Mechanics of superfluids; phase transitions; phonon interactions in solids and liquids. *Mailing Add:* Dept of Physics Univ of Mo St Louis MO 63121

MOSS, GERALD, b New York, NY, Feb 1, 31; m 63; c 1. BIOMEDICAL ENGINEERING, SURGERY. *Educ:* NY Univ, BA, 51, MS, 56; Union Univ, NY, PhD(biochem), 61; Albany Med Col, MD, 61. *Prof Exp:* Res phys chemist, Vitro Labs, Inc, 56; resident surg, Albany Med Ctr Hosp, 61-68; PROF BIOMED ENG, RENSSELAER POLYTECH INST, 68- *Concurrent Pos:* Clin asst prof surg, Albany Med Col, 68- *Res:* Biochemistry; postoperative protein metabolism and wound healing; cerebral glucose metabolism; circulatory physiology; gastrointestinal physiology. *Mailing Add:* Biomed Eng Lab Rensselaer Polytech Inst Troy NY 12181

MOSS, GERALD ALLEN, b Milwaukee, Wis, Jan 24, 40. NUCLEAR PHYSICS. *Educ:* Univ Wis, BS, 61; Univ Ore, MS, 63, PhD(physics), 66. *Prof Exp:* Fel nuclear physics, Univ Man, 67-69; asst prof, 69-72, assoc prof, 72-80, PROF NUCLEAR PHYSICS, UNIV ALTA, 80- *Concurrent Pos:* Vis scientist, Saclay Nuclear Res Ctr, France, 75-76. *Mem:* Am Asn Physics Teachers. *Res:* Nuclear reactions; spectroscopy; intermediate energy experimental nuclear physics. *Mailing Add:* Nuclear Res Ctr Univ Alta Edmonton AB T6G 2G7 Can

MOSS, GERALD S, b Cleveland, Ohio, Mar 4, 35; m; c 3. SURGERY, EXPERIMENTAL SURGERY. *Educ:* Ohio State Univ, BA, 56, MD, 60. *Prof Exp:* Teaching fel anat, Sch Med, Harvard Univ, 62; tutor surg, Manchester Royal Infirmary, Eng, 64; head exp surg, US Naval Res Inst, 66-68; from asst prof to assoc prof, 68-72, PROF SURG, UNIV ILL, CHICAGO, 73-; CHMN DEPT SURG, MICHAEL REESE HOSP & MED CTR, 77- *Concurrent Pos:* Asst chief surg, Vet Admin West Side Hosp, Chicago, 68-70; attend surg, Cook County Hosp, 70-72, chmn dept, 72-; dir surg res, Hektoen Inst Med Res, Chicago, 72- *Mem:* Soc Univ Surgeons; fel Am Col Surgeons; Asn Acad Surg (pres, 76-); Nat Soc Med Res; Int Cardiovasc Soc. *Res:* Shock and resuscitation; blood preservation; blood component therapy and blood substitutes; cardiopulmonary physiology. *Mailing Add:* Dept Surg Michael Reese Hosp 2929 S Ellis Ave Chicago IL 60616

MOSS, HERBERT IRWIN, b Brooklyn, NY, Mar 8, 32; m 60; c 3. INORGANIC CHEMISTRY, CERAMICS. *Educ:* Univ Louisville, BS, 53; Indiana Univ, PhD(chem), 60. *Prof Exp:* MEM TECH STAFF, DAVID SARNOFF RES CTR, RCA LABS, 59- *Mem:* Am Chem Soc; Electrochem Soc; Am Powder Metall Inst; Am Ceramic Soc. *Res:* Pressure sintering of magnetic, electronic and optically active materials; synthesis and properties of electronically active materials; thin films; materials for magnetic recording heads. *Mailing Add:* David Sarnoff Res Ctr RCA Labs Princeton NJ 08540

MOSS, LLOYD KENT, b Los Angeles, Calif, Aug 8, 24; m 50; c 4. BIOCHEMISTRY. *Educ:* Univ Calif, Los Angeles, BS, 50; Stanford Univ, PhD(chem), 57. *Prof Exp:* Chemist, Aerojet-Gen Corp, Gen Tire & Rubber Co, 50-52; assoc chemist, Stanford Res Inst, 56-58, biochemist, 58-66; from asst prof to assoc prof, 66-70, PROF CHEM, FOOTHILL COL, 70- *Mem:* AAAS; Am Chem Soc; NY Acad Sci. *Res:* Protein characterization; preparative chromatography; continuous flow electrophoresis; periodate oxidations; photosynthetic energy transfer mechanisms; allergens, hemagglutinins and toxins. *Mailing Add:* Dept of Chem Foothill Col 12345 El Monte Rd Los Altos CA 94022

MOSS, MARTIN E, civil engineering, see previous edition

MOSS, MARVIN, b New York, NY, Dec 8, 29; m 57; c 2. SOLID STATE PHYSICS. *Educ:* Queens Col, NY, BS, 51; Cornell Univ, PhD(eng physics), 63. *Prof Exp:* Jr engr, Sylvania Elec Prod, Inc, 51-54; asst physics, Cornell Univ, 54-62; STAFF MEM, SANDIA LABS, 63- *Mem:* AAAS; Am Phys Soc. *Res:* Thermophysical properties of solids; solar energy. *Mailing Add:* Div 5842 Sandia Labs Albuquerque NM 87185

MOSS, MELVIN LANE, b Deerfield, Ohio, July 3, 15; m 52; c 1. BIOCHEMISTRY, SCIENCE ADMINISTRATION. *Educ:* Mt Union Col, BS, 38; Purdue Univ, MS, 40, PhD(anal chem), 42. *Prof Exp:* Asst instr chem, Purdue Univ, 38-41; res chemist, Hercules Powder Co, 42-48; asst div head, Alcoa Res Labs, Aluminum Co Am, 48-62; NIH fel, Inst Neurobiol, Univ Gothenburg, 63-64; sr scientist staff mem, Oak Ridge Nat Lab, 69-73; assoc mem, Inst Muscle Dis, Inc, 64-69, actg dir, 73-74, DIR RES & DEVELOP, MUSCULAR DYSTROPHY ASN, INC, 73- *Mem:* AAAS; Am Chem Soc; Histochem Soc; Am Micrchem Soc. *Res:* Analytical methods and instrumentation; chemical and metallurgical process control; analysis of isolated nerve, muscle and amniotic cells; prenatal detection of genetic disorders; biochemistry of muscle disease. *Mailing Add:* Muscular Dystrophy Asn Inc 810 7th Ave New York NY 10019

MOSS, MELVIN LIONEL, b New York, NY, Jan 3, 23; m 70; c 2. ANATOMY. *Educ:* NY Univ, AB, 42; Columbia Univ, DDS, 46, PhD, 54. *Prof Exp:* From asst anat to assoc prof, 52-67, dean, Sch Dent & Oral Surg, 68-73, PROF ANAT, COLUMBIA UNIV, 68-, PROF ORAL BIOL, COL PHYSICIANS & SURGEONS, 67- *Concurrent Pos:* Lederle med fac award, 54-56; mem int comt standardization human biol. *Mem:* AAAS; Am Soc Zoologists; Am Asn Anatomists; Am Asn Phys Anthrop; Int Asn Dent Res. *Res:* Skeletal morphology and physiology; physical anthropology. *Mailing Add:* Dept of Anat Columbia Univ 630 W 168th St New York NY 10032

MOSS, RANDY HAYS, b Searcy, Ark, Aug 7, 53; m 78. PATTERN RECOGNITION, IMAGE PROCESSING. *Educ:* Univ Ark, BS, 75, MS, 77; Univ Ill, PhD(elec eng), 81. *Prof Exp:* ASST PROF ELEC ENG, UNIV MO-ROLLA, 81- *Concurrent Pos:* Vis instr, Univ Ill, 79, vis lectr, 80. *Mem:* Inst Elec & Electronics Engrs; Sigma Xi. *Res:* Vision systems for industrial robots; computer aided design and manufacturing; pattern recognition; image processing; digital systems, including microprocessor systems. *Mailing Add:* Elec Eng Dept Univ Mo Rolla MO 65401

MOSS, RICHARD WALLACE, b Charlotte, NC, June 12, 41; m 62; c 2. ELECTRONIC ENGINEERING, COMMUNICATIONS. *Educ:* Ga Inst Technol, BEE, 65, MSEE, 68. *Prof Exp:* Asst res engr, 65-68, res engr, 68-73, SR RES ENGR, 73- & HEAD, COMMUN TECHNOL GROUP ELEC ENG SECT, GA INST TECHNOL, 74- *Concurrent Pos:* Consult engr, 73- *Mem:* Sigma Xi; Inst Elec & Electronics Engrs; Nat Soc Prof Engrs. *Res:* Communications systems and technology; signal monitoring systems, spectrum utilization management; simulation modeling. *Mailing Add:* GA Inst Technol Eng Exp Sta Atlanta GA 30332

MOSS, ROBERT ALLEN, b Brooklyn, NY, May 27, 40; m 67. ORGANIC CHEMISTRY. *Educ:* Brooklyn Col, BS, 60; Univ Chicago, MS, 62, PhD(chem), 63. *Prof Exp:* Nat Acad Sci-Nat Res Coun res fel chem, Columbia Univ, 63-64; from asst prof to assoc prof, 64-73, PROF CHEM, RUTGERS UNIV, 73- *Concurrent Pos:* Vis scientist, Mass Inst Technol, 71-72; Alfred P Sloan Found fel, 71-73; acad vis, Univ Oxford, 76-77. *Mem:* Am Chem Soc; Royal Soc Chem. *Res:* Organic and bioorganic chemistry in the micellar phase; deamination; chemistry of alkyl diazotate salts and alkyldiazonium ions; carbenes and carbenoids. *Mailing Add:* Sch of Chem Rutgers Univ New Brunswick NJ 08903

MOSS, ROBERT HENRY, b New York, NY, July 26, 22; m 52; c 4. PHYSICAL INORGANIC CHEMISTRY, SOLID STATE CHEMISTRY. *Educ:* Univ NH, BS, 43; Univ Ark, MS, 48; Univ Conn, PhD(phys chem), 55. *Prof Exp:* Res asst indust eng, Eng Exp Sta, Univ NH, 43-46; res asst chem, Univ Conn, 53-54, asst instr, 54-55; prin chemist, Mine Safety Appliances Co, 55-56; engr, Westinghouse Elec Corp, 56-58, sr engr, 58-64; sr scientist, 64-69, sect head res & develop purification & supt prod purification, 69-77, SKILL GROUP LEADER PURIFICATION, CRYSTALS & ELECTRONIC PARTS DEPT, HARSHAW CHEM CO, 77- *Mem:* Am Chem Soc; Electrochem Soc. *Res:* Materials preparation and purification of soild state materials; semiconductor, thermoelectric, electro-optical, scintillation and optical materials. *Mailing Add:* 3018 E Overlook Rd Cleveland OH 44118

MOSS, ROBERT L, b Brooklyn, NY, Aug 24, 40. NEUROPHYSIOLOGY, NEUROENDOCRINOLOGY. *Educ:* Villanova Univ, BS, 62; Claremont Grad Sch & Univ Ctr, MA, 67; PhD(neurophysiol, neuropsychol), 69. *Prof Exp:* Res asst, Inst Behav Res, Silver Spring, Md, 63-64; res asst grade I operant behav, Patton State Hosp, Calif, 64-65; res assoc anat, Med Sch, Univ Bristol, 69-71; asst prof, 71-77, ASSOC PROF PHYSIOL, SOUTHWESTERN MED SCH, UNIV TEX HEALTH SCI CTR DALLAS, 77- *Concurrent Pos:* NIMH fel, Dept Anat, Med Sch, Univ Bristol, 69-71; Instnl grant, Dept Physiol, Southwestern Med Sch, Univ Tex Health Sci Ctr, Dallas, 71-72, NIH grant, 72-78, NSF grant, 74-76 & Ayerst Labs Inc grant, 74-; NIH career develop award, 76-81. *Honors & Awards:* Young Scientist Award, Am Psychol Asn, 69. *Mem:* AAAS; Am Physiol Soc; Endocrine Soc; Int Soc Neuroendocrinol; Soc Neurosci. *Res:* Neural and biochemical mechanisms involved in hypothalamic control over pituitary function(s) and reproductive behavior. *Mailing Add:* Dept Physiol Southwestern Med Sch Univ of Tex Health Sci Ctr Dallas TX 75235

MOSS, RODNEY DALE, b Oakdale, Nebr, Apr 9, 27; m 50; c 2. ORGANIC CHEMISTRY, ANALYTICAL CHEMISTRY. *Educ:* Univ Nebr, BS, 48, MS, 49; Indiana Univ, PhD(chem), 51. *Prof Exp:* Res chemist, 51-60, proj leader, 60-63, group leader, 63-65, head pharm chem res dept, 65-68, dir chem, 68-76, dir prod develop, Agr Prod Ctr, Dow Chem, USA, 76-81, DIR AGR CHEM RES & DEVELOP, DOW CHEM PAC LTD, 81- *Mem:* Am Chem Soc. *Res:* Organic sulfur and phosphorus chemistry; residue analysis and environmental studies. *Mailing Add:* Dow Chem Pac Ltd PO Box 711 Hong Kong 48640 Hong Kong

MOSS, RONNIE LEE, statistics, operations research, see previous edition

MOSS, SANFORD ALEXANDER, III, environmental physiology, marine biology, see previous edition

MOSS, SIMON CHARLES, b Woodmere, NY, July 31, 34; m 58; c 4. MATERIALS SCIENCE, SOLID STATE PHYSICS. *Educ:* Mass Inst Technol, SB, 56, SM, 59, ScD(metall), 62. *Prof Exp:* Mem res staff metall, Res Div, Raytheon Mfg Co, 56-57; from asst prof to assoc prof, Mass Inst Technol, 62-70; dir sci dept, Energy Conversion Devices, Inc, 70-72; PROF PHYSICS, UNIV HOUSTON, 72- *Concurrent Pos:* Ford fel eng, Mass Inst Technol, 62-64; Guggenheim fel, 68-69; Alexander von Humboldt sr scientist grant, Univ Munich, 79. *Res:* X-ray and neutron diffraction; structure of disordered and defective solids; crystallography and thermodynamics of phase transformations; amorphous semiconductors; hydrogen in metals; biological structures. *Mailing Add:* Dept of Physics Univ of Houston Houston TX 77004

MOSSER, JOHN SNAVELY, b Canton, Ohio, Apr 7, 28. PHYSICAL CHEMISTRY, ENVIRONMENTAL MANAGEMENT. *Educ:* Case Western Reserve Univ, BS, 50, MS, 52, PhD(phys chem), 63; Univ Akron, MBA, 77. *Prof Exp:* Res engr, Indust Rayon Corp, 52-54; sr res chemist, Gen Tire & Rubber Co, 62-70; WASTEWATER QUAL COORDR, CITY OF AKRON, 72- *Mem:* Am Chem Soc; Sigma Xi. *Res:* Cryogenic measurement and calculation of thermodynamic properties; preparation and characterization of polymers and latices. *Mailing Add:* Water Pollution Control 2460 Akron Peninsula Rd Akron OH 44313

MOSSMAN, ARCHIE STANTON, b Madison, Wis, Feb 5, 26; m; c 3. WILDLIFE ECOLOGY. *Educ:* Univ Wis, BA, 49, PhD(zool, wildlife mgt), 55; Univ Calif, MA, 51. *Prof Exp:* Biologist, Dept Fish & Game, Alaska, 55-57; instr, Exten Div, Univ Wis, 57-58; asst prof, Univ Wyo, 58-59; Fulbright res scholar, Nat Mus Southern Rhodesia, 59-61; from asst prof to assoc prof, 61-71, PROF WILDLIFE ECOL, SCH NATURAL RESOURCES, HUMBOLDT STATE UNIV, 71- *Concurrent Pos:* Sr lectr, Univ Col Rhodesia & Nyasaland, 63-65; Food & Agr Orgn consult, Malawi, 69; prin investr evaluation game ranching in southern Africa, Int Union Conserv Nature & Natural Resources & World Wildlife Found Joint Proj, 74-75. *Mem:* Ecol Soc Am; Wildlife Soc; Am Soc Mammal; Cooper Ornith Soc; Am Inst Biol Sci. *Res:* Animal behavioral response to environment; food production from wildlife; predation. *Mailing Add:* Sch of Natural Resources Humboldt State Univ Arcata CA 95521

MOSSMAN, DAVID JOHN, b Mar 9, 38; Can citizen; m 63; c 1. MINERALOGY, GEOLOGY. *Educ:* Dalhousie Univ, BSc, 59, MSc, 63; Univ Otago, NZ, PhD(geol), 70. *Prof Exp:* Field geologist, Anglo Am Corp, SAfrica, 59-62; party chief groundwater res, NS Govt, Can, 64; lectr appl geol, Univ Otago, NZ, 70; geologist, Dept Natural Resources, NB, Can, 71; asst prof, 71-76, ASSOC PROF ECON GEOL, UNIV SASK, 76- *Mem:* Geol Soc NZ; Mineral Asn Can; Can Inst Mining & Metall. *Res:* Economic geology; petrology of basic and ultrabasic rocks; low grade metamorphism; petrology of coal. *Mailing Add:* Dept Geol Sci Univ Sask Saskatoon SK S7N 0W0 Can

MOSSMAN, KENNETH LESLIE, b Windsor, Ont, Apr 14, 46; US citizen; m 70. RADIATION BIOLOGY. *Educ:* Wayne State Univ, BS, 68; Univ Tenn, MS, 70, PhD(radiation biol), 73. *Prof Exp:* RADIATION BIOLOGIST & ASST PROF RADIOL, MED CTR, GEORGETOWN UNIV, 73- *Concurrent Pos:* Consult, OMNI Res Corp, 75-76, George Washington Univ, 75-78 & Best Indust, 77-; asst prof, Howard Univ, 76- *Mem:* Radiation Res Soc; Sigma Xi; Am Soc Therapeut Radiologists; Radiol Soc NAm. *Res:* Human radiobiology; radiation effects on taste acuity and saliva; radiation effects of oral tissues in small animals. *Mailing Add:* Dept of Radiation Oncol Georgetown Univ Hosp Washington DC 20007

MOSSMAN, REUEL WALLACE, b Fresno, Calif, Aug 18, 14; m 40. GEOPHYSICS. *Educ:* Columbia Univ, AB, 35, MA, 39. *Prof Exp:* County Supvr, Okla State Mineral Surv, 35-36; survr-comput, Geophys Res Corp, 37; supvr, 39-50, chief geophysicist, 50-55, ASST V PRES, SEISMOGRAPH SERV CORP, 55- *Mem:* Am Asn Petrol Geologists; Soc Explor Geophys; Am Geophys Union; Europ Asn Explor Geophys. *Mailing Add:* Seismograph Serv Corp Box 1590 Tulsa OK 74102

MOSSOP, GRANT DILWORTH, b Calgary, Alta, Apr 15, 48; m 69; c 2. SEDIMENTOLOGY, SEDIMENTARY PETROLOGY. *Educ:* Univ Calgary, BSc, 70, MSc, 71; Univ London, PhD(sedimentary geol), & DIC, 73. *Prof Exp:* Fel geol, Univ Calgary, 74; res officer oil sand geol, 75-80, HEAD, ALTA GEOL SURV, ALTA RES COUN, 80- *Mem:* Can Soc Petrol Geologists; Geol Asn Can; Soc Econ Paleontologists & Mineralogists. *Res:* Detailed sedimentology and petrology of the Athabasca Oil Sands, Alberta. *Mailing Add:* Alta Res Coun 4445 Calgary Trail S Edmonton AB T6H 5R7 Can

MOSS-SALENTIJN, LETTY, b Amsterdam, Netherlands, Apr 14, 43; m 70. ANATOMY, DENTAL RESEARCH. *Educ:* State Univ Utrecht, DDS, 67, PhD(anat), 76. *Prof Exp:* Chief instr oral hist growth & develop, Holland Lab Hist & Micros Anat, State Univ Utrecht, 67-68; asst prof anat, 68-74, assoc prof oral biol, 74-78, ASSOC PROF OROFACIAL GROWTH & DEVELOP, COLUMBIA UNIV, 78- *Mem:* AAAS; Int Asn Dent Res; Am Soc Zool; Int Soc Stereology; fel Royal Micros Soc. *Res:* Growth and development of skeletal tissues; growth of cartilages; orofacial embryology; comparative odontology. *Mailing Add:* Dept of Anat Columbia Univ 630 W 168th St New York NY 10032

MOST, DAVID S, b Boston, Mass, Feb 7, 29; m 52; c 4. PAPER CHEMISTRY. *Educ:* Boston Univ, AB, 52; Lawrence Col, MS, 54, PhD(chem), 57. *Prof Exp:* Group leader, Res Dept, Albemarle Paper Co Div, Ethyl Corp, 57-60; dept mgr appl res, Itek Corp, 60-62; vpres & gen mgr, New Eng Labs, Inc, Rahn Corp, 62-65; consult paper chem, 65-70; pres, M/K Systs, Inc, 70-75; CONSULT, 75- *Mem:* AAAS; Am Chem Soc; Tech Asn Pulp & Paper Indust; Soc Photog Sci & Eng. *Res:* Reproduction technology; development of special papers for use in recording and communications applications including copy papers and facsimile. *Mailing Add:* 435 Atlantic Ave Marblehead MA 01945

MOST, JOSEPH MORRIS, b New York, NY, Apr 24, 43; m 65; c 2. PHYSICAL CHEMISTRY. *Educ:* Rutgers Univ, AB, 64, PhD(inorg chem), 74. *Prof Exp:* Chemist, NL Industs, Inc, 64-66; instr chem, Rutgers Col, Rutgers Univ, 71-74; ASST PROF CHEM, UPSALA COL, 74- *Mem:* Am Chem Soc. *Res:* Chemical education, especially course development. *Mailing Add:* Upsala Col Dept of Chem 2 Upsala Ct East Orange NJ 07019

MOSTARDI, RICHARD ALBERT, b Bryn Mawr, Pa, July 1, 38; m 62; c 4. PHYSIOLOGY. *Educ:* Kent State Univ, BS, 60, MEd, 64; Ohio State Univ, PhD(physiol), 68. *Prof Exp:* Res asst physiol, Aviation Med Lab, Ohio State Univ, 66-68; ASSOC PROF PHYSIOL, UNIV AKRON, 68- *Concurrent Pos:* NIH fel, Milan, Italy, 72-73. *Mem:* NY Acad Sci; Sigma Xi. *Res:* Acoustic diagnosis of arthritis; effects of drag reducing polymers in the vertebrate system; exercise in humans. *Mailing Add:* Dept of Biol Univ of Akron Akron OH 44325

MOSTELLER, C FREDERICK, b Clarksburg, WVa, Dec 24, 16; m 41; c 2. MATHEMATICAL STATISTICS. *Educ:* Carnegie Inst Technol, BS, 38, MS, 39; Princeton Univ, AM, 42, PhD(math), 46. *Hon Degrees:* DSc, Univ Chicago, 73 & Carnegie-Mellon Univ, 74. *Prof Exp:* Instr math, Princeton Univ, 42-44; res mathematician, Statist Res Group, 44-45; chmn dept statist, 57-69, 75-76, MEM FAC, DEPT SOCIAL RELS, HARVARD UNIV, 46-, PROF MATH STATIST, 51-, CHMN DEPT BIOSTATIST, 77- MEM FAC, J F K SCH GOVT, 70- *Concurrent Pos:* Fund Advan Educ fel, Univ Chicago, 54-55; mem staff probability & statist, NBC's Continental Classroom TV Course, 60-61; fel, Ctr Advan Study Behav Sci, 62-63; chmn bd dirs, Soc Sci Res Coun, 66-68; Guggenheim fel, 69-70; vchmn, President's Comn Fed Statist, 71; Miller res prof, Univ Calif, 74-75. *Mem:* Nat Acad Sci; Inst of Med of Nat Acad Sci; AAAS; Am Philos Soc; Am Acad Arts & Sci. *Res:* Theoretical statistics and its applications to social science, medicine, public policy and industry. *Mailing Add:* Rm 603 Sci Ctr Harvard Univ One Oxford St Cambridge MA 02138

MOSTELLER, RAYMOND DEE, b Austin, Tex, Dec 30, 41. BIOCHEMISTRY. *Educ:* Univ Tex, Austin, BA, 64, PhD(biochem), 68. *Prof Exp:* Asst prof, 70-81, ASSOC PROF BIOCHEM, SCH MED, UNIV SOUTHERN CALIF, 81- *Concurrent Pos:* Fel molecular biol, Stanford Univ, 68-70; NSF res grants, 71-73 & 73-75; NIH res grant, 73-76. *Mem:* Am Soc Microbiol; AAAS. *Res:* Mechanism of protein biosynthesis; control of gene expression; regulation of protein degradation. *Mailing Add:* Dept of Biochem Univ of Southern Calif Sch Med Los Angeles CA 90033

MOSTELLER, ROBERT COBB, b Lynchburg, Va, Oct 14, 38; m 60; c 2. BIOMETRICS. *Educ:* Randolph-Macon Col, BA, 61; Emory Univ, MS, 67, PhD(statist), 76. *Prof Exp:* Res assoc biostatist, Biomet Unit, Dept Plant Breeding, Cornell Univ, 65; instr biometry, Univ Kans Med Ctr, 68-70; assoc, Dept Biometry & Statist, 70-73, CHIEF STATIST UNIT BIOMETRY, MAMMOGRAPHY SECT, DEPT RADIOL, EMORY UNIV, 73- *Res:* Statistical evaluation of breast cancer data aimed at the identification of women with a high risk of either current or future breast cancer. *Mailing Add:* Mammography Sect Emory Univ Atlanta GA 30322

MOSTERT, PAUL STALLINGS, b Morrilton, Ark, Nov 27, 27; m 47; c 4. MATHEMATICS. *Educ:* Southwestern at Memphis, BS, 50; Univ Chicago, MS, 51; Purdue Univ, PhD(math), 53. *Prof Exp:* Asst math, Purdue Univ, 51-53; res instr, Tulane Univ La, 53-54, from asst prof to prof, 54-70, chmn dept, 68-70; chmn dept, 70-73, PROF MATH, UNIV KANS, 70- *Concurrent Pos:* Vis prof, Univ Tubingen, 62-63 & 66; NSF sr fel & mem, Inst Advan Study, 67-68; mem selection of postdoctoral fels panel, Nat Res Coun, 69-71; managing ed & co-founder, Semigroup Forum, exec ed, 74-; chmn comt acad freedom, tenure and employment security, Am Math Soc, 72-77. *Mem:* Nat Acad Sci; Am Acad Arts & Sci. *Res:* Topological semigroups; transformation groups; category theory. *Mailing Add:* Dept of Math Univ of Kans Lawrence KS 66044

MOSTOLLER, MARK ELLSWORTH, b Somerset, Pa, Sept 13, 41; m 63; c 2. SOLID STATE PHYSICS. *Educ:* Harvard Col, AB, 62; Harvard Univ, SM, 63, PhD(appl physics), 69. *Prof Exp:* MEM RES STAFF, OAK RIDGE NAT LAB, 69- *Mem:* Am Phys Soc. *Res:* Lattice dynamics; disordered systems; defects in solids; electronic structure and properties. *Mailing Add:* Solid State Div Oak Ridge Nat Lab PO Box X Oak Ridge TN 37830

MOSTOW, GEORGE DANIEL, b Boston, Mass, July 4, 23; m 47; c 4. MATHEMATICS. *Educ:* Harvard Univ, BA, 43, MA, 46, PhD(math), 48. *Prof Exp:* Instr math, Princeton Univ, 47-48; asst prof, Syracuse Univ, 49-52; from asst prof to prof, Johns Hopkins Univ, 52-61; prof, 61-63, chmn dept, 71-74, JAMES E ENGLISH PROF MATH, YALE UNIV, 63- *Concurrent Pos:* Mem staff, Inst Advan Study, 47-49, 56-57, 75; vis prof, Inst Pure & Appl Math, Brazil, 53-54; Guggenheim fel & Fulbright res scholar, State Univ Utrecht, 57-58; ed, Am J Math, 63-67, assoc ed, 67-; exchange prof, Univ Paris, 66; vis prof, Hebrew Univ, Israel, 67; Tata Inst Fundamental Res, India, 69; Inst Advan Study Sci, 71 & 75; chmn, US Nat Comt Math, 73-74; chmn, Off Math Sci, Nat Acad Sci-Nat Res Coun, 75-78. *Mem:* Am Acad Arts & Sci; Nat Acad Sci. *Res:* Lie groups; discrete subgroups of algebraic groups. *Mailing Add:* Dept of Math Yale Univ New Haven CT 06520

MOSZKOWSKI, STEVEN ALEXANDER, b Berlin, Ger, Mar 13, 27; nat US; m 52; c 3. THEORETICAL PHYSICS. *Educ:* Univ Chicago, BS, 46, MS, 50, PhD(physics), 52. *Prof Exp:* Jr physicist, Argonne Nat Lab, 50-51; res asst, Columbia Univ, 52-53; from asst prof to assoc prof physics, 53-63, PROF PHYSICS, UNIV CALIF, LOS ANGELES, 63- *Concurrent Pos:* Consult, Rand Corp, 53-71 & Oak Ridge Nat Lab, 62-68; Guggenheim fel, 61-62. *Mem:* Fel Am Phys Soc. *Res:* Nuclear shell structure; many-body problem. *Mailing Add:* Dept of Physics Univ of Calif Los Angeles CA 90024

MOSZYNSKI, JERZY ROBERT, b Lwow, Poland, May 12, 25; m 50. MECHANICAL ENGINEERING. *Educ:* Univ London, BSc, 49, MSc, 52, PhD, 58. *Prof Exp:* Asst lectr mech eng, Woolwich Polytech, London, 49-52, lectr thermodyn, 52-54; sr design engr gas turbines, English Elec Co, Ltd, 54-55; res assoc, Brown Univ, 55-58; from asst prof to assoc prof mech eng, Case Inst Technol, 58-63, prof eng, 63-66; PROF MECH & AEROSPACE ENG, UNIV DEL, 66- *Concurrent Pos:* Consult, Babcock & Wilcox Co, 60- & Nat Bur Standards, 77-; vis prof, Polish Acad Sci, 72-73; Humboldt Found sr fel, 74-75. *Mem:* Am Soc Mech Engrs; Brit Inst Mech Engrs. *Res:* Measurement of thermodynamic properties; theoretical and experimental heat transfer; magnetohydrodynamic power generation. *Mailing Add:* 501 N Country Club Dr Newark DE 19711

MOTARD, R(ODOLPHE) L(EO), b Ottawa, Ont, May 26, 25; m 47; c 4. CHEMICAL ENGINEERING. *Educ:* Queen's Univ, Ont, BSc, 47; Carnegie Inst Technol, MS, 48, DSc(chem eng), 52. *Prof Exp:* Res engr, Shell Oil Co, 51-56, group leader, 56-57; from assoc prof to prof chem eng, Univ Houston, 57-78; PROF CHEM ENG & CHMN DEPT, WASHINGTON UNIV, 78- *Concurrent Pos:* Nat Acad Sci-NASA sr fel, 66-67. *Mem:* AAAS; Am Inst

Chem Engrs; Am Chem Soc; Am Soc Eng Educ; Simulation Coun. *Res:* Applied reaction kinetics; thermodynamics; computer science; systems engineering; computer aided design. *Mailing Add:* Dept of Chem Eng Washington Univ St Louis MO 63130

MOTAWI, KAMAL EL-DIN HUSSEIN, food science, see previous edition

MOTCHAN, HAROLD LLOYD, b St Louis, Mo, June 2, 25; m 46; c 2. ELECTRONIC ENGINEERING. *Educ:* Iowa State Col, BSEE, 46. *Prof Exp:* Asst engr, 46-48, engr, 48-50, sr engr, 50-52, group mgr, 52-56, proj electronics engr, 56-59, sect mgr, 59-61, mgr electronics eng dept, 61-68, dir avionics, 68-74, DIR ENG, McDONNELL DOUGLAS ASTRONAUTICS CORP, 74- *Mem:* Inst Elec & Electronics Engrs; Am Defense Preparedness Asn; Am Inst Aeronaut & Astronaut. *Mailing Add:* McDonnell Douglas Astronautics Corp PO Box 516 St Louis MO 63166

MOTCHENBACHER, CURTIS D, b Canby, Minn, Nov 19, 31; m 53; c 3. ELECTRONIC ENGINEERING. *Educ:* SDak State Col, BS, 53. *Prof Exp:* Eval engr, Controls Div, 56-57, res scientist, Res Ctr, 57-62, sr res scientist, 62-68, sr prin res scientist, 68-73, sr prin design engr, 73-78, STAFF ENGR, HONEYWELL, INC, 78- *Honors & Awards:* H W Sweatt Engr-Scientist Award, Honeywell, Inc, 66. *Mem:* Fel AAAS; Am Inst Elec & Electronics Engrs; Nat Soc Prof Engrs. *Res:* Problems of design of optimum low noise transistor amplifiers for specialized applications. *Mailing Add:* 4844 Woodridge Ct Minnetonka MN 55343

MOTE, C(LAYTON) D(ANIEL), JR, b San Francisco, Calif, Feb 5, 37; m 62; c 2. ENGINEERING MECHANICS, MECHANICAL ENGINEERING. *Educ:* Univ Calif, Berkeley, BSc, 59, MSc, 60, PhD(eng mech), 63. *Prof Exp:* Asst mech engr & lectr mech eng, Univ Calif, Berkeley, 62-63; NSF res fel mech eng, Univ Birmingham, 63-64; asst prof, Carnegie Inst Technol, 64-67; from asst prof to assoc prof, 67-72, assoc res engr, Forest Prod Lab, 67-72, PROF MECH ENG, UNIV CALIF, BERKELEY, 72-, V CHMN MECH ENG, 76- *Concurrent Pos:* Consult, Westinghouse Elec Corp, Calif Cedar Prod Co & Teknekron. *Honors & Awards:* Blackall Award, Am Soc Mech Engrs, 75. *Mem:* AAAS; Am Soc Mech Engrs; Am Inst Aeronaut & Astronaut; Forest Prod Res Soc; Am Soc Biomech. *Res:* Mechanics of solids, dynamics and dynamic systems. *Mailing Add:* Dept of Mech Eng Univ of Calif Berkeley CA 94720

MOTE, JIMMY DALE, b Sheridan, Ark, Nov 4, 30; m 51; c 1. METALLURGY. *Educ:* Univ Calif, BS, 57, PhD(metall), 64. *Prof Exp:* Res metallurgist, Lawrence Radiation Lab & Inst Eng Res, Univ Calif, Berkeley, 57-64; tech staff mem, Sandia Corp, NMex State Univ, 64-65; assoc res scientist, Denver Div, Martin Co, 65-68, chief mat sci, 66-68, dir ctr high energy forming, Martin Marietta Corp, 68-71; vpres opers, E F Industs Inc, Univ Louisville, 71-77; SR RES METALL, METALL & MAT SCI DIV, DENVER RES INST, UNIV DENVER, 77- *Mem:* Am Inst Mining, Metall & Petrol Engrs; Am Soc Metals; Am Soc Testing & Mat; Soc Mining Engrs. *Res:* Explosive forming and composite materials; fundamental deformation mechanisms of deformation in metals and alloys under static and dynamic loading. *Mailing Add:* Metall & Mat Sci Div Univ Denver Denver CO 80208

MOTE, MICHAEL ISNARDI, b San Francisco, Calif, Feb 5, 35; m 65; c 2. NEUROPHYSIOLOGY. *Educ:* Univ Calif, Berkeley, AB, 58; San Francisco State Col, MA, 63; Univ Calif, Los Angeles, PhD(zool), 68. *Prof Exp:* NIH fel biol, Yale Univ, 68-70; asst prof, 70-74, ASSOC PROF BIOL, TEMPLE UNIV, 74-, NIH FEL, EYE INST & NSF FEL PSYCHOBIOL, 71- *Concurrent Pos:* Res fel, Swiss Nat Sci Found, 77 & Roche Res Found, Basel, 77; vis prof, Univ Zurich, 77. *Mem:* Fel AAAS; Am Soc Zool; Soc Gen Physiol; Asn Res Vision & Opthal. *Res:* Integrative neurophysiology of invertebrate nervous systems with emphasis on vision in arthropods. *Mailing Add:* Dept of Biol Temple Univ Philadelphia PA 19122

MOTEFF, J(OHN), b Youngstown, Ohio, Aug 8, 23; m 51; c 1. PHYSICS, MATERIALS SCIENCE. *Educ:* Univ Youngstown, BS, 50; Kent State Univ, MA, 51; Univ Cincinnati, PhD(mat sci), 65. *Prof Exp:* Tech engr, Aircraft Nuclear Propulsion Dept, Gen Elec Co, 51-53, supvr shield systs, Design & Eval, 55-61, mgr radiation effects to metals, Nuclear Mat & Propulsion Oper, 61-69; assoc prof, 69-77, PROF MAT SCI, UNIV CINCINNATI, 77- *Mem:* Am Nuclear Soc; Health Phys Soc; Am Soc Metals; Am Inst Mining, Metall & Petrol Engrs. *Res:* Reactor shielding; dosimetry; standardization; high temperature mechanical properties of metals; electron microscopy. *Mailing Add:* Dept of Mat Sci & Metall Eng Univ of Cincinnati Cincinnati OH 45221

MOTHERSILL, JOHN SYDNEY, b Ottawa, Ont, Mar 24, 31; m 79; c 1. GEOLOGY. *Educ:* Carleton Univ, Can, BSc, 53; Queen's Univ, Ont, BSc, 56, PhD(geol), 67. *Prof Exp:* Geologist, Esso Standard Turkey, Inc, Stand Oil Co NJ, 56-58; geologist, Mobil Explor Nigeria, Inc, Mobil Int Oil Co, Inc, 58-61, sect head admin stratig, Colombia Petrol Co, 61-62, sr geologist, Mobil Explor Nigeria, Inc, 62-64; asst prof, 66-70, assoc prof stratig & sedimentation, 70-75, PROF GEOL & DEAN SCI, LAKEHEAD UNIV, 75- *Concurrent Pos:* Reader, Univ Nigeria, 72-73; mem staff, Limnol Surv Lake Superior, Can Ctr Inland Waters. *Mem:* Int Asn Sedimentologists; Geol Asn Can; Am Asn Petrol Geologists. *Res:* Stratigraphy; sedimentation; paleomagnetic studies; nearshore clastic sedimentation. *Mailing Add:* Fac of Sci Lakehead Univ Thunder Bay ON P7B 5E1 Can

MOTHERWAY, JOSEPH E, b Providence, RI, Jan 28, 30; m 55; c 9. MECHANICAL ENGINEERING. *Educ:* Brown Univ, ScB, 55; Univ Conn, MS, 61, PhD, 70. *Prof Exp:* Mech engr, Esso Bayway Refinery, 55-56; design engr, Elec Boat Div, Gen Dynamics Corp, 56-58, design group leader, 58-59; sr proj engr, Remington Rand Univac Labs, 59-60; chief engr res & develop, CHI Div, Speidel Corp, 60-63; chief engr, CHI Div, Textron, Inc, 63-64; from asst prof to assoc prof mech eng, 64-70, head dept, 71-75, BULLARD PROF ENG DESIGN, UNIV BRIDGEPORT, 70- *Concurrent Pos:* Lectr, Brown Univ, 62-64; indust consult, 64- *Mem:* Am Soc Mech Engrs; Soc Exp Stress Anal; Instrument Soc Am. *Res:* Stress wave propagation; nonlinear mechanics; machinery dynamics. *Mailing Add:* 4637 Congress St Fairfield CT 06430

MOTICKA, EDWARD JAMES, b Oak Park, Ill, May 21, 44; m 69; c 1. IMMUNOLOGY. *Educ:* Kalamazoo Col, BA, 66; Univ Ill, PhD(anat), 70. *Prof Exp:* Vis scientist immunol, Czech Acad Sci, Inst Microbiol, 71-72; asst prof cell biol, Univ Tex Health Sci Ctr, Dallas, 72-78; assoc prof, Sch Med, Southern Ill Univ, Carbondale, 78-80; ASSOC PROF, SCH MED, SOUTHERN ILL UNIV, SPRINGFIELD, 80- *Mem:* Am Asn Immunologists; Am Soc Zoologists. *Res:* Development and control of polyclonal immunoglobulin synthesis and the controlling functions of thymus-derived lymphocytes in immune responses. *Mailing Add:* PO Box 3926 Souther Ill Univ Springfield IL 62708

MOTILL, RONALD ALLEN, b Feb 5, 41; US citizen. THEORETICAL PHYSICS, COSMOLOGY. *Educ:* Syracuse Univ, BS, 61, MS, 63, PhD(physics), 75. *Prof Exp:* Technician physics, Syracuse Univ, 58, Bausch & Lomb Optical Co, 60; asst prof physics, Furman Univ, 74-80; MEM FAC, DEPT PHYSICS, VA MILITARY INST, 80- *Mem:* Am Phys Soc; Am Asn Physics Teachers; AAAS. *Res:* Construction of a quantum field theory of the gravitational field based on commutators within characteristic, or null, hypersurfaces; general relativity; quantum field theory. *Mailing Add:* Dept of Physics Va Military Inst Lexington VA 24450

MOTLEY, DAVID MALCOLM, b Long Beach, Calif, June 4, 29; m 52; c 4. COMMUNICATIONS SCIENCE. *Prof Exp:* Staff engr, Collins Radio Co, 52-63; SUPVR COMMUN RES GROUP, ADVAN TECHNOL DEPT, AUTONETICS DIV, N AM ROCKWELL CORP, ANAHEIM, 63- *Mem:* Inst Elec & Electronics Engrs. *Res:* Digital communications; adaptive equalization for data modems; high frequency transmission; communication systems. *Mailing Add:* 16841 Armstrong Santa Ana CA 92705

MOTLEY, ROBERT W, plasma physics, see previous edition

MOTOYAMA, ETSURO K, b Japan, Apr 11, 32; US citizen. ANESTHESIOLOGY, RESPIRATORY PHYSIOLOGY. *Educ:* Chiba Univ, Japan, BS, 53; Chiba Univ Med Sch, Japan, MD, 57. *Prof Exp:* Res assoc pediat, Med Sch, Yale Univ, 64-66, asst prof anesthesiol & pediat, 66-70, assoc prof, 70-79; PROF ANESTHESIOL & PEDIAT, SCH MED, UNIV PITTSBURGH, 79-; DIR, PULMONOLOGY PROG & ATTEND ANESTHESIOLOGIST & PEDIATRICIAN, CHILDREN'S HOSP, PITTSBURGH, 79- *Concurrent Pos:* Fel respiratory physiol, Harvard Med Sch, 62-64; attend anesthesiologist & pediatrician, Yale-New Haven Hosp, 66-; prin investr lung res ctr, Yale Univ, 71-77. *Mem:* Am Physiol Soc; Am Pediat Soc; Soc Pediat Res; Am Soc Anesthesiol; Asn Univ Anesthetists. *Res:* Developmental physiology of lung in fetus, newborn and infant; pediatric pulmonary function in health and disease; pediatric anesthesiology. *Mailing Add:* Dept Anesthesiol & Pediat Sch Med Univ Pittsburgh Pittsburgh PA 15213

MOTSAVAGE, VINCENT ANDREW, b Scranton, Pa, May 10, 34; m 57; c 5. PHARMACY, PHYSICAL CHEMISTRY. *Educ:* Philadelphia Col Pharm, BS, 55; Temple Univ, MS, 57, PhD(pharm), 62. *Prof Exp:* Res assoc pharmaceut develop, Merck Sharp & Dohme Res Labs, Merck & Co, Inc, 57-59, pharm res, 61-63; asst instr pharm, Temple Univ, 59-60, res asst, 60-61; sr phys chemist, Avon Prod, Inc, 64-67, sect head chem res, 67-69; head, Dept Cosmetic & Toiletries Develop, 69-80, ASSOC DIR RES & DEVELOP, MENLEY & JAMES LABS, INC, SMITH KLINE & FRENCH LABS, 80- *Mem:* Am Chem Soc; Am Pharmaceut Asn; Soc Cosmetic Chemists. *Res:* Physical and colloid chemistry as applied to the research and development of cosmetics and pharmaceuticals. *Mailing Add:* Smith Kline & French Labs One Franklin Plaza Philadelphia PA 19101

MOTSINGER, RALPH E, b Carthage, NC, May 10, 31; m 52; c 2. PLANT PATHOLOGY. *Educ:* NC State Univ, BS, 56; Univ Md, MS, 60; Auburn Univ, PhD(plant path), 64. *Prof Exp:* Asst county agent, NC Agr Exten Serv, 56-58; asst county agent, Md Agr Exten Serv, 58-59, exten tobacco specialist, 59-61; exten plant pathologist, La Coop Exten Serv, 64-70; EXTEN PLANT PATHOLOGIST, GA COOP EXTEN SERV, UNIV GA, 70- *Concurrent Pos:* Ford Found vis prof, Col Agr, Selangor Malaysia, 69-70; exten nematologist, Ga Coop Exten Serv, 70- *Mem:* Am Phytopath Soc; Soc Nematol. *Res:* Nematode population dynamics; grower acceptance of plant disease control information. *Mailing Add:* 120 Doe Run Athens GA 30605

MOTT, DAVID LOWE, b Springfield, Vt, Apr 28, 25; m 45; c 3. PHYSICS. *Educ:* Tex Western Col, BS, 58; NMex State Univ, MS, 60, PhD(physics), 63. *Prof Exp:* Asst prof physics, Univ, 65-76, PHYSICIST, PHYS SCI LAB, NMEX STATE UNIV, 63-, ASSOC PROF PHYSICS, NMEX STATE UNIV, 76- *Mem:* Am Asn Physics Teachers. *Res:* X-ray spectroscopy; classical mechanics. *Mailing Add:* Dept of Physics NMex State Univ Las Cruces NM 88003

MOTT, FREDERICK DODGE, b Wooster, Ohio, Aug 3, 04; m 30; c 3. PREVENTIVE MEDICINE. *Educ:* Princeton Univ, AB, 27; McGill Univ, MD & CM, 32. *Hon Degrees:* LLD, Univ Sask, 55. *Prof Exp:* From med officer to chief med officer, US Farm Security Admin, 37-46; chmn, Health Serv Planning Comn, Sask, 46-51; dep minister, Dept Pub Health, Sask, 51; med adminr, Miners Mem Hosp Asn, Washington, DC, 52-57; exec dir, Community Health Asn, Detroit, Mich, 57-64; consult med care, NY Acad Med, 64-66; prof med care, Sch Hyg, Univ Toronto, 66-72; CONSULT, 72- *Concurrent Pos:* Chief health serv br, Off of Labor, War Food Admin, 43-45; actg dept minister, Dept Pub Health, Sask, 49-51; mem expert adv panel on orgn of med care, WHO, 51-77. *Mem:* Fel Am Pub Health Asn. *Res:* Rural health and medical care; organization and financing of health services; planning of hospital and health facilities; medical administration. *Mailing Add:* 19 E Jefferson Circle Pittsford NY 14534

MOTT, GEORGE ROBSON, physics, see previous edition

MOTT, HAROLD, b Harris, NC, June 16, 28; m 59; c 1. ELECTRICAL ENGINEERING. *Educ:* NC State Univ, BEE, 51, MSEE, 53, PhD(elec eng), 60. *Prof Exp:* Asst elec eng, NC State Univ, 51-53, instr, 54-60; engr, Wright Mach Co, NC, 53-54; assoc prof, 60-64, PROF ELEC ENG, UNIV ALA, TUSCALOOSA, 64- *Concurrent Pos:* Consult, Troxler Elec Labs, NC, 56-59 & US Army Missile Res & Develop Command. *Mem:* Inst Elec & Electronics Engrs; Am Soc Eng Educ. *Res:* Antennas; radio wave propagation; electromagnetic theory; radar. *Mailing Add:* Dept of Elec Eng Univ of Ala University AL 35486

MOTT, JACK EDWARD, b Hammond, Ind, May 4, 37; m 59; c 2. ENGINEERING PHYSICS. *Educ:* Univ Chicago, MS, 60; Northwestern Univ, PhD(physics), 67. *Prof Exp:* Assoc scientist, Bettis Atomic Power Div, Westinghouse Elec Co, 60-63; res asst physics, Northwestern Univ, Evanston, 63-67, res assoc, 67-68; from asst prof to assoc prof, Indiana Univ, 68-75; SR PHYSICIST, ENERGY SYSTS & TECHNOL DIV, GEN ELEC CO, 75- *Mem:* Am Phys Soc; Sigma Xi; Am Nuclear Soc. *Res:* Fundamental particle research and teaching; nuclear physics research and teaching; nuclear reactor and energy systems research. *Mailing Add:* Energy Systs & Technol Div GE Co 310 DeGuinge Dr Sunnyvale CA 94086

MOTT, JOE LEONARD, b Linden, Tex, Apr 1, 37; m 60; c 2. ALGEBRA. *Educ:* E Tex Baptist Col, BS, 58; La State Univ, MS, 60, PhD(math), 63. *Prof Exp:* Asst prof math, Univ Kans, 63-65; assoc prof, 65-75, PROF MATH, FLA STATE UNIV, 75- *Concurrent Pos:* Vis prof, Mich State Univ, 73-74 & Univ Tenn, 78- *Mem:* Am Math Soc; Am Math Asn. *Res:* Ideal theory of commutative rings; partially ordered Abelian groups. *Mailing Add:* Dept of Math Fla State Univ Tallahassee FL 32306

MOTT, JULIAN EDWARD, b Lebanon, Mo, Aug 22, 29; m 54; c 2. NUCLEAR ENGINEERING. *Educ:* Univ Tenn, BS, 56; Univ Minn, PhD(aeronaut eng), 66. *Prof Exp:* Test engr, Pratt & Whitney Aircraft Co, 56-57; engr, Oak Ridge Nat Lab, 57-59; from asst prof to assoc prof, 59-72, PROF NUCLEAR ENG, UNIV TENN, KNOXVILLE, 72- *Concurrent Pos:* Consult, Oak Ridge Nat Lab, 59-76, Oak Ridge Assoc Univs, 66-67, Oak Ridge Gaseous Diffusion Plant, 67-74; mgr mech eng, Technol for Energy Corp, 76- *Mem:* Am Nuclear Soc; Am Soc Eng Educ; Am Soc Mech Engrs. *Res:* Two-phase heat transfer and fluid mechanics; nuclear reactor safety and loss of coolant accidents; scientific use of mini-computers. *Mailing Add:* Technol for Energy Corp 10770 Dutchtown Rd Knoxville TN 37922

MOTT, THOMAS, b Oswego, NY, Feb 14, 26; m 77; c 7. MATHEMATICS. *Educ:* Union Col, AB, 50; Univ Pa, AM, 52; Pa State Univ, PhD, 67. *Prof Exp:* Jr mathematician, Cornell Aeronaut Lab, Buffalo, NY, 52-53; instr math, Pa State Univ, Erie, 53; instr, Clarkson Inst Technol, 53-55; instr, Pa State Univ, Hazleton, 55-57, University Park, 57-62; assoc prof, State Univ NY Col Fredonia, 62-67; PROF MATH, STATE UNIV NY COL BUFFALO, 67- *Concurrent Pos:* Math Asn Am lectr, 70- *Mem:* Math Asn Am. *Res:* Analysis; integration theory; limit theorems. *Mailing Add:* Dept of Math State Univ NY Col Buffalo NY 14222

MOTTA, JEROME J, b Los Angeles, Calif, July 6, 33. MYCOLOGY. *Educ:* San Francisco State Col, AB, 58, MA, 64; Univ Calif, Berkeley, PhD(bot), 68. *Prof Exp:* Res plant pathologist, Univ Calif, Berkeley, 68-69; ASSOC PROF BOT, UNIV MD, COLLEGE PARK, 69- *Mem:* AAAS; Mycol Soc Am; Bot Soc Am. *Res:* Cytology and ultrastructure of fungi. *Mailing Add:* Dept of Bot Univ of MD College Park MD 20742

MOTTELER, ZANE CLINTON, b Wenatchee, Wash, July 4, 35; m 60; c 4. MATHEMATICS, COMPUTER SCIENCE. *Educ:* Stanford Univ, BS, 57, MS, 62, PhD(math), 64. *Prof Exp:* NSF fel, Univ Minn, 57-58 & Univ NMex, 58-59; res asst math, Los Alamos Sci Lab, Univ Calif, 58-60, staff mem, 60-65; from asst prof to assoc prof math, Gonzaga Univ, 65-72, chmn dept, 66-71; PROF & HEAD DEPT MATH & COMPUT SCI, MICH TECHNOL UNIV, 72- *Concurrent Pos:* NSF vis scientist prog lectr, 60-61, 65-66; consult, Northwest Col & Univ Asn Sci, 70; nat lectr, Soc Indust & Appl Math, 70-72. *Mem:* Soc Indust & Appl Math; Math Asn Am. *Res:* Existence theory for non-linear elliptic partial differential equations of second order; quantitative and qualitative behavior of polynomials near roots; computer systems. *Mailing Add:* Dept of Math & Comput Sci Mich Technol Univ Houghton MI 49931

MOTTER, ROBERT FRANKLIN, b Early, Iowa, June 29, 33; m 55; c 3. PHOTOGRAPHY, CHEMISTRY. *Educ:* Morningside Col, BS, 55; Univ Minn, PhD(org chem), 58. *Prof Exp:* Res chemist, Dow Chem Co, 55; asst, Univ Minn, 55-58; RES CHEMIST, EASTMAN KODAK CO, 58- *Mem:* Am Chem Soc; Soc Photog Sci & Eng; Soc Motion Picture & TV Engrs. *Res:* Organic synthesis in hetercyclics and sulfur chemistry. *Mailing Add:* 142 El Mar Dr Rochester NY 14616

MOTTERN, JOHN WALLACE, chemical engineering, see previous edition

MOTTET, N KARLE, b Renton, Wash, Jan 8, 24; m 52; c 3. PATHOLOGY, TERATOLOGY. *Educ:* Wash State Univ, BS, 47; Yale Univ, MD, 52; Am Bd Path, dipl, 57. *Prof Exp:* Instr physiol, Yale Univ, 51-52 & path, 55-59; from asst prof to assoc prof, 59-66, dir hosp path, 59-74, PROF PATH, SCH MED, UNIV WASH, 66- *Concurrent Pos:* Nat Found Infantile Paralysis fel, Cambridge Univ, 52-53; USPHS trainee path, 54-55; pathologist & dir lab, Griffin Hosp, Derby, Conn, 55-59; vis scientist, Strangeways Res Lab, Eng, 69-70; consult ed, McGraw-Hill Encycl Sci & Technol & Yearbk Sci. *Mem:* NY Acad Sci; Am Asn Pathologists; Teratology Soc. *Res:* Controls of morphogenesis; metals teratology. *Mailing Add:* D403 Health Sci Bldg Univ Wash Seattle WA 98195

MOTTINGER, JOHN P, b Detroit, Mich, Nov 28, 38. CYTOGENETICS. *Educ:* Ohio Wesleyan Univ, BA, 61, Indiana Univ, PhD(cytogenetics), 68. *Prof Exp:* Instr, 67-68, asst prof, 68-75, ASSOC PROF BOT, UNIV RI, 75- *Mem:* AAAS; Genetics Soc Am. *Res:* Cytogenetics of maize and study of endosperm mutants in tissue culture. *Mailing Add:* Dept of Bot Univ RI Kingston RI 02881

MOTTLEY, CAROLYN, b Palestine, Tex, Oct 29, 47. PHYSICAL CHEMISTRY. *Educ:* Wayland Col, BS, 69; Univ NC, Chapel Hill, PhD(chem), 73. *Prof Exp:* Res assoc chem, Univ Ala, Tuscaloosa, 74-75; ASST PROF CHEM, LUTHER COL, 75- *Mem:* Am Chem Soc; Am Phys Soc. *Res:* Study of molecular motion and structure through the use of magnetic resonance techniques. *Mailing Add:* Dept of Chem Luther Col Decorah IA 52101

MOTTMANN, JOHN, b Alsfeld, WGer, Apr 6, 44; US citizen. ASTRONOMY. *Educ:* Univ Calif, Los Angeles, BA, 66, MS, 67, PhD(astron), 72. *Prof Exp:* Astron, Aerospace Corp, 70-74; lectr astron, Santa Monica Community Col, 72-74; ASSOC PROF ASTRON, CALIF POLYTECH UNIV, 74- *Mem:* Am Astron Soc; Astron Soc Pac; AAAS. *Res:* Galaxies; radio properties of extra-galactic sources. *Mailing Add:* Dept of Physics Calif Polytech State Univ San Luis Obispo CA 93407

MOTTO, JEROME (ARTHUR), b Kansas City, Mo, Oct 16, 21. PSYCHIATRY. *Educ:* Univ Calif, AB, 48, MD, 51. *Prof Exp:* Intern, San Francisco Gen Hosp, 51-52; resident psychiat, Henry Phipps Psychiat Clin, Johns Hopkins Hosp, 52-55; sr resident, Langley Porter Neuropsychiat Inst, 55-56; from instr to asst prof, 56-64, lectr, 64-67, assoc clin prof, 67-69, assoc prof, 69-73, PROF PSYCHIAT, SCH MED, UNIV CALIF, SAN FRANCISCO, 73- *Concurrent Pos:* Attend psychiatrist, Langley Porter Neuropsychiat Inst, 56-; chief psychiat serv, San Francisco Gen Hosp, 71. *Res:* Clinical psychiatry. *Mailing Add:* Dept of Psychiat Univ of Calif Med Ctr San Francisco CA 94143

MOTTOLA, HORACIO ANTONIO, b Buenos Aires, Arg, Mar 22, 30; m 58; c 2. ANALYTICAL CHEMISTRY. *Educ:* Indust Tech, Indust Nat Sch, Arg, 49; Univ Buenos Aires, MS, 57, PhD(chem), 62. *Prof Exp:* Teaching asst chem, Univ Buenos Aires, 56-57, instr, 57-58, 60-63; res assoc, Univ Ariz, 63-64; asst prof, Elbert Covell Col, Univ of the Pac, 64-67; from asst prof to assoc prof, 67-75, PROF CHEM, OKLA STATE UNIV, 75- *Concurrent Pos:* Lectr, Univ Ariz, 66-67. *Mem:* Am Chem Soc; Sigma Xi. *Res:* Separation and determination of traces of metals; mechanisms of liquid-liquid distribution; chemistry of metal chelates; reaction rate methods; fast analyzers. *Mailing Add:* Dept of Chem Okla State Univ Stillwater OK 74074

MOTTS, WARD SUNDT, b Cleveland, Ohio, Oct 31, 24; m 51; c 2. GEOLOGY. *Educ:* Columbia Univ, BA, 49; Univ Minn, MS, 51; Univ Ill, PhD(geol), 57. *Prof Exp:* Geologist, US Bur Reclamation, 51-53; geologist, US Geol Surv, 53-60 & Okla Geol Surv, 60-61; ASSOC PROF GEOL, UNIV MASS, AMHERST, 61- *Concurrent Pos:* Asst, Univ Ill, 55-57. *Mem:* Fel Geol Soc Am; Am Geophys Union. *Res:* Hydrogeology; environmental geology; geomorphology; engineering geology. *Mailing Add:* Dept of Geol Univ of Mass Amherst MA 01002

MOTTUS, EDWARD HUGO, b Eckville, Alta, June 12, 22; m 45; c 3. ORGANIC CHEMISTRY. *Educ:* Univ Alta, BSc, 49; Univ Ill, PhD(chem), 52. *Prof Exp:* Teacher pub schs, Can, 41-42; asst, Univ Ill, 49-51; fel, Nat Res Coun Can, 52-53; res chemist, 53-67, scientist, 67-71, SR SCI FEL, MONSANTO CO, 71- *Mem:* AAAS; Am Chem Soc; The Chem Soc. *Res:* Electrolytic reduction of bicyclic aminoketones; polarographic reduction of diketones; lycopodine; protopine; polyethylene, ionic ringopening polymerizations; polyethers; polyamides; catalysis; polymer syntheses. *Mailing Add:* Monsanto Co M2QID 800 N Lindbergh Blvd St Louis MO 63166

MOTULSKY, ARNO GUNTHER, b Fischhausen, Ger, July 5, 23; nat US; m 45; c 3. INTERNAL MEDICINE, MEDICAL GENETICS. *Educ:* Univ Ill, BS, 45, MD, 47. *Prof Exp:* Res assoc internal med, Sch Med, George Washington Univ, 52-53; from instr to assoc prof, 53-61, PROF MED & GENETICS, SCH MED, UNIV WASH, 61- *Concurrent Pos:* Clin investr, Army Med Serv Grad Sch, Walter Reed Army Med Ctr, DC, 52-53; attend physician, King County & Vet Admin Hosps, Seattle, 54-; consult, Madigan Army Hosp, Tacoma, 55-74; Commonwealth Fund fel, Univ London, 57-58; Markle scholar, 57-62; mem subcomt transfusion probs, Nat Res Coun, 58-63; attend physician, Univ Wash Hosp, 59-; mem human ecol study sect, NIH, 61-65 & hemat study, 69-72; mem, US Panel Methods Eval Environ Mutagenesis & Carcinogenesis, Nat Inst Allergy & Infectious Dis, 72-76; mem, Nat Heart, Lung & Blood Inst Lipid Metab Adv Comt, 76-; mem, Nat Res Coun Comt on Study of Nat Needs for Biomed & Behav Res Personnel, 77- *Mem:* Inst Med-Nat Acad Sci; Am Acad Arts & Sci; Asm Am Physicians; fel Am Col Physicians; Am Fedn Clin Res. *Res:* Role of genetic factors in disease etiology; genetics of coronary heart disease; hereditary hemolytic anemias; abnormal hemoglobins; genetics of drug reaction and response; human population genetics. *Mailing Add:* Div of Med Genetics Univ of Wash Sch of Med Seattle WA 98195

MOTZ, HENRY THOMAS, b St Louis, Mo, June 10, 23; m 47; c 3. NUCLEAR PHYSICS. *Educ:* Yale Univ, BS, 44, MS, 48, PhD, 49. *Prof Exp:* Physicist, Brookhaven Nat Lab, 49-56; physicist, 56-61, group leader res reactor group, 61-65, assoc physics div leader, 65-71, PHYSICS DIV LEADER, LOS ALAMOS SCI LAB, 71- *Concurrent Pos:* Res fel, Univ Zurich, 53-54; guest lectr, Netherlands-Norweg Reactor Sch, 63; secy & chmn nuclear cross sect adv comt & controlled thermonuclear res standing comt, USAEC; mem, Europ-Am Nuclear Data Comt; adv to US mem, Int Nuclear Data Comt, Int Atomic Energy Agency & US mem, Nuclear Energy Agency-Nuclear Data Comt, 73-; Univ Calif contractor to Energy Res & Develop Admin. *Mem:* Am Phys Soc; NY Acad Sci. *Res:* Cyclotron bombardment; si reactions; slow neutron capture gamma rays. *Mailing Add:* Los Alamos Sci Lab PO Box 1663 Los Alamos NM 87545

MOTZ, JOSEPH WILLIAM, b Binghamton, NY, Nov 11, 18; m 45; c 2. PHSYICS. *Educ:* Univ Wis, BS, 41; Cornell Univ, MS, 42; Ind Univ, PhD(physics), 49. *Prof Exp:* Physicist, Armour Res Found, 43-46; PHYSICIST, X-RAY DIV, NAT BUR STANDARDS, 49- *Mem:* Fel Am Phys Soc. *Res:* Radiation physics; photon and electron scattering processes. *Mailing Add:* Nat Bur of Standards X-Ray Div Washington DC 20234

MOTZ, KAYE LA MARR, b Bluffton, Ind, Aug 10, 32; m 59. INDUSTRIAL ORGANIC CHEMISTRY. *Educ:* Univ Colo, BA, 54; Univ Ill, PhD(chem), 58. *Prof Exp:* Instr chem, Mich State Univ, 58-59; res assoc, Univ Mich, 59-60; RES ASSOC, CONTINENTAL OIL CO, 60- *Mem:* Am Chem Soc; Royal Soc Chem. *Res:* Reactions of aluminum alkyls; antioxidants; tertiary oil recovery. *Mailing Add:* Res & Develop Dept Continental Oil Co Drawer 1267 Ponca City OK 74602

MOTZ, LLOYD, b Susquehanna, Pa, June 5, 10; m 34; c 2. ASTROPHYSICS, NUCLEAR PHYSICS. *Educ:* City Col NY, BS, 30; Columbia Univ, PhD(physics), 36. *Prof Exp:* Instr physics, City Col New York, 31-40; dir res & optical design, Dome Precision Corp, NY, 42-46; dir, Park Instrument Co, NJ, 46-49; from asst prof to assoc prof, 50-62, PROF ASTRON, COLUMBIA UNIV, 62- *Concurrent Pos:* Lectr, Columbia Univ, 35-49; adj prof, Polytech Inst Brooklyn, 50-; consult, AMF, Inc, Grumman Aerospace Corp, Polarad Electronics Corp & Razdow Labs; mem bd dirs, Geosci Instrument Corp & Thexon Corp. *Honors & Awards:* Award, Gravity Res Found, 60; Boris Pregel Award in Astron & Physics, NY Acad Sci, 72. *Mem:* AAAS; fel Am Phys Soc; Am Astron Soc; Royal Astron Soc; NY Acad Sci (pres, 70-71). *Res:* Internal constitution of stars; unified field theory; design of optical instruments; geometrical optics; structure of elementary particles; cosmology. *Mailing Add:* 815 W 181st St New York NY 10033

MOTZ, ROBIN OWEN, b New York, NY, Mar 9, 39; m 59. PLASMA PHYSICS, INTERNAL MEDICINE. *Educ:* Columbia Univ, AB, 59, AM, 60, PhD(physics), 65, MD, 75. *Prof Exp:* Asst astron, Columbia Univ, 58-63; lectr physics, City Col New York, 63-65; asst prof, Stevens Inst Technol, 65-71; lectr, Columbia Univ, 71-75; med house staff mem & dept head, Presby Hosp, New York, 75-78; ASST PROF CLIN MED, COLUMBIA UNIV, 78- *Concurrent Pos:* Astron ed, Am Oxford Encyclop, 62-63; assoc ed, Am J Physics, 69-72. *Mem:* Fel NY Acad Sci; AAAS; Am Phys Soc; AMA; Am col Physicians. *Res:* Magnetohydrodynamic drag; Alfven waves; plasma radiation; optical diagnostics. *Mailing Add:* 404 Tenafly Rd Tenafly NJ 07670

MOTZKIN, SHIRLEY M, b New York, NY, Jan 12, 27; m 52; c 3. ANATOMY, DEVELOPMENTAL BIOLOGY. *Educ:* Brooklyn Col, BS, 47; Columbia Univ, AM, 49; NY Univ, PhD(anat), 58. *Prof Exp:* Instr biol, Brooklyn Col, 47-52; instr histol, NY Univ, 51-59, asst prof, 59-66; assoc prof, 66-78, PROF BIOL, POLYTECH INST NEW YORK, 81-, DIR LIFE SCI, 66- *Concurrent Pos:* Adj instr & prof, Brooklyn Col, 52-; guest lectr, Guggenheim Dent Clin, 60-; partic, interdisciplinary prog, NIH basic res prog, 62-66. *Mem:* Sigma Xi; NY Acad Sci; Int Asn Dent Res. *Res:* Interactive effects of millimeter waves on living systems; effects of ionizing radiation on development; developmental teratologic studies of bone formation, palate and tooth development and tissue interactions using biochemical, embryological, histological, cytological, histochemical, cytochemical and radioisotopic techniques. *Mailing Add:* Polytech Inst of New York 333 Jay St Brooklyn NY 11201

MOU, DUEN-GANG, b China, Nov 5, 48; m 72; c 2. BIOCHEMICAL ENGINEERING, INDUSTRIAL MICROBIOLOGY. *Educ:* Nat Taiwan Univ, BS, 70; Univ RI, MS, 75; Mass Inst Technol, PhD(biochem eng), 79. *Prof Exp:* Res engr, Food Indust Res Develop Inst, 71-72; develop engr, Indust Div, Bristol-Myers Co, 79-80; RES ENGR, RES LABS, EASTMAN KODAK CO, 80- *Mem:* Am Chem Soc; Am Inst Chem Engrs. *Res:* Development, automation and control of industrial fermentations, specifically, fed-batch and continuous fermentation processes; application of computer-coupled process monitoring and control. *Mailing Add:* 295 Bonnie Brae Ave Rochester NY 14618

MOUDGIL, VIRINDER KUMAR, b Ludhiana, India. BIOCHEMICAL ENDOCRINOLOGY. *Educ:* Panjab Univ, BSc, 67; Banaras Hindu Univ, MSc, 69, PhD(zool), 72. *Prof Exp:* Res fel biochem, Banaras Hindu Univ, 69-71, asst res officer, 71-73, sr res fel, 73; fel molecular med, Mayo Clin, 73-76; asst prof, 76-82, ASSOC PROF BIOL SCI, OAKLAND UNIV, 82- *Concurrent Pos:* Prin investr, NIH, 78- *Mem:* Am Physiol Soc; Am Soc Biol Chemists; Endocrine Soc; Biophys Soc; Am Chem Soc. *Res:* Investigating the mode of action of steroid hormones with particular emphasis on the role of nucleotides in the process of activation of steroid hormone-receptor complexes. *Mailing Add:* Dept Biol Sci Oakland Univ Rochester MI 48063

MOUK, ROBERT WATTS, b Trenton, NJ, June 23, 40; m 65. POLYMER CHEMISTRY, SYNTHETIC ORGANIC CHEMISTRY. *Educ:* Wittenberg Univ, BS, 63; Bowling Green State Univ, MA, 67; Mich State Univ, PhD(chem), 70. *Prof Exp:* SR RES CHEMIST, ASHLAND CHEM CO, ASHLAND OIL INC, 69- *Mem:* Sigma Xi; Am Chem Soc. *Res:* Emulsion polymerization; new polymers and intermediates; adhesives. *Mailing Add:* Res & Develop Lab Ashland Chem Co PO Box 2458 Columbus OH 43216

MOULD, RICHARD A, b Reading, Pa, Mar 4, 27. THEORETICAL PHYSICS. *Educ:* Lehigh Univ, BS, 51; Yale Univ, MS, 55, PhD(physics), 57. *Prof Exp:* Asst prof, 57-64, master, Learned Hand Col, 70-78, ASSOC PROF PHYSICS, STATE UNIV NY STONY BROOK, 64- *Mem:* Am Asn Physics Teachers. *Res:* General relativity quantum theory of measurements. *Mailing Add:* Dept of Physics State Univ of NY Stony Brook NY 11794

MOULDEN, TREVOR HOLMES, b Leicester, Eng. ENGINEERING. *Educ:* Imperial Col, London, BSc, 61; Univ London, MPhil, 68; Univ Tenn, PhD(aeronaut eng), 73. *Prof Exp:* Sci officer aeronaut eng, Nat Phys Lab, Eng, 61-66; res engr aeronaut eng, Lockheed-Georgia Co, 66-69; res fel, 69-73, asst prof, 73-78, ASSOC PROF AERONAUT ENG, UNIV TENN, SPACE INST, 78- *Mem:* Am Acad Mech; Soc Indust Appl Math; Am Inst Aeronaut & Astronaut. *Res:* Fluid motion with special reference to viscous flow and transonic flows. *Mailing Add:* Univ Tenn Space Inst Tullahoma TN 37388

MOULDER, JAMES WILLIAM, b Burgin, Ky, Mar 28, 21; m 42; c 4. MICROBIOLOGY. *Educ:* Univ Chicago, SB, 41, PhD(biochem), 44. *Prof Exp:* Res assoc malaria, Off Sci Res & Develop Proj, 44-45, Logan fel, 46, instr biochem, Dept Microbiol & Biochem, 46-47, from asst prof to assoc prof, 47-57, chmn dept, 60-69, PROF MICROBIOL, UNIV CHICAGO, 57- *Concurrent Pos:* Fulbright scholar & Guggenheim fel, Oxford Univ, 52-53; Ciba lectr microbial biochem, 63; ed, J Infectious Dis, 57-68. *Honors & Awards:* Lilly Award, 54. *Mem:* AAAS; Am Soc Biol Chem; Am Soc Microbiol; Am Acad Microbiol. *Res:* Biochemistry of intracellular parasitism. *Mailing Add:* Dept of Microbiol Univ of Chicago Chicago IL 60637

MOULDER, JERRY WRIGHT, b Bowling Green, Ky, Sept 2, 42; m 67; c 1. PHYSICS. *Educ:* Western Ky Univ, BS, 64; Univ Tenn, PhD(physics), 70. *Prof Exp:* Asst prof physics, WVa Inst Technol, 70-75; asst prof, 75-77, ASSOC PROF PHYSICS, TRI-STATE COL, 77- *Concurrent Pos:* NSF Acad Yr exten grant, WVa Inst Technol, 71-73. *Mem:* Am Asn Physics Teachers. *Res:* The interaction of low energy K mesons with nuclei. *Mailing Add:* Dept of Physics Tri-State Col Angola IN 46703

MOULDER, PETER VINCENT, JR, b Jackson, Mich, Jan 26, 21; m 46; c 4. CARDIOVASCULAR SURGERY. *Educ:* Univ Notre Dame, BS, 42; Univ Chicago, MD, 45; Am Bd Surg, dipl, 54; Am Bd Thoracic Surg, dipl, 56. *Hon Degrees:* MS, Univ Pa, 72. *Prof Exp:* Intern surg, Univ Chicago Clins, 45-46, resident gen surg, 48-51; resident, Univ Ill, 52; from instr to prof surg, Univ Chicago Clins, 52-68; prof thoracic & cardiovasc surg & dir dept, Pa Hosp, Sch Med, Univ Pa, 68-72; prof thoracic & cardiovasc surg, Univ Fla, 72-80; MEM STAFF, SCH MED, TULANE UNIV, 80- *Concurrent Pos:* Resident thoracic surg, Univ Chicago Clins, 52-53, chief resident surgeon, 53-54, secy dept surg, 59-64; consult & lectr, Great Lakes Naval Hosp, Chicago, 59-68; consult, Philadelphia Naval Hosp, 68-; med investr, Vet Admin Hosp, 73-74 & 76-82. *Mem:* Am Physiol Soc; Am Asn Thoracic Surg; Am Surg Asn; Am Col Surg; Soc Clin Surg. *Res:* Biochemical and physiological studies on the heart; pulmonary hypertension; myocardial hypertrophy; time series analysis of cardiovascular phenomena; computer science. *Mailing Add:* Sch Med Tulane Univ 1430 Tulane Ave New Orleans LA 70112

MOULE, DAVID, b Hamilton, Ont, Nov 17, 33; m 62; c 2. PHYSICAL CHEMISTRY, MOLECULAR SPECTROSCOPY. *Educ:* McMaster Univ, BSc, 58, PhD(chem), 62. *Prof Exp:* Asst res officer chem, Atomic Energy Comn Can, 64-66; asst prof, 66-70, assoc prof, 70-76, PROF CHEM, BROCK UNIV, 76- *Concurrent Pos:* NATO fel, 62-64. *Res:* spectroscopy of polyatomic molecules in excited electronic states; isotope equilibria. *Mailing Add:* Dept of Chem Brock Univ St Catherines ON L2S 3A1 Can

MOULIS, EDWARD JEAN, JR, b Natchitoches, La, July 26, 40; m 67; c 2. MATHEMATICS. *Educ:* Harvard Univ, BA, 62; Univ Del, MS, 67, PhD(math), 71. *Prof Exp:* Instr math, US Navy Nuclear Power Sch, Md, 62-66; asst prof, Frostburg State Col, 71-75; ASST PROF MATH, US NAVAL ACAD, 75- *Mem:* Math Asn Am; Am Math Soc. *Res:* Complex analysis; univalent function theory; conformal mapping. *Mailing Add:* Dept of Math US Naval Acad Annapolis MD 21402

MOULTHROP, PETER HILL, energy conversion, see previous edition

MOULTON, ARTHUR B(ERTRAM), b Rochester, NH, Nov 29, 20. ELECTRICAL ENGINEERING. *Educ:* Univ Maine, BS, 43. *Prof Exp:* Electronic scientist, US Dept Defense, 46-52; sr electronic engr, Gen Dynamics/Convair, 52-55; assoc engr, Scripps Inst, Univ Calif, 55-56; asst prof elec eng, Univ Maine, 56-59; sr electronic engr, Litton Industs, 59; sr commun engr, Holmes & Narver, 60-61; engr, Lawrence Radiation Lab, Univ Calif, 61-63 & ACF Industs Inc & Link Group, Gen Precision Inc, 64-67, field eng dept, Systs Div, 67-68, ENGR, LINK DIV, SINGER-GEN PRECISION, 68- *Mem:* Inst Elec & Electronics Engrs. *Res:* Communications; digital computers; navigation. *Mailing Add:* Link Div 11800 Tech Rd Silver Spring MD 20904

MOULTON, BRUCE CARL, b Oneida, NY, Nov 6, 40; m 67; c 2. ENDOCRINOLOGY, BIOCHEMISTRY. *Educ:* Hamilton Col, AB, 62; Cornell Univ, MS, 65, PhD(endocrinol), 68. *Prof Exp:* Fel, Reprod Biol Training Prog, Col Med, Univ Nebr, Omaha, 68-70, res asst prof obstet-gynec & biochem, 70; asst prof obstet-gynec & biol chem, 70-75, ASSOC PROF RES OBSTET-GYNEC, COL MED, UNIV CINCINNATI, 75- *Mem:* AAAS; Endocrine Soc; Soc Study Reprod; Am Physiol Soc. *Res:* Biochemical mechanisms of hormone action in reproductive physiology. *Mailing Add:* Dept of Obstet-Gynec Univ of Cincinnati Col of Med Cincinnati OH 45267

MOULTON, DAVID GILLMAN, b Bombay, India, Nov 29, 28; m 55; c 3. PHYSIOLOGY. *Educ:* Glasgow Univ, BSc, 54; Univ Birmingham, PhD(anat), 58. *Prof Exp:* Thomas Welton Stanford fel psychol, Stanford Univ, 58-59; res assoc physiol, Fla State Univ, 60-63, vis assoc prof, 63-65; from assoc prof to prof, Clark Univ, 65-69; assoc prof, 69-77, PROF PHYSIOL, SCH MED, UNIV PA, 77-; MEM MONELL CHEM SENSES CTR, 69-; RES PHYSIOLOGIST, VET ADMIN HOSP, 69- *Mem:* AAAS; Brit Soc Exp Biol; Am Physiol Soc; Brit Inst Biol; Soc Neurosci. *Res:* Olfaction; sensory physiology; neurophysiology. *Mailing Add:* Monell Chem Senses Ctr Univ of Pa Philadelphia PA 19104

MOULTON, EDWARD Q(UENTIN), b Kalamazoo, Mich, Nov 16, 26; m 54; c 4. CIVIL ENGINEERING, EDUCATION ADMINISTRATION. *Educ:* Mich State Univ, BS, 47; La State Univ, MS, 48; Univ Calif, Berkeley, PhD(environ eng), 56. *Prof Exp:* Instr civil eng, Mich State Univ, 47; asst prof, Auburn Univ, 48-50; lectr, Univ Calif, 51-54; from asst prof to assoc prof civil eng, Ohio State Univ, 54-64, prof eng mech, 64-66, asst dean, Grad Sch, 58-62, assoc dean, 62-64, assoc dean arts & sci & chmn, Dept Geod Sci, 62-64, assoc dean acad affairs & dean off campus educ, 64-66; pres, Univ SDak, 66-68; prof civil eng, Ohio State Univ, 68-79, secy bd trustees, 68-79, exec asst to pres, 68-69, vpres admin opers, 69-70, exec vpres, 70-73, vpres bus & admin, 73-79; CHANCELLOR, OHIO BD REGENTS, 79- *Mem:* Am Soc

Civil Engrs. *Res:* Water resources; effects of toxic ions of waste water recovery procedures; application of electrodialysis to the removal of saline and waste waters; acid mine drainage. *Mailing Add:* Ohio Bd Regents 30 East Broad St Columbus OH 43215

MOULTON, GRACE CHARBONNET, b New Orleans, La, Nov 1, 23; m 47; c 2. BIOPHYSICS, EXPERIMENTAL SOLID STATE PHYSICS. *Educ:* Tulane Univ, BA, 44; Univ Ill, MS, 48; Univ Ala, PhD(physics), 62. *Prof Exp:* Asst biophys, Univ Ill, 50-52; physicist, Argonne Cancer Res Hosp, Ill, 52; asst physics, Univ Ala, 59-61, asst prof, 61-65; asst prof, 65-74, ASSOC PROF PHYSICS, FLA STATE UNIV, 74- *Mem:* Sigma Xi; Am Phys Soc. *Res:* Radiation effects in materials of biological importance with emphasis on the mechanisms involved, as studied by electron spin resonance and electron nuclear double resonance. *Mailing Add:* Dept of Physics Fla State Univ Tallahassee FL 32306

MOULTON, JACK E, veterinary pathology, see previous edition

MOULTON, JAMES FRANK, JR, b Wash, DC, Nov 9, 21; m 44; c 2. RESEARCH ADMINISTRATION. *Educ:* Georgetown Univ, BS, 43. *Prof Exp:* Res physicist, Underwater & Air Explosion Effects, US Dept Navy, 43-46, sr res assoc, Shock Wave Phenomena in Air, Naval Ord Lab, 46-58, chief, Air-Ground Explosions Div, 58-65, chief, Naval Effects Br, Defense Atomic Support Agency, 65-67, CHIEF, AEROSPACE SYSTS DIV, DEFENSE NUCLEAR AGENCY, 67- *Concurrent Pos:* Sci consult, Energy Res & Develop Admin, Dept Navy, Armed Serv Explosives Safety Bd & Nat Mat Adv Bd; mem working group, S2-54 Atmospheric Blast Effects, Am Nat Standards Comt, 71- *Honors & Awards:* Newmann Award, 40; Meritorious Civilian Serv Award, US Navy, 51, 59; Sustained Superior Performance, Defense Nuclear Agency, 74. *Mem:* AAAS; Am Phys Soc. *Res:* Detection and measurement of blast and shock phenomena in high explosive and nuclear explosion environments; impulsive irradiation and response of aerospace systems materials and structures; research and development resource management. *Mailing Add:* 4105 Glenrose St Kensington MD 20795

MOULTON, JAMES MALCOLM, b West Haven, Conn, July 25, 21; m 49; c 3. VERTEBRATE MORPHOLOGY. *Educ:* Univ Mass, BS, 47; Harvard Univ, MA, 50, PhD(zool), 52. *Prof Exp:* Asst biol, Williams Col, 47-48; instr, Brown Univ, 51; instr anat, Sch Med, Johns Hopkins Univ, 51-52; from instr to assoc prof, 52-65, actg chmn dept, 59-60 & 66-67, chmn, 70-73, premed adv, 69-77, prof biol, 65-77, GEORGE LINCOLN SKOFIELD, JR PROF BIOL, BOWDOIN COL, 77- *Concurrent Pos:* Res assoc, Woods Hole Oceanog Inst, 55-72; NSF grant, 57-63; Fulbright res scholar & Guggenheim fel, Univ Queensland, 60-61; mem conf animal orientation, Univ Munich, 62; Wenner-Gren Conf Animal Communication, 65; partic, Southeast Pac Biol Oceanog Prog, cruise 18A of Anton Bruun, 66; vis scientist, Inst Animal Genetics, Edinburgh Univ, 67; vis prof, Mus Comp Zool, Harvard Univ, 74. *Mem:* Am Micros Soc; Am Inst Biol Sci; Int Acad Fishery Sci; Fisheries Soc Brit Isles; Royal Micros Soc. *Res:* Animal morphology and development; acoustical biology of animals. *Mailing Add:* Dept of Biol Bowdoin Col Brunswick ME 04011

MOULTON, PETER FRANKLIN, b Springfield, Mass, May 27, 46; m 70; c 2. SOLID STATE LASERS, SOLID STATE SPECTROSCOPY. *Educ:* Harvard Univ, BA, 68; Mass Inst Technol, MS, 71, PhD(elec eng), 75. *Prof Exp:* Physicist, Arthur D Little, Inc, 68-69; MEM STAFF, LINCOLN LAB, MASS INST TECHNOL, 75- *Res:* Quantum electronics. *Mailing Add:* Lincoln Lab Mass Inst Technol Lexington MA 02173

MOULTON, WILLIAM G, b Waverly, Ill, Jan 4, 25; m 47; c 2. SOLID STATE PHYSICS, LOW TEMPERATURE PHYSICS. *Educ:* Western Ill State Col, BS, 46; Univ Ill, MS, 48, PhD(physics), 52. *Prof Exp:* Asst physics, Univ Ill, 46-51; instr, Chicago Div, Univ Ill, 51-53, asst prof, 53-56; from asst prof to prof, Univ Ala, 56-65; PROF PHYSICS, FLA STATE UNIV, 65- *Mem:* Am Phys Soc. *Res:* Superconductivity; magnetic resonance; magnetic ordered states; solid state and low temperature physics. *Mailing Add:* Dept of Physics Fla State Univ Tallahassee FL 32306

MOUNCE, TROY G(ASPARD), b Luftkin, Tex, Mar 12, 26; m 53; c 1. CHEMICAL ENGINEERING, CHEMISTRY. *Educ:* Lamar State Col, BS, 53; WVa Univ, MS, 72; Ohio Univ, PhD(chem eng), 79. *Prof Exp:* Jr engr, BF Goodrich Chem Co, 53-56, engr, 56-63, sr engr, 63-65; sr engr, Borg-Warner Chem & Plastics, 65-67, develop specialist, 67-68, sr develop specialist, 68-76; MGR, CHEM ENG RES, RES CTR, US INDUST CHEM, 76- *Mem:* Am Chem Soc. *Res:* Process development. *Mailing Add:* 3407 York Lane Cincinnati OH 45215

MOUNT, DAVID WILLIAM ALEXANDER, b Bromley, Eng, Jan 15, 38; m 60; c 2. GENETICS, MOLECULAR BIOLOGY. *Educ:* Univ Alta, BSc, 60; Univ Toronto, MA, 63, PhD(med biophys), 66. *Prof Exp:* asst prof, 69-81, PROF MICROBIOL, COL MED, UNIV ARIZ, 81- *Concurrent Pos:* Fel genetics, Univ Alta, 67-68; USPHS fel molecular biol, Univ Calif, Berkeley, 68-69; lectr, Univ Ottawa, 66, Carleton Univ, 66-67 & Univ Alta, 67-68. *Mem:* AAAS; Genetics Soc Am; Am Soc Microbiol. *Res:* Genetics of bacteria and bacterial viruses; radiation biology; biophysics. *Mailing Add:* Dept of Microbiol Univ of Ariz Col of Med Tucson AZ 85721

MOUNT, DONALD I, b Miamisburg, Ohio, Sept 20, 31; m 53; c 2. FISH BIOLOGY. *Educ:* Ohio State Univ, BS, 53, MS, 57, PhD(zool, fish physiol), 60. *Prof Exp:* Fisheries res biologist, R A Taft Sanit Eng Ctr, Fed Water Pollution Control Admin, 60-67, dir, Nat Water Qual Lab, 67-79, RES AQUATIC BIOLOGIST, US ENVIRON PROTECTION AGENCY, 79- *Honors & Awards:* Superior Serv Award, US Dept Health, Educ & Welfare, 65; Gold Medal, US Environ Protection Agency, 73. *Mem:* AAAS; Am Fisheries Soc; Int Asn Great Lakes Res. *Res:* Fish toxicology and physiology; effects of water pollution on fishes, especially the chronic effects of pollutants. *Mailing Add:* Environ Res Lab US Environ Protection Agency 6201 Congdon Duluth MN 55804

MOUNT, ELDRIDGE MILFORD, III, b Springfield, Pa, Jan 22, 50; m 72; c 2. POLYMER ENGINEERING. *Educ:* West Chester State Col, BA, 72; Rensselaer Polytech Inst, ME, 76, PhD(chem eng), 79. *Prof Exp:* Asst res chem, Sterling Winthrop Res Inst, 72-74; process develop engr, Films Res & Develop, ICI Americas, 78-81; SR DEVELOP ENGR, FILMS RES & DEVELOP, MOBIL CHEM, 81- *Concurrent Pos:* Mem bd dir, Extrusion Div, Soc Plastics Engrs, 81. *Mem:* Soc Plastics Engrs; Am Chem Soc; Soc Rheology. *Res:* Mechanism of polymer melting in signle screw extgrudes, both theoretical and experimental; film properties versus processing conditions and polymer composition. *Mailing Add:* Mobil Tech Ctr Rt 31 Macedon NY 14502

MOUNT, GARY A, medical entomology, see previous edition

MOUNT, KENNETH R, b Champaign, Ill, Apr 29, 33; m 66; c 2. MATHEMATICS. *Educ:* Univ Ill, BA, 54, MA, 55; Univ Calif, Berkeley, PhD(math), 60. *Prof Exp:* From instr to asst prof, 60-66, ASSOC PROF MATH, NORTHWESTERN UNIV, ILL, 66- *Concurrent Pos:* NSF res grant, France, 64-65; NATO grant, 74. *Mem:* Am Math Soc. *Res:* Algebraic geometry and commutative algebra; economics. *Mailing Add:* Dept of Math Northwestern Univ Evanston IL 60201

MOUNT, LLOYD GORDON, b Central Square, NY, Mar 29, 16; m 41; c 3. INDUSTRIAL ORGANIC CHEMISTRY. *Educ:* Cornell Univ, AB, 37; Yale Univ, PhD(org chem), 40. *Prof Exp:* Res chemist, Calco Chem Div, Am Cyanamid Co, NJ, 40-41, group leader process develop, 45-51; chief, Pyrotech Res & Develop Sect, Picatinny Arsenal, 51-52; tech liason mkt res, Chemstrand Corp, 52-55; commercial develop, Food Mach & Chem Corp, 55-58; head chem res & develop dept, Vitro Labs, 58-60; pres, Carnegies Fine Chem of Kearny, NJ, 60-62; dir bus res, Thiokol Chem Corp, 62-65; vpres planning & develop, Clarkson Col Technol, 65-67; dir res & develop, 67-68, tech dir, 68-71, dir mfg, 71-72, VPRES PROD, RUETGERS-NEASE CHEM CO, INC, 72- *Concurrent Pos:* Lectr, Rutgers Univ, 46-47. *Mem:* Am Chem Soc; Chem Mkt Res Asn; Am Inst Chem. *Res:* Sulfa compounds; vat dyes; military explosives; synthetic fibers; planning, development and marketing research. *Mailing Add:* Ruetgers-Nease Chem Co Inc Box 221 State College PA 16801

MOUNT, MARK SAMUEL, b Crawfordsville, Ind, Nov 18, 40; m 63; c 1. PLANT PATHOLOGY, PLANT PHYSIOLOGY. *Educ:* Ill Wesleyan Univ, BS, 63; Mich State Univ, MS, 65, PhD(bot, plant path), 68. *Prof Exp:* Res assoc, Cornell Univ, 68-69; asst prof, 69-76, ASSOC PROF PLANT PATH, UNIV MASS, AMHERST, 76- *Concurrent Pos:* NSF res grant, Univ Mass, Amherst, 70-72, NIH res grant, 73-76. *Mem:* Am Phytopath Soc; Am Soc Plant Physiol. *Res:* Physiology of plant disease development; nucleic acid metabolism in diseased plants. *Mailing Add:* Dept of Plant Path Univ of Mass Amherst MA 01003

MOUNT, RAMON ALBERT, b Lohrville, Iowa, May 4, 39; m 62; c 2. ORGANIC CHEMISTRY. *Educ:* Ariz State Univ, BS, 61; Mich State Univ, PhD(org chem), 67; St Louis Univ, MBA, 72. *Prof Exp:* Chemist, Dow Chem Co, 61-64; res specialist, 67-75, SR RES SPECIALIST, MONSANTO CO, 75- *Mem:* AAAS; Am Chem Soc. *Res:* Catalytic oxidation of hydrocarbons; heterogeneous catalysis; industrial process research in organic chemistry. *Mailing Add:* 4810 Broad Oak Dr St Louis MO 63128

MOUNT, ROBERT HUGHES, b Lewisburg, Tenn, Dec 25, 31; m 61; c 2. VERTEBRATE ZOOLOGY. *Educ:* Auburn Univ, BS, 54, MS, 56; Univ Fla, PhD(biol), 61. *Prof Exp:* From asst prof to assoc prof biol, Ala Col, 61-66; assoc prof, 66-72, PROF ZOOL, AUBURN UNIV, 72- *Mem:* Am Soc Ichthyologists & Herpetologists; Soc Study Amphibians & Reptiles. *Res:* Herpetology; natural history of reptiles and amphibians of southern United States. *Mailing Add:* Dept of Zool & Entom Auburn Univ Auburn AL 36830

MOUNTAIN, CLIFTON FLETCHER, b Toledo, Ohio, Apr 15, 24; m 45; c 3. THORACIC SURGERY. *Educ:* Harvard Col, AB, 47; Boston Univ, MD, 54; Am Bd Surg, dipl, 62. *Prof Exp:* Dir dept statist res, Univ Boston, 47-50; consult & res analyst, Mass Dept Pub Health, 51-53; resident surgeon, Univ Chicago Clins, 54-58; instr surg, Univ Chicago, 58-59; asst prof, 60-63, assoc prof surg, 63-76, PROF SURG & CHIEF SECT THORACIC SURG, UNIV TEX SYST CANCER CTR, M D ANDERSON HOSP & TUMOR INST, 76- *Concurrent Pos:* Fel surg physiol, Univ Chicago, 55-58; sr fel thoracic surg, Univ Tex M D Anderson Hosp & Tumor Inst, 59-60; prin investr & mem solid tumor study group, Cancer Chemother Nat Serv Ctr, NIH, 61-72, prin investr, Cancer Res Progs, Nat Cancer Inst, 63-; sect ed chest dis, Yearbk Cancer, 61-; sr investr & chmn prog biomath & comput sci, Univ Tex, 62-64; consult med sci adv comt, Systs Develop Corp, Calif, 63-68; mem, Am Joint Comt Cancer Staging & End Result Reporting; chmn, Task Force Lung & Esophageal Cancer & Nat Working Party Lung Cancer; chmn, Task Force Surg. *Mem:* AAAS; Am Col Chest Physicians; Am Radium Soc; Soc Surg Oncol; Soc Thoracic Surgeons. *Res:* Thoracic malignant diseases; surgical techniques and adjunctive therapeutic programs in cancer chemotherapy and supervoltage irradiation; quantitative biology through biomathematics and computer sciences. *Mailing Add:* Univ of Tex M D Anderson Hosp & Tumor Inst Houston TX 77030

MOUNTAIN, DAVID CHARLES, JR, b Boston, Mass, Oct 3, 46. NEUROPHYSIOLOGY, BIOMEDICAL INSTRUMENTATION. *Educ:* Mass Inst Technol, BS, 68; Univ Wis, Madison, MS, 73, PhD(elec eng), 78. *Prof Exp:* Med engr, Mass Gen Hosp, 68-70; ASST PROF BIOMED ENG & ASST RES PROF OTOLARYNGOL, BOSTON UNIV, 79- *Mem:* AAAS; Asn Res Otolaryngol; Am Asn Eng Educ; NY Acad Sci. *Res:* Physiology of the auditory system and development of related instrumentation. *Mailing Add:* Boston Univ 110 Cummington St Boston MA 02215

MOUNTAIN, RAYMOND DALE, b Great Falls, Mont, Mar 28, 37; m 61; c 3. THEORETICAL PHYSICS. *Educ:* Mont State Col, BS, 59; Case Western Reserve Univ, MS, 61, PhD(physics), 63. *Prof Exp:* Physicist, 63-68, CHIEF STATIST PHYSICS SECT, NAT BUR STANDARDS, 68- *Concurrent Pos:* Nat Acad Sci-Nat Res Coun fel, 63-65; John Simon Guggenheim Mem Found fel, 74. *Mem:* Am Phys Soc. *Res:* Statistical mechanics; physics of liquids. *Mailing Add:* Nat Bur Standards Statist Physics B318 Phys Bldg Washington DC 20234

MOUNTAIN, WILLIAM BUCKINGHAM, b Kamsack, Sask, Dec 3, 22; m 48; c 2. NEMATOLOGY. *Educ:* Univ Western Ont, BSc, 50; Univ Toronto, PhD(plant path), 53. *Prof Exp:* Nematologist, Harrow Res Sta, 50-59, head nematol sect, 59-64; dir, Vineland Res Sta, 64-69; dir, Entom Res Inst, Agr Can, 69-73, asst dir gen, Res Br, 73-78, dir gen, 78-80; ASST DEP MINISTER, ENVIRON CAN, 80- *Mem:* Soc Nematol (vpres, 63, pres, 64); Agr Inst Can; Soc Europ Nematol. *Res:* Phytonematology; management and administration of research. *Mailing Add:* Environ Conserv Serv Environ Can Place Vincent Massey Ottawa ON K1A 0E7 Can

MOUNTCASTLE, VERNON BENJAMIN, b Shelbyville, Ky, July 15, 18; m 45; c 3. PHYSIOLOGY. *Educ:* Roanoke Col, BS, 38; Johns Hopkins Univ, MD, 42. *Hon Degrees:* DSc, Roanoke Col, 68, Univ Pa, 76. *Prof Exp:* House officer surg, Johns Hopkins Hosp, 42-43; resident fel physiol, 46-48, from asst prof to assoc prof, 48-59, PROF PHYSIOL, SCH MED, JOHNS HOPKINS UNIV, 59-, DIR DEPT, 64- *Concurrent Pos:* Mem physiol study sect, NIH, 57-58, chmn, 58-63, chmn physiol training comt, 58-63; Lilly lectr & spec univ lectr, Univ London, 59; vis lectr, Col France, 59; chief ed, J Neurophysiol, 62-64; mem vis comt psychol & mem neurosci res prog, Mass Inst Technol, 66-; mem bd biol & med, NSF, 70-73; Wilder Penfield Mem lectr, Am Univ Beirut, 71; mem coun, Nat Eye Inst, 71-74; chmn sect physiol, Nat Acad Sci, 71-74; mem comn neurophysiol, Int Union Phys Sci; Sherrington lectr, Univ Liverpool, 74; Stevenson lectr, Univ Western Ont, 76; Rector's lectr, Univ Helsinki, 77; Mellon lectr, Univ Pittsburgh, 77; Hughlings Jackson lectr, McGill Univ, 78. *Honors & Awards:* Lashley Prize, Am Philos Soc, 74; F O Schmitt Prize & Medal, Inst Tech, 75; Horwitz Prize, Columbia Univ, 78. *Mem:* Nat Acad Sci; AAAS; Am Neurol Asn; Am Asn Neurol Surg; Soc Neurosci (pres, 70-71). *Res:* Central nervous mechanisms in emotion; neurophysiology of the great afferent systems; sensation. *Mailing Add:* Dept of Physiol Johns Hopkins Univ Sch of Med Baltimore MD 21205

MOUNTCASTLE, WILLIAM R, JR, b Smyrna, Ga, Oct 31, 21; m 50; c 2. PHYSICAL CHEMISTRY, ANALYTICAL CHEMISTRY. *Educ:* Ga Inst Technol, BS, 43; Univ Ala, MS, 56, PhD(chem), 58. *Prof Exp:* Rubber chemist, Goodyear Tire & Rubber Co, Ala, 43-53; chem engr, Southeastern Exp Sta, US Bur Mines, 54-56; instr chem, Univ Ala, 57-58; assoc prof anal & phys chem, Birmingham-Southern Col, 58-65, prof, 65-66; ASST PROF CHEM, AUBURN UNIV, 66- *Concurrent Pos:* Consult res ctr, Med Col, Univ Ala, 58-60; participation contract, Oak Ridge Assoc Univs, 61-; res assoc, Union Carbide Nuclear Corp, 63; dir, NSF-Undergrad Res Chem, 64-66. *Mem:* Am Chem Soc. *Res:* Solvent extraction using phenyl phosphate diester and applications of electrochemical and spectrographic methods to this study; coulometry; spectroscopy. *Mailing Add:* Dept of Chem Auburn Univ Auburn AL 36830

MOUNTFORD, KENT, b Plainfield, NJ, July 23, 38; m 71. MARINE ECOLOGY. *Educ:* Rutgers Univ, BS, 60, MS, 69, PhD(bot), 71. *Prof Exp:* Res asst bur biol res, Rutgers Univ, 67-71, teaching asst bot & zool, 69-70; asst cur, Benedict Estuarine Lab, Acad Natural Sci, Philadelphia, 71-78; res assoc, Chesapeake Biol Lab, Univ Md, 78-79; mgr, Aquatic Toxicol Biospherics, Inc, 79-80; ENVIRON SCIENTIST QUALITY ASSURANCE, DC GOVT, 80- *Concurrent Pos:* Lectr, var Cols, Univs & Co; State Govt contract officer. *Mem:* Am Soc Limnol & Oceanog; Am Littoral Soc; Sigma Xi; Estuarine Res Fedn; Atlantic Estuarine Res Soc. *Res:* Human estuary interactions, field and lab studies on ecology of estuarine plankton systems, multi-media public information programs. *Mailing Add:* Barnegat Assocs Box 10 Breeden Rd Lushby MD 20657

MOUNTJOY, ERIC W, b Calgary, Alta, Nov 28, 31; m 58. GEOLOGY, STRATIGRAPHY. *Educ:* Univ BC, BASc, 55; Univ Toronto, PhD(stratig, struct geol), 60. *Prof Exp:* Tech officer field geol, Geol Surv Can, 57-60, geologist, 60-63; from asst prof to assoc prof, 63-74, PROF SEDIMENTATION STRATIG, McGILL UNIV, 74- *Mem:* Soc Econ Paleont & Mineral (vpres, 78-79); Am Asn Petrol Geol; fel Geol Soc Am; fel Geol Asn Can; Int Asn Sedimentologists. *Res:* Sedimentation; structural geology of Alberta Rocky Mountains; Devonian Reef complexes; carbonate sedimentology; recent carbonates. *Mailing Add:* Dept of Geol Sci McGill Univ 3450 University St Montreal PQ H3A 2A7 Can

MOUNTNEY, GEORGE JOSEPH, poultry science, food technology, see previous edition

MOUNTS, RICHARD DUANE, b San Diego, Calif, Nov 15, 41; m 75; c 2. ANALYTICAL CHEMISTRY. *Educ:* Wheaton Col, Ill, BS, 64; Ariz State Univ, MS, 68; Univ Ariz, PhD(anal chem), 74. *Prof Exp:* Res chemist, J T Baker Chem Co, 67-69 & Grefco, Inc, 69-70; asst prof chem, Wake Forest Univ, 74-75; ASST PROF CHEM, FLA INST TECHNOL, 75- *Mem:* Am Chem Soc. *Res:* Voltammetric methods of analysis and electronic modules for instruction in analytical chemistry instrumentation. *Mailing Add:* Dept of Chem Fla Inst of Technol Melbourne FL 32901

MOUNTS, TIMOTHY LEE, b Peoria, Ill, Sept 14, 37; m 58; c 3. AGRICULTURAL CHEMISTRY, RADIOCHEMISTRY. *Educ:* Bradley Univ, BS, 59, MS, 68. *Prof Exp:* Res chemist, 57-75, leader edible oils prod & processes, 75-80, CHIEF, OILSEED CROPS LAB, NORTHERN REGIONAL RES CTR, USDA, 80- *Honors & Awards:* Bond Award, Am Oil Chemists Soc, 69 & 71. *Mem:* Am Oil Chemists Soc; Am Chem Soc; Inst Food Technologists. *Res:* Development of improved edible oil products and processes so as to maintain a safe and nutritious food supply; hydrogenation and refining of edible oils, organoleptic evaluation of oils for flavor and stability, oils from damaged soybeans. *Mailing Add:* 2223 N North Peoria IL 61604

MOURAD, A GEORGE, b Bludan, Syria, Nov 6, 31; US citizen; m 58; c 1. GEODESY, PETROLEUM ENGINEERING. *Educ:* Ohio State Univ, BSc, 57, MSc, 59. *Prof Exp:* Res asst gravity & geod, Inst Geod, Ohio State Univ Res Found, 56-59, res assoc, 59-62; sr engr, NAm Aviation, 62-64; res geodesist, 64-66, SR GEODESIST, BATTELLE MEM INST, 66-, PROG DIR MARINE GEOD, 68-, PROJ MGR GEOD & OCEAN PHYSICS, 72- *Concurrent Pos:* Vchmn navig subcomt antisubmarine warfare, Nat Security Indust Asn, 70-; chmn spec study group on marine geod, Int Asn Geod, 70-; chmn comt marine geod, Int Asn Geod, 75-79. *Mem:* Marine Technol Soc; Am Geophys Union; Am Inst Navig. *Res:* Research and management ain in programs on satellite applications to earth and ocean dynamics disciplines; satellite altimetry for determining mean sea level; radar techniques for sea state measurements; satellite interferometry techniques for navigation; traffic control; data transfer; search and rescue applications. *Mailing Add:* 3680 Dublin Rd Columbus OH 43220

MOURITSEN, T(HORVALD) EDGAR, b Waukegan, Ill, Aug 13, 26; m 60; c 3. MECHANICAL ENGINEERING. *Educ:* Univ Ill, BS, 48; Univ Tex, MS, 54. *Prof Exp:* Propulsion & flight test engr, Gen Dynamics Corp, 50-53; res asst, Univ Tex, 53-54; propulsion engr, Chance Vought Aircraft, Inc, 54-59, res specialist, Vought Res Ctr, 59-63, SR SPECIALIST, VOUGHT AERONAUTICS CO, LTV AEROSPACE CORP, 63- *Mem:* Am Soc Mech Engrs. *Res:* Aerospace propulsion and environmental control; heat transfer and fluid mechanics. *Mailing Add:* 4739 Harvest Hill Dallas TX 75234

MOURNING, MICHAEL CHARLES, b Jerseyville, Ill, Oct 6, 40; m 67; c 2. CHEMISTRY. *Educ:* Univ Ill, Urbana, BS, 63; Univ NC, Chapel Hill, PhD(chem), 68. *Prof Exp:* Chemist, GAF Corp, 68-80; CHEMIST, ANITEC IMAGE CORP, 80- *Mem:* Am Chem Soc; Soc Photog Sci & Eng. *Res:* Organic synthesis. *Mailing Add:* Anitec Image Corp 44-2 Binghamton NY 13902

MOURSUND, DAVID G, b Eugene, Ore, Nov 3, 36; m 61; c 4. COMPUTER SCIENCE, MATHEMATICS EDUCATION. *Educ:* Univ Ore, BA, 58; Univ Wis, MS, 60, PhD(math), 63. *Prof Exp:* From asst prof to assoc prof math, Mich State Univ, 63-67; res assoc, Comput Ctr, 67-70, head dept comput sci, 69-75, assoc prof, 67-76, PROF COMPUT SCI, UNIV ORE, 76- *Mem:* Am Math Asn; Asn Comput Mach. *Res:* Computers in education, with major emphasis upon uses of computers in pre-college education; computer literacy. *Mailing Add:* Dept of Comput Sci Univ of Ore Eugene OR 94703

MOUSCHOVIAS, TELEMACHOS CHARALAMBOUS, b Famagusta, Cyprus, Dec 29, 45. THEORETICAL ASTROPHYSICS, MAGNETOHYDRODYNAMICS. *Educ:* Yale Univ, BS, 68; Univ Calif, Berkeley, PhD(physics), 75. *Prof Exp:* Res assoc astrophys, Princeton Univ, 75-76; spec proj scientist solar physics, Nat Ctr Atmospheric Res, 76-77; ASST PROF PHYSICS & ASTRON, UNIV ILL, URBANA-CHAMPAIGN, 77- *Concurrent Pos:* Prin investr, NSF, 78-80; proj dir, NASA, 79-81. *Honors & Awards:* Trumpler Award, Astron Soc Pac, 77. *Mem:* Am Astron Soc; Int Astron Union. *Res:* Interstellar gas dynamics; star formation; galactic structure; dynamics of solar corona. *Mailing Add:* Dept of Physics & Astron Univ Ill Urbana IL 61801

MOUSHEGIAN, GEORGE, b Detroit, Mich, Jan 19, 23; m 52; c 3. PHYSIOLOGICAL PSYCHOLOGY. *Educ:* Wayne State Univ, BS, 47, MA, 51; Univ Tex, PhD, 57. *Prof Exp:* Res scientist, Defense Res Lab, Univ Tex, 56-59; res fel hearing, neurophysiol & psychol, Walter Reed Army Inst Res, 59-64; prof physiol psychol, Lab Sensory Commun, Syracuse Univ, 64-68; actg dean & actg dir, Sch Human Develop & Callier Ctr, 76-77, DIR RES, CALLIER CTR COMMUN DIS, UNIV TEX, DALLAS, 68-, PROF COMMUN DISORDERS, 73-, DEAN & DIR, SCH HUMAN DEVELOP & CALLIER CTR, 77- *Concurrent Pos:* Adj prof, Dept Physiol, Univ Tex Southwest Med Br, 69- *Mem:* AAAS; Am Psychol Asn; Acoust Soc Am; Am Physiol Soc; Soc Neurosci. *Res:* Electrophysiological study of responses from the brain stem to acoustic stimulation, using micro and macro electrodes; study of human responses to sounds; neurophysiology; psychophysics. *Mailing Add:* Callier Ctr for Commun Dis 1966 Inwood Rd Dallas TX 75235

MOUSTAKAS, THEODORE D, b Greece, Jan 28, 40; m 74; c 2. SOLID STATE PHYSICS, MATERIAL SCIENCE. *Educ:* Univ Salonika, Greece, BS, 64; Columbia Univ, NY, MPhil, 74, PhD(solid state sci), 74. *Prof Exp:* Res fel amorphous semiconductors, Harvard Univ, 74-77; SR PHYSICIST SOLAR ENERGY, EXXON RES & ENG CO, 77- *Concurrent Pos:* Fel, IBM Corp, 74-75. *Mem:* Am Phys Soc; Sci Res Soc NAm. *Res:* Optical and electronic properties of amorphous semiconductors (chalcogenide glasses and tetrahedrally corrdinated); photovoltaic studies of amorphous silicon and related materials. *Mailing Add:* Exxon Res & Eng Co PO Box 8 Linden NJ 07036

MOUW, DAVID RICHARD, b Carlisle, Pa, Aug 22, 42; c 2. PHYSIOLOGY. *Educ:* Hope Col, BA, 64; Univ Mich, Ann Arbor, PhD(physiol), 69. *Prof Exp:* Instr biol, Hampton Inst, 67-68; NIH fel exp physiol, Howard Florey Labs Exp Physiol, Melbourne, Australia, 70-71; asst prof physiol, 71-75, ASSOC PROF PHYSIOL, UNIV MICH, ANN AROBR, 75- *Concurrent Pos:* Fogarty Int fel, Howard Floney Inst, Melbourne, 77-78. *Mem:* Am Physiol Soc; AAAS. *Res:* Central nervous system control of electrolyte metabolism. *Mailing Add:* 6812 Med Sci II Univ of Mich Ann Arbor MI 48104

MOVAT, HENRY ZOLTAN, b Temesvar, Romania, Aug 11, 23; nat Can; m 56; c 3. PATHOLOGY. *Educ:* Innsbruck Univ, MD, 48; Queen's Univ, Ont, MSc, 54, PhD, 56; Royal Col Physicians & Surgeons Can, cert path, 59; FRCP(C), 67. *Prof Exp:* From asst prof to assoc prof, 57-65, PROF PATH, UNIV TORONTO, 65-, HEAD DIV EXP PATH, 68-, MEM INST IMMUNOL, 71- *Concurrent Pos:* Career investr, Med Res Coun, 60- *Mem:* Am Asn Path; Am Asn Immunol; Soc Exp Biol & Med; Int Acad Path. *Res:* Acute inflammatory reaction; chemical mediators of acute inflammation and hypersensitivity; disseminated intravascular coagulation. *Mailing Add:* Div of Exp Path Med Sci Bldg Univ of Toronto Toronto ON M5S 1A8 Can

MOVIUS, WILLIAM GUST, b Portland, Ore, Jan 15, 43. INORGANIC CHEMISTRY. *Educ:* Univ Ore, BA, 65; Pa State Univ, PhD(chem), 68. *Prof Exp:* Fel, Univ Calif, San Diego, 68-69; ASST PROF CHEM, KENT STATE UNIV, 70- *Res:* Oxidation-reduction reactions, especially those involving uncommon oxidation states; coordination compounds in nonaqueous electrolyte solutions, especially those incompatible with water. *Mailing Add:* Dept of Chem Kent State Univ Kent OH 44242

MOVSHON, J ANTHONY, b New York, NY, Dec 10, 50; m 75. NEUROPHYSIOLOGY, PSYCHOPHYSICS. *Educ:* Univ Cambridge, BA, 72, MA, 76, PhD(psychol), 75. *Prof Exp:* Asst prof, 75-78, ASSOC PROF PSYCHOL, NY UNIV, 78- *Mem:* Soc Neurosci; Asn Res Vision Opthamol; NY Acad Sci. *Res:* Neurophysiology and psychophysics of vision and visual development. *Mailing Add:* Dept Psychol NY Univ 6 Washington Place New York NY 10003

MOW, C(HAO) C(HOW), b Nanking, China, Apr 28, 30; US citizen; m 54; c 4. APPLIED MECHANICS, MATHEMATICS. *Educ:* Rensselaer Polytech Inst, BME, 53, MS, 56, PhD(appl mech), 59. *Prof Exp:* Teaching asst appl mech, Rensselaer Polytech Inst, 53-56, instr, 56-59; chief stress anal unit, Watervliet Arsenal, 59-60; mem staff, Mitre Corp, 61-62, sub-dept head appl mech, 62-63; mem staff, 63-65, Rand Corp, mech group leader eng sci dept, 65-72, dep dept head, 72-77, sr staff mem, 77-78; CHMN BD & CHIEF EXEC OFFICER, CENTURY WEST DEVELOP, INC, 78- *Concurrent Pos:* Lectr, Univ Calif, Los Angeles, 64 & Univ Southern Calif, 68. *Mem:* Am Soc Mech Engrs; NY Acad Sci. *Res:* Shell stability; stress wave propagation and scattering phenomena; bio-mechanics; environmental impact of transportation systems; electricity demand forecast methodology. *Mailing Add:* Century West Development Inc 3340 Ocean Park Blvd #3070 Santa Monica CA 90405

MOW, MAURICE, b China, June 24, 40; US citizen; m 66; c 2. CIVIL ENGINEERING, APPLIED MECHANICS. *Educ:* Rensselaer Polytech Inst, BCE, 63, MS, 64, PhD(appl mech), 68. *Prof Exp:* Tech staff struct mech, TRW Inc, 68-71; vpres, Doch Corp, 71-73; partner, Design & Planning Assoc, 73-76; asst prof eng technol, Ulster Co Community Col, 75-76; asst prof civil technol, Univ Maine, 76-78; ASSOC PROF CIVIL ENG, CALIF STATE UNIV, CHICO, 78- *Mem:* Am Soc Civil Engrs; Am Soc Eng Educrs; Sigma Xi. *Res:* Marketing freshwater resources. *Mailing Add:* Dept of Civil Eng Calif State Univ Chico CA 95929

MOW, VAN C, b China, Jan 10, 39; US citizen; m 63; c 2. MECHANICS, BIOMEDICAL ENGINEERING. *Educ:* Rensselaer Polytech Inst, BAE, 62, PhD(mech), 66. *Prof Exp:* Asst prof mech, Rensselaer Polytech Inst, 66-67; vis mem electromagnetic div, Courant Inst Math Sci, NY Univ, 67-68; mem tech staff, Bell Tel Labs, 68-69; assoc prof, 69-76, PROF MECH, RENSSELAER POLYTECH INST, 76-, DIR BIOMECH RES LAB, 71- *Concurrent Pos:* Consult, Mech Technol, Inc, 66-67; NATO sr fel, 76; adj prof orthop, Albany Med Col, 77-; lectr, Harvard Med Col, 78- *Mem:* Orthop Res Soc; Am Asn Univ Prof; AAAS; Am Soc Mech Engrs; Am Inst Physics. *Res:* Continuum mechanics; classical elasticity and thermoelasticity theory; fluid mechanics; applied mathematics; lubrication biomechanics; biomechanics of synovial joints; study of mechanical processes in various degenerative arthritic diseases. *Mailing Add:* Dept of Mech Eng Rensselaer Polytech Inst Troy NY 12181

MOWAT, JOHN GORDON, physics, see previous edition

MOWAT, RICHARD J, b Honolulu, Hawaii, Aug 29, 43; US citizen; m 63; c 2. EXPERIMENTAL ATOMIC PHYSICS. *Educ:* Univ Calif, Berkeley, AB, 66, PhD(physics), 69. *Prof Exp:* Res assoc physics, Brandeis Univ, 69-72; res assoc physics, Univ Tenn, 72-73, asst prof, 73-74; asst prof physics, City Col New York, 74-76; asst prof, 76-80, PROF PHYSICS, NC STATE UNIV, 80- *Concurrent Pos:* Invited assignee, Oak Ridge Nat Lab, 72-74, mem tandem accel users group, 72-; mem tandem accel users group, Brookhaven Nat Lab, 74-, res collabr, 75-; users group, Holifield Heavy Ion Res Facil, 74- *Mem:* Am Phys Soc; Sigma Xi. *Res:* Experimental atomic physics; inner shell phenomena; x-ray and auger electron spectroscopy of highly ionized atoms; excited state lifetimes. *Mailing Add:* Dept Physics NC State Univ Raleigh NC 27607

MOWATT, THOMAS C, b Orange, NJ, Apr 24, 36; m 59; c 1. GEOCHEMISTRY, GEOLOGY. *Educ:* Rutgers Univ, BA, 59; Univ Mont, PhD(geol), 65. *Prof Exp:* Res scientist, Pan Am Petrol Corp, Okla, 65-67; asst prof geol, Winona State Col, 67-68 & Univ SDak, 68-70; supvr minerals anal & res, Alaska Geol Surv, 70-74; geologist, Bur Land Mgt, 74-75, GEOLOGIST, BUR MINES, US DEPT INTERIOR, 75- *Concurrent Pos:* Lectr, Univ Tulsa, 67; res assoc, SDak State Geol Surv, 68-70; adj assoc prof, Inst Marine Sci, Univ Alaska, 73- *Mem:* Geochem Soc; Mineral Soc Am; Clay Minerals Soc; Mineral Asn Can; Soc Econ Paleontologists & Mineralogists. *Res:* Petrology; sedimentology; environmental studies; economic geology; geochemistry, mineralogy and petrology in the contexts of economic geology, environmental science and marine science. *Mailing Add:* US Dept Interior Bur Mines PO Box 550 Juneau AK 99802

MOWBRAY, DONALD F, b Duluth, Minn, July 29, 37; m 62. ENGINEERING MECHANICS. *Educ:* Univ Minn, BS, 60, MS, 62; Rensselaer Polytech Inst, PhD(mech), 68. *Prof Exp:* Asst mech, Univ Minn, 60-62; engr, Knolls Atomic Power Lab, 62-68, engr mat & processes lab, 68-71, mgr, Gas Turbine, 71-74, mgr mech mat, Mat & Processes Lab, 74-79, MGR SOLID MECHS, RES LAB, GEN ELEC CO, 79- *Mem:* Am Soc Testing & Mat; Am Soc Mech Engrs. *Res:* Material damping; metal fatigue; fracture of metals; dynamic thermoelasticity. *Mailing Add:* Gen Elec Co Bldg 37-319 Schenectady NY 12345

MOWBRAY, THOMAS BRUCE, b Duluth, Minn, Mar 1, 40; m 66. BOTANY, PLANT ECOLOGY. *Educ:* Univ Minn, Duluth, BA, 62; Duke Univ, MA, 64, PhD(bot), 67. *Prof Exp:* Instr biol, Duke Univ, 67-68; from asst prof to assoc prof biol & chairperson pop dynamics, Univ Wis-Green Bay, 68-78; mem fac, 78-80, ASSOC PROF BIOL, SALEM COL, 80- *Mem:* Ecol Soc Am; Am Inst Biol Sci. *Res:* Plant community analysis; vegetation gradient analysis. *Mailing Add:* Dept of Biol Salem Col Winston-Salem NC 27108

MOWER, HOWARD FREDERICK, b Chicago, Ill, Aug 25, 29; m; c 2. ORGANIC CHEMISTRY. *Educ:* Calif Inst Technol, BS, 51, PhD(org chem), 56. *Prof Exp:* Res chemist, Cent Res Dept, E I du Pont de Nemours & Co, Del, 56; assoc prof, 65-69, PROF BIOCHEM, UNIV HAWAII, 69- *Res:* Ferredoxins; hydrogenase enzymes; biological nitrogen fixation. *Mailing Add:* Dept of Biochem Univ of Hawaii Honolulu HI 96822

MOWER, LYMAN, b Berkeley, Calif, June 15, 27; m 48; c 3. PHYSICS. *Educ:* Univ Calif, BS, 49; Mass Inst Technol, PhD(physics), 53. *Prof Exp:* Eng specialist, Sylvania Elec Prod Inc, 53-57; from asst prof to assoc prof, 57-64, PROF PHYSICS, UNIV NH, 64- *Concurrent Pos:* Vis fel, Joint Inst Lab Astrophys, 64-65. *Mem:* AAAS; Am Phys Soc. *Res:* Atomic and plasma physics; quantum electronics. *Mailing Add:* Dept of Physics Univ of NH Durham NH 03824

MOWER, ROBERT G, b Gasport, NY, Sept 27, 28. FLORICULTURE, ORNAMENTAL HORTICULTURE. *Educ:* Cornell Univ, BS, 56, MS, 59, PhD(turf dis), 61. *Prof Exp:* Asst prof, 61-67, assoc prof, 67-77, PROF WOODY ORNAMENTALS, CORNELL UNIV, 77- *Mem:* AAAS; Am Soc Hort Sci; Int Soc Hort Sci. *Res:* Taxonomy, evaluation of woody plants for landscape use. *Mailing Add:* Dept of Floriculture & Ornamental Hort Plant Sci Bldg Cornell Univ Ithaca NY 14853

MOWERY, DWIGHT FAY, JR, b Moorehead, Minn, May 1, 15; m 43. CARBOHYDRATE CHEMISTRY, CHEMICAL KINETICS. *Educ:* Harvard Univ, AB, 37; Mass Inst Technol, PhD(org chem), 40. *Prof Exp:* Res chemist, E I du Pont de Nemours & Co, Del, 40-42; res chemist, Hercules Powder Co, 42-43; head chem dept, Elms Col, 43-46; head dept, Franklin Tech Inst, 46-49; asst prof, Trinity Col, Conn, 49-53; chmn dept chem, Ripon Col, 53-57; prof chem & dir grad prog, New Bedford Inst Tech, 57-64; chmn dept, 64-70, COMMONWEALTH PROF CHEM, SOUTHEASTERN MASS UNIV, 65- *Concurrent Pos:* Researcher, J B Williams Co, Conn, 52-53, WTM Mfg Co, Wis, 54-56, Aerovox Corp, Mass, 62, Acushnet Process Corp, Mass, 65-67 & Tibbetts Eng Corp, Mass, 78- *Mem:* Am Chem Soc. *Res:* Seed disinfectants and bactericides; carbohydrate chemistry; chromatographic adsorption; gas chromatography; organic microanalysis; chemical kinetics and computer programming; environmental analysis. *Mailing Add:* Dept of Chem Southeastern Mass Univ North Dartmouth MA 02747

MOWERY, RICHARD ALLEN, JR, b Newboston, Ohio, June 2, 38. ANALYTICAL CHEMISTRY. *Educ:* Univ Calif, Los Angeles, BS, 63; Univ Southern Calif, MAOM, 69; Ariz State Univ, PhD(chem), 74. *Prof Exp:* RES CHEMIST, APPL AUTOMATION, INC, PHILLIPS PETROL CO, 74- *Mem:* Am Chem Soc; The Chem Soc. *Mailing Add:* 1343 SE Greystone Bartlesville OK 74003

MOWITZ, ARNOLD MARTIN, b New York, NY, Jan 14, 23; m 46; c 2. ANALYTICAL CHEMISTRY, TOXICOLOGY. *Educ:* Univ Buffalo, MA, 53. *Prof Exp:* Supvr control analysts, Nat Aniline Div, Allied Chem & Dye Corp, 46-48, chief analyst res & develop, 48-50, anal res chemist, 50-53, chief anal res, 53-55; group leader, Anal Dept, Interchem Corp, 55-65, prog mgr, 66-67, mgr res serv dept, 67-70, mgr, Opers Dept, 70-77, CORP MGR, INDUST TOXICOL & PROD SAFETY, CENT RES LABS, INMONT CORP, 77- *Mem:* Am Chem Soc; Am Microchem Soc; Soc Appl Spectros; Am Soc Test & Mat; NY Acad Sci. *Res:* Instrumental analysis; infrared and ultraviolet absorption analysis; spectrographic and microchemical analysis; x-ray diffraction; gas chromatography; light and electron microscopy; physical testing; nuclear magnetic resonance spectroscopy; research management; environmental chemistry. *Mailing Add:* Res Serv Dept Cent Res Labs Inmont Corp 1255 Broad St Clifton NJ 07015

MOWLE, FREDERIC J, b Orange, NJ, Aug 4, 37; m 63; c 3. ELECTRICAL ENGINEERING. *Educ:* Univ Notre Dame, BS, 59, MS, 61, PhD(elec eng), 66. *Prof Exp:* ASSOC PROF ELEC ENG, PURDUE UNIV, WEST LAFAYETTE, 66- *Mem:* Inst Elec & Electronics Engrs; Asn Comput Mach; Am Soc Eng Educ. *Res:* Sequential machine theory, in particular the stability and cycle structure of nonlinear feedback shift registers; design and organization of small special purpose digital hardware for computational and coding applications. *Mailing Add:* Dept of Elec Eng Purdue Univ West Lafayette IN 47907

MOWLES, THOMAS FRANCIS, b Boston, Mass, Feb 26, 34; m 56; c 4. PHARMACOLOGY, IMMUNOLOGY. *Educ:* Boston Univ, BA, 55; NY Univ, MS, 64; Rutgers Univ, PhD(zool), 68. *Prof Exp:* Lab supvr, Ciba Pharmaceut Co, 56-68; sr res biochemist, 68-74, res group chief, 75-81, RES SECT HEAD, HOFFMANN-LA ROCHE INC, 81- *Mem:* AAAS; Am Chem Soc; Int Soc Psychoneurol Endocrinol; NY Acad Sci. *Res:* Mechanism of hormone action; psychoneuroendocrinology; biochemical pharmacology; steroid biosynthesis; peptide hormones. *Mailing Add:* 266 Changebridge Rd Pine Brook NJ 07058

MOWRY, DAVID THOMAS, b Pyengyang, Korea, Mar 11, 17; US citizen; m 38; c 3. INDUSTRIAL CHEMISTRY. *Educ:* Col Wooster, BS, 38; Ohio State Univ, MSc, 40, PhD(org chem), 41. *Prof Exp:* Chemist, Ohio State Univ, 38-41; res mgr, Cent Res Labs, Monsanto Co, 41-52, mgr chem develop, Phosphate Div, 52-53, mgr fine chem, Org Div, Develop Dept, 54-57, asst dir, 57-58, dir res & eng div, 58-61, mgr plastics div, 61-64, mgr planning East Asia, Int Div, 64-68, dir, Monsanto Japan Ltd & Ryoko Chemstrand Ltd, 68-74; prin engr, Int Opers Div, Nus Corp, 74-77; PROG MGR, PATENT

LICENSING & INFO, NAT TECH INFO SERV, US DEPT COM, 77- *Mem:* Am Chem Soc; Com Develop Asn; Licensing Exec Soc; Technol Transfer Soc. *Res:* Structure of natural products; synthesis and reactions of nitriles; exploratory organic synthesis; high polymers; agricultural chemicals; commercial development; patent and know-how licensing; energy economics. *Mailing Add:* Nat Tech Info Serv 5285 Port Royal Rd Springfield VA 22161

MOWRY, JAMES B, b Peoria, Ill, Oct 3, 20; m 46; c 2. HORTICULTURE. *Educ:* Univ Ill, BS, 48; Purdue Univ, MS, 49; Rutgers Univ, PhD(genetics, fruit breeding), 51. *Prof Exp:* Asst fruit breeding, Univ Ill, 47-48; asst bot & plant path, Purdue Univ, 48-49; asst fruit breeding, Rutgers Univ, 49-51; from asst prof to assoc prof, 51-62, PROF HORT, DEPT PLANT & SOIL SCI, UNIV ILL, URBANA & SOUTHERN ILL UNIV, CARBONDALE, 62-; SUPT, ILL HORT EXP STA, 51- *Honors & Awards:* Shepard Award, 60. *Mem:* Am Pomol Soc (secy-treas, 65-); AAAS; Genetics Soc Am; Am Soc Hort Sci; Am Phytopath Soc. *Res:* Cross inoculation of prunus with coccomyces; embryology and cytology of pear; peach and apple genetics and breeding for disease resistance; climatic adaptation, phenology, bud hardiness and disease susceptibility of peaches and apples; root stock-scion interactions affecting apples. *Mailing Add:* Dept of Plant & Soil Sci Southern Ill Univ Carbondale IL 62901

MOWRY, ROBERT WILBUR, b Griffin, Ga, Jan 10, 23; m 49; c 3. PATHOLOGY. *Educ:* Birmingham Southern Col, BS, 44; Johns Hopkins Univ, MD, 46. *Prof Exp:* Intern, Med Col Ala, 46-47, asst resident path, 47-48; sr asst surgeon, NIH, 48-52; asst prof path, Sch Med, Washington Univ, 52-53; from asst prof to assoc prof path, Med Ctr, 53-57, dir grad progs path, 64-72, sr scientist, Inst Dent Res, 67-72, PROF PATH, MED CTR, UNIV ALA, BIRMINGHAM, 58-, PROF HEALTH SERV ADMIN, 76- *Concurrent Pos:* Fel, Mallory Inst Path, Boston Univ, 49-50; dir, Anat Path Lab, Univ Ala Hosp, 60-64 & 75-79; assoc ed, J Histochem & Cytochem, 61-76, & Stain Technol, 65-; mem, Path A Study Sect, USPHS, 64-68, trustee, Biol Stain Comn, 66-, vpres, 74-76, pres, 76-81, vis scientist, Dept Path, Cambridge Univ, 72-73; consult, Food & Drug Admin, 77-81. *Mem:* Am Soc Exp Path; Histochem Soc; Am Asn Path; Biol Stain Comn; Int Acad Path. *Res:* Histochemistry and its applications to pathology; histopathologic technic; methods for detection and characterization of complex carbohydrates, microbial agents, amyloids and insulin in cells and tissues. *Mailing Add:* Dept of Path Univ of Ala Med Ctr Birmingham AL 35294

MOWSHOWITZ, ABBE, b Liberty, NY, Nov 13, 39; m 64; c 2. COMPUTER SCIENCE. *Educ:* Univ Chicago, SB, 61; Univ Mich, Ann Arbor, MA, 65, MS, 66, PhD(comput sci), 67. *Prof Exp:* Res assoc methodology, Human Sci Res, Inc, 62-63; res asst appl math, Ment Health Res Inst, Univ Mich, 63-67, asst res mathematician, 67-68; asst prof comput sci & indust eng, Univ Toronto, 68-69; asst prof comput sci, Univ BC, 69-74, assoc prof, 74-79; vis prof, Grad Sch Mgt, Delft, Netherlands, 79-80; DIR, CROTON RES GROUP, INC, 80- *Concurrent Pos:* Res assoc, Inst Social Res & lectr, Dept Commun & Comput Sci, Univ Mich, 67-68; vis res assoc, Dept Comput Sci, Cornell Univ, 75-76. *Mem:* Asn Comput Mach. *Res:* Social impact of science and technology; science and technology policy; effects of information technology on economic and political organization, decision-making, and ethics. *Mailing Add:* 212 Hessian Hills Rd Croton-on-Hudson NY 10520

MOXHAM, ROBERT LYNN, b Burlington, Ont, July 2, 33; m 61; c 3. GEOCHEMISTRY. *Educ:* McMaster Univ, BA, 55, MSc, 58; Univ Chicago, PhD(geochem), 63. *Prof Exp:* Field geologist, Int Nickel Co, Can, 55-57, 58-59; Nat Res Coun Can fel, Univ Man, 63-64; geochemist, NY State Mus & Sci Serv, 64-69; geochemist, Off Tech Coop, UN, 69-75; GEOCHEMIST, INT ATOMIC ENERGY AGENCY, 75- *Mem:* Geol Soc Am; Soc Econ Geol; Mineral Asn Can; Am Inst Prof Geologists; Asn Explor Geochemists. *Res:* Geochemical exploration; geochemistry of ore deposits; instrumental analysis of rocks; trace element abundances. *Mailing Add:* 16 Fernbank Ave Delmar 12054 Austria

MOY, JAMES HEE, b Canton, China, Feb 20, 29; US citizen; m 67; c 2. FOOD SCIENCE, CHEMICAL ENGINEERING. *Educ:* Univ Wis-Madison, BSChE, 57, MSChE, 58; Rutgers Univ, New Brunswick, PhD(food sci), 65. *Prof Exp:* Chem engr, Esso Res & Eng Co, 58-60 & Lipton Co, 60-61; asst prof, 65-72, assoc prof, 72-80, PROF FOOD ENG, UNIV HAWAII, 80- *Concurrent Pos:* USAEC res grant, 68-71; Int Sugar Res Found res grant, 72-76; US Dept Energy res grant, 76-82; US NSF sea grant, 77-81. *Mem:* Inst Food Technologists; Am Inst Chem Engrs; Am Soc Agr Engrs. *Res:* Food engineering; tropical foods and root crops processing including solar dehydration, freeze dehydration, freezing and ionizing radiation. *Mailing Add:* Dept of Food Sci & Technol Univ Hawaii 1920 Edmundson Rd Honolulu HI 96822

MOY, MAMIE WONG, b San Antonio, Tex, Sept 4, 29; m 58; c 1. SCIENCE EDUCATION. *Educ:* Univ Tex, Austin, BA, 50; Univ Houston, MS, 52. *Prof Exp:* Instr, 52-56, asst prof, 56-76, ASSOC PROF CHEM, UNIV HOUSTON, CENT CAMPUS, 76- *Mem:* Am Chem Soc; AAAS; Nat Sci Teachers Asn. *Mailing Add:* Dept Chem Univ Houston Cent Campus Houston TX 77004

MOY, RICHARD HENRY, b Chicago, Ill, Feb 2, 31; m 54; c 2. MEDICINE, HEALTH SCIENCE. *Educ:* Univ Chicago, BA, 53, BS, 54, MD, 57; Am Bd Internal Med, dipl, 66. *Prof Exp:* Intern med, Univ Chicago, 57-68; clin assoc endocrinol, USPHS, 58-60; res internal med, Univ Chicago Clins, 60-62, instr & chief res med, 62-63, from instr to assoc prof, 63-70; PROF MED, DEAN & PROVOST, SCH MED, SOUTHERN ILL UNIV, 70- *Concurrent Pos:* Nat Cancer Inst spec fel, 63-64; res assoc, Univ Chicago, 64-68; dir, Univ Health Serv, Univ Chicago, 64-70; consult, HEW, 77-78; consult, Vet Admin, Washington, DC, 77-78. *Mem:* Fel Am Col Physicians; Am Med Asn; Soc Health Human Values. *Mailing Add:* Southern Ill Univ PO Box 3926 Springfield IL 62708

MOY, WILLIAM A(RTHUR), b St Paul, Minn, June 16, 31; m 54; c 2. INDUSTRIAL ENGINEERING, OPERATIONS RESEARCH. *Educ:* Univ Minn, BIE, 54, MS, 56; Northwestern Univ, PhD(indust eng, mgt sci), 65. *Prof Exp:* Dept mgr, Proctor & Gamble Mfg Co, 56-57, methods engr, 57-58; from asst prof to assoc prof mech eng, Univ Wis-Madison, 58-69, prof indust eng, 69-74, chmn dept, 69-71; dean sch mod indust, 72-76, PROF INDUST ENG, UNIV WIS-PARKSIDE, 73- *Mem:* Opers Res Soc Am; Inst Mgt Sci; Am Inst Indust Engrs; Am Soc Qual Control; Am Prod & Inventory Control Soc. *Res:* Operations research and management science especially digital computer simulation methods. *Mailing Add:* Dept of Indust Eng Univ of Wis-Parkside Kenosha WI 53141

MOYE, ANTHONY JOSEPH, b McAdoo, Pa, Oct 15, 33; m 57; c 3. ACADEMIC ADMINISTRATION, PHYSICAL ORGANIC CHEMISTRY. *Educ:* Upsala Col, BS, 55; Iowa State Univ, MS, 57, PhD(org chem), 62. *Prof Exp:* Prof chem & dean acad planning & grad studies, Calif State Col, Los Angeles, 62-71; prof chem & vpres acad affairs, Quinnipiac Col, 71-72; state univ dean, 72-79, ASST VCHANCELLOR, EDUC PROGS & RESOURCES, CALIF STATE UNIV, 79- *Mem:* AAAS; Am Chem Soc; Royal Soc Chem. *Res:* Free radicals in solution; chemiluminescence. *Mailing Add:* Calif State Univ & Cols 400 Golden Shore Long Beach CA 90802

MOYE, HUGH ANSON, b Mobile, Ala, Oct 18, 38. ANALYTICAL CHEMISTRY. *Educ:* Spring Hill Col, BS, 61; Univ Fla, PhD(chem), 65. *Prof Exp:* Asst prof, 65-75, assoc prof, 75-78, ASSOC CHEMIST PESTICIDE RES, PESTICIDE RES LAB, UNIV FLA, 75-, PROF CHEM, 78- *Mem:* Am Chem Soc; Asn Offs Anal Chem. *Res:* Analaytical methods for pesticides; reaction gas chromatography of pesticides; gas chromatography detectors. *Mailing Add:* 2208 SW 43rd Pl Gainesville FL 32608

MOYED, HARRIS S, b Philadelphia, Pa, May 15, 25; m 54; c 2. BACTERIOLOGY, BIOCHEMISTRY. *Prof Exp:* Nat Found res fel biochem, Mass Gen Hosp, 54-55 & bact, Harvard med Sch, 55-57; from instr to asst prof bact, Harvard Med Sch, 57-63; Hastings prof microbiol, Sch Med, Univ Southern Calif, 63-69; PROF MICROBIOL, COL MED, UNIV CALIF, IRVINE, 69- *Concurrent Pos:* Lederle award, 58-60; Vis prof, Rockefeller Univ, 81-82. *Mem:* Am Soc Microbiol; Am Soc Biol Chem. *Res:* Biochemistry of bacteria; regulation of biosynthetic reactions; action of plant auxin. *Mailing Add:* Dept of Med Microbiol Univ of Calif Irvine CA 92717

MOYER, CALVIN LYLE, b Philadelphia, Pa, Nov 2, 41; m 63; c 2. ORGANIC CHEMISTRY. *Educ:* Ursinus Col, BS, 63; Harvard Univ, MA, 65, PhD(chem), 68. *Prof Exp:* Res chemist, Benger Lab, 68-72, sr res chemist end use res, 72-73, col recruiter, 74-75, prog coordr, Col Rels, 76-77, col rels supvr, 77-78, staff asst, 78-81, EMPLOYEE RELS SUPT, PLASTIC PROD & RESINS DEPT, MFG DIV, E I DU PONT DE NEMOURS & CO, INC, 81- *Mem:* Am Chem Soc. *Mailing Add:* 2011 Foulk Rd Wilmington DE 19810

MOYER, CARL EDWARD, b Dayton, Ohio, Dec 24, 26; m 50; c 4. PHYSIOLOGICAL CHEMISTRY. *Educ:* Univ Dayton, BS, 53; Ohio State Univ, MS, 57, PhD, 59. *Prof Exp:* Clin biochemist & head clin lab, Res Labs, Parke Davis & Co, 63-77, clin biochemist & head clin lab, Pharmaceut Res Div, 77-81, MGR, CLIN PATHOL LAB, DEPT PATHOL & EXP TOXICOL, WARNER-LAMBERT/PARKE-DAVIS, 81- *Concurrent Pos:* Supvr clin labs, Riverside Methodist Hosp, Columbus, Ohio, 59-63. *Mem:* Am Chem Soc; Am Asn Clin Chem. *Res:* Clinical biochemistry. *Mailing Add:* Warner-Lambert/Parke-Davis 2800 Plymouth Rd Ann Arbor MI 48105

MOYER, DEAN LA ROCHE, b Pa, Mar 17, 25; m 53; c 5. PATHOLOGY. *Educ:* Lehigh Univ, BA, 48; Univ Rochester, MD, 52. *Prof Exp:* From instr to prof path, Med Ctr, Univ Calif, Los Angeles, 56-69; PROF PATH, OBSTET & GYNEC, MED SCH, UNIV SOUTHERN CALIF, 69-, HEAD, EXP PATH SECT, 69- *Concurrent Pos:* Fel oncol, Mass Gen Hosp, 55-56; dir labs, Harbor Gen Hosp, Torrance, 61-69. *Res:* Early reproduction. *Mailing Add:* Sect of Exp Path Univ of Southern Calif Med Sch Los Angeles CA 90033

MOYER, FRANK H, cytology, environmental science, see previous edition

MOYER, H(ALLARD) C(HARLES), b Crawford, Nebr, Dec 27, 18; m 47; c 2. PETROLEUM ENGINEERING & TECHNOLOGY. *Educ:* Univ Nebr, BS, 40. *Prof Exp:* Chem engr, Sinclair Refining Co, 41-42; exp engr, S C Johnson & Son, Inc, 47-52; sr res engr, Sinclair Res, Inc, 52-69; dir indust prod res, Atlantic Richfield Co, 69-71, mgr tech support, Asphalt & Process Oils, 71-75, mgr indust lubricants & asphalt res, Develop & Tech Serv, 75-80; RETIRED. *Concurrent Pos:* Mem, Hwy Res Bd, Nat Acad Sci-Nat Res Coun. *Mem:* Asn Asphalt Paving Technol; Am Inst Chemists; Am Chem Soc; Am Soc Testing Mat. *Res:* Processing and functionality of refined petroleum oils and waxes; composition and physical properties of asphalts. *Mailing Add:* 1537 186 Place Homewood IL 60430

MOYER, JAMES EARL, microbiology, see previous edition

MOYER, JAMES ROBERT, b Kitchener, Ont, June 28, 42; m 74; c 2. AGRICULTURE. *Educ:* Univ Waterloo, BSc, 66; Univ Guelph, MSc, 68; Univ Sask, PhD(soil sci), 72. *Prof Exp:* Res assoc soil sci, Univ Sask, 72 & Univ Guelph, 72-75; RES SCIENTIST WEED SCI, AGR CAN, 75- *Mem:* Int Weed Sci Soc; Can Soc Soil Sci; Weed Sci Soc Am. *Res:* Control of weeds in rangeland and pastures and the effect of soil physical properties on the persistence and efficacy of herbicides. *Mailing Add:* Lethbridge Res Sta Agr Can Lethbridge AB T1J 4B1 Can

MOYER, JAMES WARD, b Chicago, Ill, June 29, 44; m 69. INORGANIC CHEMISTRY. *Educ:* Univ Rochester, BS, 66; Univ Wis-Madison, PhD(inorg chem), 71. *Prof Exp:* RES CHEMIST, LIGHTING BUS GROUP, GEN ELEC CO, 70- *Mem:* Am Chem Soc; AAAS; Sigma Xi. *Res:* High purity inorganic chemicals; reduced oxidation state of transition metals; metal-halide chemistry; chemical transport phenomenon; molten salt chemistry. *Mailing Add:* LR & TSO Bldg 336 Lamp Bus Group Gen Elec Co Nela Park East Cleveland OH 44112

MOYER, JOHN ALLEN, b Lebanon, Pa, Oct 20, 51; m 77. NEUROPSYCHOPHARMACOLOGY, PSYCHOBIOLOGY. *Educ:* Albright Col, BS, 73; Bucknell Univ, MS, 75; Temple Univ, PhD(psychobiol), 78. *Prof Exp:* Res asst psychol, Bucknell Univ, 73-75; res asst psychobiol, Temple Univ, 75-78; fel neuropharmacol, Sch Med, Univ Pa, 78-80; SUPVR PSYCHOPHARMACOL, WYETH LABS, INC, 80- *Concurrent Pos:* Vis scientist, Lab Clin Sci, NIMH, 75-76. *Mem:* Soc Neurosci; Int Soc Psychoneuroendocrinol; AAAS. *Res:* Neuropsychopharmacology of central nervous system disorders; behavioral pharmacology, neurochemistry, and neuropharmacology. *Mailing Add:* Neuropsychopharmacol Sect Wyeth Labs Inc PO Box 8299 Philadelphia PA 19101

MOYER, JOHN CLARENCE, b Chicago, Ill, Jan 9, 46; m 75. MATHEMATICS. *Educ:* Christian Bros Col, BS, 67; Northwestern Univ, MS, 69, PhD(math educ), 74. *Prof Exp:* Teacher math, St Patrick High Sch, Chicago, 67-69 & St Joseph High Sch, Chicago, 69-72; asst prof, 74-80, ASSOC PROF MATH, MARQUETTE UNIV, 80- *Mem:* Math Asn Am; Am Math Soc; Nat Coun Teachers Math. *Res:* Problem solving research with children ages 9-14. *Mailing Add:* Dept of Math & Statist Marquette Univ Milwaukee WI 53233

MOYER, JOHN HENRY, b Hershey, Pa, Apr 1, 19; m; c 7. MEDICINE. *Educ:* Lebanon Valley Col, BS, 39; Univ Pa, MD, 43; Am Bd Internal Med, dipl. *Hon Degrees:* DSc, Lebanon Valley Col, 68. *Prof Exp:* Intern, Pa Hosp, 43; resident, Belmont Hosp, Worcester, Mass, 44-45; asst instr tuberc & contagious dis, Univ Vt, 44-45; chief resident med, Brooke Gen Hosp, 47; fel pharmacol & med, Sch Med, Univ Pa, 48-50; from asst prof to prof pharmacol, Col Med, Baylor Univ, 50-57; prof med, Hahnemann Med Col & Hosp, 57-74, chmn dept med, 57-71, vpres acad affairs, 71-73; VPRES, DIR PROF & EDUC AFFAIRS, CONEMAUGH VALLEY MEM HOSP, 74-, PROF MED, SCH MED, TEMPLE UNIV, 76- *Concurrent Pos:* From attend physician to sr attend, Jefferson Davis Hosp, Houston, 50-57; consult, Vet Admin Hosp, Houston & Houston Tuberc Hosp, 50-57; vis prof, Sch Med, La State Univ, 52; consult, Vet Admin Hosp, Philadelphia, 58-68, Philadelphia Naval Hosp, 58-, Bd Vet Appeals, 63- & comn drugs, AMA, 68-; deleg at large, AMA, 70-75; adv & consult, Hypertension Info & Educ Adv Comt, US Dept Health, 72-75; pres bd trustees, US Pharmacopeia, 70-75; adv, Gov Task Force Hypertension, State of Pa, 74-; ed consult, Am J Cardiol; ed cardiovasc sect, Cyclopedia Med, Surg & Specialties; Milliken lect, Pa Hosp, 58; chmn adv group, Pa High Blood Pressure Control Prog, 79-81. *Honors & Awards:* Hunter Award, Am Therapeut Soc, 59; Clyde M Fish Mem Lect, 60; Mayo Found Honor Lect, 60; Susan & Theodore Cummings Humanitarian Award, 62, 65 & 66; Presidential Citation, 64. *Mem:* Fel Am Col Cardiol; Am Soc Clin Pharmacol & Therapeut (pres, 65); Am Acad Tuberc Physicians (pres, 61); fel Am Col Clin Pharmacol & Chemother (pres, 64-66); fel NY Acad Sci. *Res:* Hypertension and pharmacodynamics of the cardiovascular system; renal function. *Mailing Add:* Conemaugh Valley Mem Hosp 1086 Franklin St Johnstown PA 15905

MOYER, JOHN RAYMOND, b Buffalo, NY, June 9, 31; m 52; c 4. INORGANIC CHEMISTRY. *Educ:* Eastern Mich Univ, AB, 52; Univ Mich, PhD(phys inorg chem), 58. *Prof Exp:* Res chemist, Electro-inorg Res Lab, 59-63, sr res chemist, 63-68, assoc scientist, 68-70, environ res lab, 70-74, assoc scientist, 74-76, RES SCIENTIST, CENT RES-INORG LAB, DOW CHEM, USA, 76- *Mem:* Am Chem Soc. *Res:* Aqueous chemistry of halogens; peroxide chemistry. *Mailing Add:* Dow Chem USA 1776 Bldg Midland MI 48640

MOYER, JOSEPH DONALD, b Dunbar, Pa, Jan 15, 20; m 46; c 3. ORGANIC CHEMISTRY. *Educ:* Pa State Col, BS, 48, MS, 49; Univ Md, PhD(org chem), 58. *Prof Exp:* Chemist, Nat Bur Standards, 49-60; CHEMIST, W R GRACE & CO, 60- *Mem:* Am Chem Soc. *Res:* Carbohydrates; isotopic tracers in organic chemistry; polymer research; synthesis of monomers for photopolymers. *Mailing Add:* 10707 Francis Dr Silver Spring MD 20902

MOYER, KENNETH EVAN, b Chippewa Falls, Wis, Nov 19, 19; m 43; c 2. PHYSIOLOGICAL PSYCHOLOGY. *Educ:* Park Col, AB, 43; Wash Univ, MA, 48, PhD(psychol), 51. *Prof Exp:* Dir phys educ, Park Col, 42-43; instr psychol & phys educ, Pearl River Col, 46-47; vet counr psychol, Wash Univ, 47-49; instr psychol, Carnegie Inst Technol, 49-50, assoc prof, 54-61; PROF PSYCHOL, CARNEGIE-MELLON UNIV, 61- *Concurrent Pos:* Actg dept head, Dept Psychol, Carnegie-Mellon Univ, 61; consult higher educ, govt Norway, 54; ed-in-chief, Aggressive Behav, 74-78. *Honors & Awards:* Carnegie Found Award, 54. *Mem:* Fel Am Psychol Asn; Psychonomic Soc; fel AAAS. *Res:* Physiology of aggressive behavior. *Mailing Add:* Dept of Psychol Carnegie-Mellon Univ Pittsburgh PA 15213

MOYER, KENNETH HAROLD, b Poughkeepsie, NY, Sept 30, 29; m 51; c 7. METALLURGICAL ENGINEERING. *Educ:* Polytech Inst Brooklyn, BS, 59, MS, 62. *Prof Exp:* Jr staff mem metall, US Hoffman Mach Corp, 53-54 & Int Nickel Res Lab, 54-55; proj engr, Grumman Aircraft Eng Corp, 55-58, Sylvania Corning Nuclear Corp, 58-60 & Beryllium Corp Am, 60-62; mgr beryllium opers, Gen Astrometals Corp, 62-66; mgr spec alloys res & develop, 66-80, NEW PROD ENG, HOEGANAES CORP, 80- *Concurrent Pos:* Consult; instr, Spring Garden Col Eve Div, 73- *Mem:* Fel Am Soc Metals; Am Inst Mining, Metall & Petrol Engrs; Am Ord Asn. *Res:* Fabrication of beryllium; high alloy iron powders. *Mailing Add:* 4 Green Briar Lane Cinnaminson NJ 08077

MOYER, MARY PAT SUTTER, b Arlington, Mass, Apr 27, 51; m 74; c 1. VIROLOGY, ONCOLOGY. *Educ:* Fla Atlantic Univ, BS, 72, MS, 74, PhD, 81. *Prof Exp:* Dir tissue culture res virol, Equine Res Inst, 70-73; cancer res scientist viral oncol, Thorman Cancer Res Lab, Trinity Univ, 74-81; INSTR, DEPT SURG, UNIV TEX HEALTH SCI CTR, 81- *Mem:* Asn Women Sci; Am Soc Microbiol; AAAS; Tissue Culture Asn; Am Soc Cell Biol. *Res:* Experimental oncology; biological activity of simian virus 40 DNA fragments; persistent virus infections in vitro; animal tumorigenesis models; tumor immunology. *Mailing Add:* Univ Tex Health Sci Ctr San Antonio TX 78284

MOYER, MELVIN ISAAC, b Newton, Kans, June 30, 21; m 61. ORGANIC CHEMISTRY. *Educ:* Bethel Col, AB, 42; Univ Okla, MS, 44; Univ Kans, PhD(chem), 52. *Prof Exp:* Asst, Univ Okla, 42-44; res chemist, Cities Serv Oil Co, 46-48; asst instr, Univ Kans, 48-50; develop chemist, 52-57, chief chemist mfg, 57-62, sr chemist, NJ, 62-73, SR CHEMIST, AM CYANAMID CO, W VA, 73- *Mem:* AAAS; Am Chem Soc. *Res:* Manufacturing. *Mailing Add:* Box 23 Willow Island WV 26190

MOYER, PATRICIA HELEN, b Greensboro, NC, Sept 30, 27; m 50; c 3. ORGANIC CHEMISTRY. *Educ:* Northwestern Univ, BA, 49; Univ Wis, PhD(chem), 54. *Prof Exp:* Res chemist, Phillips Petrol Co, 53; sr chemist, Clevite Corp, 55-56; sr res chemist, Res Ctr, B F Goodrich Co, 56-63; head biochem lab, Midwest Med Res Found, 65-66; sr res chemist, Frontier Chem Co, 66-67; chem div, Vulcan Mat Co, 67-68, group leader chem res, 68-73; instr vis staff, 74-78, RES FAC, DEPT CHEM, PHOENIX COL, 78- *Mem:* AAAS; Am Asn Univ Women; Am Chem Soc; Sigma Xi. *Res:* Rates and mechanisms of organic reactions; polymerization; organometallics. *Mailing Add:* 8102 N 6th St Phoenix AZ 85020

MOYER, RALPH OWEN, JR, b New Bedford, Mass, May 19, 36. INORGANIC CHEMISTRY. *Educ:* Southeastern Mass Univ, BS, 57; Univ Toledo, MS, 63; Univ Conn, PhD(inorg chem), 69. *Prof Exp:* Develop engr, Union Carbide Corp, 57-64; asst prof, 69-75, ASSOC PROF CHEM, TRINITY COL, CONN, 75- *Concurrent Pos:* Res collabr, Brookhaven Nat Lab, 77-80. *Mem:* Am Chem Soc; Sigma Xi. *Res:* Preparation, structure, magnetic and electrical properties of ternary hydrides. *Mailing Add:* Clement Chem Lab Trinity Col Hartford CT 06106

MOYER, REX CARLTON, b Elkhart, Ind, Dec 8, 35; m 58; c 4. CANCER, MICROBIOLOGY. *Educ:* Purdue Univ, BS, 57; Univ Nebr, MS, 61; Univ Tex, PhD(microbiol), 65. *Prof Exp:* Asst bacteriologist, Miles-Ames Res Labs, 57-58; lab instr gen microbiol, Univ Nebr, 58-61; trainee molecular biol, Univ Tex, 61-65; Nat Acad Sci-Nat Res Coun res fel microbial genetics & bacteriophagy, Ft Detrick, 65-66; res microbiologist, Ft Detrick, 66-69; co-dir, Bettye Thorman Cancer Res Lab, 70-75, asst prof, 69-77, ASSOC PROF BIOL, TRINITY UNIV, 77- DIR, BETTYE THORMAN CANCER RES LAB, 75- *Concurrent Pos:* Assoc ed, Tex J Sci. *Mem:* Am Soc Microbiol; Int Study Group for Detection and Prevention of Cancer. *Res:* Cancer virology and nutrition; microbial genetics; nucleic acids. *Mailing Add:* Dept of Biol Trinity Univ San Antonio TX 78284

MOYER, ROBERT (FINDLEY), b New York, NY, May 12, 37; m 61; c 3. RADIATION PHYSICS. *Educ:* Pa State Univ, BS, 59, MS, 61; Univ Calif, Los Angeles, PhD(med physics), 65. *Prof Exp:* Inst radiol physics, State Univ NY Upstate Med Ctr, 65-70, asst prof radiol, 70-81; CHIEF PHYSICIST, READING HOSPITAL, 81- *Concurrent Pos:* Consult medical radiation physicist. *Mem:* Am Asn Physicists in Med. *Res:* Radiological physics and biology. *Mailing Add:* Dept of Radiol Reading Hosp & Med Ctr Reading PA 19603

MOYER, ROBERT DALE, b Allentown, Pa, Sept 5, 38; m 63; c 4. MATHEMATICAL ANALYSIS. *Educ:* Pa State Univ, BS, 60; Univ Calif, Berkeley, MS, 62, PhD(appl math), 64. *Prof Exp:* Mem tech staff, Bellcomm, Inc, 64-65; asst prof math, Pa State Univ, 65-67; ASSOC PROF MATH, UNIV KANS, 67- *Concurrent Pos:* Assoc prof, Purdue Univ, 73-74. *Mem:* Am Math Soc; Inst Advan Study. *Res:* Partial differential equations; functional analysis; global analysis; complex analysis. *Mailing Add:* Dept of Math Univ of Kans Lawrence KS 66044

MOYER, RUDOLPH HENRY, b Sask, June 1, 35; m 57; c 2. BIOCHEMISTRY. *Educ:* Univ BC, BSA, 58, MSc, 62; Univ Calif, Los Angeles, PhD(biochem), 66. *Prof Exp:* Food technologist, Fisheries Res Bd, Can, 58-60; sr biochemist, Aerojet-Gen Corp Div, 65-69; SR SCIENTIST, GEOMET, INC, 69- *Mem:* AAAS; Am Chem Soc. *Res:* Development of instrument systems for bio-medical, geochemical and environmental applications; detection and quantitation of aerosols and other atmospheric pollutants. *Mailing Add:* Geomet Inc 2814A Metropolitan Pl Pomona CA 91767

MOYER, SAMUEL EDWARD, b Hershey, Pa, Oct 5, 34; m 59; c 2. POPULATION GENETICS. *Educ:* Pa State Univ, BS, 56; Univ NH, MS, 59; Univ Minn, PhD(genetics), 64. *Prof Exp:* Asst geneticist, NC State Univ, 64-65; asst prof genetics, Northeastern Univ, 66-71; ASSOC PROF BIOL, BURLINGTON COUNTY COL, 71- *Mem:* Genetics Soc Am; Am Genetic Asn. *Res:* Genetic traits of economic importance in poultry; effects of linkage on survival; genetic loads of populations. *Mailing Add:* Dept of Biol Burlington County Col Pemberton NJ 08068

MOYER, VANCE EDWARDS, b Orwigsburg, Pa, Nov 22, 14; m 53; c 2. METEOROLOGY. *Educ:* Pa State Univ, BS, 50, MS, 51, PhD(meteorol), 54. *Prof Exp:* Res asst meteorol, Pa State Univ, 51, res assoc, 52-54; asst prof, Univ Tex, 54-58; assoc prof, 58-61, chmn instruct meteorol, 60-66, actg head dept, 66-67, head dept, 67-75, prof, 61-80, EMER PROF METEOROL, TEX A&M UNIV, 80- *Concurrent Pos:* NSF lectr, 58-64; mem earth sci curriculum proj, 65. *Mem:* Am Meteorol Soc; Am Geophys Union. *Res:* Cloud and precipitation physics; physical and radar meteorology; satellite determination of atmospheric structure. *Mailing Add:* Dept of Meteorol Tex A&M Univ College Station TX 77843

MOYER, WALTER ALLEN, JR, b Philadelphia, Pa, Nov 16, 22; m 46; c 2. ORGANIC CHEMISTRY. *Educ:* Philadelphia Col Pharm, BSc, 43; Middlebury Col, MSc, 48; Univ Del, PhD(org chem), 51. *Prof Exp:* From instr to assoc prof, 51-67, PROF CHEM, MIDDLEBURY COL, 67-, ASSOC DEAN, COL INST RES & SPEC ADMIS, 71-, DIR, CAREER COUN & PLACEMENT, 74-, ASSOC DEAN SCI, 81- *Mem:* Nat Asn Adv Health Professions; Am Chem Soc. *Res:* Carbohydrates; natural products; organic synthesis. *Mailing Add:* Sci Ctr 113 Middlebury Col Middlebury VT 05753

MOYER, WAYNE A, b Brooklyn, NY, Mar 9, 30; m 54; c 1. CELL ADHESION. *Educ:* Bucknell Univ, BS, 52; Syracuse Univ, MS, 55; Brown Univ, ScM, 64; Princeton Univ, PhD(develop biol), 73. *Prof Exp:* Dept chmn biol, East Brunswick Bd Educ, 55-69; asst prof develop biol, City Univ NY, 73-76, Trenton State Col, 76-77 & Seton Hall Univ, 77-79; EXEC DIR, NAT ASN BIOL TEACHERS, 79- *Concurrent Pos:* Teacher gen sci, Fair Lawn Bd Educ, NJ, 55-58. *Mem:* AAAS; Am Inst Biol Sci; Nat Sci Teachers Asn; Soc Develop Biol; Nat Asn Biol Teachers. *Res:* Sequestered mRNA in sea urchin embryos as revealed by actinomycin block to RNA synnthesis; rate studies of cell adhesion between various cell types derived from embryonic chick tissues; strength of adhesion as measured by hierarchical envelopment, interpreted by the differential adhesion hypothesis. *Mailing Add:* Nat Asn Biol Teachers 11250 Roger Bacon Dr #19 Reston VA 22090

MOYER, WILLIAM C, JR, b Dallas, Tex, Apr 5, 37. UNDERWATER ACOUSTICS. *Educ:* Southern Methodist Univ, BS, 59; Univ Tex, PhD(mech eng), 66. *Prof Exp:* Mem tech staff, Hughes Aircraft Co, 59; sr scientist, 66-68, asst dir res dept, 68-69, dir anal dept, 69-71, asst vpres appl technol div, 71-74, vpres, Anal & Appl Res Div, 74-76, VPRES APPL SCI, TRACOR INC, 76- *Res:* Sonar system performance analysis; radiation associated with underwater arrays; transducer and baffle interactions; specialized underwater sensor systems. *Mailing Add:* Tracor Inc 6500 Tracor Lane Austin TX 78721

MOYERMAN, ROBERT MAX, b Atlantic City, NJ, Sept 14, 25; m 51; c 3. ORGANIC CHEMISTRY, ANALYTICAL CHEMISTRY. *Educ:* Rutgers Univ, BS, 49; Univ Ala, MS, 51. *Prof Exp:* Chemist high temperature nuclear reactors, Nuclear Develop Assocs, Inc, 51-52; assoc chemist carbohydrate & anal chem, Johns Hopkins Univ, 52-53, chem kinetics, Appl Physics Lab, 53-55; res investr, Am Smelting & Ref Co, 55-58; res chemist anal chem & org separations, Ansul Co, Wis, 58-63, sr res chemist process res, Org Res & Sect Head Anal Dept, 63-65; sr chemist, Scholler Bros, Inc, Pa, 65-68; group leader, Chem Div, Sun Chem Corp, RI, 68-70; mgr res & develop, Hydrolabs, Inc, Paterson, 74-75; OWNER & NEW PROD MGR, WARWICK LABS, 70- *Concurrent Pos:* Tech serv dir, Org Chem Corp, 70-72. *Mem:* Am Chem Soc; Am Microchem Soc; Am Asn Textile Chemists & Colorists; Sigma Xi. *Res:* Organic syntheses; organic arsenic. *Mailing Add:* 118 Edmond Dr Warwick RI 02886

MOYERS, JACK, b Sidney, Iowa, Dec 7, 21; m 45; c 2. ANESTHESIOLOGY. *Educ:* Univ Iowa, BS, 43, MD, 45; Am Bd Anesthesiol, dipl, 53. *Prof Exp:* Intern med, Mt Carmel Mercy Hosp, Detroit, 45-46; resident anesthesiol, Col Med, Univ Iowa, 48-50; instr, WHO Anesthesiol Training Ctr, Univ Copenhagen, 50-51; instr, 51-52, assoc, 52-53, from asst prof to assoc prof, 53-66, actg head dept, 67-68, head dept, 68-77, PROF ANESTHESIA, COL MED, UNIV IOWA, 66-, ATTEND ANESTHESIOLOGIST, VET ADMIN HOSP, 52- *Mem:* Am Soc Anesthesiol; Asn Univ Anesthetists; fel Am Col Anesthesiol; Am Heart Asn; NY Acad Sci. *Res:* Clinical and laboratory investigation in field of anesthesiology. *Mailing Add:* Dept of Anesthesia Univ of Iowa Col of Med Iowa City IA 52240

MOYERS, JARVIS LEE, b Houston, Tex, Sept 7, 43; m 66; c 1. CHEMISTRY. *Educ:* Marshall Univ, BS, 65; Univ Hawaii, PhD(chem), 70. *Prof Exp:* LAB DIR, DEPT CHEM, UNIV ARIZ, 71- *Mem:* AAAS; Am Chem Soc; Am Geophys Union; Am Soc Testing & Mat. *Res:* Analytic environmental chemistry; atmospheric chemistry. *Mailing Add:* Univ Anal Ctr Dept Chem Univ of Ariz Tucson AZ 85721

MOYERS, ROBERT EDISON, b Sidney, Iowa, Nov 19, 19; m 56; c 2. ORTHODONTICS, HUMAN DEVELOPMENT. *Educ:* Univ Iowa, BS & DDS, 42, MS, 47, PhD(physiol), 49. *Prof Exp:* Assoc orthod, Col Dent, Univ Iowa, 45-47, instr, 47-49; prof & head dept, Fac Dent, Univ Toronto, 49-53; head dept orthod, 53-65, PROF DENT, SCH DENT, UNIV MICH, ANN ARBOR, 53-, DIR CTR HUMAN GROWTH & DEVELOP, 65- *Concurrent Pos:* Fulbright scholar, Nat Univ Athens, 51, vis prof, 64; consult, WHO, 57- *Honors & Awards:* Milo Hellman Res Award, 50; mem, Order Brit Empire; Order of Phoenix. *Mem:* AAAS; Am Asn Orthod; Am Dent Asn; Int Asn Dent Res; Int Soc Craniofacial Biol. *Res:* Electromyography; facial growth. *Mailing Add:* 1035 Country Club Ann Arbor MI 48105

MOYLE, DAVID DOUGLAS, b Wilkes-Barre, Pa, Dec 10, 42; m 64; c 2. BIOMECHANICS, BIOMATERIALS. *Educ:* Wilkes Col, BS, 64; Rensselaer Polytech Inst, PhD(physics), 69. *Prof Exp:* Fel biomech, Rensselaer Polytech Inst, 69-71; asst prof, 71-75, ASSOC PROF BIOENG, CLEMSON UNIV, 75- *Mem:* Sigma Xi; AAAS. *Res:* Mechanics of skeletal tissue including properties of bone and bone replacement materials. *Mailing Add:* 301 Rhodes Eng Dept Res Ctr Clemson Univ Clemson SC 29631

MOYLE, PETER BRIGGS, b Minneapolis, Minn, May 29, 42; m 66. ICHTHYOLOGY, AQUATIC ECOLOGY. *Educ:* Univ Minn, BA, 64, PhD(zool), 69; Cornell Univ, MS, 66. *Prof Exp:* Asst prof biol, Fresno State Col, 69-72; asst prof, 72-77, ASSOC BIOL, DEPT WILDLIFE & FISHERIES BIOL, UNIV CALIF, DAVIS, 77- *Mem:* AAAS; Ecol Soc Am; Am Fisheries Soc; Am Soc Ichthyol & Herpet. *Res:* Ecology of freshwater and estuarine fishes; distribution and ecology of freshwater fishes of California. *Mailing Add:* Dept of Wildlife & Fisheries Biol Univ Calif Davis CA 95616

MOYLE, RICHARD W, b American Fork, Utah, Mar 22, 30; m 57; c 2. PALEONTOLOGY, GEOLOGY. *Educ:* Brigham Young Univ, BS, 52, MS, 57; Univ Iowa, PhD(gen geol), 63. *Prof Exp:* Instr geol, Western State Col Colo, 61-63, asst prof, 63-65; from asst prof to assoc prof, 65-71, actg head dept geol & geog, 68-69, chmn dept, 69-72, PROF GEOL, WEBER STATE COL, 71- *Concurrent Pos:* Geologist mat eng, Region 4, Regional Off, US Forest Serv, 78- *Mem:* Geol Soc Am; Nat Asn Geol Teachers; Soc Econ Paleont & Mineral; Paleont Asn. *Res:* Mississippian and Pennsylvanian sponges; paleoecology of Upper Mississippian and Lower Pennsylvanian sediments in west central Utah; ammonoids of Wolfcampian from the Glass Mountains of west Texas and continguous areas; microcrystals and photography of same; Mississippian Blastoids of Utah. *Mailing Add:* Dept of Geol & Geog Box 2507 Ogden UT 84408

MOYLE, SUSAN MARY, see Studlar, Susan Moyle

MOYLS, BENJAMIN NELSON, b Vancouver, BC, May 1, 19; m 42, 76; c 2. ALGEBRA. *Educ:* Univ BC, BA, 40, MA, 41; Harvard Univ, AM, 42, PhD(math), 47. *Prof Exp:* From instr to assoc prof, 47-59, asst dean grad studies, 67-76, PROF MATH, UNIV BC, 59-, HEAD MATH DEPT, 78- *Mem:* Am Math Soc; Math Asn Am; Soc Indust & Appl Math; Edinburgh Math Soc; Can Math Soc (vpres, 81-). *Res:* Linear algebra. *Mailing Add:* Dept Math Univ BC Vancouver BC V6T 1W5 Can

MOYNE, JOHN ABEL, b Yezd, Iran, July 6, 20; m 63; c 3. COMPUTER SCIENCE, COMPUTATIONAL LINGUISTICS. *Educ:* Georgetown Univ, BA, 59, MA, 60; Harvard Univ, PhD(ling), 70. *Prof Exp:* Res assoc mach transl, Georgetown Univ, 56-63; mgr appl ling, IBM Corp, 63-71; assoc prof, 71-75, PROF COMPUT SCI & CHMN DEPT, QUEENS COL, CITY UNIV NEW YORK, 75- *Concurrent Pos:* Researcher, Europ AEC, Italy, 61-63; teaching fel, Harvard Univ, 69-70. *Mem:* Asn Comput Mach; Ling Soc Am; NY Acad Sci; Asn Computational Ling; Brit Inst Eng Technol. *Res:* Linguistic theory; formal languages automata; programming languages and compilers. *Mailing Add:* Dept of Comput Sci Queens Col Flushing NY 11367

MOYNIHAN, CORNELIUS TIMOTHY, b Inglewood, Calif, Feb 2, 39; m 63; c 2. GLASS SCIENCE, PHYSICAL CHEMISTRY. *Educ:* Univ Santa Clara, BS, 60; Princeton Univ, MA, 62, PhD(chem), 65. *Prof Exp:* From asst prof to assoc prof chem, Calif State Col Los Angeles, 64-69; assoc prof chem, Cath Univ Am, 68-69, assoc prof chem eng, 69-75, prof chem eng, 75-81; PROF MAT ENG, RENSSELAER POLYTECHNIC INST, 81- *Concurrent Pos:* Res assoc, Purdue Univ, 68-69. *Mem:* Am Chem Soc; Am Ceramic Soc; Electrochem Soc. *Res:* Physical chemistry of molten salts, electrolyte solutions and glasses; materials engineering of glasses; hydrocarbon fuels. *Mailing Add:* Dept Mat Eng Rennselaer Polytech Inst Troy NY 12181

MOYNIHAN, MARTIN HUMPHREY, b Chicago, Ill, Feb 5, 28. ANIMAL BEHAVIOR. *Educ:* Princeton Univ, AB, 50, DPhil(zool), Oxford Univ, 53. *Prof Exp:* Vis fel, Cornell Univ, 53-55; res fel, Harvard Univ, 55-57; DIR SMITHSONIAN TROP RES INST, 57- *Mem:* Soc Study Evolution; Am Ornith Union; Asn Trop Biol. *Res:* Behavior, ecology and evaluation. *Mailing Add:* Smithsonian Trop Res Inst PO Box 2072 Balboa Panama

MOZELL, MAXWELL MARK, b Brooklyn, NY, May 20, 29; m 55; c 4. SENSORY PHYSIOLOGY, PSYCHOPHYSIOLOGY. *Educ:* Brown Univ, AB, 51, MSc, 53, PhD(phsiol psychol), 56. *Prof Exp:* Fel physiol, Fla State Univ, 59-61; from asst prof to assoc prof, 61-70, assoc dean, 71-77, PROF PHYSIOL, STATE UNIV NY UPSTATE MED CTR, 70- *Concurrent Pos:* Mem sensory physiol & perception study panel, NSF, 74-78; mem commun disorders rev comt, NIH, 81-85. *Mem:* Am Physiol Soc; Am Psychol Asn; Soc Neurosci; Sigma Xi; Asn Chemoreceptum Sci. *Res:* Sensory psychophysiology; oflaction; electrophysiology; determine the physical, chemical, physiological mechanisms basic to olfactory discriminations. *Mailing Add:* Dept of Physiol State Univ of NY Upstate Med Ctr Syracuse NY 13210

MOZER, BERNARD, b Denver, Colo, Dec 2, 25; m 57; c 3. PHYSICS. *Educ:* Univ Denver, BS, 50; Univ Colo, MS, 52; Carnegie Inst Technol, PhD(physics), 60. *Prof Exp:* Res assoc physics, Univ Denver, 52-53; jr physicist, Brookhaven Nat Lab, 53-55; res asst physics, Carnegie Inst Technol, 55-59; res assoc, Brookhaven Nat Lab, 59-61, from asst physicist to assoc physicist, 61-67; PHYSICIST, NAT BUR STAND, 67- *Mem:* Am Phys Soc. *Res:* Theoretical plasma physics; theoretical and experimental aspects of Mossbauer effect; inelastic neutron scattering experiments on liquids, metals and alloys; vibrational and electronic effects of impurities in solids. *Mailing Add:* Reactor Bld Nat Bur Stand Washington DC 20234

MOZER, FORREST S, b Lincoln, Nebr, Feb 13, 29; m 58; c 3. SPACE PHYSICS. *Educ:* Univ Nebr, BS, 51; Calif Inst Technol, MS, 53, PhD(physics), 56. *Prof Exp:* Fel, Calif Inst Technol, 56-57; res scientist, Lockheed Res Lab, 57-61 & Aerospace Corp, 62-63; res dir space physics, Univ Paris, 63-66; from asst prof to assoc prof, 66-70, PROF PHYSICS, UNIV CALIF, BERKELEY, 70- *Mem:* Am Geophys Union; Am Phys Soc. *Mailing Add:* Dept of Physics Univ of Calif Berkeley CA 94720

MOZERSKY, SAMUEL M, b Sask, Can, Sept 19, 24; US citizen; m 55; c 2. BIOCHEMISTRY, ENZYMOLOGY. *Educ:* Univ Calif, Los Angeles, BA, 47; Univ Southern Calif, PhD(biochem), 57. *Prof Exp:* Sr lab asst turnover of plasma proteins, Col Med, Univ Ill, 52-55; grad res physiol chemist, Med Ctr, Univ Calif, Los Angeles, 56-57, asst res physiol chemist, 57-61; RES BIOCHEMIST, EASTERN REGIONAL LAB, USDA, WYNDMOOR, 63- *Concurrent Pos:* USPHS spec fel, Dept Biol, Brookhaven Nat Lab, 61-63. *Mem:* Biophys Soc; Am Chem Soc; NY Acad Sci. *Res:* Biosynthesis of plasma proteins; purification and characterization of hyaluronidases; protein modification; mechanisms of enzyme action; structure and enzymatic properties of contractile proteins. *Mailing Add:* Eastern Regional Lab USDA 600 E Mermaid Lane Wyndmoor PA 19118

MOZINGO, HUGH NELSON, b Monongahela, Pa, Apr 23, 25; m 49. BOTANY. *Educ:* Univ Pittsburgh, BS, 46, MS, 47; Columbia Univ, PhD(bot), 50. *Prof Exp:* Asst biol, Univ Pittsburgh, 46-47; asst bot, Columbia Univ, 47-50; instr, Univ Tenn, 50-51; assoc prof biol & bot & chmn sci div, Fla Southern Col, 51-55; asst prof, Mich State Univ, 55-59; assoc prof, 59-68, chmn dept, 69-76, PROF BIOL, UNIV NEV, RENO, 68- *Concurrent Pos:* Herbarium Cur, 59. *Mem:* AAAS; Bot Soc Am; Am Soc Plant Physiol; Am Bryol & Lichenological Soc; Electron Micros Soc Am. *Res:* Plant morphogenesis; plant systematics; Nevada bryophytes. *Mailing Add:* Dept of Biol Univ of Nev Reno NV 89507

MOZLEY, JAMES MARSHALL, JR, b Marion, Ill, Nov 1, 22; m 44; c 1. BIOMEDICAL ENGINEERING. *Educ:* Washington Univ, BS, 43, MS, 47, PhD(chem & elec eng), 50. *Prof Exp:* Instr chem eng, Washington Univ, 47-49; assoc chemist sec oil recovery, Atlantic Refining Co, Tex, 49-51; sr instr chem eng, Polytech Inst Brooklyn, 51-52; res engr, automatic control, E I du Pont de Nemours & Co, Del, 51-57; assoc prof radiol, Johns Hopkins Univ, 57-65, dir div radiation chem, Sch Pub Health & Hyg, 59-65; dir, Div Radiol Physics & Eng, 75-78, PROF RADIOL, UNIV HOSP, STATE UNIV NY UPSTATE MED CTR, 65-; PROF CHEM ENG, SYRACUSE UNIV, 67- *Concurrent Pos:* Pres, Radiation Assocs Md, Inc, 59-; ed, Trans, Instrument Soc Am, 62-68; vis prof biomed eng, Wash Univ, St Louis, 74-75; adj prof elec eng, Syracuse Univ, 80- *Mem:* AAAS; Am Inst Chem Eng; Am Chem Soc; Am Soc Mech Eng; sr mem Instrument Soc Am. *Res:* Automatic control of chemical processes; radiological instrumentation; data processing; computation; nuclear medicine. *Mailing Add:* Dept of Radiol State Univ NY Upstate Med Ctr Syracuse NY 13210

MOZLEY, ROBERT FRED, b Boston, Mass, Apr 18, 17; c 2. NUCLEAR PHYSICS, ELEMENTARY PARTICLE PHYSICS. *Educ:* Harvard Univ, AB, 38; Univ Calif, MS & PhD(physics), 50. *Prof Exp:* Elec engr radar, Sperry Gyroscope Co, 41-45; asst radiation lab, Univ Calif, 45-50; from instr to asst prof physics, Princeton Univ, 50-53; assoc prof, 53-62, PROF PHYSICS, STANFORD UNIV, 62- *Mem:* Fel Am Phys Soc. *Res:* Elementary particle physics. *Mailing Add:* Stanford Linear Accelerator Ctr Stanford Univ Stanford CA 94305

MOZLEY, SAMUEL CLIFFORD, b Atlanta, Ga, Aug 13, 43; m 64; c 2. AQUATIC ECOLOGY. *Educ:* Emory Univ, BS, 64, MS, 66, PhD(animal ecol), 68. *Prof Exp:* NATO fel, Max Planck Inst Limnol, Ger, 68-69, NSF fel, 69-70; Nat Res Coun Can fel, Univ Toronto, 70; asst res scientist, Great Lakes Res Div, Univ Mich, Ann Arbor, 76-77, assoc res scientist, 76-77; ASSOC PROF ZOOL, NC STATE UNIV, 77- *Mem:* Am Soc Limnol & Oceanog; NAm Benthological Soc. *Res:* Taxonomy and morphology of Chironomidae; community structure of benthic animals; benthos and pollution in fresh waters; methodology of benthic sampling. *Mailing Add:* Dept Zool NC State Univ Raleigh NC 27650

MOZUMDER, ASOKENDU, b Baherok, India, June 2, 31; m 61. RADIATION CHEMISTRY, RADIATION PHYSICS. *Educ:* Univ Calcutta, BSc, 50, MSc, 53; Indian Inst Technol, Kharagpur, PhD(physics). 61. *Prof Exp:* From assoc lectr to lectr physics, Indian Inst Technol, Kharagpur, 54-62; assoc, 62-65, from assoc res scientist to res scientist, 65-69, ASSOC FAC FEL, RADIATION LAB, UNIV NOTRE DAME, 69- *Mem:* Am Phys Soc; Radiation Res Soc. *Res:* Theoretical radiation chemistry; application of the methods of theoretical physics to problems involving interaction of radiation with matter. *Mailing Add:* Radiation Lab Univ of Notre Dame Notre Dame IN 46556

MOZZI, ROBERT LEWIS, b Meriden, Conn, Dec 8, 31; m 56; c 1. EXPERIMENTAL SOLID STATE PHYSICS. *Educ:* Villanova Univ, BS, 53; Univ Pittsburgh, MS, 56; Mass Inst Technol, PhD(physics), 68. *Prof Exp:* Physicist, Pratt & Whitney Aircraft Div, United Aircraft Corp, 55-57; PRIN SCIENTIST, RES DIV, RAYTHEON CO, 57- *Mem:* Am Phys Soc. *Res:* X-ray diffraction studies of the structure of glass and imperfections in crystals; ion implantation in semiconductors; gallium arsenide microwave device technology; high resolution lithography. *Mailing Add:* Res Div Raytheon Co Waltham MA 02154

MRAW, STEPHEN CHARLES, b Trenton, NJ, Jan 27, 50; m 71; c 4. THERMODYNAMICS. *Educ:* Fordham Univ, BS, 70; Univ Calif, Berkeley, PhD(phys chem), 74. *Prof Exp:* NATO fel chem, Inorg Chem Lab, Oxford Univ, 74-75; fel res assoc chem eng, Rice Univ, 75-76; STAFF CHEMIST, EXXON RES & ENG CO, 76- *Concurrent Pos:* Dir, Calorimetry Conf, 80-82. *Mem:* Am Chem Soc. *Res:* Thermodynamics, principally calorimetry of pure compounds and complex systems at high temperatures as related to fossil fuel technology; study of the structure of coal as related to other porous systems. *Mailing Add:* Corp Res Sci Labs Exxon Res & Eng Co PO Box 45 Linden NJ 07036

MRAZ, FRANK RUDOLPH, b New York, NY, Feb 25, 25. NUTRITION, BIOCHEMISTRY. *Educ:* Rutgers Univ, BS, 51; Pa State Univ, MS, 53, PhD(agr & biol chem, poultry husb), 54. *Prof Exp:* From asst scientist to assoc scientist, 55-65, assoc prof nutrit biochem, 55-65, SCIENTIST & PROF METAB & NUTRIT, UNIV TENN-DEPT OF ENERGY COMP ANIMAL RES LAB, OAK RIDGE, 65- *Mem:* Soc Exp Biol & Med; Poultry Sci Asn; Am Inst Nutrit; Radiation Res Soc. *Res:* Comparative metabolism and influence of diet on metabolic pathways of fission products and industrial pollutants in avian and mammalian species; mechanisms of discrimination between the elements at physiological interfaces. *Mailing Add:* 1299 Bethel Valley Rd Oak Ridge TN 37830

MRAZEK, ROBERT VERNON, b Chicago, Ill, Jan 15, 36; m 59; c 3. CHEMICAL ENGINEERING. *Educ:* Purdue Univ, BS, 57; Rensselaer Polytech Inst, PhD(chem eng), 60. *Prof Exp:* From asst prof to assoc prof, 60-67, PROF CHEM ENG, ORE STATE UNIV, 67- *Concurrent Pos:* Consult, Albany Metall Res Sta, US Bur Mines, 63- *Mem:* Am Inst Chem Engrs. *Res:* Thermodynamics; applied mathematics. *Mailing Add:* Dept of Chem Eng Ore State Univ Corvallis OR 97330

MRAZEK, RUDOLPH G, b Chicago, Ill, May 23, 22; m 44; c 3. SURGERY. *Educ:* Univ Ill, BA, 41, MD, 44, MS, 45. *Prof Exp:* Resident surg, MacNeal Hosp, 45-46 & Hines Vet Admin Hosp, 49-52; from instr to clin assoc prof, 52-73, PROF CLIN SURG, UNIV ILL COL MED, 73-; DIR MED EDUC, MACNEAL HOSP, 71- *Mem:* AMA; Am Asn Cancer Res; fel Am Col Surg; Soc Surg Alimentary Tract; Soc Surg Oncol. *Res:* Cancer chemotherapy. *Mailing Add:* Macneal Prof Bldg 3231 S Euclid Ave Berwyn IL 60402

MROCZKOWSKI, STANLEY, b Poland, Mar 29, 25; US citizen; m 54; c 1. SOLID STATE CHEMISTRY. *Educ:* Adam Mickiewicz Univ, Poznan, MPH, 52; Univ Warsaw, Cand Sci & PhD(inorg chem), 56. *Hon Degrees:* Doctorate, Arts & Lett, 73. *Prof Exp:* Group leader rare earth compounds, Inst Electron Technol, Polish Acad Sci, Warsaw, 56-58; head anal sect, Weitzman Inst, Albar Kvar-Saba, 59-61; res assoc chem, Columbia Univ, 61-63; SR RES ASSOC & LECTR APPL PHYSICS, CHEM RARE EARTH COMPOUND & SEMICONDUCTORS MAT, YALE UNIV, 63- *Concurrent Pos:* Tech consult, David Sarnoff Res Ctr, RCA Corp, 67- & Autoclave Engrs, Inc, Erie, Pa, 74- *Mem:* Am Chem Soc; Inst Elec & Electronics Engrs; Am Crystal Growth Asn. *Res:* Crystallization processes under high pressure and high temperature; crystal growth from high temperature solution; vapor transport reaction. *Mailing Add:* Yale Univ Dept of Eng & Appl Sci 427 Becton Ctr New Haven CT 06520

MROTEK, JAMES JOSEPH, b Loyal, Wis, Mar 19, 39; m 67. CELL BIOLOGY, ENDOCRINOLOGY. *Educ:* Univ Wis-Madison, BS, 64, MS, 65; Clark Univ, PhD(biol), 73. *Prof Exp:* Res technician qual control, Barley & Malt Lab, USDA, 60-61; res scientist adrenal physiol, Worcester Found Exp Biol, 68-69; fel adrenal physiol, Dept Physiol, Calif Col Med, Univ Calif, Irvine, 73-76; ASST PROF CELLULAR & MOLEC BIOL, DEPT BIOL SCI, N TEX STATE UNIV, 76- *Mem:* Soc Study Reprod; AAAS. *Res:* Cellular and molecular mechanisms of steroidogenesis; age-related changes in adrenal physiology; biochemistry of microfilaments; toxicological effects of cigarettes on cultured cells; cellular changes occurring in neoplastic cells. *Mailing Add:* Dept of Biol Sci N Tex State Univ Denton TX 76203

MROWCA, JOSEPH J, b Taylor, Pa, Jan 25, 39; m 60; c 3. ORGANOMETALLIC CHEMISTRY. *Educ:* Univ Scranton, BS, 60; Columbia Univ, MA, 62, PhD(chem), 65. *Prof Exp:* RES CHEMIST, BIOCHEM DEPT, E I DU PONT DE NEMOURS & CO, INC, 65- *Mem:* Am Chem Soc. *Res:* Transition metal catalysis. *Mailing Add:* Biochem Dept E I du Pont de Nemours & Co Inc 1007 Market St Wilmington DE 19898

MROZIK, HELMUT, b Habelschwerdt, Ger, Oct 23, 31; m 57; c 2. ORGANIC CHEMISTRY. *Educ:* Univ Basel, PhD(chem), 58. *Prof Exp:* Asst chem, Columbia Univ, 59-60; SR INVESTR, MERCK & CO, 60- *Mem:* Am Chem Soc. *Res:* Chemotherapy of parasitic diseases; medicinal chemistry; natural product chemistry. *Mailing Add:* 159 Idlebrook Lane Matawan NJ 07747

MROZINSKI, PETER MATTHEW, b Chicago, Ill, Apr 22, 47; m 70; c 1. APPLIED PHYSICS, LOW TEMPERATURE PHYSICS. *Educ:* St Mary's Col, Minn, BA, 69; Ohio State Univ, MS, 72, PhD(physics), 75- *Prof Exp:* RES PHYSICIST, E I DU PONT DE NEMOURS & CO, INC, 74- *Mem:* Am Phys Soc. *Res:* Applications of x-ray fluorescence. *Mailing Add:* Exp Sta B-357 E I du Pont de Nemours & Co Inc Wilmington DE 19898

MRTEK, MARSHA BEDFORD, pharmacy, see previous edition

MRTEK, ROBERT GEORGE, b Oak Park, Ill, Sept 2, 40; m 66. PHARMACY, HISTORY OF PHARMACY. *Educ:* Univ Ill, BS, 62, PhD(pharm), 67. *Prof Exp:* Resident res assoc chem, Argonne Nat Lab, 64-66; from asst prof to assoc prof pharm, 67-73, coordr educ res develop, 70-73, asst dean educ develop, 73-79, PROF PHARM, COL PHARM, UNIV ILL, CHICAGO, 73-, SPECIAL ASST, CHANCELLOR'S OFFICE, MED CTR, 80- *Concurrent Pos:* Consult, Walter Reed Army Inst Res, 66-69 & Health Sci Educ Planning, Off Pres, Univ Calif, Berkeley, 79; Univ Ill res bd grants, 68-69; consult & examr, Civil Serv Comn, City of Chicago, 69; US Vitamin & Pharmaceut Co res grant, 70; spec proj prog, Health Professions, Bur Health Manpower Educ grant, 72-74; vis prof, Health Sci Ctr, Univ Wis, Madison, 75-76. *Honors & Awards:* C P van Schaak Chem Award, Lehn & Fink Gold Medal Award & Elich Prize, 62; Citation Hist Res, Am Inst Hist Pharm, 72; Kremers Award, Am Inst Hist Pharm, 81. *Mem:* AAAS; Am Pharmaceut Asn; Am Inst Hist Pharm; Am Asn Col Pharm. *Res:* History of pharmacy in Illinois; history of pharmaceutical education and of American pharmacy practice; self study resources for pharmaceutical education; higher education administration. *Mailing Add:* Dept of Pharm Prac Col of Pharm Univ of Ill Med Ctr PO Box 6998 Chicago IL 60680

MUAN, ARNULF, b Lokken Verk, Norway, Apr 19, 23; nat US; m 60; c 2. SLAG-REFRACTORY CHEMISTRY, HIGH-TEMPERATURE THERMODYNAMICS. *Educ:* Tech Univ Norway, dipl, 48; Pa State Univ, PhD(geochem), 55. *Prof Exp:* Instr anal chem, Tech Univ Norway, 48-49; asst geochem, 50-51, res assoc, 52-55, from asst prof to prof metall, 55-66, PROF MINERAL SCI, PA STATE UNIV, 66-, ASSOC DEAN RES, 76- *Concurrent Pos:* Head dept geochem & mineral, Pa State Univ, 66-71, head dept geosci, 71-73. *Honors & Awards:* Ross Coffin Purdy Award, Am Ceramic Soc, 59, Jeppson Award, 78. *Mem:* Fel Mineral Soc Am (secy, 69-70, vpres, 73-74, pres, 74-75); fel Am Ceramic Soc; Am Inst Mining, Metall & Petrol Engrs; fel Geol Soc Am; AAAS. *Res:* Heterogeneous equilibria and thermodynamics at high temperatures with special emphasis on oxide systems; applications to mineralogy-petrology, slags and refractories and to the use of materials in high-temrperature environments; application of these principles to petrology, ore deposits, slag and refractory problems. *Mailing Add:* 1121 Mayberry Lane State Col Pa State College PA 16801

MUCCI, JOSEPH FRANCIS, b Southington, Conn, Apr; m 53; c 3. PHYSICAL CHEMISTRY. *Educ:* Cent Conn State Col, BS, 50; Wesleyan Univ, MA, 53; Yale Univ, PhD, 57. *Prof Exp:* Asst, Yale Univ, 54-57; from instr to assoc prof, 57-66, PROF CHEM, VASSAR COL, 66-, CHMN DEPT, 75- *Mem:* AAAS; Am Chem Soc; NY Acad Sci; fel Am Inst Chem. *Res:* Complexions in various media by spectrophotometric, conductometric, polarographic, ion exchange, extraction and radiochemical methods; quantum chemical studies employing self consistent field-linear combination of atomic orbitals-molecular orbitals; statsitical mechanics. *Mailing Add:* Dept of Chem Vassar Col Poughkeepsie NY 12601

MUCCINO, RICHARD ROBERT, b West New York, NJ, May 19, 46; m 71; c 2. ORGANIC CHEMISTRY. *Educ:* Rutgers Univ, BA, 67, PhD(chem), 71. *Prof Exp:* NIH fel, Stanford Univ, 71-73; ASST RES GROUP CHIEF ISOTOPE SYNTHESIS, HOFFMANN-LA ROCHE, INC, 73- *Concurrent Pos:* Roche-Basel exchange scientist, 79-80. *Mem:* Am Chem Soc; AAAS. *Res:* Use of stable and radioactive isotopes in determining reaction mechanisms and utilization of isotope effects to induce metabolic switching and influence stereoselectivity of reactions. *Mailing Add:* Dept of Chem Res Hoffmann-LaRoche Inc Nutley NJ 07110

MUCENIEKS, PAUL RAIMOND, b Riga, Latvia, Feb 3, 21; US citizen; m 56; c 1. PHYSICAL CHEMISTRY, ELECTROCHEMISTRY. *Educ:* Johns Hopkins Univ, MA, 61, PhD(phys chem), 64. *Prof Exp:* Prin physicist, Litton Systs, Litton Indust, Inc, 64; sr res chemist, 64-80, RES ASSOC, FMC CORP, 81- *Mem:* Am Chem Soc; Electrochem Soc. *Res:* Studies of reaction kinetics and mechanisms; x-ray diffraction in heavy metal salt solutions; synthesis of stable free radicals; electrochemical synthesis and electrodialysis; chemical instrumentation; elimination of industrial pollutants; physical properties of solids. *Mailing Add:* 338 Glenn Ave Lawrenceville NJ 08648

MUCHMORE, HAROLD GORDON, b Ponca City, Okla, Mar 8, 20; m 54; c 4. INTERNAL MEDICINE. *Educ:* Rice Univ, BA, 43; Univ Okla, MD, 46, MS, 56; Am Bd Internal Med, dipl, 62. *Prof Exp:* Intern, Jersey City Med Ctr, 46-47; univ fel, Univ Okla, 47-48, instr pharmacol, Sch Med, 48-49, instr med, 49-52, resident, Univ Hosps, 54-56, asst prof, 57-62; assoc prof, Med Sch, Univ Minn, 62-66; assoc prof med, microbiol & immunol, 66-70, chief infectious dis sect, 66-68, Carl Puckett assoc prof pulmonary dis, 68-70, prof microbiol & immunol, 71-79, CARL PUCKETT PROF PULMONARY DIS & PROF MED, MED SCH, UNIV OKLA, 70-, ADJ PROF MICROBIOL & IMMUNOL, 80- *Concurrent Pos:* Clin investr, Vet Admin, 57-60, chief tuberc & infectious dis sect, Vet Admin Hosp, Oklahoma City, 60-62 & 66-; chief infectious dis sect, Ancker Hosp, St Paul, Minn, 62-66. *Mem:* Fel Am Col Physicians; Am Fedn Clin Res; Am Thoracic Soc; Med Mycol Soc Americas; Int Soc Human & Animal Mycol. *Res:* Infectious diseases, especially fungus disease; Antarctic medical research. *Mailing Add:* Univ Okla Health Sci Ctr 800 NE 13th St Oklahoma City OK 73104

MUCHMORE, ROBERT B(OYER), b Augusta, Kans, July 8, 17; m 44; c 2. ELECTRONIC ENGINEERING. *Educ:* Univ Calif, BS, 39; Stanford Univ, EE, 42. *Prof Exp:* Proj engr, Sperry Gyroscope Co, 42-46; sr mem tech staff, Res & Develop Labs, Hughes Aircraft Co, 46-54; mem tech staff, TRW Systs, 54-60, dir electronics div, 60-61, dir phys res div, 61-65, vpres & assoc dir syst labs, 65-69, vpres & gen mgr, 69-71, vpres & chief scientist, Software & Info Systs Div, 71-73; CONSULT, 73- *Concurrent Pos:* Lectr, Univ Calif, Los Angeles, 53-58. *Mem:* Sigma Xi; fel Inst Elec & Electronics Engrs. *Res:* Microwave; stochastic processes; system analysis; radio propagation. *Mailing Add:* 4311 Grove St Sonoma CA 95476

MUCHMORE, WILLIAM BREULEUX, b Cincinnati, Ohio, July 7, 20; m 43; c 2. ARACHNOLOGY. *Educ:* Oberlin Col, AB, 42; Washington Univ, PhD(zool), 50. *Prof Exp:* From instr to assoc prof, 50-70, PROF BIOL, UNIV ROCHESTER, 70- *Concurrent Pos:* Res assoc, Fla State Collection Arthropods, 74. *Mem:* Am Micros Soc; Am Soc Zool; Am Arachnolog Soc; Brit Arachnolog Soc. *Res:* Systematics and biogeography of pseudoscorpions. *Mailing Add:* Dept of Biol Univ of Rochester Rochester NY 14627

MUCHOW, GORDON MARK, b Evanston, Ill, June 15, 21; m 44; c 3. PHYSICAL CHEMISTRY. *Educ:* Northwestern Univ, Ill, BS, 42, MS, 51; St Louis Univ, PhD(chem), 54. *Prof Exp:* Res chemist, Pure Oil Co, 46-48; chemist, Graymills Corp, 48; res chemist, Monsanto Co, 53-62; from res scientist to sr res scientist, Owens-Ill, Inc. 62-73; staff technologist, Brush Wellman, Inc, 73-75; SR MAT ENGR, PRESTOLITE CO, 75- *Res:* Silicates; x-ray crystallography; crystal chemistry. *Mailing Add:* 5923 Winding Way Sylvania OH 43560

MUCHOWSKI, JOSEPH MARTIN, b Odessa, Sask, Jan 30, 37; m 65; c 3. ORGANIC CHEMISTRY. *Educ:* Univ Sask, BSc, 58, MSc, 59; Univ Ottawa, PhD(org chem), 59. *Prof Exp:* Nat Res Coun Can overseas fel with Prof A Eschenmoser, Swiss Fed Inst Technol, 62-63; sr res chemist, Bristol Labs of Can, Que, 63-71; sr chemist, Syntex, SA, Mexico City, 71-72, asst dir res, 72-73, DIR CHEM RES, SYNTEX, SA, MEXICO CITY, 73-, ASST DIR RES, SYNTEX RES CENTER, PALO ALTO, 75- *Concurrent Pos:* Prof extraordinary, Iberoamerican Univ, Mex, 74-76. *Mem:* Am Chem Soc; Chem Soc Mex; Mex Acad Sci Res; Chem Inst Can. *Res:* Mechanistic and synthetic organic chemistry; medicinal chemistry. *Mailing Add:* Syntex Res Inst Org Chem 3401 Hillview Ave Palo Alto CA 94304

MUCK, DARREL LEE, b Larned, Kans, Jan 26, 38; m 81; c 2. PHYSICAL ORGANIC CHEMISTRY. *Educ:* Wichita State Univ, BS, 59, MS, 62; Univ Fla, PhD(phys org chem), 65. *Prof Exp:* Res chemist, Procter & Gamble Co, 65-71 & Pfizer, Inc, 71-72; tech mgr detergents res, 72-74, prod mgr detergent chem, 74-77, mgr polymer additives, 77-80, MGR ZEOLITE VENTURE, PHILADELPHIA QUARTZ CO, VALLEY FORGE, PA, 81- *Mem:* Am Oil Chemists Soc. *Res:* Chelating and/or sequestering tendencies of organic hydroxy Soc Plastics Engrs; acids and inorganic polymers to heavy metal ions. *Mailing Add:* PO Box 840 Valley Forge PA 19482

MUCK, GEORGE A, b Fillmore, Ill, Sept 28, 37; m 59; c 2. DAIRY SCIENCE, BIOCHEMISTRY. *Educ:* Univ Ill, BS, 59, MS, 61, PhD(dairy tech), 62. *Prof Exp:* Res asst food tech, Univ Ill, 59-62; head prod develop sect, Res Dept, Dean Foods Co, 62-67, dir res, 67-70, VPRES, RES & DEVELOP, RES DEPT, DEAN FOODS CO, 70- *Mem:* Am Dairy Sci Asn; Inst Food Technol; Am Chem Soc; Am Oil Chemist Soc. *Res:* Dairy technology; isolation and identification of flavors; effect of high heat treatment on model milk systems; development of new dairy and food products. *Mailing Add:* Res Dept Dean Foods Co 1126 Kilburn Ave Rockford IL 61101

MUCKENFUSS, CHARLES, b Cleveland, Ohio, May 2, 27; m 54; c 2. THEORETICAL CHEMISTRY. *Educ:* Univ Wis, PhD(chem), 57. *Prof Exp:* Nat Res Coun fel, Nat Bur Standards, Washington, DC, 57-58; res assoc, Gen Elec Res & Develop Ctr, NY, 58-67; ASSOC PROF CHEM ENG, RENSSELAER POLYTECH INST, 67- *Res:* Kinetic theory; statistical mechanics; irreversible thermodynamics; transport phenomena. *Mailing Add:* Div of Chem Eng Rensselaer Polytech Inst Troy NY 12181

MUCKENHOUPT, BENJAMIN, b Newton, Mass, Dec 22, 33; m 64; c 2. MATHEMATICAL ANALYSIS. *Educ:* Harvard Univ, AB, 54; Univ Chicago, MS, 55, PhD(math), 58; from instr to asst prof math, DePaul Univ, 58-60; from asst prof to assoc prof, 60-70, PROF MATH, RUTGERS UNIV, 70- *Concurrent Pos:* Vis assoc prof, Mt Holyoke Col, 63-65; visitor, Inst Advan Study, 68-69 & 75-76; vis prof, Stat Univ NY, Albany, 70-71. *Mem:* Am Math Soc; Math Asn Am. *Res:* Singular transformations; Fourier series. *Mailing Add:* Dept of Math Rutgers Univ New Brunswick NJ 08903

MUCKENTHALER, FLORIAN AUGUST, b McFarland, Kans, July 31, 33; m 69; c 3. GENETICS, DEVELOPMENTAL BIOLOGY. *Educ:* Spring Hill Col, BS, 59; Catholic Univ, PhD(zool), 64. *Prof Exp:* USPHS fel cell biol, Johns Hopkins Univ, 64-65; asst prof biol, State Univ NY Albany, 65-71; from asst prof to assoc prof biol, 71-79, PROF BIOL, BRIDGEWATER STATE COL, 79- *Concurrent Pos:* Vis prof med sci, Brown Univ, 80. *Mem:* AAAS; Am Soc Cell Biol; Am Genetics Asn; Am Inst Biol Sci; Am Soc Zool. *Res:* Developmental genetics; cell biology; nucleic acid synthesis in spermatogenesis and oogenesis; mechanisms in meiosis and development. *Mailing Add:* Dept of Biol Sci Bridgewater State Col Bridgewater MA 02324

MUCKERMAN, JAMES T, b St Louis, Mo, Jan 10, 43. THEORETICAL CHEMISTRY. *Educ:* Carleton Col, BA, 65; Univ Wis-Madison, PhD(phys chem), 70. *Prof Exp:* Assoc chemist, 69-73, CHEMIST RES, BROOKHAVEN NAT LAB, 73- *Concurrent Pos:* Lectr chem, Columbia Univ, 75; adj assoc prof, Res Inst Eng Sci, Wayne State Univ, 76- *Mem:* Am Chem Soc; Sigma Xi. *Res:* Energetics and dynamics of molecular collisons; molecular collison theory; potential energy surfaces; classical and semiclassical calculations of collison phenomena; reactive collisions; chemical kinetics. *Mailing Add:* Dept of Chem Brookhaven Nat Lab Upton NY 11973

MUDD, J GERARD, b St Louis, Mo, Apr 7, 21; m 46; c 5. CARDIOLOGY. *Educ:* Col Holy Cross, BS, 43; St Louis Univ, MD, 45. *Prof Exp:* Intern med, 45-46, resident, 48-50, instr, 51-55, sr instr, 55-56, from asst prof to assoc prof med, 56-76, PROF INTERNAL MED, ST LOUIS UNIV, 76- *Concurrent Pos:* Fel, Johns Hopkins Univ, 50-51; St Louis Heart Asn fel cardiol, 51-52; Nat Heart Inst fel, 52-54. *Mem:* Am Heart Asn; Am Col Cardiol; Am Fedn Clin Res. *Res:* Cardiac catheterization, including right heart, left, retrograde and coronary arteriography. *Mailing Add:* Dept of Internal Med St Louis Univ Sch of Med St Louis MO 63104

MUDD, JOHN BRIAN, b Darlington, Eng, Aug 31, 29; m 74; c 1. BIOCHEMISTRY. *Educ:* Cambridge Univ, BA, 52; Univ Alta, MSc, 55; Univ Wis, PhD(biochem), 58. *Prof Exp:* Jane Coffin Childs Mem Fund Med Res fel, Univ Calif, Davis, 59-60; from assst prof to prof biochem, Univ Calif, Riverside, 61-80; GROUP LEADER, ARCO PLANT CELL RES INST, 81- *Mem:* Am Chem Soc; Am Soc Plant Physiol; Brit Biochem Soc; Am Soc Biol Chem. *Res:* Lipid metabolism in plants; mechanism of enzyme action; biochemical effects of toxic oxidants. *Mailing Add:* ARCO Plant Cell Res Inst 6560 Trinity Court Dublin CA 94566

MUDD, STUART HARVEY, b Bryn Mawr, Pa, Apr 29, 27; m 55; c 3. BIOCHEMISTRY. *Educ:* Harvard Univ, BS, 49, MD, 53. *Prof Exp:* Intern med, Mass Gen Hosp, 53-54; MED DIR, LAB GEN & COMP BIOCHEM, NAT INST MENT HEALTH, 56- *Concurrent Pos:* NSF res fel, Biochem Res Lab, Mass Gen Hosp, Boston, 54-56. *Mem:* Am Soc Biol Chemists. *Res:* Oxidative phosphorylation; transmethylation; plant metabolism; mechanism of enzyme action. *Mailing Add:* 9507 Wadsworth Dr Bethesda MD 20014

MUDGE, GILBERT HORTON, b Brooklyn, NY, Apr 19, 15; m 41; c 4. PHYSIOLOGY, MEDICINE. *Educ:* Amherst Col, BA, 36; Columbia Univ, MD, 41, Med Sci Dr, 45. *Prof Exp:* Instr med, Columbia Univ, 48-49, assoc, 49-51, from asst prof to assoc prof, 51-55; prof pharmacol & exp therapeut & dir dept, Johns Hopkins Univ, 55-62, dean, 62-65, actg chmn dept med, 65-66, chmn dept, 66-67; prof, 65-81, EMER PROF MED, DARTMOUTH MED SCH, 81- *Concurrent Pos:* Mem pharmacol study sect, USPHS, 57-60, Life Ins Med Res Fund, 60-64 & Nat Res Coun, 60-62; assoc dean, Johns Hopkins Univ, 60-62, prof exp therapeut, 62-66; mem regulatory biol panel, NSF, 61-65. *Mem:* Soc Exp Biol & Med; Am Physiol Soc; Am Soc Clin Invest; Am Soc Pharmacol & Exp Therapeut; Asn Am Physicians. *Res:* Renal function; electrolyte physiology. *Mailing Add:* Lyme NH 03768

MUDGE, JOSEPH WILLIAM, b Gridley, Kans, Apr 12, 21; m 47; c 2. ANIMAL BREEDING, GENETICS. *Educ:* Kans State Univ, BS, 42, MS, 57, PhD(animal breeding), 66. *Prof Exp:* Instr dairy husb, Kans State Univ, 46-47; dairy farmer, 48-55; res asst dairy husb, Kans State Univ, 56-60; from instr to assoc prof, 60-72, PROF DAIRY HUSB, UNIV MINN, ST PAUL, 72-, EXTEN DAIRYMAN, 60- *Mem:* Am Dairy Sci Asn; Am Genetic Asn. *Res:* Dairy cattle breeding; extension activities in dairy management. *Mailing Add:* 3007 N Pascal St Paul MN 55116

MUDGETT, MEREDITH, immunochemistry, see previous edition

MUDHOLKAR, GOVIND S, b Aurangabad, India, Jan 5, 34. MATHEMATICAL STATISTICS. *Educ:* Univ Poona, BSc, 56, MSc, 57 & 58; Univ NC, PhD(statist), 63. *Prof Exp:* Lectr math & statist,SP Col, Poona, 57-60; from asst prof to assoc prof, 63-75, PROF STATIST & BIOSTATIST, MED SCH, UNIV ROCHESTER, 75- *Concurrent Pos:* Vis prof, Stanford Univ, 68-69 & KUL, Belgium, 78-79. *Mem:* Fel Inst Math Statist; Am Statist Asn; Am Math Soc; Math Asn Am; Biomet Soc. *Res:* Multivariate analysis; inequalities; goodness of fit problems; robust inference; statistical inference and methodology; biostatistics; quantal response problems. *Mailing Add:* Med Sch Univ Rochester Rochester NY 14627

MUDREY, MICHAEL GEORGE, JR, b Pinebluff, Ark, Sept 22, 45; m 70; c 2. PRECAMBRIAN GEOLOGY, ORE DEPOSITS. *Educ:* Princeton Univ, AB, 67; Northern Ill Univ, MS, 69; Univ Minn, PhD(geol), 73. *Prof Exp:* Geologist precambrian geol, Minn Geol Surv, 69-72; proj scientist, Dry Valley Drilling Proj, Northern Ill Univ, 73-75, asst prof environ geol, 75; sect head geol, 79-81, GEOLOGIST, WIS GEOL SURV, 76- *Concurrent Pos:* Geologist mineral res, US Geol Surv, 74; adj asst prof, Dept Geol, Northern Ill Univ, 76-; asst prof, Dept Environ Sci, Unvi Wis, Extension, 76-; asst prof, Dept Geol Sci, Univ Wis, Madison, 76- *Mem:* Fel Geol Asn Can; Soc Econ Geologists; Geochem Soc; Am Polar Soc; Soc Explor Geophysicists. *Res:* Geologic evolution of the Lake Superior region, and the relationship of that history to mineral deposits. *Mailing Add:* 1502 Rae Lane Madison WI 53711

MUDRICK, STEPHEN EDWARD, dynamic meteorology, see previous edition

MUDROCH, ALENA, b Prague, Czech, Nov 4, 30; Can citizen; m 50; c 2. GEOCHEMISTRY, LIMNOLOGY. *Educ:* State Col, Prague, BSc, 48; McMaster Univ, MSc, 73. *Prof Exp:* Lab asst chem, State Res Inst Metal Finishing & Corrosion, Prague, 48-52 & Acad Sci, Prague, 64-68; lab asst limnol, 68-73, PHYS SCIENTIST GEOCHEM, CAN CTR INLAND WATERS, 73- *Res:* Effects of toxic substances originated from dredge spoil disposal on existing aquatic ecosystem; evaluation the release and/or retention of nutrients and toxic metals by different type of marshes; pathways of environmental contaminants in aquatic ecosystem. *Mailing Add:* Nat Water Res Inst Burlington ON L7R 4A6 Can

MUDRY, KAREN MICHELE, b Philadephia, Pa, Nov 3, 48; m 72. BIOENGINEERING, BIOMEDICAL ENGINEERING. *Educ:* Villanove Univ, BEE, 70; Johns Hopkins Univ, MS, 72; Cornell Univ, PhD(bioeng), 78. *Prof Exp:* Elec engr, Dept Defense, 70-72; fel neurophysiol, Eye & Ear Hosp, Pittsburgh, Pa, 78-79; ASST PROF ELEC ENG, UNIV AKRON, 79- *Concurrent Pos:* Prin investr grants, Neurol & Commun Disorders & Stroke, NIH, 81-, Deafness Res Found, 81- *Mem:* Soc Neurosci; Sigma Xi; AAAS; Acoustical Soc Am; Inst Elec & Electronic Engrs. *Res:* Processing of sensory information in the peripheral and central nervous system of vertebrates; determination of organizational principles for central nervous system analysis of sensory information through a combination of neurophysiological, anatomical, and behavioral studies. *Mailing Add:* Dept Elec Eng Univ Akron Akron OH 44325

MUECKE, HERBERT OSCAR, b Kenedy, Tex, Jan 14, 40; m 61. MATHEMATICS. *Educ:* Univ Tex, Austin, BS & MA, 62, PhD(math), 68. *Prof Exp:* Asst prof, 68-74, ASSOC PROF MATH, SAM HOUSTON STATE UNIV, 74- *Res:* Complex analysis; symbolic logic; history and philosophy of science. *Mailing Add:* Dept of Math Sam Houston State Univ Huntsville TX 77340

MUEGGLER, WALTER FRANK, b Enterprise, Ore, May 22, 26; m 58; c 6. PLANT ECOLOGY, RANGE SCIENCE. *Educ:* Univ Idaho, BS, 49, Univ Wis, MS, 53; Duke Univ, PhD, 61. *Prof Exp:* Plant ecologist, 49-74, PROJ LEADER, INTERMOUNTAIN FOREST & RANGE EXP STA, US FOREST SERV, 74- *Mem:* Ecol Soc Am; Soc Range Mgt. *Res:* Range and wildlife habitat research; plant synecology and autecology. *Mailing Add:* Forestry Sci Lab US Forest Serv 860 N 12 E Logan UT 84321

MUEHLBAUER, FREDERICK JOSEPH, b Buffalo, NY, Feb 22, 40; m 62; c 4. PLANT BREEDING. *Educ:* Univ Ga, BS, 63; Pa State Univ, MS, 65, PhD(genetics), 69. *Prof Exp:* Instr agron, Pa State Univ, 68-69; RES GENETICIST PLANT BREEDING, AGR RES SERV, USDA, 69- *Mem:* Crop Sci Soc Am; Pisum Genetics Asn; Nat Pea Improv Asn; Lentil Res Orgn; Coun Agr Sci & Technol. *Res:* Genetics and breeding of dry-edible legumes including dry peas, lentils and chickpeas. *Mailing Add:* Dept of Agron & Soils Wash State Univ Pullman WA 99163

MUEHLBERGER, WILLIAM RUDOLF, b New York, NY, Sept 26, 23; m 49; c 2. GEOLOGY. *Educ:* Calif Inst Technol, BS & MS, 49, PhD(geol), 54. *Prof Exp:* From asst prof to prof geol, 54-62, chmn dept geol sci, 66-70, PROF GEOL, UNIV TEX, AUSTIN, 62- *Concurrent Pos:* Geologic field asst, US Geol Surv, 48-49, geologist, 49 & 71-; geologist, State Bur Mines & Mineral Resources, NMex, 53-61, dir crustal studies lab, 61-66; prin investr, Apollo Field Geol Invests, Apollo 16 & 17, 71-74; dir, Tectonic Map NAm Proj, 80-86. *Honors & Awards:* Matson Award, Am Asn Petrol Geologists, 64. *Mem:* AAAS; Geol Soc Am; Am Asn Petrol Geol; Am Geophys Union. *Res:* Structural, areal and lunar geology; analysis of global tectonics; tectonics of North America. *Mailing Add:* Dept of Geol Sci Univ of Tex Austin TX 78712

MUELLER, AUGUST P, b Fargo, NDak, July 30, 33; m 58; c 2. IMMUNOLOGY, SEROLOGY. *Educ:* Moorhead State Col, BSc, 55; Univ Wis, MSc, 57, PhD(zool, chem), 60. *Prof Exp:* Res assoc zool, Univ Wis, 60 & 62; fel, Univ Edinburgh, 61-62; asst prof, 62-67, ASSOC PROF BIOL, STATE UNIV NY BINGHAMPTON, 67- *Concurrent Pos:* NIH res grant, 63-66. *Mem:* AAAS; Am Soc Zool; Reticuloendothelial Soc; Genetics Soc Am; Am Inst Biol Sci. *Res:* Immune unresponsiveness in juvenile and adult animals; development of the immune system; bursa of Fabricus in chickens and the thymus in mammals; genetics; biometry. *Mailing Add:* Dept Biol State Univ NY Binghamton NY 13901

MUELLER, CHARLES CARSTEN, b Glenwood Springs, Colo, July 11, 37; m 59, 73. GEOTECHNICAL FOUNDATIONS ENGINEERING. *Educ:* Calif State Polytech Col, San Luis Obispo, BS, 63; Mich State Univ, MS, 65, PhD(agr eng), 69. *Prof Exp:* Res asst agr eng, Mich State Univ, 63-67; asst prof agr eng & asst agr engr, Wash State Univ, 68-73; lectr, 73-74, assoc prof, 74-78, PROF CIVIL ENG, DIV ENG, CALIF STATE UNIV, CHICO, 78- *Mem:* Am Soc Civil Engrs; Am Soc Agr Engrs; Am Soc Testing & Mat. *Res:* Building foundations, irrigation and drainage; soil mechanics. *Mailing Add:* Div of Eng Calif State Univ Chico CA 95929

MUELLER, CHARLES FREDERICK, b Sharon, Pa, Oct 3, 39; m 64; c 2. ECOLOGY. *Educ:* Ind Univ Pa, BSEd, 62; Ohio Univ, MS, 65; Mont State Univ, PhD(zool), 67. *Prof Exp:* Assoc prof, 67-76, PROF BIOL, SLIPPERY ROCK STATE COL, 76-, CHMN DEPT, 75- *Concurrent Pos:* NSF res grant, Slippery Rock State Col, 69-71; consult herpetol, Aquatic Ecol Assocs, Pittsburgh. *Mem:* Soc Study Amphibians & Reptiles; Am Soc Ichthyologists & Herpetologists. *Res:* Temperature and energy characteristics; bioenergetics of poikilotherms. *Mailing Add:* Dept of Biol Slippery Rock State Col Slippery Rock PA 16057

MUELLER, CHARLES RICHARD, b St Louis, Mo, June 22, 25; m 47; c 2. THEORETICAL CHEMISTRY, PHYSICAL CHEMISTRY. *Educ:* Washington Univ, AB, 48; Univ Utah, PhD(chem), 51. *Prof Exp:* From instr to assoc prof, 51-64, PROF CHEM, PURDUE UNIV, 64- *Mem:* Am Chem Soc; Sigma Xi. *Res:* Intermolecular forces and molecular beam methods; scattering theory. *Mailing Add:* Dept of Chem Purdue Univ Lafayette IN 47907

MUELLER, CHARLES W(ILLIAM), b New Athens, Ill, Feb 12, 12; m 41; c 2. ELECTRONICS. *Educ:* Univ Notre Dame, BS, 34; Mass Inst Technol, MS, 36, ScD(physics), 42. *Prof Exp:* Prod engr, Raytheon Prod Corp, Mass, 36-37, develop engr, 37-38; res asst, Off Sci Res & Develop Proj, Mass Inst Technol, 40-41; RES PHYSICIST, RCA LABS, 42- *Honors & Awards:* David Sarnoff Sci Award, 66; J J Ebers Award, Inst Elec & Electronics Engrs, 72. *Mem:* Am Phys Soc; fel Inst Elec & Electronics Engrs. *Res:* Development of transistors; single-crystal silicon films on insulators; silicon-target image and storage tubes; ion implantation. *Mailing Add:* RCA Labs Princeton NJ 08540

MUELLER, DALE M J, b Grand Forks, NDak, June 24, 39; m 64; c 2. BOTANY, BRYOLOGY. *Educ:* Sch Forestry, NDak State, AS, 60; NDak Univ, Fargo, BS, 62; Okla State Univ, Stillwater, MS, 64; Univ Calif, Berkeley, PhD(bot), 70. *Prof Exp:* Mus technician res, Dept Bot, Univ Calif, Berkeley 70-71, actg asst prof & fel, 71; vis asst prof, Univ Minn, 71-72; asst prof, 72-78, ASSOC PROF BIOL, TEX A&M UNIV, COLLEGE STATION, 78- *Concurrent Pos:* Ed, Bryologist, Am Bryological & Lichenological Soc, 75-79. *Mem:* Sigma Xi; Am Bryological & Lichenological Soc; Bot Soc Am; Int Asn Bryologists. *Res:* Studies of the anatomy-morphology (including ultrastructure) and phylogeny of bryophytes, specifically, sporophyte development, sporogenesis, mechanisms of spore dispersal and methods of asexual propagation (reproductive biology). *Mailing Add:* Dept Biol Tex A&M Univ College Station TX 77843

MUELLER, DELBERT DEAN, b Claremore, Okla, Oct 22, 33; m 59; c 3. PHYSICAL BIOCHEMISTRY. *Educ:* Univ Okla, BS, 62, PhD(phys chem), 66. *Prof Exp:* Res assoc phys biochem, Northwestern Univ, 66-68; asst prof, 68-75, ASSOC PROF BIOCHEM, KANS STATE UNIV, 75- *Concurrent Pos:* Vis staff mem, Los Alamos Sci Lab, 74- *Mem:* AAAS; Am Soc Biol Chemists; Am Chem Soc. *Res:* Physical studies on biopolymers with emphasis on the applications of carbon-13 and phosphorus-31 nuclear magnetic resonance spectroscopy and hydrogen exchange techniques to conformational change and binding problems. *Mailing Add:* Dept of Biochem Kans State Univ Manhattan KS 66506

MUELLER, DONALD SCOTT, b Cleveland, Ohio, May 8, 47; m 69; c 1. PLASTICS CHEMISTRY, POLYMER CHEMISTRY. *Educ:* Hiram Col, BA, 69; Univ Ill, PhD(org chem), 73. *Prof Exp:* Teaching asst org chem, Univ Ill, 69-73; CHEMIST, ROHM AND HAAS CO, 73- *Mem:* Am Chem Soc. *Res:* Synthesis and development of new polymeric systems, especially in reference to the production of new plastics; aqueous coatings; development and promotion of new floor polish systems. *Mailing Add:* Rohm and Haas Co Norristown & McKean Rds Spring House PA 19477

MUELLER, EDWARD E(UGENE), b Wood River, Ill, July 26, 24; m 46; c 3. CERAMICS. *Educ:* Univ Mo, BS, 48; Rutgers Univ, MS, 52, PhD(ceramics), 53. *Prof Exp:* Instr, Rutgers Univ, 48-53; assoc prof ceramic eng, Univ Wash, 53-59; dir ceramics res, Chem Group, Glidden Co, Md, 59-65; prof ceramics & dean, 65-73, PROF CERAMIC ENG, NY STATE COL CERAMICS, ALFRED UNIV, 73- *Concurrent Pos:* Consult, Boeing Airplane Co, United Control Corp, US Army Corps Engrs, Gladding, McBean & Co, Inc, Gen Elec Co, du Pont, Union Carbide & Xerox. *Mem:* Fel Am Ceramic Soc; Nat Inst Ceramic Engrs (pres, 65-66); Am Soc Eng Educ; Soc Women Engrs. *Res:* Ceramic engineering, science education. *Mailing Add:* NY State Col Ceramics Alfred Univ Alfred NY 14802

MUELLER, FRED(ERICK) M(ARION), b Urich, Mo, May 25, 16. ELECTRICAL ENGINEERING. *Educ:* Univ Mo, Rolla, BS, 38, EE, 44. *Prof Exp:* With elec & eng consult, Mo, 37-40; elec clerk & checker, Union Elec Co Mo, Stone & Webster Eng Corp, 40-41, elec supvr, Pac Gas & Elec Co, 47-49, chief line route surv party, Mo, 56; field engr, Ebasco Servs, Inc, 49-51, 54-55; chief elec engr, Bokaro Thermal Power Sta construct, Damodar Valley Corp, India, 51-53; sr testing & oper engr, Naval Reactors Facility, Bettis Atomic Power Div, 56-67, SR ENGR, ATOMIC POWER DIV, BETTIS ATOMIC POWER LAB, IDAHO NAT ENG LAB, WESTINGHOUSE ELEC CORP, IDAHO, 67-81; RETIRED. *Concurrent Pos:* Mem tech asst recruitment serv, UN. *Res:* Construction supervision and technology of nuclear and thermal central electrical power generating stations; electrical power supply systems. *Mailing Add:* 336 1/2 W 18th Idaho Falls ID 83402

MUELLER, FRED MICHAEL, b Chicago, Ill, Oct 8, 38; div. SOLID STATE PHYSICS. *Educ:* Univ Chicago, SB, 61, SM, 62, PhD(physics), 66. *Prof Exp:* Assoc physicist, Argonne Nat Lab, 66-73, sr scientist, 73-75; PROF, PHYSICS LAB, NIJMEGEN, NETH, 75- *Concurrent Pos:* Consult, Northwestern Univ, 69-, Univ Chicago, 69-, Stanford Univ, 70- & Am Photo Copying Equip Co, 71-; prof physics, Northern Ill Univ, 69-75. *Mem:* Fel Am Phys Soc. *Res:* Electronic structure of transition metal compound; phonon spectra; superconductivity. *Mailing Add:* Toernooiveld Nijmegen Netherlands

MUELLER, GEORGE E(DWIN), b St Louis, Mo, July 16, 18. COMMUNICATIONS, ELECTRONICS. *Educ:* Univ Mo, BS, 39; Purdue Univ, MS, 40; Ohio State Univ, PhD(physics), 51. *Hon Degrees:* PhD(eng), Univ Mo & Wayne State Univ, 64, Purdue Univ, 65; PhD(laws), NMex State Univ, 64. *Prof Exp:* Mem tech staff, Bell Tel Labs, Inc, 40-46; prof elec eng, Ohio State Univ, 46-57; vpres & dir space systs, Space Technol Labs, Calif, 47-63; assoc adminr manned space flight, NASA, DC, 63-69; sr vpres, Gen Dynamics Corp, NY, 69-71; chmn bd & pres, 71-80, CHMN & CHIEF EXEC OFFICER, SYST DEVELOP CORP, 81-; SR VPRES, BURROUGHS CORP, 81- *Concurrent Pos:* vpres, Int Astronaut Fedn. *Honors & Awards:* Nat Sci Medal, 71. *Mem:* Nat Acad Eng; fel Am Inst Aeronaut & Astronaut (pres, 79-80); fel Inst Elec & Electronics Engrs; fel Am Geophys Union; NY Acad Sci. *Mailing Add:* Syst Develop Corp 2500 Colorado Ave Santa Monica CA 90406

MUELLER, GEORGE PETER, b Atchison, Kans, Aug 7, 18; m 46; c 1. ORGANIC CHEMISTRY. *Educ:* Univ Nebr, BSc, 40, MSc, 41; Univ Ill, PhD(org chem), 43. *Prof Exp:* Chemist, State Hwy Testing Lab, Nebr, 38-40 & Eastman Kodak Co, 42; asst, Univ Ill, 44; res assoc, Harvard Univ, 44-46; chemist, Wyeth Inst Appl Biochem, Pa, 46-47; assoc prof chem, Univ Tenn, 47-52; res supvr, G D Searle & Co, 52-62, coordr, Searle Chem Inc, Ill & Mex, 59-62; dir res, Marine Colloids, Inc, Maine, 62-68; CONSULT, 68- *Concurrent Pos:* Fel, Univ Ill, 44-45; consult, Oak Ridge Nat Lab & Oak Ridge Inst Nuclear Studies, 49-52. *Mem:* AAAS; Am Chem Soc; NY Acad Sci. *Res:* Synthetic and steroidal estrogens; barbiturates; insecticides; alicyclic synthesis; androgens; corticoids; isolation, pharmacology; structure of botanical isolates; sources, chemistry steroidal sapogenins; seaweed sources; structure, modification, utilization of seaweed colloids; polysaccharides. *Mailing Add:* 5 Cedar St Camden ME 04843

MUELLER, GERALD CONRAD, b Centuria, Wis, May 22, 20; m 44; c 3. BIOCHEMISTRY. *Educ:* Univ Wis, BS, 43, MD, 46, PhD(biochem, physiol), 50. *Prof Exp:* Intern, Med Col, Va Hosp, 47; from instr to assoc prof oncol, 50-58, asst prof acad affairs, Univ, 63-67, PROF ONCOL, MCARDLE LAB CANCER RES, UNIV WIS-MADISON, 58-, PROF HEALTH SCI MED, 77- *Concurrent Pos:* Schering scholar, Max Planck Inst Virus Res, 58; mem drug eval panel, Cancer Chemother Nat Serv Ctr, 60-61, chmn, 61-62, mem biochem comt, 60-62; USPHS res career award, Univ Wis-Madison, 62-; mem bd sci coun, Nat Cancer Inst, 65-69, mem organizational task force, 68, mem chemother adv comt, 69-; vis prof, Univ Sao Paulo, 71. *Mem:* Am Soc Biol Chem; Am Asn Cancer Res. *Res:* Mechanism of action of estrogenic hormones; molecular processes regulating animal cell replication; intermediate metabolism of growth regulation. *Mailing Add:* McArdle Lab for Cancer Res Univ of Wis Madison WI 53706

MUELLER, GERALD SYLVESTER, b Nurnberg, Ger, June 18, 41; Can citizen; m 62; c 2. CHEMICAL ENGINEERING, AUTOMATIC CONTROL SYSTEMS. *Educ:* Univ Waterloo, BASc, 66; Univ Manchester, MSc, 67, PhD(automatic control), 69. *Prof Exp:* Asst prof mech eng, Sir George Williams Univ, 69-71; asst prof, 71-76, ASSOC PROF CHEM ENG, UNIV WATERLOO, 76-, ASSOC CHMN DEPT, 78- *Concurrent Pos:* Nat Res Can sr indust fel, Esso Chem Can, 78. *Res:* Application of multivariable control theory and optimization to chemical processes; computer control of processes. *Mailing Add:* Dept Chem Eng Univ Waterloo Waterloo ON N2L 3G1 Can

MUELLER, HELMUT, b Schneeberg, Ger, Jan 2, 26; US citizen; m 53; c 2. BIOCHEMISTRY. *Educ:* Univ Würzburg, MD, 52; Univ Birmingham, PhD(biochem), 61. *Prof Exp:* Univ fel, Univ Colo, 53-54; resident physician, Northwestern Univ, 54-56; Am Heart Asn res fel, Inst Muscle Res, Mass, 57-58, adv res fel, 58-60; asst res prof biochem, Univ Pittsburgh, 61-64, assoc res prof, 64-65; sr fel, Mellon Inst, 65-68; HEALTH SCI ADMINR & MED OFFICER DRUG SURVEILLANCE, CTR POP RES, NAT INST CHILD HEALTH & HUMAN DEVELOP, 68- *Concurrent Pos:* Am Heart Asn estab investr, Univ Birmingham, 60-61 & Univ Pittsburgh, 61-65. *Mem:* AAAS; Am Soc Biol Chem; Soc Gen Physiol; Biophys Soc. *Res:* Structure and function of contractile proteins; cardiovascular disease; epidemiology of adverse drug effects; drug-nutrient interactions. *Mailing Add:* Ctr for Pop Res Nat Inst of Child Health & Human Develop Bethesda MD 20205

MUELLER, HELMUT CHARLES, b Milwaukee, Wis, Mar 20, 31; m 59; c 1. ZOOLOGY, ANIMAL BEHAVIOR. *Educ:* Univ Wis-Madison, BS, 53, MS, 58, PhD(zool), 62. *Prof Exp:* Res assoc zool, Univ Wis-Madison, 62-65, lectr, 66; asst prof, 66-70, assoc prof, 70-77, PROF ZOOL, UNIV NC, CHAPEL HILL, 77- *Concurrent Pos:* Vis prof, Univ Vienna, 75. *Mem:* Fel AAAS; fel Am Ornithologists Union; Wilson Ornith Soc; Ecol Soc Am; Animal Behav Soc. *Res:* Behavioral aspects of the predator-prey interaction; hawk behavior; bird migration; behavioral ecology. *Mailing Add:* Dept of Zool Univ of NC Chapel Hill NC 27514

MUELLER, HERBERT J, b Vienna, Austria, Dec 1, 23; US citizen; m 50; c 1. PHYSICS, MATERIAL SCIENCE. *Educ:* Univ Vienna, PhD(physics), 49. *Prof Exp:* Asst prof physics, II Inst Physics, Univ Vienna, 49-58; asst dir basic res lab, US Army Eng Res & Develop Lab, Va, 58-67; RES ADMINR, NAVAL AIR SYSTS COMMAND, 67- *Mem:* Sigma Xi (pres, Sci Res Soc Am, 65-66); Austrian Phys Soc; Austrian Phys-Chem Soc (secy, 56-58). *Res:* Solid state and metal physics; x-ray diffraction; exo-electron emission; luminescence. *Mailing Add:* Naval Air Systs Command AIR-310 Washington DC 20361

MUELLER, HILTRUD S, b Amorbach-Heidelberg, Ger, July 4, 26; US citizen. CARDIOLOGY, INTERNAL MEDICINE. *Educ:* Univs Jena & Heidelberg, MD, 50. *Prof Exp:* Fac mem, USPHS training prog, St Vincent's Hosp, NY, 67-68, dir intensive care & shock unit, Hosp & Med Ctr, 69-73; dir div cardiol, St Vincent's Hosp, Mass, 73-75; chief div cardiol & prof med, Sch Med, St Louis Univ, 76-81; ASSOC CHIEF, DIV CARDIOL, MONTEFIORE HOSP & PROF MED, ALBERT EINSTEIN COL, BRONX, NY, 81- *Concurrent Pos:* Fel cardiol, Univ Hosp Minn, 65-66 & St Vincent's Hosp & Med Ctr, NY, 66-67; mem cardiol adv comt, Nat Inst Heart, Lung & Blood Inst, 76-80, Cardiovasc & Renal Study Sect, Div Res Grants; consult, Ischemic Sci Ctr Res Comt, Nat Inst Heart, Lung & Blood Inst, 76- *Mem:* Fel Am Col Chest Physicians; fel Am Col Cardiol; fel Am Col Physicians; fel NY Acad Sci; Fedn Clin Res. *Res:* Acute ischemic heart disease; influence of sympathetic nervous systems on ischemia; myocardial metabolism; coronary blood flow; beta adrenergic blockade. *Mailing Add:* Dept Cardiol N-2 Montefiore Hosp Med Ctr 111 E 210 St Bronx NY 10467

MUELLER, IRENE MARIAN, b St Libory, Nebr, July 12, 04. PLANT ECOLOGY. *Educ:* Nebr Cent Col, AB, 27; Univ Nebr, AM, 37, PhD(plant ecol), 40. *Prof Exp:* Teacher high schs, Nebr, 27-35; asst bot, Univ Nebr, 36-39; instr biol sci, Wis State Teachers Col, Platteville, 40-43; from assoc prof to prof, 43-75, EMER PROF BIOL, NORTHWEST MO STATE UNIV, 75- *Res:* Rhizomes of prairie plants; drought resistance in prarie plants. *Mailing Add:* 728 West Third St Maryville MO 64468

MUELLER, IVAN I, b Budapest, Hungary, Jan 9, 30; US citizen; m 50; c 2. GEODESY, GEOPHYSICS. *Educ:* Budapest Tech Univ, dipl eng, 52; Ohio State Univ, PhD(geod sci), 60. *Prof Exp:* Asst prof geod, Budapest Tech Univ, 52-56; design engr, C H Sells Consult Engr, NY, 57-58; from instr to assoc prof, 59-66, PROF GEOD, OHIO STATE UNIV, 66- *Concurrent Pos:* Mem geod-cartog working group, Manned Space Sci Coord Comt, NASA, 65-66, prin investr, Nat Geod Satellite Prog, 65-74, mem adv group satellite geod, 66-67, geod & cartog subcomt & space sci & appln steering comt, 67-68; panel solid earth geophys & earthquake eng, comt adv to Environ Sci Serv Admin, Nat Acad Sci-Nat Acad Eng, 67-69; assoc ed J geophys res, 67-74; consult, UN Develop Prog, Ctr Survey Training & Map Prod, Hyderabad, India, 71 & 72; Ed in chief, Bull Geodesique, Paris, 75-; vis prof, Univ Berlin, 65, 69, Univ Parana, Brazil, 72-74, 78 & Univ Stuttgart, 80; chmn subcomt, Int Asn Geodesy, mem, US Nat Comn, Int Union of Geodesy & Geophys, 76-, vchmn, 80-; mem comt geod, Nat Acad Sci, 76-81, chmn, 78-81; corres mem, Ger Geod Comn, Bavarian Acad Sci, Munich, 80. *Honors & Awards:* Alexander von Humboldt Prize, Bonn-Munich, 77. *Mem:* Am Soc Photogram; fel Am Geophys Union (pres/geod, 74). *Res:* Geodetic astronomy; gravimetric and satellite geodesy. *Mailing Add:* Dept Geod Sci & Surv Ohio State Univ Columbus OH 43210

MUELLER, JAMES I(RVING), b Cincinnati, Ohio, June 26, 16; m 42; c 4. CERAMIC ENGINEERING. *Educ:* Ohio State Univ, BCerE, 39; Univ Mo, PhD(ceramic eng), 49. *Prof Exp:* Head dept, 76-81, from asst prof to PROF CERAMIC ENG, UNIV WASH, 49- *Concurrent Pos:* Consult, Pratt & Whitney Aircraft Div, United Aircraft Corp, 56-61, Lawrence Radiation Lab, Univ Calif, 59-63, Sci Res Lab, Boeing Co, 60-62, Weyerhaueser Co, 61-64, Gulf Res & Develop Co, 62-70, Avco Corp, 63-68, Bell Aerosysts, 63-67 & NASA, 68-72 & 79-81; prin investr, Brittle Mat Design, 76- *Honors & Awards:* Jeppson Medal. *Mem:* Sigma Xi; Nat Inst Ceramic Engrs; fel Am Ceramic Soc (vpres, 59-60, treas, 76-78, pres, 81-82); Am Defense Preparedness Asn. *Res:* Reactions and structure of ceramic materials. *Mailing Add:* Div of Ceramic Eng Univ of Wash FB-10 Seattle WA 98105

MUELLER, JAMES LOWELL, b Thief River Falls, Minn, Dec 10, 40; m 67; c 2. REMOTE SENSING, OCEAN OPTICS. *Educ:* US Coast Guard Acad, New London, Conn, BS, 62; Ore State Univ, PhD(phys oceanog), 74. *Prof Exp:* Res assoc, Goddard Space Flight Ctr, NASA, 73-74, res oceanog, 74-80; ADJ PROF OCEANOG, NAVAL POSTGRAD SCH, 81- *Concurrent Pos:* Proj scientist, Goddard Space Flight Ctr, Nat Oceanic Satellite Syst Proj, NASA, 79-80. *Mem:* Am Geophys Union. *Res:* Remote sensing of oceanographic phenomena with emphasis on uses of Nimbus-7 Coastal Zone Color Scanner; phytoplankton distributions, patchiness, and distributions of atmospheric aerosols. *Mailing Add:* Oceanog Dept Code 68MY Naval Postgrad Sch Monterey CA 93940

MUELLER, JOHN FREDERICK, b Goshen, Ind, June 15, 22; m 45; c 4. INTERNAL MEDICINE. *Educ:* Capital Univ, BA, 44; Univ Cincinnati, MD, 46. *Prof Exp:* Intern, King's County Hosp, Brooklyn, NY, 46-47; resident internal med & fel hemat & nutrit, Univ Cincinnati, 47-50; fel hemat, Western Reserve Univ, 50-51; from instr to assoc prof med, Sch Med, Univ Cincinnati, 51-62, assoc dir lab hemat & nutrit, 55, co-dir, 57-62; prof med, Univ Colo, 62-64; prof, State Univ NY Downstate Med Ctr, 64-73; PROF MED, UNIV COLO MED CTR, DENVER, 73- *Concurrent Pos:* Chief Clinician, Outpatient Dept, Cincinnati Gen Hosp, 57-62; chief med, Denver Vet Admin Hosp, 62-64; physician-in-chief, Brooklyn-Cumberland Med Ctr, 64-73; consult, Surgeon Gen, NIH; dir internal med, St Lukes Hosp, 73-81; dir acad affairs, Presbyterian/St Lukes Med Ctr, 81- *Mem:* Am Soc Clin Invest; Am Fedn Clin Res; Am Soc Clin Nutrit (secy-treas, 63-66); Am Heart Asn. *Res:* General field of lipid chemistry of blood and tissues as related to various disease states; nutrition and hematology. *Mailing Add:* St Lukes Hosp Dept of Med 601 E 19th Ave Denver CO 80203

MUELLER, JOSEPH ROBERT, b Appleton, Wis, Oct 23, 42. BIOCHEMISTRY, ENDOCRINOLOGY. *Educ:* St Procopius Col, BS, 64; Med Univ SC, PhD(biochem), 75. *Prof Exp:* Res assoc endocrinol, Univ Iowa, 67-70; assoc fac biochem & endocrinol, Med Univ SC, 74-75; NIH res fel, 75-76, res instr, Washington Univ, 76-77; ASSOC PROF CHEM & BIOL, ST LOUIS COMMUNITY COL, FOREST PARK, 77- *Honors & Awards:* Cert Merit, Am Chem Soc, 64. *Mem:* Am Chem Soc; AAAS. *Res:* The elucidation of the topography of steroid binding sites of steroid converting enzymes and steroid receptor proteins via affinity labeling steroid derivatives. *Mailing Add:* St Louis Community Col Dept Chem 5600 Oakland Ave St Louis MO 63110

MUELLER, JUSTUS FREDERICK, b Baltimore, Md, Nov 20, 02. ZOOLOGY. *Educ:* Johns Hopkins Univ, AB, 23; Univ Ill, MA, 26, PhD(zool), 28. *Prof Exp:* Sci asst, Bur Fisheries, 23-24; asst zool, Univ Ill, 24-28; from instr to assoc prof zool, State Univ NY Col Forestry, Syracuse Univ, 28-42, assoc prof parasitol, Col Med, Univ, 42-50; assoc prof parasitol, 50-56, actg chmn dept microbiol, 54-57, prof microbiol, 56-72, EMER PROF, STATE UNIV NY UPSTATE MED CTR, 72- *Concurrent Pos:* Field naturalist, Roosevelt Wild Life Forest Exp Sta, 28-35; mem trop med & parasitol study sect, NIH, 62-66; leader Ore Biol Colloquium, 65; fel trop med, Cent Am Prog, La State Univ, 65; consult Merck Inst Therapeut Res, 68-69; lectr, Col Med, Syracuse Univ, 30-42, Med Sch, Marquette Univ, 56-60, Univ Pittsburgh, 65 & Yale Univ, 67; ed, J Parasitol, 62-78. *Mem:* Am Soc Parasitol (pres elect, 72, pres, 73); Am Micros Soc; Am Soc Trop Med & Hyg. *Res:* Invertebrates; fish and human parasites; pseudophyllidean tapeworms; sparganosis; visual education; models; in vitro culture of cestodes; growth-promoting substances in cestodes; parasite-induced obesity. *Mailing Add:* Dept of Microbiol State Univ of NY Upstate Med Ctr Syracuse NY 13210

MUELLER, KARL HUGO, JR, b Ft Worth, Tex, May 27, 43; m 65; c 2. SOLID STATE PHYSICS. *Educ:* Rice Univ, BA, 65; Duke Univ, PhD(physics), 72. *Prof Exp:* Res assoc physics, Duke Univ, 71-73; staff mem, Kernforschungsanlage Julich GMBH, 73-75; STAFF MEM PHYSICS, LOS ALAMOS SCI LAB, 75- *Mem:* Am Phys Soc. *Res:* Shock wave data of cryogenic fluids; high pressure phase transitions that are shock induced. *Mailing Add:* MS 942 PO Box 1663 Los Alamos NM 87544

MUELLER, MARVIN MARTIN, b Broken Arrow, Okla, Sept 29, 28; m 54, 67. PHYSICS. *Educ:* Univ Okla, BS, 51, MS, 54, PhD(physics), 59. *Prof Exp:* STAFF MEM, LOS ALAMOS NAT LAB, UNIV CALIF, 59- *Mem:* AAAS; Am Asn Physics Teachers; Am Phys Soc. *Res:* Laser-generated plasmas; x-ray plasma diagnostics; radiation physics. *Mailing Add:* 409 Estante Way Los Alamos NM 87544

MUELLER, MARY CASIMIRA, see Mueller, Rita Marie

MUELLER, MELVIN H(ENRY), b Spencer, Iowa, Feb 22, 18; m 42; c 4. CHEMISTRY, METALLURGY. *Educ:* Univ Northern Iowa, BA, 40; Univ Ill, PhD(chem), 49. *Prof Exp:* Asst chem, Univ Northern Iowa, 41; chemist, Deere & Co, 42; chemist & metallurgist, US Rubber Co, 43-45; asst, Univ Ill, 45-49; assoc metallurgist, 49-60, SR METALLURGIST, ARGONNE NAT LAB, 60- *Mem:* Am Chem Soc; Am Phys Soc; Am Crystallog Asn; Am Inst Mech Engrs; Am Inst Mining, Metall & Petrol Engrs. *Res:* X-ray and neutron diffraction; solid state physics; chemical and magnetic structure determination. *Mailing Add:* Argonne Nat Lab Bldg 212 Argonne IL 60439

MUELLER, N(ORMAN) F(RANCIS), b St Louis, Mo, Sept 18, 22; m 57; c 1. CHEMICAL ENGINEERING. *Educ:* Univ Notre Dame, BS, 43; Washington Univ, St Louis, MS, 47, PhD, 50. *Prof Exp:* Chem engr, Reilly Tar & Chem Corp, 43-45; instr, Washington Univ, St Louis, 47-50; chem engr, Am Cyanamid Co, 50-53; CHEM ENGR, MONSANTO CO, 53- *Mem:* Am Inst Chem Engrs. *Res:* Process development at laboratory scale. *Mailing Add:* Monsanto Co 800 N Lindbergh Blvd St Louis MO 63166

MUELLER, NANCY SCHNEIDER, b Wooster, Ohio, Mar 8, 33; m 59; c 1. DEVELOPMENTAL BIOLOGY, IMMUNOLOGY. *Educ:* Col Wooster, AB, 55; Univ Wis, MS, 57, PhD(zool), 62. *Prof Exp:* Hon fel, Univ Wis, Madison, 65-66, instr develop biol, 66; vis asst prof zool, NC State Univ, 68 & zool & poultry sci, 68-71; vis prof, 71-72, assoc prof, 72-79, PROF BIOL, NC CENT UNIV, 79- *Mem:* Women Cell Biol; Am Soc Zool; Am Ornith Union; Sigma Xi. *Res:* Genetic and hormonal influences on sexual differentiation of birds; sex determination and differentiation in bird embryos; hematology and immunology of birds. *Mailing Add:* Dept of Biol NC Cent Univ Durham NC 27707

MUELLER, PAUL ALLEN, b Anniston, Ala, Sept 9, 45. GEOCHEMISTRY. *Educ:* Washington Univ, AB, 67; Rice Univ, MA & PhD(geol), 71. *Prof Exp:* Advan res projs agency res assoc geochem, Mat Res Ctr, Univ NC, Chapel Hill, 71-73; asst prof, 73-78, ASSOC PROF GEOL, UNIV FLA, 78- *Concurrent Pos:* sr res assoc, Nat Res Coun, 81-82. *Honors & Awards:* Nininger Prize, 69. *Mem:* Geol Soc Am; Geochem Soc; Am Geophys Union. *Res:* Petrology, geochemistry, isotopic geochemistry and geochronology of igneous and metamorphic rocks. *Mailing Add:* Dept of Geol Univ of Fla Gainesville FL 32611

MUELLER, PETER KLAUS, b Hanover, Ger, Dec 30, 26; US citizen; m 50; c 3. ENVIRONMENTAL SCIENCE, BIOCHEMISTRY. *Educ:* George Washington Univ, BS, 50; Rutgers Univ, MS, 53, PhD(sanit biochem), 55. *Prof Exp:* Res asst environ sci, Rutgers Univ, 52-55; res chemist, Komline-Sanderson Eng Corp, NJ, 55-57; res chemist, Calif State Dept Pub Health, 57-63, chief, Air & Indust Hyg Lab, 63-77; mem staff, Environ Res & Technol Inc, 77-80; MEM STAFF, ENVIRON ASSESSMENT DEPT, ELEC POWER RES INST, INC, 80- *Concurrent Pos:* Mem tech adv comt instrumentation, Calif Motor Vehicle Control Bd, 65-; tech adv comt motor vehicle emissions, Calif Div Indust Safety, 66; consult, NIH, 66 & Nat Inst Occup Safety & Health, 71; air pollution res grants adv comt mem, Environ Protection Agency, 67-71; Nat Acad Sci measurements for air qual eval panel, 71-72 & air chem panel, 74-76; mem, Calif Air Resources Bd, 75. *Mem:* AAAS; Am Chem Soc; Air Pollution Control Asn. *Res:* Air pollution composition and analysis; aerosols; effects on man and animals. *Mailing Add:* Environ Assessment Dept Elec Power Res Inst Inc PO Box 10412 Palo Alto CA 94304

MUELLER, PETER STERLING, b New York, NY, Dec 28, 30; m 58; c 4. METABOLISM, PSYCHIATRY. *Educ:* Princeton Univ, AB, 52; Univ Rochester, MD, 56. *Prof Exp:* Intern Bellevue Hosp, 56-57; clin assoc metab serv, Gen Med Br, Nat Cancer Inst, 57-59; clin assoc, Off Chief, Unit Psychosom, Lab Clin Sci, NIMH, 59-63; asst resident psychiat, Phipps Psychiat Clin, Johns Hopkins Univ, 63-66; asst prof, Sch Med, Yale Univ, 66-72; assoc prof, 72-77, CLIN PROF PSYCHIAT, RUTGERS MED SCH, COL MED & DENT NJ, 77- *Concurrent Pos:* Consult to resident supvr psychother, Conn Valley Hosp, 66-72; staff, Princeton House, Princeton Med Ctr, 76-; consult psychiat, Carrier Clinic, Belle Mead, 73- & Vet Admin Hosp, Lyons, 75-; consult, Rehab Unit & Ctr Indust Human Resources, Community Mental Health Ctr, Piscataway, 73- *Mem:* Am Psychosom Soc; Am Psychiat Asn; AAAS. *Res:* Free fatty acid and neurohormone metabolism in cancer and mental illness; psychoendocrinology; family therapy of schizophrenia; psychosomatic medicine. *Mailing Add:* Dept of Psychiat Rutgers Med Sch PO Box 101 Piscataway NJ 08854

MUELLER, RAYMOND KARL, b East St Louis, Ill, Oct 18, 41; m 67. APPLIED MATHEMATICS. *Educ:* Washington Univ, BS, 63, MS, 65, DSc(appl math), 67. *Prof Exp:* Mem tech staff, Bell Tel Labs, 67-70; asst prof, 70-78, assoc prof math, 78-80, PROF METALL ENG & HEAD DEPT, COLO SCH MINES, 80- *Mem:* Opers Res Soc Am; Inst Math Statist. *Res:* Applied probability; probability and stochastic processes; operations research. *Mailing Add:* Dept of Math Colo Sch of Mines Golden CO 80401

MUELLER, RITA MARIE, b Cincinnati, Ohio, July 16, 18. PHYSICAL CHEMISTRY, THEORETICAL CHEMISTRY. *Educ:* Villa Madonna Col, BA, 41; Cath Univ Am, MS, 42; Univ Cincinnati, PhD(chem), 62. *Prof Exp:* From asst prof to assoc prof, 42-52, PROF CHEM, THOMAS MORE COL, 52-, CHMN DEPT, 73- *Mem:* Am Chem Soc. *Res:* Physics and mathematics. *Mailing Add:* Dept of Chem Thomas More Col Ft Mitchell KY 41017

MUELLER, ROBERT ANDREW, b Rockville Center, NY, July 29, 52. COMPUTER SCIENCE. *Educ:* Colo State Univ, BS, 74, MS, 76; Univ Colo, PhD(comput sci), 80. *Prof Exp:* Res asst, Colo State Univ, 74-76; sci programmer, Tex Instruments Inc, 76-77; mem staff algorithms, Univ Colo, 77-80; ASST PROF COMPUT SCI, COLO STATE UNIV, 80- *Concurrent Pos:* Consult, Pinon Syst & Technol, 81-; NSF grant prin investr, 81- *Mem:* Asn Comput Mach; Inst Elec & Electronics Engrs; Soc Comput Simulation; EuroMicro Asn. *Res:* Automatic microprogramming; algorithms; computer engineering; simulation; logic programming; formal methods. *Mailing Add:* Dept Comput Sci Colo State Univ Ft Collins CO 80523

MUELLER, ROBERT ARTHUR, b Fond du Lac, Wis, July 24, 38; m 62; c 4. ANESTHESIOLOGY, PHARMACOLOGY. *Educ:* Univ Wis-Madison, BS, 60, MS, 63; Univ Minn, Minneapolis, MD, 65, PhD(pharmacol), 66. *Prof Exp:* Am Cancer Soc fel, Univ Minn, Minneapolis, 65-66, intern surg, Hosps, 66-67, resident anesthesiol, 67; res assoc pharmacol & toxicol, Lab Clin Sci, NIMH, 67-69; resident anesthesia, Med Sch, Northwestern Univ, Ill, 69-70; assoc prof anesthesiol & asst prof pharmacol, Med Sch, Univ NC, Chapel Hill, 70-75, prof anesthesiol & assoc prof pharmacol, prof anesthesiol & pharmacol, 78-81. *Mem:* Am Soc Pharmacol & Exp Therapeut; Fedn Am Socs Exp Biol; Soc Neurosci; Am Soc Anesthesiol. *Res:* Adrenergic pharmacology. *Mailing Add:* Rm 223 Burnett-Womack Bldg Chapel Hill NC 27514

MUELLER, ROBERT KIRK, b St Louis, Mo, July 25, 13; m 40; c 3. CHEMICAL ENGINEERING. *Educ:* Washington Univ, BS, 34; Univ Mich, MS, 35. *Prof Exp:* Plant chemist, Monsanto Co, 35-38, gen supt plastics div, 40-42; chmn, Shawinigan Resins Corp, Mass, 38-40; supt, Longhorn Ord Works, Tex, 42-44, plant mgr, 44-46; prod supt plastics div, Monsanto Co, 46-48, asst prod mgr, 48-49, prod mgr, 49-50, asst gen mgr, 50-52, gen mgr, 52-54, vpres, 54-68; vpres, 73-77, CHMN, ARTHUR D LITTLE, INC, 77-, DIR, ARTHUR D LITTLE, LTD, 68- *Concurrent Pos:* Mem bd dirs exec comt, Monsanto Co, 61-68, exec comn, Mass Mutal Life Ins Co, 68-; dir, BayBanks Inc, Boston, 69-; trustee, Colby-Sawyer Col, 69-; chmn fac & lectr, Salsburg Sem Am Studies, Austria, 70; trustee, Cheswick Ctr, Boston, 78- *Mem:* Fel AAAS; Am Chem Soc; Am Inst Chem Engrs; Am Mgt Asn; NY Acad Sci. *Res:* Chemicals and plastics; fibers; international business; management consulting and writing. *Mailing Add:* Arthur D Little Inc Acorn Park Cambridge MA 02140

MUELLER, ROLF KARL, b Zurich, Switz, Aug 30, 14; nat US; m 42; c 3. APPLIED PHYSICS, ACOUSTIC IMAGING. *Educ:* Munich Tech Univ, Dipl phys, 39, Dr rer nat, 42, habil, 50. *Prof Exp:* Asst prof appl physics, Univ Jena, 39-45; asst prof theoret physics, Stuttgart Tech Univ, 47-48; dozent, Munich Tech Univ, 48-52; consult, Air Force Cambridge Res Ctr, Mass, 52-55; sr tech specialist & head solid state res sect, Gen Mills, Inc, 56-63; mgr, Gen Sci & Technol Lab, Bendix Corp, 63, Lab dir, Bendix Ctr, 63-74; PROF ELEC ENG, UNIV MINN, 74- *Mem:* AAAS; fel Am Phys Soc; Soc; sr mem Inst Elec & Electronics Engrs. *Res:* Acoustic imaging and image processing applied to biomedical diagnostic instrumentation; nondestructive materials evaluation and sonar processing. *Mailing Add:* 9707 Manning Ave Stillwater MN 55082

MUELLER, SABINA GERTRUDE, b Binghamton, NY, Apr 29, 40; m 70; c 2. BOTANY. *Educ:* Swarthmore Col, BA, 61; Univ NC, Chapel Hill, PhD(bot), 68. *Prof Exp:* From asst prof to assoc prof bot, Shippensburg State Col, 66-70; staff mem plant records, Cox Arboretum, Dayton, 72-73, botanist, Educ Serv, 73-75; botanist, Fullmer's Landscape Serv, Dayton, 75-76; prof bot, Wilberforce Univ, 77-80; PRES & DIR, IVY RES CTR, COX ABORE, 80- *Concurrent Pos:* Vis prof, Miami Univ, Middletown, 78, 79 & 80; registrar, Ivy Soc, 77- *Mem:* Int Asn Plant Taxon; Am Daffodil Soc; Am Ivy Soc; Am Hort Soc; Am Hosta Soc. *Res:* Plant nomenclature; Hedera cultivars. *Mailing Add:* 5512 Woodbridge Lane Dayton OH 45429

MUELLER, STEPHEN NEIL, b New York, NY, Mar 17, 47. CELL BIOLOGY. *Educ:* LeMoyne Col, BS, 69; Syracuse Univ, PhD(biol), 76. *Prof Exp:* Fel, 76-78, res investr, 78-80, RES ASSOC, WISTAR INST ANAT & BIOL, 80- *Mem:* Tissue Cult Asn. *Res:* Growth control; cellular senescence. *Mailing Add:* Wistar Inst Anat & Biol 36th & Spruce Sts Philadelphia PA 19104

MUELLER, THEODORE ARNOLD, b St Louis, Mo, Jan 29, 38; m 63; c 2. BIOPHYSICS. *Educ:* Cent Methodist Col, AB, 59; NMex Highlands Univ, MS, 62, PhD(biophys chem), 65. *Prof Exp:* PROF SCI, ADAMS STATE COL, 65-, HEAD DEPT PHYSICS & ASTRON, 77- *Mem:* Asn Physics Teachers; Biophys Soc; Air Pollution Control Asn. *Res:* Cellular and photochemical ultraviolet effects; photobiology; environmental pollution; pollution monitoring. *Mailing Add:* Div Sci & Math Adams State Col Alamosa CO 81102

MUELLER, THEODORE ROLF, b Ft Wayne, Ind, Dec 14, 28; m 51; c 3. ANALYTICAL CHEMISTRY, INSTRUMENTATION. *Educ:* Valparaiso Univ, BA, 50; Univ Kans, PhD(anal chem), 63. *Prof Exp:* Instr math & sci, Lutheran High Sch, Houston, Tex, 50-51; instr chem, Concordia Col Inst,

Bronxville, NY, 51-53; CHEMIST, OAK RIDGE NAT LAB, 61- *Mem:* AAAS; Am Chem Soc; Sigma Xi. *Res:* Application of electroanalytical techniques to environmental problems; research and development in analytical procedures; instruments for automated analyses. *Mailing Add:* Oak Ridge Nat Lab PO Box Y Oak Ridge TN 37830

MUELLER, THOMAS D(ELBERT), b Lakewood, Ohio, July 11, 22; m 43; c 6. PETROLEUM ENGINEERING, NUMERICAL ANALYSIS. *Educ:* Univ Mich, BS, 43; Univ Southern Calif, MS, 53, PhD(eng), 59. *Prof Exp:* Assoc petrol engr, Standard Oil Co Calif, 46-48, assoc res engr, Calif Res Corp Div, 48-53, res engr, 53-57, group supvr, 57-58, supv comput analyst, Electronic Comput Ctr, 58-61, asst mgr, 61-66, dep mgr, Systs Develop & Appln Div, 66-68, mgr, Develop & Appln Div, 68-74; coordr comput appln, 74-78, proj mgr, 78-81, SR ENGR CONSULT, ARABIAN AM OIL CO, 81- *Concurrent Pos:* Lectr, Univ Calif, 59-70; lectr, Stanford Univ, 60-74, res assoc, 61-74; consult, W Australian Petrol Proprietary Ltd, 71-72. *Mem:* Sigma Xi; Soc Petrol Engrs; Asn Comput Mach. *Res:* Gas and oil pipeline mathematical modeling; electric power and oil and gas dispatching systems. *Mailing Add:* ARAMCO Box 2655 Dhahran Saudi Arabia

MUELLER, THOMAS J, b Chicago, Ill, May 25, 34; m 61; c 3. GAS DYNAMICS, FLUID MECHANICS. *Educ:* Ill Inst Technol, BS, 56; Univ Ill, MS, 58, PhD(gas dynamics), 61. *Prof Exp:* Res assoc thermodyn & gas dynamics, Univ Ill, 60-61, asst prof gas dynamics, 61-63; sr res scientist, United Aircraft Res Labs, 63-65; assoc prof gas dynamics, 65-69, PROF FLUID MECH, UNIV NOTRE DAME, 69- *Concurrent Pos:* Vis res prof, von Karman Inst Fluid Dynamics, 73-74; consult, US Army, Md, 76-77, Coachmen Indust, Inc, 77 & Lockheed-Georgia Co, 80-81. *Mem:* Am Inst Aeronaut & Astronaut; fel Am Soc Mech Engrs; Am Soc Eng Educ. *Res:* Compressible and incompressible laminar and turbulent separated or wake flows; propulsive exhaust nozzles; numerical and biofluid mechanics. *Mailing Add:* Dept of Aerospace & Mech Eng Univ of Notre Dame Notre Dame IN 46556

MUELLER, THOMAS JOSEPH, b Evanston, Ill, June 2, 46. NEUROBIOLOGY. *Educ:* Loyola Univ, BS, 69; Univ Southern Calif, PhD(biol), 81. *Prof Exp:* ASST PROF BIOL, HARVEY MUDD COL, 81- *Concurrent Pos:* Consult comput & statist, Univ Southern Calif, 78- *Mem:* Inst Elec & Electronics Engrs; Soc Neurosci; Sigma Xi. *Res:* Mauthner cell; neurobiology and behavior of lower vertebrates and invertebrates. *Mailing Add:* 1706 Chattanooga Ct Claremont CA 91711

MUELLER, W(HEELER) K(AY), b Decatur, Ill, July 25, 25; m 50; c 1. MECHANICAL ENGINEERING. *Educ:* Iowa State Univ, BS, 45; Univ Ill, MS, 52, PhD(mech eng), 56. *Prof Exp:* Engr, Monsanto Chem Co, 46-48 & Gen Motors Corp, 48-50; asst, Univ Ill, 50-52; prof mech eng, NY Univ, 53-73; PROF MECH & AEROSPACE ENG, POLYTECH INST NEW YORK, 73- *Mem:* Am Soc Mech Engrs. *Res:* Convection heat transfer; fluid dynamics; thermodynamics. *Mailing Add:* Dept of Mech & Aerospace Eng Polytech Inst of New York Brooklyn NY 11201

MUELLER, WALTER A, b Koenigshofen, Ger, Jan 16, 10; Can citizen; m 38; c 3. PHYSICAL CHEMISTRY, METALLURGY. *Educ:* Univ Heidelberg, PhD(phys chem), 34. *Prof Exp:* Fel metall, Univ Gottingen, 34-36; head lab, Siemens-Schuckertwerke, Ger, 36-47; consult, Brit Mil Forces, 47-50; corrosion specialist, Mannesman Roehren Werke, AG, Ger, 50-51; sr scientist, Pulp & Paper Res Inst Can, 51-72, prin scientist, 72-75; CONSULT CORROSION & ENERGY CONSERV, 75- *Honors & Awards:* Weldon Medal, Can Pulp & Paper Asn, 60; Willis Rodney Whitney Award, Nat Asn Corrosion Engrs, 78. *Mem:* Electrochem Soc; Nat Asn Corrosion Eng; Tech Asn Pulp & Paper Indust; Can Pulp & Paper Asn. *Res:* Corrosion; polarization curves; anodic protection; corrosion studies in: Kraft liquor recovery, bleaching solutions and paper machines; new method of producing chlorine monoxide as bleaching chemical. *Mailing Add:* 138 Mimosa Ave Dorval PQ H9S 3J9 Can

MUELLER, WALTER CARL, b Newark, NJ, Nov 29, 34; m 56; c 3. PLANT PATHOLOGY. *Educ:* Rutgers Univ, BS, 56; Cornell Univ, PhD(plant path), 61. *Prof Exp:* From asst prof to assoc prof, 61-74, PROF PATH-ENTOM, UNIV RI, 74- *Mem:* AAAS; Am Phytopath Soc; Electron Micros Soc Am. *Res:* Viruses and virus diseases of plants; electron microscopy. *Mailing Add:* Dept of Plant Path-Entom Univ of RI Kingston RI 02881

MUELLER, WAYNE PAUL, b Evansville, Ind, July 27, 33; m 57; c 2. ECOLOGY. *Educ:* Univ Evansville, BA, 56; Ind Univ, MA, 61, PhD(zool), 62. *Prof Exp:* From asst prof to assoc prof, 62-72, PROF BIOL, UNIV EVANSVILLE, 72-, HEAD DEPT BIOL, 77- *Mem:* Nat Asn Biol Teachers. *Res:* Protozoan ecology. *Mailing Add:* Dept of Biol Univ of Evansville Evansville IN 47702

MUELLER, WENDELIN HENRY, III, b St Louis, Mo, Feb 12, 41; m 66; c 2. CIVIL & STRUCTURAL ENGINEERING. *Educ:* St Louis Univ, BS, 62; Univ Mo-Rolla, MS, 66, PhD(civil eng), 72. *Prof Exp:* Engr flood struct, US Army Corps Engrs, St Louis, 62-65; asst civil eng, Univ Mo-Rolla, 65-66; res engr aerospace, Boeing Airplane Co, Seattle, 66-68; engr/programmer civil mech eng, Nat Comput Serv, St Ann, Mo, 68-69; instr civil eng, Univ Mo-Rolla, 69-72; struct engr flood struct, US Army Corps Engrs, Portland, 72-73; asst prof, 73-75, assoc prof civil struct, 75-80, PROF, PORTLAND STATE UNIV, 80- *Concurrent Pos:* Fel, Am Inst Steel Construct, 72. *Mem:* Am Soc Civil Engrs; Am Soc Eng Educrs; Sigma Xi. *Res:* Investigation of non-linear performance of steel structures using computer analysis; bio-medical engineering, particularly mechanical improvement of artificial joint systems and monitoring and control using micro-processors. *Mailing Add:* Dept of Eng PO Box 751 Portland OR 97207

MUELLER, WERNER JULIUS, poultry science, physiology, see previous edition

MUELLER, WILLIAM HODGE, b El Paso, Tex, Mar 12, 34; m 59; c 1. CHEMICAL ENGINEERING. *Educ:* Rice Univ, BS, 55, BS, 56, PhD(chem eng), 60. *Prof Exp:* Engr, Esso Res & Eng Co, 60-63, sr engr, 63-65, sect head, 65-69, div mgr, 69-71; sr adv logistics dept, Standard Oil Co, NJ, 71-77; ASST GEN MGR RES & ENG DIV, EXXON CORP, 77- *Res:* Refinery planning and economics; hydrocarbon pyrolysis; fertilizer research and development. *Mailing Add:* Res & Eng Div PO Box 101 Florham Park NJ 07932

MUELLER, WILLIAM M(ARTIN), b Denver, Colo, Jan 14, 17; m 42; c 2. PHYSICAL METALLURGY. *Educ:* Colo Sch Mines, MetE, 40, MS, 49, DSc(phys metall), 52. *Prof Exp:* Metallurgist, Aluminum Co Am, 40-45; metall engr, Gates Rubber Co, 45-47; instr, Colo Sch Mines, 47-52; metallurgist, Dow Chem Co, 52-57; mgr phys metall lab, Denver Res Inst, 57-59, head metall div, 59-65, prof metall & chmn dept, Univ Denver, 61-65; dir educ, Am Soc Metals, 65-74; prof metall eng & head dept, 74-79, VPRES, ACAD AFFAIRS, COLO SCH MINES, 79- *Concurrent Pos:* Consult, Climax Molybdenum Co & Res Found, Colo Sch Mines, 49-52, Sundstrand Aviation, 60-61, Gordon & Breach Sci Publ, 62-65 & Western Forge Corp, 75-; mem, US-Indonesian Workshop, Nat Acad Sci, 71; vis, Beijing Univ Iron & Steel Technol, China, 80. *Honors & Awards:* Distinguished Achievement Medal, Colo Sch Mines, 72. *Mem:* Am Soc Metals; Am Soc Nondestructive Testing; Am Inst Mining, Metall & Petrol Engrs; Am Soc Eng Educ; Am Soc Testing & Mat. *Res:* Spectrochemical analysis of ores; eutectic aluminum-silicon alloys; synthetic mica; radioactive metals; metal hydrides; metallurgical and industrial development; engineering education. *Mailing Add:* Vpres Acad Affairs Colo Sch Mines Golden CO 80401

MUELLER-DOMBOIS, DIETER, b Bethel, Ger, July 26, 25; nat Can; m 51; c 5. PLANT ECOLOGY. *Educ:* Univ Gottingen, BS, 51; Hohenheim Agr Univ, dipl, 51; Univ BC, BS, 55, PhD, 60. *Prof Exp:* Asst biol & bot, Univ BC, 55-57; forest ecologist, Res Div, Can Dept Forestry, 58-63; forest ecologist, Dept Bot, Univ Hawaii, 63-66; prin field investr, Smithsonian-Ceylon Ecol Proj, Univ Ceylon, 67-69; PRIN FIELD INVESTR, UNIV HAWAII, 69-, PROF BOT & ECOL, 71- *Concurrent Pos:* Co-dir & sci coordr, Island Ecosysts Integrated Res Prog, Int Biol Prog, 70-71, dir, 72- *Mem:* Fel AAAS; Asn Trop Biol; Ecol Soc Am; Int Soc Trop Ecol. *Res:* Agriculture; botany; soil science; climatology; forest site classification; vegetation and environmental studies; synecology and autecology; tree physiology; soil water-plant growth relations; ecology of vegetation on recent volcanic matter; tropical and ecosystems ecology; animal-vegetation interactions. *Mailing Add:* Dept Bot Univ Hawaii Honolulu HI 96822

MUENCH, DONALD LEO, b Rochester, NY, Jan 31, 34; m 60; c 4. MATHEMATICS. *Educ:* St John Fisher Col, BS, 55; St John's Univ, NY, MS, 60; Idaho State Univ, DA(math), 74. *Prof Exp:* Asst prof math, US Naval Acad, 60-66; assoc prof, 66-81, chmn math dept, 68-80, dir comput sci prog, 81-82, PROF MATH, ST JOHN FISHER COL, 81- *Mem:* Math Asn Am. *Res:* Linear Algebra; matrix theory; computer science education. *Mailing Add:* Dept of Math St John Fisher Col Rochester NY 14618

MUENCH, JOHN, JR, b Annapolis, Md, July 26, 30; m 54; c 2. FORESTRY, FOREST ECONOMICS. *Educ:* Pa State Univ, BS, 53, MF, 58; Duke Univ, DFor, 64. *Prof Exp:* From instr to asst prof forestry, Pa State Univ, 57-65; forest economist, 65-73, DIR ECON, NAT FOREST PRODS ASN, 73- *Mem:* Soc Am Foresters; Am Econ Asn; Nat Asn Bus Econ. *Res:* Public forestry programs for private landowners; impact of public versus private ownership of forest land on a rural economy; management of even-aged forest stands. *Mailing Add:* Nat Forest Prods Asn 1619 Massachusetts Ave NW Washington DC 20036

MUENCH, KARL HUGO, b St Louis, Mo, May 3, 34; m 76; c 5. BIOCHEMISTRY, GENETICS. *Educ:* Princeton Univ, AB, 56; Washington Univ, MD, 60. *Prof Exp:* Intern med, Barnes Hosp, St Louis, 60-61; USPHS fel biochem, Stanford Univ, 61-65; from instr to assoc prof med & biochem, 65-73, PROF MED, SCH MED, UNIV MIAMI, 73-, CHIEF GENETIC MED, 68- *Concurrent Pos:* Am Cancer Soc fac res assoc, Univ Miami, 65-70; Markle scholar acad med, 69-74; Leukemia Soc Am scholar, 71-76; USPHS res career develop award, 71-76; ed bd, Year Book of Cancer, 73-; NSF adv, Panel Molecular Biol, 78-81. *Mem:* Am Soc Biol Chem; Am Chem Soc; Am Soc Human Genetics. *Res:* Amino acyl-transfer RNA synthetases; transfer RNA; protein synthesis; medicine. *Mailing Add:* Dept of Med Univ of Miami Sch of Med Miami FL 33101

MUENCH, NILS LILIENBERG, b Houston, Tex, Feb 27, 28; m 50; c 1. PHYSICS. *Educ:* Rice Univ, BA, 49, MA, 50, PhD(physics), 55; S Tex Col, LLB, 59. *Prof Exp:* Sr res engr, Humble Oil & Ref Co, 55-59; chief scientist, Army Rocket & Guided Missile Agency, 59-62; mem Inst Defense Anal, 62-63; head physics dept, 63-69, TECH DIR GEN MOTORS RES LABS, 69- *Mem:* Am Phys Soc; Am Inst Aeronaut & Astronaut. *Res:* Solid state physics; management of research. *Mailing Add:* Gen Motors Res Labs Warren MI 48090

MUENCH, ROBIN DAVIE, b North Conway, NH, Sept 16, 42; m 66; c 2. PHYSICAL OCEANOGRAPHY. *Educ:* Bowdoin Col, AB, 64; Dartmouth Col, MA, 66; Univ Washington, PhD(oceanog), 70. *Prof Exp:* From res asst oceanogr to oceanogr, Univ Washington, 68-70; from asst prof to assoc prof oceanog, Inst Marine Sci, Univ Alaska, 75-76; res oceanogr, Pac Marine Environ Lab, Nat Oceanog & Atmospheric Admin, 76-79; SR RES OCEANOGR, SCI APPLN INC, 79- *Mem:* AAAS; Am Geophys Union; Am Meteorol Soc. *Res:* Physical oceanography of estuarine and inshore waters; air-sea interaction. *Mailing Add:* Sci Appln Inc/Northwest 13400B Northrup Way #36 Bellevue WA 98005

MUENDEL, CARL H(EINRICH), b New York, NY, July 27, 30; m 61; c 3. CHEMICAL ENGINEERING. *Educ:* Columbia Univ, BS, 52, MS, 54, EngScD(chem eng), 59. *Prof Exp:* Instr chem eng, Columbia Univ, 55-56; chem engr, 57-66, sr res engr, 66-68, res supvr, Res Div, 68-78, TECH SERV SUPVR, CHEM PIGMENTS DEPT, E I DU PONT DE NEMOURS & CO, INC, 78- *Mem:* Am Inst Chem Engrs; Am Chem Soc. *Res:* Pigments; industrial chemicals. *Mailing Add:* E I du Pont de Nemours & Co Inc Chestnut Run Lab 1007 Market St Wilmington DE 19898

MUENOW, DAVID W, b Chicago, Ill, May 28, 39. PHYSICAL CHEMISTRY, GEOCHEMISTRY. *Educ:* Carleton Col, BA, 61; Purdue Univ, PhD(chem), 67. *Prof Exp:* Welch fel mass spectrometry, Rice Univ, 67-70; asst prof, 70-74, ASSOC PROF CHEM, UNIV HAWAII, 75- *Mem:* Am Chem Soc; Am Geophys Union. *Res:* High temperature mass spectrometry; thermodynamics; silicate chemistry; geochemistry; magmatic volatiles. *Mailing Add:* 2545 The Mall Dept Chem Univ Hawaii Honolulu HI 96822

MUENTENER, DONALD ARTHUR, b Pigeon, Mich, Apr 24, 26; m 52; c 2. BACTERIOLOGY. *Educ:* Alma Col, BSc, 50; Mich State Univ, MS, 53. *Prof Exp:* Instr biol, Alma Col, 50; asst, Mich State Univ, 53-55; microbiologist, 56-60, asst dir, 61-75, actg dir, 75-76, STATE ANALYST & DIR LAB DIV, MICH DEPT AGR, 76- *Mem:* Regist Nat Registry Microbiol; Am Soc Microbiol; Brit Soc Appl Bact; Asn Food & Drug Off; Asn Off Anal Chemists. *Res:* Laboratory administration; agricultural, industrial, food, dairy and sanitation microbiology. *Mailing Add:* 3312 Inverary Dr Lansing MI 48910

MUENTER, ANNABEL ADAMS, b New York, NY, Dec 3, 44; m 68. PHOTOGRAPHIC CHEMISTRY, PHYSICAL CHEMISTRY. *Educ:* Univ Mich, BSChem, 66; Harvard Univ, PhD(chem physics), 72. *Prof Exp:* SR RES CHEMIST, EASTMAN KODAK RES LABS, 70- *Mem:* Soc Photog Scientists & Engrs; Am Chem Soc. *Res:* Dyes and spectral sensitization of silver halide using various spectroscopic techniques, including sub nanosecond fluorescence lifetime measurements. *Mailing Add:* Eastman Kodak Res Labs Bldg 81 Kodak Park Rochester NY 14650

MUENTER, JOHN STUART, b Cleveland, Ohio, May 10, 38; m 68. PHYSICAL CHEMISTRY, SPECTROSCOPY. *Educ:* Kenyon Col, BA, 60; Stanford Univ, PhD(chem). 65. *Prof Exp:* Fel Stanford Univ, 65-66; NIH fel, Harvard Univ, 66-68; asst prof, 69-75, assoc prof, 75-81, PROF PHYS CHEM, UNIV ROCHESTER, 81- *Mem:* Am Inst Physics. *Res:* Spectroscopic studies of the electronic structure of small molecules utilizing microwave and molecular beam electric resonance and laser spectroscopy. *Mailing Add:* Dept of Chem Univ of Rochester Rochester NY 14627

MUENZENBERGER, THOMAS BOURQUE, b New Orleans, La, Aug 13, 43; m 67. TOPOLOGY. *Educ:* Univ Fla, BS, 65, MS, 67; Univ Wyo, PhD(math), 72. *Prof Exp:* Asst prof, 73-80, ASSOC PROF MATH, KANS STATE UNIV, 80- *Mem:* Am Math Soc; Math Asn Am; Sigma Xi. *Res:* Mathematics; general topology; fixed point theory; partially ordered spaces. *Mailing Add:* Dept of Math Kans State Univ Manhattan KS 66506

MUESER, WILLIAM HENRY, b New York, NY, Apr 10, 00; m 25. CIVIL ENGINEERING. *Educ:* Mass Inst Technol, BS, 22. *Prof Exp:* Mem staff, 23-37, sr partner, 37-75, CONSULT CIVIL ENG, MUESER, RUTLEDGE, WESTWORTH & JOHNSTON, 75- *Mem:* Nat Acad Eng; Am Soc Civil Engrs; Am Soc Mil Engrs; Am Rd Bldg Soc. *Res:* Advancing the design technology of deep foundations as applied to major buildings, bridges and drydocks. *Mailing Add:* Quarry Lane RD 2 Box 52 Bedford Village NY 10506

MUESSIG, PAUL HENRY, b Philadelphia, Pa, June 22, 49; m 72. AQUATIC ECOLOGY, FISH PHYSIOLOGY. *Educ:* La Salle Col, BA, 71; Fla State Univ, MS, 74. *Prof Exp:* Group leader & scientist, Ecol Serv, Tex Instruments Inc, 74-77; PROG MGR & SCIENTIST AQUATIC TOXICOLOGY IMPACT ASSESSMENT THERMAL ECOL, ECOL ANALYSTS INC, 77- *Mem:* Ecol Soc Am; Estuarine Res Fedn; Can Soc Zoologists. *Res:* Aquatic Toxicology; industry environmental impact assessment and mitigation; thermal and stress physiology of fish; aquaculture. *Mailing Add:* Ecol Analysts Inc RD 2 Goshen Turnpike Middletown NY 10940

MUESSIG, SIEGFRIED JOSEPH, b Freiburg, Ger, Jan 19, 22; nat US; m 49; c 2. ECONOMIC GEOLOGY. *Educ:* Ohio State Univ, BSc, 47, PhD(geol), 51. *Prof Exp:* Instr field geol, Ohio State Univ, 50; geologist, Mineral Deposits Br, US Geol Surv, 51-59; chief geologist, US Borax & Chem Corp, 59-66; minerals explor mgr, Tidewater Oil Co, Calif, 66-67; MINERALS EXPLOR MGR, GETTY OIL CO, 67-, PRES, GETTY OIL DEVELOP CO, LTD, 73- *Concurrent Pos:* Consult, Borax Consol, Ltd, 55; regional dir, Nat Defense Exec Reserve, 71-; dir region 9, Emergency Minerals Admin, Dept Interior, 71-, Nat Acad Sci Comt Geol, 78-82. *Mem:* AAAS; Am Inst Mining, Metall & Petrol Eng; Geol Soc Am; Soc Econ Geologists (vpres, 73-74, pres, 78-79); Am Asn Petrol Geologists. *Res:* Stratigraphy and structure; geology of saline deposits; geology of northeastern Washington; economic geology; geology of northwest Argentina. *Mailing Add:* Getty Oil Development Co Ltd PO Box 54050 Terminal Annex Los Angeles CA 90054

MUETHER, HERBERT ROBERT, b Winfield, NY, Sept 27, 21; m 51; c 6. NUCLEAR PHYSICS. *Educ:* Queens Col, NY, BS, 42; Princeton Univ, AM, 47, PhD(physics), 51. *Prof Exp:* Instr physics, Princeton Univ, 49-50; lectr, Queens Col, NY, 50-52, instr, 52-55, asst prof, 55-59; assoc prof, 59-61, assoc chmn dept, 68-75, PROF PHYSICS, STATE UNIV NY STONY BROOK, 61-, DIR UNDERGRAD PROG PHYSICS, 75- *Concurrent Pos:* Res collabr, Brookhaven Nat Lab, 51-; consult, Frankford Arsenal, Pa, 58- *Mem:* AAAS; Am Phys Soc; Am Asn Physics Teachers. *Res:* Neutron physics. *Mailing Add:* Dept of Physics State Univ of NY Stony Brook NY 11790

MUETTERTIES, EARL LEONARD, b Elgin, Ill, June 23, 27; m 56; c 6. INORGANIC CHEMISTRY. *Educ:* Northwestern Univ, BS, 49; Harvard Univ, AM, 51, PhD(inorg chem), 52. *Prof Exp:* Res chemist, Cent Res Dept, E I Du Pont de Nemours & Co, Inc, 52-57, res supvr, 57-65, assoc res dir, 65-73; prof chem, Cornell Univ, 73-78; PROF CHEM, UNIV CALIF, BERKELEY, 78- *Concurrent Pos:* Adj prof dept chem & assoc mem Monell Chem Senses Ctr, Univ Pa, 69-73. *Honors & Awards:* Award, Am Chem Soc, 65 & 79. *Mem:* Nat Acad Sci; Am Chem Soc; Am Acad Arts & Sci; hon fel Royal Soc Chem; Am Phys Soc. *Res:* organometallics; catalysis; stereochemistry; coordination chemistry of surfaces. *Mailing Add:* 12120 Tartan Way Oakland CA 94619

MUFFLER, LEROY JOHN PATRICK, b Alhambra, Calif, Sept 19, 37; m 66; c 1. GEOLOGY, GEOCHEMISTRY. *Educ:* Pomona Col, BA, 58; Princeton Univ, MA, 61, PhD(geol), 62. *Prof Exp:* Geologist, Southwest States Br, 62, Alaska Geol Br, 62-64, GEOLOGIST, FIELD GEOCHEM & PETROL BR, US GEOL SURV, 64- *Concurrent Pos:* vis scientist, NZ Dept Sci & Indust Res Geophys Div, 70, Ital Elec Agency, 76-77; mem, US Continental Sci Drilling Comt, Nat Res Coun, 81- *Mem:* Geol Soc Am; Mineral Soc Am; Am Geophys Union; Geothermal Resources Coun; Soc Econ Geologists. *Res:* Geothermal resources; hydrothermal alteration; hot springs; Cenozoic volcanic rocks. *Mailing Add:* Mail Stop 18 US Geol Surv 345 Middlefield Rd Menlo Park CA 94025

MUFFLEY, HARRY CHILTON, b Urbana, Ill, Dec 2, 21; m 50. BIOLOGY, ORGANIC CHEMISTRY. *Educ:* Milliken Univ, BS, 49. *Prof Exp:* Res chemist, Fine Chem Div, Glidden Co, 50-52; res chemist, Rock Island Arsenal, 52-63, res phys scientist, US Army Weapons Command, 63-70; res phys scientist, Gen Thomas J Rodman Lab, 70-77; HEAD HYDRAUL FUILDS & LUBRICANTS DIV, US ARMY ARMAMENT RES & DEVELOP COMMAND, 77- *Honors & Awards:* Wilbur Deutsch Mem Award, Am Soc Lubrication Eng, 67. *Mem:* AAAS; Am Chem Soc (pres, 61); Am Soc Lubrication Engrs (pres, 65); Am Defense Preparedness Asn. *Res:* Biomechanics; study of the unique or unusual characteristics of animal leading to new concepts in weapons or weapons systems; hydraulic fluids; corrosion preventives. *Mailing Add:* 20 Cobblestone Irvine CA 92715

MUFSON, DANIEL, b Bronx, NY, Dec 24, 42; m 64; c 2. PHARMACEUTICAL CHEMISTRY. *Educ:* Columbia Univ, BS, 63, MS, 65; Univ Mich, PhD(pharmaceut chem), 68. *Prof Exp:* Res pharmacist, Parke Davis & Co, 68-71; sr scientist pharmaceut chem, Smith Kline & French Labs, 71-73, group leader, 73-74; mgr biopharmaceut & drub metab, 74-76, dir, Pharm Res & Develop Dept, USV Pharmaceut Corp, Div Revlon, 76-80, DIR, PHARMACEUT RES & DEVELOP DEPT, REVLON HEALTH CARE RES & DEVELOP, 80- *Mem:* Am Pharmaceut Asn; Acad Pharmaceut Sci; Am Soc Hosp Pharmacists. *Res:* Solubilization and dissolution studies on pharmaceuticals and endogenous lipids; biopharmaceutics and drug metabolism; pharmaceutical development. *Mailing Add:* Revlon Health Care 1 Scarsdale Rd Tuckahoe NY 10707

MUFSON, STUART LEE, b Philadelphia, Pa, May 16, 46; m 72; c 2. HIGH ENERGY & EXTRAGALCTIC OBJECTS. *Educ:* Univ Pa, BA & MS(physics), 68; Univ Chicago, MS(astron), 70, PhD(astron), 74. *Prof Exp:* Res assoc, Nat Radio Astron Observ, 73-75; Nat Res Coun assoc, Marshall Space Flight Ctr, NASA, 75-77; ASST PROF ASTRON, IND UNIV, 77- *Concurrent Pos:* Prin investr, NASA, 77- *Mem:* Am Astron Soc; Int Astron Union. *Res:* Physical properties and evolution of high-energy, extragalactic sources known as quasars; structure and kinematics of large active regions of star formation in our Milky Way galaxy. *Mailing Add:* Astron Dept Ind Univ 319 Swain W Bloomington IN 47405

MUFTI, IZHAR-UL HAQ, b Batala, India, June 15, 31; Can citizen; m 61; c 2. APPLIED MATHEMATICS. *Educ:* D J Col, Univ Karachi, Pakistan, BSc, 51, MSc, 53; Univ BC, PhD(appl math), 60. *Prof Exp:* Lectr math, DJ Col, Univ Karachi, 51-56; asst, Univ BC, 56-60; asst res officer, Nat Res Coun Can, Ottawa, 60-66, assoc res officer, 66-76, SR RES OFFICER ANAL LAB, DIV MECH ENG, NAT RES COUN CAN, OTTAWA, 76- *Mem:* Soc Indust & Appl Math. *Res:* Multi-body dynamics; manipulator dynamics; numerical mathematics; stability; optimization. *Mailing Add:* Anal Lab Div of Mech Eng Nat Res Coun of Can Ottawa ON K1A 0R6 Can

MUGA, MARVIN LUIS, b Dallas, Tex, Mar 1, 32. NUCLEAR CHEMISTRY. *Educ:* Southern Methodist Univ, BS, 53, MS, 54; Univ Tex, PhD, 57. *Prof Exp:* Res nuclear chemist, Lawrence Radiation Lab, Univ Calif, 57-60; from asst prof to assoc prof nuclear chem, 60-77, PROF CHEM, UNIV FLA, 77- *Concurrent Pos:* Fulbright lectr, 60. *Mem:* Am Chem Soc; Am Phys Soc. *Res:* Thin film scintillator detectors for dE dx measurements of energetic heavy ions; fission decay phenomena. *Mailing Add:* Dept of Chem & Physics Univ of Fla Gainesville FL 32601

MUGGENBURG, BRUCE AL, b St Paul, Minn, May 2, 37; m 60; c 3. VETERINARY PHYSIOLOGY. *Educ:* Univ Minn, BS, 59, DVM, 61; Univ Wis, Madison, MS, 64, PhD(vet sci), 66. *Prof Exp:* From instr to asst prof vet sci, Univ Wis, Madison, 64-69; VET PHYSIOLOGIST, INHALATION TOXICOL RES INST, LOVELACE FOUND, 69- *Mem:* Am Thoracic Soc; Am Vet Med Asn; Am Phsiol Soc; Health Physics Soc. *Res:* Therapy of radiation induced disease; deposition and clearance of particles from the lung; toxicity of inhaled radionuclides. *Mailing Add:* Inhalation Toxicol Res Inst Lovelace Found PO Box 5890 Albuquerque NM 87185

MUGGLI, ROBERT ZENO, b Richardton, NDak, Dec 6, 29; m 54; c 8. ORGANIC CHEMISTRY, CHEMICAL MICROSCOPY. *Educ:* St John's Univ, Minn, BA, 51; NDak State Univ, MS, 56; Kans State Univ, PhD(org chem). 60. *Prof Exp:* Paint chemist, Western Paint & Varnish, Minn, 53-54; anal chemist, Standard Oil Co (Ind), NDak, 54-55; res chemist, Sinclair Res Inc, Ill, 60-65; SR RES CHEMIST, WALTER C McCRONE ASSOCS, INC, CHICAGO, 65- *Mem:* Am Chem Soc; Sigma Xi. *Res:* Paint, petroleum, biological and organic chemistry; electron microscopy; x-ray diffraction; non-routine microanalytical chemistry; optical microscopy. *Mailing Add:* Walter C McCrone Assocs Inc 28205 Michigan Ave Chicago IL 60616

MUGHABGHAB, SAID F, b Beirut, Lebanon, July 4, 34; m 63. NUCLEAR PHYSICS. *Educ:* Am Univ Beirut, BSc, 56, MSc, 59; Univ Pa, PhD(nuclear physics), 63. *Prof Exp:* Res assoc physics, 63-65, asst physicist, 65-67, assoc physicist, 67-73, physicist, 73-79, SR PHYSICIST, BROOKHAVEN NAT LAB, 80- *Concurrent Pos:* Adj assoc prof, Dowling Col, 70-73. *Mem:* Am Phys Soc. *Res:* Evaluation of nuclear data; compilation of nuclear data in the neutron field; photonuclear reactions; neutron total cross section measurements, study of nuclear structure and reaction mechanism with n, Gamma reactions. *Mailing Add:* Dept of Nuclear Energy Brookhaven Nat Lab Upton NY 11973

MUGLER, DALE H, b Denver, Colo, Nov 8, 48; m 72. MATHEMATICAL ANALYSIS. *Educ:* Univ Colo, BA, 70; Northwestern Univ, MA, 71, PhD(math), 74. *Prof Exp:* Asst prof math, Syracuse Univ, 74-75; ASST PROF MATH, UNIV SANTA CLARA, 75- *Mem:* Am Math Soc; Math Asn Am; Soc Indust & Appl Math. *Res:* Complex function theory and related parts of applicable mathematics, especially differential and integral equations. *Mailing Add:* Dept of Math Univ of Santa Clara Santa Clara CA 95053

MUGNAINI, ENRICO, b Siena, Italy, Dec 10, 37; m 61; c 2. NEUROANATOMY. *Educ:* Univ Pisa, MD, 62. *Prof Exp:* Trainee neuroanat, Univ Oslo, 63; asst prof anat, Med Sch, Univ Bergen, 64-66; assoc prof, Med Sch, Univ Oslo, 67-69; PROF BIOBEHAV SCI & HEAD LAB NEUROMORPHOL, UNIV CONN, 69- *Concurrent Pos:* Vis prof, Harvard Med Sch, 70. *Mem:* AAAS; Soc Neurosci; Am Asn Anat; Am Asn Cell Biol. *Res:* Developmental neurobiology with special reference to cerebellum and laminated gray matters; circuitry of cerebellum and precerebellar nuclei; vestibular system; acoustic system; myelin and glial cells; immunocytochemistry. *Mailing Add:* Lab of Neuromorphol Univ of Conn U-154 Storrs CT 06268

MUGWIRA, LUKE MAKORE, b Selukwe, Rhodesia, Mar 21, 40; m 65; c 2. SOIL CHEMISTRY. *Educ:* Lewis & Clark Col, BS, 65; Mich State Univ, MS, 67, PhD(soil chem), 70. *Prof Exp:* Teaching asst soil chem, Mich State Univ, 65-67, res asst, 67-70, fel, 70-71; assoc prof soil chem, 71-81, PROF SOIL SCI, ALA A&M UNIV, 81- *Concurrent Pos:* Consult, Biochem Labs, 74 & Hayes Int Corp, City Investing Co, 75- *Mem:* Am Soc Agron; Soil Sci Soc Am. *Res:* Triticale adaptation to acid soils, its mineral nutrition and physiological characteristics related to fertilizer efficiency utilization; organic waste evaluation for crop production and role in environmental pollution. *Mailing Add:* Ala A&M Univ PO Box 137 Normal AL 35762

MUHLBAUER, KARLHEINZ CHRISTOPH, b Heidelberg, Ger, Dec 29, 30; US citizen; div; c 2. ENGINEERING MECHANICS. *Educ:* Mo Sch Mines, BS, 56, MS, 58; Vanderbilt Univ, PhD(struct mech), 68. *Prof Exp:* From instr to assoc prof eng mech, Univ Mo-Rolla, 56-73, prof, 73-81; MEM STAFF, MTS AEROSPACE CORP, EL SEGUNDO, CALIF, 81- *Concurrent Pos:* Consult, Naval Weapons Ctr, Calif, 69-72 & McDonnell Douglas Aircraft Co; Undergrad Educ Improv grant, Univ Mo-Rolla, 70-71. *Mem:* Am Soc Eng Educ; Am Soc Civil Engrs. *Res:* Stress analysis, folded plates, composite systems; individualized instruction techniques for undergraduate engineering education. *Mailing Add:* 6600 Beadview Apt 232 Rancho Palos Verdes CA 90274

MUHLEMAN, DUANE OWEN, b Maumee, Ohio, Mar 7, 31; m 55; c 2. RADIO ASTRONOMY, PLANETARY SCIENCES. *Educ:* Univ Toledo, BS, 53; Harvard Univ, PhD(astron), 64. *Prof Exp:* Aeronaut res engr aerodyn, Nat Adv Comt Aeronaut, 53-55; commun res engr radar, Jet Propulsion Lab, Calif Inst Technol, 55-66; vis prof radar astron, Cornell Univ, 66-67; PROF PLANETARY SCI RADIO ASTRON, CALIF INST TECHNOL, 67- *Concurrent Pos:* Consult, Jet Propulsion Lab, 66-; staff mem, Owens Valley Radio Observ, Calif Inst Technol, 67-; NASA & NSF grants, 67-; US deleg gen assembly, Int Union Radio Sci, 76, 77 & 78. *Mem:* Am Astron Soc. *Res:* Planetary radio astronomy; galactic radio astronomy; experimental general relativity; celestial mechanics; radio propagation in electron plasmas. *Mailing Add:* Dept of Planetary Sci Calif Inst Technol Pasadena CA 91125

MUHLENBRUCH, CARL W(ILLIAM), b Decatur, Ill, Nov 21, 15; m 39; c 2. ENGINEERING MANAGEMENT. *Educ:* Univ Ill, BS, 37, CE, 45; Carnegie Inst Technol, MS, 43. *Prof Exp:* Res engr, Aluminum Co Am, Pa, 37-39; from instr to assoc prof civil eng, Carnegie Inst Technol, 39-48; assoc prof, Northwestern Technol Inst, 48-54; pres, 54-67, CHMN, TEC-SEARCH, INC, 67- *Honors & Awards:* Thompson Award, Am Soc Testing & Mat, 45. *Mem:* Am Soc Eng Educ; Am Soc Civil Engrs; Nat Soc Prof Engrs; Am Econ Develop Coun. *Res:* Mechanics and properties of engineering materials; engineering and industrial management; plant location; transportation engineering; city planning; regional studies of economic potential. *Mailing Add:* 4071 Fairway Dr Wilmette IL 60091

MUHLER, JOSEPH CHARLES, b Ft Wayne, Ind, Dec 22, 23; m 49; c 2. BIOCHEMISTRY. *Educ:* Ind Univ, BS, 45, DDS, 48, PhD(chem), 51. *Prof Exp:* From asst prof to prof chem, Ind Univ, Indianapolis, 51-61, res prof basic sci, Sch Dent, 61-72; RES PROF DENT SCI & DIR PREV DENT RES INST, SCH DENT, IND UNIV, FT WAYNE, 72- *Concurrent Pos:* Consult, Procter & Gamble Co, 49-; chmn biochem sect, Am Asn Dent Schs, 58; chmn dept prev dent, Sch Dent, Ind Univ, Indianapolis, 58-72, dir prev dent res inst, 68-72; consult, US Air Force Sch Aviation Med, 59-61, Off Surgeon Gen, US Army, 61-, Ft Knox, 62-, Mead Johnson Co, 61-, Gen Foods Corp, 64-69, Bur Med & Surg, US Navy, 64-, White Labs, 66-, & Dentsply Corp, 70- *Honors & Awards:* Award, Int Asn Dent Res, 68. *Mem:* Fel AAAS; fel Am Col Dent; fel Am Inst Chem; Am Chem Soc; Am Dent Asn. *Res:* Essentiality of trace elements; lipid metabolism. *Mailing Add:* Ind Univ at Ft Wayne 2101 Coliseum Blvd E Ft Wayne IN 46805

MUHS, MERRILL ARTHUR, b San Francisco, Calif, May 9, 26; m 52; c 3. ORGANIC CHEMISTRY, ANALYTICAL CHEMISTRY. *Educ:* Univ Calif, BS, 49; Univ Wash, PhD(chem), 54. *Prof Exp:* Res chemist, 54-73, SUPVR SR STAFF, SHELL DEVELOP CO, 73- *Mem:* Am Chem Soc. *Res:* Gas chromatography; applied spectroscopy; characterization of odors; analysis of air and water pollutants; liquid chromatography; polymer analysis. *Mailing Add:* Shell Develop Co PO Box 1380 Houston TX 77001

MUIR, ARTHUR H, JR, b San Antonio, Tex, Aug 26, 31. SOLID STATE SCIENCE. *Educ:* Williams Col, BA, 53; Calif Inst Technol, MS, 55, PhD(physics), 60. *Prof Exp:* Sr physicist, Atomics Int Div, NAm Rockwell Corp, 60-62, specialist Mossbauer effect, 62-63, mem tech staff, Sci Ctr, 63-69, mem technol advan staff, 69-70, mgr int technol prog, 70-74, dir physics & chem dept, 74-76, mgr, Com & Univ Progs, 76-80, PROJ MGR, SPACE SHUTTLE PROG, ROCKWELL INT SCI CTR, 80- *Mem:* Am Phys Soc; Sigma Xi. *Res:* Applications of Mossbauer effect to solid state physics; nuclear spectroscopy; reactor physics; low energy nuclear physics; solar energy; research administration; minority engineering and science programs. *Mailing Add:* Rockwell Int Sci Ctr PO Box 1085 Thousand Oaks CA 91360

MUIR, BARRY SINCLAIR, b Belleville, Ont, July 21, 32; m 61; c 2. ZOOLOGY. *Educ:* Univ Toronto, BA, 56, MA, 58, PhD(zool), 61. *Prof Exp:* From asst prof to assoc prof zool, Univ Hawaii, 61-67; sr res scientist, Hydronautics, Inc, Md, 67-68; scientist, 68-71, asst dir res, Fisheries Res Bd Can, Marine Ecol Lab, Bedford Inst, 71-76; dir, Resource Br, Fisheries Mgt, Maritimes Region, Halifax, 76-79; DIR GEN, RESOURCE SERV DIRECTORATE, DEPT FISHERIES & OCEANS, OTTAWA, 79- *Concurrent Pos:* Prin investr, NSF grant, 63-68. *Mem:* Sigma Xi; Am Fisheries Soc; Am Soc Ichthyologists & Herpteologists; Can Sos Zoologists. *Res:* Dynamics of fish populations; environmental influence on energy metabolism of fish, especially processes of growth and reproduction. *Mailing Add:* Dept Fisheries & Oceans 240 Sparks St Ottawa ON K1A 0E6 Can

MUIR, DEREK CHARLES G, b Montreal, Que, Oct 13, 49. TOXICOLOGY, ANALYTICAL CHEMISTRY. *Educ:* McGill Univ, BSc, 70, MSc, 73, PhD(agr chem), 77. *Prof Exp:* RES SCIENTIST ORG CHEMICALS TOXICOL, DEPT FISHERIES & OCEANS CAN, 77- *Concurrent Pos:* Adj prof soil sci dept, Univ Man, 78- *Mem:* Am Chem Soc; Chem Inst Can; Soc Environ Toxicol & Chem. *Res:* Persistence and degradation of xenobiotics in aquatic ecosystems; field and lab experiments; methodology development; uptake and metabolism of trace organics by aquatic animals. *Mailing Add:* Freshwater Inst 501 University Crescent Winnipeg MB R3T 2N6 Can

MUIR, DONALD EARL, b Seattle, Wash, Apr 15, 33; m 56; c 2. MATHEMATICS. *Educ:* Univ Idaho, BS, 56; Stanford Univ, MS, 74. *Prof Exp:* Instr math, Univ Idaho, 56-57; design specialist, Martin Co, 57-61; sr engr, Raytheon Co, 61-62; res engr, Boeing Co, 62; opers analyst, Tech Opers, Inc, 62-64; MEM PROF STAFF, CTR NAVAL ANAL, 64- *Mem:* Am Math Soc; Am Astron Soc; Math Soc Am; Am Geophys Union; Opers Res Soc Am. *Res:* Military operations analysis; computer sciences. *Mailing Add:* 6607 Degen Dr Burke VA 22015

MUIR, DONALD RIDLEY, b Toronto, Ont, Jan 3, 29; m 54; c 2. PHYSICAL CHEMISTRY, RESEARCH ADMINISTRATION. *Educ:* Univ Toronto, BA, 51, MA, 52, PhD(phys chem), 54. *Prof Exp:* Mem staff, Res & Develop, Johnson & Johnson Ltd, 54-62; dir res & develop div, Columbia Cellulose Co, Ltd, BC, 62-69; dir res & develop, Oxford Paper Co, 69-73; PRES, SULPHUR DEVELOP INST CAN, 73- *Mem:* Am Chem Soc; Tech Asn Pulp & Paper Indust; Can Pulp & Paper Asn; fel Chem Inst Can. *Res:* Research and development of new uses for sulphur. *Mailing Add:* 3325 Lassiter Ct SW Calgary AB T3E 6JB Can

MUIR, DOUGLAS WILLIAM, b Kalamazoo, Mich, May 18, 40; m 67; c 2. APPLIED NUCLEAR DATA, PARTICLE TRANSPORT CALCULATIONS. *Educ:* Southern Ill Univ, BA, 62; NMex State Univ, MS, 65, PhD(physics), 68. *Prof Exp:* Mem staff, Los Alamos Sci Lab, 68-78; nuclear data specialist, Int Atomic Energy Agency, 78-80; MEM STAFF, LOS ALAMOS NAT LAB, 80- *Mem:* Am Nuclear Soc; Am Phys Soc. *Res:* Measurement, compilation, processing and testing of nuclear data for calculations of neutron/photon transport and radiation effects. *Mailing Add:* Los Alamos Nat Lab MS 243 Los Alamos NM 87545

MUIR, FOREST VERN, poultry science, see previous edition

MUIR, JAMES ALEXANDER, b Jamestown, NY, Oct 29, 38; m 62; c 2. PHYSICS. *Educ:* Univ Rochester, BA, 60; Northwestern Univ, PhD(physics), 66. *Prof Exp:* From asst prof to assoc prof, 66-78, PROF PHYSICS, UNIV PR, RIO PIEDRAS, 78-, DIR ACAD SERV, COMPUT CTR, 80- *Concurrent Pos:* Assoc scientist, PR Nuclear Ctr, 66-67; sr vis scholar, Univ Cambridge, 73-74; vis prof, Mich State Univ, 75-77; energy consult, PR Ctr Energy Environ Res, 76-; user servs coordr, Comput Ctr, Univ PR, 78-80. *Mem:* Am Phys Soc; Am Crystallog Asn; Am Optical Soc; Asn Comput Mach. *Res:* Crystallography; optical properties of solar selective surfaces; management of academic computing. *Mailing Add:* Dept Physics Univ PR Rio Piedras PR 00931

MUIR, LARRY ALLEN, b Warren, Ohio, May 31, 42; m 65; c 3. ANIMAL NUTRITION & PHYSIOLOGY. *Educ:* Ohio State Univ, BS, 64, MS, 66, PhD(ruminant nutrit), 70. *Prof Exp:* Res assoc ruminant nutrit, Ohio State Univ, 64-70; sr res physiologist, 70-75, res fel, 75-77, SR RES FEL, BASIC ANIMAL SCI RES, MERCK & CO, INC, 77- *Mem:* Am Dairy Sci Asn; Am Soc Animal Sci. *Res:* Ruminant nutrition and physiology. *Mailing Add:* Merck Inst Therapeut Res Merck & Co Inc Rahway NJ 07065

MUIR, MARIEL MEENTS, b Sioux Falls, SD, Nov 18, 39; m 62; c 2. CHEMISTRY. *Educ:* Grinnell Col, BA, 61; Northwestern Univ, PhD(chem), 65. *Prof Exp:* Instr chem, Univ Ill, Chicago Circle, 65-66; from asst prof to assoc prof, 66-77, PROF CHEM, UNIV PR, RIO PIEDRAS, 77-, DIR, DEPT CHEM, 80- *Concurrent Pos:* Assoc scientist, PR Nuclear Ctr, Rio Piedras, 66-68; sr vis scholar, Univ Cambridge, Eng, 73-74; grad prog coordr, Chem Dept, Univ PR, Rio Piedras, 78-80. *Mem:* Am Chem Soc; Sigma Xi. *Res:* Photochemistry and thermal reaction rates of transition metal complexes and interactions of complexes with molecules of biological importance. *Mailing Add:* Dept Chem Univ PR Box AW Univ Sta Rio Piedras PR 00931

MUIR, MELVIN K, b Johannesburg, SAfrica, Jan 25, 32; US citizen; m 57; c 2. SOIL CHEMISTRY, PLANT NUTRITION. *Educ:* Brigham Young Univ, BSc, 61; Pa State Univ, MSc, 63, PhD(agron), 66. *Prof Exp:* Mine officer, Johannesburg City Deep Mines, SAfrica, 52-57; asst soils, Pa State Univ, 61-66; asst prof, Mont State Univ, Univ, 57-59; ENVIRON ASSOC SCIENTIST, KENNECOTT MINERALS CO, 69- *Mem:* Am Soc Agron; Soil Sci Soc Am. *Res:* Environmental research; amounts of hydrogen fluorine extractable ammonium in Pennsylvania soils; evaluation of slags as soil liming materials; minor element availability for plant growth; correlations of plant growth factors; influence of pollutants on air, water, soil and vegetation; methods development on analytical techniques for environment and biological samples. *Mailing Add:* Kennecott Res & Develop Ctr PO Box 11248 Salt Lake City UT 84147

MUIR, ROBERT DONALD, b Sharon. Pa, June 27, 14; m 40; c 2. MICROBIOLOGY. *Educ:* Allegheny Col, AB, 36; Yale Univ, PhD(bact), 42. *Prof Exp:* Instr med bact, Sch Med, St Louis Univ, 42-43; microbiologist, Bristol Labs, 43-53; microbiologist, 53-69, asst dir biol res, 69-78, DIR MICROBIOL DEVELOP, G D SEARLE & CO, 78- *Mem:* AAAS; Am Soc Microbiol; Mycol Soc Am; Soc Indust Microbiol. *Res:* Fermentation; mycology; product development and control; pharmaceutical bacteriology; control microbiology; antibiotics. *Mailing Add:* G D Searle & Co Box 5110 Chicago IL 60680

MUIR, ROBERT MATHEW, b Laramie, Wyo, Oct 15, 17; m 47; c 3. PLANT PHYSIOLOGY. *Educ:* Univ Wyo, BA, 38; Univ Mich, MA, 41, PhD(bot), 46. *Prof Exp:* Asst prof bot, Pomona Col, 46-48; from asst prof to assoc prof, 48-61, PROF BOT, UNIV IOWA, 61- *Mem:* Bot Soc Am; Am Soc Plant Physiol; Soc Exp Biol & Med. *Res:* Relation of chemical constitution to growth regulator action; role of hormones in fruit development; vernalization; abscission; gibberellin and auxin physiology. *Mailing Add:* Dept of Bot Univ of Iowa Iowa City IA 52242

MUIR, THOMAS GUSTAVE, JR, b San Antonio, Tex, Aug 3, 38; m 66; c 2. ACOUSTICS. *Educ:* Univ Tex, Austin, BS, 61, MA, 65, PhD(mech eng), 71. *Prof Exp:* RES SCIENTIST ACOUST, APPL RES LABS, UNIV TEX, AUSTIN, 61-, LECTR, DEPT MECH ENG, 77- *Mem:* Fel Acoust Soc Am; Am Soc Mech Engrs; AAAS; fel Brit Inst Acoust. *Res:* Underwater and airborne sonar and nonlinear acoustics; biomedical ultrasonics; sound propagation and scattering. *Mailing Add:* Appl Res Labs Univ of Tex PO Box 8029 Austin TX 78712

MUIR, WILLIAM A, b Pittsburgh, Pa, Dec 8, 37; m 62; c 1. HUMAN GENETICS, ANATOMY. *Educ:* George Washington Univ, BS, 60, MS, 62; Univ Rochester, PhD(anat), 66. *Prof Exp:* Instr anat & human genetics, Sch Med, Univ Rochester, 65-66; fel human genetics, 66-74, ASST PROF MED, CASE WESTERN RESERVE UNIV, 74-, DIR HUMAN GENETICS, UNIV HOSPS, 76- *Mem:* Am Soc Human Genetics; NY Acad Sci. *Res:* Genetic and biochemical investigation of the thalassemias; hematology; biochemistry. *Mailing Add:* Dept of Med Case Western Reserve Univ Cleveland OH 44106

MUIR, WILLIAM ERNEST, b Portage la Prairie, Man, Sept 6, 40; m 68; c 2. AGRICULTURAL ENGINEERING. *Educ:* Univ Sask, BE, 62, PhD(agr eng), 67; Univ Ill, Urbana, MS, 64. *Prof Exp:* Jr res off food technol, Nat Res Coun Can, 62-63; from asst prof to assoc prof, 67-77, PROF AGR ENG, UNIV MAN, 77- *Concurrent Pos:* Res grants, Nat Res Coun Can, 68-69 & 73-83, Ctr Transp Studies, 68-71 & Can Dept Agr, 68-82; ed, Can Agr Eng, 81- *Mem:* Can Soc Agr Eng; Am Soc Agr Eng; Agr Inst Can; Am Soc Eng Educ. *Res:* Storage of cereal grains and oil seeds. *Mailing Add:* Dept of Agr Eng Univ of Man Winnipeg MB R3T 2N2 Can

MUIR, WILLIAM HOWARD, b Sharon, Pa, May 26, 28; m 52; c 4. PLANT PATHOLOGY, PHYSIOLOGY. *Educ:* Allegheny Col, BS, 49; Johns Hopkins Univ, MA, 51; Univ Wis, PhD(plant path, physiol), 55. *Prof Exp:* Res assoc plant path, Univ Wis, 55-57; asst prof biol, 57-62, assoc prof bot, 62-66, chmn dept biol, 64-69, PROF BOT, CARLETON COL, 66- *Concurrent Pos:* NSF res grants, 58-65, eval panelist, 62-69. *Mem:* AAAS; Bot Soc Am; Tissue Cult Asn; Am Phytopath Soc; Am Soc Plant Physiol. *Res:* Morphogenesis; development of plant tissue cultures from single cells; morphogenesis in tissue cultures; auxin relations; phylogeny and development of cryptogams; mycology; boreal ecology. *Mailing Add:* Dept of Biol Carleton Col Northfield MN 55057

MUIR, WILLIAM W, III, b Bay City, Mich, July 8, 46. ANESTHESIOLOGY, ELECTROPHYSIOLOGY. *Educ:* Mich State Univ, BS, 68, DVM, 70; Ohio State Univ, MS, 72, PhD(physiol), 74; Am Col Vet Anesthesiol, dipl, 77; Am Col Vet Physiol & Pharm, dipl, 80. *Prof Exp:* Res assoc physiol, 70-74, asst prof 74-77, ASSOC PROF PHYSIOL & PHARM, OHIO STATE UNIV, 77- *Concurrent Pos:* Ed, Am Vet Med Asn J, 78-, Am J Vet Res, 78- *Mem:* Am Chem Soc; Am Col Cardiol Vet. *Res:* Electrophysiologic and hemodynamic effects of drugs, which effect the cardiovascular system. *Mailing Add:* 1935 Coffey Rd Columbus OH 43210

MUIR, WILSON BURNETT, b Montreal, Que, Can, July 20, 32; m 55; c 3. SOLID STATE PHYSICS. *Educ:* McGill Univ, BSc, 53; Univ Western Ont, MSc, 55; Ottawa Univ, PhD(solid state physics), 62. *Prof Exp:* Sci officer, Radioactivity Div, Dept Mines & Tech Surv, Can, 55-57; physicist, Franklin Inst Labs, 61-64 & Noranda Res Centre, 64-66; physicist, 66-68, asst prof, 68-69, ASSOC PROF PHYSICS, MCGILL UNIV, 69- *Mem:* Am Phys Soc; Can Asn Physicists. *Res:* Electron transport; magnetization and Mossbauer effect in metals, alloys, semiconductors and minerals. *Mailing Add:* Dept Physics McGill Univ 3600 University St Montreal PQ H3A 2T5 Can

MUIRHEAD, JOHN F, b Munson, Pa, Sept 12, 37; m 60; c 3. PETROLEUM ENGINEERING. *Educ:* Pa State Univ, BS, 60, MS, 61. *Prof Exp:* Engr, Gulf Res & Develop Co, 61-65, res engr, 65-67, sr res engr, 67, sect supvr well completion & simulation, 68-70, sect supvr drilling surface equip, 70-71, sect supvr abrasive jet drilling, 71-77, ENG MGR, GULF MINERAL RESOURCES, 77- *Concurrent Pos:* Inspector petrol eng curric, Eng Coun Prof Develop, 69- *Mem:* Soc Petrol Engrs. *Res:* Petroleum production problems; well cementing; sand control; fracturing; thermal stimulation techniques; drilling; natural gas engineering. *Mailing Add:* 28131 Man O'War Dr Evergreen Denver CO 80439

MUIRHEAD, ROBB JOHN, b Adelaide, S Australia, July 7, 46; m 70; c 2. MATHEMATICAL STATISTICS. *Educ:* Univ Adelaide, BSc, 68, PhD(statist), 70. *Prof Exp:* From asst prof to assoc prof statist, Yale Univ, 70-78; assoc prof, 78-81, PROF STATIST, UNIV MICH, 81- *Mem:* Am Statist Asn; Inst Math Statist; Royal Statist Soc. *Res:* Multivariate analysis and distribution theory; asymptotic methods; linear models. *Mailing Add:* Dept of Statist 1447 Mason Hall Ann Arbor MI 48109

MUIRHEAD, VINCENT URIEL, b Dresden, Kans, Feb 6, 19; m 43; c 3. AEROSPACE ENGINEERING. *Educ:* US Naval Acad, BS, 41; US Naval Postgrad Sch, BSAE, 48; Calif Inst Technol, AE, 48. *Prof Exp:* From asst prof to assoc prof aerodyn, 61-76, PROF AEROSPACE ENG & CHMN DEPT, UNIV KANS, 76- *Concurrent Pos:* Consult, Black & Veatch, Consult Engrs, Mo, 64- *Mem:* Am Inst Aeronaut & Astronaut; Am Soc Eng Educ; NY Acad Sci; Am Acad Mech. *Res:* Subsonic and supersonic aerodynamics; tornado vortices; tornado damage to buildings and wind loadings on buildings from severe winds; shock tubes. *Mailing Add:* Dept of Aerospace Eng Univ of Kans Lawrence KS 66044

MUJUMDAR, ARUN SADASHIV, b Karwar, India, Jan 14, 45. CHEMICAL ENGINEERING. *Educ:* Univ Bombay, BChemEng, 65; McGill Univ, MEng, 68, PhD(chem eng), 71. *Prof Exp:* Mech engr, Res Div, Carrier Corp, NY, 69-71; res assoc & univ fel, 71-74, asst prof, 74-78, ASSOC PROF, McGILL UNIV & PULP & PAPER RES INST, CAN, 78- *Concurrent Pos:* Sabbatical leave, India. *Mem:* Am Inst Chem Engrs; Am Soc Mech Engrs; Can Pulp & Paper Asn; Can Soc Chem Engrs. *Res:* Turbulence; heat and mass transfer; aerodynamics of turbomachines; mixing. *Mailing Add:* Dept of Chem Eng McGill Univ 3480 University St Montreal PQ H3A 2A7 Can

MUKA, ARTHUR ALLEN, b Adams, Mass, Oct 23, 24; m 52; c 5. ENTOMOLOGY. *Educ:* Univ Mass, BS, 50; Cornell Univ, MS, 52, PhD(econ entom), 54. *Prof Exp:* Asst entom, Cornell Univ, 50-54; assoc entomologist, Va Agr Exp Sta, 54-56; from asst prof to assoc prof, 56-65, PROF ENTOM, CORNELL UNIV, 65- *Concurrent Pos:* Rockefeller Found entomologist, Int Rice Res Inst, 65-66. *Mem:* Entom Soc Can. Am; Entom Soc Can. *Res:* Field and forage crop insect pests; vegetable insect pests; pest management; extension entomology; international agricultural development. *Mailing Add:* Dept of Entom Cornell Univ Ithaca NY 14853

MUKAI, CROMWELL DAISAKU, b Bostonia, Calif, Apr 13, 17; m 44; c 4. CHEMISTRY. *Educ:* Univ Calif, BS, 43; NY Univ, MS, 49, PhD(org chem), 55. *Prof Exp:* Res chemist, Gelatin Prods Corp Mich, 44-46; res chem chemist, Boyle-Midway Div, Am Home Prods Corp, 46-67, res assoc, 67-75; mgr, Anal Lab, Polychrome Corp, Yonkers, 75-80; RES MGR, DELEET MERCHANDISING CORP, NEWARK, 80- *Mem:* AAAS; Am Chem Soc. *Res:* Synthesis of amino acids; emulsion technology as applied to waxes; petroleum additives; plastics; mechanisms of Grignard reactions; instrumental analysis; characterization and synthesis of resins; lithographic ink vehicles; graphic arts chemicals; aerosol technology; cleaners; detergents; emulsion polymerization. *Mailing Add:* Deleet Merchandising Corp 26 Blanchard St Newark NJ 07105

MUKERJEE, BARID, b Suri, India, Oct 27, 28; m 59. GENETICS. *Educ:* Univ Calcutta, BSc, 51; Brigham Young Univ, MS, 56; Univ Utah, PhD(genetics), 58. *Prof Exp:* Demonstr biol, Vidyasagar Col, India, 51-55; asst prof, Westminster Col, 58-59; asst res prof, Univ Utah, 60-61; res assoc genetics, Columbia Univ, 61-63; from asst prof to assoc prof, 63-70, prof genetics, 70-80, PROF BIOL, MCGILL UNIV, 80- *Res:* Relationship of embryonic differentiation and malignancy; mechanism of chromosome differentiation. *Mailing Add:* Dept of Biol McGill Univ Montreal PQ H3A 2T5 Can

MUKERJEE, PASUPATI, b Calcutta, India, Feb 13, 32; m 64. SURFACE CHEMISTRY, COLLOID CHEMISTRY. *Educ:* Univ Calcutta, BSc, 49, MSc, 51; Univ Southern Calif, PhD(colloid chem), 57. *Prof Exp:* Lab asst chem, Univ Southern Calif, 52-54, res fel, 54-56, lectr & res fel, 56-57; res assoc, Brookhaven Nat Lab, 57-59; reader phys chem, Indian Asn Cultivation Sci, 59-64; guest scientist chem, Van't Hoff Lab, Univ Utrecht, 64; sr scientist, Univ Southern Calif, 64-66; vis assoc prof, 66-67, PROF, SCH PHARM, UNIV WIS-MADISON, 67- *Concurrent Pos:* Vis asst prof, Univ Southern Calif, 57; hon lectr, Univ Calcutta, 61-64; vis prof, Indian Inst Technol, Kharagpur, India, 71-72. *Mem:* Fel AAAS; Am Chem Soc; Royal Soc Chem; Am Pharmaceut Asn; Sigma Xi. *Res:* Structure and properties of micelles; molecular microenvironment at interfaces; aggregation of dyes, drugs and bile salts; solubilization and chemical reactions in micellar systems; adsorption phenomena; model membrane systems. *Mailing Add:* Sch Pharm Univ Wis 425 N Charter St Madison WI 53706

MUKERJI, AMBUJ, b Calcutta, India, Mar 1, 19; m 54; c 2. NUCLEAR PHYSICS. *Educ:* Univ Calcutta, BS, 40, MS, 42; Swiss Fed Inst Technol, DrScNat(nuclear physics), 52. *Prof Exp:* Res fel nuclear spectros, Tata Inst Fundamental Res, India, 52-55, fel, 59-61; res assoc nuclear physics, Univ Wis, 55-56; physicist, Bartol Res Found, Franklin Inst, 56-57; assoc prof physics, Tex A&M Univ, 57-59; vis assoc prof, Univ Ala, 61-64, prof, 64-68; chmn dept physics & astron, 73-76, PROF PHYSICS, LEHMAN COL, 68-, MEM GRAD FAC, CITY UNIV NEW YORK, 69- *Concurrent Pos:* Consult, Phys Sci Lab, US Army Missile Command, Redstone Arsenal, 64-73. *Mem:* AAAS; Am Phys Soc; Swiss Phys Soc. *Res:* Nuclear spectroscopy by the study of the decay of radioactive nuclei; determination of the fluorescent yields in the K and L shells; nuclear and solid state properties with help of Mossbauer effect experiments; Mossbauer effect investigations on hemoglobin. *Mailing Add:* Dept Physics Herbert H Lehman Col Bronx NY 10468

MUKERJI, MUKUL KUMAR, b India, Jan 6, 38; Can citizen. ENTOMOLOGY, POPULATION ECOLOGY. *Educ:* Univ Calcutta, BSc, 57, MSc, 59; McGill Univ, PhD(entom), 65. *Prof Exp:* Res scientist insect pop, 67-80, SR RES SCIENTIST, RES BR AGR CAN, 80- *Concurrent Pos:* Nat Res Coun Can fel, 65-66; assoc ed, Can Entom, Entom Soc Can, 77- *Mem:* Entom Soc Can; Japanese Soc Pop Ecol; Entom Soc Am. *Res:* Insect population ecology; biocontrol; pest management; modelling; bioenergetics; insect morphology; survey. *Mailing Add:* Res Sta Res Br 107 Science Crescent Saskatoon SK S7N 0X2 Can

MUKHEDKAR, DINKAR, b Hyderabad, India, Feb 2, 36; Can citizen; m 64; c 2. ELECTRICAL ENGINEERING. *Educ:* Osmania Univ, India, BS, 57; Univ Nancy, DSc(power), 62. *Prof Exp:* Design engr, Bhilai Steel Works, India, 57-59; Govt of France grant, Inst Radium, Paris, 62-63; asst prof elec eng, Indian Inst Technol, Bombay, 63-64; sr engr, Surveyer, Nenineger & Chenevert, 64-68; from asst prof to assoc prof, 68-74, PROF ELEC ENG, POLYTECH SCH, UNIV MONTREAL, 74- *Concurrent Pos:* Consult, Surveyer, Nenineger & Chenevert, 68- *Mem:* Sr mem Inst Elec & Electronics Engrs; Fr Soc Electricians; fel Eng Inst Can; Can Elec Asn; fel Inst Engrs, India. *Res:* Power systems; simulation techniques. *Mailing Add:* Ecole Polytech PB 6079 Sta A Montreal PQ H3C 3J7 Can

MUKHERJEA, ARUNAVA, b Calcutta, India, Aug 14, 41; m 71; c 1. MATHEMATICS. *Educ:* Univ Calcutta, MSc, 61; Wayne State Univ, PhD(math), 67. *Prof Exp:* Asst prof math, Eastern Mich Univ, 67-69; from asst prof to assoc prof, 69-75, PROF MATH, UNIV SOUTH FLA, 75- *Mem:* Am Math Soc. *Res:* Probability; measure theory; analysis on semigroups. *Mailing Add:* Dept Math Univ South Fla Tampa FL 33620

MUKHERJEE, AMAL, b Titagarh, West Bengal, India, Apr 27, 44; US citizen; m 75; c 1. HORMONE RECEPTORS, ENZYMOLOGY. *Educ:* Calcutta Univ, BS, 65, MS, 67, PhD(physiol), 72. *Prof Exp:* ASST PROF MED, ISCHEMIC HEART CTR, UNIV TEX HEALTH SCI CTR, DALLAS, 80- *Concurrent Pos:* Consult, Int Immunoassay Lab, 79-; prin investr, Am Heart Asn, 81- *Mem:* Am Physiol Soc; Int Soc Heart Res. *Res:* Involvement of autonomic receptors in cardiac excitation and contraction; development of radioimmunoassay of enzymes used as markers for detecting heart diseases. *Mailing Add:* Ischemic Heart Ctr Univ Tex Health Sci Ctr Dallas TX 75235

MUKHERJEE, AMIYA K, b Purnea, India, June 1, 36; m 62; c 2. MATERIALS SCIENCE, METALLURGY. *Educ:* Univ Calcutta, BSc, 54; Univ Sheffield, MSc, 59; Oxford Univ, DPhil(metall), 62. *Prof Exp:* Mgt trainee, Indian Iron & Steel Co, 54-56 & Stewart & Lloyds Ltd, Eng, 56-57; res metallurgist, Lawrence Radiation Lab, 62-65; sr scientist, Battelle Mem Inst, 65-66; from asst prof to assoc prof eng, 66-69, PROF ENG, UNIV CALIF, DAVIS, 69- *Concurrent Pos:* Fel, Univ Calif, 62-65; consult, Lawrence Radiation Lab, 68- & IBM Corp. *Mem:* Am Inst Mining, Metall & Petrol Engrs; Am Soc Metals; Brit Inst Metals; Brit Inst Metall; fel Am Inst Chemists. *Res:* Deformation mechanisms of crystalline materials as a function of temperature strain-rate and crystal structure; elevated temperature strength properties of alloys; fracture characteristics of engineering materials; environmental behavior of structural materials. *Mailing Add:* Dept of Mech Eng Col of Eng Univ of Calif Davis CA 95616

MUKHERJEE, ASIT B, b Suri, India, Apr 6, 40. CYTOGENETICS, SOMATIC CELL GENETICS. *Educ:* Univ Utah, BS, 65, MS, 66, PhD(zool), 68. *Prof Exp:* Teaching asst biol, Univ Utah, 65-67; res assoc human genetics, State Univ NY Upstate Med Ctr, 68-69; fel genetics, Med Ctr, Columbia Univ, 69-70; instr, Albert Einstein Col Med, 70-72; asst prof, 72-77, ASSOC PROF, DEPT BIOL, FORDHAM UNIV, 77- *Mem:* AAAS; Tissue Cult Asn; Am Soc Cell Biol; Am Soc Human Genetics. *Res:* Genetics of aging; somatic cell genetics; human genetics. *Mailing Add:* Dept Biol Fordham Univ Bronx NY 10458

MUKHERJEE, DEBI PRASAD, b Krisnanagar, India, Oct 26, 39. CHEMICAL ENGINEERING, POLYMER SCIENCE. *Educ:* Jadavpur Univ, India, BChE, 61; Mass Inst Technol, SM, 65, ScD(chem eng), 69, Univ Conn, MBA, 79. *Prof Exp:* Asst chem eng, Mass Inst Technol, 65-68; sr res engr, Basic Polymer Res Sect, Goodyear Tire & Rubber Co, 69-74; SR RES ENGR & GROUP LEADER, DAVIS & GECK, AM CYANAMID CO, 74- *Mem:* Am Chem Soc; Rheology Soc; Am Inst Chem Engrs. *Res:* Viscoelastic properties of elastin; molecular structure and physical properties of elastin; biopolymers; structure and property of polymers; fiber spinning; polymer melt rheology; medical products development. *Mailing Add:* Am Cyanamid Co 1 Casper St Danbury CT 06810

MUKHERJEE, KALINATH, b Calcutta, India, Feb 19, 32; US citizen; m 59; c 3. SOLID STATE PHYSICS. *Educ:* Univ Calcutta, BE, 56; Univ Ill, Urbana, MS, 59, PhD(metall), 63. *Prof Exp:* Engr, Indian Iron & Steel Co, 56-57; res asst, Univ Ill, Urbana, 57-63, res assoc, 63-64; asst prof mat sci, State Univ NY Stony Brook, 64-67; assoc prof metall, Polytech Inst NY, 67-72, prof, 72-80, head, Dept Physics & Eng Metall, 74-80; PROF, MICH STATE UNIV, 80- *Concurrent Pos:* Indian Inst Metals Awards, 56; NSF grant, 66-67; ed, Metall/Mat Yearbk, 75-; NSF fac res fel, Grumman Aerospace, 76. *Mem:* fel Am Soc Metals; fel AAAS; Am Inst Mining, Metall & Petrol Engrs; Am Phys Soc. *Res:* Thermodynamics of point defects; diffusion-less phase transformations; solid state reactions kinetics; dental and bio-materials; laser interactions with metals and alloys; lattice vibrations. *Mailing Add:* Dept of Phys & Eng Metall 333 Jay St Brooklyn NY 11201

MUKHERJEE, MUKUNDA DEV, b Calcutta, India, July 5, 42; m 73; c 3. NUTRITION, PEDIATRICS. *Educ:* King's Col, Durham, Eng, MB & BS, 66; State Univ NY, MD, 72; Am Bd Pediat, FAAP, 74; Am Bd Family Pract, dipl, 78. *Prof Exp:* Jr asst resident, Children's Med Ctr, Harvard Univ, 68-69; asst resident pediat, Mass Gen Hosp, Harvard Univ, Boston, 69-70; res assoc Nutrit & Food Sci Dept, Mass Inst Technol, 70-71; instr pediat, Albert Einstein Col Med, 71-73; asst clin prof pediat, Boston Univ, 73-76; assoc prof, Univ NDak, 76-78; ASSOC PROF PEDIAT & FAMILY PRACT & RES DIR, DEPT FAMILY PRACT, WRIGHT STATE UNIV, 78- *Concurrent Pos:* Clin instr community med, Tufts Univ, 73-76; assoc vis physician, Boston City Hosp, 73-76, vis physician, Children's Hosp, St Elizabeth Hosp, Good Samaritan Hosp & Miami Valley Hosp, 78-; AMA award, 81-84. *Mem:* Fel Am Acad Pediat; AMA; Soc Teachers Family Med; Am Pub Health Asn; Am Cancer Soc. *Res:* Maternal and fetal nutrition; trace metals; effect of maternal plasma zinc on feto-maternal complications in human; prediction of fetal weight from maternal plasma nutrients. *Mailing Add:* St Elizabeth Hosp 601 Miami Blvd West Dayton OH 45408

MUKHERJEE, TAPAN KUMAR, b Gorakhpur, India, Jan 5, 29; m 57; c 2. ORGANIC CHEMISTRY, SOLID STATE SCIENCE. *Educ:* Patna Univ, BS, 48, MS, 50, DSc(chem), 74; Wayne State Univ, PhD(chem), 56. *Prof Exp:* Lectr chem, Patna Univ, 50-52; asst, Wayne State Univ, 52-55, res fel, 55-56; lectr, Univ Bihar, 57-58; res chemist, Mass Inst Technol, 58-60, Gen Aniline & Film Corp, 60-61, Retina Found, 61-62 & Air Force Cambridge Res Lab, 62-74; prog mgr, Solar Energy Conversion, 74-75, prog mgr, Advan Energy & Resources, prog mgr div appl res, 78-81, DIR MINERALS & PRIMARY MAT PROCESSING PROG, NSF, 81- *Mem:* Am Chem Soc; Am Inst Mining, Metall & Petrol Engrs; Indian Chem Soc. *Res:* Syntheses of organic compounds; mechanism of reactions; stable free radicals; organic semiconductors; photoconductors; high temperature laser window materials, photovoltaic materials and devices. *Mailing Add:* Div Chem & Process Eng NSF 1800 G St NW Washington DC 20550

MUKHERJI, KALYAN KUMAR, b Calcutta, India, May 30, 39; m 65. GEOLOGY, GEOPHYSICS. *Educ:* Univ Calcutta, BSc, 59, MSc, 61; Univ Leeds, Dipl, 63; Univ Western Ont, PhD(geol), 68. *Prof Exp:* Demonstr geol, Univ Western Ont, 63-67; asst prof, 68-73, PROF GEOL, CONCORDIA UNIV, LOYOLA, MONTREAL, 73- *Concurrent Pos:* Fel, Carleton Univ, Ont, 68; Nat Res Coun Can grant, 69-; Geol Surv Can res grant, 69-70. *Mem:* Can Soc Petrol Geologists; Int Asn Sedimentologists; Indian Soc Earth Sci; Soc Econ Paleont & Mineral; Geol Asn Can. *Res:* Ordovician stratigraphy and sedimentation in southwest Ontario; carbonate sedimentation and petrology of Sicker Group, Vancouver Islands; thermo luminescence study of Middle Ordovician limestones and recent sediments; exploration geophysics; carbonate trace element geochemistry. *Mailing Add:* Dept of Geol Concordia Univ Loyola Montreal PQ H3G 1M8 Can

MUKHOPADHYAY, NIAMAI CHAND, b Maharampur, West Bengal, Jan 17, 42; m 78; c 1. THEORETICAL PHYSICS. *Educ:* Univ Calcutta, BSc, 63, MSc, 65; Univ Chicago, SM, 70, PhD(physics), 72. *Prof Exp:* Vis mem res nuclear physics, Tata Inst Fundamental Res, Bombay, India, 66-68; resident assoc theoret physics, Argonne Nat Lab, 68-72; fel, Univ Md, 72-74; vis scientist, Europ Orgn Nuclear Res, Geneva, Switz, 74-75; physicist, Swiss Inst Nuclear Res, Villigen, 75-80, Swiss Fed Inst Reactor Res, Wurenlingen, 80-81; ASSOC PROF TEACHING & RES PHYSICS, RENSSELAER POLYTECH INST, 81- *Concurrent Pos:* Vis prof, Univ de Louvain, Belg, 75 & Int Sch Nuclear Physics, Erice, Italy, 76; vis scientist, Inst Nuclear Res, Holland, 77; vis prof, Joint Inst Nuclear Res, Dubna, USSR, 78, Phys Res Lab, Ahmedabad, India, 78 & Technion, Haifa, Israel, 79-80; invited lectr, Univ Fribourg, Switz, 81. *Mem:* Sigma Xi. *Res:* Theoretical medium energy physics as studied in lepton and meson factories; manifestations of fundamental interactions in atomic, nuclear and astrophysical phenomena. *Mailing Add:* Dept Physics Rensselaer Polytech Inst Troy NY 12181

MUKHOPADHYAY, NITIS, b West Bengal, Dec 22, 50; m 78; c 1. PATTERN RECOGNITION, MULTIVARIATE ANALYSIS. *Educ:* Univ Calcutta, BSc, 70; Indian Statist Inst, MStat, 72, PhD(statist), 76. *Prof Exp:* Tutor, Monash Univ, Australia, 76-77, vis asst prof statist, Univ Minn, Minneapolis, 77-78, Univ Mo, Columbia, 78-79; asst prof, 79-81, ASSOC PROF STATIST, OKLA STATE UNIV, 81- *Mem:* Am Statist Asm; Inst Math Statist; Inst Math Statist; NY Acad Sci. *Res:* Applied and theoretical statistics using sequential analysis for reliability or clinical trials. *Mailing Add:* Statist Dept 301 Math Sci Bldg Okla State Univ Stillwater OK 74078

MUKI, ROKURO, b Morioka, Japan, Apr 27, 28; m 56; c 2. SOLID MECHANICS. *Educ:* Keio Univ, Japan, BS, 51, PhD(eng), 59. *Prof Exp:* Lectr math, Keio Univ, Japan, 56-58 & 60-61, assoc prof eng, 61-65; res assoc, Brown Univ, 58-60; vis assoc prof, Calif Inst Technol, 65-66, sr res fel, 66-67; assoc prof, 67-69, PROF APPL MECH, UNIV CALIF, LOS ANGELES, 69- *Mem:* Am Soc Mech Engrs. *Res:* Three dimensional theory of elasticity; thermal stress problems; linear viscoelasticity; elastic load diffusion problems; micromechanics of composite materials. *Mailing Add:* Sch of Eng & Appl Sci Boelter Hall 5732 Los Angeles CA 90024

MUKKADA, ANTONY JOB, b Kerala, India. MICROBIOLOGY, BIOCHEMISTRY. *Educ:* Univ Kerala, BSc, 57; Univ Delhi, MSc, 59, PhD(bot), 62. *Prof Exp:* Fel, Nat Inst Sci, India, 62-63; fel, St Thomas Inst Advan Studies, Ohio, 64-67; vis asst prof bact, 67-68, res assoc, 69-71, asst prof, 71-75, assoc prof biol, 75-79, PROF BIOL & MICROBIOL, UNIV CINCINNATI, 79- *Mem:* Am Soc Microbiol; Am Soc Parasitologists; AAAS; Int Soc Plant Morphologists. *Res:* Microbial physiology and metabolic regulation; biochemistry of intracellular parasitism with special reference to membrane transport and enzyme regulation in haemoflagellates. *Mailing Add:* Dept Biol Sci Univ Cincinnati Cincinnati OH 45221

MUKUNNEMKERIL, GEORGE MATHEW, b Kerala, India, Jan 10, 39; m 73; c 2. DEVELOPMENTAL BIOLOGY. *Educ:* Univ Kerala, BSc, 60; DePaul Univ, MS, 69; Univ Notre Dame, PhD(biol), 73. *Prof Exp:* Demonstr zool, St Berchmans' Col, 60-61; teacher biol, St Josephs High Sch, 61-65; NIH grant, DePaul Univ, 66-68; NSF fel, Univ Notre Dame, 71-73, res assoc radiation lab, 73-76; asst prof biol, NCent Col, 76-81; ASST PROF BIOL, UNIV ILL, CHICAGO CIRCLE, 81- *Mem:* AAAS; Am Soc Zoologists; Sigma Xi. *Res:* Cytochemical and ultrastructural aspects of gametogenesis in insects with emphasis on mosquitoes; ontogenesis of hormonal control during vertebrate embryogenesis, particularly chick embryos; ultrastructure of hemopoiesis. *Mailing Add:* Dept Biol Univ Ill Chicago Circle Chicago IL 60680

MULAR, A(NDREW) L(OUIS), b Beulah, NDak, Dec 10, 30; m 57; c 3. METALLURGICAL ENGINEERING. *Educ:* Mont Col Mineral Sci & Technol, BSc, 57, MSc, 58. *Prof Exp:* Res engr metall, Mass Inst Technol, 58-60, Mich Technol Univ, 60-62 & Univ Calif, Berkeley, 62-63; from assoc prof to prof mineral eng, Queen's Univ, Ont, 63-72; PROF MINERAL ENG, UNIV BC, 72- *Concurrent Pos:* Consult, 80- *Mem:* Am Inst Mining, Metall & Petrol Engrs; Can Inst Mining & Metall. *Res:* Comminution; flotation; process simulation; optimization; control; unit operations. *Mailing Add:* Dept Mineral Eng Univ BC Vancouver BC V6T 1W5 Can

MULARIE, WILLIAM MACK, b Duluth, Minn, Dec 4, 38; m 61; c 2. SOLID STATE PHYSICS. *Educ:* Univ Minn, Duluth, BA, 61; Univ Minn, Minneapolis, MSEE, 66, PhD(elec eng), 71. *Prof Exp:* Physicist, Minn Mining & Mfg Co, 61-63; res scientist solid state physics, Res Inst Advan Studies, 71-74; sr res engr, 3M Co, 74-77, res specialist, 77-79, supvr, Cent Res Lab, 79-80; corp res dir, Am Hoist & Derrick, 80-81; VPRES & GEN MGR, INTERBOND TECHNOL, INC, 81- *Mem:* Sigma Xi. *Res:* Physics of semiconductor surfaces; auger electron spectroscopy; glass corrosion; infrared detectors; optics; materials science engineering. *Mailing Add:* Interbond Technol Inc 225 Roselawn Ave St Paul MN 55117

MULARZ, EDWARD JULIUS, b Lakewood, Ohio, Nov 24, 43; m 67; c 2. COMBUSTION, AEROSPACE ENGINEERING. *Educ:* Univ Detroit, BS, 66; Northwestern Univ, PhD(mech eng), 71. *Prof Exp:* Engr combustion, 71-75, sr engr, 75-78, prog mgr combustion, 78-81, HEAD, COMBUSTION SECTION, PROPULSION LAB, US ARMY RES & TECH LABS, NASA, 81- *Mem:* Am Inst Aeronaut & Astronaut; Sigma Xi; Am Soc Mech Engrs. *Res:* Heat transfer; thermo-dynamics; aircraft propulsion. *Mailing Add:* Propulsion Lab USARTL 21000 Brook Park Rd Cleveland OH 44135

MULAS, PABLO MARCELO, b Atlixco, Mex, Apr 26, 39. PHYSICAL CHEMISTRY, NUCLEAR ENGINEERING. *Educ:* Univ Ottawa, BS, 60; Princeton Univ, PhD(chem eng), 65. *Prof Exp:* Resident res assoc, Jet Propulsion Lab, Nat Acad Sci, 67-68; asst vis prof, Grad Sect, Sch Eng, Univ Calif, Los Angeles, 68; prof nuclear sci, Nat Polytech Inst, Mex, 67-71, head dept nuclear eng, 69-71; dir, Reactor Lab, Nat Inst Nuclear Energy, Mex, 71-73; prof phys chem, CIEA Res, Nat Polytech Inst, Mex, 73-76; DIR, ENERGY RESOURCES DIV, MEX ELEC RES INST, MEX, 76- *Concurrent Pos:* Mem comt, Nat Prog Basic Sci, Nat Coun Sci & Technol, Mex & consult, Nat Energy Comn, Mex, 75- *Mem:* Am Phys Soc; Am Nuclear Soc; Am Chem Soc; Acad Sci Res Mex; Mex Phys Soc. *Res:* Microscopic studies of interfacial phenomena, mass and energy transport; direct conversion of solar electromagnetic radiation to chemical fuels. *Mailing Add:* Mexicali 36 Mexico 11 DF Mexico

MULAY, LAXMAN NILAKANTHA, b Rahuri, India, Mar 5, 23; m 45. PHYSICAL CHEMISTRY, INORGANIC CHEMISTRY. *Educ:* Univ Bombay, MS, 46, PhD(phys chem), 50. *Prof Exp:* Daxina Merit fel, Karnatak Col, Bombay, 43-45, demonstr & lectr chem, 46-48, lectr, Inst Sci, 48-53 & 57-58; res assoc, Northwestern Univ, 53-55; res fel, Harvard Univ, 55-57; asst prof, Univ Cincinnati, 58-63; assoc prof, 63-67, chmn, Solid State Sci Prog, 67-77, prof chem, 67-77, PROF SOLID STATE SCI, PA STATE UNIV, 77- *Mem:* Am Chem Soc; Am Phys Soc; assoc Royal Inst Chem. *Res:* Magneto-chemistry applied to inorganic polymeric systems; nuclear and electron magnetic resonance studies on metallocenes and biological systems; adsorption; coordination compounds; superparamagnetic systems. *Mailing Add:* Mat Res Lab Pa State Univ University Park PA 16802

MULCAHEY, THOMAS P, b Gary, Ind, Sept 14, 31; div; c 1. CHEMICAL & NUCLEAR ENGINEERING. *Educ:* Purdue Univ, BSChE, 54, MSE, 59, PhD(nuclear eng), 63. *Prof Exp:* Assoc engr, 61-70, MGR INSTRUMENTATION & CONTROL, ARGONNE NAT LAB, 70- *Mem:* Inst Elec & Electronics Engrs. *Res:* Coal conversion process and nuclear reactor instrumentation and control. *Mailing Add:* Argonne Nat Lab 9700 S Cass Ave Argonne IL 60439

MULCAHY, DAVID LOUIS, b Manchester, NH, Oct 16, 37; m 63; c 2. ECOLOGY, EVOLUTION. *Educ:* Dartmouth Col, BA, 59; Vanderbilt Univ, PhD(bot), 63. *Prof Exp:* Asst prof bot, Univ Ga, 63-66; vis scientist, Brookhaven Nat Lab, 66-68; asst prof, 68-71, assoc prof, 71-81, PROF BOT, UNIV MASS, AMHERST, 81- *Mem:* Ecol Soc Am; Genetics Soc Am; Am Genetic Asn; Soc Study Evolution; Bot Soc Am. *Res:* Gametophytic competition; population structure of trees; evolution of heterostyly; pollination systems. *Mailing Add:* Dept of Bot Univ of Mass Amherst MA 01003

MULCAHY, GABRIEL MICHAEL, b Jersey City, NJ, Feb 16, 29; m 58; c 7. PATHOLOGY. *Educ:* St Peter's Col, NJ, AB, 50; Georgetown Univ, MD, 54. *Prof Exp:* USPHS med officer, Navajo Indian Reservation, 55-57; resident path, USPHS Hosp, Seattle, Wash, 57-59, USPHS Hosp, Staten Island, NY, 59-61; chief path, USPHS Hosp, Detroit, Mich, 61-62; from instr to assoc prof path, Sch of Med, Creighton Univ, 62-69, actg chmn dept, 67; DIR PATH, JERSEY CITY MED CTR, 69-; PROF GEN & ORAL PATH, NJ DENT SCH & ASSOC CLIN PROF PATH, NJ MED SCH, COL MED & DENT NJ, 71- *Mem:* Am Soc Clin Pathologists; Int Acad Path; Am Soc Human Genetics; AAAS; AMA. *Res:* Pathology of familial tumors; cytogenetics. *Mailing Add:* Dept of Path Jersey City Med Ctr 50 Baldwin Ave Jersey City NJ 07304

MULCAHY, JOHN JOSEPH, b New York, NY, Jan 7, 41; m 70; c 2. UROLOGY. *Educ:* Georgetown Univ, MD, 66; Univ Minn, MS, 74; Univ Mich, PhD(physiol), 72. *Prof Exp:* Asst prof surg, Univ Ky, 74-78; ASSOC PROF UROL, IND UNIV MED CTR, 78-; CHIEF UROL, WISHARD MEM HOSP, 78- *Mem:* Am Urol Asn; Am Fertal Soc; Soc Univ Urol; AMA. *Res:* Renal perfusion from a physiologic standpoint; post-obstructive diuresis; compensatory renal hypertrophy. *Mailing Add:* Dept of Surg 1001 W Tenth St Indianapolis IN 46202

MULCARE, DONALD J, b New York, NY, July 27, 38; m 68; c 4. ZOOLOGY, DEVELOPMENTAL BIOLOGY. *Educ:* St Procopius Col, BS, 62; Univ Notre Dame, PhD(biol), 68. *Prof Exp:* Teaching asst biol, Univ Notre Dame, 62-66; lectr, St Mary's Col, Ind, 66-67; Nat Cancer Inst fel zool, Univ Mich, Ann Arbor, 68-69; asst prof, 69-76, ASSOC PROF BIOL, SOUTHEASTERN MASS UNIV, 76- *Mem:* Sigma Xi; Am Soc Zoologists; Soc Develop Biol. *Res:* Oncology in amphibians; transmission of the Lucke renal adenocarcinoma in Rana pipiens; Rana palustris and their hybrids. *Mailing Add:* Dept of Biol Southeastern Mass Univ North Dartmouth MA 02747

MULCHI, CHARLES LEE, b Warren County, NC, Dec 2, 41; m 62; c 2. AGRONOMY, PLANT PHYSIOLOGY. *Educ:* NC State Univ, BS(crop sci) & BS(soil sci), 64, MS, 67, PhD(plant physiol), 70. *Prof Exp:* Instr soil-plant rels & biochem, NC State Univ, 66-70; asst prof, 70-75, ASSOC PROF CROP PHYSIOL, UNIV MD, COLLEGE PARK, 75- *Concurrent Pos:* Consult power plant impact on crops and soils. *Mem:* Am Soc Agron; Crop Sci Soc Am. *Res:* Soil-plant relations; plant physiology with special interest in photosynthesis and photo-respiration; air pollution effects on plants; aerosol salt effects on crops or cooling tower salt drift effects on vegetation; particulates and metals deposition on crops near power plants. *Mailing Add:* Dept Agron Univ Md College Park MD 20740

MULCRONE, THOMAS FRANCIS S J, b Chicago, Ill, Aug 5, 12. MATHEMATICS. *Educ:* Spring Hill Col, BS, 39; Catholic Univ, MS, 42; St Mays Col, Kans, STL, 47. *Prof Exp:* Instr math, Spring Hill Col, 40-41 & 42-43; spec lectr, St Louis Univ, 43-47; asst prof, Spring Hill Col, 48-54; asst prof Loyola Univ, La, 54-60; assoc prof, Spring Hill Col, 61-75; assoc prof, 75-77, EMER PROF MATH, CITY COL, LOYOLA UNIV, LA, 80- *Mem:* Math Asn Am; Nat Coun Teachers Math. *Res:* Modern geometry and algebra; semigroups; history of mathematics; statistics. *Mailing Add:* Dept Math Loyola Univ 6363 St Charles Ave New Orleans LA 70118

MULDAWER, LEONARD, b Philadelphia, Pa, Aug 6, 20; m 50; c 3. SOLID STATE PHYSICS, MEDICAL PHYSICS. *Educ:* Temple Univ, AB, 42, AM, 44; Mass Inst Technol, PhD(physics), 48. *Prof Exp:* Instr eng, Sci & Mgt War Training, Temple Univ, 42-44, from asst prof to assoc prof, 48-61, PROF PHYSICS, TEMPLE UNIV, 61- *Concurrent Pos:* Consult, Labs, Meret Co; staff, Diag Radiol Res Lab, Temple Univ Med Sch, 72-; field ctr dir, Short Course Prog, NSF, 80- *Mem:* Am Phys Soc; Am Soc Metals; Am Crystallog Asn; Am Asn Physics Teachers; Sigma Xi. *Res:* X-ray diffraction studies of order, particle size and strain; electron diffraction studies of oxides; physiological acoustics; optical and transport properties of alloys; phase transformations; science education; radiological physics. *Mailing Add:* Dept of Physics Temple Univ Philadelphia PA 19122

MULDER, CAREL, b Arnhem, Neth, Mar 19, 28; m 61; c 4. VIROLOGY, MOLECULAR BIOLOGY. *Educ:* Univ Leiden, BS, 51, Drs, 55; Oxford Univ, DPhil(microbiol), 63. *Prof Exp:* Instr molecular biol, Sch Med, Leiden Univ, 60-65; res assoc, Dept Chem, Harvard Univ, 65-67; NIH spec fel tumor virol, Sch Med, St Louis Univ, 67-68 & Salk Inst Biol Studies, 68-70; sr staff investr, Cold Spring Harbor Lab, 70-75; assoc prof microbiol & pharmacol, 75-80, PROF MOLOCULAR GENETICS & MICROBIOL & PHARMACOL, SCH MED, UNIV MASS, 80- *Concurrent Pos:* Vis prof, Sch Med, Univ Leiden, 75; res assoc prof microbiol & molecular genetics, Harvard Med Sch, 78- *Mem:* Am Soc Microbiol; Soc Gen Microbiol; Neth Soc Biochem. *Res:* Molecular biology of DNA tumor viruses and herpesvirus latency; restriction endonucleases. *Mailing Add:* Dept Pharmacol Sch Med Univ Mass Worcester MA 01605

MULDER, DONALD WILLIAM, b Rehoboth, NMex, June 30, 17; m 43. CLINICAL NEUROLOGY. *Educ:* Calvin Col, AB, 40; Marquette Univ, MD, 43; Univ Mich, MS, 46. *Prof Exp:* Asst prof neurol, Univ Colo, 49-50; from instr to assoc prof, Mayo Grad Sch Med, Univ Minn, 50-64; chmn sect neurol, 66-71, pres staff, 70-71, SR CONSULT, MAYO CLIN, 50-; PROF NEUROL, MAYO MED SCH, UNIV MINN, 64- *Mem:* Am Neurol Asn; Am Psychiat Asn; fel Am Acad Neurol. *Res:* Amyotropic lateral sclerosis; epilepsy; neuromuscular disease. *Mailing Add:* Mayo Clin 200 First St SW Rochester MN 55901

MULDOON, THOMAS GEORGE, b Brooklyn, NY, May 13, 38. BIOCHEMISTRY. *Educ:* Queens Col, NY, BS, 60; Univ Louisville, PhD(biochem), 67. *Prof Exp:* Fel biochem, Med Ctr, Univ Kans, 67-69; from asst prof to assoc prof, 69-78, PROF ENDOCRINOL, MED COL GA, 78- *Concurrent Pos:* Mem biochem endocrinol study sect, NIH. *Mem:* Am Soc Biol Chemists; Endocrine Soc; NY Acad Sci; Soc Study Reprod; Soc Exp Biol & Med. *Res:* Tissue-specific interactions of steroid hormones and proteins; regulation of hormone receptor activity. *Mailing Add:* Dept Endocrinol Med Col Ga Augusta GA 30902

MULDREW, DONALD BOYD, b Winnipeg, Man, Oct 17, 34; m 60; c 3. IONOSPHERIC PHYSICS, WAVE PROPAGATION. *Educ:* Univ Man, BSc, 57. *Prof Exp:* Sci officer, Defence Res Bd, Defence Res Telecommun Estab, 60-69; RES SCIENTIST, COMMUN RES CTR, DEPT COMMUN, 69- *Mem:* Am Geophys Union; Can Asn Physicists. *Res:* Electromagnetic and electrostatic wave propagation in plasmas; ionospheric-magnetospheric field-aligned irregularities; F-layer trough; ocean backscatter; plasma resonances and echoes; hot-plasma dispersion curves; HF-enhanced plasma lines; long-delay echoes. *Mailing Add:* Commun Res Ctr Box 11490 Sta H Ottawa ON K2H 8S2 Can

MULDREW, JAMES ARCHIBALD, b Winnipeg, Man, Oct 9, 25; m 58; c 4. FOREST ENTOMOLOGY. *Educ:* Univ Manitoba, BSc, 49, MSc, 52. *Prof Exp:* Agr res officer forest entom, Can Dept Agr, 49-61; res officer forestry, Can Dept Forestry, Winnipeg, 61-71; RES SCIENTIST, CAN DEPT ENVIRON, 71- *Mem:* AAAS; Entom Soc Can; Can Inst Forestry. *Res:* Biological control of forest insects; resistance of insects to parasites; population dynamics. *Mailing Add:* 3843 112A St Edmonton AB T6J 1K4 Can

MULDROW, CHARLES NORMENT, JR, b Washington, DC, 1930; m 58; c 3. POLYMER CHEMISTRY. *Educ:* Col Charleston, BS, 50; Univ NC, MA, 54; Univ Va, PhD(phys chem), 58. *Prof Exp:* Instr chem, Univ NC, 51-52; res chemist, Shell Develop Co, 58-59; from res chemist to sr res chemist, Am Enka Corp, 59-65, head polyester develop sect, 65-70, head polymer develop, 70-76; PROJ LEADER, NL INDUSTS, 76- *Mem:* Am Chem Soc. *Res:* Synthesis of dielectric materials; magnetochemistry; stabilizers for PVC; organic and inorganic solution thermodynamics; process development of plastics and synthetic rubber; reaction kinetics; synthetic fibers; synthetic inorganic and organometallic chemistry. *Mailing Add:* 5 Knollwood Dr E Windsor NJ 08520

MULE, SALVATORE JOSEPH, b Trenton, NJ, Apr 7, 32; m 56; c 4. PHARMACOLOGY, BIOCHEMISTRY. *Educ:* Col Wooster, BA, 54; Rutgers Univ, MS, 55; Univ Mich, PhD(pharmacol), 61. *Prof Exp:* Fel biochem & pharmacol, Univ Wis, 61-63; res pharmacologist, Addiction Res Ctr, NIMH, Ky, 63-68; DIR, OFF DRUG ABUSE SERV, TESTING & RES LAB, 68- *Concurrent Pos:* Consult to govt & indust. *Mem:* AAAS; Am Chem Soc; Am Soc Pharmacol & Exp Therapeut; Am Acad Forensic Sci; fel Am Inst Chem. *Res:* Drug metabolism as related to biochemical mechanisms associated with the action of narcotic analgesics; development of analytical techniques to detect drugs in biological materials. *Mailing Add:* Off Drug Abuse Serv Testing & Res Lab 80 Hanson Pl Brooklyn NY 11217

MULFORD, DWIGHT JAMES, b Greenville, Ill, Feb 9, 11; m 37. BIOCHEMISTRY. *Educ:* Greenville Col, BS, 33; St Louis Univ, PhD(biochem), 42. *Prof Exp:* Res assoc phys chem, Harvard Univ, 42-47, assoc, 47-49; from asst prof to assoc prof biochem, Univ Kans, Lawrence, 49-56; actg chmn dept, Univ Kans Med Ctr, Kansas City, 57-58, asst dean, 67-71, prof biochem, 56-77, dean, 71-77; RETIRED. *Concurrent Pos:* Tutor, Harvard Univ, 42-46; chief blood processing lab, Mass Dept Pub Health, 45-47, asst dir, 47-49; asst prof, Boston Univ, 46-47. *Mem:* Am Soc Biol Chem; Soc Exp Biol & Med. *Res:* Choline metabolism; plasma fractionation; stability of proteins; blood bank. *Mailing Add:* 6231 Glenfield Dr Shawnee Mission KS 66205

MULFORD, ROBERT ALAN, b Camden, NJ, Dec 13, 47; m 69; c 1. METALLURGY, MATERIALS SCIENCE. *Educ:* St Josephs Col, BS, 69; Univ Pa, MSE, 72, PhD(metall), 74. *Prof Exp:* asst metallurgist, Argonne Nat Lab, 74-79; metallurgist, Gen Elec Res & Develop Ctr, 79-81, METALLURGIST, KNOLLS ATOMIC POWER LAB, GEN ELEC CO, 81- *Mem:* Am Inst Mining, Metall & Petrol Engrs; AAAS. *Res:* Effects of microstructure and trace impurity segregation on fracture, corrosion and stress corrosion; auger spectroscopy; x-ray photoelectron spectroscopy. *Mailing Add:* Gen Elec Co Knolls Atomic Power Lab Box 1072 Schenectady NY 12301

MULFORD, ROBERT NEAL RAMSAY, b US, Oct 2, 22; m 51; c 1. PHYSICAL CHEMISTRY, PHYSICAL METALLURGY. *Educ:* Hofstra Col, BA, 47; Brown Univ, PhD(chem), 50. *Prof Exp:* Asst, Brown Univ, 46-49; staff chemist, 50-69, alt group leader, 69-74, GROUP LEADER, LOS ALAMOS NAT LAB, 74- *Res:* Hydride chemistry; gas-metal equilibria; high temperature chemistry; plutonium chemistry. *Mailing Add:* Los Alamos Nat Lab Los Alamos NM 87544

MULHAUSEN, HEDY ANN, b Cleveland, Ohio, Dec 5, 40. BIOCHEMISTRY, INFORMATION SCIENCE. *Educ:* Ursuline Col, Ohio, AB, 62; Ohio State Univ, MS, 65, PhD(biochem), 67. *Prof Exp:* Res assoc biochem, Ohio State Univ, 68; assoc, Univ Ga, 68-69; BIOCHEM ED ANALYST, CHEM ABSTR SERV, OHIO STATE UNIV, 69-, TECH SERV REP, 80- *Mem:* Am Chem Soc. *Res:* Mechanisms of control in mammalian carbohydrate metabolism. *Mailing Add:* Chem Abstracts Serv Ohio State Univ Columbus OH 43210

MULHAUSEN, ROBERT OSCAR, b Chicago, Ill, June 7, 30; m 54; c 4. INTERNAL MEDICINE, MEDICAL ADMINISTRATION. *Educ:* Univ Ill, BS, 51, MD, 55; Univ Minn, MS, 64. *Prof Exp:* Fel internal med, Univ Minn, Minneapolis, 56-59; from instr to assoc prof internal med, 59-73, from asst dean to assoc dean med sch, 67-73, PROF INTERNAL MED, UNIV MINN, MINNEAPOLIS, 73-; CHIEF MED, ST PAUL RAMSEY HOSP, 73- *Concurrent Pos:* Fulbright res award grant, Rigshospitalet, Copenhagen, 65-66. *Mem:* AAAS; fel Am Col Physicians; Am Fedn Clin Res; NY Acad Sci; Am Soc Nephrol. *Res:* Fluid, electrolyte and acid-base physiology; renal physiology. *Mailing Add:* St Paul Ramsey Hosp 640 Jackson St St Paul MN 55101

MULHERN, JOHN E, JR, b Chicago, Ill, Mar 26, 26; m 50; c 3. PHYSICS. *Educ:* Okla State Univ, BS, 48; Boston Univ, MS, 49, PhD, 54. *Prof Exp:* Semiconductor physicist, Gen Elec Co, 51-54; from asst prof to assoc prof, 54-66, PROF PHYSICS, UNIV NH, 66- *Concurrent Pos:* Vis asst prof, Brandeis Univ, 57-58; consult, NASA Cambridge Res Ctr, 65-69; NIH spec res fel, 69-70; sr vis fel, Cavendish Lab, Eng, 69-70. *Mem:* Am Phys Soc. *Res:* Solid state physics; use of an electron microprobe to analyse the elemental content of biological tissue. *Mailing Add:* Dept of Physics Univ of NH Durham NH 03824

MULHOLLAND, GEORGE, b Philadelphia, Pa, July 12, 38; m 62; c 2. MECHANICAL ENGINEERING. *Educ:* NMex State Univ, BS, 61, MS, 62; Okla State Univ, PhD(mech eng), 67. *Prof Exp:* Sr engr, Jet Propulsion Labs, 65-66; asst prof, 66-76, assoc prof, 76-80, PROF MECH ENG, NMEX STATE UNIV, 80- *Mem:* Am Soc Mech Engrs. *Res:* Heat transfer and fluid mechanics. *Mailing Add:* Dept of Mech Eng NMex State Univ Las Cruces NM 88001

MULHOLLAND, JOHN DERRAL, b Muncie, Ind, Sept 28, 34; m 57; c 2. ASTRONOMY, ASTRONAUTICS. *Educ:* Purdue Univ, BSAE, 57; Univ Cincinnati, MS, 61, PhD, 65; Yale Univ, MS, 64. *Prof Exp:* Asst proj engr, Kett Tech Ctr, US Indust Inc, 57-58; staff engr, Ketco, Inc, 58-59; res asst & lectr aerodynamics, Univ Cincinnati, 59-60, instr astronaut, 60-64, res assoc astron, 64-65, asst prof, 65-66; mem tech staff, Jet Propulsion Lab, Calif Inst Technol, 66-71; RES SCIENTIST, MCDONALD OBSERV, UNIV TEX, AUSTIN, 71- *Concurrent Pos:* Consult, CTL Div, Studebaker-Packard Corp, 61-62; consult, Aerospace Res Lab, Wright-Patterson AFB, 65; consult mem working group on ephemerides for space res, Int Astron Union, 67-70; mem lunar laser ranging panel, Comt Space Res, Int Coun Sci Unions, chmn panel 1D, 75-79; res assoc, Res Group Space Geodesy & Paris Observ, France, 73-74, 76-77, 79, 80 & 81; consult, Encycl Britannica, 74-; sci counr, Ctr Res in Geodyn & Astron, Grasse, France; sr fel, NATO, 79-81. *Honors & Awards:* Bronze Medal, Nat Ctr Space Studies, France, 74. *Mem:* AAAS; Am Geophys Union; Am Astron Soc; Int Astron Union. *Res:* Celestial mechanics; theory of differential correction processes; orbital and rotational dynamics of the earth-moon system; astrometry and dynamics of natural satellites; geophysical application of laser ranging; planetary astrophysics. *Mailing Add:* Dept of Astron Univ of Tex Austin TX 78712

MULHOLLAND, ROBERT J(OSEPH), b St Louis, Mo, Jan 18, 40; m 72, 81. ELECTRICAL ENGINEERING, SYSTEMS THEORY. *Educ:* Washington Univ, BS, 61, MSc, 64, DSc(elec eng), 68. *Prof Exp:* Radar equip engr, Westinghouse Elec Corp, 61-62; instr elec eng, Washington Univ, 64-66; NSF fel, Univ Calif, Los Angeles, 68-69; from asst prof to assoc prof, 69-77, PROF ELEC ENG, OKLA STATE UNIV, 77- *Mem:* AAAS; Inst Elec & Electronics Engrs; Soc Indust & Appl Math; Ecol Soc Am. *Res:* Linear and nonlinear system theory; systems ecology; problems of energy and the environment. *Mailing Add:* Sch of Elec Eng Okla State Univ Stillwater OK 74074

MULIERI, BERTHANN SCUBON, b Menticle, Pa, May 4, 37; m 60. PHYSIOLOGY. *Educ:* Pa State Univ, BS, 58; Univ Vt, PhD(physiol, biophys), 68. *Prof Exp:* Asst prof biol sci, Hunter Col, 67-70; USPHS fel, pharmacol inst, Univ Lund, 71-72; from instr to asst prof biol, Trinity Col, Vt, 72-74; res assoc, 74-77, RES ASST PROF PHYSIOL & BIOPHYS, PHYSIOL & BIOPHYS, UNIV VT, 77- *Concurrent Pos:* Health Educ & Welfare res fel physiol & biophys, Univ Vt, 74-75; mem bd, Creamery Educ Found. *Mem:* Biophys Soc; NY Acad Sci; Sigma Xi. *Res:* Mechanics of muscle contraction; desensitization at neuromuscular junction; electrophysiology of hypertrophied myocardium. *Mailing Add:* Dept of Physiol & Biophys Univ Vt Col of Med Burlington VT 05401

MULINOS, MICHAEL GEORGE, b Cairo, Egypt, Nov 24, 97; nat US; m 27; c 2. CLINICAL PHARMACOLOGY. *Educ:* Columbia Univ, AB, 21, AM, 22, MD, 24, PhD(physiol), 29. *Prof Exp:* Intern, St Vincent's Hosp, Pa, 24-25; instr pediat, Univ Minn, 25-26; vis asst, Univ Chicago, 26; from instr to assoc prof pharmacol, Col Physicians & Surgeons, Columbia Univ, 27-44; assoc prof, NY Med Col, 44-45; dir med res, Interchem Corp, NJ, 45-47; med dir, Com Solvents Corp, 53-63; consult & med dir, McCann-Erickson, Inc, 66-69; med dir, Erwin Wasey, Inc, 69-73; CONSULT, LIFE EXTEN INST, NEW YORK, 75-; MED DIR, RES CONSULTS, INC, NJ, 75-; MED DIR, UNIMED, INC, NJ, 77- *Concurrent Pos:* Asst, Inst Child Guid, Minneapolis, Minn, 26; asst med dir, Life Exten Inst New York. *Mem:* AAAS; Am Soc Pharmacol & Exp Therapeut; Asn Med Dirs (past pres); Soc Exp Biol & Med; Harvey Soc. *Res:* Pharmacology of gastrointestinal tract; toxicology of pharmaceuticals and irritation; physiology of autonomic nervous systems; clinical testing of drugs. *Mailing Add:* 869 Standish Ave Westfield NJ 07090

MULKERN, GREGORY BENEDICT, b Tulsa, Okla, Mar 27, 31; m 54; c 6. ENTOMOLOGY. *Educ:* Univ Ill, BS, 53; Kans State Univ, MS, 54, PhD(entom), 57. *Prof Exp:* From asst prof to assoc prof, 57-69, PROF ENTOM, N DAK STATE UNIV, 69- *Mem:* Entom Soc Am. *Res:* Insect morphology and physiology; insect ecology; host plant selection; biology of orthoptera; acrididae. *Mailing Add:* Dept Entom NDak State Univ Fargo ND 58102

MULKEY, JAMES ROBERT, JR, agronomy, see previous edition

MULLAN, DERMOTT JOSEPH, b Omagh, Northern Ireland, Jan 10, 44; m 70; c 7. ASTROPHYSICS. *Educ:* Queen's Univ, Belfast, BS, 64, BS, 65; Univ Md, PhD(astron), 69. *Prof Exp:* Astronr, Armagh Observ, Northern Ireland, 69-72; presidential intern fel astron, 72-73, asst prof, 73-78, ASSOC PROF ASTROPHYS, BARTOL RES FOUND, UNIV DEL, 78- *Mem:* Am Astron Soc; Int Astron Union. *Res:* Physics of stellar flares; formation of sunspots and starspots; structure of magnetic fields in late-type stars; coronal propagation of cosmic rays; mass loss; magnetic convection; cosmic ray composition. *Mailing Add:* Bartol Res Found Univ of Del Newark DE 19711

MULLAN, JOHN F, b County Derry, NIreland, May 17, 25; US citizen; m 59; c 3. NEUROSURGERY. *Educ:* St Columbus Col, Ireland, BAO, 42; Queen's Univ, Belfast, MB & BCh, 47; FRCS, 51; Am Bd Neurol Surg, dipl, 57. *Hon Degrees:* DSc, Queen's Univ, Belfast, 76. *Prof Exp:* Resident surg, Royal Victoria Hosp, Belfast, Ireland, 50-51; resident neurol surg, Montreal Neurol Inst, 53-55; from asst prof to assoc prof, 55-63, PROF NEUROL SURG, UNIV CHICAGO, 63-, CHMN DEPT, 67- *Concurrent Pos:* Fel, Middlesex Hosp, Univ London, 49-50 & Guys Hosp, 51. *Mem:* Fel Am Col Surg; Am Asn Neurol Surg; Am Acad Neurol Surg. *Res:* Head injury, intracranial aneurysm and pain; epilepsy. *Mailing Add:* Div Neurol Surg 950 E 59th St Chicago IL 60637

MULLANE, JOHN F, b New York, NY, Mar 10, 37; m 62; c 5. MEDICINE, PHARMACOLOGY. *Educ:* State Univ NY, MD, 63, PhD(physiol), 68; Fordham Univ, JD, 77. *Prof Exp:* NY Heart Asn fel, State Univ NY, 66-68; chief exp surg, Walter Reed Army Inst Res, 70-73; asst med dir, 73-75, dir clin res, 75-76, vpres clin res, 77, V PRES SCI AFFAIRS, AYERST LABS, 77- *Mem:* Fel Am Col Clin Pharmacol; Am Soc Nephrol; Am Asn Study Liver Dis; Am Col Law & Med. *Res:* New drug development; clinical pharmacology. *Mailing Add:* Ayerst Labs 685 Third Ave New York NY 10017

MULLANEY, HENRY WENDELL, b Boston, Mass, July 6, 43; m 70; c 3. ELECTROMAGNETICS, IONOSPHERIC PHYSICS. *Educ:* Providence Col, BS, 65; Boston Univ, MA, 67, PhD(physics & astron), 72. *Prof Exp:* Res asst physics & astron, Boston Univ, 68-71; mem tech staff physics, Sanders Assocs, Inc, 71-75; sci officer, 75-80, GROUP LEADER, OFF NAVAL RES, 80- *Mem:* Am Geophys Union; Am Inst Physics; Int Union Radio Sci. *Res:* Ionospheric and magnetospheric physics; solar terrestrial effects; electromagnetics, primarily antennas, antenna arrays and adaptive beamforming; radio and electromagnetic propagation including guided and ducted modes, propagation through plasma including irregularity effects, waveguides and optical fibers; communications, radar and electronic warfare. *Mailing Add:* 6316 25th St N Arlington VA 22207

MULLANEY, PAUL F, b New York, NY, Jan 26, 38; m 63; c 2. PHYSICS, BIOPHYSICS. *Educ:* Iona Col, BS, 59; Univ Del, MS, 63, PhD(physics), 65. *Prof Exp:* Asst prof physics, St Bonaventure Univ, 65-66; staff mem, Bio-Med Res Group, Los Alamos Sci Lab, 66-72, sect leader biophys, 72-73, group leader, biophys & instrumentation group H-10, 73-80; MGR BIOPHYS, BIOL DIV, OAK RIDGE NAT LAB, OAK RIDGE, TENN, 80- *Concurrent Pos:* Consult, Photoconductor Devices Div, Sylvania Elec Prod, Inc, Pa, 65-66; Nat Cancer Inst, Comt Cytol Automation, 73-75; vis scientist, Battelle Inst,Frankfurt, WGer, 78-79. *Honors & Awards:* Alexander von Humboldt Sr Am Scientist Prize, Bonn, WGer, 78. *Mem:* AAAS; Biophys Soc; Am Asn Physics Teachers (pres-elect, 78-80, pres, 80-82). *Res:* Cellular biophysics; light scattering and fluorescence of cells; high speed cell analysis by flow methods; biomedical engineering. *Mailing Add:* Biol Div Oak Ridge Nat Lab Oak Ridge TN 37830

MULLEN, ANTHONY J, b Jermyn, Pa, Sept 2, 27. ELECTROMAGNETISM. *Educ:* Villanova Univ, BS, 50; Cath Univ Am, MS, 54; Bryn Mawr Col, PhD, 68. *Prof Exp:* Teacher, Archbishop Carroll High Sch, 54-59; prof elec eng, Villanova Univ, 59-71, chmn dept, 59-67; sr engr flying qual, Vertol Div, 72, ENG SUPVR ELECTROMAGNETIC PULSE ANAL ENG, BOEING AEROSPACE CO, 72- *Concurrent Pos:* Consult, Reentry Systs Div, Gen Elec Corp, 66-67; res assoc, Geophys Inst, Univ Alaska, 70-71. *Mem:* Am Phys Soc. *Res:* Electromagnetic radiation in plasmas; geomagnetic micropulsations. *Mailing Add:* 17327 158th Ave Se Renton WA 98055

MULLEN, DAVID ANTHONY, zoology, see previous edition

MULLEN, GARY LEE, b Meadville, Pa, Apr 9, 47. NUMBER THEORY, GINITE MATH & COMBINATORICS. *Educ:* Allegheny Col, BS, 69; Pa State Univ, MA, 70, PhD(math), 74. *Prof Exp:* Grad asst, 69-74, from instr to asst prof, 74-78, ASSOC PROF MATH, PA STATE UNIV, 78- *Mem:* Am Math Soc; Math Asn Am. *Res:* Algebra and number theory, particularly polynomials and matrices over finite fields and their relations to combinatorics. *Mailing Add:* Dept of Math Pa State Univ Sharon PA 16146

MULLEN, GARY RICHARD, b Ogdensburg, NY, Nov 16, 45; m 69; c 2. MEDICAL-VETERINARY ENTOMOLOGY, ECOLOGY. *Educ:* Northeastern Univ, BA, 68; Cornell Univ, MS, 70, PhD(entom), 74. *Prof Exp:* Med entomologist & adminr, Allegheny County Health Dept, Vector Control Prog, Pittsburgh, 74-75; asst prof, 75-80, ASSOC PROF, DEPT ZOOL & ENTOM, AUBURN UNIV, 80- *Concurrent Pos:* Consult, Environ Sci Div, QLM Labs, Inc, 73-, Ecol Sci Div, NUS Corp, 75- *Mem:* Entom Soc Am; Am Mosquito Control Asn; Acarological Soc Am; Am Arachnological Soc. *Res:* Ecology of insects and mites of medical and veterinary importance; general acarology with emphasis on the Parasitengona, their evolution and host-parasite relationship with arthropods; acarine parasites of mosquitoes and other nematocerous flies. *Mailing Add:* Dept Zool Entom & Agr Exp Sta Auburn Univ Auburn AL 36849

MULLEN, GEORGE HENRY, b Hackensack, NJ, Nov 10, 34; m 58; c 5. THEORETICAL PHYSICS. *Educ:* Rutgers Univ, BA, 56; Syracuse Univ, MS, 58, PhD(physics), 61. *Prof Exp:* Nat Acad Sci-Nat Res Coun res assoc, US Naval Ord Lab, Md, 61-63; asst prof physics, Univ NH, 63-69, PROF PHYSICS & CHMN DEPT, MANSFIELD STATE COL, 69- *Mem:* Am Phys Soc. *Res:* Theoretical investigations in planetary atmospheres. *Mailing Add:* Dept of Physics Grant Sci Bldg Mansfield State Col Mansfield PA 16933

MULLEN, JAMES A, b Malden, Mass, May 28, 28; m 61; c 4. APPLIED PHYSICS. *Educ:* Providence Col, BS, 50; Harvard Univ, MA, 51, PhD, 55. *Prof Exp:* Mem res staff, 55-65, prin scientist, 65-69, CONSULT SCIENTIST, RES DIV, RAYTHEON CO, 69- *Mem:* Am Phys Soc; Soc Indust & Appl Math; Inst Elec & Electronics Engrs; Am Math Soc. *Res:* Statistical communication theory; noise in non-linear circuits and oscillators; adaptive detection theory; pattern recognition. *Mailing Add:* 337 S Main St Cohasset MA 02025

MULLEN, JAMES G, b St Louis, Mo, Sept 17, 33; m 58; c 3. SOLID STATE PHYSICS. *Educ:* Univ Mo-Rolla, BS, 55; Univ Ill, MS, 57, PhD(physics), 60. *Prof Exp:* From asst physicist to assoc physicist, Argonne Nat Lab, 60-64; from asst prof to assoc prof, 64-75, PROF PHYSICS, PURDUE UNIV, LAFAYETTE, 75- *Concurrent Pos:* Consult, Argonne Nat Lab, 64-65; mem, Ad Hoc Panel Mossbauer Data; Pres, World Technologies, Inc. *Mem:* Am Phys Soc; Am Asn Physics Teachers. *Res:* Studies of solid state diffusion in ionic and metallic crystals; Mossbauer studies of properties of solids. *Mailing Add:* Dept Physics Purdue Univ Lafayette IN 47907

MULLEN, JAMES L, b Norristown, Pa, Jan 8, 42; m 71; c 2. NUTRITION. *Educ:* Harvard Univ, BA, 63; Univ Pa, MD, 67. *Prof Exp:* Surg resident, 67-73, asst prof, 75-78, ASSOC PROF SURG, SCH MED, UNIV PA, 78- *Concurrent Pos:* Chief surg, Philadelphia Vet Admin Med Ctr, 78- *Mem:* Am Soc Parental & Enteral Nutrit; Am Col Surgeons; Soc Univ Surgeons; Soc Surg Alimentary Tract. *Res:* Clinical nutrition; gastrointestinal surgery; nutrition and cancer; anorexia nervosa. *Mailing Add:* 3400 Spruce St Philadelphia PA 19104

MULLEN, JOSEPH DAVID, b Green Isle, Minn, Jan 6, 34; m 56; c 4. BIOCHEMISTRY, FOOD SCIENCE. *Educ:* Col St Thomas, BS, 56; Univ Minn, PhD(biochem), 62. *Prof Exp:* group head, 61-72, dept head, 72-80, SR PRIN SCIENTIST, GEN MILLS, INC, 80- *Mem:* AAAS; Am Chem Soc; Am Asn Cereal Chem; Inst Food Technologists. *Res:* Protein chemistry; relation of protein structures to function in foods; new food product development including extruded protein and gum systems, edible protein films, gel technology, low calorie foods and nutrition; relation of food to dental health; satiety and appetite. *Mailing Add:* Gen Mills Inc Bell Res Ctr 9000 Plymouth Ave N Minneapolis MN 55427

MULLEN, JOSEPH MATTHEW, b Washington, DC, June 1, 44; m 65. CHEMICAL PHYSICS, ASTROPHYSICS. *Educ:* Old Dom Univ, BS, 66; Univ Fla, PhD(physics), 72. *Prof Exp:* Asst prof physics, Valdosta State Col, 71-72; fel, Univ Fla, 72-74; prin staff oper anal, Oper Res Inc, Silver Spring, Md, 74-76; MEM STAFF, JEM ASSOCS, RESTON, VA, 76- *Mem:* AAAS; Sigma Xi; Am Phys Soc. *Res:* Determination of intermolecular potentials; development of instrumentation for ion-molecule reaction studies; theory of mass transfer in close binary star systems. *Mailing Add:* 2159 Greenskeeper Ct Reston VA 22091

MULLEN, KENNETH, b London, Eng, Feb 28, 39; US citizen; m 61; c 3. STATISTICS, MATHEMATICS. *Educ:* Western Reserve Univ, BA, 61; Va Polytech Inst & State Univ, PhD(statist), 66. *Prof Exp:* Asst prof math, Radford Col, 64-65; asst prof biometry, Med Col Va, 65-67; sr statistician, Ciba, Ltd, 20 Switz, 67-69; asst prof, 69-71, ASSOC PROF STATIST, UNIV GUELPH, 71- *Concurrent Pos:* Consult, Am Tobacco Co, 65-67 & Albemarle Paper Co, 66-67. *Mem:* Am Statist Asn. *Res:* Estimation problems associated with censored and truncated data; development of non-parametric procedures. *Mailing Add:* 31 Kendrick Guelph ON N16 2P5 Can

MULLEN, LEO VINCENT, JR, b Paterson, NJ, June 4, 26; m 53; c 2. RUBBER CHEMISTRY. *Educ:* Univ NC, BS, 47, MS, 49. *Prof Exp:* Sect head petrol additives, Exxon Res Eng Co, 54-60, MGR, US TECH SERV ELASTOMERS, EXXON CHEM CO, 60- *Mem:* Am Chem Soc; Soc Automotive Engrs. *Res:* Elastomers product applications and development. *Mailing Add:* Elastomers Technol Div PO Box 45 Linden NJ 07036

MULLEN, PATRICIA ANN, b Flushing, NY, July 10, 35. COSMETIC CHEMISTRY. *Educ:* Seton Hill Col, BA, 57; Mt Holyoke Col, MA, 61. *Prof Exp:* Res chemist, Charles Bruning Co, 57-59; res asst spectros, Mt Holyoke Col, 59-61; res chemist, Am Cyanamid Co, 63-74, group leader, 74-77; mgr, 77-80, DIR, FRAGRANCE APPLN LAB, NAARDEN INT USA, INC, 80-, MGR HOUSEHOLD PROD LINE, 81- *Mem:* Am Chem Soc; Soc Cosmetic Chemists. *Res:* Ultraviolet and vacuum spectroscopy; photochemistry; spectropolarimetry; cosmetic chemistry; fragrances. *Mailing Add:* Naarden Int 919 Third Ave New York NY 10022

MULLEN, RICHARD JOSEPH, b Leominster, Mass, Aug 15, 41; m 64; c 3. DEVELOPMENTAL GENETICS, NEUROSCIENCES. *Educ:* Fitchburg State Col, BS, 63; Univ NH, MS, 69, PhD(genetics), 71. *Prof Exp:* USPHS fel develop genetics, Harvard Med Sch, 71-74, RES ASSOC NEUROSCI, CHILDREN'S HOSP MED CTR, 73-; ASST PROF NEUROPATHOL, HARVARD MED SCH, 76- *Concurrent Pos:* Instr neuropathol, Harvard Med Sch, 73-76. *Res:* Mammalian developmental genetics; culture and manipulation of preimplantation embryos; use of experimental chimeric mice in studies of brain development. *Mailing Add:* Dept of Neurosci Children's Hosp Med Ctr Boston MA 02115

MULLEN, ROBERT KEECH, physiological ecology, radiation ecology, see previous edition

MULLEN, ROBERT TERRENCE, b Chicago, Ill, Sept 25, 35; m 55; c 4. PHYSICAL CHEMISTRY. *Educ:* Univ Ill, BS, 57; Univ Calif, PhD(phys chem), 61. *Prof Exp:* Res assoc chem, Brookhaven Nat Lab, 61-63; sr chemist, Res Lab, Merck & Co, Inc, 63-65, sect leader, 65-67, res fel, 67-68, supvr automation & control dept, 68-70, mgr automation & control lab automation, 70-75, mgr lab & gen automation, 75-78, dir, 78-79, EXEC DIR AUTOMATION & CONTROL SYSTS, MERCK & CO, INC, 79- *Mem:* AAAS; Am Chem Soc; Soc Appl Spectros; NY Acad Sci. *Res:* Hot atom chemistry; photochemistry; Mossbauer spectroscopy; radioisotope tracer applications; laboratory and process automation. *Mailing Add:* Automation & Control Dept Merck & Co Inc Rahway NJ 07065

MULLEN, WESLEY GRIGG, b Richmond, Va, Nov 30, 22; m 51; c 2. CONSTRUCTION MATERIALS. *Educ:* Va Mil Inst, BS, 49; Univ Md, MS, 51; Purdue Univ, PhD(civil eng), 63. *Prof Exp:* Field engr heavy construct, Madigan-Hyland Consult Engrs, 51-59; instr civil eng, Univ Md, 59-61, Purdue Univ, 61-62; res engr highways, Md State Roads Comn, 63-65; PROF CIVIL ENG, NC STATE UNIV, 65- *Concurrent Pos:* Coordr, Highway Res Prog, NC State Univ, 65-81. *Honors & Awards:* Charles B Dudley Medal, Am Soc Testing Mat, 66. *Mem:* Am Soc Testing Mat; Am Soc Civil Eng; Am Concrete Inst; Asn Asphalt Paving Technologists. *Res:* Properties of Portland cement concrete; skid resistance of pavements including maintenance, testing and prediction. *Mailing Add:* NC State Univ PO Box 5993 Raleigh NC 27650

MULLENAX, CHARLES HOWARD, b Sterling, Colo, Feb 5, 32; m 54; c 4. ECOLOGY, RANGE SCIENCE & MANAGEMENT. *Educ:* Colo State Univ, BS, 53, DVM, 56; Cornell Univ, MS, 61. *Hon Degrees:* DVM, Cent Univ, Ecuador, 66. *Prof Exp:* Owner & vet, Mountain Parks Vet Hosp, 56-59; asst vet physiol, NY State Vet Col, Cornell, 59-61; res vet, Nat Animal Dis Lab, USDA, 61-64; lectr vet med & dir clins, Fulbright Binational Educ Comn, US Dept State, Cent Univ, Ecuador, 64-66; assoc pathologist, Agr Sci Prog, Rockefeller Found, Bogota, Colombia, 66-69; animal prod training specialist, Int Ctr Trop Agr, Cali, Colombia, 69-71; tech dir, Colombia Livestock Proj, Int Bank Reconstruction & Develop, 71-73; pres & gen mgr, Concordia Int Ltda, 73-79; COORDR, NUTRIT RES, META LIVESTOCK ASN, 80- *Concurrent Pos:* Consult, Bahamas Livestock Co, 56-57. *Mem:* NY

Acad Sci; Asn Trop Biol. *Res.* Ruminant intermediary metabolism; physiopathology; veterinary epidemiology; tropical livestock diseases; livestock production; range ecology; nutritional diseases of cattle in tropics. *Mailing Add:* Concordia Int Ltda Apartado Aereo 21-18 Villavicencio Meta Colombia

MULLENDORE, A(RTHUR) W(AYNE), b River Falls, Wis, Aug 5, 28; m 60. METALLURGY. *Educ:* Univ Wis, BS, 50; Mass Inst Technol, SM, 53, ScD(metall), 60. *Prof Exp:* Asst prof metall, Mass Inst Technol, 60-64; staff mem, Sandia Corp, 64-69; DIV SUPVR, SANDIA LABS, 69- *Mem:* Am Inst Mining, Metall & Petrol Eng; Electron Micros Soc Am. *Res:* High temperature metallurgy; electron microscopy; carbon materials. *Mailing Add:* Div 5315 Sandia Labs Sandia Park Albuquerque NM 87107

MULLENDORE, JAMES ALAN, b Greenwood, Wis, Dec 6, 32; m 62; c 2. METALLURGICAL ENGINEERING. *Educ:* Univ Wis, BS, 54, MS, 55; Univ Ill, PhD(metall eng), 61. *Prof Exp:* Sr scientist, Avco Res & Develop Lab, 59-60, lead scientist, 60-61; asst prof metall eng, Univ Wis-Madison, 61-66; engr specialist, Sylvania Elec Prod, Inc, 66-71, head metals res, 71-80, SR ENGR SPECIALIST & HEAD REFRACTORY METALS RES, CHEM & METAL DIV, GTE SYLVANIA, 66- *Concurrent Pos:* Mem, Am Powder Metall Inst. *Mem:* Am Inst Mining, Metall & Petrol Engrs; Am Soc Metals. *Res:* Physical and process metallurgy of refractory metals and alloys. *Mailing Add:* Chem & Metals Div GTE Sylvania Towanda PA 18848

MULLENDORE, JAMES MYERS, b Ft Wayne, Ind, Aug 15, 19; m 42; c 4. SPEECH PATHOLOGY, AUDIOLOGY. *Educ:* Northwestern Univ, BS, 41, MA, 42, PhD(speech path), 48. *Prof Exp:* Instr speech correction, Northwestern Univ, 44-45; from asst prof to assoc prof speech, Univ Va, 45-61; prof audiol & speech path, Vanderbilt Univ, 61-63 & WVa Univ, 63-67; dir sch speech & hearing sci, 67-78, PROF SPEECH & HEARING SCI, BRADLEY UNIV, 67-, DEAN, COL HEALTH SCI, 78- *Concurrent Pos:* Ed consult, State Farm Mutual Ins Co, 56-61; prof, George Peabody Col, 61-63; dir, Bill Wilkerson Hearing & Speech Ctr, 61-63. *Mem:* Fel Am Speech & Hearing Asn; Am Soc Allied Health Prof. *Res:* Stuttering; supervision and administration; voice disorders. *Mailing Add:* 203 W Northgate Rd Peoria IL 61614

MULLER, BURTON HARLOW, b New York, NY, May 11, 24; m 52; c 2. PHYSICS. *Educ:* Wesleyan Univ, BA, 44; Yale Univ, MS, 45; Univ Ill, PhD(physics), 54. *Prof Exp:* Asst physics, SAM Labs, Columbia Univ, 45; from asst prof to assoc prof, 53-62, PROF PHYSICS, UNIV WYO,62- *Concurrent Pos:* NSF fac fel, Univ BC, 59-60 & Univ Nottingham, 65-66; vis prof, Univ Kent, 71-72; cong sci fel, Am Phys Soc, 81. *Mem:* Am Phys Soc. *Res:* Nuclear magnetic resonance; molecular motion. *Mailing Add:* Dept of Physics Univ of Wyo Laramie WY 82071

MULLER, CORNELIUS HERMAN, b Collinsville, Ill, July 22, 09; m 39; c 1. PLANT ECOLOGY, ALLELOPATHY. *Educ:* Univ Tex, BA, 32, MA, 33; Univ Ill, PhD(plant ecol), 38. *Prof Exp:* Asst bot, Univ Tex, 29-33; asst Univ Ill, 34-38; ecologist, Ill State Natural Hist Surv, 38; asst botanist, Div Plant Explor & Introd, Bur Plant Indust, USDA, 38-42, rubber plant invests, 42, assoc botanist, Spec Guayule Res Proj, 42-45; from asst prof to prof, 45-76, EMER PROF BOT, UNIV CALIF, SANTA BARBARA, 76- *Concurrent Pos:* Instr grad sch, USDA, 41-42, collabr, 45-46; res assoc, Inst Tech & Plant Indust, Southern Methodist Univ, 45 & Santa Barbara Bot Garden, 48-76; fac res lectr, Univ Calif, Santa Barbara, 57, actg dean grad div, 61-62; adj prof bot, Univ Tex, Austin, 74- *Mem:* Eminent ecologist, Ecol Soc Am. *Res:* Vegetation of the southwestern United States, Mexico and Central America; basic nature of the biotic community; biochemical inhibition among higher plants; plant competition and community interactions; taxonomy and evolution of American Quercus. *Mailing Add:* Dept of Biol Sci Univ of Calif Santa Barbara CA 93106

MULLER, DAVID EUGENE, b Austin, Tex, Nov 2, 24; m 44; c 2. APPLIED MATHEMATICS. *Educ:* Calif Inst Technol, BS, 47, PhD(physics), 51. *Prof Exp:* Res fel physics, Calif Inst Technol, 51-52; fel electronic digital comput, 52-53, res asst prof appl math, 53-56, res assoc prof, 56-60, res prof, 60-64, PROF MATH, UNIV ILL, URBANA, 64- *Concurrent Pos:* Consult, IBM Corp, 59-; Fulbright res scholar, Univ Tokyo, 61-62. *Mem:* AAAS; Am Phys Soc; Am Math Soc. *Res:* Switching and automata theory; error correcting codes. *Mailing Add:* Dept of Math 273 Atgeld Hall Univ Ill Urbana IL 61801

MÜLLER, DIETRICH, b Leipzig, Ger, Sept 14, 36; m 68; c 2. PHYSICS, ASTROPHYSICS. *Educ:* Univ Bonn, Dipl physics, 61, PhD(physics), 64. *Prof Exp:* Res assoc physics, Univ Bonn, 64-68; res assoc physics, Univ Chicago, 68-70, asst prof, 70-77, ASSOC PROF, ENRICO FERMI INST & DEPT PHYSICS, 77- *Mem:* Am Phys Soc. *Res:* Experimental physics; mass spectroscopy; aeronomy; high energy astrophysics; cosmic ray research. *Mailing Add:* Enrico Fermi Inst Univ of Chicago 933 E 56th St Chicago IL 60637

MULLER, ERIC RENE, b Morija, Lesotho, Nov 5, 38; Can citizen; m 65; c 2. MATHEMATICS, PHYSICS. *Educ:* Univ Natal, BSc, 60, MSc, 62; Univ Sheffield, PhD(theoret physics), 67. *Prof Exp:* Lectr math, Rhodes Univ, SAfrica, 61-64; lectr col appl arts & technol, Univ Sheffield, 64-67; asst prof math & physics, 67-71, ASSOC PROF MATH & PHYSICS, BROCK UNIV, 71- *Concurrent Pos:* Consult, Steltner Develop, 70- & Transp Develop Agency, Can Ministry Transport, 73- *Mem:* Math Soc Can; Am Asn Physics Teachers; Math Asn Am; Soc Indust & Appl Math. *Res:* Mathematical models and analyses of transportation systems; theoretical solid state physics. *Mailing Add:* Dept of Math Brock Univ St Catharines ON L2S 3A1 Can

MULLER, ERNEST HATHAWAY, b Tabriz, Iran, Mar 4, 23; US citizen; m 51; c 3. GEOLOGY. *Educ:* Col Wooster, AB, 47; Univ Ill, MS, 49, PhD(geol), 52. *Prof Exp:* Geologist mil geol br, US Geol Surv, Alaska, 48, proj head, Bristol Bay Area, 49-54; asst prof geol, Cornell Univ, 54-59; assoc prof, 59-65, interim chmn, 70-71 & 80-81, PROF GEOL, SYRACUSE UNIV, 65- *Concurrent Pos:* Geologist, NY State Sci Serv, 56-; mem SChile exped, Am Geog Soc, 59; mem exped, Katmai Nat Monument, Alaska, 63-64; res assoc, Mus Natural Hist, Reykjavik, Iceland, 68-69 & Churchill Falls Power Proj, Labrador, 70; Erskine fel, Univ Canterbury, Christchurch, NZ, 73-74; vis prof, Alaska Pac Univ, 79. *Mem:* AAAS; Geol Soc Am; Nat Asn Geol Teachers; Am Asn Univ Professors; Glaciol Soc. *Res:* Geomorphology; glacial, engineering and environmental geology; permafrost; denudation; drumlin origins; glacial geology of New York, Southwestern Alaska, Iceland, and South Island of New Zealand. *Mailing Add:* Dept of Geol 204 Heroy Geol Lab Syracuse Univ Syracuse NY 13210

MULLER, GEORGE HEINZ, b Ger, June 6, 19; US citizen; m 49. VETERINARY DERMATOLOGY. *Educ:* Tex A&M Univ, DVM, 43; Am Col Vet Internal Med, dipl & cert dermat, 74. *Prof Exp:* Dir, Pittsburg Vet Hosp, 46-56; DIR, MULLER VET HOSP, 56-, DIR, VET DERMATOL CLIN, 79-; CLIN PROF DERMAT, SCH MED, STANFORD UNIV, 58- *Concurrent Pos:* Ed dermat, Current Vet Ther, 66-75; pres, Dermat Specialty Group, Am Col Vet Internal Med, 74-76. *Honors & Awards:* McCoy Mem Award, Wash State Univ, 69; Merit Award Dermat, Am Animal Hosp Asn, 70. *Mem:* Am Acad Vet Dermat (pres); affil Am Acad Dermat; Am Animal Hosp Asn. *Res:* Small animal veterinary dermatology; comparative dermatology; canine and human demodicosis. *Mailing Add:* Dept of Dermat Stanford Univ Med Sch Stanford CA 94305

MULLER, KARL FREDERICK, b Glen Ridge, NJ, Sept 5, 35; m 61; c 2. APPLIED MATHEMATICS, COMPUTER SCIENCE. *Educ:* Lafayette Col, BSME, 57; Syracuse Univ, MSEE, 65, PhD(appl math), 70. *Prof Exp:* Field engr, Leeds & Northrup Co, Philadelphia, 57-63; res engr, Syracuse Univ Res Corp, 64-66, group leader appl math, 66-69; mem tech staff, Mitre Corp, Bedford, Mass, 69-76; prin res engr, Avco Everett Res Labs, 76-79; MEM STAFF, C S DRAPER LAB INC, CAMBRIDGE, MASS, 79- *Concurrent Pos:* Mem weather '85 study group, US Air Force Systs Command, 71-72; consult, PHI Comput Serv, Inc, Arlington, Mass, 72. *Res:* Detailed mathematical analysis, modeling and computer simulation of physical and probabalistic phenomena associated with seismic, and acoustic propagation, weather predictability, optimal control systems, high-sensitivity electro-optical sensors and detection, especially identification algorithms; fault tolerant digital architecture. *Mailing Add:* 9 San Jose Terr Stoneham MA 02180

MULLER, KENNETH JOSEPH, b Altadena, Calif, July 29, 45; m 75; c 1. NEUROBIOLOGY, BIOPHYSICS. *Educ:* Univ Chicago, SB, 66; Mass Inst Technol, PhD(biol), 71. *Prof Exp:* Fel neurobiol anat, Harvard Med Sch, 71-75; STAFF MEM NEUROBIOL, CARNEGIE INST WASHINGTON, 75-; assoc prof, 77-81, ASSOC PROF, DEPT BIOPHYS, JOHNS HOPKINS UNIV, 81- *Mem:* AAAS; Am Physiol Soc; Soc Neurosci; Soc Gen Physiologists. *Res:* Developmental neurobiology; synapse regeneration; neuronal signaling and integration; synaptic transmission. *Mailing Add:* Dept of Embryol 115 W University Pkwy Baltimore MD 21210

MULLER, LAWRENCE DEAN, b Peoria, Ill, Nov 26, 41; m 65; c 1. DAIRY HUSBANDRY. *Educ:* Univ Ill, Urbana, BS, 64, MS, 66; Purdue Univ, Lafayette, PhD(animal sci), 69. *Prof Exp:* Asst prof animal sci, Purdue Univ, 69-71; assoc prof dairy sci, SDak State Univ, 71-76; assoc prof, 76-80, PROF DAIRY SCI, PA STATE UNIV, 80- *Mem:* Am Dairy Sci Asn; Am Soc Animal Sci; Am Inst Nutrit. *Res:* Animal production with emphasis on interrelationships between nutrition, physiology and management on animal productivity. *Mailing Add:* Dept of Dairy & Animal Sci Pa State Univ University Park PA 16802

MULLER, MARCEL WETTSTEIN, b Vienna, Austria, Nov 1, 22; nat US; m 47; c 3. PHYSICS. *Educ:* Columbia Univ, BS, 49, AM, 52; Stanford Univ, PhD(physics), 57. *Prof Exp:* Sr scientist, Varian Assocs, Calif, 52-66; PROF ELEC ENG, WASHINGTON UNIV, 66- *Concurrent Pos:* Lectr, Univ Zurich, 62-63; vis prof, Univ Colo, 68; Humboldt award, 76; vis scientist, Max Planck Inst Metals Res, Stuttgart, 76-77. *Mem:* Optical Soc Am; Am Phys Soc; Inst Elec & Electronics Eng. *Res:* Microwave electronics; quantum electronics; solid state physics. *Mailing Add:* Dept Elec Eng Washington Univ Lindell & Skinker Blvds St Louis MO 63130

MULLER, MERVIN EDGAR, b Hollywood, Calif, June 1, 28; m 63; c 3. COMPUTER SCIENCE, STATISTICS. *Educ:* Univ Calif, Los Angeles, PhD(math), 54. *Prof Exp:* Instr math, Cornell Univ, 54-56; res assoc, Princeton Univ, 56-59; mem staff control planning, Data Processing Div, Int Bus Mach Corp, 59-60, mgr proj weld, 60-64; prof comput sci, Univ Wis-Madison, 64-70, prof comput sci & statist, 70-71, dir comput ctr, 64-70; DIR DEPT COMPUT ACTIV, WORLD BANK, 71- *Concurrent Pos:* Mem bd dir, Am Fedn Info Processing, 71-73, chmn finance comt, 71-75; chmn comt statist comput, Int Statist Inst, 75-77; mem steering comt, Nat Res Coun panel sci computing, Nat Bur Standards, 80-82. *Mem:* Am Math Soc; Int Statist Inst; Math Asn Am; fel Am Statist Asn; Asn Comput Mach. *Res:* Monte Carlo procedures and simulation; statistical design of experiments; use of computers in statistics, data processing and statistical control procedures; computer information systems and languages; management information systems; data base management systems. *Mailing Add:* 5303 Mohican Rd Washington DC 20016

MULLER, MIKLOS, b Budapest, Hungary, Nov 24, 30; m 73; c 2. BIOLOGICAL CHEMISTRY, PARASITOLOGY. *Educ:* Med Univ Budapest, MD, 55. *Prof Exp:* Instr biol & histol, Med Univ Budapest, 50-55, asst prof, 55-64; res assoc biochem cytol, Rockefeller Inst, 64-65; Rask-Orsted fel & guest investr cell biol, Dept Physiol, Carlsberg Lab, Copenhagen, 65-66; asst prof biochem cytol, 66-68, ASSOC PROF BIOCHEM CYTOL, ROCKEFELLER UNIV, 68- *Concurrent Pos:* Ed, J Molecular & Biochem Parasitol, 80-; mem, Steering Comt Sci Working Group, Leishmaniasis World Health Orgn Spec Prog on Trop Dis, 77- *Honors & Awards:* S H Hutner Prize, Soc Protozool, 77. *Mem:* Soc Protozool (pres-elect, 81-82, pres, 82-83); Am Soc Parasitol; Med Soc Study Venereal Dis; Am Microbiol Soc; Am Venerial Dis Asn. *Res:* Physiology and biochemistry of parasitic and free living protozoa; peroxisomes; hydrogenosomes; action of antiprotozoal drugs; lysosomes in intracellular digestion and in host-parasite relationships. *Mailing Add:* Rockefeller Univ 1230 York Ave New York NY 10021

MULLER, NORBERT, b Hamburg, Ger, Jan 25, 29; nat US; m 58; c 10. PHYSICAL CHEMISTRY. *Educ:* Univ Calif, BS, 49; Harvard Univ, MA, 51, PhD(chem physics), 53. *Prof Exp:* Instr chem, 53-54, from asst prof to assoc prof, 56-68, PROF CHEM, PURDUE UNIV, LAFAYETTE, 68- *Mem:* Am Chem Soc; Royal Soc Chem. *Res:* Molecular structure and spectra; nuclear magnetic resonance; surfactant chemistry. *Mailing Add:* Dept of Chem Purdue Univ Lafayette IN 47907

MULLER, OLAF, b Tallinn, Estonia, Jan 14, 38; US citizen. INORGANIC CHEMISTRY, SOLID STATE CHEMISTRY. *Educ:* Western Reserve Univ, BA, 60, MS, 61; Pa State Univ, PhD(solid state sci), 68. *Prof Exp:* Res assoc solid state sci, Pa State Univ, 68-72; inorg chemist, Corp Res & Develop Ctr, Gen Elec Co, 72-75; SCIENTIST SOLID STATE SCI, WEBSTER RES CTR, XEROX CORP, 75- *Mem:* Am Chem Soc; Am Ceramic Soc. *Res:* Synthesis and crystal chemistry of inorganic materials; property-composition relationships; magnetic materials; thin films. *Mailing Add:* Webster Res Ctr Bldg 201 Xerox Corp 800 Phillips Rd Webster NY 14580

MULLER, OTTO HEINRICH, b Esslingen, Ger, Sept 20, 08; nat US; m 41; c 6. PHYSIOLOGY. *Educ:* Stanford Univ, BA, 33; Charles Univ, Prague, RNDr(phys chem), 35. *Prof Exp:* Res asst physiol, Stanford Univ, 35-37, res assoc chem, 37-38; res assoc surg & assoc physiol, Med Col, Cornell Univ, 38-40, res assoc anat, 40-45; from instr to asst prof physiol & pharmacol, Col Med, Univ Nebr, 45-47; from asst prof to assoc prof physiol, Syracuse Univ, 47-50; from assoc prof to prof, 50-77, EMER PROF PHYSIOL, STATE UNIV NY UPSTATE MED CTR, 77- *Concurrent Pos:* Upjohn fel, Stanford Univ, 37-38; instr physiol, Med Col, Cornell Univ, 42-45. *Mem:* Am Chem Soc; Am Physiol Soc; fel NY Acad Sci; Harvey Soc. *Res:* Polarographic studies of passivity; overvoltage; oxid-red systems; buffer action; proteins; enzymes; respiratory gases; organic chemistry. *Mailing Add:* Dept of Physiol State Univ of NY Upstate Med Ctr Syracuse NY 13210

MULLER, PAMELA HALLOCK, b Pierre, SDak, June 2, 48; m 69. PALEONTOLOGY, STRATIGRAPHY-SEDIMENTATION. *Educ:* Univ Mont, BA, 69; Univ Hawaii, Manoa, MS, 72, PhD(oceanog), 77. *Prof Exp:* ASST PROF EARTH SCI, UNIV TEX PERMIAN BASIN, 78- *Concurrent Pos:* Environ consult, Hawaiian Elec Co Inc, 75-77; res fel, Univ Copenhagen, 78 & Kiel Univ, 79; consult, Cities Serv Co, 81; prin investr, NSF grant, 81-83; mem, Cushman Found Foraminiferal Res. *Mem:* Geol Soc Am; Soc Econ Paleontologists & Mineralogists; Asn Women Sci. *Res:* Carbonate production; algal symbiosis; morphology of foraminifera; carbonate paleoenvironments; population dynamics. *Mailing Add:* Fac of Earth Sci Univ Tex of the Permian Basin Odessa TX 79762

MULLER, RICHARD A, b New York, NY, Jan 6, 44; m 66; c 2. EXPERIMENTAL PHYSICS. *Educ:* Columbia Univ, AB, 64; Univ Calif, Berkeley, PhD(physics), 69. *Prof Exp:* Asst res physicist, Space Sci Lab, 69-75, assoc res physicist, 75-78, assoc prof physics, 78-80, PROF PHYSICS, UNIV CALIF, BERKELEY, 80-, FAC SR SCIENTIST, LAWRENCE BERKELEY LAB, 78- *Concurrent Pos:* Lectr physics, Univ Calif, Berkeley, 72-74; consult to US Govt, 73- *Honors & Awards:* Tex Instruments Found Founders Prize, 77; Alan T Waterman Award, NSF, 78. *Mem:* Am Phys Soc; Am Astron Soc; AAAS; Sigma Xi; Int Astron Union. *Res:* Cosmic microwave anisotropy; radioisotope dating using accelerators; adaptive optics; elementary particles; automated supernova search; instrumentation. *Mailing Add:* 2831 Garber St 50/232 Univ of Calif Berkeley CA 94720

MULLER, RICHARD S, b Weehawken, NJ, May 5, 33; m 57; c 2. SOLID-STATE DEVICE PHYSICS, SENSOR DEVICES. *Educ:* Stevens Inst Technol, MechE, 55; Calif Inst Technol, MSEE, 57, PhD(physics), 62. *Prof Exp:* Res engr, Hughes Aircraft Co, 57-58; from asst prof to assoc prof, 62-73, vchmn admin, Dept of Elec Eng & Comput Sci, 73-75, PROF ELEC ENG, UNIV CALIF, BERKELEY, 73- *Concurrent Pos:* Consult, Pac Semiconductors Inc, 59-62, Stanford Res Inst & Lawrence Berkeley Lab, 62-, Hughes Micro-electronics Labs, 63-64, Signetics Corp, 71-, Xerox Corp, 77-; NATO fel, Munich Tech Univ, 68-69. *Mem:* Sr mem Inst Elec & Electronics Engrs. *Res:* Solid-state device research; integrated sensing devices. *Mailing Add:* Dept of Elec Eng & Comput Sci Cory Hall Univ of Calif Berkeley CA 94720

MULLER, ROBERT ALBERT, b Passaic, NJ, Dec 5, 28; m 50; c 2. CLIMATOLOGY, PHYSICAL GEOGRAPHY. *Educ:* Rutgers Univ, BA, 58; Syracuse Univ, MA, 59, PhD(geog), 62. *Prof Exp:* Phys geogr, Pac Southwest Forest & Range Exp Sta, Calif, 62-64; lectr climat, Univ Calif, Berkeley, 64; from asst prof to assoc prof geog, Rutgers Univ, 64-68; assoc prof, 69-72, chmn dept geog & anthrop, 78-81, PROF GEOG, LA STATE UNIV, 72-, STATE CLIMATOLOGIST, 78- *Mem:* Asn Am Geog; Am Geophys Union; Am Meteorol Soc. *Res:* Water balance and synoptic climatology evaluations of evapotranspiration loss, water yield, and river basin regimen including flooding. *Mailing Add:* Dept of Geog La State Univ Baton Rouge LA 70803

MULLER, ROBERT E, b Brooklyn, NY, June 27, 21; m 49; c 4. CHEMICAL ENGINEERING. *Educ:* Polytech Inst Brooklyn, BChemE, 41, MChemE, 42, DSc(chem eng), 47. *Prof Exp:* Res engr plastics & atomic physics, Bakelite Co Div, Union Carbide & Carbon Corp, 42-46; res fel adsorption, Am Sugar Ref Co, 46-47; dir res & prod, Luxene, Inc, 47-54; from asst res dir to div res mgr, US Gypsum Co, 54-63; dir res & develop, MacAndrews & Forbes Co, 63-65; corp dir res & develop, Nat Can Corp, 65-67; PRES, ASTRON DENT CORP, 67- *Mem:* Am Chem Soc; Am Inst Chem Engrs. *Res:* High polymer and atomic research; paper and wood; research management. *Mailing Add:* Astron Dental Corp 280 Holbrook Dr Wheeling IL 60090

MULLER, ROBERT NEIL, b Santa Barbara, Calif, Aug 29, 46; m 70. PLANT ECOLOGY. *Educ:* Univ Calif, Riverside, BA, 69; Yale Univ, MFS, 72, PhD(plant ecol), 75. *Prof Exp:* Appointee ecol, Argonne Nat Lab, 74-76, asst ecologist, 76-78; ASST PROF, DEPT FORESTRY, UNIV KY, 78- *Mem:* Ecol Soc Am. *Res:* Adaptations of species to their environment; factors affecting distributions of species within plant communities; structure and function of terrestrial ecosystems. *Mailing Add:* Dept of Forestry Univ of Ky Lexington KY 40506

MULLER, ROLF HUGO, b Aarau, Switz, Aug 6, 29; nat US; m 62; c 2. ELECTROCHEMISTRY, CHEMICAL ENGINEERING. *Educ:* Swiss Fed Inst Technol, Dipl sc nat, 53, Dr sc nat(phys chem), 57. *Prof Exp:* Res chemist polychem, E I du Pont de Nemours & Co, 57-60; res assoc electrochem eng, Univ Calif, Berkeley, 61-62; asst head inorg mat res div, 70-75, PRIN INVESTR PHYSICS & CHEM OF PHASE BOUNDARIES, LAWRENCE BERKELEY LAB, UNIV CALIF, 62-, LECTR CHEM ENG, 66-, ASST HEAD MAT & MOLECULAR RES DIV, 75-, STAFF SR SCIENTIST, 78- *Concurrent Pos:* Secy ad hoc planning subcomt, Nat Battery Adv Comt, 77- *Mem:* AAAS; Am Chem Soc; Optical Soc Am; Int Soc Electrochem; Electrochem Soc. *Res:* Scale-dependent processes in electrochemistry; optical observation of surfaces, thin films and boundary layers; electrolytic metal dissolution and crystallization; electrochemical processes at high current densities, mass transport; film formation in batteries and fuel cells. *Mailing Add:* Mat & Molecular Res Div Lawrence Berkeley Lab Bldg 62 Berkeley CA 94720

MULLER, WALTER HENRY, b New York, NY, Jan 30, 21; m 46; c 4. PLANT PHYSIOLOGY, ALLELOPATHY. *Educ:* Queens Col, NY, BS, 42; Cornell Univ, PhD(plant physiol), 50. *Prof Exp:* Bacteriologist, Appl Res Labs, Inc, NJ, 42; instr bot, Cornell Univ, 49-50; from instr to assoc prof, 50-65, PROF BOT, UNIV CALIF, SANTA BARBARA, 65- *Mem:* AAAS; Am Soc Plant Physiol; Bot Soc Am; Am Inst Biol Sci. *Res:* Natural inhibitors in vascular plants; influence of natural inhibitors on plant growth, development and metabolism. *Mailing Add:* Dept Bio-Sci Univ Calif Santa Barbara CA 93106

MULLER, WILLIAM A, b New York, NY, Aug 16, 42. MARINE BIOLOGY, MARINE ECOLOGY. *Educ:* Queens Col, NY, BS, 64, MS, 68; City Univ New York, PhD(biol), 72. *Prof Exp:* Res asst marine biol, Am Mus Natural Hist, 60-69; chmn dept, 76-78, ASSOC PROF LIFE SCI, NY INST TECHNOL, 72-, ASSOC DIR NATURAL SCI CTR, 78- *Concurrent Pos:* Pres, New York Sportfishing Coun, 77-78; consult, NY Dept Environ Conserv Shellfish Leasing, 77-; chmn squid/butterfish subpanel & mem bluefish subpanel, Mid Atlantic Fisheries Mgt Coun, 78-81; adv, Long Island State Parks & Recreation Comn, 79-; res assoc marine biol, City Univ New York, 69-78. *Mem:* Sigma Xi; Soc Protozool; Am Soc Limnol & Oceanog; Am Fisheries Soc. *Res:* Salt marsh ecology, productivity and fisheries management; niche theory environmental stress. *Mailing Add:* Dept Life Sci Wheatley Rd Old Westbury NY 11568

MULLER, WILLIAM HENRY, JR, b Dillon, SC, Aug 19, 19; m 46; c 3. SURGERY. *Educ:* The Citadel, BS, 40; Duke Univ, MD, 43; Am Bd Surg, dipl; Am Bd Thoracic Surg, dipl. *Prof Exp:* Intern, Johns Hopkins Hosp, 44, asst resident & asst surg, 44-46, instr surg & resident gen surg, 48-49, resident cardiovasc surg, 49; from asst prof to assoc prof surg, Sch Med, Univ Calif, Los Angeles, 49-54; Steven H Watts prof surg & chmn dept, 54-76, surgeon-in-chief, Hosp, 54-76, VPRES HEALTH SCI, SCH MED, UNIV VA, 76-, STEVEN H WATTS PROF SURG & CHMN DEPT SURG, 80- *Concurrent Pos:* Attend specialist, Wadsworth Vet Admin Hosp, Los Angeles, chief sect cardiovasc surg, Los Angeles County Gen Hosp, Torrence, consult, St John's Hosp, Santa Monica & Santa Monica Hosp, 49-54; mem exam bd, Am Bd Surg; chmn surg study sect, NIH; mem, President's Panel on Heart Dis, 72; mem Nat Joint Practice Comn of Med & Nursing, 72; mem bd trustees, Duke Univ & Duke Univ Med Ctr. *Mem:* Soc Vascular Surg (pres, 66-67); Soc Clin Surg; Am Asn Thoracic Surg; AMA; fel Am Col Surg. *Res:* Surgery of cardiovascular deformities; pulmonary hypertension; enzymatic debridement of wounds. *Mailing Add:* Dept of Surg Univ of Va Hosp Charlottesville VA 22901

MULLER-EBERHARD, HANS JOACHIM, b Magdeburg, Ger, May 5, 27; m 53, 77; c 2. IMMUNOLOGY, BIOCHEMISTRY. *Educ:* Univ Gottingen, MD, 53. *Prof Exp:* Asst physician, Dept Med, Univ Gottingen, 53-54; asst & asst physician, Rockefeller Inst, 54-57; fel, Swedish Med Res Coun, Dept Clin Chem, Univ Uppsala, 57-59; from asst prof to assoc prof biochem & immunol, Rockefeller Inst, 59-63; mem dept exp path, 63-74, CECIL H & IDA M GREEN INVESTR MED RES, SCRIPPS CLIN & RES FOUND, 72-, CHMN DEPT MOLECULAR IMMUNOL, 74-, ASSOC DIR, RES INST OF SCRIPPS CLIN, 78- *Concurrent Pos:* Assoc physician, Rockefeller Inst, 59-62; mem allergy & immunol A study sect, NIH, 65-69; adj prof, Univ Calif, San Diego, 68-; Harvey lect, 70. *Honors & Awards:* Parke Davis Meritorious Award, 66; Squibb Award, Infectious Dis Soc Am, 70; T Duckett Jones Mem Award, Helen Hay Whitney Found, 71; Modern Med Distinguished Achievement Award, 74; Karl Landsteiner Mem Award, Am Asn Blood Banks, 74; Annual Int Award, Gairdner Found, Can, 74. *Mem:* Nat Acad Sci; Am Soc Clin Invest; Am Asn Immunol; Am Soc Biol Chemists; Asn Am Physicians. *Res:* Molecular biology and biochemistry of complement; cellular cytotoxicity; modulation of cellular functions by effector molecules. *Mailing Add:* Dept Molecular Immunol Scripps Clin & Res Found La Jolla CA 92037

MULLER-EBERHARD, URSULA, hematology, biochemistry, see previous edition

MÜLLER-SCHWARZE, DIETLAND, b Grosshartmannsdorf, Ger, Oct 4, 34; m 65. ANIMAL BEHAVIOR. *Educ:* Univ Freiburg, PhD(zool), 63. *Prof Exp:* Asst prof zool, Univ Freiburg, 63-65; asst prof biol, San Francisco State Col, 65-68; assoc prof animal behav, Utah State Univ, 68-73; assoc prof, 73-78, PROF, COL ENVIRON SCI & FORESTRY, STATE UNIV NY, 78- *Mem:* Animal Behav Soc; Ger Zool Soc; Europ Chemoreception Res Orgn; Sigma Xi; Am Soc Mammalogists. *Res:* Vertebrate pheromones; behavioral adaptations in birds and mammals; behavior development; human ethology. *Mailing Add:* State Univ of NY Col of Environ Sci & Forestry Syracuse NY 13210

MULLHAUPT, JOSEPH TIMOTHY, b St Marys, Pa, Feb 25, 32; m 57; c 5. PHYSICAL CHEMISTRY. *Educ:* Univ Rochester, BS, 54; Brown Univ, PhD(phys chem), 58. *Prof Exp:* From res chemist to sr res chemist, 58-67, res supvr phys chem, 67-69, SR RES SCIENTIST PHYS CHEM, LINDE DIV, UNION CARBIDE CORP, 69- *Mem:* AAAS; Am Phys Soc; Sigma Xi; Am Chem Soc. *Res:* Solid state chemistry; adsorption and surface chemistry; thermodynamics of phase equilibria. *Mailing Add:* 61 E Park Dr Tonawanda NY 14150

MULLIGAN, BENJAMIN EDWARD, b Greensboro, NC, May 17, 36; m 63; c 2. SENSORY PSYCHOLOGY. *Educ:* Univ Ga, BA, 58; Univ Miss, MA, 61, PhD(sensory psychol), 64. *Prof Exp:* Asst prof, 64-69, ASSOC PROF SENSORY PSYCHOL, UNIV GA, 69- *Concurrent Pos:* Nat Inst Neurol Dis & Stroke grant, 65-70; partic, Int Cong Physiol Sci, 65. *Mem:* Acoust Soc Am; Optical Soc Am; Am Soc Cybernet; Soc Neurosci. *Res:* Sensory processes; psychophysics; mathematical models; noise pollution; communication. *Mailing Add:* Dept of Psychol Univ of Ga Athens GA 30602

MULLIGAN, BERNARD, b Montgomery, Ala, Aug 31, 34; m 64. THEORETICAL PHYSICS, NUCLEAR PHYSICS. *Educ:* Univ Ala, BS, 56; Mass Inst Technol, PhD(theoret physics), 62. *Prof Exp:* Vis asst prof, 61-63, from asst prof to assoc prof, 63-77, PROF PHYSICS, OHIO STATE UNIV, 77- *Res:* Theory of nuclear phenomena; mathematical physics. *Mailing Add:* Dept of Physics Ohio State Univ Columbus OH 43210

MULLIGAN, JAMES ANTHONY, b Denver, Colo, Aug 31, 24. ANIMAL BEHAVIOR. *Educ:* St Louis Univ, AB, 47, STL, 57; Univ Calif, Berkeley, PhD(zool), 63. *Prof Exp:* From instr to asst prof, 63-68, ASSOC PROF BIOL, ST LOUIS UNIV, 68- *Concurrent Pos:* Frank M Chapman Mem Fund res grant, 64; NSF res grant, 65-71; fel, Woodrow Wilson Int Ctr Scholars, 71-72. *Mem:* Animal Behav Soc; Ecol Soc Am; Am Soc Zoologists; Am Ornith Union. *Res:* Social behavior and communication in animals by means of sound; field study and physical analysis of avian vocalizations; ontogeny and genetic analysis of bird vocalizations; vertebrate ecology; conservation of natural areas; ethics of the environmental crisis. *Mailing Add:* St Louis Univ St Louis MO 63103

MULLIGAN, JAMES EDWARD, JR, b Boston, Mass, Apr 26, 27; m 47; c 2. MATHEMATICS. *Educ:* Univ Mich, AB, 49, AM, 50. *Prof Exp:* Math statistician, US Census Bur, 50-51; mathematician hydrographic off, US Dept Navy, 51-52, mathematician, Naval Weapons Lab, 53-58, supvry opers res analyst, 59-60; MATHEMATICIAN, GEN ELEC CO, 61- *Mem:* Fel AAAS; Opers Res Soc Am; Math Asn Am. *Res:* Computer simulation; numerical analysis; operations research; systems design. *Mailing Add:* 27 Red Coat Lane Trumbull CT 06611

MULLIGAN, JAMES H(ENRY), JR, b Jersey City, NJ, Oct 29, 20; m 47; c 2. ELECTRICAL ENGINEERING. *Educ:* Cooper Union, BEE, 43, EE, 47; Stevens Inst Technol, MS, 45; Columbia Univ, PhD, 48. *Prof Exp:* Mem tech staff, Bell Tel Labs, Inc, 41-44; sr engr, A B du Mont Labs, Inc, 45-47, chief engr, Transmitter Div, 48-49; from asst prof to prof elec eng, NY Univ, 49-68, chmn dept, 52-68; secy & exec officer, Nat Acad Eng, 68-74; dean, Sch Eng, 74-77, PROF ELEC ENG, UNIV CALIF, IRVINE, 74- *Concurrent Pos:* Consult, Res & Develop Bd, Off Secy Defense, Bell Tel Labs & Sprague Elec Co; mem comn human resources, Nat Res Coun, 79- *Honors & Awards:* Haraden Pratt Award, Inst Elec & Electronics Engrs. *Mem:* Nat Acad Eng (secy, 68-78); fel Inst Elec & Electronics Engrs (vpres, 70, pres, 71); fel Brit Inst Elec Engrs; Am Phys Soc; Nat Soc Prof Engrs. *Res:* Network theory; feedback systems; solid state electronics; applied mathematics in electrical engineering. *Mailing Add:* 12121 Sky Lane Santa Ana CA 92705

MULLIGAN, JOSEPH FRANCIS, b New York, NY, Dec 12, 20; m 68. ATOMIC PHYSICS, MOLECULAR PHYSICS. *Educ:* Boston Col, AB, 45, MA, 46; Cath Univ, PhD(physics), 51. *Prof Exp:* Instr physics, St Peter's Col, 46-47; instr, Fordham Univ, 55-57, from asst prof to assoc prof, 57-68, chmn dept, 57-64, dean grad sch arts & sci & dean fac, 64-67; PROF PHYSICS & DEAN GRAD STUDIES & RES, UNIV MD, BALTIMORE COUNTY, 68- *Concurrent Pos:* Mem adv comt grad fels, Nat Defense Educ Act, 59-63, mem adv comt grad educ, NY State, 63-68; NSF fac fel, Univ Calif, San Diego, 61-62. *Mem:* AAAS; Am Phys Soc; Am Asn Physics Teachers; Sigma Xi. *Res:* Fundamental constants of physics; physics of energy. *Mailing Add:* Dept of Physics Univ of Md Baltimore County Baltimore MD 21228

MULLIKEN, ROBERT SANDERSON, b Newburyport, Mass, June 7, 96; m 29; c 2. PHYSICS, CHEMISTRY. *Educ:* Mass Inst Technol, BS, 17; Univ Chicago, PhD(phys chem), 21. *Hon Degrees:* ScD, Columbia Univ, 39, Marquette Univ, 67, Cambridge Univ, 67, Gustavus Adolphus Col, 75; PhD, Univ Stockholm, 60. *Prof Exp:* Jr chem eng bur mines, US Dept Interior, Washington, DC, 17-18; asst rubber res, NJ Zinc Co, Pa, 19; Nat Res Coun fel, Univ Chicago & Harvard Univ, 21-25; asst prof physics, Wash Sq Col, NY Univ, 26-28; from assoc prof to prof, 28-37, dir ed work & info, Plutonium Proj, 42-45, Ernest DeWitt Burton distinguished serv prof, 57-61, DISTINGUISHED SERV PROF PHYSICS & CHEM, UNIV CHICAGO, 61- *Concurrent Pos:* Guggenheim fel, 30 & 32; Fulbright scholar, Oxford Univ, 52-53; sci attache, London, 55; Baker lectr, Cornell Univ, 60; lectr, Atomic Energy Estab, Trombay, India & Indian Inst Tech, Kanpur, 62; Silliman lectr, Yale Univ, 65; Jan Van Geuns vis prof, Univ Amsterdam, 65; distinguished res prof, Fla State Univ, Winters, 65-71. *Honors & Awards:* Nobel Prize in Chem, 66; Lewis Gold Medal, Am Chem Soc, 60, Richards Gold Medal, 60, Debye Award, 63, Kirkwood Medal, 64, City Col New York Alumni Asn Gold Medal, 65, Willard Gibbs Gold Medal, 65. *Mem:* Nat Acad Sci; AAAS; fel Am Phys Soc; fel Am Acad Arts & Sci; hon mem Royal Soc Chem. *Res:* Separation of isotopes; molecular spectra; diatomic molecules; theory of molecular spectra and electronic structure of molecules; electron donor-acceptor interactions and charge-transfer spectra. *Mailing Add:* Dept of Chem Univ of Chicago Chicago IL 60637

MULLIKIN, H(ARWOOD) F(RANKLIN), b Baltimore, Md, June 27, 08; m; c 2. MECHANICAL & NUCLEAR ENGINEERING. *Educ:* Johns Hopkins Univ, BS, 30; Yale Univ, MS, 31, ME, 32, PhD(mech eng), 34. *Prof Exp:* Test engr, Gen Elec Co, 35; anal engr, Babcock & Wilcox Co, NY, 36-42; instr, City Univ New York, 42-44; design engr, Ebasco Servs, Inc, 44-46; assoc prof, Ill Inst Technol, 46-47; head dept mech eng, Mont State Univ, 47-67; chmn dept mech eng, 67-76, CONSULT, CTR NUCLEAR STUDIES, MEMPHIS STATE UNIV, 76- *Concurrent Pos:* Consult mech engr. *Mem:* Am Soc Mech Engrs. *Res:* Heat transfer; thermodynamics; dimensional analysis; metrication conversion; powerplant design; nuclear power. *Mailing Add:* Ctr for Nuclear Studies Memphis State Univ Memphis TN 38152

MULLIKIN, RICHARD V(ICKERS), b Wilmington, Del, Apr 13, 23; m 49; c 2. CHEMICAL ENGINEERING. *Educ:* Mass Inst Technol, BS, 44. *Prof Exp:* Indust engr, E I du Pont de Nemours & Co, 44-48, plant assistance engr, 48-51, prod supvr, 51-55; res engr, Monsanto Co, 56-60, res specialist, 60-78; sr design engr, Cities Serv Co, 78-80; RETIRED. *Mem:* Am Inst Chem Engrs; Am Chem Soc. *Res:* Polymer process research. *Mailing Add:* 407 Karen Lane San Antonio TX 78209

MULLIKIN, THOMAS WILSON, b Tenn, Jan 9, 28; m 52; c 3. APPLIED MATHEMATICS. *Educ:* Univ Tenn, AB, 50; Harvard Univ, MA, 54, PhD(math), 58. *Prof Exp:* Asst math, Oak Ridge Nat Lab, 47-48; mathematician, Rand Corp, 57-64; PROF MATH, PURDUE UNIV, 64- *Mem:* AAAS; Am Math Soc; Soc Indust & Appl Math. *Res:* Differential and integral equations; functional analysis. *Mailing Add:* Dept of Math Purdue Univ West Lafayette IN 47906

MULLIN, BETH CONWAY, b Philadelphia, Pa, Oct 28, 45. PLANT PHYSIOLOGY, CELL BIOLOGY. *Educ:* Earlham Col, BA, 67; NC State Univ, PhD(plant physiol), 72. *Prof Exp:* Investr RNA tumor viruses, Oak Ridge Nat Lab, 73-75, Nat Cancer Inst fel, 75-76; asst prof biochem, Wilmington Col, 76-77; ASST PROF PLANT PHYSIOL, UNIV TENN, 77- *Concurrent Pos:* NIH biomed res grant, 77-78; Lilly Found fel, Univ Tenn, 78-79; consult molecular carcinogenesis, Oak Ridge Nat Lab, 77- *Mem:* Am Soc Plant Physiologists. *Res:* Regulation of DNA synthesis; tRNA metabolism; molecular biology of symbiotic nitrogen fixation; characterization of amino acid analog resistant mutants in cereals. *Mailing Add:* Hesler Biol Bldg Dept of Bot Univ of Tenn Knoxville TN 37916

MULLIN, BRIAN ROBERT, b Columbus, Ga, June 16, 45. MULTIPLE SCLEROSIS RESEARCH, MEDICAL STUDENT TEACHING. *Educ:* Univ Scranton, BS, 66; State Univ NY, Upstate Med Ctr, MD, 70; Am Bd Path, dipl, 73. *Prof Exp:* Researcher endocrinol, Sloan-Kettering Inst Cancer Res, 69-70; internship, Cleveland Metrop Gen Hosp, 70-71; residency path, Nat Cancer Inst, NIH, 71-73, fel biochem, Nat Inst Arthritis, Metabolism & Digestive Dis, 74-77; asst prof, Sch Med, Case Western Reserve Univ, 77-81; ASSOC PROF PATH, UNIFORMED SERV UNIV HEALTH SCI, 81- *Mem:* Paleopath Asn. *Res:* Gangliosides as autoantigens in multiple sclerosis. *Mailing Add:* Dept Path Uniformed Serv Univ Health Sci 4301 Jones Bridge Rd Bethesda MD 20814

MULLIN, CHARLES R, physical chemistry, see previous edition

MULLIN, MICHAEL MAHLON, b Galveston, Tex, Nov 17, 37; m 64; c 3. BIOLOGICAL OCEANOGRAPHY, ECOLOGY. *Educ:* Shimer Col, AB, 57; Harvard Univ, AB, 59, MA, 60, PhD(biol), 64. *Prof Exp:* NSF fel, 64; instr oceanog & res biologist, 64-65, asst prof & asst res biologist, 65-71, assoc prof oceanog & assoc res biologist, Inst Marine Resources, 71-77, chmn grad dept, 77-80, PROF OCEANOG, SCRIPPS INST OCEANOG & RES BIOLOGIST, INST MARINE RESOURCES, UNIV CALIF, SAN DIEGO, 77-, ASSOC DIR, 80- *Concurrent Pos:* Mem, Ocean Sci Bd, Nat Res Coun, 79- *Mem:* Am Soc Limnol & Oceanog. *Res:* Ecology of marine plankton, especially energetics and population dynamics of zooplankton. *Mailing Add:* Inst of Marine Resources Univ Calif San Diego A-018 La Jolla CA 92093

MULLIN, ROBERT SPENCER, b Tazewell, Va, May 19, 12; m 38; c 2. PLANT PATHOLOGY. *Educ:* Hampden-Sydney Col, BS, 34; Va Polytech Inst, MS, 37; Univ Minn, PhD, 50. *Prof Exp:* Agt directing grain rust control, USDA, Va, 36-41, state leader, 41-44; assoc pathologist, Truck Exp Sta, Univ, Va, 45-46, plant pathologist & head dept, 48-58; assoc prof plant path, physiol & bot, Va Polytech Inst, 46-48; prof & plant pathologist, 58-77, EMER PROF & PLANT PATHOLOGIST, COOP EXTEN SERV, UNIV FLA, 77- *Concurrent Pos:* Consult plant path. *Mem:* Am Phytopath Soc. *Res:* Control of plant diseases, especially vegetable, ornamental and fruit crops. *Mailing Add:* 1132 SW 11 Ave Gainesville FL 32601

MULLIN, RONALD CLEVELAND, b Guelph, Ont, Aug 15, 36. MATHEMATICS. *Educ:* Univ Western Ont, BA, 59; Univ Waterloo, MA, 60, PhD(math), 64. *Prof Exp:* Lectr math, Univ Waterloo, 60-64, from asst prof to assoc prof, 64-68; prof, Fla Atlantic Univ, 68-69; assoc dean grad studies, 71-75, chmn dept combinatorics & optimization, 75-78, PROF MATH, UNIV WATERLOO, 69- *Mem:* Math Asn Am; Am Math Soc. *Res:* Combinatorial mathematics; design theory. *Mailing Add:* Dept Combinatorics Optimization Univ of Waterloo Waterloo ON N2L 3G1 Can

MULLIN, WILLIAM JESSE, b Brentwood, Mo, Dec 8, 34; m 61; c 3. THEORETICAL SOLID STATE PHYSICS. *Educ:* St Louis Univ, BS, 56; Washington Univ, PhD(theoret solid state physics), 65. *Prof Exp:* Res physicist, Aerospace Res Labs, Wright-Patterson AFB, Ohio, 64-65; res assoc physics, Univ Minn, Minneapolis, 65-67; asst prof theoret solid state physics, 67-71, ASSOC PROF THEORET SOLID STATE PHYSICS, UNIV MASS, AMHERST, 71- *Concurrent Pos:* Sci Res Coun fel, Univ Sussex, Eng, 73-74. *Mem:* Am Phys Soc. *Res:* Many-body theory; analysis of properties of quantum solids and liquids at low temperatures. *Mailing Add:* Dept of Physics Univ of Mass Amherst MA 01003

MULLINAX, PERRY FRANKLIN, b Quebec, Que, June 7, 31; US citizen; m 57; c 2. RHEUMATOLOGY, IMMUNOLOGY. *Educ:* Duke Univ, BA, 51; Med Col Va, MD, 55; Am Bd Internal Med, dipl; Subspecialty Bd Rheumatol, dipl. *Prof Exp:* Clin & res fel med, Mass Geh Hosp, 59-61; Helen Hay Whitney res fel, Sch Med, Washington Univ, 61-62; Helen Hay Whitney res fel, Mass Inst Technol, 62-63; asst prof, 63-67, asst dir, Clin Res Ctr, 70-75, assoc prof, 67-76, PROF MED, MED COL VA, 76- *Concurrent Pos:* Fel med, Harvard Med Sch, 59-61; res fel, Arthritis Found, 59-61. *Mem:* AAAS; Am Fedn Clin Res; Am Rheumatism Asn; fel Am Col Physicians. *Res:* Clinical immunology; immunochemistry; rheumatic diseases. *Mailing Add:* Dept of Med Med Col of Va Richmond VA 23298

MULLINEAUX, DONAL RAY, b Weed, Calif, Feb 16, 25; m 51; c 3. GEOLOGY. *Educ:* Univ Wash, Seattle, BS, 47 & 49, MS, 50, PhD(geol), 61. *Prof Exp:* Field asst, 50, GEOLOGIST, ENG GEOL BR, US GEOL SURV, 50- *Mem:* Geol Soc Am; Am Quaternary Asn. *Res:* Geology of Puget Sound Basin; engineering geology; volcanic hazards in western United States and Hawaii; eruptive histories and productrs of Cascade Range volcanoes; Mount St Helens eruptions and effects. *Mailing Add:* US Geol Surv Denver Fed Ctr Denver CO 80225

MULLINEAUX, RICHARD DENISON, b Portland, Ore, Feb 23, 23; m 47; c 2. ORGANIC CHEMISTRY. *Educ:* Univ Wash, Seattle, BS, 48; Univ Wis, PhD(org chem), 51. *Prof Exp:* Chemist, Shell Develop Co, 51-59, res supvr, 60-63, spec technologist, Wilmington Refinery, Shell Oil Co, 63-64, mgr aromatics dept, Wood River Refinery, 65-66, asst mgr head off tech dept, 66-67, dir, Gen Sci Div, Shell Develop Co, Calif, 67-69, gen mgr, Mfg, Transport & Mkt, Shell Oil Co, 69-74, gen mgr, Mfg, Transport & Mkt/Chem Res & Develop, 74, gen mgr res & develop prod, 75-78, GEN MGR HEALTH SAFETY & ENVIRON SUPPORT, SHELL OIL CO, 78- *Mem:* Am Chem Soc; NY Acad Sci; Am Asn Advan Sci. *Res:* Hydrocarbon chemistry; organo metallics; engine lubricants; petroleum refining; organic chemical products and processes. *Mailing Add:* Shell Oil Co One Shell Plaza Houston TX 77002

MULLINIX, KATHLEEN PATRICIA, b Boston, Mass, Mar 19, 44; m 66. BIOCHEMISTRY, ENDOCRINOLOGY. *Educ:* Trinity Col, DC, AB, 65; Columbia Univ, PhD(chem biol), 69. *Prof Exp:* NIH fel, Harvard Univ, 69-71, res assoc biol, 71-72; staff fel, Nat Inst Arthritis, Metab & Digestive Dis, NIH, 72-73, sr staff fel, 73-75, res chemist, Nat Cancer Inst, 75-79, asst dir intramural planning, 79-81; DEP PROVOST HEALTH SCI, COLUMBIA UNIV, 81- *Mem:* AAAS; Am Chem Soc; Am Soc Microbiol; Am Soc Biol Chemists. *Res:* Regulation of gene expression; mechanisms of controlling RNA synthesis; effects of steroid hormones on gene expression. *Mailing Add:* Columbia Univ 630 W 168th St P&S 2-460 New York NY 10032

MULLINS, DAIL W, JR, b St Louis, Mo, Feb 9, 44; m 67; c 1. MOLECULAR BIOLOGY. *Educ:* Southwestern at Memphis, BA, 66; Memphis State Univ, MS, 69; Univ Ala, Birmingham, PhD(biochem), 75. *Prof Exp:* Lectr genetics, Dept Biol, Univ Ala, Birmingham, 74-75; res assoc biochem, Dept Biochem, Med Sch, Georgetown Univ, Washington, DC, 75-77; res assoc molecular biol, 77-79, sr res assoc, 79-81, SR RES ASSOC BIOCHEM, UNIV ALA, BIRMINGHAM, 82- *Concurrent Pos:* Lectr genetics, Dept Biol, Univ Ala, Birmingham, 77-78, prin investr, Nat Cancer Inst grant, Dept Biochem, 81-83. *Mem:* Int Soc Study Orgin Life; Planetary Soc. *Res:* Orgin of life biochemistry; eukaryotic gene regulation. *Mailing Add:* Dept Biochem Univ Ala University Station Birmingham AL 35294

MULLINS, DONALD EUGENE, b La Junta, Colo, Nov 2, 44; m 68; c 2. INSECT PHYSIOLOGY. *Educ:* Univ Colo, BA, 66; Colo State Univ, MS, 68; Va Polytech Inst & State Univ, PhD(entom), 72. *Prof Exp:* Lectr zool, Univ Western Ont, 71-73; from instr to asst prof, 73-79, ASSOC PROF ENTOM, VA POLYTECH INST & STATE UNIV, 79- *Mem:* Sigma Xi; AAAS; Entom Soc Am. *Res:* Physiology and biochemistry of nitrogen metabolism in insects as it relates to osmoregulation and excretion, particularly the role of stored urates; pesticide disposel using biological methods. *Mailing Add:* Dept of Entom Va Polytech Inst & State Univ Blacksburg VA 24061

MULLINS, HENRY THOMAS, b Ghent, NY, Dec 14, 51; m 77. CARBONATE SEDIMENTATION, SEISMIC STRATIGRAPHY. *Educ:* State Univ NY, Oneonta, BS, 73; Duke Univ, MS, 75; Univ NC, Chapel Hill, PhD(oceanog), 78. *Prof Exp:* ASST PROF OCEANOG, MOSS LANDING MARINE LABS, 78- *Concurrent Pos:* Assoc ed, Geo-Marine Letters. *Mem:* Am Asn Petrol Geol; AAAS; Geolog Soc Am; Sigma Xi; Soc Econ Paleontologists & Mineralogists. *Res:* Marine geology and geophysics; carbonate sedimentology; seismic stratigraphy; sedimentary petrology (phsophorites). *Mailing Add:* Moss Landing Marine Labs PO Box 223 Moss Landing CA 95039

MULLINS, JAMES MICHAEL, b San Deigo, Calif, Sept 22, 45; m 70; c 1. CELL BIOLOGY. *Educ:* Grinnell Col, BA, 68; Univ Tex, Austin, MA, 72, PhD(zool), 75. *Prof Exp:* Fel cell biol, Univ Colo, Boulder, 75-78; ASST PROF BIOL, CATH UNIV AM, 78- *Concurrent Pos:* NIH fel molecular, cellular & develop biol, Univ Colo, Boulder, 75-77. *Mem:* Am Soc Cell Biol. *Res:* Cell division; cellular motility. *Mailing Add:* Dept of Biol Cath Univ of Am Washington DC 20064

MULLINS, JEANETTE SOMERVILLE, b Salem, Ohio, Aug 1, 32; c 2. MICROBIAL ECOLOGY, PLANT TAXONOMY. *Educ:* Wayne State Univ, BA, 55, MS, 62; NDak State Univ, PhD(bot), 75. *Prof Exp:* Sr bacteriologist, Henry Ford Hosp, Detroit, 55-66; bacteriologist, Providence Hosp, Southfield, Mich, 68; plant physiologist & res asst, Metab & Radiation Res Lab, Agr Res Serv, USDA, Fargo, NDak, 69-74; asst prof biol sci, 75-80, ASSOC PROF BIOL, CALIFORNIA STATE COL, PA, 80- *Mem:* AAAS; Am Inst Biol Sci; Am Soc Microbiol; Sigma Xi. *Res:* Enumeration and identification of leaf surface bacteria; effects of surface applied herbicides on phyllpplane bacteria. *Mailing Add:* Dept of Biol Sci Calif State Col California PA 15419

MULLINS, JOHN A, b Philadelphia, Pa, Feb 16, 31. CHEMISTRY. *Educ:* Univ Pa, BS, 58, PhD(chem), 64. *Prof Exp:* Fel photochem, Brandeis Univ, 64-66; lectr chem, Bucknell Univ, 66-67; asst prof, 67-74, assoc prof, 74-80, PROF NATURAL SCI, MICH STATE UNIV, 80- *Res:* Biophysical chemistry; history and philosophy of science. *Mailing Add:* Dept of Natural Sci Kedzie Lab Mich State Univ East Lansing MI 48824

MULLINS, JOHN DOLAN, b Avon, Mass, May 2, 24; m 45. PHARMACY. *Educ:* Mass Col Pharm, BS, 50, MS, 52; Univ Fla, PhD, 55. *Prof Exp:* Res assoc, Merck Sharp & Dohme Res Labs, 55-61; asst dir prod develop, Mead Johnson Res Ctr, 61-64; dir prod develop, 64-68, dir develop, 68-71, dep gen mgr sci & technol, 71-74, dir, Dermat Res & Develop, 74-81, DIR PHARM SCI, ALCON LABS, INC, 81- *Mem:* Am Chem Soc; Am Pharmaceut Asn; NY Acad Sci; Int Soc Pharm Eng. *Res:* Pharmaceutical dosage forms; colloids; emulsion technology. *Mailing Add:* 4801 Westlake Dr Ft Worth TX 76132

MULLINS, JOHN THOMAS, b Richmond, Va, Nov 18, 32; m 55; c 3. BOTANY. *Educ:* Univ Richmond, BS, 55, MS, 57; Univ NC, PhD(bot), 60. *Prof Exp:* Asst prof bot & biol sci, Univ Fla, 59-64; NIH spec res fel, Harvard Univ, 64-65; assoc prof, 65-73, assoc chmn dept, 75-80, PROF BOT, UNIV FLA, 73- *Mem:* AAAS; Bot Soc Am; Mycol Soc Am; Sigma Xi; Am Soc Plant Physiologist. *Res:* Regulatory mechanisms in hormonal control of sexual morphogenesis in fungi. *Mailing Add:* Dept of Bot Univ of Fla Gainesville FL 32611

MULLINS, JOSEPH CHESTER, b Thomaston, Ga, Dec 5, 31; m 58; c 3. CHEMICAL ENGINEERING. *Educ:* Ga Inst Technol, BS, 54, MS, 60, PhD(chem eng), 65. *Prof Exp:* Res asst micromeritics, Eng Exp Sta, Ga Inst Technol, 58-62, asst res engr, 62-64; from asst prof to assoc prof chem eng, 65-77, PROF CHEM ENG, CLEMSON UNIV, 77- *Mem:* Am Inst Chem Engrs. *Res:* Thermodynamics and cryogenic engineering. *Mailing Add:* Dept Chem Eng Clemson Univ Clemson SC 29631

MULLINS, LAWRENCE J, JR, b New York, NY, Nov 7, 21; m 46; c 4. PHYSICAL CHEMISTRY. *Educ:* Queen's Col, NY, BS, 43; Univ NMex, PhD(chem), 57. *Prof Exp:* STAFF MEM, LOS ALAMOS SCI LAB, 46- *Mem:* Fel Am Inst Chem; Am Chem Soc; Am Nuclear Soc. *Res:* Plutonium chemistry and metallurgy; electrochemistry and electrorefining of plutonium metals; thermodynamic properties of nuclear materials; plutonium fuel cycles; fused salt chemistry; high temperature chemistry of plutonium, uranium, americum and rare earths; plutonium 238 heat sources. *Mailing Add:* 505 Rover Blvd Los Alamos NM 87544

MULLINS, LORIN JOHN, b San Francisco, Calif, Sept 23, 17; m 46; c 2. BIOPHYSICS. *Educ:* Univ Calif, BS, 37, PhD(biophys), 40. *Prof Exp:* Asst, Univ Calif, 38-40; asst physiol, Sch Med & Dent, Univ Rochester, 40-41, instr, 41-43; res assoc, Med Sch, Wayne State Univ, 46; Am-Scand Found fel, Inst Theoret Physics, Copenhagen, 47-48; Nat Res Coun Merck fel, Zool Sta, Naples & Johnson Res Found, Sch Med, Univ Pa, 48-49; Nat Res Coun Merck fel biophys, Johns Hopkins Univ, 49-50; assoc prof biol sci, Purdue Univ, 50-58; PROF BIOPHYS & HEAD DEPT, SCH MED, UNIV MD, BALTIMORE CITY, 59- *Concurrent Pos:* Mem Corp Bermuda Biol Sta, 51-; mem, Marine Biol Lab, Woods Hole, Mass, 56-; USPHS fel, Zoophysiol Lab, Univ Copenhagen, 56-57; mem bd sci counr, Nat Inst Neurol Dis & Stroke, 69-73; chmn, J Neurosci Res, 75-; ed, Ann Rev Biophys & Bioeng, 72- *Mem:* Am Physiol Soc; Biophys Soc; Am Chem Soc; Soc Gen Physiol; Sigma Xi. *Res:* Permeability of cells to ions; applications of radioisotopes to biological problems; active transport of ions; modes of anesthetic action. *Mailing Add:* Dept of Biophys Univ of Md Baltimore MD 21201

MULLINS, ROBERT EMMET, b New York, NY, Sept 24, 37; m 64; c 2. MATHEMATICAL ANALYSIS. *Educ:* Iona Col, BS, 58; Univ Notre Dame, MS, 60; Northwestern Univ, PhD(function algebras), 65. *Prof Exp:* Instr, 64-65, asst prof, 65-70, ASSOC PROF MATH, MARQUETTE UNIV, 70- *Mem:* Am Math Soc. *Res:* Algebras of functions. *Mailing Add:* Dept of Math Marquette Univ Milwaukee WI 53233

MULLINS, WILLIAM WILSON, b Boonville, Ind, Mar 5, 27; m 48; c 4. PHYSICS, METALLURGY. *Educ:* Univ Chicago, MS, 51, PhD(physics), 55. *Prof Exp:* Res physicist, Res Labs, Westinghouse Elec Corp, 55-59, adv physicist, 59-60; assoc prof metall eng, Carnegie Inst Technol, 60-63; prof & head dept, 63-66, dean, 66-70; PROF APPL SCI, CARNEGIE-MELLON UNIV, 70-, DIR, CTR JOINING OF MAT, 81- *Honors & Awards:* Mathewson Gold Medal, Am Inst Mining, Metall & Petrol Engrs, 63; Philip M McKenna Mem Award, 81. *Mem:* Am Phys Soc; Am Inst Mining, Metall & Petrol Engrs. *Res:* Metallic surfaces and interfaces; physical metallurgy; statistical mechanics of alloys; morphology of solid state transformations; diffusion; defect structures in crystalline lattices; particle flow and soil mechanics. *Mailing Add:* Carnegie-Mellon Univ Pittsburgh PA 15213

MULLISON, WENDELL ROXBY, b Philadelphia, Pa, Sept 24, 13; m. PLANT PHYSIOLOGY. *Educ:* Univ NMex, BA, 34; Univ Chicago, PhD(plant physiol), 38. *Prof Exp:* Instr biol, Purdue Univ, 40-44; plant physiologist olericult, Curacaosche Petrol Indust Maatschappij, Neth WIndies, 44-46; plant physiologist, Dow Chem Co, 45-50, asst tech dir in chg agr chem, Dow Chem Int, Ltd, 50-59, prod mgr, 59-62, dir info serv, Bioprod Dept, 62-65, mgr govt contract res & develop, 66-72, registr specialist, 72-; CONSULT PUB AFFAIRS & GOVT ISSUES, 79- *Mem:* Am Soc Plant Physiol; Bot Soc Am; Am Soc Hort Sci; Am Soc Agron; Soil Sci Soc Am. *Res:* Plant nutrition and hormones; herbicides. *Mailing Add:* Dow Chem Co PO Box 1706 Midland MI 48640

MULLOOLY, JOHN P, b Manhattan, NY, July 8, 37; m 69. BIOSTATISTICS, BIOMATHEMATICS. *Educ:* St Francis Col, BS, 59; Mich State Univ, MS, 61; Cath Univ Am, PhD(math statist), 66. *Prof Exp:* Math statistician, NIH, Md, 66-68; prof statist, Ore State Univ, 68-73; SR BIOSTATISTICIAN, KAISER FOUND HOSP, HEALTH SERV RES

CTR, PORTLAND, ORE, 73- *Mem:* Biomet Soc; Am Statist Asn; Am Pub Health Asn. *Res:* Epidemiology, medical care and health services research; statistical methods in epidemiology; statistical inference; applied stochastic processes. *Mailing Add:* Kaiser Found Hosp 4610 SE Belmont Portland OR 97215

MULRENNAN, CECILIA AGNES, b Everett, Mass, Aug 4, 25. BIOLOGY. *Educ:* Regis Col, Mass, AB, 46; Fordham Univ, MA, 57, PhD(genetics), 59. *Prof Exp:* Instr biol, 59-63, PROF BIOL & CHMN DEPT, REGIS COL, MASS, 63- *Concurrent Pos:* NIH res grant, 60-61; Grass Found res grant, 68-71. *Res:* Genetics of Drosophila; philosophy of science. *Mailing Add:* Dept of Biol Regis Col Wellesley St Weston MA 02193

MULRENNAN, JOHN ANDREW, JR, b Tallahassee, Fla, Mar 2, 34; m 59; c 3. MEDICAL ENTOMOLOGY, PARASITOLOGY. *Educ:* Univ Fla, BS, 57, MS, 59; Okla State Univ, PhD(entom & parasitol), 68. *Prof Exp:* US Navy, 59-, officer-in-chg, Dis Vector Ecol & Control Ctr, Alameda, Calif, 73-76, head vector control sect, Bur Med & Surg, 76-79, MED ENTOMOLOGIST, US NAVY, 59-; DIR OFF ENTOM, FLA DEPT HEALTH & REHAB SERV, 79- *Concurrent Pos:* Chmn, Armed Forces Pest Control Bd, 77-78. *Mem:* Am Mosquito Control Asn. *Res:* Mosquito control; cockroach control; toxicology of pesticides. *Mailing Add:* PO Box 210 Fla Dept Health & Rehab Serv Jacksonville FL 32231

MULROW, PATRICK J, b New York, NY, Dec 16, 26; m 53; c 4. MEDICINE. *Educ:* Colgate Univ, AB, 47; Cornell Univ, MD, 51; Am Bd Internal Med, dipl, 58, recert, 74; Endocrinol & Metab Spec Bd, dipl, 77. *Hon Degrees:* MSc, Yale Univ, 69. *Prof Exp:* Instr physiol, Med Col, Cornell Univ, 54-55; from instr to assoc prof med, Sch Med, Yale Univ, 57-69, chief, Endocrine Sect, 66-75, prof internal med, 69-75; PROF MED & CHMN DEPT, MED COL OHIO, 75- *Concurrent Pos:* USPHS res fel, 54-56, res grant, 57-66; Arthritis Res Found res fel, 56-57; clin investr, Vet Admin Hosp, West Haven, Conn, 58-61; attend, Yale-New Haven Hosp, 68-75; mem study sect, NIH, 70-74. *Mem:* Am Soc Clin Invest; Am Physiol Soc; Endocrine Soc; Am Fedn Clin Res; Asn Am Physicians. *Res:* Hypertension and endocrinology. *Mailing Add:* Dept of Med C S 10008 Toledo OH 43699

MULROY, JULIANA CATHERINE, b Pomona, Calif, June 12, 48. PLANT ECOLOGY, BOTANY. *Educ:* Pomona Col, BA, 70; Duke Univ, AM, 72, PhD(plant ecol), 79. *Prof Exp:* Res asst plant ecol, Duke Univ, 70-74, teaching asst bacteriol, 75-76, technician photobiol, 76-77; instr, 77-79, ASST PROF BIOL, DENISON UNIV, 79- *Mem:* Am Inst Biol Sci; Ecol Soc Am; Brit Ecol Soc; Am Asn Plant Taxonomists; Sigma Xi. *Mailing Add:* Dept of Biol Denison Univ Granville OH 43023

MULROY, MICHAEL JOSEPH, b Wyandotte, Mich, July 26, 31; m 65; c 1. ANATOMY. *Educ:* Our Lady of the Forest Sem, AB, 57; DePaul Univ, MS, 60; Univ Calif, San Francisco, PhD(anat), 68. *Prof Exp:* NIH fel auditory physiol, Harvard Med Sch-Mass Inst Technol, 68-70; instr anat, Harvard Med Sch, 72-74; asst prof, 74-77, assoc prof anat, Med Ctr, Univ Mass, 77-80; res assoc otolaryngol, Mass Eye & Ear Infirmary, Eaton Peabody Lab, 71-80; ASSOC PROF ANAT, MED COL GA, 80- *Concurrent Pos:* Teaching fel gross anat, Harvard Med Sch, 71- *Mem:* Am Asn Anatomists. *Res:* Structure and function of comparative vertebrate hearing. *Mailing Add:* Sch Med Med Col Ga Augusta GA 30912

MULROY, THOMAS WILKINSON, b Pomona, Calif, Sept 1, 46. PLANT ECOLOGY & TAXONOMY. *Educ:* Pomona Col, BA, 68; Univ Ariz, MS, 71; Univ Calif, Irvine, PhD(ecol & evolutionary biol), 76. *Prof Exp:* Instr bot, Pomona Col, 73-76, asst prof, 76-77; MGR NATURAL SCI & SR ECOLOGIST, HENNINGSON, DURHAM & RICHARDSON, SCI DIV, 77- *Mem:* Ecol Soc Am; Am Soc Naturalists; Am Inst Biol Sci; AAAS. *Res:* Plant biogeography, evolution and systematics; desert ecology; ecology and evolution of succulent plants; systematics and ecology of Dudleya; adaptive morphology of plants; environmental impact analysis in terrestrial environments. *Mailing Add:* Henningson Durham & Richardson Ecosci Div 804 Anacapa St Santa Barbara CA 93101

MULSON, JOSEPH F, b Milwaukee, Wis, Feb 6, 29; m 49; c 2. ELECTRON PHYSICS. *Educ:* Rollins Col, BS, 56; Pa State Univ, MS, 61, PhD(physics), 63. *Prof Exp:* From asst prof to assoc prof physics, 63-73, chmn sci div, 70-72, PROF PHYSICS, ROLLINS COL, 73- *Concurrent Pos:* Cotrell grant, 64-65; mem, Nat Sci Stud Res Partic, 65-66. *Res:* Holography and laser applications. *Mailing Add:* Dept of Physics A G Bush Sci Ctr Rollins Col Winter Park FL 32789

MULTER, H GRAY, b Syracuse, NY, July 7, 26; m 50; c 2. GEOLOGY. *Educ:* Syracuse Univ, AB, 49, MS, 51; Ohio State Univ, PhD(geol), 55. *Prof Exp:* Petrol geologist, Tex Co, Calif, 51-53; prof geol, Col Wooster, 55-69; dir, West Indies Lab, 69-75, CHMN DEPT EARTH SCI, FAIRLEIGH DICKINSON UNIV, MADISON, NJ, 75-, PROF MARINE GEOL, 80- *Mem:* Geol Soc Am; Nat Asn Geol Teachers; Am Asn Petrol Geol. *Res:* Sedimentation; marine geology; enrivonmental geology. *Mailing Add:* Dept of Earth Sci Fairleigh Dickinson Univ Madison NJ 07940

MULVANEY, JAMES EDWARD, b Brooklyn, NY, Aug 4, 29; m 52; c 4. ORGANIC CHEMISTRY. *Educ:* Polytech Inst Brooklyn, BS, 51, PhD(chem), 59. *Prof Exp:* Res chemist gen chem div, Allied Chem & Dye Corp, 51-53; asst, Polytech Inst Brooklyn, 55-59; res assoc chem, Univ Ill, 59-61; from asst prof to assoc prof, 61-71, PROF CHEM, UNIV ARIZ, 71- *Mem:* AAAS; Am Chem Soc; Royal Soc Chem. *Res:* Organic synthesis; synthesis and mechanism of high polymer formation. *Mailing Add:* Dept of Chem Univ of Ariz Tucson AZ 85721

MULVANEY, JOHN FRANCIS, organic chemistry, deceased

MULVANEY, THOMAS RICHARD, b Bellevue, Mich, July 4, 33; m 54; c 4. FOOD SCIENCE. *Educ:* Mich State Univ, BS, 56, MS, 59, PhD(food sci), 62. *Prof Exp:* Asst food eng, Mich State Univ, 56-59, asst food sci, 59-61, asst instr, 61-62, asst, 62; res engr, Alcoa Res Labs, Aluminum Co Am, Pa, 62-67, sr res scientist, 67-68; assoc prof food sci & technol, Univ Mass, Amherst, 68-71; sr scientist, 71-72, CHIEF FOOD PROCESSING SECT, FOOD & DRUG ADMIN, 72- *Mem:* AAAS; Am Chem Soc; Inst Food Technologists; fel Am Inst Chemists. *Res:* Thermal processing of foods and beverages; effect of sequestering agents on metals; chemical and physical changes in foods induced by packaging materials; nature of metallic flavors; consumer protection. *Mailing Add:* 8307 Forrester Blvd Springfield VA 22152

MULVEY, DENNIS MICHAEL, b Lockport, NY, Nov 17, 38; div; c 2. ORGANIC CHEMISTRY. *Educ:* Univ Pa, AB, 60; State Univ NY Buffalo, PhD(org chem), 65. *Prof Exp:* Res assoc, Columbia Univ, 64-65; sr res chemist, Sharp & Dohme Res Labs, Rahway, 65-73, res fel, 73-77; GROUP LEADER, ORTHO PHARMACEUT CORP, RARITAN, 77- *Mem:* Am Chem Soc. *Res:* Heterocyclic compounds; reaction mechanisms; synthesis of nonclassical aromatic systems; photochemistry; chemistry of natural products. *Mailing Add:* One Middle Rd New Hope PA 18938

MULVEY, MARGARET, b Waterbury, Conn, Apr 12, 52. POPULATION BIOLOGY. *Educ:* Univ Conn, BA, 74, MS, 77; Rutgers Univ, PhD(zool), 81. *Prof Exp:* VIS RESEARCHER, SAVANNAH RIVER ECOL LAB, 81- *Mem:* Am Genetic Soc; Genetics Soc Am; Soc Study Evolution. *Res:* Population genetics; evolutionary aspects of host-parasite relationships. *Mailing Add:* Drawer E Savannah River Ecol Lab Aiken SC 29801

MULVEY, PHILIP FRANCIS, JR, b Worcester, Mass, Dec 22, 31; m 55; c 4. RADIOBIOLOGY, PHYSIOLOGY. *Educ:* Clark Univ, AB, 53; Bowling Green State Univ, MA, 55; Univ Buffalo, PhD(biol), 59; Suffolk Univ Sch Law, JD, 74. *Prof Exp:* Asst biol, Bowling Green State Univ, 54-55; res biochemist radioisotope serv, Vet Admin Hosp, 58-65; res physiologist, Electronics Res Ctr, NASA, Mass, 66; res physiologist, US Army Natick Labs, 66-68; lectr, 59-68, PROF BIOL, SUFFOLK INST, 68- *Concurrent Pos:* Asst, Sch Med, Boston Univ, 59-66. *Mem:* AAAS; Am Soc Zoologists; Am Physiol Soc. *Res:* Use of radioisotopes and antithyroid agents to study thyroid gland physiology; environmental law and management; use of activation analysis to determine trace element concentrations in biological systems. *Mailing Add:* Dept of Biol Suffolk Inst Boston MA 02114

MULVIHILL, JOHN JOSEPH, b Washington, DC, Aug 20, 43; m 66; c 3. EPIDEMIOLOGY, PEDIATRICS. *Educ:* Col of the Holy Cross, BS, 65; Dartmouth Med Sch, BMS, 67; Univ Wash, MD, 69. *Prof Exp:* Staff assoc epidemiol, 70-74, CHIEF CLIN GENETICS SECT, CLIN EPIDEMIOL BR, NAT CANCER INST, 74- *Concurrent Pos:* Mem, Comt Biol Effects Ionizing Radiation, Nat Acad Sci, 70-73; fel pediat, Sch Med, Johns Hopkins Univ, 72-74. *Mem:* Teratology Soc; Soc Pediat Res; Am Acad Pediat; Am Soc Human Genetics. *Res:* Epidemiology of cancer and congenital defects in man, especially genetic and familial factors; animal models of congenital and genetic disease; medical genetics. *Mailing Add:* Clin Epidemiol Br Landow Bldg Nat Cancer Inst Bethesda MD 20814

MULVIHILL, MARY LOU JOLIE, b Chicago, Ill, Sept 28, 28. HUMAN PHYSIOLOGY. *Educ:* St Xavier Col, Ill, BA, 60; Purdue Univ, PhD(physiol), 67. *Prof Exp:* From asst prof to assoc prof biol, St Xavier Col, Ill, 67-72, chmn div natural sci, 69-72, vpres student affairs, 70-72; assoc prof, Harper Col, 72-77, prof biol, 77-81. *Concurrent Pos:* Consult physiol, W C Brown, Harper & Row & Scott, Foresman, 73-81. *Mem:* Am Inst Biol Sci. *Res:* Effect of a vitamin A deficiency on the ultrastructure of the mosquito eye; human anatomy and disease. *Mailing Add:* Dept of Biol William Rainey Harper Col Palatine IL 60067

MULY, EMIL CHRISTOPHER, JR, b Baltimore, Md, Mar 24, 34; m 60; c 3. PHYSICAL ELECTRONICS, MASS SPECTROMETRY. *Educ:* Johns Hopkins Univ, BES, 56; Northwestern Univ, MS, 58, PhD(elec eng), 62. *Prof Exp:* Scientist electronics div, Martin Co, Md, 62-64; assoc prof elec eng, George Washington Univ, 64-65; asst dir res, Nat Res Corp, 65-76; PROG MGR, LEEDS & NORTHRUP CO, 76- *Mem:* Inst Elec & Electronics Engrs; Am Phys Soc; NY Acad Sci. *Res:* High power electron beam production; gaseous electronics; electron optics. *Mailing Add:* Leeds & Northrup Co Sumnaytown Pike North Wales PA 19454

MUMA, MARTIN HAMMOND, b Topeka, Kans, July 24, 16; m 40; c 6. ARACHNOLOGY, DESERT ECOLOGY. *Educ:* Univ Md, BS, 39, MS, 40, PhD(entom), 43. *Prof Exp:* Lab asst, USDA, Md, 37-38; asst, Univ Md, 41-43, instr entom, 43-44, asst entomologist, 44-45; assoc exten entomologist, Univ Nebr, 45-48, assoc prof entom & assoc entomologist, 48-51; from assoc prof entom & assoc entomologist to prof & entomologist, 51-71, EMER PROF ENTOM & EMER ENTOMOLOGIST, CITRUS EXP STA, UNIV FLA, 71-; RES ASSOC, DIV PLANT INDUST, FLA DEPT AGR & CONSUMER SERV & WESTERN NMEX UNIV, 71- *Mem:* Southwest Asn Naturalists; Am Arachnol Soc. *Res:* Taxonomy, systematics, biology, behavior and ecology of arid-land arachnids. *Mailing Add:* PO Box 135 Portal AZ 85632

MUMBACH, NORBERT R, b Buffalo, NY, June 6, 20; m 48; c 5. APPLIED CHEMISTRY. *Educ:* Canisius Col, BS, 42. *Prof Exp:* Instr phys chem, Canisius Col, 42-43; instr chem oper, Lake Ont Ord Works, 43; anal chemist, Manhattan Proj, Linde Air Prods Co, 43-46, res chemist, 46-52, mass spectrometrist, Linde Div, Union Carbide Corp, 52-56, spectroscopist, 59-61, res chemist, Linde Div, 61-77; RETIRED. *Mem:* Am Chem Soc; Sigma Xi. *Res:* Synthetic gemstones; hydrothermal methods; new silicate phases created at high pressures and temperatures. *Mailing Add:* Genessee Rd East Concord NY 14055

MUMFORD, DAVID BRYANT, b Worth, Eng, June 11, 37; m 59; c 4. MATHEMATICS. *Educ:* Harvard Univ, BA, 57, PhD, 61. *Prof Exp:* Jr fel, 58-61, assoc prof, 62-66, PROF MATH, HARVARD UNIV, 66- *Honors & Awards:* Fields Medal, Int Cong Mathematicians, 74. *Mem:* Nat Acad Sci. *Res:* Geometric invariant theory; algebraic geometry. *Mailing Add:* Dept of Math Harvard Univ Cambridge MA 02138

MUMFORD, DAVID LOUIS, b Salt Lake City, Utah, May 2, 32; m 55; c 5. PLANT PATHOLOGY. *Educ:* Brigham Young Univ, BS, 56, MS, 58; Univ Minn, PhD(plant path), 62. *Prof Exp:* Plant pathologist, USDA, Mich State Univ, 63-67; PLANT PATHOLOGIST, USDA, CROPS RES LAB, UTAH STATE UNIV, 67- *Mem:* Am Phytopath Soc. *Res:* Virus diseases of sugar beets; disease resistance in sugar beets. *Mailing Add:* Crops Res Lab Utah State Univ Logan UT 84322

MUMFORD, GEORGE, b Sydney, Australia, Apr 4, 27; US citizen; c 3. PROSTHODONTICS. *Educ:* Univ Sydney, BDS, 53, MDS, 61, DDSc, 61; Ind Univ, DDS, 64. *Prof Exp:* Sr lectr oper dent, Univ Sydney, 58-59; from asst prof to assoc prof crown & bridge, Sch Dent, Ind Univ & dir ceramics sect, 65-68; assoc prof restorative dent & chmn dept, 68-72, prof gen dent, 72-75, PROF & HEAD DEPT RESTORATIVE DENT, HEALTH CTR, UNIV CONN, FARMINGTON, 75- *Mem:* Int Asn Dent Res; fel Am Col Dent; fel Australian Col Dent Surg. *Res:* Material sciences and restorative dentistry. *Mailing Add:* Dept Restorative Dent Sch Dent Univ of Conn Health Ctr Farmington CT 06032

MUMFORD, GEORGE SALTONSTALL, III, b Milton, Mass, Nov 13, 28; m 49; c 4. ASTRONOMY. *Educ:* Harvard Univ, AB, 50; Ind Univ, MA, 52; Univ Va, PhD(astron), 55. *Prof Exp:* Instr math, Randolph-Macon Woman's Col, 52-53; instr, 55-56, from asst prof to assoc prof, 56-68, PROF MATH, TUFTS UNIV, 68-, DEAN COL LIBERAL ARTS, 69- *Concurrent Pos:* Vis astronr, Kitt Peak Nat Observ, 62- *Mem:* AAAS; Am Astron Soc; Am Asn Variable Star Observers; Am Phys Soc; Int Astron Union. *Res:* Cataclysmic variable stars; close binaries. *Mailing Add:* Ballou Hall Tufts Univ Medford MA 02155

MUMFORD, RUSSELL EUGENE, b Casey, Ill, May 26, 22; m 47; c 3. ANIMAL ECOLOGY. *Educ:* Purdue Univ, BS, 48, MS, 52, PhD, 61. *Prof Exp:* Res biologist, State Dept Conserv, Ind, 48-50; teacher natural hist, Fla Audubon Soc, 50-51; res biologist, State Dept Conserv, Ind, 52-55; asst mus zool, Univ Mich, 55-57; PROF VERT NATURAL HIST, PURDUE UNIV, LAFAYETTE, 58- *Mem:* Am Soc Mammal; Wilson Ornith Soc; Am Ornith Union. *Res:* Life history and distribution of birds and mammals; bat banding. *Mailing Add:* Dept Forestry Natural Resources Purdue Univ Lafayette IN 47907

MUMM, ROBERT FRANKLIN, b Urbana, Ill, Oct 16, 35. BIOMETRICS, GENETICS. *Educ:* Univ Ill, BS, 57, MS, 58; Univ Nebr, PhD(quant genetics), 67. *Prof Exp:* Assoc dir res, Crow's Hybrid Corn Co, Ill, 61-65; instr biomet, 65-67, from asst prof to assoc prof agron, 67-75, PROF AGRON & CONSULT BIOMET CTR, UNIV NEBR, LINCOLN, 75- *Mem:* Am Soc Agron; Crop Sci Soc Am; Am Statist Asn. *Res:* Genetic variance components; computer simulation studies of their distribution and effect of choice of mating deisgn on their estimation. *Mailing Add:* Rm 103 Miller Hall Univ of Nebr Col of Agr Lincoln NE 68503

MUMM, WALTER JOHN, b Sidney, Ill, Nov 20, 95; m 21; c 1. GENETICS. *Educ:* Univ Ill, BS, 19, MS, 28, PhD(agron, plant breeding), 40. *Prof Exp:* Asst agron, Univ Ill, 27-28, instr, 28-31, assoc, 31-38; dir res & plant breeding, 38-67, RES CONSULT, CROW'S HYBRID CORN CO, 67- *Mem:* Am Soc Agron; AAAS. *Res:* Genetics of dent corn; breeding multiple-ear and dwarf corn; new approaches to maize inbreeding. *Mailing Add:* 510 E Jones St Milford IL 60953

MUMMA, ALBERT G, b Findlay, Ohio, June 2, 1906; m 27; c 3. ENGINEERING. *Educ:* Newark Col Eng, DEng, 70. *Prof Exp:* Chief bur ships & coordr shipbuilding, conversion & repair, Dept Defense, 55-59; vpres & group exec, Worthington Corp, 59-64, exec vpres & dir-in-chg all domestic opers, 64-67, pres & chief operating officer, 67, chmn bd, 67-71; chmn, Am Shipbuilding Comn, 71-73; CONSULT MGT, 73- *Concurrent Pos:* Past mem res coun, Nat Acad Sci, past chmn numerous comts; past mem maritime transp res bd, Eng & Indust Res Comt, Nat Res Coun; trustee, Drew Univ & St Barnabas Med Ctr, Livingston, NJ. *Honors & Awards:* Jerry Land Gold Medal. *Mem:* Nat Acad Eng; hon mem & fel Soc Naval Architects & Naval Engrs (past pres); hon mem Am Soc Naval Engrs (past pres). *Mailing Add:* 66 Minnisink Rd Short Hills NJ 07078.

MUMMA, MARTIN DALE, b Gideon, Mo, Jan 21, 36; m 56; c 3. GEOLOGY. *Educ:* Univ Mo, AB, 58, MA, 60; La State Univ, PhD(geol), 65. *Prof Exp:* Field geologist, Magnolia Petrol Co, 58; geologist, Esso Prod Res Co, Standard Oil Co, NJ, 65-66; sr geologist, Humble Oil & Refining Co, 66-68; assoc prof geol, Eastern Ky Univ, 68-69; asst prof, 69-71, assoc prof, 71-80, PROF GEOL, EASTERN WASH STATE COL, 80- *Mem:* Soc Econ Paleont & Mineral; Am Asn Petrol Geologists; Paleont Soc. *Res:* Sedimentary petrology and environments; biostratigraphy; micropaleontology. *Mailing Add:* Dept of Geol Eastern Wash State Col Cheney WA 99004

MUMMA, MICHAEL JON, b Lancaster, Pa, Dec 3, 41; m 66; c 2. ATOMIC & MOLECULAR PHYSICS. *Educ:* Franklin & Marshall Col, AB, 63; Univ Pittsburgh, PhD(physics), 70. *Prof Exp:* Space scientist, 70-76, HEAD INFRARED & RADIO ASTRON BR, GODDARD SPACE FLIGHT CTR, NASA, 76- *Concurrent Pos:* Adj sr res assoc, Physics Dept, Pa State Univ, 79-; expert witness, various Univs, 80-, lectr, 70-; mem working/study groups, NASA, Nat Bur Standards, Nat Acad Sci, 74-; prin investr, Infrared Heterodyne Spectroscopy, 74- *Mem:* Am Geophys Union; Am Phys Soc; Am Inst Physics; AAAS; Am Astron Asn. *Res:* Doppler limited infrared spectroscopy of planets, stars and terrestrial atmosphere; natural infrared lasers on Jupiter and Mars and measured fundamental molecular cross-sections and ultraviolet and infrared spectra; author or coauthor of over 40 publications. *Mailing Add:* Code 693 Infrared & Radio Astron Br Goddard Space Flight Ctr NASA Greenbelt MD 20771

MUMMA, RALPH O, b Mechanicsburg, Pa, June 20, 34; m 58; c 2. BIOCHEMISTRY, ENTOMOLOGY. *Educ:* Juniata Col, BS, 56; Pa State Univ, PhD(chem), 60. *Prof Exp:* Fel biochem, 60-61, asst prof, 61-66, from asst prof to assoc prof chem pesticides, 66-72, PROF CHEM PESTICIDES, PA STATE UNIV, 72- *Mem:* Am Chem Soc; Am Oil Chemist Soc; Entom Soc Am; AAAS; Am Inst Biol Sci. *Res:* Lipid, sulfur, pesticide and insect metabolism. *Mailing Add:* Pesticide Res Lab Dept Entom Pa State Univ University Park PA 16802

MUMME, KENNETH IRVING, US citizen. CHEMICAL ENGINEERING. *Educ:* Lawrence Col, BS, 54; Univ Maine, Orono, MS, 66, PhD(chem eng), 70. *Prof Exp:* Instrumentation engr, Kimberly-Clark Corp, Wis, 56-58, physicist, 58-63; lectr mach comput, 63-70, ASSOC PROF CHEM ENG, UNIV MAINE, ORONO, 70- *Concurrent Pos:* Royal Norweg Coun Sci & Indust Res fel, Norweg Inst Technol, 71-72. *Mem:* Am Inst Chem Engrs. *Res:* Chemical process control and optimization; river pollution control systems. *Mailing Add:* Dept of Chem Eng Univ of Maine Orono ME 04473

MUMMERT, HAROLD B, b South Whitley, Ind, Nov 13, 09; m 41; c 2. MECHANICAL ENGINEERING. *Educ:* Purdue Univ, BS, 30, ME, 45; Univ Colo, MS, 55. *Prof Exp:* Asst field engr, Commonwealth Edison Co, Ill, 30-43; asst prof eng, Valparaiso Tech Inst, 43-46; from assoc prof to prof, 46-70, EMER PROF MECH ENG, COLO STATE UNIV, 70- *Concurrent Pos:* Consult & designer, solar energy heating systs, 75- *Mem:* Am Soc Mech Engrs; Am Soc Eng Educ; Am Sect Int Solar Energy Soc. *Res:* Instrumentation; equipment design; air conditioning; energy conversion; solar energy; thermodynamics. *Mailing Add:* 508 Peterson Ft Collins CO 80524

MUMPTON, FREDERICK ALBERT, b Rome, NY, Dec 14, 32; m 54; c 5. MINERALOGY. *Educ:* St Lawrence Univ, BS, 54; Pa State Univ, MS, 56, PhD(geochem), 58. *Prof Exp:* Res chemist, Linde Div, Union Carbide Corp, 58-60, res geochemist, Nuclear Div, 60-65; mineral group leader, Mining & Metals Div, NY, 65-69; assoc prof, 69-74, PROF, DEPT EARTH SCI, STATE UNIV NY COL BROCKPORT, 74- *Concurrent Pos:* Chmn, Int Comt Natural Zeolites, 76-; ed-in- chief, Clays & Clay Minerals, 78- *Mem:* Geochem Soc; fel Mineral Soc Am; Clay Minerals Soc; Sigma Xi; Int Zeolite Asn. *Res:* Silicate chemistry; synthetic and clay mineralogy; mineralogy and utilization of zeolite minerals; mineralogy of asbestos and serpentinites; mineral resources; environmental mineral science. *Mailing Add:* Dept of the Earth Sci State Univ of NY Col Brockport NY 14420

MUN, ALTON M, b Honolulu, Hawaii, Apr 1, 23; m 55; c 5. DEVELOPMENTAL BIOLOGY. *Educ:* Univ Southern Calif, BA, 49; Univ Ill, MS, 51; Ind Univ, PhD(zool), 56. *Prof Exp:* Res assoc avian embryol, Wash State Univ, 56-59; asst invest exp embryol, Carnegie Inst, 59-61; assoc prof zool, 61-70, PROF ZOOL, UNIV MAINE, 70- *Mem:* Am Soc Zool; Sigma Xi; Soc Develop Biol. *Res:* Experimental embryology; zoology; effects of antisera on chick embryos; enhancement of growth of chick host spleens by homologous adult organ fragments; homograft reaction in the chick embryo; parthenogenetic development in unfertilized turkey eggs; teratological effects of trypan blue in the chick embryo. *Mailing Add:* Dept Zool Murray Hall Univ Maine Orono ME 04473

MUNA, NADEEM MITRI, b Jerusalem, Palestine, Apr 8, 28; US citizen; m 69; c 2. IMMUNOLOGY, MICROBIOLOGY. *Educ:* Univ Dubuque, BSc, 51; Univ SDak, MA, 54; Univ Utah, PhD(microbiol), 68. *Prof Exp:* Clin Sacred Heart Hosp, Yankton, SDak, 54-56, Thomas D Dee Mem Hosp, Ogden, Utah, 58-65; pres & dir res mfg, Microbiol Res Corp, 68-78; PRES & DIR IMMUNOL PROD, IMMUNO-DIAG PROD INC, 78- *Mem:* Am Soc Microbiol; Sigma Xi. *Res:* Cancer immunology by immunofluorescence; answers to this approach will identify and localize cancer material which then can be isolated and possibly used for immunization as a means of prevention and treatment. *Mailing Add:* Immuno-Diag Prod Inc 54 S 130th St North Salt Lake UT 84054

MUNAN, LOUIS, b New York, NY, Feb 10, 21; m 47; c 4. EPIDEMIOLOGY. *Educ:* City Col New York, BA, 48; George Washington Univ, AB, 48, MSc, 50. *Prof Exp:* Res analyst, Nat Acad Sci-Nat Res Coun, 49-51; res analyst, Prev Med Div, Off Surgeon Gen, Dept Army, 51-55, chief res & develop sect, Med Info & Intel Div, 55-56; Fulbright exchange prof, Schs Med, Lima & Guayaquil, 57-58; statistician, Pan-Am Sanit Bur, WHO, 58-61, res scientist, Off Res Coord, Pan-Am Health Orgn, 61-68; chmn dept, 68-75, ASSOC PROF EPIDEMIOL, FAC MED, UNIV SHERBROOKE, 68- *Concurrent Pos:* Assoc, Sch Med, George Washington Univ, 50-58; vis prof, Malaria Eradication Training Ctr, Kingston, Jamaica, 62 & 63, Univ Nancy, 77, Univ Toronto, 79 & Univ McGill, 80. *Mem:* Fel Am Pub Health Asn; Can Asn Teachers Social & Prev Med (secy-treas); fel NY Acad Sci; Soc Epidemiol Res; Int Epidemiol Asn. *Mailing Add:* Epidemiol Lab Fac Med Univ of Sherbrooke Sherbrooke PQ J1H 5H4 Can

MUNCH, GUIDO, b San Cristobal, Mex, June 9, 21; m 47; c 4. ASTROPHYSICS, ASTRONOMY. *Educ:* Nat Univ Mex, BS, 38, MS, 44; Univ Chicago, PhD(astron, astrophys), 47. *Prof Exp:* Instr astrophys, Yerkes Observ, Univ Chicago, 47-48, asst prof, 48-51; from asst prof to assoc prof astrophys, Calif Inst Technol, 51-59, prof, 59-77; DIR, MAX PLANCK INST FUER ASTRON, 78- *Mem:* Nat Acad Sci; fel Am Acad Arts & Sci. *Res:* Stellar atmospheres; interstellar matter; planetary atmospheres. *Mailing Add:* Max Planck Inst fuer Astron Konigstuhl 6900 Heidelberg West Germany

MUNCH, JESPER, b Denmark, Sept 6, 45. EXPERIMENTAL PHYSICS. *Educ:* Mass Inst Technol, BS, 68; Univ Chicago, MS, 70, PhD(physics), 74. *Prof Exp:* Res asst electron optics & holography, Univ Chicago, 68-74; MEM TECH STAFF, LASERS & COHERENT OPTICS, TRW SYSTS, 75- *Concurrent Pos:* Lectr, Sch Eng, Univ Calif, Los Angeles, 78- *Res:* Experimental research in lasers; coherent optics; frequency stability; electron holography; free electron lasers. *Mailing Add:* 7215 Rindge Ave Playa Del Ray CA 90291

MUNCH, JOHN HOWARD, b St Louis, Mo, Feb 9, 38; m 65. ORGANIC CHEMISTRY. *Educ:* Swarthmore Col, BA, 60; Univ Wis, Madison, PhD(org chem), 66. *Prof Exp:* Asst prof chem, Dickinson Col, 65-69; RES CHEMIST, TRETOLITE DIV, PETROLITE CORP, ST LOUIS, 69- *Mem:* AAAS; Am Chem Soc; Royal Soc Chem. *Res:* Organic reaction mechanisms and synthesis; electrophilic substitution reactions; Mannich reactions; surface-active compounds. *Mailing Add:* 9 Douglass Lane Kirkwood MO 63122

MUNCH, RALPH HOWARD, b Lafayette, Ind, May 5, 11; m 35; c 5. PHYSICAL CHEMISTRY. *Educ:* Univ NC, BS, 31, MS, 32; Northwestern Univ, PhD(phys chem), 35. *Prof Exp:* Res asst, Rockefeller Found, Chicago, 35-37; res chemist ord div, Res Dept, Monsanto Chem Co, 37-41, group leader, 41-54, sect leader, 54-56, asst dir res, 56-60, res assoc, 60-64, sr res specialist, Monsanto Co, 64-67, advan scientist, 67-70, sr sci fel, 70-74, distinguished sci fel, Monsanto Indust Chem Co, 74-76; CONSULT, 76- *Concurrent Pos:* Vchmn, Gordon Res Conf Instrumentation, 53, chmn, 54. *Mem:* AAAS; Am Chem Soc; fel Instrument Soc Am (vpres, 46). *Res:* Spectroscopy; process control instrumentation; gas chromatography; dielectrics. *Mailing Add:* 303 Planthurst Rd Webster Groves MO 63119

MUNCH, THEODORE, b Columbus, Ohio, Nov 9, 19; m 60. BACTERIOLOGY, SCIENCE EDUCATION. *Educ:* Ohio State Univ, BS, 41 & 46; Colo State Univ, MEd, 48; Stanford Univ, EdD(sci educ), 52. *Prof Exp:* Instr, Balboa High Sch, CZ, 49-50; instr sci & educ, San Francisco State Col, 52; instr life sci, Fullerton Jr Col, 53; asst prof sci educ, Univ Tex, 54-58; assoc prof, 59-63, PROF SCI EDUC, ARIZ STATE UNIV, 63- *Mem:* Fel AAAS; Nat Sci Teachers Asn. *Res:* Science books for children. *Mailing Add:* Dept of Physics Ariz State Univ Tempe AZ 85282

MUNCHAUSEN, LINDA LOU, b New Orleans, La, Aug 30, 46. ORGANIC CHEMISTRY. *Educ:* Southeastern La Univ, BS, 68; Univ Ark, PhD(chem), 73. *Prof Exp:* Fel biol, Oak Ridge Nat Lab, 73-75; fel chem, La State Univ, 75; INSTR ORG CHEM, DEPT CHEM, SOUTHEASTERN LA UNIV, 75- *Mem:* Am Chem Soc; Royal Soc Chem; Am Soc Photobiol. *Mailing Add:* Dept of Chem Southeastern La Univ Hammond LA 70402

MUNCHMEYER, FREDERICK CLARKE, b Washington, DC, Mar 26, 22; m 64; c 4. NAVAL ARCHITECTURE, MARINE ENGINEERING. *Educ:* US Coast Guard Acad, BS, 42; Mass Inst Technol, MS, 48; Univ Mich, PhD(naval archit & marine eng), 78. *Prof Exp:* Comn officer, US Coast Guard, 42-63; prof mech eng, Univ Hawaii, 63-82; PROF NAVAL ARCHIT & MARINE ENG, UNIV NEW ORLEANS, 82- *Concurrent Pos:* Sr engr, Westinghouse Ocean Res & Eng Ctr, 68-69; vis prof, Tech Univ, Berlin, 78-79; prin investr, Univ Hawaii, 75-82. *Mem:* Sigma Xi; Soc Naval Archit & Marine Engrs; Am Soc Eng Educ. *Res:* Computer aided design of doubly curved surfaces; applications of classic differential geometry and of Morse theory to the design and analysis of surfaces. *Mailing Add:* Univ New Orleans New Orleans LA 70122

MUNCK, ALLAN ULF, b Buenos Aires, Arg, July 4, 25; US citizen; m 57; c 3. ENDOCRINOLOGY. *Educ:* Mass Inst Technol, BS, 48, MS, 49, PhD(biophys), 56. *Prof Exp:* Nat Cancer Inst fel steroid biochem, Worcester Found Exp Biol, 57-58; from asst prof to assoc prof, 59-67, PROF PHYSIOL, DARTMOUTH MED SCH, 67- *Concurrent Pos:* Res career develop award, Dartmouth Med Sch, 63-72; assoc ed, J Steroid Biochem, 67- *Mem:* Biophys Soc; Endocrine Soc; Physiol Soc. *Res:* Physiological and molecular mechanisms of action of glucocorticoids. *Mailing Add:* Dept of Physiol Dartmouth Med Sch Hanover NH 03755

MUNCY, ROBERT JESS, b Narrows, Va, Apr 13, 29; m 54; c 1. ZOOLOGY. *Educ:* Va Polytech Inst & State Univ, BS, 50, MS, 54; Iowa State Col, PhD(fishery biol), 57. *Prof Exp:* Asst zool, Iowa State Col, 54-57; fishery biologist, Chesapeake Biol Lab, Md, 57-59; asst prof wildlife mgt, La State Univ, 59-65; asst prof, Colo State Univ, 65-66; prof zool & entom & unit leader, Iowa Coop Fishery Unit, Fish & Wildlife Serv, Iowa State Univ, 66-79; UNIT LEADER & PROF, MISS COOP FISH & WILDLIFE RES UNIT, MISS STATE UNIV, 79- *Concurrent Pos:* Vis lectr, Univ Md, 58-59 & Mt Lake Sta, Va, 64; fishery biologist, Food & Agr Orgn, UN, Zambia, Africa, 72-73. *Mem:* Am Fisheries Soc; Am Soc Limnol & Oceanog; Wildlife Soc. *Res:* Fishery biology and limnology. *Mailing Add:* Coop Fish & Wildlife Res Unit Miss State Univ Mississippi State MS 39762

MUNCZEC, HERMAN J, b Buenos Aires, Arg, June 9, 27; m 54; c 2. PHYSICS. *Educ:* Univ Buenos Aires, Lic, 54, PhD(physics), 58. *Prof Exp:* Res investr, AEC, Arg, 54-60; from asst prof to assoc prof physics, Univ Buenos Aires, 61-66; vis assoc prof, Northwestern Univ, 66-69; assoc prof, 69-71, PROF PHYSICS & ASTRON, UNIV KANS, 71- *Concurrent Pos:* Univ Buenos Aires res fel elem particle physics, Univ Rome, 58-60. *Mem:* Am Phys Soc. *Res:* Theory of elementary particles. *Mailing Add:* Dept of Physics & Astron Univ of Kans Lawrence KS 66044

MUNDAY, J(OHN) C(LINGMAN), b Keithville, La, June 17, 07; m 33; c 3. CHEMISTRY. *Educ:* Centenary Col, BS, 27; Syracuse Univ, MS, 29; Columbia Univ, PhD(chem eng), 34. *Prof Exp:* High sch teacher, La, 27-28; instr chem, Syracuse Univ, 28-29; asst, Columbia Univ, 29-30; chemist, State Motor Fuel Lab, La, 35; chem engr, Standard Oil Co (La), 35-40 & Standard Oil Develop Co, 40-58; res assoc, Esso Res & Eng Co, 58-68; INDUST CONSULT, 68- *Mem:* AAAS; Am Chem Soc. *Res:* Petroleum cracking, thermal and catalytic; alkylation; polymerization; hydroforming; fluidized solids; lubricants; static electricity; soil stabilization. *Mailing Add:* 19 Hampton St Cranford NJ 07016

MUNDAY, JOHN CLINGMAN, JR, b Plainfield, NJ, June 10, 40; m 65; c 3. REMOTE SENSING, WATER QUALITY. *Educ:* Cornell Univ, AB, 62; Univ Ill, PhD(biophys), 68. *Prof Exp:* Res asst photosynthesis, Univ Ill, 65-68, res assoc, 68; physicist, Air Force Missile Develop Ctr, Holloman Air Force Base, NMex, 68-69; assoc marine scientist, Va Inst Marine Sci, 69-71; asst prof geog, Univ Toronto, 71-75; ASSOC MARINE SCIENTIST, VA INST MARINE SCI, 75- *Concurrent Pos:* Nat Res Coun res associateship, 68-69; asst prof, Univ Va & Col William & Mary, 69-71; assoc prof marine sci, Col William & Mary, 75-81, prof 81- *Mem:* AAAS; Am Soc Photogram; Asn Am Geographers; Int Asn Energy Economists. *Res:* Spectroscopy, photosynthesis and membrane physiology of algae; missile reentry spectral photography; estuarine oil pollution; remote sensing of coastal water quality and circulation; land sattelite data processing. *Mailing Add:* Va Inst Marine Sci Gloucester Point VA 23062

MUNDAY, THEODORE F, b Baton Rouge, La, July 7, 37; m 63; c 3. INORGANIC CHEMISTRY. *Educ:* Cornell Univ, AB, 59; Iowa State Univ, PhD(inorg chem), 64. *Prof Exp:* Res chemist, 64-68, sr res chemist, 68-78, RES ASSOC, FMC CORP, 78- *Res:* Process development; phase equilibria; high temperature reactions; molten salts; sol stability; distillation; phosphorus and phosphates; hydrogen peroxide; peroxide monopropellant catalysts; aluminosilicates. *Mailing Add:* 16 Steven Rd Kendall Park NJ 08824

MÜNDEL, HANS-HENNING, b Kosten, Poland, Mar 31, 42; Can citizen; m 68; c 3. PLANT BREEDING, PLANT PHYSIOLOGY. *Educ:* Univ BC, BScAg, 64; Univ Calif, Davis, MS, 66; Univ Man, PhD(plant breeding), 73. *Prof Exp:* Farm mgr tribal rehab farm colony, Nilgiris Adivasi Welfare Asn, India, Can Univ Serv Overseas, 66-67, res agronomist safflower breeding & field experimentation, Nimbkar Agr Res Inst, Phaltan, India, 67-69; plant breeder wheat breeding, Can Int Develop Agency, Kenya, Univ Man, 72-74; proj mgr plant genetic resources ctr, Ger Agency Tech Coop, Ethiopia Proj, 75-77; RES SCIENTIST NEW CROPS, BREEDING & MGT SOYBEANS & SAFFLOWER, LETHBRIDGE RES STA, AGR CAN, 78- *Concurrent Pos:* chmn, Int Safflower Continuing Comt, 81-85. *Mem:* Agr Inst Can; Am Soc Agron; Crop Sci Soc Am; Can Soc Agron. *Res:* Research into adaptability of diverse crops for the area of southern Alberta, particularly screening and breeding soybeans for this latitude and agroclimatic zone; crop genetic resources world-wide. *Mailing Add:* Agr Can Res Sta Lethbridge AB T1J 4B1 Can

MUNDEL, M(ARVIN) E(VERETT), b New York, NY, Apr 20, 16; c 2. ENGINEERING. *Educ:* NY Univ, BS, 36; Univ Iowa, MS, 38, PhD(indust eng), 39. *Prof Exp:* Asst mech eng, Univ Iowa, 36-39, res engr & instr indust eng, 39; indust engr, Tung-Sol Lamp Works, NJ, 39-40; asst prof gen eng, Bradley Polytech Inst, 40-42; asst prof indust eng, Purdue Univ, 42-46, from assoc prof to prof, 46-52, chmn dept, 50-52; dir, US Army Ord Mgt Eng Training Prog, 52-54; vdir mgt ctr & prof indust mgt, Marquette Univ, 54-58; dir, 58-63, PRES, M E MUNDEL & ASSOCS, 65- *Concurrent Pos:* Vis prof, Univ Birmingham, 51 & Keo Univ, Japan, 60-63; prin staff officer indust eng & work measurement, Bur Budget, Exec Off President, 63-65. *Honors & Awards:* Gilbreth Medal, Am Soc Advan Mgt, 53; APO Award, Asian Productivity Orgn, Tokyo, 80. *Mem:* Fel Soc Advan Mgt; fel Am Inst Indust Engrs (pres-elect, 78-80); Am Soc Mech Engrs; hon mem Inst Indust Engrs Australia. *Res:* Systematic motion and time study; testing for skill; hand motions and rhythm in factory work; principles and practice of motion and time; management control systems; motion and time study-improving productivity; measuring and enhancing the productivity of goverment and service organizations. *Mailing Add:* 821 Loxford Terr Silver Spring MD 20901

MUNDELL, PERCY MELDRUM, b Vancouver, BC, Dec 14, 21; m 50; c 3. ORGANIC CHEMISTRY. *Educ:* Univ BC, BA, 43, MA, 45; Ohio State Univ, PhD(chem), 53. *Prof Exp:* Asst chem, Univ BC, 42-45, instr, 45-46; asst, Ohio State Univ, 47-51; from asst prof to assoc prof, 52-67, PROF CHEM, MIAMI UNIV, 67- *Mem:* Am Chem Soc. *Res:* Structural studies of natural products. *Mailing Add:* Dept of Chem Miami Univ Oxford OH 45056

MUNDELL, ROBERT DAVID, b Greensburg, Pa, Aug 30, 36; m 62; c 2. ANATOMY, CELL BIOLOGY. *Educ:* Waynesburg Col, BS, 57; Univ Pittsburgh, PhD(anat, cell biol), 65. *Prof Exp:* Instr anat & histol, Sch Med, Tufts Univ, 64-66; asst prof histol, 66-68, head dept, 68-70, assoc prof histol & anat, 68-72, PROF HISTOL & ANAT, SCH DENT MED, UNIV PITTSBURGH, 72-, HEAD DEPT ANAT, 70- *Concurrent Pos:* NSF res grant, Tufts Univ & Univ Pittsburgh, 66-68. *Mem:* Am Asn Anatomists; AAAS; Sigma Xi; NY Acad Sci; Am Asn Dent Schs. *Res:* Craniofacial development. *Mailing Add:* 630 Salk Hall Sch of Dent Med Univ of Pittsburgh Pittsburgh PA 15261

MUNDERLOH, ULRIKE GERTRUD, b Schwaig-Nurnberg, Ger, Apr 25, 51. INVERTEBRATE CELL CULTURE, INVERTEBRATE-TRANSMITTED PARASITES. *Educ:* Univ Munich, Ger, Vet, 75, DrMedVet, 77. *Prof Exp:* Clinician, Dept Large Animal Surg, Vet Fac, Univ Munich, Ger, 77; fel, Int Lab Res Training Animal Dis, Kenya, 78-79; FEL, WAKSMAN INST MICROBIOL, RUTGERS UNIV, NJ, 79- *Concurrent Pos:* Adj fac, W Alton Jones Cell Sci Ctr, Lake Placid, NY, 80. *Res:* Arboviruses, Nairobi sheep disease virus; immunoparasitology: sporozoite antigens, tick antigens; tissue culture: vertebrate cell culture, mosquito and tick tissue culture; cultivation of the mammalian and vector stages of parsitic protozoa--Babesia, Theileria and Plasmodium. *Mailing Add:* Inst Microbiol Rutgers Univ PO Box 759 Piscataway NJ 08854

MUNDIE, LLOYD GEORGE, b Udney, Ont, Dec 15, 16; nat US; m 42; c 2. OPTICS. *Educ:* Univ Sask, BSc, 35, MSc, 37; Purdue Univ, PhD(physics), 43. *Prof Exp:* Instr physics, Purdue Univ, 39-47; infrared physicist, Naval Ord Lab, 47-51; physicist, Nat Bur Standards, 51-54; physicist, Univ Mich, 54-57; head infrared & optics dept, Bendix Systs Div, 57-61; dir basic res lab, Lockheed-Calif Co, 61-65; PHYSICIST, RAND CORP, 65- *Mem:* Fel AAAS; fel Optical Soc Am. *Res:* Spectroscopy; infrared. *Mailing Add:* Rand Corp 1700 Main St Santa Monica CA 90406

MUNDKUR, BALAJI, b Mangalore, India, Dec 27, 24; nat US; m 46. CYTOLOGY. *Educ:* Univ Bombay, India, BSc, 45; Washington Univ, PhD(bot, genetics), 51. *Prof Exp:* Assoc mycol, Indian Agr Res Inst, 47; res assoc, Univ Southern Ill, 50-53; sr sci officer, Indian Cancer Res Ctr, 53-55; assoc bacteriologist, Univ PR, 55-58; spec res fel anat, USPHS, Chicago, 58-60; ASSOC PROF BIOL SCI, UNIV CONN, 60- *Res:* Electron microscopy; application of cytological freeze-drying techniques in cytochemistry and electron microscopy. *Mailing Add:* Biol Sci Group Univ of Conn Storrs CT 06268

MUNDT, PHILIP A, b Sioux Falls, SDak, Oct 2, 27; m 51; c 3. PETROLEUM GEOLOGY. *Educ:* SDak Sch Mines & Technol, BS, 51; Washington Univ, MA, 53; Stanford Univ, PhD(geol), 55. *Prof Exp:* Geologist, Mobil Producing Co, 55-58, subsurface supvr, Mobil Mediterranean Inc, 58-63, staff geologist, Mobil Oil Corp, 63-65, explor supvr, Libya, 65-67, geol supvr, 67-69; explor mgr, US Nat Resources, Inc, 69-72; mgr geol & geochem res, Mobil Res Develop Corp, Mobile Prod Nigeria, 72-77, explor mgr, 77-79; EXPLOR MGR, MOBIL OIL INDONESIA, 79- *Res:* Petroleum exploration. *Mailing Add:* 1221 Rock Springs Rd Duncanville TX 75110

MUNDY, BRADFORD PHILIP, b Warrensburg, NY, Nov 9, 38; m 63; c 3. CHEMISTRY. *Educ:* State Univ NY Albany, BS, 61; Univ Vt, PhD(chem), 65. *Prof Exp:* Res assoc chem, Univ Calif, Berkeley, 65-66; NIH fel, 66-67; asst prof, 67-71, assoc prof, 71-75, PROF CHEM, MONT STATE UNIV, 75- *Mem:* Am Chem Soc. *Res:* Synthesis of natural products; heterocyclic chemistry; biosynthesis. *Mailing Add:* Dept of Chem Mont State Univ Bozeman MT 59717

MUNDY, GREGORY ROBERT, b Melbourne, Australia, June 16, 42; m 66; c 3. METABOLISM, ENDOCRINOLOGY. *Educ:* Univ Melbourne, BM, BS, 66; Univ Tasmania, MD, 73. *Prof Exp:* Resident med officer internal med, Royal Hobart Hosp, 67-70; lectr, Univ Tasmania, 70-72; res assoc clin pharmacol, Univ Rochester, 72-74; asst prof, 74-77, ASSOC PROF ENDOCRINOL, HEALTH CTR, UNIV CONN, 77- *Concurrent Pos:* Consult physician, Vet Admin Hosp, Newington, Conn, 74-; consult endocrinologist, Newington Children's Hosp & St Francis Hosp, Hartford, Conn, 77- *Mem:* Fel Royal Australasian Col Physicians; Am Fedn Clin Res; AAAS; Endocrine Soc. *Res:* Calcium and bone metabolism; chemotaxis; lymphokines; bone resorption. *Mailing Add:* Dept of Med Rm L 2080 Univ of Conn Health Ctr Farmington CT 06032

MUNDY, ROY LEE, b Charlottesville, Va, Mar 4, 22; m 41; c 3. PHARMACOLOGY, TOXICOLOGY. *Educ:* Howard Col, BS, 48; Univ Ala, MS, 50; Univ Va, PhD(pharmacol), 57. *Prof Exp:* Asst prof pharmacol, Howard Col, 50-51; chief pharmacol dept, Walter Reed Army Inst Res, 55-66; assoc prof, 66-71, PROF PHARMACOL, MED CTR, UNIV ALA, BIRMINGHAM, 71- *Mem:* Soc Toxicol; Soc Exp Biol & Med; Am Soc Pharmacol & Exp Therapeut. *Res:* Pharmacology of sulfhydryl radio-protectant chemicals; removal of radiation agents from the animal body; autonomic pharmacology. *Mailing Add:* Dept of Pharmacol Univ of Ala Med Ctr Birmingham AL 35294

MUNETA, PAUL, b Harlowton, Mont, Apr 21, 31; m 56; c 2. FOOD SCIENCE. *Educ:* Mont State Col, BS, 53; Cornell Univ, PhD(veg crops), 59. *Prof Exp:* Asst agr chem, 59-68, asst prof, 61-68, ASSOC PROF FOOD SCI & ASSOC FOOD SCIENTIST, UNIV IDAHO, 68- *Mem:* Am Chem Soc; Inst Food Technol; Int Asn Milk, Food & Environ Sanit. *Res:* Changes in nitrate and nitrite in cured meats; factors affecting microbiol conversion of nitrate to nitrite in foods; determination of chemical and physical methods to control nitrate reduction. *Mailing Add:* Food Res Bldg Univ Idaho Moscow ID 83843

MUNGALL, ALLAN GEORGE, b Vancouver, BC, Mar 12, 28; m 50; c 3. EXPERIMENTAL ATOMIC PHYSICS. *Educ:* Univ BC, BASc, 49, MASc, 50; McGill Univ, PhD(physics), 54. *Prof Exp:* Geophysicist, Calif Stand Co, Alta, 50; jr res officer physics, Nat Res Coun Can, 50-52; asst, McGill Univ, 54; from asst res officer to assoc res officer, 54-67, sr res officer, 67-81, PRIN RES OFFICER, NAT RES COUN CAN, 81- *Mem:* Can Asn Physicists; fel Inst Elec & Electronics Engrs. *Res:* Atomic frequency and time standards. *Mailing Add:* Physics Div M-36 Nat Res Coun Montreal Rd Ottawa ON K1A 0R6 Can

MUNGALL, WILLIAM STEWART, b Buffalo, NY, July 24, 45; m 67; c 2. SYNTHETIC ORGANIC CHEMISTRY. *Educ:* State Univ NY Buffalo, BA, 67; Northwestern Univ, PhD(org chem), 70. *Prof Exp:* Asst prof chem, 71-74, ASSOC PROF CHEM, HOPE COL, 74- *Concurrent Pos:* Consult, Org Chem Inc & Hexcel Inc. *Mem:* Am Chem Soc; Sigma Xi. *Res:* Synthesis of biologically active organic compounds; phosphoramidate chemistry. *Mailing Add:* Dept of Chem Hope Col Holland MI 49423

MUNGAN, NECMETTIN, b Mardin, Turkey, Mar 1, 34; m 62; c 4. PETROLEUM ENGINEERING, MATHEMATICS. *Educ:* Univ Tex, BS, 56, BA, 57, MS, 58, PhD(petrol eng), 62. *Prof Exp:* Scientist, Sinclair Res, Inc, 61-63, res scientist, 63-65 & Sinclair Oil & Gas Co, 65-66, sr res scientist, 66; chief res officer, Petrol Recovery Inst, Univ Calgary, 66-78; CONSULT, MUNGAN PETROL CONSULTS LTD, 78- *Honors & Awards:* Cedric K Ferguson Award, Soc Petrol Engrs, 66; Presentation Award, Am Inst Chem Engrs, 66. *Mem:* Soc Petrol Engrs; Can Inst Mining & Metall; Am Chem Soc; Am Inst Chem Engrs. *Res:* Application of surface chemistry to flow of fluids in petroleum reservoirs; formation damage due to clays; reservoir engineering and well logging; mathematical modeling of fluid flow in reservoirs; enhanced recovery of oil and gas from underground deposits. *Mailing Add:* Mungan Petrol Consults Ltd 540 Fifth Ave SW Calgary AB T2P 0M2 Can

MUNGER, BRYCE LEON, b Everett, Wash, May 20, 33; m 57; c 4. HUMAN ANATOMY, CELL BIOLOGY. *Educ:* Washington Univ, MD, 58. *Prof Exp:* Intern path, Johns Hopkins Hosp, 58-59; asst prof anat, Washington Univ, 61-65; assoc prof, Univ Chicago, 65-66; PROF ANAT & CHMN DEPT, HERSHEY MED CTR, PA STATE UNIV, 66- *Mem:* AAAS; Am Asn Anat; Am Soc Cell Biol; Am Diabetes Asn; NY Acad Sci. *Res:* Cytology of secretion, especially pancreatic islets and comparative ultrastructure of sensory nerve endings, particularly mechanoreceptors. *Mailing Add:* Dept of Anat Hershey Med Ctr Pa State Univ Hershey PA 17033

MUNGER, GEORGE DONALD, b Wilmington, Del, May 21, 23; m 50; c 2. PLANT PATHOLOGY. *Educ:* Univ Del, BS, 48, MS, 49; Ohio State Univ, PhD(bot, plant path), 55. *Prof Exp:* Tech serv rep, E I du Pont de Nemours & Co, 49-50; sr res biologist, Battelle Mem Inst, 50-54; plant pathologist, B F Goodrich Co, 55-56; plant pathologist, Diamond Shamrock Corp, 56-58; plant pathologist fungicide develop coord, Am Cyanamid Co, 58-66; supvr field res, T R Evans Res Ctr, 66-69, MGR COM DEVELOP, AGR CHEM, DIAMOND SHAMROCK CORP, 69- *Mem:* Am Phytopath Soc. *Res:* Agricultural pesticides; field research and development. *Mailing Add:* Diamond Shamrock Corp Agr Chem Div 1100 Superior Ave Cleveland OH 44114

MUNGER, HAMNETT P(ITZER), b Spartansburg, SC, Nov 1, 03; m 33; c 1. CHEMICAL ENGINEERING. *Educ:* Ga Inst Technol, BS, 25; Columbia Univ, MA, 27; Univ Pittsburgh, PhD(phys chem), 29. *Prof Exp:* Indust res fel, Mellon Inst, 26-28; asst, Univ Pittsburgh, 28-29; metallurgist steel res, Armco Steel Corp, 29-36; supt electroplating, Repub Steel Corp, 36-44; plant mgr chromium plating, Van der Horst Corp Am, 44-45; supt tin finishing, Youngstown Sheet & Tube Co, 45-48; tech adv res, Battelle Mem Inst, 48-55; chmn dept chem eng & metall, Syracuse Univ, 55-58; head metall div, Res Ctr, Repub Steel Corp, 58-63, mgr spec mat develop, 63-68; METALL & CHEM ENG CONSULT, 68- *Concurrent Pos:* Consult, NY State Air Pollution Control Bd, 56-58; Int Exec Serv Corps consult, Turkey, 69-70, AID Mission consult, 70-71; consult, UN Develop Prog, Thailand, 72; instr metall, Am Soc Metals, 76-78. *Mem:* Am Chem Soc; Am Soc Eng Educ; Am Soc Metals; fel Am Inst Chem Engrs; Am Inst Mining, Metall & Petrol Engrs. *Res:* Metallurgical research in flat rolled steel and coated products; high temperature and high strength alloys; air pollution control and prevention; chemical engineering pilot plant work; development and expansion of steel mill production in developing countries. *Mailing Add:* 7562 Sugarbush Trail Hudson OH 44236

MUNGER, STANLEY H(IRAM), b Detroit, Mich, Apr 29, 20; m 55; c 3. RESEARCH MANAGEMENT, CHEMICAL ENGINEERING. *Educ:* Purdue Univ, BSChE, 42. *Prof Exp:* Res engr, 42-44 & 46-52, res supvr, 52-58, res mgr, 58-70, MGR PHOTO PROD ENG RES, E I DU PONT DE NEMOURS & CO, INC, 70- *Mem:* AAAS; Am Chem Soc. *Res:* Polymer processing; photopolymerization; photographic films. *Mailing Add:* 33 Wardell Ave Rumson NJ 07760

MUNI, INDU A, b Amreli, India, Oct 24, 42; m 69. TOXICOLOGY. *Educ:* Univ Nagpur, BS, 64; NDak State Univ, MS, 66; Univ Miss, PhD(biochem, pharmacol), 68. *Prof Exp:* NIMH res fel, Univ Miss, 68-69; clin biochemist dept path, St Joseph's Hosp, Milwaukee, 69-74; sr res scientist, Miles, Inc, 74-76; mgr regulatory & clin affairs, J T Baker Diag, 77-78; dir spec serv, Ind Bio-Test Labs, 78-81; DIR TOXICOL, BIOASSAY SYSTS CORP, 81- *Mem:* Am Asn Clin Chemists; Am Chem Soc; Regulatory Affairs Prof Soc; Soc Toxicol. *Res:* Clinical chemistry; immunochemical and biochemical toxicology. *Mailing Add:* Bioassay Systs Corp Woburn MA 01801

MUNIES, ROBERT, b New York, NY, Oct 19, 35. INDUSTRIAL PHARMACY, RESEARCH ADMINISTRATION. *Educ:* Columbia Univ, BS, 56; Univ Wis, PhD(pharm), 65. *Prof Exp:* Sr pharmaceut scientist, Vick Div Res & Develop, Richardson-Merrell, Inc, 65-71, group supvr sci info, 71; mgr, 71-79, DIR REGULATORY AFAIRS, BOEHRINGER INGELHEIM LTD, 79- *Mem:* Am Pharmaceut Asn; Acad Pharm Sci; NY Acad Sci. *Res:* Factors influencing percutaneous absorption through human skin; etiology and treatment of acne; food and drug law; clinical research. *Mailing Add:* Boehringer Ingelheim Ltd 90 E Ridge Ridgefield CT 06877

MUNIGLE, JO ANNE, b Los Angeles, Calif, Nov 14, 34. TOXICOLOGY. *Educ:* Conn Col, BA, 57; Cornell Univ, PhD(anat), 67. *Prof Exp:* Fel anat, McGill Univ, 66-68; mgr reprod & mutagenesis, 68-78, DIR TOXICOL, SAFETY HEALTH & ECOL DEPT, CIBA-GEIGY CORP, 78- *Mem:* AAAS; Genetics Soc Am. *Res:* Developmental biology and genetics. *Mailing Add:* Dept of Safety Health & Ecol Ciba-Geigy Corp Ardsley NY 10502

MUNIR, ZUHAIR A, b Iraq, July 7, 34; m 63; c 1. CERAMIC ENGINEERING. *Educ:* Univ Calif, Berkeley, BS, 56, MS, 58, PhD(mat sci), 63. *Prof Exp:* Chem engr, Mt Copper Co, 56-57; from asst prof to prof mat sci, San Jose State Col, 62-73; PROF MECH ENG, UNIV CALIF, DAVIS, 73- *Concurrent Pos:* Consult, Molectro Corp, 63-64, Lawrence Livermore Lab, 73-, Rockwell-Int, 75 & State Calif Energy Comn, 77; engr, IBM Corp, 64, consult, 65-; engr, Gen Elec Co, 65; vis mem fac, Sch Eng Sci, Fla State Univ, 67-68; vis prof, Univ Calif, Davis, 72-73. *Mem:* AAAS; Am Inst Mining, Metall & Petrol Engrs. *Res:* High temperature chemistry and thermodynamic properties; thermodynamics and kinetics of solid-gas reactions; surface phenomena and corrosion. *Mailing Add:* Dept of Mech Eng Univ of Calif Davis CA 95616

MUNK, BENEDIKT AAGE, b Fredericia, Denmark, Dec 3, 29. ELECTRICAL ENGINEERING. *Educ:* Tech Univ Denmark, MScEE, 54; Ohio State Univ, PhD, 68. *Prof Exp:* Res & develop engr, Rhode & Schwarz, Ger, 57-58; engr, A/S Nordisk Antenne Fabrik, Denmark, 59-60; res & develop engr, Andrew Corp, 61-63; sr res engr, NAm Aviation, Inc, 63-64; res assoc, ElectroSci Lab, 64-68, asst supvr, 68-69, asst prof elec eng, 71-77, ASSOC SUPVR ELECTROSCI LAB, OHIO STATE UNIV, 69-, ASSOC PROF ELEC ENG, 77- *Mem:* Inst Elec & Electronics Engrs. *Res:* Electromagnetic theory; antennas; scattering; arrays; radomes; absorbers; radar; camouflage; periodic surfaces. *Mailing Add:* ElectroSci Lab Ohio State Univ 1320 Kinnear Rd Columbus OH 43212

MUNK, MINER NELSON, b Napa, Calif, Nov 17, 34; m 55; c 2. APPLIED PHYSICS. *Educ:* Univ Calif, Berkeley, AB, 57, MA, 59, PhD(physics), 67. *Prof Exp:* Physicist, Aerojet Gen Corp, Calif, 59-62; sr physicist, Varian Aerograph, 67-75; physicist, Milton Roy Co, 75-78; CHIEF SCIENTIST, LDC/MILTON ROY, 78- *Mem:* Sigma Xi; Optical Soc Am; Am Chem Soc. *Res:* Physical methods of analysis; mass spectroscopy; liquid chromatography. *Mailing Add:* LDC/Milton Roy PO Box 10235 Riviera Beach FL 33404

MUNK, PETR, b Praha, Czech, Oct 31, 32; m 61; c 2. POLYMER CHEMISTRY. *Educ:* Col Chem Technol, Prague, Czech, MS, 56; Inst Macromolecular Chem, Czech Acad Sci, PhD(phys chem macromolecules), 60, DSc(phys chem macromolecules), 67. *Prof Exp:* Head dept molecular hydrodyn, Inst Macromolecular Chem, Czech Acad Sci, 56-67; res scientist, Res Triangle Inst, NC, 68; vis assoc prof chem, 69-71, asst prof, 71-72, ASSOC PROF CHEM, UNIV TEX, AUSTIN, 72- *Mem:* Am Chem Soc. *Res:* Thermodynamics of macromolecular solutions; sedimentation analysis; viscometry; streaming birefringence. *Mailing Add:* Dept of Chem Univ of Tex Austin TX 78712

MUNK, VLADIMIR, b Pardubice, Czech, Feb 27, 25; m 50; c 2. MICROBIOLOGY, BIOCHEMISTRY. *Educ:* Prague Tech Univ, MS, 50, PhD(biochem), 55. *Prof Exp:* Head anal dept, Cent Res Inst Food Indust, 53-57, head microbiol dept, 58-63; sr microbiologist, Inst Microbiol, Czech Acad Sci, 63-69; PROF BIOL, STATE UNIV NY COL PLATTSBURGH, 69- *Concurrent Pos:* Univ fel & grant-in-aid, 70-71, Chase Chem Co fel, 71-72; exchange scholar, State Univ NY, 74. *Honors & Awards:* State Prize, Govt Czech Socialistic Repub, 68. *Mem:* AAAS; Am Soc Microbiol. *Res:* Industrial use of microorganisms; microbial production of vitamins and enzymes; fermentation of hydrocarbons; continuous cultivation of microorganisms. *Mailing Add:* Fac of Sci State Univ of NY Col Plattsburgh NY 12901

MUNK, WALTER HEINRICH, b Vienna, Austria, Oct 19, 17; nat US; m 53; c 2. PHYSICAL OCEANOGRAPHY. *Educ:* Calif Inst Technol, BS, 39; Univ Calif, MS, 40, PhD(oceanog), 47. *Hon Degrees:* Doctor Philosophiae Honoris Causa, Univ Bergen, Norway, 75. *Prof Exp:* From asst prof to assoc prof geophys, 47-54, PROF GEOPHYS, UNIV CALIF, SAN DIEGO, 54-, ASSOC DIR, INST GEOPHYS, 59- *Concurrent Pos:* Guggenheim Found fel, Univ Oslo, 48, Cambridge Univ, 55 & 62. *Honors & Awards:* Arthur L Day Medal, Am Geol Soc; Sverdrup Gold Medal; Gold Medal, Royal Astron Soc; Maurice Ewing Medal; Agassiz Medal; Capt Robert Dexter Conrad Award; Josiah Willard Gibbs Lectr. *Mem:* Nat Acad Sci; Am Acad Arts & Sci; Am Philos Soc; foreign mem Royal Soc London; Leopoldina Ger Acad Res Natural Sci. *Res:* Ocean waves; tides; wind stress and ocean currents; rotation of the earth; ocean acoustics. *Mailing Add:* Inst of Geophys & Planetary Sci Univ of Calif San Diego La Jolla CA 92093

MUNKACSI, ISTVAN, b Budapest, Hungary, Apr 15, 27; m 54; c 1. ANATOMY. *Educ:* Med Univ Budapest, Dr med, 53; Univ Khartoum, Dr philos, 64. *Prof Exp:* Lectr anat, Med Univ Budapest, 53-57, sr lectr, 57-60; sr lectr, Univ Khartoum, 60-64; sr lectr, Med Univ Budapest, 64-66; vis asst prof, 66-68, assoc prof, 68-74, PROF ANAT, UNIV SASK, 74- *Mem:* Anat Soc Gt Brit & Ireland; Can Asn Anat; Int Soc Nephrology; Pan Am Asn Anat (secy gen, 72-75). *Res:* Comparative morphology; innervation of the kidney and distribution of the type of nephrons investigated in desert and laboratory mammals; blood vessels and arterio-venous connections of the kidney; dynamics of synapse formation in the sympathetic nervous tissue in tissue culture. *Mailing Add:* Dept of Anat Univ of Sask Saskatoon SK S7N 0W0 Can

MUNKRES, JAMES RAYMOND, b Omaha, Nebr, Aug 18, 30; m 64. MATHEMATICS. *Educ:* Nebr Wesleyan Univ, AB, 51; Univ Mich, AM, 52, PhD(math), 56. *Prof Exp:* Instr math, Univ Mich, 55-57; instr, Princeton Univ, 57-58, Fine instr, 58-60; from asst prof to assoc prof, 60-66, PROF MATH, MASS INST TECHNOL, 66- *Concurrent Pos:* Sloan res fel, 65-67. *Mem:* Am Math Soc; Math Asn Am. *Res:* Differential and combinatorial topology. *Mailing Add:* 2-242 Mass Inst of Technol Dept of Math Cambridge MA 02139

MUNN, CARYL GWYNETH, b London, Eng, Sept 2, 46; m 76. IMMMUNOLOGY. *Educ:* London Univ, BSc, 73; NY Univ, MS, 79, PhD(immunol), 82. *Prof Exp:* RES ASST, SLOAN-KETTERRING INST, 73- *Mem:* British Soc Immunol. *Res:* Role of iron and iron binding proteins in the function of the lymphonyeloid system with particular reference to B-cell differentiation. *Mailing Add:* Sect 6154 Sloan-Ketterinig Inst 1275 York Ave New York NY 10021

MUNN, DAVID ALAN, b Elyria, Ohio, Mar 27, 47; m 69; c 2. SOIL CHEMISTRY, AGRONOMY. *Educ:* Ohio State Univ, BS, 70, MS, 72, PhD(agron), 74. *Prof Exp:* Teaching & res assoc, Soils Agron Dept, Ohio State Univ, 70-74; vis asst prof & res assoc, Soil Sci Dept, NC State Univ, 74-76; ASST PROF SOILS & AGRON, AGR TECH INST, OHIO STATE UNIV, 76- *Mem:* Soil Sci Soc Am; Am Soc Agron; Sigma Xi. *Res:* Plant nutrition, including phosphorus, potassium, nitrogen, lime and acidity. *Mailing Add:* Agr Tech Inst US Rte 250 Wooster OH 44691

MUNN, GEORGE EDWARD, b Lawrence Co, Pa, Nov 29, 24. ORGANIC CHEMISTRY. *Educ:* Westminster Col, Pa, BS, 45; Univ Ill, PhD(org chem), 48. *Prof Exp:* Asst, Univ Ill, 45-47; Du Pont fel, Mass Inst Technol, 48-49; CHEMIST, E I DU PONT DE NEMOURS & CO, INC, 49- *Mem:* Am Chem Soc. *Res:* Synthetic organic chemistry; polymer chemistry. *Mailing Add:* Polymer Prod Dept Exp Sta Wilmington DE 19898

MUNN, JOHN IRVIN, b Pittsburgh, Pa, Oct 28, 22; m 48; c 3. ENVIRONMENTAL HEALTH, PHARMACOLOGY. *Educ:* Ind Univ Pa, BS, 48; George Washington Univ, MS, 52; Georgetown Univ, PhD(biochem), 57. *Prof Exp:* Res biochemist, US Naval Med Res Inst, 48-52; res hematologist, Walter Reed Army Inst Res, 52-58; biochemist, Food & Drug Admin, 58-61; scientist adminr-pharmacologist, NIH, Md, 61-71; sr scientist, WHO, 71-76; asst to sci coordr environ cancer, Nat Cancer Inst, NIH, 76-80; CONSULT, 80- *Honors & Awards:* Superior Performance Award, Walter Reed Army Inst Res, 57. *Mem:* Soc Toxicol; Am Soc Pharmacol & Exp Therapeut. *Res:* Metabolism of gallium; biochemical methodology; hemoglobin; fatty acids and surface areas of erythrocytes; toxicity of emulsifiers in foods; food standardization and contaminant monitoring; international and national environmental health policies; identification, assessment and control of carcinogenic environmental agents. *Mailing Add:* 11022 Marcliff Rd Rockville MD 20852

MUNN, ROBERT EDWARD, b Winnipeg, Man, July 26, 19; m 44; c 4. METEOROLOGY, AIR POLLUTION. *Educ:* McMaster Univ, BA, 41; Univ Toronto, MA, 45; Univ Mich, PhD(meteorol), 62. *Prof Exp:* Meteorologist, Meteorol Serv Can, 41-77; PROF, INST ENVIRON STUDIES, UNIV TORONTO, 77- *Concurrent Pos:* Vis prof, Univ Stockholm, 70; ed, Problems Environ, Int Coun Sci Unions & J Boundary Layer Meteorol; chmn, Sci Adv Comm, Monitoring & Assessment Res Ctr, Chelsea Col, London, Eng. *Honors & Awards:* Applied Meteorol Award, Am Meteorol Soc, 74, Paterson Medal, 75. *Mem:* Fel Am Meteorol Soc; Fel Royal Meteorol Soc; Can Meterol & Oceanog Soc. *Res:* Micrometeorology; regional air pollution; environmental monitoring; environmental impact assessment. *Mailing Add:* Inst for Environ Studies Univ of Toronto Toronto ON M5S 1A4 Can

MUNN, ROBERT JAMES, b Southampton, Eng, Jan 31, 37; m 62; c 2. CHEMICAL PHYSICS. *Educ:* Bristol Univ, BSc, 57, PhD(chem), 61. *Prof Exp:* Res fel chem, Bristol Univ, 61-63; Harkness fel of Commonwealth Fund, Univ Md, 63-64; lectr chem, Bristol Univ, 64-65; lectr math, Queen's Univ, Belfast, 65-66; from asst prof to assoc prof chem physics, 66-72, PROF CHEM, UNIV MD, COLLEGE PARK, 72-, DIR, 70-, ASST DEAN, 75- *Concurrent Pos:* Consult, Lockheed Electronics, 70-71 & NSF, 70- *Mem:* AAAS; Am Phys Soc. *Res:* Scattering; educational technology; computer aided instruction. *Mailing Add:* Dept of Chem Univ of Md College Park MD 20742

MUNNECKE, DONALD EDWIN, b St Paul, Minn, May 30, 20; m 42; c 4. PHYTOPATHOLOGY. *Educ:* Univ Minn, BA, 42, MS, 49, PhD(plant path), 50. *Prof Exp:* Instr & jr plant pathologist, Univ Calif, Los Angeles, 51-53, from asst prof & asst plant pathologist to assoc prof & assoc plant pathologist, 53-61; assoc prof & assoc plant pathologist, 61-65, PROF & PLANT PATHOLOGIST, UNIV CALIF, RIVERSIDE, 65- *Concurrent Pos:* Guggenheim fel & Fulbrigh res scholar, Univ Gottingen, 65-66. *Mem:* Am Phytopath Soc; Bot Soc Am. *Res:* Ornamental plant diseases; chemical soil treatments for disease control; fungicide action in soils; ecological relations in control of Armillaria mellea. *Mailing Add:* Dept Plant Path Univ Calif Riverside CA 92502

MUNNELL, EQUINN W, b Sayville, NY, June 28, 13; m 37; c 3. MEDICINE. *Educ:* Amherst Col, BA, 35; Cornell Univ, MD, 39; Am Bd Obstet & Gynec, dipl, 48. *Prof Exp:* Asst instr obstet & gynec, Col Med, NY Univ, 45-47; from asst prof to assoc prof, 50-59, PROF OBSTET & GYNEC, COL PHYSICIANS & SURGEONS, COLUMBIA UNIV, 69- *Concurrent Pos:* Asst gynecologist, Mem Hosp, New York, 45-47; asst obstetrician & gynecologist, Presby Hosp, New York, 47-57, assoc obstetrician & gynecologist, 57-69, attend obstetrician & gynecologist, 69-; assoc attend gynecologist, Francis Delafield Hosp, 53-62, attend gynecologist, 62- *Mem:* Fel Am Col Surg; fel Am Col Obstet & Gynec; Am Asn Obstet & Gynec; Am Cancer Soc; soc Gynec Theologists. *Res:* Obstetrics and gynecology; gynecologic cancer. *Mailing Add:* 842 Park Ave New York NY 10021

MUNNO, FRANK J, b New Castle, Pa, Jan 5, 36; m 58; c 3. NUCLEAR ENGINEERING. *Educ:* Waynesburg Col, BS, 57; Univ Fla, MS, 62, PhD(nuclear eng), 64. *Prof Exp:* From asst prof to assoc prof, 65-72, PROF NUCLEAR ENG, UNIV MD, COLLEGE PARK, 72- *Concurrent Pos:* Consult, Gen Physics Corp, 66-69 & Harry Diamond Lab, 70- *Mem:* Am Nuclear Soc; Am Inst Chem Engrs. *Res:* Heat transfer in two phase flow; nuclear radiation shielding and neutral particle transport; nuclear reactor dynamics. *Mailing Add:* Dept of Chem Eng Univ of Md Col Eng College Park MD 20742

MUNNS, DONALD NEVILLE, b Sydney, Australia, Sept 6, 31; m 60; c 3. PLANT NUTRITION, SOIL SCIENCE. *Educ:* Univ Sydney, BScAgr, 54; Univ Calif, Berkeley, PhD(soil sci), 61. *Prof Exp:* Asst chemist, NSW Dept Agr, Australia, 54-57; res asst, Univ Calif, Berkeley, 57-60; from res officer to sr res officer, Commonwealth Sci & Indust Res Orgn, Canberra, 60-66; asst chemist, 66-68, assoc prof soils & plant nutrit, 68-76, PROF SOIL SCI, UNIV CALIF, DAVIS, 76- *Concurrent Pos:* Vis soil scientist, Univ Hawaii, 73-74. *Mem:* AAAS; Soil Sci Soc Am; Am Soc Agron. *Res:* Plant and soil analysis; soil phosphate, acidity, and legume growth; nodulation and nitrogen fixation; salinity; genetic variations in response of plants and thizobia to substrate factors. *Mailing Add:* Dept of Soils & Plant Nutrit Univ of Calif Davis CA 95616

MUNNS, THEODORE WILLARD, b Peoria, Ill, June 11, 41. BIOCHEMISTRY. *Educ:* Bradley Univ, BS, 63; St Louis Univ, PhD(biochem), 70. *Prof Exp:* Res assoc biochem, 70-74, instr, 74-76, ASST RES PROF, BIOCHEM, ST LOUIS UNIV, 76-; ASST RES PROF, WASHINGTON UNIV, 80- *Concurrent Pos:* NSF fel, St Louis Univ, 70-71, NIH fel, 72- *Mem:* Am Chem Soc; Sigma Xi; NY Acad Sci; Am Soc Biol Chemists. *Res:* Nucleic acid and protein metabolism in neoplastic systems; immunochemistry. *Mailing Add:* 4566 Scott Box 8045 St Louis MO 63104

MUNNS, W(ILLIAM) O, b Tuxford, Sask, Dec 16, 26; m 53; c 5. CHEMICAL ENGINEERING. *Educ:* Univ Sask, BSc, 49; Univ Toronto, MBA, 76. *Prof Exp:* Res engr, Res & Develop Labs, 49-56, group leader chem develop, 56-57, group leader food & pharmaceut, 57-65, new prod mgr, 65-71, chief chemist, 71-80, NAT QUALITY ASSURANCE MGR, CAN PACKERS LTD, 80- *Concurrent Pos:* Chmn res policy comt, Meat Packers Coun Can, 65-; pres, Innovation Can Inc, 77-; consult, Int Develop Res Ctr. *Mem:* Am Inst Chem Engrs; fel Chem Inst Can; Can Inst Food Technol; Inst Food Technol; Am Soc Qual Control. *Res:* Food processing; pharmaceutical processing; product planning and new product development; quality assurance; chemical laboratories, microbiological laboratories and quality control; innovation management; entrepreneurship; product and service development in the public and private sectors. *Mailing Add:* 2 Woodark Rd Weston ON M9P 1M1 Can

MUNOZ, JAMES LOOMIS, b East Orange, NJ, Oct 31, 39. GEOCHEMISTRY. *Educ:* Princeton Univ, AB, 61; Johns Hopkins Univ, PhD(geol), 66. *Prof Exp:* Fel, Carnegie Inst Geophys Lab, 66-68; asst prof geol, 68-74, ASSOC PROF GEOL, UNIV COLO, BOULDER, 74- *Mem:* AAAS; Am Geophys Union; Mineral Soc Am; Geochem Soc. *Res:* Application of thermodynamics to petrology; geochemistry of fluorine in igneous, metamorphic, and ore-forming processes. *Mailing Add:* Dept of Geol Sci Univ of Colo Boulder CO 80309

MUNOZ, JOHN JOAQUIN, b Guatemala, Dec 23, 18; nat US; m 47; c 4. IMMUNOLOGY, MICROBIOLOGY. *Educ:* La State Univ, BS, 42; Univ Ky, MS, 45; Univ Wis, PhD(med bact), 47; Am Bd Microbiol, dipl. *Prof Exp:* Jr & sr technician bact, Univ Ky, 42-44; asst microbiol, Univ Wis, 44-47; asst prof med bact, Sch Med, Univ Ill, 47-51; res assoc, Merck Sharp & Dohme Res Labs, 51-57; prof microbiol & pub health, chmn dept & dir Stella Duncan Mem Labs, Univ Mont, 57-61; RES MICROBIOLOGIST, ROCKY MOUNTAIN LAB, NAT INST ALLERGY & INFECTIOUS DIS, 61- *Concurrent Pos:* Spec assignment, Pasteur Inst, Paris, 66-67. *Mem:* AAAS; fel Am Acad Microbiol; Am Soc Microbiol; Am Asn Immunol; Soc Exp Biol & Med. *Res:* Biologically active substances from Bordetella pertussis; mechanisms of action of B pertussis active substances; mechanism of anaphylaxis and hypersensitivity; purification of bacterial antigens; serological techniques. *Mailing Add:* Rocky Mountain Lab Nat Inst Allergy & Infect Dis Hamilton MT 59840

MUNOZ-CANDELARIO, RAFAEL, chemical engineering, see previous edition

MUNRO, DONALD W, JR, b Philadelphia, Pa, Dec 27, 37; m 61; c 2. PHYSIOLOGY, GENETICS. *Educ:* Wheaton Col, BS, 59; Pa State Univ, MS, 63, PhD(zool), 66. *Prof Exp:* Assoc prof zool, 66-71, PROF BIOL & HEAD DEPT, HOUGHTON COL, 71- *Mem:* Am Soc Zool; Am Physiol Soc; Am Inst Biol Sci; NY Acad Sci; AAAS. *Res:* Effects of cold exposure and hibernation on the respiration rates and oxidative phosphorylation of various tissues of carp, trout, frogs, rats, hamsters and chipmunks. *Mailing Add:* Dept of Biol Houghton Col Houghton NY 14744

MUNRO, HAMISH N, b Edinburgh, Scotland, July 3, 15; m 46; c 4. BIOCHEMISTRY, NUTRITION. *Educ:* Glasgow Univ, BSc, 36, MB, 39, DSc(biochem), 56. *Prof Exp:* Clin tutor med, Victoria Infirmary, Glasgow, Scotland, 40-45, asst dir path, 42-45; lectr physiol, Glasgow Univ, 45-47, sr lectr biochem, 47-56, reader nutrit biochem, 56-64, prof biochem, 64-66; PROF PHYSIOL CHEM, MASS INST TECHNOL, 66-; PROF MED & NUTRIT & DIR, USDA HUMAN NUTRIT RES CTR, TUFTS UNIV, 79- *Concurrent Pos:* Rockefeller traveling fel, 48; Fleck lectr, Glasgow Univ, 60; mem protein requirements comt, WHO-Food & Agr Orgn, 63; chmn food & nutrit bd, US Nat Res Coun, 75-; chmn, Dietary Allowances Comt. *Honors & Awards:* Osborne & Mendel Award, Am Inst Nutrit, 68; Bordan Award; Bristol-Myers Award. *Mem:* Nat Acad Sci; Am Inst Nutrit; fel Royal Soc Edinburgh; fel, Brit Inst Biol; Brit Biochem Soc. *Res:* Mammalian protein metabolism, notably nutritional aspects; protein synthesis control mechanisms and actions of hormones on protein and RNA metabolism; tissue analysis of mammals; nutrition and aging. *Mailing Add:* Dept of Nutrit & Food Sci Mass Inst of Technol Cambridge MA 02139

MUNRO, MICHAEL BRIAN, b Calgary, Alta, Oct 12, 48; m 71. MECHANICAL ENGINEERING, BIOMEDICAL ENGINEERING. *Educ:* Univ Waterloo, BASc, 71, PhD(mech eng), 77; Mass Inst Technol, SM, 73. *Prof Exp:* ASST PROF MECH ENG, UNIV OTTAWA, 78- *Concurrent Pos:* Nat Res Coun Can scholar, 73-76; Nat Res Coun Can fel, Univ Cambridge, 77. *Mem:* Assoc mem Am Soc Mech Engrs; Can Med & Biol Eng Soc; Am Soc Metals; Soc Adv Mat & Process Eng; Am Soc Testing & Mat. *Res:* Fracture of fibre-reinforced composite materials; engineering applications of composite materials (flywheels, filament winding). *Mailing Add:* Dept of Mech Eng Univ of Ottawa Ottawa ON K1N 6N5 Can

MUNRO, RICHARD HARDING, b Pasadena, Calif, Jan 28, 43; m 67; c 2. SOLAR PHYSICS, ASTRONOMY. *Educ:* Harvey Mudd Col, BS, 64; Harvard Univ, MA, 69, PhD(astron), 73. *Prof Exp:* SCIENTIST SOLAR PHYSICS, HIGH ALTITUDE OBSERV, NAT CTR ATMOSPHERIC RES, 72- *Concurrent Pos:* Prin investr, Joint Lyman Alpha/White Light Rocket Exp, 79-; lectr, Univ Colo, 81. *Mem:* Am Astron Soc; Am Geophys Union; Int Astron Union; Sigma Xi. *Res:* Investigation of the physical properties, the dissipation and transport of non-radiative energy and the initial acceleration of the solar wind in the transition region and corona of the solar atmosphere. *Mailing Add:* High Altitude Observ PO Box 3000 Boulder CO 80307

MUNRO, RONALD GORDON, US citizen. PHYSICS. *Educ:* Univ Mich, BS, 69, MS, 70; Univ Ore, PhD(physics), 76. *Prof Exp:* Nat Bur Standards/Nat Res Coun res assoc fel physics & solid state mat, 76-78, RES PHYSICIST PHYSICS AT HIGH PRESSURE, NAT BUR STANDARDS, 78- *Mem:* Am Phys Soc. *Res:* Theory of condensed matter at high pressure; theory of magnetism; materials research. *Mailing Add:* Ctr for Mat Sci Nat Bur Standards Washington DC 20234

MUNRO, WILLIAM DELMAR, b Cedaredge, Colo, Nov 22, 16; m 51; c 3. NUMERICAL ANALYSIS. *Educ:* Univ Colo, BA, 38; Univ Minn, MA, 40, PhD(math), 47. *Prof Exp:* Asst math, 38-41, instr, 41-43, asst prof math & mech, 45-49, from assoc prof to prof math, 49-69, PROF COMPUT, INFO & CONTROL SCI & ASSOC HEAD DEPT, UNIV MINN, MINNEAPOLIS, 69- *Concurrent Pos:* Proj engr, Honeywell Inc, 43-; consult, Radio Corp Am, 45-, Maico Corp, 58-, Viron Div, GCA Corp, 65- & North Star Res Corp, 70-; vis res mathematician, Univ Calif, Los Angeles, 57-58; vis prof, Johns Hopkins Univ, 59-60. *Mem:* Am Math Soc; Math Asn Am; Soc Indust & Appl Math; Asn Comput Mach. *Res:* Theory of approximation; computers; numerical methods and analysis research; navigation computer for aircraft; orthogonal trigonometric sums with auxiliary conditions; high order precision by exact arithmetic. *Mailing Add:* Dept Comput Sci 120 Lind Hall Univ of Minn Minneapolis MN 55455

MUNROE, EUGENE GORDON, b Detroit, Mich, Sept 8, 19; nat Can; m 44; c 4. ENTOMOLOGY, ECOLOGY. *Educ:* McGill Univ, BSc, 40, MSc, 41; Cornell Univ, PhD(entom), 48. *Prof Exp:* Lectr & res asst, Inst Parasitol, Macdonald Col, McGill Univ, 46-50; agr res officer, Can Dept Agr, 50-65; sci adv, Sci Secretariat, Off Privy Counr, 65-67, head studies, 67-68; res scientist, Biosyst Res Inst, Can Dept Agr, 68-79; RES ASSOC, LYMAN ENTOM MUS, MCGILL UNIV, 81- *Concurrent Pos:* Vis lectr, Univ Calif, Berkeley, 60-61; mem, Steering Comt, Biol Coun Can, 65-66; res assoc, Entom Res Inst, Can Dept Agr, 65-68 & 80-81. *Mem:* Royal Soc Can; hon mem Lepidop Soc (pres, 59-60); Entom Soc Can (pres, 63-64); Entom Soc Am; Royal Entom Soc London. *Res:* Science policy; research planning and management; management and conservation of renewable resources; ecology; biogeography; taxonomy; systematics. *Mailing Add:* Lyman Entom Mus Macdonald Campus McGill Univ Ste Anne de Bellevue PQ H9X 1C0 Can

MUNROE, MARIAN HALL, botany, see previous edition

MUNROE, MARSHALL EVANS, b Gainesville, Ga, 18; m 47; c 1. MATHEMATICS. *Educ:* Univ Tex, BA, 40; Brown Univ, ScM, 41, PhD(math), 45. *Prof Exp:* Instr math, Brown Univ, 43-45; from instr to assoc prof, Univ Ill, 45-58; PROF MATH & CHMN DEPT, UNIV NH, 59- *Concurrent Pos:* Vis prof, Cairo Univ, 65-66; vis prof, Univ Col Galway, 75-76. *Mem:* Am Math Soc; Math Asn Am. *Res:* Abstract integration theory; measure theory; modernization of calculus. *Mailing Add:* Dept of Math Univ of NH Durham NH 03824

MUNROE, STEPHEN HORNER, b Baltimore, Md, June 3, 46; m 78; c 1. MOLECULAR BIOLOGY, BIOCHEMISTRY. *Educ:* Haverford Col, BA, 68; Ind Univ, PhD(biol chem), 74. *Prof Exp:* Res fel genetics, Harvard Med Sch, 74-77; res assoc cell biol, Worcester Found Exp Biol, 77-78; ASST PROF BIOL, MARQUETTE UNIV, 78- *Concurrent Pos:* Res fel genetics, Children's Hosp Med Ctr, Boston, 74-77. *Mem:* Am Chem Soc; Am Soc Cell Biol; AAAS. *Res:* Organization and transcription of eucaryotic chromosomes. *Mailing Add:* Dept of Biol Marquette Univ Milwaukee WI 53233

MUNSE, WILLIAM H(ERMAN), b Chicago, Ill, July 10, 19; m 42; c 2. CIVIL ENGINEERING. *Educ:* Univ Ill, BS, 42, MS, 44. *Prof Exp:* Engr, Champaign, Ill, 41; struct draftsman, Am Bridge Co, Ind, 42-43; spec asst civil eng, Univ Ill, 43-44; res engr, Lehigh Univ, 46-47; spec res asst prof, 47-52, res assoc prof, 52-55, prof, 55-81, EMER PROF CIVIL ENG, UNIV ILL, URBANA, 81- *Concurrent Pos:* Mem, Hwy Res Bd, Nat Acad Sci-Nat Res Coun. *Honors & Awards:* Adams Mem Award, Am Welding Soc, 61; W L Huber Res Prize, Am Soc Civil Engrs, 62; Distinguished Serv Award, Japan Welding Soc, 76. *Mem:* Am Soc Testing & Mat; Am Welding Soc; Am Rwy Eng Asn; Am Concrete Inst; Am Soc Eng Educ. *Res:* Design of structures of concrete and steel; metal structure; fatigue; riveted, bolted and welded structures; brittle fracture. *Mailing Add:* 2129 Civil Eng Bldg Univ of Ill Urbana IL 61801

MUNSEE, JACK HOWARD, b Niagra Falls, NY, Sept 27, 34; m 62; c 4. PHYSICS. *Educ:* Col Wooster, BA, 56; Case Western Reserve Univ, MS, 62, PhD(physics), 68. *Prof Exp:* Jr engr, Aeroprod Opers, 56-57; asst physics, Case Western Reserve Univ, 58-62, part-time instr, 64-68; instr physics & math, Col Wooster, 62-64; asst prof, 68-71, ASSOC PROF PHYSICS, CALIF STATE UNIV, LONG BEACH, 71- *Mem:* Am Phys Soc; Am Asn Physics Teachers. *Res:* Low energy nuclear physics; neutrinos; physics education. *Mailing Add:* Dept of Physics Calif State Univ Long Beach Long Beach CA 90801

MUNSELL, MONROE WALLWORK, b New London, Conn, Jan 8, 25; m 54; c 2. ORGANIC CHEMISTRY, PETROLEUM TECHNOLOGY. *Educ:* Carnegie-Mellon Univ, BS, 47, MS, 50, PhD, 55. *Prof Exp:* Res chemist, Esso Res & Eng Co, 55-64, sr chemist & proj leader, 64-68, res assoc, Esso Kagaku kk, Japan, 68-72, RES ASSOC, EXXON CHEM CO, 72- *Mem:* Am Chem Soc; Sigma Xi; Soc Automotive Eng. *Res:* Lubrication oil and fuel additives; technical service and product application in field of detergents and viscosity improvers; conduct lubricant technology training seminars for government oil companies in Asia and Latin America. *Mailing Add:* 180 Sutton Dr Berkeley Heights NJ 07922

MUNSICK, ROBERT ALLIOT, b Glen Ridge, NJ, Oct 21, 28; m 53, 65; c 3. OBSTETRICS & GYNECOLOGY. *Educ:* Cornell Univ, AB, 50; Columbia Univ, MD, 54, PhD(pharmacol), 62; Am Bd Obstet & Gynec, dipl, 66. *Prof Exp:* Intern med, Roosevelt Hosp, New York, 54-55; resident obstet & gynec, Sloane Hosp Women, 59-62; asst prof, Sch Med, Univ Colo, 62-65; prof, Sch Med, Univ NMex, 65-74, chmn dept, 64-73; PROF OBSTET & GYNEC, SCH MED, IND UNIV, INDIANAPOLIS, 74- *Concurrent Pos:* Josiah Macy, Jr Found fel, 57-62; NIH res grant, 62- *Mem:* Soc Gynec Invest; fel Am Col Obstet & Gynec; Asn Planned Parenthood Physicians; Am Asn Obstetricians & Gynecologists; Am Gynec & Obstet Soc. *Res:* Education. *Mailing Add:* Dept Obstet & Gynec Sch Med Ind Univ Indianapolis IN 46202

MUNSON, ALBERT G, b Baton Rouge, La, Jan 10, 31; m 64. AERONAUTICAL ENGINEERING, AEROACOUSTICS. *Educ:* La State Univ, BS, 51; Calif Inst Technol, MS, 52, AeroEng, 56; Stanford Univ, PhD(aeronaut & astronaut eng), 64. *Prof Exp:* Aerodyn engr, Hughes Aircraft Co, Calif, 56-58; aeronaut res scientist, Ames Res Ctr, Moffet Field, 58-62; mem tech staff, Nat Eng Sci Co, Calif, 64-65, mem sr staff, 66; prin staff engr, Martin Co, Fla, 66-67, dept staff engr, 67-69, sr staff engr, Denver Div, 69-73; prin scientist, 73-77, sect chief acoustic res, 77-78, SECT CHIEF EXTERIOR ACOUSTIC DESIGN, DOUGLAS AIRCRAFT CO, MCDONNELL DOUGLAS CORP, 78- *Res:* Hypersonic aerodynamics. *Mailing Add:* Douglas Aircraft Co 6859 Citriadora Ct Garden Grove CA 92645

MUNSON, ARVID W, b Paterson, NJ, Aug 22, 33; m 54; c 2. AGRICULTURAL STATISTICS. *Educ:* Iowa State Univ, BS, 55, MS, 57; Okla State Univ, PhD(animal breeding), 66. *Prof Exp:* Anal statistician, Biomet Serv Staff, Agr Res Serv, USDA, 65-66, biometrician, 66-67, asst dir, 67-68, actg dir data processing, Data Syst Appln Div, 68; dir, Res Serv Div, 68-78, PRES, RALTECH SCI SERV DIV, RALSTON PURINA CO, 78- *Mem:* AAAS; Am Soc Animal Sic; Am Statist Asn; Am Mgt Asn; Inst Food Technologists. *Res:* Statistical methodology and computer techniques in animal science research and improvement. *Mailing Add:* Raltech Sci Serv Box 7545 Madison WI 53707

MUNSON, BENJAMIN RAY, b Tonawanda, NY, Sept 19, 37; m 63; c 2. BIOCHEMISTRY, ONCOLOGY. *Educ:* Houghton Col, BA, 60; State Univ NY Buffalo, PhD(biochem, pharmacol), 67. *Prof Exp:* Teacher, NY High Schs, 60-62; sr cancer res scientist, Springville Labs, Roswell Park Mem Inst, 70-76, cancer res scientist IV, Exp Biol Dept, 76-81. *Concurrent Pos:* NIH res fel biochem, Springville Labs, Roswell Park Mem Inst, 68-70, fel physiol, Inst, 70-, Nat Cancer Inst res grant, 71- *Mem:* AAAS; Am Chem Soc; Int Soc Biochem Pharmacol; NY Acad Sci. *Res:* Bacteriology; molecular biology; biochemistry; molecular genetics. *Mailing Add:* Dept Exp Biol Roswell Park Mem Inst 666 Elm St Buffalo NY 14263

MUNSON, BURNABY, b Wharton, Tex, Mar 20, 33. PHYSICAL CHEMISTRY, ANALYTICAL CHEMISTRY. *Educ:* Univ Tex, BA, 54, MA, 56, PhD(phys chem), 59. *Prof Exp:* Res chemist, Humble Oil & Refining Co, 59-62, sr res chemist, 62-64, sr res chemist, Esso Res & Eng Co, 64-66, res specialist, Tex, 66-67; assoc prof chem, 67-72, PROF CHEM, UNIV DEL, 72- *Mem:* AAAS; Am Chem Soc; Am Inst Chem; Am Soc Mass Spectros; Sigma Xi. *Res:* Kinetics; mass spectrometry; reactions of gaseous ions and excited species. *Mailing Add:* Dept of Chem Univ of Del Newark DE 19711

MUNSON, DARRELL E(UGENE), b Rapid City, SDak, Jan 18, 33; m 69; c 2. METALLURGY. *Educ:* SDak Sch Mines & Technol, BS, 54; Stanford Univ, MS, 56, PhD(metall eng), 60. *Prof Exp:* Asst, Stanford Univ, 56-57, actg instr, 57-58; asst prof metall, Wash State Univ, 59-61; staff mem technol, 61-67, DIV SUPVR, SANDIA CORP, 67- *Concurrent Pos:* Jr metallurgist, Stanford Res Inst, 56-57. *Mem:* Am Soc Metals; Am Soc Eng Educ; Am Inst Mining, Metall & Petrol Engrs. *Res:* Structural metallurgy and deformation, particularly high temperature kinetics and mechanisms of deformation and shock wave propagation; wave propagation and fracture in composites. *Mailing Add:* Shock Wave Phenomena Div 5163 Sandia Labs Albuquerque NM 87115

MUNSON, DONALD ALBERT, b New York, NY, May 13, 41; m 79. ZOOLOGY, PARASITOLOGY. *Educ:* Colgate Univ, AB, 63; Adelphi Univ, MS, 66; Univ NH, PhD(zool), 70. *Prof Exp:* Teaching asst zool, Univ NH, 66-68, teaching fel, 68-70; NIH fel parasitol, Med Sch, Tulane Univ, 70-72; asst prof biol, Hood Col, 72-76; ASST PROF BIOL, WASHINGTON COL, 76- *Mem:* Am Soc Parasitol; Am Soc Trop Med & Hyg; Wildlife Dis Asn; Am Microscop Soc; Soc Protozoologists. *Res:* Histological, histochemical and histopathological studies of medically important parasites; host-parasite relations of fish parasites; ecology of estuarine and marine protozoa. *Mailing Add:* Dept of Biol Washington Col Chestertown MD 21620

MUNSON, EDWIN STERLING, b Akron, Ohio, Dec 29, 33. ANESTHESIOLOGY. *Educ:* Univ Tenn, MD, 57. *Prof Exp:* Intern, State Univ Iowa, 57-58; NIH trainee anesthesia, 63-64, from clin instr to asst clin prof anesthesia, Univ Calif, San Francisco, 63-65; asst prof, Univ Va, Charlottesville, 65-67; asst prof, Univ Calif, Davis, 67-71, assoc prof anesthesia & guest investr, Nat Ctr Primate Biol, 67-71; dir res training, 71-78, PROF ANESTHESIOL, COL MED, UNIV FLA, 71-; CHIEF, ANESTHESIOL SERV, VET ADMIN MED CTR, GAINESVILLE, 78- *Concurrent Pos:* NIH trainee anesthesia, Univ Calif, San Francisco, 64. *Mem:* Am Soc Anesthetists; Asn Univ Anesthetists; Asn Vet Admin Anesthesiologists. *Res:* Pharmacology of anesthetic drugs. *Mailing Add:* Dept Anesthesiol Col Med Univ Fla Box J-254 Gainesville FL 32610

MUNSON, H RANDALL, JR, b Washington, DC, Sept 2, 34. ORGANIC CHEMISTRY. *Educ:* Univ Md, College Park, BS, 58; Georgetown Univ, PhD(org chem), 69. *Prof Exp:* Res asst biochem pharmacol, Med Sch, Georgetown Univ, 62-64; Walter Reed Army Inst Res fel, Univ Va, 68-69; sr res chemist, 69-74, res assoc, 74-79, GROUP MGR, GASTROINTESTINAL CHEM GROUP, A H ROBINS C0, 79- *Mem:* Am Chem Soc; Sigma Xi. *Res:* Medicinal chemistry; synthesis of antimalarials, antivirals and nucleosides; quantitative structure-activity relationships. *Mailing Add:* A H Robins Co Chem Res Dept 1211 Sherwood Ave Richmond VA 23220

MUNSON, J(OHN) C(HRISTIAN), b Clinton, Iowa, Oct 9, 26; m 50; c 2. ELECTRONIC ENGINEERING. *Educ:* Iowa State Col, BS, 49; Univ Md, MS, 52, PhD, 62. *Prof Exp:* Electronic scientist, Naval Ord Lab, 49-68; SUPT ACOUST DIV, NAVAL RES LAB, 68- *Concurrent Pos:* Asst prof exten sch, Univ Md, 64-67. *Mem:* Sr mem Inst Elec & Electronics Engrs; fel Acoust Soc Am; Sigma Xi; Acoust, Speech & Signal Processing Soc. *Res:* Application of information theory and computer techniques to underwater acoustic system developments; understanding of sound propagation characteristics of the ocean, especially its effect on acoustic systems. *Mailing Add:* 119 Marine Terr Silver Spring MD 20904

MUNSON, JAMES WILLIAM, b Perrysburg, Ohio, Aug 13, 43; m 66; c 2. ANALYTICAL CHEMISTRY. *Educ:* Ohio State Univ, BS, 67; Univ Wis, MS, 69, PhD(pharmaceut), 71. *Prof Exp:* Asst prof pharm, Univ Conn, 71-73; from asst prof to assoc prof pharm, Univ Ky, 73-77; res scientist, 78-80, RES HEAD, UPJOHN CO, 80- *Mem:* Am Pharmaceut Asn; Acad Pharmaceut Sci. *Res:* Analysis of drugs in biological fluids and dosage forms. *Mailing Add:* Qual Control Upjohn Co Kalamazoo MI 49001

MUNSON, JOHN BACON, b Clifton Springs, NY, Nov 15, 32; m 59; c 3. NEUROSCIENCES. *Educ:* Union Col, NY, AB, 57; Univ Rochester, PhD(neurobiol), 65. *Prof Exp:* Fel neurophysiol, Inst Physiol, Univ Pisa, 65-66; res assoc physiol, 66-68, from instr to asst prof physiol & psychol, 69-73, asst prof neurosci, 71-73, ASSOC PROF NEUROSCI, PHYSIOL, NEUROSURG & PSYCHOL, COL MED, UNIV FLA, 73- *Concurrent Pos:* Vis scientist, Duke Med Ctr, 73 & Neurol Sci Inst, Portland, Ore, 75. *Mem:* AAAS; Am Physiol Soc; Soc Neurosci; Int Brain Res Orgn; Asn Res Vision & Ophthal. *Res:* Disfunction and recovery of function in damaged spinal motoneurons; spinal cord damage; effects and recovery; anatomy and physiology of the epilepsies; central correlates of eye movements. *Mailing Add:* Dept of Neurosci Univ of Fla Col of Med Gainesville FL 32610

MUNSON, PAUL LEWIS, b Washta, Iowa, Aug 21, 10; m 31; c 1; m 48; c 2. PHARMACOLOGY, ENDOCRINOLOGY. *Educ:* Antioch Col, BA, 33; Univ Wis, MA, 37; Univ Chicago, PhD(biochem), 42. *Hon Degrees:* MA, Harvard Univ, 55. *Prof Exp:* Asst biochem, Univ Chicago, 39-42; res biochemist, Wm S Merrell Co, Ohio, 42-43; res biochemist & head endocrinol res, Armour & Co, Ill, 43-48; from res asst to res assoc pharmacol, Yale Univ, 48-50; from asst prof to prof, Sch Dent Med, Harvard Univ, 50-65; prof pharmacol, 65-70, chmn, Dept Pharmacol, 65-77, Sarah Graham Kenan Prof, 70-81, EMER SARAH GRAHAM KENAN PROF PHARMACOL & ENDOCRINOL, SCH MED, UNIV NC, CHAPEL HILL, 81- *Concurrent Pos:* Mem, Corticotropin Assay Study Panel, US Pharmacopoeia, 51-55; tutor, Harvard Univ, 55-58, lectr, 65-66; Claude Bernard vis prof, Univ Montreal, 64; mem, Gen Med B Study Sect, USPHS, 66-70, chmn, 69-70; sr adv comt, Laurentian Hormone Conf, 66-; mem pharmacol test comt, Nat Bd Med Exam, 67-71; ed, Vitamins & Hormones, 68-81, Pharmacol Reviews, 77-81; mem pharmacol-toxicol prog comt, Nat Inst Gen Med Sci, 72-76; chairperson, Task Force Bone & Mineral, NIH Eval. *Honors & Awards:* Fred Conrad Koch Award, Endocrine Soc, 76. *Mem:* Am Soc Pharmacol & Exp Therapeut (secy-treas, 71-72); Am Chem Soc; Endocrine Soc; Am Soc Biol Chemists; Asn Med Sch Pharmacol (secy, 72-73, pres, 74-76). *Res:* Isolation, bioassay and mechanism of action of hormones, especially hypothalamic, pituitary, androgenic, parathyroid and calcitonin; steroid metabolism; calcium metabolism; mechanism of stimulation of adrenocorticotropic hormone secretion. *Mailing Add:* Dept Pharmacol FLO Bldg 231H Univ NC Sch of Med Chapel Hill NC 27514

MUNSON, ROBERT DEAN, b Stockport, Iowa, Mar 14, 27; m 50; c 3. SOIL FERTILITY, PLANT NUTRITION. *Educ:* Univ Minn, BS, 51; Iowa State Univ, MS, 54, PhD(soil fertil, agr econ), 57. *Prof Exp:* Instr high sch, Minn, 51-52; agr economist, Tenn Valley Authority, 57-58; agronomist, Am Postash Inst, 58-67, midwest dir, 67-81, NORTHCENTRAL DIR, POTASH & PHOSPHATE INST, INC, 81- *Concurrent Pos:* Assoc ed, J Agron Educ, 73; mem panel fertilizer use res needs, NSF, 75; assoc ed, Soil Sci Soc Am J; study, Potassium, Calcium and Magnesium in Tropical & Subtropical Soils, Int Fertilizer Develop Ctr, 79. *Honors & Awards:* Agronomic Serv Award, Am Soc Agron, 76. *Mem:* Fel AAAS; fel Am Soc Agron; fel Soil Sci Soc Am; Int Soil Sci Soc; Crop Sci Soc Am. *Res:* Factors influencing the availability of phosphorus; interaction of plant nutrient and management proactices in crop production; potassium availability, movement in soils and physiological function in plants and animals; cation balance and interrelationship of plant nutrients; diagnostic techniques in crop production; soil and plant analysis; availability of soil and fertilizer nitrogen as affected by residues; economics of fertilizer use and research methodology. *Mailing Add:* Potash & Phosphate Inst Inc 2147 Doswell Ave St Paul MN 55108

MUNSON, RONALD ALFRED, b Lancaster, Pa, Aug 12, 33; m 67; c 4. PHYSICAL CHEMISTRY. *Educ:* Franklin & Marshall Col, BS, 55; Northwestern Univ, PhD(phys chem), 59. *Prof Exp:* NSF fel, Max Planck Inst Phys Chem, Gottingen, WGer, 58-59; phys chemist, Gen Elec Co Res & Develop Ctr, 60-67; res chemist, 67-72, STAFF CHEMIST, US BUR MINES, 72- *Mem:* Am Inst Mining, Metall & Petrol Eng; Am Chem Soc. *Res:* Chemical kinetics; electrochemistry; ultra high pressure synthesis; zeolites. *Mailing Add:* Metall Res US Bur Mines 2401 E St NW Washington DC 20241

MUNTZ, ERIC PHILLIP, b Hamilton, Ont, May 18, 34; m 64; c 2. GAS DYNAMICS, ENVIRONMENTAL SCIENCES. *Educ:* Univ Toronto, BASc, 56, MASc, 57, PhD(aerophys), 61. *Prof Exp:* Physicist, Gen Elec Space Sci Lab, 61-65, group leader, 65-69; assoc prof aerospace eng, 69-71, assoc dir environ eng, 71-74, PROF AEROSPACE ENG, UNIV SOUTHERN CALIF, 71-, PROF RADIOL, 74- *Concurrent Pos:* Consult numerous corp, 69- *Mem:* Am Asn Physicists in Med; Am Inst Aeronaut & Astronaut; Am Phys Soc. *Res:* Statistical nature of gas flows; development of electron beam fluorescence technique for the study of rarefied gas flows; gaseous separation phenomena; high altitude exhaust plumes; gas dynamic lasers; radiological imaging techniques; radiation physics. *Mailing Add:* Dept Aerospace Eng Univ Southern Calif Los Angeles CA 90007

MUNTZ, RICHARD ROBERT, b Jersey City, NJ, Mar 6, 41; m 64. COMPUTER SCIENCE. *Educ:* Pratt Inst, BEE, 63; NY Univ, MEE, 66; Princeton Univ, PhD(elec eng), 69. *Prof Exp:* Elec engr commun facilities, Indust Mgr Off, US Navy, 63-64; mem tech staff comput, Bell Tel Labs, Inc, 64-66; asst prof, 69-76, ASSOC PROF COMPUT SCI, UNIV CALIF, LOS ANGELES, 76- *Mem:* Asn Comput Mach; Inst Elec & Electronics Engrs. *Res:* Computer operating systems; computer system modeling and analysis. *Mailing Add:* Rm 3731 Boelter Hall Univ of Calif Los Angeles CA 90024

MUNTZ, RONALD LEE, b Bonaparte, Iowa, Sept 19, 45; m 66; c 3. ORGANOMETALLIC CHEMISTRY, ORGANIC CHEMISTRY. *Educ:* Iowa State Univ, BS, 68; Univ Ill, PhD(org chem), 72. *Prof Exp:* Res chemist, 72-78, supvr org res, 78-80, TECH MGR SWS SILICONES, DIV TECH CTR, STAUFFER CHEM CO, 80- *Mem:* Am Chem Soc. *Res:* Flame retardant synthesis; organic intermediates and organometallics; silicones. *Mailing Add:* Stauffer Chem Co Eastern Res Ctr Dobbs Ferry NY 10522

MUNUSHIAN, JACK, b Binghamton, NY, Sept 6, 23. ELECTRICAL ENGINEERING. *Educ:* Univ Rochester, BS, 47; Univ Calif, Berkeley, PhD(elec eng), 54. *Prof Exp:* Head appl physics dept, Component Div, Hughes Aircraft Co, 54-61; head solid state electronics dept, Labs Div, Aerospace Corp, 61-67; PROF ELEC ENG, UNIV SOUTHERN CALIF, 67-, DIR GRAD CTR ENG SCI, 76- *Concurrent Pos:* Lectr, Univ Southern Calif, 54-62, chmn comput sci prog, 69-76; dir, Instr Television Network, 72- *Mem:* AAAS; Inst Elec & Electronics Engrs; Am Phys Soc. *Res:* Solid state electronics; educational technology. *Mailing Add:* SSC 510 Sch of Eng Univ of Southern Calif Los Angeles CA 90007

MUNYAN, ARTHUR CLAUDE, b Lexington, Ky, May 31, 08; m 32; c 1. GEOLOGY, ENGINEERING GEOLOGY. *Educ:* Univ Ky, BS, 30; Univ Cincinnati, AM, 31, PhD(geol), 51. *Prof Exp:* Jr geologist, US Geol Surv, 34-36; asst state geologist, Ky, 36-37; asst state geologist, Ga, 37-41; from asst prof to assoc prof geol, Emory Univ, 41-51; staff geologist, Sohio Petrol Co, Can & US, 51-56, div geologist, 56-60, explor geologist, 60; chmn dept geol, 61-70, prof, 61-73, EMER PROF GEOL & GEOPHYS, OLD DOM UNIV, 73-; CONSULT GEOLOGIST, 60-; PRES, GEOSERV CO, INC, 65- *Mem:* Fel Geol Soc Am; Soc Econ Paleont & Mineral; Am Asn Petrol Geol; Int Geol Cong; Am Inst Prof Geologists (pres, 64, vpres, 68). *Res:* Structure; petroleum; sedimentology. *Mailing Add:* 3204 Blue Ridge Ct Virginia Beach VA 23452

MUNYER, EDWARD ARNOLD, b Chicago, Ill, May 8, 36; m 60; c 3. ZOOLOGY, SCIENCE EDUCATION. *Educ:* Ill State Univ, BSEd, 58, MS, 62. *Prof Exp:* Teacher pub schs, Ill, 58-59; asst biol, Ill State Univ, 59-60; teacher pub schs, Ill, 60-63; instr, Ill State Univ, 63-64; cur zool, Ill State Mus, 64-67; assoc prof sci, Vincennes Univ, 67-70; coord educ, 70-80, ASSOC CUR EDUC, FLA STATE MUS, UNIV FLA, 80- *Mem:* Am Inst Biol Sci; Am Asn Mus; Wilson Ornith Soc. *Res:* Museum education; vertebrate natural history; raptor ecology; comparative anatomy; perceptual learning; science education. *Mailing Add:* Fla State Mus Univ of Fla Gainesville FL 32611

MUNZ, FREDERICK WOLF, b Pomona, Calif, Sept 3, 29; m 54; c 3. VISUAL PHYSIOLOGY. *Educ:* Pomona Col, BA, 50; Univ Calif, Los Angeles, MA, 52, PhD(zool), 58. *Prof Exp:* Asst zool, Univ Calif, Los Angeles, 50-52, from actg instr to instr, 57-58; USPHS fel, Inst Ophthal, London, 58-59; from asst prof to assoc prof biol, 59-71, PROF BIOL, UNIV ORE, 71- *Concurrent Pos:* Guggenheim fel, 67-68. *Mem:* AAAS; Am Soc Zool. *Mailing Add:* Dept of Biol Univ of Ore Eugene OR 97403

MURA, TOSHIO, b Kanazawa, Japan, Dec 7, 25; m 54; c 2. MECHANICS. *Educ:* Univ Tokyo, BS, 49, PhD(mech), 59. *Prof Exp:* Asst prof eng, Meiji Univ, Japan, 54-58; Air Force Off Sci Res fel & res assoc mat sci, 58-61, from asst prof to assoc prof, 61-66, PROF CIVIL ENG, NORTHWESTERN UNIV, 66- *Mem:* Am Phys Soc; Am Soc Mech Engrs; Soc Eng Sci; fel Am Acad Med. *Res:* Micromechanics; dislocations; disclinations; plasticity; variational principle; thermostresses. *Mailing Add:* Dept of Civil Eng Northwestern Univ Evanston IL 60201

MURACA, RAFFAELE FRANCESCO, b Easton, Pa, July 27, 21. ANALYTICAL CHEMISTRY, PHYSICS. *Educ:* Lehigh Univ, BS, 44, MS, 47, PhD(chem physics), 50. *Prof Exp:* Asst chem cent res labs, Gen Aniline & Film, Inc, 43-44; assoc prof & head dept, Concord Col, 47-48; asst, Lehigh Univ, 48-50, instr, 50-51, asst prof & div head, 51-55; group leader chem & physics, Jet Propulsion Lab, Calif Inst Technol, 55-56, sect chief chem, 56-59; asst div head propulsion, Stanford Res Inst, 59-61, dir space sci, 61-62, asst gen mgr phys sci, 62-64, dir anal & instrumentation, 64-69; pres, Western Appl Res & Develop, Inc, 69-78; PROF CHEM & PHYSICS, COL NOTRE DAME, BELMONT, CALIF, 75-, CHMN DEPT, 78- *Concurrent Pos:* Ed, Chemist-Analyst, 53-55; chmn, Joint Army-Navy-Air Force Panel Anal Chem, 58-63. *Honors & Awards:* C E Heussner Award, 55; Cert of Recognition, NASA, 75. *Mem:* AAAS; Am Chem Soc. *Res:* Analytical chemistry; mass spectroscopy of natural products; high vacuum techniques; electrochemistry; electronics; instrument design; instrumental analysis; space sciences; applications. *Mailing Add:* Dept of Chem Col of Notre Dame Belmont CA 94002

MURACA, RALPH JOHN, b Dunmore, Pa, June 5, 35. FLUID MECHANICS, DYNAMICS. *Educ:* Drexel Inst Technol, BS, 59; Univ Va, MS, 70; Va Polytech Inst & State Univ, PhD(aerospace eng), 72. *Prof Exp:* Engr prod support, Convair Astronautics, 59-60; engr struct dynamics, Martin Marietta Co, 60-62; aerospace technician, Aerospace & Dynamics, 62-76, mgr laminar flow control proj, 76-79, mgr shuttle test procedure specification life assessment, 79-81, ASST CHIEF SYST ENG DIV, LANGLEY RES CTR, NASA, 81- *Concurrent Pos:* Instr, George Washington Univ-Tidewater Campus, 73-75 & Hampton Inst, Va, 75-76. *Honors & Awards:* Spec Achievement Award, NASA Langley Res Ctr, 72. *Mem:* Am Inst Astronaut & Aeronaut. *Res:* Boundary layer flows; laminar flow control for commercial transport aircraft. *Mailing Add:* Mail Stop 158 NASA Langley Res Ctr Hampton VA 23665

MURAD, EDMOND, b Bagdad, Iraq, Nov 29, 34; US citizen. PHYSICAL CHEMISTRY. *Educ:* NY Univ, BA, 55; Univ Rochester, PhD(phys chem), 59. *Prof Exp:* Res assoc phys chem, Nat Bur Standards, DC, 59-60; res assoc, Univ Wis, 60-61; res assoc chem phys, Univ Chicago, 61-63; res assoc phys chem, Cornell Univ, 63-64; res scientist, Aeronutronic Div, Ford Motor Co, 64-66; RES CHEMIST, AIR FORCE GEOPHYSICS LAB, 66- *Mem:* AAAS; Am Chem Soc; Am Geophys Union; Am Phys Soc. *Res:* Mass spectrometry; high temperature thermodynamics; ion-neutral collision phenomena; aeronomy. *Mailing Add:* Air Force Geophysics Lab/LKD Hanscom AFB Bedford MA 01731

MURAD, EMIL MOISE, b Detroit, Mich, May 10, 26. OPERATIONS RESEARCH. *Educ:* Univ Southern Calif, AB, 49, MS, 51. *Prof Exp:* Res chemist, Standard Coil Prod, Inc, 51-53; res chemist, Hydroaire Div, Crane Co, 53-55; chief chemist, Marvelco Electronics Div, Nat Aircraft Corp, 55-57; prin scientist, Stromberg-Carlson Div, Gen Dynamics Corp, 57-59; res specialist, Autonetics Div, NAm Aviation, Inc, 59; dir res, Orbitec Corp, 60-62; sr tech specialist space div, NAm Rockwell Corp, 62-68; PRES, QUANTADYNE ASSOCS, INC, 66- *Mem:* AAAS; Am Phys Soc; Electrochem Soc; Inst Elec & Electronics Eng; Opers Res Soc Am. *Res:* Development of computer technology for the application of data processing techniques to industrial electronic systems design. *Mailing Add:* Exec Off Quantadyne Assocs Inc 1929 Livonia Ave Los Angeles CA 90034

MURAD, FERID, b Whiting, Ind, Sept 14, 36; m 58; c 5. CLINICAL PHARMACOLOGY. *Educ:* DePauw Univ, BA, 58; Western Reserve Univ, MD & PhD(pharmacol), 65. *Prof Exp:* From intern to resident med, Mass Gen Hosp, 65-67; sr asst surg, Nat Heart & Lung Inst, 67-69, sr staff fel res, 69-70; assoc prof pharmacol & internal med, Sch Med, Univ Va, 70-75, prof, 75-81, dir, Clin Res Ctr, 71-81, dir, Div Clin Pharmacol, 73-81; PROF MED & PHARMACOL, STANFORD UNIV, 81-, CHIEF MED, VET ADMIN MED CTR, 81- *Concurrent Pos:* Nat Inst Arthritis & Metab Dis grant, Sch Med, Univ Va, 71-; USPHS res career develop award, 72-; Nat Heart & Lung Inst res grant, 75- *Mem:* Am Soc Biol Chem; Asn Am Physicists; Endocrine Soc; Am Soc Pharmacol & Exp Therapeut; Am Soc Clin Invest. *Res:* Cyclic adenosine monophosphate and cyclic guanosine monophosphate metabolism; endocrinology. *Mailing Add:* Dept Med Stanford Univ Ved Admin Med Ctr 3801 Maranda Ave Palo Alto CA 94304

MURAD, JOHN LOUIS, b Tyler, Tex, Dec 15, 32; m 58; c 4. ZOOLOGY. *Educ:* Austin Col, BA, 56; NTex State Univ, MA, 58; Tex A&M Univ, PhD(zool), 65. *Prof Exp:* Asst microbiol, NTex State Univ, 56-58; teaching res med br, Univ Tex, 58-59; instr biol, Stephen F Austin State Col, 59-61; instr, Tex A&M Univ, 61-65; asst prof zool, 65-71, PROF ZOOL & DIR RES, COL LIFE SCI, LA TECH UNIV, 71- *Concurrent Pos:* Res partic, NSF-NAtlantic Treaty Orgn, Ger, 72, Eng, 74. *Mem:* AAAS; Soc Nematol; Am Soc Microbiol; Am Soc Testing & Mat; Am Inst Biol Sci. *Res:* Parasitology of wild and domestic animals, especially helminthic parasites; nematodes of soil, water and sewage; medical parasitology. *Mailing Add:* Col Life Sci La Tech Univ Box 10198 Ruston LA 71272

MURAD, TARIQ MOHAMMED, b Karbalaa, Iraq, July 28, 36; US citizen; m 69; c 3. PATHOLOGY. *Educ:* Univ Baghdad, MB ChB, 59; Ohio State Univ, MSc, 65, PhD(path), 67; Am Bd Path, cert anat path & clin path, 68. *Prof Exp:* From instr to assoc prof path, Ohio State Univ, 65-72; dir, Div Surg Path & Cytol, 75-79, PROF PATH, MED CTR, UNIV ALA, 72- *Concurrent Pos:* Dir div clin cytol, Ohio State Univ, 71-72. *Mem:* Int Acad Path; Am Soc Cytol; Am Asn Pathologists & Bacteriologists; fel, Int Acad Cytol; Soc Surg Oncol. *Res:* Classification of breast cancers according to cell of origin and application of electron microscopy and identification of tumor. *Mailing Add:* Med Ctr Univ Ala 619 S 19th St Birmingham AL 35233

MURAD, TURHON ALLEN, b Hammond, Ind, July 27, 44; m 68. BIOLOGICAL ANTHROPOLOGY. *Educ:* Ind Univ, Bloomington, AB, 68, MA, 71, PhD(bio-anthrop), 75. *Prof Exp:* assoc prof, 72-80, PROF PHYS ANTHROP, CALIF STATE UNIV, CHICO, 80- *Mem:* Int Dermatoglyphic Asn; Am Asn Phys Anthropologists; Sigma Xi. *Res:* North Alaskan Eskimo intrapopulation variation for palmar dermatoglyphics; skeletal biology; forensic medicine; general physical anthropology. *Mailing Add:* Dept of Anthrop Calif State Univ Chico CA 95929

MURAI, KOTARO, b San Francisco, Calif, Jan 10, 25; m 54; c 1. ORGANIC CHEMISTRY. *Educ:* Univ Nebr, BSc, 44, MSc, 45; Univ Minn, PhD(org chem), 49. *Prof Exp:* Asst, Univ Nebr, 44-45; asst, Univ Minn, 45-48; mem res staff, Pfizer, Inc, 49-73, SR RES INVESTR, PFIZER CENT RES, PFIZER MED RES LABS, 73- *Mem:* AAAS; Am Chem Soc; NY Acad Sci; Am Inst Chem. *Res:* Physico-organic approaches to kinetics, antibiotics, alkaloids and steroids. *Mailing Add:* Pfizer Med Res Labs Groton CT 06340

MURAI, MARY MIYEKO, b San Francisco, Calif, Jan 16, 13. NUTRITION. *Educ:* Univ Calif, BA, 34, MS, 50, MPH, 60, DrPH, 64. *Prof Exp:* Staff dietitian, St Luke's Int Med Ctr, Tokyo, Japan, 35-39; chief dietitian, Kaukini Hosp, Honolulu, Hawaii, 41-47; lab technician, Univ Calif, 50; technician res proj, US Dept Navy, 51; asst prof home econ, Univ Hawaii, 53-60; fel pub health nutrit, Sch Pub Health, Univ Calif, Berkeley, Children's Br, 59-64, lectr, Sch Pub health, 64-66, asst prof, 66-77, assoc clin prof pub health, 77-80; RETIRED. *Concurrent Pos:* Nat Res Coun fel, Pac Sci Bd, 51; mem, Food & Agr Orgn-WHO, 55; consult, Off Surg Gen, US Army. *Mem:* AAAS; Am Pub Health Asn; Am Dietetic Asn; NY Acad Sci. *Res:* Nutrition survey and food habits of Micronesia; food values of South Pacific foods; training public health nutritionists; development and improvement of the criteria for selection of public health nutrition students. *Mailing Add:* 419 Earl Warren Hall Sch of Pub Health Univ of Calif Berkeley CA 94720

MURAKAMI, MASANORI, b Kyoto, Japan, Nov 28, 43; m 71; c 2. PHYSICAL METALLURGY, DIFFUSION. *Educ:* Kyoto Univ, BS, 66, MS, 68, PhD, 71. *Prof Exp:* Fel, Univ Calif, Los Angeles, 71-75; MEM RES STAFF, THOMAS J WATSON RES CTR, IBM CORP, 75- *Mem:* Am Vacuum Soc; Japan Inst Metals. *Res:* Physical properties in thin films; phase transformations in metals; phase diagrams; x-ray diffraction techniques; low temperature physics; thin films. *Mailing Add:* IBM Thomas J Watson Res Ctr Yorktown Heights NY 10598

MURAKAMI, TAKIO, b Kanazawa, Japan, Mar 17, 21; m 49; c 2. METEOROLOGY. *Educ:* Meteorol Col, dipl, 43 & 49; Univ Tokyo, ScD(meteorol), 60. *Prof Exp:* Chief gen circulation, Meteorol Res Inst, Tokyo, 53-67; res meteorologist, Meteorol Satellite Lab, Washington, DC, 67-69; PROF METEOROL, UNIV HAWAII, 69- *Concurrent Pos:* Fel, Sch Advan Study, Mass Inst Technol, 60-62; res meteorologist, Inst Trop Meteorol, Poona, India, 66-67. *Honors & Awards:* Meteorol Soc Japan Award, 54. *Mem:* Am Meteorol Soc; Meteorol Soc Japan. *Res:* Synoptic and theoretical tropical meteorology. *Mailing Add:* Dept of Meteorol Univ of Hawaii Honolulu HI 96822

MURAKISHI, HARRY HARUO, b San Francisco, Calif, Oct 21, 17; m 48; c 3. PLANT PATHOLOGY. *Educ:* Univ Calif, BS, 40; Univ NC, MS, 47; Univ Minn, PhD(plant path), 48. *Prof Exp:* Asst plant path, Univ NC, 44-45; asst, Univ Minn, 46-48; from asst plant pathologist to plant pathologist, Univ Hawaii, 48-56, head dept plant path, 52-56; assoc prof bot & plant path, 56-63, PROF BOT & PLANT PATH, MICH STATE UNIV, 63- *Concurrent Pos:* Agent, USDA, 44; Guggenheim Mem Found fel & assoc plant path, Univ Calif, 55-56. *Honors & Awards:* Ruth Allen Award, Am Phytopathol Soc, 80. *Mem:* Am Phytopath Soc; Tissue Culture Asn. *Res:* Plant virology; virus diseases of vegetables and orchids; plant tissue culture. *Mailing Add:* Dept of Bot & Plant Path Mich State Univ East Lansing MI 48824

MURAMOTO, HIROSHI, b Hilo, Hawaii, June 6, 22; m 56; c 2. PLANT BREEDING, GENETICS. *Educ:* NMex Col Agr & Mech Arts, BS, 55; Univ Ariz, PhD(agron), 58. *Prof Exp:* Asst plant breeder, 58-64, assoc prof, 64-75, assoc plant breeder, 64-80, ASSOC PROF PLANT SCI & ASSOC RES SCIENTIST PLANT BREEDING, AGR EXP STA, UNIV ARIZ, 80- *Res:* Cotton breeding and genetics. *Mailing Add:* Dept of Plant Sci Univ of Ariz Tucson AZ 85721

MURANO, GENESIO, b Cairano, Italy, Oct 23, 41. PHYSIOLOGY, BIOCHEMISTRY. *Educ:* Univ Mass, BA, 64; Wayne State Univ, MS, 66, PhD(physiol), 68. *Prof Exp:* Res assoc, 68-70, from asst prof to assoc prof physiol, Wayne State Univ, 71-77; sr staff fel, 77-78, PHYSIOLOGIST, BUREAU BIOLOGICS, FOOD & DRUG ADMIN, 78-; ASSOC PROF PHYSIOL, UNIFORMED SERV UNIV HEALTH SCI, 78- *Concurrent Pos:* NIH fel, Karolinska Inst, Sweden, 70-71. *Mem:* NY Acad Sci; Int Soc Thrombosis & Haemostasis. *Res:* Biochemical interactions of clotting factors; fibrinogen structure; fibrinolytic agents; antithrombin. *Mailing Add:* Bur Biologics Bldg #29 8800 Rockville Pike Bethesda MD 20205

MURANY, ERNEST ELMER, b Avella, Pa, Mar 28, 23; m 57; c 2. EXPLORATION GEOLOGY. *Educ:* Kent State Univ, BS, 50; Univ Utah, PhD(geol), 63. *Prof Exp:* Photogrammeter, Corps Engrs, US Army, 51-52; stratigr, US Geol Surv, 52-53; sect chief, Mene Grande Oil Co, Gulf Oil Corp, 53-60; explor mgr & dist geologist, Sinclair Venezuelan Oil Co, Sinclair Oil Co, 63-68; vpres, Collman Indust, 69-70; consult geologist, Dallas, Tex, 70-71, staff consult, Venezuelan Petrol Corp, 71-73; sr staff geologist, Belco Petrol Corp, 73-77; mem staff, Tetra Tech Int, Inc, 77; sr explor adv, Ministry Petrol, Sultanate Oman, 77-80; DISTRICT MGR, BOIS D'ARC CORP, 81- *Mem:* AAAS; Am Asn Petrol Geologists; Asn Venezuelan Mineralogists & Petrologists; Am Geophys Union. *Res:* Structural, geochemical, sedimentological and stratigraphic implication of plate tectonics mountain building as related to generation, migration and accumulation of oil in Middle East, South America and eastern United States. *Mailing Add:* Bois d'Arc Corp 6660 Doubletree Suite 2 Columbus OH 43229

MURASHIGE, TOSHIO, b Kapoho, Hawaii, May 26, 30; m 53; c 5. PLANT PHYSIOLOGY. *Educ:* Univ Hawaii, BS, 52; Ohio State Univ, MS, 54; Univ Wis, PhD(plant physiol), 58. *Prof Exp:* Res assoc, Univ Wis, 58-59; asst prof, Univ Hawaii, 59-64; from asst plant physiologist to assoc plant physiologist, 64-72, assoc prof plant sci, 67-72, PROF HORT SCI & PLANT PHYSIOLOGIST, UNIV CALIF, RIVERSIDE, 72- *Concurrent Pos:* Elvenia Slosson fel ornamental hort, 72-77. *Mem:* AAAS; Am Soc Plant Physiol; Bot Soc Am; Am Soc Hort Sci; Tissue Culture Asn. *Res:* Plant tissue culture; experimental morphogenesis; growth regulators. *Mailing Add:* Dept of Plant Sci Univ of Calif Riverside CA 92502

MURASKIN, MURRAY, b Brooklyn, Ny, Aug 7, 35; m; c 3. PHYSICS. *Educ:* Mass Inst Technol, BS, 57; Univ Ill, MS, 59, PhD(physics), 61. *Prof Exp:* Res assoc physics, Univ Minn, 61-63; asst prof, Univ Nebr, Lincoln, 63-69; assoc prof, 69-74, PROF PHYSICS, UNIV NDAK, 74- *Mem:* Am Phys Soc. *Res:* Elementary particle physics. *Mailing Add:* Dept of Physics Univ of NDak Grand Forks ND 58201

MURASUGI, KUNIO, b Tokyo, Japan, Mar 25, 29; m 55; c 3. MATHEMATICS. *Educ:* Tokyo Univ Educ, BSc, 52, DSc(math), 61; Univ Toronto, MA, 61. *Prof Exp:* Lectr math, Hosei Univ, 55-59, asst prof, 59-61; res asst, Univ Toronto, 61-62; res assoc, Princeton Univ, 62-64; asst prof, 64-66, assoc prof, 66-69, PROF MATH, UNIV TORONTO, 69- *Concurrent Pos:* Res grants, Nat Res Coun Can, 61-62, NSF, 62-64 & Can Coun grant; vis scientist, Princeton Univ, 71-72; ed, Can J Math, 69-71. *Mem:* Am Math Soc; Can Math Soc; Math Soc Japan; fel Royal Soc Can. *Res:* Knot theory in combinatorial topology; infinite group theory. *Mailing Add:* 611 Cummer Ave Willowdale ON M2K 2M5 Can

MURATA, TADAO, b Takayama, Japan, June 26, 38; m 64; c 2. COMPUTER SYSTEMS, GRAPH THEORY. *Educ:* Tokai Univ, Tokyo, BS, 62; Univ Ill, Urbana, MS, 64, PhD(elec eng), 66. *Prof Exp:* Res asst, Coordinated Sci Lab, Univ Ill-Urbana, 62-66; asst prof elec eng, Univ Ill-Chicago, 66-68; assoc prof commun eng, Tokai Univ, Tokyo, 68-70; asst prof, 70-72, assoc prof, 72-78, PROF ELEC ENG & COMPUT SCI, UNIV ILL-CHICAGO, 78- *Concurrent Pos:* Vis assoc prof, Univ Calif, Berkeley, 76-77; prin investr, NSF, 78-; guest researcher, Ges fur Math und Datenuerarbeitung, Bonn, WGer, 79; vis scientist, Centre Nat de la Recherche Sci, France, 81; panel mem, Nat Res Coun, Nat Acad Sci, 81- *Mem:* Inst Elec & Electronic Engrs; Asn Comput Mach; Info Processing Soc Japan; Europ Asn Theoret Corp Sci. *Res:* Petri nets and related computation models; concurrent/distributed computer systems; data flow computers; very-large-scale integration systems and computations; applied graph theory; circuit and system theory. *Mailing Add:* Dept Info Eng Univ Ill Box 4348 Chicago IL 60680

MURATA, YORIHIRO, b Tokyo, Japan, May 18, 22; m 49; c 4. CERAMIC ENGINEERING. *Educ:* Tokyo Metrop Col, BS, 43; Tokyo Inst Technol, MS, 45, PhD(ceramic mat), 60. *Prof Exp:* Asst prof metall eng, Tokyo Metrop Col, 47-48; res assoc ceramic eng, Tokyo Inst Technol, 48-55, from asst prof to assoc prof, 55-60; sr res assoc, 60-70, SR DEVELOP ASSOC, RES & DEVELOP DIV, CARBORUNDUM CO, 71- *Honors & Awards:* Niagara Frontier Inventor Award, Tech Soc Coun & Patent Law Asn, 77. *Mem:* Am Ceramic Soc; Chem Soc Japan. *Res:* Basic and applied research of high temperature materials and dielectric ceramics such as ceramic cutting tools, refractory foam bricks, ferroelectric ceramics, boron nitrides, sintered silicon carbides, highway materials, aluminas, and ceramic fiber composites. *Mailing Add:* Carborundum Co Res & Develop Div Buffalo Ave Niagara Falls NY 14302

MURAY, JULIUS J, b Budapest, Hungary, Mar 22, 31; US citizen; m 56; c 2. PHYSICS. *Educ:* Eotvos Lorand Univ, Budapest, dipl, 54; Univ Calif, Berkeley, MA, 60, PhD(physics), 61. *Prof Exp:* Asst prof physics, Eotvos Lorand Univ, 53-56; asst, Univ Calif, Berkeley, 57-61; physicist, Stanford Univ, 61-65; physicist, Hewlett-Packard Co, Palo Alto, 65-67; exec vpres, Cintra Inc, Physics Int Co, 67-71; exec Sloan fel, Grad Sch Bus, Stanford Univ, 71-72; mgr, Phys Electronics Lab, Cent Eng Lab, FMC Corp, 72-77; STAFF SCIENTIST, STANFORD RES INST, 77- *Concurrent Pos:* Consult, Appl Radiation Co, Calif, 60-65. *Mem:* Am Phys Soc; sr mem Inst Elec & Electronics Eng. *Res:* Electron and radiation physics; atomic and molecular physics; electro-optics; microscience and microelectronics. *Mailing Add:* 890 Madonna Los Altos CA 94022

MURAYAMA, MAKIO, b San Francisco, Calif, Aug 10, 12; m 45. BIOCHEMISTRY. *Educ:* Univ Calif, BA, 39, MA, 40, PhD(immunochem), 53. *Prof Exp:* Asst biochem, Univ Calif, 39-42; res chemist, Bellevue Hosp, NY, 43-45; res biochemist, Univ Hosp, Univ Mich, 45-48; res biochemist res div, Harper Hosp, 50-54; res fel chem, Calif Inst Technol, 54-56; res assoc biochem, Univ Pa, 55-58; Nat Cancer Inst spec res fel, Cavendish Lab, Cambridge Univ, 58; BIOCHEMIST, NIH, 58- *Mem:* AAAS; Am Soc Biol Chem. *Res:* Protein chemistry; chemistry and structure of hemoglobin, especially electron microscopic studies of human sickle cell hemoglobin cable; molecular mechanism of human red cell sickling with hemoglobin S; etiology of acute mountain sickness; molecular mode of action of 2-oxo-1 pyrrolidine acetamide. *Mailing Add:* Nat Inst of Health Bethesda MD 20014

MURAYAMA, TAKAYUKI, b Tokyo, Japan, Mar 29, 32; US citizen. POLYMER SCIENCE. *Educ:* Tokyo Univ Agr & Technol, BS, 54; Lowell Technol Inst, MS, 62; Kyushu Univ, PhD(polymer sci), 68. *Prof Exp:* Res asst eng, Tokyo Univ Agr & Technol, 54-59; mech engr, Chemstrand Res Ctr, 62-66, from res physicist to sr res physicist, 66-72; res specialist, 72-77, FEL, TRIANGLE PARK DEVELOP CTR, MONSANTO CO, 72- *Concurrent Pos:* Adj prof, NC State Univ, 76- *Mem:* Soc Rheol; Am Chem Soc; Fiber Soc. *Res:* Dynamic mechanical analyses on material; studies on differential thermoproperties relating to molecular structure on polymers; dynamic anisotropic viscoelasticity on material. *Mailing Add:* PO Box 12274 Research Triangle Park NC 27709

MURBACH, EARL WESLEY, b Almira, Wash, Oct 10, 22; m 48; c 2. INORGANIC CHEMISTRY. *Educ:* Gonzaga Univ, BS, 43; Wash State Univ, MS, 49, PhD(chem), 52. *Prof Exp:* Anal chemist, Kaiser Aluminum Co, 46-47; chem engr div indust res, Wash State Univ, 49-50; chemist, Calif Res & Develop Corp Div, Standard Oil Co, Calif, 52-53; chemist, Nat Carbon Co, 53-54; sr chemist, Phillips Petrol Co, Idaho, 54-56; sr res engr, Atomics Int Div, NAm Aviation, Inc, 56-57, supvr chem develop, 57-70; mgr nuclear process develop, Allied Gulf Nuclear Serv, 70-74, MGR NUCLEAR PROCESS DEVELOP, ALLIED GEN NUCLEAR SERV, 74- *Mem:* Am Chem Soc. *Res:* High temperature methods for reprocessing reactor fuel; chemical reaction kinetics at high temperatures. *Mailing Add:* 877 Sycamore Dr Aiken SC 29801

MURCH, LAURENCE EVERETT, b Beverly, Mass, Nov 18, 42; m 68; c 3. MICRO-COMPUTERS. *Educ:* Northeastern Univ, BSME, 65; Clarkson Col Technol, MSME, 68; Univ Mass, PhD(mech eng), 72. *Prof Exp:* Methods engr, United Shoe Mach Corp, 65; instr, Clarkson Col Technol, 67-68; res asst, 68-70, instr, 70-72, asst prof, 72-76, ASSOC PROF MECH ENG, UNIV MASS, 76- *Concurrent Pos:* Vis prof, Cramfield Inst Technol, Eng, 78-79. *Mem:* Soc Mfg Engrs; Am Soc Eng Educ. *Res:* Automatic assembly; programmable assembly. *Mailing Add:* Mech Eng Dept Eng Lab Bldg Univ Mass Amherst MA 01003

MURCH, ROBERT MATTHEWS, b Lackawanna, NY, June 27, 24; m 51; c 4. POLYMER CHEMISTRY, ORGANOMETALLIC CHEMISTRY. *Educ:* Univ Mich, BS, 48; Pa State Univ, MS, 50; Univ Wis, PhD(inorg chem), 66. *Prof Exp:* Chem engr, Dow Corning Corp, 50-54, res chemist, 54-58, proj leader, 58-62; sr chemist, 65-67, res supvr, 67-71, RES ASSOC, WASHINGTON RES CTR, W R GRACE & CO, 71- *Mem:* Am Chem Soc; Sigma Xi. *Res:* Organosilicon; organophosphorus; organofluorine; inorganic polymers; fire retardant urethanes and polyester resins; flammability and smoke testing research. *Mailing Add:* Washington Res Ctr W R Grace & Co Columbia MD 21044

MURCH, S(TANLEY) ALLAN, b Grand Mere, Que, July 29, 29; US citizen; div; c 2. ENGINEERING MECHANICS. *Educ:* Wayne State Univ, BS, 52; Univ Mich, MS, 54, PhD(eng mech), 58. *Prof Exp:* Res asst, Eng Res Inst, Univ Mich, 54-58; asst res engr, Inst Eng Res, Univ Calif, Berkeley, 58-61; STRUCT ENG GROUP HEAD, CHEM SYSTS DIV, UNITED TECHNOLOGIES CORP, 61- *Mem:* AAAS; Am Soc Mech Engrs; Soc Eng Sci. *Res:* Mechanical behavior of solid propellants; viscoelasticity; failure analysis; plasticity; continuous media; fracture; shell theory. *Mailing Add:* Struct Anal Sect United Technologies Corp Sunnyvale CA 94088

MURCHISON, PAMELA W, b Pittsburgh, Pa, June 14, 43; m 70; c 2. PHYSICAL CHEMISTRY. *Educ:* Carnegie Inst Technol, BS, 65; Univ Minn, PhD(phys chem), 69. *Prof Exp:* Vis lectr chem, Hamline Univ, 69-70; ASST PROF PHYS CHEM, CENT MICH UNIV, 70-71, 72-74 & 75- *Mem:* Am Chem Soc. *Res:* Effective undergraduate chemical education. *Mailing Add:* 606 W Meadowbrook Midland MI 48640

MURCHISON, THOMAS EDGAR, b Kingsville, Tex, Aug 7, 32. VETERINARY PATHOLOGY. *Educ:* Tex A&M Univ, DVM, 55; Ohio State Univ, MSc, 57, PhD, 59. *Prof Exp:* Instr vet path, Ohio State Univ, 55-59; head path dept, Fla Dept Agr, 59-62; head exp path, Orange Mem Hosp, 62-65; head, Dawson Res Inst, 60-65, PRES, DAWSON RES CORP, 65- *Concurrent Pos:* Pres, Temson Co, 65- *Mem:* Am Vet Med Asn; Am Col Vet Path; Int Acad Path; Am Bd Toxicol. *Res:* Pharmaceutical toxicology; veterinary pathology; comparative pathology; research administration. *Mailing Add:* Dawson Res Corp Box 8272 Orlando FL 32856

MURCRAY, DAVID GUY, b Leadville, Colo, Jan 19, 24; m 45; c 2. ATMOSPHERIC PHYSICS. *Educ:* Univ Denver, BS, 48, PhD, 63; Okla State Univ, MS, 50. *Prof Exp:* Fel, Univ Kans, 50-51; res mathematician, Phillips Petrol Co, 51-52; res physicist res inst, 52-63, asst prof, 63, assoc prof, 66-69, PROF PHYSICS, UNIV DENVER, 69-, SR RES PHYSICIST, 63- *Mem:* AAAS; Optical Soc Am; Am Geophys Union; Royal Meteorol Soc. *Res:* Upper atmospheric physics; infrared transmission in the upper atmosphere; radiation balance of the atmosphere; infrared spectroscopy; operations analysis. *Mailing Add:* Dept of Physics Univ of Denver Denver CO 80210

MURCRAY, FRANK JAMES, b Stillwater, Okla, Mar 12, 50. ATMOSPHERIC & PLANETARY PHYSICS. *Educ:* Univ Denver, BS, 72; Harvard Univ, AM, 73, PhD(physics), 78. *Prof Exp:* Res physicist physics, 78-80, ASST RES PROF, UNIV DENVER, 80- *Mem:* Optical Soc Am. *Res:* Infrared measurements; stratospheric composition and radiation budget. *Mailing Add:* Dept of Physics University Park Campus Denver CO 80210

MURDAUGH, HERSCHEL VICTOR, JR, b Columbia, SC, Mar 4, 28; 48; c 3. INTERNAL MEDICINE. *Educ:* Duke Univ, MD, 50. *Prof Exp:* Intern med, Grady Mem Hosp, Atlanta, Ga, 50-51; from asst resident to sr asst resident, Duke Univ Hosp, 53-56, instr, 56-57, assoc, 57-58; from asst prof to assoc prof med, Med Col Ala, 58-65, dir renal & electrolyte div, 58-61; assoc prof med & dir renal div, Sch Med, Univ Pittsburgh, 65-77; PROF & CHMN MED, UNIV SC, VET ADMIN HOSP, 77- *Concurrent Pos:* Res fel, Duke Univ & USPHS Hosp, 54-55; chief res, Vet Admin Hosp, Durham, NC, 56-57, clin investr, 57-58; trustee, Mt Desert Island Biol Lab, 62- *Mem:* Am Physiol Soc; Am Fedn Clin Res; Am Soc Clin Invest; fel Am Col Physicians; Soc Exp Biol & Med. *Res:* Renal physiology and disease; physiology of aquatic mammals. *Mailing Add:* Rm 212 Bldg T-28 Univ SC Columbia SC 29201

MURDAY, JAMES STANLEY, b Trenton, NJ, Sept 16, 42; m 67; c 3. SURFACE PHYSICS, SURFACE CHEMISTRY. *Educ:* Case Inst Technol, BS, 64; Cornell Univ, PhD(physics), 70. *Prof Exp:* Res physicist, 69-75, sect surface anal, 75-81, HEAD SURFACE CHEM BR, NAVAL RES LAB, 81- *Concurrent Pos:* Consult, Off Naval Res, 73- *Mem:* AAAS; Am Chem Soc; Am Phys Soc; Am Vacuum Soc. *Res:* Interaction of energy forms with surfaces, surface chemical analysis, surface reactions; conduction mechanisms in conjugated carbonaceous materials. *Mailing Add:* Code 6170 Naval Res Lab Washington DC 20375

MURDEN, W(ILLIAM) P(AUL), b Newport News, Va, Mar 13, 24; m 47; c 3. MECHANICS, OPERATIONS ANALYSIS. *Educ:* Va Polytech Inst, BS, 49, MS, 51. *Prof Exp:* Instr appl mech, Va Polytech Inst, 49-51; sr analyst, Southwest Res Inst, 51-54; combat opers res group, Tech Opers, Inc, 55-56, dep dir, 56-58, mgr, Monterey Res Off, 58-60, dep dir proj Omega, 60-61, dir, Washington Res Off, 61-62, dep dir, Washington Res Ctr, 62-63; mgr opers anal, 64-71, dir opers & reliability anal, 71-76, DIR ENG TECHNOL, McDONNELL AIRCRAFT CO, 76- *Mem:* Sigma Xi; Am Inst Aeronaut & Astronaut. *Res:* Matrix stress analysis, rigid frames; rocket ballistics; six degree of freedom elastic impact; electromechanical transducers; operational simulation and experiments; war gaming; military operations analysis; weapon systems and cost-effectiveness analysis. *Mailing Add:* Dept 390 McDonnell Aircraft Co PO Box 516 St Louis MO 63166

MURDESHWAR, MANGESH GANESH, b Bombay, India, Mar 25, 33; m 61; c 3. TOPOLOGY. *Educ:* Univ Bombay, BA, 54, MA, 56; Univ Alta, PhD(math), 64. *Prof Exp:* Lectr math, Wilson Col, Univ Bombay, 56-57, Khalsa Col, 58-59 & Parle Col, 59-61; asst prof, 64-77, ASSOC PROF MATH, UNIV ALTA, 78- *Concurrent Pos:* Nat Res Coun Can overseas fel, Univ Bombay, 66-68. *Mem:* Math Asn Am. *Res:* Point-set topology. *Mailing Add:* Dept of Math Univ of Alta Edmonton AB T6G 2G1 Can

MURDICK, PHILIP W, b Akron, Ohio, Nov 13, 28; m 52; c 4. VETERINARY MEDICINE. *Educ:* Ohio State Univ, DVM, 52, MS, 58, PhD(physiol), 64. *Prof Exp:* Instr vet med, 56-64, from asst prof to assoc prof, 64-69, PROF VET MED, OHIO STATE UNIV, 69-, CHMN DEPT VET CLIN SCI, 71- *Mem:* Am Vet Med Asn. *Res:* Veterinary obstetrics and diseases of the genitalia; development of methods for the detection of drugs illegally administered to race horses. *Mailing Add:* Col of Vet Med Ohio State Univ 1935 Coffey Rd Columbus OH 43210

MURDOCH, ARTHUR, b DuBois, Nebr, Aug 25, 34; m 57; c 2. ORGANIC CHEMISTRY. *Educ:* Westmar Col, BA, 56; Yale Univ, MS, 58, PhD(org chem), 64. *Prof Exp:* Asst prof chem, Morningside Col, 62-65; assoc prof, 65-68, PROF CHEM, MT UNION COL, 68-, CHMN DEPT, 65- *Mem:* Fed Am Scientists; Am Asn Univ Professors; Am Chem Soc. *Res:* Organic reduction-oxidation polymers. *Mailing Add:* Dept Chem Mt Union Col Alliance OH 44601

MURDOCH, BRUCE THOMAS, b Prague, Okla, Mar 15, 40; m 69; c 2. NUCLEAR WELL LOGGING. *Educ:* Carleton Col, BA, 62; Rice Univ, MA, 66; Utah State Univ, PhD(physics), 75. *Prof Exp:* Develop engr, Goodyear Aerospace Corp, 67-70; fel nuclear physics, Univ Man, 74-76, prof assoc, 76-77; PROJ DEVELOP ENGR, SCHLUMBERGER WELL SERV, 78- *Mem:* Am Phys Soc; Soc Petrol Engrs. *Res:* Medium energy experimental nuclear physics; cryogenic targets; nuclear techniques in oil well logging. *Mailing Add:* 12607 Hunting Briar Dr PO Box 2175 Houston TX 77099

MURDOCH, CHARLES LORAINE, b Atkins, Ark, Aug 23, 32; m 66; c 2. HORTICULTURE. *Educ:* Univ Ark, BS, 59, MS, 60; Univ Ill, PhD(agron), 66. *Prof Exp:* Res asst agron, Southwest Br Exp Sta, Univ Ark, 60-62 & Univ Ill, 62-66; res assoc, Univ Ark, 66-70; from asst prof to assoc prof, 70-78, PROF HORT, UNIV HAWAII, HONOLULU, 78- *Mem:* Am Soc Agron. *Res:* Turfgrass management; ecological and physiological aspects of turfgrass growth and development. *Mailing Add:* Dept of Hort Univ of Hawaii Honolulu HI 96822

MURDOCH, DAVID CARRUTHERS, b Tunbridge Wells, Eng, Mar 31, 12; m 50; c 3. MATHEMATICS. *Educ:* Univ BC, BA, 31, MA, 33; Univ Toronto, PhD(math), 37. *Prof Exp:* Sterling fel math, Yale Univ, 37-38, instr, 38-40; instr, Univ Sask, 40-42, asst prof, 42-44; from assoc prof to prof, 44-77, EMER PROF MATH, UNIV BC, 77- *Concurrent Pos:* Vis prof, Ford Found, Mass Inst Technol Proj, Birla Inst Math & Sci, Pilani, India, 66-68. *Mem:* Am Math Soc; Math Asn Am; Can Math Soc. *Res:* Non-commutative ideal theory and theory of rings; abstract algebra. *Mailing Add:* Dept of Math Univ of BC Vancouver BC V6T 1W5 Can

MURDOCH, JOSEPH B(ERT), b Cleveland, Ohio, Jan 31, 27; m 51; c 5. ELECTRICAL ENGINEERING. *Educ:* Case Inst Technol, BS, 50, PhD, 62; Univ NH, MS, 55. *Prof Exp:* Engr, Gen Elec Co, 50-52; from instr to assoc prof, 52-65, chmn dept, 66-77, PROF ELEC ENG, UNIV NH, 65- *Concurrent Pos:* Prof lectr, Case Inst Technol, 59-60; Phillips fel admin, Ore State Univ, 65-66. *Mem:* Inst Elec & Electronics Engrs; Am Soc Eng Educ. *Res:* Network synthesis and analysis; illumination and circuits. *Mailing Add:* Dept of Elec Eng Univ of NH Durham NH 03824

MURDOCH, JOSEPH RICHARD, b Portland, Ore, Sept 15, 46; m 71. ORGANIC CHEMISTRY. *Educ:* Univ Calif, Santa Barbara, BA, 68; Univ Calif, Berkeley, PhD(chem), 73. *Prof Exp:* Damon Runyon Cancer Found fel, Dept Chem, Stanford Univ, 73-75; res assoc chem, Univ Calif, Berkeley, 75-76; ASST PROF CHEM, UNIV CALIF, LOS ANGELES, 76- *Mem:* Am Chem Soc. *Res:* Solid state chemistry, dynamics of chemical reactions in solution and condensed phases, applications to biological systems. *Mailing Add:* Dept of Chem Univ of Calif Los Angeles CA 90024

MURDOCH, WILLIAM W, b Glassford, Scotland, Jan 28, 39; m 63; c 1. POPULATION BIOLOGY, ECOLOGY. *Educ:* Univ Glasgow, BSc, 60; Oxford Univ, DPhil(ecol), 63. *Prof Exp:* Res assoc & instr ecol, Univ Mich, 63-65; from asst prof to assoc prof, 65-75, PROF BIOL SCI, UNIV CALIF, SANTA BARBARA, 75- *Concurrent Pos:* Vis lectr, Univ BC, 65. *Mem:* Ecol Soc Am; Brit Ecol Soc; Japanese Soc Pop Biol. *Res:* Population and community dynamics of organisms. *Mailing Add:* Dept of Biol Sci Univ of Calif Santa Barbara CA 93106

MURDOCK, ARCHIE LEE, b Arcola, Mo, Nov 5, 33; m 53; c 3. BIOCHEMISTRY. *Educ:* Southwest Mo State Univ, BS, 57; Univ Mo, MS, 60, PhD(biochem), 63. *Prof Exp:* Res assoc fel biochem, Brookhaven Nat Lab, 63-65; ASST PROF BIOCHEM, MED CTR, UNIV KANS, 65- *Mem:* Am Chem Soc; Sigma Xi. *Res:* Protein chemistry; molecular mechanisms of thermophily in bacteria; methodology. *Mailing Add:* Dept of Biochem Univ of Kans Med Ctr Kansas City KS 66103

MURDOCK, FENOI R, b Blackfoot, Idaho, Feb 2, 17; m 42; c 3. ANIMAL NUTRITION. *Educ:* Univ Idaho, BS, 38; Pa State Univ, PhD(agr), 43. *Prof Exp:* Res chemist, Borden Co, 43-49; asst prof dairy sci, Western Wash Exp Sta, 49-52, assoc prof dairy sci & assoc dairy scientist, 52-60, PROF DAIRY SCI & DAIRY SCIENTIST, WESTERN WASH RES & EXTEN CTR, WASH STATE UNIV, 60- *Mem:* Am Dairy Sci Asn. *Res:* Dairy cattle nutrition, utilization of forages and by-products as feeds, animal waste management to conserve nutrients and prevent air and water pollution. *Mailing Add:* Western Wash Res & Exten Ctr Puyallup WA 98371

MURDOCK, GORDON ALFRED, b Minneapolis, Minn, Jan 4, 23; m 50; c 5. PHYSICAL CHEMISTRY. *Educ:* Willamette Univ, BS, 50; Univ Ore, MA, 51, PhD, 54. *Prof Exp:* Asst, Univ Ore, 49-53; res chemist, 53-57, prof leader, 57-60, supvr printing grades develop, 60-68, supvr reprographic res, 68-69, TECH MGR, REPROGRAPHIC PROD, CROWN ZELLERBACH CORP, 69- *Mem:* Am Chem Soc; Tech Asn Pulp & Paper Indust; Soc Photog Sci & Eng. *Res:* Electrochemistry; corrosion studies; polarography; paper products; graphic arts; electrophotography and reproduction papers. *Mailing Add:* Electrographic Papers Div Crown Zellerbach Corp PO Box 17128 Portland OR 97217

MURDOCK, GORDON ROBERT, b Redlands, Calif, Jan 4, 43; m 68; c 1. INVERTEBRATE ZOOLOGY. *Educ:* Reed Col, AB, 65; Duke Univ, PhD(zool), 72. *Prof Exp:* Asst prof zool, Ariz State Univ, 70-75; fel, Duke Univ, 75-77; vis assoc prof zool, Clemson Univ, 77-78; dir, NC Marine Res Ctr, Ft Fisher, 78-81; CUR PUB EDUC, BELL MUS NATURAL HIST, UNIV MINN, 81- *Concurrent Pos:* Fel, Univ Manchester, 74-75; vis fac, West Indies Lab, Farleigh Dickinson Univ, 76. *Mem:* AAAS; Am Soc Zoologists; Sigma Xi. *Res:* Prey capture and utilization by sessile invertebrates, biological fluid mechanics, biomechanics, and functional morphology, especially of invertebrates. *Mailing Add:* 10 Church St SE Minneapolis MN 55455

MURDOCK, JOHN THOMAS, b Lynn Grove, Ky, Nov 21, 27; m 49; c 3. SOIL SCIENCE. *Educ:* Univ Ky, BS, 52, MS, 53; Univ Wis, PhD(soils), 56. *Prof Exp:* Assoc prof, 55-72, asst dir int agr progs, 68-70, PROF SOILS, UNIV WIS-MADISON, 72-, ASSOC DIR INT AGR PROGS, 74- *Concurrent Pos:* Soils specialist, Univ Wis Contract, Univ Rio Grande do Sul, Brazil, 64-68; proj coordr, Midwestern Univs Consortium Int Activities Higher Agr Educ Proj, Bogor, Indonesia, 70-72; sr res adv spec prog agr res, Brasilia, Brazil, 72-73; dir, Int Agr Progs, 73-78; exec dir, Midwest Univs Consortium for Int Activities, 75-78. *Mem:* Soil Sci Soc Am. *Res:* Soil fertility and management. *Mailing Add:* 1003 WARF Bldg Univ of Wis Madison WI 53706

MURDOCK, JOSEPH RICHARD, b Provo, Utah, Apr 25, 21; m 47; c 4. PLANT ECOLOGY. *Educ:* Brigham Young Univ, BS, 49, MS, 51; Wash State Univ, PhD(bot), 56. *Prof Exp:* From asst prof to assoc prof, 52-69, PROF BOT, BRIGHAM YOUNG UNIV, 69- *Concurrent Pos:* Res assoc radiation ecol proj, Nev Test Site, AEC, 59-60. *Res:* Microenvironmental studies of plant habitats; temperature and moisture. *Mailing Add:* Dept of Bot Brigham Young Univ Provo UT 84601

MURDOCK, KEITH CHADWICK, b Garfield, Utah, Feb 5, 28; m 53; c 2. SYNTHETIC ORGANIC CHEMISTRY, MEDICINAL CHEMISTRY. *Educ:* Univ Utah, BA, 48, MA, 50; Univ Ill, PhD(chem), 53. *Prof Exp:* Asst pharmacol & chem, Univ Utah, 48; asst chem, Univ Ill, 50-53; chemist, Res Div, Am Cyanamid Co, NJ, 53-54 & Army Chem Ctr, Edgewood, Md, 55-56; res chemist, 56-63, SR RES CHEMIST, LEDERLE DIV, AM CYANAMID CO, 63- *Mem:* Am Chem Soc. *Res:* Mannich reaction; copolymerization; pharmaceutical and medicinal chemistry; heterocyclics; cancer and antiviral chemotherapy; nucleic acids; DNA intercalating agents. *Mailing Add:* 15 Birch St Pearl River NY 10965

MURDOCK, LARRY LEE, physiology, biochemistry, see previous edition

MURDY, WILLIAM HENRY, b New Bedford, Mass, Dec 25, 28; m 52; c 2. BOTANY. *Educ:* Univ Mass, BS, 56; Washington Univ, PhD(bot), 59. *Prof Exp:* From instr to assoc prof, 59-71, chmn Biol Dept, 71-74, PROF BIOL, EMORY UNIV, 71- *Concurrent Pos:* Scholar, Harvard Univ, 67-68. *Mem:* Bot Soc Am; Soc Study Evolution. *Res:* Systematics of plant species of granite outcrop communities in the Southeastern Piedmont; effect of sulfur dioxide on plant reproduction and the evolution of tolerance in plant populations. *Mailing Add:* Dept of Biol Emory Univ Atlanta GA 30322

MUREIKA, ROMAN A, b Lithuania, Aug 9, 44; Can citizen; m 66; c 2. MATHEMATICS. *Educ:* Cath Univ Am, BA, 64, MA, 67, PhD(math), 69. *Prof Exp:* Asst prof math, Univ Alta, 68-76; asst prof statist, 76-78, ASSOC PROF STATIST, UNIV NB, 78- *Mem:* Can Math Soc; Inst Math Statist; Statist Soc Can. *Res:* Probability theory; empirical characteristic functions; stochastic processes; sampling theory; entropy. *Mailing Add:* Dept of Math Univ of NB Fredericton NB E3B 5A3 Can

MURIE, JAN O, b Okanogan, Wash, July 24, 39; m 61; c 2. ANIMAL BEHAVIOR, ECOLOGY. *Educ:* Colo State Univ, BS, 59; Univ Mont, MA, 63; Pa State Univ, PhD(zool), 67. *Prof Exp:* Fel & lectr, 67-69, asst prof, 69-75, ASSOC PROF ZOOL, UNIV ALTA, 75- *Mem:* Ecol Soc Am; Animal Behav Soc; Am Soc Zoologists; Am Soc Mammal; Am Soc Naturalists. *Res:* Ecology and behavior of small mammals, especially social behavior of sciurid rodents. *Mailing Add:* Dept of Zool Univ of Alta Edmonton AB T6G 2G7 Can

MURIE, RICHARD A, b Mt Pleasant, Ohio, Oct 3, 23; m 50; c 2. ANALYTICAL CHEMISTRY. *Educ:* Ohio Univ, BS, 50; Iowa State Univ, MS, 52, PhD(anal chem), 55. *Prof Exp:* Assoc prof chem, Drake Univ, 51-52; res chemist, Monsanto Chem Co, 55-60; sr res chemist, Res Ctr, Diamond Alkali Chem Co, 60, group leader, 60-63; prin scientist, Allison Div, 63-68, supvr appl math res, Tech Ctr, 68-70, SR RES CHEMIST, GEN MOTORS RES LABS, 70- *Concurrent Pos:* Instr, Eve Div, WVa State Col, 55-60; vis prof, Univ Guadalajara, 72-75; instr, Eve Div, Lawrence Inst Technol, Southfield, Mich, 72- *Mem:* Am Chem Soc; Instrument Soc Am; Soc Appl Spectros. *Res:* Instrumental methods of analysis, especially gas chromatography, differential thermal analysis and ultraviolet and infrared spectroscopy; development of high temperature battery systems and materials to serve as insulators in such systems. *Mailing Add:* RCEL Dept 37 Gen Motors Res Ctr Warren MI 48090

MURINO, CLIFFORD JOHN, b Yonkers, NY, Feb 10, 29; m 54; c 3. METEOROLOGY. *Educ:* St Louis Univ, BS, 50, MS, 54, PhD(geophys), 57. *Prof Exp:* From assoc prof to prof geophysics, Inst Technol, St Louis Univ, 67-77, vpres finance & res, 71-75; dir Atmospheric Technol Div, Nat Ctr Atmospheric Res, 75-80; PRES, DESERT RES INST, UNIV NEV SYST, 80- *Concurrent Pos:* Vpres res, St Louis Univ, 69-71; sci consult, Div Environ Sci, NSF, Washington, DC, 67-69. *Mem:* Am Meteorol Soc. *Res:* Satellite meteorology; radiation physics; atmospheric energetics; severe storms. *Mailing Add:* Desert Res Inst Univ Nev Syst PO Box 60220 Reno NV 89506

MURINO, VINCENT S, b New York, NY, July 30, 24; m 50; c 1. METEOROLOGY, RESEARCH ADMINISTRATION. *Educ:* St Louis Univ, BS, 51, MS, 52; Am Univ, MA, 67. *Prof Exp:* Meteorologist, 52-64, meteorol syst analyst, 64-73, exec officer systs develop off, 73-76, EXEC OFFICER, NAT WEATHER SERV, NAT OCEANIC & ATMOSPHERIC ADMIN, 73- *Concurrent Pos:* Environ Sci Serv Admin fel, 66-67. *Mem:* Am Meteorol Soc; Am Geophys Union. *Res:* Administration of national weather service programs. *Mailing Add:* Nat Weather Serv 8060 13th St Silver Spring MD 20910

MURISON, GERALD LEONARD, b SAfrica, May 16, 39; US citizen; m 69; c 2. CELL BIOLOGY, DEVELOPMENTAL BIOLOGY. *Educ:* Univ Witwatersrand, BSc, 61, MSc, 63; Johns Hopkins Univ, PhD(biol), 69. *Prof Exp:* Jr lectr biochem, Univ Witwatersrand, 61-64; Pa Plan scholar & instr histol, Med Sch, Univ Pa, 69-70; asst prof biol, Univ Miami, 70-73; ASSOC PROF BIOL, FLA INT UNIV, 73- *Mem:* AAAS; Soc Develop Biol; Am Soc Cell Biologists. *Res:* Biochemistry of development with emphasis on protein synthesis in tissues before and after birth; regulation of liver metabolism; protein biosynthesis; chemical carcinogenesis in mammalian cells in vitro. *Mailing Add:* Dept of Biol Sci Fla Int Univ Miami FL 33199

MURMAN, EARLL MORTON, b Berkeley, Calif, May 12, 42. FLUID MECHANICS, AERODYNAMICS. *Educ:* Princeton Univ, BSE, 63, MA, 65, PhD(aerospace eng), 67. *Prof Exp:* Aerospace engr aerodyn, Boeing Co, 67-71 & NASA-Ames Res Ctr, 71-74; sr res scientist fluid mech, Flow Industs Inc, 74-76, vpres, 76-80; PROF, MASS INST TECHNOL, 80- *Concurrent Pos:* Lectr, Stanford Univ, 73. *Mem:* Am Inst Aeronaut & Astronaut. *Res:* Transonic flow, electrostatic precipitators; computational fluid dynamics. *Mailing Add:* Mass Inst Technol 77 Massachusetts Ave Cambridge MA 02139

MURMANN, ROBERT KENT, b Chicago, Ill, Oct 7, 27; m 55; c 2. INORGANIC CHEMISTRY. *Educ:* Monmouth Col, BS, 49; Northwestern Univ, MS, 51, PhD(chem), 53. *Prof Exp:* Res assoc, Univ Chicago, 53-54; from instr to asst prof chem, Univ Conn, 54-57; assoc prof, 58-60, PROF CHEM, UNIV MO-COLUMBIA, 60- *Mem:* AAAS; Am Chem Soc. *Res:* Coordination compounds; rhenium chemistry; 0-18 isotopic exchange kinetics. *Mailing Add:* Dept of Chem Univ of Mo Columbia MO 65202

MURNANE, THOMAS GEORGE, b Dallas, Tex, May 5, 26; m 53; c 5. VETERINARY MEDICINE, RESOURCE MANAGEMENT. *Educ:* Agr & Mech Col Tex, DVM, 47. *Prof Exp:* Pvt pract, Tex, 47-48; vet, Foot & Mouth Campaign, Joint US-Mex Comn, Mex, 48-49; US Army, 49-, vet lab officer, Area Med Labs, 49-56, vet adv, US Mil Mission, Repub Panama, 56-59, dir defense subsistence testing lab, Ill, 59-63, dep dir div vet med, Walter Reed Army Inst Res, 63-66, chief vet dept, Ninth Med Field Lab, 66-67, chief vet res div, US Army Med Res & Develop Command, 67-72, sr vet corps staff officer, Off Surgeon Gen, 72-74, chief vet corps career activities off, Army Med Dept Personnel Support Agency, Off Surgeon Gen, 74-76; brigadier gen & chief, US Army Vet Corps, 76-80; ANIMAL HEALTH SPECIALIST, INTERAMERICAN INST AGR SCI, MEX, 80- *Concurrent Pos:* Consult vet pub health, Surgeon Gen, Dept Army, Washington, DC, 74-76. *Mem:* Am Vet Med Asn; US Animal Health Asn; Asn Mil Surgeons US; Am Asn Vet Lab Diagnosticians; Conf Res Workers Animal Dis. *Res:* Food hygiene; rabies; leptospirosis; encephalomyocarditis virus; foot and mouth disease; military participation in emergency animal disease programs; career management of health professionals. *Mailing Add:* Interamerican Inst Agr Sci Apartado Postal 61-148 Mexico 6 D F Mexico

MURNANE, THOMAS WILLIAM, b Cambridge, Mass, July 18, 36; m 65; c 2. ORAL SURGERY, ANATOMY. *Educ:* Tufts Univ, BS, 58, DMD, 62, PhD(anat), 68; Am Bd Oral Surg, dipl. *Prof Exp:* Fel anesthesia, Tufts Univ-Boston City Hosp, 63-64; fel, Queen Victoria Hosp, Eng, 65; NIH fel, Med Col Va, 65-66; sr instr anat, Sch Med, 67-68, asst prof oral surg, Sch Dent Med, 67-71, actg dean, 71-72, assoc dean, Sch Dent Med, & chmn steering comt, Univ, 72-76, asst to pres, 76-78, vpres health progs develop, 78-79, ASSOC PROF ORAL SURG, SCH DENT MED, TUFTS UNIV, 71-, LECTR ANAT, SCH MED, 71-, VPRES, UNIV DEVELOP, 79- *Concurrent Pos:* Vis assoc oral surgeon, Boston City Hosp & Tufts New Eng Med Ctr, 68; consult, Coun Dent Educ, Am Dent Asn; mem coun oral surg, Pan-Am Med Asn. *Mem:* Am Dent Asn; Am Soc Oral Surg. *Res:* Joints; synovial membrane; connective tissue; electron and light microscopy; experimental pathology. *Mailing Add:* Off Pres Tufts Univ 193 Harrison Ave Boston MA 02111

MURNIK, MARY RENGO, b Manistee, Mich, Aug 30, 42; m 70; c 1. GENETICS. *Educ:* Mich State Univ, BS, 64, PhD(zool, genetics), 69. *Prof Exp:* Asst prof biol & genetics, Fitchburg State Col, 68-70; from asst prof to assoc prof, Western Ill Univ, 70-80; PROF BIOL SCI & DEAD DEPT, FERRIS STATE COL, 80- *Mem:* AAAS; Genetics Soc Am; Environ Mutagen Soc; Genetics Soc. *Res:* Mutagen assays, reproductive behavior and meiotic drive in Drosophila. *Mailing Add:* Dept Biol Sci Ferris State Col Big Rapids MI 49307

MUROGA, SABURO, b Numazu, Japan, Mar 15, 25; m 56; c 4. COMPUTER SCIENCE. *Educ:* Univ Tokyo, BE, 47, PhD(info theory), 58. *Prof Exp:* Mem res staff, Nat Railway Pub Corp, Japan, 47-49; mem eng staff, Govt Radio Regulatory Comn, Japan, 50-51; mem res staff, Elec Commun Lab, Nippon Tel & Tel Pub Corp, Japan, 51-60 & IBM Res Ctr, Yorktown Heights, NY, 60-64; PROF COMPUT SCI, UNIV ILL, URBANA, 64- *Mem:* Fel Inst Elec & Electronic Engrs; Asn Comput Mach; Info Processing Soc Japan; Inst Electronics & Commun Engrs Japan. *Res:* Logical design; switching theory; integrated circuits; mathematical programming; integrated programming. *Mailing Add:* Dept of Comput Sci Univ of Ill Urbana IL 61801

MUROV, STEVEN LEE, b Los Angeles, Calif, Oct 16, 40; m 66. PHOTOCHEMISTRY. *Educ:* Harvey Mudd Col, BS, 62; Univ Chicago, PhD(photochem), 67. *Prof Exp:* NIH fel photochem, Calif Inst Technol, 67-68; asst prof org chem, State Univ NY Stony Brook, 68-73; assoc prof phys sci, Sangamon State Univ, 73-78; vis assoc prof chem, Moorhead State Univ, 77-78; lectr chem, Calif State Col, Bakersfield, 78-79; INSTR CHEM, MODESTO JR COL, 79- *Mem:* Am Chem Soc. *Res:* Organic photochemistry; methods in science education at the elementary school level. *Mailing Add:* Dept Chem Modesto Jr Col Modesto CA 93350

MURPHEY, BYRON FREEZE, b Great Falls, Mont, Aug 12, 18; m 41; c 2. PHYSICS. *Educ:* Univ Mont, BA, 39; Univ Minn, MA, 41, PhD(physics), 48. *Prof Exp:* Physicist underwater ord, Naval Ord Lab, 41-45; physicist, Minn Mining & Mfg Co, 48-49, physics sect leader, 53-58; div supvr weapons effects, Sandia Corp, NMex, 49-53, div supvr underground explosions, 58-61, div supvr appl phys sci, 61-62, dept mgr nuclear burst physics, 62-67, dir underground exp, 67-71; DIR APPL RES, SANDIA LABS, 71- *Mem:* Fel Am Phys Soc; Am Asn Physics Teachers. *Res:* Magnetism; solid state physics; effects of nuclear weapons. *Mailing Add:* 1822 Vancouver Way Livermore CA 94550

MURPHEY, ROBERT STAFFORD, b Littleton, NC, Oct 29, 21; m 46; c 2. MEDICINAL CHEMISTRY. *Educ:* Univ Richmond, BS, 42; Univ Va, MS, 47, PhD(org chem), 49. *Prof Exp:* Res chemist medicinal chem, 48-53, dir chem res, 53-55, asst dir res, 55-57, dir res, 57-60, dir int res, 60-66, dir sci develop, 66-80, asst vpres, 67-73, vpres, 73-81, VPRES SCI AFFAIRS & CORP DEVELOP, A H ROBINS & CO, INC, 82- *Mem:* AAAS; Am Chem Soc. *Res:* Organic chemistry. *Mailing Add:* 1405 Cummings Dr PO Box 26609 Richmond VA 23261

MURPHEY, RODNEY KEITH, b Minneapolis, Minn, May 6, 42; m 64; c 2. NEUROBIOLOGY. *Educ:* Univ Minn, Minneapolis, BA, 65, MS, 67; Univ Ore, PhD(biol), 70. *Prof Exp:* NIH fel, Univ Calif, Berkeley, 70-71; asst prof zool, Univ Iowa, 71-74; vis asst prof biol, Univ Ore, 74-75; res assoc, Ctr for Neurobiol, 75-77, ASSOC PROF BIOL, STATE UNIV NY ALBANY, 77- *Mem:* AAAS; Brit Soc Exp Biol; Soc Neurosci; Am Soc Zoologists. *Res:* Neural mechanisms of animal behavior; mechanisms of orientation in animals; neurophysiology of invertebrates; developmental neurobiology. *Mailing Add:* Ctr for Neurobiol State Univ NY Albany NY 12222

MURPHEY, WAYNE K, b Glenolden, Pa, Sept 5, 27; m 52; c 5. WOOD TECHNOLOGY. *Educ:* Pa State Univ, BS, 52, MF, 53; Univ Mich, PhD, 61. *Prof Exp:* Engr res, Koppers Co, Inc, 53-55; instr forest prod, Ohio Agr Exp Sta, 55-60; asst prof wood utilization, 60-67, head dept wood sci & technol & in chg forestry res lab, 67-68, actg asst dean resident instr, Col Agr, 68-70, prof wood technol & asst dir sch forest resources, Pa State Univ, University Park, 70-78; head & prof forest sci, Tex A&M Univ, College Station, 78-81; FOREST PROD TECHNOLOGIST, SCI & EDUC, COOP STATE RES SERV, USDA, WASHINGTON, DC, 81- *Concurrent Pos:* Consult wood surg, Philippines, Morocco, Brazil & Dominican Repub. *Res:* Physical and mechanical properties of wood; adhesives; wood preservation and seasoning; biomass utilization; energy; effects of environment on wood and fiber properties. *Mailing Add:* Sci & Educ Coop State Res Serv USDA Washington DC 20590

MURPHEY, WILBUR ALFORD, research administration, polymer chemistry, deceased

MURPHEY, WILLIAM HOWARD, biochemistry, microbiology, see previous edition

MURPHREE, HENRY BERNARD SCOTT, b Decatur, Ala, Aug 11, 27; m 53; c 3. CLINICAL PHARMACOLOGY. *Educ:* Yale Univ, BA, 50; Emory Univ, MD, 59. *Prof Exp:* Instr pharmacol, Emory Univ, 59-61, intern med, Grady Mem Hosp, 59-61; asst chief pharmacol sect, Bur Res Neurol & Psychiat, NJ Neuropsychiat Inst, 61-68, mem staff, Inst, 62-68; assoc prof psychiat, 68-71, mem prof staff, Rutgers Ctr Alcohol Studies, 68-72, assoc, Grad Fac Psychol, 69-72, prof pharmacol, 71-81, dir liaison psychiat, 72-77, actg chmn, 77-78, assoc dean acad affairs, 77-81, PROF PSYCHIAT, COL MED & DENT NJ-RUTGERS MED SCH, 71-, MEM GRAD FAC PSYCHOL, 72-, CHMN DEPT PSYCHIAT, 78- *Concurrent Pos:* Consult, Princeton Hosp, NJ, 64-75, Comt Impaired Physicians, Med Soc NJ, 77-, hon consult staff, Carrier Found, 79-; lectr, Hahnemann Med Col, 65-73; chief psychiat, Raritan Valley Hosp, 72-77, consult staff psychiat, 77-81; vis prof, Ctr Alcohol Studies, Rutgers Univ, 75-; mem, State NJ Sci Adv Comt, 81-; dir, Corp J Alcohol Studies, 81-; mem bd trustees, Carrier Found, 81- *Mem:* AAAS; Am Soc Pharmacol & Exp Therapeut; NY Acad Sci; Soc Biol Psychiat; Am Col Neuropsychopharmacol. *Res:* Human psychopharmacology, psychophysiology, psychometrics, electronics, computer techniques, as all these come together in the understanding of the biological correlates and determinants of behavior. *Mailing Add:* Dept of Psychiat Rutgers Med Sch Piscataway NJ 08854

MURPHY, ALEXANDER JAMES, b New York, NY, May 19, 39; m 60; c 1. BIOCHEMISTRY. *Educ:* Brooklyn Col, BS, 62; Yale Univ, PhD(biochem), 67. *Prof Exp:* Am Heart Asn spec fel, Univ Calif, San Francisco, 67-70; asst mem dept contractile proteins, Inst Muscle Dis, 70-72; asst prof physiol, 72-74, asst prof, 74-77, ASSOC PROF & CHAIRPERSON DEPT BIOCHEM, SCH DENT, UNIV OF THE PAC, 77- *Concurrent Pos:* NIH career develop award, 72-77. *Mem:* Biophys Soc; NY Acad Sci. *Res:* Protein structure; active sites of contractile and membrane proteins; synthesis of nucleotide analogs. *Mailing Add:* Dept of Biochem Sch of Dent Univ of the Pac 2155 Webster San Francisco CA 94115

MURPHY, ALLAN HUNT, b Cambridge, Mass, Oct 29, 31; m 60; c 4. STATISTICAL METEOROLOGY, APPLIED METEOROLOGY & CLIMATOLOGY. *Educ:* Mass Inst Technol, SB, 54; Univ Mich, MS, 60, AM, 63, PhD(atmos & oceanic sci), 74. *Prof Exp:* Res asst, Mass Inst Technol, 49-54; meteorologist, Northeast Weather Serv, Mass, 54-55; phys sci asst, US Army Electronic Proving Ground, Ariz, 55-58; res asst, Univ Mich, 58-59; res assoc, Travelers Res Ctr, Conn, 59-61, consult, 61-63; res meteorologist, Univ Mich, 61-67, lectr, 64-67; res scientist, Travelers Res Corp, 67-69; res assoc & lectr, Univ Mich, 69-71; mem staff, Nat Ctr Atmospheric Res, 71-79; assoc prof, 79-81, PROF, ORE STATE UNIV, 81-, DIR, STATIST & CLIMATIC IMPACTS LAB, 80-; CLIMATOLOGIST, STATE ORE, 81- *Concurrent Pos:* Fac mem, Univ Hartford, 67-69; vis scholar, Inst Behav Sci, Univ Colo, 71-75; res scholar, Int Inst Appl Syst Anal, Austria, 74-75, consult, 75-76; adj prof, Grad Sch Bus Admin, Univ Colo, 75-79; vis scientist, Europ Ctr Medium Range Weather Forecasts, 80 & 81, Royal Neth Meteorol Inst, 81. *Mem:* AAAS; fel Am Meteorol Soc; Nat Weather Asn; Am Statist Asn; Opers Res Soc Am. *Res:* Application of methodology of statistics and operations research in atmospheric sciences, especially statistical and probabilistic forecasting, forecast evaluation and value and use of weather and climate information. *Mailing Add:* Dept of Atmospheric Sci Ore State Univ Corvallis OR 97331

MURPHY, ALLEN EMERSON, b Barnesville, Ohio, Aug 9, 21; m 43; c 3. GEOLOGY. *Educ:* Mt Union Col, AB, 43; WVa Univ, MS, 48; Syracuse Univ, PhD, 55. *Prof Exp:* Topog engr, US Coast & Geod Surv, 43; geol engr, Guy B Panero, 48; from asst prof to assoc prof geol, 48-61, PROF GEOL & GEOG, POTOMAC STATE COL, WVA UNIV, 61-, HEAD DEPT, 48- *Mem:* Geol Soc Am. *Res:* Physical, historical geomorphology and general geology. *Mailing Add:* Dept of Geol Potomac State Col Keyser WV 26726

MURPHY, ARTHUR THOMAS, b Hartford, Conn, Feb 15, 29; m 52; c 7. SYSTEMS ENGINEERING. *Educ:* Syracuse Univ, BEE, 51; Carnegie-Mellon Univ, MS, 52, PhD(elec eng), 57. *Prof Exp:* Asst & assoc prof & head elec eng, Wichita State Univ, 56-61; vis assoc prof mech eng, Mass Inst Technol, 61-62; prof & dean eng, Widener Col, 62-71, vpres & dean, 71-75; Brown prof mech eng & head dept, Carnegie-Mellon Univ, 75-80; MGR COMPUT & AUTOMATED SYSTS, BERG ELECTRONICS DIV, E I DU PONT DE NEMOURS & CO, INC, 80- *Concurrent Pos:* Consult, Boeing Co, 57-67, Educ Career Systs, 71-75 & Cyclops Corp, E G Smith Div, 76; ed eng systs, Pergamon Press, 66-; vis prof control eng, Univ Manchester Inst Sci & Technol, Eng, 68-69; bd dir, Rumford Press, 75-; prof-in-indust, E I du Pont de Nemours & Co, Inc, 79-80. *Honors & Awards:* Western Elec Fund Award, Am Soc Eng Educ, 65. *Mem:* Am Soc Mech Engrs; AAAS; Soc Mfg Engrs; Inst Elec & Electronics Engrs; Am Soc Eng Educ. *Res:* Control systems; computer aided design and manufacturing; electronic interconnections and effects on computer performance including electromagnetic interference. *Mailing Add:* E I du Pont de Nemours & Co Inc 30 Hunter Lane Camp Hill PA 17011

MURPHY, BERNARD T, b Hull, Eng, May 30, 32; m 59; c 2. PHYSICS. *Educ:* Univ Leeds, BSc, 53, PhD(physics), 59. *Prof Exp:* Physicist-engr, Mullard Res Labs, Eng, 56-59; supvry engr, Westinghouse Elec Co, Pa, 59-62; dir develop, Siliconix, Inc, Calif, 62-63; DEPT HEAD, BELL TEL LABS, INC, 63- *Mem:* Am Phys Soc; fel Inst Elec & Electronics Engrs. *Res:* Medical physics; electron beam studies; integrated circuit structures. *Mailing Add:* Bell Tel Labs Inc 600 Mountain Ave Murray Hill NJ 07974

MURPHY, BEVERLEY (ELAINE) PEARSON, biochemistry, endocrinology, see previous edition

MURPHY, BRIAN BORU, b Detroit, Mich, Dec 17, 47. MATHEMATICS. *Educ:* Wayne State Univ, BS, 68, MA, 69, PhD(math), 74. *Prof Exp:* NDEA Title IV fel, Wayne State Univ, 69-72; exchange fel, Univ Munich, 73-74; instr math, Wayne State Univ, 74-75; sr res analyst, Blue Cross & Blue Shield, Mich, 76-77, proj leader, 77-78, res assoc, 78-80; ACTUARY, GABRIEL, ROEDER, SMITH & CO, 80- *Mem:* Am Math Soc; Soc Actuaries. *Res:* Numerical analysis; applied statistics; health care system dynamics. *Mailing Add:* Gabriel Roeder Smith & Co 2090 First Nat Bldg Detroit MI 48226

MURPHY, BRIAN DONAL, b Dublin, Ireland, May 31, 39; US citizen; m 67; c 2. PHYSICS, LONG RANGE ATMOSPHERIC DISPERSION. *Educ:* Nat Univ Ireland, BSc, 61, MSc, 63; Univ Va, PhD(physics), 73. *Prof Exp:* Res officer, Agr Inst, Dublin, 63-65; res assoc radiation physics, Med Col Va, 65-66; res asst physics, Univ Va, 68-72; res assoc, Univ Wis-Madison, 72-74; analyst comput appln, 74-77, sect head, 77-81, DEPT HEAD PHYSICS, TECH APPLN & COMPUT SCI, NUCLEAR DIV, UNION CARBIDE CORP, 81- *Mem:* Am Phys Soc; AAAS. *Res:* Applications of computers in physics; computer modeling and analysis of modeling errors; long range atmospheric transport of pollutants; nuclear and radiation physics. *Mailing Add:* Oak Ridge Nat Lab PO Box X Oak Ridge TN 37830

MURPHY, BRIAN LOGAN, b Hartford, Conn, Apr 24, 39; m 61; c 6. AIR POLLUTION, SCIENCE POLICY. *Educ:* Brown Univ, ScB, 61; Yale Univ, MS, 63, PhD(physics), 66. *Prof Exp:* Physicist, Mt Auburn Res Assocs, Inc, 65-75; cheif scientist & dep mgr, Air Qual Studies Div, 75-80, GEN MGR PHYS SCI, ENVIRON RES & TECHNOL, INC, CONCORD, 80- *Res:* Air quality diffusion modeling; fluid mechanics; meteorology; energy and environmental policy analysis. *Mailing Add:* 101 Avalon Rd Waban MA 02168

MURPHY, BRUCE DANIEL, b Denver, Colo, Mar 16, 41; m 67. REPRODUCTIVE PHYSIOLOGY. *Educ:* Colo State Univ, BSc, 65, MSc, 69; Univ Sask, PhD(physiol), 73. *Prof Exp:* Asst prof zool, Univ Idaho, 72-73; asst prof, 73-77, assoc prof, 77-82, PROF BIOL, UNIV SASK, 82- *Concurrent Pos:* Res consult, Ctr Nat Sci Invest, Cuba, 73-77; assoc mem vet physiol sci, Univ Sask. *Mem:* Soc Study Reprod; Can Physiol Soc; Can Soc Endocrinol & Metab. *Res:* Reproductive physiology of ovulation; tubal function; implantation and sexual maturation in mammals. *Mailing Add:* RR #5 Saskatoon SK S7K 3J8 Can

MURPHY, C(HARLES) H(ENRY), JR, b Chicago, Ill, Sept 1, 27; m 52; c 6. AERONAUTICAL ENGINEERING. *Educ:* Georgetown Univ, BS, 47; Johns Hopkins Univ, MA, 48, MS, 52, PhD(aeronaut), 57. *Prof Exp:* Instr, Univ Hawaii, 49-50; aeronaut res engr, Ballistic Res Labs, 50-70, chief exterior ballistic lab, 70-76, CHIEF, LAUNCH & FLIGHT DIV, BALLISTIC RES LAB, ABERDEEN PROVING GROUND, 76- *Concurrent Pos:* Vis prof, Univ Ill, 60 & Univ Va, 69. *Honors & Awards:* Mech & Control Flight Award, Am Inst Aeronaut & Astronaut, 76. *Mem:* Fel Inst Aeronaut & Astronaut. *Res:* Motion of symmetric configurations acted on by nonlinear aerodynamic forces and moments; effect of liquid payloads on projectile stability; use of vertical fire guns for upper atmosphere research. *Mailing Add:* 7806 Chapman Rd Kingsville MD 21087

MURPHY, CATHERINE MARY, b Cambridge, Mass, Oct 16, 40; m 71; c 2. DISCRETE MATHEMATICAL STRUCTURES. *Educ:* Regis Col, AB, 62; Catholic Univ Am, AM, 65, PhD(algebra), 68. *Prof Exp:* Asst prof, 66-68, ASSOC PROF MATH, PURDUE UNIV, 68- *Mem:* Math Asn Am; Am Math Soc; Soc Indust & Appl Math; Sigma Xi. *Res:* Application of permutation groups and combinatorics to the characterization of specified sets of linear rankings. *Mailing Add:* Dept Math Sci Purdue Univ Hammond IN 46323

MURPHY, CHARLES FRANKLIN, b Des Moines, Iowa, Dec 13, 33; m 61; c 1. PLANT BREEDING. *Educ:* Iowa State Univ, BS, 56, PhD(crop breeding), 61; Purdue Univ, MS, 57. *Prof Exp:* Asst prof, 60-67, assoc prof, 67-78, PROF CROP SCI, NC STATE UNIV, 78- *Concurrent Pos:* Prog coordr germplasm, USDA, 81. *Mem:* AAAS; Am Soc Agron. *Res:* Effects of diverse polygenic systems on yield; yield components and other quantitative characters in oats; small grain breeding. *Mailing Add:* Dept Crop Sci NC State Univ Raleigh NC 27650

MURPHY, CHARLES FRANKLIN, b Ithaca, NY, June 9, 40; m 63. MEDICINAL CHEMISTRY. *Educ:* Rochester Inst Technol, BS, 63; Iowa State Univ, PhD(org chem), 66. *Prof Exp:* NSF fel org chem, Inst Chem, Strasbourg, France, 66-67; sr chemist, 71-77, asst dir res, 77-79, head, Org Chem Dept, Surrey, Eng, 79-80, DIR MICROBIOL & FERMENTATION PROD RES, ELI LILLY & CO, INDIANAPOLIS, 80- *Mem:* Am Chem Soc. *Res:* Natural products chemistry; medicinal chemistry. *Mailing Add:* 307 E McCarty St Indianapolis IN 46285

MURPHY, CHARLES THORNTON, b Boston, Mass, May 20, 38; m 69; c 4. ELEMENTARY PARTICLE PHYSICS. *Educ:* Princeton Univ, AB, 59; Univ Wis, MA, 61, PhD(physics), 63. *Prof Exp:* Res assoc physics, Univ Wis, 63-64; asst prof, Univ Mich, Ann Arbor, 64-68; from asst prof to assoc prof, Carnegie-Mellon Univ, 68-73; PHYSICIST, FERMI NAT ACCELERATOR LAB, 73- *Mem:* Am Phys Soc. *Res:* Experimental high energy physics; weak interactions; bubble chamber and particle beam technology. *Mailing Add:* Fermilab Box 500 Batavia IL 60510

MURPHY, CLARENCE JOHN, b Manchester, NH, Apr 20, 34; m 60; c 3. ORGANIC CHEMISTRY, INORGANIC CHEMISTRY. *Educ:* Univ NH, BS, 55, MS, 57; Univ Buffalo, PhD(organometallic chem), 62. *Prof Exp:* Res assoc chem, Mass Inst Technol, 60-61; from asst prof to assoc prof & chmn dept, Ithaca Col, 61-69; PROF CHEM & CHMN DEPT, E STROUDSBURG STATE COL, 69- *Concurrent Pos:* NSF res vis prof, Cornell Univ, 67-69; vis scientist & chem consult, Lehigh Univ, 81- *Mem:* AAAS; Am Chem Soc; Soc Appl Spectros; Am Inst Chemists; Coblenz Soc. *Res:* Infrared spectroscopy; polymer syntheses using monomers derived from natural products. *Mailing Add:* Dept of Chem E Stroudsburg State Col East Stroudsburg PA 18301

MURPHY, CLIFFORD ELYMAN, b Blocher, Ind, Apr 2, 12; m 40; c 2. BIOLOGY. *Educ:* Hanover Col, AB, 36; Univ Ill, MS, 48; Univ Okla, PhD(limnol), 62. *Prof Exp:* Pub sch teacher, Ind, 36-44, 46-47; instr zool, Univ Ill, 47-48; from asst prof to assoc prof biol, 48-68, prof, 68-77, EMER PROF BIOL, TEX CHRISTIAN UNIV, 77-; EXEC VPRES, TALEM, INC, 76- *Mem:* AAAS; Am Soc Limnol & Oceanog; Am Micros Soc; World Maricult Soc; Am Water Resources Asn. *Res:* Ecology of impoundments; water pollution, especially industrial effluents and their effects on aquatic ecology. *Mailing Add:* 5836 Waltham Ave Ft Worth TX 76133

MURPHY, COLLIN GRISSEAU, b Dayton, Ohio, Oct 25, 40; m 62; c 2. CELL BIOLOGY, DEVELOPMENTAL BIOLOGY. *Educ:* Ohio State Univ, BS, 62; Univ Calif, Berkeley, MA, 6S, PhD(zool), 66. *Prof Exp:* Res asst zool, 66-69, asst res zoologist, 69-70, NIH trainee genetics, 70-71, NIH spec fel, 71-73, asst res geneticist, Univ Calif, Berkeley, 73-76; RES ASSOC ELECTRON MICROS, DEPT OPHTHAL, UNIV CALIF, SAN FRANCISCO, 77- *Concurrent Pos:* Lectr biol, San Francisco State Univ, 74-77. *Mem:* AAAS; Am Soc Cell Biol; Electron Micros Soc Am; Soc Develop Biol. *Res:* Developmental genetics; ultrastructure and cell biology of the vertebrate eye, glaucoma, corneal morphology; Drosophila developmental genetics; pattern formation. *Mailing Add:* Dept Ophthal Univ Calif San Francisco CA 94143

MURPHY, CORNELIUS BERNARD, b Worcester, Mass, Dec 10, 18; m 43; c 4. CHEMISTRY. *Educ:* Col of the Holy Cross, BS, 41, MS, 42; Clark Univ, PhD(chem), 52. *Prof Exp:* From instr to asst prof chem, Col of the Holy Cross, 45-52; res chemist, Stamford Labs, Am Cyanamid Co, 52-55; develop chemist, Gen Eng Lab, Gen Elec Co, 55-57, mgr anal chem, 57-58, mgr anal & phys chem, 58-63, proj engr, 63-65; mgr mat anal, 65-70, prog mgr, 70-72, mgr chem eng, 72-73, mgr toner processing, 73-75, prin scientist, 76-77, mat coordr, 76-78, CONTRIB SCIENTIST, XEROX CORP, 78- *Concurrent Pos:* Mem bd dirs, Delta Labs, NY. *Mem:* Am Chem Soc; Electrochem Soc; NY Acad Sci; Int Confedn Thermal Anal (pres, 68-71); AAAS. *Res:* Chelation; phase equilibria; differential thermal analysis. *Mailing Add:* Webster Res Ctr Xerox Corp 800 Phillips Rd Webster NY 14580

MURPHY, DANIEL BARKER, b Richmond Hill, NY, Apr 7, 28; m 51; c 4. ORGANIC CHEMISTRY, CARBON & GRAPHITE. *Educ:* Fordham Univ, BS, 47, MS, 49; Pa State Univ, PhD(fuel technol), 58. *Prof Exp:* Asst chem, Fordham Univ, 47-49; instr, Univ Scranton, 49-51; res chemist, Picatinny Arsenal, US Dept Army, 51-54; asst fuel technol, Pa State Univ, 54-57; from instr to assoc prof, 57-70, PROF CHEM, LEHMAN COL, 70- *Mem:* Am Chem Soc; Royal Soc Chem; Am Carbon Soc. *Res:* Organic synthesis; nitrogen heterocyclics; propellants and explosives; carbon and graphite; kinetics and mechanism of the formation of solid carbon by pyrolysis of hydrocarbons in a flow system. *Mailing Add:* Dept of Chem Herbert H Lehman Col Bronx NY 10468

MURPHY, DANIEL JOHN, b New York, NY, July 16, 12; m 35; c 2. PHYSICAL METALLURGY. *Educ:* US Mil Acad, BS, 35; Mass Inst Technol, MS, 39; Columbia Univ, PhD(phys metall), 52. *Prof Exp:* Head Pitman-Dunn labs, Frankford Arsenal, US Dept Army, 50-52, chief ord indust planning opers, Far East Command, 52-54; res metallurgist, Los Alamos Sci Lab, 54-57; prof, 57-80, EMER PROF, UNIV ARIZ, 80- *Concurrent Pos:* Consult, Los Alamos Sci Lab, 57- *Mem:* Sigma Xi; Am Soc Metals. *Res:* Crystal imperfections by precision density measurements; effects of alloy additions and transformation characteristics in uranium; hot laboratory metallurgy; high temperature properties of metals. *Mailing Add:* 2625 E Southern Ave Tempe AZ 85282

MURPHY, DANIEL JOHN, b Fall River, Mass, Dec 23, 35; m 61; c 3. ELECTRICAL ENGINEERING. *Educ:* Southeastern Mass Univ, BS, 60; Northeastern Univ, MS, 66, PhD(elec eng), 69. *Prof Exp:* Assoc engr, Appl Physics Lab, Johns Hopkins Univ, 60-62; instr elec eng, New Bedford Inst Technol, 62-65; from asst prof to assoc prof, 65-73, chmn dept, 70-74, PROF ELEC ENG, SOUTHEASTERN MASS UNIV, 73-, CHMN DEPT, 81- *Concurrent Pos:* Consult, Bristol Electronics, 63-65 & Naval Underwater Systs Ctr, Newport, 67-; chmn bd, Mitili, Inc, 81- *Mem:* Inst Elec & Electronics Engrs; Am Soc Eng Educ. *Res:* Linear systems; applications of optimal control and estimation theory; engineering education. *Mailing Add:* Dept of Elec Eng Southeastern Mass Univ North Dartmouth MA 02748

MURPHY, DONALD G, b New York, NY, July 14, 34; m 56; c 2. BIOMEDICAL RESEARCH, CELL BIOLOGY. *Educ:* Ore State Univ, BS, 56, PhD(nematol), 61. *Prof Exp:* NSF grant & asst prof nematol, Ore State Univ, 61-62; NIH fel & spec fel, Univ Hamburg, 62-65; res nematologist, Agr Res Serv, USDA, 65-67; grants assoc, NIH, 67; health scientist adminr, Nat Inst Child Health & Human Develop, 68-74 & Nat Inst Aging, 75-77, chief basic aging prog, Nat Inst Aging, 77-81, DIR, OFF SPEC EMPHASIS AREAS, DIGESTIVE DIS & NUTRIT PROG, NAT INST ARTHRITIS, DIABETES & DIGESTIVE KIDNEY DIS, NIH, 81- *Concurrent Pos:* Fel, Dept Path, Johns Hopkins Univ, 71-73. *Mem:* AAAS; Geront Soc; Tissue Cult Asn. *Res:* Gerontology; genetics; cellular aging; nematode phylogeny and bionomics; evolution; research administration. *Mailing Add:* Westwood Bldg Rm 606 NIH NIADDK 5333 Westbard Ave Bethesda MD 20014

MURPHY, DONALD HENRY, bioengineering, see previous edition

MURPHY, DOUGLAS BLAKENEY, b Jan 25, 45; US citizen; m 67; c 2. CELL & DEVELOPMENTAL BIOLOGY. *Educ:* Univ Rochester, AB, 67; Syracuse Univ, MS, 69; Univ Pa, PhD(biol), 73. *Prof Exp:* NIH fel molecular biol, Univ Wis, 73-76; asst prof biol, Kansas State Univ, 76-78; ASST PROF CELL BIOL & ANAT, JOHNS HOPKINS UNIV SCH MED, 78- *Mem:* Am Soc Cell Biol. *Res:* Cell biology of microtubules and cytoplasmic filaments; molecular mechanisms of cytoplasmic motility and intracellular transport. *Mailing Add:* Dept of Cell Biol & Anat 725 N Wolfe St Baltimore MD 21205

MURPHY, DOUGLAS RICHARD, b Sunapee, NH, Dec 28, 21; m 43; c 3. PLANT PATHOLOGY. *Educ:* Univ NH, BS, 49, MS, 51; Iowa State Univ, PhD(plant path), 54. *Prof Exp:* Res asst plant path, Univ NH, 49-51; tech sales mgr, 54-58, PROD MGR, AGR CHEM DIV, STAUFFER CHEM CO, 59-, GROUP PROD MGR, 73- *Mem:* Weed Sci Soc Am; Am Entom Soc. *Res:* Control of oak wilt. *Mailing Add:* Stauffer Chem Co Westport CT 06880

MURPHY, EDUARDO S, pathology, oncology, see previous edition

MURPHY, EDWARD G, b Sheffield, Eng, Dec 6, 21; Can citizen; m 47; c 1. MEDICINE, PEDIATRICS. *Educ:* Univ London, MB & BS, 45; Royal Col Physicians & Surgeons, dipl, 50; Royal Col Physicians & Surgeons Can, cert, 53; FRCPS(C), 72. *Prof Exp:* Intern med & surg, Guy's Univ, County Hosp, Pembury, Eng, 45; intern surg, St Mary's Hosp, Roehampton, 46; intern med, Edgware Gen Hosp, 49; intern, Evelina Children's Hosp, 49-50; intern med & pediat, 52-53, ELECTROENCEPHALOGRAPHER, HOSP SICK CHILDREN, TORONTO, ONT, 55-, CONSULT, 56-; ASSOC PROF MED & PEDIAT, UNIV TORONTO, 74- *Concurrent Pos:* Fel neurol serv, Hosp Sick Children, Toronto, Ont, 53-55; neurol consult, Ont Crippled Children's Ctr, 63-; assoc, Univ Toronto, 67-71, asst prof, 71-74. *Mem:* Can Med Asn; Can Pediat Soc; fel Can Soc Electroencephalog; assoc Can Neurol Soc; Brit Med Asn. *Res:* Neuromuscular disorders. *Mailing Add:* Hosp for Sick Children Toronto ON M5G 1X8 Can

MURPHY, EDWARD JOSEPH, b Moosomin, Sask, Apr 6, 98; m 34; c 1. BIOPHYSICS. *Educ:* Univ Sask, BSc, 18. *Prof Exp:* Asst, Univ Sask, 18-19 & Harvard Univ, 22-23; mem tech staff, Bell Tel Labs, Inc, 23-58; guest investr, Rockefeller Inst, 58-64; RES SCIENTIST, STANLEY-THOMPSON LAB SURFACE STUDIES, COLUMBIA UNIV, 64- *Mem:* Sigma Xi; Am Phys Soc; Biophys Soc; NY Acad Sci. *Res:* Ionic conduction and dielectric polarization in hydrogen-bonded solids; ionic conduction in water-sorbing dielectrics such as the fibrous proteins and cellulose; molecular basis for some biological processes. *Mailing Add:* 217 E 66th St New York NY 10021

MURPHY, EDWIN DANIEL, b Brooklyn, NY, July 30, 17; m 42; c 7. EXPERIMENTAL PATHOLOGY. *Educ:* St John's Univ, NY, BS, 39; Yale Univ, MD, 43. *Prof Exp:* Intern surg, New Haven Hosp & Yale Univ, 43; instr path, Col Med, Univ Tenn, 46-48; pathologist, Nat Cancer Inst, 48-53; res assoc, 53-57, sci dir, 56-57, asst dir res, 57-58, staff scientist, 57-70, SR STAFF SCIENTIST, JACKSON LAB, 70- *Concurrent Pos:* Childs fel clin & exp oncol, Sch Med, Yale Univ, 44-46; Guest prof & Fulbright sr res award, Univ Frankfurt, 63-64; Japan Soc Prom Sci fel, 73; vis scientist, Aichi Cancer Ctr Res Inst, Nagoya, Japan, 73-74; Nat Cancer Inst spec res fel, 74. *Mem:* Am Asn Cancer Res. *Res:* Experimental tumorigenesis; pathologic anatomy of inbred mice. *Mailing Add:* Jackson Lab Bar Harbor ME 04609

MURPHY, ELIZABETH WILCOX, b Ionia, Mich, Feb 11, 27; m 55; c 2. NUTRITION, FOOD CHEMISTRY. *Educ:* Cent Mich Col Educ, BS, 48; Univ Chicago, MS, 55. *Prof Exp:* Lab technician, Dept Home Econ, Univ Chicago, 48-51 & Nutrit Lab, Quaker Oats Co, Ill, 51-54; nutrit specialist, Human Nutrit Res Div, 54-56, res chemist, 56-65, res chemist, Consumer & Food Econ Inst, Agr Res Serv, 65-76, nutritionist, Meat & Poultry Standards & Labeling Div, Food Safety & Qual Serv, 76-79, CHIEF, NUTRIT BR, FOOD INGREDIENT ASSESSMENT DIV, FOOD SAFETY & INSPECTION SERV, USDA, 79- *Mem:* Am Inst Nutrit; Am Dietetic Asn; Inst Food Technol; Am Chem Soc; Soc Environ Geochem & Health. *Res:* Nutritional aspects of policies related to labeling of and standards for and poultry products. *Mailing Add:* Food Safety & Inspecting Serv USDA 300 12th St SW Washington DC 20250

MURPHY, EUGENE F(RANCIS), b Syracuse, NY, May 31, 13; m 55; c 2. MATERIALS SCIENCE ENGINEERING, SCIENCE COMMUNICATIONS. *Educ:* Cornell Univ, ME, 35; Syracuse Univ, MME, 37; Ill Inst Technol, PhD, 48. *Prof Exp:* Asst mech eng, Syracuse Univ, 35-36; mech engr, Ingersoll-Rand Co, 37-39; instr heat power, Ill Inst Technol, 39-41; from instr to asst prof mech eng, Univ Calif, 41-48; staff engr comt artificial limbs, Nat Acad Sci, Wash, 45-48; asst dir res, Prosthetic & Sensory Aids Serv, 48-54, chief res & develop div, 54-73, dir, Res Ctr Prosthetics, 73-78, DIR, OFF TECHNOL TRANSFER, VET ADMIN, 78- *Concurrent Pos:* Adv fel, Mellon Inst, 47-48; Fulbright lectr, Soc & Home for Cripples, Denmark, 57-58; actg dep dir, Rehabilitative Eng Res & Develop Serv, Vet Admin, Wash, 75-77; ed, Bulletin Prosthetics Res, 77- *Honors & Awards:*

Silver Medal, City of Paris, France, 61; Meritorious Serv Award, Vet Admin, 71. *Mem:* Nat Acad Eng; fel Am Soc Mech Engrs; Acoust Soc Am; assoc fel NY Acad Med; Am Soc Testing & Mat. *Res:* Rehabilitative engineering, including prostheses, orthoses, sensory aids, mobility aids, and surgical implants; mechanical engineering. *Mailing Add:* Off of Technol Transfer Vet Admin 252 Seventh Ave New York NY 10001

MURPHY, FREDERICK A, b New York, NY, June 14, 34; m 60; c 4. VIROLOGY, IMMUNOLOGY. *Educ:* Cornell Univ, BS, 57, DVM, 59; Univ Calif, Davis, PhD(comp path), 64. *Prof Exp:* Chief viral path br, Ctr Dis Control, HEW, 64-78; ASSOC DEAN, COL VET MED & BIOMED SCI, COLO STATE UNIV, FT COLLINS, 78- *Concurrent Pos:* Mem, Int Comt Taxonomy of Viruses; chmn, Am Comt Arthropod-borne Viruses; hon fel, John Curtin Sch Med Res, Australian Nat Univ, 70-71; chmn virol div, Int Union Microbiol Socs, 81-84; chmn prog comt, Fifth Int Cong Virol, 78-81. *Mem:* Am Soc Virol; Am Asn Immunol; Soc Exp Biol & Med; Am Soc Microbiol; Infectious Dis Soc Am. *Res:* Pathogenesis of viral diseases and encephalitis; electron microscopy; veterinary medicine; viral ultrastructure. *Mailing Add:* Off of the Dean Colo State Univ Ft Collins CO 80523

MURPHY, FREDERICK VERNON, b Washington, DC, Mar 26, 38; m 65; c 2. EXPERIMENTAL PHYSICS. *Educ:* Georgetown Univ, BS, 59; Princeton Univ, MA, 61, PhD(physics), 67. *Prof Exp:* Instr physics, Princeton Univ, 66-67; asst res physicist, Univ Calif, Santa Barbara, 67-75; mem staff, Varian Assoc Inc, Palo Alto, 75-80, mgr, Res X-ray Imaging Div, 77-80; RES SCIENTIST, TELESENSORY SYSTS, INC, 80- *Res:* Technology for the handicapped; tactile displays; elementary particle physics; K meson scattering and decays; photoproduction and total photon cross sections; counters; spark and streamer chamber techniques; x-ray computerized tomography; secondary particle beam design. *Mailing Add:* 430 Sherwood Way Menlo Park CA 94025

MURPHY, GEORGE EARL, b Portland, Ore, Oct 17, 22; c 2. PSYCHIATRY. *Educ:* Ore State Univ, BS, 49; Washington Univ, MD, 52. *Prof Exp:* From intern to asst resident med, Highland-Alameda County Hosp, Oakland, Calif, 52-54; fel psychosom med, Sch Med, Washington Univ, 54-55; clin & res fel psychiat, Mass Gen Hosp, 55-56; asst resident, Renard Hosp, Barnes Hosp Group, St Louis, Mo, 56-57; from instr to assoc prof, 57-69, PROF PSYCHIAT, SCH MED, WASHINGTON UNIV, 69-, DIR PSYCHIAT OUTPATIENT DEPT, 76- *Concurrent Pos:* Consult forensic psychiat, St Louis County Med Exam Off, 74-79, forensic psychiatrist, 79- *Mem:* Fel Am Psychiat Asn; Psychiat Res Soc; Am Psychopath Asn; Sigma Xi. *Res:* Clinical and epidemiologic studies in suicide, alcoholism, drug addiction, affective disorder and life stress; problems of psychotherapy. *Mailing Add:* Dept Psychiat Sch Med Wash Univ St Louis MO 63110

MURPHY, GEORGE EDWARD, b Kansas City, Mo, Aug 22, 18; m 43. EXPERIMENTAL PATHOLOGY. *Educ:* Univ Kans, AB, 39; Univ Pa, MD, 43. *Prof Exp:* Intern, Univ Kans Hosp, 43; asst resident & res pathologist, Hosp & asst path, Sch Med, Johns Hopkins Univ, 44-45; asst physician, Rockefeller Inst Hosp, 46-53; assoc prof path, Med Col, Cornell Univ, 53-68; assoc attend pathologist, 61-67, ATTEND PATHOLOGIST, NY HOSP, 68-, PROF PATH, MED COL, CORNELL UNIV, 68- *Concurrent Pos:* Mem coun on arteriosclerosis & coun cardiovasc dis of the young, Am Heart Asn; Life Ins Med Res Fund fel rheumatic fever, 46-49; Helen Hay Whitney Found fel rheumatic fever, 49-53; Lederle med fac award, 54-57. *Honors & Awards:* William Osler Medal, Am Asn Hist Med, 43. *Mem:* Am Asn Path; Soc Exp Biol & Med; Harvey Soc; NY Acad Med; NY Acad Sci. *Res:* Experimental and histopathologic studies on nature of rheumatic fever, especially rheumatic heart disease, glomerulonephritis, and arteriosclerosis; medical education. *Mailing Add:* Dept of Path Cornell Univ Med Col New York NY 10021

MURPHY, GEORGE GRAHAM, b Clarksville, Tenn, Aug 31, 43; div; c 1. HERPETOLOGY. *Educ:* Austin Peay State Univ, BS, 65; Miss State Univ, MS, 67, PhD(zool), 70. *Prof Exp:* Assoc prof, 69-80, PROF BIOL & CHMN DEPT, MID TENN STATE UNIV, 80- *Mem:* Sigma Xi; Soc Study Amphibians & Reptiles; Herpetologist's League; Am Soc Ichthyologists & Herpetologists. *Res:* Behavior of turtles; reproductive biology of turtles. *Mailing Add:* Dept of Biol Mid Tenn State Univ Murfreesboro TN 37130

MURPHY, GEORGE WASHINGTON, b Hot Springs, Ark, Jan 2, 19; m 45, 67; c 4. PHYSICAL CHEMISTRY. *Educ:* Univ Ark, AB, 40; Univ NC, PhD(phys chem), 46. *Prof Exp:* Asst chem, Univ NC, 40-42; res chemist, US Naval Res Lab, 42-45; from instr to asst prof chem, Univ Wis, 46-51; assoc chemist, Argonne Nat Lab, 51-53; prof chem & chmn dept, State Univ NY Col Teachers, Albany, 53-56; assoc prof, 56-59, chmn dept, 60-68, PROF CHEM, UNIV OKLA, 59- *Mem:* Am Chem Soc; Electrochem Soc. *Res:* Theory of solutions; thermodynamics; photochemical conversion of solar energy; electrochemistry. *Mailing Add:* Dept Chem Univ Okla Norman OK 73019

MURPHY, GORDON J, b Milwaukee, Wis, Feb 16, 27; m 48; c 2. ELECTRICAL ENGINEERING, COMPUTER SCIENCE. *Educ:* Milwaukee Sch Eng, BS, 49; Univ Wis, MS, 52; Univ Minn, PhD, 56. *Prof Exp:* Asst prof elec eng, Milwaukee Sch Eng, 49-51; syst engr automatic control & inertial guid, AC Spark Plug Div, Gen Motors Corp, 51-52; from instr to asst prof elec eng, Univ Minn, 52-57; assoc prof, 57-60, chmn dept, 60-70, PROF ELEC ENG, NORTHWESTERN UNIV, EVANSTON, 60- *Concurrent Pos:* Consult, Aeronaut Div, Minneapolis-Honeywell Regulator Co, 54-57 & AC Spark Plug Div, Gen Motors Corp, 59-62. *Mem:* fel Inst Elec & Electronics Engrs. *Res:* Automatic control; analog and digital computers; digital systems; solid state motor drives. *Mailing Add:* Dept of Elec Eng Northwestern Univ Evanston IL 60201

MURPHY, GRATTAN PATRICK, b Parsons, Kans, Sept 15, 35; m 61; c 3. MATHEMATICS. *Educ:* Rockhurst Col, BS, 57; St Louis Univ, MS, 62, PhD(math), 66. *Prof Exp:* Tech analyst comput prog & data reduction, McDonnell Aircraft Co, 59-61; instr math, St Louis Univ, 62-65; from asst prof to assoc prof, 65-81, PROF MATH, UNIV MAINE, ORONO, 81- *Concurrent Pos:* Guest prof, Univ Freiburg, 71-72. *Mem:* Am Math Soc; Math Asn Am. *Res:* Geometry of generalized metric spaces. *Mailing Add:* Dept of Math Univ of Maine Orono ME 04473

MURPHY, HENRY D, b Hartshorne, Okla, Mar 21, 29. HISTOLOGY, ANATOMY. *Educ:* Univ Calif, Berkeley, AB, 58, MA, 60; Univ Calif, San Francisco, PhD(anat), 65. *Prof Exp:* From asst prof to assoc prof anat & physiol, 65-77, PROF BIOL, SAN JOSE STATE UNIV, 77- *Res:* Endocrine research on role of follicle stimulating hormone on the testes of rats; comparative histological study of marine mammals, seals, sea-lions, porpoises and various whales. *Mailing Add:* Dept of Biol San Jose State Univ San Jose CA 95114

MURPHY, JAMES A, b Philadelphia, Pa, July 28, 35; m 63; c 4. PHYSICAL CHEMISTRY, SURFACE CHEMISTRY. *Educ:* St Joseph's Col, BS, 57; Iowa State Univ, PhD(phys chem), 63. *Prof Exp:* Sr chemist, 63-66, res chemist, 66-69, sr res chemist, 69-72, proj leader, 72-76, RES ASSOC, CORNING GLASS WORKS, 76- *Concurrent Pos:* Ed, Newsletter, Corning Sect, Am Chem Soc, 74-80. *Mem:* Am Chem Soc; Am Inst Chemists. *Res:* Materials research, especially thin films; surface chemistry and the interaction of solid, liquids and gases with solids; optical wave guide process research. *Mailing Add:* 106 Fairview Ave Painted Post NY 14870

MURPHY, JAMES CLAIR, b Salt Lake City, Utah, July 29, 31. PATHOLOGY. *Educ:* Utah State Univ, BS, 57; Wash State Univ, DVM, 61; Colo State Univ, PhD(path), 66. *Prof Exp:* Fel path, Col Vet Med, Colo State Univ, 62-66; res fel, Harvard Med Sch, 66-67; pathologist, Hazleton Labs, Va, 67-68, supvr teratol sect, 67-68; instr, Sch Med, Tufts Univ, 68-74, asst prof surg, 74-75; VET PATHOLOGIST MED DEPT & DIR RES ANIMAL LAB, DIV LAB ANIMAL MED, MASS INST TECHNOL, 75- *Concurrent Pos:* Mem spec sci staff, New Eng Med Ctr Hosps, 68-75, vet & dir res animal lab, 70-75. *Mem:* Am Vet Med Asn; Am Col Vet Path; Int Acad Path. *Res:* Pathogenesis of infectious diseases. *Mailing Add:* Div Lab Animal Med Mass Inst Technol Cambridge MA 02139

MURPHY, JAMES FRANCIS, b Lethbridge, Alta, Aug 19, 22; nat US; m 49; c 4. PHYSICAL CHEMISTRY. *Educ:* Univ Alta, BS, 45, MS, 46; Univ Calif, PhD(chem), 50. *Prof Exp:* Asst prof chem, Univ Idaho, 49-51; res chemist, Dept Metall Res, Kaiser Aluminum & Chem Corp, 51-55; mgr phys chem, Gen Eng Lab, Gen Elec Co, 55-58; chief chem sect, Metall Labs, Olin Mathieson Chem Corp, 58-66; res assoc, Kaiser chem Res Labs, 66-68, lab mgr, 68-71; mgr chem res, 71-75, ASST RES DIR, KAISER ALUMINUM & CHEM CORP, 75- *Mem:* Am Chem Soc; Electrochem Soc; Int Soc Gen Semantics. *Res:* Surface chemistry and physics; electrochemistry; inorganic chemistry; corrosion and finishing reactions; welding and fusion reactions; adhesion. *Mailing Add:* Kaiser Aluminum & Chem Corp PO Box 877 Pleasanton CA 94566

MURPHY, JAMES GILBERT, b Brooklyn, NY, July 25, 19; m 47; c 8. ORGANIC CHEMISTRY. *Educ:* St Francis Col, NY, BS, 47; Polytech Inst Brooklyn, MS, 50; Georgetown Univ, PhD(chem), 59. *Prof Exp:* Asst chemist, Nat Oil Prod Co, NJ, 40-42; chemist, Evans Res & Develop Corp, NY, 45-51; res chemist, NIH, 52-71; CONSULT CHEMIST, 72- *Mem:* Am Chem Soc. *Res:* Organic sulfur compounds; medicinal chemistry; biological substrates. *Mailing Add:* 829 Robert St Venice FL 33595

MURPHY, JAMES JOHN, b Scranton, Pa, Apr 1, 39; m 69; c 2. TOXICOLOGY. *Educ:* Lafayette Col, AB, 61; St John's Univ, MA, 66; Temple Univ, PhD(physiol/biophys), 79; Am Bd Toxicol, dipl, 80. *Prof Exp:* Asst prof psychol, Bloomsburg State Col, 67-70; fel, Temple Univ Health Sci Ctr, 70-74, lectr anat & physiol, 75; toxicologist, Stanford Res Inst, 76-78; TOXICOLOGIST, OFF TOXIC SUBSTANCE, US ENVIRON PROTECTION AGENCY, 79- *Concurrent Pos:* Lab instr physiol & histol, Pa Col Podiat Med, 73-75; consult, indust hyg & toxicol, 78. *Mem:* Soc Toxicol; Soc Risk Analysis. *Res:* Hazard identification and risk assessment; industrial toxicology; hydrogen sulfide as a geothermal and petrochemical air pollutant; gastrointestinal models of adrenergic pharmacology, cell cycle in tumors. *Mailing Add:* 12802 Colby Dr Woodbridge VA 22192

MURPHY, JAMES JOSEPH, b New York, NY, Apr 29, 38; m 61; c 3. EXPERIMENTAL SOLID STATE PHYSICS. *Educ:* St Joseph's Col, Pa, BS, 59; Fordham Univ, MS, 61, PhD(physics), 71. *Prof Exp:* From instr to assoc prof, 61-76, chmn dept, 66-75, PROF PHYSICS, IONA COL, 76-, DIR ACAD DEVELOP SCI & TECHNOL, 82- *Concurrent Pos:* Mem adj fac, Bergen Community Col, 69-76. *Mem:* AAAS; Am Asn Physics Teachers; NY Acad Sci. *Res:* Magnetism in transition metals; spin echo studies of ferromagnetic alloys. *Mailing Add:* Dept of Physics Iona Col New Rochelle NY 10801

MURPHY, JAMES L, b Pasadena, Calif, May 21, 27; m 55; c 4. FOREST ECONOMICS, FORESTRY. *Educ:* Utah State Univ, BS, 58, MS, 59; Univ Mich, PhD(forest mgt-econ), 65. *Prof Exp:* Fire control aid, US Forest Serv, 45-48, forester, 58-61, res forester, Calif, 61-68, proj leader forest fire sci proj, Wash, 68-71, asst to dep chief res, Washington, DC, 71-74, proj leader nat forest fire prev proj, 73-74; MEM STAFF, PAC SOUTHWEST EXP STA, US FOREST SERV, 74- *Concurrent Pos:* Assoc prof, Col Forest Resources, Univ Wash, 68-; consult, US Peace Corps, 71 & Repub Chile, 71-; chmn, Nat Interagency Wildfire Prev Anal Task Force, 73-74. *Mem:* AAAS; Soc Am Foresters. *Res:* Forest fire research and economics; wildfire prevention; evaluation systems; early warning systems; behavioral studies. *Mailing Add:* 5605 Daukie Ave Ewa Beach HI 96706

MURPHY, JAMES LEE, b Grand Ledge, Mich, Aug 29, 40; m 65; c 4. MATHEMATICS. *Educ:* Univ Detroit, BA, 64; Mich State Univ, MS, 66, PhD(math), 70. *Prof Exp:* Admin asst math, Mich State Univ, 66-69, instr, 69-70; asst prof math, Calif State Col, San Bernardino, 70-80; ASST PROF MATH, CALIF STATE UNIV, CHICO, 80- *Mem:* Math Asn Am. *Res:* Piecewise linear topology in Euclidean four-space. *Mailing Add:* Dept Math Calif State Univ Chico CA 92929

MURPHY, JAMES SLATER, b New York, NY, June 2, 21; m 48, 64; c 6. MICROBIOLOGY. *Educ:* Johns Hopkins Univ, MD, 45. *Prof Exp:* Intern med, Johns Hopkins Univ, 45-46; USPHS fel, 48-50, Am Cancer Soc fel, 50-51; from asst to asst prof, 51-60, ASSOC PROF VIROL & MED, ROCKEFELLER UNIV, 60- *Mem:* AAAS; Soc Exp Biol & Med; Am Soc Microbiol; Harvey Soc; Am Asn Immunologists. *Res:* Virology; influenza; virus development cycle; genetics; mammalian cell cycle kinetics; bacteriophage; aging and nutrition of Crustacea. *Mailing Add:* 177 E 64th St New York NY 10021

MURPHY, JOHN CORNELIUS, b Wilmington, Del, Feb 28, 36; m 58; c 7. PHYSICS. *Educ:* Cath Univ Am, BA, 57, PhD(physics), 71; Univ Notre Dame, MS, 59. *Prof Exp:* Prin res assoc, Dept Mat, Sci & Eng, 80, PHYSICIST, APPL PHYSICS LAB, JOHNS HOPKINS UNIV, 59- *Mem:* Am Phys Soc; Optical Soc Am. *Res:* Microwave-optical double resonance experiments on excitation migration in solids; photocatalysis; elastic wave propagation in soils using electro-optical methods; photo acoustic spectroscopy; electron spin resonance of electro generated radical ions in solution, including double resonance in chemiluminescence; photothermal imaging; corrosion. *Mailing Add:* Johns Hopkins Appl Physics Lab Johns Hopkins Rd Laurel MD 20707

MURPHY, JOHN FRANCIS, b Cranston, RI, Aug 27, 22; m 45; c 2. GEOLOGY. *Educ:* Dartmouth Col, AB, 47, AM, 49. *Prof Exp:* Geologist, 51-65, chief org fuels br, Colo, 65-66, geologist, Heavy Metals Br, 67-68, dep assoc chief geologist, 68-72, dep chief off energy resources, US Geol Surv, Potomac Md, 72-77; MEM STAFF, OFF ENERGY RESOURCES, US GEOL SURV, DENVER, 77- *Mem:* AAAS; Geol Soc Am; Am Asn Petrol Geologists; Soc Econ Geologists. *Res:* Structural geology; stratigraphy; petrology. *Mailing Add:* US Geol Surv Denver Fed Ctr MS 937 Denver CO 80225

MURPHY, JOHN JOSEPH, b Tucson, Ariz, July 28, 40; m 64; c 4. BIOCHEMISTRY, PESTICIDE METABOLISM. *Educ:* Univ Ariz, BS, 62, MS, 63; Purdue Univ, Lafayette, PhD(biochem), 66. *Prof Exp:* NSF fel, King's Col, Univ London, 66-67; res biochemist, Agr Res Ctr, Stauffer Chem Co, Calif, 67-74; SR RES BIOCHEMIST, CHEMAGRO AGR DIV, MOBAY CHEM CORP, 74- *Mem:* Am Chem Soc; Am Inst Biol Sci; Am Soc Plant Physiologists; Am Soc Agron; Weed Sci Soc Am. *Res:* Metabolism and mechanisms of action of pesticides in plants, animals and soil. *Mailing Add:* Mobay Chem Corp PO Box 4913 Kansas City MO 64120

MURPHY, JOHN JOSEPH, b New York, NY, July 10, 34; m 65; c 2. ORGANIC POLYMER CHEMISTRY, PHOTOCHEMISTRY. *Educ:* Manhattan Col, BS, 56; Niagara Univ, MS, 58. *Prof Exp:* Res chemist, E I du Pont de Nemours & Co, Inc, 62-69; SR RES ASSOC CHEM, INT PAPER CO, 69- *Mem:* Am Chem Soc. *Res:* Investigation of polymeric systems, curable by high energy radiation sources, mainly ultraviolet and electron beam with application of these systems to organic coatings, inks. *Mailing Add:* Int Paper Co Corp Res Ctr Tuxedo Park NY 10987

MURPHY, JOHN JOSEPH, b Scranton, Pa, Oct 2, 20; m 44; c 6. UROLOGY, SURGERY. *Educ:* Univ Scranton, BS, 42; Univ Pa, MD, 45. *Prof Exp:* Asst instr surg, Harrison Dept Surg Res, Sch Med, Univ Pa, 48-52; sr instr surg, Dept Urol, Sch Med, Univ Mich, 52-53; assoc urol, Hosp, 53-56, instr, 56-58, from asst prof to assoc prof, 56-64, PROF UROL, SCH MED, UNIV PA, 64- *Concurrent Pos:* Fel, Harrison Dept Surg Res, Sch Med, Univ Pa, 48-51, Am Cancer Soc fel, 51-52; Harrison fel urol surg & Am Cancer Soc fel, Dept Urol, Sch Med, Univ Mich, 52-53; Ravidin traveling fel, 52-53; consult urologist, Vet Admin Hosp, 53- & Children's Seashore House, Atlantic City, NJ; consult, Univ Hosp, Pa. *Mem:* Am Soc Exp Path; Am Surg Asn; Am Urol Asn; Am Col Surg; Am Asn Genito-Urinary Surg. *Res:* Lymphatic system of the kidney; hydrodynamics of the urinary tract; hypertension as related to the kidney; renal healing; pyelonephritis; cineradiography in urology. *Mailing Add:* Div of Urol Univ of Pa Sch of Med Philadelphia PA 19104

MURPHY, JOHN MICHAEL, b Madison, Wis, May 30, 35; m 59; c 4. MECHANICAL & AERONAUTICAL ENGINEERING. *Educ:* Purdue Univ, BS, 57, MS, 59, PhD(mech eng), 64. *Prof Exp:* Asst, Jet Propulsion Ctr, Purdue Univ, 55-56, asst aeronaut eng, 57-59, asst & instr mech eng, 60-64; tech opers officer, Missile & Space Off, US Army Eng Res & Develop Labs, Ft Belvoir, Va, 59-60; sr engr & prin engr, Thiokol Chem Corp, Ala, 64; chief tech group, air augmented rocket task team, 64-66; sr res scientist, air augmented rocket studies, Martin Co, 66-69; sr res scientist, Propulsion Systs Res & Develop, 69-73, mgr external tank propulsion, 73-75, mgr amine fuels, 75-78, mgr propulsion eng, 78-79, mgr space shuttle reaction control syst propellnt tanks, 79-81, MGR PROPELLANT SYSTS, MARTIN MARIETTA CORP, 81- *Concurrent Pos:* Asst prof, Univ Ala, 64-66; lectr, Univ Colo, 67-; mem, Joint Army-Navy-NASA-Air Force Air Augmented Performance Comt; consult, Baumgartner Co, 73- *Honors & Awards:* Thomas Jefferson Award, Martin Marietta Corp, 68. *Mem:* Assoc fel Am Inst Aeronaut & Astronaut; Combustion Inst; Am Inst Chem Engrs. *Res:* Liaison and design of large space environment simulator; means of reclaiming water in space; radial flow turbines; chemical laser mixing dynamics; rocket combustion; air augmented rocket technology; liquid and solid rocket fuel combustion; liquid propellant feed systems. *Mailing Add:* 6185 W Summit Dr Littleton CO 80123

MURPHY, JOHN N, b Pittsburgh, Pa, July 14, 39; m 62. MINING ENGINEERING, ELECTRICAL ENGINEERING. *Educ:* Univ Pittsburgh, BS, 61; Duquesne Univ, MBA, 67. *Prof Exp:* Res supvr indust hazards & commun, 61-78, RES DIR, PITTSBURGH RES CTR, US BUR MINES, 78- *Mem:* Sr mem Inst Elec & Electronics Engrs; Am Inst Mining, Metall & Petrol Engrs. *Res:* Surface and underground mines: dust control, life support, fires and explosions, methane control and ventilation, roof support, industrial type hazards and communications, explosives, and environmental problems such as acid mine drainage, subsidence, mine closure, reclamation and abandoned mine fire control. *Mailing Add:* US Bur Mines Cochrans Mill Rd PO Box 18070 Pittsburgh PA 15236

MURPHY, JOHN RICHARD, organic chemistry, see previous edition

MURPHY, JOHN RIFFE, b Hooker, Okla, Apr 12, 42; m 62; c 3. EXPERIMENTAL STATISTICS. *Educ:* Panhandle State Col, BS, 64; Okla State Univ, MS, 67, PhD(statist), 73. *Prof Exp:* Math statistician, Control Systs Div, Environ Protection Agency, Research Triangle Park, NC, 71-72; SR STATISTICIAN, ELI LILLY & CO, 74- *Concurrent Pos:* Lectr statist, Butler Univ, 75. *Mem:* Am Statist Asn; Biomet Soc. *Res:* Development and study of statistical procedures for obtaining an objective grouping in a set of observed means, especially multiple decision procedures. *Mailing Add:* Eli Lilly & Co Dept MC730 307 EMcCarty St Indianapolis IN 46285

MURPHY, JOHN THOMAS, b Yonkers, NY, Mar 14, 38; c 4. MEDICAL PHYSIOLOGY, NEUROLOGY. *Educ:* Columbia Univ, MD, 63; McGill Univ, PhD(neurol & neurosurg), 68. *Prof Exp:* Intern med, Columbia Univ, 63-64, resident surg, 64-65; fel electroencephalography & clin neurophysiol, Montreal Neurol Inst, McGill Univ, 65-66, res fel neurol & neurosurg, 65-68, lectr physiol, 68; asst prof, State Univ NY, 68-70; assoc prof, 70-73, PROF PHYSIOL, UNIV TORONTO, 73-, CHMN DEPT, 75- *Concurrent Pos:* Invited res lectr, Int Conf Nat Ctr Sci Res, Aix-Marseille, 74. *Mem:* Am Physiol Soc; Can Physiol Soc; Soc Neurosci; Int Brain Res Orgn; Can Soc Electroencephalographers, Electromyographers & Clin Neurophysiologists. *Res:* Brain mechanisms in control of voluntary movement. *Mailing Add:* Dept Physiol Univ Toronto Toronto ON M5S 1A8 Can

MURPHY, JOSEPH, b Montreal, Que, Nov 6, 32; m 58; c 2. SOLID STATE PHYSICS. *Educ:* McGill Univ, BSc, 56, MSc, 58, PhD(physics), 63. *Prof Exp:* Sr physicist, US Naval Ord Lab, Calif, 60-63; sr physicist, Solid State Sci Dept, 63-70, SR PHYSICIST, PHYSICS DEPT, WESTINGHOUSE RES & DEVELOP CTR, 70- *Mem:* Am Phys Soc. *Res:* Theoretical nuclear physics; microwave and optical properties of solids; theory of interaction of localized defects with each other and with lattice vibrations. *Mailing Add:* Westinghouse R&D Ctr Physics Dept 401 4621 Beulah Rd Pittsburgh PA 15235

MURPHY, JOSEPH FRANCIS, b Riverside, Ill, Apr 15, 48; m 70; c 3. CONTINUUM MECHANICS, TRANSPORT PHENOMENA. *Educ:* Northwestern Univ, BS, 70, MS, 73, PhD(theoret appl mech), 76. *Prof Exp:* Res engr fracture mech, 76-80, RES ENGR & PROJ LEADER CREEP-RUPTURE, FOREST PROD LAB, USDA FOREST SERV, 80- *Mem:* Am Soc Civil Engrs. *Res:* Fracture and solid mechanics of anisotropic, nonhomogenous viscoelastic material. *Mailing Add:* Forest Prod Lab USDA Forest Serv Gifford Pinchot Dr Madison WI 53705

MURPHY, JOSEPH ROBISON, b Salt Lake City, Utah, June 14, 25; m 46; c 5. ZOOLOGY. *Educ:* Brigham Young Univ, AB, 50, MA, 51; Univ Nebr, PhD(zool), 57. *Prof Exp:* From instr to asst prof zool, Univ Nebr, 51-60; from asst prof to assoc prof, 60-68, chmn dept, 68-74, PROF ZOOL, BRIGHAM YOUNG UNIV, 68- *Mem:* Raptor Res Found (pres, 74-78); Sigma Xi; Cooper Ornith Soc; Am Ornithologists Union. *Res:* Ecology of predatory birds, especially American eagles. *Mailing Add:* Dept of Zool 167 WIDB Brigham Young Univ Provo UT 84602

MURPHY, JUNEANN WADSWORTH, b Chickasha, Okla, Mar 13, 37; m 67; c 2. MEDICAL MICROBIOLOGY, IMMUNOLOGY. *Educ:* Univ Okla, BS, 59, MSS, 61, MS, 65, PhD(microbiol), 69. *Prof Exp:* Res asst, Sch Med, Tulane Univ, 59; med technologist, Cent State Hosp, 61, instr, 63-64; res asst med mycol, 62-63, vis asst prof, 69-70, asst prof, 70-81, ASSOC PROF MICROBIOL, UNIV OKLA, 81-, DIR MED TECHNOL, 78- *Concurrent Pos:* Vis asst prof clin immunol, Univ Colo Health Sci Ctr, 80. *Mem:* Am Soc Microbiol; Med Mycol Soc Am; Am Soc Med Technol. *Res:* Host-parasite relationships in systemic mycotic diseases, with a primary interest in host defense mechanisms and their regulation in Cryptococcosis. *Mailing Add:* Dept of Bot-Microbiol Univ of Okla 770 Van Vleet Oval Norman OK 73069

MURPHY, KEITH LAWSON, b Toronto, Ont, June 12, 32; m 53; c 4. SANITARY ENGINEERING. *Educ:* Univ Toronto, BASc, 54; Univ Wis, MSc, 59, PhD(civil eng), 61. *Prof Exp:* Jr design engr, City of Hamilton, Can, 54-55; asst proj engr, Greater Winnipeg Water & Sanit Dist, 55-57; instr civil eng, Univ Wis, 58-59, proj assoc, 59-60; from asst prof to assoc prof, 61-71, PROF CIVIL ENG, MCMASTER UNIV, 71- *Concurrent Pos:* Vis prof, Univ Newcastle, 67-68. *Mem:* Am Water Works Asn; Water Pollution Control Fedn; Chem Inst Can; Am Soc Civil Engrs. *Res:* Process of water and waste water treatment involving phase separation and biological treatments; effects of flow patterns. *Mailing Add:* Dept of Chem Eng McMaster Univ Hamilton ON L8S 4K1 Can

MURPHY, KENNETH ROBERT, b Oneonta, NY, Oct 13, 40; m 80; c 1. ENVIRONMENTAL ENGINEERING, ATMOSPHERIC SCIENCE. *Educ:* Syracuse Univ, AB, 62; Rensselaer Polytech Inst, MS, 64, PhD(environ eng), 69. *Prof Exp:* Res engr, Dow Chem Co, 68-69; air pollution control engr, Real Estate Div, 69-72, sr proj engr, Serv Eng Div, 72-77, sr environ engr, Energy Systs Div, 77-81, MGR, ADVAN DEVELOP PROJ, GEN ELEC ENVIRON SERV INC, GEN ELEC CO, 81- *Mem:* AAAS; Air Pollution Control Asn; Am Chem Soc; Water Pollution Control Fedn. *Res:* Advanced systems for measurement and control of atmospheric emissions from energy utilization processes. *Mailing Add:* Gen Elec Environ Serv Inc 200 N 7th St Lebanon PA 17072

MURPHY, LARRY S, b Greenfield, Mo, Dec 15, 37; m 59; c 2. AGRONOMY, PLANT PHYSIOLOGY. *Educ:* Univ Mo, BS, 59, MS, 60, PhD(agron), 65. *Prof Exp:* Instr soils, Univ Mo, 60-65; from asst prof to prof agron, Kans State Univ, 65-78; GREAT PLAINS DIR, POTASH & PHOSPHATE INST, 78- *Concurrent Pos:* Res assoc, Mich State Univ, 71-72. *Honors & Awards:* Geigy Award, Am Soc Agron, 73. *Mem:* Hon mem Nat Fertilizer Solutions Asn; fel Am Soc Agron; fel Soil Sci Soc Am. *Res:* Nitrate accumulation in forage crops and water supplies; wheat, corn, grain sorghum, forage production and quality; micronutrient nutrition of plants; evaluation of P fertilizers; water pollution; animal waste disposal. *Mailing Add:* 200 Res Dr Manhattan KS 66502

MURPHY, LEA FRANCES, b Hutchinson, Kans, Dec 11, 54. POPULATION DYNAMICS, CONTINUUM MECHANICS. *Educ:* Temple Univ, BA, 76; Carnegie-Mellon Univ, MS & PhD(math), 80. *Prof Exp:* Res asst, Math Dept, Carnegie-Mellon Univ, 76-80; ASST PROF MATH, ORE STATE UNIV, 80- *Concurrent Pos:* Res asst, Mech Dept, Johns Hopkins Unvi, 79; mathematician, Naval Undersea Warfare Eng Sta, 81. *Mem:* Am Math Soc; Soc Indust & Appl Math; Soc Natural Philos. *Res:* Continuous mathematical modeling of biological phenomenon, including harvesting of age structured populations and variation of individual growth rates within age structured populations. *Mailing Add:* Dept Math Ore State Univ Corvallis OR 97331

MURPHY, LESLIE CARLTON, b Mercer, NDak, May 28, 13; m 38; c 3. MICROBIOLOGY. *Educ:* Univ Idaho, BS, 35; State Col Wash, DVM, 39; Am Bd Vet Prev Med, dipl, 69. *Prof Exp:* Asst vet, Western Wash Exp Sta, 39-40; res vet, Carnation Res Labs, Wis, 40; vis investr, Rockefeller Inst, NY, 49-50, chief dept bact, Vet Div, Walter Reed Army Inst Res, Washington, DC, 53-58, chief br IV, Virus & Rockettsia Div, 58-61; head cancer virol sect, Virol Res Resources Br, Nat Cancer Inst, 61-64; dir res develop, 64-68, assoc dean res & develop, 68-78, EMER ASSOC DEAN & EMER PROF, COL VET MED, UNIV MO-COLUMBIA, 79- *Mem:* Am Vet Med Asn; Conf Res Workers Animal Dis; Conf Pub Health Vets; Am Col Vet Microbiol; Am Asn Lab Animal Sci. *Res:* Veterinary medicine. *Mailing Add:* W203 Vet Med Univ Mo Col Vet Med Columbia MO 65201

MURPHY, MARJORY BETH, b Page, Nebr, July 21, 25. CELL PHYSIOLOGY, BIOCHEMISTRY. *Educ:* Nebr Wesleyan Univ, BA, 47; Univ Colo, MA, 53; Univ Ill, PhD(cell physiol), 61. *Prof Exp:* PROF CHEM, PHILLIPS UNIV, 53- *Mem:* AAAS. *Res:* Enzymes involved in membrane transport; active sites of enzymes. *Mailing Add:* Dept of Chem Phillips Univ Enid OK 73701

MURPHY, MARTIN JOSEPH, JR, b Colorado Springs, Colo, Dec 29, 42; m 65; c 5. EXPERIMENTAL HEMATOLOGY. *Educ:* Regis Col, Colo, BS, 64; NY Univ, MS, 67, PhD(physiol, hemat), 69. *Prof Exp:* Reader & lect asst, Grad Sch Arts & Sci, NY Univ, 65-68; instr biol, Nassau Community Col, 68-69; asst mem, St Jude Children's Res Hosp, Memphis, 73-75; assoc, Sloan-Kettering Inst Cancer Res, 75-79; ASSOC PROF MED, SCH MED, WRIGHT STATE UNIV, DAYTON, OHIO, 79- *Concurrent Pos:* Damon Runyon res fel, Inst Cellular Path, Hopital Bicetre, Kremlin-Bicetre, France, 69-70; NIH res fel, Paterson Labs, Christie Hosp & Holt Radium Inst, Manchester, Eng, 70-71; Leukemia Soc Am spec fel immunol, John Curtin Sch Med Res, Australian Nat Univ, 71-73; dir hemat training prog, Sloan-Kettering Inst Cancer Res & Bob Hipple Lab Cancer Res, Mem Sloan-Kettering Cancer Ctr, 77-79; dir, Bob Hipple Lab Cancer Res, Dayton, Ohio, 79- *Mem:* NY Acad Sci; Electron Micros Soc Am; Soc Exp Biol & Med; Am Asn Cancer Res; Sigma Xi. *Res:* Physiology of blood cell production in health and disease. *Mailing Add:* Bob Hipple Lab Cancer Res 3525 Southern Blvd Dayton OH 45429

MURPHY, MARY ELLEN, b Hartford, Conn, Sept 10, 28. GEOCHEMISTRY, ANALYTICAL CHEMISTRY. *Educ:* St Joseph Col, Conn, BS, 50; Wesleyan Univ, MA, 56; Fordham Univ, PhD(chem), 65. *Hon Degrees:* DSc, Univ Hartford, 75. *Prof Exp:* Chemist, Naugatuck Chem Div, US Rubber Co, 50-51 & Travelers Ins Co, 51-54; res chemist, Monsanto Chem Co, 56-58; from asst prof to assoc prof, 65-73, PROF CHEM, ST JOSEPH COL, CONN, 73- *Concurrent Pos:* NASA fel, Univ Glasgow, 66-67, Oil & Gas Br, US Geol Surv, Denver, Colo, 80 & Inst Chimie, Univ Louis Pasteur, Strasbourg, France, 81. *Mem:* AAAS; Am Chem Soc; Geochem Soc. *Res:* Geochemistry of organic matter in rocks and meteorites; oil shales; correlation of petroleum and source rocks. *Mailing Add:* Dept of Chem St Joseph Col West Hartford CT 06117

MURPHY, MARY LOIS, b Nebr, Oct 16, 16. MEDICINE. *Educ:* Univ Nebr, BA, 39, MD, 44; Am Bd Pediat, dipl, 51. *Prof Exp:* Asst bacteriologist, Minn State Dept of Health, 42-43; intern, Woman's Med Col, Pa, 44-45; resident pediat, St Christopher's Hosp Children, Philadelphia, 45-46; resident path, Children's Hosp, Washington, DC, 46-47; asst instr clin path, Med Sch, Georgetown Univ, 47-48; asst instr pediat, Med Sch, Univ Pa, 49-52; instr med, Cornell Univ, 52-53, res assoc, 53-54, asst prof med, 54-57, from asst prof to assoc prof pediat, 57-70; asst attend pediatrician, 54-58, assoc attend pediatrician, 58-66, chmn dept, 66-76, ATTEND PEDIATRICIAN, MEM HOSP, 66-, PROF PEDIAT THERAPEUT RES, 76-; PROF PEDIAT, MED COL, CORNELL UNIV, 70- *Concurrent Pos:* Res fel, Children's Hosp, Philadelphia, 49-51; res fel, Sloan-Kettering Inst Cancer Res, 51-54; from resident to asst chief resident, Children's Hosp, Philadelphia, 47-49, asst vis physician, 49; chief resident, Camden Munic Hosp Contagious Dis, 49-51; asst mem, Sloan-Kettering Inst Cancer Res, 54-60, assoc mem, 60-70, mem, 70- *Mem:* Harvey Soc; AMA; Am Asn Cancer Res; Am Fedn Clin Res; Am Acad Pediat. *Res:* Pediatrics; leukemia; cancer; teratogenesis. *Mailing Add:* Dept Pediat Mem Hosp 1275 York Ave New York NY 10021

MURPHY, MARY NADINE, b Waucoma, Iowa, June 22, 33. MICROBIOLOGY. *Educ:* Clarke Col, AB, 54; Purdue Univ, NSF fel, 61-64, MS, 64, PhD(biol sci), 65. *Prof Exp:* Instr, 59-61 & 65-66, asst prof, 66-70, assoc prof, 70-78, PROF BIOL, MUNDELEIN COL, 78-, CHMN DEPT, 66- *Concurrent Pos:* Shell Merit fel, Stanford Univ, 70; consult- evaluator, NCent Asn Cols & Schs, 73-; Am Coun Educ fel, 74-75. *Mem:* AAAS; Am Soc Microbiol. *Res:* Cellular differentiation; physiology of aquatic fungi. *Mailing Add:* Dept of Biol Mundelein Col Chicago IL 60660

MURPHY, MICHAEL A, b Spokane, Wash, Mar 11, 25; m 47; c 2. GEOLOGY, STRATIGRAPHY. *Educ:* Univ Calif, Los Angeles, PhD, 54. *Prof Exp:* Subsurface geologist, Shell Oil Co, 53-54; from asst prof to assoc prof geol, 54-67, PROF GEOL, UNIV CALIF, RIVERSIDE, 67- *Concurrent Pos:* NSF grant, 58, 61, 67 & 69; prof, Univ Cenap, Brazil, 59-60. *Mem:* Paleont Soc; fel Geol Soc Am. *Mailing Add:* Dept of Geol Sci Univ of Calif Riverside CA 92507

MURPHY, MICHAEL JOHN, b Milwaukee, Wis. COMBUSTION ENGINEERING, FUEL CHEMISTRY. *Educ:* Marquette Univ, BS, 70; Univ Wis, MS(chem), 72, MS(eng), 74, PhD(mech eng), 78. *Prof Exp:* Res asst, Univ Wis, 72-78; RES SCIENTIST, BATTELLE COLUMBUS LABS, 78- *Mem:* Am Chem Soc; Combustion Inst; Am Soc Mech Engrs; Am Soc Advan Sci. *Res:* Combustion systems, flames, analysis of energy use, fuel-generated air pollution. *Mailing Add:* Battelle Columbus Labs 505 King Ave Columbus OH 43201

MURPHY, MICHAEL JOSEPH, b Butte, Mont, Feb 12, 23. PHYSICAL GEOLOGY. *Educ:* Univ Notre Dame, AB, 45, BS, 51; Univ Calif, Berkeley, MS, 53. *Prof Exp:* From instr to asst prof, 53-65, asst chmn dept, 66-70, ASSOC PROF GEOL, UNIV NOTRE DAME, 65-, CHMN DEPT, 70- *Concurrent Pos:* NSF fel, Columbia Univ, 60-61. *Mem:* AAAS; fel Geol Soc Am; Mineral Soc Am; Nat Asn Geol Teachers; Sigma Xi. *Res:* Isomorphic mineral systems. *Mailing Add:* Dept of Earth Sci Univ of Notre Dame Notre Dame IN 46556

MURPHY, MICHAEL JOSEPH, b Albany, NY, Feb 2, 53. FETAL ENDOCRINOLOGY, COMPARATIVE PHYSIOLOGY. *Educ:* Siena Col, Loudonville, BS, 75; Col St Rose, Albany, MS, 80; State Univ NY, PhD(biol), 82. *Prof Exp:* Teaching asst embrol & histol, Siena Col, 75; res asst embrol, State Univ NY, Albany, 75-80; instr anat & histol, State Univ NY, Cobleskill, 80; instr embrol, Col St Rose, 81-82; ASST PROF HISTOL, SIENA COL, LOUDONVILLE, 82- *Concurrent Pos:* Researcher, State Univ NY, Albany, 82. *Mem:* AAAS; Am Soc Zoologists. *Res:* Hormonal control of osmoregulation during avian development; effects of arginine vasotocin and prolactin on embyonic fluids and renal function. *Mailing Add:* RD#2 Stovepipe Rd Voorheesville NY 12186

MURPHY, PATRICIA A, b Eureka, Calif, July 27, 51. FOOD PROTEINS, FOOD TOXICOLOGY. *Educ:* Univ Calif, Davis, BS, 73, MS, 75; Mich State Univ, PhD(food sci), 79. *Prof Exp:* Sea grant trainee food sci, Inst Marine Resources, Univ Calif, Davis, 73-75; asst, Dept Food Sci & Human Nutrit, Mich State Univ, 75-78, NIH asst, 78-79; ASST PROF FOOD TECHNOL, IOWA STATE UNIV, 79- *Mem:* Inst Food Technologists; Am Chem Soc; AAAS; Am Soc Plant Physiologists; Am Oil Chemists Soc. *Res:* Maximizing use of soy protein for human consumption by understanding basic interactions of soy protein with non-protein constituents, off-flavors, phytoestrogens, complex protein food systems through basic research on individual soy proteins. *Mailing Add:* Dept Food Technol Iowa State Univ Ames IA 50011

MURPHY, PATRICK AIDAN, b Liverpool, Eng, June 4, 37; m 64; c 4. MICROBIOLOGY, MEDICINE. *Educ:* Univ Liverpool, BSc, 57, MB & ChB, 60; Oxford Univ, DPhil, 66. *Prof Exp:* UK Med Res Coun fel, Oxford Univ, 64-67; fel microbiol, 67-68, from instr to asst prof, 68-76, ASSOC PROF MICROBIOL & MED, SCH MED, JOHNS HOPKINS UNIV, 76- *Res:* Pathogenesis of fever. *Mailing Add:* Dept Microbiol Sch Med Johns Hopkins Univ Baltimore MD 21205

MURPHY, PATRICK JOSEPH, b Chicago, Ill, June 11, 40; m 66; c 4. BIOCHEMISTRY. *Educ:* Loyola Univ Chicago, BS, 62; San Diego State Col, MS, 64; Univ Calif, Los Angeles, PhD(biochem), 67. *Prof Exp:* Sr scientist, 67-73, res scientist, 73-77, res assoc, 77, head, drug disposition, 77-79, HEAD, CARDIOVASC PHARMACOL & DRUG DISPOSITON, ELI LILLY & CO, 79- *Concurrent Pos:* Vchmn, Gordon Conf Drug Metabolism, 80, chmn, 81. *Mem:* AAAS; Am Chem Soc; Am Soc Pharmacol & Exp Therapeut. *Res:* Drug metabolism; biochemical pharmacology; studies of enzymes involved in metabolism of endogenous and exogenous compounds. *Mailing Add:* Eli Lilly & Co Dept MC906 Indianapolis IN 46285

MURPHY, PAUL HENRY, b Boston, Mass, July 7, 42; m 65; c 3. NUCLEAR MEDICINE, MEDICAL PHYSICS. *Educ:* Univ Kans, MS, 68, PhD(radiation biophys), 70. *Prof Exp:* asst prof, 71-79, ASSOC PROF NUCLEAR MED & PHYSICS, BAYLOR COL MED, 79- *Concurrent Pos:* Advan sr fel med physics, Univ Tex M D Anderson Hosp & Tumor Inst Houston, 70-71. *Mem:* Soc Nuclear Med; Health Physics Soc; Am Asn Physicists in Med. *Res:* Nuclear medicine imaging; radionuclide pulmonary function and cardiovascular tests; computer applications in nuclear medicine. *Mailing Add:* Dept Radiol Baylor Col Med Houston TX 77030

MURPHY, PETER GEORGE, b New York, NY, Feb 23, 42; m 67. ECOLOGY, BOTANY. *Educ:* Syracuse Univ, BS, 63, MS, 68; Univ NC, Chapel Hill, PhD(plant ecol), 70. *Prof Exp:* Res assoc trop ecol, PR Nuclear Ctr, Rio Piedras, 63-66; asst prof, 70-75, assoc prof, 75-81, PROF BOT & ECOL, MICH STATE UNIV, 81- *Concurrent Pos:* AID ecol adv, Indonesia, 73-74; mem directorate, US Man & Biosphere Prog, Trop Forest Panel, 75-; ed, Trop Ecol, 81-; prin investr, Man & Biosphere Prog, Dept Energy, 80- & NSF, 81- *Mem:* AAAS; Ecol Soc Am; Am Inst Biol Sci; Asn Trop Biol; Int Soc Trop Ecol. *Res:* Structure and function of tropical and temperate forest ecosystems; primary productivity; sand dune ecosystems; radiation ecology. *Mailing Add:* Dept of Bot & Plant Path Mich State Univ East Lansing MI 48824

MURPHY, PETER JOHN, b Brooklyn, NY, July 29, 39. HYDRAULIC ENGINEERING, FLUID MECHANICS. *Educ:* Webb Inst Naval Archit, BS, 62; Johns Hopkins Univ, PhD(fluid mech), 68. *Prof Exp:* Vis prof, Univ Valle, Colombia, 68-74; asst prof, Cornell Univ, 74-78; ASST PROF CIVIL ENGR, UNIV MASS, 78- *Mem:* Am Soc Civil Engrs; Am Phys Soc. *Res:* Sediment transport; environmental turbulence; measurement techniques. *Mailing Add:* Dept of Civil Eng Univ of Mass Amherst MA 01003

MURPHY, RANDALL BERTRAND, b Pasadena, Calif, May 6, 54. BIOPHYSICAL CHEMISTRY, BIOCHEMISTRY. *Educ:* Univ Southern Calif, BS, 70; Univ Calif, Los Angeles, PhD(phys chem), 75. *Prof Exp:* Res chemist dept chem, Univ Calif, 74-75; Marion & Eugene Bailey fel biochem, Bone Res Lab, Univ Calif, Los Angeles, 75-76; res chemist, US Nat Bur Standards, 76-77; ASST PROF CHEM, NEW YORK UNIV, 77- *Concurrent*

Pos: NIH res fel, Lab Biophys Chem, 76-77. *Mem:* Am Chem Soc; Biophys Soc; AAAS; NY Acad Sci. *Res:* Molecular biochemistry of receptors; molecular olfaction; high pressure chemistry; tracer biochemistry. *Mailing Add:* Dept of Chem 4 Washington Pl New York NY 10003

MURPHY, RAY BRADFORD, b USA, June 7, 22; m 54; c 5. MATHEMATICAL STATISTICS, APPLIED STATISTICS. *Educ:* Princeton Univ, AB, 43, MA, 48, PhD(math), 51. *Prof Exp:* From instr to asst prof math, Carnegie Inst Technol, 49-52; mem tech staff, 52-58, dept head qual theory, 58-67, dept head appl statist, 67-77, STATIST CONSULT, BELL LABS, HOLMDEL, 77- *Mem:* Am Math Soc; Am Soc Testing & Mat; Am Statist Asn; Inst Math Statist. *Mailing Add:* Bell Labs Holmdel NJ 07733

MURPHY, RICHARD ALAN, b Twin Falls, Idaho, July 4, 38; m 61; c 2. PHYSIOLOGY. *Educ:* Harvard Univ, AB, 60; Columbia Univ, PhD(physiol), 64. *Prof Exp:* NIH fel physiol, Max Planck Inst Med Res, Heidelberg, 64-66; res assoc, Univ Mich, 66-68; from asst prof to assoc prof, 68-77, PROF PHYSIOL, SCH MED, UNIV VA, 77- *Concurrent Pos:* NIH career develop award, 71. *Mem:* AAAS; Am Physiol Soc; Biophys Soc; Soc Gen Physiologists. *Res:* Biochemistry of the contractile proteins of vascular smooth muscle; contractile properties of arterial smooth muscle. *Mailing Add:* Dept of Physiol Univ of Va Sch of Med Box 449 Charlottesville VA 22908

MURPHY, RICHARD ALLAN, b Evergreen Park, Ill, Feb 23, 41; m 65; c 3. MEDICAL MICROBIOLOGY. *Educ:* Loyola Univ, BS, 63; Univ Ill, MS, 66, PhD(microbiol), 71. *Prof Exp:* Teaching asst, 64-70, asst prof, 70-76, ASSOC PROF ORAL DIAG, UNIV ILL MED CTR, 76- *Concurrent Pos:* Mem bd dirs, Int Found Microbiol. *Mem:* Am Soc Microbiol; Int Found Microbiol (exec secy). *Res:* Role of bacterial enzymes and toxins in pathogenesis; microbiology of periodontal diseases; microbiology of endodontic pathologies; dental microbiology. *Mailing Add:* Dept of Oral Diag Univ of Ill Med Ctr Chicago IL 60612

MURPHY, RICHARD ERNEST, b Hibbing, Minn, Sept 21, 20; m 49; c 3. PHYSICAL GEOGRAPHY. *Educ:* St Lawrence Univ, BA, 43; George Washington Univ, MA, 52; Clark Univ, PhD(geog), 57. *Prof Exp:* Cartographic aide, US Army Map Serv, 46-48; head reference sect, Map Div, Libr Cong, 49-54; from asst prof to assoc prof geog, George Washington Univ, 55-59; from assoc prof to prof, Univ Wyo, 59-63; vis prof, Univ Hawaii, 63-64; NSF sci fac fel, Inst Geog, Univ Paris, 64-65; PROF GEOG & CHMN DEPT, UNIV NMEX, 65- *Concurrent Pos:* Consult theory group, George Washington Univ-US Army Logistics Res Proj, 55-56; res scientist, George Washington Univ-US Army Qm Intel Res Proj, 58-59; consult, Univ NMex Technol Appln Ctr, NASA, 67-; Fulbright lectr, Inst Geog, Tohoku Univ, Japan, 68-69; hon supernumerasy mem, Jesus Col, Eng, 81-82. *Mem:* Asn Am Geogr; Int Geog Union. *Res:* Classification and distribution of world ethnic groups; the raison d'etre of nation-states; classification and distribution of world landform regions; conservation, especially wilderness areas. *Mailing Add:* Dept of Geog Univ of NMex Albuquerque NM 87106

MURPHY, ROBERT CARL, b Wheeler, Pa, Dec 18, 19; m 45; c 3. ANATOMY. *Educ:* Geneva Col, BS, 49; Univ Wis, MS, 52, PhD, 55. *Prof Exp:* Asst zool, Univ Wis, 49-52, asst anat, 52-54, instr, 54-55; asst prof, Univ Iowa, 55-57; from asst prof to assoc prof, 57-72, PROF ANAT, TERRE HAUTE CTR MED EDUC, IND UNIV SCH MED, 72- *Res:* Cells and tissues of the lymphoid system; immunology. *Mailing Add:* Terre Haute Ctr for Med Educ Ind Univ Sch of Med Terre Haute IN 47809

MURPHY, ROBERT CARL, b Seymour, Ind, Dec 15, 44; m 65; c 2. ORGANIC CHEMISTRY, PHARMACOLOGY. *Educ:* Mt Union Col, BS, 66; Mass Inst Technol, PhD(org chem), 70. *Prof Exp:* NIH trainee & Harvard Univ fel, Mass Inst Technol & Harvard Univ, 70-71; asst prof, 71-76, assoc prof, 76-80, PROF PHARMACOL, UNIV COLO MED CTR, DENVER, 80- *Concurrent Pos:* Assoc ed, Org Mass Spectrometry, 74-76; career develop award, NIH, 76-81. *Mem:* Am Chem Soc; Am Soc Mass Spectrometry; Am Soc Pharmacol & Exp Therapeut. *Res:* Application of stable isotopes and mass spectrometry to biomedical research; drug metabolism; structure determination of complex lipids and pharmacologically active molecules by mass spectrometry; pharmacologic studies of leukotrienes and lipoxygenase products. *Mailing Add:* Dept of Pharmacol Univ of Colo Med Ctr Denver CO 80262

MURPHY, ROBERT EMMETT, b Chicago, Ill, Jan 28, 27; m 71; c 4. MEAT SCIENCES. *Educ:* Univ Ill. BS, 51. *Prof Exp:* Meat technologist, 53-61, proj leader, 61-75, assoc scientist, 76-79, HEAD, FRESH MEATS DIV, RES & DEVELOP CTR, SWIFT & CO, 79- *Concurrent Pos:* Meat technol consult, Consortium Develop Technol, Brazil, 74. *Mem:* Inst Food Technologists; Am Meat Sci Asn. *Res:* International application of antemortem and postmortem enzymatic meat tenderization in Australia, New Zealand, Korea, Brazil, Costa Rica and Canada; fresh meat products and processing. *Mailing Add:* Res & Develop Ctr Swift & Co 1919 Swift Dr Oak Brook IL 60521

MURPHY, ROBERT T, b Washington, DC, Nov 17, 31; m 54; c 1. PESTICIDE CHEMISTRY. *Educ:* Univ Md, BS, 58. *Prof Exp:* Res chemist, USDA, 58-63; chemist, Univ Calif, Riverside, 63-65; res chemist, 65-68, dir anal chem, NY, 68-78, dir registration & toxicol, Ag Div, 78-81, MGR RESIDUE INVESTIGATIONS, CIBA-GEIGY CORP, 81- *Mem:* Am Chem Soc; Entom Soc Am; Weed Sci Soc Am. *Res:* Agricultural chemicals; metabolic pathway and dissipation of pesticides; toxicology and safety aspects of pesticides; state and federal registration of pesticides. *Mailing Add:* Biochem Dept Ag Div Ciba-Geigy Corp Greensboro NC 27419

MURPHY, ROYSE PEAK, b Norton, Kans, May 2, 14; m 41; c 3. PLANT BREEDING. *Educ:* Kans State Univ, BS, 36; Univ Minn, MS, 38, PhD(plant breeding, genetics), 41. *Prof Exp:* Asst, Div Agron & Plant Genetics, Univ Minn, 36-37, from instr to asst prof, 37-42; assoc prof, Mont State Univ, 42-46; assoc prof plant breeding, 46-48, prof, 48-79, head dept, 53-64, dean univ fac, 64-67, EMER PROF PLANT BREEDING, CORNELL UNIV, 79- *Mem:* AAAS; Am Soc Agron; Genetics Soc Am; Am Inst Biol Sci. *Res:* Plant genetics and breeding with perennial forage legumes and grasses. *Mailing Add:* Dept Plant Breeding & Biometry Cornell Univ Ithaca NY 14853

MURPHY, SAMUEL G, cancer, immunology, see previous edition

MURPHY, SHELDON DOUGLAS, b Forestburg, SDak, July 16, 33; m 54; c 1. TOXICOLOGY, PHARMACOLOGY. *Educ:* SDak State Col, BS, 55; Univ Chicago, PhD(pharmacol), 58. *Prof Exp:* Technician pharmacol, Univ Chicago, 55-58; asst scientist, Occup Health Field Hqs, USPHS, 58-59, chief pharmacol & toxicol sect, Div Air Pollution, 59-63; from asst prof to assoc prof toxicol, Sch Pub Health, Harvard Univ, 63-77, dir toxicol training prog, 67-77; PROF TOXICOL & DIR DIV TOXICOL, MED SCH, UNIV TEX, HOUSTON, 77- *Concurrent Pos:* Mem toxicol study sect, NIH, 69-73, chmn, 72-73; mem marine food resources comt, Nat Acad Sci-Nat Res Coun; mem pesticide bd, Dept Pub Health, Commonwealth of Mass, 70-77; mem WHO expert comt pesticide residues, Food & Agr Orgn-WHO, Rome, 72, chmn, Geneva, Switz, 73, temporary adv, Rome, 74; mem expert adv panel food additives, WHO, 72-; mem bd sci counr, Nat Inst Environ Health Sci, 73-77; mem panel oxidants med biol effects environ pollutants, Nat Acad Sci-Nat Res Coun, 73-75, mem, Food Protection Comn, 77-80, mem safe drinking water comn, 78-79, mem comn, Priority Mechanisms Res Agents Potentially Hazardous to Human Health, 81- & mem comn, Response Strategies to Unusual Chem Hazards, 78-81; mem toxicol adv comt, US Food & Drug Admin, 75-76; mem hazardous mat adv comt, Environ Protection Agency, 75-77, mem adv comn environ health, 78-81; mem, Intergovt Maritime Consult Orgn, Bergen, Norway, 78, London, Eng, 79 & 81 Houston, Tex, 80. *Mem:* AAAS; Soc Toxicol (pres, 74-75); Am Soc Pharmacol & Exp Therapeut; Soc Exp Biol & Med; NY Acad Sci. *Res:* Metabolism and interaction of drugs and chemicals by mammalian organisms; environmental toxicology; comparative pesticide toxicology; environmental health. *Mailing Add:* Div Toxicol Dept Pharmacol PO Box 20708 Houston TX 77025

MURPHY, STANLEY REED, b Guthrie, Okla, Nov 3, 24; m 57; c 1. PHYSICS. *Educ:* Fresno State Col, BA, 48; Univ Wash, PhD(physics), 59. *Prof Exp:* Res engr, Boeing Airplane Co, 50-52; assoc physicist, Appl Physics Lab, 52-54, physicist, 54-57, sr physicist, 57-64, asst dir, 64-68, PROF OCEANOG, COL ARTS & SCI, PROF MECH & OCEAN ENG, COL ENG & DIR DIV, MARINE RESOURCES, UNIV WASH, 68- *Concurrent Pos:* Mem, Wash Comn Oceanog, 69-, vchmn, 70-71; adj prof, Inst Marine Study, Univ Wash, 73- *Mem:* Am Phys Soc. *Res:* Acoustics; oceanography; instrumentation. *Mailing Add:* Div of Marine Resources Univ of Wash Seattle WA 98195

MURPHY, TED DANIEL, b Stanley, NC, Apr 21, 36; m 57; c 1. BIOLOGY, ZOOLOGY. *Educ:* Duke Univ, AB, 58, MA, 60, PhD(zool), 63. *Prof Exp:* Asst prof biol, State Univ NY Binghamton, 63-70; assoc prof, Siena Col, 70-72; PROF BIOL, CALIF STATE COL, BAKERSFIELD, 72-, DIR ENVIRON STUDIES AREA & FACIL ANIMAL CARE & TREATMENT, 80- *Mem:* AAAS; Am Soc Ichthyologists & Herpetologists; Ecol Soc Am. *Res:* Ecology of amphibians and reptiles. *Mailing Add:* Dept Biol Calif State Col Bakersfield CA 93309

MURPHY, TERENCE MARTIN, b Seattle, Wash, July 1, 42; m 69. PLANT BIOCHEMISTRY, PHYSIOLOGY. *Educ:* Calif Inst Technol, BS, 64; Univ Calif, San Diego, PhD(cell biol), 68. *Prof Exp:* USPHS fel, Univ Wash, 69-70; asst prof, 71-76, ASSOC PROF BOT, UNIV CALIF, DAVIS, 76- *Res:* Photochemistry and photobiology of RNA and DNA and plant cell membranes; immunochemical characterizations of plant enzymes. *Mailing Add:* Dept of Bot Univ of Calif Davis CA 95616

MURPHY, THOMAS DANIEL, III, b Franklin, Pa, Apr 30, 34; m 58; c 3. APPLIED STATISTICS, CHEMICAL ENGINEERING. *Educ:* Univ Md, BS, 57; Rutgers Univ, New Brunswick, MS, 64. *Prof Exp:* Process develop engr chem eng, Hercules Inc, 57-62, control lab supvr anal chem, 62-67; statistician statist, 67-71, group leader automation, 71-76, sr statistician statist, 76-80, GROUP LEADER, AM CYANAMID CO, 80- *Concurrent Pos:* Adj lectr, Rutgers Univ, 69- *Mem:* Am Statist Asn; Am Soc Qual Control; Am Inst Chem Engrs. *Res:* Industrial consultant in applied statistics; experimental design and analysis in chemical, engineering and toxicology studies; methodology in data analysis and statistical inference. *Mailing Add:* 308 Ellis Pkwy Piscataway NJ 08854

MURPHY, THOMAS JAMES, b Brooklyn, NY, Feb 17, 42; m 68; c 2. STATISTICAL MECHANICS. *Educ:* Fordham Univ, BS, 63; Rockefeller Univ, PhD(physics), 68. *Prof Exp:* Res staff physicist, Yale Univ, 68-69; asst prof, 69-75, ASSOC PROF CHEM, UNIV MD, COLLEGE PARK, 75- *Res:* Equilibrium and non-equilibrium statistical mechanics of Coulomb systems; Brownian motion of interacting particles; density dependence of transport coefficients of gases. *Mailing Add:* Dept of Chem Univ of Md College Park MD 20742

MURPHY, THOMAS JOSEPH, b Pittsburgh, Pa, Oct 4, 41; m. WATER CHEMISTRY. *Educ:* Univ Notre Dame, BS, 63; Iowa State Univ, PhD(photochem), 67. *Prof Exp:* NIH fel org chem, Ohio State Univ, 67-68; asst prof org chem, 68-77, ASSOC PROF CHEM, DEPAUL UNIV, 77- *Mem:* Am Chem Soc; Int Asn Great Lakes Res; Int Soc Limnol; AAAS. *Res:* Collection and measurement of atmospheric deposition and its effect on bodies of water. *Mailing Add:* Dept of Chem DePaul Univ Chicago IL 60614

MURPHY, WALTER THOMAS, b Medford, Mass, Oct 5, 28; m 55; c 5. ORGANIC CHEMISTRY, POLYMER CHEMISTRY. *Educ:* Boston Col, BS, 50, MS, 52. *Prof Exp:* Lab supvr, Main Plant, 52-53, jr res chemist, Res Ctr, 53-57, res chemist, 57-64, sr res chemist, 64-78, RES ASSOC, RES CTR, B F GOODRICH CO, 78- *Mem:* Am Chem Soc. *Res:* Polyurethane polymers; catalysis; structure versus mechanical properties; spandex fiber; adhesives; coatings, poromeric films; formulation and processing of reactive liquid polymers of epoxy, butadiene and acrylonitrile. *Mailing Add:* 1091 Taft Ave Cuyahoga Falls OH 44223

MURPHY, WILLIAM FREDERICK, b Dunkirk, NY, June 10, 39; m 61; c 3. MOLECULAR SPECTROSCOPY. *Educ:* Case Inst Technol, BS, 61; Univ Wis, PhD(phys chem), 66. *Prof Exp:* Fel, 66-68, asst res officer, 68-72, assoc res officer, 72-81, SR RES OFFICER, NAT RES COUN, CAN, 81- *Mem:* Am Phys Soc; Optical Soc Am; Soc Appl Spectros; Coblentz Soc; Sigma Xi. *Res:* Raman spectroscopy; Raman gas phase intensities and band contours; instrumentation for Raman spectroscopy. *Mailing Add:* Div Chem Nat Res Coun of Can 100 Sussex Dr Ottawa ON K1A 0R6 Can

MURPHY, WILLIAM G(ROVE), b Pittsburgh, Pa, July 19, 21; m 42; c 2. CIVIL ENGINEERING. *Educ:* Univ Ill, BS, 43, MS, 48. *Prof Exp:* Instr eng drawing, Univ Ill, 46, instr theoret & appl mech, 46-49; from asst prof to assoc prof, 49-67, asst chmn dept, 56-57, chmn dept theoret & appl mech, 57-66, PROF CIVIL ENG, MARQUETTE UNIV, 67-, CHMN DEPT, 76- *Mem:* Am Soc Testing & Mat; Am Soc Civil Engrs; Am Soc Eng Educ; Am Rwy Eng Asn; Am Concrete Inst. *Res:* Soil mechanics; foundation engineering; structural mechanics; material behavior. *Mailing Add:* Col of Eng Marquette Univ 1131 W Wisconsin Ave Milwaukee WI 53233

MURPHY, WILLIAM HENRY, JR, b New York, NY, June 26, 25; m 48; c 4. MICROBIOLOGY. *Educ:* Pa State Univ, BS, 50, MS, 51; Univ Minn, PhD, 54. *Prof Exp:* Instr microbiol, Univ Minn, 54-56; from asst prof to assoc prof, 56-67, PROF MICROBIOL, UNIV MICH, ANN ARBOR, 67- *Concurrent Pos:* Rockefeller exchange prof, Colombia, SAm, 58. *Mem:* AAAS; Am Soc Microbiol; Am Asn Immunologists. *Res:* Virology; immunology; leukemia, infectious diseases; immunology and immunopathology of leukemia. *Mailing Add:* Dept of Microbiol 6706 MS II Univ of Mich Ann Arbor MI 48104

MURPHY, WILLIAM J(AMES), b Lansing, Mich, Dec 21, 27; m 76; c 3. METALLURGICAL ENGINEERING, RESEARCH MANAGEMENT. *Educ:* Wayne State Univ, BS, 49; Lehigh Univ, MS, 51, PhD(metall eng), 55. *Prof Exp:* Metall engr, Aircraft Gas Turbine Div, Gen Elec Co, 51-52; asst prof metall eng, Lehigh Univ, 53-57; div chief, 59-72, mgr steel prod develop, 72-81, DIR CORP RES, RES LAB, US STEEL CORP, 81- *Mem:* Fel Am Soc Metals; Am Inst Mining, Metall & Petrol Engrs; Am Welding Soc; Iron & Steel Inst. *Res:* Physical metallurgy, structure and properties of steel, steel processing. *Mailing Add:* US Steel Res Lab Monroeville PA 15146

MURPHY, WILLIAM MICHAEL, b West DePere, Wis, Oct 17, 41; m 66; c 2. CROP PRODUCTION, SOIL FERTILITY. *Educ:* Univ Wis, BS, 65, MS, 69, PhD(crop sci), 72. *Prof Exp:* Res asst forages & soils, Univ Wis, 67-70; res fel, Ford Found, 70-72; forage specialist, Southern Ill Univ, 72-74; res agronomist forages, Ore State Univ, 74-79; ASSOC PROF PLANT SOIL SCI, UNIV VT, 79- *Concurrent Pos:* Prin investr, Symbiotic Nitrogen Fixation Prog, Chile, 77- *Mem:* Am Soc Agron; Soil Sci Soc Am; Sigma Xi. *Res:* Legume inoculation and nodulation, soil fertility, pasture renovation and plant introductions for new forage, seed and oil crops. *Mailing Add:* Plant Soil Sci Dept Univ Vt Burlington VT 05401

MURPHY, WILLIAM PARRY, JR, b Boston, Mass, Nov 11, 23; c 3. MEDICINE. *Educ:* Univ Ill, MD, 47. *Prof Exp:* Instr med, Harvard Med Sch, 49-51, res assoc, 53-55; dir res, Dade Reagents, 55-57; pres, 57-77, BD CHMN, CORDIS CORP, 77- *Concurrent Pos:* Res fel med, Peter Bent Brigham Hosp, Boston, 49-51, asst med, 53-55; chief engr, Fenwal Labs, Mass, 49 & 54; with lab biol control, NIH, 51-53; res assoc, Miami Heart Inst, 56-68; res assoc prof biophys & chmn div, Med Sch, Univ Miami, 58-70; pres, Cordis Dow Corp, 70-75, bd chmn, 75-80. *Honors & Awards:* Award, Am Roentgen Ray Soc, 48. *Mem:* AAAS; AMA; Inst Elec & Electronics Engrs. *Res:* Artificial internal organs; transfusion; biology instrumentation; heart disease; biophysics. *Mailing Add:* Cordis Corp PO Box 525700 Miami FL 33172

MURPHY, ZATIS LUAIN, organic chemistry, see previous edition

MURR, BROWN L, JR, b Atlanta, Ga, Feb 23, 31; m 53, 73; c 2. PHYSICAL ORGANIC CHEMISTRY. *Educ:* Emory Univ, AB, 52, MS, 53; Ind Univ, PhD(chem), 61. *Prof Exp:* NSF fel org chem, Mass Inst Technol, 61-62, res assoc, 62; from asst prof to assoc prof, 62-71, chmn dept, 73-76, PROF ORG CHEM, JOHNS HOPKINS UNIV, 71- *Concurrent Pos:* Vis scientist, Dept Embryol, Carnegie Inst, Washington, DC, 76- *Mem:* Am Chem Soc; Royal Soc Chem. *Res:* Reaction mechanisms; kinetics; stereochemistry; kinetic isotope effects. *Mailing Add:* Dept of Chem Johns Hopkins Univ Baltimore MD 21218

MURR, LAWRENCE EUGENE, b Lancaster, Pa, Apr 7, 39; m 58; c 2. METALLURGY, MATERIALS SCIENCE. *Educ:* Pa State Univ, BS, 62, MS, 64, PhD(solid state sci), 67; Albright Col, BSc, 63. *Prof Exp:* Instr eng mech, Pa State Univ, 62-66, res asst solid state sci, Mat Res Lab, 66-67; asst prof mat sci & elec eng, Univ Southern Calif, 67-72; prof metall & mat eng, John D Sullivan Ctr For In-Situ Mining Res, NMex Inst Mining & Technol, 72-81, head dept & dir, 72-80; VPRES, ACAD AFFAIRS & RES & PROF MAT SCI, ORE GRAD CTR, 81- *Concurrent Pos:* Consult, Res Div, US Naval Weapons Lab, 66-67; vpres res, NMex Tech Res Found, 73-80, pres, 80-81; consult metall, Los Alamos Sci Labs, 75-; vchmn, NMex Joint Ctr for Mat Sci, 76-79, chmn, 79-80. *Honors & Awards:* Phys Sci Award, Electromicros Soc Am, 72. *Mem:* Inst Elec & Electronics Engrs; Electron Micros Soc Am; fel Am Soc Metals; Am Inst Metal Engrs Metall Soc; Int Metallograph Soc. *Res:* Biophysics-effects of electric fields on plants; metal physics; transmission electron microscopy in the study of structure and properties of solids; studies of solid interfacial free energy; hydrometallurgy, environmental metallurgy. *Mailing Add:* 19600 NW Walker Rd Beaverton OR 97006

MURRAY, BERTRAM GEORGE, JR, b Elizabeth, NJ, Sept 24, 33. ORNITHOLOGY. *Educ:* Rutgers Univ, AB, 61; Univ Mich, MS, 63, PhD(zool), 67. *Prof Exp:* Lectr biol, Cornell Univ, 67-68; asst prof natural sci, Mich State Univ, 68-71; asst prof, 71-74, assoc prof, 74-81, PROF BIOL, RUTGERS UNIV, NEW BRUNSWICK, 81- *Mem:* Am Ornithologists Union. *Res:* Ecology, behavior and evolution of birds; migration; orientation; territoriality; paleontology. *Mailing Add:* Dept Biol Sci Livingston Col Rutgers Univ New Brunswick NJ 08903

MURRAY, BRUCE C, b New York, NY, Nov 30, 31; m 54, 71; c 4. ASTRONOMY, GEOLOGY. *Educ:* Mass Inst Technol, SB, 53, SM, 54, PhD(geol), 55. *Prof Exp:* Explor & exploitation geologist, Calif Co, La, 55-58; geophysicist, Geophys Res Directorate, L G Hanscom Field, Mass, 58-60; res fel, 60-63, assoc prof, 63-68, PROF PLANETARY SCI, CALIF INST TECHNOL, 68-, DIR JET PROPULSION LAB, 76- *Concurrent Pos:* Guest observer, Mt Wilson & Palomar Observ, 60-65, staff assoc, 65-69; consult, Rand Corp, 61-75; co-investr, TV Exp, Mariner 4, 65, Mariner 6 & 7, 69, Mariner 9, 71, leader imaging team, Mariner Venus Mercury 73 Mission; Guggenheim fel, 75-76. *Honors & Awards:* Except Sci Achievement Award, NASA, 69 & Distinguished Pub Serv Medal, 74. *Mem:* AAAS; Am Astron Soc; Am Geophys Union. *Res:* Planetary exploration; geology and geophysics of the surfaces of the moon and planets; techniques of space photography. *Mailing Add:* Div of Geol & Planetary Sci Calif Inst of Technol Pasadena CA 91125

MURRAY, CALVIN CLYDE, b Oakboro, NC, Aug 5, 07; m 34; c 1. AGRONOMY. *Educ:* NC State Col, BS, 32; Univ Ga, MS, 38; Cornell Univ, PhD(plant breeding), 45. *Prof Exp:* High sch teacher, NC, 32-35; asst agronomist, Soil Conserv Serv, USDA, NC, 35; from asst prof to prof agron, Univ Ga, 36-46; prof & agronomist, La State Univ, 46-48; dir exp sta, 48-50, dean col agr, 50-68, regents prof int educ, dir inter-instnl progs, int affairs & exec dir southern consortium int educ, 68-74, EMER DEAN COL AGR & REGENTS PROF INT EDUC, UNIV GA & EMER DIR INT AFFAIRS, UNIV GA SYST, 74- *Concurrent Pos:* Consult, AID, World Bank, 74- & Inter Am Develop Bank, 75-; mem, Int Exec Serv Corps, 75- *Res:* International education; administration; institutional development overseas. *Mailing Add:* 236 West View Dr Athens GA 30606

MURRAY, CHRISTOPHER BROCK, b Meadville, Pa, Jan 16, 37; m 61; c 2. MATHEMATICS. *Educ:* Rice Univ, BA, 58; Univ Tex, PhD(math), 64. *Prof Exp:* Spec instr math, Univ Tex, 61-63; engr scientist, Tracor, Inc, 64-66; ASST PROF MATH, UNIV HOUSTON, 66- *Mem:* Am Math Soc; Math Asn Am. *Res:* Mathematical analysis. *Mailing Add:* Dept of Math Univ of Houston Houston TX 77004

MURRAY, DAVID WILLIAM, b Calgary, Alta, July 19, 30; m 56; c 4. CIVIL ENGINEERING, MECHANICS. *Educ:* Univ Alta, BSc, 52; Univ London, MSc, 54, Univ Calif, PhD(civil eng), 67. *Prof Exp:* Design engr, T Lamb, F N McManus & Assoc, 54-56, Montreal Eng Co Ltd, 56-57 & Green Blankstien, Russel & Assoc, 57-60; asst prof struct, Univ Man, 57-60; from asst prof to assoc prof civil eng, 60-70, PROF CIVIL ENG, UNIV ALTA, 70- *Honors & Awards:* Gold Medal in Civil Eng, Asn Prof Engrs Alta, 52. *Mem:* Am Soc Civil Engrs; Can Soc Civil Engrs. *Res:* Finite elements; inelastic buckling; soil consolidation; permafrost thermal analysis; inelastic analysis of nuclear containments; concrete constitutive theory; structures. *Mailing Add:* Dept of Civil Eng Univ of Alta Edmonton AB T6G 2G7 Can

MURRAY, DONALD EDWARD, food biochemistry, see previous edition

MURRAY, DONALD SHIPLEY, b Philadelphia, Pa, June 30, 16; m 38; c 3. ACADEMIC ADMINISTRATION, APPLIED STATISTICS. *Educ:* Univ Pa, BS, 37, AM, 40, PhD(statist), 44. *Prof Exp:* Instr statist & acct, 37-44, from asst prof to assoc prof statist, 45-57, prof, 57-80, chmn dept, 64, EMER PROF STATIST, UNIV PA, 80- *Concurrent Pos:* Treas, Am Inst Indian Studies, 64-73, pres asst for Indian opers, 73-80, treas & asst secy, 80-; dir, Nat Conf Admin Res, 66-72; mem, Nat Adv Coun Arthritis & Metab Dis, 69-72; mem, Grants Admin Adv Comt, Dept Health, Educ & Welfare, 69-72, chmn, 70-72; asst chmn, Dept S Asia Regional Studies, Univ Pa, 77-79, chmn, 79-80; secy-treas, La Napoule Found, La Napoule, France & Philadelphia, 78-81. *Mem:* Am Statist Asn. *Res:* Development of models for financial management of private institutions of higher education. *Mailing Add:* 120 Berkeley Rd Glenside PA 19038

MURRAY, EDWARD CONLEY, b Mullen, Nebr, Sept 25, 31; m 53; c 2. INORGANIC CHEMISTRY. *Educ:* Nebr State Teachers Col, Kearney, AB, 52; Univ Colo, Boulder, MS, 63, PhD(inorg chem), 69. *Prof Exp:* Jr chemist, Ames Lab, AEC, Iowa, 52-55; proj engr, Aeronaut Res Lab, Wright-Patterson AFB, Ohio, 59-60; sr res chemist, Am Potash & Chem Corp, 69-70; sr res chemist, Kerr-McGee Corp, 70-78; PRES, MURLIN CHEM INC, 78- *Mem:* Am Chem Soc. *Res:* Preparation of high purity inorganic chemicals; surface chemistry of titanium dioxide pigments; calcium phosphate compounds. *Mailing Add:* Murlin Chem Inc Balligomingo Rd West Conshohocken PA 19428

MURRAY, FINNIE ARDREY, JR, b Burgaw, NC, May 30, 43; m 64; c 3. REPRODUCTIVE IMMUNOLOGY, REPRODUCTIVE PHYSIOLOGY. *Educ:* NC State Univ, BS, 66, MS, 68; Univ Fla, PhD(reproductive physiol), 71. *Prof Exp:* Res assoc, Dept Molecular, Cellular & Develop Biol, Univ Colo, 70-71; instr, Dept Zool, Univ Tenn, 71-72, asst prof, 72-74; asst prof, 74-77, ASSOC PROF, DEPT ANIMAL SCI, OHIO AGR RES & DEVELOP CTR, WOOSTER, 77- *Concurrent Pos:* Assoc prof, Dept Animal Sci, Ohio State Univ, 77- *Mem:* Am Soc Animal Sci; AAAS; Soc Study Reproduction; SIGMA XI; Am Dairy Sci Asn. *Res:* Immunology of maternal-fetal relationship; regulatory immunology of reproduction and lactation; function of the uterus in embryonic development; biochemistry of uterine secretions; endocrine control of uterine and ovarian function. *Mailing Add:* Dept Animal Sci Ohio Agr Res & Develop Ctr Wooster OH 44691

MURRAY, FRANCIS E, b Grande Prairie, Alta, Nov 17, 18; m 39; c 4. PHYSICAL CHEMISTRY. *Educ:* Univ Alta, BSc, 50; McGill Univ, PhD(phys chem), 53. *Prof Exp:* Asst prof phys chem, Univ Man, 53-55; asst prof, Can Serv Col, Royal Roads, 55-56; res chemist, BC Res Coun, 56-61;

res coord, Consol Paper Corp, 61-62; head div chem, BC Res Coun, 62-68; assoc prof chem eng, 68-70, PROF CHEM ENG & HEAD DEPT, FAC APPL SCI, UNIV BC, 70- *Concurrent Pos:* Consult, Air Pollution Br, USPHS. *Mem:* Can Pulp & Paper Asn; Tech Asn Pulp & Paper Indust; Air Pollution Control Asn. *Res:* Molecular association forces; critical temperature phenomena; Kraft pulping chemical recovery and pulp purification. *Mailing Add:* Dept of Chem Eng Univ of BC Fac of Appl Sci Vancouver BC V6T 1W5 Can

MURRAY, FRANCIS JOSEPH, b New York, NY, Feb 3, 11; m 35; c 6. MATHEMATICS. *Educ:* Columbia Univ, AB, 32, MA, 33, PhD(math), 35. *Prof Exp:* From instr to prof math, Columbia Univ, 36-60; prof math, Duke Univ, 60-80, dir spec res numerical anal, 60-70, dir undergrad studies, 76-80; RETIRED. *Concurrent Pos:* Consult ed, Math Tables & Other Aids to Comput, Div Math, Nat Res Coun, 53-57. *Mem:* Am Math Soc; Asn Comput Mach. *Res:* Partial differential equations; linear spaces; rings of operators; Hilbert space; mathematical machines; aids to computation. *Mailing Add:* Dept of Math Duke Univ Durham NC 27706

MURRAY, FRANCIS JOSEPH, b Jersey City, NJ, Oct 16, 20; m 47; c 5. MEDICAL SCIENCE, HEALTH SCIENCES. *Educ:* St Peters Col, BS, 42; Purdue Univ, PhD(bact), 48. *Prof Exp:* Asst bact, Lederle Labs, Am Cyanamid Co, NY, 44; asst serol, Purdue Univ, 44-46; asst chief bacteriologist, Wm S Merrell Co, 48-51, head dept microbiol, 51-56, exec asst to dir res, 56-59, dir sci rels, 60-67, dir sci & com develop & cent sci serv, 67-69, vpres, Richardson-Merrell Inc, 69-81, VPRES, MERRELL-DOW PHARMACEUT INC, 81- *Mem:* AAAS; Am Soc Microbiol; Am Asn Immunol; Am Soc Clin Pharmacol & Therapeut; Lic Exec Soc. *Res:* Antibiotics; immunology; virology; chemotherapy. *Mailing Add:* 2110 E Galbraith Rd Merrell Dow Pharmaceut Inc Cincinnati OH 45215

MURRAY, FRANCIS WILLIAM, b San Antonio, Tex, July 29, 21; m 54; c 1. METEOROLOGY. *Educ:* Univ Tex, BA, 41; Univ Calif, Los Angeles, MA, 48; Mass Inst Technol, PhD(meteorol), 60. *Prof Exp:* Sr res scientist, Douglas Aircraft Co, Inc, 63-66; phys scientist, 66-80, SR PHYS SCIENTIST, RAND CORP, 80- *Concurrent Pos:* Weather officer, Air Weather Serv, DC, Marshall Islands & Morocco. *Mem:* Am Meteorol Soc; Am Geophys Union; Royal Meteorol Soc. *Res:* Atmospheric science; cloud dynamics; dynamic meteorology; numerical weather prediction. *Mailing Add:* Rand Corp 1700 Main St Santa Monica CA 90406

MURRAY, FREDERICK NELSON, b Tulsa, Okla, Apr 21, 35; m 67. STRUCTURAL GEOLOGY, STRATIGRAPHY. *Educ:* Univ Tulsa, BS, 57; Univ Wash, BS, 62; Univ Colo, MS, 62, PhD(geol), 66. *Prof Exp:* Jr geologist, Pan Am Petrol Corp, 57-58; asst geologist, Ill State Geol Surv, 65-67; asst prof geol, Allegheny Col, 68-71; geologist, US Geol Surv, 71-72; MGR EXPLOR & LAND, MAPCO INC, 72- *Mem:* Am Asn Petrol Geologists; Am Geophys Union; Geol Soc Am. *Res:* Computer application in geology; geologic mapping; coal geology. *Mailing Add:* 3734 E 81st Pl Tulsa OK 74136

MURRAY, GARY JOSEPH, b Toronto, Ont, Aug 26, 50. GLYOCPROTEINS, RECEPTORS. *Educ:* Univ Waterloo, BSc, 72, PhD(chem), 77. *Prof Exp:* Lectr, Univ Waterloo, 77; vis fel, NIMH, Bethesda, 77-80; VIS ASSOC, BIOCHEM, NAT INST NEUROL & COMMUN DISORDERS & STROKE, 80- *Mem:* Am Chem Soc; NY Acad Sci. *Res:* Modification of proteins with carbohydrate or oligosaccharide chains; various lectin receptors on cell membranes. *Mailing Add:* Nat Inst Neurol & Commun Disorders & Stroke Nat Inst Health Bldg 10 Rm 4N248 Bethesda MD 20205

MURRAY, GEORGE CLOYD, b Minneapolis, Minn, May 20, 34; m 57; c 2. NEUROPHYSIOLOGY, PHYSICS. *Educ:* George Washington Univ, BS, 59; Univ Colo, MS, 62; Johns Hopkins Univ, PhD(biophys), 68. *Prof Exp:* Assoc staff engr, Appl Physics Lab, Johns Hopkins Univ, 54-59; instr & teaching assoc physics, Univ Colo, 59-62; asst prof, George Washington Univ, 62; instr & res assoc biophys, Johns Hopkins Univ, 62-68; staff fel neurophysiol, Lab Neurophysiol, Nat Inst Neurol Dis & Blindness, 68-72, head, Communicative Disorders Sect & Biomed Eng Sect, C & FR, Nat Inst Neurol Dis & Stroke, 72-74, spec asst to dir & dept dir div blood dis & resources, Nat Heart, Lung & Blood Inst, 74-76, DIR, OPPE, NAT INST NEUROL & COMMUN DIS & STROKE, NIH, 76- *Res:* Biophysical study of the mechanisms of excitable biological membrane systems. *Mailing Add:* 1706 Mark Lane Rockville MD 20852

MURRAY, GEORGE GRAHAM, JR, b Detroit, Mich, Feb 23, 24; m 51; c 3. MATHEMATICS. *Educ:* Harvard Univ, AB, 44, MA, 48, PhD(math), 51. *Prof Exp:* Mathematician, Appl Physics Lab, Johns Hopkins Univ, 51-55; systs engr, Radio Corp Am, 55-57, mgr digital systs group, Missile & Surface Radar Div, 57-63; dir adv tech, Librascope Div, Gen Precision, Inc, 63-65, chief engr, Kearfott-San Marcos Div, 65-69; PARTNER & COMPUT CONSULT, DATA-WARE DEVELOP, 69- *Mem:* Am Math Soc; Soc Indust & Appl Math; Asn Comput Mach. *Res:* Analysis; digital computer systems; Walsh and Fourier transforms; special processor design and development. *Mailing Add:* 8650 Kilbourn Dr La Jolla CA 92037

MURRAY, GEORGE R(AYMOND), JR, b Dayton, Ohio, Sept 4, 30; m 54; c 3. DECISION ANALYSIS, OPERATIONS RESEARCH. *Educ:* Mass Inst Technol, PhD(phys chem), 56. *Prof Exp:* NSF fel, Oxford Univ, 56-57; asst prof chem, Pa State Univ, 57-59; opers res analyst, Arthur D Little, Inc, 59-63; res assoc, Opers Res Ctr, Mass Inst Technol, 63-65; assoc prof systs eng, Stanford Univ, 65-69; vpres, Klainer, Murray & Copenhagen, 69-74; SR DECISION ANALYST, SRI INT, 74- *Concurrent Pos:* Dir, Off Planning & Policy, Energy Res & Develop Admin, 75- *Mem:* Inst Mgt Sci; Opers Res Soc Am. *Res:* Design of experiments; research allocation; analysis of industrial systems; research and development planning. *Mailing Add:* 1248 Shafter St San Mateo CA 94402

MURRAY, GEORGE T(HOMAS), b Waynesburg, Ky, Feb 6, 27; m 58; c 2. METALLURGY. *Educ:* Univ Ky, BS, 49; Univ Tenn, MS, 51; Columbia Univ, ScD(metall), 58. *Prof Exp:* Metallurgist, Oak Ridge Nat Lab, 49-52, res lab, Bendix Aviation Co, 52-54 & Bridgeport Brass Co, 54-55; vpres, Mat Res Corp, 57-78; PROF METALL ENG, CALIF POLYTECH STATE UNIV, 78- *Concurrent Pos:* Res assoc, Columbia Univ, 54-57; lectr, Cooper Union, 57- *Mem:* Am Ceramic Soc; Am Soc Metals; Am Inst Mining, Metall & Petrol Engrs. *Res:* Solid state diffusion and reactions; irradiation effects in metals. *Mailing Add:* Dept of Metall Eng Calif Polytech State Univ San Luis Obispo CA 93401

MURRAY, GLEN A, b Sidney, Mont, Mar 1, 39; m 61; c 2. CROP PHYSIOLOGY, AGRONOMY. *Educ:* Mont State Univ, BS, 62, MS, 64; Univ Ariz, PhD(agron), 67. *Prof Exp:* Assoc prof & assoc crop physiologist, 67-77, PROF PLANT SCI & CROP PHYSIOLOGIST, UNIV IDAHO, 77- *Mem:* Am Soc Agron; Crop Sci Soc Am. *Res:* Cold hardiness of grass seedlings; photoperiodic studies on legumes; associating changes from vegetative to reproductive states; regulation of nitrogen distribution in wheat plants; protein and yield studies on Austrian winter peas, growth regulators; alternative crops for Idaho, especially sunflower, safflower and meadowfoam; row spacing, date of seeding and photoperiod studies. *Mailing Add:* Dept of Plant & Soil Sci Univ of Idaho Moscow ID 83843

MURRAY, GROVER ELMER, b Maiden, NC, Oct 26, 16; m 41; c 2. GEOLOGY. *Educ:* Univ NC, BS, 37; La State Univ, MSc, 39, PhD(geol), 42. *Prof Exp:* Res geologist, State Geol Surv, La, 38-41; geologist, Magnolia Petrol Co, 41-48; prof stratig geol, La State Univ, 48-55, chmn dept, 50-53, Boyd prof geol, 55-66, vpres & dean, 63-65, vpres acad affairs, La State Univ Syst, 65-66; pres, 66-76, pres, Sch Med, 69-76, UNIV PROF & PROF GEOSCI, SCH MED, TEX TECH UNIV, LUBBOCK, 76- *Concurrent Pos:* With Ark Fuel Oil Corp, 51-60; dir, Orgn Trop Studies, Inc, 64-65 & Gulf Univs Res Corp, 64-66, pres, 65-66; consult, 49-; mem, Am Comn Stratig Nomenclature, 51-54 & 57-63; ed, J Paleont, 52-54; mem, Int Comn Stratig Nomenclature, 54-; ed, Bull Am Asn Petrol Geologists, 59-63; mem, US Nat Comt Geol, 65-69, chmn, 64-68; deleg, House Soc Reps, Am Geol Inst, 58-63 & 65-68; mem bd gov, ICASALS, Inc, 67-76; mem, Nat Sci Bd, 68-80; bd dirs, Tex Partners of Americas, 71-; mem, Nat Adv Comt Oceans & Atmosphere, 75-77; dir, Ashland Oil, Inc, 76-; pres & dir, Global Explor, Inc, 78- *Mem:* Geol Soc Am; hon mem Soc Econ Paleontologists & Mineralogists (pres, 62-63); Paleont Soc; hon mem Am Asn Petrol Geologists (pres, 64-65); Am Geophys Union. *Res:* Structural and field geology; geomorphology; geophysics; micropaleontology; stratigraphy of the Gulf coast and southern Appalachians; petroleum geology of coastal plain. *Mailing Add:* Off of the Pres Tex Tech Univ Lubbock TX 79409

MURRAY, HAROLD DIXON, b Neodesha, Kans, May 25, 31; m 554; c 1. MALACOLOGY. *Educ:* Ottawa Univ, BA, 52; Kans State Col Pittsburg, MSc, 53; Univ Kans, PhD(zool), 60. *Prof Exp:* Asst biol, zool & parasitol, Univ Kans, 55-60, instr limnol & invert zool, 60-61; from asst prof to assoc prof, 61-74, PROF BIOL, TRINITY UNIV, TEX, 74-, CHMN DEPT, 75- *Mem:* AAAS; Am Malacol Union (vpres, pres, 74); Sigma Xi; Am Soc Parasitol. *Res:* Geographical distribution of Unionidae and Unionicolidae; biology and ecology of Thiaridae. *Mailing Add:* Dept Biol Trinity Univ San Antonio TX 78284

MURRAY, HAYDN HERBERT, b Kewanee, Ill, Aug 31, 24; m 44; c 3. CLAY MINERAOLOGY, ECONOMIC GEOLOGY. *Educ:* Univ Ill, BS, 48, MS, 50, PhD(geol), 51. *Prof Exp:* From asst prof to assoc prof geol, Ind Univ, 51-57; dir appl res, Ga Kaolin Co, 57-59, dir res & mfg, 59-63, vpres, 63-64, exec vpres, 64-73; CHMN DEPT GEOL, IND UNIV, 73- *Concurrent Pos:* Clay mineralogist, State Geol Surv, Ind, 51-57; mem exec comt, Working Comt Genesis & Age of Kaolins, UNESCO, 73- *Honors & Awards:* Hal Williams Hardinge Award, Am Inst Mining, Metall & Petrol Engr, 76. *Mem:* Fel Am Ceramic Soc (vpres, 74-75); Am Chem Soc; Mineral Soc Am; distinguished mem Am Inst Mining, Metall & Petrol Engr; distinguished mem Clay Minerals Soc (pres, 65-66). *Res:* Geology, economic uses and chemistry of clay minerals; beneficiation of metallic, non-metallic, and coals using high intensity magnetic separation. *Mailing Add:* Dept Geol Ind Univ Bloomington IN 47401

MURRAY, IRWIN MACKAY, b NS, Can, Nov 20, 19; m 44; c 4. ANATOMY. *Educ:* Dalhousie Univ, MD, 44. *Prof Exp:* From asst prof to assoc prof anat, Dalhousie Univ, 47-50; from asst prof to assoc prof, 51-68, PROF ANAT, COL MED, STATE UNIV NY DOWNSTATE MED CTR, 68-, ASSOC CHMN ANAT & CELL BIOL, 80- *Mem:* Gerontol Soc; Am Asn Anat; NY Acad Sci. *Res:* Physiologic aspects of aging; physiologic functions of reticuloendothelial system; human anatomy. *Mailing Add:* Dept of Anat State Univ NY Downstate Med Ctr Brooklyn NY 11203

MURRAY, JAMES GORDON, b Flint, Mich, July 8, 27; m 47; c 4. ORGANIC POLYMER CHEMISTRY. *Educ:* Univ Mich, BS, 50; Dartmouth Univ, MA, 52; Duke Univ, PhD(chem), 55. *Prof Exp:* Chemist, Monsanto Chem Co, 55-59 & Gen Elec Co, 59-67; group leader polyolefins, 67-74, RES ASSOC, MOBIL CHEM CO, 74- *Mem:* Am Chem Soc. *Res:* Polymers; organometallics; catalysis; petroleum chemistry. *Mailing Add:* Mobil Chem Co PO Box 240 Edison NJ 08817

MURRAY, JAMES W, b Berwyn, Alta, Sept 11, 33; m 60. GEOLOGY. *Educ:* Univ Alta, BSc, 56; Princeton Univ, MA, 63, PhD(geol), 64. *Prof Exp:* Geologist, Texaco Explor Co, Alta, 57-61; fel, Inst Oceanog, 64-65, asst prof geol, 65-69, assoc prof geol & oceanog, 69-74, actg head, Dept Geol, 71-72, PROF GEOL SCI, UNIV BC, 74- *Concurrent Pos:* Mem subcomt stratig, paleont & fossil fuels res, Nat Adv Comt Can, 65-68; co-chmn, Marine Geol Prog Int Geol Cong, Montreal, 72. *Mem:* Fel Geol Soc Am; Am Asn Petrol Geologists; Soc Econ Paleontologists & Mineralogists. *Res:* Origin and distribution of recent marine sediments in fjords and delta; origin of continental shelves and slopes. *Mailing Add:* Dept Geol Sci Univ BC Vancouver BC V6T 1W5 Can

MURRAY, JAY CLARENCE, b Lapoint, Utah, June 27, 29; m 49; c 2. GENETICS, AGRONOMY. *Educ:* Utah State Univ, BS, 51; Colo Agr & Mech Col, MS, 55; Cornell Univ, PhD, 59. *Prof Exp:* Asst agron, Colo Agr & Mech Col, 53-55; asst genetics, Cornell Univ, 55; from asst prof to assoc prof, 59-67, PROF AGRON, OKLA STATE UNIV, 67-, ASSOC DIR AGR EXP STA, 68- *Res:* Physiological genetics of neurospora and photoperiodism in Gossypium; geneome complementation in the tetraploid species of Gossypium; genetics of fiber differentiation in cotton; quantitative genetic studies of fiber properties and earliness of cotton; genetics, cytogenetics, and breeding of forage grasses and legumes. *Mailing Add:* Okla Agr Exp Sta Okla State Univ Stillwater OK 74074

MURRAY, JOAN BAIRD, b Rochester, NY, Nov 20, 26; m 52; c 2. VERTEBRATE ZOOLOGY. *Educ:* Alfred Univ, BA, 48; Syracuse Univ, MA, 50, PhD, 53. *Prof Exp:* Asst prof biol, Western Col, 60-68; TEACHER BIOL, DEKALB COL, 68- *Concurrent Pos:* Grammar sch teacher & demonstr, Ibadan, 65-66. *Mem:* AAAS; Am Inst Biol Sci; Am Soc Zoologists. *Res:* Biogeography; biological education. *Mailing Add:* Dept of Biol DeKalb Col Clarkston GA 30021

MURRAY, JOHN FREDERIC, b Mineola, NY, June 8, 27; m 49; c 3. INTERNAL MEDICINE. *Educ:* Stanford Univ, AB, 49, MD, 53. *Prof Exp:* From intern to asst resident med, San Francisco Hosp, 52-54; from resident to sr resident, Kings County Hosp, New York, 54-56; res fel, Am Col Physicians, Post-Grad Sch Med, Univ London, 56-57; from instr to assoc prof med & physiol, Univ Calif, Los Angeles, 57-59; assoc prof, 66-69, PROF MED, UNIV CALIF, SAN FRANCISCO, 69-, STAFF MEM CARDIOVASC RES INST, SCH MED, 66-; CHIEF CHEST SERV, SAN FRANCISCO HOSP, 66- *Concurrent Pos:* Attend specialist, Vet Admin, 59-; chmn pulmonary training comt, Nat Heart & Lung Inst, 70-72; ed, Am Rev Respiratory Dis; chmn pulmonary acad award comt, Nat Heart & Lung Inst, 74-, mem pulmonary dis adv comt, 75- *Mem:* Asn Am Physicians; Am Soc Clin Invest; Am Fedn Clin Res; Am Physiol Soc; Am Theol Soc (pres, 81). *Res:* Cardiopulmonary physiological techniques in clinical medicine. *Mailing Add:* Chest Serv San Francisco Hosp San Francisco CA 94110

MURRAY, JOHN JOSEPH, b New York, NY, Oct 16, 37; m 60; c 3. ORGANIC CHEMISTRY. *Educ:* Manhattan Col, BS, 59; Fordham Univ, PhD(org chem), 64. *Prof Exp:* Res chemist, Gen Chem Div, Allied Chem Corp, NJ, 64-70; from asst prof to assoc prof, 70-76, PROF CHEM, MIDDLESEX COUNTY COL, 76- *Mem:* Am Chem Soc. *Res:* Synthesis of new fluorinated compounds; chemistry of carbenes and their diazo precursors. *Mailing Add:* Dept of Chem Middlesex County Col Edison NJ 08817

MURRAY, JOHN RANDOLPH, b PEI, Aug 18, 16; m 42; c 2. PHARMACOLOGY. *Educ:* Univ Alta, BSc, 40, MSc, 50; Ohio State Univ, PhD(pharmacol), 55. *Prof Exp:* Asst dispenser, Dunford Drug Co, Ltd, Alta, 40-41; asst dept mgr, Parke, Davis & Co, Ont, 41-42; from lectr pharm to prof, Sch Pharm, Univ Alta, 46-59; dir, Sch Pharm, Univ Man, 59-70, dean fac pharm, 70-81; RETIRED. *Mem:* AAAS; Pharmacol Soc Can; Can Pharmaceut Asn; Asn Fac Pharmaceut Can; Can Found Adv Pharm. *Res:* Hypertension and the antihypertensive drugs. *Mailing Add:* Fac of Pharm Univ of Man Winnipeg MB R3T 2N2 Can

MURRAY, JOHN WOLCOTT, b Flushing, NY, Jan 9, 09; m 38; c 2. CHEMISTRY. *Educ:* Colgate Univ, AB, 30; Johns Hopkins Univ, PhD(chem), 33. *Prof Exp:* Asst chem, Johns Hopkins Univ, 32-33, instr, 33-34; asst, Rockefeller Inst, 34-39; chief chemist, Thomasville Stone & Lime Co, 39-42; from asst prof to prof, 42-71, EMER PROF CHEM, VA POLYTECH INST & STATE UNIV, 71- *Mem:* Am Chem Soc. *Res:* Raman spectra; molecular models; dissociation of phenols; movement of water in cell models; factors controlling nature of cave deposits. *Mailing Add:* 701 York Dr NE Blacksburg VA 24060

MURRAY, JOSEPH BUFORD, b Birmingham, Ala, July 29, 33; m 55; c 2. GEOLOGY. *Educ:* Univ Chattanooga, BS, 55; Univ Tenn, Knoxville, MS, 60; Case Western Reserve Univ, PhD(geol), 71. *Prof Exp:* Asst prof geol & geog, Grove City Col, 60-66; CHIEF GEOLOGIST, DEPT NATURAL RESOURCES, DIV GEOL & WATER RESOURCES, GEOL SURV, 69- *Mem:* Geol Soc Am; Soc Econ Paleontologists & Mineralogists. *Res:* Precambrian and Paleozoic stratigraphy of the southern and central Appalachian Mountains. *Mailing Add:* Dept of Natural Resources Geol Surv Atlanta GA 30334

MURRAY, JOSEPH JAMES, JR, b Lexington, Va, Mar 13, 30; m 57; c 3. ZOOLOGY. *Educ:* Davidson Col, BS, 51; Oxford Univ, BA, 54, MA, 57, DPhil(zool), 62. *Prof Exp:* Instr biol, Washington & Lee Univ, 56-58; from asst prof to assoc prof, 62-73, PROF BIOL, UNIV VA, 73-, CO-DIR, MOUNTAIN LAKE BIOL STA, 64- *Mem:* AAAS; Soc Study Evolution; Am Soc Naturalists; Am Soc Ichthyologists & Herpetologists; Genetics Soc Am. *Res:* Genetics of populations of gastropods. *Mailing Add:* Dept of Biol Univ of Va Charlottesville VA 22903

MURRAY, KENNETH MALCOLM, JR, b Philadelphia, Pa, July 17, 25; div; c 2. NUCLEAR PHYSICS. *Educ:* Univ Miami, BSc, 49; Univ Md, MS, 63; Georgetown Univ, PhD(physics), 69. *Prof Exp:* Instr physics, Univ Miami, 49-51, oceanogr, Marine Lab, 51-52; oceanogr, 52-56, physicist, 56-70, HEAD X-RAY APPLN SECT, RADIATION TECHNOL DIV, NAVAL RES LAB, 70- *Concurrent Pos:* Edison mem grad training prog, Naval Res Lab, 64-66. *Mem:* Am Phys Soc. *Res:* Measured short period current variations in Florida Current between Miami and Gun Cay; photonuclear reactions in light elements; applications of nuclear physics. *Mailing Add:* Code 6633 Naval Res Lab Washington DC 20375

MURRAY, LAWRENCE P(ATTERSON), JR, b Hollins, Va, Nov 30, 30; m 52; c 3. CHEMICAL ENGINEERING. *Educ:* Va Polytech Inst, BSc, 52, MSc, 54, PhD(chem eng), 56. *Prof Exp:* Sr engr tech develop, 55-61, supvr, 61-66, sr res supvr, Spunbonded Div, 65-76, SR RES ENGR, E I DU PONT DE NEMOURS & CO, INC, 76- *Mem:* Am Inst Chem Engrs. *Res:* High polymer development; synthetic fibers and elastomers; textile operations; solvent recovery; spunbonded technology. *Mailing Add:* Dacron Div E I du Pont de Nemours & Co Inc Old Hickory TN 37138

MURRAY, LEO THOMAS, b New York, NY, May 15, 37; m 60; c 5. INORGANIC CHEMISTRY, ORGANIC CHEMISTRY. *Educ:* Manhattan Col, BS, 58; Purdue Univ, PhD(inorg chem), 63. *Prof Exp:* Res chemist, 62-63, sr res chemist, 63-66, sect head oral prod, 66-70, sect head laundry res, 70-72, tech coordr mkt, 72-73, dir contract purchasing, 73-74, mgr household specialties res, 74-78, assoc dir, 78-80, DIR DEVELOP, COLGATE-PALMOLIVE CO, 80- *Mem:* Am Chem Soc; Asn Res Dir; Indust Res Inst. *Res:* Chemistry organoboranes, specifically amine-boranes; chemistry of oxidizing agents, specifically N-kalo and peroxide types; development of household and toiletries consumer products. *Mailing Add:* Colgate-Palmolive Co 909 River Rd Piscataway NJ 08854

MURRAY, MARGARET RANSONE, b Mathews Co, Va, Nov 16, 01; m 41. NEUROSCIENCES. *Educ:* Goucher Col, AB, 22; Washington Univ, MS, 24; Univ Chicago, PhD(zool), 26. *Prof Exp:* Nat Res Coun fel, Univ Chicago, 26-28; assoc prof biol & physiol, Fla State Col Women, 28-29; from instr surg to prof anat, 29-70, EMER PROF ANAT, COL PHYSICIANS & SURGEONS, COLUMBIA UNIV, 70-; res biologist & sr scientist, NIH, 73-81; RETIRED. *Concurrent Pos:* Mem fel rev panel, NIH, 60-63; NIH res career award, 62-72; Commonwealth Fund traveling fel, Europe & Asia, 63-64. *Honors & Awards:* Sci Medal, Univ Brussels, 64. *Mem:* Am Soc Cell Biologists; hon mem Tissue Cult Asn (secy, 46-50, pres, 54-56); Am Asn Anat; Soc Neurosci; hon mem Am Asn Neuropath. *Res:* Neurobiology; organotypic culture of the nervous system; functional differentiation of nerve and muscle in vitro; degenerative diseases of the nervous system; active transport, cerebrovascular. *Mailing Add:* Box 221 Mathews VA 23109

MURRAY, MARION, b Evanston, Ill, Feb 27, 37. NEUROBIOLOGY. *Educ:* McGill Univ, BSc, 59; Harvard Univ, MA, 61; Univ Wis-Madison, PhD(physiol), 64. *Prof Exp:* Res asst neurobiol, Rockefeller Univ, 67-69; asst prof anat, Pritzker Sch Med, Univ Chicago, 69-77; MEM STAFF, DEPT ANAT, MED COL PA, PRITZKER SCH MED, UNIV CHICAGO, 77- *Concurrent Pos:* NIH fel anat, McGill Univ, 64-67. *Mem:* Am Asn Anat; Soc Neurosci. *Res:* Structure and function of nerve cells with special emphasis on synthesis and transport of protein. *Mailing Add:* Med Col of Pa Dept of Anat 3300 Henry Ave Philadelphia PA 19179

MURRAY, MARVIN, b Milwaukee, Wis, June 10, 27; m 59; c 2. CLINICAL PATHOLOGY. *Educ:* Marquette Univ, BS, 48; Mich State Univ, MS, 50, PhD(physiol), 56; Wayne State Univ, MD, 55. *Prof Exp:* Res path resident path, Univ Wis, 56-59; from asst prof to assoc prof, 59-71, dir clin path, 59-78, PROF PATH, SCH MED, UNIV LOUISVILLE, 71-, ADJ ASSOC PROF CHEM, 65- *Concurrent Pos:* Nat Cancer Inst trainee, Univ Wis, 56-59, dir clin labs, Louisville Gen Hosp, 59-78. *Honors & Awards:* Lederle Med Fac award, 64. *Res:* Blood coagulation; protein chemistry; clinical analytical chemistry. *Mailing Add:* 323 E Chestnut St Louisville KY 40202

MURRAY, MARY AILEEN, b Washington, DC, Nov 11, 14. BOTANY. *Educ:* Univ Ariz, BA, 36, MS, 38; Univ Chicago, PhD(bot), 45. *Prof Exp:* Pub sch teacher, Ariz, 37-43; asst bot, Univ Chicago, 43-45, res assoc & instr, 45-48; asst prof, 48-55, ASSOC PROF BOT, DePAUL UNIV, 55- *Mem:* AAAS; Bot Soc Am; Am Inst Biol Sci; Sigma Xi. *Res:* Plant morphology and anatomy. *Mailing Add:* Dept of Biol DePaul Univ Chicago IL 60614

MURRAY, MARY PATRICIA, b Milwaukee, Wis, July 27, 23; m 63. KINESIOLOGY, MEDICAL RESEARCH. *Educ:* Ripon Col, BA, 45; Marquette Univ, MS, 56, PhD(anat), 61. *Prof Exp:* Resident phys ther, Mayo Clin, 45; staff phys therapist, Curative Workshop of Milwaukee, 45-48; staff phys therapist, 48-51, supvr, 51-53, asst chief, 53-54, clin training supvr, 55-58, res & educ supvr, 59-64, CHIEF KINESIOLOGY RES LAB, VET ADMIN CTR, 64- *Concurrent Pos:* From instr to clin prof phys ther, Marquette Univ, 54-; assoc prof, Med Col Wis, 67-80, assoc prof anat, 75-, prof, 80-; grants, NIH, 62-63 & 67-, Vet Admin, 62- & Dept Health, Educ & Welfare, 63-66; mem appl physiol & bioeng study sect, NIH, 71-76; Mary Eleanor Brown Award, Tex Inst Rehab & Res, 81. *Honors & Awards:* Sci Exhibit Award, Am Phys Ther Asn, 64, Marian Williams Res Award, 67. *Mem:* Am Phys Ther Asn; Am Cong Rehab Med; Soc Behav Kinesiology. *Res:* Normal and abnormal human motion; locomotion, postural steadiness and upright stability, muscle strength and joint mobility in patients with neuro-musculo-skeletal disabilities. *Mailing Add:* Kinesiology Res Lab Vet Admin Med Ctr Wood WI 53193

MURRAY, MURRAY J, b Palmerston North, NZ, Oct 30, 22; m 46; c 4. MEDICINE. *Educ:* Univ NZ, MB & ChB, 46, MD, 53; Univ Otago, NZ, DSc, 70; Royal Australasian Col Physicians, dipl, 67; Royal Col Physicians Edinburgh, dipl, 69. *Prof Exp:* Registr, St Stephens Hosp, London, Eng, 50-51; asst physician, Wellington Hosp, NZ, 52-55; from instr to assoc prof, 56-69, PROF MED, UNIV MINN, MINNEAPOLIS, 69-, DIR MED SERV, UNIV HOSP, 70- *Concurrent Pos:* Hartford Found res grant, 68-69. *Mem:* Fel Am Col Cardiol; Am Gastroenterol Asn; Royal Col Physicians; fel Royal Soc Med. *Res:* Coronary artery disease; portal hypertension; iron absorption. *Mailing Add:* 200 N Meadow Lane Minneapolis MN 55422

MURRAY, PETER, b Rotherham, Yorks, UK, Mar 13, 20; m 47; c 3. METALLURGY, CERAMICS. *Educ:* Univ Sheffield, BSc, 41, PhD(metall, ceramics), 49. *Prof Exp:* Res chemist, Steetley Co, Ltd, 41-46; sr sci off ceramics sect, Atomic Energy Res Estab, 49-51, prin sci off, 51-55, sr prin scientist, 55-60, head metall div, 60-64, asst dir-mem bd mgt, 64-67; sr consult, 67-68, tech dir, 68-69, mgr fuels, mats & sodium technol, 69-70, mgr technol, Advan Reactors Div, 70-74, dir, Res Lab, 74-75, mgr technol, Advan Reactors Div, 75-76, mgr bus develop, Advan Nuclear Systs Div, 76-77, chief scientist, Advan Power Systs Div, 77-81, DIR NUCLEAR PROGS, ADVAN ENERGY PROGS DEPT, WESTINGHOUSE ELEC CORP, 81- *Mem:* Nat Acad Eng; Am Nuclear Soc; Am Ceramic Soc; fel Royal Inst Chem; Brit Ceramic Soc (pres, 65). *Res:* Nuclear reactor technology; materials science and technology. *Mailing Add:* Westinghouse Elec Corp 1801 K Street NW Washington DC 20006

MURRAY, RAYMOND CARL, b Fitchburg, Mass, July 2, 29; m 55; c 2. SEDIMENTARY PETROLOGY. *Educ:* Tufts Col, BS, 51; Univ Wis, MS, 52, PhD, 55. *Prof Exp:* Asst, Tufts Col, 50-51 & Univ Wis, 52-55; res geologist, Shell Develop Co Div, Shell Oil Co, 55-62, mgr prod geol res, 62-66; assoc prof geol, Univ NMex, 66-67; prof geol & chmn dept, Rutgers Univ, 67-77; ASSOC V PRES RES & DEAN GRAD SCH, UNIV MONT, MISSOULA, 77- *Concurrent Pos:* Sr field geologist, State Geol Surv, Wis, 52, 54 & Buchans Mining Co, Ltd, 53; instr, Edgewood Col, 53 & 55; vis lectr, Univ Calif, 62; vis scientist, Rijswijk, Neth, 63-64; vis prof, Univ Mont, 75. *Mem:* Fel Geol Soc Am; Soc Econ Paleontologists & Mineralogists; Am Asn Petrol Geologists. *Res:* Petrology of recent sediments and carbonate and evaporite rocks; forensic geology. *Mailing Add:* Univ of Mont Missoula MT 59801

MURRAY, RAYMOND GORBOLD, b Tokyo, Japan, May 12, 16; m 38, 56, 75; c 6. HISTOLOGY. *Educ:* Monmouth Col, SB, 37; Univ Chicago, PhD(histol), 42. *Prof Exp:* Asst histol, Univ Chicago, 39-43, res assoc, 43-46; instr, Med Sch, Tufts Col, 46-48; asst prof path, Dent Sch, Northwestern Univ, 48-49; assoc prof, 49-65, chmn dept anat & physiol, 73-76, PROF ANAT, MED SCH, IND UNIV, BLOOMINGTON, 65- *Mem:* AAAS; Electron Micros Soc Am; Am Soc Cell Biol; Am Asn Anat; Soc Neurosci. *Res:* Tissue culture of thymus; parenteral nutrition; histopathology of x-rays; histopathology and distribution of radioisotopes; morphology and function of lymphocytes; fine structure of taste buds. *Mailing Add:* 1910 E First St Bloomington IN 47401

MURRAY, RAYMOND HAROLD, b Cambridge, Mass, Aug 17, 25; m 48; c 8. CARDIOLOGY. *Educ:* Univ Notre Dame, BS, 45; Harvard Univ, MD, 48; Am Bd Internal Med, dipl, 55; Am Bd Cardiovasc Dis, dipl, 60. *Prof Exp:* Intern med, Peter Bent Brigham Hosp, Boston, Mass, 48-49; resident, Roosevelt Hosp, New York, 49-50; res assoc cardiol, Nat Heart Inst, 50-53; instr med, Univ Mich, 53-54; from assoc prof to prof med, Sch Med, Ind Univ Indianapolis, 67-77, chmn dept community health sci, 72-77; PROF & CHMN DEPT MED, COL HUMAN MED, MICH STATE UNIV, EAST LANSING, 77- *Concurrent Pos:* Fel coun clin cardiol, Am Heart Asn, 64. *Mem:* Cent Soc Clin Res; Am Fedn Clin Res; Am Col Physicians. *Res:* Health care delivery; cardiovascular physiology. *Mailing Add:* Dept of Med Col of Human Med East Lansing MI 48824

MURRAY, RAYMOND L(EROY), b Lincoln, Nebr, Feb 14, 20; m 41, 67, 79; c 7. PHYSICS, NUCLEAR ENGINEERING. *Educ:* Univ Nebr, BS, 40, MA, 41; Univ Tenn, PhD(physics), 50. *Prof Exp:* Asst physics, Univ Nebr, 40-41 & Univ Calif, 41-43, res physicist, Radiation Lab, 42-43; asst dept supt, Tenn Eastman Corp, 43-47; res physicist, Carbide & Carbon Chem Co, 47-50; prof, 50-57, head dept physics, 60-63, head dept nuclear eng, 63-74, Burlington prof, 57-80, EMER PROF PHYSICS, NC STATE UNIV, 80- *Concurrent Pos:* Instr, Oak Ridge Adult Educ Prog, 45-46 & Univ Tenn, 46-47; consult, Oak Ridge Nat Lab, 50-68, AMF Atomics, Conn, 55-64, Alco Prod, Inc, 56-62, Lockheed Aircraft Corp, Ga, 58-62 & Westinghouse Elec Corp, Pa, 58-62; mem, Gov Sci Adv Comt, NC, 61-62; consult, Int Atomic Energy Agency, 63 & 80; exec ed for US, J Nuclear Energy, 63-73; consult, Atomic Power Develop Assocs, Mich, 70-72, Duke Power Co, NC, 71-, US Arms Control & Disarmament Agency, 77-78 & Dept Energy, 80-81. *Honors & Awards:* Oliver Max Gardner Award, Univ NC, 65; Arthur Holly Compton Award, Am Nuclear Soc, 70; Glenn Murphy Award, Am Soc Eng Educ, 76. *Mem:* Fel Am Phys Soc; fel Am Nuclear Soc; Am Soc Eng Educ. *Res:* Nuclear reactor theory, design analysis and radioactive waste management; basic physics; teaching, writing and consulting in nuclear engineering. *Mailing Add:* Dept of Nuclear Eng NC State Univ Raleigh NC 27650

MURRAY, RICHARD BENNETT, b Marietta, Ga, Dec 5, 28; m 56; c 2. SOLID STATE PHYSICS. *Educ:* Emory Univ, AB, 47; Ohio State Univ, MS, 50; Univ Tenn, PhD(physics), 55. *Prof Exp:* Asst physics, Oak Ridge Gaseous Diffusion Plant, 47-48; physicist, Oak Ridge Nat Lab, 55-66; assoc prof, 66-68, actg chmn dept, 75-76, PROF PHYSICS, UNIV DEL, 69-, UNIV COORDR GRAD STUDIES, 79- *Concurrent Pos:* Vis assoc prof, Univ Del, 62-63; lectr, Univ Tenn, 63-66; councr, Oak Ridge Assoc Univs; prin investr, Dept Energy res grant. *Mem:* AAAS; Am Asn Physics Teachers; Sigma Xi; fel Am Phys Soc. *Res:* Luminescence and scintillation phenomena in solids; color centers; channeling; ion penetration and radiation damage; graduate studies administration. *Mailing Add:* Dept of Physics Univ of Del Newark DE 19711

MURRAY, ROBERT EDWARD, biochemistry, virology, see previous edition

MURRAY, ROBERT FULTON, JR, b Newburgh, NY, Oct 19, 31; m 56; c 4. MEDICAL GENETICS. *Educ:* Union Col, NY, BS, 53; Univ Rochester, MD, 58; Am Bd Internal Med, dipl, 66; Univ Wash, MS, 68. *Prof Exp:* Resident med, Colo Gen Hosp, 59-62; sr surgeon, USPHS, NIH, 62-65; fel med genetics, Univ Wash, 65-67; from asst prof to assoc prof pediat & med, 67-74, prof genetics, Sch Arts & Sci, 76, prof oncol, 77, PROF PEDIAT & MED, COL MED, HOWARD UNIV, 74- *Concurrent Pos:* Mem nat adv coun, Nat Inst Gen Med Sci, 71-75; chmn ad hoc comt sickel cell trait, Armed Forces, 72; mem comt inborn errors metab, Nat Res Coun, Nat Acad Sci, 72-75. *Mem:* Nat Inst Med; Am Soc Human Genetics; fel AAAS; fel Am Col Physicians; fel Inst Soc Ethics & Life Sci. *Res:* Studies of factors influencing genetic counseling; genetic and developmental variations in isoenzymes; bioethics; inherited susceptibility to disease. *Mailing Add:* Div of Med Genetics Box 75 Howard Univ Col of Med Washington DC 20059

MURRAY, ROBERT GEORGE EVERITT, b Ruislip, Eng, May 19, 19; m 44; c 3. BACTERIOLOGY. *Educ:* Cambridge Univ, BA, 41, MA, 45; McGill Univ, MD, CM, 43. *Prof Exp:* Lectr, 45-47, from asst prof to assoc prof, 47-49, head dept, 49-74, PROF BACT & IMMUNOL, UNIV WESTERN ONT, 49- *Concurrent Pos:* Ed, Can J Microbiol, 54-60; hon consult, St Joseph's Hosp, London, Ont, 60-; mem, Bergey's Manual Trust, 64-; mem, Int Comt Bact Nomenclature, 66-; gov bd, Biol Coun Can, 66-72; ed, Bact Rev, 69-79. *Honors & Awards:* Coronation Medal, 53; Harrison Prize, Royal Soc Can, 57 & Award, 60-61; Prize, Can Soc Microbiol, 63; Centennial Medal, Govt Can, 67; Jubilee Medal, 78. *Mem:* Fel Am Acad Microbiol; Am Soc Microbiol (vpres, 71-72, pres, 72-73); Am Soc Cell Biologists; fel Royal Soc Can; Can Soc Microbiol (pres, 51-52). *Res:* Bacterial cytology and physiology; ultrastructure of bacteria and relation of structure to function, with emphasis on the cell wall and macromolecular arrangement. *Mailing Add:* Fac of Med Univ of Western Ont London ON N6A 5B8 Can

MURRAY, ROBERT KINCAID, b Glasgow Scotland, Dec 18, 32; m 59; c 4. BIOCHEMISTRY. *Educ:* Glasgow Univ, MB, ChB, 56; Univ Mich, MS, 58; Univ Toronto, PhD(biochem), 61. *Prof Exp:* From asst prof to assoc prof, 61-73, PROF BIOCHEM, UNIV TORONTO, 73- *Res:* Biochemistry of glycosphingolipids; biochemistry of cancer. *Mailing Add:* Dept of Biochem Univ of Toronto Toronto ON M5S 2R8 Can

MURRAY, ROBERT MARIE, b New London, Conn, Mar 5, 27. RUBBER CHEMISTRY. *Educ:* Mass Inst Technol, BS, 48. *Prof Exp:* Rubber chemist, B F Goodrich Co, 49-53; rubber chemist, 53-63, group leader, Elastomers Lab, 63-80, SR SUPVR, EXP STA, E I DU PONT DE NEMOURS & CO, INC, 80- *Mem:* Am Chem Soc. *Res:* Development of new synthetic elastomers, especially compounding and applications. *Mailing Add:* E I du Pont de Nemours & Co Inc Rd 3 Box 250 Bldg C Unit 4-C Hockessin DE 19707

MURRAY, ROBERT WALLACE, b Brockton, Mass, June 20, 28; m 51; c 7. PHYSICAL ORGANIC CHEMISTRY. *Educ:* Brown Univ, AB, 51; Wesleyan Univ, MA, 56; Yale Univ, PhD(chem), 60. *Prof Exp:* Asst chem, Wesleyan Univ, 54-56 & Yale Univ, 56-57; res chemist polymer chem, Olin-Mathieson Chem Corp, 56-57; mem tech staff chem, Bell Tel Labs, Inc, 59-63, res supvr, 63-68; prof chem, 68-80, chmn dept, 75-80, CURATORS' PROF CHEM, UNIV MO-ST LOUIS, 81- *Concurrent Pos:* Mem, Nat Adv Comt Air Pollution Res Grants, 70-73; consult, Panel Vapor Phase Org Air Pollutants from Hydrocarbons, Nat Acad Sci. *Honors & Awards:* Am Chem Soc Award, 74. *Mem:* AAAS; Am Chem Soc; Int Ozone Asn; The Chem Soc; Am Inst Chemists. *Res:* Oxidation of organic compounds; singlet oxygen and ozone chemistry; air pollution chemistry; chemistry of aging; carbene chemistry; reaction mechanisms; enzyme modelling. *Mailing Add:* 1810 Walnutway Dr Creve Coeur MO 63141

MURRAY, ROGER KENNETH, JR, b Buffalo, NY, July 9, 42; c 1. SYNTHESIS, PHOTOCHEMISTRY. *Educ:* Cornell Univ, AB, 64; Mich State Univ, MS, 66, PhD(chem), 69. *Prof Exp:* Fel chem, Princeton Univ, 69-70, instr, 70-71; asst prof, 71-76, ASSOC PROF CHEM, UNIV DEL, 76- *Concurrent Pos:* Teacher & scholar, Camille & Henry Dreyfus Found, 76-81; vis prof, Fulbright-Hayes Found, Univ De Reims, France, 77-78; Lank exchange prof, Universite De Montreal, 81. *Mem:* Am Chem Soc; Sigma Xi. *Res:* Synthesis and chemistry of cage compounds related to adamantane and its derivatives; chemistry of compounds containing strained rings; organic photochemistry; conformational influences on mass spectrometric behavior. *Mailing Add:* Dept Chem Univ Del Newark DE 19711

MURRAY, ROYCE WILTON, b Birmingham, Ala, Jan 9, 37; m 57; c 5. ANALYTICAL CHEMISTRY. *Educ:* Birmingham-Southern Col, BS, 57; Northwestern Univ, PhD(anal chem), 60. *Prof Exp:* From instr to assoc prof, 60-69, actg chmn dept, 70-71, prof, 70-79, KENAN PROF CHEM, UNIV NC, CHAPEL HILL, 79-, CHMN DEPT, 80- *Concurrent Pos:* Alfred P Sloan res fel, 69-72; prog dir chem anal, NSF, 71-72; Guggenheim fel, 80-81; mem, Japan Soc Promotion Sci. *Mem:* Am Chem Soc. *Res:* Electroanalytical chemistry, including surface chemistry, instrumentation and nonaqueous media. *Mailing Add:* Dept Chem Univ NC Chapel Hill NC 27514

MURRAY, STEPHEN PATRICK, b New York, NY, Oct 4, 38; m 62; c 3. PHYSICAL OCEANOGRAPHY. *Educ:* Rutgers Univ, AB, 60; La State Univ, MS, 63; Univ Chicago, PhD(geophys), 66. *Prof Exp:* NSF fel, 66-67; from asst prof to assoc prof, 67-77, PROF MARINE SCI, COASTAL STUDIES INST, LA STATE UNIV, BATON ROUGE, 77-, ASST DIR, COASTAL STUDIES INST, 75- *Concurrent Pos:* Consult, Bangladesh, 80. *Mem:* Am Geophys Union; Am Meteorol Soc; Sigma Xi; Estuarine Res Fedn. *Res:* Coastal oceanography, including generation and trajectories of coastal currents; land-sea interaction and the turbulent diffusion of solid particles under shoaling waves; dynamics of straits; dynamical oceanography of coastal currents and currents in straits in middle east environments such as Egypt, Saudi Arabia and Sudan. *Mailing Add:* Coastal Studies Inst La State Univ Baton Rouge LA 70803

MURRAY, STEPHEN S, b New York, NY, Aug 28, 44; m 65; c 2. X-RAY ASTRONOMY, COSMOLOGY. *Educ:* Columbia Univ, BS, 65; Calif Inst Technol, PhD(physics), 71. *Prof Exp:* Staff scientist x-ray astron, Am Sci & Eng, Inc, 71-73; ASTROPHYSICIST, CTR ASTROPHYS, SMITHSONIAN ASTROPHYS OBSERV, 73- *Concurrent Pos:* Assoc, Harvard Col Observ, 74- *Mem:* Am Astron Soc. *Res:* Observational x-ray astronomy, particularly extragalactic objects; development and use of high sensitivity, high resolution x-ray imaging detectors for extragalactic observations. *Mailing Add:* Ctr Astrophys 60 Garden St Cambridge MA 02138

MURRAY, STEVEN NELSEN, b Los Angeles, Calif, Sept 7, 44; m 66; c 2. MARINE ECOLOGY, PHYCOLOGY. *Educ:* Univ Calif, Santa Barbara, BA, 66, MA, 68; Univ Calif, Irvine, PhD(phycol), 71. *Prof Exp:* From asst prof biol to assoc prof, 71-77, PROF BIOL, CALIF STATE UNIV,

FULLERTON, 78- *Concurrent Pos:* Calif State Univ grants, 72, 73, 75. *Mem:* Phycol Soc Am; Int Phycol Soc; Am Soc Limnol & Oceanog; Ecol Soc Am; AAAS. *Res:* Marine algal ecology, including studies of seaweed distributions and production; successional events in intertidal communities; physiological ecology of seaweeds; marine pollution. *Mailing Add:* Dept of Biol Sci Calif State Univ Fullerton CA 92634

MURRAY, THOMAS PINKNEY, b Charleston, SC, Oct 8, 42; m 65; c 2. ORGANIC CHEMISTRY. *Educ:* Western Carolina Univ, BS, 64; Appalachian State Univ, MA, 66; Va Polytech Inst & State Univ, PhD(chem), 69. *Prof Exp:* Res assoc chem, Univ Alta, 69-71, Vanderbilt Univ, 71-72; asst prof, 72-77, ASSOC PROF CHEM, UNIV NORTH ALA, 77- *Concurrent Pos:* Consult, Tenn Valley Authority, 76-; consult org nitrogen fertilizers, Int Fertilizer Develop. *Mem:* Am Chem Soc; Sigma Xi. *Res:* Biosynthesis of phenolic plant metabolites, isolation and characterization of new metabolites; organic synthesis; beneficiation of phosphate rock by foam floatation. *Mailing Add:* Dept of Chem Univ of N Ala Florence AL 35630

MURRAY, WALLACE JASPER, b Quantico, Va, July 13, 40; m 64; c 3. MEDICINAL CHEMISTRY. *Educ:* San Diego State Univ, BS, 64; Univ Calif, San Francisco, PhD(pharmaceut chem), 74. *Prof Exp:* Instr chem, Mass Col Pharm, 74-75; asst prof med chem, 75-78, ASSOC PROF BIOMED CHEM, MED CTR, UNIV NEBR-OMAHA, 78- *Mem:* Sigma Xi; Am Chem Soc; sci assoc Am Pharmaceut Asn. *Res:* Topological indices in structure-activity relationships; molecular orbital approach to drug-receptor interactions; pharmaceutical analysis. *Mailing Add:* Dept of Biomed Chem Univ Nebr Col Pharm Med Ctr Omaha NE 68105

MURRAY, WILLIAM DOUGLAS, b Guelph, Ont, Sept 14, 50. BIOTECHNOLOGY, MICROBIOLOGY. *Educ:* Univ Waterloo, BSc, 74, MSc, 76, PhD(microbiol), 79. *Prof Exp:* Res assoc, 79-81, ASST RES OFFICER, NAT RES COUN CAN, 81- *Honors & Awards:* W B Pearson Medal, 79. *Mem:* Can Soc Microbiol; Am Soc Microbiol. *Res:* Anaerobic conversion of biomass to energy fuels and chemical feedstock; mechanisms that regulate carbon and electron flow to specific fermentation products. *Mailing Add:* Div Biol Sci Nat Res Coun Can Ottawa ON K1A 0R6 Can

MURRAY, WILLIAM R, b Ottawa, Ont, Dec 4, 24; US citizen; m; c 2. ORTHOPEDIC SURGERY. *Educ:* St Patrick's Col, Ottawa, BSc, 47; McGill Univ, MD & CM, 52. *Prof Exp:* From instr to assoc prof, 58-72, chief orthop out patient surg clin, 58-73, vchmn orthop surg, 76-78, PROF ORTHOP SURG, SCH MED, UNIV CALIF, SAN FRANCISCO, 72-, CHMN DEPT, 78- *Concurrent Pos:* Adv, Bur Hearings & Appeals, Soc Security Admin, Dept Health, Educ & Welfare, 64-72; mem, Arthritis Found. *Mem:* AMA; Am Acad Orthop Surg; Am Orthop Asn; Am Rheumatism Asn; dipl mem Pan Am Med Asn. *Res:* Total hip joint replacement arthroplasty; rheumatoid arthritis. *Mailing Add:* Dept of Orthop Surg Univ of Calif San Franicsco CA 94143

MURRAY, WILLIAM SINGLER, b Chicago, Ill, Aug 16, 17; m 50; c 4. CHEMISTRY. *Educ:* Univ Notre Dame, BS, 39, MS, 40, PhD(org chem), 42. *Prof Exp:* Res chemist, Jackson Lab, E I du Pont de Nemours & Co, Del, 42-51, chief supvr, Plant Technol Sect, Chambers Works, NJ, 51-60, div head, Jackson Lab, Del, 60-64, div head, Process Dept, Chambers Works, NJ, 64-70, tech supt, Petrolchem Div, 70-79; RETIRED. *Mem:* AAAS; Am Chem Soc. *Res:* Fluorinated hydrocarbons; organometallics. *Mailing Add:* 116 Canterbury Dr Wilmington DE 19803

MURRAY, WILLIAM SPARROW, b Wilkes Barre, Pa, July 15, 26; m 52; c 2. SCIENCE ADMINISTRATION. *Educ:* Juniata Col, BS, 50; Univ Md, MS, 52, PhD(entom), 63. *Prof Exp:* Agt entomologist, USDA, 51; dist entomologist, US Army Corps Engrs, 52-55; entomologist, Norfolk Dist, US Dept Navy, 55-58, dist entomologist, River Commands, Washington, DC, 58-62, entomologist, Dept Navy, 63-64; consult, Nat Pesticide Prob, House of Rep, US Cong, 64-65; asst exec secy, Fed Comt Pest Control, 65-69; exec secy, Working Group Pesticides, President's Cabinet Comt Environ, 69-71; staff dir hazardous mat adv comt, 71-72, phys sci adminr, Off Pesticide Progs, 73-78, assoc dep asst adminr, 78-79, DIR TOXICS & PESTICIDES, OFF HEALTH & ECOL EFFECTS, OFF RES & DEVELOP, ENVIRON PROTECTION AGENCY, 79- *Concurrent Pos:* Consult, Nat Plant & Animal Dis & Quarantine Probs, House Appropriations Comt, US Cong, 67. *Honors & Awards:* Qual Increase Award, Off of Pesticide Progs, Environ Protection Agency, 74. *Mem:* AAAS; Sigma Xi; Am Inst Biol Sci; Entom Soc Am. *Res:* National pesticide problem; incidence and effects of pesticides and other pollutants on human health and the environment. *Mailing Add:* 1281 Bartonshire Way Potomac Woods Rockville MD 20854

MURRELL, JAMES THOMAS, JR, b Dickson, Tenn, Mar 17, 42; m 60; c 2. SYSTEMATIC BOTANY. *Educ:* Austin Peay State Col, BS, 64; Vanderbilt Univ, PhD(syst bot), 69. *Prof Exp:* NIH trainee, Univ Miami, 68-69; asst prof biol, George Peabody Col, 69-75; asst prof, 75-78, ASSOC PROF BIOL & DEAN, GRAD SCH, MISS UNIV WOMEN, 78-, DEAN ARTS & SCI, 80- *Res:* Chemotaxonomy; pollination biology. *Mailing Add:* Dept of Biol Miss Univ for Women Columbus MS 39701

MURRELL, KENNETH DARWIN, b Burley, Idaho, Jan 19, 40; m 65; c 2. PARASITOLOGY, IMMUNOLOGY. *Educ:* Chico State Col, AB, 62; Univ NC, Chapel Hill, MSPH, 63, PhD(parasitol), 69. *Prof Exp:* NIH trainee microbiol, Univ Chicago, 69-71; res zoologist, Naval Med Res Inst, 71-78; CHIEF, NON-RUMINANT PARASITE DIS LAB, ANIMAL PARASITOL INST, USDA, 78- *Mem:* Am Asn Vet Parasitol; Am Soc Parasitol; Am Asn Immunol. *Res:* Fundamental mechanisms of immunity to animal parasites; immunochemistry of parasite antigens; epidemiology and diagnoses of food; parasite diseases. *Mailing Add:* Helminth Dis Lab Animal Parasitol Inst USDA Beltsville MD 20705

MURRELL, LEONARD RICHARD, b Stamford Centre, Ont, June 17, 33. ANATOMY. *Educ:* McMaster Univ, BSc, 57, MSc, 58; Univ Minn, Minneapolis, PhD(anat), 64. *Prof Exp:* Asst biol, McMaster Univ, 57-58; from instr to asst prof anat, Univ Minn, Minneapolis, 64-67; from asst prof to assoc prof, 67-74, PROF ANAT, UNIV TENN CTR HEALTH SCI, 74- *Concurrent Pos:* Am Diabetes Asn res fel, Univ Minn, Minneapolis, 64-66; ed-in-chief, J Tissue Cult Methods, 80- *Mem:* Am Asn Anat; Am Diabetes Asn; Brit Soc Cell Biol; Tissue Cult Asn; Can Asn Anat. *Res:* Human anatomy; experimental diabetes; functional cytodifferentiation; organ culture; carcinogenesis model systems. *Mailing Add:* Dept of Anat Univ of Tenn Ctr for Health Sci Memphis TN 38163

MURRILL, EVELYN A, b Sheffield, Ala, April 14, 30. ORGANIC CHEMISTRY. *Educ:* Fontbonne Col, BS, 50; Univ Minn, PhD(organic chem), 66. *Prof Exp:* Instr chem, Avila Col, 65-68; assoc, Chem Dept, Midwest Res Inst, 68-70; res fel, Univ Kans, 70-71; SR PRIN & SR ADV, CHEM SCI DEPT, MIDWEST RES INST, 71- *Concurrent Pos:* Nat Sci Fel, Univ Minn, 64; Nat Sci Res Fel, Ill Inst Technol, 67-68. *Mem:* Am Chem Soc; Sigma Xi. *Res:* Development of methods for analysis of organic molecules in biological motives or complex mixtures. *Mailing Add:* 7521 E 100th St Kansas City MO 64134

MURRILL, PAUL W(HITFIELD), b St Louis, Mo, July 10, 34; m 59; c 3. CHEMICAL ENGINEERING. *Educ:* Univ Miss, BS, 56; La State Univ, MS, 62, PhD(chem eng), 63. *Prof Exp:* Engr, Pittsburgh Plate Glass Co, 59-60 & Ethyl Corp, 62: lectr process control, 62-63, from asst prof to assoc prof chem eng & mech, indust & aerospace eng, La State Univ, Baton Rouge, 63-67, assoc prof chem eng, 67-68, head dept, 67-69, dean acad affairs, 69-70, vchancellor, 69-74, provost, 70-74, prof chem eng, 68-80, chancellor, 74-80; SR VPRES & DIR, ETHYL CORP, 81- *Concurrent Pos:* Consult ed, Intext Educ Publ, NY, 65-72; proj mgr & prin investr, US Dept Defense Proj Themis Study in Digital Automata, 67-70; dir, Nuclear Systs, Inc, 68-71, 74-77; dir, United Way, 69-, pres, 77-79; dir, STL Electronics, Inc, 70-71, 71-; trustee, Gulf South Res Inst, 70-; dir, Boy Scouts Am, 71-77, Foxboro Co, 74-; mem, Comn Future Blacks in Higher Educ & Black Cols & Univs, HEW & Air Univ Bd Visitors, US Air Force; indust consult numerous companies. *Honors & Awards:* Nat Donald Eckman Award, Instrument Soc Am, 76. *Mem:* Am Soc Eng Educ; Am Inst Chem Engrs; Instrument Soc Am; Sigma Xi. *Res:* Process control and dynamics; formulation of mathematical models and simulation techniques; dynamic aspects of unit operations in chemical process industries; automatic control theory; systems engineering; computer applications; digital control. *Mailing Add:* 206 Sunset Blvd Baton Rouge LA 70808

MURRIN, LEONARD CHARLES, b Iowa City, Iowa, Oct 9, 43; m 68; c 3. PHARMACOLOGY. *Educ:* St John's Col, Calif, BA, 65; Yale Univ, PhD(pharmacol), 75. *Prof Exp:* Fel, Dept Pharmacol & Exp Ther, Johns Hopkins Univ Sch Med, 75-78; ASST PROF PHARMACOL, UNIV NEBR MED CTR, OMAHA, 78- *Mem:* AAAS; Soc Neurosci; Am Soc Pharmacol & Exp Therapeut; Am Soc Neurochem; Int Soc Neurochem. *Res:* Neurotransmitter systems in the central nervous system and their development; factors involved in control of neurotransmitter synthesis, release and catabolism. *Mailing Add:* Dept of Pharmacol 42nd & Dewey Ave Omaha NE 68105

MURRISH, C(HARLES) H, electrical engineering, see previous edition

MURRISH, DAVID EARL, b Glasgow, Mont, Jan 28, 37; m 65. COMPARATIVE PHYSIOLOGY. *Educ:* Calif State Col, Los Angeles, BA, 53, MA, 65; Univ Mont, PhD(comp physiol), 68. *Prof Exp:* Res assoc comp physiol, Duke Univ, 68-70; asst prof biol, Case Western Reserve Univ, 70-77; ASSOC PROF BIOL, STATE UNIV NY BINGHAMTON, 77- *Mem:* Am Physiol Soc; Am Soc Zoologists. *Res:* Temperature regulation in birds; transcapillary fluid exchange in birds. *Mailing Add:* Dept of Biol Sci State Univ of NY Binghamton NY 13901

MURRMANN, RICHARD P, b South Bend, Ind, Aug 3, 40; m 61; c 2. PHYSICAL CHEMISTRY, SOIL SCIENCE. *Educ:* Purdue Univ, BS, 62; Cornell Univ, MS, 63, PhD(soil sci chem), 66. *Prof Exp:* Res assoc soil chem, Cornell Univ, 66; res chemist, US Army Cold Regions Res & Eng Lab, NH, 66-74; asst area dir, 74-79, ASSOC CTR DIR, AGR RES SERV, USDA, 79- *Mem:* Am Soc Agron; Soil Sci Soc Am; Sigma Xi. *Res:* Inorganic phosphate in soil; electrical conductivity and diffusivity of ions; adsorption of heavy metal ions by minerals; chemistry of trace components in atmosphere, soil and water; land treatment wastewater. *Mailing Add:* Western Regional Res Ctr USDA Berkeley CA 94710

MURSKY, GREGORY, b Ukraine, Feb 13, 29; Can citizen; m 52; c 2. GEOLOGY. *Educ:* Univ BC, BSc, 56; Stanford Univ, MS, 60, PhD(geol), 63. *Prof Exp:* Geologist, Eldorado Mining & Refining, Ont, 56-57, chief geologist, 57-59; Nat Res Coun Can fel, 63-64; from asst prof to assoc prof geol, 64-68, chmn dept geol sci, 66-68, PROF GEOL, UNIV WIS-MILWAUKEE, 68- *Concurrent Pos:* Geol Surv Can res grant, 65-66; NSF instructional improv grants, 65-68, in-serv inst grant, 67; Univ Wis res grants, 65-71. *Mem:* AAAS; Soc Econ Geol; Mineral Soc Am; Mineral Asn Can; Can Inst Mining & Metall. *Res:* Mineralogy; economic geology; petrology; geochemistry. *Mailing Add:* Dept of Geol Sci Univ of Wis Milwaukee WI 53201

MURTAGH, FREDERICK REED, b Philadelphia, Pa, Nov 20, 44; m 68; c 2. NEURORADIOLOGY. *Prof Exp:* ASST PROF RADIOL, UNIV SOUTH FLA, TAMPA, 79- *Concurrent Pos:* Fel neuroradiol, Jackson Mem Hosp & Univ Miami, 78. *Mem:* Am Med Asn; Radiol Soc NAm. *Res:* Computed tomography, hydrocephalus, aneurysms and cerebral circulation, spinal stenosis. *Mailing Add:* Dept of Radiol Univ of SFla Tampa FL 33612

MURTAUGH, WALTER A, b Providence, RI, Apr 7, 03. NUCLEAR PHYSICS, AERONAUTICS. *Educ:* Providence Col, BA, 24; Cath Univ Am, MS, 43. *Hon Degrees:* MA, Providence Col, 53, DSc, 64. *Prof Exp:* Chmn physics, Aquinas Col High Sch, 33-43; chmn dept, 43-68, PROF PHYSICS,

PROVIDENCE COL, 68- *Concurrent Pos:* Partic, Oper Plumbbob, Nev Test Site, 57; mem staff, Oak Ridge Inst Nuclear Studies, 59; mem adv comt radiation & merit award, Indust Code Comn Safety & Health, 64; mem, RI State Atomic Energy Comn. *Mem:* Fel AAAS; Am Phys Soc; Am Nuclear Soc; Am Meteorol Soc; Am Optical Soc. *Res:* Scattering processes; nuclear materials testing; optical methods of material testing; stability phenomena. *Mailing Add:* Dept Physics Providence Col Providence RI 02918

MURTHA, JOSEPH P, b Connellsville, Pa, July 18, 31; m 54; c 5. CIVIL ENGINEERING. *Educ:* Carnegie Inst Technol, BS, 53, MS, 55; Univ Ill, PhD(civil eng), 61. *Prof Exp:* Instr civil eng, Carnegie Inst Technol, 54-55; res assoc, Univ Ill, 58-61, from asst prof to prof, 61-66, dir water resources ctr, 63-66; dir, Amphibious & Harbor Div, US Naval Civil Eng Lab, Calif, 66-67; sr staff mem, Nat Eng Sci Co, 67-68; mgr ocean eng, Western Offshore Drilling & Explor Co, 68-69; PROF STRUCT & HYDRAUL ENG, UNIV ILL, URBANA, 69- *Concurrent Pos:* Fulbright-Hays sr res fel, US-UK Ed Comn, 76; vis prof eng, Heriot-Watt Univ, 76-77. *Mem:* Am Soc Civil Engrs; Am Geophys Union; Seismol Soc Am. *Res:* Hydraulic engineering; structural dynamics; ocean engineering; water resources. *Mailing Add:* Dept of Civil Eng Univ of Ill Urbana IL 61801

MURTHY, A S KRISHNA, b Bangalore, India, Feb 8, 32; m 65; c 1. HISTOCHEMISTRY, EXPERIMENTAL PATHOLOGY. *Educ:* Univ Mysore, BSc, 50; Univ Bombay, MSc, 55, PhD(biochem), 61. *Prof Exp:* Res asst histochem & exp path, Indian Cancer Res Ctr, Bombay, 52-57, asst res officer endocrinol, 57-61; res assoc morphol, Chicago Med Sch, 61-63; res assoc histochem, Children's Cancer Found, Boston, 63-65; res officer, Indian Coun Med Res, New Delhi, 65-67; res assoc histochem, exp path & biochem, Children's Cancer Res Found, Boston, 67-73; SR SCIENTIST, EG&G MASON RES INST, WORCESTER, 73- *Concurrent Pos:* Ill Rheumatism & Arthritis Found fel, Chicago Med Sch, 61-62, Chicago Heart Asn fel, 62. *Honors & Awards:* Dr Khanolkar Prize, Indian Asn Path & Bact, 63. *Mem:* AAAS; Am Soc Zoologists; Am Asn Cancer Res; Endocrine Soc. *Res:* Functional endocrine tumors and their induction in animals; endocrine interrelationships; carcinogens; chemical analysis of tumors. *Mailing Add:* EG&G Mason Res Inst Worcester MA 01608

MURTHY, ANDIAPPAN KUMARESA SUNDARA, b Sivakasi, India. CHEMICAL ENGINEERING, COMPUTER SCIENCE. *Educ:* Indian Inst Technol, BTech, 66; Columbia Univ, MS, 68, EngScD, 74. *Prof Exp:* Engr res, Digvijay Cement Co, Jamnagar, India, 66-67; res engr inorganic, 68-69, sr engr process, 69-76, engr assoc simulation, 76-78, mgr process, 78-80, MGR FUELS RES, ALLIED CHEM CORP, 80- *Concurrent Pos:* Adj prof, Columbia Univ & NJ Inst Tech. *Mem:* Am Inst Chem Engrs. *Res:* Mathematical modeling of processes; computer simulation; chemical reaction engineering; separation processes; chemical thermodynamics; numerical methods; fuels and synfuels res. *Mailing Add:* 53 Ridgewood Ave Lake Hiawatha NJ 07034

MURTHY, GOPALA KRISHNA, b Bangalore, India, Mar 13, 25; nat US; m 57. DAIRYING. *Educ:* Univ Mysore, BSc, 44; Univ Ill, MS, 53, PhD(dairy technol, biochem), 56. *Prof Exp:* Chemist, Indian Dairy Res Inst, Bangalore, 44-50; asst dairy technol, Univ Ill, 50-56; res assoc dairy chem, Iowa State Col, 56-57; RES CHEMIST MILK & FOODS RES, ROBERT A TAFT SANIT ENG CTR, 57-; RES CHEMIST, BUR FOODS, US FOOD & DRUG ADMIN, 69- *Mem:* AAAS; Am Chem Soc; Am Dairy Sci Asn; Am Inst Chemists; Inst Food Technologists. *Res:* Milk and food biochemical research. *Mailing Add:* Div of Microbiol Bur of Foods 1090 Tusculum Ave Cincinnati OH 45226

MURTHY, GUMMULURU SATYANARAYANA, paleomagnetism, see previous edition

MURTHY, MAHADI RAGHAVANDRARAO V, b Bangalore, India, Nov 3, 29. BIOCHEMISTRY, NEUROCHEMISTRY. *Educ:* Univ Mysore, BSc, 49; Indian Inst Sci, Bangalore, PhD(biochem), 55. *Prof Exp:* Res assoc biochem, Med Br, Univ Tex, 61-63; from asst prof to assoc prof, 64-69, PROF BIOCHEM, FAC MED, LAVAL UNIV, 69-, DIR MOLECULAR NEUROBIOL LAB, 69- *Concurrent Pos:* Fel biochem, Texas A&M Univ, 55-58; fel, Sch Med, Yale Univ, 58-59; Welch Found fel biochem & entom, Med Br, Univ Tex, 59-61. *Honors & Awards:* M Sreenivasaya Award, Coun Indian Inst Sci, 53. *Mem:* AAAS; Can Biochem Soc; Brit Biochem Soc; Fedn Europ Biochem Socs; Chem Inst Can. *Res:* Regulation of protein and nucleic acid synthesis in tissues during growth; metabolism of biological macromolecules; biochemical mechanisms of memory. *Mailing Add:* Dept of Biochem Laval Univ Fac of Med Quebec G1K 7P4 PQ G1K 7P4 Can

MURTHY, RAJASEKARA CHANDRAPPA, b Morale Bevukuppe, India, May 8, 36; m 71. LIMNOLOGY, FLUID MECHANICS. *Educ:* Univ Col Eng, Bangalore, BE, 58; Indian Inst Sci, Bangalore, ME, 60; Univ Waterloo, PhD(mech eng), 67. *Prof Exp:* Asst prof mech eng, Birla Inst Tech, Ranchi, 60-61; lectr, Indian Inst Technol, Madras, 61-64; fel, Univ Waterloo, 67; RES SCIENTIST, CAN CENTRE INLAND WATERS, 68- *Mem:* AAAS; Air Pollution Control Asn; Inst Asn Gt Lakes Res. *Res:* Physical limnology; geophysical fluid mechanics; turbulence and turbulent diffusion in fluids, particularly dispersal of pollutants in the natural environment such as the atmosphere, Great Lakes and oceans. *Mailing Add:* Can Centre for Inland Waters PO Box 5050 Burlington ON L7R 4A6 Can

MURTHY, RAMAN CHITTARAM, b Bangalore, India, US citizen; c 1. BIOLOGY, ENVIRONMENTAL HEALTH. *Educ:* Univ Mysore, BSc, 57, MSc, 61; Univ Notre Dame, MS, 66; Univ Cincinnati, PhD(biol), 72. *Prof Exp:* Fel toxicol, Dept Environ Health, Med Ctr, Univ Cincinnati, 70-74, res assoc, 74-76; ASST PROF BIOL, CENT STATE UNIV, 74-; ADJ ASST PROF ENVIRON HEALTH, MED CTR, UNIV CINCINNATI, 76- *Concurrent Pos:* Asst prof zool, Univ Mysore, 61-64; teaching asst biol, Univ Notre Dame, 64-66 & Univ Cincinnati, 68-70; res assoc biol, Univ Chicago, 66-68. *Mem:* Environ Mutagen Soc; Am Genetic Asn; Genetics Soc Am; Sigma Xi; Acad Kettering Fels. *Res:* Toxicology, genetic toxicology and teratogenic studies; physiological and biochemical responses to environmental pollutante; effects of drugs on the hemotological changes and membrane changes in red blood cells; effects as seen by light and electron microscope. *Mailing Add:* 662 Doepke Lane Cincinnati OH 45231

MURTHY, VADIRAJA VENKATESA, b Bombay, India, Mar 27, 40; US citizen; m 69; c 2. ENZYMOLOGY, AROMATIC AMINO ACID METABOLISM. *Educ:* Univ Bombay, BSc Hons, 59, MSc, 61; Univ Md, PhD(biol chem), 68. *Prof Exp:* Res asst biochem, Purdue Univ, 61-63; res fel, Med Sch, Univ Md, 63-68; sci off pharmacol, St Johns Med Col, Bangalore, India, 68-69; sr res biochemist & asst group leader, USV Pharmaceut Corp, 70-71; res assoc toxicol, Toxicol Ctr, Pharmacol Dept, Univ Iowa, 71-72; vis scientist environ toxicol, Nat Inst Environ Health, 72-74; sr res assoc, Pharmacol Dept, Emory Univ, 74-75; adj asst prof biochem, Chem Dept, Atlanta Univ, 75-76; ASSOC PROF, BIOL DEPT & CO-DIR, MINORITY BIOMED SUPPORT PROG, TALLADEGA COL, 76- *Concurrent Pos:* Guest lectr, Seminar Dermatol, Med Sch, Harvard Univ, 68; minority biomed support consult anal chem, Stillman Col, 80. *Mem:* Am Asn Cancer Res; Am Chem Soc; NY Acad Sci; Am Fedn Clin Res; Sigma Xi. *Res:* Role of tyrosine metabolizing enzymes in the process of hardening of the vitelline membrane following in vitro fertilization of sea urchin eggs and the possible role of melanin. *Mailing Add:* 111 Dogwood Circle Talladega AL 35160

MURTHY, VARANASI RAMA, b Visakhapatnam, India, July 2, 33; m 59. GEOCHEMISTRY. *Educ:* Andhra Univ, India, BSc, 51; Yale Univ, MS, 55, PhD, 57. *Prof Exp:* Res fel geol, Calif Inst Technol, 57-59; res asst geochem, Univ Calif, San Diego, 59-62, asst prof, 62-65; assoc prof, 65-69, PROF GEOCHEM, UNIV MINN, MINNEAPOLIS, 69-, CHMN DEPT, 71- *Mem:* Am Geophys Union; Geochem Soc; Geol Soc Am. *Res:* Petrology; cosmochemistry and lunar investigation; early crustal and mantle evolution in the earth. *Mailing Add:* Dept of Geol & Geophys Univ of Minn Minneapolis MN 55455

MURTHY, VEERARAGHAVAN KRISHNA, b Pudukottah, India, Feb 27, 34; c 3. BIOCHEMISTRY, PHYSIOLOGY. *Educ:* Univ Madras, BS, 53; Univ Bombay, MS, 60, PhD(biochem), 64. *Prof Exp:* Res asst biochem, Vallabhbhai Patel Chest Inst, Univ Delhi, 55-57; sci officer, Indian Cancer Res Ctr, AEC, Govt India, 57-64; ASST PROF MED & BIOCHEM, UNIV NEBR MED CTR, OMAHA, 74- *Concurrent Pos:* Res fels, Univ Fla, 64-68 & Univ Toronto, 68-74. *Mem:* Royal Inst Chemists; Can Biochem Soc; Am Diabetes Asn. *Res:* Diabetes and lipid metabolism; hormones and lipids; cardiac muscle metabolism; muscle contraction; drug metabolism in cancer. *Mailing Add:* 3410 Jones Omaha NE 68105

MURTHY, VISHNUBHAKTA SHRINIVAS, pharmacology, see previous edition

MURTY, DANGETY SATYANARAYANA, b Visakhapatnam, India, Dec 28, 27; m 52; c 2. PHYSICS. *Educ:* Govt Arts Col, India, BSc, 48; Presidency Col, MA, 50; Andhra Univ, MSc, 51, DSc(ionosphere physics), 56. *Prof Exp:* Lectr appl physics, Andhra Univ, India, 52-57; Colombo Plan res scholar, 57-58; lectr appl physics, Andhra Univ, 58-60; assoc prof physics & actg head dept, Tex Southern Univ, 60-63; assoc prof, 63-69, chmn dept, 63-72, PROF PHYSICS, ST MARY'S UNIV, NS, 69- *Concurrent Pos:* Vis scholar, Univ Calif, Berkeley, 77-78. *Mem:* Can Asn Physicists; Inst Elec & Electronics Engrs; Am Asn Physics Teachers; fel Brit Inst Elec Engrs; fel Brit Inst Electronics & Radio Engrs. *Res:* Mossbauer effect; radio astronomy; low energy nuclear physics. *Mailing Add:* St Mary's Univ Robie St Halifax NS B3H 3C3 Can

MURTY, DASIKA RADHA KRISHNA, b Guntur, India, Dec 13, 31; m 49; c 4. ORGANIC CHEMISTRY. *Educ:* Andhra Univ, India, BSc, 51, MSc, 52; Fla State Univ, PhD(org chem), 60. *Prof Exp:* Asst org chem, Fla State Univ, 55-60; fel, Wayne State Univ, 60; sr chemist, Tracerlab Div, Lab for Electronics, Inc, 61-63; sr res scientist, 63-68, supvr, Radiomed Synthesis Sect, 68-70, head, Radiopharmaceut Res Sect, 70-72, head, In-Vitro Diag Sect, 72-79, ASST DIR CLIN ASSAY RES & DEVELOP, E R SQUIBB & SONS, 79- *Mem:* AAAS; Am Inst Clin Chemists; Am Chem Soc; Soc Nuclear Med. *Res:* Heterocyclics synthesis, reaction mechanisms; synthesis of radiochemicals and radiopharmaceuticals; clinical radioassay research and development. *Mailing Add:* 755 Hoover Dr North Brunswick NJ 08902

MURTY, HARI SRIRAM, biochemistry, see previous edition

MURTY, KATTA GOPALAKRISHNA, b Pandillapalli, India, Sept 9, 36; m 64; c 2. OPERATIONS RESEARCH. *Educ:* Madras Univ, BSc, 55; Univ Calif, Berkeley, MS, 66, PhD(opers res), 68. *Prof Exp:* Consult asst prof statist & opers res, Indian Statist Inst, Calcutta, 58-65; prog adv, Dept Indust & Opers Eng, 75-78, assoc prof, 68-80, PROF OPERS RES, UNIV MICH, ANN ARBOR, 80- *Concurrent Pos:* Fulbright travel grant, 61-62. *Mem:* Assoc mem Opers Res Soc Am; Math Prog Soc; Sigma Xi. *Res:* Mathematical programming; branch and bound algorithms; complementarity problem; network flows; convex polyhedra. *Mailing Add:* Dept Indust & Opers Eng Univ Mich Ann Arbor MI 48109

MURTY, RAMA CHANDRA, b Vizianagaram, India, July 1, 28; Can citizen; m 62; c 1. PHYSICS. *Educ:* Andhra Univ, India, BSc, 47; Univ Bombay, MSc, 50, dipl librarianship, 51; Univ Western Ont, MSc, 58, PhD(physics), 62. *Prof Exp:* Demonstr physics, Wilson Col, Bombay, 47-52; librn, Express Newspapers Ltd, India, 52; sr master physics, Harrison Col, Barbados, West Indies, 52-57; demonstr, 57-58, sr demonstr, 58-61, res assoc geophys, 59-61, lectr physics, 61-63, asst prof, 63-68, ASSOC PROF PHYSICS, UNIV WESTERN ONT, 68- *Concurrent Pos:* Scanner, Tata Inst Fundamental Res, India, 50; Nat Res Coun Can grant, 65-; contract, Meteorol Br, Can Dept Transportation, 65-72; chmn comn VII, Can Div, Int Sci Radio Union. *Mem:* NY Acad Sci; Am Asn Physics Teachers; Am Meteorol Soc; Can Asn Physicists; Brit Inst Physics. *Res:* Physics of lightning; atmospheric electricity; sferics and meteorology. *Mailing Add:* Dept of Physics Univ of Western Ont London ON N6A 5B8 Can

MURTY, TADEPALLI SATYANARAYANA, b Rambhotlapalem, India, Aug 5, 37; m 67. PHYSICAL OCEANOGRAPHY. *Educ:* Andhra Univ, India, BSc, 55, MSc, 59; Univ Chicago, MS, 62, PhD(geophys), 67. *Prof Exp:* Lectr physics, Osmania Col, India, 59-60; res asst geophys, Univ Chicago, 60-67; res scientist I, 67-69, RES SCIENTIST II, CAN DEPT ENVIRON, 69- *Concurrent Pos:* Can mem int tsunami comt, Int Union Geod & Geophys, 71- *Honors & Awards:* Distinguished Res Medal, Univ Chicago, 67. *Mem:* Am Geophys Union; Am Meteorol Soc; Am Soc Limnol & Oceanog; Seismol Soc Am; Am Math Soc. *Res:* Theoretical research in physical oceanography using numerical integration techniques. *Mailing Add:* Inst of Ocean Sci PO Box 6000 9860 W Saanic Sidney BC V8L 4B2 Can

MURVOSH, CHAD M, b Toronto, Ohio, Aug 10, 31; m 65; c 3. AQUATIC ECOLOGY. *Educ:* Kent State Univ, BS, 53; Ohio State Univ, MS, 58, PhD(zool, entom), 60. *Prof Exp:* Instr entom, Ohio State Univ, 60-61; instr zool, Ohio Wesleyan Univ, 61; med entomologist, Entom Res Div, USDA, 62-64; from asst prof to assoc prof zool, 64-78, PROF BIOL, UNIV NEV, LAS VEGAS, 78- *Concurrent Pos:* Grant, Desert Res Inst, Univ Nev, 65-66. *Mem:* Entom Soc Am; Ecol Soc Am; Soc Study Evolution; Soc Syst Zool; Am Mosquito Control Asn. *Res:* Aquatic insect ecology and medical entomology. *Mailing Add:* Dept of Biol Sci Univ of Nev Las Vegas NV 89154

MUSA, SAMUEL A, electrical engineering, applied mathematics, see previous edition

MUSACCHIA, X, b Brooklyn, NY, Feb 11, 23; m 50; c 4. PHYSIOLOGY, ZOOLOGY. *Educ:* St Francis Col, NY, BS, 44; Fordham Univ, MS, 47, PhD(biol), 49. *Prof Exp:* Instr biol, Marymount Col, NY, 47-49; instr comp physiol, St Louis Univ, 49-51, from asst prof to prof, 51-65; prof physiol, Univ Mo-Columbia, 65-78, assoc dean, grad sch & assoc dir res, 72-78, dir, Dalton Res Ctr, 74-78; PROF PHYSIOL & BIOPHYS & DEAN GRAD SCH, UNIV LOUISVILLE, 78- *Concurrent Pos:* Co-dir, Arctic Res Projs, St Louis Univ, 49-52, actg dir, Biol Labs, 52-53; vis scientist, Am Physiol Soc, 63-65; sr investr, Dalton Res Ctr, 65-74. *Mem:* Fel AAAS; Am Physiol Soc; Am Soc Zoologists; Sigma Xi; Soc Exp Biol Med. *Res:* Environmental physiology; biochemistry of hibernation in reptiles and mammals; radiation biology and comparative physiology of intestinal absorption; physiology of depressed metabolism, hypothermia and hibernation; gravitational physiology. *Mailing Add:* Grad Sch Univ of Louisville Louisville KY 40292

MUSAL, HENRY M(ICHAEL), JR, b Chicago, Ill, Aug 18, 31; m 52; c 4. ELECTRICAL ENGINEERING, ELECTROMAGNETIC PHYSICS. *Educ:* Ill Inst Technol, BS, 54, MS, 57, PhD(elec eng), 65. *Prof Exp:* Jr engr, Sinclair Res Labs, 53-54; instr elec eng, Ill Inst Technol, 54-56; sr engr, Cook Res Labs, 56-58 & Bendix Systs Div, 58-61; staff scientist, GM Defense Res Labs, Calif, 61-67; STAFF SCIENTIST, LOCKHEED PALO ALTO RES LAB, 67- *Mem:* Inst Elec & Electronics Engrs; Am Phys Soc. *Res:* Laboratory generation of plasma for basic investigations; plasma diagnostics; gas lasers; radar systems and electromagnetic wave scattering; interaction of electromagnetic fields and laser radiation with plasmas and materials. *Mailing Add:* Dept 52-56 Bldg 205 3251 Hanover St Palo Alto CA 94304

MUSCARI, JOSEPH A, b Chicago, Ill, May 13, 35; m 60; c 6. PHYSICS. *Educ:* Beloit Col, BS, 57; Johns Hopkins Univ, MS, 63; Wash State Univ, PhD(physics), 66. *Prof Exp:* Teacher high sch, 59-63; chief, Optical Physics Sect, 66-70, RES SCIENTIST, MARTIN MARIETTA CORP, 70- *Concurrent Pos:* Prin investr, Skylab Prog Exp, Martin Marietta Corp. *Mem:* Optical Soc Am; Am Vacuum Soc. *Res:* Nuclear physics; gamma ray spectroscopy; optical physics; vacuum ultraviolet spectroscopy. *Mailing Add:* 2413 W Costilla Littleton CO 80120

MUSCATELLO, ANTHONY CURTIS, b Princeton, WVa, Sept 25, 50. SEPARATIONS CHEMISTRY, RADIOCHEMISTRY. *Educ:* Concord Col, BS, 72; Fla State Univ, PhD(inorg chem), 79. *Prof Exp:* Res assoc, Argonne Nat Lab, 79-81; SR RES CHEMIST, ROCKY FLATS PLANT, ROCKWELL INT, 81- *Mem:* Am Chem Soc. *Res:* Separations chemistry of actinides and lanthandes-solvent extraction using bifunctional organophosphorus compounds, ion-exchange chromatography; formation and dissociation kinetics of transplutonium element chelates; radiochemical techniques. *Mailing Add:* Rocky Flats Plant Rockwell Int PO Box 464 Golden CO 80401

MUSCATINE, LEONARD, b Trenton, NJ, Sept 7, 32; m 57; c 4. INVERTEBRATE ZOOLOGY, COMPARATIVE PHYSIOLOGY. *Educ:* Lafayette Col, BA, 54; Univ Calif, Berkeley, MA, 56, PhD(zool), 61. *Prof Exp:* Fel biochem, Howard Hughes Med Inst, 61-62; fel plant biochem, Scripps Inst Oceanog, 62-63, res biologist, 63-64; assoc prof, 64-74, PROF BIOL, UNIV CALIF, LOS ANGELES, 74-, CHMN DEPT, 76- *Concurrent Pos:* NIH fel, 61-63; NSF res grant, 63-64 & 65-77; Guggenheim fel, Oxford Univ, 70-71. *Mem:* Am Soc Zoologists; Brit Soc Exp Biol; Marine Biol Asn UK. *Res:* Coelenterate physiology; symbiosis of invertebrates and unicellular algae; biology of corals and coral reefs. *Mailing Add:* Dept of Biol Univ of Calif Los Angeles CA 90024

MUSCHEK, LAWRENCE DAVID, b Philadelphia, Pa, Apr 28, 43; m 64; c 3. BIOCHEMICAL PHARMACOLOGY. *Educ:* Philadelphia Col Pharm & Sci, BSc, 65; Mich State Univ, PhD(biochem), 70. *Prof Exp:* Mich Heart Asn fel cardiovasc pharmacol, Mich State Univ, 70-72; res scientist, 72-73, sr scientist, 73-76, group leader cardiovasc biochem, 76-78, head biochem mechanisms sect, 78-79, DIR, DEPT BIOL RES, MCNEIL LABS, INC, 76- *Mem:* Am Chem Soc; AAAS. *Res:* Discovery and development of new agents effective in the treatment and/or prevention of thrombosis; mechanisms responsible for myocardial ischemia and infarction. *Mailing Add:* Dept of Biochem McNeil Labs Inc Ft Washington PA 19034

MUSCHEL, LOUIS HENRY, b New York, NY, July 4, 16; m 46; c 1. IMMUNOLOGY. *Educ:* NY Univ, BS, 36; Columbia Univ, AM, 38; Yale Univ, MS, 51, PhD(microbiol), 53. *Prof Exp:* Asst supvr, Serum Diag Dept, Div Labs & Res, NY State Dept Health, 39-41 & 46; chief, Dept Spec Serol & exec officer, Fourth Area Lab, Brooke Med Ctr, US Army Med Serv Corps, Tex, 46-47, chief lab serv, 20th Sta Hosp, Clark Field, PI, 47-48, Depts Serol & Chem, Second Area Lab, Ft Meade, Md, 48-50, 406th Med Gen Lab, Far East Command, 53-56, Exp Immunol Sect, Dept Appl Immunol, Walter Reed Army Inst Res, Washington, DC, 56-58, Dept Serol, 58-62; from assoc prof to prof microbiol, Med Sch, Univ Minn, Minneapolis, 62-70; MEM STAFF, RES DEPT, AM CANCER SOC, 70- *Concurrent Pos:* Abstractor, Biol Abstr, 47-48 & Chem Abstr, Am Chem Soc, 55-62; mem, Bact & Mycol Study Sect, Div Res Grants, NIH, 59- & Grants Rev Comt, Minn Chap, Arthritis & Rheumatism Found, 65-70; consult, Walter Reed Army Inst Res, Washington, DC, 63- & Vet Admin Hosp, Minneapolis, 65-; adj prof microbiol, Columbia Univ, 77- *Mem:* Am Soc Microbiol; Soc Exp Biol & Med; Am Asn Immunol; Am Asn Cancer Res; NY Acad Sci. *Res:* Immunochemistry; natural resistance; bactericidal reactions; serology of syphilis; immunohematology. *Mailing Add:* Res Dept Am Cancer Soc 777 Third Ave New York NY 10017

MUSCHIK, GARY MATHEW, b Rice Lake, Wis, July 22, 44; m 70; c 2. ORGANIC & ANALYTICAL CHEMISTRY. *Educ:* Wis State Univ, River Falls, BS, 66; Kans State Univ, PhD(chem), 72. *Prof Exp:* Chemist, Agr Res Serv, USDA, 72-73; scientist, 73-77, HEAD CHEM SYNTHETICS & ANAL, FREDERICK CANCER RES CTR, NAT CANCER INST, 77- *Mem:* Am Chem Soc; Am Soc Mass Spectrometry; AAAS. *Res:* Polycyclic aromatic hydrocarbon synthesis, separation, identification, metabolism and carcinogenicity studies; synthesis and development of liquid crystal GLC liquid phases for novel separations; development of new methodologies in analytical chemistry and organic syntheses. *Mailing Add:* Frederick Cancer Res Ctr PO Box B Frederick MD 21701

MUSCHIO, HENRY M, b New York, NY, Apr 25, 31; m 57; c 4. HUMAN GENETICS. *Educ:* Syracuse Univ, AB, 52; Fordham Univ, MS, 57, PhD(biol), 63. *Prof Exp:* Instr biol sci, Fairleigh Dickinson Univ, 58-62; asst prof, Montclair State Col, 62-66; assoc prof, 66-68, PROF BIOL SCI, DUTCHESS COMMUNITY COL, 68-, HEAD DEPT, 66- *Concurrent Pos:* Dir & lectr, NSF Inserv Inst Modern Biol, Montclair State Col, 65-66; dir, NSF grant, Norrie Point Proj, Dutchess Community Col, 79-82; mem bd dirs, Rehab Progs Inc, Poughkeepsie & Anderson Sch, Staatsburg, NY. *Mem:* AAAS; NY Acad Sci; Nat Sci Teachers Asn. *Res:* Human cytogenetics and cytological research related to the effects of chemical agents and their effects on the human karyotype and various human cell lines in vitro, with consideration of ethical and moral issues and values. *Mailing Add:* Dept of Biol Sci Dutchess Community Col Poughkeepsie NY 12601

MUSCHLITZ, EARLE EUGENE, JR, b Palmerton, Pa, Apr 23, 21; m 53; c 2. PHYSICAL CHEMISTRY, CHEMICAL PHYSICS. *Educ:* Pa State Univ, BS, 41, MS, 42, PhD(phys chem), 47. *Prof Exp:* Asst, Pa State Univ, 43-46; instr phys chem, Cornell Univ, 47-51; asst res prof, Col Eng, Univ Fla, 51-53, assoc prof, Univ Fla, 53-58, chmn dept, 73-77, PROF CHEM, UNIV FLA, 58- *Concurrent Pos:* NSF sr fel, 63-64; vis fel, Joint Inst Lab Astrophys, Boulder, Colo, 68; Alexander von Humboldt sr scientist award, Gottingen, WGer, 78. *Mem:* AAAS; Am Chem Soc; fel Am Phys Soc. *Res:* Ion, electron and excited atom scattering in gases; negative ions; molecular beams; mass spectrometry; molecular structure; upper atmosphere phenomena. *Mailing Add:* Dept Chem Univ Fla Gainesville FL 32611

MUSCOPLAT, CHARLES CRAIG, b St Paul, Minn, Aug 13, 48; m 69; c 2. IMMUNOLOGY, VETERINARY MEDICINE. *Educ:* Univ Minn, BA, 70, PhD(vet microbiol), 75. *Prof Exp:* Instr, Cornell Med Sch, 75-76; assoc, Sloan-Kettering Inst, NY, 75-76; res assoc immunol, Univ Minn, 76-78, assoc prof, 78-81; VPRES MED PROD, MOLECULAR GENETICS, INC, MINNETONKA, MINN, 81- *Concurrent Pos:* Consult, Kallestad Labs, 78- *Mem:* Am Asn Immunologists; Am Soc Microbiol; Conf Res Workers Animal Dis. *Res:* Immunology of respiratory disease in cattle; immunology of cancer and immune regulation. *Mailing Add:* Molecular Genetics Inc Minnetonka MN 55343

MUSE, JOEL, JR, b Williamston, NC, July 11, 41; div; c 2. INDUSTRIAL ORGANIC CHEMISTRY. *Educ:* Univ NC, Chapel Hill, AB, 63; Univ Md, College Park, PhD(chem), 68. *Prof Exp:* Sr res chemist, 68-77, sect head, 77-80, MGR, GOODYEAR TIRE & RUBBER CO, AKRON, 80- *Mem:* Am Chem Soc. *Res:* Process and product development; rubber chemicals; hydroquinone and derivates. *Mailing Add:* 1089 Kevin Dr Kent OH 44240

MUSGRAVE, ALBERT WAYNE, b Eads, Colo, Jan 22, 23; m 43; c 4. GEOPHYSICS, ENGINEERING. *Educ:* Colo Sch Mines, ScD(geophys eng), 52. *Prof Exp:* from geophys trainee to interpreter, Seismic Surv, Magnolia Petrol Co, Socony Mobil Oil Co, Inc, 47-49, seismologist seismic interpretation, Mobil Oil Corp, 50, seismic party chief, Seismic Surv, 52-53, res geophysicist geophys explor, 54-60, supt spec probs, 60-65, sr geophys scientist, Geophys Serv Ctr, 65-72, sr scientist, Seismic Res, Mobil Res & Develop, 72-80; RETIRED. *Honors & Awards:* Van Diest Gold Medal, Colo Sch Mines, 61. *Mem:* Soc Explor Geophys; Sigma Xi; Am Asn Petrol Geologists. *Res:* Geophysical engineering; physics; geology; mathematics; electronics; seismology; gravity; magnetism; well logging. *Mailing Add:* 6404 Lavendale Dallas TX 75230

MUSGRAVE, CAROL ANN, b Riverside, Calif, Sept 30, 48. ENTOMOLOGY. *Educ:* Boise State Col, BS, 71; Ore State Univ, PhD(entom), 74. *Prof Exp:* Res aide entom, Ore State Univ, 74; ASST PROF ENTOM & NEMATOL, UNIV FLA, 74- *Mem:* Entom Soc Am; Am Inst Biol Sci; Sigma Xi; AAAS. *Res:* Biology and ecology of parasitic insects and agriculturally important arthropod pests; biology, ecology and systematics of leafhoppers (Homoptera Cicadellidae). *Mailing Add:* Dept of Entom & Nematol 339 Archer Rd Lab Univ Fla Gainesville FL 32611

MUSGRAVE, F STORY, b Boston, Mass, Aug 19, 35; m; c 5. PHYSIOLOGY, SURGERY. *Educ:* Syracuse Univ, BS, 58; Univ Calif, Los Angeles, MBA, 59; Marietta Col, BA, 60; Columbia Univ, MD, 64; Univ Ky, MS, 66. *Prof Exp:* Intern surg, Med Ctr, Univ Ky, 64-65; SCIENTIST-ASTRONAUT, JOHNSON SPACECRAFT CTR, NASA, 67- *Concurrent Pos:* US Air Force fel aerospace physiol & med & Nat Heart Inst fel, Univ Ky, 65-67; instr physiol & biophys, Med Ctr, Univ Ky, 69-; fel surg, Denver Gen Hosp, 69- *Honors & Awards:* Except Serv Medal, NASA, 74. *Mem:* AAAS; Aerospace Med Asn; Am Inst Aeronaut & Astronaut; AMA; Civil Aviation Med Asn. *Res:* Design and development of Space Shuttle extravehicular activity equipment and procedures. *Mailing Add:* NASA Code CB Houston TX 77058

MUSGRAVE, STANLEY DEAN, b Hutsonville, Ill, Jan 26, 19; m 44; c 2. ANIMAL BREEDING, ANIMAL NUTRITION. *Educ:* Univ Ill, BS, 47, MS, 48; Cornell Univ, PhD(animal breeding), 51. *Prof Exp:* Asst animal husb, Cornell Univ, 47-50; asst prof dairy prod, Univ Ill, 50-51; from asst prof to prof dairying & head dept, Okla State Univ, 51-68; chmn dept, 68-73, PROF ANIMAL & VET SCI, UNIV MAINE, ORONO, 68-, CHMN DEPT, 80- *Concurrent Pos:* Prog chmn, Am Dairy Sci Asn, 66; chmn, Dept Animal & Vet Sci, Univ Maine, Orono, 68-73; consult, Mossoro Advan Sch Agr, Brazil, 74- & Univ Mosul, Iraq, 73- *Mem:* AAAS; Am Soc Animal Sci; Am Genetics Asn; Am Registry Cert Animal Scientists; Am Dairy Sci Asn. *Res:* Milk component analysis; dairy cattle nutrient, health requirements; scanning electron microscopic studies of feed and age effect on gastrointestinal epithelium; dairy management systems development and analysis; animal production. *Mailing Add:* Dept Animal & Vet Sci Univ Maine Orono ME 04473

MUSGRAVE, TED RUSSELL, inorganic chemistry, see previous edition

MUSHAK, PAUL, b Dunmore, Pa, Dec 9, 35. BIOCHEMISTRY, CHEMISTRY. *Educ:* Univ Scranton, BS, 61; Univ Fla, PhD(chem), 70. *Prof Exp:* Res asst clin biochem & toxicol, Clin Res Labs, Sch Med, Univ Fla, 67-69; NIH res assoc metalloenzym, Dept Molecular Biophys & Biochem, Yale Univ, 69-71; ASST PROF METAL BIOCHEM & PATH, UNIV NC, CHAPEL HILL, 71- *Concurrent Pos:* Sr mem, Nat Inst Environ Health Sci proj prog heavy metal path, Univ NC, Chapel Hill, 71-, Environ Protection Agency & Inter-univ Consortium Environ Studies grants, 71-; consult, Nat Inst Environ Health Studies, 71-; mem & consult, Inter-univ Consortium Environ Studies, 71- *Mem:* AAAS; Am Chem Soc. *Res:* Metalloenzymology; trace metal analysis; metabolism and biochemical effects of metal chelating agents; heavy metal toxicology; organometallic chemistry of the nickel triad metals. *Mailing Add:* Dept of Path Univ of NC Sch of Med Chapel Hill NC 27514

MUSHER, DANIEL MICHAEL, b New York, NY, Feb 27, 38; m 67; c 3. MEDICINE, INFECTIOUS DISEASES. *Educ:* Harvard Univ, BA, 59; Columbia Univ, MD, 63. *Prof Exp:* Intern resident med, Columbia Div, Bellevue Hosp, New York, 63-65; chief internal med, USAF Hosp, Laredo AFB, Tex, 65-67; resident NIH trainee infectious dis, Tufts-New England Med Ctr, 67-71; asst prof, 71-73, assoc prof, 73-76, PROF MED MICROBIOL & IMMUNOL, BAYLOR COL MED, 76- *Mem:* Am Asn Immunologists; Am Fedn Clin Res; Am Soc Clin Invest; Am Soc Microbiol; Soc Exp Biol & Med. *Res:* Infectious diseases and host response; immunologic aspects of syphilis; urinary tract infections. *Mailing Add:* Vet Admin Hosp 2002 Holcombe Blvd Houston TX 77211

MUSHETT, CHARLES WILBUR, b Elizabeth, NJ, Apr 1, 14; m 39. PATHOLOGY. *Educ:* NY Univ, AB, 39, MS, 41, PhD(vert morphol), 44. *Prof Exp:* Technician, Merck Inst Therapeut Res, Merck & Co Inc, 33-35, lab asst, 35-37, sr worker, Bact & Path Dept, 37-40, assoc hemat & path, 40-43, from assoc head to head dept path, 43-56, from asst dir to dir sci rels, Merck Sharp & Dohme Res Labs, 57-66, dir int sci rels, 66-70, dir sci indust liaison, Merck Sharp & Dohme Res Labs, 70-79; CONSULT, 79- *Concurrent Pos:* Merck foreign fel, Denmark & Ger, 52-53. *Mem:* AAAS; Endocrine Soc; Am Soc Exp Path; fel NY Acad Sci; fel Int Soc Hemat. *Res:* Experimental animal pathology and hematology in relation to nutrition, infection and toxicology of drugs; blood coagulation and anticoagulants. *Mailing Add:* 82 Parkway Dr Clark NJ 07066

MUSHINSKI, JOSEPH FREDERIC, b New Brighton, Pa, Mar 18, 38; m 71. BIOCHEMISTRY, CANCER. *Educ:* Yale Univ, BA, 59; Harvard Med Sch, MD, 63. *Prof Exp:* Intern med, Med Ctr, Duke Univ, 63-64; res assoc biochem, 65-70, SR INVESTR, LAB CELL BIOL, NAT CANCER INST, 70- *Concurrent Pos:* USPHS fel, Res Training Prog, Med Ctr, Duke Univ, 64-65; William O Moseley traveling fel from Harvard Univ, Max Planck Inst Exp Med, 69-70. *Mem:* Am Asn Cancer Res; AAAS; Am Soc Biol Chemists. *Res:* Molecular biology of cancer; immunology; messenger RNA; genomic DNA; transfer RNA. *Mailing Add:* Lab of Cell Biol Nat Cancer Inst Bldg 8 Rm 120 NIH Bethesda MD 20205

MUSHINSKY, HENRY RICHARD, ecology, behavioral biology, see previous edition

MUSHOTZKY, RICHARD FRED, b New York, NY, June 18, 47; m 81. ASTROPHYSICS. *Educ:* Mass Inst Technol, BS, 68; Univ Calif, San Diego, MS, 70, PhD(physics), 76. *Prof Exp:* Res assoc physics, Univ Calif, San Diego, 69-76, res fel, 76-77; Nat Res Coun assoc, 77-79, ASTROPHYSICIST, GODDARD SPACE FLIGHT CTR, NASA, 79- *Mem:* Am Astron Soc. *Res:* X-ray astronomy concentrating on x-ray observations; clusters of galaxies, seyfert galaxies, BL Lac objects. *Mailing Add:* Goddard Space Flight Ctr 661 Greenbelt MD 20771

MUSIC, JOHN FARRIS, b Childress, Tex, Oct 5, 21; m 42; c 2. PHYSICAL CHEMISTRY, PHYSICS. *Educ:* Univ Tex, BA, 46, PhD(phys chem), 51. *Prof Exp:* Res scientist, Gen Elec Co, 51-52, supvr graphite & mat develop, 52-54, process tech, 54-56, mgr, 56-60, proj analyst, 60-61, consult analyst, 61-65, mgr, Div Anal & Planning, 65-68, mgr aerospace anal & planning, Aerospace Group, Valley Forge Space Technol Ctr, 68-69, mgr, Group Planning Oper, Info Systs Group, 69-71; PRES, MACRO OPERS INC, 71- *Mem:* Am Chem Soc; Am Phys Soc; Inst Mgt Sci. *Res:* Properties of matter; chemicals, materials, nuclear energy, aerospace, computers, economics; management of research and development; coupling of science and technology to business; leadership and management of the enterprise. *Mailing Add:* 590 Bair Rd Berwyn PA 19312

MUSICK, GERALD JOE, b Ponca City, Okla, May 24, 40; m 62; c 2. ENTOMOLOGY, INSECT PEST MANAGEMENT. *Educ:* Okla State Univ, BS, 62; Iowa State Univ, MS, 64; Univ Mo-Columbia, PhD(entom), 69. *Prof Exp:* Asst entom, Iowa State Univ, 62-64; instr, Univ Mo-Columbia, 64-69; from asst prof to assoc prof entom, Ohio Agr Res & Develop Ctr, 69-76; assoc prof & head dept entom & fisheries, Univ Ga, Coastal Plain Exp Sta, Tifton, 76-79; PROF & HEAD DEPT ENTOM, UNIV ARK, FAYETTEVILLE, 79- *Mem:* Sigma Xi; Entom Soc Am. *Res:* Biology and control of insect pests of corn. *Mailing Add:* Dept Entom Univ Ark Fayetteville AR 72701

MUSICK, HUGH BRADLEY, JR, b Houston, Tex, Oct 13, 47; m 68. REMOTE SENSING. *Educ:* Univ Calif, Santa Barbara, BA, 69, MA, 72; Univ Ariz, PhD(biol), 77. *Prof Exp:* Instr biol, Millsaps Col, 77-80; ARID LANDS ECOLOGIST, EARTH RESOURCES LAB, NAT SPACE TECHNOL LAB, NASA, 80- *Mem:* Ecol Soc Am; British Ecol Soc; Bot Soc Am; Am Soc Photogrammetry. *Mailing Add:* Earth Resources Lab Nat Space Technol Labs NASA NSTL Station MS 39529

MUSICK, JACK T(HOMPSON), b Cleveland, Va, Oct 6, 27; m 55; c 3. AGRICULTURAL ENGINEERING. *Educ:* Va Polytech Inst, BS, 53; Okla State Univ, MS, 55. *Prof Exp:* Res agr engr, 55-65, res agr engr & dir, 66-67, agr engr, Southwestern Great Plains Res Ctr, 68-80, AGR ENGR, CONSERV & PROD RES LAB, AGR RES SERV, USDA, 80- *Mem:* Am Soc Agr Engrs; Am Soc Agron; Soil Conserv Soc Am. *Res:* Irrigation water management research in the southwestern Great Plains. *Mailing Add:* Conserv & Prod Res Lab USDA PO Drawer 10 Bushland TX 79012

MUSICK, JAMES R, b Mendota, Ill, Mar 24, 46; div. NEUROPHYSIOLOGY, NEUROCHEMISTRY. *Educ:* Northwestern Univ, BA, 68, PhD(biol), 75. *Prof Exp:* Res assoc, 73-74, res instr, 74-75, instr, Dept Physiol, 75-80, ASST PROF PHYSIOL, UNIV UTAH COL MED, 80- *Concurrent Pos:* Fel, Muscular Dystrophy Asn, 75-76; investr, Marine Biol Lab, Woods Hole, Mass, 76. *Mem:* AAAS; Soc Neurosci; NY Acad Sci; Sigma Xi. *Res:* Mechanisms of short and long term regulation of synaptic transmission; neurotrophism; mechanisms of action of toxins. *Mailing Add:* Dept of Physiol Univ Utah Sch Med 410 Chipeta Way Salt Lake City UT 84108

MUSICK, JOHN A, b 1941; m. ICHTHYOLOGY, ECOLOGY. *Educ:* Rutgers Univ, AB, 62; Harvard Univ, MA, 64, PhD, 69. *Prof Exp:* Fisheries biologist, US Fish & Wildlife Serv, 62; teaching fel comp anat & gen biol, Harvard Univ, 62-63, anthrop, 63-64, ichthyol, 65 & 67; asst prof, 67-76, ASSOC PROF MARINE SCI, COL WILLIAM & MARY & UNIV VA, 77- *Concurrent Pos:* Assoc marine scientist, Va Inst Marine Sci, 67-; sci collabr, Capes Hatteras & Lookout Nat Seashores, US Park Serv; mem, Adv Comt Vertebrates, Smithsonian Inst Oceanog Sorting Ctr, 77-, Rev Panel Biol Oceanog, Nat Sci Found & Rev Panel Oceanog Facil Support, 77. *Mem:* AAAS; Am Soc Ichthyologists & Herpetologists; Ecol Soc Am; Am Fisheries Soc. *Res:* Community ecology of demersal fishes; structure and function of deep-sea ecosystems; systematics and zoogeography of fishes and reptiles. *Mailing Add:* Va Inst of Marine Sci Gloucester Point VA 23062

MUSIEK, FRANK EDWARD, b Union City, Pa, July 4, 47; m 72; c 1. AUDITORY NEUROPHYSIOLOGY, AUDITORY PSYCHOPHYSICS. *Educ:* Edinborough Col, BS, 68; Kent State Univ, MA, 71; Case Western Reserve Univ, PhD(audiol), 75. *Prof Exp:* ASSOC PROF AUDIOL, DARTMOUTH-HITCHCOCK MED CTR, DARTMOUTH COL, 75- *Concurrent Pos:* Adj asst prof psychol, Dartmouth Col, 77- *Mem:* Acoust Soc Am; Am Speech, Language & Hearing Asn; Soc Neurosci; Deafness Res Found. *Res:* Auditory neurophysiology and its clinical application to neuroaudiology; electrophysiological measures and psychophysical measures to evaluate dysfunction of the higher auditory system; vestibular physiology, particularly electronystagmography; development of various test procedures to monitor higher auditory function. *Mailing Add:* 2 Maynard St Hanover NH 03755

MUSINSKI, DONALD LOUIS, b Winsted, Conn, Mar 29, 46; m 71. PHYSICS, ENGINEERING. *Educ:* Trinity Col, BS, 68; Univ Rochester, MA, 70, PhD(physics), 73. *Prof Exp:* Fel, Dept Appl Physics, Cornell Univ, 73-75; sr res scientist physics & eng, 75-79, mgr, 79-80, SR MGR MAT ENG DEPT, DIV MAT SCI, KMS FUSION INC, 80- *Mem:* Am Phys Soc; Am Vacuum Soc. *Res:* Target technology for inertial confinement fusion experiments. *Mailing Add:* 4365 Central Blvd Ann Arbor MI 48104

MUSKA, CARL FRANK, b Milwaukee, Wis, Feb 3, 48; m 70. AQUATIC TOXICOLOGY, PHYSIOLOGICAL ECOLOGY. *Educ:* Univ Tex, Austin, BA, 70; Tex A&M Univ, MS, 73; Ore State Univ, PhD(fishery biol), 77. *Prof Exp:* Staff res asst toxicol, Ore State Univ, 76-77; RES TOXICOLOGIST, HASKELL LAB TOXICOL & INDUST MED, E I DU PONT DE NEMOURS & CO, 77- *Concurrent Pos:* Mem comt environ, US Chamber Com, 80- *Mem:* Am Fisheries Soc; Am Soc Testing & Mat. *Res:* Interactive effects of toxicants and environmental parameters on biological systems; growth and bioenergetics of aquatic organisms; comparative vertebrate pharmacology; use of aquatic organisms as animal models for carcinogenicity research. *Mailing Add:* Haskell Lab Toxicol & Indust Med Elkton Rd PO Box 50 Newark DE 19711

MUSKAT, JOSEPH BARUCH, b Marietta, Ohio, Sept 20, 35; m 59. NUMBER THEORY, COMPUTER SCIENCE. *Educ:* Yale Univ, AB, 55; Mass Inst Technol, SM, 56, PhD(math), 61. *Prof Exp:* From asst prof to assoc prof math, Univ Pittsburgh, 61-69; vis assoc prof, 69-70, ASSOC PROF MATH, BAR-ILAN UNIV, ISRAEL, 70- *Concurrent Pos:* NSF fel, 63-69; res assoc comput, Univ Pittsburgh, 61-69; chmn dept math, Bar-Ilan Univ, 71-74. *Mem:* Am Math Soc; Math Asn Am; Asn Comput Mach. *Res:* Reciprocity laws; cyclotomy; use of computers in number theory. *Mailing Add:* Dept of Math Bar-Ilan Univ Ramat-Gan Israel

MUSKER, WARREN KENNETH, b Chicago, Ill, Apr 17, 34; c 2. INORGANIC CHEMISTRY. *Educ:* Bradley Univ, BS, 55; Univ Ill, PhD(org chem), 59. *Prof Exp:* Asst boron hydrides, Univ Mich, 61-62; from asst prof to assoc prof, 62-70, PROF INORG CHEM, UNIV CALIF, DAVIS, 75- *Concurrent Pos:* Von Humboldt fel, 70-71. *Mem:* Am Chem Soc. *Res:* Influence of ligand structure on the stereochemistry and reactivity of metal complexes; copper II oxidations; medium ring complexes of transition metals; thioether cation radicals and dications; organosulfur chemistry. *Mailing Add:* Dept of Chem Univ of Calif Davis CA 95616

MUSMAN, STEVEN ABEL, solar physics, see previous edition

MUSS, DANIEL R, b Birmingham, Ala, Apr 5, 28; m 65; c 2. PHYSICS. *Educ:* Mass Inst Technol, BS, 48; Calif Inst Technol, MS, 53; Univ Pittsburgh, PhD(physics), 61. *Prof Exp:* Sr physicist, 48-64, mgr silicon device develop, 64-69, dir solid state res, 72-75, res dir, Pub Systs Co, 75-77, MGR SOLID STATE RES & DEVELOP DIV, WESTINGHOUSE RES LABS, 77- *Concurrent Pos:* Assoc ed, IEEE Transactions on Electron Devices. *Mem:* Am Phys Soc; sr mem Inst Elec & Electronics Eng. *Res:* Defect structure of metals; semiconductors; semiconductor devices. *Mailing Add:* Westinghouse Res Labs Churchill Borough Pittsburgh PA 15235

MUSSELL, HARRY W, b Paterson, NJ, Nov 10, 41; m 64. PLANT PATHOLOGY, PLANT BIOCHEMISTRY. *Educ:* Drew Univ, AB, 65; Duke Univ, MF, 65; Purdue Univ, PhD(bot), 68. *Prof Exp:* PLANT PATHOLOGIST, BOYCE THOMPSON INST PLANT RES, INC, 68- *Honors & Awards:* Ciba Sci Res Award, 62. *Mem:* AAAS; Am Phytopath Soc; Am Soc Plant Physiol; Bot Soc Am; Am Inst Biol Sci. *Res:* Physiology of parasitism, particularly enzymology of pathogenesis in plants; disease tolerance. *Mailing Add:* Boyce Thompson Inst for Plant Res Tower Rd Cornell Univ Ithaca NY 14853

MUSSELMAN, NELSON PAGE, b Luray, Va, Mar 20, 17. TOXICOLOGY, ANALYTICAL CHEMISTRY. *Educ:* Western Md Col, AB, 38. *Prof Exp:* Teacher, Baltimore Dept Educ & social investr, Dept Pub Welfare, 38-42; mem sales & mgt staff, Chrysler Air Temp, Frigidaire div, Gen Motors Corp , 46-51; chemist, Armco Steel Corp, 51-54; res chemist, US Army Edgewood Arsenal, 54-73; ENVIRON HEALTH ASST, AIR MGT ADMIN, STATE OF MD, 75- *Mem:* Fel AAAS; Am Chem Soc. *Res:* Vapor and carbon monoxide toxicity; chemical analysis and methods; evaluation of chemical protective devices; air pollution. *Mailing Add:* 1101 N Calvert St Baltimore MD 21202

MUSSEN, ERIC CARNES, b Schenectady, NY, May 12, 44; m 69; c 2. APICULTURE, INSECT PATHOLOGY. *Educ:* Univ Mass, BS, 66; Univ Minn, MS, 69, PhD(entomol), 75. *Prof Exp:* EXTENSION APICULTURIST, UNIV CALIF, 76- *Mem:* Entomol Soc Am. *Res:* Honey bee diseases; crop pollination; judicious use of bee-toxic insecticides. *Mailing Add:* Entomol Exten Univ Calif Davis CA 95616

MUSSER, A WENDELL, b Herrick, Ill, Dec 15, 30; m 53; c 2. PATHOLOGY. *Educ:* Purdue Univ, BS, 52; Ind Univ, MD, 56; Am Bd Path, dipl, 61. *Prof Exp:* Res instr, Med Ctr, Ind Univ, 57-61, lectr clin path, 61; from asst prof to assoc prof path, Med Ctr, Duke Univ, 63-74; PROF PATH, MED CTR, UNIV KY, 74-, ASSOC DEAN VET ADMIN AFFAIRS, 74- *Concurrent Pos:* Nat Cancer Inst fel, Med Ctr, Ind Univ, 58-61; chief lab serv, Vet Admin Hosp, NC, 63-70; dir allied health educ prog, Duke Univ, 67-70; chmn, Nat Coun Med Technol Educ, 68-; asst chief med dir planning & eval, Cent Off, Vet Admin, Washington, DC, 70-74; chief staff, Vet Admin Hosp, Lexington, Ky, 74-; vpres, Bd Dirs, Nat Registry Clin Chem, 75-; mem bd trustees, Hunter Found, 78. *Mem:* AAAS; AMA; Col Am Path; Am Soc Clin Path; Int Acad Path. *Res:* Clinical pathology and chemistry; medical education. *Mailing Add:* Vet Admin Hosp Lexington KY 40507

MUSSER, DAVID MUSSELMAN, b Bowmansville, Pa, Apr 30, 09; m 38; c 2. ORGANIC CHEMISTRY. *Educ:* Pa State Col, BS, 31; Ga Inst Technol, MS, 33; Univ Wis, PhD(org chem), 37. *Prof Exp:* Indust fel, Mellon Inst, 37-42; res chemist, Pac Mills, NJ, 42-46; sr chemist, Deering Milliken Res Trust, Conn, 46-47; head textile res & develop, Onyx Oil & Chem Co, 47-52; dir res, Refined Prods Corp, 52-62; DIR RES, RAYTEX CHEM CORP, 62- *Mem:* Am Chem Soc; Am Asn Textile Chemists & Colorists. *Res:* Cellulose; textile finishing agents. *Mailing Add:* 821 Lawrence Dr Emmaus PA 18049

MUSSER, DAVID REA, b Sherman, Tex, Aug 24, 44; m 66; c 2. COMPUTER SCIENCE. *Educ:* Austin Col, BA, 66; Univ Wis, MA, 68, PhD(comput sci), 71. *Prof Exp:* Asst prof comput sci, Univ Tex, Austin, 70-73; vis asst prof comput sci & res staff mem, Math Res Ctr, Univ Wis, Madison, 73-74; res staff mem comput sci, Info Sci Inst, Univ Southern Calif, 74-79; COMPUT SCIENTIST, GEN ELEC RES & DEVELOP CTR, SCHENECTADY, NY, 79- *Mem:* Asn Comput Mach. *Res:* Program verification; formal specification of programs; automatic theorem proving; computer algebra; analysis of algorithms. *Mailing Add:* Gen Elec Res & Develop Ctr 1 River Rd Schenectady NY 12345

MUSSER, MICHAEL TUTTLE, b Williamsport, Pa, Jan 31, 42; m 66; c 3. ORGANIC CHEMISTRY. *Educ:* Purdue Univ, BS, 63, PhD(org chem), 68. *Prof Exp:* Res chemist, Intermediates Div, Plastics Dept, Exp Sta, E I Du Pont De Nemours & Co, 67-72 & Nylon Intermediates Div, Polymer Intermediates Dept, 72-74, sr res chemist, 74-80, RES ASSOC, SABINE RIVER WORKS, E I DU PONT DE NEMOURS & CO, INC, TEX, 80- *Mem:* Am Chem Soc; Sigma Xi. *Res:* Homogeneous catalysis as a route to organic intermediates. *Mailing Add:* 1529 Lindenwood Dr Orange TX 77630

MUSSER, SAMUEL JOHN, b South Haven, Mich, Nov 22, 16; m 51; c 3. BIOCHEMISTRY. *Educ:* Mich State Univ, BS, 49, MS, 51. *Prof Exp:* Res assoc virol, Upjohn Co, 52-58; assoc dir biol res, Anchor Serum Co div, Philips Roxane, Inc, 58-64, dir res, 64-69, VPRES, PHILIPS ROXANE, INC, 69- *Mem:* Soc Cryobiol; NY Acad Sci. *Res:* Human or veterinary virus vaccines; measles vaccine; blood fractionation; physical properties of viruses. *Mailing Add:* Philips Roxane Inc 2621 N Belt Highway St Joseph MO 64502

MUSSINAN, CYNTHIA JUNE, b Elizabeth, NJ, Dec 23, 46. ANALYTICAL CHEMISTRY. *Educ:* Georgian Court Col, BA, 68; Rutgers Univ, MS, 75. *Prof Exp:* Sr chemist, 68-76, RES CHEMIST, INT FLAVORS & FRAGRANCES, INC, 76- *Mem:* Am Chem Soc. *Res:* Isolation, identification and synthesis of the volatile and nonvolatile flavor constituents of foods. *Mailing Add:* Int Flavors & Fragrances 1515 Hwy 36 Union Beach NJ 07735

MUSSON, ALFRED LYMAN, b Honolulu, Hawaii, Aug 31, 11; m 35; c 3. ANIMAL SCIENCE. *Educ:* Univ Conn, BS, 33; Iowa State Univ, MS, 34, PhD(animal breeding), 51. *Prof Exp:* Res assoc & asst prof swine breeding, Iowa State Univ, 46-52; prof, 52-73, EMER PROF ANIMAL SCI, SDAK STATE UNIV, 73- *Concurrent Pos:* Head dept animal sci, SDak State Univ, 52-60, from asst dir to assoc dir, Exp Sta, 59-73. *Mem:* Am Soc Animal Sci. *Res:* Swine breeding. *Mailing Add:* 715 Sixth Ave Brookings SD 57006

MUSTACCHI, PIERO OMAR, b Cairo, Egypt, May 29, 20; nat US; m 48; c 2. MEDICINE. *Educ:* Italian Lyceum, Cairo, BS, 37; Fuad 1st Univ, Cairo, MB, ChB, 44. *Prof Exp:* Asst resident path, Med Sch, Univ Calif, 49-51; clin instr med, 53-58, clin asst prof med & prev med, 58-66, consult, Hemat Clin, 54-58, asst dir continuing educ med & health sci, 64-69, assoc dir, 69-74, vchmn dept prev med, 65-66, assoc dir spec serv extended prog med educ, 74-75, clin assoc prof, 66-75, CLIN PROF MED & PREV MED, MED SCH, UNIV CALIF, SAN FRANCISCO, 75- *Concurrent Pos:* Res fel, Am Cancer Soc, 49-52; fel, Sloan-Kettering Inst, 51-53; vis instr, Fac Med, Cairo Univ, 50; resident, Mem Hosp Cancer & Allied Dis, New York, 51-53; physician-in-chg, Hemat & Lymphoma Clin, St Mary's Hosp, San Francisco, 54-56, consult, 68; mem consult tumor bd, Children's Hosp, San Francisco, 55-56, consult, 58-, head off epidemiol & biomet, 60-; consult, staff, Franklin Hosp, 70-; physician, Ital Consulate, San Francisco, hon vconsul Italy, 71-; chmn, Comt Continuing Educ, Children's Hosp, 72-78; med consult, Work Clin, Univ San Francisco Med Ctr, 74-75. *Honors & Awards:* Knight Officer, Order of Merit, Italy, 71, Commander, 76. *Mem:* AAAS; Am Soc Clin Invest; AMA; fel Am Col Physicians; Am Soc Environ & Occup Health. *Res:* Epidemiology of cancer; general ecology and education. *Mailing Add:* Sch Med Univ Calif San Francisco CA 94143

MUSTAFA, MOHAMMED G, b Bangladesh, Nov 3, 41; US citizen; m 68; c 3. NUCLEAR PHYSICS. *Educ:* Univ Dacca, BSc, 62; Yale Univ, MS, 67, PhD(physics), 70. *Prof Exp:* Res assoc physics, Oak Ridge Nat Lab, 70-73, Univ Md & Goddard Space Flight Ctr, 73-77; PHYSICIST, LAWRENCE LIVERMORE LAB, 77- *Concurrent Pos:* Nat Res coun fel, 75-77. *Mem:* Am Phys Soc; fel Int Atomic Energy Agency. *Res:* Theoretical studies of the physics and chemistry of nuclear fission and heavy-ion collisions. *Mailing Add:* Lawrence Livermore Lab L-234 PO Box 808 Livermore CA 94550

MUSTAFA, SYED JAMAL, b Lucknow, India, July 10, 46; m 73; c 1. MEDICAL RESEARCH. *Educ:* Lucknow Univ, BS, 62, MS, 65, PhD(biochem), 70. *Prof Exp:* Fel, Indust Toxicol Res Ctr, Lucknow Res Ctr, Lucknow, India, 70-71, Dept Physiol, Univ Va, 71-74; asst prof, 74-77, ASSOC PROF PHARMACOL, COL MED, UNIV SOUTH ALA, 77- *Concurrent Pos:* Fel, Coun Sci & Indust Res & Indian Coun Med Res, New Delhi, India, 70-71, NIH, 71-74. *Mem:* Am Physiol Soc; Sigma Xi; NY Acad Sci; Am Heart Asn; Int Study Group Res Cardiac Metab. *Res:* The field of cardiology; the study of the relationship between vasoactive agents and blood flow. *Mailing Add:* Dept of Pharmacol Col of Med Univ SAla Mobile AL 36688

MUSTARD, JAMES FRASER, b Toronto, Ont, Oct 16, 27; m 52; c 6. PATHOLOGY. *Educ:* Univ Toronto, MD, 53; Cambridge Univ, PhD, 56; FRCP, 65. *Prof Exp:* Can Heart Found sr res assoc med, Univ Toronto, 58-63, from asst prof to assoc prof path, 63-66, assoc med, 63-66, asst prof med, 65; chmn dept path, 66-72, PROF PATH, FAC MED, MCMASTER UNIV, 66-, DEAN FAC MED, 72-, DEAN FAC HEALTH SCI, 75- *Concurrent Pos:* Mem, Coun Arteriosclerosis, Am Heart Asn, 65-, mem, Coun Thrombosis; mem, Int Comt Haemostasis & Thrombosis; chmn, Health Res Comt, Ont Coun Health, 66-73, chmn, Task Force Health Planning, Ont Coun Health, 73-74; chmn, Med Adv Comt, Can Heart Found, 72-76, dir, 71-; mem, Expert Adv Panel Cardiovasc Dis, WHO, 72; chmn, Ont Adv Coun Occup Health & Occup Safety, 77- *Honors & Awards:* Gairdner Found Int Award, 67. *Mem:* Fel Royal Soc Can; Can Soc Clin Invest (pres, 65-66); fel Am Asn Physicians; Am Soc Hemat (secy, 64-67, pres, 70); Am Soc Exp Path. *Res:* Blood and vascular disease. *Mailing Add:* McMaster Univ Med Ctr 1200 Main St W Hamilton ON L8N 4K1 Can

MUSTARD, MARGARET JEAN, b Bayfield, Ont, Feb 18, 20; nat US. BOTANY, HORTICULTURE. *Educ:* Univ Miami, Bs, 42, MS, 50; Ohio State Univ, PhD(hort), 58. *Prof Exp:* Lab technician, Sub-trop Exp Sta, Univ Fla, 42-45; instr hort, 45-50, from asst prof to assoc prof, 50-68, PROF TROP BOT, UNIV MIAMI, 68- *Mem:* AAAS; Am Soc Hort Sci; Bot Soc Am; Sigma Xi. *Res:* Anatomical and morphological aspects of botany; fruit setting in horticultural plants. *Mailing Add:* Dept Biol Univ Miami PO Box 249118 Coral Gables FL 33124

MUSTER, DOUGLAS FREDERICK, b Milwaukee, Wis, Nov 2, 18; m 44; c 5. MECHANICAL ENGINEERING, APPLIED MECHANICS. *Educ:* Marquette Univ, BS, 40; Ill Inst Technol, MS, 49, PhD(appl mech), 55. *Prof Exp:* Asst mech, Ill Inst Technol, 46-48, instr, 48-50, asst prof mech eng, 50-53; vibrations engr, Gen Eng Lab, Gen Elec Co, 53-60, mech systs engr, 60-61; chmn dept mech eng, 63-72, PROF MECH ENG, UNIV HOUSTON, 61-, BROWN & ROOT PROF ENG, 67-, DIR, OFF ENG PRACT PROGS, 77- *Concurrent Pos:* Pres tech comt 108, mech vibration & shock, Int Standards Orgn, 67- *Mem:* Am Soc Eng Educ; fel Am Soc Mech Engrs; fel Inst Mech Engrs; fel Acoust Soc Am; fel Inst Acoust. *Res:* Vibration; structure borne sound; rotor dynamics; underwater acoustics. *Mailing Add:* Dept of Mech Eng Univ of Houston Houston TX 77004

MUT, STUART CREIGHTON, b Dallas, Tex, July 27, 24; m 47; c 5. GEOPHYSICS. *Educ:* Rice Inst, BS, 47, MS, 48. *Prof Exp:* Asst physicist, Atlantic Refining Co, 48-49, admin asst, Res Admin, 49-51, sr physicist, 51-56, supvry physicist, 56-59, dir res & develop, Explor Sect, 59-61, mgr, Eng Div, Producing Dept, 61-63, Eastern Dist, 63-66, vpres eastern region, NAm Producing Div, 66-81, SR VPRES RES & ENG, ATLANTIC RICHFIELD CO, 81- *Mem:* Soc Explor Geophysicists; Soc Petrol Engrs; Inst Elec & Electronics Engrs. *Res:* Petroleum exploration geophysics; petroleum engineering; geology. *Mailing Add:* Atlantic Richfield Co PO Box 2819 Dallas TX 75221

MUTCH, GEORGE WILLIAM, b Ann Arbor, Mich, June 22, 43; m 66. CHEMICAL KINETICS, PHYSICAL CHEMISTRY. *Educ:* Andrews Univ, BA, 66; Univ Calif, Davis, PhD(chem), 73. *Prof Exp:* Teaching asst chem, Univ Calif, Davis, 67-70, res asst, 70-73; asst prof, 73-77, ASSOC PROF CHEM, ANDREWS UNIV, 77- *Mem:* Am Chem Soc; Am Phys Soc. *Res:* Chemical dynamics of high energy unimolecular decomposition processes. *Mailing Add:* Dept of Chem Andrews Univ Berrien Springs MI 49104

MUTCH, PATRICIA BLACK, b Alexandria, La, Sept 5, 43; m 66. NUTRITION POLICY, RESEARCH. *Educ:* Andrews Univ, BS, 65; Loma Linda Univ, dietetic internship cert, 66; Univ Calif, Davis, PhD(nutrit), 72. *Prof Exp:* Therapeut dietitian, Hinsdale Sanitarium & Hosp, 66-67; res asst nutrit, Univ Calif, Davis, 67-72; asst prof home econ, 72-76, coordr health maj, 75-77, DIR DIETETIC EDUC, ANDREWS UNIV, 73-, PROF HOME ECON, 76- *Concurrent Pos:* Mem nutrit adv coun, Seventh-day Adventist Church, 75-; comnr, State Mich Nutrit Comn, 77-80. *Mem:* Am Home Econ Asn; Am Dietetic Asn; Seventh-day Adventist Dietetic Asn (pres, 77-78); Soc Nutrit Educ; Am Soc Allied Health Professions. *Res:* Interaction of ethanol and caffeine; methods of dietetic education and practice; nutrition education; cost-benefit and cost-effective analysis of nutrition services. *Mailing Add:* Dept Home Econ Andrews Univ Berrien Springs MI 49104

MUTCH, THOMAS ANDREW, geology, deceased

MUTCHLER, CALVIN KENDAL, b Oceola, Ohio, Jan 25, 26; m 51; c 6. SOIL EROSION, SEDIMENT YIELD. *Educ:* Ohio State Univ, BAgrEng, 51, MS, 52; Univ Minn, PhD, 70. *Prof Exp:* Instr soil & water struct, Univ Conn, 52-53; tech man, B F Goodrich Co, Ohio, 53-54; agent, Miss, 54-56, agr engr, 56-58, agr engr, Minn, 58-72, HYDRAUL ENGR, SEDIMENTATION LAB, AGR RES SERV, USDA, MISS, 72- *Mem:* Am Soc Agr Engrs; Soil Conserv Soc Am. *Res:* Mechanics of erosion, especially raindrop splash erosion; soil and water conservation; applied research using erosion plots; sediment yield research. *Mailing Add:* USDA Sedimentation Lab Oxford MS 38655

MUTCHLER, GORDON SINCLAIR, b Iowa City, Iowa, Mar 18, 38; m 63; c 1. NUCLEAR PHYSICS. *Educ:* Mass Inst Technol, BS, 60, PhD(physics), 66. *Prof Exp:* Res assoc nuclear physics, Los Alamos Sci Lab, Univ Calif, 66-68; from res assoc to sr res assoc, 68-73, asst prof, 73-76, ASSOC PROF PHYSICS, T W BONNER NUCLEAR LABS, RICE UNIV, 76- *Concurrent Pos:* Sabbatical leave, Sweizerisches Inst Nuclear Forschung, Switzerland, 81-82. *Mem:* Am Phys Soc. *Res:* Investigation of nuclear structure and nucleon-nucleon interactions using intermediate energy particles. *Mailing Add:* T W Bonner Nuclear Labs Rice Univ Houston TX 77001

MUTCHMOR, JOHN A, b Ft William, Ont, Aug 21, 29; m 55; c 1. INSECT PHYSIOLOGY. *Educ:* Univ Alta, BSc, 50; Univ Minn, MS, 55, PhD(entom), 61. *Prof Exp:* Tech officer entom, Sci Serv Lab, Can Dept Agr, 50-51 & Chatham Entom Lab, 56-61; from asst prof to assoc prof zool & entom, 62-70, PROF ZOOL & ENTOM, IOWA STATE UNIV, 70- *Mem:* Entom Soc Am. *Res:* Low temperature adaption of poikilotherms and the influence of temperature and thermal adaptation on their dispersion and physiology. *Mailing Add:* Dept Zool Iowa State Univ Ames IA 50011

MUTEL, ROBERT LUCIEN, b St Albans, NY, June 22, 46; m 70; c 1. RADIO ASTRONOMY. *Educ:* Cornell Univ, AB, 68; Univ Colo, PhD(astro-geophys), 75. *Prof Exp:* Physicist, Environ Sci Serv Admin, Dept of Com, 68-70; asst prof, 75-80, ASSOC PROF ASTRON, UNIV IOWA, 80- *Concurrent Pos:* Mem, US Very Long Baseline Interferometer Network Users Group, 75- *Honors & Awards:* Antarctic Serv Metal US, NSF, 73. *Mem:* Am Astron Soc; Royal Astron Soc; AAAS; Int Astron Union. *Res:* Radio astronomy, including very long baseline interferometry, stellar masers, radio binary stars and scintillations. *Mailing Add:* Dept of Physics & Astron Univ of Iowa Iowa City IA 52242

MUTH, CHESTER WILLIAM, b Antioch, Ohio, May 23, 22; m 49; c 5. ORGANIC CHEMISTRY. *Educ:* Ohio Univ, BS, 43; Ohio State Univ, PhD(chem), 49. *Prof Exp:* Synthetic org chemist, Eastman Kodak Co, 43-44, jr chemist, Tenn Eastman Corp, 44-45; asst, Ohio State Univ, 45-49; from asst prof to assoc prof chem, 49-63, PROF CHEM, WVA UNIV, 63- *Mem:* Am Chem Soc. *Res:* Synthetic organic chemistry with emphasis on tertiary amine-N-oxides and antimalarials. *Mailing Add:* Dept of Chem WVa Univ Morgantown WV 26506

MUTH, EGINHARD JOERG, b Beuthen, Ger, Sept 12, 28; US citizen; div; c 4. MICROCOMPUTERS, ROBOTICS. *Educ:* Karlsruhe Tech Univ, Dipl Ing, 51; Polytech Inst Brooklyn, MS, 65, PhD(syst sci), 67. *Prof Exp:* Test engr, Oerlikon Eng Co, Switz, 51-55; develop engr, Allen Bradley Co, 55-56; design engr, Gen Elec Co, 56-63, sr analyst comput, 63-65, consult engr, 65-67, mgr process control, 67-69; assoc prof indust & systs eng, 69-73, PROF INDUST & SYSTS ENG, UNIV FLA, 73- *Concurrent Pos:* Adj lectr, Univ Fla, 65-67 & Polytech Inst Brooklyn, 68. *Mem:* Inst Elec & Electronics Engrs; Opers Res Soc Am. *Res:* Stochastic processes; reliability modeling; industrial applications of microcomputers. *Mailing Add:* Dept Indust & Systs Eng Univ Fla Gainesville FL 32611

MUTH, ERIC ANTHONY, b Bethesda, Md, July 23, 48; m 74; c 2. PSYCHOPHARMACOLOGY, NEUROCHEMISTRY. *Educ:* Cornell Univ, BA, 73; George Washington Univ, PhD(pharmacol), 81. *Prof Exp:* NIMH biologist, 74-80; SUPVR NEUROCHEM, WYETH LABS, 81- *Mem:* AAAS. *Res:* Neurochemical mechanism of action of psychoactive drugs, especially neuroleptics and antidepressants; central nervous system receptor activity and effects on neurotransmitter activity of psychoactive drugs. *Mailing Add:* Wyeth Labs PO Box 8299 Philadelphia PA 19101

MUTH, GILBERT JEROME, b Modesto, Calif, Mar 1, 38; m 59; c 2. BOTANY, FLORISTICS. *Educ:* Pac Union Col, BA, 61, MA, 67; Univ Calif, Davis, PhD(bot), 76. *Prof Exp:* Teacher biol & math, Napa Jr Acad, 61-66; from instr to assoc prof, 66-80, PROF BIOL, PAC UNION COL, 80- *Concurrent Pos:* Sci fac fel, NSF, 71-72. *Mem:* Sigma Xi. *Res:* Computerizing herbarium label data for interactive instant retrieval to a terminal or line printer of raw or summarized data with the primary use being toward rare and endangered plants. *Mailing Add:* Dept of Biol Pac Union Col Angwin CA 94508

MUTH, WAYNE ALLEN, b Denver, Colo, Mar 25, 32; m 54; c 3. ENGINEERING, COMPUTER SCIENCE. *Educ:* Univ Colo, BS, 54; Iowa State Univ, MS, 60, PhD(mech eng & math), 63. *Prof Exp:* Asst prof naval sci, Iowa State Univ, 57-59, asst prof mech eng, 59-63; res scientist, Aerospace Div, Martin-Marietta Corp, 63-65; asst prof info processing sci, Southern Ill Univ, Carbondale, 65-69; PROF COMPUT SCI & DIR COMPUT CTR, W VA UNIV, 69- *Mailing Add:* Comput Ctr WVa Univ Morgantown WV 26506

MUTHA, SHANTILAL CHHOTMAL, b Ujjain, India, July 12, 34; m 54; c 4. ANALYTICAL CHEMISTRY, FORMULATION. *Educ:* Birla Col, Pilani, India, BPharm, 56; Banaras Hindu Univ, India, MPharm, 57; Univ Calif, San Francisco, PhD(pharmaceut chem), 68; St Mary's Col, Moraga, Calif, MBA, 80. *Prof Exp:* Lectr pharmaceut chem, D A V Col, Kanpur, 57-58 & Banaras Hindu Univ, India, 58-64; teaching asst, Sch Pharm, Univ Calif, San Francisco, 64-68, Nat Inst Ment Heallth res chemist, 68; from anal chemist to sr anal chemist, 68-73, supvr chem anal res, 73-75, mgr anal serv, 75-78, sr scientist/mgr, Formulation & Prod Eval Lab, 79-80, MGR MED PROD NUTRIT & TECH SERV, CUTTER LABS, 81- *Mem:* Am Chem Soc; Asn Off Anal Chemists; Am Pharmaceut Asn; Am Inst Chemists. *Res:* Pharmaceutical and medicinal chemistry; protein chemistry; intravenous emulsion and solutions development; applied clinical chemistry. *Mailing Add:* Cutter Labs Inc 4th & Parker St Berkeley CA 94710

MUTHARASAN, RAJAKKANNU, b India, Jan 1, 47; m 74; c 2. CHEMICAL ENGINEERING, BIOCHEMICAL ENGINEERING. *Educ:* Indian Inst Technol, BS, 69; Drexel Univ, MS, 71, PhD(chem eng), 73. *Prof Exp:* Fel, Univ Toronto, 73-74; asst prof, 74-79, ASSOC PROF CHEM ENG, DREXEL UNIV, 79- *Concurrent Pos:* Consult, Metals & Biochem Indust, 80- *Mem:* Am Inst Chem Engrs; Am Chem Soc; Am Inst Metall Engrs. *Res:* Chemical process control; biochemical process engineering; bio-instrumentation; filtration of micron-sized particles with application in fermentation and metallurgical industries. *Mailing Add:* Dept of Chem Eng Drexel Univ Philadelphia PA 19104

MUTHUKRISHNAN, SUBBAR.ATNAM, b India, Dec 27, 42; m 77; c 2. BIOCHEMISTRY. *Educ:* Univ Madras, BS, 63, MS, 65; Indian Inst Sci, Bangalore, PhD(biochem), 70. *Prof Exp:* Res assoc, Univ Chicago, 71-73; res fel, Roche Inst Molecular Biol, 73-76; vis scientist, NIH, 76-80; ASST PROF BIOCHEM, KANS STATE UNIV, 80- *Res:* Hormonal control of gene expression in plants; messenger RNA structure and function. *Mailing Add:* Dept Biochem Kans State Univ Manhattan KS 66506

MUTHUKUMAR, MURUGAPPAN, Indian citizen. POLYMER DYNAMICS. *Educ:* Univ Madras, India, BSc, 70, MSc, 72; Univ Chicago, PhD(chem), 79. *Prof Exp:* Fel physics, Cavendish Lab, Univ Cambridge, 79-81; ASST PROF CHEM, ILL INST TECHNOL, 80- *Res:* Polymerdynamics and hydrodynamics of solutions; viscoelasticity of polymers; flow through porous media; diffusion controlled chemical reactions; energy transport in solution. *Mailing Add:* Dept Chem Ill Inst Technol Chicago IL 60616

MUTIS-DUPLAT, EMILIO, b Cucuta, Colombia, Sept 6, 32; m 58; c 3. GEOLOGY, PETROLOGY. *Educ:* Nat Univ Colombia, geologist, 60; Tex A&M Univ, MS, 69; Univ Tex, Austin, PhD(geol), 72. *Prof Exp:* From asst prof to assoc prof geol, Nat Univ Colombia, 61-67, dean fac, 64-65, chmn dept, 65-67; explor geologist, Tex Land & Trading Co, Austin, 73-74; assoc prof earth sci, 74-81, PROF GEOL, UNIV TEX, PERMIAN BASIN, 81- *Concurrent Pos:* Fel, Univ Tex, Austin, 72-73. *Mem:* Fel Geol Soc Am; fel Geol Soc London; Geochem Soc; Mineral Soc Am; Mineral Soc London. *Res:* Origin of migmatites; origin of augen gneiss; amphibolite facies in regional metamorphism; marbles in regional metamorphic rocks. *Mailing Add:* Fac of Earth Sci Univ of Tex Permian Basin Odessa TX 79762

MUTMANSKY, JAN MARTIN, b New Rochelle, NY, Apr 26, 41; m 65; c 3. MINE SYSTEMS ANALYSIS, OPERATIONS RESEARCH. *Educ:* PA State Univ, BS, 64, MS, 66, PhD(mining eng), 68. *Prof Exp:* Trainee mining eng, Ingersoll-Rand Co, 60-62 & US Bur Mines, 63-64; systs analyst, Kennecott Copper Corp, 68-69; asst prof, Univ Utah, 69-73; assoc prof, WVa Univ, 73-77; ASSOC PROF MINERAL ENG, PA STATE UNIV, FAYETTE CAMPUS, 81-, COORDR, MINING CTR, 77- *Concurrent Pos:* US Bur Mines fel, 70-71; opers res analyst, Dept Energy, 76- *Mem:* Am Inst Mining, Metall & Petrol Engrs. *Res:* Mine materials transport systems, mine ventilation, mine operations research. *Mailing Add:* Pa State Univ Fayette Campus PO Box 519 Uniontown PA 15401

MUTO, PETER, b Chicago, Ill, Apr 23, 24; m 45; c 5. SCIENCE EDUCATION. *Educ:* Wis State Univ, Stevens Point, BS, 48; Phillips Univ, MEd, 51. *Prof Exp:* Teacher high sch, Okla, 49-51 & Iowa, 51-54; asst prof chem, 54-61, ASSOC PROF PHYS SCI, UNIV WIS-RIVER FALLS, 62- *Mem:* Nat Sci Teachers Asn. *Res:* Improvement of instruction in science for non-scientists at the college level. *Mailing Add:* Dept of Chem Univ of Wis River Falls WI 54022

MUTSCH, EDWARD L, b Madelia, Minn, Mar 15, 39; m 61. ORGANIC CHEMISTRY. *Educ:* St Olaf Col, BS, 61; Univ Minn, PhD(org chem), 65. *Prof Exp:* Sr res investr, G D Searle & Co, Ill, 65-67; sr res chemist, Biochem Res Cent Res Lab, Minn Mining & Mfg Co, 67-74; mgr med chem, 74-76, mgr chem res & develop, 76-78, LAB MGR, NEW MOLECULE RES, RIKER LABS, INC, 78- *Mem:* Am Chem Soc. *Res:* Synthesis of nucleoside antimetabolites. *Mailing Add:* Riker Labs Inc Chem Res & Develop 3M Ctr Bldg 218-1 St Paul MN 55101

MUTSCHLECNER, JOSEPH PAUL, astrophysics, hydrodynamics, see previous edition

MUTTER, WALTER EDWARD, b New York, NY, Nov 13, 21; m 63; c 2. PHYSICS. *Educ:* Polytech Inst Brooklyn, BS, 42; Mass Inst Technol, PhD(physics), 49. *Prof Exp:* Engr, Radio Corp Am, 42-46; res assoc physics, Mass Inst Technol, 46-49; engr, 49-59, SR ENGR, IBM CORP, 59- *Honors & Awards:* Sr Medal, Am Inst Chemists, 42. *Mem:* Am Phys Soc; Am Chem Soc; Electrochem Soc; Inst Elec & Electronics Engrs. *Res:* Electronic processes in crystals and semiconductors; semiconductor devices; vacuum tubes. *Mailing Add:* Dept 084 Bldg 300-48 A IBM Corp Hopewell Junction NY 12533

MUTTER, WILLIAM HUGH, b Orange, NJ, July 28, 34. MECHANICAL ENGINEERING. *Educ:* US Merchant Marine Acad, BS, 56; Columbia Univ, MS, 57. *Prof Exp:* Mem tech staff power systs lab, Bell Tel Labs, 62-66; sr proj engr vending mach systs, Trodyne Corp, 66-69; proj mgr auto typewriter systs, Quindar Electronics, 69-73; mech eng group leader pneumatic tube systs, Airmatic Systs Div, Mosler Safe Co, 73-75; MGR SYSTS DESIGN & MFR, TECH INFO SYSTS DIV, AM HOECHST CORP, 75- *Res:* Machine design and associated control circuitry. *Mailing Add:* Tech Info Systs Div Am Hoechst Corp PO Box 3700 Somerville NJ 08876

MUTTON, DONALD BARRETT, b New Toronto, Ont, Oct 29, 27; m 53; c 2. CHEMISTRY. *Educ:* Univ Toronto, BASc, 49, MASc, 51, PhD(cellulose chem), 53. *Prof Exp:* Asst res chemist, Int Cellulose Res, Ltd, 52-55, asst in-chg, Pioneering Res Div, 55-58, asst mgr, Basic Res Div, 58-60, mgr, 60-62, dir basic res & spec serv, 62-70, dir sci, 70-71, DIR RES, CIP RES LTD, 71-, VPRES & DIR RES, 72- *Mem:* Can Pulp & Paper Asn; Chem Inst Can (treas, 62-64); Tech Asn Pulp & Paper Indust; Asn Sci, Tech & Eng Community Can; Can Soc Chem Eng. *Res:* Pulp and paper technology; wood and cellulose chemistry. *Mailing Add:* CIP Res Ltd Hawkesbury ON K6A 2H4 Can

MUUL, ILLAR, b Tallinn, Estonia, Feb 18, 38; US citizen; m 61, 74; c 2. ECOLOGY, ANIMAL BEHAVIOR. *Educ:* Univ Mass, BS, 60; Univ Mich, MS, 62, PhD(zool), 65. *Prof Exp:* Researcher ecol virus transmission, Walter Reed Army Inst Res, Washington, DC, 65-68, chief, Dept Ecol, Army Med Res Unit, Inst Med Res, Malaysia, 68-74, chief, Environ Res Requirements Br, US Army Med Bioeng Lab, 74-77, exec officer & res prog mgr, Armed Forces Res Inst Med Sci, Bangkok, Thailand, 77-80, COORDR INT PROGS, US ARMY MED RES & DEVELOP COMMAND, FT DETRICK, MD, 80- *Concurrent Pos:* Lectr, Eastern Mich Univ, 65. *Honors & Awards:* A Brazier Howell Award, Am Soc Mammal. *Mem:* Am Soc Mammal; Ecol Soc Am; Malaysian Soc Parasitol & Trop Med. *Res:* Environmental physiology; ethology; systematics of flying squirrels of the world; ecological factors involved in disease transmission; tropical ecology; population dynamics of mammals; zoogeography; environmental quality; coordination of international research programs. *Mailing Add:* USA Med Bioeng Res & Dev Lab Ft Detrick Frederick MD 21701

MUUS, JYTTE MARIE, b Copenhagen, Denmark, Sept 21, 04. BIOCHEMISTRY. *Educ:* Univ Copenhagen, Mag Sci, 30. *Prof Exp:* Instr biochem, Univ Copenhagen, 30-36; Rockefeller fel, Harvard Med Sch, 36-37, asst, 37-39, fel, 39-40; from asst prof to prof, 40-70, EMER PROF BIOL SCI, MT HOLYOKE COL, 70- *Concurrent Pos:* Instr, Sch Pub Health, Harvard Univ, 42-46; Am Asn Univ Women fel, Carlsberg Lab, Copenhagen, 51-52; vis investr, Rockefeller Inst, 53; Fulbright lectr, Univ Col, Rhodesia & Nyasaland, 58-59 & 65-66. *Mem:* AAAS; Am Soc Biol Chem. *Res:* Tissue metabolism; chemical changes in burns; enzyme chemistry. *Mailing Add:* 54 Amherst Rd South Hadley MA 01075

MUVDI, BICHARA B, b Barranquilla, Colombia, Aug 16, 27; nat US; m 52; c 2. MECHANICS. *Educ:* Syracuse Univ, BME, 52, MME, 54; Univ Ill, PhD, 61. *Prof Exp:* Instr & res assoc, Syracuse Univ, 52-56; sr engr, Martin Co, 56-58; assoc prof eng mech, Mich Technol Univ, 58-63; actg dean col eng & technol, 70-72, PROF CIVIL ENG & ENG MECH & CHMN DEPT, BRADLEY UNIV, 64- *Mem:* Am Soc Eng Educ; Am Soc Civil Engrs. *Res:* Influence of environment on materials behavior. *Mailing Add:* Col of Eng & Technol Bradley Univ Peoria IL 61606

MUZIK, THOMAS J, b Lorain, Ohio, Dec 21, 19; m 45; c 3. PLANT PHYSIOLOGY. *Educ:* Univ Mich, AB, MS, 42, PhD(bot), 50. *Prof Exp:* Res botanist, Firestone Plantations, Liberia, 42-47; plant physiologist, Fed Exp Sta, PR, 49-56; assoc prof agron, 56-62, PROF AGRON & AGRONOMIST, WASH STATE UNIV, 62- *Concurrent Pos:* Vis prof, Univ Madrid, 70-71; distinguished vis prof, US Air Force Acad, 76-77. *Mem:* AAAS; Bot Soc Am; Weed Sci Soc Am; Am Soc Agron. *Res:* Growth and development; environmental relationships; growth-regulators and herbicides. *Mailing Add:* Dept of Agron & Soils Wash State Univ Pullman WA 99164

MUZINICH, IVAN J, theoretical high energy physics, see previous edition

MUZYCZKO, THADDEUS MARION, b Chicago, Ill, Jan 14, 36; m 65; c 2. POLYMER CHEMISTRY. *Educ:* Mich State Univ, BA, 59; Roosevelt Univ, MS, 68. *Prof Exp:* Proj engr, Chicago Pump Div, FMC Corp, 60-61; chemist & supvr chem, Richardson Co, 61-69, mgr & tech dir graphic arts, Res & Develop Div, Melrose Park, Ill, 70-78; V PRES RES & DEVELOP, SAMUEL BINGHAM CO, CHICAGO, 78- *Concurrent Pos:* Lectr polymer chem, Roosevelt Univ, 69-; instr polymer technol, Col DuPage, 71-, coordr plastics technol prog, 75-76; mem, Plastics Technol Adv Comt, Col Dupage, 77- *Mem:* Am Chem Soc; Soc Plastics Engrs; Fedn Socs Coatings & Technol. *Res:* Polymer morphology; photopolymers; polymer characterizations; surface coatings; polymer design and engineering. *Mailing Add:* 530 W 36th St Downers Grove IL 60515

MUZYKA, DONALD RICHARD, b Northampton, Mass, Aug 23, 38; m 61; c 3. METALLURGY, MATERIALS SCIENCE. *Educ:* Univ Mass, BS, 60; Rensselaer Polytech Inst, MS, 66; Dartmouth Col, PhD(mat sci), 67. *Prof Exp:* Metallurgist, Pratt & Whitney Aircraft, United Technol Corp, 60-63; supvr high temperature alloy res, 66-73, mgr alloy res & develop, 73-75, mgr high temperature alloy metall, 75-76, gen mgr res & develop lab, 76-77, gen mgr distrib, 77-79, DIV V PRES-TECH, CARPENTER TECHNOL CORP, 79- *Mem:* Fel Am Soc Metals; Am Inst Mining, Metall & Petrol Engrs; Am Iron & Steel Inst; Am Inst Steel Engrs. *Res:* High temperature alloys; superalloys; powder and process metallurgy. *Mailing Add:* Carpenter Technol Corp PO Box 662 Reading PA 19603

MYATT, DONALD J(OSEPH), communications, engineering, deceased

MYCEK, MARY J, b Shelton, Conn, Dec 19, 26. BIOCHEMISTRY, PHARMACOLOGY. *Educ:* Brown Univ, BA, 48; Yale Univ, PhD(biochem), 55. *Prof Exp:* Instr biochem, Yale Univ, 54-55; sr res biochemist, NY State Psychiat Inst, 57-61; res assoc biochem, Col Physicians & Surgeons, Columbia Univ, 59-61; res assoc, 61-63, asst prof, 63-69, assoc prof, 69-76, PROF PHARMACOL, COL MED & DENT, NJ, NJ MED SCH, 76- *Concurrent Pos:* USPHS fel, Rockefeller Inst, 55-57; USPHS grants, 61-66, 67-71 & 72-; mem pharmacol study sect, NIH, 74-78, Pharmacol Sci Study Sect, Nat Inst Gen Med Sci, 80-84. *Mem:* AAAS; Am Chem Soc; Am Soc Pharmacol & Exp Therapeut; fel NY Acad Sci; Sigma Xi. *Res:* Effect of drugs on nucleic acid metabolism; mechanism of barbiturate tolerance in CNS; drug metabolism. *Mailing Add:* Dept of Pharmacol I-673 NJ Med Sch Newark NJ 07103

MYCIELSKI, JAN, b Wisniowa, Poland, Feb 7, 32; m 59. MATHEMATICS. *Educ:* Wroclaw Univ, MA, 55, PhD(math), 57. *Prof Exp:* Full researcher, Nat Ctr Sci Res, Paris, 57-58; adjunkt, Inst Math, Polish Acad Sci, 58-63, docent, 63-68, prof, 68-69; PROF MATH, UNIV COLO, BOULDER, 69- *Concurrent Pos:* Vis prof, Univ Calif, Berkeley, 61-62 & 70, Case Western Reserve Univ, 67 & Univ Colo, Boulder, 67. *Honors & Awards:* Polish Math Soc Award, 56, Stefan Banach Prize, 66. *Mem:* Am Math Soc; Math Asn Am; Polish Math Soc. *Res:* Logic and foundations; artificial intelligence; theory of games; measure theory; varia. *Mailing Add:* Dept of Math Univ of Colo Boulder CO 80309

MYER, DONAL GENE, b Toledo, Ohio, May 4, 30; m 51; c 3. FISH PARASITES, PARASITE LIFE-HISTORIES. *Educ:* Ohio State Univ, BSc, 51, MSc, 53, PhD(zool), 58. *Prof Exp:* Asst instr zool, Ohio State Univ, 57-58; from asst prof to assoc prof, 58-70, chmn dept diol sci, 74-77, PROF ZOOL, SOUTHERN ILL UNIV, 70- *Concurrent Pos:* Asst dean, Grad Sch, Southern Ill Univ, 64-70; Am Coun Educ acad admin intern, Fla State Univ, 67-68; fel trop med, Med Sch, La State Univ, 70; prin investr, Ill Water Res Ctr grant, Univ Ill, Urbana Champaign, 79-81. *Mem:* Am Soc Parasitol; Am Micros Soc; Sigma Xi; Am Soc Zoologists; NAm Benth Soc. *Res:* Investigations into the influence of environmental factors (physico-chemical and biotic) on functioning of a waste stabilization pond; taxonomy, distribution, life history and ecology of parasites of fish. *Mailing Add:* Dept of Biol Sci Southern Ill Univ Edwardsville IL 62025

MYER, GEORGE HENRY, b Bronx, NY, Dec 25, 37; m 76; c 1. GEOLOGY, MINERALOGY. *Educ:* Univ Calif, Santa Barbara, BA, 59; Yale Univ, PhD(geol), 65. *Prof Exp:* Asst prof geol, Univ Maine, 65-70; asst prof, 70-77, ASSOC PROF GEOL, TEMPLE UNIV, 77- *Concurrent Pos:* Consult, 79- *Mem:* Am Crystallog Asn; Mineral Soc Am; Geol Soc Am. *Res:* Mineralogy and metamorphic petrogenesis: claysources in the Isthmus of Ierapetra, Eastern Crete and mineralogical ceramic analysis of Bronze Age Pottery. *Mailing Add:* Dept Geol Temple Univ Philadelphia PA 19122

MYER, GLENN EVANS, b Kingston, NY, Sept 16, 41; m 61. OCEANOGRAPHY, METEOROLOGY. *Educ:* State Univ NY Plattsburgh, BS, 65; State Univ NY Albany, MS, 69, PhD(atmospheric physics), 71. *Prof Exp:* Teacher physics, Plattsburgh High Sch, NY, 65-66; asst prof meteorol, 71-76, ASSOC PROF EARTH SCI, STATE UNIV NY PLATTSBURGH, 76-, DIR NORTH COUNTRY PLANETARIUM, 71-, DIR & CHMN LAKES & RIVERS RES LAB, 72- *Mem:* Am Phys Soc; Am Asn Physics Teachers; Am Soc Limnol & Oceanog; Int Asn Great Lakes Res; Royal Astron Soc Can. *Res:* Computer modeling and field measurements related to turbulent transport processes; applications of fluid dynamics to problems of physical limnology, atmospheric transport and modeling of planetary atmospheres. *Mailing Add:* Hudson Hall State Univ of NY Plattsburgh NY 12901

MYER, JON HAROLD, b Heilbronn, Ger, Sept 29, 22; nat US; m 48; c 4. EXPERIMENTAL PHYSICS. *Educ:* Hebrew Tech Col, BEE, 41. *Prof Exp:* Instrument maker, Anglo Iranian Oil Co, Iran, 42-44; instrument designer, Hebrew Tech Col, 44-46; eng consult, 46-47; instrumentologist, Dept Chem, Univ Southern Calif, 47-53; sub-lab head, Semiconductor Div, Hughs Aircraft Co, 53-60, mgr laser metall, 60-66, sr staff engr, Theoret Studies Dept, Hughes Res Labs, Malibu, Calif, 66-70, sr staff engr, Chem Physics Dept, 70-74, sr staff engr, Opto Electronics Dept, 74-77, sr staff engr, Optical Physics Dept, 77-80, SR STAFF ENGR, OPTICAL CIRCUITS DEPT, HUGHES RES LABS, HUGHES AIRCRAFT CO, 80- *Concurrent Pos:* Lectr, Calif State Lutheran Col, 73-78. *Mem:* Sigma Xi; Am Phys Soc; sr mem Inst Elec & Electronics Engrs; Optical Soc Am. *Res:* Physical instrumentation and apparatus design; semiconductor devices; laser applications; bubble domains; forensic science and technology; fiber optics and optical circuits. *Mailing Add:* 22931 Gershwin Dr Woodland Hills CA 91364

MYER, YASH PAUL, b Jullundur City, India, May 5, 32; m 59; c 2. PHYSICAL BIOCHEMISTRY. *Educ:* Punjab Univ, BSc, 53, MSc, 55; Univ Ore, PhD(chem), 61. *Prof Exp:* Lectr chem, SD Col, Punjab, India, 53-55; jr sci officer, Coun Sci & Indust Res, Punjab Univ, 55-57; res assoc biochem, Sch Med, Yale Univ, 61-66; from asst prof to assoc prof, 66-74, PROF CHEM, STATE UNIV NY ALBANY, 74- *Mem:* Am Chem Soc; Am Soc Biol Chem; Biophys Soc. *Res:* Macromolecular conformation and structure. *Mailing Add:* Dept of Chem State Univ of NY Albany NY 12222

MYERHOLTZ, RALPH W, JR, b Bucyrus, Ohio, July 29, 26; m 51; c 2. POLYMER CHEMISTRY. *Educ:* Purdue Univ, BS, 50; Northwestern Univ, PhD(org chem), 54. *Prof Exp:* Asst proj chemist, Standard Oil Co, Ind, 54-55, proj chemist, 55-58, group leader high polymers, 58-60; group leader, 60-66, res assoc, 66-69, DIR POLYMER PROPERTIES DIV, AMOCO CHEM CORP, 69- *Mem:* Am Chem Soc; Soc Plastics Engrs. *Res:* Structure-property relationships of high polymers; rheology, dynamic mechanical properties, stability and crystallization of high polymers; anionic polymerization processes; catalysis and hydrocarbon isomerization. *Mailing Add:* Amoco Chem Corp PO Box 400 Naperville IL 60540

MYERLY, RICHARD CREBS, b Westminster, Md, Aug 6, 28; m 49; c 1. ORGANIC CHEMISTRY. *Educ:* Franklin & Marshall Col, BS, 48; Pa State Col, MS, 50, PhD(chem), 52. *Prof Exp:* Proj leader, Process Develop Labs, Carbide & Carbon Chem Co Div, Union Carbide & Carbon Corp, 52-58, group leader, Union Carbide Chem Co Div, Union Carbide Corp, 58-63, mgr res & develop detergents & specialty chem, Chem Div, WVa, 63-67, tech mgr soaps & detergents, 67-69, TECH MGR AGR & BIOCHEM INTERMEDIATES, CHEM DIV, UNION CARBIDE CORP, 69- *Mem:* Am Chem Soc. *Res:* Production of organic chemicals by biological processes. *Mailing Add:* 1578 Nottingham Rd Charleston WV 25314

MYERS, ALAN LOUIS, b Cincinnati, Ohio, Sept 26, 32; m 57; c 2. CHEMICAL ENGINEERING. *Educ:* Univ Cincinnati, BS, 60; Univ Calif, Berkeley, PhD(chem eng), 64. *Prof Exp:* Chem engr, Andrew Jergens Co, Ohio, 49-51, 55-59; from asst prof to assoc prof, 64-71, chmn chem & biochem eng, 77-80, PROF CHEM ENG, SCH CHEM ENG, UNIV PA, 71- *Concurrent Pos:* NSF grants, 65-67, 70-72; consult, Sun Oil Co, 67-68 & Atlantic Refining Co, 67-68; exchange scientist, Inst Phys Chem, USSR Acad Sci, Moscow, 69-70; vis prof, Univ Graz, Austria, 75-76. *Honors & Awards:* Distinguished Alumnus Award, Univ Cincinnati, 77. *Mem:* Am Inst Chem Engrs; Am Chem Soc. *Res:* Adsorption and surface science; thermodynamics; statistical mechanics. *Mailing Add:* Dept Chem & Biochem Eng Univ Pa Philadelphia PA 19104

MYERS, ARTHUR JOHN, b South Haven, Mich, Aug 27, 18. GEOMORPHOLOGY. *Educ:* Kalamazoo Col, BA, 41; Mich Col Mining, BS & MS, 49; Univ Mich, PhD(geol), 57. *Prof Exp:* Asst prof, 51-61, assoc prof, 61-73, PROF GEOL, UNIV OKLA, 73- *Mem:* AAAS; Geol Soc Am; Am Asn Petrol Geol. *Res:* Permian and Pleistocene fluviatile deposits of northwestern Oklahoma; geomorphology as it reflects rock types, structure, climate and time; geologic mapping using aerial photographs and field observations; photogrammetry. *Mailing Add:* Okla Geol Surv 830 Van Vleet Oval Norman OK 73019

MYERS, BARBARA ELLEN, b Urbana, Ill, Feb 5, 51. STATISTICS, RESEARCH DESIGN. *Educ:* Southern Ill Univ, Carbondale, BS, 72, MS, 74, PhD(statist), 78. *Prof Exp:* asst prof biostatist, Boston Univ, 78-80. *Mem:* Am Educ Res Asn; Nat Coun Measurement Educ; Am Statist Asn. *Res:* Hypothesis testing theory and non-central sampling distributions; indices of effect size in various scientific fields; statistical computer software applications. *Mailing Add:* PO Box 655 Kingston NH 03848

MYERS, BASIL R, b Yorkshire, Eng, Sept 11, 22; m 45. ENGINEERING, MATHEMATICS. *Educ:* Univ Birmingham, BSc, 50; Univ Ill, MS, 51, PhD(elec eng), 59. *Prof Exp:* Asst elec eng, Univ Ill, 50-51, from instr to asst prof, 56-59, assoc prof, 61-62; mem tech staff, Bell Tel Labs, Inc, 51-56; prof elec eng, chmn dept & dir univ comput ctr, Univ Waterloo, 59-61; prof elec eng & head dept, Univ Iowa, 62-63; prof elec eng & mem staff radiation lab, Univ Notre Dame, 63-74, head dept, 63-73; dean col eng & sci & dir Maine technol exp sta, 74-77, PROF ELEC ENG, UNIV MAINE, ORONO, 74- *Concurrent Pos:* Mem steering comt, Midwest Symp Circuit Theory, 59-68, actg chmn, 62-63, chmn, 63-64, 67-68; mem awards comt & fel comt, Nat Electronics Conf, 63-65, chmn, 65, mem bd trustees, 64-67; US deleg & lectr, Advan Study Inst Network & Switching Theory, NATO, Trieste, Italy, 66, UK deleg & lectr, Conf Commun Networks, L'Ile de Bendor, France, 68; vis prof, Oxford Univ, 67-68, Univ Chile, 69, Univ BC, 73-74 & Naval Postgrad Sch, 78; assoc ed, Technos, Am Soc Eng Educ, 72-75; mem bd dir, N New Eng Clin Eng Prog, 75-77; mem, USSR Popov Soc Cong Deleg, 76; mem reg surv educ dir, New Eng, Am Cong Surv & Mapping, 76-77. *Mem:* Fel Inst Elec & Electronics Engrs; fel Brit Inst Elec Engrs; Math Asn Am; Soc Indust & Appl Math; Am Asn Univ Professors. *Res:* Circuit and graph theory. *Mailing Add:* Dept of Elec Eng Barrows Hall Univ of Maine Orono ME 04469

MYERS, BENJAMIN FRANKLIN, JR, b Steelton, Pa, Sept 3, 26; m 56; c 2. PHYSICAL CHEMISTRY. *Educ:* Pa State Univ, BS, 50; Northwestern Univ, PhD(chem), 55. *Prof Exp:* Res chemist, Union Oil Co, Calif, 55-59; res assoc & instr phys chem, Princeton Univ, 59-62; staff scientist, Gen Dynamics/Convair, 62-69 & Sci Applications, Inc, 69-74; STAFF SCIENTIST, GEN ATOMIC CO, 74- *Concurrent Pos:* Consult, Sci Applications, Inc, 74-78. *Mem:* AAAS; Am Chem Soc; Am Phys Soc; Combustion Inst. *Res:* Shock phenomena; chemical kinetics; energy exchange processes; atmospheric chemistry; nuclear reactor fission product transport. *Mailing Add:* Gen Atomic Co 10955 John Jay Hopkins Dr San Diego CA 92121

MYERS, BETTY JUNE, b Ashland, Ohio, Apr 18, 28. PARASITOLOGY. *Educ:* Ashland Col, BA & BSc, 49; Univ Nebr, MA, 51; McGill Univ, PhD(parasitol), 59. *Prof Exp:* Lab asst biol, Ashland Col, 47-49, instr, 51-52; asst biol, Univ Nebr, 49-51; instr parasitol, McGill Univ, 52-53, res assoc, 53-59, asst prof parasitol, 59-64; parasitologist, Southwest Found Res & Educ, 64-69, asst found scientist, 69-73; HEALTH SCI ADMINR, DIV RES GRANTS, NIH, 73- *Concurrent Pos:* Fisheries Res Bd Can res grant, 54-58; consult, Food & Agr Orgn, 57-; Mem, Can Comt Freshwater Fisheries Res & Sci Adv Bd, Ashland Col, 59-; Nat Res Coun Can fel, 59-60; consult, NIH, 61; parasitologist, Arctic Unit, Fisheries Res Bd Can, 62-63; coun mem at large, Am Soc Parasitol, 74-, vpres, 75. *Mem:* AAAS; Am Soc Mammal; Am Soc Parasitol; Am Soc Trop Med & Hyg; Am Micros Soc (pres, 74). *Res:* Parasites of marine mammals, fish and primates; anisakiasis; schistosomiasis haematobium; primate ecological relationships of host and parasites; host-phylogenetic relationships; zoogeography; systematic experimental studies; helminthology. *Mailing Add:* Div Res Grants Westwood Bldg Rm 319 Bethesda MD 20014

MYERS, BLAKE, b Seattle, Wash, July 15, 23; m 44; c 2. MECHANICAL ENGINEERING. *Educ:* Univ Wash, Seattle, BSME, 47; Mass Inst Technol, SMME, 48. *Prof Exp:* Instr mech eng, Univ Wash, Seattle, 46; assoc, Mass Inst Technol, 47-48; design engr, Richmond Refinery, Standard Oil Co, Calif, 48-50; mech engr, Calif Res & Develop Co, 50-53; leader, Apparatus Eng Div, 56-58 & Propulsion Eng Div, 58-67, MECH ENGR, LAWRENCE LIVERMORE LAB, UNIV CALIF, 53-, HEAD RES PROG ENG DIV, 67- *Concurrent Pos:* Consult, Kaiser Eng, 67-; mem exec comn tech group controlled fusion, Am Nuclear Soc, 71- *Res:* Design and analysis of power, propulsion, accelerator and nuclear systems. *Mailing Add:* 4650 Almond Circle Livermore CA 94550

MYERS, CARROL BRUCE, b Asheville, NC, Sept 6, 43; m 65; c 2. ALGEBRA. *Educ:* Berea Col, BA, 65; Univ Ky, MA, 67, PhD(math), 70. *Prof Exp:* Asst prof, 70-72, assoc prof math, 72-80, PROF MATH & COMPUT SCI, AUSTIN PEAY STATE UNIV, 80- *Mem:* Math Asn Am; Nat Coun Teachers Math; Asn Comput Mach. *Res:* Ring theory; module theory. *Mailing Add:* Dept of Math & Comput Sci Austin Peay State Univ Clarksville TN 37040

MYERS, CHARLES CHRISTOPHER, b Richwood, WVa, June 12, 34; m 60; c 3. FORESTRY, BIOMETRY. *Educ:* WVa Univ, BS, 60; Syracuse Univ, MS, 62; Purdue Univ, PhD(forestry), 66. *Prof Exp:* From instr to asst prof forestry, Purdue Univ, 62-67; technician, US AID, 67-69; asst prof, Univ Vt, 69-73; ASSOC PROF FORESTRY, SOUTHERN ILL UNIV, CARBONDALE, 73- *Concurrent Pos:* NSF grant, 71. *Mem:* Soc Am Foresters. *Res:* Applications of statistics and computers to forest inventory. *Mailing Add:* Dept of Forestry Southern Ill Univ Carbondale IL 62901

MYERS, CHARLES EDWIN, b Philadelphia, Pa, Dec 15, 40; m 63; c 3. ENVIRONMENTAL ENGINEERING, SCIENCE POLICY. *Educ:* Pa State Univ, BS, 62; Univ Md, MS, 65. *Prof Exp:* Res chemist metal ceramic solution chem, Dept Interior, Bur Mines, 65-67; res assoc water transfer & membranes, AeroChem Res Labs, Inc, 67-68; res engr ion exchange & membrane technol, Permutit Co, 68-69; chemist water pollution control, Fed Water Pollution Control Admin, 69-71; chem engr water qual sanit eng, US Environ Protection Agency, 71-74; exec secy interagency arctic res coord comt, 74-78, INTERAGENCY/INT PROG COORDR, NSF, 78- *Concurrent Pos:* Partner & consult engr, Myers, Tobin, Trax & Assocs, 73-74. *Mem:* Am Inst Chem Engrs. *Res:* Membranes and ion exchange; water quality; sanitary engineering; pollution control; solid waste management; integrated utility systems; arctic; cold regions engineering; antarctic; environmental impact analysis; conservation; pollution control regulation; international science policy. *Mailing Add:* NSF 1800 G St NW Washington DC 20550

MYERS, CHARLES WILLIAM, b St Louis, Mo, Mar 4, 36. HERPETOLOGY. *Educ:* Univ Fla, BS, 60; Southern Ill Univ, MA, 62; Univ Kans, PhD(zool), 70. *Prof Exp:* Vis scientist herpet, Gorgas Mem Lab, Panama, 64-67; asst cur, 68-73, assoc cur, 73-78, CUR HERPET, AM MUS NATURAL HIST, 78-, CHMN DEPT, 80- *Mem:* Am Soc Ichthyologists & Herpetologists; Soc Study Amphibians & Reptiles. *Res:* Systematics of neotropical amphibians and reptiles. *Mailing Add:* Dept Herpet Am Mus Natural Hist New York NY 10024

MYERS, CLIFFORD ALBERT, JR, b New London, Conn, Oct 19, 20; m 42; c 1. FOREST MANAGEMENT, FOREST MENSURATION. *Educ:* Colo State Univ, BSF, 42, MF, 47; Yale Univ, PhD(forestry), 59. *Prof Exp:* Asst prof forestry, Univ WVa, 47-55; res forester, Rocky Mountain Forest & Range Exp Sta, 55-75, RES FORESTER, SOUTHERN FOREST EXP STA, US FOREST SERV, 75- *Honors & Awards:* Superior Serv Award, USDA, 72; Mgt Improv Award, US President, 75. *Mem:* Soc Am Foresters; Biometrics Soc; Soc Am Archaeol. *Res:* Systems analysis in forestry; simulation in forest management. *Mailing Add:* Southern Forest Exp Sta US Postal Serv Bldg New Orleans LA 70113

MYERS, CLIFFORD EARL, b Jefferson City, Tenn, June 1, 29; m 53; c 2. PHYSICAL INORGANIC CHEMISTRY, HIGH TEMPERATURE CHEMISTRY. *Educ:* Carson-Newman Col, BS & BA, 51; Purdue Univ, MS, 53, PhD(inorg chem), 56. *Prof Exp:* Asst, Purdue Univ, 51-54; grad res chemist, Inst Eng Res, Univ Calif, 54-55; res assoc chem eng, Univ Ill, 55-56; from asst prof to assoc prof chem, Lynchburg Col, 56-58; asst prof, State Univ NY Col Ceramics, Alfred Univ, 58-63; assoc prof, 63-78, PROF CHEM, STATE UNIV NY BINGHAMTON, 78- *Concurrent Pos:* Vis staff mem, Los Alamos Sci Lab, 64-65; vis scientist, Univ Brussels, Belg, 69-70; vis prof, Ames Lab, Iowa State Univ, 77, 78. *Mem:* Fel AAAS; Am Chem Soc; Sigma Xi. *Res:* High temperature vaporization processes; thermodynamic stabilities, structure and bonding in refractory substances and high temperature molecules. *Mailing Add:* Dept of Chem State Univ of NY Binghamton NY 13901

MYERS, DALE DEHAVEN, b Kansas City, Mo, Jan 8, 22; m 43; c 2. AERONAUTICS. *Educ:* Univ Wash, BS, 43; Whitworth Col, PhD, 70. *Prof Exp:* Chief engr, Missile Develop Div, NAm Aviation, 46-57, vpres & weapons systs mgr, 57-63, asst div dir advan systs, Rockwell Int Corp, El Segundo, Calif, 63-64, vpres & gen mgr CSM progs, 64-69, vpres & mgr space shuttle prog, 69-70; assoc adminr manned space flight, NASA, 70-74; pres, Rockwell Int Corp & corp vpres, Rockwell Int, 74-77; UNDER-SECY, DEPT ENERGY, 77- *Honors & Awards:* Pub Serv Award, NASA, 69, Distinguished Serv Medal, 71 & 74. *Mem:* Nat Acad Eng; fel Am Inst Aeronaut & Astronaut; Am Astronaut Soc. *Mailing Add:* Off Under-Secy Dept of Energy Washington DC 20585

MYERS, DALE KAMERER, organic chemistry, see previous edition

MYERS, DAVID, b Philadelphia, Pa, Sept 18, 06; m 30; c 2. MEDICINE. *Educ:* Univ Pa, 27; Temple Univ, MD, 30; Am Bd Otolaryngol, dipl, 35. *Prof Exp:* Intern, Temple Univ, 30-32, preceptor, Temple Univ & trainee, Temple Univ Hosp, 32-40, mem staff dept otorhinol, Temple Univ Med Sch, 32-55, prof & chmn dept, 55-62; prof otorhinolaryngol, 62-71, chmn dept, 64-71, prof otolaryngol, 71-76, EMER PROF OTOLARYNGOL & HUMAN COMMUN, SCH MED, UNIV PA, 76- *Concurrent Pos:* Dir inst otol, Presby Hosp, Philadelphia, 62- *Mem:* Fel Am Otol Soc; Am Laryngol, Rhinol & Otol Soc; fel Am Col Surg; fel Am Acad Ophthal & Otolaryngol. *Res:* Otolaryngology. *Mailing Add:* The Philadelphian 2401 Pennsylvania Ave Philadelphia PA 19130

MYERS, DAVID DANIEL, b Morris, Minn, Dec 19, 32; m 59; c 1. LABORATORY ANIMAL SCIENCE, ANIMAL PATHOLOGY. *Educ:* Univ Minn, BS, 55, DVM, 57; Univ Ill, MS, 62, PhD(vet path & microbiol), 65. *Prof Exp:* Poultry vet, Fla Livestock Bd, 57-58; animal pathologist, Ill Dept Agr, 58-59; instr vet path, Univ Ill, 59-61; assoc staff scientist, 65-69, staff scientist, 69-75, SR STAFF SCIENTIST, JACKSON LAB, 75- *Concurrent Pos:* Assoc ed, Lab Animal Sci; actg assoc dir lab animal resources, Wide Ctr, Cornell Univ, 80-81. *Mem:* AAAS; Am Vet Med Asn; Am Asn Lab Animal Sci; Asn Gnotobiol; Am Soc Lab Animal Practrs. *Res:* Histopathology; pathogenesis of infectious diseases. *Mailing Add:* Jackson Lab Bar Harbor ME 04609

MYERS, DAVID J, analytical chemistry, electrochemistry, see previous edition

MYERS, DAVID KENNETH, radiation biology, biochemistry, see previous edition

MYERS, DAVID RICHARD, b Harvey, Ill, Dec 16, 48; m 75. SOLID-STATE PHYSICS, ELECTRICAL ENGINEERING. *Educ:* Univ of Ill, Chicago Circle, BSE, 71; Univ Ill, Urbana-Champaign, MS, 73, PhD(elec eng), 77. *Prof Exp:* Res asst semiconductor phys, Coord Sci Lab, Univ Ill, Urbana-Champaign, 72-77; Nat Bur Standards-Nat Res Coun res assoc, Electronic Technol Div, Nat Bur Standards, 77-78, physicist, Electronic Devices Div, 78-81; MEM TECH STAFF, SANDIA NAT LABS, ALBUQUERQUE, NMEX, 81- *Mem:* Inst Elec & Electronics Engrs; Am Phys Soc; Sigma Xi. *Res:* Ion implantation; ion range particularly theory and measurement; radiation damage and annealing of semiconductors; deep levels in semiconductors; growth and characterization of compound semiconductors; lasers; superconductivity; compound semiconductor device physics; process development for compound semiconductors. *Mailing Add:* 5705 Carruthers NE Albuquerque NM 87111

MYERS, DIRCK V, b New York, NY, Aug 24, 35; m 59; c 3. BIOCHEMISTRY. *Educ:* Dartmouth Col, AB, 57; Univ Wash, PhD(biochem), 62. *Prof Exp:* Res fel biol, Harvard Univ, 62-64; sr res scientist, Squibb Inst Med Res, NJ, 64-68; sr scientist, 68-77, PRIN INVESTR, COCA-COLA CO, 77- *Mem:* Am Chem Soc. *Res:* Protein chemistry; peptide synthesis; enzymology. *Mailing Add:* Coca Cola Co PO Drawer 1734 Atlanta GA 30301

MYERS, DONALD ALBIN, b Denver, Colo, May 17, 36; m 58; c 2. PHYSIOLOGY, BIOMEDICAL ENGINEERING. *Educ:* Colo Sch Mines, PE, 58; Univ Colo, PhD(physiol), 73. *Prof Exp:* Pipeline engr, US Army Corps Engrs, 58-60; design engr, Martin Marietta Corp, 60-65; develop engr, AiResearch Mfg Co, Garrett Corp, 65-67; staff engr, Martin Marietta Corp, 67-69; CONSULT, US GOVT, WASHINGTON, DC, 73- *Mem:* AAAS; Aerospace Med Asn; Sigma Xi. *Res:* Integration of established and new technologies from both biological and physical science origin to create new applications; effects of environmental stressors on the normal functioning of the human organism. *Mailing Add:* 8537 Pepperdine Dr Vienna VA 22180

MYERS, DONALD EARL, b Chanute, Kans, Dec 29, 31; m 54; c 2. MATHEMATICS. *Educ:* Kans State Univ, BS, 53, MS, 55; Univ Ill, PhD, 60. *Prof Exp:* Asst math, Kans State Univ, 53-55 & Univ Ill, 55-58; assoc prof, Millikin Univ, 58-60; from asst prof to assoc prof, 60-68, PROF MATH, UNIV ARIZ, 68- *Concurrent Pos:* Co-dir, Sec Sci Training Prog, NSF, Univ Ariz, 61, dir, 63, mem, Adv Panel Judge Proposals, 63-66 & writing team, Minn Math & Sci Teaching Proj, Univ Minn, 63-66; vis lectr, Teachers Col, 66; consult, India Prog, NSF-AID, 67. *Mem:* AAAS; Math Asn Am; Am Math Soc; Inst Math Statist; Int Asn Math Geologists. *Res:* Analysis; theory of distributions; geostatistics. *Mailing Add:* 3322 E Waverly Tucson AZ 85716

MYERS, DONALD ROYAL, b Cleveland, Ohio, Dec 18, 13; m 40; c 1. ORGANIC CHEMISTRY. *Educ:* Ohio State Univ, AB, 35, PhD(chem), 40. *Prof Exp:* Asst anal chem, Ohio State Univ, 35-40; res engr, Battelle Mem Inst, Ohio, 40-42; fel, Carnegie Inst Technol, 42-44; res chemist, Upjohn Co, 44-54, sect head, Chem Dept, 54-60, mgr chem res prep dept, 60-79; RETIRED. *Mem:* AAAS; Am Chem Soc; NY Acad Sci. *Res:* Steroids; medicinal chemicals. *Mailing Add:* 890 E G Ave Kalamazoo MI 49004

MYERS, DREWFUS YOUNG, JR, b Corcicana, Tex, Aug 20, 46; m 79. ORGANIC POLYMER CHEMISTRY, COLLOID & SURFACE CHEMISTRY. *Educ:* Tex Lutheran Col, BS, 68; Univ Utah, PhD(org chem), 74; Univ Bristol, Eng, MSc, 79. *Prof Exp:* RES CHEMIST, EASTMAN KODAK CO, 74- *Mem:* AAAS; Am Chem Soc. *Res:* Various aspects of emulsion polymerization, latex polymer application and the colloidal stability of latex polymers; surfactant synthesis; characterization and application; surface energetics; polymer characterization. *Mailing Add:* Res Labs Eastman Kodak Co Rochester NY 14650

MYERS, EARL A(BRAHAM), b York Co, Pa, Jan 15, 29; m 56; c 2. AGRICULTURAL ENGINEERING, LAND APPLICATION OF WASTEWATER. *Educ:* Pa State Univ, BS, 50, MS, 52; Mich State Univ, PhD, 60. *Prof Exp:* From instr to prof, 51-77, EMER PROF AGR ENG, PA STATE UNIV, 77- *Concurrent Pos:* Consult land application of wastewater, 62-77; wastewater irrigation specialist, consult, Williams & Works, Grand Rapids, Mich, 77- *Honors & Awards:* Karl M Mason Award. *Mem:* Am Soc Agr Engrs; Water Pollution Control Fedn; Irrigation Asn. *Res:* Soil and water area; small watershed hydrology; terraces; tile drainage; wastewater irrigation systems design; development of heads for distributing waste water year-around, including subzero weather. *Mailing Add:* 164 W Hamilton Ave State College PA 16801

MYERS, EARL EUGENE, b Ruffsdale, Pa, Nov 5, 24; m 54; c 4. PETROLEUM CHEMISTRY. *Educ:* Thiel Col, BS, 47; Western Reserve Univ, MS, 49, PhD(org chem), 51. *Prof Exp:* Res chemist, Esso Res & Eng Co, 51-52; res chemist, 53-62, SR RES CHEMIST, GULF RES & DEVELOP CO, 62- *Mem:* AAAS; Am Chem Soc. *Res:* Preparation of chemicals for use as petroleum additives; relationships of structure to activity; oil-soluble polymers. *Mailing Add:* 1526 Sherman St Cheswick PA 15024

MYERS, EUGENE NICHOLAS, b Philadelphia, Pa, Nov 27, 33; m 56; c 2. OTOLARYNGOLOGY. *Educ:* Univ Pa, BS, 54; Temple Univ, MD, 60. *Prof Exp:* PROF OTOLARYNGOL & CHMN DEPT, SCH MED, UNIV PITTSBURGH, 72- *Concurrent Pos:* Consult, Children's Hosp & Vet Admin Hosp, Pittsburgh, 72-; chief dept otolaryngol, Eye & Ear Hosp, Pittsburgh, 72-; bd gov, Am Col Surg, 81- *Mem:* Am Acad Facial, Plastic & Reconstruct Surg; Am Acad Otolaryngol Head & Neck Surg; Am Soc Head & Neck Surg; Am Otol Soc; Asn Res Otolaryngol. *Res:* Clinical trials head and neck surgery. *Mailing Add:* 230 Lothrop St Dept Otolaryngol Univ Pittsburgh Sch Med Pittsburgh PA 15213

MYERS, FRANKLIN GUY, b Baltimore, Md, Aug 9, 18; m 37; c 3. MATHEMATICS. *Educ:* Univ Va, BA, 38, MA, 40, PhD(math), 42. *Prof Exp:* Instr math, Univ Va, 39-42; res engr, Martin Co, 42-50, supvr automatic comput, 50-53, chief servomech, 53-57, mgr advan reactor systs, 57-62; dir res, Allison Div, 62-68, chief mfg technol, Detroit Diesel Allison Div, 68-74, MGR MFG COMPUT SYSTS, DETROIT DIESEL ALLISON DIV, GEN MOTORS CORP, 74- *Res:* Gas turbine engines. *Mailing Add:* Detroit Diesel Div Gen Motors Corp Indianapolis IN 46206

MYERS, GARDINER HUBBARD, b Washington, DC, Jan 16, 39; m 63; c 2. PHYSICAL CHEMISTRY. *Educ:* Princeton Univ, AB, 59; Univ Calif, Berkeley, PhD(chem), 65. *Prof Exp:* Asst prof, 65-72, ASSOC PROF CHEM, UNIV FLA, 72- *Mem:* Am Chem Soc. *Res:* Gas kinetics; singlet oxygen; chemical education. *Mailing Add:* Dept of Chem Univ of Fla Gainesville FL 32611

MYERS, GEORGE E, b Detroit, Mich, Aug 9, 26; m 53; c 6. PHYSICAL CHEMISTRY, POLYMER CHEMISTRY. *Educ:* Univ Southern Calif, BS, 48, MS, 49; Harvard Univ, PhD, 52. *Prof Exp:* Res chemist, Oak Ridge Nat Lab, 52-56; proj scientist, Plastics Div, Union Carbide Corp, 56-63; sr tech specialist & sect chief, Lockheed Propulsion Co, Calif, 63-75; RES CHEMIST, FOREST PROD LAB, 75- *Mem:* Am Chem Soc; Forest Prods Res Soc; Sigma Xi. *Res:* Physical chemistry of proteins, clays, ion-exchange resins and polymers; solid propellants; wood adhesives. *Mailing Add:* 2210 Fox Ave Madison WI 53711

MYERS, GEORGE HENRY, b New York, NY, Feb 21, 30; m 56; c 3. ELECTRICAL ENGINEERING, BIOMEDICAL ENGINEERING. *Educ:* Mass Inst Technol, SB & SM, 52; Columbia Univ EngScD, 59. *Prof Exp:* Mem tech staff, Bell Tel Labs, Inc, 52-59, supvr guid & control, 59-65; from assoc prof to prof elec eng, NY Univ, 65-69; mgr biomed eng lab, Riverside Res Inst, New York, 69-74; TECH DIR PACEMAKER CTR, NEWARK BETH ISRAEL MED CTR, 74- *Mem:* Sr mem Inst Elec & Electronics Eng; Am Soc Artificial Internal Organs; Biomed Eng Soc. *Res:* Ultrasonics; pacemakers and control of respiration; digital and analog computers. *Mailing Add:* 190 Wyoming Ave Maplewood NJ 07040

MYERS, GEORGE SCOTT, JR, b Monte Vista, Colo, Mar 21, 34; m 61; c 8. ANIMAL NUTRITION. *Educ:* Colo State Univ, BS, 56; Univ Conn, MS, 58; Cornell Univ, PhD(animal nutrit), 66. *Prof Exp:* Asst animal nutrit, Univ Conn, 56-58 & Cornell Univ, 60-63; sr nutritionist, Ciba Res Farm, NJ, 63-69;

sr res nutritionist, Squibb Agr Res Ctr, 69-70; PRES, MYERS ANIMAL SCI CO, 70- *Concurrent Pos:* Consult sales & mkt. *Res:* Carotene; vitamins A and E requirements of cattle, sheep and swine; rumen metabolism; ration formulation; animal husbandry management; animal health research; feeding experiments. *Mailing Add:* Myers Animal Sci Co 11104 Bonney View Lane Hanford CA 93230

MYERS, GERALD ANDY, b Boelus, Nebr, Sept 23, 28; m 53; c 4. PLANT ANATOMY, SCIENCE EDUCATION. *Educ:* Kearney State Col, AB, 51; Colo State Col, AM, 57; SDak State Col, PhD(plant sci), 63. *Prof Exp:* Teacher elem sch, Nebr, 51-52; teacher, jr high sch, Idaho, 52-55, high sch, 55-56; asst bot & biol, Colo State Col, 56-57; elem teacher adminr, elem sch, Ill, 57-58; instr bot, 58-64, asst prof, 64-68, assoc prof, 68-72, head dept, 72-81, PROF BIOL, SDAK STATE UNIV, 72- *Concurrent Pos:* NSF instr, Ind Univ, 59, SDak State Col, 60, Univ Wash, 61, Fla State Univ, 67 & Pa State Univ, 68 & Ohio State Univ, 72; consult, Biol Sci Curric Study, SDak, 63-79, chmn, Testing Comt, 66-67; consult sci process approach, AAAS, 68-; consult, Intermediate Sci Curric Study, 69-79; Danforth Assoc. *Mem:* Inst Soc, Ethics & Life Sci. *Res:* Plant morphogenesis and developmental plant anatomy; internal consistency, reliability of computer managed instructional tests. *Mailing Add:* Dept Biol SDak State Univ Brookings SD 57007

MYERS, GLEN E(VERETT), b Los Angeles, Calif, Mar 6, 34; m 63; c 2. MECHANICAL ENGINEERING. *Educ:* Rensselaer Polytech Inst, BME, 56; Stanford Univ, MS, 57, PhD(mech eng), 62. *Prof Exp:* From asst prof to assoc prof, 62-71, PROF MECH ENG, UNIV WIS-MADISON, 71- *Concurrent Pos:* NSF sci fac fel, Stanford Univ, 69-70. *Mem:* Am Soc Mech Engrs; Am Soc Eng Educ. *Res:* Finite-difference and finite-element methods for conduction heat transfer. *Mailing Add:* Dept Mech Eng Univ Wis Madison WI 53706

MYERS, GORDON EDWARD, b Calgary, Alta, Oct 1, 18; m; c 2. MICROBIOLOGY. *Educ:* Univ Alta, BSc, 46, MSc, 48; McGill Univ, PhD(bact), 51. *Prof Exp:* Lectr bact, 46-49, from asst prof to prof, 51-63, microbiol, Fac Microbiol, 63-66, PROF MICROBIOL, FAC PHARM, UNIV ALTA, 67-, ASSOC DEAN, FAC PHARM & PHARMACEUT SCI, 71- *Concurrent Pos:* Asst prov bacteriologist, Alta Dept Pub Health, 46-57; head dept microbiol, Univ Alta, 63-66; consult microbiol, Pharm & Petrol Indust, Prov & Fed Depts, 51-66; Nat Res Coun Can sr res fel, Univ Hawaii, 66-67. *Mem:* Can Pharmaceut Asn. *Res:* Antimicrobial agents in medical practice and industry; industrial microbiology, especially pharmaceutical microbiology. *Mailing Add:* Fac of Pharm & Pharmaceut Sci Univ of Alberta Edmonton BC Can

MYERS, GORDON SHARP, b St John, NB, Jan 23, 21; m 47; c 5. MEDICINAL CHEMISTRY. *Educ:* Univ NB, BA, 41; Univ Toronto, MA, 42, PhD(org chem), 45. *Prof Exp:* Res chemist, Dom Rubber Co, 45-47; res assoc, Dept Biochem, Queen's Univ, Ont, 47-49; res chemist, Ayerst, McKenna & Harrison, Ltd. 49-67, mgr chem develop, 67-69, DIR CHEM DEVELOP, AYERST LABS, 69- *Mem:* Am Chem Soc; fel Chem Inst Can; Am Inst Chem Engrs. *Res:* Medicinal and pharmaceutical chemistry; synthesis of anticonvulsants, antispasmodics, analgesics and steroids. *Mailing Add:* Ayerst Labs PO Box 6115 Montreal PQ H3C 3J1 Can

MYERS, GRANT G, b Avoca, Iowa, Dec 6, 30; m 52; c 2. ELECTRICAL ENGINEERING. *Educ:* Univ Iowa, BSEE, 57, MSEE, 58, PhD(elec engr), 65. *Prof Exp:* Elec engr develop, Collins Radio Co, 58-62, res, 62-63; asst prof elec eng, Univ Nebr, Lincoln, 65-67; elec eng in internal med & physiol, Sch Med, Univ Nebr, Omaha, 67-69, assoc prof physiol, Sch Med & elec eng, Sch Eng, 69-74, asst dir cardiovasc eng, 65-70; MEM FAC, UNIV NEBR, LINCOLN, 74- *Concurrent Pos:* Nat Insts Health res grant, 67; Fulbright award, Uruguay, 67; NSF grant, 79. *Mem:* Inst Elec & Electronics Engrs. *Res:* Solid state devices and integrated circuits; bioengineering; control systems. *Mailing Add:* Dept of Elec Eng Univ of Nebr Lincoln NE 68588

MYERS, HARVEY NATHANIEL, b Tampa, Fla, Aug 26, 46; m 70; c 2. ANALYTICAL CHEMISTRY. *Educ:* Morehouse Col, BS, 69; Univ Ill, Urbana, MS, 71, PhD(chem), 74. *Prof Exp:* Fel comput based teaching, Univ Ill, Urbana, 74; asst prof chem, Chicago State Univ, 74-76, coordr comput assisted instr, 75-76; RES SCIENTIST, UPJOHN CO, 76- *Mem:* AAAS; Am Chem Soc. *Res:* Curriculum development; bio-organic chemistry for computer assisted instruction. *Mailing Add:* The Upjohn Co 7000 Portage Rd Kalamazoo MI 49001

MYERS, HENRY S, JR, b York, Pa, Jan 4, 24; m 49; c 4. CHEMICAL ENGINEERING. *Educ:* Pa State Univ, BS, 44, MS, 47, PhD(chem eng), 52. *Prof Exp:* Instr chem eng, Pa State Univ, 44-52; res engr, 52-71, HEAD RES SERV, C F BRAUN & CO, ALHAMBRA, 71- *Res:* Distillation; vacuum work; design of pilot scale equipment. *Mailing Add:* C F Braun & Co 1000 S Freemont Ave Alhambra CA 91801

MYERS, HOWARD, b New York, NY, Jan 27, 28; m 76; c 3. CHEMICAL PHYSICS. *Educ:* Univ Chicago, PhB, 48, BS, 51, MS, 58. *Prof Exp:* Mem tech staff, Hughes Res Labs, 54-56; res specialist, Douglas Aircraft Co, Inc, 56-61; mem tech staff, Aerospace Corp, 61-63, mgr reentry physics, 63-66; mem tech staff, TRW Systs Group, 66-68; mgr plasma physics, McDonnell Douglas Astronaut, 69-70, mgr planetary atmospheric physics, 70-73, proj scientist, Planetary Progs, 73-78, instrumentation mgr, Fusion Energy Progs, 78-79, sr tech specialist, 79-80; SR SYSTS ENGR, SPACE DIV, GEN ELEC CO, 80- *Concurrent Pos:* Pres & tech dir, Changed Particle Res Lab, Inc, 68- *Mem:* AAAS; Am Astron Soc; Am Phys Soc; Am Geophys Union; fel Am Inst Chemists. *Res:* Thermodynamics and reaction kinetics of solids, gases and plasmas. *Mailing Add:* 699 North Valley Rd Paoli PA 19301

MYERS, HOWARD M, b Brooklyn, NY, Dec 12, 23; m 72; c 3. PHARMACOLOGY. *Educ:* Western Reserve Univ, DDS, 49; Univ Calif, MS, 53; Univ Rochester, PhD(pharmacol), 58; San Francisco State Col, MA, 64. *Hon Degrees:* MA, Univ Pa, 74. *Prof Exp:* Asst dent med, Sch Dent, Univ Calif, San Francisco, 4951, from instr to asst prof, 51-59, assoc prof dent med & biochem, 59-65, prof oral biol & lectr biochem, 65-71, vchmn dept biochem, Sch Med, 67-71, prof biochem & biophys, 71-72; prof biochem & chmn dept, Sch Dent, Univ Pac, 71-74; dir, Ctr Oral Health Res, 74-78, PROF PHARMACOL, SCH DENT MED, UNIV PA, 74- *Concurrent Pos:* Nat Inst Dent Res spec res fel, Dept Med Physics, Karolinska Inst, Sweden, 64-65; trainee, Advan Seminar Res Educ, Am Col Dentists, 63, mentor, 64; consult, Stanford Res Inst, 63-74; mem, Dent Training Comt, Nat Inst Dent Res, 65-69; dent res consult, Vet Admin Hosp, San Francisco, 66-74; mem, Dent Study Comt, Div Res Grants, NIH, 69-73; ed, Monographs Oral Sci, 70-; consult, Cooper Labs, 74-79; invited prof, Univ Geneva, Switz, 80-81; Fogarty sr int res fel, 80-81. *Mem:* AAAS; Am Asn Dent Res (pres, 74); Int Asn Dent Res. *Res:* Mineral metabolism; composition of saliva; surface properties of tooth and bone mineral. *Mailing Add:* Sch Dent Med Univ of Pa Philadelphia PA 19174

MYERS, IRA LEE, b Madison Co, Ala, Feb 9, 24; m 43; c 4. PREVENTIVE MEDICINE, PUBLIC HEALTH. *Educ:* Howard Col, BS, 45; Univ Ala, MD, 49; Harvard Univ, MPH, 53; Am Bd Prev Med, dipl pub health, 67. *Prof Exp:* Chief epidemic intel serv officer & asst to chief epidemiol br, Commun Dis Ctr, USPHS, 49-55; admin officer & asst state health officer, 55-62, STATE HEALTH OFFICER, DEPT PUB HEALTH, ALA, 63-; ASST CLIN PROF PREV MED, MED COL ALA, 57- *Concurrent Pos:* Secy, Ala Bd Med Examrs, 62-73; chmn, Ala Water Improv Comn, 63- *Honors & Awards:* McCormack Award, Asn State & Territorial Health Offices. *Mem:* Asn State & Prov Health Authorities of NAm; Asn State & Territorial Health Offs; Am Thoracic Soc. *Res:* Epidemiology of acute and chronic disease; problems of the aged, including medical care and nursing. *Mailing Add:* State Off Bldg Rm 381 Ala Dept Pub Health Montgomery AL 36130

MYERS, IRA THOMAS, b Iona, SDak, June 10, 25; m 47; c 8. PHYSICS. *Educ:* Wash State Univ, BS, 48, MS, 52, PhD(physics), 58. *Prof Exp:* Actg chief engr, Radio Sta KWSC, 48-49; sr physicist, Gen Elec Co, 49-62, mgr radiation effects sect, 62-70, mgr power components sect, 70-76, MGR POWER DEVICES SECT, LEWIS RES CTR, NASA, 76- *Res:* High power high performance electronic components. *Mailing Add:* NASA Lewis Res Ctr 21000 Brookpark Mail Stop 501-8 Cleveland OH 44135

MYERS, JACK DUANE, b New Brighton, Pa, May 24, 13; m 46; c 5. CLINICAL MEDICINE. *Educ:* Stanford Univ, AB, 33, MD, 37. *Prof Exp:* From intern to asst resident, Stanford Univ Hosps, 36-38; from asst resident to resident, Peter Bent Brigham Hosp, Boston, 39-42; assoc, Emory Univ, 46-47; assoc prof med, Duke Univ, 47-55; prof & chmn dept, 55-70, UNIV PROF, SCH MED, UNIV PITTSBURGH, 70- *Concurrent Pos:* Chmn, Am Bd Internal Med, 67-70; mem, Nat Adv Coun Arthritis & Metab Dis, 70-74; chmn, Nat Bd Med Examrs, 71-75. *Mem:* Am Soc Clin Invest (secy-treas, 55-57); fel Am Col Physicians (pres, 76); Am Physiol Soc; Asn Am Physicians. *Res:* Clinical investigation of circulatory system of man, particularly the hepatic blood flow; diagnostic use of computers in clinical medicine. *Mailing Add:* 1291 Scaife Hall Univ Pittsburgh 3550 Terrace St Pittsburgh PA 15261

MYERS, JACK EDGAR, b Boyds Mills, Pa, July 10, 13; m 37; c 4. PHOTOBIOLOGY. *Educ:* Juniata Col, BS, 34; Mont State Col, MS, 36; Univ Minn, PhD(bot), 39. *Hon Degrees:* DSc, Juniata Col, 66. *Prof Exp:* Nat Res Coun fel, Smithsonian Inst, 39-41; asst prof physiol, 41-46, from assoc prof to prof zool, 46-55, PROF BOT & ZOOL, UNIV TEX, AUSTIN, 55- *Concurrent Pos:* Guggenheim fel, 60; sci ed, Highlights for Children, 61. *Honors & Awards:* Kettering Award, Am Soc Plant Physiologists, 74. *Mem:* Nat Acad Sci; Bot Soc Am; Am Soc Plant Physiologists; Soc Gen Physiol; Am Soc Photobiol (pres, 75). *Res:* Photosynthesis; plant pigments; biological effects of radiation; physiology of algae. *Mailing Add:* Dept of Zool Univ of Tex Austin TX 78712

MYERS, JACOB MARTIN, b Mercersburg, Pa, Aug 16, 19; m 45; c 2. PSYCHIATRY. *Educ:* Princeton Univ, AB, 40; Johns Hopkins Univ, MD, 43; Am Bd Psychiat & Neurol, dipl, 49. *Prof Exp:* Exec med officer, Pa Hosp, 51-62, med dir, 62-70, psychiatrist-in-chief, 70-81, from asst prof to assoc prof, 54-70, PROF PSYCHIAT, SCH MED, UNIV PA, 70-, PSYCHIATRIST-IN-RESIDENCE & DIR PSYCHIAT, PA HOSP, 81- *Concurrent Pos:* Consult, Vet Admin Hosp, Coatesville, 55-65; US Naval Hosp, Philadelphia, 57-75; mem, Accreditation Coun, Psychiat Facil, Joint Comn Accreditation Hosps, 76- *Mem:* AAAS; Am Psychopath Asn; AMA; fel Am Psychiat Asn; Am Col Psychiat (pres, 71-72). *Res:* Clinical evaluation of treatment of hospitalized psychiatric patients. *Mailing Add:* Inst of the Pa Hosp 111 N 49th St Philadelphia PA 19139

MYERS, JAMES HURLEY, b Memphis, Tenn, Sept 28, 40; m 63; c 2. PHYSIOLOGY. *Educ:* Memphis State Univ, BS, 63; Univ Tenn, Memphis, PhD(physiol), 69. *Prof Exp:* Instr physiol, Memphis State Univ, 68-69; asst prof, 71-77, ASSOC PROF PHYSIOL, SOUTHERN ILL UNIV, CARBONDALE, 77- SCH MED, 71-, CURRIC COORDR, SCH & REP TO AM ASN MED COLS GROUP STUDENT AFFAIRS, 71- *Concurrent Pos:* USPHS fel biol, Brookhaven Nat Lab, 69-71. *Mem:* Assoc Am Physiol Soc; Geront Soc. *Res:* Physiology of circulation; radiation injury in primates; radioisotope techniques; physiology of aging. *Mailing Add:* Dept of Physiol Southern Ill Univ Sch Med Carbondale IL 62901

MYERS, JAMES R(USSELL), b Middletown, Ohio, June 17, 33. METALLURGY. *Educ:* Univ Cincinnati, BS, 56; Univ Wis, MS, 57; Ohio State Univ, PhD(metall eng), 64. *Prof Exp:* Proj engr, Wright Air Develop Div, Wright-Patterson AFB, 59-60, mat engr, Aeronaut Systs Div, 60-62; assoc prof metall, Sch Civil Eng, US Air Force Inst Technol, 62-71, prof, 71-79; DIR, JRM ASSOCS, 79- *Concurrent Pos:* Corrosion consult, US Air Force Civil Eng, worldwide. *Mem:* Nat Asn Corrosion Engrs; Am Soc Metals; Am Inst Mining, Metall & Petrol Engrs; fel Brit Inst Corrosion Sci & Technol. *Res:* Thermodynamic activity measurements; stress-corrosion cracking; oxidation; anodic polarization behavior; corrosion in potable waters; protective coating; phase diagram determinations; cathodic protection. *Mailing Add:* US Air Force Inst Technol 4198 Merlyn Dr Franklin OH 45005

MYERS, JEFFREY, b Philadelphia, Pa, Feb 8, 32; div; c 1. PATHOLOGY, INFORMATION SCIENCE. *Educ:* Univ Pa, AB, 52; Temple Univ, MD, 57, MSc, 62; McGill Univ, PhD(path), 65. *Prof Exp:* Pathologist, Allentown Hosp, 65-66; pathologist, Philadelphia Gen Hosp, 66-69, chief surg path, 69-77; DIR LAB & CHIEF PATH, BURLINGTON COUNTY MEM HOSP, 77- *Concurrent Pos:* Asst prof, Sch Med, Temple Univ, 65-66; consult, Wyeth Labs, 66-77; asst prof path, Sch Med, Univ Pa, 66-78. *Mem:* AAAS; fel Col Am Path; NY Acad Sci. *Res:* Use of computers to analyze pathology data; sources of errors in medical information systems; validity of computerized information. *Mailing Add:* 175 Madison Ave Mount Holly NJ 08060

MYERS, JOHN ADAMS, b Elk Point, SDak, June 12, 32; m 58; c 5. CHEMICAL ENGINEERING, APPLIED MATHEMATICS. *Educ:* Univ Kans, BS, 58, MS, 60, PhD(heat transfer), 64. *Prof Exp:* Instr, Univ Kans, 59-63; asst prof, 63-68, ASSOC PROF CHEM ENG, VILLANOVA UNIV, 68- *Mem:* Am Inst Chem Engrs; Am Soc Eng Educ. *Res:* Heat transfer accompanied by phase change; optimal design. *Mailing Add:* Dept of Chem Eng Villanova Univ Villanova PA 19085

MYERS, JOHN ALBERT, b Sandusky, Ohio, Mar 13, 43; m 73; c 3. ORGANIC CHEMISTRY. *Educ:* Carson-Newman Col, BS & BA, 65; Univ Fla, PhD(chem), 70. *Prof Exp:* Res grant, Mich State Univ, 70-71; assoc prof, 71-80, PROF CHEM, NC CENT UNIV, 80- *Mem:* Am Chem Soc. *Res:* Heterocyclic synthesis; radiation sensitizers; dipolar cycloaddition reactions. *Mailing Add:* Dept Chem NC Cent Univ Durham NC 27707

MYERS, JOHN E(ARLE), b Swalwell, Alta, Sept 14, 23; nat US; m 46; c 2. CHEMICAL ENGINEERING. *Educ:* Univ Alta, BSc, 44; Univ Toronto, MASc, 46; Univ Mich, PhD(chem eng), 52. *Prof Exp:* Lectr chem eng, Univ Toronto, 46-47; instr, Univ Mich, 47-50; from asst prof to prof, Purdue Univ, 50-66; chmn dept chem & nuclear eng, 66-76, PROF CHEM ENG, UNIV CALIF, SANTA BARBARA, 66-, DEAN COL ENG, 76- *Concurrent Pos:* Fulbright lectr, Univ Leeds, 56-57 & Univ Toulouse, 63-64. *Mem:* Am Chem Soc; Am Inst Chem Engrs. *Res:* Heat transfer; fluid flow. *Mailing Add:* Dept of Chem & Nuclear Eng Univ of Calif Santa Barbara CA 93106

MYERS, JOHN MARTIN, b Portland, Ore, June 8, 35; m 59; c 3. APPLIED PHYSICS, SYSTEMS THEORY. *Educ:* Calif Inst Technol, BS, 56; Harvard Univ, MS, 57, PhD(appl physics), 62. *Prof Exp:* Jr engr, Raytheon Co, 56-57, engr, 57-60, res scientist, 60-62, sr res scientist, 62-65, prin res scientist, 65-67; opers res analyst, Off Asst Secy Defense, 67-68; asst adminr, Model City Admin, Boston, 68-70; CONSULT PROCESS CONTROL & REPORTING SYSTS, 70- *Res:* Boundary value problems; transformational generating principles for biological structure; systems research; concurrency, choice. *Mailing Add:* 18 Joy St Boston MA 02114

MYERS, JOSEPH B, b Indianapolis, Ind, Dec 30, 27; m 49; c 5. PHYSIOLOGY. *Educ:* WVa State Col, BS, 49; Atlanta Univ, MS, 64; Howard Univ, PhD(zool), 71. *Prof Exp:* Res assoc exp path, Sch Med, Ind Univ, 51-58; instr biol, Indianapolis Pub Sch Syst, 58-63; asst prof, St Joseph Col, 64-68; asst prof, 71-77, ASSOC PROF BIOL, ATLANTA UNIV, 77- *Mem:* AAAS. *Res:* Renal hypertension; physiological variation during hypertensive state; the physiology of insect body fluids. *Mailing Add:* Dept of Physiol Atlanta Univ Atlanta GA 30314

MYERS, JULIAN MOSTELLA, b Olanta, SC, Nov 22, 21; m 43; c 2. AGRICULTURAL ENGINEERING. *Educ:* Clemson Univ, BS, 43; Univ Fla, MS, 52. *Prof Exp:* Assoc prof agr eng & assoc agr engr, 47-60, PROF AGR ENG & AGR ENGR, UNIV FLA, 60- *Mem:* Am Soc Agr Engrs; Nat Soc Prof Engrs. *Res:* Soil and water engineering; agricultural land drainage and irrigation; processing agricultural crops. *Mailing Add:* Dept of Agr Eng Univ of Fla Gainesville FL 32601

MYERS, LAWRENCE STANLEY, JR, b Memphis, Tenn, Apr 29, 19; m 42; c 3. RADIATION BIOPHYSICS, ENVIRONMENTAL SCIENCES. *Educ:* Univ Chicago, 41, PhD(phys chem), 49. *Prof Exp:* Asst chem, Metall Lab, Manhattan Eng Dist, Chicago, 42-44; assoc chemist, Clinton Lab, Tenn, 44-46; asst, Inst Nuclear Studies, Univ Chicago, 46-48, chemist, Univ, 48-49; assoc chemist, Argonne Nat Lab, 49-52; asst prof biophys, nuclear med & radiol, Sch Med, Univ Calif, Los Angeles, 53-70, res radiobiologist, Lab Nuclear Med & Radiation Biol, 53-76, lectr radiol, Sch Med, 70-76, adj prof radiol sci, 76-82, adj prof radiation oncol, 80-82; SCI DIR, ARMED FORCES RADIOBIOL RES INST, 82- *Concurrent Pos:* Biophysicist, Biol Br, Div Biol & Med, AEC, 72-74; assoc ed, Radiation Res, 74-77. *Mem:* Am Soc Photobiol; AAAS; Radiation Res Soc; Biophys Soc. *Res:* Effects of ionizing radiation and environmental contaminants on nucleic acids, nucleoproteins and simple biological systems. *Mailing Add:* Armed Forces Radiobiol Res Inst Bethesda MD 20014

MYERS, LEE THOMAS, b Lykens, Pa, Sept 1, 49; m 70; c 1. GAMMA RAY SPECTROSCOPY. *Educ:* Franklin & Marshall Col, BA, 71; Georgetown Univ, MS, 78, PhD(physics), 78. *Prof Exp:* RES PHYSICIST, NAVAL RES LAB, 78- *Mem:* Sigma Xi; Am Nuclear Soc; Am Phys Soc. *Res:* Direct atom counting; tritum sampling; gamma-ray spectroscopy. *Mailing Add:* Naval Res Lab Code 6614 Washington DC 20375

MYERS, LLOYD E(LDRIDGE), b Ellensburg, Wash, Nov 25, 17; m 42; c 4. LAND & WATER RESOURCES. *Educ:* Utah State Univ, BS, 49, MS, 50. *Prof Exp:* Drainage engr, US Bur Reclamation, Utah, 50-51; irrig engr pub health, USPHS, Calif, 51-53; mgr, Merced County Mosquito Abatement Dist, Calif, 53-54; irrig engr drainage res, Western Soil & Water Mgt Sect, Agr Res Serv, USDA, 54-56, staff specialist, 56-57, head, Irrig & Drainage Facil Sect, 57-58, dir, US Water Conserv Lab, 58-72, assoc dep adminr, 72-76, area dir sci & educ admin, 76-80; CONSULT, 80- *Concurrent Pos:* Consult, US State Dept, 72, US Acad Sci, 74 & WHO, 81. *Mem:* Am Soc Civil Engrs. *Res:* Conservation and management of land and water resources. *Mailing Add:* 1910 W Cassim Lane Tucson AZ 85704

MYERS, LYLE LESLIE, b Salem, Ore, June 11, 38; m 60; c 3. BIOCHEMISTRY, IMMUNOCHEMISTRY. *Educ:* Ore State Univ, BS, 60; Mont State Univ, MS, 62; Purdue Univ, PhD(biochem), 66. *Prof Exp:* Asst prof, 66-71, ASSOC PROF VET BIOCHEM, VET RES LAB, MONT STATE UNIV, 71- *Mem:* Conf Res Workers Animal Dis; Am Soc Microbiol. *Res:* Immunological and biochemical aspects of neonatal enteritis of the bovine; antigenic structure of the vibrio fetus bacteria. *Mailing Add:* Vet Res Lab Mont State Univ Bozeman MT 59717

MYERS, MARCUS NORVILLE, b Boise, Idaho, May 30, 28; m 50; c 3. ANALYTICAL CHEMISTRY. *Educ:* Brigham Young Univ, BS, 50, MS, 52; Univ Utah, PhD(phys chem), 65. *Prof Exp:* Engr, Hanford Works, Gen Elec Co, 51-57, chemist, Idaho, 57-61, Vallecitos Atomic Lab, 61-62; res asst, 62-65, res assoc, 65-67, asst res prof, 67-68, ASSOC RES PROF PHYS CHEM, UNIV UTAH, 78- *Mem:* AAAS; Am Chem Soc. *Res:* High pressure gas chromatography; theory of all forms of chromatography; field flow fractionation; activation analysis. *Mailing Add:* Dept Chem Univ Utah Salt Lake City UT 84112

MYERS, MARK B, b Winchester, Ind, Oct 14, 38; m 59; c 4. MATERIALS SCIENCE, CERAMICS. *Educ:* Earlham Col, AB, 60; Pa State Univ, PhD(solid state technol), 64. *Prof Exp:* Mem sci staff, Xerox Res Labs, NY, 64-68, mgr mat sci br, 68-71, mgr mat res lab, 71-75, mgr, Res Ctr Can Ltd, 75-78, VPRES, MAT ENG DEPT, XEROX RES LABS, NY, 78- *Concurrent Pos:* Assoc prof, Univ Rochester, 70-75. *Mem:* Am Phys Soc; Am Ceramic Soc. *Res:* Thermodynamics and kinetics of glass formation; phase transitions; glass transition phenomena; two phase glass ceramics; chalcogenide materials. *Mailing Add:* Xerox Corp W129 Rochester NY 14644

MYERS, MAX H, b Lynchburg, Va, July 2, 36; m 59; c 2. BIOMETRICS, STATISTICS. *Educ:* Bridgewater Col, BA, 58; Va Polytech Inst, MS, 60; Univ Minn, PhD(biomet), 71. *Prof Exp:* USPHS officer, End Results Sect, Biomet Br, 60-62, math statistician, 62-73, HEAD END RESULT SECT, BIOMET BR, FIELD STUDIES & STATIST, DIV CANCER CAUSE & PREV, NAT CANCER INST, 73- *Mem:* Am Statist Asn; Biomet Soc. *Res:* Epidemiology of cancer patient survival including detailed study of factors related to prognosis; statistical methodology for evaluating multifactor relationships to survival. *Mailing Add:* Nat Cancer Inst 9000 Rockville Pike Bethesda MD 20014

MYERS, MELVIL BERTRAND, JR, b New Orleans, La, Sept 12, 28; m 54; c 3. MEDICINE. *Educ:* Tulane Univ, MD, 51; Am Bd Surg, dipl, 58. *Prof Exp:* Clin instr, 56-71, assoc prof, 71-75, PROF SURG, SCH MED, LA STATE UNIV MED CTR, NEW ORLEANS, 75-; PRIN INVESTR SURG RES, VET ADMIN HOSP, NEW ORLEANS, 63-, SR SURGEON, TOURO INFIRMARY, 65- *Concurrent Pos:* Grants, Am Cancer Soc, Southeast Surg Cong, Ethicon, Inc, Warren-Teed, Inc & John A Hartford Found; sr surgeon, Charity Hosp, New Orleans, 61-; attend physician, US Vet Admin Hosp, 66-71, staff physician, 71- *Mem:* Fel Am Col Surgeons; Am Heart Asn; Plastic Surg Res Coun; Southern Surg Asn; Am Soc Plastic & Reconstruct Surgeons. *Res:* Wound healing and revascularization; cause of tissue necrosis; tissue changes following devascularization and revascularization; mechanism of ventricular fibrillation following ischemia; various clinical surgical problems. *Mailing Add:* Vet Admin Hosp 1601 Perdido St New Orleans LA 70140

MYERS, MICHAEL KENNETH, b Portland, Ore, May 18, 39; m 62; c 2. FLUID MECHANICS, ACOUSTICS. *Educ:* Willamette Univ, BS, 62; Columbia Univ, BS, 62, MS, 63, PhD(eng mech), 66. *Prof Exp:* From asst prof to assoc prof civil eng & eng mech, Columbia Univ, 66-73; assoc prof, 73-78, PROF, JOINT INST ADVAN FLIGHT SCI, GEORGE WASHINGTON UNIV, 78- *Mem:* Assoc fel Am Inst Aeronaut & Astronaut; Soc Eng Sci. *Res:* Wave propagation; propagation of sonic booms; asymptotic solution of hyperbolic partial differential equations; linear and nonlinear acoustics; duct acoustics; atmospheric sound propagation. *Mailing Add:* NASA Langley Res Ctr JIAFS Mail Stop 169 Hampton VA 23665

MYERS, OVAL, JR, b Roachdale, Ind, July 28, 33; m 59; c 2. PLANT GENETICS, PLANT BREEDING. *Educ:* Wabash Col, BA, 58; Dartmouth Col, MA, 60; Cornell Univ, PhD(genetics), 63. *Prof Exp:* From instr to asst prof bot & bact, Univ Ark, Fayetteville, 63-68; assoc prof bot & plant indust, 68-75, PROF PLANT & SOIL SCI, SOUTHERN ILL UNIV, CARBONDALE, 75- *Concurrent Pos:* Educ specialist, Southern Ill Univ & Food & Agr Orgn, Brazil, 72-74. *Mem:* Fel AAAS; Am Genetic Asn; Genetics Soc Am; Sigma Xi; Am Soc Agron. *Res:* Genetics and plant breeding of Zea mays, Glycine max and Impatiens; developmental plant morphology. *Mailing Add:* Dept of Plant & Soil Sci Southern Ill Univ Carbondale IL 62901

MYERS, PAUL WALTER, b Schenectady, NY, Jan 15, 23; m 44; c 4. NEUROSURGERY. *Educ:* Albany Med Col, MD, 46; Am Bd Neurol Surg, dipl, 60. *Prof Exp:* Intern med, Ellis Hosp, Schenectady, NY, 46-47; US Air Force, 51-, resident surg, Ellis Hosp, 52-53, resident neurol surg, Albany Med Ctr, 53-56, chief neurol surg, 58-71, commander, Wilford Hall Air Force Med Ctr, 71, PROF NEUROSURG, UNIV TEX MED SCH, SAN ANTONIO, 69-, SURGEON GEN, US AIR FORCE, 78- *Concurrent Pos:* Hon flight surgeon designation, Govt Chile, 68. *Mem:* AMA; Cong Neurol Surgeons; Am Asn Neurol Surg; Am Col Surgeons. *Res:* Cervical injuries; neuroanatomy. *Mailing Add:* Off of Surgeon Gen US Air Force Washington DC 20314

MYERS, PETER BRIGGS, b Washington, DC, Apr 24, 26; m 48; c 2. PHYSICS. *Educ:* Worcester Polytech Inst, BSEE, 46; Oxford Univ, DPhil(physics), 50. *Hon Degrees:* DHumLitt, Col Idaho, 73. *Prof Exp:* Mem tech staff, Switching Res Dept, Bell Tel Labs, Inc, 50-59; staff scientist, Motorola, Inc, 59-62; mgr res & advan technol, Martin Co, 62-64; mgr res & advan technol, Bunker-Ramo Corp, 64-65, vpres res & develop, 65-66; mgr advan technol, Magnavox Res Labs, Calif, 66-74, dir, Advan Systs Anal Off,

Magnavox Co, Md, 74-78, dir fed liaison, 78-80; MEM STAFF, NAT RES COUN-NAT ACAD SCI, 80- *Mem:* Fel AAAS; Inst Mgt Sci; Opers Res Soc Am; Am Phys Soc; fel Inst Elec & Electronics Engrs. *Res:* Solid state device physics; solid state circuits; magnetic logic and memory; communications navigation and position location systems analysis and technology; solid state integrated circuits. *Mailing Add:* Magnavox Co 8750 Georgia Ave Silver Spring MD 20910

MYERS, PHILIP, b Baltimore, Md, June 10, 47; m 69; c 1. MAMMALOGY. *Educ:* Swarthmore Col, BA, 69; Univ Calif, Berkeley, PhD(zool), 75. *Prof Exp:* ASST PROF ZOOL, UNIV MICH, ANN ARBOR, 75- *Mem:* Assoc Sigma Xi; Am Soc Mammalogists; Asn Syst Collections; Soc Syst Zool. *Res:* Ecology and evolution of mammals; population biology; biosystematics of mammals. *Mailing Add:* Mus of Zool Univ of Mich Ann Arbor MI 48109

MYERS, PHILIP CHERDAK, b Elizabeth, NJ, Nov 18, 44; m 72; c 1. RADIO ASTRONOMY. *Educ:* Columbia Univ, AB, 66; Mass Inst Technol, PhD(physics), 72. *Prof Exp:* Staff scientist radio physics & astron, Res Lab Electronics, 72-75, asst prof, 75-79, ASSOC PROF PHYSICS, MASS INST TECHNOL, 79- *Concurrent Pos:* Sr res assoc, Goddard Inst Space Studies, NASA, 80-81; vis scientist, Ctr Astrophys, 82. *Mem:* Am Astron Soc; Int Union Radio Sci; Int Astron Union; AAAS. *Res:* Radio astronomy of interstellar medium, particularly spectral lines in dark clouds; microwave radiometry of human tissue for purposes of medical diagnosis. *Mailing Add:* Dept Physics Mass Inst Technol Cambridge MA 02139

MYERS, PHILLIP S(AMUEL), b Webber, Kans, May 8, 16; m 43; c 5. MECHANICAL ENGINEERING. *Educ:* McPherson Col, BS, 40; Kans State Col, BS, 42; Univ Wis, PhD(mech eng), 47. *Prof Exp:* From instr to assoc prof, 42-55, PROF MECH ENG, UNIV WIS-MADISON, 55- *Concurrent Pos:* Consult, US Army, Dupont & Diesel Engine Mfrs Asn. *Honors & Awards:* Horning Mem Award, Soc Automotive Engrs. *Mem:* Nat Acad Eng; AAAS; fel Am Soc Mech Engrs; fel Soc Automotive Engrs (pres, 69). *Res:* Combustion in internal combustion engines; diesel combustion; thermodynamics; heat power; flame-temperature measurements in internal combustion engines; pyrolysis of propane; fuel sprays and vaporization; welding heat transfer. *Mailing Add:* Dept of Mech Eng Univ of Wis 1513 University Ave Madison WI 53706

MYERS, PHILLIP WARD, otolaryngology, audiology, see previous edition

MYERS, R(ALPH) THOMAS, b Maidsville, WVa, Mar 28, 21; m 54; c 2. PHYSICAL INORGANIC CHEMISTRY. *Educ:* WVa Univ, AB, 41, PhD(phys org chem), 49. *Prof Exp:* Asst, Manhattan Proj, Columbia Univ, 44-46; assoc prof chem & head dept, Waynesburg Col, 48-51; asst prof phys chem & consult, Res Found, Colo Sch Mines, 51-56; from asst prof to assoc prof chem, 56-77, PROF CHEM, KENT STATE UNIV, 77- *Mem:* AAAS; Am Chem Soc. *Res:* Nonaqueous solvents; dielectric constant; forces between molecules in liquids. *Mailing Add:* Dept Chem Kent State Univ Kent OH 44242

MYERS, RALPH, b Ft Smith, Ark, Nov 25, 38; m 63; c 1. GEOLOGY. *Educ:* Okla State Univ, BS, 55; Harvard Univ, AM, 62; Univ Tex, Austin, PhD(biostratig), 65. *Prof Exp:* NSF fel, Univ Tex, Austin, 65-67; asst prof geol, East Tex State Univ, 67-68; consult, Compania Dominicana de Desarrollo y Fomento, 68; res geologist, 69-71, SR RES GEOLOGIST, MOBIL RES & DEVELOP CORP, 71- *Mem:* AAAS; Geol Soc Am; Am Asn Petrol Geologists; Paleont Soc. *Res:* Habitat of oil; mesozoic stratigraphy of Mexico and the Carribean; evolution of rudists; plate tectonics. *Mailing Add:* MEPSI PO Box 900 Dallas TX 75221

MYERS, RAYMOND HAROLD, b Charleston, WVa, Oct 13, 37; m 59; c 2. MATHEMATICAL STATISTICS. *Educ:* Va Polytech Inst, BSc, 59, MSc, 61, PhD(statist), 64. *Prof Exp:* From asst prof to assoc prof, 63-71, PROF STATIST, VA POLYTECH INST & STATE UNIV, 71- *Mem:* Am Statist Asn. *Res:* Experimental design and analysis; response surface techniques. *Mailing Add:* Dept of Statist Va Polytech Inst & State Univ Blacksburg VA 24060

MYERS, RAYMOND J, b Bellevue, Ohio, Dec 5, 03; m 32; c 1. ZOOLOGY. *Educ:* Heidelberg Col, AB, 27; Univ Pa, PhD(zool), 33. *Prof Exp:* Asst, Univ Ind, 27-30; instr, Univ Pa, 30-34; instr, 34-42, from asst prof to prof, 42-72, chmn, Dept Biol, 71-72, EMER PROF ZOOL, COLGATE UNIV, 72- *Concurrent Pos:* Instr, LI Col Med, 44-46. *Mem:* AAAS; assoc Am Soc Zoologists. *Res:* Reproduction and taxonomy of Hirudinea; human hair growth. *Mailing Add:* 13 Payne St Hamilton NY 13346

MYERS, RAYMOND REEVER, b New Oxford, Pa, Jan 23, 20; m 43; c 3. CHEMISTRY. *Educ:* Lehigh Univ, AB, 41, PhD(chem), 52; Univ Tenn, MS, 42. *Prof Exp:* Res chemist, Cent Res Labs, Monsanto Co, 42-46 & Jefferson Chem Co, 46-50; asst chem, Lehigh Univ, 50-52, res assoc, 52-53, from res asst prof to res prof, 53-65; prof & chmn dept, 65-77, UNIV PROF CHEM, KENT STATE UNIV, 77- *Concurrent Pos:* Res dir, Paint Res Inst, 64-; former consult, Nat Bur Standards, R T Vanderbilt Co & Air Reduction Co; ed, J Rheol; Matiello lectr, Fedn Socs Coatings Technol, 75. *Honors & Awards:* Borden Award, Am Chem Soc, 71; Morrison Award, NY Acad Sci, 58; Heckel Award, Fedn Soc Coatings Technol, 73. *Mem:* Am Chem Soc; fel Am Inst Chemists; Soc Rheol fel NY Acad Sci; Brit Soc Rheol. *Res:* Rheology of coatings; adhesion; application of spectra in catalysis; structure of matter; research administration. *Mailing Add:* Dept of Chem Kent State Univ Kent OH 44242

MYERS, RICHARD F, b Hammond, Ind, Feb 1, 31; m 51; c 4. VERTEBRATE ZOOLOGY, ACADEMIC ADMINISTRATION. *Educ:* Earlham Col, AB, 52; Cornell Univ, MS, 54; Univ Mo, PhD, 64. *Prof Exp:* From asst prof to assoc prof zool, Cent Mo State Col, 59-67; assoc prof zool & ecol, Univ Mo-Kansas City, 67-72; DIR, NAT WEATHER SERV TRAINING CTR, 72- *Concurrent Pos:* Inst Int Educ-US AID consult, Bangladesh, 69-70; US consult training & educ, Iranian Meteorol Orgn, 78. *Mem:* AAAS; Am Soc Mammal; Sigma Xi. *Res:* Mammalogy; wildlife biology; movement and migration patterns; population ecology, especially bats. *Mailing Add:* Nat Weather Serv 617 Hardesty Kansas City MO 64124

MYERS, RICHARD HEPWORTH, b Austin, Tex, Nov 1, 47; m 78. BEHAVIOR GENETICS, CYTOGENETICS. *Educ:* Univ Kans, BA, 69; Ga State Univ, MEd, 73, MA, 76, PhD(psychol), 79. *Prof Exp:* Teacher spec educ, 69-74; psychol tech, Genetics Lab, Ga Mental Health Inst, 75-80; clin asst prof, Dept Psychiat, Emory Med Sch, 80; NEUROPSYCHOLOGIST, UNIV HOSP, BOSTON UNIV MED CTR, 80-, ASST PROF, DEPT NEUROL, 80- *Concurrent Pos:* Consult psychol, Dept Neurol, Mass Gen Hosp, 80-; lectr, Dept neurol, Harvard Med Sch, 80- *Mem:* Behavior Genetics Asn; AAAS; Soc Study Social Biol. *Res:* Midlife onset inherited neurological disorders and factors related to age of onset; comparative cytogenetics and chromosomal mechanisms in speciation and gene regulation. *Mailing Add:* Dept Neurol Boston Univ Med Ctr 80 E Concord St Boston MA 02118

MYERS, RICHARD LEE, b Doylestown, Pa, Oct 26, 44; m 66. ANALYTICAL CHEMISTRY, ENVIRONMENTAL SYSTEMS & TECHNOLOGY. *Educ:* Calif Inst Technol, BS, 66; Univ Wis-Madison, PhD(anal chem), 71. *Prof Exp:* Mem tech staff, NAm Rockwell Sci Ctr, 71-73, prog mgr, Air Monitoring Ctr, Rockwell Int Corp, 73-75, cent region dir, Environ Monitoring & Serv Ctr, 75-80; mem staff, 80-81, PRES, MEAD COMPUCHEM, MEAD TECH LABS, 81- *Mem:* Am Chem Soc; Electrochem Soc. *Res:* Application of gas chromatography-mass spectrometry and minicomputers to chemical and physical measurements; ambient air and water pollution measurement techniques and instrumentation. *Mailing Add:* Mead CompuChem PO Box 12652 Research Triangle Park NC 27709

MYERS, RICHARD SHOWSE, b Jackson, Miss, Oct 26, 42; m 65; c 2. PHYSICAL CHEMISTRY. *Educ:* Miss Col, BS, 64; La State Univ, MS, 66; Emory Univ, PhD(chem), 68. *Prof Exp:* From asst prof to assoc prof, 68-77, PROF CHEM, DELTA STATE UNIV, 77- *Mem:* Am Chem Soc. *Res:* Surface thermodynamics and surface tension of nonelectrolyte solutions; determination of activity coefficients of nonelectrolyte solutions by Rayleigh light scattering techniques. *Mailing Add:* Dept of Chem Delta State Univ Cleveland MS 38733

MYERS, RICHARD THOMAS, b Macon, Ga, Dec 25, 18; m 59; c 4. SURGERY. *Educ:* Univ NC, AB, 39; Univ Pa, MD, 43. *Prof Exp:* From asst prof to assoc prof, 50-68, PROF SURG & CHMN DEPT, BOWMAN GRAY SCH MED, 68- *Mem:* AMA; Am Col Surg. *Res:* Upper gastrointestinal tract; pancreas and biliary tract. *Mailing Add:* Dept of Surg Bowman Gray Sch of Med Winston-Salem NC 27103

MYERS, ROBERT ANTHONY, b Brooklyn, NY, Feb 22, 37. SOLID STATE PHYSICS. *Educ:* Harvard Univ, AB, 58, AM, 59, PhD(appl physics), 64. *Prof Exp:* Physicist, IBM Watson Res Ctr, NY, 63-68, mem corp tech comt staff, IBM Corp, 68-72, MGR TERMINAL TECHNOL, IBM WATSON RES CTR, 73- *Concurrent Pos:* Secy, Sci Adv Comt, IBM Corp, 71-72. *Mem:* Am Phys Soc; Inst Elec & Electronics Engrs. *Res:* Application of solid state technology to computer input/output devices. *Mailing Add:* IBM Watson Res Ctr PO Box 218 Yorktown Heights NY 10598

MYERS, ROBERT DURANT, b Philadelphia, Pa, Oct 25, 31; m 53; c 4. PSYCHOBIOLOGY, NEUROBIOLOGY. *Educ:* Ursinus Col, BS, 53; Purdue Univ, MS, 54, PhD, 56. *Prof Exp:* Asst psychol, Purdue Univ, 54-55; from asst prof to assoc prof & dir res coun, Colgate Univ, 56-64; fel, Neurol Sci Group, Sch Med, Johns Hopkins Univ, 60-61; prof psychol, Purdue Univ, 65-72, prof psychol & biol sci, 72-78, coordr neurobiol training prog, 70-78, dir psychobiol prog, 73-78; PROF PSYCHIAT & PHARMACOL, UNIV NC SCH MED, 78- *Concurrent Pos:* Res psychologist, Rome Air Develop Ctr, Griffiss AFB, 57-58; vis scientist, Nat Inst Med Res Eng, 63-65 & 69-70; Sigma Xi res award, Purdue Univ, 71; vis prof, La Trobe Univ, Australia, 75. *Mem:* AAAS; Int Brain Res Orgn; NY Acad Sci; Am Col Neuropharmacol; Am Physiol Soc. *Res:* Neural mechanisms controlling feeding, drinking, emotional behavior and thermoregulation; transmitter synthesis, turnover and release in brain stem; physiology and pharmacology of hypothalamus; role of amives and ions; alcohol and drug administration. *Mailing Add:* Dept of Psychiat & Pharmacol Univ of NC Sch Med Chapel Hill NC 27514

MYERS, ROBERT FREDERICK, b Trenton, NJ, Feb 23, 16; m 40; c 3. METEOROLOGY, CHEMICAL ENGINEERING. *Educ:* Va Polytech Inst, BS, 36. *Prof Exp:* Observer, US Weather Bur, 39-41, jr instrument engr, 41-42; sr inspector eng, Bur Ord, US Navy, 42-43; meteorologist, US Weather Bur, 45-57, liaison officer, Ga, 47-48, meteorologist, Tenn, 48-54, meteorologist in charge res, 54-55; chief data handling br, US Air Force Cambridge Res Lab, 55-60, sr res engr, 60-81, CONSULT, AIR FORCE GEOPHYS LAB, 81- *Mem:* Am Meteorol Soc. *Res:* Meteorological instrumentation including data acquisition, communication and display; micrometeorological research; ozone research; meteorological satellite ground stations with integral interactive computer. *Mailing Add:* 80 Willow Rd Nahant MA 01908

MYERS, ROLLIE JOHN, JR, b Nebr, July 15, 24; m 50; c 2. PHYSICAL CHEMISTRY. *Educ:* Calif Inst Technol, BS, 47, MS, 48; Univ Calif, PhD(chem), 51. *Prof Exp:* From instr to assoc prof, 51-62, PROF CHEM, UNIV CALIF, BERKELEY, 62-, ASST DEAN COL CHEM, 73-, PRIN INVESTR, INORG MAT RES DIV, 73- *Concurrent Pos:* Guggenheim fel, 57-58; int fac award, Am Chem Soc-Petrol Res Fund, 65-66. *Mem:* Am Chem Soc; Am Phys Soc. *Res:* Spectroscopy; magnetic resonance; microwave and molecular structure. *Mailing Add:* Dept of Chem Univ of Calif Berkeley CA 94720

MYERS, RONALD ELWOOD, b Chicago Heights, Ill, Sept 24, 29; m 57, 81; c 4. NEUROLOGY. *Educ:* Univ Chicago, AB, 50, PhD(neuroanat), 55, MD, 56. *Prof Exp:* Intern, Univ Chicago Clins, 56-57; res officer, Walter Reed Army Inst Res, 57-60; dir, Lab Neurol Sci, Spring Grove State Hosp, Baltimore, Md, 63-64; chief Lab Perinatal Physiol, Nat Inst Neurol Dis & Stroke, 64-80; ASSOC CHIEF STAFF & RES, CINCINNATI VET ADMIN MED CTR, 80- *Concurrent Pos:* Spec fel physiol & neurol med, Sch Med, Johns Hopkins Univ, 60-63; guest lectr, First Mem Ignatz Semmelweis Seminar, 75, Am Psychol Asn, 76, Int Neuropsychol Cong, 78 & Can Investr Reproduction, 80; distinguished lectr, Women & Infants' Hosp RI, 75; spec lectr, Swiss Asn Neuropathologists, 78. *Honors & Awards:* Purkinje lectr, Slovak Acad Sci, 63; 14th Crittenden Mem lectr, Kansas City, 74; Hershenson lectr, Boston Hosp Women, 78. *Mem:* Am Soc Neuropath; Am Physiol Soc; Am Acad Neurol; Soc Gynec Invest; Pavlovian Soc NAm. *Res:* Physiological pyschology; fiber connections of the brain; experimental neuropathology; perinatalogy. *Mailing Add:* Lab Perinatal Physiol NIH 9000 Rockville Pike Bethesda MD 20014

MYERS, RONALD FENNER, b East Haven, Conn, July 22, 30; m 59; c 3. NEMATOLOGY. *Educ:* Univ Conn, BS, 57, MS, 59; Univ Md, PhD(plant path, nematol), 64. *Prof Exp:* Nematologist, USDA, Md, 59-61; asst bot, Univ Md, 61-63; asst prof, Univ Conn, 64-65; from asst prof to assoc prof nematode physiol, 65-75, dir, Rhiz Res Group, 79-81, PROF PLANT PATH, RUTGERS UNIV, NEW BRUNSWICK, 75- *Concurrent Pos:* Res prof, Mem Univ Nfld, 73-74. *Mem:* Soc Nematol; Soc Europ Nematol. *Res:* Physiology and biochemistry of nematodes; culture and nutrition of nematodes; nematode detection, chemical control, and control recommendations. *Mailing Add:* Dept Plant Path Cook Col Rutgers Univ New Brunswick NJ 08903

MYERS, RONALD G, b Eldon, Mo, Aug 12, 33; m 55; c 7. ELECTRICAL ENGINEERING. *Educ:* Univ Mo, BS, 56, MS, 57. *Prof Exp:* Res asst elec eng, Univ Mo, 56-57; asst, Argonne Nat Labs, 57-59; radar engr, Emerson Elec Co, 59-65; res specialist, Monsanto Co, Mo, 65-66, eng group leader digital prod, 66-69, eng mgr, Boulder Tech Ctr, 69-70; VPRES ENG & MEM BD DIRS, TECNETICS, INC, 70- *Concurrent Pos:* Consult digital instrument design & develop. *Mem:* Inst Elec & Electronics Engrs. *Res:* Electromagnetic testing of metals; radar display and video processing; transient testing of systems; digital voltmeters, counter-timers and instruments; power supplies. *Mailing Add:* 879 Laurel Ave Boulder CO 80303

MYERS, ROY MAURICE, b Scottdale, Pa, Sept 24, 11; m 39; c 4. BOTANY. *Educ:* Ohio State Univ, BSc, 34, MA, 37, PhD(plant physiol), 39. *Prof Exp:* Teacher high sch, Ohio, 34-35; asst bot, Ohio State Univ, 35-38 & Northwestern Univ, 38-40; instr, Boise Jr Col, 40-42; instr biol, Denison Univ, 42-45; from asst prof to prof biol, 45-78, cur, Herbarium, 69-78, EMER PROF BIOL, WESTERN ILL UNIV, 78- *Concurrent Pos:* Chmn, Dept Biol Sci, Western Ill Univ, 53-69. *Mem:* AAAS; Am Inst Biol Sci; Soc Econ Bot. *Res:* Economic botany; plant taxonomy, flora of coastal west central Florida. *Mailing Add:* 1173 Westchester Blvd Port Charlotte FL 33952

MYERS, SAMUEL MAXWELL, JR, b Florence, SC, Jan 30, 43. SOLID STATE PHYSICS. *Educ:* Duke Univ, BS, 65, PhD(physics), 70. *Prof Exp:* Sandia Corp fel, 70-72, MEM STAFF, SANDIA NAT LABS, 72- *Mem:* Am Phys Soc; Am Inst Metall Engrs Metall Soc. *Res:* Ion implantation and ion beam analysis are employed in fundamental studies of metals; hydrogen effects, diffension and tapping of solutes; phase diagrams, metastalle phases and corrosion. *Mailing Add:* Div 5111 Sandia Nat Labs Albuquerque NM 87185

MYERS, THOMAS DEWITT, b Wilmington, Del, Apr 8, 38; m 61; c 3. INVERTEBRATE ZOOLOGY, OCEANOGRAPHY. *Educ:* Bridgewater Col, BA, 59; Univ NC, MA, 65; Duke Univ, PhD(zool), 68. *Prof Exp:* Fishery biologist, Biol Lab, US Bur Commercial Fisheries, 61-62; asst prof biol sci, Univ Del, 67-70, asst prof marine studies, 70-74; mgr, Life Systs Dept, Roy F Weston, Inc, 74-77; RES DIR, BOOZ-ALLEN & HAMILTON, INC, 77- *Concurrent Pos:* Adj asst prof marine sci, Univ Del, 74-78. *Mem:* AAAS; Ecol Soc Am; Marine Technol Soc. *Res:* Biology and distribution of pelagic molluscs; migration of marine animals; environmental impact of advanced energy technology; marine pollution and ocean waste disposal. *Mailing Add:* Booz-Allen & Hamilton 4330 East West Hwy Bethesda MD 20814

MYERS, THOMAS WILMER, b Lamar, Mo, Nov 25, 39; m 61; c 3. MECHANICAL ENGINEERING. *Educ:* Univ Mo, BS, 61, MS, 63, PhD(mech eng), 65. *Prof Exp:* Instr thermodyn heat transfer, Univ Mo, 64-65; vis res assoc, Aerospace Res Labs, Wright-Patterson AFB, 65-66; res scientist, 66-76, GROUP LEADER, TECH CTR, DEERE & CO, 76- *Mem:* Am Soc Mech Engrs; Sigma Xi. *Res:* Fluid mechanics; hydraulic and electrohydraulic controls and control systems. *Mailing Add:* Tech Ctr Eng Sci Div Deere & Co Moline IL 61265

MYERS, VERNE STEELE, b Hillsdale, Mich, Apr 11, 07; m 32; c 2. STATISTICS. *Educ:* Hillsdale Col, BS, 30; Columbia Univ, BS, 32, MS, 35. *Prof Exp:* Develop engr, Tex Corp, 32-34; develop engr, M W Kellogg Co, 34; econ statistician, Tidewater Oil Co, 35-41; supvr mgt planning, Lockheed Aircraft Corp, 41-71; MGT ENG CONSULT, 71- *Concurrent Pos:* Lectr, Pasadena City Col, 54-56; lectr, Univ Southern Calif, 56-68. *Mem:* Economet Soc; Am Inst Indust Engrs. *Res:* Statistical relationships existing in economic factors in the general economy; the petroleum industry; the aircraft industry; specific corporations. *Mailing Add:* 4610 Commonwealth La Canada CA 91011

MYERS, VERNON W, b New Castle, Pa, Feb 16, 19; m 47; c 5. PHYSICS. *Educ:* Geneva Col, BS, 40; Syracuse Univ, MA, 42; Yale Univ, PhD(physics), 47. *Prof Exp:* Instr physics, Yale Univ, 43-44; physicist, Naval Res Lab, DC, 44 & Argonne Nat Lab, 47-48; from asst prof to assoc prof physics, Pa State Univ, 48-63; PHYSICIST, NUCLEAR RADIATION DIV, NAT BUR STANDARDS, 63- *Concurrent Pos:* Guest scientist, Brookhaven Nat Lab, 52-53, 60-61 & 63-66; Fulbright prof, Univ Philippines, 61-62. *Mem:* AAAS; Am Phys Soc. *Res:* Molecular quantum mechanics; nuclear physics. *Mailing Add:* 135 S Adams St Rockville MD 20850

MYERS, VICTOR (IRA), b Casa Blanca, NMex, June 8, 21; m 40; c 3. AGRICULTURAL ENGINEERING. *Educ:* Univ Idaho, BS, 49, MS, 55. *Prof Exp:* Civil engr, Soil Conserv Serv, 49-51, civil engr hydraul eng, Ore, 51-52; assoc prof agr eng, Univ Idaho, 52-56; proj supvr irrig & drainage res, Agr Res Serv, USDA, Nev, 56-60, res invests leader, Soil & Water Lab, Tex, 60-69; DIR, REMOTE SENSING INST, S DAK STATE UNIV, 69- *Concurrent Pos:* Mem comt remote sensing for agr purposes, Nat Acad Sci, 66-69, rev bd, NASA; consult, Egypt remote sensing proj, 72, 75, 78, 80 & 81, Bangladesh remote sensing training prog, 78, Syrian land use & soils classification, 79-82, Senegal Nat Plan for land use & develop, 79 & 82 & UN desertification prog. *Mem:* Am Soc Agr Engrs; Sigma Xi; Am Soc Civil Engrs; Am Soc Photogram. *Res:* Irrigation; water resources management; drainage; hydrology; remote sensing. *Mailing Add:* Remote Sensing Inst SDak State Univ Brookings SD 57006

MYERS, W(ILLIAM) A(LVIN), b Lac du Flambeau, Wis, July 8, 01; m 25; c 1. CHEMICAL ENGINEERING. *Educ:* Univ Mich, BSE, 23, MSE, 24. *Prof Exp:* Anal & res chemist, Nizer Corp, Mich, 24-25; chem engr, Atlantic Refining Co, 24-30; refinery supt, Elk Refining Co, WVa, 30-31; chem engr & eng supvr, 31-47, asst gen mgr, Res & Develop Dept, 47-58, actg gen mgr, 58-61, CONSULT, ATLANTIC REFINING CO, 61- *Mem:* Am Chem Soc; Am Inst Chem Engrs. *Res:* Petroleum refining; entrainment separator for fractioning towers; solvent recovery system for dewaxing process; solvent extraction process for lubricating oils. *Mailing Add:* 42 N Hillcrest Rd Springfield PA 19064

MYERS, WALTER LOY, b Joliet, Ill, Mar 13, 33; m 59. IMMUNOLOGY. *Educ:* Univ Ill, BS, 55, DVM, 57, MS, 59; Univ Wis, PhD(vet sci), 61. *Prof Exp:* From asst prof to prof vet path & hyg, Univ Ill, Urbana, 61-73; PROF IMMUNOL, SCH MED, SOUTHERN ILL UNIV, SPRINGFIELD, 73-, CHMN, DEPT MED MICRO & IMMUNOL, 80- *Mem:* AAAS; Am Asn Immunologists; Am Soc Microbiol. *Res:* Role of cellular immunity in neoplasia; clinical immunology. *Mailing Add:* Southern Ill Univ Sch of Med PO Box 3926 Springfield IL 62708

MYERS, WARD R(ALSTON), b Harrisonburg, Va, Nov 28, 07; m 37; c 2. METALLURGY. *Educ:* Bridgewater Col, BA, 29; Vanderbilt Univ, MS, 32, PhD(inorg chem, metall), 37. *Prof Exp:* Instr chem, Bridgewater Col, 27-29; metallurgist, Youngstown Sheet & Tube Co, 29-31; instr chem, Vanderbilt Univ, 35-37; metall engr, 37-51, mgr mech eng sect, Eng Dept, 51-55, dir consults, 55-57, asst dir res, Mech Develop Lab, 58-60, dir, Mech Res Lab, 60-63 & Eng Tech & Mat Res, 63-69, DIR ENG PHYSICS RES, EXP STA, E I DU PONT DE NEMOURS & CO, INC, 69- *Concurrent Pos:* With Metals & Mineral Bur, Nat Prod Authority, 52; civilian with Atomic Energy Comn, 44. *Mem:* Am Soc Metals; Am Soc Mech Engrs; Am Soc Testing & Mat; Nat Asn Corrosion Engrs. *Res:* Stainless steels; precious metal alloys; corrosion behavior of metals and alloys; carbides of manganese; welding by the inert gas tungsten arc process; engineering application of plastics. *Mailing Add:* Holly Farm Bear DE 19701

MYERS, WARREN POWERS LAIRD, b Philadelphia, Pa, May 2, 21; m 44; c 4. INTERNAL MEDICINE, ONCOLOGY. *Educ:* Yale Univ, BS, 43; Columbia Univ, MD, 45; Univ Minn, MS, 52; Am Bd Internal Med, dipl, 53 & 77. *Prof Exp:* Intern, Philadelphia Gen Hosp, 45-46; intern med, Maimonides Hosp, NY, 48-49; from asst prof to assoc prof, 54-68, PROF MED, MED COL CORNELL UNIV, 68- *Concurrent Pos:* Fel, Mem Hosp, NY, 48; Eleanor Roosevelt Found fel, Cambridge, Eng, 62-63; clin asst, Mem Hosp, NY, 52-54, from asst attend physician to attend physician, 54-59, assoc chmn dept med, 64-67, chmn dept med, 68-77, vpres for educ affairs, 77-81, chmn clin educ affairs, 81-; asst, Sloan-Kettering Inst Cancer Res, 52-56, assoc, 56-60, assoc mem, 60-69, mem, 69-; head metab & renal studies sect, Div Clin Invest, 57-66, head calcium metab lab, 67-78; asst attend physician, NY Hosp, 59-68, attend physician, 68-; vis physician, Bellevue Hosp, 60-68; consult, Grasslands Hosp, Valhalla, 66-68; mem clin cancer training comt, Nat Cancer Inst, 70-73, chmn, 71-73, mem & chmn clin cancer educ comt, 75-78; Eugene Kettering prof, Mem Sloan Kettering Cancer Ctr, 79- *Mem:* AAAS; Endocrine Soc; Harvey Soc; AMA; Am Asn Cancer Res. *Res:* Medical oncology; calcium metabolism; clinical endocrinology. *Mailing Add:* Mem Hosp 1275 York Ave New York NY 10021

MYERS, WAYNE LAWRENCE, b Adrian, Mich, Sept 17, 42; m 62; c 3. FORESTRY, BIOMETRY. *Educ:* Univ Mich, Ann Arbor, BS, 64, MF, 65, PhD(forestry), 67. *Prof Exp:* Res scientist, Forest Res Lab, Can Dept Fisheries & Forestry, Ont, 66-69; from asst prof to assoc prof forestry, Mich State Univ, 69-78; ASSOC PROF FOREST BIOMETRICS, PA STATE UNIV, 78- *Mem:* Soc Am Foresters; Am Soc Photogram; Am Statist Asn. *Res:* Forest biometry; quantitative ecology; remote sensing. *Mailing Add:* Sch of Forest Resources Pa State Univ University Park PA 16802

MYERS, WILLARD GLAZIER, JR, b Albany, NY, Aug 9, 35; m 62; c 4. ENVIRONMENTAL SCIENCES. *Educ:* Rensselaer Polytech Inst, BChE, 58, MS, 65, PhD(environ eng), 69. *Prof Exp:* Design engr, Boeing Co, Wash, 58-64; RES ASSOC ENVIRON SCI, RENSSELAER POLYTECH INST, 69- *Mem:* Am Chem Soc; Am Nuclear Soc; Am Soc Mass Spectrometry. *Res:* Application of mass spectrometry to environmental science. *Mailing Add:* 18 Kelton Ct Albany NY 12209

MYERS, WILLIAM HOWARD, b Dodge Co, Nebr, Nov 17, 08; m 32; c 3. MATHEMATICS. *Educ:* Stanford Univ, AB, 34, PhD(math), 39; Univ Calif, MA, 35. *Prof Exp:* Asst math, Stanford Univ, 35-36, instr, 36-39; instr, Univ Utah, 39-40; from asst prof to prof, 40-74, EMER PROF MATH, SAN JOSE STATE UNIV, 74- *Mem:* Math Asn Am. *Res:* Linear groups; algebra; analysis. *Mailing Add:* 2352 Sunny Vista Dr San Jose CA 95128

MYERS, WILLIAM HOWARD, b Oak Ridge, Tenn, Jan 26, 46; m 67; c 2. INORGANIC CHEMISTRY. *Educ:* Houston Baptist Col, BA, 67; Univ Fla, PhD(chem), 72. *Prof Exp:* Instr chem, Univ Fla, 68-69; fel, Ohio State Univ, 72-73; ASST PROF CHEM, UNIV RICHMOND, 73- *Concurrent Pos:* Res chemist, Ethyl Corp, '81-82. *Mem:* Am Chem Soc; Sigma Xi. *Res:* Halogenation reactions of amine-boranes and amine-alanes and investigations of steric effects on reactivity in such systems. *Mailing Add:* Dept of Chem Univ of Richmond Richmond VA 23173

MYERSON, ALBERT LEON, b New York, NY, Nov 14, 19; m 53; c 3. PHYSICAL CHEMISTRY. *Educ:* Pa State Univ, BS, 41; Univ Wis, PhD(phys chem), 48. *Prof Exp:* Asst org chem, Off Sci Res & Develop & Nat Defense Res Comt, Columbia Univ, 41-42, org chem & phys chem, Manhattan Proj, SAM labs, 42-45; asst chem, Univ Wis, 46-48; mem staff, Franklin Inst, 48-56; mgr phys chem, Missile & Space Vehicle Dept, Gen Elec Co, 56-60; prin res phys chemist, Cornell Aeronaut Lab, Inc, 60-69; res assoc, Exxon Res & Eng Res Labs, 69-79; SR STAFF SCIENTIST & HEAD, PHYS CHEM DIV, MOTE MARINE LAB, 79- *Mem:* Am Chem Soc; Am Phys Soc; Combustion Inst; fel Am Inst Chemists. *Res:* Airborne marine pollution; reduction of nitric oxide as a pollutant; reactions and properties of uranium hexafluoride; combustion mechanisms; chemical kinetics; recombination of atoms on surfaces; waterborne pollution. *Mailing Add:* Mote Marine Lab 1600 City Island Park Sarasota FL 33577

MYERSON, GERALD IRA, b New York, NY, July 10, 51. MATHEMATICS. *Educ:* Harvard Col, AB, 72; Stanford Univ, MS, 75; Univ Mich, PhD(math), 77. *Prof Exp:* ASST PROF MATH, STATE UNIV NY, BUFFALO, 77- *Mem:* Am Math Soc; Math Asn Am. *Res:* Number and distribution of solutions of equations and systems of equations over finite fields; relations between average values and zero-sets of polynomials. *Mailing Add:* Dept Math State Univ NY Buffalo NY 14214

MYERSON, RALPH M, b New Britain, Conn, July 21, 18; m 43; c 2. INTERNAL MEDICINE. *Educ:* Tufts Univ, BS, 38, MD, 42. *Prof Exp:* Intern, Boston City Hosp, 42-43, resident med, 46-48; ward physician, Vet Admin Hosp, Wilmington, Del, 48-52, asst chief med serv, Vet Admin Hosp, Philadelphia, 53-67, chief med serv, 67-72, chief staff, 72-75; assoc dir, Clin Serv Dept, 75-77, GROUP DIR MED AFFAIRS, SMITH KLINE & FRENCH LABS, PA, 77-; CLIN PROF MED, MED COL PA, 75- *Concurrent Pos:* Instr, Sch Med, Tufts Univ, 47-48; clin prof, Med Col Pa, 77-66, prof med, 66-75. *Mem:* Fel Am Col Physicians; Am Fedn Clin Res; Int Soc Internal Med; fel Am Col Gastroenterol; Am Gastroenterol Asn. *Res:* Alcoholism; liver disease; application of new diagnostic techniques and evaluation in clinical medicine; gastroenterology; hepatology. *Mailing Add:* Smith Kline & French Labs 1500 Spring Garden St Philadelphia PA 19101

MYHILL, JOHN, b Birmingham, Eng, Aug 11, 23; m 69; c 4. MATHEMATICS. *Educ:* Harvard Univ, PhD(philos), 49. *Prof Exp:* Instr philos, Vassar Col, 48-49, Temple Univ, 49-51 & Yale Univ, 51-53; asst prof, Univ Chicago, 53-54; from asst prof to assoc prof, Univ Calif, 54-60; prof philos & math, Stanford Univ, 60-63 & Univ Ill, 63-66; PROF MATH, STATE UNIV NY BUFFALO, 66- *Concurrent Pos:* Guggenheim fel, 53-54; mem, Inst Advan Study, 57-59 & 63; res assoc, Moore Sch Elec Eng & assoc prof, Univ Pa, 59; vis prof, Univ Mich, 69-70 & Univ Leeds, 71-72; consult, air weapons res, Univ Chicago, 56-57, Stanford Res Inst, 60, Hughes Aircraft Corp, 66-68 & IBM Corp, 68-70; NSF fel, 57-59 & 68-75. *Mem:* Am Math Soc. *Res:* Constructive foundations of mathematics; computer music; electrical computer science; mathematical linguistics; cognitive psychology. *Mailing Add:* Dept of Math State Univ of NY Buffalo NY 14226

MYHRE, BYRON ARNOLD, b Fargo, NDak, Oct 22, 28; m 53; c 2. PATHOLOGY, IMMUNOHEMATOLOGY. *Educ:* Univ Ill, BS, 50; Northwestern Univ, MS, 52, MD, 53; Univ Wis, PhD, 62. *Prof Exp:* Resident path, Univ Wis, 56-60; asst prof med microbiol & immunol, Sch Med, Marquette Univ, 62-64, asst prof path, 64-66; assoc clin prof, Univ Southern Calif, 66-69, assoc prof path, 69-72; PROF PATH, UNIV CALIF, LOS ANGELES, 72-; DIR, BLOOD BANK, HARBOR MED CTR, 72- *Concurrent Pos:* Nat Inst Arthritis & Metab Dis fel, Univ Wis, 60-62; res grants, Ortho Found, 63-64, NIH, 65-66 & 72-73, Am Nat Red Cross, 67-68, Nat Heart Inst, 73-75; assoc med dir, Milwaukee Blood Ctr, Wis, 62-65; sci dir, Los Angeles-Orange Counties Res Cross Blood Ctr, 66-72. *Mem:* Am Soc Clin Path; Am Soc Exp Path; Am Asn Blood Banks; Col Am Pathologists. *Res:* Blood banking; immunopathology; histochemistry; cryobiology. *Mailing Add:* 1000 W Carson Torrance CA 90509

MYHRE, DAVID V, b Lloydminster, Sask, Jan 4, 32; m 57; c 2. FOOD CHEMISTRY. *Educ:* Concordia Col, Moorhead, Minn, BA, 54; NDak State Univ, MS, 55; Univ Minn, PhD(biochem), 62. *Prof Exp:* RES BIOCHEMIST, MIAMI VALLEY LABS, PROCTER & GAMBLE CO, 62- *Mem:* Am Chem Soc. *Res:* Flavor and food chemistry; carbohydrate chemistry. *Mailing Add:* Miami Valley Labs Procter & Gamble Co Cincinnati OH 45239

MYHRE, JANET M, b Tacoma, Wash, Sept 24, 32; m 54; c 1. MATHEMATICAL STATISTICS. *Educ:* Pac Lutheran Univ, BA, 54; Univ Wash, MA, 56; Univ Stockholm, Fil Lic, 68. *Prof Exp:* Res engr, Boeing Co, 56-58; lectr math, Harvey Mudd Col, 61-62; PROF MATH, CLAREMONT MCKENNA COL, 62- *Concurrent Pos:* Consult, US Navy, 68-; assoc ed, Technometrics, 70-75; guest prof math, Univ Stockholm & Eidgenossische Tech Hochschule, Zurich, 71-72; pres, Math Anal Res Corp, 74-; dir, Inst Decision Sci, 75- *Mem:* Am Statist Asn; Inst Math Statist. *Res:* Reliability theory. *Mailing Add:* Dept Math Claremont McKenna Col Claremont CA 91711

MYHRE, PHILIP C, b Tacoma, Wash, Mar 13, 33; m 54; c 1. ORGANIC CHEMISTRY. *Educ:* Pac Lutheran Univ, BA, 54; Univ Wash, PhD(chem), 58. *Prof Exp:* NSF fel, Nobel Inst Chem, Stockholm, 58-60; from asst prof to assoc prof, 60-69, PROF CHEM, HARVEY MUDD COL, 69- *Concurrent Pos:* Vis assoc, Calif Inst Technol, 67-68; guest prof, Swiss Fed Inst Technol, 71-72; chmn dept chem, Harvey Mudd Col, 74-75, 81- *Mem:* AAAS; Am Chem Soc. *Res:* Mechanisms of organic reactions; nuclear magnetic resonance spectroscopy. *Mailing Add:* Dept of Chem Harvey Mudd Col Claremont CA 91711

MYHRE, RICHARD JOHN, b Tacoma, Wash, Dec 11, 20; m 49; c 4. FISHERIES MANAGEMENT. *Educ:* Univ Wash, BS, 50, MS, 60. *Prof Exp:* Jr scientist, 49-54, asst scientist, 54-55, assoc scientist, 55-57, biologist, 57-64, sr biologist, 64-70, ASST DIR, RESOURCE MGT, INT PAC HALIBUT COMN, 70- *Concurrent Pos:* Consult, Int NPac Fisheries Comn, 63-81. *Mem:* AAAS; Am Inst Fishery Res Biologists; Am Fisheries Soc; Biomet Soc. *Res:* Population dynamics; tagging studies; biometrics; mortality estimation; population models. *Mailing Add:* PO Box 5009 University Station Seattle WA 98105

MYINT, THAN, b Moulmein, Burma, June 5, 18; US citizen; m 66; c 5. BIOCHEMISTRY. *Educ:* Univ Rangoon, BS, 41; Utah State Univ, MS, 48, PhD(biochem), 50. *Prof Exp:* Res assoc nutrit, Wash State Univ, 50-51; liaison personnel, US Tech Corp Admin, Burma, 52-53; pub analyst, Dept Pub Health, Govt of Union of Burma, 53-57; res asst chem, Utah State Univ, 57-58; res assoc radiation biol, Mass Inst Technol, 58-59; res fel radiol, Mass Gen Hosp, Boston, 59; protein chemist, Armour & Co, Ohio, 59-60; biochemist, Case Western Reserve Univ, 60-68; HEAD CLIN CHEM DIV, ST VINCENT CHARITY HOSP, 68-; DIR CLIN CHEM, LINCOLN HOSP, ALBERT EINSTEIN COL MED, 68- *Concurrent Pos:* Lectr, Mass Ed Ctr, Burma, 52-53; Sch Health Asst, Burma, 57. *Honors & Awards:* Cleveland Obstet & Gynec Soc Award, 68. *Mem:* AAAS; Am Chem Soc; Am Asn Clin Chem. *Res:* Clinical biochemistry; microbiology chemistry; vitamins; methodology. *Mailing Add:* PO Box 154 Riverdale NY 10471

MYKKANEN, DONALD L, b Bovey, Minn, Jan 7, 32; m 56; c 5. MATERIALS SCIENCE, MECHANICAL ENGINEERING. *Educ:* Univ Calif, Los Angeles, BS, 54; Univ Ill, MS, 55, PhD(mech eng), 61. *Prof Exp:* Instr mech eng, Univ Ill, 56-61; res & develop specialist, Missiles & Space Systs Div, Douglas Aircraft Co, Inc, 61-63, sect chief Saturn prod design, 63-65, sect chief nonmetall res proj, 64-68, prog mgr nuclear effects, McDonnell Douglas Astronaut Co, 68-75; PRES, ETA CORP, 75- *Mem:* Am Soc Metals; AAAS; Am Inst Aeronaut & Astronaut. *Res:* Research and development and engineering analysis of high technology, military and commercial systems. *Mailing Add:* 18301 Churchill Lane Villa Park CA 92667

MYLES, CHARLES WESLEY, b Bethesda, Md, Nov 21, 47; m 69; c 2. THEORETICAL SOLID STATE PHYSICS. *Educ:* Univ Mo-Rolla, BS, 69; Wash Univ, MA, 71, PhD(physics), 73. *Prof Exp:* Fel solid state theory, Battelle Mem Inst, 73-75; res assoc & instr, Swiss Fed Inst Technol, Lausanne, Switz, 75-77; res asst prof, Physics Dept, Univ Ill, Urbana-Champaign, 77-78; ASST PROF SOLID STATE THEORY DEPT PHYSICS, TEX TECH UNIV, 78- *Concurrent Pos:* Consult, Mat Res Lab & Dept Physics, Univ Ill, Urbana-Champaign, 78- & Dept Elec Eng, Univ Southern Calif, 81- *Mem:* Am Phys Soc. *Res:* Deep impurity levels in semiconductors; photon and electronic properties of alloys; properties of magnetic materials; spin-phonon interactions; magnetic resonance; quantum size effects in metal particles; solid molecular hydrogen. *Mailing Add:* Dept of Physics & Eng Physics Tex Tech Univ Lubbock TX 79409

MYLES, DIANA GOLD, b Topeka, Kans, May 8, 44. MEMBRANE BIOLOGY, REPRODUCTIVE BIOLOGY. *Educ:* Univ Calif, Berkeley, BA, 67, PhD(bot), 72. *Prof Exp:* Fel, Dept Biol Sci, Stanford Univ, 73-77, res assoc, Depts Physiol & Anat, Lab Human Reprod & Reprod Biol, 77-81; ASST PROF PHYSIOL, HEALTH CTR, UNIV CONN, 81- *Mem:* Sigma Xi; Am Soc Cell Biol. *Res:* Topographical organization of the mammalian sperm cell surface studies with monoclonal antibodies; role of the sperm cell surface in fertilization. *Mailing Add:* Dept Physiol Health Ctr Univ Conn Farmington CT 06032

MYLES, KEVIN MICHAEL, b Chicago, Ill, July 18, 34; m 56; c 3. COAL COMBUSTION & CONVERSION, ALTERNATIVE FUELS. *Educ:* Univ Ill, Urbana, BS, 56, MS, 57, PhD(phys metall), 63. *Prof Exp:* Asst mgr, Nuclear Fuel Reprocessing Prog, 78-80, PHYS METALLURGIST, CHEM ENG DIV, ARGONNE NAT LAB, 57-, SECT HEAD, 81-, LEADER COAL COMBUSTION & CONVERSION, 80-, MGR THERMAL SYSTS ENERGY MUNICIPAL WASTE, 81- *Concurrent Pos:* Prof mat sci, Midwest Col Eng, 70- *Mem:* Am Soc Metals; Am Inst Mining, Metall & Petrol Engrs; Sigma Xi. *Res:* Nuclear fuel reprocessing; high temperature lithium/metal sulfide batteries; sodium chemistry; physical metallurgy of nuclear materials; thermodynamics of transition elements; fluidized-bed combustion coal; combustion emissions control technologies; thermal destruction of municipal solid waste. *Mailing Add:* Chem Eng Div Argonne Nat Lab 9700 S Cass Argonne IL 60439

MYLONAS, CONSTANTINE, b Athens, Greece, June 24, 16; m 55; c 2. ENGINEERING. *Educ:* Athens Tech Univ, ScB, 39; London Univ, PhD(eng), 49. *Prof Exp:* Construct engr, Ergon Construct Co, Greece, 39-41; design engr struct, Off Struct Design, Greek Ministry Pub Works, 41-44; res engr stress anal, Aero-Res, Ltd, Eng, 48-51; prof & dir lab testing mat, Athens Tech Univ, 51-53; assoc prof, 53-60, PROF ENG, BROWN UNIV, 60- *Concurrent Pos:* Lectr, Athens Tech Univ, 41-44; Guggenheim fel, 59-60; expert, Am del, Int Inst Welding, 62- *Mem:* AAAS; Am Soc Mech Engrs; Soc Exp Stress Anal; Am Soc Testing & Mat; Adams Memorial mem Am Welding Soc. *Res:* Stress analysis; photoelasticity; plasticity; structures; mechanical properties of materials under static and dynamic locating; mechanics of fracture; radiation damage in solids; strength of cemented structures. *Mailing Add:* Div of Eng Brown Univ Providence RI 02912

MYLROIE, JOHN EGLINTON, b Philadelphia, Pa, June 13, 49; m 70. GEOMORPHOLOGY, PALEOECOLOGY. *Educ:* Syracuse Univ, BS, 71; Rensselaer Polytech Inst, PhD(geol), 77. *Prof Exp:* Tech specialist biol, State Univ NY Albany, 72-74; ASST PROF GEOL, MURRAY STATE UNIV, 77- *Concurrent Pos:* Ed, Western Ky Speleol Surv, 77-; chmn, Nat Speleol Soc Comt Cave Ownership & Mgt, 78-81. *Mem:* Fel Nat Speleol Soc; Cave Res Found; Am Geol Inst. *Res:* Karst geomorphology and hydrology, evolution of karst systems, effects of glaciation on karst systems; origin of life, interaction of paleoecosystem parameters. *Mailing Add:* Dept Geosci Murray State Univ Murray KY 42071

MYLROIE, WILLA W, b Seattle, Wash, May 30, 17; m 40, 66; c 2. TRANSPORTATION ENGINEERING, REGIONAL PLANNING. *Educ:* Univ Wash, BS, 40, MS, 52. *Prof Exp:* Checker, Planning Div, State Hwy Dept Wash, 40-41; jr & asst engr, mil & civil construct, US Army Engrs, 41-45; assoc static mech courses, Univ Wash, 48-50, res engr hwys, 51-55; assoc prof civil eng, Purdue Univ, 56-58; res engr, Wash State Dept Transp, 58-69, head, Res & Spec Assignments Div, 69-81. *Concurrent Pos:* Assoc mem, Transp Res Bd, Nat Acad Sci-Nat Res Coun, coun mem opers & maintenance, 73-76; res consult, Univ Wash & King County Design Comn, 81-; invitational res partic, Nat Conf Future Nat Safety Prog, 77. *Honors & Awards:* Edmund Friedman Award, Am Soc Civil Engrs, 78. *Mem:* Inst Transp Engrs; Am Soc Civil Engrs; Sigma Xi. *Res:* Comprehensive land use planning; transportation research; resource management; transportation and land use. *Mailing Add:* 7501 Boston Harbor Rd NE Olympia WA 98506

MYODA, TOSHIO TIMOTHY, b Mukden, Manchuria, Mar 17, 29; m 63; c 2. MICROBIOLOGY, MOLECULAR BIOLOGY. *Educ:* Hokkaido Univ, BS, 49, MS, 52; Iowa State Univ, PhD(bact), 59. *Prof Exp:* Asst microbiol, Hokkaido Univ, 52-54, instr, 54-59; asst bact, Iowa State Univ, 56-59; res fel, Nat Res Coun Can, 59-60; res fel microbiol, Western Reserve Univ, 60-64; chief microbiol, Inst Microbial Chem, Japan, 64-66; res assoc & instr, La Rabida-Univ Chicago Inst, 66-67; assoc chief microbiol & immunochemist, 67-73, dir burn res, 77-78, CHIEF MICROBIOL DEPT, ALFRED I DU PONT INST, 73-, AFFIL MED STAFF, 72- *Concurrent Pos:* Vis prof, Valparaiso Univ, 67; ed asst, Int Union Microbiol Soc, 77- *Mem:* AAAS; Am Soc MIcrobiol; The Biochem Soc; Am Chem Soc; Am Acad Microbiol. *Res:* Molecular biology of group A streptococcal M antigens; molecular genetics, recombinant DNA, cloning, mapping and expression of genes; burns. *Mailing Add:* Dept of Microbiol Aflred I du Pont Inst Wilmington DE 19899

MYRBERG, ARTHUR AUGUST, JR, b Chicago Heights, Ill, June 28, 33; m; c 2. ANIMAL BEHAVIOR, MARINE BIOLOGY. *Educ:* Ripon Col, BS, 54; Univ Ill, MS, 58; Univ Calif, Los Angeles, PhD(zool), 61. *Prof Exp:* Asst, Ill Natural Hist Surv, 57; asst zool, Univ Ill, 57-58 & Univ Calif, Los Angeles, 58-61; fel, Max Planck Inst Behav Physiol, Seewiesen, Ger, 61-64; from asst prof to assoc prof, 64-71, PROF MARINE SCI, UNIV MIAMI, 71- *Mem:* Am Soc Zoologists; Am Soc Ichthyol & Herpet; Animal Behav Soc; Am Inst Biol Sci; fel Am Inst Fishery Res Biologists. *Res:* Ichthyology; comparative behavior of fishes, particularly those of tropical waters with emphasis on the families Cichlidae and Pomacentridae; underwater acoustics and its biological significance; bioacoustics; sensory biology and behavior of sharks. *Mailing Add:* Sch Marine Atmospheric Sci 4600 Rickenbracker Univ Miami Miami FL 33149

MYRES, MILES TIMOTHY, b London, Eng, May 16, 31. ECOLOGY, ORNITHOLOGY. *Educ:* Univ Cambridge, BA, 53, MA, 58; Univ BC, MA, 57, PhD(zool), 60. *Prof Exp:* Res officer, Edward Grey Inst Field Ornith, Oxford Univ, 59-61; asst prof biol, Lakehead Col, 62-63; asst prof zool, 63-69, ASSOC PROF ZOOL, UNIV CALGARY, 69- *Concurrent Pos:* Can Wildlife Serv res grant, 67-68; nat dir, Can Nature Fedn, 72-74; mem coun, Pac Seabird Group, 73-74. *Mem:* Am Ornithologists Union; Can Soc Environ Biol; Brit Ornithologists Union. *Res:* Bird migration; ecology of birds; North Pacific seabirds; man-land-fauna interactions; cultural aspects of environmental conservation at different times in history; relationship between amateur naturalists and professional biologists. *Mailing Add:* Dept of Biol Univ of Calgary Calgary AB T2N 1N4 Can

MYRIANTHOPOULOS, NTINOS, b Cyprus, July 24, 21; m 55; c 3. HUMAN GENETICS. *Educ:* George Washington Univ, BS, 52; Univ Minn, MS, 54, PhD(genetics), 57. *Prof Exp:* Res assoc neurol, Univ Ill, 55-57; res geneticist, 57-63, proj consult, 55-57, HEAD SECT EPIDEMIOL & GENETICS, DEVELOP NEUROL BR, NAT INST NEUROL & COMMUN DIS & STROKE, 63- *Concurrent Pos:* Assoc prof neurol, George Washington Univ, 58-; instr grad prog, NIH, 58-; dir, Genetic Counseling Ctr, 58- *Mem:* Am Soc Human Genetics; NY Acad Sci; Soc Study Social Biol; Teratology Soc. *Res:* Genetics and epidemiology of neurological disease; congenital malformations, prevalence, incidence and mutation rates; metabolic etiology; clinical and behavioral genetics. *Mailing Add:* Develop Neurol Br Inst of Neurol & Commun Dis & Stroke Bethesda MD 20014

MYRICK, ALBERT CHARLES, JR, b Visalia, Calif, July 8, 39. MARINE MAMMAL AGE DETERMINATION, MARINE MAMMAL ECOLOGY. *Educ:* George Wash Univ, BA, 71; Univ Calif, Los Angeles, MA, 74, PhD(biol), 79. *Prof Exp:* Mus specialist, Dept Paleobiol, Smithsonian Inst, Washington, DC, 64-72; teaching fel vertebrate paleo mammal evolution comp anat, Dept Biol, Univ Calif, Los Angeles, 72-75; Smithsonian fel, Dept Paleobiol, Smithsonian Inst, 75; curatorial asst earth sci, Los Angeles County Mus Natural Hist, 74-76; WILDLIFE BIOLOGIST, NAT MARINE FISHERIES SERV, DEPT COMMERCE, LAJOLLA, CALIF, 77- *Res:* Age determination and age-related biological parameters of marine mammals especially small species of odontocetes and serenians; time calibration of layers and etiology of layered tissue in teeth and bones of mammals. *Mailing Add:* Southwest Fisheries Ctr Nat Marine Fisheries Serv LaJolla CA 92038

MYRICK, HENRY NUGENT, b Cisco, Tex, Apr 30, 35. ENVIRONMENTAL SCIENCES. *Educ:* Lamar Univ, BS(chem) & BS(biol), 57; Rice Univ, MS, 59; Washington Univ, St Louis, ScD, 62. *Prof Exp:* Instr environ sci, Rice Univ, 62-63; instr, Harvard Univ, 63-65, fel, 63-64; asst prof, Cullen Col Eng, Univ Houston, 65-68, assoc prof, 68-74; PRES, PROCESS CO INC & RESOURCE CONVERSION SYSTS, INC, 74-; VPRES, AM PROCESS EQUIP INC, 80- *Honors & Awards:* H P Eddy Award, Water Pollution Control Fedn, 61. *Mem:* Am Inst Chem Engrs; Am Inst Chemists; Am Water Works Asn; Air Pollution Control Asn; Water Pollution Control Fedn. *Res:* Environmental engineering; process kinetics of processes for air, water and solid waste conversion or treatment; analytical chemical and biological methods for waste characterization. *Mailing Add:* Process Co Inc 2123 Winnock Blvd Houston TX 77057

MYRON, DUANE R, b Birmingham, Ala, Jan 3, 43; m 62; c 2. BIOCHEMISTRY, NUTRITION. *Educ:* Univ NDak, BS, 65, PhD(biochem), 70. *Prof Exp:* Fel biochem, St Jude Children's Res Hosp, 70-72 & Mem Univ Nfld, 72-73; fel biochem & nutrit, 73-74, RES ASSOC BIOCHEM & NUTRIT, HUMAN NUTRIT LAB, AGR RES SERV, UNIV NDAK, USDA, 74- *Mem:* Sigma Xi; AAAS; Am Chem Soc. *Res:* Biochemical and metabolic role of trace mineral nutrients in laboratory animals and in humans. *Mailing Add:* USDA Human Nutrit Lab Univ of NDak Dept of Biochem Grand Forks ND 58201

MYRON, HAROLD WILLIAM, b New York, NY, Apr 28, 47. THEORETICAL SOLID STATE PHYSICS. *Educ:* City Univ New York, BA, 67; Iowa State Univ, PhD(physics), 72. *Prof Exp:* Res asst physics, Ames Lab, US AEC, 69-72; res assoc, Dept Physics, Magnetic Theory Group, Northwestern Univ, 72-74, vis asst prof, 74-75; SCIENTIST PHYSICS, INST METAL PHYSICS, UNIV NIJMEGEN, NETH, 75- *Mem:* Am Phys Soc. *Res:* Ab initio calculations of electron and phonon properties in metals including dielectric functions of transition metal compounds. *Mailing Add:* Inst Metal Physics Univ Nijmegen Nijmegen Netherlands

MYRON, THOMAS L(EO), b Pittsburgh, Pa, June 12, 23; m 49; c 11. CHEMICAL ENGINEERING. *Educ:* Univ Pittsburgh, BS, 48, MS, 49. *Prof Exp:* Asst lab instr chem eng, Univ Pittsburgh, 48-49; asst chief raw mat eng div, Res Lab, 59-61, chief, Raw Mat Div, 61-76, CHIEF, CHEM DIV, RES LAB, US STEEL CORP, UNIVERSAL, 76- *Mem:* Am Inst Chem Engrs; Am Inst Mining, Metall & Petrol Engrs. *Res:* Ore agglomeration and reduction; pollution abatement; coal and coke; chemicals. *Mailing Add:* 650 Broughton Rd Bethel Park PA 15102

MYRONUK, DONALD JOSEPH, b Kapuskasing, Ont; m 66; c 3. MECHANICAL ENGINEERING, FIRE RESEARCH. *Educ:* Queen's Univ, Ont, BSc, 61, MSc, 65; Univ Ill, Urbana, PhD(mech eng), 69. *Prof Exp:* Design engr, Chalk River Proj, Atomic Energy Can Ltd, 61-62; res asst, Univ Ill, Urbana, 64-69; from asst prof to prof mech eng, 69-81, ASSOC DEAN ENG, SAN JOSE STATE UNIV, 81- *Concurrent Pos:* Res engr fire & earthquake induced fire damage, Sci Serv Inc. *Mem:* Soc Automotive Eng; Air Pollution Control Asn; Am Soc Mech Eng; Am Soc Eng Educ. *Res:* Clean air cars; compressible gas dynamics; biomedical engineering, especially devices for the handicapped; fire research, flammability of fuels hydraulic fluids and lubricants; fire resistant materials; disaster mitigation. *Mailing Add:* Sch Eng 143 125 S Seventh St San Jose CA 95192

MYRVIK, QUENTIN NEWELL, b Minneota, Minn, Nov 9, 21; m 44; c 1. MICROBIOLOGY, IMMUNOLOGY. *Educ:* Univ Wash, BS, 48, MS, 50, PhD(microbiol), 52. *Prof Exp:* From asst prof to assoc prof microbiol, Univ Va, 52-63; prof microbiol & chmn dept, 63-81, PROF MICROBIOL & IMMUNOL, BOWMAN GRAY SCH MED, WAKE FOREST UNIV, 81- *Mem:* Am Soc Microbiol; Am Asn Immunol; Reticuloendothelial Soc; Am Acad Microbiol; Am Thoracic Soc. *Res:* Mechanisms of natural immunity to infectious agents and emphasis on role of lysozyme; cell mediated immunity with emphasis on the structure and function of alveolar macrophages; allergic pulmonary granulomas and mechanisms of necrosis; T lymphocyte subsets. *Mailing Add:* Dept Microbiol & Immunol Bowman Gray Sch Med Wake Forest Univ Winston-Salem NC 27103

MYSAK, LAWRENCE ALEXANDER, b Saskatoon, Sask, Jan 22, 40; m 74; c 2. APPLIED MATHEMATICS, PHYSICAL OCEANOGRAPHY. *Educ:* Univ Alta, BSc, 61; Univ Adelaide, MSc, 63; Harvard Univ, AM, 64, PhD(appl math), 66. *Prof Exp:* US Navy fel, Harvard Univ, 66-67; from asst prof to assoc prof math & oceanog, 67-76, PROF MATH & OCEANOG, UNIV BC, 76- *Concurrent Pos:* Vis res assoc, Ore State Univ, 68; sr visitor, Cambridge Univ, 71-72; travel fel, Nat Res Coun Can, 71-72 & 76-77; vis lectr, Soc Indust & Appl Math, 75-76 & 78-79; consult scientist & guest lectr, Inst Ocean Sci, Patricia Bay, 76; vis scientist, Nat Ctr Atmospheric Res, 77; vis prof, Naval Postgrad Sch, Monterrey, 81. *Honors & Awards:* Pres Prize, Can Meteorol & Oceanog Soc, 80. *Mem:* Can Appl Math Soc; Can Meteorol & Oceanog Soc; Am Meteorol Soc. *Res:* Analytical and probabilistic methods of applied mathematics; waves and currents in rotating stratified fluids; dynamical oceanography; relationship between physical and biological fluctuations in the ocean. *Mailing Add:* Dept of Math Univ of BC Vancouver BC V6T 1W5 Can

MYSELS, ESTELLA KATZENELLENBOGEN, b Berlin, Ger, Jan 12, 21; nat US; m 53. CHEMISTRY. *Educ:* Univ Calif, BS, 42, PhD(chem), 46. *Prof Exp:* Chemist, Richfield Oil Co, 42-44; instr chem, Univ Calif, 46-47 & Univ Southern Calif, 47-50; asst, Sloan-Kettering Inst Cancer Res, 50-53; res assoc chem, Univ Southern Calif, 54-66; lectr chem, Salem Col, 67, prof, 67-70; lectr chem, Univ Calif, San Diego, 75; CONSULT, 80- *Concurrent Pos:* Chmn dept chem, Salem Col, 68-70. *Mem:* Am Chem Soc. *Res:* Infrared and ultraviolet spectroscopy; electrophoresis; surfactant solutions; organic and physical chemistry. *Mailing Add:* 8327 La Jolla Scenic Dr La Jolla CA 92037

MYSELS, KAROL JOSEPH, b Krakow, Poland, Apr 14, 14; nat US; m 53. COLLOID CHEMISTRY, SURFACE CHEMISTRY. *Educ:* Univ Lyon, Lic-es-sc Ing chim, 37; Harvard Univ, PhD(inorg chem), 41. *Prof Exp:* Res asst chem, Stanford Univ, 41-42, res assoc, 43-45; instr, NY Univ, 45-47; from asst prof to prof, Univ Southern Calif, 47-66; assoc dir res, R J Reynolds Industs, 66-70; sr res adv, Gen Atomic Co, 70-79; RES CONSULT, 79- *Concurrent Pos:* Mem staff, Shell Develop Co, 40-42; NSF fac fel, 57-58, sr fel, Strasbourg Ctr Macromolecule Res, France, 62-63; Guggenheim fel, 65-66; Rennebohm lectr, Univ Wis, 64, Pharm Alumni lectr, 67; John Watson Mem Lectr, Va Polytech Inst, 68; assoc mem, Comn Colloid & Surface Chem, Int Union Pure & Appl Chem, 65-69, titular mem, 69-73, chmn, 73-79, mem, Div Comt Phys Chem Div, 75-79; Phi Lambda Upsillon Lectr, Univ Okla, 74; Am Chem Soc tour lectr, 71, 74, 77, 78 & 80-81; res chemist, Sch Med, Univ Calif, San Diego, 80- *Honors & Awards:* Kendall Award, Am Chem Soc, 64. *Mem:* AAAS; Am Chem Soc. *Res:* Surfactant solutions; surface tension; soap films; evaporation control; osmosis; conductivity; electrophoresis; diffusion; rheology; intermolecular forces; thermochemical water splitting; gas-cooled nuclear reactor design and applications; membranology; research tactics. *Mailing Add:* 8327 La Jolla Scenic Dr La Jolla CA 92037

MYSEN, BJORN OLAV, b Oslo, Norway, Dec 20, 47; m 75; c 2. PETROLOGY, GEOCHEMISTRY. *Educ:* Univ Oslo, BSc, 69, MA, 71; Pa State Univ, PhD(geochem), 74. *Prof Exp:* Res assoc geochem, Mineral Mus Univ Oslo, 70-71; fel exp petrol, Geophys Lab, Carnegie Inst Wash, 74-77; lectr petrol, Johns Hopkins Univ, 74-76; STAFF MEM GEOCHEMIST GEOCHEM & PETROL, GEOPHYS LAB, CARNEGIE INST WASHINGTON, 77- *Honors & Awards:* F W Clarke Award, Geochem Soc, 77; Reusch Medal, Geol Soc Norway, 79. *Mem:* Am Geophys Union; fel Mineral Soc Am; Geochem Soc. *Res:* Experimental petrology relevant to igneous processes in the earth and terrestrial planets with emphasis on the role of volatiles, trace element partitioning, phase equilibria and physical properties of silicate melts at high pressure and temperature. *Mailing Add:* Geophys Lab 2801 Upton St NW Washington DC 20008

MYSER, WILLARD C, b Cuyahoga Falls, Ohio, Apr 22, 23; m 43; c 4. ZOOLOGY. *Educ:* Kent State Univ, BS, 44; Ohio State Univ, MS, 47, PhD, 52. *Prof Exp:* Asst zool, 45-47, asst instr, 47-48, from instr to assoc prof, 48-61, asst chmn dept, 61-68, PROF ZOOL, OHIO STATE UNIV, 61- *Concurrent Pos:* Res assoc, Argonne Nat Lab, 56. *Mem:* Radiation Res Soc. *Res:* Radiation biology; cytology. *Mailing Add:* Dept of Zool Ohio State Univ Columbus OH 43210

MYTELKA, ALAN IRA, b Somerville, NJ, Jan 30, 35; m 56; c 2. ENVIRONMENTAL SCIENCES, CHEMICAL ENGINEERING. *Educ:* Polytech Inst Brooklyn, BChE, 58; Newark Col Eng, MSChE, 61; Rutgers Univ, PhD(environ sci), 67. *Prof Exp:* Instr chem, Newark Col Eng, 58-64; environ scientist, Aero Chem Res Labs, Inc, Ritter-Pfaudler Corp, Princeton, 66-70; ASST INVESTR & ASST CHIEF ENGR, INTERSTATE SANITATION COMN, 70- *Mem:* Am Inst Chemists; Air Pollution Control Asn; Am Inst Chem Engrs; Water Pollution Control Asn. *Res:* Oxidation in aqueous systems, especially ionizing-radiation treatment of industrial wastes. *Mailing Add:* 9 Redwood Rd Martinsville NJ 08836

MYTON, BECKY ANN, ethology, ecology, see previous edition

MYTTON, JAMES W, b Kansas City, Mo, Feb 18, 27; m 69; c 1. GEOLOGY. *Educ:* Dartmouth Col, AB, 49; Univ Wyoming, MA, 51. *Prof Exp:* Geologist, US Geol Surv, 51-58; photogeologist, Knox, Bergman & Shearer, 61-63; GEOLOGIST, US GEOL SURV, 63- *Mem:* AAAS; Geol Soc Am; Am Asn Petrol Geologists. *Res:* Investigation of fissionable materials in sedimentary rocks; coal resource studies; regional stratigraphic studies; photogeologic interpretation; evaluation of mineral resources on a regional scale; investigation of phosphate and related commodities; waste disposal studies; studies related to underground nuclear testing; geologic studies related to geothermal energy. *Mailing Add:* US Geol Surv Fed Ctr Denver CO 80225

N

NA, GEORGE CHAO, b Liao-Ning, China, March 23, 47; US citizen; m 73. PHYSICAL BIOCHEMISTRY. *Educ:* Tunghai Univ, BS, 69; Boston Univ, PhD(chem), 76. *Prof Exp:* Fel biochem res, Grad Dept Biochem, Brandeis Univ, 75-81; RES CHEMIST, EASTERN REGIONAL RES CTR, USDA, 81- *Mem:* Am Chem Soc; AAAS; Biophys Soc. *Res:* Protein physical biochemistry. *Mailing Add:* Eastern Regional Res Ctr USDA 600 E Mermaid Lane Philadelphia PA 19118

NAAE, DOUGLAS GENE, b Graettinger, Iowa, Dec 24, 46; m 67; c 2. ORGANIC CHEMISTRY, POLYMER CHEMISTRY. *Educ:* Univ Iowa, BS, 69, MS, 71, PhD(org chem), 72. *Prof Exp:* Res assoc solid state org chem, Univ Minn, Minneapolis, 73-74; from asst prof org chem to prof, Univ Ky, 74-80; RES CHEMIST, GULF OIL CHEMICALS CO, 80- *Mem:* Am Chem Soc. *Res:* Polymer chemistry; Ziegler-Natt catalysis; properties and synthesis of polyolefins; transition metal chemistry; organometallic chemistry; organic chemistry; spectroscopy. *Mailing Add:* Gulf Oil Chemicals Co 13401 Katy Freeway Houston TX 77084

NAAKE, HANS JOACHIM, b Leipzig, Ger, Jan 2, 25; nat; m 56; c 3. ACOUSTICS, SOLID STATE PHYSICS. *Educ:* Univ Gottingen, dipl, 51, PhD(physics), 53. *Prof Exp:* Sci co-worker physics, Physics Inst, Univ Gottingen, 53-57; physicist, 57-69, mgr appl physics, Major Appliance Labs, 69-79, SR SCIENTIST APPL PHYSICS, APPL SCI & TECHNOL LABS, GEN ELEC CO, 80- *Concurrent Pos:* Adj prof, Univ Louisville, 69- *Mem:* Acoust Soc Am; Ger Phys Soc. *Res:* General acoustics; vibrations; sound propagation in liquids and solids; solid state and semiconductor physics; thermoelectricity, especially thermoelectric refrigeration. *Mailing Add:* Appl Sci & Technol Labs Gen Elec Co Louisville KY 40225

NAAR, JACQUES, b Salonica, Greece, Aug 15, 30; nat US; m 53; c 3. CIVIL ENGINEERING. *Educ:* Free Univ Brussels, Ing Civ, 54, PhD, 60; Mass Inst Technol, MS & CE, 58. *Prof Exp:* Asst, Free Univ Brussels, 54-56 & Mass Inst Technol, 56-58; proj engr, Gulf Res & Develop Co, 58-61; res assoc, Olin Mathieson Chem Corp, 61-62; DIR SYSTS EVAL DEPT, SRI INT, 62- *Concurrent Pos:* McCarty-Little chair gaming & res tech, US Naval War Col, 72-74. *Mem:* Am Soc Civil Engrs; Sigma Xi; Royal Belg Fedn Eng Asn. *Res:* Systems evaluation and analysis. *Mailing Add:* Systs Eval Dept SRI Int 333 Ravenswood Menlo Park CA 94025

NAAR, RAYMOND ZACHARIAS, b Salonica, Greece; US citizen. POLYMERS, MECHANICAL ENGINEERING. *Educ:* Advan Sch Textiles, Verviers, Belg, Ingenieur, 55; Mass Inst Technol, SM, 57, ScD(mat sci), 74. *Prof Exp:* Engr polymers, Dewey & Almy, 58-60; res mgr, Cabot Corp, 60-68; res fel polymers & mat, Mass Inst Technol, 68-72; asst prof chem eng, Tufts Univ, 72-77; MGR NEW PROD RES, HUYCK RES CTR, HUYCK CORP, 77- *Concurrent Pos:* Tech consult, 68-72; mkt consult, 73-77. *Mem:* Soc Plastics Engrs; Am Chem Soc; Am Inst Chem Engrs. *Res:* Polymers; biocompatible materials; fibers and fibrous structures. *Mailing Add:* 43 Marlboro Rd Delmar NY 12054

NABER, EDWARD CARL, b Mayville, Wis, Sept 12, 26; m 53; c 2. POULTRY NUTRITION. *Educ:* Univ Wis, BS, 50, MS, 52, PhD(biochem & poultry sci), 54. *Prof Exp:* Asst poultry husb, Univ Wis, 53-54; asst poultry nutritionist, Clemson Col, 54-56; from asst prof to assoc prof, 56-63, PROF POULTRY SCI, OHIO STATE UNIV, 63-, CHMN DEPT, 69-, PROF FOOD SCI & NUTRIT, 76- *Concurrent Pos:* Vis prof, Univ Wis, 64-65; mem, Animal Nutrit Comt, Nat Res Coun, 72-77. *Mem:* Am Chem Soc; Worlds Poultry Sci Asn; Poultry Sci Asn (pres, 76-77); Am Inst Nutrit; Am Inst Biol Sci. *Res:* Nutrition and metabolism in the avian species; vitamin metabolism and protein formation in the avian embryo; energy utilization in the chick; amino acid and lipid metabolism in the laying hen. *Mailing Add:* Dept of Poultry Sci Ohio State Univ Columbus OH 43210

NABER, JAMES ALLEN, radiation physics, solid state physics, see previous edition

NABIGHIAN, MISAC N, b Bucharest, Rumania, Dec 5, 31; US citizen; m 66; c 2. GEOPHYSICS. *Educ:* Mining Inst Bucharest, BS, 54; Columbia Univ, PhD(geophys), 67. *Prof Exp:* Geophysicist, Geol Comt, Bucharest, 55-57; res scientist, Geophys Inst, Rumanian Acad Sci, 57-62; res asst, Lamont Geol Observ, NY, 63-67; geophysicist, 67-80, SR RES GEOPHYSICIST, NEWMONT EXPLOR LTD, 80- *Concurrent Pos:* Adj prof geophysics, Columbia Univ, 67-76 & Univ Ariz, 76- *Mem:* Soc Explor Geophys; Europ Asn Explor Geophys; Am Geophys Union; Royal Acad Sci. *Res:* Theoretical research for the development of new exploration and interpretive techniques in geophysical prospecting. *Mailing Add:* Newmont Explor Ltd 200 W Desert Sky Rd Tucson AZ 85704

NABOR, GEORGE W(ILLIAM), b Chippewa Falls, Wis, Dec 17, 29; m 52; c 3. PETROLEUM ENGINEERING. *Educ:* Univ Wis, BS, 50; Purdue Univ, PhD(chem eng), 53. *Prof Exp:* Sr res technologist, 52-63, res assoc, 63-64, sect supvr, 64-70, MGR, RESERVOIR MECH TECH SERV, FIELD RES LAB, RES DIV, MOBIL RES & DEVELOP CORP, 70- *Mem:* Am Inst Mining, Metall & Petrol Engrs. *Res:* Fluid flow in porous media; reservoir engineering; digital computation; applied mathematics and physics. *Mailing Add:* 4138 Allencrest Dallas TX 75234

NABORS, CHARLES J, JR, b Cleveland, Ohio, Jan 11, 34; m 61; c 3. CYTOLOGY, ANATOMY. *Educ:* Wabash Col, AB, 55; Univ Utah, PhD(anat), 65. *Prof Exp:* Instr, 65-66, ASST PROF ANAT, COL MED, UNIV UTAH, 66-, ASST DEAN, 76- *Concurrent Pos:* Markle scholar acad med, 69-74. *Mem:* AAAS; Endocrine Soc; Reticuloendothelial Soc; Radiation Res Soc; NY Acad Sci. *Res:* Steroid hormone effects on fibroblasts and reticuloendothelial cells; steroid biochemistry; endocrinology; circadian rhythms; radiobiology. *Mailing Add:* Dept of Anat Univ of Utah Med Ctr Salt Lake City UT 84132

NABORS, MURRAY WAYNE, b Carlisle, Pa, Oct 4, 43; m 66. PLANT PHYSIOLOGY, PLANT BREEDING. *Educ:* Yale Univ, BS, 65; Mich State Univ, PhD(bot), 70. *Prof Exp:* NSF grant & vis asst prof biol, Univ Ore, 70; asst prof, Univ Santa Clara, 70-72; ASSOC PROF BIOL, COLO STATE UNIV, 72- *Mem:* AAAS; Am Soc Plant Physiol. *Res:* Phytochrome; water relations; tissue culture. *Mailing Add:* Dept of Bot Colo State Univ Ft Collins CO 80521

NABOURS, ROBERT EUGENE, b Tucson, Ariz, Nov 27, 34; m 54; c 3. ELECTRICAL ENGINEERING. *Educ:* Univ Ariz, BSEE, 57, PhD(elec eng), 65; Stanford Univ, MS, 59. *Prof Exp:* Engr, Lenkurt Elec Co, Calif, 57-58; instr elec eng, Stanford Univ, 58-59; instr, Univ Ariz, 59-62, engr, Appl Res Lab, 62-63; res engr, Tucson Res Lab, Bell Aerosysts Co, 63-65; sr engr, Burr-Brown Res Corp, 65-66, chief engr & mgr eng dept, 66-68; vpres, Kinnison & Nabours Consult Engrs, Inc, 68-71; prin, Robert E Nabours Consult Elec Engr, 71-78; sr vpres, Johannessen & Grand Consult Engrs, 78-80; DIR ELEC ENG, FINICAL & DOMBROWSKI, ARCHITECTS & ENGRS, 80- *Mem:* Inst Elec & Electronics Engrs; Nat Soc Prof Engrs; Instrument Soc Am; Illum Eng Soc. *Res:* Adaptive communication systems; synthesis of optimum systems; analog/hybrid computer systems for random process simulation; construction electrical engineering; forensic engineering. *Mailing Add:* 5201 Salida Del Sol Tucson AZ 85718

NABRIT, SAMUEL MILTON, b Macon, Ga, Feb 21, 05; m. MORPHOLOGY, PHYSIOLOGY. *Educ:* Morehouse Col, BS, 25; Brown Univ, MS, 28, PhD(biol), 32. *Prof Exp:* Instr zool, Morehouse Col, 25-27, prof, 28-31; prof, Atlanta Univ, 32-55; pres, Tex Southern Univ, 55-66; comnr, US AEC, 66-67; exec dir, Southern Fels Fund, 67-81. *Concurrent Pos:* Exchange prof, Atlanta Univ, 30, dean grad sch; Gen Educ Bd fel, Columbia Univ, 43; res fel, Univ Brussels, 50; coordr, Carnegie Exp Grant-in-Aid Res Prog; mem sci bd, NSF, 56-60; mem corp, Marine Biol Lab, Woods Hole. *Mem:* Inst of Med of Nat Acad Sci; Am Soc Zool; Soc Develop Biol; Nat Asn Res Sci Teaching; Nat Inst Sci (pres, 45). *Res:* Neuroembryology; role of fin rays in regeneration of tail-fins of fishes. *Mailing Add:* 686 Beckwith St SW Atlanta GA 30314

NACAMU, ROBERT LARRY, b New York, NY, Oct 17, 44; m 66; c 3. CERAMIC SCIENCE. *Educ:* Rutgers Univ, BS, 66, PhD(ceramics), 69. *Prof Exp:* Res scientist, Lavino Div, Int Minerals & Chem, 69-74; STAFF RES ENGR, KAISER REFRACTORIES DIV, KAISER ALUMINUM & CHEM CORP, 74- *Mem:* Am Ceramic Soc; Nat Inst Ceramic Eng; Am Inst Mining, Metall & Petrol Eng. *Res:* Basic refractory brick and monolithics. *Mailing Add:* Kaiser Aluminum & Chem Corp Ctr Technol PO Box 877 Pleasanton CA 94566

NACARRATO, WILLIAM FRANK, biochemistry, lipid chemistry, see previous edition

NACE, DONALD MILLER, b Hanover, Pa, Nov 28, 24; m 45; c 2. PHYSICAL CHEMISTRY. *Educ:* Lehigh Univ, BS, 47, MS, 49; Pa State Univ, PhD(chem), 56. *Prof Exp:* Asst, Nat Printing Ink Res Inst, 47-49; res chemist, 49-58, sr res chemist, 58-74, RES ASSOC, MOBIL RES & DEVELOP CORP, 74- *Mem:* Am Chem Soc. *Res:* Catalysis in petroleum processing. *Mailing Add:* Mobil Res & Develop Corp Res Dept Paulsboro NJ 08066

NACE, GEORGE WILLIAM, b Connellsville, Pa, Apr 1, 20; m 46; c 4. DEVELOPMENTAL BIOLOGY, IMMUNOLOGY. *Educ:* Reed Col, BA, 43; Univ Calif, Los Angeles, MA, 48, PhD(embryol), 50. *Prof Exp:* NIH fel, Brussels, Belg, 50-51; asst prof, Duke Univ, 51-57; assoc prof, 57-61, PROF ZOOL, UNIV MICH, ANN ARBOR, 61-, DIR AMPHIBIAN FACILITY, 68-, FEL, CTR HUMAN GROWTH & DEVELOP, 69- *Concurrent Pos:* Staff asst, Div Biol & Agr, Nat Res Coun, 52-53; vis prof, Kyoto Univ, 64, adv, 64-; consult, NIH, 65; vis prof, Hiroshima Univ, 66, 68, 70; vis lecturers' trust fund vis prof, Univ Witwatersrand, 71; chmn subcomt amphibian standards, Comt Standards, Inst Lab Animal Resources, Nat Acad Sci-Nat Res Coun. *Mem:* Soc Develop Biol; Genetics Soc Am; Am Soc Zoologists; Am Asn Anatomists; fel NY Acad Sci. *Res:* Proteins in fertilization and ontogeny of amphibia; biology of neoplasia in the frog; development and maintenance of defined strains of amphibia; influence of microgravity on development. *Mailing Add:* Div of Biol Sci Natural Sci Bldg Univ of Mich Ann Arbor MI 48109

NACE, HAROLD RUSS, b Collingswood, NJ, July 5, 21; m 44. ORGANIC CHEMISTRY. *Educ:* Lehigh Univ, BS, 43; Mass Inst Technol, PhD(org chem), 48; Brown Univ, MS, 57. *Prof Exp:* Res chemist, Merck & Co, Inc, 44-45; from instr to assoc prof, 48-59, PROF CHEM, BROWN UNIV, 59- *Concurrent Pos:* Res chemist, Jackson Lab, E I du Pont de Nemours & Co, 56-57, consult, 57-60; consult, William S Merrell Co div, Richardson-Merrell Inc, 60-68, Wyeth Labs, 68- & Bd Rev, US Pharmacopeia, 80- *Mem:* AAAS; Am Chem Soc; fel Am Inst Chemists; fel NY Acad Sci. *Res:* Stereochemistry and partial synthesis of steroids; dipole moment studies of organic compounds; prostaglandin syntheses. *Mailing Add:* Dept of Chem Brown Univ Providence RI 02912

NACHAMKIN, JACK, b New York, NY, Mar 23, 40; div; c 2. MATHEMATICAL PHYSICS. *Educ:* Polytech Inst Brooklyn, BS, 60; Rensselaer Polytech Inst, PhD(physics), 64. *Prof Exp:* Physicist fel appl nuclear, Univ Kans, 64-66, Chalk River Lab, Can, 66-68; physicist appl nuclear, Los Alamos Nat Lab, 68-80; MEM STAFF, EXXON ENTERPRISES, 80- *Mem:* Am Phys Soc. *Res:* Nuclear structure; hydrodynamics; radiation transport; space charge electronics; electric vehicle research. *Mailing Add:* Exxon Enterprises 328 Gilbralton Dr Sunnyvale CA 94086

NACHBAR, MARTIN STEPHEN, b New York, NY, July 17, 37; m 62; c 1. MEDICINE, MICROBIOLOGY. *Educ:* Union Col, BS, 58; NY Univ, MD, 62. *Prof Exp:* From intern to resident, Bellevue Hosp, New York, 62-66; USPHS med scientist training fel, 66-69, from instr to asst prof med, 69-72, asst prof med & microbiol, 72-74, ASSOC PROF MED & MICROBIOL, MED CTR, NY UNIV, 75- *Concurrent Pos:* NY Heart Asn sr investr, 69. *Honors & Awards:* Career Scientist Award, Irma T Hirschl Trust, 74. *Res:* Dietary effects of lectins. *Mailing Add:* Dept of Med & Microbiol Med Ctr NY Univ 550 First Ave New York NY 10016

NACHBAR, WILLIAM, b Brooklyn, NY, Apr 25, 23; m 52; c 1. APPLIED MATHEMATICS. *Educ:* Cornell Univ, BME, 44; NY Univ, MS, 48; Brown Univ, PhD(appl math), 51. *Prof Exp:* Res assoc appl math, Brown Univ, 49-51; staff mem, Math Servs Unit, Boeing Airplane Co, 51-55; sect head mech, Appl Math Dept, Missiles & Space Div, Lockheed Aircraft Corp, 55-60, staff scientist, 60-63; assoc prof, Dept Aeronaut & Astronaut, Stanford, 63-65; PROF APPL MECH & ENG SCI, UNIV CALIF, SAN DIEGO, 65- *Concurrent Pos:* Res assoc, Stanford Univ, 61-63. *Mem:* Assoc fel, Am Inst Aeronaut & Astronaut; Am Soc Mech Eng; Combustion Inst. *Res:* Solid mechanics and structural analysis; stability theory; energy policy and technology. *Mailing Add:* 6551 Avenida Manana La Jolla CA 92037

NACHBIN, LEOPOLDO, b Recife, Brazil, Jan 7, 22; m 56; c 4. MATHEMATICS. *Educ:* Univ Brazil, MS, 43, PhD(math), 47. *Hon Degrees:* Dr, Univ Pernambuco, 66. *Prof Exp:* Prof math, Univ Brazil, 50-61; vis prof, Univ Paris, 61-63; prof, 63-67, GEORGE EASTMAN PROF MATH, UNIV ROCHESTER, 67- *Concurrent Pos:* Fels, Guggenheim Found, 49-50, 57-58 & Rockefeller Found, 56-57; head div math res, Nat Res Coun Brazil, 55-56, mem gen bd, 60-61; mem, Inter-Am Comt Math Educ, 61-75. *Honors & Awards:* Moinho Santista Found Prize, 62. *Mem:* Brazilian Acad Sci; Lisbon Acad Sci. *Res:* Approximation theory; holomorphy; functional analysis. *Mailing Add:* Dept of Math Univ of Rochester Rochester NY 14627

NACHLINGER, R RAY, b Taylor, Tex, Dec 4, 44; m 65. ENGINEERING MECHANICS. *Educ:* Univ Tex, BEngS, 66, MS, 67, PhD(eng mech), 68. *Prof Exp:* Res engr, Univ Tex, 66-68; ASST PROF MECH ENG, UNIV HOUSTON, 68- *Mem:* Am Soc Mech Engrs. *Res:* Theoretical and applied solid and continuum mechanics. *Mailing Add:* Dept of Mech Eng Univ of Houston Houston TX 77004

NACHMAN, JOSEPH F(RANK), b Toledo, Ohio, Jan 22, 18; m 43; c 2. PHYSICAL METALLURGY. *Educ:* Univ Toledo, BS, 40; Ohio State Univ, MSc, 47. *Prof Exp:* Metallurgist phys metall, US Naval Ord Lab, 48-56; mgr alloy develop, Denver Res Inst, 56-63; specialist, Atomics Int Div, Rockwell Int, Inc, 63-66; chief appl sci, advan methods & mat, Solar Div, Int Harvester Co, 66-81, RES STAFF SPECIALIST, SOLAR TURBINES INT, INT HARVESTER CO, 81-; PRES, METALL CONSULT SERV, INC, 81- *Honors & Awards:* Letter Commendation, Chief Navy Bur Ord, 45; Civilian Meritorious Award, US Dept Navy, 53. *Mem:* AAAS; Am Soc Metals; Nat Asn Corrosion Engrs. *Res:* Nonstrategic aluminum-iron base alloys; research on magnetic alloys; dispersion hardening of metals; turbine superalloys; high-damping alloys; rare earth metals; nuclear materials and cladding alloys; metal hydrides. *Mailing Add:* 7060 Murray Park Dr San Diego CA 92119

NACHMAN, RALPH LOUIS, b Bayonne, NJ, June 29, 31; m 58; c 2. MEDICINE. *Educ:* Vanderbilt Univ, AB, 53, MD, 56. *Prof Exp:* From instr to asst prof, 63-68, assoc prof, 68-80, PROF MED, MED COL, CORNELL UNIV, 80-, CHIEF DIV HEMAT, 70-; ASSOC ATTEND PHYSICIAN, NY HOSP, 70- *Concurrent Pos:* Res fel med, New York Hosp-Cornell Med Ctr, 62-63; dir labs clin path, NY Hosp, 63-70. *Mem:* AAAS; Am Fedn Clin Res; Am Soc Hemat; Am Physiol Soc. *Res:* Immunological aspects of hematologic diseases, particularly platelet abnormalities. *Mailing Add:* Dept of Med Cornell Univ Col of Med New York NY 10021

NACHMANSOHN, DAVID, b Jekaterinoslaw, Russia, Mar 17, 99; nat US; m 29; c 1. NEUROLOGY. *Educ:* Univ Berlin, MD, 26. *Hon Degrees:* MD, Free Univ Berlin, 64; Dr, Univ Liege, 78; DSc, Tufts Univ, 78. *Prof Exp:* Res fel, Kaiser Wilhelm Inst Biol, Ger, 26-30; asst med, Univ Frankfurt, 30-31; independent investr, Paris, 33-39; instr, Sch Med, Yale Univ, 39-42; res assoc neurol, 42-47, from asst prof to assoc prof, 47-55, prof biochem, 55-68, EMER PROF BIOCHEM & SPEC LECTR, COL PHYSICIANS & SURGEONS, COLUMBIA UNIV, 68- *Concurrent Pos:* Hon fel, Weizmann Inst Sci, Israel, 72. *Honors & Awards:* Pasteur Medal, Paris, 52; Neuberg Medal, 53; Gold Medal, Spanish Superio Coun Sci Invest, Madrid, 75. *Mem:* Nat Acad Sci; life mem New York Acad Sci; hon mem Berliner Medizinische Gesellschaft; Am Acad Arts & Sci; hon mem Spanish Superior Coun Sci Invest. *Res:* Chemical and molecular basis of nerve activity; role of acetylcholine cycle in control of ion movements across excitable membranes; transduction of chemical into electrical energy, also nerve excitability and bioelectricity; molecular forces in enzymes and proteins associated with function of acetylcholine; electric fish; organophosphorous compounds. *Mailing Add:* Dept of Neurol Col of Phys & Surgeons Columbia Univ New York NY 10032

NACHREINER, RAYMOND F, b Richland Center, Wis, Apr 29, 42; m 68; c 3. VETERINARY PHYSIOLOGY, ENDOCRINOLOGY. *Educ:* Iowa State Univ, DVM, 66; Univ Wis, PhD(endocrinol), 72. *Prof Exp:* Res asst endocrinol, Univ Wis, 68-72; asst prof physiol, Auburn Univ, 72-77; DIR, ENDOCRINE DIAG SECT, ANIMAL HEALTH DIAG LAB, MICH STATE UNIV, 77- *Honors & Awards:* Burr Beach Award, Univ Wis, 72. *Mem:* Soc Study Fertil; Soc Study Reprod; Am Vet Med Asn. *Res:* Population control in animals; porcine stress syndrome and porcine agalactia syndrome; endocrine diagnostic procedures in domestic animals; endocrine pharmacokinetics; bovine cystic ovarian disease. *Mailing Add:* 1874 Penobscot Dr Okemos MI 48864

NACHTIGAL, CHESTER LEE, b Hutchinson, Kans, Sept 11, 41; m 71; c 3. MECHANICAL ENGINEERING. *Educ:* Bethel Col, Newton, Kans, AB, 63; Kans State Univ, BS, 64; Mass Inst Technol, MS & ME, 66, PhD(mech eng), 69. *Prof Exp:* Asst prof mech eng, Purdue Univ, 69-73, assoc prof, 73-78; ENG SPECIALIST II, WEYERHAEUSER CO, 78- *Concurrent Pos:* Chief engr, GLN, Inc, 70-78; vis assoc prof, Univ Wash, 76-77. *Mem:* Am Soc Mech Engrs; Am Soc Eng Educ; Soc Mfg Engrs; Sigma Xi. *Res:* Automation concepts and technology in the wood products industry, particularly in the area of automated lumber manufacturing. *Mailing Add:* Weyerhaeuser Tech Ctr 1H5 Weyerhaeuser Co Tacoma WA 98477

NACHTIGALL, GUENTER WILLI, b Hamburg, Ger, Jan 1, 29; nat US; m 50; c 1. ORGANIC CHEMISTRY. *Educ:* Columbia Univ, BS, 62; Univ Colo, PhD(org chem), 68. *Prof Exp:* Chemist, Indust Chem Div, 61, chemist cent res div, 62-63, res chemist, 64-74, SR RES CHEMIST, CHEM RES DIV, AM CYANAMID CO, 74- *Mem:* Am Chem Soc; Sigma Xi. *Res:* Carbonium ion reactions, particularly those of bridged polycyclic compounds; asymmetric organic pharmaceuticals; industrial organic process research and development. *Mailing Add:* 66 N Main St Georgetown CT 06829

NACHTMAN, ELLIOT SIMON, b Cleveland, Ohio, June 8, 23; m 45; c 3. MECHANICAL METALLURGY, TRIBOLOGY. *Educ:* Wooster Col, BA, 45; Ill Inst Technol, MS, 50, PhD(metall eng), 69; cert mgt, Univ Chicago, 56. *Prof Exp:* Jr chemist, Harshaw Chem Co, Ohio, 45-46; res chemist, Manhattan Proj, Univ Chicago, 46-48; instr metall, Ill Inst Technol, 48-50; prod engr, LaSalle Steel Co, Ind, 50-52, mgr prod eng, 52-56, dir res & develop, 56-66, vpres res & develop, 66-71; MGR INDUST TECHNOL DIV, TOWER OIL & TECHNOL CO, 71- *Concurrent Pos:* Mem adv panel metall, NSF, 70-; adj prof, Univ Ill, Chicago Circle, 75- *Mem:* Fel Am Soc Metals; Metall Soc; Am Inst Mining, Metall & Petrol Engrs; Soc Lubrication Engrs. *Res:* Plastic deformation of metals; surface reactions; ferrous metallurgy; machinability of metals; lubrication. *Mailing Add:* Tower Oil & Technol Co 300 W Washington St Chicago IL 60606

NACHTRIEB, NORMAN HARRY, b Chicago, Ill, Mar 4, 16; m 41, 53; c 1. PHYSICAL CHEMISTRY. *Educ:* Univ Chicago, BS, 36, PhD(chem), 41. *Prof Exp:* Anal chemist, State Geol Surv, Ill, 37-38; head, Anal Sect, Columbia Chem Div, Pittsburgh Plate Glass Co, Ohio, 41-43; res chemist, Manhattan Dist, Metall Lab, Chicago, 43-44; alternate group leader anal group, Los Alamos Sci Lab, NMex, 44-46; from asst prof to assoc prof, 46-53, prof chem, James Franck Inst, 46-81, chmn dept, 62-71, master, Phys Sci Col Div & assoc dean, Div Phys Sci, 73-81, PROF CHEM, UNIV CHICAGO, 53- *Concurrent Pos:* Adv ed, Encyclopaedia Britannica, 55-; NSF fel, 59-60, mem adv panel, Sci Educ Div, 65-68. *Mem:* Am Chem Soc; fel Am Phys Soc. *Res:* Spectrochemical analysis of solutions; fused salts; metals; extraction of metal halides by organic solvents; electrode potentials; diffusion in crystalline solids and liquids; high pressure chemistry; nuclear magnetic resonance; solid state chemistry; magnetic, electrical and optical properties of metal-molten salt solutions. *Mailing Add:* Dept of Chem Univ of Chicago 5735 Ellis Ave Chicago IL 60637

NACHTSHEIM, PHILIP ROBERT, b New York, NY, Dec 26, 28; m 56; c 4. AERONAUTICAL ENGINEERING. *Educ:* Ohio State Univ, BS, 52; Case Inst Technol, MS, 58, PhD(aeronaut eng), 63. *Prof Exp:* Instr mech eng, Case Inst Technol, 55-61; res engr, Lewis Res Ctr, Ohio, 61-65, asst chief, Thermal Protection Br, 65-80, ASST CHIEF, ENTRY TECHNOL BR,

AMES RES CTR, NASA, 80- *Mem:* Am Inst Aeronaut & Astronaut. *Res:* Planetary entry technology; interaction of intense radiation with material; patterned ablation effects; hydrodynamic stability. *Mailing Add:* 563 Dublin Way Sunnyvale CA 94087

NACHTWEY, DAVID STUART, b Seattle, Wash, Aug 9, 29; m; c 3. PHOTOBIOLOGY, RADIOBIOLOGY. *Educ:* Univ Wash, BA, 51; Univ Tex, MA, 56; Stanford Univ, PhD(biol sci), 61. *Prof Exp:* Nat Cancer Inst fel, Biol Inst, Carlsberg Found, Denmark, 61-62; res biologist, Cellular Radiobiol Br, US Naval Radiol Defense Lab, 62-68; assoc prof radiation biol, Ore State Univ, 68-74; ed, Climatic Impact Assessment Prog Monograph 5, 74-75; bioenviron effects officer, 75-81, CHIEF, BIOMED APPLICATIONS BR, NASA, 81- *Concurrent Pos:* Mem comt photobiol, Nat Res Coun. *Mem:* AAAS; Sigma Xi; Radiation Res Soc; Am Soc Photobiol. *Res:* Cell division processes in protozoa, algae, and mammalian cells; effects of ultraviolet and ionizing radiation on cells; mutagenesis; recovery from radiation damage; ecosystem responses to solar ultraviolet radiation; skin cancer incidence modeling. *Mailing Add:* Biomed Applns Br Mail Code SD5 NASA Johnson Space Ctr Houston TX 77058

NACOZY, PAUL E, b Los Angeles, Calif, Apr 15, 42. ASTRONOMY, CELESTIAL MECHANICS. *Educ:* San Diego State Col, BA, 64; Yale Univ, MS, 66, PhD(astron), 68. *Prof Exp:* Asst prof, 68-74, ASSOC PROF AEROSPACE ENG, UNIV TEX, AUSTIN, 74- *Mem:* Am Astron Soc; Int Astron Soc; Am Inst Aeronaut & Astronaut. *Res:* Celestial mechanics and aerospace mechanics, especially series-solutions of the motions of space vehicles, asteroids, and comets; earth-moon-space vehicle dynamical system. *Mailing Add:* Dept of Aerospace Eng Univ of Tex Austin TX 78712

NADAS, ALEXANDER SANDOR, b Budapest, Hungary, Nov 12, 13; US citizen; m 41; c 3. PEDIATRIC CARDIOLOGY. *Educ:* Med Univ Budapest, MD, 37; Wayne State Univ, MD, 45; Am Bd Pediat, dipl & cert pediat cardiol. *Prof Exp:* Intern, Fairview Park Hosp, Cleveland, Ohio, 39-40 & Wilmington Gen Hosp, Del, 40-41; resident pediat, Mass Mem Hosps, Boston, 41-42; vol asst med serv, Children's Hosp, Boston, 42-43, asst resident, 43; chief resident, Children's Hosp, Mich, 43-45; pvt pract, Greenfield, Mass, 45-49; instr pediat, 50-52, clin assoc, 52-55, from asst clin prof to clin prof, 55-69, PROF PEDIAT, HARVARD MED SCH, 69-; CHIEF CARDIOL DEPT, CHILDREN'S HOSP MED CTR, 69- *Concurrent Pos:* Res fel pediat, Harvard Med Sch, 49; Guggenheim fel, 70; instr, Wayne State Univ, 43-45; asst physician & assoc chief cardiol div, Children's Hosp Med Ctr, 49-50, from assoc physician to physician, Sharon Sanatorium, 50-51; assoc physician & assoc cardiologist, Sharon Cardiovasc Unit, 51-52, cardiologist, 52-66, sr assoc med & Good Samaritan Div, 62-, chief cardiol div, 66-69; Fulbright prof, State Univ Groningen, 56-57; consult, Brigham & Women's Hosp, Mass Gen Hosp, Boston & Newton Wellesley Hosp. *Mem:* Am Heart Asn; Am Acad Pediat; Soc Pediat Res; Am Pediat Soc. *Res:* Applied cardiovascular physiology and physiology of congenital heart disease; natural history of congenital heart disease with special emphasis on clinical-physiologic correlations; multicenter clinical trials in congenital heart disease. *Mailing Add:* Children's Hosp Med Ctr 300 Longwood Ave Boston MA 02115

NADAS, ARTHUR, mathematical statistics, see previous edition

NADDOR, ELIEZER, b Jerusalem, Israel, Sept 23, 20; US citizen; m 54; c 3. OPERATIONS RESEARCH, SOFTWARE SYSTEMS. *Educ:* Israel Inst Technol, BS, 51, CE, 52; Columbia Univ, MS, 53; Case Inst Technol, PhD(opers res), 57. *Prof Exp:* Asst opers res, Case Inst Technol, 53-55, instr bus admin, 55-56; from asst prof to assoc prof opers res, 56-64, PROF OPERS RES, JOHNS HOPKINS UNIV, 64- *Concurrent Pos:* Consult, Cleveland Graphite Bronze Co, 53-55, Am Airlines, Inc, 55-56 & Chesapeake & Potomac Tel Co Md, 57-66; consult, Res Labs, Gen Motors Corp, 59-, Bell Tel Labs, 63-64 & Gen Acct Off, 73-; Fulbright lectr, Finland, 64-65; consult, Gen Elec Co & US Naval Acad, 66-70. *Mem:* Opers Res Soc Am; Inst Mgt Sci (secy-treas, 64-66); Math Asn Am. *Res:* Inventory systems; information storage and retrieval. *Mailing Add:* Dept of Math Sci Johns Hopkins Univ Baltimore MD 21218

NADDY, BADIE IHRAHIM, b Haifa, Palestine, Dec 31, 33; US citizen; m 63; c 3. PHYSICAL CHEMISTRY, SOIL CHEMISTRY. *Educ:* Am Univ Beirut, BS, 57; Kans State Univ, PhD(soil & phys chem), 63. *Prof Exp:* Chmn div sci, Henderson State Col, 63-65; dir labs, Jordan Govt, 65-67; CHMN DIV MATH & SCI, COLUMBIA STATE COMMUNITY COL, 68- *Mem:* Am Chem Soc; Sigma Xi. *Res:* Effect of cation exchange on the dielectric constants of minerals; x-ray diffraction of minerals saturated with different cations. *Mailing Add:* Div of Math & Sci Columbia State Community Col Columbia TN 38401

NADEAU, GERARD, b Quebec, Que, Oct 28, 25; m 53; c 5. THEORETICAL PHYSICS. *Educ:* Laval Univ, BS, 48, MS, 49. *Prof Exp:* From asst prof to assoc prof, 49-62, PROF PHYSICS, LAVAL UNIV, 63- *Mem:* French-Can Asn Advan Sci; Can Asn Physicists. *Res:* Theory of elasticity. *Mailing Add:* Dept of Physics Fac Sci Laval Univ Quebec PQ G1K 7P4 Can

NADEAU, HERBERT GERARD, b Cranston, RI, Aug 1, 28; m 51; c 4. PHYSICAL CHEMISTRY, COMBUSTION TECHNOLOGY. *Educ:* Providence Col, BS, 51. *Prof Exp:* Anal res chemist, Geigy Chem Corp, 51-55; chief, Sect Anal Chem, Olin Mathieson Chem Corp, 55-65; head anal res serv, 65, mgr cellular plastics, 66-68, mgr anal & phys res, 68-74, MGR PHYS & FLAMMABILITY RES, UPJOHN CO, 74- *Concurrent Pos:* Mem, Prods Res Comt, 75-80. *Honors & Awards:* Distinguished Serv Award, Citation & Cert Appreciation, Soc Plastics Indust, 75. *Mem:* Am Chem Soc; Int Isocyanate Inst; Soc Plastics Indust. *Res:* Organic analysis; infrared; vapor phase chromatography; high vacuum techniques; boron compounds; commercial products; urethane chemistry; polymers; flammability testing and research. *Mailing Add:* 1 Carolyn Ct North Haven CT 06473

NADEAU, JOHN S, b Detroit, Mich, July 19, 29; m 56, 78; c 4. CERAMICS. *Educ:* Univ Notre Dame, BS, 51; Univ Calif, Berkeley, MS, 52, PhD(phys metall), 60. *Prof Exp:* Res engr, Univ Calif, Berkeley, 59-60; metallurgist, Gen Elec Res Lab, 60-70; PROF METALL, UNIV BC, 70- *Concurrent Pos:* Metallurgist, Imp Col, Univ London, 67-68. *Mem:* Am Ceramic Soc; Can Ceramic Soc; Nat Inst Ceramic Engrs; Am Soc Metals; Ceramic Educ Coun. *Res:* Mechanical properties of engineering materials. *Mailing Add:* Dept of Metall Univ of BC Vancouver BC V6T 1W5 Can

NADEAU, REGINALD ANTOINE, b St Leonard, NB, Dec 18, 32; m 57; c 2. CARDIOVASCULAR PHYSIOLOGY, CARDIOLOGY. *Educ:* Loyola Col, Can, BA, 52; Univ Montreal, MD, 57; FRCP(C), 62. *Prof Exp:* From asst prof to assoc prof, 64-70, prof physiol, 72-75, PROF MED, FAC MED, UNIV MONTREAL, 75- *Concurrent Pos:* Assoc, Med Res Coun Can, 65; dir res, Cardiol Hosp Sacre Coeur, Montreal. *Mem:* Can Physiol Soc; Can Cardiovasc Soc; Am Col Cardiol. *Res:* Clinical cardiology. *Mailing Add:* Dept Med Fac Med Univ Montreal Montreal PQ H3C 3J7 Can

NADEL, ELI MAURICE, physiology, pathology, deceased

NADEL, ETHAN RICHARD, b Washington, DC, Sept 3, 41. PHYSIOLOGY. *Educ:* Williams Col, BA, 63; Univ Calif, Santa Barbara, MA, 66, PhD(biol), 69. *Prof Exp:* Asst prof, 70-76, ASSOC PROF, DEPTS EPIDEMIOL & PUB HEALTH & PHYSIOL, SCH MED, YALE UNIV, 76- *Concurrent Pos:* NIH fel, Sch Med, Yale Univ, 69-70, USPHS grant, 70-; from asst fel to assoc fel, John B Pierce Found Lab, 70-; partic, US-Japan Prog Human Adaptability, 72-73; mem, Environ Physiol Comn, Int Union Physiol Sci, 77-; Hall Mem lectr, Univ Louisville, 79. *Mem:* AAAS; Am Physiol Soc; fel Am Col Sports Med. *Res:* Physiological regulations against hyperthermia. *Mailing Add:* John B Pierce Found Lab 290 Congress Ave New Haven CT 06519

NADEL, JAY A, b Philadelphia, Pa, Jan 21, 29; m 60; c 3. PULMONARY PHYSIOLOGY, PHARMACOLOGY. *Educ:* Temple Univ, AB, 49; Jefferson Med Col, MD, 53. *Prof Exp:* Trainee heart & lung res, 58-62, clin instr med, 61-62, asst clin prof, 62-64, from asst prof to assoc prof, 64-70, PROF MED & RADIOL, CARDIOVASC RES INST, MED CTR, UNIV CALIF, SAN FRANCISCO, 70-, MEM STAFF, 64- *Concurrent Pos:* Mem, Cardiovasc B Study Sect, Nat Heart & Lung Inst, 71-75; adv, Comn State-Wide Air Pollution Res, Univ Calif; mem, Comn Surv Prof Manpower Pulmonary Dis; dir, Multidisciplinary Res Training Prog in Pulmonary Dis, Nat Heart, Lung & Blood Inst, 74-, prog dir, Neuro Humoral Control of Lungs & Airway, 78-, mem, Pulmonary Dis Adv Comt, 81-85. *Mem:* Am Physiol Soc; Asn Am Physicians; Thoracic Soc (pres, 73-); Am Soc Clin Invest. *Res:* Control of airways, mucous secretion, respiration, ion transport smooth muscle and automic nerves; pulmonary radiology. *Mailing Add:* Dept of Med & Physiol Univ of Calif Med Ctr San Francisco CA 94143

NADELHAFT, IRVING, b New York, NY, Nov 4, 28; m 56; c 2. NEUROBIOLOGY. *Educ:* City Col New York, BS, 49; Syracuse Univ, PhD, 56. *Prof Exp:* Res assoc, Carnegie Inst Technol, 58-61, asst prof physics, 61-67; ASST PROF NEUROL SURG, MED SCH, UNIV PITTSBURGH, 74-; RES PHYSICIST, VET ADMIN HOSP, PITTSBURGH, 69. *Concurrent Pos:* Ford Found fel, Europ Orgn Nuclear Res, 56-57; NIH spec fel, Dept Anat & Cell Biol, Sch Med, Univ Pittsburgh & Dept Biol, Mass Inst Technol, 67-69; guest res physicist, Brookhaven Nat Lab, 62-63; adj asst prof pharmacol, Med Sch, Univ Pittsburgh, 69- *Mem:* AAAS; Biophys Soc; Soc Neurosci; Am Phys Soc. *Res:* High energy physics; weak interactions; particle physics; axoplasmic flow; tracer techniques; computer simulation. *Mailing Add:* Gen Med Res University Dr Pittsburgh PA 15240

NADER, ALLAN E, b Chicago, Ill, Dec 24, 37; m 65; c 1. ORGANIC CHEMISTRY. *Educ:* Ill Inst Technol, BS, 60; Western Mich Univ, MA, 63; Purdue Univ, PhD(org chem), 67. *Prof Exp:* Res chemist, 66-71, sr res chemist, Petrochem Dept, 71-80, SR RES CHEMIST, CENT RES DEPT, E I DU PONT DE NEMOURS & CO, INC, 80- *Mem:* Am Chem Soc; Sigma Xi. *Res:* Reaction mechanism studies; hydrocarbon nitration and oxidation; metal catalysis; polymer degradation; chemical process research. *Mailing Add:* Central Res Dept Exp Sta E I du Pont de Nemours & Co Inc Wilmington DE 19898

NADER, JOHN S(HAHEEN), b Farrell, Pa, Nov 16, 21; m 54; c 6. AIR POLLUTION MEASUREMENT, INSTRUMENT DESIGN. *Educ:* Univ Cincinnati, EE, 44, MS, 53. *Prof Exp:* Proj engr instrumentation, Sperti, Inc, 45; develop engr, Russell R Gannon Co, 45-46; instr physics, Univ Cincinnati, 46-49; physicist measurements & instrumentation, Robert A Taft Sanit Eng Ctr, 49-57, chief instrumentation air pollution eng res, 57-62, chief phys res develop, lab eng & phys sci, 62-64, chief phys measurements, Div Air Pollution, 64-67; chief, Nat Ctr Air Pollution Control, Ohio, 67-70; chief stationary source emissions measurement methods, Optics & Radiation Sect, Nat Environ Res Ctr, Environ Protection Agency, 70-74, chief, Stationary Source Emissions Res Br, Environ Sci Res Lab, 75-79; CONSULT AIR QUALITY MEASUREMENTS, 79- *Mem:* Air Pollution Control Asn; Int Standards Orgn. *Res:* Nuclear physics; air pollution; automation and control instrumentation; aerosol physics. *Mailing Add:* 2336 New Bern Ave Raleigh NC 27610

NADKARNI, MORESHWAR VITHAL, b Bombay, India, July 1, 18; nat US; m 50; c 5. BIOCHEMICAL PHARMACOLOGY. *Educ:* Univ Bombay, BS, 37; Univ Iowa, MS, 47, PhD(pharmaceut chem), 49. *Prof Exp:* Asst res prof pharmacol, George Washington Univ, 54-58; pharmacologist, 58-59, head pharmacol sect, Drug Eval Br, 59-65, dir pharmacol prog, extramural activities, 65-80, CHIEF, EXTRAMURAL RES & RES BR, DEVELOP THERAPEUT PROG, DIV CANCER TREATMENT, NAT CANCER INST, 80- *Concurrent Pos:* Fel, Nat Cancer Inst, 49-51; Am Cancer Soc fel, George Washington Univ, 52-54. *Mem:* Am Chem Soc; Am Pharmaceut Asn; Am Asn Cancer Res; NY Acad Sci. *Res:* Chemotherapy of cancer; pharmacology and toxicology; drug metabolism; isotope tracer techniques. *Mailing Add:* Develop Therapeut Prog Nat Cancer Inst Bethesda MD 20205

NADKARNI, RAMACHANDRA ANAND, b Karwar, India, Oct 28, 38; US citizen; m 70; c 2. ANALYTICAL CHEMISTRY, RADIOCHEMISTRY. *Educ:* Univ Bombay, BSc, 59, MSc, 61, PhD(anal chem), 65. *Prof Exp:* Res assoc radiochem, Univ Ky, 67-70; res officer, Univ Bombay, 70-72; res mgr anal chem, Cornell Univ, 72-78; SR CHEMIST ANAL CHEM, EXXON RES & ENG CO, 78- *Honors & Awards:* Fulbright Award, US Educ Found in India, 67. *Mem:* Am Chem Soc; AAAS; Sigma Xi; Soc Appl Spectros. *Res:* Geochemistry; trace elements in bio-environmental processes; environmental chemistry; coal and shale analysis. *Mailing Add:* Exxon Res & Eng Co PO Box 4255 Baytown TX 77520

NADLER, CHARLES FENGER, b Chicago, Ill, Nov 8, 29; m 53; c 3. INTERNAL MEDICINE, ZOOLOGY. *Educ:* Dartmouth Col, AB, 51; Northwestern Univ, MD, 55. *Prof Exp:* From intern to asst resident med, Barnes Hosp, St Louis, Mo, 55-57 & 59-60; instr, 61-63, assoc, 63-67, asst prof, 67-71, ASSOC PROF MED, MED SCH, NORTHWESTERN UNIV, 71; RES ASSOC, DIV MAMMALS, FIELD MUS NATURAL HIST, 65- *Concurrent Pos:* Fel hemat, Med Ctr, Univ Colo, 60-61; attend physician, Passavant Mem Hosp, Chicago, Ill, 61-72; attend physician, Northwestern Mem Hosp, Chicago, 73-; assoc mammal, Mus Natural Hist, Univ Kans, 73-; activity leader, US-USSR Environ Agreement, 77- *Mem:* Am Fedn Clin Res; Soc Exp Biol & Med; Am Soc Mammal; Soc Syst Zool; Am Col Physicians. *Res:* Hematology; application of cytogenetics and comparative biochemistry of proteins to the evolution of Asian and North American mammals. *Mailing Add:* Dept of Med Northwestern Univ Med Sch Chicago IL 60611

NADLER, GERALD, b Cincinnati, Ohio, Mar 12, 24; m 47; c 3. INDUSTRIAL ENGINEERING. *Educ:* Purdue Univ, BSc, 45, MSc, 46, PhD(indust eng), 49. *Prof Exp:* Asst indust eng, Purdue Univ, 46-48; plant indust engr, Cent Wis Canneries, 48; instr indust eng, Purdue Univ, 48-49; from asst prof to prof, Wash Univ, 49-64, head dept, 55-64; chmn dept, 64-67, 71-75, PROF INDUST ENG, UNIV WIS-MADISON, 64- *Concurrent Pos:* Consult indust engr, 49-; vis prof, Univ Birmingham, Eng, 59, Waseda Univ, Japan, 63-64, Ind Univ, 64, Univ Louvain, Belg, 75 & Technion-Israel Inst Technol, 75-76; vpres gen opers, Artcraft Mfg Co, 56-57; chmd bd, Planning, Design & Improv Methods Group, 66; mem bd dirs, Intertherm Inc, 69-; vis lectr numerous US & foreign univs; planning facilitator, Nat Gypsy Moth Pest Mgt Syst, 77-79. *Honors & Awards:* Gilbreth Medal, 61; Ed Award, Hosp Mgt Mag, 66; Distinguished Eng Alumnus Award, Purdue Univ, 75. *Mem:* AAAS; fel Am Inst Indust Engrs; Am Soc Eng Educ; Inst Mgt Sci; Sigma Xi. *Res:* System design strategies; health care and hospital systems; planning largescale complex systems; engineering concepts for nonengineers; planning and design methods; author or coauthor of numerous publications. *Mailing Add:* Indust Eng Dept Univ of Wis 1513 University Ave Madison WI 53706

NADLER, HENRY LOUIS, b New York, NY, Apr 15, 36; m 57; c 4. PEDIATRICS, HUMAN GENETICS. *Educ:* Colgate Univ, AB, 57; Northwestern Univ, MD, 61; Univ Wis, MS, 65. *Prof Exp:* From intern to resident pediat, Med Ctr, NY Univ, 61-63, chief resident & inst pediat, 63-64; instr, Sch Med, Univ Wis, 64-65; assoc, Med Sch, 65-66, from asst prof to assoc prof, 67-70, PROF PEDIAT, MED SCH & GRAD SCH & CHMN DEPT PEDIAT, MED SCH, NORTHWESTERN UNIV, 70-; HEAD DIV GENETICS, CHILDREN'S MEM HOSP, 69-, CHIEF OF STAFF PEDIAT, 70- *Concurrent Pos:* Res fel pediat, Children's Mem Hosp, Chicago, 64-65. *Honors & Awards:* Irene Heinz Given & John La Porte Given Res Prof Pediat, Children's Mem Hosp, Chicago; E Mead Johnson Award, Am Acad Pediat, 73. *Mem:* Am Soc Clin Invest; Am Soc Human Genetics; Am Pediat Soc; Soc Pediat Res; Soc Exp Biol & Med. *Res:* Human biochemical genetics; chromosomal disorders and inborn errors of metabolism; prenatal detection of genetic diseases. *Mailing Add:* Dept of Pediat Northwestern Univ Sch of Med Evanston IL 60201

NADLER, KENNETH DAVID, b Bronx, NY, Sept 18, 42; m 67. PLANT PHYSIOLOGY, BIOCHEMISTRY. *Educ:* Rensselaer Polytech Inst, BSc, 63; Rockefeller Univ, PhD(life sci), 68. *Prof Exp:* NIH res fel biol, Revelle Col, Univ Calif, San Diego, 68-70; asst prof, 70-77, ASSOC PROF BOT, MICH STATE UNIV, 70- *Concurrent Pos:* Lectr, Univ Calif, San Diego, 68; sabbitical leave, Dept Genetics, John Innes Inst, UK, 79-80. *Mem:* AAAS; Am Soc Microbiol; Am Soc Plant Physiologists. *Res:* Biochemical mechanisms with which subcellular activities are integrated into cellular metabolism; heme formation in legume root nodules and root nodule bacteria; biochemistry of chlorophylls and hemes; control of differentiation of plastids, mitochondria and cells in relation to porphyrin biosynthesis; genetics of the Rhizobilem-legume root rodule symbiosis. *Mailing Add:* Dept of Bot Mich State Univ East Lansing MI 48823

NADLER, MELVIN PHILIP, b Malden, Mass, May 20, 40; m 71. PHYSICAL CHEMISTRY. *Educ:* Northeastern Univ, AB, 63; Cornell Univ, PhD(phys chem), 69. *Prof Exp:* NSF fel under R Weiner, Northeastern Univ, 61-63; res assoc, State Univ NY Binghamton, 68-70; supvr air & water pollution control, Remington Rand Div, Sperry Rand Corp, 71-72; RES CHEMIST, NAVAL WEAPONS CTR, 72- *Mem:* Am Chem Soc. *Res:* Kinetics, spectroscopy and photochemistry of boron systems and flames; infrared emission; combustion of solid propellants. *Mailing Add:* 525 S Sanders Ridgecrest CA 93555

NADLER, NORMAN JACOB, b Montreal, Que, Dec 24, 27; m 53. ENDOCRINOLOGY, ANATOMY. *Educ:* McGill Univ, BSc, 47, MD, CM, 51, PhD(thyroid), 55. *Prof Exp:* Lectr, 57-59, asst prof, 59-64, ASSOC PROF ANAT, McGILL UNIV, 65- *Concurrent Pos:* Consult med, Jewish Gen Hosp, Montreal, 59- *Mem:* Endocrine Soc; Am Asn Anatomists; Am Diabetes Asn; Can Asn Anat. *Res:* Biophysical approach to morphological physiological aspects of thyroid gland. *Mailing Add:* 4141 Sherbrooke West Suite 540 Montreal PQ H3Z 1B8 Can

NADLER, RONALD DAVID, b Newark, NJ, Jan 19, 36; m 79; c 3. ANIMAL BEHAVIOR, PRIMATOLOGY. *Educ:* Univ Calif, Los Angeles, BA, 60, MA, 63, PhD(physiol psychol), 65. *Prof Exp:* USPHS res fels, Oxford Univ, 65-66 & Univ Wash, 66-67; asst prof psychiat, State Univ NY Downstate Med Ctr, 67-71; develop biologist primatol, 71-80, ASSOC RES PROF BEHAV BIOL, YERKES PRIMATE RES CTR, EMORY UNIV, 80- *Concurrent Pos:* State Univ NY Res Found grant, State Univ NY Downstate Med Ctr, 68-70, NSF grant, 69-71, USPHS grants, 69-70 & 71-72; NSF grants, Yerkes Primate Res Ctr, Emory Univ, 71-73 & 71-74; NSF res grant, 75-79 & 80-83. *Mem:* Int Soc Psychoneuroendocrinol; Int Primatol Soc; AAAS; Int Acad Sex Res; Am Soc Primatologists. *Res:* Comparative, developmental research on socio-sexual behavior of the great apes, chimpanzee, gorilla and orang-utan; emphasis is placed on physiological correlates of behavior, especially hormonal. *Mailing Add:* Yerkes Regional Primate Res Ctr Emory Univ Atlanta GA 30322

NADOL, BRONISLAW JOSEPH, JR, b Cambridge, Mass, Oct 2, 43; m 70; c 2. OTOLARYNGOLOGY. *Educ:* Harvard Col, BA, 66; Johns Hopkins Univ, MD, 70; Am Bd Otolaryngol, dipl, 75. *Prof Exp:* Intern surg, Beth Israel Hosp, 70-71, residency surg, 71-72, residency otolaryngol, 72-75; instr, 75-76, asst prof, 76-80, ASSOC PROF OTOLARYNGOL, HARVARD MED SCH, 80- *Concurrent Pos:* Asst surgeon otolaryngol, Mass Eye & Ear Infirmary, 75-80, assoc surgeon, 80- *Mem:* Am Acad Ophthal & Otolaryngol. *Res:* Electron microscopy of the human inner ear; clinical electrocochleography. *Mailing Add:* Mass Eye & Ear Infirmary 243 Charles St Boston MA 02114

NAEGELE, EDWARD WISTER, JR, b Philadelphia, Pa, Sept 30, 23; m 50; c 1. ORGANIC CHEMISTRY. *Educ:* Temple Univ, AB, 48, MA, 50, PhD(chem), 55. *Prof Exp:* Technologist, E I du Pont de Nemours & Co, 55-57; supvr basic res, Acheson Dispersed Pigments Co, 57-58; assoc prof chem, 58-62, PROF CHEM & CHMN DEPT, GROVE CITY COL, 62- *Mem:* AAAS; Am Chem Soc. *Res:* Heterocyclic compounds. *Mailing Add:* Dept of Chem Grove City Col Grove City PA 16127

NAEGER, LEONARD L, b St Louis, Mo, July 19, 41; m 66; c 2. PHARMACOLOGY. *Educ:* St Louis Col Pharm, BS, 63, MS, 65; Univ Fla, PhD(pharmacol), 70. *Prof Exp:* Asst prof, Sch Dent Med, Wash Univ, 72-77; ASST PROF PHARMACOL, ST LOUIS COL PHARM, 70- *Concurrent Pos:* Lectr, Med Ctr, St Louis Univ, 71- *Res:* Ethanol metabolism. *Mailing Add:* Dept of Pharmacol St Louis Col of Pharm St Louis MO 63110

NAESER, CHARLES RUDOLPH, b Mineral Point, Wis, Nov 13, 10; m 36; c 2. INORGANIC CHEMISTRY. *Educ:* Univ Wis, BS, 31; Univ Ill, MS, 33, PhD(inorg chem), 35. *Prof Exp:* Asst gen chem, Univ Ill, 32-35; from instr to asst prof inorg chem, 35-42, from assoc prof to prof chem, 45-76, chmn dept, 48-50, 51-53 & 56-76, EMER PROF CHEM, GEORGE WASHINGTON UNIV, 76- *Concurrent Pos:* Chief, Chem Group, US Geol Surv, 53-56, consult, 56-75; consult, Off Saline Water, 62-72. *Honors & Awards:* Am Inst Chem Honor Award, 62. *Mem:* AAAS; Am Inst Chem; Am Chem Soc; Geochem Soc. *Res:* Inorganic chemistry of rare earths, beryllium, uranium, rhenium and selenium; electro reduction of less common metals; fluoroplatinates; geochemistry; radioactive waste disposal; desalinization. *Mailing Add:* 6654 Van Winkle Dr Falls Church VA 22044

NAESER, CHARLES WILBUR, b Washington, DC, July 2, 40; div; c 2. GEOLOGY. *Educ:* Dartmouth Col, AB, 62, MA, 64; Southern Methodist Univ, PhD(geol), 67. *Prof Exp:* GEOLOGIST, US GEOL SURV, 67- *Concurrent Pos:* Vis prof, Univ Alaska, 72, Univ Wash, 75 & Univ Ariz, 78. *Mem:* Fel Geol Soc Am; Am Geophys Union. *Res:* Geochronology, specifically the use of fission track dating of minerals. *Mailing Add:* US Geol Surv Box 25046 Denver Fed Ctr Stp 424 Denver CO 80225

NAESER, NANCY DEARIEN, b Morgantown, WVa, Apr 15, 44; m 82. FISSION-TRACK DATING. *Educ:* Univ Ariz, BS, 66; Victoria Univ, PhD(geol), 73. *Prof Exp:* Geol field asst & phys sci technician, US Geol Surv, Flagstaff, Ariz, 66; sci ed, New Zealand Dept Sci & Indust Res, Wellington, 74-76; res assoc, Univ Toronto, 76-79; res assoc, 79-81, GEOLOGIST, US GEOL SURV, DENVER, COLO, 81- *Mem:* Geol Soc Am; Am Asn Petrol Geologists; Am Quaternary Asn. *Res:* Fission-track dating applied to geologic studies, including tephrochronology and thermal history of sedimentary basins. *Mailing Add:* Mail Stop 424 US Geol Surv Fed Ctr Denver CO 80225

NAEYE, RICHARD L, b Rochester, NY, Nov 27, 29; m 55; c 3. PATHOLOGY. *Educ:* Colgate Univ, AB, 51; Columbia Univ, MD, 55; Am Bd Path, cert, anat path & clin path. *Prof Exp:* Instr path, Col Physicians & Surgeons, Columbia Univ, 57-58; trainee, Med Col, Univ Vt, 58-60, from asst prof to prof, 60-67; PROF PATH & CHMN DEPT, HERSHEY MED CTR, PA STATE UNIV, 67- *Concurrent Pos:* Marckle scholar, 60-65; asst attend pathologist, Mary Fletcher Hosp, Burlington, Vt, 60-63, assoc attend pathologist, 63-67; mem path A study sect, NIH, 68-72; mem adv bd, Armed Forces Inst Path, 72-76; mem comt epidemiol & vet follow-up, Nat Acad Sci, 72-75; mem, Coun Cardiopulmonary Dis, Am Heart Asn, Inc, 72-; consult, World Health Orgn. *Mem:* Col Am Path; Am Soc Exp Path; Am Soc Clin Path; Int Acad Path. *Res:* Prenatal and neonatal disorders; fetal growth and development; pulmonary vascular disease; sudden infant death syndrome. *Mailing Add:* Dept of Path Pa State Univ Hershey Med Ctr Hershey PA 17033

NAFE, JOHN ELLIOTT, b Seattle, Wash, July 22, 14; m 41; c 2. PHYSICS, GEOPHYSICS. *Educ:* Univ Mich, BS, 38; Wash Univ, MS, 40; Columbia Univ, PhD(physics), 48. *Prof Exp:* Asst physics, Wash Univ, 38-39; asst, Columbia Univ, 40-41, instr, 46-49; asst prof, Univ Minn, 49-51; dir res, Hudson Lab, 51-53, res assoc, Lamont-Doherty Geol Observ, 53-55, adj assoc prof geophys, 55-58, chmn dept geol, 62-65, prof, 58-80, EMER PROF GEOPHYS, LAMONT-DOHERTY GEOL OBSERV, COLUMBIA UNIV, 80- *Concurrent Pos:* Vis fel, Cambridge Univ, 71-72; hon prof, Dept Geophys & Astron, Univ BC, Can, 80- *Mem:* Fel AAAS; fel Am Geophys Union; fel

Am Phys Soc; fel Geol Soc Am; Seismol Soc Am. *Res:* Atomic beams; hyperfine structure of deuterium and hydrogen; seismology; marine geophysics; underwater sound. *Mailing Add:* 5775 Toronto Rd Vancouver BC V6T 1X4 Can

NAFF, JOHN DAVIS, b Atlanta, Ga, Nov 12, 18; m 42; c 5. GEOLOGY. *Educ:* Univ Ala, AB, 39, MA, 40; Univ Kans, PhD, 60. *Prof Exp:* Assoc prof, 50-65, PROF GEOL, OKLA STATE UNIV, 65- *Concurrent Pos:* Staff geologist, Juneau Icefield Res Prog, NSF lect series; ed, Geol Sect, Okla Acad Sci, 68- *Mem:* Soc Econ Paleont & Mineral; Am Asn Petrol Geologists; Nat Asn Geol Teachers (secy). *Res:* Invertebrate paleontology; stratigraphy; mountaineering; photography; electronics; miniaturization and packaging of equipment. *Mailing Add:* Dept of Geol Okla State Univ Stillwater OK 74074

NAFF, MARION BENTON, b Lexington, Ky, Mar 23, 18; m 46. ORGANIC CHEMISTRY. *Educ:* Univ Ky, BS, 41, MS, 46; Ore State Col, PhD(org chem), 50. *Prof Exp:* Asst prof chem, Western Carolina State Col, 50-51 & Bowling Green State Univ, 51-55; assoc prof, Loyola Univ, La, 55-58 & Dickinson Col, 58-66; CHEMIST, DRUG SYNTHESIS & CHEM NAT CANCER INST, 66- *Concurrent Pos:* Vis assoc prof chem, Brown Univ, 64-65. *Mem:* Fel AAAS; Am Chem Soc. *Res:* Synthesis of heterocyclics; acetylenic chemistry; chemical kinetics; medicinal chemistry; organic synthesis and analysis; instrumentation. *Mailing Add:* Drug Synthesis & Chem Nat Cancer Inst NIH Bethesda MD 20814

NAFIE, LAURENCE ALLEN, b Detroit, Mich, Aug 9, 45; m 68; c 2. PHYSICAL CHEMISTRY. *Educ:* Univ Minn, Minneapolis, BChem, 67; Univ Ore, MS, 69, PhD(chem), 73. *Prof Exp:* Sci & eng asst nuclear physics, Nuclear Effects Lab, Edgewood Arsenal, Md, 69-71; res assoc infrared circular dichroism, Univ Southern Calif, 73-75; asst prof, 75-79, ASSOC PROF PHYS CHEM, SYRACUSE UNIV, 79- *Concurrent Pos:* Alfred P Sloan fel, 78-82. *Honors & Awards:* Coblentz Soc Award, 81. *Mem:* Am Chem Soc; Optical Soc Am. *Res:* Vibrational optical activity, including experimental and theoretical research in vibrational circular dichroism and Raman circular intensity differential scattering; resonance Raman spectroscopy and the theory of Raman line shapes; fourier transform infrared spectroscopy. *Mailing Add:* Dept Chem Syracuse Univ Syracuse NY 13210

NAFISSI-VARCHEI, MOHAMMAD MEHDI, b Arak, Iran, Sept 23, 36; m 69; c 1. ORGANIC CHEMISTRY. *Educ:* Tehran Univ, Iran, Licentiate, 60; Miami Univ, Ohio, MSc, 66; Mass Inst Technol, PhD(org chem), 69. *Prof Exp:* Instr chem, Tehran Univ, 60-65; res assoc spectros, Mass Inst Technol, 69-70; sr scientist med chem, 71-74, PRIN SCIENTIST, SCHERING CORP, 74- *Mem:* Am Chem Soc; Chem Soc Eng. *Res:* Medicinal chemistry; anti-infective agents. *Mailing Add:* Schering Corp 60 Orange St Bloomfield NJ 07003

NAFOOSI, A AZIZ, b Mosul, Iraq, June 2, 22; m 50; c 5. MATHEMATICS. *Educ:* Univ Baghdad, BA, 44; Univ Mich, MA, 50; Univ Colo, PhD(math), 60. *Prof Exp:* High sch teacher, Iraq, 44-48; instr, Higher Teachers Col, 50-56; instr, Univ Colo, 56-59; asst prof, Kans State Col, 59-62; assoc prof, Tulsa, 62-63; design specialist, Hayes Int Corp, 63-65, eng specialist, 65-67; PROF MATH, CHICAGO STATE UNIV, 67- *Mem:* Am Math Soc; Opers Res Soc Am; Iraq Math Soc. *Res:* Pure mathematics, particularly the theory of numbers and nonlinear differential equations; applied mathematics; guidance; optimization technique; application of calculus of variation for obtaining optimum trajectory equations; operation research, especially mathematical models for lethal area and related areas of research. *Mailing Add:* Dept of Math Chicago State Univ Chicago IL 60628

NAFPAKTITIS, BASIL G, b Athens, Greece, Dec 23, 29; m 64; c 2. BIOLOGY. *Educ:* Am Univ Beirut, BSc, 62, MS, 63; Harvard Univ, PhD(biol), 69. *Prof Exp:* Asst prof, 67-71, assoc prof, 71-81, PROF BIOL, UNIV SOUTHERN CALIF, 81- *Mem:* Am Soc Ichthyologists & Herpetologists; Am Soc Zoologists; Soc Syst Zool. *Res:* Ichthyology, particularly distribution, systematics and ecology of deep-sea fishes; bioluminescence. *Mailing Add:* Dept of Biol Sci Univ of Southern Calif Los Angeles CA 90007

NAFTOLIN, FREDERICK, b New York, NY, Apr 7, 36; m 57; c 2. OBSTETRICS & GYNECOLOGY, ENDOCRINOLOGY. *Educ:* Univ Calif, Berkeley, BA, 58, San Francisco, MS, 61; Oxford Univ, Eng, DPhil(neuroendocrinol), 70. *Prof Exp:* Asst chief gynec serv, USPHS Hosp, Seattle, Wash, 66-68; from asst prof to assoc prof obstet & gynecol, Univ Calif, San Diego, 70-73; assoc prof, Harvard Med Sch, 73-75; prof & chmn, Fac Med, McGill Univ, 75-78; PROF & CHMN OBSTET & GYNECOL, SCH MED, YALE UNIV, 78- *Concurrent Pos:* Res fel, Univ Wash, 66-68, NIH, Oxford Univ, 68-70; chief obstet & gynecol, Royal Victoria Hosp, 75-78, Yale-New Haven Hosp, 78- *Mem:* Endocrine Soc; Soc Gynecol Invest; Soc Psychoneuroendocrinol; Int Soc Neuroendocrinol; Am Soc Androl. *Res:* Investigation of the relationship of hormones to reproductive function; brain/pituitary-sex steroid interaction; molecular biology; cell biology; infestility. *Mailing Add:* Dept Obstet & Gynecol Sch Med Yale Univ 333 Cedar St Box 3333 New Haven CT 06510

NAFUS, DONALD MARVIN, entomology, ecology, see previous edition

NAFZIGER, RALPH HAMILTON, b Minneapolis, Minn, Aug 9, 37. CHEMICAL METALLURGY. *Educ:* Univ Wis, BS, 60; Pa State Univ, PhD(geochem), 66. *Prof Exp:* Geol asst, US Geol Surv, 63; res assoc geochem, Pa State Univ, 66-67; res chemist, 67-79, RES SUPVR, US BUR MINES, 79- *Concurrent Pos:* Mem electroslag & plasma arc melting, Nat Mat Adv Bd, 74-75. *Mem:* Mineral Soc Am; Am Inst Mining & Metall Engrs; Am Soc Metals. *Res:* Thermochemistry of metal-nonmetal systems; electroslag melting of metals; electric furnace smelting of lower-grade titaniferous, chromite and ferrous ores. *Mailing Add:* US Bur of Mines PO Box 70 Albany OR 97321

NAGAI, JIRO, b Nagano, Japan, Sept 26, 27; Can citizen; m 59; c 2. ANIMAL BREEDING. *Educ:* Univ Tokyo, BA, 52, DAgr(animal breeding), 61. *Prof Exp:* Instr animal breeding, Univ Tokyo, 55-65; RES SCIENTIST ANIMAL GENETICS, AGR CAN, 65- *Concurrent Pos:* Vis prof, NC State Univ, 74-75. *Mem:* Genetics Soc Can; Genetics Soc Am; Can Asn Lab Animal Sci; Japan Exp Animal Res Asn; Am Soc Animal Sci. *Res:* Animal breeding through experiments using mice; selection for nursing ability, mature weight and index combining the two, and long-term performance of crosses from the selected lines of mice. *Mailing Add:* 28 Kinnear St Ottawa ON K1A 3R6 Can

NAGAI, TOSHIO, b Osaka, Japan, Jan 23, 22; m 48; c 3. PHYSIOLOGY, ZOOLOGY. *Educ:* Univ Tokyo, MEng, 45, MSc, 50, DSc(physiol), 60. *Prof Exp:* Asst prof zool & physiol, Natural Sci Div, Int Christian Univ, Tokyo, 58-63, prof, 63-67; RES SCIENTIST, RES INST, CAN DEPT AGR, 67- *Concurrent Pos:* Fulbright travel grant, 60-62; res assoc, Dept Physiol, Univ Ill, 60-62, vis scientist, 64-67; hon lectr, Univ Western Ont, 71- *Mem:* AAAS; Am Inst Biol Sci; NY Acad Sci; Am Soc Zool; Zool Soc Japan. *Res:* Electrophysiological study of smooth muscle; neuromuscular activity of intestinal muscle; mode of action of insect pheromone. *Mailing Add:* Univ Sub PO Can Dept Agr London ON N6A 5B7 Can

NAGAMATSU, HENRY T, b Garden Grove, Calif, Feb 13, 16; m 42; c 2. FLUID PHYSICS, PLASMA PHYSICS. *Educ:* Calif Inst Technol, BS, 38 & 39, MS, 40, PhD(aeronaut), 49. *Prof Exp:* Asst, Calif Inst Technol, 38-41; theoret aerodynamicist, Douglas Aircraft Co, 41-42; theoret aerodynamicist, Curtiss-Wright Aircraft Corp, 42-43, head aeronaut res, Res Lab, 43-46; asst sect head, Jet Propulsion Lab, Calif Inst Technol, 46-49, sr res fel & dir hypersonic res, Aeronaut Dept, 49-55; res assoc, Res & Develop Ctr, Gen Elec Co, 55-78; res prof, 78-80, PROF AERONAUT ENG, RENSSELAER POLYTECH INST, 80- *Concurrent Pos:* Consult, US Naval Ord Test Sta, 49-56, Rand Corp, 50-59, Atlas Proj, Gen Dynamics/Convair, 50-53, Midwest Res Inst, 52-55, Off Sci Res, US Dept Air Force, 57- & Aeronaut Lab, Wright-Patterson AFB, 60-; adj prof, Rensselaer Polytech Inst, 56-64; mem, Eng Noise Subcomt, Nat Acad Sci, 68-71. *Mem:* AAAS; fel Am Phys Soc; fel Am Inst Aeronaut & Astronaut; NY Acad Sci. *Res:* High temperature gas dynamics associated with intercontinental ballistic missiles, satellites and space vehicles; applied mathematics; magnetohydrodynamics; high temperature physics; physical chemistry; fluid mechanics; rockets and missiles; jet noise and acoustics; transonic flows; arc physics. *Mailing Add:* 1046 Cornelius Ave Schenectady NY 12309

NAGASAWA, HERBERT TSUKASA, b Hilo, Hawaii, May 31, 27; m 51; c 2. MEDICINAL CHEMISTRY. *Educ:* Western Reserve Univ, BS, 50; Univ Minn, PhD(org chem), 55. *Prof Exp:* Fel biochem, Univ Minn, 55-57; sr chemist, Radioisotope Serv, 57-61, sr scientist, Lab Cancer Res, 61, PRIN SCIENTIST, MED RES LABS, VET ADMIN HOSP, MINNEAPOLIS, 61- *Concurrent Pos:* From asst prof to assoc prof, Col Pharm, Univ Minn, 59-72, prof, 73-; assoc ed, J Med Chem, 72-, actg ed, 73. *Mem:* AAAS; Am Chem Soc; Am Asn Cancer Res; NY Acad Sci; Soc Toxicol. *Res:* Synthesis on rational biochemical basis of cytotoxic agents and of amino acid antimetabolites, and evaluation of their biochemical pharmacology. *Mailing Add:* Vet Admin Hosp 54th St & 48th Ave S Minneapolis MN 55417

NAGATANI, KUNIO, b Manchuria, Jan 23, 36; Japanese citizen; m 59; c 2. NUCLEAR PHYSICS. *Educ:* Tohoku Univ, BS, 58, MS, 60; Yale Univ, PhD(physics), 65. *Prof Exp:* Res assoc physics, Mass Inst Technol, 65-66; res fel physics, Calif Inst Technol, 67-68; from asst physicist to physicist, Brookhaven Nat Lab, 68-72; assoc prof, 72-79, PROF PHYSICS, TEX A&M UNIV, 79- *Concurrent Pos:* Physicist, Dept Physics, Ctr Atomic Studies, Saclay, France, 77- *Mem:* Am Phys Soc; Sigma Xi. *Res:* Experimental nuclear physics, especially heavy ion reaction studies. *Mailing Add:* Cyclotron Inst Tex A&M Univ College Station TX 77843

NAGEL, CHARLES WILLIAM, b St Helena, Calif, Dec 8, 26; m 51; c 5. FOOD SCIENCE. *Educ:* Univ Calif, BA, 50, PhD(microbiol), 60. *Prof Exp:* Bacteriologist, US Dept War, Dugway Proving Grounds, Utah, 51-52; lab technician food technol, Univ Calif, 52-54; sr lab technician & coop agt food technol & preserv of refrig poultry, USDA & Univ Calif, 54-60; from asst prof to prof fruit & veg processing, Wash State Univ, 60-71; res dir, United Vintners Inc, Calif, 71-73; actg chmn dept, 78-79, PROF FOOD SCI & TECHNOL, WASH STATE UNIV, 73- *Concurrent Pos:* Chmn food sci exec comt, Wash State Univ, 64-68. *Mem:* Inst Food Technologists; Am Soc Enol; Sigma Xi (secy-treas, 75-77). *Res:* Sanitation; fruit and vegetable products processing; pectic enzymes of bacteria; food fermentations; enology; phenolic compounds. *Mailing Add:* Dept of Food Sci & Technol Wash State Univ Pullman WA 99164

NAGEL, DONALD LEWIS, b Blue Island, Ill, May 24, 41; m 63; c 1. CHEMICAL CARCINOGENESIS, ORGANIC CHEMISTRY. *Educ:* Knox Col, BA, 67; Univ Nebr-Lincoln, PhD(org chem), 71. *Prof Exp:* Chemist, Libby, McNeill & Libby, 63-67; asst org chem, Univ Nebr-Lincoln, 67-71; from instr to asst prof, 71-79, ASSOC PROF CANCER, EPPLEY INST RES CANCER, UNIV NEBR MED CTR, OMAHA, 79- *Mem:* Am Chem Soc; Sigma Xi. *Res:* Chemical carcinogenesis with special emphasis on problems relating to mechanisms of action, organic chemical applications, nuclear magnetic resonance and mass spectrometry. *Mailing Add:* Eppley Inst Res Cancer Univ Nebr Med Ctr Omaha NE 68105

NAGEL, EDGAR HERBERT, b San Diego, Calif, Mar 24, 38; m 69; c 2. ANALYTICAL CHEMISTRY. *Educ:* Valparaiso Univ, BS, 60; Northwestern Univ, PhD(chem), 65. *Prof Exp:* From instr to asst prof, 63-69, assoc prof, 69-76, PROF CHEM, VALPARAISO UNIV, 76- *Concurrent Pos:* Consult, Argonne Nat Lab, 65-79. *Mem:* Am Chem Soc. *Res:* Gas chromatography; electrochemistry; computer applications in teaching. *Mailing Add:* Dept Chem Valparaiso Univ Valparaiso IN 46383

NAGEL, ERNEST, b Novemesto, Czech, Nov 16, 01; nat US; m 35; c 2. PHILOSOPHY OF SCIENCE. *Educ:* City Col New York, BS, 23; Columbia Univ, AM, 25, PhD, 31. *Hon Degrees:* LHD, Bard Col, 64 & City Univ New York, 72; DSc, Brandeis Univ, 65; DLitt, Rutgers Univ, 67, Case Western Reserve Univ, 70 & Columbia Univ, 71. *Prof Exp:* Teacher pub schs, New York, 23-29; instr philos, City Col New York, 30-31; from instr to prof, 31-55, John Dewey prof, 55-66, univ prof, 67-70, EMER PROF PHILOS, COLUMBIA UNIV, 70- *Concurrent Pos:* Guggenheim fels, 34-35 & 50-51; ed, J Symbolic Logic, 39-45, J Philos, 40-56 & Philos of Sci, 56-59; chmn, Conf Methods Philos Sci, 46-47; fel, Ctr Advan Study Behav Sci, 59-60. *Mem:* Nat Acad Sci; fel AAAS (vpres, Sect L, 51, 73); fel Am Acad Arts & Sci; fel Am Philos Soc; Asn Symbolic Logic (pres, 47-49). *Res:* Logic of measurements; sovereign reason; logic without metaphysics. *Mailing Add:* 25 Claremont Ave New York NY 10027

NAGEL, EUGENE L, b Quincy, Ill, Aug 12, 24; c 3. ANESTHESIOLOGY. *Educ:* Cornell Univ, BEE, 49; Wash Univ, MD, 59. *Prof Exp:* Intern, St Luke's Hosp, St Louis, Mo, 59-60; resident anesthesiol, Presby Hosp, New York, 60-62; from asst prof to assoc prof, Sch Med, Univ Miami, 65-73; prof anesthesiol, Univ Calif, Los Angeles, 74-77; PROF ANESTHESIOL & CHMN DEPT, JOHNS HOPKINS UNIV SCH MED, 77- *Concurrent Pos:* Attend physician, Jackson Mem Hosp, Miami, Fla, 63-74, clin dir anesthesiol, 66-74; consult, Am Heart Asn, 69, Nat Registry of Emergency Med Technicians, 71-, Am Col Surgeons, Robert Wood Johnson Found & Bur Med Serv, Dept Health, Educ & Welfare, 72-; chmn sect clin care, Am Soc Anesthesiol, 73-74; chmn comn emergency med serv, AMA, 74- *Mem:* AMA; Am Physiol Soc; Am Soc Anesthesiol; Am Col Cardiol; Soc Critical Care Med. *Res:* Emergency care; telemetry; sudden cardiac death. *Mailing Add:* Dept of Anesthes Johns Hopkins Univ Sch of Med Baltimore MD 21205

NAGEL, FRITZ JOHN, b Ger, Oct 20, 19; nat US; m 53; c 3. ORGANIC CHEMISTRY. *Educ:* Univ Notre Dame, BSChE, 41, MS, 42. *Prof Exp:* Engr mat, Gen Elec Co, 50-52; tech dir, Capac Plastics, Inc, 52-53; dir res, Congoleum-Nairn, Inc, 53-56; vpres, Polymer Processes, Inc, 56-68; res & develop mgr, Signal Oil & Gas Co, 68-70; VPRES, CHAPMAN CHEM CO, 70- *Concurrent Pos:* Res engr, Res Labs, Westinghouse Elec Corp, 43-68. *Mem:* Am Chem Soc. *Res:* High polymers; laminates; insulating varnishes; adhesives; protective coatings; plastics; electrical insulation; fungicides. *Mailing Add:* 1264 E Massey Rd Memphis TN 38138

NAGEL, G(EORGE) W(OOD), b Pittsburgh, Pa, Jan 28, 15; m 40; c 5. ELECTRONICS. *Educ:* Carnegie Inst Technol, BS, 36; Univ Pittsburgh, MS, 41. *Prof Exp:* Res engr electronics, Res Labs, 36-38, design engr, Radio Div, 39-46, res engr electronics, 46-52, adv engr, 52-55, new prod, 55-62 & appl physics, 62-65, ADV ENGR, SOLID STATE APPLNS, WESTINGHOUSE ELEC CORP, 65- *Res:* Television; pulse and frequency modulation radar; industrial electronics; military vehicle guidance; document scanners. *Mailing Add:* 234 Cascade Rd Pittsburgh PA 15221

NAGEL, GLENN M, b Blue Island, Ill, Apr 16, 44; m 66. BIOCHEMISTRY. *Educ:* Knox Col, BA, 66; Univ Ill, PhD(biol chem), 71. *Prof Exp:* Scholar molecular biol & biochem, Univ Calif, Berkeley, 70-72; asst prof chem & molecular biol, 72-76, ASSOC PROF CHEM & MOLECULAR BIOL, CALIF STATE UNIV, FULLERTON, 76- *Concurrent Pos:* NIH res fel, 70-72. *Mem:* Am Chem Soc. *Res:* Structure and function of oligomeric enzymes; metabolic control; specific interactions between proteins and nucleic acids. *Mailing Add:* Dept of Chem Calif State Univ Fullerton CA 92634

NAGEL, HAROLD GEORGE, b Natoma, Kans, May 17, 40; m 69. ECOLOGY, ENTOMOLOGY. *Educ:* Ft Hays Kans State Col, BS, 62, MS, 64, Kans State Univ, PhD(entom), 69. *Prof Exp:* Instr biol, Ft Hays Kans State Col, 64-65; res asst entom, Kans State Univ, 66-69; PROF BIOL, KEARNEY STATE COL, 69- *Mem:* Central States Entom Soc; Am Water Resources Asn; NAm Benthol Soc; Mosquito Control Asn. *Res:* Prairie plant insect interrelationships; ant ecology. *Mailing Add:* Dept of Biol Kearney State Col Kearney NE 68847

NAGEL, RONALD LAFUENTE, b Santiago, Chile, Jan 18, 36; US citizen; m 60; c 3. HEMATOLOGY. *Educ:* Univ Chile, MD, 60. *Prof Exp:* Asst resident, Hosp Salvador, Sch Med, Univ Chile, 60-63; int fel, NIH, 63-64; res fel, 64-67, assoc med, 67-69, from asst prof to assoc prof, 69-78, PROF MED, ALBERT EINSTEIN COL MED, 78- *Concurrent Pos:* Mem, Exec Comt, Hemolytic Anemia Study Group, 74- *Honors & Awards:* Award in Black, Found Res & Educ Sickle Cell Dis, 73. *Mem:* Am Soc Clin Invest; Am Soc Biol Chemists; Am Soc Hemat; Int Soc Hemat. *Res:* The molecular, cellular and clinical aspects of sickle cell anemia and other hemoglobinopathies; the structural and functional relationships in hemoglobin. *Mailing Add:* Dept of Med 1300 Morris Park Ave Albert Einstein Col of Med Bronx NY 10461

NAGEL, SIDNEY ROBERT, b New York, NY, Sept 28, 48. SOLID STATE PHYSICS. *Educ:* Columbia Univ, BA, 69; Princeton Univ, MA, 71, PhD(physics), 74. *Prof Exp:* Res assoc solid state physics, div eng, Brown Univ, 74-76; asst prof, 76-81, ASSOC PROF, JAMES FRANCK INST & DEPT PHYSICS, UNIV CHICAGO, 81- *Mem:* Am Phys Soc. *Res:* Electronic structure of metals and alloys; transport in metals; amorphous materials. *Mailing Add:* James Franck Inst Univ of Chicago Chicago IL 60637

NAGEL, TERRY MARVIN, b Rochester, Minn, Mar 25, 43. INORGANIC CHEMISTRY, PHYSICAL CHEMISTRY. *Educ:* Macalester Col, BA, 65; Univ Minn, Minneapolis, PhD(chem), 70. *Prof Exp:* Asst prof chem, Monmouth Col, 70-74; asst prof, Kalamazoo Col, 74-75; asst prof chem, Lakeland Col, 75-80; MEM FAC, CHEM DEPT, COL IDAHO, 80- *Mem:* Am Chem Soc. *Res:* Mechanisms of electron-transfer reactions. *Mailing Add:* Chem Dept Col Idaho Caldwell ID 83605

NAGEL, THEODORE J, b Andes, NY, 1913. ELECTRICAL ENGINEERING. *Educ:* Columbia Univ, BA, 32, MSEE, 34. *Prof Exp:* Mem staff, 39-75, SR EXEC V PRES, AM ELEC POWER SERV CORP, 75- *Mem:* Nat Acad Eng; fel Inst Elec & Electronics Engrs. *Res:* Future electrical power demands and necessary power supply facilities for meeting such demands. *Mailing Add:* Am Elec Power Serv Corp 2 Broadway New York NY 10004

NAGELBERG, ALAN SCOTT, b Philadelphia, Pa, Dec 1, 51. CORROSION SCIENCE. *Educ:* Univ Pa, BS, 73, PhD(mat sci), 78. *Prof Exp:* MEM TECH STAFF, SANDIA NAT LAB, LIVERMORE, 78- *Mem:* Electrochem Soc; Am Inst Mining, Metall & Petrol Engrs; Nat Asn Corrosion Engrs. *Res:* Interactions of metals and other structural materials with their environment; development of new techniques to analyse these events. *Mailing Add:* Div 8313 Sandia Nat Lab Livermore CA 94550

NAGELE, ROBERT GEORGE, b Philadelphia, Pa, Nov 4, 53; m 75; c 2. MOLECULAR BIOLOGY. *Educ:* Rutgers Univ, BA, 75, MS, 77, PhD(zool), 80. *Prof Exp:* FEL HUMAN HISTOL, RUTGERS MED SCH, 80- *Concurrent Pos:* Adj fac mem, Rutgers Grad Sch, 81- *Res:* The early development of the central nervous system; the mechano-chemical basis of nonmuscle cell motility; the role of cytoplasmic contractile elements in nerve growth and axoplastic transport. *Mailing Add:* Dept Anat Rutgers Med Sch Univ Med & Dent Piscataway NJ 08854

NAGELL, RAYMOND H, b Rochester, NY, Apr 10, 27; m 49; c 1. GEOLOGY. *Educ:* Univ Rochester, BS, 51, MA, 52; Stanford Univ, PhD(geol), 58. *Prof Exp:* Geologist, Cerro Corp, 52-55 & Cia Minera Cuprum, 56-57; chief geologist, Industria e Comercio de Minerios SAm, 57-61; geologist, Shenon & Full, 61-62 & US Geol Surv, 63-70; geologist, 70-76, GEOLOGIST COAL INVESTS, BETHLEHEM STEEL 76- *Concurrent Pos:* Tech consult, Industria e Comercio de Minerios, SAm, 72-76. *Mem:* Soc Econ Geol; Geol Soc Am; Am Inst Mining, Metall & Petrol Engrs; Brazilian Geol Soc. *Res:* Economic geology; ore deposits. *Mailing Add:* Geol Dept Bethlehem Steel Corp Bethlehem PA 18016

NAGER, GEORGE THEODORE, b Zurich, Switz, Dec 1, 17; m 50; c 2. OTOLARYNGOLOGY. *Educ:* Zurich Univ, MD, 47; Swiss Bd Otolaryngol, dipl, 54; Am Bd Otolaryngol, dipl, 59. *Prof Exp:* PROF LARYNGOL & OTOL, SCH MED, JOHNS HOPKINS UNIV, 68-, CHMN DEPT, 70-, CHIEF OTOL, JOHNS HOPKINS HOSP, 70- *Concurrent Pos:* Consult Baltimore City Hosps, Greater Baltimore Med Ctr, Good Samaritan Hosp & USPHS Hosp, Baltimore. *Honors & Awards:* Sir Win Wilde Medal, 80. *Mem:* Am Acad Ophthal & Otolaryngol; Am Col Surg; Am Laryngol, Rhinol & Otol Soc; Am Otol Soc; hon mem Egyptian & Irish Otol Soc. *Res:* Monographs, chapters and numerous articles concerned with the clinical, radiological and pathological aspects of diseases, tumors, malformations and trauma involving the ear. *Mailing Add:* Dept Laryngol & Otol Johns Hopkins Univ Sch Med Baltimore MD 21205

NAGER, URS FELIX, b Zurich, Switz, May 15, 22; nat US; m 51; c 3. ORGANIC CHEMISTRY, BIOCHEMISTRY. *Educ:* Swiss Fed Inst Technol, Chem Eng, 45, PhD(org chem), 49. *Prof Exp:* Res biochemist, Com Solvents Corp, Ind, 59-52; sr res chemist, Burke Res Co, Mich, 52-58; res assoc, Squibb Inst Med Res, 58-60, res supvr, 60-69, ASST DIR, SQUIBB CORP, 69- *Mem:* Am Chem Soc; NY Acad Sci; Swiss Chem Soc. *Res:* Antibiotics; enzymes; steroids; designed experimentation. *Mailing Add:* Bunkerhill Rd RD 1 Princeton NJ 08540

NAGERA, HUMBERTO, b Havana, Cuba, May 23, 27; Brit citizen; m 52; c 3. PSYCHIATRY, PSYCHOANALYSIS. *Educ:* Maristas Col, BS, 45; Havana Univ, MD, 52. *Prof Exp:* Mem staff, Hampstead Clin, London, 58-68; prof psychiat, 68-73, prof child psychiat & chief youth serv, 73-79, dir child psychoanal study prog, 68-79, CLIN PROF PSYCHIAT, UNIV MICH, 79-; TRAINING PSYCHOANALYST, MICH PSYCHOANAL INST, 68- *Mem:* Brit Psychoanal Soc; Am Psychoanal Asn; Int Psychoanal Asn; Asn Prof Child Psychiatrists. *Res:* Child development and psychopathology. *Mailing Add:* Children's Psychiat Hosp Ann Arbor MI 48104

NAGHDI, P(AUL) M(ANSOUR), b Iran, Mar 29, 24; nat US; m 47; c 3. MECHANICS. *Educ:* Cornell Univ, BS, 46; Univ Mich, MS, 48, PhD(eng mech), 51. *Prof Exp:* From instr to prof eng mech, Univ Mich, 49-58; res prof, Miller Inst, 63-64 & 71-72, chmn div appl mech, 64-69, PROF ENG SCI, UNIV CALIF, BERKELEY, 58- *Concurrent Pos:* Mem adv comt, Sch Math Study Group, NSF, 58-64; Guggenheim fel, 58; ed, Proc, US Nat Cong Appl Mech, 54; mem, US Nat Comt Theoret & Appl Mech, 72-, chmn, 78-80. *Honors & Awards:* George Westinghouse Award, Am Soc Eng Educ, 62; Timoshenko Medal, Am Soc Mech Engrs, 80. *Mem:* Am Soc Mech Engrs; Acoust Soc Am; Am Soc Eng Educ; Soc Rheol; Soc Eng Sci. *Res:* Continuum mechanics; theory of elasticity; elastic shells and plates; theory of plasticity. *Mailing Add:* Dept of Mech Eng Etcheverry Hall Univ of Calif Berkeley CA 94720

NAGI, ANTERDHYAN SINGH, b Lahore, India, Apr 1, 33; Can citizen; m 64; c 2. THEORETICAL PHYSICS. *Educ:* Panjab Univ, India, BSc Hons, 56, MSc, 57; Univ Delhi, PhD(physics), 61. *Prof Exp:* From asst prof to assoc prof, 67-78, PROF PHYSICS, UNIV WATERLOO, 78- *Concurrent Pos:* Alexander Von Humboldt fel, Inst Theoret Physics, Univ Frankfurt, 70; Nat Res Coun Can grant, 67-79; Nat Sci & Eng Res Coun Can grant, 79- *Mem:* Can Asn Physicists; Am Phys Soc. *Res:* Superfluid liquid 3He and liquid 4He; superconductivity; solid state physics. *Mailing Add:* Physics Dept Univ of Waterloo Waterloo ON N2L 3G1 Can

NAGIN, DANIEL STEVEN, b Philadelphia, Pa, Nov 29, 48; m 72. STATISTICAL ANALYSIS. *Educ:* Carnegie-Mellon Univ, BS & MS, 71, PhD(urban & pub affairs), 75. *Prof Exp:* Systs analyst health, 71-72, RES ASSOC URBAN & PUB AFFAIRS, CARNEGIE-MELLON UNIV, 74-, ASST PROF TRANSP, 75- *Concurrent Pos:* Prin staff mem panel on deterrence & incapacitation, Nat Acad Sci, 75- *Res:* Determining the deterrent effects of criminal sanctions; factors which influence an individual's choice among alternative transportation modes and alternative sources for receiving primary care. *Mailing Add:* Sch of Urban & Pub Affairs Carnegie-Mellon Univ Pittsburgh PA 14213

NAGLE, BARBARA TOMASSONE, b Philadelphia, Pa, Dec 8, 47; m 72. PHARMACOLOGY. *Educ:* Drexel Univ, BS, 70; Hahnemann Med Sch, MS, 72, PhD(pharmacol), 75. *Prof Exp:* Res technician pharmacol clin lab, Hahnemann Med Col, 70-72; res, Wills Eye Res Inst, 75-76; ASST PROF PHARMACOL & PHYSIOL, PHILADELPHIA COL OSTEOP MED, 76- *Concurrent Pos:* Investr, Fight for Sight Inc grant, Wills Eye Res Inst, 77-78. *Mem:* NY Acad Sci; Am Physiol Soc; Sigma Xi; AAAS. *Res:* Pharmacokinetics of systemically administered drugs within special tissues of the body such as aqueous humor within the eye and parotid salivary secretions. *Mailing Add:* Dept of Pharmacol & Physiol 4150 City Line Ave Philadelphia PA 19131

NAGLE, DARRAGH (EDMUND), b New York, NY, Feb 25, 19; m 49; c 3. PHYSICS. *Educ:* Calif Inst Technol, BS, 40; Columbia Univ, AM, 42; Mass Inst Technol, PhD(physics), 47. *Prof Exp:* Lectr, Columbia Univ, 41-42; res assoc, Metall Lab, Univ Chicago, 43; group leader, Argonne Nat Lab, 43-44; asst group leader, Los Alamos Sci Lab, 44-45; res assoc, Mass Inst Technol, 45-47, instr, 47-48; Fulbright fel, Cambridge Univ, 48-49; asst prof physics, Univ Chicago, 49-55; mem staff, 55-62, group leader, 62-65, assoc div leader, 65-68, ALT DIV LEADER MEDIUM ENERGY PHYSICS, LOS ALAMOS NAT LAB, 68- *Concurrent Pos:* Guggenheim fel, 53; mem, Stanford Linear Accelerator Policy Bd, 70-73 & Bates Linac Prog Comt, Mass Inst Technol, 73- *Mem:* Fel Am Phys Soc. *Res:* Physics of particles; nuclear physics; accelerator design; plasma physics. *Mailing Add:* Los Alamos Nat Lab Los Alamos NM 87545

NAGLE, DENNIS CHARLES, b Dolgeville, NY, Jan 13, 45; m 69; c 5. CARBON TECHNOLOGY. *Educ:* Alfred Univ, BS, 67; Pa State Univ, PhD(mats sci), 72. *Prof Exp:* Sr engr, Pratt & Whitney Aircraft, 72-76; MGR, RES & DEVELOP, MARTIN MARIETTA CORP, 76- *Res:* Characterization of pyrolytic graphities; development of carbon and graphite materials for fuel cell and alumunium reduction cell applications; development of refractory materials for steel making vesels. *Mailing Add:* 6618 Hunters Wood Cir Catonsville MD 21228

NAGLE, FRANCIS J, b Lynn, Mass, July 1, 24; m 60; c 11. EXERCISE PHYSIOLOGY, CARDIOVASCULAR PHYSIOLOGY. *Educ:* Univ Nebr, BS, 51, MA, 53; Boston Univ, EdD(health, phys educ), 59; Univ Okla, PhD(physiol), 66. *Prof Exp:* Asst prof phys educ, Univ Fla, 56-62; sect chief biodynamics br, Civil Aeromed Res Inst, Fed Aviation Agency, 62-64; from asst prof to assoc prof, 66-75, PROF PHYSIOL & PHYS EDUC, BIODYNAMICS LAB, UNIV WIS-MADISON, 75-, DIR LAB, 73- *Mem:* AAAS; Am Asn Health Phys Educ & Recreation; Am Asn Univ Prof; Am Physiol Soc. *Res:* Cardiovascular physiology and metabolism in stress. *Mailing Add:* Dept of Phys Educ Univ of Wis 2000 Observatory Dr Madison WI 53706

NAGLE, FREDERICK, JR, b Queens, NY, Jan 30, 37; m 57; c 2. PETROLOGY, MINERALOGY. *Educ:* Lafayette Col, BA, 58; Princeton Univ, MA, 61, PhD(geol), 66. *Prof Exp:* Asst prof geol, Juniata Col, 64-68; from asst prof to assoc prof geol, 68-78, PROF GEOL, UNIV MIAMI, 78- *Concurrent Pos:* NSF col teacher res fel, 67-68. *Mem:* AAAS; Mineral Soc Am; Geol Soc Am; Am Geophys Union. *Res:* Igneous and metamorphic petrology; K-Ar dating; Caribbean Island arc geology. *Mailing Add:* Dept of Geol Univ of Miami PO Box 249176 Coral Gables FL 33124

NAGLE, JAMES JOHN, b Wilkes-Barre, Pa, Nov 10, 37; m 60. GENETICS, EVOLUTION. *Educ:* Bloomsburg State Col, BS, 62; NC State Univ, MS, 65, PhD(genetics), 67. *Prof Exp:* Instr genetics, NC State Univ, 66-67; from asst prof to assoc prof zool & bot, 67-78, PROF ZOOL & BOT, DREW UNIV, 78- *Concurrent Pos:* Adj prof, Hunter Col, City Univ New York, 71-74. *Res:* Experimental evolution; biological education, especially biology for non-majors; social implications of biology. *Mailing Add:* Dept of Zool Drew Univ Madison NJ 07940

NAGLE, JOHN F, b Easton, Pa, Sept 29, 39; m 80. PHYSICS, BIOPHYSICS. *Educ:* Yale Univ, BA, 60, MS, 62, PhD(physics), 65. *Prof Exp:* NATO fel physics & statist mech, King's Col, London, 65-66; res assoc statist mech, Cornell Univ, 66-67; asst prof physics, 67-72, assoc prof physics & biol sci, 72-78, PROF PHYSICS & BIOL SCI, CARNEGIE-MELLON UNIV, 78- *Concurrent Pos:* A P Sloan Found fel, 69-71; Guggenheim fel, 79-80. *Mem:* Fel Am Phys Soc; Biophys Soc; Sigma Xi; NY Acad Sci. *Res:* Phase transitions; condensed matter physics and chemistry; membranes. *Mailing Add:* Dept Physics Carnegie-Mellon Univ Pittsburgh PA 15213

NAGLE, RICHARD KENT, b Detroit, Mich, Feb 19, 47; m 69. NONLINEAR DIFFERENTIAL EQUATIONS. *Educ:* Univ Mich BS, 68, MA, 69, PhD(math), 75. *Prof Exp:* Asst prof, Univ Mich, Dearborn, 75-76; asst prof, 76-80, ASSOC PROF MATH, UNIV SOUTH FLA, 80-, ASSOC DIR, CTR MATH SERV, 80- *Mem:* Am Math Soc; Soc Indust & Appl Math; Math Asn Am. *Res:* Nonlinear partial differential equations; nonlinear ordinary differential equations; nonlinear functional analysis; bifurcation theory. *Mailing Add:* Dept of Math 4202 Fowler Ave Tampa FL 33620

NAGLE, WILLIAM ARTHUR, b W Reading, Pa, May 16, 43; m 70. RADIATION BIOPHYSICS, MOLECULAR BIOLOGY. *Educ:* Albright Col, BS, 65; Univ Okla, Norman, MS, 66; Univ Tex Southwestern Med Sch, PhD(radiation biol), 72. *Prof Exp:* Fel, Harvard Med Sch, 72-74; ASST PROF RADIOL & PHYSIOL-BIOPHYS, UNIV ARK MED SCI, 74- *Concurrent Pos:* Student travel grant, Radiation Res Soc, 71; molecular biologist, Med Res Serv, Vet Admin Hosp, Little Rock, 74-; consult, Nat Cancer Inst, 77, consult radiation study sect AHR, 78. *Mem:* Biophys Soc; Radiation Res Soc. *Res:* Molecular radiobiology of mammalian cells; DNA damage and repair; influence of cell energy metabolism on recovery from radiation and hyperthermia injury. *Mailing Add:* Dept of Radiol Univ of Ark for Med Sci Little Rock AR 72201

NAGLER, ARNOLD LEON, b New York, NY, Aug 18, 32; m 61; c 2. PATHOLOGY, PHYSIOLOGY. *Educ:* City Col New York, BS, 53; NY Univ, MD, 58, PhD(path), 60. *Prof Exp:* Res assoc, Col Med, NY Univ, 58-60; res assoc, Mt Sinai Hosp, 60-61; asst prof surg & path, 61-76, ASSOC PROF SURG, ALBERT EINSTEIN COL MED, 76- *Concurrent Pos:* NIH fel, NY Univ, 60-61; prin investr, NIH grant, Albert Einstein Col Med, 70- *Mem:* NY Acad Sci; Fedn Am Socs Exp Biol. *Res:* Pathophysiology of shock; determination of the mechanisms involved in the pathogenesis of shock and the mortality therefrom; methods of circumventing lethality; choline and nutritional deficiencies and the pathology resulting therefrom. *Mailing Add:* Dept of Surg Albert Einstein Col of Med Bronx NY 10461

NAGLER, CHARLES ARTHUR, b Whitsett, Pa, May 10, 16; m 47; c 2. PHYSICAL METALLURGY. *Educ:* Univ Mich, BSE, 38, MSE, 39; Univ Minn, PhD(phys metall), 45. *Prof Exp:* Metallurgist, Eng Res Inst, Univ Mich, 38-39; asst phys metall, Univ Minn, 39-41, from instr to asst prof, 41-46; assoc prof metall eng, Wayne State Univ, 46-80; RETIRED. *Concurrent Pos:* Chief metallurgist, Twin City Cartage Corp, 42-45; pres, Metall Consult, Inc, 46-; mem, Hwy Res Bd, Nat Acad Sci-Nat Res Coun. *Mem:* Am Soc Metals; Soc Automotive Engrs; Am Soc Testing & Mat; fel Am Inst Chem; NY Acad Sci. *Res:* Physical and extractive metallurgy; failure of materials of engineering in service. *Mailing Add:* 16369 Melrose Ave Detroit MI 48075

NAGLER, ROBERT CARLTON, b Iowa City, Iowa, July 4, 23; m 47; c 5. ORGANIC CHEMISTRY. *Educ:* William Penn Col, BS, 47; Univ Mo, MA, 49; Univ Iowa, PhD(chem), 53. *Prof Exp:* Asst chem, Univ Mo, 47-49; asst, Univ Iowa, 49-51, instr, 52-53; asst prof, Purdue Univ, 53-56; from asst prof to assoc prof, 56-69, asst chmn dept, 68-78, PROF CHEM, WESTERN MICH UNIV, 69-, CHMN DEPT, 78- *Concurrent Pos:* USAID sci adv, Nigeria, 62-64. *Mem:* AAAS; Sigma Xi; Am Chem Soc. *Res:* Nitrogen-magnesium-halide reagents; Grignard reactions; synthesis of anti-tumor agents; fluoride analysis. *Mailing Add:* Dept of Chem Western Mich Univ Kalamazoo MI 49008

NAGLIERI, ANTHONY N, b New York, NY, Apr 15, 30; m 55; c 1. INDUSTRIAL ORGANIC CHEMISTRY. *Educ:* Fordham Univ, BS, 51, MS, 53; Columbia Univ, PhD(chem), 59. *Prof Exp:* Proj leader, 59-64, res assoc, 64-68, sect head res & develop, 68-74, asst dir res, 74-76, DIR EXPLOR RES, HALCON RES, MONTVALE, NJ, 76- *Mem:* Am Chem Soc. *Res:* Liquid and vapor phase oxidations; catalysis; carbonyletim; free radical chemistry. *Mailing Add:* 32 Breton Dr Pine Brook NJ 07058

NAGODE, LARRY ALLEN, b New Deal, Mont, Nov 15, 38; m 63; c 2. VETERINARY PATHOLOGY. *Educ:* Colo State Univ, DVM, 63; Ohio State Univ, MSc, 65, PhD(vet path), 68. *Prof Exp:* Morris Animal Found res fel vet path, Ohio State Univ, 63-65, Nat Cancer Inst res fel, 65-68; Nat Cancer Inst res fel biochem, Med Sch, Univ Pa, 69-70; asst prof vet path, 70-77, ASSOC PROF VET PATH, COL VET MED, OHIO STATE UNIV, 77- *Res:* Metabolism and mechanism of action of vitamin D in normal and diseased states; mechanism of action of enterotoxins of escherichia coli. *Mailing Add:* Dept Vet Path Ohio State Univ Col Vet Med 1925 Coffey Rd Columbus OH 43210

NAGY, ANDREW F, b Budapest, Hungary, May 2, 32; m 65. AERONOMY, ATMOSPHERIC PHYSICS. *Educ:* Univ New South Wales, BE, 57; Univ Nebr, MSc, 59; Univ Mich, MSE, 60, PhD(elec eng), 63. *Prof Exp:* Design engr, Elec Control & Eng Co, 56-57; instr elec eng, Univ Nebr, 57-59; asst res engr, 60-63, from asst prof to assoc prof elec eng, 63-71, PROF ATMOSPHERIC SCI & PROF ELEC ENG, UNIV MICH, ANN ARBOR, 71- *Concurrent Pos:* Ed, Rev Geophys Space Physics; mem comt solar space physics, Nat Res Coun. *Mem:* Inst Elec & Electronics Eng; Am Geophys Union; AAAS. *Res:* Theoretical and experimental studies of the chemistry and physics of the terrestrial and planetary atmospheres. *Mailing Add:* Dept of Atmos & Oceanic Sci Univ of Mich Ann Arbor MI 48109

NAGY, BARTHOLOMEW STEPHEN, b Budapest, Hungary, May 11, 27; nat US; m 52, 67; c 2. ORGANIC GEOCHEMISTRY. *Educ:* Pazmany Peter Univ, Hungary, BA, 48; Columbia Univ, MA, 50; Pa State Univ, PhD(mineral), 53. *Prof Exp:* Asst, Pa State Univ, 49-53; res engr, Pan Am Oil Co, 53-55; res assoc & supvr geophys res, Cities Serv Res & Develop Co, Okla, 55-57; from asst prof to assoc prof chem, Fordham Univ, 57-65; assoc res geochemist, Univ Calif, San Diego, 65-68; PROF GEOSCI, UNIV ARIZ, 68- *Concurrent Pos:* Vis assoc prof, Univ Calif, San Diego, 63-65; mem adv comt, Lunar Sci Inst, 72; managing ed, Precambrian Res, Elsevier Pub Co, Amsterdam, Neth, 72- *Mem:* Geochem Soc; Am Chem Soc; NY Acad Sci; fel Am Inst Chemists; Int Soc Study Origin Life. *Res:* Origin of life on earth; amino acids; hydrocarbons; meteorites; clay mineralogy; x-ray crystallography; petroleum geochemistry and exploration. *Mailing Add:* 533 Space Sci Dept Geosci Univ Ariz Tucson AZ 85721

NAGY, BELA FERENC, b Nagybanhegyes, Hungary, May 15, 26; US citizen; m 58; c 2. BIOCHEMISTRY. *Educ:* Eotvos Lorand Univ, Budapest, dipl biol & chem, 53; Brandeis Univ, PhD(biocehm), 64. *Prof Exp:* Asst prof biochem, Eotvos Lorand Univ, 53-56; Nat Acad Sci res fel, Rockefeller Inst, 57, res assoc, 57-59; res assoc, NY Univ, 59-60; Muscular Dystrophy Asn Am spec fel, Inst Muscle Dis, 60; NIH spec fel, Brandeis Univ, 61-64; res assoc, Retina Found, 64-70, staff scientist, Boston Biomed Res Inst, 70-78; ASSOC PROF, DEPT NEUROL & DEPT PHARMACOL & CELL BIOPHYS, UNIV CINCINNATI, COL MED, 78- *Concurrent Pos:* NIH res grant, 67-69 & career develop award, 67-72; res assoc neuropath, Harvard Univ, 68-69; prin assoc neurol (biochem), Harvard Univ, 69-78. *Mem:* AAAS; Am Chem Soc; Brit Biochem Soc; Biophys Soc; Am Soc Biol Chem. *Res:* Chemistry and physiology of muscle contraction; chemistry and physical chemistry of proteins. *Mailing Add:* Dept Neurol 4010 Med Sci Bldg Cincinnati OH 45267

NAGY, DENNIS J, b Perth Amboy, NJ, Oct 8, 50; m 74; c 1. POLYMER CHEMISTRY. *Educ:* Lebanon Valley Col, BS, 72, MA, 75; Lehigh Univ, PhD(chem), 79. *Prof Exp:* Sr res asst, E R Squibb & Sons, Inc, 74-76; SR RES CHEMIST, AIR PROD & CHEM, INC, 79- *Mem:* Am Chem Soc. *Res:* Polymer characterization and analysis; correlation of polymer structure with properties and performance. *Mailing Add:* Air Prod & Chem Inc PO Box 538 Allentown PA 18105

NAGY, GEORGE, b Budapest, Hungary, July 7, 37; Can citizen; m 63; c 1. COMPUTER SCIENCE, ELECTRIC ENGINEERING. *Educ:* McGill Univ, BEng, 59, MEng, 60; Cornell Univ, PhD(elec eng), 62. *Prof Exp:* Res assoc cognitive systs, Cornell Univ, 62-63; staff mem comput sci, Watson Res Ctr, IBM Corp, 63-72; PROF & CHMN, UNIV NEBR, 72- *Concurrent Pos:* Res assoc, Cornell Univ, 66; vis lectr, Univ Nebr, 67; vis prof, Univ Montreal, 68-69; vis scientist, IBM Watson Res Ctr & IBM San Jose Res Lab, 76. *Mem:* Sr mem Inst Elec & Electronics Engrs; Asn Comput Mach. *Res:* Pattern recognition; optical character recognition; speech; remote sensing; image processing; man-computer interface; geographic data processing; computation geometry. *Mailing Add:* Ferguson Hall Univ of Nebr Lincoln NE 68588

NAGY, JULIUS G, b Balatonboglar, Hungary, Aug 7, 25; US citizen; m 49; c 2. NUTRITION, BACTERIOLOGY. *Educ:* Wayne State Univ, BS, 60; Colo State Univ, MS, 63, PhD(wildlife nutrit), 66. *Prof Exp:* Animal scientist, 63-65, from instr to assoc prof, 65-77, PROF WILDLIFE BIOL, COLO STATE UNIV, 77- *Mem:* Wildlife Soc. *Res:* Wildlife nutrition and physiology, especially the rumen microbiological digestion of wild ruminants. *Mailing Add:* Dept of Fishery & Wildlife Biol Colo State Univ Ft Collins CO 80521

NAGY, KENNETH ALEX, b Santa Monica, Calif, July 1, 43; m 67; c 2. ENVIRONMENTAL PHYSIOLOGY. *Educ:* Univ Calif, Riverside, AB, 67, PhD(biol), 71. *Prof Exp:* Actg asst prof zool, 71-72, adj asst prof biol, Dept Biol & asst res zoologist environ biol, Nuclear Med & Radiation Biol Lab, 72-77, ASSOC PROF, DEPT BIOL & ASSOC RES ZOOLOGIST ENVIRON BIOL, BIOMED ENVIRON SCI LAB, UNIV CALIF, LOS ANGELES, 77- *Mem:* Sigma Xi; AAAS; Am Soc Ichthyologists & Herpetologists; Am Inst Biol Sci; Ecol Soc Am. *Res:* Physiology and behavior of desert vertebrates as these relate to the animal's survival in nature, including water, mineral, nitrogen and energy balance in field animals measured with isotopically-labeled water. *Mailing Add:* Lab Biomed & Environ Sci Univ of Calif Los Angeles CA 90024

NAGY, STEPHEN MEARS, JR, b Yonkers, NY, Apr 1, 39; c 2. ALLERGY, IMMUNOLOGY. *Educ:* Princeton Univ, AB, 60; Tufts Univ, MD, 64; Am Bd Internal Med, dipl, 71; Am Bd Allergy & Immunol, dipl, 74. *Prof Exp:* Intern med, Baltimore City Hosps, 64-65, resident, 65-66, 68-69; fel allergy & immunol, Johns Hopkins Hosp, 69-71; asst prof, 73-80, ASSOC CLIN PROF MED, SCH MED, UNIV CALIF, DAVIS, 80- *Concurrent Pos:* Fel med, Sch Med, Johns Hopkins Univ, 64-66, 68-71. *Mem:* Am Acad Allergy & Clin Immunol; AMA. *Res:* Evaluation and management of allergic and asthmatic diseases of adults and children. *Mailing Add:* 4801 J St Sacramento CA 95819

NAGY, STEVEN, b Fords, NJ, Apr 7, 36; m 80; c 1. CITRUS CHEMISTRY. *Educ:* La State Univ, BS, 60; Rutgers Univ, MS, 62, PhD(physiol & biochem), 65; Univ SFla, ME, 77. *Prof Exp:* Anal chemist, US Pub Health Serv, 62-65; res assoc, Lever Brothers, 65-67; res chemist, USDA, 68-78; RES SCIENTIST, FLA DEPT CITRUS, 79- *Concurrent Pos:* Adj prof, Univ Fla, 79- *Mem:* Am Chem Soc (vchmn, Agr & Food Div, 81-82, chmn elect, 82-83, chmn, 83); Am Oil Chemists Soc; Phytochem Soc NAm; Am Soc Hort Sci. *Res:* Methods development of monitor storage abuse of product; nutrient stability; off-flavor development; can corrosion of citrus products; lipid chemistry of mycorrhizal infections; citrus chemosystematics and leaf proteins. *Mailing Add:* 103 Arietta Shores Dr Auburn Dale FL 33823

NAGY, THERESA ANN, b Wheeling, WVa, July 16, 46. ASTROPHYSICS. *Educ:* West Liberty State Col, BS, 68; Tex A&M Univ, MS, 70; Univ Pa, PhD(astron), 74. *Prof Exp:* Analyst & programmer, Anal Inc, 72-73; STAFF SCIENTIST, COMPUT SCI CORP, NASA GODDARD SPACE FLIGHT CTR, 73- *Mem:* Am Astron Soc; Sigma Xi. *Res:* Data reduction and retrieval of space satellite data; computation of synthetic light curves for contact binary star systems; computer generation and manipulation for stellar and nonstellar astronomical data; image processing; cosmic ray muon intensity research. *Mailing Add:* Code 681 NASA Goddard Space Flight Ctr Greenbelt MD 20771

NAGY, ZOLTAN, b Budapest, Hungary, Aug 16, 33; US citizen; m 56; c 1. ELECTROCHEMISTRY. *Educ:* Univ Veszprem, Hungary, dipl chem eng, 56; Univ Akron, MS, 62; Univ Pa, PhD(phys chem), 72. *Prof Exp:* Res chemist, Chem Div, PPG, Inc, 57-63; sr res engr, Philadelphia Div, Honeywell, Inc, 63-65; res group leader, Betz Lab, Inc, 65-67; res fel, Univ Pa, 67-71; res assoc, Diamond Shamrock Corp, 72-76; STAFF CHEMIST, ARGONNE NAT LAB, 76- *Mem:* Am Chem Soc; Electrochem Soc; Int Soc Electrochem; AAAS. *Res:* Electrode phenomena; electrode kinetics; metal deposition-dissolution reactions; application of computers to electrode kinetic investigations; electrochemical aspects of corrosion; electrochemical technology; thermodynamics of ionic solutions. *Mailing Add:* Argonne Nat Lab 9700 S Cass Ave Argonne IL 60439

NAGYLAKI, THOMAS ANDREW, b Budapest, Hungary, Jan 29, 44; US citizen; m 69. THEORETICAL POPULATION GENETICS. *Educ:* McGill Univ, BS, 64; Calif Inst Technol, PhD(physics), 69. *Prof Exp:* Res assoc physics, Univ Colo, 69-71; vis asst prof, Ore State Univ, 71-72; proj assoc med genetics, Univ Wis-Madison, 72-74, asst scientist med genetics & math res ctr, 74-75; asst prof biophys & theoret biol, 75-77, ASSOC PROF BIOPHYS & THEORET BIOL, UNIV CHICAGO, 77- *Res:* Theoretical population genetics; geographical structure of populations; stochastic processes in population genetics; linkage and selection. *Mailing Add:* Dept of Biophys & Theoret Biol Univ of Chicago Chicago IL 60637

NAGYVARY, JOSEPH, b Szeged, Hungary, Apr 18, 34; m 63; c 3. ORGANIC CHEMISTRY. *Educ:* Univ Zurich, PhD(org chem), 62. *Prof Exp:* Res asst peptide synthesis, CIBA, Ltd, Switz, 62; fel nucleotides, Univ Cambridge, 62-64; res asst prof nucleotides synthesis, Univ Conn, 64-65; asst prof nucleic acids, Sch Med, Creighton Univ, 65-68; assoc prof biochem, 68-74, PROF BIOCHEM, COL AGR, TEX A&M UNIV, 74- *Concurrent Pos:* Swiss Regional Scholar fel, 62-63; NIH grant, 64-66; consult, CIBA, Ltd, 64. *Mem:* Am Chem Soc; Am Soc Biol Chem. *Res:* Nucleic acid chemistry; synthesis of nucleotide di-and triesters; nutrient-fiber interactions; Italian violin varnish. *Mailing Add:* Dept of Biochem & Biophys Tex A&M Univ Col of Agr College Station TX 77840

NAHABEDIAN, KEVORK VARTAN, b Boston, Mass, Oct 31, 28; m 57; c 1. CHEMISTRY. *Educ:* Mass Inst Technol, SB, 52; Univ Vt, MS, 54; Univ NH, PhD(chem), 59. *Prof Exp:* Asst chem, Univ Vt, 52-54, instr, 62-63; instr, Lafayette Col, 54-55; asst, Univ NH, 55-57, fel, 57-59; res assoc, Brown Univ, 59-61; res chemist, Qm Res & Eng Ctr, 61-62; asst prof chem, Union Col, NY, 63-68; PROF CHEM & CHMN DEPT, STATE UNIV NY COL GENESEO, 68- *Mem:* Am Chem Soc. *Res:* Physical organic chemistry; electrophilic and nucleophilic aromatic substitution; acid and base catalysis; donor functions for basic media. *Mailing Add:* 10 Melody Lane Geneseo NY 14454

NAHAS, GABRIEL GEORGES, b Alexandria, Egypt, Mar 4, 20; nat US; m 54; c 3. PHARMACOLOGY. *Educ:* Univ Toulouse, BA, 37, MD, 44; Univ Rochester, MS, 49; Univ Minn, PhD(physiol), 53. *Prof Exp:* Chief lab exp surg, Marie Lannelongue Hosp, Paris, 53-55; asst prof physiol, Univ Minn, 55-57; chief respiratory sect, Walter Reed Army Inst Res, 57-59; assoc prof anesthesiol, 59-62, RES PROF ANESTHESIOL, COL PHYSICIANS & SURGEONS, COLUMBIA UNIV, 62- *Concurrent Pos:* Mem med adv bd, Coun Circulation & Basic Sci, Am Heart Asn; mem comt trauma, Nat Res Coun, 64; consult, Oceanog Inst, Monaco; adj prof anesthesiol res, Univ Paris, 68. *Honors & Awards:* Mem, Order Brit Empire; Officer, Order Orange Nassau; Presidential Medal Freedom with Gold Palm; Officer, Legion of Honor. *Mem:* Am Physiol Soc; Am Soc Pharmacol & Exp Therapeut; Brit Pharmacol Soc; Harvey Soc. *Res:* Acid-base equilibrium, catecholamines metabolism; mechanism of action of drugs; marihuana and drug abuse. *Mailing Add:* Dept of Anesthesiol Columbia Univ New York NY 10032

NAHHAS, FUAD MICHAEL, b Sidon, Lebanon, Jan 29, 27; m 53; c 3. PARASITOLOGY, MEDICAL MICROBIOLOGY. *Educ:* Univ of the Pac, AB, 58, MA, 60; Purdue Univ, PhD(biol sci), 63. *Prof Exp:* Res fel parasitol, Fla State Univ, 63-64; from asst prof to assoc prof, 64-71, PROF BIOL, UNIV OF THE PAC, 71- *Mem:* Am Inst Biol Sci; Am Soc Parasitol; Am Soc Microbiol. *Res:* Parasites of vertebrates; taxonomy and life history studies; geographic distribution of parasites; the antibiogram as an aid in the identification of bacteria. *Mailing Add:* Dept of Biol Sci Univ of the Pac Stockton CA 95211

NAHMAN, NORRIS S(TANLEY), b San Francisco, Calif, Nov 9, 25; m 53; c 4. ELECTRONICS ENGINEERING, APPLIED PHYSICS. *Educ:* Calif State Polytech Col, BS, 51; Stanford Univ, MS, 52; Univ Kans, PhD, 61. *Prof Exp:* Res engr, Stanford Univ & electronics engr, San Francisco Naval Shipyard, 52; instr elec eng, Univ Kans, 55-61, from assoc prof to prof, 61-66, dir electronics res lab, 58-66, prin investr, Proj Jayhawk, 56-64; sci consult, Radio Stand Lab, Nat Bur Standards, 66-70, chief, Pulse & Time Domain Sect, Electromagnetics Div, 70-73; prof elec eng & chmn dept, Univ Toledo, 73-75; chief, Time Domain Metrol Sect, Electromagnetics Div, 75-76, group leader, Picosecond Transition Phenomena, 76-77, chief, Time Domain Metrol Sect, Electromagnetic Technol Div, 78-79, SR SCIENTIST, ELECTROMAGNETIC WAVEFORM METROL, NAT BUR STANDARDS, 80- *Concurrent Pos:* Tech adv, Dept Defense, 58-61; consult, Space Tech Labs, Calif, 62, Martin Co, MD, 61-62 & Wilcox Elec Co, Mo, 63-66; adj prof, Univ Colo, Boulder, 66-73 & 75- *Mem:* Fel Inst Elec & Electronics Engrs. *Res:* Transient response of distributed networks; generation, transmission and measurement of electrical and optical picosecond pulses; interaction of electromagnetic waves and materials; dielectric dispersion; low temperatures; normal and super conductors. *Mailing Add:* Time Domain Metrol Sect 724-04 Nat Bur of Standards Boulder CO 80302

NAHMIAS, ANDRE JOSEPH, b Alexandria, Egypt, Nov 20, 30; US citizen; m 56; c 3. VIROLOGY, PEDIATRICS. *Educ:* Univ Tex, Austin, BA, 50, MA, 52; Univ Mich, MPH, 53; George Washington Univ, MD, 57. *Prof Exp:* Intern, USPHS Hosp, Staten Island, NY, 57-58; resident pediat, Boston City Hosp, Mass, 60-62, clin assoc, 62-64; from asst prof to assoc prof pediat & prev med, 64-70, PROF PEDIAT, SCH MED, EMORY UNIV, 70-, CHIEF DIV INFECTIOUS DIS, ALLERGY & IMMUNOL, 64-, PROF PATH, 77- *Concurrent Pos:* NIH spec res fel virol, Mass Mem Hosp & res assoc microbiol, Sch Med, Boston Univ, 62-64; var study grants, USPHS, Am Cancer Soc, Surgeon Gen, US Army & Nat Found & lectr var univs, US, Europe & Australia, 64-; NIH res career develop award, 66-71; consult, Am Red Cross, 68-72; mem study sect, Grants Rev Bd, Nat Commun Dis Ctr, 69-70; Macy fac award, Univ Western Australia, 76. *Honors & Awards:* Mead Johnson Award Pediat Res, 74; P R Edwards Award, Am Soc Microbiol, 77. *Mem:* AAAS; fel Am Pub Health Asn; fel Am Acad Pediat; Soc Pediat Res; Infectious Dis Soc Am. *Res:* Bacterial infections, particularly staphylococcus, pertussis and leptospirosis; viral infections, particularly herpes viruses and relation to cancer; serological techniques, particularly immunofluorescence; immune mechanisms, particularly cellular immunity; clinical and epidemiological aspects of infectious diseases; fetal and neonatal diseases and neurological diseases. *Mailing Add:* Emory Univ Sch of Med Atlanta GA 30303

NAHMIAS, STEVEN, b New York, NY, June 19, 45; m 72. OPERATIONS RESEARCH, STATISTICS. *Educ:* Queens Col, BA, 68; Columbia Univ, BS, 68; Northwestern Univ, MS, 71, PhD(opers res), 72. *Prof Exp:* Asst prof indust eng, Univ Pittsburgh, 72-76, assoc prof, 76-78; PROF INDUST ENG,

DEPT DECISION & INFO SCI, UNIV SANTA CLARA, 80- *Concurrent Pos:* Programmer & Analyst, IBM Corp, 67-68; consult, Ingalls Shipbuilding Div, Litton Indust, 74-75; vis assoc prof opers res & indust eng, Stanford Univ, 78-79, vis prof indust eng, 81; vis assoc, Xerox Res Ctr & Lexington Automotive. *Mem:* Opers Res Soc Am; Inst Mgt Sci. *Res:* Stochastic inventory models with emphasis on perishable inventories and reparable item systems; fuzzy systems theory. *Mailing Add:* Dept Decision & Info Sci Univ Santa Clara Santa Clara CA 95053

NAHORY, ROBERT EDWARD, b McKeesport, Pa, Mar 1, 38; m 60; c 3. PHYSICS. *Educ:* Carnegie-Mellon Univ, BS, 60; Purdue Univ, MS, 62, PhD(physics), 67. *Prof Exp:* MEM TECH STAFF PHYSICS, BELL TEL LABS, 67- *Mem:* Am Phys Soc. *Res:* Semiconductor physics, especially optical properties; characteristics of new semiconductor materials; behavior of semiconductors under high excitation; lasers; oscillatory photoconductivity. *Mailing Add:* Bel Tel Labs Room 4d-409 Holmdel NJ 07733

NAHRWOLD, DAVID LANGE, b St Louis, Mo, Dec 21, 35; m 58; c 4. SURGERY, GASTROENTEROLOGY. *Educ:* Ind Univ, AB, 57, MD, 60. *Prof Exp:* Intern surg, Med Ctr, Ind Univ, Indianapolis, 60-61, resident, 61-65, asst prof, Sch Med, 68-70; assoc prof surg, 70-73, assoc dean patient care, 78-80, PROF SURG, VCHMN DEPT & CHIEF DIV GEN SURG, COL MED, PA STATE UNIV, 73-, ASSOC PROVOST & DEAN HEALTH AFFAIRS, 81- *Concurrent Pos:* Scholar, Univ Calif, Los Angeles, 65-66; mem, Surg & Bioeng Study Sect, NIH, 78- *Mem:* Am Surg Asn; Soc Clin Surg; fel Am Col Surgeons; Soc Surg Alimentary Tract; Soc Univ Surgeons. *Res:* Gastrointestinal physiology. *Mailing Add:* Dept of Surg Pa State Univ Hershey Med Ctr Hershey PA 17033

NAIB, ZUHER M, b Aleppo, Syria, Dec 10, 27; US citizen; m 58; c 3. PATHOLOGY. *Educ:* Univ Geneva, BS, 49, MD, 52; Am Bd Path, dipl, 60. *Prof Exp:* From instr to asst prof cytopath, Univ Md, 58-63; assoc prof, 63-67, PROF PATH & PROF GYNEC & OBSTET, EMORY UNIV, 67- *Concurrent Pos:* Fel path, Univ Va, 54-58; mem staff, Cytopath Div, Grady Mem Hosp, Atlanta, Ga. *Mem:* Am Cytol Soc. *Res:* Exfoliative cytopathology. *Mailing Add:* Dept of Path Emory Univ Atlanta GA 30322

NAIBERT, ZANE ELVIN, b Cedar Rapids, Iowa, Nov 19, 31; m 58. SCIENCE EDUCATION, CHEMISTRY. *Educ:* Coe Col, BA, 54; Univ Iowa, MS, 57, PhD(sci educ, chem), 64. *Prof Exp:* Asst anal chem, La State Univ, 54-55; asst, Univ Iowa, 55-57, asst & teacher, Lab Schs, 59-61; teacher, Algona Community Schs, 58-59; asst prof chem, State Univ NY Col Cortland, 61-67; assoc prof & chmn div sci & math, 67-71, PROF CHEM, MONTGOMERY COL, 71- *Mem:* AAAS; Am Chem Soc. *Mailing Add:* Dept of Chem Montgomery Col Takoma Park MD 20012

NAIDE, MEYER, b Russia, Mar 13, 07; nat US; m 33; c 2. MEDICINE. *Educ:* Univ Pa, AB, 29, MD, 32. *Prof Exp:* In chg vascular clin, Woman's Med Col Pa, 52-58, assoc prof med, 58-67; dir peripheral vascular div, Grad Hosp, 64-77, asst prof med, Univ, 67-77, EMER DIR PERIPHERAL VASCULAR DIV, GRAD HOSP, UNIV PA, 77- *Concurrent Pos:* In chg vascular clin, Einstein Med Ctr, 36-72; assoc, Univ Pa, 46-; pvt practr. *Mem:* AAAS; AMA; Am Col Physicians; Am Col Angiol; Int Cardiovasc Soc. *Res:* Peripheral vascular disease. *Mailing Add:* 2034 Spruce St Philadelphia PA 19103

NAIDU, ANGI SATYANARAYAN, b Sundargarh, India, Oct 21, 36; m 69; c 2. SEDIMENTOLOGY, MARINE GEOLOGY. *Educ:* Andhra Univ, India, BSc, 59, MSc, 60, PhD(geol), 68. *Prof Exp:* Demonstr geol, Andhra Univ, India, 60-61, Univ Grants Comn jr res fel, 66-69; asst prof marine sci, 69-71, marine geochemist, Inst Marine Sci, 71-76, ASSOC PROF MARINE SCI, UNIV ALASKA, FAIRBANKS, 76- *Concurrent Pos:* Geol consult Arctic environ. *Mem:* AAAS; Soc Econ Paleont & Mineral; Geochem Soc; Clay Minerals Soc; Int Asn Study Clays. *Res:* Marine geochemistry; lithological and chemical facies changes in recent sediments of arctic and tropical deltas and in subarctic fjordal environment, their present and paleoenvironmental implications; Cenozoic sedimentary history of Arctic Ocean; clay mineralogy. *Mailing Add:* Inst Marine Sci Univ Alaska Fairbanks AK 99701

NAIDU, JANAKIRAM RAMASWAMY, b Bangalore, India, Nov 15, 31; US citizen; m 64. RADIOECOLOGY, ENVIRONMENTAL POLLUTION. *Educ:* Univ Bombay, BS, 55; Univ Washington, MS, 63; Ore State Univ, PhD(oceanog radioecol), 74. *Prof Exp:* Jr res scholar marine wood borers, Forest Res Inst, Dehra Dun, India, 56-59; sr scientist radioecol, Bhabha Atomic Res Ctr, Bombay, India, 59-68; proj ecologist, Dames & Moore, Los Angeles, 74-75; ECOLOGIST ENVIRON MONITORING & DOSES ASSESSMENT, BROOKHAVEN NAT LAB, 75- *Concurrent Pos:* Res scholar, US Atomic Energy Comn, 61-63 & 69-74; adj prof, Marine Sci Res Ctr, State Univ NY, Stony Brook, 76- *Mem:* Marine Biol Asn UK; plenary mem Health Physics Soc. *Res:* Effect on wood treated by preservatives against the attack of marine wood borers; distribution of radioactivity in the marine environment; effects of nuclear fallout on human beings. *Mailing Add:* 4 Thornwood Circle Setauket NY 11733

NAIDUS, HAROLD, b New York, NY, Apr 11, 21; m 43; c 2. CHEMISTRY. *Educ:* Univ Ill, AB, 41, MS, 42; Polytech Inst Brooklyn, PhD(org chem), 44. *Prof Exp:* Sr res chemist, Publicker Industs, Pa, 44-48; res dir, Am Polymer Corp Div, Borden Co, 48-55, tech dir & vpres, Polyvinyl Chem, Inc, 55-62; assoc prof chem, 62-69, asst dean, 69-76, dir lib arts progs, 76-79, ASSOC DEAN, NORTHEASTERN UNIV, 76-, DIR, SCI & HEALTH PROGS, 79- *Mem:* Am Chem Soc; AAAS; NY Acad Sci; Sigma Xi. *Res:* Kinetics of polymerization; physical properties and preparation of polymers; monomer synthesis; organic synthesis. *Mailing Add:* Northeastern Univ Boston MA 02115

NAIK, DATTA VITTAL, b Goa, India, Mar 5, 47; m 71; c 2. ANALYTICAL CHEMISTRY, INORGANIC CHEMISTRY. *Educ:* Univ Bombay, BSc, 67; Univ Notre Dame, PhD(chem), 72. *Prof Exp:* Asst prof pharmaceut anal, Col Pharm, Univ Fla, 73-75; asst prof anal chem, Manhattanville Col, 75-77; asst prof, 77-82, ASSOC PROF ANAL CHEM, MONMOUTH COL, NJ, 82- *Concurrent Pos:* Assoc chem, Univ Fla, 72-73. *Mem:* Am Chem Soc; Sigma Xi; Acad Pharmaceut Sci. *Res:* Development of new and sensitive analytical methods using spectroscopic techniques; study of interaction of small molecules with biological macromolecules. *Mailing Add:* Dept of Chem Monmouth Col West Long Branch NJ 07764

NAIK, TARUN RATILAL, b Ahmedabad, India, April 22, 40; US citizen; m 66; c 2. STRUCTURAL ENGINEERING, GEOTECHNICAL ENGINEERING. *Educ:* Gujarat Univ, India, BE, 62; Univ Wis, Madison, MS, 64, PhD(struct eng), 72. *Prof Exp:* Jr engr, Consult Eng Co, Chicago & Madison, 64-67; researcher & lectr struct eng & mech, Univ Wis, Madison, 67-72; exec vpres, Soils & Eng Serv, Inc, 72-75; ASSOC PROF STRUCT ENG & GEOTECH, UNIV WIS, MILWAUKEE, 75- *Concurrent Pos:* Consult var spec proj, NAm, 72-; lectr, Univ Wis, Esten, 67- & Mex Cement & Concrete Inst, Mexico City, 77- *Mem:* Am Soc Civil Engrs; Am Concrete Inst; Am Soc Testing & Mat; Nat Soc Prof Engrs. *Res:* Properties of concrete (eg nondestructive testing of concrete and rapid testing of plastic concrete); machinery foundations; deep foundations; structures subjected to dynamic loads. *Mailing Add:* Dept Civil Eng Univ Wis PO Box 784 Milwaukee WI 53211

NAIL, BILLY RAY, b Roby, Tex, Jan 19, 33; m 52; c 3. ALGEBRA. *Educ:* Hardin-Simmons Univ, BA, 56; Univ Ill, Urbana, MA, 62, PhD(math), 67. *Prof Exp:* Teacher math, High Sch, Tex, 57-61; instr, Wayland Baptist Col, 62-64; from assoc prof to prof, Morehead State Univ, 67-72, chmn div math sci, 67-72; PROF MATH & DEAN, CLAYTON JR COL, 72- *Mem:* Math Asn Am. *Res:* Lie algebras. *Mailing Add:* Clayton Jr Col Morrow GA 30260

NAIMAN, BARNET, b Baltimore, Md, Mar 21, 00; m 34; c 1. ANALYTICAL CHEMISTRY. *Educ:* Univ NC, BS, 21, MS, 22; Columbia Univ, PhD(org chem), 34. *Prof Exp:* Asst chemist, State Dept Agr, NC, 22-24; from instr to prof, 25-70, EMER PROF CHEM, CITY COL NEW YORK, 70- *Concurrent Pos:* Res consult, Lewkowitz Dye Co, 30-31; sci text recorder for blind students, NJ Comn Blind; mem & past pres, Teaneck Student Loan Asn. *Mem:* AAAS; Am Chem Soc; NY Acad Sci; Sigma Xi; Am Asn Univ Profs. *Res:* Synthesis and structure of benzothiazoles; analytical methods; organic reagents in quantitative analysis; okra seed oil; male hormone; quantitative analysis. *Mailing Add:* 945 Ward Dr Sp 176 Santa Barbara CA 93111

NAIMAN, ROBERT JOSEPH, b Pasadena, Calif, July 31, 47. AQUATIC ECOLOGY. *Educ:* Calif State Polytech Univ, BS, 69; Univ Calif, Los Angeles, MA, 71; Ariz State Univ, PhD(zool), 74. *Prof Exp:* Nat Res Coun Can fel estuarine ecol, Pac Biol Sta, Fisheries & Oceans, Can, 74-76, 78; res assoc stream ecol, Dept Fisheries & Wildlife, Ore State Univ, 76-77; asst cur estuarine & fish ecol, Acad Natural Sci Philadelphia, 77-78; ASSOC SCIENTIST, WOODS HOLE OCEANOG INST, 78- *Concurrent Pos:* Dir, Matamek Res Sta, Que, Can. *Mem:* Am Fisheries Soc; Am Soc Ichthyologists & Herpetologists; Am Soc Limnol & Oceanog; Ecol Soc Am; Desert Fishes Coun. *Res:* Aquatic ecology with emphasis on lotic ecosystem dynamics; terrestrial-aquatic interactions mediated by beavers, periphyton and macrophytal primary production; detritus dynamics; carbon and nutrient expont from watersheds; decompositon dynamics of wood and leves; biology of Atlantic salmon and brook trout; stream ecology. *Mailing Add:* Dept of Biol Woods Hole Oceanog Inst Woods Hole MA 02543

NAIMARK, GEORGE MODELL, b New York, NY, Feb 5, 25; m 46; c 3. BIOCHEMISTRY. *Educ:* Bucknell Univ, BS, 47, MS, 48; Univ Del, PhD(biochem), 51. *Prof Exp:* Res fel ultrasonics & biochem, Biochem Res Found, 48-51; res biochemist, Clevite-Brush Develop Co, 51; asst dir biochem labs, Strong, Cobb & Co, Inc, 51-53, asst dir control, 53-54, dir, 54; asst to dir med res dept, White Labs, Inc, 54-58, dir sci serv, 58-60; dir, Burdick & Becker, Inc, 60-61; vpres & dir res & develop, Dean L Burdick Assocs, Inc, New York, 61-66; PRES, NAIMARK & BARBA, INC, NEW YORK, 66- *Mem:* AAAS; Am Chem Soc; Am Inst Chem; NY Acad Sci. *Res:* Product development; promotional utilization of scientific and medical information. *Mailing Add:* 87 Canoe Brook Pkwy Summit NJ 07901

NAIMPALLY, SOMASHEKHAR AMRITH, b Bombay, India, Aug 31, 31; m 55; c 3. TOPOLOGY. *Educ:* Univ Bombay, BSc, 52, MSc, 54 & 58; Mich State Univ, PhD(math), 64. *Prof Exp:* Lectr math, Ruparel Col, India, 52-58; prof, Kirti Col, India, 59-61; teaching asst, Mich State Univ, 61-64; asst prof, Iowa State Univ, 64-65; assoc prof, Univ Alta, 65-69; prof, Indian Inst Technol, 69-71; vis prof, 71-74, PROF MATH, LAKEHEAD UNIV, 74- *Concurrent Pos:* Fel, Inst Sci India, 52-53. *Mem:* Am Math Soc; Math Asn Am; Indian Math Soc; Can Math Cong. *Res:* General topology; proximity and uniform spaces; function spaces; semi-metric, developable spaces; compactifications; convexity; proximity. *Mailing Add:* Dept of Math Lakehead Univ Thunder Bay ON P7B 5E1 Can

NAINES, JOSEPH B, JR, operations research, economics, see previous edition

NAIR, GANGADHARAN V M, b Madras, India, Jan 26, 30; m 71. PLANT PATHOLOGY, MYCOLOGY. *Educ:* Univ Madras, BSc, 51; Aligarh Muslim Univ, MSc, 53; Univ Wis-Madison, PhD(plant path, mycol), 64. *Prof Exp:* Mycologist, Indian Agr Res Inst, New Delhi, 55-59; res scientist, Univ Wis-Madison, 64-68; asst prof environ sci, Univ Wis-Green Bay, 68-69; UN expert, Food & Agr Orgn, UN Develop Prog, Italy, 69-71; assoc prof environ control, 71-79, PROF PLANT & FOREST PATH & MOCOL & INT CONSERV NATURAL RESOURCES, UNIV WIS-GREEN BAY, 79-, DIR INT PROGS, 74- *Concurrent Pos:* NSF fel plant path, Univ Wis-Madison, 64-66, NSF sr fel, 66-68; external exam doctoral thesis, Aligarh Muslim Univ, 69-81; UN expert, Food & Agr Orgn, UN Italy, 69-71. *Mem:*

Am Phytopath Soc; Am Inst Biol Sci; Indian Phytopath Soc; Forestry Asn Nigeria; Int Union Forest Res Orgn. *Res:* International control programs of plant-forest tree diseases; weedicide-Sylvicide applications in the establishment of exotic tree species in developing countries; host parasite interactions of vascular wilt pathogens; electron microscopy and chemotherapy. *Mailing Add:* Col Environ Sci Univ Wis Green Bay WI 54302

NAIR, K AIYAPPAN, b Trivandrum, India, Jan 7, 36; m 66; c 1. MATHEMATICAL STATISTICS. *Educ:* Univ Kerala, BSc, 56, MSc, 58; State Univ NY Buffalo, PhD(statist), 70. *Prof Exp:* Statist asst, Damodar Valley Corp, India, 59; res off statist, Univ Kerala, 59-63, lectr, 63-66; ASSOC PROF MATH, EDINBORO STATE COL, 70- *Mem:* Am Statist Asn. *Mailing Add:* Dept of Math Edinboro State Col Edinboro PA 16412

NAIR, PADMANABHAN, b Singapore, Nov, 9, 31; m 59; c 3. BIOCHEMISTRY. *Educ:* Univ Travancore, India, BSc, 51; Univ Bombay, MSc, 55, PhD(biochem), 57. *Prof Exp:* Res officer chem path, All India Inst Med Sci, 58-60; res assoc biol, McCollum-Pratt Inst, Johns Hopkins Univ, 60-62; res assoc biochem, 62-64, DIR BIOCHEM RES DIV, SINAI HOSP, BALTIMORE, 64- *Concurrent Pos:* Fel, Indian Coun Med Res, 57-58; Fulbright res grant, 60-63; instr, Sch Med, Johns Hopkins Univ, 64-69, lectr, 72-80, asst prof, Sch Hyg & Pub Health, 80- *Mem:* AAAS; Am Inst Nutrit; Am Oil Chem Soc; NY Acad Sci; Am Soc Biol Chem. *Res:* Biochemistry of fat soluble vitamins; fatty acids, sterols and bile acids; biochemistry and nutrition in cancer. *Mailing Add:* Dept Res Med Sinai Hosp Biochem Res Div Baltimore MD 21215

NAIR, RAMACHANDRAN MUKUNDALAYAM SIVARAMA, b North Parur, India, Nov 15, 38; m 73. NATURAL PRODUCT CHEMISTRY. *Educ:* Kerala Univ, India, BSc, 57, MSc, 59; Poona Univ, PhD(chem), 64. *Prof Exp:* Sr res fel org synthesis & natural prod, Nat Chem Lab, Poona, India, 64-66; res fel fungal metabolites, NY Bot Garden, 66-69; sr researcher org synthesis, Univ Paris, France, 69-70; sci pool officer org synthesis, Indian Inst Technol, Bombay, 70-71; res fel, NY Bot Garden, NY, 71-73, res assoc fungal prod, 73-80; CHEMIST BIO-ORG, MARINE NATURAL PROD, NY AQUARIUM, 81- *Concurrent Pos:* Jr res fel, Coun Sci & Indust Res, India, 61-64, sr res fel, 64-66. *Mem:* Am Chem Soc; Am Inst Chemists; Am Soc Pharmacog. *Res:* Study of the structure, chemistry, biogenesis and biological activity of secondary metabolites of fungi and of certain higher plants; synthesis of natural products. *Mailing Add:* Osborn Labs Marine Sci NY Aquarium Bdwlk & W 8th St Brooklyn NY 11224

NAIR, SHANKAR P, b Calicut, India, Apr 16, 26; m 62; c 2. POPULATION GENETICS, CYTOGENETICS. *Educ:* Univ Madras, BSc, 48, MSc, 61; Wash Univ, PhD(genetics), 66. *Prof Exp:* Asst prof zool, Madras Univ, 61-68; res assoc genetics, Univ Tex, Austin, 68-70; ASSOC PROF GENETICS, SOUTHERN ILL UNIV, EDWARDSVILLE, 70-, CHMN DEPT BIOL, 80- *Concurrent Pos:* Vis prof, Univ Hawaii, 73-74 & Wash Univ, 72-73. *Mem:* AAAS; Genetics Soc Am; Soc Study Evolution; Scientists' Inst Pub Info. *Res:* Cytogenetic effect of environmental agents on cell cultures. *Mailing Add:* E Southern Ill Univ Edwardsville IL 62025

NAIR, SREEDHAR, b Trivandrum, India, July 28, 28; nat US; m 54; c 3. PULMONARY PHYSIOLOGY, PHARMACOLOGY. *Educ:* Univ Travancore, India, ISc, 45; Univ Madras, MB, BS, 51; Am Bd Internal Med & Am Bd Pulmonary Dis, dipl. *Prof Exp:* Res physician med & pulmonary dis, Metrop Hosp & NY Med Col, 54-57, res assoc med, 57-58; asst prof physiol & pharmacol, NY Med Col, 58-64, asst clin prof med, 64-77; ASSOC CLIN PROF MED, SCH MED, YALE UNIV, 77-; PROF RESPIRATORY TECHNOL, UNIV BRIDGEPORT, 78- *Concurrent Pos:* Sr attend physician, Norwalk Hosp, Conn, 68-, dir, Dept Chest Dis, 70- *Mem:* Fel Am Col Physicians; Am Thoracic Soc; fel Am Col Chest Physicians; AMA. *Res:* Pulmonary diseases; physiology of respiration. *Mailing Add:* Dept of Chest Dis Norwalk Hosp Norwalk CT 06856

NAIR, SREEKANTAN S, b Trivandrum, India, May 2, 41; m 71; c 2. STATISTICS, OPERATIONS RESEARCH. *Educ:* Univ Kerala, BSc, 61, MSc, 63; Purdue Univ, West Lafayette, MS, 69, PhD(math statist), 70. *Prof Exp:* Teaching asst statist, Purdue Univ, 66-70; asst prof, 70-74, assoc prof, 74-81, PROF MATH, AUGUSTINE'S COL, 81-, CHMN DEPT, 78- *Mem:* Math Asn Am. *Res:* Applied probability; theory of queues; mathematical statistics. *Mailing Add:* Dept Math St Augustine's Col Raleigh NC 27611

NAIR, VASAVAN N P, b Trivandrum, India, April 25, 34; Can citizen; m 58; c 3. PSYCHONEUROENDOCRINOLOGY, PSYCHOPHARMACOLOGY. *Educ:* Univ Kerale, MD, 59; Univ Mysore, DPM, 63; Glasgow Col, MRCP, 65; FRCP(C), 72; FRCPsych, 81; FRCPRCPS, 81. *Prof Exp:* Dir res & med educ psychiat, Saskatchewan Hosp, Weyburn, 68-69, NBattleford, 69-71; coordr res & lectr, 72, asst prof, 72-76, dir res, 76-79, DIR PSYCHIAT, DOUGLAS HOSP RES CTR, MCGILL UNIV, 80-, ASSOC PROF, 81- *Concurrent Pos:* Chmn, Prog Comt, Can Col Neuropsychopharmacol, 79-; temp adv, WHO, 81- *Mem:* AAAS; Can Col Neuropsychopharmacol; Collegium Internationale Neuropsychopharmacologicum; Am Psychiat Asn; NY Acad Sci. *Res:* Clinical psychopharmacology; neuroendocrine effects of psychotropic drugs in schizophrenia and tardive dyskinesia; new psychotropic drugs. *Mailing Add:* 6875 LaSalle Blvd Verdun PQ H4H 1R3 Can

NAIR, VASU, b Suva, Fiji Islands, Jan 7, 39; m 78; c 1. ORGANIC CHEMISTRY, BIO-ORGANIC CHEMISTRY. *Educ:* Univ Otago, NZ, BS, 63; Univ Adelaide, PhD(org chem), 66. *Prof Exp:* USPHS res fel org chem, Univ Sydney, 66-67; res assoc chem, Univ Ill, Urbana, 67-68; res fel, Harvard Univ, 68-69; asst prof, 69-73, assoc prof, 73-80, PROF CHEM, UNIV IOWA, 80- *Mem:* Am Chem Soc; Royal Australian Chem Inst. *Res:* Synthetic, natural products, bioorganic, and heterocyclic chemistry. *Mailing Add:* Dept of Chem Univ of Iowa Iowa City IA 52240

NAIR, VELAYUDHAN, b India, Dec 29, 28; US citizen; m 57; c 3. PHARMACOLOGY. *Educ:* Benares Univ, BPharm, MS, 48; Univ London, PhD(med), 56, DSc, 76. *Prof Exp:* Res assoc pharmacol, Col Med, Univ Ill, Chicago, 56-58; asst prof, Univ Chicago, 58-63; assoc prof, 63-66, PROF PHARMACOL & THERAPEUT, CHICAGO MED SCH, 66-, VCHMN DEPT, 71-, DEAN SCH GRAD & POSTDOCTORAL STUDIES, 77- *Concurrent Pos:* Dir lab neuropharmacol & biochem, Psychiat Inst, Michael Reese Hosp, 63-66, dir therapeut res, 66-70. *Honors & Awards:* Morris Parker Award, 72. *Mem:* Am Soc Pharmacol & Exp Therapeut; Radiation Res Soc; Soc Toxicol; Int Soc Chronobiol; Int Brain Res Orgn. *Res:* Blood-brain barrier; effects of environmental toxicants in pregnancy on biochemical and functional development in the offspring; radiation effects on the nervous system; radiation pharmacology; circadian rhythms in drug action. *Mailing Add:* Sch of Grad & Postdoctoral Studies Chicago Med Sch Univ of Health Sci NChicago IL 60064

NAIR, VIJAY, b Konny, India, Oct 5, 41; m 75; C 1. ORGANIC SYNTHESIS. *Educ:* Univ Kerala, BSc, 60; Banaras Hindu Univ, MSc, 62, PhD(org chem), 67; Univ BC, PhD, 69. *Prof Exp:* Fel org synthesis, Univ Chicago, 69-71, Univ Toronto, 71-72 & Columbia Univ, 72-74; SR RES CHEMIST, LEDERLE LABS, DIV AM CYANAMID CO, 74- *Concurrent Pos:* Vis scholar, Columbia Univ, 78-79. *Mem:* Am Chem Soc; Royal Soc Chem. *Res:* Total synthesis of modified steroids; steroidal alkaloids; macrolides; methods for thiocarbamylation; synthesis of sulfur and nitrogen heterocycles; glycosides; polyanionic immunomodulators; circular dichroism studies; enzymatic reactions of organic compounds. *Mailing Add:* Lederle Lab Am Cyanamid Co Pearl River NY 10965

NAIRN, ALAN EBEN MACKENZIE, b Newcastle on Tyne, Eng, Sept 9, 27. GEOLOGY. *Educ:* Univ Durham, BSc, 51; Glasgow Univ, PhD(geol), 54. *Prof Exp:* Asst geophys, Cambridge Univ, 54-55; asst, King's Col, Univ Durham, 56-58, Turner & Newall fel, 58-62, lectr, 62-65; vis prof, 63-64, from assoc prof to prof geol & geophys, Case Western Reserve Univ, 65-73; PROF GEOL, UNIV SC, 73- *Concurrent Pos:* Brit Geol Soc Lyell Fund grant, 63; guest prof, Univ Bonn, 65-66. *Mem:* Am Geophys Union; Geol Soc London; Royal Astron Soc; Am Geol Soc. *Res:* Paleomagnetism of Mediterranean rocks for interpretation of continental drift, megatectonic deformation; paleoclimates and origin of glaciations; development and changes of climatic belts. *Mailing Add:* Earth Sci & Resources Inst Univ SC Columbia SC 29208

NAIRN, JOHN GRAHAM, b Toronto, Ont, Aug 23, 28; m 54; c 4. PHARMACY, PHYSICAL PHARMACY. *Educ:* Univ Toronto, BScPharm, 52; State Univ NY Buffalo, PhD(chem), 59. *Prof Exp:* Retail pharmacist, 52-54; from asst prof to assoc prof, 58-72, PROF PHARM, UNIV TORONTO, 73- *Concurrent Pos:* Grants, Can Found Adv Pharm, 61-65, Nat Res Coun Can, 63-66, Nu Chapter, Rho Phi Fraternity, 62 & 65, Univ Toronto, 64-65, Med Res Coun Can, 67, Ont Ministry Natural Resources, 80 & Ont Ministry Health, 81. *Mem:* Asn Faculties Pharm Can; Can Pharmaceut Asn; Ont Col Pharmacists. *Res:* Ion exchange resins in pharmacy; surface active agents in pharmaceutical systems; kinetics of drug decomposition and stabilization; microencapsulation. *Mailing Add:* Fac of Pharm Univ of Toronto 19 Russell St Toronto ON M5S 1A1 Can

NAISTAT, SAMUEL SOLOMON, b Worcester, Mass, Mar 6, 17; m 42; c 3. PHYSICAL CHEMISTRY. *Educ:* Worcester Polytech Inst, BS, 37, MS, 39; Univ Wis, PhD(chem), 44. *Prof Exp:* Asst physics, Worcester Polytech Inst, 37-39; asst chem, Univ Wis, 39-41, instr physics, 43-44; res engr, Westinghouse Elec Corp, NJ, 44-45; res chemist, Congoleum-Nairn, Inc, 45-50; res chemist, Buffalo Electro-Chem Co, Inc, 50-55; group leader & asst to mgr, Becco Chem Div, FMC Corp, 55-57, sect mgr, Inorg Res & Develop Dept, 57-61, proj evaluator & tech consult, 61-63; supvr propulsion tech, Rocketdyne Solid Rocket Div, NAm Aviation, Inc, Tex, 63, res specialist, 64-65; from asst prof to assoc prof chem, 65-74, PROF CHEM, STEPHEN F AUSTIN STATE UNIV, 74- *Mem:* Am Chem Soc. *Res:* Physical chemistry of macromolecules; manufacture and applications of peroxygen chemicals; chemistry and energetics of propellants; energy conversion processes. *Mailing Add:* Dept of Chem Stephen F Austin State Univ Nacogdoches TX 75962

NAITOH, PAUL YOSHIMASA, b Japan, Feb 1, 31; US citizen; m 59; c 2. PSYCHOPHYSIOLOGY. *Educ:* Yamaguchi Univ, BA, 53; Univ Minn, MA, 56, PhD(psychol), 64. *Prof Exp:* Asst psychol, Univ Minn, 53-56, psychiat, 57-58 & vet radiol, 58-61; head psychophysiol lab, Neuropsychiat Inst, Univ Calif, Los Angeles, 65-67, staff psychologist, Inst & asst prof med psychol, Univ, 66-67; head, Behav Res Br, Psychophysiol Div, US Navy Med Neuropsychiat Res Unit, 67-74, head, Behav Res Br, Psychophysiol Div, 74-79, SUPVRY RES PSYCHOLOGIST, ENVIRON PHYSIOL DEPT, NAVAL HEALTH RES CTR, 79-, GROUP LEADER, APPL PSYCHOPHYSIOL GROUP, 79- *Concurrent Pos:* Trainee, Nat Inst Ment Health interdisciplinary res training prog, 64-66; res assoc, Nat Ctr Sci Res, France, 74-75; liaison psychologist, Off Naval Res, Tokyo, 80-81; adj prof, US Int Univ, 81- *Mem:* Am Electroencephalographic Soc; Int Soc Chronobiol; Biomet Soc; Asn Psychophysiol Study Sleep. *Res:* Psychophysiological analyses of electroencephalography; psychophysiological correlates of alcoholism; psychophysiology of sleep and sleep loss. *Mailing Add:* Naval Health Res Ctr PO Box 85122 San Diego CA 92138

NAITOVE, ARTHUR, b New York, NY, Mar 25, 26; m 46; c 5. SURGERY, PHYSIOLOGY. *Educ:* Dartmouth Col, BA, 45; NY Univ, MD, 48; Am Bd Surg, dipl, 58. *Prof Exp:* Asst chief surg, White River Junction Vet Admin Hosp, Vt, 58; from instr to assoc prof, 59-81, PROF SURG, DARTMOUTH MED SCH, 81-, DIR SURG LABS, 71- *Concurrent Pos:* USPHS fel physiol, Dartmouth Med Sch, 59-61; attend, White River Junction Vet Admin Hosp, 58-, consult surg, 70-; prin investr, USPHS res grant, Dartmouth Med Sch, 61-76; consult, Hitchcock Clin, Hanover, NH, 70-; assoc dean, Acad & Student Affairs, Dartmouth Med Sch, Hanover, NH, 80. *Mem:* Fel Am Col Surg; Am Gastroenterol Asn; NY Acad Sci. *Res:* Abdominal surgery; gastrointestinal tract and physiology of gastrointestinal tract, particularly relating to hemodynamic events, their control and their influence on secretory processes. *Mailing Add:* 20 Rip Rd Hanover NH 03755

NAJAR, RUDOLPH MICHAEL, b San Fernando, Calif, June 11, 31; m 70; c 1. MATHEMATICS, PHYSICS. *Educ:* St Mary's Col Calif, BS, 54; Univ Calif, Berkeley, MA, 61; Univ Notre Dame, MS, 62, PhD(math), 69. *Prof Exp:* From instr to asst prof math, St Mary's Col Calif, 67-70, chmn dept, 69-70; ASST PROF MATH, UNIV WIS-WHITEWATER, 70- *Mem:* Am Math Soc; Math Asn Am. *Res:* Homological algebra and category theory; cohomology of finite groups. *Mailing Add:* Dept of Math Univ of Wis Whitewater WI 53190

NAJARIAN, HAIG HAGOP, b Nashua, NH, Jan 5, 25; m 57; c 3. PARASITOLOGY. *Educ:* Univ Mass, BS, 48; Boston Univ, MA, 49; Univ Mich, PhD(zool), 53. *Prof Exp:* Asst biol, Boston Univ, 49; asst zool, Univ Mich, 49-51; asst prof biol, Northeastern Univ, 53-55; assoc res parasitologist, Parke, Davis & Co, 55-57; scientist, Bilharziasis Control Proj, WHO, Iraq, 58-59; USPHS trainee trop med & parasitol, Med Br, Univ Tex, 59-60, asst prof microbiol, 60-66; assoc prof, 66-68, chmn div sci & math, 67-71, chmn dept biol, 71-75, PROF BIOL, UNIV SOUTHERN MAINE, 68- *Mem:* AAAS; Am Soc Parasitol; Am Micros Soc; Am Soc Trop Med & Hyg. *Res:* Life histories of digenetic trematodes; morphology of aspidogastrid trematodes and parasitic copepods; experimental chemotherapy of schistosomiasis, malaria, amebiasis, paragonimiasis and intestinal helminths; biharziasis control; ecology of bulinid snails; filariasis; haemobartonellae; haemoflagellates; experimental amebiasis. *Mailing Add:* Dept of Biol Univ of Southern Maine Portland ME 04103

NAJARIAN, JOHN SARKIS, b Oakland, Calif, Dec 22, 27; m; c 4. SURGERY. *Educ:* Univ Calif, AB, 48, MD, 52; Am Bd Surg, dipl. *Prof Exp:* From intern to resident surg, Sch Med, Univ Calif, 52-60; prof surg & vchmn dept, dir surg res labs & chief transplantation serv, Sch Med, Univ Calif, San Francisco, 63-67; PROF SURG & CHMN DEPT, COL MED SCI, UNIV MINN, MINNEAPOLIS, 67- *Concurrent Pos:* NIH spec res fel immunopath, Sch Med, Univ Pittsburgh, 60-61; NIH assoc & sr fel tissue transplantation immunol, Scripps Clin & Res Found, La Jolla, Calif, 61-63; Markle Award, 64-69; NIH spec consult clin res training comt, Nat Inst Gen Med Sci, 65-69. *Mem:* AAAS; fel Am Col Surgeons; Soc Exp Biol & Med; Am Soc Exp Path; Am Fedn Clin Res. *Mailing Add:* Univ of Minn Health Sci Ctr Mayo Mem Bldg Box 195 Minneapolis MN 55455

NAJFELD, IGOR, b Bosanska Krupa, SRBiH, Yugoslavia, June 28, 44. APPLIED MATHEMATICS. *Educ:* Univ Beograd, Jugoslavia, Dipl Ing, 69; Weizmann Inst Sci, Israel, MSc, 74; Brown Univ, PhD(appl math), 78. *Prof Exp:* Numerical analyst appl math dept, Weizmann Inst Sci, 74-75; asst prof appl math, Polytech Inst New York, 78-80; STAFF SCIENTIST, INST COMPUT APPLICATIONS SCI & ENG, LANGLEY RES CTR, NASA, HAMPTON, VA, 80- *Mem:* Am Math Soc. *Res:* Numerical analysis; control theory; matrix theory; computational geometry. *Mailing Add:* Inst Comput Applications Sci & Eng Nasa Langley Res Ctr Hampton VA 23665

NAJJAR, TALIB A, b Baghdad, Iraq, July 1, 38; US citizen; m 65; c 4. DENTISTRY, MAXILLOFACIAL SURGERY. *Educ:* Univ Baghdad, BDS, 60; Ala Univ, DMD, 72; NY Univ, MSc, 65; McGill Univ, PhD(path), 65; Am Bd Oral & Maxillofacial Surg & Am Bd Oral Path, dipl. *Prof Exp:* Instr oral surg, Univ Baghdad, 60-62; asst teacher, Yale Univ, 63-65; asst teacher oral path, McGill Univ, 65-67; asst prof, Montreal Univ, 67-70, Ala Univ, 70-73; PROF MAXILLOFACIAL SURG, COL MED & DENT, NJ, 76- *Concurrent Pos:* Intern, Yale New Haven Hosp, 63-64, residency, 64-65; Med Res Coun Can fel, 65-67. *Mem:* Int Asn Dent Res; fel Int Asn Maxillofacial Surgeons; Int Asn Oral Pathologists; Am Asn Maxillofacial Surgeons; fel Am Acad Oral Path. *Res:* Experimental osteomycitis; electron microscopy of oral and maxillofacial pathologic lesion bone healing and remodeling both clinical and experimental. *Mailing Add:* Col Med & Dent NJ 100 Bergen St Newark NJ 07103

NAJJAR, VICTOR ASSAD, b Zalka, Lebanon, Apr 15, 14; nat US; div; c 3. PEDIATRICS, BIOCHEMISTRY. *Educ:* Am Univ, Beirut, MD, 35; Am Bd Nutrit, dipl. *Prof Exp:* From instr to assoc prof pediat, Harriet Lane Home, Johns Hopkins Univ, 39-57; prof microbiol & head dept, Sch Med, Vanderbilt Univ, 57-68; AM CANCER SOC PROF MOLECULAR BIOL, PROF PEDIAT & CHMN DIV PROTEIN CHEM, SCH MED, TUFTS UNIV, 68- *Concurrent Pos:* Nat Res Coun fels, Sch Med, Washington Univ, 46-48 & Sch Biochem, Cambridge Univ, 48-49; Irving McQuarrie lectr, 57; ed-in-chief, Molecular & Cellular Biochem, 72- *Honors & Awards:* Mead Johnson Award, 51; Fulbright-Hays Award, 76. *Mem:* NY Acad Sci; Am Soc Biol Chemists; Am Pediat Soc; Am Soc Clin Invest; Pediat Res Soc. *Res:* Vitamin metabolism and human requirement; mammalian and bacterial enzymology; mechanism of enzyme action; immunochemistry. *Mailing Add:* Div Protein Chem Tufts Univ Sch Med Boston MA 02111

NAKA, F(UMIO) ROBERT, b San Francisco, Calif, July 18, 23; m 49; c 4. ELECTRONICS, SPACE SYSTEMS. *Educ:* Univ Mo, BS, 45; Univ Minn, MS, 47; Harvard Univ, ScD(elec eng, electron optics), 51; Harvard Grad Sch Bus Admin, cert, 67. *Prof Exp:* Asst math, Univ Mo, 44-45; instr elec eng, Univ Minn, 45-47; staff mem radar develop, Lincoln Lab, Mass Inst Technol, 51-54, assoc group leader, 54-56, group leader, 56-59; dept head, Mitre Corp, Mass, 59-60, assoc tech dir, Appl Sci Labs, 60-62, tech dir, 62-68, chief scientist, 68-69; dep under secy Air Force for space systs, US Air Force, 69-72; dir, Detection & Instrumentation Systs, Raytheon Co, 72-75; chief scientist, US Air Force, 75-80; MEM STAFF, SCI APPLICATIONS INC, 80- *Concurrent Pos:* Mem, Space Prog Adv Coun, Nat Aeronaut & Space Admin, 70-77 & Air Force Studies Bd, Nat Acad Sci, 72-75. *Mem:* Inst Elec & Electronics Engrs; Sigma Xi. *Res:* Radar; space systems; electron optics; electromagnetic wave propagation; radar techniques. *Mailing Add:* Sci Applications Inc 1710 Goodridge Dr McLean VA 22102

NAKADA, DAISUKE, b Osaka, Japan, July 23, 25; m 58; c 2. BIOCHEMISTRY, MICROBIOLOGY. *Educ:* Kyoto Univ, BS, 48; Osaka Univ, PhD(bact), 55. *Prof Exp:* Lectr bact, Osaka Univ, 55-56, asst prof, 56-58; vis asst prof microbial genetics, Columbia Univ, 58-61; vis asst prof biol, Mass Inst Technol, 61-63; res proj leader molecular biol, E I du Pont de Nemours & Co, Inc, 63-67; assoc prof, 67-71, PROF BIOCHEM, SCH MED, UNIV PITTSBURGH, 71- *Concurrent Pos:* Fulbright exchange fel, Columbia Univ, 58-61; NIH res grant, 68-75. *Mem:* Am Soc Biol Chem; Am Soc Microbiol; Am Chem Soc. *Res:* Control of macromolecule synthesis in bacteria and bacteriophage; ribosomal function. *Mailing Add:* Dept of Biochem Univ of Pittsburgh Sch of Med Pittsburgh PA 15261

NAKADA, HENRY ISAO, b Los Angeles, Calif, Oct 12, 22; m 45; c 3. BIOCHEMISTRY. *Educ:* Temple Univ, BA, 48, PhD, 53. *Prof Exp:* Res assoc, Inst Cancer Res, Philadelphia, 50-54; mem, Scripps Clin & Res Found, 54-62; from assoc prof to prof, 62-78, EMER PROF BIOCHEM, UNIV CALIF, SANTA BARBARA, 62- *Mem:* Am Soc Biol Chemists; Soc Exp Biol & Med; Am Chem Soc. *Res:* Mucopolysaccharide, carbohydrate and amino acid metabolism; commercial fishing; research on octopus; oil spills; public relations of fishermen and Alaska's natives. *Mailing Add:* PO Box 908 Homer AK 99603

NAKADA, MINORU PAUL, b Los Angeles, Calif, Jan 15, 21; m 53; c 3. PHYSICS. *Educ:* Univ Calif, AB, 47, PhD(cosmic rays, physics), 52. *Prof Exp:* Physicist, Lawrence Radiation Lab, Univ Calif, 52-61 & Jet Propulsion Lab, Calif Inst Technol, 61-62; PHYSICIST, GODDARD SPACE FLIGHT CTR, NASA, GREENBELT, 62- *Mem:* Am Phys Soc; Am Geophys Union. *Res:* Space plasma physics. *Mailing Add:* c/o Goddard Space Flight NASA Greenbelt MD 20771

NAKADA, YOSHINAO, b Osaka, Japan, Apr 5, 34; US citizen; m 59; c 3. MATERIAL SCIENCE. *Educ:* Harvard Univ, AB, 58, SM, 59, PhD(appl physics), 63. *Prof Exp:* Res fel metall, Harvard Univ, 63-64; scientist, E C Bain Lab, US Steel Corp, 64-68; MEM TECH STAFF, BELL TEL LABS, 68- *Mem:* AAAS; Am Ceramic Soc; Int Soc Hybrid Electronics. *Res:* Physical metallurgy; thin films; ceramics; hybrid microelectronics; electric discharge phenomena. *Mailing Add:* Bell Tel Labs 555 Union Blvd Allentown PA 18103

NAKADA, YOSHINAO, b Los Angeles, Calif, Mar 14, 18; m 44; c 2. PHYSICS. *Educ:* Calif Inst Technol, BS, 40, MS, 41. *Prof Exp:* Chief chemist, Nobell Res Found, 46-48; res physicist, West Precipitation Corp, 48-55, Magnavox Co, 55-56, Hughes Aircraft Co, 56-59 & A C Spark Plug Div, Gen Motors Corp, 59-61; res physicist, Hughes Aircraft Co, 61-78; RETIRED. *Mem:* Am Phys Soc. *Res:* Real time data processing; electrical discharge; infrared. *Mailing Add:* 4227 Don Mariano Dr Los Angeles CA 90008

NAKADOMARI, HISAMITSU, b Japan, Sept 15, 35; US citizen; m 67; c 2. ELECTROCHEMISTRY. *Educ:* Kans State Col of Pittsburgh, BA, 61; Ft Hays Kans State Col, MS, 65; Colo State Univ, PhD(chem), 74. *Prof Exp:* Asst prof chem, St Gregory's Col, 65-68; sr res assoc bioelectrochem, Brookhaven Nat Lab, 74-76; asst prof chem, George Mason Univ, 76-81; VPRES RES, SAFETY DEVICES, INC, 81- *Concurrent Pos:* Fel, Colo State Univ, 73-74. *Mem:* Sigma Xi; Am Chem Soc; AAAS. *Res:* Ion transport phenomena in lipid bilayer membranes; studies of the electrode-solution interfaces; thermodynamic studies of the solvent effects on the properties of electrolyte solutions; the investigation of new ion selection electrodes; electrochemical studies of corrosion inhibition. *Mailing Add:* Safety Devices Inc 8805 Telegragh Rd Lorton VA 22079

NAKAGAWA, T WILLIAM, organic chemistry, polymer chemistry, see previous edition

NAKAHARA, SHOHEI, b Hiroshima. Japan, Jan 3, 42; m 78. MATERIALS SCIENCE. *Educ:* Hiroshima Univ, BE, 65, ME, 67; Stevens Inst Technol, PhD(metall), 73. *Prof Exp:* MEM TECH STAFF, BELL LABS, 73- *Mem:* Electrochem Soc; Phys Soc Japan. *Res:* Electron microscopy; electrodeposition; thin film phenomena. *Mailing Add:* Bell Labs Murray Hill NJ 07974

NAKAI, SHURYO, b Kanazawa, Japan, Dec 13, 26; m 52; c 3. FOOD CHEMISTRY, PROTEIN CHEMISTRY. *Educ:* Univ Tokyo, BSc, 50, PhD(dairy tech), 62. *Prof Exp:* Res chemist, Okayama Plant, Meiji Milk Prod Co Ltd, 50-51, sect head dairy chem, Cent Res Lab, Meiji Milk Prod Co, 52-62; res assoc, Univ Ill, 62-66; asst prof dairying, 66-70, assoc prof food chem, 70-75, PROF FOOD CHEM, UNIV BC, 75- *Mem:* Am Dairy Sci Asn; Can Inst Food Sci & Technol; Inst Food Technol. *Res:* Chemistry of food proteins; chemical studies on food products. *Mailing Add:* Dept Food Sci 233 MacMillan Bldg Univ of BC Vancouver BC V6T 2A2 Can

NAKAJIMA, NOBUYUKI, b Tokyo, Japan, Nov 3, 23; c 3. POLYMER CHEMISTRY, POLYMER PHYSICS. *Educ:* Univ Tokyo, BS, 45; Polytech Inst Brooklyn, MS, 55; Case Inst Technol, PhD(phys chem), 58. *Prof Exp:* Asst polymer & phys chem, Naval Air Force Res Ctr, Japan, 44-45; prod engr, Chem Div, Osaka Gas Co, 45-51; from res asst to res assoc, Case Inst Technol, 55-60; res chemist, W R Grace & Co, 60-63, sect leader, Polymer Chem Div, 63-66, asst to vpres chem, Res Div, 65-66; tech supvr plastics div, Allied Chem Corp, NJ, 66-67, mgr polymer physics & anal plastics div, 67-71; MEM STAFF, TECH CTR, B F GOODRICH CHEM CO, 71- *Concurrent Pos:* Assoc ed, Rubber Chem & Technol. *Mem:* AAAS; Am Chem Soc; Soc Rheol; Am Phys Soc; Sigma Xi. *Res:* Elastomer rheology and processing; polymer solution thermodynamics; rheology of polymer melts and solution; molecular weight distribution of polymers; polymer morphology, processing and structural analysis. *Mailing Add:* B F Goodrich Chem Co Tech Ctr PO Box 122 Avon Lake OH 44012

NAKAJIMA, SHIGEHIRO, b Kobe, Japan, July 13, 31; nat US; m 57; c 2. NEUROBIOLOGY. *Educ:* Univ Tokyo, MD, 55, PhD(physiol), 61. *Prof Exp:* Instr physiol, Sch Med, Univ Tokyo, 60-65; assoc prof, Sch Med, Juntendo Univ, Japan, 65-69; assoc prof, 69-73, PROF BIOL & NEUROPHYSIOL, PURDUE UNIV, 73- *Concurrent Pos:* United Cerebral Palsy Res & Educ Found fel neurophysiol, Col Physicians & Surgeons,

Columbia Univ, 62-64; asst zoologist, Brain Res Inst, Univ Calif, Los Angeles, 64-65; Wellcome Trust fel physiol, Univ Cambridge, 67-69; mem, Corp Marine Biol Lab, Woods Hole; ad hoc mem, Physiol Study Sect, NIH, 81. *Mem:* Am Physiol Soc; Biophys Soc; Soc Neurosci; Soc Gen Physiol. *Res:* Electrophysiology of nerves and muscles; developmental neurobiology on tissue cultured nerves and muscles. *Mailing Add:* Dept Biol Sci Purdue Univ Lafayette IN 47907

NAKAJIMA, YASUKO, b Osaka, Japan, Jan 8, 32; m 57; c 2. ANATOMY, NEUROBIOLOGY. *Educ:* Univ Tokyo, MD, 55, PhD(anat), 62. *Prof Exp:* Instr anat, Univ Tokyo, 62-67; vis res fel zool, Univ Cambridge, 67-69; assoc prof, 69-76, PROF NEUROBIOL, PURDUE UNIV, WEST LAFAYETTE, 76- *Concurrent Pos:* Vis res fel anat, Col Physicians & Surgeons, Columbia Univ, 62-64; asst res anat, Med Sch, Univ Calif, Los Angeles, 64-65; vis res, Univ Col, London, 78-79; mem, Marine Biol Lab, Woods Hole. *Mem:* Am Asn Anat; Am Soc Cell Biol; Soc Neurosci. *Res:* Neurobiology at the cellular level; electron microscopy, electrophysiology, and tissue culture. *Mailing Add:* Dept of Biol Sci Purdue Univ West Lafayette IN 47907

NAKAMOTO, KAZUO, b Kobe, Japan, Mar 1, 22; m 50; c 3. PHYSICAL CHEMISTRY. *Educ:* Osaka Univ, BS, 45, DSc, 53. *Prof Exp:* Res asst chem, Osaka Univ, 45-46, res assoc, 46-51, lectr, 51-57, assoc prof, 57; res fel, Clark Univ, 57-58, asst prof, 58-61; from asst prof to prof, Ill Inst Technol, 61-69; WEHR PROF CHEM, MARQUETTE UNIV, 69- *Concurrent Pos:* Res fel, Iowa State Univ, 53-55. *Mem:* Am Chem Soc; Chem Soc Japan; Soc Appl Spectros; Sigma Xi. *Res:* Electronic and vibrational spectra. *Mailing Add:* Dept of Chem Marquette Univ Milwaukee WI 53233

NAKAMOTO, TOKUMASA, b Kohala, Hawaii, July 8, 28; m 50; c 3. BIOCHEMISTRY. *Educ:* Univ Chicago, BA, 56, PhD(biochem), 59. *Prof Exp:* Res assoc biochem, Univ Chicago, 59-62; res assoc, Rockefeller Inst, 62-64, asst prof, 64-65; asst prof, 65-67, ASSOC PROF BIOCHEM, SCH MED, UNIV CHICAGO, 67- *Concurrent Pos:* Mem, Franklin McLean Mem Res Inst. *Res:* Biosynthesis of proteins. *Mailing Add:* Dept of Biochem Univ of Chicago Sch of Med Chicago IL 60637

NAKAMURA, EUGENE LEROY, b San Diego, Calif, June 8, 26; m 61. BIOLOGICAL OCEANOGRAPHY, FISH BIOLOGY. *Educ:* Univ Ill, BS, 50, MS, 51. *Prof Exp:* Res asst zool, Univ Hawaii, 51-56; fishery biologist, Biol Lab, US Bur Com Fisheries, Hawaii, 56-70; DIR, PANAMA CITY LAB, NAT MARINE FISHERIES SERV, 70- *Mem:* AAAS; Am Fisheries Soc; Am Soc Ichthyologists & Herpetologists; Am Soc Limnol & Oceanog; Am Inst Fishery Res Biol. *Res:* Biology, ecology and fishery of marine fishes. *Mailing Add:* Nat Marine Fish Serv 3500 Delwood Beach Rd Panama City FL 32407

NAKAMURA, KAZUO, b Fukuoka, Japan, June 30, 29; m 60; c 2. MICROBIAL GENETICS, PHYCOLOGY. *Educ:* Kyushu Univ, BS, 54, MS, 56, DSc, 67; Univ Mo, PhD(genetics), 64. *Prof Exp:* Res assoc bot, Univ Mo, 64-65; scholar, Univ Calif, Los Angeles, 65-67; res fel, Kyushu Univ, 67-69; prof, Fukuoka Univ, Japan, 69-70; vis asst prof, 69-70, asst prof, 70-74, ASSOC PROF BOT, UNIV LETHBRIDGE, 74- *Concurrent Pos:* Vis prof, Univ Mo-Columbia, 75-76; Nat Res Coun Can travel fel, 75. *Mem:* Genetics Soc Am; Int Phycol Soc; Genetics Soc Can; Can Soc Microbiol; Am Soc Microbiol. *Res:* Genetics and physiology of Chlamymonas and Neurospora. *Mailing Add:* Dept of Biol Sci Univ of Lethbridge Lethbridge AB T1K 3M4 Can

NAKAMURA, MITSURU J, b Los Angeles, Calif, Dec 17, 26; m 51; c 3. MICROBIOLOGY. *Educ:* Univ Calif, Los Angeles, AB, 49; Univ Southern Calif, MS, 50, PhD(med sci), 56; Am Bd Med Microbiol, dipl, 62. *Prof Exp:* Asst, Sch Med, Univ Calif, S0-52; from asst prof to assoc prof, Northeastern Univ, 52-56; assoc prof, 57-63, PROF MICROBIOL & CHMN DEPT, UNIV MONT, 63- *Concurrent Pos:* Res assoc, Sch Med, Boston Univ, 55-56; responsible investr, Comn Enteric Infections, Armed Forces Epidemiol Bd, Off Surgeon Gen, US Dept Army, 57-62; fel, Sch Med, La State Univ, 59 & 60; fel, Univ Costa Rica, 63; Am Acad Microbiol fel, 67; Nat Acad Sci interacad awards to visit Poland, 76, Yugoslavia, 78 & Hungary, 82. *Mem:* Fel AAAS; fel Am Pub Health Asn; Am Soc Microbiol; Am Soc Trop Med & Hyg; Soc Exp Biol & Med. *Res:* Physiology of Shigella; water pollution; effects of ultraviolet irradiation on bacteria; cultivation of Protozoa; Clostridium perfringens food poisoning. *Mailing Add:* Dept of Microbiol Univ of Mont Missoula MT 59801

NAKAMURA, ROBERT MASAO, b Los Angeles, Calif, Sept 18, 35; m 66; c 3. REPRODUCTIVE BIOLOGY, BIOPHYSICS. *Educ:* Occidental Col, BA, 59; Univ Southern Calif, MS, 64, PhD(biochem), 68. *Prof Exp:* Res asst biochem, Univ Southern Calif, 59-61, res assoc biophys, Allan Hancock Found, 66-67; asst res biochemist, Dept Obstet & Gynec, Harbor Gen Hosp, Torrance, Calif, 67-68, res biochemist, 68-69; asst prof reprod biol, 69-76, ASSOC PROF OBSTET & GYNEC & PATH & PHYSIOL, SCH MED, UNIV SOUTHERN CALIF, 76- *Concurrent Pos:* Consult, Ford Found, 69-; mem task force human reproduction, WHO; managing ed, Contraception, 69- *Mem:* AAAS; Royal Soc Chem; Am Chem Soc; NY Acad Sci; Endocrine Soc. *Res:* Hormonal profiles in normal menstruating women; effects of contraceptive steroids on the serum hormone levels; biophysical properties of cervical mucus; properties of protein hormones. *Mailing Add:* Dept of Obstet & Gynec Univ of Southern Calif Sch Med Los Angeles CA 90007

NAKAMURA, ROBERT MOTOHARU, b Montebello, Calif, June 10, 27; m 57; c 2. PATHOLOGY, IMMUNOLOGY. *Educ:* Whittier Col, AB, 49; Temple Univ, MD, 54. *Prof Exp:* Chief clin path, Long Beach Vet Admin Hosp, 59-60; pathologist, Atomic Bomb Casualty Comn, Japan, 60-61; instr path, Sch Med, Univ Calif, Los Angeles, 61-62, asst prof, 62-65; pathologist, St Joseph Hosp, Orange, Calif, 68-69; from assoc prof to prof path & dir clin labs, Orange County Med Ctr, Univ Calif, Irvine, 69-74; HEAD DEPT PATH, HOSP SCRIPPS CLIN, 74-, ASSOC MEM, DEPT MOLECULAR IMMUNOL, SCRIPPS CLIN & RES FOUND, 74-, ADJ PROF PATH, UNIV CALIF, SAN DIEGO, 75- *Concurrent Pos:* USPHS spec fel exp path, Scripps Clin & Res Found, Univ Calif, 65-68; pathologist, Los Angeles County Harbor Gen Hosp, Calif, 61-65; consult dept path, Orange County Gen Hosp, 62-65; adj prof path, Univ Calif, Irvine, 74- *Mem:* AAAS; AMA; fel Am Col Path; fel Am Soc Clin Path; Am Soc Exp Path. *Res:* Clinical pathology; general area of cell proliferation; immunopathology, specifically autoimmune diseases and immunological tolerance. *Mailing Add:* Dept Path Hosp Scripps Clin La Jolla CA 92037

NAKAMURA, SHOICHIRO, b Osaka, Japan, Oct 20, 35; m 64; c 2. NUCLEAR ENGINEERING, APPLIED MATHEMATICS. *Educ:* Kyoto Univ, BS, 58, PhD(nuclear eng), 67. *Prof Exp:* Vis res fel nuclear eng, Univ Calif, Berkeley, 66-70; engr nuclear reactor design, Hitachi Ltd, Tokyo, 58-69; fel nuclear eng, 69-70, asst prof, 70-73, assoc prof, 73-78, PROF MECH ENG, OHIO STATE UNIV, 78- *Mem:* Am Nuclear Soc; Am Inst Aeronaut & Astronaut. *Res:* Nuclear reactor analysis; numerical methods; computational fluid dynamics; nuclear fuel management; electric power generating system planning. *Mailing Add:* Dept of Mech Eng 206 W 18th Ave Columbus OH 43210

NAKANE, PAUL K, b Yokahama, Japan, Oct 20, 35; m 59; c 3. HISTOCHEMISTRY, ELECTRON MICROSCOPY. *Educ:* Huntingdon Col, BA, 58; Brown Univ, MS, 61, PhD(cytol), 63. *Prof Exp:* Res assoc histochem, Sch Med, Stanford Univ, 63-65; instr path, Univ Mich, Ann Arbor, 65-67, asst prof cell biol in path, 67-68; asst prof, 68-69, assoc prof, 69-72, PROF PATH, SCH MED, MED CTR, UNIV COLO, DENVER, 73- *Concurrent Pos:* Cancer Inst trainee, 59-63. *Mem:* Am Asn Cell Biol; Histochem Soc (pres, 78-79); Fedn Am Soc Exp Biol; AAAS. *Res:* Ultrastructural localization of antigens by enzyme-labeled antibody. *Mailing Add:* Dept of Path Sch of Med Univ of Colo Med Ctr Denver CO 80262

NAKANISHI, KEITH KOJI, b Honolulu, Hawaii, Mar 20, 47; m 71; c 1. SEISMOLOGY. *Educ:* Occidental Col, BA, 69; Univ Calif, Los Angeles, MS, 71, PhD(geophysics & space physics), 78. *Prof Exp:* SEISMOLOGIST, EARTH SCI DIV, LAWRENCE LIVERMORE NAT LAB, UNIV CALIF, 77- *Mem:* Seismol Soc Am; Am Geophys Union. *Res:* Seismic waves for the purpose of determining source mechanisms; techniques to discriminate between earthquakes and underground nuclear explosions; modelling of data using synthetic seismograms. *Mailing Add:* L-205 Lawrence Livermore Nat Lab Univ Calif Livermore CA 94550

NAKANISHI, KOJI, b Hong Kong, May 11, 25; m 47; c 2. ORGANIC CHEMISTRY. *Educ:* Nagoya Univ, BSc, 47, PhD(chem), 54. *Prof Exp:* Garioa fel, Harvard Univ, 50-52; asst prof chem, Nagoya Univ, 55-58; prof, Tokyo Kyoiku Univ, 58-63 & Tohoku Univ, Japan, 63-69; PROF CHEM, COLUMBIA UNIV, 69- *Concurrent Pos:* Consult, Syntex/Zoecon Corp, 65- & Lederle Labs, 69- *Honors & Awards:* Chem Soc Japan Award, 54 & 79; Cult Award, Asahi Press, Japan, 68; E Guenther Award, Am Chem Soc, 78. *Mem:* Am Chem Soc; Chem Soc France; Royal Soc Chem; Chem Soc Japan; fel Am Acad Arts & Sci. *Res:* Isolation and structural studies of physiologically active natural products; applications of spectroscopy to structure determination; visual pigments. *Mailing Add:* Dept Chem Columbia Univ New York NY 10027

NAKANO, JAMES HIROTO, b Hiroshima, Japan, Jan 17, 22; nat US; m 47; c 3. MICROBIOLOGY, EXPERIMENTAL PATHOLOGY. *Educ:* Stanford Univ, AB, 47, MA, 51, PhD(bact), 53. *Prof Exp:* Asst dir labs clin path, Kaiser Found Hosp, 54-59; virologist, Commun Dis Ctr, 59-65, chief vesicular dis virus lab, 65-67, res microbiologist, Enterovirus Infections Unit, 67-71, chief vesicular dis lab & poliovirus strain characterization lab, 71-72, chief viral vaccine invest sect, 72-74, CHIEF VIRAL EXANTHEMS BR, CTR DIS CONTROL, USPHS, 74-; DIR, COLLAB REF CTR SMALLPOX & OTHER POXVIRUS INFECTIONS, WHO, 74- *Concurrent Pos:* Consult vaccine assoc poliomyelitis, 65-75; dir, Regional Ref Ctr Smallpox, WHO, 71-72, dir, Int Ref Ctr Smallpox, 72-74, consult pox virus, WHO, 71- *Mem:* AAAS; fel Am Acad Microbiol; Sigma Xi; Am Soc Microbiol; NY Acad Sci. *Res:* Enteroviruses; poxviruses; viral immunology. *Mailing Add:* Rm 230 Bldg 7 Viral Exanthems Br Ctr for Dis Control Atlanta GA 30333

NAKASHIMA, TADAYOSHI, b Yokkaichi, Japan, Dec 1, 22; m 47; c 1. BIOCHEMISTRY. *Educ:* Nagoya Pharmaceut Col, BP, 43; Taihoku Imp Univ, BS, 46; Kyushu Univ, PhD(biochem), 61. *Prof Exp:* Fel biochem, Univ Hawaii, 62-64; res scientist biochem, Inst Molecular Evolution, 65-73, res asst prof, 73-77, res assoc prof, 77-81, RES PROF BIOCHEM, INST MOLECULAR & CELLULAR EVOLUTION, UNIV MIAMI, 81- *Concurrent Pos:* Vis res scientist, Inst Animal Physiol, Univ Bonn, Ger, 66-69. *Mem:* Int Soc Study Origin Life; Am Chem Soc; Japanese Soc Food & Nutrit; Sigma Xi. *Res:* Nucleic acid-protein interaction, genetic code, protein synthesis on the model ribosomes, including prebiological chemistry. *Mailing Add:* Inst of Molecular & Cellular Evol Univ of Miami Coral Gables FL 33134

NAKASONE, HENRY YOSHIKI, b Kauai, Hawaii, July 6, 20; m 48; c 2. HORTICULTURE. *Educ:* Univ Hawaii, BA, 43, MS, 52, PhD(genetics), 60. *Prof Exp:* Asst hort, Agr Exp Sta, 48-52, instr plant propagation, Col Agr & jr horticulturist, Agr Exp Sta, 52-58, asst prof plant propagation & trop pomol & asst horticulturist, 58-60, assoc prof & assoc horticulturist, 60-69, chmn dept, 75-80, PROF HORT, COL AGR & HORTICULTURIST, AGR EXP STA, UNIV HAWAII, 69- *Concurrent Pos:* Consult, Heinz Alimentos, Mex, 66-72, Comn Fruit Cult, Mex Govt & DaCosta Bros, Jamaica, 72- *Honors & Awards:* Best Paper Award, Am Soc Hort Sci, 73 & Res Excellence Award, 77. *Mem:* Fel AAAS; Am Soc Hort Sci. *Res:* Plant breeding and culture of tropical crops; genetics of tropical crops. *Mailing Add:* Dept of Hort Univ of Hawaii 3190 Maile Way Honolulu HI 96822

NAKATA, HERBERT MINORU, b Pasadena, Calif, Mar 10, 30; m 60; c 3. BACTERIOLOGY. *Educ:* Univ Ill, BS, 52, MS, 56, PhD, 59. *Prof Exp:* From instr to assoc prof, 59-71, PROF BACT, WASH STATE UNIV, 71-, CHMN DEPT BACT & PUB HEALTH, 68- *Mem:* AAAS; Am Soc Microbiol; Sigma Xi. *Res:* Bacterial physiology, particularly the biochemical processes associated with sporulation of aerobic bacilli. *Mailing Add:* Dept of Bacteriol & Pub Health Wash State Univ Pullman WA 99164

NAKATA, SHIGERU, b Honolulu, Hawaii, Nov 15, 19; m 47; c 2. PLANT PHYSIOLOGY. *Educ:* Univ Hawaii, BS, 47, MS, 49, PhD(bot), 65. *Prof Exp:* Asst plant physiologist, 59-67, ASSOC PLANT PHYSIOLOGIST, UNIV HAWAII, 67- *Concurrent Pos:* Mem staff, Purdue Univ, 65-66. *Mem:* AAAS; Bot Soc Am. *Res:* Growth and development of plants, especially floral initiation in subtropical plants; mineral nutrition and water stress. *Mailing Add:* Dept of Plant Physiol Univ of Hawaii 3190 Maile Way Honolulu HI 96822

NAKATANI, ROY E, b Seattle, Wash, June 8, 18; m 55; c 5. FISH BIOLOGY. *Educ:* Univ Wash, BS, 47, PhD(fisheries), 60. *Prof Exp:* Fishery biologist, Fisheries Res Inst, 47-48; res assoc blood chem salmonoids, Univ Wash, 52-58, anal past Alaskan fisheries data, 58-59; biol scientist, Hanford Labs, Gen Elec Co, 59-62, mgr aquatic biol, 62-66; mgr ecol, Pac Northwest Labs, Battelle Mem Inst, 66-70; assoc prof fisheries, 70-73, PROF FISHERIES, UNIV WASH, 73-, ASSOC DIR FISHERIES RES INST & PROG DIR, DIV MARINE RESOURCES, 70- *Concurrent Pos:* Consult, Wash Pub Power Supply Syst, ARCO & Puget Power & Light; mem panel radioactivity in marine environ & biol effects of ionizing radiation subcomt environ effects, Nat Acad Sci-Nat Res Coun. *Mem:* AAAS; Am Inst Fishery Res Biol; Am Soc Limnol & Oceanog; Int Acad Fishery Sci; Am Fisheries Soc. *Res:* Radiation biology of aquatic organisms; water pollution; nuclear power plant siting; oil pollution. *Mailing Add:* Fisheries Res Inst Univ of Wash Seattle WA 98195

NAKATO, TATSUAKI, b Okayama, Japan, Jan 17, 42; m 79; c 1. HYDRAULIC MODELING, SEDIMENT TRANSPORT. *Educ:* Nagoya Univ, Japan, BS, 66, MS, 68; Univ Iowa, PhD(mech & hydraul), 74. *Prof Exp:* Res asst, 71-74, asst res scientist, 75-78, RES SCIENTIST, INST HYDRAUL RES, UNIV IOWA, 78- *Concurrent Pos:* Adj asst prof hydraul, Inst Hydraul Res, Univ Iowa, 77- *Mem:* Japan Soc Civil Eng; Am Soc Civil Engrs; Sigma Xi. *Res:* Hydraulic models, including pump-intake structures and thermal-discharge schemes; analyzing mathematical models of various types of sediment-transport phenomena. *Mailing Add:* 806 9th Ave Coralville IA 52241

NAKATSU, KANJI, b Greenwood, BC, June 19, 45; m 71; c 2. PHARMACOLOGY. *Educ:* Univ Alta, BSc, 64, MSc, 68; Univ BC, PhD(pharmacol), 71. *Prof Exp:* Student pharmacol, Univ Alta, 66-68, Univ BC, 68-71; fel, Stanford Univ, 71-73; asst prof, 73-79, ASSOC PROF PHARMACOL, QUEEN'S UNIV, 79- *Concurrent Pos:* Consult, Dept Med, Div Respirology, Queen's Univ, 76-; vis scientist, Baylor Col Med, 79-80. *Mem:* Can Pharmacol Soc; Am Soc Pharmaceut & Exp Therapeut. *Res:* Pharmacology of morphone esters; pharmacological characteristics of adenine derivative receptors and physiological role of the receptors; pharmacokinetics of anti-asthmatic drugs; environmental toxins. *Mailing Add:* Dept Pharmacol Queen's Univ Kingston ON K7L 3N6 Can

NAKATSUGAWA, TSUTOMU, b Kochi-Ken, Japan, Apr 17, 33; m 65; c 3. ENVIRONMENTAL TOXICOLOGY, INSECTICIDE TOXICOLOGY. *Educ:* Univ Tokyo, BAgr, 57; Iowa State Univ, MS, 61, PhD(insect toxicol), 64. *Prof Exp:* Asst entomologist, Nat Inst Agr Sci, Tokyo, 57-60; res assoc insect toxicol, Iowa State Univ, 64-68; from asst to assoc prof, 68-76, PROF INSECTICIDE TOXICOL, COL ENVIRON SCI & FORESTRY, STATE UNIV NY, 76- *Mem:* AAAS; Am Chem Soc; Entom Soc Am; Soc Toxicol; Soc Environ Toxicol & Chem. *Res:* Detoxication and health effects of insecticides and environmental toxicants with emphasis on liver toxicology. *Mailing Add:* Dept of Environ & Forest Biol Col Environ Sci & Forestry Syracuse NY 13210

NAKAYAMA, FRANCIS SHIGERU, b Honolulu, Hawaii, July 1, 30. SOIL CHEMISTRY. *Educ:* Univ Hawaii, BS, 52; Iowa State Univ, MS, 55, PhD(soil fertil), 58. *Prof Exp:* Asst, Iowa State Univ, 53-58; CHEMIST, US WATER CONSERV LAB, USDA, 58- *Mem:* AAAS; Am Inst Chem; Am Soc Agron; Am Chem Soc. *Res:* Solubility of calcium constituents of soil and calcium complex formation; interrelation between water quality, trickle irrigation operation and soil water movement; neutron soil moisture equipment. *Mailing Add:* US Water Conserv Lab 4331 E Broadway Phoenix AZ 85040

NAKAYAMA, ROY MINORU, b Dona Ana, NMex, Sept 11, 23. PLANT BREEDING, HORTICULTURE. *Educ:* NMex Col, BS, 48; Iowa State Univ, MS, 50, PhD, 60. *Prof Exp:* Asst plant path, Exp Sta, NMex Col, 51-53; asst plant pathologist, Plant Path Bur, State Dept Agr, Calif, 53-56; asst prof agr sci, 56-60, asst prof hort, 60-69, assoc prof, 69-80, PROF HORT, NMEX STATE UIV, 80- *Mem:* Am Hort Soc. *Res:* Breeding of chile peppers and pecans. *Mailing Add:* Dept of Hort NMex State Univ Las Cruces NM 88003

NAKAYAMA, TAKAO, b Sacramento, Calif, Sept 19, 13; m 41; c 2. PHYTOPATHOLOGY, HORTICULTURE. *Educ:* Univ Calif, BS, 37. *Prof Exp:* Plant pathologist, Ohara Inst Agr Res, 40-46; agriculturist & dir, Chofu Hydroponic Farm, Japan, 46-61; horticulturist, US Army Procurement Agency Japan, 62-74; horticulturist, Pac Air Force Procurement Ctr, Japan, 74-81. *Concurrent Pos:* Agr consult, Land Auth, Govt PR, 59, Repub Korea, 64-65 & Repub China, Thailand & SVietnam, 66-68. *Mem:* Am Phytopath Soc; Phytopath Soc Japan. *Res:* Wheat scab and vegetable diseases; vegetable production; hydroponic vegetable production; technical and economical implications surrounding production of fresh fruits and vegetables in Japan and far eastern countries. *Mailing Add:* 1-61 Nishishiba Kanazawa-Ku Yokohama 236 Japan

NAKAYAMA, TOMMY, b Ballico, Calif, Mar 15, 28; m 57; c 4. FOOD SCIENCE. *Educ:* Univ Calif, Berkeley, BS, 51, MS, 52, PhD(agr chem), 57. *Prof Exp:* Jr specialist, Univ Calif, Berkeley, 54-57, asst specialist, 57-58; asst prof food sci & technol, Univ Calif, Davis, 59-63; res supvr, Miller Brewing Co, 63-66; assoc prof food sci, Univ Ga, 66-70; prof, Univ Hawaii, 70-77; PROF FOOD SCI & HEAD DEPT, UNIV GA, 77- *Mem:* Inst Food Technol; Am Chem Soc; Am Soc Advan Sci; Sigma Xi. *Res:* Carotenoids and polyphenolic compounds in foods; agricultural waste utilization; small scale processing of foods. *Mailing Add:* Dept Food Sci Ga Sta Experiment GA 30212

NAKON, ROBERT STEVEN, b Brooklyn, NY, May 1, 44. INORGANIC CHEMISTRY. *Educ:* DePaul Univ, BS, 65; Tex A&M Univ, PhD(inorg chem), 71. *Prof Exp:* Fel inorg chem, Iowa State Univ, 71-73 & Memphis State Univ, 73-74; asst prof, 74-78, ASSOC PROF INORG CHEM, WVA UNIV, 79- *Mem:* Am Chem Soc; AAAS. *Res:* Metal complexes as catalysts for biomimetic reactions; metal ion interactions with "Good's" buffers and other biologically important substances; correlation of reactivity with the structures of metal chelates as intermediates. *Mailing Add:* Dept Chem WVa Univ Morgantown WV 26506

NALBANDIAN, JOHN, b Providence, RI, Nov 26, 32; m 70. ORAL PATHOLOGY, ELECTRON MICROSCOPY. *Educ:* Brown Univ, AB, 54; Harvard Univ, DMD, 58. *Prof Exp:* Res assoc periodont, Sch Dent Med, Harvard Univ, 62-63, assoc, 63-64, asst prof oper dent, 64-69; prof gen dent, Sch Dent Med, Hosp, Univ Conn, Hartford, 69-74, head dept, 69-71; PROF PERIODONT, HEALTH CTR, UNIV CONN, FARMINGTON, 74- *Concurrent Pos:* Fel periodont, Sch Dent Med, Harvard Univ, 58-61; USPHS spec fel, Nat Inst Dent Res, 61-62; actg head dept periodont, Health Ctr, Univ Conn, 74-75; Fogarty Sr Int fel, 77-78. *Mem:* AAAS; Int Asn Dent Res. *Res:* Dental aspects of aging; dental embryology; ultrastructure of oral tissues and of bone; bone resorption; dental caries; dental plaque. *Mailing Add:* Dept of Periodont Univ of Conn Health Ctr Farmington CT 06032

NALDRETT, ANTHONY JAMES, b London, Eng, June 23, 33; m 60; c 3. GEOLOGY. *Educ:* Cambridge Univ, BA, 56, MA, 62; Queen's Univ, MSc, 61, PhD(geol), 64. *Prof Exp:* Geologist, Falconbridge Nickel Mines Ltd, 57-59; fel geochem, Geophys Lab, Carnegie Inst Wash, 64-67; from asst prof to assoc prof, 67-72, PROF GEOL, UNIV TORONTO, 72- *Concurrent Pos:* Mem, Comn Exp Petrol, Int Union Geol Sci; ed, J Petrol, 73-; mem, Earth Sci Grant Selection Comt, Nat Res Coun, 75-78, chmn, 77-78; mem, Panel Geochem & Petrol, NSF. *Honors & Awards:* Barlow Medal, Can Inst Mining & Metall, 74; Dun Derry Medal, Geol Asn Can, 80. *Mem:* Geol Soc Am; Can Inst Mining & Metall; Geol Asn Can; Soc Econ Geol; Mineral Asn Can. *Res:* Geology and geochemistry of nickel deposits; geology of the Sudbury area; petrology of mafic and ultramafic rocks; experimental geochemistry of sulfide, sulfide-oxide and sulfide-silicate systems. *Mailing Add:* Dept of Geol Univ of Toronto Toronto ON M55 1A1 Can

NALEWAJA, JOHN DENNIS, b Browerville, Minn, Oct 7, 30; m 59; c 3. WEED SCIENCE. *Educ:* Univ Minn, BS, 53, MS, 59, PhD(agron), 62. *Prof Exp:* PROF WEED SCI, NDAK STATE UNIV, 62- *Mem:* Weed Sci Soc Am. *Res:* Basic and applied aspects of weed science. *Mailing Add:* Dept of Agron NDak State Univ Fargo ND 58105

NALIN, DAVID ROBERT, b New York, NY, Apr 22, 41. MEDICAL RESEARCH. *Educ:* Cornell Univ, AB, 61; Albany Med Col, MD, 65. *Prof Exp:* Intern & resident med, Montefiore Hosp, New York, 66-67; res assoc, Cholera Res Hosp, Off Int Res, NIH, 67-70; sr resident, Boston City Hosp, 70-71; instr, Sch Med, Dept Med & res assoc pathobiol, Sch Hyg & Pub Health, Johns Hopkins Univ, 71-72, asst prof med & pathobiol, 72-76; ASSOC PROF, INT HEALTH & ASSOC PROF EPIDEMIOLOGY & PREV MED, UNIV MD MED COL, BALTIMORE, 76- *Concurrent Pos:* Guest scientist, Cholera Res Lab, Dacca, Bangladesh & sr consult, Int Rescue Comt, 72-75; dir, Univ Md Pakistan Med Res Ctr, Lahore, 1979082. *Mem:* Royal Soc Trop Med & Hyg; Infectious Dis Soc; Am Soc Microbiol. *Res:* Infectious diseases, particularly enteric, including treatment and pathophysiology; tropical diseases and adaptation of medical technology to needs of developing countries. *Mailing Add:* Dept Int Health Univ Md Rm 8-36 10 S Pine St Baltimore MD 21201

NALL, RAY(MOND) W(ILLETT), b Flaherty, Ky, Nov 21, 39; c 3. LIMNOLOGY, BOTANY. *Educ:* Western Ky Univ, BS, 61; Univ Louisville, PhD(bot), 65. *Prof Exp:* Staff biologist, 65, RESOURCE PROJS MGR, TENN VALLEY AUTHORITY, 73- *Concurrent Pos:* Asst prof, Murray State Univ, 70-72, adj prof, 70-73. *Mem:* Am Soc Limnol & Oceanog; Sigma Xi; Nat Management Asn. *Res:* Water pollution ecology; life histories of deer and wild turkey; improved techniques for management of natural resources. *Mailing Add:* Forestry Bldg Tenn Valley Authority Norris TN 37828

NALLEY, DONALD WOODROW, b Easley, SC, Aug 14, 32; c 2. ELECTRICAL ENGINEERING, COMPUTER SCIENCE. *Educ:* Clemson Univ, BSEE, 61, PhD(elec eng), 71; Univ Ark, MS, 65. *Prof Exp:* Engr, Naval Ord Lab, Md, 61-65 & Union Bleachery, SC, 65; instr elec eng, Clemson Univ, 66-68; consult, Comput Sci Corp, Ala, 69; asst prof elec eng & dir Burton Comput Ctr, McNeese State Univ, 70-76; SUBSYSTS MGR, UNITED SPACE BOOSTERS, INC, 76- *Concurrent Pos:* Burton Found grant, Burton Comput Ctr, McNeese State Univ, 71-74. *Mem:* Inst Elec & Electronics Engrs; Simulation Coun. *Res:* Fault isolation; feature extraction; x-ray diagnostics. *Mailing Add:* United Space Boosters Inc Bldg 4666 MSFC Huntsville AL 35812

NALLEY, SAMUEL JOSEPH, b Benton, Ark, May 5, 43; m 62; c 2. ATOMIC PHYSICS, MOLECULAR PHYSICS. *Educ:* State Col Ark, BS, 65; Univ Tenn, Knoxville, MS, 67, PhD(physics), 71. *Prof Exp:* Asst prof, 71-74, ASSOC PROF PHYSICS, CHATTANOOGA STATE TECH COMMUNITY COL, 74- *Mem:* Am Phys Soc; Am Asn Physics Teachers. *Res:* Atomic and molecular collision. *Mailing Add:* Dept Physics Chattanooga State Tech Com Col Chattanooga TN 37406

NALOS, ERVIN JOSEPH, b Prague, Czech, Sept 10, 24; nat US; m 47; c 3. PHYSICS. *Educ:* Univ BC, BASc, 46, MASc, 47; Stanford Univ, PhD(elec eng), 51. *Prof Exp:* Res assoc microwave physics, 50-54; group leader microwave tube develop & res, Microwave Lab, Gen Elec Co, Calif, 54-59, sci rep to Europe, Res Lab, 59-62; staff engr, Off Vpres Res & Develop, 62-69, mgr appl technol, Military Airplane Systs Div, 69-71, supvr civil & com systs, 71-78, SUPVR ELECTROMAGNETICS & ENG TECHNOL, BOEING AEROSPACE CO, 78- *Honors & Awards:* Baker Award, Inst Radio Eng, 59. *Mem:* Sr mem Inst Elec & Electronics Eng; Sigma Xi. *Res:* Electron physics and electronics; high power microwave devices. *Mailing Add:* M/S 8C-62 Boeing Aerospace Co PO Box 3999 Seattle WA 98124

NAMBA, RYOJI, b Honolulu, Hawaii, Jan 31, 22; m 48; c 4. ENTOMOLOGY. *Educ:* Mich State Col, BS, 48, MS, 50; Univ Minn, PhD(entom), 53. *Prof Exp:* From asst entomologist to assoc entomologist, 53-68, ENTOMOLOGIST, AGR EXP STA, UNIV HAWAII, 68-, PROF ENTOM, 76- *Mem:* Entom Soc Am. *Res:* Leafhoppers; insect transmission of plant pathogens. *Mailing Add:* Dept Entom Univ Hawaii 3050 Maile Way Honolulu HI 96822

NAMBA, TATSUJI, b Changchun, China, Jan 29, 27. NEUROLOGY, PHARMACOLOGY. *Educ:* Okayama Univ, MD, 50, PhD(med), 56. *Prof Exp:* Asst med, Med Sch, Okayama Univ, 56-57, lectr, 57-62; res assoc, 62-64, from asst attend physician to assoc attend physician, 64-71, dir neuromuscular dis labs, 66-71, ATTEND PHYSICIAN, MAIMONIDES MED CTR, 71-, HEAD ELECTROMYOGRAPHY CLIN, 66-, DIR NEUROMUSCULAR DIS DIV, 71-; PROF MED, STATE UNIV NY DOWNSTATE MED CTR, 76- *Concurrent Pos:* Res fel, Maimonides Med Ctr, 59-62; Fulbright fel, 59-62; consult, Fukuyama Defense Force Hosp, Japan, 57-59; from instr to assoc prof, State Univ NY Downstate Med Ctr, 59-76; from asst vis physician to assoc vis physician, Kings County Hosp Ctr, 65-73, vis physician, 73-; from asst attend physician to assoc attend physician, Coney Island Hosp, 66-74, attend physician, 74-; attend physician, State Univ Hosp, 66-; mem, Med Adv Bd, Myasthenia Gravis Found. *Mem:* Am Col Physicians; Am Acad Neurol; Am Soc Pharmacol & Exp Therapeut; Am Soc Clin Pharmacol & Chemother; AMA. *Res:* Basic and clinical research of skeletal muscle and neuromuscular diseases; clinical pharmacology of neuromuscular agents. *Mailing Add:* Maimonides Med Ctr 4802 Tenth Ave Brooklyn NY 11219

NAMBOODIRI, MADASSERY NEELAKANTAN, b Kothamangalam, India, Oct 18, 35; m 63; c 1. NUCLEAR CHEMISTRY. *Educ:* Kerala Univ, India, BSc, 57; State Univ NY Stony Brook, PhD(chem), 72. *Prof Exp:* Sci officer radiochem, Bhabha Atomic Res Ctr, Bombay, India, 58-67; RES SCIENTIST NUCLEAR CHEM, CYCLOTRON INST, TEX A&M UNIV, 72- *Concurrent Pos:* Res affil chem, Argonne Nat Lab, 60-61. *Mem:* Am Phys Soc; AAAS. *Res:* Nuclear reactions, especially heavy ion induced reactions, with emphasis on fission, heavy ion fusion, deep inelastic reactions and related phenomena. *Mailing Add:* Cyclotron Inst Tex A&M Univ College Station TX 77843

NAMBU, YOICHIRO, b Tokyo, Japan, Jan 18, 21; m 45; c 2. THEORETICAL PHYSICS. *Educ:* Univ Tokyo, BS, 42, ScD, 52. *Prof Exp:* Asst, Univ Tokyo, 45-49; from asst prof to prof, Osaka City Univ, 49-56; res assoc, 54-56, from assoc prof to prof, 56-71, DISTINGUISHED SERV PROF PHYSICS, ENRICO FERMI INST NUCLEAR STUDIES, UNIV CHICAGO, 71-, HARRY PRATT JUDSON DIST SERV PROF, 77- *Concurrent Pos:* Mem, Inst Advan Study, 52-54. *Honors & Awards:* Dannie Heineman Prize Math Physics, Am Phys Soc, 70; J Robert Oppenheimer Prize, 76. *Mem:* Nat Acad Sci; Am Phys Soc; Am Acad Arts & Sci. *Res:* Field theory; theory of elementary particles; theory of superconductivity. *Mailing Add:* Dept Physics E Fermi Inst for Nuclear Studies Univ of Chicago Chicago IL 60637

NAMER, IZAK, b Istanbul, Turkey, Nov 14, 52; US citizen; m 75; c 1. COMBUSTION, FLUID MECHANICS. *Educ:* City Col New York, BE, 75; Univ Calif, Berkeley, MS, 76, PhD(mech eng), 80. *Prof Exp:* Res asst, Univ Calif, Berkeley, 75-80; ASST PROF MECH ENG, DREXEL UNIV, 80- *Concurrent Pos:* Consult, Lotepro Corp, New York, 81, Gen Eng Assoc, Philadelphia, 81. *Mem:* Am Inst Aeronaut & Astronaut; Am Soc Mech Engrs; Combustion Inst. *Res:* Studies on impinging jets, turbulent flames, spray combustion, free convection flows, and incineration of hazardous waste. *Mailing Add:* 1168 Barbara Dr Cherry Hill NJ 08003

NAMEROFF, MARK A, b Philadelphia, Pa, May 16, 39. DEVELOPMENTAL BIOLOGY. *Educ:* Univ Pa, BA, 60, MD, 65, PhD(anat embryol), 66. *Prof Exp:* Instr anat, Sch Med, Univ Pa, 66-67; staff mem, Armed Forces Inst Path, Washington, DC, 67-70; asst prof, 70-75, ASSOC PROF BIOL STRUCT, UNIV WASH, 75- *Res:* Cell differentiation; embryonic chondrocytes and muscle cells. *Mailing Add:* Dept of Biol Struct Univ of Wash Seattle WA 98195

NAMIAS, JEROME, b Bridgeport, Conn, Mar 19, 10; m 38; c 1. METEOROLOGY. *Educ:* Mass Inst Technol, MS, 41. *Hon Degrees:* ScD, Univ RI, 72. *Prof Exp:* Asst aerology, Blue Hill Meteorol Observ, Harvard Univ, 33-36; res assoc, Mass Inst Technol, 35-40; chief extended forecast div, US Weather Bur, Nat Oceanic & Atmospheric Agency, 41-71; RES METEOROLOGIST, SCRIPPS INST OCEANOG, UNIV CALIF, SAN DIEGO, 72- *Concurrent Pos:* Meteorologist, Trans World Airlines, Inc, 34; lectr, Univ Stockholm, 50; assoc, Woods Hole Oceanog Inst, 54-, mem sci vis comt, 64-; distinguished lectr, Pa State Univ, 62; res meteorologist, Scripps Inst Oceanog, 68-71; vis scholar, Rockefeller Study & Conf Ctr, Bellagio, Italy, 77. *Honors & Awards:* Meisinger Award, 38; Sverdrup Gold Medal, Am Meteorol Soc, 81. *Mem:* Fel Am Meteorol Soc; fel AAAS; fel Am Geophys Union; fel NY Acad Sci; Royal Meteorol Soc. *Res:* Long range weather forecasting and general circulation of atmosphere; aerology; large scale air-sea interaction. *Mailing Add:* Scripps Inst of Oceanog Univ of Calif at San Diego La Jolla CA 92093

NAMKOONG, GENE, b New York, NY, Jan 25, 34; m 56; c 3. FOREST GENETICS, EVOLUTION. *Educ:* State Univ NY, BS, 56, MS, 58; NC State Univ, PhD(genetics), 63. *Prof Exp:* Res forester, 58-60, plant geneticist, 63-71, PIONEERING RES SCIENTIST POP GENETICS, FOREST SERV, USDA, 71- *Concurrent Pos:* From asst prof to assoc prof genetics & forestry, NC State Univ, 63-71, prof, 71-; vis prof, Univ Chicago, 68; consult, BC Forest Serv, 72- & Repub Korea Forest Serv, 74-; adj prof, Shaw Univ, 75-; group leader genetics, Int Union Forest Res Orgn, 76-; sci policy adv, Dept Admin, NC, 77-78; chmn genetics working group, Soc Am Foresters, 78-80; vis prof, Oxford Univ, 79. *Honors & Awards:* Sci Achievement Award, Int Union Forest Res Orgns, 71. *Mem:* Biomet Soc; Genetics Soc Am; Am Soc Nat; Soc Study Evolution. *Res:* Mathematical, population genetics, particularly with respect to forest tree species. *Mailing Add:* 811 Beaver Dam Rd Raleigh NC 27607

NAMM, DONALD H, b Hamden, Conn, Feb 10, 40; m 63; c 2. PHARMACOLOGY. *Educ:* Rensselaer Polytech Inst, BS, 61; Albany Med Col, PhD(pharmacol), 65. *Prof Exp:* Instr pharmacol, Emory Univ, 67-68; asst prof, Sch Med, Univ Okla, 68-69; sr res pharmacologist, 69-75, GROUP LEADER, RES LABS, BURROUGHS-WELLCOME CO, 75- *Concurrent Pos:* Fel pharmacol, Emory Univ, 65-67. *Mem:* Am Soc Pharmacol & Exp Therapeut. *Res:* Heart metabolism; blood vessel metabolism; drug-enzyme interactions. *Mailing Add:* Dept of Pharmacol Wellcome Res Labs Research Triangle Park NC 27709

NAMMINGA, HAROLD EUGENE, b Scotland, SDak, July 26, 45; m 73; c 1. FISHERIES ECOLOGY, LIMNOLOGY. *Educ:* Univ SDak at Springfield, BS, 67; Univ SDak at Vermillion, MA, 69; Okla State Univ, PhD(zool), 75. *Prof Exp:* Instr biol, Kearney State Col, 69-71; environ scientist-ecol, technol res & develop, Inc Div, Benham-Blair & Affil, 75-78; ASST CHIEF RES, FISH DIV, OKLA DEPT WILDLIFE CONSERV, 78- *Mem:* Am Fisheries Soc; Am Soc Limnol & Oceanog; Am Inst Biol Sci. *Res:* Fish commmunity structure, predator-prey relationships and effects of fishing mortality on populations of sportfish; secondary interests include heavy metals in aquatic ecosystems and the effects of metals on aquatic community structure. *Mailing Add:* Okla Dept Wildlife Conserv Fish Div PO Box 53465 Oklahoma City OK 73152

NAMY, JEROME NICHOLAS, b Cleveland, Ohio, Aug 11, 38; m 63; c 3. PETROLOGY, STRATIGRAPHY. *Educ:* Western Reserve Univ, BA, 60; Univ Tex, Austin, PhD(geol), 69. *Prof Exp:* Explor geologist, Pan Am Petrol Corp, Standard Oil Co, Ind, 67-70; asst prof, Baylor Univ, 70-73, assoc prof geol, 73-80; MEM STAFF, TAXLAND PETROL, 80- *Mem:* Nat Asn Geol Teachers; Geol Soc Am; Am Asn Petrol Geologists; Sigma Xi; Soc Econ Paleontologists & Mineralogists. *Res:* The stratigraphy and petrology of carbonate and sedimentary rocks. *Mailing Add:* Taxland Petrol 3402 Ft Worth Nat Bank Building Fort Worth TX 76102

NANCARROW, WARREN GEORGE, b Texarkana, Tex, Aug 10, 23; m 47; c 4. PETROLEUM ENGINEERING. *Educ:* Tex A&M Univ, BS, 47. *Prof Exp:* Petrol engr, Standard Oil Co, Ind, 47-54; petrol engr, 54-66, vpres, 66-68, sr vpres petrol eng, 68-78, CHMN BD, DE GOLYER & MACNAUGHTON, INC, 78- *Mem:* Am Petrol Inst; Am Inst Mining, Metall & Petrol Engrs. *Res:* Petroleum drilling, production and reservoir study. *Mailing Add:* One Energy Sq Dallas TX 75206

NANCE, DWIGHT MAURICE, b Bartlesville, Okla, Jan 31, 43. NEUROSCIENCE, PSYCHOBIOLOGY. *Educ:* Okla State Univ, BS, 65, MS, 67, PhD(psychol), 69. *Prof Exp:* Fel physiological psychol, Univ Houston, 69-70; fel reproductive physiol, Worcester Found Exp Biol, 70-72; res anatomist neuroendocrinol, Univ Calif, Los Angeles, 72-77; asst prof anat, Univ SFla, 77-79; ASSOC PROF ANAT, DALHOUSIE UNIV, 79- *Concurrent Pos:* NIMH sr fel, Worcester Found Exp Biol, 70-71; trainee reproductive physiol, 71-72; co-prin investr, Nat Inst Arthritis & Metab Dis, NIH grant, Univ Calif, Los Angeles, 72-77; co-investr, Nat Inst Child Health & Human Develop, NIH grant, Univ SFla, 77-80; prin investr, Can Med Res Coun, Dalhousie Univ, 81- *Mem:* Soc Neurosci; Am Asn Anatomists. *Mailing Add:* Dept Anat Col Med Dalhousie Univ Halifax NS B3H 4H7 Can

NANCE, FRANCIS CARTER, b Manila, Philippines, Jan 1, 32; US citizen; m 59; c 4. SURGERY, PHYSIOLOGY. *Educ:* Univ Tenn, MD & MS, 59. *Prof Exp:* Instr surg, 65-67, from asst prof to assoc prof surg & physiol, 67-73, PROF SURG & PHYSIOL, LA STATE UNIV SCH MED, NEW ORLEANS, 73- *Concurrent Pos:* Am Cancer Soc fel, Univ Pa, 63-64. *Mem:* AAAS; Am Gastroenterol Soc; Am Col Surgeons; Am Asn Surg Trauma; Am Surg Asn. *Res:* Gastrointestinal physiology; effects of microbial flora on various gastrointestinal functions and diseases; burns. *Mailing Add:* Dept of Surg 1542 Tulane Ave New Orleans LA 70112

NANCE, JOHN ARTHUR, b Ralls, Tex, Jan 26, 19; m 44; c 3. NUTRITION. *Educ:* Tex A&M Univ, BS, 41; Iowa State Univ, MS, 47; Okla State Univ, PhD(animal sci), 52. *Prof Exp:* Instr animal sci, Navarro Jr Col, 47-48; asst prof, Tex A&I Univ, 48-49; PROF AGR, SAM HOUSTON STATE UNIV, 52- *Mem:* Am Soc Animal Sci. *Res:* Ruminant nutrition; roughage substitutes. *Mailing Add:* Dept of Agr Sam Houston State Univ Huntsville TX 77340

NANCE, JON ROLAND, physics, see previous edition

NANCE, RICHARD E, b Raleigh, NC, July 22, 40; m 62; c 2. COMPUTER SCIENCE, OPERATIONS RESEARCH. *Educ:* NC State Univ, BS, 62, MS, 66; Purdue Univ, PhD(opers res), 68. *Prof Exp:* From asst prof to assoc prof comput sci & opers res, Southern Methodist Univ, 68-73; head, Dept Comput Sci, Va Polytech Inst & State Univ, 73-79; comput scientist, Naval Surface Weapons Ctr, 79-80; PROF, DEPT COMPUT SCI, VA POLYTECH INST & STATE UNIV, 80- *Concurrent Pos:* Area ed comput struct & technol, Opers Res & simulation, gaming & info systs, Am Inst Indust Engrs Trans; sr res assoc, Imp Col, UK, 80. *Mem:* Asn Comput Mach; Opers Res Soc Am; Inst Mgt Sci; Am Soc Info Sci; Am Inst Indust Engrs. *Res:* Digital simulation theory; mathematical models of information networks; theory of information retrieval; computer systems modeling and performance evaluation. *Mailing Add:* Dept Comput Sci Va Polytech Inst & State Univ Blacksburg VA 24061

NANCE, WALTER ELMORE, b Manila, Philippines, Mar 25, 33; US citizen; m 57; c 2. HUMAN GENETICS, INTERNAL MEDICINE. *Educ:* Univ of South, SB, 54; Harvard Univ, MD, 58; Univ Wis, PhD(med genetics), 68. *Prof Exp:* From intern to resident med, Sch Med, Vanderbilt Univ, 58-61, asst prof, Sch Med, Vanderbilt Univ, 64-69; prof genetics & med, Sch Med, Ind Univ, Indianapolis, 69-75; PROF HUMAN GENETICS & CHMN DEPT, MED COL VA, 75-, PROF MED & PEDIAT, 76- *Concurrent Pos:* Mem, Genetics Training Comt, Nat Inst Gen Med Sci, 71-74; prin investr, Ind Univ Human Genetics Ctr, 74-75; consult, Nat Inst Neurol Dis & Stroke, Annual Surv Hearing Impaired Children & Youth & Genetics Sect, WHO; mem, Epidemiol & Dis Control Study Sect, NIH, 75-79. *Mem:* AAAS; Math Asn Am; Am Soc Human Genetics (secy, 71-74); Int Soc Twin Studies; fel Am Col Physicians. *Res:* Medical genetics; hereditary deafness; human twin studies; population genetics; analysis of human genetic polymorphisms; genetically determined disorders of metabolism. *Mailing Add:* Dept Genetics Med Col Va Box 33 Richmond VA 23298

NANCOLLAS, GEORGE H, b Wales, Brit, Sept 24, 28; m 54; c 2. PHYSICAL CHEMISTRY, INORGANIC CHEMISTRY. *Educ:* Univ Wales, BSc, 48, PhD(phys chem), 51; Glasgow Univ, DSc, 63. *Prof Exp:* Res assoc, Univ Manchester, 51-53; lectr, Glasgow Univ, 53-65; provost fac natural sci & math, 70-75, PROF CHEM, STATE UNIV NY BUFFALO, 65- *Concurrent Pos:* Fel, Univ Wales, 51-52; vis scientist, Brookhaven Nat Lab, 63-64; adj prof chem, Sch Dent, State Univ NY, Buffalo, 70-; chmn anal chem comn on equilibria, Int Union Pure & Appl Chem. *Honors & Awards:* Schoellkopf Medal, Am Chem Soc, 77. *Mem:* AAAS; Faraday Soc; Am Chem Soc; Royal Soc Chem; fel Royal Inst Chem. *Res:* Formation of metal complexes and ion-pairs; inorganic ion exchangers; kinetics of crystal growth and dissolution; the electrical double layer. *Mailing Add:* Dept of Chem State Univ of NY Buffalo NY 14214

NANDA, DEVENDER KUMAR, b Mandibahudin, India, Mar 15, 38; m 66; c 1. PLANT BREEDING, GENETICS. *Educ:* Cent Col Agr, New Delhi, India, BSc, 58; Indian Agr Res Inst, New Delhi, MSc, 60; Univ Wis-Madison, PhD(agron), 64. *Prof Exp:* Res asst sorghum breeding, Rockefeller Found, 60, in-charge field collection corn & millets, 60-61; res agronomist, DeKalb AgRes, Inc, 64-65; dir res corn breeding & genetics, Edward J Funk & Sons, Inc, 65-68; res dir, Eastern Area, Pfizer Genetics Inc, 68-80; DIR RES, O'S GOLD SEED CO, 80- *Mem:* Am Soc Agron; Crop Sci Soc Am; Soil Sci Soc Am. *Res:* Botany; cytology; plant pathology; fungicides; herbicides; teaching; extension; seed production; marketing of seeds; quality control in seeds; crop management; fertilizers; statistics; economics; entomology. *Mailing Add:* O's Gold Seed Co PO Box 460 Parkersburg IA 46076

NANDA, JAGDISH L, b Punjab, India, Feb 1, 33; m 63; c 2. MATHEMATICS. *Educ:* Univ Delhi, BA, 53, MA, 55; Ind Univ, PhD(geom), 61. *Prof Exp:* Asst math, Govt India, New Delhi, 55-57; res assoc, Wright-Patterson AFB, Ohio, 60-62; asst prof, Univ Dayton, 61-63; assoc prof, Villanova Univ, 63; assoc prof, Univ Delhi, 63-64; PROF MATH, EASTERN ILL UNIV, 64- *Mem:* Math Asn Am; Am Math Soc. *Res:* Geometry; relativity. *Mailing Add:* Dept of Math Eastern Ill Univ Charleston IL 61920

NANDA, RAVINDER, b Bombay, India, Sept 12, 36; m 62; c 2. INDUSTRIAL ENGINEERING. *Educ:* Banaras Hindu Univ, BSc, 60; Univ Ill, MS, 60, PhD(indust eng), 62. *Prof Exp:* Asst indust eng, Univ Ill, 59-62; asst prof, Univ Miami, Fla, 62-67; from asst prof to assoc prof, NY Univ, 67-73; ASSOC PROF, POLYTECH INST NY, 73-, DIR INDUST ENG PROG, 75- *Concurrent Pos:* Consult, Case & Co Ohio, 62, Trans World Airlines, 69-70, Port Authority NY & NJ, 69-78, Nashua Corp, 77 & Am Mgt Asn, 80; NSF Inst res grants, 65-67 & initiation res grant, 65-67; mem, Vol Int Tech Assistance; Danforth Assoc. *Mem:* Sr mem Am Inst Indust Engrs; Inst Mgt Sci. *Res:* System analysis and design; operational planning and control; work measurement and productivity improvement, safety and management training. *Mailing Add:* Polytech Inst of NY 333 Jay St Brooklyn NY 11201

NANDA, RAVINDRA, b Layallpur, India, Feb 19, 43; m 66; c 2. ORTHODONTICS, TERATOLOGY. *Educ:* Univ Lucknow, BDS, 64, MDS, 66; Roman Cath Univ, Nijmegen, PhD(med), 69. *Prof Exp:* Res assoc orthod, Roman Cath Univ, Nijmegen, 67-70; asst prof, Col Dent Surg, Loyola Univ, Chicago, 70-73; assoc prof orthod, 73-79, PROF ORTHOD, UNIV CONN HEALTH CTR, FARMINGTON, 79- *Mem:* Teratol Soc; Int Asn Dent Res; Europ Orthod Soc; Indian Dent Asn; Am Asn Orthod. *Res:* Clinical orthodontics; growth and development of face; tooth development; radiotracer studies; craniofacial orthopedics. *Mailing Add:* 3 Wintergreen Lane West Simsbury CT 06092

NANDEDKAR, ARVINDKUMAR NARHARI, b Nagpur, India, Apr 8, 37; m 64; c 2. BIOCHEMISTRY, CLINICAL CHEMISTRY. *Educ:* Univ Nagpur, BSc, 59, MSc, 61; Univ Delhi, PhD(med biochem), 66. *Prof Exp:* Asst res officer, Indian Coun Med Res, V Patel Chest Inst, Univ Delhi, 66; NIH res assoc biochem, Georgetown Univ, 66-68; from instr to asst prof, 68-74, asst dir acad reinforcement prog, 73-81, ASSOC PROF BIOCHEM, HOWARD UNIV, 74-, ACTG CHMN DEPT BIOCHEM, 78- *Concurrent Pos:* AEC fel, Howard Univ, 68-71; vis assoc prof, Cornell Univ Med Ctr, 75-; consult clin biochem, New York Hosp, 75-; consult, Path Lab, Doctors Hosp, Lanham, Md, 76- *Mem:* Am Asn Clin Chemists; fel Am Acad Clin Toxicol; AAAS; Am Chem Soc; fel Am Inst Chem. *Res:* Lipid biochemistry, including clinical application to tuberculosis and anaphylaxis; metabolism of fatty acids in mammary gland; protein chemistry; binding and carrier of metals in body fluids. *Mailing Add:* Dept of Biochem Howard Univ Col of Med Washington DC 20059

NANDI, SATYABRATA, b North Lakhimpur, India, Dec 1, 31; nat US; m 57. ZOOLOGY, ENDOCRINOLOGY. *Educ:* Univ Calcutta, BSc, 49, MSc, 51; Univ Calif, PhD(zool), 58. *Prof Exp:* Demonstr zool, Bethune Col, India, 49-53; lectr, City Col Calcutta, 53; asst biophys, Saha Inst Nuclear Physics, Calcutta, 53-54; asst zool, 54-56, res zoologist, 56-57, jr res zoologist & lectr, 58-59, asst res endocrinologist, 59-61, actg asst prof zool, 61-62, from asst prof to prof, 62-70, Miller prof, 70-71, res endocrinologist, Cancer Res Lab, 68-74, chmn dept zool, 71-73, PROF ZOOL, UNIV CALIF, BERKELEY, 71-, DIR CANCER RES LAB, 74- *Concurrent Pos:* Guggenheim fel, Netherlands Cancer Inst, Amsterdam, 67-68; vis scientist, Virus Res Inst, Kyoto Univ, 65; bd gov, Int Asn for Breast Cancer Res. *Mem:* Am Soc Zoologists; Endocrine Soc; Am Asn Cancer Res. *Res:* Tumor biology, including endocrinology, virology, genetics and hormone receptor. *Mailing Add:* Dept of Zool Univ of Calif Berkeley CA 94720

NANDI, SATYENDRA PROSAD, b Aug 1, 27; US citizen; m 59; c 2. FUEL SCIENCE & TECHNOLOGY, PHYSICAL CHEMISTRY. *Educ:* Dacca Univ, BSc, 49, MSc, 50; Pa State Univ, PhD(fuel technol), 63. *Prof Exp:* Scientist phys chem, Central Fuel Res Inst, 52-60; res assoc fuel sci, Pa State Univ, 63-65, sr res assoc, 68-74; chemist fuel chem, Argonne Nat Lab, 74-76; CHEMIST FUEL PROCESS RES, INST GAS TECHNOL, 76- *Concurrent Pos:* Consult, St Regis Paper Co, 69-71. *Mem:* Am Chem Soc; Am Carbon Soc. *Res:* Surface chemistry of coals; preparation and characterization of active carbons and molecular line carbons; kinetics of gas solid reactions; Fischer Tropsch synthesis. *Mailing Add:* Inst of Gas Technol 3424 S State St Chicago IL 60616

NANDY, KALIDAS, b Calcutta, India, Oct 1, 30; m 61; c 2. GERIATRICS, NEUROANATOMY. *Educ:* Univ Calcutta, MD, 53; Univ Lucknow, MSurg, 60; Emory Univ, PhD(anat), 63. *Prof Exp:* Lectr anat, Univ Calcutta, 54-57, asst prof, 57-60, reader, 60-61; from asst prof to prof anat, Emory Univ, 63-75; DEP DIR & DIR RES, GERIATRIC RES EDUC & CLIN CTR, BEDFORD VET ADMIN HOSP, 75-; prof, 75-81, RES PROF ANAT & NEUROL, BOSTON UNIV, 81- *Concurrent Pos:* Indian Coun Med Res-Rockefeller Found fel, 59-60; Tull fel, 62-63. *Mem:* Am Asn Anat; Geront Soc; Soc Neurosci. *Res:* Neurobiology of aging and senile dementia; gero-pharmacological agents. *Mailing Add:* Geriatric Res Educ & Clin Ctr Vet Admin Hosp 200 Springs Rd Bedford MA 01730

NANES, ROGER, b Brooklyn, NY, Jan 25, 44; m 68; c 3. MOLECULAR SPECTROSCOPY. *Educ:* Harpur Col, BA, 65; Johns Hopkins Univ, PhD(phys chem), 70. *Prof Exp:* Nat Res Coun Can fel spectros, Div Pure Physics, Nat Res Coun Can, Ont, 70-71 & Univ Western Ont, 71-72; asst prof, 72-75, assoc prof, 75-80, PROF PHYSICS, CALIF STATE UNIV, FULLERTON, 80- *Mem:* Am Chem Soc; Am Phys Soc; Soc Appl Spectros. *Res:* Spectroscopy and molecular structure; vapor phase electronic spectroscopy of polyatomic molecules; electric and magnetic field effects on spectra; air pollution. *Mailing Add:* Dept of Physics Calif State Univ Fullerton CA 92634

NANEVICZ, JOSEPH E, b Buckley, Wash, Sept 11, 25; m 55; c 4. ELECTRICAL ENGINEERING. *Educ:* Univ Wash, BS, 51, MS, 53; Stanford Univ, PhD(elec eng), 58. *Prof Exp:* Instr elec eng, Univ Wash, 52-53; engr, Boeing Co, 53-54; res engr, 54-67, prog mgr, 67-79, DEP DIR, ELECTROMAGNETIC SCI LAB, SRI INT, 79- *Concurrent Pos:* NAm ed, J Electrostatics. *Mem:* Sr mem Inst Elec & Electronics Engrs. *Res:* Electromagnetics; noise; plasmas; electrostatics; spacecraft charging. *Mailing Add:* SRI Int 333 Ravenswood Menlo Park CA 94025

NANICHE, GEORGE RENE, b Algiers, France, Jan 5, 26; US citizen; m 55; c 2. CHEMICAL ENGINEERING. *Educ:* Ecole Centrale, Paris, BS, 50; Petrol Sch, Paris, BS, 51; Univ Houston, MS, 53. *Prof Exp:* Jr technologist, Shell Oil Co, Tex, 51-53; design engr, Royal Dutch/Shell, Netherlands, 53-56; process engr, Iranian Oil Refining Co, Iran, 56-58; res engr, Chevron Res Co, 59-67, sr res engr, 67-69, sr econ analyst, 69-73, staff economist, 73-78, sr econ advr, 78-81, MGR, PRICE FORECASTING DIV, STANDARD OIL CO CALIF, 81- *Res:* Oil refining; refining economics; facilities planning; process integration. *Mailing Add:* Standard Oil Co Calif 225 Bush St San Francisco CA 94104

NANKERVIS, GEORGE ARTHUR, b Meriden, Conn, Apr 1, 30; m 54; c 2. PEDIATRICS, MICROBIOLOGY. *Educ:* Princeton Univ, AB, 52; Univ Rochester, PhD(microbiol), 59, MD, 62. *Prof Exp:* From asst prof to assoc prof pediat, Case Western Reserve Univ, 67-76, prof, 76-79; PROF & CHMN, DEPT PEDIAT, MED COL OHIO, 79- *Concurrent Pos:* Teaching fel pediat, Harvard Univ, 64-65; res fel infectious dis, Case Western Reserve Univ, 65-67. *Res:* Diagnostic virology and vaccine evaluation; study of pediatric populations with respect to immune status to infectious diseases; congenital viral infections. *Mailing Add:* Dept Pediat CS 10008 Med Col Ohio Toledo OH 43699

NANKIVELL, JOHN (ELBERT), b Mt Vernon, NY, Jan 31, 21; m 45; c 3. PHYSICS. *Educ:* Stevens Inst Technol, ME, 43, MS, 51, PhD, 62. *Prof Exp:* Mech engr, Gen Elec Co, 43-46; asst prof physics, Stevens Inst Technol, 46-58, res assoc, 58-63; PROF MECH TECHNOL, COL STATEN ISLAND, 63- *Mem:* Am Phys Soc; Int Solar Energy Soc; Am Soc Eng Educ. *Res:* Plasma physics; solar energy. *Mailing Add:* Dept of Mech Technol Col Staten Island Staten Island NY 10301

NANN, HERMANN, b Cologne, WGer, Oct 8, 40; m 68; c 2. NUCLEAR STRUCTURE. *Educ:* Univ Frankfurt, WGer, dipl, 65, PhD(physics), 67, Dr habil, 74. *Prof Exp:* Asst res, Inst Kernphysik, Univ Frankfurt, 68-72, dozent, Dept Physics, 72-74; vis asst prof, Physics Dept, Mich State Univ, 74-76, vis assoc prof, 76-77; sr res assoc, Physics Dept, Northwestern Univ, 77-79; ASSOC PROF, PHYSICS DEPT, IND UNIV, 79- *Mem:* Am Phys Soc; Sigma Xi. *Res:* One, two and three nucleon transfer; inelastic proton scattering; mass measurements; proton induced pion production; pion induced double charge exchange. *Mailing Add:* Physics Dept Ind Univ Bloomington IN 47405

NANNELLI, PIERO, b Montelupo, Italy, Sept 29, 35; m 61; c 2. POLYMER CHEMISTRY. *Educ:* Univ Florence, DSc(org chem), 61. *Prof Exp:* Res assoc inorg polymers, Univ Ill, 61-63; asst prof coord chem, Univ Florence, 63-65; sr res chemist, 65-70, proj leader, 70-72, GROUP LEADER, PENNWALT CORP, 72- *Mem:* Am Chem Soc. *Res:* Inorganic polymers; coordination compounds; high performance structural materials and coatings; conductive polymers; lubricant additives. *Mailing Add:* Pennwalt Corp Technol Ctr 900 First Ave King of Prussia PA 19406

NANNEY, DAVID LEDBETTER, b Abingdon, Va, Oct 10, 25; m 51; c 2. GENETICS. *Educ:* Okla Baptist Univ, AB, 46; Ind Univ, PhD(zool), 51. *Prof Exp:* From asst prof to assoc prof zool, Univ Mich, 51-58; fel, Calif Inst Technol, 58-59; prof zool, 59-76, PROF GENETICS & DEVELOP, UNIV ILL, URBANA, 76- *Mem:* Am Genetics Soc (pres, 82-83); Genetics Soc Am; Soc Protozool; Am Soc Zool; fel Am Acad Arts & Sci. *Res:* Formal genetics, cytogenetics, developmental genetics and evolutionary genetics of ciliated protozoa. *Mailing Add:* Dept Genetics & Develop Univ Ill 505 S Gregory Ave Urbana IL 61801

NANNEY, THOMAS RAY, b Concord, NC, Apr 21, 31; m 54; c 2. PHYSICAL CHEMISTRY, COMPUTER SCIENCE. *Educ:* Univ NC, BS, 53; Univ SC, PhD(phys chem), 62. *Prof Exp:* Chemist, E I du Pont de Nemours & Co, Inc, 53-54; asst prof chem, 60-66, assoc prof chem, 66-77, dir comput ctr, 67-73, assoc prof, 70-72, PROF COMPUT SCI, FURMAN UNIV, 72-, CHMN DEPT, 73- *Concurrent Pos:* Vis asst prof & USPHS & Dept Defense Advan Res Projs Agency fel, 64-65; consult. *Mem:* AAAS; AAAS; Asn Comput Mach. *Res:* Information retrieval; programming languages; artificial intelligence. *Mailing Add:* Comput Ctr Furman Univ Greenville SC 29613

NANZ, ROBERT AUGUSTUS ROLLINS, b Baltimore, Md, Apr 3, 15; m 39. FOOD SCIENCE, NUTRITION. *Educ:* Rutgers Univ, BS, 37; Columbia Univ, MS, 39. *Prof Exp:* Food chemist, Quaker Maid Co, Inc, Great Atlantic & Pac Tea Co, NY, 37-38; biochemist, Watchung Labs, NJ, 38-39; nutrit specialist, Walker-Gordon Lab Co, Inc, 39-43; asst to coordr res, Spec Prod Div, Borden Co, NY, 46-47; dir food tech sect, Foster D Snell, Inc, 47-50; res chemist, Fla Citrus Canners Coop, 50-51; tech rep, Crown Can Co Div, Crown Cork & Seal Co, Fla, 51-53; pres, Fla Chemists & Engrs, Inc, 53-60; pres, Sci Assocs, Inc, 60-62; aerospace technologist, Food & Nutrit Group, Biomed Res Off, Manned Spacecraft Ctr, NASA, Tex, 62-67; asst dir, Nat Ctr Fish Protein Concentrate, US Dept Com, DC, 67-68; proj dir tech develop, Aquatic Sci Inc, Fla, 69-70; CONSULT FOODS & NUTRIT, 70- *Concurrent Pos:* Instr, Col Boca Raton, 71-74; instr, Palm Beach Jr Col, 78. *Mem:* Inst Food Technologists. *Res:* Food processing, formulations; marketing; nutritional factors in food; food service management systems. *Mailing Add:* Apt 701 300 NE 20th St Boca Raton FL 33431

NANZ, ROBERT HAMILTON, JR, b Shelbyville, Ky, Sept 14, 23; m; c 2. GEOLOGY. *Educ:* Miami Univ, AB, 44; Univ Chicago, PhD(geol), 52. *Prof Exp:* Res geologist, Shell Develop Co, 47-58, mgr geol dept, 58-59, dir explor res, 59-64, explor mgr, 64-67, vpres explor & prod res div, 67-70, vpres explor, Shell Oil Co, 70-75, VPRES WESTERN E&P REGION, SHELL OIL CO, 75- *Mem:* Geol Soc Am; Am Asn Petrol Geol. *Res:* Petroleum geology. *Mailing Add:* Shell Oil Co PO Box 576 Houston TX 77001

NANZETTA, PHILIP NEWCOMB, b Wilmington, NC, June 4, 40; m 62; c 2. MATHEMATICS, ACADEMIC ADMINISTRATION. *Educ:* NC State Univ, BS, 62; Univ Ill, MS, 63, PhD(math), 66. *Prof Exp:* Res assoc math, Case Western Reserve Univ, 66-67; asst prof, Univ Fla, 67-70; assoc prof, St Mary's Col Md, 70-74; dean, Fac Natural Sci & Math, 74-79, dir, Ctr Environ Res, 78-79, VPRES ACAD AFFAIRS, STOCKTON STATE COL, 79- *Concurrent Pos:* Mem, NJ Natural Resource Coun, 78-80, NJ Pinelands Comn, 80- & gov sci adv panel, 81- *Mem:* AAAS; Am Math Soc. *Res:* Topology; structure spaces; lattice theory; genetics. *Mailing Add:* Stockton State Col Pomona NJ 08240

NAPHTALI, LEONARD MATHIAS, b Brooklyn, NY, Aug 6, 27; m 58; c 2. SYNTHETIC FUELS, COMPUTER AIDED DESIGN. *Educ:* Cooper Union, BChE, 49; Univ Mich, MSE, 50, PhD(chem eng), 54. *Prof Exp:* Res engr process metall, Sci Lab, Ford Motor Co, 54-56; prof, Polytech Inst Brooklyn, 56-66; mgr comput appln comput serv, Realtime Syss Inc, 66-68; dir petrochem, Sci Resources Corp, 68-70; dep city adminr urban admin, Off of Mayor, New York, NY, 71-72; chief process engr chem processes, Heyward-Robinson Co, 72-74; mgr process anal, Chem Construc Corp, 74-75; PROG MGR COAL GASIFICATION & ASST SECY FOSSIL ENERGY, US DEPT ENERGY, 76- *Concurrent Pos:* Adj prof, Wayne State Univ, 55-56, NY Univ, 54-76 & Columbia Univ, 75-77; consult, var clients, 56-; vis prof, Israel Inst Technol, 65-66. *Mem:* Am Inst Chem Engrs; Am Chem Soc; AAAS. *Res:* Fossil fuel processes; coal gasification; process synthesis; process design; separation processes; distillation; chemical reactor design. *Mailing Add:* 575 West End Ave New York NY 10024

NAPIER, ROGER PAUL, b Rochester, NY, Apr 1, 38; m 65. ORGANIC CHEMISTRY. *Educ:* St John Fisher Col, BS, 59; Univ Rochester, PhD(chem), 63. *Prof Exp:* Fel organophosphorus chem, Rutgers Univ, 63-65; PROJ LEADER, MOBIL CHEM CO, 65- *Mem:* Sr mem Am Chem Soc. *Res:* Natural products; nitrogen heterocycles; organophosphorus chemistry; pesticide chemistry. *Mailing Add:* Rt 1 Box 445 Califon NJ 07830

NAPKE, EDWARD, b Zahle, Lebanon, Jan 21, 24; Can citizen; m 61; c 3. MEDICINE, PHYSIOLOGY. *Educ:* Univ NB, Fredericton, BSc, 45; Univ Toronto, MD, 51, dipl pub health, 68. *Prof Exp:* Res officer aviation physiol, Defence Med Res Labs, 57-58; med officer, Dept Health & Welfare, Food & Drug Directorate, 63-65, MED OFFICER, DRUG ADVERSE REACTION & POISON CONTROL PROGS, DEPT HEALTH & WELFARE, HEALTH PROTECTION BR, GOVT CAN, 65- *Concurrent Pos:* Res fels, Karolinska Inst, Sweden, 5861 & C H Best Inst, 61-63; consult, Drug Monitoring Prog, WHO, 68- *Mem:* AAAS; Am Asn Poison Control Ctrs; NY Acad Sci; Can Soc Forensic Sci; Int Soc Biometeorol. *Res:* G stress and unconsciousness; drug reaction and interreaction detection by program methods; poison control and prevention; human toxicology; hypnosis; fatty tissue studies; biometeorological studies; blood clotting. *Mailing Add:* Dept Health & Welfare Health Protection Br Ottawa ON K2E 2E8 Can

NAPLES, FELIX JOHN, b Quadrelle, Italy, July 7, 12; nat US; m 41; c 3. ORGANIC CHEMISTRY. *Educ:* Youngstown Col, AB, 33; Univ Vt, MS, 34; Ind Univ, PhD(org chem), 36. *Prof Exp:* Asst, Ind Univ, 34-36; instr chem & physics, Youngstown Col, 36-37, assoc prof, 40-43; head dept chem, Springfield Jr Col, 37-40; res chemist, Goodyear Tire & Rubber Co, 43-45, sr res chemist, 45-77; RETIRED. *Concurrent Pos:* Instr, Akron Univ, 78- *Mem:* Am Chem Soc. *Res:* Polymerization; solubility of amino acids; chemical equilibrium; organic synthesis; synthetic rubber; chemical derivatives of diene rubbers. *Mailing Add:* 466 Roslyn Ave Akron OH 44320

NAPLES, JOHN OTTO, b Long Beach, Calif, Apr 2, 47; m 69; c 2. ORGANIC CHEMISTRY, POLYMER CHEMISTRY. *Educ:* Stanford Univ, BS, 69; Univ Calif, Los Angeles, PhD(org chem), 74. *Prof Exp:* SR SCIENTIST, ROHM AND HAAS CO, 74- *Mem:* Am Chem Soc. *Res:* Synthesis of ion exchange resins of unusual selectivity, of superior mechanical, thermal and chemical stability; solid phase organic synthesis; solid phase organic photosensitization. *Mailing Add:* Rohm and Haas Co Norristown & McKean Rds Spring House PA 19477

NAPLES, VIRGINIA L, b Worcester, Mass. FUNCTIONAL MORPHOLOGY, VERTEBRATE PALEONTOLOGY. *Educ:* Univ Mass, BS, 72, MS, 75, PhD(zool), 80. *Prof Exp:* Biol fac biol comp & vert anat, Dept Biol, Mt Holyoke Col, 78-79; FEL GROSS ANAT, DEPT ORAL ANAT, UNIV ILL MED CTR, 80- *Concurrent Pos:* Prin investr, NSF grants, 81- *Mem:* Paleont Soc; Am Soc Zoologists; Sigma Xi; Soc Study Evolution; Am Soc Mammalogists. *Res:* Functional morphology, paleontoloy, evolution and systematics of the Xenarthra. *Mailing Add:* Dept Oral Anat Univ Ill Med Ctr 801 S Pavlina St Chicago IL 60612

NAPOLIELLO, MICHAEL J, b New York, NY, Feb 14, 42. PSYCHIATRY, PSYCHOPHARMACOLOGY. *Educ:* Fordham Univ, BS, 62; NY Univ, MD, 66; Am Bd Psychiat & Neurol, cert, 75; Xavier Univ, MBA, 80. *Prof Exp:* Intern, Univ NMex Affil Hosps, 66-67, chief resident, 69, resident psychiat, 67-70; asst prof psychiat, Sch Med, Univ NMex, 73-74; asst prof clin psychiat, Dartmouth Med Sch, 74-76; GROUP DIR CENT NERVOUS SYST MED, MERRELL DOW RES CTR, 76-; ASSOC CLIN PROF PSYCHIAT, COL MED, UNIV CINCINNATI, 80- *Concurrent Pos:* Attend psychiatrist, Bernalillo County Ment Health & Ment Retardation Ctr, Bernalillo County Med Ctr & Albuquerque Vet Admin Hosp, 73-74; dir behavioral med, Sch Med, Univ NMex, 73-74; chmn med recs comt, Bernalillo County Ment Health & Ment Retardation Ctr, 74; dir emerg & walk-in servs, Dartmouth-Hitchcock Ment Health Ctr, Hanover, NH, 74-75; attend psychiatrist, Mary Hitchcock Mem Hosp & Dartmouth-Hitchcock Ment Health Ctr, Hanover, NH, 74-76; consult psychiatrist, Vet Admin Hosp, White River Jct, Vt, 75; examr, Am Bd Psychiat & Neurol, 76-; consult psychiatrist, Rollman Psychiat Inst, Cincinnati, Ohio, 76-; lectr, Sch Bus, Xavier Univ; asst clin prof, Col Med, Univ Cincinnati, 76-80. *Honors & Awards:* AMA Physician's Recognition Award, 69, 72 & 76. *Mem:* Am Med Asn; Am Psychiat Asn; Am Geriatric Soc. *Mailing Add:* Merrell Res Ctr 2110 East Galbraith Rd Cincinnati OH 45215

NAPOLITANO, JOSEPH J, b New York, NY, Feb 15, 35; m 58; c 3. BIOLOGY, PROTOZOOLOGY. *Educ:* Iona Col, BS, 56; St John's Univ, NY, MS, 59; NY Univ, PhD(biol), 63. *Prof Exp:* From instr to asst prof biol, Iona Col, 58-63; asst prof, 63-72, PROF BIOL, ADELPHI UNIV, 72- *Mem:* Soc Protozool; Am Micros Soc; NY Acad Sci; AAAS. *Res:* Morphogenesis and taxonomy of amoeboflagellates; biology of soil amoebae. *Mailing Add:* Dept of Biol Adelphi Univ Garden City NY 11530

NAPOLITANO, LEONARD MICHAEL, b Oakland, Calif, Jan 8, 30; m 55; c 3. ANATOMY. *Educ:* Univ Santa Clara, BS, 51; St Louis Univ, MS, 54, PhD(anat), 56. *Prof Exp:* Instr anat, Med Col, Cornell Univ, 56-58; from instr to asst prof, Sch Med, Univ Pittsburgh, 58-64; assoc prof, 64-70, PROF ANAT, SCH MED, UNIV N MEX, 70-, DEAN SCH MED, 72-, DIR MED CTR, 77- *Mem:* Am Asn Anat; Am Asn Cell Biol; Electron Micros Soc Am. *Res:* Autonomic nervous system; fine structure of adipose tissue, heart and myelin. *Mailing Add:* Deans Off Univ of NMex Sch of Med Albuquerque NM 87131

NAPOLITANO, RAYMOND L, b New York, NY, Feb 7, 47; m 70; c 1. MICROBIOLOGY, BIOCHEMISTRY. *Educ:* Manhattan Col, BS, 68; St John's Univ, MS, 70, PhD(biochem), 73. *Prof Exp:* Fel elec microbiol, Brooklyn Col, City Univ New York, 73-74, asst prof biol, New York City Col, 74-78; asst prof biol, Manhattanville Col, 78-80; MEM STAFF, ANIMAL HOSP, NEW YORK ZOOL SOC, 80- *Concurrent Pos:* Adj asst prof biol, C W Post Col, Long Island Univ, 74-; res assoc, NY Zool Soc, 75- *Mem:* Sigma Xi; Am Soc Microbiol; Am Soc Protozoologists; Am Soc Zoologists; NY Acad Sci. *Res:* Isolation and axenic cultivation of free living ciliates from various sources and parasitic amoebae with special emphasis on the importance of lipids in the physiological role. *Mailing Add:* Animal Hosp New York Zool Soc Bronx Southern Blvd New York NY 10401

NAPORA, THEODORE ALEXANDER, b Ridgewood, NJ, Sept 14, 27. BIOLOGICAL OCEANOGRAPHY. *Educ:* Columbia Univ, BS, 51; Univ RI, MS, 53; Yale Univ, PhD(biol), 64. *Prof Exp:* ASSOC PROF OCEANOG, UNIV RI, 64-, ASST DEAN GRAD SCH OCEANOG, 71-, DEAN STUDENTS, 77- *Mem:* AAAS; Am Soc Limnol & Oceanog. *Res:* Plankton ecology; composition and distribution of oceanic zooplankton; physiology of deep-sea organisms. *Mailing Add:* Grad Sch of Oceanog Univ of RI Kingston RI 02881

NAPPI, ANTHONY JOSEPH, b New Britain, Conn, Oct 21, 37; m; c 3. INSECT PHYSIOLOGY, PATHOLOGY. *Educ:* Cent Conn State Col, BS, 59, MS, 64; Univ Conn, PhD(entom, zool), 68. *Prof Exp:* Instr biol, Cent Conn State Col, 64-65; res asst entom, Univ Conn, 65-67; univ res grant, State Univ NY Col Oswego, 68-69, NSF res grant, 71-72, asst prof biol, 68-70, assoc prof, 71-76, prof, 76-81, PROF BIOL & CHMN DEPT, LOYOLA UNIV, CHICAGO, 81- *Concurrent Pos:* NIH res grant, 74; Am Cancer Soc scholarship, 75. *Mem:* AAAS; Am Inst Biol Sci; Am Soc Zool; Soc Invertebrate Path; Am Soc Parasitologists. *Res:* Cellular immune mechanisms of insects against metazoan parasites; insect pathology; parasitology. *Mailing Add:* Dept Biol Loyola Univ Chicago IL 60626

NAPTON, LEWIS KYLE, b Bozeman, Mont, Nov 15, 33; m 60; c 2. ARCHAEOLOGY, PHYSICAL ANTHROPOLOGY. *Educ:* Mont State Univ, BS, 59; Univ Mont, MA, 65; Univ Calif, Berkeley, PhD(anthrop), 70. *Prof Exp:* Wenner-Gren fel, Univ Calif, Berkeley, 68-69, asst prof anthrop, 70-71; assoc prof, 72-74, prof anthrop, 74-81, PROF ARCHAEOL, CALIF STATE COL, STANISLAUS, 81- *Concurrent Pos:* NSF fel, Univ Calif, Berkeley, 70-; NSF res assoc, Cent Australian Exped, 73-74. *Res:* North American archaeology; paleoanthropology; environmental archaeology, prehistoric man in arid environments. *Mailing Add:* Dept of Anthrop Calif State Col Stanislaus Turlock CA 95380

NAQVI, IQBAL MEHDI, b New Delhi, India, Jan 6, 39; m 64; c 2. DEVICE PHYSICS, SOLID STATE ELECTRONICS. *Educ:* Univ Panjab, WPakistan, BS, 58; Youngstown Univ, BEng, 60; Univ Pa, MS, 61; Cornell Univ, PhD(electrophys), 69. *Prof Exp:* Sr engr electronic data processing div, Honeywell, Inc, 61-66; res asst elec eng, Cornell Univ, 66-69; asst prof elec eng, Univ Hawaii, 70-73; device physicist, Rockwell Int, 76-78; HEAD DEVICE CHARACTERIZATION LAB, HUGHES AIRCRAFT CO, 78- *Concurrent Pos:* vis lectr, Calif State Univ, Fullerton, 77, Calif State Polytech Univ, Pomona, 78 & Univ Calif, Irvine, 82- *Mem:* AAAS; Inst Elec & Electronics Engrs. *Res:* Microwave solid state devices; noise in semiconductor devices; semiconductor device processing; integrated circuit technology; semiconductor memories; electronic circuit design; computer aided circuit design. *Mailing Add:* Hughes Aircraft Co 500 Superior Ave MS A-2408 Newport Beach CA 92663

NAQVI, SAIYID ISHRAT HUSAIN, b Saharanpur, India, June 29, 31; m 58; c 3. NUCLEAR PHYSICS, ASTRONOMY. *Educ:* Univ Lucknow, BSc, 51, MSc, 53; Univ Man, MSc, 56, PhD(nuclear physics), 61. *Prof Exp:* Lectr physics, Univ Man, 56-61; asst prof, St Paul's Col, Man, 61-65 & Univ Man, 65-66; asst prof, 66-68, assoc prof physics, 68-77, PROF PHYSICS & ASTRON, UNIV REGINA, 77- *Concurrent Pos:* Vis prof, Copenhagen Univ Observ, 72-73, Atomic Energy Can, Ltd, Chalk River, 62, & Mass Inst Technol, 63. *Mem:* Int Astron Union; Royal Astron Soc Can; Can Asn Univ Teachers. *Res:* Beta and gamma ray spectroscopy; low and medium energy nuclear physics; photoelectric photometry; low-mass pseudo-scalar boson. *Mailing Add:* Dept of Physics & Astron Univ of Regina Regina SK S4S 0A2 Can

NARA, HARRY R(AYMOND), b New York Mills, Minn, Sept 19, 21; m 46; c 3. ENGINEERING MECHANICS. *Educ:* Case Inst Technol, BS, 46, MS, 48, PhD(eng mech), 51. *Prof Exp:* From instr to assoc prof eng mech, 46-57, prof struct & mech & head dept, 57-61, assoc head eng div, 61-64, vprovost, 64-67, assoc dean, Sch Eng, 68-73, PROF ENG, CASE WESTERN RESERVE UNIV, 61- *Concurrent Pos:* Pres, Dicar Corp, 72-76. *Mem:* Am Soc Civil Engrs; Am Soc Mech Engrs; Soc Exp Stress Anal; Am Soc Eng Educ; Sigma Xi. *Res:* Structures; soil mechanics; dynamics; reinforced plastics. *Mailing Add:* Sch of Eng Case Western Reserve Univ University Circle Cleveland OH 44106

NARAHARA, HIROMICHI TSUDA, b Tokyo, Japan, Oct 24, 23; US citizen; m 54; c 4. BIOCHEMISTRY, METABOLISM. *Educ:* Columbia Univ, BA, 43, MD, 47; Am Bd Internal Med, dipl, 55. *Prof Exp:* USPHS res fel med, Univ Wash, 53-56, res instr, 56-58; USPHS spec res fel biol chem, Wash Univ, 58-60, from asst prof to assoc prof, 60-70; MEM STAFF, DIV LABS & RES, NY STATE DEPT HEALTH, 70-; ASSOC PROF BIOCHEM, ALBANY MED COL, 70- *Mem:* Am Diabetes Asn; Endocrine Soc; Am Soc Biol Chem. *Res:* Intermediary metabolism of carbohydrates; muscle physiology; effect of hormones and muscle contraction on carbohydrate metabolism; cell membranes. *Mailing Add:* Div of Labs & Res NY State Dept of Health Albany NY 12201

NARAHASHI, TOSHIO, b Fukuoka, Japan, Jan 30, 27; m 56; c 2. NEUROPHYSIOLOGY, NEUROPHARMACOLOGY. *Educ:* Univ Tokyo, BS, 48, PhD(insect neurotoxicol), 60. *Prof Exp:* Res assoc physiol, Univ Chicago, 61-62, asst prof, 62; asst prof, 62-63, from asst prof to prof, 65-69, vchmn dept, 73-75, prof physiol & pharmacol, Med Ctr, Duke Univ, 69-77; PROF & CHMN, PHARMACOL DEPT, MED SCH, NORTHWESTERN UNIV, CHICAGO, 77- *Concurrent Pos:* Res assoc, Fac Agr, Univ Tokyo, 51-65. *Honors & Awards:* Japanese Soc Appl Entom & Zool Prize, 55; Cole Award, Biophys Soc, 81. *Mem:* Soc Neurosci; Am Soc Pharmacol & Exp Therapeut; Am Physiol Soc; Soc Toxicol; Biophys Soc. *Res:* Electrophysiology and pharmacology of nerve and muscle membrane and synaptic junctions in general; basic insect neurophysiology; neurotoxicology of insecticides; neurotoxicology of environmental toxicants. *Mailing Add:* Dept Pharmacol Northwestern Univ Med Sch 303 E Chicago Ave Chicago IL 60611

NARANG, SARAN A, b Agra, India, Sept 10, 30; m; c 1. ORGANIC CHEMISTRY, MOLECULAR BIOLOGY. *Educ:* Panjab Univ, India, BSc, 51, MSc, 53; Univ Calcutta, PhD(org chem), 60. *Prof Exp:* Sr res fel chem, Indian Asn Cultivation Sci, Calcutta, 59-62; res assoc, Johns Hopkins Univ, 62-63; proj assoc molecular biol, Inst Enzyme Res, Univ Wis-Madison, 63-66; asst res officer, Div Pure Chem, 66-67, assoc res officer, Div Biochem & Molecular Biol, 67-73, SR RES OFFICER, DIV BIOL SCI, NAT RES COUN CAN, 73- *Concurrent Pos:* Adj prof, Carleton Univ, 73- *Honors & Awards:* Coochbihar Professorship Mem Award, Indian Asn Cultivation Sci, Calcutta, 74. *Res:* Chemico-enzymatic synthesis of DNA and RNA and their biological roles; DNA-protein recognition and studies viroids. *Mailing Add:* Div Biol Sci Nat Res Coun Can Montreal Rd Ottawa ON K1A 0R6 Can

NARASIMHAN, MANDAYAM A, b Tarikere, India, July 5, 49; m 77. ELECTRICAL ENGINEERING, COMPUTER SCIENCE. *Educ:* Bangalore Univ, BE, 69; Indian Inst Sci, Bangalore, ME, 71; Univ Tex, Arlington, PhD(elec eng), 75. *Prof Exp:* Lectr elec eng, Bangalore Univ, 72-73; mem tech staff, elec eng, 74-79, MGR, RES & DEVELOP, TEX INSTRUMENTS, 79-, SR MEM TECH STAFF, 81- *Mem:* Sigma Xi; Inst Elec & Electronics Engrs. *Res:* Digital image processing; pattern recognition; artificial intelligence; robotics and industrial automation; intelligent systems. *Mailing Add:* Box 225621 Ms452 Tex Instruments Inc Dallas TX 75265

NARASIMHAN, MYSORE N L, b Mysore City, India, July 7, 28; US citizen; m 49; c 3. APPLIED MATHEMATICS, ENGINEERING SCIENCE. *Educ:* Univ Mysore, MSc, 51; Indian Inst Technol, Kharagpur, PhD(math), 58. *Prof Exp:* Lectr math, Lingaraj Col, India, 51-55; asst lectr, Indian Inst Technol, Kharagpur, 55-58; lectr, Indian Inst Technol, Bombay, 58-61, asst prof, 61-62, assoc prof, 64-65; res prof, Math Res Ctr, Univ Wis, 62-64; assoc prof, Univ Calgary, 65-66; PROF MATH, ORE STATE UNIV, 66- *Concurrent Pos:* Vis prof, Princeton Univ, 72-73. *Honors & Awards:* Iyengar Mem Prize, Mysore, 51. *Mem:* Am Math Soc; Soc Indust & Appl Math; US Soc Eng Sci; Indian Soc Theoret & Appl Mech. *Res:* Non-Newtonian fluid flows; flow through elastic tubes; porous channel and magnetohydrodynamic flows; stability of fluid flows; microcontinuum theory; liquid crystal theory; thermodynamics; nonlinear continuum-mechanics. *Mailing Add:* Dept of Math Ore State Univ Corvallis OR 97331

NARASIMHAN, THIRUPPUDAIMARUDHUR N, b Madras City, India, Oct 6, 35; m 62; c 1. HYDROGEOLOGY, CIVIL ENGINEERING. *Educ:* Univ Madras, BSc, 56; Univ Calif, Berkeley, MS, 71, PhD(eng sci), 75. *Prof Exp:* Geol asst, Geol Surv India, 56-57, asst geologist, 57-64, geologist, 64-70; res engr, 75-76, staff scientist, 76-80, STAFF SR SCIENTIST, LAWRENCE BERKELEY LAB, 80- *Concurrent Pos:* Res hydrologist, Nat Coun Appl Econ Res, New Delhi, India, 68-; lectr, Dept Mat Sci & Mineral Eng, Univ Calif, Berkeley, 77- *Mem:* Fel Geol Soc India; life mem Am Geophys Union; fel Geol Soc Am. *Res:* Flow through porous media; mathematical modeling of groundwater systems; geothermal reservoir engineering; well testing; flow in fractured rocks; chemical transport in groundwater systems; hydrology and water resources. *Mailing Add:* Div of Earth Sci Lawrence Berkeley Lab Berkeley CA 94720

NARATH, ALBERT, b Berlin, Ger, Mar 5, 33; US citizen; m 58; c 4. SOLID STATE PHYSICS. *Educ:* Univ Cincinnati, BS, 55; Univ Calif, Berkeley, PhD(phys chem, molecular spectros), 59. *Prof Exp:* Dept mgr solid state res, 59-68, dir solid state sci res, 68-71, managing dir phys sci, 71-73, VPRES, SANDIA NAT LABS, 73- *Mem:* Fel Am Phys Soc. *Res:* Nuclear magnetic resonance in nonmetallic magnetic crystals and in transition metals and intermetallic compounds; properties of ferromagnets and antiferromagnets. *Mailing Add:* Orgn 4000 Sandia Nat Labs Albuquerque NM 87185

NARAYAN, JAGDISH, b Kanpur, India, Oct 15, 48; US citizen; m 73; c 1. MATERIALS SCIENCE, SOLID STATE PHYSICS. *Educ:* Indian Inst Technol, BTech, 69; Univ Calif, Berkeley, MS, 70, PhD(mat sci), 71. *Prof Exp:* Res metallurgist mat sci; Lawrence Berkeley Lab & Univ Calif, Berkeley, 71-72; MEM RES STAFF MAT SCI & SOLID STATE PHYSICS, OAK RIDGE NAT LAB, 72- *Honors & Awards:* India President's Gold Medal, Indian Inst Technol, Kanpur & Govt India, 69; Best in Class Medal, Am Soc Metals, 71; Sustained Basic Res Award, Dept Energy, 81. *Mem:* Am Phys Soc; Am Soc Electron Micros; Am Inst Mining, Metall & Petrol Engrs. *Res:* Defects in oxides; radiation damage in metals; ion implantation and defect physics of semiconductors. *Mailing Add:* Div of Solid State Physics Oak Ridge Nat Lab Oak Ridge TN 37830

NARAYAN, KRISHAMURTHI ANANTH, b Secunderabad, India, Oct 1, 30; m 61; c 2. NUTRITIONAL BIOCHEMISTRY, FOOD SCIENCE. *Educ:* Madras Univ, BS, 49; Osmania Univ, India, MS, 51; Univ Ill, Urbana, PhD(food technol), 57. *Prof Exp:* Res assoc phys chem, Wash State Univ, 57-60, res assoc agr chem, 61-62; sci officer, Nutrit Res Lab, 60-61; from asst prof to assoc prof food chem, Univ Ill, Urbana, 62-71; RES NUTRITIONIST, FOOD LABS, US ARMY NATICK LABS, 71- *Concurrent Pos:* Nat Cancer Inst career develop award, 66- *Mem:* AAAS; Am Oil Chem Soc; Am Inst Nutrit; NY Acad Sci; Brit Biochem Soc. *Res:* Lipids in cancer; lipoprotein metabolism; disc electrophoresis and lipoproteins; wheat and serum proteins; oxidized lipid-protein complexes; lipoproteins in cancer; liver plasma membranes; essential fatty acid deficiency; absorption, transport and utilization of lipids. *Mailing Add:* Biochem & Nutrit Group US Army Natick R&D Command Natick MA 01760

NARAYAN, OPENDRA, b Essequibo, Guyana, Nov 28, 36; Can citizen; m 63; c 3. VIROLOGY. *Educ:* Univ Toronto, DVM, 63; Univ Guelph, PhD(virol), 70. *Prof Exp:* Veterinarian, pvt pract, Man, 63-65; Can Med Res Coun fel, 70-72; asst prof neurol, 72-74, ASSOC PROF COMP MED, SCH MED, JOHNS HOPKINS UNIV, 74- *Mem:* AAAS; Am Asn Microbiol; Am Asn Neuropath. *Res:* Slow virus infections; mechanisms of virus infections of the brain; viral teratology. *Mailing Add:* Dept of Neurol Sch of Med Johns Hopkins Univ Baltimore MD 21205

NARAYAN, TV LAKSHMI, b Udamalpet, India, June 5, 37; m 68; c 2. ORGANIC CHEMISTRY, POLYMER CHEMISTRY. *Educ:* Univ Madras, BSc, 58; Annamalai Univ, Madras, MSc, 61; Univ 21 Pa, PhD(chem), 65. *Prof Exp:* Fel polymer chem, Univ Ariz, 65-66; res chemist, Am Cyanamid Co, Conn, 66-69; sr res chemist, 69-80, RES ASSOC, BASF WYANDOTTE CORP, 80- *Mem:* Am Chem Soc; The Chem Soc. *Res:* Organophosphorous and sulfur chemistry; thermostable polymers; engineering thermoplastics; flame retardant polymers; isocyanate chemistry; polyurethane chemistry. *Mailing Add:* Cent Res BASF Wyandotte Corp Wyandotte MI 48192

NARAYANA, TADEPALLI VENKATA, b Madras, India, Apr 23, 30; m 60. MATHEMATICS. *Educ:* Univ Madras, MA, 50; Univ Bombay, MA, 51; Univ NC, PhD, 53. *Prof Exp:* Statistician, Indian Coun Agr Res, India, 54; asst prof math, McGill Univ, 55-58; assoc prof, 58-66, PROF MATH, UNIV ALTA, 66- *Res:* Probability and statistics; number theory. *Mailing Add:* Dept of Math Univ of Alta Edmonton AB T6G 2G7 Can

NARAYANAMURTI, VENKATESH, b Bangalore, India, Sept 9, 39; m 61; c 2. EXPERIMENTAL SOLID STATE PHYSICS. *Educ:* Univ Delhi, BS, 58, MS, 60; Cornell Univ, PhD(physics), 65. *Prof Exp:* Res assoc physics, Cornell Univ, 64-65, instr, 67-68; asst prof, Indian Inst Technol, Bombay, 65-66; mem tech staff physics, 68-76, head, Semiconductor Electronics Res Dept, 76-81, DIR, SOLID STATE ELECTRONICS RES LAB, BELL LABS, 81- *Mem:* Fel Am Phys Soc; Assoc Inst Physics London; Fel Acad Sci India; AAAS; sr mem Inst Elec & Electronics Engrs. *Res:* Phonons in solids and liquid helium; second sound and sound propagation in matter; superconductivity; metal-insulator transitions under pressure; energy transport in semiconductors. *Mailing Add:* Bell Labs Murray Hill NJ 07974

NARAYANASWAMY, ONBATHIVELI S, b Madras, India, May 13, 36; m 67. ENGINEERING MECHANICS. *Educ:* Univ Madras, BE, 58; Univ Sask, MS, 62; Case Western Reserve Univ, PhD(eng mech), 65. *Prof Exp:* Jr sci officer, Atomic Energy Estab, India, 59-60; lectr, Indian Inst Technol, 60-61; sr res scientist, 65-69, sr res engr, 69-72, assoc prin res engr, 72-81, STAFF SCIENTIST, FORD MOTOR CO, 81- *Honors & Awards:* Ross Coffin Purdy Award, Am Ceramic Soc, 73. *Mem:* Fel Am Ceramic Soc; Soc Exp Stress Anal. *Res:* Viscoelasticity applied to glass fabrication problems; glass science; theoretical and experimental stress analysis. *Mailing Add:* Metallurg Dept Sci Res Lab Ford Motor Co Dearborn MI 48121

NARAYANASWAMY, PADMANABHA, b Madras, India, July 25, 36; m 63; c 2. THEORETICAL HIGH ENERGY PHYSICS. *Educ:* Univ Delhi, BS, 56, MS, 58, PhD(physics), 63. *Prof Exp:* Res fel theoret physics, Univ Delhi, 63-64; fel, Tata Inst Fundamental Res, India, 64-65; vis scientist, Int Ctr Theoret Physics, Trieste, 65-66 & Ctr Europ Nuclear Res, Switz, 66-67. fel theoret physics, Tata Inst Fundamental Res, India, 67-68; asst prof physics, Am Univ Beirut, 68-69; from asst prof, to assoc prof, 69-72, PROF PHYSICS, SOUTHERN ILL UNIV, EDWARDSVILLE, 78- *Concurrent Pos:* Vis scientist, Ctr Particle Theory, Univ Tex, Austin, 74-75. *Mem:* Am Phys Soc; Ital Phys Soc. *Res:* Field theory; theory of elementary particles. *Mailing Add:* Dept of Physics Southern Ill Univ Edwardsville IL 62025

NARCISI, ROCCO S, b Bristol, Pa, Apr 4, 31; m 57; c 1. AERONOMY. *Educ:* Pa State Univ, BS, 53; Harvard Univ, MS, 55, PhD(physics), 59. *Prof Exp:* Supvry physicist, 60-74, PROJ SCIENTIST, UPPER ATMOSPHERE COMPOS PROJ & PROG MGR, MIDDLE ATMOSPHERE TECHNOL PROJ, AIR FORCE GEOPHYSICS LAB, 74- *Concurrent Pos:* Lectr, Int Sch Atmospheric Physics, Erice, Sicily, 70. *Honors & Awards:* Marcus D O'Day Award, Air Force Cambridge Res Labs, 66 & Guenter Loeser Mem Award, 70. *Mem:* Sigma Xi; Am Geophys Union; AAAS; NY Acad Sci; Explorers Club. *Res:* Ionospheric and upper atmospheric structure and dynamics; mass spectrometry; rocket and satellite instrumentation to measure composition and density of the neutral and ionized constituents of the atmosphere; experimental and theoretical research on the composition of the atmosphere and the associated physical and chemical processes; study of the earth's stratosphere. *Mailing Add:* Code LKD Air Force Geophysics Lab Bedford MA 01731

NARCOWICH, FRANCIS JOSEPH, b Gary, Ind, Jan 23, 46. PARTIAL DIFFERENTIAL EQUATIONS, OPERATOR THEORY. *Educ:* De Paul Univ, BS, 68; Princeton Univ, MA, 70, PhD(math physics), 72. *Prof Exp:* NSF fel, Princeton Univ, 68-71, fel, 71-72; asst prof, 72-78, ASSOC PROF MATH, TEX A&M UNIV, 78- *Concurrent Pos:* Appl mathematician, Zenith Radio Corp, 69, 70 & 71; consult. *Mem:* Am Math Soc. *Res:* Partial differential equations that arise in quantum field theory when general relativity is taken account of; C-algebras; numerical methods. *Mailing Add:* Dept Math Tex A&M Univ College Station TX 77843

NARDACCI, JOSEPH L, chemical engineering, see previous edition

NARDI, JAMES BENJAMIN, b Clinton, Ind, Oct 9, 48. DEVELOPMENTAL BIOLOGY. *Educ:* Purdue Univ, BS, 70; Harvard Univ, PhD(biol), 75. *Prof Exp:* Postdoc fel biol, Med Res Coun, Lab Molecular Biol, 75-76; RES ASSOC BIOL, DEPT GENETICS & DEVELOP, UNIV ILL, 76- *Concurrent Pos:* NATO fel, NSF, 75-76; vis asst prof, Univ Ill, 78-79. *Mem:* Soc Exp Biol; AAAS; Soc Develop Biol. *Res:* Cell interactions during development. *Mailing Add:* Dept of Genetics & Develop Univ of Ill Urbana IL 61801

NARDI, VITTORIO, b Ravenna, Italy, Oct 9, 30; m 56; c 4. STATISTICAL PHYICS, PLASMA PHYSICS. *Educ:* Univ Rome, Italy, PhD(physics & field theory), 54; Italian Ministry Educ, Rome, Libero Docente, 67. *Prof Exp:* Fel res scientist, Univ Rome, 54-55, Univ Amsterdam, 55-56, Univ Padua, 56-59; lectr & prof statist mech & thermodynamics, Univ Padua & Ferrara, Italy, 59-63; vis res scientist, NY Univ, 62-63 & Courant Inst Math Sci, NY Univ, 64-67; vis res prof electrodynamics, waves propagation & gen physics, 67-79, RES PROF PHYSICS, STEVENS INST TECHNOL, 79- *Concurrent Pos:* Consult, Nat Inst Nuclear Physics, Rome, 57-64, Nat Inst Electrotech, Turin, 72-78 & Lawrence Livermore Lab, 76-78; prin investr particle beam physics, plasma focus & particle beam generators res, Physics Dept, Stevens Inst Technol, 72-; ed, Energy, Storage, Compression & Switching Conf Proceedings, 74- *Honors & Awards:* Davis Res Award, Stevens Inst Technol, 73. *Res:* Dynamics and structure of particle beams; propagation of relativistic electron beams of high density; plasma focus and pulsed power systems. *Mailing Add:* Stevens Inst Technol Castle Point Sta Hoboken NJ 07030

NARDO, SEBASTIAN V(INCENT), b Brooklyn, NY, Dec 25, 17; m 42; c 4. AEROSPACE ENGINEERING. *Educ:* Polytech Inst Brooklyn, BME, 40, MAE, 42, PhD(appl mech), 49. *Prof Exp:* Aeronaut engr, Chance Vought Aircraft, Tex, 42-45; from instr to assoc prof aeronaut eng, 46-60, PROF AEROSPACE ENG, POLYTECH INST NEW YORK, FARMINGDALE, 60- *Mem:* Soc Exp Stress Anal; Am Inst Aeronaut & Astronaut; Am Soc Eng Educ; NY Acad Sci. *Res:* Heat conduction; stability and stresses in plate and shell structures; dynamics; solar energy. *Mailing Add:* Dept of Mech & Aerospace Eng Polytech Inst New York Rte 110 Farmingdale NY 11735

NARDONE, JOHN, b Passaic, NJ, Mar 30, 34; m 57; c 2. MATERIALS ENGINEERING, MECHANICAL ENGINEERING. *Educ:* Newark Col Eng, BS, 56; Stevens Inst Technol, MS, 67. *Prof Exp:* Mech engr missiles, US Army Picatinny, 59-63; MAT ENGR POLYMERS, US ARMY ARMAMENT RES & DEVELOP COMMAND, 63- *Mem:* Soc Plastics Engrs. *Res:* Applications engineering directed at the effective utilization of polymeric materials; areas include research, design, development processing and evaluation of materials. *Mailing Add:* Plastics Tech Eval Ctr US Army Dover NJ 07801

NARDONE, ROLAND MARIO, b Brooklyn, NY, Mar 29, 28; m 51; c 4. PHYSIOLOGY. *Educ:* Fordham Univ, BS, 47, MS, 49, PhD(biol), 51. *Prof Exp:* Instr, St Francis Col, 48-51 & St Louis Univ, 51-52; from asst prof to assoc prof, 52-63, PROF BIOL, CATH UNIV AM, 63- *Mem:* Tissue Cult Asn (secy, 72-76). *Res:* Cell division; physiology of cells in culture; cytotoxicity in nitro. *Mailing Add:* Dept of Biol Cath Univ of Am Washington DC 20064

NARDUCCI, LORENZO M, b Torino, Italy, May 25, 42; m 65; c 3. QUANTUM OPTICS. *Educ:* Univ Milan, PhD(physics), 64. *Prof Exp:* Asst prof quantum electronics, Univ Milan, 65-66; from asst prof physics, to assoc prof Worcester Polytech Inst, 66-76; assoc prof, 76-79, PROF PHYSICS, DREXEL UNIV, 79- *Concurrent Pos:* Consult, Am Optical Corp, 67-68 &Phys Sci Directorate, Redstone Arsenal, 72- *Honors & Awards:* Drexel Univ Res Award, 80. *Mem:* Am Phys Soc; fel Optical Soc Am. *Res:* Laser theory; interaction of radiation and matter; quantum statistics; light scattering and phase transitions; bistability; nonlinear optics. *Mailing Add:* Dept Physics & Atmospheric Sci Drexel Univ Philadelphia PA 19104

NARENDRA, KUMPATI S, b Madras, India, Apr 14, 33; m 61. CONTROL SYSTEMS. *Educ:* Univ Madras, BE, 54; Harvard Univ, SM, 55, PhD(appl physics), 59; Yale Univ, MA, 68. *Prof Exp:* Lectr appl physics, Harvard Univ, 59-61, asst prof, 61-65; assoc prof appl sci, 65-68, PROF APPL SCI, YALE UNIV, 68- *Concurrent Pos:* Consult, Boston Div, Minneapolis Honeywell Regulator Co, Mass, 59-61, Sperry Rand Res Ctr, 61-64, Dynamics Res Corp, 65-67, Bell Aerosysts Co, NY, 66-67, Sikorsky Aircraft, 67-73, Long Lines Div, Am Tel & Tel Co, 75-81 & Borg-Warner Corp, 79-81; vis assoc prof, Indian Inst Sci, Bangalore, 64-65; ed, J Cybernetics & Info Sci; assoc ed, Inst Elec & Electronics Engrs-Control Systs Soc & Trans Automatic Control. *Honors & Awards:* Franklin V Taylor Award, Inst Elec & Electronics Engrs-SMC Soc, 72. *Mem:* Fel Inst Elec & Electronics Engrs; fel Inst Electronics & Telecommun Engrs India. *Res:* Stability theory; large scale systems; adaptive control learning automata. *Mailing Add:* 35 Old Mill Rd Woodbridge CT 06525

NARIBOLI, GUNDO A, b Dharwar, India, Sept 2, 25; m 47; c 4. APPLIED MATHEMATICS. *Educ:* Univ Bombay, BSc, 47, MSc, 52; Karnatak Univ, India, MSc, 54; Indian Inst Technol, Kharagpur, PhD(appl math), 59. *Prof Exp:* Lectr math, Col Eng & Technol, Hubli, India, 52-55 & Indian Inst Technol, Kharagpur, 56-59; reader, Univ Bombay, 59-62; assoc prof, Iowa State Univ, 62-64; reader, Univ Bombay, 64-66; assoc prof math & eng mech, 66-69, PROF ENG MECH, IOWA STATE UNIV, 69- *Concurrent Pos:* Reviewer, Appl Math Rev. *Mem:* Soc Indust & Appl Math; Math Asn Am; Am Math Soc; Sigma Xi. *Res:* Linear and nonlinear waves; group-invariant solutions; Baeklund transformations; perturbation methods; method of perturbation for waves in bounded media; traffic flow theory. *Mailing Add:* Eng Sci & Mech Dept Iowa State Univ Ames IA 50010

NARICI, LAWRENCE ROBERT, b Brooklyn, NY, Nov 15, 41. MATHEMATICAL ANALYSIS. *Educ:* Polytech Inst Brooklyn, BS, 62, MS, 63, PhD(math), 66. *Prof Exp:* From instr to asst prof math, Polytech Inst Brooklyn, 65-67; assoc prof, 67-72, PROF MATH, ST JOHN'S UNIV, NY, 72- *Mem:* Am Math Soc; Math Asn Am; Mex Math Soc; Math Soc France; Israel Math Union. *Res:* Non-Archimedean Banach spaces and algebras; topological algebras; functional analysis; valuation theory. *Mailing Add:* Dept of Math St John's Univ Jamaica NY 11439

NARINS, DORICE MARIE, b Chicago, Ill, Oct 9, 32; m 70. NUTRITIONAL BIOCHEMISTRY. *Educ:* Northwestern Univ, BS, 54; Mass Inst Technol, PhD(nutrit biochem), 66. *Prof Exp:* NIH fel overnutrit, Rockefeller Univ, 66-68; asst prof nutrit biochem, Mich State Univ, 68-74; ASSOC PROF NUTRIT BIOCHEM, RUSH UNIV, 74- *Concurrent Pos:* Chmn, Task Force Nutrit Pregnancy & Childhood, Ill State Coun Nutrit. *Mem:* Inst Food Technologists; Soc Nutrit Educ; Am Inst Nutrit; Sigma Xi; AAAS. *Res:* Undernutrition and overnutrition, particularly effects on brain and liver; trace mineral metabolism; world nutrition problems; normal growth. *Mailing Add:* Dept of Clin Nutrit Rush Univ Chicago IL 60612

NARO, PAUL ANTHONY, b Scranton, Pa, Aug 17, 34; m 57; c 2. ORGANIC CHEMISTRY, TOXICOLOGY. *Educ:* Temple Univ, AB, 56; Pa State Univ, PhD(chem), 60. *Prof Exp:* Res chemist, Socony Mobil Oil Co, Inc, 59-61, sr res chemist, Mobil Oil Corp, 61-72, asst supvr, 64-66, admin mgr, Mobil Res & Develop Corp, 72-78, MGR TOXICOL OPERS, MOBIL OIL CORP, 78- *Mem:* Am Chem Soc. *Res:* Hydrocarbon synthesis; organic sulfur compounds; polymer chemistry; heterogeneous catalysis; computer applications. *Mailing Add:* Mobil Res & Develop Corp Cent Res Div Box 1025 Princeton NJ 08540

NAROTSKY, SAUL, b Brooklyn, NY, May 19, 22; m 50; c 4. VETERINARY MEDICINE, POULTRY PATHOLOGY. *Educ:* Univ Conn, BS, 44; Kans State Univ, DVM, 47. *Prof Exp:* Instr bact & poultry path, Mich State Univ, 47-49; dir regional vet lab, Cornell Univ, 49-71; DIR, AVIAN VET SERV, 71- *Mem:* Am Asn Avian Path; Am Vet Med Asn. *Res:* Prevention and control of poultry disease; poultry immunology and nutrition; clinical evaluation of vaccines, drugs and nutrition in poultry disease. *Mailing Add:* Avian Vet Serv 239 Capen Blvd Buffalo NY 14226

NARROD, MARIAN FREEMAN, pharmacology, see previous edition

NARROD, STUART ALLAN, b Chicago, Ill, Apr 9, 25; m 58; c 2. BIOCHEMISTRY. *Educ:* Univ Ill, BS, 48, PhD(dairy sci, bact), 55, MD, 76. *Prof Exp:* Asst, Univ Ill, 51-55; res assoc, Am Dent Asn, NIH, 55-58; chemist, NIH, 61-64; resident internal med, Albert Einstein Med Ctrt, 77-79, fel rheumatology, 80-81; ASSOC PROF BIOCHEM, MED COL PA, 64-, ACTG CHMN DEPT, 69- *Mem:* Am Soc Microbiol; Am Chem Soc; Am Rheumatology Asn. *Res:* Biochemistry and bacterial physiology in relation to metabolic processes and enzyme chemistry; therapeutic level and distribution of drugs in the body. *Mailing Add:* 961 Steven Ln Wayne PA 19087

NARSKE, RICHARD MARTIN, b Berwyn, Ill, July 4, 42; m 65; c 2. ORGANIC CHEMISTRY. *Educ:* Augustana Col, BA, 64; Univ Iowa, MS, 66, PhD(chem), 68. *Prof Exp:* Asst prof chem, Univ Tampa, 68-70, assoc prof, 70-78; head, Anal & Microbiol Lab, Ophthal Res & Develop, Milton Roy Co, 78-80; MEM FAC, CHEM DEPT, AUGUSTANA COL, 80- *Concurrent Pos:* Consult, Erny Supply Co, 69-78; chief chem consult, Intersci Inc, 70-78. *Mem:* Am Chem Soc (treas-secy, 69-71); Am Inst Chemists; Sigma Xi. *Res:* Gas chromatographic analysis of pesticide residues; forensic chemistry; organic metallic complexes; new ophthalmologic analysis and testing methods; ophthalmology and eye care solutions. *Mailing Add:* Chem Dept Augustana Col Rock Island IL 61201

NARTEN, PERRY FOOTE, b Cleveland, Ohio, July 24, 21; m 46; c 2. GEOGRAPHIC MAPPING SYSTEMS, ORNAMENTAL HORTICULTURE. *Educ:* Col Wooster, BA, 43; Wash Univ, MS, 49. *Prof Exp:* Geologist, Pa State Geol Surv, 47 & US Geol Surv, 48-63; opers analyst, Res Anal Corp, 63-72; staff environmentalist, Gen Res Corp, 72-74; environ consult, 74-75; GEOLOGIST, US GEOL SURV, 75- *Concurrent Pos:* Dir, Coover Arboretum, 54- *Mem:* Royal Hort Soc; World Future Soc; AAAS; Geol Soc Am. *Res:* Environmental and engineering geology; land use planning; mine reclamation; environmental impact analysis; ornamental horticulture; plant breeding. *Mailing Add:* 3708 N Randolph St Arlington VA 22207

NARULA, SUBHASH CHANDER, b Bannu, India, Jan 20, 44; US citizen. APPLIED STATISTICS, OPERATIONS RESEARCH. *Educ:* Univ Delhi, BE, 65; Univ Iowa, MS, 69, PhD(indust & mgt eng), 71. *Prof Exp:* Supvr prod, Hindustan Mach Tools Ltd, 65-68; asst prof indust eng, State Univ NY, Buffalo, 71-77; vis assoc prof, 77-78, ASSOC PROF, SCH MGT, RENSSELAER POLYTECH INST, 78- *Mem:* Am Statist Asn; Royal Statist Soc; Opers Res Soc Am; Inst Mgt Sci; Math Prog Soc. *Mailing Add:* Sch of Mgt Rensselaer Polytech Inst Troy NY 12181

NARVAEZ, RICHARD, b New York, NY, May 4, 30; m 63; c 7. POLYMER CHEMISTRY. *Educ:* City Col New York, BS, 51; NY Univ, PhD(phys chem), 63. *Prof Exp:* Chemist, Savannah River Lab, 51-55, 57-58, res chemist, 63-65, res chemist, Carothers Lab, 65-69, sr res chemist, 69-75, res chemist, 76-81, SR RES CHEMIST PIONEERING RES LAB, EXP STA, E I DU PONT DE NEMOURS & CO, INC, 81- *Res:* Basic studies leading to improved polyester and polyamide products including development of new characterization techniques for polymers. *Mailing Add:* Pioneering Res Lab E I du Pont de Nemours & Co Wilmington DE 19898

NASAR, SYED ABU, b Gorakhpur, India, Dec 25, 32; m 61; c 2. ELECTRICAL ENGINEERING. *Educ:* Agra Univ, BSc, 51; Univ Dacca, BScEE, 55; Tex A&M Univ, MS, 57; Univ Calif, Berkeley, PhD(elec eng), 63. *Prof Exp:* Lectr elec eng, Ahsanullah Eng Col, Dacca Univ, Pakistan, 55-63; from asst prof to assoc prof, EPakistan Univ Eng & Technol, 63-66; assoc prof, Gonzaga Univ, 66-68; assoc prof, 68-70, PROF ELEC ENG, UNIV KY, 70- *Concurrent Pos:* Brit Coun visitor, Imp Col, Univ London, 64; Sigma Xi-Sci Res Soc Am res award, 64-65; Sigma Xi res awards, 66-67 & 69-70; NSF res grants, 67-68, 69-70, 70-72 & 74-; Ford Motor Co res grant, 69; consult, Ford Motor Co, TRW Systs & Marathon LeTourneau Co, 76- *Mem:* Inst Elec & Electronics Engrs; Brit Inst Elec Engrs. *Res:* Linear electric machines; novel electric machines. *Mailing Add:* Dept of Elec Eng Univ of Ky Lexington KY 40506

NASATIR, MAIMON, b Chicago, Ill, Apr 16, 29; div; c 3. CELL BIOLOGY. *Educ:* Univ Chicago, PhB, 50; Univ Pa, PhD(bot), 58. *Prof Exp:* Instr biol, Univ Pa, 58-59; lectr, Haverford Col, 59; USPHS fel, Univ Brussels, 59-60 & Univ Ill, 60-61; asst prof bot, Brown Univ, 61-66, asst to dean, Pembroke Col, 63-65; chmn dept biol, 66-70, PROF BIOL, UNIV TOLEDO, 66- *Concurrent Pos:* Lalor fel, 62 & 63; adj prof dept physiol, Med Col Ohio, 68-71; vis scientist, Brandeis Univ, 76. *Mem:* AAAS; NY Acad Sci; Bot Soc Am; Am Soc Cell Biol. *Res:* Biochemical cytology; plant physiology; cellular biology. *Mailing Add:* Dept of Biol Univ of Toledo Toledo OH 43606

NASCI, ROGER STANLEY, b Pittsburgh, Pa, Jan 30, 52; m 80. BEHAVIORAL ECOLOGY, MEDICAL ENTOMOLOGY. *Educ:* Ohio Univ, BS, 74, MS, 76; Univ Mass, PhD(entom), 80. *Prof Exp:* Fel, 79-80, NIH FEL, VECTOR BIOL LAB, UNIV NOTRE DAME, 80- *Mem:* AAAS; Am Soc Trop Med & Hyg; Mosquito Control Asn; Entom Soc Am; Sigma Xi. *Res:* Mosquito behavior under natural conditions with emphasis on host/mosquito interaction; variations in behavior that may influence the dynamics of mosquito-borne disease system. *Mailing Add:* Vector Biol Lab Biol Dept Univ Notre Dame Notre Dame IN 46556

NASH, CARROLL BLUE, b Louisville, Ky, Jan 29, 14; m 41. BIOLOGY, PARAPSYCHOLOGY. *Educ:* George Washington Univ, BS, 34; Univ Md, MS, 36, PhD, 39. *Prof Exp:* Instr zool, Univ Ariz, 39-41; assoc prof biol, Pa Mil Col, 41-44; asst prof, Am Univ, 44-45; prof, Washington Col, Md, 45-48; prof biol, 48-80, EMER PROF BIOL, ST JOSEPH'S UNIV, PA, 80-, DIR PARAPSYCHOL LAB, 56- *Honors & Awards:* William McDougall Award, Parapsychol Lab, Duke Univ, 60. *Mem:* AAAS; Parapsychol Asn. *Res:* Extrasensory perception; precognition; psychokinesis. *Mailing Add:* Dept of Biol St Joseph's Univ Philadelphia PA 19131

NASH, CHARLES DUDLEY, JR, b New York, NY, May 28, 26; m 49; c 4. MECHANICAL ENGINEERING. *Educ:* Yale Univ, BE, 49; Ohio State Univ, MS, 51, PhD(mech eng), 59. *Prof Exp:* Mech engr, Rocket Sect, Armament Lab, Air Develop Ctr, Wright-Patterson AFB, 49-50, aircraft armament engr, 50-51, rocket design engr, 51-52, ord engr, 52-53, physicist, Ballistics & Terminal Effects Sect, 53-54; from instr to asst prof mech eng, Ohio State Univ, 55-62; assoc prof, Univ Maine, 62-64; actg chmn dept mech eng & appl mech, 66-67, mem, pres selection comt, 67-68, dir, univ honors colloquium, 69-70, PROF MECH ENG, UNIV RI, 64- *Concurrent Pos:* Consult, US Naval Underwater Systs Ctr-Newport Lab, 65- *Mem:* Am Soc Eng Educ; Am Soc Mech Engrs; Am Inst Aeronaut & Astronaut; Soc Eng Sci; Am Math Soc. *Res:* Socio-technological and socio-economic problems; fatigue failure; reliability; vibrations; materials science; thermodynamics; applied mechanics and mathematics; systems analysis. *Mailing Add:* Dept of Mech Eng & Appl Mech Univ of RI Kingston RI 02881

NASH, CHARLES PRESLEY, b Sacramento, Calif, Mar 15, 32; m 55; c 3. PHYSICAL CHEMISTRY. *Educ:* Univ Calif, BS, 52; Univ Calif, Los Angeles, PhD(chem), 58. *Prof Exp:* Actg instr chem, Univ Calif, Los Angeles, 56; instr, 57, assoc prof, 65-70, PROF CHEM, UNIV CALIF, DAVIS, 70- *Concurrent Pos:* Consult, Lawrence Livermore Lab, Univ Calif, 57-68; vis sr lectr, Imp Col, Univ London, 68; distinguished vis prof, US Air Force Acad, 79. *Mem:* Am Phys Soc; Am Chem Soc. *Res:* Exploding wires; solution chemistry; vibrational spectroscopy; amino acids. *Mailing Add:* Dept of Chem Univ of Calif Davis CA 95616

NASH, CLAUDE HAMILTON, III, microbial physiology, see previous edition

NASH, CLINTON BROOKS, b Gunnison, Miss, Jan 3, 18; m 46; c 1. PHARMACOLOGY. *Educ:* Univ Tenn, BS, 50, MS, 52, PhD(pharmacol), 55. *Prof Exp:* Sr pharmacologist, Res Labs, Mead Johnson & Co, 54-57, group leader pharmacol, 57-58; from asst prof to assoc prof, 58-65, PROF PHARMACOL, UNIV TENN CTR HEALTH SCI, MEMPHIS, 65- *Mem:* Am Soc Pharmacol & Exp Therapeut; Am Heart Asn; Soc Exp Biol & Med; Soc Toxicol. *Res:* Cardiovascular effects of anesthetic agents; intraocular pressures; peripheral vasodilators; catecholamine content of various tissues; coronary blood flow; antiarrhythmic agents; cardiovascular actions of vasopressin, reserpine and digitalis. *Mailing Add:* Dept of Pharmacol Univ of Tenn Ctr for Health Sci Memphis TN 38163

NASH, COLIN EDWARD, b Liverpool, Eng, Jan 23, 37; m 61; c 3. RESOURCE MANAGEMENT. *Educ:* Univ Leeds, BS, 59, PhD(textile technol), 62. *Prof Exp:* Res fel textile technol, Int Wood Secretariat, 62-63; res officer aquacult, White Fish Authority, Eng, 63-67, asst prin officer, 67-71; dir, Multunna Lab, Wash, 71-72; dir, 72-78, vpres, oceanic inst, Hawaii, 75-78; MGR APPL SCI, KRAMER, CHIN & MAYO, 78- *Concurrent Pos:* Deleg, S Pac Comn, UN, 71 & 72; consult, US AID, Rockefeller Found, Nat Sea Grant Prog & Int Aquacult Consultancy, 72-; mem comn, Dept Commerce Aquacult Surv, Nat Oceanic & Atmospheric Admin, 72, Marine Resources Subcomt, State of Hawaii, 73; adv, Int Ctr Living Aquatic Resources Mgt, 74-; Aquacult Adv Coun, Hawaii, 77; Int Coun for the Explor of the Seas, 67, 76, 77; Indo-Pac Fisheries Coun, 74; mem, Smithsonian Inst & Int Atlantic Salmon Found. *Mem:* Challenger Soc; Am Fisheries Soc; World Maricult Soc. *Res:* Fish culture science and technology, embracing the interdisciplinary fields of reproductive physiology, nutrition, environmental and aquatic biology, engineering and economics, relating the whole to aquatic resources management for increased animal protein production. *Mailing Add:* Kramer Chin & Mayo Inc 1917 First Ave Seattle WA 98101

NASH, DAVID, b London, Eng, Sept 10, 37. BIOCHEMICAL GENETICS, CYTOGENETICS. *Educ:* Univ London, BSc, 60; Univ Cambridge, PhD(genetics), 63. *Prof Exp:* Wis Alumni Res Found fel zool, Univ Wis, 63-64; asst prof genetics, 65-70, assoc prof genetics, 70-75, assoc chmn, 78-79, PROF GENETICS, UNIV ALTA, 75- *Mem:* Genetics Soc Am; Genetics Soc Can; Am Soc Cell Biol; Can Soc Cell Biol. *Res:* Nucleotide metabolism in Drosophila; studies on auxotrophic mutants of Drosophila. *Mailing Add:* Dept of Genetics Univ of Alta Edmonton AB T6G 2E1 Can

NASH, DAVID BYER, b Cambridge, Mass, Jan 21, 49. QUATERNAY AGE DATING, THERMAL REMOTE SENSING. *Educ:* Colo Col, BA, 71; Univ Mich, MS, 74, PhD(geol), 77. *Prof Exp:* ASST PROF GEOMORPHOL, UNIV CINCINNATI, 77- *Concurrent Pos:* Nat Res Coun res fel, Jet Propulsion Lab, NASA, 81- *Mem:* Geol Soc Am; Sigma Xi; Am Soc Photogram. *Res:* Morphologic dating and computer modeling of fault scarps and other hillslopes; thermal remote sensing of buried bedrock faults; stabilization of landslide prone areas by tree roots; catastrophism in fluvial systems. *Mailing Add:* Dept Geol Univ Cincinnati Cincinnati OH 45221

NASH, DAVID HENRY GEORGE, b Ash Vale, Eng, June 19, 43. APPLIED MATHEMATICS, SOFTWARE DEVELOPMENT. *Educ:* Univ Calif, Riverside, BA, 65; Univ Calif, Berkeley, MA, 67, PhD(math), 70. *Prof Exp:* Actg asst prof math, Univ Hawaii, 69-70; Woodrow Wilson intern, Va State Col, 70-71; lectr, Univ Calif, Berkeley, 71; assoc sr res mathematician, Res Labs, Gen Motors Corp, 72-77, sr staff anal, Corp Prod Planning Group, 77-81; PRES, SCI MKT CORP, 81-; PRES, SCIENTIFIC SOFTWARE ASSOCS, INC, 82- *Concurrent Pos:* Adj assoc prof math, Drexel Univ, 81- *Mem:* Am Math Soc; Math Asn Am. *Res:* Functional analysis. *Mailing Add:* PO Box 461 Bala Cynwyd PA 19106

NASH, DONALD JOSEPH, b New York, NY, Dec 20, 30; m 54; c 3. GENETICS, ZOOLOGY. *Educ:* Univ Mich, BS, 51; Univ Kans, MA, 57; Iowa State Univ, PhD(genetics), 60. *Prof Exp:* Asst prof genetics, Pa State Univ, 60-62; asst prof zool, Rutgers Univ, 62-65; assoc prof radiation biol & zool, 65-66, assoc prof zool, 66-71, PROF ZOOL, COLO STATE UNIV, 71- *Mem:* AAAS; Genetics Soc Am; Am Genetic Asn; Am Soc Mammal; Soc Study Evolution. *Res:* Physiological and quantitative genetics; radiation biology. *Mailing Add:* Dept of Zool Colo State Univ Ft Collins CO 80521

NASH, DONALD ROBERT, b Pittsfield, Mass, Nov 15, 38; m 63; c 1. IMMUNOBIOLOGY. *Educ:* Am Int Col, BA, 61; Boston Col, MS, 63; Univ NC, Chapel Hill, PhD(bact, immunol), 67. *Prof Exp:* Asst prof immunol, Univ Hawaii, 69-70; head immunobiol res, 72-78, RES ASSOC PROF & ACTG CHMN, IMMUNOL/MICROBIOL DEPT, UNIV TEX HEALTH CTR, 78-, ADJ PROF MED MICROBIOL, 78- *Concurrent Pos:* Res fel immunol, Univ NC, Chapel Hill, 67-68; Belg Am Educ Fund res fel, Cath Univ Louvain, 68-69; sr res fel immunol, Ref & Training Ctr, WHO, Switz, 70-72; consult, M D Anderson Hosp & Tumor Inst, 75-78. *Mem:* Am Thoracic Soc; Am Asn Immunologists; NY Acad Sci; Int Asn Study Lung Cancer. *Res:* Humoral and cellular immunity. *Mailing Add:* Univ Tex Health Ctr Box 2003 Tyler TX 75701

NASH, DOUGLAS B, b Elgin, Ill, Dec 2, 32; m 64. GEOLOGY, SPACE PHYSICS. *Educ:* Univ Calif, Berkeley, AB, 60, MA, 62. *Prof Exp:* From assoc scientist to sr scientist, 62-68, res group supvr, 68-70, prin investr, Lunar Sample Anal, 69-74, consult, 74-76, res scientist, 76-81, MGR, PLANETOLOGY & OCEANOGRAPHY SECT, JET PROPULSION LAB, CALIF INST TECHNOL, 81- *Mem:* AAAS; Am Geophys Union; Geol Soc Am; Am Astron Soc. *Res:* Lunar luminescence; lunar surface optical properties; proton irradiation effects on rocks; x-ray diffraction analysis of rock glass; instrument development for lunar and planetary geological analysis; surface properties of Galilean satellites; spectroscopy of planetary materials; planetary sciences. *Mailing Add:* Space Sci Div Jet Propulsion Lab Pasadena CA 91103

NASH, EDMUND GARRETT, b Manitowoc, Wis, Nov 19, 36; m 61; c 2. ORGANIC CHEMISTRY. *Educ:* Lawrence Col, BS, 59; Univ Colo, PhD(chem), 65. *Prof Exp:* Sr res chemist, Gen Mills, Inc. 65-66; res assoc, Johns Hopkins Univ, 66-67; asst prof, 67-70, assoc prof, 70-76, PROF CHEM, FERRIS STATE COL, 77-, ASST VPRES ACAD AFFAIRS, 79- *Mem:* AAAS; Am Chem Soc. *Res:* Chemistry of organic nitrogen compounds; nuclear magnetic resonance of systems with restricted rotation; organic polymer chemistry. *Mailing Add:* Acad Affairs Off Ferris State Col Big Rapids MI 49307

NASH, EDWARD THOMAS, b New York, NY, July 31, 43; m 70. EXPERIMENTAL HIGH ENERGY PHYSICS. *Educ:* Princeton Univ, AB, 65; Columbia Univ, MA, 67, PhD(physics), 70. *Prof Exp:* Res assoc physics, Nevis Cyclotron Lab, Columbia Univ, 70 & Lab Nuclear Sci, Mass Inst Technol, 70-71; staff physicist, 71-82, head internal target lab, 76-77, proj mgr, tagged photon spectrometer, 77-80, DEP CHMN, PHYSICS DEPT, FERMI NAT ACCELERATOR LAB, 79- *Mem:* Am Phys Soc. *Res:* Fundamental forces and symmetries; searches for and studies of the properties of new particles; study of the interaction of photons with matter at very high energy; study of charmed particle dynamics. *Mailing Add:* Fermi Nat Accelerator Lab PO Box 500 Batavia IL 60510

NASH, FRANKLIN RICHARD, b Brooklyn, NY, July 23, 34. PHYSICS. *Educ:* Polytech Inst New York, BS, 55; Columbia Univ, PhD(physics), 62. *Prof Exp:* MEM TECH STAFF PHYSICS RES, BELL LABS, 63- *Mem:* Am Phys Soc; Inst Elec & Electronics Engrs. *Res:* Semiconductor lasers. *Mailing Add:* Bell Labs 600 Mountain Ave Murray Hill NJ 07974

NASH, HAROLD ANTHONY, b Corvallis, Ore, Sept 28, 18; m 46; c 2. BIOCHEMISTRY. *Educ:* Ore State Col, BS, 40; Purdue Univ, PhD(biochem), 47. *Prof Exp:* Asst agr chem, Purdue Univ, 40-44, asst chemist, 42-44 & 46-47; res chemist, Pitman-Moore Co, 47-55, dir chem res, 55-60, dir pharmaceut res, 60-61, asst to tech dir, 61-63; dir res biosci, NStar Res & Develop Inst, 63-64, dir biosci div, 64-70; staff assoc, 70-71, ASSOC DIR, CTR BIOMED RES, POP COUN, 72- *Mem:* Am Chem Soc. *Res:* Chemistry of natural products; medicinal chemicals; mechanism of drug action; biochemistry of chronic diseases; fertility control; contraceptive development. *Mailing Add:* Pop Coun Rockefeller Univ York Ave & 66th St New York NY 10021

NASH, HAROLD EARL, b Lindsay, Calif, July 14, 14; m 40. PHYSICS. *Educ:* Univ Calif, Berkeley, BA, 38. *Prof Exp:* Radio engr, US Signal Corps, McClellan Field, Calif, 42-44; res assoc, Underwater Sound Lab, Harvard Univ, 44-45; sect leader, US Naval Underwater Sound Lab, 45-50, div head, 50-60, assoc tech dir systs develop, 60-63, tech dir, 63-70, tech dir, US Naval Underwater Systs Ctr, Conn, 70-75; CONSULT, UNDERWATER ACOUSTICS, 75- *Mem:* Fel Acoust Soc Am; fel Inst Elec & Electronics Engrs. *Res:* Sonar systems; laboratory administration. *Mailing Add:* PO Box 314 Quaker Hill CT 06375

NASH, HARRY CHARLES, b Cleveland, Ohio, Mar 24, 27; m 51; c 12. SOLID STATE PHYSICS, OPTICS. *Educ:* John Carroll Univ, BS, 50, MS, 51; Case Inst Technol, PhD(physics), 58. *Prof Exp:* From instr to assoc prof, 51-64, PROF PHYSICS, JOHN CARROLL UNIV, 64-, CHMN DEPT, 71- *Mem:* Optical Soc Am; Am Asn Physics Teachers. *Res:* Optical properties of absorbing thin films; elastic constants of single crystals; spectroscopy; emission spectroscopy. *Mailing Add:* Dept of Physics John Carroll Univ Cleveland OH 44118

NASH, J FRANK, pharmaceutical chemistry, physical pharmacy, see previous edition

NASH, J(OHN) THOMAS, b Glen Cove, NY, July 30, 41; m 66; c 1. GEOLOGY, GEOCHEMISTRY. *Educ:* Amherst Col, BA, 63; Columbia Univ, MA, 65, PhD(geol), 67. *Prof Exp:* GEOLOGIST, US GEOL SURV, 67- *Mem:* Geol Soc Am; Am Inst Mining, Metall & Petrol Engrs; Mineral Soc Am; Mineral Asn Can. *Res:* Geochemistry of mineral deposits; fluid inclusions; geology of uranium deposits; clay mineralogy; exploration geochemistry. *Mailing Add:* US Geol Surv Fed Ctr Box 25046 Denver CO 80225

NASH, JAMES LEWIS, JR, b Drakesboro, Ky, Sept 24, 26; m 51; c 2. POLYMER CHEMISTRY. *Educ:* Western Ky State Col, BS, 48; Univ Fla, MS, 50, PhD(chem), 53. *Prof Exp:* Asst chem, Univ Fla, 48-49, 51-53; sr chemist, 53-56, group supvr, 56-60, sr res chemist, 60-69, tech serv specialist, 69-79, SR TECH SERV SPECIALIST, TEXTILE FIBERS DEPT, E I DU PONT DE NEMOURS & CO, INC, 79- *Mem:* Am Chem Soc; Sigma Xi. *Res:* Textile chemistry. *Mailing Add:* Textile Fibers Dept E I du Pont De Nemours Co Inc PO Box 34249 Charlotte NC 28234

NASH, JAMES RICHARD, b Trenton, NJ, Nov 9, 31. PHYSICAL CHEMISTRY, ENGINEERING. *Educ:* Mt St Mary's Col, BS, 53; Univ Notre Dame, PhD(diffusion kinetics), 58. *Prof Exp:* Res asst reaction kinetics, Univ Notre Dame, 53-57, res assoc radiation, 59-61; guest scientist for Frankford Arsenal, Brookhaven Nat Lab, 58-59; supvr subsyst eng, Space Div, NAm Rockwell Corp, 61-67, syst engr, 67-69; syst engr, Systs Group, TRW, Inc, 69-74; mgr, Shuttle Power Systs, Space Div, Rockwell Int, 74-78; SR PROJ ENGR, TRW SYSTS, 78- *Mem:* Am Chem Soc; Radiation Res Soc; Am Inst Aeronaut & Astronaut. *Res:* Space studies; Apollo spacecraft fuel cell system; radiation chemistry; photochemistry; kinetics. *Mailing Add:* 8745 Delgany Playa Del Ray CA 90291

NASH, JONATHON MICHAEL, b Little Rock, Ark, Aug 10, 42; m 72; c 2. ENERGY SYSTEMS. *Educ:* Univ Miss, BSME, 66, MS, 70, PhD(mech eng), 73. *Prof Exp:* Eng officer, US Army Corps Engrs, 68-70; fel, Univ Miss, 70-73; sr assoc engr, 73-74, staff engr, 75-77, proj develop engr, 77-80, adv engr, 80-81, MGR TECH PLANNING, FED SYST DIV, INT BUS MACH CORP, 81- *Concurrent Pos:* Res & develop reserve officer, US Army Mobility Equip Res & Develop Command, 71- *Honors & Awards:* Tudor Medal, Soc Am Military Engr, 78; New Technol Award, NASA, 79. *Mem:* Am Soc Mech Engrs; Am Soc Heating, Refrig & Air Conditioning Engrs; assof fel Am Inst Aeronaut & Astronaut; Am Inst Chem Engrs; Soc Am Mil Engrs. *Res:* Analysis and evalutation of energy conversion processes and their applications including synthetic fuel processes and solar thermal systems. *Mailing Add:* 300 Rockwell Terrace Frederick MD 21701

NASH, LEONARD KOLLENDER, b New York, NY, Oct 27, 18; m 45; c 2. PHYSICAL CHEMISTRY. *Educ:* Harvard Univ, BS, 39, MA, 41, PhD(anal chem), 44. *Prof Exp:* Asst chem, Harvard Univ, 43-44; res assoc, Columbia Univ, 44-45; instr, Univ Ill, 45-46; from instr to assoc prof, 46-59, chmn dept, 71-74, PROF CHEM, HARVARD UNIV, 59- *Mem:* Am Acad Arts & Sci. *Res:* Chemical education; statistical mechanics. *Mailing Add:* Dept of Chem Harvard Univ Cambridge MA 02138

NASH, MURRAY L, b Brooklyn, NY, Dec 28, 17; m 40; c 3. PHYSICAL CHEMISTRY, CHEMICAL ENGINEERING. *Educ:* Brooklyn Col, BS, 39. *Prof Exp:* Phys sci aide, Nat Bur Standards, DC, 41-42; jr chemist, US Bur Mines, Md, 42-44; res assoc, SAM Labs, Columbia Univ, 44; chemist & maj supvr, Carbide & Carbon Chem Corp, Tenn, 44-46; sci analyst, AEC, 46-49, tech asst, 49-55, chief classification analyst, 55-56, chief classification br, 56-64, asst dir opers, Div Classification, 64-67, DEP DIR DIV CLASSIFICATION, US DEPT OF ENERGY, 67- *Mem:* Am Chem Soc; Am Nuclear Soc; NY Acad Sci. *Res:* Separation of isotopes; mass and emission spectroscopy; spectrographic methods of analysis and production of uranium. *Mailing Add:* Div of Classification US Dept of Energy Washington DC 20545

NASH, PETER, b St Paul, Minn, July 11, 45; m 68; c 2. MEDICAL MICROBIOLOGY, IMMUNOLOGY. *Educ:* Lawrence Univ, BA, 67; Univ Hawaii, MS, 69; Colo State Univ, PhD(microbiol), 72. *Prof Exp:* Res asst microbiol, Colo State Univ, 69-72; environ control & safety officer, Ball State Univ, 72-77, assoc prof biol, 72-77; ASSOC PROF BIOL, MANKATO STATE UNIV, 77- *Concurrent Pos:* Researcher fac res grants, Ball State Univ, 73-77, Mankato State Univ, 77-, CORE res grant, 76-77; consult, Marsh Supermkts, Inc, 74-77, Process Supplies, Inc, 76-77 & Muncie Clin, Inc, 75-77. *Honors & Awards:* Gordon Rosene Cancer Award, Am Cancer Soc, Ball State Univ, 76; Nat Registry Microbiol Award, Am Soc Microbiol, 77. *Mem:* Sigma Xi; Am Soc Microbiol; Am Soc Testing & Mat; Wildlife Dis Asn; Nat Environ Health Asn. *Res:* Medical microbiology in vaccine development; tumor immunology and the effect of nutrition on tumor development and immune response repression. *Mailing Add:* Dept of Biol 34 Mankato State Univ Mankato MN 56001

NASH, PETER HOWARD, b Sidcup, Eng, Feb 20, 17; Can citizen; m 51; c 4. RESEARCH ADMINISTRATION. *Educ:* Cambridge Univ, BA, 38, MB, BCh, 41, MA, 45, MD, 50; Univ London, DPH, 47, DIH, 53. *Prof Exp:* Intern surg, Middlesex Hosp, London, 41-42; resident internal med, Metrop Hosp, London, 49-50; asst dir, Slough Indust Health Serv, 50-53; regional med dir occup health, Bell Tel Co Can, 54-57; med dir, Abbott Labs, Ltd, 57-64, DIR SCI AFFAIRS, ABBOTT LABS, LTD, 64- *Concurrent Pos:* Rockefeller fel prev med, 46-48; res fel indust toxicol, Harvard Med Sch, 48; lectr indust health, London Sch Hyg & Trop Med, 50-53; asst physician, Royal Victoria Hosp, Montreal, Can, 57- *Mem:* Fel Indust Med Asn; NY Acad Sci; Can Med Asn; Brit Med Asn; Pharmacol Soc Can. *Res:* Pharmaceutical, medical and research development; quality control. *Mailing Add:* 228 Portland TMR Montreal PQ H3R 1V2 Can

NASH, RALPH GLEN, b Del Norte, Colo, July 26, 30; m 57; c 3. SOIL SCIENCE, CHEMISTRY. *Educ:* Colo State Univ, BS, 58, MS, 61, PhD(soil sci), 63. *Prof Exp:* SOIL SCIENTIST, AGR ENVIRON QUAL INST, SCI & EDUC ADMIN-AGR RES, USDA, 65- *Mem:* Am Soc Agron; Soil Sci Soc Am; Weed Sci Soc Am; Am Chem Soc; Soc Environ Toxicol & Chem. *Res:* Weed science; toxic and residual interactions which result from a combination of two or more pesticides added to soils; plant absorption of pesticides; pesticide degradation; persistence and movement in soil and plants; design and development of an agricultural terrestrial microcosm for following fate of pesticides in plant, soil, water and air; soil and plant analytical pesticide methods; comparative volatization of pesticides from soils. *Mailing Add:* Agr Environ Qual Inst USDA BARC-West Bldg 050HH1 Beltsville MD 20705

NASH, RALPH ROBERT, b South Bend, Ind, May 17, 16; m 42; c 2. PHYSICAL METALLURGY. *Educ:* Purdue Univ, BS, 42; Rensselaer Polytech Inst, MS, 48, PhD(metall), 55. *Prof Exp:* Metallurgist, Aluminum Co Am, 42-44; from instr to assoc prof phys metall, Rensselaer Polytech Inst, 48-57; phys metallurgist, Div Res, Atomic Energy Comn, Washington, DC, 57-60; sci liaison, Off Naval Res, London & Washington, DC, 60-63; mgr solid state mat res prog, NASA, 63-67, chief mat sci br, Div Res, 67-71, exec secy, Off Advan Res & Technol Res Coun, 71-77, MGR INDEPENDENT RES & DEVELOP, NASA, 77- *Concurrent Pos:* Consult, Rensselaer Polytech Inst, 50-58 & Dow Chem Co, 55-58. *Mem:* Am Phys Soc; Am Soc Metals; Am Inst Mining, Metall & Petrol Engrs. *Res:* Plastic deformation of solids; solid state physics and chemistry of solids; surface phenomena; interaction of radiation with matter. *Mailing Add:* Hq NASA 600 Independence Ave SW Washington DC 20546

NASH, REGINALD GEORGE, b LaValle, Wis, Nov 20, 22; m 52; c 3. PARASITOLOGY. *Educ:* William Penn Col, BA, 48; Univ Iowa, MS, 52; Mich State Univ, PhD(zool), 64. *Prof Exp:* Asst prof biol, Northern Ill Univ, 52-54; instr natural sci, Mich State Univ, 54-58; PROF BIOL, UNIV WIS-WHITEWATER, 58- *Res:* Immunologic studies involving infections with roundworms Trichinella spiralis, Ascaris lumbricoides and Toxocara canis. *Mailing Add:* Dept of Biol Univ of Wis Whitewater WI 53190

NASH, ROBERT ARNOLD, b Brooklyn, NY, July 6, 30; m 52; c 3. PHARMACEUTICS, INDUSTRIAL CHEMISTRY. *Educ:* Brooklyn Col Pharm, BS, 52; Rutgers Univ, MS, 54; Univ Conn, PhD, 58. *Prof Exp:* Asst, Rutgers Univ, 53-54 & Univ Conn, 54-57; res assoc, Merck, Sharp & Dohme Res Labs, 57-60; proj leader, mgr pharmaceut prod develop, Lederle Labs Div, Am Cyanamid Co, 60-76; dir pharmaceut develop, Purdue Frederick Co, 76-81; ASSOC PROF INDUST PHARM, ST JOHN'S UNIV, 81- *Concurrent Pos:* Consult pharmaceut & indust pharm. *Honors & Awards:* Richardson Award, 57. *Mem:* Acad Pharmaceut Sci; Am Chem Soc; Int Pharmaceut Fedn. *Res:* Application of the principles of physical chemistry and chemical engineering to industrial pharmaceutical technology; professional industrial manager. *Mailing Add:* St John's Univ Jamaica NY 11439

NASH, ROBERT JOSEPH, b Coventry, Eng, Sept 12, 39; m 63; c 2. SURFACE CHEMISTRY. *Educ:* Univ Wales, BSc, 62; Bristol Univ, PhD(phys chem), 66. *Prof Exp:* Res assoc surface chem, Amherst Col, 65-66, asst prof chem, 66-67; res assoc surface chem, Case Western Reserve Univ, 67-69; scientist, 70-73, SR SCIENTIST, XEROX CORP, 73- *Concurrent Pos:* Ed, CHEMunications, 78- *Mem:* Am Chem Soc. *Res:* Palladium-hydrogen system; hysteresis in absorption processes; surface chemistry of metals; uses of gas chromatography in surface chemistry; surface chemistry of pigments and polymers; surface potentials; xerographic materials. *Mailing Add:* Xerox Corp 800 Phillips Rd Bldg 139 Webster NY 14580

NASH, ROBERT T, b Columbus, Ohio, Sept 20, 29; m 61; c 3. ELECTRICAL ENGINEERING. *Educ:* Ohio State Univ, BSc, 52, MSc, 55, PhD(elec eng), 61. *Prof Exp:* From instr to assoc prof elec eng, Ohio State Univ, 57-66; ASSOC PROF ELEC ENG, VANDERBILT UNIV, 66- *Mem:* Am Astron Soc; Inst Elec & Electronics Engrs. *Res:* Radio astronomy; decision theory. *Mailing Add:* 201 Mockingbird Rd Nashville TN 37205

NASH, STANLEY WILLIAM, b Yakima County, Wash, Oct 8, 15; Can citizen. MATHEMATICAL STATISTICS. *Educ:* Col Puget Sound, BA, 39; Univ Calif, Berkeley, MA, 46, PhD(math statist), 50. *Prof Exp:* From asst prof to assoc prof, 50-66, PROF MATH, UNIV BC, 66- *Concurrent Pos:* Vis assoc prof, Dept Statist, Iowa State Univ, 60-61. *Mem:* Biomet Soc; Am Statist Asn; Inst Math Statist; Am Math Soc; Math Asn Am. *Res:* Classification problems; dissection of mixed distributions; contingency tables in several dimensions; least squares estimation in the singular case; growth curves. *Mailing Add:* Dept of Math Univ of BC Vancouver BC V6T 1W5 Can

NASH, VICTOR E, b Frankfort, Ky, Sept 27, 28; m 56; c 4. SOIL CHEMISTRY, MINERALOGY. *Educ:* Univ Ky, BS, 51, MS, 52; Univ Mo, PhD(soils), 55. *Prof Exp:* Res geochemist, Cities Serv Res & Develop Co, 56-59; from asst prof to assoc prof soils, 59-68, assoc agronomist, 59-68, PROF SOILS & AGRONOMIST, MISS STATE UNIV, 68- *Mem:* Am Soc Agron; Clay Minerals Soc; Soil Sci Soc Am; Int Soil Sci Soc. *Res:* Cation exchange of soil colloids and interaction of soil colloids; soil micromorphology and mineralogy; non-crystalline minerals in soils. *Mailing Add:* Dept Agron Miss State Univ PO Box 5248 Mississippi State MS 39762

NASH, WILLIAM A(RTHUR), b Chicago, Ill, Sept 5, 22; m 53; c 2. MECHANICS. *Educ:* Ill Inst Technol, BS, 44, MS, 46; Univ Mich, PhD(eng mech), 49. *Prof Exp:* Asst engr, Armour Res Found, Ill Inst Technol, 44-45, instr mech inst, 45-46; instr, Univ Mich, 47-49; asst prof, Univ Notre Dame, 49-50; head, Plates & Shells Sect, David Taylor Model Basin, US Dept Navy, 50-54; from assoc prof to prof mech, Univ Fla, 54-67, chmn eng sci & mech, 64-67; PROF CIVIL ENG, UNIV MASS, AMHERST, 67- *Concurrent Pos:* Ed, Int J Nonlinear Mech, 65- *Honors & Awards:* Award, Am Soc Eng Educ, 58. *Mem:* Fel Am Soc Mech Engrs; Am Soc Eng Educ; Am Inst Aeronaut & Astronaut; Int Asn Shell & Spatial Struct. *Res:* Mathematical investigations in the theory of elasticity and the theory of plates and shells; theoretical and applied mechanics; earthquake engineering. *Mailing Add:* Dept of Civil Eng Univ of Mass Amherst MA 01002

NASH, WILLIAM DONALD, b Shreveport, La, Jan 17, 47; m 69; c 2. SYNTHETIC ORGANIC CHEMISTRY. *Educ:* McNeese State Univ, La, BS, 70; Tex A&M Univ, PhD(org chem), 74. *Prof Exp:* RES CHEMIST, EL PASO PROD CO, 74- *Mem:* Am Chem Soc. *Mailing Add:* El Paso Prod Co PO Box 3986 Odessa TX 79760

NASH, WILLIAM HART, b Oct 8, 25; US citizen; c 3. ELECTRICAL ENGINEERING, PLASMA PHYSICS. *Educ:* Univ Wis-Madison, BS, 49, MS, 56; Univ Chicago, MBA, 74. *Prof Exp:* Trainee, McGraw Edison Power Systs, 49-50, jr engr, 50-51, asst engr, 51-52, engr, 52-60, chief engr, 60-67, mgr new prod, 67-68, mgr advan develop, 68-71, mgr res & develop, Power Systs Div, 71-76, DIR, THOMAS A EDISON TECH CTR, MCGRAW EDISON CO, 76- *Mem:* Sr mem Inst Elec & Electronics Engrs; fel Brit Inst Elec Engrs. *Res:* Plasma physics applied to power vacuum interrupters; solid state physics applied to high voltage lightning arresters. *Mailing Add:* PO Box 100 Franksville WI 53126

NASH, WILLIAM PURCELL, b Boston, Mass, Mar 20, 44; m 66; c 2. PETROLOGY, GEOCHEMISTRY. *Educ:* Univ Calif, Berkeley, BA, 65, PhD(geol), 71. *Prof Exp:* From asst prof to assoc prof, 70-78, PROF GEOL, UNIV UTAH, 78-, CHMN, DEPT GEOL & GEOPHYS, 80- *Mem:* Am Geophys Union; Mineral Soc Am; Geochem Soc. *Res:* Field, chemical and thermodynamic methods applied to the origin, evolution and crystallization of igneous rocks. *Mailing Add:* Dept of Geol & Geophys Univ of Utah Salt Lake City UT 84112

NASHED, MOHAMMED ZUHAIR ZAKI, b Aleppo, Syria, May 14, 36; m 59; c 4. MATHEMATICS. *Educ:* Mass Inst Technol, SB, 57, SM, 58; Univ Mich, MS & PhD(math), 63. *Prof Exp:* From asst prof to prof math, Ga Inst Technol, 63-76; vis prof, Univ Mich, 76-77; PROF MATH, UNIV DEL, 77- *Concurrent Pos:* Assoc prof, Am Univ Beirut, 67-69; vis prof, Math Res Ctr, Univ Wis-Madison, 67, 70-72; ed-in-chief, J Numerical Functional & Optimization & J Integral Equations. *Honors & Awards:* Lester Ford Award, Math Asn Am, 67. *Mem:* AAAS; Am Math Soc; Math Asn Am; Soc Indust & Appl Math; Opers Res Soc Am. *Res:* Nonlinear functional analysis; iterative methods for operator equations; numerical analysis; optimization; mathematical programming; integral equations; generalized inverses; ill-posed problems; random operators. *Mailing Add:* Dept of Math Sci Univ of Del Newark DE 19711

NASHED, WILSON, b Damanhour, Egypt, Feb 16, 19; nat US; m 54; c 1. PHARMACY. *Educ:* Univ Cairo, BS, 39; Purdue Univ, MS, 51, PhD(pharm), 54. *Prof Exp:* Hosp pharmacist, Egyptian Govt, 40-41; tech dir, Delta Labs, Egypt, 41-50; sr res chemist, 54-55, res group leader, 56-62, asst dir prod coord, 62-65, mgr regulatory affairs, 65-69, dir sci info, 69-74, assoc dir res, 74-75, dir tech serv & res facil, 75-78, dir sci affairs, 78-79, DIR NEW TECHNOL, JOHNSON & JOHNSON, 79- *Mem:* Am Pharmaceut Asn. *Res:* Pharmaceutical research and product development. *Mailing Add:* Johnson & Johnson New Brunswick NJ 08903

NASHOLD, BLAINE S, b Lennox, SDak, Nov 12, 23; m 48; c 4. NEUROSURGERY, NEUROPHYSIOLOGY. *Educ:* Ind Univ, AB, 43; Ohio State Univ, MSc, 44; Univ Louisville, MD, 49; McGill Univ, MSc, 54. *Prof Exp:* Instr neuroanat, McGill Univ, 53; asst neurosurg, Bowman Gray Sch Med, 56-57; from asst prof to assoc prof, 57-75, PROF NEUROSURG, SCH MED, DUKE UNIV, 75- *Concurrent Pos:* Chief neurosurg sect, Vet Admin Hosp, Durham, NC, 57-59; chmn, Coop Studies Intervertebral Disc Dis & Parkinsonism, Vet Admin, 60-; mem, Cong French Speaking Neurosurgeons, 64. *Mem:* Am Asn Neurol Surg; Am Acad Neurol; Asn Res Nerv & Ment Dis; Am Acad Cerebral Palsy. *Res:* Stereotactic neurosurgical problems in relation to extrapyramidal diseases and problems of central pain; neurochemistry of brain function. *Mailing Add:* Dept Neurosurg Duke Univ Med Ctr Durham NC 27716

NASIM, MOHAMMED ANWAR, b Pasrur, Pakistan, Dec 7, 35; Can citizen. GENETICS. *Educ:* Punjab Univ, BS, 55, MS, 57; Univ Edinburgh, PhD(genetics), 66. *Prof Exp:* Res officer genetics, Atomic Energy Can Ltd, 66-73; res res officer, 73-80, SR RES OFFICER GENETICS, NAT RES COUN CAN, 80- *Mem:* Environ Mutagen Soc; Genetics Soc Can. *Res:* Mechanisms of mutagenesis; DNA repair in yeast; genetic hazards; recombinant DNA, genetic engineering. *Mailing Add:* Div of Biol Sci Nat Res Coun 100 Sussex Dr Ottawa ON Can

NASJLETI, CARLOS EDUARDO, b San Juan, Arg, Apr 24, 21; US citizen; m 55; c 3. CYTOGENETICS, TERATOLOGY. *Educ:* San Juan Nat Col, BA & BS, 41; Nat Univ Cordoba, DDS, 45. *Prof Exp:* Pvt practr dent, San Juan, 45-55; res asst, Dept Nuclear Med, Med Ctr, 55-63, res biologist, 63-69, RES ASSOC DENT, SCH DENT, UNIV MICH, ANN ARBOR, 63; DIR DENT RES & EDUC TRAINEE PROG, 69-, COORDR PROG, 71- *Concurrent Pos:* Partic, Nat Inst Dent Res-Am Col Dent Inst Dent Res, Nat Inst Dent Res, Bethesda, Md & Rockefeller Inst, New York, 65. *Mem:* AAAS; Am Dent Asn: Int Asn Dent Res; Soc Nuclear Med; NY Acad Sci. *Res:* Human cytogenetics, especially investigation of the effects of ionizing radiation and certain chemotherapeutic agents on human chromosomes, both in vivo and invitro. *Mailing Add:* Vet Admin Hosp Ann Arbor MI 48105

NASKALI, RICHARD JOHN, b Jefferson, Ohio, Dec 11, 35. BOTANY. *Educ:* Ohio State Univ, BSc, 57, MSc, 61, PhD(bot), 69. *Prof Exp:* Instr bot, Ohio State Univ, 60-67; ASST PROF BOT, UNIV IDAHO, 67- *Mem:* AAAS; Bot Soc Am. *Res:* Developmental plant anatomy, particularly of flowering and plant chimeras; internode elongation in monocotyledons; aquatic macrophytes of Pacific Northwest. *Mailing Add:* Dept of Biol Sci Univ of Idaho Moscow ID 83843

NASON, HOWARD KING, b Kansas City, Mo, July 12, 13; m 34. CHEMISTRY. *Educ:* Univ Kans, AB, 34. *Prof Exp:* Chief chemist, Anderson-Stolz Corp, 35-36; res chemist, Org Div, Monsanto Chem Co, 36-39, asst dir res plastics div, 39-44, dir develop cent res dept, 44-46, assoc dir, 46-48, dir, 48-50, asst to vpres, 50-51, dir res org div, 51-56, vpres & gen mgr res & eng div, 56-60, pres, Monsanto Res Corp, 60-76; pres, 76-80, CONSULT, IRI RES CORP, 76- *Concurrent Pos:* Mem adv comt isotopes & radiation develop, AEC, 64-68, labor-mgt adv comt, 65; mem, President's Comn Patent Syst, 65-68; mem patent adv comt, US Patent Off, 68; trustee-at-large, Univs Res Asn, Inc, 71-76; vpres & mem exec comt, Atomic Indust Forum, Inc, 71-73; chmn, Aerospace Safety Adv Panel, 72-77, trustee, Charles F Kettering Found, 73-; mem, Nat Mat Adv Bd, Nat Acad Eng, 73-77; consult, 76- *Mem:* AAAS; Am Chem Soc; Am Soc Testing & Mat; Soc Rheol; Am Inst Chem Engrs. *Res:* Plastics; plasticizers; industrial microbiology; physical testing; water treatment; industrial application of chemicals; protective coatings; management of innovation. *Mailing Add:* IRI Res Corp 7800 Bonhomme Ave St Louis MO 63105

NASON, ROBERT DOHRMANN, b San Francisco, Calif, Dec 9, 39. SEISMOLOGY. *Educ:* Calif Inst Technol, BS, 61; Univ Calif, San Diego, PhD, 71. *Prof Exp:* Seismologist, Earthquake Mechanism Lab, Nat Oceanic & Atmospheric Admin, Calif, 66-73; EARTHQUAKE GEOPHYSICIST, US GEOL SURV, 73- *Mem:* Am Geophys Union; Geol Soc Am; Seismol Soc Am; Earthquake Eng Res Inst. *Res:* Heat-flow and marine tectonics; earthquakes and earthquake tectonics; movement on the San Andreas fault; fault creep; earthquake damage and seismic intensity. *Mailing Add:* US Geol Surv 345 Middlefield Rd Menlo Park CA 94025

NASRALLAH, MIKHAIL ELIA, b Kafarmishky, Lebanon, Feb 1, 39; c 3. BIOLOGY, GENETICS. *Educ:* Am Univ Beirut, BSc, 60; Univ Vt, MS, 62; Cornell Univ, PhD, 65. *Prof Exp:* Res assoc physiol genetics, Cornell Univ, 65-66; asst prof plant breeding & biol, Cornell Univ & State Univ NY Col Cortland, 66-67; from asst prof to assoc prof biol, 67-74, PROF BIOL, STATE UNIV NY COL CORTLAND, 74- *Res:* Physiological genetics of self-incompatible plants; characterization of self-incompatibility antigens; cytochemical, enzymatic and immunogenetic studies with pollen and stigmatic proteins involved in cell-cell recognition. *Mailing Add:* Dept of Biol Sci State Univ NY Col Cortland NY 13045

NASS, HANS GEORGE, agronomy, plant science, see previous edition

NASS, ROGER DONALD, b Merrill, Wis, Nov 9, 32; m 54; c 2. WILDLIFE MANAGEMENT. *Educ:* Univ Wis, BS, 60; Univ Mo, MS, 63. *Prof Exp:* Biologist animal damage control res, Tex, 63-65, biologist forest animal res, Colo, 65-66, biologist rodent res, Hawaii, 66-72, biologist predator res, Idaho, 72-74, PROJ LEADER PREDATOR RES, US FISH & WILDLIFE SERV, IDAHO, 74- *Mem:* Wildlife Soc; Am Soc Mammologists. *Res:* Predator-prey relationships; animal damage control methodology. *Mailing Add:* Rte 2 Twin Falls ID 83301

NASSAU, KURT, b Stockerau, Austria, Aug 25, 27; US citizen; m 49. SOLID STATE CHEMISTRY, PHYSICS. *Educ:* Bristol Univ, BSc, 48; Univ Pittsburgh, PhD(phys chem), 59. *Prof Exp:* Res chemist, Glyco Prod Co, Inc, Pa, 49-54; chemist, Dept Metab, Walter Reed Army Med Ctr, Washington, DC, 54-56; MEM TECH STAFF, BELL LABS, MURRAY HILL, 59- *Mem:* Am Chem Soc; Am Crystallog Asn; Am Asn Crystal Growth. *Res:* Growth of crystals and their physical and chemical properties; solid state and crystal chemistry and physics; crystallography; laser, magnetic, piezoelectric, ferroelectric and vitreous materials. *Mailing Add:* 170 Round Top Rd Bernardsville NJ 07924

NASSER, DELILL, microbiology, microbial genetics, see previous edition

NASSER, KARIM WADE, b Shweir, Lebanon, Dec 9, 27; Can citizen; m; c 5. CIVIL ENGINEERING. *Educ:* Am Univ Beirut, BA, 48, BSc, 49; Univ Kans, MSc, 52; Univ Sask, PhD(civil eng), 65. *Prof Exp:* Engr, Trans-Arabian Pipe Line Co, Lebanon, 49-51, design engr, 51-53, supvr engr, Pump Sta, 53-54, maintenance supvr, 54-56; res asst prestressed concrete, Lehigh Univ, 56-59; gen mgr, J M Wright Ltd, Can, 59-62; lectr civil eng, 62-64, from asst prof to assoc prof, 64-71, PROF CIVIL ENG, UNIV SASK, 71- *Concurrent Pos:* Pres, Victory Construct Ltd, 64; consult, 66-; pres, NHF Eng, 76-; pres, Int Construct Co Ltd, 81. *Honors & Awards:* Wason Medal for Res, Am Concrete Inst, 71. *Mem:* Am Concrete Inst; Am Soc Civil Engrs; Eng Inst Can; Can Standards Asn; Am Soc Testing & Mat. *Res:* Concrete and structures; creep of concrete at elevated temperatures; behavior of prestressed concrete members; behavior and design criterion for beams with large openings; K-slump tester, K-5 strength tester and K-situ air tester and fluid level controller. *Mailing Add:* Dept of Civil Eng Univ of Sask Saskatoon SK S7H 0W0 Can

NASSI, ISAAC ROBERT, b New York City, NY, Feb 24, 49; m 70; c 2. SOFTWARE SYSTEMS. *Educ:* State Univ NY, Stony Brook, BS, 70, MS, 72, PhD(comput sci), 74. *Prof Exp:* Sr software engr, Softech, Inc, 74-76; prin software engr, Digital Equip Corp, 76-78, consult software engr, 78-82; VPRES SYST ENG, ONTEL CORP, 82- *Concurrent Pos:* Consult, US Army, 78-79; distinguished rev, Defense Advan Res Proj Agency, 79-; assoc ed, J Comput Languages, 79-; adj instr, Boston Univ, 74-79; prog comt, Boston Sicplan, 76-82. *Mem:* Asn Comput Mach; Inst Elec & Electronics Engrs. *Res:* Design and implementation of programming languages; distributed systems; software engineering; personal computing. *Mailing Add:* Ontel Corp 250 Crossways Park Dr Woodbury NY 11797

NASSOS, PATRICIA SAIMA, b San Francisco, Calif, Sept 10, 51; m 81. FOOD MICROBIOLOGY, CLINICAL MICROBIOLOGY. *Educ:* Univ Calif, Berkeley, AB, 73, PhD(microbiol), 81. *Prof Exp:* Med technologist, Ralph K Davies Med Ctr, San Francisco, 73-76; RES MICROBIOLOGIST, WESTERN REGIONAL RES LAB, USDA, 81- *Mem:* Am Soc Microbiol; Am Soc Clin Pathologists. *Res:* Effect of dietary fiber on ureolytic gut microflora; incipient bacterial spoilage in ground beef products. *Mailing Add:* US Dept Agr 800 Buchanan Berkeley CA 94710

NASTUK, WILLIAM LEO, b Passaic, NJ, June 17, 17; m 50; c 3. PHYSIOLOGY. *Educ:* Rutgers Univ, BSc, 39, PhD(physiol), 45. *Prof Exp:* Asst chem, Rutgers Univ, 39-40, asst physiol, 40-43, instr elec & radio eng, 43-44, asst, Off Sci Res & Develop Proj, 44-45; from instr to assoc prof physiol, 45-60, PROF PHYSIOL, COL PHYSICIANS & SURGEONS, COLUMBIA UNIV, 60- *Concurrent Pos:* Mem, Physiol Study Sect, USPHS, 60-64 & Physiol Training Comt, 64-66; mem, Sci Adv Bd, Myasthenia Gravis Found, 63-; dir, Bioeng Inst, Columbia Univ, 74-78. *Mem:* Soc Neurosci; Am Physiol Soc; Biophys Soc. *Res:* Membrane potentials, neuromuscular transmission; instruments for electrophysiology; gravity and hemorrhagic shock; myasthenia gravis; neuromuscular pharmacology; muscle contraction. *Mailing Add:* Dept Physiol Columbia Univ Col Phys & Surg New York NY 10032

NATALE, NICHOLAS ROBERT, b Philadelphia, Pa, Oct 30, 53; m 74. ASYMMETRIC SYNTHESIS, ANTHANIDE CHEMISTRY. *Educ:* Drexel Univ, BS, 76, PhD(org chem), 79. *Prof Exp:* Res fel, Colo State Univ, 79-81; ASST PROF ORG CHEM, UNIV IDAHO, 81- *Mem:* Am Chem Soc; Sigma Xi. *Res:* Use of heterocycles as masked annulating agents; synthesis of spirocyclic terpenes; selective reductions. *Mailing Add:* Dept Chem Univ Idaho Moscow ID 83843

NATALINI, JOHN JOSEPH, b Norristown, Pa, Apr 27, 44. BIOLOGICAL RHYTHMS, VERTEBRATE BIOLOGY. *Educ:* Villanova Univ, BS, 66; Northwestern Univ, MS & PhD(biol), 71. *Prof Exp:* Asst prof biol, 71-75, ASSOC PROF BIOL, QUINCY COL, 75-, CHMN DEPT, 78- *Concurrent Pos:* Instr anat & physiol, Blessing Hosp Sch Nursing, Quincy, Ill, 74- *Mem:* Sigma Xi; Int Soc Chroniobiol; Int Soc Biometerol; Animal Behavior Soc; AAAS. *Res:* Phase response curves to light and the means of entrainment of biological rhythms to various zeitgebers; circannual rhythms of gerbils. *Mailing Add:* Dept of Biol Quincy Col Quincy IL 62301

NATANSOHN, SAMUEL, b Rzeszow, Poland, June 18, 29; US citizen; m 51; c 4. INORGANIC CHEMISTRY, MATERIALS SCIENCE. *Educ:* Brooklyn Col, BA, 55, MA, 59. *Prof Exp:* MEM TECH STAFF CHEM, GEN TEL & ELEC LAB INC, 55- *Mem:* Am Chem Soc; Sigma Xi; Am Ceramic Soc. *Res:* Complexation reactions in solutions; magnetic materials; luminescent phenomena in solids; crystal growth; inorganic synthesis; hydrometallurgy. *Mailing Add:* GTE Labs 40 Sylvan Rd Waltham MA 02154

NATAPOFF, MARSHALL, b New York, NY, May 5, 25; m 78; c 2. PHYSICS, ELECTRONICS. *Educ:* Cornell Univ, BA, 48; NY Univ, MS, 56; Stevens Inst Technol, PhD(physics), 68. *Prof Exp:* Tech writer electronics, Warner Inc, 59-60; instr physics, City Univ New York, 57-60 & NJ Inst Technol, 60-63; engr electronics, Radio Corp Am, 57-63; ASSOC PROF PHYSICS, NJ INST TECHNOL, 63- *Mem:* Am Phys Soc; Am Asn Physics Teachers. *Res:* Solid state physics; properties of dilute metallic alloys; determination of activation energies theoretically; calculation of atomic radii; influence of time on quantum mechanical systems; cancellation in pseudo potential theory. *Mailing Add:* Dept Physics NJ Inst Technol 323 High St Newark NJ 07102

NATARAJAN, KOTTAYAM VISWANATHAN, b Cochin, India, Apr 21, 33; m; c 4. OCEANOGRAPHY, MICROBIOLOGY. *Educ:* Univ Travancore, India, BS, 52; Benaras Hindu Univ, MS, 55; Univ Alaska, PhD(marine sci), 65. *Prof Exp:* Demonstr bot, NSS Col, Kerala, 52-53 & Vivekananda Col, Madras, 55-56; lectr, Mar Ivanios Col, Kerala, 56-57; res asst, Indian Agr Res Inst, 57-60; scientist, Kaiser Found Res Inst, Calif, 60-61; res asst bot, Univ Calif, Berkeley, 61-62; sr res asst marine sci, Univ Alaska, 62-65, asst prof, 65-70; PROF SCI, GREATER HARTFORD COMMUNITY COL, 70- *Concurrent Pos:* Mem sci fac fel panel, NSF, 74 & mem Comprehensive Assistance Undergrad Sci, 76. *Mem:* AAAS; Am Soc Limnol & Oceanog; Int Phycol Soc. *Res:* Nitrogen fixation by blue-green algae; general physiology of algae; vitamins of the sea. *Mailing Add:* Dept of Sci Greater Hartford Community Col Hartford CT 06105

NATARAJAN, VISWANATHAN, b Chidambaram, India, Aug 15, 48; m 77; c 1. NEUROCHEMISTRY, LIPID METABOLISM. *Educ:* Univ Bombay, India, BSc, 68, MSc, 70; Indian Inst Sci, Bangalore, PhD(biochem), 75. *Prof Exp:* Res fel, 75-78, res assoc, 78-81, ASST PROF BIOCHEM, HORMEL INST, UNIV MINN, 81- *Mem:* Am Soc Neurochem. *Res:* Structure, function and metabolism of phospholipids in biological membranes; lipid metabolism in ischemia; diabetes and peripheral neuropathy; drug-induced phospholipidoses; metabolism and function of inositol lipids. *Mailing Add:* Hormel Inst Univ Minn 801-16th Ave NE Austin MN 55912

NATELSON, SAMUEL, b New York, NY, Feb 28, 09; m 37; c 4. CLINICAL CHEMISTRY. *Educ:* NY Univ, MS, 30, PhD(chem), 31. *Prof Exp:* Instr chem, NY Univ, 28-31; res chemist in-chg, NY Testing Lab, 31-32; res biochemist, Jewish Hosp Brooklyn, 33-49; chmn dept biochem, Rockford Mem Hosp, 49-57, St Vincent's Hosp, New York, 57-58 & Roosevelt Hosp, New York, 58-65; chmn, Dept Biochem, Michael Reese Hosp, 65-79; ADJ PROF ENVIRON PRACT, COL VET MED, UNIV TENN, KNOXVILLE, 79- *Concurrent Pos:* Lectr, Grad Sch, Brooklyn Col, 47-49 & 57-65, New York Polyclin Med Sch & Hosp, 62-65 & Ill Inst Technol, 71-79. *Honors & Awards:* Van Slyke Award Clin Chem, 61; Ames Award, Am Asn Clin Chemists, 65. *Mem:* AAAS; Am Microchem Soc; Harvey Soc; Soc Appl Spectros; Am Chem Soc. *Res:* Citric acid metabolism in humans; infant feeding; radiopaques; surface tension; vapor pressure; sterols; vitamin D; resins; alkaloids; synthetic organic chemistry; organic analysis; microanalysis; instrumentation; nitrogen metabolism. *Mailing Add:* 925 Southgate Rd Knoxville TN 37914

NATH, AMAR, b Agra, India, Nov 28, 29; m 57; c 1. PHYSICAL CHEMISTRY, SOLID STATE CHEMISTRY. *Educ:* Agra Univ, MSc, 50, DSc, 70; Moscow State Univ, PhD(chem), 61. *Prof Exp:* Sci officer, Bhabha Atomic Res Ctr, 51-66; assoc geophysicist, Inst Geophys & Planetary Physics, Univ Calif, Los Angeles, 66-67; res chemist, Lawrence Radiation

Lab, Univ Calif, Berkeley, 67-69; PROF CHEM, DREXEL UNIV, 69- *Mem:* Fel Am Inst Chemists; Am Chem Soc; NY Acad Sci. *Res:* Hot-atom chemistry of solids; isotopic exchange in solid cobalt chelates; injection of electrons or holes and study of thermally stimulated luminescence; current and exo-electron emission; Mossbauer studies of after-effects of Auger events; Mossbauer spectroscopy of vitamin B12 and hemoglobin. *Mailing Add:* Dept Chem Drexel Univ Philadelphia PA 19104

NATH, DILIP K, b Calcutta, India, Dec 4, 33; US citizen; m 66; c 3. MATERIALS SCIENCE. *Educ:* Univ Calcutta, PhD(ceramics), 64. *Prof Exp:* Sr res scientist mat sci, Gen Elec Co, 68-80; MGR OPTICAL FIBER RES & DEVELOP, ITT CORP, 80- *Concurrent Pos:* Fel Zementforshung, Dusseldorf, WGer, 64-65 & Pa State Univ, 65-68. *Mem:* Am Ceramic Soc; Electrochem Soc. *Res:* To discover and understand the inorganic luminescent materials with regards to phosphor technology; high quality quartz for lamps and other applications. *Mailing Add:* ITT Corp 7635 Plantation Rd Roanoke VA 24019

NATH, JOGINDER, b Joginder nagar, India, May 12, 32; m 69; c 1. CYTOLOGY. *Educ:* Panjab Univ, India, BS, 53, MS, 55; Univ Wis, PhD(agron), 60. *Prof Exp:* Res assoc cryobiol, Am Found Biol Res, Wis, 60-63; asst prof cytol & res grant, Southern Ill Univ, 64-66; asst prof genetics, 66-72, PROF GENETICS & REPROD PHYSIOL, WVA UNIV, 72- *Concurrent Pos:* NSF res grant, WVa Univ, 67- *Mem:* Electron Micros Soc Am; Soc Cryobiol; Am Soc Agron; Indian Soc Genetics & Plant Breeding. *Res:* Cytology of genus Selaginella; cytogenetic studies of some species of Paniceae and Phleum; cytogenetics and origin of wheat; cryobiological studies on blood cells, plasma, heart, intestines, mesentery and embryo; electron microscopy of frog oocytes; cryobiological studies on semen, pollen grains and bacteria. *Mailing Add:* Dept Genetics/Plant & Soil Sci WVa Univ Morgantown WV 26506

NATH, K RAJINDER, b Ferozepur, India, May 26, 37; m 73; c 1. DAIRY MICROBIOLOGY, FOOD SCIENCE. *Educ:* Delhi Univ, BSc Hons, 59; Agra Univ, MSc, 61; Cornell Univ, PhD(food sci), 69. *Prof Exp:* Res assoc dairy technol, Ohio State Univ, 69-70; res assoc food sci, Cornell Univ, 70-75; RES MICROBIOLOGIST, KRAFT INC, 75- *Concurrent Pos:* Proj leader & secy, Qual Assurance Consumer Foods Proj, NE-83, 72-75. *Mem:* Am Dairy Sci Asn; Inst Food Technologists. *Res:* Development of microbial culture for food use; microbial interaction in foods; stimulation and inhibition of lactic acid bacteria; protein hydrolysis and protein modification. *Mailing Add:* Kraft Inc Res & Dev 801 Waukegan Rd Glenview IL 60025

NATH, NRAPENDRA, b Meerut, India, Oct 13, 40; US citizen; m 74; c 2. MICROBIOLOGY, VETERINARY SCIENCE. *Educ:* Agra Univ, BVSc, 63, MVSc, 65; All-India Inst Med Sci, PhD(microbiol), 70. *Prof Exp:* Instr vet virol, Univ Guelph, 70-71; res fel coagulation, McMaster Univ, 71-72; res instr, Temple Univ Med Ctr, 72-74; res scientist hepatitis, 74-81, SR RES SCIENTIST, HEPATITIS & TISSUE CULTURE, AM RED CROSS BLOOD SERV LAB, 81- *Concurrent Pos:* Res fel, Dir Gen Health Serv, 66-68 & Indian Coun Med Health, 68-70. *Mem:* Am Soc Microbiol; AAAS. *Res:* Studies in the natural history of hepatitis B virus. *Mailing Add:* Am Red Cross Blood Serv Lab 9312 Old Georgetown Rd Bethesda MD 20814

NATH, RAVINDER KATYAL, b Jullundar, India, Apr 9, 42; m 71; c 1. RADIOLOGICAL PHYSICS. *Educ:* Univ Delhi, BS, 63, MS, 65; Yale Univ, PhD(physics), 71. *Prof Exp:* Res staff physicist, 71-73, res assoc, 73-76, asst prof, 76-79, ASSOC PROF PHYSICS, YALE UNIV, 79- *Honors & Awards:* Med Physics Award, Am Asn Physicists Med, 75. *Mem:* Am Phys Soc; Am Asn Physicists Med; Health Physics Soc; Radiation Res Soc; AAAS. *Res:* Radiological physics related to radiation therapy. *Mailing Add:* Dept Therapeut Radiol PO Box 3333 New Haven CT 06510

NATHAN, ALAN MARC, b Rumford, Maine, Sept 17, 46; m 70. EXPERIMENTAL NUCLEAR PHYSICS. *Educ:* Univ Md, BS, 68; Princeton Univ, MA, 72, PhD(physics), 75. *Prof Exp:* Res assoc physics, Brookhaven Nat Lab, 75-77; asst prof, 77-80, asst dean, Col Eng, 80-81, ASSOC PROF PHYSICS, UNIV ILL, URBANA, 80- *Mem:* Am Phys Soc. *Res:* Nuclear spectroscopy and fundamental interactions of nuclei and nucleons; photonuclear reactions; intermediate energy nuclear physics. *Mailing Add:* Dept Physics Univ Ill Urbana IL 61820

NATHAN, CHARLES C(ARB), b Ft Worth, Tex, Oct 15, 19; m 48; c 4. PHYSICAL CHEMISTRY, CHEMICAL ENGINEERING. *Educ:* Rice Univ, BSChE, 40; Univ Pittsburgh, MS, 42, PhD(chem), 49. *Prof Exp:* Asst chem, Univ Pittsburgh, 40-42; chemist & chem engr, Monsanto Chem Co, 42-44; asst, Purdue Univ, 44; group leader & res assoc petrol prod res, Texaco, Inc, 48-63; mgr coating res & eng, AMF Tuboscope, 63-64; consult, Proj Mohole, 65; process specialist petrol prod & utilization, Monsanto Co, 65-67; sr res assoc, Betz Labs, Inc, 67-68, sect head, 68-71, sr corrosion engr, 71-77; DIR, N MEX ENERGY INST, N MEX INST MINING & TECHNOL, SOCORRO, 77- *Concurrent Pos:* Observer & lectr, Bikini Atom Bomb Tests, 46; mem, Fossil Energy Adv Comt, US Dept Energy, 78- *Mem:* Fel Am Inst Chem Engrs; Nat Asn Corrosion Engrs; Am Soc Qual Control; NY Acad Sci; Nat Soc Prof Engrs. *Res:* Corrosion of ferrous metals; water treatment; industrial quality control; thermodynamics of boron hydrides and hydrocarbons; atomic energy; nuclear physics; statistics; energy research and applications. *Mailing Add:* NMex Inst of Mining & Technol Socorro NM 87801

NATHAN, HENRY C, b New York, NY, Aug 16, 24; m 57; c 1. BIOLOGY. *Educ:* NY Univ, BA, 50; Columbia Univ, PhD(histochem, path), 66. *Prof Exp:* Microbiologist, Personality & Celebrity Printing Co, 51-53; res biologist, Wellcome Res Labs, 53-65; cytopharmacologist, Union Carbide Res Inst, NY, 65-68; instr biol sci, anat & physiol, Hunter Col, 68-74; ADJ PROF BIOL, PACE UNIV, 74- *Concurrent Pos:* Instr, NY Inst Dietetics, 56-57; consult, Darwin Animal Labs, Brooklyn, NY, 60-65. *Mem:* AAAS; Am Soc Zoologists; Am Soc Microbiol; Fedn Am Scientists; NY Acad Sci. *Res:* Nutrition and disease; antibacterials; experimental cancer chemotherapy; metabolism and disease; chemical suppression of immune response; nature of immune mechanisms. *Mailing Add:* Dept of Biol Pace Univ New York NY 10038

NATHAN, KURT, b Essen, Ger, June 27, 20; nat US; m 48; c 1. AGRICULTURAL ENGINEERING, HYDROLOGY. *Educ:* Cornell Univ, BS, 46, MS, 48; Rutgers Univ, BSAE, 55. *Prof Exp:* Asst agr eng & mod lang, Cornell Univ, 46-48; asst prof agr eng, Nat Agr Col, 48-51; res assoc, 51-55, from asst prof to assoc prof, 55-74, PROF AGR ENG, RUTGERS UNIV, 74- *Concurrent Pos:* Pres & prin engr, Conserv Eng, Pa, 81- *Mem:* Nat Soc Prof Engrs; Am Soc Agr Engrs. *Res:* Irrigation and drainage; engineering aspects of soil and water conservation; site development engineering; surface water hydrology; water resources. *Mailing Add:* 144 Dayton Ave Somerset NJ 08873

NATHAN, LAWRENCE CHARLES, b Corning, Calif, Nov 26, 44; m 66; c 2. INORGANIC CHEMISTRY. *Educ:* Linfield Col, BA, 66; Univ Utah, PhD(inorg chem), 71. *Prof Exp:* ASSOC PROF CHEM, UNIV SANTA CLARA, 70- *Concurrent Pos:* Petrol Res Fund res grant, 71. *Mem:* Sigma Xi; Am Chem Soc. *Res:* Preparation and characterization of new transition metal coordination complexes. *Mailing Add:* Dept of Chem Univ of Santa Clara Santa Clara CA 95053

NATHAN, MARC A, b Great Falls, Mont, Sept 14, 37; m 57; c 4. NEUROPHYSIOLOGY, CARDIOVASCULAR PHYSIOLOGY. *Educ:* Wash State Univ, BS, 60; Univ Wash, MS, 62, PhD(psychol), 67. *Prof Exp:* Res assoc physiol psychol, Sch Med, Univ Wash, 67-68, res psychologist radiobiol, Sch Aerospace Med, 68-71; instr, Med Col, Cornell Univ, 72-73, asst prof neurol, 73-78; ASSOC PROF PHARMACOL, UNIV TEX HEALTH SCI CTR, SAN ANTONIO, 78- *Concurrent Pos:* Dir field neurobiol & behav, Med Col, Cornell Univ, 73-77; res career develop award, 76-81. *Mem:* AAAS; Am Physiol Soc; Inst Elec & Electronics Engrs; Soc Neurosci; Am Heart Asn. *Res:* Neural control of the cardiovascular system; neurogenic hypertension; emotional behavior. *Mailing Add:* Dept Pharmacol Univ Tex Health Sci Ctr San Antonio TX 78284

NATHAN, MARSHALL I, b Lakewood, NJ, Jan 22, 33; m 55, 71; c 2. PHYSICS. *Educ:* Mass Inst Technol, BS, 54; Harvard Univ, PhD(physics), 58. *Prof Exp:* Staff mem, 58-71, mgr coop phenomena group, 71-74, consult to dir res, 74-75, mgr optical solid state technol group, 75-77, mgr, Semiconductor Physics & Device Dept, 77-79, MGR, SEMICONDUCTOR MICROSTRUCT DEVICE PHYSICS GROUP, IBM CORP, 79- *Honors & Awards:* David Sarnoff Prize, Inst Elec & Electronics Engrs, 80. *Mem:* Fel Am Phys Soc; fel Inst Elec & Electronics Engrs. *Res:* Solid state physics; semiconductor devices; optics. *Mailing Add:* IBM Corp Res Ctr Box 218 Yorktown Heights NY 10598

NATHAN, PAUL, b Chicago, Ill, June 18, 24; m 53; c 4. PHYSIOLOGY. *Educ:* Univ Chicago, PhB, 46, PhD(physiol), 53. *Prof Exp:* Biochemist, Galesburg State Res Hosp, Ill, 53-55; from instr to assoc prof, 55-77, PROF PHYSIOL, COL MED, UNIV CINCINNATI, 77- ASST PROF EXP SURG, 66-, DIR DEPT CELL BIOL & IMMUNOL, SHRINERS BURNS INST, 66- *Concurrent Pos:* Advan res fel, Am Heart Asn, 59-61; res assoc, May Inst Med Res, Cincinnati Jewish Hosp, 55-65; estab investr, Am Heart Asn, 61-66; res collabr, Brookhaven Nat Lab, 64-71. *Mem:* AAAS; Am Physiol Soc; Int Soc Burn Injuries. *Res:* Transplantation; physiology of digestion; immunology; burn injury. *Mailing Add:* Dept of Physiol Univ of Cincinnati Col of Med Cincinnati OH 45267

NATHAN, RICHARD ARNOLD, b New York, NY, Sept 25, 44; m 66; c 2. ORGANIC CHEMISTRY. *Educ:* Mass Inst Technol, BS, 65; Polytech Inst Brooklyn, PhD(org chem), 69. *Prof Exp:* Chemist, Rohm and Haas Co, 65 & Polaroid Corp, 69; proj leader, Org Chem Div, 70-74, assoc mgr, Org & Struct Chem Sect, 74-76, mgr, Org, Anal & Environ Chem Sect, 76-79, ASSOC DIR, CORP TECH DEVELOP, COLUMBUS LABS, BATTELLE MEM INST, 79- *Mem:* Am Mgt Asn; Am Defense Preparedness Asn; AAAS; Am Nuclear Soc; Atomic Indust Forum. *Res:* Photochemistry and bioorganic chemistry. *Mailing Add:* Nuclear Technol & Phys Sci Dept Battelle Mem Inst Columbus OH 43201

NATHANIEL, EDWARD J H, b Guntur, India, Apr 21, 28; m 53; c 3. ANATOMY. *Educ:* Univ Madras, MB, BS, 52; Univ Calif, Los Angeles, MS, 58, PhD(anat), 62. *Prof Exp:* Demonstr anat, Christian Med Col, Vellore, 52-54; civil asst surgeon & actg chief med officer, Leprosy Treatment & Study Ctr, Turukoilur, 55-56; res anatomist, Sch Med, Univ Calif, Los Angeles, 57-62; chief electron micros lab path, Cedars of Labanon Hosp, 62-64; assoc prof anat & path, Med Col Ga, 64-66; asst prof anat, McGill Univ, 66-68; ASSOC PROF ANAT, SCH MED, UNIV MAN, 68- *Concurrent Pos:* Med Res Coun Can fel, Sch Med, Univ Man, 60-72, Nat Cancer Inst Can fel, 69-72; USPHS fel, Cedars of Lebanon Hosp, Los Angeles, 63-66; USPHS fel, Med Col Ga, 64-66. *Mem:* Am Asn Anatomists; Can Asn Anat; Electron Micros Soc Am; Am Soc Cell Biol; Am Soc Exp Path. *Res:* Electron microscopic research in experimental neurology with emphasis on demyelination and remyelination, postnatal development of nervous system, platelet morphology in artificially induced thrombi in experimental situations and chemotherapy of experimental mouse tumors. *Mailing Add:* Dept of Anat Univ of Man Sch of Med Winnipeg MB R3T 2N2 Can

NATHANS, DANIEL, b Wilmington, Del, Oct 30, 28; m 56; c 3. MICROBIOLOGY, MOLECULAR BIOLOGY. *Educ:* Univ Del, BS, 50; Washington Univ, MD, 54. *Prof Exp:* Resident, Columbia-Presby Med Ctr, 57-59; from asst prof to prof microbiol, 62-76, Boury prof microbiol, 76-80, BOURY PROF MOLECULAR BIOL & GENETICS, JOHNS HOPKINS UNIV, 80-, DIR, 72- *Concurrent Pos:* USPHS grant, Rockefeller Univ, 59-62. *Honors & Awards:* Nobel Prize Cowinner in Med, 78. *Res:* Tumor viruses. *Mailing Add:* Dept of Microbiol Johns Hopkins Univ Baltimore MD 21205

NATHANS, MARCEL WILLEM, physical chemistry, see previous edition

NATHANS, ROBERT, solid state physics, urban studies, see previous edition

NATHANSON, BENJAMIN, b New York, NY, Jan 9, 29. AIR & WATER POLLUTION, CHEMICAL INSTRUMENTATION. *Educ:* City Col New York, BS, 47; Columbia Univ, MA, 49; NY Univ, PhD(chem), 65. *Prof Exp:* Grad asst chem, NY Univ, 50-54; lectr, Chem Dept, Hunter Col, 54-55; instr, Finch Col, 66-67; lectr, Pace Col, 67-68; SR CHEMIST, DEPT ENVIRON PROTECTION, CITY OF NEW YORK, 68- *Concurrent Pos:* Adj asst prof, Pratt Inst, 67-68, Chem Dept, Cooper Union, 76-77. *Mem:* Am Chem Soc; Soc Appl Spectros. *Res:* Instrumental analysis of air and water pollutants and toxic wastes utilizing atomic absorption; x-ray fluorescence; gas chromatography; high-pressure liquid chromatography; gas chromatography-mass spectroscopy; ion chromatography; analysis of airborne particulates for trace metals and organic components; analyzing gasoline for lead; trace gas analysis; freon analysis in air; fuel oil contaminants. *Mailing Add:* 470 W 24th St #7G New York NY 10011

NATHANSON, FRED E(LIOT), b Baltimore, Md, Jan 12, 33; m 56; c 2. ELECTRICAL ENGINEERING. *Educ:* Johns Hopkins Univ, BS, 55; Columbia Univ, MS, 56. *Prof Exp:* Assoc engr, Appl Physics Lab, Johns Hopkins Univ, 56-60, sr staff engr, 60-63, prin staff engr & asst supvr advan radar technol, 63-70; MGR WASH OPERS, TECHNOL SERV CORP, 70- *Concurrent Pos:* Assoc mem, Adv Group Electron Devices. *Mem:* Inst Elec & Electronics Engrs. *Res:* Radar design; radar signal processing; optical electronic techniques. *Mailing Add:* Technol Serv Corp 8555 16th St Silver Spring MD 20910

NATHANSON, H(ARVEY) C(HARLES), b Pittsburgh, Pa, Oct 22, 36; m 63; c 1. SOLID STATE ELECTRONICS. *Educ:* Carnegie Inst Technol, BSEE, 58, MSEE, 59, PhD(elec eng), 62. *Prof Exp:* Instr elec eng, Carnegie Inst Technol, 59-60; sr engr, 62-66, fel eng, 66-67, mgr silicon junction physics, 67-72, MGR MICROELECTRONIC DEVICES, RES LABS, WESTINGHOUSE ELEC CORP, 72- *Mem:* Inst Elec & Electronics Engrs; Electron Dence Soc (pres, 78-80). *Res:* Solid state devices; hyper-abrupt pn semiconductor junctions; surface controlled pn junction breakdown; silicon-silicon dioxide surface stability; mechanically resonant metal-insulator-semiconductor systems; microwave diodes; imaging devices. *Mailing Add:* Westinghouse Res & Develop Ctr 1310 Beulah Rd Pittsburgh PA 15235

NATHANSON, MELVYN BERNARD, b Philadelphia, Pa, Oct 10, 44. MATHEMATICS. *Educ:* Univ Pa, BA, 65; Univ Rochester, MA, 68, PhD(math), 72. *Prof Exp:* PROF MATH, SOUTHERN ILL UNIV, CARBONDALE, 71- *Concurrent Pos:* Asst IREX fel, fac Mech & Math, Moscow State Univ, 72-73; asst to Andre Weil, Inst Advan Study, 74-75; assoc prof math, Brooklyn Col, 75-76; guest, Rockefeller Univ, 75-76; hon res fel math, Harvard Univ, 77-78. *Mem:* Am Math Soc; Math Asn Am. *Res:* Number theory; algebra; combinatorial theory. *Mailing Add:* Dept of Math Southern Ill Univ Carbondale IL 62901

NATHANSON, NEAL, b Boston, Mass, Sept 1, 27; m 54; c 3. VIROLOGY, EPIDEMIOLOGY. *Educ:* Harvard Univ, AB, 49, MD, 53. *Prof Exp:* Chief poliomyelitis surveillance unit, USPHS Commun Dis Ctr, 55-57; res assoc anat & asst prof, Sch Med, Johns Hopkins Univ, 57-63, assoc prof epidemiol, 63-70, prof, 70-79; CHMN, DEPT MICROBIOL, SCH MED, UNIV PA, 79- *Concurrent Pos:* Ed-in-chief, Am J Epidemiol, 64-79. *Mem:* Am Epidemiol Soc; Am Asn Immunol; Am Soc Microbiol; Am Soc Trop Med & Hyg; Am Pub Health Asn. *Res:* Neurotropic viruses; neuropathology. *Mailing Add:* Dept Microbiol Sch Med Univ Pa Philadelphia PA 19104

NATHANSON, NEIL MARC, neurobiology, see previous edition

NATHANSON, WESTON IRWIN, b Detroit, Mich, May 2, 38; m 58; c 2. MATHEMATICS. *Educ:* Univ Calif, Los Angeles, BA, 61, MA, 63, PhD(math), 70. *Prof Exp:* Aeronaut engr, Douglas Aircraft Co, 61-66; prof math, Calif State Univ, Northridge, 66-81; ADV ENGR, FED SYST DIV, IBM CORP, CALIF, 81- *Concurrent Pos:* Eng analyst, Litton Aero Prod, 78-81. *Mem:* Am Math Soc; Math Asn Am. *Res:* Control theory; calculus of variations and the mathematical theory of control processes. *Mailing Add:* 748 Townsgate Rd Westlake CA 94015

NATHENSON, MANUEL, b Charleroi, Pa, Feb 17, 44; m 68; c 1. ENGINEERING, GEOPHYSICS. *Educ:* Carnegie-Mellon Univ, BS, 65; Stanford Univ, MS, 67, PhD(aeronaut eng), 71. *Prof Exp:* MECH ENGR GEOTHERMAL ENERGY, US GEOL SURV, 72- *Mem:* Am Phys Soc; Am Geophys Union; AAAS. *Res:* Geothermal energy. *Mailing Add:* US Geol Surv 345 Middlefield Rd MS 18 Menlo Park CA 94025

NATHENSON, STANLEY G, b Denver, Colo, Aug 1, 33; m 59; c 2. IMMUNOBIOLOGY, IMMUNOCHEMISTRY. *Educ:* Reed Col, BA, 55; Washington Univ, MD, 59. *Prof Exp:* From asst prof to assoc prof microbiol & immunol, 66-73, PROF CELL BIOL, MICROBIOL & IMMUNOL, ALBERT EINSTEIN COL MED, 73- *Concurrent Pos:* Nat Found fel pharmacol, Washington Univ, 60-62; Helen Hay Whitney Found fel, Queen Victoria Hosp, Sussex, Eng, 64-67. *Mem:* Am Asn Immunologists; Transplantation Soc. *Res:* Immunogenetics of transplantation antigens; immunochemistry and biochemistry of mammalian cell membranes; cellular regulation and biosynthetic mechanisms of membrane macromolecules. *Mailing Add:* Dept of Microbiol & Immunol Albert Einstein Col of Med Bronx NY 10461

NATHER, ROY EDWARD, b Helena, Mont, Sept 23, 26; m 62; c 3. ASTRONOMY, PHYSICS. *Educ:* Whitman Col, BA, 49; Univ Cape Town, PhD(astron), 72. *Prof Exp:* Physicist, Hanford Works, Gen Elec Co, 47-51, Calif Res & Develop Corp, 51-53, Tracerlab, Inc, 53-56 & Gen Atomics Div, Gen Dynamics Corp, 56-60; programmer comput div, Royal McBee, Inc, 60-61 & Packard Bell Comput Co, 61-62; tech dir, Sharp Lab, Beckman Inst, 62-67; spec res assoc, 67-73, assoc prof, 73-80, PROF ASTRON, UNIV TEX, AUSTIN, 80- *Res:* Application of high speed electronic techniques to study of short timescale astronomical phenomena, in particular, the evolution of interacting binary stars. *Mailing Add:* Dept of Astron Univ of Tex Austin TX 78712

NATION, JAMES EDWARD, b Springfield, Ill, Aug 22, 33. SPEECH LANGUAGE PATHOLOGY, NEUROLINQUISTICS. *Educ:* Ill State Univ, BS, 60; Univ Wis, MS, 60, PhD(speech path), 64. *Prof Exp:* Asst prof speech path, Univ Ga, 64-66; asst prof, 66-69, assoc prof, 77-80, PROF SPEECH PATH & CHMN DEPT, DEPT COMMUN SCI, CASE WESTERN RESERVE UNIV, 80- *Concurrent Pos:* Assoc dir org dis, Cleveland Hearing & Speech Ctr, 66-67, dir, Dept Speech Path, 70-74; assoc adj prof, Dept Speech Path, Cleveland State Univ, 70-74 & Kent State Univ, 76-77; consult speech path, Dept Pediat, Cleveland Metrop Gen Hosp, 70-; speech path craniofacial team, Univ Hosps, Cleveland, 78-; proj dir, Rehab Serv Admin Training grant, 77-; sr clin instr, Dept Pediat, Case Western Reserve Univ, 79-; mem, Nat Coun Grad Prog Speech-Language Path & Audiol, 78-, secy & treas, 80- *Mem:* Am Speech & Hearing Asn; Am Cleft Palate Asn. *Res:* Speech and language disorders of children and adults with emphasis on the underlying physical and biological processes that account for normal and disordered behavior. *Mailing Add:* Dept Speech Commun Sci Case Western Reserve Univ Cleveland OH 44106

NATION, JAMES LAMAR, b Webster Co, Miss, Mar 3, 36; m 59; c 3. INSECT PHYSIOLOGY. *Educ:* Miss State Univ, BS, 57; Cornell Univ, PhD(entom), 60. *Prof Exp:* From asst prof to assoc prof biol sci, 60-70, assoc prof entom & nematol, 70-72, PROF ENTOM & NEMATOL, UNIV FLA, 72- *Concurrent Pos:* NSF grants, 61-65; mem staff, Univ Guelph, 69-70; USDA Coop grant, 70-72 & 80-83; Environ Protection Agency grant, 80-83. *Mem:* AAAS; Entom Soc Am. *Res:* Nitrogen metabolism and purine excretion in insects; insect nutrition; sex pheromones in insects; insect-plant interactions. *Mailing Add:* Dept of Entom & Nematol Univ of Fla Gainesville FL 32611

NATION, JOHN, b Bridgwater, Eng, Aug 8, 35; m 61; c 2. RELATIVISTIC BEAMS, COLLECTIVE ACCELERATORS. *Educ:* Univ London, BSc & ARCS, 57, DIC & PhD(plasma physics), 60. *Prof Exp:* Consult plasma physics, Nat Comt for Nuclear Energy, Rome, Italy, 60-62; staff scientist, Cen Elec Generating Bd, Eng, 62-65; from asst prof to assoc prof plasma physics, 65-77, asst dir, Lab Plasma Studies, 75-80, PROF ELEC ENG, CORNELL UNIV, 78-, ASSOC DIR, LAB PLASMA STUDIES, 80- *Concurrent Pos:* Lectr, Chelsea Col Sci & Technol, Eng, 64-65; sr vis fel, Sci Res Coun, London, Eng, 73-76; consult phys dynamics, La Jolla Inst, La Jolla & Jaycor, Del Mar, Calif. *Mem:* Sr mem Inst Elec & Electronics Engrs; Am Phys Soc. *Res:* Investigation of the physics of intense electron and ion beams and their applications to accelerators; relativistic electron beams; collective ion accelerators; high power microwave generation. *Mailing Add:* 212 Phillips Hall Cornell Univ Ithaca NY 14853

NATIONS, CLAUDE, b Marlow, Okla, July 9, 29; m 53; c 4. CELL BIOLOGY. *Educ:* Univ Okla, BS, 53; Okla State Univ, MS, 58, PhD(bot), 67. *Prof Exp:* Teacher, Okla City Bd Educ, Okla, 55-57; teacher, Wichita Bd Educ, Kans, 58-62; consult sci educ, Mo State Dept Educ, 63-64; instr biol, bot & plant physiol, Okla State Univ, 64-66; asst prof bot, Univ Tex, Arlington, 66-68; asst prof, 68-76, ASSOC PROF BIOL, SOUTHERN METHODIST UNIV, 76- *Concurrent Pos:* Fel, Lab Cancer Res, Univ Wis, 72-73. *Mem:* Am Soc Cell Biol. *Res:* Gene regulation by nuclear proteins. *Mailing Add:* Dept of Biol Southern Methodist Univ Dallas TX 75275

NATIONS, JACK DALE, b Prairie Grove, Ark, Oct 18, 34; m 57; c 4. PALEOECOLOGY. *Educ:* Ariz State Univ, BS, 56; Univ Ariz, MS, 62; Univ Calif, Berkeley, PhD(paleont), 69. *Prof Exp:* Geologist, Stand Oil Co Tex, 61-64, Pan Am Petrol Corp, 64, Bur Land Mgt, 79-80; ASSOC PROF GEOL, NORTHERN ARIZ UNIV, 69- *Concurrent Pos:* Grant paleoecol & biostratig of Cenozoic Basins, 75-76; cretaceous biostratig & paleoecol of Ariz, 76-81. *Mem:* Am Asn Petrol Geol; Paleont Soc; Soc Econ Paleont & Mineral; Int Paleont Union. *Res:* Paleoecology and biostratigraphy of freshwater mollusks; systematics, phylogeny and paleobiogeography of fossil crabs. *Mailing Add:* Dept of Geol Northern Ariz Univ Flagstaff AZ 86001

NATOLI, JOHN, b Clearfield, Pa, July 5, 50. SURFACE & COLLOID SCIENCE. *Educ:* Univ Pittsburgh, BS, 72; Carnegie-Mellon Univ, MS, 77, PhD(chem eng), 80. *Prof Exp:* Anal biochemist, Biodecision Labs, Div Mylan Pharmaceut, 73-74; asst prof chem eng, Pa State Univ, 79-81; SR SCIENTIST, ROHM & HAAS CO, 81- *Mem:* Am Inst Chem Engrs; Am Chem Soc; AAAS. *Res:* Water soluble polymers; emulsion polymerization; phase behavior of surfactant solutions; membranes and membrane bound transport systems. *Mailing Add:* Rohm & Haas Res Labs 727 Norristown Rd Spring Hease PA 19477

NATOWITZ, JOSEPH BERNARD, b Saranac Lake, NY, Dec 24, 36; m 61; c 2. NUCLEAR CHEMISTRY. *Educ:* Univ Fla, BS, 58; Univ Pittsburgh, PhD(chem), 65. *Prof Exp:* Asst chem, Univ Pittsburgh, 61-65; res assoc, State Univ NY Stony Brook, 65-67; from asst prof to assoc prof, 67-76, PROF CHEM, TEX A&M UNIV, 76-, HEAD DEPT, 81- *Concurrent Pos:* Res collabr, Brookhaven Nat Lab, 65-67; vis scientist, Max Planck Inst; Alexander von Humboldt sr scientist award, 78; vis prof, Tokyo Univ, 79. *Mem:* Am Chem Soc; Chem Inst Can; Am Phys Soc. *Res:* Nuclear reaction studies; fission, light fragment emission, angular momentum effects. *Mailing Add:* Dept Chem Tex A&M Univ College Station TX 77840

NATOWSKY, SHELDON, b Brooklyn, NY, May 6, 44; m 68; c 2. INDUSTRIAL ORGANIC CHEMISTRY. *Educ:* Brooklyn Col, BS, 66; Cornell Univ, PhD(phys org chem), 73. *Prof Exp:* Res specialist surfactants, GAF Corp, 73-75; dir res & develop labs, Carson Chem Inc, Div Quad Chem Corp, 75-78; prod develop chemist, Clorox Co, 78-79; MGR OIL FIELD CHEM, PROD DEVELOP & ANAL SERV, ARCO CHEM CO, 79- *Mem:* Am Chem Soc; Am Oil Chemists Soc; Soc Cosmetic Chemists. *Res:* Management of synthesis, formulation, analysis and governmental regulations relating to oil field production, chemicals manufacture, sales and applications; surfactant formulation cosmetics; consumer products. *Mailing Add:* Arco Chem Co PO Box 370 Sand Springs OK 74063

NATT, MICHAEL PHILIP, b New York, NY, Sept 30, 25; m 55; c 4. INFORMATION SCIENCE, COMMUNICATION SCIENCE. *Educ:* Univ Wis, BA, 47, MA, 48, PhD(zool, biochem), 51. *Prof Exp:* Res asst, Univ Wis, 48-51; res assoc, Hektoen Inst Med Res, Cook County Hosp, 51-52 & Trop Res Found Chicago & Mex, 52; chief sect parasitol, Eaton Labs Inc Div, Norwich Pharmacal Co, 52-59, sr info scientist, 59-60; sr info scientist, Ciba Pharmaceut Prod, Inc, NJ, 60-64; MGR INFO SERV SECT, WYETH LABS, AM HOME PROD CORP, 64- *Mem:* AAAS; Am Soc Parasitol; Am Soc Trop Med & Hyg; Am Asn Vet Parasitol; Am Soc Info Sci. *Res:* Biochemistry, physiology and chemotherapy of parasites; manual and machine documentation; storage and retrieval of scientific information; administration; data processing; data cost analysis; information management. *Mailing Add:* 404 Yorkshire Rd Rosmount PA 19010

NATTIE, EUGENE EDWARD, b Alexandria, Va, June 15, 44; m 70. PULMONARY PHYSIOLOGY. *Educ:* Dartmouth Col, BA, 66, BMS, 68; Harvard Univ, MD, 71. *Prof Exp:* Intern med, Peter Bent Brigham Hosp, 71-72; fel, 72-75, ASST PROF PHYSIOL, SCH MED, DARTMOUTH COL, 75- *Res:* The relationship of brain intra and extra-cellular acid-base and electrolyte balance and the control of breathing in newborn and adults with special emphasis on metabolic acid base disturbances and potassium. *Mailing Add:* Dept of Physiol Dartmouth Med Sch Hanover NH 03755

NATTRESS, JOHN ANDREW, b Lansdowne, Pa, June 16, 20; m 43, 75; c 5. INDUSTRIAL ENGINEERING. *Educ:* Drexel Inst Tech, BS, 43; Ga Inst Technol, MS, 50. *Hon Degrees:* DEng, Embry-Riddle Aeronaut Univ, 69. *Prof Exp:* Head indust tech dept, Southern Tech Inst, Ga, 49-53; chief indust eng, Norwood Mfg Co, 53-54; dir, Charlotte Tech Inst, 54-55; asst prof indust eng, NC State Col, 56-57; assoc prof, 57-65, actg dean col eng, 66-68, assoc dean, 68-78, PROF INDUST ENG, UNIV FLA, 65-, EXEC V PRES, 78- *Mem:* Am Soc Eng Educ; Am Inst Indust Engrs; Nat Soc Prof Engrs. *Res:* Critical path scheduling and schedule evaluation techniques; work measurement and simplification; engineering economics. *Mailing Add:* 226 Tigert Hall Univ of Fla Gainesville FL 32611

NATZKE, ROGER PAUL, b Greenleaf, Wis, June 15, 39; m 64; c 2. DAIRY SCIENCE, PHYSIOLOGY. *Educ:* Univ Wis, BS, 62, MS, 63, PhD(dairy sci), 66. *Prof Exp:* Asst prof, 66-71, ASSOC PROF DAIRY SCI, CORNELL UNIV, 71- *Mem:* Am Dairy Sci Asn; Nat Mastitis Coun; Int Asn Milk, Food & Environ Sanit. *Res:* Factors affecting screening tests; effect of sanitary practices on mastitis; free stall management factors. *Mailing Add:* Dept of Animal Sci Cornell Univ Ithaca NY 14853

NAU, CARL AUGUST, b Yorktown, Tex, June 25, 03; m 25; c 2. PREVENTIVE MEDICINE. *Educ:* Univ Tex, BA, 23, MA, 24; Rush Med Col, MD, 34. *Prof Exp:* Asst zool, Univ Tex, 22, from asst chem to asst prof, 23-27, asst prof physiol, Sch Med, 27-29; from asst prof to assoc prof, Sch Med, Univ Okla, 29-36; dir div indust hyg, State Dept Health, Tex, 36-41; prof physiol, prev med & pub health, Sch Med, Univ Tex, 41-43, prof prev med & pub health, Med Br, 43-61; prof prev med & pub health & dir inst environ health, 61-73, EMER PROF PREV MED & PUB HEALTH, COL MED, UNIV OKLA, 73-; consult to dean, 74-80, PROF CLIN TOXICOL, SCH MED, TEX TECH UNIV, 74- *Concurrent Pos:* Mem, Occup Med & Indust Hyg Adv Comt to Surgeon Gen. *Mem:* Fel Am Pub Health Asn; fel Indust Med Asn; Am Indust Hyg Asn; Am Conf Govt Indust Hygienists. *Res:* Occupational medicine; toxicology; public health. *Mailing Add:* 5209 27th St Lubbock TX 79407

NAU, DANA S, b Urbana, Ill, Dec 29, 51. ARTIFICIAL INTELLIGENCE. *Educ:* Univ Mo-Rolla, BS, 74; Duke Univ, AM, 78, PhD(comput sci), 79. *Prof Exp:* Consult, IBM Res, 77; ASST PROF COMPUT SCI, UNIV MD, 79- *Concurrent Pos:* Comput scientist, Nat Bur Standards, 81. *Mem:* Asn Comput Mach; Am Asn Artificial Intelligence. *Res:* Artificial intelligence research, especially searching and problem-solving techniques, knowledge-based computer systems and expert computer systems. *Mailing Add:* Comput Sci Dept Univ Md College Park MD 20742

NAU, RICHARD WILLIAM, b Lakefield, Minn, May 28, 41; m 63; c 2. MATHEMATICS. *Educ:* SDak Sch Mines & Technol, BS, 63, MS, 65; Univ Va, PhD(appl math), 70. *Prof Exp:* Res assoc, Boeing Co, 65-66; asst prof math, Clarkson Col, 66-67; actg asst prof comput sci, Univ Va, 70; assoc prof, 70-80, PROF MATH & COMPUT SCI, CARLETON COL, 80- *Concurrent Pos:* Fulbright lectr, 80-81. *Mem:* Math Asn Am; Asn Comput Mach; Soc Indust & Appl Math. *Res:* Asymptotic methods; optimization methods; computer graphics. *Mailing Add:* Dept of Math Carleton Col Northfield MN 55057

NAU, ROBERT H(ENRY), b Burlington, Iowa, Apr 21, 13; m 50; c 3. ELECTRICAL ENGINEERING. *Educ:* Iowa State Col, BS, 35, EE, 41; Agr & Mech Col, Tex, MS, 37. *Prof Exp:* Instr physics, Agr & Mech Col, Tex, 35-36, instr elec eng, 36-37; design & develop engr, Westinghouse Elec Corp, Pa, 37-42, design & develop engr heating & vent, NY, 46-47; design & develop engr & consult, Allis-Chalmers Mfg Co, Mass, 46-47; asst prof elec eng, Univ Ill, 47-52; prof in charge power & circuit courses, Dept Elec Eng, Univ Santa Clara, 52-55; head prof elec eng, Ohio Northern Univ, 55-57; PROF ELEC ENG, UNIV MO-ROLLA, 57- *Mem:* Am Soc Eng Educ; Nat Soc Prof Engrs; fel Inst Elec & Electronics Engrs. *Res:* Magnetic fluxes in three-phase circuits; arc interruption by magnetic means in free air, by compressed air and by oil flow; mechanical vibration of electric power transmission lines; electric and magnetic circuits; educational methods; circuits; network analysis and synthesis; solid state physics; servomechanisms. *Mailing Add:* Dept of Elec Eng Univ of Mo Rolla MO 65401

NAUENBERG, MICHAEL, b Berlin, Ger, Dec 19, 34; US citizen; m 69; c 2. ELEMENTARY PARTICLE PHYSICS. *Educ:* Mass Inst Technol, BS, 55; Cornell Univ, PhD(physics), 59. *Prof Exp:* Asst prof physics, Columbia Univ, 61-64; vis res prof, Stanford Univ, 64-66; PROF PHYSICS, UNIV CALIF, SANTA CRUZ, 66- *Concurrent Pos:* Consult, Brookhaven Nat Lab, 62-64 & NSF; Guggenheim fel, 63-64; A P Sloan fel, 64-66; NSF grant, 66- *Mem:* Am Phys Soc. *Res:* Elementary particles and their interactions; astrophysics. *Mailing Add:* Div of Natural Sci Univ of Calif Santa Cruz CA 95060

NAUGHTEN, JOHN CHARLES, b Chicago, Ill, Jan 29, 42; m 66. ZOOLOGY, EMBRYOLOGY. *Educ:* Univ Chicago, AB, 64; Univ Iowa, MS, 68, PhD(zool), 71. *Prof Exp:* Res assoc neuroembryol, Univ Iowa, 71-72; asst prof biol, Univ Wis-Eau Claire, 72-77; asst prof biol, 77-78, ASST PROF ANAT, SCH MED, UNIV SDAK, 78- *Mem:* AAAS; Am Soc Zool; Soc Develop Biol. *Res:* Vertebrate embryology, tissue interactions and differentiation, neuroembryology, metamorphosis. *Mailing Add:* Sch of Med Univ of SDak Vermillion SD 57069

NAUGHTON, MICHAEL A, b UK, June 23, 26; US citizen; c 4. BIOPHYSICS, OBSTETRICS & GYNECOLOGY. *Educ:* Univ St Andrews, BSc, 52; Cambridge Univ, PhD, 59. *Prof Exp:* Res asst, Cambridge Univ, 54-56; res assoc, Mass Inst Technol, 59-62; assoc prof biophys, Johns Hopkins Univ, 62-67; sr prin res scientist, Div Animal Genetics, Commonwealth Sci, Indust & Res Orgn, 67-70; PROF BIOPHYS, OBSTET & GYNEC, SCH MED, UNIV COLO, DENVER, 70- *Concurrent Pos:* NIH career develop award, 64. *Mem:* Brit Biochem Soc; Am Soc Biol Chemists. *Res:* Molecular biology and immunology of proteins. *Mailing Add:* Div of Perinatal Med Box B-198 Univ of Colo Med Ctr Denver CO 80262

NAUGLE, DONALD, b Wetumpka, Okla, Apr 23, 36; m 58; c 2. LOW TEMPERATURE, SOLID STATE PHYSICS. *Educ:* Rice Univ, BA, 58; Tex A&M Univ, PhD(physics), 65. *Prof Exp:* Res fel physics, Tex A&M Univ, 65-66; res assoc, Univ Md, College Park, 67-69; asst prof, 69-75, assoc prof, 75-81, PROF PHYSICS, TEX A&M UNIV, 81- *Concurrent Pos:* NATO fel, Univ Gottingen, 66-67. *Mem:* Am Phys Soc. *Res:* Ultrasonics; fluid transport properties; superconductivity; amorphous metals. *Mailing Add:* Dept Physics Tex A&M Univ College Station TX 77843

NAUGLE, JOHN EARL, b Belle Fourche, SDak, Feb 9, 23; m 45; c 3. PHYSICS. *Educ:* Univ Minn, BS, 49, MS, 50, PhD(physics), 53. *Prof Exp:* Sr staff scientist, Convair Sci Res Lab, 56-59; head nuclear emulsion sect, Goddard Space Flight Ctr, 59-60, head energetic particles prog, satellite & sounding rocket progs, Off Space Flight Progs, 60-61, chief physics, geophys & astron progs, Off Space Sci, 61-62, dir physics & astron progs, Off Space Sci & Appln, 62-66, from dep assoc adminr to assoc adminr space sci & appln, 66-67, assoc adminr space sci, 67-74, dep assoc adminr, 74-75, actg assoc adminr, 75, assoc adminr, 75-77, chief scientist, 77-81, CONSULT, NASA, 81- *Mem:* Am Phys Soc; Am Inst Aeronaut & Astronaut; Am Geophys Union. *Res:* Cosmic rays; high energy physics; trapped radiation. *Mailing Add:* 7211 Rollingwood Dr Chevy Chase MD 20015

NAUGLE, NORMAN WAKEFIELD, b Saginaw, Tex, Jan 9, 31; m 55; c 2. NUMERICAL ANALYSIS, APPLIED MATHEMATICS. *Educ:* Tex A&M Univ, AB, 53, MS, 58, PhD(physics), 65. *Prof Exp:* Asst math, Tex A&M Univ, 55-57 from instr to asst prof, 57-64; mathematician, Manned Spacecraft Ctr, NASA, 64-68; ASSOC PROF MATH, TEX A&M UNIV, 68- *Concurrent Pos:* Teacher, Allen Mil Acad, 57-59 & Alvin Jr Col, 65-67; consult, Appl Res Corp, Tex, 68-72. *Mem:* Math Asn Am; Soc Indust & Appl Math. *Res:* Numerical analysis; digital picture data processing; photoclinometry; molecular structure calculations for vibrational and rotational analysis. *Mailing Add:* Dept of Math Tex A&M Univ College Station TX 77843

NAULT, LOWELL RAYMOND, entomology, see previous edition

NAUMAN, CHARLES HARTLEY, b Philadelphia, Pa, June 6, 37; m 68. RADIATION BIOLOGY. *Educ:* Davis & Elkins Col, BS, 62; Univ Ark, Fayetteville, MS, 65; Northwestern Univ, Evanston, PhD(biol), 72; Columbia Univ, MPH, 79. *Prof Exp:* Assoc radiobiol, Brookhaven Nat Lab, 65-68, tech collabr, Brookhaven Nat Lab-Columbia Univ, 71-72, asst biologist, Brookhaven Nat Lab, 73-74, assoc biologist, 75-79; ENVIRON TOXICOLOGIST, US ENVIRON PROTECTION AGENCY, 79- *Mem:* AAAS; Environ Mutagen Soc; Radiation Res Soc; Am Chem Soc. *Res:* Health and environmental risk analyses for energy-related and other environmental pollutants. *Mailing Add:* 8001 Ronald Rd Manassas VA 22111

NAUMAN, EDWARD BRUCE, b Kansas City, Mo, Oct 3, 37; m 59; c 2. CHEMICAL ENGINEERING. *Educ:* Kans State Univ, BS, 59; Univ Tenn, MS, 61; Univ Leeds, PhD(chem eng), 63. *Prof Exp:* Demonstr chem eng, Univ Leeds, 62-63; engr, Union Carbide Corp, Bound Brook, 63-65, proj scientist, 66-67, res scientist, 67-69, group leader & technol mgr, 69-73, bus strategy mgr, New York, 73-75, prod mgr, 75-77; DIR RES & DEVELOP, XEROX CORP, ROCHESTER, NY, 77- *Mem:* AAAS; Am Inst Chem Engrs; Sigma Xi. *Res:* Chemical reaction engineering with emphasis on mixing phenomena and residence time distribution theory; numerical analysis, simulation and process control; polymer processing. *Mailing Add:* 324 Avalon Dr Rochester NY 14618

NAUMAN, EDWARD FRANKLIN, b Kansas City, Mo, May 1, 15; m 35; c 3. CHEMISTRY, MATERIALS ENGINEERING. *Educ:* Univ Kansas City. *Prof Exp:* Chem engr, Remington Arms Co Div, E I du Pont de Nemours & Co, 41-45; tech dir, J A Folger & Co, 45-55; gen mgr, Longhorn Div, Thiokol Chem Co, 55-60 & Wasatch Div, 60-62, vpres & gen mgr, Co, 62-65; dir develop, Champion Papers, Inc, 65-66, dir corp res & develop, US Plywood-Champion Papers, Inc, 66-68, vpres & dir res & develop, 68-71; pres, Disposal Systs, Inc, 71-77; PRES, NAUMAN ELECTRONICS CO, 74- *Concurrent Pos:* Consult res mgt, 70-; chmn bd, Disposal Technol, Inc, 71, D S Properties, Inc & D S Mfg, Inc, 72. *Mem:* Fel AAAS; Am Inst Chem Engrs; Am Chem Soc. *Res:* Explosives; rocket propulsion; chemical processing; corporate management; solid state electronics and electro-mechanical devices. *Mailing Add:* 508 Highland Blvd Brigham City UT 84302

NAUMAN, ROBERT KARL, b Allentown, Pa, Feb 26, 41; m 68; c 2. MICROBIOLOGY. *Educ:* Pa State Univ, BS, 63; Univ Mass, MS, 65, PhD(microbiol), 68. *Prof Exp:* Res asst microbiol, Univ Mass, 63-68; res assoc, Med Ctr, WVa Univ, 68-69, instr, 69-70; asst prof, 70-78, ASSOC PROF MICROBIOL, SCH DENT, UNIV MD, BALTIMORE, 78- *Mem:*

Am Soc Microbiol; Electron Micros Soc Am. *Res:* General microbiology; microbial cytology, oral microbiology and periodontal diseases; motility, ultrastructure and function; ultrastructure of mammalian tumors and tumor viruses. *Mailing Add:* Dept of Microbiol Univ of Md Sch of Dent Baltimore MD 21201

NAUMAN, ROBERT VINCENT, b East Stroudsburg, Pa, Dec 6, 23; m 55; c 4. PHYSICAL CHEMISTRY. *Educ:* Duke Univ, BS, 44; Univ Calif, PhD(chem), 47. *Prof Exp:* Res assoc chem, Cornell Univ, 47-52; asst prof, Univ Ark, 52-53; from asst prof to assoc prof, 53-63, PROF CHEM, LA STATE UNIV, BATON ROUGE, 63-, DIR, GRAD STUDIES, 81- *Concurrent Pos:* Fulbright-Hays lect award, Santa Maria Tech Univ, Valparaiso, Chile, 66-67; vis prof, Fac Sci, Univ Chile, 71-72. *Mem:* AAAS; Am Chem Soc; Am Phys Soc. *Res:* Molecular spectra; internal energy conversion; photochemistry; light scattering; sodium silicates; structure, size and shape of molecules; detergents; photoacoustic spectroscopy. *Mailing Add:* Dept Chem La State Univ Baton Rouge LA 70803

NAUMANN, ALFRED WAYNE, b Farmington, Iowa, May 8, 28; m 52; c 4. PHYSICAL CHEMISTRY. *Educ:* Grinnell Col, BA, 51; Iowa State Univ, PhD, 56. *Prof Exp:* Asst, Iowa State Univ, 51-56; assoc chemist, 56-71, SR RES SCIENTIST, UNION CARBIDE CORP, 71- *Mem:* AAAS; Am Chem Soc; Am Ceramic Soc. *Res:* Hydrometallurgical separation processes; surface and colloid chemistry; preparation and properties of high performance ceramics; heterogeneous catalysis. *Mailing Add:* 1587 Virginia St E Charleston WV 25311

NAUMANN, HUGH DONALD, b Newport, Ark, Oct 26, 23; m 45; c 2. FOOD MICROBIOLOGY. *Educ:* Univ Mo, BS, 49, MS, 50, PhD(meat technol), 56. *Prof Exp:* From asst instr to instr animal husb, Univ Mo, 50-53; asst prof, Cornell Univ, 53-55; from asst prof to prof animal husb, 55-68, PROF FOOD SCI & NUTRIT, UNIV MO-COLUMBIA, 68-, CHMN DEPT, 75- *Concurrent Pos:* Fulbright sr res scholar, Commonwealth Sci & Indust Orgn, 65-66, Fulbright sr lectr, Gida Fermantasyon Teknolojisi Kurusu Ege Univ, Turkey, 74-75; res fel, Animal & Dairy Sci Res Inst, Irene, SAfrica, 82. *Mem:* Inst Food Technologists; Food Distrib Res Soc; Am Soc Animal Prod. *Res:* Meat technology; evaluation of quality attributes of meat, formulation of meat food products and processing meats, particularly the effects of sanitation, temperature environment, gas environment, and packaging upon the stability of fresh, frozen and cured meats. *Mailing Add:* 228 Eckles Hall Univ of Mo Columbia MO 65211

NAUMANN, ROBERT ALEXANDER, b Dresden, Ger, June 7, 29; nat US; m 61; c 2. PHYSICAL CHEMISTRY. *Educ:* Univ Calif, BS, 49; Princeton Univ, MA, 51, PhD(phys chem), 53. *Prof Exp:* From instr to assoc prof, 52-73, PROF CHEM & PHYSICS, PRINCETON UNIV, 73- *Concurrent Pos:* Procter & Gamble fac fel, 59-60. *Honors & Awards:* Alexander von Humboldt Stiftung Sr US Scientist Award, 78. *Mem:* Fel AAAS; Am Chem Soc; fel Am Phys Soc; NY Acad Sci. *Res:* Radioactivity; inorganic chemistry; nuclear physics. *Mailing Add:* Dept of Physics Jadwin Hall Princeton Univ PO Box 708 Princeton NJ 08540

NAUMANN, ROBERT JORDAN, b Gillespie, Ill, July 1, 35; m 59; c 3. SOLID STATE PHYSICS, MATERIALS SCIENCES. *Educ:* Univ Ala, BS, 57, MS, 62, PhD(physics), 70. *Prof Exp:* Physicist, Army Ballistic Missile Agency, 57-60; physicist, 60-64, br chief, 64-70, div chief instrumentation sci, 70-77, DIV CHIEF & PROG SCIENTIST MAT SCI, SPACE SCI LAB, MARSHALL SPACE FLIGHT CTR, NASA, 77- *Concurrent Pos:* Instr, Athens State Col, 64-; instr, Univ Ala, Huntsville, 70- *Mem:* AAAS; Am Phys Soc; Sigma Xi; Am Inst Aeronaut & Astronaut; Mat Res Soc. *Res:* Crystal growth and characterization; solidification phenomena; fluid-chemical processes; bio and chemical physics; cell and protein separation. *Mailing Add:* ES-71 NASA Huntsville AL 35812

NAUNTON, RALPH FREDERICK, b London, Eng, Sept 26, 21; m; c 2. OTOLARYNGOLOGY. *Educ:* Univ London, MB, BS, 45. *Prof Exp:* Resident surg & dir audiol, Univ Col Hosp, Univ London, 47-50; Med Res Coun res fel, Cent Inst for Deaf, Mo, 51; sci officer, Med Res Coun Eng, 51-52; res asst, Cent Inst for Deaf, Mo, 52-53; sci officer, Med Res Coun Eng, 53-54; instr surg, Sch Med, Univ Chicago, 54-57, from asst prof to prof otolaryngol, 57-80, chmn dept, 68-80; DIR COMMUN DISORDERS PROG, NAT INST NEUROL & COMMUN DISORDERS & STROKE, NIH, 80- *Concurrent Pos:* Asst surgeon, St John's Hosp, London, 47-50; Univ London fel, Holland, 49; clin asst, Royal Nat Throat, Nose & Ear Hosp, 51-54. *Mem:* Am Speech & Hearing Asn; fel Royal Soc Med. *Res:* Otology. *Mailing Add:* Nat Inst Neurol & Commun Disorders & Stroke 7550 Wisconsin Ave Bethesda MD 20205

NAUS, JOSEPH IRWIN, b New York, NY, Mar 14, 38; m 61; c 4. APPLIED STATISTICS, SURVEY SAMPLING. *Educ:* City Col New York, BBA, 59; Harvard Univ, MS, 61, PhD(statist), 64. *Prof Exp:* Analyst opers res, Appl Sci Div, Mass Inst Technol, 62-63 & Inst Naval Studies, Franklin Inst, 63-64; assoc prof statist, City Col New York, 67-68; asst prof, 64-66, assoc prof, 67-74, PROF STATIST, RUTGERS UNIV, 74- *Concurrent Pos:* Dir statist, Rutgers Univ, 73-77 & 81-82. *Mem:* Am Statist Asn; Inst Math Statists. *Res:* Applied probability and statistics; distributional theoretic problems, particularly with the unusual clustering of points in time or space; approaches for screening and editing data for errors. *Mailing Add:* Dept Statist Rutgers Univ-State Univ NJ New Brunswick NJ 08903

NAUTA, WALLE J H, b Medan, Indonesia, June 8, 16; US citizen; m 42; c 3. ANATOMY. *Educ:* State Univ Utrecht, MD, 42, PhD(anat), 45. *Hon Degrees:* Dr, Univ Rochester, 75. *Prof Exp:* Lectr anat, State Univ Utrecht, 42-46; assoc prof, State Univ Leiden, 46-47 & Univ Zurich, 47-51; neurophysiologist, Walter Reed Army Inst Res, 51-64; PROF NEUROANAT, MASS INST TECHNOL, 64-, INST PROF, 73- *Concurrent Pos:* Mem bd, Found Fund Res Psychiat, 59-62; mem res career develop awards comt, NIMH, 66-; mem Biol Stain Comn, 57- *Honors & Awards:* Karl Spencer Lashley Award, Am Philos Soc, 64; Henry Gray Award, Am Asn Anat, 73. *Mem:* Nat Acad Sci; Am Philos Soc; Am Asn Anat; Am Acad Arts & Sci; Swiss Asn Anat. *Res:* Neuroanatomy; neurophysiology. *Mailing Add:* Dept Psychol Rm E10-104 Mass Inst Technol Cambridge MA 02139

NAVALKAR, RAM G, b Bombay, India, May 7, 24; m 66; c 2. MICROBIOLOGY, IMMUNOLOGY. *Educ:* St Xavier's Col, India, BSc, 46; Univ Bombay, PhD(microbiol), 56. *Prof Exp:* Res officer leprosy, Acworth Leprosy Hosp, Bombay, 58-60; proj assoc tuberc, Sch Med, Univ Wis, 60-63; res assoc, Gothenburg Univ, 64-65; proj assoc tuberc & leprosy, Sch Med, Univ Wis, 66-67; from asst prof to prof med microbiol, Meharry Med Col, 67-80; PROF & CHMN, DEPT MICROBIOL & IMMUNOL, MOREHOUSE SCH MED, ATLANTA, GA, 80- *Concurrent Pos:* Fel microbiol, Sch Med, Stanford Univ, 56-58; NIH grant, 67-; consult, Stanford Res Inst, 57-58. *Mem:* Fel Am Acad Microbiol; Soc Exp Biol Med; AAAS; Am Soc Microbiol; Int Leprosy Asn. *Res:* Antigenic studies on mycobacteria; study of Mycobacterium leprae by comparative analysis, using various immunochemical techniques; specific antigens of Mycobacterium leprae in relation to their biological activity; immune mechanisms in Mycobacterial infections. *Mailing Add:* Morehouse Sch Med 830 Westview Dr Southwest Atlanta GA 30314

NAVAR, LUIS GABRIEL, b El Paso, Tex, Mar 24, 41; m 65; c 4. PHYSIOLOGY, BIOPHYSICS. *Educ:* Agr & Mech Col, Tex, BS, 62; Univ Miss, PhD(biophys, physiol), 66. *Prof Exp:* Instr physiol & biophys, Sch Med, Univ Miss, 66-67, from asst prof to assoc prof, 67-74; assoc prof, 75-76, PROF PHYSIOL & BIOPHYS, SCH MED, UNIV ALA, BIRMINGHAM, 76- *Concurrent Pos:* Nat Inst Arthritis & Metab Dis fel physiol & biophys, Med Ctr, Univ Miss, 66-69 & spec fel med, Duke Univ, 72; Nat Heart & Lung Inst res career develop award, 74; mem, Coun Kidney & Cardiovasc Dis, Am Heart Asn. *Mem:* Am Soc Nephrology; Am Heart Asn; Am Physiol Soc; NY Acad Sci; Sigma Xi. *Res:* Control of renal hemodynamics; regulation of sodium excretion; pathophysiology of high blood pressure; regulation of extracellular fluid volume. *Mailing Add:* CDLD Bldg 727 Univ of Ala Med Sch Birmingham AL 35294

NAVARRA, JOHN GABRIEL, b Bayonne, NJ, July 3, 27; m 47; c 2. EARTH SCIENCES, SCIENCE EDUCATION. *Educ:* Columbia Univ, AB, 49, MA, 50, EdD(sci educ), 54. *Prof Exp:* Assoc prof chem, physics & sci educ, ECarolina Univ, 54-58; prof sci & chmn dept, 58-68, PROF GEOSCI, JERSEY CITY STATE COL, 68-; DIR, LEARNING RESOURCES LABS, 67- *Concurrent Pos:* Consult, NC State Bd Educ Sci Curriculum Study, 58, State of Calif NDEA Workshops Strengthening Elem Sch Sci, 60-61 & State Adv Comt on Sci, 60-62; partic, White House Conf Children & Youth Golden Anniversary, 60; teacher educ study, Nat Asn State Dir Teacher Educ & Cert, 60-61; Am Inst Physics coordr vis scientists prog physics for high schs, NJ, 61-64; sci ed, Arabian-Am Oil Co, Saudi Arabia, 63. *Mem:* Am Geol Soc; AAAS. *Res:* Applications of chromatography; development and refinement of broad areas of science in elementary, junior high school and college curriculum. *Mailing Add:* Learning Resources Labs PO Box 647 Farmingdale NJ 07727

NAVARRO, JOSEPH ANTHONY, b New Britain, Conn, July 6, 27; m 51; c 3. MATHEMATICAL STATISTICS. *Educ:* Cent Conn State Col, BS, 50; Purdue Univ, MS, 52, PhD(math statist), 55. *Prof Exp:* Asst math, Purdue Univ, 51, math statist, 51-55; consult statistician, Gen Elec Co, 55-59; mem res staff, IBM Corp, 59-64; mem res staff, Inst Defense Anal, 64-70, asst dir systs eval div, 70-72; EXEC VPRES, SYST PLANNING CORP, 72- *Mem:* Sigma Xi; Opers Res Soc Am; Am Statist Asn. *Res:* Use of operations research, probability and mathematical statistics in analysis weapon system acquisition; systems analysis. *Mailing Add:* 7825 Fulbright Ct Bethesda MD 20034

NAVARRO-BERMUDEZ, FRANCISCO JOSE, b San Jose, Costa Rica, Aug 4, 35. MATHEMATICS. *Educ:* Mass Inst Technol, BS, 59; Harvard Univ, AM, 60; Bryn Mawr Col, PhD(math), 77. *Prof Exp:* Prof math, Univ Costa Rica, 61-63; ASSOC PROF MATH, WIDENER COL, 64- *Mem:* Am Math Soc; Math Asn Am; Sigma Xi. *Res:* Real variables; measure theory. *Mailing Add:* Dept Math Widener Col Chester PA 19013

NAVE, CARL R, b Newport, Ark, July 21, 39; m 62; c 2. PHYSICS. *Educ:* Ga Inst Technol, BEE, 61, MS, 64, PhD(physics), 66. *Prof Exp:* Fel physics, Univ Col NWales, 66-67; asst prof, 68-71, ASSOC PROF PHYSICS, GA STATE UNIV, 71- *Mem:* Am Phys Soc; AAAS; Audio Eng Soc; Am Asn Physics Teachers. *Res:* Determination of molecular structure and study of intramolecular interactions by microwave spectroscopy; electron spin resonance studies of radiation damage in organic crystals. *Mailing Add:* Dept of Physics Ga State Univ University Plaza Atlanta GA 30303

NAVE, FLOYD ROGER, b Moline, Ill, Oct 7, 25; m 49; c 4. GEOMORPHOLOGY, PALEONTOLOGY. *Educ:* Augustana Col, AB, 49; Univ Iowa, MS, 52; Ohio State Univ, PhD, 68. *Prof Exp:* Instr geol, Augustana Col, 51-52; geologist, Gen Petrol Corp, Calif, 52-53; asst prof geol, 53-61, assoc prof, 62-69, chmn dept, 64-74, PROF GEOL, WITTENBERG UNIV, 69- *Concurrent Pos:* NSF sci fac fel, 58-59. *Mem:* Geol Soc Am; Am Asn Petrol Geol; Nat Asn Geol Teachers; Sigma Xi; Am Quaternary Asn. *Res:* Environmental geology. *Mailing Add:* Dept of Geol Wittenberg Univ Springfield OH 45501

NAVE, PAUL MICHAEL, b Lancaster, Pa, June 3, 43; m 65; c 2. ORGANIC CHEMISTRY. *Educ:* Memphis State Univ, BS, 65; Iowa State Univ, PhD(org chem), 69. *Prof Exp:* Asst prof, 69-74, ASSOC PROF CHEM, ARK STATE UNIV, 74- *Mem:* Am Chem Soc. *Res:* Metal ion oxidation of organic compounds; ligand transfer oxidation of free radicals. *Mailing Add:* Dept of Chem Ark State Univ State University AR 72467

NAVES, RENEE G, b Toulouse, France, Nov 18, 27. ORGANIC CHEMISTRY. *Educ:* Univ Grenoble, BS, 48, PhB, 49; Univ Geneva, MS, 52, PhD(biol), 55. *Prof Exp:* Instr, Univ Geneva, 52-55; res fel org chem, Mass Gen Hosp & Harvard Med Sch, 55-57; res asst, Univ Fla, 57-58; prof & chmn dept, Newton Col Sacred Heart, 58-72; researcher, Am Univ, 72-74; Am Chem Soc fel chem & pub affairs, serv in House of Rep, 75-76; CONSULT, 76- *Concurrent Pos:* Res asst, Harvard Med Sch, 58-59; abstractor, Chem Abstr, 65-69; consult, Sci Curriculum in East Boston Schs, 71; vis scientist, Duke Univ, 74-75. *Mem:* AAAS; Am Chem Soc; NY Acad Sci. *Res:* Carbohydrate chemistry and synthesis, specifically examinations for determinations of carbohydrate content of microorganisms cell walls; carbohydrate research through use of nuclear magnetic resonance. *Mailing Add:* 1131 University Blvd W Suite 1010 Wheaton MD 20902

NAVIA, JUAN MARCELO, b Havana, Cuba, Jan 16, 27; US citizen; m 50; c 4. NUTRITION. *Educ:* Mass Inst Technol, BS & MS, 50, PhD, 65. *Prof Exp:* Tech dir, Cuba Indust & Com Co, 50-52; assoc prof nutrit & food sci, Univ Villanueva, Cuba, 55-61; res assoc, Mass Inst Technol, 61-65, assoc prof nutrit biochem, 66-69; SR SCIENTIST, INST DENT RES & PROF BIOCHEM, COMP MED, ORAL BIOL & NUTRIT SCI, UNIV ALA, BIRMINGHAM, 69-, DIR RES TRAINING, SCH DENT, 73- *Concurrent Pos:* Dir, FIM Nutrit Lab, 52-55; asst dir, Cuban Inst Tech Invest, 55-61. *Mem:* Int Asn Dent Res; Am Soc Microbiol; Am Inst Nutrit; Inst Food Technologists; Am Inst Chemists. *Res:* Nutritional biochemistry; mineral metabolism; oral biology. *Mailing Add:* Univ of Ala Sch of Dent University Station Birmingham AL 35294

NAVIA, MANUEL ALBERTO, biophysics, x-ray diffraction, see previous edition

NAVON, DAVID H, b New York, NY, Oct 28, 24; m 47; c 2. ELECTRONIC PHYSICS, MICROELECTRONICS. *Educ:* City Col New York, BEE, 47; NY Univ, MS, 50; Purdue Univ, PhD(physics), 53. *Prof Exp:* Instr physics, Mohawk Col, 47 & Queen's Univ, NY, 47-50; res assoc, Purdue Univ, 53-54; asst dir res, Transition Electronic Corp, 54-60, dir semiconductor res, 60-65; vis assoc prof elec eng, Mass Inst Technol, 65-68; PROF ELEC ENG, UNIV MASS, AMHERST, 68- *Concurrent Pos:* Lectr, Hebrew Univ, Jerusalem, 74, Nanjing Inst Technol & Futan Univ, Shanghi, 81. *Mem:* Inst Elec & Electronics Engrs. *Res:* Solar energy; semiconductor electronics; microelectronics. *Mailing Add:* Dept of Elec Eng Univ of Mass Amherst MA 01002

NAVRATIL, GERALD ANTON, b Troy, NY, Sept 5, 51. PLASMA PHYSICS. *Educ:* Calif Inst Technol, BS, 73; Univ Wis-Madison, MS, 74, PhD(plasma physics), 76. *Prof Exp:* Proj assoc physics, Univ Wis-Madison, 76-77; asst prof eng sci, Mech & Nuclear Eng Dept, 77-78, ASST PROF APPL PHYSICS, DEPT APPL PHYSICS & NUCLEAR ENG, COLUMBIA UNIV, 78- *Mem:* Am Phys Soc. *Res:* Trapped particle instabilities in plasma; high pressure limits of plasma confinement in tokamaks; controlled fusion research. *Mailing Add:* 215 SW Mudd Bldg Columbia Univ New York NY 10027

NAVRATIL, JAMES DALE, b Denver, Colo, Jan 20, 41; m 67; c 4. INDUSTRIAL CHEMISTRY, ANALYTICAL CHEMISTRY. *Educ:* Univ Colo, Boulder, BA, 70, MSc, 72, PhD(anal chem), 75. *Prof Exp:* Anal lab technician anal chem, Dow Chem USA, 61-66, chem res & develop master technician, 66-68, sr chemist, 70-73, res chemist, 73-75; sr res chemist res & develop, Rockwell Int, 75-76, res specialist, 76-77, group leader I, 77-78; first officer, Int Atomic Energy Agency, 78-81; MGR CHEM RES, ROCKWELL INT, 81- *Concurrent Pos:* Res assoc, Univ Colo, Boulder, 75-76, instr, 76-78. *Honors & Awards:* Rockwell Int Engr of Year, 77. *Mem:* AAAS; Am Chem Soc; Am Nuclear Soc. *Res:* Chemical separations methods; ion exchange chromatography; liquid chromatography; solvent extraction research; chemical synthesis and characterization; actinide chemistry. *Mailing Add:* Rockwell Int PO Box 464 Golden CO 80401

NAVROTSKY, ALEXANDRA, b New York, NY, June 20, 43. CHEMISTRY. *Educ:* Univ Chicago, BS, 63, MS, 64, PhD(chem), 67. *Prof Exp:* Res assoc theoret metall, Clausthal Tech Univ, 67-68; res assoc geochem, Pa State Univ, 68-69; from asst prof to assoc prof, 69-77, prof chem, 77-81, PROF CHEM & GEOL, ARIZ STATE UNIV, 81- *Concurrent Pos:* Alfred P Sloan Found fel, 73. *Mem:* Am Geophys Union; Mineral Soc Am; Am Ceramic Soc. *Res:* Thermodynamics; phase equilibria and high temperature calorimetry; oxides and oxide solid solutions; order-disorder; geochemistry; geothermal fluids. *Mailing Add:* Dept of Chem Ariz State Univ Tempe AZ 85281

NAWAR, TEWFIK, b Cairo, Egypt, Sept 6, 39; Can citizen. NEPHROLOGY. *Educ:* Einshams Univ, Cairo, MB, BCh, 63; McGill Univ, MSc, 72; Col Physicians & Surgeons Can, FRCP(C), 72; Am Bd Internal Med, dipl nephrol, 78. *Prof Exp:* Med Res Coun fel, Montreal Clin Res Inst, 70-72; asst prof, 72-77, ASSOC PROF MED, MED SCH, UNIV SHERBROOKE, 77- *Concurrent Pos:* Med Res Coun fel, Renal Div, Med Sch, Wash Univ, 71-72. *Mem:* Can Soc Nephrol; NY Acad Sci; Am Soc Nephrol; Int Soc Nephrol; Can Soc Clin Invest. *Res:* Renal handling of adenosine 3',5' cyclic monophosphate in health and disease; hypertension. *Mailing Add:* Univ Hosp Ctr Univ of Sherbrooke Sherbrooke PQ J1K 2R1 Can

NAWAR, WASSEF W, b Cairo, Egypt, May 17, 26; m 53; c 1. FOOD CHEMISTRY. *Educ:* Univ Cairo, BSc, 47, MS, 50; Univ Ill, PhD(food sci), 59. *Prof Exp:* Asst dairy tech, Univ Ill, 50-52 & 57-59; from asst prof to assoc prof, 59-70, PROF FOOD SCI, UNIV MASS, AMHERST, 70- *Concurrent Pos:* Res grants, Sigma Xi, 61, USPHS, 65-69 & AEC, 65-; mem comt food irradiation, Nat Acad Sci-Nat Res Coun, 74- *Mem:* Am Chem Soc; Am Oil Chem Soc; AAAS; Inst Food Technol. *Res:* Flavor chemistry; thermal decomposition of fats; effects of ionizing radiation on fats. *Mailing Add:* Dept of Food Sci Univ of Mass Amherst MA 01003

NAWORSKI, JOSEPH SYLVESTER, JR, b Glassmere, Pa, May 3, 37; m 65; c 3. CHEMICAL ENGINEERING. *Educ:* Univ Pittsburgh, BS, 59, MS, 62; Cornell Univ, PhD(chem eng), 66. *Prof Exp:* Res engr, Res Labs, Aluminum Co Am, 59-62 & Res & Develop Div, Sun Oil Co, 66-68; asst prof chem eng, Va Polytech Inst & State Univ, 68-72; supvr process develop, 72-77, SECT MGR PROCESS DEVELOP, STAUFFER CHEM CO, 77- *Mem:* Am Inst Chem Engrs. *Res:* Chemical reaction engineering; preparative gas-liquid chromatography; oxychlorination of ethylene; chemical process development. *Mailing Add:* Stauffer Chem Co 1200 S 47th St Richman CA 94801

NAWROCKY, ROMAN JAROSLAW, b Przemysl, Poland, Apr 30, 32; US citizen; m 66; c 1. ELECTRICAL ENGINEERING. *Educ:* Univ Man, BSEE, 56; Polytech Inst Brooklyn, MSEE, 63; Polytech Inst New York, PhD(elec eng), 75. *Prof Exp:* Develop engr elec eng, Can Gen Elec Co, 56-58, Nat Co, 58-59, Mass Inst Technol, 59-61 & Bendix Corp, 63-64; DEVELOP ENGR ELEC ENG, BROOKHAVEN NAT LAB, 64- *Mem:* Sigma Xi; Inst Elec & Electronics Engrs. *Res:* Automatic control; communications; instrumentation. *Mailing Add:* ISABELLE Prog Bldg 902-A Brookhaven Nat Lab Upton NY 11973

NAWY, EDWARD GEORGE, b Baghdad, Iraq, Dec 21, 26; US citizen; m 49; c 2. CIVIL & STRUCTURAL ENGINEERING. *Educ:* Univ Baghdad, Dipl, 48; Imp Col, Univ London, Dipl, 51; Mass Inst Technol, CE, 59; Univ Pisa, DrEng(concrete), 67. *Prof Exp:* Dep head struct div, Israel Water Planning Authority, Tel Aviv, 51-57; res engr, Mass Inst Technol, 57-59; PROF CIVIL ENG, RUTGERS UNIV, NEW BRUNSWICK, 59-, CHMN, DEPT CIVIL ENVIRON ENG, 80- *Concurrent Pos:* Chmn, Nat Comt on Cracking, Am Concrete Inst, 66-; adv, Fed Aviation Admin, Washington, DC, 69- *Honors & Awards:* H L Kennedy Award of Excellence, Am Concrete Inst. *Mem:* Fel Am Soc Civil Engrs; Nat Soc Prof Engrs; NY Acad Sci; fel Brit Inst Civil Eng. *Res:* Concrete structural systems, particularly cracking in two-way slabs; ultimate load of large diameter concrete pipes; plastic hinge rotation in reinforced and prestressed concrete systems; off-shore airports; fiber glass reinforcement in concrete. *Mailing Add:* Dept of Civil Eng Rutgers Univ New Brunswick NJ 08903

NAYAK, DEBI PROSAD, b West Bengal, India, Apr 1, 37; m 65; c 2. VIROLOGY, GENETIC ENGINEERING. *Educ:* Univ Calcutta, BVSc, 57; Univ Nebr, Lincoln, MS, 63, PhD(virol), 64. *Prof Exp:* Actg asst prof virol, 64-66, asst res virologist, 66-68, from asst prof to assoc prof, 68-76, PROF VIROL, UNIV CALIF, LOS ANGELES, 77- *Concurrent Pos:* Cancer Res Coord Comt & Calif Inst Cancer Res fels, Univ Calif, Los Angeles, 69, Calif Div Am Cancer Soc sr Dernham fel, 69-74, Am Cancer Soc res grant, 72-74, Nat Cancer Inst res grant, 74-78, Nat Inst Allergy & Infectious Dis res grant, 75- & NSF, 79-81. *Mem:* AAAS; Am Soc Microbiol. *Res:* Influenza virus genome and its translation, transcription, and replication; structure and genesis of defective interfering influenza viral genome; mechanism of interference; cloning, sequencing and expression of viral genes in both bacterial and eukaryotic systems; manipulation of cloned genes for producing medically important products. *Mailing Add:* Dept Med Microbiol & Immunol Univ Calif Ctr Health Sci Los Angeles CA 90024

NAYAK, RAMCHANDRA KESHAV, pharmaceutical chemistry, see previous edition

NAYAK, RAMESH KADBET, b Udipi, India, Sept 6, 34; US citizen; m 58; c 2. REPRODUCTIVE PHYSIOLOGY, CELL BIOLOGY. *Educ:* Univ Madras, BS, 54; Univ Bombay, MS, 56; Univ RI, MS, 64; Ore State Univ, PhD(physiol), 70. *Prof Exp:* Lectr zool, Inst Sci, Bombay, 56-61; res asst biol, Childrens Cancer Res Found, 64-65; fel, Univ Nebr, 70-72; res assoc anat, George Washington Univ, 72-75; assoc prof zool, Kuwait Univ, 75-78; HEALTH SCIENTIST ADMINR, NIH, BETHESDA, 78- *Concurrent Pos:* Scientist biol, Smithsonian Sci Info Exchange, 72-75. *Mem:* Electron Micros Soc Am; Am Soc Cell Biol; Am Soc Animal Sci; Am Inst Biol Sci; Am Anat Soc. *Res:* Electron microscopic studies of mammalian oviduct; effect of contraceptive steroids on the cardiovascular system. *Mailing Add:* 9000 Rockville Pike Div Res Grants Westwood Bldg Rm 233 Bethesda MD 20205

NAYAK, RAMNATH V, medicine, endocrinology, see previous edition

NAYAR, JAI KRISHEN, b Kisumu, East Africa, Jan 3, 33; US citizen; m 64; c 3. INSECT PHYSIOLOGY, MEDICAL ENTOMOLOGY. *Educ:* Univ Delhi, BSc, 54, MSc, 56; Univ Ill, Urbana, PhD(entom), 62. *Prof Exp:* Sr res asst entom, Indian Agr Res Inst, Delhi, 56-58; med entomologist, Div Health, Fla Med Entom Lab, Vero Beach, Fla, 63-79; MED ENTOMOLOGIST, FLA MED ENTOM LAB, UNIV FLA, VERO BEACH, 79- *Concurrent Pos:* Nat Res Coun Can award, Univ Man, 62-63; adj assoc prof entom & nematol, Univ Fla, Gainesville, 75-, affil assoc prof preventive med, Col Vet Med, 81- *Mem:* Entom Soc Am; Am Soc Trop Med & Hyg. *Res:* Biology and physiology of mosquitoes of medical and veterinary importance. *Mailing Add:* Fla Med Entom Lab PO Box 520 Vero Beach FL 32960

NAYFEH, ALI HASAN, b Shuweikah, Jordan, Dec 21, 33; m 65; c 1. MECHANICS, APPLIED MATHEMATICS. *Educ:* Stanford Univ, BS, 62, MS, 63, PhD(aeronaut, astronaut), 64. *Prof Exp:* Prin res scientist, Heliodyne Corp, Calif, 64-68; mgr math physics dept, Aerotherm Corp, 68-71; prof eng mech, 71-74, UNIV DISTINGUISHED PROF ENG MECH, VA POLYTECH INST & STATE UNIV, 75- *Mem:* Am Inst Aeronaut & Astronaut; Am Phys Soc; Am Soc Mech Engrs. *Res:* Perturbation methods; linear and nonlinear hydrodynamic stability; nonlinear vibrations; nonlinear waves; aerodynamics; acoustics; missible dynamics. *Mailing Add:* Dept of Eng Mech Va Polytech Inst & State Univ Blacksburg VA 24061

NAYFEH, MUNIR HASAN, b Shuweikah-Tulkarem, Jordan, Dec 13, 45; m 73; c 4. ATOMIC PHYSICS. *Educ:* Am Univ Beirut, BSc, 68, MSc, 70; Stanford Univ, PhD(physics), 74. *Prof Exp:* Fel physics, Oak Ridge Nat Lab, 74-76, res physicist, 76-77; lectr, Yale Univ, 77-78; asst prof, 78-80, ASSOC

PROF PHYSICS, UNIV ILL, URBANA-CHAMPAIGN, 80- *Honors & Awards:* Indust Res-100 Award. *Res:* High resolution laser spectroscopy; atomic collisions; coherence and quantum optics; multiphoton ionization of atoms and molecules. *Mailing Add:* Dept of Physics Univ Ill Urbana-Champaign Urbana IL 61801

NAYFEH, SHIHADEH NASRI, b Merj 'Youn, Lebanon. BIOCHEMISTRY, ENDOCRINOLOGY. *Educ:* Am Univ Beirut, BS & teaching dipl, 59, MS, 61; Univ NC, Chapel Hill, PhD(biochem), 64. *Prof Exp:* Fel, Harvard Univ, 64-65; investr biochem, Lebanese Agr Res Inst, 65-67 & Univ Pa, 67-68; asst prof biochem & endocrinol & dir endocrinol lab, NC Mem Hosp, 68-72, ASSOC PROF BIOCHEM, NUTRIT & PEDIAT, SCH MED, UNIV NC, CHAPEL HILL, 72- *Mem:* AAAS; Soc Study Reproduction; Endocrine Soc; NY Acad Sci; Am Soc Biol Chemists. *Res:* Mechanisms of action of polypeptide hormones in normal and tumour cells. *Mailing Add:* Dept of Biochem Univ of NC Sch of Med Chapel Hill NC 27514

NAYLOR, ALFRED F, b South River, NJ, Oct 17, 27; m 50; c 3. GENETICS. *Educ:* Univ Chicago, AB, 50, PhD(zool), 57. *Prof Exp:* Asst, Univ Chicago, 51-54 & 55-57; asst prof zool, Univ Okla, 57-60; asst prof genetics, McGill Univ, 60-64; GENETICIST, NAT INST NEUROL DIS & STROKE, 64- *Mem:* Am Soc Human Genetics. *Res:* Population and human genetics; biometry; population ecology. *Mailing Add:* 6303 Bannockburn Dr Bethesda MD 20014

NAYLOR, AUBREY WILLARD, b Union City, Tenn, Feb 5, 15; m 40; c 2. PLANT PHYSIOLOGY. *Educ:* Univ Chicago, BS, 37, MS, 38, PhD(bot), 40. *Prof Exp:* Rockefeller asst, Univ Chicago, 38; mem staff, Bur Plant Indust, USDA, 38-40; instr bot, Univ Chicago, 40-44, naval radio, 42-44; instr bot, Northwestern Univ, 44-45; Nat Res Coun fel biol sci, Boyce Thompson Inst, 45-46; asst prof plant physiol, Univ Wash, 46-47 & Yale Univ, 47-52; from assoc prof to prof, 52-72, JAMES B DUKE PROF PLANT PHYSIOL, DUKE UNIV, 72- *Concurrent Pos:* Res partic & consult, Oak Ridge Inst Nuclear Studies, 54-64; consult, Oak Ridge Nat Lab, 57-58, NSF, 60-65, Res Triangle Inst, 68-, Biol Div, Tenn Valley Authority, 69-75 & Educ Testing Serv, 72-; NSF sr fel & vis prof, Univ Bristol, 58-59, prog dir metab biol, NSF, 61-62; mem, Comn Undergrad Educ in Biol Sci, chmn panel interdisciplinary activ; chmn comt examr, Grad Rec Exam Biol, 66-72; mem bd, Southeastern Plant Environ Labs, 68-; Charles Reid Barnes Life Mem Award, Am Soc Plant Physiol, 81. *Mem:* Am Am Soc Plant Physiol (secy, 53-55, vpres, 56, pres, 61); Japanese Soc Plant Physiologists; Australian Soc Plant Physiologists; Biochem Soc; Sigma Xi. *Res:* Photophysiology; growth regulation; enzymes; amino acid metabolism. *Mailing Add:* Dept Bot Duke Univ Durham NC 27706

NAYLOR, BENJAMIN FRANKLIN, b Gilroy, Calif, Nov 15, 17; m 46; c 3. CHEMISTRY. *Educ:* San Jose State Col, AB, 40; Stanford Univ, MA & PhD(phys chem), 43. *Prof Exp:* Phys chemist, US Bur Mines, Calif, 43-45; chemist, Stand Oil Co Calif, 45; from instr to assoc prof chem, San Jose State Univ, 45-61, head dept, 50-61, prof chem & coordr gen chem, 61-80. *Concurrent Pos:* Adj prof chem, San Jose State Univ, 80- *Mem:* Am Chem Soc. *Res:* Chemical thermodynamics; high-temperature heat contents of titanium carbide and titanium nitride; specific heats of metals at high temperatures by AC-DC method. *Mailing Add:* Dept of Chem San Jose State Univ San Jose CA 95192

NAYLOR, BRUCE GORDON, b Midale, Sask, Aug 19, 50. VERTEBRATE PALEONTOLOGY, HERPETOLOGY. *Educ:* Univ Sask, BSc, 72; Univ Alta, PhD(vert paleont), 78. *Prof Exp:* Fel vert paleont, Univ Toronto, 78-80; LECTR, UNIV CALIF, BERKELEY, 79-; ASST PROF GEOL ZOOL, UNIV ALBERTA, 80- *Concurrent Pos:* Nat Res Coun Can fel, 78-80. *Mem:* Soc Vert Paleont; Soc Study Evolution; Soc Study Amphibians & Reptiles; Am Soc Ichthyologists & Herpetologists. *Res:* Phylogenetic relationships and functional morphology of fossil and recent salamanders and lizards. *Mailing Add:* Lab Vert Paleo Dept Geol & Zool Univ Alberta Edmonton ON T6G 2E3 Can

NAYLOR, CARTER GRAHAM, b Denver, Colo, May 22, 42; m 64; c 3. PETROLEUM CHEMISTRY, SURFACTANTS. *Educ:* Calif Inst Technol, BS, 64; Univ Colo, PhD(org chem), 69. *Prof Exp:* Res chemist, 69-70, sr res chemist, Jefferson Chem Co, 70-80, SR RES CHEMIST, TEXACO CHEM CO, 80- *Mem:* Am Chem Soc; Am Oil Chemists Soc. *Res:* Petrochemicals, especially surfactants; enhanced oil recovery. *Mailing Add:* Texaco Chem Co Box 15730 Austin TX 78761

NAYLOR, DENNY VE, b Twin Falls, Idaho, Oct 26, 37; m 59; c 2. SOIL CHEMISTRY. *Educ:* Univ Idaho, BS, 59, MS, 61; Univ Calif, Berkeley, PhD(soil sci), 66. *Prof Exp:* Assoc prof, 66-77, PROF SOILS, UNIV IDAHO, 77- *Mem:* AAAS; Am Soc Agron; Soil Sci Soc Am. *Res:* Nutrients in soil-water systems; water quality and agricultural practices; soil organic matter chemistry. *Mailing Add:* Dept of Plant & Soil Sci Univ of Idaho Moscow ID 83843

NAYLOR, DEREK, b Eng, Nov 9, 29; m 60; c 2. APPLIED MATHEMATICS. *Educ:* Univ London, BSc, 51, PhD(aerodyn), 53. *Prof Exp:* Res assoc, Brown Univ, 53-54; aerodynamicist, A V Roe & Co, 54-56; asst prof appl math, Univ Toronto, 56-62; sr lectr, Royal Col Sci, Glasgow, 62-63; assoc prof, 63-65, PROF APPL MATH, UNIV WESTERN ONT, 65- *Mem:* London Math Soc; fel Brit Inst Math & Appln. *Res:* Integral transforms. *Mailing Add:* Dept of Appl Math Univ of Western Ont London ON N6A 5B8 Can

NAYLOR, FLOYD EDMOND, b Becker, NMex, Feb 9, 22; m 52; c 4. POLYMER CHEMISTRY. *Educ:* Wash State Col, BS, 51; Univ Md, PhD(org chem), 56. *Prof Exp:* RES CHEMIST & GROUP LEADER, PHILLIPS PETROL CO, 55- *Mem:* Am Chem Soc. *Res:* Chemistry of high polymers; rubber; plastics. *Mailing Add:* 145 CPL-PRC Phillips Petrol Co Bartlesville OK 74004

NAYLOR, GERALD WAYNE, b Keener, Ala, Feb 15, 22; m 44; c 3. AGRONOMY, PLANT PHYSIOLOGY. *Educ:* Auburn Univ, BS, 47, MS, 49; NC State Univ, PhD(agron), 53; Southeastern Baptist Theol Sem, BD, 56. *Prof Exp:* Minister & hosp chaplain, NC Baptist Hosp, 53-60, res fel, 60-61; assoc prof, 61-71, PROF BIOL, CARSON-NEWMAN COL, 71- *Concurrent Pos:* Partic, NSF res prog, Univ Tex, 64-66 & acad year exten, 64-66, 67-69; proj dir, NSF Student Sci Training Prog, 72-79. *Mem:* AAAS; Am Soc Plant Physiol. *Res:* Water pollution studies of Lake Cherokee and the resultant serious problem of fish kill. *Mailing Add:* Dept of Biol Carson-Newman Col Jefferson City TN 37760

NAYLOR, HARRY BROOKS, b Minn, Mar 30, 14; m 40; c 3. BACTERIOLOGY. *Educ:* Univ Minn, BS, 38; Cornell Univ, PhD(bact), 43. *Prof Exp:* Dairy chemist, Sheffield Farms Co, 46-47; prof dairy indust, 47-50, prof bact, 50-77, EMER PROF MICROBIOL, CORNELL UNIV, 77- *Concurrent Pos:* Fulbright-Hays lectureship, Univ Alexandria, 66-67; Orgn Am States lectureship, Univ Campinas, Brazil, 72, 73, sabbatical res leave, Univ Campinas, 75; spec assignment at Fed Univ Rio de Janeiro, 78; mem staff, Pasco Lab, Inc, 78- *Mem:* Am Soc Microbiol; Am Acad Microbiol. *Res:* Bacterial physiology; virology. *Mailing Add:* Pasco Lab Inc 12750 W 42nd Ave Wheat Ridge CO 80033

NAYLOR, JAMES MAURICE, b Hawarden, Sask, Feb 22, 20; nat Can; m 43; c 2. BOTANY. *Educ:* Univ Wis, PhD(bot), 53. *Prof Exp:* From asst prof to assoc prof field husb, 53-64, prof biol, 64-74, head dept, 68-77, RAWSON PROF BIOL, UNIV SASK, 74- *Res:* Genetic and physiological control of growth in higher plants. *Mailing Add:* Dept of Biol Univ of Sask Saskatoon SK S7H 0W0 Can

NAYLOR, MARCUS A, JR, b Oberlin, Ohio, Apr 27, 20; m 43; c 2. ORGANIC CHEMISTRY. *Educ:* Col Wooster, BA, 42; Johns Hopkins Univ, MA, 43, PhD(org chem), 45. *Prof Exp:* Lab instr chem, Johns Hopkins Univ, 42-44; res chemist, Plastics Dept, E I Du Pont de Nemours & Co, Inc, 44-50, supvr, Res Div, Polychem Dept, 50-55, com investr, Planning Div, 55-56, sect mgr, Res Div, 56-58, dir gen prod res & develop, 58-59, asst dir, Res Div, Indust & Biochem Dept, 59-67, asst dir, Indust Chem Sales Div, 67-72, dir lab, Chem Dyes & Pigments Dept, 73-80; RETIRED. *Mem:* Am Chem Soc. *Res:* Research administration; organic synthesis; reaction mechanisms; chemistry of high polymers. *Mailing Add:* 4706 Washington St Ext Wilmington DE 19809

NAYLOR, PAUL HENRY, b Easton, Md, Jan 11, 48; m 70. BIOCHEMICAL ENDOCRINOLOGY. *Educ:* Washington Col, Md, Bs, 70; Johns Hopkins Univ, MA, 72; Univ Tex, Galveston, PhD(biochem), 77. *Prof Exp:* Instr chem, Univ Md, Baltimore County, 72-74; res affil biochem endocrinol, Roswell Park Mem Inst, 78-80; res fel, 80-82, RES ASSOC BIOL CHEM, HARVARD MED SCH, 82- *Concurrent Pos:* McLaughland fel, Univ Tex Med Br, 77-78; training fel, Nat Cancer Inst, 78-80. *Mem:* Endocrine Soc; AAAS; NY Acad Sci. *Res:* Immunological and endocrinological roles of the thymus; role of steroids, especially corticosteroids and thymic factors (thymosin) in neoplasia; steroid mechanisms of action on target cells, using antiglucocorticoids and estrogens in normal and neoplastic hormone responsive models; mechanism of neoplastic transformation by hormones and chemical carcinogens. *Mailing Add:* Dept Biol Chem Harvard Med Sch Boston MA 02115

NAYLOR, RICHARD STEVENS, b Lakeland, Fla, July 15, 39. GEOLOGY, GEOCHEMISTRY. *Educ:* Mass Inst Technol, BS, 61; Calif Inst Technol, PhD(geol), 67. *Prof Exp:* Asst prof geol, Mass Inst Technol, 67-74; ASSOC PROF EARTH SCI & CHMN DEPT, NORTHEASTERN UNIV, 74- *Mem:* Geol Soc Am; Am Geophys Union; Geochem Soc. *Res:* Geology and geochronology of northern Appalachian Mountain system; geology and geochronology of mantled gneiss domes. *Mailing Add:* Dept Earth Sci 14HO Northeastern Univ Boston MA 02115

NAYLOR, ROBERT ERNEST, JR, b Nashville, Ark, July 14, 32; m 63; c 1. CHEMICAL PHYSICS. *Educ:* Univ SC, BS, 51; Harvard Univ MA, 54, PhD(chem physics), 56. *Prof Exp:* Res chemist, Film Dept, E I du Pont de Nemours & Co, Inc, 56-62, res supvr, 62-64, res mgr, 64-66, tech supt, 66-67, lab dir, 67-71, tech mgr, 71-74, prod & tech dir, Film Dept, 74-76, tech dir, Atomic Energy Div, 76-79, dir, Res & Develop Planning, Corp Plans Dept, 79-80, dir res, Cent Res & Develop Dept, 81; VPRES & CORP DIR RES, ROHM & HAAS CO, 82- *Res:* Polymer science; nuclear energy. *Mailing Add:* Rohm & Haas Co Res Lab 727 Norristown Rd Spring House PA 19477

NAYMARK, SHERMAN, b Duluth, Minn, May 12, 20; m 42; c 2. NUCLEAR ENGINEERING. *Educ:* US Naval Acad, BS, 41; Mass Inst Technol, MS, 46. *Prof Exp:* Asst chief engr, USS Saratoga, 41-44; repair supt, Norfolk Naval Shipyard, 46-48; sr scientist, Argonne Nat Labs, 48-52; dir Naval Reactors Schenectady Opers, Off AEC, 52-54; proj engr & mgr submarine intermediate reactor, Knolls Atomic Power Lab, Gen Elec Co, Schenectady, 54-56, mgr reactor design, Atomic Power Equip Dept, San Jose, 56-60, mgr fuel develop, 60-65, mgr nuclear mat & propulsion opers, Cincinnati, 65-67, mgr & engr turnkey opers, Atomic Power Equip Dept, San Jose, 67-69; PRES, QUADREX CORP, 70- *Mem:* Fel Am Nuclear Soc; AAAS; assoc Am Public Power Asn. *Res:* Nuclear power. *Mailing Add:* Quadrex Corp 1700 Dell Ave Campbell CA 95008

NAYMIK, DANIEL ALLAN, b Lorain, Ohio, Mar 8, 22; m 44. MATHEMATICS, QUANTUM PHYSICS. *Educ:* Univ Mich, BS, 47, MS, 48, PhD(physics), 58. *Prof Exp:* Mem tech staff semiconductor adv develop, Bell Tel Labs, NJ, 58-64; mem sr staff physics of thin films, Gen Dynamics/Electronics, 64-66, prin engr, Comput Sci Dept, 66-69; SR RES SCIENTIST, COMPUT RES DEPT, AMOCO PROD CO, 69- *Mem:* Am Phys Soc. *Res:* Computer and management sciences; thin film physics; high energy and mathematical physics; quantum mechanics; electron scattering; semiconductor device development; computer graphics systems. *Mailing Add:* Res Ctr Amoco Prod Co PO Box 591 Tulsa OK 74102

NAYUDU, Y RAMMOHANROY, b Masulipatam-Andhr, India, Jan 13, 22; US citizen; m 43; c 3. MARINE GEOLOGY, PETROLOGY. *Educ:* Univ Bombay, BS, 45, MSc, 47; Univ Wash, PhD(geol), 59. *Prof Exp:* Lectr geol, Univ Rangoon, 51-53; geologist, Burma Geol Dept, Ministry Mines, 54-55; res instr geol oceanog, Univ Wash, 59-61; res asst geologist, NSF fel, Scripps Inst, Univ Calif, 61-63; res asst prof marine geol, Univ Wash, 63-65, res assoc prof, 65-68; dep dir, Inst Marine Sci, Alaska, 68-69; prof marine geol, Univ Alaska, 69-71; dir div marine & coastal zone mgt, Alaska Dept Environ Conserv, 71-74; SCI ADV TO GOV, ALASKA, 70-; DIR DIV FISHERIES & NATURAL RESOURCES, CENT COUN TLINGIT & HAIDA INDIANS OF ALASKA, 77- *Concurrent Pos:* NSF grants, 59-63, 65 & 66-67; dir, Ore Coastal Zone Mgt Asn, 76-77. *Mem:* Am Asn Petrol Geologists; Soc Econ Paleontologists & Mineralogists; Geol Soc Am; fel Brit Geol Asn; Int Asn Sedimentol. *Res:* Deep sea sediments and submarine volcanics. *Mailing Add:* Div of Fisheries & Natural Resources PO Box 323 Juneau AK 99802

NAYYAR, RAJINDER, b Khanna, India, June 14, 36; m 69; c 1. NEUROLOGY, MICROSCOPIC ANATOMY. *Educ:* Panjab Univ, India, BSc, 57, MSc, 59; Univ Delhi, PhD(zool), 64. *Prof Exp:* Asst lectr zool, Univ Delhi, 63-64, chmn dept zool, H R Col, 64-65; asst prof neurol & anat, Med Sch, Northwestern Univ, Chicago, 67-77; MEM STAFF, LOYOLA UNIV, CHICAGO, 77-; RES BIOLOGIST & ELECTRON MICROSCOPIST, NEUROL SERV, VET ADMIN HOSP, 67- *Concurrent Pos:* Joseph P Kennedy fel anat, Univ Western Ont, 65-66, Med Res Coun fel, 66-67. *Mem:* Electron Micros Soc Am; Am Asn Anat; Am Soc Cell Biol; Histochem Soc. *Res:* Fish chromosome studies; histochemistry of fish oocytes; sex-chromatin studies; histochemistry of the diabetic retina; electron microscopy and histochemistry; the effect of antibiotics on the brain; cytogenesis of lysosomes; electromagnetic autoradiography; chemically induced myelopathy; preputial gland secretion; effect of castration. *Mailing Add:* Loyola Univ Chicago IL 60611

NAZARIAN, GIRAIR MIHRAN, b Trenton, NJ, Sept 5, 26; m 52; c 4. PHYSICAL CHEMISTRY. *Educ:* Rutgers Univ, BS, 46, MS, 48; Calif Inst Technol, PhD(chem, physics), 57. *Prof Exp:* Asst chem, Rutgers Univ, 46-47, Cornell Univ, 47-48 & Calif Inst Technol, 48-49; sr engr, Physics Lab, Sylvania Elec Prod, Inc, 51-55; res fel chem & lectr statist mech, Calif Inst Technol, 57-58; mem tech staff, Res Lab, Thompson Ramo Wooldridge, Inc, 58-61; assoc prof, 61-65, PROF CHEM, CALIF STATE UNIV, NORTHRIDGE, 65- *Concurrent Pos:* Instr, Univ Southern Calif, 58-61 & exten, Univ Calif, Los Angeles, 59-60; consult, Space Technol Labs, 61-62. *Res:* Statistical mechanics of liquid-vapor interface, molecular friction constant and gas adsorption; luminescence phenomena; electron diffraction calculations; ultracentrifuge; ionic propulsion; radiolytic gas in nuclear reactors; protein diffusion through liquid-liquid interfaces. *Mailing Add:* Dept of Chem Calif State Univ Northridge CA 91330

NAZAROFF, GEORGE VASILY, b San Francisco, Calif, Apr 12, 38; m 63; c 1. THEORETICAL CHEMISTRY. *Educ:* Univ Calif, Berkeley, BS, 59; Univ Wis-Madison, PhD(chem), 65. *Prof Exp:* NSF fel, 65-66; asst prof chem, Col Natural Sci, Mich State Univ, 66-72; ASSOC PROF CHEM & CHMN DEPT, IND UNIV, SOUTH BEND, 72- *Concurrent Pos:* Res Corp starter grant, 66- *Mem:* Am Chem Soc. *Res:* Perturbation theory; generalized Hartree-Fock formalisms; natural spin orbitals; resonant scattering; electron-diatomic collision theory. *Mailing Add:* Dept of Chem Ind Univ South Bend IN 46615

NAZEM, FARAMARZ FRANZ, b Rasht, Iran, Jan 22, 43; US citizen; m 69; c 2. RHEOLOGY, CHEMICAL ENGINEERING. *Educ:* Ohio State Univ, BSChE, 68; Washington Univ, MS, 71, DSc(chem eng), 73. *Prof Exp:* Proj assoc rheology, Univ Wis-Madison, 73-74, asst scientist, 74-75; staff res scientist rheology, 75-80, res scientist, 80-81, GROUP LEADER, UNION CARBIDE CORP, 81- *Mem:* Am Inst Chem Engrs; Soc Rheol; Soc Plastics Engrs. *Res:* Flow and deformation of viscoelastic materials; fundamentals of melt spinning; elongational viscosity of composite materials; rheology of liquid crystals. *Mailing Add:* Union Carbide Corp PO Box 6116 Cleveland OH 44101

NAZERIAN, KEYVAN, b Tehran, Iran, Dec 21, 34; m 59; c 3. VIROLOGY, ELECTRON MICROSCOPY. *Educ:* Univ Tehran, DVM, 58; Mich State Univ, MS, 60, PhD(virol), 65. *Prof Exp:* Asst virol, Mich State Univ, 59-60; vis scientist, Pub Health Inst, Padua, 60-62; asst virol, Mich State Univ, 63-65; head electron micros lab, South Jersey Med Res Found, 65-66; MICROBIOLOGIST, REGIONAL POULTRY RES LAB, USDA, 66- *Mem:* AAAS; Am Soc Microbiol; Electron Micros Soc Am; NY Acad Sci. *Res:* Biochemical, biophysical and morphological studies of animal viruses, particularly oncogenic viruses and their interaction with susceptible hosts. *Mailing Add:* Regional Poultry Res Lab USDA 3606 E Mt Hope Rd East Lansing MI 48823

NAZY, JOHN ROBERT, b Alamosa, Colo, July 12, 33; m 56; c 5. INDUSTRIAL ORGANIC CHEMISTRY. *Educ:* Regis Col, Colo, BS, 54; Northwestern Univ, PhD(org chem), 59. *Prof Exp:* Chemist, Union Carbide Chem Co, 58-60; proj leader, 60-66, tech supvr, 66-69, sect leader, Tech Serv Dept, 69-73, tech dir, 73-76, marketing mgr petroleum, 76-77, dir indust mgrs, 77-79, DIR PROD MGRS, WATER SOLUBLE POLYMERS, HENKEL CORP, 79- *Mem:* Tech Asn Pulp & Paper Indust; Am Chem Soc; Soc Petrol Eng. *Res:* Organoboron and fatty acid chemistry; polymer synthesis; guar and natural gums. *Mailing Add:* Henkel Corp 4620 W 77th St Minneapolis MN 55435

NEADERHOUSER, CARLA CECILIA, b Rome, NY, June 15, 45; m 68, 82; c 2. LIMIT THEOREMS, STATISTICAL MECHANICS. *Educ:* Cornell Univ, BA, 67; Univ Ill, Urbana, MA, 69, PhD(math), 75. *Prof Exp:* ASST PROF MATH, TEX A&M UNIV, 75- *Concurrent Pos:* Prin investr NSF grants, 76-77. *Mem:* Am Math Soc; Math Asn Am. *Res:* Limit behavior of ramdom fields with application to statistical mechanics; asymptotic expansions and clustering behavior, along with related computational problems. *Mailing Add:* Math Dept Tex A&M Univ College Station TX 77843

NEAGLE, LYLE H, b Mutual, Okla, Nov 6, 31; m 64; c 2. ANIMAL NUTRITION, BIOCHEMISTRY. *Educ:* Okla State Univ, BS, 53; Iowa State Univ, PhD(animal nutrit), 60. *Prof Exp:* Asst dir animal nutrit & res, Supersweet Feeds Div, Int Milling Co, Minn, 60-67; mgr res, Allied Mills, Inc, 67-72, dir res, 72-81, VPRES RES & DEVELOP, CONTINENTAL GRAIN CO, 81- *Mem:* Am Soc Animal Sci. *Mailing Add:* Continental Grain Co PO Box 459 Libertyville IL 60048

NEAL, DONALD WADE, b Hopewell, Va, June 23, 51. BASIN ANALYSIS, CARBONATE PETROLOGY. *Educ:* Col William & Mary, BS, 73; Eastern Ky Univ, MS, 75; WVa Univ, PhD(geol), 79. *Prof Exp:* Res assoc stratig, WVa Geol & Encon Surv, 77-79; ASST PROF GEOL, EAST CAROLINA UNIV, 79- *Mem:* Geol Soc Am; Soc Econ Paleontologists & Mineralogists; Paleont Soc. *Res:* Basin analysis of upper paleozoic sediments in the Central Appalachians-includes stratigraphy, petrology, geochemistry and paleontology. *Mailing Add:* Dept Geol East Carolina Univ Greenville NC 27834

NEAL, HOMER ALFRED, b Franklin, Ky, June 13, 42; m 62; c 2. EXPERIMENTAL HIGH ENERGY PHYSICS. *Educ:* Ind Univ, BS, 61; Univ Mich, MS, 63, PhD(physics), 66. *Prof Exp:* NSF fel, Europ Orgn Nuclear Res, 66-67; from asst prof to assoc prof physics, Ind Univ, Bloomington, 67-72, prof, 72-81, dean res & grad develop, 76-81; PROVOST, STATE UNIV NY, STONY BROOK, 81- *Concurrent Pos:* Alfred P Sloan Found fel, Ind Univ, Bloomington, 68-; chmn zero gradient synchrotron accelerator users orgn, mem zero gradient synchrotron prog comt, 70-72; mem bd trustees, Argonne Univs Asn, 71-74; J S Guggenheim fel, Stanford Univ, 80-81. *Mem:* Fel Am Phys Soc; Sigma Xi; AAAS. *Res:* Application of spark chamber and scintillation counter techniques in the study of elementary particle interactions. *Mailing Add:* Off Provost State Univ NY Stony Brook NY 11794

NEAL, J(AMES) P(RESTON), III, b St Louis, Mo, July 16, 08; m 32; c 3. ELECTRICAL ENGINEERING. *Educ:* Univ Cincinnati, EE, 30; Univ Ill, MS, 50, PhD(elec eng), 55. *Prof Exp:* Test ctr supvr, Cincinnati Bell, Inc, 27-36, mfg specialties, 36-37; engr equip, Fosdick & Hilmer, Inc, 37-40; from asst prof to assoc prof elec eng, 47-74, EMER PROF ELEC ENG, UNIV ILL, URBANA, 74- *Concurrent Pos:* Consult, Gen Elec Co, 53-56, Energy Conversion Corp, 59-60 & N Am Aviation, Inc, 62-63; res assoc, Nat Bur Standards-Nat Res Coun, Colo, 64-65. *Mem:* Soc Urban Residential Environ (pres, 74-). *Res:* Computer-guided experimentation research developing a system and demonstrating its worth for automatically modifying computer-aided instruction in accordance with electrically sensed and fedback reports of a student's actual experimentation activities. *Mailing Add:* 2003 S Vine Urbana IL 61801

NEAL, JAMES THOMAS, b Detroit, Mich, Feb 9, 36; m 60; c 4. GEOLOGY. *Educ:* Mich State Univ, BS, 57, MS, 59. *Prof Exp:* Geologist, Can Cliffs Ltd, 57 & Albanel Minerals Ltd, 59; US Air Force, 60-79, proj officer geol res, Air Force Cambridge Res Labs, 60-63, proj scientist, 63-66, chief geotech br, 66-68, from instr to assoc prof geog, US Air Force Acad, 68-73, chief ground shock & cratering, Civil Eng Res Div, US Air Force Weapons Lab, 73-78, staff scientist, Air Force Systs Command Hq, 78-79; MEM TECH STAFF, SANDIA NAT LAB, 80- *Honors & Awards:* Outstanding Res & Develop Award, US Air Force, 66. *Mem:* Sigma Xi; fel Geol Soc Am. *Res:* Engineering and military geology; geology of playas; remote sensing; site selection and evaluation methodology. *Mailing Add:* PO Box 5668 Albuquerque NM 87185

NEAL, JOHN ALEXANDER, b Aliquippa, Pa, Aug 7, 40; m 64; c 2. INORGANIC CHEMISTRY. *Educ:* Eastern Wash State Col, BA, 66; Univ Wash, PhD(inorg chem), 70. *Prof Exp:* Res assoc chem, Wash State Univ, 71-72; res chemist, 72-75, group leader, 75-76, RES DIR, GA-PAC CORP, 76- *Mem:* Am Chem Soc. *Res:* Factors which influence formation and stability of transition metal complexes in polydentate systems; sterochemistry of polydentate complexes; oxidative degradation of metal complexes. *Mailing Add:* Bellingham Div Ga-Pac Corp 300 W Laurel St Bellingham WA 98225

NEAL, JOHN ALVA, b Omaha, Nebr, Mar 6, 38; m 61; c 3. CIVIL ENGINEERING, MATERIALS SCIENCE. *Educ:* Ga Inst Technol, BME, 61; Univ Ill, Urbana, MS, 62, PhD, 65. *Prof Exp:* Asst prof civil eng, 65-70, dir construct & rehab, Off Facil Planning, 70-73, asst vpres facil planning, 73-78, ASSOC PROF CIVIL ENG, STATE UNIV NY BUFFALO, 70-, VPRES FACIL PLANNING, 78- *Mem:* Am Concrete Inst; assoc Am Soc Civil Engrs; Am Soc Eng Educ. *Res:* Fatigue of plain concrete. *Mailing Add:* Dept Civil Eng State Univ NY Buffalo NY 14260

NEAL, JOHN LLOYD, JR, b Concordia, Kans, Oct 18, 37; m 62; c 2. MICROBIOLOGY, SOIL SCIENCE. *Educ:* Ore State Univ, BSc, 60, MSc, 63, PhD(soil microbiol), 68. *Prof Exp:* Res asst microbiol, Ore State Univ, 60-67; res scientist, Can Agr Res Sta, 67-77; ASST PROF MICROBIOL, VA POLYTECH & STATE UNIV, 77- *Mem:* Am Soc Microbiol; Sigma Xi; AAAS; Soil Sci Soc Am. *Res:* Asymbiotic and symbiotic nitrogen fixation; interrelationship between plant roots and soil microorganisms; soil biochemistry microbial transformations in soil. *Mailing Add:* Dept of Biol VA Polytech Inst & State Univ Blacksburg VA 24060

NEAL, JOHN WILLIAM, JR, b St Louis, Mo, Nov 17, 37; m 73. ENTOMOLOGY. *Educ:* Univ Mo-Columbia, BS, 61, MS, 64; Univ Md, College Park, PhD(entom), 70. *Prof Exp:* Mus aid & entomologist, Dept Mammals (Iran), US Nat Mus, 63-65; fac res asst alfalfa weevil, Univ Md, College Park, 66-68, instr biol control, 68-70; RES ENTOMOLOGIST, FLORIST & NURSERY CROPS LAB, HORT SCI INST, AGR RES SERV, USDA, 70- *Mem:* Entom Soc Am; Sigma Xi. *Res:* Biological and chemical control pests of ornamental plants; screening germplasm for insect-host resistance. *Mailing Add:* Agr Res Serv USDA Ornamentals Bldg 470 Beltsville MD 20705

NEAL, MARCUS PINSON, JR, b Columbia, Mo, Apr 22, 27; m 61; c 3. RADIOLOGY. *Educ:* Univ Mo, AB, 49, BS, 51; Univ Tenn, MD, 53; Am Bd Radiol, cert radiol, 58 & radiol in nuclear med, 59. *Prof Exp:* Intern, Med Col Va Hosp, 53-54; res assoc path, Sch Med, Univ Mo, 54; resident radiol, Univ Wis Hosps, 54-57, from instr to asst prof, Sch Med, 57-63; assoc prof radiol, 63-66, chmn, Div Diag Radiol, 65-71, asst dean health sci div & dir, Regional Med Progs, 68-71, dir housestaff educ & dir continuing educ med & grad educ med, 69-71, interim dean sch med, 71, asst vpres health sci, 71-73, provost health sci, 73-78, assoc dean, Sch Med, Med Educ Quality Assurance, 78-79, PROF RADIOL, MED COL VA, VA COMMONWEALTH UNIV, 66-, DIR RADIOL, HOUSESTAFF EDUC, 79- *Concurrent Pos:* Radiologist, Cent Wis Colony, Madison, 59-63 & Vet Admin Hosp, 61-63; consult, Wis Diag Ctr, 61-63, US Air Force Hosp, Truax Field, 63 & Vet Admin Hosp, Richmond, Va, 63-; pres, Va Coun Health & Med Care, 70-74 & 78-80. *Mem:* Am Col Radiol; AMA; Radiol Soc NAm; Brit Inst Radiol; Southern Med Asn (pres elect). *Res:* Diagnostic radiology in medical research. *Mailing Add:* Med Col of Va Va Commonwealth Univ Richmond VA 23298

NEAL, RALPH BENNETT, b Mankato, Minn, Nov 29, 20; m 41; c 1. ENGINEERING. *Educ:* Naval Postgrad Sch, BS, 53, MS, 54. *Prof Exp:* Group leader tech support, Kaiser Westcoast Electronics Lab, 59-60; proj mgr data syst div, 60-62, prog mgr, 62-64, dir prod support dept, 65-66, dir sci support iab, 66-68, dir defense sci labs, Mellonics Systs Develop Div, 68-69, prog dir sci support lab, 69-76, PROG MGR, LITTON INDUST, INC, 76- *Mem:* Inst Elec & Electronics Engrs. *Res:* Military operations research; electronic systems development. *Mailing Add:* Litton Indust Inc 8000 Woodley Ave Van Nuys CA 91406

NEAL, RICHARD ALLAN, b Waverly, Iowa, July 27, 39; m 62; c 3. FISHERIES. *Educ:* Iowa State Univ, BS, 61, MS, 62; Univ Wash, PhD(invert fishery biol), 67. *Prof Exp:* Supvry fishery biologist, Nat Marine Fisheries Serv, 66-77; aquacult adv, Agency for Int Develop, 77-80; DEP DIR GEN, INT CTR LIVING AQUATIC RESOURCES MGT, 80- *Mem:* Am Soc Zoologists; Am Fisheries Soc; World Maricult Soc. *Res:* Freshwater fishery biology; ecological studies of paralytic shellfish poisoning; fishery population dynamics; penaeid shrimp culture; aquaculture research; international fisheries development. *Mailing Add:* Int Ctr Living Aquatic Resources Shell Rock IA 50670

NEAL, RICHARD B, b Lawrenceburg, Tenn, Sept 5, 17; m 44; c 2. PHYSICS. *Educ:* US Naval Acad, BS, 39; Stanford Univ, PhD(physics), 53. *Prof Exp:* Field serv engr, Sperry Gyroscope Co, 41-42, fire control serv supt, 42-46, res engr, 46-47; res assoc, 50-62, ASSOC DIR TECH DIV, LINEAR ACCELERATOR CTR, STANFORD UNIV, 62- *Mem:* Sigma Xi; Am Phys Soc. *Res:* Microwave and accelerator physics; high energy linear electron accelerators. *Mailing Add:* 1351 N Lemon Ave Menlo Park CA 94025

NEAL, ROBERT A, b Casper, Wyo, Apr 21, 28; m 58; c 3. TOXICOLOGY, BIOCHEMISTRY. *Educ:* Univ Denver, BS, 49; Vanderbilt Univ, PhD(biochem), 63. *Prof Exp:* From asst prof to assoc prof, biochem, Sch Med, Vanderbilt Univ, 64-75, dir, ctr environ toxicol, 73-81, prof, 75-81; PRES, CHEM INDUST INST TOXICOL, 81- *Concurrent Pos:* NIH res fel toxicol, Univ Chicago, 63-64; mem, Food Protection Comt & Toxciol Subcomt, Nat Acad Sci; mem, Toxicol Study Sect, Prog Comt Multiple Factors Causation Environ Induced Dis & bd Toxicol & environ Health Hazards, NIH. *Mem:* AAAS; Am Soc Pharmacol & Exp Therapeut; Soc Toxicol; Am Inst Nutrit; Am Asn Biol Chemists. *Res:* Natural product chemistry; isolation and identification of natural products; detoxification mechanisms. *Mailing Add:* PO Box 12137 Chem Indust Inst Toxicol Research Triangle Park NC 27709

NEAL, SCOTTY RAY, b Redlands, Calif, July 12, 37; m 58; c 2. APPLIED MATHEMATICS, TELECOMMUNICATIONS. *Educ:* Univ Calif, Riverside, BA, 61, MA, 63, PhD(math), 65. *Prof Exp:* Res mathematician, US Naval Weapons Ctr, China Lake, Calif, 64-67; mem tech staff, 67-73, SUPVR, TRAFFIC RES GROUP, BELL TEL LABS, 73- *Mem:* Am Math Soc; Oper Res Soc. *Res:* Optimal design strategy for stochastic networks. *Mailing Add:* Bell Tel Labs Crawford Corner Rd Holmdel NJ 07733

NEAL, THOMAS EDWARD, b Royal Oak, Mich, May 2, 42; m 67; c 2. ANALYTICAL CHEMISTRY, TEXTILE CHEMISTRY. *Educ:* Univ Mich, BS, 64; Univ NC, PhD(anal chem), 70. *Prof Exp:* Res asst inorg chem, Univ Mich, 64-65; res chemist, 70-73, sr res chemist, Textile Fibers Dept, 73-78, mkt develop rep, 78-80, TECH SERV SUPVR, E I DU PONT DE NEMOURS & CO, INC, 80- *Res:* Electroanalytical chemistry in non-aqueous systems; end use research of synthetic polymer products in textile applications; high modulus fiber applications in rigid structures. *Mailing Add:* Textile Fibers Dept E I du Pont de Nemours & Co Inc Wilmington DE 19898

NEAL, VICTOR THOMAS, b Dell Rapids, SDak, Nov 1, 24; m 48; c 2. PHYSICAL OCEANOGRAPHY. *Educ:* Univ Notre Dame, BS, 48; Univ NDak, MEd, 54; Ore State Univ, PhD(phys oceanog), 65. *Prof Exp:* Geophysicist, Carter Oil Co, 48-49; teacher, Various Sec Schs & Jr Cols, 50-62; instr phys oceanog, Ore State Univ, 64; asst prof, US Naval Postgrad Sch, 64-66; asst prof, 66-74, ASSOC PROF OCEANOG, ORE STATE UNIV, 74-, DIR LATIN AM OCEANOG PROG & MARINE RESOURCE MGT PROG, 70- *Mem:* Am Geophys Union; CoastalSoc. *Res:* Estuarine, coastal and arctic oceanography. *Mailing Add:* Sch Oceanog Ore State Univ Corvallis OR 97331

NEAL, WILLIAM JOSEPH, b Princeton, Ind, Nov 19, 39; m 59; c 3. SEDIMENTARY PETROLOGY, MINERALOGY. *Educ:* Univ Notre Dame, BS, 61; Univ Mo, MA, 64, PhD(geol), 68. *Prof Exp:* Fel geol, McMaster Univ, 67-68; asst prof, Ga Southern Col, 69-71; asst prof, 71-73, chmn dept, 75-79, ASSOC PROF GEOL, GRAND VALLEY STATE COL, 73- *Concurrent Pos:* Adj prof, Skidaway Inst Oceanog, Ga, 69-71; fel, Duke Univ 76-77, vis scientist, 80-81. *Mem:* Am Asn Petrol Geol; Soc Econ Paleont & Mineral; Int Asn Sedimentologists; Nat Asn Geol Teachers. *Res:* Heavy minerals; recent and Pleistocene deep-sea sediments; coastal hazards; carbonate petrology; Pennsylvanian cyclothems; ancient turbidites. *Mailing Add:* Dept Geol Grand Valley State Col Allendale MI 49401

NEALE, ELAINE ANNE, b Philadelphia, Pa, May 20, 44; m 67; c 2. ELECTRON MICROSCOPY, NEUROCYTOLOGY. *Educ:* Rosemont Col, AB, 65; Georgetown Univ, PhD(biol), 69. *Prof Exp:* Asst res neuromorphologist, Ment Health Res Inst, Univ Mich, Ann Arbor, 70-75; NEUROCYTOLOGIST, BEHAV BIOL BR, NEUROBIOL SECT, NAT INST CHILD HEALTH & HUMAN DEVELOP, NIH, 75- *Concurrent Pos:* NIH staff fel, Nat Cancer Inst, 69-70 & Nat Inst Child Health & Human Develop, 73-; NIH fel, Univ Mich, Ann Arbor, 70-73. *Mem:* Am Soc Cell Biol; Am Asn Women Sci; Sigma Xi. *Res:* Structure-function relationships in the nervous system; techniques for the ultrastructural localization of specific macromolecules; ultrastructural anatomy. *Mailing Add:* Nat Insts of Health Bldg 36 Rm 2A-21 Bethesda MD 20014

NEALE, ERNEST RICHARD WARD, b Montreal, Que, July 3, 23; m 50; c 2. GEOLOGY. *Educ:* McGill Univ, BSc, 49; Yale Univ, MS, 50, PhD(geol), 52. *Hon Degrees:* LLD, Univ Calgary, 77. *Prof Exp:* Asst, Yale Univ, 51-52; asst prof, Rochester Univ, 52-54; geologist, Geol Surv Can, 54-60, 65-67, head Pre-Cambrian shield sect, 67-68; prof geol & head dept, Mem Univ Nfld, 68-76; head geol info, Inst Sedimentary & Petrol Geol, 76-81; ACAD VPRES, MEM UNIV NFLD, 82- *Concurrent Pos:* Field geologist, Que Dept Mines, 47-53; actg head, Appalachian Sect, Geol Surv Can 59-60, head, 60-62; Brit Commonwealth Geol Liaison Off, Eng, 63-65; ed, Can J of Earth Sci, 74-; vis prof, Univ BC, 74-75; adj prof, Univ Calagary, 76- *Honors & Awards:* Bancroft Award, Royal Soc Can, 75; Queen's Anniversary Medal, 77. *Mem:* Am Geol Soc; Royal Soc Can; Geol Asn Can (pres, 72); Can Inst Mining & Metall; Can Geosci Coun, (vpres, 72-73, 74-75, pres, 75-76). *Res:* Appalachian geology and mineral resources; Canadian science policy. *Mailing Add:* Mem Univ Nfld St John's NF A1C 5S7 Can

NEALE, ROBERT S, b Abington, Pa, Mar 19, 36; m 57; c 3. ORGANIC CHEMISTRY. *Educ:* Amherst Col, AB, 57; Univ Ill, PhD(org chem), 61. *Prof Exp:* Org chemist, Union Carbide Res Inst, 60-67, RES SCIENTIST, UNION CARBIDE CHEM & PLASTICS, 67- *Mem:* Am Chem Soc. *Res:* Chemistry of nitrogen free radicals, especially those derived from N-Halo compounds; chemistry of hydroperoxide oxidations; synthesis of organosilicon compounds; organosilicon chemistry. *Mailing Add:* Robin Dr Ossining NY 10562

NEALE, WILLIAM MCC(ORMICK), JR, b Greensboro, NC, May 18, 20; m 43; c 7. SYSTEM ANALYSIS, MANAGEMENT INFORMATION SYSTEMS. *Educ:* NC State Univ, BS, 43, MS, 51. *Prof Exp:* From instr to asst prof mech eng, NC State Univ, 46-53; armament instrumentation engr, Vitro Corp Am, 53-56, paraflight group leader & sr engr, 56-58; asst dir bur eng res, Univ Ala, 58-63; sr scientist, Systs Sci Div, Spindletop Res, Inc, 63-67; res projs mgr, Vitro Corp Am, 67-69; assoc prof systs sci, Univ 69-78, DIR EGLIN-FT WALTON BEACH EDUC CTR, UNIV WEST FLA, 78- *Concurrent Pos:* Fan proj engr, Bohnson Co, 52; consult, Monarch Elevator Co, 52-53; instr & consult syst anal & data processing, Eglin Educ Ctr, Eglin AFB. *Mem:* Am Soc Mech Engrs; Instrument Soc Am; Am Soc Eng Educ. *Res:* Operations and systems analysis; mechanical, electrical and photographic instrumentation; digital and hybrid computer applications to business and scientific systems. *Mailing Add:* Eglin-Ft Walton Beach Educ Ctr PO Box 1492 Eglin AFB FL 32542

NEALEY, RICHARD H, b Lawrence, Mass, May 30, 36; m 60; c 4. ORGANIC CHEMISTRY. *Educ:* Merrimack Col, BSc, 57; Univ Conn, MSc, 59; Brown Univ, PhD(chem), 63. *Prof Exp:* Res chemist, Ethyl Corp, Mich, 62-63; sr res chemist, Monsanto Res Corp, 63-68; mgr org chem res, Tech Opers Inc, 68-69; TECH MFG SPEC, ADVAN MFG & ENG|N AM MFG DIV, XEROX CORP, 69- *Res:* Organometallic chemistry; heterocyclic synthesis; photo-sensitizing dyes; solvent recovery; manufacturing research; synthesis of novel imaging materials. *Mailing Add:* Xerox Corp 800 Phillips Rd W218L Webster NY 14580

NEALON, THOMAS F, JR, b Jessup, Pa, Feb 24, 20; m 46; c 4. SURGERY, THORACIC SURGERY. *Educ:* Scranton Univ, BS, 41; Jefferson Med Col, MD, 44. *Prof Exp:* Am Cancer Soc fel surg, Jefferson Med Col, 51-53; from instr to prof, 55-68; PROF SURG, NY UNIV, 68-; DIR SURG, ST VINCENT'S HOSP & MED CTR, NEW YORK, 68- *Concurrent Pos:* Consult, Greenwich Hosp, Conn, Holy Name Hosp, Teaneck, NJ, St Agnes Hosp, White Plains, NY & St Vincent's Med Ctr of Richmond, Staten Island. *Mem:* Am Col Chest Physicians; Am Surg Asn; Am Asn Thoracic Surg; Am Col Surg; Am Soc Artificial Internal Organs. *Res:* Cancer; cardiorespiratory physiology during operations; gastrointestinal surgery. *Mailing Add:* Dept of Surg St Vincent's Hosp & Med Ctr New York NY 10011

NEALSON, KENNETH HENRY, b Iowa City, Iowa, Oct 8, 43. MARINE MICROBIOLOGY. *Educ:* Univ Chicago, BS, 65, MS, 66, PhD(microbiol), 69. *Prof Exp:* NIH fel, Harvard Univ, 69-71; asst prof biol, Univ Mass, Boston, 71-73; ASST PROF MARINE BIOL, SCRIPPS INST OCEANOG, 73- *Mem:* AAAS; Am Soc Microbiol. *Res:* Physiology, biochemistry and genetics of luminous bacteria; study of the symbiotic relationship between luminous bacteria and marine luminous fishes; physiology and biochemistry of manganese oxidizing bacteria. *Mailing Add:* Scripps Inst of Oceanog A-002 La Jolla CA 92037

NEALY, CARSON LOUIS, b Natchitoches, La, Dec 24, 38; m; c 1. ANALYTICAL CHEMISTRY. *Educ:* Northwestern State Col, La, BS, 60; Fla State Univ, MS, 63, PhD(nuclear & inorg chem), 65. *Prof Exp:* Nuclear chemist, Shell Develop Co, Houston, 65-70, anal chemist, Shell Oil Co, 70-72; MGR ANAL CHEM ENERGY SYST GROUP, ROCKWELL INT CORP, 72- *Mem:* Am Chem Soc; Sigma Xi. *Res:* Nuclear reaction spectroscopy in nuclear structure studies; neutron activation analysis; gas chromatography; instrument development; nuclear fuel analysis; nuclear methods in analytical chemistry. *Mailing Add:* 5912 Adler Ave Woodland Hills CA 91367

NEALY, DAVID LEWIS, b Monticello, NY, June 29, 36; m 62; c 2. ORGANIC CHEMISTRY. *Educ:* Duke Univ, BS, 58; Cornell Univ, PhD(org chem), 63. *Prof Exp:* NSF fel org chem, Mass Inst Technol, 63-64; res chemist, Tenn Eastman Co, 64-65, sr res chemist, 65-69, res assoc, 70, head phys & anal chem div, 71-73, supt, Fiber Develop Div, 74-76, mkt staff, 76-77, asst supt, Organic Chem Div, 78-79, DIR, CHEM RES DIV, EASTMAN CHEM DIV, EASTMAN KODAK CO, 79- *Mem:* Am Chem Soc. *Res:* Organic polymer chemistry; synthetic Organic chemistry; chemical kinetics. *Mailing Add:* 102 Crown Colony Kingsport TN 37660

NEARN, WILLIAM THOMAS, b Middletown, NY, Dec 2, 20; m 46; c 4. FOREST PRODUCTS. *Educ:* State Univ NY, BS, 43; Yale Univ, MF, 47, DF, 54. *Prof Exp:* From instr to assoc prof, Pa State Univ, 47-60; prof specialist, 60-73, mgr sci serv, 76-80, MGR WOOD SCI & MORPHOL, WEYERHAEUSER CO, 73-, MGR INSTRUMENTATION & TEST, 74-, MGR CONTROL TECHNOL, 80- *Mem:* Soc Wood Sci & Technol. *Res:* Wood-moisture relations; wood adhesives; composite wood products; scanning and transmission electron microscopy. *Mailing Add:* Res Div Weyerhaeuser Co Tacoma WA 98401

NEARY, MICHAEL PAUL, b Pueblo, Colo, Aug 16, 35. ANALYTICAL CHEMISTRY. *Educ:* Univ Colo, BA, 65; Univ Ga, PhD(anal chem), 75. *Prof Exp:* Res chemist anal chem, Beckman Instruments Inc, 65-71; STAFF MEM ANAL & PHOTOCHEM, LOS ALAMOS SCI LABS, 76-, PRES, SANTA FE RES & DEVELOP INC, 80- *Concurrent Pos:* Consult, Southern Calif Gas Co, 79-, Minerals Recovery Ltd, 79- & Solar Storage Technol Inc, 78- *Mem:* Am Chem Soc. *Res:* Chemiluminescence in analysis; photochemicaly synthesized reactants in analysis; photochemical solar energy storage and retrieval, metal coatings. *Mailing Add:* Los Alamos Sci Labs MS 920 Los Alamos NM 87545

NEAS, CHARLES C(LEVELAND), chemical engineering, see previous edition

NEAS, ROBERT EDWIN, b Sheldon, Mo, May 7, 35; m 57; c 3. ANALYTICAL CHEMISTRY. *Educ:* Cent Methodist Col, AB, 57; Southern Ill Univ, Carbondale, MS, 65; Univ Mo-Columbia, PhD(chem), 70. *Prof Exp:* Analyst chem, Mallinckrodt Chem Works, 57-58, chemist, 58-59, supvr, 59-61, asst to dir qual control, 61-62, res asst chem, 62-63; instr, Univ Mo-Mo Exp Sta Lab, 65-66; asst prof, 69-74, ASSOC PROF CHEM, WESTERN ILL UNIV, 74- *Concurrent Pos:* Univ res coun grant, Western Ill Univ, 70-71. *Mem:* Am Chem Soc. *Res:* Analytical chemistry of anions; spectrophotometry; ion selective electrodes; trace analysis. *Mailing Add:* Rt One Macomb IL 61455

NEASE, ROBERT F, b Walters, Okla, June 4, 31. ELECTRICAL ENGINEERING. *Educ:* Tex Tech Col, BS, 51; Mass Inst Technol, SM, 53, ScD, 57. *Prof Exp:* Asst, Mass Inst Technol, 51-52 & 54-55, instr, 56; sr res engr & supvr autonetics, N Am Aviation, Inc, 57-60; mgr systs integration dept, aeronutronic, Ford Motor Co, 60-63; SR TECH STAFF & CHIEF SCIENTIST, AUTONETICS DIV, ROCKWELL INT, 63- *Res:* Autonatic control; avionics and space systems analysis. *Mailing Add:* 701 W Lamark Dr Anaheim CA 92802

NEATHERY, MILTON WHITE, b Chapel Hill, Tenn, Apr 15, 28; m 50; c 1. ANIMAL NUTRITION. *Educ:* Univ Tenn, BS, 50, MS, 55; Univ Ga, PhD(animal nutrit), 73. *Prof Exp:* Farm mgr dairy, Minglewood Farm, Tenn, 50-51; fieldman dairy, Nashville Pure Milk Co, 53-54; asst dairy, Univ Tenn, 55-56; asst animal husbandman animal nutrit, Ga Mountain Exp Sta, 56-59; asst prof, 59-79, ASSOC PROF DAIRY SCI, UNIV GA, 79- *Mem:* Sigma Xi; Am Dairy Sci Asn; Am Soc Animal Sci. *Res:* Mineral metabolism in animals; primarily trace mineral metabolism in ruminants using radioisotopes. *Mailing Add:* Animal & Dairy Sci Dept Univ Ga Livestock-Poultry Bldg Athens GA 30602

NEATHERY, RAYMOND FRANKLIN, b Conroe, Tex, Aug 31, 39; m 62; c 3. MECHANICAL ENGINEERING, MECHANICS. *Educ:* John Brown Univ, BS, 61; NMex State Univ, MSME, 64; Univ Ark, Fayetteville, PhD(eng sci), 70. *Prof Exp:* Asst prof mech eng, John Brown Univ, 64-67; assoc prof, LeTourneau Col, 67-71; sr res engr, Biomed Sci Dept, Gen Motors Res Labs, 71-76; assoc prof & head, 76-80, PROF & CHAIRMAN MECH DESIGN TECHNOL, OKLA STATE UNIV, 80- *Concurrent Pos:* NASA-Am Soc Eng Educ Systs Design Inst fel, NASA Manned Spacecraft Ctr, 70. *Mem:* Am Soc Mech Engrs; Am Soc Eng Educ. *Res:* Solid mechanics; mechanical modeling of humans for crash testing; machine design. *Mailing Add:* Mech Design Technol Okla State Univ Stillwater OK 74074

NEATHERY, THORNTON LEE, b Atlanta, Ga, Mar 12, 31; m 56; c 3. GEOLOGY. *Educ:* Univ Ala, BS, 56, MS, 64. *Prof Exp:* Geologist, Reynolds Metals Co, 56-62; asst vpres, Textile Rubber & Chem Co, 63; geologist, 64-73, chief geologist, 73-76, ASST STATE GEOLOGIST & DIR BUDGET & RES DEVELOP, GEOL SURV ALA, 76- *Mem:* Sigma Xi; fel Geol Soc Am; Soc Econ Geologist; Mineral Soc Am; Soc Mining Engrs. *Res:* Regional geologic mapping in southern Piedmont and folded Appalachians with emphasis on sedimentation, metamorphism, and structural evolution as applied to distribution of ore deposits. *Mailing Add:* PO Drawer 0 Geol Surv of Ala University AL 35486

NEAVEL, RICHARD CHARLES, b Philadelphia, Pa, Oct 21, 31; m 58; c 3. FUEL SCIENCE. *Educ:* Temple Univ, BA, 54; Pa State Univ, MS, 57, PhD(geol), 66. *Prof Exp:* Coal petrologist, Ind Geol Surv, 57-61; res assoc, Dept Geol, Pa State Univ, 61-66; staff geologist, Humble Oil & Refining Co, 67; geologist, Synthetic Fuel Lab, 68-69, group leader, 70, res assoc, Gasification Lab, 71-75, sr res assoc, 75-79, SCI ADV, COAL RES LAB, EXXON RES & ENG CO, 79- *Concurrent Pos:* Consult, Inst Gas Technol, 59-63; chmn fuels sci, Gordon Res Conf, 75. *Honors & Awards:* R A Glenn Award, Am Chem Soc, 79 & Storch Award, 80. *Mem:* Am Chem Soc-Fuel Chem Div; AAAS; Sigma Xi; Am Soc Testing & Mat. *Res:* Characterization of coals and relationships between coal properties and utilization, emphasizing synthetic fuels processes. *Mailing Add:* Exxon Res & Eng Co PO Box 4255 Baytown TX 77520

NEAVES, WILLIAM BARLOW, b Spur, Tex, Dec 25, 43; m 65; c 2. ANATOMY, CELL BIOLOGY. *Educ:* Harvard Univ, AB, 66, PhD(anat), 69. *Prof Exp:* Lectr vet anat, Univ Nairobi, 70-71; lectr anat, Med Sch, Harvard Univ, 72; asst prof, 72-74, assoc prof & dir anat, 74-77, assoc dean grad sch, 77-80, PROF CELL BIOL, UNIV TEX HEALTH SCI CTR DALLAS, 77-, DEAN, GRAD SCH, 80- *Concurrent Pos:* Rockefeller Found fel anat, Harvard Univ & Univ Nairobi, 70-71; res assoc, Los Angeles County Mus, 70-73; consult, Ford Found, 73-74; assoc ed, Anat Record, 75-; vis prof, Univ Nairobi, 78. *Mem:* AAAS; Am Asn Anat; Soc Study Reproduction. *Res:* Reproductive biology; androgenic tumors; testicular endocrinology; contraception. *Mailing Add:* Dept of Cell Biol Univ of Tex Health Sci Ctr Dallas TX 75235

NEBEKER, ALAN V, b Salt Lake City, Utah, Apr 8, 38; m 60; c 3. ENTOMOLOGY, AQUATIC ECOLOGY. *Educ:* Univ Utah, BS, 61, MS, 63, PhD(zool), 55. *Prof Exp:* Res aquatic biologist entom, Nat Water Qual Lab, 66-71, RES AQUATIC BIOLOGIST, ENVIRON PROTECTION AGENCY, ENTOM & FISHERIES, WESTERN FISH TOXICOL LAB, 71- *Mem:* Entom Soc Am; Am Entom Soc; Am Fisheries Soc. *Res:* Water pollution toxicology; systematics of aquatic insects; water quality criteria for protection of aquatic life; bioassay analysis. *Mailing Add:* 1350 S E Goodnight Ave Corvallis OR 97330

NEBEKER, EUGENE BYRD, b Santa Monica, Calif, Nov 30, 36. CHEMICAL ENGINEERING. *Educ:* Stanford Univ, BS, 59; Calif Inst Technol, MS, 60, PhD(chem & nuclear eng), 65. *Prof Exp:* Tech specialist, Rocketdyne Div, NAm Rockwell Corp, 65-68, tech staff mem, Autonetics Div, 68-69; PRES, SCI ASSOCS, INC, 69- *Mem:* AAAS; Am Inst Chem Engrs; Am Chem Soc; Am Inst Aeronaut & Astronaut. *Res:* Thermodynamics; transport phenomena. *Mailing Add:* 400 N Rockingham Ave Los Angeles CA 90049

NEBEKER, THOMAS EVAN, b Richfield, Utah, May 10, 45; m 64; c 3. FOREST ENTOMOLOGY. *Educ:* Col Southern Utah, BS, 67; Utah State Univ, MS, 70; Ore State Univ, PhD(entom), 74. *Prof Exp:* Teaching asst zool & entom, Utah State Univ, 67-70; NSF trainee pest pop ecol, Ore State Univ, 70-73; fel pop ecol, Utah State Univ, 73-74; asst prof, 74-78, ASSOC PROF FOREST ENTOM, MISS STATE UNIV, 78- *Mem:* Entom Soc Am; Ecol Soc Am; Sigma Xi; Can Entom Soc. *Res:* Population biology of forest insects with emphasis on the dynamics of southern pine beetle populations; parasite and predator efficiency studies utlizing behavior patterns. *Mailing Add:* Dept of Entom Miss State Univ Drawer EM Mississippi State MS 39762

NEBEL, CARL WALTER, b Dover, NJ, July 25, 37; m 60; c 1. ORGANIC CHEMISTRY, ENVIRONMENTAL SCIENCE. *Educ:* Tusculum Col, BS, 58; Cornell Univ, MS, 61; Univ Del, PhD(org chem), 65. *Prof Exp:* Von Humboldt fel, Govt Ger, Univ Karlsruhe, 68; asst prof chem, Univ Del, 68-70; asst gen mgr, Welsbach Corp, 70-76; VPRES & CHIEF OPERATING OFFICER OZONE TECHNOL, PCI OZONE CORP, 76- *Mem:* Am Chem Soc; Water Pollution Control Fedn. *Res:* Organic ozone reactions; application of ozone to air and water purification. *Mailing Add:* PCI Ozone Corp One Fairfield Crescent East Caldwell NJ 07006

NEBENZAHL, LINDA LEVINE, b Duluth, Minn, Oct 4, 49; m 71. PHYSICAL ORGANIC CHEMISTRY, SURFACE CHEMISTRY. *Educ:* Univ Minn, Minneapolis, BA, 71; Univ Calif, Berkeley, PhD(org chem), 75. *Prof Exp:* STAFF CHEMIST, IBM CORP, 75- *Mem:* Am Chem Soc. *Res:* Light scattering of surfactants and polymer solutions; fluid flow through porous media. *Mailing Add:* E06/025 IBM Corp San Jose CA 95193

NEBERT, DANIEL WALTER, b Portland, Ore, Sept 26, 40; m 60, 81; c 2. PEDIATRICS, PHARMACOLOGY. *Educ:* Univ Ore, BA, 61, MS & MD, 64. *Prof Exp:* From intern to resident pediat, Ctr Health Sci, Univ Calif, Los Angeles, 64-66; res assoc biochem, Lab Chem, Etiology Br, Nat Cancer Inst, 66-68; res investr pharmacol, Sect Develop Enzym, 68-70, head sect develop pharmacol, Lab Biomed Sci, 70-74, chief neonatal & pediat med br, 74-75, CHIEF DEVELOP PHARMACOL BR, NAT INST CHILD HEALTH & HUMAN DEVELOP, NIH, 75- *Honors & Awards:* Pfizer hon lectr, 78. *Mem:* AAAS; Am Soc Pharmacol & Exp Therapeut; Am Soc Biol Chemists; Sigma Xi; Am Soc Clin Invest. *Res:* Application of recombinant DNA technology, mammalian cell culture, and inbred animal strains to molecular genetics, clinical pharmacology, toxicology, cancer research and pharmacogenetic disorders. *Mailing Add:* Rm 13 N-266 Bldg 10 Nat Inst Child Health & Human Dev Bethesda MD 20205

NEBGEN, JOHN WILLIAM, b Independence, Mo, May 20, 3S; div; c 2. PHYSICAL CHEMISTRY, INORGANIC CHEMISTRY. *Educ:* Washington Univ, AB, 56; Univ Pa, PhD(chem), 60. *Prof Exp:* Assoc chemist, 60-65, sr chemist, 65-68, prin chemist, 68-78, SR ADV CHEM, MIDWEST RES INST, 78- *Mem:* Am Chem Soc; Water Pollution Control Fedn. *Res:* Molecular structure; infrared, nuclear magnetic resonance and electron spin resonance spectroscopy; inorganic synthesis; portland cement manufacture; wastewater treatment; water pollution abatement; environmental systems analysis; water desalting and reuse; waste utilization; corrosion chemistry. *Mailing Add:* Midwest Res Inst 425 Volker Blvd Kansas City MO 64110

NEBIKER, JOHN HERBERT, b Eastport, Maine, May 26, 36; m 62; c 2. ENVIRONMENTAL ENGINEERING. *Educ:* Mass Inst Technol, SB, 58; Swiss Fed Inst Technol, DSc(environ eng), 66. *Prof Exp:* Asst prof sanit & water resources eng, Vanderbilt Univ, 65-67; asst prof civil eng, Univ Mass, 67-69; vpres, Curran Assocs, Inc, 69-72; sanit engr, WHO, 72-75; mgr environ planning, Malcolm Pirnie, Inc, 75-79; SANIT ENGR, WORLD BANK, 79- *Mem:* Am Soc Civil Engrs; Am Water Works Asn; NY Acad Sci. *Res:* Physical processes in sanitary engineering; public health engineering. *Mailing Add:* 8204 Lillystone Dr Bethesda MD 20014

NEBOLSINE, PETER EUGENE, b Annapolis, Md, Apr 6, 45; m 67; c 2. PHYSICS, OPTICS. *Educ:* Lafayette Col, BS, 67; Univ Rochester, PhD(optics), 72. *Prof Exp:* Sr scientist physics, Avco Everett Res Lab, 72-73; prin scientist physics, 74-80, MGR EXP RES, PHYS SCI INC, 80- *Mem:* Optical Soc Am. *Res:* Laser applications especially laser propulsion, material interaction and sound generation; hypervelocity impact experimentalist. *Mailing Add:* Phys Sci Inc 30 Commerce Way Woburn MA 01801

NECE, RONALD ELLIOTT, b Seattle, Wash, May 25, 27; m 51; c 2. CIVIL ENGINEERING. *Educ:* Univ Wash, BS, 49; Lehigh Univ, MS, 51; Mass Inst Technol, ScD(civil eng), 58. *Prof Exp:* Instr civil eng, Rutgers Univ, 51-52; instr fluid mech & civil eng, Mass Inst Technol, 52-56, asst prof hydraul & civil eng, 56-59; from asst prof to assoc prof civil eng, 59-67, PROF CIVIL ENG, UNIV WASH, 67- *Mem:* Am Soc Civil Engrs; Am Soc Mech Engrs; Int Asn Hydraul Res. *Res:* Fluid mechanics; hydraulic engineering; hydrodynamics in natural bodies of water. *Mailing Add:* Dept of Civil Eng Univ of Wash Seattle WA 98195

NECHAMKIN, HOWARD, b Brooklyn, NY, Aug 18, 18; m 56; c 1. INORGANIC CHEMISTRY. *Educ:* Brooklyn Col, BA, 39; Polytech Inst Brooklyn, MS, 49; NY Univ, EdD, 61. *Prof Exp:* Chemist, R H Macy Co, NY, 39-41 & US Naval Supply Depot, 41-42; head res chemist, Hazeltine Electronics Corp, 42-45; instr chem, Brooklyn Col, 45-46; from instr to assoc prof chem, Pratt Inst, 46-61; PROF CHEM, TRENTON STATE COL, 61-, CHMN DEPT, 68- *Honors & Awards:* Professional Chemist Award, Am Inst Chemists, 74. *Mem:* Fel Am Inst Chem; Am Chem Soc. *Res:* Analysis of synthetic fibers; metal coatings research; plastics development; detection of vanillin flavor; chemistry of rhenium; volumetric analysis of sulfate; chemistry of recyclable materials. *Mailing Add:* Dept of Chem Trenton State Col Trenton NJ 08625

NECHAY, BOHDAN ROMAN, b Prague, Czech, Nov 26, 25; nat US; m; c 2. PHARMACOLOGY, THERAPEUTICS. *Educ:* Univ Minn, DVM, 53. *Prof Exp:* Pvt practr, Minn, 53-56; asst prof pharmacol, Col Med, Univ Fla, 61-66; asst prof pharmacol & urol, Med Ctr, Duke Univ, 66-68; assoc prof, 68-78, PROF PHARMACOL & TOXICOL, UNIV TEX MED BR GALVESTON, 78- *Concurrent Pos:* Fel pharmacol, Col Med, Univ Fla, 56-60; Am Heart Asn fel, 58-60; NIH fel pharmacol, Univ Uppsala, 60-61; vis mem grad fac, Tex A&M Univ, 81- *Mem:* Soc Toxicol; Am Soc Nephrology; Am Soc Pharmacol & Exp Therapeut. *Res:* Electrolyte physiology and pharmacology; environmental occupational toxicology; kidney and cardiovascular system. *Mailing Add:* Dept of Pharmacol & Toxicol Univ of Tex Med Br Galveston TX 77550

NECHELES, THOMAS, b Hamburg, Ger, Oct 1, 33; US citizen; m 55; c 5. PEDIATRICS, PHYSIOLOGY. *Educ:* Univ Chicago, BA, 53, BS, 57, MS, 58, MD & PhD(biol, physiol), 61. *Prof Exp:* Instr med, 65-67, asst prof pediat, 67-70, ASSOC PROF PEDIAT, SCH MED, TUFTS UNIV, 70- *Concurrent Pos:* USPHS hemat fel, Blood Res Lab, New Eng Med Ctr Hosps, 63-66; asst hematologist, Boston Floating Hosp, 65-67; consult & sr instr, Blood Res Lab, New Eng Med Ctr Hosps, 66-, hematologist, 67-70, chief pediat hemat, 70-; estab investr, Am Heart Asn, 66-71; consult, Springfield Hosp, Mass, 72-, St Elizabeth Hosp, Brighton, 73- & Kennedy Mem Hosp, 74- *Mem:* Am Soc Clin Oncol; AAAS; Am Fedn Clin Res; Am Soc Hemat; Am Soc Exp Path. *Res:* Control of cellular proliferation; hemoglobin synthesis; red cell metabolism. *Mailing Add:* Dept of Pediat Hemat New Eng Med Ctr Hosps Boston MA 02111

NECHVATAL, STANLEY RUDOLPH, b Cleveland, Ohio, Oct 30, 28; m 55; c 3. ENGINEERING. *Educ:* Case Western Reserve, BS, 52. *Prof Exp:* Develop engr, Indust Rayon Corp, 52-57, sr engr, 57-61; proj engr, 61-67, group leader, 67-73, RES SCIENTIST, HERCULES INC, 73- *Res:* Development and design of processes and equipment for olefin (polypropylene) fiber production. *Mailing Add:* 2462 Fieldstone Dr Conyers GA 30208

NECKER, WALTER LUDWIG, history of biology, history of medicine, deceased

NECKERS, DOUGLAS, b Corry, Pa, Aug 15, 38; m 60; c 2. ORGANIC CHEMISTRY, PHOTOCHEMISTRY. *Educ:* Hope Col, AB, 60; Univ Kans, PhD(org chem), 63. *Prof Exp:* From asst prof to assoc prof chem, Hope Col, 64-71; assoc prof, Univ NMex, 71-73; PROF CHEM & CHMN DEPT, BOWLING GREEN STATE UNIV, 73- *Concurrent Pos:* Fel, Harvard Univ, 63-64; vis lectr, Ohio State Univ, 65 & Univ Ill, 70; vis prof, State Univ Groningen, 68-69 & Roman Cath Univ Nijmegen, 75; Alfred P Sloan Found fel, 71. *Mem:* Sigma Xi (vpres, 76-77, pres, 77-78); Am Chem Soc; Am Asn Univ Prof. *Res:* Polymer chemistry; polymer based reagents in synthesis; photopolymerization. *Mailing Add:* Dept Chem Bowling Green State Univ Bowling Green OH 43404

NEDDENRIEP, RICHARD JOE, b Leipsic, Ohio, June 3, 30; m 57; c 2. PHYSICAL CHEMISTRY. *Educ:* Miami Univ, BA, 53; Univ Wis, PhD(phys chem), 58. *Prof Exp:* Res chemist, Linde Div, Union Carbide Corp, NY, 57-65, group leader, 65-69; group leader, 69-72, mgr prod res, 72-73, asst dir res, 73-74, ASST VPRES, BETZ LABS, INC, 74- *Mem:* Am Chem Soc. *Res:* Reaction kinetics, particularly free radical reactions and the radiolysis of organic materials; adsorption; catalysis, particularly with molecular sieves; water and air purification; corrosion and scale inhibition. *Mailing Add:* Res Dept Betz Labs Inc 4636 Somerton Rd Trevose PA 19047

NEDDERMAN, HOWARD CHARLES, b Mishawaka, Ind, Apr 11, 19; m 40; c 4. PHYSICS. *Educ:* Purdue Univ, BS, 42, MS, 44; Columbia Univ, PhD(physics), 56. *Prof Exp:* Instr chem, Purdue Univ, 42-46; engr microwave tubes, Radio Corp Am, Pa, 46-48; res assoc, Radiation Lab, Columbia Univ, 48-53; sr physicist thermionics, Gen Elec Co, 53-56; res specialist, Stromberg-Carlson Div, Gen Dynamics Corp, NY, 56-57, mgr res, 57-61, from assoc dir to dir res, Electronics Div, 61-66; pres & gen mgr, Megadyne Industs, Inc, 66-70; indust consult, 70-75; vpres, Interstate Circuits, Inc, 75-77; PRIN ENG, KOLLSMAN INSTRUMENT CO, 77- *Mem:* Am Phys Soc. *Mailing Add:* 88 Mammoth Rd Londonderry NH 03053

NEDDERMEYER, PETER ARTHUR, b Elze, Hannover, Ger, Mar 5, 41; US citizen; m 65; c 3. ANALYTICAL CHEMISTRY. *Educ:* Union Col, NY, BS, 63; Purdue Univ, PhD(anal chem), 68. *Prof Exp:* SUPVR CHROMATOGRAPHY SECT, EASTMAN KODAK CO, 68- *Mem:* Am Chem Soc. *Res:* Liquid chromatography, molecular weight characterization, surface chemistry, photographic science. *Mailing Add:* Indust Lab Eastman Kodak Co 343 State St Rochester NY 14650

NEDELSKY, LEO, b Russia, Oct 28, 03; nat US; m 41; c 3. THEORETICAL PHYSICS. *Educ:* Univ Wash, Seattle, BS, 28; Univ Calif, MS, 31, PhD(theoret physics), 32. *Prof Exp:* Instr physics, Univ Calif, 32-35 & Hunter Col, 35-40; fel Gen Educ Bd, 40-41, dir res basic nursing educ, 54-55, PROF PHYS SCI & EXAM, UNIV CHICAGO, 41- *Concurrent Pos:* Lectr, Baker & Ottawa Univs, 48, Univ Pa, 52-53, Univ Wash, Seattle, 56, Univ Mo, 58, Northern Mich Col, 58-59, Univs Colombia, El Salvador, Guatemala, Israel, Mex, Puerto Rico, Venezuela, Cuba & Brazil, 66; consult, Univ Wash, Seattle, 54-57, NY State Univ, 57, Am Bd Radiol, 58, CBS-TV, 58, Univ Ill, 59-60, Michael Reese Hosp, 60; res assoc dent educ, Univ Ill, 65-71; consult, WHO, 66-68. *Mem:* AAAS; Am Phys Soc; Am Asn Physics Teachers. *Res:* Physical sciences in general education. *Mailing Add:* Univ of Chicago 5811 S Ellis Ave Chicago IL 60637

NEDICH, RONALD LEE, b Chicago, Ill. PHYSICAL PHARMACY, INDUSTRIAL PHARMACY. *Educ:* St Louis Col Pharm, BS, 65; Purdue Univ, MS, 68, PhD(phys pharm), 70. *Prof Exp:* Sr res pharmacist, 70-73, mgr pharm develop, 73-76, sr mgr pharm develop, 76-78, DIR PHARM DEVELOP, BAXTER LABS, INC, 78- *Mem:* Acad Pharmaceut Sci; Am Pharmaceut Asn; Am Chem Soc. *Res:* Dosage form design; physical chemical principles associated with pharmaceutical dosage forms; pharmacokinetics. *Mailing Add:* 812 Pembrooke Rd Libertyville IL 60048

NEDOLUHA, ALFRED K, b Vienna, Austria, Sept 13, 28; m 57; c 1. THEORETICAL SOLID STATE PHYSICS. *Educ:* Univ Vienna, PhD(physics), 51. *Prof Exp:* Staff mem, Felten & Guilleaume, A G, Austria, 51-56, head high voltage lab, 56-57; physicist, White Sands Missile Range, NMex, 57-59; Naval Ord Lab, Corona, 59-62, res physicist, Naval Electronics Lab Ctr, 62-70, res physicist, San Diego, 70-75; CHIEF ELECTRONICS BR, EUROP RES OFF, US ARMY, 75- *Mem:* Am Phys Soc. *Res:* Solid state theory. *Mailing Add:* 223 Old Marylebone Rd London NW1 5TH United Kingdom

NEDWICK, JOHN JOSEPH, b Ranshaw, Pa, Jan 11, 22; m 61; c 3. INDUSTRIAL ORGANIC CHEMISTRY, CHEMICAL ENGINEERING. *Educ:* Univ Louisville, AB, 47; Univ Pa, MS, 53. *Prof Exp:* Chemist, 48-56, group leader high pressure chem, 56-63, GROUP LEADER POLYMER CHEM, ROHM AND HAAS CO, 63-, PROJ LEADER, CHEM PROCESS ENG DEPT, 73- *Mem:* Am Chem Soc; Am Inst Chem Engrs. *Res:* High pressure research and process development; acetylene reactions; continuous bench scale pilot plants; polymer chemistry; plastics; coatings; process development of agricultural chemicals and health products. *Mailing Add:* Rohm and Haas Co PO Box 219 Bristol PA 19007

NEDZEL, V ALEXANDER, b Constantinople, Turkey, Sept 20, 21; nat US; m 45; c 3. PHYSICS. *Educ:* Univ Chicago, SB, 41, SM, 50, PhD(nuclear physics), 53. *Prof Exp:* Physicist, Metall Lab, Manhattan Dist, 42-44; assoc scientist, Los Alamos Sci Lab, 44-47; asst physics, Univ Chicago, 47-51; syst anal & eval, 53-55, group leader, 55-65, assoc head data systs div, 65-69, HEAD AEROSPACE DIV, LINCOLN LAB, MASS INST TECHNOL, 69- *Concurrent Pos:* Asst to dir, Los Alamos Group, Bikini Tests, 46. *Mem:* AAAS; fel Am Phys Soc; Opers Res Soc Am; Am Inst Aeronaut & Astronaut; AAAS. *Res:* Radar and computer systems; defense sciences. *Mailing Add:* Lincoln Lab Mass Inst of Technol Lexington MA 02173

NEE, M COLEMAN, b Taylor, Pa, Nov 14, 17. MATHEMATICS. *Educ:* Marywood Col, AB, 39, MA, 43; Univ Notre Dame, MS, 59. *Prof Exp:* Teacher math & Latin, Marywood Sem, 43-55; asst prof math, 59-70, PRES MARYWOOD COL, 70- *Res:* Group theory of algebra. *Mailing Add:* Marywood Col Scranton PA 18509

NEE, VICTOR W, b Soochow, China, Apr 8, 35; m 61; c 4. FLUID MECHANICS. *Educ:* Univ Taiwan, BS, 57; Johns Hopkins Univ, PhD(fluid mech), 67. *Prof Exp:* Asst civil eng, Univ Taiwan, 57-60; asst fluid mech, Johns Hopkins Univ, 60-65; from asst prof to assoc prof, 65-73, PROF FLUID MECH, UNIV NOTRE DAME, 73- *Concurrent Pos:* Mem adv comt, Environ Protection Agency, USA, 74- *Mem:* Am Phys Soc. *Res:* Fluid mechanics; turbulence; turbulent boundary layers; laminar flows; air pollution; heat and mass transfer. *Mailing Add:* Dept of Aerospace & Mech Eng Univ of Notre Dame Notre Dame IN 46556

NEECE, GEORGE A, b Pine Bluff, Ark, Sept 18, 39; m 62. PHYSICAL CHEMISTRY. *Educ:* Rice Univ, AB, 61; Duke Univ, PhD(phys chem), 64. *Prof Exp:* Chemist, US Army Res Off-Durham, 64-67; res assoc chem, Cornell Univ, 67-68; asst prof, Univ Ga, 68-71; CHEMIST, OFF NAVAL RES, 71-, DIR CHEM PROG, 72- *Res:* Statistical mechanics. *Mailing Add:* Off of Naval Res 800 N Quincy Arlington VA 22217

NEEDHAM, CHARLES D, b Chicago, Ill, Sept 17, 37. PHYSICAL CHEMISTRY. *Educ:* Carnegie Inst Technol, BS, 59; Univ Minn, PhD(chem), 65. *Prof Exp:* Staff fel phys biol, NIH, 65-67; ADV CHEMIST, GEN TECHNOL DIV, IBM CORP, 67- *Mem:* Am Chem Soc. *Res:* Raman spectroscopy and optical analysis techniques. *Mailing Add:* Zip 57A IBM Corp Hopewell Jct NY 12533

NEEDHAM, GERALD MORTON, b Caldwell, Idaho, Aug 4, 17; m 42; c 2. BACTERIOLOGY. *Educ:* Col Idaho, BS, 40; Univ Minn, PhD(bact), 47; Am Bd Med Microbiol, dipl. *Prof Exp:* Bacteriologist, State Dept Health, Minn, 41-42; instr bact, Med Sch, Univ Minn, 41-46; med bacteriologist, Mayo Clin, 46-68; ASSOC DIR DIV EDUC, MAYO SCH HEALTH REL SCI, MAYO

FOUND, 68-; ASSOC DEAN STUDENT AFFAIRS, MAYO MED SCH, UNIV MINN, 71- *Concurrent Pos:* Consult bacteriologist, Econ Labs, St Paul, 41-46. *Mem:* AAAS; Am Soc Microbiol; fel Am Acad Microbiol; fel Am Pub Health Asn. *Res:* Medical bacteriology; antibiotics; tuberculosis; action of a few antibacterial substances on resting cells. *Mailing Add:* Mayo Clin Rochester MN 55901

NEEDHAM, GLEN RAY, b Lamar, Colo, Dec 25, 51. ACARINE PHYSIOLOGY, ENTOMOLOGY. *Educ:* Southwestern Okla State Univ, BS, 73; Okla State Univ, MS, 75, PhD(entom), 78. *Prof Exp:* ASST PROF ACAROL, OHIO STATE UNIV, 78- *Mem:* Entom Soc Am; Acarol Soc Am; AAAS; Sigma Xi. *Res:* Ion and water balance in ticks and mites; disease transmission by ticks. *Mailing Add:* Col of Biol Sci Acarol Lab 484 W 12th Ave Columbus OH 43210

NEEDHAM, THOMAS E, JR, b Newton, NJ, Apr 12, 42. PHARMACEUTICS. *Educ:* Univ RI, BS, 65, MS, 67, PhD(pharmaceut sci), 70. *Prof Exp:* Pharmacist, Galen Drug, Inc, 65-68; instr pharm, Univ RI, 67-69; pharmacist, Pinault Drug, Inc, 69-70; asst prof pharm, Sch Pharm, Univ Ga, 70-74, assoc prof, 74-80; ASSOC DIR, PHARMACEUT DEVELOP, TRAVENOL LABS, 80- *Mem:* Am Pharmaceut Asn; Acad Pharmaceut Sci; Am Asn Cols of Pharm. *Res:* Effects of selected variables on the dissolution and absorption of drugs; particulate and incompatibilities in glass and plastic parenteral containers. *Mailing Add:* Travenol Labs 6301 Lincoln Ave Morton Grove IL 60053

NEEDLEMAN, SAUL BEN, b Chicago, Ill, Sept 25, 27; m 54; c 4. BIOCHEMISTRY, NEUROCHEMISTRY. *Educ:* Ill Inst Technol, BS, 50, MS, 55; Northwestern Univ, PhD(med & biochem), 57. *Prof Exp:* Res assoc biochem, Col Med, Univ Ill, 52-53; asst chem, Ill Inst Technol, 53-55; asst chem, Northwestern Univ, 55-57, from instr to asst prof neurobiochem, 57-72; prof biochem & head dept, Roosevelt Univ, 72-74; clin diag specialist, Abbott Labs, 74-76, coordr clin res, 76-79; dir clin affairs, Consumers Prod Div, Schering-Plough, 79-81; DIR MED AFFAIRS, HOLLISTER INC, 81- *Concurrent Pos:* Group leader, Helene Curtis Industs, Inc, 57-58; sr res chemist, Nalco Chem Co, 58-62; sr res biochemist, Abbott Labs, 62-66; asst chief radioisotope serv, Vet Res Hosp, Chicago, 66-71. *Mem:* Am Chem Soc; Sigma Xi; Am Soc Biol Chemists; Am Soc Cell Biol; Biophys Soc. *Res:* Protein sequence determination; mechanism of enzyme action; lysosomal enzyme diseases; Wilson's disease; organic synthesis of biochemically active substances; Collagen disease metabolism. *Mailing Add:* Dir med affairs Hollister Inc 2000 Hollister Dr Libertyville IL 60048

NEEDLER, GEORGE TREGLOHAN, b Sommerxide, PEI, Feb 2, 35; m 59; c 4. DYNAMICAL OCEANOGRAPHY, DEEP SEA POLLUTION. *Educ:* Univ BC, BSc, 58, MSc, 59; McGill Univ, PhD(theoret physics), 63. *Prof Exp:* Res scientist phys oceanog, 62-79, DIR, ATLANTIC OCEANOG LAB, BEDFORD INST OCEANOG, 80- *Concurrent Pos:* Res assoc phys oceanog, Dalhousie Univ, 67- *Mem:* Can Meteorol & Oceanog Soc; Int Union Geodesy & Geophysics. *Res:* Large-scale dynamical oceanography including thermocline theory, climate research, and the interpretation of geochemical data; deep ocean pollution, especially as related to the disposal of radio-active wastes. *Mailing Add:* Atlantic Oceanog Lab Bedford Inst Oceanog PO Box 1006 Dartmouth NS B2Y 4A2 Can

NEEDLES, HOWARD LEE, b Bloomington, Calif, June 26, 37; m 60; c 4. POLYMER CHEMISTRY, TEXTILE CHEMISTRY. *Educ:* Univ Calif, Riverside, AB, 59; Univ Mo, PhD(org chem), 63. *Prof Exp:* Res chemist, Western Regional Res Lab, USDA, 63-69; asst prof textile sci & asst textile chemist, Agr Exp Sta, 69-74, assoc prof, 74-77, PROF TEXTILE SCI, UNIV CALIF, DAVIS, 77- *Mem:* Fiber Soc; Am Asn Textile Chem & Colorists; Am Chem Soc. *Res:* Modification of fibers and polymers; photo and heat induced changes in fibers; textile flammability; physical and chemical properties of modified fibers; color relationships in dyed fibers. *Mailing Add:* Div of Textiles & Clothing Univ of Calif Davis CA 95616

NEEL, JAMES VAN GUNDIA, b Middletown, Ohio, Mar 22, 15; m 43; c 3. GENETICS. *Educ:* Col Wooster, AB, 35; Univ Rochester, PhD(genetics), 39, MD, 44. *Hon Degrees:* DSc, Col Wooster, 59, Univ Rochester, 74, Med Col Ohio, 81. *Prof Exp:* Asst, Univ Rochester, 35-39; instr zool, Dartmouth Col, 39-41; from intern to asst resident med, Strong Mem Hosp & Rochester Munic Hosp, NY, 44-46; dir field studies, Atomic Bomb Casualty Comn, Nat Res Coun, 47-48; assoc geneticist, Inst Human Biol, 48-56, from asst prof to assoc prof internal med, 49-56, prof human genetics & internal med, Sch Med, 56-66, chmn, Dept Human Genetics, 56-81, LEE R DICE UNIV PROF HUMAN GENETICS & INTERNAL MED, SCH MED, UNIV MICH, ANN ARBOR, 66- *Concurrent Pos:* Mem comt res probs sex, Nat Res Coun, 49-56, panel genetics, Comt Growth, 51-56, comt atomic casualties, 51-54, adv comt, Atomic Bomb Casualty Comn, 57-, comt epidemiol & vet follow-up studies, 65-; mem comt genetic effects of atomic radiation, Nat Acad Sci, 55-, comt int biol prog, 65-, selection comt sr res fels, NIH, 56-60 & gen res training grant comt, 57-58, chmn genetic training grant comt, 58-63, mem comt int ctrs for med res & training, 61-65, comt int res, 65-69, expert adv panel radiation, WHO, 57-61, expert adv panel human genetics, 61, mem coun, Nat Acad Sci, 70-73; US deleg, US-Japan Coop Med Sci Prog, 71-78. *Honors & Awards:* Lasker Award, Am Pub Health Asn, 60; Allen Award, Am Soc Human Genetics, 65; Nat Medal of Sci, 74. *Mem:* Nat Acad Sci; Am Acad Arts & Sci; Asn Am Physicians; Am Philos Soc; Am Soc Naturalists. *Res:* Genetics of man. *Mailing Add:* Dept Human Genetics Univ Mich Ann Arbor MI 48109

NEEL, JAMES WILLIAM, b Turlock, Calif, July 20, 25; m 56. SOIL SCIENCE, BOTANY. *Educ:* Univ Calif, Berkeley, BS, 49, Univ Calif, Los Angeles, PhD(bot sci), 64. *Prof Exp:* From lab technician to prin lab technician, Atomic Energy Proj, Univ Calif, Los Angeles, 49-59, asst plant physiol, Dept Irrig & Soil Sci, 59-63; from asst prof to assoc prof, 63-69, chmn dept, 69-71, PROF BIOL, SAN DIEGO STATE UNIV, 69- *Concurrent Pos:* Consult, Rand Corp, Calif, 63-71. *Mem:* AAAS; Am Soc Agron; Soil Sci Soc Am; NY Acad Sci. *Res:* Fate of soluble and insoluble forms of radionuclides in soils and availability to plants; effects of heavy metals on plant systems. *Mailing Add:* Dept of Biol San Diego State Univ San Diego CA 92182

NEEL, JOE KENDALL, SR, b Tacoma, Va, June 12, 15; m 42; c 1. LIMNOLOGY. *Educ:* Univ Ky, BS, 37, MS, 38; Univ Mich, PhD(limnol), 47. *Prof Exp:* Instr zool, Univ Ky, 38-39; teaching fel, Univ Mich, 41-42; med entomologist, USPHS, 42-46; Rackham fel, Univ Mich, 46-47; asst prof zool, Univ Ky, 47-50; basin biologist, Div Water Pollution Control, USPHS, 50-53, biologist, 53-58, chief water quality sect, 58-63; dir potamological inst, Louisville, Ky, 63-66; prof biol, 66-81, chmn dept, 74-76, EMER PROF BIOL, UNIV NDAK, 81- *Concurrent Pos:* Prin investr, 67-81. *Mem:* AAAS; Am Inst Biol Sci; Am Soc Limnol & Oceanog; Am Micros Soc; Water Pollution Control Fedn. *Res:* Psammon; stream limnology; waste treatment; eutrophication; reservoirs. *Mailing Add:* 2221 Chestnut St Grand Forks ND 58201

NEEL, PERCY LANDRETH, ornamental horticulture, see previous edition

NEEL, WILLIAM WALLACE, b Thomasville, Ga, Feb 4, 18; m 52; c 2. ENTOMOLOGY. *Educ:* Emory Univ, BA, 40; Univ Fla, MS, 49; Tex A&M Univ, Tex, PhD(entom), 54. *Prof Exp:* Field supvr, Disease Control, USPHS, 45-47; asst entomologist, Inter-Am Inst of Agr Sci, 48-49, 52-53; asst prof entom & asst entomologist, Agr Exp Sta, Miss State Univ, 54-62; field res, Chemagro Corp, 62-63; asst prof entom & asst entomologist, Agr Exp Sta, Univ WVa, 63-66; assoc prof & assoc entomologist, 66-77, PROF ENTOM & ENTOMOLOGIST, AGR EXP STA, MISS STATE UNIV, 77- *Mem:* Entom Soc Am; Sigma Xi. *Res:* Forest and pecan entomology with special interest in seed and cone insects; toxicant research on pecan and seed and cone insects; pheromone isolation of pecan weevil. *Mailing Add:* Dept of Entom PO Drawer EM Mississippi State MS 39762

NEELEY, CHARLES MACK, b Pine Bluff, Ark, Mar 7, 42; m 68. PHYSICAL CHEMISTRY, POLYMER CHEMISTRY. *Educ:* Univ Ark, Fayetteville, BS, 65, PhD(chem), 69. *Prof Exp:* Lab technician, Houston Chem Corp, 62-63; asst phys chem, Univ Ark, Fayetteville, 65-69; fel, Univ Fla, 69-70; res chemist polymer phys chem, Plastics Lab, 70-75, sr chemist, Polymer Develop Polyethylene & Polypropylene Divs, Polymer Develop Div, 75-77, MGT STAFF ASST, TEX EASTMAN CO, 77- *Mem:* AAAS; Am Chem Soc. *Res:* Pyrolysis gas chromatography; rheology; gas phase photochemistry; gas phase kinetics. *Mailing Add:* 1600 Pineridge St Longview TX 75604

NEELEY, JOHN CHARLES, genetics, see previous edition

NEELIN, JAMES MICHAEL, b London, Ont, Dec 4, 30; m 53; c 4. BIOCHEMISTRY, CELL DIFFERENTIATION. *Educ:* Univ Toronto, BA, 53, PhD(biochem), 58. *Prof Exp:* Jr scientist, Atlantic Tech Sta, Fisheries Res Bd, Can, 53-54, asst scientist, 54-55; Coun fel, Div Appl Biol, Nat Res Coun Can, 58-59, asst res officer, 59-62; res assoc chicken histones, Stanford Univ, 62-63; assoc res officer, Div Biosci, Nat Res Coun Can, 64-70, sr res officer, 71; chmn dept biol, 71-74 & 75-78, PROF BIOL & BIOCHEM, CARLETON UNIV, 71-, DIR, BIOCHEM INST, 79- *Concurrent Pos:* co-ed, Can J Biochem, 81- *Mem:* Can Biochem Soc; Can Soc Cell Biol; Can Fedn Biol Sci; Can Hist Sci Technol Asn. *Res:* Chemistry and biological implication of histones, especially of nucleated erythrocytes. *Mailing Add:* Dept Biol Carleton Univ Ottawa ON K1S 5B6 Can

NEELY, BROCK WESLEY, b London, Ont, Apr 28, 26; nat US; m 53; c 3. BIOCHEMISTRY, PHYSICAL CHEMISTRY. *Educ:* Univ Toronto, BS, 48; Mich State Univ, PhD(biochem), 52. *Prof Exp:* Res Found fel chem, Ohio State Univ, 52-53; Rockefeller fel, Univ Birmingham, 53-54; res assoc, G D Searle & Co, Ill, 54-55; RES ASSOC BIOCHEM, DOW CHEM CO, 57-, RES ASSOC ENVIRON SCI, 73- *Mem:* Am Chem Soc; Sigma Xi; NY Acad Sci; Soc Environ Toxicol & Chem. *Res:* Structure- activity relationships; environment research; math modeling. *Mailing Add:* 1702 Bldg Dow Chem Co Midland MI 48640

NEELY, CHARLES LEA, JR, b Memphis, Tenn, Aug 3, 27; m 57; c 2. MEDICINE, HEMATOLOGY. *Educ:* Princeton Univ, AB, 50; Washington Univ, MD, 54. *Prof Exp:* Intern, Bellevue Hosp, New York, 54-55; resident, Barnes Hosp, St Louis, 55-57, fel med & NIH trainee chemother, 57-58; from instr to assoc prof, 58-71, chief, Dept Oncol, 76 & Dept Hemat, 81, PROF MED, COL MED, UNIV TENN, MEMPHIS, 71- *Concurrent Pos:* Actg dir, Memphis Regional Cancer Ctr, 79- & Cancer Prog, Univ Tenn, 79- *Mem:* Am Soc Hemat; fel Am Col Physicians; Am Fedn Clin Res; Am Soc Clin Oncol; AMA. *Res:* Hemolytic anemias and oncology. *Mailing Add:* Dept of Med Univ of Tenn 800 Madison Ave Memphis TN 38163

NEELY, JAMES ROBERT, b Tenn, June 11, 35; m 54; c 5. CARDIOVASCULAR PHYSIOLOGY. *Educ:* Tenn Tech Univ, BS, 61, MA, 62; Vanderbilt Univ, PhD(physiol), 66. *Prof Exp:* Tenn Heart Asn fel, Vanderbilt Univ, 66-67; from instr to assoc prof, 67-76, PROF PHYSIOL, M S HERSHEY MED CTR, COL MED, PA STATE UNIV, 76- *Concurrent Pos:* Mem, Int Study Group Res in Cardiac Metab. *Mem:* Am Physiol Soc; Cardiac Muscle Soc. *Res:* Cardiac metabolism. *Mailing Add:* M S Hershey Med Ctr Pa State Univ Hershey PA 17033

NEELY, JAMES W, physical inorganic chemistry, see previous edition

NEELY, PETER MUNRO, b Los Angeles, Calif, Dec 31, 27; m 65; c 2. SYSTEMATICS, ECOLOGY. *Educ:* Univ Calif, Los Angeles, BA, 52, PhD(bot), 60. *Prof Exp:* Asst bot, Univ Calif, Los Angeles, 52-63; asst prof bot & res assoc, Biol Sci Comput Ctr, Chicago, 63-68; assoc prof statist biol, Dept Bot, 68-71, assoc dir comput ctr, 69-77, ASSOC PROF SYSTS & ECOL, UNIV KANS, 71- *Concurrent Pos:* USPHS fel, Sch Pub Health, Univ Calif, Los Angeles, 61-62. *Res:* Application of computer processing and statistical techniques to biological problems; grouping algorithms and development of general theory of classifications; development of interactive pedagogic programs; bioethics and ecological scarcity. *Mailing Add:* Dept of Systs & Ecol Univ of Kans Lawrence KS 66045

NEELY, ROBERT DAN, b Senath, Mo, Oct 6, 28; m 53; c 2. PLANT PATHOLOGY. *Educ:* Univ Mo, BS, 50, PhD(bot), 57. *Prof Exp:* PLANT PATHOLOGIST, ILL NATURAL HIST SURV, 57- *Concurrent Pos:* Adj prof plant path, Univ Ill, Urbana-Champaign, 72- *Honors & Awards:* Author's Citation, Int Soc Arboriculture, 74. *Mem:* Mycol Soc Am; Am Phytopath Soc. *Res:* Diseases of shade and forest trees and woody ornamentals. *Mailing Add:* 382 Natural Resources Bldg Ill Natural Hist Surv Urbana IL 61801

NEELY, STANLEY CARRELL, b Abilene, Tex, Sept 11, 37; m 59; c 3. PHYSICAL CHEMISTRY. *Educ:* Southern Methodist Univ, BS, 60; Yale Univ, PhD(phys chem), 65. *Prof Exp:* Asst prof, 65-69, ASSOC PROF CHEM, UNIV OKLA, 69-, ASST CHMN CHEM, 81- *Mem:* Am Chem Soc. *Res:* Molecular and solid state spectroscopy; molecular interactions. *Mailing Add:* 4 Bingahm Place Norman OK 73069

NEELY, WILLIAM CHARLES, b Cave City, Ark, Nov 22, 31; m 57; c 2. PHYSICAL CHEMISTRY. *Educ:* Miss State Col, BS, 53; La State Univ, MS, 60, PhD(chem), 62. *Prof Exp:* Chemist, Nylon Div, Chemstrand Corp, 53-54, res chemist, Chemstrand Res Ctr, Inc, 62-66; asst prof, 66-70, ASSOC PROF CHEM, AUBURN UNIV, 70- *Mem:* Am Chem Soc. *Res:* Molecular spectroscopy and photochemistry of uranyl compounds; amides; azo compounds; anthraquinones; electronic excitation energy transfer processes. *Mailing Add:* Dept of Chem Auburn Univ Auburn AL 36830

NEEMAN, MOSHE, b Latvia, Apr 1, 19; nat US; m 60; c 4. ORGANIC CHEMISTRY, BIOCHEMISTRY. *Educ:* Univ London, BSc, 43; Hebrew Univ, MSc, 45, PhD, 47. *Prof Exp:* Asst, D Sieff Res Inst, Israel, 36-44; with indust, 45-46; indust safety & hyg expert, Govt Israel, 48-52; dep dir, Israel Res Coun & dir, Lab Appl Org Chem, 52-56; sr lectr, Israel Inst Technol, 56; vis res assoc chem, Univ Wis, 56-59; assoc res prof chem, 64-72, co-chmn chem prog, 69-73, ASSOC CANCER RES SCIENTIST, ROSWELL PARK MEM INST, 59-, RES PROF CHEM, 72-, HEAD, CARCINOGENESIS LAB, 73- *Concurrent Pos:* Chmn standards comt, Israel Standards Inst, 48-50; dir, Inst Indust Hyg, 50-52; res prof chem, Niagara Univ, 69-; res prof biol, Canisuis Col, 69- *Honors & Awards:* Szold Award, Israel, 57. *Mem:* Am Chem Soc; fel Royal Soc Health; fel Am Inst Chemists; fel Royal Soc Chem. *Res:* Heterocyclic syntheses; diazoalkanes; medicinal chemistry; mechanism of carcinogenesis and tumor promotion; chemistry and reaction mechanisms of steroids; steroidal alkaloids; steroid hormone metabolism. *Mailing Add:* Roswell Park Mem Inst 666 Elm St Buffalo NY 14263

NEENAN, JOHN PATRICK, b Detroit, Mich, Nov 3, 43; US citizen. NUCLEIC ACID CHEMISTRY, ENZYMOLOGY. *Educ:* Wayne State Univ, BS, 69; Univ Calif, Santa Barbara, PhD(chem), 73. *Prof Exp:* Fel pharmacol, Sch Med, Yale Univ, 73; fel med chem, Sch Med, Univ Pa, 74; sr res chemist, Asn Stevens Inc, Detroit, 74-75; res assoc chem, Mich Cancer Found, 75-77; asst prof biochem, Ill Benedictine Col, 77-79; res assoc, Univ Ariz, 79-81; RES ASSOC BIOCHEM, BOWLING GREEN STATE UNIV, 81- *Concurrent Pos:* Adj lectr, Univ Mich, Dearborn, 76-79; mem fac, Argonne Nat Lab, 78; prin investr, US Army contract, Ill Benedictine Col, 78-79; prin investr, US Army contract, Univ Ariz, 80-81. *Mem:* Am Chem Soc. *Res:* Design of nucleoside and nucleotide analogs as enzyme inhibitors and antiviral, antitumor and antiparasite agents. *Mailing Add:* Dept of Chem Bowling Green State Univ Bowling Green OH 43403

NEEPER, DONALD ANDREW, b New York, NY, Aug 9, 37. SOLAR ENERGY. *Educ:* Pomona Col, BA, 58; Univ Wis, MS, 60, PhD(physics), 64. *Prof Exp:* Res assoc, James Franck Inst, Univ Chicago, 66-68; staff mem, 68-79, GROUP LEADER, LOS ALAMOS NAT LAB, 79- *Mem:* Am Phys Soc; Int Solar Energy Soc; AAAS. *Res:* Thermal transport; solar energy collection. *Mailing Add:* 2708 Walnut St Los Alamos NM 87544

NEER, EVA JULIA, b Warsaw, Poland; US citizen. BIOCHEMISTRY. *Educ:* Barnard Col, BA, 59; Col Physicians & Surgeons, Columbia Univ, MD, 63. *Prof Exp:* Intern med, Georgetown Univ Hosp, DC, 63-64; fel biol, Yale Univ, Conn, 65-66; fel, 66-68, res assoc, 67-76, asst prof med, 76-79, ASSOC PROF MED, HARVARD MED SCH, BOSTON, 79- *Concurrent Pos:* Estab investr, Am Heart Asn, 71-76; tutor biochem sci, Harvard Univ, Cambridge, 72-; ed, J Biol Chem, 78- & J Cyclase Nuclear Res, 81- *Mem:* Am Soc Biol Chemists; Endocrine Soc; Soc Neurosci. *Res:* Chemistry of the early events in the action of hormones which activate adenylate cyclase; defining the structure and subunit interactions of adenylate cyclase from the heart and from the brain. *Mailing Add:* Cardiovasc Div Brigham & Womens Hosp 75 Francis St Boston MA 02115

NEER, KEITH LOWELL, b Springfield, Ohio, Feb 18, 49; m 71. MEAT SCIENCE. *Educ:* Ohio State Univ, BSc, 72, MSc, 73; Univ Nebr, PhD(animal sci), 75. *Prof Exp:* Technician meats, Ohio State Univ, 72-73; instr animal sci, Univ Nebr, Lincoln, 75-76; asst prof animal sci, Va Polytech Inst & State Univ, 76-77; MEM STAFF RES & DEVELOP, KROGER CO, 77- *Mem:* Am Meat Sci Asn; Am Soc Animal Sci; Inst Food Sci; Sigma Xi. *Res:* Investigating various feeding regimes and their effect on beef palatability; evaluating mechanical tenderization, pressing, power cleaving and cooking methods on beef palatability. *Mailing Add:* Kroger Co 1212 State Ave Cincinnati OH 45204

NEESBY, TORBEN EMIL, b Copenhagen, Denmark, Apr 21, 09; nat US; m 39; c 3. CLINICAL CHEMISTRY. *Educ:* Tech Univ Denmark, MSc, 32; Columbia Pac Univ, PhD, 79. *Prof Exp:* Consult chemist, 32-40; tech dir, Norsk Sulfo, Norway, 40-43; private bus, Denmark, 43-48; tech dir, Am Sulfo, Inc, NY, 48-51; head org chem, Carroll Dunham Smith Pharmacal Co, 51-56; head lab, E F Drew & Co, 56-58; asst dir tech servs, Bristol Myers, Inc, 58; sr scientist, Schieffelin & Co, 58-61; sr biochemist surg res, Harbor Gen Hosp, Univ Calif, 61-68; CLIN BIOCHEMIST, VALLEY MED CTR, 68- *Mem:* AAAS; Am Chem Soc; Soc Clin Ecol. *Res:* Structure-activity relationship; isotopes; investigation of mediator compounds; research on exogenous and endogenous polypeptide factors with effect on growth of fibroblasts and connective tissue, in vitro; ecology. *Mailing Add:* Valley Med Ctr 445 S Cedar St Fresno CA 93702

NEESON, JOHN FRANCIS, b Buffalo, NY, Dec 9, 36; m 63; c 1. NUCLEAR PHYSICS. *Educ:* Canisius Col, BS, 58; Univ Mich, MS, 60; State Univ NY Buffalo, PhD(physics), 65. *Prof Exp:* From asst prof to assoc prof physics, St Bonaventure Univ, 65-68; assoc prof, State Univ NY Col Brockport, 68-69; assoc prof, 69-74, assoc dean col arts & sci, 69-74, dir instnl res, 74-77, PROF PHYSICS, ST BONAVENTURE UNIV, 74-, CHMN DEPT, 77- *Concurrent Pos:* Consult, Clarke Bros Co Div, Dresser Industs, 65-67 & Dresser-Clark Div, 67-; sr scientist, Western NY Nuclear Res Ctr, 69- *Mem:* Am Phys Soc; Am Nuclear Soc; Am Asn Physics Teachers; Am Asn Higher Educ. *Res:* Low energy nuclear physics, especially nuclear structure of spherical nuclei; ultrasonics, light sound wave interaction. *Mailing Add:* Dept of Physics St Bonaventure Univ St Bonaventure NY 14778

NEET, KENNETH EDWARD, b St Petersburg, Fla, Sept 24, 36; m 60; c 4. BIOCHEMISTRY. *Educ:* Univ Fla, BSCh, 58, MS, 60, PhD(biochem), 65. *Prof Exp:* Fel biochem, Univ Calif, Berkeley, 65-67; from asst prof to assoc prof, 67-78, PROF BIOCHEM, SCH MED, CASE WESTERN RESERVE UNIV, 78- *Concurrent Pos:* Macy fac scholar vis prof, Stanford Univ, 80-81. *Mem:* AAAS; Am Chem Soc; Am Soc Biol Chemists; NY Acad Sci. *Res:* Protein chemistry; enzyme regulation and mechanisms; subunit interactions; neurobiology. *Mailing Add:* Dept Biochem Sch Med Case Western Reserve Univ Cleveland OH 44106

NEFF, ALVEN WILLIAM, b Lafayette, Ind, Sept 13, 23; m 48; c 4. BIOCHEMISTRY. *Educ:* Kans State Col, BS, 47, MS, 48; Purdue Univ, PhD, 52. *Prof Exp:* BIOCHEMIST, UPJOHN CO, 52- *Mem:* AAAS; Am Chem Soc. *Res:* Drug and pesticide metabolism; drug residue in animals; pesticide residues in plants. *Mailing Add:* Upjohn Co 301 Henrietta St Kalamazoo MI 49001

NEFF, BEVERLY JEAN, virology, epidemiology, see previous edition

NEFF, BRUCE LYLE, b Philadelphia, Pa, Apr 15, 50; m 76; c 1. POLYMER CHARACTERIZATION, POLYMER PHYSICAL CHEMISTRY. *Educ:* Tulane Univ, BS, 72; Mass Inst Technol, PhD(phys chem), 77. *Prof Exp:* Res chemist polymer spectros, Tenn Eastman Co, 77-79, RES CHEMIST POLYMER PHYSICAL CHEM, EASTMAN CHEM DIV, EASTMAN KODAK CO, 79- *Mem:* Am Phys Soc. *Res:* Investigations of polymer structure and branching by gauge pressure control; light scattering and viscosity techniques; solid state nuclear magnetic resonance spectroscopy, techniques and applications. *Mailing Add:* Res Labs B-150 Eastman Chem Div Kingsport TN 37662

NEFF, CARROLL FORSYTH, b Pigeon, Mich, Jan 10, 08; m 30, 57; c 2. NUTRITION. *Educ:* Washington Univ, AB, 29; Univ Calif, MA, 30. *Prof Exp:* With res lab, Ralston Purina Co, Mo, 26-28 & 30-31; head biol lab, Anheuser-Busch, Inc, 31-38; mgr plant & labs, Sterling Drug, Inc, Ga, 38-50, plant mgr, SAfrica, 50-51, consult chemist, Ga, 51-56; with res dept, New Prod Liaison, Foremost Dairies, Inc, 57-62; TECH CONSULT FOOD, DRUGS & COSMETICS, 62- *Concurrent Pos:* Scholar, Food Law Inst, Emory Univ, 54; western rep, Food & Drug Res Labs, Inc, NY, 68-72; lectr-consult, Nat Agr Col Chapingo, Mex, 74-76. *Mem:* Am Chem Soc; Am Pharmaceut Asn; Am Mkt Asn; Inst Food Technologists. *Res:* Chemotherapy of poultry coccidiosis; yeast vitamins; diet and immunity; milk derivatives; special dietary use foods; food and drug regulations. *Mailing Add:* 4260 Clayton Rd No 27 Concord CA 94521

NEFF, EARL L(OCK), b Marfa, Tex, Jan 7, 28; m 50; c 3. CIVIL & HYDRAULIC ENGINEERING. *Educ:* Univ Nebr, BSc, 53; Univ Idaho, MSc, 67. *Prof Exp:* Hydraul engr, Soil Conserv Serv, 53-55, HYDRAUL ENGR, AGR RES SERV, USDA, 55- *Mem:* Am Soc Agr Engrs; Soil Conserv Soc Am; Soc Range Mgt. *Res:* Hydrologic performance of small watersheds; problems of precipitation measurement; water supply forecasting; sediment transport. *Mailing Add:* Agr Res Serv-USDA PO Box 1109 Sidney MT 59270

NEFF, HERBERT PRESTON, JR, b Knoxville, Tenn, Jan 1, 30; m 53; c 4. ELECTRICAL ENGINEERING. *Educ:* Univ Tenn, Knoxville, BS, 53, MS, 56; Auburn Univ, PhD(elec eng), 67. *Prof Exp:* Jr engr, Univ Tenn, Knoxville, 52-56, asst prof elec eng, 56-65; asst, Auburn Univ, 65-66; ASSOC PROF ELEC ENG, UNIV TENN, KNOXVILLE, 66- *Concurrent Pos:* Consult, Auburn Univ, 66-68, Oak Ridge Nat Labs, 69- & Goddard Space Flight Ctr, NASA, 72- *Mem:* Inst Elec & Electronics Engrs. *Res:* Electromagnetic fields; antennas and propagation. *Mailing Add:* Dept of Elec Eng Univ of Tenn Knoxville TN 37916

NEFF, JOHN DAVID, b Cedar Rapids, Iowa, July 30, 26; m 52. MATHEMATICS. *Educ:* Marquette Univ, BNS, 46; Coe Col, BA, 49; Kans State Univ, MS, 51; Univ Fla, PhD(math), 56. *Prof Exp:* Mem tech staff, Bell Tel Labs, NY, 52-53; instr math, Univ Fla, 53-55; from instr to asst prof, Case Inst Technol, 56-61; from asst prof to assoc prof, 61-72, actg dir math, 70-72, dir, 72-78, PROF MATH, GA INST TECHNOL, 72- *Mem:* Am Math Soc; Math Asn Am; Inst Math Statist; Soc Indust & Appl Math; Nat Coun Teachers Math. *Res:* Differential equations; probability. *Mailing Add:* Sch of Math Ga Inst of Technol Atlanta GA 30332

NEFF, JOHN S, b Milwaukee, Wis, Nov 24, 34; m 60; c 2. ASTRONOMY, ASTROPHYSICS. *Educ:* Univ Wis, BS, 57, MS, 58, PhD(astron), 61. *Prof Exp:* Res assoc, Yerkes Observ, Chicago, 61-64; asst prof, 64-68, ASSOC PROF ASTRON, UNIV IOWA, 68- *Concurrent Pos:* NSF res grant, 65-67. *Mem:* Am Astron Soc; fel Royal Astron Soc; Int Astron Union. *Res:* Stellar photometry and spectrophotometry; planetary spectrophotometry; design of astronomical instruments; stellar classification and investigation of galactic structure. *Mailing Add:* Dept of Physics & Astron Univ of Iowa 704 Physics Bldg Iowa City IA 52240

NEFF, LAURENCE D, b Santa Ana, Calif, Jan 11, 38; m 60; c 2. PHYSICAL CHEMISTRY. *Educ:* John Brown Univ, BA, 59; Univ Ark, MS, 62, PhD(phys chem), 64. *Prof Exp:* Sr chemist, NAm Aviation, Inc, 64; res chemist, Beckman Instruments, Inc, 64-66; res specialist mat sci, NAm Rockwell Corp, 66-68; from asst prof to assoc prof chem, ETex State Univ, 68-78, prof, 78-81; PROJ CHEMIST, TEXACO, USA, 81- *Mem:* AAAS; Am Chem Soc. *Res:* Heterogeneous catalysis; application of infrared spectroscopy to gas-solid phase interactions. *Mailing Add:* Texaco Res & Tech Dept PO Box 1608 Port Arthur TX 77640

NEFF, LOREN LEE, b Seattle, Wash, Sept 14, 18; m 40; c 1. CHEMISTRY. *Educ:* Univ Wash, Seattle, BS, 39, PhD(chem), 43. *Prof Exp:* Asst chem, Univ Wash, Seattle, 39-43; supvr res dept, Union Oil Co Calif, 43-81; RETIRED. *Mem:* Am Chem Soc. *Res:* Lubricating oil additives; lubricating oils; activity of colloidal electrolytes; determination of the thermodynamic activity of 1-dodecane sulfonic acid in aqueous solutions at forty degrees Centigrade by electromotive force measurements; petroleum industry corrosion; chemicals. *Mailing Add:* 425 W Brookdale Dr Fullerton CA 92632

NEFF, MARY MUSKOFF, b Jacksonville, Fla, Jan 20, 30; m 52. MATHEMATICS. *Educ:* Purdue Univ, BS, 51, MS, 52; Univ Fla, PhD(math), 56. *Prof Exp:* Instr math, Univ Fla, 55-56; from instr to asst prof, John Carroll Univ, 56-61; asst prof, 61-68, ASSOC PROF MATH, EMORY UNIV, 68- *Mem:* Math Asn Am; Am Math Soc. *Res:* Identities in lattices; groups given by generators and relations; near-rings. *Mailing Add:* Dept of Math Emory Univ Atlanta GA 30322

NEFF, RAYMOND KENNETH, b New York, NY, May 1, 42; m 69. BIOMETRICS. *Educ:* Dartmouth Col, AB, 64; Harvard Univ, SM, 67, ScD, 77. *Prof Exp:* Lectr biostatist, Harvard Univ, 74-78 & 81-82, asst prof, 78-81; ASSOC PROF BIOSTATIST, DARTMOUTH COL, 82- *Concurrent Pos:* Pres, New Eng Regional Comput, 73-76; dir sci comput, Sidney Farber Cancer Inst, Boston, 79-82, Health Sci Comput Facil, Harvard Univ, 71-82; consult, Nat Toxicol Prog, NIH, 80-81; dir acad comput, Dartmouth Col, 82- *Mem:* Am Public Health Asn; Asn Comput Mach; Biomet Soc; AAAS; Am Statist Asn. *Res:* Multivariate analysis of epidemiologic data; statistical and interactive computing. *Mailing Add:* Off Acad Comput Kiewit Comput Ctr Dartmouth Col Hanover NH 03755

NEFF, RICHARD D, b Elmo, Mo, Oct 7, 32; m 54; c 4. HEALTH PHYSICS. *Educ:* Northwest Mo State Col, BS, 57; Univ Kans, MS, 59; Univ Calif, Los Angeles, PhD(biophys), 64; Am Bd Health Physics, cert, 73. *Prof Exp:* Res biophysicist, Lab Nuclear Med & Radiation Biol, Univ Calif, Los Angeles, 59; health physicist, Atomics Int, 59-60; radiation physicist, Tison-Pease Inc, 60-61; asst prof radiol health, Mich State Univ, 64-66; from asst prof to assoc prof, 66-73, PROF NUCLEAR ENG, TEX A&M UNIV, 73-, RADIOL SAFETY OFFICER, 66- *Mem:* AAAS; Health Physics Soc; Am Nuclear Soc. *Res:* Mammalian radiation biology; environmental radioactivity. *Mailing Add:* Dept Nuclear Eng Tex A&M Univ College Station TX 77843

NEFF, RICHMOND C(LARK), b DeKalb, Ill, July 30, 23; m 44; c 4. ENGINEERING MECHANICS. *Educ:* Purdue Univ, BS, 43, MS, 48, PhD(eng mech), 54. *Prof Exp:* Instr eng mech, Purdue Univ, 47-52; from asst prof to assoc prof civil eng, 52-58, PROF CIVIL ENG, UNIV ARIZ, 58- *Mem:* Soc Exp Stress Anal; Am Soc Eng Educ. *Res:* Photoelastic analysis of structural and machine components; numerical solutions of elasticity and plasticity equations. *Mailing Add:* Dept of Civil Eng Univ of Ariz Tucson AZ 85721

NEFF, ROBERT JACK, b Kansas City, Mo, Jan 22, 21; m 48; c 3. BIOLOGY, PHYSIOLOGY. *Educ:* Univ Mo, AB, 42, MA, 48, PhD(zool), 51. *Prof Exp:* Instr anat, Sch Med, Johns Hopkins Univ, 51-52; from asst prof to assoc prof biol, 52-64, ASSOC PROF MOLECULAR BIOL, VANDERBILT UNIV, 64- *Concurrent Pos:* Vis assoc prof, Univ Calif, 57-58; NIH spec fel, Biol Inst, Carlsberg Found, Copenhagen, 65-66. *Mem:* AAAS; Soc Protozool; Am Soc Cell Biol; NY Acad Sci. *Res:* Cellular physiology; nuclear-cytoplasmic control mechanisms; cellular osmoregulation; macromolecular organization of protoplasm; cytodifferentiation; encystment; cell growth-division cycle. *Mailing Add:* Dept of Molecular Biol Vanderbilt Univ Nashville TX 37235

NEFF, STUART EDMUND, b Louisville, Ky, Oct 3, 26; m 48; c 3. BIOLOGY. *Educ:* Univ Louisville, BS, 54; Cornell Univ, PhD(limnol), 60. *Prof Exp:* Asst limnol, Cornell Univ, 54-59, instr, 60; from asst prof to assoc prof, Va Polytech Inst, 60-68; assoc res prof, 68-72, RES PROF BIOL, WATER RESOURCES LAB, UNIV LOUISVILLE, 72- *Mem:* Soc Syst Zool; Entom Soc Am; Royal Entom Soc London. *Res:* Hydrobiology; immature stages of aquatic insects; taxonomy and biology of acalyptrate Diptera; biology of Chironomidae. *Mailing Add:* Water Resources Lab Univ of Louisville Louisville KY 40208

NEFF, THOMAS O'NEIL, b Jacksonville, Fla, Nov 19, 09; m 39; c 3. ENGINEERING MECHANICS. *Educ:* Univ Fla, BSEE, 32, MSE, 52, CE, 56. *Prof Exp:* Inspector, State Rd Dept, Fla, 32-38; party chief, State Hwy Dept Ga, 38-39; dist engr, Works Projs Admin, Fla, 39-41; sect head, US Corps Engrs, 41-43, assoc engr, Dist Off, 45-46; resident engr, G S Broadway, Consult Engrs, 43-44; prof eng mech, 46-67, prof mech eng, 67-76, EMER ASSOC PROF MECH ENG, UNIV FLA, 76-; PRES, NEFF & ASSOCS, INC, 80- *Mem:* Fel Am Soc Civil Engrs. *Res:* Structural design and analysis. *Mailing Add:* 1708 SW 35th Pl Gainesville FL 32608

NEFF, THOMAS RODNEY, b Salt Lake City, Utah, Sept 22, 37; m 70. GEOLOGY. *Educ:* Univ Utah, BS, 60, MS, 63; Stanford Univ, PhD(geol), 69. *Prof Exp:* Field asst, Utah Geol & Mineral Surv, 59-60 & Humble Oil & Ref Co, 63; ASST PROF GEOL, WEBER STATE COL, 68- *Concurrent Pos:* Vis res prof, Mineral-Geol Mus, Oslo, Norway, 73-74. *Mem:* Geol Soc Am; Sigma Xi. *Res:* Structural geology; petrography; petrology of Norwegian granitic rocks. *Mailing Add:* Dept of Geol & Geog Weber State Col Ogden UT 84403

NEFF, VERNON DUANE, b Rochester, NY, Sept 16, 32; m 55; c 4. PHYSICAL CHEMISTRY. *Educ:* Syracuse Univ, BS, 53, PhD(phys chem), 60. *Prof Exp:* Spectroscopist, Gen Tire & Rubber Co, 59-61; from asst prof to assoc prof, 61-81, PROF PHYS CHEM, KENT STATE UNIV, 81- *Concurrent Pos:* Consult, Gen Tire & Rubber Co, 61- *Mem:* Am Chem Soc; Am Phys Soc. *Res:* Infrared spectroscopy; quantum chemistry. *Mailing Add:* Dept of Chem Kent State Univ Kent OH 44242

NEFF, WILLIAM DAVID, b Portland, Ore, Mar 25, 45; div; c 2. ATMOSPHERIC PHYSICS. *Educ:* Lewis & Clark Col, BA, 67; Univ Wash, MS, 68; Univ Colo, PhD, 80. *Prof Exp:* Commissioned officer, 68-73, physics scientist, 73-80, SUPVRY PHYSICIST, ATMOSPHERIC STUDIES, NAT OCEANIC & ATMOSPHERIC ADMIN, 81- *Mem:* Am Meteorol Soc. *Res:* Applications of acoustic remote sensing techniques to boundary layer meteorology, particularly relating to air quality meteorology in complex terrain. *Mailing Add:* Wave Propagation Lab R45X7 Nat Oceanic & Atmospheric Admin Boulder CO 80302

NEFF, WILLIAM DUWAYNE, b Lomax, Ill, Oct 27, 12; m 37; c 2. NEUROSCIENCES. *Educ:* Univ Ill, AB, 36; Univ Rochester, PhD(psychol), 40. *Prof Exp:* Res assoc psychol, Swarthmore Col, 40-42; from asst prof to prof, Univ Chicago, 46-59, psychol & physiol, 59-61; dir, Lab Physiol Psychol, Bolt, Beranek, Newman, Inc, Mass, 61-63; prof psychol, 63-64, dir, Ctr Neural Sci, 65-68, RES PROF, IND UNIV, BLOOMINGTON, 64- *Concurrent Pos:* Consult, Nat Acad Sci, Nat Res Coun, NSF, NIH, & NASA; mem, Otolaryngol Res Group, Int Brain Res Orgn & sci liaison off, London Br, Off Naval Res, 53-54. *Honors & Awards:* Hearing Res Award, Beltone Inst. *Mem:* Nat Acad Sci; fel AAAS; fel Am Physiol Soc; fel Acoust Soc Am; Soc Exp Psychol (secy-treas, 52-59). *Res:* Brain functions; neural mechanisms of sensory discrimination; physiological acoustics. *Mailing Add:* Ctr for Neural Sci Ind Univ Bloomington IN 47401

NEFF, WILLIAM H, b May 13, 31; US citizen; m 50; c 6. ZOOLOGY, PHYSIOLOGY. *Educ:* Pa State Univ, BS, 56, MS, 59, PhD(zool), 66. *Prof Exp:* Instr anat & physiol, 59-65, asst prof zool, 66-75, ASSOC PROF BIOL, PA STATE UNIV, 75-, COORDR BIOL SCI, COMMONWEALTH CAMPUSES, 66- *Res:* Adaptation to environmental stress; gross metabolic and electrolyte response during cold acclimation; histological changes in reproductive tract of season breeding mammals. *Mailing Add:* Dept of Biol Pa State Univ University Park PA 16802

NEFF, WILLIAM MEDINA, b San Francisco, Calif, Oct 27, 29; m 52; c 4. EMBRYOLOGY. *Educ:* Stanford Univ, AB, 51, PhD(biol sci, statist), 58. *Prof Exp:* From instr to assoc prof biol, Knox Col, 56-68; assoc prof, Chico State Col, 68-70; assoc prof embryol, 70-81, ASSOC PROF BIOL SCI & OCEANOG, CITY COL SAN FRANCISCO, 81- *Mem:* Western Soc Naturalists; Nat Asn Underwater Instrs; Sigma Xi. *Res:* Development of the skin; cells of the dermis. *Mailing Add:* Dept of Biol City Col of San Francisco San Francisco CA 94112

NEFT, NIVARD, b Shooks, Minn, Apr 1, 22. BIOCHEMISTRY, MEDICAL TECHNOLOGY. *Educ:* Col St Benedict, BS, 46; St Cloud Univ, MT, 52; Utah State Univ, PhD(biochem), 72. *Prof Exp:* Sci instr, Cathedral High Sch, St Cloud, 48-51; med technologist, St Cloud Hosp, 52-56 & Clinica Font Martelo, Humacao, PR, 56-58; chief med technologist & teaching supvr, St Benedict's Hosp, Ogden, 59-64; sci instr anat, physiol & chem, St Benedict's Sch Nursing, 64-68; assoc prof integrated sci core, Sch Allied Health, Weber State Col, 73-77; ASSOC PROF ORG & BIOCHEM, COL ST BENEDICT, 77- *Mem:* AAAS; affil mem Am Soc Clin Pathologists; Am Chem Soc. *Res:* Chemistry of antimycin A and antimicrobial agents; integrated science core curriculum. *Mailing Add:* Dept of Chem Col of St Benedict St Joseph MN 56374

NEGELE, JOHN WILLIAM, b Cleveland, Ohio, Apr 18, 44; m 67. THEORETICAL PHYSICS. *Educ:* Purdue Univ, Lafayette, BS, 65; Cornell Univ, PhD(theoret physics), 69. *Prof Exp:* NATO fel & vis physicist, Niels Bohr Inst, Copenhagen, Denmark, 69-70; vis asst prof, 70-71, asst prof, 71-72, assoc prof, 72-79, PROF PHYSICS, MASS INST TECHNOL, 79- *Concurrent Pos:* Alfred P Sloan Foun res fel, 72; consult, Los Alamos Sci Lab, 73, Argonne Nat Lab, 77 & Lawrence Livermore Lab, 77; mem, Brookhaven Nat Lab, Tandem Prog Adv Comt, 73-77, co-ed, Advan Nuclear Physics, 77-; fel, Japan Soc Prom Sci. *Mem:* Am Phys Soc. *Res:* Theoretical nuclear physics; many-body theory; microscopic theory of nuclear structure. *Mailing Add:* Rm 6-302 Dept Physics Mass Inst Technol Cambridge MA 02139

NEGGERS, JOSEPH, b Amsterdam, Netherlands, Jan 10, 40; US citizen; m 65. MATHEMATICS. *Educ:* Fla State Univ, BS, 59, MS, 60, PhD(math), 63. *Prof Exp:* Asst prof math, Fla State Univ, 63-64; sci asst math, Univ Amsterdam, 64-65; lectr pure math, King's Col, London, 65-66; vis assoc prof, Univ PR, 66-67; asst prof, 67-68, ASSOC PROF MATH, UNIV ALA, 68- *Mem:* Am Math Soc. *Res:* Algebra; derivations and automorphisms on local-rings, associated structures; partially ordered sets. *Mailing Add:* Dept of Math Univ of Ala University AL 35486

NEGIN, MICHAEL, b Tampa, Fla, Dec 19, 42; m 63; c 3. ELECTRICAL ENGINEERING, BIOMEDICAL ENGINEERING. *Educ:* Univ Fla, BEE, 64, MSE, 65, PhD(elec eng), 68; Temple Univ, MS, 75. *Prof Exp:* Asst prof, 68-71, ASSOC PROF ELEC ENG, DREXEL UNIV, 71- *Concurrent Pos:* Nat Inst Gen Med Sci spec fel, 72-74. *Mem:* AAAS; Sigma Xi; Inst Elec & Electronics Engrs. *Res:* Early detection of breast cancer by computerized thermography and radiography; sleep electroencephalographic analysis by computer; digital simulation of biosystems; electromyographic and electroencephalographic studies and the relationship between these bioelectric events; dental radiography by digital computer. *Mailing Add:* Biomed Eng & Sci Prog Drexel Univ Philadelphia PA 19104

NEGISHI, EI-ICHI, b Shinkyo, Repub China, July 14, 35; Japanese citizen; m 60; c 2. ORGANIC CHEMISTRY, ORGANOMETALLIC CHEMISTRY. *Educ:* Univ Tokyo, BE, 58; Univ Pa, PhD(chem), 63. *Prof Exp:* Res chemist, Teijin Ltd, 58-66; res assoc, Purdue Univ, 66-72; asst prof, Syracuse Univ, 72-76, assoc prof, 76-79; PROF, PURDUE UNIV, 79- *Mem:* Am Chem Soc; Sigma Xi. *Res:* Organic and organometallic chemistry; development of new selective synthetic methods and applications to the synthesis of natural products of biological and medicinal interest. *Mailing Add:* Dept Chem Purdue Univ West Lafayette IN 47907

NEGUS, NORMAN CURTISS, b Portland, Ore, Sept 20, 26; m 48; c 4. ZOOLOGY. *Educ:* Miami Univ, BA, 48, MA, 50; Ohio State Univ, PhD(zool), 56. *Prof Exp:* Asst zool, Miami Univ, 48-50; res fel, Ohio State Univ, 51-55; from instr to prof, Tulane Univ, 55-70; prof zool, 70-76, PROF BIOL, UNIV UTAH, 76- *Concurrent Pos:* Vis investr, SEATO Med Res Lab, Thailand, 65-66. *Mem:* Am Soc Mammalogists; Ecol Soc Am; Am Soc Zoologists; Am Asn Anatomists; Wildlife Soc. *Res:* Mammalian population dynamics; reproductive physiology; molting in mammals; orientation and movements of mammals. *Mailing Add:* Dept of Biol Univ of Utah Salt Lake City UT 84112

NEHARI, ZEEV, mathematics, deceased

NEHER, CLARENCE M, b Twin Falls, Idaho, May 14, 16; m 39; c 4. ORGANIC CHEMISTRY. *Educ:* Manchester Col, AB, 37; Purdue Univ, MS, 39, PhD(chem), 41. *Prof Exp:* Asst, Purdue Univ, 37-40; res chemist, Ethyl Corp, 41-45, res supvr, 45-51, asst dir res & develop labs, 51-54, proj mgr, 54-57, dir com develop, 57-63, spec assignment, 63-64, vpres & gen mgr, Plastics Div, 64-69, sr vpres, 69-81, mem bd dirs, 70-81; RETIRED. *Mem:* Mfg Chem Asn; Am Chem Soc; Chem Mkt Res Asn; Com Chem Develop Asn; Soc Plastics Indust. *Res:* Chlorination; polymers; chlorination of aliphatics and aromatics; cracking of chlorocarbons; chlorination methane and ethane. *Mailing Add:* 861 Delgado Dr Baton Rouge LA 70808

NEHER, DAVID DANIEL, b McCune, Kans, July 12, 23; m 50; c 3. SOILS. *Educ:* Kans State Univ, BS, 46, MS, 48; Utah State Univ, PhD(soil sci), 59. *Prof Exp:* Instr soils, Kans State Univ, 48-49; from asst prof to assoc prof, 49-65, PROF SOILS, TEX A&I UNIV, 65- *Mem:* Soil Sci Soc Am; Am Soc Agron; Crop Sci Soc Am; Soil Conserv Soc Am. *Mailing Add:* Col of Agr PO Box 156 Tex A&I Univ Kingsville TX 78363

NEHER, DEAN ROYCE, b Enterprise, Kans, Feb 10, 29; m 53; c 4. PHYSICS, COMPUTER SCIENCE. *Educ:* McPherson Col, BS, 54; Univ Kans, MS, 59, PhD(physics), 64. *Prof Exp:* From asst prof to assoc prof, 61-68, PROF PHYSICS, BRIDGEWATER COL, 68-, DIR COMPUT CTR, 70- *Mem:* Am Asn Physics Teachers. *Res:* Nuclear physics; use of computers in teaching. *Mailing Add:* 210 E College St Bridgewater VA 22812

NEHER, GEORGE MARTIN, b Chicago, Ill, June 4, 21; m 45. VETERINARY SCIENCE. *Educ:* Purdue Univ, BS, 47, MS, 50, PhD(endocrinol), 53, DVM, 67. *Prof Exp:* From asst prof to assoc prof vet sci, 54-66, PROF VET PHYSIOL & PHARMACOL, SCH VET SCI & MED, PURDUE UNIV, WEST LAFAYETTE, 66- *Mem:* Assoc Am Vet Radiol Soc; assoc Am Rheumatism Asn; Conf Res Workers Animal Dis; Am Vet Med Asn; Soc Study Reproduction. *Res:* Histochemistry and pathogenesis of the arthritides of animals; experimental hypopituitarism in swine; physiologic effects of noise. *Mailing Add:* Dept of Physiol & Pharmacol Purdue Univ Sch Vet Sci & Med West Lafayette IN 47906

NEHER, LELAND K, b Porterville, Calif, Dec 2, 20; m 43; c 7. NUCLEAR PHYSICS. *Educ:* Pomona Col, BA, 43; Univ Calif, PhD(physics), 53. *Prof Exp:* MEM STAFF, LOS ALAMOS NAT LAB, 53- *Mem:* AAAS; Am Phys Soc. *Res:* Nuclear science. *Mailing Add:* 205 Rio Bravo W R Los Alamos NM 87544

NEHER, MAYNARD BRUCE, b Greenville, Ohio, Apr 2, 23; m 44; c 3. CHEMISTRY. *Educ:* Manchester Col, AB, 44; Purdue Univ, PhD(chem), 47. *Prof Exp:* Asst chem, Purdue Univ, 44-47; asst prof, Univ Ohio, 47-51; res chemist, 51-56, asst div chief, 56-71, res chemist, 71-78, QUAL ASSURANCE COORDR CHEM DEPT, COLUMBUS DIV, BATTELLE MEM INST, 78- *Mem:* Am Chem Soc; AAAS. *Res:* Nitroparaffin derivatives as insecticidal compounds; aldol condensation of fluoroform with acetone; preparation of selected diaryl nitroalkanes and their derivatives; leather treatments; application of computer techniques in organic analysis; structural organic chemistry; mass spectroscopy; analytical quality control and quality assurance; gas-liquid chromatography. *Mailing Add:* 3911 Bickley Pl Columbus OH 43220

NEHER, ROBERT TROSTLE, b Mt Morris, Ill, Nov 1, 30; m 54; c 3. PLANT TAXONOMY, ENVIRONMENTAL BIOLOGY. *Educ:* Manchester Col, BS, 53; Univ Ind, MAT, 55, PhD(bot), 66; Bethany Sem, MRE, 57. *Prof Exp:* From asst prof to assoc prof, 57-67, chmn dept, 67-78, PROF BIOL, LA VERNE COL, 67-, CHMN NATURAL SCI DIV, 72- *Concurrent Pos:* NSF fac fel, 62-63; mem environ qual comn, City of La Verne, 72-76, mem city coun, 76-; aquaculture consult, Am/China, 81. *Mem:* AAAS; Sigma Xi; Am Soc Plant Taxon. *Res:* Systematic studies in Tagetes, stressing chemotaxonomy and cytogenetics; study and development of environmental control models; development of multi-stage aquaculture systems. *Mailing Add:* Dept of Biol La Verne Col 1950 Third St La Verne CA 91750

NEHLS, JAMES WARWICK, b Memphis, Tenn, June 30, 26; m 53; c 3. INORGANIC CHEMISTRY. *Educ:* Univ Tenn, BS, 48, MS, 49, PhD(chem), 52. *Prof Exp:* Asst chem, Univ Tenn, 49-52; chemist, E I du Pont de Nemours & Co Tenn, 52, Ind, 52-53, & SC, 53-60; chemist, Oak Ridge Opers, US Atomic Energy Comn, 60-65, asst to dir, Res & Develop Div, 65-73; chemist, Res & Tech Support Div, 73-78, MGR ISOTOPE PROD & DISTRIBUTION, US DEPT ENERGY, 81- *Mem:* AAAS; Am Chem Soc. *Res:* Transplutonium elements; radioisotope production; exchange reactions; radiochemistry. *Mailing Add:* 121 Balboa Circle Oak Ridge TN 37830

NEHLSEN, WILLA CLARK, plant development, see previous edition

NEI, MASATOSHI, b Miyazaki, Japan, Jan 2, 31; m 63; c 2. POPULATION GENETICS, EVOLUTION. *Educ:* Miyazaki Univ, BS, 53; Kyoto Univ, MS, 55, PhD(genetics), 59. *Hon Degrees:* DSc, Kyushu Univ, 77- *Prof Exp:* Instr, Kyoto Univ, 58-62; geneticist, Nat Inst Radiol Sci, Japan, 62-64, chief geneticist, 65, head lab, 65-69; from assoc prof to prof, Brown Univ, 69-72; actg dir, 78-80, PROF POP GENETICS, CTR DEMOG & POP GENETICS, UNIV TEX, HOUSTON, 72- *Mem:* AAAS; Am Soc Naturalists; Am Soc Human Genetics; Soc Study Evolution; Genetics Soc Am. *Res:* Population dynamics of mutant genes; genetic structure of populations; molecular evolution. *Mailing Add:* Ctr for Demog & Pop Genetics Univ Tex PO Box 20334 Houston TX 77030

NEIBLING, WILLIAM HOWARD, b Highland, Kans, Mar 6, 52; m 77; c 2. EROSION MECHANICS, SEDIMENT TRANSPORT. *Educ:* Kans State Univ, BS, 74, MS, 76; Purdue Univ, PhD(agr eng), 83. *Prof Exp:* AGR ENGR, ARG RES SERV, USDA, 76- *Mem:* Am Soc Agr Engrs; Soil Conservation Soc Am; Sigma Xi. *Res:* Erosion mechanics; sediment transport; identify variables important in the erosion/deposition process and quantify relationships relating these variables to prediction of the detachment of soil by raindrop impact and overland flow and subsequent transport or deposition of sediment. *Mailing Add:* USDA Nat Sci Erosion Lab Purdue Univ W Lafayette IN 47907

NEIBURGER, MORRIS, b Hazleton, Pa, Dec 5, 10; m 32, 76; c 1. METEOROLOGY, CLOUD PHYSICS. *Educ:* Univ Chicago, BS, 36, PhD(meteorol), 45. *Prof Exp:* Observer meteorol, US Weather Bur, Ill, 30-38, from jr meteorologist to asst meteorologist, Washington, DC, 39-40; instr meteorol, Mass Inst Technol, 40-41; from instr to prof, 41-78, chmn dept, 56-62, EMER PROF METEOROL, UNIV CALIF, LOS ANGELES, 78- *Concurrent Pos:* Instr grad sch, USDA, 39-40; sr meteorologist, Air Pollution Found, 54-56; trustee, Univ Corp Atmospheric Res, Univ Calif, Los Angeles, 59-67, members' rep, 67-76; consult, World Meteorol Orgn, Los Angeles County Air Pollution Control Dist & other orgns. *Honors & Awards:* Meisinger Award, Am Meteorol Soc, 46. *Mem:* Fel AAAS; Am Meteorol Soc (pres, 62-64); Am Geophys Union; for mem Royal Meteorol Soc. *Res:* Physics of clouds; air pollution; synoptic meteorology; upper wind dynamics and temperature forecasting; atmospheric radiaton; evaporation. *Mailing Add:* 1510 Oak Creek Dr (Apt 403) Palo Alto CA 94304

NEIDELL, NORMAN SAMSON, b New York, NY, Mar 11, 39; m 63; c 5. GEOPHYSICS. *Educ:* NY Univ, BA, 59; Univ London, DIC, 61; Cambridge Univ, PhD(geod, geophys), 64. *Prof Exp:* Res geophysicist, Gulf Res & Develop Co, 64-68; geophys researcher, Seismic Comput Corp, 68-72; CHMN & PRES, N S NEIDELL & ASSOCS, CONSULT, 73-; ASSOC PROF, UNIV HOUSTON, 80- *Concurrent Pos:* Consult & dir, Geoquest Int, Inc, 73-80; assoc ed marine opers, Geophysics, 76-80; exec vpres, founder & dir, Zenith Explor Co, Inc, 77-; managing founder & partner, Delphian Signals Ltd, 80- *Honors & Awards:* Best Presentation Award, Soc Explor Geophysicists, 74. *Mem:* Soc Explor Geophysicists; Europ Asn Explor Geophysicists; Soc Photo-optical Instrument Engrs. *Res:* Signal analysis and computer processing in the earth sciences; digital computer applications in geology and geophysics; oil and gas explorations. *Mailing Add:* 13054 Taylorcrest Houston TX 77079

NEIDERHISER, DEWEY HAROLD, b Masontown, Pa, Jan 22, 35. BIOCHEMISTRY. *Educ:* Duquesne Univ, BS, 56; Univ Pittsburgh, MS, 59; Univ Wis, PhD(biochem), 63. *Prof Exp:* ASST PROF BIOCHEM & RES CHEMIST, VET ADMIN MED CTR, SCH MED, CASE WESTERN RESERVE UNIV, 62- *Mem:* Res Soc Alcoholism; AAAS. *Res:* Biochemistry of human cholesterol gallstone formation; alcoholism. *Mailing Add:* Res Dept Vet Admin Med Ctr Cleveland OH 44106

NEIDERS, MIRDZA ERIKA, b Riga, Latvia, Aug 21, 33; US citizen; div; c 2. ORAL PATHOLOGY, IMMUNOLOGY. *Educ:* Univ Mich, DDS, 58; Univ Chicago, MS, 61; State Univ NY Buffalo, cert periodont, 74. *Prof Exp:* Instr dent, Zoller Dent Clin, Univ Chicago, 61-62; from asst prof to assoc prof oral path, 62-70, PROF ORAL PATH, SCH DENT, STATE UNIV NY BUFFALO, 70- *Concurrent Pos:* Consult oral path, Vet Admirn Hosp, 65-73; res assoc, Roswell Park Mem Inst, 63-72; counr, Am Acad Oral Path, 73-76; guest scientist immunol, NIH, 74-77, mem OBMS sect, NIH grant review bd, 77-81. *Mem:* Am Acad Oral Path; Am Acad Periodont; Am Dent Asn; Int Asn Dent Res; Sigma Xi. *Res:* Immunoglobulin systesis; cell detachment; in vitro and in vivo studies on bone resorption; periodontal disease; cellular immunology. *Mailing Add:* 246 Farber Hall Sch of Dent State Univ NY Buffalo NY 14214

NEIDHARDT, FREDERICK CARL, b Philadelphia, Pa, May 12, 31; m 56, 77; c 1. MICROBIOLOGY, BIOCHEMISTRY. *Educ:* Kenyon Col, BA, 52; Harvard Univ, PhD(bact), 56. *Prof Exp:* Am Cancer Soc res fel, Inst Pasteur, Paris, 56-57; Harold C Ernst res fel, Harvard Med Sch, 57-58, instr bact & immunol, 58-59, assoc, 59-61; from assoc prof biol sci to prof & assoc head dept, Purdue Univ, 61-70; PROF MICROBIOL & CHMN DEPT, MED SCH, UNIV MICH, ANN ARBOR, 70- *Concurrent Pos:* Mem microbial chem study sect, NIH, 65-69; NSF sr fels, Univ Inst Microbiol, Copenhagen, 68-69; mem comn scholars, Ill Bd Higher Educ, 73-80; mem microbiol comt, Nat Bd Med Examr, 75-80; sr US scientist award, Alexander Von Humboldt, Fed Rep Ger, 79. *Honors & Awards:* Award Bact & Immunol, Eli Lilly & Co, 66. *Mem:* AAAS; Am Soc Microbiol; Am Soc Biol Chemists; Soc Gen Physiol; NY Acad Sci. *Res:* Regulation of gene expression in bacteria; regulation of bacterial metabolism; regulation of macromolecule synthesis in bacteria; genetics; molecular biology. *Mailing Add:* Dept Microbiol 6643 Med Sci II Univ of Mich Med Sch Ann Arbor MI 48109

NEIDHARDT, WALTER JIM, b Paterson, NJ, June 19, 34; m 62; c 2. LOW TEMPERATURE PHYSICS, QUANTUM PHYSICS. *Educ:* Stevens Inst Technol, ME, 56, MS, 58, PhD(physics), 62. *Prof Exp:* Instr, Newark Col Eng, 62-63, asst prof, 63-67, ASSOC PROF PHYSICS, NJ INST TECHNOL, 67- *Concurrent Pos:* Consult ed, J Am Sci Affil, 68- *Mem:* Am

Phys Soc; Am Inst Physics Teachers; fel Am Sci Affil; Sigma Xi; NY Acad Sci. *Res:* Application of quantum physics to low temperature phenomena; examination of the nature of science, its proper domains and limits; emphasis on those integrative concepts that are common to science, philosophy and religion. *Mailing Add:* 146 Park Ave Randolph NJ 07869

NEIDIG, DONALD FOSTER, b Harrisburg, Pa, Aug 6, 44; m 79. ASTRONOMY. *Educ:* Dickinson Col, BS, 66; Pa State Univ, MS, 68, PhD(astron), 76. *Prof Exp:* Fac mem sci, East Pennsboro High Sch, Pa, 68-69; instr math & physics, Alliance Col, 71-73; ASTROPHYSICIST SOLAR PHYSICS, AIR FROCE GEOPHYS LAB, 76- *Concurrent Pos:* Partic, Skylab Solar Flare Workshops, NASA & NSF, 76-77. *Mem:* Am Astron Soc; Sigma Xi. *Res:* Physics of solar flares; solar activity forecasting. *Mailing Add:* Sacramento Peak Observ Sunspot NM 88349

NEIDIG, HOWARD ANTHONY, b Lemoyne, Pa, Jan 25, 23; m 46, 72; c 4. PHYSICAL CHEMISTRY, ORGANIC CHEMISTRY. *Educ:* Lebanon Valley Col, BS, 43; Univ Del, MS, 46, PhD(chem), 48. *Prof Exp:* Instr chem, Univ Del, 46-48; from asst prof to assoc prof, 48-59, HEAD DEPT, LEBANON VALLEY COL, 51-, PROF CHEM, 59- *Concurrent Pos:* Prog ed, Modular Lab Prog Chem, 70- *Mem:* AAAS; Am Chem Soc; Am Inst Chemists; Nat Sci Teachers Asn. *Res:* Reaction mechanism; molecular rearrangements; mechanism of oxidation and reduction reactions in organic chemistry. *Mailing Add:* Dept of Chem Lebanon Valley Col Annville PA 17003

NEIDLE, ENID ANNE, b New York, NY, Apr 6, 24; m 49; c 2. PHARMACOLOGY, PHYSIOLOGY. *Educ:* Vassar Col, AB, 44; Columbia Univ, PhD(physiol), 49. *Prof Exp:* Assoc pharmacol, Jefferson Med Col, 49-50; instr biol, Brooklyn Col, 50-54; from instr to prof physiol & pharmacol, 55-78, PROF PHARMACOGY & CHMN, COL DENT & GRAD FAC ARTS & SCI, NY UNIV, 78- *Concurrent Pos:* USPHS grant, 60. *Mem:* AAAS; Am Asn Dent Schs; Sigma Xi; Am Physiol Soc; Harvey Soc. *Res:* Vasomotor innervation of orofacial structures; circulation in the dental pulp; contribution of the mandibular nerve to growth, development and vasomotion in orofacial structures. *Mailing Add:* NY Univ Col of Dent 421 First Ave New York NY 10010

NEIDLEMAN, SAUL L, b New York, NY, Oct 3, 29; m 56; c 4. BIOCHEMISTRY. *Educ:* Mass Inst Technol, MS, 52; Univ Ariz, PhD(biochem), 59. *Prof Exp:* Biophysicist, Peter Bent Brigham Hosp, Boston, 53-54; res assoc agr biochem, Univ Ariz, 58-59; sr res microbiologist, Squibb Inst Med Res Div, Olin Corp, 59-67, res assoc, 67-69, sect head microbial biochem, 69-72; sr scientist, 73-80, DEPT DIR, NEW VENTURES RES, CETUS CORP, 80- *Mem:* NY Acad Sci; Am Soc Microbiol; Soc Indust Microbiol; Am Chem Soc. *Res:* Antibiotic biosynthesis; microbial metabolism; enzyme reactions; oil microbiology. *Mailing Add:* Cetus Corp 600 Bancroft Way Berkeley CA 94710

NEIE, VAN ELROY, b Clifton, Tex, Nov 1, 38; m 63; c 2. PHYSICS EDUCATION. *Educ:* McMurry Col, BA, 61; NTex State Univ, MS, 66; Fla State Univ, PhD(sci educ), 70. *Prof Exp:* Instr physics, NTex State Univ, 64-67; teacher, Fla High Sch, Tallahassee, 68-69; asst prof, 70-76, ASSOC PROF PHYSICS & EDUC, PURDUE UNIV, WEST LAFAYETTE, 76- *Concurrent Pos:* Mem sci adv comt, Ind Dept Pub Instr, 71- *Mem:* Nat Asn Res Sci Teaching; Nat Sci Teachers Asn; Asn Educ Teachers Sci; Am Asn Physics Teachers; Soc Col Sci Teachers. *Res:* Information theory and its application to lexical communication in science; problem solving in science. *Mailing Add:* Dept of Physics Purdue Univ West Lafayette IN 47907

NEIGHBOURS, JOHN ROBERT, solid state physics, see previous edition

NEIHEISEL, JAMES, b Cincinnati, Ohio, June 3, 27; m 53; c 2. ENGINEERING GEOLOGY, GEOCHEMISTRY. *Educ:* Ohio State Univ, BS, 50; Univ SC, MS, 58; Ga Inst Technol, PhD(geophys sci), 73. *Prof Exp:* Chemist, Va Carolina Chem Corp, SC, 55-57; chief geol & petrog sect, South Atlantic Div Lab, Corps Eng, US Army, 58-77; GEOLOGIST, ENVIRON PROTECTION AGENCY, 77- *Concurrent Pos:* spec lectr, Ga Inst Technol, 65-71; instr, Ga State Univ, 66-77, George Mason Univ, 81- *Mem:* Fel Geol Soc Am; affil Am Soc Civil Engrs. *Res:* Standard development for high level radioactive waste and low level radioactive waste; ocean disposal investigations of radioactive waste. *Mailing Add:* Environ Protection Agency Off of Radiation Prog Washington DC 20460

NEIHOF, REX A, b Ponca City, Okla, Oct 31, 21; m 49; c 3. HYDROCARBON FUEL CONTAMINATION, MICROBIAL BIOCHEMISTRY. *Educ:* Tex Technol Col, BS, 43; Univ Minn, PhD(biochem), 50. *Prof Exp:* Chem engr, Gates Rubber Co, Colo, 43-45; asst, Univ Minn, 46-48, instr physiol chem, 48-49; phys chemist, NIH, 49-55, 57-58; Nat Heart Inst spec fel, Physiol Inst, Univ Uppsala, 55-57; RES CHEMIST, US NAVAL RES LAB, 58- *Concurrent Pos:* Vis scientist, Univ Calif, San Diego, 70-71. *Mem:* Am Soc Microbiol; Am Chem Soc; Sigma Xi. *Res:* Physical chemistry and electrochemistry of membrane processes; permselective membranes; biophysical studies on biological membranes; microbial cell walls; marine fouling; microbial deterioration of hydrocarbons; microbial ecology. *Mailing Add:* Environ Biol Br US Naval Res Lab Washington DC 20375

NEIL, DONALD E, b Alliance, Nebr, Jan 15, 28; m 51; c 3. PHYSICAL CHEMISTRY. *Educ:* Univ SDak, AB, 50, MA, 54; Rensselaer Polytech Inst, PhD(phys chem), 59. *Prof Exp:* Jr res assoc, Brookhaven Nat Lab, 55-58; res fel, Reactor Div, Brookhaven Nat Lab & Rensselaer Polytech Inst, 58-60; res scientist, Union Carbide Olefins Co, 60-63; assoc chemist, Argonne Nat Lab, 63-64; tech sales rep, Instrument Prod Div, 64-68, prod mgr, 68-69, sales mgr, Instrument & Equip Div, 69-73, mkt mgr, Sci & Process Div, 73-74, mgr, 74-78, DIR, ANAL INSTRUMENTS DIV, PHOTO PROD DEPT, E I DU PONT DE NEMOURS & CO, INC, 78- *Mem:* Am Chem Soc. *Res:* High temperature thermodynamics; fused salts; radiation chemistry; analytical and process instrumentation. *Mailing Add:* Anal Instruments Div Photo Prod Dept E I du Pont de Nemours & Co Inc Wilmington DE 19898

NEIL, GARY LAWRENCE, b Regina, Sask, June 13, 40; m 62; c 2. ORGANIC CHEMISTRY, BIOCHEMICAL PHARMACOLOGY. *Educ:* Queen's Univ, Ont, BSc, 62; Calif Inst Technol, PhD(chem), 66. *Prof Exp:* Res assoc cancer res, 66-74, res head cancer res, 74-79, res mgr, Exp Biol Res, 79-81, RES MGR CANCER RES, UPJOHN CO, KALAMAZOO, 82- *Mem:* Am Asn Cancer Res; Am Soc Pharmacol & Exp Therapeut; Am Chem Soc. *Res:* Enzyme kinetics; mode of action of antitumor agents; drug metabolism and pharmacokinetics. *Mailing Add:* Upjohn Co 700 Portage Rd Kalamazoo MI 49001

NEIL, GEORGE RANDALL, b Springfield, Mo, Apr 11, 48; m 78. ELECTRON LASERS. *Educ:* Univ Va, BS, 70; Univ Wis, MS, 73, PhD(nuclear eng), 77. *Prof Exp:* SCIENTIST, TRW CORP, 77- *Concurrent Pos:* Prin investr, Free Electron Laser Prog, TRW Corp, 80- *Mem:* Am Phys Soc; Sigma Xi; Soc Photo-Optical Instrumentation Engrs. *Res:* Free electron lasers; lasers and plasma physics research including controlled fusion and isotope separation, neutron and x-ray sources. *Mailing Add:* TRW Corp R1/1196 1 Space Park Redondo Beach CA 90278

NEIL, THOMAS C, b Tacoma, Wash, Dec 21, 34; m 63; c 5. ORGANIC CHEMISTRY, ANALYTICAL CHEMISTRY. *Educ:* Earlham Col, AB, 56; Pa State Univ, MS, 60, PhD(org chem), 64. *Prof Exp:* Asst prof chem, Baldwin-Wallace Col, 64-66; assoc prof, 66-80, PROF CHEM, KEENE STATE COl, 80- *Concurrent Pos:* Mem, Bd Dir, Harsyd Chem, Inc. *Mem:* Am Chem Soc. *Res:* Photochemistry; reactions of carbenes, waxes and macromolecules. *Mailing Add:* Dept Chem Keene State Col Keene NH 03431

NEILAND, BONITA, b Eugene, Ore, June 5, 28; m 55. PLANT ECOLOGY, RESOURCE MANAGEMENT. *Educ:* Univ Ore, BS, 49; Ore State Univ, BA, 51; Univ Col Wales, dipl rural sci, 52; Univ Wis, PhD(bot), 54. *Prof Exp:* Instr biol, Univ Ore, 54-55; asst prof, Gen Exten Div, Ore State Syst Higher Educ, 55-60; from asst prof to assoc prof, 61-68, head dept land resources & agr sci, 71-73, PROF BOT & LAND RESOURCES, UNIV ALASKA, 68-, DIR INSTRUCTION & PUB SERV, SCH AGR & LAND RESOURCES MGT, 75- *Concurrent Pos:* NSF grant, 55-57 & 62-70; mem contract group, Proj Chariot, AEC, Alaska, 61-62; McIntire-Stennis Fund grant, 70-; Bur Land Mgt grant, 71-78; US Forest Serv contracts, 74-; co-prin investr proj, Arctic Willow Reestab, Alyeska Pipeline Serv Co, 78-81. *Mem:* Fel AAAS; Ecol Soc Am; Arctic Inst NAm; Brit Ecol Soc; Soil Conserv Soc Am. *Res:* Comparisons of burned and unburned forest lands; analysis of forest and bog communities; vegetation, topography and ground ice correlations in the Fairbanks area; revegetation of denuded lands. *Mailing Add:* Sch of Agr & Land Resources Mgt Univ Ala Fairbanks AK 99701

NEILAND, KENNETH ALFRED, b Portland, Ore, Feb 18, 29; m 55; c 1. INVERTEBRATE ZOOLOGY. *Educ:* Reed Col, BA, 50; Univ Ore, MA, 53. *Prof Exp:* Asst parasitol, Reed Col, 50-51; asst physiol, Univ Ore, 51-53; asst zool, physiol & parasitol, Univ Calif, Los Angeles, 53-54; res fel physiol, Univ Ore, 55-56; instr biol sci, Ore Col Educ, 57-59; RES BIOLOGIST PARASITOL & COMP PHYSIOL, ALASKA DEPT FISH & GAME, 59- *Mem:* Am Soc Parasitologists. *Res:* Comparative parasitology; biology of helminth parasites; comparative physiology of molting in Crustacea. *Mailing Add:* PO Box 10095 Fairbanks AK 99701

NEILANDS, JOHN BRIAN, b Glen Valley, BC, Sept 11, 21; nat US. BIOCHEMISTRY, MICROBIOLOGY. *Educ:* Univ Toronto, BS, 44; Dalhousie Univ, MSc, 46; Univ Wis, PhD(biochem), 49. *Prof Exp:* Nat Res Coun chemist, SAM Med Inst, Stockholm, 49-51; instr biochem, Univ Wis, 51-52; from asst prof to assoc prof, 52-61, PROF BIOCHEM, UNIV CALIF, BERKELEY, 61- *Concurrent Pos:* Guggenheim Found fel, 58-59. *Mem:* Am Chem Soc; Am Soc Biol Chem; Biochem Soc; Bertrand Russell Soc. *Res:* Bioinorganic chemistry; chemistry and biochemistry of iron compounds; microbial iron transport; membranes; cell surface receptors. *Mailing Add:* Dept of Biochem Univ Calif Berkeley Berkeley CA 94720

NEILD, A(LTON) BAYNE, b Woolford, Md, Apr 14, 21; m 50; c 3. ENGINEERING, MECHANICAL ENGINEERING. *Educ:* Johns Hopkins Univ, BE, 43. *Prof Exp:* Sr draftsman, Goodyear Aircraft Corp, 43-44; mech engr, US Naval Eng Exp Sta, Naval Ship Res & Develop Ctr, 46-51, supvr marine power plant eng, Naval Marine Eng Lab, 51-60, energy conversion br head, 60-63, supvr marine eng, 63-67, energy conversion br head, Naval Ship Res & Develop Ctr, 67-69, power transmission br head, 69-80, ; MECH TRANSMISSION & ELECTROCHEM SYST BR HEAD, DAVID W TAYLOR NAVAL SHIP RES & DEVELOP CTR, 80- *Concurrent Pos:* Mem, Interagency Adv Power Group, 63- *Honors & Awards:* US Navy Superior Accomplishment Awards, 55, 57, 63 & 73. *Mem:* Am Soc Mech Engrs; Am Soc Naval Engrs; Soc Automotive Engrs. *Res:* Development on gas turbines, free-piston machinery, tracked vehicles, thermoelectric power and cooling and thermionics; radioisotope thermoelectric generators for space, surface and undersea environments; marine propulsion power transmission systems; marine electrochemical systems. *Mailing Add:* Propulsion & Auxiliary Syst Dept & Develop Ctr Annapolis MD 21402

NEILD, RALPH E, b Georgetown, Ill, Apr 14, 24; m 49; c 4. HORTICULTURE, AGRICULTURAL CLIMATOLOGY. *Educ:* Univ Ill, Urbana, BS, 49; Iowa State Univ, MS, 51; Kans State Univ, PhD, 70. *Prof Exp:* Agr & opers researcher, Libby McNeill & Libby, 51-64; assoc prof, 64-74, PROF HORT, UNIV NEBR-LINCOLN, 74- *Concurrent Pos:* Consult, Libby McNeil & Libby, Imp Govt, Iran & Hashemite Kingdom, Jordan. *Mem:* Am Soc Hort Sci. *Res:* Crop ecology; operations research; crop geography. *Mailing Add:* Dept of Hort Univ of Nebr Lincoln NE 68588

NEILER, JOHN HENRY, b Mt Oliver, Pa, Dec 21, 22; m 47; c 3. NUCLEAR PHYSICS. *Educ:* Univ Pittsburgh, BS, 47, MS, 50, PhD(physics), 53. *Prof Exp:* Instr physics, Univ Pittsburgh, 47-51; physicist, Oak Ridge Nat Lab, 53-62, vpres-tech dir, Oak Ridge Tech Enterprises Corp,

62-67, VPRES-TECH DIR, ORTEC INC, 67- *Concurrent Pos:* Lectr, Univ Tenn, 57-; vis scientist, Am Inst Physics-Am Asn Physics Teachers Prog, 57-63. *Mem:* Am Asn Physics Teachers. *Res:* Neutron and gamma ray spectrometry; nanosecond pulsing and timing techniques; neutron cross section measurements; nuclear spectrometry with semiconductor diode detectors; fission fragment energy correlations. *Mailing Add:* Ortec Inc PO Box C Oak Ridge TN 37830

NEILL, ALEXANDER BOLD, b Jersey City, NJ, Sept 27, 19; m 47; c 4. ORGANIC CHEMISTRY. *Educ:* Lehigh Univ, BS, 41, MS, 47, PhD(chem), 49. *Prof Exp:* Chemist, Hercules Powder Co, 41, shift supvr smokeless powder, 42-44, shift supvr rocket powder, 44-45; develop chemist, Carwin Co, 49-50; sr res chemist, 51-58, admin asst to dir res, 58-62, admin asst to vpres res, 62-65, chief scheduling & control, 65-67, chief document, 67, mgr info serv, 67-74, dir regulatory affairs, 74-77, DIR RES OPER, NORWICH-EATON PHARMACEUT, 77- *Mem:* Am Chem Soc; Sigma Xi. *Mailing Add:* 17 Ridgeland Rd Norwich NY 13815

NEILL, JIMMY DYKE, b Merkel, Tex, Mar 6, 39; m 60; c 2. PHYSIOLOGY, ENDOCRINOLOGY. *Educ:* Tex Tech Col, BS, 61; Univ Mo, MS, 63, PhD(physiol), 65. *Prof Exp:* Nat Inst Child Health & Human Develop res fel physiol, Sch Med, Univ Pittsburgh, 65-67, instr, 67-69; from asst prof to assoc prof, Sch Med, Emory Univ, 69-76, William Patterson Timmie prof, Div Basic Health Sci, 76-79; PROF & CHMN DEPT PHYSIOL & BIOPHYSICS, UNIV ALA, BIRMINGHAM, 79- *Concurrent Pos:* Nat Inst Child Health & Human Develop career develop award, 70-75. *Mem:* Soc Study Reproduction; Am Physiol Soc; Endocrine Soc. *Res:* Pituitary-ovarian relationships; hormone levels in various reproductive states. *Mailing Add:* Dept of Physiol Sch of Med Univ Ala Birmingham AL 35294

NEILL, JOHN MUIR, nuclear engineering, see previous edition

NEILL, ROBERT LEE, b Sedan, Kans, July 25, 41; m 63; c 1. BOTANY, ORNITHOLOGY. *Educ:* Kans State Teachers Col, BSE, 63, MS, 68; Univ Okla, PhD(bot), 70. *Prof Exp:* ASSOC PROF BIOL, UNIV TEX, ARLINGTON, 70- *Concurrent Pos:* Res partic, NSF Res Partic Prog, 66; res dir, Univ Tex Syst Cancer Ctr, 72-75. *Mem:* Sigma Xi; AAAS; Wilson Ornith Soc; Ecol Soc Am; Nat Audobon Soc. *Res:* Plant allelopathic studies; plant bird interactions and investigation of causes of high incidence of bill abnormalities in birds. *Mailing Add:* Dept of Biol Univ of Tex Arlington TX 76019

NEILL, WILLIAM ALEXANDER, b Nashville, Tenn. MEDICINE, CARDIOLOGY. *Educ:* Amherst Col, BA, 51; Cornell Univ, MD, 55. *Prof Exp:* NIH fel, Peter Bent Brigham Hosp, Boston, 59-61; instr med, Mass Mem Hosp, 61-63; assoc prof, Sch Med, Univ Ore, 63-76; PROF MED, SCH MED, TUFTS UNIV, 76-; CHIEF CARDIOL, BOSTON VET ADMIN MED CTR, 76- *Concurrent Pos:* Mem staff, USPHS Commun Dis Ctr, 56-68; fel, Physiol Inst, Dusseldorf, Ger, 69-70; fel coun clin cardiol, Am Heart Asn. *Mem:* Am Fedn Clin Res; Am Physiol Soc. *Res:* Coronary circulation; muscle metabolism; tissue oxygen supply; exercise physiology. *Mailing Add:* Vet Admin Hosp Boston MA 02130

NEILL, WILLIAM HAROLD, b Wynne, Ark, Oct 21, 43; m 64; c 1. FISH BIOLOGY. *Educ:* Univ Ark, BS, 65, MS, 67; Univ Wis, PhD(zool), 71. *Prof Exp:* Res fishery biologist, Nat Marine Fisheries Serv, Nat Oceanog & Atmospheric Admin, US Dept Commerce, 71-74; ASSOC PROF FISHERIES, TEX A&M UNIV, 74- *Concurrent Pos:* Affil prof zool, Univ Hawaii, 73- *Honors & Awards:* Spec Achievement Award, Nat Marine Fisheries Serv, 74. *Mem:* Am Fisheries Soc; Am Inst Fishery Res Biologists; AAAS; Sigma Xi. *Res:* Behavioral and physiological ecology of fishes, with emphasis on behavioral regulation of environment and intra-habitat distribution. *Mailing Add:* Dept Wildlife & Fisheries Sci Tex A&M Univ College Station TX 77843

NEILSEN, GERALD HENRY, b Kingston, Ont, Jan 1, 48; m 72; c 2. SOIL FERTILITY, PLANT NUTRITION. *Educ:* Queen's Univ, BSc, 70, MSc, 72; McGill Univ, PhD(soil sci), 77. *Prof Exp:* Lectr soil sci, Fac Agr, McGill Univ, 72-73; res scientist, Soil Res Inst Agr Can, 77-78; RES SCIENTIST SOIL SCI, AGR CAN RES STA, SUMMERLAND, BC, 78- *Mem:* Can Soil Sci Soc; Int Soil Sci Soc; Am Soc Agron. *Res:* Soil fertility; nutrient leaching; runoff water quality; fruit tree nutrition. *Mailing Add:* Res Sta Agr Can Summerland BC V0H 1Z0 Can

NEILSEN, IVAN ROBERT, b Rulison, Colo, Aug 12, 15; m 37; c 2. PHYSICS. *Educ:* Pac Union Col, AB, 36; Stanford Univ, MS, 48, PhD(physics), 52. *Prof Exp:* Instr physics, Glendale Union Acad, 36-38, San Diego Union Acad, 38-40 & Modesto Union Acad, 40-43; from instr to asst prof, Pac Union Col, 43-48; res assoc, Microwave Lab, Stanford Univ, 48-51; assoc prof, Pac Union Col, 51-52, prof & chmn phys sci div, 52-64, dir data processing lab, 58-64; prof physiol & biophys, 64-69, coordr, Sci Comput Facil, 65-76, prof biomath & chmn dept, 69-81, PROF RADIOL & PHYSIOL, SCH MED, LOMA LINDA, 81- *Concurrent Pos:* Res consult, Hansen Labs, Stanford Univ, 52-; consult, Calif State Dept Educ, 64. *Mem:* AAAS; Am Phys Soc; Am Asn Physics Teachers; Asn Comput Mach; Inst Elec & Electronics Engrs; Radiation Res Soc. *Res:* Applied electromagnetic field theory; high power pulsed klystrons; linear electron accelerators; chemical and biological reactions induced by ionizing radiation; computer models of living systems. *Mailing Add:* Dept of Biomath Loma Linda Univ Sch of Med Loma Linda CA 92354

NEILSON, GEORGE CROYDEN, b Vancouver, BC, Apr 4, 28; m; c 3. NUCLEAR PHYSICS. *Educ:* Univ BC, BA, 50, MA, 52, PhD(physics), 55. *Prof Exp:* Physicist, Radiation Sect, Defence Res Bd, 55-58, head radiation sect, 58-59; from asst prof to assoc prof, 59-66, PROF PHYSICS, UNIV ALTA, 66- *Mem:* Am Phys Soc; Can Asn Physicists. *Res:* Measurement of the energy angular distribution, gamma ray correlation and polarization of neutrons and protons produced by deuteron bombardment of light nuclei; angular correlation of cascade gamma rays. *Mailing Add:* Nuclear Res Ctr Dept of Physics Univ of Alta Edmonton AB T6G 2E1 Can

NEILSON, GEORGE FRANCIS, JR, b Portland, Ore, Jan 19, 30; m 55; c 3. PHYSICAL CHEMISTRY. *Educ:* Ore State Univ, BS, 51, MS, 53; Ohio State Univ, PhD, 62. *Prof Exp:* Res chemist, Cent Res Dept, E I du Pont de Nemours & Co, 58-62; res scientist, 62-67, sr scientist, Owens-Ill, Inc, 67-78; MEM TECH STAFF, JET PROPULSION LAB, 78- *Mem:* Am Chem Soc; Am Phys Soc; Am Crystallog Asn. *Res:* Small-angle x-ray scattering; kinetics and mechanisms of nucleation and crystallization; phase transformation processes in glass systems; microstructure of amorphous and polycrystalline materials; space processing of glass. *Mailing Add:* Jet Propulsion Lab 4800 Oak Grove Dr Pasadena CA 91103

NEILSON, JAMES MAXWELL, b Shellbrook, Sask, Apr 5, 12; m 45; c 3. GEOLOGY. *Educ:* Queen's Univ, Ont, BSc, 36; McGill Univ, MSc, 47; Univ Minn, PhD(geol), 50. *Prof Exp:* Mining engr, Perron Gold Mines, Ltd, 37-39; mine mgr, Senore Gold Mines, Ltd, 39-40; chief geologist, Mistassini Explor, Ltd, 46-47; geologist, Que Dept Mines, 48-50; from asst prof to assoc prof geol & geol eng, Mich Technol Univ, 50-57, prof geol eng, 57-66, asst dean fac, 60-64; prof, 66-77, EMER PROF GEOL SCI, QUEEN'S UNIV, ONT, 77-; PRES, JAMES NEILSON & ASSOC, INC, 78- *Concurrent Pos:* Consult geologist, Dames & Moore, UN & Asian Develop Bank. *Mem:* Fel Geol Soc Am; Am Inst Mining, Metall & Petrol Engrs; Can Inst Mining & Metall; Soc Econ Geologists. *Res:* Precambrian regional, glacial and engineering geology; iron ore deposits. *Mailing Add:* Dept Geol Sci Queen's Univ Kingston ON K7L 3N6 Can

NEILSON, JOHN WARRINGTON, b Saskatoon, Sask, Feb 13, 18; m 47; c 3. DENTISTRY. *Educ:* Univ Sask, BA, 39; Univ Alta, DDS, 41; Univ Mich, MSc, 46; Am Bd Periodont, dipl. *Prof Exp:* From asst prof to assoc prof periodont & oral path, Univ Alta, 45-47; assoc prof periodont, Univ Wash, 52-57; dean fac dent, 57-77, PROF ORAL BIOL UNIV MAN, 57- *Concurrent Pos:* Consult, USPHS Hosp, Seattle, Wash, 54-57, Royal Can Dent Corps, 60, Winnipeg Gen & Children's Hosps, 60; examr oral med, Nat Dent Exam Bd Can, 58-60; mem assoc comt dent res, Nat Res Coun Can, 59-60; mem dent adv comt, Nat Health & Welfare, 65-; mem coun higher learning, Prov Man, 65- *Mem:* Fel Am Col Dent; Am Acad Oral Path; Am Acad Periodont; Can Dent Asn; Can Acad Periodont (pres, 61-62). *Res:* Oral pathology and medicine; periodontology; effect of irritation on supporting tissues of the dentition. *Mailing Add:* Univ of Man Fac of Dent 780 Bannatyne Ave Winnipeg MB R3T 2N2 Can

NEILSON, ROBERT HUGH, b Pittsburgh, Pa, Jan 24, 48. INORGANIC CHEMISTRY. *Educ:* Carnegie-Mellon Univ, BS, 69; Duke Univ, PhD(chem), 73. *Prof Exp:* Res assoc inorg chem, Univ Tex, Austin, 74-75; asst prof, Duke Univ, 75-78; asst prof inorg chem, 78-81, ASSOC PROF CHEM, TEX CHRISTIAN UNIV, 81- *Concurrent Pos:* US Army Res Off grant, 77-84, Off Naval Res grant, 79-84. *Mem:* Am Chem Soc; Sigma Xi. *Res:* Preparative chemistry of the main group elements including inorganic polymers. *Mailing Add:* Dept of Chem Tex Christian Univ Ft Worth TX 76129

NEIMAN, BENJAMIN H, b Toronto, Ont, Oct 12, 10; US citizen; m 31; c 3. PATHOLOGY. *Educ:* Univ Chicago, BS, 26; Rush Med Col, MD, 30; Univ Ill, MS, 34. *Prof Exp:* From assoc prof to prof path, Chicago Med Sch, 46-48, clin prof, 68-76. *Concurrent Pos:* Dir labs, MacNeal Mem Hosp, 37-76; attend pathologist, Cook County Hosp, 45-76. *Mem:* Col Am Path; Am Col Physicians; Am Soc Clin Path; AMA. *Mailing Add:* 1315 Verano Dr Palm Springs CA 92262

NEIMAN, GARY SCOTT, b Chicago, Ill, Oct 2, 47; m 72; c 2. CRANIOFACIAL ANOMALIES, VOICE DISORDERS. *Educ:* Univ Ill, Urbana, BS, 69, MA, 71, PhD(speech sci), 73. *Prof Exp:* Speech pathologist, Facial Deformity Tear, Carle Found Hosp, 73-77; asst prof speech path, Kans State Univ, 73-77, clin dir, Speech & Hearing Clin, 74-77; ASSOC PROF SPEECH PATH, KENT STATE UNIV, 77-, PROG DIR, DIV SPEECH PATH & AUDIOL, 79-; SPEECH PATHOLOGIST, AKRON CRANIOFACIAL CLIN, 77- *Concurrent Pos:* mem med adv bd, Kent Vis Nurse Assoc, 79- *Mem:* Am Speech & Hearing Asn; Am Cleft Palate Asn; Int Asn Logopedics & Phoniatrics. *Res:* Normal and abnormal aspects of speech and voice production; psychosocial aspects of esophageal speech and cleft palate speech; pre-linguistic variables affecting the acquisition of language in children with orofacial anomalies. *Mailing Add:* 1167 Erin Dr Kent OH 44240

NEIMARK, HAROLD CARL, b Detroit, Mich, July 25, 32; m 69. MICROBIOLOGY, IMMUNOLOGY. *Educ:* Univ Calif, Los Angeles, BA, 54, PhD(microbiol), 60. *Prof Exp:* Res assoc, Inst Microbiol, 59-60; from instr to asst prof, 60-71, ASSOC PROF MICROBIOL & IMMUNOL, STATE UNIV NY DOWNSTATE MED CTR, 72- *Concurrent Pos:* NIH grants, 67-77; collabr, USDA. *Honors & Awards:* Fogerty Sr Int fel, 78. *Mem:* AAAS; Am Soc Microbiol; Brit Soc Gen Microbiol. *Res:* Genetics and physiology of microorganisms; L forms and mycoplasmas; infectious diseases; bacterial evolution. *Mailing Add:* Dept Microbiol & Immunol State Univ NY Downstate Med Ctr Brooklyn NY 11203

NEIMS, ALLEN HOWARD, b Chicago, Ill, Oct 24, 38; m 61; c 3. BIOCHEMISTRY, PEDIATRICS. *Educ:* Univ Chicago, BA & BS, 57; Johns Hopkins Univ, MD, 61, PhD(physiol chem), 66. *Prof Exp:* NIH fel, Lab Neurochem, Nat Inst Neurol Dis & Stroke, 68-70; asst prof pediat, Johns Hopkins Univ, 70, asst prof physiol chem, 70-72; from asst prof to prof pharmacol & assoc prof to prof pediat, McGill Univ, 72-78; assoc prof, 74-78, PROF PHARMACOL & PEDIAT & CHMN PHARMACOL, UNIV FLA, 78- *Concurrent Pos:* Physician, Johns Hopkins Hosp & J F Kennedy Inst, Baltimore, 70-72. *Honors & Awards:* Henry Strong Denison Award, 61. *Mem:* Soc Pediat Res; Am Fedn Clin Res; Am Soc Pharmacol & Exp Therapeut; Can Soc Clin Invest. *Res:* Developmental pharmacology and therapeutics; developmental biology; clinical pharmacology; pharmacology. *Mailing Add:* Dept Pharmacol Univ Fla Gainesville FL 32610

NEISH, GORDON ARTHUR, b Saskatoon, Sask, May 1, 49; m 78; c 2. MYCOLOGY, BOTANY. *Educ:* Acadia Univ, BSc, 70; Univ BC, PhD(bot), 77. *Prof Exp:* Asst prof bot, Univ RI, 77-78; RES SCIENTIST MYCOL, CAN DEPT AGR, 78- *Mem:* Mycol Soc Am; Brit Mycol Soc; Sigma Xi; Can Phytopath Soc. *Res:* Hyphomycete systematics; toxigenic potential of fusarium species. *Mailing Add:* Agr Can Biosysts Res Inst Cent Exp Farm Ottawa ON K1A 0C6 Can

NEISWENDER, DAVID DANIEL, b Palmdale, Pa, Oct 6, 30; m 55; c 2. PETROLEUM CHEMISTRY. *Educ:* Lebanon Valley Col, BS, 53; Pa State Univ, MS, 55, PhD(chem), 57. *Prof Exp:* Res chemist, Cent Res Div, Mobil Oil Corp, 57-60, sr res chemist, 60-62, asst supvr, 62-64, res assoc, Paulsboro Lab, 64-80, ADMIN MGR, PROD RES DIV, MOBIL RES & DEVELOP CORP, 80- *Mem:* Am Chem Soc. *Res:* Development and testing of automotive engine, transmission and gear oils; chemistry of electrical discharges; synthesis of petrochemicals; preparation and reactions of organoboron compounds; hydrocarbon oxidation; design and testing of synthetic lubricants; lubricant contributions to fuel economy. *Mailing Add:* Paulsboro Lab Mobil Res & Develop Corp Paulsboro NJ 08066

NEITHAMER, RICHARD WALTER, b Wesleyville, Pa, Aug 3, 29; m 58; c 1. INORGANIC CHEMISTRY. *Educ:* Allegheny Col, BS, 51; Univ Ind, PhD(inorg chem), 57. *Prof Exp:* Asst prof chem, Lebanon Valley Col, 55-59, East Tex State Univ, 59-61, Rose Polytech Inst, 61-64; assoc prof & coord chem, 64-67, PROF CHEM, ECKERD COL, 67-, CHMN, COLLEGIUM NATURAL SCI, 72- *Concurrent Pos:* Vis scientist, Ind Acad Sci, 63-64 & Fla Acad Sci, 65-66; consult, US Naval Weapons Lab, 65-66, contract res, 66-69. *Mem:* AAAS; Am Chem Soc; fel Am Inst Chem. *Res:* Coordination and metal chelate compounds; polarography. *Mailing Add:* Dept of Chem Eckerd Col St Petersburg FL 33733

NEL, LOUIS DANIEL, b Barkly West, SAfrica, June 5, 34; m 56; c 4. CATEGORICAL ASPECTS FUNCTIONAL ANALYSIS, TOPOLOGY. *Educ:* Univ Stellenbosch, BSc, 54, MSc, 58; Cambridge Univ, PhD(math), 62. *Prof Exp:* Lectr math, Univ Stellenbosch, 56-62; sr lectr, Univ Cape Town, 62-65; prof, Port Elizabeth Univ, 66-68; assoc prof, 68-76, PROF MATH, CARLETON UNIV, 76- *Mem:* SAfrican Math Soc (secy, 63-67); Am Math Soc; Can Math Soc. *Res:* Functional analysis and exponential laws; categories in functional analysis; topology and topological algebra which uphold an exponential laws; application of the intrinsic functorial calculus of such categories to solve various problems. *Mailing Add:* Dept of Math Carleton Univ Ottawa ON K1S 5B6 Can

NELAN, DONALD ROYCE, organic chemistry, deceased

NELB, GARY WILLIAM, b Waterbury, Conn, Sept 8, 52. POLYMER PHYSICAL CHEMISTRY. *Educ:* Dartmouth Col, AB, 74; Univ Wis, PhD(chem), 78. *Prof Exp:* RES CHEMIST, E I DU PONT DE NEMOURS & CO INC, 78- *Mem:* Am Chem Soc; Sigma Xi. *Res:* Polymer chemistry especially fibers and fibrous materials. *Mailing Add:* E I du Pont de Nemours & Co Inc Textile Fibers E302/132 Wilmington DE 19898

NELB, ROBERT GILMAN, b Lawrence, Mass, Dec 4, 23; m 45; c 5. ORGANIC CHEMISTRY. *Educ:* Dartmouth Col, BA, 45, MA, 46; Univ Rochester, PhD(chem), 49. *Prof Exp:* Instr chem, Dartmouth Col, 45-46; asst, Univ Rochester, 46-48; res chemist, Chem Div, US Rubber Co, 49-52, group leader new prod, 52-53, mgr vibrin polyester develop, 53-57, mgr vibrin polyester & vibrathane polyurethane res & develop, 57-60, mgr kralastic res & develop, 60-65; group mgr plastics res & develop, Indust Prods Co, Uniroyal, Inc, 65-66, dir res & develop Consumer, Indust & Plastics Div, 66-74, dir res & develop, 74-77; TECH DIR BAILEY DIV, USM CORP, 77- *Mem:* Am Chem Soc. *Res:* High temperature and reinforced polyesters; polyurethane elastomers; emulsion polymerization; thermoplastics; elastomers and plastics-fabrication of rubber products; fabrication of elastomeric and plastic automotive body components. *Mailing Add:* 40 Alehson Rd PO Box 33 Rye NH 03870

NELKIN, MARK, b New York, NY, May 12, 31; m 52; c 2. THEORETICAL PHYSICS. *Educ:* Mass Inst Technol, SB, 51; Cornell Univ, PhD, 55. *Prof Exp:* Res assoc, Knolls Atomic Power Lab, Gen Elec Co, 55-57; mem res staff, Gen Atomic Div, Gen Dynamics Corp, 57-62; assoc prof eng physics, 62-67, PROF APPL PHYSICS, CORNELL UNIV, 67- *Concurrent Pos:* Vis res assoc, State Univ Utrecht, 60-61; Guggenheim fel, Orsay, Paris, 68-69; vis prof, Col France, Paris, 76. *Mem:* Am Phys Soc. *Res:* Statistical physics; turbulent fluid flow. *Mailing Add:* Sch of Appl & Eng Physics Cornell Univ Ithaca NY 14853

NELLES, JOHN SUMNER, b Regina, Sask, Dec 2, 20; m 43; c 1. MECHANICAL ENGINEERING. *Educ:* Univ Sask, BSc, 49. *Prof Exp:* Design engr, Dom Eng Works, Que, 49-51, prod engr, 51-53; work shops engr, Atomic Energy Can Ltd, 54-55, develop engr, 55-75, head indust liaison, 75-78; indust contracts officer, 78-79, COMMERCIAL OPERS OFFICER, CHALK RIVER NUCLEAR LAB, ATOMIC ENERGY CAN RES CO, 79- *Mem:* Eng Inst Can. *Res:* Development of nuclear fuels. *Mailing Add:* Atomic Energy of Can Res Co Chalk River Nuclear Lab Chalk River ON K0J 1J0 Can

NELLES, MAURICE, b Madison, SDak, Oct 19, 06; m 29; c 3. PHYSICAL CHEMISTRY. *Educ:* Univ SDak, AB, 27, AM, 28; Harvard Univ, PhD(phys chem), 34. *Hon Degrees:* DSc, Univ SDak, 55. *Prof Exp:* Prof physics, Columbus Col, SDak, 28-29; instr chem, Univ SDak, 29-30; res chemist, Nat Aniline Chem Co, 32-34 & Union Oil Co, 34-36; camp dir, Civilian Conserv Corps, Ft Lewis, Wash, 36-37; res engr, Riverside Cement Co, 37-39; engr, Permanente Corp, 39-40; staff asst, Lockheed Aircraft Corp, 40-47; prof aeronaut eng, Univ Southern Calif, 46-49, res mgr, Allan Hancock Found, 49-50; prof & dir eng exp sta, Pa State Univ, 50-51; vpres petro-mech div & dir res, Borg-Warner Corp, 51-54; dir res & diversification & mgr, Graphic Arts Div, Technicolor Corp, 54-57; vpres eng, Crane Co, 57-59; dir Lamb-Weston Div, 57-71, vpres, Am Electronics Corp, 59-61; mgr mfg res & develop, Westinghouse Defense Ctr, 64-66; prof bus admin, Univ Va, 66-70. *Concurrent Pos:* Dep dir, War Prod Bd, 44-45; pres, Corwith Co, Crane Co, 57-59; dir, MER & D Corp, 61-, Hydro-Aire Co & Crane, Ltd, Can; mem expeds; chief engr, Off Prod Res & Develop; mem tech adv comt, Calif Air Resources Bd. *Mem:* AAAS; Am Soc Mech Eng; Soc Automotive Eng; Am Chem Soc; Am Soc Metals. *Res:* Electronics; radio transmitter design; structures; petroleum; catalytic reactions; design of mechanisms; preliminary design for a mass production factor for frozen stuffed quail. *Mailing Add:* 5522 Rutgers Rd La Jolla CA 92037

NELLIGAN, WILLIAM BRYON, b Northampton, Mass, Jan 19, 20; m 42. PHYSICS. *Educ:* Rensselaer Polytech Inst, BS, 50, MS, 51. *Prof Exp:* Designer elec power, Gen Elec Co, Mass, 42-44; asst physics, Rensselaer Polytech Inst, 50-51; physicist, Res Lab, Schlumberger Well Surv Corp, 51-53, sr res physicist, 53-65, res proj physicist, 65-67, RES PROJ PHYSICIST, SCHLUMBERGER TECH CORP, 67- *Mem:* AAAS; Am Phys Soc; Am Nuclear Soc; Soc Petrol Engrs; Sigma Xi. *Res:* Applied nuclear physics; electronic instrumentation; mathematics. *Mailing Add:* PO Box 307 Schlumberg Well Survey Corp Ridgefield CT 06877

NELLIS, LOIS FONDA, b Dayton, Ohio, Nov 30, 26. MICROBIOLOGY. *Educ:* Hobart & William Smith Cols, BA, 46; Smith Col, MA, 48; Purdue Univ, PhD(bact), 62. *Prof Exp:* From instr to assoc prof, 48-68, chmn dept, 69-74, PROF BIOL, HOBART & WILLIAM SMITH COLS, 68- *Concurrent Pos:* Res mem, Bergey's Manual Comn, 53-55 & 61; Geneva City bacteriologist, 50-52; United Health Found of western NY grant, 68-70; NIH co-proj dir, Dept Pharmacol, Med Sch, State Univ NY Buffalo, 70-76; vis prof med, Univ Rochester, 75-76. *Mem:* AAAS; Am Soc Microbiology; Am Inst Biol Sci. *Res:* Myxobacteria; R factors and tetracycline resistance in Escherichia coli. *Mailing Add:* Dept of Biol Hobart & William Smith Cols Geneva NY 14456

NELLOR, JOHN ERNEST, b Omaha, Nebr, Oct 31, 22; m 46; c 3. PHYSIOLOGY, ENDOCRINOLOGY. *Educ:* Univ Calif, BS, 50, PhD(comp physiol), 55. *Prof Exp:* From instr to prof physiol, Col Human Med & Natural Sci, Mich State Univ, 55-69, dir, Endocrine Res Unit, 64-69, asst to assoc vpres res develop & dir, Ctr Environ Qual, 71-76; DEAN, GRAD SCH & COORDR RES, UNIV NEV, RENO, 76- *Concurrent Pos:* Mem staff, NSF, 66-67, prog dir metals biol, 67-68; mem, US Nat Comn for UNESCO Man & Biosphere Prog, 75- *Mem:* Am Physiol Soc; Soc Study Reproduction; Sigma Xi. *Res:* Comparative reproductive physiology; hormones and body defense; adrenal-pituitary hormones and aging. *Mailing Add:* Grad Sch Univ of Nev Reno NV 89557

NELLUMS, ROBERT (OVERMAN), b Nashville, Tenn, Sept 19, 21; m 47; c 4. CHEMICAL ENGINEERING. *Educ:* Vanderbilt Univ, BSChE, 42. *Prof Exp:* Control analyst, Org Div, Monsanto Co, 42-43, asst prod supvr, 43-44, proj engr, 46-48, prod supvr, 48-51, group leader pilot plant, 51-55, sect leader chem eng, 55-57, asst dir res, 58-59, asst dir eng, 59-62, mgr purchasing, 62-66, dir purchasing admin & control, 66-71, dir intermediates, Monsanto Textiles Co, 71-76, dir textile intermediates, Monsanto Intermediates Co, 76-80, PROD DIR TEXTILE INTERMEDIATES, MONSANTO INT DIV-EUROPE, MONSANTO CO, 80- *Mem:* Am Chem Soc; Sigma Xi; Am Mgt Asn; Am Inst Chem Engrs; Soc Chem Indust. *Res:* Process development; scale-up; plant design. *Mailing Add:* Monsanto Textiles Co 800 N Lindbergh Blvd St Louis MO 63166

NELMS, GEORGE E, b Ark, Feb 6, 27; m 50; c 4. ANIMAL BREEDING. *Educ:* Ark State Col, BS, 51; Ore State Col, MS, 54, PhD(genetics), 56. *Prof Exp:* Instr animal husb, Ore State Col, 55-56; asst prof animal sci, Univ Ariz, 56-59; ASST PROF ANIMAL BREEDING, UNIV WYO, 59- *Mem:* Am Soc Animal Sci; Am Genetic Asn; Sigma Xi; Coun Agr Sci & Tech. *Res:* Reproductive and environmental physiology; genetics of beef cattle. *Mailing Add:* Div of Animal Sci Univ of Wyo Box 3354 Univ Sta Laramie WY 82071

NELP, WIL B, b Pittsburgh, Pa, July 30, 29; m 52, 69; c 4. INTERNAL MEDICINE, NUCLEAR MEDICINE. *Educ:* Franklin Col, BA, 51; Johns Hopkins Univ, MD, 55. *Hon Degrees:* DSc, Franklin Col, 67. *Prof Exp:* NIH fel med & radiol, Johns Hopkins Univ, 60-62; from asst prof to assoc prof, 62-71, PROF MED & RADIOL, UNIV WASH, 71-, CHIEF DIV NUCLEAR MED & HEAD CLIN NUCLEAR MED, UNIV HOSP, 62- *Concurrent Pos:* Instr, Johns Hopkins Univ, 61-62; Nat Inst Arthritis & Metab Dis training grant, 63-69; consult, Providence Hosp, Seattle, Wash, 64-68, Nat Heart Inst, 67-68 & Nat Heart & Lung Inst, 68-; consult adv radiopharmaceut, Food & Drug Admin, 70; consult, Children's Orthop Hosp, Seattle Vet Admin Hosp, Harborview Med Ctr & USPHS Hosp, Seattle. *Mem:* Am Fedn Clin Res; Soc Nuclear Med (vpres, 69-70, pres, 73-74); fel Am Col Physicians; fel Am Col Nuclear Physicians. *Res:* Physiologic and clinical investigations in nuclear medicine. *Mailing Add:* BB20 Univ Hosp RC-70 Univ of Wash Seattle WA 98195

NELSEN, ROGER BAIN, b Chicago, Ill, Dec 20, 42; m 79. MATHEMATICS. *Educ:* DePauw Univ, BA, 64; Duke Univ, PhD(math), 69. *Prof Exp:* ASSOC PROF MATH & CHMN DEPT, LEWIS & CLARK COL, 69- *Mem:* Math Asn Am. *Res:* Stochastic processes. *Mailing Add:* Dept of Math Lewis & Clark Col Box LC110 Portland OR 97219

NELSEN, STEPHEN FLANDERS, b Chicago, Ill, Apr 17, 40; m 62; c 1. ORGANIC CHEMISTRY. *Educ:* Univ Mich, BS, 62; Harvard Univ, PhD(chem), 65. *Prof Exp:* From asst prof to assoc prof, 65-75, PROF ORG CHEM, UNIV WIS-MADISON, 75- *Concurrent Pos:* Vis scientist, Hafn-Meituer Inst, Berlin, 79 & 81. *Mem:* Am Chem Soc. *Res:* Physical organic chemistry; physical and chemical properties of free radicals; electrochemistry; conformational analysis. *Mailing Add:* 1101 W University Ave Madison WI 53706

NELSEN, THOMAS SLOAN, b Tacoma, Wash, Aug 4, 26; m 45; c 2. SURGERY. *Educ:* Univ Wash, BS, 47, MD, 51; Am Bd Surg, dipl, 59. *Prof Exp:* From instr to asst prof, Univ Chicago, 57-60; from asst prof to assoc prof, 60-71, PROF SURG, SCH MED, STANFORD UNIV, 71- *Mem:* Am Col Surgeons; Inst Elec & Electronics Engrs. *Res:* Surgery of neoplasms; gastrointestinal physiology and surgery. *Mailing Add:* Dept of Surg Stanford Univ Sch of Med Stanford CA 94305

NELSESTUEN, GARY LEE, b Galesville, Wis, Sept 10, 44; m 67; c 2. BIOCHEMISTRY. *Educ:* Univ Wis-Madison, BS, 66; Univ Minn, St Paul, PhD(biochem), 70. *Prof Exp:* NIH fel biochem, Univ Wis, 70-72; asst prof biochem, Univ Minn, St Paul, 72-76, assoc prof, 76-80. *Concurrent Pos:* Estab investr, Am Heart Asn, 75-80. *Mem:* Am Chem Soc. *Res:* Function of the carbohydrate portion of glycoproteins; role of vitamin K and the vitamin K-dependent amino acid, gamma-carboxyglutamic acid. *Mailing Add:* Dept Biochem Univ Minn Col Biol Sci St Paul MN 55108

NELSON, A CARL, JR, b West Chester, Pa, Jan 2, 26; m 50; c 4. MATHEMATICAL STATISTICS, MATHEMATICS. *Educ:* Mass Inst Technol, SB, 46; Univ Del, MS, 48. *Prof Exp:* Instr math, Univ Del, 48-50, 51-52 & 53-56; scientist, Bettis Atomic Power Div, Westinghouse Elec Corp, Pa, 56-60, fel scientist, 60; statistician, Res Triangle Inst, 60-63, sr statistician, 63-73; statist consult, 73-75; SR PROF SCIENTIST, PED CO-ENVIRON SPECIALISTS, INC, 75- *Mem:* Statist Asn; Biomet Soc; Soc; Am Soc Qual Control. *Res:* Applied research in application of statistics to physical sciences, particularly the fields of environmental analysis, occupational and highway safety, quality assurance, systems analysis, and the statistical design of experiments for developing mathematical models. *Mailing Add:* 5414 Highland Dr Durham NC 27712

NELSON, A GENE, b Galesburg, Ill, Sept 9, 42; m 64; c 3. AGRICULTURAL ECONOMICS. *Educ:* Western Ill Univ, BS, 64; Purdue Univ, MS, 67, PhD(agr econ), 69. *Prof Exp:* Asst prof, 69-74, assoc prof, 74-79, PROF AGR ECON, ORE STATE UNIV, 79- *Mem:* Am Agr Econ Asn; Am Soc Farm Mgrs & Rural Appraisers. *Res:* Systems analysis of beef and forage production; decision making under risk and uncertainty. *Mailing Add:* Dept Agr & Resource Econ Ore State Univ Corvallis OR 97331

NELSON, AARON LOUIS, b Deer Lodge, Mont, June 23, 20; m 51; c 3. ORGANIC CHEMISTRY. *Educ:* Harvard Univ, BS, 42, MS, 46, PhD(org chem), 49. *Prof Exp:* Asst prof org chem, Case Univ, 49-55; res chemist, E I du Pont de Nemours & Co, Inc, 55-61; mem res staff, Wright Lab, 61-67, ASSOC PROF CHEM, UNIV COL, RUTGERS UNIV, NEW BRUNSWICK, 67- *Concurrent Pos:* Rutgers res coun vis fel, Princeton Univ, 70-71. *Mem:* AAAS; Am Chem Soc; The Chem Soc. *Res:* Heterocyclic and aromatic chemistry and synthesis. *Mailing Add:* Dept of Chem Rutgers Univ New Brunswick NJ 08903

NELSON, ALAN R, b Logan, Utah, June 11, 33; m 59; c 3. MEDICAL QUALITY ASSESSMENT. *Educ:* Northwestern Univ, BS, 55, MD, 58. *Prof Exp:* Pres, Utah Prof Rev Orgn, 71-75; ASSOC, MEM MED CTR, 64- *Concurrent Pos:* Mem, Nat Prof Stand Rev Coun, 73-77. *Honors & Awards:* Recognition Award, Am Soc Int Med, 73. *Mem:* Inst Med of Nat Acad Sci. *Res:* Medical utilization review and quality assessment. *Mailing Add:* Mem Med Ctr 2000 S 900 E Salt Lake City UT 84108

NELSON, ALBERT WENDELL, b Boston, Mass, June 2, 35; m 59; c 3. CARDIOVASCULAR DISEASES. *Educ:* Cornell Univ, DVM, 59; Colo State Univ, MS, 62, PhD(path), 65; Am Col Vet Surgeons, dipl, 74. *Prof Exp:* Vet, private practice, 59-60; asst prof, 65-69, assoc prof surg, 69-75, PROF CLIN SCI, COLO STATE UNIV, 75- *Concurrent Pos:* NIH res grants, Colo State Univ, 65-68, 71-73; Colo Heart Asn res grant, 71-73; Nat Heart & Lung Inst Contract, 73-77. *Mem:* Am Vet Med Asn. *Res:* Cardiovascular pathology and physiology, primarily in relation to the microcirculation; reconstructive surgery relative to animal and human problems. *Mailing Add:* Vet Teaching Hosp Colo State Univ Ft Collins CO 80521

NELSON, ALLEN CHARLES, b Plum City, Wis, July 13, 32; m 54; c 4. MYCOLOGY, MICROBIOLOGY. *Educ:* Wis State Univ, River Falls, BS, 54; Univ SDak, MA, 61; Univ Wis, PhD(bot), 64. *Prof Exp:* From asst prof to assoc prof, 64-68, chmn dept biol, 67-73, PROF BOT, UNIV WIS-LA CROSSE, 68- *Mem:* Mycol Soc Am; Bot Soc Am; Sigma Xi; Am Soc Microbiol. *Res:* Ascomycetes; morphological and cytological studies. *Mailing Add:* Dept of Biol Univ of Wis-LaCrosse La Crosse WI 54601

NELSON, ARNOLD BERNARD, b Valley Springs, SDak, Aug 26, 22; m 43; c 4. ANIMAL NUTRITION. *Educ:* SDak State Col, BS, 43, MS, 48; Cornell Univ, PhD(animal husb), 50. *Prof Exp:* Asst animal husb, SDak State Col, 46-47, asst animal husbandman, 47-48; asst, Cornell Univ, 48-50; from asst prof to assoc prof, Okla State Univ, 50-62; prof, 63-71, PROF ANIMAL RANGE SCI & HEAD DEPT, NMEX STATE UNIV, 71- *Mem:* AAAS; Am Soc Animal Sci; Soc Range Mgt; Am Dairy Sci Asn. *Res:* Ruminant nutrition; applied cattle nutrition. *Mailing Add:* Dept of Animal Range Sci NMex State Univ Las Cruces NM 88003

NELSON, ARTHUR ALEXANDER, JR, b New Roads, La, June 12, 46; m 78; c 2. PHARMACY. *Educ:* Northeast La Univ, BS, 69, MS, 71; Univ Iowa, PhD(pharm), 73. *Prof Exp:* Asst prof pharm, Med Ctr, Univ Ill, 73-76; ASSOC PROF PHARM, UNIV SC, 76- *Concurrent Pos:* Proj dir, Ill Dept Ment Health & Deviation Disabilities, 75-76; consult, Ill State Pharmaceut Asn, 74-76 & Col Pharm, Univ Nebr, 75-76. *Mem:* Am Soc Hosp Pharmacists; Acad Pharmaceut Sci. *Res:* Behavioral and administrative practices of pharmacists; economics of health care delivery with particular interest in the pharmaceutical component. *Mailing Add:* Col of Pharm Univ of SC Columbia SC 29208

NELSON, ARTHUR EDWARD, b Orange, NJ; m 52; c 3. STRUCTURAL GEOLOGY, METAMORPHIC GEOLOGY. *Educ:* Upsala Col, BS, 49; Univ Tenn, MS, 54. *Prof Exp:* GEOLOGIST, US GEOL SURV, 50- *Mem:* Geol Soc Am. *Res:* Volcanic geology and stratigraphy of Puerto Rico; stratigraphy of medium to high grade metamorphic rocks; tectonics and structural geology of Appalachian orogenic belt. *Mailing Add:* MS 926 US Geol Surg Nat Ctr Reston VA 22092

NELSON, ARTHUR KENDALL, b Washburn, Wis, Aug 28, 32; m 61; c 1. CHEMISTRY. *Educ:* Univ Wis, BS, 54; Univ Minn, PhD(chem), 59. *Prof Exp:* Asst prof, Macalester Col, 59-60; res chemist, Stauffer Chem Co, 60-64; sr tech specialist, Nalco Chem Co, 64-68; mem staff, Rauland Div, Zenith Radio Corp, 68-76; mgr bus develop, Carus Chem Co, 77-81, VPRES & GEN MGR, LA SALLE TRANSPORT CO, SUBSID CARUS CORP, 81- *Mem:* Am Chem Soc. *Mailing Add:* 1267 W Highland Ave Elgin IL 60120

NELSON, ARTHUR L(EE), b Dallas, Tex, Jan 29, 15; m 35; c 2. ENGINEERING. *Educ:* Univ Ark, BSEE, 38. *Prof Exp:* Engr, RCA Mfg Co, Inc, 35-37; proj engr, Farnsworth TV & Radio Corp, 38-41; chief engr & prod mgr, Aircraft Accessories Corp, 41-43; pres, Nelson Elec Corp, 43-49; engr, Fla Power Corp, 49-51; tech adv, US Air Force, 51-53; consult engr, 53-54; consult, RCA Serv Co, Inc, 54-56; sr engr, Scripps Inst, Univ Calif, 56-59; supvry engr, US Navy Electronics Lab, 59-63; founder & pres, Electro Oceanics, Inc, 63-65; founder & chmn bd dirs, Hotsplicer Corp, 68-74. *Concurrent Pos:* Consult ocean engr; founder & owner, Arthur L Nelson & Co, 65- *Mem:* Marine Technol Soc. *Res:* Oceanography; high-voltage engineering; development of methods and equipment for splicing and terminating high-voltage underground cables. *Mailing Add:* 954 Candlelight Pl La Jolla CA 92037

NELSON, ARTHUR ROBERT, optics, see previous edition

NELSON, BERNARD ANDREW, b Chicago, Ill, Jan 10, 10; m 36. ORGANIC CHEMISTRY. *Educ:* Wheaton Col, Ill, BS, 31; Northwestern Univ, MS, 38, PhD(org chem), 42. *Prof Exp:* Asst chem, Wheaton Col, Ill, 28-31; instr, Maine Twp Jr Col, Ill, 39-42; asst prof, Baylor Univ, 42-43; from asst prof to assoc prof, 43-53, chmn chem dept, 69-76, prof, 53-78, EMER PROF CHEM, WHEATON COL, ILL, 78- *Mem:* Fel AAAS; Nat Sci Teachers Asn; Am Chem Soc; Am Inst Chem. *Res:* Cyclic acetals and ethers; Grignard reagents; acridine and anthracene derivatives; absorption spectra in ultraviolet range; chromanones; pyrazolines. *Mailing Add:* 1018 N Scott Wheaton IL 60787

NELSON, BERNARD CLINTON, b Cass Lake, Minn, June 2, 34; m 64; c 2. MEDICAL ENTOMOLOGY. *Educ:* Wis State Univ, Superior, BS, 56; Univ Mich, MS, 60; Univ Calif, Berkeley, PhD(parasitol), 68. *Prof Exp:* Fel ecol avian lice, McMaster Animal Health Lab, Nat Inst Gen Med Sci, Australia, 68-70; PUB HEALTH BIOLOGIST ZOONOTIC DIS INVEST, VECTOR BIOL & CONTROL SECT, CALIF DEPT HEALTH SERV, 71- *Concurrent Pos:* Assoc exp sta, Div Entomol & Parasitol, Univ Calif, Berkeley, 71- *Mem:* Am Soc Mammal; Wildlife Dis Soc; Am Soc Trop Med & Hyg; AAAS; Am Nature Study Soc. *Res:* Biology and taxonomy of avian lice; ecology of bubonic plague and tick-borne diseases in California; parasites of fleas; ecology of fleas. *Mailing Add:* Vector Biol & Control Sect Calif Dept Health Serv 2151 Berkeley Way Berkeley CA 94704

NELSON, BRUCE PHILIP, elementary particle physics, see previous edition

NELSON, BRUCE WARREN, b Cleveland, Ohio, Mar 17, 29; m 56; c 1. SEDIMENTOLOGY, CLAY MINERALOGY. *Educ:* Harvard Col, AB, 51; Pa State Univ, MS, 54; Univ Ill, PhD(geol), 55. *Prof Exp:* From assoc prof to prof geol, Va Polytech Inst, 55-63; prof & head dept, Univ SC, 63-74, dean col arts & sci, 66-72, dean grad sch & vprovost advan studies & res, 72-74; prof environ sci, dean & asst provost, 74-77, assoc provost, 77-81, PROF ENVIRON SCI, SCH CONTINUING EDUC, UNIV VA, 81- *Concurrent Pos:* Geologist, US Geol Surv, 51-55; geologist, Ohio Geol Surv, 52-54; vis scientist, Am Geol Inst, 64-69; vis prof, Univ Va, 70-71. *Mem:* Fel AAAS; fel Mineral Soc Am; fel Geol Soc Am; Soc Econ Paleontologists & Mineralogists. *Res:* Sedimentary mineralogy, geochemistry, and petrology; recent sedimentary processes; diagenesis; chemistry of natural waters; estuarine environment. *Mailing Add:* 36 University Circle Univ of Va Charlottesville VA 22903

NELSON, BURT, b Milwaukee, Wis, Mar 10, 22; m 47. ASTRONOMY. *Educ:* Univ Wis, BS, 51, MS, 52, PhD(philos), 59. *Prof Exp:* Asst prof astron & phys sci, 57-61, assoc prof astron, 61-66, PROF ASTRON, SAN DIEGO STATE COL, 66- *Mem:* Am Astron Soc. *Res:* Astronomical photoelectric photometry. *Mailing Add:* Dept of Astron San Diego State Univ San Diego CA 92182

NELSON, (JOHN) BYRON, b Buffalo Center, Iowa, Feb 7, 37; m 63, 81; c 3. INDUSTRIAL & HUMAN FACTORS ENGINEERING. *Educ:* Iowa State Univ, BSIE, 59; Purdue Univ, MSIE, 65, PhD(indust eng), 69. *Prof Exp:* Qual control engr, US Gypsum Co, 59-60, personnel supvr, 60-61; indust engr, Sylvania Electronics Prod, Inc, 61-63; indust engr, Radio Corp Am, 66; instr indust eng, Purdue Univ, 66-68; asst prof indust eng & opers res, Va Polytech Inst & State Univ, 68-73; PROF ENG MGT, UNIV MO-ROLLA, 73-, EXTEN CONSULT, 76- *Honors & Awards:* Res Award, Am Inst Indust Engrs, 66. *Mem:* Am Inst Indust Engrs; Human Factors Soc; Am Soc Eng Educ. *Res:* Dynamic visual perception; occupational safety and health; life cycle costing and inflation of engineering projects; engineering economics. *Mailing Add:* 317 Eng Res Lab Univ of Mo Rolla MO 65401

NELSON, CARL WILLIAM, b Troy, NY. PHYSICAL CHEMISTRY, APPLIED PHYSICS. *Educ:* Rensselaer Polytech Inst, BChE, 59, MChE, 64. *Prof Exp:* RES PHYS SCIENTIST PHYS CHEM, US ARMY BALLISTIC RES LABS, 71- *Mem:* Am Inst Chem Engrs; AAAS. *Res:* Combustion of propellants. *Mailing Add:* US Army Ballistic Res Lab Aberdeen Proving Ground MD 21005

NELSON, CARLTON HANS, b Wabasha, Minn, Dec 16, 37; m 62; c 2. GEOLOGY. *Educ:* Carleton Col, BA, 59; Univ Minn, MS, 62; Ore State Univ, PhD(oceanog), 68. *Prof Exp:* Ranger naturalist, Nat Park Serv, 59-61 & 63; teaching asst, Lehigh Univ, 61-62; field asst, US Geol Surv, 62; instr phys sci, Portland State Col, 62-63; res asst, Ore State Univ, 63-67; GEOLOGIST, US GEOL SURV, 66- *Concurrent Pos:* Vis asst prof, Chapman Col, 66, San Jose State Col, 68-69 & Calif State Col, Hayward, 70-71; actg asst prof, Stanford Univ, 73; vis prof, Univ Barcelona, Spain & Univ Utrecht, The Netherlands, 81. *Mem:* AAAS; Soc Econ Paleont & Mineral; Int Asn Sedimentol; fel Geol Soc Am. *Res:* Geological limnology; Pleistocene geology; sedimentology; geological oceanography; epicontinental shelf and deep-sea fan sedimentation; placer and trace metal dispersal in marine sediments; marine geology. *Mailing Add:* US Geol Surv 345 Middlefield Rd Menlo Park CA 94025

NELSON, CAROLYNN, b Jacksonville, Fla, Oct 16, 51; m 82. VIBRATIONAL SPECTROSCOPY, GLASSES. *Educ:* Univ NMex, BS, 74; Univ Calif, San Diego, MS, 77; Pa State Univ, PhD(geochem), 81. *Prof Exp:* MEM TECH STAFF CERAMIC DEVELOP, SANDIA NAT LAB, 81- *Mem:* Am Geophys Union; Am Ceramic Soc. *Mailing Add:* Div 5845 Sandia Nat Lab Albuquerque NM 87185

NELSON, CECIL MORRIS, b Rock Island, Ill, Nov 12, 22; m 46; c 2. PHYSICS, CHEMISTRY. *Educ:* Univ Chicago, BS, 44, MS, 48; Univ Tenn, PhD(chem), 52. *Prof Exp:* Anal chemist, Clinton Lab, 44-46; phys chemist, Argonne Nat Lab, 46-48 & Oak Ridge Nat Lab, 48-60; chmn sci div, 70-77, PROF PHYSICS, EMORY & HENRY COL, 60- *Mem:* Am Asn Physics Teachers. *Res:* Radiation effects in ionic crystals. *Mailing Add:* Dept of Physics Emory & Henry Col Emory VA 24327

NELSON, CHARLES A, b Buffalo, NY, June 26, 36; m 64; c 2. BIOCHEMISTRY. *Educ:* Cornell Col, BS, 57; Univ Iowa, MS, 60, PhD(biochem), 62. *Prof Exp:* Res assoc, Duke Univ, 61-66; ASST PROF BIOCHEM, MED CTR, UNIV ARK, LITTLE ROCK, 66- *Concurrent Pos:* NIH fel, 62-64. *Res:* Subunit structure of serum lipoproteins and xanthine oxidase; detergent effects on proteins, their activity and dissociation to subunits; further effect of combining detergents with other denaturants. *Mailing Add:* 235 Markwood Dr Ark Med Ctr Little Rock AR 72205

NELSON, CHARLES ARNOLD, b Chadron, Nebr, Oct 11, 43; m 71. HIGH ENERGY & THEORETICAL PHYSICS. *Educ:* Univ Colo, BS, 65; Univ Md, PhD(theoret physics), 68. *Prof Exp:* Res assoc high energy theoret physics, City Col New York, 68-70 & La State Univ, Baton Rouge, 70-72; Nat Res Coun-Nat Bur Standards fel, Nat Bur Standards, Washington DC, 72-73; asst prof physics, 73-78, ASSOC PROF PHYSICS, STATE UNIV NY, BINGHAMTON, 78- *Concurrent Pos:* Consult, Ctr Particle Theory, Univ Tex, Austin, 70-72 & Ctr Theoret Physics, Univ Md, 72-73. *Mem:* Am Phys Soc. *Res:* Particles and fields in theoretical high energy physics; mathematical physics. *Mailing Add:* Dept of Physics State Univ of NY Binghamton NY 13901

NELSON, CHARLES G(ARTHE), b Northport, Mich, Mar 4, 33. ELECTRICAL ENGINEERING. *Educ:* Mich State Univ, BS, 55; Stanford Univ, MS, 59, PhD(elec eng), 62. *Prof Exp:* Proj engr, Microwave Sect, Zenith Radio Res Corp, 62-64; asst prof elec eng, 65-71, PROF ELEC ENG, CALIF STATE UNIV, SACRAMENTO, 71- *Mem:* Inst Elec & Electronics Engrs; Inst Noise Control Eng. *Res:* High efficiency microwave tubes; acoustics and noise pollution measurements; instrumentation. *Mailing Add:* Dept of Eng 6000 J St Calif State Univ Sacramento CA 95819

NELSON, CHARLES HENRY, b Boston, Mass, July 28, 41; m 66. ENTOMOLOGY. *Educ:* Univ Mass, BS, 63, MS, 67, PhD(entom), 69. *Prof Exp:* From asst prof to assoc prof, 69-78, PROF BIOL, UNIV TENN, CHATTANOOGA, 78- *Mem:* Entom Soc Am; Am Entom Soc; Soc Syst Zool. *Res:* Systematics and morphology of the Plecoptera; systematic entomology. *Mailing Add:* Dept of Biol Univ of Tenn Chattanooga TN 37403

NELSON, CHARLES JAY, polymer chemistry, see previous edition

NELSON, CLARENCE NORMAN, b Starbuck, Minn, June 6, 09; m 35; c 2. PHYSICS. *Educ:* St Olaf Col, BA, 31; Ohio State Univ, MA, 33. *Prof Exp:* Physicist, Res Labs, Eastman Kodak Co, 33-53, res assoc, 53-74; RETIRED. *Concurrent Pos:* Lectr image sci, Rochester Inst Technol, 81-82. *Mem:* Optical Soc Am; Soc Photog Scientists & Engrs. *Res:* Optics; physics of the photographic process; sensitometry; vision; tone reproduction; modulation transfer; communication theory; image science; American standards on image evaluation; theory of the photographic process. *Mailing Add:* 73 Sagamore Dr Rochester NY 14617

NELSON, CLIFFORD MELVIN, JR, b Chicago, Ill, Nov 8, 37. PALEONTOLOGY, HISTORY OF GEOLOGY. *Educ:* Univ Ill, Urbana, BS, 60; Mich State Univ, MS, 63; Univ Calif, Berkeley, PhD(paleontol), 74. *Prof Exp:* Asst geol, Mich State Univ, 61-63; asst paleontol, Univ Calif, Berkeley, 63-66; instr geol, Cabrillo Col, 67-69 & 75-76; lectr geol, Calif State Univ, Hayward, 70-71; assoc historian, 76-80, GEOLOGIST, US GEOL SERV, 76- *Concurrent Pos:* Res fel, Smithsonian Inst, 74-75; res assoc, Mus Paleontol, Univ Calif, Berkeley, 75- *Mem:* Sigma Xi; AAAS; Geol Soc Am; Paleontol Soc; Hist Sci Soc. *Res:* Cenozoic marine invertebrate paleontology and stratigraphy; molluscan zoogeography, paleobiology and taxonomy; history of geology and paleontology, especially United States Geological Survey and predecessor agencies from 1867. *Mailing Add:* US Geol Surv 904 National Ctr Reston VA 22092

NELSON, CLIFFORD VINCENT, b Boston, Mass, Sept 23, 15; m 41; c 2. CARDIOVASCULAR PHYSIOLOGY. *Educ:* Mass Inst Technol, BS, 42; Univ London, PhD(eng electrocardiol), 53. *Prof Exp:* Asst biol eng, Mass Inst Technol, 40; spec res fel, Nat Cancer Inst, 41; engr, Submarine Signal Co, Mass, 42-47; res engr, Sanborn Co, 48; researcher, EEG Lab, Mass Gen Hosp, 49; asst res prof med & biophys, Col Med, Univ Utah, 54-56; RES ASSOC CARDIOL & RES, MAINE MED CTR, 56- *Concurrent Pos:* Am Heart Asn fel, 53-55, estab investr, 56-61; Nat Heart Inst res career award, 62-; adj assoc res prof, Boston Univ, 66-70; hon res fel, Baker Med Res Inst, Royal Melbourne Hosp, Australia, 69-70. *Mem:* Fel Am Col Cardiologists; Biophys Soc; Am Physiol Soc; Inst Elec & Electronics Engrs; Biomed Eng Soc. *Res:* Vector-cardiology; electrophysiology. *Mailing Add:* Dept Res Maine Med Ctr Portland ME 04102

NELSON, CRAIG EUGENE, b Concordia, Kans, May 21, 40; m 62; c 2. ECOLOGY, EVOLUTIONARY BIOLOGY. *Educ:* Univ Kans, AB, 62; Univ Tex, PhD(zool), 66. *Prof Exp:* Asst prof zool, 66-71, dir environ studies, 71-77, ASSOC PROF ZOOL, PUB & ENVIRON AFFAIRS, IND UNIV, BLOOMINGTON, 71- *Mem:* Soc Study Evolution; Ecol Soc Am; Am Soc Naturalists; Soc Study of Amphibians & Reptiles; Sigma Xi. *Res:* Ecological and evolutionary theory; community structure; speciation; evolutionary processes in amphibia; microhylid frogs. *Mailing Add:* Dept Biol Ind Univ Bloomington IN 47401

NELSON, CURTIS JEROME, b Mitchell Co, Iowa, Mar 25, 40; m 60; c 2. AGRONOMY. *Educ:* Univ Minn, St Paul, BS, 61, MS, 63; Univ Wis-Madison, PhD(agron), 66. *Prof Exp:* Res asst forage mgt, Univ Minn, 61-63; forage physiol, Univ Wis, 63-66; res assoc, Cornell Univ, 66-67; from asst prof to assoc prof, 67-75, PROF FORAGE PHYSIOL, UNIV MO-COLUMBIA, 75- *Concurrent Pos:* Fel, Welsh Plant Breeding Sta, Aberystwyth Wales, UK, 73-74; NSF fel, NATO, 73-74; assoc ed, Crop Science, 75-78; vis prof, Swiss Fed Inst Technol, 80-81. *Mem:* Am Forage & Grassland Coun; fel Am Soc Agron; Crop Sci Soc Am; Am Soc Plant Physiol; Brit Grassland Soc. *Res:* Crop physiology and biochemistry; genetic control of photosynthesis; carbon metabolism; yield expression of forage grasses; management of forage legumes and grasses. *Mailing Add:* Dept Agron Univ Mo Columbia MO 65201

NELSON, CURTIS NORMAN, b Rochester, NY, Jan 31, 41; m 61; c 3. NEUROSURGERY, BRAIN RESEARCH. *Educ:* Princeton Univ, BSE, 63; Univ Rochester, PhD(physiol), 70, MD, 72. *Prof Exp:* Intern surg, Mary Hitchcock Mem Hosp, 72-73; resident neurosurg, Mass Gen Hosp, 73-78; ASST PROF NEUROSURG, UNIV ROCHESTER & CTR BRAIN RES, 78- *Res:* Cerebral blood flow and stroke. *Mailing Add:* Neurosurgery Box 661 601 Elmwood Ave Rochester NY 14642

NELSON, D KENT, b Ft Collins, Colo, Mar 8, 39; m 60; c 4. ANIMAL NUTRITION. *Educ:* Colo State Univ, BS, 61; Mich State Univ, MS, 64; Iowa State Univ, PhD(animal nutrit), 68. *Prof Exp:* Asst prof dairy sci, Wash State Univ, 68-69; assoc prof dairy sci, Iowa State Univ, 69-77; PRES, NELSON FARM CONSULT, INC, 77- *Mem:* Am Soc Animal Sci; Am Dairy Sci Asn. *Res:* Calf nutrition; nonprotein nitrogen utilization; dairy cattle nutrition. *Mailing Add:* Nelson Farm Consult Inc 901 Ridge Rd Decorah IA 52101

NELSON, DALLAS LEROY, b Clay Center, Kans, Oct 4, 28; m 51; c 2. TOXICOLOGY, PARASITOLOGY. *Educ:* Kans State Univ, BS, 53, DVM, 53, MS, 59, PhD(parasitol), 63. *Prof Exp:* Instr path, Kans State Univ, 56-64; MGR TOXICOL RES, MOBAY CORP, 64- *Mem:* Am Vet Med Asn; Soc Toxicol; Am Col Vet Toxicol; Am Asn Vet Parasitol. *Res:* Host-parasite relationships; toxicology of agricultural chemicals. *Mailing Add:* 1013 Lennox Dr Olathe KS 66061

NELSON, DARRELL WAYNE, b Aledo, Ill, Nov 28, 39; m 61; c 2. SOIL CHEMISTRY, SOIL MICROBIOLOGY. *Educ:* Univ Ill, Urbana, BS, 61, MS, 63; Iowa State Univ, PhD(soil chem), 67. *Prof Exp:* asst & assoc prof, 68-77, PROF SOIL MICROBIOL, PURDUE UNIV, WEST LAFAYETTE, 77- *Honors & Awards:* Agronomy Award, Ciba-Geigy Inc, 75. *Mem:* Fel Am Soc Agron; fel Soil Sci Soc Am; Int Soil Sci Soc; AAAS. *Res:* Chemistry of nitrogen in soils and sediments; effect of fertilizer use on the environment; nature and properties of soil organic matter. *Mailing Add:* Dept of Agron Purdue Univ West Lafayette IN 47906

NELSON, DARREN MELVIN, b Lincoln, Nebr, Aug 15, 25; m 53; c 4. ANIMAL PHYSIOLOGY, ENDOCRINOLOGY. *Educ:* Univ Nebr, BS, 54; Univ Ill, PhD(animal physiol), 65. *Prof Exp:* Res asst animal sci, Univ Nebr, 54; asst prof animal husb, Calif State Polytech Col, 54-58; instr animal sci, Purdue Univ, 58-60; res asst, Univ Ill, 60-65; NIH fel as trainee in endocrinol, Sch Med, Univ Kans, 65-66; assoc res prof gynec & obstet, Med Ctr, Univ Okla, 66-67; assoc prof biol, Univ Redlands, 67-68; PROF ANIMAL SCI, CALIF STATE UNIV, FRESNO, 68- *Mem:* AAAS; Soc Exp Biol & Med; Am Fertil Soc; Am Soc Animal Sci; Poultry Sci Asn. *Res:* Neuroendocrine regulation of reproductive processes in mammals of both sexes; early neonatal differentiation of the central nervous system as influenced by steroid administration in mammals and avian species. *Mailing Add:* Dept of Animal Sci Calif State Univ Fresno CA 93710

NELSON, DAVID, b Cape Girardeau, Mo, Jan 2, 18. MATHEMATICAL LOGIC. *Educ:* Univ Wis, BA, 39, MA, 40, PhD, 46. *Prof Exp:* Asst prof math, Amherst Col, 42-46; from asst prof to assoc prof, 46-58, chmn dept, 56-68, PROF MATH, GEORGE WASHINGTON UNIV, 59- *Concurrent Pos:* Consult, Nat Res Coun, 60-63. *Mem:* Am Math Soc; Math Asn Am; Asn Symbolic Logic. *Res:* Theory of recursive functions; intuitionistic mathematics. *Mailing Add:* Dept of Math George Washington Univ Washington DC 20006

NELSON, DAVID ALAN, b Melrose, Mass, June 13, 31; m 56; c 3. CHEMISTRY. *Educ:* Mass Inst Technol, BS, 53; Univ RI, MS, 55; Univ NH, PhD(chem), 60. *Prof Exp:* Res assoc chem, Univ Ore, 60-62; asst prof, 62-67, assoc prof, 67-81, PROF CHEM, UNIV WYO, 81- *Concurrent Pos:* Petrol Res Fund grant, 62-63; USPHS grants, 65-68 & 69-71; NSF grant, 74-78; Dept Energy grant, 79-82. *Mem:* Am Chem Soc. *Res:* Photochemistry of organic nitrogen compounds; nucleophilic substitution of substituted pyridines; high performance liquid chromatography; synthesis of surface modified silica gels; analysis of petroleum products; water tracing compounds. *Mailing Add:* Dept Chem Box 3838 Univ Sta Laramie WY 82071

NELSON, DAVID B, b Elgin, Ill, Feb 22, 32; m 56; c 3. CHEMICAL ENGINEERING. *Educ:* Purdue Univ, BS, 53; Washington Univ, St Louis, MBA, 61. *Prof Exp:* Eng aide, Monsanto Chem co, 53-56, chem engr, 56-57, prod supvr, 57-63, group leader, Pilot Plant, Monsanto Res Corp, 63-66, sr res & develop mkt rep, 66-72, specialist air pollution monitoring & environ control serv, 72-73, MGR RES & DEVELOP MKT, MONSANTO ENVIROCHEM SYSTS, 73- *Mem:* Fel Am Inst Chem Engrs; Water Pollution Control Fedn. *Mailing Add:* 5276 Newell Circle Kettering OH 45440

NELSON, DAVID BRIAN, b Lincoln, Nebr, Oct 23, 40; m 64; c 2. PLASMA PHYSICS. *Educ:* Harvard Univ, AB, 62; NY Univ, MA, 65, PhD(math), 67. *Prof Exp:* Elec engr, Guy B Panero Engrs, 63-64; res asst, Courant Inst, NY Univ, 64-66; res staff mem eng physics, Oak Ridge Nat Lab, 66-71, res staff mem plasma physics, 71-79; CHIEF, FUSION THEORY & COMPUT SERV BR, OFF FUSION ENERGY, US DEPT ENERGY, 79- *Concurrent Pos:* Adv comt civil defense, Nat Acad Sci, 69-72; vis mem plasma physics, Courant Inst, NY Univ, 75-76. *Mem:* Am Phys Soc. *Res:* Theoretical plasma physics and applications to contolled nuclear fusion. *Mailing Add:* Off Fusion Energy ER-541 US Dept Energy Washington DC 20545

NELSON, DAVID HERMAN, b Houston, Tex, Mar 28, 43; m 65; c 2. VERTEBRATE ECOLOGY, AQUATIC ECOLOGY. *Educ:* Baylor Univ, BA, 66, MA, 68; Mich State Univ, PhD(zool), 74. *Prof Exp:* Asst prof biol, Adrian Col, 73-75; res assoc ecol, Savannah River Ecol Lab, Univ Ga, 75-77; asst prof, 77-80, ASSOC PROF BIOL, UNIV SOUTH ALA, 80- *Honors & Awards:* Roosevelt Mem Award, Am Mus Natural Hist, 69; Pres Award, Am Soc Ichthyologists & Herpetologists, 70. *Mem:* Ecol Soc Am; Am Inst Biol Sci; Am Soc Ichthyologists & Herpetologists; Soc Study Amphibians & Reptiles; AAAS. *Res:* Thermal ecology of aquatic organisms; biological effects of heated reactor effluents; temperature tolerances, temperature prefences and thermal stress; ecology, movements and activity patterns of amphibians and reptiles. *Mailing Add:* Dept Biol Univ South Ala Mobile AL 36688

NELSON, DAVID LYNN, b Sacramento, Calif, Dec 6, 42. PHYSICAL CHEMISTRY. *Educ:* Augustana Col, BA, 65; Univ Waterloo, PhD(phys chem), 69. *Prof Exp:* Vis asst prof phys chem, Univ Windsor, 70-72 & Rensselaer Polytech Inst, 72-75; SCI OFFICER PHYS CHEM, OFF NAVAL RES, 75- *Mem:* Am Chem Soc; Sigma Xi. *Res:* Spectroscopy and instrumentation; electrochemistry; surface chemistry and photochemistry. *Mailing Add:* Off of Naval Res 472 800 N Quincy Arlington VA 22217

NELSON, DAVID MICHAEL, b Madison, Wis, Nov 21, 46; m 69. BIOLOGICAL OCEANOGRAPHY, CHEMICAL OCEANOGRAPHY. *Educ:* Dartmouth Col, AB, 69; Univ Alaska, PhD(oceanog), 75. *Prof Exp:* Scholar biol, Woods Hole Oceanog Inst, 75-76, investr, 76-77; ASST PROF OCEANOG, ORE STATE UNIV, 77- *Mem:* Am Soc Limnol & Oceanog; Phycol Soc Am. *Res:* Nutrient dynamics of the near surface ocean; marine silicon cycle; silicon metabolism in marine diatoms; chemistry and biology of the southern ocean. *Mailing Add:* Sch of Oceanog Ore State Univ Corvallis OR 97331

NELSON, DAVID ROBERT, b Stuttgart, Ger, May 9, 51; m 75. THEORETICAL PHYSICS, PHYSICAL CHEMISTRY. *Educ:* Cornell Univ, AB, 72, MS, 74, PhD(physics), 75. *Prof Exp:* Res assoc chem dept, Cornell Univ, 75; jr fel physics, Harvard Soc, 75-78; assoc prof, 78-80, PROF PHYSICS, HARVARD UNIV, 80- *Mem:* Am Phys Soc. *Res:* Static and dynamic critical phenomena, superfluidity and melting; turbulence; properties of glasses. *Mailing Add:* Dept Physics Harvard Univ Cambridge MA 02138

NELSON, DAVID TORRISON, b Decorah, Iowa, May 16, 27; m 57; c 4. OPTICS. *Educ:* Luther Col, Iowa, BA, 49; Univ Rochester, MA, 55; Iowa State Univ, PhD(physics), 60. *Prof Exp:* Asst physics, Univ Rochester, 49-53; instr, Luther Col, Iowa, 54-57; asst, Iowa State Univ, 58-60; from asst prof to assoc prof, 60-67, PROF PHYSICS, LUTHER COL, IOWA, 67-, CHMN DEPT, 72- *Concurrent Pos:* NSF sci fac fel, Stanford Univ, 67-68; vis prof eng, Ariz State Univ, 74; mem, Govt Sci Adv Coun, 79- *Mem:* Am Phys Soc; Am Asn Physics Teachers; Optical Soc Am; Acoustical Soc Am; Int Solar Energy Soc. *Res:* Solar energy. *Mailing Add:* Dept of Physics Luther Col Decorah IA 52101

NELSON, DEANNA JEAN, physical organic chemistry, radiation chemistry, see previous edition

NELSON, DENNIS RAYMOND, b New Rockford, NDak, Feb 7, 36; m 61; c 3. BIOCHEMISTRY. *Educ:* NDak State Univ, BS, 58, MS, 59; Univ NDak, PhD(biochem, chem, physiol), 64. *Prof Exp:* Res chemist, 64-71, RES LEADER METAB & RADIATION RES LAB, AGR RES, USDA, 71- *Concurrent Pos:* Assoc prof biochem, NDak State Univ, 72- *Mem:* Am Chem Soc; Sigma Xi; Am Soc Biol Chemists; AAAS. *Res:* Structure, biosynthesis and hormonal control of insect cuticular hydrocarbons; mass spectra of insect methylalkanes; biochemistry of photoperiodic induction of dispause; mode of action of insect hormones. *Mailing Add:* Metab & Radiation Res Lab Agr Res USDA Fargo ND 58105

NELSON, DEWART ERLE, archaeometry, physics, see previous edition

NELSON, DIANE RODDY, b Knoxville, Tenn, July 10, 44; m 66. INVERTEBRATE ZOOLOGY. *Educ:* Univ Tenn, Knoxville, BS, 66, MS, 68, PhD(invert zool), 73. *Prof Exp:* Instr biol, 68-69, instr gen sci, 69-72, from asst prof to assoc prof gen sci, 72-78, ASSOC PROF BIOL SCI, EAST TENN STATE UNIV, 78- *Mem:* Am Inst Biol Sci; Am Micros Soc; Am Soc Zoologists; Soc Syst Zool; Int Soc Meiobenthologists. *Res:* Systematics and ecology of tardigrades or water bears, Phylum: Tardigrada. *Mailing Add:* Box 22900A E Tenn State Univ Johnson City TN 37601

NELSON, DON B, organic chemistry, see previous edition

NELSON, DON HARRY, b Salt Lake City, Utah, Nov 28, 25; m 49; c 3. MEDICINE. *Educ:* Univ Utah, BA, 45, MD, 47. *Prof Exp:* Res instr biochem, Univ Utah, 50, asst res prof, 52; res assoc med, Harvard Med Sch, 55-56, instr, 57, assoc, 58-59; dir metab ward, Peter Bent Brigham Hosp, Boston, 57-58; from assoc prof to prof med, Sch Med, Univ Southern Calif, 59-66; PROF MED, SCH MED, UNIV UTAH, 66- *Mem:* Endocrine Soc; Am Soc Clin Invest; Am Physiol Soc. *Res:* Endocrinology; control of adrenal secretion; mechanism of action of adrenal steroids. *Mailing Add:* Dept of Med Univ of Utah Med Ctr Salt Lake City UT 84112

NELSON, DON JEROME, b Pilger, Nebr, Aug 17, 30. ELECTRICAL ENGINEERING. *Educ:* Univ Nebr, BSc, 53, MSc, 58; Stanford Univ, PhD(elec eng), 62. *Prof Exp:* Mem tech staff, Bell Tel Labs, Inc, 53-55; instr elec eng, 55-58, from asst prof to assoc prof, 60-63, DIR COMPUT CTR, UNIV NEBR, LINCOLN, 63-, PROF ELEC ENG, 67- *Mem:* Inst Elec & Electronics Engrs; Asn Comput Mach. *Mailing Add:* Comput Ctr Univ of Nebr Lincoln NE 68588

NELSON, DONALD CARL, b Minneapolis, Minn, June 28, 31; m 53; c 3. HORTICULTURE, PLANT PHYSIOLOGY. *Educ:* Univ Minn, BS, 53, PhD(hort), 61. *Prof Exp:* Asst veg crops, Univ Minn, 53-55; from asst prof to assoc prof, 61-73, PROF HORT, N DAK STATE UNIV, 73- *Mem:* Europ Asn Potato Res; Potato Asn Am; Weed Soc Am. *Res:* Physiology and culture of potatoes. *Mailing Add:* Dept Hort NDak State Univ Fargo ND 58102

NELSON, DONALD DEWEY, animal nutrition, see previous edition

NELSON, DONALD FREDERICK, b East Grand Rapids, Mich, July 4, 30; m 54; c 2. PHYSICS. *Educ:* Univ Mich, BS, 52, MS, 53, PhD(physics), 59. *Prof Exp:* Fel physics, Univ Mich, 58-59; mem tech staff, Bell Tel Labs, Inc, 59-67; prof physics, Univ Southern Calif, 67-68; MEM TECH STAFF, RES DIV, BELL TEL LABS, 68- *Concurrent Pos:* Vis lectr, Princeton Univ, 76. *Mem:* Fel Am Phys Soc; Acoust Soc Am; Optical Soc Am. *Res:* Scattering of polarized electrons; laser properties; diode lasers and electroluminescence; electro-optic diode light modulators; optical waveguides; semiconductor and dielectric luminescence; nonradiative recombination; acousto-optic interactions; Brillouin scattering; electrodynamics of elastic dielectrics; nonlinear electroacoustics; continuum mechanics; drift velocities in semi-conductors. *Mailing Add:* Res Div 1C 332 Bell Tel Labs Murray Hill NJ 07974

NELSON, DONALD J, b Harvey, Ill, Feb 2, 38; m 60; c 2. BIOCHEMICAL PHARMACOLOGY. *Educ:* Oberlin Col, BA, 60; Yale Univ, PhD(pharmacol), 65. *Prof Exp:* Fel pharmacol, Case Western Reserve Univ, 65-67, instr, 67-69; sr res biochemist, 69-80, GROUP LEADER, BURROUGHS WELLCOME CO, 80- *Concurrent Pos:* Adj prof pharmacol, Univ NC, 76- *Mem:* NY Acad Sci; Am Soc Biol Chemists. *Res:* Synthesis of pyrimidine antimetabolites; purification and kinetics of thymidylate kinase from tumors and Escherichia coli; metabolism of thiopurines; control mechanisms in purine and pyrimidine biosynthesis; metabolic effects of allopurinol; adenosine deaminase inhibitors; anti-parasitic drugs and Leishmania. *Mailing Add:* Dept of Exp Ther Burroughs Wellcome Co Research Triangle Park NC 27709

NELSON, DONALD JOHN, b Perth Amboy, NJ, July 24, 45; m 67; c 2. BIOCHEMISTRY. *Educ:* Rutgers Univ, BS, 67; Univ NC, Chapel Hill, PhD(biochem), 72. *Prof Exp:* Fel biochem, Dept Pharmacol, Stanford Univ, 72-74 & Dept Chem, Univ Va, 74-75; ASST PROF CHEM, CLARK UNIV, 75- *Concurrent Pos:* NIH fel gen med sci, 74-75. *Mem:* Am Chem Soc. *Res:* Metal ion and small molecule binding to proteins by nuclear magnetic resonance and fluorescence spectroscopy; protein evolution and polymorphism; intermolecular associations in nucleoside-drug complexes. *Mailing Add:* Dept of Chem Clark Univ Worcester MA 01610

NELSON, DOUGLAS A, b Windom, Minn, Jan 20, 27; m 56; c 4. CLINICAL PATHOLOGY, HEMATOLOGY. *Educ:* Univ Minn, BA, 50, BS & MD, 54. *Prof Exp:* Intern, Philadelphia Gen Hosp, 54-55; resident path anat, Mallory Inst Path, Boston City Hosp, 55-58; med fel specialist & res clin path, Univ Minn, 58-60, instr lab med, 60-63, asst prof & asst dir clin labs, 63-64; assoc prof path & assoc dir clin path, 64-69, PROF PATH & ASSOC DIR CLIN PATH, DIV CLIN PATH, STATE UNIV NY UPSTATE MED CTR, 69- *Concurrent Pos:* Sr teaching fel path, Sch Med, Boston Univ, 57-58 & Harvard Med Sch, 57-58; hon consult hemat, Royal Postgrad Med Sch, Hammersmith Hosp, London, Eng, 70-71. *Mem:* Am Soc Clin Path; Am Soc Cell Biol; NY Acad Sci; AMA; Acad Clin Lab Physicians & Scientists. *Res:* Cellular pathology and cytochemistry of hematopoietic system. *Mailing Add:* Div of Clin Path State Univ Hosp Syracuse NY 13210

NELSON, EARL C(HARLES), chemical engineering, see previous edition

NELSON, EARL EDWARD, b New Richmond, Wis, Jan 11, 35; m 60; c 1. PLANT PATHOLOGY. *Educ:* Ore State Univ, BS, 57, PhD(plant path), 62. *Prof Exp:* Res forester, Pac Northwest Forest Exp Sta, US Forest Serv, 57-59, plant pathologist, 59-63; ASST PROF PLANT PATH, ORE STATE UNIV, 70-, US FOREST SERV PLANT PATHOLOGIST, FORESTRY SCI LAB, 63-, PROJ LEADER, 74- *Mem:* Mycol Soc Am; Am Phytopath Soc. *Res:* Forest disease; root diseases of northwest conifers; ecology of root pathogens emphasizing antagonism by soil fungi; dwarf mistletoes of northwest conifers. *Mailing Add:* Rte 2 Box 277 Corvallis OR 97330

NELSON, EDWARD A, b Cedar City, Utah, May 8, 25; m 48; c 6. ANIMAL BREEDING. *Educ:* Utah State Univ, BS, 52, MS, 53; Kans State Univ, PhD(animal breeding), 58. *Prof Exp:* Mgr, Br Agr Col Valley Farm, 49-51; asst animal breeding, Kans State Univ, 55-58; PROF ANIMAL SCI, CALIF STATE POLYTECH UNIV, POMONA, 58- *Mem:* Am Soc Animal Sci. *Res:* Reproductive activity in rams; synchronization of estrus in ewes; artificial insemination of ewes. *Mailing Add:* Dept of Animal Sci Calif State Polytech Univ Pomona CA 91766

NELSON, EDWARD BLAKE, b Altoona, Pa, Dec 12, 43; m 64; c 2. MEDICINE, PHARMACOLOGY. *Educ:* Pa State Univ, BS, 65; Mich State Univ, PhD(biochem), 70; Univ Tex Med Br, MD, 74. *Prof Exp:* Nat Heart & Lung Inst fel biochem, Univ Tex Southwestern Med Sch, Dallas, 70-71; sr scientist endocrinol, Univ Tex Med Br, Galveston, 71-76; asst prof internal med, pharmacol & therapeut, State Univ NY Buffalo, 77-79; ASST PROF INTERNAL MED, BAYLOR COL MED, 79- *Mem:* Am Col Physicians; Am Soc Clin Pharm. *Res:* Biochemical pharmacology; clinical pharmacology. *Mailing Add:* Dept Med Baylor Col Med Houston TX 77030

NELSON, EDWARD BRYANT, b McHenry, Ky, July 26, 16; m 41; c 2. PHYSICS. *Educ:* Western Ky State Col, BS, 37; Vanderbilt Univ, MS, 38; Columbia Univ, PhD, 49. *Prof Exp:* Asst physics, Columbia Univ, 38-41, lectr, 41-43; asst prof, Western Ky State Col, 43-44; res physicist, Manhattan Proj, 44-46; lectr physics, Columbia Univ, 46-49; from asst prof to assoc prof, 49-63, PROF PHYSICS & ASSOC HEAD DEPT, UNIV IOWA, 63-, PROF ASTRON, 77- *Concurrent Pos:* NSF sr fel, Cambridge Univ, 56-57; vis lectr, Univ Exeter, 61-62. *Mem:* Am Phys Soc; Am Asn Physics Teachers. *Res:* Nuclear physics; reactions in light nuclei; nuclear models. *Mailing Add:* Dept of Physics & Astron Univ of Iowa Iowa City IA 52240

NELSON, EDWARD MONS, b Milwaukee, Wis, Sept 20, 15; m 40; c 2. ANATOMY. *Educ:* Univ Wis, BA, 37, MA, 39, PhD(anat, zool), 47. *Prof Exp:* Asst zool, Univ Wis, 37-42; instr, Yale Univ, 47-49; assoc & asst prof anat, Stritch Sch Med, Loyola Univ, Ill, 49-59; from assoc prof to prof, Sch Med, Univ PR, 59-64; assoc prof, 64-67, PROF ANAT, DIV MED & SURG, ACAD HEALTH SCI, US, 67- *Mem:* Am Asn Anatomists. *Res:* Comparative and functional anatomy. *Mailing Add:* Div of Med & Surg Acad of Health Sci US Ft Sam Houston TX 78234

NELSON, ELDON CARL, b Dunkirk, Ohio, Dec 13, 35; m 57; c 2. BIOCHEMISTRY, NUTRITION. *Educ:* Ohio State Univ, BSc, 57, MSc, 60, PhD(nutrit), 63. *Prof Exp:* From instr to assoc prof, 63-75, PROF BIOCHEM, OKLA STATE UNIV, 75- *Concurrent Pos:* Vis assoc res biochemist, Univ Calif, Davis, 75. *Mem:* Am Inst Nutrit; Am Chem Soc; Am Soc Animal Sci; Am Soc Biol Chemists. *Res:* Metabolism and metabolic function of the vitamins A; nutrition; lipid metabolism. *Mailing Add:* Dept Biochem Okla State Univ Stillwater OK 74078

NELSON, ELDON LANE, JR, b Morehead City, NC, May 10, 42; m 67; c 1. MEDICAL PHYSIOLOGY. *Educ:* E Carolina Univ, BS & BA, 64, MA, 71; Univ Fla, PhD(med physiol), 74. *Prof Exp:* Fel physiol, Col Med, Univ Fla, 75; asst prof physiol, Okla Col Osteop Med & Surg, 75-80; MEM FAC, DEPT BIOCHEM, OKLA STATE UNIV, 80- *Mem:* AAAS; Sigma Xi. *Res:* Thirst mechanisms and how thirst is affected by alteration of renal and endocrine mechanisms. *Mailing Add:* Dept Biochem Okla State Univ Stillwater OK 74074

NELSON, ELDRED (CARLYLE), b Starbuck, Minn, Aug 14, 17; m 46, 63; c 1. PHYSICS. *Educ:* St Olaf Col, AB, 38; Univ Calif, PhD(physics), 42. *Prof Exp:* Instr physics & res assoc, Radiation Lab, Univ Calif, 42-43; group leader theoret physics div, Los Alamos Sci Lab, NMex, 43-46; asst prof physics, Univ Chicago, 46-47; partner & consult math physics, Frankel & Nelson, 47-48; head comput systs dept, Res & Develop Labs, Hughes Aircraft Co, 48-54, head adv electron lab & assoc dir res & develop labs, 54; assoc dir comput systs div, Ramo Wooldridge Corp, 54-58, head Army data processing systs proj, 58-60, dir intellectronic systs lab, 60-61, prog & appl math lab, TRW Systs, 62, dir comput & data reduction ctr, 63-69, DIR TECHNOL PLANNING & RES, TRW SYSTS, 69- *Concurrent Pos:* Res assoc, Calif Inst Technol, 46; lectr, Univ Calif, 47-48; prof, Univ Southern Calif, 52-53. *Mem:* Am Phys Soc; Inst Mgt Sci; NY Acad Sci; Asn Comput Mach; Sigma Xi. *Res:* Nuclear physics; quantum field theory; electronic digital computer; computer software; research on computer software technology, including the theoretical basis for software reliability, program structure, data structures and computer security. *Mailing Add:* 1808 Melhill Way Los Angeles CA 90049

NELSON, ELTON GLEN, b Elgin Ore, Sept 15, 10; m 50; c 2. TEXTILES. *Educ:* Ore State Col, BS, 37, MS, 46; Univ Minn, PhD, 61. *Prof Exp:* Shipping point inspector, State Dept Agr, Ore, 36; coop fiber flax, USDA & Ore State, 37-48; consular attache, US Dept State, India, 48-49; proj leader field crops res br, Agr Res Serv, USDA, 49-57, head, Cordage Fibers Sect, 57-60; asst chief agron & soils br, Off Food, Agency Int Develop, 60-61, asst sci adv, Latin Am, 61-63; asst dir bus serv & anal div, Off Textiles, US Dept Commerce, 63-70; FIBER SPECIALIST, PLANT GENETICS & GERMPLASM INST, AGR RES SERV, USDA, 70-; CONSULT, CORDAGE INST, 72- *Mem:* Soc Econ Bot; Am Soc Agron. *Res:* Long vegetable fibers, hard and soft fibers; cordage and industrial textiles. *Mailing Add:* 7813 Chester Rd Bethesda MD 20817

NELSON, ELVIN CLIFFORD, b Boulder, Colo, Aug 18, 07; m 32; c 1. PARASITOLOGY. *Educ:* Univ Colo, BS, 29, MA, 30; Johns Hopkins Univ, ScD(parasitol), 33. *Prof Exp:* From instr to asst prof zool, Univ Maine, 33-40; parasitologist, State Inland Fisheries & Game Dept, Maine, 40-43; assoc prof bact & parasitol, 47-65, prof microbiol, 65-76, EMER PROF MICROBIOL, MED COL VA, 76- *Mem:* AAAS; Am Soc Parasitol; Am Soc Trop Med & Hyg; Soc Protozool. *Res:* Cultivation of Entamoeba histolytica; mosquito cycle of Wuchereria bancrofti; laboratory diagnosis of Schistosoma japonicum; laboratory diagnosis of primary amebic meningoencephalitis. *Mailing Add:* Apt 712 2956 Hathaway Rd Richmond VA 23225

NELSON, ERIC ALAN, b San Bernardino, Calif, May 28, 49; m 71. PLANT PHYSIOLOGY, FORESTRY. *Educ:* Occidental Col, BA, 71; Ore State Univ, MS, 74, PhD(forest sci), 78. *Prof Exp:* Lab instr, Ore State Univ, 72, res asst, 72; forestry technician res, Forest Serv, USDA, 72; res asst, Ore State Uni Univ, 72-77; plant physiologist res, US Forest Serv, USDA, 78-79; res assoc, NDak State Univ, 79-80; RES PHYSIOLOGIST, WESTVACO CORP, 80- *Mem:* Am Soc Plant Physiologists; Sigma Xi; Soc Am Foresters. *Res:* Seedling physiology; physiology during dormancy; storage compounds; endogenous plant hormones; water relations; nursery production of seedlings for reforestation; photoperiodic responses. *Mailing Add:* Cent Forest Res Ctr Westvaco Corp PO Box 458 Wickliffe KY 42087

NELSON, ERIC LOREN, b Los Angeles, Calif, June 29, 24; m 48; c 3. MOLECULAR PHARMACOLOGY. *Educ:* Univ Calif, Los Angeles, BA, 47, PhD(microbiol), 51. *Prof Exp:* Asst bact, Univ Calif, Los Angeles, 48-51, assoc infectious dis, Med Sch, 51-52, instr, 52-55, asst prof, 55-58, asst prof bact, 58-60; sci dir, Allergan Pharmaceut Corp, Calif, 61-63, vpres, 63-72; PRES, NELSON RES & DEVELOP CO, 72- *Concurrent Pos:* Res assoc, Univ Chicago, 55-57. *Mem:* Am Soc Microbiol; Soc Exp Biol & Med; Int Soc Chemotherapy. *Res:* Speciation and brucellaphage of brucella; hemoglobin particles; radiation infection; cellular immunity; ophthalmology; bioreceptors and molecular design. *Mailing Add:* Nelson Res & Develop Co 19722 Jamboree Blvd Irvine CA 92715

NELSON, ERIC V, b Green Bay, Wis, Jan 9, 40; m 61; c 4. ENTOMOLOGY, APICULTURE. *Educ:* Univ Wis, BS, 61, MS, 63; Univ Man, PhD(entom), 66. *Prof Exp:* Res entomologist, Entom Res Apicult Br, Agr Res Serv, USDA, 66-67; asst prof, 67-70, assoc prof, 70-79, PROF BIOL, OHIO NORTHERN UNIV, 80- *Concurrent Pos:* Vis assoc prof entom, Univ Man, 73-74. *Mem:* Entom Soc Am; Sigma Xi. *Res:* Physiology of bee diseases; diets for bees. *Mailing Add:* Dept of Biol Ohio Northern Univ Ada OH 45810

NELSON, ERLAND, b Blair, Nebr, June 4, 28. NEUROLOGY, NEUROPATHOLOGY. *Educ:* Carthage Col, BA, 47; Columbia Univ, MD, 51; Univ Minn, PhD(neurol, path), 61. *Hon Degrees:* DSc, Carthage Col, 73. *Prof Exp:* Armed Forces Inst Path fel, Max Planck Inst, Munich, Ger, 55-57, NIH fel, 59-60; assoc prof neurol & neuropath, Univ Minn, 61-64; prof neurol & head dept, Sch Med, Univ Md, Baltimore City, 64-81; PROF & VCHMN AFFIL HOSP, RUSH MED COL, 81- *Concurrent Pos:* Chmn, Dept Neurol, Mount Sinai Hosp Med Ctr, 81- *Mem:* Asn Univ Professors Neurol (secy-treas, 68-72); Am Acad Neurol; Am Neurol Asn; Am Asn Neuropath. *Res:* Clinical neurology; electron microscopy of central nervous system infections, neoplasms and leukoencephaopathy; ultrastructure of intracranial arteries; atherosclerosis; cerebrovascular disease. *Mailing Add:* Dept Neurol Univ Md Sch Med Baltimore MD 21201

NELSON, EVELYN MERLE, b Can citizen; m 63; c 2. ALGEBRA, THEORETICAL COMPUTER SCIENCE. *Educ:* McMaster Univ, PhD(algebra), 70. *Prof Exp:* Fel, 70-73, res assoc, 73-78, ASSOC PROF MATH, MCMASTER UNIV, 78- *Mem:* Am Math Soc; Can Math Soc; Can Soc Hist & Philos Math; Asn Symbolic Logic; Asn Women Math. *Res:* Equational compactness in algebras and relational structures; applications of model theory to universal algebra, in particular, first order properties of algebras of continuous functions; formal language theory. *Mailing Add:* Dept of Math McMaster Univ Hamilton ON L8S 4L8 Can

NELSON, FRANK EUGENE, b Harlan, Iowa, Dec 5, 09; m 40; c 3. FOOD MICROBIOLOGY. *Educ:* Univ Minn, BS, 32, MS, 34; Iowa State Col, PhD(dairy bact), 36. *Prof Exp:* Lab technician, Univ Minn, 32-33, instr dairy bact, 36-37; from asst prof to assoc prof bact, Kans State Col, 37-43; prof dairy bact & res prof, Iowa State Univ, 43-60; food scientist, Agr Exp State & prof food sci, 60-77, prof microbiol & med technol, 69-77, EMER PROF NUTRIT, FOOD SCI & MICROBIOL, UNIV ARIZ, 77- *Concurrent Pos:* Ed, Am Dairy Sci Asn J, 47-52. *Honors & Awards:* Borden Award, Am Dairy Sci Asn, 53, Award of Honor, 71. *Mem:* Am Soc Microbiol; Am Dairy Sci Asn (vpres, 64-65, pres, 65-66); Inst Food Technol; Int Asn Milk, Food & Environ Sanit; Brit Soc Appl Bact. *Res:* Lipolytic and proteolytic activities of bacteria; factors affecting resistance to heat; psychrophilic bacteria. *Mailing Add:* 3960 E Ina Rd Tucson AZ 85718

NELSON, FREDERICK CARL, b Braintree, Mass, Aug 8, 32; m 55; c 4. MECHANICAL ENGINEERING. *Educ:* Tufts Univ, BS, 54; Harvard Univ, MS, 55, PhD(mech eng), 61. *Prof Exp:* ?From instr to assoc prof mech eng, 55-71, chmn dept, 69-80, PROF MECH ENG, TUFTS UNIV, 71-, DEAN ENG, 80- *Concurrent Pos:* NSF res grants, Tufts Univ, 63-64, 66-68; vis res fel, Inst Sound & Vibration Res, Univ Southampton, 67; vis prof, Nat Inst Appl Sci, Lyon France, 77. *Mem:* AAAS; Am Soc Mech Engrs; Acoust Soc Am. *Res:* Structural dynamics and damping; mechanical acoustics & noise control. *Mailing Add:* Dept of Mech Eng Tufts Univ Medford MA 02155

NELSON, GARETH JON, ichthyology, see previous edition

NELSON, GARY JOE, b Oakland, Calif, Sept 27, 33; m 59; c 1. BIOPHYSICS, BIOCHEMISTRY. *Educ:* Univ Calif, Berkeley, BS, 55, PhD(biophys), 60. *Prof Exp:* Res fel heart dis, Donner Lab, Univ Calif, Berkeley, 60-63; sr staff scientist, Lawrence Livermore Lab, Univ Calif, 63-73; assoc res scientist, NY State Inst Basic Res in Ment Retardation, 73-74; grants assoc, NIH, 74-75; HEALTH SCIENTIST ADMINR, NAT HEART, LUNG & BLOOD INST, 75- *Concurrent Pos:* Nat Heart Inst fel, 60-62; estab investr, Am Heart Asn, 62-63; ed, Coun Arteriosclerosis Newsletter, 78- *Mem:* AAAS; Am Soc Biol Chemists. *Res:* Science policy and administration; membrane structure and function; lipid biochemistry; analytical instrumentation; chromatography; spectroscopy; heart disease and atherosclerosis; disorders of lipid metabolism. *Mailing Add:* Lipid Metab-Atherogenesis Br Rm 401 Fed Bldg Nat Heart Lung & Blood Inst NIH Bethesda MD 20205

NELSON, GAYLE HERBERT, b Dayton, Wash, Mar 17, 26; m 46; c 2. ANATOMY. *Educ:* Walla Walla Col, BA, 47; Univ Md, MS, 53; Univ Mich, PhD(anat), 57. *Prof Exp:* Asst biol, Walla Walla Col, 47-49; instr, Washington Missionary Col, 49-51, instr & actg head dept, 51-53; from instr to assoc prof anat, Loma Linda Univ, 57-66; from assoc prof to prof anat, Kansas City Col Osteop Med, 66-79, chmn dept, 71-79; prof anat, 79-80, ASST DEAN BASIC SCI, COL OSTEOP MED PACIFIC, 80- *Res:* Lymphatic system; biology and taxonomy of Coleoptera. *Mailing Add:* Col Osteop Med Pacific 309 Pomona Mall E Pomona CA 91766

NELSON, GEORGE DRIVER, b Charles City, Iowa, July 13, 50; m 71; c 2. ASTRONOMY, SOLAR PHYSICS. *Educ:* Harvey Mudd Col, BS, 72; Univ Wash, MS, 74, PhD(astron), 78. *Prof Exp:* Researcher solar physics, Sacramento Peak Observ, 75-76; researcher astrophys, Astron Inst Netherlands, Utrecht, 76-77; fel, Joint Inst Lab Astrophys, Univ Colo, 78; ASTRONAUT, JOHNSON SPACE CTR, NASA, 78- *Mem:* AAAS; Am Astron Soc. *Res:* Convection in stellar atmospheres, radiation driven hydrodynamics. *Mailing Add:* 714 Redway Houston TX 77062

NELSON, GEORGE HUMPHRY, b Charleston, SC, Nov 24, 30; m 56; c 4. BIOCHEMISTRY, OBSTETRICS & GYNECOLOGY. *Educ:* Col Charleston, AB, 51; Med Col SC, MS, 53, PhD(biochem), 55; WVa Univ, MD, 62. *Prof Exp:* USPHS res fel, 55-56; asst prof biochem, Univ SDak, 56-58; instr, WVa Univ, 58-62; asst prof biochem, 62-68, from instr to asst prof obstet & gynec, 62-68, assoc prof biochem & obstet & gynec, 68-74, PROF OBSTET & GYNEC, MED COL GA, 74- *Concurrent Pos:* Intern, Eugene Talmadge Mem Hosp, 64. *Mem:* AMA; Soc Gynec Invest; Sigma Xi. *Res:* Lipid metabolism in normal and abnormal pregnancy; fetal maturity evaluation. *Mailing Add:* Dept Obstet & Gynec Med Col Ga Augusta GA 30912

NELSON, GEORGE LEONARD, b Marshall, Minn, Dec 8, 43; m 64. ORGANIC CHEMISTRY. *Educ:* St John's Univ, Minn, BS, 65; Univ Wis-Madison, PhD(chem), 69. *Prof Exp:* NIH fel, Columbia Univ, 69-70; asst prof, 70-76, assoc prof, 76-80, PROF ORGANIC CHEM, ST JOSEPH'S COL, 80- *Concurrent Pos:* Cottrell Res Corp grant, 70-71; vis prof, Hahneman Med Col, 75-, Univ Wis, 75 & Univ Pa, 81-82. *Mem:* Am Chem Soc; NY Acad Sci; Sigma Xi. *Res:* Mechanistic organic chemistry; thermal rearrangements; synthetic organic chemistry; development of new synthetic techniques; heart and brain chemistry; preparation of biologically active compounds. *Mailing Add:* Dept Chem St Joseph's Col Philadelphia PA 19131

NELSON, GEORGE WILLIAM, b Mansfield, Ohio, Apr 27, 38; m 61; c 4. NUCLEAR ENGINEERING. *Educ:* Case Inst Technol, BS, 60, MS, 65, PhD(nuclear eng), 66. *Prof Exp:* Engr, Los Alamos Sci Lab, 61-62; asst prof nuclear eng, 66-70, ASSOC PROF NUCLEAR ENG, UNIV ARIZ, 70-, DIR, NUCLEAR REACTOR LAB, 76- *Mem:* Am Soc Nondestructive Testing; Inst Elec & Electronics Engrs; Am Nuclear Soc. *Res:* Cavity nuclear reactors; pulsed neutron experimentation; neutron thermalization; nuclear materials safeguards. *Mailing Add:* Dept of Nuclear Eng Univ of Ariz Tucson AZ 85721

NELSON, GERALD CLIFFORD, b Benson, Minn, Aug 21, 40; m 64. NUCLEAR PHYSICS. *Educ:* St Olaf Col, BA, 62; Iowa State Univ, PhD(physics), 67. *Prof Exp:* Res assoc, Iowa State Univ, 67-68; res assoc, Lawrence Radiation Lab, Univ Calif, Berkeley, 68-70; RES ASSOC, SANDIA LABS, 70- *Mem:* AAAS; Am Phys Soc. *Res:* Properties of x-rays from high atomic number elements; gamma ray energies, intensities and internal conversion of coefficients. *Mailing Add:* Sandia Labs Albuquerque NM 87115

NELSON, GERALD DUANE, b Detroit Lakes, Minn, July 9, 33; m 57; c 3. ELECTRICAL ENGINEERING. *Educ:* Univ Minn, BEE, 59; Univ Iowa, MSEE, 62, PhD(elec eng), 68. *Prof Exp:* Engr, Collins Radio Co, 59-60; teaching asst elec eng, Univ Iowa, 60-62; res engr, Honeywell, Inc, 62-66; teaching asst elec eng, Univ Iowa, 67; prin res engr, Honeywell, Inc, 68-69; assoc prof elec eng, SDak State Univ & pattern recognition specialist, Remote Sensing Inst, 69-78; PRIN ENGR SYSTS DESIGN, SPERRY UNIVAC, 78- *Mem:* Pattern Recognition Soc; Inst Elec & Electronics Engrs. *Res:* Pattern recognition systems and theory; statistical communication theory; information processing; dynamic and integer programming approaches to the selection of pattern features. *Mailing Add:* MS U2U19 Univac Park PO Box 3525 St Paul MN 55165

NELSON, GIDEON EDMUND, JR, b Jacksonville, Fla, Feb 21, 24; m 48; c 3. BIOLOGY. *Educ:* Univ Fla, MS, 50, PhD(zool), 54. *Prof Exp:* Asst zool, Univ Fla, 49; from instr to assoc prof, Ala Col, 52-60; asst prof zool & gen biol, 60-61, assoc prof biol, 61-67, prof, 67-81, EMER PROF BIOL, UNIV SOUTH FLA, 81- *Mem:* AAAS. *Res:* Ecology. *Mailing Add:* Dept Biol Univ South Fla Tampa FL 33620

NELSON, GILBERT HARRY, b Manhattan, NY, Sept 20, 27; m 55; c 3. CLINICAL CHEMISTRY. *Educ:* Wagner Lutheran Col, BS, 52; Purdue Univ, MS, 56, PhD(biochem), 58. *Prof Exp:* Biochemist, Christian Hansen's Lab, Inc, Wis, 57-58 & New Castle State Hosp, 58-64; CLIN CHEMIST, MIAMI VALLEY HOSP, 64- *Concurrent Pos:* Assoc prof clin chem, Univ Dayton, 69-79; pres, Clin Chem Consults, Inc. *Mem:* AAAS; Am Chem Soc; Am Asn Clin Chemists; NY Acad Sci. *Mailing Add:* Diagnostic Labs 1 Wyoming St Miami Valley Hosp Dayton OH 45409

NELSON, GORDON ALBERT, b Bentley, Alta, Nov 29, 25; m 54; c 3. PLANT PATHOLOGY. *Educ:* Univ Alta, BSc, 49, MSc, 51; SDak State Univ, PhD(plant path), 61. *Prof Exp:* Res officer bact, Defense Res Bd, Alta, 54-55; lab scientist, Prov Dept Agr, 55-57; res asst plant path, SDak State Univ, 57-61; res scientist, Nfld, 61-66, RES SCIENTIST, RES STA, CAN DEPT AGR, ALTA, 66- *Concurrent Pos:* Nat Res Coun Can res fel, 61; vis lectr, Mem Univ, 63-65. *Mem:* Am phytopath Soc; Can Phytopath Soc; Potato Asn Am. *Res:* Dairy bacteriology; bacterial plant diseases; soil-borne plant diseases and ecology of plant pathogens. *Mailing Add:* Agr Can Res Sta Lethbridge AB T1J 4B1 Can

NELSON, GORDON L(EON), b Maynard, Minn, Dec 28, 19; m 42; c 5. AGRICULTURAL ENGINEERING. *Educ:* Univ Minn, BAgrE, 42; US Naval Acad, cert, 45; Okla State Univ, MS, 51; Iowa State Univ, PhD(theoret & appl mech, agr eng), 57. *Prof Exp:* Sr agr engr, Portland Cement Asn, 46-47; from assoc prof to prof agr eng, Okla State Univ, 47-69; chmn dept, 69-81, PROF AGR ENG, OHIO STATE UNIV, 69- *Concurrent Pos:* NSF sr fel, Univ Calif, Berkeley & Davis, 64-66; dir, Ford Found proj through Ohio State Univ, Punjab Agr Univ, India, 69-73; consult, Okla Agr Exp Sta; mem bd dirs, Coun Agr Sci & Technol, 75-82, Am Soc Agr Engrs, 69-71 & 78-81. *Honors & Awards:* Award, Am Soc Agr Eng-Metal Bldg Mfrs Asn, 60. *Mem:* Fel Am Soc Agr Engrs; Am Soc Eng Educ. *Res:* Light structures engineering; environmental control engineering for livestock; wind force effects on low structures; similitude and theory of models; process engineering for agricultural products; development of agricultural engineering educational and research programs; mechanical engineering; author of over 115 technical papers. *Mailing Add:* Dept of Agr Eng 2073 Neil Ave Columbus OH 43210

NELSON, GREGORY VICTOR, b Minneapolis, Minn, Nov 16, 43; m 67. INORGANIC CHEMISTRY, MATHEMATICAL STATISTICS. *Educ:* St Olaf Col, BA, 65; Univ Calif, Berkeley, PhD(chem), 68. *Prof Exp:* Asst prof chem, Drew Univ, 68-73, assoc prof, 73-79; MEM STAFF, CELANESE RES CO, 80- *Concurrent Pos:* Vis prof, Inst Org Chem, Univ Fribourg, Switz, 74-75; consult, Chem Solve, Inc, Morristown, NJ, 78. *Mem:* AAAS; Am Chem Soc; Sigma Xi. *Res:* Organometallic complexes of transition metal carbonyls, metalolefin complexes; aids to chemical education, stereoscopic computer drawing, single-concept films; aromatic radical anions; crown complexes; electron spin resonance; computer modelling. *Mailing Add:* Celanese Res Co 86 Morris Ave Summit NJ 07901

NELSON, HARLAN FREDERICK, b Otranto Twp, Iowa, Aug 6, 38; m 61; c 3. AERONAUTICAL ENGINEERING. *Educ:* Iowa State Univ, BS, 61; Purdue Univ, MS, 64, PhD(aeronaut eng), 68. *Prof Exp:* PROF AEROSPACE ENG, UNIV MO-ROLLA, 68- *Mem:* Am Inst Aeronaut & Astronaut; Combustion Inst. *Res:* Thermophysics; radiation transfer in shock waves. *Mailing Add:* Dept of Mech & Aerospace Eng Univ of Mo Rolla MO 65401

NELSON, HAROLD CHRISTOPHER, b Brooklyn, NY, Sept 24, 46; m 79; c 1. CATALYST EVALUATION, ANALYTICAL EVALUATION. *Educ:* Brooklyn Col, BS, 68, MA, 72; City Univ New York, PhD(chem), 76. *Prof Exp:* Fel chem, Lehman Col, 73-76; lectr, Brooklyn Col, 71-72, adj lectr, 68-70; ROBERT A WELCH FEL, UNIV TEX, AUSTIN, 76- *Mem:* Am Chem Soc; AAAS; NY Acad Sci; Sigma Xi. *Res:* Synthesis and chemical characterization of transition metal complexes containing nucleic acid bases, hallucinogens and amino acids; EPR and variable temperature magnetic susceptibility measurements; stability constant measurements using potentiometry; IR spectroscopy. *Mailing Add:* W R Grace & Co Davison Div 7379 Route 32 Columbia MD 21044

NELSON, HAROLD STANLEY, b New Britain, Conn, Jan 17, 30; m 53; c 3. MEDICINE. *Educ:* Harvard Univ, AB, 51; Univ Mich, MS, 69; Emory Univ, MD, 55. *Prof Exp:* Chmn dept med, US Army Hosp, Ft Rucker, 62-64 & 5th Gen Hosp, 64-67; CHMN ALLERGY-IMMUNOL SERV, FITZSIMONS ARMY MED CTR, 69- *Concurrent Pos:* Fel allergy-immunol, Univ Mich, 67-69. *Mem:* Fel Am Acad Allergy; fel Am Col Physicians; fel Am Col Allergists; Am Asn Immunologists; Am Thoracic Soc. *Res:* Beta-adrenergic bronchodilators, efficacy and subsensitivity; allergy extract stability, compotent allergens and efficiacy of therapy; biologic effects of air ions. *Mailing Add:* Allergy-Immunol Serv Fitzsimons Army Med Ctr Denver CO 80240

NELSON, HARRY ERNEST, b Rockford, Ill, Sept 21, 13; m 41; c 3. MATHEMATICS, ASTRONOMY. *Educ:* Augustana Col, AB, 35; Univ Wis, PhM, 40; Univ Iowa, PhD(math), 50. *Prof Exp:* Teacher high sch, Ill, 35-37; teacher math, Luther Col, 37-42; teacher, Gustavus Adolphus Col, 42-46; prof math, 46-81, DIR, JOHN DEERE PLANETARIUM, AUGUSTANA COL, ILL, 67- *Concurrent Pos:* Mem Univ Ky team, Int Coop Admin, Indonesia, Bandung, 58-60. *Mem:* Math Soc Am; Int Planetarium Soc; Planetary Soc. *Res:* Meteors. *Mailing Add:* John Deere Planetarium Augustana Col Rock Island IL 61201

NELSON, HARRY GLADSTONE, b Chicago, Ill, Feb 4, 22; m 44; c 2. ZOOLOGY. *Educ:* Univ Chicago, BS, 45. *Prof Exp:* Asst zool, Univ Chicago, 45-47; instr biol, Gary Col, 47-48; teacher zool, Herzl Br, Chicago City Jr Col, 48-51; from lectr to assoc prof, 51-69, actg chmn dept, 65-66, chmn, 66-72, PROF BIOL, ROOSEVELT UNIV, 69- *Concurrent Pos:* Teacher, Herzl Br, Chicago City Jr Col, 54; assoc, Field Mus Natural Hist, 58- *Mem:* Celeopterits Soc; Soc Syst Zool; AAAS; NAm Benthol Soc. *Res:* Aquatic biology; invertebrate zoology and entomology; evolution, ecology, distribution, taxonomy and morphology of the Dryopoidea. *Mailing Add:* Dept of Biol Roosevelt Univ 430 S Michigan Ave Chicago IL 60605

NELSON, HARVARD G, b Logan, Utah, Aug 29, 19; m 47; c 1. DAIRY SCIENCE. *Educ:* Utah State Univ, BS, 41; Ohio State Univ, MS, 42; Univ Minn, PhD(dairy indust), 52. *Prof Exp:* Explosives chemist, Pantex Ord Plant, 42-43; PROF FOOD SCI, SOUTHEASTERN LA UNIV, 50- *Concurrent Pos:* Tech dir, Hammond Milk Corp, 51-58; consult, Brown's Velvet Dairy Prod, Inc, 55-; lab dir, Goldhill Foods Corp, 61-64. *Mem:* Am Dairy Sci Asn; Sigma Xi; Inst Food Technol. *Res:* Quality control work in seafood, vegetable and dairy products. *Mailing Add:* Box 370 College Station Hammond LA 70401

NELSON, HERBERT LEROY, b Eddyville, Iowa, June 15, 22; m 43; c 4. PSYCHIATRY. *Educ:* Univ Iowa, BA, 43, MD, 46; Am Bd Neurol & Psychiat, dipl psychiat, 53. *Prof Exp:* Intern, Univ Hosps, Iowa City, Iowa, 46-47; psychiat physician, US Vet Admin Hosp, Knoxville, Iowa, 49-51; chief acute treatment serv, Ore State Hosp, Salem, 51-55, clin dir, 55-63, asst supt, 58-63; dir, Iowa Ment Health Authority, 68-82; from asst prof to assoc prof psychiat, 63-73, PROF PSYCHIAT, UNIV IOWA, 73- *Concurrent Pos:* Proj dir, Iowa Comprehensive Ment Health Planning, 63-66; asst dir, State Psychiat Hosp, Iowa City, 66-74. *Mem:* AMA; fel Am Psychiat Asn. *Res:* Mental health administration; therapeutic community organization; community psychiatry. *Mailing Add:* Psychiat Hosp 500 Newton Rd Iowa City IA 52242

NELSON, HOMER MARK, b Malad, Idaho, Dec 11, 32; m 69; c 4. SOLID STATE PHYSICS. *Educ:* Brigham Young Univ, BS, 53, MS, 54; Harvard Univ, PhD(physics), 60. *Prof Exp:* Assoc prof, 59-71, PROF PHYSICS, BRIGHAM YOUNG UNIV, 71- *Mem:* Am Phys Soc. *Res:* Magnetic resonance under high pressure; molecular beams; plasma physics. *Mailing Add:* Dept of Physics Brigham Young Univ Provo UT 84602

NELSON, HOWARD GUSTAVE, b St Paul, Minn, Jan 61, 38; m 70; c 2. MATERIALS SCIENCE. *Educ:* Wash State Univ, BS, 60, MS, 63; Univ Calif, Los Angeles, PhD(mat sci), 70. *Prof Exp:* Process metallurgist, NAm Aviation, Rockwell Int Corp, 60-62; RES SCIENTIST, AMES RES CTR, NASA, 63- *Honors & Awards:* Except Sci Achivement Medal, NASA, 75. *Mem:* Am Soc Metals; Am Inst Mining, Metall & Petrol Engrs. *Res:* Understanding the influences of the chemical environment on the fracture behavior of materials. *Mailing Add:* Ames Res Ctr 230-3 NASA Moffett Field CA 94035

NELSON, IRAL CLAIR, b Eugene, Ore, Apr 18, 27; m 55; c 3. HEALTH PHYSICS. *Educ:* Univ Ore, BS, 51, MA, 55; Am Bd Health Physics, dipl, 62, recert, 81. *Prof Exp:* engr, Hanford Atomic Prod Opers, Gen Elec Co, 55-64, mgr external dosimetry, 64-65; sr res scientist, 65-67, res assoc, 67-72, mgr radial health res sect, 72-76, mgr environ technol, 76-80, PAC NORTHWEST LABS, BATTELLE MEM INST, 80- *Mem:* Health Physics Soc; Soc Risk Analysis. *Res:* Radiation dosimetry; methods for determining the fate of radionuclides deposited in the body from accidental intake; environmental consequences of construction, operation and decommissioning of nuclear power production and commercial and natural defense waste management facilities. *Mailing Add:* 2105 Putnam Richland WA 99352

NELSON, IVORY VANCE, b Curtiss, La, June 11, 34; m 60; c 2. ANALYTICAL CHEMISTRY. *Educ:* Grambling Col, BS, 59; Univ Kans, PhD(chem), 63. *Prof Exp:* From assoc prof to prof chem, Southern Univ, Baton Rouge, 63-67, chmn div natural sci, Shreveport, 67-68; asst dean, 68-71, V PRES RES & SPEC PROGS, PRAIRIE VIEW A&M UNIV, 71- *Concurrent Pos:* Vis prof, Loyola Univ, 67-68; consult, Oak Ridge Assoc Univs, 69-70. *Mem:* AAAS; Am Chem Soc; NY Acad Sci. *Res:* Higher education; administration; behavior of metal ions in nonaqueous solvent. *Mailing Add:* Prairie View A&M Univ Prairie View TX 77445

NELSON, JACK RAYMOND, b Fargo, NDak, July 25, 34; m 55; c 5. RANGE ECOLOGY, WILDLIFE ECOLOGY. *Educ:* NDak State Univ, BS, 60, MS, 61; Univ Idaho, PhD(range ecol), 69. *Prof Exp:* Instr range sci, 64-69, asst prof range & wildlife ecol, 69-74, ASSOC PROF WILDLIFE HABITAT MGT, WASH STATE UNIV, 74- *Concurrent Pos:* Consult, Spokane Indian Tribe, Bur Indian Affairs, 69-70 & Key Chem Inc, Wash, 70- *Mem:* Ecol Soc Am; Wildlife Soc; Soc Range Mgt. *Res:* Big game range ecology; big game livestock competition; multiple land-use management; habitat management. rehabilitation. *Mailing Add:* Dept of Forestry & Range Mgt Wash State Univ Pullman WA 99164

NELSON, JAMES ARLY, b Livingston, Tex, Feb 8, 43; m 63; c 3. PHARMACOLOGY. *Educ:* Univ Houston, BS, 65, MS, 67; Univ Tex Med Br Galveston, PhD(pharmacol), 70. *Prof Exp:* Res assoc pharmacol, Brown Univ, 70-72; sr biochemist, Southern Res Inst, 72-76; asst prof pharmacol & toxicol, Univ Tex Med Br Galveston, 76-; ASSOC PROF PEDIAT PHARMACOL, SYST CANCER CTR, UNIV TEX M D ANDERSON HOSP & TUMOR INST. *Concurrent Pos:* Assoc prof pharmacol, Med Sch, Univ Tex, Houston, 79- *Mem:* Am Asn Cancer Res; Am Soc Pharmacol & Exp Therapeut. *Res:* Biochemical pharmacology; cancer chemotherapy; ion and drug transport; environmental toxicology. *Mailing Add:* Dept Exp Pediat Syst Cancer Ctr Univ Tex M D Anderson Hosp & Tumor Inst Houston TX 77030

NELSON, JAMES DONALD, b Paducah, Ky, Apr 30, 43. MATHEMATICS. *Educ:* Univ Ky, BS, 65, MS, 67, PhD(math), 70. *Prof Exp:* ASSOC PROF MATH, WESTERN MICH UNIV, 70- *Mem:* Am Math Soc; Math Asn Am. *Res:* Analysis. *Mailing Add:* Dept of Math Western Mich Univ Kalamazoo MI 49001

NELSON, JAMES H, JR, b Marietta, Ohio, June 28, 26; m; c 2. OBSTETRICS & GYNECOLOGY. *Educ:* Marietta Col, BS, 49; NY Univ, MD, 54. *Prof Exp:* Spec fel, Gynec Tumor Serv, State Univ NY Downstate Med Ctr, 57-58, from instr to prof obstet & gynec, 61-76, chmn dept, 69-76, dir gynec tumor serv, 64-76; JOE V MEIGS PROF GYNEC, HARVARD MED SCH, 76-; CHIEF GYNEC & VINCENT MEM HOSP, MASS GEN HOSP, 76- *Concurrent Pos:* Am Cancer Soc adv clin fel, 61-64; from asst attend physician to assoc attend, Kings County Hosp, 61-66, vis attend, 66-76; fel med, Cancer Chemother Div, Mem Ctr Cancer & Allied Dis, 62-63; res fel, Sloan-Kettering Res Inst, 62-63, vis investr chemother, 63-68; consult, US Naval Hosps, St Albans, NY, 63-65, Bethesda, Md, 66 & consult & lectr, Philadelphia, Pa, 67; mem div gynec oncol, Am Bd Obstet & Gynec. *Mem:* AAAS; Am Cancer Soc; Am Col Surgeons; Am Asn Obstet & Gynec; Am Gynec Soc. *Res:* Gynecologic malignancy; thymo-lymphatic system. *Mailing Add:* Dept of Gynec Fruit St Boston MA 02114

NELSON, JAMES S, b St Louis, Mo, Mar 19, 33; m 56; c 2. NEUROPATHOLOGY. *Educ:* St Louis Univ, MD, 57. *Prof Exp:* Asst path, St Louis Univ, 57-59; instr neuropath, Columbia Univ, 59-60; asst path, St Louis Univ, 60-61; Nat Inst Neurol Dis & Blindness spec fel neurochem, 61-63; instr path, Washington Univ, 63-64; state neuropathologist, Div Ment Dis, Mo, 64-65; from asst prof to assoc prof path, Sch Med, St Louis Univ, 65-73; assoc prof path & assoc prof path in pediat, 73-75, PROF PATH, PROF PATH IN PEDIAT & DIR DIV NEUROPATH, DEPT PATH, SCH MED, WASHINGTON UNIV, 75- *Concurrent Pos:* Consult, St Louis State Hosp, 65-66; neuropathologist, St Louis Univ Hosps & Glennon Mem Hosp Children, 65-73; consult neuropath, St Louis City Hosp, St John's Mercy Hosp & St Luke's Hosp, 68-79; asst pathologist, Barnes & Allied Hosps & St Louis Children's Hosp, 73-75, assoc pathologist, 75-; vis scientist, Inst Neuropath, Frei Univ Berlin, 79-80; Alexander von Humboldt Found US sr scientist award, WGer, 79. *Mem:* AAAS; Am Asn Neuropath; Int Soc Neurochem; Am Inst Nutrit; Am Asn Pathologists. *Res:* Neuropathology of nutritional disorders and microcirculation; effects of vitamine E deficiency on the mammalian nervous system. *Mailing Add:* Dept Path Sch Med Washington Univ 660 S Euclid Ave St Louis MO 63110

NELSON, JERRY ALLEN, b Durango, Colo, Feb 22, 23; m 44; c 3. ORGANIC CHEMISTRY. *Educ:* Univ Wash, BS, 46, PhD(chem), 50. *Prof Exp:* Res chemist, 50-53, res supvr, 53-56, head, Textile Chem & Intermediate Res Div, 56-60, head textile & indust chem, Res & Develop Div, 60-69, head, New Prod Div, Org Chem Dept, Res & Develop Div, 69-76, head, Dyes Prod Develop Div, 76-78, RES & DEVELOP STAFF, CHEM & PIGMENT DEPT, E I DU PONT DE NEMOURS & CO, INC, WILMINGTON, 78- *Mem:* AAAS; Am Chem Soc. *Res:* Polymer, surface and fluorine chemistry. *Mailing Add:* 1012 Baylor Dr Newark DE 19711

NELSON, JERRY EARL, b Glendale, Calif, Jan 15, 44; m 65; c 2. ASTROPHYSICS, EXPERIMENTAL HIGH ENERGY PHYSICS. *Educ:* Calif Inst Technol, BS, 65; Univ Calif, Berkeley, PhD(physics), 72. *Prof Exp:* Fel particle physics, 72-75, DIV FEL ASTROPHYS, LAWRENCE BERKELEY LAB, UNIV CALIF, 75- *Mem:* Am Phys Soc; Am Astron Soc. *Res:* Pulsars, x-ray sources and black holes; optical pulsars; electron-positron colliding beam physics. *Mailing Add:* Lawrence Berkeley Lab Univ of Calif Berkeley CA 94720

NELSON, JERRY REES, b Payson, Utah, Apr 22, 47; m 67; c 2. MICROBIOLOGY, IMMUNOLOGY. *Educ:* Univ Utah, BS, 69, MS, 73, PhD(microbiol & immunol), 76. *Prof Exp:* Cult cur microbiol, Univ Utah, 69-74; technician, Deseret Pharmaceutical, 74-75; LAB DIR QUAL CONTROL, MICROBIOL DEVELOP & CONTROL INC, 75- *Mem:* Am Soc Microbiol; Am Pub Health Asn; Am Asn Lab Animal Sci; AAAS. *Res:* Biomaterials toxicology; tissue culture toxicology; bacterial aerosols, enumeration and sizing; barrier properties of nonwoven materials, endotoxin detection. *Mailing Add:* Microbiol Develop & Control Inc Univ of Utah Res Park Salt Lake City UT 84108

NELSON, JOHN ARCHIBALD, b Can, Nov 25, 16; m 46; c 3. ORGANIC CHEMISTRY. *Educ:* Univ Alta, MSc, 39; McGill Univ, PhD(org chem), 45. *Prof Exp:* Biochemist, Animal Dis Res Inst, Can, 45-46; chemist, Ciba Co, Ltd, Can, Ciba-Geigy Corp, 46-49, Ciba Pharmaceut Prod, Inc, 49-69, mgr process res, Ciba-Beigy Corp, 69-72, asst dir clin prep process res, 72-77, asst vpres develop & control, 77-79, dir tech doc, 80-81; RETIRED. *Mem:* Am Chem Soc; NY Acad Sci; Sigma Xi. *Res:* Process research in pharmaceuticals. *Mailing Add:* Develop & Control Div Pharmaceut Div Ciba-Geigy Corp Summit NJ 07901

NELSON, JOHN ARTHUR, b Sturgeon Bay, Wis, Jan 16, 38; m 62; c 2. CHEMISTRY, CHEMICAL ENGINEERING. *Educ:* Univ Wis-Madison, BS, 60; Univ Ariz, PhD(chem), 66. *Prof Exp:* Metallurgist, Res Dept, Inland Steel Co, Ind, 60-62, res engr, 66-68, sr res engr, 68-69; sr phys chemist, Res Dept, Whirlpool Corp, 69-70, sr res chemist, 71-80; MEM STAFF, CIBA PHARMACEUT INC, 80- *Mem:* Am Chem Soc; Electrochem Soc; Nat Asn Corrosion Engrs; Sigma Xi. *Res:* Corrosion of metals; treatment and processing of metals; physics and chemistry of processing systems. *Mailing Add:* CIBA Pharmaceut Inc 558 Morris Ave Summit NJ 07901

NELSON, JOHN D, b Duluth, Minn, Sept 16, 30. PEDIATRICS. *Educ:* Univ Minn, BS, 52, MS, 54. *Prof Exp:* Fel infectious dis, Univ Tex Southwestern Med Sch, 59-60; from instr to assoc prof, 60-70, PROF PEDIAT, UNIV TEX HEALTH SCI CTR, DALLAS, 70- *Concurrent Pos:* Nat Inst Allergy & Infectious Dis res fel, 60-62 & res career develop award, 63-73; vis prof, Med Ctr, Univ Colo, Denver, 62; mem antibiotics panel drug efficacy study, Nat Acad Sci-Nat Res Coun, 66-68; consult staff, John Peter Smith Hosp, Ft Worth, Tex, 74- *Mem:* Am Soc Microbiol; Infectious Dis Soc Am; Soc Pediat Res; Am Pediat Soc. *Res:* Pediatric infectious diseases. *Mailing Add:* Dept of Pediat Univ of Tex Health Sci Ctr Dallas TX 75235

NELSON, JOHN FRANKLIN, b Twin Falls, Idaho, Sept 27, 34; m 58; c 2. ORAL PATHOLOGY, ORAL MEDICINE. *Educ:* Univ Minn, BS, 57, DDS, 59; George Washington Univ, MAEd, 78. *Prof Exp:* Officer, Dent Corp, US Army, 59-62 & 63-79; PROF ORAL PATH & MED, COL DENT, UNIV IOWA, 79- *Concurrent Pos:* Consult oral med & path, numerous orgns including Repub of Vietnam, Univ Saigon, and various US Army installations. *Mem:* Am Dent Asn; fel Am Acad Oral Path; Int Asn Dent Res; Asn Dent Schs; Asn Military Surgeons. *Res:* Case reports epidemiological analysis, clinical features and applications of oral lesions and conditions; healing; osteogenesis grafting principles; effects of trauma as related to oral structures. *Mailing Add:* Col Dent Univ Iowa Iowa City IA 52240

NELSON, JOHN HENRY, b Ogden, Utah, Mar 25, 40; m 64; c 3. INORGANIC CHEMISTRY, ORGANOMETALLIC CHEMISTRY. *Educ:* Weber State Col, AS, 61; Univ Utah, BS, 64, PhD(chem), 68. *Prof Exp:* Teaching asst, Univ Utah, 64-65; Esso fel, Tulane Univ La, 68-70; asst prof, 70-74, assoc prof, 74-81, PROF CHEM, UNIV NEV, RENO, 81- *Concurrent Pos:* Univ Nev Res Adv Bd Grant, Univ Nev, Reno, 71-73, 73-76, 77-79; Petrol Res Fund grant, 71-74, 75-77; Res Corp grant, 74-76. *Mem:* AAAS; Am Chem Soc; The Chem Soc; Sigma Xi. *Res:* Synthesis, physical properties and reactions of coordination and organometallic compounds. *Mailing Add:* Dept of Chem Univ of Nev Reno NV 89557

NELSON, JOHN HOWARD, b Chicago, Ill, May 29, 30; m 52; c 3. BIOCHEMISTRY. *Educ:* Purdue Univ, BS, 52, MS, 53; Univ Minn, PhD(biochem), 61. *Prof Exp:* Res biochemist, Gen Mills, Inc, Minn, 60-61, supvr chem, microbiol & phys testing, 61-64, dept head refrig foods res, James Ford Bell Res Ctr, 65-66, head frozen food res, 66-68; dir corp res, 68, vpres res & develop, Peavey Co, Minn, 68-76, dir int ventures res div, 71-76; partner, Johnson, Powell & Co & Sci prog advisor, Charles F Kettering Res

Lab, 76-77; VPRES RES, AM MAIZE PROD CO, 77- *Concurrent Pos:* Mem gen comt on DOD Food Prog & chmn comt on cereal & gen prods, Adv Bd Mil Personnel Supplies, Nat Acad Sci, 73- *Mem:* Am Asn Cereal Chemists (past pres, 73-74 & 75); Am Chem Soc; Inst Food Technologists; Am Oil Chemists Soc; AAAS. *Res:* Lipids of cereal grain; new instrumental methods of analysis for food ingredients and products; new food product research and development; market and business planning. *Mailing Add:* 113th & Indianapolis Blvd 11 Peavey Rd Hammond IN 55318

NELSON, JOHN HOWARD, b Bozeman, Mont, Feb 5, 26; m 52; c 3. FOOD SCIENCE. *Educ:* Mont State Col, BS, 50; Univ Wis, MS, 51, PhD(dairy & food indust), 53. *Prof Exp:* Res fel, Univ Wis, 53-54; dir res, 54-61, vpres res & develop, 61-72, vpres corp develop, 72-75, vpres sci affairs, Dairyland Food Labs, Inc, 75-77; mgr, regulatory compliance, 77-78, corp dir, 79-81, VPRES QUAL ASSURANCE & REGULATORY COMPLIANCE, KRAFT INC, 81- *Concurrent Pos:* Mem food stand adv comt, State of Wis, 67-73, 77- *Mem:* Asn Food & Drug Off, Am Chem Soc; Am Dairy Sci Asn; Inst Food Technol. *Res:* Industrial enzymes for food and dairy field; enzyme modified food ingredients; flavors; food law; enzymes and fermentations in food processing. *Mailing Add:* 2230 Swainwood Dr Glenview IL 60025

NELSON, JOHN MARVIN, JR, b Richmond, Mo, May 19, 33; m 62; c 4. ENTOMOLOGY. *Educ:* North Cent Bible Col, BA, 56; Evangel Col, BS, 64; Southern Ill Univ, Carbondale, MS, 66, PhD(zool), 70. *Prof Exp:* Asst prof gen zool, Glenville State Col, 69-71; asst prof, 71-74, ASSOC PROF BIOL, ORAL ROBERTS UNIV, 74- *Mem:* Entom Soc Am; Am Arachnol Soc; Am Inst Biol Sci; Lepidopterists Soc. *Res:* Nest ecology and nest symbionts of Polistes wasps; morphology of Polistes larvae; spider distribution and ecology; butterfly distribution in Oklahoma. *Mailing Add:* Dept Natural Sci Oral Roberts Univ Tulsa OK 74171

NELSON, JOHN WILLIAM, b St Louis, Mo, July 18, 26; m 53; c 3. ENVIRONMENTAL PHYSICS, EXPERIMENTAL NUCLEAR PHYSICS. *Educ:* Univ Calif, Los Angeles, BA, 47; Wash Univ, BA, 49; Univ Tex, MA, 52, PhD(physics), 59. *Prof Exp:* Flight forecaster meteorol, US Weather Bur, La, 50-51; res assoc physics, Fla State Univ, 59-62; asst prof, Kans State Univ, 62-66; from asst prof to assoc prof, 66-77, PROF PHYSICS, FLA STATE UNIV, 77- *Mem:* Am Phys Soc; Inst Elec & Electronics Engrs; Am Asn Physics Teachers. *Res:* Low energy nuclear physics; application of nuclear techniques to environmental problems. *Mailing Add:* Dept of Physics Fla State Univ Tallahassee FL 32306

NELSON, JOSEPH EDWARD, b Decatur, Ga, May 4, 32; m 52. MATHEMATICS. *Educ:* Univ Chicago, AM, 53, PhD(math), 55. *Prof Exp:* Mem, Inst Advan Study, 56-59; from asst prof to assoc prof, 59-70, PROF MATH, PRINCETON UNIV, 70- *Mem:* Am Math Soc. *Res:* Functional analysis. *Mailing Add:* Dept of Math Princeton Univ Princeton NJ 08540

NELSON, JOSEPH SCHIESER, b San Francisco, Calif, Apr 12, 37; Can citizen; m 63; c 4. ICHTHYOLOGY. *Educ:* Univ BC, BSc, 60, PhD(zool), 65; Univ Alta, MSc, 62. *Prof Exp:* Res assoc zool, Indiana Univ, 65-67, asst dir univ biol stas, 67-68; from asst prof to assoc prof, 68-78, assoc chmn dept, 76-81, PROF ZOOL, UNIV ALTA, 78- *Concurrent Pos:* Mem, Fisheries & Oceans Res Adv Coun, Gov Can, 81- *Mem:* Soc Study Evolution; Am Soc Ichthyol & Herpet; Am Fisheries Soc; Can Soc Zool; Can Soc Environ Biol (pres, 72-74). *Res:* Hybridization in cyprinid and catostomid fishes; systematics of gasterosteid, psychrolutid, creediid, and percophid fishes; classification of world fishes; pelvic skeleton absence in sticklebacks. *Mailing Add:* Dept Zool Univ Alta Edmonton AB T6G 2E9 Can

NELSON, JUDD OWEN, b Stoughton, Wis, Sept 10, 47; m 68; c 2. ENVIRONMENTAL TOXICOLOGY, PESTICIDE CHEMISTRY. *Educ:* Univ Wis-Madison, BS, 69, MS, 72, PhD(entom), 74. *Prof Exp:* Proj asst, Dept Entom, Univ Wis, 68-69, res asst, 69-74; res assoc, 74-76, asst prof, 76-81, ASSOC PROF, DEPT ENTOM, UNIV MD, 81- *Mem:* Am Chem Soc; Entom Soc Am; AAAS; Sigma Xi. *Res:* Chemistry, metabolism and toxicology of pesticides and environmental contaminants; insect pheromone perception; insecticide resistance; chemical mutagenesis and carcinogenesis. *Mailing Add:* Dept Entom Univ Md College Park MD 20742

NELSON, KAREN ANN, b Spokane, Wash, Feb 16, 48. IMMUNE REGULATION, TUMOR IMMUNOLOGY. *Educ:* Univ Wash, BS, 70, PhD(path), 75. *Prof Exp:* Fel, Wallenberg Lab, Univ Lund, Sweden, 75-77; RES ASSOC TUMOR IMMUNOL, FRED HUTCHINSON CANCER RES CTR, 78- *Mem:* AAAS; Asn Women Sci. *Res:* Identification of the cells, molecules and genes involved in regulation of the immune response to neoplastic cells and manipulation of this response towards rejection of tumors. *Mailing Add:* Fred Hutchinson Cancer Res Ctr 1124 Columbia St Seattle WA 98104

NELSON, KARIN BECKER, b US. CHILD NEUROLOGY. *Educ:* Univ Chicago, MD, 57. *Prof Exp:* Assoc neurologist, Children's Hosp, Washington, DC, 67-71; asst prof, 70-72, ASSOC CLIN PROF NEUROL, GEORGE WASHINGTON UNIV, 72-; CHIEF CEREBRAL PALSY & OTHER MOTOR DIS SECT, NIH, 73- *Concurrent Pos:* Child Neurol Soc liaison, Nat Inst Neurol & Commun Dis & Stroke, 75-, mem clin res panel, 77-; Nat Inst Neurol & Commun Dis & Stroke rep, Interagency Group Metal Retardation, 75- & Interagency Collab Group Hyperactiv, 76-79; consult, Nat Inst Child Health & Human Develop, 76-79; mem, Food & Drug Admin Peripheral & Cent Nerv Syst Drug Adv Comn, 78-80, chmn, 81- *Honors & Awards:* Spec Recognition Award, USPHS, 77. *Mem:* Child Neurol Soc; Am Acad Neurol; Am Acad Cerebral Palsy; Am Epilepsy Soc. *Res:* Epidemiologic studies of the etiology of childhood neurologic disorders. *Mailing Add:* Nat Insts of Health 7550 Wisconsin Ave Rm 8CO4 Bethesda MD 20205

NELSON, KAY LEROI, b Richmond, Utah, Apr 4, 26; m 47; c 4. PHYSICAL ORGANIC CHEMISTRY. *Educ:* Utah State Univ, BS, 48; Purdue Univ, PhD(chem), 52. *Prof Exp:* Asst chem, Purdue Univ, 48-50, instr, 53-54; fel org chem, Off Naval Res, Univ Calif, Los Angeles, 52-53; asst prof, Wayne State Univ, 54-56; assoc prof, 56-61, chmn dept, 68-71, PROF ORG CHEM, BRIGHAM YOUNG UNIV, 61- *Concurrent Pos:* Vis prof, Ore State Univ, 71-72. *Mem:* AAAS; Am Chem Soc. *Res:* Directive effects in electrophilic aromatic substitution; rearrangement of aminoketones; olefin bromination and hydrochlorination; kinetics and mechanisms of organic reactions; natural products by selective extraction from bark and berries. *Mailing Add:* Dept of Chem Brigham Young Univ Provo UT 84602

NELSON, KEITH, b San Francisco, Calif, Nov 25, 34; div; c 2. ZOOLOGY, PSYCHOLOGY. *Educ:* Univ Calif, Berkeley, AB, 56 & 59, MA, 61, PhD(zool), 63. *Prof Exp:* NIMH res fel zool, State Univ Leiden, 63-65; asst prof, Univ Md, College Park, 65-68; assoc prof biol, San Francisco State Col, 68-69; dir, Int Dirtyupsquird Found, 69-73; RES ASSOC, UNIV CALIF, DAVIS & BODEGA MARINE LAB, 73- *Concurrent Pos:* Vis assoc prof, Tel-Aviv Univ, 71; adj prof, Sonoma State Univ, 72- *Mem:* World Maricult Soc; AAAS; Am Soc Naturalists. *Res:* Temporal patterning of behavior; motivation and memory; genesis of biological patterning; population genetics and evolution; ecological theory; marine biology; growth inhibitor substances and pheromones; crustacean growth and reproduction; biogeography; aquacultural genetics. *Mailing Add:* Bodega Marine Lab PO Box 247 Bodega Bay CA 94923

NELSON, KENNETH FRED, b Council Grove, Kans, Sept 18, 42; m 65; c 1. MEDICINAL CHEMISTRY. *Educ:* Univ Kans, BSc, 65; Univ Wash, PhD(med chem), 70. *Prof Exp:* ASST PROF PHARM, UNIV WYO, 70- *Mem:* AAAS; Am Chem Soc. *Res:* Medicinal chemistry, especially in the field of analgetics. *Mailing Add:* Sch of Pharm Univ of Wyo Box 3375 Univ Sta Laramie WY 82070

NELSON, KENNETH GORDON, b Chicago, Ill, May 29, 40; m 62; c 2. PHARMACEUTICS. *Educ:* Univ Wis, Madison, BS, 63; Univ Mich, Ann Arbor, MS, 64, PhD(pharmaceut chem), 68. *Prof Exp:* Asst prof pharmaceut, Col Pharm, Univ Minn, Minneapolis, 68-74, assoc prof, 74-79; SR RES SCIENTIST, UPJOHN CO, KALAMAZOO, MICH, 79- *Mem:* Fel Acad Pharmaceut Sci. *Res:* Drug transport mechanisms; fluoride reactions with hydroxyapatite. *Mailing Add:* Col of Pharm Univ of Minn Minneapolis MN 55455

NELSON, KENNETH WILLIAM, b Superior, Wis, Sept 27, 17; m 42; c 2. INDUSTRIAL HYGIENE. *Educ:* Superior State Col, Wis, BEd, 38; Univ Utah, MS, 57. *Prof Exp:* Teacher high sch, Wis, 38-39; lab asst toxicol, US Food & Drug Admin, Washington, DC, 40-41, jr chemist, 41-42; indust hygienist, 46-50, chief hygienist, 50-57, dir dept hyg, 58-66, dir dept environ sci, 66-74, V PRES ENVIRON AFFAIRS, ASARCO INC, 74- *Mem:* AAAS; Am Chem Soc; Am Indust Hyg Asn (pres, 58); Am Acad Indust Hyg (pres, 75); NY Acad Sci. *Mailing Add:* ASARCO Inc 3422 S 700 West Salt Lake City UT 84119

NELSON, KLAYTON EDWARD, b Vivian, SDak, May 15, 17; m 42; c 2. PLANT PATHOLOGY. *Educ:* SDak State Col, BS, 39; Univ Calif, PhD(plant path), 49. *Prof Exp:* Teacher high sch, SDak, 39-41; asst plant path, 47-49, from lectr to assoc prof viticult, 50-64, from jr viticulturist to assoc viticulturist, 50-64, PROF VITICULT & VITICULTURIST, UNIV CALIF, DAVIS, 64- *Concurrent Pos:* Agent-plant pathologist, Bur Plant Indust, USDA, 49- *Mem:* Am Phytopath Soc; Am Soc Hort Sci; Am Soc Enol. *Res:* Post-harvest pathological and physiological problems of table grapes. *Mailing Add:* Dept Viticulture Univ Calif Davis CA 95616

NELSON, KURT HERBERT, b Sweden, Dec 8, 24; US citizen; m 49; c 3. ANALYTICAL CHEMISTRY. *Educ:* Reed Col, BA, 48; Univ Wash, PhD(anal chem), 53. *Prof Exp:* Anal res chemist, Phillips Petrol Co, 53-60; res chemist, Tektronix, Inc, 60-62; res specialist, Autonetics Div, NAm Aviation, Inc, 62-64, mem tech staff, Rocketdyne Div, NAm Rockwell Corp, Calif, 64-70; sr res chemist, Burlington Industs, 70-72; SR RES ASSOC, INT PAPER CO, 72- *Mem:* Am Chem Soc; Am Inst Chemists; Tech Asn Pulp & Paper Indust; Can Pulp & Paper Asn. *Res:* Analytical methods development; high pressure liquid chromatography; nondispersive x-ray analysis; instrument research; paper and textile analysis; environmental chemistry and pollution; ultratrace analysis; gas chromatography; spectrophotometry; data correlation; quality control. *Mailing Add:* 14 Virginia Ave Monroe NY 10950

NELSON, KYLER FISCHER, b Litchfield, Minn, Sept 16, 38; m 61; c 3. ELECTROOPTICS. *Educ:* Hamline Univ, BS, 60; Purdue Univ, MS, 62; Univ Utah, PhD(physics), 68. *Prof Exp:* Fel, Univ Utah, 68; SCIENTIST, WEBSTER RES CTR, XEROX CORP, 69- *Mem:* Am Phys Soc; Sigma Xi. *Res:* Charge transport in insulating media; liquid crystals; photoelectrophoresis; photoconductivity. *Mailing Add:* Webster Res Ctr-114 Xerox Corp Xerox Square Rochester NY 14644

NELSON, LARRY DEAN, b Newton, Kans, Aug 5, 37; m 72. APPLIED MATHEMATICS, COMPUTER SCIENCE. *Educ:* Phillips Univ, BA, 59; Kans State Univ, MS, 62; Ohio State Univ, PhD(math), 65. *Prof Exp:* Part-time mathematician, Battelle Mem Inst, Ohio, 62-65; res assoc comput sci, Ohio State Univ Res Found, 65; mem tech staff, Bellcomm, Inc, DC, 65-68, supvr numerical methods & systs studies group, Appl Math Dept, 68-70, supvr data applns group, Data Systs Develop Dept, 70-72; supvr, Mgt Info Systs Dept, Bell Tel Labs, 72-77; Supvr rate & tariff planning div, Tariffs & Cost Dept, Am Tel & Tel, 77-79; dep adminr, Res & Spec Progs Admin, US Dept Transp, 79-81; PRES, MCS, INC, 81- *Mem:* Asn Comput Mach; Math Prog Soc; Am Math Soc; Inst Elec & Electronics Eng; NY Acad Sci. *Res:* Information systems; computers; telecommunications. *Mailing Add:* MCS Inc 440 New Jersey Ave SE Washington DC 20003

NELSON, LAWRENCE BARCLAY, b New York, NY, Jan 9, 31; m 55; c 2. CHEMISTRY. *Educ:* NY Univ, BA, 51, PhD(chem), 55. *Prof Exp:* Res investr, NJ Zinc Co, Pa, 55-56; res assoc, Socony Mobil Oil Co, Inc, 56-60; asst to vpres res & mfg, 60-62, corp res dir, 62-76, vpres tech, Sonnenborn Div, 76-80, CORP VPRES TECH & GEN MGR, SONNENBORN DIV, WITCO CHEM CORP, 81- *Mem:* AAAS; Am Chem Soc. *Res:* Industrial and petroleum chemistry; isotope tracer techniques; fused salt electrolysis; crystal growth; technical management. *Mailing Add:* Witco Chem Corp 277 Park Ave New York NY 10017

NELSON, LENIS ALTON, b Walnut Grove, Minn, Sept 22, 40; m 65; c 2. AGRONOMY. *Educ:* SDak State Univ, BS, 62; NDak State Univ, MS, 68, PhD(agron), 70. *Prof Exp:* Voc agr instr, Pub Sch, Minn, 62-64; asst supt agron, Southeast SDak Exp Farm, SDak State Univ, 64-66; res asst, NDak State Univ, 66-68; ASSOC PROF AGRON, PANHANDLE STA, UNIV NEBR, LINCOLN, 70- *Mem:* Am Soc Agron; Crop Sci Soc Am. *Res:* Variety improvement of proso millet; variety testing of grain crops such as corn, oats, wheat, barley and sorghum. *Mailing Add:* Panhandle Station Univ of Nebr Scottsbluff NE 69361

NELSON, LEONARD, b Philadelphia, Pa, Oct 29, 20; m 43; c 1. PHYSIOLOGY, REPRODUCTIVE PHYSIOLOGY. *Educ:* Univ Pa, AB, 42; Univ Minn, MA, 50, PhD, 53. *Prof Exp:* Asst zool, Washington Univ, 46-47; asst zool, Univ Minn, 47-48; from instr to asst prof physiol, Univ Nebr, 48-56; res assoc & asst prof anat, Univ Chicago, 56-58; Lalor Found fel, 58-59; assoc prof physiol, Emory Univ, 59-66; PROF PHYSIOL & CHMN DEPT, MED COL OHIO, 67- *Concurrent Pos:* Mem corp, Marine Biol Lab, Woods Hole, Mass, 54; Pop Coun, Inc fel, 56-58; USPHS sr res fel, Emory Univ, 59-60; USPHS career develop award, 60-66; Commonwealth Found fel, Cambridge Univ, 63-64; vis prof, Physiol Labs, Cambridge Univ, 63-64; prog dir develop biol, NSF, 67; Josiah Macy, Jr Found fac scholar award, 75-76. *Mem:* Fel AAAS; Soc Gen Physiol; Soc Study Fertil; Am Physiol Soc; Soc Study Reproduction. *Res:* Physiology of reproduction; gamete transport and fertilization. *Mailing Add:* Dept Physiol Med Col Ohio Toledo OH 43699

NELSON, LEONARD C(ARL), b Albia, Iowa, Aug 26, 20; m 46; c 4. MECHANICAL ENGINEERING. *Educ:* Iowa State Col, BS, 43; Mo Sch Mines, MS, 49; Northwestern Univ, PhD(eng), 54. *Prof Exp:* Asst prof mech eng, Mo Sch Mines, 47-50; lectr, Northwestern Univ, 53-54; assoc prof mech eng, NC State Col, 54-56; prof eng & dean, 56-61, PRES, WVA INST TECHNOL, 61- *Mem:* Am Soc Mech Engrs; Am Soc Eng Educ; Sigma Xi. *Res:* Thermodynamics and heat transfer. *Mailing Add:* Off Pres WVa Inst Technol Montgomery WV 25136

NELSON, LLOYD RUSSEL, plant breeding, see previous edition

NELSON, LLOYD STEADMAN, mathematics, see previous edition

NELSON, LOUISE MARY, b Kirkland Lake, Ont, May 13, 51; m 80. SOIL MICORBIOLOGY. *Educ:* Univ Western Ont, BSc, 72; Univ Calgary, PhD(microbiol ecol), 76. *Prof Exp:* Fel soil microbiol, Dept Microbiol, McGill Univ, 76-78; Rhodes vis fel soil microbiol, Dept Agr Sci, Univ Oxford, Eng, 78-79; res assoc, 79-80, ASST RES OFFICER, PRAIRIE REGIONAL LAB, NAT RES COUN CAN, SASK, 80- *Concurrent Pos:* Assoc ed, Can J Microbiol, 82- *Mem:* Can Soc Microbiologists; Am Soc Microbiol. *Res:* Physiology of dinitrogen fixation in symbiotic system between Rhizobium and a legume host, including dihydrogen metabolism in Rhizobium and interaction between dinitrogen fixation and alternate sources of nitrogen. *Mailing Add:* Prairie Regional Lab Nat Res Coun Can Saskatoon SK S7N 0W9 Can

NELSON, LYLE ENGNAR, b Donnybrook, NDak, Jan 6, 21. SOILS. *Educ:* Cornell Univ, MS, 52, PhD(soils), 59. *Prof Exp:* Soil scientist, USDA, 48; asst, Cornell Univ, 49-52; asst prof agron & asst agronomist, Agr Exp Sta, Miss State Univ, 52-55; vis assoc prof soils, Univ Philippines, 55-57; assoc prof agron & assoc agronomist, Agr Exp Sta, 57-60, PROF AGRON & AGRONOMIST, AGR EXP STA, MISS STATE UNIV, 60- *Concurrent Pos:* Vis prof, NC State Univ, 65; vis scientist, Rothamsted Exp Sta, Eng, 71-72; vis scientist, Int Rice Res Inst & vis prof, Univ Philippines-Los Banos, 78-79. *Mem:* AAAS; Soil Sci Soc Am; Am Soc Agron; Soil Conserv Soc Am; Int Soc Soil Sci. *Res:* Soil fertility; soil reaction and plant growth; nutrition and nutrient cycling in forest stands. *Mailing Add:* Dept of Agron Box 5248 Mississippi State MS 39762

NELSON, MARGARET CHRISTINA, b Louisville, Ky, Nov 13, 43. NEUROPHYSIOLOGY, ETHOLOGY. *Educ:* Swarthmore Col, BA, 65; Univ Pa, MA, 67, PhD(physiol psychol), 70. *Prof Exp:* Nat Inst Ment Health fel biol, Tufts Univ, 70-72; asst prof psychol, Brandeis Univ, 72-75; res fel neurobiol, Harvard Med Sch, 75-80; MEM STAFF, LANGMUIR LAB, CORNELL UNIV, 80- *Mem:* AAAS; Am Soc Zool; Animal Behav Soc; Soc Neurosci. *Res:* Behavior and neurophysiological correlates of behavior in insects. *Mailing Add:* Langmuir Lab Cornell Univ Ithaca NY 14850

NELSON, MARITA LEE, b Torrance, Calif. HUMAN ANATOMY, ENDOCRINOLOGY. *Educ:* Univ Calif, Los Angeles, BS, 57, MS, 59; Univ Calif, Berkeley, PhD(anat), 68. *Prof Exp:* Assoc phys educ, Univ Calif, Los Angeles, 59-60; instr, Ill State Univ, 60-64; actg asst prof anat, Univ Calif, Berkeley, 68-69; asst prof, Schs Med & Dent, Georgetown Univ, 69-72; actg asst prof, Univ Calif, Berkeley, 72-74; asst prof, Sch Dent, Univ Pac, 73-74; ASSOC PROF ANAT, SCH MED, UNIV HAWAII, 74-, ASSOC PROF REPRODUCTIVE BIOL, 81- *Mem:* Am Asn Anatomists; Sigma Xi; Endocrine Soc; Soc Study Reprod; Asn Women Sci. *Res:* Hormonal regulation of puberty; effects of high altitude on growth and pituitary function; effects of stress on reproductive maturation. *Mailing Add:* Dept Anat & Reprod Biol Univ Hawaii 1960 East-West Rd Honolulu HI 96822

NELSON, MARK RADFORD, b Salt Lake City, Utah, Jan 8, 46; m 68; c 2. PHYSICS. *Educ:* Harvard Univ, BA, 68; Princeton Univ, PhD(physics), 72. *Prof Exp:* From instr to asst prof physics, Univ Ill, Urbana, 72-76; DIR, LOS ANGELES OPERS, PATTERN ANAL & RECOGNITION CORP, 76- *Mem:* Am Phys Soc. *Res:* Speckle interferometry; signal processing; pattern recognition; computer systems; radar data processing. *Mailing Add:* Pattern Anal & Recognition Technol Corp 5410 W Imperial #500 Los Angeles CA 90045

NELSON, MARTIN EMANUEL, b Tacoma, Wash, Oct 21, 15; m 42; c 3. PHYSICS. *Educ:* Col Puget Sound, BS, 37; Univ Hawaii, MS, 39; Ohio State Univ, PhD(physics), 42. *Prof Exp:* Asst physics, Univ Hawaii, , 37-39; asst, Ohio State Univ, 39-41; physicist, Nat Defense Res Comt, Princeton Univ, 42; instr physics, Univ Ill, 42-44; physicist, Ord Bur, US Naval Res Lab, Washington, DC, 44-46; from asst prof to assoc prof physics, Col Puget Sound, 46-52; res engr, Boeing Airplane Co, 52-56; dir div natural sci, Univ Puget Sound, 70-74, chmn dept physics, 56-70, prof physics, 56-81; RETIRED. *Concurrent Pos:* NSF sci fac fel, Univ Wash, 66-67. *Mem:* AAAS; Am Phys Soc; Am Asn Physics Teachers. *Res:* Artificial radioactivity; cosmic rays; nuclear reactions. *Mailing Add:* 4436 Memory Lane Tacoma WA 98466

NELSON, MARY LOCKETT, b New Orleans, La, July 24, 14; m 68. CELLULOSE CHEMISTRY. *Educ:* Newcomb Col, BA, 34; Tulane Univ, MS, 36, PhD(phys chem), 57. *Prof Exp:* Plant physiologist, Forest Serv, La, USDA, 36-40, seed technologist, Agr Mkt Serv, Washington, DC, 40-42, chemist, Southern Regional Res Lab, 42-64, sr res chemist, Southern Regional Res Ctr, 64-80; RETIRED. *Mem:* Fel AAAS; fel Am Inst Chem; Fiber Soc; Am Chem Soc; Sigma Xi. *Res:* Cellulose fine structure; crystallinity; accessibility; IR spectra; swelling; crosslinking; changes in cotton fiber during growth; heat damage to cotton; heats of combustion and solution; storage of pine seed. *Mailing Add:* 6848 Louisville St New Orleans LA 70124

NELSON, MERRITT RICHARD, b New Richmond, Wis, Oct 11, 32; m 56; c 3 . PLANT PATHOLOGY. *Educ:* Univ Calif, Berkeley, BS, 55; Univ Wis, PhD, 58. *Prof Exp:* Asst, Univ Wis, 55-57; asst plant pathologist, 58-61, assoc prof, 61-67, PROF PLANT PATH, AGR EXP STA, UNIV ARIZ, 67-, HEAD DEPT, 76- *Mem:* Am Phytopath Soc; Soc Gen Microbiol. *Res:* Plant virology, specifically epidemiology of native and cultivated plant virus diseases and biophysical and serological studies of viruses that infect plants. *Mailing Add:* Dept of Plant Pathology Univ of Ariz Tucson AZ 85721

NELSON, NEAL STANLEY, b Chicago, Ill, Jan 1, 34; m 66. PHARMACOLOGY, RADIOBIOLOGY. *Educ:* Univ Ill, BS, 55, DVM, 57; Univ Chicago, PhD(pharm), 64. *Prof Exp:* Res assoc pharmacol, Univ Chicago, 63-65; Nat Cancer Inst spec fel, Milan, 65-66; res scientist, Div Radiol Health, Robert A Taft Sanit Eng Ctr, Ohio, 66-67; dep chief toxicol studies sect, Div Biol Effects, Bur Radiation Health, Hazelton Lab, USPHS, Va, 67-71, res scientist & dep chief toxicol studies sect, Off Res & Monitoring, Twinbrook Res Lab, 71-73, RADIOBIOLOGIST, OFF RADIATION PROGS, ENVIRON PROTECTION AGENCY, 73- *Concurrent Pos:* Mem comt guide rev, Inst Lab Animal Resources, Nat Acad Sci-Nat Res Coun, 65 & mem comt stand for cats, 72-76. *Mem:* AAAS; Am Vet Med Asn; Am Soc Lab Animal Practitioners; NY Acad Sci. *Res:* Metabolism of radioisotopes; pathology of alpha-emitting isotopes; effects of ionizing radiation; high resolution autoradiography and intracellular localization of labeled compounds. *Mailing Add:* 8102 Ashtonbirch Dr Springfield VA 22152

NELSON, NEIL DOUGLAS, b Yankton, SDak, Sept 22, 44; c 1. FORESTRY, PLANT PHYSIOLOGY. *Educ:* Iowa State Univ, BS, 66; Univ Wis-Madison, MS, 68, PhD(forestry), 73. *Prof Exp:* Wood scientist plant physiol, Forest Prod Lab, US Forest Serv, Madison, 71-77; RES PLANT PHYSIOLOGIST TREE PHYSIOL, FORESTRY SCI LAB, US FOREST SERV, 77- *Concurrent Pos:* Fulbright fel, Forest Prod Lab, Melbourne, Australia, 75-76. *Honors & Awards:* Wood Award, Forest Prod Res Soc, 73. *Mem:* Soc Am Foresters; Am Soc Plant Physiologists; Sigma Xi; Plant Growth Regulatory Soc Am. *Res:* Photosynthesis, translocation and growth in woody plants; heartwood formation physiology; plant growth regulators; leaf and xylem senescence; secondary metabolism in woody plants. *Mailing Add:* Forestry Sci Lab PO Box 898 Rhinelander WI 54501

NELSON, NELS M, b Baker, NDak, May 30, 19; m 57; c 1. MICROBIOLOGY. *Educ:* Jamestown Col, BS, 41; Univ Wash, MS, 53, PhD(microbiol), 55. *Prof Exp:* From asst prof to assoc prof, 55-69, PROF MICROBIOL, MONT STATE UNIV, 69- *Mem:* AAAS; Am Soc Microbiol. *Res:* Microbial physiology. *Mailing Add:* Dept of Bot & Microbiol Mont State Univ Bozeman MT 59715

NELSON, NILS KEITH, b Leadwood, Mo, Nov 10, 26. ORGANIC CHEMISTRY. *Educ:* Mo Sch Mines, BS, 46; Univ Ill, MS, 47, PhD(chem), 49. *Prof Exp:* Asst gen & org chem, Univ Ill, 46-49; instr, Univ Maine, 49-51; res chemist, Shell Oil Co, 51-62; asst prof, 62-66, ASSOC PROF ORG CHEM, PURDUE UNIV, CALUMET, 66- *Mem:* Am Chem Soc. *Res:* Stereochemistry of substituted aryl amines; Darzens reaction. *Mailing Add:* Dept Chem Purdue Univ Calumet Hammond IN 46323

NELSON, NORMAN ALLAN, b Edmonton, Alta, July 26, 27; nat US; m 55. PHARMACEUTICAL CHEMISTRY. *Educ:* Univ Alta, BSc, 49; Univ Wis, PhD(chem), 52. *Prof Exp:* Res assoc, Mass Inst Technol, 52-53, instr, 53-55, asst prof chem, 55-59; res assoc, 59-81, RES HEAD CARDIOVASC DIS RES, UPJOHN CO, 81- *Mem:* Am Chem Soc. *Res:* Steroidal hormone analogs; organic synthesis; prostaglandin chemistry; ionophores. *Mailing Add:* 7243-209-7 Upjohn Co Kalamazoo MI 49001

NELSON, NORMAN CROOKS, b Hibbing, Minn, July 24, 29; m 55; c 3. SURGERY, ENDOCRINOLOGY. *Educ:* Tulane Univ, BS, 51, MD, 54. *Prof Exp:* Clin & res fel surg, Harvard Med Sch & Mass Gen Hosp, Boston, 62-63; from instr to prof surg, Sch Med, Univ New Orleans, 63-73, from assoc dean to dean sch med, 69-73; PROF SURG, MED CTR, UNIV MISS, 73-,

VCHANCELLOR HEALTH AFFAIRS & DEAN SCH MED, 73- *Mem:* Endocrine Soc; Am Diabetes Asn; Am Surg Asn; Soc Univ Surgeons; Soc Head & Neck Surgeons. *Res:* Mineral and carbohydrate metabolism. *Mailing Add:* Sch of Med Univ Miss Med Ctr Jackson MS 39216

NELSON, NORMAN NEIBUHR, b Boody, Ill, July 17, 37; m 67. MATHEMATICS EDUCATION. *Educ:* Eastern Ore Col, BS, 59; Univ Ill, MA, 64; Univ Northern Colo, EdD(math, educ), 70. *Prof Exp:* Teacher physics-chem, high sch, Ore, 59-61; from instr to asst prof math, Eastern Ore Col, 61-68; asst prof, 70-73, ASSOC PROF MATH, ORE COL EDUC, 73- *Mem:* Math Asn Am. *Res:* Development and testing of mathematics teaching materials through utilization of audio and AV media. *Mailing Add:* Dept of Math Ore Col of Educ Monmouth OR 97361

NELSON, NORTON, b McClure, Ohio, Feb 6, 10; m 36; c 3. ENVIRONMENTAL MEDICINE, BIOCHEMISTRY. *Educ:* Wittenberg Col, AB, 32; Univ Cincinnati, PhD(biochem), 38. *Hon Degrees:* DSc, Wittenberg Col, 64. *Prof Exp:* Res asst, Children's Hosp Res Found, Ohio, 34-38; biochemist, May Inst Med Res, Jewish Hosp, Ohio, 38-42; asst prof biochem, Univ Cincinnati, 46-47; assoc prof environ med, 47-53, chmn dept & dir, Inst Environ Med, 54-80, PROF ENVIRON MED, MED CTR, NY UNIV, 53- *Concurrent Pos:* Res assoc, Children's Hosp Res Found, Ohio, 46-47; dir res, Inst Environ Med, NY Univ, 47-54, actg dir, Univ Valley Sterling Forest, 62-66, dir, 67-, provost, Heights Ctr, 66-67; mem study group smoking & health, Am Cancer Soc-Am Heart Asn-Nat Cancer Inst-Nat Heart Inst, 57 & comn environ health, Armed Forces Epidemiol Bd, 60-; mem man in space comt, Nat Acad Sci-Nat Res Coun, 61, working group Gemini-Apollo manned orbiting lab exp, 64, chmn comt air qual stand in space flight, mem space sci bd, ad hoc comt on sci qualification & selection of scientist-astronauts; mem panel air pollution, Gross Comt, Dept Health, Educ & Welfare, 61, mem, Nat Adv Dis Prev & Environ Control Coun, 67-69, bd trustees, Indust Health Found, 69-75; mem expert panel carcinogenicity, Int Union Against Cancer, 62; regent's lectr, Univ Calif, Davis, 63; consult, Calif Health Dept; mem, Nat Adv Comt Commmunity Air Pollution, Surgeon Gen, mem panel non-neoplastic dis & Surgeon Gen adv comt smoking & health, USPHS, 63-64, nat adv environ health comt, 63-67; chmn, Nat Health Forum, Nat Health Coun, 64; mem comt on motor vehicle emission and comt microchem pollutants, WHO, 64-68, chmn expert comt manual on methods of toxicity eval of chem, 75-; chmn comt protocols for safety eval, Food & Drug Admin, 66-71; mem environ sci & eng study sect, NIH & Nat Inst Environ Health Sci Adv Comt, 67-71 & 74-77, chmn task force res planning environ health sci, 69-70 & 75-80; mem, White House Task Force Air Pollution, 69; mem panel herbicides, US Off Sci & Technol, 69, chmn task force hazardous trace substances, mem ad hoc comt environ health res, Off Sci & Technol-Coun Environ Qual, 71; mem comt environ physiol & comt nitrate accumulation, Nat Res Coun, 70-72, chmn comt toxicol & mem comt atmospheric & indust hyg, mem assembly life sci, Exec Comt, 75-, chmn bd toxicol & environ health hazards, 77-, mem comn natural resources, 77-; mem hazardous mat adv comt, Environ Protection Agency, 70-74, consult, Sci Adv Comt, 74-, mem sci adv bd exec comt & chmn environ health adv comt, 75-; mem vis comt for bd overseers, Harvard Sch Pub Health, 70-76; mem, President's Sci Adv Comt Panel on Chem & Health, 70-73; mem vis comt dept nutrit & food sci, Mass Inst Technol, 71-74; mem res adv comt, Boyce Thompson Inst Plant Res, 70-; consult, NSF, 71-72 & 74-75; mem etiology adv comt, Nat Cancer Inst, 71-73 & Indust Hyg Round Table; consult ed, Environ Res; mem energy policy proj adv bd, Ford Found, 72-74. *Mem:* Sr mem Inst Med-Nat Acad Sci; hom mem NY Acad Sci; hon mem Am Acad Occup Med; hon mem Soc Toxicol; Am Soc Biol Chemists. *Mailing Add:* NY Univ Med Ctr 550 First Ave New York NY 10016

NELSON, NORVELL JOHN, US citizen. MATERIALS SCIENCE, ELECTRONIC INSTRUMENTATION. *Educ:* Ill Inst Technol, BS, 64; Stanford Univ, PhD(chem), 67. *Prof Exp:* Res assoc & instr inorg chem, Northwestern Univ, 67-69; res assoc organometallic chem, Stanford Univ, 69-70; sr res chemist org photochem, Eastman Kodak Co, 70-74; sr engr solid state chem, Varian Assocs, Inc, 74-78; sr res chemist, Catalytica Assocs, Inc, 78-80. *Mem:* Am Chem Soc; Electrochem Soc; AAAS. *Res:* Industrial process chemistry; development of new analytical techniques; III-V semiconductor materials preparation, particularly optoelectronic devices; catalysis. *Mailing Add:* 3445 Greer Rd Palo Alto CA 94303

NELSON, OLIVER EVANS, b Seattle, Wash, Aug 16, 20; m 63. GENETICS. *Educ:* Colgate Univ, AB, 41; Yale Univ, MS, 43, PhD, 47. *Hon Degrees:* Dr Agr, Purdue Univ. *Prof Exp:* Assoc geneticist, Purdue Univ, 47-54, geneticist, 54-69; PROF GENETICS, UNIV WIS-MADISON, 69- *Concurrent Pos:* Vis investr, Nat Forest Res Inst & Biochem Inst, Univ Stockholm, 54-55; NSF sr fel biol, Calif Inst Technol, 61-62. *Honors & Awards:* John Scott Medal; Hoblitzelle Award; Browning Award; Donald F Jones Medal. *Mem:* Nat Acad Sci; Am Acad Arts & Sci; Am Soc Plant Physiologists; Crop Sci Soc Am; Am Genetics Asn. *Res:* Physiological genetics. *Mailing Add:* Genetics Lab Univ of Wis Madison WI 53706

NELSON, OSCAR TIVIS, JR, mathematics, see previous edition

NELSON, OWEN LLOYD, electrical engineering, physics, see previous edition

NELSON, PAUL A, chemical engineering, see previous edition

NELSON, PAUL EDWARD, b Franklin Twp, Wis, May 26, 27; m 50; c 3. PLANT PATHOLOGY. *Educ:* Univ Calif, BS, 51, PhD(plant path), 55. *Prof Exp:* From asst prof to assoc prof plant path, Cornell Univ, 55-65; assoc prof, 65-67, PROF PLANT PATH, PA STATE UNIV, 67- *Mem:* Am Phytopath Soc; Mycol Soc Am; Bot Soc Am. *Res:* Root-disease fungi, especially those causing vascular wilt diseases of plants; pathological anatomy of diseased plants; Fusarium species. *Mailing Add:* 211 Buckhout Lab Dept Plant Path Pa State Univ University Park PA 16802

NELSON, PAUL VICTOR, b Somerville, Mass, May 4, 39; m 64. HORTICULTURE, PLANT NUTRITION. *Educ:* Univ Mass, BS, 60; Pa State Univ, MS, 61; Cornell Univ, PhD(floricult), 64. *Prof Exp:* Staff res specialist, Geigy Chem Corp, NY, 64-65; from asst prof to assoc prof, 65-73, PROF HORT SCI, NC STATE UNIV, 73- *Concurrent Pos:* NSF travel grant, Int Hort Cong, Israel, 70; leave of absence, Lab Plant Physiol Res, Agr Univ, Wageningen, Holland, 71-72. *Mem:* Am Soc Hort Sci; Soc Am Florists; Int Soc Hort Sci; Coun Soil Test & Plant Anal. *Res:* Foliar analysis and fertilization of floricultural crops; efficiency of uptake and utilization of nitrogen and phosphorus in plants; plant root media. *Mailing Add:* Dept of Hort Sci NC State Univ Raleigh NC 27607

NELSON, PETER REID, b Norwich, Conn, Aug 11, 49; m 81. MATHEMATICAL STATISTICS. *Educ:* Case Inst Technol, BS, 71; Case Western Reserve Univ, MS, 73, PhD(math & statist), 75. *Prof Exp:* Vis asst prof statist, Ohio State Univ, 75-76, asst prof, 76-81; SR STATISTICIAN, G D SEARLE & CO, 81- *Concurrent Pos:* Prin investr res libr type Markov chains, NSF grant, 78-79. *Mem:* Am Statist Asn; Am Soc Qual Control. *Res:* The analysis of means. *Mailing Add:* G D Searle & Co Box 5110 Chicago IL 60680

NELSON, PHILIP EDWIN, b Shelbyville, Ind, Nov 12, 34; m 55; c 3. FOOD SCIENCE, AGRICULTURE. *Educ:* Purdue Univ, BS, 56, PhD(food sci), 67. *Prof Exp:* Plant mgr food processing, Blue River Packing Co, 56-60; from instr to asst prof food sci, 60-70, PROF FOOD SCI, PURDUE UNIV, 74-, DIR, FOOD SCI INST, 75- *Concurrent Pos:* Guest specialist, US Info Agency, 75-76; chmn subcomt world food & nutrit study, Nat Acad Sci, 76-77, food additive surv, 80-; consultant, 80- *Mem:* Sigma Xi; fel Inst Food Technologists; AAAS; Coun Agr Sci & Technol. *Res:* Fruit and vegetable preservation including aseptic processing and prevention of food losses. *Mailing Add:* Food Sci Inst Smith Hall Purdue Univ West Lafayette IN 47907

NELSON, PHILLIP GILLARD, b Albert Lea, Minn, Dec 3, 31; m 55; c 4. NEUROSCIENCES, CELL BIOLOGY. *Educ:* Univ Chicago, MD, 56, PhD(physiol), 57. *Prof Exp:* Intern, Philadelphia Gen Hosp, 57-58; from sr surgeon to surgeon, USPHS, 58-67; actg chief sect spinal cord, Nat Inst Neurol Dis & Blindness, 64-69; chief behav biol br, 69-75, CHIEF, LAB DEVELOP NEUROBIOL, NAT INST CHILD HEALTH & HUMAN DEVELOP, 76- *Concurrent Pos:* Hon res asst, Dept Biophys, Univ Col, Univ London, 62-63; lectr physiol, George Washington Univ, 64- *Mem:* AAAS; Am Physiol Soc; Biophys Soc; Am Soc Cell Biol; Soc Neurosci. *Res:* Single unit and integrative activity in the central nervous system; tissue culture of nervous tissue. *Mailing Add:* NIH Lab Develop Neurobiol Bldg 36 Rm 2A21 Bethesda MD 20205

NELSON, R WILLIAM, b Logan, Utah, May 23, 31; m 52; c 9. HYDROLOGY, EARTH SCIENCE. *Educ:* Univ Idaho, BS, 54; Colo State Univ, MS, 59. *Prof Exp:* Drainage engr, Agr Res Serv, USDA, Idaho, 54-56, engr, Colo, 56-60; engr, Hanford Atomic Prod, Gen Elec Co, 60-63, sr engr, 63-65; sr res scientist, Pac Northwest Lab, Battelle Mem Inst, Wash, 65-66, res assoc, 66-68; sr staff specialist, Sci Systs Dept, Comput Sci Corp, 68-75 & Boeing Comput Serv Richland Inc, 75-78; staff scientist, Geosci Sect, 78-80, STAFF SCIENTIST, HYDROLOGIC SYSTEMS SECT, PAC NORTHWEST LABS, BATTELLE MEM INST, 80- *Concurrent Pos:* Deleg, Int Conf Ground Disposal Radioactive Wastes, Chalk River, 61; US rep, Int Radioisotopes Hydrol Conf, Int Atomic Energy Agency, Tokyo, 63; mem int adv comt, Inventory Groundwater Models, Int Asn Sci Union, 75-77. *Honors & Awards:* Meinzer Award, Geol Soc Am, 78. *Mem:* Am Geophys Union; Soil Sci Soc Am; Sigma Xi. *Res:* Research and development in application of mathematics to flow liquids in porous media including contaminant transport methods for application in groundwater quality management; evaluation of subsurface pollution problems. *Mailing Add:* Battelle Mem Inst Pac Northwest Labs Richland WA 99352

NELSON, RALPH A, b Minneapolis, Minn, June 19, 27; m 54; c 5. NUTRITION, PHYSIOLOGY. *Educ:* Univ Minn, BA, 50, MD, 53, PhD(physiol), 61; Am Bd Internal Med, dipl, 81. *Prof Exp:* Intern med, Cook County Hosp, 53-54; fel path, Hosps, Minn, 54-55, res assoc neurophysiol, Univ, 55-56, fel physiol, Mayo Found, 57-60; asst prof nutrit, Cornell Univ, 61-62; assoc physiol, Med Sch, Case Western Reserve Univ, 62-67; asst prof physiol, Mayo Grad Sch, 67-73; asst prof physiol, Mayo Med Sch, 73-78, assoc prof nutrit, 74-78; chmn sect nutrit, Mayo Clin, 67-78; assoc prof internal med & chmn nutrit sect, Sch Med, Univ SDak, 78-79; PROF NUTRIT, COL MED, UNIV ILL, URBANA-CHAMPAIGN, 79- *Concurrent Pos:* Dir med res, George H Scott Res Lab, Fairview Park Hosp, Cleveland, 62-67; consult internal med, Danville Vet Admin Hosp, 79-; dir res & head, Nutrit Support Serv, Carle Found Hosp, Urbana, 80- *Mem:* Am Physiol Soc; Am Inst Nutrit; Am Soc Clin Nutrit; Am Med Asn; Am Gastroenterol Soc. *Res:* Gastroenterology, membrane transport, physiology and structural aspects of vitamin function; applied nutrition of obesity and chronic renal disease. *Mailing Add:* Nutrit Dept Col Med Univ Ill Urbana IL 61801

NELSON, RALPH FRANCIS, b Hartford, Conn, Sept 20, 45; m 72; c 2. NEUROPHYSIOLOGY, NEUROANATOMY. *Educ:* Amherst Col, BA, 67; Johns Hopkins Univ, PhD(biophysics), 72. *Prof Exp:* Fel, 72-74, staff fel, 74-78, RES PHYSIOLOGIST, DEPT HEALTH & HUMAN SERV, NAT EYE INST, NIH, 78- *Concurrent Pos:* Fel, Max Planck Inst Physcol & Clin Res, Bad Narheim, Fed Repub Ger, 81. *Mem:* Asn Res Vision & Opthamol; Soc Gen Physiologists; AAAS. *Res:* Electrophysiology and neuroanatomy of retinal neurons; neural circuitry and neuronal interactions, structure and function. *Mailing Add:* Bldg 9 Rm 1E112 Nat Eye Inst NIH Bethesda MD 20205

NELSON, RANDALL BRUCE, b Swissvale, Pa, Feb 15, 48; m 78; c 2. ORGANIC & NATURAL PRODUCTS CHEMISTRY. *Educ:* Washington & Jefferson Col, BA, 70; Dartmouth Col, PhD(org chem), 75. *Prof Exp:* NIH fel dept chem, Columbia Univ, 75-76; res chemist, Arapahoe Chem Div,

Syntex Corp, 76-78; res chemist chem, 78-80, RES GROUP LEADER, OLYMPIC RES DIV, ITT RAYONIER, 80- *Mem:* Sigma Xi; Am Chem Soc. *Res:* New synthetic methods in organic and heterocyclic chemistry; process development and modern synthetic reagents in production scale equipment; chemistry of metal hydrides; pulping and bleaching processes; paper and dissolving pulp chemistry. *Mailing Add:* ITT Rayonier 409 E Harvard Ave Shelton WA 98584

NELSON, RAYMOND ADOLPH, b Spokane, Wash, Apr 24, 26; m 52, 78; c 5. RADIOPHYSICS. *Educ:* Wash State Univ, BS, 50, MS, 52; Stanford Univ, PhD(physics), 61. *Prof Exp:* Mem tech staff, Bell Tel Labs, Inc, 52-55; res engr, 55-61, physicist, 61-70, SR RES PHYSICIST, RADIO PHYSICS LAB, SRI INT, 70- *Mem:* Am Phys Soc; Am Geophys Union; Sigma Xi. *Res:* Foundations of statistical mechanics; ionospheric physics. *Mailing Add:* Radio Physics Lab SRI Int 333 Ravenswood Menlo Park CA 94025

NELSON, RAYMOND JOHN, b Chicago, Ill, Oct 8, 17; m 42; c 3. MATHEMATICS. *Educ:* Grinnell Col, AB, 41; Univ Chicago, PhD(philos), 49. *Prof Exp:* Prof philos, Univ Akron, 46-52; mathematician, Int Bus Mach Corp, 52-55; staff engr, Link Aviation, Inc, 55-56; prof math, 56-65, dir comput ctr, 56-65, PROF PHILOS, CASE WESTERN RESERVE UNIV, 65- *Concurrent Pos:* Mem bd dirs, CHI Corp, Ohio; consult, Rockefeller Found, 74- *Mem:* Am Math Soc; Asn Symbolic Logic; Asn Comput Mach; Am Philos Asn. *Res:* Mathematical logic; automata theory; philosophy of science; application of mathematical models to psychological attitudes such as belief and perception. *Mailing Add:* 2400 Demington Dr Cleveland Heights OH 44106

NELSON, REGINALD DAVID, organic chemistry, see previous edition

NELSON, REX ROLAND, b Greenville, Mich, Sept 14, 24; m 54; c 2. ACOUSTICS. *Educ:* Kenyon Col, BA, 49; Univ Calif, Los Angeles, MS, 51; Pa State Univ, PhD(high pressure physics), 59. *Prof Exp:* PROF PHYSICS, OCCIDENTAL COL, 59- *Mem:* Am Phys Soc; Am Asn Physics Teachers; Acoust Soc Am. *Res:* Polymorphic transitions and phase transitions at high pressure; acoustics; acoustics of musical instruments. *Mailing Add:* Dept of Physics Occidental Col Los Angeles CA 90041

NELSON, RICHARD BARTEL, b Weiser, Idaho, Sept 13, 40. CIVIL ENGINEERING, ENGINEERING MECHANICS. *Educ:* Willamette Univ, BA, 63; Columbia Univ, BS, 63, MS, 64, DEngSc(civil eng), 68. *Prof Exp:* Asst prof, 68-76, ASSOC PROF ENG, UNIV CALIF, LOS ANGELES, 76- *Mem:* Am Inst Aeronaut & Astronaut. *Res:* Structural analysis; optimum structural design; wave propagation in elastic media; structural stability. *Mailing Add:* 6731-H Boelter Hall Univ of Calif Los Angeles CA 90024

NELSON, RICHARD BURTON, b Powell, Wyo, Dec 10, 11; c 1. ELECTRONIC ENGINEERING. *Educ:* Calif Inst Technol, BS, 35; Mass Inst Technol, PhD(physics), 38. *Prof Exp:* Mem electron optics lab, Radio Corp Am Mfg Co, 38-41; asst res physicist, Nat Res Coun Can, 41-42; res assoc, Gen Elec Co, 42-50; sr engr, Litton Industs, 50-51; sr engr, 51-57, mgr klystron develop, 57-60, mgr tube res & develop, 60-63, chief engr, Tube Div, 63-74, CONSULT PATENT DEPT, VARIAN ASSOCS, 74- *Mem:* Fel Inst Elec & Electronics Eng. *Res:* Vacuum tubes; high-power magnetrons and klystrons. *Mailing Add:* 27040 Dezahara Way Los Altos Hills CA 94022

NELSON, RICHARD CARL, b Stillwater, Minn, May 1, 15; m 43; c 2. PHYSICS, BIOPHYSICS. *Educ:* Univ Minn, AB, 35, PhD(plant physiol), 38. *Prof Exp:* Agent tung res, USDA, 39; res fel plant physiol, Univ Minn, 40-42; spectroscopist, Armour & Co, 42-43; chief chemist, Citrus Concentrates, Inc, Fla, mgr Pectin Prods Div, 45-46; res assoc, Northwestern Univ, 46-49; assoc prof, 49-62, PROF PHYSICS, OHIO STATE UNIV, 62- *Concurrent Pos:* Mem comt heat attenuation in clothing systs, Qm Res & Develop Adv Bd, 59-62; conuslt, Minn Mining & Mfg Co, 60-70; USPHS res career prog award, 64-74; vis prof, Phys Chem Inst, Univ Marburg, 65. *Mem:* Fel Am Phys Soc. *Res:* Photoconductivity; sensitization by dyes; electronic processes in organic solids. *Mailing Add:* Dept of Physics Ohio State Univ Columbus OH 43210

NELSON, RICHARD DAVID, physical chemistry, see previous edition

NELSON, RICHARD DOUGLAS, b Modesto, Calif, Apr 17, 41; m 61; c 3 ENTOMOLOGY, PLANT PATHOLOGY. *Educ:* Univ Calif, Davis, BS, 63, MS, 66, PhD(entom), 68. *Prof Exp:* Asst res biologist, Biol Res Div, Stauffer Chem Co, 63-64; ENTOMOLOGIST, PLANT PATHOLOGIST & DIR RES, RES DIV, DRISCOLL STRAWBERRY ASSOC, INC, 68- *Mem:* AAAS; Entom Soc Am; Entom Soc Can; Acaralogical Soc Am; Int Soc Hort Sci. *Res:* Biology, population dynamics, and integrated pest management strategies used for control of insects, mites, diseases, and weeds in strawberries; physiological studies with strawberries, including nutrition and tissue culturing. *Mailing Add:* 404 San Juan Rd Watsonville CA 95076

NELSON, RICHARD L(LOYD), b Mansfield, Ohio, Nov 18, 34; m 53; c 2. ELECTRICAL ENGINEERING, ECONOMICS. *Educ:* Univ Cincinnati, EE, 57; Ohio State Univ, MSc, 64. *Prof Exp:* Sr res engr, Battelle Mem Inst, 60-63; mgr prod & mkt, Ray Data Corp, 63-64; adminstr mgt, Battelle Develop Corp, Ohio, 64-67; dir res, Gilbarco Inc, 68-69; mgr new bus develop group, Jersey Enterprises, Standard Oil Co NJ, 69-72; founder & pres, QWIP Systs Div, 72-78, VPRES, EXXON ENTERPRISES, INC, 78-, CHIEF EXEC, ADVAN PROJS DIV, 78- *Concurrent Pos:* Consult, US Navy, 60-61 & Battelle Mem Inst, 63-64. *Mem:* Fel AAAS; sr mem Inst Elec & Electronics Engrs; Am Soc Naval Engrs. *Res:* Cost-effectiveness analysis; development of techniques for application of digital systems to management reporting; control systems; management of research and new technology business-venture development. *Mailing Add:* 69 W Ninth St Apt 4F New York NY 10011

NELSON, RICHARD ROBERT, b Austin, Minn, May 23; m 52; c 4. PLANT PATHOLOGY. *Educ:* Augsburg Col, BA, 50; Univ Minn, MS, 52, PhD(plant path), 54. *Prof Exp:* Res fel fungal genetics, Univ Minn, 53-55; plant pathologist corn diseases, USDA, NC State Univ, 55-66; prof, 66-74, EVAN PUGH PROF PLANT PATH, PA STATE UNIV, 74- *Concurrent Pos:* Regional Sigma Xi lectr. *Mem:* Fel Am Phytopath Soc; Mycol Soc Am. *Res:* Evolution of fungi; heterothallism and homothallism in fungi; sexuality of fungi; pathogen variation and host resistance; epidemiology of plant diseases; mycology; pest management. *Mailing Add:* 733 N McKee St State College PA 16801

NELSON, ROBERT A, b Tracy, Minn, Mar 26, 35; m 60; c 4. VETERINARY MEDICINE, TOXICOLOGY. *Educ:* Univ Minn, BS, 58, DVM, 60. *Prof Exp:* Vet, Hanover Animal Hosp, Forest Park, Ill, 60-62 & Albrecht Animal Hosp, Denver, 62; instr vet surg, Col Vet Med, Univ Minn, 62-63; sr vet, Biochem Res Lab, 63-68, supvr animal lab, 68-71, supvr animal lab & toxicol, Riker Res Lab, 71-72, mgr animal lab & toxicol, 72-75, mgr safety eval, 75-78, lab mgr safety eval, 78-79, mgr, Develop Labs, 79-81, DIR REGULATORY AFFAIRS & QUAL ASSURANCE, RIKER RES LAB, 3M CO, 81- *Concurrent Pos:* Guest lectr, Col Med, Univ Minn, 68- *Mem:* Am Asn Lab Animal Sci; Soc Toxicol. *Res:* Laboratory animal care; biopolymer surgery and toxicology; testing of potential drugs, agrichemicals, biopolymers and industrial chemicals. *Mailing Add:* Riker Res Lab 3M Co 3M Ctr Bldg 270-3A St Paul MN 55144

NELSON, ROBERT ANDREW, b Detroit, Mich, Apr 16, 43; m 68. POLYMER CHEMISTRY, CELLULOSE CHEMISTRY. *Educ:* Wayne State Univ, BS, 67; Univ Mich, MS, 70, PhD(polymer chem), 72. *Prof Exp:* Group leader alloy anal, Detroit Testing Lab, 67; assoc scientist polymer chem, 72-74, scientist cellulose chem, 75-76, scientist polymer chem, 76-80, SR SCIENTIST POLYMER CHEM, XEROX CORP, 80- *Mem:* Am Chem Soc; AAAS; Sigma Xi. *Res:* Basic physicochemical properties of cellulose and paper including cellulose/water interactions, electrical conduction mechanisms and mechanical properties; polymer synthesis; kinetics, structure-property relationships. *Mailing Add:* 103 Alpine Knoll Fairport NY 14450

NELSON, ROBERT B, b Casper, Wyo, Apr 2, 35; m 58; c 2. PHARMACOLOGY. *Educ:* Univ Wyo, BS, 57; Univ Calif, San Francisco, MS, 63, PhD(pharmacol), 65. *Prof Exp:* Asst prof, Idaho State Univ, 65-70; assoc prof, 70-77, PROF PHARMACOL, SCH PHARM, UNIV WYO, 77- *Mem:* Am Col Pharm. *Res:* Actions of narcotic analgesics on respiration and other general functions. *Mailing Add:* Dept of Pharmacol Univ of Wyo Sch of Pharm Laramie WY 82070

NELSON, ROBERT B, b July 13, 29; US citizen; m 56; c 2. STRUCTURAL GEOLOGY. *Educ:* Ore State Univ, BS, 51; Univ Wash, MS, 56, PhD(structure, petrog), 59. *Prof Exp:* From instr to assoc prof, 60-74, PROF GEOL, UNIV NEBR-LINCOLN, 74- *Mem:* Fel Geol Soc Am; Am Geophys Union; fel Geol Soc London. *Res:* Deformations in sedimentary and metamorphic strata. *Mailing Add:* Dept of Geol Univ of Nebr Lincoln NE 68508

NELSON, ROBERT JOHN, b Minot, NDak, Dec 12, 39; m 63; c 2. MATHEMATICS, STATISTICS. *Educ:* Mont State Univ, BS, 61, MS, 64; Purdue Univ, Lafayette, PhD(math), 69. *Prof Exp:* Instr math & statist, Mont State Univ, 63-64; instr math, St Cloud State Col, 64-66; instr, Purdue Univ, Lafayette, 66-69; from asst prof to assoc prof, St Cloud State Col, 69-74, asst dean lib arts & scis, 72-74; VPRES ACAD AFFAIRS, MO WESTERN STATE COL, 74- *Concurrent Pos:* Consult, NCent Asn Cols. *Mem:* Math Asn Am. *Res:* Linear algebra; curriculum development at undergraduate and graduate level. *Mailing Add:* Mo Western State Col St Joseph MO 64506

NELSON, ROBERT LEON, b Billings, Mont, Aug 17, 45; m 70; c 2. MEDICAL ONCOLOGY, CLINICAL PHARMACOLOGY. *Educ:* Ore State Univ, BS, 68, MS & MD, 71; Am Bd Internal Med, dipl, 75; Am Bd Med Oncol, dipl, 77. *Prof Exp:* Intern internal med, Albert Einstein Col Med, 71-72, resident, 72-73; fel med oncol, Nat Cancer Inst, 73-75, fel clin pharmacol, 74-75; CLIN PHARMACOLOGIST ONCOL, LILLY RES LABS, 75- *Concurrent Pos:* Assoc prof med & consult oncol, Sch Med, Ind Univ, 75-, assoc prof pharmacol, 78- *Mem:* Am Col Physicians; Am Fedn Clin Res. *Res:* Clinical pharmacology and initial clinical trials of new anticancer drugs; pharmacokinetics and optimization of clinical dosage regimens. *Mailing Add:* 3729 E Carmel Dr Carmel IN 46032

NELSON, ROBERT M, Los Angeles, Calif. PLANETARY SATELLITES, SOLID STATE SPECTROSCOPY. *Educ:* City Univ NY, BS, 66; Wesleyan Univ, MA, 69; Univ Pittsburgh, PhD(earth & planetary sci), 77. *Prof Exp:* Nat Acad Sci res assoc, NASA, 78-80; SR SCIENTIST, JET PROPULSION LAB, CALIF INST TECHNOL, 80-; PROF, DEPT PHYSICS, CALIF STATE UNIV, LOS ANGELES, 81- *Mem:* Am Astron Soc; Am Geophys Union; Am Inst Physics; AAAS. *Res:* Telescope and spacecraft observations of planetary satellites, particularly those of Jupiter and Saturn; laboratory spectroscopy of solid state materials of planetary interest. *Mailing Add:* 183-301 Jet Propulsion Lab 4800 Oak Grove Dr Pasadena CA 91103

NELSON, ROBERT MELLINGER, b Burlington, Iowa, May 17, 18. ORTHODONTICS. *Educ:* Univ Iowa, BA, 41, DDS, 50, MA, 51. *Prof Exp:* Practicing orthodontist, Chicago, 51-52; assoc prof orthod, 53-65, PROF ORTHOD & HEAD DEPT, SCH DENT, UNIV NC, CHAPEL HILL, 65- *Res:* Facial growth and development. *Mailing Add:* Sch of Dent Univ of NC Chapel Hill NC 27514

NELSON, ROBERT NORTON, b Cincinnati, Ohio, Nov 1, 41; m 68; c 2. PHYSICAL CHEMISTRY. *Educ:* Brown Univ, ScBChem, 63; Mass Inst Technol, PhD(phys chem), 68. *Prof Exp:* Fel molecular collisions, Dept Chem, Univ Fla, 68-70, interim asst prof chem, 69-70; ASST PROF CHEM, GA SOUTHERN COL, 70- *Concurrent Pos:* Vis asst prof chem, Colgate

Univ, 77-78; vis lectr, Univ Ga, 81. *Mem:* Am Chem Soc; Am Phys Soc; Sigma Xi; Soc Appl Spectros. *Res:* Molecular collisions at thermal and near thermal energies; effusive flow of gases; laser spectroscopy. *Mailing Add:* Dept Chem Ga Southern Col Statesboro GA 30460

NELSON, ROBERT S, b Atlantic City, NJ, Apr 7, 11; m 36; c 3. MEDICINE. *Educ:* Univ Minn, BS & BM, 34, MD, 35. *Prof Exp:* Chief Europ Hepatitis Res Ctr & consult, US Army, 50-53; chief gastroenterol, Brooke Army Hosp, San Antonio, Tex, 53-55; assoc prof med, 56-65, PROF MED, GRAD SCH BIOMED SCI, TEX MED CTR, UNIV TEX, HOUSTON, 65-; INTERNIST, DEPT MED & CHIEF GASTROENTEROL SERV, UNIV TEX M D ANDERSON HOSP & TUMOR INST, 64- *Concurrent Pos:* From clin asst prof to clin assoc prof, Baylor Col Med, 55-; consult, Vet Admin & Jefferson Davis Hosps, Houston & Brooke Army Hosp. *Honors & Awards:* Schindler Award, Am Soc Gastrointestinal Endoscopy, 60; William H Rorer Award, Am J Gastroenterol, 66; Seale Harris Award, Southern Med Asn, 74. *Mem:* Am Soc Gastrointestinal Endoscopy; Am Gastroenterol Asn; fel Am Col Physicians. *Res:* Gastroenterology. *Mailing Add:* Dept of Med M D Anderson Hosp & Tumor Inst Houston TX 77025

NELSON, RODNEY ALDEN, physical chemistry, chemical engineering, see previous edition

NELSON, ROGER EDWIN, b New York, NY, Feb 1, 40; m 64; c 2. TECHNICAL MANAGEMENT, APPLIED RESEARCH. *Educ:* Rutgers Univ, BS, 62; Seton Hall Univ, MS, 66, PhD(phys chem), 69. *Prof Exp:* Develop scientist prod develop, Lever Bros Co, 64-75; res & develop assoc, PQ Corp, 75-79; ASST TECH DIR, REHEIS CHEM CO, 79- *Mem:* Am Chem Soc; Am Oil Chemists' Soc. *Res:* Management of inorganic chemical research on aluminum and other light metal compounds for applications in the cosmetic, pharmaceutical and other specialty chemicals industries. *Mailing Add:* 1526 Leon Dr Hatfield PA 19440

NELSON, ROGER PETER, b Bridgeport, Conn, Dec 15, 42; m 64; c 3. ORGANIC CHEMISTRY. *Educ:* Fairfield Univ, BS, 64; Univ Mich, PhD(org chem), 67. *Prof Exp:* Sr res scientist, Chem Res & Develop, 72-74, proj leader food chem res & develop, 74-78, PROJ LEADER PROCESS RES & DEVELOP, PFIZER, INC, 78- *Mem:* Am Chem Soc. *Res:* Construction and conformational properties of bridged bicyclic systems; chemistry and mode of action of antihypertensives; agents affecting gastrointestinal function; food protein research; immobilized enzymes; chemical bioprocess development. *Mailing Add:* Process Res & Develop Pfizer Inc Eastern Point Rd Groton CT 06340

NELSON, RONALD HARVEY, b Union Grove, Wis, Aug 10, 18; m 40; c 4. ANIMAL HUSBANDRY. *Educ:* Univ Wis, BA, 39; Okla Agr & Mech Col, MS, 41; Iowa State Col, PhD(animal breeding), 44. *Prof Exp:* From asst prof to assoc prof, 46-49, PROF ANIMAL HUSB, MICH STATE UNIV, 49-, HEAD DEPT, 50- *Concurrent Pos:* Chief of party, Agr Proj, Balcarce, 66-68. *Honors & Awards:* Animal Sci Award in Int Animal Agr, 78. *Mem:* AAAS; fel Am Soc Animal Sci. *Res:* Sheep and beef cattle breeding; lamb mortality and factors affecting it; effect of inbreeding on a herd of Holstein-Friesian cattle. *Mailing Add:* Dept Animal Husb Mich State Univ East Lansing MI 48823

NELSON, RUSSELL ANDREW, b Grand Forks, NDak, May 13, 13; m 39. MEDICINE. *Educ:* Univ Minn, AB, 33; Johns Hopkins Univ, MD, 37; Univ Miami, DSc, 72. *Prof Exp:* Intern, asst resident & resident med, Johns Hopkins Hosp, 37-44, dir med clins, 45-50, dir admin, 52-63, pres, 63-72; CONSULT MED EDUC, 72- *Concurrent Pos:* Mem fac, Sch Med, Johns Hopkins Univ, 40-52, asst dir, Hosp, 45-47, assoc admin, 47-48, adj prof pub health admin, Sch Hyg & Pub Health, 52-55, lectr, 55-57; chmn adv comt hosp facil & serv, USPHS, 56-; mem, President's Comn Health Manpower, 61; Nuffield Trust fel, London, 73. *Mem:* Inst Med-Nat Acad Sci; master Am Col Physicians; AAAS; AMA; Am Asn Med Cols. *Mailing Add:* 605 Ocean Dr Key Biscayne FL 33149

NELSON, RUSSELL C, b Hackensack, NJ, Nov 3, 25; m 52; c 2. METALLURGICAL ENGINEERING. *Educ:* Lehigh Univ, BS, 48; Colo Sch Mines, MS, 49, DSc(metall), 51. *Prof Exp:* Asst metall, Colo Sch Mines, 49-51; mineral engr, Oak Ridge Nat Lab, 51-53; sr engr, Chem & Metall Div, Sylvania Elec Prod, Inc, 53-54, engr in chg chem develop lab, 54-55, metall testing lab, 55-58, head metall res lab, 58-61; assoc prof, 61-65, PROF MECH ENG, UNIV NEBR, LINCOLN, 65-, MEM GRAD FAC, 62-, ASSOC DEAN GRAD STUDIES & APPT DENT, 78- *Concurrent Pos:* Consult metall eng. *Mem:* Am Inst Mining, Metall & Petrol Engrs; Am Soc Metals; Am Soc Eng Educ; Soc Biomat. *Res:* Powder metallurgy, mechanical behavior of materials, metallurgical aspects of fracture; biomaterials. *Mailing Add:* 900 Moraine Dr Lincoln NE 68510

NELSON, RUSSELL MARION, b Salt Lake City, Utah, Sept 9, 24; m 45; c 10. SURGERY. *Educ:* Univ Utah, BA, 45, MD, 47; Univ Minn, PhD(surg), 54; Am Bd Surg, dipl; Am Bd Thoracic Surg, dipl. *Hon Degrees:* ScD, Brigham Young Univ, 70. *Prof Exp:* From intern to sr resident, Univ Minn Hosps, 47-55; from asst prof to assoc clin prof surg, Col Med, 55-69, res prof, 70, DIR TRAINING PROG CARDIOVASC & THORACIC SURG, UNIV UTAH AFFIL HOSPS, 67- *Concurrent Pos:* Nat Heart Inst res fel, 49-50; first asst resident, Mass Gen Hosp, 53-54; Nat Cancer Inst trainee, 53-55; Markle scholar, 57-59; mem, White House Conf Youth & Children, 60; chmn div thoracic & cardiovasc surg, Latter-day Saints Hosp, 66-72; dir med serv, Utah Biomed Test Lab, 70-73; mem bd dirs, Am Bd Thoracic Surg, 72- & Int Cardiol Found; pvt pract, 59- *Mem:* Am Surg Asn; Soc Univ Surgeons; Am Asn Thoracic Surg; AMA; fel Am Col Surgeons. *Res:* Development of artificial heart-lung machine for open heart surgery; cardiovascular surgery; physiology of shock; physiological mechanisms involved in the etiology and treatment of ventricular fibrillation and other cardiac arrhythmias. *Mailing Add:* 324 Tenth Ave Suite 160 Salt Lake City UT 84103

NELSON, S(TUART) O(WEN), b Pilger, Nebr, Jan 23, 27; m 53, 79; c 2. AGRICULTRUAL ENGINEERING, PHYSICS. *Educ:* Univ Nebr, BSc, 50, MSc, 52, MA, 54; Iowa State Univ, PhD, 72. *Prof Exp:* Asst physics, Univ Nebr, 52-54; proj leader, Farm Electrification Res Br, Agr Res Serv, 54-59, invest leader, 59-72, res leader, Lincoln, Nebr, 72-76, RES AGR ENGR, AGR RES SERV, USDA, ATHENS, GA, 76- *Concurrent Pos:* Res assoc, Univ Nebr-Lincoln, 54-59, from assoc prof to prof agr eng, 60-76; adj prof, Univ Ga, 76-; assoc ed, Int Microwave Power Inst, 76-; mem sci adv coun, Am Seed Res Found. *Honors & Awards:* Tech Paper Award, Am Soc Agr Engrs, 65. *Mem:* AAAS; Am Soc Agr Engrs; Int Microwave Power Inst; Inst Elec & Electronics Engrs. *Res:* Electromagnetic energy for insect control and seed treatment to improve germination; electrical properties of agricultural products; radiofrequency dielectric properties of insects, grain and seeds; frequency and moisture dependence of dielectric properties; methods and techniques for measuring dielectric properties; agricultural microwave power applications. *Mailing Add:* Russell Agr Res Ctr USDA PO Box 5677 Athens GA 30613

NELSON, SAMUEL JAMES, b Vancouver, BC, June 2, 25; m 54; c 2. STRATIGRAPHY, PALEONTOLOGY. *Educ:* Univ BC, BASc, 48, MASc, 50; McGill Univ, PhD(stratig, paleont), 52. *Prof Exp:* Asst prof geol, Univ NB, 52-54; from asst prof to assoc prof, 54-62, PROF GEOL, UNIV CALGARY, 62- *Concurrent Pos:* Consult to var oil industs. *Mem:* Fel Geol Asn Can. *Res:* Ordovician and Permocarboniferous stratigraphy and paleontology. *Mailing Add:* Dept Geol Univ Calgary Calgary AB T2N 1N4 Can

NELSON, SHELDON DOUGLAS, b Idaho Falls, Idaho, Aug 12, 43; m 65; c 5. SOIL CONSERVATION, SOIL MORPHOLOGY. *Educ:* Brigham Young Univ, BS, 67; Univ Calif, Riverside, PhD(soil sci), 71. *Prof Exp:* Soil scientist, Agr Res Serv, USDA, 67-72; ASSOC PROF AGRON, BRIGHAM YOUNG UNIV, 72- *Concurrent Pos:* Environ consult, Eryring Res Inst, 75-76. *Mem:* Am Soc Agron; Soil Sci Soc Am; Int Soil Soc; Coun Agr Sci & Technol; Sigma Xi. *Res:* Subsurface and drip irrigation practices; dairy waste pollution; water quality; water movement in soils; soil physics; soil salinity. *Mailing Add:* Dept of Agron Brigham Young Univ Provo UT 84601

NELSON, SIGURD OSCAR, JR, b Marquette, Mich, Jan 5, 37; m 60. ARACHNOLOGY. *Educ:* Northern Mich Univ, BS, 64; Mich State Univ, MS, 66, PhD(zool), 71. *Prof Exp:* Asst prof biol, Adrian Col, Mich, 71-72; ASSOC PROF ZOOL & CHMN DEPT, STATE UNIV NY COL OSWEGO, 72- *Mem:* Sigma Xi; Am Arachnological Soc; Am Micros Soc. *Res:* Systematics and ecology of pseudoscorpions. *Mailing Add:* Dept of Zool State Univ of NY Oswego NY 13126

NELSON, STANLEY REID, b Kidder, SDak, Dec 20, 28; m 58; c 3. PHARMACOLOGY, NEUROSURGERY. *Educ:* Univ SDak, BA, 49, MS, 57; Tulane Univ, MD, 59. *Prof Exp:* Intern surg, Univ NC, 59-60; resident neurosurg, Univ Miss, 60-64; fel neurochem, Washington Univ, 64-66; from instr to assoc prof pharmacol & neurosurg, 66-73, prof pharmacol & assoc prof neurosurg, 73-81, PROF & CHMN, DEPT ANAT, UNIV KANS MED CTR, KANSAS CITY, 81- *Mem:* Soc Neurosci; Am Soc Pharmacol & Exp Therapeut. *Res:* Effect of drugs on brain glycolysis; neurochemistry of head injury; effect of anticholinesterase; agents on regional brain activity. *Mailing Add:* Dept of Pharmacol Univ of Kans Med Ctr Kansas City KS 66103

NELSON, STEPHEN GLEN, b Frederick, Okla, July 22, 47. AQUATIC ECOLOGY, AQUACULTURE. *Educ:* San Diego State Univ, BS, 70, MS, 75; Univ Calif, Davis, PhD(ecol), 76. *Prof Exp:* Res assoc water sci & eng, Univ Calif, Davis, 76-77; asst prof, 77-80, ASSOC PROF BIOL, MARINE LAB, UNIV GUAM, 80- *Mem:* Ecol Soc Am; Am Soc Limnol & Oceanog; Phycol Soc Am; AAAS; World Maricult Soc. *Res:* Physiological ecology; nitrogen metabolism of aquatic species. *Mailing Add:* Marine Lab Univ Guam Mangilao GU 96913

NELSON, STUART HARPER, b Richmond, Ont, May 21, 26; m 52; c 3. HORTICULTURE. *Educ:* Univ Toronto, BSA, 48; Mich State Univ, MS, 50, PhD(hort), 55. *Prof Exp:* Res officer & horticulturist, Hort Div, Cent Exp Farm, Can Dept Agr, 48-54, res officer propagation, 54-59, propagation & nursery mgt, Plant Res Inst, 59-60; assoc prof, 61-66, PROF HORT, UNIV SASK, 66-, HEAD DEPT, 61- *Res:* Propagation of horticultural plants; fruit breeding; turf research; water usage at different stages of growth by horticultural plants; temperature effects on hollow heart in potatoes. *Mailing Add:* Dept of Hort Sci Univ of Sask Saskatoon SK S7H 0W0 Can

NELSON, TALMADGE SEAB, b Booneville, Ark, Jan 25, 28. ANIMAL NUTRITION. *Educ:* Univ Ark, BSA, 52; Univ Ill, MS, 52; Cornell Univ, PhD(animal nutrit), 59. *Prof Exp:* Res farm mgr, Western Condensing Co, Wis, 51-52; field supvr feed & fertilizer inspection, State Plant Bd, Ark, 52-54; res assoc poultry husb, Cornell Univ, 54-58, asst, 58-59; sr res biochemist, Int Minerals & Chem Corp, 59-63, supvr animal nutrit res, 63-68; PROF ANIMAL SCI, UNIV ARK, FAYETTEVILLE, 68- *Mem:* Am Soc Animal Sci; Poultry Sci Asn; Am Inst Nutrit; Animal Nutrit Res Coun. *Res:* Animal nutrition, especially requirements and functions; amino acids and minerals. *Mailing Add:* Dept Animal Sci Univ Ark Fayetteville AR 72701

NELSON, TERENCE JOHN, b Sioux City, Iowa, May 12, 39; m 63; c 2. THEORETICAL PHYSICS. *Educ:* Iowa State Univ, BS, 61, PhD(physics), 67; NY Univ, MEE, 63. *Prof Exp:* Mem tech staff, Bell Tel Labs, 61-63; AEC fel physics, Ames Lab, Iowa State Univ, 67-68 & Lawrence Radiation Lab, Univ Calif, 68-69; instr, Iowa State Univ, 69-70; MEM TECH STAFF, BELL TEL LABS, 70- *Mem:* Am Phys Soc. *Res:* Lasers; magnetic domain research and device development; mathematical physics in particle and group theory. *Mailing Add:* Bell Tel Labs Mountain Ave Murray Hill NJ 07974

NELSON, THEODORA S, b Phillips, Nebr, Dec 18, 13. MATHEMATICS. *Educ:* Nebr State Teachers Col, Kearney, BS, 42; Univ Ill, Urbana, BS, 46; Univ Nebr, EdD, 59. *Prof Exp:* Teacher pub schs, Nebr, 32-41; teacher high sch, Nebr, 42-45; asst math, Univ Ill, Urbana, 45-46; from asst prof to prof, 46-79, EMER PROF MATH, KEARNEY STATE COL, 79- *Concurrent Pos:* Part-time asst, Univ Ill, 45-46 & Univ Nebr, 57-58. *Mem:* Math Asn Am. *Res:* Mathematics seminar and research; projective geometry; history of mathematics. *Mailing Add:* Bruner Hall of Sci Kearney State Col Kearney NE 68847

NELSON, THOMAS CHARLES, b Wautoma, Wis, Aug 11, 23; m 44; c 2. FORESTRY. *Educ:* Univ Wis, BS, 43; Mich State Univ, MS, 47, PhD(silvicult), 50. *Prof Exp:* Res biologist, State Dept Conserv, Mich, 49-50; res forester, Southeastern Forest Exp Sta, US Forest Serv, 50-57; admin forester, Kirby Lumber Corp, Tex, 57-59; asst chief, Div Forest Mgt Res, Southeast Forest Exp Sta, US Forest Serv, 59-63, branch chief, Timber Mgt Res, Wash Off, 63-64, asst to dep chief, 64-66, dir, South Forest Exp Sta, 66-70, assoc dep chief, 70-71, dept chief, 71-80; ASST TO PRES, AM MINING CONG, 81- *Concurrent Pos:* Mem, Bd Agr & Renewable Resources, Nat Acad Sci, 73- *Honors & Awards:* Superior Serv Award, USDA, 70. *Mem:* Fel Soc Am Foresters. *Res:* Natural resource administration. *Mailing Add:* 8326 Briar Creek Dr Annandale VA 22003

NELSON, THOMAS CLIFFORD, b Columbus, Ohio, July 24, 25. MICROBIOLOGY. *Educ:* Queens Col, NY, BS, 46; Columbia Univ, MA, 46, PhD, 51. *Prof Exp:* Asst prof, Vanderbilt Univ, 51-52; proj assoc genetics, Univ Wis-Madison, 52-53, USPHS res fel, 53-54, proj assoc bot, 55-57; USPHS res fel microbiol, Rutgers Univ, 54-55; sr microbiologist, Eli Lilly & Co, 57-65; asst prof microbiol, 65-70, ASSOC PROF BOT & ZOOL, UNIV WIS-MILWAUKEE, 70- *Res:* Microbial genetics; industrial microbiology; algal biochemistry. *Mailing Add:* Dept Bot Univ Wis Box 413 Milwaukee WI 53211

NELSON, THOMAS EUSTIS, JR, b Sharon, Mass, May 3, 22; m 47; c 3. PHARMACOLOGY, PHYSIOLOGY. *Educ:* Antioch Col, BA, 47; Univ Southern Calif, MS, 51, PhD(med physiol), 56. *Prof Exp:* Asst physiol, Sch Med, Univ Southern Calif, 50-56, instr, 56-57; from asst prof to assoc prof pharmacol, Sch Med & Dent, Univ PR, 57-61, actg head dept, 59-60; asst prof, Med Ctr, Univ Colo, 61-68; assoc prof, Univ Tex Dent Br Houston, 68-70; chmn dept pharmacol, 70-76, PROF PHARMACOL & CHMN DEPT BIOMED SCI, SCH DENT MED, SOUTHERN ILL UNIV, EDWARDSVILLE, 76-, DIR RES ADMIN, 80- *Concurrent Pos:* Consult, Am Dent Asn Comn & Coun Dent Educ, 80- *Mem:* Am Soc Pharmacol & Exp Therapeut; Int Asn Dent Res; Microcirculatory Soc; Am Physiol Soc; Sigma Xi. *Res:* Physiology and pharmacology of the cardiovascular and nervous systems. *Mailing Add:* Dept of Biomed Sci Southern Ill Univ Sch Dent Med Edwardsville IL 62026

NELSON, THOMAS EVAR, b Chicago, Ill, Oct 13, 34; m 59. BIOCHEMISTRY. *Educ:* Univ Ill, Urbana, BS, 57, MS, 59; Univ Minn, St Paul, PhD(biochem), 65. *Prof Exp:* Asst, Univ Ill, Urbana, 58-59; asst, Univ Minn, St Paul, 59-64, instr, 63; instr, Univ Minn, Minneapolis, 66-67; ASST PROF BIOCHEM, BAYLOR COL MED, 68- *Concurrent Pos:* Res fel, Univ Minn, Minneapolis, 65-68; USPHS fel, 66-68. *Mem:* Sigma Xi; AAAS; Am Chem Soc; fel Am Inst Chemists; Am Soc Biol Chemists. *Res:* Action pattern, specificity, mode to attack, transglucosylation and cleavage mechanisms of carbohydrases; fine structure of polysaccharides; enzyme purification techniques; carbohydrate chemistry; enzyme interrelationships in glycogen storage diseases; glycogen debranching enzyme; control of glycogen metabolism; specificity and mechanism of hormone action; cystic fibrosis factor. *Mailing Add:* Tex Med Ctr Baylor Col of Med Houston TX 77030

NELSON, THOMAS LOTHIAN, b Baranquilla, Colombia, Jan 17, 22; US citizen; m 55; c 2. PEDIATRICS, ALLERGY. *Educ:* Univ Calif, Berkeley, AB, 43; Univ Calif, San Francisco, MD, 46. *Prof Exp:* Resident pediat, Med Ctr, Univ Calif, San Francisco, 49-51, instr, 51-56, asst clin prof pediat & lectr psychiat, Sch Med, 56-61; from assoc prof to prof pediat, Col Med, Univ Ky, 61-64; chmn dept, 64-78, PROF PEDIAT, UNIV CALIF, IRVINE-CALIF COL MED, 64-, ASSOC DEAN ACAD AFFAIRS, 78- *Concurrent Pos:* Pediatrician, Sonoma State Hosp, Eldridge, 51-52, chief physician, 52-54, asst supt med serv, 54-56, supt & med dir, 56-61; chief physician pediat & contagious dis serv, Los Angeles County Gen Hosp Unit II, 64-68; prog consult, Nat Inst Child Health & Human Develop, 64-68; mem, Fed Hosp Coun, 64-67; dir pediat prog, Orange County Med Ctr, 68- *Res:* Clinical immunology; mental retardation. *Mailing Add:* Off of the Dean Univ Calif Col of Med Irvine CA 92717

NELSON, VERNON A, b Norwood, Mass, Apr 17, 39; m 61; c 2. ENTOMOLOGY. *Educ:* Univ Mass, BS, 63, MS, 64; Pa State Univ, PhD(entom), 68. *Prof Exp:* Instr entom, Pa State Univ, 64-68; asst prof, 68-77, ASSOC PROF BIOL, SOUTHERN CONN STATE COL, 77- *Mem:* Entom Soc Am. *Res:* Arthropods of public health importance; taxonomy and biology; aquatic entomology. *Mailing Add:* Dept Biol Southern Conn State Col New Haven CT 06515

NELSON, VERNON RONALD, b Webster, SDak, Jan 20, 21; m 45; c 1. ELECTRONICS. *Educ:* Augustana Col, BA, 44; Univ Colo, MA, 51, DrSc(sci educ), 53. *Prof Exp:* Assoc prof, 46-54, PROF PHYSICS, AUGUSTANA COL, SDAK, 54- *Mem:* Am Asn Physics Teachers; Nat Sci Teachers Asn; Inst Elec & Electronics Engrs. *Res:* Wave analysis; electronics in music; square wave generator. *Mailing Add:* Dept of Physics Augustana Col Sioux Falls SD 57105

NELSON, VICTOR EUGENE, b Denver, Colo, Jan 8, 36; m 58; c 3. ZOOLOGY. *Educ:* Augustana Col, Ill, BA, 59; Univ Colo, PhD(zool, physiol), 64. *Prof Exp:* Asst biol, Univ Colo, 60-63, asst acarine physiol, 61-63; res assoc, Univ Kans, 64-65, asst prof & res assoc acarine physiol & entom, 65-66, asst prof biol, entom & insect biochem, 66-71; assoc prof, 71-76, PROF BIOL, BAKER UNIV, 76-, CHMN DEPT, 72- *Concurrent Pos:* Res grant, Univ Kans, 66-67. *Mem:* AAAS; Am Inst Biol Sci; Am Soc Zoologists; Sigma Xi. *Res:* Physiological ecology of terrestrial arthropods, particularly water relations. *Mailing Add:* Dept of Biol Baker Univ Baldwin City KS 66006

NELSON, W(INSTON) L(OWELL), b Logan, Utah, Apr 21, 27; m 49; c 2. ELECTRICAL ENGINEERING. *Educ:* Univ Utah, BS, 50; Columbia Univ, MS, 53, PhD(elec eng), 59. *Prof Exp:* Asst, Columbia Univ, 50-51 & 52-54, staff engr electronics res labs, 54-57, from instr to asst prof elec eng, univ, 57-60; mem tech staff, 60-62, supvr commun theory & control studies group, 62-66, supvr systs anal group, Radar Res Dept, 66-67, supvr control systs res group, 67-70, supvr systs anal group, Ocean Systs Anal Dept, 70-77, MEM TECH STAFF, BELL TEL LABS, INC, 77- *Concurrent Pos:* Chmn appln comt, Am Automatic Control Coun. *Mem:* Inst Elec & Electronics Engrs; Instrument Soc Am. *Res:* Control system theory; computer-aided system design; optimal control techniques; system performance evaluation; cybernetics; computer data analysis; estimation technique. *Mailing Add:* Bell Tel Labs 600 Mountain Ave Murray Hill NJ 07974

NELSON, WALLACE WARREN, soils, see previous edition

NELSON, WALTER GARNET, b London, Eng, Oct 26, 50; m 75. MARINE ECOLOGY. *Educ:* Duke Univ, AB, 72, PhD(zool), 78. *Prof Exp:* Fel marine ecol, Harbor Br Inst, 78-79, oil pollution, Royal Norwegian Coun Indust & Sci Res, 79-80; res assoc math model of population, Nat Res Coun, US Environ Protection Agency, 80-81; ASST PROF BIOOCEANOG, DEPT OCEANOG & OCEAN ENG, FLA INST TECHNOL 81- *Mem:* AAAS; Ecol Soc Am; Am Soc Zoologists. *Res:* Ecosystem dynamics of marine benthic cummunities; benthic and pelagic community relationships in estuarine and near-shore ecosystems. *Mailing Add:* Dept Oceanog & Ocean Eng Fla Inst Technol Melbourne FL 32901

NELSON, WALTER RALPH, b St Paul, Minn, Mar 24, 37; m 60; c 2. HEALTH PHYSICS. *Educ:* Univ Calif, Berkeley, AB, 63; Univ Wash, MS, 64; Stanford Univ, PhD(health physics & dosimetry), 73. *Prof Exp:* STAFF MEM HEALTH PHYSICS, STANFORD LINEAR ACCELERATOR CTR, 64- *Concurrent Pos:* Consult, Varian Assocs, Calif, 67-75 & McCall Assocs, 69-; lectr, Sch Radiation Protection & Dosimetry, Italy, 75; dir, Sch Comput Shielding & Dosimetry, Italy, 78; sci assoc, Europ Orgn Nuclear Res, 78-79. *Mem:* Health Physics Soc. *Res:* Electromagnetic cascade calculations; muon production and transport; radiation dosimetry; electron accelerator shielding; medical physics calculations. *Mailing Add:* Stanford Linear Accelerator Ctr PO Box 4349 Stanford CA 94305

NELSON, WARREN G(EORGE), b Brooklyn, NY, Oct 7, 31; m 56; c 4. MECHANICAL ENGINEERING. *Educ:* Mass Inst Technol, SB & SM, 54, ScD(mech eng), 59. *Prof Exp:* Instr mech eng, Mass Inst Technol, 55-57 & 58-59; asst prof, Univ Pa, 59-60 & 62-64; ASSOC PROF MECH ENG, NORTHEASTERN UNIV, 64- *Mem:* Am Soc Eng Educ. *Res:* Boundary layer theory; gas dynamics; unsteady laminar flow; biomedical heat transfer. *Mailing Add:* Dept of Mech Eng 360 Huntington Ave Boston MA 02115

NELSON, WAYNE BRYCE, b Chicago, Ill, Aug 17, 36; m 58; c 3. STATISTICS. *Educ:* Calif Inst Technol, BS, 58; Univ Ill, Urbana, MS, 59, PhD(statist), 65. *Prof Exp:* STATISTICIAN, CORP RES & DEVELOP, GEN ELEC CO, 65- *Concurrent Pos:* Adj prof, Union Col, 66- & Rensselaer Polytech Inst, 69-; Am Statist Asn fel, 73; pvt consult & instr, 63- *Honors & Awards:* Brumbaugh Award, Am Soc Qual Control, 69, Youden Prize, 70, Wilcoxon Prize, 72; Brumbaugh Award & Publ Award, GE Corp, 81. *Mem:* Am Statist Asn; Biomet Soc; Inst Elec & Electronics Engrs; Am Soc Quality Control. *Res:* Accelerated life testing, life data analysis, statstatistical computing and prediction methods. *Mailing Add:* 37-578 Gen Elec Co Corp Res & Develop Schenectady NY 12345

NELSON, WAYNE FRANKLIN, b Altona, Ill, Jan 16, 20; m 45; c 2. INORGANIC CHEMISTRY, PHYSICAL CHEMISTRY. *Educ:* Augustana Col, Ill, AB & BS, 41. *Prof Exp:* Asst chemist, Am Container Corp, Ill, 40-41, plant chemist, NY, 41-43, asst plant mgr, 43-47, plant mgr, 47-49, dir res, WVa, 49-57; DIR RES & DEVELOP, A SCHULMAN, INC, 57- *Mem:* Am Chem Soc; Soc Plastics Engrs; fel Am Inst Chemists. *Res:* Soft and hard rubber compounds; styrene plastics; colors and blends; polyolefins; polypropylene-natural; special compounds. *Mailing Add:* A Schulman Inc 3550 W Market St Akron OH 44313

NELSON, WENDEL LANE, b Mason City, Nebr, Apr 7, 39; m 68; c 2. MEDICINAL CHEMISTRY. *Educ:* Idaho State Univ, BS, 62; Univ Kans, PhD(pharmaceut chem), 65. *Prof Exp:* From asst prof to assoc prof, 65-76, prof pharmaceut chem, 76-80, PROF MED CHEM, UNIV WASH, 80- *Mem:* Am Chem Soc; NY Acad Sci; Am Asn Cols Pharm; Am Pharmaceut Asn. *Res:* Mechanisms of drug action; stereochemistry and conformational analysis; drug metabolism. *Mailing Add:* Sch Pharm BG-20 Univ Wash Seattle WA 98195

NELSON, WERNER LIND, b Sheffield, Ill, Oct 17, 14; m 40; c 2. AGRONOMY. *Educ:* Univ Ill, BS, 37, MS, 38; Ohio State Univ, PhD(soil physics), 40. *Prof Exp:* Instr, Univ Idaho, 40-41; asst agronomist, Agr Exp Sta, NC State Univ, 41-44, assoc agronomist, 44-47, prof agron, 47-54, in charge soil fertil res, 51-54; midwest dir, Am Potash Inst, 55-67, regional dir, 62-67; sr vpres, Potash Inst, 67-77, SR V PRES, POTASH & PHOSPHATE INST, 77- *Concurrent Pos:* Dir soil testing div, State Dept Agr, NC, 49-52; chmn soil test work group, Int Soil Fertil Cong, Ireland; mem fertilizer surv team, Food & Agr Orgn, UN, Asia & Far East Region, 59, fertilizer indust adv panel, 60-75; bd of dirs, Coun Agr Sci Technol, 72-81; adj prof agron, Purdue Univ, 73- *Honors & Awards:* Merit Cert, Am Forage & Grassland Coun, 71; Agron Serv Award, Am Soc Agron, 64. *Mem:* AAAS; fel Am Soc Agron (pres, 68-69); fel Soil Sci Soc Am (pres, 60-61); hon mem, Nat Fertilizer Solutions Asn. *Res:* Plant nutrition; soil fertility evaluation and management; fertilizers; limiting factors in crop production; maximum yield; maximum economic yield. *Mailing Add:* Potash & Phosphate Inst 402 Northwestern West Lafayette IN 47906

NELSON, WILBUR C, b Flint, Mich, May 9, 13; m 37; c 6. AERODYNAMICS. *Educ:* Univ Mich, BSE, 35, MSE, 37. *Prof Exp:* Aeronaut engr, Lockheed Aircraft Corp, Calif, 35-36; asst aeronaut engr, Civil Aeronaut Admin, Washington, DC, 37-39; proj engr, Eng Proj, Inc, Ohio, 39-40; asst prof aeronaut eng, Iowa State Col, 40-42, prof & head dept, 42-46; prof eng, 46-77, chmn dept, 53-68, prof, 77-81, EMER PROF AEROSPACE ENG, UNIV MICH, ANN ARBOR, 81- *Concurrent Pos:* Group supvr appl physics lab, Johns Hopkins Univ, 45; Navy tech rep, Eng, 48; consult, Swedish Govt, 49, Army Air Force, Europe, 50-51, Bell Aircraft Co, 52 & Advan Group Aeronaut Res & Develop, NATO, 53-68; mem adv comt launch vehicle, NASA, 63-65; mem adv comt supersonic transport, Fed Aviation Admin, 66-67. *Mem:* Fel Am Inst Aeronaut & Astronaut. *Res:* Aircraft and spacecraft design. *Mailing Add:* Dept of Aerospace Eng Univ of Mich Ann Arbor MI 48109

NELSON, WILFRED H, b Evanston, Ill, May 23, 36; m 74; c 3. INORGANIC CHEMISTRY. *Educ:* Univ Chicago, BSc & MSc, 59; Univ Minn, PhD(inorg chem), 63. *Prof Exp:* Res assoc inorg chem, Univ Ill, Urbana, 63-64; from asst prof to assoc prof, 64-77, PROF CHEM, UNIV RI, 77- *Concurrent Pos:* Res Corp grant, 65-66; grant, Sydney Univ, 70-71; NSF grant, 66-68 & 68-72. *Mem:* Am Chem Soc; Soc Appl Spectros; Sigma Xi. *Res:* Structure of organometallics with metal-oxygen bonds; synthesis of post-transition metal coordination compounds; dynamic light scattering and bond polarizability studies; solution thermodynamics; resonance Raman study of microorganisms. *Mailing Add:* Dept of Chem Univ of RI Kingston RI 02881

NELSON, WILLIAM ARNOLD, b Lethbridge, Alta, June 24, 18; m 48; c 3. ENTOMOLOGY. *Educ:* Univ Alta, BSc, 44; McGill Univ, MSc, 48, PhD(med entom), 57. *Prof Exp:* Asst wheat stem sawfly, Field Crop Entom Sect, 43-47, RES SCIENTIST, VET MED SECT, RES STA, CAN DEPT AGR, 48- *Mem:* Am Soc Parasitologists. *Res:* Physiology of host-parasite relationships; humoral factors. *Mailing Add:* Animal Parasitol Sect Can Agr Res Sta Lethbridge AB T1J 4B1 Can

NELSON, WILLIAM FRANK, b Cleveland, Ohio, May 4, 24. PHYSICS. *Educ:* Univ Akron, BS, 48, MS, 49; Wash State Univ, PhD(physics), 56. *Prof Exp:* Head, Mat Res Group, Long Beach Div, Douglas Aircraft Co, 53-60; sr res scientist & head solid state physics group fundamental res, Owens-Ill, Inc, 60-64, dir fundamental res, Tech Ctr, 64-69, ASSOC DIR RES & DIR ADVAN TECHNOL LAB, GTE LABS, INC, 69- *Concurrent Pos:* Adj prof, Univ Toledo, 63-69. *Mem:* AAAS; fel Am Phys Soc; Sigma Xi. *Res:* Physics of solids. *Mailing Add:* GTE Labs Inc One Stamford Forum Stamford CT 06904

NELSON, WILLIAM HENRY, b Huntsville, Ala, Nov 24, 43. MAGNETIC RESONANCE. *Educ:* Auburn Univ, BS, 66; Duke Univ, PhD(physics), 70. *Prof Exp:* Asst prof physics, Hollins Col, Va, 70-73; instr, Duke Univ, 73-74; asst prof, 74-81, ASSOC PROF PHYSICS, GA STATE UNIV, 81- *Concurrent Pos:* Res assoc, Microwave Lab, Duke Univ, 73-74. *Mem:* Am Phys Soc; Am Asn Physics Teachers; Sigma Xi; Radiation Res Soc. *Res:* Use of magnetic resonance, electron spin resonance and electron-nuclear double resonance, for study of radiation damage and molecular structure. *Mailing Add:* Dept of Physics Ga State Univ Atlanta GA 30303

NELSON, WILLIAM PIERREPONT, III, b New Orleans, La, Jan 9, 20; m 44; c 3. MEDICINE, INTERNAL MEDICINE. *Educ:* Wesleyan Univ, BA, 41; Cornell Univ, MD, 44; Am Bd Internal Med, dipl, 52. *Prof Exp:* Life Ins Med Res Fund fel metab, Sch Med, Yale Univ, 50-51; instr med, Albany Med Col, 51-53; asst prof, 53-56, asst dean col, 56-66, PROF MED & PROF POSTGRAD MED, ALBANY MED COL, 56- *Concurrent Pos:* Chief metab & endocrine sect, Vet Admin Hosp, 52-54, chief med serv, 54-56, chief ambulatory care, 74-77, assoc chief staff educ, 77- *Mem:* Fel Am Col Physicians; Am Soc Int Med. *Res:* Metabolism and endocrinology. *Mailing Add:* Font Grove Rd Slingerlands NY 12159

NELSON, WOODROW ENSIGN, b Mesa, Ariz, Apr 23, 18; m 43; c 3. FOOD TECHNOLOGY, MICROBIOLOGY. *Educ:* Utah State Univ, BS, 47; Univ Wis-Madison, MS, 60, PhD(dairy foods, microbiol), 67. *Prof Exp:* Dir qual control, Hi-Land Dairymen Asn, 47-51; plant supt, Clark County Dairymen, Nev, 51-56; owner & operator dairy herd, Clark County, Nev & Cache County, Utah, 56-58; dir food technol, 63-72, DIR, THERACON, INC, 72- *Mem:* AAAS; Inst Food Technol; Am Dairy Sci Asn. *Res:* Reconstitution characteristics of dried milk; ultra high temperature sterilization of foods; effect of ultra high temperature sterilization on the degradation of food nutrients. *Mailing Add:* Theracon Inc PO Box 1493 Topeka KS 66601

NELSON-REES, WALTER ANTHONY, b Havana, Cuba, Jan 11, 29; US citizen. GENETICS, CYTOLOGY. *Educ:* Emory Univ, AB, 51, MA, 52; Univ Calif, Berkeley, PhD(genetics), 60. *Prof Exp:* NIH training grant & res assoc genetics, Univ Calif, Berkeley, 60-61, from asst res geneticist to assoc res geneticist, Naval Biosci Lab, Sch Pub Health, 61-73, CONSULT, NAVAL BIOSCI LAB, SCH PUB HEALTH, UNIV CALIF, BERKELEY, 63-, ASSOC CHIEF CELL CULT DIV, 69-, LECTR CYTOL & CYTOGENETICS, 71- *Concurrent Pos:* Fulbright res scholar cytogenetics, Max Planck Inst Marine Biol, Ger, 61-62; consult, Breast Cancer Task Force, Nat Cancer Inst, NIH, 75-; co-prin investr, Nat Cancer Inst-NIH-Univ Calif, Berkeley, 76-; adj fac mem, W A Jones Cell Sci Ctr, 77. *Mem:* AAAS; Tissue Cult Asn. *Res:* Induction of chromosome aberrations in Tradescantia; factors influencing sex determination in coccid insects; heterochromatin and fertility factors in male mealy bugs; cinemicrography of animal cells; chromosome banding and other methods for cell line identification and detection of cellular cross contamination. *Mailing Add:* 6000 Contra Costa Rd Oakland CA 94618

NEMAT-NASSER, SIAVOUCHE, b Tehran, Iran, Apr 14, 36; m 65; c 3. APPLIED & STRUCTURAL MECHANICS, GEOMECHANICS. *Educ:* Sacramento State Col, BS, 60; Univ Calif, Berkeley, MS, 61, PhD(struct mech), 64. *Prof Exp:* Asst prof eng, Sacramento State Col, 61-62; fel struct mech, Northwestern Univ, 64-65, sr res fel, 65-66; asst prof appl mech, Univ Calif, San Diego, 66-69, assoc prof, 69-70; PROF CIVIL ENG & APPLIED MATH, NORTHWESTERN UNIV, 70- *Concurrent Pos:* Mem, Ctr Study Democratic Insts; vis prof dept solid mech, Tech Univ Denmark, 72-73; ed, Mech Today; chief ed int jour, Mech Mat; Alburz Educ Found, 75. *Mem:* Am Soc Mech Engrs; Am Soc Civil Engrs; Soc Eng Sci (vpres-pres, 78-80); fel Am Acad Mech; Earthquake Eng Res Inst. *Res:* Vibration and stability; continuum mechanics; elasticity; plasticity; waves in composites; flow, fracture and general constitutive behavior of geophysical, geotechnical and technological materials (experiment and theory); earthquake and geothermal energy research. *Mailing Add:* Dept of Civil Eng Technol Inst Northwestern Univ Evanston IL 60201

NEMATOLLAHI, JAY, b Astara, Azerbaijan, Dec 21, 25; US citizen; m 52; c 3. MEDICINAL CHEMISTRY, MICROBIOLOGY. *Educ:* Univ Tehran, PharmD, 48; Univ Calif, MA, 54, PharmD, 58, PhD(pharmaceut chem), 63. *Prof Exp:* Fel, Univ Calif, 63; asst prof, prof pharmaceut chem, Univ RI, 63-64; assoc prof, Tex Southern Univ, 64-65; asst prof, 67-71, ASSOC PROF PHARMACEUT CHEM, COL PHARM, UNIV TEX, AUSTIN, 71- *Concurrent Pos:* Adj grad fac, Univ Houston; Fulbright fel, USSR, 80. *Mem:* Am Chem Soc; AAAS. *Res:* Synthesis of organic medicinals; spectroscopy. *Mailing Add:* Col of Pharm Univ of Tex Austin TX 78712

NEMEC, JOSEF, b Ostresany, Czech, Sept 7, 29; m 75; c 1. ORGANIC CHEMISTRY. *Educ:* Inst Chem Technol, Czech Acad Sci, MS, 54; Czech Acad Sci, PhD(org chem), 58. *Prof Exp:* Scientist org chem, Czech Acad Sci, 54-61; sr res chemist, Inst Chem Technol, Czech Acad Sci, 61-69; res fel org chem, Wayne State Univ, 69-70; sr res scientist, Squibb Inst Med Res, 70-75; MEM, ST JUDE CHILDREN'S RES HOSP, 75-; PROF, DEPT MED CHEM, UNIV TENN, MEMPHIS, 79- *Mem:* Am Chem Soc; Royal Soc Chem. *Res:* Stereochemistry and synthesis of deoxy sugars, amino sugars, antibiotics and analogs; drug metabolism; nucleosides; nucleotides; design and synthesis of potential antineoplastic agents. *Mailing Add:* St Jude Children's Res Hosp Memphis TN 38101

NEMEC, JOSEPH WILLIAM, b Philadelphia, Pa, Mar 24, 22; m 48; c 3. ORGANIC CHEMISTRY. *Educ:* Temple Univ, AB, 43; Ind Univ, MA, 44; Pa State Univ, PhD(chem), 49. *Prof Exp:* Sr org chemist, 49-61, lab head, 61-69, res supvr, 69-73, MGR PROCESS RES, ROHM AND HAAS CO, 73- *Mem:* AAAS; Am Chem Soc. *Res:* Process research and development; catalysis; acrylate monomer technology. *Mailing Add:* Rohm and Haas Co Independence Mall W Philadelphia PA 19105

NEMEC, STANLEY, b St Louis, Mo, Feb 3, 35; m 60; c 2. PLANT PATHOLOGY. *Educ:* Auburn Univ, BS, 60; Okla State Univ, MS, 64; Ore State Univ, PhD(plant path), 67. *Prof Exp:* Landscape technician, Harland Bartholomew & Assoc, City Planners, 60-61; plant pathologist, Ore Dept Agr, 63-66; res plant pathologist, Southern Ill Univ, Carbondale, 66-72, RES PLANT PATHOLOGIST, USDA, FLA, 72- *Mem:* Am Phytopath Soc; Soc Nematol. *Res:* Botany; horticulture; biochemistry. *Mailing Add:* Agr Res Serv USDA US Hort Field Lab 2120 Camden Rd Orlando FL 32803

NEMENZO, FRANCISCO, b Pinamungajan, Philippines, Sept 17, 05; m 31; c 3. ZOOLOGY. *Educ:* Univ Philippines, BS, 29, MS, 34, ScD, 81; Univ Mich, AM, 48. *Prof Exp:* Registr, Cebu Col, 45-50, dean, 50, asst prof zool, 52-55, assoc prof & head dept, 55-60, prof zool, 60-69, chmn div natural sci, 60-63, dean col arts & sci, 63-69, EMER PROF ZOOL, UNIV PHILIPPINES, 71- *Concurrent Pos:* Mem, Nat Res Coun, Philippines. *Res:* Philippines recent scleractinians; systematics and ecology of stony reef corals. *Mailing Add:* 12 Sampaguita St Cebu City Philippines

NEMER, MARTIN JOSEPH, b Philadelphia, Pa, Nov 26, 29. BIOCHEMISTRY. *Educ:* Kenyon Col, BA, 52; Harvard Univ, MS, 55, PhD(biochem), 58. *Prof Exp:* Fel, Univ Brussels, 58-59; res fel, Stazione Zool, Naples, Italy, 59-60; res assoc biochem, 60-63, from asst mem to assoc mem, 63-77, MEM, INST CANCER RES, 78- *Mem:* AAAS; Am Soc Biol Chemists; Soc Develop Biol. *Res:* Chemical embryology; regulation of protein and nucleic acid synthesis. *Mailing Add:* Inst Cancer Res 7701 Burholme Ave Philadelphia PA 19111

NEMERGUT, PAUL JOSEPH, JR, applied mechanics, see previous edition

NEMEROW, NELSON L(EONARD), b Syracuse, NY, Apr 16, 23; m 47; c 3. SANITARY ENGINEERING. *Educ:* Syracuse Univ, BSChE, 44; Rutgers Univ, MS, 49, PhD(sanit eng), 51. *Prof Exp:* Res engr, Johns Manville Corp, 44, 46; from asst prof to assoc prof civil eng, NC State Col, 51-57; prof, Syracuse Univ, 58-76; RES PROF, UNIV MIAMI, 76- *Concurrent Pos:* Lectr, Stanford Univ, 65-66; consult, Environ Protection Agency, 67-78, UN Indust Develop Orgn, Vienna, Austria, 74-78 & Nat Water Comn, 75-76. *Mem:* Am Soc Civil Engrs; Am Soc Sanit Engrs; Am Acad Environ Engrs. *Res:* Water; sewage; industrial wastes; stream pollution; solid wastes disposal; economics of water resources; oil pollution of beaches; aquaculture; industrial complexes. *Mailing Add:* Dept of Civil Eng Univ of Miami Coral Gables FL 33124

NEMERSON, YALE, b New York, NY, Dec 15, 31; m 58; c 3. HEMATOLOGY, BIOCHEMISTRY. *Educ:* Bard Col, BA, 53; NY Univ, MD, 60. *Prof Exp:* Intern, Lenox Hill Hosp, 60-61; resident, Bronx Vet Admin Hosp, 61-62; fel hemat, Montefiore Hosp, 62-64; from instr to prof, Sch Med, Yale Univ, 64-75; prof med, State Univ NY Stony Brook, 75-77; PHILLIP J & HARRIET L GOODHART PROF MED, MT SINAI SCH MED, 77- *Concurrent Pos:* Leukemia Soc fel, 63-64; NIH res grant, 64-76; investr, Am Heart Asn, 67-72, res grant, 67-73. *Mem:* AAAS; Am Soc Hemat; Am Soc Exp Path; Am Soc Clin Invest. *Res:* Lipid-protein interactions in blood coagulation. *Mailing Add:* Mt Sinai Sch of Med 100th St & Fifth Ave New York NY 10029

NEMES, MARJORIE M, bacteriology, see previous edition

NEMETH, ABRAHAM, b New York, NY, Oct 16, 18; m 44. MATHEMATICS, COMPUTER SCIENCE. *Educ:* Brooklyn Col, BA, 40; Columbia Univ, MA, 42; Wayne State Univ, PhD(math), 64. *Prof Exp:* Instr math, Brooklyn Col, 46, Manhattan Col, 53-54 & Manhattanville Col, 54-55; from instr to assoc prof, 55-76, PROF MATH, UNIV DETROIT, 76- *Mem:* Math Asn Am; Asn Comput Mach. *Res:* Computer science; Nemeth braille code of mathematics and scientific notation. *Mailing Add:* Dept of Math Univ of Detroit Detroit MI 48221

NEMETH, ANDREW MARTIN, b Philadelphia, Pa, Sept 13, 26; m 61; c 4. ANATOMY. *Educ:* Johns Hopkins Univ, AB, 49, MD, 53. *Prof Exp:* Intern pediat, Johns Hopkins Hosp, 53-54; NSF fel biochem, Col Physicians & Surgeons, Columbia Univ, 54-56; assoc anat, 56-59, from asst prof to assoc prof, 59-68, PROF ANAT, SCH MED, UNIV PA, 68- *Mem:* Am Asn Anatomists. *Res:* Regulation of enzyme formation in developing tissues; induction of enzymes; fetal development. *Mailing Add:* Dept of Anat Univ of Pa Sch of Med Philadelphia PA 19104

NEMETH, EVI, b Cooperstown, NY, June 7, 40; m 63; c 1. COMBINATORIAL MATHEMATICS, COMPUTER SCIENCE. *Educ:* Pa State Univ, BA, 61; Univ Waterloo, PhD(math), 71. *Prof Exp:* Gen mgr oceanog, Estuarine & Oceanic Technol Corp, 72-75; asst prof math & comput sci, Fla Atlantic Univ, 75-76; ASST PROF MATH & COMPUT SCI, STATE UNIV NY COL TECHNOL, 76- *Concurrent Pos:* Mathematician math & comput sci, US Dept Com, 76-; HEW grant, 78; consult, Pattern Anal & Recognition Corp, 77- *Mem:* Math Asn Am; Asn Comput Mach. *Res:* Combinatorics; existence theorems for designs; combinatorial algorithms; information retrieval. *Mailing Add:* Dept of Comput Sci State Univ NY Col of Technol Utica NY 13502

NEMETH, JOSEPH, b Ithaca, NY, Dec 29, 40; m 76; c 3. MATERIALS ENGINEERING. *Educ:* Alfred Univ, BS, 63, MS, 66; Univ Windsor, PhD(mat eng), 71. *Prof Exp:* Res assoc mech properties, Air Force Lab, State Univ NY Col Ceramics, Alfred Univ, 63-66; res assoc crystal growth, Univ Windsor, 66-70; RES ENGR, CHAMPION SPARK PLUG CO, 70- *Concurrent Pos:* Lectr, Univ Windsor, 68-70. *Mem:* Am Ceramic Soc; Nat Inst Ceramic Engrs; Am Soc Metals. *Res:* Mechanical and electrical properties of insulating and semiconducting materials; microstructure and fracture behavior of oxide materials. *Mailing Add:* Ceramic Div 20000 Conner Ave Detroit MI 48234

NEMETH, LASZLO K, b Szeged, Hungary, June 7, 32; m 56; c 4. PETROLEUM ENGINEERING. *Educ:* Rensselaer Polytech Inst, BS, 55; Pa State Univ, MS, 57; Tex A&M Univ, PhD(petrol & natural gas eng), 66. *Prof Exp:* Reservoir & sec recovery engr, Texaco, Inc, 57-63; consult, Nat Oil Co Arg, 66-70; sr res engr, Tenneco Oil Co, 70-71; consult engr, Butler, Miller & Lents Ltd, 71-76; exec vpres, 76-80, PRES, J R BUTLER & CO, 80- *Concurrent Pos:* Univ Ind lectr, US, Arg & Chile; sr vpres, GeoQuest Int, Inc. *Mem:* Soc Petrol Engrs; Am Inst Mining, Metall & Petrol Engrs; Int Oil Scouts Asn. *Res:* Reservoir engineering and simulation; secondary recovery; improved recovery methods; miscible flooding; gas and condensate recovery. *Mailing Add:* 5542 Dumfries Houston TX 77096

NEMETH, RONALD LOUIS, b Endicott, NY, Mar 4, 41; m 66. COLLOID AND SURFACE SCIENCE. *Educ:* Clarkson Col Technol, BS, 64, MS, 66, PhD(phys chem), 69. *Prof Exp:* res chemist, 68-80, SR TECHNOL SPECIALIST, MONSANTO CO, 80- *Mem:* Am Chem Soc. *Res:* Stability of aqueous dispersions; molecular structure and mechanical property relationships of polymers. *Mailing Add:* Res Dept Monsanto Co Indian Orchard MA 01051

NEMETH, ZOLTAN ANTHONY, b Sopron, Hungary, Apr 27, 31; US citizen; m 54; c 2. CIVIL & TRANSPORTATION ENGINEERING. *Educ:* Budapest Tech Univ, Dipl, 54; Ohio State Univ, MS, 63, PhD(transp eng), 68. *Prof Exp:* Design engr, Design Off, Ministry Mining, Hungary, 54-56, Truscon Steel Co, Can, 57-60 & P A Benn & Assoc Consult, 60-61; res assoc transp eng, 61-68, ASST PROF CIVIL ENG, TRANSP RES CTR, OHIO STATE UNIV, 68- *Concurrent Pos:* Secy comt, Hwy Res Bd, Nat Acad Sci-Nat Res Coun, 71-, chmn, 71. *Mem:* Inst Traffic Engrs. *Res:* Application of photographic data collection and digital simulation to the investigation of traffic flow characteristics at intersections, on freeway ramps and on signalized arterials. *Mailing Add:* Dept of Civil Eng Transp Res Ctr 2070 Neil Ave Columbus OH 43210

NEMETHY, GEORGE, b Budapest, Hungary, Oct 11, 34; US citizen; m 75; c 2. PHYSICAL CHEMISTRY. *Educ:* Lincoln Univ, Pa, BA, 56; Cornell Univ, PhD(phys chem), 62. *Prof Exp:* Phys chemist, Gen Elec Res Lab, NY, 62-63; asst prof phys chem, Rockefeller Univ, 63-72; vis prof, Dept Biochem, Univ Paris, Orsay, 72-74; vis assoc prof, Dept Chem, State Univ NY Binghamton, 74-75; SR RES ASSOC, DEPT CHEM, CORNELL UNIV, 75- *Concurrent Pos:* NATO fel & vis lectr, Instituto Superiore di Sanita, Rome, 70; lectr, Med Ctr, NY Univ, 71-72; mem biophys sci training comt, Nat Inst Biomed Sci, 71-72. *Honors & Awards:* Pius XI Gold Medal, Pontifical Acad Sci, 72; Europ Molecular Biol Orgn sr scientist fel, 73-74. *Mem:* Am Soc Biol Chemists; NY Acad Sci; Am Chem Soc. *Res:* Statistical thermodynamics, liquid structure; thermodynamic properties of aqueous solutions; structure of proteins, conformations, thermodynamics, structure and enzymatic activity; protein conformation; statistical thermodynamics. *Mailing Add:* Baker Lab Chem Cornell Univ Ithaca NY 14853

NEMHAUSER, GEORGE L, b New York, NY, July 27, 37; m 59; c 2. OPERATIONS RESEARCH. *Educ:* City Col New York, BChE, 58; Northwestern Univ, MS, 59, PhD(opers res), 61. *Prof Exp:* From asst prof to assoc prof opers res, Johns Hopkins Univ, 61-69; PROF OPERS RES, CORNELL UNIV, 69-, DIR, SCH OPERS RES & INDUST ENG, 77- *Concurrent Pos:* Vis lectr, Univ Leeds, 63-64; vis res prof, Ctr Opers Res & Economet, Cath Univ Louvain, 69-70; NSF fac fel, 69-70; dir res ctr opers res & economet, Cath Univ Louvain, 75-77; ed-in-chief Opers Res, J Opers Res Soc Am, 75-78; found ed, Oper Res Letters, 81- *Mem:* Opers Res Soc Am (vpres, 80-81 & pres, 81-82); Inst Mgt Sci; Soc Indust & Appl Math; Math Prog Soc; Am Inst Indust Engrs. *Res:* Theory and computational aspects of mathematical programming; mathematical modelling of complex systems. *Mailing Add:* Sch Opers Res & Indust Eng Upson Hall Cornell Univ Ithaca NY 14853

NEMIR, PAUL, JR, b Navasota, Tex, Aug 30, 20; m 49; c 3. SURGERY. *Educ:* Univ Tex, AB, 40, MD, 44. *Prof Exp:* From instr to assoc prof surg, 48-69, dean grad sch med, 59-64, dir div grad med, 64-69, PROF SURG, SCH MED, UNIV PA, 69- *Concurrent Pos:* Surgeon-in-chief, Grad Hosp & consult cardiovasc surg, US Naval Hosp, 48- *Mem:* AMA; Soc Univ Surgeons; Soc Vascular Surg; Am Asn Thoracic Surg; Soc Surg Alimentary Tract. *Res:* Pulmonary function and embolism; diseases of the esophagus and esophageal motor function; mechanism of toxicity of hemoglobin derivatives; studies on vascular prosthetics. *Mailing Add:* Grad Hosp 19th & Lombard Sts Philadelphia PA 19146

NEMIR, ROSA LEE, b Waco, Tex, July 16, 05; m 34; c 3. PEDIATRICS. *Educ:* Univ Tex, BA, 26; Johns Hopkins Univ, MD, 30. *Hon Degrees:* DSc, Colgate Univ, 74. *Prof Exp:* From instr to assoc prof, Med Col, 33-50, assoc prof, Postgrad Med Sch, 50-53, PROF PEDIAT, SCH MED, NY UNIV, 53- *Concurrent Pos:* Lectr, Sch Nursing, Bellevue Hosp, 34-49, from asst vis pediatrician to vis pediatrician, 37-; attend pediatrician, Univ Hosp, 50-, vis physician & in chg chest unit, Children's Med Serv, 60, dir children's chest clin, 61-; attend pediatrician, Gouvernour Hosp, 50-58, consult, 58; consult, NY Infirmary, 54-82, dir pediat educ & res, 66-73; vis prof, Col Physicians & Surgeons, Columbia Univ, 58-59; dir cont med educ, Am Med Womens Asn, 77-81. *Honors & Awards:* New York Dept Hosps Award, 59; Off, Medal of Cedars of Lebanon, Repub Lebanon; Elizabeth Blackwell Award, Am Med Women's Asn, 70. *Mem:* Soc Pediat Res; Am Pediat Soc; Am Col Chest Physicians; Am Med Women's Asn (pres, 64); Med Women's Int Asn (vpres, 70-74). *Res:* Pneumonia in children; nutrition; tuberculosis; virology. *Mailing Add:* NY Univ Sch of Med 550 First Ave New York NY 10016

NEMITZ, WILLIAM CHARLES, b Memphis, Tenn, July 27, 28. PURE MATHEMATICS. *Educ:* Southwestern at Memphis, BS, 50; Ohio State Univ, MS, 56, PhD(math), 59. *Prof Exp:* Instr math, Ohio State Univ, 59-60; asst prof, Univ Kans, 60-61; from asst prof to assoc prof, 61-70, PROF MATH, SOUTHWESTERN AT MEMPHIS, 70- *Concurrent Pos:* NSF grant, 63-64, 71-73. *Mem:* Am Math Soc; Am. *Res:* Algebraic structures related to intuitionistic logics, particularly implicative semi-lattices. *Mailing Add:* Dept of Math Southwestern at Memphis Memphis TN 38112

NEMPHOS, SPEROS PETER, b New York, NY, July 8, 30; m 55; c 3. POLYMER CHEMISTRY. *Educ:* Ursinus Col, BS, 52; Univ Del, MS, 55, PhD(phys chem), 57. *Prof Exp:* Res chemist, 56-63, specialist, 63-65, group leader, 65-74, res mgr, 74-77, MGR RES, MONSANTO CO, 77- *Mem:* Am Chem Soc. *Res:* Polymer synthesis; kinetics and characterization of vinyl polymers; polymer degradations and stabilization; plastic foams; emulsion and suspension polymerizations; graft polymer systems; barrier resins; plastics fire safety; membrane science; separational technology. *Mailing Add:* 104 Coorsdale Dr Cary NC 27511

NEMUTH, HAROLD I, b Norfolk, Va, Mar 12, 12; m 47; c 3. PREVENTIVE MEDICINE. *Educ:* Columbia Univ, BA, 34; Med Col Va, MD, 39. *Prof Exp:* Actg chmn dept prev med, 59-62, assoc prof, 62-73, CLIN PROF PREV MED, MED COL VA, 73-, ASSOC MED, HOME CARE PROG, 57- *Concurrent Pos:* Mem bd visitors, Va Commonwealth Univ, 78. *Mem:* AAAS; AMA; Asn Am Med Cols; Asn Teachers Prev Med; Geront Soc. *Mailing Add:* Dept of Prev Med Med Col of Va Richmond VA 23219

NENNO, ROBERT PETER, b Buffalo, NY, Mar 3, 22; m; c 4. PSYCHIATRY. *Educ:* Univ Notre Dame, BS, 43; Loyola Univ, MD, 47; Am Bd Psychiat & Neurol, dipl. *Prof Exp:* Intern, E J Meyer Mem Hosp, Buffalo, NY, 47-48; resident psychiat, Vet Admin Hosp, Minneapolis, 48-50; resident, Vet Admin Hosp, Downey, Ill, 50-51; asst prof psychiat & asst dir dept, Sch Med, Georgetown Univ, 53-56, assoc prof, 56-58; prof psychiat & chmn dept, Seton Hall Col Med, 58-63; med dir & chief exec officer, NJ State Hosp, Marlboro, 63-68; interim med dir, Raritan Bay Ment Health Ctr, 70; prof psychiat, NJ Med Sch, Col Med & Dent NJ, Newark, 73-76; attend, Martland Hosp, 76-77; dir dept psychiat, Jersey City, Med Ctr, 73-76, actg med dir, 75-76; clin prof psychiat, NJ Med Sch, 76-77; CLIN PROF PSYCHIAT, SCH MED, E CAROLINA UNIV, 77-; MED DIR, PITT COUNTY MENTAL HEALTH CTR, 77- *Concurrent Pos:* Asst dir psychiat div, Georgetown Univ Hosp, 53-56; consult, DC Gen Hosp, Mt Alto Vet Admin Hosp & Cent Intel Agency, 53-58; asst examr, Am Bd Psychiat & Neurol, 56-; clin prof psychiat, Sch Med, Rutgers Univ, 66-73; pvt pract psychiat, 68-; mem staff, Overlook Hosp, Summit, NJ, 68-77; attend, Pitt County Mem Hosp, Greenville, NC, 77- *Mem:* Fel Am Psychiat Asn; Am Pub Health Asn; Am Asn Social Psychiat; Acad Psychoanal. *Res:* Vocational and social rehabilitation of the mentally ill; nicotinic acid in the treatment of schizophrenia; use of librium analogs in psychiatry. *Mailing Add:* Sch of Med E Carolina Univ Greenvile NC 27834

NEPTUNE, JOHN ADDISON, b Barnesville, Ohio, Nov 27, 19; m 47; c 1. INORGANIC CHEMISTRY. *Educ:* Muskingum Col, BS, 42; Univ Wis, MS, 49, PhD(chem), 52. *Prof Exp:* Instr chem, Muskingum Col, 43-44, 45-48; shift foreman, Chem Refining Div, Tenn Eastman Corp, 44-45; asst prof chem, Bowling Green State Univ, 49-50; instr pharmaceut chem, Univ Wis, 52-55; from asst prof to assoc prof chem, 55-61, PROF CHEM, SAN JOSE STATE UNIV, 61-, CHMN DEPT, 73- *Mem:* Am Chem Soc. *Res:* Reaction kinetics of oxidation-reduction reactions; reactions in non-aqueous solvents. *Mailing Add:* 50 Cherokee Lane San Jose CA 95127

NEPTUNE, WILLIAM EVERETT, b Lawton, Okla, Apr 24, 28; m 50; c 2. PHYSICAL CHEMISTRY. *Educ:* Okla Baptist Univ, BS, 50; Univ Okla, MS, 52, PhD(chem), 54. *Prof Exp:* From asst prof to assoc prof, 54-60, PROF CHEM, OKLA BAPTIST UNIV, 60-, DEAN LIB ARTS, 61-, VPRES ACADEMIC AFFAIRS, 73-, PROVOST, 78- *Concurrent Pos:* Consult, Saline Waters Proj, US Dept Interior, 60-61, dir, 61-65; consult, NCent Asn Cols & Sec Schs, 63-, mem, Comn Insts Higher Educ, 69- & Coun Res & Serv, 78- *Mem:* AAAS; Am Chem Soc; Royal Soc Chem; NY Acad Sci. *Res:* Electrochemistry; chemistry of carbon; history and philosophy of science; chemchemical education. *Mailing Add:* Dept of Chem Okla Baptist Univ Shawnee OK 74801

NERBUN, ROBERT CHARLES, JR, b Waukegan, Ill, Apr 19, 46; m 72; c 2. EXPERIMENTAL NUCLEAR PHYSICS. *Educ:* Univ Wis-River Falls, BS, 68; Case Western Reserve Univ, MS, 71, PhD(exp nuclear physics), 73. *Prof Exp:* Lectr, Col Physics, Case Western Reserve Univ, 69-70; ASST PROF PHYSICS, UNIV SC, SUMTER, 73- *Mem:* Am Phys Soc; Am Asn Physics Teachers. *Res:* Measurements of reaction cross sections for (d,n) stripping reactions at 2.5 to 4.0 MeV bombarding energies. *Mailing Add:* Dept of Physics Univ of SC Miller Rd Sumter SC 29150

NEREM, ROBERT MICHAEL, b Chicago, Ill, July 20, 37; m 58, 78; c 4. BIOMEDICAL ENGINEERING, FLUID MECHANICS. *Educ:* Univ Okla, BS, 59; Ohio State Univ, MS, 61, PhD(aeronaut eng), 64. *Prof Exp:* From instr to assoc prof, Ohio State Univ, 61-72, prof aeronaut & astronaut eng, 72-79, assoc dean, Grad Sch, 75-79; PROF & CHMN MECH ENG, UNIV HOUSTON, 79- *Concurrent Pos:* Consult, Goodyear Aerospace Corp, Ohio, 62-74, Aro, Inc, Tenn, 64-65 & Space & Info Systs Div, NAm Aviation, Inc, Calif, 65; Sci Res Coun sr vis fel, Imp Col, Univ London, 70; consult, Gen Elec Co, 71-72 & Technol Inc, 80. *Mem:* Am Inst Aeronaut & Astronaut; Am Phys Soc; AAAS; Am Soc Mech Engrs; Am Physiol Soc. *Res:* Biological fluid mechanics; arterial blood flow; hemodynamics and atherogenesis; heart disease; unsteady flow phenomena. *Mailing Add:* Dept Mech Eng Univ Houston Houston TX 77004

NERESON, NORRIS (GEORGE), b Gaylord, Minn, Nov 4, 18; m; c 2. LASERS. *Educ:* Concordia Col, Minn, BA, 39; Univ Denver, MS, 41; Cornell Univ, PhD(nuclear physics), 43. *Prof Exp:* Asst physics, Cornell Univ, 42-43; mem staff, Physics Div, Los Alamos Sci Lab, 43-45; asst prof physics, Univ NMex, 46-47; MEM STAFF, LASER DIV, LOS ALAMOS SCI LAB, 48- *Concurrent Pos:* Int Atomic Energy Agency vis prof, Brazil, 64-65. *Res:* Solid state physics and lasers; application of molecular spectroscopy to isotope separation employing diode lasers. *Mailing Add:* PO Box 366 Los Alamos NM 87544

NERI, ANTHONY, b Italy, Jan 15, 48; US citizen; m 76; c 2. TISSUE CULTURE. *Educ:* Loyola Univ, BS, 71; Calif State Univ, Northridge, MS, 75; Univ Calif, Irvine, PhD(cell biol), 81. *Prof Exp:* Res assoc cancer res, Sch Med, Univ Calif, Los Angeles, 71-75; asst instr, Univ Calif, Irvine, 75-80; RES FEL, UNIV SOUTHERN CALIF CANCER CTR, 81- *Mem:* Sigma Xi. *Res:* Cellular and biochemical events associated with the process of cancer metastasis and detection. *Mailing Add:* Univ Southern Calif Cancer Ctr CRL 208 1303 N Mission Rd Los Angeles CA 90033

NERI, FILIPPO, b Cesena, Italy, April 18, 51. SUPER SYMMETRY, MAGNETIC MONOPOLES. *Educ:* Univ Parma, Italy, Laurea, 75, NY Univ, PhD(physics), 79. *Prof Exp:* FEL, RUTGERS UNIV, 80- *Res:* Field theory and particle physics; magnetic monopoles; supersymmetric theories. *Mailing Add:* Dept Physics & Astron Rutgers Univ Piscataway NJ 08854

NERI, RUDOLPH ORAZIO, b Barre, Mass, Sept 11, 28; m 55; c 4. ENDOCRINOLOGY. *Educ:* Col Holy Cross, BS, 50; NY Univ, MS, 58, PhD(biol), 63. *Prof Exp:* Asst biologist, Worcester Found Exp Biol, 51-55; from asst scientist to prin scientist, 55-70, res fel, 70-79, ASSOC DIR, CLIN RES, SCHERING CORP, 79- *Concurrent Pos:* Adj prof physiol, Farleigh Dickinson Univ Dental Sch, 72- *Mem:* AAAS; Am Physiol Soc; Endocrine Soc; Am Soc Dermat. *Res:* Effects of anti-estrogens, anti-androgens and anti-progesterones on reproductive processes in laboratory animals; rat skin homotransplantation studies, immune and reticuloendothelial response. *Mailing Add:* Dept Clin Res Schering Corp Bloomfield NJ 07003

NERI, UMBERTO, b Rimini, Italy, Sept 7, 39; m 64; c 1. MATHEMATICS. *Educ:* Univ Chicago, BS, 61, MS, 62, PhD(math), 66. *Prof Exp:* Asst prof, 66-70, assoc prof, 70-81, PROF MATH, UNIV MD, COLLEGE PARK, 81- *Concurrent Pos:* NSF fel, Univ Md, College Park, 68-69; Nat Res Coun Italy fel, Univ Genoa, 69-70, Univ Pisa, 73-74, Univ Bari, 75, Univ Cagliari, 77 & 79, Univ Minn, 80 & Ind Univ, 82. *Mem:* Am Math Soc. *Res:* Singular integral operators; partial differential equations; harmonic analysis. *Mailing Add:* Dept of Math Univ of Md College Park MD 20742

NERING, EVAR DARE, b Gary, Ind, July 18, 21; m 42; c 2. MATHEMATICS. *Educ:* Ind Univ, AB, 42, AM, 43; Princeton Univ, AM, 47, PhD(math), 48. *Prof Exp:* Asst, Ind Univ, 42-44; jr physicist, Appl Physics Lab, Johns Hopkins Univ, 44-45; instr math, Princeton Univ, 45-46, asst, 46-47; instr, Rutgers Univ, 47-48; from asst prof to assoc prof, 60-74, chmn dept, 62-70, PROF MATH, ARIZ STATE UNIV, 74-, DIR DEPT, 78- *Concurrent Pos:* Technician, Manhattan Proj, Ind Univ, 43-44; mathematician, Goodyear Aircraft Corp, 53-54. *Mem:* Am Math Soc; Math Asn Am. *Res:* Algebraic function and game. *Mailing Add:* Dept of Math Ariz State Univ Tempe AZ 85281

NERKEN, ALBERT, b New York, NY, Aug 21, 12. CHEMISTRY. *Educ:* Cooper Union, BS, 33. *Prof Exp:* chemist, Sinclair Ref Co, Pa, 33-35; jr physicist, Nat Adv Comt Aeronaut, Langley Field, Va, 35-37; chief chemist, Polin Labs, NY, 37-43; res chemist, Kellex Corp, 43-45; partner & engr, 45-61, chmn bd & treas, 61-71, vchmn bd, 71-75, CHMN BD, VEECO INSTRUMENTS INC, 75- *Mem:* Am Chem Soc; Am Vacuum Soc. *Res:* Airplane dynamics; plastics from agricultural products; high vacuum techniques; gas analysis. *Mailing Add:* Veeco Instruments Inc Terminal Dr Plainview Hicksville NY 11803

NERLICH, WILLIAM EDWARD, b Los Angeles, Calif, May 6, 23; m 57; c 4. MEDICINE. *Educ:* Univ Southern Calif, MD, 47; Am Bd Internal Med, dipl, 55. *Prof Exp:* From head physician to chief physician, 52-66, DIR INTERN TRAINING, LOS ANGELES COUNTY HOSP, 66-; DIR OFF EDUC & ASST MED DIR, LOS ANGELES COUNTY-UNIV SOUTHERN CALIF MED CTR, 69-; PROF MED, SCH MED, UNIV SOUTHERN CALIF, 71- *Concurrent Pos:* From asst prof med & asst dean student affairs to assoc prof med & assoc dean student affairs & assoc dean admis, Univ Southern Calif, 58-81; mem, Physician's Asst Exam Comt, Calif State Bd Med Examr, 71-79. *Mem:* Asn Am Med Cols; Am Col Physicians. *Res:* Medical education; physical diagnosis. *Mailing Add:* Los Angeles County & Univ of Southern Calif Med Ctr Los Angeles CA 90033

NERO, ANTHONY V, b Salisbury, Md, Apr 11, 42. NUCLEAR PHYSICS. *Educ:* Fordham Univ, BS, 64; Stanford Univ, PhD(physics), 71. *Prof Exp:* Res fel nuclear physics, Kellogg Radiation Lab, Calif Inst Technol, 70-72; asst prof physics, Princeton Univ, 72-75; PHYSICIST, ENERGY & ENVIRON DIV, LAWRENCE BERKELEY LAB 75 *Concurrent Pos:* phys sci officer, US Arms Control & Disarmament Agency, 78. *Mem:* Am Phys Soc; AAAS; Sigma Xi. *Res:* Health and safety impacts, as well as general environmental effects of energy technologies, with emphasis on nuclear power and energy conservation; instrumentation for environmental radiation monitoring; alternative nuclear reactor types. *Mailing Add:* 2738 Benvenue Ave Berkeley CA 94705

NERODE, ANIL, b Los Angeles, Calif, June 4, 32; m 70; c 3. MATHEMATICS. *Educ:* Univ Chicago, BA, 49, BS, 52, MS, 53, PhD, 56. *Prof Exp:* Sr mathematician, Inst Syst Res, Univ Chicago, 54-56, group leader, 56-57; mem, Inst Adv Study, 57-58, 62-63; vis asst prof math, Univ Calif, 58-59; from asst prof to assoc prof, 59-65, actg dir, Ctr Appl Math, 65-66, PROF MATH, CORNELL UNIV, 65- *Concurrent Pos:* NSF fel, Cornell Univ, 57-58; mem consult bur, Math Asn Am, 61-; prin investr, NSF grants, 61-; mem comt appln math, Nat Res Coun, 67-70; ed, J Symbolic Logic, 68-; vis prof, Monash Univ, Australia, 70, 74 & 78, Univ Chicago, 76; mem math sci adv comt, NSF, 72-75; vis prof, Mass Inst Technol, 80 & Univ Calif, San Diego, 81. *Mem:* Am Math Soc; Math Asn Am; Soc Indust & Appl Math; Asn Symbolic Logic. *Res:* Mathematical logic; recursive functions; automata. *Mailing Add:* White Hall Cornell Univ Ithaca NY 14850

NERSASIAN, ARTHUR, b Salem, Mass, July 14, 24; m 46; c 3. ORGANIC CHEMISTRY. *Educ:* Mass Inst Technol, BS, 49; Univ Mich, MS, 51, PhD(org chem), 54. *Prof Exp:* Asst, Dow Chem Co for Univ Mich, 50-51, res fel & instr chem, 52-53; res chemist, Org Chem Dept, 54-57, Elastomer Chem Dept, 57-79, RES CHEMIST, POLYMER PROD DEPT, ELASTOMERS DIV, E I DU PONT DE NEMOURS & CO, INC, 80- *Mem:* Am Chem Soc. *Res:* rubber chemicals; Hypalon synthetic rubbers; polymer structural analysis; resilient foams; thermoplastic polyurethanes; Viton fluorohydrocarbon rubbers; effect of sour fuels and alcohol containing fuels on rubber properties; rubbers in automotive applications; oil additives-rubber compatibility; fluids interactions and solubility parameters of rubber. *Mailing Add:* 335 Spalding Rd Wilmington DE 19803

NERTNEY, ROBERT JAMES, system safety, nuclear engineering, see previous edition

NERVIK, WALTER EDWARD, b New York, NY, Mar 11, 23; m 51; c 2. NUCLEAR CHEMISTRY. *Educ:* Univ Calif, BS, 51, PhD(chem), 54. *Prof Exp:* NUCLEAR CHEMIST, LAWRENCE LIVERMORE LAB, UNIV CALIF, 54- *Mem:* AAAS. *Res:* Nuclear chemistry of fission product and transuranium elements; ion exchange phenomena; fission and stability of nuclei; inorganic chemistry of all elements. *Mailing Add:* Lawrence Livermore Lab Univ of Calif Livermore CA 94551

NES, WILLIAM DAVID, b Bethesda, Md, Aug 16, 53; m 76; c 2. PLANT LIPID BIOCHEMISTRY. *Educ:* Gettysburg Col, BA, 75; Drexel Univ, MS, 77; Univ Md, PhD(plant physiol), 79. *Prof Exp:* Fel, Univ Calif, Berkeley, 79-80; fel, 80-81, RES CHEMIST & PROJ LEADER, USDA, BERKELEY, 82- *Concurrent Pos:* Instr, Berkeley Exten Sch, Univ Calif, 80-81. *Mem:* NY Acad Sci; Sigma Xi; Soc Plant Physiol; Phytochem Soc NAm; Am Oil Chemists Soc. *Res:* Chemistry, biological functions and phylogenetic significance of steroids and triterpenoids in plants. *Mailing Add:* Plant Physiol & Chem Res Unit US Dept Agr 800 Buchanan St Berkeley CA 94710

NES, WILLIAM ROBERT, b Oxford, Eng, May 16, 26; US citizen; m 46; c 2. BIOCHEMISTRY. *Educ:* Univ Okla, BA, 46; Univ Va, MS, 48, PhD(chem), 50. *Prof Exp:* Fel, Mayo Clin, 50-51; vis scientist, NIH, 51, staff mem, Nat Inst Arthritis & Metab Dis, 51-58; assoc prof biochem, Clark Univ, 58-64; prof chem & pharmaceut chem, Univ Miss, 64-67; prof, 67-73, W L OBOLD PROF BIOL SCI & DIR INST POP STUDIES, DREXEL UNIV, 73- *Concurrent Pos:* Res fels, Forrestal Res Ctr, Princeton Univ, 54, Univ Heidelberg, 55-56 & Univ Wales, 56; sr scientist & dir training prog steroid biochem, Worcester Found Exp Biol, 58-64; mem adv panel metab biol, NSF, 66-69; vis prof obstet & gynec, Hahnemann Med Col & Hosp, 70-; partic scientist, Franklin Inst Res Lab, 71-; mem res comt, Norristown State Hosp, 75-77, phys chem study sect, NIH, 79-80 & fel eval panel biochem & biophys, Nat Acad Sci, 79. *Mem:* AAAS; Am Chem Soc; Am Soc Biol Chem; Endocrine Soc; Am Oil Chemists Soc. *Res:* Biosynthesis and metabolism of steroids, terpenes and other lipids; biochemistry of hormones; phylogeny; role of sterols in membranes; biochemistry of steroids and other isopentenoids; structure-activity relationships. *Mailing Add:* Dept of Biol Sci Drexel Univ Philadelphia PA 19104

NESBEDA, PAUL, b Trieste, Italy, June 20, 21; nat US; m 49; c 5. SYSTEM ENGINEERING. *Educ:* Univ Pisa, PhD(math), 43. *Prof Exp:* Asst prof math anal, Univ Trieste, 44-46; fel, Univ Paris, 46-47; mem staff, Inst Adv Study, 47-48; instr math anal, Catholic Univ, 48-52; mathematician & engr, RCA Corp, 52-58, leader tech staff, 58-64, staff eng scientist, Aerospace Div, 65-74; MEM TECH STAFF, THE MITRE CORP, 74- *Concurrent Pos:* Lectr,

Boston Col, 59-60. *Mem:* Am Math Soc; Soc Indust & Appl Math; Math Asn Am; Sigma Xi. *Res:* Functional and combinatorial analysis; probability; information processings and decision theory; detection communications and imaging systems; electro-optical systems; biomathematics; system analysis; robotics. *Mailing Add:* 10 Blodgett Rd Lexington MA 02173

NESBET, ROBERT KENYON, b Cleveland, Ohio, Mar 10, 30; m 58; c 3. THEORETICAL PHYSICS. *Educ:* Harvard Univ, AB, 51; Cambridge Univ, PhD(physics), 54. *Prof Exp:* Mem staff, Lincoln Lab, Mass Inst Technol, 54-56; asst prof physics, Boston Univ, 56-62; STAFF MEM, RES LAB, IBM CORP, 62- *Concurrent Pos:* Nat Cancer Inst spec res fel, Inst Pasteur, France, 60-61; exchange prof, Univ Paris, 73; assoc ed, J Chem Physics, 71-73 & J Computational Physics, 70-74; vis prof, Univ Kaiserslautern, WGer, 79-80. *Mem:* Fel Am Phys Soc; AAAS; Sigma Xi. *Res:* Theoretical atomic and molecular physics; quantum theory of finite many-particle systems; computational physics. *Mailing Add:* IBM Res Lab San Jose CA 95193

NESBITT, BRUCE EDWARD, b Crawfordsville, Ind, Aug 28, 51. ECONOMIC GEOLOGY. *Educ:* Carleton Col, BA, 73; Univ Mich, MS, 76, PhD(econ geol), 79. *Prof Exp:* Teaching fel geol, Univ Mich, 73-78, lectr econ geol, 78-79; assoc res, Pa State Univ, 79-80; ASST PROF ECON GEOL, UNIV ALBERTA, 80- *Mem:* Soc Econ Geol; Mineral Soc Am; Sigma Xi; Am Geophys Union; Can Mineral Asn. *Res:* Metamorphosed ore deposits and the geochemistry of sediment-hosted lead-zinc deposits. *Mailing Add:* Dept Geol Univ Alberta Edmonton AB T6G 2E3 Can

NESBITT, CECIL JAMES, b Ft William, Ont, Oct 10, 12; nat US; m 38. ACTUARIAL MATHEMATICS. *Educ:* Univ Toronto, BA, 34, MA, 35, PhD(math), 37. *Prof Exp:* Mem, Inst Advan Study, 37-38; from instr to assoc prof, 38-52, prof, 52-80, assoc chmn dept, 62-67, chmn, 70-71, EMER PROF MATH, UNIV MICH, ANN ARBOR, 80- *Concurrent Pos:* Coun mem, Conf Bd Math Sci, 68-75; co-chmn data registry comt, Cystic Fibrosis Found, 73-78; res dir, Actuarial Educ & Res Found, 80- *Mem:* Am Math Soc; Inst Math Statist; Soc Actuaries. *Res:* Actuarial theory. *Mailing Add:* Dept Math Univ Mich Ann Arbor MI 48104

NESBITT, HERBERT HUGH JOHN, b Ottawa, Ont, Feb 7, 13; m 44; c 4. ENTOMOLOGY. *Educ:* Queen's Univ, Ont, BA, 37; Univ Toronto, MA, 39, PhD(invert zool), 44; Univ Leiden, DSc, 51. *Hon Degrees:* DSc, Carleton Univ. *Prof Exp:* Agr scientist, Div Entom, Dept Agr, Ont, 39-48; from asst prof to assoc prof, 48-56, dir div sci, 60-63, dean fac sci, 63-74, clerk senate, 75-81, PROF BIOL, CARLETON UNVI, 56- *Concurrent Pos:* Bd Govs, Algonquin Col, 81- *Mem:* Soc Syst Zool; fel Royal Entom Soc London; Zool Soc London; fel Linnean Soc London; fel Entom Soc Can. *Res:* Nervous system of insects; comparative morphological and taxonomic work on Acari. *Mailing Add:* Fac of Sci Tory Bldg Carleton Univ Colonel By Dr Ottawa ON K1S 5B6 Can

NESBITT, JOHN B, b State College, Pa, Apr 18, 24; div; c 3. SANITARY ENGINEERING. *Educ:* Pa State Univ, BS, 48; Mass Inst Technol, SM, 49, ScD, 52. *Prof Exp:* Asst sanit eng, Mass Inst Technol, 49-52; instr hydraul, McCoy Col, Johns Hopkins Univ, 52-53; from asst prof to assoc prof civil eng, 53-65, PROF CIVIL ENG, PA STATE UNIV, 65- *Concurrent Pos:* Sanit eng designer, Whitman, Requardt & Assocs, Md, 52-53; mem USA nat comt, Int Asn Water Pollution Res, 69-78. *Mem:* Am Soc Civil Engrs; Water Pollution Control Fedn; Asn Environ Eng Prof; Am Water Works Asn. *Res:* Liquid and solid municipal and industrial wastes; removal of radioactive contaminants from water supplies; treatment of industrial wastes containing the cyanide ion; water filtration; removal of phosphorus from municipal wastewaters. *Mailing Add:* Dept of Civil Eng Pa State Univ University Park PA 16802

NESBITT, LYLE EDWIN, physical chemistry, inorganic chemistry, see previous edition

NESBITT, ROBERT EDWARD LEE, JR, b Albany, Ga, Aug 21, 24; m 47; c 2. OBSTETRICS & GYNECOLOGY. *Educ:* Vanderbilt Univ, BA, 44, MD, 47; Am Bd Obstet & Gynec, dipl, 56. *Prof Exp:* Asst instr, Johns Hopkins Hosp, 48-52; obstetrician & gynecologist in chief, US Army Hosp, Ger, 52-54; asst prof, Sch Med, Johns Hopkins Univ, 54-56; prof & chmn dept, Albany Med Col, 58-61; PROF OBSTET & GYNEC & CHMN DEPT, STATE UNIV NY UPSTATE MED CTR, 61- *Concurrent Pos:* Fel, Am Asn Maternal & Child Health Dirs; obstetrician & gynecologist in chief, Albany Hosp, 56-61 & Crouse-Irving Hosp, 63-70; mem, Pub Health Coun State NY, 62-67; chief obstet & gynec, State Univ Hosp, 64-; assoc examr, Am Bd Obstet & Gynec. *Mem:* Soc Gynec Invest; Pan-Am Med Asn; fel Am Col Obstet & Gynec; fel Am Col Surg; NY Acad Sci. *Res:* Cytologic, cytochemical and histochemical study and diagnosis of early cervical cancer; prenatal and placental pathology; cytohormonal diagnosis; experimental production of abruptio placenta; reproductive endocrinology; animal experimentation; hormonal influence on placentation; fetal anoxia; immunoglobulin patterns in normal and toxemic pregnancy; in vitro placental perfusion studies; infertility. *Mailing Add:* State Univ NY Upstate Med Ctr 750 E Adams St Syracuse NY 13210

NESBITT, STUART STONER, b Aledo, Ill, Jan 29, 21; m 51; c 2. CHEMISTRY. *Educ:* Monmouth Col, BS, 43; Univ Tex, MA, 44, PhD(chem), 49. *Prof Exp:* Lab asst, Monmouth Col, 42-43; lab instr, Univ Tex, 43-44, asst, 46-49; res chemist, Mid-Continent Petrol Corp, 49-55; supvr prod res, Sunray D-X Oil Co, 55-69, mgr fuels & indust prod res, DX Div, 69-70, chief prod develop, Appl Res Dept, Tulsa Lab, 70-71, mgr, 71-72, chief prod serv, 72-79, MGR, TULSA REFINERY LAB, SUN OIL CO, 79- *Mem:* Am Chem Soc. *Res:* Alkoxyacetaldehydes; allylic chlorides; petroleum. *Mailing Add:* Tulsa Refinery Lab Sun Oil Co PO Box 2039 Tulsa OK 74102

NESBITT, WILLIAM BELTON, b Tryon, NC, Mar 22, 32; m 64; c 1. HORTICULTURE, PLANT BREEDING. *Educ:* NC State Univ, BS, 54, MS, 62; Rutgers Univ, PhD(hort, genetics), 65. *Prof Exp:* ASSOC PROF HORT, NC STATE UNIV, 65- *Mem:* Am Soc Hort Sci. *Res:* Breeding and production of grapes. *Mailing Add:* Dept of Hort Sci NC State Univ Raleigh NC 27650

NESENBERGS, MARTIN, b Jelgava, Latvia, Nov 8, 28; m 54; c 1. COMMUNICATIONS THEORY, COMPUTER NETWORKS. *Educ:* Univ Denver, BS, 52; NY Univ, MS, 58; Univ Colo, PhD(appl math), 67. *Prof Exp:* Mem tech staff commun res, Bell Tel Labs, 53-60; MATHEMATICIAN COMMUN RES, INST TELECOMMUN SCI, DEPT COMMERCE, 60- *Concurrent Pos:* Mem, US Delegation, Int Telecommun Union/Int Radio Consult Comt, Geneva, 67-72, Comn C, US Nat Int Union Radio Sci, 81-; ed, Commun Mag, Inst Elec & Electron Engrs, 74-75; vis prof, elec eng & telecommun, Univ Colo, 80-; mem, Armed Forces Commun & Electronics Asn. *Mem:* Sr mem Inst Elec & Electronics Engrs. *Res:* Communications theory subareas such as random processes, error-coding, applied mathematics, traffic theory and topology synthesis have been applied to various communication networks. *Mailing Add:* Nat Telecommun & Info Admin Inst Telecommun Sci-4 325 Broadway Boulder CO 80303

NESER, WILLIAM BERNARD, epidemiology, see previous edition

NESHEIM, MALDEN CHARLES, b Rochelle, Ill, Dec 19, 31; m 77; c 3. NUTRITION. *Educ:* Univ Ill, BS, 53, MS, 54; Cornell Univ, PhD, 59. *Prof Exp:* Asst animal sci, Univ Ill, 53-54; asst poultry husbandry, 56-59, asst prof animal nutrit, 59-64, assoc prof, 64-74, PROF & DIR, DIV NUTRIT SCI, CORNELL UNIV, 74- *Concurrent Pos:* NIH spec fel, Cambridge Univ, 72-73, overseas fel, Churchill Col, 72-73. *Mem:* Am Inst Nutrit; Brit Nutrit Soc. *Res:* Amino acid metabolism; amino acid and protein requirements; gastrointestinal physiology; nutrition and parasitic infection. *Mailing Add:* Div Nutrit Sci Savage Hall Cornell Univ Ithaca NY 14853

NESHEIM, ROBERT OLAF, b Monroe Center, Ill, Sept 13, 21; m 81; c 3. NUTRITION. *Educ:* Univ Ill, BS, 43, MS, 50, PhD(animal nutrit), 51. *Prof Exp:* Swine res specialist, Gen Mills, Inc, 51-52; head swine feed res, Quaker Oats Co, 52-59, mgr livestock feed res, 59-64; prof animal sci & head dept, Univ Ill, 64-67; assoc dir, 67-69, dir, 69, vpres res & develop, 69-77, VPRES SCI & TECHNOL, QUAKER OATS CO, 77- *Concurrent Pos:* Chmn, Animal Nutrit Res Coun, 65-66; mem US nat comt, Int Union Nutrit Sci, 68-74; mem food industs adv comt & chmn food & nutrit liason comt, Nutrit Found, mem bd trustees, 78-80; mem adv comt, US Meat Animal Res Ctr, USDA, 71-75; mem food & nutrit bd, Nat Acad Sci, 72-78, mem exec comt, 72-76; mem, Comt Food Sci & Technol; mem food indust liaison comt, Am Med Asn; mem food adv comt, Off Technol Assessment, US Cong, 75-80; mem bd trustees, Food Safety Coun & mem exec comt, 76-79; mem bd trustees, BioSci Info Serv, 78-, vchmn, 80, chmn, 82; mem gen comt food prog, Nat Res Coun, 80- *Mem:* Am Soc Animal Sci; Am Inst Nutrit; Fedn Am Soc Exp Biol (treas, 74-78); Soc Nutrit Educ; Am Pub Health Asn. *Res:* Amino acid nutrition; energy utilization. *Mailing Add:* Quaker Oats Co Merchandise Mart Plaza Chicago IL 60654

NESHEIM, STANLEY, b Chicago, Ill, Apr 24, 30; m 58; c 4. ANALYTICAL CHEMISTRY. *Educ:* Brooklyn Col, BS, 56; George Washington Univ, MS, 62. *Prof Exp:* Chemist, US Bur Mines, 56-57; RES CHEMIST, US FOOD & DRUG ADMIN, 57- *Mem:* AAAS; Am Chem Soc; Am Oil Chem Soc. *Res:* Edible fats and oil characterization and chemical analysis; food contaminants; mycotoxin chemistry and analysis. *Mailing Add:* 3008 Tennyson St NW Washington DC 20015

NESHYBA, STEVE, b Jourdanton, Tex, Oct 8, 27; m 50; c 6. PHYSICAL OCEANOGRAPHY. *Educ:* Univ Tex, BSEE, 49, MS, 54; Tex A&M Univ, PhD(phys oceanog), 65. *Prof Exp:* Res engr, Elec Eng Res Lab, Univ Tex, 53-54; aerophys engr, Gen Dynamics/Convair, 54-57, sr aerophys engr, 57-60; asst prof elec eng, Arlington State Col, 60-62; fel oceanog, Tex A&M Univ, 62-64; assoc prof, 65-81, PROF PHYS OCEANOG, ORE STATE UNIV, 81- *Res:* Deep sea hydrography; analyses of time-dependent motions of water bodies. *Mailing Add:* Dept of Oceanog Ore State Univ Corvallis OR 97331

NESLINE, FREDERICK WILLIAM, JR, b Baltimore, Md, Dec 31, 26; m 57; c 3. ELECTRICAL ENGINEERING. *Educ:* Univ Md, BSEE, 51; Yale Univ, MSEE, 52, PhD(elec eng), 56; Northeastern Univ, MBA, 75. *Prof Exp:* From instr to asst prof elec eng, Mass Inst Technol, 55-58; asst mgr systs anal dept, Missile Systs Div, Raytheon Co, 58-61, performance dept mgr, 61-63, mgr systs performanc dept, Space & Info Systs Div, 63-64, mgr systs eng ctr, 64-66; pres, Appl Anal, Inc, 66-68; consult aerospace systs eng, 68-70; CONSULT SCIENTIST, MISSILE SYSTS DIV, RAYTHEON CO, 70- *Mem:* Am Inst Aeronaut & Astronaut; Inst Elec & Electronics Engrs. *Res:* Digital and analog smoothing, filtering and prediction using noisy measurement data; automatic feedback control system design, analysis and synthesis; homing missile guidance, navigation and autopilot control; computer optimization of large scale systems. *Mailing Add:* 53 Baskin Rd Lexington MA 02173

NESNOW, STEPHEN CHARLES, b New York, NY, Dec 19, 41. ONCOLOGY, BIO-ORGANIC CHEMISTRY. *Educ:* Bucknell Univ, BS, 63; NY Univ, MS, 66, PhD(org chem), 68. *Prof Exp:* Fel cancer res, Sloan-Kettering Inst Cancer Res, 68-70; res assoc, McArdle Inst Cancer Res, 70-74; asst scientist human oncol, Univ Wis, 74-76; ASST PROF CANCER RES, UNIV NC, 77-; chief metab effects sect, 77-79, CHIEF, CARCINOGENESIS & METAB BR, US ENVIRON PROTECTION AGENCY, 79- *Concurrent Pos:* Am Cancer Soc grant, 74-75; mem, Cancer Res Ctr, Univ NC, 77-; adj mem, W Alton Jones Cell Sci Ctr, 78-79. *Honors & Awards:* Bronze Medal, US Environ Protection Agency, 80. *Mem:* Am Chem Soc; Am Asn Cancer Res; Tissue Culture Asn. *Res:* Chemical carcinogenesis; biochemical oncology; environmental carcinogenesis; oncogenic transformation of cells in culture; carcinogen metabolism. *Mailing Add:* Health Effects Res Lab US Environ Protection Agency Research Triangle Park NC 27711

NESS, GENE CHARLES, b Bemidji, Minn, Dec 17, 44; m 66; c 2. BIOCHEMISTRY. *Educ:* Bemidji State Univ BS, 66; Univ NDak, PhD(biochem), 71. *Prof Exp:* Fel lipid metabolism, Dept Physiol Chem, Vet Admin Hosp, 71-73; sr scientist clin chem, Div Am Hosp Supply, Dade, 74; asst prof, 74-80, ASSOC PROF BIOCHEM, UNIV SOUTH FLA, 80- *Concurrent Pos:* Consult, Metabolism Study Sect, NIH, 82; prin investr, NIH, 75- *Mem:* Am Soc Biol Chemists. *Res:* Regulation of cholesterol biosynthesis and whether hydroxymethylglutaryl-coenzyme A reductase, the rate-limiting enzyme, is regulated by changes in enzyme protein or by other means. *Mailing Add:* Dept Biochem Col Med Univ SFla 12901 N 30th St Tampa FL 33612

NESS, JOHN RAGNAR, b Denver, Colo, May 2, 28; m 53; c 4. ANALYTICAL CHEMISTRY. *Educ:* Univ Denver, BS, 53. *Prof Exp:* Chemist, 53-58, res chemist, 58-65, sr res chemist, 65-78, RES ASSOC ANAL CHEM, E I DU PONT DE NEMOURS & CO, INC, 78- *Mem:* Sigma Xi. *Mailing Add:* Exp Sta E I du Pont de Nemours & Co Inc Wilmington DE 19898

NESS, LINDA ANN, b Albert Lea, Minn, Oct 29, 47. MATHEMATICS. *Educ:* St Olaf Col, BA, 69; Harvard Univ, MA & PhD(math), 75. *Prof Exp:* asst prof math, Univ Wash, 75-80; MEM FAC MATH, HARVARD UNIV, 80- *Res:* Algebraic and differential geometry. *Mailing Add:* Harvard Univ Cambridge MA 02138

NESS, NATHAN, b New York, NY, Jan 18, 16; m 53; c 1. FLUID MECHANICS. *Educ:* Polytech Inst Brooklyn, BAeroEng, 43, MS, 49, PhD(appl mech), 52. *Prof Exp:* Stress analyst, Lockheed Aircraft Corp, Calif, 44-45, flight test analyst, 46-47; res asst prof fluid mech, Polytech Inst Brooklyn, 52-56; res engr, Gen Elec Co, Pa, 56-59 & Radio Corp Am, NJ, 59-64; prof, 64-81, EMER PROF AEROSPACE ENG, WVA UNIV, 81- *Concurrent Pos:* Consult, Gen Elec Co, 55-56. *Mem:* Am Inst Aeronaut & Astronaut. *Res:* Mass addition effects on skin friction and heat transfer; wake studies on hypersonic reentry missiles; circulation control of bluff-ended bodies; theory of bubble formation in gas-particulate fluidized beds. *Mailing Add:* 417 Pocahontas Ave Morgantown WV 26505

NESS, NORMAN FREDERICK, b Springfield, Mass, Apr 15, 33; m 56; c 2. SPACE PHYSICS. *Educ:* Mass Inst Technol, BS, 55, PhD(geophys), 59. *Prof Exp:* Res geophysicist inst geophys, Univ Calif, Los Angeles, 59-60, asst prof geophys, 60-61; res physicist, 61-66, staff scientist, 66-68, head extraterrestrial physics br, 68-69, CHIEF LAB EXTRATERRESTRIAL PHYSICS, GODDARD SPACE FLIGHT CTR, NASA, 69- *Concurrent Pos:* Nat Acad Sci-Nat Res Coun res assoc, 60-61; consult, 57-; vis assoc prof, Univ Md, 65-68. *Honors & Awards:* Exceptional Sci Achievement Medal, NASA, 66; Flemming Medal, US Govt, 68; Space Sci Award, Am Inst Aeronaut & Astronaut, 72; John Adam Fleming Medal, Am Geophys Union, 65. *Mem:* AAAS; fel Am Geophys Union. *Res:* Experimental investigation of magnetic fields in the magnetosphere and interplanetary space; satellite and space probe studies; measurement of planetary magnetic fields. *Mailing Add:* 4321 Woodbury St University Park MD 20872

NESS, ROBERT KIRACOFE, b York, Pa, Apr 29, 22; m 44; c 3. CARBOHYDRATE CHEMISTRY. *Educ:* Lebanon Valley Col, BS, 43; Ohio State Univ, MS, 45, PhD(org chem), 48. *Prof Exp:* Asst, Ohio State Univ, 43-45; assoc prof, Lebanon Valley Col, 47-48; fel, 48-50, sr asst scientist, 50-54, from scientist to sr scientist, 54-63, SCIENTIST DIR, NIH, 63- *Concurrent Pos:* USPHS, 50- *Mem:* AAAS; Am Chem Soc; NY Acad Sci; The Chem Soc. *Res:* Carbohydrates; reaction mechanisms; sugar benzoates; chemistry of ribose and deoxyribose; synthesis of deoxynucleosides; glycals; vinyl glycosides; amino sugars. *Mailing Add:* 4216 Dresden St Kensington MD 20795

NESSEL, ROBERT J, b Bronx, NY, Dec 28, 36; m 60; c 2. PHARMACY, PHARMACEUTICAL CHEMISTRY. *Educ:* Columbia Univ, BS & MS, 60; Purdue Univ, PhD(indust pharm), 63. *Prof Exp:* Pharmacist, Mt Sinai Hosp, NY, 58-59; asst pharm, Purdue Univ, 60-61; sr res pharmacist, Squibb Inst Med Res, 63-66; head med prod tech serv, Merck & Co, 66-69, head animal formulations res & develop, 69-74, assoc dir regulatory affairs, Int, 74-75, dir regulatory affairs, 75-81, SR DIR REGULATORY AFFAIRS, MERCK, SHARP & DOHME RES LABS, 81- *Mem:* Am Pharmaceut Asn; Acad Pharmaceut Sci. *Res:* Industrial pharmacy. *Mailing Add:* Merck Sharp & Dohme Res Labs Rahway NJ 07065

NESSELSON, EUGENE J(OSEPH), b Omaha, Nebr, May 30, 28; m 54; c 2. ENVIRONMENTAL & CHEMICAL ENGINEERING. *Educ:* Univ Omaha, BS, 49; Univ NC, MS, 51; Univ Wis, PhD(sanit eng), 53. *Prof Exp:* Chem engr waste disposal, Standard Oil Co Ind, 54-55; chief process develop, Taft Sanit Eng Ctr, USPHS, 55-57; sr chem engr, Gen Elec Co, 57-61; prin chem engr, Am-Standard Corp, 61-64; dir air & water mgt, Velsicol Chem Corp, 64-68; CONSULT ENVIRON MGT, 68- *Mem:* Am Chem Soc; Am Water Works Asn; Am Inst Chem Engrs; Water Pollution Control Fedn; Air Pollution Control Asn. *Res:* Water treatment; industrial wastes; air and water pollution abatement; industrial hygiene; chemical process engineering; solid hazardous waste disposal; industrial environmental affairs. *Mailing Add:* 2620 W Fitch Ave Chicago IL 60645

NESSLER, CRAIG LEE, plant anatomy, plant morphology, see previous edition

NESSMITH, JOSH T(HOMAS), JR, b Bulloch Co, Ga, June 18, 23; m 48; c 4. ELECTRICAL ENGINEERING. *Educ:* Ga Sch Technol, BEE, 47; Univ Pa, MSEE, 57, PhD(elec eng), 65. *Prof Exp:* Engr, Civil Aeronaut Admin, 47-52; design engr, 52-53, proj engr, 53-59, syst & proj leader, 59-60, syst & proj mgr, 60-63, RCA Tradex-Press prog mgr, 63-64, MGR SYST ENG, MISSILE & SURFACE RADAR DIV, RCA CORP, 65- *Concurrent Pos:* Mem, Franklin Inst. *Mem:* Inst Elec & Electronics Engrs; assoc Am Inst Aeronaut & Astronaut. *Res:* Air navigation; advanced radars; scatterers; signal processing; phased arrays; wide band radar operation; weapon system engineering. *Mailing Add:* Missile & Surface Radar Div RCA Corp Moorestown NJ 08057

NESTE, SHERMAN LESTER, b Decorah, Iowa, Sept 23, 43; m 72; c 1. METEORITICS. *Educ:* Luther Col, BA, 65; Mich State Univ, MS, 67; Drexel Univ, PhD(physics), 75. *Prof Exp:* RES PHYSICIST METEORITICS, SPACE SCI LAB, GEN ELEC CO, 67- *Mem:* AAAS; Am Geophys Union. *Res:* Establishing an experimental model of the asteroid/meteoroid environment in the region of space between the orbits of Earth and Jupiter. *Mailing Add:* Space Sci Lab Gen Elec Co PO Box 8555 Philadelphia PA 19101

NESTELL, MERLYND KEITH, b Fletcher, NC, Oct 27, 37; m 57; c 2. MATHEMATICS. *Educ:* Andrews Univ, BA, 57; Univ Wis, MA, 59; Ore State Univ, PhD(math), 66. *Prof Exp:* Instr math, Southern Missionary Col, 59-61; instr, Ore State Univ, 63-65; sr res scientist, Pac Northwest Lab, Battelle Mem Inst, 65-69; ASSOC PROF MATH & GEOL, UNIV TEX, ARLINGTON, 69- *Mem:* Am Math Soc; Paleont Soc; Soc Econ Paleont & Mineral. *Res:* Functional analysis; integral and integro-differential equations, radiative transfer theory; paleontology; Upper Paleozoic biostratigraphy. *Mailing Add:* Dept of Math Univ of Tex Arlington TX 76019

NESTER, EUGENE WILLIAM, b Johnson City, NY, Sept 15, 30; m 59; c 2. MICROBIOLOGY. *Educ:* Cornell Univ, BS, 52; Western Reserve Univ, PhD, 59. *Prof Exp:* Am Cancer Soc res fel genetics, Sch Med, Stanford Univ, 59-62; instr microbiol, 62-63, from asst prof to assoc prof microbiol & genetics, 63-72, PROF MICROBIOL & IMMUNOL, UNIV WASH, 72- *Mem:* Am Soc Microbiol. *Res:* Genetics and biochemistry of enzyme regulation; bacterial-plant relationships. *Mailing Add:* Dept of Microbiol Univ of Wash Seattle WA 98195

NESTER, JAMES MICHAEL, b Nesquehoning, Pa, Jan 2, 43. RELATIVITY. *Educ:* Univ Md, BSc, 70, MSc, 72, PhD(physics), 77. *Prof Exp:* Fel physics, Univ Sask, 77-78; res assoc physics, Univ Md, 79; FEL PHYSICS & MATH, UNIV ALTA, 80- *Res:* Classical general relativity and other general geometrodynamical field theories and gauge theories, especially torsion and their associated variational principles; canonical Hamiltonian formalism; symplectic formulation; dirac constraint theory. *Mailing Add:* Dept Physics Univ Alta Edmonton AB T6G 2J1 Can

NESTOR, JOHN JOSEPH, JR, b Miami, Fla, Jan 21, 45; m 74; c 1. POLYPEPTIDE CHEMISTRY. *Educ:* Polytech Inst NY, BS, 66; Univ Ariz, PhD(org chem), 71. *Prof Exp:* Assoc fel, Cornell Univ, 71-74; staff researcher, 74-78, SR STAFF RESEARCHER, SYNTEX RES, 78- *Mem:* Am Chem Soc. *Res:* Agonists and antagonist of oxytocin and vasopressin; immunostimulatory glycopeptide adjuvant analogs; agonists and antagonists of luteinizing hormone-releasing hormone; unnatural amino acid synthesis; asymmetric synthesis of amino acids; immunostimulatory peptides. *Mailing Add:* Inst Bio-Org Chem Syntex Res 3401 Hillview Ave Palo Alto CA 94304

NESTOR, JOHN W(ESLEY), JR, b Darby, Pa, Mar 25, 36. CHEMICAL ENGINEERING. *Educ:* Cornell Univ, BChE, 59; Mass Inst Technol, ScD(chem eng), 64. *Prof Exp:* Sr scientist, Res & Adv Develop Div, Avco Corp, 64-65, group leader, 65-67, sect chief, Space Systs Div, 67-68; mgr mfg support, 68-73, LAB MGR, POLAROID CORP, 73- *Mem:* Am Inst Chem Engrs; Am Chem Soc. *Res:* Kinetics and catalysis; ferromagnetic fluids; reinforcing fibers for high strength composites; diffusion transfer photographic processes and products. *Mailing Add:* Polaroid Corp 28 Osborne St Cambridge MA 02139

NESTOR, KARL ELWOOD, b Kasson, WVa, Dec 17, 37; m 58; c 2. GENETICS. *Educ:* Univ WVa, BS, 59, MS, 61; Ohio State Univ, PhD(genetics), 64. *Prof Exp:* Asst genetics, Univ WVa, 59-61; asst, 61-64, asst instr, 65, from asst to assoc prof, 65-78, PROF GENETICS, OHIO AGR RES & DEVELOP CTR, 78- *Mem:* Poultry Sci Asn; Worlds Poultry Sci Asn. *Res:* Physiological genetics of chickens and turkeys; poultry physiology. *Mailing Add:* Dept of Poultry Sci Ohio Agr Res & Develop Ctr Wooster OH 44691

NESTOR, ONTARIO HORIA, b Youngstown, Ohio, Sept 20, 22; m 43; c 2. PHYSICS. *Educ:* Marietta Col, AB, 43; Univ Minn, MS, 49; Univ Buffalo, PhD(physics), 60. *Prof Exp:* Instr physics, Marietta Col, 42-43; res asst, SAM Labs, Columbia Univ, 43-44; res asst, Univ Minn, 47-48; res assoc, Linde Div, Union Carbide Corp, 49-68, sr res assoc, 68-71; dir technol, Crystal Optics Res, Inc, 71-74; MGR CRYSTAL DEVELOP, HARSHAW CHEM CO, 74- *Mem:* Am Phys Soc; Am Asn Crystal Growth. *Res:* Crystal growth and properties. *Mailing Add:* Harshaw Chem Co 6801 Cochran Rd Solon OH 44139

NESTRICK, TERRY JOHN, US citizen. ORGANICS ANALYSIS, CHROMATOGRAPHIC SEPARATIONS. *Educ:* Oakland Univ, BS, 68, MS, 72. *Prof Exp:* RES LEADER, MICH DIV ANAL LABS, DOW CHEM CO, 72- *Mem:* Am Chem Soc. *Res:* Environmental and commercial product trace level organic analyses, specializing in chlorinated dibenzo-p-dioxins and related compounds. *Mailing Add:* Mich Div Anal Labs Bldg 574 Dow Chem Co Midland MI 48640

NESTVOLD, ELWOOD OLAF, b Minot, NDak, Mar 19, 32; m 55; c 2. INFORMATION SCIENCE, GEOPHYSICS. *Educ:* Augsburg Col, BA, 52; Univ Minn, MS, 59, PhD(physics), 62. *Prof Exp:* Asst physics, Univ Minn, 56-59, instr, 59-61; physicist, Shell Develop Co, 62-63, res physicist, 63-65, res assoc & sect head, 65-68, mgr geophys dept, 68-71, sr staff geophysicist, 71-72, mgr geophysics, Western Region, 72-74, Int Region, 74-75, sr staff geophysicist, Pecten Cameroon, 76; chief geophysicist & dep mgr explor, Woodside Petrol Develop Pty, Ltd, Perth, Australia, 77-78; mgr, Explor & Prod Processing Ctr, Koninklijke/Shell Explor & Prod Lab, Rijswijk, Neth, 79-81, CHIEF GEOPHYSICIST, ROYAL DUTCH/SHELL GROUP, THE HAGUE, NETH, 81- *Concurrent Pos:* Consult, Lighting & Transients Res Inst, Minn, 57-62. *Mem:* Inst Elec & Electronics Engrs; Soc Explor Geophys; Europ Asn Explor Geophysicists. *Res:* Prediction and filter theory; digital-computer techniques for acoustic and seismic signal processing; application of probability theory to hydrocarbon detection; performance evaluation of computer systems for geophysical processing. *Mailing Add:* SIPM PO Box 162 2501 An The Hague Netherlands

NETA, PEDATSUR, b Tripoli, Libya, Jan 1, 38; m 59; c 2. PHYSICAL CHEMISTRY, ORGANIC CHEMISTRY. *Educ:* Hebrew Univ, Jerusalem, MSc, 60; Weizmann Inst Sci, PhD(phys chem), 65. *Prof Exp:* Res assoc radiation chem, Soreq Nuclear Res Ctr, Israel, 60-66; Nat Res Coun Can fel, Univ Toronto, 66-67; AEC fel, Ohio State Univ, 67-68; Nat Acad Sci-Nat Res Coun fel, US Army Natick Labs, 68-69; res fel, Radiation Res Labs, Mellon Inst Sci, Carnegie-Mellon Univ, 69-74, sr res chemist radiation chem, 74-76; assoc prof specialist, Radiation Lab, 76-80, ASSOC FAC FEL, UNIV NOTRE DAME, 80- *Concurrent Pos:* Assoc ed, Radiation Res, 75-79. *Mem:* AAAS; Am Chem Soc; Sigma Xi; Radiation Res Soc. *Res:* Physical organic chemistry; free radical reactions; radiation chemistry of aqueous systems; electron spin resonance; electron transfer processes. *Mailing Add:* Radiation Lab Univ of Notre Dame Notre Dame IN 46556

NETA, RUTH, b Lodz, Poland; US citizen; m 59; c 2. IMMUNOLOGY. *Educ:* Tel-Aviv Univ, MS, 67; Univ Notre Dame, PhD(immunol), 79. *Prof Exp:* Res assoc immunol, Ohio State Univ, 67-68; res assoc, Sch Med, Univ Pittsburgh, 69-77; RES ASSOC IMMUNOL, UNIV NOTRE DAME, 79- *Concurrent Pos:* Nat res serv award, NIH, 79-82. *Mem:* Am Asn Immunologists. *Res:* Cell-mediated immunity; delayed hypersensitivity; immune regulation; lymphokines; interferon. *Mailing Add:* Dept Microbiol Univ Notre Dame Notre Dame IN 46556

NETER, ERWIN, b Mannheim, Ger, May 26, 09; nat US; m 45; c 1. BACTERIOLOGY, IMMUNOLOGY. *Educ:* Univ Heidelberg, MD, 33; Am Bd Path, dipl, 55. *Hon Degrees:* MD, Univ Heidelberg, 74. *Prof Exp:* From assoc bact & immunol to instr, Sch Med, 36-53, from bacteriologist to chief res microbiol, Children's Hosp, 36-38, dir bact, 36-81, consult, Inst, 37-68, prof microbiol & pediat, 68-79, from asst prof to assoc prof microbiol, Sch Nursing, 46-68, from asst prof to assoc prof bact, immunol & pediat, Sch Med, 53-56, prof clin microbiol, Dept Pediat, 56-68, EMER PROF MICROBIOL & PEDIAT, SCH MED, ROSWELL PARK MEM INST, STATE UNIV NY BUFFALO, 79- *Concurrent Pos:* Consult bact, Children's Hosp, 81- *Honors & Awards:* Wyeth Award Clin Microbiol, Am Soc Microbiol, 77. *Mem:* AAAS; Am Soc Microbiol; Soc Exp Biol & Med; Am Asn Immunologists; hon mem Reticuleondothelial Soc. *Res:* Chemotherapy; Escherichia. *Mailing Add:* Children's Hosp 219 Bryant St Buffalo NY 14222

NETER, JOHN, b Ger, Feb 8, 23; US citizen; m 51; c 2. APPLIED STATISTICS. *Educ:* Univ Buffalo, BA, 43; Univ Pa, MBA, 47; Columbia Univ, PhD(bus statist), 52. *Prof Exp:* Asst prof bus statist, Syracuse Univ, 49-55; prof quant anal, Univ Minn, Minneapolis, 55-75; PROF MGT SCI & STATIST, COL BUS ADMIN, UNIV GA, 75- *Concurrent Pos:* Ford Found fac res fel, Univ Minn, 57-58; supvry math statistician, US Bur Census, 59-60, consult, 61-65; ed, The Am Statistician, 76-80. *Mem:* Fel AAAS; fel Am Statist Asn; Inst Mgt Sci; Inst Math Statist; fel Am Inst Decision Sci (pres, 78-79). *Res:* Uses of statistics in accounting; measurement errors; decision theory. *Mailing Add:* Col of Bus Admin Univ of Ga Athens GA 30602

NETHAWAY, DAVID ROBERT, b San Diego, Calif, Aug 6, 29; m 64; c 3. NUCLEAR CHEMISTRY. *Educ:* Univ Calif, BS, 51, MS, 57; Wash Univ, PhD(chem), 59. *Prof Exp:* Chemist, Gen Elec Co, Wash, 51-53; chemist, Calif Res & Develop Co, 53; CHEMIST, LAWRENCE LIVERMORE LAB, UNIV CALIF, 53- *Mem:* Am Chem Soc; Am Phys Soc. *Res:* Nuclear charge distribution in fission; nuclear reactions; decay scheme studies. *Mailing Add:* Lawrence Livermore Lab Livermore CA 94550

NETHERCOT, ARTHUR HOBART, JR, b Evanston, Ill, June 16, 23; m 44; c 4. PHYSICS. *Educ:* Northwestern Univ, BA, 44, MS, 46; Univ Mich, PhD, 50. *Prof Exp:* Union Carbide & Carbon Corp fel, Columbia Univ, 51-52, res assoc physics, 52-57; PHYSICIST RES CTR, IBM CORP, 57- *Mem:* Fel Am Phys Soc. *Res:* Microwave physics; solid state physics; materials science. *Mailing Add:* 107 Mt Hope Blvd Hastings NY 10706

NETHERCUT, PHILIP EDWIN, b Indianapolis, Ind, Apr 3, 21; m 49; c 3. ORGANIC CHEMISTRY. *Educ:* Beloit Col, BS, 42; Lawrence Col, MS, 44, PhD(org chem), 49. *Prof Exp:* Res chemist, Watervliet Paper Co, Mich, 49-50; process control engr, Scott Paper Co, Pa, 51, res group leader, 52-54, res mgr, 55-56; tech secy, 57-58, exec secy, 59-74, treas, 63-74, EXEC DIR, TECH ASN PULP & PAPER INDUST, 75- *Concurrent Pos:* Pres, Coun Eng & Sci Soc Execs, 69. *Mem:* Fel Tech Asn Pulp & Paper Indust; Am Soc Asn Execs. *Res:* Pulp and paper technology; industrial research administration. *Mailing Add:* Tech Asn Pulp & Paper Indust 1 Dunwoody Park Atlanta GA 30338

NETHERTON, LOWELL EDWIN, b Fairfield, Ill, Feb 9, 22; m 46; c 4. INORGANIC CHEMISTRY, PHYSICAL CHEMISTRY. *Educ:* Western Ill Univ, BS, 44; Univ Wis, PhD(chem), 50. *Prof Exp:* Anal chemist, Sinclair Refining Co, 44; asst, Univ Wis, 48-50; res chemist, Victor Chem Co, 50-57, dir res, Victor Chem Div, Stauffer Chem Co, 57-63, mgr prod, 63-65; dir res, Mich, 65-78, DIR SCI & TECH RELS, BASF WYANDOTTE CORP, 78- *Mem:* Am Chem Soc; Soc Plastics Indust; Indust Res Inst; Am Inst Chem Engrs; Am Inst Chemists. *Res:* Phosphorus compounds; electrochemistry of rare elements; chemistry of rhenium, tungsten and tantalum; chlor-alkali electrochemistry; urethanes, polyethers, isocyanates, alkyleneoxides and auxiliaries; foamed plastics; textile and paper specialties; surfactants and detergents. *Mailing Add:* BASF Wyandotte Corp 100 Cherry Hill Rd Parsippany NJ 07054

NETI, RADHAKRISHNA MURTY, b Nandigama, India, June 20, 33; m 60; c 1. PHYSICAL CHEMISTRY. *Educ:* Hindu Col, Masulipatam, India, BS, 53; Banaras Hindu Univ, MS, 55, dipl mod Europ lang, 56, PhD(chem), 60. *Prof Exp:* Lectr chem, Banaras Hindu Univ, 60; res assoc radiation chem, Univ Notre Dame, 60-62; res assoc bot & biophys, Univ Ill, 62-66; RES SCIENTIST, BECKMAN INSTRUMENTS, INC, 66- *Honors & Awards:* John C Vaaler Award, 70. *Mem:* AAAS; Am Chem Soc. *Res:* Photo, radiation and electro-analytical chemistry; air and water quality instrumentation. *Mailing Add:* Dept 762 Beckman Instruments Inc 2500 Harbor Blvd Fullerton CA 92634

NETRAVALI, ARUN NARAYAN, b Bombay, India, May 26, 46; m 74. ELECTRICAL ENGINEERING. *Educ:* Indian Inst Technol, Bombay, BS, 67; Rice Univ, MS, 69, PhD(elec eng), 70. *Prof Exp:* Asst elec eng, Rice Univ, 67-70; asst dir elec eng, Optimal Data Corp, 70-72; mem tech staff picture processing, 72-78, HEAD, VISUAL COMMUN RES DEPT, BELL LABS, 78- *Concurrent Pos:* Adj prof, Dept Elec Eng, Rutgers Univ, 79-; ed, Signal Processsing & Commun Electronics, Inst Elec & Electronics Engrs Trans Communs. *Mem:* Sr mem Inst Elec & Electronics Engrs. *Res:* Processing of television and graphical images for the purpose of efficient transmission, enhancement and restoration; digital signal processing. *Mailing Add:* Bell Labs Holmdel NJ 07733

NETSKY, MARTIN GEORGE, b Philadelphia, Pa, May 15, 17; m 46. NEUROLOGY, NEUROPATHOLOGY. *Educ:* Univ Pa, AB, 38, MS, 40, MD, 43. *Prof Exp:* From intern to resident neurol, Hosp Univ Pa, 43-44; Weil fel neuropath, Montefiore Hosp, New York, 46-47; from asst neuropathologist to assoc neuropathologist, Montefiore Hosp, 47-54; from assoc prof to prof neurol, Bowman Gray Sch Med, 55-61, prof neuropath, 55-61, dir sect neurol, 57-59, chmn dept, 59-61; vis prof path, Univ Med Sci, Thailand, 61; prof neuropath, Sch Med, Univ Va, 62-75; PROF PATH, SCH MED, VANDERBILT UNIV, 74- *Concurrent Pos:* Lectr, US Naval Hosp, St Albans, NY, 48, consult pathologist, 50-54; from adj attend physician to assoc attend physician, Montefiore Hosp, 49-54; assoc, Col Physicians & Surgeons, Columbia Univ, 52-54; mem sci adv bd, Armed Forces Inst Path. *Mem:* Am Neurol Asn; Am Asn Neuropath (pres, 63); Asn Res Nerv & Ment Dis; Am Acad Neurol; Am Soc Exp Path. *Res:* Permeability of living membranes; autonomic nervous system; clinicopathologic aspects of human brain tumors; congenital and degenerative neurologic disorders; medical education; learning. *Mailing Add:* Dept of Path Vanderbilt Univ Sch of Med Nashville TN 37232

NETTEL, STEPHEN J E, b Prague, Czech, Aug 12, 32; US citizen. SOLID STATE PHYSICS. *Educ:* McGill Univ, BEng, 54; Mass Inst Technol, PhD(physics), 60. *Prof Exp:* Jr res physicst, Univ Calif, San Diego, 60-61; staff mem, Int Bus Mach Corp, Switz, 61-65; res fel appl physics, Harvard Univ, 65-66; asst prof physics, 66-69, ASSOC PROF PHYSICS, RENSSELAER POLYTECH INST, 69- *Res:* Theoretical solid state physics. *Mailing Add:* Dept of Physics Rensselaer Polytech Inst Troy NY 12181

NETTERVILLE, JOHN T, analytical chemistry, see previous edition

NETTING, M(ORRIS) GRAHAM, b Wilkinsburg, Pa, Oct 3, 04; m 30; c 2. HERPETOLOGY. *Educ:* Univ Pittsburgh, BS, 26; Univ Mich, AM, 29; Waynesburg Col, ScD, 50. *Prof Exp:* Asst herpet, 25-28, asst cur, 28-31, cur, 31-54, asst dir, 49-53, actg dir, 53-54, dir herpet, 54-75, EMER DIR, CARNEGIE MUS NATURAL HIST, 75- *Concurrent Pos:* Leader, Carnegie Mus Exped, Venezuela, 29-30; asst prof, Univ Pittsburgh, 44-63. *Mem:* AAAS; Am Soc Ichthyologists & herpetologists (secy, 31-48, pres, 48-50); Asn Sci Mus Dirs; Ecol Soc Am. *Res:* Herpetology; zoogeography; museology; conservation. *Mailing Add:* Powdermill Nature Reserve Star Rte S Rector PA 15677

NETTLES, JOHN BARNWELL, b Dover, NC, May 19, 22; m 56; c 3. OBSTETRICS & GYNECOLOGY. *Educ:* Univ SC, BS, 41; Med Col SC, MD, 44. *Prof Exp:* Intern gen med, Garfield Mem Hosp, DC, 44-45; res fel path, Med Col Ga, 46-47; res staff obstet & gynec, Univ Ill Hosps, 47-51, from instr to asst prof, Univ, 51-57; asst prof, Sch Med, Univ Ark, 57-60, assoc prof & med educ nat defense coordr, 60-67, prof obstet & gynec, 67-69; PROF OBSTET & GYNEC, TULSA MED COL, UNIV OKLA, 69-, CHMN DEPT, 75- *Concurrent Pos:* Dir, Tulsa Residency Training Prog Obstet & Gynec & Tulsa Obstet & Gynec Educ Found, 69- *Mem:* AAAS; AMA; Asn Mil Surgeons US; Am Col Obstet & Gynec; Int Soc Advan Humanistic Studies Gynec. *Res:* Renal function and structure; kidney biopsy; newborn and fetal morbidity and mortality; genital malignancy; obstetric anesthesia and analgesia; physiology and toxemia of pregnancy. *Mailing Add:* Tulsa Med Col Univ of Okla 2727 E 21st St Tulsa OK 74114

NETTLES, WILLIAM CARL, b Sumter, SC, Aug 11, 07; m 38; c 3. ECONOMIC ENTOMOLOGY. *Educ:* Clemson Col, BS, 30; Ohio State Univ, MS, 32. *Prof Exp:* Asst entomologist exp sta, 30-34, exten entomologist, 34-46, leader exten entom & plant dis, 46-65, state chem info leader, 65-68, exten specialist entom & plant path, 68-69, exten prin specialist, 69-72, EMER ASSOC PROF ENTOM, CLEMSON UNIV, 72- *Mem:* Entom Soc Am (secy, 36). *Res:* Biology and control of insects and plant diseases. *Mailing Add:* 119 Folger St Clemson SC 29631

NETTLES, WILLIAM CARL, JR, b Anderson, SC, Dec 21, 34; m 67. ENTOMOLOGY. *Educ:* Clemson Univ, BS, 55, MS, 59; Rutgers Univ, PhD(entom), 62. *Prof Exp:* Res asst agr chem, Clemson Univ, 57-59; RES ENTOMOLOGIST, COTTON INSECTS BR, AGR RES SERV, USDA, 62- *Mem:* AAAS; Entom Soc Am. *Res:* Physiology and biochemistry of insects; biological control. *Mailing Add:* PO Drawer DG College Station TX 77840

NETTLESHIP, ANDERSON, pathology, deceased

NETTLETON, DONALD EDWARD, JR, b New Haven, Conn, Mar 16, 30; m 57; c 4. ORGANIC CHEMISTRY, BIOCHEMISTRY. *Educ:* Yale Univ, BS, 52; Rice Inst, PhD, 56. *Prof Exp:* Res assoc biochem, Med Col, Cornell Univ, 56-58; SR CHEMIST, DEPT BIOCHEM, BRISTOL LABS, INC DIV, BRISTOL-MYERS CO, 58- *Mem:* Am Chem Soc; Am Soc Pharmacog. *Res:* Isolation of antitumor and antibiotic agents from fermentation liquors and higher plants; syntheses of derivatives and analogs of physiologically active natural products. *Mailing Add:* RFD 1 Box 524 Jordan NY 13080

NETTLETON, (GARY) STEPHEN, b Albert Lea, Minn, May 7, 46; m 68; c 2. ANATOMY, HISTOCHEMISTRY. *Educ:* McPherson Col, BS, 68; Univ Minn, PhD(anat), 76. *Prof Exp:* From instr to asst prof, 76-82, ASSOC PROF ANAT, SCH MED, UNIV LOUISVILLE, 82- *Concurrent Pos:* Ed asst, Stain Technol, 77-80, asst ed, 80- *Mem:* Histochem Soc; Biol Stain Comn; Soc Appl Spectros; Sigma Xi; Am Chem Soc. *Res:* Chemical reaction mechanisms of biological stains; histochemical approaches to the study of tissues. *Mailing Add:* Dept of Anat Health Sci Ctr Univ Louisville Louisville KY 40292

NETTLETON, WILEY DENNIS, b Noble, Ill, June 8, 32; m 56; c 4. SOIL SCIENCE, GEOLOGY. *Educ:* Univ Ill, BS, 57, MS, 58; NC State Univ, PhD(soil classification & genesis), 66. *Prof Exp:* Trainee, Western Soil Surv Invest Unit, Soil Conserv Serv, 56, soil scientist, 57 & 58-65, res soil scientist, Soil Surv Lab, 65-72, supvry res soil scientist, 72-76, RES SOIL SCIENTIST, NAT SOIL SURV LAB, USDA, 77- *Concurrent Pos:* Res asst, NC State Univ, 60-65; lectr, Univ Calif, Riverside, 70. *Mem:* Soil Sci Soc Am; Am Soc Agron. *Res:* Use of mineralogy and micromorphology in the laboratory and geomorphology in the field as tools for studying genesis and classification of soils from the Midwest, Southeast and Western United States. *Mailing Add:* Fed Bldg Rm 345 Nat Soils Surv Lab Lincoln NE 68508

NETZEL, DANIEL ANTHONY, b Chicago, Ill, Feb 16, 34; m 58; c 3. PHYSICAL CHEMISTRY. *Educ:* Univ Ill, BS, 57; Univ Mo-Kansas City, MS, 61; Northwestern Univ, PhD(phys & anal chem), 75. *Prof Exp:* Assoc res chemist, Midwest Res Inst, 58-67; res chemist, DeSoto Inc, 67-69; supvr spectros, Northwestern Univ, 69-74; RES ASSOC CHEM & SUPVR SECT, LARAMIE ENERGY TECH CTR, 75- *Mem:* Am Chem Soc; Soc Appl Spectros; Res Soc Am; Sigma Xi. *Res:* Identification, structural characterization and analytical applications of nuclear magnetic and electron spin resonances to fossil fuels. *Mailing Add:* Laramie Energy Tech Ctr PO Box 3395 Univ Sta Laramie WY 82071

NETZEL, RICHARD G, b Shawano, Wis, May 13, 28; m 51; c 3. PHYSICS, ACADEMIC ADMINISTRATION. *Educ:* Univ Wis, BS, 50, MS, 56, PhD(physics), 60. *Prof Exp:* From asst prof to prof physics, Univ Wis-Oshkosh, 60-68, asst vpres prog develop & staffing, 68-70, asst acad vpres, 70-71; actg dep dir educ, AAAS, 71-72; vpres acad affairs, Metrop State Col, 72-78, actg pres, 78-79; ASSOC VPRES, CONSORTIUM STATE COL, COLO, 79- *Mem:* AAAS; Am Phys Soc; Am Asn Higher Educ. *Res:* Low temperature physics; superconducting transition temperatures of titanium; science education. *Mailing Add:* Metrop State Col 1006 11th St Denver CO 80204

NETZEL, THOMAS LEONARD, b Wausau, Wis, Dec 5, 46; m 68; c 3. CHEMICAL PHYSICS, BIOPHYSICS. *Educ:* Univ Wis-Madison, BS, 68; Yale Univ, MPhil, 70, PhD(chem), 72. *Prof Exp:* Mem tech staff chem physics & appl econ, Bell Labs, 72-77; assoc chemist, 77-80, CHEMIST, BROOKHAVEN NAT LAB, 80- *Mem:* Inter Am Photochem Soc; Am Chem Soc. *Res:* Development and application of picosecond spectroscopic techniques to probe the dynamics of chemical and biological systems; observation and modeling of electron and energy transfer processes; construction of molecular, solar energy transducers; photochemistry; inorganic chemistry. *Mailing Add:* Dept of Chem Bldg 555A Brookhaven Nat Lab Upton NY 11973

NETZER, DAVID WILLIS, b Washington, DC, Feb 25, 39; m 61; c 1. AERONAUTICAL & MECHANICAL ENGINEERING. *Educ:* Va Polytech Inst, BSME, 60; Purdue Univ, MSME, 62, PhD, 68. *Prof Exp:* Engr, Aerojet Gen Corp, 62-64; assoc prof, 68-80, PROF AERONAUT, NAVAL POSTGRAD SCH, 80- *Mem:* Combustion Inst; Am Inst Aeronaut & Astronaut. *Res:* Solid propellant combustion-acceleration sensitivity; particulate behavior; hybrid rocket and solid fuel ramjet internal ballistics; numerical analysis of reacting flows; pollution from turbojet test cells. *Mailing Add:* Dept of Aeronautics Code 67Nt Naval Postgrad Sch Monterey CA 93940

NEU, ERNEST LUDWIG, b Frankfurt, Ger, Aug 19, 15; nat US; m 46; c 2. CHEMISTRY. *Educ:* Univ Nancy, BS, 37; Univ Caen, MS, 38. *Prof Exp:* Res chemist, Celotex Corp, 38-42; chief chemist dicalite & perlite, Great Lakes Carbon Corp, 52-59, asst tech dir, Mining & Mineral Prod Div, Grefco Inc, 59-62, tech dir, 62-66, managing dir, Dicalite Europe Nord, 59-73, gen mgr, Int Div, 66-73, vpres, 73-81, managing dir, Permalite Europe, SA, 73-81; RETIRED. *Mem:* Am Chem Soc; Am Inst Chem Eng; NY Acad Sci. *Res:* Filteraids; diatomite; perlite; acoustical and thermal insulation; fungi diseases. *Mailing Add:* Grefco Inc 2340 Wilshire Blvd Los Angeles CA 90010

NEU, HAROLD CONRAD, b Omaha, Nebr, Aug 19, 34; m 62; c 3. MEDICINE, PHARMACOLOGY. *Educ:* Creighton Univ, AB, 56; Johns Hopkins Univ, MD, 60. *Prof Exp:* From intern to resident med, Columbia-Presby Med Ctr, 60-62; res assoc biochem, Nat Inst Arthritis & Metab Dis, 62-64; chief resident med, Columbia-Presby Med Ctr, 64-65; assoc, 65-66, from asst prof to assoc prof med, 66-75, PROF MED & PHARMACOL, COL PHYSICIANS & SURGEONS, COLUMBIA UNIV, 70-, HEAD DIV INFECTIOUS DIS, COLUMBIA-PRESBY MED CTR, 71-, ATTEND PHYSICIAN, 75- *Concurrent Pos:* Career scientist, New York Health Res Coun, 65-71; attend, Harlem Hosp, New York, 67; assoc attend, Columbia-Presby Med Ctr, 70-75. *Honors & Awards:* Borden Award, Borden Found, 60. *Mem:* Am Soc Microbiol; Am Soc Biol Chemists; Am Soc Clin Invest; Am Col Physicians. *Res:* Resistance of bacteria to antibiotics; bacterial surface enzymes. *Mailing Add:* Dept of Med Columbia Univ Col of Physicians & Surgeons New York NY 10032

NEU, JOHN TERNAY, b Commerce, Tex, Apr 23, 20; div; c 2. AEROSPACE RESEARCH. *Educ:* Agr & Mech Col, Tex, BS, 42; Univ Calif, Berkeley, PhD(phys chem), 49. *Prof Exp:* Instr chem, Univ Calif, Berkeley, 49; res chemist, Calif Res Corp, 49-56; sr staff scientist & chief optics technol, Gen Dynamics/Convair Aerospace, 56-75; PRIN PHYSICIST, IRT CORP, 75- *Res:* Space physics; optical properties of surfaces; space optical instrumentation; vehicle signatures; vehicle survivability. *Mailing Add:* 4544 Bancroft St San Diego CA 92116

NEUBAUER, BENEDICT FRANCIS, b Bird Island, Minn, Mar 14, 38; m 61; c 3. PLANT ANATOMY. *Educ:* St John's Univ, Minn, BA, 60; Iowa State Univ, PhD(plant anat), 65. *Prof Exp:* Asst prof bot & plant anat, 65-70, ASSOC PROF BOT, UNIV MAINE, ORONO, 70- *Mem:* Sigma Xi; Bot Soc Am. *Res:* Anatomy of vascular plants. *Mailing Add:* Dept of Bot & Plant Path Univ of Maine Orono ME 04473

NEUBAUER, L(OREN) W(ENZEL), b St James, Minn, June 23, 04; m 46; c 1. AGRICULTURAL & CIVIL ENGINEERING. *Educ:* Univ Minn, BS, 26, MS, 32, PhD(civil eng), 48. *Prof Exp:* Instr math, Col Eng, Univ Minn, 26-28, instr agr eng, 29-39; from asst prof to prof, 40-71, EMER PROF AGR ENG, UNIV CALIF, DAVIS, 71- *Honors & Awards:* L J Markwardt Wood Eng Res Award, Forest Products Res Soc, 74. *Mem:* Am Soc Agr Engrs; Am Soc Testing & Mat; Am Geophys Union; Forest Prod Res Soc. *Res:* Farm structures; adobe construction; wood durability; strength of wood, wood beams and wood columns, and concrete; solar heating and cooling. *Mailing Add:* 3422 Monte Vista Ave Davis CA 95616

NEUBAUER, RUSSELL HOWARD, b Detroit, Mich, Feb 15, 44; m 69; c 4. LYMPHOCYTE FUNCTIONS, MONOCLONAL ANTIBODIES. *Educ:* Mich State Univ, BS, 66, MS, 68; Univ Md, PhD(microbiol), 72. *Prof Exp:* Virologist, Litton Bionetics, Inc, 72-76; IMMUNOLOGIST, FREDERICK CANCER RES FACIL, NAT CANCER INST, 76- *Concurrent Pos:* Mem, Herpesvirus Adv Team-1, Simian Herpeviruses, World Health Orgn, Int Agency Res Cancer, 71-77. *Mem:* Am Asn Cancer Res; Am Asn Immunologists; Am Soc Microbiol; Int Asn Comp Res Leukemia & Related Dis; Tissue Cult Asn. *Res:* Use of monoclonal antibodies to identify norman and malignant cell populations; the effect of growth factors on normal and transformed cells; the effect of lymphoid disease on normal immunological functions. *Mailing Add:* Frederick Cancer Res Facil Nat Cancer Inst PO Box B Bldg 560 Frederick MD 21701

NEUBAUER, WERNER GEORGE, b White Plains, NY, Apr 18, 30; m 54; c 2. PHYSICS. *Educ:* Roanoke Col, BS, 52; Cath Univ Am, PhD(acoust), 68. *Prof Exp:* Physicist, Electronics Br, Sound Div, 53-57, physicist, Propagation Br, 57-58, sect head microacoust sect, Acoust Res Br, 58-69, actg br head, Phys Acoust Br, Acoust Div, 69-70, sect head micro acoust sect, Phys Acoust Br, 70-79, SPEC ASST TARGET CHARACTERISTICS, ACOUST DIV, NAVAL RES LAB, 79- *Honors & Awards:* Applied Res Award, Sigma Xi, 81. *Mem:* Fel Acoust Soc Am; AAAS; Sigma Xi. *Res:* Radiation, reflection and diffraction of waves; properties of elastic media; optical visualization of acoustic waves; underwater acoustic radiation, reflection and scattering. *Mailing Add:* 4603 Quarter Charge Dr Annandale VA 22003

NEUBECK, CLIFFORD EDWARD, b Erie, Pa, Nov 6, 17; m 43; c 8. CHEMISTRY. *Educ:* Univ Pittsburgh, BS, 39, PhD(biochem), 43. *Prof Exp:* Asst chem, Univ Pittsburgh, 39-41, asst biochem, 41-43; biochemist, Rohm and Haas Co, 43-50, sr chemist, 50-59, sr scientist, 59-71, sr biochemist, 71-76, head, Enzyme Lab, 76-82; RETIRED. *Mem:* Am Chem Soc; Soc Indust Microbiol; Am Soc Enologists. *Res:* Commercial production of enzymes; utilization of enzymes; microbial fermentations. *Mailing Add:* 45 Horsham Rd Hatboro PA 19040

NEUBECKER, ROBERT DUANE, b Lackawanna, NY, Oct 10, 25; m 50; c 5. PATHOLOGY. *Educ:* Univ Rochester, AB, 46, MD, 49; Am Bd Path, dipl, 56. *Prof Exp:* Intern med, Vanderbilt Univ Hosp, 49-50; intern path, Strong Mem Hosp, Rochester, NY, 50; asst, Sch Med & Dent, Univ Rochester, 52-54, instr, 54-55; pathologist, Armed Forces Inst Path, 55-57, chief obstet, gynec & breast path br, 57-61; pathologist & dir res & develop, St Joseph's Hosp, Marshfield, Wis, 61-66; ASSOC DIR LABS, MERCY HOSP, 66- *Mem:* Am Asn Path & Bact; Int Acad Path. *Res:* Pathologic anatomy with clinical pathologic correlations in the field of female genital diseases. *Mailing Add:* Dept of Lab Med Mercy Hosp Oshkosh WI 54901

NEUBERGER, DAN, b Zagreb, Yugoslavia, Feb 19, 29; nat US; m 56; c 2. PHOTOGRAPHIC CHEMISTRY. *Educ:* Columbia Univ, BA, 50; Univ Rochester, PhD(phys chem), 53. *Prof Exp:* Asst, Univ Rochester, 50-52; sr res chemist, 53-63, RES ASSOC, EASTMAN KODAK CO, 63- *Mem:* Soc Photog Sci & Eng. *Res:* Photographic science. *Mailing Add:* 95 Wendover Rd Rochester NY 14610

NEUBERGER, HANS HERMANN, b Mannheim, Ger, Feb 17, 10; nat US; m 39, 57; c 2. METEOROLOGY. *Educ:* Univ Hamburg, DSc(meteorol), 36. *Prof Exp:* Res asst to Dr Christian Jensen, Univ Hamburg, 36-37; instr geophys, 37-41, asst prof, 41-43, from assoc prof to prof meteorol, 43-70, chief div, 45-54, head dept, 54-61 & 65-67, EMER PROF METEOROL, PA STATE UNIV, 70- *Concurrent Pos:* Tech ed, Weatherwise, 48-53; consult, US Weather Bur, Turkey, 54-55; assoc, Army-Navy Vision Comt & mem subcomt visibility & atmospheric optics, Nat Res Coun; Am Meteorol Soc rep div earth sci, Nat Acad Sci-Nat Res Coun, 57-60; UN tech expert, Pakistan, 61; vis prof, Univ SFla, 71-74, emer prof geog, 74- *Mem:* Fel Am Meteorol Soc; Am Geophys Union. *Res:* Design of mine safety device and meteorological equipment; atmospheric optics and pollution. *Mailing Add:* 1805 Burlington Circle Sun City Center FL 33570

NEUBERGER, JACOB, b Ger, June 8, 27; nat US; m; c 5. SOLID STATE PHYSICS. *Educ:* Johns Hopkins Univ, BS, 50; NY Univ, MS, 53, PhD(physics), 58. *Prof Exp:* Res scientist, NY Univ, 54-57; asst prof physics, Rutgers Univ, 57-60; asst prof, 60-66, ASSOC PROF PHYSICS, QUEEN'S COL, NY, 66- *Concurrent Pos:* Lectr, City Col New York, 54-61; guest, Brookhaven Nat Lab, 67-68. *Mem:* AAAS; Am Phys Soc; Am Asn Physics Teachers. *Res:* surface states of solids; defects and diffusion in solids. *Mailing Add:* Dept of Physics Queens Col Flushing NY 11367

NEUBERGER, JOHN STEPHEN, b New York, NY, June 29, 38; m 80; c 1. ENVIRONMENTAL EPIDEMIOLOGY, OCCUPATIONAL EPIDEMIOLOGY. *Educ:* Cornell Univ, BME, 61; Columbia Univ, MBA, 67; Johns Hopkins Univ, MPH, 74, DrPH, 77. *Prof Exp:* Consult systs analyst, Rand Corp, 68-69; researcher, Riverside Res Inst, 69-71; consult analyst, Inst Space Studies, NASA, 71-75; environ epidemiologist & environ health specialist, Environ Sci Lab, 76-77, ASST PROF EPIDEMIOL & ENVIRON HEALTH, MED SCH, UNIV KANS, 78- *Concurrent Pos:* Consult, Md Dept Health & Ment Hyg, 73-74, Reg Planning Coun, 75-76 & Reg VII, US Environ Protection Agency, 79- *Mem:* Am Pub Health Asn; NY Acad Sci; Soc Epidemiol Res; Soc Occup & Environ Health. *Res:* Environmental and occupational carcinogenesis; environmental and occupational agents causing congenital malformations; lung cancer epidemiology. *Mailing Add:* Dept Community Heath Sch Med Univ Kans Rainbow Blvd at 39th Kansas City KS 66103

NEUBERGER, JOHN WILLIAM, b Ventura, Iowa, Aug 14, 34; m 59; c 2. MATHEMATICS. *Educ:* Univ Tex, BA, 54, PhD(math), 57. *Prof Exp:* Spec instr math, Univ Tex, 56-57; instr, Ill Inst Technol, 57-59; asst prof, Univ Tenn, 59-63; from assoc prof to prof, Emory Univ, 67-77; PROF MATH, N TEX STATE UNIV, 77- *Concurrent Pos:* Mem, Inst Air Weapons Res, Univ Chicago, 57-59, consult, Oak Ridge Nat Lab, 59, 65 & 79- ; Alfred P Sloan res fel, 67-69; mem, Inst Advan Study, 68; NSF res grant, 70-72 & 74; mem, Inst Defense Anal, 73; vis prof, Univ Ky, 73; ed, Houston J Math, 75-; NSF res grant, 77-79. *Mem:* Am Math Soc; Soc Indust & Appl Math; Edinburgh Math Soc; London Math Soc. *Res:* Partial differential equations; numerical analysis; functional analysis; hydrodynamics. *Mailing Add:* Dept Math N Tex State Univ Denton TX 76203

NEUBERT, JEROME ARTHUR, b Mankato, Minn, Dec 1, 38; m 66. PHYSICS. *Educ:* Univ Kans, BS, 62; Calif State Col, Los Angeles, MS, 66; Pa State Univ, PhD(eng acoust), 70. *Prof Exp:* SR RES PHYSICIST, NAVAL OCEAN SYSTS CTR, 63- *Mem:* Acoust Soc Am. *Res:* Engineering acoustics; applied mathematics and physics; sound propagation in stochastic media; underwater acoustics. *Mailing Add:* 250 Murray Dr Fletcher Hills El Cajon CA 92020

NEUBERT, RALPH LEWIS, b St Louis, Mo, Jan 30, 22; m 44; c 6. RESEARCH ADMINISTRATION. *Educ:* Univ Mo, Rolla, BS, 42; grad, Advan Mgt Prog, Harvard Univ, 70. *Hon Degrees:* Prof Eng, Univ Mo, Rolla, 71. *Prof Exp:* Plant engr, Monsanto Co, Carondelet, 42-44, various eng & mfg positions, Mo, Ala, Tenn & Mass, 46-62, mgr opers & planning, Agr Div, 62-64, area dir, Latin Am & Can Int Div, 64-67, dir admin & planning, Int Div, 67-68, vpres, Monsanto Res Corp & dir, Mound Lab, 68-72, mgr corp planning & develop, 72-74, DIR, STRATEGIC PLANNING, MONSANTO CO, 74- *Mem:* AAAS; Planning Exec Inst; Am Soc Corp Planning. *Res:* Research and development management; chemical production; international business; business planning. *Mailing Add:* Monsanto Co 800 N Lindbergh Blvd St Louis MO 63166

NEUBERT, THEODORE JOHN, b Rochester, NY, Jan 10, 17. PHYSICAL CHEMISTRY. *Educ:* Univ Rochester, BS, 39; Brown Univ, PhD(phys chem), 42. *Prof Exp:* Res assoc, US Naval Res Lab, 42; chemist, Manhattan Proj, Chicago, 42-45; scientist, Argonne Nat Lab, 45-47, fel inst nuclear studies, 47-49; from asst prof to assoc prof chem, 49-61, PROF CHEM, ILL INST TECHNOL, 61- *Concurrent Pos:* Consult, Argonne Nat Lab, 49-60. *Mem:* AAAS; Am Chem Soc; Am Phys Soc. *Res:* Physics and chemistry of solid state. *Mailing Add:* Dept Chem Ill Inst Technol Chicago IL 60616

NEUBERT, VERNON H, b Cabot, Pa, Dec 23, 27; m 50; c 5. MECHANICS. *Educ:* Carnegie Inst Technol, BS, 48, MS, 49; Yale Univ, DEng, 57. *Prof Exp:* Design engr, struct, Pittsburgh Indust Eng Corp, 49-50; res engr, Res Labs, Aluminum Co Am, 52-54; part-time instr appl mech, Yale Univ, 54-57; supvr appl mech, Elec Boat Div, Gen Dynamics Corp, 57-62; assoc prof eng mech, 62-66, PROF ENG MECH, PA STATE UNIV, 66- *Concurrent Pos:* Lectr eve sch, New London Exten, Univ Conn, 57-62. *Mem:* Am Soc Civil Engrs; Am Soc Mech Engrs; Acoust Soc Am. *Res:* Applied and solid mechanics, especially stress and vibration analysis. *Mailing Add:* Dept Eng Sci & Mech Pa State Univ University Park PA 16802

NEUBORT, SHIMON, b New York, NY, Aug 21, 42; m 67; c 5. CANCER BIOLOGY, RADIOBIOLOGY. *Educ:* Yeshiva Univ, BA, 64; Albert Einstein Col Med, PhD(biochem), 71. *Prof Exp:* Res fel biochem, Albert Einstein Col Med, 71-72, res assoc radiobiol, 72-74, instr, 74-76, asst prof, 76-80; SR BIOCHEMIST CANCER BIOL, NY UNIV, 80- *Concurrent Pos:* Chief chemist, Crown-Kesser Wine Cellars, 81- *Mem:* Am Asn Cancer Res; Radiation Res Soc. *Res:* Response of mammalian cells and their nucleic acid metabolism to ionizing radiation and chemical agents; radiosensitizers; hyperthermia; chemical carcinogens; chemical analysis of cell components and metabolites. *Mailing Add:* Dept Biol NY Univ 952 Brown Bldg Wash Square New York NY 10003

NEUCERE, JOSEPH NAVIN, b Hessmer, La, Feb 21, 32; m 71; c 1. BIO-ORGANIC CHEMISTRY, IMMUNOCHEMISTRY. *Educ:* La State Univ, Baton Rouge, BS, 60. *Prof Exp:* Chemist, 61-68, RES CHEMIST PLANT BIOCHEM, SOUTHERN REGIONAL RES CTR, USDA, 68- *Mem:* Am Chem Soc; AAAS; Am Asn Cereal Chemists; Inst Food Technol. *Res:* General characterization of proteins and enzymes in relation to species differentiation, biological value, and other factors leading to improved quality of plant foods. *Mailing Add:* Southern Regional Res Ctr USDA PO Box 19687 New Orleans LA 70179

NEUDECK, GEROLD W(ALTER), b Beach, NDak, Sept 25, 36; m 62; c 2. ELECTRICAL ENGINEERING, SOLID STATE ELECTRONICS. *Educ:* Univ NDak, BSEE, 59, MSEE, 60; Purdue Univ, PhD(elec eng), 69. *Prof Exp:* Asst prof elec eng, Univ NDak, 60-64; from instr to assoc prof, 64-76, PROF ELEC ENG, PURDUE UNIV, WEST LAFAYETTE, 76- *Concurrent Pos:* Consult, CTS Corp, 66-; lectr, Western Elec Co, Inc, 69-71, Delco Electronics, 80, Bell Telephone Labs, 81 & Int Electrodynamics, 81. *Honors & Awards:* D D Ewing Award; A A Potter Award. *Mem:* Inst Elec & Electronics Engrs; Am Vacuum Soc. *Res:* Integrated circuits and devices, germanium-silicon heterojunctions, high frequency noise in diodes, transistor and intergrated circuit fabrication, amorphous silicon thin films, zinc silicon sputtered on silicon substrated, very large scale integration technology. *Mailing Add:* Sch of Elec Eng Purdue Univ West Lafayette IN 47907

NEUDECK, LOWELL DONALD, b Billings, Mont, Aug 28, 37; m 66; c 2. PHYSIOLOGY, ENDOCRINOLOGY. *Educ:* Univ Mont, BA, 64, MA, 68; Univ Conn, PhD(zool), 77. *Prof Exp:* Asst prof, 76-80, ASSOC PROF BIOL, NORTHERN MICH UNIV, 80- *Mem:* Sigma Xi; Am Soc Zool; Am Soc Mammalogists. *Res:* Mammalian, renal physiology; mammalian kidneys, physiology, morphology changes during growth and aging including hormonal effects on these changes; sexual dimorphism in mammalian kidneys. *Mailing Add:* Dept of Biol Northern Mich Univ Marquette MI 49855

NEUENDORFFER, JOSEPH ALFRED, b New York, NY, Feb 28, 18; m 42; c 3. PHYSICS, OPERATIONS ANALYSIS. *Educ:* Mass Inst Technol, SB & SM, 41; Johns Hopkins Univ, PhD(physics), 51. *Prof Exp:* Staff mem, Acoustics Lab, Mass Inst Technol, 41-42; opers analyst, Columbia Res Group M, 42-43; opers analyst naval opers, Off Sci Res & Develop, 43-46, opers analyst, Opers Eval Group, 48-51, dep dir, 51-56; opers analyst, Staff Comdr in Chief Naval Opers, 58-61; staff comdr, Submarine Force, Atlantic, 61-62; dir naval objectives group, Ctr Naval Analyses, 63-64; analyst staff comdr, US Sixth Fleet, 65-66, sr scientist, Ctr Naval Anal, 67-68, staff comdr in chief, Atlantic Fleet, 69-70, sr scientist, Ctr Naval Anal, 71-74, staff comdr, Surface Forces, Atlantic, 75-76, sr scientist, Ctr Naval Anal, Univ Rochester, 77-80; CONSULT, CTR NAVAL ANAL & METRON, INC, 81- *Mem:* Oper Res Soc Am; Am Phys Soc. *Res:* Development comparison and testing of naval tactics and equipment; sonar research, war gaming, simulation of military operations and search theory; angular distribution of the products of nuclear reactions. *Mailing Add:* 911 Allison St Alexandria VA 22302

NEUFELD, ABRAM HERMAN, b Russia, Apr 26, 07; nat US; m 37; c 2. CLINICAL PATHOLOGY. *Educ:* Univ Man, BSc, 34, MSc, 35, PhD(med biochem), 37; McGill Univ, MD & CM, 50. *Prof Exp:* Instr biochem, Univ Man, 35-36; lectr, McGill Univ, 36-41, asst prod prof endocrinol, 41-43; med biochemist, Queen Mary Vet Hosp, Montreal, 46-55, chief of serv biochem & radioisotopes, 55-6O; prof, 60-72, EMER PROF CLIN PATH, FAC MED, UNIV WESTERN ONT, 72- *Concurrent Pos:* Hon lectr, McGill Univ, 58-60; sr consult, Can Dept Vet Affairs, 50-60; ed, Med Serv J, Can, 47-59. *Mem:* Can Soc Clin Invest; Can Biochem Soc; Can Med Asn; Chem Inst Can; Can Physiol Soc. *Res:* Metabolism of normal and pathological lipids and proteins, especially in arteriosclerosis, myelomatosis and lipidoses; hemoglobins; radioactive isotopes in clincal investigation; chemical pathology. *Mailing Add:* 1071 Colborne St London ON N6A 4B4 Can

NEUFELD, BERNEY ROY, b Sask, Aug 3, 41; US citizen; m 63; c 2. MOLECULAR BIOLOGY. *Educ:* Columbia Union Col, BA, 63; Loma Linda Univ, MA, 65; Ind Univ, Bloomington, PhD, 68. *Prof Exp:* asst prof biol, Loma Linda Univ, 68-78; PROF BIOL, SOUTHWESTERN ADVENTIST COL, 78- *Concurrent Pos:* Mem extended day fac, Riverside City Col, 70-71; lectr, Univ Calif Exten, 71; NIH spec res fel, Calif Inst Technol, 71-73, vis fel, 73-74; assoc prof biol & head dept, Mid East Col, Beirut, Lebanon, 75-76. *Mem:* Genetics Soc Am; Am Soc Microbiol. *Res:* Evolution of restriction enzyme genes in salmonella. *Mailing Add:* Southwestern Adventist Col Keene TX 76059

NEUFELD, CORNELIUS HERMAN HARRY, b Scottdale, Pa, Apr 15, 23; m 51; c 3. ORGANIC CHEMISTRY. *Educ:* Dalhousie Univ, BSc, 47; Univ Notre Dame, PhD(chem), 51. *Prof Exp:* Asst prof chem, Am Univ, 51-53; chemist biol active chem compounds sect, Eastern Utilization Res Br. 53-54, chemist, Western Utilization Res & Develop Div, 54-68, asst to dir, 58-59, asst dir, 59-68, dir, Richard B Russell Agr Res Ctr, 68-72, AREA DIR, SOUTHERN REGIONAL SCI & EDUC ADMIN-AGR RES, USDA, 72- *Concurrent Pos:* Vis prof, Univ Ariz, 65-66. *Mem:* Am Chem Soc; Am Oil Chem Soc; Inst Food Technol. *Res:* Plant growth modifiers; organic reaction mechanisms; synthetic organic protein chemistry; food technology; carbohydrate and polymer chemistry. *Mailing Add:* Richard B Russell Agr Res Ctr PO Box 5677 Athens GA 30604

NEUFELD, DANIEL ARTHUR, b Fresno, Calif, Aug 26, 45; m 77; c 2. HUMAN ANATOMY, EXPERIMENTAL MORPHOLOGY. *Educ:* Univ Calif, Los Angeles, BA, 68; Calif State Univ, Long Beach, MA, 72; Tulane Univ, PhD(human anat), 75. *Prof Exp:* Asst prof human anat, George Washington Univ Med Ctr, 75-77; asst prof 77-80, ASSOC PROF ANAT, SCH MED, UNIV SDAK, 80- *Mem:* Am Asn Anat; AAAS; Soc Develop Biol. *Res:* Attempted induction of extremity regeneration in mammals. *Mailing Add:* Dept of Anat Univ SDak Sch Med Vermillion SD 57069

NEUFELD, ELIZABETH FONDAL, b Paris, France, Sept 27, 28; nat US; m 51; c 2. BIOCHEMISTRY, HUMAN GENETICS. *Educ:* Univ Calif, PhD(comp biochem), 56. *Hon Degrees:* DHC, Univ Rene' Descartes, Paris, 78; DSc, Russell Sage Col, Troy, NY, 81. *Prof Exp:* Asst res biochemist, 63-73, res biochemist, 73-79, CHIEF, SECT HUMAN BIOCHEM GENETICS, NAT INST ARTHRITIS, METAB & DIGESTIVE DIS, 79-, CHIEF GENETICS & BIOCHEM BR, 80- *Concurrent Pos:* USPHS fel, Univ Calif, Berkeley, 57-63, asst biochemist, 63- *Honors & Awards:* Dickson Prize, Univ Pittsburgh, 74; Hillebrand Award, 75; Gardner Found Award. *Mem:* Nat Acad Sci; Am Acad Arts & Sci; Am Soc Human Genetics; Am Chem Soc; Am Soc Biol Chemists. *Res:* Sugar nucleotides; human biochemical genetics; mucopolysaccharidoses; lysosomes. *Mailing Add:* Nat Inst of Arthritis Diabetes Digestive & Kidney Dis Bldg 10/GNZ38 Bethesda MD 20205

NEUFELD, GAYLEN JAY, b Beaver Co, Okla, Feb 25, 39; m 61; c 3. CELL PHYSIOLOGY. *Educ:* Tabor Col, BA, 61; Kans State Univ, MS, 63; Univ Tex, Austin, PhD(protein chem), 66. *Prof Exp:* Damon Runyon Cancer Fund fel dept genetics, Univ Melbourne, 66-67; asst prof, 67-71, assoc prof, 71-78, PROF BIOL, EMPORIA STATE UNIV, 78- *Concurrent Pos:* Res physiologist, NIH, Res Triangle Park, NC, 77-78. *Mem:* AAAS; Sigma Xi; Am Soc Zoologists; Am Inst Biol Sci. *Res:* Structural characteristics of phycocyanin and phycoerythrin; effects of molting hormone on protein and ribonucleic acid synthesis in the third instar larvae of Calliphora; role of sodium potassium-atpase in osmoegulation in the blue crab. *Mailing Add:* Div of Biol Sci Emporia State Univ Emporia KS 66801

NEUFELD, HAROLD ALEX, b Paterson, NJ, Mar 23, 24; m 50; c 4. BIOCHEMISTRY. *Educ:* Rutgers Univ, BS, 49; Univ Rochester, PhD(biochem), 53. *Prof Exp:* Res fel biochem, Sch Med, Univ Rochester, 53-54, instr, 54-55; biochemist crops div, US Dept Army, 55-57, biochemist chem br, 57-70; teacher, Frederick County Sch Syst, 70-72; BIOCHEMIST PHYS SCI DIV, US ARMY INST INFECTIOUS DIS, FT DETRICK, 72-, PRIN INVESTR, 80- *Concurrent Pos:* Lectr, Frederick Community Col, 57-65; lectr biochem, Hood Col, Frederick, Md, 74-79. *Honors & Awards:* Award, US Dept Army, 59, 64 & 81. *Mem:* Am Chem Soc; Am Soc Biol Chem; Sigma Xi; Soc Exp Biol Med. *Res:* Purification and kinetics of enzymes concerned with biological oxidation; properties of enzymes in proliferating tissue; relationship between hormones and enzymes; respiratory enzymes in bacteria and fungi; chemiluminescence and bioluminescence; relationship between endocrine effects and ketone body formation during the inflammatory state. *Mailing Add:* 117 W 14th St Frederick MD 21701

NEUFELD, JERRY DON, b Isabella, Okla, Jan 20, 40; m 60; c 2. ANALYTICAL CHEMISTRY, FORENSIC CHEMISTRY. *Educ:* Tabor Col, BA, 61; Univ Hawaii, PhD(chem), 72. *Prof Exp:* Teacher math & chem, Hillsboro High Sch, Kans, 61-63 & Kodaikanal Sch, S India, 63-67; fel & res assoc chem, Univ NC, 72-73; prof & chmn dept, Anderson Col, 73-80; LECTR, CALIF STATE UNIV, FRESNO, 80- *Mem:* Am Chem Soc; Soc Appl Spectros: Nat Sci Teachers Asn; Am Sci Affil. *Res:* Infrared optic properties of polyatomic substances; development of low cost instrumental analysis experiments for a chemistry laboratory; trace analysis in forensic chemistry. *Mailing Add:* Calif State Univ Fresno CA 93740

NEUFELD, RONALD DAVID, b Brooklyn, NY, Feb 10, 47; m 68; c 3. ENVIRONMENTAL ENGINEERING, INDUSTRIAL WASTE TREATMENT. *Educ:* Cooper Union, BEChE, 67; Northwestern Univ, MS, 68, PhD(civil eng), 73; Am Acad Environ Engrs, dipl, 80. *Prof Exp:* Sanit engr environ eng, Hydrotechnic Corp, 67; USPHS trainee, Northwestern Univ, 67-68; chem engr, Rohm & Haas Corp, 68-70; NSF trainee civil & environ eng, Northwestern Univ, 70-73; asst prof civil eng, 73-77, ASSOC PROF CIVIL ENG, UNIV PITTSBURGH, 77- *Concurrent Pos:* NSF res grant, 74-76; chem engr, US Dept Energy, 76-78, res contract, 77-; Am Iron & Steel Inst res grant, 77-; Environ Protection Agency res grant, 78-; consult design firms, A-C Valley Corps. *Mem:* Am Soc Civil Engrs; Am Inst Chem Engrs; Water Pollution Control Fedn; Int Asn Water Pollution. *Res:* Asn Environ Eng Profs. Res: Industrial and advanced waste treatment; environmental process control technology; biological and physical chemical processes; hazardous sludge and solid waste disposal; coal gasification and liquefaction waste treatment; biological nitrification; thiocyanate bio-degradation; heavy metal wastes. *Mailing Add:* 6573 Rosemoor St Pittsburgh PA 15217

NEUFER, JOHN E, physical chemistry, see previous edition

NEUFFER, MYRON GERALD, b Preston, Idaho, Mar 4, 22; m 43; c 7. GENETICS. *Educ:* Univ Idaho, BS, 47; Univ Mo, MA, 48, PhD(genetics), 52. *Prof Exp:* Asst field crops, 47-51, from asst prof to assoc prof, 51-66, prof genetics, 66-70, chmn dept, 67-69, PROF BIOL SCI, UNIV MO-COLUMBIA, 70- *Mem:* AAAS; Genetics Soc Am; Am Genetic Asn. *Res:* Gene mutation in maize. *Mailing Add:* Div of Biol Sci 202 Curtis Hall Univ of Mo Columbia MO 65201

NEUGEBAUER, CHRISTOPH JOHANNES, b Dessau, Ger, Apr 21, 27; nat US; m 58; c 3. MATHEMATICS. *Educ:* Univ Dayton, BS, 50; Ohio State Univ, MS, 52, PhD(math), 54. *Prof Exp:* From instr to assoc prof, 54-62, PROF MATH, PURDUE UNIV, WEST LAFAYETTE, 62- *Mem:* Am Math Soc. *Res:* Analysis. *Mailing Add:* Div of Math Sci Purdue Univ West Lafayette IN 47907

NEUGEBAUER, CONSTANTINE ALOYSIUS, b Dessau, Ger, Apr 20, 30; nat US; m 58; c 2. PHYSICAL CHEMISTRY. *Educ:* Union Univ, NY, BS, 53; Univ Wis, PhD(chem), 57. *Prof Exp:* Fel phys chem, Univ Wis, 57; res assoc, Info Sci Lab, Res & Develop Ctr, 57-76, MGR, POWER MODULE & HYBRID UNIT, CORP RES & DEVELOP, GEN ELEC CO, 76- *Mem:* Inst Elec & Electronics Engrs; Am Phys Soc; Am Vacuum Soc. *Res:* Calorimetry; thermodynamics; structure and properties of thin films; large scale integration; hybrids; power semiconductor packaging. *Mailing Add:* Corp Res & Develop Gen Elec Co 37-2077 Schenectady NY 12345

NEUGEBAUER, GERRY, b Gottingen, WGer, Sept 3, 32; US citizen; m 56; c 2. ASTROPHYSICS. *Educ:* Cornell Univ, AB, 54; Calif Inst Technol, PhD, 60. *Prof Exp:* US Army, Sta Jet Propulsion Lab, 60-62; from asst prof to assoc prof, 62-70, PROF PHYSICS, CALIF INST TECHNOL, 70- *Concurrent Pos:* Mem, NASA Astron Missions Bd, 69-70; prin investr infrared radiometer, Mariner, 69 & 71; dir, Asn Univ Res Astron Bd, 70-73; co-investr, Mariner 2 infrared radiometer, Pioneer F & G infrared radiometer, Mariner Venus-Mercury, 73; staff mem, Hale Observ, 70-80; KPNO time allocation comt, 73-76; mem, Intermediate Range Task Force, Infrared Telescope Design Comt, NASA, 74-79; chmn, Study on Infrared & Submillimeter Astron from Space, Nat Acad Sci, 75; US prin scientist, Infrared Astron Satellite; vis comt, Asn Univ Res Astron, 77-80; exec mem, Interdisciplinary Sci Comn E Res Astrophysics from Space, Comt Space Res, 79-; mem infrared subcomt ultraviolet, optical & infrared panel, Astron Surv Comt, 79. *Mem:* Nat Acad Sci; Am Acad Arts & Sci; Am Astron Soc; Royal Astron Soc; Int Astron Union. *Mailing Add:* Down Lab Physics 320-47 Calif Inst Technol Pasadena CA 91125

NEUGEBAUER, RICHARD, b New York, NY, Aug 18, 44; m 74. EPIDEMIOLOGY. *Educ:* Univ Chicago, BA, 65; Columbia Univ, MA, 68, PhD(hist), 76, MPH, 79. *Prof Exp:* Instr hist, Alfred Univ, 68-70; SERGIEVSKY SCHOLAR NEURO-EPIDEMIOL, GERTRUDE H SERGIEVSKY CTR, FAC MED, COLUMBIA UNIV, 79- *Concurrent Pos:* NIMH res training fel hist, Columbia Univ, 76-78 & NIMH res training fel epidemiol, 78-79; prin investr, NIH grants, 78-79, 79-80 & 81-84; res scientist, NY State Psychiat Inst; instr, Prog Health & Soc, Barnard Col. *Mem:* Am Pub Health Asn; Soc Epidemiol Res; AAAS. *Res:* Psychosocial and biological factors in organic and functional psychiatric disorders. *Mailing Add:* Gertrude H Sergievsky Ctr 630 West 168th St New York NY 10032

NEUHARDT, JOHN BERNARD, statistics, operations research, see previous edition

NEUHAUS, FRANCIS CLEMENS, b Huntington, WVa, May 5, 32; m 55; c 4. BIOCHEMISTRY. *Educ:* Duke Univ, BS, 54, PhD(biochem), 58. *Prof Exp:* NSF fel, Univ Newcastle-on-Tyne, Eng, 58-59 & Univ Ill, 59-60, instr biochem div, 59-60, asst prof chem, 60-61; from asst prof to assoc prof, 61-70, prof chem, 70-74, PROF BIOCHEM & MOLECULAR BIOL, NORTHWESTERN UNIV, 74- *Concurrent Pos:* USPHS res career develop award, 66-71. *Mem:* Am Chem Soc; Am Soc Microbiol; Am Soc Biol Chem. *Res:* Biosynthesis of bacterial cell wall components; mechanism of antibiotic action; membrane reactions. *Mailing Add:* Dept of Biochem & Molecular Biol Northwestern Univ 2145 Sheridan Evanston IL 60201

NEUHAUS, OTTO WILHELM, b Ger, Nov 18, 22; nat US; m 47; c 3. BIOCHEMISTRY. *Educ:* Univ Wis, BS, 44; Univ Mich, MS, 47, PhD(biochem), 53. *Prof Exp:* Res chemist, Merck & Co, 44-46; asst biochem, Univ Mich, 46-49; res chemist, Huron Milling Co, 51-54; instr physiol chem, Col Med, Wayne State Univ, 54-58, res assoc anat, 54-58, asst prof physiol chem, 58-65, assoc prof biochem, 65-66; chmn dept biochem, 66-75, PROF BIOCHEM, SCH MED, UNIV SDAK, 66-, CHMN DEPT BIOCHEM, PHYSIOL & PHARMACOL, 76- *Mem:* AAAS; Am chmn dept, 66-76, Chem Soc; Soc Exp Biol & Med; Am Soc Biol Chemists. *Res:* Proteins of biological fluids; control of plasma protein biosynthesis; transport of amino acids. *Mailing Add:* Div of Biochem Univ of SDak Sch of Med Vermillion SD 57069

NEUHOLD, JOHN MATHEW, b Milwaukee, Wis, May 18, 28; m 52; c 1. AQUATIC ECOLOGY. *Educ:* Utah State Univ, BS, 52, MS, 54, PhD(fish biol), 59. *Prof Exp:* Biologist, State Dept Fish & Game, Utah, 52-55, asst fed aide coord, 55-56; asst fish toxicol, 56-58, from asst prof to assoc prof fish biol, 58-66, actg dir ecol ctr, 66-68, dir, Ecol Ctr, 68-78, PROF FISH BIOL, UTAH STATE UNIV, 61- *Concurrent Pos:* Prog dir ecosyst anal, NSF, 71-72; trustee, Inst Ecol, 73-74, dir, 74-76; sci adv bd, Environ Protection Agency, 74- *Mem:* AAAS; Am Fisheries Soc; Am Soc Limnol & Oceanog; Ecol Soc Am. *Res:* Fish toxicology, production in aquatic habitat, population dynamics; pollution biology. *Mailing Add:* Dept of Wildlife Sci Utah State Univ Logan UT 84322

NEUHOUSER, DAVID LEE, b Leo, Ind, Mar 28, 33; m 54; c 4. MATHEMATICS. *Educ:* Manchester Col, BS, 55; Univ Ill, MS, 59; Fla State Univ, PhD(math educ), 64. *Prof Exp:* High sch teacher, Iowa, 55-57 & Ind, 57-58; from instr to assoc prof math & head dept, Manchester Col, 59-71; PROF MATH & HEAD DEPT, TAYLOR UNIV, 71- *Concurrent Pos:* Consult to sch systs, Northern Ind, 64- *Mem:* Math Asn Am. *Res:* Methods of teaching mathematics, particularly the discovery method. *Mailing Add:* Taylor Univ Upland IN 46989

NEUMAN, CHARLES HERBERT, b Los Angeles, Calif, Feb 8, 37; m 58; c 2. PHYSICS. *Educ:* Calif Inst Technol, BS, 58; Univ Ill, MA, 60, PhD(physics), 63. *Prof Exp:* Res assoc physics, Univ Calif, Riverside, 63-65; res physicist, 65-76, sr res physicist, 76-80, SR RES ASSOC, CHEVRON OIL FIELD RES CO, 80- *Mem:* Am Phys Soc; Soc Petrol Engrs; Soc Prof Well Log Analysts. *Res:* Defects in solids; effects of pressure on transition metal oxides; nuclear spin echo in liquids; x-ray diffraction of minerals; radioactive measurement of liquid content in porous media. *Mailing Add:* Chevron Oil Field Res Box 446 La Habra CA 90631

NEUMAN, CHARLES P(AUL), b Pittsburgh, Pa, July 26, 40; m 67. APPLIED MATHEMATICS, ELECTRICAL ENGINEERING. *Educ:* Carnegie-Mellon Univ, BS, 62; Harvard Univ, SM, 63, PhD(appl math), 68. *Prof Exp:* Mem tech staff, Bell Tel Labs, Inc, 67-69; from asst prof to assoc prof elec eng, 69-78, PROF ELEC ENG, CARNEGIE-MELLON UNIV, 78- *Mem:* AAAS; Inst Elec & Electronics Engrs; Soc Indust & Appl Math; Inst Mgt Sci; Sigma Xi. *Res:* Control engineering and adaptive control; microcomputer control; control and systems science; Lyapunov stability theory; sensitivity analysis of dynamic systems. *Mailing Add:* Dept of Elec Eng Carnegie-Mellon Univ Pittsburgh PA 15213

NEUMAN, MARGARET WRIGHTINGTON, b Lexington, Mass, May 31, 17; m 43; c 3. PHARMACOLOGY. *Educ:* Vassar Col, BA, 38; Univ Rochester, MS, 40, PhD(pharmacol), 43. *Prof Exp:* Vol asst path, Histol Lab, Harvard Univ, 38-39; asst, 39-43, asst toxicol & instr pharmacol, Sch Med & Dent & asst biochem sect, Atomic Energy Proj, 43-60, instr radiation biol, 60-64, ASST PROF RADIATION BIOL & BIOPHYS, UNIV ROCHESTER, 64- *Res:* Toxicology of organic nitrates, choline and uranium; biochemistry of bone; chemical evolution. *Mailing Add:* Dept of Radiation Biol & Biophys Univ of Rochester Med Ctr Rochester NY 14642

NEUMAN, MICHAEL R, b Milwaukee, Wis, Nov, 25, 38; m 73; c 1. BIOENGINEERING & BIOMETRICAL ENGINEERING. *Educ:* Case Inst Technol, BS, 61, MS, 63, PhD, 66; Case Western Reserve Univ, MD, 74. *Prof Exp:* Asst prof, 66-70, ASSOC PROF, CASE WESTERN RESERVE UNIV, 70- *Concurrent Pos:* Res assoc, Dept Obstet & Gynecol, Cleveland Metrop Gen Hosp, 66-, Univ Hosp Cleveland, 74-; guest prof, Universitat Frauenklinik, Zurich, 80. *Mem:* Am Vacuum Soc; Inst Elec & Electronics Engrs; AAAS; Soc Gynec Invest; Biomed Eng Soc. *Res:* Design, development and application of biomedical electronic instrumentation and transducers for clinical and basic science measurements and basic patient monitoring; blood gas measurement; perinatology; obstetrics; gynecology; pediatrics. *Mailing Add:* Electronics Design Ctr Case Western Reserve Univ Clevland OH 44106

NEUMAN, RICHARD STEPHEN, b San Francisco, Calif, June 12, 45; Can citizen; m 69; c 2. PHARMACOLOGY. *Educ:* San Francisco State Col, BA, 68; Univ Alta, PhD(pharmacol), 74. *Prof Exp:* Asst prof, 74-79, ASSOC PROF PHARMACOL, MEM UNIV NFLD, 79- *Concurrent Pos:* Asst prof res grants, Res Drug Abuse, 77-78, Med Res Coun Can, 78-80 & Med Res Coun, 80-82. *Mem:* Pharmacol Soc Can; Neurosci Soc. *Res:* 5-hydroxytryptamine and norepinephrine as modulators on spinal motoneuronec; synaptic transmission in the mammalian central nervous system. *Mailing Add:* Fac Med Mem Univ Nfld St John's NF A1B 3V6 Can

NEUMAN, ROBERT BALLIN, b Washington, DC, Feb 28, 20; m 49; c 2. GEOLOGY. *Educ:* Univ NC, BS, 41; Johns Hopkins Univ, PhD(geol), 49. *Prof Exp:* GEOLOGIST, US GEOL SURV, 49- *Concurrent Pos:* Lectr, Johns Hopkins Univ, 56-57 & Univ Oslo, 70-71; chmn US working group, Appalachian-Caledonide Orogen Proj int working group, Int Geol Correlation Prog, 74-82; adj prof, Va Tech, 80-; res assoc, Dept Paleobiol, Smithsonian Inst. *Mem:* AAAS; Paleont Soc; Geol Soc Am; Soc Econ Paleont & Mineral. *Res:* Ordovician paleontology and paleogeography of the region bordering the North Atlantic Ocean. *Mailing Add:* US Geol Surv Room E-304 Nat Mus Washington DC 20560

NEUMAN, ROBERT C, JR, b Chicago, Ill, Aug 21, 38; m 81; c 2. PHYSICAL ORGANIC CHEMISTRY. *Educ:* Univ Calif, Los Angeles, BS, 59; Calif Inst Technol, PhD(org chem), 63. *Prof Exp:* NSF res fel, Columbia Univ, 62-63; from asst prof to assoc prof chem, 63-72, PROF CHEM, UNIV CALIF, RIVERSIDE, 72- *Concurrent Pos:* Vis lectr dept chem, Princeton Univ, 71-72; NIH spec res fel, 71-72. *Mem:* Am Chem Soc; Sigma Xi. *Res:* Effects of high pressure on chemical systems; free radical chemistry. *Mailing Add:* Dept of Chem Univ of Calif Riverside CA 92521

NEUMAN, SHLOMO PETER, b Zilina, Czech, Oct 26, 38; US citizen; m 65; c 2. HYDROLOGY, HYDROGEOLOGY. *Educ:* Hebrew Univ, Jerusalem, BSc, 63; Univ Calif, Berkeley, MS, 66, PhD(eng sci), 68. *Prof Exp:* Asst res engr, Univ Calif, Berkeley, 68-70, actg asst prof civil eng, 70; res scientist hydrol, Agr Res Orgn, Israel, 70-74; vis assoc prof civil eng, Univ Calif, Berkeley, 74-75; PROF HYDROL, UNIV ARIZ, 75- *Concurrent Pos:* Res consult, Israel Inst Technol, 70-74 & Lawrence Berkeley Lab, 75- *Honors & Awards:* Robert E Horton Award, Am Geophys Union, 69; O E Meinzer Award, Geol Soc Am, 76. *Mem:* Am Geophys Union; Nat Water Well Asn. *Res:* Groundwater modeling; finite element techniques; well hydraulics; applications of systems theory in hydrology; geothermal studies and modeling. *Mailing Add:* Dept of Hydrol & Water Resources Univ of Ariz Tucson AZ 85721

NEUMAN, WILLIAM FREDERICK, biochemistry, biophysics, deceased

NEUMANN, A CONRAD, b Oak Bluffs, Mass, Dec 21, 33; m 62; c 3. OCEANOGRAPHY. *Educ:* Brooklyn Col, BS, 55; Tex A&M Univ, MS, 58; Lehigh Univ, PhD(geol), 63. *Prof Exp:* Res assoc sedimentary geol, Woods Hole Oceanog Inst, 58-60; asst prof marine geol, Lehigh Univ, 63-65; asst prof marine sci, Univ Miami, 65-69; prog dir marine geol & geophys, NSF, 69-70; assoc prof marine sci, Univ Miami, 69-72; actg dir marine sci curric, 73-74, PROF MARINE SCI, MARINE SCI PROG, UNIV NC, 72- *Concurrent Pos:* Trustee, Bermuda Biol Sta Res, Inc, 72-76. *Mem:* AAAS; Soc Econ Paleont & Mineral; Geol Soc Am; Sigma Xi; Am Asn Petrol Geologists. *Res:* Sedimentology; recent carbonate sediments of the Bermudas, Bahamas and Florida; biological erosion of limestone; marine geology by research submersibles; Quaternary history of sea level; deep flanks of carbonate platforms. *Mailing Add:* Marine Sci Prog 12-5 Venable Hall Univ NC Chapel Hill NC 27514

NEUMANN, ALVIN LUDWIG, b Granite, Okla, July 9, 15; m 38. ANIMAL NUTRITION. *Educ:* Okla State Univ, BS, 38, MS, 39; Univ Ill, PhD(animal sci, nutrit), 49. *Prof Exp:* Asst, Okla State Univ, 38-39; instr high sch, Okla, 39-41; head agr div, Cameron State Agr Col, Okla, 41-44; county farm agent, Comanche County, Okla, 44-45; asst prof animal indust, Univ Ark, 45-47; asst, Univ Ill, 47-48; prof animal indust, Univ Ark, 49-50; from assoc prof to prof beef cattle nutrit, Univ Ill, 50-64; prof animal, range & wildlife sci & head dept, NMex State Univ, 64-71; prof, 71-76, EMER PROF ANIMAL SCI, UNIV ILL, URBANA-CHAMPAIGN, 76- *Concurrent Pos:* Consult, beef cattle prod, nutrit. *Mem:* AAAS; Am Soc Animal Sci. *Res:* Nutrient requirements of beef cattle; use of hormones, antibiotics and other additives in feeding beef cattle; management of beef cattle farms. *Mailing Add:* 41 Sherwin Dr Urbana IL 61801

NEUMANN, CALVIN LEE, b Coldwater, Mich, Sept 13, 38; m 61; c 1. PHYSICAL ORGANIC CHEMISTRY. *Educ:* Wayne State Univ, BS, 62, PhD(org chem), 66. *Prof Exp:* Technician res labs, Ethyl Corp, Mich, 58-59; sr chemist res dept, R J Reynolds Indust, Inc, 66-70, group leader, 70-74, group leader res dept, 74-80, SR RES & DEVELOP CHEMIST, R J REYNOLDS TOBACCO CO, 80- *Mem:* Am Chem Soc. *Res:* Conformational analysis; tobacco and health relationships; research and development of tobacco and tobacco related products. *Mailing Add:* Res & Develop Dept R J Reynolds Tobacco Co Winston-Salem NC 27102

NEUMANN, FRED ROBERT, b Chicago, Ill, June 3, 00; wid. GEOLOGY. *Educ:* Univ Chicago, BS, 21, MS, 23; Cornell Univ, PhD(geol), 26. *Prof Exp:* Instr geol, Univ SC, 24-25; geologist, Shell Oil Co, 27-28; prof geol & geog, Ill Wesleyan Univ, 28-31; asst prof, Bowling Green Univ, 31-32; supvr, Chicago Bd Educ, 32-35; instr geol & geog, Drury Col, 35-36 & Mesaba Col, 36-42; instr geol & sci, Col of the Sequoias, 42-44; geologist, Standard Oil Co Calif, 44-46; prof, 46-70, EMER PROF GEOL, CHICO STATE UNIV, 70- *Mem:* Geol Soc Am; Am Asn Petrol Geol; AAAS; Sigma Xi; Nat Asn Geol Teachers. *Res:* Geology of Butte County, California. *Mailing Add:* Dept Geol Chico State Univ Chico CA 95929

NEUMANN, FRED WILLIAM, b Chicago, Ill, Sept 28, 18; m 44; c 3. ORGANIC CHEMISTRY, ANALYTICAL CHEMISTRY. *Educ:* Univ Ill, BS, 40; Ind Univ, PhD(org chem), 44. *Prof Exp:* Jr chemist, Merck & Co, NJ, 40-41; asst chem, Ind Univ, 41-43; chemist, Gen Aniline & Film Corp, 44-55; group leader, 55-68, anal specialist, 68-72, RES SPECIALIST, DOW CHEM, USA, 72- *Mem:* Am Chem Soc; Sigma Xi. *Res:* Phenol and bisphenol A processes; synthetic organic chemistry of diazotypes, amidines and phenols; identification of dyes, diazotypes and organic commercial products; organic air-borne pollutants; iodine and bromine processes. *Mailing Add:* 213 Norfolk Midland MI 48640

NEUMANN, GERHARD, b Frankfort, Ger, Oct 8, 17; US citizen. AIRCRAFT ENGINEERING. *Prof Exp:* Gen mgr, Flight Propulsion Div, Gen Elec Co, 61-68, vpres & group exec, 68-78. *Honors & Awards:* Collier Trophy, 58; Goddard Gold Medal, 69; French Legion of Honor, 78; Guggeheim Medal, 79. *Mem:* Nat Acad Eng; hon fel Am Inst Aeronaut & Astronaut. *Mailing Add:* Gen Elec Co 1000 Western Ave Lynn MA 01910

NEUMANN, HELMUT CARL, b Berlin, Ger, Dec 24, 16; nat US; m 46; c 4. PHARMACEUTICAL CHEMISTRY. *Educ:* Polytech Inst Brooklyn, BS, 38; Fed Inst Technol, Zurich, DSc(chem), 49. *Prof Exp:* Anal & develop chemist, Fritzsche Bros Inc, 38-42, asst lab head, 45-46; res fel, Univ Pa, 49-50; res chemist, White Labs, Inc, 50-51; res assoc, Sterling-Winthrop Res Inst, 51-59, sr res chemist, 59-82; RETIRED. *Concurrent Pos:* Ed, Eastern New York Chemist, 65-68. *Mem:* AAAS; Am Chem Soc. *Res:* Terpenes; steroids; antifertility agents; research on steroids and related compounds in search for medicinal applications. *Mailing Add:* 12 Point View Dr East Greenbush NY 12061

NEUMANN, HENRY MATTHEW, b Minneapolis, Minn, July 15, 24. INORGANIC CHEMISTRY. *Educ:* Col St Thomas, BS, 47; Univ Calif, PhD(chem), 50. *Prof Exp:* Instr chem, Northwestern Univ, 50-54, asst prof, 54-56; assoc prof, 56-60, PROF CHEM, GA INST TECHNOL, 60- *Mem:* Am Chem Soc. *Res:* Radioactive exchange reactions; kinetics and reaction mechanisms of complex ions and of organometallic compounds. *Mailing Add:* Sch of Chem Ga Inst of Technol Atlanta GA 30332

NEUMANN, HERSCHEL, b San Bernardino, Calif, Feb 3, 30; m 51; c 2. ATOMIC & MOLECULAR PHYSICS. *Educ:* Univ Calif, Berkeley, BA, 51; Univ Ore, MA, 59; Univ Nebr, Lincoln, PhD(theoret phys), 65. *Prof Exp:* Physicist, Hanford Labs, Gen Elec Co, Wash, 51-57; instr phys, Univ Nebr, Lincoln, 65; asst prof, 65-71, ASSOC PROF PHYS, UNIV DENVER, 71- *Mem:* Am Asn Physics Teachers; Am Phys Soc. *Res:* Atomic and molecular collision theory; numerical analysis; physics education. *Mailing Add:* Dept of Physics Univ of Denver Denver CO 80208

NEUMANN, JOACHIM PETER, b Berlin, Ger, June 15, 31; US citizen; m 62; c 2. METALLURGY. *Educ:* Tech Univ, Berlin, Dipl Ing, 56; Univ Calif, Berkeley, PhD(metall), 65. *Prof Exp:* Metall engr, Sherritt Gordon Mines, Ltd, 56-57 & Aluminum Co of Can, 57-58; asst prof metall, Univ Calif, Los Angeles, 63-69; tech adv, UNESCO, Spain & Venezuela, 69-74; sr scientist, Univ Wis-Milwaukee, 74-78; metallurgist, Bur Mines, Albany, 78-80; ASSOC PROF METALL ENG, UNIV ALA, TUSCALOOSA, 80- *Mem:* Am Soc Metals; Am Inst Mining, Metall & Petrol Engrs; Am Soc Eng Educ. *Res:* Chemical metallurgy; physical metallurgy; relationship between structure and properties of materials. *Mailing Add:* Dept Chem & Metall Eng Univ Ala PO Box G University AL 35486

NEUMANN, MARGUERITE, b West Bend, Wis, May 7, 14. ORGANIC CHEMISTRY, MEDICINAL CHEMISTRY. *Educ:* Mundelein Col, BS, 42; Univ Iowa, MS, 43; St Louis Univ, PhD(chem), 54. *Prof Exp:* Asst prof chem, Mundelein Col, 43-50 & 54-57; chmn dept, 57-70, PROF CHEM, CLARKE COL, 57- *Mem:* Am Chem Soc; Sigma Xi; Am Asn Univ Women. *Res:* Biochemistry. *Mailing Add:* Dept of Chem Clarke Col Dubuque IA 52001

NEUMANN, NORBERT PAUL, b Chicago, Ill, Oct 13, 31; m 56; c 3. BIOCHEMISTRY. *Educ:* St Peters Col, BS, 53; Okla State Univ, MS, 55; Univ Wis, PhD(biochem), 58. *Prof Exp:* Res assoc biochem, Rockefeller Inst, 58-61; from instr to asst prof microbiol, Rutgers Univ, 61-67, asst prof sch med, 67-70; dir biochem, 70-74, asst dir res, 74-81, DIR IMMUNOL RES, ORTHO RES INST MED SCI, 81- *Mem:* AAAS; Am Chem Soc; Am Soc Human Genetics; Soc Complex Carbohydrates; NY Acad Sci. *Res:* Relationship between structure and function in enzymes; methods of protein isolation and characterization; diagnostic chemistry and immunology; lymphokines and immunoregulation. *Mailing Add:* Ortho Res Inst of Med Sci Raritan NJ 08869

NEUMANN, PAUL GERHARD, b Insterburg, Ger, June 26, 11; nat US; m 48; c 3. OCEANOGRAPHY, METEOROLOGY. *Educ:* Univ Berlin, Dr rer nat(geophys), 39. *Prof Exp:* Res scientist, Ger Marine Observ, 39-45 & Ger Hydrographic Off, 45-47; docent, Univ Hamburg, 47-51; from assoc prof to prof oceanog, NY Univ, 51-73; prof earth & planetary sci, 73-80, EMER PROF & RESIDENT PROF, CITY COL NEW YORK, 80- *Concurrent Pos:* Consult, NSF, 66, 67 & 72. *Mem:* Am Meteorol Soc; Am Geophys Union; Ger Geophys Soc. *Res:* Air-sea interaction; ocean waves and currents; internal waves; physical oceanography; oceanography of the tropical Atlantic Ocean. *Mailing Add:* 11 Goodwin St Hastings-on-Hudson NY 10706

NEUMANN, STEPHEN MICHAEL, b La Porte, Ind, Aug 7, 52; m 74. ORGANOMETALLIC CHEMISTRY. *Educ:* Ind Univ, BS, 74; Univ Wis, PhD(org chem), 78. *Prof Exp:* RES CHEMIST, EASTMAN KODAK CO, 78- *Mem:* Am Chem Soc. *Res:* Organometallic chemistry, specifically transition metal formyl complexes and their properties; properties of dyes for photographic image transfer. *Mailing Add:* Eastman Kodak Co Res Labs Bldg 82 Rochester NY 14615

NEUMARK, GERTRUDE FANNY, b Nueremberg, Ger, Apr 29, 27; nat US; m 50. SEMICONDUCTOR PHYSICS. *Educ:* Columbia Univ, BA, 48, PhD(chem), 51; Radcliffe Col, MA, 49. *Prof Exp:* Asst chem, Columbia Univ, 48, asst, Barnard Col, 50-51; adv res physicist, Sylvania Elec Prod, Inc, Gen Tel & Electronics Corp, 52-60; STAFF PHYSICIST PHILIPS LABS, NORTH AM PHILIPS CO, INC, 60- *Concurrent Pos:* Anderson fel, Am Asn Univ Women, 51-52; adj assoc prof, Fairleigh Dickinson Univ, 73-74. *Mem:* Am Chem Soc; Am Phys Soc; NY Acad Sci. *Res:* Luminescence and electroluminescence; non-radiative recombination; conductivity in wide band-gap semiconductors; influence of dielectric screening on semiconductor transport and recombination properties; photovoltaic effect. *Mailing Add:* Philips Lab NAm Philips Co Inc Briarcliff Manor NY 10510

NEUMEIER, LEANDER ANTHONY, b St Louis, Mo, Feb 15, 33; m 63; c 1. METALLURGICAL ENGINEERING, PHYSICAL METALLURGY. *Educ:* Univ Mo-Rolla, BS, 59, MS, 60. *Prof Exp:* Technician metall, Uranium Div, Mallinckrodt Chem Works, 58; metallurgist, 60-74, actg res dir, 79, SUPVRY METALLURGIST, US BUR MINES, 74- *Mem:* Sigma Xi; Am Soc Metals; Am Inst Mining, Metall & Petrol Engrs; Am Foundrymen's Soc. *Res:* Physical and process metallurgy; ferrous and nonferrous; cast irons; magnesium alloys; secondary materials; powder metallurgy; relation structure and composition to properties. *Mailing Add:* US Bur Mines PO Box 280 Rolla MO 65401

NEUMEYER, JOHN L, b Munich, Ger, July 19, 30; US citizen; m 56; c 3. MEDICINAL CHEMISTRY. *Educ:* Columbia Univ, BS, 52; Univ Wis, PhD(med chem), 61. *Prof Exp:* Pharmaceut chemist, Ethicon, Inc Div, Johnson & Johnson, 52-53, group leader pharmaceut res, 55-57; sr res chemist, Cent Res Labs, Niagara Chem Div, FMC Corp, NJ, 61-63; sr staff chemist, Arthur D Little, Inc, 63-69; PROF MED CHEM, NORTHEASTERN UNIV, 69-, PROF CHEM, 75-, DIR, GRAD SCH PHARM & ALLIED HEALTH PROF, 76- *Concurrent Pos:* Adj prof, Mass Col Pharm, 64-69; mem adv panel secy comn on pesticides & their relationship to environ health, HEW, 69-70; mem comt rev, US Pharmacopeia, 69-; consult, Arthur D Little, Inc, 69- & Environ Protection Agency, 70-72; mem, Mass State Pesticide Bd, 73-75; bk rev ed, J Med Chem, 74-; vis prof chem, Univ Konstanz, WGer, 75-76; mem study sect, NIH, 81. *Mem:* Am Chem Soc; Am Pharmaceut Asn; AAAS; fel Acad Pharmaceut Sci. *Res:* Chemistry of biologically-active compounds of natural and synthetic origin; aporphines; isoquinolines; chemistry of heterocyclics, antimalarials; central nervous system active compounds, cancer chemotherpy, pesticides. *Mailing Add:* Dept Med Chem Northeastern Univ Boston MA 02115

NEUMILLER, HARRY JACOB, JR, b Peoria, Ill, Dec 25, 29; m 57; c 4. ORGANIC CHEMISTRY. *Educ:* Knox Col, BA, 51; Univ Ill, MS, 52, PhD(org chem), 56. *Prof Exp:* Res chemist, Eastman Kodak Co, NY, 55-59; asst prof, 59-65, ASSOC PROF CHEM, KNOX COL, ILL, 65- *Mem:* Am Chem Soc. *Res:* Orientations in additions to quinones and quinone-like compounds. *Mailing Add:* Dept of Chem Knox Col Galesburg IL 61401

NEUNZIG, HERBERT HENRY, b Richmond Hill, NY, May 11, 27; m 55; c 2. ENTOMOLOGY. *Educ:* Cornell Univ, MS, 55, PhD(entom), 57. *Prof Exp:* From asst res prof to assoc res prof entom, 57-68, PROF ENTOM, NC STATE UNIV, 68- *Mem:* Entom Soc Am; Lepidopterists' Soc. *Res:* Taxonomy of lepidotera and megaloptera. *Mailing Add:* Dept of Entom NC State Univ Raleigh NC 27650

NEUPERT, WERNER MARTIN, b Worcester, Mass, Dec 19, 31; m 59; c 2. SPECTROSCOPY, SOLAR PHYSICS. *Educ:* Worcester Polytech Inst, BS, 54; Cornell Univ, PhD(physics), 60. *Prof Exp:* Vis asst prof physics, Univ Calif, Santa Barbara, 59-60; PHYSICIST, GODDARD SPACE FLIGHT CTR, NASA, 60- *Mem:* Int Astron Union; Am Phys Soc; Am Astron Soc. *Res:* Studies of the solar extreme ultraviolet and x-ray spectrum using rocket and satellite-borne instrumentation. *Mailing Add:* Lab for Solar Physics Code 682 Goddard Space Flight Ctr NASA Greenbelt MD 20771

NEURATH, ALEXANDER ROBERT, b Bratislava, Czech, May 8, 33; US citizen. VIROLOGY. *Educ:* Inst Tech, Bratislava, Czech, DiplIng, 57; Vienna Tech Univ, ScD(microbiol), 68. *Prof Exp:* Res scientist, Plant Physiol Inst, Czech Acad Sci, 57-59; dept head vet virol, Bioveta, Nitra, Czech, 59-61; res scientist, Inst Virol, Czech Acad Sci, 61-64; res fel virol, Wistar Inst, 64-65; sr virologist, Wyeth Labs, Inc, 65-72; INVESTR, L KIMBALL RES INST, NEW YORK BLOOD CTR, 72- *Mem:* AAAS; Am Soc Microbiol; Brit Soc Gen Microbiol. *Res:* Analysis of trace elements in plants; analytical biochemistry; biochemistry of viruses including, myxoviruses, adenoviruses, rabies and pseudorabies; hepatitis B. *Mailing Add:* New York Blood Ctr 310 E 67th St New York NY 10021

NEURATH, HANS, b Vienna, Austria, Oct 29, 09; nat US; m 36, 60; c 1. BIOCHEMISTRY. *Educ:* Univ Vienna, PhD(colloid chem), 33. *Hon Degrees:* DSc, Univ Geneva, 70; Dr, Univ Tokushima, 77. *Prof Exp:* Res fel, Univ Col, Univ London, 34-35; res fel biochem, Univ Minn, 35-36; instr & Baker res fel chem, Cornell Univ, 36-38; from asst prof to assoc prof biochem sch med, Duke Univ, 38-46, prof phys biochem, 46-50; chmn dept biochem, 50-75, prof biochem, 50-80, sci dir, Ger Cancer Res Ctr, 80-81, EMER PROF BIOCHEM, UNIV WASH, 82- *Concurrent Pos:* Mem comt biol chem, Div Chem & Chem Eng, Nat Res Coun, 54-58, mem exec comt, Off Biochem Nomenclature, 64-; consult, NIH, 54-; Guggenheim fel, 55-56; Phillips visitor, Haverford Col, 59; Darling lectr, Allegheny Col, 60; ed, Biochem, 61-; mem, US Nat Comt Biochem, 62-63 & US-Japan Coop Sci Prog Adv Panel on Med Sci, 64-65; comn ed, Int Union Biochem, 65-; mem comt res life sci, Nat Acad Sci, 66-70; mem, Nat Bd Grad Educ, 71-74; guest prof, Alexander von Humboldt Found, WGer & Univ Heidelberg, 75; 1st distinguished fac lectr, Univ Wash, 76; vis prof, Japan Soc Prom Sci & Kelly lectr, Purdue Univ, 77; Smith, Kline & French distinguished lectr, Univ Mich, NSF vis prof, Univ Hawaii & co-chmn, Int Symp Proteins, Taipei, 78; hon prof, Univ Heidelberg. *Honors & Awards:* Awardee, Alexander von Humboldt Found, WGer & Univ Heidelberg, 75. *Mem:* Nat Acad Sci; fel AAAS; fel Am Acad Arts & Sci; hon mem Biochem Soc Japan; fel NY Acad Sci. *Res:* Protein structure and function; enzymes; proteolytic enzymes; evolution; physical biochemistry of macromolecules. *Mailing Add:* Dept of Biochem Univ of Wash Seattle WA 98195

NEUREITER, NORMAN PAUL, b Macomb, Ill, Jan 24, 32; m 59. SCIENCE POLICY. *Educ:* Univ Rochester, AB, 52; Northwestern Univ, PhD, 57. *Prof Exp:* Instr basic sci, Northwestern Univ, 56-57; res chemist, Humble Oil & Refining Co, Tex, 57-63; asst prog dir off int sci activ, NSF, Washington, DC, 63-64; actg prog dir, US-Japan Coop Sci Prog, 64-65; dep sci attache, US Dept State, Am Embassy, Bonn, 65-67, sci attache, Am Embassy, Warsaw, 67-69, tech asst off sci & technol, Exec Off of the President, 69-73; dir, East-West Bus Develop, 73-74, mgr int bus develop, Tex Instruments Inc, 74-77, pres & mgr Europe Div, 77-80, MGR, CORP RELATIONS, TEX INSTRUMENTS INT TRADE CORP, 80- *Concurrent Pos:* Guide, Am Nat Exhib, Moscow, 59; mem bd int orgn & prog, Nat Acad Sci, Off For Secy, Washington, DC, 73-77; mem, Adv Comt Int Progs, NSF, 78- *Mem:* AAAS; Am Chem Soc. *Res:* International cooperation in science; relationships of science to foreign policy; role of technology in international trade; East-West trade. *Mailing Add:* PO Box 225012 M/S 77 Dallas TX 75265

NEURINGER, JOSEPH LOUIS, b Brooklyn, NY, Jan 16, 22; m 46; c 2. MATHEMATICAL PHYSICS. *Educ:* Brooklyn Col, BA, 43; Columbia Univ, MA, 48; NY Univ, PhD(physics), 51. *Prof Exp:* Asst jet propulsion, NY Univ, 47-51; eng specialist, Repub Aviation Corp, 51-55; prin scientist res & adv develop div, Avco Corp, 55-56; chief scientist plasma propulsion & power lab, Repub Aviation Corp, 56-62; sr consult scientist res & tech labs, Avco Space Systs Div, 62-67, prin staff scientist, 67-70; PROF MATH, UNIV LOWELL, 70- *Mem:* AAAS; Am Phys Soc; assoc fel Am Inst Aeronaut & Astronaut. *Res:* Magnetohydrodynamics; ferrohydrodynamics; application of plasma physics and aerophysics to propulsion; generation of electricity; space flight; differential equations. *Mailing Add:* 39 Vine St Reading MA 01867

NEURINGER, LEO J, b New York, NY, Nov 20, 28; m 54; c 3. HIGH FIELD NUCLEAR MAGNETIC RESONANCE, BIOMEMBRANES. *Educ:* Rensselaer Polytech Inst, BS, 51; Univ Pa, PhD(physics), 57. *Prof Exp:* Physicist optics, Nat Bur Standards, 51-52; staff scientist infrared detectors, Res Div, Raytheon Co, 56-63; staff mem semiconductors, 63-67, SR SCIENTIST HIGH FIELD SUPERCONDUCTORS, FRANCIS BITTER NAT MAGNET LAB, MASS INST TECHNOL, 67-, GROUP LEADER MOLECULAR BIOPHYS, 73-, DIR, HIGH FIELD NUCLEAR MAGNETIC RESONANCE FACILITY, 76- *Concurrent Pos:* Instr physics, Tufts Univ, 57-58, vis prof, 69-70; vis prof, Hebrew Univ, Jerusalem, 71, Univ Chile, 73. *Mem:* AAAS; fel Am Phys Soc; Sigma Xi; Biophys Soc. *Res:* High field nuclear magnetic resonance of biomembranes, proteins and tissue; high field superconductivity. *Mailing Add:* Francis Bitter Nat Magnet Lab 170 Albany St Cambridge MA 02139

NEUSE, EBERHARD WILHELM, b Berlin, Ger, Mar 7, 25; m 63. POLYMER CHEMISTRY, ORGANOMETALLIC CHEMISTRY. *Educ:* Hanover Tech Univ, BS, 48, MS, 50, PhD(org chem), 53, DSc(polymer chem), 76. *Prof Exp:* Res asst chem heterocyclics, Hanover Tech Univ, 51-53; head appln lab, O Neynaber & Co, AG, Ger, 54-57; res assoc plastics lab, Princeton Univ, 57-59; head polymer lab missile & space systs div, Douglas Aircraft Co, 60-70, chief plastics & elastomers develop sect, 67-70; sr lectr chem, 71-73, READER & PROF POLYMER CHEM, UNIV WITWATERSRAND, 73- *Concurrent Pos:* Mem, Nat Adv Comt Plastics Educ; Mem comt, Macromolecular Div, Int Union Pure & Appl Chem, 75- *Mem:* Am Chem Soc; NY Acad Sci; SAfrican Chem Inst. *Res:* Organic and organometallic chemistry of monomeric and polymeric compounds; development of polymeric materials for high temperature applications; organo-sulfur chemistry; charge-transfer complexes; carbohydrate modification. *Mailing Add:* Dept Chem Univ the Witwatersrand Johannesburg South Africa

NEUSHUL, MICHAEL, JR, b Shanghai, China, Dec 27, 33; nat US. BOTANY. *Educ:* Univ Calif, Los Angeles, BA, 55, PhD(bot), 59. *Prof Exp:* Asst bot, Univ Calif, Los Angeles, 55-56; res biologist, Scripps Inst, 56-58; asst bot, Univ Calif, Los Angeles, 58-59; NSF fel, Univ London, 59-60; from instr to asst prof bot, Univ Wash, 60-63; from asst prof to assoc prof, 63-73, PROF BOT, UNIV CALIF, SANTA BARBARA, 73-, PROF MARINE PHYCOL, 77- *Concurrent Pos:* Botanist, Arg Antarctic Exped, 57-58; vis fel, Swiss Fed Inst Technol, Zurich, 69-70; partic, Scripps Mex Oceanog Cruises. *Mem:* Am Phycol Soc; Bot Soc Am; Brit Phycol Soc; Int Soc Plant Morphol; Arg Antarctic Asn. *Res:* Marine algology; ultrastructure; development; sublittoral ecology; antarctic marine algae; algae development. *Mailing Add:* Dept of Biol Univ of Calif Santa Barbara CA 93106

NEUSTADT, BERNARD RAY, b Washington, DC, May 7, 43; m 64; c 5. MEDICINAL CHEMISTRY. *Educ:* Columbia Univ, AB, 64; Brandeis Univ, PhD(org chem), 69. *Prof Exp:* Jr chemist, Arthur D Little, Inc, 66; sr chemist, 69-74, prin scientist, 74-78, RES SECT LEADER, SCHERING CORP, 78- *Mem:* Am Chem Soc. *Res:* Medicinal organic chemistry. *Mailing Add:* Schering Corp Bloomfield NJ 07003

NEUSTADTER, SIEGFRIED FRIEDRICH, b Ger, July 5, 23; nat US. MATHEMATICS. *Educ:* Univ Calif, PhD(math), 48. *Prof Exp:* Lectr math, Univ Calif, 48-49; Peirce instr, Harvard Univ, 49-52; mem staff, Lincoln Lab, Mass Inst Technol, 52-58; PROF MATH, SAN FRANCISCO STATE UNIV, 58- *Concurrent Pos:* Mem staff res lab, Sylvania Elec Prod, Inc, Mass, 62-65. *Mem:* Am Math Soc; Opers Res Soc Am. *Res:* Applied mathematics; mathematical analysis. *Mailing Add:* Dept of Math 1600 Holloway Ave San Francisco CA 94132

NEUSTEIN, HARRY (BERNARD), b Pittsburgh, Pa, June 13, 24. PATHOLOGY. *Educ:* Univ Pittsburgh, BS, 47; Univ Cincinnati, MD, 49; Am Bd Path, dipl, 57. *Prof Exp:* From intern to asst resident path, Cincinnati Gen Hosp, 49-51; resident, Children's Hosp of Pittsburgh, 53-54 & Colo Gen Hosp, 54-55; asst, Sch Med, Univ Colo, 55-56, from instr to asst prof, 56-63; USPHS spec fel, Univ Calif, Los Angeles, 63-66; assoc prof, 66-71, PROF PATH, UNIV SOUTHERN CALIF, 71- *Concurrent Pos:* Pathologist, Los Angeles Children's Hosp, 66- *Mem:* Electron Micros Soc Am; NY Acad Sci; Int Acad Path. *Res:* Kidney disease; electron microscopy; pulmonary disease in the newborn. *Mailing Add:* Dept of Path Los Angeles Children's Hosp Los Angeles CA 90054

NEUSTEIN, JOSEPH, mechanical engineering, see previous edition

NEUTRA, MARIAN R, b Chicago, Ill, Aug 31, 38; m 64, 77; c 3. INTESTINAL PHYSIOLOGY, ELECTRON MICROSCOPY. *Educ:* Univ Mich, BA, 60; McGill Univ, PhD(cell biol & anat), 66. *Prof Exp:* Vis asst prof cell biol, Univ Del Valle, Colombia, 71-73; asst prof, 73-80, ASSOC PROF ANAT, HARVARD MED SCH, 80- *Concurrent Pos:* Prin investr, Cystic Fibrosis Found, 74-77 & 81- & NIH res grant, 78-; res comt, Cystic Fibrosis Found, 79-; assoc ed, Anatomical Rec, 82- *Mem:* Am Soc Cell Biol; Am Asn Anatomists; Electron Microscope Soc Am; Fedn Am Scientists. *Res:* Cell biology of the intestinal epithelium; glycoprotein secretion, macromolecular transport, bacterial adherance, intercellular junctions and membrane specializations in humans and other mammals. *Mailing Add:* Dept Anat Harvard Med Sch 25 Shattuck St Boston MA 02115

NEUTS, MARCEL FERNAND, b Ostend, Belg, Feb 21, 35; m 59; c 4. STATISTICS, OPERATIONS RESEARCH. *Educ:* Univ Louvain, Lic math, 56; Stanford Univ, MSc, 59, PhD(statist), 61. *Prof Exp:* Instr math, Univ Lovanium, Leopoldville, 56-57; from asst prof to prof math & statist, Purdue Univ, 62-76; UNIDEL CHAIR PROF STATIST & COMPUT SCI, UNIV DEL, 76- *Concurrent Pos:* Consult, Gen Motors Res Labs, 64-66 & Bell Labs, 80; vis prof, Cornell Univ, 68-69; dept ed appl stochastic model, Mgt Sci, 74-80; ed, J Appl Probability, 79-; fac vis, IBM Res Ctr, 81. *Honors & Awards:* Lester R Ford Award, Math Asn Am. *Mem:* Fel Inst Math Statist; Math Asn Am; Opers Res Soc Am; Int Statist Inst; Statist Asn Can. *Res:* Probability theory; biological models, order statistics and numerical methods in probability; queueing theory; Markov chains; general stochastic processes. *Mailing Add:* Dept of Math Sci Univ of Del Newark DE 19711

NEUVAR, ERWIN W, b Hallettsville, Tex, Mar 13, 30; m 56; c 2. INORGANIC CHEMISTRY. *Educ:* Tex A&M Univ, BS, 52, PhD(inorg chem), 62. *Prof Exp:* Chemist, Hanford Atomic Prod Oper, Gen Elec Co, 55-58; SR CHEMIST, MINN MINING & MFG CO, 62- *Res:* Ion exchange membrane technology; radiochemical analysis; microwave spectroscopy; fluorine and polymer chemistry; gas chromatography. *Mailing Add:* Minn Mining & Mfg Co Bus Commun Prod Div 3M Ctr St Paul MN 55119

NEUWIRTH, JEROME H, b Brooklyn, NY, Mar 7, 31; m 57; c 2. MATHEMATICS. *Educ:* City Col New York, BS, 52; Univ Ill, MS, 54; Mass Inst Technol, PhD(math), 59. *Prof Exp:* Asst prof math, Rutgers Univ, 59-63; mathematician, NASA, 63-65; assoc prof math, Hunter Col, 65-67; assoc prof, 67-73, PROF MATH, UNIV CONN, 73- *Mem:* Am Math Soc. *Res:* Harmonic analysis. *Mailing Add:* Dept of Math Univ of Conn Storrs CT 06268

NEUWIRTH, PAUL, b Salzburg, Austria, July 6, 20; US citizen; m 46; c 3. ELECTRONICS. *Educ:* NY Univ, BS, 46, MS, 51. *Prof Exp:* Engr, RCA Indust Serv Labs, 46-48; sr engr, Teletone Corp, 48-49; proj engr, Emerson Radio Corp, 49-52 & Teleking Corp, 52-54; proj mgr, CBS Columbia Div, Columbia Broadcasting Co, 54-56; mgr display systs, Autometric Corp, 56-63; mgr, Newtek Inc, 63-69; electro-optics mgr, Aeroflex Labs, Inc, 69-72; MEM TECH STAFF, MITRE CORP, 72- *Concurrent Pos:* Mem, Nat TV Systs Comt, 53-54. *Mem:* Inst Elec & Electronics Engrs. *Res:* Television systems, receivers and instrumentation; display and electro-optical systems engineering; graphic data reduction systems; correlation; real time computer systems; air traffic control engineering. *Mailing Add:* Mitre Corp Westgate Research Park McLean VA 22102

NEUWIRTH, ROBERT SAMUEL, b New York, NY, July 11, 33; m 57; c 4. OBSTETRICS & GYNECOLOGY. *Educ:* Yale Univ, BS, 55, MD, 58. *Prof Exp:* Intern surg, Columbia-Presby Med Ctr, 58-59, resident obstet & gynec, 59-64; from asst prof to assoc prof, Columbia Univ, 64-71; prof, Albert Einstein Col Med, 71-72; PROF OBSTET & GYNEC, COLUMBIA UNIV, 72-; DIR OBSTET & GYNEC, WOMAN'S HOSP, ST LUKE'S MED CTR, 74- *Concurrent Pos:* Am Cancer Soc grant, Columbia Univ, 63-64; dir obstet & gynec, Bronx-Lebanon Hosp Ctr, 67-72; consult, Nat Inst Child Health & Human Develop, 71- & Fertil Control, WHO, 72-; consult, Wausau Ins Co. *Mem:* Soc Gynec Invest; Am Col Obstet & Gynec. *Res:* Gynecologic endoscopy; fertility control; methods of female sterilization; infertility and reproductive failure. *Mailing Add:* St Luke's Med Ctr Woman's Hosp 1111 Amsterdam Ave New York NY 10025

NEUZIL, EDWARD F, b Chicago, Ill, Oct 12, 30; m 55; c 2. NUCLEAR CHEMISTRY. *Educ:* NDak State Col, BS, 52; Purdue Univ, MS, 54; Univ Wash, PhD(nuclear chem), 59. *Prof Exp:* From asst prof to assoc prof, 59-66, PROF CHEM, WESTERN WASH UNIV, 66- *Mem:* Am Chem Soc; Fedn Am Scientists. *Res:* Nuclear fission of lighter elements; geochemistry; chemical kinetics; radiation damage. *Mailing Add:* Dept of Chem Western Wash Univ Bellingham WA 98225

NEUZIL, JOHN PAUL, b Decorah, Iowa, Aug 8, 42; m 66; c 1. MATHEMATICS. *Educ:* Univ Iowa, BA, 64, MS, 66, PhD(math), 69. *Prof Exp:* Asst prof math, 69-77, ASSOC PROF MATH, KENT STATE UNIV, 77- *Mem:* Am Math Soc. *Res:* Geometric topology. *Mailing Add:* Dept of Math Kent State Univ Kent OH 44242

NEUZIL, RICHARD WILLIAM, b Chicago, Ill, Sept 4, 24; wid; c 2. CHEMISTRY. *Educ:* Roosevelt Univ, BS, 50. *Prof Exp:* Spectroscopist, Universal Oil Prod Co, 50-55, supvr, 55-58, proj leader radiation chem, 58-59, proj leader air pollution control, 59-63, assoc res coordr catalyst eval, 63-66, res coordr, Catalyst Eval, 66-76, RES MGR SEPARATIONS RES, UOP INC, 76- *Mem:* AAAS; Am Chem Soc. *Res:* Determination of physical and thermochemical constants; thermodynamic properties; continuous process instrumentation; methods for separation and purification of chemical compounds for use on an industrial scale. *Mailing Add:* UOP Inc 10 UOP Plaza Algonquin & Mt Prospect Rds Des Plaines IL 60016

NEVA, FRANKLIN ALLEN, b Cloquet, Minn, June 8, 22; m 47; c 3. MICROBIOLOGY, INTERNAL MEDICINE. *Educ:* Univ Minn, MD, 46; Am Bd Internal Med, dipl, 54. *Prof Exp:* House officer med, Boston City Hosp, 46-47, asst resident internal med, Harvard Med Servs, 49-50; Nat Res Coun fel poliomyelitis, Dept Microbiol, Sch Pub Health, Harvard Univ, 50-51, Nat Found Infantile Paralysis fel virol, Res Div, Infectious Dis, Children's Hosp, Harvard Med Sch, 51-53; asst prof res bact & instr res med, Sch Med, Univ Pittsburgh, 53-55; from asst prof to assoc prof trop pub health, Sch Pub Health, Harvard Univ, 55-64, John Laporte Given prof, 64-69; CHIEF LAB PARASITIC DIS, NAT INST ALLERGY & INFECTIOUS DIS, 69- *Concurrent Pos:* Area consult, Vet Admin, 57-64; mem comn parasitic dis & assoc mem comn virus infections, Armed Forces Epidemiol Bd, 60-68 & 65-68; mem, Latin Am Sci Bd, Nat Acad Sci-Nat Res Coun, 63-68; mem bd sci counr, Nat Inst Allergy & Infectious Dis, 66-69, mem study sect virus & rickettsial dis, 68-70; mem med adv bd, Leonard Wood Mem Found, 68- *Honors & Awards:* Bailey K Ashford Award, 65. *Mem:* Soc Exp Biol & Med; Asn Am Physicians; Infectious Dis Soc Am; Am Soc Trop Med & Hyg. *Res:* Virus, rickettsial and parasitic diseases; clinical infectious diseases. *Mailing Add:* Bldg 5 Rm 114 NIH Bethesda MD 20014

NEVALAINEN, DAVID ERIC, b Moose Lake, Minn, June 30, 44; m 66; c 1. LABORATORY MEDICINE, DIAGNOSTICS. *Educ:* Univ Minn, Minneapolis, BS, 66, PhD(anat), 72. *Prof Exp:* Instr lab sci, Hibbing Area Tech Inst, Minn, 69-72; res assoc lab med, Hibbing Gen Hosp, Minn, 69-72; lab supvr, Fairbanks Mem Hosp, Alaska, 72-73; asst prof med technol, Mich Technol Univ, 73-76, assoc prof, 76-79, assoc dir dept, 73-79; assoc prof med technol, Univ Wis-Milwaukee, 79-81, sr hematologist, 81-82, CLIN PROJ MGR, ABBOTT DIAGNOSTICS, ABBOTT LABS, 82- *Concurrent Pos:* Consult, Diag Div, Abbott Labs, Dallas, 76-79; assoc ed, Am J Med Technol. *Mem:* Am Soc Med Technol; Am Soc Clin Pathologists; Am Asn Blood Banks; Soc Anal Cytol; Am Soc Qual Control. *Res:* Development, manufacture and testing of diagnostic products for use in the clinical laboratory. *Mailing Add:* 5011 N Berkeley Blvd Whitefish Bay WI 53217

NEVE, RICHARD ANTHONY, b Los Angeles, Calif, Nov 3, 23; m 53; c 2. BIOCHEMISTRY, MARINE CHEMISTRY. *Educ:* Loyola Univ, BS, 48; Univ San Francisco, MS, 51; Univ Ore, PhD(biochem), 56. *Prof Exp:* Biologist, US Naval Radiol Defense Lab, Calif, 49-51; asst biochem, Med Sch, Univ Ore, 51-56, res assoc, 56-58; USPHS fel, Univ Calif, 58-60; dir chem lab, Providence Hosp, 60-62; assoc prof biol & chmn dept, Seattle Univ, 62-66; prof biochem & dean grad sch, Cent Wash State Col, 66-70; PROF MARINE PATH & TOXICOL, UNIV ALASKA, 70- *Mem:* Am Chem Soc; Am Fisheries Soc. *Res:* Porphyrin metabolism; hemoglobin synthesis; iron metabolism; application of enzymology; biochemical evolution of hemoglobins; marine carotenoids; biochemical behavior patterns; paralytic shellfish poisoning; aquaculture; stress and disease in aquatic fish and invertebrates; arctic resources. *Mailing Add:* Inst Marine Sci Univ Alaska Fairbanks AK 99701

NEVELS, ROBERT DUDLEY, b Hopkinsville, Ky, Apr 14, 46; m 76. ANTENNA THEORY, MILLIMETER WAVE DEVICES. *Educ:* Univ Ky, BS, 69; Ga Inst Technol, MS, 73; Univ Miss, PhD(elec eng), 79. *Prof Exp:* Asst prof electromagnetics, Univ Miss, 77-78; ASST PROF ELECTROMAGNETICS, TEX A&M UNIV, 78- *Mem:* Inst Elec & Electronics Engrs; Sigma Xi; Electromagnetics Soc. *Res:* Electromagnetic scattering from both electrically large and small bodies; equivalance method for formulation of integral equations with solution methods ranging from asymptotic techniques to geometrical theory of diffraction and moment methods. *Mailing Add:* Dept Elec Eng Tex A&M Univ College Station TX 77843

NEVENZEL, JUDD CUTHBERT, b Tucson, Ariz, Oct 8, 20. LIPID CHEMISTRY. *Educ:* Univ Ariz, BS, 41, MS, 42; Calif Inst Technol, PhD(chem), 49. *Prof Exp:* Res chemist, Wood Conversion Co, 42; chemist, Nat Defense Res Comt Proj, Calif Inst Technol, 43; jr chemist, Los Alamos Sci Lab, 43-46; res fel chem, Ohio State Univ, 49-50; assoc res biochemist, Scripps Inst Oceanog, Univ Calif, San Diego, 70-73; assoc res biochemist, Lab Nuclear Med & Radiation Biol, Univ Calif, Los Angeles, 51-73, res biochemist, 73-76; RES BIOCHEMIST, SCRIPPS INST OCEANOG, UNIV CALIF, SAN DIEGO, 77- *Concurrent Pos:* Mem subcomt lipids, Comt Biol Chem, Nat Acad Sci-Nat Res Coun, 59-77. *Mem:* Am Chem Soc; Am Oil Chem Soc. *Res:* Synthesis of C-14 labeled fatty acids; composition, biosynthesis and function of waxes; lipids of deep-sea organisms. *Mailing Add:* Marine Biol Res Div A-002 Scripps Inst of Oceanog La Jolla CA 92093

NEVEU, DARWIN D, b Green Bay, Wis, Feb 26, 33. ANALYTICAL CHEMISTRY. *Educ:* Wis State Univ, Oshkosh, BS, 58. *Prof Exp:* Chemist, Freeman Chem Co, 63-65; asst chief chemist, WVa Pulp & Paper Co, 65-66; chemist, Newport Army Ammunition Ctr, FMC Corp, 66-67 & Celanese Plastics, 67-69; mgr org lab, Crobaugh Labs, 69-70; LAB DIR CHEM ANAL & CONSULT, NALIN LABS, 70- *Concurrent Pos:* Fac adv, Wooster Agr Tech Inst, 73-79. *Mem:* Am Chem Soc; Am Electroplaters Soc; Nat Asn Corrosion Engrs; Soc Plastics Engrs; Electrochem Soc. *Mailing Add:* Nalin Labs 2641 Cleveland Ave Columbus OH 43211

NEVEU, MAURICE C, b Nashua, NH, Feb 3, 29; m 55; c 5. THERMODYNAMICS, BIOCHEMISTRY. *Educ:* Univ NH, BS, 52, MS, 55; Ill Inst Technol, PhD(chem), 59. *Prof Exp:* Asst, Univ NH, 53-54; asst, Ill Inst Technol, 54-58; instr, Ohio Northern Univ, 58-59, asst prof chem, 59-60; asst prof, Longwood Col, 60-64; ASSOC PROF CHEM, STATE UNIV NY COL FREDONIA, 64- *Mem:* Am Chem Soc. *Res:* Mechanisms of organic reactions; chemical kinetics; catalysis; isotope effects; mechanism of ester hydrolysis; enzymology; metabolic pathways by carbon-14 tracers; differential scanning calorimetry; measurement of freezing points of binary and ternary hydrocarbon systems and construction of their phase diagrams. *Mailing Add:* Dept Chem State Univ NY Col Fredonia NY 14063

NEVILL, GALE E(RWIN), JR, b Houston, Tex, Nov 17, 33; m 54; c 2. ENGINEERING MECHANICS. *Educ:* Rice Univ, BA, 54, BSME, 55, MSME, 57; Stanford Univ, PhD(eng mech), 61. *Prof Exp:* Res engr, McEvoy Co, 58; res asst mech, Stanford Univ, 59-60; sr res engr, Southwest Res Inst, 60-64; from assoc prof to prof mech, Univ Fla, 60-73, chmn dept, 68-73, prof eng sci, 73-81. *Concurrent Pos:* Consult, Lawrence Livermore Nat Lab, 76-81. *Mem:* Am Soc Mech Engrs; Am Soc Eng Educ; Am Inst Aeronaut & Astronaut; Inst Mat Sci. *Res:* Modeling and decision making in complex systems; energy policy; robotics. *Mailing Add:* Dept Eng Sci & Mech Col Eng Univ Fla Gainesville FL 32611

NEVILL, WILLIAM ALBERT, b Indianapolis, Ind, Jan 1, 29; m 79; c 5. ORGANIC CHEMISTRY. *Educ:* Butler Univ, BS, 51; Calif Inst Technol, PhD(chem biol), 54. *Prof Exp:* Res chemist, Procter & Gamble Co, 54; from asst prof to assoc prof chem, Grinnell Col, 56-67, chmn dept, 64-67; prof, Purdue Univ & chmn dept chem, Indianapolis Campus, 67-70; asst dean acad affairs, 70-71, actg dean, 38th St Campus, 71-72, actg dean, Sch Eng & Technol, 72-74, dean, Sch Sci, 72-79, DIR GRAD STUDIES, IND UNIV-PURDUE UNIV, INDIANAPOLIS, 79- *Concurrent Pos:* Consult, Eli Lilly, 71-81 & Lilly Indust Coatings, 80- *Mem:* Am Chem Soc. *Res:* Mechanisms of organic reactions relating to small ring compounds, synthesis of nitrogen heterocycles and industrial coating polymers. *Mailing Add:* 11514 Dona Dr Carmel IN 46032

NEVILLE, DONALD EDWARD, b Los Angeles, Calif, Apr 5, 36; m 77; c 1. THEORETICAL HIGH ENERGY PHYSICS. *Educ:* Loyola Univ, Los Angeles, BS, 57; Univ Chicago, SM, 60, PhD(physics), 62. *Prof Exp:* Fel physics, Univ Calif, Berkeley, 62-64, Europ Orgn Nuclear Res, Geneva, 64-65 & Lawrence Radiation Labs, Livermore, 65-67; assoc prof, 67-80, PROF PHYSICS, TEMPLE UNIV, 80- *Mem:* Am Phys Soc; AAAS. *Res:* Theoretical particle physics, especially constraints imposed by duality and symmetries obeyed by scattering amplitudes; impact of particle physics on cosmology and astrophysics; quantum gravity. *Mailing Add:* Dept of Physics Temple Univ Philadelphia PA 19122

NEVILLE, JAMES RYAN, b San Jose, Calif, May 13, 25; m 49; c 2. MEDICAL PHYSIOLOGY. *Educ:* Stanford Univ, AB, 49, MA, 51, PhD(physiol), 55. *Prof Exp:* Teaching asst physiol, Stanford Univ, 52-55; aviation physiologist, US Air Force Sch Aerospace Med, 55-57, from asst prof to assoc prof biophys, 57-63, chief biophys sect, 63-70; clin res physiologist, 70-79, ASST DIR RES CONTRACT, LETTERMAN ARMY INST RES, 79- *Mem:* AAAS; Biophys Soc; Instrument Soc Am; Aerospace Med Asn; Am Physiol Soc. *Res:* Respiratory physiology; gas transport; enzymes; methodology and bioinstrumentation; polarography. *Mailing Add:* Off Comdr Letterman Army Inst of Res Presidio San Francisco CA 94129

NEVILLE, JANICE NELSON, b Schenectady, NY, Dec 1, 30; m 53; c 2. NUTRITION. *Educ:* Carnegie Inst Technol, BS, 52; Univ Ala, MS, 53; Univ Pittsburgh, MPH, 62, DSc(hyg), 64. *Prof Exp:* Instr diet ther & clin dietitian, Sch Nursing, Hillman Clins, Univ Ala, 54; res dietitian, Grad Sch Pub Health, Univ Pittsburgh, 56-61, res asst nutrit, 61-64, asst res prof, 64-65; from asst prof to assoc prof, 65-74, PROF NUTRIT & CHMN DEPT, CASE WESTERN RESERVE UNIV, 74- *Concurrent Pos:* Mem, Coun on Epidemiol, Am Heart Asn. *Mem:* AAAS; Am Heart Asn; NY Acad Sci; Am Pub Health Asn; Soc Nutrit Educ. *Res:* Diet therapy; community health. *Mailing Add:* Dept of Nutrit Case Western Reserve Univ Cleveland OH 44106

NEVILLE, JOHN F, JR, medicine, see previous edition

NEVILLE, MARGARET COBB, b Greenville, SC, Nov 4, 34; m 57; c 2. PHYSIOLOGY. *Educ:* Pomona Col, BA, 56; Univ Pa, PhD(physiol), 62. *Prof Exp:* Res assoc cell physiol, Dept Molecular Biol, Pa Hosp, Philadelphia, 64-68; from instr to asst prof, 68-75, ASSOC PROF PHYSIOL, MED CTR, UNIV COLO, DENVER, 75- *Concurrent Pos:* Prin investr, NIH grant, 74- *Mem:* Am Physiol Soc; Biophys Soc; Soc Cell Biol. *Res:* Mammary gland biology; hormonal control of cellular transport of nutrients; calcium ATPase. *Mailing Add:* Dept of Physiol Univ of Colo Med Ctr Denver CO 80262

NEVILLE, MELVIN EDWARD, microbiology, see previous edition

NEVILLE, WALTER EDWARD, JR, b Rabun Gap, Ga, May 5, 24; m 48; c 2. ANIMAL SCIENCE. *Educ:* Univ Ga, BS, 47; Univ Mo, MS, 50; Univ Wis, PhD(genetics, animal husb), 57. *Prof Exp:* Asst county agr agent agr exten, Univ Ga, 47-49; asst animal breeding, 50-51, assoc, 51-77, PROF ANIMAL BREEDING, COASTAL PLAIN EXP STA, 77- *Honors & Awards:* Sigma Xi Res Award, 75. *Mem:* AAAS; Am Soc Animal Sci; Coun Agr Sci & Technol. *Res:* Crossbreeding of beef cattle and heritability estimates among various economic traits in beef cattle; physiology of reproduction in farm animals; nutritive requirements of beef cattle and their calves. *Mailing Add:* Coastal Plain Exp Sta Tifton GA 31393

NEVILLE, WILLIAM E, b Fairbury, Nebr, Apr 13, 19; m 58; c 5. SURGERY. *Educ:* Univ Nebr, BS & MD, 43. *Prof Exp:* Assoc prof surg, Univ Ill Col Med, 62-71; PROF SURG & DIR CARDIOTHORACIC SURG, COL MED & DENT NJ, 71- *Mem:* Fel Am Col Surg; Soc Thoracic Surg; Am Asn Thoracic Surg; Int Cardiovasc Soc; Am Surg Asn. *Res:* Cardiothoracic surgery. *Mailing Add:* Col of Med & Dent of NJ Newark NJ 07103

NEVIN, FLOYD REESE, b Long Eddy, NY, Feb 24, 04; m 34, 80; c 1. ACAROLOGY. *Educ:* Temple Univ, AB, 27; Univ Pa, MA, 29; Cornell Univ, PhD(med entom), 34. *Prof Exp:* Asst, Temple Univ, 27-29; instr biol, Ursinus Col, 29-30; asst biol, Cornell Univ, 30-34, instr, 34-44; prof & head sci, Rider Col, 44-46; prof biol, 46-73, chmn dept sci & math, 50-64, EMER PROF BIOL, STATE UNIV COL ARTS & SCI, PLATTSBURGH, NY, 73- *Concurrent Pos:* Fel sch hyg & pub health, Johns Hopkins Univ, 43-44; asst bur entom, USDA. *Mem:* Entom Soc Am; Nat Asn Biol Teachers; Am Inst Biol Sci. *Res:* Medical entomology; taxonomy of Oribatid mites; parasitology. *Mailing Add:* 49 Prospect Ave Plattsburgh NY 12901

NEVIN, ROBERT STEPHEN, b New York, NY, Oct 20, 33; m 55. ORGANIC CHEMISTRY, POLYMER CHEMISTRY. *Educ:* Queens Col, NY, BS, 55; St John's Univ, NY, MS, 57; State Univ NY Col Forestry, Syracuse, PhD(chem), 61. *Prof Exp:* Res chemist, Esso Res & Eng Co, 61-63; sr res chemist, J T Baker Chem Co, 63-67; sr res chemist, 67, RES SCIENTIST, LILLY RES LAB, ELI LILLY & CO, 67- *Mem:* Am Chem Soc. *Res:* Organic chemistry of polymers; ionic polymerization; monomer synthesis; chemical modification of polymers. *Mailing Add:* Lilly Res Lab MC525 Eli Lilly & Co Indianapolis IN 46206

NEVIN, THOMAS ANDREW, b New York, NY, Oct 20, 17; m 43; c 2. BACTERIOLOGY. *Educ:* Stetson Univ, BS, 49; Univ Ala, MS, 52; Univ Southern Calif, PhD(bact), 57. *Prof Exp:* Res assoc bact, Eastman Dent Dispensary, 49-50; instr, Exten Div, Univ Ala, 52-53; dir control labs, Delta Labs, 53-54; res bacteriologist, Nat Inst Dent Res, 57-60; asst dir, Germfree Life Res Ctr, 60-63; chief bact physiol & chem lab, Venereal Dis Res Lab, Communicable Dis Ctr, 63-68; res prof microbiol, Fla Inst Technol, 68-75. *Mem:* Am Soc Microbiol; Sigma Xi. *Res:* Bacterial physiology; nutritional bases of bacterial interactions; physiology and nutrition of spirochetes. *Mailing Add:* PO Box 486 Melbourne FL 32901

NEVINS, ARTHUR JAMES, b New York, NY, Sept 22, 37; m 60; c 2. COMPUTER SCIENCE. *Educ:* Mass Inst Technol, BS, 59; Univ Rochester, MA, 62, PhD(econ), 65. *Prof Exp:* Fel, Carnegie Inst Technol, 64-65; sr scientist logistics res proj, George Washington Univ, 65-69, sr staff scientist, Inst Mgt Sci, 69-72; res scientist, Artificial Intel Lab, Mass Inst Technol, 72-74; MEM FAC, DEPT INFO SYSTS, GA STATE UNIV, 74- *Mem:* Asn Comput Mach. *Res:* Artifical intelligence. *Mailing Add:* 5343 O'Reilly Lane Stone Mountain GA 30088

NEVINS, DONALD JAMES, b San Luis Obispo, Calif, July 6, 37; m 62; c 2. PLANT PHYSIOLOGY. *Educ:* Calif State Polytech Col, BS, 59; Univ Calif, Davis, MS, 61, PhD(plant physiol), 65. *Prof Exp:* NIH res assoc chem, Univ Colo, 65-67; from asst prof to assoc prof bot, 67-74, PROF BOT, IOWA STATE UNIV, 74- *Concurrent Pos:* Vis prof, Osaka City Univ, Japan Soc Prom Sci, 74-75. *Mem:* AAAS; Am Soc Plant Physiol; Am Chem Soc; Japanese Soc Plant Physiologists. *Res:* Physiology of cell walls, growth and development. *Mailing Add:* Dept Bot Iowa State Univ Ames IA 50011

NEVIS, ARNOLD HASTINGS, b Albuquerque, NMex, Aug 3, 31; m 52; c 3. NEUROLOGY, BIOPHYSICS. *Educ:* Calif Inst Technol, BS, 47; Harvard Med Sch, MD, 51; Mass Inst Technol, PhD(biophys), 56. *Prof Exp:* Asst prof physiol & coordr muscular dystrophy res, Med Br, Univ Tex, 56-57; clin fel neurol, Med Ctr, Univ Calif, Los Angeles, 58-60; asst prof neurol, 60-67, assoc prof neurol & elec eng, 67-69, PROF BIOPHYS & BIOMED ENG, COL MED, UNIV FLA, 69- *Mem:* Soc Nuclear Med; Biophys Soc. *Res:* Neurophysiology, especially tissue impedance in relation to electrophysiology, ultrastructure and water and electrolyte transport across membranes; disease of muscle. *Mailing Add:* Dept of Physics Univ of Fla Gainesville FL 32611

NEVITT, MICHAEL VOGT, b Lexington, Ky, Sept 7, 23; m 46; c 4. METAL PHYSICS. *Educ:* Univ Ill, BS, 44, PhD(metall eng), 54; Va Polytech Inst, MS, 51. *Prof Exp:* Res metallurgist, Olin Mathieson Chem Corp, 46-48; from asst prof to assoc prof metall eng, Va Polytech Inst, 48-55 & head dept, 53-55; assoc phys metallurgist, Metall Div, 55-64, group leader, 55-66, sr phys metallurgist, 64, dir metall div, 66-69, dep lab dir, 69-81, SR SCIENTIST, ARGONNE NAT LAB, 81- *Concurrent Pos:* Mem adv comt, Polysci Corp, 54; vis prof, Univ Sheffield, 65-66; mem univ adv comts, Lehigh Univ, 76- & Univ Ky, 78-; consult ed, J Contemp Physics, 77- & Res Mechanica Lett, 80-; mem adv comt mat res, NSF, 80-82. *Mem:* Fel Am Soc Metals; Sigma Xi; Am Inst Mining, Metall & Petrol Engrs. *Res:* Physical and engineering metallurgy of nuclear materials; alloy theory of transition and actinide elements; magnetic properties. *Mailing Add:* Argonne Nat Lab 9700 S Cass Ave Argonne IL 60439

NEVITT, THOMAS D, b Kewanee, Ill, July 22, 25; m 49; c 3. ORGANIC CHEMISTRY, PETROLEUM CHEMISTRY. *Educ:* Bradley Univ, BS, 47; Iowa State Col, MS, 50, PhD(phys org chem), 53. *Prof Exp:* PROJ MGR, AMOCO OIL CO, 54- *Mem:* Am Chem Soc; Royal Soc Chem. *Res:* Catalysis; chemical kinetics; reaction engineering. *Mailing Add:* Amoco Oil Co PO Box 400 Naperville IL 60566

NEVLING, LORIN IVES, JR, b St Louis, Mo, Sept 23, 30; m 57; c 5. PLANT TAXONOMY. *Educ:* St Mary's Col, BS, 52; Wash Univ, AM, 57, PhD(bot), 59. *Prof Exp:* Researcher, Mo Bot Garden, 59; from asst cur to assoc cur, Arnold Arboretum, Harvard Univ, 59-69, cur, 69-73, supvr, Gray Herbarium, 63-72, assoc cur, 63-69, coordr bot syst collections, 72-73; cur & chmn dept bot, 73-77, ASST DIR SCI & EDUC, FIELD MUS NATURAL HIST, 78-, LECTR BIOL SCI, NORTHWESTERN UNIV, 74- *Concurrent Pos:* Asst cur vascular plants, Northeast Bot Club, 62-73; lectr biol, Harvard Univ, 68-69 & 71-73; mem, Conserv Comn, City Boston, 73; adj prof biol sci, Northern Ill Univ, 74- *Honors & Awards:* George R Cooley Prize, 70. *Mem:* Bot Soc Am; Asn Trop Biol; Am Soc Plant Taxon (secy, 66-71, pres, 77); Int Asn Plant Taxon; Am Inst Biol Sci. *Res:* Taxonomy of the Thymelaeaceae; flora of Veracruz, Mexico. *Mailing Add:* Field Mus Natural Hist Roosevelt Rd & Lake Shore Dr Chicago IL 60605

NEW, JOHN COY, JR, b Little Rock, Ark, Jan 14, 48; m 75; c 2. VETERINARY MEDICINE, EPIDEMIOLOGY. *Educ:* Tex A&M Univ, BS, 70, DVM, 71; Univ Minn, MPH, 77. *Prof Exp:* Res assoc vet econ, Univ Minn, 75-77; ASST PROF PUB HEALTH, UNIV TENN, KNOXVILLE, 77- *Mem:* Am Vet Med Asn; Am Pub Health Asn; Am Col Vet Prev Med; Conf Pub Health Veterinarians; Asn Teachers Vet Pub Health & Prev Med. *Res:* Zoonotic diseases; economics of animal diseases; diseases of raptors and pet birds; food hygiene; environmental health; diseases of fish. *Mailing Add:* Dept of Environ Pract PO Box 1071 Knoxville TN 37901

NEW, JOHN G, b New York, NY, Jan 16, 27; m 50; c 4. ENVIRONMENTAL SCIENCES, VERTEBRATE ZOOLOGY. *Educ:* Cornell Univ, BS, 50, MS, 51, PhD(vert zool), 56. *Prof Exp:* Assoc prof, 56-60, PROF SCI, STATE UNIV NY COL ONEONTA, 60- *Mem:* AAAS; Am Soc Mammal; Wilson Ornith Soc; Am Soc Ichthyol & Herpet; Ecol Soc Am. *Res:* Environment, ecology, systematics, evolution, and life histories of vertebrates, particularly freshwater fishes and mammals. *Mailing Add:* Dept of Biol State Univ of NY Col Oneonta NY 13820

NEW, MARIA IANDOLO, b New York, NY, Dec 11, 28; m 49; c 3. PEDIATRICS. *Educ:* Cornell Univ, AB, 50; Univ Pa, MD, 54; Am Bd Pediat, dipl, 60. *Prof Exp:* Intern med, Bellevue Hosp, New York, 54-55; asst resident pediat, 55-57, asst pediatrician, Clin Res Ctr, 57-59, pediatrician, Outpatient Dept, 59-63, res investr diabetic study group, Comprehensive Care & Teaching Prog, 58-61, instr pediat, 58-63, asst prof & asst attend pediatrician, 63-68, assoc prof & assoc attend pediatrician, 68-71, PROF PEDIAT & ATTEND PEDIATRICIAN, NEW YORK HOSP-CORNELL MED CTR, 71-, DIR PEDIAT METAB & ENDOCRINE CLIN & DIV HEAD PEDIAT ENDOCRINOL, 64-, ASSOC DIR PEDIAT CLIN RES CTR, 66-, VCHMN DEPT PEDIAT, 74- *Concurrent Pos:* Fel pediat metab & renal dis, New York Hosp-Cornell Med Ctr, 57-58, res fel med, 62-64, Harold & Percy Uris prof pediat endocrinol & metab, 78; vis physician, Rockefeller Univ, 71-, consult, Albert Einstein Col Med, 74- & United Hosp, Port Chester, NY, 77- *Mem:* AAAS; Am Acad Pediat; Am Pediat Soc; Soc Pediat Res; Am Fedn Clin Res. *Res:* Pediatric endocrinology and renal diseases; juvenile hypertension; pediatric pharmacology; growth and development from the biochemical viewpoint. *Mailing Add:* New York Hosp Dept of Pediat 525 E 68th St New York NY 10021

NEWBERGER, BARRY STEPHEN, b Huntington, WVa, June 19, 45; m 75. PLASMA PHYSICS. *Educ:* Carnegie Inst Technol, BS, 67; Princeton Univ, PhD(astrophys sci), 76. *Prof Exp:* Staff mem plasma physics, Laser Theory Group, 72-77, STAFF MEM PLASMA PHYSICS, INTENSE PARTICLE BEAM THEORY GROUP, LOS ALAMOS SCI LAB, 77- *Mem:* Am Phys Soc; Sigma Xi. *Res:* Theoretical plasma physics with emphasis on the linear theory of instability in relativistic beam-plasma systems and low frequency instabilities in toroidal plasmas. *Mailing Add:* Los Alamos Nat Lab X-3 MS-608 Los Alamos NM 87545

NEWBERGER, EDWARD, b New York, NY, Feb 15, 40. MATHEMATICS. *Educ:* City Col New York, BS, 61; Ind Univ, PhD(partial differential equations), 69. *Prof Exp:* Asst prof, 70-74, ASSOC PROF MATH, STATE UNIV NY COL BUFFALO, 74- *Mem:* Am Math Soc; Am Math Asn; NY Acad Sci; Math Soc France. *Res:* Pseudo-differential operators; Gevrey classes; asymptotic Gevrey classes; partial differential equations. *Mailing Add:* Dept of Math State Univ of NY Col Buffalo NY 14222

NEWBERGER, MARK, b Brooklyn, NY, Mar 26, 42. CHEMICAL ENGINEERING. *Educ:* Cooper Union, BChE, 62; Univ Mich, MS, 63, PhD, 67. *Prof Exp:* From develop engr to sr dev engr, 63-69; sr process engr, Eng Div, 69-74, process supvr, 75-79, MGR PROCESS ANALYSIS, AM CYANAMID CO, WAYNE, NJ, 79- *Concurrent Pos:* Adj instr, Jersey City State Col, 68-71, consult, 70-71; sr lectr, Stevens Inst Technol, 75-79. *Mem:* Am Inst Chem Engrs. *Res:* Process control; dynamics; optimization and optimal control; large system simulation; mathematical modeling; chemical reactor engineering; computer applications. *Mailing Add:* Am Cyanamid Co Eng & Construct Div Wayne NJ 07470

NEWBERGER, STUART MARSHALL, b New York, NY, Oct 4, 38; m 64; c 1. MATHEMATICS. *Educ:* City Col New York, BEE, 60; Mass Inst Technol, PhD(math), 64. *Prof Exp:* From instr to asst prof math, Univ Calif, Berkeley, 64-69; ASSOC PROF MATH, ORE STATE UNIV, 69- *Mem:* Am Math Soc; Math Asn Am. *Res:* Functional analysis, integration theory, including integration in linear space; operator theory, including unbounded operators in Hilbert Space and partial differential operators; generalized function theory; applications of operators to quantum theory. *Mailing Add:* Dept of Math Ore State Univ Corvallis OR 97331

NEWBERNE, JAMES WILSON, b Adel, Ga, Dec 1, 23; m 49; c 3. VETERINARY PATHOLOGY. *Educ:* Ala Polytech Inst, DVM, 50, MS, 54. *Prof Exp:* Instr path, Ala Polytech Inst, 52-55; pathologist, Pitman-Moore Co, 55-57, asst dir path dept, 57-61; ASSOC CLIN PROF PATH, COL MED, UNIV CINCINNATI, 63-; head dept path & toxicol, Wm S Merrell Co, 62-69, dir drug safety & metab, Richardson-Merrell Inc, 69-76, vpres drug safety assessment, Merrell Nat labs div, Richardson-Merrell Inc, 76-80, VPRES & DIR, DRUG SAFETY ASSESSMENT, MERRELL DOW RES CTR, MERRELL DOW PHARMACEUT INC, 81-; CLIN PROF LAB MED, MED CTR, UNIV CINCINNATI, 74- *Concurrent Pos:* Consult, Toxicol Protocol Comt, Nat Acad Sci-Nat Res Coun, 75-; mem health ministry, France, 76- *Mem:* Am Vet Med Asn; Am Col Vet Path; Am Asn Lab Animal Sci; NY Acad Sci; Soc Toxicol. *Res:* Toxicopathology; experimental pathology. *Mailing Add:* Merrell Res Ctr Merrell Dow Chem Co Cincinnati OH 45215

NEWBERNE, PAUL M, b Adel, Ga, Nov 4, 20; m 45; c 2. NUTRITION, PATHOLOGY. *Educ:* Auburn Univ, DVM, 50, MSc, 51; Univ Mo, PhD(biochem, nutrit), 58. *Prof Exp:* Instr path, Auburn Univ, 50-51; instr microbiol, Univ Mo, 54-56, instr agr chem, 56-57, fel, NIH, 57-58; animal pathologist, Auburn Univ, 58-62; PROF NUTRIT PATH, MASS INST TECHNOL, 62- *Mem:* AAAS; Am Inst Nutrit; Am Col Vet Path; Am Vet Med Asn. *Res:* Nutritionally-induced experimental cancer; cardiovascular disease; nutritionally-induced teratology; nutritional pathology and toxicology; interaction of nutrition and toxicology. *Mailing Add:* Dept of Nutrit & Food Sci Mass Inst of Technol Cambridge MA 02139

NEWBERRY, ANDREW TODD, b Orange, NJ, Aug 30, 35; m 58; c 2. INVERTEBRATE ZOOLOGY. *Educ:* Princeton Univ, AB, 57; Stanford Univ, PhD(biol), 65. *Prof Exp:* Nat Acad Sci-Nat Res Coun fel, 64-65; assoc prof, 65-81, PROF BIOL, COWELL COL, UNIV CALIF, SANTA CRUZ, 81- *Res:* Invertebrate reproduction and development; biology of colonial animals; biology of ascidian tunicates; invertebrate colonies; ascidian anatomy, developmental morphology. *Mailing Add:* Cowell Col Univ of Calif Santa Cruz CA 95064

NEWBERRY, GILLIAN, lichenology, taxonomy, see previous edition

NEWBERRY, J(AMES) R(AYMOND), b Forest Grove, Ore, Dec 31, 11; m 47; c 1. CHEMICAL ENGINEERING, WASTE TREATMENT. *Educ:* Ore State Col, BS, 34. *Prof Exp:* Jr engr surv, US Engr Dept, Ore, 35-37; jr chemist testing, Nat Bur Standards, Calif, 37-42; control supvr, Remington Arms Co, Utah, 42-43; tech proj off, Bur Ord, US Navy, Washington, DC, 43-46; chem engr process develop, Olin Mathieson Chem Corp, NY, 46-50; vpres, Trichemco, Inc, 50-53; group leader electrochem, Res & Develop Dept, Energy Div, Olin Mathieson Chem Corp, 53-55, sect chief process develop, 55-59, sect chief electrochem develop, 59-65, sr chem engr, Res Dept, Chem Div, 65-69; plant supt, Strow Chem, 69-70; develop specialist, Olin Corp, 70-77; assoc, Lupton Eng Assocs, Chattanooga, 77-82; ASSOC, J R NEWBERRY ENG, CLEVELAND, 82- *Mem:* AAAS; Electrochem Soc; Am Chem Soc; Am Inst Chem Engrs; Nat Soc Prof Engrs. *Res:* Electrolysis of fused salts and anhydrous solutions; organic-phosphorus compounds; boron hydrides; plating; alkali-chlorine technology; waste treatment. *Mailing Add:* 1965 Chambliss Ave Cleveland TN 37311

NEWBERRY, TRUMAN ALBERT, b St Paul, Minn, July 19, 20; m 45; c 3. CANCER. *Educ:* Univ Minn, BS, 45, MB, 47, MD, 48, PhD(cancer biol), 53. *Prof Exp:* Intern, Univ Mich Hosp, 47-48, surg resident, 48-49; Am Cancer Soc fel, Univ Minn, 49-52, instr physiol, 52-53; resident gen surg & Nat Cancer Inst trainee, Ancker Hosp, St Paul, Minn, 53-57; pvt pract, 57-58; surgeon, Mendocino State Hosp, 59-61; GEN SURGEON & ASST SUPT, STOCKTON STATE HOSP, 63- *Concurrent Pos:* Mem exec comt, Union Am Physicians & Dentists. *Mem:* AAAS. *Res:* General surgery. *Mailing Add:* Stockton State Hosp 510 E Magnolia Stockton CA 95202

NEWBERRY, WILLIAM MARCUS, b Columbus, Ga, Nov 13, 38; m 65; c 3. INTERNAL MEDICINE. *Educ:* Northwestern Univ, BA, 60; Emory Univ, MD, 64. *Prof Exp:* Asst prof int med, Southwestern Med Sch, Univ Tex, 70-71; assoc prof, 71-75, DEAN COL MED & PROF INT MED, MED UNIV SC, 75- *Concurrent Pos:* Actg dean col med, Med Univ SC, 74-75. *Mem:* Am Fedn Clin Res; Reticuloendothelial Soc; Southern Soc Clin Invest. *Res:* Infectious diseases, specifically the epidemiology of the systemic mycoses, and the cellular immune responses to the granulomatous infections. *Mailing Add:* Col Med Med Univ SC Charleston SC 29425

NEWBERY, A CHRIS, b Broxbourne, Eng, July 12, 23; Can citizen; m 54; c 2. MATHEMATICS. *Educ:* Cambridge Univ, BA, 48; Univ London, BA, 53, PhD(math), 62; Univ BC, MA, 58. *Prof Exp:* Lectr math, Univ BC, 56-62; mathematician, Boeing Co, 62-63; asst prof, Univ Alta, Calgary, 63-65; assoc prof math & comput, Univ Ky, 65-67; mathematician, Boeing Co, Wash, 67-69; assoc prof math, 69-72, PROF COMPUT SCI, UNIV KY, 72- *Mem:* Soc Indust & Appl Math; Asn Comput Mach; Can Math Cong. *Res:* Numerical analysis; application of computers to problems, particularly in curve-fitting; linear algebra and polynomial problems. *Mailing Add:* Dept of Comput Sci Univ of Ky Lexington KY 40506

NEWBOLT, WILLIAM BARLOW, b Berea, Ky, Sept 29, 34; m 62; c 1. PHYSICS. *Educ:* Berea Col, BA, 56; Vanderbilt Univ, MS, 59, PhD(physics), 63. *Prof Exp:* From instr to assoc prof, 62-73, PROF PHYSICS, WASHINGTON & LEE UNIV, 73- *Mem:* Am Phys Soc; Am Asn Physics Teachers; Health Physics Soc. *Res:* Nuclear spectroscopy; Mossbauer effect. *Mailing Add:* Dept Physics Washington & Lee Univ Lexington VA 24450

NEWBORG, MICHAEL FOXX, b Philadelphia, Pa, Mar 23, 48; m 72; c 2. CELLULAR IMMUNOBIOLOGY, IMMUNOPARASITOLOGY. *Educ:* Univ Md, BS, 70, PhD(zool), 77. *Prof Exp:* res assoc immunol, 77-80, ASST PROF MICROBIOL, TRUDEAU INST, INC, 80- *Mem:* Am Soc Microbiologists. *Res:* Effects of infection on the subsequent generation of immune responses. *Mailing Add:* New Eng Col Osteophathic Med 11 Hills Beach Rd Biddeford ME 04005

NEWBOULD, FRANCIS HENRY SAMUEL, b Berwick-on-Tweed, Eng, May 20, 12; Can citizen; m 36; c 4. VETERINARY MICROBIOLOGY, VETERINARY IMMUNOLOGY. *Educ:* Univ Toronto, BSA, 36, MSA, 57; Univ Reading, PhD(staphylococcal mastitis), 64. *Prof Exp:* Owner, Newbould Labs, Guelph, Ont, 38-46; exten asst bact, Ont Agr Col, 46-48, lectr microbiol, 48-53, lectr, 54-56, from asst prof to prof bact, 56-77, EMER PROF BACT, DEPT VET MICROBIOL & IMMUNOL, ONT VET COL, UNIV GUELPH, 78- *Concurrent Pos:* Asst supvr blood serum drying, Connaught Med Res Labs, Univ Toronto, 43-44; vis worker, Nat Inst Res Dairying, Univ Reading, 61-63; chmn, Conf Res Workers Bovine Mastitis, US, 66-67; tech consult, West Agro-Chem Inc, NY, 66-78. *Mem:* Can Soc Microbiologists; Brit Soc Appl Bact. *Res:* Staphylococcal mastitis prevention by sanitation; penetration of teat duct by staphylococci; phagocytosis by milk leucocytes; methods of leucocyte counting. *Mailing Add:* Dept of Vet Microbiol & Immunol Ont Vet Col Univ of Guelph Guelph ON N1G 2W1 Can

NEWBOUND, KENNETH BATEMAN, b Winnipeg, Man, Mar 12, 29; m 47; c 4. PHYSICS. *Educ:* Univ Man, BSc, 40, MSc, 41; Mass Inst Technol, PhD(physics), 48. *Prof Exp:* Physicist naval res, Nat Res Coun Can, 41-43; assoc prof physics, 48-59, assoc dean sci, 64-76, dean sci, 76-81, PROF PHYSICS, UNIV ALTA, 59- *Mem:* Can Asn Physicists. *Res:* Atomic spectroscopy; spectrographic analysis; precision wave-length measurements; underwater acoustics. *Mailing Add:* 8910 Windsor Rd Edmonton AB T6G 2A2 Can

NEWBRUN, ERNEST, b Vienna, Austria, Dec 1, 32; US citizen; m 56; c 3. ORAL BIOLOGY, BIOCHEMISTRY. *Educ:* Univ Sydney, BDS, 54; Univ Rochester, MS, 57; Univ Ala, DMD, 59; Univ Calif, San Francisco, PhD(biochem), 65. *Prof Exp:* Res assoc, Eastman Dent Dispensary, Rochester, NY, 56-57 & Med Ctr, Univ Ala, 57-59; lectr biochem, 65, assoc res dentist & assoc prof oral biol, 65-70, chmn sect biol sci, 72-77, PROF ORAL BIOL, SCH DENT, UNIV CALIF, SAN FRANCISCO, 70- *Concurrent Pos:* Nat Health & Med Res Coun dent res fel, 60-61; res teacher trainee, Med Ctr, Univ Calif, San Francisco, 61-63, fel, 63-64; biochem consult oral calculus study, Sect Epidemiol, USPHS, San Francisco, 64-65; Am Col Dent trainee, Phys Biol Sect, Inst Advan Educ Dent Res, 65; USPHS res career develop award, 65-70; vis scientist, Sch Dent, Univ Lund, 67-68; mem, Nat Caries Prog Adv Comt, Nat Inst Dent Res, 72-75 & Dent Drug Prod Adv Comt, Food & Drug Admin, 74-78. *Mem:* Am Inst Oral Biol; Int Asn Dent Res; Europ Orgn Caries Res; AAAS; Am Soc Microbiol. *Res:* Dental caries; microradiography and microhardness of enamel; chemistry; mucoprotein chemistry and biosynthesis; bacterial polysaccharides, chemistry and synthesis; dental plaque, chemistry and microbiology. *Mailing Add:* Dept of Oral Med Hosp Dent Univ of Calif Sch of Dent San Francisco CA 94143

NEWBURG, EDWARD A, b Indianapolis, Ind, Dec 22, 29; m 59. APPLIED MATHEMATICS. *Educ:* Purdue Univ, BS, 52, MS, 53; Univ Ill, PhD(math), 58. *Prof Exp:* Mathematician, Nuclear Div, Combustion Eng, Inc, 58-61; res scientist, Travelers Res Ctr, Inc, 61-66; assoc prof math, Worcester Polytech Inst, 66-70; assoc prof, Va Commonwealth Univ, 70-74; PROF MATH & HEAD DEPT, ROCHESTER INST TECHNOL, 74- *Concurrent Pos:* From adj asst prof to adj assoc prof, Hartford Grad Ctr, Rensselaer Polytech Inst, 60-70. *Mem:* Soc Indust & Appl Math. *Mailing Add:* Dept of Math Rochester Inst Technol Rochester NY 14623

NEWBURGER, JEROLD, b Saskatoon, Can, Oct 18, 23; US citizen; m 57; c 2. PHARMOCOKINETICS. *Educ:* Temple Univ, BS, 51, MS, 54; Univ Ky, PhD(pharm), 74. *Prof Exp:* Instr physics, Temple Univ Col Pharm, 53-68; instr, Univ Ky Col Pharm, 68-73; asst prof, 73-80, ASSOC PROF PHARM, UNIV TEX COL PHARM, 80- *Concurrent Pos:* Consult, Southwest Res Inst, 81- *Mem:* Sigma Xi; Am Asn Col Pharm; AAAS. *Res:* Biopharmaceutics; photochemistry. *Mailing Add:* 7400 Mesa Dr Austin TX 78731

NEWBURGH, ROBERT WARREN, b Sioux City, Iowa, Mar 22, 22; m 47, 79; c 2. BIOCHEMISTRY. *Educ:* Univ Iowa, BS, 49; Univ Wis, MS, 51, PhD(biochem), 53. *Prof Exp:* Asst biochem, Univ Wis, 49-53; res assoc, Sci Res Inst, Ore State Univ, 53-54, from asst prof to assoc prof, 54-61, asst dir, Sci Res Inst, 62-72, chmn, Dept Biochem & Biophys, 68-76, dean, Grad Sch, 76-80, prof biochem, 61-80; SECT HEAD, MOLECULAR GENETICS BIOSCI, NSF, 79- *Concurrent Pos:* Am Cancer Soc grant & assoc prof, Univ Conn, 60-61; vis prof, Univ Calif, San Diego, 70-71; consult, NIH, 66-74. *Mem:* Am Chem Soc; Am Soc Biol Chem; Am Soc Neurochem; Toxicol Soc. *Res:* Neural development; insect biochemistry. *Mailing Add:* 9600 Overlea Dr Rockville MD 20850

NEWBURGH, RONALD GERALD, b Boston, Mass, Feb 21, 26; m 57, 70; c 2. ELECTROMAGNETISM. *Educ:* Harvard Univ, AB, 45; Mass Inst Technol, PhD(physics), 59. *Prof Exp:* Sr chemist, Electronics Corp Am, 49-53, consult, 53-55 & 57-59; res physicist, Comstock & Wescott, Inc, 59-61; res physicist, Air Force Cambridge Res Labs, 61-76; SECT CHIEF, ROME AIR DEVELOP CTR, HANSCOM AFB, 76- *Mem:* Am Phys Soc. *Res:* Physics of rotating systems; special and general relativity. *Mailing Add:* Rome Air Develop Ctr/EEC Hanscom AFB Bedford MA 01731

NEWBURN, RAY LEON, JR, b Rock Island, Ill, Jan 9, 33; m 68; c 2. ASTRONOMY. *Educ:* Calif Inst Technol, BS, 54, MS, 55. *Prof Exp:* Res engr, 56-60, sr scientist lunar & planetary sci sect, 60-62, sci specialist, 62-65, sci group supvr, 65-72, mem tech staff, 73-80, STAFF SCIENTIST, PLANETARY ATMOSPHERES SECT, SPACE SCI DIV, JET PROPULSION LAB, CALIF INST TECHNOL, 72-, SCI TEAM LEADER, 80-, LEADER, INT HALLEY WATCH & MGR INT HALLEY WATCH, PASADENA OFF, 81- *Mem:* AAAS; Am Astron Soc; Am Geophys Union; Int Astron Union. *Res:* Ground based and space probe research in astronomy of the solar system, especially photometry and physical modeling of comets. *Mailing Add:* 3226 Emerald Isle Dr Glendale CA 91206

NEWBURY, DALE ELWOOD, b Danville, Pa, May 15, 47; m 69; c 2. MATERIALS SCIENCE, ANALYTICAL CHEMISTRY. *Educ:* Lehigh Univ, BS, 69; Oxford Univ, DPhil(metall), 72. *Prof Exp:* Res staff metall, 72-79, GROUPLEADER, MICROANALYSIS RES GROUP, NAT BUR STANDARDS, 79- *Concurrent Pos:* Nat Res Coun fel & res metallurgist, Nat Bur Standards, 72-73; tech chmn, Microbeam Anal Soc, 78-79 & Nat Coun, Microbeam Anal Soc, 79-81. *Honors & Awards:* Hardy Gold Medal, Am Inst Metall Engrs, 73; Corning Award, Microbeam Anal Soc, 75; US Dept Com Bronze Medal, 80 & Silver Medal, 81. *Mem:* Microbeam Anal Soc; Am Soc Testing & Mat. *Res:* Development of techniques of microanalysis by electron and ion microbeams; calculation of the properties of electron interactions in solids by Monte Carlo simulation techniques; studies of contrast mechanisms in scanning electron microscopy; analytical electron microscopy. *Mailing Add:* Chem Bldg (222)/A121 Nat Bur of Standards Washington DC 20234

NEWBURY, ROBERT W(ILLIAM), b Winnipeg, Man, June 16, 39; m 61; c 2. HYDROLOGY, ENGINEERING. *Educ:* Univ Man, BSc, 62, MSc, 64; Johns Hopkins Univ, PhD(eng sci), 68. *Prof Exp:* Res engr, Man Hydrol, 66-68; prof eng & earth sci, Univ Man, 68-75; SR RES SCIENTIST, CAN DEPT FISHERIES & ENVIRON, 75- *Concurrent Pos:* Mem, Int Hydrol Decade; vis prof, Univ Man, 75- *Res:* Physical hydrology; geomorphology; water resources engineering; permafrost hydrology; reservoir erosion and sedimentation. *Mailing Add:* Freshwater Inst 501 University Crescent Winnipeg MB R3T 2N6 Can

NEWBY, FRANK ARMON, JR, b Columbus, Kans, Dec 4, 32; m 61; c 4. PHYSICAL CHEMISTRY. *Educ:* Univ Kans, BS, 54, PhD(chem), 64. *Prof Exp:* From asst prof to assoc prof phys chem, 59-70, PROF PHYS CHEM, E TENN STATE UNIV, 70- *Mem:* AAAS; Am Chem Soc. *Res:* Coordination compound equilibria in non-aqueous solvents by phase rule and spectrophotometric studies. *Mailing Add:* ETenn State Univ Box 23350A Johnson City TN 37614

NEWBY, NEAL D(OW), b Alden, Kans, Mar 7, 99; m 24; c 1. ELECTRICAL ENGINEERING. *Educ:* Univ Kans, BS, 22, EE, 48. *Prof Exp:* Engr, Develop & Res Dept, Am Tel & Tel Co, New York, 22-34; mem tech staff, Bell Tel Labs, 34-63; RES CONSULT, 63- *Concurrent Pos:* Mem, Am Inst Physics. *Mem:* Asn Comput Mach; sr mem Inst Elec & Electronics Engrs; Am Phys Soc. *Res:* High speed machine switching and signaling systems; electronic circuitory and data storage; electronic computers and data processing systems; microwave logic; radar; magnetic devices and circuitry. *Mailing Add:* 228 E Cordova Rd Santa Fe NM 87501

NEWBY, NEAL DOW, JR, b New York, NY, Mar 18, 26; m 64; c 2. THEORETICAL PHYSICS. *Educ:* Columbia Univ, BS, 49; Harvard Univ, MA, 51; Ind Univ, PhD(physics), 59. *Prof Exp:* Instr math, Univ Ohio, 52-53; res assoc physics, Univ Calif, Berkeley, 59-61; asst prof, Univ Southern Calif, 61-63; physicist, Autonetics, 64-67; lectr, Calif State Col, 69; prof physics, Edinboro State Col, 69-80. *Concurrent Pos:* Tutor, San Juan-Santa Clara Indian Pueblos, 81- *Mem:* Am Phys Soc. *Res:* Classical mechanics; relativity. *Mailing Add:* Box 1072 San Juan Pueblo NM 87566

NEWBY, WILLIAM EDWARD, b Kansas City, Mo, Nov 17, 23; m 49; c 3. PHYSICAL CHEMISTRY, ORGANIC CHEMISTRY. *Educ:* Univ Kans City, BA, 47; Northwestern Univ, PhD(chem), 50. *Prof Exp:* Res chemist, Jackson Lab, 50-52, res supvr, 53-58, res supvr petrol lab, 58-59, res supvr plant tech sect, 59-60, res supvr, Jackson Lab, 60-68, supvr mkt res, 68-70, mkt planning mgr, Org Chem Dept, Dyes & Chem Div, 70-78, MKT RES ASSOC, CHEM & PIGMENTS DEPT, E I DU PONT DE NEMOURS & CO, INC, 78- *Mem:* Am Chem Soc; Chem Mkt Res Asn. *Res:* Catalytic hydrogenation; fuel deposit and combustion phenomena; synthesis and application of dyes for synthetic fibers. *Mailing Add:* Chem & Pigments Dept E I du Pont de Nemours & Co Inc Wilmington DE 19898

NEWCOMB, ELDON HENRY, b Columbia, Mo, Jan 19, 19; m 49; c 3. PLANT CYTOLOGY. *Educ:* Univ Mo, AB, 40, AM, 42; Univ Wis, PhD(bot), 49. *Prof Exp:* From asst prof to assoc prof, 49-58, PROF BOT, UNIV WIS-MADISON, 58- *Concurrent Pos:* Guggenheim fel, Univ Calif, 51-52; NSF sci fac fel, Harvard Univ, 63-64; consult, Shell Develop Co, 54-59; US managing ed, Protoplasma, 69-73; mem photorespiration exped of R/V Alpha Helix to Great Barrier Reef, 73; Fulbright sr res scholar, Australian Nat Univ, 76; mem, Univ Nations Oceanog Lab Syst R/V Alpha Helix Rev Comt, 78-79; dir, Inst Plant Develop, Univ Wis-Madison, 79- *Mem:* Bot Soc Am; Am Soc Cell Biol; Am Soc Plant Physiologists. *Res:* Plant cell fine structure in relation to function; plant microbodies; green prokaryotic algae associated with didemnid ascidians. *Mailing Add:* Dept of Bot Univ of Wis Madison WI 53706

NEWCOMB, HARVEY RUSSELL, b Bismarck, NDak, Oct 6, 16; m 53; c 2. MICROBIOLOGY. *Educ:* Denison Univ, AB, 39; Syracuse Univ, MS, 52, PhD(microbiol), 54. *Prof Exp:* Res bacteriologist, Borden Co, NY, 53-55; res asst prof microbiol, Dept Bact & Bot & Biol Res Labs, Syracuse Univ, 55-64; lab dir, Raritan Bay & Hudson-Champlain Water Pollution Control Projs, USPHS, NJ, 64-65; PROF MICROBIOL & CHMN DEPT, COL OSTEOP MED & SURG, 65- *Mem:* AAAS; Am Soc Microbiol; Am Pub Health Asn; NY Acad Sci. *Res:* Radiation effects on microorganisms; bacterial spores; preservation and wholesomeness of irradiated foods; physiology and industrial production of lactic acid bacteria; physiology of wood-rotting basidiomycetes; gnotobiotic technology; metabolic functions of serotonin. *Mailing Add:* Dept of Microbiol Col of Osteop Med & Surg Des Moines IA 50312

NEWCOMB, MARTIN, b Mishawaka, Ind, Nov 17, 46; m 67; c 1. CHEMISTRY. *Educ:* Wabash Col, BA, 69; Univ Ill, PhD(chem), 73. *Prof Exp:* Fel chem, Univ Calif, Los Angeles, 73-75; asst prof, 75-81, ASSOC PROF CHEM, TEX A&M UNIV, 81- *Concurrent Pos:* Camille & Henry Dreyfus teacher-scholar, Dreyfus Found, 80-85. *Mem:* Am Chem Soc; Royal Chem Soc; AAAS; NY Acad Sci; Sigma Xi. *Res:* Synthetic and mechanistic organic chemistry; electrophilic asymmetric syntheses; electron transfer reactions and host-guest chemistry. *Mailing Add:* Dept Chem Tex A&M Univ College Station TX 77843

NEWCOMB, ROBERT LEWIS, b Oceanside, Calif, Aug 2, 32; m 58; c 3. STATISTICS, SURVEY SAMPLE DESIGN. *Educ:* Univ Redlands, BA, 59; Univ Calif, Santa Barbara, PhD(math), 67. *Prof Exp:* Res assoc statist, Univ Calif, Santa Barbara, 68-69; LECTR STATIST, UNIV CALIF, IRVINE, 69- *Mem:* Math Asn Am; Am Statist Asn. *Res:* Computer-graphics in statistics education. *Mailing Add:* Sch of Soc Sci Univ of Calif Irvine CA 92717

NEWCOMB, ROBERT WAYNE, b Glendale, Calif, June 27, 33; m 54; c 2. ELECTRICAL ENGINEERING. *Educ:* Purdue Univ, BS, 55; Stanford Univ, MSc, 57; Univ Calif, Berkeley, PhD(elec eng), 60. *Prof Exp:* Assoc prof elec eng, Stanford Univ, 63-70; PROF ELEC ENG, UNIV MD, COLLEGE PARK, 70- *Concurrent Pos:* Fulbright fel, Australia, 63-64; invited prof, Cath Univ Louvain, 67-68; Fulbright fel, Malaysia, 76. *Mem:* Fel Inst Elec & Electronics Eng; Soc Indust & Appl Math; Math Asn Am; Australian Inst Radio & Electronics Engrs. *Res:* Network theory; microsystems and systems theory; nonliners systems via the semistate, design of hysteresis; new number bases for computers, especially the fibonacci computer; adaptive hearing aids, surface acoustic wave theory; neurol-type microsystems; systems theoryas applied to university administration. *Mailing Add:* Dept of Elec Eng Univ of Md College Park MD 20742

NEWCOMB, THOMAS F, b Buffalo, NY, June 22, 27; m 51; c 6. INTERNAL MEDICINE, HEMATOLOGY. *Educ:* Univ Pittsburgh, BS, 49, MD, 51; Am Bd Internal Med, dipl. *Prof Exp:* From intern med to resident hemat, Univ Pa, 51-53; resident med, Vet Admin Hosp, Seattle, Wash, 53-54; res fel hemat, Univ Wash, 54-55; Fulbright scholar med, Rikshospitalet Coagulation Lab, Oslo, Norway, 55-56; sr asst resident, Peter Bent Brigham Hosp, Boston, 56-57, jr assoc med, Hosp & investr, Howard Hughes Med Inst, 57-59, assoc dir, Richard C Curtis Hemat Lab, 58-59; from asst prof to prof med, Col Med, Univ Fla, 59-76, prof biochem, 71-74, dir hemat, 59-64, head div, 64-68, actg chmn dept biochem, 69-71; dir res serv, 72-73, asst chief med dir res & develop, Cent Off, Vet Admin, 73-78; CHIEF STAFF, AUDIE L MURPHY VET ADMIN MED CTR, 78- *Concurrent Pos:* Instr, Harvard Med Sch, 58-59; consult, Vet Admin Hosp, Lake City, Fla, 62-68, assoc chief of staff res & educ & chief research serv, Gainesville, 68-72; prof med, Univ Tex Med Sch, 78- *Mem:* Fel Am Col Physicians; Am Soc Hemat; Am Fedn Clin Res; Int Soc Hemat. *Res:* Hemostasis. *Mailing Add:* Audie L Murphy 7400 Merton Minter Blvd San Antonio TX 78284

NEWCOMB, WILLIAM A, b San Jose, Calif, Sept 4, 27; m 64; c 2. MAGNETOHYDRODYNAMICS. *Educ:* Cornell Univ, BA, 48, PhD(theoret physics), 52. *Prof Exp:* Physicist, Proj Matterhorn, Forrestal Res Ctr, Princeton Univ, 52-55; PHYSICIST, LAWRENCE LIVERMORE LAB, UNIV CALIF, 55- *Concurrent Pos:* Adj prof, Univ Calif, Davis. *Mem:* Am Phys Soc; Math Soc Am. *Res:* Magneto-hydrodynamics and plasma physics. *Mailing Add:* Lawrence Livermore Nat Lab Univ of Calif Livermore CA 94550

NEWCOMBE, DAVID S, environmental health sciences, arthritis, see previous edition

NEWCOMBE, HOWARD BORDEN, b Kentville, NS, Sept 19, 14; m 42; c 3. RADIATION GENETICS, HUMAN GENETICS. *Educ:* Acadia Univ, BSc, 35; McGill Univ, PhD(genetics), 39. *Hon Degrees:* DSc, McGill Univ, 66, Acadia Univ, 70. *Prof Exp:* 1851 sci res scholar, John Innes Hort Inst, Eng, 39-40; sci officer, Brit Ministry Supply, 40-41; res assoc genetics, Carnegie Inst Technol, 46-47; head, Biol Br, Atomic Energy Can, Ltd, 47-70, head, Pop Res Br, 70-79; CONSULT, 79- *Concurrent Pos:* Sci adv, Sci Comt Atomic Radiation, UN, 55-66; mem expert adv panel human genetics, WHO, 61-, mem, Int Comn Radiol Protection, 65-77; vis prof, Ind Univ, 63. *Mem:* Am Soc Human Genetics (pres, 65); Genetics Soc Am (secy, 56-58); Radiation Res Soc; Genetics Soc Can (pres, 64-65); Royal Soc Can. *Res:* Genetics; epidemiology; public health. *Mailing Add:* 67 Hillcrest Ave PO Box 135 Deep River ON K0J 1P0 Can

NEWCOME, MARSHALL MILLAR, b Chicago, Ill, Nov 22, 26; m 49; c 2. ANALYTICAL CHEMISTRY. *Educ:* Ill Inst Technol, BS, 49; Univ Wash, Seattle, PhD(chem), 54. *Prof Exp:* Res chemist, 54-74, SUPVR ANAL CHEM, MORTON CHEM CO, 74- *Mem:* Am Chem Soc. *Res:* Electronic instrumentation in chemical analysis. *Mailing Add:* 546 W Kimball Ave Woodstock IL 60098

NEWCOMER, WILBUR STANLEY, b Turbotville, Pa, Nov 25, 19; m 46; c 4. PHYSIOLOGY. *Educ:* Pa State Univ, BS, 41; Cornell Univ, MS, 42, PhD(zool), 48. *Prof Exp:* Asst chem, Lycoming Col, 38-39; asst zool, Cornell Univ, 42-44 & 46-47; from instr to asst prof biol, Hamilton Col, NY, 47-50; from asst prof to assoc prof, 50-58, PROF PHYSIOL, OKLA STATE UNIV, 58- *Concurrent Pos:* NIH spec res fel, 62. *Honors & Awards:* Hutyra Medal, Univ Vet Sci, Hungary. *Mem:* Soc Exp Biol & Med; Am Physiol Soc. *Res:* Physiology of thyroid and adrenal glands, especially in birds. *Mailing Add:* Dept of Physiol Sci Okla State Univ Stillwater OK 74074

NEWELL, ALLEN, b San Francisco, Calif, Mar 19, 27; m 47; c 1. COMPUTER SCIENCE, PSYCHOLOGY. *Educ:* Stanford Univ, BS, 49; Carnegie Inst Technol, PhD(indust admin), 57. *Prof Exp:* Res scientist, Rand Corp, 50-61; res scientist inst prof systs & commun sci, 61-67, UNIV PROF COMPUT SCI, CARNEGIE-MELLON UNIV, 67- *Concurrent Pos:* Lectr, Carnegie-Mellon Univ, 57-61; consult, Rand Corp, 61-; mem adv comt comput, Stanford Univ, 66-70; mem comput sci study sect, NIH, 67-71; chmn panel comput, Comt Res Life Sci, Nat Acad Sci, 67-69; consult, Xerox Res Lab, Calif, 71- *Honors & Awards:* Harry Goode Mem Award, Am Fedn Info Processing Socs, 71; John Danz Lectr, Univ Wash, 72; A M Turing Award, Asn Comput Mach, 75. *Mem:* Nat Acad Sci; AAAS; Asn Comput Mach; Am Psychol Asn; Inst Elec & Electronics Eng. *Res:* Computer programs that exhibit intelligence; information processing psychology; programming systems and computer structures. *Mailing Add:* Carnegie-Mellon Univ Pittsburgh PA 15213

NEWELL, DARRELL E, b Audubon, Iowa, Sept 24, 26; m 47; c 2. ELECTRICAL ENGINEERING. *Educ:* Iowa State Univ, BS, 52; Univ Iowa, MS, 56, PhD(elec eng), 58. *Prof Exp:* Engr, Collins Radio, 52-54 & 58-59; from instr to assoc prof elec eng, Univ Iowa, 54-61; eng mgr, Bendix Corp, 61-65; pres, Newell Labs, Inc, 65-66, dir eng, CTS Knights Corp, 66-68; assoc prof indust & technol, 69-77, PROF INDUST & TECHNOL, NORTHERN ILL UNIV, 77- *Concurrent Pos:* Mem bd dirs, CTS Knights Corp, 69- & Bodelle Corp, 71- *Mem:* Inst Elec & Electronics Engrs (treas). *Res:* Originated temperature compensated crystal oscillators. *Mailing Add:* Dept of Indust & Technol Northern Ill Univ DeKalb IL 60115

NEWELL, FRANK WILLIAM, b St Paul, Minn, Jan 14, 16; m 42; c 4. OPHTHALMOLOGY. *Educ:* Loyola Univ, Ill, MD, 39; Univ Minn, MSc, 42; Am Bd Ophthal, dipl. *Prof Exp:* Fel, Univ Minn, 40-42; res fel, Northwestern Univ, 46-47, instr, 47-50, assoc, 50-53; assoc prof, 53-55, chmn dept ophthal, 53-81, PROF OPTHAL, SCH MED, UNIV CHICAGO, 55- *Concurrent Pos:* Ed in chief, Am J Ophthal, 65- *Mem:* Am Ophthal Soc; Soc Exp Biol & Med; Pan-Am Asn Ophthal (pres, 81-83); Am Acad Ophthal & Otolaryngol (pres, 75). *Res:* Pharmacology and physiology of the eye. *Mailing Add:* Univ of Chicago Eye Res Labs 939 E 57th St Chicago IL 60637

NEWELL, GORDON FRANK, b Dayton, Ohio, Jan 26, 25; m 49; c 2. APPLIED MATHEMATICS. *Educ:* Union Col, BS, 45; Univ Ill, PhD(physics), 50. *Prof Exp:* Lectr physics & math, Union Col, 45-46; asst physics, Univ Ill, 46-49, fel, 50; fel appl math, Univ Md, 50-51, res assoc, 51-52; res assoc, Brown Univ, 53-54, from asst prof to prof, 54-66; PROF TRANSP ENG, UNIV CALIF, BERKELEY, 66- *Concurrent Pos:* Sloan res fel, 56-59; Fulbright fel, 63-; vis prof, Univ Calif, Berkeley, 65-66. *Mem:* Soc Indust & Appl Math; Opers Res Soc Am. *Res:* Operations research; transportation and traffic engineering. *Mailing Add:* Inst Transp Studies Univ of Calif Berkeley CA 94720

NEWELL, GORDON WILFRED, b Madison, Wis, Aug 27, 21; m 48; c 4. TOXICOLOGY. *Educ:* Univ Wis, BA, 43, MS, 44, PhD(biochem), 48; Am Bd Indust Hyg, dipl. *Prof Exp:* Novadel-Agene fel, Univ Wis, 48-49; res biochemist, Wallace & Tiernan Co, Inc, 49-50; sr biochemist, Stanford Res Inst, 50-66, dir div indust biol, 66-68, dir, Dept Toxicol, 68-78, assoc dir, Bd Toxicol & Environ Health Hazards, 78-80; MEM STAFF, NAT RES COUN, NAT ACAD SCI, 80- *Concurrent Pos:* Consult adv comn animal resources, NIH, 65-68; coun mem, Am Asn Accreditation Animal Care, 67-78; assoc ed, J Lab Animal Care, 64- *Mem:* Am Acad Indust Hyg; Soc Toxicol; Environ Mutagen Soc; Am Inst Nutrit; NY Acad Sci. *Res:* Animal nutrition and metabolism; toxicological studies on chemicals and food products; biochemical toxicology of food additives, environmental, industrial, and military chemicals, drugs, and pesticides; toxicity of pollutants to fish and wildlife; nutrition and metabolism; mutagenesis, carcinogenesis, teratology, and inhalation toxicology. *Mailing Add:* Nat Res Coun Nat Acad Sci 2101 Constitution Ave Washington DC 20418

NEWELL, JON ALBERT, b St Louis, Mo, Aug 5, 41; div; c 1. BIOCHEMISTRY. *Educ:* Okla State Univ, BS, 63, PhD(biochem), 67. *Prof Exp:* Technician anal chem, Enid Bd Trade Lab, 59-62; res asst toxicol, Okla State Univ, 60-63, asst flavor chem, 63-67; sr res chemist food & fermentation res, 67-75, res mgr biochem, 75-80, RES MGR PROCESS OPTIMIZATION, ANHEUSER-BUSCH, INC, 80- *Concurrent Pos:* Nestle fel, Inst Food Technologists, Univ Chicago, 66. *Mem:* Am Chem Soc. *Res:* Use of unconventional protein sources in foods; identification of flavorful constituents of foods; process control using microprocessors. *Mailing Add:* Yeast Prod Res Dept 721 Pestalozzi St St Louis MO 63118

NEWELL, JONATHAN CLARK, b Worcester, Mass, Oct 13, 43; m; c 2. PHYSIOLOGY, BIOMEDICAL ENGINEERING. *Educ:* Rensselaer Polytech Inst, BEE, 65, MEngr, 68; Albany Med Col, PhD(physiol), 74. *Prof Exp:* Supv engr, 70-72, asst prof biomed eng, Rensselaer Polytech inst, 74-79, asst prof, 74-79, ASSOC PROF PHYSIOL, ALBANY MED COL, 79-; ASSOC PROF BIOMED ENG, RENSSELAER POLYTECH INST, 79- *Concurrent Pos:* Consult, Trauma Res Unit, Albany Med Col, 74- *Mem:* Am Physiol Soc; Inst Elec & Electronics Engrs; NY Acad Sci; Am Thoracic Soc; Biomed Eng Soc. *Res:* Pulmonary hemodynamics and mechanics; modelling of physiological systems. *Mailing Add:* Ctr for Biomed Eng Rensselaer Polytech Inst Troy NY 12181

NEWELL, KATHLEEN, b Stafford, Kans, Sept 1, 22. NUTRITION. *Educ:* Kans State Univ, BS, 44; Univ Wis, MS, 51; Univ Tenn, PhD(nutrit), 73. *Prof Exp:* Admin ther & teaching dietitian, Butterworth Hosp, Grand Rapids, Mich, 45-47; ther & teaching dietitian, Univ Colo Med Ctr, 47-49, educ dir dietetic intern, 52-56; asst prof dietetics, Loretto Heights Col & Glockner Penrose Hosp, Colo Springs, 56-58; asst prof home econ, Univ Wyo, 58-62; asst prof, 62-69 & 72-77, ASSOC PROF FOODS & NUTRIT, KANS STATE UNIV, 77- *Mem:* Am Dietetic Asn; Sigma Xi; Geront Soc; Soc Nutrit Educ; Nutrit Today Soc. *Res:* Nutrition education; human nutrition. *Mailing Add:* Dept Foods & Nutrit Kans State Univ Manhattan KS 66506

NEWELL, LAURENCE CUTLER, b Alexandria, Nebr, Apr 12, 05; m 28; c 3. AGRONOMY. *Educ:* Hastings Col, AB, 26; Univ Nebr, MSc, 33, PhD(agron), 40. *Prof Exp:* Teacher & prin, Davenport High Sch, Nebr, 27-31; asst agron, Univ Nebr, 31-33; county agr agt, Saunders & Stanton Counties, Nebr, 33-34; agt, Div Plant Explor & Introd, 34, asst agronomist, Soil Conserv Nurseries, Ames, Iowa, 35, from asst agronomist to agronomist, Forage & Range Res Br, Crops Res Div, Nebr, 36-54, RES AGRONOMIST, NCENT REGION, AGR RES SERV, USDA, 54-; EMER PROF AGRON, UNIV NEBR-LINCOLN, 74- *Concurrent Pos:* From asst to prof agron, Univ Nebr-Lincoln, 36-74. *Honors & Awards:* Soc Range Mgt Award. *Mem:* AAAS; fel Am Soc Agron; hon mem Soil Conserv Soc Am; Soc Range Mgt. *Res:* Grass breeding and pasture management, especially development of breeding procedures and seed production practices resulting in the release and propagation of improved varieties of forage grasses for seeding pastures and rangelands. *Mailing Add:* 1315 N 37th St Lincoln NE 68503

NEWELL, MARJORIE PAULINE, b Holden, Alta; nat US. ORGANIC CHEMISTRY. *Educ:* Univ Fla, BS, 53, PhD(biochem), 58. *Prof Exp:* Asst biochem, Univ Fla, 55-58; res chemist org chem, 58-69, SR SCIENTIST, RES DEPT, R J REYNOLDS TOBACCO CO, 69- *Mem:* AAAS; Am Chem Soc. *Res:* Physical and chemical properties of tobacco and smoke; tracer techniques with radioisotopes. *Mailing Add:* 3901 Guinevere Lane Winston-Salem NC 27104

NEWELL, NANETTE, b Pensacola, Fla, Aug 20, 51. RECOMBINANT DNA TECHNOLOGY. *Educ:* Lewis & Clark Col, BS, 73; Johns Hopkins Sch Med, PhD(biochem), 78. *Prof Exp:* Fel, Univ Wis, 78-80; asst prof genetics, Reed Col, 80-81; ANALYST, OFF TECHNOL ASSESSMENT, 81- *Mem:* AAAS. *Res:* Scientific aspects of genetic screening in the workplace and the commercial development of biotechnology. *Mailing Add:* Off Technol Assessment Congress US Washington DC 20510

NEWELL, NORMAN DENNIS, b Chicago, Ill, Jan 27, 09; m 28, 72, 73. GEOLOGY. *Educ:* Univ Kans, BS, 29, AM, 31; Yale Univ, PhD(geol), 33. *Prof Exp:* Asst geologist, Geol Surv, Kans, 29-33; from instr to asst prof geol, Univ Kans, 34-37; assoc prof, Univ Wis, 37-45; prof, 45-78, EMER PROF

GEOL, COLUMBIA UNIV, 78-; EMER CUR INVERT FOSSILS & HIST GEOL, AM MUS NATURAL HIST, 78- *Concurrent Pos:* Sterling fel, Yale Univ, 33-34; geologist, Geol Surv, Kans, 35-37; lectr, Univ Pa, City Col New York & Yale Univ; US Dept State deleg, Int Geol Cong, Moscow, 37; co-ed, Paleont, 39-42; consult, Govt Peru, 42-43; leader, Exped Geol & Petrol Resources Lake Titicaca, Peru-Bolivia, 43-44, Am Mus Natural Hist-Columbia Univ Exped, Peru, 47 & Andros Island, Behamas, 50 & 51; cur invert fossils & hist geol, Am Mus Natural Hist, 45-78; leader invests limestone reefs, WTex, 49-52; leader, Pac Sci Bds, Nat Res Coun Exped Coral Atoll, Raroia, Tuamotu Group, SPac, 52; mem, Smithsonian Coun, 66-; mem, Scripps Inst Oceanog Exped Carmarsel, Micronesia, 67; exchange scholar, Nat Acad Sci, USSR, 78. *Honors & Awards:* Mary Thompson Clark Medal, Nat Acad Sci, 60; Distinguished Serv Citation, Univ Kans, 61; Medal, Univ Hiroshima, 64; Hayden Mem Award, Acad Natural Sci, Philadelphia, 65; Verrill Medal, Yale Univ, 66; Paleont Soc Medal, 79; Raymond C Moore Medal, Soc Econ Paleontologist & Mineralogists, 80. *Mem:* Nat Acad Sci; fel Geol Soc Am; Soc Econ Paleontologists & Mineralogists; fel Paleont Soc (vpres, 48, pres, 61); Soc Study Evolution (pres, 49). *Res:* Invertebrate paleontology; micropaleontology; stratigraphy; petroleum geology; coral reefs; geology of South America. *Mailing Add:* Am Mus Natural Hist Central Park W & 79 St New York NY 10024

NEWELL, REGINALD EDWARD, b Peterborough, Eng, Apr 9, 31; m 54; c 4. METEOROLOGY. *Educ:* Univ Birmingham, BSc, 54; Mass Inst Technol, SM, 56, ScD(meteorol), 60. *Prof Exp:* Res asst meteorol, 54-60, mem staff, Div Sponsored Res, 60-61, from asst prof to assoc prof, 61-69, PROF METEOROL, MASS INST TECHNOL, 69- *Concurrent Pos:* Pres, Int Comn Climat, Int Asn Meteorol & Atmospheric Physics 77-; mem, Int Comn Atmospheric Chem & Global Pollution, Int Asn Meteorol & Atmospheric Physics, 71- *Mem:* Int Asn Meteorol & Atmospheric Physics; Am Meteorol Soc; Am Geophys Union; Sigma Xi; fel Royal Meteorol Soc. *Res:* Climate variations; atmospheric trace constituents. planetary circulations. *Mailing Add:* Dept Meteorol 54-1520 Mass Inst Technol Cambridge MA 02139

NEWELL, RUSSELL A, engineering, see previous edition

NEWELL, WILLIAM ANDREWS, b Holyoke, Mass, Mar 3, 20; m 42; c 3. TEXTILES. *Educ:* NC State Col, BS, 47. *Prof Exp:* Managing ed, Textile World, McGraw-Hill Publ Co, 47-52; dir res, Sch Textiles, NC State Col, 52-61; mgr prod eng, Whitin Mach Works, 61-65; tech dir, Textile Div, Kendall Co, 65-71, dir gen, Mulsant, SA, France, 71-74, mgr cent qual control & regulatory compliance, 74-82; RETIRED. *Mem:* Am Asn Textile Technol. *Res:* Textile engineering and technology. *Mailing Add:* Kendall Co 1 Federal St Boston MA 02110

NEWELL-MORRIS, LAURA, b Whitehall, NY, May 16, 33. PHYSICAL ANTHROPOLOGY. *Educ:* Univ NMex, BA, 54; Northwestern Univ, MA, 57; Univ Wash, PhD(anthrop), 66. *Prof Exp:* Asst cur archaeol, State Mus NY, 54-55; res asst phys anthrop, Fels Res Inst, 59-60; from instr to assoc prof, 64-81, PROF PHYS ANTHROP, UNIV WASH, 81- *Concurrent Pos:* Assoc ed, Am J Phys Anthrop & NIH res award, 75; consult ed, Am J Primatal. *Mem:* Am Anthrop Asn; Am Asn Phys Anthrop; Brit Soc Study Human Biol; Int Primatol Soc. *Res:* Growth, especially of lower primates and population as a unit of study. *Mailing Add:* Dept of Anthrop Univ of Wash Seattle WA 98195

NEWEY, HERBERT ALFRED, b Logan, Utah, June 11, 16; m 41; c 3. ORGANIC POLYMER CHEMISTRY. *Educ:* Utah State Col, BS, 38; Mass Inst Technol, PhD(org chem), 41. *Prof Exp:* Res chemist, Am Cyanamid Co, 41-46; chemist, Shell Develop Co Div, Shell Oil Co, 46-62, supvr res, 62-73; CONSULT CHEMIST, 73- *Res:* Epoxy and polyester resins for surface coatings, laminates and adhesives. *Mailing Add:* 730 Los Palos Dr Lafayette CA 94549

NEWHOUSE, ALBERT, b Cambrai, France, May 31, 14; nat US; wid; c 2. MATHEMATICS, COMPUTER SCIENCE. *Educ:* Univ Chicago, PhD(math), 40. *Prof Exp:* Asst Math, Tulane Univ, 39-41; instr, Univ Ala, 41-42, Univ Nebr, 42-44 & Rice Inst, 44-46; from instr to asst prof, 46-48, from assoc prof to prof math, 48-70, chmn dept math, 52-54, asst dir comput & data processing ctr, 56-60, prof comput sci, 70-78, EMER PROF COMPUT SCI, UNIV HOUSTON, 78- *Concurrent Pos:* Consult, Res Lab, Humble Oil & Ref Co, 58, Camco, Inc, 61-70 & Symbiotics Int, 70-74. *Mem:* AAAS; Asn Comput Mach; Am Math Soc; Soc Indust & Appl Math; Math Asn Am. *Res:* Modern algebra; theory of groups; numerical methods; formal languages. *Mailing Add:* 7907 Braesview Lane Houston TX 77071

NEWHOUSE, KEITH N, b Chambers, Nebr, Mar 11, 24; m 47; c 3. MECHANICAL ENGINEERING. *Educ:* Univ Nebr, BS, 48, MS, 49. *Prof Exp:* Instr mech eng, Univ Nebr, 48-51, asst prof mech eng & asst utilities engr, 51-56, assoc prof & power plant engr, 56-60; res engr, Jet Propulsion Lab, Calif Inst Technol, 63-65; PROF MECH ENG, UNIV NEBR, LINCOLN, 65- *Honors & Awards:* Western Elec Fund Award, 65, res grant, 65-66; Engrs Distinction, Engrs Joint Coun, 70. *Mem:* Am Soc Mech Engrs; Nat Soc Prof Engrs; Am Soc Heating, Refrig, Air Conditioning Engrs. *Res:* Heat transfer. *Mailing Add:* Dept of Mech Eng Univ of Nebr Lincoln NE 68588

NEWHOUSE, RUSSELL C(ONWELL), b Clyde, Ohio, Dec 17, 06; m 36; c 1. ELECTRICAL ENGINEERING. *Educ:* Ohio State Univ, BEE, 29, MS, 30. *Prof Exp:* Dir Kwajalein Field Sta, Bell Tel Labs, Inc, 30-67, dir, Nike-X Radar Systs Lab, 67-71; consult engr & mgr radar dept, 71-74, CONSULT ENGR, TELEDYNE BROWN ENG, 74- *Concurrent Pos:* Consult, Air Navig Develop Bd, 54; mem President's Task Force air traffic control, Proj Beacon, 61; off electronics, Mutual Weapons Develop Prog, Off Asst Secy Defense. *Mem:* Fel Inst Elec & Electronics Engrs; Sigma Xi; AAAS. *Res:* Radio altimeters; radar; electronic computers; air navigation and traffic control. *Mailing Add:* 13 Dale Dr Chatham NJ 07928

NEWHOUSE, VERNE FREDERIC, b Tulsa, Okla, May 7, 30; m 53; c 5. MEDICAL ENTOMOLOGY. *Educ:* Pac Lutheran Col, AB, 53; Wash State Univ, MS, 55, PhD(entom), 60. *Prof Exp:* Asst zool, Wash State Univ, 54-55 & 56-57; med entomologist, Rocky Mountain Lab, 57-63, res entomologist, Arbovirus Vector Lab, 64-75, res entomologist, Leprosy & Rickettsia Br, Virol Div, 75-80, VIRAL RICKETTSIAL ZOONOSES BR, CTR DIS CONTROL, USPHS, 81- *Honors & Awards:* Best Sci Paper Year Lab Sect Group Award, Am Pub Health Asn, 68; Superior Achievement Group Award, US Dept Health, Educ & Welfare, 72. *Res:* Ecology of arthropod-borne rickettsial and viral agents and their vectors. *Mailing Add:* US Pub Health Serv Ctr Dis Control 1600 Clifton Rd Stone Mountain GA 30087

NEWHOUSE, VERNON LEOPOLD, b Mannheim, Ger, Jan 30, 28; US citizen; m 50; c 4. BIOMEDICAL ENGINEERING. *Educ:* Univ Leeds, BSc, 49, PhD(physics), 52. *Prof Exp:* Mem staff, Ferranti Comput Lab, 51-54; mem staff, Res Lab, Radio Corp Am, 54, proj engr, Comput Dept, 54-57; physicist, Gen Elec Res & Develop Ctr, NY, 57-67; prof elec eng, Sch Elec Eng, Purdue Univ, 67-73, prof med eng & coordr, 73-81; DISTINGUISHED PROF ELEC ENG, DREXEL UNIV, 82- *Concurrent Pos:* Consult, NSF, 74. *Mem:* Am Phys Soc; fel Inst Elec & Electronics Engrs; Am Inst Ultrasound Med. *Res:* Acoustic flow measurement and imaging for medical and industrial applications. *Mailing Add:* Biomed Eng & Sci Inst Drexel Univ Philadelphia PA 19104

NEWHOUSE, W JAN, b Boston, Mass, Feb 6, 26; m 50; c 4. PHYCOLOGY, SCIENCE EDUCATION. *Educ:* Dartmouth Col, BA, 49; Univ NH, MS, 52; Univ Hawaii, PhD(bot), 67. *Prof Exp:* Asst botanist, Pac Sci Bd, Nat Acad Sci, 52, botanist & phycologist, 54; dir pineapple res, Hawaiian Canneries Co, Ltd, 56-59; fruit qual analyst, Dole Corp, 59-63, dir tech serv, Philippines, 63-65; asst prof, 66-71, ASSOC PROF GEN SCI, UNIV HAWAII, HONOLULU, 71- *Concurrent Pos:* Res initiation grant, Univ Hawaii, 66, Res Coun grant, 68; chief scientist, Stanford Oceanog Exped, 68. *Mem:* AAAS; Am Soc Limnol & Oceanog; Phycol Soc Am. *Res:* Primary productivity of the oceans; biogeography of tropical Pacific Phaeophyta; ecology of marine Myxophyta; ciguatera fish toxin. *Mailing Add:* Dept of Gen Sci Univ of Hawaii 2450 Campus Rd Honolulu HI 96822

NEWILL, VAUN ARCHIE, b Mt Pleasant, Pa, Nov 11, 23; m 55; c 3. EPIDEMIOLOGY, INTERNAL MEDICINE. *Educ:* Juaniata Col, BS, 43; Univ Pittsburgh, MD, 47; Harvard Univ, SMHyg, 60. *Prof Exp:* Intern, St Francis Hosp, Pittsburgh, Pa, 47-48; resident, Harrisburg Polyclin Hosp, 48-50; resident med, Vet Admin Hosps, Buffalo, NY, 52-53 & Cleveland, Ohio, 53-54, mem staff geriat serv, 55; from instr prev med & med to sr instr, Sch Med, Western Reserve Univ, 55-60, sr instr med, 60-68, from asst prof prev med to assoc prof, 60-68; chief ecol res sect, Health Effects Res Prog, Nat Ctr Air Pollution Control, USPHS, Ohio, 67-68; chief health effects res prog, Nat Air Pollution Control Admin, NC, 68-71; mem staff, Environ Protection Agency, 71-72; tech asst, Off Sci & Technol, Exec Off of President, 72-73; spec asst to adminr, Environ Protection Agency, 73-74; asst dir, 74-78, assoc dir, 78-81, dir res & environ health div, 78-81, ASSOC DIR, MED & ENVIRON HEALTH DEPT, EXXON CORP, 81-, DIR, OPER DIV, 81- *Concurrent Pos:* Asst physician, Univ Hosps, Cleveland, 55-68 & Benjamin Rose Hosp, 57-68; attend metab, Vet Admin Hosp, Cleveland, 58-63, sr attend, 63-64; spec consult epidemiol training prog med students, Calif Dept Health, 62; vis lectr, Sch Pub Health, Harvard Univ, 62-65; med officer, Field Studies Br, Div Air Pollution, USPHS, Japan, 65; adj assoc prof, Dept Epidemiol, Sch Pub Health, Univ NC, Chapel Hill, 68-75; clin prof environ health, NY Univ. *Mem:* AAAS; Am Fedn Clin Res; Am Pub Health Asn. *Res:* Epidemiology of chronic diseases and effects of environmental pollutant exposures; information retrieval. *Mailing Add:* Med Dept Exxon Corp 1251 Ave of the Americas New York NY 10020

NEWITT, EDWARD JAMES, b Scranton, Pa, Mar 18, 27; m 48; c 5. PHYSICAL ORGANIC CHEMISTRY. *Educ:* Imp Col, Univ London, BSc, 53, PhD, 57. *Prof Exp:* Works chemist indust chem, Boots Pure Drug Co, Eng, 48-49; asst chem, Brit Coal Utilization Res Asn, 49-53; lectr inorg & phys chem, Imp Col, Univ London, 53-57; res chemist, Plastics Dept, Exp Sta, 57-59, res supvr, 59-61, sr res chemist, Wash Works, 61-62, res supvr, Electrochem Dept, Exp Sta, 62-69, prod mgr mkt, 69-70, res supvr, 70-71, develop supvr polymer prod mkt, Plastics Dept, 72-73, new prod specialist, 73-74, consult, Energy & Math Dept, 74-76, specialist, feedstocks, Central Res & Develop Dept, 76-77, SPECIALIST, PATENT DIV, E I DU PONT DE NEMOURS & CO, INC, 77- *Mem:* Am Chem Soc; Royal Inst Chemists. *Res:* Chemical kinetics; high temperature chemistry and polymer chemistry; alternate raw materials and energy sources. *Mailing Add:* Exp Sta Bldg 307 E I du Pont de Nemours & Co Inc Wilmington DE 19898

NEWKIRK, DAVID DUDLEY, polymer chemistry, organic chemistry, see previous edition

NEWKIRK, DAVID ROYAL, b Arlington, Va, Dec 16, 50; m 76; c 2. ORGANIC CHEMISTRY, BIOCHEMISTRY. *Educ:* Am Univ, BS, 74, PhD, 82. *Prof Exp:* Chemist, 74-77, RES CHEMIST ORG & BIOCHEM, US FOOD & DRUG ADMIN, 77- *Mem:* Asn Off Anal Chemists; AAAS. *Res:* Cholesterol; fatty acid and other lipids studies of food products and their nutritional effects; methods development for the analysis of animal drugs in animals. *Mailing Add:* 8204 Shady Spring Dr Gaithersburg MD 20877

NEWKIRK, GARY FRANCIS, b Paterson, NJ, June 25, 46; m 68; c 3. AQUACULTURAL BREEDING, ECOLOGICAL GENETICS. *Educ:* Rutgers Univ, BSc, 68; Duke Univ, PhD(zool), 74. *Prof Exp:* Fel ecol genetics, 73-75, RES ASSOC ECOL GENETICS, DALHOUSIE UNIV, 75- *Mem:* Soc Study Evolution; World Maricult Soc; Nat Shellfish Asn. *Res:* Ecological genetics of marine species especially those of importance to mariculture. *Mailing Add:* Dept of Biol Dalhousie Univ Halifax NS B3H 4J1 Can

NEWKIRK, GORDON ALLEN, JR, b Orange, NJ, June 12, 28; m 56; c 3. ASTROPHYSICS. *Educ:* Harvard Univ, AB, 50; Univ Mich, MA, 52, PhD(astrophys), 53. *Prof Exp:* Asst, Observ, Univ Mich, 50-53; astrophysicist, Upper Air Res Observ, 53; adj prof astrogeophys, 61-65, adj prof physics & astrophys, 65-76, dir, 68-79, SR MEM STAFF, HIGH ALTITUDE OBSERV, UNIV COLO, 55- *Concurrent Pos:* Prin investr, ATM White Light Coronagraph, 64-70; mem solar physics subcomt, NASA, 65-68, astron missions bd, Solar Panel, 69-70; mem orgn comt, Comn 10 Solar Activ, Inst Astron Union, 67-73, vpres, 73, actg pres, 75-76, pres, 77-79; mem consult group potentially harmful effects on space res panel 3B & Comn V, Int Sci Radio Union. *Honors & Awards:* Boulder Scientist Award, 65; Publ Prize, Nat Ctr Atmospheric Res, 67, Technology Award, 73. *Mem:* AAAS; Int Astron Union; Sigma Xi; Am Astron Soc; Am Geophys Union. *Res:* Solar physics; corona, prominences and solar radio radiation; scattering of light in terrestrial atmosphere; space observations; solar magnetic fields; solar and galactic cosmic rays. *Mailing Add:* High Altitude Observ PO Box 3000 Boulder CO 80307

NEWKIRK, HERBERT WILLIAM, b Jersey City, NJ, Nov 23, 28; m 52; c 2. INORGANIC CHEMISTRY, PHYSICAL CHEMISTRY. *Educ:* Polytech Inst Brooklyn, BS, 51; Ohio State Univ, PhD(chem), 56. *Prof Exp:* Res chemist, Allied Chem & Dye Corp, 51-52; res engr, Gen Elec Co, 56-59; mat scientist, Radio Corp Am, 59-60 & Lawrence Livermore Lab, Univ Calif, 60-69; guest prof, Philips Res Lab, Aachen, WGer, 69-71; PROG MGR, LAWRENCE LIVERMORE LAB, UNIV CALIF, 71- *Res:* High energy density and high temperature chemistry; irradiation chemistry of nuclear fuels and structural materials; electronic properties of solids; inorganic synthesis, characterization and single crystal growth of materials; technology transfer processes. *Mailing Add:* 1141 Madison Ave Livermore CA 94550

NEWKIRK, JOHN BURT, b Minneapolis, Minn, Mar 24, 20; m 51:; c 4. PHYSICAL METALLURGY, BIOENGINEERING. *Educ:* Rensselaer Polytech Inst, BMetE, 41; Carnegie Inst Technol, MS, 47, DSc(phys metall), 50. *Prof Exp:* Fulbright fel crystallog, Cavendish Lab, Cambridge Univ, 50-51; res metallurgist, Res Lab, Gen Elec Co, 51-59; prof phys metall, Cornell Univ, 59-64; Phillipson prof phys metall, 64-75, PROF PHYS CHEM, UNIV DENVER, 75- *Concurrent Pos:* Consult, Gen Elec Co, 60-65, Atomics Int, Inc, 63-65, Jet Propulsion Lab, 64-65, 3M Co, 75-77 & Denver Med Specialties, Inc, 75-; pres, Denver Biomat Inc, 68- *Honors & Awards:* V C Huffsmith Res Award, Denver Res Inst, 73. *Mem:* AAAS; Am Soc Mining, Metall & Petrol Engrs; fel Am Soc Metals; Sigma Xi; Am Chem Soc. *Res:* Characterization of solids, with special emphasis on heat resisting alloys; biomaterials and implantable biodevices for flow control of abnormal body liquids. *Mailing Add:* Space Sci Lab Dept of Chem Univ of Denver Denver CO 80208

NEWKIRK, LESTER LEROY, b Kansas City, Kans, June 2, 20; m 44; c 3. SPACE PHYSICS. *Educ:* Kans State Col, BS, 43, MS, 48; Iowa State Univ, PhD(physics), 51. *Prof Exp:* Physicist microwave lab, Res & Develop Dept, Hughes Aircraft Co, 51-53; mem staff, Lawrence Radiation Lab, Univ Calif, 53-58 & Los Alamos Sci Lab, 58-61; MEM STAFF, LOCKHEED MISSILES & SPACE CO, PALO ALTO, 61- *Mem:* Am Phys Soc; Am Geophys Union. *Res:* Space physics; nuclear weapons physics; solar x-ray physics. *Mailing Add:* 240 Silvia Ct Los Altos CA 94022

NEWKIRK, RICHARD ALBERT MICHAEL, b Quincy, Ill, Dec 19, 25; m 68; c 4. ACAROLOGY, SCIENTIFIC BIBLIOGRAPHY. *Educ:* Univ Miami, BS, 56. *Prof Exp:* Biol aid insect taxon, USDA, 56-57, plant pest control inspector, 57-63, agriculturist insect status reporter, 63-70; PROG SPECIALIST PESTICIDES, REGULATION DIV, ENVIRON PROTECTION AGENCY, 70- *Mem:* AAAS; Entom Soc Am. *Res:* Insect and mite-host relationships; ecology of phytophagous insects and mites; systematics and nomenclature of Eriophyoidea. *Mailing Add:* 3421 Toledo Terrace Hyattsville MD 20782

NEWKOME, GEORGE R, b Akron, Ohio, Nov 26, 38; m 62; c 1. ORGANIC CHEMISTRY, ORGANOMETALLIC CHEMISTRY. *Educ:* Kent State Univ, BS, 61, PhD(org chem), 66. *Prof Exp:* Chemist, Firestone Tire & Rubber Co, 61-62; res assoc, Princeton Univ, 66-67, NIH fel, 67-68; from asst prof to assoc prof chem, 68-78, PROF CHEM, LA STATE UNIV, BATON ROUGE, 78- *Concurrent Pos:* La State Univ Alumni distinguished fac fel, 70-71; NATO sr fac fel, 76-77. *Mem:* AAAS; Am Chem Soc; Royal Soc Chem; NY Acad Sci; Swiss Chem Soc. *Res:* Synthetic and structural organic chemistry relating to natural products and biochemical mimics, including organic-biochemistry; stereochemistry; synthesis of compounds with potential pharmacological properties; molecular rearrangements; macrocyclic chemistry. *Mailing Add:* Dept of Chem La State Univ Baton Rouge LA 70803

NEWLAND, GORDON CLAY, b Kingsport, Tenn, Feb 26, 27; m 53; c 2. POLYMER CHEMISTRY, PHOTOCHEMISTRY. *Educ:* ETenn State Univ, BS, 49. *Prof Exp:* Res chemist, 50-57, SR RES CHEMIST, TENN EASTMAN RES LAB DIV, EASTMAN KODAK, 57- *Mem:* Am Chem Soc; AAAS. *Res:* Photochemistry of polymer degradation and stabilization mechanisms; photoinitiated polymerization. *Mailing Add:* Tenn Eastman Co Box 511 Kingsport TN 37664

NEWLAND, HERMAN WILLIAM, b Hastings, Mich, Jan 26, 17; m 41; c 3. ANIMAL HUSBANDRY. *Educ:* Mich State Univ, BS, 40, MS, 49; Univ Fla, PhD(animal nutrit), 55. *Prof Exp:* From instr to assoc prof animal husb, Mich State Univ, 46-67; assoc prof, 67-70, PROF ANIMAL SCI, OHIO STATE UNIV, 70- *Res:* Animal production and nutrition. *Mailing Add:* Dept of Animal Sci Ohio State Univ Columbus OH 43210

NEWLAND, LEO WINBURNE, b Nocona, Tex, Sept 15, 40. SOIL CHEMISTRY, WATER CHEMISTRY. *Educ:* Tex A&M Univ, BS, 64; Univ Wis, MS, 66, PhD(soils), 69. *Prof Exp:* Agr res specialist, Frito Lay Inc, 64-66; res asst soils & water, Univ Wis, 66-68; fel biol, 68-69, ASST RES SCIENTIST & ASST PROF GEOL & BIOL, TEX CHRISTIAN UNIV, 69-, DIR ENVIRON SCI PROG, 71- *Mem:* Am Chem Soc; Soil Sci Soc Am; Water Pollution Control Fedn; Am Soc Agron. *Res:* Chemical pollution of surficial waters and soils, specifically pesticidal pollution. *Mailing Add:* Dept of Biol & Geol Tex Christian Univ Ft Worth TX 76129

NEWLAND, ROBERT JOE, b Lansing, Mich, Jan 30, 46; m 67; c 2. ORGANIC CHEMISTRY. *Educ:* Kalamazoo Col, BA, 68; Wayne State Univ, PhD(chem), 74. *Prof Exp:* Chemist, Res & Develop Dept, Dupont, 73-75; vis asst prof, Univ Ill, 75-77; ASST PROF, LAFAYETTE COL, 77- *Mem:* Am Chem Soc; AAAS. *Res:* Synthetic organic chemistry; medicinal chemistry; biochemistry. *Mailing Add:* Dept Chem Lafayette Col Easton PA 18042

NEWLANDS, MICHAEL JOHN, b London, Eng, Mar 10, 31; m 54; c 2. INORGANIC CHEMISTRY, ANALYTICAL CHEMISTRY. *Educ:* Cambridge Univ, BA, 53, PhD(chem), 57. *Prof Exp:* Fel, Inst Sci & Technol, Manchester, 58-60, lectr, 60-67; assoc prof, 67-72, PROF CHEM, MEM UNIV NFLD, 72- *Concurrent Pos:* Vis prof, Latrobe Univ, 81. *Mem:* Sigma Xi; Am Chem Soc; Chem Inst Can; Royal Soc Chem. *Res:* Organometallic chemistry of main group elements, analytical chemistry of environmental pollutants, especially organometallics. *Mailing Add:* Dept Chem Mem Univ Nfld St John's NF A1C 5S7 Can

NEWLIN, CHARLES W(ILLIAM), b Terre Haute, Ind, Feb 3, 24; m 47; c 2. CIVIL ENGINEERING. *Educ:* Rose Polytech Inst, BS, 47; Harvard Univ, MS, 49; Northwestern Univ, PhD, 65. *Prof Exp:* Asst prof civil eng, Swarthmore Col, 49-61; from assoc prof to prof, Ariz State Univ, 61-76, chmn dept, 68-76; CIVIL ENGR, DAMES & MOORE, 76- *Concurrent Pos:* Civil engr, Soil Conserv Serv, 58-61; fac fel, NSF, 65- *Mem:* Am Soc Civil Engrs; Am Soc Eng Educ; Nat Soc Prof Engrs. *Res:* Soil mechanics; earth dams; shear and consolidation of soils. *Mailing Add:* Dames & Moore 234 N Cent Ave Suite 111 Phoenix AZ 85004

NEWLIN, OWEN JAY, b Des Moines, Iowa, Feb 6, 28; m 52; c 4. AGRONOMY. *Educ:* Iowa State Univ, BS, 51, MS, 53; Univ Minn, PhD, 55. *Prof Exp:* Asst agron, Iowa State Univ, 51-53; asst agron & plant genetics, Univ Minn, 53-55; asst prof res, Pioneer Seed Co, 55-56, dir prod res, 56-60, asst prod mgr & dir prod res, 60-64, prod mgr, 64-67, pres, Cent Div, 67-78, VPRES, PIONEER HI-BRED INT, INC, 78-, MEM BD DIRS, 63- *Mem:* Am Soc Agron. *Res:* Corn production and breeding. *Mailing Add:* 3315 48th Pl Des Moines IA 50310

NEWLIN, PHILIP BLAINE, US citizen. CIVIL ENGINEERING. *Educ:* Univ Ariz, BS, 46; Mo Sch Mines, MS, 49. *Prof Exp:* From instr to assoc prof, 46-70, PROF CIVIL ENG, UNIV ARIZ, 70- *Concurrent Pos:* Hwy res engr, US Forest Serv; consult, US Army Signal Corps & Pima County Hwy Dept; consult, earth resource observational systs prog, earth resources survs, US Geol Surv. *Mem:* Am Soc Civil Engrs; Am Soc Eng Educ; Am Soc Photogram; Am Cong Surv & Mapping. *Res:* Photogrammetry and highway engineering; legal aspects of land surveying and boundaries. *Mailing Add:* Dept of Civil Eng Univ of Ariz Tucson AZ 85721

NEWMAN, A KIEFER, b Boston, Mass, Jan 20, 36. ELECTRICAL ENGINEERING, COMPUTER SCIENCE. *Educ:* Ohio State Univ, BEE, 59, MSc, 61, PhD(elec eng, controls), 64. *Prof Exp:* Asst instr math, Ohio State Univ, 60-64; asst prof elec eng, Moore Sch Elec Eng, Univ Pa, 64-70 & Univ NH, 70-73; PRIN ENGR & DEPT MGR CONTROL SYSTS ENG, MISSILE SYSTS LAB, MISSILE SYSTS DIV, RAYTHEON CO, 73- *Concurrent Pos:* Mem, Franklin Inst, 64-; vis asst prof, Univ Calif, Berkeley, 67; consult, Leeds & Northrup Corp, Pa, 68-70; fac fel, Stanford Univ, 69 & Case Western Reserve Univ, 70. *Mem:* Soc Indust & Apppl Math; Inst Elec & Electronics Engrs. *Res:* Mathematical control theory and engineering; stability theory; linear and dynamic programming; optimal control; estimation theory; decoupling theory; acoustic sediment identification; mathematical oceanography; serro system design and simulation; microprocessor control engineering; mini-computer data acquisition system design and programming; system modeling and identification from test data. *Mailing Add:* Raytheon Co MSD Hartwell Rd Bedford MA 01730

NEWMAN, B(ARRY) G(EORGE), b Manchester, Eng, May 23, 26; Can citizen; m 55; c 3. AERODYNAMICS, FLUID MECHANICS. *Educ:* Cambridge Univ, BA, 47; Univ Sydney, PhD(aerodyn), 51. *Prof Exp:* Sci officer flight res, Royal Australian Air Force, 51-53; res officer, Nat Aeronaut Estab, Nat Res Coun Can, 53-55; lectr aeronaut, Cambridge Univ, 55-58; chmn dept aerodyn & mech eng, 69-72, PROF AERODYN & MECH ENG, MCGILL UNIV, 59-, CANADAIR CHAIR, 59- *Concurrent Pos:* Vis prof, Laval Univ, 58-59; consult, Canadair Ltd, 58-70; Defence Res Bd Can grants, 59-74; mem, assoc comt aerodyn, Nat Res Coun Can, 61-64, 66-69 & 78-; mem, Can nat comt, Int Union Theoret & Appl Mech, 65-68; consult, Can Pratt & Whitney, 73- & Pulp & Paper Res Inst Can, 74-; invited lectr, Cancam, 81. *Honors & Awards:* Busk Mem Prize, Royal Aeronaut Soc, 60; Turnbull lectr, Can Aeronaut & Space Inst, 69. *Mem:* Fel Can Aeronaut & Space Inst; fel Royal Aeronaut Soc. *Res:* Turbulent boundary layer separation; separation control by geometric and aerodynamic means; Coanda effect; aerodynamics of air-cushion vehicles; jets and wakes in streaming flow; insect flight; flow past flexible structures. *Mailing Add:* Dept Mech Eng 817 Sherbrooke St W Montreal PQ H3A 2K6 Can

NEWMAN, BERNARD, b New York, NY, Sept 17, 13; m 46; c 2. CHEMISTRY. *Educ:* City Col New York, BS, 35, MS, 43; NY Univ, PhD, 55. *Prof Exp:* Lab technician, Bronx County Anal Labs, NY, 35-37; chief lab technician, Morrisania City Hosp, 37-38; biochemist, Hosp Daughters Jacob, 38-42, dir chem labs, 46; chief biochemist, Rystan Co, Inc, NY, 46-47; chief biochemist, Vet Admin Hosp, NY, 47-48; biochemist, S Shore Res Lab, 48-58; dir, Newing Labs, Inc, 58-78; sr res scientist, Res Div, NY Univ, 56-74; dir, Marine Sci Grad Dept, Long Island Univ, 74-79. *Concurrent Pos:* Dir, Police Lab, Police Dept, Suffolk County, 60-74; adj assoc prof, Suffolk

Community Col, 62-67; pres, Nat Asn Police Labs, 67-68; prof, Grad Dept Marine Sci, Long Island Univ, 67-78; consult, Kings Park State Hosp, NY; vis prof, Chem Dept, State Univ NY, Stony Brook, 80-81; vis prof, chem dept, State Univ NY, Stony Brook, 80-81. *Mem:* AAAS; Am Soc Microbiol; Am Chem Soc; fel Am Pub Health Asn; fel Am Acad Forensic Sci. *Res:* Criminalistics; toxicology. *Mailing Add:* 52 Church Ave Islip NY 11751

NEWMAN, BERTHA L, b Caldwell, Idaho, Mar 29, 26. ANATOMY. *Educ:* Col Idaho, BS, 48; Univ Ore, MA, 50; Univ Iowa, PhD(anat), 58. *Prof Exp:* Instr zool, Idaho State Col, 49-53; asst prof neuroanat, Univ NDak, 58; res fel neurophysiol, Univ Wash, 58-60; asst prof, 60-65, ASSOC PROF NEUROANAT, SCH MED, UNIV SOUTHERN CALIF, 65- *Mem:* Soc Neurosci; Am Asn Anatomists; Am Physiol Soc. *Res:* Electrophysiological changes associated with electrical self-stimulation; ultrastructure of the median eminence of neonatal and adult rats; subcellular changes of blood vessels in hypertension; electronmicroscopy of subcellular fractions of hypertensive rat brains. *Mailing Add:* Dept of Anat Sch of Med Univ of Southern Calif Los Angeles CA 90033

NEWMAN, CHARLES MICHAEL, b Chicago, Ill, Mar 1, 46; m 70; c 2. STATISTICAL MECHANICS, STOCHASTIC PROCESSES. *Educ:* Mass Inst Technol, BS(math) & BS(physics), 66; Princeton Univ, MA, 68, PhD(physics), 71. *Prof Exp:* Asst prof math, New York Univ, 71-73; asst prof, Ind Univ, 73-75, assoc prof, 75-79; PROF MATH, UNIV ARIZ, 79- *Concurrent Pos:* Consult, Bell Telephone Labs, 75; vis assoc prof, Technion Israel Inst Technol, 75-76, Univ Ariz, 79; assoc ed, J Statist Physics, 81- *Mem:* Am Math Soc. *Res:* Mathematical physics and probability theory with an emphasis on statistical mechanics and stochastic processes. *Mailing Add:* Dept Math Univ Ariz Tucson AZ 85721

NEWMAN, CLARENCE WALTER, b Lake Providence, La, Aug 3, 32; m 54; c 2. ANIMAL NUTRITION. *Educ:* La State Univ, BS, 54; Tex A&M Univ, MS, 58; La State Univ, PhD(animal sci), 65. *Prof Exp:* Instr animal sci, La Agr Exp Sta, 58-60; spec lectr animal nutrit, La State Univ, 61-62; assoc prof, 64-75, PROF ANIMAL SCI, MONT STATE UNIV, 75- *Mem:* AAAS; Am Soc Animal Sci. *Res:* Nutritive value of barley varieties, barley variety isogenes and high-lysine barley mutants as related to their nutrient composition and availability of these nutrients to swine and laboratory animals. *Mailing Add:* Dept of Animal & Range Sci Mont State Univ Bozeman MT 59717

NEWMAN, DAVID EDWARD, b Lilybrook, WVa, June 4, 47. PHYSICS. *Educ:* Mass Inst Technol, BS & MS, 70; Princeton Univ, PhD(physics), 75. *Prof Exp:* Scholar, 74-77, ASST RES SCIENTIST PHYSICS, UNIV MICHIGAN, 77- *Mem:* Am Phys Soc; AAAS. *Res:* Precision measurements of electron g-factor positron polarization in nuclear beta decay; tests of time-reversal invariance; search for the axion particle. *Mailing Add:* Physics Dept Univ Mich Ann Arbor MI 48109

NEWMAN, DAVID JOHN, b Grays, UK, May 2, 39; m 69. BIOCHEMISTRY, MICROBIOLOGY. *Educ:* Univ Liverpool, MSc, 63; Univ Sussex, DPhil(biochem), 68; Drexel Univ, MSLS, 77. *Prof Exp:* Analyst chem & biochem, J Bibby & Sons, 56-61; res chemist, Ilford Ltd, 63-64; asst exp off biochem & microbiol, Agr Res Coun, Univ Sussex, 64-68; res assoc biochem, Univ Ga, 68-70; assoc sr investr, 70-79, SR INVESTR, SMITH KLINE & FRENCH LABS, 79- *Mem:* Fel Royal Soc Chem; Inst Biol; Am Chem Soc; Am Soc Microbiol; Biochem Soc. *Res:* Chemistry, biochemistry and enzymology of metalloproteins; metabolic regulation at enzyme level; bioenergetics; roles of cyclic nucleotides in normal and diseased states; isolation and classification of antibiotics; differential biochemistry of prokaryotes and eukaryotes. *Mailing Add:* Smith Kline & French Labs 1500 Spring Garden St Philadelphia PA 19101

NEWMAN, DAVID S, b New York, NY, Sept 18, 36; m 59; c 4. PHYSICAL CHEMISTRY. *Educ:* Earlham Col, AB, 57; NY Univ, MS, 60; Univ Pa, PhD(chem), 65. *Prof Exp:* Teacher, Newtown High Sch, 59-60; instr chem & physics, Bronx Community Col, 60; teacher, Roosevelt High Sch, 60; res assoc phys chem, Princeton Univ, 64-65; from asst prof to assoc prof phys chem, 65-74, PROF PHYS CHEM, BOWLING GREEN STATE UNIV, 74- *Concurrent Pos:* Prof adv continuing educ appointee, Argonne Nat Lab, 67, consult, Chem Div; Cotrell res grant, Res Corp, 67-68; sr Fulbright fel, 74-75; sr Fulbright lectr, US Govt, 74-75; NSF fac resident, Argonne Nat Lab, 79, fossil fuels res fel, 80, vis scientist, 81. *Mem:* Am Chem Soc; Electrochem Soc. *Res:* Chemistry of fused salts; structure of electrolyte solutions; electrochemistry; chemistry of solid electrolytes. *Mailing Add:* Dept of Chem Bowling Green State Univ Bowling Green OH 43403

NEWMAN, DAVID WILLIAM, b Pleasant Grove, Utah, Oct 26, 33; m 56. PLANT PHYSIOLOGY. *Educ:* Univ Utah, BS, 55, MS, 57, PhD, 60. *Prof Exp:* Asst bot, Univ Utah, 54-55; from asst prof to assoc prof, 60-74, PROF BOT, MIAMI UNIV, 74- *Mem:* Am Soc Plant Physiol; Am Chem Soc. *Res:* Lipid and protein metabolism of plants. *Mailing Add:* Dept of Bot Miami Univ Oxford OH 45056

NEWMAN, EUGENE, b New York, NY, Sept 14, 30; m 52; c 2. NUCLEAR PHYSICS. *Educ:* Polytech Inst Brooklyn, BS, 52; Yale Univ, MS, 57, PhD(physics), 60. *Prof Exp:* Physicist, 52-54 & 60-74, SECT HEAD ISOTOPES, OAK RIDGE NAT LAB, 74- *Mem:* Am Phys Soc; Am Nuclear Soc. *Res:* Use of low to medium energy cyclotron produced nucleons to investigate nuclear spectroscopy and reaction mechanisms; methods of isotopic enrichment and production of radioisotopes and enriched stable isotopes. *Mailing Add:* Opers Div Bldg 3047 Oak Ridge Nat Lab Oak Ridge TN 37830

NEWMAN, EZRA, b New York, NY, Oct 17, 29; m 58; c 2. THEORETICAL PHYSICS. *Educ:* NY Univ, BA, 51; Syracuse Univ, MA, 55, PhD, 56. *Prof Exp:* Asst physics, Syracuse Univ, 52-56; from instr to assoc prof, 57-66, PROF PHYSICS, UNIV PITTSBURGH, 66- *Concurrent Pos:* Vis lectr, Syracuse Univ, 60-61; vis prof, King's Col, Univ London, 64-65 & 68-69; mem, Comt Int Soc Gen Relativity & Gravitation. *Mem:* Fel Am Phys Soc. *Res:* General theory of relativity with emphasis on gravitational radiation and the theory of twistors. *Mailing Add:* Dept of Physics Univ of Pittsburgh Pittsburgh PA 15260

NEWMAN, FRANKLIN SCOTT, b Rozel, Kans, July 31, 31; m 54; c 4. MICROBIOLOGY, VIROLOGY. *Educ:* Southwestern Col Kans, AB, 53; Kans State Univ, MS, 57, PhD(bact), 62. *Prof Exp:* Asst prof microbiol, Mont State Univ, 61-65; asst prof, Med Br, Univ Tex, 65-68; assoc prof microbiol, 68-75, PROF VET VIROL, VET RES LAB, MONT STATE UNIV, 75- DIR WAMI MED PROG, 74- *Concurrent Pos:* Asst dean, Univ Wash Sch Med, 75- *Mem:* AAAS; Am Soc Microbiol; Sigma Xi. *Res:* Infectious diseases of domestic animals; bacterial virology; phage-host relationships in pathogenic bacteria. *Mailing Add:* Vet Res Lab Mont State Univ Bozeman MT 59717

NEWMAN, GEORGE ALLEN, b Las Cruces, NMex, Mar 15, 41; m 64; c 2. ECOLOGY, ORNITHOLOGY. *Educ:* Baylor Univ, BSc, 64, MSc, 66; Tex A&M Univ, PhD(wildlife sci), 75. *Prof Exp:* From asst prof to assoc prof, 75-79, Cullen prof, 80-81, PROF BIOL, HARDIN-SIMMONS UNIV, 79- *Concurrent Pos:* Collabr, Nat Park Serv, 72-; mem citizens adv coun, Tex Air Control Bd, 72-74; consult, Ecol Audits Inc, 73. *Mem:* Fel Welder Wildlife Found; Ecol Soc Am; Am Ornithologists Union; Wilson Ornith Soc; Cooper Ornith Soc. *Res:* Avian population studies of Guadalupe Mountain Range, Texas and West Texas. *Mailing Add:* Dept Biol Hardin-Simmons Univ Abilene TX 79601

NEWMAN, GERALD HENRY, b New York, NY, June 21, 32; m 57; c 2. PHYSICAL & ELECTROCHEMISTRY. *Educ:* Hofstra Univ, BA, 54; Lehigh Univ, MS, 57; Pa State Univ, PhD(phys chem), 61. *Prof Exp:* Sr res chemist, Battery Div, Union Carbide Corp, 61-74; STAFF CHEMIST PHYS CHEM, EXXON RES & ENG CO, 74- *Mem:* Am Chem Soc; Electrochem Soc. *Res:* Research and development of organic solvent based lithium battery systems and of electrolytes employed therein. *Mailing Add:* 728 Crescent Pkwy Westfield NJ 07090

NEWMAN, HOWARD ABRAHAM IRA, b Chicago, Ill, July 5, 29; m 55; c 4. BIOCHEMISTRY, PHYSIOLOGY. *Educ:* Univ Ill, BS, 51, MS, 56, PhD(food technol), 58; Am Bd Clin Chem, dipl. *Prof Exp:* Asst, Univ Ill, 54-58, res assoc, 58; res assoc physiol, Univ Tenn, 58-59, asst prof, 59-65; asst prof biochem, Case Western Reserve Univ, 66-68; assoc prof path, 68-79, PROF PATH, OHIO STATE UNIV, 79-, ASSOC PROF PHYSIOL CHEM, 68- *Concurrent Pos:* Mem coun arteriosclerosis, Am Heart Asn. *Mem:* AAAS; Am Physiol Soc; NY Acad Sci; Am Inst Chem; Am Asn Clin Chem. *Res:* Cholesterol, triglyceride and phospholipid metabolism in the intact animal, especially in the atherosclerotic intima; cholesterol esterases; analytical lipid techniques; lipoprotein phenotyping in clinical chemistry; mycobacterial phage lipids; hypolipoproteinemic drugs; cell membrane changes in carcinogenesis; childhood autism. *Mailing Add:* Starling Loving Hall M 352 Ohio State Univ 320 W Tenth Ave Columbus OH 43210

NEWMAN, J(OHN) NICHOLAS, hydrodynamics, see previous edition

NEWMAN, JACK HUFF, b Roanoke, Va, Aug 15, 29; m 56; c 3. BACTERIOLOGY, BIOCHEMISTRY. *Educ:* Va Polytech Inst, BS, 56, MS, 59. *Prof Exp:* Jr biochemist, Smith Kline & French Labs, 58-62; biochemist, 62-77, GROUP MGR, A H ROBINS CO, INC, 77- *Mem:* Am Chem Soc. *Res:* Radioisotopes; drug metabolism; quantitatively administer radioactive experimental drugs to different animal species by different routes, collect biological samples, process and use appropriate radioactive analyses procedures; calculate raw data. *Mailing Add:* 8106 Diane Lane Richmond VA 23227

NEWMAN, JAMES BLAKEY, b Little Rock, Ark, Jan 10, 17; m 42; c 3. PHYSICS. *Educ:* Va Mil Inst, BS, 39; Cornell Univ, PhD(physics), 51. *Prof Exp:* Instr, 39-42, from asst prof to assoc prof, 49-56, PROF PHYSICS, VA MIL INST, 56- *Mem:* Am Phys Soc; Am Asn Physics Teachers; Am Nuclear Soc. *Res:* Atomic and nuclear physics. *Mailing Add:* Dept of Physics Va Mil Inst Lexington VA 24450

NEWMAN, JAMES CHARLES, JR, b Memphis, Tenn, Oct 12, 42; m 64; c 4. ENGINEERING MECHANICS, MATERIALS SCIENCE. *Educ:* Univ Miss, BS, 64; Va Polytech Inst & State Univ, MS, 69, PhD(eng mech), 74. *Prof Exp:* RES ENGR FATIGUE & FRACTURE, NASA, 64- *Concurrent Pos:* Lectr fracture mech, Fed Avaiation Admin. *Honors & Awards:* Sci Achievement Award, NASA, 77; George Rankin Irwin Award, Am Soc Testing & Mat, 81. *Mem:* Am Soc Testing & Mat. *Res:* Fatigue, crack propagation and fracture of materials under service loading and environmental conditions. *Mailing Add:* Langley Res Ctr NASA Mail Stop 188E Hampton VA 23665

NEWMAN, JAMES EDWARD, b Brown Co, Ohio, Dec 22, 20; m 49; c 3. AGRONOMY. *Educ:* Ohio State Univ, BS, 47, MS, 49. *Prof Exp:* Asst, Ohio Agr Exp Sta, 47-49; from asst prof to assoc prof agron & climat, 49-69, PROF AGRON, PURDUE UNIV, WEST LAFAYETTE, 69- *Concurrent Pos:* Partic comn agr meteorol, World Meteorol Orgn, Ont, Can, 62; New World ed, Jour Agr Meteorol, 63; vis prof, Univ Calif, Riverside, 65-66; vis scientist, Inst Agr Sci, Univ Alaska, 70; ed-in-chief, Int J Agr Meteorol, 74-76; mem select comt, Nat Defense Univ, 77-78. *Honors & Awards:* Soils & Crops Award, Am Soc Agron, 65. *Mem:* Fel AAAS; fel Am Soc Agron; Am Meteorol Soc; Ecol Soc Am; Int Soc Biometeorol. *Res:* Radiant energy flux and plant responses in both natural and mono culture phyto-environments; adaptation of cereal grains; crop modeling; climatic variability/changes on world food production. *Mailing Add:* Dept of Agron Purdue Univ West Lafayette IN 47906

NEWMAN, JAMES MARTIN, b New York, NY, Dec 8, 37. MATHEMATICS. *Educ:* Cornell Univ, BA, 59; Harvard Univ, AM, 60; NY Univ, PhD(math), 69. *Prof Exp:* Math analyst, Gen Elec Co, Pa, 61-62; lectr math, Brooklyn Col, 66-68; asst prof, Fla Atlantic Univ, 68-71; asst prof math, Baruch Col, 71-75; mathematician, Geophys Fluid Dynamics Lab, 76-80; ASST PROF DECISION SCI & COMPUT, RIDER COL, 80- *Mem:* Math Asn Am; Asn Comput Mach. *Res:* Partial differential equations; computer science; mathematical economics. *Mailing Add:* 12 Bolfmar Ave RD #1 Cranbury NJ 08512

NEWMAN, JOHN ALEXANDER, b Lethbridge, Alta, Jan 23, 32; m 59; c 4. ANIMAL BREEDING, ANIMAL GENETICS. *Educ:* Univ Alta, BSc, 55; Univ Edinburgh, dipl animal genetics, 58, PhD(animal genetics), 60. *Prof Exp:* RES SCIENTIST ANIMAL BREEDING, AGR CAN RES STA, 55- *Concurrent Pos:* Chmn, Can Beefcattle Record Performance Tech Comt, 75-81; mem, Can Agr Res Coun, 75-79; assoc ed, Can J Animal Sci, 77-80. *Mem:* Agr Inst Can (vpres, 74-75); Genetics Soc Can; Am Soc Animal Sci; Can Soc Animal Sci (pres, 72-73). *Res:* Beef cattle breeding and genetics. *Mailing Add:* Res Sta Agr Can PO Box 1420 Lacombe AB T0C 1S0 Can

NEWMAN, JOHN B(ULLEN), b Okmulgee, Okla, Sept 27, 38; m 73; c 4. APPLIED MECHANICS, ENGINEERING MECHANICS. *Educ:* Stanford Univ, BS, 61, MS, 62, PhD(eng mech), 65. *Prof Exp:* Assoc engr, Lockheed Missiles & Space Co, 62-63; sr engr, 65-73, fel engr, 73-80, ADV ENGR, BETTIS ATOMIC POWER LAB, WESTINGHOUSE ELEC CORP, 80- *Mem:* Am Soc Mech Engrs; Am Inst Aeronaut & Astronaut; Am Acad Mech; Am Nuclear Soc; Sigma Xi. *Res:* Elastic-plastic instabilities; approximation methods in solid mechanics; constitutive relations in continuum mechanics; modelling of behavior of nuclear reactor fuel rods; fluid-solid interactions; non-linear, time dependent, stuctural analysis methods and computational techniques for engineering application. *Mailing Add:* 4830 McAnulty Rd Pittsburgh PA 15236

NEWMAN, JOHN BROWN, physics, see previous edition

NEWMAN, JOHN JOSEPH, b Wolf Point, Mont, Jan 15, 36; m 64; c 4. ELECTRICAL ENGINEERING, MAGNETISM. *Educ:* Mont State Col, BSEE, 58; Univ NMex, MSEE, 61; Univ Santa Clara, PhD(elec eng), 68. *Prof Exp:* Staff mem res & develop, Sandia Corp, 58-61; sr elec engr reliability, Lockheed Missiles & Space Co, 61-64; teaching asst, Univ Santa Clara, 64-67; SR STAFF MEM ELEC ENG, MEMOREX CORP, 67- *Mem:* Inst Elec & Electronics Engrs. *Res:* Magnetic recording, especially theory, media and processes; magnetic measurements; instrumentation development and design. *Mailing Add:* Memorex Corp MS 1407 San Thomas at Cent Expressway Santa Clara CA 95052

NEWMAN, JOHN SCOTT, b Richmond, Va, Nov 17, 38. ELECTROCHEMISTRY, CHEMICAL ENGINEERING. *Educ:* Northwestern Univ, BS, 60; Univ Calif, Berkeley, MS, 62, PhD(chem eng), 63. *Prof Exp:* From asst prof to assoc prof chem eng, 63-70, PROF CHEM ENG, UNIV CALIF, BERKELEY, 70-, PRIN INVESTR MAT & MOLECULAR RES DIV, 63- *Honors & Awards:* Young Author's Prize, Electrochem Soc, 66 & 69. *Mem:* Am Inst Chem; Electrochem Soc. *Res:* Design and analysis of electrochemical systems; transport properties of concentrated electrolytic solutions; mass transfer. *Mailing Add:* Dept Chem Eng Univ Calif Berkeley CA 94720

NEWMAN, JOSEPH HERBERT, b Brooklyn, NY, Feb 2, 25; m 50; c 2. CHEMICAL ENGINEERING. *Educ:* Polytech Inst New York, BchE, 45, MchE, 47. *Prof Exp:* Res engr, Flintkote Co, 45-51; sect head, M W Kellogg Co, 51-53; asst mgr aeronaut div, Curtiss Wright Co, Woodridge, NJ, 53-59; gen mgr, 59-65, vpres, 66-72, sr vpres, 73-76, exec vpres, 77-78, PRES, TISHMAN RES CORP, 79- *Concurrent Pos:* Mem adv panel bldg res sect, Nat Bur Standards, 65-68; mem comt urban technol, Nat Res Coun, 67-69; vpres, Tishman Realty & Construct Co, Inc, 67-73, 1st vpres, 74-76, sr vpres, 79-; mem panel housing technol, US Dept Com, 68-70; chmn bldg res adv bd, Nat Acad Sci, 72-73, mem comn sociotech systs, 74-77; chmn comt tech transfer, Nat Acad Eng, 73-74; dir, Nat Inst Building Sci, 76-; sr vpres, Tishman Construct & Res Co, Inc, 77-78; chmn, Nat Inst Building Sci, 80-81. *Mem:* Nat Acad Eng; Am Inst Chem Engrs; Nat Inst Bldg Sci; Am Chem Soc. *Res:* Building science and construction technology innovation. *Mailing Add:* Tishman Res Corp 666 Fifth Ave New York NY 10019

NEWMAN, KARL ROBERT, b Mt Pleasant, Mich, Feb 26, 31; m 61; c 3. GEOLOGY. *Educ:* Univ Mich, BS, 53, MS, 54; Univ Colo, PhD(geol), 61. *Prof Exp:* Geologist, Magnolia Petrol Co, 54 & Palynological Res Lab, 59-61; sr res geologist, Pan-Am Petrol Corp, 61-66; asst prof geol, Mont Col Mineral Sci & Technol, 66-67; assoc prof, Cent Wash State Col, 67-71, chmn dept, 69-71; assoc prof, 71-80, PROF GEOL, COLO SCH MINES, 80- *Concurrent Pos:* Consult geologist, Geol Explor Assoc, Ltd, 66- *Mem:* Soc Econ Paleontologists & Mineralogists; Am Asn Petrol Geologist; Geol Soc Am; Am Inst Prof Geologists. *Res:* Stratigraphy; geology and palynology of Rocky Mountain basins; field geology; upper Cretaceous and lower Tertiary palynomorphs; geology of coal and oil shale. *Mailing Add:* Dept of Geol Colo Sch of Mines Golden CO 80401

NEWMAN, KENNETH WILFRED, b Lincoln, Nebr. ALGEBRA. *Educ:* City Univ New York, BS, 65; Cornell Univ, PhD(math), 70. *Prof Exp:* Fel math, McGill Univ, 69-71; asst prof math, Univ Ill, Chicago Circle, 71-78; ASSOC PROF MATH, UNIV MASS, BOSTON, 78- *Mem:* Am Math Soc. *Res:* Theory of Hopf algebras. *Mailing Add:* Dept of Math Univ of Mass Boston MA 02116

NEWMAN, LEONARD, b New York, NY, Jan 15, 31; m 53; c 2. ATMOSPHERIC CHEMISTRY, ANALYTICAL CHEMISTRY. *Educ:* Polytech Inst Brooklyn, BS, 52; Mass Inst Technol, PhD(chem), 56. *Prof Exp:* Asst, Mass Inst Technol, 52-55; scientist, Nat Lead Co, 56-57; scientist, 58-63, sr scientist, 63-80, assoc head, Atmospheric Sci Div, 77, HEAD, ENVIRON CHEM DIV, BROOKHAVEN NAT LAB, 78- *Concurrent Pos:* Vis scientist, Royal Inst Technol, Sweden, 62-63; mem comt on nuclear methods for investigating air pollution, Nat Acad Sci, 68; consult, Gen Pub Utilities Corp, 74, Public Serv Comn, Wis, 75, Environ Criteria Assessment Off, Environ Protection Agency, 80, Empire State Elec Energy Res Corp & State Univ Res Found, NY, 81. *Mem:* AAAS; Am Chem Soc; Am Soc Testing & Mat; NY Acad Sci; Air Pollution Control Asn. *Res:* Complex ion equilibria of simple and mixed ligand complexes; atmospheric chemistry; analytical chemistry of air pollutants; hydrolysis reactions; solvent extraction; chemistry of actinide and less familiar elements; kinetic mechanisms; nuclear reactor chemistry and fuel processing; electrochemistry. *Mailing Add:* Dept Energy & Environ Bldg 426 Brookhaven Nat Lab Upton NY 11973

NEWMAN, LESTER JOSEPH, b St Louis, Mo, June 15, 33. CYTOGENETICS. *Educ:* Wash Univ, BA, 55; Univ Mich, MA, 60; Wash Univ, PhD(zool), 63. *Prof Exp:* NIH trainee, Wash Univ, 60-63; asst prof zool, Ore State Univ, 63-64; actg head dept, 65-66, from asst prof to assoc biol, 64-78, PROF BIOL, PORTLAND STATE UNIV, 78- *Mem:* AAAS; Genetics Soc Am. *Res:* Cytogenetics of Diptera. *Mailing Add:* Dept of Biol Portland State Univ Portland OR 97207

NEWMAN, LOUIS BENJAMIN, b New York, NY. REHABILITATION MEDICINE. *Educ:* Ill Inst Technol, ME, 21; Rush Med Col, MD, 33; Am Bd Phys Med & Rehab, dipl, 47. *Prof Exp:* Attend physician, Cook County Hosp, Ill, 33-42; PROF REHAB MED, MED SCH, NORTHWESTERN UNIV, CHICAGO, 46- *Concurrent Pos:* Chief rehab med serv, Vet Admin Hosps, Hines, 46-53 & Vet Res Hosp, Chicago, 53-67; consult rehab med, Vet Admin Med Centers & several community hosps, Chicago Area, 67-; mem med adv bd, Vis Nurse Asn, Nat Found, Arthritis Found, Rehab Comt of Inst Med, United Parkinson Found & others; lectr rehab med, Col Med, Univ Ill & Stritch Sch Med, Loyola Univ Chicago; lectr, Chicago Med Sch, Univ Health Sci. *Honors & Awards:* Davis Award, Asn Phys & Ment Rehab, 56. *Mem:* AMA; Am Cong Rehab Med (vpres, 60); Am Acad Phys Med & Rehab (pres, 59); Am Asn Electromyog & Electrodiag; Int Soc Rehab Disabled. *Mailing Add:* 400 E Randolph St Chicago IL 60601

NEWMAN, M(ORRIS) M, b Poland, Sept 7, 09; nat US; m 38; c 3. ELECTRICAL ENGINEERING. *Educ:* Univ Minn, BSEE, 31, MSEE, 37. *Prof Exp:* Asst prof elec eng, Univ Minn, 44-46; res dir, Lightning & Transients Res Inst, Minneapolis, 46-71; res prof & dir, Lightning Res Oceanic Lab, 72-76; res prof & dir, Lightning & Transients Res Inst, 76-80; RES PROF & DIR, LIGHTNING & OCEANICS INST, 80- *Concurrent Pos:* Assoc res prof, Univ Fla, 60-63; vis prof, Univ Miami, 63-72 & Friends World Col, 66- *Mem:* AAAS; Am Meteorol Soc; Inst Elec & Electronics Engrs; Am Geophys Union. *Res:* High voltage engineering; lightning studies and radio interference. *Mailing Add:* Lightning & Oceanics Inst 164 MacArthur Causeway Miami Beach FL 33139

NEWMAN, MELVIN MICKLIN, b Chicago, Ill, Dec 20, 21; m 49; c 2. SURGERY, PULMONARY PHYSIOLOGY. *Educ:* Univ Chicago, BS, 41, MD, 44. *Prof Exp:* From asst resident to instr surg, Univ Chicago, 46-52; from asst prof to assoc prof, State Univ NY Downstate Med Ctr, 54-59; chief, Nat Jewish Hosp, 59-68; ASSOC PROF SURG, MED CTR, UNIV COLO, DENVER, 61- *Concurrent Pos:* Nat Res Coun fel, Univ Chicago, 52; NIH grants, Nat Jewish Hosp, Denver, Colo, 62-68; NIH grant, Univ Colo, Denver, 70- *Mem:* Am Soc Artificial Internal Organs (pres, 60); Soc Univ Surgeons; Am Asn Thoracic Surg; Soc Thoracic Surg; Am Thoracic Soc. *Res:* Shock; microcirculation; pulmonary ventilation and circulation; vascular prostheses. *Mailing Add:* Dept of Surg Univ of Colo Med Ctr Denver CO 80220

NEWMAN, MELVIN SPENCER, b New York, NY, Mar 10, 08; m 33; c 4. ORGANIC CHEMISTRY. *Educ:* Yale Univ, BS, 29, PhD(chem), 32. *Hon Degrees:* DSc, Univ New Orleans, 75. *Prof Exp:* Nat Tuberc Asn fel, Yale Univ, 32-33; Nat Res Coun fel chem, Col Physicians & Surgeons, Columbia Univ, 33-34 & Harvard Univ, 34-36; instr chem, 36-39, Elizabeth Clay Howald scholar, 39-40, from asst prof to prof, 40-65, REGENTS PROF CHEM, OHIO STATE UNIV, 65- *Concurrent Pos:* Guggenheim fel, 49 & 51; Fulbright lectr, Glasgow Univ, 57 & 67; ed, J, Am Chem Soc. *Honors & Awards:* Award, Am Chem Soc, 61; Wilbur Cross Medal, Yale Univ, 70. *Mem:* Nat Acad Sci; AAAS; Am Chem Soc; The Chem Soc. *Res:* Synthetic and theoretical organic chemistry. *Mailing Add:* 2239 Onandaga Dr Columbus OH 43221

NEWMAN, MICHAEL JOHN, b Oak Park, Ill, Apr 12, 48. ASTROPHYSICS, PHYSICS. *Educ:* Rice Univ, BA, 70, MS, 73, PhD(astrophysics), 75; La State Univ, Baton Rouge, MS, 71. *Prof Exp:* Res assoc astrophysics, Rice Univ, 75; res fel physics, W K Kellogg Radiation Lab, Calif Inst Technol, 75-77; staff mem, Max Planck Inst Physics & Astrophysics, Munich, WGer, 77-78; STAFF MEM ASTROPHYSICS, LOS ALAMOS NAT LAB, 78- *Mem:* Am Astron Soc; fel Royal Astron Soc; Astron Soc Pac; fel Am Phys Soc; AAAS. *Res:* Nuclear astrophysics; theoretical astrophysics; stellar structure and evolution; star formation; nucleosynthesis; interactions with the interstellar medium; astronomical influences on terrestrial climate. *Mailing Add:* Los Alamos Nat Lab T-DOT Mail Stop 288 PO Box 1663 Los Alamos NM 87545

NEWMAN, MORRIS, b New York, NY, Feb 25, 24; m 48; c 2. MATHEMATICS. *Educ:* NY Univ, BA, 45; Columbia Univ, MA, 46; Univ Pa, PhD(math), 52. *Prof Exp:* Lectr math, Columbia Univ, 45; Instr, Univ Del, 48-51; res mathematician, 51-63, chief numerical anal sect, 63-70, sr res mathematician, Nat Bur Standards, 70-76; PROF MATH, UNIV CALIF, SANTA BARBARA, 76- *Concurrent Pos:* Ed, Math Comput, 75-; assoc ed, J Linear & Multilinear Algebra, 73- & Letters in Linear Algebra, 79- *Honors & Awards:* Dept Commerce Gold Medal Award, 66. *Mem:* Am Math Soc; Math Asn Am; London Math Soc. *Res:* Number theory; group theory; matrix theory; structure of matrix groups over rings; automorphic and modular functions. *Mailing Add:* Dept of Math Univ Calif Santa Barbara CA 93106

NEWMAN, MURRAY ARTHUR, b Chicago, Ill, Mar 6, 24; m 52; c 1. ICHTHYOLOGY. *Educ:* Univ Chicago, BS, 49; Univ Calif, MA, 51; Univ BC, PhD(zool), 60. *Prof Exp:* Cur fishes, Univ Calif, Los Angeles, 51-53; cur inst fishes, Univ BC, 53-56; DIR, VANCOUVER PUB AQUARIUM, 56- *Mem:* Am Soc Ichthyologists & Herpetologists; Can Mus Asn. *Res:* Behavior of fishes; marine ecology; systematic ichthyology. *Mailing Add:* Vancouver Pub Aquarium Box 3232 Vancouver BC V6B 3X8 Can

NEWMAN, NORMAN, b Brooklyn, NY, Mar 13, 39; m 62; c 2. ORGANIC CHEMISTRY. *Educ:* Brooklyn Col, BS, 59; Univ Minn, PhD(org chem), 64. *Prof Exp:* Res specialist, 63-80, DIV SCIENTIST, MINN MINING & MFG CO, 80- *Mem:* Am Chem Soc; Soc Photog Sci & Eng. *Res:* Photographic science and chemistry; photochemical systems; reaction mechanisms. *Mailing Add:* Minn Mining & Mfg Co 3M Ctr 209-2C St Paul MN 55101

NEWMAN, PAUL HAROLD, b Washington, DC, Apr 25, 33; m 58; c 3. INFORMATION SCIENCE. *Educ:* Antioch Col, BSc, 56. *Prof Exp:* Sr res assoc human eng, Am Insts Res, 56-60; res engr, Boeing Co, 60-61; systs specialist info processing systs design, Syst Develop Corp, 61-72, mgr control staff, 73; systs design mgr, 73-75, asst chief, Off Info Systs, 75-80, MGR, SYSTS ENG, DEPT SOCIAL & HEALTH SERV, STATE WASH, 80- *Mem:* AAAS; Soc Eng Psychol; Human Factors Soc; Asn Comput Mach. *Res:* information processing systems design and control; educational requirements; systems analyses; human factors analyses. *Mailing Add:* Dept Social & Health Serv Mail Stop OB-12 Olympia WA 98504

NEWMAN, PAULINE, b New York, NY, June 20, 27. INDUSTRIAL CHEMISTRY, LAW. *Educ:* Vassar Col, AB, 47; Columbia Univ, AM, 48; Yale Univ, PhD(chem), 52; NY Univ, LLB, 58. *Prof Exp:* Lab instr, Columbia Univ, 48 & Yale Univ, 48-50; res chemist, Am Cyanamid Co, 51-54; patent atty, 54-69, DIR PATENT & LICENSING DEPT, FMC CORP, 69- *Concurrent Pos:* Specialist natural sci, UNESCO, 61-62; mem patent adv comt, Res Corp, 72-; mem nat bd, Med Col Pa, 76-; mem adv comt, Indust Innovation, Domestic Policy Rev, 79; mem adv comt, Int Intellectual Proj, State Dept, 74- *Mem:* AAAS; Am Chem Soc; Am Inst Chem; Soc Chem Indust; fel NY Acad Sci. *Res:* Chemistry of high polymers; oxidation-reduction reactions; patent law; physical organic chemistry. *Mailing Add:* FMC Corp 2000 Market St Philadelphia PA 19103

NEWMAN, PHILIP E(DWARDS), b St Louis, Mo, Mar 4, 18; m 50; c 1. CHEMICAL ENGINEERING. *Educ:* Univ Mich, BS, 40, MS, 47; Univ Pittsburgh, PhD(chem eng), 48. *Prof Exp:* Asst fel, Mellon Inst, 40-41; chem engr, Plant Opers Probs Res, Hercules Powder Co, 41-43; chief chem eng, Pechiney, 48-52; vpres & Europ mgr, Sci Design Co, 52-63; sr vpres, Halcon Int, Inc, 63-73, exec vpres, 74-75; SR ADV, IMHANSEN CHEMIE GMBH, 76- *Concurrent Pos:* Prof, Ecole des Poudres, 50-51. *Mem:* Am Chem Soc; Am Inst Chem Engrs. *Res:* Heat transfer; fractionation of petrolatum; drying. *Mailing Add:* Viale B0220-Costa 91 6035 Rapallo Italy

NEWMAN, R(OBERT) W(EIDENTHAL), b Cleveland, Ohio, May 14, 14; m 50; c 1. CHEMICAL ENGINEERING. *Prof Exp:* Works engr glass tech, Pitney Glass Works, Gen Elec Co, Ohio, 36-41, works engr electron tube mfg, Buffalo Tube Works, 41-47, mfg engr, Schenectady Tube Works, 47-55, consult oper res & synthesis, Mgt Consult, Serv, NY, 55-62; econ decision models, Acct Serv, 62-69; MGR PLANNING SERV, GEN ELEC CO, 69- *Concurrent Pos:* Assoc prof, NY Univ, 69- *Mem:* AAAS; Am Chem Soc; Am Soc Qual Control; Inst Elec & Electronics Engrs. *Res:* Electron tube technology; cathode materials and processes; operations research and management science; management and decision making process; corporate planning. *Mailing Add:* 381 Eden Ave Springdale CT 06907

NEWMAN, RICHARD HOLT, b Mebane, NC, Aug 12, 32; m 55; c 3. RADIOCHEMISTRY. *Educ:* Elon Col, BA, 54; Univ SDak, MA, 60. *Prof Exp:* Chemist I water anal, NC State Bd Health, 54-55, Chemist II pollution control, 57-58; assoc scientist anal res, 60-67, res prof radiochem, 68-74, PROJ LEADER SMOKE MECHANISM, PHILIP MORRIS, INC, 74- *Mem:* Am Chem Soc; Sigma Xi. *Res:* Study of precursor product relationship between tobacco and smoke and elucidating mechanisms for smoke formation utilizing both radioactive and stable isotopes as tracers. *Mailing Add:* Philip Morris Inc PO Box 26583 Richmond VA 23261

NEWMAN, ROBERT ALWIN, b Winchester, Mass, July 11, 48. BIOCHEMISTRY, PHARMACOLOGY. *Educ:* Univ RI, BS, 70; Univ Conn, MS, 73, PhD(pharmacol), 75. *Prof Exp:* Res fel cell & molecular biol, Med Col Ga, 75-76; res assoc biochem, 76-77, ASST PROF PHARMACOL, DEPT PHARMACOL, COL MED, & STAFF MEM VT REG CANCER CTR, UNIV VT, 77- *Mem:* Am Asn Cancer Res; Am Soc Contemporary Opthalmol; Am Cancer Soc; Sigma Xi; Am Soc Pharmacol & Exp Therapeut. *Res:* Connective tissue biochemistry and pharmacology; experimental cancer chemotherapy (basic and clinical); cancer biology. *Mailing Add:* Dept of Pharmacol Col Med Univ Vt Given Bldg Burlington VT 05405

NEWMAN, ROBERT BRADFORD, b Ungkung, China, Nov 5, 17; US citizen; m 41, 55; c 3. ACOUSTICS. *Educ:* Univ Tex, BA, 38, MA, 39; Mass Inst Technol, MArch, 49. *Hon Degrees:* ScD, Lawrence Col, 63. *Prof Exp:* Engr, Radio Corp Am, 41; civilian scientist, Naval Air Exp Sta, Pa, 43-45; partner, 48-53, VPRES, BOLT BERANEK & NEWMAN, INC, 53- *Concurrent Pos:* From instr to asst prof, Mass Inst Technol, 49-56, assoc prof, 56-76, adj prof, 76- vis lectr, 55-71, PROF, Harvard Univ, 71-; Fulbright vis lectr, Royal Acad Fine Arts, Copenhagen, 59; mem bd governors, Bldg Res Inst, Nat Res Coun, 57-60; US specialist to Singapore, US Dept State, 61 & 65. *Honors & Awards:* Brown Medal, Franklin Inst, 66. *Mem:* Fel Acoust Soc Am. *Res:* Architecture; integration of acoustics principles into design of buildings (theaters, concert halls, office buildings, hotels and apartment houses). *Mailing Add:* Bolt Beranek & Newman Inc 50 Moulton St Cambridge MA 02138

NEWMAN, ROGER, chemistry, see previous edition

NEWMAN, ROGERS J, b Ramar, Ala, Dec 22, 26; m 51; c 3. MATHEMATICS. *Educ:* Morehouse Col, AB, 48; Atlanta Univ, MA, 49; Univ Mich, PhD(math), 61. *Prof Exp:* Instr physics & math, Bishop Col, 49-50; instr math, Grambling Col, 50-51; instr math & physics, Jackson State Col, 51-53; instr, Southern Univ, 53-55; jr instr math, Univ Mich, 59-60; chmn dept math, 61-74, PROF MATH, SOUTHERN UNIV, BATON ROUGE, 60- *Concurrent Pos:* NSF fac fel, Imp Col, Univ London, 70-71. *Mem:* Am Math Soc; Math Asn Am; Nat Inst Sci (vpres, 64). *Res:* Complex variables. *Mailing Add:* Dept of Math Southern Univ Baton Rouge LA 70813

NEWMAN, SANFORD BERNHART, b New York, NY, July 26, 14; m 42; c 2. MATERIALS SCIENCE. *Educ:* Long Island Univ, BS, 36; George Washington Univ, MS, 41; Univ Md, PhD(biophys), 51. *Prof Exp:* Mat engr, 40-46, microanalyst, 46-54, plastics technologist, 54-58, consult, 58-64, chief mat eval & testing sect, 64-67, chief mat eval div, 67-69, spec asst to dir inst appl technol, 69-70, SR PROG ANALYST, OFF ASSOC DIR PROGS, NAT BUR STANDARDS, 70- *Concurrent Pos:* Vis scientist, Cavendish Lab, Cambridge Univ, 59. *Honors & Awards:* Meritorious Award, US Dept Com, 53. *Mem:* AAAS; Am Soc Testing & Mat; fel Royal Micros Soc. *Res:* Electron microscopy; physics of solids; microstructure of polymers; fracture morphology; applied light and x-ray microscopy. *Mailing Add:* 3508 Woodbine St Chevy Chase MD 20015

NEWMAN, SEYMOUR, b New York, NY, July 9, 22; m 43; c 2. POLYMER SCIENCE, PLASTICS. *Educ:* City Col New York, BS, 42; Columbia Univ, MA, 47; Polytech Inst Brooklyn, PhD, 49. *Prof Exp:* Res assoc, Southern Regional Res Labs, USDA, 49-51, Cornell Univ, 51-52 & Allegany Ballistics Lab, Hercules Powder Co, 52-55; group leader & scientist, Monsanto Co, 56-67; staff scientist sci res staff, 67-69, mgr, Polymer Sci Dept, 69-73, SR STAFF SCIENTIST, 73- & MGR ADV FUNCTIONAL COMPONENTS, PLASTICS DEVELOP CTR, FORD MOTOR CO, DETROIT, 77- *Concurrent Pos:* Adj assoc prof, Univ Mass, Amherst, 67-; mem technol assessment panel, Engrs Joint Coun, 75-; adj prof, Univ Detroit, 80-81; mem bd dir, Engr Prop Div Specialities, 80-81, Ad Hoc Panel, Polymer Sci & Engr, Nat Res Coun, 80-81. *Mem:* Am Chem Soc; Am Phys Soc; Soc Plastic Engrs. *Res:* Physical chemistry of high polymers; dynamic mechanical behavior; crystallinity; dilute solution behavior; fiber and film properties; strength properties; rheology; coatings; processing; composites; plastic materials; design; automotive component development. *Mailing Add:* 29395 Sharon Lane Southfield MI 48076

NEWMAN, SIMON M(EIER), b Rockville Center, NY, Feb 3, 06; m 30; c 3. INFORMATION SCIENCE, COMMUNICATION. *Educ:* Columbia Univ, AB, 27, BS, 28, ME, 29; Am Univ, LLB & MPL, 32, JD, 68. *Prof Exp:* Exam, US Patent Off, 29-37, classifier, 37-55, researcher doc, 55-61; DOC CONSULT, 61- *Concurrent Pos:* US del from Nat Acad Sci, Int Fedn Doc, 60 & 67, mem, Nat Acad Sci Nat Comt, 64-70; Nat Acad Sci consult, Off Doc, 61-66; prof lectr, Am Univ, 62-66. *Honors & Awards:* Watson Davis Award, Am Soc Info Sci, 77. *Mem:* Fel AAAS; Am Soc Info Sci; fel Brit Inst Info Sci. *Res:* Linguistic problems in automation of information retrieval of scientific information from expository prose; classification and indexing problems in documentation. *Mailing Add:* 1411 Hopkins St NW Washington DC 20036

NEWMAN, STANLEY RAY, b Idaho Falls, Idaho, Mar 5, 23; m 61; c 5. ORGANIC CHEMISTRY. *Educ:* Univ Utah, BS, 47, PhD(chem), 52. *Prof Exp:* Chemist, 51-59, res chemist, 59-61, group leader, 61-64, sr res chemist, 64-68, group leader, 68-73, technologist, 73-77, SR TECHNOLOGIST, TEXACO RES CTR, TEXACO, INC, 77- *Concurrent Pos:* Mem Solid Waste Mgt, Dutchess County, NY, 74-76. *Mem:* AAAS; NY Acad Sci; Sigma Xi. *Res:* Organic carbonates; organic phosphorus chemistry; lead appreciators; tertiary esters of organic acids; organic synthesis; fuel additives; petrochemicals; recrystallization using surface active agents; effect of lead antiknocks on health; residual fuel technology; fuel technology. *Mailing Add:* 24 Virginia Ave Fishkill NY 12524

NEWMAN, STEVEN BARRY, b New York, NY, May 19, 52; m 73; c 1. CLOUD PHYSICS, ATMOSPHERIC SCIENCE. *Educ:* City Col New York, BS, 73; State Univ NY Albany, MS, 75, PhD(atmospheric sci), 78. *Prof Exp:* Teaching asst atmospheric sci, State Univ NY Albany, 73-77, instr meteorol, Col Oneonta, 77-78; ASST PROF METEOROL & EARTH SCI, CENT CONN STATE COL, 78- *Concurrent Pos:* Fac res fel, Air Force Geophys Lab, Hanscom AFB, Mass, 81. *Mem:* Am Meteorol Soc. *Res:* Hail and hail dynamics; cloud-precipitation physics and weather modification. *Mailing Add:* Dept of Physics & Earth Sci Cent Conn State Col New Britain CT 06050

NEWMAN, STUART ALAN, b New York, NY, Apr 4, 45; m 68; c 2. DEVELOPMENTAL BIOLOGY. *Educ:* Columbia Univ, AB, 65; Univ Chicago, PhD(chem physics), 70. *Prof Exp:* Fel theoret biol, Univ Chicago, 70-72; vis fel biol sci, Univ Sussex, Eng, 72-73; instr anat, Univ Pa, 73-75; asst prof biol sci, State Univ NY Albany, 75-79; ASSOC PROF ANAT, NY MED COL, 79- *Concurrent Pos:* Consult, Friends of The Earth & Nat Coun Churches; exec coun, Coalition Responsible Genetic Technol; prin investr, NSF, 76-79, NIH, 79- *Mem:* Am Soc Cell Biol; AAAS; NY Acad Sci. *Res:* Cell differentiation; chromatin structure; cellular pattern formation; embryological mechanisms of evolution; dynamics of biochemical networks. *Mailing Add:* Dept Anatomy Elmwood Hall NY Med Col Valhalla NY 10595

NEWMAN, THEODORE JOSEPH, physics, electronics, see previous edition

NEWMAN, WALTER HAYES, b Birmingham, Ala, Mar 15, 38; m 63; c 3. PHARMACOLOGY. *Educ:* Auburn Univ, BS, 62, MS, 63; Med Col SC, PhD(pharmacol), 67. *Prof Exp:* Instr, 66-67, assoc, 67-68, asst prof, 68-72, assoc prof, 72-78, PROF PHARMACOL, MED UNIV SC, 78- *Mem:* Am Soc Pharmacol & Exp Therapeut; Sigma Xi. *Res:* Cardiac hypertrophy & heart failure. *Mailing Add:* Dept of Pharmacol Med Univ of SC Charleston SC 29425

NEWMAN, WALTER S, b New York, NY, May 24, 27; m 55; c 2. QUATERNARY GEOLOGY. *Educ:* Brooklyn Col, BS, 50; Syracuse Univ, MS, 59; NY Univ, PhD, 66. *Prof Exp:* Geophysicist, Lake Mead Seismol Surv, US Coast & Geod Surv, 51; eng geologist, Corps Engrs, US Army, 51-56; explor geologist, Ramapo Uranium Corp, 56-57; eng geologist, Frederic R Harris, Inc, Consult Engrs, 57-58 & Moran, Proctor, Museser & Rutledge, Consult Engrs, 58-59; asst, Lamont Geol Observ, Columbia Univ, 59-60; lectr geol, 60-66, asst prof, 66-68, chmn dept, 68-71, assoc prof, 68-78, PROF EARTH & ENVIRON SCI, QUEENS COL NY, 78- *Concurrent Pos:* Geologist, US Geol Surv; sr res assoc, Goddard Inst Space Sci, NASA. *Mem:* AAAS; fel Geol Soc Am; Am Quaternary Asn; Soc Am Archaeol; fel Geol Asn Can. *Res:* Late quaternary environments of Northeastern United States. *Mailing Add:* Dept of Earth & Environ Sci Queens Col Flushing NY 11367

NEWMAN, WILEY CLIFFORD, JR, b Europa, Miss, Apr 15, 31; m 58; c 1. PHYSIOLOGY. *Educ:* Vanderbilt Univ, AB, 53; Univ Tenn, PhD(physiol), 65. *Prof Exp:* Instr, Univ Tenn, Memphis, 66-68; asst prof physiol, 68-76, ASSOC PROF PHYSIOL, SCH MED, TULANE UNIV, 76- *Mem:* AAAS. *Res:* Endocrine physiology; experimental mammary cancer induction. *Mailing Add:* Dept of Physiol Tulane Univ Sch of Med New Orleans LA 70112

NEWMAN, WILLIAM ALEXANDER, b Colebrook, NH, Nov 14, 34; m 60; c 2. GLACIAL & PLEISTOCENE GEOLOGY, GEOHYDROLOGY. *Educ:* Boston Univ, AB, 57, AM, 59; Syracuse Univ, PhD(geol), 71. *Prof Exp:* Instr, 60-64, asst prof, 68-78, ASSOC PROF GEOL, NORTHEASTERN UNIV, 78- *Mem:* Asn Eng Geologists; Sigma Xi; Nat Water Well Asn; Int Glaciol Soc. *Res:* Pleistocene geology of northern New England; groundwater aquifers associated with Pleistocene sediments. *Mailing Add:* Dept Earth Sci 103 GR Bldg Northeastern Univ Boston MA 02115

NEWMAN, WILLIAM ANDERSON, b San Francisco, Calif, Nov 13, 27; div; c 4. MARINE BIOLOGY. *Educ:* Univ Calif, Berkeley, AB, 53, MA, 54, PhD(zool), 62. *Prof Exp:* Actg instr zool, Univ Calif, Berkeley, 60-61, asst prof oceanog, Univ Calif, San Diego, 62-63; asst prof marine biol, Harvard Univ, 63-65; asst prof biol oceanog, 65-71, assoc prof oceanog, 71-74, PROF OCEANOG, SCRIPPS INST OCEANOG, UNIV CALIF, SAN DIEGO, 74- *Concurrent Pos:* NSF fel, 62; mem adv comt arthropods, Smithsonian Oceanog Sorting Ctr, 64-67; mem comt ecol of interoceanic canal, Nat Acad Sci, 69-70; mem biol sci comt, World Book Encyclop, 71- *Mem:* AAAS; Marine Biol Asn India; Am Inst Biol Sci. *Res:* Systematics and biogeography of the Crustacea, especially the Cirripedia; biology and near surface geology of oceanic islands; oceanography. *Mailing Add:* Scripps Inst of Oceanog A-002 Univ of Calif San Diego La Jolla CA 92093

NEWMARK, HAROLD LEON, b New York, NY, July 21, 18; m 49; c 2. ORGANIC CHEMISTRY, BIOCHEMISTRY. *Educ:* City Col New York, BS, 39; Polytech Inst Brooklyn, MS, 50. *Prof Exp:* Res dir, Vitarine Co, Inc, NY, 50-59; res chemist & group leader appl res, Hoffman-LaRoche, Inc, Nutley, NJ, 59-66, asst dir prod develop, 66-81, consult, 81; CONSULT, LUDWIG INST CANCER RES, TORONTO, 81- *Concurrent Pos:* Mem, XV revision, US Pharmacopoeia. *Mem:* AAAS; Am Chem Soc; Am Pharmaceut Asn; NY Acad Sci; Am Pharm Asn. *Res:* Biochemistry nutrition, vitamins, carotenoids, parenterals and aneroid health drugs; applications to foods and pharmaceuticals. *Mailing Add:* Ludwig Inst Cancer Res 9 Earl St Toronto ON M4Y 1M4 Can

NEWMARK, MARJORIE ZEIGER, b Cheyenne, Wyo, Aug 6, 22; m 47; c 3. BIOCHEMISTRY. *Educ:* Univ Colo, AB, 44, PhD(biochem), 54. *Prof Exp:* Res asst, Wash Univ, 50-52; res assoc anat, Sch Med, 54-62, vis lectr comp biochem & physiol, 62-63, vis asst prof, 63-64, asst prof, 64-68, asst prof biochem, 68-74, ASSOC PROF BIOCHEM, UNIV KANS, 74- *Mem:* AAAS; Am Chem Soc; Am Soc Cell Biol. *Res:* Biochemistry of arterial tissues. *Mailing Add:* Dept of Biochem Univ of Kans Lawrence KS 66045

NEWMARK, N(ATHAN) M(ORTIMORE), civil engineering, deceased

NEWMARK, RICHARD ALAN, b Urbana, Ill, Nov 11, 40; m 65; c 2. ANALYTICAL CHEMISTRY. *Educ:* Harvard Univ, AB, 61; Univ Calif, Berkeley, PhD(chem), 65. *Prof Exp:* NSF fel, Mass Inst Technol, 64-66; asst prof chem, Univ Colo, Boulder, 66-69; res chemist, 69-72, res specialist, 72-76, sr res specialist, 76-81, STAFF SCIENTIST, 3M CO, 81- *Mem:* Am Chem Soc; Soc Appl Spectros. *Res:* Nuclear magnetic resonance studies. *Mailing Add:* Cent Res Labs 3M Co St Paul MN 55101

NEWMEYER, DOROTHY, b Philadelphia, Pa, May 28, 22; m 52; c 1. GENETICS. *Educ:* Philadelphia Col Pharm, BS, 43; Yale Univ, MS, 48; Stanford Univ, PhD(biol), 51. *Prof Exp:* Fel, NY Univ, 51-52; RES ASSOC BIOL SCI, STANFORD UNIV, 52- *Mem:* Genetics Soc Am. *Res:* Neurospora genetics. *Mailing Add:* Dept of Biol Sci Stanford Univ Stanford CA 94305

NEWNAN, DONALD G(LENN), b San Jose, Calif, Dec 31, 28. INDUSTRIAL ENGINEERING. *Educ:* San Jose State Col, BS, 51; Stanford Univ, MS, 52, MBA, 59, PhD, 65. *Prof Exp:* Design engr, Standard Oil Co Calif, 52-55; asst bus, Stanford Univ, 59; asst prof gen eng, 59-62, assoc prof indust eng, 62-66, interim dean eng, 78-79, PROF INDUST ENG, SAN JOSE STATE UNIV, 66- *Mem:* Am Inst Indust Engrs; Am Soc Eng Educ. *Res:* Applications of economic analysis to public and private sectors; digital computer solution of models of engineering-economic systems. *Mailing Add:* Dept of Indust Eng San Jose State Univ San Jose CA 95192

NEWNHAM, ROBERT EVEREST, b Amsterdam, NY, Mar 28, 29. PHYSICS. *Educ:* Hartwick Col, BS, 50; Colo State Univ, MS, 52; Pa State Univ, PhD(physics), 56; Cambridge Univ, PhD(crystallog), 60. *Prof Exp:* Assoc prof elec eng, Mass Inst Technol, 59-66; assoc prof solid state sci, 66-71, PROF SOLID STATE SCI, PA STATE UNIV, UNIVERSITY PARK, 71-, SECT HEAD, 77- *Mem:* Am Phys Soc; Am Crystallog Asn; Am Ceramic Soc; Mineral Soc Am. *Res:* Crystal and solid state physics; x-ray crystallography. *Mailing Add:* Dept of Mat Sci Pa State Univ University Park PA 16802

NEWNHAM, ROBERT MONTAGUE, b Bromley, Eng, Aug 11, 34; m 59; c 3. FOREST MANAGEMENT, FOREST MENSURATION. *Educ:* Univ Wales, BS, 56; Univ BC, MF, 58, PhD(forestry), 64. *Prof Exp:* Asst exp officer forest ecol, Nature Conservancy, Grange over Sands, Eng, 60-62; res scientist forest mgt & forest mensuration, Forest Mgt Inst, Ottawa, 64-79, DIR, PETAWAWA NAT FORESTRY INST, CAN FORESTRY SERV, DEPT ENVIRON, CHALK RIVER, ONT, 79- *Mem:* Can Inst Forestry; Commonwealth Forestry Asn; Int Union Forest Res Orgn. *Res:* Planning logging operations; systems analysis; applications of computers to forest research; development of forest stand growth models; forest biomass for energy. *Mailing Add:* Petawawa Nat Forestry Inst Can Forestry Serv Dept Environ Chalk River ON K0J 1J0 Can

NEWROCK, RICHARD SANDOR, b New York, NY, Aug 7, 42; div; c 1. SOLID STATE PHYSICS. *Educ:* Rensselaer Polytech Inst, BS, 64; Rutgers Univ, MS, 66, PhD(physics), 70. *Prof Exp:* Res fel physics, Cornell Univ, 70-73; ASST PROF PHYSICS, UNIV CINCINNATI, 73- *Mem:* Am Phys Soc; Sigma Xi. *Res:* Metals and alloys; electrical and thermal magnetoresistivity; magnetic susceptibility; superconductivity; thin films, cermets and inhomogeneous materials; electrical and thermal properties. *Mailing Add:* Dept of Physics Univ of Cincinnati Cincinnati OH 45221

NEWROTH, PETER RUSSELL, b Sheffield, Eng, Oct 12, 45; Can citizen. MARINE BOTANY, WATER RESOURCE MANAGEMENT. *Educ:* Univ NB, BS, 66, PhD(marine biol), 70. *Prof Exp:* Fel bot, Univ BC, 70-72; biologist, Water Invest Br, Water Resources Serv, BC, 72-80; BIOLOGIST & MGR, AQUATIC STUDIES BR, MINISTRY ENVIRON, 80- *Mem:* Aquatic Plant Mgt Soc; NAm Lake Mgt Soc; Int Asn Aquatic Plant Biologists; Int Phycol Soc. *Res:* Life histories, taxonomy and morphology of marine Rhodophyta; management and ecology of freshwater macrophytes. *Mailing Add:* Littoral Studies Sec Aquatic Studies Br Ministry Environ Victoria BC V8V 1X5 Can

NEWSOM, BERNARD DEAN, b Oakland, Calif, Feb 8, 24; m 45; c 2. ENVIRONMENTAL PHYSIOLOGY. *Educ:* Univ Calif, AB, 49, PhD(physiol), 60; Univ San Francisco, MS, 54. *Prof Exp:* Investr & physiologist, US Naval Radiol Defense Lab, 49-61; sr staff scientist, Life Sci Lab, Gen Dynamics/Convair, 61-68; res analyst, Med Res & Opers Directorate, Manned Spacecraft Ctr, 68-72, proj mgr biomed res, Ames Res Ctr, NASA, 72-77; CONSULT, RES PLANNING & MGT, 77- *Mem:* AAAS; Am Physiol Soc; Radiation Res Soc; Aerospace Med Asn; Am Inst Aeronaut & Astronaut. *Res:* Physiological and performance changes of man in a rotational environment; adaptation and tolerance to prolonged exposures to angular velocities and perturbations; biological interpretation of complex space stresses of vibration, acceleration, null gravity and radiation; effect of abnormal environments on radiation sequela in terms of stress tolerance, performance and longevity; Apollo; Skylab; environmental impact of proposed space power satellite; biological effects of power transmission by microwaves. *Mailing Add:* 26645 Altamont Rd Los Altos Hills CA 94022

NEWSOM, DONALD WILSON, b Shongaloo, La, Nov 14, 18; m 44; c 2. HORTICULTURE. *Educ:* La State Univ, BS, 47, MS, 48; Mich State Univ, PhD(hort), 52. *Prof Exp:* Asst prof agr, Tex Col Arts & Indust, 50; assoc horticulturist, Clemson Col, 51-54; horticulturist, USDA, 54-57; PROF HORT, LA STATE UNIV, BATON ROUGE, 57-, HEAD DEPT, 66- *Mem:* Fel AAAS; fel Am Soc Hort Sci (vpres, 80); Am Soc Plant Physiol; Am Forestry Asn. *Res:* Post harvest physiology and chemical composition of fruits and vegetables, especially flavor components. *Mailing Add:* Dept of Hort La State Univ Baton Rouge LA 70803

NEWSOM, GERALD HIGLEY, b Albuquerque, NMex, Feb 11, 39. ASTRONOMY, ATOMIC & MOLECULAR PHYSICS. *Educ:* Univ Mich, Ann Arbor, BA, 61; Harvard Univ, MA, 63, PhD(astron), 68. *Prof Exp:* Res asst, Imperial Col, Univ London, 68-69; asst prof, 69-73, ASSOC PROF ASTRON, OHIO STATE UNIV, 73- *Concurrent Pos:* Res asst, Physikalisches Inst Univ of Bonn, W Ger, 78. *Mem:* Am Astron Soc; Int Astron Union. *Res:* Observation and interpretation of the spectrum of SS 433; classification of energy levels in neutral atoms; measurement of oscillator strengths for neutral and singly ionized atomic spectral lines. *Mailing Add:* Dept of Astron Ohio State Univ 174 W 18th Ave Columbus OH 43210

NEWSOM, HERBERT CHARLES, b Whittier, Calif, Oct 25, 31; m 55; c 2. ORGANIC CHEMISTRY, PESTICIDE CHEMISTRY. *Educ:* Whittier Col, BA, 53; Univ Southern Calif, PhD(org chem), 59. *Prof Exp:* Asst chem, Univ Southern Calif, 55-59; res chemist, 59-65, sr res chemist, 65-80, MGR CHEM ECON, US BORAX RES CORP, 80- *Mem:* AAAS; Am Chem Soc; Nat Asn Corrosion Engrs. *Res:* Organoboron and free radical chemistry; kinetics; herbicide residue analysis; photolysis; herbicide degradation; process development; EPA pesticide registration studies; corrosion testing; engineering economics. *Mailing Add:* 1702 Greenmeadow Ave Tustin CA 92680

NEWSOM, LEO DALE, b Shongaloo, La, Feb 23, 15; m 46; c 4. ENTOMOLOGY. *Educ:* La State Univ, BS, 40; Cornell Univ, PhD(econ entom), 48. *Prof Exp:* Asst forage crop insects res, Cornell Univ, 40-42, in-chg field lab, 46-48; asst entomologist in-chg cotton insect res, Exp Sta, 48-51, ASSOC ENTOMOLOGIST IN-CHG, COTTON INSECT RES, EXP STA, LA STATE UNIV, BATON ROUGE, 51-, HEAD ENTOM RES, EXP STA, 54-, BOYD PROF ENTOM, 66- *Concurrent Pos:* Prof entom, La State Univ, Baton Rouge, 64-66, head dept, 64-77; mem panel cotton insects, President's Sci Adv Comt, 64, sub-panel mem restoring qual of our environ, 65-, mem panel world food supplies, 66-; sub-comt insect pests, Nat Acad Sci-Nat Res Coun, 64-; secy agr comt agr sci. *Mem:* AAAS; Entom Soc Am. *Res:* Biology and ecology of insects; physiology and ecology of diapause in insects; biological and ecological consequences of pesticide usage. *Mailing Add:* Agr Exp Sta La State Univ Baton Rouge LA 70803

NEWSOM, RAYMOND A, b Tarrant Co, Tex, Jan 8, 31; m 50; c 2. ORGANIC CHEMISTRY. *Educ:* Ariz State Univ, BS, 53; Univ Ariz, MS, 57; Univ Iowa, PhD(org chem), 60. *Prof Exp:* Res chemist, Plastics Div Res, 60-61 & Hydrocarbons Div, 62-65, process chemist, Process Technol Dept, 65-75, SR PROCESS SPECIALIST, PROCESS TECHNOL DEPT, MONSANTO CO, TEXAS CITY, TEX, 75- *Mem:* Am Chem Soc. *Res:* Organic syntheses and reaction mechanisms; product and process development for monomers. *Mailing Add:* 1209 Plantation Dr Dickinson TX 77539

NEWSOM, WILLIAM S, JR, b Wynne, Ark, Dec 31, 18; m 46; c 3. AGRICULTURAL CHEMISTRY. *Educ:* Univ Ark, BS, 48. *Prof Exp:* Chemist, Lion Oil Co, 48-55 & Monsanto Chem Co, 55-57; sr res chemist, Int Minerals & Chem Corp, Ill, 57-67; sr res engr, Ga Inst Technol, 67-68; SECT HEAD, OCCIDENTAL CHEM CO, 68- *Mem:* Am Chem Soc; Brit Fertilizer Soc. *Res:* Fertilizer technology; pesticides; plant growth regulators. *Mailing Add:* Agr Res Lab Occidental Chem Co PO Box 300 White Springs FL 32096

NEWSOME, DAVID ANTHONY, b Winston-Salem, NC, Apr 16, 42. OPHTHALMOLOGY. *Educ:* Duke Univ, AB, 64; Col Physicians & Surgeons, Columbia Univ, MD, 68. *Prof Exp:* Resident opthal, Harvard Univ, 73-76; lectr physiol, Simmons Col, Boston, 75-77; fel, Bascom Palmer Eye Inst, Univ Miami, 77; sr staff opthalmologist, Nat Eye Inst, 77-79, chief, Sect Retinal & Ocular Connective Tissue Dis, 79-82; DIR, LAB RETINAL DEGENESTIONS, WILMER INST, JOHNS HOPKINS UNIV, 82- *Concurrent Pos:* Res fel med, Mass Gen Hosp, 73-76; consult, Pan Am Health Orgn, 79 & Nat Geog Soc, 81; lectr macular dis, Wilmer Ophthal Inst, 80-; comt mem res sect, Asn Res Vision & Ophthal, 80- *Mem:* AAAS; Asn Res Vision & Ophthal; Am Acad Ophthal; Am Soc Cell Biol. *Res:* Clinical and laboratory investigations into the cellular and tissue mechanisms of serious eye diseases affecting retina, vitreous, choroid and other ocular tissues. *Mailing Add:* Wilmer Ophthal Inst 600 N Wolfe St Baltimore MD 21205

NEWSOME, JAMES FREDERICK, b Winton, NC, Mar 24, 23; m 56; c 3. SURGERY. *Educ:* Univ NC, AB, 44, cert, 47; Vanderbilt Univ, MD, 49. *Prof Exp:* Intern, Med Col Va Hosp, 49-50; from asst resident to chief resident, 52-56, from instr to assoc prof, 64-71, PROF SURG, SCH MED, UNIV NC, CHAPEL HILL, 71- *Concurrent Pos:* Consult, Vet Admin Hosp, Fayetteville, NC, 56- *Mem:* Soc Surg Alimentary Tract; Am Asn Cancer Res; AMA; Am Col Surgeons; Am Asn Cancer Educ. *Res:* Cancer, especially breast carcinoma; chemotherapy of cancer; cystic disease of breast. *Mailing Add:* Dept of Surg Univ of NC Sch of Med Chapel Hill NC 27514

NEWSOME, RICHARD DUANE, b Kalamazoo, Mich, Aug 19, 31; m 54; c 2. PLANT ECOLOGY, BOTANY. *Educ:* Western Mich Univ, BS, 54; Univ Sask, MS, 63, PhD(plant ecol), 65. *Prof Exp:* From instr to asst prof, 65-70, ASSOC PROF BOT & ECOL, BELOIT COL, 70- *Mem:* Ecol Soc Am; Am Inst Biol Scientists; Nat Sci Teachers Asn. *Res:* Plant ecological research on the structure and dynamics of communities in ecotonal situations; assessment of plant ecologic condition of disturbed watersheds in southern Wisconsin; grassland ecology; environmental education. *Mailing Add:* 1716 Oakwood Ave Beloit WI 53511

NEWSOME, ROSS WHITTED, b Lynchburg, Va, Nov 6, 35. PHYSICS. *Educ:* Mass Inst Technol, SB, 57; Univ Mich, Ann Arbor, MS, 58, PhD(physics), 63. *Prof Exp:* Univ Mich res asst high energy physics, Lawrence Radiation Lab, Univ Calif, Berkeley, 59-60; from res asst to res assoc exp nuclear physics, Univ Mich, Ann Arbor, 60-64; mem staff, Los Alamos Sci Lab, Univ Calif, 64-66; mem tech staff systs eng, Bellcomm, Inc, Washington, DC, 66-72; MEM TECH STAFF CUSTOMER SYSTS ENG CTR, BELL LABS, 72- *Mem:* AAAS; Am Phys Soc; Sigma Xi; NY Acad Sci. *Res:* Transmission of infrared radiation through the atmosphere; capabilities of thermal infrared instruments for remote sensing of surface targets from satellites; measurements and analyses of telephone traffic for small business customers; utilization of hierarchical data bases to store and extract large quantities of information. *Mailing Add:* Customer Systs Eng Ctr Bell Labs Inc Holmdel NJ 07733

NEWSON, HAROLD DON, b Salt Lake City, Utah, July 11, 24; m 48; c 4. MEDICAL ENTOMOLOGY. *Educ:* Univ Utah, BA, 49, MS, 50; Univ Md, PhD(entom), 59; Am Registry Prof Entomologists. *Prof Exp:* From res entomologist to med entom consult to Surgeon Gen, US Army, 51-70; assoc prof, 70-76, PROF ENTOM, MICROBIOL & PUB HEALTH, MICH STATE UNIV, 76- *Concurrent Pos:* Mem, US Armed Forces Pest Control Bd, 62-70, chmn, 63-67; mem res subcomt, Fed Comt Pest Control, 64-66; mem study group, Off Environ Sci, Smithsonian Inst, 72-74; chmn region V, USPHS Vector Control Group, 73-76; res consult, US Army Res & Develop Command, 79- *Mem:* Am Soc Trop Med & Hyg; Am Mosquito Control Asn; Entom Soc Am. *Res:* Ecology; transmission and control of arthropod-borne diseases of medical and veterinary importance. *Mailing Add:* Dept of Entom Mich State Univ East Lansing MI 48824

NEWSTEAD, JAMES DUNCAN MACINNES, b Camberley, Eng, Oct 11, 30; m 62; c 1. CELL BIOLOGY, HISTOLOGY. *Educ:* Univ BC, BA, 54, MA, 56; Ore State Univ, PhD(cell biol), 62. *Prof Exp:* From instr to asst prof zool, Ore State Univ, 60-63; USPHS fel fine structure, Univ Wash, 63-65; from asst prof to assoc prof anat, 65-74, PROF ANAT, UNIV SASK, 74- *Mem:* AAAS; Am Soc Zoologists; Am Soc Cell Biol. *Res:* Circulation and ion transport in gills of fish; fine structure of cell division in protozoa. *Mailing Add:* Dept of Anat Univ of Sask Saskatoon SK S7N 0W0 Can

NEWSTEIN, HERMAN, b Philadelphia, Pa, May 4, 18; m 53; c 1. METEOROLOGY. *Educ:* Temple Univ, BS, 48, MEd, 51; NY Univ, MS, 53, PhD(meteorol), 57. *Prof Exp:* Meteorologist, US Weather Bur, 41-53, res meteorologist, 53-62; PROF PHYSICS & ATMOSPHERIC SCI, DREXEL UNIV, 62- *Concurrent Pos:* Sci consult, Nat Acad Sci, 58; adj assoc prof, NY Univ, 58-62. *Mem:* AAAS; Am Meteorol Soc; Am Geophys Union; Air Pollution Control Asn; Am Asn Physics Teachers. *Res:* Experimental and theoretical atmospheric physics. *Mailing Add:* Dept of Physics Drexel Univ Philadelphia PA 19104

NEWSTEIN, MAURICE, b Philadelphia, Pa, Feb 13, 26; m 57; c 2. THEORETICAL PHYSICS. *Educ:* Temple Univ, AB, 49; Mass Inst Technol, PhD(physics), 54. *Prof Exp:* Asst univ observ, Harvard Univ, 54-55; physicist, Tech Res Group, Inc, 55-67; res scientist electrophys, 67-70, ASSOC PROF ELECTROPHYS, GRAD CTR, POLYTECH INST NEW YORK, 70- *Res:* Atomic scattering problems; plasma physics; applications of microwave and optical spectroscopy; quantum electronics. *Mailing Add:* Dept of Electrophys Grad Ctr 333 Jay St Brooklyn NY 11201

NEWTON, ALWIN B, b Athol, Mass, Aug 8, 07; m 31; c 3. MECHANICAL ENGINEERING. *Educ:* Syracuse Univ, BSME, 30; Mass Inst Technol, MS, 32. *Prof Exp:* Test engr, Gen Elec Co, Mass, 30-31; develop engr, York Ice Mach Corp, Pa, 32-36; mgr refrig controls div, Minneapolis-Honeywell Regulator Co, Minn, 36-44; chief engr, Airtemp Div, Chrysler Corp, Ohio, 44-49; vpres eng, Acme Industs, Inc, Mich, 49-53; vpres & dir eng, Coleman Co, Kans, 53-58; vpres & dir res, York Div, Borg-Warner Corp, 58-72, consult & dir res, 72-76; CONSULT, 76- *Concurrent Pos:* US deleg, 12th Int Cong Refrig, Madrid, 67; chmn, 13th Int Cong Refrig, Washington, DC, 71; pres comt E-1, Int Inst Refrig. *Honors & Awards:* Distinguished Serv Award, Am Soc Heat, Refrig & Air-Conditioning Engrs, 63. *Mem:* Am Soc Mech Engrs; fel Am Soc Heat, Refrig & Air-Conditioning Engrs; Solar Energy Soc; Am Ord Asn; Int Inst Refrig. *Res:* Aircraft control; thermoelectric heat pumping; multiphase jet flow and power utilization; research in patterns of temperature and humidity for human comfort. *Mailing Add:* 136 Shelbourne Dr York PA 17403

NEWTON, AMOS SYLVESTER, b Shingletown, Calif, July 26, 16; m 42; c 2. CHEMISTRY. *Educ:* Univ Calif, BS, 38; Univ Mich, MS, 39, PhD(phys chem), 41. *Prof Exp:* Chemist, Eastman Kodak Co, NY, 41-42, Manhattan Proj, Iowa State Col, 42-46 & Eastman Kodak Co, NY, 46-62; CHEMIST, LAWRENCE BERKELEY LAB, UNIV CALIF, 62- *Concurrent Pos:* Consult, Lawrence Berkeley Lab, Univ Calif, 46-62. *Mem:* AAAS; Am Soc Mass Spectros; Am Chem Soc. *Res:* Use of radioisotopes as tracer; chemistry of heavy elements; radiochemistry of fission products; radiation chemistry; mass spectrometry; molecular beam studies; environmental chemistry; marine chemistry; fuel science. *Mailing Add:* Lawrence Berkeley Lab Univ Calif Energy & Environ Div Berkeley CA 94720

NEWTON, (WILLIAM) AUSTIN, US citizen. DEVELOPMENTAL GENETICS. *Educ:* Univ Calif, PhD(biochem), 64. *Prof Exp:* Asst prof, 66-72, ASSOC PROF BIOL, PRINCETON UNIV, 72- *Res:* Biochemistry and genetics of gene expression and development in microorganisms. *Mailing Add:* Dept of Biol Princeton Univ Princeton NJ 08540

NEWTON, CAROL MARILYN, medicine, computer science, see previous edition

NEWTON, CHESTER WHITTIER, b Los Angeles, Calif, Aug 17, 20; m 48; c 4. METEOROLOGY. *Educ:* Univ Chicago, SB, 46, SM, 47, PhD(meteorol), 51. *Prof Exp:* Weather observer, US Weather Bur, 39-41, meteorologist, 48; asst meteorol, Univ Chicago, 47-48, synoptic analyst, 48-51; synoptic analyst, Univ Stockholm, 51-53 & Woods Hole Oceanog Inst, 53; res assoc meteorol, Univ Chicago, 53-56, asst prof, 56-61; chief scientist, Nat Severe Storms Proj, US Weather Bur, 61-63; SR SCIENTIST, NAT CTR ATMOSPHERIC RES, 63- *Concurrent Pos:* Affil prof, Pa State Univ, 65-67; mem steering comt, Earth Sci Curric Proj, 65-68. *Honors & Awards:* Editor's Award, Am Meteorol Soc, 70. *Mem:* AAAS; fel Am Meteorol Soc (pres, 79); Am Geophys Union; foreign mem, Royal Meteorol Soc; Meteorol Soc Japan. *Res:* Synoptic meteorology; atmospheric general circulation and global energy balance; aerological analysis of atmospheric current systems; structure of and physical processes in cyclone formation; thunderstorms and severe local storms. *Mailing Add:* Nat Ctr for Atmospheric Res Box 3000 Boulder CO 80307

NEWTON, DAVID C, b Middletown, Conn, Apr 27, 39; m 58; c 2. APICULTURE, ANIMAL BEHAVIOR. *Educ:* Cent Conn State Col, BS, 61; Wesleyan Univ, MALS, 65; Univ Ill, PhD(entom), 67. *Prof Exp:* Teacher pub schs, 61 & high sch, 61-64; ASSOC PROF BIOL, CENT CONN STATE COL, 67- *Concurrent Pos:* Conn Res Comn grant, 68-71; USDA study grant, 73-76. *Mem:* AAAS; Animal Behav Soc; Bee Res Asn; Am Inst Biol Sci. *Res:* Behavior studies of honey bees; behavior studies of honey bees relating to nest cleaning and disease resistance. *Mailing Add:* Dept Biol Sci Cent Conn State Col New Britain CT 06050

NEWTON, DAVID EDWARD, b Grand Rapids, Mich, June 18, 33. SCIENCE WRITING, SCIENCE EDUCATION. *Educ:* Univ Mich, BS, 55, MA, 61; Harvard Univ, EdD(sci educ), 71. *Prof Exp:* Teacher math & sci, Ottawa Hills Sch, Mich, 55-67; PROF CHEM & PHYSICS, SALEM STATE COL, 69- *Concurrent Pos:* Vis prof sci educ, Western Wash Univ, 80- *Honors & Awards:* Star Award, Nat Sci Teachers Asn, 60; Outstanding Sci Educator of Year, Asn Educ Teachers Sci, 68. *Mem:* AAAS; Asn Educ Teachers Sci; Sex Educ & Info Coun US. *Res:* Social and ethical issues in science and their role in secondary and college education; human sexuality; gay studies; science education in the schools. *Mailing Add:* 12 Ober St Beverly MA 01915

NEWTON, GEORGE C(HENEY), JR, b Milwaukee, Wis, May 14, 19; m 46; c 3. ELECTRICAL ENGINEERING. *Educ:* Mass Inst Technol, SB, 41, ScD, 50. *Prof Exp:* Asst, Mass Inst Technol, 41-42; sr engr, York Safe & Lock Co, Pa, 42-43; from asst to sr proj engr, Sperry Gyroscope Co, NY, 43-46; from instr to assoc prof elec eng, 46-64, PROF ELEC ENG, MASS INST TECHNOL, 64- *Concurrent Pos:* Chmn working group control systs, guid & control panel, guided missiles comt, Res Develop Bd, 52-53; chmn educ comt, Am Automatic Control Coun, 63-68. *Honors & Awards:* Levy Medal, Franklin Inst, 53. *Mem:* Inst Elec & Electronics Engrs. *Res:* Automatic control; instrumentation; electronics. *Mailing Add:* Lab for Info & Decision Syst 35-414 Mass Inst of Technol Cambridge MA 02139

NEWTON, GEORGE LARRY, b Lincolnton, NC, Mar 29, 45; m 68; c 1. ANIMAL NUTRITION, WASTE MANAGEMENT. *Educ:* NC State Univ, BS, 67, PhD(animal sci), 72; Va Polytech Inst & State Univ, MS, 70. *Prof Exp:* Res assoc animal sci, Univ Ky, 72-73; asst prof, 73-80, ASSOC PROF ANIMAL SCI, UNIV GA, 80- *Mem:* Am Soc Animal Sci; Am Registry Cert Animal Scientists. *Res:* Ruminant and non-ruminant nutrition; environmental and nutritional interactions; livestock waste management. *Mailing Add:* Dept of Animal Sci Coastal Plain Sta Tifton GA 31794

NEWTON, H CALVIN, JR, plant pathology, plant breeding, see previous edition

NEWTON, HOWARD JOSEPH, b Oneida, NY, June 16, 49; m 70. STATISTICAL ANALYSIS. *Educ:* Niagara Univ, BS, 71; State Univ NY Buffalo, MA, 73, PhD(statist sci), 75. *Prof Exp:* res asst prof statist sci & tech specialist surg, statist lab, Res Found State NY, State Univ NY Buffalo, 75-78; ASST PROF STATIST, TEXAS A&M UNIV, 78- *Mem:* Am Statist Asn; Asn Comput Mach. *Res:* Statistical computing with particular emphasis on the analysis of multiple time series having rational spectra. *Mailing Add:* Inst of Statist Texas A&M Univ College Station TX 77843

NEWTON, JAMES HENRY, physical chemistry, see previous edition

NEWTON, JOHN CHESTER, b Grainfield, Kans, May 30, 33; div; c 1. ANALYTICAL CHEMISTRY. *Educ:* Univ Kans, BS, 54; Univ Colo, Boulder, BA, 59; Univ Calif, Berkeley, PhD(chem), 65. *Prof Exp:* Mem staff chem, Forest Prod Lab, Univ Calif, 59-60 & Los Alamos Sci Lab, Univ Calif, 65-69; MEM STAFF CHEM, LAWRENCE LIVERMORE LAB, UNIV CALIF, 69- *Mem:* Am Soc Mass Spectrometry. *Res:* Mass spectrometry; computer automation; gas analyses. *Mailing Add:* Lawrence Livermore Nat Lab Univ of Calif Livermore CA 94550

NEWTON, JOHN MARSHALL, b Popejoy, Iowa, May 20, 13; m 41; c 3. CARBOHYDRATE CHEMISTRY. *Educ:* Iowa State Col, BS, 36, PhD(chem), 41. *Prof Exp:* Res chemist, Clinton Indust, 41-42, from asst supvr to res supvr, 42-49; dir tech sales serv, 49-63, tech asst to vpres sales, Clinton Corn Processing Co, 63-78; RETIRED. *Mem:* AAAS; Am Asn Cereal Chem; Am Chem Soc; Tech Asn Pulp & Paper Indust; Am Asn Textile Chem & Colorists. *Res:* Carbohydrate and enzyme chemistry; concentration, characterization and properties of soybean amylase; chemistry of starch, lactic acid, oil and plant proteins; fermentation of lactic acid. *Mailing Add:* 1425 Seventh St NW Clinton IA 52732

NEWTON, JOHN S, b Oneonta, NY, Sept 21, 08; m 30, 46; c 6. ELECTRICAL & MECHANICAL ENGINEERING. *Educ:* Ore State Col, BS, 30. *Prof Exp:* Design engr, East Pittsburgh Works, Westinghouse Elec Corp, 30-39, mgr appl eng, Steam Div, 39-44, asst mgr eng, 44-48; vpres eng, Baldwin-Lima-Hamilton Corp, 48-51, locomotive div, 51-54, testing mach div, 54-55; vpres eng, Goodman Mfg Co, 55-62, exec vpres, 62-63, pres, 63-65, vpres & gen mgr, Goodman Div, Westinghouse Air Brake Co, 65-66; pres & chief exec off, Poor & Co, Ill, 66-69; pres, chief exec off & dir, Portec, Inc, 69-74; PRES, NEWTON ENG, 76- *Mem:* Am Soc Mech Engrs; Am Inst Mining, Metall & Petrol Engrs. *Res:* Removal of hard cemented materials from the earth, especially mining of ores and tunneling. *Mailing Add:* Newton Eng Co 22 W 450 Ahlstrand Dr Glen Ellyn IL 60137

NEWTON, JOSEPH EMORY O'NEAL, b Orlando, Fla, Apr 5, 27; m 58; c 2. PSYCHIATRY, PHYSIOLOGICAL PSYCHOLOGY. *Educ:* Emory Univ, BS, 52, MD, 55. *Prof Exp:* Fel psychiat, Pavlovian Lab, Phipps Psychiat Clin, Sch Med, Johns Hopkins Univ, 56-57, USPHS fel, 58-61; instr psychiat, Pavlovian Lab, Phipps Psychiat Clin, Sch Med, Johns Hopkins Univ, 62-66, asst prof, 66-68; res physiologist, 68-74, PHYSIOLOGIST, NEUROPSYCHIAT RES LAB, VET ADMIN HOSP, NORTH LITTLE ROCK, ARK, 74- *Concurrent Pos:* Investr psychophysiol res lab, Vet Admin Hosp, Perry Point, Md, 58-61. *Mem:* AAAS; Am Physiol Soc; Soc Psychophysiol Res; Pavlovian Soc NAm. *Res:* Conditional reflex studies in dogs and opossums; cardiovascular conditioning; effects of cerebral cortical ablations on acquired emotional reactions. *Mailing Add:* Neuropsychiat Res Lab Vet Admin Hosp North Little Rock AR 72116

NEWTON, MARSHALL DICKINSON, b Boston, Mass, July 15, 40; m 63; c 2. THEORETICAL CHEMISTRY. *Educ:* Dartmouth Col, BA, 61, MA, 63; Harvard Univ, PhD(chem), 66. *Prof Exp:* NSF fel chem, Oxford Univ, 66-67; NIH fel, Carnegie-Mellon Univ, 67-68, res assoc, 68-69; assoc chemist, 69-73, chemist, 73-81, SR CHEMIST, BROOKHAVEN NAT LAB, 81- *Concurrent Pos:* Carnegie-Mellon Univ & Mellon Inst res fel, 68. *Mem:* Am Chem Soc. *Res:* Calculation of molecular potential energy surfaces; analysis of molecular bonding in terms of electronic structure; theory of solvation phenomena. *Mailing Add:* Chem Dept Brookhaven Nat Lab Upton NY 11973

NEWTON, MELVIN GARY, b Millen, Ga, Feb 18, 39. ORGANIC CHEMISTRY. *Educ:* Ga Inst Technol, BS, 61, PhD(chem), 66. *Prof Exp:* Asst prof, 67-77, ASSOC PROF CHEM, UNIV GA, 77- *Concurrent Pos:* Fel, Univ Ill, 65-67. *Mem:* Am Chem Soc. *Res:* Structural chemistry, single crystal X-ray diffraction; structure and mechanism in organophosphorus chemistry; organometallic structural chemistry. *Mailing Add:* Dept of Chem Univ of Ga Athens GA 30602

NEWTON, MICHAEL, b Hartford, Conn, Oct 24, 32; m 54; c 3. FOREST ECOLOGY, WEED SCIENCE. *Educ:* Univ Vt, BS, 54; Ore State Univ, BS, 59, MS, 60, PhD(bot), 64. *Prof Exp:* Res asst forest herbicides, 59-60, instr forest mgt, 60-64, asst prof forest sci, 64-68, assoc prof forest mgt, 68-75, PROF FOREST ECOL, ORE STATE UNIV, 75- *Concurrent Pos:* Consult to numerous corps, 62-; fel, Univ Tenn, 69-70; consult comt effects of herbicides in Vietnam, Nat Acad Sci, 72-73, mem study of pest problems, 73-74. *Mem:* AAAS; Soc Am Foresters; Ecol Soc Am; Weed Sci Soc Am. *Res:* Quantitative forest ecology; usage of herbicides to manipulate components of forest ecosystems; development of theory and practice in forest manipulation. *Mailing Add:* Sch of Forestry Ore State Univ Corvallis OR 97331

NEWTON, R(OBERT) E(UGENE), b St Louis, Mo, Oct 16, 17; m 42; c 2. MECHANICAL ENGINEERING. *Educ:* Wash Univ, BS, 38, MS, 39; Univ Mich, PhD(eng mech), 51. *Prof Exp:* Asst math, Wash Univ, 38-39, instr, 39-41; stress analyst, Curtiss-Wright Corp, Mo, 41-42, flutter analyst, 42-43, head struct methods unit, 43-45; res engr, McDonnell Aircraft Corp, 45; from asst prof to assoc prof appl mech, Wash Univ, 45-51; chmn dept, 53-67, PROF MECH ENG, NAVAL POSTGRAD SCH, 51- *Concurrent Pos:* Vis prof, Univ Wales, 68-69 & Univ Nantes, 81; consult, Western Cartridge Co, Firestone Tire & Rubber Co, Monterey Res Lab & Ryan Aeronaut Co. *Mem:* Am Soc Mech Engrs; Am Soc Eng Educ; Soc Exp Stress Anal. *Res:* Applied mechanics; theory of structures; thermal stresses; shock and vibration. *Mailing Add:* Dept of Mech Eng Naval Postgrad Sch Monterey CA 93940

NEWTON, RICHARD WAYNE, b Baytown, Tex, Aug 26, 48; m 68; c 2. ELECTRICAL ENGINEERING. *Educ:* Tex A&M Univ, BS, 70, MS, 71, PhD(elec eng), 77. *Prof Exp:* Engr & scientist, Lockheed Electronics Co, Inc, 71-73; prog mgr, Remote Sensing Ctr, 73-77; asst prof, 77-81, assoc dir, Remote Sensing Ctr, 77-80, ASSOC PROF ELEC ENG, TEX A&M UNIV, 81-, DIR, REMOTE SENSING CTR, TEX ENG EXP STA, 80- *Concurrent Pos:* Prin, Innovative Develop Eng Assocs, 80-; pres, Aerial Surveys, Inc, 77-; consult, Zesco, Inc, 80-; Univ Space Res Asn representative, Landsat D Tech Users Comt, NASA, 81-; mem, various workshops, comts & working groups, NASA, 74-; mem, Automated In-Situ Water Quality Workshop, Enivron Protection Agency, 77. *Mem:* Am Geophys Union; Inst Elec & Electronics Engrs; Sigma Xi. *Res:* Techniques of extracting agricultural, hydrologic and oceanographic information from remote sensing measurements ranging from microwave to visible wavelengths; automated sensor systems for remote sensing applications. *Mailing Add:* Remote Sensing Ctr 326 Teague Bldg Tex A&M Univ College Station TX 77843

NEWTON, ROBERT ANDREW, b Oakville, Wash, Sept 23, 22; m 46; c 4. PHYSICAL ORGANIC CHEMISTRY. *Educ:* Univ Wash, BS, 47, PhD(chem), 53. *Prof Exp:* Mem staff res, E I du Pont de Nemours & Co, 53-56; chemist, 56-57, from res chemist to sr res chemist, 57-68, res specialist, 68-74, sr res specialist, 74-80, ASSOC SCIENTIST, DOW CHEM CO, 80- *Mem:* Am Chem Soc; Sigma Xi; AAAS. *Res:* Aklylene oxide chemistry and polymerization products; chromatography; chemical kinetics; isolation and identification of trace components; process studies, especially related to productivity and quality enhancement. *Mailing Add:* 53 Pin Oak Ct Lake Jackson TX 77566

NEWTON, ROBERT CHAFFER, b Bellingham, Wash, June 11, 33; m 67; c 2. PETROLOGY. *Educ:* Univ Calif, Los Angeles, AB, 56, MA, 58, PhD(geol), 63. *Prof Exp:* From asst prof to assoc prof, 63-71, PROF GEOL, DEPT GEOPHYS SCI, UNIV CHICAGO, 71- *Mem:* Am Geophys Union; Am Mineral Soc. *Res:* Experimental investigation of the high-temperature, high-pressure stabilities of minerals. *Mailing Add:* Dept of Geophys Sci Univ of Chicago Chicago IL 60637

NEWTON, ROBERT MORGAN, b Salem, Mass, Jan 3, 48; m 69; c 1. GLACIAL GEOLOGY. *Educ:* Univ NH, BA, 70; State Univ NY Binghamton, MA, 72; Univ Mass, PhD(geol), 78. *Prof Exp:* Vis prof geol, Brock Univ, 76-78; ASST PROF GEOL, SMITH COL, 78- *Mem:* Geol Soc Am; Int Glaciological Soc; Clay Minerals Soc. *Res:* Geomorphology; groundwater geology; low temperature geochemistry and clay petrology. *Mailing Add:* Dept of Geol Smith Col Northampton MA 01063

NEWTON, ROBERT RUSSELL, b Chattanooga, Tenn, July 7, 18; m 44; c 2. PHYSICS. *Educ:* Univ Tenn, BS, 40; Ohio State Univ, MS, 42, PhD(physics), 46. *Prof Exp:* Instr physics, Univ Tenn, 42-44; res assoc, George Washington Univ, 44-45; mem tech staff, Bell Labs, Inc, 46-48; assoc prof physics, Univ Tenn, 48-54; prof, Tulane Univ, 55-57; MEM PRIN STAFF, APPL PHYSICS LAB, JOHNS HOPKINS UNIV, 57-, BR SUPVR, SPACE RES & ANALYSIS, 64- *Concurrent Pos:* Consult, Oak Ridge Nat Lab, 49- *Mem:* Am Phys Soc; Am Geophys Union; Int Astron Union. *Res:* Exterior ballistics; molecular spectra; Townsend discharges in gases; electron conduction in and emission from solids; satellite dynamics and geodesy; astronomy. *Mailing Add:* Space Res & Anal Appl Phys Lab Johns Hopkins Univ J Hop Rd Laurel MD 20707

NEWTON, ROGER GERHARD, b Ger, Nov 30, 24; nat US; m 53; c 3. THEORETICAL PHYSICS. *Educ:* Harvard Univ, AB, 49, AM, 50, PhD(physics), 53. *Prof Exp:* Mem, Inst Advan Study, 53-55; from asst prof to assoc prof, 55-60, prof physics, 60-78, chmn dept, 73-80, DISTINGUISHED PROF PHYSICS, IND UNIV, BLOOMINGTON, 78-. *Concurrent Pos:* Jewett fel, 53-55; NSF sr fel, Univ Rome, 62-63, Univ Montpellier, 71-72, Inst Advan Study, Princeton Univ, 79. *Mem:* AAAS; fel Am Phys Soc; Sigma Xi; Fed Am Scientists; NY Acad Sci. *Res:* Field and scattering theories; nuclear and high energy physics; elementary particles; quantum mechanics. *Mailing Add:* Dept Physics Ind Univ Bloomington IN 47401

NEWTON, SEABORN ALTON, JR, b Statesboro, Ga, Sept 13, 29; m 53; c 5. CHEMICAL ENGINEERING, PHYSICAL CHEMISTRY. *Educ:* Ga Inst Technol, BChE, 48, MS, 49; Oxford Univ, PhD(phys chem), 53. *Prof Exp:* Chem engr, Esso Standard Oil Co, 53-57, chem res supvr, Esso Res Labs, 57-59; nuclear specialist, Sci & Tech Intel Ctr, US Dept Navy, Washington, DC, 59-63; ADMINR, US GOVT, 63- *Res:* Nuclear engineering; scientific intelligence. *Mailing Add:* 9808 Inglemere Dr Bethesda MD 20817

NEWTON, STEPHEN BRUINGTON, b Freeport, Ill, Dec 24, 34; m 58; c 3. TECHNICAL WRITING, TECHNICAL EDITING. *Educ:* Univ Mo, BA, 56; Univ Ill, MS, 61, PhD(bact), 65. *Prof Exp:* Prod develop scientist, Pillsbury Co, 64-71; sr group leader, Quaker Oats Co, 71-76; assoc ed, Food Prod Develop, 76-79; sr food technologist, Sara Lee, 79-81; TECH WRITER, 81- *Mem:* Inst Food Technologists. *Res:* Production of polysaccharides and extracellular enzymes by microbes; food product development. *Mailing Add:* 862 Coventry Lane Crystal Lake IL 60014

NEWTON, THOMAS ALLEN, b Buffalo, NY, May 30, 43. ORGANIC CHEMISTRY. *Educ:* Hobart Col, BS, 65; Bucknell Univ, MS, 68; Univ Del, PhD(org chem), 73. *Prof Exp:* Res assoc, Rensselaer Polytech Inst, 73-76, asst prof, Williams Col, 76-78; ASST PROF COLBY COL, 78- *Mem:* Am Chem Soc. *Res:* The synthesis of nucleoside analogues as potential antitumor/antiviral agents; the photochemistry of enaminonitriles; orbital symmetry controlled reactions; sigmatropic rearrangements. *Mailing Add:* 16 1/2 Dalton St Waterville ME 04901

NEWTON, THOMAS HANS, b Berlin, Ger, May 9, 25; US citizen; c 2. RADIOLOGY. *Educ:* Univ Calif, Berkeley, BA, 49; Univ Calif, San Francisco, MD, 52. *Prof Exp:* From asst prof to assoc prof, 59-68, PROF RADIOL, MED CTR, UNIV CALIF, SAN FRANCISCO, 68-, CHIEF SECT NEURORADIOL, 77- *Concurrent Pos:* Consult, Ft Miley Vet Admin Hosp & Letterman Gen Hosp, San Francisco, Martinez Vet Admin Hosp & Oaknoll Naval Hosp, Oakland. *Mem:* Asn Univ Radiol; Am Soc Neuroradiol; Neurosurg Soc Am. *Res:* Neuroradiology. *Mailing Add:* Dept of Radiol Univ of Calif Med Ctr San Francisco CA 94122

NEWTON, THOMAS WILLIAM, b Berkeley, Calif, June 26, 23; m 48; c 3. INORGANIC CHEMISTRY, PHYSICAL CHEMISTRY. *Educ:* Univ Calif, Berkeley, BS, 43, PhD(chem), 49. *Prof Exp:* Chemist, Manhattan Proj, Univ Calif & Tenn Eastman, 44-46; CHEMIST STAFF MEM, LOS ALAMOS SCI LAB, 49- *Concurrent Pos:* Vis prof, State Univ NY Stonybrook, 67. *Mem:* AAAS; Am Chem Soc. *Res:* Actinide chemistry; equilibrium and kinetics of reactions in aqueous solutions. *Mailing Add:* Los Alamos Sci Lab Univ of Calif Box 1663 Los Alamos NM 87544

NEWTON, TYRE ALEXANDER, b Morris, Okla, Dec 28, 21; m 46; c 2. MATHEMATICAL ANALYSIS. *Educ:* Colo State Univ, BS, 49; Univ Ga, MA, 51, PhD(math), 52. *Prof Exp:* Instr math, Univ Nebr, 52-55; from asst prof to assoc prof, Colo State Univ, 55-58; asst prof, 58-72, assoc prof, 72-78, PROF MATH, WASH STATE UNIV, 78- *Mem:* Am Math Soc; Soc Indust & Appl Math; Math Asn Am; Am Soc Eng Educ. *Res:* Infinite series; finite differences; functional analysis; qualitative theory of ordinary differential equations; using the analog computer to illustrate mathematical concepts. *Mailing Add:* Dept of Math Wash State Univ Pullman WA 99163

NEWTON, VICTOR JOSEPH, b Boston, Mass, Apr 9, 37. THEORETICAL NUCLEAR PHYSICS. *Educ:* Spring Hill Col, BS, 61, MA, 62; Mass Inst Technol, PhD(physics), 66. *Prof Exp:* Lectr physics, Loyola Col Md, 68-69; asst prof, 69-73, ASSOC PROF PHYSICS, FAIRFIELD UNIV, 73-, CHMN DEPT, 76- *Mem:* AAAS; Am Phys Soc; Am Asn Physics Teachers; Fed Am Scientists; Sigma Xi. *Res:* Many channel scattering theory; three and four nucleon systems as applied to nuclear systems, including weak interactions. *Mailing Add:* Dept of Physics Fairfield Univ Fairfield CT 06430

NEWTON, WILLIAM ALLEN, JR, b Traverse City, Mich, May 19, 23; m 45; c 4. PEDIATRICS, PATHOLOGY. *Educ:* Alma Col, Mich, BSc, 43; Univ Mich, MD, 46. *Prof Exp:* Intern, Wayne County Gen Hosp, Eloise, Mich, 47; fel pediat path, Children's Hosp Mich, 48, fel pediat hemat, 49-50; resident pediat, Children's Hosp Philadelphia, 50; from instr to asst prof path, 52-59, assoc prof path, 59-66, PROF PATH & PEDIAT, OHIO STATE UNIV, 66-; DIR LABS, CHILDREN'S HOSP, 52- *Mem:* Soc Pediat Res; Am Asn Cancer Res; Am Soc Exp Path. *Res:* Cancer chemotherapy in children, particularly leukemia and brain tumors; red cell enzyme deficiency of glucose 6-phosphate dehydrogenase. *Mailing Add:* Children's Hosp Columbus OH 43205

NEWTON, WILLIAM EDWARD, b London, Eng, Nov 10, 38; m 77; c 3. NITROGEN FIXATION, BIOINORGANIC. *Educ:* Nottingham Univ, Eng, BSc, 61; Royal Inst Chem, grad, 65; Univ London, PhD(chem), 68. *Prof Exp:* Anal chemist, Rayner & Co, Ltd, London, 62-66; teaching asst chem, Northern Polytechnic, London, 66-68; res fel chem, Harvard Univ, 68-69; staff scientist, 69-71, sect head, 71-73, investr, 73-77, RESEARCH MGR & SR INVESTR, NITROGEN FIXATION MISSION, CHARLES F KETTERING RES LAB, 77- *Mem:* Royal Soc Chem; Royal Inst Chem; Am Chem Soc. *Res:* Bioinorganic and organometallic chemistry; studies of the early transition metals, particularly molybdenum and tungsten, as an aid in elucidating the role of molybdenum in enzymes; molybdenum cofactors; mechanism of biological nitrogen fixation. *Mailing Add:* Charles F Kettering Res Lab 150 E South College St Yellow Springs OH 45387

NEWTON, WILLIAM MORGAN, b Moline, Ill, May 30, 21; m 49; c 2. LABORATORY ANIMAL MEDICINE, PHYSIOLOGY. *Educ:* Univ Ill, BS, 50, DVM, 52, PhD(physiol), 65; Am Col Lab Animal Med, dipl, 74. *Prof Exp:* Pvt pract, 52-61; from instr to assoc prof vet physiol, Univ Ill, Urbana, 64-79, dir lab animal care, 67-79; PROF SURG & DIR LAB ANIMAL RESOURCES, UNIV SOUTH CAROLINA, 79- *Concurrent Pos:* Mem vet drug rev panel, Nat Acad Sci, 66-68. *Mem:* Am Vet Med Asn; Am Col Lab Animal Med; Am Soc Lab Animal Practioners; Am Asn Lab Animal Sci. *Res:* Diseases and management of laboratory animals. *Mailing Add:* Animal Resource Facil Sch Med BTW Ctr Univ SC Columbia SC 29208

NEY, EDWARD PURDY, b Minneapolis, Minn, Oct 28, 20; m 42; c 4. PHYSICS. *Educ:* Univ Minn, BS, 42; Univ Va, PhD(physics), 46. *Prof Exp:* Asst physics, Univ Minn, 40-42; res assoc, Univ Va, 43-46, from asst prof to assoc prof, 46-47; from asst prof to assoc prof, 47-50, prof physics, 50-74, chmn astron dept, 74-78, REGENT'S PROF PHYSICS & ASTRON, UNIV MINN, MINNEAPOLIS, 74- *Concurrent Pos:* Consult, Naval Res Lab, DC, 43-44 & Gen Dynamics/Convair. *Mem:* Nat Acad Sci; AAAS; fel Am Phys Soc; Am Astron Soc; Am Geophys Union. *Res:* Mass spectroscopy; cosmic rays; atmospheric physics; astrophysics; infrared astronomy. *Mailing Add:* Dept of Astron Univ of Minn Minneapolis MN 55455

NEY, PETER E, b Brno, Czech, July 6, 30; US citizen; m 55; c 2. MATHEMATICS. *Prof Exp:* Instr math, Cornell Univ, 58-60, asst prof indust eng, 60-63; vis asst prof statist, Stanford Univ, 63-64; assoc prof indust eng, Cornell Univ, 64-65; assoc prof math, 65-69, chmn dept, 74-77, PROF MATH, UNIV WIS-MADISON, 69- *Concurrent Pos:* Grants, Off Naval Res & NSF, 58-65; prin investr, NIH grant, 65-; Guggenheim fel, 71-72; vis prof, Israel Inst Technol & Weizmann Inst Sci, 71-72. *Mem:* Am Math Soc; Inst Math Statist. *Res:* Probability; stochastic processes; branching processes; Markov chains. *Mailing Add:* Dept of Math Univ of Wis Madison WI 53706

NEY, ROBERT LEO, b Brno, Czech, May 22, 33; US citizen; m 56; c 3. MEDICINE, ENDOCRINOLOGY. *Educ:* Harvard Univ, AB, 54; Cornell Univ, MD, 58. *Prof Exp:* Fel endocrinol & instr med, Vanderbilt Univ, 61-63; investr endocrinol, Nat Heart Inst, 63-65; asst prof med, Vanderbilt Univ, 65-67; assoc prof, Univ NC, Chapel Hill, 67-70, prof med, 70-80, chmn dept, 72-80; PROF MED & DIR DIV ENDOCRINOL & METAB, SCH MED, JOHNS HOPKINS UNIV, BALTIMORE, MD, 81- *Mem:* AAAS; Am Fedn Clin Res; Endocrine Soc; Am Soc Clin Invest; Am Physiol Soc; Asn Am Physicians; Am Col Physicians. *Res:* Regulation of pituitary-adrenal function; structure and function of ACTH, melanocyte stimulating hormone and related polypeptides; regulation of endocrine tumor function. *Mailing Add:* Dept of Med Sch Med Johns Hopkins Univ Baltimore MD 21205

NEY, WILBERT ROGER, b Rockford, Ill, Nov 28, 29; m 58; c 2. PHYSICS. *Educ:* Yale Univ, BS, 57; George Washington Univ, JD, 64. *Prof Exp:* Physicist, Nat Bur Stand, 58-60, sci asst, 60-64; EXEC DIR, NAT COUN RADIATION PROTECTION & MEASUREMENTS, 64- *Concurrent Pos:* Secy, Nat Comt Radiation Protection & Measurements, 61-64; tech secy, Int Comn Radiation Units & Measurements, 61-79, exec dir, 79- *Mem:* AAAS; Health Physics Soc; Radiation Res Soc; Am Nuclear Soc; Soc Nuclear Med. *Res:* Law; radiation, protection, quantities, units and effects. *Mailing Add:* Nat Coun Rad Prot & Meas Suite 1016 7910 Woodmont Ave Washington DC 20014

NEYMAN, JERZY, statistics, deceased

NEYNABER, ROY H(AROLD), b Highland Park, Mich, July 4, 26; m 51; c 4. ATOMIC PHYSICS. *Educ:* Univ Wis, BS, 49, MS, 51, PhD(physics), 55. *Prof Exp:* Asst physics, Univ Wis, 51-55; sr staff scientist, Gen Dynamics/Convair, 55-69; mgr atomic physics br, Gulf Energy & Environ Systs Co, 69-73; mgr, Atomic Physics Dept, IRT Corp, 73-77, sci adv, 78-80; STAFF SCIENTIST, LA JOLLA INST, 80- *Concurrent Pos:* Physicist, Liberty Powder Co, 53; adj prof physics, Univ Calif, San Diego, 80- *Mem:* AAAS; Sigma Xi; fel Am Phys Soc. *Res:* Gaseous electronics; atomic beams; atomic scattering experiments; particle-surface interactions; small angle scattering of x-rays; lattice imperfections in solids. *Mailing Add:* 4471 Braeburn Rd San Diego CA 92116

NEZRICK, FRANK ALBERT, b Mansfield, Ohio, Apr 1, 37; m 60; c 3. ELEMENTARY PARTICLE PHYSICS. *Educ:* Case Inst, BS, 59, MS, 62, PhD(physics), 65. *Prof Exp:* Vis scientist grant elem particle physics, Europ Orgn Nuclear Res, 65-68; PHYSICIST, NAT ACCELERATOR LAB, 68- *Mem:* Am Phys Soc. *Res:* Weak interaction physics; neutrino-bubble chamber research; magnetic monopole search; development of neutrino focussing systems. *Mailing Add:* Nat Accelerator Lab PO Box 500 Batavia IL 60510

NG, BARTHOLOMEW SUNG-HONG, b Canton, China, Sept 10, 46; m 73. APPLIED MATHEMATICS, FLUID DYNAMICS. *Educ:* St Josephs Col, Ind, BS, 68; Univ Chicago, MS, 70, PhD(appl math), 73. *Prof Exp:* Syst engr, Int Bus Mach Corp, 68; res asst math, Univ Chicago, 68-69, teaching asst & lectr, 69-73; fel, Univ Toronto, 73-75; res assoc, Indianapolis Ctr Advan Res, 75-76; asst prof, 75-79, ASSOC PROF MATH, IND UNIV-PURDUE UNIV, INDIANAPOLIS, 79- *Concurrent Pos:* Vis asst prof math, Rensselaer Polytech Inst, 79 & vis assoc prof, 80; assoc prof math, Old Dominion Univ, 79-80. *Mem:* Am Math Soc; Soc Indust & Appl Math; Sigma Xi. *Res:* Hydrodynamic stability; asymptotic and numerical techniques in applied mathematics. *Mailing Add:* Dept Math Sci Ind Univ-Purdue Univ PO Box 647 Indianapolis IN 46223

NG, EDWARD WAI-KWOK, US citizen. APPLIED MATHEMATICS, COMPUTER SCIENCE. *Educ:* Univ Minn, BA, 62; Columbia Univ, MA, 65, PhD(astrophysics), 67. *Prof Exp:* Sr engr, 67-68, sr scientist, 68-70, MEM TECH STAFF APPL MATH, JET PROPULSION LAB, CALIF INST TECHNOL, 70- *Concurrent Pos:* Adj assoc prof, Univ Southern Calif, 74-77. *Mem:* Asn Comput Mach; Soc Indust & Appl Math; fel AAAS. *Res:* Mathematical software; mathematics of computation; numerical and symbolic computation; computer science applications. *Mailing Add:* Jet Propulsion Lab Calif Inst Technol Pasadena CA 91103

NG, HENRY, b San Francisco, Calif, Nov 6, 29; m 57; c 5. MICROBIOLOGY, FOOD SCIENCE. *Educ:* Univ Calif, Davis, BS, 54, MS, 60, PhD(microbiol), 63. *Prof Exp:* Res microbiologist low temperature microbiol, Eastern Utilization Res & Develop Div, 63-65, RES MICROBIOLOGIST HEAT RESISTANCE SALMONELLA, WESTERN REGIONAL RES CTR, USDA, 65- *Mem:* Am Soc Microbiol; Brit Soc Gen Microbiol. *Res:* Low temperature microbiology; lactic acid and bread fermentations and thermal resistance of pathogenic bacteria found in foods. *Mailing Add:* Western Regional Res Ctr USDA 800 Buchanan St Berkeley CA 94710

NG, LORENZ KENG-YONG, b Singapore, Aug 6, 40; US citizen. NEUROPSYCHIATRY. *Educ:* Stanford Univ, AB, 61; Columbia Univ, MD, 65. *Prof Exp:* Intern med, Mt Sinai Hosp, Los Angeles, Calif, 65-66; resident neurol, Hosp Univ Pa, Philadelphia, 66-69; spec fel neuropsychopharmacol, Lab Clin Sci, NIMH, 69-72, spec asst to dir, Div Narcotic Addiction & Drug Abuse, 72-74, CHIEF, INTRAMURAL RES LAB, NAT INST DRUG ABUSE, 74-, RES SCIENTIST, NIMH, 72- *Concurrent Pos:* Consult, Vet Admin Hosp, 75-; pres, World Man Found. *Honors & Awards:* S Weir Mitchell Award, Am Acad Neurol, 71; A E Bennett Award, Soc Biol

Psychiat, 72; Acupuncture Res Award, Am Soc Chinese Med, 75. *Mem:* World Acad Art & Sci; AAAS; Am Acad Neurol; Soc Neurosci. *Res:* Neurology and behavioral biology of pain states; stress management and preventive medicine; clinical, experimental and theoretical aspects of acupuncture; chemical and non-chemical approaches to treatment of drug and alcohol dependence. *Mailing Add:* Nat Inst on Drug Abuse 11400 Rockville Pike Rockville MD 20852

NG, RAYMOND YEW-HAY, solid state physics, chemistry, see previous edition

NG, (SIMON) S F, Can citizen. CIVIL ENGINEERING. *Educ:* Univ BC, BS, 62; Univ Windsor, MS, 64, PhD(civil eng), 67. *Prof Exp:* Engr, Hydroelec Design Div, Int Power & Eng Consult, 62-63; scientist, IBM Corp, 66-67; from asst prof to assoc prof, 67-75, PROF CIVIL ENG, UNIV OTTAWA, 75- *Mem:* Am Acad Mech. *Res:* Static and dynamic behavior of plates and shells; experimental stress analysis; sandwich construction; material behavior at abnormal temperatures; vibration of bridge structures. *Mailing Add:* Dept Civil Eng Univ Ottawa Ottawa ON K1N 6N5 Can

NG, TIMOTHY J, b Oakland, Calif, Apr 15, 50; m 76. PLANT BREEDING, HORTICULTURE. *Educ:* Univ Calif, Berkeley, BS, 69; Purdue Univ, MSc, 72, PhD(plant breeding), 76. *Prof Exp:* Lab technician chem, Eng Sci Inc, 69-70; res asst hort, Purdue Univ, 70-76; asst prof, 77-81, ASSOC PROF HORT, UNIV MD, COLLEGE PARK, 81- *Concurrent Pos:* Instr, Ore State Univ, 74-75. *Honors & Awards:* Meadows Award, Am Soc Hort Sci, 78. *Mem:* AAAS; Am Genetic Asn; Am Soc Hort Sci; Crop Sci Soc Am. *Res:* Vegetable breeding and improvement; breeding for disease resistance, improved horticultural characteristics and improved nutritional quality; investigations in postharvest physiology, ripening and storage life. *Mailing Add:* Dept Hort Univ Md College Park MD 20742

NGAI, KIA LING, b Canton, China, May 20, 40; US citizen; m 67; c 3. CONDENSED MATTER PHYSICS, POLYMER PHYSICS. *Educ:* Univ Hong Kong, BSc, 62; Univ Southern Calif, MS, 64; Univ Chicago, PhD(physics), 69. *Prof Exp:* Staff mem, Lincoln Lab, Mass Inst Technol, 69-71; SUPVRY RES PHYSICIST, NAVAL RES LAB, 71- *Mem:* Am Phys Soc; Am Chem Soc. *Res:* Physics of microelectronic interfaces; polymer physics; 1/f noise; dielectric response; amorphous materials; universal and unified low frequency responses of condensed matter. *Mailing Add:* Code 6807 Naval Res Lab Washington DC 20375

NGAI, SHIH HSUN, b China, Sept 15, 20; nat US; m 48; c 3. ANESTHESIOLOGY. *Educ:* Nat Cent Univ, China, MD, 44. *Prof Exp:* From instr to assoc prof, 49-65, PROF ANESTHESIOL, COL PHYSICIANS & SURGEONS, COLUMBIA UNIV, 65-, PROF PHARMACOL, 74- *Concurrent Pos:* Asst anesthesiologist, Presby Hosp, New York, 49-54, from asst attend anesthesiologist to attend anesthesiologist, 57- *Mem:* Am Soc Anesthesiol; Am Physiol Soc; Am Soc Pharmacol & Exp Therapeut; Asn Univ Anesthetists. *Res:* Neural control of respiration and circulation; pharmacology of anesthetics and agents affecting respiration and circulation. *Mailing Add:* Dept Anesthesiol Columbia Univ Col Physicians & Surgeons New York NY 10032

NGO, THAT TJIEN, b Indonesia, Mar 10, 44; m 77. IMMUNOCHEMISTRY. *Educ:* Univ Sask, BSc, 70, PhD(biochem), 74. *Prof Exp:* Sr investr, Clin Res, Inst Montreal, 76-78; sr res scientist, Miles Lab, 78-79; biochemist, Univ Calif, Irvine, 79-81; DIR, IMMUTRON, INC, 81- *Mem:* Am Chem Soc. *Res:* Enzymology; analytical chemistry; clinical chemistry; biotechnology. *Mailing Add:* 15 Deer Creek Irvine CA 92714

NGUYEN, DONG HUU, b Quang Tri, Vietnam, Jan 1, 31; m 63; c 2. NUCLEAR SCIENCE & ENGINEERING. *Educ:* Purdue Univ, BS, 60, MS, 61; Univ Calif, Berkeley, PhD(nuclear eng), 65. *Prof Exp:* Res engr, Res Estab Riso, Danish Atomic Energy Comn, 65-66; asst prof nuclear eng, Univ Tex, 66-69; asst prof nuclear eng, Naval Postgrad Sch, 69-71, assoc prof, 71-76; mem tech staff, Sandia Labs, 76-78; PRIN ENGR, HANFORD ENG DEVELOP LAB, 78- *Concurrent Pos:* Res Found res grant, 69-72. *Mem:* Am Nuclear Soc; Sigma Xi; AAAS. *Res:* Physics of fast and thermal reactors; particle and radiation transport; fast reactor safety. *Mailing Add:* 214 Pinetree Lane Richland WA 99352

NGUYEN, HIEN VU, b Saigon, Vietnam, Dec 15, 43; m 72; c 3. POLYMER CHEMISTRY, CHEMICAL ENGINEERING. *Educ:* Mont State Univ, BS, 66; Univ Wis-Madison, MS, 68, PhD(chem eng), 70. *Prof Exp:* Fel chem eng, McGill Univ, Montreal, 71-72; res assoc polymer chem, Univ Montreal, 72-74; sr develop engr non woven, Res & Develop Div, Johnson & Johnson, Montreal, 74-76; res assoc specialty paper, Polyfibron Div, W R Grace & Co, Cambridge, Mass, 76-78; SR TECHNOL COUNR ABSORBENTS RES, JOHNSON & JOHNSON, 78- *Mem:* Am Chem Soc; Am Phys Soc; Tech Asn Pulp & Paper Inst. *Res:* Morphology of polymers, especially single crystals, fibers and elastomers; polymer chain conformation in the solid and solution states; non-woven and paper technology; radiation chemistry; mathematical and computer simulation of fluid transport; software systems. *Mailing Add:* Absorbent Technol 21 Lake Dr East Windsor NJ 08520

NGUYEN, THUAN VAN, b Namdinh, Vietnam, Oct 7, 29; m 57; c 3. ELECTRICAL ENGINEERING, COMPUTER SCIENCE. *Educ:* Chu Van An Col, Hanoi, Baccalaureat Complet, 51; Univ Hanoi, Lic en Droit, I, 52; Univ NMex, MA, 60, PhD(elec eng), 69; Stanford Univ, MS, 62. *Prof Exp:* Instr, US Army Lang Sch, 55-59; asst prof elec eng, Univ Alta, 62-65; assoc prof, 69-75, actg head dept, 71-73, PROF ELEC ENG, UNIV OF THE PAC, 75- *Concurrent Pos:* Lectr, Univ Alta Community Col, 63-65; off res grant, Univ of the Pac, 70-72; Nat Sci Found Regional Comput Network grant, Stanford Univ, 71-73. *Mem:* Am Soc Eng Educ; Inst Elec & Electronics Engrs; Sigma Xi. *Res:* Network theory; bioelectronics; communications systems; computer simulation and applications; astronomy; existence of extra sensory perception; electricity; basic tools of network analysis. *Mailing Add:* Dept of Elec Eng Univ of the Pac Stockton CA 95211

NGUYEN-HUU, XUONG, b Thai-Binh, Vietnam, July 14, 33; US citizen; m 60. CRYSTALLOGRAPHY, BIOPHYSICS. *Educ:* Sch Indust Elec, Marseille, France, BS, 55; Advan Sch Elec, Paris, MS, 57; Univ Paris, MA, 58; Univ Calif, Berkeley, MA & PhD(physics), 62. *Prof Exp:* Physicist, Lawrence Radiation Lab, Univ Calif, Berkeley, 62; asst res physicist, 62-63, from asst prof to assoc prof physics, 64-77, PROF PHYSICS, CHEM & BIOL, UNIV CALIF, SAN DIEGO, 77- *Concurrent Pos:* Guggenheim fel, 65-66. *Mem:* Am Phys Soc. *Res:* Elementary particle physics; data reduction using digital computer. *Mailing Add:* Dept of Physics Univ of Calif San Diego La Jolla CA 92037

NI, CHEN-CHOU, b Feb 1, 27; US citizen; m 64. OPTICS, FLUIDS. *Educ:* Nat Taiwan Univ, BS, 55; Univ Minn, MS, 60; Ill Inst Technol, PhD(physics), 70. *Prof Exp:* Eng officer civil eng, Bur Pub Works, Chinese Navy, China, 55-57; jr lectr, Nat Taiwan Univ, 57-58; civil engr, Ill State Hwy, 60-66; RES PHYSICIST, US NAVAL RES LAB, 70- *Mem:* Am Phys Soc; Sigma Xi. *Res:* Fluid dynamics; fiber optics; mechanics. *Mailing Add:* Naval Res Lab 4555 Overlook Ave SW Washington DC 20375

NIAZY, NAGLA NADOURI, physical chemistry, electrochemistry, see previous edition

NIBLACK, JOHN FRANKLIN, b Oklahoma City, Okla, Mar 5, 39; m 77; c 2. PHARMACOLOGY, BIOCHEMISTRY. *Educ:* Okla State Univ, BS, 60; Univ Ill, Urbana, MS, 65, PhD(biochem), 68. *Prof Exp:* Res biochemist, 68-69, res projs leader, 69-72, res mgr, 72-75, asst dir, Dept Pharmacol, 75-76, dir, Dept Pharmacol, cent Res Div, 76-80, DIR RES MED PROD, PFIZER, INC, 81- *Mem:* Am Soc Microbiol. *Res:* Biochemical mechanisms of drugs; drugs affecting immune responses and general lymphoreticular function; immunology. *Mailing Add:* Cent Res Div Pfizer Inc Groton CT 06340

NIBLER, JOSEPH WILLIAM, b Silverton, Ore, May 9, 41; m 64; c 2. PHYSICAL CHEMISTRY. *Educ:* Ore State Univ, BS, 63; Univ Calif, Berkeley, PhD(chem), 66. *Prof Exp:* NSF fel chem, Cambridge Univ, 66-67; from asst prof to assoc prof, 67-78, PROF CHEM, ORE STATE UNIV, 78- *Mem:* Am Optical Soc; Am Phys Soc; Am Chem Soc. *Res:* Infrared and Raman spectroscopy of matrix isolated molecules; nonlinear optical spectroscopy of gases; energy transfer in solids. *Mailing Add:* Dept of Chem Ore State Univ Corvallis OR 97331

NIBLETT, CHARLES LESLIE, b Wolfeboro, NH, Feb 15, 43; m 61; c 2. PLANT PATHOLOGY, VIROLOGY. *Educ:* Univ NH, BS, 65; Univ Calif, PhD(plant path), 69. *Prof Exp:* Asst prof plant path, Kans State Univ, 69-74, assoc prof, 74-80; PROF & CHMN, DEPT PLANT PATH, UNIV FLA, 80- *Concurrent Pos:* Vis prof, Cornell Univ, 77-78. *Mem:* Am Phytopath Soc. *Res:* Plant and cell and tissue culture; plant virology; viroids. *Mailing Add:* Plant Path Dept Univ Fla Gainesville FL 32611

NIBLETT, EDWARD RONALD, geophysics, see previous edition

NICCOLAI, NILO ANTHONY, b Pittsburgh, Pa, May 21, 40; m 64; c 4. SOFTWARE DESIGN, SYSTEMS SOFTWARE. *Educ:* Carnegie-Mellon Univ, BS, 62, MS, 63, PhD(math), 68. *Prof Exp:* Mathematician, US Bur Mines, Pa, 67-68; math analyst, Off Chief Staff, US Army, 68-70; asst prof, 70-77, ASSOC PROF MATH, UNIV NC, CHARLOTTE, 77- *Concurrent Pos:* Consult. *Honors & Awards:* Army Commendation Medal. *Mem:* Comput Soc; Sigma Xi; Asn Comput Mach. *Res:* Programming languages; operating systems; data base; theorem-proving. *Mailing Add:* Univ of NC University Sta Charlotte NC 28223

NICE, CHARLES MONROE, JR, b Parsons, Kans, Dec 21, 19; m 40; c 6. RADIOLOGY. *Educ:* Univ Kans, AB, 39, MD, 43; Univ Colo, MS, 48; Univ Minn, PhD(radiol), 56. *Prof Exp:* From instr to assoc prof, Univ Minn, 51-58; PROF RADIOL, SCH MED, TULANE UNIV, 58- *Mem:* AAAS; Radiol Soc NAm; Am Roentgen Ray Soc; AMA; Asn Am Med Cols. *Res:* Acquired radioresistance in mouse tumors; clinical diagnostic radiology. *Mailing Add:* Dept of Radiol Tulane Univ Sch of Med New Orleans LA 70112

NICELY, KENNETH AUBREY, b Slab Fork, WVa, Feb 25, 38; m 64. BOTANY. *Educ:* WVa Univ, AB, 59, MS, 60; NC State Univ, PhD(bot), 63. *Prof Exp:* Asst prof bot, Va Polytech Inst, 63-64; from asst prof to assoc prof, 64-77, PROF BOT, WESTERN KY UNIV, 77- *Mem:* Am Soc Plant Taxon; Int Asn Plant Taxon. *Res:* Taxonomy of flowering plants. *Mailing Add:* Dept of Biol Western Ky Univ Bowling Green KY 42101

NICELY, VINCENT ALVIN, b Botetourt Co, Va, Feb 10, 43; m 66; c 1. PHYSICAL CHEMISTRY, ANALYTICAL CHEMISTRY. *Educ:* WVa Wesleyan Col, BS, 65; Mich State Univ, PhD(phys chem), 69. *Prof Exp:* Res assoc quantum chem, Mich State Univ, 69-70; res chemist, 70-72, sr res chemist, 72-78, RES ASSOC TENN EASTMAN CO DIV, EASTMAN KODAK CO, 70- *Mem:* Am Chem Soc. *Res:* Spectroscopy; quantum chemistry; applications of computers in chemistry. *Mailing Add:* B-150 Tenn Eastman Co Eastman Kodak Co Kingsport TN 37662

NICHAMAN, MILTON Z, public health nutrition, cardiovascular diseases, see previous edition

NICHOALDS, GEORGE EDWARD, b Harrison, Ark, Jan 15, 40; m 61; c 2. BIOCHEMISTRY, NUTRITION. *Educ:* Ouachita Baptist Univ, BS, 62; Univ Ark, MS, 64, PhD(biochem), 67. *Prof Exp:* Instr chem, Univ Ark, Little Rock, 65-68; lab asst biol chem, Univ Mich, Ann Arbor, 68-69; res assoc biochem, Vanderbilt Univ, 69-70, dir clin nutrit lab, 70-78, asst prof biochem, 72-78; ASSOC PROF, DEPT OBSTET/GYNEC & BIOCHEM, UNIV TENN, MEMPHIS, 78- *Concurrent Pos:* NIH fel, Univ Mich, Ann Arbor, 68-69; nutrit biochemist, Meharry Med Col, 72- *Mem:* Am Asn Clin Chemists; Am Col Nutrit; Am Pub Health Asn. *Res:* Nutritional biochemistry; assessment of nutritional status and development of methodology; vitamin and trace mineral requirements of total parenteral nutrition. *Mailing Add:* Dept of Obstet/Gynec & Biochem 800 Madison Ave Memphis TN 38163

NICHOL, CHARLES ADAM, b Fergus, Ont, May 3, 22; nat US; m 47; c 3. PHARMACOLOGY, BIOCHEMISTRY. *Educ:* Univ Toronto, BS, 44; McGill Univ, MS, 46; Univ Wis, PhD(biochem), 49. *Prof Exp:* From instr to asst prof, Western Reserve Univ, 49-52; asst prof, Sch Med, Yale Univ, 53-56; res prof, State Univ NY Buffalo, 56-70; DIR RES PHARMACOL, WELLCOME RES LABS, 69- *Concurrent Pos:* Am Cancer Soc scholar, 52-56; dir dept exp therapeut, Roswell Park Mem Inst, 56-70; mem biochem-pharmacol panel, Cancer Chemother Nat Serv Ctr, NIH, 57-58, mem drug eval panel, 58-60, chmn exp therapeut comt, 59-60, consult grants & fels div, 59-62, mem cancer chemother study sect, 59-62, spec adv comt, 64-69; adj prof, Duke Univ, 70- *Mem:* Am Soc Biol Chem; Am Chem Soc; Soc Pharmacol & Exp Therapeut; Soc Exp Biol & Med; Am Asn Cancer Res. *Res:* Cancer chemotherapy; mechanism of action of folic acid antagonists; metabolism of folic acid and vitamin B-12; drug resistance in bacterial and mammalian cells; nutrition and tumor growth; corticosteroids and transaminase enzymes; drug-metabolizing enzymes. *Mailing Add:* Wellcome Res Labs 3030 Corwallis Rd Research Triangle Park NC 27709

NICHOL, CHRISTINA JANET, biochemistry, see previous edition

NICHOL, FRANCIS RICHARD, JR, b Baltimore, Md, Feb 27, 42; m 60; c 3. VIROLOGY. *Educ:* Pa State Univ, BA, 64, MS, 66, PhD(microbiol), 68. *Prof Exp:* Res scientist, Upjohn Co, 67-72, clin res assoc, 72-74, sr res scientist, 74-75; PRES, INST BIOL RES & DEVELOP, INC, 75- *Mem:* AAAS; assoc mem Am Soc Clin Pharmacol & Therapeut; Am Soc Microbiol. *Res:* Research and development of interferon stimulators; inhibitors of tumor virus enzymes; chemotherapeutic agents for virus infections; stimulators of host-defense mechanisms; cell mediated immunity; post-marketing surveillance; clinical trials, phase II, III. *Mailing Add:* Inst Biol Res & Develop Inc Suite 165 901 Dove St Newport Beach CA 92660

NICHOL, JAMES CHARLES, b Onoway, Alta, Apr 6, 22; nat US; m 48; c 2. PHYSICAL CHEMISTRY. *Educ:* Univ Alta, BSc, 43, MSc, 45; Univ Wis, PhD(phys chem), 48. *Prof Exp:* Instr Univ Alta, 44-46; proj assoc, Univ Wis, 48-49; assoc prof chem, Willamette Univ, 49-57; from asst prof to assoc prof, 57-62, PROF CHEM, UNIV MINN, DULUTH, 62- *Concurrent Pos:* Calif Res Corp fel, Yale Univ, 53-54; vis prof, Inst Enzyme Res, Univ Wis, 65-66. *Mem:* Am Chem Soc; The Chem Soc. *Res:* Transport properties of electrolytes; physical chemistry of proteins. *Mailing Add:* Dept Chem Univ Minn Duluth MN 55812

NICHOLAIDES, JOHN J, III, b Statesville, NC, Aug 1, 44; m 67; c 1. SOIL FERTILITY. *Educ:* NC State Univ, BS, 66, MS, 69; Univ Fla, PhD(soil chem), 73. *Prof Exp:* Peace Corps vol agron, 69-70; vis asst prof soil fertil eval, Int Soil Fertil Eval & Improv Proj, 73-75, vis asst prof soil fertil, 75-77, asst prof, 77-81, ASSOC PROF & COORDR, TROP SOILS RES PROG, NC STATE UNIV, 81- *Concurrent Pos:* NDEA Title IV fel, US Govt/Univ Fla, 70-73; mem, Nat Soil Fertil Adv Comn, Govt Costa Rica, 74-75; mem, Nat Agr Adv Comn, Govt Nicaragua, 74-75; coordr consortium on soils of the tropics, Title XII Activ, 77-81; consult, World Bank, US & foreign govts, tech adv comt, private indust & Rockefeller Found, 76- *Mem:* Sigma Xi. *Res:* developing economical agronomic systems for soils of the tropics; Relationships and correlations of soil test values and plant tissue nutrient content with crop response to fertilizers. *Mailing Add:* Dept of Soil Sci NC State Univ PO Box 5907 Raleigh NC 27607

NICHOLAS, HAROLD JOSEPH, b St Louis, Mo, Mar 1, 19; m 52; c 2. BIOCHEMISTRY. *Educ:* Univ Mo, BS, 41; St Louis Univ, PhD(biochem), 50. *Prof Exp:* Res chemist, Hercules Powder Co, 41-44 & Parke, Davis & Co, 44-45; asst prof biochem, Univ Kans, 50-53, asst prof obstet, Med Ctr, 55-63; DIR EXP MED, INST MED EDUC & RES & PROF BIOCHEM, SCH MED, ST LOUIS UNIV, 63- *Mem:* Am Chem Soc; Sigma Xi; Am Soc Biol Chemists; Am Acad Neurol; Int Soc Neurochem. *Res:* Metabolism of plant and animal steroids; terpene biosynthesis; chemistry of the central nervous system. *Mailing Add:* Inst of Med Educ & Res 1604 S 14th St St Louis MO 63104

NICHOLAS, JAMES A, b Portsmouth, Va, Apr 15, 21; m 52; c 1. SURGERY. *Educ:* NY Univ, BA, 42; Long Island Col Med, MD, 45; Am Bd Orthop Surg, dipl, 55. *Prof Exp:* From instr to asst prof surg & orthop, 53-70, PROF ORTHOP, MED COL, CORNELL UNIV, 70-; ADJ PROF PHYS EDUC, NY UNIV, 70- *Concurrent Pos:* Attend orthop surgeon, New York Hosp, 53-; attend, Hosp for Spec Surg, 53-, chief metab bone dis clin, 59-64; adj attend orthop surg, Lenox Hill Hosp, 53-, dir dept orthop surg, 70-, dir, Inst Sports Med & Athletic Trauma; secy bd trustees, Philip D Wilson Res Found; pvt pract; mem exec subcomt athletic injuries skeletal systs, Nat Acad Sci, Presidents' Coun on Phys Fitness. AEC res grant; NIH res grant. *Honors & Awards:* Am Roentgen Ray Soc Cert of Merit, 59. *Mem:* AAAS; Am Orthop Asn; Am Trauma Soc; Am Orthop Soc Sports Med (pres); Am Acad Orthop Surg. *Res:* Disturbances of knee joint, especially prosthetics, instability and replacement; athletic injuries; muscle physiology; radioisotope study of metabolic bone disease; osteoporosis; metabolic response to injury; sports medicine research. *Mailing Add:* 130 E 77th St New York NY 10021

NICHOLAS, KENNETH M, b Jamaica, NY, July 20, 47; m 71; c 2. HOMOGENEOUS CATALYSIS. *Educ:* State Univ NY Stony Brook, BS, 69; Univ Tex, Austin, PhD(chem), 72. *Prof Exp:* Res fel org chem, Dept Chem, Brandeis Univ, 72-73; asst prof, 73-79, ASSOC PROF ORG & INORG CHEM, DEPT CHEM, BOSTON COL, 79- *Concurrent Pos:* Vis prof, Celanese Res Co, 81. *Mem:* Am Chem Soc. *Res:* Organometallic complexes as synthetic intermediates and reagents; activation of small molecules by coordination; homogeneous catalysis. *Mailing Add:* Dept Chem Boston Col Chestnut Hill MA 02167

NICHOLAS, LESLIE, b Philadelphia, Pa, Dec 22, 13. DERMATOLOGY, SYPHILOLOGY. *Educ:* Temple Univ, BS, 35, MD, 37. *Prof Exp:* Assoc prof, 52-59, PROF DERMAT, HAHNEMANN MED COL, 59- *Concurrent Pos:* Lectr, Div Grad Med, Univ Pa, 49-67; venereal dis prog specialist, Philadelphia Dept Pub Health, 65-72; tech counr, Int Union Against the Venereal Dis & the Treponematoses, 78-80. *Mem:* Am Venereal Dis Asn (pres, 77-78); Soc Invest Dermat; Am Acad Dermat; Acad Psychosom Med. *Res:* Necrobiosis lipoidica diabeticorum; demodex folliculorum; erysipeloid; syphilis. *Mailing Add:* 1521 Locust St Philadelphia PA 19102

NICHOLAS, PAUL PETER, b Ohrid, Yugoslavia, Aug 6, 38; US citizen; m 62; c 1. ORGANIC CHEMISTRY. *Educ:* Univ Ill, Urbana, BS, 60; Cornell Univ, PhD(org chem), 64. *Prof Exp:* Sr res chemist org chem, 64-67, sect leader polymer chem res, 67-69, res assoc, 69-73, sr res assoc, 73-78, MGR NEW TECHNOL, CORP RES, B F GOODRICH RES CTR, 78- *Mem:* Sigma Xi; Am Chem Soc. *Res:* Synthesis and reaction mechanisms; chemistry of nitrenes; phase transfer catalysis; heterogeneous high temperature catalysis; halogenation; polymer crosslinking and stabilization. *Mailing Add:* 4775 Canterbury Lane Broadview Heights OH 44147

NICHOLAS, RICHARD CARPENTER, b Minneapolis, Minn, Dec 13, 26; m 52, 74. FOOD SCIENCE. *Educ:* Pa State Univ, BS, 48, MS, 50; Mich State Univ, PhD(agr eng), 58. *Prof Exp:* Instr physics, Pa State Univ, 48, instr physics & math, 51-52; from instr to asst prof agr eng, 56-60, from asst prof to assoc prof food sci, 60-71, PROF FOOD SCI, MICH STATE UNIV, 71- *Mem:* Inst Food Technol; Am Soc Qual Control. *Res:* Quality assurance control. *Mailing Add:* Dept of Food Sci & Human Nutrit Mich State Univ East Lansing MI 48824

NICHOLAS, THEODORE, engineering mechanics, see previous edition

NICHOLES, PAUL SCOTT, b American Fork, Utah, Apr 28, 16; m 41; c 3. BACTERIOLOGY. *Educ:* Brigham Young Univ, AB, 41; Univ Cincinnati, PhD(bact), 46. *Prof Exp:* Asst bact, Brigham Young Univ, 40-41; from asst prof to prof bact, 47-76, PROF MICROBIOL & MED TECHNOL IN APPL PHARMACEUT SCI, UNIV UTAH, 76- *Concurrent Pos:* Consult, Amalgamated Sugar Co & Deseret Pharmaceut Co. *Mem:* AAAS; Am Soc Microbiol; NY Acad Sci. *Res:* Immunology; bacterial metabolism; antigenic structure of bacterium tularense; aerobiology; microbiology. *Mailing Add:* Dept of Microbiol Univ of Utah Salt Lake City UT 84112

NICHOLLS, CURTIS W(AYNE), chemical engineering, see previous edition

NICHOLLS, DORIS MCEWEN, b Bayfield, Ont, Jan 24, 27; m 52. BIOCHEMISTRY, ENZYMOLOGY. *Educ:* Univ Western Ont, BSc, 49, MSc, 51, PhD(biochem), 56, MD, 59. *Prof Exp:* Demonstr bot, Univ Western Ont, 47-51; assoc physiol, George Washington Univ, 59-60; dir clin invest unit lab, Westminster Hosp, London, Ont, 60-65; assoc prof biochem, 65-70, PROF BIOCHEM, YORK UNIV, 70- *Concurrent Pos:* Consult, Nat Heart Inst, 59-60; res assoc, Univ Western Ont, 60-62. *Mem:* Am Soc Biol Chemists; Can Biochem Soc; Brit Biochem Soc; Am Chem Soc; Biophys Soc. *Res:* Protein synthesis in mammalian tissue; regulation of cell metabolism; heavy metal toxicity; muscular dystrophy. *Mailing Add:* Dept Biol York Univ Downsview ON M3J 1P3 Can

NICHOLLS, GERALD P, b Orange, NJ, Nov 12, 43; m 65; c 2. HEALTH PHYSICS, RADIOECOLOGY. *Educ:* Trenton State Col, BA, 65, MA, 68; Temple Univ, MS, 73, PhD(radioecol), 79. *Prof Exp:* From instr to asst prof, 68-80, ASSOC PROF PHYSICS, TRENTON STATE COL, 80-; RES SCIENTIST HEALTH PHYSICS, BUR RADIATION PROTECTION, NJ, 81- *Mem:* Health Physics Soc; AAAS; Am Asn Physics Teachers. *Res:* Gamma spectrometry applied to environmental monitoring for natural and man made radioactive materials; movement of radioactive materials in the food chain leading to man and the application of computers to these problems. *Mailing Add:* 361 W Burlington St Bordentown NJ 08505

NICHOLLS, J(AMES) A(RTHUR), b Detroit, Mich, Feb 12, 21; m 45; c 3. AERONAUTICAL ENGINEERING. *Educ:* Wayne State Univ, BS, 50; Univ Mich, MS, 51, PhD(aeronaut eng), 60. *Prof Exp:* From asst to res engr, Aeronaut Eng Labs, 50-64, instr aeronaut & astronaut eng, Univ, 55-58, lectr, 58-60, assoc prof, 60-64, PROF AEROSPACE ENG, UNIV MICH, ANN ARBOR, 64-, HEAD GAS DYNAMICS LABS, 61- *Concurrent Pos:* Consult, 58- *Honors & Awards:* S S Attwood Award, 80. *Mem:* Am Inst Aeronaut & Astronaut; Combustion Inst. *Res:* Gas dynamics; heterogeneous and homogeneous combustion; engine generated pollutants. *Mailing Add:* Dept of Aerospace Eng Univ of Mich Ann Arbor MI 48109

NICHOLLS, JOHN GRAHAM, neurophysiology, see previous edition

NICHOLLS, PETER JOHN, b Kent, Gt Brit, Nov 29, 45; m 68; c 3. PURE MATHEMATICS. *Educ:* Imp Col, Univ London, BSc, 67; Cambridge Univ, PhD(math), 70. *Prof Exp:* Tutorial fel math, Univ Lancaster, 70-71; asst prof, 71-77, ASSOC PROF MATH, NORTHERN ILL UNIV, 77- *Mem:* Am Math Soc; London Math Soc. *Res:* Functions of a complex variable; discrete groups and Riemann surfaces. *Mailing Add:* Dept of Math Northern Ill Univ De Kalb IL 60115

NICHOLLS, RALPH WILLIAM, b Richmond, Eng, May 3, 26; m 52. PHYSICS. *Educ:* Univ London, BSc, 46, PhD(physics), 51, DSc(spectros), 61. *Prof Exp:* Demonstr physics, Imp Col, Univ London, 45-46, sr demonstr astrophys, 46-48; instr physics, Univ Western Ont, 48-50, lectr, 50-52, from asst prof to prof, 52-62, sr prof, 62-65; chmn dept physics, 65-69, PROF PHYSICS & SCI & DIR CTR RES EXP SPACE SCI, YORK UNIV, 65- *Concurrent Pos:* Consult, Nat Bur Standards, 59-60; vis prof, Stanford Univ, 64 & 68. *Mem:* Int Astron Union; fel Am Phys Soc; fel Royal Astron Soc Can; fel Royal Astron Soc; Royal Soc Can. *Res:* Spectroscopy; astrophysics; aeronomy; chemical physics. *Mailing Add:* Ctr for Res in Exp Space Sci 4700 Keele St Downsview ON M3J 1P3 Can

NICHOLLS, ROBERT LEE, b Lincoln, Nebr, June 11, 29; m 58; c 3. GEOTECHNICAL & CONSTRUCTION MATERIALS ENGINEERING, SYSTEMS ENGINEERING. *Educ:* Univ Colo, BS, 51; Iowa State Univ, MS, 52, PhD(civil eng), 57. *Prof Exp:* Res asst construct mat, Iowa State Univ, 55-57; mat & geotech engr, Gannett, Gleming, Corddry & Carpenter, 57-59; from asst prof to assoc prof, 59-70, PROF CIVIL ENG, UNIV DEL, 70- *Concurrent Pos:* Geotech & construct mat consult, E I du Pont de Nemours & Co, Inc, 61- *Mem:* Am Soc Civil Engrs; Transp Res Bd; Am Concrete Inst. *Res:* Composite construction materials; civil engineering systems. *Mailing Add:* Dept of Civil Eng Univ of Del Newark DE 19711

NICHOLS, ALEXANDER VLADIMIR, b San Francisco, Calif, Oct 9, 24; m 55; c 3. MEDICAL PHYSICS, BIOPHYSICS. *Educ:* Univ Calif, AB, 49, PhD(biophys), 55. *Prof Exp:* Res biophysicist, 55-59, lectr med physics & biophys, 59-61, from asst prof to prof, 61-77, vchmn div med physics, 67-71, chmn, 71-72, PROF BIOPHYSICS, DONNER LAB, UNIV CALIF, BERKELEY, 77- *Res:* Structure and function of lipoproteins; atherosclerosis; biophysics of lipid-protein structures. *Mailing Add:* Dept of Med Physics Univ of Calif Berkeley CA 94720

NICHOLS, AMBROSE REUBEN, JR, b Corvallis, Ore, June 21, 14; m 38; c 3. PHYSICAL CHEMISTRY. *Educ:* Univ Calif, BS, 35; Univ Wis, PhD(inorg chem), 39. *Prof Exp:* Asst chem, Univ Wis, 36-39; instr, San Diego State Col, 39-43; res chemist, Radiation Lab, Manhattan Proj, Univ Calif, 43-45; from asst prof to prof chem, San Diego State Col, 45-61; pres, 61-70, prof chem, 70-76, EMER PROF CHEM, SONOMA STATE COL, 76- *Concurrent Pos:* Analyst, Procter & Gamble Co, Ohio, 37; asst physicist, Radio & Sound Lab, US Dept Navy, 42-43; prin chemist, Oak Ridge Nat Lab, 51-52; res collabr, Brookhaven Nat Lab, 70. *Mem:* Am Chem Soc. *Res:* Chemistry of manganese; solution chemistry of uranium; autoxidation of manganous hydroxide; high temperature electrochemistry. *Mailing Add:* Dept of Chem Sonoma State Univ Rohnert Park CA 94928

NICHOLS, BARBARA ANN, b Long Beach, Calif, Nov 16, 21. CELL BIOLOGY, EXPERIMENTAL PATHOLOGY. *Educ:* Univ Calif, Los Angeles, BA, 43; Univ Calif, Berkeley, PhD(zool), 68. *Prof Exp:* Teaching asst zool, Univ Calif, Berkeley, 63-66, instr, 66-67; res fel path, Sch Med, 68-72, asst prof microbiol, 72-79, CHIEF ELECTRON MICROS LAB, PROCTOR RES FOUND OPHTHAL, SCH MED, UNIV CALIF, SAN FRANCISCO, 72-, ASSOC PROF MICROBIOL, UNIV, 79- *Concurrent Pos:* NIH training grant, Sch Med, Univ Calif, San Francisco, 68-69, NIH fel, 69-71, Nat Tuberc & Respiratory Dis Asn fel, 71-72. *Honors & Awards:* US Pub Health Serv Res Career Develop Award, Nat Inst of Allergy & Infectious Dis. *Mem:* Am Soc Cell Biol; Electron Micros Soc Am; Reticuloendothelial Soc; AAAS. *Res:* Use of electron microscopy and cytochemistry to investigate the development and function of monocytes and macrophages in normal and pathologic states. *Mailing Add:* Proctor Found for Res in Ophthal Univ of Calif Med Sch San Francisco CA 94143

NICHOLS, BENJAMIN, b Staten Island, NY, Sept 20, 20; m 42; c 2. ELECTRICAL ENGINEERING. *Educ:* Cornell Univ, BEE, 46, MEE, 49; Univ Alaska, PhD(geophys), 58. *Prof Exp:* From instr to assoc prof elec eng, 46-59, dir elem sci study, 64-65, PROF ELEC ENG, CORNELL UNIV, 59-, ASST DEAN ENG, 80- *Concurrent Pos:* Ford Found fel, 50-51; mem, US comt, Int Sci Radio Union, 57-; lectr, Cornell Aeronaut Lab, 59-60. *Mem:* AAAS; Sigma Xi; Am Soc Eng Educ. *Res:* Science education; science policy. *Mailing Add:* Col Eng Cornell Univ Ithaca NY 14853

NICHOLS, BUFORD LEE, JR, b Ft Worth, Tex, Dec 21, 31; m; c 3. MEDICINE, NUTRITION. *Educ:* Baylor Univ, BA, 55, MS, 59; Yale Univ, MD, 60; Am Bd Pediat, dipl; Am Bd Nutrit, dipl. *Prof Exp:* Instr physiol, Col Med, Baylor Univ, 56-57; instr pediat, Sch Med, Yale Univ, 63-64; instr physiol & pediat, 64-66, from asst prof to assoc prof pediat, 66-77, instr physiol, 66-74, ASSOC PROF COMMUNITY MED & CHIEF SECT NUTRIT & GASTROENTEROL, BAYLOR COL MED, 70-, PROF PHYSIOL & PEDIAT, 77- *Concurrent Pos:* Sci dir, Children's Nutrit Res Ctr, Baylor Col Med. *Mem:* Am Acad Pediat; Am Soc Clin Nutrit; Am Col Nutrit (vpres, 75-76). *Res:* Environmental effects upon growth and development in the infant, especially alterations in body composition and muscle physiology in malnutrition; diarrhea and infectious diseases. *Mailing Add:* Dept Pediat Baylor Col Med Tex Med Ctr Houston TX 77030

NICHOLS, CARL WILLIAM, b State Center, Iowa, June 1, 24; m 55; c 3. PLANT PATHOLOGY. *Educ:* Mich State Col, BS, 48; Univ Idaho, MS, 49; Univ Calif, PhD(plant path), 52. *Prof Exp:* Tech plant path, Univ Idaho, 48-49; asst, Univ Calif, 49-51, jr specialist, 51-53; from assoc plant pathologist to plant pathologist, 53-62, prog supvr, 62-66, chief bur plant path, 66-71, chief spec serv & asst to div chief, Div Plant Indust, 71-72 & 76-78, asst dir plant indust, 72-76, CHIEF LAB SERV, DIV OF PLANT INDUST, CALIF DEPT FOOD & AGR, 78- *Concurrent Pos:* Assoc, Exp Sta, Univ Calif, Davis, 67-; mem, Western Plant Bd, 72-, Nat Plant Bd, 74-, Interstate Pest Control Compact Tech Adv Comt, 75- *Mem:* AAAS; Am Phytopath Soc; Am Inst Biol Sci; Int Asn Plant Path. *Res:* Regulatory plant pest control. *Mailing Add:* Div Plant Indust Calif Dept Food & Agr Sacramento CA 95814

NICHOLS, CHESTER ENCELL, b Boston, Mass, Dec 28, 35; m 63; c 2. GEOPHYSICS, STRUCTURAL GEOLOGY. *Educ:* Cornell Univ, AB, 60; Univ Iowa, MS, 65; Univ Mo-Rolla, PhD, 77; Nat Cert Comn Chem, cert. *Prof Exp:* Teaching asst geol, Univ Iowa, 61-62; geologist, US Bur Mines, 62-63; teaching asst geol, Univ Mo-Rolla, 64-66; explor geologist, 68-73, sr mines geologist, 73-75, proj geologist/geochemist, 75-78, sr explor geologist, Grand Junction, Colo, 78-80, SR STAFF GEOLOGIST, UNION CARBIDE CORP, RENO, NEV, 81- *Concurrent Pos:* V H McNutt res award, 65, 66 & 67. *Mem:* Asn Explor Geochemists; Sigma Xi; AAAS; Geol Soc Am; fel Am Inst Chemists. *Res:* Tungsten exploration in Great Basin; uranium exploration in Wyoming (Precambrian), Colorado Plateau (Jurassic) and Texas Gulf Coast (tertiary); applied geochemistry; exploration geophysics; astrogeology; structural geology. *Mailing Add:* Union Carbide Corp 751 Ryland St Reno NV 89502

NICHOLS, COURTLAND GEOFFREY, b Wilmington, Del, May 16, 34; m 59; c 3. PLANT BREEDING. *Educ:* Pa State Univ, BS, 56; Univ Wis, PhD(hort, plant path), 63. *Prof Exp:* Res assoc tomato breeding, Campbell Inst Agr Res, 63-68; PLANT BREEDER, FERRY MORSE SEED CO, 69- *Mem:* Am Phytopath Soc; Am Soc Hort Sci; Sigma Xi; Sci Soc. *Res:* Onion breeding, especially inheritance of pink root resistance; tomato breeding, especially heat tolerance in Texas and mechanical harvesting in Illinois and California; carrot breeding, especially hybrids. *Mailing Add:* Ferry Morse Seed Co Res Div PO Box 1010 San Juan Bautista CA 95045

NICHOLS, DAVID EARL, b Covington, Ky, Dec 23, 44; m 66; c 2. MEDICINAL CHEMISTRY. *Educ:* Univ Cincinnati, BS, 69; Univ Iowa, PhD(med chem), 73. *Prof Exp:* Fel pharmacol, Univ Iowa, 73-74; asst prof, 74-80, ASSOC PROF MED CHEM, SCH PHARM, PURDUE UNIV, WEST LAFAYETTE, 80- *Mem:* Am Chem Soc; Soc Neurosci; Am Asn Col Pharm; Am Pharm Asn. *Res:* Synthesis and study of structure-activity relationships of centrally active drugs and neurotransmitter congeners; study of mode of action of psychotomimetic and antipsychotic drugs; molecular pharmacology. *Mailing Add:* Dept of Med Chem & Pharmacog Purdue Univ Sch Pharm & Pharmacal Sci West Lafayette IN 47907

NICHOLS, DAVIS BETZ, b Carlisle, Ky, Nov 19, 40; m 65; c 3. LASER EFFECTS, LASERS. *Educ:* Wheaton Col Ill, BS, 62; Univ Ky, PhD(nuclear physics), 66. *Prof Exp:* Res assoc nuclear physics, Van de Graaff Lab, Ohio State Univ, 66-67, fel, Van de Graaff Accelerator Lab, 67-68; res fel physics, Kellogg Radiation Lab, Calif Inst Technol, 68-70; MEM STAFF, BOEING AEROSPACE CO, 70- *Mem:* Am Phys Soc. *Res:* Laser damage of optical components, laser-induced gas breakdown, laser effects and pulsed chemical lasers; radiation physics; nuclear spectroscopy; particle-gamma ray correlations; inelastic neutron scattering; on-line computers. *Mailing Add:* Boeing Aerospace Co Mail Stop 88-46 PO Box 3999 Seattle WA 98124

NICHOLS, DONALD RAY, b Omaha, Nebr, Mar 26, 27; m 48; c 4. ENGINEERING GEOLOGY. *Educ:* Univ Nebr, BS, 50. *Prof Exp:* Geologist & geomorphologist, US Geol Surv, Menlo Park, Calif, 51-64, staff geologist, Eng Geol Subdiv, 64-67, supvr geologist, 67-755, chief earth sci applications prog, 75-79, hazards info coordr, 77-79, CHIEF BR ENG GEOL, US GEOL SURV, DENVER, COLO, 79- *Concurrent Pos:* Vchmn land use planning adv group, Joint Calif Legis Comt Seismic Safety, 70-74; mem, Earthquake Hazards Reduction Implementation Plan Working Group, 77-78. *Mem:* Geol Soc Am; Asn Eng Geol. *Res:* Engineering and glacial geology; permafrost; geomorphology; earth sciences applications to land-use planning. *Mailing Add:* 978 Coneflower Dr Golden CO 80401

NICHOLS, DONALD RICHARDSON, b Minneapolis, Minn, Feb 22, 11; wid; c 6. CLINICAL MEDICINE. *Educ:* Amherst Col, AB, 33; Univ Minn, MD, 38, MS, 42; Am Bd Internal Med, dipl. *Prof Exp:* From asst prof to prof clin med, Mayo Grad Sch Med, Univ Minn, 48-72, prof med, Mayo Med Sch, 72-81, sr consult med, Mayo Clin, 73-81. *Concurrent Pos:* Consult, Mayo Clin, 43-, head sect infectious dis, 61-69, chmn div infectious dis & internal med, 70-73. *Mem:* AMA; Cent Soc Clin Res; fel Am Col Physicians; Infectious Dis Soc Am. *Res:* Clinical investigation of antibiotic agents and the treatment of infectious diseases. *Mailing Add:* Mayo Clin 102 Second Ave SW Rochester NY 55902

NICHOLS, DOUGLAS JAMES, b Jamaica, NY, Feb 19, 42; m 64; c 3. PALEONTOLOGY. *Educ:* NY Univ, BA, 63, MS, 66; Pa State Univ, PhD(geol), 70. *Prof Exp:* Sci asst micropaleont, Am Mus Natural Hist, 63-65; lectr geol, City Col New York, 65-66; asst prof, Ariz State Univ, 70 & State Univ NY Col Geneseo, 70-74; palynologist, Chevron Oil Co, 74-78; GEOLOGIST, US GEOL SURV, 78- *Mem:* Soc Econ Paleontologists and Mineralogists; Brit Palaeont Asn; Am Asn Stratig Palynologists (pres, 81-83); Int Asn Angiosperm Paleobot. *Res:* Palynology; biostratigraphy; evolution; paleoecology. *Mailing Add:* US Geol Surv MS 919 Box 25046 Denver CO 80225

NICHOLS, DUANE GUY, b Middlebourne, WVa, July 18, 37; m 63; c 2. CHEMICAL ENGINEERING. *Educ:* WVa Univ, BSChE, 59; Univ Del, MChE, 63, PhD(chem eng), 68. *Prof Exp:* Asst prof physics, Del State Col, 63-68; from asst prof to assoc prof chem eng, WVa Univ, 68-77; sr chem engr, Res Triangle Inst, 78-80; SR RES ENGR, CONOCO, INC, 80- *Concurrent Pos:* Vis lectr, Del Acad Sci, 66-68 & Am Inst Chem Engrs, 77-79; tech chmn, Am Inst Chem Engrs & Air Pollution Control Asn, 5th & 6th Nat Conf on Energy & Environ, 77-79; vis assoc prof, WVa Univ, 78. *Mem:* Am Inst Chem Engrs; Am Chem Soc. *Res:* Mass transfer; digital and analog computer simulation; fluidized bed applications; coal conversion processes; environmental and biomedical engineering. *Mailing Add:* Coal Res Div 400 Brownsville Rd Conoco Inc Library PA 15129

NICHOLS, EUGENE DOUGLAS, b Rovno, Poland, Feb 6, 23; US citizen; m 51. MATHEMATICS. *Educ:* Univ Chicago, BS, 49; Univ Ill, MA, 53, MEd, 54, PhD(math educ), 56. *Prof Exp:* Instr math, Roberts Wesleyan Col, 50-51, Univ Ill, 51-53, Urbana High Sch, 53-54 & Univ Ill, 54-56; PROF & LECTR

MATH EDUC & MATH, FLA STATE UNIV, 56- *Mem:* Am Math Soc; Math Asn Am; Asn Comput Mach; AAAS. *Res:* Foundations of mathematics, with emphasis on linguistics of mathematics. *Mailing Add:* 3386 W Lake Shore Dr Tallahassee FL 32312

NICHOLS, FREDERIC HONE, b Boston, Mass, Nov 28, 37; m 71; c 2. BIOLOGICAL OCEANOGRAPHY. *Educ:* Hamilton Col, AB, 60; Univ Wash, MS, 68, PhD(oceanog), 72. *Prof Exp:* Teaching asst oceanog, Univ Wash, 66-69, res assoc, 69-72; OCEANOGR, US GEOL SURV, 71- *Concurrent Pos:* Mem, NSF Comt Syst Resources Invert Zool, 74-; vis scientist, Inst Oceanog & Univ Kiel, 75-76; mem, Calif Water Resources Control Bd, San Francisco Bay & Estuary Adv Comt, 76-78; mem gov bd, Tiburon Ctr Environ Studies, San Francisco State Univ, 77-; actg chief, Pac-Arctic Br Marine Geol, US Geol Surv, 78- *Mem:* Am Soc Limnol & Oceanog; Ecol Soc Am; Marine Biol Asn UK; Sigma Xi. *Res:* Marine and estuarine benthic ecology. *Mailing Add:* US Geol Surv 345 Middlefield Rd Menlo Park CA 94025

NICHOLS, G(EORGE) STARR, b Argyle, Wis, Aug 11, 18; m 41; c 3. CHEMICAL ENGINEERING. *Educ:* Univ Wis, BS, 41, PhD(chem eng), 52. *Prof Exp:* RES ENGR, E I DU PONT DE NEMOURS & CO, INC, 41- *Concurrent Pos:* Res engr, Argonne Nat Lab, 51-52; instr, Augusta Col. *Mem:* AAAS; Am Chem Soc; Am Inst Chem Engrs. *Res:* Chemical kinetics; prevention of hazardous reaction. *Mailing Add:* 1224 Johns Rd Augusta GA 30904

NICHOLS, GEORGE, JR, b New York, NY, May 15, 22; m 44, 77; c 4. BIOCHEMISTRY, OCEANOGRAPHY. *Educ:* Columbia Univ, MD, 45. *Prof Exp:* Intern med, Presby Hosp, New York, 45-46; asst resident, Peter Bent Brigham Hosp, Boston, 48-50; res biochemist, Baker Clin Res Lab, 50; res fel pediat, Harvard Med Sch, 50-52, instr med, 52-53, dir student health & med care prog, 53-55, assoc med, 53-59, consult univ health serv, 55-57, from asst dean & secy fac med to assoc dean, 59-65, from asst prof to assoc clin prof med, 59-65, clin prof med, 65-80; dir, Cancer Res Inst, New Eng Deaconess Hosp, 69-73; PRES, OCEAN RES & EDUC SOC, BOSTON, 80- *Concurrent Pos:* Fel, Harvard Med Sch, 48-50; assoc, Peter Bent Brigham Hosp, 53-58, sr assoc, 58-; investr, Howard Hughes Med Inst, 55-57; Markle scholar med sci, 57-62; chief dept, Cambridge City Hosp, 65-68; pres, Ocean Res & Educ Soc, Boston, 80- *Mem:* Am Physiol Soc; Am Soc Clin Invest; Asn Am Physicians; Am Col Physicians; Endocrine Soc. *Res:* Electrolyte and water metabolism; endocrinology; biochemistry and physiology of bone. *Mailing Add:* 51 Commercial Wharf Boston MA 02110

NICHOLS, GEORGE MORRILL, b Seattle, Wash, July 17, 28; m 57; c 3. PHYSICAL CHEMISTRY. *Educ:* Univ Wash, BS, 52; Ill Inst Technol, PhD(chem), 57. *Prof Exp:* Res fel solid state chem, Argonne Nat Lab, 57-58; res chemist, E I du Pont de Nemours & Co, 58-62; sr res chemist, Stauffer Chem Co, 63-66; SCIENTIST, RES CTR, BORG-WARNER CORP, 66- *Mem:* Electrochem Soc; Am Chem Soc; Sigma Xi; Sci Res Soc; Combustion Inst. *Res:* Dielectrics; color centers; inorganic polymers; thermally stable fluids; organophosphorus compositions; electrochemistry; fire retardance. *Mailing Add:* 1120 South Blvd Evanston IL 60202

NICHOLS, HERBERT WAYNE, b Bessemer, Ala, Feb 24, 37. BIOLOGY, PHYCOLOGY. *Educ:* Univ Ala, BS, 59, MS, 60, PhD(phycol), 63. *Prof Exp:* Asst prof, 63-65, assoc prof bot & co-chmn dept biol, 65-76, ASSOC PROF BIOL, WASH UNIV, 76- *Concurrent Pos:* Instr, Marine Biol Lab, Woods Hole, 64-65; vis lectr, Univ Tex, 63; NSF grant, 65-67; Am Cancer Soc grant, 65; USPHS res grant, 67-; Off Naval Res res grant, 67- *Mem:* AAAS; Bot Soc Am; Am Micros Soc; Am Phycol Soc (treas, 70-72, vpres, 72-73); Int Phycol Soc. *Res:* Morphogenetic studies of algae. *Mailing Add:* Dept of Biol Wash Univ St Louis MO 63130

NICHOLS, JACK LORAN, b Drumheller, Can, Dec 3, 39. BIOCHEMISTRY. *Educ:* Univ Alta, BS, 60, MS, 63, PhD(biochem), 67. *Prof Exp:* Res fel, Lab Molecular Biol, Cambridge, Eng, 68-70; assoc prof microbiol, Med Ctr, Duke Univ, 70-76; ASSOC PROF MICROBIOL, UNIV VICTORIA, BC, 76- *Mem:* Am Soc Microbiol; Am Soc Biol Chemists. *Res:* Structure and function of nucleic acids. *Mailing Add:* Dept of Biochem & Microbiol Univ of Victoria Victoria BC V8W 2Y2 Can

NICHOLS, JAMES OTIS, b Rochester, NY, Mar 26, 29; m 53; c 3. FOREST ENTOMOLOGY. *Educ:* State Univ NY Col Forestry, BS, 51, MS, 57. *Prof Exp:* Entomologist, Dept Agr, 57-61 & Dept Environ Resources, 62-81, CHIEF, DIV FOREST PEST MGT, COMMONWEALTH OF PA, 74- *Mem:* Soc Am Foresters; Entom Soc Am. *Res:* Forest insects. *Mailing Add:* Pa Dept Environ Resources 34 Airport Dr Middletown PA 17057

NICHOLS, JAMES RANDALL, b Wilmington, Del, Mar 10, 31; m 54; c 3. PHYSICAL CHEMISTRY. *Educ:* Univ Del, BS, 53; Pa State Univ, MS, 57, PhD(fuel technol), 61. *Prof Exp:* Sr chemist, Chem Res Dept, Atlas Chem Industs, Inc, 61-67, res chemist, 67-72, RES CHEMIST, CHEM RES DEPT, ICI AMERICAS, INC, 72- *Mem:* AAAS; Am Chem Soc. *Res:* Physical-chemical structure studies on activated carbon; chemical nature of carbon surface; characterization of supported catalysts; thermal analysis; x-ray diffraction and electron microscopy of polymer and pharmaceutical products. *Mailing Add:* ICI Americas Inc Concord Pike & New Murphy Rd Wilmington DE 19897

NICHOLS, JAMES ROSS, b Kansas City, Mo, June 26, 44; m 65; c 3. ZOOLOGY. *Educ:* Abilene Christian Col, BS, 66; Univ Mich, Ann Arbor, MS, 68; Univ Mo-Columbia, PhD(zool), 73. *Prof Exp:* Asst prof, 72-75, assoc prof, 78-81, PROF BIOL, UNIV CENT ARK, 81- *Mem:* Am Soc Zoologists; Am Inst Biol Sci; AAAS; Nat Asn Biol Teachers. *Res:* Cellular and comparative physiology, especially ionic and water regulation; effects of antibiotics and endocrine control; temperature and light effects. *Mailing Add:* Dept of Biol Univ of Cent Ark Conway AR 72032

NICHOLS, JAMES T, b Salina Kans, Jan 5, 30; m 59; c 6. RANGE MANAGEMENT, AGRONOMY. *Educ:* Ft Hays Kans State Col, BS, 60, MS, 61; Univ Wyo, PhD(range mgt), 64. *Prof Exp:* Asst prof range mgt, SDak State Univ, 64-69; assoc prof, 69-74, PROF AGRON, UNIV NEBR, 74- *Mem:* Soc Range Mgt; Soc Agron; Am Forage & Grassland Coun. *Res:* Range improvement through grazing management and range renovation; soil vegetation relationship; irrigated pasture production; pasture management. *Mailing Add:* Dept of Agron Univ Nebr N Platte Sta North Platte NE 69101

NICHOLS, JOE DEAN, b Skiatook, Okla, July 14, 31; m 55; c 1. SOIL SCIENCE. *Educ:* Okla A&M Col, BS, 55, MS, 56. *Prof Exp:* Party leader soil sci, Soil Conserv Serv, Pawhuska, Okla, 59-62, soil scientist specialist, Pauls Valley, 62-65, soil correlator, Stillwater, 65-69, state soil scientist, Denver, Colo, 69-71, asst prin soil correlator, 71-76, HEAD SOILS STAFF, SOIL CONSERV SERV, USDA, 76- *Concurrent Pos:* geologist, Selieh Archeol Exped, Fayoum, Egypt, Brigham Young Univ & Univ Calif, Berkeley, 81. *Honors & Awards:* Cert of Merit, Soil Conserv Serv, USDA, 68, 73 & 78. *Mem:* Soil Conserv Soc Am; Soil Sci Soc Am; Int Soc Soil Sci. *Res:* Soil genesis, morphology and soil classification. *Mailing Add:* PO Box 6567 Ft Worth TX 76115

NICHOLS, JOHN C, b Chicago, Ill, Feb 28, 39; m 61; c 2. MATHEMATICS. *Educ:* Blackburn Col, BA, 60; Southern Ill Univ, MS, 62; Univ Iowa, PhD(math), 66. *Prof Exp:* Asst prof math, Monmouth Col, Ill, 66-71; ASSOC PROF MATH, THIEL COL, 71- *Mem:* Math Asn Am; Am Math Soc. *Res:* Homological algebra as related to the theory of local rings. *Mailing Add:* Dept of Math Thiel Col Greenville PA 16125

NICHOLS, JOSEPH, b New York, NY, July 9, 17; m 51; c 2. ORGANIC CHEMISTRY. *Educ:* City Col New York, BS, 38; Univ Minn, PhD(org chem), 43. *Prof Exp:* Asst physiol chem, Univ Minn, 39-42, Nat Defense Res Coun res fel, 42-43; res chemist, Interchem Corp, NY, 43-49; chief, Dept Org Chem, Ethicon, Inc, 51-57, assoc dir res, 57-65, dir res, Collagen Prod, 65-68; pres, Princeton Biomedix Inc, 68-76; PRES, HELITREX INC, 76- *Mem:* AAAS; Am Chem Soc; NY Acad Sci; Soc Biomaterials; Am Soc Artificial Internal Organs. *Res:* Quinones; fatty acids; biomaterials medical products. *Mailing Add:* Helitrex Inc PO Box 2041 Princeton NJ 08540

NICHOLS, K(ENNETH) D(AVID), b Cleveland, Ohio, Nov 13, 07; m 32; c 2. ENGINEERING. *Educ:* US Mil Acad, BS, 29; Cornell Univ, CE, 32, MCE, 33; Univ Iowa, PhD(hydraul), 37. *Prof Exp:* Asst dir, US Waterways Exp Sta, US Army, Miss, 33-34 & 35-36, instr civil & mil eng, US Mil Acad, 37-41, prof mech, 47-48, area engr, Rome Air Depot, NY & Pa Ord Wroks, 41-42, dep dist engr, Manhattan Dist, 42-43, dist engr, 43-47, chief armed forces spec weapons proj & Army mem mil liaison comt to US Atomic Energy Comn, 48-50, dep dir guided missiles, Off Secy Defense, 50-53, chief res & develop, US Army, 52-53; gen mgr, US Atomic Energy Comn, 53-55; CONSULT ENGR, 55- *Concurrent Pos:* Dir, Atomic Indust Forum, 56-59 & 64-70, Detroit Edison Co, 62-80 & Fruehauf Corp, 64- *Honors & Awards:* Collinwood Prize, Am Soc Civil Engrs, 38; Nicaraguan Medal of Merit; Comdr, Order of the Brit Empire. *Mem:* Nat Acad Engrs; fel Am Nuclear Soc. *Res:* Hydraulic model; atomic energy; nuclear engineering management. *Mailing Add:* 16715 Thurston Rd Dickerson MD 20842

NICHOLS, KATHLEEN MARY, b Amsterdam, NY, May 29, 48. CELL BIOLOGY, ANIMAL BEHAVIOR. *Educ:* State Univ NY, Albany, BS, 70, PhD(biophysics), 76; Col St Rose, MS, 72. *Prof Exp:* Res assoc fel biophys cell biol, State Univ NY, Albany, 76-79; res assoc fel toxicol, Albany Med Col, 79-80; ASST PROF BIOL, RUSSELL SAGE COL, NY, 80- *Concurrent Pos:* Res assoc, State Univ NY, Albany, 80, 81 & 82. *Mem:* Biophys Soc; Am Soc Cell Biol; AAAS. *Res:* Control of the mobility of cellular flagella. *Mailing Add:* Biol Dept Russell Sage Col Troy NY 12180

NICHOLS, KATHRYN MARION, b Santa Monica, Calif, Apr 30, 46. STRATIGRAPHY, SEDIMENTARY PETROLOGY. *Educ:* Univ Calif, Riverside, BS, 68; Stanford Univ, PhD(geol), 72. *Prof Exp:* NSF res asst, Stanford Univ, 70-72, NSF res assoc, 73-74, lectr geol, 75-76; GEOLOGIST, US GEOL SURV, 78- *Concurrent Pos:* Petrol Res Fund fel, 74-76; Nat Res Coun fel, 76-77. *Mem:* Geol Soc Am; Soc Econ Paleontologists & Mineralogists. *Res:* Sedimentology of carbonate rocks; Mississippian stratigraphy of the northern rocky mountains. *Mailing Add:* Fed Ctr US Geol Surv Denver CO 80225

NICHOLS, KENNETH E, b Brems, Ind, Dec 17, 20; m 41; c 4. PLANT PHYSIOLOGY. *Educ:* Valparaiso Univ, AB, 49; Univ Chicago, MS, 53, PhD(physiol), 61. *Prof Exp:* Assoc prof biol, 53-67, PROF BIOL, VALPARAISO UNIV, 67- *Mem:* Am Soc Plant Physiol; Phycol Soc Am; Int Phycol Soc. *Res:* Biosynthesis of plant pigments. *Mailing Add:* Dept of Biol Valparaiso Univ Valparaiso IN 46383

NICHOLS, LEE L(OCHHEAD), JR, b Richmond, Va, June 5, 23; m 49; c 3. ELECTRICAL ENGINEERING. *Educ:* Va Mil Inst, BS, 47; Ohio State Univ, MS, 51; Va Polytech Inst, PhD, 70. *Prof Exp:* PROF ELEC ENG, VA MIL INST, 47-, DIR ENG & HEAD DEPT ELEC ENG, 71- *Mem:* Am Soc Eng Educ; Inst Elec & Electronics Engrs. *Res:* Instrumentation and measurement of physical quantities by electrical means and analog devices as applied to basic physical problems. *Mailing Add:* Dept of Elec Eng Va Mil Inst Lexington VA 24451

NICHOLS, LOWELL LEWIS, health physics, accelerator physics, see previous edition

NICHOLS, MAYNARD M, marine geology, oceanography, see previous edition

NICHOLS, MICHAEL CHARLES, b Minneapolis, Minn, Jan 24, 51; m 81. HYDROBIOLOGY. *Educ:* Univ Mich, Flint, AB, 73; Univ Ga, MS, 78. *Prof Exp:* Res asst, Inst Ecol, Univ Ga, 77-78; SR BIOLOGIST, ENVIRON AFFAIRS CTR, GA POWER CO, 78- *Mem:* Am Soc Limnol & Oceanog; AAAS; Soc Power Indust Biologists. *Res:* Monitoring environmental effects of nuclear power plant operations; investigation of effects of hypolimnetic releases form hydroelectric impoundments on downstream water quality. *Mailing Add:* Ga Power Co 791 DeKalb Indust Way Decatur GA 30030

NICHOLS, NATHAN LANKFORD, b Jackson, Mich, Nov 16, 17; m 41; c 5. PHYSICS. *Educ:* Western Mich Univ, AB, 39; Univ Mich, MS, 45; Mich State Univ, PhD(physics), 53. *Prof Exp:* Teacher high sch, SDak, 39-40 & Mich, 40-43; instr physics, Ill Col, 43-44 & Univ Mich, 44-45; asst, Mich State Univ, 46-48; prof & head dept, Alma Col, 49-55; from assoc prof to prof physics, Western Mich Univ, 55-81; RETIRED. *Mem:* Optical Soc Am; Am Asn Physics Teachers. *Res:* Near infrared spectroscopy; optics. *Mailing Add:* 2420 Frederick Ave Kalamazoo MI 49008

NICHOLS, PARKS MONTGOMERY, rubber chemistry, deceased

NICHOLS, ROBERT LESLIE, b Boston, Mass, June 10, 04; m 35; c 1. GEOLOGY. *Educ:* Tufts Univ, BS, 26; Harvard Univ, MA, 30, PhD(geol), 40. *Hon Degrees:* DSc, Eastern Ky Univ, 74, Tufts Univ, 78. *Prof Exp:* Master, Montpelier Sem, 26-27 & Milton Acad, 27-28; asst geol, Harvard Univ, 28-30; instr, 29-36, from asst prof to prof, 36-74, actg head dept geol, 36-40, head dept, 40-69, distinguished prof, 69-74, EMER PROF GEOL, TUFTS UNIV, 74- *Concurrent Pos:* Ranger naturalist, Nat Park Serv, 30-31; instr, Boston Adult Educ Ctr, 33-35; res assoc, Mus Northern Ariz, 40-41; from asst geologist to assoc geologist, US Geol Surv, 40-74; geologist, Ronne Antarctic Res Exped, 47-48; geologist, US Navy Arctic Task Force, 48; geologist, Am Geog Soc-Nat Hist Mus Arg Exped, Patagonia, 49; mem, Juneau, Alaska Ice Cap Exped, 50; leader, US Army Transp Corps Exped, Inglefieldland, Greenland, 53; geologist, Oper Deep Freeze, Antarctica, US Navy, 57-58 & Int Geophys Year, 58-59; leader, Tufts Col-NSF Antarctic Exped, 59-60 & 60-61, Northwest Greenland Exped, 63 & 65; field worker, NMex, Wash, Ore, New Eng, Alaska, Antarctica, Arctic & Patagonia. *Honors & Awards:* Bellingshausen Mem Medal, Acad Sci Soviet Union, 75. *Mem:* AAAS (secy, Geol & Geog Sect, 55-56); fel Geol Soc Am; fel Am Geog Soc; Nat Asn Geol Teachers (vpres, 59); fel Royal Geog Soc. *Res:* Geomorphology; vulcanology; high-alumina clay. *Mailing Add:* 15 Pleasant St Harwich Port MA 02646

NICHOLS, ROBERT LORING, b Newton, NJ, Mar 3, 46; m 76; c 3. AGRONOMY, WEED SCIENCE. *Educ:* Yale Univ, BA, 68; Univ Conn, MS, 77, PhD(agron), 80. *Prof Exp:* Sr lang analyst, US Army Security Agency, 68-72; tech dir polymer sci, Tech Rubber, Inc, 72-73; teaching fel soil sci, Univ Conn, Storrs, 74-76; instr, Univ Conn, Torrington, 76; res asst, Univ Conn, Storrs, 77-80; RES AGRONOMIST FORAGE WEED CONTROL, AGR RES SERV, UNIV GA, USDA, 80- *Mem:* Am Soc Agron; Crop Sci Soc; Soil Sci Soc; Weed Sci Soc Am. *Res:* Forages; weed science. *Mailing Add:* Nematode & Weed Res Ctr Agr Res Serv Univ Ga Coastal Plain Exp Sta USDA Tifton GA 31753

NICHOLS, ROBERT TED, b Lewis, Iowa, Dec 30, 25; m 55; c 3. PHYSICS. *Educ:* Iowa State Univ, BS, 50, MS, 55, PhD(physics), 60. *Prof Exp:* Asst beta & gamma ray spectros, Ames Lab, AEC, 50-51; instr physics & math, Bethel Col, Minn, 54-56; asst prof physics, Gustavus Adolphus Col, 60-63; mem tech staff & physicist, Hughes Res Labs, Calif, 63-66; assoc prof physics, 66-74, chmn dept, 74-78, PROF PHYSICS, CALIF LUTHERAN COL, 74- *Concurrent Pos:* Consult mil prod group, Minneapolis-Honeywell Regulator Co, 62-63. *Mem:* Am Asn Physics Teachers; Sigma Xi. *Res:* Radiation physics; linear energy transfer for dosimetry; small angle beta scattering; beta and gamma ray spectroscopy; computer generation of random number distributions. *Mailing Add:* Dept of Physics Calif Lutheran Col Thousand Oaks CA 91360

NICHOLS, ROGER LOYD, b Waverly, Iowa, Apr 29, 26; m 49; c 3. MICROBIOLOGY. *Educ:* Cornell Col, BA, 48; Univ Iowa, MD, 53. *Hon Degrees:* MA, Harvard Univ, 71. *Prof Exp:* Res fel med, Sch Med, 55-56, res fel microbiol, Sch Pub Health, 57-60, res assoc, 61-63, from asst prof to assoc prof appl microbiol, 63-69, IRENE HEINZ GIVEN PROF MICROBIOL, SCH PUB HEALTH, HARVARD UNIV, 69-; PRES, UNIV ASSOCS INT HEALTH, INC, 73- *Concurrent Pos:* Med consult, Ministry Health, Gov of Saudi Arabia & Supreme Coun Univs of Saudi Arabia, 74-75. *Mem:* AAAS; Am Fedn Clin Res; Am Soc Microbiol; Am Epidemiol Soc; fel Am Col Epidemiol. *Res:* Field and laboratory research in trachoma; clinical research in new antibiotics; trachoma; venereal diseases; international health. *Mailing Add:* Dept of Microbiol Harvard Univ Sch Pub Health Boston MA 02115

NICHOLS, ROY ELWYN, b Leonardsville, NY, July 10, 09; m 32; c 2. VETERINARY PHYSIOLOGY. *Educ:* Univ Toronto, DVM, 33, DVSc, 43; Ohio State Univ, MSc, 34, PhD(vet hemat), 41. *Prof Exp:* Asst vet surg, Col Vet Med, Ohio State Univ, 34-35, instr, 35-41; asst prof col agr & assoc, Agr Exp Sta, Purdue Univ, 41-42 & 45-47; dean col vet med, State Col Wash, 47-50; lectr & res assoc, 50-51, prof vet sci, 51-72, EMER PROF VET SCI, UNIV WIS-MADISON, 72- *Mem:* Am Soc Animal Sci; Am Vet Med Asn; Am Dairy Sci Asn; Conf Res Workers Animal Dis. *Res:* Veterinary hematology, physiology and surgery; instrument for photographic recording of erythrocyte sedimentation; ruminology. *Mailing Add:* 5605 Taychopera Rd Madison WI 53705

NICHOLS, RUDOLPH HENRY, b Bellaire, Mich, Dec 6, 11; m 39; c 1. ACOUSTICS. *Educ:* Hope Col, AB, 32; Univ Mich, AM, 33, PhD(physics), 39. *Prof Exp:* Lab asst physics, Univ Mich, 35-36, asst acoust & physics, 36-38, res assoc, 39; physicist, Owens-Ill Glass Co, 40-41; spec res assoc, Cruft Lab, Harvard Univ, 41-44, from asst dir to assoc dir, Electro-Acoust Lab, 44-46; mem tech staff, Bell Labs, 46-76; CONSULT ACOUST, 76- *Mem:* Fel Acoust Soc Am. *Res:* Audio communications; sound reduction in vehicles; vibration isolation; acoustical materials; hearing and hearing aids; underwater acoustics. *Mailing Add:* Bell Labs Whippany NJ 07981

NICHOLS, WARREN WESLEY, b Collingswood, NJ, May 16, 29; m 53; c 3. CYTOGENETICS, PEDIATRICS. *Educ:* Rutgers Univ, BS, 50; Jefferson Med Col, MD, 54; Univ Lund, PhD(med cytogenetics), 64, DrPhil, 66. *Prof Exp:* Intern, Cooper Hosp, Camden, NJ, 54-55; fel, Children's Hosp Philadelphia, 55-56; chief pediat, Lake Charles AFB, 57-59; assoc, Sch Med & instr, Grad Sch Med, 59-67, from asst prof to assoc prof, Sch Med, 64-73, PROF HUMAN GENETICS & PEDIAT, SCH MED, UNIV PA, 73-; asst dir, 63-81, VPRES RES, INST MED RES, 81-, S EMLEN STOKES PROF GENETICS, 75- *Concurrent Pos:* Chief med staff, Camden Munic Hosp Contagious Dis, 59-61; assoc mem, SJersey Med Res Found, 59-65; asst physician, Children's Hosp Philadelphia, 59-65, assoc physician & assoc hematologist, 65-73, sr physician, Div Metab & Genetics, 73-81, univ assoc, Div Human Genetics & Teratol, 81-; mem pediat staff, Cooper Hosp, Camden, NJ, 59-65, consult staff, 65-; consult staff, Our Lady of Lourdes Hosp, Camden, 59-66, assoc pediat, 66-; NIH res career develop award, 63-72; assoc prof, Univ Lund, 66-; mem, Human Cytogenetics Study Group, 66-; consult secy comn pesticides & their relationship to environ health, Dept Health, Educ & Welfare, 69; mem human embryol & develop study sect, NIH, 73-78; mem panel, US-Japan Coop Med Sci Prog, 72-74; co-chmn USA-USSR Prog on Mammalian Somatic Cell Genetics Related to Neoplasia, 76-80; clin prof pediat, NJ Col Med & Dent, 79-; mem bd sci counsrs, Div Cancer Cause & Prev, Nat Cancer Inst, 79-82. *Mem:* AAAS; Environ Mutagen Soc (secy, 73-76); AMA; Soc Pediat Res; Genetics Soc Am. *Res:* Spontaneous and induced gene and chromosome mutations and their role in carcinogenesis, aging and hereditary disease; emphasis is on virus induced cellular genetic changes and high risk cancer individuals and families. *Mailing Add:* Inst for Med Res Copewood St Camden NJ 08103

NICHOLS, WILLIAM B(URT), chemical engineering, see previous edition

NICHOLS, WILLIAM HERBERT, b Cleveland, Ohio, Mar 15, 28. STATISTICAL MECHANICS, FIBER OPTICS. *Educ:* West Baden Col, AB, 50; Mass Inst Technol, SB, 55, PhD(physics), 58; Weston Col, STL, 61. *Prof Exp:* Instr physics & algebra, Loyola Acad, 52-53; res asst physics, Inst Theoret Physics, Univ Vienna, 62-63; asst prof, Univ Detroit, 63-67; from asst prof to assoc prof, 67-74, PROF PHYSICS, JOHN CARROLL UNIV, 74- *Mem:* Am Phys Soc. *Res:* Theory of optical fibers as sound sensors. *Mailing Add:* Dept of Physics John Carroll Univ Cleveland OH 44118

NICHOLS, WILLIAM KENNETH, b Seattle, Wash, Sept 25, 43; m 73. PHARMACOLOGY. *Educ:* Univ Wash, BS, 66; Univ Minn, PhD(phamacol), 71. *Prof Exp:* asst prof, 71-78, ASSOC PROF PHARMACOL, DEPT BIOCHEM PHARMACOL & TOXICOL, COL PHARM & COL MED, UNIV UTAH, 78- *Concurrent Pos:* NIH career develop award, Nat Inst Arthritis, Metabol & Digestive Dis, 78-83. *Mem:* Am Asn Col Pharmacol; Am Soc Pharmacol Exp Therapeut. *Res:* Biochemical pharmacology; endocrinology; diabetes; immunology; leukocyte metabolism and function; cyclic nucleotides; allergy; hormonal and cyclic nucleotide modulation of cellular functions; alterations in cellular immune responses and vascular tissue in the diabetic state. *Mailing Add:* Dept Biochem Pharmacol & Toxicol Col Pharm Univ Utah Salt Lake City UT 84112

NICHOLS, WILMER WAYNE, b Booneville, Miss, Aug 12, 34; m 62; c 2. CARDIOVASCULAR PHYSIOLOGY. *Educ:* Delta State Col, BS, 60; Univ Southern Miss, MS, 66; Univ Ala, PhD(physiol, biophys), 70. *Prof Exp:* Instr physiol, Med Sch, Univ Ala, 70-71; asst prof med physics, Inst Med Physics, Holland, 71-72; asst prof physiol, Sch Med, Johns Hopkins Univ, 72-74; ASST PROF PHYSIOL & ASSOC PROF CLIN CARDIOL, COL MED, UNIV FLA, 74- *Concurrent Pos:* Consult, Millar Instruments Inc, Tex, 74-; mem, Cardiovasc Catheter Standards Subcomt, 74- *Mem:* Am Fedn Clin Res; Am Physiol Soc; Cardiol Soc Holland; Am Heart Asn; Asn Advan Med Instrumentation. *Res:* Pulsatile hemodynamics in man. *Mailing Add:* Dept Med Col Med Univ Fla Gainsville FL 32610

NICHOLS-DRISCOLL, JEAN ANN, biological oceanography, see previous edition

NICHOLSON, ARNOLD EUGENE, b Jasper, Ind, Apr 9, 30. PHARMACEUTICAL CHEMISTRY. *Educ:* Purdue Univ, BS, 52, MS, 54, PhD(pharmaceut chem), 56. *Prof Exp:* Sr res chemist, Smith Kline & French Labs, 56-64; asst to tech dir pharmaceut develop, Stuart Div, Atlas Chem Industs, Inc, 64-72; PROJ ADMINR REGIONAL AFFAIRS, HYLAND LABS, DIV BAXTER LABS & MEM STAFF, TRAVENOL LAB DIV, BAXTER TRAVENOL LABS, INC, 72- *Mem:* Am Chem Soc; Am Pharmaceut Asn; Am Soc Hosp Pharmacists; Int Asn Biol Standardization. *Res:* Pharmaceutical research and development. *Mailing Add:* Hyland Thereapeutics PO Box 1976 Glendale CA 91202

NICHOLSON, BASIL J(OHN), physics, solid state electronics, see previous edition

NICHOLSON, BRUCE LEE, b Baltimore, Md, Feb 13, 43; m 65. MICROBIOLOGY. *Educ:* Univ Md, College Park, BS, 65, PhD(microbiol), 69. *Prof Exp:* Asst prof microbiol, 69-74, assoc prof, 74-79, PROF MICROBIOL & ZOOL & CHMN, DEPT MICROBIOL, UNIV MAINE, 79- *Mem:* Am Soc Microbiol; AAAS; Wildlife Dis Asn; Tissue Culture Asn; Am Fisheries Soc. *Res:* Biochemical and biophysical characteristics of fish viruses and their interactions with susceptible cells; serological methods for detection and identification of fish viruses. *Mailing Add:* Dept Microbiol Univ Maine Orono ME 04473

NICHOLSON, (JOHN) CHARLES (GODFREY), b Great Malvern, Eng, Feb 8, 42. NEUROBIOLOGY. *Educ:* Univ Birmingham, BSc, 63; Univ Keele, PhD(commun), 68. *Prof Exp:* Sci officer math physics, UK Atomic Energy Authority, 63-65; vis investr neurobiol, Inst Biomed Res, Am Med Asn-Educ & Res Found, Ill, 67-69, asst mem, 69-70; from asst prof to assoc prof, Univ Iowa, 70-76; PROF PHYSIOL & BIOPHYS, MED CTR, NY UNIV, 76- *Mem:* NY Acad Sci; Soc Neurosci; Inst Elec & Electronics Eng.

Res: Neuronal organization and function as revealed by anatomical, physiological and mathematical analysis with emphasis on cerebellum; electrical and ionic properties of brain cell microenvironment. *Mailing Add:* Dept of Physiol & Biophys 550 First Ave NY Univ Med Ctr New York NY 10016

NICHOLSON, D ALLAN, b Waterloo, Iowa, June 22, 39; m 62; c 2. ORGANOMETALLIC CHEMISTRY, ANALYTICAL CHEMISTRY. *Educ:* Cornell Col, BA, 60; Northwestern Univ, PhD(inorg chem), 65. *Prof Exp:* Staff chemist, 65-70, sect head anal chem, 70-72, sect head toxicol, 72-74, assoc dir soap & toilet goods technol div, 74-79, ASSOC DIR PACKAGED SOAP & DETERGENTS DIV, PROCTER & GAMBLE CO, 79- *Mem:* Am Chem Soc. *Res:* Non-transition metals such as germanium, silicon; organophosphorus chemistry. *Mailing Add:* Procter & Gamble Co 5299 Spring Grove Cincinnati OH 45217

NICHOLSON, DANIEL ELBERT, b Waco, Tex, Sept 1, 26; m 51. PHYSICAL CHEMISTRY. *Educ:* Baylor Univ, BS, 46; Univ Tex, MA, 48, PhD(phys chem), 50. *Prof Exp:* Tutor, Univ Tex, 46-48; chemist, Oak Ridge Nat Lab, 50-51; from res chemist to sr res chemist, Humble Oil & Ref Co, 52-61; staff mem, Los Alamos Sci Lab, 62; res assoc, Richfield Oil Corp, 63-67; sect head optical spectros, Micro Data Opers, 67-68, sect mgr, Electro-Optical Systs, Inc, 68-76; tech coord, Witco Chem Co, 76-78; MEM STAFF, ENG DIV-ENFORCEMENT, SOUTH COAST AIR QUAL MGT DIST, 78- *Res:* Kinetics of hydrocarbon decomposition; precision calorimetry; infrared spectroscopy of absorbed species; electrical and magnetic properties of catalysts; Raman spectroscopy; thermodynamic properties; catalytic studies of hydrode-sulfurization; hydrogenation of aromatic hydrocarbons. *Mailing Add:* 2209 California Blvd San Marino CA 91108

NICHOLSON, DAVID WILLIAM, b Boston, Mass, May 9, 44. MECHANICS. *Educ:* Mass Inst Technol, SB, 66; Yale Univ, MS, 67, PhD(mech), 71. *Prof Exp:* Sr physicist mech, Goodyear Tire & Rubber Co, 71-77; MECH ENGR, NAVAL SURFACE WEAPONS CTR, 77- *Concurrent Pos:* Reviewer, Appl Mech Revs, 74. *Mem:* Am Acad Mech; Adhesive Soc Am; Soc Automotive Engrs. *Res:* Plasticity; viscoelasticity; fracture mechanics; tire mechanics; numerical analysis. *Mailing Add:* Naval Surface Weapons Ctr Silver Spring MD 20910

NICHOLSON, DONALD PAUL, b Pershing, Iowa, Jan 3, 30; m 54; c 2. MICROBIOLOGY, VIROLOGY. *Educ:* Iowa State Col, BS, 51; Univ SDak, BSM, 59; Univ Iowa, MD, 61. *Prof Exp:* Asst radiation res, 56-57, clin intern med, 61-62, USPHS fel, 62-65, from instr to asst prof microbiol, 62-68, asst dir clin lab serv, 68-71, asst prof path & supvr clin microbiol, 71-76, investr res, develop, eval for clin microbiol, 76-81, ASST PROF PATH, UNIV IOWA, 81- *Mem:* AAAS; Am Soc Microbiol; AMA. *Res:* Areas related to clinical microbiology. *Mailing Add:* Rm 382 MRC Univ of Iowa Dept of Path Iowa City IA 52242

NICHOLSON, DOUGLAS GILLISON, b Joliet, Ill, Dec 29, 08; m 32; c 2. INORGANIC CHEMISTRY. *Educ:* Univ Ill, BS, 30, MS, 31, PhD(inorg chem), 34. *Prof Exp:* Asst chem, Univ Ill, 30-34, instr, 35-37, assoc, 37-42; res chemist, E I du Pont de Nemours & Co, 34-35; assoc prof chem, Univ Pittsburgh, 45-49; dir ed serv, Fisher Sci Co, 49-53; assoc prof inorg chem, 53-57, prof chem & chmn dept, 57-74, EMER CHMN DEPT CHEM, EAST TENN STATE UNIV, 74- *Mem:* Am Chem Soc. *Res:* White pigments, especially titanium dioxide; titanium compounds; reactions in non-aqueous solvents. *Mailing Add:* 2200 N Greenwood Dr Johnson City TN 37601

NICHOLSON, DWIGHT ROY, b Racine, Wis, Oct 3, 47; m 69. PLASMA PHYSICS. *Educ:* Univ Wis-Madison, BS, 69; Univ Calif, Berkeley, PhD(plasma physics), 75. *Prof Exp:* Res assoc plasma physics, 75-77, asst prof Astro-Geophys Dept, Univ Colo, Boulder, 77-78; asst prof, 78-81, ASSOC PROF PHYSICS, DEPT PHYSICS & ASTRO, UNIV IOWA, IOWA CITY, 81- *Mem:* AAAS; Union Radio Sci Int; Am Phys Soc. *Res:* Plasma theory; nonlinear waves in plasma; plasma turbulence. *Mailing Add:* Dept Physics & Astron Univ Iowa Iowa City IA 52242

NICHOLSON, EDWARD W(HEELOCK) S(TEELE), b Chicago, Ill, July 1, 13; m 36; c 2. ENERGY SYSTEMS, PLANNING. *Educ:* Univ Chicago, BS, 34; Mass Inst Technol, MS, 36. *Prof Exp:* Instr chem eng, Mass Inst Technol, 36-37; chem eng planning mgr, Esso Res Labs, Standard Oil Co, NJ, La, 37-46, sect head, 46-47, asst dir, 47-55, asst head chem prod div, Baton Rouge Ref, 55, head petrol tech serv dept, 55-56, asst dir process res div, Esso Res & Eng Co, NJ, 56, asst mgr ref liaison, 57, Netherlands, 57-59 & NJ, 59-60, asst dir prod res div, 60-61, dir chem develop div, 61-62, res coord-plastics chem staff, 62-65, sr adv, Enjay Chem Co, NY, 65, Esso Chem Co, Inc, 66, Esso Chem Co SA, Brussels, 66-68 & Esso Chem Co, Inc, NY, 68-69, res coord planning corp res staff, Esso Res & Eng Co, 69-77, planning mgr, Exxon Enterprises, 73-77, consult energy systems, 77-79; RETIRED. *Mem:* Am Chem Soc; Am Inst Chem Engrs. *Res:* Energy systems, planning, process development and technical administration. *Mailing Add:* 18 Devon Rd Summit NJ 07901

NICHOLSON, EUGENE HAINES, b St Louis, Mo, Nov 10, 07. MATHEMATICS, PHYSICS. *Educ:* Wash Univ, BS, 31, MS, 37, PhD(math, physics), 41. *Prof Exp:* Elec engr, Union Elec Co, 41-60; CONSULT, 60- *Mem:* AAAS; Am Math Soc. *Res:* Applied mathematics; mathematical physics; energy conversion; systems engineering; nuclear power. *Mailing Add:* 5232 Lansdowne Ave St Louis MO 63109

NICHOLSON, HOWARD WHITE, JR, b Brooklyn, NY, Dec 18, 44; m 71. HIGH ENERGY PHYSICS. *Educ:* Hamilton Col, BA, 66; Mass Inst Technol, BA, 66; Calif Inst Technol, PhD(physics), 71. *Prof Exp:* asst prof, 71-77, ASSOC PROF PHYSICS, MT HOLYOKE COL, 77- *Concurrent Pos:* Res Corp grants, Mt Holyoke Col, 72, 75; Dept Energy Contract, 78- *Mem:* Am Phys Soc. *Res:* Experimental high energy particle physics. *Mailing Add:* Dept of Physics Shattuck Hall Mt Holyoke Col South Hadley MA 01075

NICHOLSON, HUGH HAMPSON, b Lloydminster, Sask, Sept 30, 23; m 64; c 2. ANIMAL NUTRITION, ANIMAL GENETICS. *Educ:* Univ BC, BSA, 50, MSA, 54; Ore State Univ, PhD(genetics), 58. *Prof Exp:* Res officer animal nutrit & range mgt, Can Res Sta, BC, 50-62; assoc prof, 62-76, PROF BEEF CATTLE NUTRIT & MGT, UNIV SASK, 76- *Mem:* Soc Range Mgt; Agr Inst Can; Can Soc Animal Prod; Nutrit Soc Can. *Res:* Productivity of range land; irrigated pasture production with beef cattle; record of performances of beef cattle; nutrition and management of feed lot cattle; mill processing of beef cattle feeds. *Mailing Add:* Dept of Animal Poultry Sci Univ of Sask Saskatoon SK S7H 0W0 Can

NICHOLSON, ISADORE, b Philadelphia, Pa, Apr 28, 25. ORGANIC CHEMISTRY. *Educ:* Temple Univ, BA, 49; Rutgers Univ, MSc, 52, PhD(chem), 54. *Prof Exp:* Res instr chem, Univ Minn, 54-55; sr res chemist, US Rubber Co, 55-57, sr res specialist, 57-58; from asst prof to assoc prof chem, 58-68, PROF CHEM, C W POST COL, LONG ISLAND UNIV, 68- *Res:* Theoretical and biological organic chemistry. *Mailing Add:* Dept of Chem C W Post Col Long Island Univ Greenvale NY 11548

NICHOLSON, J W G, b Crapaud, PEI, Jan 19, 31; c 4. ANIMAL NUTRITION. *Educ:* McGill Univ, BS, 51; Cornell Univ, MS, 56, PhD(animal nutrit), 59. *Prof Exp:* RES SCIENTIST ANIMAL NUTRIT, CAN DEPT AGR, 51- *Mem:* Can Soc Animal Sci; Agr Inst Can; Am Soc Animal Sci; Am Dairy Sci Asn. *Res:* Nutrition of ruminant animals. *Mailing Add:* Res Sta Agr Can PO Box 20280 Fredericton NB E3D 4Z7 Can

NICHOLSON, LARRY MICHAEL, b Nevada, Mo, Nov 22, 41; m 64; c 2. BIOCHEMISTRY. *Educ:* Kans State Univ, BS, 63, PhD(biochem), 68. *Prof Exp:* Asst prof chem, Univ Mo-Rolla, 67-75; asst prof, 76-79, ASSOC PROF, FT HAYS STATE UNIV, 79- *Mem:* Am Chem Soc; Sigma Xi. *Res:* Enzyme chemistry; peroxidase enzymes; biological halogenation; biosynthesis of thyroxine. *Mailing Add:* Dept Chem Ft Hays State Univ 600 Park St Hays KS 67601

NICHOLSON, MARGIE MAY, b San Antonio, Tex, June 10, 25; m 51. PHYSICAL CHEMISTRY. *Educ:* Univ Tex, BS, 46, MA, 48, PhD(phys chem), 50. *Prof Exp:* Phys chemist, US Naval Ord Lab, 51-52; res chemist, Humble Oil & Refining Co, 52-56, sr res chemist, 56-62; electrochemist, Stanford Res Inst, 62-64; res specialist, Rocketdyne Div, NAm Aviation, Inc, 64-65, sr tech specialist, 65, mem tech staff, Atomic Int Div, NAm Rockwell Corp, Canoga Park, 65-74, mem tech staff, Electronics Res Ctr, 74-77, mgr org electron devices, 77-79, MEM TECH STAFF, AUTONETICS STRATEGIC SYSTS DIV, ROCKWELL INT, ANAHEIM, 80- *Mem:* Am Chem Soc; Electrochem Soc; Sigma Xi. *Res:* Electrochemistry; theory and applications of voltammetric techniques; electrochemical power sources; electrode kinetics; nonaqueous electrochemistry; semiconductor electrodes; electrochromic displays; organic solid state electrochemistry. *Mailing Add:* 2209 California Blvd San Marino CA 91108

NICHOLSON, MORRIS E(MMONS), JR, b Indianapolis, Ind, Feb 15, 16; m 43; c 3. PHYSICAL METALLURGY, CORROSION. *Educ:* Mass Inst Technol, SB, 39, ScD, 47. *Prof Exp:* Res asst, Mass Inst Technol, 39-41 & 46-47; res metallurgist, Standard Oil Co, Ind, 47-48, sect head, Phys Metall, 48-50; asst prof, Inst Study of Metals, Univ Chicago, 50-55; dept head, 56-62, PROF METALL, UNIV MINN, MINNEAPOLIS, 56-, DIR CONT ED ENG & SCI, 73- *Mem:* Am Soc Metals; Metall Soc; Corrosion Soc; Am Soc Eng Educ. *Res:* Ferrous metals and alloys; plastic flow and fracture; X-ray metallography; transformations in metals textures and recrystallization mechanisms in low carbon steels; corrosion mechanisms in phosphate solutions; pitting corrosion. *Mailing Add:* 1776 N Pascal Ave Falcon Heights MN 55113

NICHOLSON, NANCY LYNNE, natural sciences, botany, see previous edition

NICHOLSON, NICHOLAS, b New York, NY, June 9, 38; m 64. EXPERIMENTAL NUCLEAR PHYSICS. *Educ:* Polytech Inst Brooklyn, BS, 60; WVa Univ, MS, 62, PhD(physics), 65. *Prof Exp:* Half-time instr physics, WVa Univ, 63-64, asst, 64-65; physicist, Div Res, USAEC, Washington, DC, 65-67; PHYSICIST, LOS ALAMOS SCI LAB, 67- *Res:* Nuclear spectroscopy, alpha, beta, and gamma; angular correlations; x-ray physics; x-ray spectroscopy; nuclear safeguards; radiography. *Mailing Add:* Los Alamos Sci Lab Group Q-2 PO Box 1663 Los Alamos NM 87544

NICHOLSON, RALPH LESTER, b Lynn, Mass, Aug 25, 42; m 74. PHYTOPATHOLOGY. *Educ:* Univ Vt, BA, 64; Univ Maine, MS, 67; Purdue Univ, PhD(plant path), 72. *Prof Exp:* Asst prof, 72-76, ASSOC PROF PLANT PATH, PURDUE UNIV, WEST LAFAYETTE, 77- *Concurrent Pos:* Purdue rep, NCent Region, Corn & Sorghum Dis Comt, USDA-Coop State Res Serv, 72- *Mem:* Am Phytopath Soc; Sigma Xi; Can Phytopath Soc; Brazilian Phytopath Soc. *Res:* Study of host biochemical response to infection with emphasis on stress compounds; recognition of the pathogen by the host, and histopathology related to disease physiology and time of host response; phenolic compound metabolism and synthesis; integrated pest management. *Mailing Add:* Dept of Bot & Plant Path Purdue Univ West Lafayette IN 47907

NICHOLSON, RICHARD BENJAMIN, b Tacoma, Wash, Sept 8, 28; m 52; c 4. NUCLEAR PHYSICS. *Educ:* Univ Puget Sound, BS, 50; Cornell Univ, MS, 60; Univ Mich, PhD(nuclear sci), 63. *Prof Exp:* Physicist mat lab, Puget Sound Naval Shipyard, 51-53; physicist, Atomic Power Develop Assocs, 54-58 & 59-61; assoc prof nuclear eng, Univ Wis, 63-66; assoc physicist, Argonne Nat Lab, 66-69, sr physicist, 69-72; prof nuclear eng, Ohio State Univ, 72-74; mgr licensing uranium enrichment, Exxon Nuclear Co Inc, 74-79; physicist, Laser Enrichment, 79-81; CONSULT PHYSICS, 81- *Concurrent Pos:* Consult, Atomic Power Develop Assocs, 61-; physicist, Lawrence Radiation Lab, Univ Calif, 65; consult adv comt reactor safeguards, AEC. *Mem:* Fel Am Nuclear Soc; Am Phys Soc. *Res:* Physics and safety of fast nuclear reactors, especially theoretical problems in Doppler effect and accident analysis; theory of high temperature plasmas; uranium laser enrichment. *Mailing Add:* 150 Spengler Richland WA 99352

NICHOLSON, RICHARD SELINDH, b Des Moines, Iowa, Apr 5, 38; m 58; c 1. CHEMISTRY. *Educ:* Iowa State Univ, BS, 60; Univ Wis-Madison, PhD(chem), 64. *Prof Exp:* Res assoc chem, Iowa State Univ, 59-60; NSF fel, Univ Wis, 60-61, res assoc, 63-64; from asst prof to assoc prof, Mich State Univ, 64-71; prog dir, 71-75, actg head Chem Synthesis & Anal Sect & dept dir, Chem Div, 75-76; spec asst to dir, 76-77, DIR, CHEM DIV, NSF, 77-, DEP ASST DIR MATH & PHYS SCI, 80- *Concurrent Pos:* NSF fel, 64-71; consult, US Army Electronic Command, 67; guest worker, NIH, 71-; exec secy, President's Comt on Nat Medal of Sci, 77-, consult, Off Sci & Technol Policy, Exec Off Pres, 78-81. *Honors & Awards:* Eastman Kodak Award, Univ Wis, 64; NSF Meritorious Serv Award, 77. *Mem:* Fel AAAS; Am Chem Soc; Brit Polarographic Soc; Int Electrochem Soc. *Res:* Electrochemistry; electrode kinetics; applications of computers in instrumentation; mass spectrometry, especially chemical ionization. *Mailing Add:* Chem Div NSF 1800 G St NW Washington DC 20550

NICHOLSON, THOMAS DOMINIC, b New York, NY, Dec 14, 22; m 46; c 4. ASTRONOMY, NAVIGATION. *Educ:* US Merchant Marine Acad, BS, 50; St John's Univ, NY, BA, 50; Fordham Univ, MS, 53, PhD(educ admin), 61. *Prof Exp:* Asst prof nautical sci & asst to dept chmn, US Merchant Marine Acad, 46-53; assoc astronr, Hayden Planetarium, 54-58, asst chmn, 58-64, chmn, 64-68, asst dir, Mus, 68-69, DIR, AM MUS NATURAL HIST, 69- *Concurrent Pos:* Lectr, Hayden Planetarium, 51-54 & US Mil Acad, 54-64; instr, US Naval Reserve Officer's Sch, 54-60; adj instr, Hunter Col, 63-67; weather forecaster, WNBC-TV, New York, 67-73. *Mem:* Fel AAAS; Am Astron Soc; Am Meteorol Soc; Am Inst Navig (pres, 71-72); Royal Astron Soc. *Res:* Geodetic astronomy, specifically in arctic regions; spherical astronomy; astronomy education. *Mailing Add:* Am Mus Natural Hist 79th St Central Park W New York NY 10024

NICHOLSON, VICTOR ALVIN, b Stafford, Kans, Dec 16, 41; m 70; c 3. MATHEMATICS. *Educ:* Okla State Univ, BS, 62, MS, 64; Univ Iowa, PhD(math), 68. *Prof Exp:* Asst prof math, Park Col, 64-65; asst prof, 68-76, ASSOC PROF MATH, KENT STATE UNIV, 76- *Concurrent Pos:* Software develop consult, 80-81. *Mem:* Am Math Soc; Math Asn Am; Sigma Xi. *Res:* Geometric topology; topology of manifolds. *Mailing Add:* Dept of Math Kent State Univ Kent OH 44240

NICHOLSON, W(ILLIAM) J(OSEPH), b Tacoma, Wash, Aug 24, 38; m 64; c 4. CHEMICAL ENGINEERING. *Educ:* Mass Inst Technol, SB, 60, SM, 61; Cornell Univ, PhD(chem eng), 65; Pac Lutheran Univ, MBA, 69. *Prof Exp:* Sr develop engr, Hooker Chem Corp, 64-69 & Battelle Northwest, Battelle Mem Inst, 69-70; planning analyst, Potlatch Forests, Inc, 70-75, CORP ENERGY COORDR, POTLATCH CORP, 75- *Mem:* Tech Asn Pulp & Paper Indust; Am Chem Soc; Am Inst Chem Engrs; Sigma Xi; AAAS. *Res:* Corporate planning; application of planning to systematic business management; chemical process development; energy development, supply, use, and economics. *Mailing Add:* Potlatch Corp PO Box 3591 San Francisco CA 94119

NICHOLSON, WESLEY LATHROP, b Andover, Mass, Jan 31, 29; m 52; c 4. STATISTICS. *Educ:* Univ Ore, BA, 50, MA, 52; Univ Ill, PhD(math statist), 55. *Prof Exp:* Asst math, Univ Ore, 50-52 & Univ Ill, 52-55; instr, Princeton Univ, 55-56; statistician, Gen Elec Co, 56-64; sr res assoc, Pac Northwest Lab, 65-71, SR STAFF SCIENTIST, BATTELLE-NORTHWEST, BATTELLE MEM INST, 71- *Concurrent Pos:* Lectr, Univ Wash, Richland Campus, 56-71, chmn math prog, 71-79; adj prof math, Wash State Univ, 66- *Mem:* Fel Am Statist Asn; Math Asn Am; Inst Math Statist; Int Soc Stereol. *Res:* Derivation and application of statistical methodology to physical and engineering sciences; construction of stochastic models; analysis of large data sets; statistical graphics. *Mailing Add:* PO Box 999 Richland WA 99352

NICHOLSON, WILLIAM JAMIESON, b Seattle, Wash, Nov 21, 30; m 57; c 4. PHYSICS, ENVIRONMENTAL HEALTH. *Educ:* Mass Inst Technol, BS, 52; Univ Wash, PhD(physics), 60. *Prof Exp:* Instr, Univ Wash, 60; physicist, Watson Res Lab, Int Bus Mach Corp, NY, 60-68; asst prof, 69-73, ASSOC PROF COMMUNITY MED, MT SINAI SCH MED, 73- *Concurrent Pos:* Adj assoc prof, Fordham Univ, 64. *Mem:* AAAS; Am Phys Soc; NY Acad Sci. *Res:* Occupational and environmental health; analysis and effect of airborne micro-particulates. *Mailing Add:* Environ Sci Lab Mt Sinai Sch of Med New York NY 10029

NICHOLSON, WILLIAM ROBERT, b Camden, NJ, Jan 25, 25; m 50; c 4. FISHERIES. *Educ:* Rutgers Univ, BSc, 50; Univ Maine, MSc, 53. *Prof Exp:* Proj leader water fowl biol, Md Game & Inland Fish Comn, 51-55; FISHERY RES BIOLOGIST, CTR ESTUARINE & FISHERIES RES, NAT MARINE FISHERIES SERV, 56- *Mem:* Am Inst Biol Sci; Am Fisheries Soc; Am Inst Fishery Res Biologists. *Res:* Population dynamics of marine fishes. *Mailing Add:* Atlantic Estuarine Fisheries Ctr Nat Marine Fisheries Serv Beaufort NC 28516

NICHOLSON-GUTHRIE, CATHERINE SHIRLEY, b Jackson, Miss; m 61; c 1. GENETICS. *Educ:* Auburn Univ, BS, 57; Fla State Univ, MS, 60; Ind Univ, Bloomington, PhD(genetics), 72. *Prof Exp:* Res asst molecular biol, Calif Inst Technol, 60-62; instr biol, Boston State Col, 63-64; vis asst prof biol, Univ Evansville, 72-73; mem adj fac, 74-76, MEM FAC MED GENETICS, SCH MED, IND UNIV, INDIANAPOLIS, 76- *Concurrent Pos:* Consult, Mead Johnson & Co, 76; Sarah Berliner fel, Am Asn Univ Women, 78-79; mass media sci fel, AAAS, 79; prof staff mem commun sci & tech, US House Rep, 81. *Mem:* Sigma Xi; AAAS; Genetics Soc Am. *Res:* Inheritance of chlorophyll and lamellae; chloroplast function; relationship between membrane structure and function. *Mailing Add:* 700 Drexel Dr Evansville IN 47712

NICKANDER, RODNEY CARL, b Aitkin, Minn, July 5, 38; m 57; c 2. PHARMACOLOGY. *Educ:* SDak State Univ, BS, 60; Purdue Univ, MS, 63, PhD(pharmacol), 64. *Prof Exp:* Pharmacol res assoc, 64-77, head, Dept Immunol & Connective Tissue Res,77-80, DIR IMMUNOL, CONNECTIVE TISSUE & PULMONARY RES, LILLY RES LABS, ELI LILLY & CO, 80- *Res:* Detection and pharmacological evaluation of new anti-inflammatory agents and analgesics; pharmacological role of metabolites. *Mailing Add:* Dept MC 771 Lilly Res Labs Eli Lilly & Co Indianapolis IN 46206

NICKEL, ERNEST HENRY, b Louth, Ont, Aug 31, 25; m 49; c 3. MINERALOGY. *Educ:* McMaster Univ, BSc, 50, MSc, 51; Univ Chicago, PhD(geol), 53. *Prof Exp:* Sci officer, Mines Br, Dept Mines & Tech Surv, 53-59, sr sci officer, 59-65, head mineral sect, Mineral Sci Div, Can Dept Energy, Mines & Resources, 65-71; CHIEF RES SCI DIV MINERAL, COMMONWEALTH SCI & INDUST RES ORGN, AUSTRALIA, 71- *Honors & Awards:* Hawley Award, Mineral Asn Can, 67 & 73. *Mem:* Mineral Asn Can (pres, 69-70); Geol Soc Australia; Australasian Inst Mining & Metall; Australian New Zealand Asn Advan Sci; Mineral Soc Am. *Res:* Determinative and descriptive mineralogy by means of microscopy; x-ray diffraction and crystallography; sulfide weathering; ore mineralogy. *Mailing Add:* Commonwealth Sci & Indust Orgn Div of Mineral Pvt Bag PO Wembly Western Australia 6014 Australia

NICKEL, GEORGE H(ERMAN), b Brawley, Calif, Mar 10, 37; m 63; c 3. PHYSICS, NUCLEAR ENGINEERING. *Educ:* San Diego State Univ, AB, 58; Univ Ill, MS, 60; Univ Calif, Davis, PhD(appl sci & eng), 66. *Prof Exp:* Proj officer physics, Air Force Weapons Lab, 61-70; mil staff mem, Los Alamos Sci Lab, 70-72; proj officer, Air Force Tech Appln Ctr, 72-77; asst prof physics, Air Force Inst Technol, Wright-Patterson AFB, 77-81; STAFF MEM, LOS ALAMOS NAT LAB, LOS ALAMOS, NMEX, 81- *Concurrent Pos:* Adj instr, Univ Albuquerque, 67-69; adj prof, Brevard Community Col, 73-77 & Fla Inst Technol, 73-77; adj asst prof, Wright State Univ, 78-81. *Mem:* Am Asn Physics Teachers. *Res:* Lasers; geophysics; statistical mechanics. *Mailing Add:* 1150 Grinnell Circle Yellow Springs OH 45387

NICKEL, JAMES ALVIN, b Grants Pass, Ore, Sept 27, 25; m 52; c 3. APPLIED MATHEMATICS. *Educ:* Willamette Univ, BA, 49; Ore State Col, MS, 51, PhD(appl math, anal), 57. *Prof Exp:* Asst math, Ore State Col, 49-50; asst appl math, Ind Univ, 51-53, asst math, 53; instr, Willamette Univ, 53-57, asst prof, 57-59; from assoc prof to prof & chmn dept, Oklahoma City Univ, 59-67; sr res mathematician, Dikewood Corp, 67-69, prin res mathematician, 69-70; mgr anal sect, Technol Inc, 70-71; math physicist, Lockheed Electronics Co, 71-72; PROF MATH, UNIV TEX PERMIAN BASIN, 72-, CHMN, DEPT MATH & COMPUT SCI, 79- *Concurrent Pos:* Statistician, State Hwy Dept, Ore, 56-59; consult, Systs Res Ctr, Okla. *Mem:* Am Math Soc; Math Asn Am; Am Statist Asn. *Res:* Systems design and simulation; applied mathematics and statistics. *Mailing Add:* 3942 Monclair Ave Odessa TX 79762

NICKEL, PHILLIP ARNOLD, b Deadwood, SDak, Oct 10, 37; m 59; c 2. PARASITOLOGY, ORNITHOLOGY. *Educ:* Ore State Univ, BS, 62; Kans State Univ, MS, 66, PhD(entom), 69. *Prof Exp:* Asst prof, 69-74, ASSOC PROF BIOL SCI, CALIF LUTHERAN COL, 74- *Concurrent Pos:* Dir, Med Technol Prog, Calif State Univ, Northridge, mem, Health Adv Comt & assoc prof, Dept Biol, 80- *Mem:* Am Inst Biol Sci; Am Asn Biol Teachers; Am Soc Parasitologist; AAAS. *Res:* Mites associated with insects; helminths of bats; medical technology; invertebrate zoology. *Mailing Add:* Dept of Biol Sci Calif Lutheran Col Thousand Oaks CA 91360

NICKEL, VERNON L, b Sask, Can, May 1, 18; US citizen; m 41; c 3. ORTHOPEDIC SURGERY. *Educ:* Loma Linda Univ, MD, 44; Univ Tenn, MSc, 49. *Prof Exp:* Fel orthop surg, Campbell Clin, Memphis, Tenn, 48-49; head orthopedist & chief surg serv, Rancho Los Amigos Hosp, Downey, Calif, 53-64, med dir, 64-69; dir dept orthop surg & rehab, 69-75, prof orthop surg & rehab, Loma Linda Univ, 69-78; adj prof orthop & med, George Washington Univ & dir, Rehab Eng Res & Develop Serv, Vets Admin, 78-80; adj prof surg & rehab, Loma Linda Univ, 69-80; MED DIR, SHARP REHAB CTR, 80-; PROF SURG, ORTHOP & REHAB, UNIV CALIF MED CTR, SAN DIEGO, 80- *Concurrent Pos:* Pvt pract, 50-78; Fulbright lectr, Cairo Univ, 61; clin prof, Univ Southern Calif, 65- & Univ Calif, Irvine-Calif Col Med, 66-78. *Mem:* Am Orthop Asn; Am Acad Orthop Surg; Am Soc Surg Hand; hon mem British Orthop Asn. *Mailing Add:* Rehab Sharp Rehab Ctr 7901 Frost St San Diego CA 92123

NICKELL, CECIL D, b Rochester, Ind, Jan 9, 41; m 62; c 2. PLANT GENETICS, BIOMETRY. *Educ:* Purdue Univ, BS, 63; Mich State Univ, MS, 65, PhD(biomet), 67. *Prof Exp:* Asst instr plant genetics, Mich State Univ, 63-67; asst prof plant breeding & genetics, Kans State Univ, 67-74, assoc prof, 74-79; ASSOC PROF PLANT BREEDING, UNIV ILL, URBANA, 79- *Mem:* Crop Sci Soc Am; Am Soc Agron. *Res:* Statistical studies concerned with evolutionary changes in plant populations under extreme stresses; biometrical application of selection procedures. *Mailing Add:* Dept Agron Turner Hall Univ Ill Urbana IL 61801

NICKELL, LOUIS G, b Little Rock, Ark, July 10, 21; m 42; c 3. PLANT PHYSIOLOGY. *Educ:* Yale Univ, BS, 42, MS, 47, PhD(physiol), 49. *Prof Exp:* Res assoc plant physiol, Brooklyn Bot Garden, 49-51; plant physiologist, Pfizer Co, 51-53, head phytochem lab, 53-61; head dept physiol & biochem, Exp Sta, Hawaiian Sugar Planters Asn, 61-65, asst dir, 65-75; vpres, res div, W R Grace & Co, 75-78; V PRES, RES & DEVELOP, VELSICOL CHEM CORP, 78- *Concurrent Pos:* Responsible scientist, Cell Nutrit Exhibit, Worlds Fair, Brussels, 58; trustee, Hawaiian Bot Gardens Found, 62-65; mem, Gov Adv Comt Sci & Technol, Hawaii, 64-70, chmn, 70-75; mem, State Task Force Energy Policy, Hawaii, 73-75, vchmn, 74-75. *Mem:* Am Soc Plant Physiol (treas, 75-); Bot Soc Am; Am Chem Soc; Soc Develop Biol; Plant Growth Regulator Soc Am (vpes, 80, pres, 81). *Res:* Sugarcane physiology and biochemistry; tissue and cell culture; medicinal and economic botany; antibiotics; plant growth substances; pesticides; research administration; microbiology. *Mailing Add:* Velsicol Chem Corp 341 E Ohio St Chicago IL 60611

NICKELL, WILLIAM EVERETT, b Hazel Green, Ky, July 29, 16; m 42. PHYSICS. *Educ:* Berea Col, BA, 40; Univ Iowa, MS, 43, PhD(physics), 54. *Prof Exp:* Researcher, Univ Iowa, 43-44, res assoc, 44-45, instr physics, 47-51, res assoc, 51-52; from asst prof to prof, SDak State Univ, 53-63; assoc prof, 63-69, PROF PHYSICS & ASTRON, SOUTHERN ILL UNIV, 69- *Mem:* Sigma Xi; Am Phys Soc; Am Asn Physics Teachers. *Res:* Nuclear physics; radio proximity fuze; missile vibrations. *Mailing Add:* Dept of Physics Southern Ill Univ Carbondale IL 62901

NICKELSEN, RICHARD PETER, b Lynbrook, NY, Oct 1, 25; m 50; c 3. STRUCTURAL GEOLOGY. *Educ:* Dartmouth Col, BA, 49; Johns Hopkins Univ, MA, 51, PhD, 53. *Prof Exp:* Asst, Johns Hopkins Univ, 51-53; asst prof geol, Pa State Univ, 53-59; assoc prof, 59-63, chmn dept geol & geog, 59-76, PROF GEOL, BUCKNELL UNIV, 64- *Concurrent Pos:* NATO fel, Norway, 65-66, NSF res grant, 68-69; consult, Amoco Prod Co, 79- *Mem:* AAAS; Geol Soc Am; Soc Econ Paleont & Mineral; Am Geophys Union. *Res:* Genesis of joints and rock cleavage; Appalachian tectonics; regional joint patterns, regional strain variation and stages of deformation; caledonide stratigraphy and tectonics (Norway); ambient environmental parameters of deforming rocks; pressure and temperature of deformation from fluid inclusion studies in syntectonic veins. *Mailing Add:* 432 Pheasant Ridge Rd Lewisburg PA 17837

NICKELSON, RANZELL, II, food microbiology, see previous edition

NICKELSON, ROBERT L(ELAND), b Livingston, Mont, Sept 13, 27; m 52; c 5. CHEMICAL ENGINEERING. *Educ:* Mont State Col, BS, 51, MS, 52; Univ Minn, PhD(chem eng), 57. *Prof Exp:* Asst, Univ Minn, 52-53; from asst prof to assoc prof chem eng, 56-64, PROF CHEM ENG, MONT STATE UNIV, 64- *Mem:* Am Soc Eng Educ; Am Inst Chem Engrs. *Res:* Reverse osmosis; mass transfer in fluid beds; reaction kinetics; application of mathematics to chemical engineering. *Mailing Add:* Col of Eng Mont State Univ Bozeman MT 59717

NICKERSON, DOROTHY, b Boston, Mass, Aug 5, 00. COLOR SCIENCE. *Prof Exp:* Asst, Munsell Res Lab & asst mgr, Munsell Color Co, 21-26; color technologist, USDA, 27-64; consult, 65-74; RETIRED. *Concurrent Pos:* Trustee, Munsell Color Found, 42-79, pres, 73-75; US expert color rendering, Int Comn Illum, 56-67. *Honors & Awards:* Superior Serv Award, USDA, 51; Gold Cert, Am Hort Coun, 57; Godlove Award, Int Soc Color Coun, 61; Distinguished Achievement Award, Instrument Soc Am, 64; Gold Medal, Illum Eng Soc, 70; Deane B Judd-AIC Gold Medal Award, Int Color Asn, 75. *Mem:* AAAS; Optical Soc Am; Int Soc Color Coun (secy, 38-52, pres, 54); Illum Eng Soc. *Res:* Color measurement related to grade standards for agricultural products; colorimetry; color tolerances and small-color-difference specification; color spacing; automatic cotton colorimeter; color-rendering properties of light sources; color-fan chart for horticulture. *Mailing Add:* 4800 Fillmore Ave 450 Alexandria VA 22311

NICKERSON, HELEN KELSALL, b New York, NY, July 2, 18; div; c 1. MATHEMATICS. *Educ:* Vassar Col, BA, 39; Radcliffe Col, MA, 40, PhD(math), 49. *Prof Exp:* From instr to asst prof math & physics, Wheaton Col, Mass, 43-50; res assoc math, Princeton Univ, 51-61; lectr, Douglass Col, 60-61, assoc prof, 61-63, ASSOC PROF MATH, RUTGERS COL, RUTGERS UNIV, 63- *Mem:* Am Math Soc; Math Asn Am; NY Acad Sci. *Res:* Differentiable manifolds. *Mailing Add:* 184 Washington Rd Princeton NJ 08540

NICKERSON, JOHN CHARLES, III, b McMinnville, Tenn, Nov 5, 43; m 65; c 1. PHYSICS. *Educ:* Princeton Univ, BSE, 65; Stanford Univ, MS, 69, PhD(physics), 71. *Prof Exp:* Res asst physics, Stanford Univ, 67-71; asst prof, 71-77, ASSOC PROF PHYSICS, MISS STATE UNIV, 77- *Mem:* Am Phys Soc. *Res:* Relativity theory; teaching methods and approaches; solid state physics-magnetism. *Mailing Add:* Dept of Physics Miss State Univ Mississippi State MS 39762

NICKERSON, JOHN DAVID, b Halifax, NS, Feb 12, 27; m 52; c 2. PHYSICAL CHEMISTRY. *Educ:* Mt Allison Univ, BSc, 48; Dalhousie Univ, MSc, 50; Univ Toronto, PhD(chem), 54. *Prof Exp:* Chemist fatty acid hydrogenation, Fisheries Res Bd Can, 48-50; demonstr, Univ Toronto, 51-53; develop chemist carbon & graphite, Nat Carbon Co, 53-57; prin res chemist, Agr Prod, Int Minerals & Chem Corp, Fla, 57-62; mem staff, Southern Nitrogen Co, Ga, 62-64; mgr chem res, Armour Agr Chem Co, 64-68; dir res & develop, 68-75, DIR DEVELOP & TECH SERV, AGRI CHEM DIV, USS, 75- *Mem:* Am Chem Soc; Chem Inst Can. *Res:* Fatty acid hydrogenation; dielectric constants of low boiling liquids; oxidation of carbon and graphite; alkali resistance of carbon and graphite; fertilizer chemistry and animal feed supplements. *Mailing Add:* USS Agri-Chem PO Box 1685 Atlanta GA 30303

NICKERSON, JOHN LESTER, b Halifax, NS, Oct 8, 03; nat US; m 29. PHYSIOLOGY. *Educ:* Dalhousie Univ, BA, 25, MA, 28; Princeton Univ, PhD(physics), 35. *Prof Exp:* Substitute prof physics & chem, Mem Univ Nfld, 25-26; instr physics, Princeton Univ, 28-31; from asst prof to prof, Mt Allison Univ, 31-39, assoc dean men, 36-39; from asst prof to prof physiol, Col Physicians & Surgeons, Columbia Univ, 39-56; chmn dept physiol, 56-70, dir div biophys, 61-70, from actg dean to dean sch grad & postdoctoral studies, 68-75, PROF PHYSIOL & BIOPHYS, CHICAGO MED SCH-UNIV HEALTH SCI, 56- *Concurrent Pos:* Consult physicist, Enamel & Heating, Ltd, 37-39; sci liaison officer, US Off Naval Res, London, 52-53; responsible investr res contracts, USPHS & US Air Force. *Mem:* Ballistocardiographic Res Soc (pres, 62-65); Am Phys Soc; Am Physiol Soc; Soc Exp Biol & Med; Harvey Soc. *Res:* Radioactivity; vacuum spectroscopy; body fluid status during trauma; ballistocardiography; response of body to mechanical stress; vibration; impact; cardiovascular dynamics. *Mailing Add:* Dept of Physiol Chicago Med Sch-Univ Health Sci Chicago IL 60612

NICKERSON, KENNETH WARWICK, b Attleboro, Mass, Nov 19, 42; m 72; c 2. MICROBIAL BIOCHEMISTRY. *Educ:* Rutgers Univ, BS, 63; Univ Cincinnati, PhD(chem), 69. *Prof Exp:* USPHS fel biophys, Ore State Univ, 69-70, genetics, Univ Wis, 70-71; fel microbial insecticides, Northern Regional Res Lab, Sci & Educ Admin-Agr Res Serv, USDA, Nat Acad Sci/Nat Res Coun, 71-73; fel plant path, 73-75, ASSOC PROF LIFE SCI, UNIV NEBR-LINCOLN, 75- *Concurrent Pos:* NIH res career develop award, Univ Nebr-Lincoln, 79- *Mem:* Am Soc Microbiol; Biophys Soc; Am Soc Biol Chemists; Soc Gen Microbiol. *Res:* Bacillus thuringiensis; microbial insecticides; fungal dimorphism; polyamines; sclerotia. *Mailing Add:* Sch of Life Sci Univ of Nebr Lincoln NE 68588

NICKERSON, MARK, b Montevideo, Minn, Oct 22, 16; Can citizen; m 42; c 3. PHARMACOLOGY, THERAPEUTICS. *Educ:* Linfield Col, AB, 39; Brown Univ, ScM, 41; Johns Hopkins Univ, PhD(embryol), 44; Univ Utah, MD, 50. *Hon Degrees:* DSc, Med Col Wis, 74. *Prof Exp:* Res biochemist, Nat Defense Res Comn, Johns Hopkins Univ, 43-44; instr pharmacol, Col Med, Univ Utah, 44-47, from asst prof to assoc prof, 47-51; assoc prof, Univ Mich, 51-54; prof pharmacol & med res, Fac Med, Univ Man, 54-57, prof pharmacol & therapeut & chmn dept, 57-67; chmn dept pharmacol & therapeut, 67-75, PROF PHARMACOL & THERAPEUT, MCGILL UNIV, 67- *Honors & Awards:* Abel Award, 49; Upjohn Award, 78. *Mem:* Am Soc Pharmacol & Exp Therapeut (pres); Soc Exp Biol & Med; Pharmacol Soc Can (pres); Can Physiol Soc; Royal Soc Can. *Res:* Drugs blocking sympathetic nervous system; cardiovascular and autonomic nervous system physiology and pharmacology; shock; clinical pharmacology. *Mailing Add:* Dept Pharmacol & Therapeut McGill Univ Montreal PQ H3A 2T6 Can

NICKERSON, MAX ALLEN, vertebrate biology, histochemistry, see previous edition

NICKERSON, NORTON HART, b Quincy, Mass, Apr 14, 26; m 54; c 3. PLANT MORPHOLOGY, PLANT ECOLOGY. *Educ:* Univ Mass, BS, 49; Univ Tex, MA, 51; Wash Univ, PhD(bot), 53. *Prof Exp:* Instr bot, Univ Mass, 53-56 & Cornell Univ, 56-58; from asst prof to assoc prof, Wash Univ, 58-63; assoc prof bot, 63-81, PROF ENVIRON STUDIES, TUFTS UNIV, 81- *Concurrent Pos:* Res fel, Calif Inst Technol, 54 & 55; NSF sci fac fel, 58; morphologist, Mo Bot Garden, 58-63; mem Mass Bd Environ Mgt; chmn, Mass Agr Lands Preserv Comt, Hazardous Waste Facil Site Safety Coun. *Mem:* AAAS; Soc Trop Ecol; Soc Study Evolution; Bot Soc Am; Ecol Soc Am. *Res:* ethnobotany; conservation; ecology of wetlands and coasts; mangroves. *Mailing Add:* Dept Biol Tufts Univ Medford MA 02155

NICKERSON, PETER AYERS, b Hyannis, Mass, Feb 19, 41. PATHOLOGY, ENDOCRINOLOGY. *Educ:* Brown Univ, AB, 63; Clark Univ, MA, 65, PhD(biol), 68. *Prof Exp:* Res instr, 67-69, res asst prof, 69-70, asst prof, 70-74, assoc prof, 74-80, PROF PATH, STATE UNIV NY BUFFALO, 80- *Mem:* Am Soc Cell Biol; Endocrine Soc; Am Soc Exp Path; Electron Micros Soc Am; Am Soc Zool. *Res:* Structure and function of the adrenal cortex; adrenal ultrastructure; adrenocorticotropic hormone secreting cell; transplantable pituitary tumor, hypertension and the adrenal cortex; gerbil adrenal cortex; oxygen toxicity and lung. *Mailing Add:* Dept of Path State Univ of NY Buffalo NY 14214

NICKERSON, ROBERT FLETCHER, b Stoneham, Mass, Mar 25, 30; m 60; c 1. COMPUTER SCIENCES, TECHNICAL MANAGEMENT. *Educ:* Tufts Univ, BS, 52, MS, 53; Univ Calif, PhD(chem), 58. *Prof Exp:* Asst chem, Tufts Univ, 52-53; asst, Univ Calif, 53-58, chemist, Lawrence Livermore Lab, 58-71; comput analyst, Calif Inst Technol, 72-81; MGR SYSTS DEVELOP, SIERRA GEOPHYSICS, INC, 81- *Res:* Small computer applications. *Mailing Add:* Sierra Geophysics Inc 15446 Bell-Red Rd Suite 400 Redmond WA 98052

NICKESON, RICHARD L, horticulture, see previous edition

NICKLAS, ROBERT BRUCE, b Lakewood, Ohio, May 29, 32; m 60. CELL BIOLOGY. *Educ:* Bowling Green State Univ, BA, 54; Columbia Univ, MA, 56, PhD(zool), 58. *Prof Exp:* From instr to asst prof zool, Yale Univ, 58-64, fel sci, 63-64, assoc prof zool, 64-65; assoc prof, 65-71, PROF ZOOL, DUKE UNIV, 71- *Concurrent Pos:* Fel J S Guggenheim Found, Max Planck Inst, Tobingen, Ger, 72-73; mem exec subcomt, Adv Comt Physiol, Cellular & Molecular Biol, NSF, 79. *Mem:* Fel AAAS; Am Soc Cell Biol; Am Soc Zool; Genetics Soc Am; Am Soc Naturalists. *Res:* Cell biology; chromosome movement in mitosis; evolution of chromosome cycles; developmental cytology. *Mailing Add:* Dept Zool Duke Univ Durham NC 27706

NICKLE, DAVID ALLAN, b Portland, Ore, May 18, 44; m 74; c 3. SYSTEMATIC ENTOMOLOGY. *Educ:* Temple Univ, BA, 70; Univ Fla, MS, 73, PhD(entom), 76. *Prof Exp:* Res scientist insect attractants, behav & basic biol, Res Lab, 76-79, RES ENTOMOLOGIST, SYST ENTOM LAB, USDA, 79- *Concurrent Pos:* Res scientist stored prod entom, Univ Fla, 76-79. *Honors & Awards:* Bailey Award, Am Peanut Res & Educ Asn, 79. *Mem:* Soc Syst Zool (treas, 80-); Entom Soc Am; Sigma Xi. *Res:* Systematics and acoustic behavior of Tettigoniidae; systematics of Blattaria and Isoptera. *Mailing Add:* NHB 168 Syst Entom Lab USDA c/o Nat Mus Natural Hist Smithsonian Inst Washington DC 20560

NICKLE, WILLIAM R, b Bridgeport, Conn, July 20, 35; m 64. NEMATOLOGY. *Educ:* State Univ NY Col Forestry, Syracuse, BS, 56; Univ Idaho, MS, 58; Univ Calif, PhD(nematol), 63. *Prof Exp:* Res officer entomophilic nematodes, Res Inst, Can Dept Agr, 62-65; NEMATOLOGIST, NEMATOL INVEST, CROPS RES DIV, AGR RES SERV, USDA, 65- *Mem:* Soc Nematol; Soc Syst Zool; Entom Soc Can. *Res:* Taxonomy, morphology and biology of plant parasitic, insect parasitic and mycophagus nematodes. *Mailing Add:* 11201 Montgomery Rd Beltsville MD 20705

NICKLES, ROBERT JEROME, b Madison, Wis, Mar 22, 40; m 63; c 1. NUCLEAR PHYSICS, MEDICAL PHYSICS. *Educ:* Univ Wis, BS, 62, PhD(nuclear physics), 68; Univ Sao Paulo, MS, 67. *Prof Exp:* Res assoc nuclear physics, Sch Med, Univ Wis-Madison, 68-69; James A Picker Found res fel, Niels Bohr Inst, Copenhagen Univ, 69-71; James A Picker Found res fel med physics, 71-73, asst prof radiol, 73-77, ASSOC PROF RADIOL, SCH MED, UNIV WIS-MADISON, 77- *Mem:* Am Phys Soc. *Res:* Study of heavy ion transfer reactions; short-lived isotope production utilizing the helium-jet technique; development of an intense neutron source for cancer therapy. *Mailing Add:* Dept of Radiol & Med Physics Univ of Wis Sch of Med Madison WI 53706

NICKLIN, ROBERT CLAIR, b Gordon, Nebr, May 23, 36; m 58; c 2. SOLID STATE PHYSICS. *Educ:* SDak Sch Mines & Technol, BS, 58; Iowa State Univ, PhD(physics), 67. *Prof Exp:* Assoc prof physics, 67-74, chmn dept, 74-77, PHYSICS, APPALACHIAN STATE UNIV, 74- *Mem:* AAAS; Am Phys Soc; Am Asn Physics Teachers. *Res:* Electron spin resonance; studies of glasses; organic crystals. *Mailing Add:* Dept of Physics Appalachian State Univ Boone NC 28608

NICKLOW, CLARK W, horticulture, see previous edition

NICKLOW, ROBERT MERLE, b St Petersburg, Fla, Oct 11, 36; m 58; c 3. SOLID STATE PHYSICS. *Educ:* Ga Inst Technol, BS, 58, MS, 60, PhD(x-ray diffraction), 64. *Prof Exp:* Asst res physicist, Eng Exp Sta, Ga Inst Technol, 63; PHYSICIST, OAK RIDGE NAT LAB, 63- *Honors & Awards:* Sidhu Award, 68. *Mem:* Fel Am Phys Soc; Am Crystallog Asn. *Res:* Crystal physics; lattice dynamics; neutron and x-ray diffraction; study of lattice dynamics and spin waves by means of coherent inelastic neutron scattering. *Mailing Add:* Solid State Div Oak Ridge Nat Lab PO Box X Oak Ridge TN 37830

NICKOL, BRENT BONNER, b Agosta, Ohio, June 22, 40; m 64; c 2. PARASITOLOGY. *Educ:* Col Wooster, BA, 62; La State Univ, MS, 63, PhD(zool), 66. *Prof Exp:* From asst prof to assoc prof, 66-75, PROF ZOOL, UNIV NEBR, LINCOLN, 75- *Mem:* Wildlife Dis Asn; Am Soc Parasitol. *Res:* Taxonomy, morphology, ecology and host-parasite relationships of the Acanthocephala. *Mailing Add:* Sch of Life Sci Univ of Nebr Lincoln NE 68588

NICKOLLS, JOHN RICHARD, b Easton, Pa, Mar 6, 50. SIGNAL PROCESSING, COMPUTER SCIENCE. *Educ:* Univ Ill, BS, 72; Stanford Univ, MS, 74, PhD(elec eng), 77. *Prof Exp:* Res assoc speech compression, Info Syst Lab, Stanford Univ, 77; MEM RES STAFF IMAGE PROCESSING, ADVAN TECHNOL DIV, AMPEX CORP, 77- *Mem:* Asn Comput Mach; Inst Elec & Electronics Engrs. *Res:* Digital signal processing; image processing and compression; language and compiler design; computer architecture. *Mailing Add:* Advan Technol Div 401 Broadway Redwood City CA 94063

NICKOLLS, KENNETH RICHARD, b Kansas City, Mo, Jan 12, 22; m 48; c 3. CHEMICAL ENGINEERING, POLYMER ENGINEERING. *Educ:* Univ Ill, BS, 43; Univ Mich, MS, 48. *Prof Exp:* Res assoc chem warfare protective devices, Mass Inst Technol-Chem Warfare Serv, 43-44; group leader res separations, GAF Corp, 48-52; FEL POLYMER ENG, MONSANTO PLASTICS & RESINS CO, 52- *Mem:* AAAS; Am Inst Chem Engrs. *Res:* Polymer film and foam process engineering; metrology; precision machining and grinding; electrolytic and electroless plating processes. *Mailing Add:* 101 Granby St Monsanto Co Bloomfield CT 06002

NICKOLS, G ALLEN, b Springfield, Ill, Apr 9, 51; m 71; c 2. PHARMACOLOGY. *Educ:* Univ Mo, BA, 73, Sch Med, PhD(pharmacol), 77. *Prof Exp:* Fel, pharmacol, Univ Va Sch Med, 77-80; ASST PROF PHARMACOL, SOUTHERN ILL UNIV SCH MED, 80- *Res:* Regulation of cellular cyclic adenosine monophosphate metabolism, endothelial and vascular smooth muscle pharmacology, calcium metabolism and parathyroid hormone-vitamin D interrelationships. *Mailing Add:* Dept Pharmacol Southern Ill Univ Sch Med PO Box 3926 Springfield IL 62708

NICKOLS, NORRIS ALLAN, b Ellensburg, Wash, July 8, 28; m 58; c 2. NUCLEAR PHYSICS. *Educ:* Cent Wash Col Educ, BA, 52; Univ Calif, Berkeley, PhD(physics), 60. *Prof Exp:* Physicist, Lawrence Radiation Lab, Univ Calif, 59-61; res scientist, Lockheed Calif Co, 61-63; res specialist, Space & Info Systs Div, NAm Aviation, Inc, 63-67; STAFF MEM, LOS ALAMOS NAT LAB, 68- *Mem:* Am Phys Soc. *Res:* High energy physics strange particles; high energy muon scattering; hyperfragments; nuclear weapons. *Mailing Add:* Los Alamos Nat Lab Los Alamos NM 87545

NICKON, ALEX, b Poland, Oct 6, 27; nat US; m 50; c 3. ORGANIC CHEMISTRY. *Educ:* Univ Alta, BSc, 49; Harvard Univ, MA, 51, PhD(chem), 53. *Prof Exp:* Vis lectr org chem, Bryn Mawr Col, 53; Nat Res Coun Can fel, Birkbeck Col, London, 53-54 & Univ Ottawa, Ont, 54-55; from asst prof to prof, 55-75, VERNON K KRIEBLE PROF CHEM, JOHNS HOPKINS UNIV, 75- *Concurrent Pos:* NSF sr fel, Imp Col, London, 63-64 & Univ Munich, 71-72; sr ed, J Org Chem, 65-71; Am exec ed, Tetrahedron Reports, 78- *Mem:* Am Chem Soc; The Chem Soc. *Res:* Carbanions and carbonium ions; stereochemistry; reaction mechanisms; syntheses and structures of natural products; biologically important reactions. *Mailing Add:* Dept of Chem Johns Hopkins Univ Baltimore MD 21218

NICKS, ORAN WESLEY, b Eldorado, Tex, Feb 2, 25; m 55; c 4. RESEARCH ADMINISTRATION, AERONAUTICS. *Educ:* Univ Okla, BS, 48. *Prof Exp:* Aeronaut engr, NAm Aviation, Inc, Calif, 48-58; proj engr, Chance-Vought Aircraft, Inc, Tex, 58-60; head lunar flight systs, NASA, Washington, DC, 60-61, dir, Lunar & Planetary Progs, Langeley Res Ctr, 61-67, dep assoc adminr space sci & appln, 67-70, acting assoc adminr advan res & technol, 70, dep dir, 70-80; RES ENGR, TEX A&M UNIV, 80- *Honors & Awards:* Except Serv Medal, NASA, 64, Outstanding Leadership Medal, 65, Distinguished Serv Medal, 71. *Mem:* Fel Am Astronaut Soc; Am Inst Aeronaut & Astronaut. *Res:* Aerodynamic research on total energy sensors for aircraft; applications of laminar flow technologies to improve wing efficiencies; automated spacecraft for scientific exploration of planets. *Mailing Add:* Aero Space Eng Tex A&M Univ College Station TX 77843

NICKSON, JAMES JOSEPH, b Portland, Ore, Dec 31, 15; m 39, 67; c 3. RADIOLOGY. *Educ:* Univ Wash, BS, 36; Johns Hopkins Univ, MD, 40. *Prof Exp:* Intern med, Baltimore City Hosp, 40-41; asst surgeon, USPHS Tumor Clin, Baltimore Marine Hosp, 41-42; physician & assoc, Metall Lab, Univ Chicago, 42-46; sr physician, Argonne Nat Lab, 46-47; assoc, Sloan-Kettering Inst, 47-50, mem, 51-65, dir radiation ther dept, Mem Hosp, 50-65; chmn dept radiation ther, Michael Reese Hosp & Med Ctr & mem, Med Res Inst, 65-72; PROF RADIATION ONCOL & CHMN DEPT, UNIV TENN CTR HEALTH SCI, 72-, DIR, MEMPHIS REGIONAL CANCER CTR, 74- *Concurrent Pos:* Am Cancer Soc & Nat Res Coun fel, Sloan-Kettering Inst, 47-48 & Royal Cancer Hosp, London, 48-49; prof radiol, Sloan-Kettering Div, Cornell Univ, 51-55, prof, Med Col, 55-65. *Mem:* Radiation Res Soc; Radiol Soc NAm; Am Radium Soc; AMA; fel Am Col Radiol. *Res:* Oncology; radiation therapy; radiobiology. *Mailing Add:* Memphis Regional Cancer Ctr Univ Tenn Ctr for Health Sci Memphis TN 38163

NICKUM, JOHN GERALD, b Rochester, Minn, Aug 7, 35; m 55; c 4. ZOOLOGY, CONSERVATION. *Educ:* Mankato State Col, BSc, 57; Univ SDak, MA, 61; Univ Southern Ill, PhD(zool), 66. *Prof Exp:* Teacher high sch, Minn, 57-59, jr high sch, 59-60; asst prof biol, Western Ky State Col, 65-66; asst prof wildlife mgt, SDak State Univ, 66-71, assoc prof wildlife & fisheries, 71-73; asst leader, NY Coop Fishery Res Unit, 73-77, leader, 77-80, asst prof natural resources, Cornell Univ, 73-80, dir aquaculture prog, 74-80; LEADER, IOWA COOP FISHERY RES UNIT & ASSOC PROF ANIMAL ECOL, IOWA STATE UNIV, 80- *Mem:* Am Fisheries Soc. *Res:* Aquaculture; application of aquaculture in the solution of recreational and environmental problems; warm-water fish management; pond management; urban recreational fisheries; use of wastewater in aquaculture; culture of cool-water fishes; ecology and management of large river systems and culture of larval fishes. *Mailing Add:* Dept Animal Ecol Sci Hall II Iowa State Univ Ames IA 50011

NICO, WILLIAM RAYMOND, b Aurora, Ill, Mar 23, 40; m 67; c 3. MATHEMATICS. *Educ:* Loyola Univ, Ill, BS, 62; Univ Calif, Berkeley, MA, 64, PhD(math), 66. *Prof Exp:* Res assoc eng mech, Stanford Univ, 66-67; asst prof, 67-73, assoc prof, 73-80, PROF MATH, TULANE UNIV LA, 80- *Mem:* Am Math Soc; Math Asn Am. *Res:* Computational complexity; secure communication protocals; programming languages; automata; semigroups; transformation monoids, extension theory of monoids and categories; homological algebra. *Mailing Add:* Dept of Math Tulane Univ of La New Orleans LA 70118

NICODEMUS, DAVID BOWMAN, b Kobe, Japan, July 1, 16; US citizen; m 48. PHYSICS. *Educ:* DePauw Univ, AB, 37; Stanford Univ, PhD(physics), 46. *Prof Exp:* Asst, Stanford Univ, 37-41, asst physicist, Off Sci Res & Develop proj, 42-43; physicist, Los Alamos Sci Lab, Calif, 43-46; instr physics, Stanford Univ, 46-49, actg asst prof, 49-50; from asst prof to assoc prof, 50-63, asst dean sch sci, 62-65, actg dean, 65-66, PROF PHYSICS, ORE STATE UNIV, 63-, DEAN FAC, 66- *Concurrent Pos:* Consult, Los Alamos Sci Lab, 56-57. *Res:* X-rays; nuclear physics. *Mailing Add:* Ore State Univ Corvallis OR 97331

NICODEMUS, FRED(ERICK) E(DWIN), b Osaka, Japan, July 25, 11; US citizen; m 35. OPTICAL PHYSICS. *Educ:* Reed Col, AB, 34. *Prof Exp:* Radio engr & physicist, Air Force Cambridge Res Labs, 46-55; advan develop engr & eng specialist, Sylvania Electronic Defense Labs, Gen Tel & Electronics Corp, Calif, 55-69; physicist, Michelson Lab, US Naval Weapons Ctr, 69-74; physicist, Nat Bur Standards, 74-81; NAT BUR STANDARDS PRIN INVESTR, CATHOLIC UNIV AM, 81- *Concurrent Pos:* Mem, Nat Acad Sci-Nat Acad Eng-Nat Res Coun adv panel to heat div, Nat Bur Standards & liaison to ad hoc panel on radiometry & photom, 70-74; consult, Int Tech Comt Photom & Radiometry, Int Comn Illum, 72-; ed self-study manual optical radiation measurements, Nat Bur Standards, 74- *Mem:* Fel Optical Soc Am; Sigma Xi; Int Comn Illum; fel Soc Photo-Optical Instrumentation Engrs. *Res:* Clarification of basic radiometric relations, definitions, and nomenclature. *Mailing Add:* A221 Physics Bldg Nat Bur of Standards Washington DC 20234

NICOL, CHARLES ALBERT, b Ft Worth, Tex, Apr 24, 25; m 56; c 1. MATHEMATICS. *Educ:* Univ Tex, PhD(math), 54. *Prof Exp:* Instr math, Univ Tex, 54-55; asst prof, Ill Inst Technol, 55-59 & Univ Okla, 59-60; asst head dept math & comp sci, 73-76, ASSOC PROF MATH, UNIV SC, 60- *Mem:* AAAS; Am Math Soc; Math Asn Am. *Res:* Number theory; algebra and combinatorial problems. *Mailing Add:* Dept of Math Univ of SC Columbia SC 29208

NICOL, DAVID, b Ottawa, Ont, Aug 16, 15; nat US; m 47; c 1. PALEONTOLOGY. *Educ:* Tex Christian Univ, BA, 37, MS, 39; Stanford Univ, MA, 43, PhD(paleont), 47. *Prof Exp:* Asst prof geol, Univ Houston, 47-48; assoc cur Mesozoic & Cenozoic inverts, US Nat Mus, 48-58; assoc prof geol, Southern Ill Univ, 58-64; assoc prof, 65-75, PROF GEOL, UNIV FLA, 75- *Mem:* Paleont Soc; Geol Soc Am; Soc Syst Zool; Soc Study Evolution; Am Asn Petrol Geol. *Res:* Pelecypods. *Mailing Add:* PO Box 14376 University Sta Gainesville FL 32604

NICOL, JAMES, b Dundee, Scotland, Aug 24, 21; nat US; m 48. ENGINEERING PHYSICS, LOW TEMPERATURE PHYSICS. *Educ:* St Andrews Univ, BSc, 46 & 48; Union Col, MS, 50; Ohio State Univ, PhD(physics), 52. *Prof Exp:* Instr physics, Ohio State Univ, 52-53; from asst prof to assoc prof, Amherst Col, 53-57; physicist, Arthur D Little, Inc, 57-62; dir res & vpres, Cryonetics Corp, 62-64; PHYSICIST, ARTHUR D LITTLE, INC, 64-, VPRES, 77- *Mem:* Am Phys Soc. *Res:* Phenomena below one degree absolute; thermal conductivity and electron tunneling in superconductors; electric power transmission; geomagnetism; underwater acoustic transmission. *Mailing Add:* 37 Miller Hill Rd Dover MA 02030

NICOL, JOSEPH ARTHUR COLIN, b Toronto, Ont, Dec 5, 15; m 41; c 1. ZOOLOGY, MARINE BIOLOGY. *Educ:* McGill Univ, BSc, 38; Univ Western Ont, MA, 40; Oxford Univ, DPhil(zool), 47, DSc(zool), 61. *Prof Exp:* Asst prof zool, Univ BC, 47-49; exp zoologist, Marine Biol Asn UK, 49-66; vis prof, 66-67, PROF ZOOL, MARINE SCI INST, UNIV TEX, 67- *Concurrent Pos:* Guggenheim fel, 53-54. *Mem:* Marine Biol Asn UK; fel Royal Soc. *Res:* Comparative physiology and neurology; bioluminescence; pigments of animals; vision, eye structure, photomechanical responses; animal camouflage; vision in animals; oil pollution, effects on animals. *Mailing Add:* Marine Sci Inst Univ of Tex Austin TX 78712

NICOL, MALCOLM FOERTNER, b New York, NY, Sept 13, 39; m 63; c 3. CHEMICAL PHYSICS. *Educ:* Amherst Col, BA, 60; Univ Calif, Berkeley, PhD(chem), 63. *Prof Exp:* Res asst, 63-64, from actg asst prof to assoc prof, 65-75, PROF CHEM, UNIV CALIF, LOS ANGELES, 75- *Concurrent Pos:* Gastprof, Univ G H Paduborn, WGer, 79; assoc ed, J Phys Chem, 80- *Mem:* Am Chem Soc. *Res:* Spectroscopy, structure and bonding in solids and macromolecules under extreme conditions of pressures; temperature and time. *Mailing Add:* Dept of Chem Univ of Calif Los Angeles CA 90024

NICOL, SUSAN ELIZABETH, b New York, NY, Apr 30, 41. NEUROCHEMISTRY, HUMAN GENETICS. *Educ:* Mt Holyoke Col, BA, 62; Columbia Univ, MA, 66; Univ Minn, PhD(behav genetics), 72. *Prof Exp:* Asst res scientist med genetics, NY State Psychiat Inst, 64-67; fel pharmacol, Univ Minn, 72-74; Nat Inst Arthritis, Metab & Digestive Dis fel endocrinol extramural prog, 74-75; res fel pharmacol, Univ Minn, 75-76; asst prof psychiat, Univ Minn, St Paul-Ramset Med Ctr, 76-80; INTERN, CLIN PSYCHOL, HENNEPIN COUNTY MED CTR, IN, 81- *Concurrent Pos:* Prin investr NIMH grant, 77-80. *Res:* Biological psychiatry; human biochemical genetics; hormone action; cyclic nucleotides; clinical psychology. *Mailing Add:* Hennepin Coun Med Ctr 701 Park Ave Minneapolis MN 55415

NICOLAENKO, BASIL, b Paris, France, Mar 23, 42; US citizen. MATHEMATICS. *Educ:* Univ Paris, Lic es sci, 65; Univ Mich, PhD(math), 68. *Prof Exp:* Staff assoc appl sci, Brookhaven Nat Lab, 68-69; prof math, Courant Inst Math Sci, NY Univ, 69-74; staff scientist, 74-81, PROF MATH, LOS ALAMOS NAT LAB, 81- *Concurrent Pos:* Prof math, Univ Paris-Orsay, France, 77-78. *Mem:* Am Math Soc; Soc Math Francaise; Soc Indust & Appl Math. *Res:* Nonlinear functional analysis and applications. *Mailing Add:* Los Alamos Sci Lab Group T-7 Math Anal Los Alamos NM 87545

NICOLAI, LLOYD A(RTHUR), chemical engineering, see previous edition

NICOLAI, VAN OLIN, b Barrington, Ill, Jan 18, 24; m 55. OPTICAL PHYSICS, LASERS. *Educ:* Univ Ill, BS, 49, MS, 51, PhD(physics), 54. *Prof Exp:* Res assoc physics, Univ Ill, 54-55; asst prof, Univ NDak, 55-57; asst prof, Southern Ill Univ, 57-59; TECH ADV PHYSICS, OFF NAVAL RES, 60- *Mem:* Am Phys Soc. *Res:* Optical properties of solids, laser applications and surface physics. *Mailing Add:* Off Naval Res Code 421 Arlington VA 22217

NICOLAIDES, ERNEST D, b Monmouth, Ill, Sept 11, 24; m 51; c 3. ORGANIC CHEMISTRY. *Educ:* Monmouth Col, BS, 48; Univ Ill, MS, 49, PhD(chem), 52. *Prof Exp:* Assoc res chemist, 51-59, sr res chemist, 59-75, sr res scientist, Parke, Davis & Co, 75-77, SR RES ASSOC, PARKE DAVIS PHARMACEUT DIV, WARNER LAMBERT CO, ANN ARBOR, 77- *Res:* Synthesis of organic compounds; natural products; amino acids; peptides; proteins. *Mailing Add:* Chem Dept Parke Davis & Co Ann Arbor MI 48105

NICOLAIDES, JOHN DUDLEY, b Washington, DC, Feb 13, 23; m 45; c 1. AERODYNAMICS. *Educ:* Lehigh Univ, BA, 46; Johns Hopkins Univ, MSE, 53; Cath Univ Am, PhD, 63. *Prof Exp:* Chief aerodynamicist, Proj Dragonfly, Gen Elec Co, 46-48; aeronaut res scientist, Ballistic Res Lab, US Army Ord Dept, 48-53; chief exterior ballistician, US Naval Bur Ord, 53-56, asst aerodyn, hydrodyn & ballistics, 56-58, sci adv astronaut, 58-59, tech dir naval astronaut, US Bur Naval Weapons, 59-61; dir prog rev & resources mgt, Off Space Sci & Applns, NASA, 61-62, spec asst to assoc adminr space sci & applns, 62-64; prof aerospace eng & chmn dept, Univ Notre Dame, 64-74; head, Dept Aeronaut Eng, 75-80, PROF AERONAUT & MECH ENG, CALIF POLYTECH STATE UNIV, 80- *Concurrent Pos:* Lectr, Univ Md, 58-64 & Cath Univ Am, 59-64; aerospace consult, Govt & Indust, 64-; pres, AERO, 69- *Mem:* Sigma Xi; assoc fel Am Inst Aeronaut & Astronaut. *Res:* Aerodynamics; space sciences; ballistics; hydrodynamics. *Mailing Add:* 2048 Skylark Lane San Luis Obispo CA 93401

NICOLAISEN, B(ERNARD) H(ENRY), b Cleveland, Ohio, Nov 12, 20; m 51; c 3. CHEMICAL ENGINEERING. *Educ:* Case Inst Technol, BS, 42, MS, 47. *Prof Exp:* Jr chem engr eng res, Monsanto Chem Co, 42-44; asst org chem, Case Inst Technol, 44-45, 46-47 & C F Prutton Assocs, 48; chem engr eng res, Mathieson Chem Corp, 48-50, asst mgr eng develop, 50-53, asst dir eng res, 53-54, asst dir res & develop, Chem Div, Olin Mathieson Chem Corp, 54-60, dir develop, 60-65, tech asst to vpres mfg, 65-66, dir process eng, 66-70, mgr automotive & org prod, 70-71, sr tech adv, 72-73, mgr process technol, 74-78, DIR ADVAN TECHNOL, OLIN CORP, 78- *Mem:* Am Inst Chem Engrs. *Res:* Organic chemical research and chemical process development. *Mailing Add:* 16410 Shady Elms Dr Houston TX 77059

NICOLAS, KENNETH ROBERT, solar physics, plasma spectroscopy, see previous edition

NICOLETTE, JOHN ANTHONY, b Chicago, Ill, Apr 2, 35; m 62; c 2. PHYSIOLOGY, ENDOCRINOLOGY. *Educ:* Dartmouth Univ, AB, 56; Univ Ill, MS, 61, PhD(physiol), 63. *Prof Exp:* USPHS fel, Nat Cancer Inst, 63-66; asst prof biol sci, 66-71, asst dean grad col, 71-73, ASSOC PROF BIOL SCI, UNIV ILL, CHICAGO CIRCLE, 71-, ASST DEAN, COL LIBERAL ARTS & SCI, 80- *Res:* Biochemical mechanism of estrogen action. *Mailing Add:* Dept of Biol Sci Univ of Ill at Chicago Circle Chicago IL 60680

NICOLI, MIRIAM ZIEGLER, see Ziegler, Miriam Mary

NICOLL, CHARLES S, b Toronto, Ont, Apr 11, 37; US citizen; m 75; c 3. PHYSIOLOGY, ENDOCRINOLOGY. *Educ:* Mich State Univ, BS, 58, MS, 60, PhD(physiol), 62. *Prof Exp:* Res zoologist, Univ Calif, Berkeley, 62, Am Cancer Soc fel endocrine-tumor probs, 62-64; staff fel tumor-endocrinol, Nat Cancer Inst, 64-66; from asst prof to assoc prof physiol, 66-74, PROF PHYSIOL, UNIV CALIF, BERKELEY, 74- *Mem:* Am Cancer Soc; Am Soc Zool; Endocrine Soc; Am Physiol Soc. *Res:* Mammary and pituitary physiology; comparative aspects of prolactin physiology; growth regulation. *Mailing Add:* Dept of Physiol & Anat Univ of Calif Berkeley CA 94720

NICOLL, JEFFREY FANCHER, b Washington, DC, Feb 25, 48; m 70; c 2. CONDENSED MATTER PHYSICS. *Educ:* Mass Inst Technol, BS(elec eng), BS(physics) & BS(math), 70, PhD(physics), 75. *Prof Exp:* Res asst physics, Ctr Mat Sci & Eng, Mass Inst Technol, 72-76, res assoc, Ctr Theoret Physics, 76-78; VIS ASST PROF PHYSICS, INST PHYS SCI & TECHNOL, UNIV MD, COLLEGE PARK, 78- *Mem:* Am Phys Soc. *Res:* Phase transitions; renormalization-group; cosmology. *Mailing Add:* Inst for Phys Sci & Technol Univ of Md College Park MD 20742

NICOLL, ROGER ANDREW, b Camden, NJ, Jan 15, 41; m 70. NEUROPHYSIOLOGY, NEUROPHARMACOLOGY. *Educ:* Lawrence Univ, BA, 63; Univ Rochester, MD, 68. *Prof Exp:* Intern med, Univ Chicago, 68-69; res assoc neurophysiol, NIMH, 69-73; assoc prof, 77-80, PROF PHARMACOL & PHYSIOL, UNIV CALIF, SAN FRANCISCO, 80- *Res:* Electrophysiology and pharmacology of nemonal circuits in vertebrate central nervous system; mechanisms of general anesthesia; neuropharmacology of presynaptic and postsynaptic inhibition in the central nervous system. *Mailing Add:* Dept Pharmacol 513 Parnassus Ave San Francisco CA 94143

NICOLLE, FRANCOIS MARCEL ANDRE, b Nancy, France, Feb 25, 37; Can citizen; m 64; c 2. CHEMISTRY, POLLUTION CONTROL. *Educ:* Advan Nat Sch Agr & Food Indust, Paris, biochem engr, 61. *Prof Exp:* Indust engr, Pernod, France, 61-62; res engr, Int Cellulose Res Ltd, 64-73, sr res engr, CIP Res Ltd, 73-76, res assoc, 76-79, ASST MGR PROCESS DEVELOP, CIP RES LTD, CIP & INT PAPER, 79- *Honors & Awards:* Douglas Jones Award, Can Pulp & Paper Asn, 74. *Mem:* Can Pulp & Paper Asn; Chem Inst Can; Can Soc Chem Eng; Asn Prof Engrs Ont. *Res:* Pulping; bleaching; by-products; pollution control involving biological treatment of newsprint and sulfite mills waste water; water and energy conservation by countercurrent washing during bleaching and water-reuse; air pollution. *Mailing Add:* CIP Res Ltd 179 Main St W Hawkesbury ON K6A 2H4 Can

NICOLLS, KEN E, b Albuquerque, NMex, Nov 28, 35; m 64; c 3. ANATOMY, BOISTATISTICS. *Educ:* Colo State Univ, BS, 59, MS, 61, PhD(anat), 69. *Prof Exp:* Res asst wildlife mgt, Colo Game & Fish Dept, 61-62; range conservationist, Worland Dist, Bur Land Mgt, 63-64; asst prof anat, Sch Med, Univ NDak, 69-76, mem fac anat, 69-76; fel, Cardiovascular Ctr, Col Med Univ Iowa, 76-78; asst prof, 78-80, ASSOC PROF ANAT, NORTHERN ARIZ UNIV SCH HEALTH PROFESSORS, 80- *Concurrent Pos:* NSF fac res grant, Univ NDak, 70, 73-76, NIH instnl res grant, Sch Med, 70-71, 74-76. *Mem:* Am Asn Anatomists. *Res:* Mechanisms of action associated with interrelationships of light, especially photoperiod and intensity; morphophysiology of endocrine organs, particularly pituitary gland and gonads; animal age; body growth and antler growth of deer. *Mailing Add:* Dept Anat & Physiol Northern Ariz Univ Sch Health Professors Flagstaff AZ 86011

NICOLOFF, DEMETRE M, b Lorain, Ohio, Aug 31, 33; m; c 3. CARDIOVASCULAR SURGERY, BIOENGINEERING. *Educ:* Ohio State Univ, BA, 54, MD, 57; Univ Minn, PhD(surg), 65, PhD(physiol), 67. *Prof Exp:* Instr surg, Univ Minn, 64-65; staff surgeon, Vet Admin Hosp, 65-69; asst prof surg, Univ Minn Hosps, Minneapolis, 69-71, assoc prof, 71-79. *Mem:* Am Med Asn; Soc Surg Alimentary Tract; Am Col Surg; Asn Acad Surg; Soc Thoracic Surg. *Mailing Add:* Dept of Surg Univ of Minn Hosps Minneapolis MN 55455

NICOLOSI, GREGORY RALPH, b Toledo, Ohio, Sept 8, 43; m 69. PHYSIOLOGY. *Educ:* Mich State Univ, BS, 65; Ohio State Univ, PhD(physiol), 71. *Prof Exp:* Instr anat & physiol, Ohio Northern Univ, 69-70; asst prof physiol, Col Med, Ohio State Univ, 71-72; asst prof, 72-77, ASSOC PROF PHYSIOL & ASSOC DEAN, COL MED, UNIV SOUTH FLA, 77- *Mem:* Am Physiol Soc; Biophys Soc. *Res:* Cardiovascular physiology; hemodynamics; spinal cord injury. *Mailing Add:* Dept Physiol Col Med Univ South Fla Tampa FL 33620

NICOLSON, MARGERY O'NEAL, b Pasadena, Calif, Mar 9, 31; m 61. BIOCHEMISTRY. *Educ:* Stanford Univ, BA, 52, MS, 54; Baylor Univ, PhD(biochem), 60. *Prof Exp:* Fel biochem, M D Anderson Hosp & Tumor Inst, Univ Tex, 60-62; res fel biol, Calif Inst Technol, 62-65; asst prof pediat, 65-72, ASSOC PROF PEDIAT & BIOCHEM, SCH MED, UNIV SOUTHERN CALIF, 72-; ASST PROF PEDIAT, CHILDREN'S HOSP LOS ANGELES, 65- *Concurrent Pos:* Am Cancer Soc fel, 62-64. *Mem:* AAAS; Am Asn Cancer Res; Brit Biochem Soc. *Res:* Biochemistry of RNA tumor viruses and human adenoviruses. *Mailing Add:* Children's Hosp PO Box 54700 Terminal Annex Los Angeles CA 90054

NICOLSON, PAUL CLEMENT, b Brooklyn, NY, June 3, 38; m 64; c 2. ANALYTICAL CHEMISTRY, SURFACTANTS POLYMERS. *Educ:* WVa Wesleyan Col, BS, 60; Ariz State Univ, MS, 65, PhD(phys-org chem), 66. *Prof Exp:* Proj leader org anal phys chem, Geigy Chem Corp, 65-69, group leader anal res, 69-71, mgr, 71-78, assoc dir cent res dept, 78-82, DIR RES, CIBA VISION CARE, CIBA-GEIGY CORP, 82- *Mem:* AAAS; Am Chem Soc; fel Am Inst Chemists. *Res:* Physical organic chemistry; instrumentation. *Mailing Add:* Cent Res Dept Ciba-Geigy Corp Ardsley NY 10502

NICOSIA, SANTO VALERIO, b Catania, Italy, Dec 12, 43; US citizen; m 69; c 3. REPRODUCTIVE PATHOBIOLOGY, CYTOPATHOLOGY. *Educ:* Catholic Univ, Sacred Heart Sch Med & Surg, Rome, Italy, MD, 67; Univ Ill, Chicago, MS, 71; Am Bd Path, dipl, 78. *Prof Exp:* Resident anat path, Michael Reese Hosp & Med Ctr, Chicago, Ill, 69-72; fel, 72-73, asst prof, 73-79, ASSOC PROF OBSTET, GYNEC & PATH, SCH MED, UNIV PA, 79- *Concurrent Pos:* Dir, Electron Micros Unit & prin investr, Div Reproductive Biol, Sch Med, Univ Pa, 73-; prin investr, Marine Biol Lab, Woods Hole, Mass, 76, 78 & 79; Ad Hoc ed, Fertil & Steril, 73-78, Biol Reproductive, 76-, Scanning Elec Microsc, Annual Symposia, 76-79, Biol Bulletin, 80- & Am J Obstet Gynecol, 81-; consult, Kimberly-Clark Corp, 80-81. *Mem:* Am Tissue Cult Asn; Soc Study Reproduction; Int Acad Path; AAAS; Am Soc Cell Biol. *Res:* Regulation of mucus secretion in vertebrate and invertebrate cells; epithelialstromal interactions in developing and adult reproductive tissues; ultrastructure of mammalian fertilization; maturation and atresia of ovarian follicles; pathobiology of ovarian surface epithelium. *Mailing Add:* Rm 305 Dept Obstet-Gynecol Div Reproductive Biol Old Med Labs Univ Pa Pennsylvania PA 19104

NIDAY, JAMES BARKER, b Nashville, Tenn, May 21, 17; m 45; c 4. NUCLEAR CHEMISTRY. *Educ:* Univ Chicago, SB, 42, SM, 60. *Prof Exp:* Jr chemist, Tenn Valley Auth, 42-45; asst radiochem, Univ Chicago, 47-52; chemist, Calif Res & Develop Co, 52-53; CHEMIST, LAWRENCE LIVERMORE LAB, UNIV CALIF, 53- *Mem:* Am Phys Soc; Am Chem Soc; Sigma Xi. *Res:* Study of the fission process through radio-chemical study of fission yields and of the ranges of fission fragments in matter; computer processing and analysis of data in gamma ray spectroscopy. *Mailing Add:* 4440 Entrada Dr Pleasanton CA 94566

NIDEN, ALBERT H, b Philadelphia, Pa, Aug 17, 27; m 55; c 3. INTERNAL MEDICINE. *Educ:* Univ Pa, AB, 49, MD, 53; Am Bd Internal Med, dipl. *Prof Exp:* Instr pharmacol, Univ Pa, 54-55; from instr to assoc prof internal med & chest dis, Sch Med, Univ Chicago, 57-68; prof med & chief pulmonary dis, Temple Univ, 69-73; PROF MED & CHIEF PULMONARY DIS DIV, CHARLES R DREW POSTGRAD MED SCH, 73-; prof med, Sch Med, Univ Southern Calif, 73-79; PROF MED, SCH MED, UNIV CALIF, LOS ANGELES, 79-; ASSOC DEAN FAC AFFAIRS, CHARLES R DREW POSTGRAD MED SCH, 80- *Concurrent Pos:* Hon res asst, Inst Path, Ger, 64; hon res assoc dept anat, Kyushu, 64-65; consult, Nat Heart & Lung Inst, 68-72; consult, Comt Med & Biol Effects of Environ Pollutants, Nat Res Coun. *Mem:* Am Thoracic Soc; Am Fedn Clin Res; fel Am Col Chest Physicians; Am Physiol Soc. *Res:* Electron microscopy of lung; chest diseases; pulmonary physiology; physiology and pharmacology of the pulmonary circulation and ventilation; effects of air pollutants on lungs; lung metabolism. *Mailing Add:* Martin Luther King Jr Gen Hosp 12021 S Wilmington Ave Los Angeles CA 90059

NIEBAUER, JOHN J, b San Francisco, Calif, July 7, 14; m 43; c 4. MEDICINE. *Educ:* Stanford Univ, BA, 37, MD, 42; Am Bd Orthop Surg, dipl, 53. *Prof Exp:* Res orthop surg, Stanford Univ Hosp, 43-44; Gibney fel, Hosp for Spec Surg, New York, 44-45; assoc clin prof, Sch Med, Stanford Univ, 46-69; CHIEF DEPT HAND SURG, PAC MED CTR, 69- *Concurrent Pos:* Adj clin asst prof surg, Sch Med, Stanford Univ, 69-; clin prof orthop surg, Univ Calif, San Francisco, 67-; dir orthop & hand surg, Res Proj, Inst Med Sci, Presby Med Ctr, San Francisco. *Mem:* AMA; Am Orthop Asn; Am Acad Orthop Surg; Am Col Surg; Am Soc Surg of Hand. *Mailing Add:* Pac Med Ctr Dept Hand Surg Clay & Webster San Francisco CA 94115

NIEBEL, B(ENJAMIN) W(ILLARD), b Hunan, China, May 7, 18; nat US; m 42; c 4. INDUSTRIAL ENGINEERING, MATERIALS SCIENCE. *Educ:* Pa State Univ, BS, 39, MS, 49, IE, 52. *Prof Exp:* Chief indust engr, Lord Mfg Co, Pa, 39-47; from instr to assoc prof, 47-57, PROF INDUST ENG & HEAD DEPT, PA STATE UNIV, 47- *Concurrent Pos:* Consult to various indust concerns; Int Coop Admin consult, Mex & Peru. *Honors & Awards:* Frank & Lillian Gilbreth Indust Eng Award, Am Inst Indust Engrs, 76. *Mem:* Fel Am Inst Indust Engrs (vpres educ, 71-73); Am Soc Eng Educ; Soc Mfg Engrs. *Res:* Product design of medical instruments, calculus disintegrator, animated intestinal tube, hemorrhoidal excisor, surgical strip stitch, mole remover; motion and time study; materials and processes and their influence on the design of products. *Mailing Add:* 334 Puddintown Rd State College PA 16801

NIEBERGALL, PAUL J, b Newark, NJ, Sept 5, 32; m 57; c 4. PHARMACY. *Educ:* Rutgers Univ, BSc, 53; Univ Mich, MSc, 58, PhD(pharm), 62. *Prof Exp:* From asst prof to prof pharm, Phila Col Pharm & Sci, 61-75; DIR CORP PROD DEVELOP, MARION LABS, 75- *Concurrent Pos:* Co-investr, Nat Inst Allergy & Infectious Dis res grant, 65-68. *Mem:* Am Pharmaceut Asn; Acad Pharmaceut Sci. *Res:* Physical pharmacy; dissolution rates; solubilization of drugs through amide fusion; metal ion-penicillin interactions. *Mailing Add:* Marion Labs 10236 Bunker Ridge Rd Kansas City MO 64137

NIEBERLEIN, VERNON ADOLPH, b Dayton, Ohio, June 28, 18; m 58; c 4. CHEMICAL ENGINEERING, MATERIALS SCIENCE. *Educ:* Univ Dayton, BChE, 39; Univ Ala, MS, 65, PhD(chem eng), 70. *Prof Exp:* Chemist, Allison Div, Gen Motors Corp, 40-43; res chemist, P R Mallory & Co, Inc, 43-48; plating engr electrochem, Mat Bearing Div, Am Brake Shoe Co, 48-53; chemist extraction metall, US Bur Mines, 53-59; CHEMIST MAT, US ARMY MISSILE COMMAND, 59- *Honors & Awards:* Outstanding Achievement Award, US Bur Mines, 59; Sci & Eng Achievement Award, US Army Missile Command, 71, Achievement Award, 77. *Mem:* Soc Advan Mat & Process Engrs. *Res:* High-temperature materials, fibers, transport phenomena. *Mailing Add:* 2419 Henry St Huntsville AL 35801

NIEBYLSKI, LEONARD MARTIN, b Detroit, Mich, Nov 11, 25; m 49; c 9. SOLID STATE CHEMICAL PHYSICS. *Educ:* Wayne State Univ, BS, 49, MS, 52. *Prof Exp:* Res assoc, 67-71, SR RES ASSOC PHYSICS, ETHYL CORP, 71- *Mem:* Am Soc Testing & Mat; Am Soc Metals; Electron Micros Soc. *Res:* Surface analysis and new material development or improvement such as metal foams, solid propellants, microfibres friction modifiers gasoline and oil additives; catalysis and products of combustion modification research. *Mailing Add:* Ethyl Corp 1600 W Eight Mile Rd Ferndale MI 48220

NIED, HERMAN ARTHUR, mechanical engineering, engineering mechanics, see previous edition

NIEDENFUHR, FRANCIS W(ILLIAM), b Chicago, Ill, Jan 23, 26; m 51; c 2. ENGINEERING MATHEMATICS. *Educ:* Univ Mich, BSc, 50, MSc, 51; Ohio State Univ, PhD(eng mech), 57. *Prof Exp:* Engr, NAm Aviation, Inc, 51-52; instr eng mech, Ohio State Univ, 52-57, assoc prof, 57-61, prof, 61-66; dir technol assessment, Defense Advan Res Projs Agency, 66-76; MEM STAFF, C3 DIV, MITRE CORP, 76- *Concurrent Pos:* Mem staff, Inst Defense Anal, 64-66; adj prof, Howard Univ, 67-74; lectr, Univ Md, 77- *Mem:* Am Soc Eng Educ; Int Asn Shell Struct; Am Acad Mech; Am Soc Mech Engrs; Am Inst Aeronaut & Astronaut. *Res:* Operations analysis and engineering mechanics. *Mailing Add:* Mitre Corp Washington C 3 Oper 1820 Dolly Madison Blvd McLean VA 22102

NIEDENZU, KURT, b Fritzlar, Ger, Mar 12, 30; m 58; c 4. INORGANIC CHEMISTRY. *Educ:* Univ Heidelberg, Dipl, 55, PhD(chem), 56. *Prof Exp:* Sci asst, Univ Heidelberg, 55-57, instr inorg & anal chem, 57; chemist, Chem Sci Div, Off Ord Res, US Dept Army, Duke Univ, 58-62, off chief scientist, Army Res Off, 62-67; res adminr, Wintershall AG, Kassel, Ger, 67-68; assoc prof, 68-73, PROF CHEM, UNIV KY, 73- *Concurrent Pos:* Vis prof, Gmelin Inst, Max-Planck Soc, 74-75; Alexander von Humboldt Found US Sr Scientist Award, 74. *Mem:* Am Chem Soc; Royal Soc Chem; Ger Chem Soc. *Res:* Synthesis and structure of phosphorus, sulfur, boron and nitrogen compounds, especially isoelectronic systems; organometallic synthesis; spectroscopy. *Mailing Add:* 724 Haverhill Dr Lexington KY 40503

NIEDERHAUSER, WARREN DEXTER, b Akron, Ohio, Jan 2, 18; m 49; c 1. ORGANIC CHEMISTRY, POLYMERS. *Educ:* Oberlin Col, AB, 39; Univ Wis, PhD(org chem), 43. *Prof Exp:* Res chemist, 43-51, head surfactant synthesis group, 51-55, head chem sect redstone div, 55-59, res supvr, 59-65, asst res dir, 66-73, DIR PIONEERING RES, ROHM & HAAS CO, 73- *Concurrent Pos:* Mem limited war comt, Dept of Defense, 61-63, mem ord sci adv panel, US Dept Army, 61-62 & mem chem & biol warfare adv comt, 61-63. *Mem:* Am Chem Soc. *Res:* Ion exchange; environmental control; petroleum chemicals; plastics; surfactants; rocket propellants. *Mailing Add:* Res Div Lab Rohm & Haas Co Spring House PA 19477

NIEDERJOHN, RUSSELL JAMES, b Schenectady, NY, June 13, 44; m 69; c 2. ELECTRICAL ENGINEERING, COMPUTER ENGINEERING. *Educ:* Univ Mass, BS, 67, MS, 68, PhD(elec eng), 71. *Prof Exp:* Comput programmer, IBM, 67; res asst elec eng, Univ Mass, 68-71; asst prof, 71-75, assoc prof elec eng, 75-80, PROF ELEC ENG & COMPUT SCI, MARQUETTE UNIV, 80- *Concurrent Pos:* Consult, Gen Elec Co, 76-78, Rome Air Develop Ctr, 77 & Eaton Corp, 78-; prin investr, US Air Force Off Sci Res grant, 78-79; dir NSF cause grant, 78-81. *Mem:* Inst Elec & Electronics Engrs; Am Soc Eng Educ; Acoust Soc Am; Audio Eng Soc; Am Asn Univ Prof. *Res:* Microcomputer applications and design; speech and signal processing; speech in noise enhancement; graduate and undergraduate educational methods. *Mailing Add:* Dept of Elec Eng Marquette Univ Milwaukee WI 53233

NIEDERKORN, JERRY YOUNG, b St Louis, Mo, Oct 31, 46; m 69; c 2. IMMUNOLOGY, PARASITOLOGY. *Educ:* Cent Methodist Col, BA, 68; Cent Mo State Univ, MS, 72; Univ Ark, PhD(zool), 77. *Prof Exp:* INSTR OPHTHAL, SOUTHWESTERN MED SCH, UNIV TEX, 77- *Mem:* Am Soc Parasitologists; AAAS. *Res:* Immunoparasitology; ocular immunology; tumor immunology. *Mailing Add:* Dept of Ophthal Univ of Tex Dallas TX 75235

NIEDERLAND, WILLIAM G, b Schippenbeil, Ger, Aug 29, 04; US citizen; m 52; c 3. PSYCHIATRY, MEDICAL SCIENCES. *Educ:* Univ Würzburg, MD, 29; Univ Genoa, MD, 34; State Univ NY, MD, 41. *Prof Exp:* Clin asst prof med, Univ Philippines, 39-40; assoc prof psychol, Univ Tampa, 45-47; clin prof, 55-77, EMER CLIN PROF PSYCHIAT, STATE UNIV NY DOWNSTATE MED CTR, 77- *Concurrent Pos:* Training psychoanalyst, State Univ NY Downstate Med Ctr, 58-74, supv psychoanalyst, 58-, emer training psychoanalyst, 75-; chief consult psychiatrist, Altro Health & Rehab Serv, New York, 58-76; ed consult, Am Imago, NY & Detroit, 63-; consult psychiatrist, Hackensack Gen Hosp, NJ, 72- *Mem:* Fel Am Psychiat Asn; Am Psychoanal Asn; Int Psychoanal Asn. *Res:* Artistic and cultural creativity; psychobiographical and psychohistorical studies; clinical research in the fields of depression and survival after social and natural catastrophes; author of more than 200 scientific articles and essays and two books. *Mailing Add:* 108 Glenwood Rd Englewood NJ 07631

NIEDERMAN, JAMES CORSON, b Hamilton, Ohio, Nov 27, 24; m 51; c 4. INTERNAL MEDICINE, EPIDEMIOLOGY. *Educ:* Johns Hopkins Univ, MD, 49; Kenyon Col, AB, 45. *Hon Degrees:* DSc, Kenyon Col, 81. *Prof Exp:* Intern med, Osler Med Serv, Johns Hopkins Hosp, 49-50; from asst resident to assoc resident, Yale-New Haven Med Ctr, 50-55; instr prev med, Sch Med, 55-58, asst prof epidemiol & prev med, 58-66, assoc clin prof, 66-76, CLIN PROF EPIDEMIOL & MED, SCH MED, YALE UNIV, 76- *Concurrent Pos:* Fel, Silliman Col, Yale Univ, 64-; mem bd counrs, Smith Col, Mass, 73-; trustee, Kenyon Col, Ohio, 73- *Mem:* Am Epidemiol Soc; Infectious Dis Soc Am; Am Fedn Clin Res; Asn Teachers Prev Med; Sigma Xi. *Res:* Infectious mononucleosis; EB virus infections; clinical epidemiological studies of virus infections. *Mailing Add:* Dept of Epidemiol & Pub Health Yale Univ Sch of Med 333 Cedar St New Haven CT 06510

NIEDERMAN, ROBERT AARON, b Norwich, Conn, Jan 19, 37. MOLECULAR BIOLOGY, BIOCHEMISTRY. *Educ:* Univ Conn, BS, 59, MS, 61; Univ Ill, Urbana, DVM, 64, PhD(bact), 67. *Prof Exp:* Atomic Energy Comn fel biochem, Mich State Univ, 67-68; fel physiol chem, Roche Inst Molecular Biol, 68-70; asst prof microbiol, 70-76, assoc prof microbiol, 76-80, PROF BIOCHEM, RUTGERS UNIV, PISCATAWAY, 80- *Concurrent Pos:* Merck Co Found fac develop award, Rutgers Univ, New Brunswick, 71-; USPHS res grant, Nat Inst Gen Med Sci, 73 & 79; NSF res grants, 74, 76 &

79; USPHS res career develop award, Nat Inst Gen Med Sci, 75-80; res fel biochem, Univ Bristol, Eng, 77-78. *Mem:* AAAS; Am Soc Biol Chem; Am Soc Microbiol; NY Acad Sci. *Res:* Membrane biochemistry; mechanisms of bacterial membrane differentiation and assembly; developmental bioenergetics; regulation of membrane synthesis. *Mailing Add:* Dept Biochem Rutgers Univ PO Box 1059 Piscataway NJ 08854

NIEDERMAYER, ALFRED O, b Munich, Ger, Aug 8, 21; US citizen; m 46; c 3. ANALYTICAL CHEMISTRY, PHARAMACEUTICAL CHEMISTRY. *Educ:* Rutgers Univ, BA, 50. *Prof Exp:* SR RES SCIENTIST, E R SQUIBB & SONS, 50-, SECT HEAD, 80- *Mem:* Am Chem Soc. *Res:* Analytical separations, particularly gas chromatography; dissolution studies of pharmaceutical dosage forms. *Mailing Add:* E R Squibb & Sons Georges Rd New Brunswick NJ 08903

NIEDERMEIER, ROBERT PAUL, b Waukesha, Wis, Sept 8, 18; m 45; c 2. DAIRY HUSBANDRY. *Educ:* Univ Wis, BS, 40, MS, 42, PhD(dairy husb, biochem), 48. *Prof Exp:* From instr to assoc prof, 47-56, PROF DAIRY HUSB, UNIV WIS-MADISON, 57-, CHMN DEPT, 63- *Mem:* Am Soc Animal Sci; Am Dairy Sci Asn (vpres, 75-76, pres, 76-77); AAAS. *Res:* Forage preservation and utilization; mineral studies of parturient paresis in dairy cattle. *Mailing Add:* 266 Animal Sci Bldg Dept Dairy Sci Univ of Wis Madison WI 53706

NIEDERMEIER, WILLIAM, b Evansville, Ind, Apr 1, 23; m 45; c 4. BIOCHEMISTRY. *Educ:* Purdue Univ, BS, 46; Univ Ala, MS, 53, PhD(biochem), 60. *Prof Exp:* Res chemist, Mead Johnson & Co, 46-49; instr nutrit, Sch Med, Northwestern Univ, 49-50; ASSOC PROF BIOCHEM, MED COL, UNIV ALA, BIRMINGHAM, 60- *Mem:* AAAS; Am Chem Soc; Soc Appl Spectros; Am Soc Biol Chem; Am Asn Immunol. *Res:* Electrolyte and trace metal metabolism; chemistry of connective tissue and hyaluronic acid; carbohydrate composition of immunoglobulins. *Mailing Add:* Rheumatol & Clin Immunol Div Univ of Ala Dept of Med Birmingham AL 35233

NIEDERMEYER, ERNST F, b Schonberg, Ger, Jan 19, 20; US citizen; m 46; c 5. NEUROLOGY. *Educ:* Innsbruck Univ, MD, 47. *Prof Exp:* Resident neurol & psychiat, Innsbruck Univ Hosp, 48-50; French Govt fel & foreign asst neurol, Salpetriere Hosp, Paris, 50-51; resident neurol, psychiat & EEG, Innsbruck Univ Hosp, 51-55, asst prof, 55-60; from asst prof to assoc prof EEG, Univ Iowa, 60-65; ASSOC PROF EEG, JOHNS HOPKINS UNIV & ELECTROENCEPHALOGRAPHER-IN-CHG, JOHNS HOPKINS HOSP, 65- *Mem:* Am EEG Soc; Am Epilepsy Soc; Austrian EEG Soc; corresp mem Ger EEG Soc; Peruvian Neuropsychol Soc. *Res:* Clinical electroencephalography with particular emphasis on epilepsy. *Mailing Add:* Dept Neurol Surg Johns Hopkins Hosp Baltimore MD 21205

NIEDERPRUEM, DONALD J, b Buffalo, NY, Sept 3, 28; m 51; c 4. MICROBIOLOGY, BIOCHEMISTRY. *Educ:* Univ Buffalo, BA, 49, MA, 56, PhD(biol), 59. *Prof Exp:* USPHS fel bact, Univ Calif, Berkeley, 59-61; from asst prof to assoc prof microbiol, 61-68, PROF MICROBIOL, MED CTR, IND UNIV, INDIANAPOLIS, 68-, PROF IMMUNOL, 77- *Concurrent Pos:* Lederle med fac award, 62-65. *Mem:* Am Soc Microbiol; Bot Soc Am; Am Soc Plant Physiol; Am Soc Biol Chem; Soc Develop Biol. *Res:* Biochemical basis of cellular regulation of differentiation and morphogenesis. *Mailing Add:* Dept of Microbiol Ind Univ Sch of Med Indianapolis IN 46202

NIEDRACH, LEONARD WILLIAM, b Weehawken, NJ, Sept 11, 21; m 50; c 3. CHEMISTRY. *Educ:* Univ Rochester, BS, 42; Harvard Univ, MA, 47, PhD(chem), 48. *Prof Exp:* Anal chemist, Gen Elec Co, Mass, 43-44; jr chemist, Univ Chicago, 44-45 & Monsanto Chem Co, Ohio, 45; res assoc, 48-58, phys chemist, 58-71, MGR MEMBRANE & SENSOR PROJS, GEN ELEC CO, 71- *Mem:* AAAS; fel Am Inst Chem; Am Chem Soc; Electrochem Soc. *Res:* Polarography of selenium and tellurium; spectroscopy as an analytical method; x-ray diffraction; inorganic preparations; electrodeposition; inorganic separations; fuel cells; electrochemical devices for medical applications. *Mailing Add:* Res & Develop Ctr Gen Elec Co PO Box 8 Schenectady NY 12301

NIEDZIELSKI, EDMUND LUKE, b Brooklyn, NY, Nov 14, 17; m 46; c 5. PETROLEUM CHEMISTRY. *Educ:* St John's Univ, NY, BS, 38; Fordham Univ, MS, 40, PhD(org chem), 43. *Prof Exp:* Asst, Fordham Univ, 38-42; res chemist 46-48, res chemist, Petrol Lab, 48-62, res chemist, Jackson Lab, 62-66, SR RES CHEMIST, PETROL LAB, E I DU PONT DE NEMOURS & CO, INC, 66- *Mem:* AAAS; fel Am Inst Chem. *Res:* Petroleum additives; synthetic fluids and lubricants; redistribution reactions; gas separation membranes. *Mailing Add:* Petrol Lab E I du Pont de Nemours & Co Inc Wilmington DE 19898

NIEFORTH, KARL ALLEN, b Melrose, Mass, July 7, 36; m 58; c 4. MEDICINAL CHEMISTRY, PSYCHOPHARMACOLOGY. *Educ:* Mass Col Pharm, BS, 57; Purdue Univ, MS, 59, PhD(med chem), 61. *Prof Exp:* From asst prof to assoc prof med chem, 61-75, asst dean, Sch Pharm, 67-76, assoc dean, Sch Pharm, 76-81, PROF MED CHEM, UNIV CONN, 75-, DEAN, SCH PHARM, 81- *Concurrent Pos:* Lectr, Yale Univ, 70-76. *Mem:* Am Chem Soc; Am Pharmaceut Asn; Am Asn Col Pharm. *Res:* Design, synthesis and biological testing of compounds in the area of psychotherapeutics; hypoglycemics or drug antagonists. *Mailing Add:* Sch of Pharm Univ of Conn Storrs CT 06268

NIEH, MARJORIE T, organic chemistry, see previous edition

NIEHAUS, MERLE HINSON, b Enid, Okla, Mar 25, 33; m 54; c 2. AGRONOMY. *Educ:* Okla State Univ, BS, 55, MS, 57; Purdue Univ, PhD(plant breeding), 64. *Prof Exp:* Instr agron, Imp Ethiopian Col Agr & Mech Arts, Harar, 59-61; instr, Purdue Univ, 63; asst dir res, Advan Seed Co, 64; from asst prof to prof agron, Ohio Agr Res & Develop Ctr, 64-78, assoc chmn dept, 75-78; PROF AGRON & HEAD DEPT, N MEX STATE UNIV, 78- *Mem:* Am Soc Agron; Crop Sci Soc Am. *Res:* Soybean breeding and variety development. *Mailing Add:* Dept Agron NMex State Univ PO Box 3Q Las Cruces NM 88003

NIEHAUS, WALTER G, JR, b Minneapolis, Minn, Dec 13, 37. BIOCHEMISTRY. *Educ:* Univ Minn, BS, 62, PhD(biochem), 64. *Prof Exp:* Nat Heart Inst fel biochem, Univ Ill, 65-66 & Karolinska Inst, Sweden, 66-67; res assoc, Univ Minn, 67-68; asst prof, Pa State Univ, 68-71, assoc prof, 71-75; ASSOC PROF BIOCHEM, VA POLYTECH & STATE UNIV, 75-, ASSOC PROF NUTRIT, 78- *Mem:* AAAS; Am Soc Biol Chem; Am Chem Soc. *Res:* Enzymatic modifications of unsaturated fatty acids; determination of stereochemistry of hydroxy fatty acids; effect of amidination on structure and function of hemoglobin. *Mailing Add:* Dept of Biochem Va Polytech & State Univ Blacksburg VA 24061

NIEKAMP, CARL WILLIAM, b Catskill, NY, Jan 12, 43; m 64; c 2. PHYSICAL CHEMISTRY, BIOCHEMISTRY. *Educ:* Hope Col, BA, 65; Purdue Univ, PhD(phys chem), 71. *Prof Exp:* Res assoc chem, Yale Univ, 71-73; asst prof, Hanover Col, 73-78; res chemist, 78-80, SR RES CHEMIST, A E STALEY MFG CO, 80- *Concurrent Pos:* Humboldt Found res fel, 76-77. *Mem:* Am Chem Soc. *Res:* Physical-chemical investigations of carbohydrate processes; energetics of protein-ligand interactions; physical understanding of chemical processes through thermochemical, thermodynamic and kinetic approaches. *Mailing Add:* Res Ctr A E Staley Mfg Co 2200 Eldorado St Decatur IL 62525

NIELL, ARTHUR EDWIN, b Lubbock, Tex, Sept 15, 42. RADIO ASTRONOMY. *Educ:* Calif Inst Technol, BS, 65; Cornell Univ, PhD(radio astron), 71. *Prof Exp:* Res fel radio astron, Queen's Univ, Ont, 71-72; resident res assoc, Nat Res Coun-Nat Acad Sci, 72-74; sr engr radio astron & earth physics, 74-76, MEM TECH STAFF, JET PROPULSION LAB, 76- *Mem:* Am Astron Soc; Int Radio Sci Union; Int Astron Union; Am Geophys Union. *Res:* Geodetic measurements using radio astronomical observations; investigation of the structure and physics of extragalactic radio sources. *Mailing Add:* Jet Propulsion Lab 264-748 4800 Oak Grove Dr Pasadena CA 91103

NIELSEN, ALLEN MADSEN, b Ft Collins, Colo, Apr 24, 45; m 68; c 3. MICROBIAL PHYSIOLOGY. *Educ:* Brigham Young Univ, BS, 70, MS, 72; Ind Univ, PhD(microbiol), 76. *Prof Exp:* Res scientist microbiol ecol, 75-80, SR RES SCIENTIST, CONOCO INC, 80- *Mem:* Am Soc Microbiol; Sigma Xi. *Res:* Oxidation and release of copper from chalcocite by Thiobacillus ferrooxidans; the metabolism of acetate by photosynthetic bacteria. *Mailing Add:* Conoco Inc PO Drawer 1267 Ponca City OK 74601

NIELSEN, ALVIN HERBORG, b Menominee, Mich, May 30, 10; m 42; c 1. PHYSICS. *Educ:* Univ Mich, BA, 31, MSc, 32, PhD(physics), 34. *Prof Exp:* Asst physics, Univ Mich, 31-34; from instr to assoc prof physics, 35-46, head dept, 56-69, dean, Col Lib Arts, 63-77, prof physics, 46-80, EMER PROF, UNIV TENN KNOXVILLE, 80-, DEAN, COL LIB ARTS, 80- *Concurrent Pos:* Fulbright scholar, Inst Astrophys, Belg, 51-52; hon fel, Ohio State Univ; consult, Union Carbide Corp, Oak Ridge Nat Lab, & Off Ord Res; mem vis sci prog, Am Inst Physics-Am Asn Physics Teachers, 64-71, Nat Acad Sci-Nat Res Coun comt basic res adv to US Army Res Off, 64-70 & div chem physics, Am Inst Physics. *Mem:* Fel AAAS; fel Am Phys Soc; fel Optical Soc Am; Am Asn Physics Teachers; Coblentz Soc. *Res:* Infrared spectra of polyatomic molecules; infrared detectors. *Mailing Add:* Dept of Physics 518 Univ of Tenn Knoxville TN 37916

NIELSEN, ARNOLD THOR, b Seattle, Wash, Sept 2, 23; m 47; c 3. ORGANIC CHEMISTRY. *Educ:* Univ Wash, BSc, 44, PhD(org chem), 47. *Prof Exp:* Res chemist, Chas Pfizer & Co, 47-48; asst prof chem, Univ Idaho, 49-52; res assoc, Purdue Univ, 52-55; instr, Rutgers Univ, 55-57; asst prof, Univ Ky, 57-59; RES CHEMIST, MICHELSON LAB, NAVAL WEAPONS CTR, 59- *Mem:* Am Chem Soc; Royal Soc Chem; Int Soc Heterocyclic Chem. *Res:* Aldol condensation; nitro compounds; stereochemistry; nitrogen heterocyclics. *Mailing Add:* Michelson Lab Code 38503 Naval Weapons Ctr China Lake CA 93555

NIELSEN, CARL EBY, b Los Angeles, Calif, Jan 22, 15; m 38; c 3. PHYSICS. *Educ:* Univ Calif, AB, 34, MA, 40, PhD(physics), 41. *Prof Exp:* Instr physics, Univ Calif, Berkeley, 41-45, lectr, 45-46; asst prof, Univ Denver, 46-47; from asst prof to assoc prof physics & astron, 47-64, PROF PHYSICS, OHIO STATE UNIV, 64- *Concurrent Pos:* Ford fel, Europ Orgn Nuclear Res, Geneva, 58-59; scientist, Midwestern Univs Res Asn, 60-61; consult thermonuclear div, Oak Ridge Nat Lab, 61-70; vis scientist, Culham Lab, UK Atomic Energy Authority, 66; consult, Los Alamos Sci Lab, 71-75 & Lawrence Livermore Lab, 74-77. *Mem:* Am Phys Soc; Int Solar Energy Soc. *Res:* Cloud chambers; collective phenomena in beams and plasmas; solar energy and solar ponds. *Mailing Add:* 8030 Sawmill Rd Dublin OH 43017

NIELSEN, DAVID GARY, b Longview, Wash, Nov 18, 43; m 64; c 2. ENTOMOLOGY. *Educ:* Willamette Univ, BA, 66; Cornell Univ, MS, 69, PhD(entom), 70. *Prof Exp:* From asst prof to assoc prof, 70-80, PROF ENTOM, OHIO AGR RES & DEVELOP CTR, OHIO STATE UNIV, 80- *Concurrent Pos:* Consult entom, Behav Chem, Urban Forest Pest Mgt. *Mem:* Entom Soc Am; Int Soc Arboricult. *Res:* Behavioral ecology and suppression of insects which attack woody ornamental plants; urban forest mangement. *Mailing Add:* Dept of Entom Ohio Agr Res & Develop Ctr Wooster OH 44691

NIELSEN, DONALD R, b Phoenix, Ariz, Oct 10, 31; m 53; c 5. SOIL PHYSICS. *Educ:* Univ Ariz, BS, 53, MS, 54; Iowa State Univ, PhD(soil physics), 58. *Prof Exp:* Res assoc soil physics, Iowa State Univ, 54-58; from asst prof to assoc prof, 58-68, dir, Kearney Found Soil Sci, 70-75, chmn dept land, air & water resources, 75-77, assoc dean, 71-80, PROF SOIL PHYSICS, UNIV CALIF, DAVIS, 68- *Concurrent Pos:* NSF sr fel, 65-66; consult, Int Atomic Energy Agency, Vienna, Austria, 74-75. *Mailing Add:* Dept Land Air & Water Resources Univ of Calif Davis CA 95616

NIELSEN, DONALD R, b Oak Park, Ill, Oct 11, 30; m 54; c 3. ORGANIC CHEMISTRY. *Educ:* Knox Col, BA, 52; Univ Kans, PhD(org chem), 56. *Prof Exp:* Res chemist, Chem Div, Pittsburgh Plate Glass Co, 56-64, res supvr, 64-68, SR RES ASSOC, CHEM DIV, PPG INDUSTS, INC, 68- *Mem:* Am Chem Soc. *Res:* Organic synthesis. *Mailing Add:* 4633 Congressional Corpus Christi TX 78413

NIELSEN, FORREST HAROLD, b Junction City, Wis, Oct 26, 41; m 64; c 2. NUTRITION, BIOCHEMISTRY. *Educ:* Univ Wis-Madison, BS, 63, MS, 66, PhD(biochem), 67. *Prof Exp:* Res chemist, Beltsville, Md, 69-70, RES CHEMIST, HUMAN NUTRIT RES CTR, AGR RES SERV, USDA, 70- *Concurrent Pos:* Adj prof biochem, Univ NDak, 71- *Mem:* Am Inst Nutrit; Soc Environ Geochem & Health; Soc Exp Biol & Med; Int Asn Bioinorgan Scientists; Sigma Xi. *Res:* Trace element nutrition and metabolism; arsenic, boron nickel, vanadium and the newer essential trace elements. *Mailing Add:* Human Nutrit Res Ctr Agr Res Serv USDA Box 7166 Univ Sta Grand Forks ND 58201

NIELSEN, GERALD ALAN, b Frederic, Wis, Nov 10, 34; m 55; c 4. SOIL SCIENCE, ECOLOGY. *Educ:* Univ Wis, BS, 58, MS, 60, PhD(soil sci), 63. *Prof Exp:* Asst prof soil sci, Univ Wyo team-US Agency Int Develop, Afghanistan, 63-67; assoc prof, 67-73, PROF SOIL SCI, MONT STATE UNIV, 73- *Mem:* AAAS; Soil Sci Soc Am; Am Soc Agron; Soil Conserv Soc Am; Int Soc Soil Sci. *Res:* Soil genesis, classification and ecology; interpretation of soil survey for land use planning; soil inventories and land potential evaluation. *Mailing Add:* Dept of Plant & Soil Sci Mont State Univ Bozeman MT 59715

NIELSEN, HARALD CHRISTIAN, b Chicago, Ill, Apr 18, 30; m 53; c 3. PHYSICAL BIOCHEMISTRY. *Educ:* St Olaf Col, BA, 52; Mich State Univ, PhD(biochem), 57. *Prof Exp:* CHEMIST, NORTHERN REGIONAL RES CTR, USDA, 57- *Mem:* AAAS; Am Chem Soc; Am Asn Cereal Chem. *Res:* Isolation and physical-chemical characterization of cereal grain proteins and related products. *Mailing Add:* Northern Regional Res Ctr USDA 1815 N University Peoria IL 61604

NIELSEN, HELMER L(OUIS), b Fredericia, Denmark, Oct 13, 21; US citizen; m 42. THERMODYNAMICS, AERONAUTICS. *Educ:* Univ Calif, Berkeley, BS, 50, MS, 52; Von Karman Inst Fluid Dynamics, Belg, Dipl Ing, 68. *Prof Exp:* Aeronaut scientist, Ames Res Ctr, NASA, 51-59; assoc prof aeronaut eng, Univ Wash, 59-61; PROF MECH ENG, SAN JOSE STATE UNIV, 61-, CHMN DEPT, 80- *Concurrent Pos:* Consult, Lockheed Aircraft Corp, 62-63, Precision Data Inc, 78 & Elec Power Res Inst, 78-80; NASA-Am Soc Eng Educ fel, 69-70. *Mem:* Assoc fel Am Inst Aeronaut & Astronaut. *Res:* Astronautical engineering; aerodynamics; boundary layer theory; energy; high speed convective heat transfer; thermodynamics; technical, social, political aspects. *Mailing Add:* Dept of Mech Eng San Jose State Univ San Jose CA 95192

NIELSEN, JAMES WILLARD, b St Michael, Nebr, July 7, 24; m 50; c 2. SOLID STATE CHEMISTRY. *Educ:* Nebr State Teachers Col, Kearney, BS, 45; Univ Minn, MS, 48; Univ Iowa, PhD(phys chem), 53. *Prof Exp:* Instr chem, Nebr State Teachers Col, Kearney, 48-50; mem tech staff, Bell Tel Labs, Inc, NJ, 53-60; mgr solid state lab, Airtron Div, Litton Industs, 60-67; SUPVR, BELL LABS, 67- *Mem:* AAAS; Am Asn Crystal Growth. *Res:* Crystal growth; crystallography; phase equilibrium in condensed systems; chemistry of solid state. *Mailing Add:* Bell Labs 7c-401 Mountain Ave Murray Hill NJ 07974

NIELSEN, JENS JUERGEN, b Bleckede, Ger, Feb 10, 27; m 58; c 4. PLANT PATHOLOGY. *Educ:* Univ Gottingen, PhD(plant path), 60. *Prof Exp:* Fel physiol parasitism, Nat Res Coun Can, 60-62 & Ger Res Asn, 62-63; RES SCIENTIST, RES BR, AGR CAN, 63- *Mem:* Can Phytopath Soc. *Res:* Cereal diseases caused by smut fungi, particularly Ustilago species. *Mailing Add:* Agr Can Res Sta 195 Dafoe Rd Winnipeg MB R3T 2M9 Can

NIELSEN, JOHN MERLE, b Logan, Utah, Aug 31, 28; m 57; c 5. SILICONES, MATERIALS SCIENCE. *Educ:* Brigham Young Univ, BS, 52, Purdue Univ, MS, 54, PhD(org chem), 57. *Prof Exp:* Res & prod develop chemist silicone fluids, Silicone Prod Dept, 56-71, mat engr plastics & chem, Corp Consult Serv, 72-75, MAT ENGR, PLASTICS & CHEM, LUBRICANTS, COATINGS HEALTH & SAFETY MAT, CORP RES & DEVELOP, GEN ELEC CO, 75- *Concurrent Pos:* Ed, Mat Safety Data Sheet Collection , GE, 76-; subj ed, (Safety, Health & Environ), PERGAMON, Encyclopedia Mat Sci & Eng, 80- *Mem:* Am Chem Soc; Am Soc Testing & Mat. *Res:* Oxidative and thermal stability of silicones; synthesis and hydrolysis of chlorosilanes; synthesis of silicone fluids; specifications, materials information and health and safety information on industrial materials. *Mailing Add:* 40 GE Mat Info Serv 120 Erie Blvd Schenectady NY 12305

NIELSEN, JOHN P(HILLIP), b Cleveland, Ohio, Nov 11, 11; m 45. PHYSICAL METALLURGY, MATERIALS SCIENCE. *Educ:* Mich Col Mining & Technol, BS, 35; Yale Univ, ME, 42, PhD(metall), 47. *Prof Exp:* Foundry engr, McGean Chem Co, 37-39; foundry consult, Seymour Mfg Co, 39-40; res metallurgist, Int Nickel Co, 42-43; assoc physicist, Philip's Lab, Inc, 43-45; from assoc prof to prof metal sci, NY Univ, 47-76, chmn dept metall & mat sci, 56-69; EMER PROF METAL SCI, POLYTECH INST NEW YORK, 76-; EXEC DIR, INT PRECIOUS METALS INST, 76- *Concurrent Pos:* Consult, J F Jelenko & Co, New Rochelle, 57- & Leach & Garner, Attleboro, 78-; adj prof dent mat, NY Univ, 76- *Honors & Awards:* Wilmer Souder Award, Int Asn Dent Res. *Mem:* Am Inst Mining, Metall & Petrol Engrs; NY Acad Sci; Am Soc Metals; AAAS. *Res:* X-ray metallography; structure of metals; surface energy of solius; grain growth and recrystallization; metallurgical engineering, especially miniature casting technology, particularly for precious metals. *Mailing Add:* One Washington Sq Village New York NY 10012

NIELSEN, JOHN PALMER, b Long Beach, Calif, Nov 20, 34; m 54; c 4. CIVIL ENGINEERING, MATHEMATICS. *Educ:* San Jose State Col, BS, 57; Univ Wyo, MSCE, 58; Colo State Univ, PhD(civil eng), 61. *Prof Exp:* Staff engr soil mech, Gribaldo, Jones & Assocs, Calif, 61-62 & Soil Mech & Found Engrs, 62-63; sr task engr, US Naval Civil Eng Lab, 63-69; prof civil eng, Univ NH, 69-74; mgr, Soils & Pavements Div, Civil Eng Res Facil, Univ NMex, 74-81; PROF CIVIL ENG, UNIV NEV, RENO, 81- *Concurrent Pos:* Lectr, Univ Southern Calif, 64-74; mem comt pavement design, Hwy Res Bd, Nat Acad Sci-Nat Res Coun, 65-; adj prof civil eng, Univ NMex, 74- *Mem:* Sigma Xi; Am Soc Civil Engrs; Am Soc Testing & Mat. *Res:* Behavior of soil systems under static loading. *Mailing Add:* Col Eng Univ Nev Reno NV 89557

NIELSEN, JULIAN MOYES, b Ogden, Utah, Mar 24, 21; m 46; c 5. ENVIRONMENTAL CHEMISTRY. *Educ:* Univ Wyo, BS, 42; Stanford Univ, MS, 48; Univ Southern Calif, PhD(phys chem), 51. *Prof Exp:* Res chemist, Naval Ord Test Sta, 50-53 & Gen Elec Co, 53-65; RES MGR, PAC NORTHWEST LABS, BATTELLE MEM INST, 65- *Mem:* Health Physics Soc; Am Chem Soc. *Res:* Diffusion of colloids and electrolytes; radiochemistry; nuclear chemistry. *Mailing Add:* 1611 Sunset St Richland WA 99352

NIELSEN, KAJ LEO, b Nyker, Denmark, Dec 3, 14; nat US; m 43; c 2. MATHEMATICS. *Educ:* Univ Mich, AB, 36; Syracuse Univ, MA, 37; Univ Ill, PhD(math), 40. *Prof Exp:* Asst math, Syracuse Univ, 36-37; asst math, Univ Ill, 37-40, instr, 40-41; Carnegie fel, Brown Univ, 41, instr, 41-42; from instr to asst prof, La State Univ, 42-45; sr mathematician, US Naval Ord Plant, Ind, 45-48, head math div, 48-58; chief opers anal, Allison Div, Gen Motors Corp, 58-60; head anal staff, Defense Systs Div, Gen Motors Corp, 60-61; prof, Butler Univ, 61-63; dir systs anal div, Battelle Mem Inst, Ohio, 63-71; lectr, 57-60, HEAD DEPT MATH, BUTLER UNIV, 71- *Concurrent Pos:* Proj anal engr, Chance Vought Aircraft, Inc, Conn, 44-45; lectr, Purdue Univ, 55-58. *Mem:* Am Math Soc; Math Asn Am; Am Comput Mach. *Res:* Partial differential equations of elliptic type; exterior ballistics; fire control; teaching of applied mathematics; numerical methods; operations and systems analysis; man-machine and management systems; computer science. *Mailing Add:* 1224 Ridge Rd Carmel IN 46032

NIELSEN, KENNETH FRED, b Cardston, Alta, July 3, 27; m 47; c 5. SOIL FERTILITY, PLANT PHYSIOLOGY. *Educ:* Brigham Young Univ, BS, 49; Ohio State Univ, PhD(soil chem & plant nutrit), 52. *Prof Exp:* Asst prof agron, Univ Maine, 52-55; head, Soil Fertil Unit, Can Dept Agr, 55-59, Soil Sect, Exp Farm, Sask, 59-65; chief agronomist, 65-66, dir planning, 66-69, dir mkt & agron, 69-72, CHIEF EXEC OFFICER & GEN MGR, WESTERN COOP FERTILIZERS LTD, 72- *Concurrent Pos:* Fel, Rothamsted Exp Sta, 62-63; pres, Can Fertilizer Inst, 77-78 & Calgary Br, Alta Inst Agrologists, 77-78; chmn bd, Can Fertilizers Ltd, 78-79. *Mem:* Soil Sci Soc Am; fel Can Soc Soil Sci (pres, 70-71); Agr Inst Can; Int Soc Soil Sci. *Res:* Plant nutrition. *Mailing Add:* PO Box 2500 Calgary AB T2P 2N1 Can

NIELSEN, KENT CHRISTOPHER, b Pocatello, Idaho, Sept 5, 45. STRUCTURAL GEOLOGY, TECTONOPHYSICS. *Educ:* Univ NC, BS, 68, MS, 72; Univ BC, PhD(geol), 78. *Prof Exp:* INstr geol, 76-78, ASST PROF GEOL, UNIV TEX, DALLAS, 78- *Concurrent Pos:* NSF prin investr, 77-79. *Mem:* Geol Soc Am; Am Geophys Union. *Res:* Field structural geology, fold analysis, cleavage development, metamorphic petrology; experimental rock deformation, high temperature creep, diffusion mechanisms, pressure solution. *Mailing Add:* Prog of Geosci Univ of Tex at Dallas Richardson TX 75080

NIELSEN, LARRY DENNIS, b Hazelwood, Minn, Feb 12, 39; m 63; c 1. BIOCHEMISTRY. *Educ:* St Olaf Col, BA, 61; Univ Colo, Denver, PhD(biochem), 66. *Prof Exp:* USPHS fel biochem, Univ Wash, 66-68, training grant, pediat, 68-71; RES SCIENTIST BIOCHEM, NAT JEWISH HOSP & RES CTR, 71- *Res:* Cell surface properties involved in intercellular adhesion of normal and malignant cells. *Mailing Add:* Nat Jewish Hosp & Res Ctr E Colfax Ave & Colorado Blvd Denver CO 80206

NIELSEN, LAWRENCE ARTHUR, b Minneapolis, Minn, Aug 7, 34; m 62; c 2. ORGANIC CHEMISTRY. *Educ:* Univ Minn, BS, 56; Univ Nebr, MS, 59, PhD(org chem), 62. *Prof Exp:* Res chemist, Chemstrand Res Ctr, Inc, Monsanto Co, 62-70; HEAD PATENT LIAISON, BURROUGHS WELLCOME CO, 70- *Mem:* Am Chem Soc; Sigma Xi. *Res:* Heterocyclic synthesis; medicinal chemistry. *Mailing Add:* Burroughs Wellcome Co 3030 Cornwallis Rd Research Triangle Park NC 27709

NIELSEN, LAWRENCE ERNIE, b Pilot Rock, Ore, Dec 17, 17; m 42; c 1. POLYMER SCIENCE, COMPOSITE MATERIALS. *Educ:* Pac Univ, AB, 40; State Col Wash, MS, 42; Cornell Univ, PhD(phys chem), 45. *Prof Exp:* Asst phys chem, State Col Wash, 40-42; lab asst, Cornell Univ, 42-45; phys chemist, Monsanto Co, 45-55, sr scientist, 55-77; POLYMER CONSULT, 77- *Concurrent Pos:* Fel, Harvard Univ, 52; leader, Juneau Ice Field Proj, Alaska, 53; affiliate prof, Wash Univ, 65-76. *Honors & Awards:* Bingham Award, Soc Rheology, 76; Int Res Award, Soc Plastics Engrs, 81. *Mem:* Am Chem Soc; Am Phys Soc; Soc Rheol; Glaciol Soc. *Res:* Molal volumes of electrolytes; Raman, infrared and ultraviolet spectroscopy; fractionation of proteins; molecular structure of high polymers and its relation to physical and mechanical properties; properties of composite materials; glaciology and flow properties of ice. *Mailing Add:* 3208 NW Lynch Way Redmond OR 97756

NIELSEN, LEWIS THOMAS, b Salt Lake City, Utah, Aug 6, 20; m 75. ENTOMOLOGY. *Educ:* Univ Utah, BA, 41, MA, 47, PhD, 55. *Prof Exp:* From instr to assoc prof, 46-66, PROF BIOL & ENTOM, UNIV UTAH, 66- *Concurrent Pos:* prin investr, Mosquito Res, Scand, 78 & 79. *Mem:* Am Mosquito Control Asn (vpres, 75-76, pres, 77); Entom Soc Am. *Res:* Systematics, biology and distribution of mosquitoes of Holarctic Region; medical entomology. *Mailing Add:* Dept of Biol Univ of Utah Salt Lake City UT 84112

NIELSEN, LOWELL WENDELL, b Weston, Idaho, Apr 23, 10; m 35; c 3. PLANT PATHOLOGY. *Educ:* Utah State Univ, BS, 35, MS, 37; Cornell Univ, PhD(plant path), 41. *Prof Exp:* Asst prof bot, Exp Sta, NC State Univ, 41-44; pathologist, Calif Packing Corp, Ill, 44-45; assoc horticulturist, Idaho Agr Exp Sta, 45-48; assoc prof plant path, 48-54, prof plant path, NC State Univ, 54-75; RETIRED. *Concurrent Pos:* Fulbright res scholar, NZ, 64-65; adv, US AID-NC State Univ mission to Peru, 66-71. *Mem:* Am Phytopath Soc; Potato Asn Am. *Res:* Plant virus diseases; diseases of Irish and sweet potatoes; bacterial decays. *Mailing Add:* Dept Plant Path NC State Univ Raleigh NC 27607

NIELSEN, MERLYN KEITH, b Omaha, Nebr, Oct 9, 48; m 70. ANIMAL BREEDING. *Educ:* Univ Nebr-Lincoln, BS, 70; Iowa State Univ, MS, 72, PhD(animal sci), 74. *Prof Exp:* Asst prof, 74-78, ASSOC PROF, UNIV NEBR-LINCOLN, 78-, MEM FAC ANIMAL SCI, 76- *Mem:* Am Soc Animal Sci; Biomet Soc. *Res:* Accurate identification of additive genetic differences in beef cattle; planning crossbreeding systems. *Mailing Add:* 215 Marvel Baker Hall Univ of Nebr Lincoln NE 68583

NIELSEN, MILO ALFRED, b Madelia, Minn, Aug, 20, 38; m 58; c 3. FOOD SCIENCE. *Educ:* Univ Minn, BS, 65, MS, 67, PhD(food sci), 71. *Prof Exp:* Sr food scientist, 71-72, mgr pet food res, 72-78, asst dir pet food res, 78-82, DIR BASIC RES, CARNATION RES LAB, VAN NUYS, CALIF, 82- *Mem:* Inst Food Technologists. *Res:* Emulsion stability and oxidation. *Mailing Add:* 8015 Van Nuys Blvd Van Nuys CA 91412

NIELSEN, N NORBY, b Denmark, Mar 29, 28; US citizen; m 54; c 2. STRUCTURAL ENGINEERING, EARTHQUAKE DESIGN. *Educ:* Tech Univ Denmark, MS, 54; Calif Inst Technol, PhD(civil eng), 64. *Prof Exp:* Instr civil eng, Univ Southern Calif, 56-58, asst prof, 58-60; asst prof, Univ Ill, Urbana, 64-66, assoc prof, 66-70; chmn, 72-81, PROF CIVIL ENG, UNIV HAWAII, 70- *Concurrent Pos:* UNESCO expert, Int Inst Seismol & Earthquake Eng, 67-68; Erskine fel, Univ Canterbury, 76. *Honors & Awards:* Moisseiff Award, Am Soc Civil Engrs, 72. *Mem:* Am Soc Civil Engrs; Am Soc Eng Educ; Am Concrete Inst; Am Acad Mech; Earthquake Eng Res Inst. *Res:* Earthquake engineering and design; behavior of reinforced concrete multistory buildings subjected to earthquakes. *Mailing Add:* Col Eng Univ Hawaii 2540 Dole St Honolulu HI 96822

NIELSEN, N OLE, b Edmonton, Alta, Mar 3, 30; m 55; c 3. VETERINARY PATHOLOGY. *Educ:* Univ Toronto, DVM, 56; Univ Minn, PhD(vet path), 63. *Prof Exp:* Private practice, 56-57; res assoc lab animal care & radiation res, Med Dept, Brookhaven Nat Lab, 60-61; from instr to assoc prof, 57-68, head dept, 68-74, dean, 74-82, PROF VET PATH, WESTERN COL VET MED, UNIV SASK, 68- *Concurrent Pos:* Med Res Coun Can vis scientist, Int Escherichia Ctr, Copenhagen, 70-71. *Mem:* AAAS; Am Col Vet Path; Am Vet Med Asn; Can Vet Med Asn (pres, 68-69). *Res:* Relationship of E coli to enteric disease; diseases of swine; enteric pathology. *Mailing Add:* Western Col of Vet Med Univ of Sask Saskatoon SK S7N 0W0 Can

NIELSEN, NORMAN RUSSELL, b Pittsburgh, Pa, Sept 8, 41; m 63; c 1. COMPUTER SYSTEM DESIGN & EVALUATION, SYSTEM SIMULATION. *Educ:* Pomona Col, BA, 63; Stanford Univ, MBA, 65, PhD(opers & systs anal), 67. *Prof Exp:* From asst prof to assoc prof opers & systs anal, Stanford Univ, 66-73; sr res engr, 73-74, mgr info systs group, Stanford Res Inst, 74-75; comput syst prog mgr, 75-79, PROG DIR, ADVAN COMPUT SYST DEPT, SRI INT, 79-; DIR, CLAREMONT CAPITAL CORP, 76- *Concurrent Pos:* From asst dir to dept dir, Stanford Comput Ctr, 66:72. *Mem:* AAAS; Asn Comput Mach; Inst Mgt Sci. *Res:* Computer system design; system simulation; computer resource allocation; computer modeling; computer aided manufacturing; computer networks; management information systems; parallel-processing computer systems; distributed systems; computer performance measurement and evaluation. *Mailing Add:* Advan Comput Syst Dept SRI Int 333 Ravenswood Ave Menlo Park CA 94025

NIELSEN, PAUL HERRON, b Berkeley, Calif, June 14, 43; m 69; c 1. SOLID STATE PHYSICS. *Educ:* Univ Chicago, BS, 64, MS, 65, PhD(physics), 70. *Prof Exp:* Assoc scientist, Xerox Corp, 69-71, scientist, 71-78, sr scientist, 78-79; scientist, 79-80, MGR ELECTRONIC MAT, UNIV DEL, 80- *Concurrent Pos:* Vpres, Nielsen-Kellerman Co, Inc, 78-; assoc prof, Bartel Res Found, 80- *Mem:* Am Phys Soc; Am Phys Soc; Am Vacuum Soc; Int Solar Energy Soc. *Res:* Ultraviolet photoemission spectroscopy; energy levels and electronics structures of molecules, solids, and interfaces; photosensitization, photovoltaic conversion, amorphous silicon. *Mailing Add:* 1817 Shipley Rd Wilmington DE 19803

NIELSEN, PAUL LIVINGSTONE, polymer chemistry, see previous edition

NIELSEN, PETER ADAMS, b Evanston, Ill, Oct 12, 26; m 52; c 2. MICROBIOLOGY. *Educ:* Williams Col, BA, 50; Columbia Univ, MA, 56, PhD(bot), 60. *Prof Exp:* Biologist, Lederle Labs, Am Cyanamid Co, 51-55; asst bot, Barnard Col, Columbia Univ, 55-56, univ, 57-59; microbiologist, Lederle Labs, Am Cyanamid Co, NY, 59-67; HEAD MICROBIOL SECT, VICK DIV RES & DEVELOP, RICHARDSON-VICKS, INC, 67- *Mem:* Am Soc Microbiol; Soc Indust Microbiol. *Res:* Microbial physiology; microbiology of skin and oral cavity; antimicrobials; preservative evaluation; microbiological quality control; quality assurance of pharmaceuticals, toiletries and nutritional products. *Mailing Add:* Vick Div Res & Develop Richardson-Vicks Inc Bradford Rd Mount Vernon NY 10553

NIELSEN, PETER JAMES, b North Platte, Nebr, Feb 21, 38; m 61; c 2. CELL PHYSIOLOGY, PROTOZOOLOGY. *Educ:* Midland Col, BS, 60; Univ Nebr, MS, 65, PhD(zool physiol), 68. *Prof Exp:* Teaching asst physiol, Univ Nebr, 64-66; asst prof biol sci, 68-77, ASSOC PROF BIOL SCI, WESTERN ILL UNIV, 77- *Mem:* AAAS; Am Soc Zool; Soc Protozool. *Res:* Effects on the phenomena of aging using the protozoan, Tetrahymena pyriformis, as a research tool; continuous culture of Tetrahymena as a tool for studying metabolism; tissue culture of chick embryo fibroblasts; studying effects of various toxins on in vitro aging. *Mailing Add:* Dept of Biol Sci Western Ill Univ Macomb IL 61455

NIELSEN, PETER TRYON, b Durham, NC, Dec 24, 33; m 60; c 2. PLANT PHYSIOLOGY, BIOPHYSICS. *Educ:* Duke Univ, BS, 57; Univ NC, Chapel Hill, PhD(algal physiol), 65. *Prof Exp:* NIH fel biophys, East Anglia, 65-66; asst prof plant physiol & biophys, State Univ NY Col Plattsburgh, 66-70; ASSOC PROF BIOL, JAMES MADISON UNIV, 70- *Mem:* Am Soc Plant Physiol; Bot Soc Am. *Res:* Ion accumulation and transport; photosynthesis and role of light reactions in ion transport; effects of heavy metal ions and algal physiology. *Mailing Add:* Dept of Biol James Madison Univ Harrisonburg VA 22807

NIELSEN, PHILIP EDWARD, b Chicago, Ill, July 18, 44; m 71; c 3. TRADE-OFF ANALYSIS, ZERO-ORDER PHYSICS. *Educ:* Ill Inst Technol, BS, 66; Case Western Reserve Univ, MS, 68, PhD(physics), 70. *Prof Exp:* Physicist, Air Force Weapons Lab, US Air Force, 70-74; asst prof physics, Air Force Inst Technol, 74-77, assoc prof, 77-79, dep head dept, 78-79; DIR, DIRECTORATE AEROSPACE STUDIES, AIR FORCE SYSTS COMMAND, 80- *Mem:* AAAS; Am Phys Soc. *Res:* System effectiveness modeling; interaction of high-intensity lasers with matter; laser-plasma interactions; transport phenomena in metals and alloys. *Mailing Add:* Directorate Aerospace Studies Air Force Contract Mgt Div Kirtland AFB NM 87117

NIELSEN, RICHARD LEROY, economic geology, see previous edition

NIELSEN, ROBERT PETER, b New Brunswick, NJ, Mar 14, 37; m 61; c 4. INDUSTRIAL CHEMISTRY. *Educ:* Rutgers Univ, BS, 58; Univ Fla, PhD(inorg chem), 62. *Prof Exp:* Chemist, Shell Develop Co, Calif, 62-66, sr technologist, Shell Chem Co, NY, 66-68, sr chemist, Tex, 68-72, staff chemist, 72-80, SR STAFF CHEMIST, SHELL DEVELOP CO, 80- *Mem:* Am Chem Soc; The Chem Soc; Sigma Xi. *Res:* Metallo-organic; transition metal homogeneous catalysis; olefin polymerization catalysis; heterogeneous catalysis; ethylene oxide chemistry; oxychlorination chemistry. *Mailing Add:* Westhollow Res Ctr-Shell Develop Co PO Box 1380 Houston TX 77001

NIELSEN, STUART DEE, b Green River, Wyo, Oct 26, 32; m 54; c 4. INDUSTRIAL HYGIENE, ANALYTICAL CHEMISTRY. *Educ:* Univ Wyo, BS, 54; Univ Wash, PhD(org chem), 62. *Prof Exp:* Sr chemist, Rohm and Haas Co, Pa, 62-66; sr res chemist, 66-68, res scientist, Gen Tire & Rubber Co, 68-78; mem staff, 78-79, SECT LEADER, LOS ALAMOS NAT LAB, 79- *Mem:* Am Chem Soc; Am Indust Hygiene Asn; Soc Appl Spectros. *Res:* Polymer synthesis and properties; kinetics and mechanisms of polymerization processes; pollution control methods and analysis. *Mailing Add:* 114 Sherwood Blvd White Rock NM 87544

NIELSEN, SUSAN THOMSON, b Astoria, Ore, Apr 26, 47; m 69. PHARMACOLOGY. *Educ:* Univ Chicago, BS, 69; Univ Rochester, PhD(pharmacol), 74. *Prof Exp:* Fel radiol biol & biophys, Univ Rochester, 75-78; fel pharmacol, ICI Americas Inc, 78-79, res pharmacologist, 80-81; SUPVR GI PHARMACOL, WYETH LABS, INC, 81- *Mem:* AAAS; Am Chem Soc; NY Acad Sci. *Res:* Pharmacology of receptors; mechanism of action of histamine, steroid and protein hormones; hormone receptors; cyclic nucleotides and hormone stimulated adenyl cyclase activity. *Mailing Add:* Dept Pharmacol Wyeth Labs PO Box 8299 Philadelphia PA 19101

NIELSEN, SVEND WOGE, b Herning, Denmark, Apr 4, 26; nat US; m 52; c 3. VETERINARY PATHOLOGY. *Educ:* Herning Gym, Denmark, Artium, 45; Royal Vet Col, DVM, 51; Ohio State Univ, MSc, 57, PhD(path), 59. *Prof Exp:* Res path, Angell Mem Animal Hosp, Boston, 51-52; res asst, Ont Vet Col, Can, 52-53, lectr, 53-55, asst prof, 55; from instr to assoc prof vet path, Ohio State Univ, 55-60; PROF PATHOBIOL, UNIV CONN, 60- *Concurrent Pos:* NIH spec fel, Univ Cambridge, 67-68; dir, WHO Collab Lab Urogenital Tumors of Animals, 68-74; dir, Northeastern Res Ctr Wildlife Dis, 72-; vis prof, Cornell Univ, 74 & Univ Calif, Davis, 81-82. *Mem:* Int Acad Path; Am Vet Med Asn; Am Col Vet Path (pres, 71-72); Wildlife Dis Asn. *Res:* Comparative oncology; pathology of vitamin A deficiency and vitamin A toxicosis in animals; diseases of wildlife in the northeastern United States; classification of urogenital neoplasms of animals. *Mailing Add:* 498 Gurleyville Rd Storrs CT 06268

NIELSEN, UDO, forestry, remote sensing, see previous edition

NIELSON, CLAIR W, b Pocatello, Idaho, Dec 10, 35. PHYSICS. *Educ:* Mass Inst Technol, SB, 57, PhD(physics), 62. *Prof Exp:* From instr to asst prof physics, Swarthmore Col, 63-68; MEM STAFF, LOS ALAMOS NAT LAB, 68- *Mem:* Am Phys Soc. *Res:* Atomic and molecular theory; numerical simulation of plasma. *Mailing Add:* Los Alamos Nat Lab Box 1663-P-18 Mail Stop 642 Los Alamos NM 87544

NIELSON, DENNIS LON, b Urbana, Ill, Jan 13, 48; m 70. ECONOMIC GEOLOGY. *Educ:* Beloit Col, BA, 70; Dartmouth Col, MA, 72, PhD(geol), 74. *Prof Exp:* staff geologist, Anaconda Co, 74-78; geologist, Earth Sci Lab, 78-79, PROJ MGR, UNIV UTAH RES INST, 79-, SECT MGR GEOL, 81- *Concurrent Pos:* Instr, Calderas & Hydrothermal Systs, Yellowstone Inst, 79- *Mem:* Geol Soc Am. *Res:* Structural controls of geothermal systems; genesis of uranium concentrations in igneous and metamorphic systems; geothermal exploration technology. *Mailing Add:* Earth Sci Lab Univ Utah Res Inst 420 Chipeta Way Salt Lake City UT 84108

NIELSON, ELDON DENZEL, b Salt Lake City, Utah, Dec 4, 20; m 42; c 3. BIOCHEMISTRY. *Educ:* Univ Utah, AB, 46; Univ Ill, PhD(biochem), 48. *Prof Exp:* Instr biochem, Univ Southern Calif, 48-49; sect head, Upjohn Co, 49-56; head biochem dept, Armour Pharmaceut Co, 56-58; head biochem, Sterling-Winthrop Res Inst, 58-62; mgr biol res div, RJ Reynolds Tobacco Co,

62-69; vpres phys sci, Mead Johnson Res Ctr, 69-75, DIR LICENSING, MEAD JOHNSON & CO, 75- *Mem:* AAAS; Soc Indust Microbiol; Am Chem Soc; NY Acad Sci. *Res:* Adrenal steroids; fermentation; natural products; tobacco; pulmonary physiology; pharmaceutical synthesis; chemical development. *Mailing Add:* Mead Johnson & Co 2404 Pennsylvania Ave Evansville IN 47721

NIELSON, GEORGE MARIUS, b Wadsworth, Ohio, May 17, 34. MATHEMATICS. *Educ:* Ohio Wesleyan Univ, BA, 56; Univ Wis, MS, 57, PhD(math), 63. *Prof Exp:* Instr math, Ohio Wesleyan Univ, 59-60; asst prof, 63-70, ASSOC PROF MATH, KALAMAZOO COL, 70- *Mem:* Am Math Soc; Math Asn Am. *Res:* Lie algebras. *Mailing Add:* Dept of Math Kalamazoo Col Kalamazoo MI 49007

NIELSON, HOWARD CURTIS, b Richfield, Utah, Sept 12, 24; m 48; c 7. STATISTICS, MATHEMATICS. *Educ:* Univ Utah, BS, 47; Univ Ore, MS, 49; Stanford Univ, MBA, 56, PhD(bus admin & statist), 58. *Prof Exp:* Actg instr math, Univ Utah, 46-47; asst, Univ Ore, 47-49; sr statistician, Calif & Hawaii Sugar Refining Corp, 49-51; res economist, Stanford Res Inst, 51-57; assoc prof econ, 57-60, assoc prof statist, 60-61, chmn dept, 60-63, PROF STATIST, BRIGHAM YOUNG UNIV, 61-, DIR, CTR BUS & ECON RES, 71- *Concurrent Pos:* Consult, Hercules Powder Co, 60-65; mgr & consult, C-E-I-R, Inc, 63-65; prin scientist, GCA Corp, 65-67 & Fairchild Semiconductor Corp, 67; consult, EG&G, Inc, 67; econ develop consult, Ford Found, Jordan, 70; mem, Gov Econ Resources Adv Coun. *Mem:* Am Statist Asn; Sigma Xi. *Res:* Economic forecasting; demographic studies and projections; statistical methods in industry; sampling survey methods; experimental design; probability; reliability; operations research. *Mailing Add:* Ctr for Bus & Econ Res Brigham Young Univ Provo UT 84601

NIELSON, LYMAN J(ULIUS), b Burley, Idaho, Oct 16, 18; m 43; c 2. SANITARY ENGINEERING, PERSONNEL ADMINISTRATION. *Educ:* St Martin's Col, BSCE, 62; Wash State Univ, MSSE, 64. *Prof Exp:* Inspector indust wastes, Wash State Pollution Control Comn, 52-53, chief inspector, 53-60, dist engr water pollution, 60-62, chief res, 62-63; chief reservoir res, Fed Water Pollution Control Admin Pac Northwest Water Lab, 64-67, chief potato processing waste res proj, NW Region, 67, chief training, 67-69, regional prog dir, Manpower & Training, 69-71; chief manpower & training br, 71-72, DIR, WASH OPERS OFF, REGION X, ENVIRON PROTECTION AGENCY, 72- *Honors & Awards:* Silver Medal, Environ Protection Agency, 72. *Mem:* Am Soc Civil Engrs; Am Acad Environ Engrs; Water Pollution Control Fedn; Nat Soc Prof Engrs. *Res:* Radiological health; effects of impoundment on water quality and the development of methods for predicting these effects; development of methods for minimizing adverse effects to water quality from impoundment. *Mailing Add:* 2835 24th Ave W Seattle WA 98199

NIELSON, MERVIN WILLIAM, b Provo, Utah, Apr 7, 27; m 56; c 3. ENTOMOLOGY. *Educ:* Utah State Univ, BS, 49, MS, 50; Ore State Univ, PhD(entom), 55. *Prof Exp:* Asst entomologist, Univ Ariz, 55-56, assoc prof, 68-77; entomologist, 56-68, RES LEADER SCI & EDUC ADMIN-AGR RES, USDA, 68- *Concurrent Pos:* Asst, Utah State Univ, 49-50; asst & instr, Ore State Univ, 51-55; adj prof, Univ Ariz, 77- *Mem:* AAAS; Entom Soc Am; Soc Syst Zool. *Res:* Taxonomy of the Cicadellidae; biology of leafhoppers and aphids; insect transmission of plant viruses; development of crop resistance to insects. *Mailing Add:* Sci & Educ Admin-Agr Res US Dept of Agr 2000 E Allen Rd Tucson AZ 85719

NIELSON, READ R, b Omaha, Nebr, Aug 4, 28; m 54; c 4. PHYSIOLOGY. *Educ:* Grinnell Col, BA, 50; Univ Iowa, MS, 52; Marquette Univ, PhD(physiol), 61. *Prof Exp:* Asst prof, 61-67, ASSOC PROF ZOOL, MIAMI UNIV, 67- *Concurrent Pos:* NIH res grant, 62-65. *Mem:* Am Physiol Soc. *Res:* Thyroid physiology and regulation of metabolism; effect of electrical stimulation on glycogen concentration in skeletal muscle during acute inanition; metabolic changes in the intact rat and excised tissues after thyroidectomy; changes in succinic dehydrogenase activity related to feeding. *Mailing Add:* Dept of Zool Miami Univ Oxford OH 45056

NIEM, ALAN RANDOLPH, b New York, NY, Mar 7, 44; m 67. GEOLOGY. *Educ:* Antioch Col, BS, 66; Univ Wis-Madison, MS, 68, PhD(geol), 71. *Prof Exp:* Asst geol, Univ Wis-Madison, 66-70; asst prof, 70-76, ASSOC PROF ORE STATE UNIV, 76- *Mem:* Am Asn Petrol Geol; Soc Econ Paleont & Mineral; Geol Soc Am. *Res:* Sedimentation; sedimentary petrography; volcaniclastic sediments; stratigraphy of geosynclinal rocks of the south-central and western United States; hydrogeology. *Mailing Add:* Dept of Geol Ore State Univ Corvallis OR 97331

NIEMAN, GEORGE CARROLL, b Dayton, Ohio, Dec 25, 38; m 60; c 3. PHYSICAL CHEMISTRY, SPECTROSCOPY. *Educ:* Carnegie Inst Technol, BS, 61; Calif Inst Technol, PhD(chem), 65. *Prof Exp:* Asst prof chem, Univ Rochester, 64-70; assoc prof, Muskingum Col, 70-76, prof chem, 76-79; ASSOC PROF, MONMOUTH COL, 79- *Mem:* Am Chem Soc. *Res:* Molecular crystals; nonradiative transitions; energy transfer; triplet states. *Mailing Add:* Dept Chem Monmouth Col Monmouth IL 61462

NIEMAN, RICHARD HOVEY, b Pasadena, Calif, Nov 7, 22; m 46; c 2. PLANT PHYSIOLOGY. *Educ:* Univ Southern Calif, AB, 49, MS, 53; Univ Chicago, PhD(plant physiol), 55. *Prof Exp:* Asst histol & morphol, Univ Chicago, 51-54, plant physiol, 54, res assoc biochem, 55-57; PLANT PHYSIOLOGIST, US SALINITY LAB, 57- *Mem:* AAAS; Am Soc Plant Physiol; Am Inst Biol Sci; Sigma Xi; NY Acad Sci. *Res:* Influence of salinity and drought on ion uptake, metabolism, and bioenergetics of plant cells; physiological-biochemical basis of salt tolerance of plants. *Mailing Add:* US Salinity Lab 4500 Glenwood Dr Riverside CA 92501

NIEMAN, TIMOTHY ALAN, b Cincinnati, Ohio, Dec 31, 48; m 70. ANALYTICAL CHEMISTRY. *Educ:* Purdue Univ, BS, 71; Mich State Univ, PhD(chem), 75. *Prof Exp:* Grad asst chem, Mich State Univ, 71-75; asst prof, 75-81, ASSOC PROF ANAL CHEM, UNIV ILL, URBANA, 81- *Mem:* Am Chem Soc; Soc Appl Spectros. *Res:* Analytical spectroscopy and kinetics; chemical instrumentation and interactive computer control; analytical chemiluminescence bipolar pulse conductance, ion selective electrodes, coulostatics. *Mailing Add:* Sch of Chem Sci Roger Adams Lab Univ of Ill Urbana IL 61801

NIEMANN, RALPH ARTHUR, b Centralia, Ill, Oct 8, 19; m 72; c 7. MATHEMATICS, COMPUTER SCIENCE. *Educ:* DePauw Univ, AB, 41; Univ Ill, MA, 42. *Prof Exp:* Programmer math, US Naval Proving Ground, Dahlgren, Va, 47-51, head comput div, 51-55; head comput & exterior ballistics dept, US Naval Weapons Lab, Dahlgren, 55-64, head warfare anal dept, 64-69, head eng & tech eval dept, 69-70; head, Strategic Systs Dept, US Naval Surface Weapons Ctr, Dahlgren, 70-79; RETIRED. *Honors & Awards:* Distinguished Civilian Serv Award, Secy Navy, 75. *Mem:* Asn Comput Mach; Am Math Asn; Fed Prof Asn. *Res:* Physics; engineering; operations research; technical management. *Mailing Add:* 25 Marshall Pl Fredericksburg VA 22401

NIEMANN, RALPH HENRY, b Farley, Mo, Mar 16, 22; m 48; c 3. MATHEMATICS. *Educ:* Park Col, BA, 47; Purdue Univ, MS, 49, PhD(math), 54. *Prof Exp:* Assoc prof math, Worcester Polytech Inst, 54-59; asst prof, 59-63, chmn math sect, Dept Math & Statist, 67-68, actg chmn dept, 68-69, PROF MATH, COLO STATE UNIV, 63- *Concurrent Pos:* Lectr, Math Asn High Sch Lectr Prog, 61, 62; consult, Summer Sci Inst Prog, India, 64-65. *Mem:* Math Asn Am. *Res:* Mathematical analysis. *Mailing Add:* Dept of Math Colo State Univ Ft Collins CO 80523

NIEMANN, THEODORE FRANK, b Burlington, Iowa, July 31, 39. POLYMER CHEMISTRY, COMPUTER SCIENCE. *Educ:* Univ Iowa, BS, 61; Univ Kans, PhD(chem), 67. *Prof Exp:* Res chemist, BF Goodrich Res Ctr, Ohio, 67-71; ASSOC SCIENTIST, DWIGHT P JOYCE RES CTR, GLIDDEN COATINGS & RESINS DIV, SCM CORP, STRONGSVILLE, 71- *Mem:* Am Chem Soc. *Res:* Computer applications in chemistry, laboratory automation and real-time systems. *Mailing Add:* 11442 Harbour Light Dr North Royalton OH 44133

NIEMCZYK, HARRY D, b Grand Rapids, Mich, July 17, 29; m 52; c 4. ENTOMOLOGY. *Educ:* Mich State Univ, BS, 57, MS, 58, PhD(entom), 61. *Prof Exp:* Asst instr entom, Mich State Univ, 60-61; entomologist, Can Dept Agr, 61-64; from asst prof to assoc prof, 64-71, PROF ENTOM, OHIO STATE UNIV & OHIO AGR RES & DEVELOP CTR, 71- *Concurrent Pos:* Consult entomologist, Chem-Lawn Corp, 74- *Mem:* Entom Soc Am; Int Turfgrass Soc. *Res:* Biology, ecology and control of insects associated with agricultural crops and turf. *Mailing Add:* 2935 Smithville Western Wooster OH 44691

NIEMCZYK, THOMAS M, b Madison, Wis, Mar 17, 47; m 81; c 1. ATOMIC SPECTROSCOPY, CHEMICAL INSTRUMENTATION. *Educ:* Univ Wis, BS, 69; Mich State Univ, PhD(chem), 73. *Prof Exp:* Asst prof, 73-80, ASSOC PROF CHEM, UNIV NMEX, 80- *Concurrent Pos:* Consult, Air Force Weapons Lab, Albuquerque, 75-77, Los Alamos Nat Lab, 81-, Denel & Assoc, 81-; vis prof, Univ Wis, 79. *Mem:* Am Chem Soc; Am Optical Soc; Soc Appl Spectros. *Mailing Add:* Dept Chem Univ NMex Albuquerque NM 87131

NIEMEIER, BERNARD AUGUST, SR, b Evansville, Ind, Oct 8, 19; m 43; c 2. MECHANICAL ENGINEERING, APPLIED PHYSICS. *Educ:* Univ Cincinnati, ME, 43; Rensselaer Polytech Inst, MME, 52. *Prof Exp:* Chief engr design, Exp Inc, 48-52; consult engr structures, Economy Cast Stone, 53-56; RES SCIENTIST METAL PHYSICS, METALL RES DIV, REYNOLDS METALS CO, 57- *Mem:* Am Soc Mech Engrs; Am Soc Testing & Mat; Am Soc Metals; Soc Exp Stress Anal; AAAS. *Res:* Structural mechanics of metals, especially reshaping metallic materials into items of utilitarian form, development of statistical mathematical models for strength, metal flow and formability. *Mailing Add:* 5208 Devonshire Rd Richmond VA 23225

NIEMEIER, RICHARD WILLIAM, b Akron, Ohio, May 16, 45; m 66; c 3. ENVIRONMENTAL HEALTH. *Educ:* Thomas More Col, AB, 67; Univ Cincinnati, MS, 69, PhD(environ health sci), 73. *Prof Exp:* NIH fel, 74-75, asst prof, Dept Environ Health, Col Med, Univ Cincinnati, 75-76; CHIEF, ACUTE & SUBCHRONIC TOXICOL SECT, EXP TOXICOL BR, DIV BIOMED & BEHAV SCI, NAT INST OCCUP SAFETY & HEALTH, HEW, 76- *Concurrent Pos:* Adj asst prof, Dept Environ Health, Col Med, Univ Cincinnati, 76-; mem, Task Force Environmental Cancer, Heart & Lung Disease, Dept Health & Human Serv & mem, Subcomt Environ Mutigens. *Mem:* Sigma Xi. *Res:* Pulmonary metabolism of carcinogens using the isolated perfused lung; industrial hygiene surveys and characterization of carcinogenic occupational environments; effects of inhaled toxicants on pulmonary alveolar macrophages; factors affecting carcinogenic response; teratology, mutagenesis; cutaneous toxicology. *Mailing Add:* Nat Inst Occup Safety & Health Robert A Taft Labs 4676 Columbia Pkwy Cincinnati OH 45226

NIEMEYER, KENNETH H, b St Louis, Mo, Sept 15, 28; m 53; c 1. VETERINARY MEDICINE. *Educ:* Univ Mo, BS & DVM, 55, MS, 62. *Prof Exp:* From instr to prof, 55-78, head small animal clins, 63-68, PROF & ASSOC CHMN VET MED & SURG, UNIV MO-COLUMBIA, 74-, ASST DEAN, COL VET MED, 76- *Mem:* Am Vet Med Asn. *Res:* Clinical veterinary medicine, especially as applied to small animals. *Mailing Add:* Dept Vet Med Univ Mo Columbia MO 65201

NIEMEYER, LAWRENCE E, b New Braunfels, Tex, Aug 6, 26; m 53; c 5. METEOROLOGY. *Educ:* Univ Tex, BA, 51; Univ Mich, MS, 65. *Prof Exp:* Observer, US Weather Bur, Nev, 55-56, res meteorologist, Ohio, 56-59, analyst forecaster, Calif, 59-61, res meteorologist, Robert A Taft Sanit Eng Ctr, Environ Sci Serv Admin, Ohio, 61-69; from asst dir to dir, Meteorol Lab, Environ Protection Agency, 69-81; CONSULT METEOROLOGIST, 82- *Mem:* AAAS; Am Meteorol Soc; Sigma Xi; Air Pollution Control Asn. *Res:* Air pollution meteorology. *Mailing Add:* 609 Compton Rd Raleigh NC 27609

NIEMEYER, SIDNEY, b Grand Rapids, Mich, Oct 27, 51; m 72. PHYSICS, SOLAR PHYSICS. *Educ:* Calvin Col, AB, 73; Univ Calif, Berkeley, PhD(physics), 78. *Prof Exp:* Asst res physicist, Univ Calif, Berkeley, 78, fel chem, 79-80, STAFF PHYSICIST, LAWRENCE LIVERMORE NAT LAB, UNIV CALIF, SAN DIEGO, 80- *Mem:* Meteoritical Soc. *Res:* History of the early solar system, as determined by isotopic analysis of meteorites, lunar rocks and terrestrial samples. *Mailing Add:* Dept of Chem Univ of Calif La Jolla CA 92037

NIEMI, ALFRED OTTO, b Grand Marais, Mich, Aug 13, 15; m 43; c 1. CONSERVATION. *Educ:* Mich State Univ, BS, 48, MA, 52, EdD(forestry ed), 60. *Prof Exp:* Teacher pub sch, Mich, 48-50; asst agr, Mich State Univ, 50-51; teacher pub sch, Mich, 51-56; asst prof agr & conserv forestry, 56-68, assoc prof conserv, 68-72, consult, Vista Training Ctr, 65, PROF CONSERV, NORTHERN MICH UNIV, 72- *Concurrent Pos:* Asst, Mich State Univ, 58-59; coordr, Upper Mich Jr Acad Sci, Arts & Letters, 59- *Mem:* Conserv Educ Asn; Soil Conserv Soc Am. *Res:* Forestry; agriculture; conservation education. *Mailing Add:* Dept of Geog Earth Sci Conserv Northern Mich Univ Marquette MI 49855

NIEMITZ, JEFFREY WILLIAM, b Orange, NJ, July 14, 50; m 73; c 3. OCEANOGRAPHY. *Educ:* Williams Col, BA, 72; Univ Southern Calif, PhD(geochem), 78. *Prof Exp:* ASST PROF GEOL, DICKINSON COL, 77- *Concurrent Pos:* Sedimentologist, Deep Sea Drilling Proj, 78-79. *Mem:* AAAS. *Res:* Geochemistry, sedimentology and tectonics of young rifting ocean basins (Gulf of California); trace element geochemistry and paleoclimate studies of various marine sediments; trace element pollution in nearshore sediments. *Mailing Add:* Dept Geol Dickinson Col Carlisle PA 17013

NIENABER, JAMES HENRY, geology, see previous edition

NIENHOUSE, EVERETT J, b Oak Park, Ill, Oct 29, 36; m 65. ORGANIC CHEMISTRY. *Educ:* Hope Col, AB, 58; Northwestern Univ, MSc, 62; State Univ NY Buffalo, PhD(org chem), 66. *Prof Exp:* asst prof org chem, 66-77, MEM FAC, FERRIS STATE COL, 77- *Mem:* Am Chem Soc; Royal Soc Chem. *Res:* Chemistry of bridged bicyclic systems; abnormal Grignard reactions; new synthetic reagents in organic chemistry; olefinic cyclizations. *Mailing Add:* Dept of Phys Sci Ferris State Col Big Rapids MI 49307

NIENHUIS, ARTHUR WESLEY, b Hudsonville, Mich, Aug 9, 41; m 68; c 4. NEMATOLOGY. *Educ:* Univ Calif, MD, 68. *Prof Exp:* Asst resident med, Mass Gen Hosp, 69-70; clin assoc, Nat Heart, Lung & Blood Inst, NIH, 70-72; clin fel hematol, Med Ctr, Children's Hosp, 72-73; chief, Clin Serv, Sect Clin Hematol, 73-77, CHIEF, CLIN HEMATOL BR, NAT HEART, LUNG & BLOOD INST, NIH, 77- *Concurrent Pos:* Deputy dir clin, Nat Heart, Lung & Blood Inst, 77- *Mem:* Asn Am Physicians; Am Soc Clin Invest; Am Soc Hematol; Am Fedn Clin Res. *Res:* Regulation of hemoglobin synthesis; structure and function of globin genes, and the molecular biology of thalassemia; evaluation and treatment of red blood cell disorders particularly thalassemia; sickle cell anemia and aplastic anemia. *Mailing Add:* Bldg 10 Rm 7D19 Clin Hematol Br Nat Heart Lung & Blood Inst NIH Bethesda MD 20205

NIENSTAEDT, HANS, b Copenhagen, Denmark, Dec 23, 22; m 49; c 5. FOREST GENETICS. *Educ:* Yale Univ, MF, 48, PhD(path), 51. *Prof Exp:* Asst geneticist, Agr Exp Sta, Univ Conn, 51-55; geneticist, Lake States Forest Exp Sta, 53-60, chief lab, N Cent Forest Exp Sta, Inst Forest Genetics, 60-76, CHIEF PLANT GENETICIST, FORESTRY SCI LAB, US FOREST SERV, 70- *Concurrent Pos:* US rep, Forest Biol Comt, Tech Asn Pulp & Paper Indust, 76; chmn, adv comt, Col Nat Res, Univ Wis, 75-81 & Lake States for Tree Improv Comt, 66-78; secy, Study Group Forest Tree Improv, NAm Forestry Comn, 76-78 & 80. *Mem:* AAAS; Soc Am Foresters; Int Union Forest Res Orgns; Tech Asn Pulp & Paper Indust. *Res:* Genetics of conifers of northern North America; breeding of spruces, and pines of northern North America. *Mailing Add:* Forestry Sci Lab Forest Serv USDA Box 898 Rhinelander WI 54501

NIER, ALFRED OTTO CARL, b St Paul, Minn, May 28, 11; m 37, 69; c 2. PHYSICS. *Educ:* Univ Minn, BE, 31, MS, 33, PhD(physics), 36. *Hon Degrees:* DSc, Univ Minn, 80. *Prof Exp:* Nat Res Coun fels, Harvard Univ, 36-38; from asst prof to assoc prof physics, Univ Minn, 38-43; physicist, Kellex Corp, NY, 43-45; chmn dept, 53-65, prof, 45-80, EMER PROF PHYSICS, UNIV MINN, MINNEAPOLIS, 80- *Honors & Awards:* Day Medal, Geol Soc Am, 56. *Mem:* Nat Acad Sci; fel Am Phys Soc; Am Philos Soc; Geochem Soc; Am Geophys Union. *Res:* Mass spectrometry; aeronomy. *Mailing Add:* Sch of Physics and Astron Univ of Minn Minneapolis MN 55455

NIERENBERG, WILLIAM AARON, b New York, NY, Feb 13, 19; m 41; c 2. PHYSICS. *Educ:* City Col New York, BS, 39; Columbia Univ, MA, 42, PhD(physics), 47. *Hon Degrees:* DSc, Univ Md, 81. *Prof Exp:* Tutor physics, City Col New York, 39-42, res scientist, Manhattan Proj, 42-45; instr physics, Columbia Univ, 46-48; asst prof, Univ Mich, 48-50; assoc prof, Univ Calif, Berkeley, 50-53, prof, 54-65; assoc prof, Univ Paris, 60-62; DIR SCRIPPS INST OCEANOG, UNIV CALIF, SAN DIEGO, 65-, VCHANCELLOR MARINE SCI, 69- *Concurrent Pos:* Dir, Hudson Labs, Columbia Univ, 53-54; mem mine adv comt, Nat Res Coun, 54-, consult comt nuclear constants, 58-; prof, Miller Inst Basic Res Sci, 57-59; consult, Nat Security Agency, 58-60 & President's Spec Proj Comt, 58-; asst secy gen sci, NATO, 60-62; adv at large, Dept of State, 68-; mem, Nat Sci Bd, 72-78; chmn nat adv comt oceans & atmosphere, 71-75; NATO sr sci fel, 69; mem, White House Task Force Oceanog, 69-70; mem oil spill panel, Off Sci & Technol, 69; chmn, NASA adv coun, 78-; mem, Space Panel, Naval Studies Bd, Nat Res Coun, 78- *Honors & Awards:* Compass Distinguished Achievement Award, Marine Technol Soc, 75; Procter Prize, Sigma Xi, 77; Richtmyer Mem lectr, Am Asn Physics Teachers, 79; Charles H Davis lectr, US Naval Postgrad Sch & Naval War Col, 81. *Mem:* Nat Acad Sci; fel Am Phys Soc; Am Acad Arts & Sci; Am Geophys Union. *Res:* Gas diffusion; molecular and atomic beams; physical oceanography; nuclear moments. *Mailing Add:* Scripps Inst Oceanog Univ Calif San Diego La Jolla CA 92093

NIERING, WILLIAM ALBERT, b Scotrun, Pa, Aug 28, 24; m 55; c 2. PLANT ECOLOGY. *Educ:* Pa State Univ, BS, 48, MS, 50; Rutgers Univ, PhD(plant ecol), 52. *Prof Exp:* From asst prof to assoc prof, 52-64, PROF BOT, CONN COL, 64- *Concurrent Pos:* Mem, Kapingamarangi Exped, Caroline Islands, 54, veg southwest, 62-64; consult, Recreation & Open Space Proj, Regional Plan Asn, Inc, 58; dir, Conn Arboretum, 65-; assoc dir environ biol prog, Nat Sci Found, 67-68. *Honors & Awards:* Mercer Award, Ecol Soc Am, 67. *Mem:* AAAS; Ecol Soc Am; Bot Soc Am; Am Inst Biol Sci. *Res:* Vegetation science; herbicides; wetland ecology; applied ecology. *Mailing Add:* Dept of Bot Conn Col Box 1511 New London CT 06320

NIERLICH, DONALD P, b Ft Lewis, Wash, Aug 10, 35; m 61; c 3. MICROBIAL PHYSIOLOGY, MOLECULAR BIOLOGY. *Educ:* Calif Inst Technol, BS, 57; Harvard Univ, PhD(bact), 62. *Prof Exp:* NSF fels, Mass Inst Technol, 63-64 & Inst Biol & Phys Chem, Paris, France, 64-65; from asst prof to assoc prof, 65-74, PROF MICROBIOL, UNIV CALIF, LOS ANGELES, 74- *Concurrent Pos:* Mem, Molecular Biol Inst, Univ Calif, Los Angeles, 74-; ed, J Bact. *Mem:* Am Soc Microbiol; Am Soc Biol Chem. *Res:* Regulation of metabolism, particularly the synthesis of RNA and its control. *Mailing Add:* Dept Microbiol Univ Calif Los Angeles CA 90024

NIES, ALAN SHEFFER, b Orange, Calif, Sept 30, 37; m 61; c 2. CLINICAL PHARMACOLOGY. *Educ:* Stanford Univ, BS, 59; Harvard Med Sch, MD, 63. *Prof Exp:* Resident & intern internal med, Univ Wash Hosp, 63-66; NIH fel clin pharmacol, Univ Calif, San Francisco, 66-68; chief clin pharmacol, Walter Reed Army Inst Res, 68-70; asst prof, 70-72, assoc prof med & pharmacol, Sch Med, Vanderbilt Univ, 72-76; PROF MED & PHARMACOL, UNIV COLO MED CTR, 77- *Mem:* AAAS; Am Fedn Clin Res; Am Soc Clin Invest; Am Soc Pharmacol & Exp Therapeut; NY Acad Sci. *Res:* Effects of disease on drug metabolism and disposition in man; prostaglandins and the circulation. *Mailing Add:* Div Clin Pharmacol C237 Univ Colo Med Ctr 4200 E Ninth Ave Denver CO 80262

NIESEN, THOMAS MARVIN, b San Diego, Calif, Apr 10, 44; m 67; c 1. MARINE ECOLOGY, POPULATION BIOLOGY. *Educ:* Univ Calif, Santa Barbara, BA, 66; San Diego State Univ, MS, 69; Univ Ore, PhD(biol), 73. *Prof Exp:* Instr, 73-75, asst prof, 75-79, ASSOC PROF BIOL, SAN FRANCISCO STATE UNIV, 79- *Concurrent Pos:* Consult, Asn Bay Area Govt, 75-77 & Oceanic Soc, 76-; proj dir, US Fish & Wildlife Serv, 78-79. *Mem:* Am Soc Limnol & Oceanog; AAAS; Ecol Soc Am; Estuarine Res Fedn. *Res:* Marine invertebrates; esturarine community ecology; intertidal and nearshore subtidal ecology. *Mailing Add:* Dept of Biol 1600 Holloway Ave San Francisco CA 94132

NIESSE, JOHN EDGAR, b Indianapolis, Ind, Nov 30, 27; m 58; c 2. MATERIALS SCIENCE. *Educ:* US Naval Acad, BS, 50; Mass Inst Technol, SM, 56, ScD(metall), 58. *Prof Exp:* Supvry engr, Crane Co, 59-60; supvry engr, Carborundum Co, 60-61, mgr process develop dept, 61-63, mgr ceramics & metall dept, 63-64, mgr technol br, NY, 64-67; chief ceramics res & develop sect, Space Systs Div, Avco Corp, Mass, 67-72; sr res group leader steel wire prod, Monsanto Co, 72-76; ENG SUPT MAT TECHNOL, MONSANTO CO, 76- *Mem:* Am Ceramic Soc; Nat Asn Corrosion Engrs; Am Soc Metals. *Res:* Abrasive materials; high temperature and wear resistant materials; corrosion resistant materials; composition, processing and application. *Mailing Add:* Monsanto Co F4EE 800 N Lindbergh Blvd St Louis MO 63167

NIETO, MICHAEL MARTIN, b Los Angeles, Calif, Mar 15, 40; m 73; c 2. THEORETICAL PHYSICS. *Educ:* Univ Calif, Riverside, BA, 61; Cornell Univ, PhD(physics), 66. *Prof Exp:* Res assoc physics, Inst Theoret Physics, State Univ NY Stony Brook, 66-68; vis physicist, Niels Bohr Inst, Copenhagen, Denmark, 68-70; lectr & asst prof physics, Univ Calif, Santa Barbara, 70-71; sr res assoc physics, Purdue Univ, Lafayette, 71-72; MEM STAFF, LOS ALAMOS NAT LAB, 72- *Mem:* Fel Am Phys Soc; Int Asn Math Phys. *Res:* Theoretical physics in fields of high energy, astrophysics and quantum mechanics; recent work on weak interactions, DKP meson and Bhabha arbitrary spin wave equations, quantum phase operators, coherent states, photon mass and law of planetary distances. *Mailing Add:* Theoretical Div MS-453 Los Alamos Nat Lab Los Alamos NM 87545

NIEVERGELT, JURG, b Lucerne, Switz, June 6, 38; US citizen; m 65; c 2. COMPUTER SCIENCE, SOFTWARE SYSTEMS. *Educ:* Swiss Fed Inst Technol, Dipl math, 62; Univ Ill, PhD(math), 65. *Prof Exp:* From asst prof to assoc prof, 65-72, prof math & comput sci, Univ Ill, Urbana, 72-77; PROF, SWISS FED INST TECHNOL, 71-72 & 75- *Mem:* AAAS; sr mem Inst Elec & Electronics Eng; Asn Comput Mach. *Res:* Computer software; program optimization; interactive systems and man-machine dialog; computers in education, in particular, computer-assisted instruction. *Mailing Add:* Informatik ETH Swiss Fed Inst Technol Zurich Switzerland

NIEWENHUIS, ROBERT JAMES, b Corsica, SDak, Sept 21, 36; m 58; c 2. ANATOMY, ELECTRON MICROSCOPY. *Educ:* Calvin Col, BS, 59; Mich State Univ, MS, 61; Univ Cincinnati, PhD(anat), 70. *Prof Exp:* Histopathologist, Procter & Gamble Co, 70-72; asst prof, 72-79, ASSOC PROF ANAT, SCH MED, UNIV CINCINNATI, 79- *Mem:* Electron Micros Soc Am; Am Asn Anatomists; Soc Study Reproduction; Sigma Xi; Am Soc Cell Biol. *Res:* Effects of cryptorchidism; vasectomy and toxins upon the ultrastructure of the testis and associated ducts; reproductive biology. *Mailing Add:* Dept Anat Med Sch Univ Cincinnati Cincinnati OH 45267

NIEWIAROWSKI, STEFAN, b Warsaw, Poland, Dec 4, 28. PHYSIOLOGICAL CHEMISTRY. *Educ:* Warsaw Univ, MD, 52, PhD(biochem), 60. *Prof Exp:* Res assoc clin biochem, Inst Hematol, Warsaw, 51-61; prof biochem, Med Sch, Brolystok, 61-68; vis prof med, Tufts Univ Med Sch, 68-70; assoc prof path, McMaster Univ Health Sci Ctr, 70-72; RES PROF MED, TEMPLE UNIV HEALTH SCI CTR, 72- & PROF PHYSIOL, 75- *Concurrent Pos:* Vis scientist, Ctr Nat Transfusion, Paris, 59 & Tufts Univ, 65; fel, Ont Heart Found, 70-71; mem, Int Comt Haemastasis Thrombosis,

68-73; consult, Res Rev Comt NIHL, 75-; NIH grants, 72-82 & Am Heart Asn grant, 78-81. *Mem:* Int Soc Hemat; Int Soc Thrombosis & Haemastasis; Am Physiol Soc; Am Soc Hemat. *Res:* Molecular biology of the platelet and its significance for hemostasis, thrombosis and atherosclerosis; platelet interaction with enzymes, drugs, and plasma proteins; platelet secretory proteins. *Mailing Add:* Thrombosis Res Health Sci Ctr Temple Univ Philadelphia PA 19140

NIEWISCH, HELGARD, b Wilkau, Ger, Aug 15, 39. VETERINARY PATHOLOGY, LABORATORY ANIMAL MEDICINE. *Educ:* Univ Hannover, Dr med vet, 64. *Prof Exp:* Asst prof res hemat, Dept Microbiol, Univ Southern Calif, 65-68; lectr macromolecular biochem, nat Ctr Sci Res, Univ Montpelier, 68-71; asst prof pulmonary path, Univ Southern Calif, 71-75; campus vet, Univ Calif, Los Angeles, 75-80, asst prof comp path, 77-80; ASSOC PROF PATH & DIR ANIMAL RES FACIL, STATE UNIV NY STONY BROOK, 80- *Mem:* Sigma Xi; World Vet Pathologists; Am Asn Lab Animal Sci; Am Vet Med Asn; Soc Lab Animals Sci. *Res:* Animal models of human disease; comparative pathology; experimental leukemias; pathology of lymphoid tumors. *Mailing Add:* Dept Path State Univ NY Stony Brook NY 11790

NIFFENEGGER, DANIEL ARVID, b Grinnell, Iowa, Apr 7, 30; m 53; c 2. BOTANY, AGRONOMY. *Educ:* Iowa State Univ, BS, 52, PhD(bot, 67; Mont State Univ, MS, 57. *Prof Exp:* Seed analyst, Mont State Univ, 55-64, asst agron, 58-62, asst prof agron, 62-64; asst agron, Iowa State Univ, 64-67; biometrician, 67-69, asst dir, Biomet Serv Staff, 69-72, prog analyst, N Cent Region, 72-76, chief prog planning & rev, Sci & Educ Admin-Agr Res, Peoria, Ill, 76-81, ASST DEP ADMINR, NAT PROG STAFF, AGR RES SERV, USDA, BELTSVILLE, MD, 81- *Mem:* Am Soc Agron; Asn Off Seed Anal; Biomet Soc; Am Statist Asn. *Res:* Seed testing methodology; use of seed test results to determine field seeding rates; development of a seed homogeneity test; seed tolerances; seed research priorities; grain sampling; tobacco fumigation. *Mailing Add:* Agr Res Serv USDA Bldg 005 Beltsville Agr Res Ctr Beltsville MD 20705

NIGAM, BISHAN PERKASH, b Delhi, India, July 14, 28; m 56; c 3. PARTICLE PHYSICS, NUCLEAR PHYSICS. *Educ:* Univ Delhi, BSc, 46, MSc, 48; Rochester Univ, PhD(theoret physics), 54. *Prof Exp:* Lectr physics, Univ Delhi, 50-52 & 55-56; asst, Rochester Univ, 52-54; res fel, Case Inst, 54-55; Nat Res Coun Can res fel, 56-59; res assoc, Rochester Univ, 59-60, asst part-time prof physics, 60-61; assoc prof, State Univ NY Buffalo, 61-64; PROF PHYSICS, ARIZ STATE UNIV, 64- *Concurrent Pos:* Prin scientist, Basic Sci Res Lab, Gen Dynamics/Electronics, 57-58; prof, Univ Wis-Milwaukee, 66-67. *Mem:* Fel Am Phys Soc. *Res:* Theoretical and elementary particle physics; field theory. *Mailing Add:* Dept of Physics Ariz State Univ Tempe AZ 85281

NIGAM, LAKSHMI NARAYAN, b Fatehpur, India, Sept 17, 34; m 58; c 3. FLUID MECHANICS, MATHEMATICS. *Educ:* Univ Allahabad, BSc, 55, MSc, 57; Indian Inst Technol, Kharagpur, PhD(fluid mech), 61. *Prof Exp:* Sr res asst appl math, Indian Inst Technol, Bombay, 60-61, from assoc lectr to lectr, 61-66, asst prof, 66-67; from asst prof to assoc prof, 67-73, chmn dept, 73-78, PROF MATH, QUINNIPIAC COL, 73- *Concurrent Pos:* Adj asst prof, New Haven Col, 68-69. *Mem:* Am Math Soc; Soc Indust & Appl Math; Math Asn Am. *Res:* Structure and propagation of shock waves in interstellar gas; gas shear flow past cylinders and wings when the effects of compressibility and viscosity are negligible. *Mailing Add:* Dept of Math Quinnipiac Col Hamden CT 06518

NIGAM, PRAKASH CHANDRA, insect toxicology, serology, see previous edition

NIGG, HERBERT NICHOLAS, b Detroit, Mich, July 9, 41; m 64; c 2. ENTOMOLOGY. *Educ:* Mich State Univ, BS, 67; Univ Ill, Urbana-Champaign, PhD(entom), 72. *Prof Exp:* Nat Res Coun-USDA fel insect endocrinol, Insect Physiol Lab, USDA, Md, 72-74; asst prof, 74-79, assoc prof insect toxicol, 79-81, ASSOC PROF ENTOM & NEMATOL, INST FOOD & AGR SCI, AGR RES & EDUC CTR, UNIV FLA, 81- *Mem:* Soc Toxicol; Entom Soc Am; Am Chem Soc; Sigma Xi. *Res:* Metabolism of insect molting hormones and the relationship between agricultural worker health and pesticides. *Mailing Add:* Inst Food & Agr Sci Univ Fla 700 Exp Sta Rd Lake Alfred FL 33850

NIGH, EDWARD LEROY, JR, b Hagerstown, Md, Aug 25, 27; m 78; c 3. PLANT PATHOLOGY, NEMATOLOGY. *Educ:* Colo Agr & Mech Col, BS, 52; Colo State Univ, MS, 56; Ore State Univ, PhD(plant path), 62. *Prof Exp:* Tech dir cotton res, Algodonera del Valle, SA, Mex, 54-62; from asst prof to assoc prof plant path & nematol, 62-67, head dept plant path, 67-76, prof plant path, assoc dean agr & assoc dir, Coop Exten Serv, 76-78, RES SCIENTIST & EXTEN NEMATOLOGIST, UNIV ARIZ, 78- *Mem:* Am Phytopath Soc; Soc Nematol. *Res:* Entomology; nematology; plant pathology. *Mailing Add:* Univ Ariz Agr Exp Sta 6425 W 8th St Yuma AZ 85364

NIGH, HAROLD EUGENE, b Parnell, Mo, May 20, 32; m 55; c 4. SOLID STATE PHYSICS. *Educ:* Northwest Mo State Col, BS, 58; Iowa State Univ, PhD, 63. *Prof Exp:* Fel physics, Inst Atomic Res, 63-64; mem tech staff, 64-68, SUPVR SURFACE PHYSICS, BELL LABS, ALLENTOWN, 68- *Mem:* Am Phys Soc; Inst Elec & Electronics Engrs. *Res:* Magnetic properties of solids; semiconductor surface physics. *Mailing Add:* 3780 Sydna St Bethlehem PA 18017

NIGH, WESLEY GRAY, physical organic chemistry, see previous edition

NIGHSWANDER, JAMES EDWARD, plant pathology, see previous edition

NIGHSWONGER, PAUL FLOYD, b Alva, Okla, Apr 14, 23; m 51; c 6. PLANT ECOLOGY. *Educ:* Northwestern State Col, Okla, BS, 49; Univ Okla, MS, 67, PhD(bot), 69. *Prof Exp:* asst prof, 69-80, ASSOC PROF BIOL, NORTHWESTERN STATE COL, OKLA, 80- *Mem:* Inland Birdbanding Asn; Southwestern Asn Naturalists; Soc Range Mgt. *Mailing Add:* Dept of Biol Northwestern Okla State Univ Alva OK 73717

NIGHTINGALE, ARTHUR ESTEN, b Millville, NJ, Dec 25, 19; m 52; c 1. HORTICULTURE. *Educ:* NJ State Teachers Col, Glassboro, BS, 42; Rutgers Univ, New Brunswick, BS & MEd, 49; Tex A&M Univ, PhD(hort), 66. *Prof Exp:* Exten agent, Rutgers Univ & USDA, 45-47; dir adult educ, Atlantic County Voc Schs, NJ, 49-51; field rep horticulturist, Calif Spray Chem Co, 51-53; area horticulturist, 54-60; dir educ progs, State NJ, 60-63; asst, 63-66, PROF HORT, TEX A&M UNIV, 66- *Mem:* Am Soc Hort Sci; Am Inst Biol Sci; Am Hort Soc; fel Royal Hort Soc. *Res:* Chemical and environmental influences on plant growth and production. *Mailing Add:* Dept of Hort Sci Tex A&M Univ College Station TX 77843

NIGHTINGALE, CHARLES HENRY, b New York, NY, June 19, 39; m 62; c 3. PHARMACOKINETICS. *Educ:* Fordham Univ, BSPharm, 61; St John's Univ, NY, MS, 66; State Univ NY Buffalo, PhD(pharmaceut), 69. *Prof Exp:* Coordr educ & res, Mercy Hosp, New York, 64-66; from asst prof to assoc prof pharm, Univ Conn, 69-76, dir clin pharm prog, Sch Pharm, 70-76; assoc prof & chmn dept, State Univ NY Buffalo, 76-78; ASSOC RES PROF PHARM, UNIV CONN, 78-; DIR PHARM SERV, HARTFORD HOSP, 78- *Mem:* AAAS; Am Pharmaceut Asn; Acad Pharmaceut Sci; fel Am Col Clin Pharmacol; Am Soc Clin Pharmacol & Therapeut. *Res:* Factors affecting drug absorption, distribution, metabolism and excretion; pharmacokinetics of drug therapy; antibiotic transport in tissue sites, protein binding; antibiotic pharmacokinetics. *Mailing Add:* Hartford Hosp Hartford CT 06116

NIGHTINGALE, DOROTHY VIRGINIA, b Ft Collins, Colo, Feb 21, 02. ORGANIC CHEMISTRY. *Educ:* Univ Mo, AB, 22, AM, 23; Univ Chicago, PhD(org chem), 28. *Prof Exp:* From instr to prof, 23-58, EMER PROF CHEM, UNIV MO-COLUMBIA, 72- *Concurrent Pos:* Hon fel, Univ Minn, 38; res assoc, Univ Calif, Los Angeles, 46-47. *Honors & Awards:* Garvan Award, Am Chem Soc, 59. *Mem:* Am Chem Soc. *Res:* Chemiluminescence of organomagnesium halides; alkylations and acylations in the presence of aluminum chloride; action of nitrous acid on alicyclic amines; reactions of nitroparaffins with alicyclic ketones. *Mailing Add:* Dept of Chem Univ of Mo Columbia MO 65201

NIGHTINGALE, ELENA OTTOLENGHI, b Livorno, Italy, Nov 1, 32; US citizen; m 65; c 2. MEDICAL GENETICS, MICROBIAL GENETICS. *Educ:* Columbia Univ, AB, 54; Rockefeller Inst, PhD(microbial genetics), 61; NY Univ, MD, 64. *Prof Exp:* Genetics training grant, 61-62; Am Cancer Soc res scholar, 62-64; instr med, NY Univ, 64-65; asst prof microbiol, Med Col, Cornell Univ, 65-70; asst prof microbiol, Sch Med, Johns Hopkins Univ, 70-73; UAP clin genetics fel, Georgetown Univ, 73-74; resident fel genetics, 74-75, sr staff officer, 75-76, dir, Div Health Prom & Dis Prev, 76-80, SR PROG OFFICER, INST MED-NAT ACAD SCI, 80-; CLIN ASST PROF PEDIAT, GEORGETOWN UNIV, 80- *Concurrent Pos:* Vis assoc prof health policy, Harvard Univ, 80-; mem, Recombinent DNA Adv Comt, US Dept Health & Human Serv, 80-; consult genetic screening, Off Technol Assessment, US Cong, 80- *Mem:* AAAS; Am Soc Human Genetics; Am Soc Microbiol; Genetics Soc Am; fel, NY Acad Sci. *Res:* Bacterial transformations; somatic cell genetics; infectious diseases. *Mailing Add:* Nat Acad Sci 2101 Constitution Ave Washington DC 20418

NIGHTINGALE, HARRY IRVING, agricultural chemistry, see previous edition

NIGHTINGALE, RICHARD EDWIN, b Walla Walla, Wash, June 3, 26; m 44; c 3. PHYSICAL CHEMISTRY, NUCLEAR ENGINEERING. *Educ:* Whitman Col, BA, 49; Wash State Univ, PhD(chem), 53. *Prof Exp:* Fel, Univ Minn, 52-54; sr engr, Hanford Labs, Gen Elec Co, 54-57, supvr nonmetallic mat, 57-65; mgr mat res & serv sect, 65-68, mgr ceramics dept, 68-69, mgr metall & ceramics dept, 69-70, MGR CHEM TECHNOL DEPT, PAC NORTHWEST LABS, BATTELLE MEM INST, 70- *Honors & Awards:* Cert Merit, Am Nuclear Soc, 65. *Mem:* Am Chem Soc; fel Am Nuclear Soc; Am Carbon Soc (mem, Exec Comt, 64-71). *Res:* Infrared spectroscopy and molecular structure; radiation damage effects; graphite structure and properties; coal research, nuclear fuel reprocessing and waste disposal. *Mailing Add:* Pac Northwest Labs Battelle Mem Inst PO Box 999 Richland WA 99352

NIGRELLI, ROSS FRANCO, b Pittston, Pa, Dec 12, 03; m 27; c 1. PROTOZOOLOGY, PARASITOLOGY. *Educ:* Pa State Univ, BS, 27; NY Univ, MS, 29, PhD(invert zool), 36. *Prof Exp:* PATHOLOGIST, NY AQUARIUM, 34-, SR SCIENTIST, OSBORN LABS MARINE SCI, 72- *Concurrent Pos:* Consult, US Food & Drug Admin, 45; dir, Lab Marine Biochem & Ecol, NY Aquarium, 57-64, aquarium dir, 66-70; adj prof, NY Univ, 58-; dir, Osborn Labs Marine Sci, 64-72; mem, Subcomt Marine Biol, Comt Oceanog, Off Sci & Technol, 65-, Adv Panel, Sea Grant Proj, Off Sea Grant Progs, 69- & President's Coun, New York Ocean Sci Lab, 71-; fel, Conserv Found. *Mem:* AAAS; NY Acad Sci. *Res:* Infectious and neoplastic diseases of fish; aquatic biology; experimental ichthyology; marine biochemistry and ecology. *Mailing Add:* Osborn Labs of Marine Sci S Boardwalk & W Eighth St Brooklyn NY 11224

NIGRO, JOHN CAMILLO, metallurgy, see previous edition

NIGRO, NICHOLAS J, b Chicago, Ill, Sept 24, 34; m 54; c 3. MECHANICS. *Educ:* Mich Technol Univ, BS, 56; Iowa State Univ, MS, 59; Univ Iowa, PhD(mech), 65. *Prof Exp:* Struct designer, Victor Chem Works, 56-57; instr eng, Southern Ill Univ, 59-62; asst prof mech, 65-69, ASSOC PROF MECH ENG, MARQUETTE UNIV, 69- *Mem:* Am Soc Eng Educ. *Res:* Vibrations; dynamics; systems; wave propagation. *Mailing Add:* 6442 W Boehlke Ave Milwaukee WI 53223

NIHEI, TAIICHI, b Aizu Wakamatzu, Japan, June 3, 29; m 60; c 1. DEVELOPMENTAL BIOLOGY. *Educ:* Hokkaido Univ, BSc, 52; Tokyo Univ, PhD(biochem), 58. *Prof Exp:* Res biologist, Tokugawa Inst Biol Res, 52-56; biochemist, Hokkaido Univ, 57-59; res assoc biochem, Dartmouth Med Sch, 59-61; vis scientist, NIH, 61-63; from asst prof to assoc prof, 63-74, PROF MED, UNIV ALTA, 74- *Mem:* Biophys Soc; Can Biochem Soc. *Res:* Muscle proteins; structure and function of muscle and nerve cells. *Mailing Add:* Dept of Med Univ of Alta Edmonton AB T6G 2G7 Can

NIJENHUIS, ALBERT, b Eindhoven, Netherlands, Nov 21, 26; US citizen. MATHEMATICS. *Educ:* Univ Amsterdam, PhD(math), 52. *Prof Exp:* Asst math, Univ Amsterdam, 48-51, sci collabr, Math Ctr, 51-52; vis fel, Princeton Univ, 52-53; mem, Inst Advan Study, 53-55; instr & res assoc, Univ Chicago, 55-56; from asst prof to prof math, Univ Wash, 56-63; PROF MATH, UNIV PA, 63- *Concurrent Pos:* Mem, Inst Advan Study & Guggenheim fel, 61-62; Fulbright lectr, Univ Amsterdam, 63-64; vis prof, Univ Geneva, 67-68, Dartmouth Col, 77-78; corresp mem, Royal Netherland Acad Sci. *Mem:* Am Math Soc; Math Asn Am; Soc Indust & Appl Math; Asn Comput Mach. *Res:* Local and global differential geometry; theory of deformations in algebra and geometry; combinatorial analysis; algorithms. *Mailing Add:* Dept Math Univ Pa Philadelphia PA 19104

NIJHOUT, H FREDERIK, b Eindhoven, Neth, Nov 25, 47. INSECT PHYSIOLOGY. *Educ:* Univ Notre Dame, BS, 70; Harvard Univ, MA, 72, PhD(biol), 74. *Prof Exp:* NIH staff fel, 75-77; asst prof, 77-81, ASSOC PROF ZOOL, DUKE UNIV, 81- *Mem:* Am Soc Zoologists; Sigma Xi. *Res:* Insect physiology, with particular emphasis on endocrinology and pattern formation. *Mailing Add:* Dept of Zool Duke Univ Durham NC 27706

NIKAIDO, HIROSHI, b Tokyo, Japan, Mar 26, 32; m 63; c 2. MICROBIOLOGY, BIOCHEMISTRY. *Educ:* Keio Univ, Japan, MD, 55, DMedSc(microbiol), 61. *Prof Exp:* Asst microbiol, Med Sch, Keio Univ, Japan, 56-60 & Inst Protein Res, Osaka Univ, 61; res fel biol chem, Harvard Med Sch, 62, assoc bact & immunol, 63-64, asst prof, 65-69; assoc prof, 69-71, PROF MICROBIOL, UNIV CALIF, BERKELEY, 71- *Concurrent Pos:* USPHS res grant, 63- & Am Cancer Soc res grant, 69-; mem, NIH Study Sect, 78- *Honors & Awards:* Ehrlich Award, 69. *Mem:* Am Soc Biol Chem; Am Soc Microbiol. *Res:* Biochemistry of bacterial cell wall and cell membrane, especially structure and functions of the outer membrane of gram-negative bacteria. *Mailing Add:* Dept Microbiol & Immunol Univ Calif Berkeley CA 94720

NIKELLY, JOHN G, b Evanston, Ill, Apr 16, 29; m 61. ANALYTICAL CHEMISTRY. *Educ:* Univ Ill, BS, 52; Cornell Univ, PhD(chem), 56. *Prof Exp:* Chemist, Exxon Res & Eng Co, 56-62; PROF CHEM, PHILADELPHIA COL PHARM, 62- *Concurrent Pos:* Sci adv, Philadelphia Dist, Food & Drug Admin, 71-75. *Mem:* AAAS; Am Chem Soc. *Res:* Gas chromatography; high pressure liquid chromatography. *Mailing Add:* Dept of Chem Philadelphia Col of Pharm & Sci Philadelphia PA 19104

NIKIFORUK, GORDON, b Redfield, Sask, Nov 2, 22; m 50; c 2. BIOCHEMISTRY, DENTISTRY. *Educ:* Univ Toronto, DDS, 47; Univ Ill, MS, 50. *Prof Exp:* Prof prev dent, Univ Toronto, 57-64, chmn div dent res, 54-64; prof pediat, Sch Med & prof pediat dent & head dept, Sch Dent, Univ Calif, Los Angeles, 64-66, prof oral biol & head dept, 66-69; dean fac dent, 70-77, PROF PREV DENT, UNIV TORONTO, 70- *Mem:* AAAS; fel Royal Col Dent; Can Dent Asn; Can Soc Dent for Children; Int Asn Dent Res. *Res:* Biochemistry of teeth and saliva; pediatric dentistry. *Mailing Add:* Fac of Dent Univ of Toronto Toronto ON M5G 1G6 Can

NIKIFORUK, P(ETER) N, b St Paul, Alta, Feb 11, 30; m 57; c 2. ENGINEERING PHYSICS. *Educ:* Queen's Univ, Ont, BSc, 52; Univ Manchester, PhD(electron eng), 55, DSc, 70. *Prof Exp:* Serv officer, Defence Res Bd, Can, 56-57; systs engr, Canadair, Ltd, 57-59; prof mech & control eng & head dept mech eng, 60-73, DEAN ENG, UNIV SASK, 73- *Concurrent Pos:* Mem, Nat Res Coun, 73-77; mem, Sask Res Coun, 77-, chmn sci coun, 78- *Mem:* Fel Brit Inst Physics; fel Brit Phys Soc; fel Brit Inst Elec Engrs; Can Soc Mech Engrs; Eng Inst Can. *Res:* Nonlinear self-adaptive control systems; very high pressure hydraulic servomechanisms; computers in process control; computer applications. *Mailing Add:* Col of Eng Univ of Sask Saskatoon SK S7H 0W0 Can

NIKITOVITCH-WINER, MIROSLAVA B, b Kraljevo, Yugoslavia, May 13, 29; US citizen; m 55; c 2. ANATOMY, ENDOCRINOLOGY. *Educ:* Univ Belgrade, BS, 45; Sorbonne, cert sci, 46; Radcliffe Col, MA, 54; Duke Univ, PhD(anat, physiol), 57. *Prof Exp:* Asst, Sch Med, Duke Univ, 57-58; USPHS fels, Univ Lund, 58, Nobel Med Inst, Karolinska Med Sch, 59 & Maudsley Hosp, Univ London, 59-60; res assoc, 60-61, from asst prof to assoc prof, 61-73, PROF ANAT, PHYSIOL & BIOPHYS, MED CTR, UNIV KY, 73-, CHMN DEPT ANAT, MED CTR, 78- *Mem:* AAAS; Am Asn Anat; Endocrine Soc; Am Physiol Soc; Int Brain Res Orgn. *Res:* Neuroendocrinology and reproduction; indirect and direct determination of neurohumoral controls of gonadotropic hormone secretion; identification of releasing versus hypophysiotropic effects of hypothalamic humoral factors concerned with hormone secretion; control of prolactin secretion; control of follicle stimulating hormone secretion by Inhibin. *Mailing Add:* Dept of Anat Univ of Ky Med Ctr Lexington KY 40536

NIKKEL, HENRY, b Munsterberg, Russia, Oct 8, 22; US citizen; m 49; c 2. PHYSICS, METALLURGY. *Educ:* Univ Mich, BS, 45, MS, 51. *Prof Exp:* Res engr, Bethlehem Steel Corp, 47-65; sr res engr, Youngstown Sheet & Tube Co, 65-69, res assoc, 69-77; microprobe analyst, 77-78, LAB DEVELOP ANALYST, FORD MOTOR CO, 78- *Mem:* Am Soc Metals; Int Metallog Soc; Sigma Xi; Microbeam Anal Soc. *Res:* Emission spectroscopy involving analytical techniques; excitation studies; instrument development and investigations in the vacuum ultraviolet; physical metallurgy, particularly electron microprobe techniques; materials evaluation and failure analysis. *Mailing Add:* Ford Motor Co Cent Lab 15000 Century Dr Dearborn MI 48121

NIKLAS, KARL JOSEPH, b New York, NY, Aug 23, 48. BIOMATHEMATICS, GEOCHEMISTRY. *Educ:* City Col New York, BS, 70; Univ Ill, Urbana-Champaign, MS, 71, PhD(bot, math), 74. *Prof Exp:* Fel bot, Univ London & Cambridge Univ, 74-75; cur palaeobot, NY Bot Garden, 74-78; asst prof, 78-81, ASSOC PROF BOT, CORNELL UNIV, 81- *Concurrent Pos:* Fulbright-Hays fel, Int Educ Comt, 74; adj prof, City Univ New York, 75. *Res:* Application of mathematical theory to selected problems in plant morphology and evolution; organic geochemistry of fossil materials and associated rock strata; paleobotanical and biological problems. *Mailing Add:* Dept of Plant Sci Cornell Univ Ithaca NY 14853

NIKLAS, WILFRID F, physics, deceased

NIKLOWITZ, WERNER JOHANNES, b Ger, Sept 14, 23; m 52; c 2. NEUROBIOLOGY, ELECTRON MICROSCOPY. *Educ:* Univ Jena, MS, 52, PhD(biol), 54. *Prof Exp:* Asst prof biol, Univ Jena, 52-54; res assoc microbiol, Acad Inst Microbiol, Jena, Ger, 54-60; res assoc path, Univ Freiburg, 61-62; res assoc, Max Planck Inst Brain Res, Frankfurt, 62-68; sr res assoc toxicol, Med Ctr, Univ Cincinnati, 68-69, from asst prof to assoc prof environ health, 69-74; res assoc neuropath, Med Ctr, Univ Ind, Indanapolis, 74-76; res assoc radiation, 78-80, SR RES ASSOC BONE RES, UNIV SAN FRANCISCO, 80- *Concurrent Pos:* NASA res grant. *Mem:* AAAS; Electron Micros Soc Am; Soc Neurosci; NY Acad Sci. *Res:* Experimental epilepsy; effects of drugs, toxic metals and radiation on the ultrastructure of brain components, enzymes, trace metals and neurotransmitters; effects of immobilization on bone. *Mailing Add:* MS 236-6 Ames Res Ctr NASA Moffett Field CA 94035

NIKODEM, ROBERT BRUCE, b Oak Park, Ill June 2, 39; m 64. PHYSICAL CHEMISTRY, INORGANIC CHEMISTRY. *Educ:* Elmhurst Col, BS, 62; Purdue Univ, Lafayette, MS, 65; Va Polytech Inst & State Univ, PhD(inorg chem), 69. *Prof Exp:* Res supvr glass films, Libbey-Owens-Ford Co, 69-77; prod mgr, Photon Power Inc, 77-81; TECH MGR FILMS, LIBBEY-OWENS-FORD CO, 81- *Mem:* Am Chem Soc. *Res:* Rare earth oxides; compound semiconductors; thin films, both oxide and metallic; solid state chemistry; photovoltaic solar energy cells. *Mailing Add:* 836 Somerset El Paso TX 79912

NIKOLAI, PAUL JOHN, b Minneapolis, Minn, Mar 2, 31; m 60; c 2. MATHEMATICS. *Educ:* Col St Thomas, BA, 53; Ohio State Univ, MSc, 55, PhD(math), 66. *Prof Exp:* Mathematician, Univac Div, Sperry Rand Corp, 55-57; mathematician, Digital Comput Br, Aeronaut Res Lab, 58-60, res mathematician, Appl Math Res Lab, Aerospace Res Lab, 60-75, MATHEMATICIAN, STRUCT & DYNAMICS DIV, FLIGHT DYNAMICS LAB, AIR FORCE WRIGHT AERONAUT LABS, US DEPT AIR FORCE, 75- *Concurrent Pos:* Asst math, Ohio State Univ, 53-57; vis scholar math, Univ Calif, Santa Barbara, 68-69; mem, Special Interest Group Numerical Math, Asn Comput Mach. *Mem:* Am Math Soc; Soc Indust & Appl Math. *Res:* Numerical linear algebra, matrix theory and combinatorial computing. *Mailing Add:* AFWAL/FIBR Wright-Patterson AFB OH 45433

NIKOLAI, ROBERT JOSEPH, b Rock Island, Ill, Apr 6, 37; m 61; c 5. ORTHODONTICS, BIOMECHANICS. *Educ:* Univ Ill, Urbana, BS, 59, MS, 61, PhD(theoret & appl mech), 64. *Prof Exp:* Teaching asst theoret & appl mech, Univ Ill, Urbana, 59-61, instr, 61-64, res assoc, 63-64; asst prof eng & eng mech, 64-68, assoc prof eng mech, 68-71, asst dean grad sch, 71-72, assoc prof biomech in orthod, 71-75, PROF BIOMECH IN ORTHOD, ST LOUIS UNIV, 75-, ASSOC DEAN GRAD SCH, 72- *Concurrent Pos:* Affil prof civil & mech eng, Washington Univ, 80-; consult, Orthoband Co, Inc, Antonia, Mo & Forestadent Pforzheim, WGer; sabbatical grant, Orthodontic Educ & Res Found, 81. *Mem:* Am Acad Mech; Am Soc Mech Eng; Int & Am Asn Dent Res; Orthod Educ & Res Found; Sigma Xi. *Res:* Force and structural analyses, and design of orthodontic appliances (braces); biomechanical interaction of the orthodontic appliance with the dentition and the facial complex. *Mailing Add:* St Louis Univ Grad Sch 221 N Grand Blvd St Louis MO 63103

NIKOLIC, NIKOLA M, b Belgrade, Yugoslavia, Sept 14, 27; US citizen; m 60; c 1. PHYSICS. *Educ:* Univ Belgrade, BS, 50; Columbia Univ, MA, 59, PhD(physics), 62. *Prof Exp:* Asst prof physics, US Naval Postgrad Sch, 62-64, La State Univ, 64-68 & Old Dom Univ, 68-69; asst prof, 69-74, PROF PHYSICS, MARY WASHINGTON COL, 74- *Mem:* Am Phys Soc. *Res:* Nuclear physics. *Mailing Add:* 12 Winston Pl Fredericksburg VA 22401

NILAN, ROBERT ARTHUR, b Can, Dec 26, 23; nat US; m 48; c 3. GENETICS. *Educ:* Univ BC, BSA, 46, MSA, 48; Univ Wis, PhD(genetics), 51. *Prof Exp:* Asst, Univ BC, 46-48 & Univ Wis, 48-51; res assoc, 51-52, from asst prof & asst agronomist to prof agron & agronomist, 52-65, chmn prog genetics, 65-79, PROF GENETICS & AGRONOMIST, WASH STATE UNIV, 65-, DEAN DIV SCI, 79- *Concurrent Pos:* Fulbright teaching scholar, 59; Guggenheim fel, 59-60; USPHS spec fel, 67-68. *Mem:* Genetics Soc Am; Am Soc Agron; Environ Mutagen Soc. *Res:* Cytogenetical, mutagenesis and breeding studies in barley. *Mailing Add:* Div Sci Wash State Univ Pullman WA 99163

NILAN, THOMAS GEORGE, b White Plains, NY, Sept 4, 26; m 61; c 6. PHYSICS. *Educ:* Columbia Univ, BS, 50; Univ Ill, MS, 56, PhD, 61. *Prof Exp:* Physicist, 50-55, sr res physicist, 60-69, ASSOC RES CONSULT, RES LAB, US STEEL CORP, 69- *Res:* Radiation damage; ultrahigh pressure; phase transformations; surface physics. *Mailing Add:* 8945 Eastwood Rd Pittsburgh PA 15235

NILES, GEORGE ALVA, b Flagstaff, Ariz, Oct 4, 26; m 48; c 4. AGRONOMY, PLANT BREEDING. *Educ:* NMex State Univ, BS, 48; Okla State Univ, MS, 49; Tex A&M Univ, PhD(plant breeding), 59. *Prof Exp:* Instr agron, NMex State Univ, 49; res assoc, Okla Agr Exp Sta, 51-53; from instr to assoc prof, 53-74, PROF AGRON, TEX A&M UNIV, 74- *Mem:* AAAS; Am Soc Agron; Crop Sci Soc Am; Int Soc Biometeorol. *Res:* Cotton genetics and breeding; host plant resistance; crop-climate studies; cotton production systems; cotton physiology; insect pest management. *Mailing Add:* Dept of Soil & Crop Sci Tex A&M Univ College Station TX 77843

NILES, JAMES ALFRED, b Eureka, Calif, Apr 24, 45; m 67; c 2. AGRICULTURAL ECONOMICS. *Educ:* Univ Calif, Davis, BS, 67, MS, 68, PhD(agr econ), 72. *Prof Exp:* Asst prof agr econ, Food & Resource Econ Dept, Univ Fla, 73-78; ASSOC PROF, INST AGRBUS, GRAD SCH BUS, UNIV SANTA CLARA, 78- *Mem:* Am Asn Agr Economists. *Res:* Commodity futures markets, emphasis on citrus futures; price forecasting of agricultural commodities and modelling; computer simulation of commodity systems. *Mailing Add:* 4188 Mystic Ct San Jose CA 95124

NILES, NELSON ROBINSON, b Southampton, NY, May 27, 24; m 51; c 5. PATHOLOGY, ANATOMY. *Educ:* Cornell Univ, MD, 47. *Prof Exp:* From instr to assoc prof, 52-67, PROF PATH ANAT, MED SCH, UNIV ORE, 67- *Concurrent Pos:* Res fel path, Royal Col Surg, 62-63. *Mem:* Int Acad Path. *Res:* Cardiovascular pathology; coronary artery disease; congenital heart disease and cardiac surgery; histochemistry. *Mailing Add:* Dept of Path Sch Med Ore Health Sci Univ Portland OR 97201

NILES, PHILIP WILLIAM BENJAMIN, b Fairfield, Calif, Jan 4, 36; m 73; c 4. MECHANICAL ENGINEERING, SOLAR ENERGY ENGINEERING. *Educ:* Univ Calif, Berkeley, BS, 57, MS, 58. *Prof Exp:* Sr res engr res & develop, Rocketdyne, NAm Aviation Corp, 58-62 & 65; consult, Dept Geophys & Astron, Rand Corp, Santa Monica, 67-68; PROF, DEPT ENVIRON ENG, CALIF POLYTECH STATE UNIV, 67- *Concurrent Pos:* Solar consult, Skytherm Processes & Eng, Los Angeles, 73-; solar thermal analyst, HUD contract, Calif Polytech State Univ Found, 73-74, NSF grant, 74-75; system design engr, Energy Res Develop Admin contract, Calif Polytech State Univ Found, 76-78, proj dir, Calif Energy Comn, 78- *Mem:* Int Solar Energy Soc; Am Soc Heating Refrig & Air Conditioning Engrs. *Res:* Application of solar energy to the environmental control of buildings, particularly passive methods and to industrial process heat applications. *Mailing Add:* Dept of Environ Eng Calif Polytech State Univ San Luis Obispo CA 93407

NILES, WESLEY E, b Taos, NMex, July 17, 32. BOTANY. *Educ:* NMex State Univ, BS, 59, MS, 61; Univ Ariz, PhD(bot), 68. *Prof Exp:* Assoc cur, New York Bot Garden, 66-68; asst prof, 68-71, ASSOC PROF BOT, UNIV NEV, LAS VEGAS, 71- *Mem:* Am Soc Plant Taxon; Int Asn Plant Taxon. *Res:* Angiosperm taxonomy. *Mailing Add:* Dept of Biol Sci Univ of Nev Las Vegas NV 89154

NILGES, MARK J, b Berea, Ohio, Aug 7, 52. ELECTRON PARAMAGNETIC RESONANCE. *Educ:* Case Western Reserve Univ, BS, 74; Univ Ill, PhD(chem), 79. *Prof Exp:* Fel, Cornell Univ, 79-81; RES BIOPHYSICIST, UNIV ILL, 81- *Mem:* Am Chem Soc. *Res:* Electron paramagnetic resonance and nuclear quadrupole coupling in transition metal ion complexes; computer simulation of electron paramagnetic resonance spectra; ultrahigh vacuum studies of metal surfaces using magnetic resonance; electron paramagnetic resonance of melanin and tree radicals involved in cancer. *Mailing Add:* Sch Basic Med Sci MS Bldg 506 S Mathews Ave Urbana IL 61801

NILSEN, WALTER GRAHN, b Brooklyn, NY, Nov 13, 27; m 59; c 3. CHEMICAL PHYSICS. *Educ:* Columbia Univ, AB, 50, PhD(phys chem), 56; Cornell Univ, MS, 52; Seton Hall Sch Law, JD, 73. *Prof Exp:* Staff mem chem, Opers Eval Group, Mass Inst Technol, 56-59; mem tech staff, 59-69, PATENT ATTORNEY, BELL LABS, NJ, 69- *Mem:* Am Chem Soc; Am Phys Soc. *Res:* Magnetic resonance; relaxation mechanisms; masers; lasers; Raman spectroscopy. *Mailing Add:* Bell Labs Inc Murray Hill NJ 07971

NILSON, ARTHUR H(UMPHREY), b Wilkinsburg, Pa, Aug 27, 26; m 81; c 4. STRUCTURAL ENGINEERING. *Educ:* Stanford Univ, BS, 48; Cornell Univ, MS, 56; Univ Calif, Berkeley, PhD, 67. *Prof Exp:* Struct eng pract, 48-54; instr civil eng, 54-56, from asst prof to assoc prof struct eng, 56-69, PROF STRUCT ENG, CORNELL UNIV, 69-, CHMN DEPT, 78- *Concurrent Pos:* Lectr, Swiss Fed Tech Inst, Lausanne, 71; vis res fel, Politecnico di Milano, 75; vis scholar, Salford Univ, 75-77; consult, H H Robertson Co, NY, Geiger Berger Asn, NY & Thompson & Lichtuer Co, Boston. *Honors & Awards:* Wason Medal for Mat Res, Am Concrete Inst, 74. *Mem:* Am Soc Civil Engrs; fel Am Concrete Inst; Prestressed Concrete Inst; Int Asn Bridge & Struct Engrs; Sigma Xi. *Res:* Teaching; research on behavior; analysis and design of structures, particularly reinforced and prestressed concrete; concrete materials, notably high-strength concrete. *Mailing Add:* Sch of Civil & Environ Eng Cornell Univ Hollister Hall Ithaca NY 14853

NILSON, EDWIN NORMAN, b Weathersfield, Conn, Feb 13, 17; m 41; c 3. MATHEMATICS. *Educ:* Trinity Col, Conn, BS, 37; Harvard Univ, MA, 38, PhD(math), 41. *Prof Exp:* Instr & tutor math, Harvard Univ, 39-41; instr, Univ Md, 41-42; asst prof, Mt Holyoke Col, 42-44; res engr aerodyn, United Aircraft Corp, Conn, 46-48; asst prof math, Trinity Col, Conn, 48-52, assoc prof, 52-56; proj engr, 56-60, chief sci staff, 60-68, MGR TECH & MGT DATA SYSTS, PRATT & WHITNEY AIRCRAFT DIV, UNITED AIRCRAFT CORP, 68- *Concurrent Pos:* Adj prof, Hartford Grad Div, Rensselaer Polytech Inst, 59-63. *Mem:* Am Math Soc; Math Asn Am. *Res:* Analysis; applied mathematics; fluid mechanics; heat conduction; elasticity. *Mailing Add:* Kenmore Rd Bloomfield CT 06002

NILSON, ERICK BOGSETH, b Aurora, Nebr, Feb 6, 27; m 55; c 2. AGRONOMY. *Educ:* Univ Nebr, BS, 50, MS, 55; Kans State Univ, PhD(agron), 63. *Prof Exp:* Soil scientist, Soil Conserv Serv, USDA, Nebr, 51-52 & Kans, 52-53; county exten agent, State Col Wash, 55-57; exten area agronomist, Iowa State Univ, 57-61; asst prof agr & biol sci, Eastern NMex Univ, 63-65; asst prof agron, 65-69, assoc prof, 69-76, PROF AGRON, KANS STATE UNIV, 76- *Mem:* Weed Sci Soc Am; Coun Agr Sci & Technol. *Res:* Crop physiology; cell length in wheat; temperature influence on DNA and RNA in grain sorghum seedings. *Mailing Add:* Dept of Agron Kans State Univ Manhattan KS 66506

NILSON, JOHN ANTHONY, b Regina, Sask, Nov 14, 36; m 59; c 2. LASERS. *Educ:* Univ Sask, BE, 59, MSc, 60; Univ London, PhD(elec eng) & dipl, Imp Col, 65. *Prof Exp:* Mem sci staff, Plasma & Space Physics Res Dept, RCA Ltd, Que, 65-71; staff scientist, 71-74, TECH DIR, LUMONICS RES LTD, 74- *Mem:* Can Asn Physicists; Inst Elec & Electronics Engrs; Optical Soc Am. *Res:* Pulsed transverse excitation TEA carbon dioxide, HF/DF, eximer, lasers; glow discharge plasmas; laser applications. *Mailing Add:* Lumonics Res Ltd 105 Schneider Rd Kanata ON K2K 1Y3 Can

NILSON, KAY MILLIGAN, b Logan, Utah, Dec 22, 28; m 49; c 6. DAIRY SCIENCE. *Educ:* Utah State Univ, BS, 53, MS, 56; Univ Nebr, PhD(dairy sci), 66. *Prof Exp:* Instr dairy sci, Univ Nebr, 56-66; from asst prof to assoc prof, 66-75, PROF DAIRY SCI, UNIV VT, 75- *Mem:* Am Dairy Sci Asn; Am Inst Food Technologists; Int Asn Milk, Food & Environ Sanitarians. *Res:* Dairy plant waste; feeding cheese whey to dairy animals; stirred curd Mozzarella cheese; manufacturing Ricotta cheese from concentrated whey; automation of Mozzarella cheese manufacturing. *Mailing Add:* Dept of Animal Sciences Univ of Vt Burlington VT 05401

NILSSON, NILS JOHN, b Saginaw, Mich, Feb 6, 33; m 58; c 2. COMPUTER SCIENCE, ELECTRICAL ENGINEERING. *Educ:* Stanford Univ, MS, 56, PhD(elec eng), 58. *Prof Exp:* Head artificial intel group, 61-67, sr res engr, 67-69, staff scientist, 69-80, DIR, ARTIFICIAL INTEL CTR, SRI INT, 80- *Mem:* Asn Comput Mach. *Res:* Learning machines; artificial intelligence; pattern recognition; radar signal processing. *Mailing Add:* 150 Coquito Way Portola Valley CA 94025

NILSSON, WILLIAM A, b New York, NY, Jan 16, 31. OCCUPATIONAL HEALTH. *Educ:* Univ Ill, Urbana, BS, 57; Univ Calif, Berkeley, PhD(org chem), 62. *Prof Exp:* Asst, Radiation Lab, Univ Calif, Berkeley, 60-61; asst prof chem, Western Wash State Col, 61-64; mgr prod develop, Purex Corp, Ltd, Calif, 65-70; teacher chem, Glendale Col, 71-73; PUB HEALTH CHEMIST, OCCUP HEALTH SECT, CALIF DEPT HEALTH, 74- *Mailing Add:* 1808 Tamerlane Dr Glendale CA 91208

NIMAN, JOHN, b Latakia, Syria, June 10, 38; US citizen. APPLIED MATHEMATICS. *Educ:* Polytech Inst Brooklyn, BS, 65; Univ Wis, MS, 68; Columbia Univ, PhD(math) & MA, 69. *Prof Exp:* Res asst geophys, Hudson Labs, Columbia Univ, 64-65; asst prof, 67-69, ASSOC PROF MATH & EDUC, HUNTER COL, 69- *Concurrent Pos:* George N Shuster fac fel, 70; consult math, More Effective Sch Prog, New York Bd Educ, 70 & Educ Assoc Prog, La Guardia Community Col, 71; res award hist math, Fed Repub Ger, 75; math consult, Metrop Mus Art, 77-78; mem, New York Bd Educ, 78. *Mem:* AAAS; Am Math Soc; Math Asn Am. *Res:* Curriculum development; Hilbert; mathematics education in the elementary school. *Mailing Add:* Dept of Math & Educ Hunter Col New York NY 10021

NIMECK, MAXWELL WILLIAM, microbiology, see previous edition

NIMER, EDWARD LEE, b Denver, Colo, Jan 1, 23; m 46; c 5. PHYSICAL CHEMISTRY. *Educ:* Univ NMex, BS, 44; Univ Utah, MS, 49, PhD(chem), 52. *Prof Exp:* Sr res chemist, Explor Process Res, 52-55, petrochem process develop & eval, 55-62, SR RES CHEMIST, POLYMER PROCESS DEVELOP, CHEVRON RES CO, STANDARD OIL CO CALIF, 62- *Mem:* Am Chem Soc; Am Soc Mech Eng. *Res:* Flow, creep and failure of solid materials; exploratory process research in petrochemicals; polarography; polymer polymerization, finishing, compounding, conversions and spinning processes; petroleum cracking processes; sulfur and applications. *Mailing Add:* 8 Alasdair Ct San Rafael CA 94903

NIMITZ, WALTER W VON, US citizen. ELECTRICAL ENGINEERING. *Educ:* Tech Univ Munich, MS, 50; Int Col, PhD, 80. *Prof Exp:* Engr, Inst Electromed, Univ Munich, 49; mem staff electronic serv, Sears Roebuck & Co, 51-57; proj leader, Indust Physics Dept, 57-60, sr res physicist & sr proj leader, Dept Appl Physics, 60-66, sect mgr, 66-69, asst dir, Dept Appl Physics, 69-74, DIR INDUST APPLNS, DIV APPL PHYSICS, SOUTHWEST RES INST, 74- *Mem:* Am Soc Mech Engrs; sr mem Instrument Soc Am. *Res:* Engineer acoustics and mechanics, machinery and plant dynamics. *Mailing Add:* Div Appl Physics PO Drawer 28510 San Antonio TX 78284

NIMLOS, THOMAS JOHN, forest soils, ecology, see previous edition

NIMMO, BRUCE GLEN, b Attleboro, Mass, Dec 14, 38; m 62; c 2. MECHANICAL ENGINEERING, SOLAR ENERGY. *Educ:* Clarkson Col Technol, BME, 60; Univ Fla, MS, 61; Stanford Univ, PhD(mech eng), 68. *Prof Exp:* Proj engr heat transfer, Brookhaven Nat Lab, 61-64; res asst, Stanford Univ, 64-68; asst prof mech eng, Clarkson Col Technol, 68-70; assoc prof, Fla Technol Univ, 70-76; PROF MECH ENG, UNIV PETROL & MINERALS, 76- *Concurrent Pos:* Chmn mech eng, Univ Petrol & Minerals, 77-78 & head res inst solar prog, 78- *Mem:* Am Soc Mech Eng; Am Soc Eng Educ; Int Solar Energy Soc; Sigma Xi. *Res:* Experimental heat transfer; thermal analysis; solar thermal applications. *Mailing Add:* Res Inst Univ of Petrol & Minerals Dhahran Saudi Arabia

NIMMO, DEL WAYNE ROY, environmental biology, see previous edition

NIMNI, MARCEL EFRAIM, b Buenos Aires, Arg, Feb 1, 31; US citizen; m 62; c 2. BIOCHEMISTRY, NUTRITION. *Educ:* Univ Buenos Aires, BS, 54, PhD(pharmacol), 60; Univ Southern Calif, MS, 57. *Prof Exp:* Biochemist, AEC, Arg, 58-60; head biol sect, Don Baxter, Inc, Calif, 62-63; asst prof biochem & nutrit, Sch Dent, 64-67, asst prof med, Sch Med, 67-68, assoc prof, 68-73, PROF MED & BIOCHEM, SCH MED, UNIV SOUTHERN CALIF, 73- *Mem:* Fel AAAS; Am Inst Nutrit; Am Soc Biol Chem; Am Rheumatism Asn; Soc Exp Biol & Med. *Res:* Biochemistry of collagen; mechanism of a defect in molecular aggregation induced by penicillamine; nature and biosynthesis of the crosslinks in collagen from skin, bone and cartilage; microtubular proteins and mitotic inhibitors. *Mailing Add:* Dept of Med Univ of South Calif Sch of Med Los Angeles CA 90033

NIMS, JOHN BUCHANAN, b Monmouth, Maine, Dec 1, 24; m 47; c 2. PHYSICS. *Educ:* Boston Univ, BA, 50, MA, 51. *Prof Exp:* Physicist reactor physics, Knolls Atomic Power Lab, Gen Elec Co, 51-54; physicist, Atomic Power Develop Assocs Inc, 54-59, sect head, 59-66, div head, 66-73; dir nuclear eng, 73-74, corp strategic planner, 74-76, MGR STRATEGIC PLANNING, DETROIT EDISON CO, 76- *Mem:* Am Phys Soc; Am Nuclear Soc; World Future Soc. *Res:* Reactor physics, kinetics and safety. *Mailing Add:* Detroit Edison Co 2000 Second Ave Detroit MI 48226

NINE, HARMON D, b Detroit, Mich, July 8, 31; m 55; c 3. METAL PHYSICS. *Educ:* Univ Mich, BS, 53, MS, 54. *Prof Exp:* Res physicist, 58-61, sr res physicist, 61-80, STAFF RES SCIENTIST, GEN MOTORS RES LABS, 80- *Mem:* Am Soc Metals. *Res:* Ultrasonics; ultrasonic attenuation in solids; fatigue of metals; spectroscopy; acoustic emission; friction in metal forming. *Mailing Add:* Dept of Physics Gen Motors Res Labs Warren MI 48090

NINE, OGDEN WELLS, JR, petroleum geology, see previous edition

NING, ROBERT YE-FONG, b Shanghai, China, Mar 12, 39; m 66; c 2. ORGANIC CHEMISTRY. *Educ:* Rochester Inst Technol, BS, 63; Univ Ill, PhD(org chem), 66; Fairleigh Dickinson Univ, MBA, 79. *Prof Exp:* Res fel, Calif Inst Technol, 66-67; sr chemist, 67-75, res fel, 75-78, GROUP LEADER, HOFFMANN-LA ROCHE INC, 78- *Mem:* Am Chem Soc; The Chem Soc. *Res:* Industrial chemical and biochemical produciton processes; synthetic organic chemistry; chemistry of heterocycles; drug design. *Mailing Add:* Hoffmann-La Roche Inc Nutley NJ 07110

NING, TAK HUNG, b Canton, China, Nov 14, 43; US citizen; m 75; c 2. SOLID STATE PHYSICS, SILICON DEVICE TECHNOLOGY. *Educ:* Reed Col, BA, 67; Univ Ill, MS, 68, PhD(physics), 71. *Prof Exp:* Fel solid state electronics, Dept Elec Eng, Univ Ill, 71-72, res asst prof, 72-73; RES STAFF MEM SEMICONDUCTOR SCI AND TECHNOLOGY, IBM RES CTR, 73- *Mem:* Am Phys Soc; Inst Elec & Electronic Engrs. *Res:* Semiconductor device physics and technology; silicon transistor device physics and technology. *Mailing Add:* IBM Thomas J Watson Res Ctr Yorktown Heights NY 10598

NININGER, ROBERT D, b Brookings, SDak, Mar 28, 19; m 43; c 4. ECONOMIC GEOLOGY. *Educ:* Amherst Col, BA, 41; Harvard Univ, MA, 42. *Prof Exp:* Geologist, Strategic Minerals Invest, US Geol Surv, 42-43; dep asst dir raw mat, AEC, 47-54, asst dir, 55-71; asst dir raw mat, Div Nuclear Fuel Cycle & Prod, US Energy Res & Develop Admin, 72-76; asst dir raw mat, Div Uranium Resources & Enrichment, 77-78, dir, 78-79, CONSULT NUCLEAR RAW MAT, US DEPT ENERGY, 79- *Mem:* Fel AAAS; fel Geol Soc Am; Am Nuclear Soc; Soc Econ Geol; Am Inst Mining, Metall & Petrol Engrs. *Res:* Geology of radioactive materials; uranium resources and supply. *Mailing Add:* US Dept Energy Washington DC 20545

NINKE, WILLIAM HERBERT, b Toledo, Ohio, Aug 25, 37; m 61; c 3. COMMUNICATIONS SCIENCE, COMPUTER SCIENCE. *Educ:* Case Inst Technol, BS, 59, MS, 61, PhD(digital systs), 64. *Prof Exp:* Mem tech staff, Bell Labs, Murray Hill, NJ, 63-69, head, Digital Systs Res Dept, Holmdel, NJ, 69-78, HEAD, IMAGE PROCESSING & DISPLAY RES DEPT, BELL LABS, HOLMDEL, NJ, 78- *Mem:* Sr mem Inst Elec & Electronics Engrs; fel Soc Info Display. *Res:* Visual telecommunications services; computer-driven display consoles; image synthesis; image analysis; robotics; computer aided design. *Mailing Add:* Bell Labs Holmdel NJ 07733

NINKOVICH, DRAGOSLAV, geology, see previous edition

NINO, HIPOLITO V, b Bogota, Colombia, Sept 28, 24; US citizen; m 55; c 3. CLINICAL & NUTRITIONAL BIOCHEMISTRY. *Educ:* Nat Univ Colombia, degree microbiol, 50; Univ Wis-Madison, MS, 52, PhD(biochem), 58. *Prof Exp:* Asst prof biochem, Nat Univ Colombia, 54-56; assoc prof, Univ Valle, Colombia, 56-57; lab dir clin chem, Citizens Hosp, Barberton, Ohio, 57-60 & St Joseph's Hosp, Syracuse, 60-63; asst prof biochem med & path & dir, Lab Clin Chem, Hosp, Univ NC, 63-70; chief nutrit biochem, Ctr Dis Control, Atlanta, 70-75; dir lab clin chem, Christ Hosp, Cincinnati, 75-78; dir res & develop diag, Beckman Instruments, Inc, 78-80; DIR, DIV CLIN LAB DEVICES, BUR MED DEVICES, FOOD & DRUG ADMIN, 80- *Concurrent Pos:* Instr biochem, State Univ NY Med Ctr, Syracuse, 60-63; consult interdept comt nutrit nat defense, NIH, 61-62. *Mem:* Am Asn Clin Chem; Am Chem Soc; Sigma Xi; Acad Clin Lab Physicians & Scientists; AAAS. *Res:* Clinical chemistry; methodology and quality assurance; hormones, vitamins and trace elements; clinical, epidemiological and analytical methods; regulatory aspects of clinical laboratory devices. *Mailing Add:* Bur Med Devices HFK-440 Food & Drug Admin Silver Spring MD 20910

NIP, WAI KIT, b Hong Kong, May 5, 41; m 70; c 2. FOOD SCIENCE AND TECHNOLOGY. *Educ:* Chung-Hsing Univ, Taiwan, BS, 62; Tex A&M Univ, MS, 65, PhD(food technol), 69. *Prof Exp:* Assoc prof food sci, Chung-Hsing Univ, Taiwan, 69-74; res assoc, Univ Wis, 74-76; ASST PROF FOOD SCI, UNIV HAWAII, 76- *Concurrent Pos:* NIH fel, Univ Wis, 75-76. *Mem:* Inst Food Technologists; Am Asn Cereal Chemists; Am Soc Hort Sci; World Maricult Soc; Sigma Xi. *Res:* Food processing technology; control of spoilage; chemical constituents in foods. *Mailing Add:* Dept Food Sci & Human Nutrit Univ Hawaii Honolulu HI 96822

NIPPER, HENRY CARMACK, b Alexander City, Ala, Mar 31, 40; m 66; c 2. CLINICAL CHEMISTRY. *Educ:* Emory Univ, AB, 60; Purdue Univ, MS, 66; Univ Md, PhD(chem), 71. *Prof Exp:* Anal chemist, E I du Pont de Nemours & Co, 60-63; teaching asst chem, Purdue Univ, 63-65, instr, 65-66; teaching asst chem, 66-68, Gillette-Harris res fel, 68-70, fel clin chem, Sch Med, 71-73, instr path, 73-74, ASST PROF PATH, SCH MED, UNIV MD, 74-; CLIN CHEMIST, VET ADMIN MED CTR, BALTIMORE, 73- *Honors & Awards:* Joseph H Roe Award, Am Asn Clin Chemists, 78. *Mem:* AAAS; Gt Brit Asn Clin Biochemists; Sigma Xi; Am Asn Clin Chem. *Res:* Gas and liquid chromatography methods; kinetic methods in clinical chemistry. *Mailing Add:* 8207 Bellona Ave Baltimore MD 21204

NIPPES, ERNEST F(REDERICK), b New York, NY, Feb 1, 18; m 39, 69; c 5. METALLURGICAL ENGINEERING. *Educ:* Rensselaer Polytech Inst, BS, 38, MetE, 40, PhD(metall), 42. *Prof Exp:* Asst metall eng, 38-39, instr, 39-45, from asst prof to assoc prof, 45-54, dir welding res, 48-61, chmn dept mat eng, 61-65, dir res div, 65-71, dir off res & sponsored progs, 71-75, PROF METALL ENG, RENSSELAER POLYTECH INST, 54- *Concurrent Pos:* Nat Acad Sci exchange visit to USSR, 61, 77, 79 & 81; pres, Rensselaer Res Corp, 65-70. *Honors & Awards:* Award, Am Soc Metals, 56; Miller Mem Medal, Am Welding Soc, 59. *Mem:* Am Soc Metals; Am Welding Soc (vpres, 65-68, pres, 68-69); Am Soc Testing & Mat; Am Soc Eng Educ; Am Inst Mining, Metall & Petrol Engrs. *Res:* Metallurgy and welding. *Mailing Add:* Dept of Mat Eng Rensselaer Polytech Inst Troy NY 12181

NIPPOLDT, BERTWIN W, b Lake Elmo, Minn, Mar 9, 22; m 48; c 3. ANALYTICAL CHEMISTRY. *Educ:* Macalester Col, BA, 47. *Prof Exp:* Chemist, Minn Mining & Mfg Co, 47-55, group supvr, Cent Res Labs, 55-64, mgr org anal chem, 65-81, LAB MGR, CENT RES LABS, 3-M CO, 81- *Mem:* Am Chem Soc. *Res:* Analytical chemistry, especially analysis of fluorinated materials; microchemical and organic functional group analysis. *Mailing Add:* Cent Res Labs 3-M Co 3-M Ctr PO Box 33221 St Paul MN 55133

NIRENBERG, LOUIS, b Hamilton, Ont, Feb 28, 25; nat US; m 48; c 2. MATHEMATICS. *Educ:* McGill Univ, BSc, 45; NY Univ, MS, 47, PhD, 49. *Prof Exp:* From res asst to res assoc, 45-54, from asst prof to assoc prof, 52-57, PROF MATH, NY UNIV, 57- *Concurrent Pos:* Nat Res Coun fel, NY Univ, 51-52; fel, Inst Advan Study, 58; Sloan Found fel, 58-60; Fulbright lectr, 65; Guggenheim fel, 66-67 & 75-76; dir, Courant Inst Math Sci, 70-72. *Honors & Awards:* Bocher Prize, Am Math Soc, 59. *Mem:* Nat Acad Sci; Am Math Soc; Am Acad Arts & Sci; Acad Dei Lincei. *Res:* Partial differential equations; differential geometry; complex analysis. *Mailing Add:* Courant Inst NY Univ 251 Mercer St New York NY 10012

NIRENBERG, MARSHALL WARREN, b New York, NY, Apr 10, 27; m. BIOCHEMISTRY. *Educ:* Univ Fla, BS, 48, MS, 52; Univ Mich, PhD(biochem), 57. *Hon Degrees:* DSc, Univ Mich, 65, Univ Chicago, 65, Yale Univ, 65, Univ Windsor, 66, George Washington Univ, 72 & Weizmann Inst, Israel, 78. *Prof Exp:* Asst zool, Univ Fla, 45-50, res assoc, Nutrit Lab, 50-52; Am Cancer Soc fel, Nat Inst Arthritis & Metab Dis, 57-59, USPHS fel, Sect Metab Enzymes, 59-60, res biochemist, 60-62; head sect biochem genetics, 62-66, RES BIOCHEMIST & CHIEF BIOCHEM GENETICS LAB, NAT HEART, LUNG & BLOOD INST, 66- *Honors & Awards:* Nobel Prize in Med, 68. *Mem:* Nat Acad Sci; Pontif Acad Sci; Am Chem Soc; Biophys Soc; Soc Develop Biol. *Mailing Add:* Lab of Biochem Genetics Nat Heart Lung & Blood Inst Bethesda MD 20014

NIRSCHL, JOSEPH PETER, b Boca Raton, Fla, Apr 27, 45; m 67; c 2. FOOD & PHARMACEUTICAL PRODUCTS, LAUNDRY PRODUCTS. *Educ:* Carnegie Inst Technol, BS, 67; Univ Wis, PhD(chem eng), 72. *Prof Exp:* Res engr detergents, Miami Valley Labs, Procter & Gamble, 71-73, process develop group leader, Bar Soap & Household Cleaning Prod Div, 74-76; mgr process eng nutrit foods, 77-80, DIR PROCESS ENG, MEAD JOHNSON & CO, EVANSVILLE, 80- *Mem:* Am Inst Chem Engrs; Inst Food Technologists; Parental Drug Asn; Am Chem Soc. *Res:* Detergents; fabric softeners; liquid cleaners; pharmaceutical process development; food process development. *Mailing Add:* 5155 W Timberwood Newburgh IN 47630

NISBET, ALEX RICHARD, b Plainview, Tex, Apr 14, 38. ELECTROANALYTICAL CHEMISTRY. *Educ:* Univ Tex, BS, 59, PhD, 63. *Prof Exp:* Assoc prof, 63-73, PROF CHEM, OUACHITA BAPTIST UNIV, 73- *Mem:* AAAS; Electrochem Soc; Am Chem Soc. *Res:* Chronopotentiometry of metals. *Mailing Add:* 1908 Sylvia St Arkadelphia AR 71923

NISBET, D(ESIRE) F(RANK), b Salt Lake City, Utah, May 20, 18; m 41; c 4. METALLURGICAL ENGINEERING. *Educ:* Univ Utah, BS, 41; Stanford Univ, MS, 46. *Prof Exp:* Engr, Stanford Univ, 47; engr, Shell Oil Co, Calif, 47-54, asst mgr eng serv, Wash, 54-60, sr res engr & asst dept mgr, Ill, 60-64, staff engr, Martinez Calif Refinery, 64-75, sr staff engr, Saudi Arabian petrochem venture, 75-80; CONSULT, 80- *Mem:* Am Soc Metals; Am Soc Mech Engrs; Nat Asn Corrosion Engrs; Am Soc Welding. *Res:* Material selection; corrosion problems relating to refinery and petrochemical plant. *Mailing Add:* 26526 Azuer Mission Viejo CA 92691

NISBET, JERRY J, b Palisade, Colo, Nov 8, 24; m 48; c 2. SCIENCE EDUCATION, PLANT ANATOMY. *Educ:* Colo State Col Educ, AB, 49, AM, 50; Purdue Univ, PhD, 58. *Prof Exp:* Instr, Ball State Teachers Col, 50-52, asst prof, 54-56; asst, Purdue Univ, 52-53, res fel, 53-54, instr, 56-58; from asst prof to assoc prof, 58-64, coordr, Univ Eval, 74-77, PROF BIOL, BALL STATE UNIV, 64- & DIR, INST ENVIRON STUDIES, 74- *Concurrent Pos:* Dir, NSF Summer Inst Biol, 60, 62-64 & 66-68, dir, NSF Acad Yr Inst, 68-71; nat dir, Outstanding Biol Teacher Awards Prog, Nat Asn Biol Teachers, 65-67, dir, Region III, 66-68; mem, Sci Adv Comt, Ind Dept Pub Instr, 72- & Ind Lt Govr's Sci Adv Comt, 73-; secy, Ind Acad Sci, 72-74; secy, Cent States Univ, Inc, 68-70, chmn, Coun, 72, pres, Bd, 76. *Mem:* Fel AAAS; Am Inst Biol Sci; Nat Asn Res Sci Teaching; Asn Midwest Col Biol Teachers; Nat Sci Teachers Asn. *Res:* Development and testing of technologically based systems of instruction; interpretation of science for the non-scientist; study of the ultrastructure of plant cell walls. *Mailing Add:* Inst for Environ Studies Ball State Univ Muncie IN 47306

NISBET, JOHN S(TIRLING), b Darval, Scotland, Dec 10, 27; US citizen; m 53; c 2. ELECTRICAL ENGINEERING. *Educ:* Univ London, BS, 50; Pa State Univ, MS, 57, PhD(elec eng), 60. *Prof Exp:* Trainer engr res & develop, Nash & Thompson Ltd, Eng, 44-51; engr, Decca Radar Ltd, 51-53 & Can Westinghouse, 53-55; res assoc, 55-60, from asst prof to assoc prof ionospheric res, 60-67, PROF ELEC ENG, PA STATE UNIV, 67-, DIR,

IONOSPHERIC RES LAB, 71- *Concurrent Pos:* Nat Sci Found fel, Belg Inst Spatial Aeronomy, 65-66; Fulbright fel, Kharkov Univ, USSR, 79; Nat Res Coun-Nat Acad Sci fel, Goddard Space Flight Ctr, 80. *Mem:* Am Geophys Union; sr mem Inst Elec & Electronics Engrs; Inst Sci Radio Union. *Res:* Physics of ionosphere. *Mailing Add:* Pa State Univ 212 Elec Eng Bldg University Park PA 16802

NISENOFF, MARTIN, b New York, NY, Dec 25, 28; m 59; c 3. LOW TEMPERATURE PHYSICS. *Educ:* Worcester Polytechnic Inst, Mass, BS, 50; Purdue Univ, MS, 52, PhD(physics), 60. *Prof Exp:* Res assoc physics, Purdue Univ, 60-61; res scientist physics, Sci Res Staff, Ford Motor Co, Dearborn, Mich, 61-70; physicist, Cryog Appln Group, Stanford Res Inst, Menlo Park, Calif, 70-72; res scientist physics, Cryog & Superconductivity Br, 72-79, RES SCIENTIST PHYSICS, MICROWAVE TECHNOL BR, NAVAL RES LAB, WASHINGTON, DC, 79- *Mem:* Am Phys Soc. *Res:* Low temperature physics; Josephson effects; superconducting magnetometry; superconducting circuit elements for use in surveillance and communication systems. *Mailing Add:* Naval Res Lab Code 6854 Washington DC 20375

NISHIBAYASHI, MASARU, b Los Angeles, Calif, May 6, 23; m 49; c 3. PHYSICAL CHEMISTRY. *Educ:* Univ Cincinnati, BS, 49, PhD(phys chem), 53. *Prof Exp:* Res chemist, Aerojet-Gen Corp, 53-60, sr res chemist, 60-63, SR CHEM SPECIALIST, AEROJET ORD CO, 63- *Mem:* Am Chem Soc; Am Ord Asn. *Res:* Physical and chemical properties of propellants and explosives; interior ballistics; gun propellants. *Mailing Add:* 1339 Beech Hill Ave Hacienda Heights CA 91745

NISHIDA, TOSHIRO, b Nagasaki, Japan, Jan 6, 26; m 60; c 3. FOOD CHEMISTRY. *Educ:* Kyoto Univ, MS, 52; Univ Ill, PhD(food chem), 56. *Prof Exp:* Res asst agr chem, Univ Osaka Prefecture, 47-49; res chemist, Osaka Soda Co, Japan, 52-53; from asst prof to assoc prof food chem, 58-70, PROF FOOD SCI, UNIV ILL, URBANA, 70- *Concurrent Pos:* Grants, NIH, 57- & Ill Heart Asn, 65- *Mem:* Am Chem Soc; Am Oil Chem Soc; Am Soc Biol Chemists; Am Inst Nutrit. *Res:* Chemistry and metabolism of lipids and lipoproteins. *Mailing Add:* 106 Burnsides Res Lab Univ of Ill Urbana IL 61801

NISHIE, KEICA, b Sao Paulo, Brazil, Sept 29, 29. PHARMACOLOGY. *Educ:* Univ Brazil, MD, 56; Northwestern Univ, MS, 59, PhD(pharmacol), 61. *Prof Exp:* NIH fel, Northwestern Univ, 59-61; sr res pharmacologist, Baxter Labs, Inc, 61-65; sr res pharmacologist, 65-73, STAFF MEM, DEPT PHARMACOL, RUSSELL RES CTR, USDA, 73- *Mem:* Am Soc Pharmacol & Exp Therapeut; NY Acad Sci. *Res:* Toxicology. *Mailing Add:* Dept of Pharmacol Russell Res Ctr USDA Athens GA 30613

NISHIHARA, MUTSUKO, microbiology, biochemistry, see previous edition

NISHIKAWA, ALFRED HIROTOSHI, b San Francisco, Calif, Apr 23, 38; m 61; c 2. BIOCHEMISTRY. *Educ:* Univ Calif, Berkeley, AB, 60; Ore State Univ, PhD(enzym), 65. *Prof Exp:* Lab technician biochem, Univ Calif, Berkeley, 60-61; res assoc, Ore State Univ, 65-69; scientist, Xerox Res Labs, NY, 69-71; sr biochemist, 71-75, res fel, Chem Res Div, 76-80, ASST DIR, BIOPOLYMER RES DEPT, HOFFMANN-LA ROCHE, INC, 81- *Mem:* AAAS; Am Chem Soc; NY Acad Sci; Sigma Xi. *Res:* Enzyme isolation and purification; physical-chemical studies of chemically modified proteins; affinity chromatography and immobilized enzyme reactors. *Mailing Add:* Chem Res Div Hoffmann-La Roche Inc Nutley NJ 07110

NISHIKAWARA, MARGARET T, b Vancouver, BC, Feb 3, 23. PHYSIOLOGY. *Educ:* Univ Toronto, BA, 47, MA, 48, PhD(physiol), 52. *Prof Exp:* Res assoc physiol, Univ Toronto, 52-54; from asst prof to assoc prof, 54-72, PROF PHYSIOL, OHIO STATE UNIV, 72- *Mem:* Sigma Xi; Am Physiol Soc; Endocrine Soc. *Res:* Physiologic and endocrine control of metabolic pathways. *Mailing Add:* Dept of Physiol Ohio State Univ Columbus OH 43210

NISHIMOTO, ROY KATSUTO, b Lihue, Hawaii, Oct 29, 44; m 70; c 1. WEED SCIENCE, VEGETABLE CROPS. *Educ:* Ore State Univ, BS, 66, MS, 67; Purdue Univ, PhD(weed sci), 70. *Prof Exp:* Asst prof, 70-74, assoc prof, 74-79, PROF WEED SCI, DEPT HORT, UNIV HAWAII, 79- *Mem:* Asian Pac Weed Sci Soc (treas, 73-); Weed Sci Soc Am; Am Soc Hort Sci. *Res:* Weed control in horticultural crops; Cyperus rotundus tuber dormancy; absorption and translocation of herbicides; phosphorus fertility in tropical soils and vegetable crops. *Mailing Add:* Dept of Hort Univ of Hawaii 3190 Maile Way Rm 102 Honolulu HI 96822

NISHIMURA, JONATHAN SEI, b Berkeley, Calif, Sept 30, 31; m 55; c 2. BIOCHEMISTRY. *Educ:* Univ Calif, AB, 56, PhD(biochem), 59. *Prof Exp:* USPHS fel biochem, Sch Med, Tufts Univ, 59-62, sr instr, 62-64, asst prof, 64-69; assoc prof, 69-71, PROF BIOCHEM, UNIV TEX HEALTH SCI CTR SAN ANTONIO, 71- *Mem:* Am Soc Biol Chem. *Res:* Mechanism of enzyme action. *Mailing Add:* 125 Mecca San Antonio TX 78232

NISHIMURA, KEIICHI, theoretical physics, see previous edition

NISHIMURA, TOSHIMITSU, electrical engineering, see previous edition

NISHIMUTA, JOHN FRANCIS, ruminant nutrition, see previous edition

NISHIOKA, DAVID JITSUO, b Los Angeles, Calif, Aug 12, 45. CELLULAR BIOLOGY, DEVELOPMENTAL BIOLOGY. *Educ:* Calif State Univ, Fullerton, AB, 71, MA, 72; Univ Calif, Berkeley, PhD(zool), 76. *Prof Exp:* Scholar biol, Univ Calif, San Diego, 76-77 & Stanford Univ, 77-78; ASST PROF BIOL, GEORGETOWN UNIV, 78- *Mem:* Am Soc Cell Biol; Soc Develop Biol. *Res:* Fertilization and activation of development; ion requirements, role of intracellular pH, initiation of DNA synthesis and synthesis of chromosomal proteins. *Mailing Add:* Dept of Biol Georgetown Univ Washington DC 20057

NISHIOKA, RICHARD SEIJI, b Hilo, Hawaii, Mar 9, 33; m 61; c 3. NEUROENDOCRINOLOGY, MICROSCOPIC ANATOMY. *Educ:* Univ Hawaii, BA, 56, MA, 59. *Prof Exp:* Res zoologist, 59-65, from asst specialist to assoc specialist, 65-72, SPECIALIST ZOOL, UNIV CALIF, BERKELEY, 72- *Mem:* Am Soc Zoologists; AAAS. *Res:* Comparative neuroendocrinology; ultrastructure and neurophysiological aspects of neurosecretion formation, transport and release; aminergic innervation of endocrine organs; effect of hormone administration to neonates; endocrinology of salmon smoltification; fish development. *Mailing Add:* 974 Tulare Ave Albany CA 94706

NISHITA, HIDEO, b Castroville, Calif, May 8, 17; m; c 4. SOIL CHEMISTRY, PLANT NUTRITION. *Educ:* Univ Calif, BS, 47, MS, 49, PhD(plant physiol), 52. *Prof Exp:* Sr lab asst bot, Univ Calif, 47-48, asst plant nutrit, 49-52; jr res soil scientist soil sci & plant physiol, Atomic Energy Proj, 52-54, asst res soil scientist, 54-58, from asst res soil scientist to assoc res soil scientist, 54-66, RES SOIL SCIENTIST, LAB NUCLEAR MED & RADIATION BIOL, UNIV CALIF, LOS ANGELES, 66- *Mem:* AAAS; Am Inst Biol Sci; Soil Sci Soc Am; Am Soc Plant Physiologists. *Mailing Add:* Lab of Nuclear Med & Rad Biol Univ of Calif Los Angeles CA 90024

NISHIZAWA, EDWARD EICHI, b Pitt Meadows, BC, Sept 25, 29. BIOCHEMISTRY, BIOLOGY. *Educ:* Univ Man, BSc, 52, MSc, 53; Univ Ottawa, PhD(org chem), 59. *Prof Exp:* Fel steroid biochem, Univ Utah, 59-63, res assoc, 61-62, res instr, 62-63; res scientist platelet biochem & Med Res Coun grant, Univ Guelph, 63-65; Med Res Coun sr fel path, McMaster Univ, 66-70; res assoc, 70-72, SR RES SCIENTIST, DIABETES & ATHEROSCLEROSIS RES UNIT, UPJOHN CO, 72- *Concurrent Pos:* Mem coun thrombosis, Am Heart Asn. *Mem:* Sigma Xi; Int Soc Thrombosis & Haemostasis; Am Heart Asn. *Res:* Elucidation of membrane function using platelets as a mode model; development of agents to combat thrombosis; mechanism of platelet aggregation. *Mailing Add:* Diabetes & Atheroscl Res Unit Upjohn Co Kalamazoo MI 49001

NISONOFF, ALFRED, b New York, NY, Jan 26, 23; m 46; c 2. IMMUNOCHEMISTRY, IMMUNOBIOLOGY. *Educ:* Rutgers Univ, BS, 42; Johns Hopkins Univ, PhD(chem), 51. *Prof Exp:* AEC fel, Med Sch, Johns Hopkins Univ, 51-52; sr res chemist, US Rubber Co, Conn, 52-54; sr cancer res scientist, Roswell Park Mem Inst, NY, 54-57, assoc cancer res scientist, 57-60; from assoc prof to prof microbiol, Univ Ill, Urbana, 60-66; prof microbiol, Univ Ill Col Med, 66-75, head dept biochem, 69-75; PROF BIOL, ROSENSTIEL RES CTR, BRANDEIS UNIV, 75- *Concurrent Pos:* NIH career res award, 62-69; mem study sects allergy & immunol, NIH & Nat Multiple Sclerosis Soc; for corresp, Belgian Royal Acad Med, 77- *Honors & Awards:* Medal, Pasteur Inst, 71. *Mem:* Am Asn Immunol; Am Soc Biol Chemists. *Res:* Mechanism of biosynthesis of antibodies and their genetic control. *Mailing Add:* Dept Biol Rosenstiel Res Ctr Brandeis Univ Waltham MA 02154

NISS, HAMILTON FREDERICK, b Milwaukee, Wis, Apr 29, 23; m 49; c 2. MICROBIOLOGY. *Educ:* Univ Wis, PhB, 45, MS, 47; Purdue Univ, PhD, 58. *Prof Exp:* Asst prof biol, Sam Houston State Col, 47-49; instr bact, Purdue Univ, 49-57; asst prof microbiol, Syracuse Univ, 57-61; SR MICROBIOLOGIST, ELI LILLY & CO, 61- *Mem:* AAAS; Am Soc Microbiol; Soc Indust Microbiol. *Res:* Biochemical microbiology; fungal physiology; antibiotic biosynthesis; chemical and microbiological assay development. *Mailing Add:* Dept K-400 Eli Lilly & Co Indianapolis IN 46206

NISSAN, ALFRED H(ESKEL), b Baghdad, Iraq, Feb 14, 14; US citizen; m 40; c 1. CHEMICAL ENGINEERING, PHYSICAL CHEMISTRY. *Educ:* Univ Birmingham, BSc, 37, PhD, 40, DSc, 43. *Prof Exp:* Lectr petrol prod, Univ Birmingham, 40-47; dir res, Bowater Pulp & Paper Co, Eng, 47-53; res prof textile eng, Univ Leeds, 53-57; chem eng, Rensselaer Polytech Inst, 57-62; corp res dir, Westvaco Corp, 62-79, vpres, 67-79; CONSULT, 79- *Concurrent Pos:* Consult, WVa Pulp & Paper Co, 57-62 & Flame Warfare Comt, Ministry of Supply, Eng, 42-57; adj prof, Rensselaer Polytech Inst, 62-69, State Univ NY Col Environ Sci & Forestry, 79-; hon vis prof, Univ Uppsala, Sweden, 7480. *Honors & Awards:* Mitscherlich Medal, Zellcheming, Germany, 82, Gold Medal, Tech Asn Pulp & Paper Indust, 82. *Mem:* Fel Am Inst Chem; fel AAAS; fel Tech Asn Pulp & Paper Indust; fel Am Inst Chem Engrs; fel Int Acad Wood Sci. *Res:* Fluid mechanics and other transport phenomena; rheology; fibers and fibrous systems. *Mailing Add:* 6A Dickel Rd Scarsdale NY 10583

NISSELBAUM, JEROME SEYMOUR, b Hartford, Conn, Dec 21, 25; m 49; c 3. BIOCHEMISTRY. *Educ:* Univ Conn, BA, 49; Tufts Univ, PhD(biochem), 53. *Prof Exp:* Asst biochem, Tufts Univ, 50-53, USPHS res fel, 53-55, instr, Sch Med, 54-57; asst, 57-60, ASSOC, SLOAN-KETTERING INST CANCER RES, 60-, ASSOC MEM, 67-; ASSOC PROF BIOCHEM, CORNELL UNIV, 68- *Concurrent Pos:* Res assoc, Sloan-Kettering Div, Cornell Univ, 57-68; asst biochemist, Mem Hosp, Mem Sloan-Kettering Cancer Ctr, 72-75, asst, 75-81, assoc attend biochemist, Mem Hosp, 75-81. *Mem:* AAAS; Am Asn Clin Chemists; Am Chem Soc; Am Soc Biol Chem. *Res:* Enzymology; clinical biochemistry; methods development; protein chemistry; immunochemistry. *Mailing Add:* 410 E 68th St New York NY 10021

NISSIM-SABAT, CHARLES, b Sofia, Bulgaria, Feb 1, 38; US citizen; m 67; c 1. COSMOLOGY, HIGH ENERGY PHYSICS. *Educ:* Columbia Univ, AB, 59, MA, 60, PhD(physics), 65. *Prof Exp:* Res assoc high energy physics, Fermi Inst, Univ Chicago, 65-67; from asst prof to assoc prof, 67-74, PROF PHYSICS & CHMN DEPT, NORTHEASTERN ILL UNIV, CHICAGO, 74- *Mem:* AAAS. *Res:* General relativity and high energy physics, particularly experimental weak interactions and mu-mesic x-rays. *Mailing Add:* Dept of Physics North Eastern Ill Univ Chicago IL 60628

NISTERUK, CHESTER JOSEPH, b New York, NY, Sept 3, 28. PHYSICS, ELECTRICAL ENGINEERING. *Educ:* Polytech Inst Brooklyn, BEE, 49, MS, 54, PhD(physics), 67. *Prof Exp:* From instr to asst prof, 51-63, head dept, 69-77, ASSOC PROF ELEC ENG, MANHATTAN COL, 63- *Concurrent Pos:* Lectr, St John's Univ, NY, 56-57. *Mem:* Inst Elec & Electronics Engrs; Am Phys Soc; Am Asn Physics Teachers. *Res:* Quantum statistical mechanics; quantum electronics; biological potentials. *Mailing Add:* Dept of Elec Eng Manhattan Col Bronx NY 10471

NISWANDER, JERRY DAVID, b Ottumwa, Iowa, Mar 1, 30; m 55; c 4. DENTISTRY, HUMAN GENETICS. *Educ:* Univ Mich, DDS, 55, MS, 62; Univ Md, cert, 76. *Prof Exp:* Dent intern, USPHS Hosp, Seattle, Wash, 55-56; mem staff clin ctr, Dent Dept, NIH, 56-57, mem staff human genetics sect, Nat Inst Dent Res, 57-58 & mem staff child health surv, Atomic Bomb Casualty Comn, 58-60; mem staff human genetics, Univ Mich, 60-63; mem staff, Human Genetics Br, 63-76, mem staff, 76-81, CHIEF, CRANIOFACIAL ANOMALIES PROG, NAT INST DENT RES, 81- *Concurrent Pos:* Prof lectr, Sch Dent, Georgetown Univ, 71-77, clin assoc prof, 77- *Mem:* AAAS; Am Soc Human Genetics; Am Pub Health Asn. *Res:* Administer research and training grants and contracts related to congenital craniofacial malformations, malocclusion, and acquired craniofacial defects; human biology; orthodontics. *Mailing Add:* Craniofacial Anomalies Prog Nat Inst Dent Res Bethesda MD 20014

NISWENDER, GORDON DEAN, b Gillette, Wyo, Apr 21, 40; m 64; c 2. REPRODUCTIVE ENDOCRINOLOGY. *Educ:* Univ Wyo, BS, 62; Univ Nebr, MS, 64; Univ Ill, PhD(animal sci), 67. *Prof Exp:* Res asst reprod physiol, Univ Nebr, 62-64 & Univ Ill, 64-65; NIH res fel, Univ Mich, Ann Arbor, 67-68, asst prof, 68-71; from asst prof to assoc prof, 71-75, PROF REPROD PHYSIOL, COLO STATE UNIV, 75- *Honors & Awards:* Animal Physiol & Endrocrinol Award, Am Asn Animal Scientists, 81. *Mem:* AAAS; Soc Study Reproduction (pres, 81); Am Soc Animal Sci; Endocrine Soc. *Res:* Reproductive biology, endocrinology, immunology. *Mailing Add:* Dept of Physiol & Biophys Colo State Univ Ft Collins CO 80523

NITECKI, DANUTE EMILIJA, b Lithuania, Apr 22, 27; US citizen; c 1. CHEMISTRY, BIOCHEMISTRY. *Educ:* Univ Chicago, MS, 56, PhD(chem), 61. *Prof Exp:* NIH fel, 61-63; asst res biochemist, Med Ctr, 63-69, assoc res biochemist, 69-77, RES BIOCHEMIST, SCH MED, UNIV CALIF, SAN FRANCISCO, 77- *Mem:* Am Chem Soc; Royal Soc Chem. *Res:* Synthesis of peptides used as haptens in immunochemical studies; synthesis of boron containing aromatic compounds of physiological interest; syntheses of well defined small molecular weight antigens used to investigate the initiation and the progress of cellular and humoral immune response. *Mailing Add:* 1555 16th Ave San Francisco CA 94122

NITECKI, MATTHEW H, b Poland, Apr 30, 25; nat US; m 64; c 2. PALEOBOTANY, INVERTEBRATE PALEONTOLOGY. *Educ:* Univ Chicago, MS, 58, PhD, 68. *Prof Exp:* Asst cur, 65-69, assoc cur, 69-75, CUR, FIELD MUS NATURAL HIST, 75-, CUR INVERT PALEONT, WALKER MUS, UNIV CHICAGO, 55- *Concurrent Pos:* Vis investr, Inst Geol & Geophys, USSR, 78; guest scientist, Acad Sci USSR, 81. *Mem:* Geol Soc Am; Am Asn Petrol Geologists; Soc Econ Paleontologists & Mineralogists; Soc Study Evolution. *Res:* Paleozoic paleobotany and invertebrate paleontology. *Mailing Add:* Field Mus Natural Hist Roosevelt Rd & Lake Shore Dr Chicago IL 60605

NITHMAN, CHARLES JOSEPH, b Belleville, Ill, Jan 14, 37; m 59; c 2. PHARMACY. *Educ:* Okla State Univ, BS, 59; Univ Okla, BSPh, 62, Univ Okla, MSc, 70; Mercer Univ, PharmD, 74. *Prof Exp:* Clin instr pharm, Univ Okla, 68-70; asst dir pharm, St Anthony Hosp, Oklahoma City, 70-72; asst prof, 72-78, ASSOC PROF PHARM, SOUTHWESTERN OKLA STATE UNIV, 72-, HEAD, CLIN PHARM DEPT, 81- *Mem:* Sigma Xi; Am Soc Hosp Pharmacists; Am Pharmaceut Asn; Am Asn Col Pharm. *Res:* Drug distribution systems in hospitals. *Mailing Add:* 4520 NW 32nd Pl Oklahoma City OK 73122

NITOWSKY, HAROLD MARTIN, b Brooklyn, NY, Feb 12, 25; m 54; c 2. MEDICINE, GENETICS. *Educ:* NY Univ, AB, 44, MD, 47; Univ Colo, MSc, 51; Am Bd Pediat, dipl, 56. *Prof Exp:* USPHS fel, Univ Colo, 50-51; from instr to assoc prof, Sch Med, Johns Hopkins Univ, 53-67; PROF PEDIAT & GENETICS, ALBERT EINSTEIN COL MED, 67- *Concurrent Pos:* Pediatrician, Johns Hopkins Hosp, 53-; res assoc & adj attend pediatrician, Sinai Hosp, 55-, dir pediat res, 58-; sr investr, Nat Asn Retarded Children, 60-65. *Mem:* AAAS; Soc Pediat Res; Sigma Xi; Am Fedn Clin Res; Am Inst Nutrit. *Res:* Somatic cell genetics; inborn errors of metabolism; genetic counseling. *Mailing Add:* Dept of Pediat Albert Einstein Col of Med Bronx NY 10461

NITSCHE, JOHANNES CARL CHRISTIAN, b Olbernhau, Ger. PARTIAL DIFFERENTIAL EQUATIONS, DIFFERENTIAL GEOMETRY. *Educ:* Univ Gottingen, dipl, 50; Univ Leipzig, PhD(math), 51. *Prof Exp:* Scientist, Max-Planck Inst, Gottingen, 50-52; prin asst, Tech Univ, Berlin-Charlottenburg, 52-55; Fulbright fel, Stanford Univ, 55-56; vis assoc prof, Univ Cincinnati, 56-57; assoc prof, 57-60, head, Sch Math, 71-78, PROF MATH, UNIV MINN, 60- *Concurrent Pos:* Prin investr, US Govt & NSF grants, 57-; vis prof, Univ Puerto Rico, 60-61, Univ Hamburg, 65, Tech Univ Vienna, 68, Univ Bonn, 71 & 75, Univ Heidelberg, 79; assoc ed, Contemporary Math, 80-; Sr US Scientist Award, Alexander von Humboldt Found, 81. *Honors & Awards:* Lester R Ford Award, Math Asn Am, 75. *Mem:* AAAS; Am Math Soc; Math Asn Am; Soc Natural Philosophy. *Res:* Mathematical analysis (approximation theory, calculus of variations, differential geometry, minimal surface theory, partial differential equations) and its applications to related disciplines; minimal surfaces. *Mailing Add:* Univ Minn Sch Math 206 Church St SE Minneapolis MN 55455

NITSCHKE, J MICHAEL, b Berlin, Ger, Apr 27, 39. NUCLEAR PHYSICS. *Educ:* Brunswick Tech Univ, MS, 65, Dr rer nat(physics), 68. *Prof Exp:* PHYSICIST NUCLEAR CHEM & PHYSICS, LAWRENCE BERKELEY LAB, 71- *Mem:* Am Phys Soc. *Res:* Physical, chemical and nuclear properties of the heaviest elements. *Mailing Add:* Lawrence Berkeley Lab 1 Cyclotron Rd Berkeley CA 94720

NITSOS, RONALD EUGENE, b Sacramento, Calif, Aug 26, 37; m 66; c 2. HORTICULTURE. *Educ:* Sacramento State Col, BA, 63; Ore State Univ, MA, 66, PhD(plant physiol), 69. *Prof Exp:* ASSOC PROF BIOL, SOUTHERN ORE STATE COL, 69- *Concurrent Pos:* Res grant, Southern Ore Col, 69-71; proj dir, Cause Grant for Greenhouse, NSF, 79-81. *Mem:* Am Soc Plant Physiologists; NAm Mycol Asn; Native Plant Soc. *Res:* Plant physiology, especially roles of univalent cations in plants; needs and effects of univalent cations in enzyme activation. *Mailing Add:* Dept of Biol Southern Ore State Col Ashland OR 97520

NITTLER, LEROY WALTER, b Shickley, Nebr, Jan 10, 21; wid; c 2. AGRICULTURE. *Educ:* Univ Nebr, BS, 49, MS, 50; Cornell Univ, PhD(plant breeding), 53. *Prof Exp:* Res asst, 50-53, from asst prof to assoc prof, 53-65, head dept seed invests, Col Agr & Life Sci, 65-81, PROF SEED INVESTS, COL AGR, CORNELL UNIV, 65- *Concurrent Pos:* Head dept seed invests Col Agr & Life Sci Cornell Univ, 68-73. *Mem:* Am Soc Agron. *Res:* Varietal purity testing of grain, forage crop and turf grass seed; response of grain, grass and legume seedlings to photoperiod, light quality, light intensity and temperature; response of seedlings to chemicals and nutrient elements. *Mailing Add:* 480 William Geneva NY 14456

NITTROUER, CHARLES A, b Philadelphia, Pa, June 20, 50; m 76. GEOLOGICAL OCEANOGRAPHY. *Educ:* Lafayette Col, BA, 72; Univ Wash, MS, 74, PhD(oceanog), 78. *Prof Exp:* Res assoc oceanog, Univ Wash, 78; ASST PROF MARINE SCI, NC STATE UNIV, 78- *Mem:* Am Geophys Union; Geol Soc Am; Soc Econ Paleontologists & Mineralogists; Int Asn Sedimentologists. *Res:* Marine sedimentology, especially sediment transport and accumulation on continental shelves and adjacent environments. *Mailing Add:* Dept Marine Sci NC State Univ Raleigh NC 27650

NITZ, OTTO WILLIAM JULIUS, b Sigourney, Iowa, June 25, 05; m 36. ORGANIC CHEMISTRY. *Educ:* Elmhurst Col, BS, 29; Univ Iowa, MS, 33, PhD(org chem), 36. *Prof Exp:* Instr, Elmhurst Col, 29-32; asst, Univ Iowa, 33-36; prof chem, Parsons Col, 36-40 & Northern Mont Col, 40-51; chief chemist, Ky Synthetic Rubber Corp, 51-52; prof, 52-71, EMER PROF CHEM, UNIV WIS-STOUT, 71- *Res:* Vanillin derivatives. *Mailing Add:* 1103 Third Ave Menomonie WI 54751

NITZSCHE, RAY NORMAN, b Walsh, Ill, Sept 23, 44; m 66; c 2. ENGINEERING MECHANICS, COMPUTER SCIENCE. *Educ:* Univ Ill, BS, 67, MS, 68, PhD(theoret & appl mech), 70. *Prof Exp:* Asst prof eng mech, Univ Mo-Rolla, 70-74; sr test engr, Caterpillar Tractor Co, 74-76; asst prof mech, Southern Ill Univ, Carbondale, 76; RES ENGR, WHIRLPOOL CORP, BENTON HARBOR, 77- *Mem:* Sigma Xi; Am Soc Eng Educ. *Res:* Finite element analysis; numerical methods of engineering. *Mailing Add:* 6209 E Becht Rd Coloma MI 49038

NIU, JOSEPH H Y, b Nanking, China, Apr 22, 32. INORGANIC CHEMISTRY, ORGANIC CHEMISTRY. *Educ:* Univ Hong Kong, BS, 55; Univ Wis-Madison, PhD(chem), 62; Univ Mich, MBA, 72. *Prof Exp:* Res chemist, BASF Wyandotte Corp, 62-66, sr res chemist, 66-73, supvr res & develop, Res Div, 73-80; GROUP LEADER, RES & DEVELOP, BETZ LAB INC, 81- *Mem:* Am Chem Soc; Soc Petrol Engrs; Tech Asn Pulp & Paper Indust. *Res:* Phosphorus, nitrogen and fluorine chemistry; surface active agents; coordination compounds; new aromatic anions; chemical additives for pulp and paper; chemical additives for petroleum industry. *Mailing Add:* Res Div Betz Lab Inc 9669 Grogans Mills Rd The Woodlands TX 77380

NIU, MANN CHIANG, b Peking, China, Oct 31, 14; nat US; m 43; c 2. DEVELOPMENTAL BIOLOGY, BIOCHEMISTRY. *Educ:* Peking Univ, AB, 36; Stanford Univ, PhD, 47. *Prof Exp:* Asst zool, Peking Univ, 36-40, lectr, 40-44; res assoc embryol, Stanford Univ, 44-52, res biologist, 52-55; asst prof gen physiol, Rockefeller Univ, 55-60; PROF BIOL, TEMPLE UNIV, 60- *Concurrent Pos:* Guggenheim fel, Rockefeller Univ, 54 & 55, vis prof, 70; mem, Academia Sinica, 70; vis prof, Inst Zool Acad Sinica, Peking, 73 & 75-78. *Honors & Awards:* Lillie Award, 57. *Mem:* Am Soc Biol Chemists; Am Tissue Culture Asn; Am Soc Cell Biol; Soc Exp Biol & Med; Soc Develop Biol; Am Soc Zoologists. *Res:* Origin of pigment cells; cell transformation and cancer; physiology of color changes; nucleocytoplasmic interactions; causal analysis of induction; physiological activity of mRNA and induced biosynthesis; RNA metabolsim in learning and aggressive behavior; genetic manipulation in higher organisms. *Mailing Add:* Dept of Biol Temple Univ Philadelphia PA 19122

NIV, YEHUDA, b Tel Aviv, Israel, May 9, 49; m 72; c 2. NUCLEAR STRUCTURE. *Educ:* Hebrew Univ, Jerusalem, Israel, BSc, 73; Weizmann Inst Sci, MSc, 75, PhD(nuclear physics), 80. *Prof Exp:* Fel, Weizmann Inst Sci, 80; DR WEIZMANN FEL, PHYSICS DEPT, RUTGERS UNIV, 80- *Concurrent Pos:* Consult, Tadiran Electronics Mfg, Holon, Israel & Israeli Aircraft Indust, 78-80; resident vis, Bell Labs, Murray Hill, NJ, 80- *Mem:* Am Phys Soc. *Res:* Hyperfine interaction in free ions; nuclear moments of excited states; laser induced nuclear orientation; optical pumping. *Mailing Add:* Dept Physics & Astron Busch Campus Rutgers Univ Piscataway NJ 08854

NIVEN, CHARLES FRANKLIN, JR, b Clemson, SC, July 22, 15; m 39; c 4. MICROBIOLOGY, FOOD SCIENCE. *Educ:* Univ Ark, BS, 35; Cornell Univ, PhD(bact), 39. *Prof Exp:* From instr to assoc prof, Cornell Univ, 39-46; bacteriologist, Hiram Walker & Sons, Inc, Ill, 46; from asst prof to prof microbiol, Univ Chicago, 46-64; DIR RES, RES CTR, DEL MONTE CORP, 64- *Concurrent Pos:* Chief, Div Bact, Am Meat Inst Found, 46-58, assoc dir,

58-61, sci dir, 61-64. *Mem:* AAAS; Am Soc Microbiol; Am Pub Health Asn; Am Chem Soc; Inst Food Technologists (pres, 74-75). *Res:* Bacterial nutrition, physiology and metabolism; food microbiology. *Mailing Add:* Del Monte Corp Res Ctr 205 N Wiget Lane Walnut Creek CA 94598

NIVEN, DONALD FERRIES, b Aberdeen, Scotland, Mar 5, 47; m 65; c 2. MICROBIOLOGY, BIOCHEMISTRY. *Educ:* Univ Aberdeen, BSc, 70, PhD(biochem), 73. *Prof Exp:* Res asst biochem, Univ Aberdeen, 70-73; res fel biol, Univ Kent, 73-76; res assoc microbiol, 76-79, ASST PROF MICROBIOL, MACDONALD COL, MCGILL UNIV, 79- *Mem:* Brit Soc Gen Microbiol; Can Soc Microbiologists; Am Soc Microbiol. *Res:* Microbiol physiology and biochemistry, especially bacterial bioenergetics; Bioenergetics and pathogenicity. *Mailing Add:* Dept Microbiol MacDonald Campus McGill Univ 21111 Lakeshore Rd Ste Anne de Bellevue PQ H9X 1C0 Can

NIX, JAMES RAYFORD, b Natchitoches, La, Feb 18, 38; m 61; c 2. THEORETICAL NUCLEAR PHYSICS. *Educ:* Carnegie Inst Technol, BS, 60; Univ Calif, Berkeley, PhD(physics), 64. *Prof Exp:* NATO fel, Niels Bohr Inst, Univ Copenhagen, 64-65; fel, Lawrence Radiation Lab, Univ Calif, Berkeley, 66-68; mem staff, 68-77, GROUP LEADER NUCLEAR THEORY, LOS ALAMOS NAT LAB, 77- *Concurrent Pos:* Chmn, SuperHILAC Prog Adv Comt, Lawrence Berkeley Lab, Univ Calif, 74-76, Gordon Res Conf Nuclear Chem, 76; mem, Physics Div Adv Comt, Oak Ridge Nat Lab, 75-77, chmn, 76; mem vis comt, Nuclear Sci Div, Lawrence Berkeley Lab, Univ Calif, 78-80, chmn, 79-80; Alexander von Humboldt US sr scientist award, 80-81; consult, Calif Inst Technol, 79. *Mem:* Fel Am Phys Soc; AAAS. *Res:* Theory of nuclear fission, very-heavy-ion reactions, super heavy nuclei, nuclear ground-state masses and deformations, large-amplitude collective nuclear motion, nuclear dissipation and relativistic heavy-ion collisions. *Mailing Add:* Nuclear Theory T-9 MS 452 Los Alamos Nat Lab Los Alamos NM 87545

NIX, JOE FRANKLIN, b Malvern, Ark, Aug 28, 39. GEOCHEMISTRY, ANALYTICAL CHEMISTRY. *Educ:* Ouachita Baptist Col, BS, 61; Univ Ark, MS, 63, PhD(chem), 66. *Prof Exp:* Assoc prof chem, 66-74, PROF CHEM, OUACHITA BAPTIST UNIV, 74- *Mem:* AAAS; Am Chem Soc; Am Geophys Union; Am Soc Limnol & Oceanog. *Res:* Radioactive fallout; neutron activation analysis of meteorites; geochemistry of hot springs and geysers; geochemistry of impoundments. *Mailing Add:* Dept of Chem Ouachita Baptist Univ Arkadelphia AR 71923

NIX, SYDNEY JOHNSTON, JR, organic chemistry, see previous edition

NIX, WILLIAM DALE, b King City, Calif, Oct 28, 36; m 58; c 3. MATERIALS SCIENCE. *Educ:* San Jose State Col, BS, 59; Stanford Univ, MS, 60, PhD(mat sci), 63. *Prof Exp:* From asst prof to assoc prof, 63-72, dir, Ctr Mat Res, 68-70, PROF MAT SCI, STANFORD UNIV, 72-, ASSOC CHMN, DEPT OF MAT SCI & ENG, 75- *Concurrent Pos:* Participant, Ford's Residencies in Eng Pract Prog, WD, Manly Stellite Div, Union Carbide Corp, Ind, 66. *Honors & Awards:* Western Elec Award Eng Teaching, 64; Bradley Stoughton Award, Am Soc Metals, 70; Mathewson Gold Medal, Am Inst Mining, Metall & Petrol Engrs, 79. *Mem:* Fel Am Soc Metals; Am Inst Mining, Metall & Petrol Engrs. *Res:* Imperfections in crystals; dislocation theory and mechanical properties of crystals; ferromagnetic perperties of metals; high temperature creep and fracture. *Mailing Add:* Dept Mat Sci & Eng Stanford Univ Stanford CA 94305

NIXON, CHARLES MELVILLE, b Newton, Mass, Jan 22, 35; m 60; c 2. WILDLIFE ECOLOGY. *Educ:* Northeastern Univ, BS, 57; Pa State Univ, MS, 59. *Prof Exp:* Res biologist, Ohio Div Wildlife, 59-70; RES BIOLOGIST WILDLIFE, ILL NAT HIST SURV, 70- *Honors & Awards:* Publ Award, Wildlife Soc, 75. *Mem:* Wildlife Soc; Am Soc Mammalogists; Soc Am fForesters. *Res:* Ecology and management of forest-dwelling wildlife. *Mailing Add:* Nat Resources Bldg Ill Nat Hist Surv 607 E Peabody Champaign IL 61820

NIXON, CHARLES WILLIAM, b Carlinville, Ill, Sept, 28, 25. GENETICS, HISTOLOGY. *Educ:* Univ Ill, BS, 46, MS, 48; Brown Univ, PhD(biol), 51. *Prof Exp:* Asst prof biol, Northeastern Univ, 51-57 & Simmons Col, 57-60; biologist, Bio-Res Inst, Inc, 60-70; pvt consult genetics, 70-73; res assoc, Mass Inst Technol, 73-79; CONSULT GENETICS, 79- *Concurrent Pos:* Ed, Sempervium Fanciers Asn Newsletter, 75- *Mem:* AAAS. *Res:* Mammalian and plant genetics. *Mailing Add:* 37 Ox Bow Lane Randolph MA 02368

NIXON, CHARLES WILLIAM, acoustics, audiology, see previous edition

NIXON, DONALD MERWIN, b Topeka, Kans, Nov 11, 35; m 62; c 3. AGRICULTURAL ECONOMICS. *Educ:* Colo State Univ, BS, 65, MS, 66, PhD(agr mkt), 69. *Prof Exp:* Instr poultry sci & mkt, Colo State Univ, 65-69; assoc prof bus & agr mkt, 69-70, assoc prof, 70-81, PROF AGR ECON, TEX A&I UNIV, 81- *Concurrent Pos:* Res grants, Houston Livestock & Rodeo Asn, 70, Rio Farms, 72 & Perry Found, 75. *Mem:* Am Mkt Asn; Am Agr Econ Asn; Inst Food Technologists; Poultry Sci Asn. *Res:* Agricultural marketing; economic analysis among beef cattle common to south Texas; taste panel evaluation; economics of crop insurance; use of grain sorghum and beef futures by south Texas producers. *Mailing Add:* Col of Agr Tex A&I Univ Kingsville TX 78363

NIXON, ELRAY S, b Escalante, Utah, Feb 5, 31; m 57; c 4. PLANT ECOLOGY, PLANT TAXONOMY. *Educ:* Brigham Young Univ, BS, 57, MS, 61; Univ Tex, PhD(bot), 63. *Prof Exp:* Asst prof biol, Chadron State Col, 63-65 & Southern Ore Col, 65-66; mem staff, 66-68, assoc prof, 68-72, PROF BIOL, STEPHEN F AUSTIN STATE UNIV, 72- *Mem:* Southwestern Asn Naturalists; Int. *Res:* Floristic ecology; soil-plant relationships. *Mailing Add:* PO Box 13003 SFA Station Nacogdoches TX 75962

NIXON, EUGENE RAY, b Mt Pleasant, Mich, Apr 14, 19; m 45; c 2. PHYSICAL CHEMISTRY. *Educ:* Alma Col, ScB, 41; Brown Univ, PhD(chem), 47. *Prof Exp:* Res chemist, Manhattan Dist, Brown Univ, 42-46, res assoc, Off Naval Res, 46-47, instr chem, 47-49; from instr to assoc prof, 49-65, dir, mat res lab, 69-72, PROF CHEM, UNIV PA, 65- *Concurrent Pos:* Vdean grad sch, Univ Pa, 58-65. *Mem:* Am Chem Soc; Coblentz Soc; Am Phys Soc. *Res:* Molecular spectroscopy and structure; laser chemistry. *Mailing Add:* Dept of Chem Univ of Pa Philadelphia PA 19104

NIXON, JOSEPH EUGENE, b Platteville, Wis, Jan 7, 38; m 65; c 2. TOXICOLOGY. *Educ:* Univ Ill, BS, 61, PhD(nutrit biochem), 65. *Prof Exp:* Res assoc biochem, Dept Physiol Chem, Univ Wis, 65-66; res biochemist, Vet Admin Hosp, Madison, Wis, 66-68; asst prof, 68-75, assoc prof, 75-81, PROF, DEPT FOOD SCI & TECHNOL, ORE STATE UNIV, 81- *Mem:* Am Inst Nutrit; Soc Toxicol. *Res:* Biochemistry of fatty acid synthesis; intermediary metabolism of lipids; nutrition and cancer, mechanisms of carcinogenesis, modification of carcinogenesis by dietary components. *Mailing Add:* Dept Food Sci Ore State Univ Corvallis OR 97331

NIXON, PAUL R(OBERT), b Kenya, EAfrica, June 23, 24; US citizen; m 50; c 1. AGRICULTURAL ENGINEERING. *Educ:* Iowa State Univ, BS, 52, MS, 55; Stanford Univ, MS, 66. *Prof Exp:* Asst soil conserv off, Kenya Dept Agr, EAfrica, 43-45; agr engr, Soil Conserv Serv, US Dept Agr, 52-54; assoc irrig res, Iowa State Univ, 55-56; proj leader hydroclimat res, 56-65, res invest leader, 65-71, agr engr, Rio Grande Soil & Water Res Ctr, 71-80, AGR ENGR, SUBTROPICAL RES LAB, AGR RES SERV, USDA, 80- *Mem:* Am Soc Agr Engrs; Am Soc Civil Engrs; Am Meteorol Soc. *Res:* Water supply and use; consumption of water as related to climate, vegetation and availability of soil water; calibration and interpretation of surface temperature maps prepared from satellite data. *Mailing Add:* Sci & Educ Admin PO Box 267 Weslaco TX 78596

NIXON, SCOTT WEST, b Philadelphia, Pa, Aug 24, 43; m 65; c 2. ECOLOGY, OCEANOGRAPHY. *Educ:* Univ Del, BA, 65; Univ NC, Chapel Hill, PhD(bot), 70. *Prof Exp:* Res assoc, 69-70, asst prof, 70-75, assoc prof, 75-80, PROF OCEANOG, UNIV RI, 80- *Mem:* Am Soc Limnol & Oceanog; Ecol Soc Am; Estuarine Res Fedn. *Res:* Ecological systems; nutrient cycling; energetics; simulation. *Mailing Add:* Sch of Oceanog Univ of RI Kingston RI 02881

NIYOGI, SALIL KUMAR, b Calcutta, India, Feb 1, 32; US citizen; m 64; c 2. NUCLEIC ACID ENZYMOLOGY. *Educ:* Univ Calcutta, BS, 53, MS, 56; Northwestern Univ, PhD(biochem), 61. *Prof Exp:* Res assoc, Dept Chem, Stanford Univ, 61-62, Dept Biochem, Univ Maryland, 63-64 & Dept Biophys, Johns Hopkins Univ, 64-66; SR SCIENTIST BIOCHEM, BIOL DIV, OAK RIDGE NAT LAB, 66- *Concurrent Pos:* Prof, Oak Ridge Grad Sch Biomed Sci, Univ Tenn, 70- *Mem:* Fel AAAS; Am Soc Biol Chemists; Am Soc Microbiol. *Res:* Enzymological aspects of RNA synthesis and degradation; molecular biology of DNA tumor viruses; chromatin structure and function; effects of metal mutagens and carcinogens on transcription. *Mailing Add:* Biol Div Oak Ridge Nat Lab PO Box Y Oak Ridge TN 37830

NIZEL, ABRAHAM EDWARD, b Boston, Mass, July 27, 17; m 42; c 2. PREVENTIVE DENTISTRY, NUTRITION. *Educ:* Tufts Univ, DMD, 40, MSD, 52. *Prof Exp:* Intern oral surg, Worcester City Hosp, 40-41; instr periodont, 52-60, asst clin prof, 61-66, assoc prof nutrit, 66-73, PROF NUTRIT & PREV DENT, SCH DENT MED, TUFTS UNIV, 73- *Concurrent Pos:* Res assoc, Mass Inst Technol, 52-70, vis assoc prof nutrit & metab, 71-73, vis prof, 73-; guest lectr, Eastman Dent Ctr, 60- & Forsyth Dent Ctr, 69-; grants, Nutrit Found, 67-72 & Nat Dairy Coun, 68-72; consult, Am Dent Asn & Food & Nutrit Bd, Nat Acad Sci; consult ed, J Am Dent Asn & J Prev Dent. *Honors & Awards:* Prev Dent Award, Am Dent Asn. *Mem:* AAAS; fel Am Col Dent; fel Am Asn Dent Sci; Int Asn Dent Res; Am Dent Asn. *Res:* Oral health-nutrition interrelationships, particularly the effect of dietary phosphate supplements on inhibition of experimental caries; model nutrition teaching program for dental schools and schools of dental hygiene; effect of calcium and vitamin D dietary supplementation on the density of alvealan ridges in the elderly. *Mailing Add:* Tufts Univ Sch of Dent Med One Kneeland St Rm 301-05 Medford MA 02155

NIZNIK, CAROL ANN, b Saratoga Springs, NY, Nov 10, 42. COMPUTER ENGINEERING. *Educ:* Univ Rochester, BSEE, 69, MSEE, 72; State Univ NY, Buffalo-Amherst, PhDEE(elec eng), 78. *Prof Exp:* Sr technician, Advan Develop, IBM, 65-68; res scientist, Eastman Kodak Corp, 69-70; engr, Xerox Corp, 71-73, sr engr commun processor cost anal, 73, comput printer design, 73-74; res asst, Lincoln Lab, Mass Inst Technol, 74-75; res asst comput networking, State Univ NY, Buffalo, 76-78, res asst prof, comput commun systs, 78-80; ASSOC PROF ELEC ENG, UNIV PITTSBURGH, 80- *Concurrent Pos:* Consult, Xerox Corp, 75-77; pres & consult, NW Systs, Xerox Corp, 78; pres & consult, NW Systs, Rochester Tel Corp, 79-80; consult postdoc prog, Griffiss AFB, Rome, NY, 81-82. *Mem:* Sigma Xi; sr mem Inst Elec & Electronics Engrs. *Res:* Computer communication networking flow and congestion control software theory and its performance evaluation; theory of software emulating the central nervous system functions in the robotic system. *Mailing Add:* 36 Panorama Trail Rochester NY 14625

NJUS, DAVID LARS, b Honolulu, Hawaii, Oct 17, 48; m 75. BIOPHYSICS. *Educ:* Mass Inst Technol, BS, 70; Harvard Univ, PhD(biophys), 75. *Prof Exp:* Fel biochem, Oxford Univ, 75-78; ASST PROF BIOL, WAYNE STATE UNIV, 78- *Concurrent Pos:* NATO fel, Oxford Univ, 75-76; NIH res, 76-78. *Mem:* AAAS; Biophys Soc. *Res:* Catecholamine transport in the adrenal medulla; membrane biophysics; circadian rhythms and biological oscillations. *Mailing Add:* Dept Biol Sci Wayne State Univ Detroit MI 48202

NOACK, MANFRED GERHARD, b Olbersdorf, Ger, Jan 25, 36; m 62; c 2. INORGANIC CHEMISTRY, INDUSTRIAL CHEMISTRY. *Educ:* Munich Tech Univ, Vordiplom, 59, Diplomchemiker, 62, Dr rer nat(chem), 64; Univ New Haven, MBA, 75. *Prof Exp:* Teaching asst chem, Munich Tech Univ,

62-64; res assoc, Univ Md, 64-67; res chemist, Olin Corp, 67-75, group leader res & develop, 75-80; CONSULT SCIENTIST, 80- *Mem:* Am Chem Soc; Nat Asn Corrosion Engrs; Sigma Xi. *Res:* Chemistry of metal carbonyls; magnetic resonance phenomena in solutions; homogeneous catalysis; corrosion inhibition; applications of redox chemistry; corrosion science and prevention. *Mailing Add:* Olin Res Ctr 275 Winchester Ave New Haven CT 06511

NOACK, T(HOMAS) L, electrical engineering, see previous edition

NOAKES, DAVID LLOYD GEORGE, b Hensall, Can, Aug 3, 42; m 66; c 1. ETHOLOGY. *Educ:* Univ Western Ont, BS, 65, MS, 66; Univ Calif, Berkeley, PhD(zool), 71. *Prof Exp:* Lectr zool, Edinburgh Univ, 70-72; asst prof, 72-80, ASSOC PROF ZOOL, UNIV GUELPH, 80- *Mem:* Animal Behav Soc; Can Soc Zoologists; Sigma Xi; Am Soc Ichthyologists & Herpetologists. *Res:* Behavioral ontogeny, social behavior and social systems, feeding and reproductive ecology, physiological basis of behavior, evolution of behavior, especially of fishes. *Mailing Add:* Dept of Zool Col of Biol Sci Univ of Guelph Guelph ON N1G 2W1 Can

NOAKES, JOHN EDWARD, b Windsor, Ont, May 21, 30; US citizen; m 61; c 2. GEOCHEMISTRY, OCEANOGRAPHY. *Educ:* Champlain Col Plattsburg, BS, 53; Tex A&M Univ, MS, 59, PhD(chem oceanog), 62. *Prof Exp:* Soils engr, NY State Soil Div, 53-55; res chemist, Clark Cleveland Pharmaceut Co, 55-57; res chemist, Tex A&M Univ, 58-59, res found, 59-61; asst prof chem oceanog, Univ Alaska, 61-62; res scientist, Oak Ridge Assoc Univs, 62-68; dir gen res servs, 70-81, ASSOC PROF GEOL & ANTHROP, UNIV GA, 68-, DIR, CTR APPL ISOTOPE STUDIES, 81- *Concurrent Pos:* Dir geochronology lab, Univ Ga, 68-70. *Mem:* Am Chem Soc. *Res:* Geochemistry of marine environment; Tritium, radioactive carbon and uranium geochronology; development of nuclear radiation analytical techniques for measuring low levels of radiation. *Mailing Add:* Dept of Geol 110 Riverbend Rd Athens GA 30601

NOALL, MATTHEW WILCOX, b Salt Lake City, Utah, Mar 16, 24; m 50; c 2. BIOCHEMISTRY. *Educ:* Univ Utah, BA, 48, MA, 49, PhD(biochem), 52. *Prof Exp:* USPHS fel, Nat Inst Arthritis & Metab Dis, 52-54; Am Cancer Soc fel, Sch Med, Tufts Univ, 54-56; asst prof obstet & gynec, Sch Med, Wash Univ, 56-62; asst prof biochem, 62-66, ASSOC PROF PATH & BIOCHEM, BAYLOR COL MED, 66- *Mem:* Am Chem Soc; NY Acad Sci. *Res:* Endocrinology; chemical carcinogenesis. *Mailing Add:* Dept of Path & Biochem Baylor Col of Med Houston TX 77030

NOBACK, CHARLES ROBERT, b New York, NY, Feb 15, 16; m 38; c 4. ANATOMY. *Educ:* Cornell Univ, BS, 36; NY Univ, MS, 38; Univ Minn, PhD(anat), 42. *Prof Exp:* Asst prof, Med Col Ga, 41-44; from asst prof to assoc prof, Long Island Col Med, 44-49; from asst prof to assoc prof anat, 49-68, actg chmn dept, 74-75, PROF ANAT, COL PHYSICIANS & SURGEONS, COLUMBIA UNIV, 68- *Concurrent Pos:* NIH res grants, 53-; James Arthur lectr, 59; mem nerv & sensory syst res eval comt, Vet Admin, 69-72. *Mem:* AAAS; Histochem Soc; Harvey Soc; Am Asn Anat; Soc Neurosci. *Res:* Development of mammalian skeleton; reproduction in the primates; histochemistry of mammalian tissue; regeneration of neural tissues; comparative neuroanatomy; nutrition and nervous system. *Mailing Add:* Dept of Anat Columbia Univ Col of Phys New York NY 10032

NOBACK, RICHARDSON K, b Richmond, Va, Nov 7, 23; m 47; c 3. INTERNAL MEDICINE. *Educ:* Cornell Univ, MD, 47; Am Bd Internal Med, dipl. *Prof Exp:* Nat Heart Inst res fel, 49-50; instr med, Col Med, Cornell Univ, 50-53; asst prof, Col Med, State Univ NY Upstate Med Ctr, 55-56; assoc prof, Med Ctr, Univ Ky, 56-63, asst dean, 56-58, dir univ health serv, 59-63; assoc dean, 64-69, dean, 69-78, PROF INTERNAL MED, MED SCH, UNIV MO-KANSAS CITY, 64-, HEAD, DIV GERIATRICS, 80- *Concurrent Pos:* Asst dir comprehensive care & teaching prog, Cornell Univ, 52-53; med dir, Syracuse Dispensary, 55-56; consult, Med Col, Univ Tenn & John Gaston Hosp, 55; exec med consult, Norfolk Area Med Ctr Authority, Va, 64-70; exec dir, Kansas City Gen Hosp & Med Ctr, 64-69. *Mem:* AMA; Asn Am Med Cols; NY Acad Sci. *Res:* Medical education; health care programs; cardiovascular and renal diseases. *Mailing Add:* 2411 Holmes St Kansas City MO 64108

NOBE, KEN, b Berkeley, Calif, Aug 26, 25; m 57; c 3. CHEMICAL ENGINEERING. *Educ:* Univ Calif, BS, 51, PhD(eng), 56. *Prof Exp:* Jr chem engr polymer res, Res Labs, Air Reduction Corp, 51-52; from asst prof to assoc prof, 57-68, PROF ENG, UNIV CALIF, LOS ANGELES, 68-, CHMN, DEPT OF CHEM & NUCLEAR ENG, 78- *Concurrent Pos:* Mem tech staff, Space Tech Labs, TRW, Inc, 58-59. *Mem:* Electrochem Sco; Nat Asn Corrosion Engrs; Am Chem Soc. *Res:* Electrochemistry; corrosion and catalysis; photoelectrochemistry. *Mailing Add:* Sch of Eng & Appl Sci Univ of Calif Los Angeles CA 90024

NOBEL, JOEL J, b Philadelphia, Pa, Dec 8, 34; c 2. MEDICINE, BIOMEDICAL ENGINEERING. *Educ:* Haverford Col, BA, 56; Univ Pa, MA, 58; Thomas Jefferson Univ, MD, 63. *Prof Exp:* Intern, Presbyterian Hosp, Philadelphia, 63-65; resident surg, Pa Hosp, Philadelphia, 64-65; submarine med officer, US Navy, 66-67, proj officer submarine rescue & survival, Mil Opers Br, Submarine Med Res Ctr, 67-68; DIR BIOMED ENG, EMERGENCY CARE RES INST, 68- *Concurrent Pos:* Consult, Foreign Policy Res Inst, 56-59; consult biomed eng, 64-68; prin investr, Pa Heart Asn grant, 65-68; fel anesthesiol, Thomas Jefferson Univ Hosp, 68-70; prin investr, HEW grant, 68-72; mem bd dir, Consumers Union, 76-79 & 80- *Mem:* Asn Advan Med Instrumentation; Biomed Eng Soc; Soc Critical Care Med; Soc Advan Med Systs; Am Hosp Asn. *Res:* National health policy; health care technology assessment; medical equipment evaluation; hospital risk management; accident investigation; biomedical engineering design and development; underwater physiology; emergency medical services. *Mailing Add:* 5200 Butler Pike Plymouth Meeting PA 19462

NOBEL, PARK S, b Chicago, Ill, Nov 4, 38; m 65; c 2. PLANT PHYSIOLOGY, ECOLOGY. *Educ:* Cornell Univ, BEP, 61; Calif Inst Technol, MS, 63; Univ Calif, Berkeley, PhD(biophys), 65. *Prof Exp:* NSF fels chloroplasts, Tokyo Univ, 65-66 & King's Col, London, 66-67; from asst prof to assoc prof molecular biol, 67-75, PROF BIOL, UNIV CALIF, LOS ANGELES, 75- *Concurrent Pos:* Guggenheim fel, Australian Nat Univ, 73-74. *Mem:* Am Soc Plant Physiologists; Ecol Soc Am; Bot Soc Am; Scand Soc Plant Physiologists. *Res:* Biophysical aspects of plant physiology, especially plant-environment interactions and ecology; emphasis on desert plants, including cacti and agaves. *Mailing Add:* Dept of Biol Univ of Calif Los Angeles CA 90024

NOBIS, JOHN FRANCIS, b Helena, Mont, Jan 23, 21; m 47; c 4. ORGANIC CHEMISTRY. *Educ:* Col St Thomas, BS, 42; Iowa State Univ, PhD(org chem), 48. *Prof Exp:* Instr org chem, Iowa State Univ, 46-48, asst prof, 48; asst prof, Xavier Univ, Ohio, 48-51; group leader, Sodium Div, Nat Distillers Chem Co, 51-56, res supvr, 56-59, asst mgr metals & sodium res, Nat Distillers & Chem Corp, US Indust Chem Co, 59; mgr, Prod Develop Dept, Armour Indust Chem Co, 59-60; dir com develop, 60-63, dir mkt serv, 63-65, asst to pres, 65-66, DIR COM DEVELOP, FORMICA CORP, AM CYANAMID CO, 66- *Mem:* AAAS; Am Chem Soc. *Res:* Sodium and organosodium chemistry; synthetic organic, organosilicon chemistry; antimalarials; anti-tuberculars; heterocycles; organometallics; polyolefins; plastics. *Mailing Add:* Formica Corp 10155 Reading Rd Cincinnati OH 45241

NOBLE, ANN CURTIS, b Harlingen, Tex, Nov 6, 43. FOOD SCIENCE. *Educ:* Univ Mass, Amherst, BS, 66, PhD(food sci), 70. *Prof Exp:* Asst prof food sci, Univ Guelph, 70-73; ASST PROF ENOL, UNIV CALIF, DAVIS, 74- *Mem:* Am Chem Soc; Inst Food Technol; Can Inst Food Sci & Technol; Am Soc Enol; Europ Chemo Receptor Orgn. *Res:* Flavor chemistry and sensory evaluation. *Mailing Add:* Dept of Viticult & Enol Univ of Calif Davis CA 95616

NOBLE, CHARLES CARMIN, b Syracuse, NY, May 18, 16; m 42; c 5. ENGINEERING. *Educ:* US Military Acad, West Point, NY, BS, 40; Mass Inst Technol, MS, 48; George Washington Univ, AM, 64. *Prof Exp:* 2nd Leiutenant, US Army, 40, from Major to General, 40-69, exec officer, Manhattan Proj, Oak Ridge, 46-47, planner, Atomic Energy Comn, 47-48, Army Gen Staff, 48-51, Supreme Hq, Allied Power Europe, 51-54, dep dist engr, NY, 54-56, comdr, Eng Combat Group, Ft Benning, Ga, 57-58, dist engr, Louisville, 58-60, dir, Atlas & Minuteman Intercontinental Ballistic Missile Construct Prog, 60-63, chief engr, UN Command, US Forces Korea, 64-66, dir constructor, Off Secy Defense, 66-67, dir civil works, Corps Engrs, 67-69, chief engr, US Forces, Europe, 69-70 & Vietnam, 70-71; pres, Miss River Comn, 71-74; proj mgr, 74-78, dir & exec vpres, 78-81, DIR, PRES & CHIEF OPER OFF, C T MAIN CORP, 81- *Concurrent Pos:* Defense rep, Mex-US Joint Comn Mutual Disaster Assistance, 68; eng agent, Atlantic-Pac Interoceanic Sea Level Canal Study Comn, 67-69; fed adv, Coun Regional Econ Develop, 67-69; def mem, Comt Multiple Uses Coastal Zone, 68-69; pres, US Army Coastal Eng Res Bd, 67-69; chmn & fel mem, Red River Compact Comn, 71-74; consult, UN Develop Orgn, 78. *Honors & Awards:* Wheeler Medal, Soc Am Military Engrs, 62. *Mem:* Nat Acad Eng; US Comt Large Dams; Am Soc Civil Engrs; Soc Am Military Engrs; Am Consult Engrs Coun. *Res:* Geomorphology and behavior of major alluvial rivers (Mississippi River, Paraguay River, etc); potomological studies to support engineering improvements for navigation and flood control. *Mailing Add:* C T Main Corp Prudential Ctr Boston MA 02199

NOBLE, DANIEL EARL, radio engineering, deceased

NOBLE, DANIEL LEE, forest & animal ecology, see previous edition

NOBLE, EDWIN AUSTIN, b Bethel, Vt, Dec 15, 22; m 48; c 3. GEOLOGY. *Educ:* Tufts Univ, BS, 46; Univ NMex, MS, 50; Univ Wyo, PhD(geol), 61. *Prof Exp:* Geologist, US Geol Surv, Boston, 52-54 & AEC, 54-62 & 63-65; adv nuclear raw mat, Int Atomic Energy Agency, Arg, 62-63; assoc prof geol, Univ NDak, 65-69, prof & chmn dept, 69-77; DEP CHIEF, OFF ENERGY RESOURCES, US GEOL SURVEY, 77- *Concurrent Pos:* Asst state geologist, NDak State Geol Surv, 65-69, state geologist & dir, 69-77; supvr oil & gas, State NDak, 69-77; ed, Asn Am State Geologists, 71-77. *Mem:* Geol Soc Am; Am Inst Mining, Metall & Petrol Engrs; Am Asn Petrol Geologists; Asn Am State Geologists; Soc Econ Geologists. *Res:* Genesis of ore deposits in sedimentary rocks. *Mailing Add:* Off Energy Resources US Geol Survey Nat Ctr Mail Stop 915 Reston VA 22090

NOBLE, ELMER RAY, b Pyong Yang, Korea, Jan 16, 09; US citizen; m 32; c 4. PARASITOLOGY. *Educ:* Univ Calif, AB, 31, AM, 33, PhD, 36. *Prof Exp:* From instr to prof, 36-74, EMER PROF ZOOL, UNIV CALIF, SANTA BARBARA, 74- *Concurrent Pos:* Chmn dept biol sci, Univ Calif, Santa Barbara, 47-51, dean div letters & sci, 51-59, actg provost, 56-58, vchancellor, 58-62; consult, Govt Indonesia, 60. *Mem:* Am Soc Parasitol (pres, 81); Soc Protozool (pres, 71-72); Am Micros Soc (vpres, 71). *Res:* Cytology pf parasitic protozoa; life history of myxosporidia, trypanosomes and amoebae; parasitism in deep-sea fishes. *Mailing Add:* Dept of Biol Sci Univ of Calif Santa Barbara CA 93106

NOBLE, GLENN ARTHUR, b Pyong Yang, Korea, Jan 16, 09; US citizen; m 35; c 3. PARASITOLOGY. *Educ:* Univ Calif, AB, 31, MA, 33; Stanford Univ, PhD(parasitol), 40. *Prof Exp:* Asst zool, Col Pac, 33-35; instr biol, San Francisco City Col, 35-46, chmn dept, 39-46; consult, US Mil Govt, Korea, 46-47; vis prof parsitol, Med Sch, Seoul Nat Univ & Severance Union Med Col, 47; prof, 47-73, head dept, 49-71, EMER PROF BIOL, CALIF POLYTECH STATE UNIV, SAN LUIS OBISPO, 73- *Concurrent Pos:* Calif Fish & Game res grant, 43; Fulbright prof, Univ Philippines, 53-54 & Nat Taiwan Univ, 61-62; res grants, NSF, 56-57 & 63-66, NIH, 59-61 & Gorgas Mem Lab, Panama, 69. Soc Protozool; Am Soc Parasitol; Philippine Soc Advan Res. *Res:* Parasitology; protozoology. *Mailing Add:* Dept of Biol Sci Calif Polytech State Univ San Luis Obispo CA 93407

NOBLE, GORDON ALBERT, b Joliet, Ill, June 20, 27. SOLID STATE PHYSICS, CHEMICAL PHYSICS. *Educ:* Univ Chicago, PhB, 47, SB, 49, SM, 51, PhD(chem), 55. *Prof Exp:* Solid state physicist, Zenith Radio Corp, 54-60; res physicist, IIT Res Inst, 60-66, sr scientist, 66-68; asst prof, 68-76, ASSOC PROF PHYSICS, N PARK COL, 76- *Mem:* AAAS; Am Phys Soc; Am Chem Soc; Am Asn Physics Teachers. *Res:* Electron paramagnetic and nuclear magnetic resonance; color centers; solid state optical spectroscopy. *Mailing Add:* North Park Col No 30 5125 N Spaulding Ave Chicago IL 60625

NOBLE, JAMES JEFFREY, b New York, NY, July 4, 39; m 78. CHEMICAL ENGINEERING. *Educ:* Rensselaer Polytech Inst, BChemE, 61; Mass Inst Technol, PhD(chem eng), 68. *Prof Exp:* Asst prof chem eng, Mass Inst Technol, 68-70; group leader, Linde Res Div, Union Carbide Corp, 70-72; lectr, Imperial Col Sci & Technol, Univ London, 72-78; GROUP LEADER, CORP RES DEPT, CABOT CORP, 78- *Mem:* Am Inst Chem Eng; Inst Chem Engrs UK; NY Acad Sci. *Res:* Radiative heat transfer and furnace design; production of flame particulates; transport phenomena; chemical process research and design; systems engineering; advanced engineering analysis; application of computational methods to chemical engineering problems. *Mailing Add:* Billerica Tech Ctr Cabot Corp Concord Rd Billerica MA 01821

NOBLE, JOHN DALE, b Glendale, Calif, Nov 21, 34; m 62; c 2. PHYSICS. *Educ:* Univ Wyo, BS, 56, MS, 59; Univ BC, PhD(physics), 65. *Prof Exp:* Elec engr, Missile Systs Div, Lockheed Aircraft Corp, 56-57; instr physics, Univ Wyo, 59-61; lectr, Univ BC, 64-65; from asst prof to assoc prof, 65-73, PROF PHYSICS, WESTERN ILL UNIV, 73-, DEPT CHMN, 77- *Concurrent Pos:* Mem fac, Univ Wyo, 71-72. *Mem:* AAAS; Am Asn Physics Teachers. *Res:* Nuclear magnetic resonance; liquid-gas critical points. *Mailing Add:* Dept of Physics Western Ill Univ Macomb IL 61455

NOBLE, JOHN F, b Salt Lake City, Utah, Mar 8, 29; m 53; c 2. PHARMACOLOGY. *Educ:* Utah State Univ, BS, 53, MS, 56; Univ Chicago, PhD(pharmacol), 59. *Prof Exp:* Asst, Utah State Univ, 53-55; asst, Univ Chicago, 56-59, instr pharmacol & res assoc, US Air Force Radiation Lab, 59-60; res pharmacologist, 60-63, res group leader, 63-65, head dept toxicol eval, 65-69, DIR TOXICOL RES SECT, LEDERLE LABS, AM CYANAMID CO, 69- *Mem:* AAAS; Soc Toxicol. *Res:* Toxicology and pharmacology; safety evaluation of new drugs; pharmacokinetics and drug metabolism; radiation biology; acute and long term effects of radiation including effects on mortality; biochemical changes and chemical means of protection against irradiation. *Mailing Add:* 67 Halley Dr Pomna NY 10970

NOBLE, JULIAN VICTOR, b New York, NY, June 7, 40; m 60; c 3. THEORETICAL PHYSICS, MATHEMATICAL BIOPHYSICS. *Educ:* Calif Inst Technol, BS, 62; Princeton Univ, MA, 63, PhD(physics), 66. *Prof Exp:* Res assoc theoret physics, Univ Pa, 66-68, asst prof, 68-71; ASSOC PROF PHYSICS, UNIV VA, 71- *Concurrent Pos:* Sloan Found fel, 71-73; mem, Prog Comt, Space Radiation Effects Lab, Va, 74- *Mem:* AAAS; Sigma Xi. *Res:* Application of quantum-mechanical collision theory to nuclear reaction studies, both to determine nuclear properties and to develop methods of handling general strong-interaction problems; nuclear reaction studies at intermediate energies; dynamics of interacting populations; functional techniques in stochastic theories. *Mailing Add:* Dept of Physics Univ of Va Charlottesville VA 22901

NOBLE, NANCY LEE, b Chattanooga, Tenn, Mar 1, 22. BIOCHEMISTRY, MEDICINE. *Educ:* Emory Univ, MS, 49, PhD(biochem), 53. *Prof Exp:* Asst, Org Res Lab, Chattanooga Med Co, Tenn, 43-48; lab asst biochem, Sch Med, Emory Univ, 49-50; res instr, 53-55, res asst prof, 55-57, asst prof, 57-63, ASSOC PROF BIOCHEM & MED, SCH MED, UNIV MIAMI, 63-, ASSOC DEAN FAC AFFAIRS, 81- *Concurrent Pos:* Dir biochem res lab, Miami Heart Inst, 53-56; investr labs cardiovasc res, Howard Hughes Med Inst, 56-70; mem coun arteriosclerosis & coun basic sci, Am Heart Asn. *Honors & Awards:* Ciba Found Awards, 57 & 58. *Mem:* Fel Geront Soc; Soc Exp Biol & Med; Biochem Soc; fel Am Inst Chemists; NY Acad Sci. *Res:* Connective tissue metabolism and disorders. *Mailing Add:* Univ of Miami Sch of Med Box 016960 Miami FL 33101

NOBLE, PAUL, JR, b Ind, Oct 16, 22; m 46; c 3. PHYSICAL CHEMISTRY. *Educ:* Reed Col, AB, 43; Rochester Univ, PhD(org chem), 50. *Prof Exp:* Jr chemist, Shell Develop Co, 43-44; asst, Reed Col, 46-47; assoc res chemist, Calif Res Corp, 50-52; res chemist & head, Phys Org Div, Merrill Co, 52-54; res chemist, Phys Org Sect, Western Labs, Arthur D Little, Inc, 54-58; res scientist, 58-62, staff scientist & group leader, 62-63, sr staff scientist & sr mem res lab, 63-70, mgr chem lab, 70-72, PROG ENGR, LOCKHEED MISSILES & SPACE CO, INC, 72- *Mem:* Am Chem Soc; assoc fel Inst Aeronaut & Astronaut; Royal Soc Chem. *Res:* Organic synthesis; kinetics and reaction mechanism; infrared applications to organic chemistry; solid propellants; composite materials; aliphatic polynitro compounds; energy conversion. *Mailing Add:* 45 Arbuelo Way Los Altos CA 94022

NOBLE, REGINALD DUSTON, b Huntington, WVa, Nov 15, 35; c 3. PLANT PHYSIOLOGY. *Educ:* Marshall Univ, AB, 57, MA, 60; Ohio State Univ, PhD(bot), 69. *Prof Exp:* Teacher high sch, 57-59, dept chmn, 59-61; asst prof biol & phys sci, Marshall Univ, 62-66; teaching assoc bot, Ohio State Univ, 66-67; asst prof, 68-74, ASSOC PROF BIOL, BOWLING GREEN STATE UNIV, 74- *Mem:* Am Soc Plant Physiologists; Am Inst Biol Sci. *Res:* Photosynthetic studies; including effects of air pollutants especially, 50Z & ozone, on photosynthesis. *Mailing Add:* Dept Biol Bowling Green State Univ Bowling Green OH 43403

NOBLE, RICHARD DANIEL, b Newark, NJ, Oct 14, 46; m 79. CHEMICAL ENGINEERING. *Educ:* Stevens Inst Technol, BE, 68, ME, 69; Univ Calif, Davis, PhD(chem eng), 76. *Prof Exp:* Proj engr, Nat Starch & Chem Co, 68-71; asst prof chem eng, Univ Wyo, 76-81; CHEM ENGR, NAT BUR STANDARDS, 81- *Concurrent Pos:* Consult, Nat Bur Standards, 80-81; adj asst prof, Univ Colo, 81- *Mem:* Am Inst Chem Eng; Am Soc Eng Educ. *Res:* Facilitated transport; chemical complexation. *Mailing Add:* Ctr Chem Eng 773.1 Nat Bur Standards Boulder CO 80303

NOBLE, ROBERT HAMILTON, b Alton, Ill, June 16, 16; m 40; c 3. OPTICAL PHYSICS. *Educ:* Antioch Col, BS, 40; Ohio State Univ, PhD(physics), 46. *Prof Exp:* Asst engr, Globe Industs, Ohio, 40-42; asst physics, Ohio State Univ, 42-46, res assoc, Univ Res Found, 46-47; asst prof physics, Mich State Col, 47-53; res physicist, Leeds & Northrup Co, 53-55; engr, Perkin-Elmer Corp, 55-64; prof optical sci, Univ Ariz, 64-74; prof & head optics dept, Nat Inst Astrophys, Optics & Electronics, Mex, 74-77; RES PHYSICIST, INST ASTRON, UNIV NAT AUTON MEX, 77- *Mem:* Fel AAAS; Am Phys Soc; fel Optical Soc Am; Mex Phys Soc; fel Soc Photo-Optical Instrumentation Engrs. *Res:* Instrumentation for astronomy. *Mailing Add:* Inst Astron Apdo Postal 70-264 Mexico City 04510 Mexico

NOBLE, ROBERT LAING, b Toronto, Ont, Feb 3, 10; m 35; c 4. PHYSIOLOGY. *Educ:* Univ Toronto, MD, 34; Royal Col Physicians, London, PhD, 37, DSc, 47. *Hon Degrees:* Univ Western Ont, DSc, 73. *Prof Exp:* Courtauld Inst Biochem, Middlesex Hosp, London, 34-39; res asst, Inst Endocrinol, McGill Univ, 39-47; prof med & assoc dir, Collip Med Res Lab, Univ Western Ont, 47-60; dir cancer res ctr, 60-75, EMER PROF PHYSIOL, UNIV BC, 75-; RES SCIENTIST, CANCER CONTROL AGENCY, BC, 80- *Concurrent Pos:* Mickle fel, Univ Toronto, 34-35; Leverhulme fel, 35-38; asst ed, J Endocrinol, 39. *Honors & Awards:* Robert M Taylor Medal, Can Cancer Soc, 80. *Mem:* Can Physiol Soc; fel Royal Soc Can; Brit Physiol Soc. *Res:* Physiology of endocrine glands and related subjects; endocrinology; motion sickness; traumatic shock; physiology and pharmacology of gastric secretion and kidney function; cancer chemotherapy; discovery of vinblastine. *Mailing Add:* Univ ov BC Animal Care Ctr Vancouver BC V6T 1W5 Can

NOBLE, ROBERT LEE, b Hominy, Okla, July 16, 23; m 47; c 4. ANIMAL NUTRITION. *Educ:* Okla State Univ, BS, 48, MS, 52; Kans State Univ, PhD(animal nutrit), 60. *Prof Exp:* From instr to assoc prof animal husb, 49-70, PROF ANIMAL SCI & INDUST, OKLA STATE UNIV, 70- *Mem:* Am Soc Animal Sci. *Res:* Applied research with sheep. *Mailing Add:* Dept of Animal Sci Okla State Univ Stillwater OK 74074

NOBLE, ROBERT VERNON, b Ithaca, NY, Jan 1, 23; m 48; c 4. ACADEMIC ADMINISTRATION. *Educ:* Cornell Univ, AB, 46; Univ Fla, MA, 50. *Prof Exp:* From instr to asst prof corresp, Univ Fla, 50-57, head dept corresp study, 57-62; assoc prof, Fla Inst Continuing Univ Studies, 62-64; educ & training officer, Div Nuclear Educ & Training, AEC, 64-67, educ & training specialist, 67-72, staff asst to dir, 72-74, asst to dir, Div Admin Serv, US ERDA, 74-76, Freedom Info & Privacy Act admin officer, US Dept Energy, 76-78; RETIRED. *Mem:* Am Nuclear Soc; Sigma Xi; NY Acad Sci. *Mailing Add:* Rte 2 Box 29-A Melrose FL 32666

NOBLE, ROBERT WARREN, JR, b Washington, DC, Feb 14, 37; m 62; c 3. BIOPHYSICAL CHEMISTRY. *Educ:* Mass Inst Technol, BA, 59, PhD(biophys), 64. *Prof Exp:* Fel biophys, Mass Inst Technol, 64; Nat Cancer Inst fel biochem, Univ Rome & Regina Elena Inst, 64-66; res assoc, Cornell Univ, 67-68; estab invest, Am Heart Asn, 73-78; asst prof, 68-72, assoc prof, 72-76, PROF MED & BIOCHEM, STATE UNIV NY BUFFALO, 76- *Mem:* Biophys Soc; Am Asn Immunologists; Am Soc Biol Chem. *Res:* Reactions of hemeproteins with ligands; interactions between subunits of allosteric proteins and the structural basis for allosteric effects; reactions of antibodies with protein antigens; kinetics of liganding reactions. *Mailing Add:* Dept of Med State Univ of NY Vet Admin Hosp Buffalo NY 14215

NOBLE, VINCENT EDWARD, b Detroit, Mich, Nov 28, 33; m 64; c 1. PHYSICAL OCEANOGRAPHY. *Educ:* Wayne State Univ, AB, 55, MS, 57, PhD(physics), 60. *Prof Exp:* Jr engr electronics & math anal, Res Labs, Bendix Aviation Corp, 54-56; res assoc solid state physics, Wayne State Univ, 58-60; assoc res physicist, Great Lakes Res Div, Univ Mich, Ann Arbor, 60-68; res physicist, US Naval Oceanog Off, 68-72, SPEC ASST FOR NAVY ENVIRON REMOTE SENSING, US NAVAL RES LAB, 72-, HEAD, SPACE SENSING APPLICATIONS BR, 79- *Mem:* Am Phys Soc; Am Geophys Union; Am Soc Limnol & Oceanog. *Res:* Physical limnology; air-sea interaction; polar and remote sensing oceanography. *Mailing Add:* 6209 Zekan Lane Springfield VA 22150

NOBLE-HARVEY, JANE, animal virology, see previous edition

NOBLES, LAURENCE HEWIT, b Spokane, Wash, Sept 28, 27; m 48; c 2. GLACIOLOGY. *Educ:* Calif Inst Technol, BS & MS, 49; Harvard Univ, PhD(geol), 52. *Prof Exp:* From instr to assoc prof, 52-67, dean admin, 72-81, PROF GEOL, NORTHWESTERN UNIV, EVANSTON, 67-, VPRES ADMIN & FINANCIAL PLANNING, 80- *Concurrent Pos:* Consult/evaluator, NCent Asn Cols & Sec Schs, 67-75; from asst dean to assoc dean, Col Arts & Sci, Northwestern Univ, Evanston, 66-70, actg dean, 70-72; pres, Chicago Acad Sci, 73-79; trustee, Adler Planetarium, 81- *Mem:* AAAS; Geol Soc Am; Am Asn Petrol Geologists; Am Geophys Union; Glaciol Soc. *Res:* Geomorphology; glacial geology. *Mailing Add:* Rebecca Crown Ctr Northwestern Univ Evanston IL 60201

NOBLES, WILLIAM LEWIS, b Meridian, Miss, Sept 11, 25; m 48; c 2. PHARMACEUTICAL CHEMISTRY. *Educ:* Univ Miss, BS, 48, MS, 49; Univ Kans, PhD(pharmaceut chem), 52. *Prof Exp:* From asst prof to prof pharm & pharmaceut chem, Univ Miss, 52-68; PRES, MISS COL, 68- *Concurrent Pos:* Pfeiffer mem res fel, 55-58 & 59-60; NSF fel, Univ Mich, 58-59; dean, Grad Sch, Univ Miss, 60-68. *Honors & Awards:* Found Award, Am Pharmaceut Asn 66; Nat Rho Chi Award in Montreal, Can, 69. *Mem:* Am Chem Soc; Am Pharmaceut Asn; NY Acad Sci; Royal Soc Chem; AAAS. *Res:* Medicinal chemistry; pharmaceutical product development. *Mailing Add:* Box 4186 Clinton MS 39058

NOBLET, RAYMOND, b Hiawassee, Ga, Aug 5, 43. INSECT PHYSIOLOGY, INVERTEBRATE PATHOLOGY. *Educ:* Univ Ga, BS, 65, MS, 67, PhD(entom), 70. *Prof Exp:* Asst prof, 70-75, assoc prof entom & econ zool, 75-77, PROF ENTOM, CLEMSON UNIV, 75- *Mem:* Entom Soc Am; Soc Invert Pathol. *Res:* Invertebrate immunity; malariology; parasitology; physiological and ecological investigations pf insect vectors of disease. *Mailing Add:* Dept of Entom Clemson Univ Clemson SC 29631

NOBUSAWA, NOBUO, b Osaka, Japan, May 15, 30; m 61; c 2. ALGEBRA. *Educ:* Osaka Univ, BS, 53, MS, 55, PhD(math), 58. *Prof Exp:* Asst prof math, Univ Alta, 62-66; assoc prof, Univ RI, 66-67; assoc prof, 67-71, PROF MATH, UNIV HAWAII, 71- *Mem:* Am Math Soc; Can Math Cong; Math Soc Japan. *Res:* Ring theory and number theory. *Mailing Add:* Dept Math Univ Hawaii Honolulu HI 96822

NOCENTI, MERO RAYMOND, b Masontown, Pa, Sept 7, 28; m 55; c 3. PHYSIOLOGY. *Educ:* Univ WVa, AB, 51, MS, 52; Rutgers Univ, PhD(endocrinol), 55. *Prof Exp:* Waksman-Merck fel, Rutgers Univ, 55-56; from instr to assoc prof, 56-75, PROF PHYSIOL, COL PHYSICIANS & SURGEONS, COLUMBIA UNIV, 75- *Concurrent Pos:* Managing ed, Proc, Soc Exp Biol & Med, 74, ed, 80. *Mem:* AAAS; Am Physiol Soc; Sigma Xi; Soc Exp Biol & Med (exec secy, 80). *Res:* Endocrine physiology; hormonal influences on electrolyte and water balance and on connective tissue. *Mailing Add:* Dept Physiol Col Phys & Surg Columbia Univ Col 630 W 168th St New York NY 10032

NOCETI, RICHARD PAUL, b Pittsburgh, Pa, Jan 16, 47; m 70; c 3. ORGANIC CHEMISTRY. *Educ:* Duquesne Univ, BS, 68, MS, 74, PhD(org chem), 79. *Prof Exp:* RES CHEMIST PROCESS SCI, PITTSBURGH ENERGY TECH CTR, US DEPT ENERGY, 75- *Mem:* Am Chem Soc. *Res:* Natural product chemistry; synthetic organic chemistry; mechanism of coal liquefaction and coal chemistry; coal conversion process water characterization, treatment and reuse. *Mailing Add:* US Dept Energy Pisstburgh Energy Technol PO Box 10940 Pittsburgh PA 15236

NOCKELS, CHERYL FERRIS, b Chicago, Ill, July 20, 35; m 57. ANIMAL NUTRITION. *Educ:* Colo State Univ, BS, 57, MS, 59; Univ Mo, PhD(animal nutrit), 65. *Prof Exp:* Res technician, 59-60, asst poultry scientist biochem, 64-70, assoc prof, 70-74, PROF ANIMAL SCI DEPT, COLO STATE UNIV, 74- *Mem:* Am Soc Animal Sci; Poultry Sci Asn; Am Inst Nutrit; NY Acad Sci. *Res:* Nutritional and biochemical studies involving both monogastric and ruminant animals. *Mailing Add:* Dept of Animal Sci Colo State Univ Ft Collins CO 80523

NODA, KAORU, b Hilo, Hawaii, Oct 16, 24; m 53; c 4. PARASITOLOGY. *Educ:* Grinnell Col, BA, 50; Univ Iowa, MS, 53, PhD(zool), 56. *Prof Exp:* Asst zool, Univ Iowa, 51-56; asst parasitologist, 57-59, asst prof sci, 59-63, assoc prof & dir Hilo Campus, 62-68, PROF BIOL, UNIV HAWAII, HILO, 69- *Concurrent Pos:* USPHS res grant, 60; scholar, Univ Calif, Los Angeles, 65-66; provost, Univ Hawaii, Hilo, 68-70, asst chancellor, 70-72; vis prof & researcher, Univ Tokyo, 72-73. *Mem:* AAAS; Am Soc Parasitol. *Res:* Trematodes, particularly the family Heterophyidae. *Mailing Add:* Univ of Hawaii PO Box 1357 Hilo HI 96720

NODA, LAFAYETTE HACHIRO, b Livingston, Calif, Mar 13, 16; m 47; c 2. BIOCHEMISTRY. *Educ:* Univ Calif, BS, 39, MA, 43; Stanford Univ, PhD, 50. *Prof Exp:* Res assoc, Stanford Univ, 50-51; asst prof, Univ Wis, 53-56; biochemist, US Naval Med Res Inst, Md, 56-57; assoc prof biochem, 57-60, chmn dept, 60-65, PROF BIOCHEM, DARTMOUTH MED SCH, 60- *Concurrent Pos:* Res fel, Enzyme Inst, Univ Wis, 51-53; Guggenheim fel, 68-69; Japan Soc Promotion Sci fel, 80. *Mem:* Am Soc Biol Chem. *Res:* Purification, kinetics, structure and mechanism of action of enzymes. *Mailing Add:* Dept of Biochem Dartmouth Med Sch Hanover NH 03755

NODAR, RICHARD (H)ENRY, b Schenectady, NY, June 15, 35. AUDIOLOGY. *Educ:* Col Geneseo, State Univ NY, BS, 62; Purdue Univ, MS, 64, PhD(audiol), 67. *Prof Exp:* Asst prof audiol, Purdue Univ, 66-67 & Mich State Univ, 67-68; assoc prof, Syracuse Univ, 68-75; HEAD, SECT COMMUN DISORDERS, DEPT OTOLARYNGOL & COMMUN DISORDERS, CLEVELAND CLIN, 75- *Mem:* Fel Am Speech-Lang-Hearing Asn; Am Acad Otolaryngol; Am Asn Ment Deficiency; Acad Rehabilitative Audiol; Am EEG Soc. *Res:* Application of brain stern auditory evoked potential testing to clinical populations; tinnitus aurium, it's origin, nature, measurement and diagnostic significance. *Mailing Add:* 9500 Euclid Ave Cleveland OH 44106

NODELMAN, NEIL H, organic chemistry, see previous edition

NODEN, DREW M, experimental embryology, neuroembryology, see previous edition

NODIFF, EDWARD ALBERT, b US, Nov 25, 26; m 50; c 2. ORGANIC CHEMISTRY. *Educ:* Temple Univ, BA, 48. *Prof Exp:* Res assoc chem, Res Inst, 49-55, proj dir, 55-60, dir org chem res, 60-80, PRIN SCIENTIST, FRANKLIN RES CTR, TEMPLE UNIV, 80- *Mem:* Am Chem Soc. *Res:* Organic fluorine and medicinal chemistry. *Mailing Add:* 1600 Placid St Philadelphia PA 19152

NODINE-ZELLER, DORIS EULALIA, b Ohio, Ill, Mar 11, 23; div. PALEONTOLOGY, STRATIGRAPHY. *Educ:* Univ Ill, AB, 46; Univ Wis, MS, 51, PhD(geol), 54. *Prof Exp:* Tech asst, Areal & Eng Geol Div, State Geol Surv Ill, 44-46; teaching asst geol, Univ Kans, 46-48; lab technician, Univ Wis, 51-54; consult, Shell Oil Co, 54-55; consult, Petroleo, Petrobras, Belem, Brasiliero, 55-56; res assoc geol, Univ Kans, 60-63; managing ed bulls & res assoc geol, 63-71, res assoc micropaleont & subsurface geol, 71-81, SR SCIENTIST SUBSURFACE GEOL, STATE GEOL SURV KANS, 81- *Concurrent Pos:* Reviewer syst biol, NSF, 61-; prof western civilization prog, Univ Kans, 63-; VChmn, Peleonzoie Foraminiferral Res Group, 79-80. *Mem:* AAAS; Asn Earth Sci Educ; Sigma Xi; Paleont Soc; Am Asn Univ Women. *Res:* Micropaleontology; taxonomic and stratigraphic work on endothyroid foraminifers, rhyncholites and other invertebrate fossils. *Mailing Add:* State Geol Surv of Kans Univ of Kans Lawrence KS 66044

NODULMAN, LAWRENCE JAY, b Chicago, Ill, May 6, 47. EXPERIMENTAL HIGH ENERGY PHYSICS. *Educ:* Univ Ill, Urbana-Champaign, BS, 69, MS, 70, PhD(physics), 73. *Prof Exp:* Res assoc physics, Univ Ill, Urbana-Champaign, 73-75; asst res physicist, Univ Calif, Los Angeles, 75-79; ASST PHYSICIST, ARGONNE NAT LAB, 79- *Mem:* AAAS; Am Phys Soc. *Res:* Particle production in electron-positron interactions; neutrino interactions; weak and electromagnetic interactions of hadrons. *Mailing Add:* Argonne Nat Lab HEP-362 Argonne IL 60439

NODVIK, JOHN S, b Canonsburg, Pa, July 2, 30; m 53; c 3. PHYSICS. *Educ:* Carnegie Inst Technol, BS(physics) & BS(math), 52, MS, 52; Univ Calif, Los Angeles, PhD(physics), 58. *Prof Exp:* From asst prof to assoc prof physics, 58-70, PROF PHYSICS, UNIV SOUTHERN CALIF, 70- *Mem:* Am Phys Soc. *Res:* Relativistic spin; nuclear optical model. *Mailing Add:* Dept of Physics University Park Los Angeles CA 90007

NOE, BRYAN DALE, b Peoria, Ill, Mar 1, 43; m 65; c 3. ANATOMY, CELL BIOLOGY. *Educ:* Goshen Col, BA, 65; WVa Univ, MA, 67; Univ Minn, PhD(anat), 71. *Prof Exp:* USPHS res fel, Univ Minn, 71-72; asst prof, 73-77, ASSOC PROF ANAT, EMORY UNIV, 77- *Mem:* Am Soc Cell Biologists; Am Asn Anatomists; Corp mem Marine Biol Lab; Am Diabetes Asn; Endocrine Soc. *Res:* Biosynthesis of glucagon, somatostatin, and insulin; proteolytic processing of precursors. *Mailing Add:* Dept Anat Emory Univ Atlanta GA 30322

NOE, ERIC ARDEN, b Bluffton, Ohio, Dec 24, 43. ORGANIC CHEMISTRY. *Educ:* Univ Cincinnati, BS, 65; Calif Inst Technol, PhD(chem), 71. *Prof Exp:* Fel chem, Univ Southern Calif, 70-71 & Univ Calif, San Francisco, 71-72; fel, Wayne State Univ, 72-75, res assoc, 75-77; ASST PROF CHEM, JACKSON STATE UNIV, 77- *Mem:* Am Chem Soc. *Res:* Conformational analysis using dynamic nuclear magnetic resonance spectroscopy; organic synthesis. *Mailing Add:* Dept of Chem Jackson State Univ Jackson MS 39217

NOE, FRANCES ELSIE, b Beacon Falls, Conn, May 23, 23; m 56; c 2. PHYSIOLOGY. *Educ:* Middlebury Col, BA, 44; Yale Univ, MN, 47; Univ Vt, MD, 54. *Prof Exp:* Intern, Mary Hitchcock Mem Hosp, 54-55; Mich Heart Asn fel, Harper Hosp, Detroit, 55-56; resident pulmonary med, Henry Ford Hosp, 56-57; Rands fel med, Wayne State Univ, 57-58, res assoc anesthesiol, Col Med, 58-59, from instr to asst prof, 59-65; res assoc, 65-70, CHIEF PULMONARY PHYSIOL SECT, DIV RES, SINAI HOSP DETROIT, 70-; ASST PROF, SCH MED, WAYNE STATE UNIV, 75- *Mem:* Sigma Xi; Int Anesthesia Res Soc; Am Soc Anesthesiol. *Res:* Anesthesiology; cardiopulmonary physiology, especially as applied to anesthesiology. *Mailing Add:* Sinai Hosp Div of Res 6767 W Outer Dr Detroit MI 48235

NOE, JERRE D(ONALD), b McCloud, Calif, Feb 1, 23; m 43; c 3. COMPUTER SCIENCE, ELECTRICAL ENGINEERING. *Educ:* Univ Calif, BS, 43; Stanford Univ, PhD(elec eng), 48. *Prof Exp:* Res assoc, Radio Res Lab, Harvard Univ, 43-45; develop engr, Hewlett-Packard Co, 46-48; res engr, Stanford Res Inst, 48-54, asst dir div eng res, 54-60, dir eng, Sci Div, 61-64, exec dir eng sci & indust develop, 64-68; chmn dept computer sci, 68-76, PROF COMPUTER SCI, UNIV WASH, 68- *Concurrent Pos:* Lectr, Stanford Univ, 52-67; mem comt, Nat Joint Comput Conf & chmn, Prof Group Electronic Comput, 56-57. *Mem:* Asn Comput Mach; sr mem Inst Elec & Eelctronics Engrs. *Res:* Computer System modeling; measurement and evaluation; computer networks. *Mailing Add:* Dept of Comput Sci FC-35 Univ of Wash Seattle WA 98195

NOE, LEWIS JOHN, b Cleveland, Ohio, Oct 26, 41; m 68; c 1. CHEMISTRY. *Educ:* Western Reserve Univ, AB, 63; Case Western Reserve Univ, PhD(chem), 67. *Prof Exp:* Fel chem, Univ Pa, 67-69; asst prof, 69-74, ASSOC PROF CHEM, UNIV WYO, 74- *Concurrent Pos:* NSF res grant, Univ Wyo, 71-73. *Mem:* Am Chem Soc. *Res:* Ultraviolet, visible and infrared spectroscopy of molecular crystals; applications of Stark and Zeeman effects to spectroscopy of molecular crystals. *Mailing Add:* Dept of Chem Univ of Wyo Laramie WY 82070

NOEHREN, THEODORE HENRY, b Buffalo, NY, Sept 6, 17; m 40; c 2. INTERNAL MEDICINE, PULMONARY DISEASES. *Educ:* Williams Col, BA, 38; Univ Rochester, MD, 42; Univ Minn, MS, 50. *Prof Exp:* Mayo Found fel, Univ Minn, 47-49; asst prof pub health & prev med, Univ Utah, 49-52; asst prof internal med, State Univ NY Buffalo, 52-69; assoc prof med, Univ Utah, 69-75; dir pulmonary dis div, Holy Cross Hosp, 74-77; PVT PRACT, 77- *Concurrent Pos:* Consult, USPHS, 50; Markle scholar, 53-58; Fulbright lectr, Univ Helsinki, 66; consult & sr cancer res internist, Roswell Park Mem Cancer Res Hosp. *Mem:* Am Thoracic Soc; AMA; Am Col Chest Physicians. *Res:* Pulmonary physiology; role of lungs as an excretory organ; action of intermittent positive pressure in pulmonary diseases; factors altering the rate of excretion of inert gases by the lungs. *Mailing Add:* Med Towers Suite 202 1060 E First South Salt Lake City UT 84102

NOEL, BRUCE WILLIAM, b York, Pa, Sept 13, 34; m 64. ELECTRONICS ENGINEERING. *Educ:* Drexel Inst Technol, BSEE, 64; Case Inst Technol, MSEE, 66; Univ NMex, PhD(elec eng), 71. *Prof Exp:* Staff mem, Sandia Labs, 66-68; res engr, Univ NMex, 71-72; STAFF MEM, LOS ALAMOS NAT LAB, 72- *Concurrent Pos:* Consult, Sandia Labs, 68-72. *Res:* Optoelectronics applications in nuclear radiation imaging and in uranium-enrrichment centrifuge diagnostics; network and spectrum analysis applications in electronics systems analysis; electronic circuit design and instrumentation; radiation effects on solid state devices; characteristics and applications of image intensifers. *Mailing Add:* Los Alamos Nat Lab PO Box 1663 Los Alamos NM 87545

NOEL, DALE LEON, b Wichita, Kans, May 21, 36; m 62; c 2. ANALYTICAL CHEMISTRY. *Educ:* Friends Univ, BA, 58; Wichita State Univ, MS, 60; Kans State Univ, PhD(chem), 70. *Prof Exp:* Asst prof chem, Friends Univ, 61-65, Eastern Nazarene Col, 67-69; assoc prof, Kearney State Col, 70-74; SR RES ASSOC CHEM, INT PAPER CO, 74- *Mem:* Am Chem Soc; Tech Asn Pulp & Paper Indust. *Res:* Polarography, anodic stripping voltammetry, gas chromatography, mass spectrometry, environmental analysis. *Mailing Add:* Corp Res Ctr Int Paper Co Box 797 Tuxedo NY 10987

NOEL, GERALD THOMAS, b West Chester, Pa, Oct 10, 34; m 62; c 3. SOLID STATE PHYSICS. *Educ:* Drexel Univ, 61; Temple Univ, MS, 66. *Prof Exp:* Mem tech staff, RCA Labs, 61-68, tech dir hybrid circuits facil, Astro Electron Div, 68-72; mem prof staff res, Univ Pa-Energy Ctr, 72-77; SR RES SCIENTIST, BATTELLE COLUMBUS LABS, 77- *Mem:* Am Inst Physics; Inst Environ Sci; Am Asn Physics Teachers. *Res:* Energy technology, primarily solar; semiconductor technology; device development; photovoltaic devices; infrared detectors; photovoltaic systems design; solar heating and cooling systems; vacuum deposition techniques; thin film materials properties. *Mailing Add:* Battelle Columbus Labs 505 King Ave Columbus OH 43201

NOEL, JAMES A, b Williamstown, Pa, Aug 11, 22; m 45; c 3. GEOLOGY. *Educ:* Lehigh Univ, BA, 49; Dartmouth Col, MA, 51; Ind Univ, PhD(geol), 56. *Prof Exp:* Sr geologist, Creole Petrol Corp, 56-60; assoc prof geol math, Northwestern State Col, La, 60-64; res assoc, Res Ctr Union Oil, 64-66; from assoc prof to prof geol & chmn dept, 66-71, asst dir, Western Ohio Br Campus, 71-73, asst dean, 73-74, PROF GEOL, WRIGHT STATE UNIV, 74- *Mem:* Am Asn Petrol Geologists; Am Inst Prof Geologists; Sigma Xi; Nat Asn Geol Teachers; Soc Explor Geophys. *Res:* Computer systems for gravity and magnetic residual calculation and automatic mapping; combined geological and gravity interpretations using computer systems; sedimentary environments. *Mailing Add:* Div of Geol Wright State Univ Dayton OH 45431

NOEL, ROBERT LEE, b Manitowoc, Wis, Mar 28, 23; m 48; c 3. MECHANICAL ENGINEERING. *Educ:* Univ Wis, BS, 50, MS, 51. *Prof Exp:* Develop engr, Micro Switch Corp, 51-54; assoc prof eng, Emmanuel Missionary Col, Andrews, 54-63; assoc prof, 63-77, PROF ENG, WALLA WALLA COL, 77- *Concurrent Pos:* Instr, Mich State Univ, 58-59. *Mem:* Am Soc Metals; Am Soc Nondestructive Testing; Am Soc Eng Educ. *Res:* Mechanical testing, particularly hot testing. *Mailing Add:* Dept of Eng Walla Walla Col College Place WA 99324

NOELKEN, MILTON EDWARD, b St Louis, Mo, Dec 5, 35; m 62; c 2. PHYSICAL CHEMISTRY. *Educ:* Washington Univ, BA, 57, PhD(phys chem), 62. *Prof Exp:* Researcher chem, Duke Univ, 62-64; assoc & res chemist, Eastern Regional Res Lab, USDA, 64-67; asst prof, 67-71, ASSOC PROF BIOCHEM, UNIV KANS MED CTR, 71- *Concurrent Pos:* Actg chmn dept biochem, Univ Kans Med Ctr, 73-74. *Mem:* AAAS; Am Chem Soc; Am Soc Biol Chem. *Res:* Physical chemistry of proteins. *Mailing Add:* Dept of Biochem Univ of Kans Med Ctr Kansas City KS 66103

NOELL, WERNER K, b Ger, June 22, 13; US citizen; c 3. PHYSIOLOGY. *Educ:* Univ Hamburg, MD, 38. *Prof Exp:* From intern to resident neurol, Univ Hamburg Clin, 39; fel physiol, Univ Berlin, 39-40; instr neurol, Med Sch Danzig, 41-43; dozent, Univ Cologne, 43-46; neurophysiologist, US Air Force Sch Aviation Med, 47-50, head neurophysiol, 50-54; assoc res prof physiol, 56-60, assoc prof, 60-62, PROF PHYSIOL, NEUROSENSORY LAB, STATE UNIV NY BUFFALO, 62- *Concurrent Pos:* Res assoc, Kaiser Wilhelm Inst, 43-46; assoc prof, Sch Aviation Med, Air Univ, 50-54; prin res scientist, Roswell Park Mem Inst, 54-60; vis prof, Sch Med, Univ Buenos Aires, 61. *Honors & Awards:* J E Hitzig Prize, Prussian Acad Sci, 44; Jonas Friedenwald Award, Asn Res Vision & Ophthal, 59. *Mem:* AAAS; Am Physiol Soc; Am Electroencephalog Asn; Asn Res Vision & Ophthal; NY Acad Sci. *Res:* Physiology of retina; visual systems; electroencephalography; cerebral circulation. *Mailing Add:* Neurosensory Lab Bldg C State Univ of NY Buffalo NY 14214

NOER, RICHARD JUUL, b Madison, Wis, July 3, 37. SOLID STATE PHYSICS, SUPERCONDUCTIVITY. *Educ:* Amherst Col, BA, 58; Univ Calif, Berkeley, PhD(physics), 63. *Prof Exp:* Physicist, Atomic Energy Res Estab, Eng, 63-64; asst prof physics, Amherst Col, 64-66; from asst prof to assoc prof, 66-75, PROF PHYSICS, CARLETON COL, 75- *Concurrent Pos:* Vis physicist, Lab de Physique des Solides, Orsay, France, 72-73, Ames Lab, Iowa State Univ, 77-80 & Univ Geneva, Switz, 80-81. *Mem:* Am Phys Soc; Am Asn Physics Teachers. *Res:* Solid state physics; low temperature, metals and superconductors. *Mailing Add:* Dept of Physics Carleton Col Northfield MN 55057

NOER, RUDOLF JUUL, b Menominee, Mich, Apr 25, 04; m 33; c 2. SURGERY. *Educ:* Univ Wis, AB, 24; Univ Pa, MD, 27. *Prof Exp:* Asst anat, Univ Wis, 32-34, resident surg, 34-37, instr, 36-37; fel surg res, Col Med, Wayne State Univ, 37-38, from instr to assoc prof surg, 38-49, prof surg & appl anat, 49-52; prof surg & head dept, Sch Med, Univ Louisville, 52-70; prof, 70-75, EMER PROF SURG, COL MED, UNIV S FLA, 75- *Concurrent Pos:* Assoc, Detroit Receiving Hosp, Mich, 46-52; consult, Detroit Marine Hosp, USPHS, 47-48; sr consult, Vet Admin Hosp, Dearborn, Mich, 48-52, area consult, Vet Admin, 55-70, Tampa, 72-; dir surg, Louisville Gen Hosp, Ky, 52-70; ed, J Trauma, 61-68. *Mem:* Am Surg Asn (vpres, 63-64); Am Asn Anatomists; Am Asn Surg of Trauma (pres, 64); Int Surg Soc; fel Am Col Surg (vpres, 64-65). *Res:* Intestinal obstruction; intestinal circulation in man and animals; physiologic responses of intestine to distention; diverticular disease of the colon; adjuvant chemotherapy for breast cancer. *Mailing Add:* Dept of Surg Univ S Fla 2901 N 30th St Tampa FL 33612

NOERDLINGER, PETER DAVID, b New York, NY, May 3, 35; m 57, 64; c 5. ASTROPHYSICS, PLASMA PHYSICS. *Educ:* Harvard Univ, AB, 56; Calif Inst Technol, PhD(physics), 60. *Prof Exp:* From instr to asst prof physics, Univ Chicago, 60-66; assoc prof, Univ Iowa, 66-68; from assoc prof to prof, NMex Inst Mining & Technol, 68-71; PROF ASTRON, MICH STATE UNIV, 71- *Concurrent Pos:* Sr resident res assoc, Nat Res Coun, NASA-Ames Res Ctr, 71, 74 & 75, NSF, 74 & 75; vis scientist, Smithsonian Astrophys Observ, Mass, 73-, High Altitude Observ, Nat Ctr Atmospheric Res, 77-78; vis prof, Univ Calif, Santa Cruz, 71; NSF fel, 77-78; vis sr res assoc, Univ Colo, 77-78; mem cosmology comn, Int Astron Union; actg chmn, Dept Astron & Astrophys, Mich State Univ, 74-75. *Mem:* Am Astron Soc; Am Asn Physics Teachers; fel Royal Astron Soc; Am Phys Soc; Fedn Am Scientists. *Res:* Quasi-stellar objects; cosmology; theoretical astrophysics; radiative transfer; comets; interstellar matter; properties of quasi-stellar objects; mass loss from stars and quasi-stellar objects; plasma processes in stars and quasars; theoretical cosmology. *Mailing Add:* Dept of Astron & Astrophys Mich State Univ East Lansing MI 48824

NOETHER, GOTTFRIED EMANUEL, b Ger, Jan 7, 15; nat US; m 42; c 1. MATHEMATICAL STATISTICS. *Educ:* Ohio State Univ, BA, 40; Univ Ill, MA, 41; Columbia Univ, PhD(math statist), 49. *Prof Exp:* Instr math, NY Univ, 49-51; from asst prof to prof math statist, Boston Univ, 51-68; HEAD DEPT STATIST, UNIV CONN, 68- *Concurrent Pos:* Fulbright lectr, Univ Tübingen, 57-58 & Univ Vienna, 65-66. *Mem:* Fel AAAS; Math Asn Am; fel Inst Math Statist; fel Am Statist Asn. *Res:* Nonparametric statistical inference. *Mailing Add:* Dept of Statist Univ of Conn Storrs CT 06268

NOETZEL, DAVID MARTIN, b Waseca, Minn, Feb 19, 29; m 50; c 6. ENTOMOLOGY, ZOOLOGY. *Educ:* Univ Minn, BA, 51, MS, 56, PhD, 66. *Prof Exp:* Asst prof agr entom, NDak State Univ, 56-65; asst prof biol, Concordia Col, Moorhead, Minn, 65-70; instr entom, 70-80, EXTEN ENTOMOLOGIST, UNIV MINN, ST PAUL, 70-, ASSOC PROF, 80- *Mem:* Entom Soc Am; Am Soc Mammal; Bee Res Asn. *Res:* Animal ecology; ornithology; economic zoology. *Mailing Add:* Dept Entom Fisheries & Wildlife Univ of Minn St Paul MN 55101

NOFFSINGER, ELLA MAE, b Center, Colo, Mar 15, 34. NEMATOLOGY, PLANT PATHOLOGY. *Educ:* Colo State Univ, BS, 56, MS, 58. *Prof Exp:* Lab asst nematol, Beet Sugar Develop Found, Ft Collins, Colo, 56-58; lab asst nematol & plant path, Dept Plant Path, Univ Wis-Madison, 58-62; lab tech nematol, Univ Calif, Davis, 62-67; nematologist, Univ Calif Coop Prog, Univ Chile, 67-69; staff res assoc, 69-76, SR MUS SCIENTIST NEMATOL, UNIV CALIF, DAVIS, 76- *Concurrent Pos:* Assoc ed, Nematropica, Trop Am Nematologists, 75-; ed, Nematol Newsletter, Soc Nematologists, 77-80. *Mem:* Soc Nematologists; Orgn Trop Nematologists; Sigma Xi; Sci Res Soc. *Res:* Taxonomy, systematics and distribution of the plant parasitic and free-living nematodes, especially fresh-water, marine and soil; taxonomic revisions of free-living marine nematodes, from genus through superfamily. *Mailing Add:* Div of Nematol Univ of Calif Davis CA 95616

NOFSINGER, C(HARLES) W(ILLIAM), mechanical engineering, deceased

NOFTLE, RONALD EDWARD, b Springfield, Mass, Mar 10, 39; m 64. INORGANIC CHEMISTRY, FLUORINE CHEMISTRY. *Educ:* Univ NH, BS, 61; Univ Wash, PhD(inorg chem), 66. *Prof Exp:* Res asst inorg chem, Univ Wash, 62-66, instr chem, 66; fel, Univ Idaho, 66-67; asst prof, 67-73, assoc prof, 73-79, PROF CHEM, WAKE FOREST UNIV, 79-, CHMN DEPT CHEM, 80- *Concurrent Pos:* Res chemist, Naval Res Lab, 75-76. *Mem:* Am Chem Soc; Royal Soc Chem; fel Am Inst Chemists; Sigma Xi. *Res:* Synthesis and properties of compounds containing fluorine; vibrational spectroscopy of halogen compounds; chemistry of the halogens. *Mailing Add:* Dept Chem Wake Forest Univ Winston-Salem NC 27109

NOFZINGER, DAVID LYNN, b Wauseon, Ohio, June 13, 44; m 68; c 2. SOIL PHYSICS, FLUID TRANSPORT. *Educ:* Goshen Col, BA, 66; Purdue Univ, MS, 70, PhD(agron), 72. *Prof Exp:* Lectr & res fel soil physics, Ahmadu Bello Univ, Nigeria, 72-74; asst prof, 74-80, ASSOC PROF SOIL PHYSICS, OKLA STATE UNIV, 80- *Mem:* Am Soc Agron; Soil Sci Soc Am; Int Soil Sci Soc. *Res:* Water movement in saturated and unsaturated soils; utilization of small computers in data acquisition annd control. *Mailing Add:* 2401 N Monroe St Stillwater OK 74074

NOGAMI, YUKIHISA, b Hamada, Japan, Oct 22, 29; m 58; c 3. THEORETICAL PHYSICS. *Educ:* Kyoto Univ, BSc, 52, DSc(physics), 61. *Prof Exp:* From asst to lectr physics, Univ Osaka Prefecture, 54-61; fel, Nat Res Coun Can, 61-63; res fel, Battersea Col Technol, 63-64; sr fel, 64-65, assoc prof, 65-69, PROF PHYSICS, McMASTER UNIV, 69- *Mem:* Can Asn Physicists; Phys Soc Japan. *Res:* Theoretical physics, nuclear forces and nuclear structure; medium energy nuclear physics. *Mailing Add:* Dept of Physics McMaster Univ Hamilton ON L8S 4L8 Can

NOGAR, NICHOLAS STEPHEN, b Chicago, Ill, Jan 19, 50; m 74; c 1. PHYSICAL CHEMISTRY, ATMOSPHERIC CHEMISTRY. *Educ:* Univ NMex, BS, 71; Univ Utah, PhD(phys chem), 76. *Prof Exp:* NSF fel chem, Univ Calif, Berkeley, 76-77; asst prof chem, Univ Nebr, 77-80; MEM STAFF, LOS ALAMOS NAT LAB, 80- *Mem:* Am Chem Soc; AAAS; Sigma Xi; Interam Photochem Soc; Laser Inst Am. *Res:* Applications of lasers in physical, analytical and biological chemistry; electronic and vibrational photochemistry and kinetics; photoacoustic measurement of trace components; CARS of biochemical systems; chemical kinetics and dynamics; application of lasers in physical and analytical chemistry. *Mailing Add:* CNC 2 MS 738 Los Alamos Nat Lab Los Alamos NM 87545

NOGES, ENDRIK, b Moisakula, Estonia, Apr 5, 27; nat US; m 51; c 3. ELECTRICAL ENGINEERING. *Educ:* Northwestern Univ, BS, 54, MS, 56, PhD(elec eng), 59. *Prof Exp:* From asst to instr elec eng, Northwestern Univ, 54-57; from asst prof to assoc prof, 58-69, asst dean eng, 66-71, PROF

ELEC ENG, UNIV WASH, 69- *Concurrent Pos:* Fulbright lectr, Finnish Inst Technol, 63-64; vis prof, Univ Karlsruhe, Ger, 72-73; consult, Boeing Co, 72- *Mem:* Am Soc Eng Educ; Inst Elec & Electronics Engrs. *Res:* Nonstationary and nonlinear feedback control systems; quantization in feedback control systems; pulse frequency modulated and other pulsed feedback systems. *Mailing Add:* Dept of Elec Eng FT10 Univ of Wash Seattle WA 98195

NOGGLE, GLENN RAY, b New Madison, Ohio, July 25, 14; m 45; c 1. PLANT PHYSIOLOGY. *Educ:* Miami Univ, AB, 35; Univ Ill, MS, 42, PhD(bot), 45. *Prof Exp:* Res assoc agron, Univ Ill, 45-46; asst prof plant physiol, Blandy Exp Farm, Va, 46-48; sr biologist, Oak Ridge Nat Lab, 48-52; sr scientist, Photosynthesis Proj, Southern Res Inst, Ala, 52-54; biochemist, C F Kettering Found & prof chem, Antioch Col, 54-57; prof bot & head dept, Univ Fla, 57-64; prof bot & head dept, NC State Univ, 64-78; BUS EXEC, AM SOC PLANT PHYSIOLOGISTS, 78- *Mem:* Am Soc Plant Physiologists (exec secy-treas, 55-58); Bot Soc Am. *Res:* Seed physiology; phenology of native and cultivated plants; primary productivity of cultivated plants. *Mailing Add:* Am Soc Plant Physiologists PO Box 1688 Rockville MD 20850

NOGGLE, JOSEPH HENRY, b Harrisburg, Pa, Mar 19, 36; m 60. PHYSICAL CHEMISTRY. *Educ:* Juniata Col, BS, 60; Harvard Univ, MS, 63, PhD(chem), 65. *Prof Exp:* Asst prof chem, Univ Wis-Madison, 65-71; assoc prof, 71-76, PROF CHEM, UNIV DEL, 76- *Mem:* AAAS; Am Chem Soc. *Res:* Nuclear magnetic resonance, including relaxation phenomena. *Mailing Add:* Dept of Chem Univ of Del Newark DE 19711

NOGGLE, THOMAS (SHERMAN), b Kansas City, Mo, Feb 13, 23; m 47; c 4. METALLURGICAL ENGINEERING. *Educ:* Univ Ill, BS, 48, MS, 51, PhD(metall eng), 55. *Prof Exp:* METALLURGIST, SOLID STATE PHYSICS DIV, OAK RIDGE NAT LAB, 55- *Mem:* AAAS; Electron Micros Soc Am; Am Inst Mining, Metall & Petrol Engrs; Am Phys Soc. *Res:* Solid state physics and metallurgy, especially radiation effects of metals. *Mailing Add:* Solid State Div Oak Ridge Nat Lab PO Box X Oak Ridge TN 37830

NOGRADY, GEORGE LADISLAUS, b Budapest, Hungary, May 2, 19; Can citizen; m 50. MICROBIOLOGY, POPULATION STUDIES. *Educ:* Univ Kolozsvar, Hungary, MD, 44; Univ Pecs, cert bact, 55; Univ Toronto, cert bact, 61; Am Bd Microbiol, dipl, 64. *Prof Exp:* Demonstr biochem, Univ Kolozsvar, 40-43, asst prof bact, 43-46; from asst prof to assoc prof, Univ Pecs, 46-54, asst dir, 54-56, State Inst Social Ins res fel, 55-56, chief diag lab, Inst Microbiol, 56; asst bact, 57-58, ASST PROF MICROBIOL, UNIV MONTREAL, 58- *Concurrent Pos:* Dir microbiol proj, Can Med Exped to Easter Island, 64-65. *Mem:* Am Soc Microbiol; Can Soc Microbiol; Can Asn Med; Int Soc Cell Biol. *Res:* Cultural diagnostic methods; bacterial morphology; microbiology of isolated populations; application of cinephotomicrography in microbiology; facial reconstruction of an Easter Island skull. *Mailing Add:* 4662 Victoria Ave Montreal PQ H3W 0N1 Can

NOGRADY, THOMAS, b Budapest, Hungary, Oct 16, 25; Can citizen; m 50; c 1. MEDICINAL CHEMISTRY. *Educ:* Eotvos Lorand Univ, Budapest, MSc, 48, PhD(org chem), 50. *Prof Exp:* Res chemist, Res Inst Pharmaceut Indust, Budapest, 50-56; res assoc org chem, Univ Vienna, 57 & Univ Montreal, 57-61; from asst prof to assoc prof, Loyola Col, Montreal, 61-70, PROF BIOCHEM, CONCORDIA UNIV, 70- *Concurrent Pos:* Rockefeller scholar, Univ Vienna, 57; consult, Delmar Chem Ltd, Montreal, 58- *Mem:* Am Chem Soc; fel Chem Inst Can. *Res:* Molecular pharmacology; nuclear magnetic resonance; biochemistry. *Mailing Add:* Dept Chem Concordia Univ Montreal PQ H3G 1M8 Can

NOHEL, JOHN ADOLPH, b Prague, Czech, Oct 24, 24; nat US; m 48; c 3. MATHEMATICS. *Educ:* George Washington Univ, BEE, 48; Mass Inst Technol, PhD(math), 53. *Prof Exp:* Asst math, George Washington Univ, 46-48; instr, Mass Inst Technol, 50-53; from asst prof to prof, Ga Inst Technol, 53-61; assoc prof, 61-64, chmn dept math, 68-70, PROF MATH, UNIV WIS-MADISON, 64-, DIR, MATH RES CTR, 79- *Concurrent Pos:* Mem, Math Res Ctr, 58-59, 77-; res sabbatical, Univ Paris, 65-66; vis prof, Ecole Polytech, Lausanne, 71-72; mem comt appl math, Nat Res Coun-Nat Acad Sci. *Mem:* AAAS; Am Math Soc; Soc Indust & Appl Math; Math Asn Am; Fedn Am Scientists. *Res:* Volterra functional differential equations, qualitative theory and applications. *Mailing Add:* Dept Math Van Vleck Hall Univ Wis Madison WI 53706

NOID, DONALD WILLIAM, b Marshalltown, Iowa, Feb 6, 49; m 77; c 2. PHYSICAL CHEMISTRY, CHEMICAL PHYSICS. *Educ:* Iowa State Univ, BS, 71; Univ Ill, MS, 73, PhD(chem), 76. *Prof Exp:* Res assoc chem, Univ Ill, 76; NSF fel, 76-77; CHEMIST, OAK RIDGE NAT LAB, 77- *Concurrent Pos:* Eugene P Wigner fel, Oak Ridge Nat Lab, 77-; adj asst prof, Univ Tenn, 81- *Mem:* Am Chem Soc; Am Phys Soc; Sigma Xi. *Res:* Chemical kinetics; molecular dynamics and laser chemistry. *Mailing Add:* Dept Chem PO Box X Oak Ridge TN 37830

NOISEUX, CLAUDE FRANCOIS, b Winchester, Mass, June 24, 53. APPLIED MATHEMATICS. *Educ:* Harvard Univ, AB, 75, MS, 77, PhD(appl math), 80. *Prof Exp:* FEL, HARVARD UNIV, 80- *Concurrent Pos:* Consult, Chase Inc, 80- *Mem:* Sigma Xi. *Res:* Study of wave propagation in harbor geometries and related Tsunami problems; modeling of turbulent boundary layer structures and the development of related approximate expansion procedures. *Mailing Add:* 65 Mt Auburn St #44 Cambridge MA 02138

NOKES, RICHARD FRANCIS, b Deerfield, Mich, Mar 16, 34; m 56; c 6. VETERINARY MEDICINE, ANATOMY. *Educ:* Mich State Univ, BS, 56, DVM, 58. *Prof Exp:* Vet, pvt pract, 58-60 & Agr Res Serv, USDA, 60-61; asst prof, 62-74, ASSOC PROF BIOL, UNIV AKRON, 74- *Concurrent Pos:* Vet, Copley Rd Animal Hosp, Akron, 62-; consult, Akron Children's Zoo, 64- & Akron Gen Med Ctr, 65- *Mem:* Am Asn Zoo Vets. *Res:* Rheological studies of blood flow; developmental studies of sense organs in the dog; excretion pathways of friction reducing agents. *Mailing Add:* Dept of Biol Univ of Akron Akron OH 44325

NOLA, FRANK JOSEPH, b Miami, Fla, June 25, 30; m 57; c 3. ELECTRONICS ENGINEERING. *Educ:* Univ Miami, BS, 58. *Prof Exp:* Elec engr, Allis Chalmers, 58-59, Martin Marietta, 59-60 & Army Ballastic Missile Agen, Dept Defense, 60-62; ELEC ENGR, MARSHALL SPACE FLIGHT CTR, NASA, 62- *Honors & Awards:* IR 100 Award, Indust Res Mag, 79; Excalibur Award, US Congress, 79. *Res:* Design and develop electronic control systems for guidance and control of missiles, for controlling earth orbiting space craft and for controlling experiments. *Mailing Add:* 117 Westbury Dr Huntsville AL 35802

NOLAN, CHRIS, b Salt Lake City, Utah, July 3, 30; m 63; c 2. BIOCHEMISTRY. *Educ:* Univ Nev, BS, 52; Univ Utah, PhD(biochem), 61. *Prof Exp:* NIH fel, Univ Wash, 61-63; RES BIOCHEMIST, ABBOTT LABS, 63- *Mem:* Am Soc Biol Chem. *Res:* Structure-function relationships in proteins. *Mailing Add:* 940 Greenleaf St Gurnee IL 60031

NOLAN, EDWARD J, b Philadelphia, Pa; m 49; c 2. THERMODYNAMICS, SCIENCE ADMINISTRATION. *Educ:* Villanova Univ, BChE, 45; Univ Del, MChE, 52; Univ Pa, PhD(chem eng & biochem eng), 81. *Prof Exp:* Proj engr, Pennwalt Chem Co, 46-48, Day & Zimmermann, Inc, 48-50 & Selas Corp, 50-56; ENG MGR, GEN ELEC CO, 56- *Concurrent Pos:* Res assoc, Med Sch, Thomas Jefferson Univ, 72-78; lectr appl math, La Salle Col, 52-56, chmn, 60- *Mem:* Am Soc Mech Engrs; Am Chem Soc; Am Inst Chem Engrs; Soc Indust & Appl Math; Am Math Soc. *Res:* Biochemical technology, including energy development and selected chemicals and fuel produced from biomass and renewable resources. *Mailing Add:* 565 Wanamaker Rd Jenkintown PA 19046

NOLAN, GEORGE JUNIOR, b Stilwell, Okla, Nov 3, 35; m 55; c 5. PHYSICAL CHEMISTRY. *Educ:* Northeastern State Col, BS, 58; Univ Ark, MS, 62, PhD(chem), 64. *Prof Exp:* Chemist, Phillips Petrol Co, 64-68; assoc prof chem, 68-73, PROF CHEM, NORTHEASTERN OKLA STATE COL, 73- *Mem:* Am Chem Soc. *Res:* Fundamental and development research in catalysis. *Mailing Add:* Northeastern Okla State Univ Tahlequah OK 74464

NOLAN, JAMES FRANCIS, b Scranton, Pa, Nov 16, 31; m 57; c 3. PHYSICS. *Educ:* Univ Scranton, BS, 54; Univ Pittsburgh, PhD(physics), 64. *Prof Exp:* Res physicist, Westinghouse Res Lab, 61-66; RES PHYSICIST, OWENS-ILL, INC, 66- *Mem:* Am Phys Soc. *Res:* Atomic collisions; medium energy ion-atom charge transfer and ionization; low energy electron-atom collisions. *Mailing Add:* Owens-Illinois Inc PO Box 1035 Toledo OH 43666

NOLAN, JAMES P, b Buffalo, NY, June 21, 29; m 56; c 4. MEDICINE. *Educ:* Yale Univ, BA, 51, MD, 55. *Prof Exp:* Instr, Yale Univ, 61-63; from asst prof to assoc prof, 63-69, PROF & ACTG CHMN MED, STATE UNIV NY BUFFALO, 69-; HEAD DEPT MED, BUFFALO GEN HOSP, 81- *Concurrent Pos:* Chief med, Buffalo Gen Hosp; actg chief, Erie Co Med Ctr. *Mem:* Am Col Physicians; Am Fedn Clin Res; Am Gastroenterol Soc; Am Asn Study Liver Dis; Reticuloendothelial Soc. *Res:* Role of bacterial endotoxins and the reticuloendothelial system in the initiation and perpetuation of liver disease. *Mailing Add:* Buffalo Gen Hosp Dept of Med 100 High St Buffalo NY 14203

NOLAN, JAMES ROBERT, b New York, NY, May 8, 23; m 46; c 3. BOTANY. *Educ:* Cornell Univ, BS, 61, PhD(plant anat & morphol), 67. *Prof Exp:* Instr biol, Antioch Col, 64-67; asst prof, 67-71, ASSOC PROF BIOL, STATE UNIV NY PLATTSBURGH, 71- *Mem:* Am Fern Soc; Bot Soc Am; Int Soc Plant Morphol; Int Soc Study Evolution. *Res:* Ontogeney and phylogeny of branching systems in plants. *Mailing Add:* Dept of Bot State Univ NY Plattsburgh NY 12901

NOLAN, JANIECE SIMMONS, b Ft Worth, Tex, June 8, 39; m 73; c 6. HOSPITAL ADMINISTRATION, PHYSIOLOGY. *Educ:* Univ Tex, BA, 61, MA, 63; Tulane Univ, PhD(biol), 68; Univ Calif, Berkeley, MPH, 75. *Prof Exp:* Res scientist aerospace med, Tex Nuclear Corp, 63-65; head cell biol, Gulf Southern Res Inst, 68-70; res physiologist, Vet Admin Hosp, 70-73, health care admin trainee, Vet Admin Hosp, Martinez & Univ Calif, Berkeley, 73-75; asst adminr ambulatory care serv, Univ Calif Med Ctr, San Francisco, 75-77; dir ambulatory care serv, 77-79, asst adminr outpatient & ancillary serv, 79-80, VPRES PROF SERV, JOHN MUIR MEM HOSP, WALNUT CREEK, 80- *Concurrent Pos:* Scholar, Dept Physiol-Anat, Univ Calif, Berkeley, 70-72. *Mem:* Am Col Hosp Adminr; Am Pub Health Asn; Geront Soc; Am Physiol Soc; Am Hosp Asn. *Res:* Delivery of outpatient health services; cell culture; cellular aging; plant senescence and growth regulators; ambulatory surgery. *Mailing Add:* John Muir Mem Hosp Walnut Creek CA 94598

NOLAN, JOHN THOMAS, JR, b Boston, Mass, Apr 15, 30; m 55; c 5. PETROLEUM CHEMISTRY, RESEARCH ADMINISTRATION. *Educ:* Cath Univ Am, AB, 51; Mass Inst Technol, PhD(org chem), 55. *Prof Exp:* Chemist, 55-58, group leader polymer res, 59-69, asst supvr ref res, 69-76, supvr coal res, 76-78, ASST MGR SCI PLANNING, TEXACO, INC, 78- *Mem:* Am Chem Soc; NY Acad Sci; Sigma Xi. *Res:* Organic syntheses; polymer syntheses, structures and testing; applied catalysis; refining processes; coal conversion. *Mailing Add:* Relyea Terr RD 6 Wappingers Falls NY 12590

NOLAN, LINDA LEE, biological chemistry, see previous edition

NOLAN, MICHAEL FRANCIS, b Evergreen Park, Ill, July 28, 47; m 73. NEUROANATOMY. *Educ:* Marquette Univ, BS, 69; Med Col Wis, PhD(anat), 75. *Prof Exp:* Staff phys therapist, Kiwanis Children's Ctr, Curative Workshop, Milwaukee, 69; instr, 75-76, asst prof, 76-81, ASSOC PROF ANAT, COL MED, UNIV SOUTH FLA, 81- *Mem:* Am Phys Ther Asn. *Res:* Neuroanatomical aspects of pain transmission, perception and appreciation; neurocytological changes in neural dysfunction. *Mailing Add:* Dept of Anat Col of Med Univ of S Fla Tampa FL 33612

NOLAN, RICHARD ARTHUR, b Omaha, Nebr, Nov 2, 37; m 67. MYCOLOGY, PHYSIOLOGY. *Educ:* Univ Nebr, Lincoln, BSc, 59, MSc, 62; Univ Calif, Berkeley, PhD(bot), 67. *Prof Exp:* NIH fel biochem, Univ Calif, Berkeley, 67-68, res biochemist, 68-69; asst prof biol, NMex State Univ, 69-70; univ fel, 70-71, asst prof, 71-75, assoc prof, 75-80, PROF BIOL, MEM UNIV NFLD, 80- *Mem:* Mycol Soc Am; Can Soc Microbiologists; Can Bot Asn; Soc Invert Path; Entomol Soc Can. *Res:* Comparative immunology and enzymology; nutritional requirements of fungal parasites of nematodes and mosquito and blackfly larvae; biological control of forest insect pests, nematodes and arthropods of medical importance; taxonomic studies with Coelomomyces. *Mailing Add:* Dept of Biol Mem Univ of Nfld St John's NF A1B 3X9 Can

NOLAN, RON SCOTT, b Goodland, Kans, Mar 4, 47. MARINE BIOLOGY, MARINE ECOLOGY. *Educ:* Univ Kans, BA, 69; Univ Calif, San Diego, PhD(marine biol), 75. *Prof Exp:* PRES, ORCA SEA FARMS, INC, 75- *Concurrent Pos:* Pres, Ocean Res Consult & Anal, Ltd, 78- *Res:* Marine shrimp farming on Molokai, Hawaii; marine shrimp farming. *Mailing Add:* Ocean Res Consult & Anal Ltd PO Box 88253 Honolulu HI 96815

NOLAN, STANTON PEELLE, b Washington, DC, May 29, 33; m 55; c 2. CARDIOVASCULAR SURGERY, CARDIOVASCULAR PHYSIOLOGY. *Educ:* Princeton Univ, AB, 55; Univ Va, Charlottesville, MD, 59, MS, 62. *Prof Exp:* From intern to resident surg, Med Ctr, Univ Va, Charlottesville, 59-65, Va Heart Asn res fel, Univ, 61-62, resident thoracic cardiovasc surg, Univ Va Hosp, 65-66; sr surgeon, Nat Heart Inst, 66-68; from asst prof to assoc prof, 68-74, surg-in-chg, 70-74, PROF SURG & SURGEON-IN-CHG THORACIC CARDIOVASC SURG DIV, UNIV VA HOSP, 74- *Concurrent Pos:* Am Cancer Soc clin fel, 63-64; estab investr, Am Heart Asn, 69-74, mem coun cardiovasc surg, 68, mem coun thrombosis, 70; attend staff, Med Ctr, Univ Va, 68-; consult cardiac surg, Vet Admin Hosp, Salem, Va, 68-; consult surg, Va State Bur Crippled Children, 68- *Honors & Awards:* John Horsley Mem Prize Med Res, 62; Am Col Chest Physicians Award of Merit, 68. *Mem:* Fel Am Col Surg; fel Am Col Cardiol; Am Heart Asn; AMA; Am Surg Asn. *Res:* Cardiovascular hemodynamics and pathophysiology. *Mailing Add:* Box 181 Univ of Va Med Ctr Charlottesville VA 22908

NOLAN, THOMAS BRENNAN, b Greenfield, Mass, May 21, 01; m 27; c 1. GEOLOGY. *Educ:* Yale Univ, PhB, 21, PhD(geol), 24. *Hon Degrees:* LLD, St Andrews, 62. *Prof Exp:* Geologist, 24-44, from asst dir to dir, 44-65, RES GEOLOGIST, US GEOL SURV, 65- *Concurrent Pos:* Vpres, Int Union Geol Sci, 65-72. *Honors & Awards:* Spendiaroff prize, Int Geol Cong, 33; Silver Medal, Tokyo Geog Soc, 65. *Mem:* Nat Acad Sci; fel Geol Soc Am; fel Soc Econ Geol; fel Mineral Soc Am; fel Am Geophysics Union. *Res:* Ore deposits of the Great Basin. *Mailing Add:* 2219 California St NW Washington DC 20008

NOLAN, VAL, JR, b Evansville, Ind, Apr 28, 20; m 46; c 3. POPULATION BIOLOGY, EVOLUTIONARY ECOLOGY. *Educ:* Ind Univ, AB, 41, JD, 49. *Prof Exp:* Dep US Marshal, 41-42; agent, US Secret Serv, 42; from asst prof to assoc prof law, 49-56, PROF LAW, IND UNIV, BLOOMINGTON, 56-, PROF ZOOL, 68- *Concurrent Pos:* Guggenheim fel, 57; res scholar zool, Ind Univ, Bloomington, 57-68. *Mem:* Fel Am Ornith Union; Ecol Soc Am; Animal Behav Soc; Ger Ornith Soc; Brit Ornith Union. *Res:* Behavior and ecology of birds. *Mailing Add:* Dept of Zool Ind Univ Bloomington IN 47401

NOLAN, WILLIAM J, chemical engineering, deceased

NOLAND, J(AMES) HUBERT, JR, b Columbia, SC, Oct 23, 22; m 48; c 4. ELECTRICAL ENGINEERING. *Educ:* Univ SC, BS, 42; Ga Inst Technol, MS, 48; Yale Univ, DEng, 61. *Prof Exp:* Adj prof physics, Univ SC, 46-47; instr elec eng, Ga Inst Technol, 47-48; adj prof, 48-50, assoc prof, 50-61, chmn div, 50-55, PROF ELEC ENG, UNIV SC, 61- *Mem:* Am Soc Eng Educ; sr mem Inst Elec & Electronics Engrs. *Res:* Control systems; computer science. *Mailing Add:* 3115 Stepp Dr Columbia SC 29204

NOLAND, JAMES STERLING, b Cape Girardeau, Mo, June 18, 33. ORGANIC POLYMER CHEMISTRY. *Educ:* Southeast Mo State Col, BS(chem), & BS(educ), 55; Univ Iowa, MS, 57, PhD(org chem), 60. *Prof Exp:* Res chemist polymer chem, 59-73, mgr aerospace adhesives res, 73-77, tech dir gen prod dept, 77-78, tech dir, Aerospace Prod Dept, Indust Chem Div, 78-80, MGR, STANFORD RES, ENG MAT DEPT, CHEM PROD DIV, AM CYANAMID CO, 80- *Mem:* Am Chem Soc; Soc Advan Mat & Process Eng; Soc Advan Educ. *Res:* New polymer systems; resin systems for structural adhesives; composites; environmental resistant resins. *Mailing Add:* Am Cyanamid Co 1937 W Main St Stanford CT 06904

NOLAND, JERRE LANCASTER, b Richmond, Ky, Feb 14, 21; m 50; c 3. BIOCHEMISTRY. *Educ:* Purdue Univ, BS, 42, MS, 44; Univ Wis, PhD(biochem, zool), 49. *Prof Exp:* Asst chem & biol, Purdue Univ, 43-44; asst biochem, Univ Wis, 48; Lalor fel, Marine Biol Lab, Woods Hole, 49; biochemist, Entom Br, Med Labs, US Army Chem Ctr, 49-54; chief biochemist, Res Lab, Wood Vet Admin Ctr, Wis, 54-58; chief med res lab, Vet Admin Hosp, Louisville, Ky, 58-73; assoc prof biochem, 59-73, RES COORDR, DEPT OBSTET & GYNEC, SCH MED, UNIV LOUISVILLE, 74- *Mem:* AAAS; Am Chem Soc; Soc Exp Biol & Med; Am Asn Clin Chem. *Res:* Endocrinology; sterol metabolism. *Mailing Add:* Dept Obstet & Gynec Univ Louisville Sch Med Louisville KY 40202

NOLAND, PAUL ROBERT, b Chillicothe, Ill, Sept 28, 24; m 47; c 4. ANIMAL NUTRITION. *Educ:* Univ Ill, BS, 47, MS, 48; Cornell Univ, PhD, 51. *Prof Exp:* Asst, Univ Ill, 48 & Cornell Univ, 51; from asst prof to assoc prof animal nutrit & husb, 51-60, PROF ANIMAL SCI, UNIV ARK, FAYETTEVILLE, 60- *Concurrent Pos:* With Ark Agr Mission, Panama, 55-57. *Mem:* Am Soc Animal Sci; Poultry Sci Asn; Am Inst Nutrit; Animal Nutrit Res Coun. *Res:* Swine nutrition and management; proteins, amino acids and mineral nutrition. *Mailing Add:* Dept of Animal Sci Univ of Ark Fayetteville AR 72701

NOLAND, WAYLAND EVAN, b Madison, Wis, Dec 8, 26. ORGANIC CHEMISTRY, HETEROCYCLIC CHEMISTRY. *Educ:* Univ Wis, BA, 48; Harvard Univ, MA, 50, PhD(phys org chem), 51. *Prof Exp:* Du Pont fel, 51-52, from asst prof to assoc prof, 52-62, PROF CHEM, UNIV MINN, MINNEAPOLIS, 62- *Concurrent Pos:* Vis instr chem, Univ BC, 56; consult, Sun Oil Co, 58-70; actg chief div org chem, Univ Minn, Minneapolis, 61-62, actg chmn dept chem, 67-69 & area coordr org chem, 72-74; secy, Org Syntheses, Inc, 69-79, vpres, 80- *Mem:* AAAS; Sigma Xi; Am Asn Univ Prof; Am Chem Soc; NY Acad Sci. *Res:* Heterocyclic nitrogen chemistry; synthesis and reactions of indoles and pyrroles; 1,3-cycloaddition reactions and ring expansions of isatogens; antimalarial compounds; rearrangements of nitronorbornenes; cycloaddition reactions of indenes; new rearrangements; reaction mechanisms; structure determination. *Mailing Add:* Sch Chem 207 Pleasant St SE Minneapolis MN 55455

NOLASCO, JESUS BAUTISTA, b Manila, Philippines, Oct 5, 17; m 42; c 4. PHYSIOLOGY. *Educ:* Univ Philippines, MD, 40. *Prof Exp:* From instr to asst prof physiol, Univ Philippines, 40-52; prof & head dept, Far Eastern Univ, Manila, 52-64, sr consult hosp, 54-64; vis prof physiol, NJ Med Sch, Col Med & Dent NJ, 64-66, assoc prof, 66-70, actg chmn dept, 74-75, prof physiol, 70-80; RETIRED. *Concurrent Pos:* Mem, Nat Res Coun Philippines, 40-; Rockefeller Found fel, Western Reserve Univ, 46-47; Williams-Waterman fel, Univ Berne, 62-63; mem comt nat med res prog, Nat Sci Develop Bd, Philippines, 62-64. *Mem:* Fel Am Col Clin Pharmacologists; Philippine Heart Asn (pres, 60-61); Am Physiol Soc. *Res:* Cardiovascular physiology, particularly electrophysiology of the heart. *Mailing Add:* Dept of Physiol NJ Med Sch Newark NJ 07103

NOLD, MAX M, radiation biology, veterinary medicine, see previous edition

NOLDE, GEORGE V, b St Petersburg, Russia, Feb 28, 00; US citizen; m 36. MECHANICAL & ELECTRICAL ENGINEERING. *Educ:* Moscow Tech Sch Higher Learning, Dipl elec eng, 23, DSc(chem eng), 29. *Prof Exp:* In res & develop, Indust Estab, Moscow, USSR, 23-33; consult engr, Calif, 34-36; res assoc, Photom Lab, Univ Calif, Berkeley, 37; develop engr, Butte Elec & Mfg Co, 38-40; res engr, Marchant Calculators, Inc, 40-44, consult engr, 46-48, res dir, 49-52; consult engr, Dalmo Victor, Inc, 45-46; proj engr & mgr comput devices unit, Radio Corp Am, NJ, 53-54, proj engr, W Coast Missile & Surface Radar Div, Calif, 58-62; sr staff engr, Aerospace Corp, 63-64; consult engr, Douglas Aircraft Co & Electro-Optical Indust, Inc, 65-66; CONSULT ENGR, 66- *Concurrent Pos:* Fel, Karpov Inst Chem, USSR, 30-33; prof elec eng, Univ Calif, Berkeley, 55-57; consult engr, Naval Electronics Lab Ctr, US Dept Navy, 67-76 & Aerospace Corp, 75-76. *Mem:* AAAS; Am Soc Mech Engrs; Nat Soc Prof Engrs; sr mem Inst Elec & Electronics Engrs. *Res:* Operations research; information theory; statistics; radar systems; light machinery design; magnetometric analysis; dynamics of metals; high speed memory devices; calculating machines and techniques. *Mailing Add:* 910 Great Western Bldg Berkeley CA 94704

NOLEN, GRANVILLE ABRAHAM, b Richmond, Ky, Apr 21, 26; m 50; c 5. TOXICOLOGY. *Educ:* Miami Univ, AB, 50. *Prof Exp:* Chief animal technician, 54-64, staff res asst animal nutrit, teratology & physiol & colony mgt, 64-70, STAFF NUTRITIONIST & TERATOLOGIST, MIAMI VALLEY LABS, PROCTER & GAMBLE CO, 70- *Mem:* AAAS; Am Asn Lab Animal Sci; Behav Teratology Soc; Teratology Soc; Am Inst Nutrit. *Res:* Animal nutrition, especially lipid and protein nutrition and metabolism; teratology, especially methods in relation to drug testing; behavioral effects of foods and chemicals; environmental effects on laboratory animals. *Mailing Add:* Miami Valley Labs Procter & Gamble Co Box 39175 Cincinnati OH 45239

NOLEN, JERRY A, JR, b Washington, DC, Nov 17, 40; m 80; c 6. NUCLEAR PHYSICS, CHARGED PARTICLE BEAM OPTICS. *Educ:* Lehigh Univ, BS, 61; Princeton Univ, PhD(physics), 65. *Prof Exp:* Instr physics, Princeton Univ, 65-66; appointee nuclear physics, Argonne Nat Lab, 66-68; asst prof physics, Univ Md, 68-70; assoc prof, 70-76, PROF PHYSICS, MICH STATE UNIV, 76- *Concurrent Pos:* Fel Max Planck Inst Nuclear Physics, Heidelberg, Ger, 77. *Mem:* Am Phys Soc. *Res:* Experimental nuclear physics; high resolution charged particle spectroscopy with cyclotrons and magnetic spectrographs; direct reactions; precision mass and excitation energy measurements; heavy ion nuclear science. *Mailing Add:* Dept Physics Mich State Univ East Lansing MI 48824

NOLF, LUTHER OWEN, b Solomon, Kans, July 16, 02. PARASITOLOGY. *Educ:* Kans State Col, BS, 26, MS, 29; Johns Hopkins Univ, ScD(med zool), 31. *Prof Exp:* Asst parasitol, Kans State Col, 27-29; asst helminth, Johns Hopkins Univ, 29-31; assoc zool, 31-37, from asst prof to prof zool, 57-70, EMER PROF ZOOL, UNIV IOWA, 70- *Concurrent Pos:* Consult, Vet Admin. *Mem:* Am Soc Trop Med & Hyg; Am Soc Parasitol; Am Micros Soc. *Res:* Helminthology; Trichinella spiralis; trematodes of fish; poultry parasites. *Mailing Add:* Dept Zool Univ Iowa Iowa City IA 52240

NOLIN, JOSEPH ARTHUR BENOIT, b Levis, Que, Apr 1, 21; m 49; c 3. POLYMER CHEMISTRY. *Educ:* Col Levis, Can, BA, 43; Laval Univ, BSc, 47, PhD(chem), 49. *Prof Exp:* Lectr, Laval Univ, 47-49; fel infrared spectros & org chem, Nat Res Coun Can, 49-51, res officer, 51-53; res assoc infrared spectros, Mass Inst Technol, 53-54; res chemist, Exp Sta, Pa, 54-80, SR RES CHEMIST, E I DU PONT DE NEMOURS & CO, INC, KINSTON, NC, 80- *Concurrent Pos:* Lectr, Univ Ottawa, 51-53. *Mem:* Am Chem Soc. *Res:* Textiles; infrared spectroscopy. *Mailing Add:* E I du Pont de Nemours & Co Box 800 Kinston NC 28501

NOLL, CLARENCE IRWIN, b Palmyra, Pa, Feb 29, 08; m 34; c 2. ORGANIC CHEMISTRY. *Educ:* Lebanon Valley Col, BS, 30; Trinity Col, Conn, MS, 32; Pa State Col, PhD(org chem), 38. *Prof Exp:* Asst chem, Trinity Col, Conn, 30-33 & Pa State Col, 34-37; res chemist, Borden Co, 37-41; from instr org res to assoc prof, 41-53, prof chem, 53-71, from asst dean to assoc dean, Col Chem & Physics, 51-63, from actg dean to dean, Col Sci, 63-71,

EMER PROF CHEM & EMER DEAN, COL SCI, PA STATE UNIV, 71- *Mem:* Am Chem Soc; AAAS; Am Inst Chemists. *Res:* Organic syntheses; chemistry of dairy products; explosives; organic nitrogen compounds. *Mailing Add:* 293 Ellen Ave State College PA 16801

NOLL, CLIFFORD RAYMOND, JR, b Providence, RI, Dec 20, 22; m 49; c 3. BIOCHEMISTRY. *Educ:* Brown Univ, AB, 44; Univ Ill, MS, 50; Univ Wis, PhD(biochem), 52. *Prof Exp:* Instr biochem, Univ Mich, 52-56; biochemist, USDA, 56-58; asst prof chem, Goucher Col, 58-62; assoc prof, Wellesley Col, 62-65; res biochemist, Hartford Hosp, 65-67; fac mem, Franconia Col, 67-68; assoc prof sci, 68-74, PROF SCI, GREATER HARTFORD COMMUNITY COL, 74- *Concurrent Pos:* Carnegie intern gen educ, Brown Univ, 55-56. *Mem:* AAAS. *Res:* History, philosophy and sociology of science. *Mailing Add:* Dept of Sci Greater Hartford Community Col Hartford CT 06105

NOLL, HANS, b Basel, Switz, June 14, 24; nat US; m 49; c 4. MOLECULAR BIOLOGY. *Educ:* Univ Basel, PhD(biochem), 50. *Prof Exp:* Fel biol standardization, State Serum Inst, Copenhagen, Denmark, 50-51; asst tuberc, Pub Health Res Inst, City of New York, Inc, 51-53, assoc, 54-56; asst res prof microbiol, Sch Med, Univ Pittsburgh, 56-58, from asst prof to assoc prof, 59-64; PROF BIOL SCI, NORTHWESTERN UNIV, EVANSTON, 64- *Concurrent Pos:* Sr res fel, USPHS, 59-63, career investr, 64, mem molecular biol study sect, NIH, 66-68; vis prof, Univ Hawaii, 69; pres, Molecular Instruments Co, 70; vis prof Basel Inst Immunol, 71; consult, Europ Molecular Biol Lab, Heidelberg, 74; vis res prof, Lab Molecular Embryol, Naples, 75 & Univ Palermo, 78. *Honors & Awards:* Lifetime Endowed Career Professorship, Am Cancer Soc, 66. *Mem:* AAAS; Am Chem Soc; Am Soc Biol Chem; NY Acad Sci. *Res:* Biochemistry of viruses; role of membrane proteins in sea urchin embryogenesis; molecular biology of nucleic acids and protein synthesis. *Mailing Add:* 2665 Orrington Ave Evanston IL 60201

NOLL, JOHN STEPHEN, b Hungary, Oct 1, 44; Can citizen. CEREAL CHEMISTRY, BIOCHEMISTRY. *Educ:* Univ Winnipeg, BSc, 69; Univ Man, PhD(cereal biochem), 77. *Prof Exp:* Cereal chemist, Plant Breeding Inst, Univ Sydney, 77-78; CEREAL PHYSIOLOGIST, CAN DEPT AGR, 78- *Mem:* Am Asn Cereal Chemists. *Res:* Screening wheat varieties that are resistant to preharvest sprouting and to identify biochemical, physiological and genetic basis of this resistance; wheat quality evaluation. *Mailing Add:* Can Dept Agr 195 Dafoe Rd Winnipeg MB R3T 2M9 Can

NOLL, KENNETH E(UGENE), b Brantwood, Wis, Aug 20, 36; m 59; c 1. ENVIRONMENTAL ENGINEERING. *Educ:* Mich Technol Univ, BSCE, 59; Univ Wash, MSCE, 66, PhD(air resources eng), 69. *Prof Exp:* Air sanit engr, Dept Pub Health, State of Calif, 63-68, sr air sanit engr, Air Resources Bd, 69-70; from assoc prof to prof air resources, Univ Tenn, Knoxville, 70-74; PROF ENVIRON ENG, ILL INST TECHNOL, 75- *Concurrent Pos:* Chmn, Knox County Air Pollution Control Bd, 72-75; dir, Environ Protection Agency Regional Air Pollution Training Ctr, 78- *Mem:* Air Pollution Control Asn; Am Soc Civil Engrs. *Res:* Atmospheric aerosol technology; air monitoring; design of air pollution control devices. *Mailing Add:* Dept of Environ Eng Ill Inst of Technol Chicago IL 60616

NOLL, LEO ALBERT, b Colordo Springs, Colo, Aug 5, 32; m 75. CALORIMETRY, ADSORPTION. *Educ:* St Benedict's Col, BS, 55; Univ Colo, MS, 62, PhD(phys chem), 76. *Prof Exp:* Instr chem & math, Abbey Sch, Colo, 55-71; instr physics & sci, Nunawading High Sch, Australia, 73-75; fel, Univ Nebr, 75-76; RES CHEMIST, US DEPT ENERGY, BARTLESVILLE ENERGY TECHNOL CTR, 76- *Mem:* Soc Prof Engrs. *Res:* Thermodynamics of enhanced oil recovery systems, especially measuring the enthalpy of adsorption of components of icellar formulations on surfaces. *Mailing Add:* 2090 S Osage Bartlesville OK 74003

NOLL, WALTER, b Berlin, Ger, Jan 7, 25; nat US; m 79; c 2. MATHEMATICS, CONTINUUM MECHANICS. *Educ:* Univ Paris, Lic es Sci, 50; Tech Univ Berlin, diplom, 51; Ind Univ, PhD(math), 54. *Prof Exp:* Instr mech, Tech Univ, Berlin, 51-55; instr math, Univ Southern Calif, 55-56; assoc prof, 56-60, PROF MATH, CARNEGIE-MELLON UNIV, 60- *Concurrent Pos:* Vis prof, Johns Hopkins Univ, 62-63. *Mem:* Am Math Soc; Math Asn Am; Soc Natural Philos. *Res:* Foundations of mechanics and thermodynamics; differential geometry; relativity. *Mailing Add:* 308 Field Club Ridge Rd Pittsburgh PA 15238

NOLLE, ALFRED WILSON, b Columbia, Mo, July 28, 19; m 46. PHYSICS. *Educ:* Southwest Tex State Teachers Col, BA, 38; Univ Tex, MA, 39; Mass Inst Technol, PhD(physics), 47. *Prof Exp:* Tutor physics, Univ Tex, 40-41; spec res assoc, Underwater Sound Lab, Harvard Univ, 41-45; asst prof eng res, Ord Res Lab, Pa State Col, 45; res assoc physics, Mass Inst Technol, 45-47, mem staff, Div Indust Coop, 47-48; from asst prof to assoc prof physics, 48-57, PROF PHYSICS, UNIV TEX, AUSTIN, 57- *Mem:* Fel Am Phys Soc; fel Acoustical Soc Am. *Res:* Solid state physics; magnetic resonance and relaxation; paramagnetic impurities and imperfections; physics of musical tone sources; ultrasonics. *Mailing Add:* Dept of Physics Univ of Tex Austin TX 78712

NOLLEN, PAUL MARION, b Lafayette, Ind, Feb 24, 34; m 66. PARASITOLOGY. *Educ:* Carroll Col, BS, 56; Univ Wis, Madison, MS, 57; Univ Purdue, PhD(parasitol), 67. *Prof Exp:* Teacher high sch, Wis, 60-62; instr biol, Univ Purdue, 62-65; from asst prof to assoc prof zool & parasitol, 67-74, PROF ZOOL & PARASITOL, WESTERN ILL UNIV, 74- *Concurrent Pos:* Fac lectr, Western Ill Univ, 75. *Honors & Awards:* Herrick Award, 67; Sigma Xi Res Award, 74. *Mem:* AAAS; Am Soc Parasitol; Am Inst Biol Sci. *Res:* Reproductive activities of digenetic trematodes; uptake and incorporation of nutrients by digenetic trematodes; egg-shell chemistry of trematodes; host-finding behavior of miracidia. *Mailing Add:* Dept Biol Sci Western Ill Univ Macomb IL 61455

NOLLER, DAVID CONRAD, b Elma, NY, Oct 1, 23; m 47; c 2. ORGANIC CHEMISTRY. *Educ:* Univ Buffalo, BA, 49, MA, 54. *Prof Exp:* Asst chem, Univ Buffalo, 49-52; res chemist, Lucidol Div, 52-57, head anal & control lab, 57-60, supvr tech serv lab, 60-64, group leader patents, lit & safety, 64-66, group leader patents & lit, 66-69, patent agent, 69-70, TECH INFO SPECIALIST, PENNWALT CORP, 70- *Mem:* Am Chem Soc; Sigma Xi. *Res:* Organic peroxides with emphasis on safety and governmental regulation. *Mailing Add:* 145 E Morris St Buffalo NY 14214

NOLLER, HARRY FRANCIS, JR, b Oakland, Calif, June 10, 39; m 64; c 2. BIOCHEMISTRY. *Educ:* Univ Calif, Berkeley, AB, 60; Univ Ore, PhD(chem), 65. *Prof Exp:* NIH fel, Lab Molecular Biol, Med Res Coun, Cambridge, Eng, 65-66 & Inst Molecular Biol, Geneva, Switz, 66-68; asst prof, 68-73, assoc prof, 73-79, PROF BIOL, UNIV CALIF, SANTA CRUZ, 79- *Res:* Protein and nucleic acid chemistry; structure and function of ribosomes. *Mailing Add:* Thimann Labs Univ of Calif Santa Cruz CA 95064

NOLTE, KENNETH GEORGE, b East Carondelet, Ill, July 20, 41; m 63; c 3. ENGINEERING MECHANICS, STRUCTURAL ENGINEERING. *Educ:* Univ Ill, BSc, 64; Brown Univ, ScM, 66, PhD(eng), 68. *Prof Exp:* Res assoc solid mech, Brown Univ, 67-68; SR RES ENGR MARINE OPERS, AMOCO PROD CO, STANDARD OIL CO, IND, 68- *Mem:* Am Soc Civil Engrs. *Res:* Marine and Arctic engineering related to structural and vessel design; solid and fluid mechanics; physical properties of ice. *Mailing Add:* 6726 S 69th East Ave Tulsa OK 74133

NOLTE, LOREN W, b Napoleon, Ohio, Dec 23, 33; m 57; c 3. ELECTRICAL ENGINEERING. *Educ:* Northwestern Univ, BSEE, 56; Univ Mich, MSE, 60, PhD(elec eng), 65. *Prof Exp:* Coop student, Cook Res Labs, Ill, 53-56, jr engr, 56-57, engr, 57-58; res asst, Willow Run Labs, Univ Mich, 58-59, asst res engr, teaching fel & lectr, Dept Elec Eng, 59-65, assoc res engr, 65-66, res fel, Univ, 65-66; from asst prof to assoc prof, Duke Univ, 66-69; vis assoc prof, Univ Colo, Boulder, 69-70; assoc prof elec & biomed eng, 71-72, PROF ELEC & BIOMED ENG, DUKE UNIV, 72- *Mem:* Inst Elec & Electronics Engrs; Acoust Soc Am. *Res:* Extension of signal detection theory to adaptive receivers, design and performance; application of statistical communications to radar, sonar and communications problems. *Mailing Add:* Dept of Elec Eng Duke Univ Durham NC 27706

NOLTE, WILLIAM ANTHONY, b Washington, DC, Nov 15, 13; m 44; c 6. BACTERIOLOGY, MICROBIOLOGY. *Educ:* Univ Md, BS, 37, MS, 39, PhD(bact), 47. *Prof Exp:* Asst bact, Univ Md, 37-42; asst bacteriologist, Meats Lab Res Ctr, USDA, 42-43; asst bact, Univ Md, 46-47; chief bacteriologist, Res Lab, Vick Chem Co, NY, 47-49; from asst prof to assoc prof path & microbiol, 48-55, PROF PATH & MICROBIOL, UNIV TEX DENT BR HOUSTON, 55- *Mem:* Am Soc Microbiol; Int Asn Dent Res; Am Asn Dent Schs. *Res:* Dental caries process; specific oral organisms associated with dental plaque; sterilization procedures for dental instruments; bacteriological culture media in endodontics. *Mailing Add:* 3723 Latma Houston TX 77025

NOLTIMIER, HALLAN COSTELLO, b Los Angeles, Calif, Mar 19, 37; m 61; c 2. GEOPHYSICS. *Educ:* Calif Inst Technol, BS, 58; Univ Newcastle, Eng, PhD(geophysics), 65. *Prof Exp:* Lectr physics & geophysics, Sch Physics, Univ Newcastle, Eng, 66-68; asst prof geol, Sch Geol & Geophys, Univ Okla, 68-71; assoc prof geol, Dept Geol, Univ Houston, 71-72; assoc prof, 72-78, PROF GEOPHYSICS, DEPT GEOL & MINERAL, OHIO STATE UNIV, 78- *Concurrent Pos:* Consult, Chevron Oil Feld Res, 70, Chevron Overseas Petrol, 71, Humble Res Lab, 72, Digital Resources Inc, 78-79 & Towner Petrol, 81- *Mem:* Fel Royal Astron Soc; Am Geophys Union; Sigma Xi; Soc Explor Geophysicists; AAAS. *Res:* Paleomagnetism of Mesozoic intrusives along the eastern margin of North America; paleomagnetism of lower Paleozoic limestones; paleomagnetism of coal; paleomagnetism of recent lake sediments with particular interest in short geomagnetic excursions. *Mailing Add:* Dept of Geol & Mineral Ohio State Univ Columbus OH 43210

NOLTMANN, ERNST AUGUST, b Gotha, Ger, June 27, 31; m 56; c 2. BIOCHEMISTRY, ENZYMOLOGY. *Educ:* Univ Münster, Physikum, 53; Med Acad Düsseldorf, Ger, MD, 56. *Prof Exp:* Jr biochemist, Inst Physiol Chem, Med Acad Dusseldorf, 56-58, asst biochemist, 58-59; fel enzyme chem, Inst Enzyme Res, Univ Wis, 59-62; from asst prof to assoc prof biochem, 62-69, PROF BIOCHEM & BIOMED SCI, UNIV CALIF, RIVERSIDE, 69- *Concurrent Pos:* USPHS & NSF res grants; chmn dept biochem, Univ Calif, Riverside, 75-77. *Mem:* Am Soc Biol Chemists; Am Chem Soc. *Res:* Isolation and characterization of enzymes and the study of their mechanisms of action. *Mailing Add:* Dept of Biochem Univ of Calif Riverside CA 92502

NOMURA, KAWORU CARL, b Deer Lodge, Mont, Apr 1, 22; m 47; c 4. SOLID STATE PHYSICS. *Educ:* Univ Minn, BPhys, 48, MS, 49, PhD(elec eng), 53; Advan Mgt Prog, Harvard Univ, grad, 72. *Prof Exp:* Sr res physicist, Corp Res Ctr, 53-54, res supvr, 54-58, staff scientist, 58-61, mgr opers semiconductor div, 61-65, VPRES & GEN MGR, SOLID STATE ELECTRONICS CTR, HONEYWELL, INC, 65- *Mem:* Fel Am Phys Soc; sr mem Inst Elec & Electronics Eng. *Res:* Electrical, optical and structural properties of semiconductors; solid state sensors and transducers; transistors and integrated circuits; research and development and manufacture. *Mailing Add:* Solid State Electronics Div Honeywell Inc 12001 State Highway 55 Minneapolis MN 55441

NOMURA, MASAYASU, b Hyogo-ken, Japan, Apr 27, 27; m 57; c 2. MOLECULAR BIOLOGY, MICROBIOLOGY. *Educ:* Univ Tokyo, BS, 51, PhD(microbiol), 57. *Prof Exp:* Res assoc microbiol, Univ Ill, 57-59; res assoc biol sci, Purdue Univ, 59-60; asst prof inst protein res, Osaka Univ, 60-63; assoc prof genetics, 63-66, prof, 66-70, PROF GENETICS & BIOCHEM, INST ENZYME RES, UNIV WIS-MADISON, 70- *Concurrent Pos:* NIH grants, 61-63 & 64-; NSF grants, 63- *Honors & Awards:* US Steel Found

Award Molecular Biol, 71; Japan Acad Award, 72. *Mem:* Nat Acad Sci; AAAS; Am Soc Microbiol; Genetics Soc Am; Am Soc Biol Chemists. *Res:* Structure, function and assembly of ribosomes; biosynthesis of nucleic acids and protein; mechanism of action of bacteriocines. *Mailing Add:* Inst for Enzyme Res Univ of Wis Madison WI 53706

NOMURA, SHIGEKO, b Tokyo, Japan, Jan 3, 29. MICROBIOLOGY, VIROLOGY. *Educ:* Toho Women's Col Med, MD, 50; Yamaguchi Univ, DMS, 60. *Prof Exp:* Intern, Tokyo Univ Hosp, 50-51; resident internal med, Tokyo Sumida Hosp, 51-53; NIH res fel virol, Tokyo, 53-61; vis assoc, NIH, Md, 61-63; res assoc, Sch Hyg & Pub Health, Johns Hopkins Univ, 63-66; sr virologist, Flow Labs, Inc, 66-67; MICROBIOLOGIST, NAT CANCER INST, 67- *Mem:* AAAS; Am Soc Microbiol. *Res:* Cancer research. *Mailing Add:* Bldg 41 S-200 Nat Cancer Inst Bethesda MD 20205

NONDAHL, THOMAS ARTHUR, b Monroe, Wis, Jan 11, 51; m 77. ELECTRICAL ENGINEERING. *Educ:* Univ Wis-Madison, BS, 73, MS, 74, PhD(elec eng), 77. *Prof Exp:* ELEC ENGR, GEN ELEC CO, 78- *Mem:* Inst Elec & Electronics Engrs; Sigma Xi. *Res:* Rotating and linear electric machines. *Mailing Add:* Bldg 37 Rm 442 PO Box 43 Schenectady NY 12301

NONNECKE, IB LIBNER, b Copenhagen, Denmark, Oct 1, 22; nat Can; m 45; c 3. HORTICULTURE. *Educ:* Univ Alta, BSc, 45, MSc, 50; Univ Ore, 50; Ore State Univ, PhD, 58. *Prof Exp:* Head hort sect, Res Sta, Can Dept Agr, 46-63; pres, Asgrow Seed Co Can, Ltd, 63-66, coordr crop improv, Asgrow Seed Co, 66-68; assoc prof hort, 68-70, PROF HORT & CHIEF VEG DIV, UNIV GUELPH, 70-, CHMN DEPT HORT SCI, 74- *Mem:* Am Soc Hort Sci; Can Soc Hort Sci; Sigma Xi; Agr Inst Can. *Res:* Plant breeding and genetics; statistics; field plot technique. *Mailing Add:* Dept Hort Sci Univ Guelph Guelph ON 1G 2W1 Can

NOODEN, LARRY DONALD, b Oak Park, Ill, June 10, 36; m 63; c 2. PLANT PHYSIOLOGY, BIOCHEMISTRY. *Educ:* Univ Ill, BSc, 58; Univ Wis, MSc, 59; Harvard Univ, PhD(biol), 63. *Prof Exp:* NIH res fel, Univ Edinburgh, 64-65; from asst prof to assoc prof, 65-76, PROF BOT, UNIV MICH, ANN ARBOR, 76- *Concurrent Pos:* NIH special res fel, Calif Inst Technol, 71-72; vis scientist, Boyce Thompson Inst, 79; vis fel, Res Sch Biol Sci, Australian Nat Univ, Canberra, 81. *Mem:* AAAS; Am Soc Plant Physiol; Bot Soc Am; Crop Sci Soc Am; Japanese Soc Plant Physiol. *Res:* Biochemistry of regulation of plant development. *Mailing Add:* Dept Bot Univ Mich Ann Arbor MI 48109

NOOKER, EUGENE L(EROY), b Cheyenne, Wyo, Oct 10, 22; m 49; c 1. ORDNANCE, MATERIALS SCIENCE. *Educ:* Univ Colo, BS, 47, MS, 49. *Prof Exp:* Res engr, Eng Exp Sta, Univ Colo, 47-51; sr engr, Appl Physics Lab, Johns Hopkins Univ, 51-58, group supvr, 58-67; vpres & dir develop eng div, G W Galloway Co, 67-73; CONSULT, 73- *Mem:* Am Soc Mech Engrs; Am Phys Soc; Newcomen Soc; Am Defense Preparedness Asn. *Res:* Warhead technology and explosive reactions; resistance welding processes; metal powder compaction. *Mailing Add:* PO Box 1383 San Luis Obispo CA 93406

NOOLANDI, JAAN, b Estonia, Aug 23, 42; Can citizen; m 72; c 2. THEORETICAL SOLID STATE PHYSICS, POLYMER PHYSICS. *Educ:* Univ Toronto, BSc, 65, PhD(physics), 70. *Prof Exp:* Nat Res Coun Can fel, Univ Oxford, 70-71 & Univ Calif, San Diego, 71-72; mem tech staff solid state physics, Bell Labs, NJ, 72-74; MEM SCI STAFF SOLID STATE PHYSICS, XEROX RES CENTRE CAN LTD, 74- *Concurrent Pos:* Vis asst prof, Univ Toronto, 75-76; vis, Ctr Rech Macromolecules, Strasbourg, France, 81. *Mem:* Am Phys Soc; Can Asn Physicists. *Res:* Electrical conduction in amorphous materials; physics and chemistry of liquid-solid interfaces; structural and electronic properties of high temperature superconductors; exciton-phonon interaction in molecular solids; multicomponent polymer systems; polymer dynamics. *Mailing Add:* Xerox Res Centre of Can Ltd 2480 Dunwin Dr Mississauga ON L5L 1J9 Can

NOONAN, CHARLES D, b San Francisco, Calif, July 16, 28; m; c 5. RADIOLOGY. *Educ:* Univ Calif, Berkeley, AB, 50; Univ Calif, San Francisco, MD, 53. *Prof Exp:* Resident, Cincinnati Gen Hosp, 56-59; from instr to assoc prof, 59-73, PROF RADIOL, SCH MED, UNIV CALIF, SAN FRANCISCO, 73- *Mailing Add:* Dept of Radiol Univ of Calif Hosp San Francisco CA 94143

NOONAN, JACQUELINE ANNE, b Burlington, Vt, Oct 28, 28. PEDIATRIC CARDIOLOGY. *Educ:* Albertus Magnus Col, BA, 50; Univ Vt, MD, 54. *Prof Exp:* Asst prof pediat, Col Med & pediat cardiologist, Hosp, Univ Iowa, 59-61; assoc prof, 61-69, PROF PEDIAT, COL MED, UNIV KY, 69-, CHMN DEPT, 74-, PEDIAT CARDIOLOGIST, UNIV HOSP, 61- *Mem:* Am Heart Asn; Am Pediat Soc; Am Acad Pediat; AMA; Am Col Cardiol. *Mailing Add:* Dept of Pediat Univ of Ky Col of Med Lexington KY 40506

NOONAN, JAMES WARING, b Fall River, Mass, Dec 21, 44. MANAGEMENT CONSULTING. *Educ:* Providence Col, AB, 66; Univ Md, College Park, MA, 69, PhD(math), 71. *Prof Exp:* Nat Res Coun res assoc, US Naval Res Lab, 70-71; asst prof math, Col of the Holy Cross, 71-78, assoc prof, 78-81, asst dean, 78-81; MGT CONSULT, DATA GEN CORP, 80- *Mem:* Am Math Soc; Math Asn Am; Sigma Xi. *Res:* Operations research; geometric function theory. *Mailing Add:* Data Gen Corp 4400 Computer Dr Westboro MA 01581

NOONAN, JOHN ROBERT, b Springfield, Mo, Sept 26, 46; m 74. PHYSICS, ELECTRICAL ENGINEERING. *Educ:* Wash Univ, BS, 68, MS, 70; Univ Ill, Urbana, PhD(elec eng), 74. *Prof Exp:* Engr comput design, Comput Sci Lab, Wash Univ, 68; NSF trainee, Univ Ill, 69-72, res asst semiconductor physics, 70-74; RES STAFF MEM SURFACE PHYSICS, SOLID STATE DIV, OAK RIDGE NAT LAB, 74- *Mem:* Sigma Xi; Inst Elec & Electronics Engrs; Am Vacuum Soc; AAAS. *Res:* Surface physics, including low energy electron diffraction and auger electron spectrscopy, optical emission from semiconductors and ultra high vacuum technology. *Mailing Add:* Solid State Div PO Box X Oak Ridge TN 37830

NOONAN, KENNETH DANIEL, b New York, NY, Jan 27, 48; m 72. BIOCHEMISTRY, CELL BIOLOGY. *Educ:* St Joseph's Col, Pa, BS, 69; Princeton Univ, PhD(biol), 72. *Prof Exp:* Jane Coffin Childs fel, Biocenter, Basel, Switz, 72-73; asst prof biochem, J Hillis Miller Health Ctr, Univ Fla, 78-81, 73-78, assoc prof, 78-81; PROF, UNIV MD, BALTIMORE CAMPUS, 81- *Concurrent Pos:* Dir mkt & prod develop, Bethesda Res Labs, Inc, 81- *Mem:* AAAS; Am Soc Cell Biol. *Res:* Role of the plasma membrane in normal and transformed cell growth; mechanisms of nuclear envelope break down and resynthesis. *Mailing Add:* 6717 Gov Circle Bethesda Res Labs Inc Gaithersburg MD 20760

NOONAN, SHARON MARIELLA, electron microscopy, cell physiology, deceased

NOONAN, THOMAS WYATT, b Glendale, Calif, July 16, 33; m 66; c 3. ASTRONOMY, PHYSICS. *Educ:* Calif Inst Technol, BS, 55, PhD(physics), 61. *Prof Exp:* Physicist, Smithsonian Astrophys Observ, 61-62; vis asst prof physics, Univ NC, Chapel Hill, 62-65, asst prof, 65-68; assoc prof, 68-71, PROF PHYSICS, STATE UNIV NY COL BROCKPORT, 71- *Concurrent Pos:* State Univ NY Res Found fel, Hale Observ, 70. *Mem:* Am Astron Soc; Royal Astron Soc. *Res:* Clusters of galaxies; cosmology. *Mailing Add:* Dept of Physics State Univ of NY Col Brockport NY 14420

NOOR, AHMED KHAIRY, b Cairo, Egypt, Aug 11, 38; US citizen; m 66; c 1. STRUCTURAL MECHANICS & ENGINEERING. *Educ:* Cairo Univ, BS, 58; Univ Ill, Urbana-Champaign, MS, 61, PhD(struct mech), 63. *Prof Exp:* Asst struct mech, Cairo Univ, 58-59; asst prof aeronaut, Stanford Univ, 63-64; sr lectr struct mech, Cairo Univ, 64-67; vis sr lectr, Baghdad Univ, 67-68; sr lectr, Univ New South Wales, 68-71; sr res assoc, 71-72, PROF ENG & APPL SCI, NASA LANGLEY RES CTR, GEORGE WASHINGTON UNIV, 72- *Concurrent Pos:* Mem comt large space systs, Nat Acad Sci, 78-, comput mech, 81- *Mem:* Am Inst Aeronaut & Astronaut; Am Soc Mech Engrs; Am Soc Civil Engrs; Am Acad Mech. *Res:* Solution strategies for structural problems on new computing systems; inproved numerical techniques for nonlinear and dynamic problems; fibrous composite structures; shell structures. *Mailing Add:* Mail Stop 246 NASA Langley Res Ctr Hampton VA 23665

NOORDERGRAAF, ABRAHAM, b Utrecht, Neth, Aug 7, 29; m 56; c 4. BIOPHYSICS, BIOENGINEERING. *Educ:* Univ Utrecht, BSc, 53, MSc, 55, PhD(biophysics), 56. *Hon Degrees:* MA, Univ Pa, 71. *Prof Exp:* Asst exp physics, Univ Utrecht, 52-53, res asst med physics, 53-55, res fel med physics, 56-58, sr res fel, 59-65; assoc prof elec eng, 64-70, chmn dept, 73-76, chmn, Grad Group Bioeng, 73-76, PROF VET MED, UNIV PA, 76-, PROF BIOMED ENG, 70- *Concurrent Pos:* Vis fel ther res, Univ Pa, 57-58, NIH res grants, 66, 68, 70, 72, 74, 76, 78 & 81, Surgeon Gen, 74; mem spec study sect, NIH, 65-68; vis prof appl physics, Delft Univ Technol, 70-71; vis prof cardiol, Erasmus Univ Med Sch, Rotterdam, 70-71; mem coun circulation, Am Heart Asn, 72-; vis prof, Univ Miami, 70-79; consult, NATO Sci Affairs Div, 73- *Mem:* Fel Inst Elec & Electronics Engrs; fel NY Acad Sci; fel AAAS; fel Explorers Club; fel Am Col Cardiol. *Res:* Mammalian cardiovascular system analysis; operation of the heart as a pump; dynamics of the microcirculation. *Mailing Add:* 620 Haydock Ln Haverford PA 19041

NOPANITAYA, WAYKIN, b Krabi, Thailand, Oct 14, 42; m 66; c 2. PATHOLOGY, ELECTRON MICROSCOPY. *Educ:* Mahidol Univ, dipl med technol, 63; Univ NC, Chapel Hill, BA, 69, PhD(path), 71. *Prof Exp:* Med technologist, Vajira Hosp, Thailand, 63; chief path & histotechnologist, US Army-SEATO Med Res Lab, Thailand, 63-67; med technologist, Univ NC, Chapel Hill, 67-69, instr electron micros, 70; consult exp path, US Army-SEATO Med Res Lab, 72; instr path, 72-74, ASST PROF PATH, MED SCH, UNIV NC, CHAPEL HILL, 74-, DIR ELECTRON MICROS & HISTOPATH TRAINING PROGS, 72-, DIR, CENT ELECTRON MICROSCOPY LABS, 77- *Concurrent Pos:* Nat Inst Gen Med Sci grant, Univ NC, Chapel Hill & Ministry Health, Thailand, 72; consult, Asn Med Technologists Thailand, 72- *Mem:* Am Soc Clin Path; Electron Micros Soc Am; Nat Soc Histotechnol; Sigma Xi; Can Micros Soc. *Res:* Gastroenterology; ultrastructural research in cellular pathology. *Mailing Add:* Dept of Path Univ of NC Sch of Med Chapel Hill NC 27514

NORA, AUDREY HART, b Picayune, Miss, Dec 5, 36; m 68; c 2. PEDIATRICS. *Educ:* Univ Miss, BS, 58, MD, 61; Am Bd Pediat, cert, 68, cert hemat & oncol, 74; Univ Calif, MPH, 78. *Prof Exp:* Fel pediat hemat & oncol, Baylor Col Med, 64-66, instr pediat, 66-70, asst prof, 70-71; asst clin prof, 78-77, ASSOC CLIN PROF PEDIAT, MED CTR, UNIV COLO, DENVER, 78-; DIR GENETICS & BIRTH DEFECTS, DENVER CHILDREN'S HOSP, 71- *Concurrent Pos:* Assoc hematologist, Tex Children's Hosp, 66-71; consult, NIH Adv Comt Arteriosclerosis & Hypertension, 75-77 & consult maternal & child health, Region VIII, Dept Health & Human Serv, 80- *Mem:* Am Fedn Clin Res; Am Soc Human Genetics; Genetics Soc Am; Teratology Soc. *Res:* Arteriosclerosis in the pediatric age group; teratology of medications, congenital malformations relating to medications taken during first trimester. *Mailing Add:* DHDS RPC MCH 1961 Stout St Denver CO 80292

NORA, JAMES JACKSON, b Chicago, Ill, June 26, 28; m 66; c 5. CARDIOLOGY, GENETICS. *Educ:* Harvard Univ, AB, 50; Yale Univ, MD, 54; Am Bd Pediat, dipl & cert Univ Calif, Berkeley, MPH, 78; Am Bd Pediat & Cardiol, dipl & cert. *Prof Exp:* Am Heart Asn res fel cardiol, Univ Wis, 62-64, from instr to asst prof pediat, 62-65; from asst prof to assoc prof, Baylor Univ, 65-71, head div human genetics & dir birth defects ctr, 67-71; assoc prof pediat, 71-74, dir pediat cardiol, 71-78, PROF PEDIAT & DIR PREVENTIVE CARDIOL, UNIV COLO MED CTR, DENVER, 78-, PROF GENETICS & PREV MED, 79-, DIR GENETICS, ROSE MED CTR, 80- *Concurrent Pos:* NIH spec fel genetics, McGill Univ, 64-65; assoc dir cardiol, Tex Children's Hosp, 65-71, chief genetics serv, 67-71. *Mem:* Am Soc Human Genetics; fel Am Acad Pediat; Am Pediat Soc; Soc Pediat Res; Teratology Soc. *Res:* Etiology of cardiovascular diseases. *Mailing Add:* Dept Pediat Univ Colo Med Ctr Denver CO 80220

NORA, PAUL FRANCIS, b Chicago, Ill, Aug 14, 29; m 56; c 5. SURGERY. *Educ:* Loyola Univ, MD, 52; Northwestern Univ, MS, 64, PhD(surg), 68. *Prof Exp:* From asst prof to assoc prof, 69-78, PROF CLIN SURG, SCH MED, NORTHWESTERN UNIV, 78- CHMN DEPT SURG, COLUMBUS-CUNEO-CABRINI MED CTR, 64- *Concurrent Pos:* Attend surgeon, Vet Admin Res Hosp, 62-; mem exec comt, Dept Surg, Med Sch, Northwestern Univ; mem, Adv Panel Nat Health Ins, Subcomt Health, Comt Ways & Means. *Mem:* Soc Surg Alimentary Tract (treas); fel Am Col Surgeons; Illum Eng Soc. *Res:* Value of operative choledochoscopy; abdominal drains; operating room lighting. *Mailing Add:* Dept Surg Columbus-Cuneo-Cabrini Med 2520 N Lakeview Ave Chicago IL 60614

NORBECK, EDWIN, JR, b Seattle, Wash, June 10, 30; m 56; c 4. NUCLEAR PHYSICS. *Educ:* Reed Col, BA, 52; Univ Chicago, MS & PhD(physics), 56. *Prof Exp:* Res assoc physics, Univ Chicago, 56-57 & Univ Minn, 57-60; from asst prof to assoc prof, 60-67, PROF PHYSICS, UNIV IOWA, 67- *Mem:* Fel Am Phys Soc. *Res:* Low energy nuclear physics; nuclear reactions with lithium and beryllium beams; use of ion beams for analysis of semiconductors; measurement of cross sections for nuclear fusion energy. *Mailing Add:* Dept of Physics & Astron Univ of Iowa Iowa City IA 52242

NORBERG, RICHARD EDWIN, b Newark, NJ, Dec 28, 22; m 47, 78; c 3. PHYSICS. *Educ:* DePauw Univ, BA, 43; Univ Ill, MA, 47, PhD(physics), 51. *Prof Exp:* Res assoc physics & control systs lab, Univ Ill, 51-53, asst prof, 53-54; vis lectr physics, 54-56, assoc - prof, 56-58, PROF PHYSICS, WASH UNIV, 58-, CHMN DEPT, 62- *Concurrent Pos:* Sloan fel, 55-59. *Mem:* Fel Am Phys Soc. *Res:* Nuclear and electron spin resonance; solid state and low temperature physics. *Mailing Add:* Dept of Physics Wash Univ St Louis MO 63130

NORBURY, KENNETH CARL, b Philadelphia, Pa, Mar 3, 49; m 68; c 3. IMMUNOLOGY, TOXICOLOGY. *Educ:* Mich State Univ, BS, 71; Univ Pa, PhD(path), 75. *Prof Exp:* Pub Health Serv trainee path, Sch Med, Univ Pa, 71-75; res asst tumor immunol, Frederick Cancer Res Ctr, Nat Cancer Inst, 75-76; sr res toxicologist, 77-79, RES FEL, MERCK INST THERAPEUT RES, DEPT SAFETY ASSESSMENT, MERCK SHARP & DOHME RES LABS, WEST POINT, 79- *Concurrent Pos:* Instr, Sch Dent Med, Univ Pa, 74-75 & Hood Col, 76- *Mem:* Am Soc Microbiol. *Res:* Immunotoxicology; relationship of immune system to nervous and endocrine systems; preclinical models for evaluating immune competence. *Mailing Add:* 2065 Stewart Dr Hatfield PA 19440

NORBY, RODNEY DALE, b Carrington, NDak, Jan 4, 45; m 68; c 1. GEOLOGY. *Educ:* Univ NDak, BS, 67; Ariz State Univ, MS, 71; Univ Ill, PhD(geol), 76. *Prof Exp:* Res asst geol, 72-76, asst geologist, 76-81, ASSOC GEOLOGIST, ILL STATE GEOL SURV, 81- *Concurrent Pos:* Fulbright fel, Australia, 67-68. *Mem:* Geol Soc Am; Soc Econ Paleont & Mineral; Paleont Soc. *Res:* Carboniferous stratigraphy; conodont biostratigraphy and taxonomy; coastal sedimentation and processes; micropaleontology. *Mailing Add:* Ill State Geol Surv 615 E Peabody Dr Champaign IL 61820

NORBY, SHONG-WAN CHAN, b Kuala Lumpur, Malaysia; US citizen; m 68; c 1. CELLULAR IMMUNOLOGY, ELECTRON MICROSCOPY. *Educ:* Univ Malaya, BSc, 67; Univ Ill, Urbana, MS, 73, PhD(zool), 79. *Prof Exp:* Res assoc cancer res, Univ Calif, San Diego, 79-80; RES ASSOC PLANT PHYSIOL, UNIV ILL, URBANA, 80- *Mem:* Sigma Xi. *Res:* In vitro and in vivo immune response to Plasmodium berghei; effects of various factors in long term cultures of human peripheral blood lymphocytes; ultrastructure and enzyme studies in soybeans. *Mailing Add:* Agron Dept Univ Ill 1102 S Goodwin Urbana IL 61801

NORCIA, LEONARD NICHOLAS, b Mountain Iron, Minn, Jan 1, 16; m 50; c 1. BIOCHEMISTRY, PHYSIOLOGY. *Educ:* Univ Minn, BChem, 46, PhD(physiol chem), 52. *Prof Exp:* Res fel biochem, Hormel Inst, Univ Minn, 52-55; from asst prof to assoc prof res biochem, Sch Med, Univ Okla, 56-60; asst prof, 60-69, assoc prof, 69-79, EMER ASSOC PROF BIOCHEM, SCH MED, TEMPLE UNIV, 79- *Concurrent Pos:* Biochemist, Okla Med Res Found, 55-60; mem coun arteriosclerosis, Am Heart Asn. *Mem:* Am Chem Soc; Am Oil Chemists Soc. *Res:* Metabolism of lipids. *Mailing Add:* 766 Castlewood Rd Glenside PA 19038

NORCROSS, BRUCE EDWARD, b Newport, Vt, Mar 14, 35; m 56; c 1. PHYSICAL ORGANIC CHEMISTRY. *Educ:* Univ Vt, BA, 56, MS, 57; Ohio State Univ, PhD(chem), 60. *Prof Exp:* Res assoc chem, Harvard Univ, 60-62; asst prof, 62-66, ASSOC PROF, STATE UNIV NY BINGHAMTON, 66- *Concurrent Pos:* Assoc dean, Harpur Col, 66-67, asst vpres, Acad Affairs, 78-80. *Mem:* AAAS; Am Chem Soc. *Res:* Organic reaction mechanisms and synthetic organic chemistry. *Mailing Add:* Dept Chem State Univ NY Binghamton NY 13901

NORCROSS, DAVID WARREN, b Cincinnati, Ohio, July 18, 41; m 67. ATOMIC PHYSICS. *Educ:* Harvard Col, AB, 63; Univ Ill, MS, 65; Univ Col, Univ London, PhD(physics), 70. *Prof Exp:* Res physicist, Sperry Rand Res Ctr, 65-67; res assoc physics, Univ Colo, 70-74; PHYSICIST, QUANTUM PHYSICS DIV, NAT BUR STANDARDS, 74- *Concurrent Pos:* Lectr, Dept Physics, Univ Colo, 74- *Mem:* Fel Am Phys Soc; Fedn Am Scientists. *Res:* Theory of electron-atom and electron-molecule interactions, atomic and molecular structure and radiative properties. *Mailing Add:* Joint Inst for Lab Astrophys Univ of Colo Boulder CO 80309

NORCROSS, MARVIN AUGUSTUS, b Tansboro, NJ, Feb 8, 31; m 56; c 2. RESEARCH ADMINISTRATION, VETERINARY PATHOLOGY. *Educ:* Univ Pa, VMD, 59, PhD(path), 66. *Prof Exp:* Gen vet pract, Md, 59-60; vet, Animal Husb Res Div, Agr Res Serv, USDA, 60-62; res fel path, USPHS training grant cancer res, Sch Vet Med, Univ Pa, 62-66; asst vet pathologist, 66-69, assoc dir clin res, 69-72, sr dir animal sci res, Merck, Sharp & Dohme Res Lab, Rahway, 72-75; dir, Div Vet Med Res, Beltsville, 75-78, ASSOC DIR RES, BUR VET MED, FOOD & DRUG ADMIN, ROCKVILLE, 78- *Concurrent Pos:* Mem animal health sci res adv bd, USDA, 78-; adj prof, Va-Md Regional Col Vet Med, Blacksburg, Va, 80- *Mem:* AAAS; Am Asn Avian Path; Am Vet Med Asn; NY Acad Sci; Soc Toxicol Path. *Res:* Chemical and viral carcinogenesis; animal health drugs and biologic. *Mailing Add:* 10100 Lakewood Dr Rockville MD 20850

NORCROSS, NEIL LINWOOD, b Derry, NH, July 18, 28; m 53; c 2. IMMUNOLOGY. *Educ:* Univ Miami, AB, 50; Univ Mass, MS, 55, PhD(bact), 58. *Prof Exp:* Immunologist, Plum Island Animal & Dis Lab, Agr Res Serv, USDA, 57-60; from asst prof to assoc prof immunochem, 60-69, PROF IMMUNOCHEM, NY STATE UNIV COL VET MED, CORNELL UNIV, 69-, SECY OF COL, 73- *Concurrent Pos:* Mem, Nat Mastitis Coun. *Mem:* Am Acad Microbiol; Am Soc Microbiol. *Res:* Immunology of foot and mouth disease virus; production of foot and mouth vaccines; mastitis; streptococci of bovine origin; immunology of equine infectious anemia; autoimmune experimental myasthenia gravis. *Mailing Add:* NY State Col Vet Med Cornell Univ Ithaca NY 14853

NORD, GORDON LUDWIG, JR, b Cincinnati, Ohio, Apr 3, 42; div; c 1. GEOLOGY. *Educ:* Univ Wis, BS, 65; Univ Idaho, MS, 67; Univ Calif, Berkeley, PhD(geol), 73. *Prof Exp:* Res assoc geol, Case Western Reserve Univ, 71-74; GEOLOGIST, US GEOL SURV, 74- *Mem:* Geol Soc Am; Am Mineral Soc; Am Geophys Union; AAAS. *Res:* The characterization and mechanisms of precipitation reactions, symmetry transitions and defect structures in natural and synthetic minerals and mineral aggregates as a function of geological history. *Mailing Add:* 959 Nat Ctr US Geol Surv Reston VA 22092

NORD, JOHN C, b Joliet, Ill, Mar 19, 38; m 68; c 3. FOREST ENTOMOLOGY. *Educ:* Univ Mich, BS, 60, MF, 62, PhD(forestry), 68. *Prof Exp:* PRIN RES ENTOMOLOGIST, SOUTHEAST FOREST EXP STA, US FOREST SERV, 64- *Mem:* Soc Am Foresters; Entom Soc Am. *Res:* Biology and ecology of forest insects; chemical control. *Mailing Add:* 345 Milledge Heights Athens GA 30606

NORDAN, HAROLD CECIL, b Vancouver, BC, Jan 21, 25; m 52; c 2. VERTEBRATE BIOLOGY. *Educ:* Univ BC, BA, 48, BSA, 50, MSA, 54; Ore State Univ, PhD(microbiol, biochem), 59. *Prof Exp:* Fel zool, 59-61, res assoc & sessional lectr, 62-65, asst prof, 65-69, ASSOC PROF ZOOL, UNIV BC, 69- *Res:* Vertebrate physiology, especially bioenergetics and growth of wild species of ungulates. *Mailing Add:* Dept Zool Univ BC Vancouver BC B6T 1W5 Can

NORDBY, GENE M, b Anoka, Minn, May 7, 26; m 49; c 3. CIVIL ENGINEERING. *Educ:* Ore State Univ, BS, 48; Univ Minn, MS, 49, PhD, 55. *Prof Exp:* Asst, St Anthony Falls Hydraul Res Lab, Minn, 48, asst civil eng, 49-50; struct designer, Pfieffer & Shultz, 50; asst prof civil eng, Univ Colo, 50-56; prog dir eng sci, NSF, 56-58; prof civil eng, head dept & dir, Transp & Traffic Inst, Univ Ariz, 59-62; prof aerospace, mech & civil eng & dean, Col Eng, Univ Okla, 62-70, vpres finance & admin, 70-77, prof civil, mech & aerospace eng, 76-77; prof civil eng & vpres bus & finance, Ga Inst Technol, 77-80; PROF CIVIL ENG & CHANCELLOR, UNIV COLO, DENVER, 80- *Concurrent Pos:* Assoc prof & res engr joint hwy res proj, Purdue Univ, 56-57; lectr, George Washington Univ, 56-58; consult ed, Macmillan Co, 62-70; mem eng educ & accreditation comt & chmn coord comt, Engrs Coun Prof Develop, 65-71, treas, Accreditation Bd Eng & Technol, 80-; pres, Tetracon Assocs, Inc, 69-; consult, NCent Asn Schs & Cols, 76-77 & 81-; mem bd dirs, Higher Educ & the Handicapped, Am Coun Educ, 80- *Mem:* Fel Am Soc Civil Engrs; Am Soc Eng Educ; Nat Soc Prof Engrs. *Res:* Structural adhesives; composite materials; reinforced concrete; structural mechanics; higher education administration; accrediation of higher education programs; research administration and finance; facilities planning. *Mailing Add:* Off Chancellor Univ Colo 1100 Fourteenth St Denver CO 80202

NORDBY, GORDON LEE, b Moscow, Idaho, Oct 3, 29; m 53; c 4. BIOCHEMISTRY, BIOMETRY. *Educ:* Stanford Univ, BS, 51, MS, 54, PhD(chem philos), 58. *Prof Exp:* Instr biochem, Stanford Univ, 58-59; res assoc, Harvard Med Sch, 60-63; asst prof biol chem & assoc res biophysicist, 63-68, ASSOC PROF BIOL CHEM, 68- *Concurrent Pos:* Am Cancer Soc res fel, 59-61. *Mem:* AAAS; Am Chem Soc; Biophys Soc; Biomet Soc. *Res:* Biophysics; digital computers; experimental design. *Mailing Add:* Dept of Biol Chem M5434 Med Sci Bldg Univ of Mich Ann Arbor MI 48109

NORDBY, HAROLD EDWIN, b New England, NDak, Nov 3, 31; m 58; c 2. ORGANIC CHEMISTRY, BIOCHEMISTRY. *Educ:* Concordia Col, Moorhead, Minn, BA, 53; Univ Ariz, MS, 59, PhD(biochem), 63. *Prof Exp:* Jr scientist lipids, Hormel Inst, Univ Minn, 53-56; res assoc dept agr biochem, Univ Ariz, 59-63; RES CHEMIST CITRUS, FRUIT & VEG LAB, AGR RES SERV, USDA, 63- *Mem:* Am Oil Chem Soc. *Res:* Isolation and characterization of bitter products in grapefruit; synthesis and isolation of cycloporpenes; lipids and natural products. *Mailing Add:* Agr Res Serv USDA 600 Ave S NW Winter Haven FL 33880

NORDELL, WILLIAM JAMES, b Chicago, Ill, June 18, 30; m 55; c 2. STRUCTURAL ENGINEERING, ENGINEERING MECHANICS. *Educ:* Univ Ill, BS, 58, MS, 59, PhD(civil eng), 63. *Prof Exp:* Struct res engr, 63-69, DIR OCEAN STRUCTURES DIV, US NAVAL CIVIL ENG LAB, 69- *Mem:* Sigma Xi; Am Soc Civil Engrs. *Res:* Behavior of materials; structural dynamics; reinforced concrete; limit design; structural mechanics; ocean structures. *Mailing Add:* 373 Maryville Ave Ventura CA 93003

NORDEN, ALLAN JAMES, b Perkins, Mich, Nov 27, 24; m 46; c 6. PLANT BREEDING, GENETICS. *Educ:* Mich State Univ, BS, 49, MS, 50; Iowa State Univ, PhD(plant breeding), 58. *Prof Exp:* Asst farm crops, Mich State Univ, 49-50, agr exten agent, 50-52, res instr crops & soils, 52-55; asst farm crops, Iowa State Univ, 55-58; from asst prof to assoc prof agron, PROF AGRON, UNIV FLA, 71- *Honors & Awards:* Golden Peanut Res Award,

Nat Peanut Coun, 73. *Mem:* Fel Am Soc Agron; AAAS; Sigma Xi; Am Genetics Asn; Am Peanut Res & Educ Soc (pres, 78-79). *Res:* Plant breeding, genetics and physiological studies with peanuts. *Mailing Add:* Dept of Agron Univ of Fla Gainesville FL 32611

NORDEN, CARROLL RAYMOND, b Escanaba, Mich, May 20, 23; m 51; c 4. ZOOLOGY. *Educ:* Northern Mich Univ, AB, 48; Univ Mich, MS, 51, PhD(zool), 58. *Prof Exp:* Asst prof biol, Univ Southwestern La, 57-63; from asst prof to assoc prof zool, 63-71, chmn dept, 69-74 & 76-78, PROF ZOOL, UNIV WIS-MILWAUKEE, 71- *Concurrent Pos:* Fishery biologist, State Dept Conserv, Mich, 53, 54 & 56; fishery biologist, US Fish & Wildlife Serv, 58 & 59. *Mem:* Am Fisheries Soc; Am Soc Ichthyologists & Herpetologists. *Res:* Ichthyology; taxonomy of fishes; fishery biology. *Mailing Add:* Dept of Zool Univ of Wis Milwaukee WI 53201

NORDEN, JEANETTE JEAN, b Ovid, Colo, Apr 15, 48. NEUROBIOLOGY. *Educ:* Univ Calif, Los Angeles, BA, 70; Vanderbilt Univ, PhD(psychol), 75. *Prof Exp:* NIH fel neuroanat, Duke Univ, 75-77; RES ASSOC, SCH MED, VANDERBILT UNIV, 77- *Concurrent Pos:* Vis res assoc histochem, Dent Res Ctr, Univ NC, Chapel Hill, 76. *Mem:* Soc Neurosci; Asn Res Vision & Ophthal. *Res:* Quantitative electron microscopy of synaptic connections of the retino-tectal projection in toads and goldfish; freeze fracture of developing retino-tectal synapses. *Mailing Add:* Dept of Anat Vanderbilt Univ Nashville TN 37232

NORDENG, STEPHAN C, b Chippewa Falls, Wis, May 24, 23; m 53; c 6. STRATIGRAPHY. *Educ:* Univ Wis, BS, 49, MS, 51, PhD(geol), 54. *Prof Exp:* Field geologist, Tex Petrol Co, 54-56; assoc prof geol, 57-71, PROF GEOL, MICH TECHNOL UNIV, 71- *Concurrent Pos:* Consult, Copper Range Co, Calumet & Hecla. *Mem:* Geol Soc Am; Paleont Soc. *Res:* Applications of statistics and computers in geology. *Mailing Add:* Dept of Geol Mich Technol Univ Houghton MI 49931

NORDGREN, RONALD PAUL, applied mechanics, petroleum engineering, see previous edition

NORDHEIM, LOTHAR WOLFGANG, b Munich, Ger, Nov 7, 99; nat US; wid; c 1. NUCLEAR SCIENCE. *Educ:* Univ Gottingen, PhD(physics), 23. *Hon Degrees:* DSc, Karlsruhe Tech Univ, 51; DSc, Purdue Univ, 62. *Prof Exp:* Rockefeller res fel, 27-28; lectr, Univ Gottingen, 28-33; res fel, Univ Paris, 34 & Univ Holland, 35; vis prof physics, Purdue Univ, 35-37; prof, Duke Univ, 37-56; physicist, Gen Atomic Div, Gen Dynamics Corp, 56-59, chmn theoret physics dept & sr res adv, 60-68; CONSULT, GEN ATOMIC CO, 68- *Concurrent Pos:* Vis prof, Ohio State Univ, 30, Moscow State Univ, 32 & Univ Heidelberg, 49; sect chief, Clinton Labs, Oak Ridge, Tenn, 43-45, dir physics div, 45-47; consult, Los Alamos Sci Lab, 50-52; mem adv comt, Reactor Physics, Atomic Energy Comn, 72. *Honors & Awards:* Armed Forces Award of Merit, 47. *Mem:* Fel AAAS; fel Am Phys Soc; fel Am Nuclear Soc; Fedn Am Scientists. *Res:* Quantum theory of matter; nuclear physics; reactor and neutron physics. *Mailing Add:* 2130 Vallecitos Apt 247 La Jolla CA 92037

NORDIN, ALBERT ANDREW, b McKeesport, Pa, Sept 7, 34; m 56; c 3. IMMUNOLOGY. *Educ:* Univ Pittsburgh, BS, 56, MS, 59, PhD(microbiol), 62. *Prof Exp:* From instr to asst prof, Dept Microbiol, Univ Pittsburgh, 63-66; from asst to assoc prof microbiol, Univ Notre Dame, 66-72; RES CHEMIST, NAT INST AGING, NIH, 72- *Concurrent Pos:* Vis scientist, Swiss Inst Exp Cancer Res, 69-70; mem adv panel regulatory biol prog, NSF, 73-75; vis prof, Basel Inst Immunol, 75 & 80-81. *Mem:* Am Asn Immunol. *Res:* Cellular aspects of antibody formation of particular interest have been the role of antigen and the description of the competent cell. *Mailing Add:* Geront Res Ctr Baltimore City Hosps Baltimore MD 21224

NORDIN, GERALD LEROY, b Rockford, Ill, Aug 14, 44; m 64; c 2. INSECT PATHOLOGY. *Educ:* Univ Ill, Urbana, BS, 62, MS, 68, PhD(entom), 71. *Prof Exp:* Tech asst entom, Ill Natural Hist Surv, 64-66, res asst, 66-71; asst prof, 71-77, PROF ENTOM, UNIV KY, 77- *Mem:* Entom Soc Am; Soc Invert Path; Sigma Xi. *Res:* Forest entomology and insect pathology; microbial control of forest insects. *Mailing Add:* S-225 Agr Sci Ctr-North Dept of Entom Univ of Ky Lexington KY 40546

NORDIN, IVAN CONRAD, b Lindsborg, Kans, May 25, 32; div; c 4. ORGANIC CHEMISTRY. *Educ:* Bethany Col, BS, 54; Univ Kans, PhD(org chem), 60. *Prof Exp:* From assoc res chemist to sr res chemist, 60-71, res scientist org chem, Parke, Davis & Co, 71-77, sect dir, chem cent nervous syst drugs, Pharm Res Div, 77-80, MGR, CHEM DEVELOP, WARNER LAMBERT/PARKE DAVIS, 80- *Concurrent Pos:* Instr, Schoolcraft Col, 71- *Mem:* Am Chem Soc. *Res:* Claisen Rearr; heterocyclic chemistry; organic chemistry of nitrogen; medicinal chemistry of central nervous system. *Mailing Add:* 2800 Plymouth Rd Holland MI 48823

NORDIN, JOHN HOFFMAN, b Chicago, Ill, Oct 11, 34; m 56; c 3. BIOCHEMISTRY. *Educ:* Univ Ill, BS, 56; Mich State Univ, PhD(biochem), 61. *Prof Exp:* NIH res fel biochem, Univ Minn, 62-65; asst prof, 65-71, assoc prof, 71-77, PROF BIOCHEM, UNIV MASS, 77- *Concurrent Pos:* NIH fel, Inst Biochem, Univ Lausanne, 71-72. *Mem:* AAAS; Soc Complex Carbohydrates; Am Chem Soc; Am Soc Biol Chem. *Res:* Carbohydrate metabolism; structure of polysaccharides and glycoproteins; chemistry of carbohydrates of biological interest; biochemistry of insect hibernation; and reproduction. *Mailing Add:* Dept of Biochem Univ of Mass Amherst MA 01002

NORDIN, PAUL, b Kansas City, Mo, Feb 12, 29; div; c 2. APPLIED PHYSICS. *Educ:* Univ Calif, Berkeley, AB, 56, MA, 57, PhD(physics), 61. *Prof Exp:* Telegrapher-clerk, Southern Pac RR, 48-52; eng draftsman, Northrop Aircraft, Inc, 52-53, radio-radar mechanic, 53; asst, Univ Calif, Berkeley, 56-61; sr scientist, Aeronutronic Div, Ford Motor Co, 61-63; mem tech staff, Aerospace Corp, 63-69; sect head, Missile Systs & Technol Dept, TRW Systs Group, 69-78, mem tech staff, Vulnerability & Hardness Lab, 78-81, MEM TECH STAFF, SYSTS ENG LAB, TRW SYSTS & ENERGY, DEFENSE & SPACE SYSTS GROUP, REDONDO BEACH, 81- *Mem:* AAAS; Am Phys Soc; Marine Technol Soc; Sigma Xi. *Res:* Nuclear weapons effects; reentry vehicles; laser weapon effects; marine technology; communication satellites. *Mailing Add:* 12 Laurel Sq Las Cruces NM 88005

NORDIN, PHILIP, b Can, Mar 21, 22; nat US; m 47; c 2. BIOCHEMISTRY. *Educ:* Univ Sask, BSA, 49, MSc, 50; Iowa State Univ, PhD, 53. *Prof Exp:* Lectr biochem, Univ Toronto, 53-54; from asst prof to assoc prof, 54-69, PROF BIOCHEM & BIOCHEMIST, AGR EXP STA, KANS STATE UNIV, 69- *Mem:* Am Chem Soc; Am Soc Biol Chem. *Res:* Carbohydrate biosynthesis. *Mailing Add:* Dept of Biochem Kans State Univ Manhattan KS 66506

NORDIN, VIDAR JOHN, b Ratansbyn, Sweden, June 28, 24; nat Can; m 47; c 2. FOREST PATHOLOGY. *Educ:* Univ BC, BA, 46, BScF, 47; Univ Toronto, PhD(forest path), 51. *Prof Exp:* Asst forest path, Forest Path Lab, Can Dept Forestry, Toronto, 47-49, officer in chg, Fredericton, NB, 49-51, Calgary, Alta, 52-57, assoc dir forest biol, 58-64, prog coordr, 65-71; PROF FOREST BIOL & DEAN FAC FORESTRY, UNIV TORONTO, 71- *Concurrent Pos:* Chmn bd, Algonquin Forestry Authority Corp, 74-; mem, Prov Parks Adv Coun, 75-77. *Mem:* NAm Forestry Comn; Int Poplar Comn; Int Union Forest Res Orgns; Soc Am Foresters; Can Inst Forestry (vpres, 65-66, pres, 67). *Res:* forestry education; research administration. *Mailing Add:* Fac Forestry Univ of Toronto Toronto ON M5S 2R8 Can

NORDINE, PAUL CLEMENS, b Grayling, Mich, Jan 7, 40; m 68; c 1. HETEROGENEOUS KINETICS, HIGH TEMPERATURE SCIENCE. *Educ:* Mich State Univ, BS, 62; Univ Kans, PhD(chem), 70. *Prof Exp:* Res assoc, 71-72, instr, 72-74, asst prof, 74-79, ASSOC PROF CHEM ENG, YALE UNIV, 79- *Mem:* Am Inst Chem Engrs; Am Chem Soc. *Res:* High temperature chemical reaction engineering; heterogeneous kinetics; fluorine corrosion and heterogeneous halogen reactions; application of laser techniques to high temperature science. *Mailing Add:* Dept Chem Eng Yale Univ PO Box 2159 Yale Sta New Haven CT 06520

NORDLANDER, JOHN ERIC, b Schenectady, NY, July 3, 34; m 65; c 2. ORGANIC CHEMISTRY. *Educ:* Cornell Univ, AB, 56; Calif Inst Technol, PhD(chem), 61. *Prof Exp:* From instr to assoc prof chem, 61-75, PROF CHEM, CASE WESTERN RESERVE UNIV, 75- *Mem:* Am Chem Soc; Royal Soc Chem. *Res:* Organic reaction mechanisms; synthetic organic chemistry. *Mailing Add:* Dept of Chem Case Western Reserve Univ Cleveland OH 44106

NORDLIE, BERT EDWARD, b Denver, Colo, July 21, 35; m 57; c 2. GEOCHEMISTRY, GEOLOGY. *Educ:* Univ Colo, BA, 60, MS, 65; Univ Chicago, PhD(geochem, petrol), 67. *Prof Exp:* Asst prof geol, Univ Ariz, 67-71, assoc prof geosci & chief scientist, 71-73; PROF GEOL & CHMN DEPT, IOWA STATE UNIV, 74- *Mem:* AAAS; Geochem Soc; Am Inst Chemists; Int Asn Volcanology & Chem Earth's Interior; Am Geophys Union. *Res:* Petrology; volcanology, especially magnetic gases. *Mailing Add:* Dept of Earth Sci Iowa State Univ Ames IA 50010

NORDLIE, FRANK GERALD, b Willmar, Minn, Jan 23, 32; m 60; c 2. ZOOLOGY. *Educ:* St Cloud State Col, BS, 54; Univ Minn, MA, 58, PhD(zool), 61. *Prof Exp:* From asst prof to assoc prof, 61-76, PROF ZOOL, UNIV FLA, 76- *Mem:* Am Soc Limnol & Oceanog; Am Soc Zool; Ecol Soc Am. *Res:* Energetics of natural aquatic communities; physiological adaptations to thermal stress; adaptations for a euryhaline existence. *Mailing Add:* Dept of Zool Univ of Fla Gainesville FL 32611

NORDLIE, ROBERT CONRAD, b Willmar, Minn, June 11, 30; m 59; c 3. BIOCHEMISTRY. *Educ:* St Cloud State Col, BS, 52; Univ NDak, MS, 57, PhD(biochem), 60. *Prof Exp:* Asst, Sch Med, Univ NDak, 55-58; Nat Cancer Inst fel, Inst Enzyme Res, Univ Wis, 60-62; Hill prof, 62-74, CHESTER FRITZ DISTINGUISHED PROF BIOCHEM, SCH MED, UNIV NDAK, 74- *Concurrent Pos:* Consult, Oak Ridge Assoc Univs. *Mem:* AAAS; Am Soc Biol Chem; Am Chem Soc; Am Inst Nutrit. *Res:* Enzymology; intermediary metabolism of carbohydrates; effects of hormones on enzymes; biological regulatory mechanisms; inorganic pyrophosphate metabolism; carbamyl phosphate metabolism; control of blood glucose levels. *Mailing Add:* Dept of Biochem Univ of NDak Sch of Med Grand Forks ND 58202

NORDLUND, R(AYMOND) L(OUIS), b Vancouver, BC, Feb 17, 29; m 54; c 3. CIVIL ENGINEERING. *Educ:* Univ BC, BASc, 51; Univ Tex, MS, 53; Univ Ill, PhD(civil eng), 56. *Prof Exp:* Sales engr, Finning Tractor Co, 51-52; asst soil mech, Univ Ill, 53-56; found engr & consult, Raymond Int Inc, 56-65; div mgr, 65-70, VPRES & CHIEF ENGR, FRANKI FOUND CO, 70- *Res:* Soil mechanics. *Mailing Add:* 4806 Bristow Dr Annadale VA 22003

NORDMAN, CHRISTER ERIC, b Helsinki, Finland, Jan 23, 25; m 52; c 4. PHYSICAL CHEMISTRY. *Educ:* Finnish Inst Technol, BS, 49; Univ Minn, PhD(phys chem), 53. *Prof Exp:* Asst phys chem, Univ Minn, 49-53; res assoc physics, Inst Cancer Res, 53-55; from instr to assoc prof chem, 55-64, PROF CHEM, UNIV MICH, ANN ARBOR, 64- *Concurrent Pos:* NIH special fel, Oxford Univ, 71-72. *Mem:* AAAS; Am Phys Soc; Am Chem Soc; Am Crystallog Asn. *Res:* X-ray crystal structure analysis. *Mailing Add:* Dept of Chem Univ of Mich Ann Arbor MI 48109

NORDMAN, JAMES EMERY, b Quinnesec, Mich, Apr 27, 34; m 59; c 6. ELECTRONIC DEVICES. *Educ:* Marquette Univ, BEE, 57; Univ Wis-Madison, MS, 59, PhD(elec eng), 62. *Prof Exp:* From instr to asst prof elec eng, Univ Wis-Madison, 59-67; mem tech staff, David Sarnoff Res Ctr, RCA Corp, NJ, 67-68; assoc prof, 68-74, PROF ELEC ENG, DEPT ELEC & COMPUT ENG, UNIV WIS-MADISON, 74- *Concurrent Pos:* Fulbright-Hayes travel grant, 72; consult, L'Air Liquide, Grenoble, France, 72-73. *Mem:* Inst Elec & Electronics Engrs; Am Vacuum Soc. *Res:* Solid state electronic devices; thin films; superconductors. *Mailing Add:* Dept Elec & Comput Eng Univ Wis Madison WI 53706

NORDMANN, JOSEPH BEHRENS, b Decatur, Ill, Apr 24, 22. CHEMISTRY. *Educ:* Bowling Green State Univ, BS, 43; Univ Southern Calif, MS, 45. *Prof Exp:* Chemist, Am Cyanamid Corp, 44; instr chem, Compton Col, 47-50; prof chem, Los Angeles Valley Col, 50-78. *Concurrent Pos:* Dir, Pac Chem Consults, 51-57. *Honors & Awards:* Medal, Mfg Chem Asn, 69. *Mem:* Am Chem Soc. *Res:* Chemical education; how to communicate science to the general public. *Mailing Add:* Dept of Chem Los Angeles Valley Col Van Nuys CA 91401

NORDMEYER, FRANCIS R, b Kankakee, Ill, Feb 1, 40; m 61; c 6. INORGANIC CHEMISTRY. *Educ:* Wabash Col, BA, 61; Wesleyan Univ, MA, 64; Stanford Univ, PhD(chem), 67. *Prof Exp:* Asst prof chem, Univ Rochester, 67-72; asst prof, 72-74, ASSOC PROF CHEM, BRIGHAM YOUNG UNIV, 74- *Mem:* AAAS; Am Chem Soc. *Res:* Mechanisms of inorganic reactions; ion chromatography. *Mailing Add:* Dept of Chem Brigham Young Univ Provo UT 84602

NORDQUIST, EDWIN C(LYDE), b Salt Lake City, Utah, Aug 7, 21; m 43, 73; c 8. CIVIL ENGINEERING. *Educ:* Univ Utah, BSCE, 43; Iowa State Univ, MS, 51. *Prof Exp:* Engr, Douglas Aircraft Co, Calif, 43-44; instr civil eng, 46-52, asst prof 52-66, ASSOC PROF CIVIL ENG, UNIV UTAH, 66- *Concurrent Pos:* Asst mat engr, Pittsburgh Testing Lab, Utah Dept Highways, 60-61, mat engr, 62, soils engr & consult, 63- *Mem:* Fel Am Soc Civil Engrs. *Res:* Soil mechanics and foundations; geotechnical. *Mailing Add:* Dept Civil Eng MEB 3012 Univ Utah Salt Lake City UT 84112

NORDQUIST, PAUL EDGARD RUDOLPH, JR, b Washington, DC, Sept 7, 36. CRYSTAL GROWTH, ANALYTICAL CHEMISTRY. *Educ:* George Washington Univ, BS, 58; Univ Minn, PhD(inorg chem), 64. *Prof Exp:* Teaching asst inorg chem, Univ Minn, 58-60, 62-63; res chemist, Monsanto Co, 64-70; RES CHEMIST, US NAVAL RES LAB, 70- *Concurrent Pos:* Chemist, Nat Bur Stand, 58-59. *Mem:* Am Chem Soc; Sigma Xi. *Res:* Materials preparation, analysis and characterization; crystal growth of III-IV compounds; trace analysis. *Mailing Add:* Code 6821 US Naval Res Lab Washington DC 20375

NORDQUIST, ROBERT ERSEL, b Oklahoma City, Okla, Sept 10, 38; m 56; c 2. PATHOLOGY, VIROLOGY. *Educ:* Oklahoma City Univ, BA, 68; Univ Okla, PhD(med sci), 71. *Prof Exp:* Res assoc electron micros, Med Sch, Univ Okla, 62-66; res assoc, Scripps Clin & Res Found, 66-67; res assoc, 67-71, ASST MEM CANCER, OKLA MED RES FOUND, 71-; ASST PROF PATH, SCH MED, UNIV OKLA, 71- *Mem:* Electron Micros Soc Am; Tissue Cult Asn; Am Asn Cancer Res. *Res:* The search for human tumor viruses, utilizing the electron microscope coupled with immunologic and virologic techniques. *Mailing Add:* Dept Anat Sci Health Sci Ctr Univ Okla PO Box 26901 Oklahoma City OK 73190

NORDSCHOW, CARLETON DEANE, b Hampton, Iowa, June 7, 26; m 50; c 3. PATHOLOGY, BIOCHEMISTRY. *Educ:* Luther Col, Iowa, AB, 49; Univ Iowa, MD, 53, PhD(biochem), 64. *Prof Exp:* From instr to assoc prof path, Univ Iowa, 54-70, dir clin labs, 63-66; PROF PATH & CHMN DEPT CLIN PATH, SCH MED, IND UNIV, INDIANAPOLIS, 70- *Concurrent Pos:* Mem, Acad Clin Lab Physicians & Scientists; USPHS res grants, 63-65 & 66-68. *Mem:* AMA; Am Soc Clin Path; Am Chem Soc; Int Acad Path. *Res:* Comparative properties of polymers in health and disease. *Mailing Add:* Dept of Clin Path Ind Univ Med Ctr 1100 W Michigan Indianapolis IN 46202

NORDSIEK, FREDERIC WILLIAM, b New York, NY, June 5, 09; m 34. NUTRITION. *Educ:* Mass Inst Technol, SB, 31; NY Univ, MS, 59; Columbia Univ, PhD(nutrit), 61. *Prof Exp:* Res bacteriologist, Borden Co, NY, 31-34 & Sanoderm Co, Inc, 34-35; exec secy, NY Diabetes Asn, 35-38; assoc nutrit dir, Am Inst Baking, 38-43; asst dir res serv dept, Standard Brands, Inc, 43-51; asst secy res Comt, Am Cancer Soc, 51-55, exec officer res dept, 55-57, prog analyst, 57-59, consult, 59-61; chief grants & fels, Sloan- Kettering Inst, 61-64, vpres, 64-67; coordr res & dir grants mgt, St Lukes Hosp Ctr, 68-72; assoc sci dir, Coun Tobacco Res, USA, 72-74; ADJ PROF PUB HEALTH NUTRIT, SCH PUB HEALTH, UNIV NC, CHAPEL HILL, 75- *Concurrent Pos:* Instr, Sch for Inspectors, New York City Health Dept, 41; NIH trainee, 59-61; lectr, Columbia Univ, 59-70, adj prof, 68-72; lectr, Syracuse Univ, 60 & NY Univ, 61-63; sci assoc, Mem Sloan-Kettering Cancer Ctr, 61-64, dir grants & contracts, 64-66; consult, USPHS, 65-68. *Mem:* AAAS; fel Am Pub Health Asn. *Res:* Nutrition; food technology; research administration; science writing. *Mailing Add:* 500 Umstead Dr 308 B Chapel Hill NC 27514

NORDSKOG, ARNE WILLIAM, b Two Harbors, Minn, Feb 21, 13; m 38; c 2. POULTRY SCIENCE. *Educ:* Univ Minn, BS, 37, MS, 40, PhD(animal breeding), 43. *Prof Exp:* Instr agr, Univ Alaska, 37-39; assoc prof animal insdust, Mont State Col, 43-45; assoc prof animal sci, 45-55, PROF ANIMAL SCI, IOWA STATE UNIV, 55- *Honors & Awards:* CPC-Int Res Award, Poultry Sci Asn, 72. *Mem:* Fel Poultry Sci Asn; hon mem Norwegian Poultry Asn; Genetics Soc Am; Biomet Soc; Poultry Sci Asn. *Res:* Poultry breeding and immunogenetics; factors affecting selection for growth rate in swine. *Mailing Add:* Dept of Animal Sci Iowa State Univ Ames IA 50010

NORDSTEDT, ROGER ARLO, b Wichita, Kans, Oct 16, 42; m 64; c 3. AGRICULTURAL ENGINEERING. *Educ:* Kans State Univ, BS, 64, MS, 66; Ohio State Univ, PhD(agr eng), 69. *Prof Exp:* Res asst feed technol, Kans State Univ, 64-65; res assoc agr eng, Ohio State Univ, 68-69; asst prof, 69-76, ASSOC PROF AGR ENG, UNIV FLA, 76- *Mem:* AAAS; Am Soc Agr Engrs. *Res:* Agriculture and quality of environment; agricultural pollution control; animal waste handling, treatment, utilization and/or disposal; lagoon treatment. *Mailing Add:* Dept of Agr Eng Rogers Hall Univ of Fla Gainesville FL 32601

NORDSTROM, DARRELL KIRK, b San Francisco, Calif, Nov 14, 46; m 73. GEOCHEMISTRY, WATER CHEMISTRY. *Educ:* Southern Ill Univ, BA, 69; Univ Colo, MS, 71; Stanford Univ, PhD(geochem), 77. *Prof Exp:* Res chemist, US Geol Surv, 74-76; asst prof environ geochem, dept environ sci, Univ Va, 76-80; GEOCHEMIST, US GEOL SURV, 80- *Concurrent Pos:* Consult, Calif State Water Qual Control Bd & US Geol Surv, 77-80. *Mem:* Sigma Xi; AAAS; Geol Soc Am; Geochem Soc; Mineral Soc Am. *Res:* Chemical modeling of natural waters; geochemistry of acid mine drainage; fluorine geochemistry. *Mailing Add:* US Geol Surv MS-21 345 Middlefield Rd Menlo Park CA 94025

NORDSTROM, J DAVID, b Minneapolis, Minn, Sept 30, 37; m 59; c 3. ORGANIC POLYMER CHEMISTRY. *Educ:* Gustavus Adolphus Col, BA, 59; Univ Iowa, PhD(chem), 63. *Prof Exp:* Res chemist polymers, Archer Daniels Midland Co, Minn, 63-68; sr res scientist, 68-70, MGR POLYMER RES & DEVELOP, PAINT PLANT, FORD MOTOR CO, 70- *Mem:* Am Chem Soc. *Res:* Synthetic organic chemistry; thermoset polymer synthesis and evaluation; Development of polymers for automotive coatings. *Mailing Add:* Dept of Polymer 400 Groesbeck Mt Clemens MI 48043

NORDSTROM, JON OWEN, b Kingsburg, Calif, July 22, 33; m 60; c 2. PHYSIOLOGY. *Educ:* Univ Calif, Davis, BS, 56, PhD(animal physiol), 66. *Prof Exp:* Asst prof physiol, Rutgers Univ, 65-69; assoc prof poultry sci, Univ Ariz, 69-75; ASSOC POULTRY SCIENTIST, WASH STATE UNIV, 75- *Mem:* Poultry Sci Asn; World's Poultry Sci Asn. *Res:* Avian physiology; environmental physiology; physiology of aging. *Mailing Add:* Western Wash Res & Exten Ctr Puyallup WA 98371

NORDSTROM, TERRY VICTOR, solid state electronics, see previous edition

NORDTVEDT, KENNETH L, b Chicago, Ill, Apr 16, 39; c 3. THEORETICAL PHYSICS. *Educ:* Mass Inst Technol, BS, 60; Stanford Univ, MS, 62, PhD(physics), 65. *Prof Exp:* Staff physicist instrumentation lab, Mass Inst Technol, 63-65; from asst prof to assoc prof physics, 65-70, PROF PHYSICS, MONT STATE UNIV, 70- *Concurrent Pos:* NASA res grants, 65-73; Sloan fel, 71-73. *Mem:* Fel Am Phys Soc. *Res:* Gravitation; relativity and cosmology. *Mailing Add:* Dept of Physics Mont State Univ Bozeman MT 59715

NORDYKE, ELLIS LARRIMORE, b Houston, Tex, June 20, 42. BIOCHEMISTRY, NEUROCHEMISTRY. *Educ:* Univ Houston, BS, 68, MS, 70, PhD(biophys sci), 72. *Prof Exp:* NIMH fel neurochem, Tex Res Inst Ment Sci, 72-74; asst prof, 74-77, ASSOC PROF BIOL, UNIV ST THOMAS, 77- *Mem:* Am Chem Soc; Sigma Xi. *Res:* Effect of ethanol on the central nervous system; diseases of amino acid metabolism; mental retardation. *Mailing Add:* Univ of St Thomas 3812 Montrose Blvd Houston TX 77006

NOREIKA, ALEXANDER JOSEPH, b Philadelphia, Pa, Feb 24, 35; m 63; c 3. SOLID STATE PHYSICS, MOLECULAR BEAM EPITAXY. *Educ:* Drexel Inst, BS, 58; Univ Reading, PhD(physics), 66. *Prof Exp:* From jr to sr physicist, Philco Sci Labs, Ford Motor Co, Pa, 59-62; SR PHYSICIST, WESTINGHOUSE RES CTR, 66- *Mem:* Am Phys Soc; Am Vacuum Soc. *Res:* Electron microscopy study of defect structures in single crystals; investigation of extended miscibility ranges in III-IV-V compounds; molecular beam epitaxy of III-V compounds; study of infrared intrinsic photodetectors. *Mailing Add:* Westinghouse Res Ctr Beulah Rd 501 2C19 Pittsburgh PA 15235

NORELL, JOHN REYNOLDS, b Hutchinson, Kans, June 25, 37; m 59; c 1. ORGANIC CHEMISTRY. *Educ:* Bethany-Nazarene Col, BS, 59; Purdue Univ, PhD(org chem), 63. *Prof Exp:* Res chemist, 64-66, group leader, 66-74, sec supvr, 74-75, sales mgr, 75-79, DIR CHEM RES, PHILLIPS PETROL CO, 79- *Concurrent Pos:* NIH fel, Inst Org Chem, Munich, Ger, 63-64. *Mem:* Am Chem Soc. *Res:* Biotechnology; organosulfur chemistry; olefins; fertilizer; petrochemicals; organic synthesis, mechanisms and spectroscopy; flame retardants; fertilizer chemistry and organic chemistry. *Mailing Add:* Phillips Petrol Co 242 Research Forum Bartleville OK 74004

NOREM, A(LLAN) G(ORDON), astronautical engineering, see previous edition

NOREN, GERRY KARL, b Minneapolis, Minn, June 22, 42; m 61; c 2. ORGANIC POLYMER CHEMISTRY. *Educ:* Univ Minn, BA, 66; Univ Iowa, PhD(org chem), 71. *Prof Exp:* Res chemist, Archer-Daniels-Midland Co, 66-67; res assoc chem, Univ Ariz, 71-72; res assoc chem, Calgon Corp, Merck Sharp & Dohme Res Labs, 72-76; supvr polymer chem, 76-79, TECH MGR INVEST RES, DESOTO INC, 79- *Mem:* Am Chem Soc. *Res:* Design and study of unique controlled release systems; synthesis and utilization of new monomers and polymeric systems; low energy crosslinking reactions; ion containing polymers; inorganic polymers; thermally stable polymers. *Mailing Add:* 1836 Sessions Walk Hoffman Estates IL 60195

NORFLEET, MORRIS L, b Nancy, Ky, Dec 15, 30; m 52; c 1. AGRICULTURE, BIOLOGY. *Educ:* Univ Ky, BS, 52; Purdue Univ, MS, 57, PhD(educ), 62. *Prof Exp:* Teacher, Spiceland Pub Schs, Ind, 52-58; pub relations asst, Ind Farm Bur Coop Asn, 58-60, market res anal, 60; instr educ, Purdue Univ, 60-62; assoc prof educ & dir student teaching, 62-65, prof educ & dir res & prog develop, 65-68, vpres res & develop, 68-76, actg pres, 76, PRES, MOREHEAD STATE UNIV, 77- *Concurrent Pos:* Dir Head Start Training prog, 66 & Proj Upward Bound, 66-68; coordr, Comput Assisted Instr Res Demonstration Proj, Ky, 67; interim dir, Appalachian Adult Basic Educ Res & Demonstration Ctr, 67; mem Steering Comt, Gov Efficiency Task Force, 66, Ky Sci & Technol Comn, 68-70 & Northeast Ky Crime Comn, 69-71; dir, Proj Newgate, 69; chmn, Gateway Comprehensive Health Planning Coun, 73, Comprehensive Planning Task Force, Ky Coun Higher Educ, 74-75, & chmn bd dir, Gateway Area Develop Dist, 77-; mem comn of gov relations of Am Coun Educ, 79- & adv comt eligibility of US Off of Educ, 78-; bd trustees, Campbellsville Col, 73-, bd dir, Area Health Educ Syst, 74-, Ky Coun Higher Educ, 77-, Gov Task Force Transp, 78- & Gov Appalachian Develop Coun, 78- consult, US Off Educ, US Off Econ Opportunity, Am Asn Jr Cols, NSF, Danforth Found, Danforth Assoc. *Mem:* Am Asn Teacher Educ; Am Asn Higher Educ; Am Educ Res Asn; Nat Col & Univ Res Adminr; Soc Col & Univ Planning. *Mailing Add:* 201 Howell-McDowell Admin Bldg Morehead State Univ Morehead KY 40351

NORFORD, BRIAN SEELEY, b Gidea Park, Eng, Sept 15, 32; Can citizen; m 62. GEOLOGY, PALEONTOLOGY. *Educ:* Cambridge Univ, BA, 55, MA, 59, ScD, 77; Yale Univ, MSc, 56, PhD, 59. *Prof Exp:* Paleontologist, Shell Oil Co, Can, 59-60; head western paleont sect, 67-72, head paleont subdiv, 72-77, GEOLOGIST, GEOL SURV CAN, 77- *Mem:* Can Soc Petrol Geologists; Am Paleont Soc; Brit Palaeont Asn; Int Palaeont Union; Geol Asn Can. *Res:* Lower Paleozoic stratigraphy; Ordovician and Silurian corals, brachiopods and trilobites. *Mailing Add:* Geol Surv of Can 3303 33rd St Calgary AB T2L 2A7 Can

NORGAARD, NICHOLAS J, b Aledo, Ill, May 28, 43; m 67; c 1. STATISTICS, COMPUTER SCIENCE. *Educ:* Univ Wis-Platteville, BS, 65, MS, 69; Univ Ga, MS, 72, PhD(statist), 75. *Prof Exp:* Asst math, Univ Wis-Platteville, 68-69; asst statist, Univ Ga, 69-70, NSF fel, 70-73; instr, 73-76, ASST PROT MATH & STATIST, WESTERN CAROLINA UNIV, 76- *Concurrent Pos:* Statist consult, Comput Ctr, Western Carolina Univ, 75- *Mem:* Am Statist Asn; Soc Qual Control. *Res:* Estimation of parameters in continuous distributions using censored samples. *Mailing Add:* Dept Math Western Carolina Univ Cullowhee NC

NORIN, ALLEN JOSEPH, b Chicago, Ill, July 30, 44; m 69; c 2. CELL BIOLOGY, TRANSPLANTATION IMMUNOLOGY. *Educ:* Roosevelt Univ, BS, 67; Univ Houston, MS, 70, PhD(biol), 72. *Prof Exp:* USPHS fel & res assoc microbiol, Univ Chicago, 72-75; ASST PROF SURG, MICROBIOL & IMMUNOL, MONTEFIORE HOSP & MED CTR, ALBERT EINSTEIN COL MED, YESHIVA UNIV, 75- *Concurrent Pos:* Immunologist, Manning Lab, NIH Prog, Proj Lung Transplantation, Montefiore Hosp, 75- *Mem:* Am Soc Microbiol; Am Inst Biol Sci; Fedn Am Scientists. *Res:* Regulation of growth and differentiation of human cells; interaction of mitogens and carcinogens with human lymphoid cells; transplantation of skin lung and bone marrow; mechanisms of allograft tolerance. *Mailing Add:* Dept of Microbiol & Immunol Albert Einstein Col of Med Yeshiva Univ Bronx NY 10461

NORING, JON EVERETT, b Pipestone, Minn, Nov 30, 54; m 78; c 1. CHEMICAL ENGINEERING. *Educ:* Univ Minn, BS, MS & PhD(mech eng). *Prof Exp:* MEM TECH STAFF, SANDIA NAT LAB, LIVERMORE, 81- *Mem:* Int Asn Hydrogen Energy; Solar Thermal Test Facil Users Asn. *Res:* Solar central receiver systems, predominately in the area of fuels and chemicals production; very high temperature thermal dissociation processes. *Mailing Add:* 4320 Baylor Way Livermore CA 94550

NORINS, ARTHUR LEONARD, b Chicago, Ill, Dec 2, 28; m 54; c 4. DERMATOLOGY. *Educ:* Northwestern Tech Inst, BS, 51; Northwestern Univ, MS, 53, MD, 55; Am Bd Dermat, dipl, 61, cert, 74. *Prof Exp:* Asst prof, Stanford Univ, 61-64; assoc prof, 64-69, PROF DERMAT, IND UNIV, INDIANAPOLIS, 69-, CHMN, DEPT DERMAT, 76- *Concurrent Pos:* Chief dermat, Riley Children's Hosp. *Mem:* Fel Am Col Physicians; Am Soc Dermatopath; Am Acad Dermat; Soc Invest Dermat; Soc Pediat Dermat. *Res:* Dermatopathology; photobiology. *Mailing Add:* Dept of Dermat Ind Univ Indianapolis IN 46202

NORK, WILLIAM EDWARD, b Shenandoah, Pa, Aug 13. 34; m 60; c 4. HYDROGEOLOGY. *Educ:* Columbia Univ, AB, 60; Univ Buffalo, MA, 61. *Prof Exp:* Asst geol, Univ Buffalo, 60-61; from asst to instr geol, Univ Ariz, 61-64; scientist, Hazelton Nuclear Sci Corp, 64-66; dep proj mgr & asst mgr hydrogeol sect isotopes, Teledyne Inc, Calif, 66-70, mgr, Teledyne Isotopes, Nev, 70-71; res assoc, Desert Res Inst, Univ Nev, Las Vegas, 71-72; consult hydrologist, Hydro-Search, Inc, 72-77; CONSULT HYDROGEOLOGIST, WILLIAM E NORK, INC, 77- *Concurrent Pos:* Consult, 60-61. *Mem:* Nat Water Well Asn; Geol Soc Am; Am Water Resources Asn; Am Geophys Union. *Res:* Optimum use and development of water, especially ground-water resources and water quality assurance for public use. *Mailing Add:* William E Nork Inc 1026 W First St Reno NV 89503

NORLING, PARRY MCWHINNIE, b Des Moines, Iowa, Apr 17, 39; m 65; c 2. SAFETY & HEALTH. *Educ:* Harvard Univ, AB, 61; Princeton Univ, PhD(polymer chem), 64. *Prof Exp:* Res assoc oxidation of polymers, Princeton Univ, 64-65; res chemist, Electrochem Dept, Del, 65-69, res supvr, 69-71, from tech supt to prod supt, Memphis Plant, 71-75, res mgr, Indust Chem Dept, Exp Sta, 75-78, dir safety & health, 78-80, LAB DIR, DEPT CHEM & PIGMENTS, EXP STA, E I DU PONT DE NEMOURS & CO INC, WILMINGTON, 80- *Mem:* Am Chem Soc. *Res:* Kinetics and mechanism of the oxidation of polymers; polymerization kinetics. *Mailing Add:* Exp Sta 336 E I du Pont de Nemours & Co Inc Wilmington DE 19898

NORLYN, JACK DAVID, b Bellflower, Calif, Dec 10, 31; m 58; c 2. PLANT PHYSIOLOGY. *Educ:* Univ Calif, Davis, BS, 55, PhD(plant physiol), 82; Calif State Univ, Fresno, MS, 76. *Prof Exp:* Lectr hydroponics, 76, STAFF RES ASSOC SALT TOLERANCE PLANTS, UNIV CALIF, DAVIS, 71- *Concurrent Pos:* Consult biomass prod, 78- *Mem:* Sigma Xi. *Res:* Physiological genetics of salt tolerance in plants; development of a crop production system using seawater on sand; improving salt tolerance of crops; biomass production for energy. *Mailing Add:* Dept Land Air & Water Resources Univ of Calif Davis CA 95616

NORMAN, ALEX, b New York, NY, Aug 7, 23; m 47; c 3. RADIOLOGY. *Educ:* NY Univ, BA, 44; Chicago Med Sch, MD, 48. *Prof Exp:* Nat Cancer Inst fel, Bellevue Hosp, 52; radiologist, Beth Israel Hosp, New York, 55-56; assoc attend radiol, Hosp Joint Dis, New York, 56-60, chief diag roentgenol, 60-66; asst prof clin radiol, Sch Med, NY Univ, 64-67; dir diag roentgenol, 66-70, DIR RADIOL, HOSP JOINT DIS/ORTHO INST, 70-, PROF RADIOL, MT SINAI SCH MED, 67- *Concurrent Pos:* NIH grant, Hosp Joint Dis, Bethesda, 62-64; consult radiologist, St Vincent's Hosp & Med Ctr, New York, 70- *Mem:* Fel NY Acad Med; fel Am Col Radiol. *Res:* Application of tomography and enlargement technique in the diagnosis of bone diseases. *Mailing Add:* Hosp Joint Dis/Orthopaedic Inst 301 E 17th St New York NY 10035

NORMAN, AMOS, b Vienna, Austria, Nov 25, 21; m 46; c 4. MEDICAL PHYSICS. *Educ:* Harvard Univ, AB, 43; Columbia Univ, MA, 47, PhD(biophys), 50. *Prof Exp:* AEC fel, Columbia Univ, 50-51; res biophysicist, 51-54, asst prof, 53-58, assoc prof, 58-63, prof radiol, 63-81, PROF RADIATION ONCOL & RADIOL SCI, UNIV CALIF, LOS ANGELES, 81- *Mem:* AAAS; Am Soc Photobiol; Am Soc Physicists in Med; Radiation Res Soc. *Res:* Cellular radiobiology; engineering in medicine. *Mailing Add:* Dept of Radiol Sci Univ of Calif Los Angeles CA 90024

NORMAN, ANDREA HAUSMAN, inorganic chemistry, see previous edition

NORMAN, ANTHONY WESTCOTT, b Ames, Iowa, Jan 19, 38. BIOCHEMISTRY. *Educ:* Oberlin Col, BA, 59; Univ Wis, MS, 61; PhD(biochem), 63. *Prof Exp:* Res assoc biochem, Univ Wis, 59-63; from asst prof to assoc prof, 63-72, PROF BIOCHEM, UNIV CALIF, RIVERSIDE, 72-, CHMN DEPT, 76- *Concurrent Pos:* NIH res grants, 64-79, spec fel, 70-71 & career develop award, 71-76; Fulbright fel, 70-71. *Honors & Awards:* Ernst Oppenheimer Award, 77; Mead Johnson Award, 77. *Mem:* Endocrinol Soc; Am Fedn Clin Res; AAAS; Am Chem Soc; Am Soc Biol Chemists. *Res:* Mechanism of action of vitamin D related to calcium metabolism; ion transport; mode of action of steroid hormones. *Mailing Add:* Dept of Biochem Univ of Calif Riverside CA 92521

NORMAN, ARLAN DALE, b Westhope, NDak, Mar 26, 40; m 66. INORGANIC CHEMISTRY. *Educ:* Univ NDak, BS, 62; Ind Univ, PhD(chem), 66. *Prof Exp:* Res assoc chem, Univ Calif, Berkeley, 65-66; from asst prof to assoc prof, 66-74, PROF CHEM, UNIV COLO, BOULDER, 74-, DEPT HEAD, 80- *Concurrent Pos:* Alfred P Sloan Found fel, 73-75. *Mem:* Am Chem Soc; Chem Soc London. *Res:* Chemistry of phosphous hydrids, phosphous-nitrogen ring and polymers, and phospine-metal complexes; photorolalipsts. *Mailing Add:* Dept of Chem Univ of Colo Boulder CO 80302

NORMAN, BILLY RAY, b Luverne, Ala, Feb 10, 35. SCIENCE EDUCATION. *Educ:* Troy State Col, BS, 57; Univ Ga, EdD(sci), 65. *Prof Exp:* Asst prof sci, Campbell Col, 65-66; assoc prof, 66-77, PROF SCI EDUC, TROY STATE UNIV, 77- *Mem:* Nat Sci Teachers Asn. *Res:* Concepts of teaching science. *Mailing Add:* Dept of Sci Educ Troy State Univ Troy AL 36081

NORMAN, CARL EDGAR, b Cokato, Minn, Feb 1, 31; m 62; c 1. STRUCTURAL GEOLOGY, ROCK MECHANICS. *Educ:* Univ Minn, Minneapolis, BA, 57; Ohio State Univ, MS, 59, PhD(geol), 67. *Prof Exp:* Geologist, Humble Oil & Refining Co, 59-62; from instr to asst prof geol, 65-71, ASSOC PROF GEOL, UNIV HOUSTON, 71- *Concurrent Pos:* NSF instr sci equip prog grant, 68-69; univ fac res support prog grant, 69. *Mem:* AAAS; Geol Soc Am; Int Soc Rock Mech. *Res:* Mechanism of failure in rocks; behavior of rocks under varying conditions of load. *Mailing Add:* Dept of Geol Univ of Houston Houston TX 77004

NORMAN, EDGAR CARL, materials science, nuclear materials, see previous edition

NORMAN, EDWARD, b New York, NY, Aug 7, 32; m 59; c 2. MATHEMATICS. *Educ:* City Col New York, BS, 54; Cornell Univ, PhD(math), 58. *Prof Exp:* Asst prof math, Mich State Univ, 58-61; res mathematician, Socony Mobil Oil Co, 61-64; asst prof math, Drexel Inst, 64-69; assoc prof math, Fla Technol Univ, 69-80; MEM FAC, DEPT MATH, UNIV CENT FLA, 80- *Mem:* Am Math Soc. *Res:* Analysis; stability of differential equations. *Mailing Add:* Dept Math Univ Cent Fla Orlando FL 32801

NORMAN, EDWARD COBB, b BC, Can, Oct 5, 13; US citizen; m 49; c 3. PUBLIC HEALTH EDUCATION, PSYCHIATRY. *Educ:* Univ Wash, BS, 35; Univ Pa, MD, 40; Tulane Univ, MPH, 65. *Prof Exp:* Psychiatrist, USPHS, 43-46; clin instr psychiat, Univ Ill Col Med, 49-53; from asst prof to assoc prof clin psychiat, 53-64, PROF PSYCHIAT & PREV MED, DEPT TROP MED & PUB HEALTH, TULANE UNIV, 64-, DIR MENT HEALTH SECT, SCH PUB HEALTH & TROP MED, 67- *Concurrent Pos:* Pvt pract, Chicago, 49-53 & New Orleans, 53-; clin physician, Michael Reese Hosp, Chicago, 49-53 & Vet Admin Hosps, Gulfport, Miss & New Orleans, 53-64; consult, Southeast La Hosp, Mandeville & East La Hosp, Jackson, 53-60; on active staff, Sara Mayo Hosp, New Orleans, 58-64; sr vis physician, Charity Hosp La, New Orleans, 64-, co-dir, Inter-Univ Forum Educr Community Psychiat, Duke Univ, 67-72; mem ad hoc grants rev comt, NIMH, 68-69; consult, New Orleans City Police Dept, 70-72 & Orleans Parish Sch Syst, 71-72; secy, Forum Improv Quality of Life, 74; mem, APA Task Force Eco-Psychiatry, 75. *Mem:* AAAS; Am Psychiat Asn; Am Acad Psychoanal; Am Pub Health Asn. *Res:* Evaluation of the education process; evaluation of mental health consultation. *Mailing Add:* 439 Pine St New Orleans LA 70112

NORMAN, ELIANE MEYER, b Lyon, France, Nov 15, 31; US citizen; m 58; c 2. BOTANY, TAXONOMY. *Educ:* Hunter Col, BA, 53; Wash Univ, MA, 55; Cornell Univ, PhD(plant taxon), 62. *Prof Exp:* Instr biol, Hobart Col, 55-56; instr natural sci, Mich State Univ, 59-60; asst prof bot, Rutgers Univ, 63-69; asst prof biol, 70-77, ASSOC PROF BIOL, STETSON UNIV, 77- *Mem:* Am Soc Plant Taxon; Asn Trop Biol; Int Asn Plant Taxon. *Res:* Taxonomic and cytological studies of the genus Buddleja; reproductive biology of Florida plants. *Mailing Add:* 1620 Druid Rd Maitland FL 32751

NORMAN, FLOYD (ALVIN), b Hallettsville, Tex, July 31, 11; m 38; c 2. MEDICINE. *Educ:* Univ Tex, MD, 35; Am Bd Pediat, dipl, 40. *Prof Exp:* Clin prof pediat, Univ Tex Southwest Med Sch Dallas, 60-72; regional health adminr, Pub Health Serv, Region VI, Dept Health, Educ & Welfare, 72-78. *Mem:* AMA; Am Acad Pediat. *Mailing Add:* 11550 Wander Lane Dallas TX 75230

NORMAN, HOWARD DUANE, b Liberty, Pa, Nov 4, 42; m 74; c 1. ANIMAL BREEDING. *Educ:* Pa State Univ, BS, 64, MS, 67; Cornell Univ, PhD(animal breeding), 70. *Prof Exp:* RES GENETICIST, ANIMAL SCI INST, BELTSVILLE AGR RES CTR, AGR RES SERV, USDA, 70- *Mem:* Am Dairy Sci Asn. *Res:* Developed procedures to improve the accuracy of estimated transmitting ability for milk thereby increasing the genetic capability of the United States dairy population. *Mailing Add:* Beltsville Agr Res Ctr-East Beltsville MD 20705

NORMAN, JACK C, b Taunton, Mass, June 16, 38; m 64. NUCLEAR CHEMISTRY, RADIOCHEMISTRY. *Educ:* Univ NH, BS, 60; Univ Wis-Madison, PhD(phys chem), 65. *Prof Exp:* Instr chem, Univ Wash, 65-66; asst prof, Univ Ky, 66-68; asst prof, 68-71, ASSOC PROF ECOSYSTS ANAL, UNIV WIS-GREEN BAY, 71-, ASSOC PROF SCI & ENVIRON CHANGE, 77- *Mem:* AAAS; Am Chem Soc; Am Phys Soc. *Res:* Neutron activation analysis of geological and environmental materials; nuclear reaction studies; radionuclides in the environment. *Mailing Add:* Col of Environ Sci Univ of Wis Green Bay WI 54302

NORMAN, JAMES EVERETT, JR, b Washington, DC, July 11, 39; m 75; c 1. EPIDEMIOLOGY, BIOSTATISTICS. *Educ:* Univ Ala, BS, 57, MS, 60; Va Polytech Inst, PhD(statist), 65. *Prof Exp:* Mathematician atmospheric res, US Army Ballistic Missile Agency, 60; physicist appl physics, Bendix Res Lab, 60-61; asst prof statist, Univ Mass, 65-67 & Univ Ga, 67-72; statistician epidemiol, Nat Acad Sci Med Follow Up Agency, 72-75; statistician epidemiol & statist dept, Radiation Effects Res Found, 75-77; statistician, Nat Res Coun-Nat Acad Sci Med Follow Up Agency, 77-81. *Mem:* Am Statist Asn. *Res:* Epidemiologic studies of chronic diseases; statistical methods and design in epidemiology. *Mailing Add:* Nat Acad of Sci Med Follow Up Agency 2101 Constitution Ave NW Washington DC 20418

NORMAN, JAY HAROLD, nuclear physics, see previous edition

NORMAN, JOE G, JR, b Brevard, NC, Aug 8, 47. TRANSITION METAL CHEMISTRY. *Educ:* Rice Univ, BA, 69; Mass Inst Technol, PhD(chem), 72. *Prof Exp:* From asst prof to assoc prof, 72-82, PROF CHEM, UNIV WASH, 82-, ASSOC DEAN GRAD SCH, 80- *Mem:* Am Chem Soc; Chem Soc; Am Crystallog Asn. *Res:* Electronic structure of large molecules containing transition metals. *Mailing Add:* Grad Sch AG-10 Univ Wash Seattle WA 98195

NORMAN, JOHN HARRIS, b Battle Creek, Mich, Apr 13, 29; m 50; c 3. PHYSICAL CHEMISTRY, NUCLEAR SCIENCE. *Educ:* Univ Mich, BS, 50; Univ Wis, PhD(chem), 54. *Prof Exp:* Chemist mass spectros, Olin Mathieson Chem Corp, 54-60; staff mem, 60-80, SR STAFF MEM CHEM, GEN ATOMIC CO, 80- *Mem:* Am Chem Soc; Am Nuclear Soc; NY Acad Sci. *Res:* Mass spectrometry; high temperature chemistry; transport phenomena; chemistry of fallout; nuclear chemistry; nuclear safety; thermochemical water splitting. *Mailing Add:* Gen Atomic Co PO Box 81608 San Diego CA 92138

NORMAN, JOHN MATTHEW, b Virginia, Minn, Nov 27, 42; m 67. MICROMETEOROLOGY, AGRICULTURAL METEOROLOGY. *Educ:* Univ Minn, BS, 64, MS, 67; Univ Wis-Madison, PhD(soil sci), 71. *Prof Exp:* Asst prof, 72-75, from asst prof to assoc prof meteorol, Pa State Univ, University Par, 72-78; PROF AGRON, UNIV NEB, LINCOLN, 78- *Concurrent Pos:* Res fel, Dept Bot, Univ Aberdeen, Scotland, 71-72. *Mem:* Sigma Xi; AAAS; Am Meteorol Soc; Am Soc Agron. *Res:* Studies of the interactions between plants and their environments including measurements of soil, plant and atmospheric characteristics and integrative modeling of the entire soil-plant-atmosphere system. *Mailing Add:* Dept of Agron Univ of Neb East Campus Lincoln NE 68583

NORMAN, L(EWIS) A(RTHUR), JR, b San Bernadino, Calif, July 6, 08; m 32; c 2. ECONOMIC GEOLOGY, MINING ENGINEERING. *Educ:* Stanford Univ, AB, 32. *Prof Exp:* Field engr ore explor, Lassen Metals, Ltd, Calif, 33; field engr mine develop, Nat Explor Co, 34; from mining engr to gen supt, Cent Eureka Mining Co, Nev & Calif, 35-43; supvr field eng, Colonial Mica Corp, 44-45; asst supvr, Chem Warfare Plant, Am Cyanamid Co, 45; plant supt, Antimony Smelter, Harshaw Chem Co, 45-46; from dist mining engr to sr mining geologist, Calif Div Mines, 47-50, supv mining geologist, 51-56; from staff engr to pres, Krebs Engrs, 56-71, chmn bd, 71-73; RETIRED. *Mem:* Soc Econ Geologists; Am Inst Mining, Metall & Petrol Engrs. *Mailing Add:* 1174 Chaparral Rd Pebble Beach CA 94953

NORMAN, LINDSAY D(EAN), b Drexel Hill, Pa, Oct 14, 37. METALLURGY. *Educ:* Univ Md, College Park, BS, 60, MS, 64, PhD(mat, physics), 70. *Prof Exp:* Metallurgist, E I du Pont de Nemours & Co, Inc, 60; instr chem, Univ Md, 60-61; metallurgist process eval, US Bur Mines, 60-62, energy conversion, 62-67, math simulation, 67-69, phys sci adminr environ & metall res, 69-75, dir planning, 75-78, asst dir, 78-79, dir, 79-81; VPRES, JONES & LAUGHLIN STEEL CORP, 81- *Concurrent Pos:* Mem, UN Working Group Environ & Mining, 71-, Comt on Mineral Res, Nat Res Coun, 74-75 & Nat Sci Found Adv Environ Res Panel, 75. *Mem:* Am Inst Mining, Metall & Petrol Engrs; Am Soc Metals; Am Iron & Steel Inst; Am Iron & Steel Engrs. *Res:* Mathematical simulation of metallurgical systems; energy conversion materials; environmental control technology. *Mailing Add:* 900 Agnew Rd Pittsburgh PA 15227

NORMAN, OSCAR LORIS, b Crawfordsville, Ind, Apr 28, 25; m 46; c 2. ORGANIC CHEMISTRY. *Educ:* Wabash Col, AB, 47; Northwestern Univ, MS, 49; Purdue Univ, PhD(chem), 53. *Prof Exp:* Sr res chemist, Int Mineral & Chem Corp, 52-58, mgr food prod res, 58-60, mgr biochem & chem res, 60-61; mgr prod develop, 61-62, sect chief basic res, 62-64, mgr, Basic Res, 65-77, MGR, PROD DEVELOP, SUN OIL CO, 77- *Mem:* AAAS; Am Chem Soc. *Res:* Biochemistry. *Mailing Add:* 2426 Graydon Rd Wilmington DE 19803

NORMAN, PHILIP SIDNEY, b Pittsburg, Kans, Aug 4, 24; m 55; c 3. IMMUNOLOGY, BIOCHEMISTRY. *Educ:* Wash Univ, MD, 51. *Prof Exp:* Intern, Barnes Hosp, St Louis, Mo, 51-52; asst resident, Vanderbilt Univ Hosp, 52-54; USPHS fel, Rockefeller Inst, 54-56; from instr to assoc prof, 56-74, PROF MED, JOHNS HOPKINS UNIV, 75-, HEAD CLIN IMMUNOL DIV, 71-, PHYSICIAN, HOSP, 59- *Concurrent Pos:* Head allergy serv & physician, Good Samaritan Hosp, Baltimore, Md, 71- *Mem:* Am Fedn Clin Res; Am Acad Allergy; Am Soc Clin Invest; Am Asn Immunol; NY Acad Sci. *Res:* Antigens of ragweed; hay fever; asthma. *Mailing Add:* Good Samaritan Hosp 5601 Loch Raven Blvd Baltimore MD 21239

NORMAN, REID LYNN, b Scott City, Kans, Feb 26, 44; m 67; c 2. NEUROENDOCRINOLOGY. *Educ:* Kans State Univ, BS, 66, MS, 68; Univ Kans, PhD(anat), 71. *Prof Exp:* Fel neuroendocrinol, Univ Calif, Los Angeles, 71-72; asst scientist reprod physiol, Ore Regional Primate Res Ctr, 72-76; asst prof, 73-77, ASSOC PROF ANAT, ORE HEALTH SCI UNIV, 77-; ASSOC SCIENTIST REPROD PHYSIOL, ORE REGIONAL PRIMATE RES CTR, 76- *Mem:* Am Asn Anatomists; Soc Study Reprod; Endocrine Soc; Am Physiol Soc. *Res:* Anatomical and physiological regulation of anterior pituitary function by the central nervous system. *Mailing Add:* Ore Regional Primate Res Ctr 505 NW 185th Ave Beaverton OR 97005

NORMAN, ROBERT DANIEL, b New York, NY, Nov 3, 38; Can citizen; m 62; c 3. MATHEMATICS. *Educ:* Univ Toronto, BA, 60; Queens Univ, Ont, MA, 62; Univ London, PhD(math), 64. *Prof Exp:* Fel math, 64-65, asst prof, 65-71, ASSOC PROF MATH, QUEENS UNIV, ONT, 71- *Mem:* Can Math Soc; Am Math Soc. *Res:* Dynamical systems. *Mailing Add:* Dept Math Queens Univ Kingston ON K7L 3N6 Can

NORMAN, ROBERT S, chemical engineering, see previous edition

NORMAN, ROBERT ZANE, b Chicago, Ill, Dec 16, 24; m 52; c 2. MATHEMATICS. *Educ:* Swarthmore Col, AB, 49; Univ Mich, AM, 50, PhD, 54. *Prof Exp:* Instr math, Princeton Univ, 54-56; assoc prof, 56-66, PROF MATH, DARTMOUTH COL, 66-, CHMN PROG IN MATH & SOC SCI, 71- *Mem:* Am Math Soc; Math Asn Am. *Res:* Theory of graphs; combinatorial analysis; mathematical models in the social sciences. *Mailing Add:* Dept of Math Dartmouth Col Hanover NH 03755

NORMAN, ROGER ATKINSON, JR, b Danville, Ky, Oct 16, 46; m 71, 80. PHYSIOLOGY, CHEMICAL ENGINEERING. *Educ:* Univ Miss, BS, 68, MS, 71, PhD(biomed eng), 73. *Prof Exp:* Res assoc physiol, 72-73, asst prof, 73-80, ASSOC PROF PHYSIOL & BIOPHYS, SCH MED, UNIV MISS, 80- *Mem:* Sigma Xi; AAAS; Am Phys Soc. *Res:* Cardiovascular physiology; hypertension. *Mailing Add:* Dept of Physiol & Biophys Univ of Miss Sch of Med Jackson MS 39216

NORMAN, WESLEY P, b Marion, Ill, Aug 14, 28. DEVELOPMENTAL BIOLOGY, NEUROANATOMY. *Educ:* Southern Ill Univ, BA, 52, MA, 54; Univ Ill, PhD(anat), 67. *Prof Exp:* Asst histologist, Am Meat Inst Found, 62-64; instr anat, Col Med, Univ Ill, 66-67; asst prof, 67-72, ASSOC PROF ANAT, GEORGETOWN UNIV, 72- *Concurrent Pos:* Consult & lectr otolaryngol basic sci course, Armed Forces Inst Path, 67- & Walter Reed Inst Dent Res & Naval Dent Sch, Bethesda, Md, 68- *Mem:* Am Asn Anat; Am Soc Cell Biol; Am Soc Zool. *Res:* Regeneration of the forelimb of the adult newt, Diemictylus viridescens, specifically skeletal muscle regeneration; histochemistry; autoradiography of fibrillogenesis; electron microscopy; analysis of denervated and reinnervated muscle spindles. *Mailing Add:* Dept of Anat Georgetown Univ 3900 Reservoir Rd Washington DC 20007

NORMANDIN, DIANE KILBOURNE, electron microscopy, see previous edition

NORMANDIN, RAYMOND O, b Lowell, Mass, May 23, 30; m 55; c 3. PLASTICS. *Educ:* St Anselm's Col, AB, 52; Boston Col, MS, 54. *Prof Exp:* Instr chem, Mt St Mary Col, NH, 54-56; instr plastics eng, 56-60, from asst prof to assoc prof plastics technol, 60-68, PROF PLASTICS ENG, UNIV LOWELL, 68- *Concurrent Pos:* Vis lectr, St Anselm's Col, 55-56; consult, numerous plastic co, 56- *Mem:* Am Chem Soc; Soc Plastics Engrs. *Res:* Plastics materials, additives and education. *Mailing Add:* 8 Moonbeam Ave Chelmsford MA 01824

NORMANDIN, ROBERT F, b Laconia, NH, July 22, 27; m 54; c 3. RADIATION BIOLOGY. *Educ:* St Anselm's Col, AB, 50; Univ NH, MS, 53; Ohio State Univ, PhD(zool), 59. *Prof Exp:* Res biologist, NH Fish & Game Dept, 53-54; cur path mus, Ohio State Univ, 56-59; res biologist, US Fish & Wildlife Serv, 59-60; assoc prof biol, 60-70, PROF BIOL, ST ANSELM'S COL, 70- *Concurrent Pos:* Consult pvt fishery, Ohio, 57-59; consult, NH Water Pollution Comn, 60-66; chmn, NH Comn Radiation Control, 62-74; consult lectr, NH Civil Defense Orgn, 64-66; chmn, NH Legis Comn Prof Nursing, 66; mem, NH Adv Comprehensive Health Planning Coun, 69. *Mem:* AAAS; Am Inst Biol Scientists. *Res:* Water pollutional control, especially algal blooms; radiation biology, especially physiology and pathology of radio-sensitivity radio-ecology. *Mailing Add:* St Anselm's Col Manchester NH 03102

NORMANN, SIGURD JOHNS, b Cincinnati, Ohio, Oct 24, 35; m 65; c 2. PATHOLOGY. *Educ:* Univ Wash, MD, 60, PhD(path), 66. *Prof Exp:* Intern surg, Univ Calif, San Francisco, 60-61; resident path, Univ Washington, 61-66; US Army Medical Corp, 66-68; from asst prof to assoc prof, 68-76, PROF PATH, UNIV FLA, 76- *Concurrent Pos:* Consult path, Vet Admin Hosp, Gainesville, 68-; Nat Insts Allergy & Infectious Dis res career develop award, Univ Fla, 70-75; vis cardiovasc path, Northwick Park Hosp, England, 75; consult, Swiss Inst Med Res, Davos, Switz, 75-; sci review comt, Gainesville Vet Admin Hosp, 77-; sci review comt, Fla Div, Am Cancer Soc, 78- *Honors & Awards:* Outstanding Achievement Res & Develop Cert, Asst Secy Defense, 68. *Mem:* AAAS; Am Asn Path; Int Acad Path; Reticuloendothelial Soc (secy, 70-73, pres-elect, 78, pres, 79). *Res:* Macrophage function in inflammation and neoplasia; phagocytosis immunology; cardiovascular pathology. *Mailing Add:* Dept Path Univ Fla Gainesville FL 32601

NORMARK, WILLIAM RAYMOND, b Seattle, Wash, Jan 21, 43; m 67. OCEANOGRAPHY, MARINE GEOLOGY. *Educ:* Stanford Univ, BS, 65; Univ Calif, San Diego, PhD(oceanog), 69. *Prof Exp:* Res oceanogr, Scripps Inst Oceanog, 69-70; asst prof geol & oceanog, Univ Minn, Minneapolis, 70-74; GEOLOGIST, PAC-ARCTIC BR MARINE GEOL, US GEOL SURV, 74- *Mem:* AAAS; Geol Soc Am; Am Geophys Union; Soc Explor Geophys. *Res:* Continental margin sedimentation, particularly deep-sea turbidites, growth patterns of deep-sea fans, structure and history of continental margins and evolution of lithospheric plate boundaries; erosion of deep-sea sediment. *Mailing Add:* US Geol Surv 345 Middlefield Rd Menlo Park CA 94025

NORMENT, BEVERLY RAY, b Whiteville, Tenn, July 23, 41; m 64; c 1. ENTOMOLOGY. *Educ:* Memphis State Univ, BS, 64, MS, 66; Miss State Univ, PhD(entom), 69. *Prof Exp:* Asst zool, Memphis State Univ, 64-66, instr, 66; from res asst to asst prof entom, 66-74, assoc prof, 74-81, PROF ENTOM, MISS STATE UNIV, 81- *Mem:* Am Soc Trop Med & Hygiene; Int Soc Toxinology; Entom Soc Am; Am Mosquito Control Asn. *Res:* Medical entomology; bioassay techniques; enzyme assays; toxinological studies; biological control. *Mailing Add:* Dept of Entom Miss State Univ Mississippi State MS 39762

NORMENT, HILLYER GAVIN, b Washington, DC, Jan 13, 28; m 73; c 3. ATMOSPHERIC SCIENCE, PHYSICAL CHEMISTRY. *Educ:* Univ Md, BS, 51, PhD(phys chem), 56. *Prof Exp:* Group leader x-ray diffraction, Callery Chem Co, 56-59; phys chemist, US Naval Res Lab, 59-62; opers res analyst nuclear fallout, Res Triangle Inst, 62-63; sr scientist nuclear fallout modeling, Tech Opers Inc, 63-67; sr scientist, Arcon Corp, 67-71; prin scientist nuclear fallout cloud physics, Mt Auburn Res Assoc, 71-75; PROPRIETOR NUCLEAR FALLOUT CLOUD PHYSICS AIR POLLUTION, ATMOSPHERIC SCI ASN, 75- *Mem:* Sigma Xi; AAAS; Air Pollution Control Asn; Am Meteorol Soc; Am Geophys Union. *Res:* Cloud physics; modeling of atmospheric transport processes; air pollution modeling; atmospheric turbulence; planetary boundary layer meteorology. *Mailing Add:* 186 Peter Spring Rd Concord MA 01742

NORMILE, HUBERT CLARENCE, b Los Angeles, Calif, Apr 16, 06; m 32; c 3. ANALYTICAL CHEMISTRY. *Educ:* Northeastern Univ, BS, 29. *Prof Exp:* Chem engr, Bethlehem Steel Co, 29-31, US Army, Philadelphia, 31-46; chemist, Vet Admin, 46-51; CHIEF CHEMIST, US AIR FORCE SPACE PROG, CAPE CANAVERAL, FLA, 51- *Mem:* Am Chem Soc; Am Inst Aeronaut & Astronaut; Am Inst Chem Engrs. *Res:* Testing of materials and contamination control for the United States Space Program. *Mailing Add:* 2727 Wickham Rd Melbourne FL 32935

NORMINTON, EDWARD JOSEPH, b Hensall, Ont, Sept 8, 38; m 63; c 2. APPLIED MATHEMATICS. *Educ:* Univ Western Ont, BA, 61, MA, 62; Univ Toronto, PhD(fluid dynamics), 65. *Prof Exp:* Asst prof math, 65-69, ASSOC PROF MATH, CARLETON UNIV, 69- *Mem:* Can Math Cong. *Res:* Mathematical software. *Mailing Add:* Dept of Math Carleton Univ Ottawa ON Can

NORNES, HOWARD ONSGAARD, b Winger, Minn, Apr 27, 31; m 58; c 3. NEUROBIOLOGY, DEVELOPMENTAL BIOLOGY. *Educ:* Concordia Col, BA, 53; Purdue Univ, Lafayette, MS, 63, PhD(biol), 71. *Prof Exp:* Teacher biol, Richfield Pub Sch, 58-66; from instr to lectr, Purdue Univ, Lafayette, 66-72; ASSOC PROF, COLO STATE UNIV, 72- *Mem:* Am Soc Zoologists; Soc Neurosci. *Res:* Developmental neurobiology. *Mailing Add:* Dept of Anat Colo State Univ Ft Collins CO 80521

NORNES, SHERMAN BERDEEN, b Winger, Minn, Jan 10, 29; m 53; c 2. SURFACE PHYSICS. *Educ:* Concordia Col, Moorhead, Minn, BA, 51; Univ NDak, MS, 56; Wash State Univ, PhD(physics), 65. *Prof Exp:* Res engr, Rocketdyne Inc Div, NAm Aviation, Inc, 56-59; assoc prof, 59-61, chmn dept, 67-81, ASSOC PROF PHYSICS, PAC LUTHERAN UNIV, 65- *Concurrent Pos:* Consult physicist, Lawrence Livermore Lab, 74- *Mem:* Am Vacuum Soc; Am Asn Physics Teachers. *Res:* X-ray photo electron spectroscopy and auger electron spectroscopy studies of surface reactions of Actinides; physics of the interaction of spectroscopically pure gases with ultra clean metal surfaces. *Mailing Add:* Dept of Physics Pac Lutheran Univ Tacoma WA 98447

NORONHA, FERNANDO M OLIVEIRA, b Portugal, Feb 10, 24; m 60; c 2. VIROLOGY. *Educ:* Lisbon Tech Univ, DVM, 49. *Prof Exp:* WHO fel, Col Med, Univ Montpellier, 50-52; French Acad bursary, Pasteur Inst, Paris, 53-55; researcher, Virus Res Inst, Eng, 56; researcher, Nat Inst Sch Higher Vet Med, Lisbon Tech Univ, 59-63; assoc prof virol, 64-66, PROF VIROL, NY STATE VET COL, CORNELL UNIV, 66- *Concurrent Pos:* Portuguese Govt scholar, Animal Virus Inst, Univ Tubingen, 59-63; resident, Portuguese Inst Vet Res, 59-63. *Honors & Awards:* Chevalier de Merite Agricole, Fr Govt, 50. *Mem:* Am Soc Microbiol; Portuguese Soc Vet Med. *Res:* Virus oncology. *Mailing Add:* NY State Col of Vet Med Ithaca NY 14853

NORR, SIGMUND CARL, developmental biology, see previous edition

NORRDIN, ROBERT W, b Brooklyn, NY, Oct 2, 37; m 63; c 4. VETERINARY PATHOLOGY. *Educ:* Brooklyn Col, BS, 58; Cornell Univ, DVM, 62, PhD(vet path), 69. *Prof Exp:* Gen pract vet med, Flemington, NJ & Locke, NY, 62-65; asst prof vet med, NY State Vet Col, Cornell Univ, 65-66, NIH trainee nutrit path, 66-69; ASSOC PROF VET PATH, DEPT PATH & COLLABR, RADIOL HEALTH LAB, COL VET MED & BIOMED SCI, COLO STATE UNIV, 69- *Concurrent Pos:* NIH & Med Res foreign fel, Res Unit 18, Hopital Lariboisiere, Paris, 75-76. *Mem:* Am Col Vet Pathologists; Am Vet Med Asn. *Res:* Multifaceted studies of nutritional and metabolic bone diseases in animals; metabolic studies; bone density and composition; histomorphometric evaluation of bone and pertinent endocrine organs. *Mailing Add:* Dept Vet Path Colo State Univ Ft Collins CO 80521

NORRED, WILLIAM PRESTON, b Tallassee, Ala, July 11, 45; m 69; c 2. PHARMACOLOGY, TOXICOLOGY. *Educ:* Emory Univ, BA, 66; Univ Ga, BS, 69, PhD(pharmacol), 71. *Prof Exp:* RES PHARMACOLOGIST, USDA-SEA-RICHARD B RUSSELL AGR RES CTR, 71- *Concurrent Pos:* Adj asst prof, Sch Pharm, Univ Ga, 76- & Grad Sch, 78- *Mem:* Am Soc Pharmacol & Exp Therapeut; Soc Toxicol; AAAS; Sigma Xi. *Res:* Drug metabolism; mycotoxins. *Mailing Add:* Pharmacol Lab USDA-SEA Russell Agr Res Ctr PO Box 5677 Athens GA 30604

NORRIE, D(OUGLAS) H, b Wellington, NZ, Dec 4, 29; m 54; c 4. MECHANICAL ENGINEERING. *Educ:* Univ Canterbury, BE, 51, Hons, 53; Univ Otago, NZ, BSc, 52; Univ Adelaide, PhD(mech eng), 65. *Prof Exp:* Design draftsman, Hamilton & Co, NZ, 53-54; grad apprentice, Rolls-Royce, Derby, UK, 54-55; tech off, Fairey Aviation, SAustralia, 55-57; lectr mech eng, Adelaide, 57-58, sr lectr, 58-66; prof & head dept, 66-71, dir info servs, 71-74, PROF MECH ENG, UNIV CALGARY, 74- *Concurrent Pos:* Mem adv comt eng res, Defence Res Bd Can, 67-74, chmn, 71 & Adv Bd Sci & Tech Info, Nat Res Coun Can, 74-77; chmn, Adv Comt Marine Physics & Eng, Defense Res Bd Can, 72-74; mem, Grant Selection Adv Comt Mech Eng, Nat Sci & Eng Res Coun Can, 80- *Mem:* Soc Naval Archit & Marine Engrs; Royal Aeronaut Soc; Brit Inst Mech Engrs; Sigma Xi; Royal Inst Naval Architects. *Res:* Fluid mechanics; finite element methods; numerical methods. *Mailing Add:* Dept Mech Eng Univ Calgary Calgary AB T2N 1N4 Can

NORRIS, A R, b Meadow Lake, Sask, May 18, 37; m 60. INORGANIC CHEMISTRY, PHYSICAL CHEMISTRY. *Educ:* Univ Sask, BE, 58, MSc, 59; Univ Chicago, PhD(chem), 62. *Prof Exp:* Res aasoc, Univ Chicago, 60; Nat Res Coun fel, Univ Col London, 62-64; asst prof chem, 64-68, ASSOC PROF CHEM, QUEEN'S UNIV, ONT, 68- *Concurrent Pos:* Vis scholar chem, Stanford Univ, 71-72. *Mem:* The Chem Soc; Can Inst Chem. *Res:* Metal ion-biomolecule interactions; oxidation, reduction and addition reactions of coordinated ligands in transition metal complexes; kinetics and mechanisms of formation of sigma complexes of polynitroaromatic compounds. *Mailing Add:* 55 Jane Ave Kingston ON K7M 3G7 Can

NORRIS, ALBERT STANLEY, b Sudbury, Ont, July 14, 26; m 50; c 3. PSYCHIATRY. *Educ:* Univ Western Ont, MD, 51. *Prof Exp:* Fel, Harvard Med Sch, 55-56; instr psychiat, Med Sch, Queen's Univ, Ont, 56-57; from asst prof to assoc prof, Col Med, Univ Iowa, 57-64; assoc prof, Med Sch, Univ Ore, 64-65; from assoc prof to prof, Col Med, Univ Iowa, 65-72; PROF PSYCHIAT & CHMN DEPT, SCH MED, SOUTHERN ILL UNIV, 72- *Mem:* AMA; fel Am Psychiat Asn. *Res:* Anatomical and physiological traits which predispose the development of mental illness; prenatal influences affecting intellectual and emotional development; capillary morphology in mental illness; psychosomatic obstetrics and gynecology; investigations of the efficacy of LSD 25 in the treatment of sexual deviation. *Mailing Add:* Dept of Psychiat Box 3926 Southern Ill Univ Sch of Med Springfield IL 62708

NORRIS, ANDREW EDWARD, b Santa Rosa, Calif, Jan 13, 37. NUCLEAR CHEMISTRY. *Educ:* Univ Chicago, SB, 58; Wash Univ, PhD(chem), 63. *Prof Exp:* Res assoc chem, Wash Univ, 63-64 & Brookhaven Nat Lab, 64-66; 64-66, STAFF MEM, LOS ALAMOS NAT LAB, 66- *Concurrent Pos:* Vis guest chemist, Lawrence Berkeley Lab, 73-74; asst for res, Off of Dir, Los Alamos Sci Lab, 75-77. *Mem:* Sigma Xi; Am Chem Soc; Am Phys Soc; AAAS. *Res:* Fission yields; heavy ion reaction; nuclear waste management. *Mailing Add:* Los Alamos Nat Lab Los Alamos NM 87545

NORRIS, BILL EUGENE, b Ft Recovery, Ohio, Jan 12, 30; m 50; c 3. BIOLOGY. *Educ:* Ball State Univ, BS, 60, MS, 65, EdD(biophys educ), 70. *Prof Exp:* Teacher high schs, Ohio & Ind, 60-68; teaching fel biol, Ball State Univ, 68-70; asst prof, 70-77, ASSOC PROF BIOL SCI, WESTERN OHIO BR CAMPUS, WRIGHT STATE UNIV, 77- *Mem:* Nat Asn Biol Teachers. *Res:* Biological survey of Grand Lake St Marys; self concepts of science teachers. *Mailing Add:* Dept of Biol Wright State Univ Celina OH 45822

NORRIS, CAROL LEE, chemical physics, see previous edition

NORRIS, CARROLL BOYD, JR, b New Orleans, La, Apr 28, 41. PHYSICS, ELECTRICAL ENGINEERING. *Educ:* Stanford Univ, BSEE, 63, MSEE, 64, PhD(elec eng), 67. *Prof Exp:* Scientist phys electronics, Lockheed Res Lab, 63; res asst device physics, Stanford Electronics Labs, 64-66, res assoc, 66-70; MEM TECH STAFF SEMICONDUCTOR PHYSICS, SANDIA LABS, 70- *Concurrent Pos:* Consult, Hewlett-Packard Assocs, 67-68, Gen Elec Res Lab, 68 & Watkins-Johnson Co, 68-70. *Mem:* Am Phys Soc. *Res:* Luminescence and the nature of optical transitions in compound semiconductors; physics of charge transport in semiconductors; irradiation and ion implantation effects in semiconductors; electron beam-semiconductor active devices. *Mailing Add:* Sandia Labs 5133 PO Box 5800 Albuquerque NM 87185

NORRIS, CHARLES H(EAD), structural engineering, deceased

NORRIS, CHARLES HAMILTON, b Cornwall, Ont, Oct 10, 14; nat US; m 39, 65; c 2. PHYSIOLOGY. *Educ:* Hamilton Col, BS, 36; Princeton Univ, PhD(biol), 39. *Prof Exp:* From instr to assoc prof biol, 39-65, assoc chmn dept, 66-70, prof, 65-81, EMER PROF BIOL, UNIV COLO, BOULDER, 81- *Res:* Physical properties of cells; kidney function in native Colorado rodents; neoteny in native Colorado salamanders; history of biology. *Mailing Add:* Dept of Biol Univ of Colo Boulder CO 80302

NORRIS, DALE MELVIN, JR, b Essex, Iowa, Aug 19, 30; wid. NEUROBIOLOGY, AGING. *Educ:* Iowa State Univ, BS, 52, MS, 53, PhD(zool, plant path), 56. Educ: Asst entomologist, Agr Exp Sta, Univ Fla, 56-57; from asst prof to assoc prof entom, 58-66, PROF ENTOM, UNIV WIS-MADISON, 66- *Concurrent Pos:* Vis lectr various univs and cols, 63-; consult, several countries. *Honors & Awards:* Foundrs Mem Award, Entom Soc Am, 75. Mem. *Mem:* AAAS; Entom Soc Am; Int Soc Neurochem; Am Soc Neurochem; Biophys Soc. *Res:* Insect transmission of microbes; systemic chemical action; insectt interactions with plants; symbiosis; chemoreception; neurobiology; aging-molecular aspects. *Mailing Add:* 642 Russell Labs Univ of Wis Madison WI 53706

NORRIS, DANIEL HOWARD, b Toledo, Ohio, Dec 29, 33; m 58. BOTANY. *Educ:* Mich State Univ, BS, 54; Univ Tenn, PhD(bot), 64. *Prof Exp:* Instr bot, Univ Tenn, 59-60; asst prof biol, Cent Methodist Col, 61-63; assoc prof, Catonsville Community Col, 64-67; asst prof biol, 67-74, PROF BOT, HUMBOLDT STATE UNIV, 74- *Mem:* AAAS; Am Bryol & Lichenol Soc; Nordic Bryol Soc; Brit Bryol Soc; Bot Soc Am. *Res:* Bryogeography and taxonomy of Dominican Republic, Newfoundland, California and the tropical Pacific Islands; bryoecology of Great Smoky Mountains National Park; phytogeography. *Mailing Add:* Dept of Bot Humboldt State Univ Arcata CA 95521

NORRIS, DAVID OTTO, b Ashtabula, Ohio, Oct 1, 39; m 66. COMPARATIVE ENDOCRINOLOGY. *Educ:* Baldwin-Wallace Col, BS, 61; Univ Wash, PhD(fish thyroid), 66. *Prof Exp:* From asst prof to assoc prof, 66-77, PROF BIOL, UNIV COLO, BOULDER, 77- *Mem:* Herpetologists League; AAAS; Am Soc Zoologists. *Res:* Comparative endocrinology of lower vertebrates; influences of environmental factors on endocrine activity; physiology and behavior in relation to life history events. *Mailing Add:* Dept of Environ Pop & Organismic Biol Univ of Colo Boulder CO 80309

NORRIS, DEAN RAYBURN, b Indianola, Iowa, Jan 21, 37; m 61; c 2. PHYCOLOGY. *Educ:* Iowa State Univ, BS, 59; Tex A&M Univ, MS, 67, PhD(oceanog), 69. *Prof Exp:* Discipline scientist, Nat Aeronaut & Space Admin, Johnson Space Ctr, 69-75; ASSOC PROF OCEANOG, FLA INST TECHNOL, 75- *Concurrent Pos:* Co-investr, Overflight Tektite II, Johnson Space Ctr, NASA, 70; mem, Oceanog Working Group, Shuttle Sortie Workshop, 72; vis scientist, Scripps Inst Oceanog, NASA, 74, aboard Res Vessel, Va Key, 73. *Mem:* Am Soc Limnol & Oceanog; Int Phycological Soc; Sigma Xi. *Res:* Ecology and taxonomy of marine phytoplankton, in particular the dinoflagellates; effects of various toxic substances on phytoplankton; effects of increased ultraviolet-light on phytoplankton; life-cycle phenomena and ecology of selected dinoflagellates. *Mailing Add:* Dept Oceanog & Ocean Eng Fla Inst Technol Melbourne FL 32901

NORRIS, DONALD EARL, JR, b Hammond, Ind, Oct 16, 40; m 64; c 1. PARASITOLOGY. *Educ:* Ind State Univ, Terre Haute, BS, 63; Tulane Univ, MS, 66, PhD(parasitol), 69. *Prof Exp:* From asst prof to assoc prof, 70-81, PROF BIOL, UNIV SOUTHERN MISS, 81- *Mem:* AAAS; Am Soc Parasitol; Am Soc Trop Med & Hyg; Royal Soc Trop Med & Hyg; Wildlife Dis Asn. *Res:* Life histories of parasites; helminthology. *Mailing Add:* Dept of Biol Univ of Southern Miss Hattiesburg MS 39401

NORRIS, DONALD KRING, b Cobourg, Ont, July 31, 24. GEOLOGY. *Educ:* Univ Toronto, BA, 47, MA, 49; Calif Inst Technol, PhD(geol), 53. *Prof Exp:* Geologist struct geol, Geol Surv Can, 53-69; MEM STAFF, INST SEDIMENT & PETROL GEOL, 69- *Honors & Awards:* Coleman Gold Medal, 47. *Mem:* Geol Soc Am; NY Acad Sci; Royal Astron Soc Can. *Res:* Geology of fuels; analysis of structural types; Mesozoic stratigraphy of Canadian Cordillera. *Mailing Add:* Inst of Sediment & Petrol Geol 3303 33rd St NW Calgary AB T2L 2A7 Can

NORRIS, EUGENE MICHAEL, b New York, NY, July 4, 38; m 69; c 3. COMPUTER SCIENCE, SOFTWARE SYSTEMS. *Educ:* Univ SFla, BA, 64, PhD(math), 69. *Prof Exp:* Lectr math, Univ Fla, 65-66 & 68-69; asst prof, WVa Univ, 69-72; asst prof math & comput sci, Univ SC, 72-78; analyst, Ketron, Inc, 78-80; ASSOC PROF COMPUT SCI, DEPT MATH SCI, GEORGE MASON UNIV, 80- *Concurrent Pos:* Consult. *Mem:* Math Asn Am; Sigma Xi; Asn Comput Mach. *Res:* Applications of neurol models ot cognition problems. *Mailing Add:* Dept Math Sci George Mason Univ Fairfax VA 22030

NORRIS, FLETCHER R, b Brownsville, Tenn, Sept 2, 34; m 60; c 2. MATHEMATICS, COMPUTER SCIENCE. *Educ:* Vanderbilt Univ, BA, 56; George Peabody Col, MA, 62, PhD(math), 68. *Prof Exp:* Teacher high sch, Tenn, 59-62; instr eng math, Vanderbilt Univ, 62-64, 66-68, asst prof, 68-70; lectr math, Univ NC, Wilmington, 70-71; Vanderbilt fel, Fla State Univ, 71-72; assoc prof, 72-77, PROF MATH, UNIV NC, WILMINGTON, 77- *Mem:* Asn Comput Mach; Am Asn Univ Prof; Nat Coun Teachers Math; Math Asn Am. *Res:* Application of computers and computing to mathematics and statistics. *Mailing Add:* Dept of Math Univ of NC Wilmington NC 28401

NORRIS, FORBES HOLTEN, JR, b Richmond, Va, May 1, 28; m 55; c 3. NEUROLOGY, NEUROPHYSIOLOGY. *Educ:* Harvard Univ, BS, 49, MD, 55. *Prof Exp:* Guest worker electromyography, NIH, 54-55; intern surg, Johns Hopkins Hosp, 55-56; med officer, NIH, 56-61; from sr instr to asst prof neurol, Univ Rochester, 61-63, assoc prof & actg chmn div, 63-66; trustee, Inst Med Sci, 69-72, 79-81, ASSOC DIR INST NEUROL SCI, PAC MED CTR, 66- *Concurrent Pos:* USPHS spec fel, 61-63; ad hoc consult, NIH, 62; sr res fel, Inst Neurol, Univ London, 66; adj prof neurol, Univ of the Pac, 70- *Mem:* AAAS; AMA; Am Acad Neurol; Am Asn Electromyog & Electrodiag; Am Neurol Asn. *Res:* Clinical and experimental studies of the function of normal and diseased nervous system. *Mailing Add:* Pac Med Ctr PO Box 7999 San Francisco CA 94120

NORRIS, FRANK ARTHUR, b Pittsburgh, Pa, July 2, 13; m 39; c 1. BIOCHEMISTRY. *Educ:* Univ Pittsburgh, BS, 35, PhD(biochem), 39. *Prof Exp:* Asst chem, Univ Pittsburgh, 36-39; Rockefeller fel, Univ Minn, 39-41; res chemist, Gen Mills, Inc, 41-44; head oil mill res, Swift & Co, 44-64, head edible oil res, 64-66; sr scientist, Res & Develop Div, Kraftco Corp, 66-69, dir res admin, 69-72, assoc mgr edible oil prod, 72-78; RETIRED. *Concurrent Pos:* Consult, 78- *Honors & Awards:* Bailey Award, Am Oil Chemist Soc, 80. *Mem:* Am Oil Chemists Soc (vpres, 72-73, pres, 73-74); AAAS; Inst Food Technologists; Am Chem Soc. *Res:* Synthetic glycerides; fatty acid chemistry; oilseed processing; vegetable proteins; edible fats and oil processing. *Mailing Add:* Apt 206A 4350 W Lake Glenview IL 60025

NORRIS, GAIL ROYAL, b Coshocton, Ohio, Jan 17, 19; m 44; c 3. RADIATION BIOPHYSICS. *Educ:* Ohio Univ, BS, 41; Ohio State Univ, MS, 47, PhD(zool), 50. *Prof Exp:* Asst zool, Ohio State Univ, 46, asst instr, 47-49; instr, Denison Univ, 49-50; from assoc prof to prof, Mt Union Col, 50-58; prof zool, 59-81, PROF BIOL, DENISON UNIV, 81- *Concurrent Pos:* Am Physiol Soc, res fel, 57-58, 60; NIH res grants, 57-60; res assoc, Ohio State Univ, 65-66; Oak Ridge Nat Lab, Tenn, 71. *Mem:* Radiation Res Soc; AAAS; Am Nuclear Soc. *Res:* Cellular physiology; red blood cell metabolism; neutron activation analysis of trace elements; neutron activation analysis of human lungs. *Mailing Add:* Dept of Biol Denison Univ Granville OH 43023

NORRIS, GEOFFREY, b Romford, Eng, Aug 6, 37; m 58; c 4. GEOLOGY, PALEONTOLOGY. *Educ:* Cambridge Univ, BA, 59, MA, 62, PhD(geol), 64. *Prof Exp:* Sci officer, NZ Geol Surv, 61-64; fel geol, McMaster Univ, 64-65; sr res scientist, Res Ctr, Pan Am Petrol Corp, Okla, 65-67; from asst prof to assoc prof, 67-74, PROF GEOL, UNIV TORONTO, 74-, CHMN, DEPT GEOL, 80- *Concurrent Pos:* Res assoc, Royal Ont Mus, Toronto, 68-; mem, Int Comn Palynology (secy, treas, 77-); Humboldt Res Fel, Univ Cologne, Ger, 78-; mem, Earth Sci Grant Selection Comt, Nat Sci Eng Res Coun Can, 80-83. *Mem:* Am Asn Stratig Palynologists (pres, 71-72); Geol Asn Can; Paleont Soc; Brit Palaeont Asn; Geol Soc Am. *Res:* Palynology; stratigraphic and paleoecologic applications; taxonomy of dinoflagellate cysts. *Mailing Add:* Dept of Geol Univ of Toronto Toronto ON M5S 1A1 Can

NORRIS, JAMES NEWCOME, IV, b Santa Barbara, Calif, Sept 8, 42; m 77; c 1. MARINE PHYCOLOGY. *Educ:* San Francisco State Col, BA, 68, MA, 71; Univ Calif, Santa Barbara, PhD(marine bot), 75. *Prof Exp:* Asst cur, Gilbert M Smith Herbarium Hopkins Marine Sta, Stanford Univ, 69-70; assoc, Dept Biol Sci, Univ Calif, Santa Barbara, 71-72; sta dir & resident marine biologist, Marine Biol Lab, Puerto Penasco, Mex, Univ Ariz, 72-74; ASSOC CUR, DEPT BOT, NAT MUS NAT HIST, SMITHSONIAN INST, 75- *Concurrent Pos:* Res assoc, Dept Ecol & Evolutionary Biol, Univ Ariz, 74-; NSF panel mem, Adv Com Syst Biol Prog, 79-80. *Mem:* Phycol Soc Am; Int Phycol Soc; Bot Soc Mex; Int Asn Plant Taxon; Asn Trop Biol. *Res:* Biosystematics and ecology of marine benthic algae; chemotaxonomy of marine algae; marine flora of the Gulf of California, Pacific Mexico, Galapagos Islands, Belize and Caribbean Panama. *Mailing Add:* Dept of Bot 166 NHB Smithsonian Inst Washington DC 20560

NORRIS, JAMES SCOTT, b Selma, Ala, Aug 6, 43; m 66. ENDOCRINOLOGY. *Educ:* Keene State Col, BS, 66; Univ Colo, PhD(zool), 71. *Prof Exp:* Ford Found fel endocrinol, Univ Ill, Urbana, 70-71, Nat Cancer Inst fel, 71, Am Cancer Soc fel, 71-74; instr cell biol, Baylor Col Med, 74-77; ASST PROF, MED SCH, UNIV ARK, 77- *Mem:* AAAS; Endocrine Soc; Am Soc Cell Biol; Tissue Cult Asn. *Res:* Cell-culture; study of abnormal endocrinology of cancer in vitro. *Mailing Add:* Dept of Med Univ Ark for Med Sci Little Rock AR 77025

NORRIS, KARL H(OWARD), b Glen Richey, Pa, May 23, 21; m 48; c 2. AGRICULTURAL ENGINEERING. *Educ:* Pa State Univ, BS, 42. *Prof Exp:* Radio engr, Airplane & Marine Instrument Co, 45-46; electronic engr, Univ Chicago, 46-49; lab dir, Instrumentation Res Lab, Agr Res Serv, 50-77, CHIEF INSTRUMENT RES LAB, SCI & EDUC ADMIN, USDA, 77- *Honors & Awards:* Superior Serv Award, USDA, 63. *Mem:* Am Soc Agr Engrs; Inst Food Technol. *Res:* Instrumentation for the measurement of quality factors of agricultural products. *Mailing Add:* Sci & Educ Admin USDA Beltsville MD 20705

NORRIS, KENNETH STAFFORD, b Los Angeles, Calif, Aug 11, 24; m 53; c 4. ZOOLOGY. *Educ:* Univ Calif, Los Angeles, MA, 51, PhD(zool), 59. *Prof Exp:* Asst ichthyol, Scripps Inst, Calif, 51-53; cur, Marineland of Pac, 54-60; lectr zool, Univ Calif, Los Angeles, 60-65, from assoc prof to prof, 65-72; dir, Coastal Marine Lab, 72-75, chemn environ studies, 76-78, PROF NATURAL HIST, UNIV CALIF, SANTA CRUZ, 72- *Concurrent Pos:* Mem sci adv comt, US Marine Mammal Comn, 72-; mem adv bd, Bur Land Mgt, Dept Interior, 75- *Mem:* AAAS; Am Soc Ichthyologists & Herpetologists; Soc Study Evolution; Ecol Soc Am; Am Soc Mammalogists. *Res:* Echolocation and natural history of cetaceans. *Mailing Add:* Coastal Marine Sci Lab Appl Sci Univ of Calif Santa Cruz CA 95064

NORRIS, LOGAN ALLEN, b Oakland, Calif, May 23, 36; m 58; c 3. PESTICIDE CHEMISTRY, WATERSHED RESEARCH. *Educ:* Ore State Univ, BS, 61, MS, 64, PhD(plant physiol, biochem), 69. *Prof Exp:* Asst biochem, Ore State Univ, 61-68; CHIEF RES CHEMIST & PROJ LEADER, FORESTRY SCI LAB, PAC NORTHWEST FOREST & RANGE EXP STA, US FOREST SERV, 68- *Mem:* Soc Am Foresters; Weed Sci Soc Am. *Res:* Woody plants; behavior and impact of chemicals in the forest environment; watershed management. *Mailing Add:* Forestry Sci Lab 3200 Jefferson Way Corvallis OR 97331

NORRIS, PAUL EDMUND, b Detroit, Mich, Nov 9, 18; m 44; c 2. PHARMACEUTICAL CHEMISTRY. *Educ:* Univ Mich, BS, 41, MS, 42, PhD(pharmaceut chem), 52. *Prof Exp:* Asst to F F Blicke, Univ Mich, 46-48, instr pharm, 48-51, asst prof, 51-54; group leader, 54-64, toxicologist, 64-76, MONITORING SYSTS COORDR, PROCTER & GAMBLE CO, 76- *Mem:* AAAS; Am Chem Soc; Soc Toxicol; Am Pharmaceut Asn. *Res:* Synthetic drugs; synthesis of organic medicinals; concentration in area of potential ergot substitutes; synthesis of esters and amides of beta-amino acids; development of anticaries agents; design of clinical tests; toxicological testing and safety evaluation. *Mailing Add:* 476 Beech Tree Dr Cincinnati OH 45224

NORRIS, RICHARD C, b Schenectady, NY, Nov 2, 35; m 58; c 3. ELECTRICAL ENGINEERING. *Educ:* Harvard Univ, AB, 57, SM, 58; Mass Inst Technol, ScD(elec eng), 62. *Prof Exp:* RES ELEC ENG, ARTHUR D LITTLE, INC, 62- *Mem:* Opers Res Soc Am. *Res:* Operations research; effectiveness analysis; computer applications; transportation. *Mailing Add:* Arthur D Little Inc 35 Acorn Park Cambridge MA 02140

NORRIS, RICHARD EARL, marine botany, see previous edition

NORRIS, ROBERT FRANCIS, b Buckinghamshire, Eng, July 4, 38; m 63; c 2. PLANT PHYSIOLOGY, WEED SCIENCE. *Educ:* Univ Reading, BSc, 60; Univ Alta, PhD(crop ecol), 64. *Prof Exp:* NIH & USPHS grants, Mich State Univ, 64-67; asst prof bot, 67-74, ASSOC PROF BOT, UNIV CALIF, DAVIS, 74- *Mem:* AAAS; Bot Soc Am; Weed Sci Soc Am; Am Soc Plant Physiologists. *Res:* Plant growth regulators; cuticle structure and penetration; weed control; ecology of crop-weed association; weed/insect interactions, integrated control; herbicide action and physiology. *Mailing Add:* Dept of Bot Univ of Calif Davis CA 95616

NORRIS, ROBERT MATHESON, b Los Angeles, Calif, Apr 24, 21; m 52; c 3. GEOLOGY. *Educ:* Univ Calif, Los Angeles, AB, 43, MA, 49; Univ Calif, San Diego, PhD(oceanog), 51. *Prof Exp:* Asst geol, Univ Calif, Los Angeles, 46-49; asst submarine geol, Scripps Inst, 49-51, assoc marine geol, 51-52; from lectr to instr, 52-55, asst prof 55-60, chmn dept, 60-63, assoc prof, 60-68, PROF GEOL, UNIV CALIF, SANTA BARBARA, 68- *Concurrent Pos:* Mem staff, US Geol Surv, 55-60; geologist, NZ Oceanog Inst, 61-62, 68-69 & 75-76. *Honors & Awards:* Neil A Miner Award, Nat Asn Geol Teachers, 81. *Mem:* Nat Asn Geol Teachers; Geol Soc Am; Soc Econ Paleontologists & Mineralogists; Am Geog Soc; Am Asn Petrol Geol. *Res:* Quaternary and marine geology; geomorphology. *Mailing Add:* Dept of Geol Sci Univ of Calif Santa Barbara CA 93106

NORRIS, ROY HOWARD, b Scammon, Kans, Apr 13, 30; m 60; c 2. REHABILITATION ENGINEERING. *Educ:* Univ Wichita, BSEE, 59, MSEE, 62; Okla State Univ, PhD(elec eng), 72. *Prof Exp:* From instr to assoc prof, 61-78, PROF ELEC ENG, WICHITA STATE UNIV, 78-, CHMN DEPT, 80- *Concurrent Pos:* Res engr, Autonetics, Downey, Calif, 59; res assoc elec eng, Univ Fla, 63-64; NSF sci fac fel, 66-67; res engr, Boeing Airplane Co, 68-72; tech engr, Boeing Co, 73-74; dir technol & eng staff, Wichita State Univ Rehab Eng Ctr, 76-78, co-dir, 78-79 & dir, 79- *Mem:* Am Soc Eng Educr; Inst Elec & Electronics Engrs; Rehab Eng Soc NAm. *Res:* Rehabilitation engineering, including the vocational prospects of the severely disabled. *Mailing Add:* 619 N 159th St E Wichita KS 67230

NORRIS, TERRY ORBAN, b NC, Apr, 29, 22; m 51; c 2. ORGANIC CHEMISTRY. *Educ:* Univ NC, PhD(chem), 54. *Prof Exp:* Anal res chemist instrumental methods, E I du Pont de Nemours & Co, 49-51, polymer systs, 54-56; asst dir res, Keuffel & Esser Co, 56-57, dir, 58-62, dir corp res, 62-63; res mgr, IBM Corp, 63-66; dir res, 66-69, VPRES RES & DEVELOP, NEKOOSA EDWARDS PAPER CO, INC, 69-, BD DIRS, 72- *Mem:* AAAS; Am Chem Soc; Am Inst Chem; Soc Photog Sci & Eng; NY Acad Sci. *Res:* Polymer systems, coating; light sensitive systems and electrophotography; recording materials technology; pulp and paper chemistry; paper coatings. *Mailing Add:* 731 Wisconsin River Dr Port Edwards WI 54469

NORRIS, THOMAS ELFRED, biochemistry, see previous edition

NORRIS, THOMAS HUGHES, b Princeton, NJ, Feb 8, 16; m 42; c 1. PHYSICAL INORGANIC CHEMISTRY, CHEMICAL KINETICS. *Educ:* Princeton Univ, AB, 38; Univ Calif, Berkeley, PhD(chem), 42. *Prof Exp:* Chemist, Linde Air Prod Co, NY, 38-39; asst chemist, Gen Elec Co, Mass, 42; res assoc, Nat Defense Res Comt, Univ Calif, Berkeley, 43, instr chem, 44-46; asst prof, Univ Minn, 46-47; from asst prof to assoc prof, 47-60, prof, 60-81, EMER PROF CHEM, ORE STATE UNIV, 81- *Mem:* Am Chem Soc; AAAS. *Res:* Radioactive tracer studies in physical and inorganic chemistry; exchange reactions and reaction mechanisms; non-aqueous ionizing solvents; complex formation in solution; nuclear magnetic resonance in solution. *Mailing Add:* Dept of Chem Ore State Univ Corvallis OR 97331

NORRIS, WILFRED GLEN, b Malmo, Sweden, Apr 21, 32; US citizen; m 55; c 3. CHEMICAL PHYSICS. *Educ:* Juniata Col, BS, 54; Harvard Univ, PhD(chem), 63. *Prof Exp:* Instr physics, 58-59, from asst prof to prof, 59-66, dean, 70-77, WILLIAM I & ZELLA B BOOK PROF PHYSICS, JUNIATA COL, 66- *Concurrent Pos:* NSF sci fac fel, Univ Md, 67-68. *Mem:* AAAS; Am Phys Soc; Am Asn Physics Teachers; Optical Soc Am. *Res:* Diffusion of hydrogen in steel; surface reactions of hydrogen on steel; photochemistry; infrared and microwave spectra of small molecules at high temperatures. *Mailing Add:* Dept Physics Juniata Col Huntington PA 16652

NORRIS, WILLIAM ELMORE, JR, b Nixon, Tex, Feb 23, 21; m 44; c 3. PLANT PHYSIOLOGY. *Educ:* Southwest Tex State Teachers Col, BS, 40; Univ Tex, PhD(physiol), 48. *Prof Exp:* Instr biol & physiol, Univ Tex, 45-47; instr physiol, biochem & bact, Bryn Mawr Col, 47-48, asst prof biol, 48-49; assoc prof, 49-52, chmn dept, 52-67, dean, Sch Sci, 65-70, Col Arts & Sci, 70-74, vpres acad affairs, 74-80, PROF BIOL, SOUTHWEST TEX STATE UNIV, 52-, DEAN, 80- *Mem:* AAAS; Am Soc Plant Physiol; Scand Soc Plant Physiol. *Res:* Bioelectrics; plant respiration; plant growth substances. *Mailing Add:* Dept of Biol Southwest Tex State Univ San Marcos TX 78666

NORRIS, WILLIAM PENROD, b Loogootee, Ind, Sept 2, 20; m 43, 77; c 3. RADIOBIOLOGY. *Educ:* DePauw Univ, AB, 41; Univ Ill, PhD(biochem), 44. *Prof Exp:* Biochemist, Dow Chem Co, Mich, 44 & Manhattan Area Engrs, 44-46; group leader biol div, Argonne Nat Lab, 46-52, assoc biochemist, 52-70, group leader div biol & med res, 70-79, scientist, 73-79; RETIRED. *Mem:* Radiation Res Soc; Am Soc Biol Chemists; Reticuloendothelial Soc; Health Physics Soc; Am Nuclear Soc. *Res:* Responses of dogs to continuous or protracted gamma-irradiation; sphingolipids; metabolism of phosphorus and alkaline earths; isolation and synthesis of dihydrosphingosine; radioautography; effects of ionizing radiations in animals; measurement and chemistry of radioactive elements; radiation chemistry; paper electrophoresis. *Mailing Add:* 63 Portwine Rd 5186 State Park Dr RR 3 Whitewater WI 53190

NORRIS, WILLIAM PHILLIP, organic chemistry, see previous edition

NORRIS, WILLIAM WARREN, b Choudrant, La, Mar 27; m 49; c 3. ZOOLOGY. *Educ:* La Polytech Inst, BS, 50; La State Univ, MS, 51, PhD, 55. *Prof Exp:* Histologist, Res Labs, Swift & Co, 55-60; assoc prof zool, Western Ky State Col, 60-65; assoc prof, 65-69, PROF BIOL, NORTHEAST LA UNIV, 69- *Mem:* Am Soc Zool. *Res:* Histology, especially as related to proteolytic action of muscle fibers and connective tissue; reproductive physiology as related to pineal gland. *Mailing Add:* Dept of Biol Northeast La Univ Monroe LA 71201

NORSTADT, FRED A, b Sidney, Iowa, Mar 15, 26; m 50; c 2. AGRICULTURAL MICROBIOLOGY, AGRICULTURAL CHEMISTRY. *Educ:* Nebr State Teachers Col, BS, 50; Univ Nebr, MS, 58, PhD(agron), 66. *Prof Exp:* Teacher high schs, Nebr, 49-56, prin, Holmesville High Sch, 51-53; instr exten div, Univ Nebr, 56-64; chemist, Soil & Water Conserv Res, 64-66, SOIL SCIENTIST, AGR RES SERV, USDA, 66- *Mem:* Soil Sci Soc Am; fel Soil Conserv Soc Am; Am Soc Agron; Crop Sci Soc Am; Int Soil Sci Soc. *Res:* Microbial crop residue decomposition; phytotoxic substances; mineralization of carbon, nitrogen, phosphorus and sulfur from soil organic matter and animal wastes; soil physical, chemical and biological effects on plant growth. *Mailing Add:* PO Box E Ft Collins CO 80522

NORSTOG, KNUT JONSON, b Grand Forks, NDak, June 11, 21; m 44; c 3. BIOLOGY. *Educ:* Luther Col, Iowa, BA, 43; Univ Mich, MS, 47, PhD(bot), 55. *Prof Exp:* Biologist, Dept Game, Fish & Parks, SDak, 47-49; instr biol, Luther Col, 49-51; assoc prof, Wittenberg Univ, 54-63; assoc prof bot & bact, Univ SFla, 63-66; prof biol sci, Northern Ill Univ, 66-77, RES ASSOC, FAIRCHILD TROP GARDEN, 78- *Concurrent Pos:* NSF fac fel, 59; res fel bot, Yale Univ, 59-60; ed-in-chief, Am J Bot, 80- *Mem:* Int Soc Plant Morphol; Torrey Bot Club; fel Linnean Soc; Bot Soc Am. *Res:* Plant morphogenesis; embryogenesis in the grasses; plant tissue culture. *Mailing Add:* Montgomery Found Northern Ill Univ Miami FL 60115

NORTH, CHARLES A, b Kingston, RI, Aug 24, 32; m 62; c 2. ZOOLOGY, ORNITHOLOGY. *Educ:* Univ Mo, BA, 54; Okla State Univ, MS, 62, PhD(zool), 68. *Prof Exp:* Asst prof, 66-76, ASSOC PROF BIOL, UNIV WIS-WHITEWATER, 76- *Concurrent Pos:* Wis State Univ res grant, 69-70; Instnl grants, 68-81; NSF travel grant, Poland, 71. *Res:* General biology; nature study; organic evolution; wildlife conservation; ecology. *Mailing Add:* Dept Biol Univ Wis Whitewater WI 53190

NORTH, CHARLES MALLORY, JR, applied mathematics, see previous edition

NORTH, DWIGHT OLCOTT, b Hartford, Conn, Sept 28, 09; m 35; c 2. THEORETICAL PHYSICS. *Educ:* Wesleyan Univ, BS, 30; Calif Inst Technol, PhD(physics), 33. *Prof Exp:* Fel tech staff, RCA Labs, 34-74; RETIRED. *Mem:* Fel Am Phys Soc; fel Inst Elec & Electronics Engrs. *Res:* Noise; solid-state; quantum theory. *Mailing Add:* 80 Random Rd Princeton NJ 08540

NORTH, EDWARD D(AVID), b Akron, Ohio, Oct 30, 18; m 42; c 2. CHEMICAL ENGINEERING. *Educ:* Univ Mich, MS, 41, PhD(chem eng), 50. *Prof Exp:* Area supt mfg, Mallinckrodt Chem Works, 50-57, plant mgr, 57-62; plant mgr, United Nuclear Corp, 62-64; asst plant mgr, Nuclear Fuel Serv, Inc, 64-65, plant mgr, 65-68, mgr environ protection & licensing, Rockville, 68-72; group leader, 76-79, MGR, COMPONENT DEVELOP, OAK RIDGE NAT LAB, 79- *Concurrent Pos:* Vchmn, Inst Nuclear Mat Mgr, 60, chmn, 61. *Mem:* Am Chem Soc; fel Am Inst Chem Engrs. *Res:* Economic processing of uranium and plutonium nuclear fuels; chemistry and technology of production of high purity inorganic compounds; nuclear fuel reprocessing and waste management. *Mailing Add:* Oak Ridge Nat Lab Oak Ridge TN 37830

NORTH, GERALD R, theoretical physics, see previous edition

NORTH, HARPER QUA, b Los Angeles, Calif, Jan 24, 17; m 69; c 2. PHYSICS. *Educ:* Calif Inst Technol, BS, 38; Univ Calif, Los Angeles, MA, 40, PhD(physics), 47. *Prof Exp:* Res asst, Gen Elec Co, 40-42, res assoc, 42-49; dir, Semiconductor Div, Hughes Aircraft Co, 49-54; pres, Pac Semiconductors, Inc, 54-62; vpres res & develop, TRW Inc, 62-69; mgr electro-optical dept, Electronics Div, Northrop Corp, 69-75; assoc dir res, Naval Res Lab, 75-81. *Concurrent Pos:* Consult, Off Dir Defense, Res & Eng, 59-75. *Honors & Awards:* Medal of Honor, Electronic Industs Asn, 66. *Mem:* Fel Am Phys Soc; fel Inst Elec & Electronics Engrs. *Res:* Semiconductor physics. *Mailing Add:* 17865 Bernardo Trails Place San Diego CA 92128

NORTH, HENRY E(RICK) T(UISKU), b Lethbridge, Alta, Nov 18, 31; m 60; c 3. FLUID MECHANICS, OPERATIONS RESEARCH. *Educ:* Queen's Univ, Ont, BSc, 55; Col Aeronaut, Dipl, 57. *Prof Exp:* Spec projs engr, United Aircraft Corp Can Ltd, 57-59; asst prof fluid mech, Univ Man, 59-66; assoc prof fluid mech & chmn sch eng, 66-77, ASSOC PROF MECH ENG, LAKEHEAD UNIV, 77- *Concurrent Pos:* Proj consult, Bristol Aero Indust Ltd, 62-64 & Hawker Siddeley Canada Ltd, 66-78; mem, comt internal aerodyn ducts, Nat Res Coun Can, 63- *Mem:* Am Soc Mech Engrs; Can Aeronaut & Space Inst. *Res:* Internal aerodynamics of straight and curved diffusers; jet interactions on lifting wings; propellor static thrust; parametric linear programming applied to projet planning; non-Newtonian fluids processing; mechanical resonant systems in high-power applications. *Mailing Add:* Sch Eng Lakehead Univ Thunder Bay ON P7B 5E1 Can

NORTH, JAMES A, b Charleston, Utah, Mar 18, 34; m 56; c 4. VIROLOGY, IMMUNOLOGY. *Educ:* Brigham Young Univ, BS, 58, MS, 60; Univ Utah, PhD(microbiol), 64. *Prof Exp:* Sr res assoc virol, Univ Cincinnati, 64-65; assoc prof, 65-72, PROF MICROBIOL, BRIGHAM YOUNG UNIV, 72- *Mem:* Am Soc Microbiol. *Res:* Viral purification and physical analysis; immunochemistry; viral etiology of cancer. *Mailing Add:* Dept of Microbiol Brigham Young Univ Provo UT 84601

NORTH, JAMES CLAYTON, solid state physics, see previous edition

NORTH, PAUL, b Coventry, Eng, Nov 5, 40; m 64; c 2. AERONAUTICAL ENGINEERING. *Educ:* Lanchester Col Technol, Eng, BS, 62; Col Aeronaut Eng, MS, 64; Univ Nottingham, PhD(fluid dynamics), 67. *Prof Exp:* Sr engr, Lockheed Ga Co, 67-68; asst prof aerothermopropulsion, Univ W Fla, 68-77; ASSOC SCI, IDAHO NAT ENG LAB, 77- *Mem:* Am Inst Aeronaut & Astronaut; Royal Aeronaut Soc; Brit Inst Mech Engrs. *Res:* Aeronautical systems; performance of conical diffusers with compressible flow; use of metal additives in tri-propellant rocket combustion. *Mailing Add:* Exp Spec & Anal/Tsb Idaho Nat Eng Lab Idaho Falls ID 83401

NORTH, RICHARD RALPH, b Hamilton, Ont, Aug 8, 34; m 55; c 4. NEUROLOGY. *Educ:* Queen's Univ, Ont, MD, CM, 59. *Prof Exp:* Fel neurophysiol, Col Med, Baylor Univ, 63-64, fel neurol, 64-66, asst prof, 66-67; from asst prof to assoc prof neurol, 67-75, clin assoc prof neurol, 75-82, CLIN PROF NEUROL, UNIV TEX HEALTH SCI CTR, DALLAS, 82- *Mem:* AAAS; Am Acad Neurol; Am EEG Soc; Am Epilepsy Soc. *Res:* Clinical electroencephalography; cerebrovascular disease; epilepsy; efficacy of levodopa therapy in parkinsonism. *Mailing Add:* 7777 Forest Ln 2420 Dallas TX 75230

NORTH, W(ALTER) PAUL TUISKU, b Vulcan, Alta, Dec 15, 34; m 57; c 3. MECHANICAL ENGINEERING. *Educ:* Queen's Univ, BSc, 58; Univ Sask, MSc, 59; Univ Ill, PhD(appl mech), 65. *Prof Exp:* Lectr mech eng, Univ Sask, 59-61, asst prof, 64-65; asst prof, 65-70, PROF MECH ENG, UNIV WINDSOR, 70- *Concurrent Pos:* Mem nat comt, Inst Union Theoret & Appl Mech, 66-67. *Mem:* Soc Exp Stress Anal. *Res:* Stress analysis including strain gages and modulated lasers in photoelastic techniques. *Mailing Add:* Dept of Mech Eng Univ of Windsor Windsor ON N9E 1P1 Can

NORTH, WHEELER JAMES, b San Francisco, Calif, Jan 2, 22; m 53; c 2. OCEANOGRAPHY. *Educ:* Calif Inst Technol, BS, 44 & 50; Univ Calif, PhD(oceanog), 53. *Prof Exp:* Electron engr, US Navy Electron Lab, 47-48; NSF fel, Cambridge Univ, 53-54; Rockefeller fel marine biol, Scripps Inst Oceanog, 55-56; asst res biologist & proj officer, Inst Marine Resources Kelp Prog, Univ Calif, 56-63; sr res scientist, Lockheed Calif Co, 63; assoc prof environ health eng, 63-68, PROF ENVIRON SCI, CALIF INST TECHNOL, 68- *Mem:* AAAS; Soc Gen Physiol; Am Soc Zool; Am Malacol Union; Am Geophys Union. *Res:* Ecology and general physiology. *Mailing Add:* W M Keck Lab Calif Inst Technol Pasadena CA 91125

NORTH, WILLIAM CHARLES, b Chungking, China, Aug 17, 25; m 71; c 9. ANESTHESIOLOGY, PHARMACOLOGY. *Educ:* DePauw Univ, BA, 45; Northwestern Univ, MS, 48, MD, 50, PhD, 52. *Prof Exp:* Intern, Chicago Mem Hosp, 49-50; from instr to asst prof pharmacol, Northwestern Univ, 50-59; asst prof anesthesiol, Sch Med, Duke Univ, 59-62, assoc prof anesthesiol & pharmacol, 63-65; PROF ANESTHESIOL & PHARMACOL & CHMN DEPT ANESTHESIOL, COL MED, UNIV TENN, MEMPHIS, 65- *Concurrent Pos:* Res anesthesia, Chicago Wesley Mem Hosp, 56-59. *Mem:* AAAS; Am Soc Anesthesiol; Am Soc Pharmacol & Exp Therapeut; AMA. *Res:* Neuropharmacology; analgesia; local anesthesia; shock; inhalation anesthesia. *Mailing Add:* Dept of Anesthesiol Univ of Tenn Col of Med Memphis TN 38163

NORTH, WILLIAM GORDON, b Woodstock, Ill, Aug 29, 42; m 64; c 2. STRATIGRAPHY. *Educ:* Carleton Col, AB, 63; Univ Ill, MS, 65, PhD(geol), 69. *Prof Exp:* Petrol geologist, Texaco, Inc, 68-75; mem staff, 77-80, ONSHORE DIST MGR, SANTA FE ENERGY, 80- *Res:* Stratigraphy, particularly subsurface stratigraphy; sedimentary petrology; statistics. *Mailing Add:* Santa Fe Energy 1616 S Voss Suite 400 Houston TX 77057

NORTHAM, EDWARD STAFFORD, b Lansing, Mich, Oct 18, 27; m 61; c 2. MATHEMATICS. *Educ:* Univ Mich, BS, 47, MS, 48; Mich State Univ, PhD(math), 53. *Prof Exp:* Mathematician, Bendix Aviation Corp, 53-54; from instr to asst prof math, Wayne State Univ, 54-64; assoc prof, 64-71, PROF MATH, UNIV MAINE, ORONO, 71-, COOP PROF ENG & SCI, 77- *Mem:* Am Math Soc; Math Asn Am. *Res:* Abstract algebra; lattice theory. *Mailing Add:* Dept of Math Univ of Maine Orono ME 04473

NORTHCLIFFE, LEE CONRAD, b Manitowoc, Wis, Mar 20, 26; m 53; c 2. NUCLEAR PHYSICS. *Educ:* Univ Wis, BS, 48, MS, 51, PhD(physics), 57. *Prof Exp:* Asst physics, Univ Wis, 51-57; from instr to asst prof, Yale Univ, 57-65; assoc prof, 65-70, PROF PHYSICS, TEX A&M UNIV, 70- *Mem:* Am Phys Soc. *Res:* Nucleon-nucleon scattering; penetration of heavy ions through matter; accelerator development and instrumentation for nuclear research; charge distributions of heavy ions; nuclear reactions and scattering. *Mailing Add:* Dept of Physics Tex A&M Univ College Station TX 77843

NORTHCOTT, JEAN, b Australia, June 26, 26; nat US. PHYSICAL CHEMISTRY, ORGANIC CHEMISTRY. *Educ:* Univ Sydney, PhD(chem), 53. *Prof Exp:* Chemist & bacteriologist, Campbell Soup Co, Can, 54-55; patent asst, Nat Aniline Div, 56-68, HEAD INFO SERV, SPECIALTY CHEM DIV, ALLIED CHEM CORP, 68- *Mem:* Am Chem Soc; Spec Libr Asn. *Res:* Chemical literature; patents. *Mailing Add:* Buffalo Res Lab PO Box 1069 Buffalo NY 14240

NORTHCUTT, RICHARD GLENN, b Mt Vernon, Ill, Aug 7, 41; m 65. NEUROANATOMY. *Educ:* Millikin Univ, BA, 63; Univ Ill, Urbana, MA, 66, PhD(zool), 68. *Prof Exp:* Asst prof anat, Case Western Reserve Univ, 68-72; assoc prof zool, 72-77, PROF BIOL SCI, UNIV MICH, ANN ARBOR, 77- *Concurrent Pos:* Res assoc, Cleveland Aquarium, 68-72; vis prof neurosci, Univ Calif, San Diego, 79; John Simon Guggenheim mem fel, 79. *Mem:* AAAS; Am Asn Anat; Am Soc Zool; Am Soc Ichthyol & Herpet; Soc Neurosci. *Res:* Evolution of the vertebrate nervous system; vertebrate paleontology, phylogeny and morphology; vertebrate behavior. *Mailing Add:* Div of Biol Sci Univ of Mich Ann Arbor MI 48109

NORTHCUTT, ROBERT ALLAN, b Luling, Tex, Sept 30, 37. MATHEMATICS. *Educ:* Univ Tex, Austin, BA, 60, MA, 62, PhD(math), 68. *Prof Exp:* Instr math, San Antonio Col, 62-64; Southwest Tex State Univ, 64-67; NSF fac fel, Univ Tex, 67-68; from asst prof to assoc prof, 68-73, chmn dept, 71-80, PROF MATH, SOUTHWEST TEX STATE UNIV, 73- *Mem:* Am Math Soc; Math Asn Am. *Res:* Differential and integral equations. *Mailing Add:* Dept of Math Southwest Tex State Univ San Marcos TX 78666

NORTHERN, JERRY LEE, b Albuquerque, NMex, Sept 13, 40; c 4. AUDIOLOGY. *Educ:* Colo Col, BA, 62; Gallaudet Col, MS, 63; Univ Denver, MA, 64; Univ Colo, PhD(audiol), 66. *Prof Exp:* Chief audiol clin, Dept Otolaryngol, Brooke Army Med Ctr, San Antonio, Tex, 66-67; asst dir, US Army Audiol & Speech Path Ctr, Walter Reed Army Med Ctr, Washington, DC, 67-70; HEAD AUDIOL SERV, DEPT OTOLARYNGOL, MED CTR, UNIV COLO, DENVER, 70- *Concurrent Pos:* Mem, Nat Registry Interpreters for the Deaf, 68- *Mem:* Am Speech & Hearing Asn; Acoust Soc Am; Am Audiol Soc; Nat Asn Deaf. *Res:* Clinical audiology; acoustic impedance of the ear. *Mailing Add:* Dept of Otolaryngol Univ of Colo Med Ctr Denver CO 80202

NORTHEY, WILLIAM T, b Duluth, Minn, Aug 10, 28; m 50; c 7. IMMUNOLOGY. *Educ:* Univ Minn, BA, 50; Univ Kans, MA, 57, PhD(immunol), 59. *Prof Exp:* Res asst, Abbott Labs, 50-51; res asst immunol & virol, Naval Med Res Unit 4, 51-55; teaching & res, Univ Kans, 55-59; from asst prof to assoc prof, 59-72, PROF IMMUNOL, ARIZ STATE UNIV, 72- *Concurrent Pos:* Mem, Allergy Found Am, 60-; consult, Iatric Corp, 70- *Mem:* Am Soc Microbiol; Am Asn Immunol; Am Asn Univ Profs. *Res:* Immune response in cold exposure; hypothermia; immunological aspects of the delayed response primarily in Coccidioidomycosis; allergenic extracts. *Mailing Add:* Dept of Bot & Microbiol Ariz State Univ Tempe AZ 85281

NORTHINGTON, DEWEY JACKSON, JR, b New Orleans, La, Jan 31, 46; c 2. ORGANIC CHEMISTRY. *Educ:* La State Univ, BS, 67; Univ Fla, PhD(org chem), 70. *Prof Exp:* Fel chem, La State Univ, 70-71 & Syva Res Inst, 71-72; res scientist, Carnation Co, 72-74; ASST TECH DIR, WEST COAST TECH SERV, INC, 74- *Mem:* Am Chem Soc. *Res:* Analysis of polymers and surfactants; organic analyses; spectral identification of organic compounds. *Mailing Add:* West Coast Tech Serv 17605 Fabrica Way Suite D Cerritos CA 90701

NORTHOUSE, RICHARD A, b Lanesboro, Minn, Apr 2, 38; m 61; c 2. COMPUTER GRAPHICS, ROBOTICS. *Educ:* Univ Wis, BS, 66, MS, 68; Purdue Univ, MS, 70, PhD(elec eng), 71. *Prof Exp:* PROF ELEC ENG, UNIV WIS, MILWAUKEE, 70- *Concurrent Pos:* Fel syst design & anal, NSF, 69-, elec eng, 70-; pres, Compco, 75- *Mem:* Inst Elec & Electronics Engrs; Asn Comput Mach; Pattern Recognition Soc. *Res:* Computers and system theory to solve agricultural problems, particularly dairy cow problems. *Mailing Add:* Univ Wis Milwaukee WI 53209

NORTHOVER, JOHN, b Keynsham, Eng, Nov 7, 37; m 70; c 2. PLANT PATHOLOGY, MYCOLOGY. *Educ:* Bristol Univ, BSc, 60; Univ London, PhD(plant path), 65. *Prof Exp:* Res asst plant path, Agr Res Coun, UK, 60-63; fel, Nat Res Coun Can, 65-66; RES SCIENTIST PLANT PATH, AGR CAN, 66- *Mem:* Can Phytopath Soc; Am Phytopath Soc. *Res:* Mycological diseases of fruit crops; epiphytology; biological and chemical control. *Mailing Add:* Res Sta Agr Can Vineland Sta ON L0R 2E0 Can

NORTHRIP, JOHN WILLARD, b Tulsa, Okla, July 7, 34; m 54; c 3. BIOPHYSICS. *Educ:* Southwest Mo State Col, BS, 54; Okla State Univ, MS, 58, PhD(physics), 64. *Prof Exp:* Staff mem phys res, Sandia Corp, 58-61; asst prof physics, Cent Mo State Col, 63-65; Fulbright lectr solid state physics, Sch Eng Sao Carlos, Univ Sao Paulo, 65-67; from asst prof to assoc prof, 67-75, PROF PHYSICS & ASTRON, SOUTHWEST MO STATE UNIV, 75- *Concurrent Pos:* Consult, Sandia Corp, 61-64. *Mem:* AAAS; Am Phys Soc; Am Asn Physics Teachers. *Res:* Study of musculoskeletal motion, especially as applied to athletics; physics of sensory perceptions. *Mailing Add:* Dept of Physics Southwest Mo State Univ Springfield MO 65802

NORTHROP, DAVID A, b New Haven, Conn, Feb 4, 38; m 60; c 2. GEOCHEMISTRY. *Educ:* Univ Chicago, BS, 60, MS, 61, PhD(chem), 64. *Prof Exp:* Tech staff mem res, 64-70, DIV SUPVR RES, SANDIA LABS, 71- *Mem:* AAAS; Soc Petrol Engrs. *Res:* Unconventional natural gas recovery; in situ conversion of fossil fuels; carbon composite materials research for aerospace applications; high temperature phase equilibria with emphasis upon vaporization phenomena; oxygen and stable isotope geochemistry. *Mailing Add:* 7207 Harwood Ave NE Albuquerque NM 87110

NORTHROP, JOHN, b New York, NY, Feb 1, 23; m 52; c 3. GEOPHYSICS. *Educ:* Princeton Univ, BA, 47; Columbia Univ, MA, 48; Univ Hawaii, PhD(solid earth geophys), 68. *Prof Exp:* Geol asst marine geol, Oceanog Inst, Woods Hole, 48-49; res assoc, Lamont Geol Observ, Columbia Univ, 49-51; head dept geol, Bates Col, 51-52; geologist, Hudson Labs, 52-61; asst specialist, Scripps Inst, Calif, 61-64; assoc geophysicist, Hawaii Inst Geophys, 64-65; assoc specialist marine geophys, Marine Phys Lab, Scripps Inst Oceanog, Univ Calif, 65-67; GEOPHYSICIST, US NAVAL OCEAN SYSTS CTR, 67- *Concurrent Pos:* Consult, Artemis Proj, 58-59. *Mem:* Am Geophys Union; Seismol Soc Am; Acoust Soc Am; NY Acad Sci. *Res:* Submarine geology; marine geophysics; underwater sound; earthquake waves; geoacoustics; hydroacoustics. *Mailing Add:* Code 5311 Catalina Blvd Naval Ocean Systs Ctr San Diego CA 92152

NORTHROP, JOHN HOWARD, b Yonkers, NY, July 5, 91; m 17; c 2. BIOCHEMISTRY, BIOLOGY. *Educ:* Columbia Univ, BS, 12, AM, 13, PhD(chem), 15, ScD, 37. *Hon Degrees:* ScD, Harvard Univ, 36, Yale Univ, 37, Princeton Univ, 49, Rutgers Univ, 41; LLD, Univ Calif, 39. *Prof Exp:* Cutting traveling fel, Columbia Univ, 15-16; asst, Rockefeller Univ, 16, assoc, 17-20, assoc mem, 20-24, mem, 24-56; Hitchcock prof, Univ Calif, Berkeley, 39, vis prof, 49-58, prof & res biophysicist, Donner Lab, 58-59, EMER PROF

BACT & PHYSIOL, UNIV CALIF, BERKELEY, 59- *Concurrent Pos:* Alvarez lectr, 32; DeLamar lectr, Sch Hyg & Pub Health, Johns Hopkins Univ, 37, Thayer lectr, 40; Jessup lectr, Columbia Univ, 38. *Honors & Awards:* Nobel Prize in Chem, 46; Stevens Prize, Columbia Univ, 31, Chandler Medal, 37, Lion Award, 49 & Alexander Hamilton Medal, 62; Elliot Medal, Nat Acad Sci, 39; Cert of Merit, 48. *Mem:* Nat Acad Sci; Am Philos Soc; Am Acad Arts & Sci; hon fel Royal Soc Chem; Franklin fel Royal Soc Arts. *Mailing Add:* PO Box 1387 Wickenburg AZ 85358

NORTHROP, ROBERT BURR, b White Plains, NY, Jan 11, 35; m 61; c 3. ELECTRICAL & BIOMEDICAL ENGINEERING. *Educ:* Mass Inst Technol, BS, 56; Univ Conn, MS, 58, PhD(physiol), 64. *Prof Exp:* Asst elec eng, 56-59, asst zool, 59-60, asst prof elec eng, 63-69, assoc prof, 69-78, PROF ELEC ENG, UNIV CONN, 78- *Concurrent Pos:* Consult, Conn State Bd Fisheries & Game, 61- & Northeast Utilities, 78. *Mem:* Am Soc Zool; Inst Elec & Electronics Engrs; Am Physiol Soc. *Res:* Neural data processing in insect compound eye vision; biomedical instrumentation; biomedical engineering education; environmental engineering. *Mailing Add:* Box U-157 Univ of Conn Storrs CT 06268

NORTHROP, ROBERT L, b Kansas City, Mo, Mar 12, 26; m 52. VIROLOGY, BIOCHEMISTRY. *Educ:* Ore State Univ, BS, 52; Univ Minn, DVM, 58; Univ Wis, PhD(microbiol), 63. *Prof Exp:* Assoc prof virol, 65-73, ASSOC PROF EPIDEMIOL, SCH PUB HEALTH, UNIV ILL MED CTR, 73-; ASSOC PROF EPIDEMIOL, COL VET MED, UNIV ILL, URBANA, 73- *Concurrent Pos:* Vis microbiologist, Rush-Presby-St Luke's Med Ctr, 65- *Mem:* Am Asn Immunol. *Res:* Infectious disease epidemiology. *Mailing Add:* Sch of Pub Health Univ of Ill Med Ctr Box 6998 Chicago IL 60680

NORTHROP, THEODORE GEORGE, b Poughkeepsie, NY, Dec 15, 24; m 49, 71; c 5. SPACE PHYSICS. *Educ:* Yale Univ, BS, 44; Cornell Univ, MS, 49; Iowa State Col, PhD(physics), 53. *Prof Exp:* Instr physics, Vassar Col, 46-47; asst, TV tube dept, Labs, Radio Corp Am, NJ, 47; instr physics, Yale Univ, 53-54; mem staff, Theoret Div, Lawrence Radiation Lab, Univ Calif, 54-65; mem staff, Goddard Space Flight Ctr, NASA, 65-67, chief lab space physics, 67-73, head theoretical group, Goddard Space Flight Ctr, NASA, 73-77. *Mem:* Fel Am Phys Soc; Am Geophys Union. *Res:* Biophysics; electronic instrumentation; plasma physics; plasma theory of planetary magnetospheres and of the solar wind. *Mailing Add:* Goddard Space Flight Ctr NASA Code 665 Greenbelt MD 20771

NORTHRUP, CLYDE JOHN MARSHALL, JR, b Oklahoma City, Okla, Apr 25, 38; m 60; c 3. THERMODYNAMICS, GEOCHEMISTRY. *Educ:* Okla State Univ, BS(math) & BS(physics), 61, PhD(physics), 66. *Prof Exp:* Staff asst, 58 & 59-60, mem tech staff, 67-77, DIV SUPVR, SANDIA LABS, 77- *Mem:* Am Asn Physics Teachers. *Res:* thermodynamics, kinetics of reaction and phase diagrams of metal alloy-hydrogen systems; physical and chemical characterization of magma; solar/hydride engines; nuclear waste stabilization; radionuclide migration in geologic formations. *Mailing Add:* Orgn 5812 Sandia Labs Albuquerque NM 87115

NORTHUP, LARRY L(EE), b Audubon, Iowa, Aug 6, 40; m 76; c 2. AEROSPACE ENGINEERING, MECHANICAL ENGINEERING. *Educ:* Iowa State Univ, BS, 62, MS, 63, PhD(aerospace & mech eng), 67. *Prof Exp:* From instr to asst prof aerospace eng, 66-73, assoc prof, 74-80, PROF FRESHMAN ENG, IOWA STATE UNIV, 80- *Mem:* Am Soc Eng Educ; Soc Mfg Engrs; Nat Acad Adv Asn. *Res:* Vibrational relaxation in high temperature gas dynamics; compressible gas dynamics; low speed aerodynamics, particularly studies of autorotation characteristics; computational fluid mechanics; fundamental engineering education. *Mailing Add:* Dept Freshman Eng Iowa State Univ 112 Marston Ames IA 50011

NORTHUP, MELVIN LEE, b Floris, Iowa, Oct 11, 41; m 65. ENVIRONMENTAL SCIENCES. *Educ:* Parsons Col, BS, 63; Purdue Univ, Lafayette, MS, 65; Univ Mo-Columbia, PhD(soil chem), 70. *Prof Exp:* Methods develop chemist, Norwich Pharmacal Co, 65-66; NSF fel soils, Univ Wis-Madison, 70-72; asst prof, 72-77, ASSOC PROF ENVIRON SCI, GRAND VALLEY STATE COLS, 77- *Mem:* Am Soc Agron; Soc Comput Simulation; Soc Gen Systs Res. *Res:* Chemistry of manganese and nitrogen in soils; nutrient cycling in nature; computer simulation of ecosystems; chemical pollution of water resources. *Mailing Add:* Grand Valley State Cols Allendale MI 49401

NORTHWOOD, DEREK OWEN, b Hitchin, Eng, July 28, 43; Can citizen; m 70; c 2. METALLURGY, ELECTRON MICROSCOPY. *Educ:* Imp Col, Univ London, BSc, 64; Univ Surrey, MSc, 66, PhD(chem physics), 68. *Prof Exp:* Investr melting & casting, Brit Non-Ferrous Metals Res Asn, London, 64-65; fel mat, Univ Windsor, 69-71; metall engr, Atomic Energy Can Ltd, Chalk River, Ont, 71-76; assoc prof mat, 76-79, PROF ENG MAT, UNIV WINDSOR, 79-, ASST DEAN RES, 80- *Mem:* Am Soc Metals; Micros Soc Can; Can Inst Mining & Metall Engrs; Can Res Mgt Asn; Metals Soc. *Res:* Materials development and performance in Canadian nuclear reactors; zirconium alloys; irradiation damage, especially characterization by electron microscopy; hydrogen storage materials; energy futures. *Mailing Add:* Dept Eng Mat Univ Windsor Windsor ON N9B 3P4 Can

NORTON, ALLEN C, b Los Angeles, Calif, Mar 20, 35; m 61; c 7. APPLIED PHYSIOLOGY, BIOMEDICAL ENGINEERING. *Educ:* Univ Calif, Santa Barbara, AB, 57; Univ Buffalo, PhD(exp psychol), 61. *Prof Exp:* Asst physiol & psychol, Univ Buffalo, 57-61; USPHS fel & instr physiol, Sch Med, Tohoku Univ, Japan, 61-63; sr res assoc neurophysiol, Develop & Sensory Physiol Lab, Children's Hosp Los Angeles, 63-64, interim dir, 64; sr investr, Inst Med Res, Huntington Mem Hosp, 64-67; asst res anatomist & physiologist, Brain Info Serv, Univ Calif Sch Med, Los Angeles, 67-68, asst prof physiol, 68-69; fel neurosci study prog, Univ Colo, Boulder, 69; SR RES PHYSIOLOGIST, BECKMAN INSTRUMENTS, INC, 70- *Concurrent Pos:* Consult, Electro Optical Systs, 65-; instr, Calif State Col, Los Angeles, 69, Otis Art Inst, 69-70 & Orange Coast Col, 75-76. *Mem:* AAAS; Instrument Soc Am; Nat Soc Cardiopulmonary Technol; Asn Advan Med Instrumentation; Am Col Sports Med. *Res:* Bioimpedance; respiratory gas analysis; cardiopulmonary physiology; application of commercial instrumentation to space station laboratories; respiratory measurements in health and disease. *Mailing Add:* Beckman Instruments Inc 1630 S State College Blvd Anaheim CA 92806

NORTON, CHARLES J, organic chemistry, anthropology, see previous edition

NORTON, CHARLES LAWRENCE, b Neponset, Ill, Dec 20, 17; m 45; c 5. DAIRY SCIENCE. *Educ:* Univ Ill, BS, 40; Cornell Univ, PhD(animal husb), 44. *Prof Exp:* Asst prof animal husb, Cornell Univ, 45-47; prof dairy husb & head dept, Univ R I, 47-50; head dept dairying, Okla State Univ, 50-58; prof dairy & poultry sci & head dept, 58-77, PROF ANIMAL SCI, KANS STATE UNIV, 77-, RES DAIRY & POULTRY SCIENTIST, AGR EXP STA, 70- *Mem:* Am Soc Animal Sci; Am Dairy Sci Asn. *Res:* Vitamin needs of dairy calves; dry calf starters; nutritive value of forages for dairy cattle. *Mailing Add:* Dept of Animal Sci & Indust Leland Call Hall Kans State Univ Manhattan KS 66502

NORTON, CHARLES WARREN, b Scranton, Pa, Aug 2, 44; m 65. MICROPALEONTOLOGY. *Educ:* Antioch Col, BA, 68; Univ Va, MA, 74; Univ Pittsburgh, PhD(geol), 75. *Prof Exp:* Res geologist, Gulf Res & Develop Corp, 74; COAL GEOLOGIST, WVA GEOL SURV, 75- *Mem:* AAAS; Paleont Soc; Palaeont Asn; Am Asn Petrol Geologists; Sigma Xi. *Res:* Coal resource and reserved study in West Virginia involving mapping, correlation, thickness and quality measures on minable seams; long-term study of interbedded marine horizons for future correlation aid. *Mailing Add:* Woodland Terrace Rte 10 Box 1 Morgantown WV 26505

NORTON, CYNTHIA FRIEND, b Shelburne Falls, Mass, Aug 18, 40. MICROBIOLOGY. *Educ:* Smith Col, AB, 61; Boston Univ, PhD(marine microbiol), 67. *Prof Exp:* Sci aide, Polaroid Corp, 61-63; res assoc microbial physiol, Univ NH, 67-68; NIH fel microbiol, Sch Med, Yale Univ, 68-71; from asst prof to assoc prof, 71-80, PROF BIOL, UNIV MAINE, AUGUSTA, 80-, CHMN, DIV MATH, SCI & SOCIAL SCI, 80- *Mem:* Am Soc Microbiol. *Res:* Microbial pigments and exoenzymes; interactions of marine organisms; ecological role of soluble exoproducts in sea. *Mailing Add:* Dept of Biol Univ of Maine Univ Heights Augusta ME 04330

NORTON, DANIEL REMSEN, b Brooklyn, NY, Jan 27, 22; m 44; c 3. ANALYTICAL CHEMISTRY. *Educ:* Antioch Col, BS, 44; Princeton Univ, MA & PhD(anal chem), 48. *Prof Exp:* Asst bacteriologist, Antioch Col, 40-41, asst org chem, 43-44; analyst, Eastern State Corp, NY, 41-42; anal chemist, Merck & Co, Inc, NJ, 42-43 & Manhattan Proj, Princeton Univ, 44-46; monitor, Radiol Surv Sect, Oper Crossroads, 46; asst prof chem, George Washington Univ, 48-52; res chemist, Sprague Elec Co, Mass, 55-70; RES CHEMIST, BUR ANAL LABS, US GEOL SURV, 52-55 & 70- *Concurrent Pos:* Res fel, Woods Hole Oceanog Inst, 50-52, assoc, 52-58; instr, Williams Col, 60-68. *Mem:* Am Chem Soc. *Res:* Solid state and surface chemistry; ceramics; thermoanalytical techniques; polarography; absorption and emission spectrometry; particle and pore size analysis; silicate rock analysis; coal analysis. *Mailing Add:* 29611 Fairway Dr Evergreen CO 80439

NORTON, DAVID JERRY, b Manhattan, Kans, Oct 23, 40; m 64; c 1. AEROSPACE ENGINEERING. *Educ:* Tex A&M Univ, BS & MS, 63; Purdue Univ, PhD(mech eng), 68. *Prof Exp:* Sr res engr, Jet Propulsion Lab, 68-70; asst prof, 70-75, assoc prof, 75-79, PROF AEROSPACE ENG, TEX A&M UNIV, 79-, ASST DIR, TEX ENG EXP STA, 81- *Concurrent Pos:* Consult, Caudill, Rowlett & Scott, 76-, Exxon Prod Res, 78- & Transworld Drilling Inc, 81- *Mem:* Assoc fel Am Inst Aeronaut & Astronaut; Am Soc Eng Educ; Am Soc Mech Engrs. *Res:* Wind engineering; flow in the atmospheric boundary layer; propulsion and gas dynamics. *Mailing Add:* Dept Aerospace Eng Tex A&M Univ College Station TX 77843

NORTON, DAVID L, b Newark, NJ, Nov 15, 45; m 73. BIOLOGICAL RHYTHMS. *Educ:* Iowa Wesleyan Col, BS, 67; Mich State Univ, MS, 70, PhD(physiol), 75. *Prof Exp:* NIH fel biorhythms, Northwestern Univ, Evanston, 75-77; vis asst prof biol, Univ Ill, Chicago Circle, 77-80; MEM FAC, BIOL SCI DEPT, NORTHWESTERN UNIV, 80- *Mem:* AAAS; Fedn Am Scientists; Sigma Xi; Int Soc Chronobiol; Am Soc Zoologists. *Res:* Estrogen receptors in rat uterii. *Mailing Add:* 110 N Kenilworth Apt 2D Oak Park IL 60302

NORTON, DAVID WILLIAM, b Mar 4, 44; US citizen; m 67; c 1. PHYSIOLOGICAL ECOLOGY. *Educ:* Harvard Col, AB, 67; Univ Alaska, MS, 70, PhD(zoophysiol), 73. *Prof Exp:* Staff ecologist environ consult, Dames & Moore, Fairbanks, 73-74; state supvr environ surveillance, Joint State-Fed Fish & Wildlife Adv Team for Surveillance Construct Trans-Alaska Oil Pipeline, 74-75; DEP PROJ MGR, BIOL, COASTAL & MARINE ECOL RES, NAT OCEANIC & ATMOSPHERIC ADMIN-OUTER CONTINENTAL SHELF ENVIRON ASSESSMENT PROG, 75- *Concurrent Pos:* Affil asst prof ecol, Inst Arctic Biol, 73-77, adj assoc prof appl sci, Geophys Inst, Univ Alaska, 77- *Mem:* Sigma Xi; Ecol Soc Am. *Res:* Ecological energetics of migrating and breeding in tundra shorebirds of Alaska. *Mailing Add:* Arctic Proj Off NOAA-OCSEP Geophys Inst Univ of Alaska Fairbanks AK 99701

NORTON, DENIS LOCKLIN, b Elba, NY, Jan 2, 39; m 60; c 3. GEOCHEMISTRY, GEOLOGY. *Educ:* Univ Buffalo, BA, 60; Univ Calif, Riverside, PhD(geol), 64. *Prof Exp:* Res asst geochem, Univ Calif, 60-64; from res geologist to sr res geologist, Kennecott Copper Corp, 64-69, chief geochem div, 69-73; asst prof, 73-76, ASSOC PROF GEOSCI, UNIV ARIZ, 76- *Mem:* Mineral Soc Am; Glaciol Soc; Am Inst Mining, Metall & Petrol Engrs; Geochem Soc; Mineral Asn Can. *Res:* Solving geological problems by developing a more thorough understanding of processes through geochemical investigations. *Mailing Add:* Dept of Geosci Univ of Ariz Tucson AZ 85721

NORTON, DON CARLOS, b Toledo, Ohio, May 22, 22; m 52; c 4. PLANT NEMATOLOGY. *Educ:* Univ Toledo, BS, 47; Ohio State Univ, MS, 49, PhD(bot), 50. *Prof Exp:* From asst prof to assoc prof plant path, Agr Exp Sta, Agr & Mech Col Tex, 51-59; assoc prof, 59-67, PROF PLANT PATH, IOWA STATE UNIV, 67- *Mem:* Am Phytopath Soc; Soc Nematol (treas, 77-80); Sigma Xi. *Res:* Nematology; root diseases; ecology of plant parasitic nematodes. *Mailing Add:* Dept Plant Path Seed & Weed Sci Iowa State Univ Ames IA 50011

NORTON, DONALD ALAN, b Mt Kisco, NY, Mar 15, 20; m 48; c 2. MATHEMATICS. *Educ:* Harvard Univ, BS, 41; Univ Wis, PhD(math), 49. *Prof Exp:* ASSOC PROF MATH, UNIV CALIF, DAVIS, 49- *Mem:* Am Math Soc; Math Asn Am; Asn Comput Math; NY Acad Sci. *Res:* Generalized groups; algorithms. *Mailing Add:* Dept of Math Univ of Calif Davis CA 95616

NORTON, EDWARD W D, b Sommerville, Mass, Jan 3, 22. MEDICINE. *Educ:* Harvard Col, BA, 43; Cornell Univ, MD, 46; Am Bd Ophthal, dipl. *Prof Exp:* Intern, Cincinnati Gen Hosp, Ohio, 46-47; asst resident neurol, Kingsbridge Vet Hosp, Bronx, NY, 49-50; from asst resident to resident ophthal, New York Hosp-Cornell Med Ctr, 50-53; from instr to asst prof surg, Cornell Univ, 53-58; assoc prof ophthal & chief div, Sch Med, 58-59, PROF OPHTHAL & CHMN DEPT, SCH MED & JACKSON MEM HOSP, UNIV MIAMI, 59- *Concurrent Pos:* Mem retina serv, Mass Eye & Ear Infirmary, Wilmer Inst Ophthal, Johns Hopkins Hosp & Mayo Clin, 53-54; res fels ophthal, Howe Lab, Boston, 53-54; asst attend surgeon, New York Hosp-Cornell Med Ctr, 54-58; consult, Hosp Spec Surg, New York, Mem Hosp Cancer & Allied Dis, Bellevue Hosp & Kingsbridge Vet Hosp, 54-58. *Mem:* Am Ophthal Soc; Retina Soc; Am Acad Ophthal & Otolaryngol. *Res:* Ophthalmology; retinal diseases; neuroophthalmology. *Mailing Add:* 1638 NW Tenth Ave Miami FL 33136

NORTON, ELINOR FRANCES, b Brooklyn, NY, July 22, 29. ANALYTICAL CHEMISTRY. *Educ:* Wellesley Col, BA, 51. *Prof Exp:* From jr chemist to assoc chemist, 51-74, CHEMIST, BROOKHAVEN NAT LAB, 74- *Mem:* Am Chem Soc. *Res:* Analytical chemistry, particularly trace elements; spectrophotometry; x-ray fluorescence; neutron activation; radiochemical separations and atomic absorption. *Mailing Add:* Brookhaven Nat Lab Upton NY 11973

NORTON, HORACE WAKEMAN, III, b Lansing, Mich, Jan 17, 14; m 37; c 4. MATHEMATICAL STATISTICS. *Educ:* Univ Wis, BS, 35; Iowa State Col, MS, 37; Univ London, PhD(math statist), 40. *Prof Exp:* Asst lectr eugenics, Univ Col, Univ London, 37-40; res assoc physics, Univ Chicago, 40-42; sr meteorologist & math statistician, US Weather Bur, 42-47; statistician, AEC, Tenn, 47-50; PROF STATIST DESIGN & ANAL, UNIV ILL, URBANA, 50- *Concurrent Pos:* Agent, Agr Mkt Serv, USDA, 40-42. *Mem:* AAAS; Biomet Soc; Am Soc Animal Sci; Am Genetic Asn. *Res:* Design of experiments; animal breeding and genetics; statistical analysis; population genetics. *Mailing Add:* Dept of Animal Sci Univ of Ill Urbana IL 61801

NORTON, JAMES AUGUSTUS, JR, b Philadelphia, Pa, Jan 3, 21; m 58; c 1. STATISTICS. *Educ:* Antioch Col, AB, 47; Purdue Univ, MS, 49, PhD, 59. *Prof Exp:* Res assoc statist, Div Educ Reference, Purdue Univ, 47-50, Statist Lab, 51-61, from instr to asst prof, 51-61; from asst prof to assoc prof statist, Dept Psychiat, Sch Med, 61-68, RES CONSULT, INST PSYCHIAT RES, IND UNIV, INDIANAPOLIS, 61-, PROF STATIST, DEPT PSYCHIAT, SCH MED, 68- *Res:* Tests of hypotheses in the case of unequal variances. *Mailing Add:* Dept of Psychiat Ind Univ Indianapolis IN 46202

NORTON, JAMES JENNINGS, b Elmira, NY, May 1, 18; m 46. GEOLOGY. *Educ:* Princeton Univ, AB, 40; Northwestern Univ, MS, 42; Columbia Univ, PhD, 57. *Prof Exp:* GEOLOGIST, US GEOL SURV, 42- *Mem:* AAAS; Mineral Soc Am; Geol Soc Am; Soc Econ Geol. *Res:* Geology of Black Hills, South Dakota; pegmatites of Black Hills and elsewhere; industrial minerals; lithium. *Mailing Add:* US Geol Surv Denver CO 80225

NORTON, JOHN LESLIE, b Chanute, Kans, June 1, 45; m 66. MATHEMATICAL PHYSICS. *Educ:* Kans State Col Pittsburg, BA, 66; Univ Kans, MS, 68, PhD(physics), 70. *Prof Exp:* Fel physics, 70-71, staff mem weapons output, 71-74, staff mem hydrodyn, 74-77, mem staff & asst group leader comput serv, 77-80, MEM STAFF & ASSOC GROUP LEADER COMPUTATIONAL PHYSICS, LOS ALAMOS NAT LAB, 80- *Mem:* Am Phys Soc; AAAS. *Res:* Numerical analysis; hydrodynamics; radiation transport; nuclear physics; computer science. *Mailing Add:* Los Alamos Nat Lab Group X-7 Box 1663 MS-625 Los Alamos NM 85745

NORTON, JOSEPH DANIEL, b Flat Rock, Ala, Oct 14, 27; m 50; c 1. GENETICS, HORTICULTURE. *Educ:* Auburn Univ, BS, 52, MS, 55; La State Univ, PhD(agron, hort), 61. *Prof Exp:* Asst hort, Auburn Univ, 54; asst veg crops specialist, Univ Fla, 54-60; from asst prof to assoc prof hort & from asst horticulturist to assoc horticulturist, 60-73, PROF HORT & HORTICULTURIST, 73- *Mem:* Am Soc Hort Sci; Am Genetic Asn. *Res:* Plant breeding, especially plum, muskmelon, watermelon, strawberry and apple; greenhouse tomato studies. *Mailing Add:* Dept Hort Auburn Univ Auburn AL 36830

NORTON, JOSEPH R(ANDOLPH), b Lisbon, Ark, Dec 23, 15; m 39; c 2. ENGINEERING MECHANICS. *Educ:* Okla State Univ, BS, 39, MS, 51; Univ Tex, PhD, 63. *Prof Exp:* Draftsman, W C Norris Mfr, Okla, 39-40, plant engr, 40-46; prof eng res, 46-51, asst dir off eng res, 51-65, head sch gen eng, 63-78, EMER HEAD SCH GEN ENG, OKLA STATE UNIV, 78- *Concurrent Pos:* Consult, Grand River Dam Auth, 76-77. *Mem:* Nat Soc Prof Engrs; Am Soc Eng Educ; Sigma Xi. *Res:* Mechanics of distributed systems; fluid and solid systems; heat transfer in distributed systems; use of hydraulic air compressors in the production of electrical power. *Mailing Add:* Rm 103 EN Okla State Univ Stillwater OK 74074

NORTON, KARL KENNETH, b London, Eng, Nov 13, 38; US citizen; m 62; c 2. MATHEMATICS. *Educ:* Yale Univ, BS, 59; Univ Chicago, MS, 61; Univ Ill, Urbana, PhD(math), 66. *Prof Exp:* Asst prof math, Univ Colo, Boulder, 66-73; INDEPENDENT RES, 73- *Concurrent Pos:* Off Naval Res res assoc, Univ Mich, Ann Arbor, 69-70; vis mem Inst Advan Study, 70-71; vis res math, Univ Geneva, 74; NSF res grant, 75; sr vis fel math, Univ York, Eng, 75; mem-at-large, Coun Am Math Soc, 75-77. *Mem:* Am Math Soc; Sigma Xi. *Res:* Number theory. *Mailing Add:* 1895 Alpine Ave Apt 36 Boulder CO 80302

NORTON, LARRY, b Bronx, NY, Apr 9, 47; m 70. CELL KINETICS, BIOELECTROCHEMISTRY. *Educ:* Univ Rochester, AB, 68; Columbia Univ, MD, 72. *Prof Exp:* Intern & resident, Albert Einstein Col Med, 72-74; clin assoc oncol, Nat Cancer Inst, 74-77; ASST PROF ONCOL, MOUNT SINAI SCH MED, 77- *Mem:* NY Acad Sci. *Res:* Treatment of human cancer including theory of tumor growth kinetics with implications in the design of chemotherapy programs; electrochemistry of tumors; enhancing chemotheraphy with induced currents. *Mailing Add:* Dept Medplastic Dis Sch Med Mount Sinai New York NY 10029

NORTON, LILBURN LAFAYETTE, b Lenoir City, Tenn, Jan 2, 27; m 46; c 4. ORGANIC POLYMER CHEMISTRY. *Educ:* Carson-Newman Col, BS, 49; Northwestern Univ, MS, 51; Univ Tenn, PhD(chem), 54. *Prof Exp:* Asst chem, Northwestern Univ, 51; sr chemist, 54-59, group supvr, 59-65, RES ASSOC, RES & DEVELOP, E I DU PONT DE NEMOURS & CO, INC, 65- *Mem:* Am Chem Soc. *Res:* Fiber forming synthetic polymers; antiarthritic and anticarcinogenic chemicals. *Mailing Add:* E I DuPont de Nemours & Co Inc 1007 Market St Wilmington DE 19898

NORTON, MAHLON H, b Denver, Colo, Nov 20, 22; m 70; c 5. ELECTRONIC ENGINEERING, COMMUNICATIONS. *Educ:* Univ Colo, BS, 44. *Prof Exp:* Elec engr, Metron Instrument Co, 44-45; electronic engr, Pilot Radio Corp, 46-47; proj engr, Fada Radio & Electronic Co, 47-52; pres & chief engr, Norton Electronics, 52-53; proj engr, Aeronaut Radio Inc, 53-57; res dir, Booz Allen Appl Res Inc, 57-63; proj leader commun command & control, Ctr Naval Anal, 63-64; sr scientist, Kaman Aircraft Corp, 64-71; staff engr, Telcom, Inc, 71-74, pres, Norton Electronics, Inc, 74-77; eng mgr, Tracor, Inc, Rockville, Md, 77-80; PRES, NORTON ENG, DC, 80- *Concurrent Pos:* Consult, Petcar Res, 50-52, Walter Kidde & Co, Thomas A Edison Co & Am Mach & Foundry Co, 52-53. *Mem:* Inst Elec & Electronics Engrs. *Res:* Communications command and control; system and cost effect effectiveness; nuclear weapons interactions; direction and planning; adaptive electronic circuitry; microprocessor applications; prototype design and fabrication; electronic warfare; special surveillance systems; high frequency radio propagation; antenna design. *Mailing Add:* 4436 45th St NW Washington DC 20016

NORTON, MATTHEW FRANK, geology, see previous edition

NORTON, NORMAN J, b DuQuoin, Ill, Apr 26, 33; m 55; c 2. BOTANY. *Educ:* Southern Ill Univ, BA, 58; Univ Minn, MS, 60, PhD(bot), 63. *Prof Exp:* Geologist, Humble Oil & Ref Co, 62-63; asst prof bot, Univ Minn, 63-64; from asst prof to prof biol, Hope Col, 64-74, chmn dept, 66-74; dean fac, 78-81, CHMN DEPT BIOL, BALL STATE UNIV, 74-, ACTG VPRES ACAD AFFAIRS, 78-, PROF, 81- *Concurrent Pos:* Consult, Gulf Oil Co; chmn bd trustees, Am Asn Stratig Palynologists Found, 76- *Mem:* Bot Soc Am; Paleont Soc; Int Asn Plant Taxon; Paleont Asn Gr Brit. *Res:* Palynology, especially Devonian spore, Acritarch and Chitinozoa assemblages; Mesozoic spore pollen assemblages. *Mailing Add:* Dept of Biol Ball State Univ Muncie IN 47306

NORTON, PAUL RAYMOND, solid state physics, electronic device physics, see previous edition

NORTON, PETER ROBERT, physical chemistry, surface physics, see previous edition

NORTON, RICHARD E, b New York, NY, Mar 2, 28; m 66; c 2. THEORETICAL PHYSICS. *Educ:* Lehigh Univ, BS, 52; Univ Pa, PhD(physics), 58. *Prof Exp:* From asst prof to assoc prof, 60-69, PROF PHYSICS, UNIV CALIF, LOS ANGELES, 69- *Concurrent Pos:* John Simon Guggenheim Found fel, 76-77. *Mem:* Am Phys Soc. *Res:* Theoretical research in field theory and elementary particle physics. *Mailing Add:* Dept of Physics Univ of Calif Los Angeles CA 90024

NORTON, RICHARD VAIL, b Hackensack, NJ, Feb 22, 40; m 62; c 2. ORGANIC CHEMISTRY. *Educ:* Rutgers Univ, BS, 61; Univ Maine, MS, 65, PhD(org chem), 67. *Prof Exp:* Chemist, Armstrong Cork Co, 61-63; sr res chemist, Mobay Chem Co, 67-68; from assoc res chemist to sr res chemist, Res & Develop Lab, Sun Oil Co, 68-77; MGR PROCESS RES & DEVELOP, ASHLAND CHEM CO, 77- *Concurrent Pos:* Tech asst to vpres, Cryog Vessel Div, Sun Shipbuilding & Drydock, Chester, Pa, 74-75. *Mem:* AAAS; Am Chem Soc. *Res:* Catalytic reactor design; reactor scale up; reaction engineering. *Mailing Add:* PO Box 275 Dublin OH 43017

NORTON, ROBERT ALAN, b Hazelton, Pa, Jan 3, 26; m 50; c 6. HORTICULTURE. *Educ:* Rutgers Univ, BS, 50, MS, 51; Mich State Univ, PhD, 54. *Prof Exp:* Asst, Mich State Univ, 51-54; from asst prof to assoc prof hort, Utah State Univ, 54-61; assoc agriculturist, Dept Pomol, Univ Calif, Davis, 61-62; supt & assoc horticulturist, 62-71, HORTICULTURIST, NORTHWESTERN WASH RES & EXTEN UNIT, WASH STATE UNIV, 71- *Concurrent Pos:* Consult, Kenai Natives Asn, Kenai, Alaska, 75-78. *Mem:* Am Soc Hort Sci; Am Pomol Soc. *Res:* Culture and physiology of horticultural plants. *Mailing Add:* Northwestern Wash Res & Exten Unit Wash State Univ Mt Vernon WA 98273

NORTON, ROBERT JAMES, b Fitchburg, Mass, May 22, 14; m 42; c 2. ECONOMIC ENTOMOLOGY, PHYTOPATHOLOGY. *Educ:* Univ NH, MSc, 39; Univ Mass, PhD(entom, plant path), 51. *Prof Exp:* Res entomologist agr chems, US Rubber Co, 40-42, tech rep, 46-47, mgr tech serv, 48; assoc dir, Crop Protection Inst, 51-54, vpres, 65-69, DIR CROP PROTECTION INST, 54-, PRES, 69- *Mem:* Entom Soc Am; Am Phytopath Soc; Weed Sci Soc Am; Royal Entom Soc London. *Res:* Detection and development of biocides as insecticides, fungicides, herbicides and nematicides. *Mailing Add:* 84 Madbury Rd Durham NH 03824

NORTON, SCOTTY JIM, b Marlow, Okla, Oct 21, 36; m 57; c 1. BIOCHEMISTRY, PESTICIDE CHEMISTRY. *Educ:* Abilene Christian Col, BS, 59; Univ Tex, Austin, PhD(chem), 63. *Prof Exp:* From asst prof to assoc prof, 63-71, PROF CHEM, NTEX STATE UNIV, 71- *Concurrent Pos:* USPHS grant, 63-68; Robert A Welch Found res grant, 63-77. *Mem:* Am Chem Soc; Am Soc Biol Chem. *Res:* Studies in amino acid metabolism; study of the glyoxalase system; membrane studies; synthesis and study of metabolite analogs; synthesis of insecticides. *Mailing Add:* Dept of Chem NTex State Univ Denton TX 76203

NORTON, STATA ELAINE, b Mt Kisco, NY, Nov 28, 22; m 49. PHARMACOLOGY, TOXICOLOGY. *Educ:* Univ Conn, BA, 43; Columbia Univ, MA, 45; Univ Wis, PhD(zool), 49. *Prof Exp:* Res scientist neuropharmacol, Burroughs Wellcome & Co, 49-62; from asst prof to assoc prof, 62-68, PROF PHARMACOL, UNIV KANS MED CTR, KANSAS CITY, 68- *Mem:* Am Soc Pharmacol & Exp Therapeut; Biomet Soc; Ecol Soc Am; Am Soc Zool; Soc Toxicol. *Res:* Neuropharmacology; animal behavior; brain development; effects of exposure to toxic substances on development and behavior. *Mailing Add:* Dept Pharmacol Univ Kans Med Ctr Kansas City KS 66103

NORTON, STEPHEN ALLEN, b Newton, Mass, May 21, 40; m 70; c 3. GEOLOGY. *Educ:* Princeton Univ, AB, 62; Harvard Univ, MA, 63, PhD(geol), 67. *Prof Exp:* Asst prof, 68-72, assoc prof geol, 72-77, PROF UNIV MAINE, ORONO, 77- *Concurrent Pos:* Geologist, US Geol Surv, 64- *Mem:* Geol Soc Am; Mineral Soc Am. *Res:* Regional geology of New England; low temperature and pressure geochemistry. *Mailing Add:* Dept Geol Sci Univ Maine Orono ME 04469

NORTON, TED RAYMOND, b Stockton, Calif, Nov 16, 19; m 44; c 3. ORGANIC CHEMISTRY, PHARMACOLOGY. *Educ:* Univ of the Pac, BA, 40; Northwestern Univ, PhD(org chem), 43. *Prof Exp:* Dir agr chem lab, Dow Chem Co, Mich, 53-57, from asst dir to dir Britton Lab, 62-66, asst dir independent labs, 66-68; PROF PHARMACOL, UNIV HAWAII, MANOA, 68- *Mem:* AAAS; Am Chem Soc. *Res:* Isolation and characterization of marine natural products for antitumor and heart stimulant properties. *Mailing Add:* Leahi-Pharmacol 3675 Kilauea Ave Honolulu HI 96816

NORTON, VIRGINIA MARINO, b Memphis, Tenn, Nov 14, 34; m 52; c 3. GERONTOLOGY, PHSYIOLOGY. *Educ:* Memphis State Univ, BS, 69, MS, 71, PhD(biol), 75; Univ Tenn, BSN, 81. *Prof Exp:* Fel & instr physiol, Dept Physiol & Biophys, Ctr Health Sci, Univ Tenn, Memphis, 75-77; asst prof anat & physiol, Dept Biol, Memphis State Univ, 77-81; NURSING STAFF, NURSING HOME CARE UNIT, VET ADMIN HOSP, MEMPHIS, 81- *Concurrent Pos:* Consult, Sci Curriculum Work Shop; instr, Memphis City Schs, 79, Nursing Inserv, 81. *Mem:* Am Inst Biol Sci; Am Soc Zool; Sci Res Soc; Am Nurses Asn. *Res:* Techniques of stress management and control in chronic and long term illness; effects of circadian rhythms on behavioral responses in the geriatric population; physiology of aging. *Mailing Add:* 5583 Ashley Sq N Memphis TN 38117

NORTON, WILLIAM THOMPSON, b Damariscotta, Maine, Jan 27, 29; m 57; c 2. NEUROCHEMISTRY. *Educ:* Bowdoin Col, AB, 50; Princeton Univ, MA, 52, PhD(org chem), 54. *Prof Exp:* Asst instr chem, Princeton Univ, 50-52; res chemist, E I du Pont de Nemours & Co, 53-57; instr biochem, 57-58, sr fel interdisciplinary prog, 57-60, assoc med & biochem, 58-59, asst prof biochem, 59-64, assoc prof neurol, 64-71, PROF NEUROL, ALBERT EINSTEIN COL MED, 71-, PROF NEUROSCI, 74- *Concurrent Pos:* Vis prof, Charing Cross Hosp Med Sch, London, 67-68; mem neurol A study sect, NIH, 71-76; chief ed, J Neurochem, 81- *Mem:* AAAS; Am Soc Biol Chem; Am Soc Neurochem; Int Soc Neurochem; Soc Neurosci. *Res:* Lipid and myelin chemistry; chemical pathology; chemistry of isolated brain components; glial cells; cytoskeleton. *Mailing Add:* Dept of Neurol Albert Einstein Col of Med New York NY 10461

NORUSIS, MARIJA JURATE, b Ansbach, Ger, Jan 3, 48; US citizen. BIOSTATISTICS. *Educ:* Univ Ill, BA, 68; Univ Mich, MPH, 71, PhD(biostatist), 73. *Prof Exp:* Res assoc statist & med, Univ Chicago, 73-76; STATISTICIAN, SPSS, INC, 76- *Mem:* Am Statist Asn; Biomet Soc. *Res:* Applications of statistics and computers to biomedical research. *Mailing Add:* SPSS Inc 444 N Michigan Ave Chicago IL 60611

NORVELL, JOHN CHARLES, b Jacksonville, Tex, Jan 11, 40; m 66; c 2. MOLECULAR BIOPHYSICS, CRYSTALLOGRAPHY. *Educ:* Rice Univ, BA, 63; Yale Univ, MS, 65, PhD(physics), 68. *Prof Exp:* Fel physics, Res Establishment Riso, Roskilde, Denmark, 68-69; fel biophysics, Biophysics Lab, Univ Wis-Madison, 70-72; res assoc biophysics, Biol Dept, Brookhaven Nat Lab, Upton, NY, 72-75; BIOPHYSICIST, REACTOR RAD DIV, NAT BUR STANDARDS, WASHINGTON, DC, 75- *Concurrent Pos:* Guest scientist, Lab Molecular Biol, Nat Inst Arthritis, Metab & Digestive Dis, NIH, 75- *Mem:* AAAS; Biophys Soc. *Res:* Neutron and x-ray diffraction studies of the structure of proteins and other biological systems. *Mailing Add:* 11525 Spring Ridge Rd Potomac MD 20854

NORVELL, JOHN EDMONDSON, III, b Charleston, WVa, Nov 18, 29; m 62; c 2. NEUROANATOMY. *Educ:* Morris Harvey Col, BS, 53; WVa Univ, MS, 56; Ohio State Univ, PhD(anat), 66. *Prof Exp:* Instr biol sci, Johnstown Col, Pittsburgh, 56-60; asst prof, Otterbein Col, 60-62; asst instr anat, Ohio State Univ, 62-65; from asst prof to assoc prof anat, Med Col Va, Va Commonwealth Univ, 66-76; PROF & CHMN DEPT ANAT, ORAL ROBERTS UNIV, 76- *Concurrent Pos:* Consult, US Naval Hosp, Portsmouth, 66-71; chmn, Okla State Anat Bd, 78-; mem, Okla Governor's Mini-Cabinet Health & Human Resources, 80- *Mem:* AAAS; Am Asn Anat; Soc Neurosci; Transplantation Soc; Am Asn Dental Schs. *Res:* Degeneration and regeneration of nerves in transplanted organs; localization of biogenic amines and transmitters in the nervous system. *Mailing Add:* Dept of Anat Oral Roberts Univ Tulsa OK 74171

NORVELL, MICHAEL JIMMY, nutrition, toxicology, see previous edition

NORWICH, KENNETH HOWARD, b Toronto, Ont, May 8, 39; m 63; c 3. BIOPHYSICS, PHYSIOLOGY. *Educ:* Univ Toronto, MD, 63, BSc, 67, MSc, 68, PhD(physics), 70. *Prof Exp:* assoc prof, 70-80, PROF PHYSIOL & APPL SCI, INST BIOMED ENG, UNIV TORONTO, 80- *Mem:* Biophys Soc; Can Physiol Soc; Can Med Asn; Can Med & Biol Eng Soc. *Res:* Mathematical studies in physiology and medicine, studies of the transport of tracers; mathematical studies of metabolism; theoretical studies of sensory perception; applications of computerrs in medical decision-making. *Mailing Add:* Dept Physiol Univ of Toronto Toronto ON M5S 1A8 Can

NORWINE, JAMES RANDOLPH, physical geography, see previous edition

NORWOOD, CHARLES ARTHUR, b Crystal City, Tex, Jan 8, 38. AGRONOMY. *Educ:* Tex A&I Univ, BS, 61; Okla State Univ, MS, 69, PhD(soil sci), 72. *Prof Exp:* Res technician soils, Agr Res Serv, USDA, Tex, 63-67; res asst soil fertil, Okla State Univ, 67-72; ASST PROF DRYLAND SOILS RES, GARDEN CITY EXP STA, KANS STATE UNIV, 72- *Mem:* Am Soc Agron; Soil Sci Soc Am. *Res:* Soil fertility; management of dryland soils-research pertaining to efficient water use under dryland conditions. *Mailing Add:* Garden City Exp Sta Kans State Univ Garden City KS 67846

NORWOOD, FREDERICK REYES, b Mexico City, Mex, May 13, 39; US citizen; m 66; c 2. SOLID MECHANICS, APPLIED MATHEMATICS. *Educ:* Univ Calif, Los Angeles, BS, 62; Calif Inst Technol, MS, 63, PhD(appl mech), 67. *Prof Exp:* MEM TECH STAFF, SANDIA LABS, 66- *Mem:* Am Soc Mech Engrs; Soc Indust & Appl Math; Am Geophys Union. *Res:* Theoretical study of transient phenomena in liquids, gases and solids. *Mailing Add:* 600 Bryn Mawr Dr NE Albuquerque NM 87106

NORWOOD, JAMES S, b Burleson, Tex, Oct 2, 32; m 62. REPRODUCTIVE PHYSIOLOGY, GENETICS. *Educ:* Tex Tech Col, BS, 54; Kans State Univ, MS, 55, PhD(reprod physiol), 63. *Prof Exp:* Instr dairy sci, Southwest Tex State Col, 55-56 & 58-60; asst prof biol, Arlington State Col, 62-63; assoc prof reprod physiol, 63-68, assoc prof biol, 68-71, PROF BIOL, E TEX STATE UNIV, 71- *Mem:* Am Soc Animal Sci; Sigma Xi. *Res:* Post-partum regression of the bovine uterus; conception rates; inhibition of estrus and effect of steroid hormones on the endometrium of the uterus. *Mailing Add:* Dept of Biol ETex State Univ ETex Sta Commerce TX 75428

NORWOOD, RICHARD E(LLIS), b Park Ridge, Ill, May 17, 34; m 58; c 3. MECHANICAL ENGINEERING. *Educ:* Mass Inst Technol, SB, 56, SM, 59, ScD(mech eng), 61. *Prof Exp:* SR ENGR, OFF PROD DIV, IBM CORP, 61- *Mem:* Am Soc Mech Engrs. *Res:* Fluid power and automatic control; fluid mechanics and logic devices; machine design. *Mailing Add:* IBM Corp 6300 Diagonal Hwy Boulder CO 80301

NOSAL, EUGENE ADAM, b Chicago, Ill, Jan 15, 42. GEOPHYSICS. *Educ:* Ill Benedictine Col, BS, 63; Univ Wyo, MS, 65, PhD(physics), 69. *Prof Exp:* SCIENTIST, DENVER RES CTR, MARATHON OIL CO, 69- *Mem:* AAAS; Am Asn Physics Teachers; Am Geophys Union; Soc Explor Geophysicists. *Res:* Analysis of digitized data for geophysical interpretation; application of probability and statistics to geological data. *Mailing Add:* Denver Res Ctr Marathon Oil Co PO Box 269 Littleton CO 80160

NOSANOW, LEWIS H, b Philadelphia, Pa, July 9, 31; m 55; c 2. THEORETICAL PHYSICS, LOW TEMPERATURE PHYSICS. *Educ:* Univ Pa, BA, 54; Univ Chicago, PhD(chem physics), 58. *Prof Exp:* NSF fel, 58-59; res assoc physics, Inst Theoret Physics, Univ Utrecht, 59-60; asst res physicist, Univ Calif, San Diego, 60-62; from asst prof to prof physics, Univ Minn, Minneapolis, 62-73; prof physics & astron & chmn dept, Univ Fla, 73-74; HEAD CONDENSED MATTER SCI SECT, DIV MAT RES, NSF, 74- *Concurrent Pos:* Guggenheim fel, 66-67; vis prof physics, Univ Sussex, Eng, 71-72, Univ Wash, Seattle & Drexel Univ, Philadelphia, 78-79; assoc provost & prof physics, Univ Chicago, 81-82. *Mem:* Am Phys Soc; AAAS. *Res:* Statistical mechanics and phase transition; macroscopic quantum systems. *Mailing Add:* Div of Mat Res NSF 1800 G St NW Washington DC 20550

NOSHAY, ALLEN, b Philadelphia, Pa, Oct 14, 33; m 56; c 2. ORGANIC CHEMISTRY, POLYMER CHEMISTRY. *Educ:* Temple Univ, BA, 55, MS, 57, PhD(polymer org chem), 59. *Prof Exp:* Chemist, Esso Res & Eng Co, 59-61, proj leader polymer chem, 61-65; res chemist, 65-69, proj scientist, 69-75, res scientist, Plastics Div, 75-79, SR GROUP LEADER, UNION CARBIDE CORP, 79- *Mem:* Am Chem Soc. *Res:* Polymer synthesis and modification; block copolymers; epoxy resins; polyolefin catalysis. *Mailing Add:* 66 Wellington Rd East Brunswick NJ 08816

NOSHPITZ, JOSEPH DOVE, b New York, NY, Aug 31, 22; m 56. CHILD PSYCHIATRY. *Educ:* Univ Louisville, MD, 45; Baltimore-DC Psychoanal Inst, grad psychoanal, 69, grad child psychoanal, 71. *Prof Exp:* Chief children's serv, Topeka State Hosp, Kans, 51-56; chief children's unit, NIMH, 56-60; dir clin inst, Hillcrest Children's Ctr, Children's Hosp, DC, 69-74; dir educ, Dept Child Psychiat, 76-79, STAFF PSYCHIATRIST, CHILDREN'S HOSP & NAT MED CTR, WASHINGTON, DC, 79- *Concurrent Pos:* prof child health & human develop, Med Sch, George

Washington Univ; med dir, Florence Crittenton Home, Washington, DC, 73-; vis prof child psychiat, Sch Med, Tel Aviv Univ, 75-76; consult, Community Ment Health Ctr, Washington, DC. *Mem:* Am Psychiat Asn; fel Am Orthopsychiat Asn; fel Am Acad Child Psychiat; Am Asn Children's Residential Ctrs. *Res:* Adolescence; delinquency; treatment of emotionally disturbed children; residential treatment. *Mailing Add:* 3141 34th St NW Washington DC 20008

NOSKOWIAK, ARTHUR FREDRICK, b Galt, Calif, Nov 14, 20. WOOD TECHNOLOGY. *Educ:* Univ Calif, Berkeley, BS, 42, MF, 49; State Univ NY Col Forestry, Syracuse, PhD(wood technol), 59. *Prof Exp:* From instr to asst prof forestry, Colo State Univ, 51-54; instr wood technol, State Univ NY Col Forestry, Syracuse Univ, 58-59; asst prof, 60-71, ASSOC PROF FORESTRY & WOOD TECHNOL, WASH STATE UNIV, 71- *Mem:* Soc Am Foresters; Forest Prod Res Soc; Soc Wood Sci & Technol. *Res:* Spiral grain in trees; strength properties of wood; anatomy of wood. *Mailing Add:* Dept of Forestry Wash State Univ Pullman WA 99164

NOSS, RICHARD ROBERT, b Chicago, Ill, May 31, 50; m 73. ENVIRONMENTAL ENGINEERING. *Educ:* Harvard Univ, AB, 72; Univ Mich, MSE, 73; Mass Inst Technol, MS, 78, PhD(civil eng), 80. *Prof Exp:* ASST PROF ENVIRON ENG, DEPT CIVIL ENG, UNIV MASS, 80- *Concurrent Pos:* Pub mem, Mass Water Resources Comn, 76-80; Kellogg Nat fel, 82-85. *Mem:* Am Soc Chem Engrs; Am Geophys Union; Am Water Resources Asn; Water Pollution Control Fedn; Asn Environ Eng Professionals. *Res:* Water quality management; environmental systems analysis; environmental policy analysis. *Mailing Add:* Dept Civil Eng Univ Mass Amherst MA 01003

NOSSAL, NANCY, b Fall River, Mass, Feb 9, 37; m 59; c 3. BIOCHEMISTRY. *Educ:* Cornell Univ, AB, 58; Univ Mich, PhD(biochem), 63. *Prof Exp:* NIH fels, Brussels, 63-64 & Bethesda, Md, 64-65, RES CHEMIST, NAT INST ARTHRITIS & METAB DIS, 66- *Mem:* Am Soc Biol Chemists. *Res:* Enzymology of nucleic acids. *Mailing Add:* Nat Inst Health Bldg 4 Room 106 Bethesda MD 20014

NOSSAL, RALPH J, b Brooklyn, NY, Dec 26, 37; m 59; c 3. BIOPHYSICS, PHYSICS. *Educ:* Cornell Univ, BEng Phys, 59; Univ Mich, MS, 61, PhD(nuclear eng), 63. *Prof Exp:* NSF fel statist mech, Brussels, 63-64; Nat Acad Sci-Nat Sci Found res assoc, Nat Bur Standards, 64-66; PHYSICIST, NIH, 66- *Concurrent Pos:* Lectr, Univ Md, 80- *Mem:* Am Phys Soc; Biophys Soc; Am Soc Cell Biol. *Res:* Statistical physics; laser scattering; membrane biophysics; cellular physiology. *Mailing Add:* Phys Sci Lab Div Comp Res Tech Nat Inst of Health Bethesda MD 20014

NOSSAMAN, NORMAN L, b Cherokee, Okla, Jan 21, 32; m 55; c 3. SOIL FERTILITY. *Educ:* Okla State Univ, BS, 53, MS, 57; Kans State Univ, PhD(soils fertil), 63. *Prof Exp:* Chg of dryland soil mgt, Garden City Br Exp Sta, Kans State Univ, 60-65; agronomist, Western Ammonia Corp, 65-69; chief agronomist, Nipak, Inc, 60-78; CONSULT AGR, 78- *Mem:* Am Soc Agron; Soil Sci Soc Am. *Res:* Dryland soil management; soil fertility; soil moisture; tillage methods. *Mailing Add:* 13411 Rolling Hills Lane Dallas TX 75240

NOSSEL, HYMIE L, b Cape Town, SAfrica, July 11, 30; m 65; c 2. HEMATOLOGY. *Educ:* Univ Cape Town, MB, ChB, 53; Oxford Univ, DPhil(med), 62. *Prof Exp:* Intern med, Groote Schuur Hosp & Univ Cape Town, 54-55, registr, 56-59, asst physician & lectr, 64-65; res bursar, Blood Coagulation Res Unit, Med Res Coun, Eng, 60-62; from res assoc to sr res asst hemat, Mt Sinai Hosp, New York, 63-66; from asst prof to assoc prof med, 66-72, PROF MED, COL PHYSICIANS & SURGEONS, COLUMBIA UNIV, 72- *Mem:* Am Fedn Clin Res; Asn Am Physicians; Am Soc Clin Invest; Am Soc Hemat; Am Soc Exp Path. *Res:* Blood coagulation. *Mailing Add:* Columbia Univ Col of Phys & Surg 630 W 168th St New York NY 10032

NOTATION, ALBERT DAVID, b Moosomin, Sask, Oct 28, 35; m 63; c 2. ENDOCRINOLOGY, BIOCHEMISTRY. *Educ:* Univ Sask, BE, 58, MSc, 59; McMaster Univ, PhD(org chem), 64. *Prof Exp:* Lab asst fats & oils, Prairie Regional Lab, Nat Res Coun Can, 53-54; NIH Steroid Training Prog fel, Sch Med, Univ Minn, Minneapolis, 64-66, res assoc biochem, 66-67, asst prof, 67-77, asst prof obstet & gynec & lab med, 71-77; chmn dept chem & phys sci, 78-81, assoc prof, 77-81, PROF CHEM, SCH ALLIED HEALTH, QUINNIPIAC COL, 81- *Concurrent Pos:* Ayerst Squibb travel fel, 68; Minn Med Found grant, 71; res affil, Dept Obstet & Gynec, Med Sch, Yale Univ, 80- *Mem:* AAAS; Am Chem Soc; Chem Inst Can; Endocrine Soc; Soc Study Reproduction. *Res:* Steroid metabolism and biochemistry; radioimmunoassay of hormones; competitive protein binding assays. *Mailing Add:* Box 370 Mt Carmel Ave Hamden CT 06518

NOTEBOOM, WILLIAM DUANE, b East Fairview, NDak, Mar 31, 33; m 67; c 1. BIOCHEMISTRY. *Educ:* Ore State Univ, BS, 55, MS, 61; Univ Ill, PhD(physiol), 65. *Prof Exp:* Fel, McArdle Inst Cancer Res, Univ Wis, 64-67; ASSOC PROF BIOCHEM, UNIV MO-COLUMBIA, 67- *Mem:* Am Chem Soc. *Res:* Regulation of cell growth and metabolism. *Mailing Add:* Dept Biochem Univ Mo Columbia MO 65212

NOTHDURFT, ROBERT RAY, b Cape Girardeau, Mo, Nov 13, 39; m 61; c 2. PHYSICS. *Educ:* Wash Univ, St Louis, AB, 61; Univ Mo-Rolla, MS, 64, PhD(physics), 67. *Prof Exp:* Res physicist, US Bur Mines, Mo, 62-67; PROF PHYSICS, NORTHEAST MO STATE COL, 67- *Res:* Kilocycle range dislocation damping, especially in magnesium single crystals. *Mailing Add:* Dept Physics Northeast Mo State Col Kirksville MO 63501

NOTHMANN, GERHARD A(DOLF), mechanical engineering, see previous edition

NOTHSTINE, LEO VAUGHN, b Mancelona, Mich, Aug 19, 16; m 41; c 4. CIVIL ENGINEERING. *Educ:* Mich State Univ, BS, 38, CE, 45; Kans State Univ, MS, 40. *Prof Exp:* Jr engr, Fed Emergency Admin Pub Works, 39; res asst appl mech, Kans State Univ, 39-40; instr, Tex Technol Col, 40-41, instr civil eng, 41-42; in charge of flight res, instrumentation & exp eng, Willow Run Plant, Ford Motor Co, 43-45; partner & engr, Gould Eng Co, 45-46; from asst prof to assoc prof civil & sanit eng, 46-59, PROF CIVIL & SANIT ENG, MICH STATE UNIV, 59- *Concurrent Pos:* Stress analyst, Ford Motor Co, 42-; consult, Gould Eng Co, 46-51, vpres, 51-; chief party, Eng Col Contract, USAID, Madras & Poona, India, 61-62, adv, 64; consult eng prog, Univ Nigeria, 63. *Mem:* Nat Soc Prof Engrs; life mem Am Soc Civil Engrs; life mem Am Soc Eng Educ. *Res:* Structural design; surveying; geodesy. *Mailing Add:* Dept of Civil & Sanit Eng Mich State Univ East Lansing MI 48823

NOTIDES, ANGELO C, b New York, NY, Dec 11, 36; m 61; c 2. ENDOCRINOLOGY, BIOCHEMISTRY. *Educ:* Hunter Col, BA, 59, MA, 62; Univ Ill, PhD(physiol), 66. *Prof Exp:* Asst prof pharmacol, 68-74, assoc prof toxicol, 74-79, PROF RADIATION BIOL & BIOPHYS, SCH MED & DENT, UNIV ROCHESTER, 79- *Mem:* Am Soc Biol Chemists; Endocrine Soc. *Res:* Mechanism of hormone action; reproductive biochemistry; receptor biochemistry. *Mailing Add:* Dept Radiation Biol & Biophys Univ Rochester Sch Med & Dent Rochester NY 14642

NOTKINS, ABNER LOUIS, b New Haven, Conn, May 8, 32; m 69. VIROLOGY, IMMUNOLOGY. *Educ:* Yale Univ, BA, 53; NY Univ, MD, 58. *Prof Exp:* Intern internal med, Johns Hopkins Hosp, 58-59, asst resident, 59-60; res assoc, Nat Cancer Inst, 60-61; investr, Lab Microbiol & Immunol, 61-67, chief virol sect, 67-73, CHIEF LAB ORAL MED, NAT INST DENT RES, 73- *Mem:* AAAS; Am Soc Exp Path; Infectious Dis Soc Am; Am Asn Immunol; Am Soc Microbiol. *Res:* Slow viruses; viral immunology and immunopathology; virus-induced diabetes. *Mailing Add:* Lab Oral Med Bldg 30 Rm 121 Nat Inst of Health Bethesda MD 20014

NOTLEY, NORMAN THOMAS, b Bristol, Eng, Apr 10, 28; US citizen. POLYMER CHEMISTRY, PHYSICAL CHEMISTRY. *Educ:* Bristol Univ, BSc, 49, PhD(phys chem), 52. *Prof Exp:* Res assoc polymer chem, Cornell Univ, 52-54; res chemist, E I du Pont de Nemours & Co, 54-59; res chemist, Metal Box Co, Eng, 59-60, dept supvr phys chem, 60-62; chief chemist, Kalvar Corp, La, 62-63, dir res photochem, 63-65, dir res, 65-66; dir chem res, Bus Equip Group, Bell & Howell, 66-69; pres, Photomedia Co, 69-78; CONSULT, 3M CO, 78- *Mem:* Am Chem Soc; Soc Photog Sci & Eng. *Res:* Solution properties of polymers; polymerization kinetics; photopolymerization; oxidation kinetics of polyolefines; permeability of plastics; unconventional photographic and reprographic systems. *Mailing Add:* Box 462 Sierra Madre CA 91024

NOTO, THOMAS ANTHONY, b Tampa, Fla, Dec 27, 31; m 63; c 3. PATHOLOGY. *Educ:* Spring Hill Col, BS, 53; St Louis Univ, MD, 57. *Prof Exp:* Instr path, Sch Med, Univ Miami, 62-64; asst prof, Med Col Ala, 64-65, clin path, 65-68; assoc prof, Med Ctr, Univ Ala, Birmingham, 68-69; assoc dir clin path, 69-77, dir clin path II, 77-78, PROF, SCH MED, UNIV MIAMI, 77-; DIR TRANSFUSION SERV, JACKSON MEM HOSP, 78- *Concurrent Pos:* Asst clin pathologist, Jackson Mem Hosp, 62-64; asst clin pathologist & dir blood bank, Med Ctr, Univ Ala, Birmingham, 64-69. *Mem:* Fel Am Soc Clin Path; Col Am Path; Am Asn Blood Banks; Int Soc Blood Transfusion. *Res:* Clinical immunology; immunohematology; protein chemistry and blood banking. *Mailing Add:* Clin Path Labs Jackson Mem Hosp Miami FL 33136

NOTTAGE, HERBERT BRADLEY, b Oakland, Calif, Dec 31, 14; m; c 2. MECHANICAL ENGINEERING. *Educ:* Univ Calif, BS, 37, MS, 39; Case Inst Technol, PhD(mech eng), 52. *Prof Exp:* Asst, Univ Calif, 37-38, asst mech eng lab, 39; instr mech eng, Ill Inst Technol, 39-41; anal engr & proj engr, Pratt & Whitney Aircraft Co, Conn, 41-45; res assoc air conditioning, Am Soc Heating & Ventilating Engrs, 45-52; lectr, 53-59, prof eng, 59-76, PROF ENG & APPL SCI, UNIV CALIF, LOS ANGELES, 76- *Concurrent Pos:* Lectr, Case Inst Technol, 48; proj mgr, Propulsion Res Corp, 52-57; res specialist, Lockheed Aircraft Corp, 57- *Mem:* Am Soc Mech Engrs; Am Soc Heat, Refrig & Air-Conditioning Engrs; Aerospace Med Asn; Am Inst Chem Engrs. *Res:* Heat transfer; fluid mechanics; thermodynamics; elasticity; biotechnology; air conditioning; combustion; aerodynamics; turbomachinery. *Mailing Add:* Dept of Eng & Appl Sci Univ of Calif Los Angeles CA 90024

NOTTER, MARY FRANCES, b Johnstown, Pa, Aug 25, 47; m 73. TISSUE CULTURE, TUMOR BIOLOGY. *Educ:* Pa State Univ, BS, 69, MS, 71, PhD(physiol), 73. *Prof Exp:* Scholar microbiol, Pa State Univ, 74-76; tech assoc infectious dis, 76-78, res assoc microbiol, 78-80, instr microbiol, 80-81, ASST PROF ANAT & MICROBIOL, UNIV ROCHESTER MED CTR, 81- *Concurrent Pos:* Teaching fel anat, Univ Rochester Med Sch, 73-74. *Res:* Tissue culture of the fetal nervous system; viral cell surface receptors; surface markers-tumor cell indentification; viral markers in tumor tissue and their visualization. *Mailing Add:* Dept Anat 601 Elmwood Ave Rochester NY 14642

NOTZ, WILLIAM IRWIN, b Washington, DC, Oct 16, 51; m 80. OPTIMAL EXPERIMENTAL DESIGN. *Educ:* Johns Hopkins Univ, BS, 73; Cornell Univ, MS, 76, PhD(statist), 78. *Prof Exp:* ASST PROF STATIST, PURDUE UNIV, 78- *Mem:* Inst Math Statist; Am Statist Asn. *Res:* Robust experimental designs for regression problems; optimal experimental designs; construction of experimental designs. *Mailing Add:* Dept Statist Purdue Univ West Lafayette IN 47907

NOUJAIM, ANTOINE AKL, b Cairo, Egypt, Feb 26, 37; m 64. NUCLEAR PHARMACY. *Educ:* Cairo Univ, BS, 58; Purdue Univ, MSc, 63, PhD(bionucleonics), 65. *Prof Exp:* Head res & statist dept, Gen Orga Drugs, Cairo Univ, 59-61; res assoc bionucleonics, Purdue Univ, 65-66; from asst prof to assoc prof bionucleonics, 66-73, chmn dept, 68-74, PROF NUCLEAR PHARM, UNIV ALTA, 73-, CHMN RADIATION CONTROL, 72-, PROF PHARMACEUT STUDIES, UNIV & MEM STAFF, CANCER RES UNIT,

77- *Concurrent Pos:* Nat Res Coun fel, Cairo Univ, 61-65; consult water resources div, Alta Dept Agr, 66-; sr vis scientist, CSIRO, Australia, 74-75; sr res fel nuclear med, Dr W W Cross Cancer Inst, 75- *Mem:* AAAS; NY Acad Sci; Am Pharmaceut Asn; Soc Nuclear Med. *Res:* Radiation effects on biological systems; drug metabolism; isotope dilution methods; activation analysis; research and development of radiopharmaceuticals; clinical applications of radioactive drugs. *Mailing Add:* Fac of Pharm Univ of Alta Edmonton AB T6G 2E1 Can

NOVACEK, MICHAEL JOHN, b Evanston, Ill, June 3, 48; m 71; c 1. EVOLUTIONARY BIOLOGY, PALEONTOLOGY. *Educ:* Univ Calif, Los Angeles, AB, 71; San Diego State Univ, MA, 73; Univ Calif, Berkeley, PhD(paleont), 77. *Prof Exp:* Res asst vert paleont, San Diego State Univ, 71-72, teaching asst, 72-73; res asst, Univ Calif, Berkeley, 73-75; lectr zool, San Diego State Univ, 76-77, asst prof, 77-79, assoc prof, 79-81; ASST CUR FOSSIL MAMMALS, AM MUS NATURAL HIST, NEW YORK, 81- *Concurrent Pos:* Res assoc, Univ Calif Mus Paleont, Berkeley, 77-; NSF fel, Am Mus Natural Hist, 79-80. *Mem:* Soc Study Evolution; Soc Syst Zool; Am Soc Mammalogists; Paleont Soc; Soc Vert Paleont. *Res:* Mammalian evolution and phylogeny; vertebrate biogeography; multivariate analysis of community structure; functional morphology of auditory features in bats and other mammals. *Mailing Add:* Am Mus Natural Hist Central Park W & 79th New York NY 10023

NOVACK, JOSEPH, b Brooklyn, NY, Mar 31, 28; m 53; c 2. CHEMICAL ENGINEERING. *Educ:* City Col New York, BChE, 49; Am Int Col, MBA, 60. *Prof Exp:* Chem engr, Nat Dairy Res Labs, 49-51; chem engr, Monsanto Chem Co, 54-64, eng specialist, Monsanto Co, 64-70, group leader, SR GROUP SUPVR, MONSANTO CO, 73- *Mem:* Am Inst Chem Engrs. *Res:* Pilot plant research and development and process scale-up of unit operations applied to polymeric and organic processes. *Mailing Add:* Monsanto Co Technol Dept 730 Worcester St Indian Orchard MA 01151

NOVACO, ANTHONY DOMINIC, b Orange, NJ, Mar 24, 43; m 66; c 2. THEORETICAL SOLID STATE PHYSICS, SURFACE PHYSICS. *Educ:* Stevens Inst Technol, BS, 64, MS, 66, PhD(physics), 69. *Prof Exp:* Assoc res scientist physics, Hudson Labs, Columbia Univ, 67-69; fel physics, Battelle Mem Inst, 69-71; asst physicist, Brookhaven Nat Lab, 71-73; asst prof, 73-80, ASSOC PROF PHYSICS, LAFAYETTE COL, 80- *Mem:* Am Phys Soc; Sigma Xi. *Res:* Theoretical research in condensed matter physics; statistical physics; physisorption and surface physics; quantum liquids and solids. *Mailing Add:* Dept of Physics Lafayette Col Easton PA 18042

NOVAK, ALFRED, b Chicago, Ill, Jan 28, 15; m 44; c 3. HEALTH SCIENCES. *Educ:* Univ Chicago, BS, 36, MS, 42; Chicago Teachers Col, ME, 40; Mich State Univ, PhD, 50. *Prof Exp:* From instr to prof biol, Mich State Univ, 44-60; chief, Div Sci & Math, Stephens Col, 60-74, dir, Div Allied Health, 74-80; PROF, UNIV MO-COLUMBIA, 80- *Concurrent Pos:* NIH spec res fel, Calif Inst Technol, 50-51; Guggenheim fel, Cambridge Univ, 57-58; adv biol ed, Encycl Americana, 59-69; consult biol sci curriculum studies, Am Inst Biol Sci, 60-62; collabr, Nat Sci Adv Bd, Encycl Britannica Films, Inc, 65-; res fel, Inst Path, Med Sch, Univ Bologna, 72. *Res:* Protein synthesis and hormonal influence. *Mailing Add:* Univ Mo Columbia MO 65201

NOVAK, ERNEST RICHARD, b Szoce, Hungary, Apr 17, 40; US citizen; m 62; c 2. ORGANIC CHEMISTRY. *Educ:* Oberlin Col, BA, 63; Univ Rochester, PhD(org chem), 67. *Prof Exp:* Res chemist, Plastics Dept, Exp Sta, Wilmington, Del, 66-73, sr res chemist, 73-78, RES ASSOC, PLASTICS PROD & RES, E I DU PONT DE NEMOURS & CO, INC, PARKERSBURG, 78- *Mem:* Am Chem Soc. *Res:* Oxonium ions; optically active compounds; monomer and polymer research; polymerization chemistry. *Mailing Add:* PO Box 1217 E I du Pont de Nemours & Co Inc Parkersburg WV 26101

NOVAK, G(EORGE) J, b New York, NY, Feb 15, 21; m 53; c 2. CHEMICAL ENGINEERING. *Educ:* Univ Ill, BS, 49. *Prof Exp:* Design engr, Air Separation Plants, 49-55, sect engr, 55-62, div engr, 62-68, opers consult, 69-72, ENG MGR, LINDE DIV, UNION CARBIDE CORP, 72- *Mem:* Am Inst Chem Engrs. *Res:* Process design of chemical process equipment for production of industrial gases such as oxygen, nitrogen, argon and hydrogen. *Mailing Add:* Linde Div Union Carbide Corp PO Box 44 Tonawanda NY 14150

NOVAK, IRWIN DANIEL, b New York, NY, June 23, 42; m 67; c 3. GEOMORPHOLOGY. *Educ:* Hunter Col, AB, 66; Univ Fla, MS, 68; Cornell Univ, PhD(geol), 71. *Prof Exp:* Asst prof, 71-75, ASSOC PROF GEOL, UNIV SOUTHERN MAINE, 75- *Concurrent Pos:* Mem adv bd, Maine Land Use Regulation Comn, 73- *Mem:* AAAS; Geol Soc Am; Soc Econ Paleontologists & Mineralogists. *Res:* Coastal and fluvial geomorphology of Maine; sedimentary processes in coastal and fluvial environments. *Mailing Add:* Univ of Southern Maine College Ave Gorham ME 04038

NOVAK, JOSEF FRANTISEK, b Ceske Budejovice, Czech, Oct 24, 42. CANCER BIOLOGY. *Educ:* Prague Univ, MS, 64; Yale Univ, PhD(biol), 74. *Prof Exp:* Res asst plant physiol, Inst Exp Bot, Czech Acad Sci, 65-68; instr biochem, Dept Biol, Princeton Univ, 73-75; res assoc cancer biol, Dept Clin & Biochem Pharmacol, St Jude Children's Res Hosp, 75-77; res assoc cancer biol, Cancer Res Unit, 77-79, DIR, ORTHOP RES LAB, ALLEGHENY GEN HOSP, 79- *Mem:* Soc Exp Biol Gt Brit; Sigma Xi; Int Soc Differentiation. *Res:* Molecular and biochemical aspects of tumor metabolism with special emphasis on endogenous and exogenous substances determining the rate of cell division in normal and tumor cells. *Mailing Add:* Orthop Res Lab Allegheny Gen Hosp Pittsburgh PA 15212

NOVAK, JOSEPH DONALD, b Minneapolis, Minn, Dec 2, 30; m 53; c 3. BIOLOGY. *Educ:* Univ Minn, BS, 52, MA, 54, PhD(bot, educ), 58. *Prof Exp:* Asst bot, Univ Minn, 52-56, instr, 56-57; asst prof biol, Kans State Teachers Col, 57-59; from asst prof biol to assoc prof biol & educ, Purdue Univ, 59-67; coordr, Shell Merit Progs, 68-72, PROF SCI EDUC & CHMN SCI & ENVIRON EDUC DIV, CORNELL UNIV, 67- *Concurrent Pos:* David Ross fel, 64; res assoc, Harvard Univ, 65-66; Fulbright-Hays sr scholar, 80. *Mem:* AAAS; Bot Soc Am; Am Asn Biol Teachers (vpres, 64); Nat Asn Res Sci Teaching (exec secy, 62-67, pres, 68); Nat Sci Teachers Asn. *Res:* Biological education; analysis of concept learning; cognitive learning theory. *Mailing Add:* Stone Hall Cornell Univ Ithaca NY 14853

NOVAK, LADISLAV PETER, b Chlum, Czech, Sept 18, 22; m 50; c 4. PHYSIOLOGICAL ANTHROPOLOGY. *Educ:* Charles Univ, Prague, BSc, 48; Univ Minn, Minneapolis, MA, 61, PhD, 62. *Prof Exp:* Fel physiol, Univ Minn, 62-64, vis asst prof physiol anthrop, 62-63, asst prof physiol anthrop, 63-66, consult, Mayo Grad Sch Med, 66-72; PROF ANTHROP, SOUTHERN METHODIST UNIV, 72- *Concurrent Pos:* NIH grants, 64-72; AMA lectr, 71-72; pres, Int Comt Standardization Phys Fitness Tests, 76-80; NIH proj officer, Foreign Res Prog; res grants, Xerox Co, 76-78 & Sun Gas Co, 78-; exchange scientist, Czech Acad Sci-US Nat Acad Sci, 78-79. *Mem:* Am Asn Phys Anthrop; NY Acad Sci; Brit Soc Study Human Biol; Am Aging Asn; Am Asn Clin Nutrit. *Res:* Physiological growth and development; body composition; physiology of exercise. *Mailing Add:* Dept of Anthrop Southern Methodist Univ Dallas TX 75222

NOVAK, MARIE MARTA, b Prague, Czechoslovakia, May 10, 40; Can citizen. ZOOLOGY. *Educ:* Univ Man, PhD(zool), 74. *Prof Exp:* asst prof, 74-79, ASSOC PROF BIOL, UNIV WINNEPEG, 79- *Mem:* Am Soc Parasitologists. *Res:* Host-parasite relationships governing the growth differentiation and morphology of populations of helminths; modification of host resistance by various immunosuppressive agents; parasite resistance by various anthelminthics. *Mailing Add:* Biol Dept Univ Winnipeg Winnipeg MB R3B 2E9 Can

NOVAK, MILOS, b Sumperk, Czech, Mar 29, 25; Can citizen. ENGINEERING SCIENCE. *Educ:* Prague Tech Univ, Ing, 49; Inst Theoret & Appl Mech, Prague, PhD(eng mech), 57. *Prof Exp:* Designer struct, Govt Consult Agency Spec Indust Struct, Bratislava, 49-52; head sect, Govt Consult Agency Heavy Indust, Prague, 52-53; scientific worker dynamics, Inst Theoret & Appl Mech, Prague, 56-67; PROF ENG SCI, UNIV WESTERN ONT, 67- *Concurrent Pos:* Consult, Can Westinghouse, 69-74, Golder Assoc, 73-75, Ont Hydro, 74-75, Law Eng, Comverse Ward Dan's, Dixon, ATEC Assocs, Harding-Lawson Assocs, Can Industs Ltd & Kraftwerk Union; researcher, Nat Res Coun res grants-in-aid, 70-; chmn task group soils & found, Can Nat Comt Earthquake Eng, 76- *Mem:* Can Nat Comt Earthquake Eng; Am Soc Civil Engrs. *Res:* Dynamics of structures, foundations and soils; wind engineering; earthquake engineering. *Mailing Add:* Fac of Eng Sci Univ of Western Ont London ON N6A 5B8 Can

NOVAK, RAYMOND FRANCIS, b St Louis, Mo. NUCLEAR MAGNETIC RESONANCE SPECTROSCOPY. *Educ:* Univ Mo-St Louis BS, 68; Case Western Reserve Univ, PhD(phys chem), 73. *Prof Exp:* Fel, chem, Case Western Reserve Univ, 73-74; fel pharmacol, 74-75, NIH fel, 75-76, assoc, 76-77, asst prof, 77-81, ASSOC PROF PHARMACOL, NORTHWESTERN UNIV MED SCH, 81- *Mem:* Am Soc Pharmacol & Exp Therapeut; Biophys Soc; Sigma Xi; AAAS; Int Soc Magnetic Resonance. *Res:* Purification of the individual enzymes and related components of the hepatic mixed function oxidase system and study of molecular level events in drug metabolism, including substrate-hemeprotein and substrate-flavoprotein interactions; role of such interactions in the formation of toxic species in the microsome and red cell. *Mailing Add:* Dept Pharmacol Northwestern Univ Med Sch 303 E Chicago Ave Chicago IL 60611

NOVAK, ROBERT EUGENE, b Spring Valley, Ill, Apr 30, 49; m 72; c 1. AUDIOLOGY. *Educ:* Univ Iowa, BS, 72, MA, 73, PhD(audiol), 77. *Prof Exp:* Audiologist, St Luke's Hosp, Cedar Rapids, Iowa, 73-74; audiol asstship, Vet Hosp, Iowa City, 76-77; ASST PROF AUDIOL, SAN DIEGO STATE UNIV, 77- *Mem:* Am Speech & Hearing Asn; Sigma Xi. *Res:* Aural rehabilitation, especially assessment and remediation of problems associated with hearing loss in the aged populations. *Mailing Add:* Dept of Commun Dis San Diego State Univ San Diego CA 92128

NOVAK, ROBERT JOHN, b Pueblo, Colo, June 5, 47; m 72; c 1. MEDICAL ENTOMOLOGY, INSECT ECOLOGY. *Educ:* Univ Southern Colo, BS, 69; Univ Utah, MS, 72; Univ Ill, Urbana-Champaign, PhD(entom), 76. *Prof Exp:* Res asst med entom, Univ Ill, 72-76; res assoc vector biol, Univ Notre Dame, 76-78; RES ENTOMOLOGIST VECTOR BIOL, BUR TROP DIS, CTR DIS CONTROL, 78- *Concurrent Pos:* Entomologist, Macon Mosquito Abatement Dist, Decatur, Ill, 72-76; NIH trainee, Univ Notre Dame, 76-78; entomologist- supvr vector control, City of Champaign, Ill, 76 & Health Dept, St Joseph County, Ind, 78; vis lectr, Purdue Univ, 77. *Mem:* Entom Soc Am; Am Mosquito Control Asn; Am Registry Prof Entomologists; Ecol Soc Am; Entom Soc Can. *Res:* Bionomics and population ecology of insect vectors of disease, especially mosquito borne. *Mailing Add:* Vector Biol CDC Div Bur of Trop Dis Atlanta GA 30333

NOVAK, ROBERT LOUIS, b Chicago, Ill, Oct 1, 37; m 65; c 1. BIOCHEMISTRY. *Educ:* Xavier Univ, Ohio, AB, 59; Univ Del, PhD(cell physiol, biochem), 64. *Prof Exp:* NIH fel, Dept Biol Sci, Purdue Univ, 63-65; asst prof biochem, Univ NH, 65-67; res fel, Harvard Univ, 67-69; asst prof, 69-74, ASSOC PROF CHEM & BIOL, DEPAUL UNIV, 74- *Concurrent Pos:* Res grants, Res Corp, 66-67 & 71-72, Am Cancer Soc, 71-72 & NIH, 71- *Mem:* Am Chem Soc. *Res:* Model polypeptides for studying biopolymer interactions; insertion sites for viral information in cancer cells; phosphorous chemistry in polynucleotides; biochemical engineering of human genes. *Mailing Add:* Dept of Chem DePaul Univ Chicago IL 60614

NOVAK, ROBERT OTTO, b Oak Park, Ill, Sept 12, 30; m 59; c 1. MYCOLOGY, PLANT PATHOLOGY. *Educ:* Mich State Univ, BS, 52; Univ Ill, MS, 56; Univ Wis, PhD(bot), 63. *Prof Exp:* Res microbiologist, Lederle Labs, 63-68; asst prof, 68-73, assoc prof, 73-81, PROF BIOL, ORE COL EDUC, 81- *Mem:* AAAS; Mycol Soc Am. *Res:* Ecology and taxonomy of soil microfungi. *Mailing Add:* Dept of Sci & Math Ore Col of Educ Monmouth OR 97361

NOVAK, ROBERT WILLIAM, b Hoboken, NJ, Aug 2, 39; m 60; c 3. ORGANIC CHEMISTRY. *Educ:* Wagner Col, BS, 60; Purdue Univ, MS, 64, PhD(org chem), 66. *Prof Exp:* Instr chem, Purdue Univ, 64-66; res chemist, 66-72, mgr paper chem tech serv, 72-74, SR RES CHEMIST, AM CYANAMID CO, 74- *Mem:* AAAS; Am Chem Soc; Tech Asn Pulp & Paper Indust. *Res:* Organic synthesis of natural products; reaction of bromine with terminal disubstituted olefins; organic synthesis and product development of paper chemicals; mechanisms of retention of chemical additives for paper application. *Mailing Add:* 32F Weed Hill Ave Stamford CT 06907

NOVAK, RONALD WILLIAM, b Elmira, NY, Dec 3, 42; m 63; c 2. EMULSION POLYMERIZATION, COATINGS. *Educ:* Univ S Fla, BA, 64; Fla State Univ, PhD(org chem), 68. *Prof Exp:* chemist, 69-81, SR RES CHEMIST, ROHM & HAAS CO, 81- *Mem:* Am Chem Soc. *Res:* Dispersion and solution polymers. *Mailing Add:* Rohm & Haas Co Spring House PA 19477

NOVAK, STEPHEN ROBERT, b Homestead, Pa, June 23, 39; m 61; c 3. MECHANICAL ENGINEERING, METALLURGICAL ENGINEERING. *Educ:* Univ Pittsburgh, BS, 61, MS, 66, PhD(metall eng, mat sci), 77. *Prof Exp:* Assoc technologist process develop, 61-65, assoc technologist res fracture mech, 65-68, res engr, 68-73, SR RES ENGR FRACTURE MECH, RES LAB, US STEEL CORP, 73- *Concurrent Pos:* Mem adv panel subcritical cracking high strength steels, US Navy, 76-; mem rev panel corrosion fatigue behav steels, Fed Hwy Admin, US Dept Transp, 78-; mem comt, Environ Assisted Cracking Test Methods for High Strength Steel Weldments, Nat Res Coun, Nat Mat Adv Bd, 80- *Mem:* Am Soc Testing & Mat; Am Soc Metals; Nat Asn Corrosion Eng; Am Soc Mech Eng. *Res:* Mechanical metallurgy; fracture mechanics; subcritical crack growth; fatigue; stress corrosion cracking; corrosion fatigue; hydrogen embrittlement; brittle fracture; ductile fracture; crack initiation; stable crack growth; r-curve technology; corrosion; physical metallurgy; engineering mechanics; materials science engineering. *Mailing Add:* Res Lab ms 90 US Steel Corp Monroeville PA 15146

NOVAL, JOSEPH JAMES, biochemistry, see previous edition

NOVALES, RONALD RICHARDS, b San Francisco, Calif, Apr 24, 28; m 53; c 2. COMPARATIVE VERTEBRATE ENDOCRINOLOGY. *Educ:* Univ Calif, Berkeley, BA, 50, MA, 53, PhD(zool), 58. *Prof Exp:* Assoc zool, Univ Calif, Berkeley, 56; from asst prof to assoc prof, 58-70, PROF BIOL SCI, NORTHWESTERN UNIV, ILL, 70- *Mem:* Fel AAAS; Endocrine Soc; Am Soc Zoologists; Int Pigment Cell Soc. *Res:* Regulation of pigment granule movements vertebrate chromatophores; action of melanocyte-stimulating hormone, catecholamines, and melatomin; action of melanocyte-stimulating hormone, catecholamines, and melatomin; role of cyclic adenusine monophosphate and calcium, using frog skin and tissue cultured melanophores; pigment cell biology. *Mailing Add:* Dept of Biol Sci Northwestern Univ Evanston IL 60201

NOVELLI, GUERINO DAVID, b Agawam, Mass, Nov 6, 18; m 43; c 2. BIOCHEMISTRY. *Educ:* Mass State Col, BS, 40; Rutgers Univ, MS, 42; Harvard Univ, PhD(biochem), 49. *Prof Exp:* Asst bact, Rutgers Univ, 40-42; chemotherapeutist, Merck Inst for Therapeut Res, 42; asst, Scripps Inst, Univ Calif, 42-44; bacteriologist, Mass Gen Hosp, 48-49, from asst biochemist to assoc biochemist, 49-53; assoc prof microbiol, Sch Med, Western Reserve Univ, 53-56; dir biol macromolecular separations prog, 65-72, PRIN BIOCHEMIST, BIOL DIV, OAK RIDGE NAT LAB, 56- *Concurrent Pos:* Tutor, Harvard Col, 49-53; mem study sect physiol chem, NIH, 61-64, 70-73, radiation, 65-; prof, Grad Sch Biomed Sci, Univ Tenn, 67-; cancer res grant, 69-70. *Mem:* AAAS; Am Cancer Soc; Am Soc Microbiol; Am Soc Biol Chemists; hon mem Lombardy Med Acad Italy. *Res:* Enzymology of protein biosynthesis; structure and function of transfer RNA; carcinogenesis; aging; macromolecular separations technology; regulation and control mechanisms; bioengineering and biomedical engineering. *Mailing Add:* 398 East Dr Oak Ridge TN 37830

NOVELLO, FREDERICK CHARLES, b Somerville, Mass, July 27, 16; m 48; c 3. ORGANIC CHEMISTRY. *Educ:* Harvard Univ, SB, 38, MA, 39, PhD(org chem), 41. *Prof Exp:* Res assoc Nat Defense Res Comt, Harvard Univ, 41-43; res chemist, Sharp & Dohme Div, Merck & Co, Inc, 43-69; sr res fel, Merck Sharp & Dohme Res Labs, 69-73, sr investr, 73-81; RETIRED. *Honors & Awards:* Modern Pioneers Award, Nat Asn Mfrs, 65; Albert Lasker Award, Albert & Mary Lasker Found, 75. *Mem:* Am Chem Soc. *Res:* Medicinal chemistry. *Mailing Add:* 786 Bair Rd Berwyn PA 19312

NOVICK, AARON, b Toledo, Ohio, June 24, 19; m 48; c 2. BIOPHYSICS. *Educ:* Univ Chicago, BS, 40, PhD(chem), 43. *Prof Exp:* Scientist, Manhattan Dist Proj, Univ Chicago, 43-46, AEC Proj, 46-47, asst prof biophys, 48-55, assoc prof biophys & microbiol, 55-58; dir inst molecular biol, 59-69, PROF BIOL, UNIV ORE, 59-, DEAN GRAD SCH, 71- *Concurrent Pos:* Guggenheim fel, Pasteur Inst, France, 53-54. *Mem:* AAAS; Genetics Soc Am; Am Soc Microbiol; Biophys Soc. *Res:* Biological regulatory mechanisms. *Mailing Add:* Inst of Molecular Biol Univ of Ore Eugene OR 97403

NOVICK, ALVIN, b Flushing, NY, June 27, 25. BEHAVIORAL PHYSIOLOGY, NEUROBIOLOGY. *Educ:* Harvard Col, AB, 47, MD. 51. *Prof Exp:* Teaching fel med, Harvard Univ, 52-53, res fel biol, 53-57; from instr to asst prof zool, 57-65, ASSOC PROF BIOL, YALE UNIV, 65- *Mem:* Am Physiol Soc; Am Soc Zool; Am Soc Mammal; Ecol Soc Am; Animal Behav Soc. *Res:* Echolocation in bats; sensory physiology; vertebrate biology. *Mailing Add:* Dept of Biol Yale Univ PO Box 2169 New Haven CT 06520

NOVICK, DAVID THEODORE, b Tucson, Ariz, Sept 25, 35; div; c 2. MATERIALS SCIENCE. *Educ:* Univ Ariz, BS, 57; Mass Inst Technol, SM, 59; Columbia Univ, PhD(mat sci), 68. *Prof Exp:* Staff metallurgist, Int Bus Mach Res Ctr, 58-60; res assoc x-ray diffraction, Columbia Univ, 60-62, res asst metall, 62-66; Columbia fel field ion micros, Battelle Mem Inst, 66; mgr, chief metallurgist, dir customer serv & assoc dir res & develop, Alpha Metals, Inc, 66-74; tech dir, Hanovia Liquid Gold Dept, 74-81, MGR NEW BUS PLANNING, ELECTRONIC MAT GROUP, ENGELHARD INSTUS DIV, ENGELHARD MINERALS & CHEM CORP, EAST NEWARK, 81- *Concurrent Pos:* Consult, Inst Printed Circuits, 69-75; spec tech consult, Corning Mus Glass, 78-80. *Mem:* Am Inst Mining, Metall & Petrol Engrs; Am Soc Metals; Int Soc Hybrid Microelectronics; Soc Glass Decorators; NY Acad Sci. *Res:* Thick film materials for hybrid microelectronics; precious metal preparations for china and glass; history of materials use in ancient technology. *Mailing Add:* Hanovia Liquid Gold One W Central Ave East Newark NJ 07029

NOVICK, RICHARD P, b New York, NY, Aug 10, 32; m 58; c 2. MICROBIAL GENETICS. *Educ:* Yale Univ, BA, 54; NY Univ, MD, 59. *Prof Exp:* Intern, Yale-New Haven Med Ctr, 59-60; Nat Found fel, Nat Inst Med Res, Eng, 60-62; asst resident, Hosp, Vanderbilt Univ, 62-63; USPHS fel, Rockefeller Univ, 63-65; assoc, 65-69, assoc mem, 69-75, MEM & CHIEF DEPT PLASMID BIOL, PUB HEALTH RES INST OF CITY OF NEW YORK, INC, 75-, DIR, 80- *Concurrent Pos:* Res asst prof, NY Univ, 66-69, res assoc prof, 69-75, res prof, 76-; lectr, Columbia Univ, 66-68; ed-in-chief, Plasmid, 77- *Mem:* Am Soc Microbiol; Genetics Soc Am; Harvey Soc. *Res:* Microbial physiology; control mechanisms in biosynthetic pathways; extrachromosomal resistance factors in Staphlylococcus aureus; genetic control of replication; misuse of science. *Mailing Add:* Dept Microbiol Pub Health Res Inst 455 First Ave New York NY 10016

NOVICK, ROBERT, b New York, NY, May 3, 23; m 47; c 3. PHYSICS. *Educ:* Stevens Inst Technol, ME, 44, MS, 49; Columbia Univ, PhD(physics), 55. *Prof Exp:* Engr microwaves, Wheeler Labs, Inc, 46-47; instr physics, Columbia Univ, 52-54, res assoc, 54-57, adj asst prof, 57; from asst prof to assoc prof, Univ Ill, 57-60; assoc prof, 60-62, dir radiation lab, 60-68, PROF PHYSICS, COLUMBIA UNIV, 62-, CO-DIR ASTROPHYS LAB, 68- *Concurrent Pos:* Sloan fel, 59-72; mem adv panel physics, NSF, 62-65; chmn subpanel atomic & molecular physics, Nat Acad Sci, 64-65; mem Nat Acad Sci Panel, adv to Nat Bur Standards Atomic Physics Div, 66-69; consult, Gen Precision Lab, Gen Time, Inc, & Perkin-Elmer Corp. *Mem:* Fel Am Phys Soc; fel Inst Elec & Electronics Eng. *Res:* Atomic physics, collisions and frequency standards; quantum electronics; nuclear moments; x-ray astronomy. *Mailing Add:* Dept of Physics Columbia Univ New York NY 10027

NOVICK, RUDOLPH G, b Warsaw, Poland, Dec 16, 10; US citizen; m 37; c 2. PSYCHIATRY. *Educ:* Northwestern Univ, BS, 31, MD, 36; Chicago Inst Psychoanal, 46-50. *Prof Exp:* Jr physician psychiat, Jacksonville State Hosp, Ill Dept Pub Welfare, 37-40; jr physician, Manteno State Hosp, Ill, 40-41; sr physician, Elgin State Hosp, Ill, 41-43; med dir, Ill Soc Ment Health, 43-55; med dir psychiat, 56-77, PSYCHIATRIST-IN-CHIEF, FOREST HOSP, 77- *Concurrent Pos:* Pvt pract, 45-; psychiat consult, Comt Community Serv, NIMH, 54-57, Chicago State Hosp, 55-56, Munic Tuberc Hosp, Chicago, 55-58 & Ill State Dept Pub Health, 69-; assoc prof psychiat & actg chmn dept, Univ Health Sci/Chicago Med Sch, 75-77. *Mem:* AMA; fel Am Psychiat Asn; Group Advan Psychiat (chmn, Comt Prev Psychiat). *Mailing Add:* Psychiatrist-in-Chief Forest Hosp 555 Wilson Lane Des Plaines IL 60016

NOVICK, STEWART EUGENE, b New York, NY, Sept 10, 45. PHYSICAL CHEMISTRY. *Educ:* State Univ Stony Brook, BS, 67; Harvard Univ, AM, 68, PhD(chem physics), 73. *Prof Exp:* Fel chem, Harvard Univ, 74-76; res assoc, Joint Inst Lab Astrophysics, Univ Colo & Nat Bur Standards, 76-78; ASST PROF CHEM, WESLEYAN UNIV, 78- *Mem:* Am Phys Soc. *Res:* Spectroscopy, structure and bonding of weakly bound complexes; molecular beams; ions. *Mailing Add:* Dept of Chem Wesleyan Univ Middletown CT 06457

NOVICK, WILLIAM JOSEPH, JR, b Revloc, Pa, Dec 14, 31; m 55; c 4. PHARMACOLOGY, BIOCHEMISTRY. *Educ:* St Francis Col, Pa, BS, 53; Duke Univ, PhD(pharmacol), 61. *Prof Exp:* Technician toxicol, Dept Pub Health, Univ Pittsburgh, 54-55; jr biochemist, Smith Kline & French Labs, 55-58, sr scientist, 61-64, group leader pharmacol, 64-65, from asst sect head to sect head, 65-67; mgr pharmacol dept, William H Rorer, Inc, Pa, 67-70; dir pharmacol dept, 70-77, DIR BIOL SCI, HOECHST ROUSSELL PHARMACEUT, INC, 77- *Mem:* Am Soc Pharmacol & Exp Therapeut; NY Acad Sci. *Res:* Effects of age and thyroid hormone on monamine oxidase; pharmacological activities of steroids; drug metabolism. *Mailing Add:* Hoechst Roussel Pharaceut Inc Rte 202-206 N Somerville NJ 08876

NOVIKOFF, ALEX BENJAMIN, b Russia, Feb 28, 13; nat US; m 39, 68; c 2. BIOCHEMISTRY. *Educ:* Columbia Univ, BS, 31, AM, 33, PhD(zool), 38. *Prof Exp:* Tutor biol, Brooklyn Col, 35-40, from instr to asst prof, 40-48; assoc prof biochem, Col Med, Univ Vt, 48-53, prof exp path, 51-53; PROF PATH, ALBERT EINSTEIN COL MED, 55- *Concurrent Pos:* Am Cancer Soc fel, Col Med, Univ Wis, 46-47; USPHS res career award, Nat Cancer Inst, 62- *Mem:* Nat Acad Sci; Am Soc Cell Biol (pres, 62-63); Histochem Soc (pres, 58-59); Electron Micros Soc Am; Soc Develop Biol. *Res:* Biochemical cytology of normal and malignant cells; hepatomas; enzyme cytochemistry; lysosomes; Golgi apparatus; peroxisomes; electron microscopy. *Mailing Add:* Dept of Path Albert Einstein Col of Med Bronx NY 10461

NOVITSKI, EDWARD, b Wilkes Barre, Pa, July 24, 18; m 43; c 4. GENETICS. *Educ:* Purdue Univ, BS, 38; Calif Inst Technol, PhD(genetics), 42. *Prof Exp:* Guggenheim fel, Univ Rochester, 45-46, res assoc, Atomic Energy Proj, 46-47; res assoc, Univ Mo, 47-48; sr res fel, Calif Inst Technol, 48-51; assoc prof zool, Univ Mo, 51-56; head biologist, Oak Ridge Nat Lab, 56-58; head dept, 64-67, PROF BIOL, UNIV ORE, 58- *Concurrent Pos:* NSF sr fel, Univs Zurich, 61-62 & Canberra, 67-68; Guggenheim fel, Univ Leiden,

74-75 & Fulbright fel, 75-76. *Mem:* Genetics Soc Am (treas, 62-66); Soc Exp Biol & Med; Am Soc Nat; Soc Human Genetics. *Res:* Chromosome behavior; speciation; statistical analysis of genetic data; use of computing methods in biology. *Mailing Add:* Dept of Biol Univ of Ore Eugene OR 97403

NOVITSKY, JAMES ALAN, b Hazleton, Pa, Nov 14, 51; m 73. MARINE MICROBIOLOGY. *Educ:* Pa State Univ, BS, 73; Ore State Univ, PhD(microbiol), 77. *Prof Exp:* Asst prof, 77-82, ASSOC PROF BIOL, DALHOUSIE UNIV, 82- *Concurrent Pos:* Res assoc oceanog, Dalhousie Univ, 78- *Mem:* Am Soc Microbiol; AAAS; Sigma Xi. *Res:* Sediment microbial ecology. *Mailing Add:* Dept of Biol Dalhousie Univ Halifax NS B3H 4J1 Can

NOVLAN, DAVID JOHN, b Colorado Springs, Colo, Dec 8, 47; m 74. METEOROLOGY, MATHEMATICS. *Educ:* Univ Colo, BS, 69; Colo State Univ, MS, 73. *Prof Exp:* Meteorologist, 73-77, sr meteorologist, 77-78, CHIEF FORECASTER, ATMOSPHERIC SCI LAB, 78- *Mem:* Am Meteorol Soc. *Res:* Improvement of operational synoptic and ballistic meteorology; improvement and computerization of regional and local weather forecasting and methods in climatology. *Mailing Add:* Atmospheric Sci Lab White Sands Missile Range NM 88002

NOVOA, WILLIAM BREWSTER, b Havana, Cuba, July 16, 30; US citizen. BIOCHEMISTRY. *Educ:* Univ Fla, BS, 55; Duke Univ, PhD, 59. *Prof Exp:* USPHS res fel, Univ Wash, 59-61; res assoc, McIlvain Lab, Med Ctr, Univ Kans, 61, from instr to asst prof biochem, 62-70; ASSOC PROF CHEM, CENT CONN STATE COL, 70- *Mem:* Am Chem Soc. *Res:* Mechanism of enzyme action. *Mailing Add:* Dept of Chem Cent Conn State Col New Britain CT 06050

NOVODVORSKY, MARK EVGENIEVICH, b Moscow, Russia, July 21, 46. PURE MATHEMATICS. *Educ:* Univ Moscow, PhD(physics, math), 71. *Prof Exp:* Asst math, Inst Advan Study, 74-75; asst prof, 75-80, ASSOC PROF MATH, PURDUE UNIV, WEST LAFAYETTE, 80- *Mem:* Am Math Soc. *Res:* Zeta functions associated to automorphic representations of reductive groups over global fields. *Mailing Add:* Dept of Math Purdue Univ West Lafayette IN 47906

NOVOSAD, ROBERT S, b Chicago, Ill, May 1, 20; m 46; c 3. MATHEMATICS. *Educ:* Ill Inst Technol, BS, 42; Univ Chicago, MS, 48, PhD(math), 52. *Prof Exp:* Instr math, Tulane Univ, 50-53; asst prof, Pa State Univ, 53-60; assoc res scientist, Denver Div, Martin-Marietta Corp, 60-67, chief space systs opers anal, 67-71; PROF PHYSICS & AERONAUT SYSTS, UNIV W FLA, 71-, PROF MATH & STATIST, 77- *Mem:* Am Math Soc; Opers Res Soc Am; Am Astronaut Soc; Am Inst Aeronaut & Astronaut. *Res:* Operations research; systems analysis. *Mailing Add:* Aeronaut Systs Fac Univ of WFla Pensacola FL 32504

NOVOTNY, ANTHONY JAMES, b Chicago, Ill, Aug 14, 32; m 53; c 2. FISHERIES, AQUACULTURE. *Educ:* Morton Col, BEd, 52; Univ Wash, BSc, 58. *Prof Exp:* Fisheries res biologist, US Bur Com Fisheries, 58-67; FISHERIES RES BIOLOGIST MARINE AQUACULT, NAT MARINE FISHERIES SERV, NAT OCEANIC & ATMOSPHERIC ADMIN, 68- *Concurrent Pos:* Nat Marine Fisheries Serv consult, Ctr Ocean Brest, France, 73- *Mem:* Am Fisheries Soc; Nat Shellfisheries Asn; Am Inst Fisheries Res Biologists. *Res:* Marine aquaculture; fish diseases; salmonid propagation and enhancement; influences of salmonid survival. *Mailing Add:* 1919 E Calhoun Seattle WA 98112

NOVOTNY, CHARLES, b New York, NY, July 27, 36; m 58; c 2. MICROBIOLOGY. *Educ:* Wis State Col Stevens Point, BS, 59; Univ Pittsburgh, PhD(bact), 65. *Prof Exp:* Fel microbiol, Sch Med, Univ Pittsburgh, 65, res assoc, 65-68; ASSOC PROF MED MICROBIOL, UNIV VT, 68- *Mem:* Am Soc Microbiol. *Res:* Transport systems in bacteria; microbial genetics. *Mailing Add:* Dept of Med Microbiol Univ of Vt Burlington VT 05401

NOVOTNY, DONALD BOB, b Cedar Rapids, Iowa, Nov 15, 37; m 67; c 2. PHYSICAL CHEMISTRY. *Educ:* Univ Iowa, BS, 59; Iowa State Univ, PhD(phys chem), 64. *Prof Exp:* Sr res chemist, Mound Lab, Monsanto Res Corp, 64-66; res assoc chem, Mass Inst Technol, 66-67; res chemist, Vacuum Measurement Sect, Nat Bur Standards, Washington, DC, 67-71, gen phys scientist, Fire Technol Div, 71-75, PHYS CHEMIST, ELECTRON DEVICES DIV, NAT BUR STANDARDS, WASHINGTON, DC, 75- *Mem:* Am Phys Soc; Inst Elec & Electronics Engrs. *Res:* Metal physics; metals; alloys; alloy phases; phase stability from thermodynamic considerations; lattice vibrations and energetics; photolithographic processes including photochemistry of resists and measurements utilizing optics; microelectronic devices and integrated circuit fabrication processes. *Mailing Add:* Nat Bur of Standards Washington DC 20234

NOVOTNY, DONALD WAYNE, b Chicago, Ill, Dec 15, 34; m 55; c 2. ELECTRICAL ENGINEERING. *Educ:* Ill Inst Technol, BS, 56, MS, 57; Univ Wis-Madison, PhD(elec eng), 61. *Prof Exp:* Instr elec eng, Ill Inst Technol, 57-58; instr, 58-60, from asst prof to assoc prof, 61-68, assoc dept, 68-76, chmn, Dept Elec & Comput Eng, 76-80, PROF ELEC ENG, UNIV WIS-MADISON, 68- *Concurrent Pos:* Consult, A O Smith Corp, 63; res grant, Marathon Elec Mfg Corp, 64, consult, 64-; consult, Hevi-Duty Equip Co, 65-67, Wis Dept Natural Resources, 70- & Borg Warner Res Lab, 73-; res grant, Allen Bradley Co, 70-71; vis prof, Eindhoven Tech Univ, 73-74; consult, Rexnord Corp, 80- & Allen Bradley Co & Eaton Corp, 81-; res grants, Gen Elec Co, 78-79 & Allen Bradley, 80; dir, Wis Elec Mach & Power Electronics Consortium, 81; Fulbright lectr, Tech Univ Gent, Belgium, 81. *Mem:* Am Soc Eng Educ; Inst Elec & Electronics Engrs. *Res:* Electromechanical devices and control systems; electric machine analysis and design; power electronics. *Mailing Add:* Dept Elec & Comput Eng Univ Wis Madison WI 53706

NOVOTNY, EVA, b Brno, Czech, May 22, 34; US citizen. ACOUSTICS, HYDRODYNAMICS. *Educ:* Barnard Col, AB, 55; Columbia Univ, PhD(astron), 61. *Prof Exp:* From instr to asst prof astron, Univ Pa, 61-68; vis scientist, Manned Spacecraft Ctr, NASA, 70-71; vis scientist, Univ Manchester, 72-73; res assoc astron, Univ Col, Cardiff, 74-78; res fel math, Univ Dundee, 79-81; RES ASSOC, UNIV LIVERPOOL, 81- *Concurrent Pos:* Lectr math, Univ Nottingham, 78-79. *Mem:* Royal Astron Soc. *Res:* Stellar interiors; binary star systems; elastic wave-scattering from a fluid cylinder (theoretical); hydrodynamics of ships in confined waters. *Mailing Add:* Dept Mech Eng Univ Liverpool Liverpool England

NOVOTNY, JAMES FRANK, b Washington, DC, May 17, 37; m 41; c 5. MICROBIOLOGY, IMMUNOLOGY. *Educ:* Univ Md, BS, 62, MS, 70, PhD(microbiol), 73. *Prof Exp:* Microbiologist, US Army Res Ctr, 62-65, USDA, 65-69 & US Army Foreign Sci & Technol Ctr, 69-70; res assoc, Washington Hosp Ctr, 70-72; dir microbiol, Woodard Res Corp, 72-75; asst prof, Col Osteop Med & Surg, 75-78; CHMN MICROBIOL, NEW ENG COL OSTEOP MED, 78- *Concurrent Pos:* Adj prof, Drake Univ, 75-78. *Mem:* Am Soc Microbiol. *Res:* Immunology of viral diseases and cell culture metabolism. *Mailing Add:* Dept Microbiol 605 Pool Rd Biddeford ME 04005

NOVOTNY, JAROSLAV, b Brtnice, Czech, Mar 11, 24; m 56; c 3. MEDICINAL CHEMISTRY. *Educ:* Univ Adelaide, BSc, 59, PhD(org chem), 63. *Prof Exp:* Demonstr, Dept Org Chem, Univ Adelaide, 62-63; res fel org & med chem, State Univ NY Buffalo, 64-65; chemist, 65, SUPVR ORG CHEM, STARKS ASSOCS, INC, 65- *Mem:* Am Chem Soc. *Res:* Synthesis and isolation of carcinogenic hydrocarbons from tars and the use of carbon 14 for them; synthesis of inhibitors of folic reductase and thymidylic synthetase; synthesis of medicinals and other organic compounds; research and development of new antimalarials. *Mailing Add:* 215 Fruitwood Terr Buffalo NY 14221

NOVOTNY, ROBERT THOMAS, b New York, NY, Nov 22, 24; m 57; c 5. MAMMALIAN ECOLOGY, PALEOECOLOGY. *Educ:* Univ Mich, BS, 50; Univ Utah, MS, 58, PhD(biol), 70. *Prof Exp:* Sci technician marine geophys, Columbia Univ-Woods Hole Oceanog Inst, 51; geophysicist uranium explor, US AEC, 51-52; geologist, E J Longyear Co, Africa, 52-55; geologist & geophysicist copper explor, Anaconda Co, New York & Salt Lake City, 55-56; spec rep oil explor, Gulf Oil Co, 59-65; asst prof biol & chem, Midwest Col, 70; head dept sci, Parsons Col West, 70-71; ASST PROF BIOL, ST MARY'S COL MD, 71- *Concurrent Pos:* Prin investr, Ecol Surv Base, US Naval Air Test Ctr, Patuxent River, Md, 75- *Mem:* AAAS; Am Inst Biol Sci; Ecol Soc Am; Animal Behav Soc; NY Acad Sci. *Res:* Tree hole protozoa and ecology; animal behavior; wildlife ecology and management. *Mailing Add:* Dept of Biol St Mary's Col of Md St Mary's City MD 20686

NOVOTNY, VLAD JOSEPH, b Vsetin, Czech, Mar 12, 44; Can citizen; m 66; c 2. PHYSICS OF INTERFACES, EXPERIMENTAL SOLID STATE PHYSICS. *Educ:* Czech Tech Univ, BSc, 65, MSc, 66; Univ Toronto, PhD(physics), 72. *Prof Exp:* Res scientist physics, Inst Physics, Czech Acad Sci, 67-68; Nat Res Coun Can fel, Univ Toronto, 72-73; Med Res Coun Can fel biophysics, Ont Cancer Inst & Univ Toronto, 73-74; sr res scientist physics, Xerox Res Ctr Can, 74-79; MGR DEVICE PHYSICS, EXXON ENTERPRISES, CALIF, 79- *Mem:* Am Chem Soc; Am Phys Soc. *Res:* Physics of interfaces: solid-liquid interfaces by light scattering and electrical measurements; solid surfaces by thermodynamic measurements, neutron and electron scattering; display devices, imaging processes and optical marking; polymer comfirmation. *Mailing Add:* Exxon Enterprises 328 Gibraltar Dr Sunnyvale CA 94086

NOVY, MILES JOSEPH, b Berlin, Ger, Nov 23, 37; c 2. PERINATAL PHYSIOLOGY, REPRODUCTIVE ENDOCRINOLOGY. *Educ:* Yale Univ, BA, 59; Harvard Med Sch, MD, 63. *Prof Exp:* Dir, Infertility Clin, Med Sch, Univ Ore, 73-77, chmn, Steering Comn, Human Seman Bank, 75; mem, Maternal Child Health Res Comn, Nat Inst Child Health Develop, NIH, 76-79; HEAD PERINATAL PHYSIOL, ORE REGIONAL PRIMATE RES CTR, 70-, SCIENTIST, 72-; PROF OBSTET & GYNEC, ORE HEALTH SCI UNIV, 78- *Mem:* Am Physiol Soc; Soc Gynec Invest; Am Fertil Soc; Soc Study Reproduction; Am Col Obsteticians & Gyecologists. *Res:* Endocrine regulation of parturiton in women and in nonhuman primates; perinatal and reproductive physiology and endocrinology; regulation of uteroplacental blood flow and placental hormone production. *Mailing Add:* Ore Regional Primate Res Ctr 505 NW 185th Ave Beaverton OR 97006

NOWACZYNSKI, WOJCIECH, b Nisko, Poland, Mar 27, 25; Can citizen; m; c 6. ENDOCRINOLOGY. *Educ:* Univ Fribourg, DSc, 52. *Prof Exp:* Mem res staff, Relationship between adrenal cortex sodium & kidney, Hotel Dieu Hosp, Montreal, 53-67; from asst prof to assoc prof med, 62-70, PROF MED, FAC MED, UNIV MONTREAL, 70-; DIR STEROID RES DEPT, CLIN RES INST MONTREAL, 67- *Concurrent Pos:* Res assoc, Med Res Coun Can, 62-65, permanent med res assoc, 65-, prin investr hypertension group, 72-76 & 77; mem adv bd, Coun High Blood Pressure Res, Am Heart Asn, 68-; lectr, Fac Med, McGill Univ, 64-70, prof, 70- *Honors & Awards:* First Marcel Piche Award. *Mem:* Int Soc Hypertension; Am Endocrine Soc; Can Soc Clin Invest; Pan Am Soc Hypertension. *Res:* Study of the pathogenesis of arterial hypertension; metabolism of steroid hormones in particular demonstration of an altered hepatic metabolism of aldosterone in primary hypertension; interaction of aldosterone and plasma and urinary macromolecules including genetic aspects. *Mailing Add:* Dept of Med Univ of BC St Paul's Hosp Vancouver BC V6Z 1Y6 Can

NOWAK, ANTHONY VICTOR, b Chicago, Ill, Aug 6, 38. ANALYTICAL CHEMISTRY. *Educ:* Loyola Univ, BS, 60; Northern Ill Univ, MS, 63; Univ Ill, Urbana, MS, 65, PhD(chem), 68. *Prof Exp:* Anal chemist, US Army QM Food & Container Inst, 60-62; SR MGR ANAL RES & COMPUT, ATLANTIC RICHFIELD CO, 67- *Concurrent Pos:* Lectr, Chicago sect, Soc Appl Spectros, 71. *Mem:* Am Chem Soc; Soc Appl Spectros. *Res:* Microprocessors in analytical instrumentation; applications of computers to laboratory automation; selective gas chromatographic detectors. *Mailing Add:* L-321 Anal Div Atlantic Richfield Co Harvey IL 60426

NOWAK, ARTHUR JOHN, b Erie, Pa, June 25, 37; m 61; c 4. PEDODONTICS. *Educ:* Univ Pittsburgh, DMD, 61; Columbia Univ, cert (pedodontics), 66, MA, 67; Am Bd Pedodont, dipl, 71. *Prof Exp:* Fel pedodontics, Columbia Univ, 64-67; asst prof, Sch Dent Med, Univ Pittsburgh, 67-70; dir pediat dent, Allegheny Gen Hosp, Pittsburgh, 70-73; assoc prof, 73-77, PROF PEDODONTICS, COL DENT, UNIV IOWA, 77- *Concurrent Pos:* Consult, President's Comt Ment Retardation, 74-75; pres, Acad Dent Handicapped, 74-75; pres, Nat Found Dent Handicapped, 75-76; exec coun mem, Am Soc Dent Children, 75-78; prof adv coun, Nat Easter Seal Soc Crippled Adults & Children, 75-; assoc ed, Pedodontic Dent, J Am Acad Pedodontics; consult comn on accreditation, Am Dent Asn. *Honors & Awards:* Am Dent Asn Preventive Dent Award. *Mem:* Am Dent Asn; Am Acad Pedodontics; Am Soc Dent Children; Am Asn Dent Sch; Int Asn Dent Res. *Res:* Effect of parent in dental treatment room; Dental management of effect of drugs on behavior of children in dental setting; effect of feeding devices on oral facial development. *Mailing Add:* Dept of Pedodontics Col Dent Univ of Iowa Iowa City IA 52242

NOWAK, EDWIN JAMES, b Chicago, Ill, Aug 12, 36; m 62; c 3. CHEMICAL ENGINEERING. *Educ:* Northwestern Univ, BS, 58; Princeton Univ, PhD(chem eng), 63. *Prof Exp:* Res engr, Calif Res Corp, 62-63; engr, Process Res Div, Esso Res & Eng Co, NJ, 63-66; asst prof chem eng, Univ NMex, 66-69; MEM TECH STAFF, SANDIA LABS, 69- *Mem:* Am Chem Soc. *Res:* Catalysis; chemical kinetics; surface phenomena; mass transport; electrochemistry. *Mailing Add:* Sandia Labs Orgn 5824 PO Box 5800 Albuquerque NM 87185

NOWAK, ROBERT MICHAEL, b South Milwaukee, Wis, Oct 28, 30; m 57; c 2. ORGANIC CHEMISTRY. *Educ:* Univ Wis, BS, 53; Univ Ill, PhD(org chem), 56. *Prof Exp:* Res chemist, Dow Chem USA, 56-64, group leader, 64-68, asst lab dir, Phys Res Lab, 68-72, res & develop mgr, Plastics Dept, 72-73, res & develop dir, Olefin & Styrene Plastics Dept, 73-78, DIR, RES & DEVELOP DIV, PLASTICS DEPT, DOW CHEM USA, 78- *Mem:* Am Chem Soc. *Res:* Grafting vinyl monomers onto polymer backbones and synthesis and study of new monomers and their polymers; new resin systems for reinforced plastics; polymer chemistry. *Mailing Add:* 1212 Bayberry Lane Midland MI 48640

NOWAK, THADDEUS STANLEY, JR, b Bloomington, Ind, Oct 24, 49. BIOCHEMISTRY. *Educ:* Mas Inst Technol, BS, 71, PhD(nutrit biochem), 79. *Prof Exp:* STAFF FEL, LAB NEUROCHEM, NAT INST NEUROL & COMMUNICATIVE DISORDERS & STROKE, 79- *Res:* Regulation of brain protein synthesis in relation to cerebral energy metabolism; in vivo and in vitro models of ischemia and amphetamine-induced hyperthermia, as experimental situations in which brain protein synthesis is affected. *Mailing Add:* Bldg 36 Rm 4D20 NIH Bethesda MD 20205

NOWAK, THOMAS, b Niagara Falls, NY, Nov 25, 42; m 67; c 1. BIOCHEMISTRY. *Educ:* Case Inst Technol, BS, 64; Univ Kans, PhD(biochem), 69. *Prof Exp:* NIH fel, Inst Cancer Res, 69-71, res assoc, 71-72. *Concurrent Pos:* Res career develop award, NIH, 79-83; vis scientist, Univ Groningen, Netherlands, 81-82. *Mem:* AAAS; Am Chem Soc; Am Soc Biol Chemists; Int Soc Magnetic Resonance; Biophys Soc. *Res:* Mechanism of action of enzymes; function of metal ions in enzymatic catalysis; protein-protein information transfer; applications of magnetic resonance to biological systems. *Mailing Add:* Dept Chem Univ Notre Dame Notre Dame IN 46556

NOWAK, WELVILLE B(ERENSON), b Hartford, Conn, Oct 6, 21; m 50; c 2. PHYSICS, MATERIALS SCIENCE. *Educ:* Mass Inst Technol, SB, 42, PhD(physics), 49. *Prof Exp:* Staff mem, Radiation Lab, Mass Inst Technol, 42-45, res assoc surface impedance metals, 47-49, staff mem, 49-52; staff mem, Microwave Assocs, Mass, 52-54; group leader appl physics, Nuclear Metals Div, Textron Corp, 54-57, mgr tech coord, 57-60, dir electronic res, 60-62; assoc prof mat sci, 62-63, PROF MAT SCI, NORTHEASTERN UNIV, 63- *Mem:* Am Phys Soc; Am Soc Metals; Am Inst Mining, Metall & Petrol Engrs; Am Vacuum Soc; Am Soc Mech Engrs; microwaves; nuclear reactor fuel-element metallurgy and fabrication; thin films; capacitors; energy conversion; material properties and deformation at high pressures. *Res:* Materials engineering; applied physics; metallurgy. *Mailing Add:* 17 Furbush Ave West Newton MA 02165

NOWAKOWSKI, JERRY, physics, mathematical physics, see previous edition

NOWATZKI, EDWARD ALEXANDER, b Bronx, NY, Feb 23, 36; m 62; c 4. CIVIL ENGINEERING, SOIL SCIENCE. *Educ:* St Joseph's Col, NY, BA, 57; Manhattan Col, BCE, 62; Univ Ariz, MSCE, 65, PhD(civil eng), 66. *Prof Exp:* Res assoc nuclear weapons effects, Univ Ariz, 65-66; res scientist geoastrophys res, Grumman Aerospace Corp, 66-68; assoc prof soil mech & civil eng, Calif State Polytech Col, 68-69; res scientist, Grumman Aerospace Corp, 69-73; tech consult, Joseph S Ward & Assocs, 73-75; ASSOC PROF CIVIL ENG, UNIV ARIZ, 75- *Concurrent Pos:* Pvt consult, var geotech eng consult firms & mining indust. *Mem:* Am Soc Civil Engrs; NY Acad Sci; Sigma Xi. *Res:* Plasticity analysis of soils; environmental effect on properties of granular materials; physicochemical aspects of soil mechanics; soil-structure interaction; soil dynamics; off-road vehicle mobility analysis; low level nuclear waste disposal--geotechnical aspects. *Mailing Add:* Dept of Civil Eng Univ of Ariz Tucson AZ 85721

NOWELL, JOHN WILLIAM, b Wake Co, NC, Aug 26, 19. CHEMISTRY. *Educ:* Wake Forest Col, BS, 40; Univ NC, PhD(phys chem), 45. *Prof Exp:* Sr physicist, Am Cyanamid Co, Conn, 44-45; from asst prof to assoc prof chem, 4S-54, chmn dept, 63-72, PROF CHEM, WAKE FOREST UNIV, 54- *Mem:* Am Chem Soc; NY Acad Sci; Sigma Xi. *Res:* Membrane permeability to gases; polarographic identification of ions; tracer methods using radioisotopes. *Mailing Add:* Box 7486 Winston-Salem NC 27109

NOWELL, PETER CAREY, b Philadelphia, Pa, Feb 8, 28; m 50; c 5. PATHOLOGY. *Educ:* Wesleyan Univ, AB, 48; Univ Pa, MD, 52. *Prof Exp:* Intern, Philadelphia Gen Hosp, 52-53; resident path, Presby Hosp, Philadelphia, 53-54; instr, 56-57, assoc, 57-60, from asst prof to assoc prof, 60-64, chmn dept, 67-73, dir cancer ctr, 72-75, PROF PATH, SCH MED, UNIV PA, 64-, ASSOC DIR, CANCER CTR, 75- *Concurrent Pos:* USPHS sr res fel & career develop award, Sch Med, Univ Pa, 56-61, USPHS res career award, 61-67; consult lab serv, Philadelphia Gen Hosp & Philadelphia Vet Admin Hosp, 70- *Honors & Awards:* Parke-Davis Award Exp Path, 65; Shubitz Prize, 80. *Mem:* Nat Acad Sci; Am Asn Cancer Res; Am Soc Exp Path (pres, 70-71); Am Asn Path & Bact; Am Asn Immunol. *Res:* Growth regulatory mechanisms and cytogenetics of normal and leukemic leukocytes; radiation carcinogenesis; cellular immunology. *Mailing Add:* Dept Path Sch Med Univ Pa Philadelphia PA 19104

NOWELL, WESLEY RAYMOND, b Oakland, Calif, Feb 9, 24; m 46; c 4. MEDICAL ENTOMOLOGY, MEDICAL ZOOLOGY. *Educ:* Stanford Univ, AB, 47, AM, 48, PhD(biol sci), 51. *Prof Exp:* Biomed Sci Corps, US Air Force, 51-78, med entomologist, 5th Air Force, Korea, 51-52, Air Res & Develop Command, 52-55, US Air Force Europe Command, 55-58, Strategic Air Command, 58-62, 4th US Air Force Epidemiol Flight, Turkey, 62-65, US Air Force Epidemiol Lab, Aerospace Med Div, Tex, 65-75 & Pac Air Forces Command, 75-78; assoc chief med entom, US Air Force Sch Aerospace Med, 68-74, dep chief, Epidemiol Div, 72-75; INSTR BIOL, UNIV CALIF, SANTA CRUZ & MONTEREY PENINSULA COL, 78- *Concurrent Pos:* Mem armed forces pest control bd, Dept Defense, 67-74. *Mem:* Sigma Xi; Entom Soc Am; Am Soc Trop Med & Hyg; Am Mosquito Control Asn. *Res:* Global medical entomology; arthropod-associated diseases; vector control program analysis and organization; scientific research and training programs administration; Diptera; Dixidae; Mariana Islands. *Mailing Add:* 357 Reindollar Ave Marina CA 93933

NOWER, LEON, b Sosnowiec, Poland, Aug 16, 27; US citizen; m 60; c 2. MATHEMATICS. *Educ:* City Col New York, BS, 53; Stanford Univ, MS, 62, PhD(math), 65. *Prof Exp:* ASSOC PROF MATH, SAN DIEGO STATE UNIV, 63- *Mem:* Am Math Soc; Math Asn Am. *Res:* Harmonic analysis; theory of distributions. *Mailing Add:* Dept of Math San Diego State Univ San Diego CA 92182

NOWICK, A(RTHUR) S(TANLEY), b US, Aug 29, 23; m 49; c 4. SOLID STATE PHYSICS, PHYSICAL METALLURGY. *Educ:* Brooklyn Col, AB, 43; Columbia Univ, AM, 48, PhD(physics), 50. *Prof Exp:* Jr instr physics, Johns Hopkins Univ, 43-44; physicist, Nat Adv Comt Aeronaut, 44-46; asst physics, Columbia Univ, 46-47; instr, Inst Study Metals, Univ Chicago, 49-51; from asst prof to assoc prof metall, Yale Univ, 51-57; mgr metall res dept, Res Ctr, Int Bus Mach Corp, NY, 57-66; adj prof, 57-66, PROF METALL, COLUMBIA UNIV, 66- *Concurrent Pos:* Consult, Oak Ridge Nat Lab, 65-70; mem, panel physics of condensed matter, Nat Res Coun, 69-; A Frank Golick mem lectureship, Univ Mo, 70; ed mat sci ser, Acad Press, Inc, 72- *Mem:* Fel Am Phys Soc; Am Inst Mining, Metall & Petrol Engrs; fel Metall Soc; Electrochem Soc; Sigma Xi. *Res:* Lattice imperfections in solids; anelasticity and internal friction; alloy thin films; ionic crystals. *Mailing Add:* Henry Krumb Sch of Mines Columbia Univ New York NY 10027

NOWICKE, JOAN WEILAND, b St Louis, Mo; m 63; c 1. PALYNOLOGY, SYSTEMATICS. *Educ:* Washington Univ, AB, 59, PhD(biosyst), 68; Univ Mo-Columbia, AM, 62. *Prof Exp:* Fel, Mo Bot Garden, 68-71; asst prof biol, Univ Mo-St Louis, 71-72; assoc cur, 72-78, CUR, BOT DEPT, SMITHSONIAN INST, 78- *Mem:* AAAS; Bot Soc Am; Am Soc Plant Taxonomists; Int Soc Plant Taxonomists; Torrey Bot Club. *Res:* Pollen morphology, structure, function and use in systematics; classification of Phytolaccaceae; Apocynaceae and Boraginaceae of Central America; pollen morphology of Onagraceae and Ranunculales. *Mailing Add:* Dept of Bot Smithsonian Inst Washington DC 20560

NOWINSKI, JERZY L, b Czestochowa, Poland, Mar 2, 05; nat US; m 29; c 1. MECHANICS. *Educ:* Warsaw Tech Inst, MS, 29, DSc(tech sci), 51. *Prof Exp:* Asst mech, Warsaw Tech Inst, 30-37; res scientist, Polish Aeronaut Inst, 37-39 & 46-50; prof appl mech, Warsaw, 54-57; vis lectr elasticity, Johns Hopkins Univ, 57-58; prof res, Math Res Ctr, Univ Wis, 58-60; prof mech eng, 60-73, EMER PROF MECH ENG, UNIV DEL, 73- *Concurrent Pos:* Dir, Bur Reconstruct, Poland, 45-49; res scientist, Inst Math, Polish Acad Sci, 50-57; ed, J Appl Mech, 51-57; prof, Univ Tex, 60-61. *Honors & Awards:* Huber Prize, Polish Acad Sci, 52; Polish State Sci Achievement Prize, 54; Knight, Cross of Reborn Poland. *Mem:* Am Math Soc; Am Soc Mech Engrs; Soc Natural Philos; NY Acad Sci; Edinburgh Math Soc. *Res:* Theory of elasticity, plasticity and viscoelasticity, especially thin-wall structures, finite elasticity, elastodynamics and variational methods. *Mailing Add:* Dept Mech & Aerospace Eng Univ Del Newark DE 19711

NOWLAN, JAMES PARKER, b NS, Can, Mar 26, 10; m 33; c 2. MINING GEOLOGY. *Educ:* Acadia Univ, BSc, 28; Univ Toronto, MA, 30, PhD(geol), 35. *Prof Exp:* Geologist, Rhokana Corp, Northern Rhodesia, 30-32 & Oro Plata Mining Corp, Can & Brazil, 33-35; geologist & geophysicist, Hans Lundberg, Ltd, 36; consult geologist & engr, 37-39; mgr, Yama Gold Mines, Ltd, 40-42; supvr ammunition div, Can Industs, Ltd, 42-45; geologist, Cochenour Williams Gold Mines, Ltd, Ont, 45-48; field supvr, Dom Gulf Co, 48-49, admin geologist, 49-53; chief geologist, McPhar Geophys, Ltd, 53-58; dep minister mines, NS, 58-73; RETIRED. *Concurrent Pos:* Mem, Nat Adv Comt Mining & Metall Res, 70-73; consult, 73-; mem, Nat Environ Adv Comt, 74-79. *Mem:* Soc Econ Geol; Can Inst Mining & Metall (pres, 73-74); Geol Asn Can (pres, 64-65). *Res:* Silurian stratigraphy of Niagaran escarpment of Ontario. *Mailing Add:* 6525 Waegwoltic Ave Halifax NS B3N 2B5 Can

NOWLIN, CHARLES HENRY, b Wilmington, Del, Feb 1, 32; m 56; c 2. APPLIED MATHEMATICS, APPLIED PHYSICS. *Educ:* Washington & Lee Univ, BS, 55; Harvard Univ, SM, 56, PhD(appl physics), 63. *Prof Exp:* Appl physicist, 63-77, group leader basic measurement sci group, 77-81, TECH CONSULT RES INSTRUMENT SECT, INSTRUMENTATION & CONTROLS DIV, OAK RIDGE NAT LAB, 81- *Mem:* Inst Elec & Electronics Engrs. *Res:* Instrumentation; information theory and signal processing; network analysis and synthesis; nuclear pulse amplifiers; image processing. *Mailing Add:* Instrumentation & Controls Div Oak Ridge Nat Lab PO Box X Oak Ridge TN 37830

NOWLIN, DUANE DALE, b Huron, SDak, Mar 14, 37; m 67. WATER CHEMISTRY. *Educ:* Macalester Col, BA, 58; Iowa State Univ, PhD(chem), 64. *Prof Exp:* Chief chemist, Lindsay Co, Union Tank Car Co, 64-65; sr chemist, Garrett Res & Develop Co, 65-66; mgr water chem, Econs Lab, Inc, 66-69; DIR RES & DEVELOP, LINDSAY CO, UNION TANK CAR CO, 69- *Mem:* Am Water Works Asn; Am Chem Soc. *Res:* Ion-exchange technology; isotope separation studies; water treatment and metal ion chelation. *Mailing Add:* Res & Develop Dept Lindsay Co 1890 Woodlane Dr St Paul MN 55125

NOWLIN, WORTH D, JR, b Smithville, Tex, Oct 1, 35; m 59; c 2. PHYSICAL OCEANOGRAPHY. *Educ:* Tex A&M Univ, BA, 58, MS, 60, PhD(phys oceanog), 66. *Prof Exp:* Instr math, Allen Jr Col, 58-59; res asst, Mobil Res Lab, 59; oceanog technician, Res Found, Tex A&M Univ, 60, res scientist, 61-63; asst prof phys oceanog, Univ, 63-67; oceanogr & prog dir, Ocean Sci & Technol Div, Off Naval Res, DC, 67-69; assoc prof, 69-74, PROF OCEANOG, TEX A&M UNIV, 74-, HEAD DEPT, 76- *Concurrent Pos:* Actg dep head, Off for Int Decade Ocean Explor, NSF, DC, 70-71, consult, 70-74, dep head, 71, mem oceanog panel, Div Environ Sci, 70-72; assoc ed, J Phys Oceanog; mem panel oceanog, Comt Polar Res, Nat Res Coun-Nat Acad Sci, 72-75; US nat rep Southern Oceans Intergovt Oceanog Comn/UNESCO, 74-; dir, Tex A&M Sea Grant Col Prog, 77-78; mem ocean sci bd, Nat Res Coun-Nat Acad Sci, 78-; co-chmn exec comt, Int Southern Ocean Studies, 75-; mem steering comt, Acad Res Fleet Study, Ocean Sci Bd, Nat Res Ctr, Nat Acad Sci, 80-81. *Mem:* fel Am Geophys Union; Sigma Xi. *Res:* Meso-scale and large-scale oceanic distributions of properties; dynamics of ocean circulation; oceanographic research management. *Mailing Add:* Dept of Oceanog Tex A&M Univ College Station TX 77843

NOWOGRODZKI, M(ARKUS), b Warsaw, Poland, Sept 13, 20; nat US; m 42; c 2. ELECTRICAL ENGINEERING. *Educ:* Polytech Inst Brooklyn, BEE, 48, MEE, 51. *Prof Exp:* Engr microwave equip, Hazeltine Electronics Corp, NY, 48-51; sr engr microwave tubes, Amperex Electronic Corp, 51-54, supv engr magnetron dept, 54-55; eng leader electronic components & devices, Radio Corp Am, 55-57, mgr microwave design & develop, 57-60, mgr prod & equip eng, 60-62, mgr microwave eng prog, 62-64, mgr traveling-wave tubes & solid-state devices oper, 64-69; mgr eng, Hicksville Div, Amperex Electronic Corp, 69-76; mgr, Liasion Div, David Sarnoff Res Ctr, 76-79, HEAD, SUBSYSTS & SPEC PROJ, RCA LABS, 79- *Mem:* Inst Elec & Electronics Engrs; NY Acad Sci. *Res:* Microwave tubes and solid-state devices. *Mailing Add:* David Sarnoff Res Ctr RCA Labs Princeton NJ 08540

NOWOTNY, ALOIS HENRY, b Gyongyos, Hungary, July 30, 22; US citizen; m 60. IMMUNOLOGY, IMMUNOCHEMISTRY. *Educ:* Pazmany Peter Univ, Budapest, dipl chem, 45, PhD(chem), 47. *Prof Exp:* Asst prof biochem, Med Sch, Univ Budapest, 47-51; res assoc immunochem, Hungarian Blood Serv Ctr, 51-54, vchmn res dept, 54-56; res assoc, A Wander Res Inst, Freiburg, WGer, 57-60; sr res assoc immunochem, City of Hope Med Ctr, Duarte, Calif, 60-62; PROF IMMUNOCHEM & IMMUNOL, MED SCH, TEMPLE UNIV, 62- *Concurrent Pos:* Mem adv bd, Cancer Res Inst, New York, 67-; guest prof, Med Sch, Univ Heidelberg, 69-70 & 72; consult, NIH, 73- *Mem:* Am Asn Immunol; Am Acad Microbiol; Am Microbiol Soc; Ger Immunol Soc; Hungarian Chem Soc. *Res:* Cellular antigens; relationship between chemical structure and biological activities; mode of action of bacterial endotoxins; immunology of erythrocyte membranes; immunology of tumor cells. *Mailing Add:* Dept of Microbiol & Immunol Temple Univ Med Sch Philadelphia PA 19104

NOWOTNY, HANS, b Linz, Austria, Sept 27, 11; m 44; c 1. PHYSICAL CHEMISTRY, MATERIALS SCIENCE. *Educ:* Vienna Tech Univ, Dipl Engr, 33, Dr Tech, 34. *Hon Degrees:* Dr Mont, Mining & Metall Col, Austria, 65. *Prof Exp:* Res asst phys chem, Vienna Tech Univ & Karlsruhe Tech Univ, 34-41; sci researcher metall, Max Planck Inst, 41-45; sci dir, Inst Metall Res, Tettnang, Ger, 45-47; assoc prof phys chem, Univ Vienna, 47-52; prof, Vienna Tech Univ, 52-58; prof & head dept, 58-77, EMER PROF PHYS CHEM, UNIV VIENNA, 77-; UNIV PROF METALL, INST MAT SCI, UNIV CONN, 77- *Concurrent Pos:* Vis prof, Univ Calif, 55, Univ Strasbourg, 57, Univ Amsterdam, 60, Univ Ill, 61, Univ Paris, 62 & Univ Conn, 68, 69 & 71; Battelle prof, Ohio State Univ, 63. *Honors & Awards:* Lavoisier Medal, Soc Chim France, 60; Medal Sci & Art, Austrian Fed Ministry Sci & Res, 78. *Mem:* Austria Acad Sci; Hungary Acad Sci; Gottingen Acad Sci; Leopoldina Acad Sci. *Res:* Structural and alloy chemistry. *Mailing Add:* U-136 Inst Mat Sci Univ Conn Storrs CT 06268

NOWOTNY, KURT A, b Vienna, Austria, Apr 8, 31; US citizen; m 60; c 2. INDUSTRIAL CHEMISTRY, INORGANIC CHEMISTRY. *Educ:* Univ Vienna, PhD(natural prod), 59. *Prof Exp:* Fel polyfunctional catalysis, Wash Univ, 59-60; from sr res chemist to proj leader functional fluids res specialist, Monsanto Co, 60-65; supvr packing res & develop, Crown Zellerbach Corp, 65-69, supvr polymer res, 69-70, mgr chem res dept, Cent Res Dept, 70-73; group vpres & dir technol & eng, Evans Prod Co, 73-77; PRES, NEUSIEDLER AG PAPIERFABRIKATION, AUSTRIA, 77- *Mem:* Am Chem Soc; Ver Oesterreichischer Chemiker; Ges Deutscher Chemiker. *Res:* Natural products; pharmaceutical and physical chemistry; oil additives; functional, aviation and fire resistant fluids; cellulose; adhesives; coatings; physics. *Mailing Add:* Haidmuehlstr 5 A 3363 Hausmening Austria

NOXON, JOHN FRANKLIN, b Pittsfield, Mass, July 7, 28; m 61; c 1. PHYSICS. *Educ:* Bowdoin Col, BA, 50; Harvard Univ, PhD(physics), 57. *Prof Exp:* Res assoc physics, Univ Sask, 57-61; res fel, Harvard Univ, 61-65, sr res assoc, 65-72; PHYSICIST, NAT OCEANIC & ATMOSPHERIC ADMIN, 72- *Res:* Atmospheric physics. *Mailing Add:* Aeronomy Lab Nat Oceanic & Atmospheric Admin Boulder CO 80302

NOY, JACK M(AX), electrical engineering, chemical engineering, deceased

NOYCE, DONALD STERLING, b Burlington, Iowa, May 26, 23; m 46; c 3. ORGANIC CHEMISTRY. *Educ:* Grinnell Col, AB, 44; Columbia Univ, MA, 45, PhD(org chem), 47. *Prof Exp:* NIH fel, Columbia Univ, 47-48; from instr to assoc prof chem, 48-60, asst dean, Col Chem, 52-60, 66-68 & 75-80, PROF CHEM, UNIV CALIF, BERKELEY, 60-, ASSOC DEAN, COL CHEM, 80- *Concurrent Pos:* Guggenheim fel, 57; NSF sr fel, 64. *Mem:* Am Chem Soc; Royal Soc Chem. *Res:* Stereochemistry; mechanisms of organic reactions; organic kinetics. *Mailing Add:* Dept of Chem Univ of Calif Berkeley CA 94720

NOYCE, ROBERT NORTON, b Burlington, Iowa, Dec 12, 27; m 75; c 4. PHYSICS. *Educ:* Grinnell Col, BA, 49; Mass Inst Technol, PhD(physics), 53. *Prof Exp:* Mem staff. Res Div, Philco Corp, 53-56; sr staff mem, Shockley Transistor Corp, 56-57; dir res & develop, Fairchild Semiconductor Corp, 57-59, vpres & gen mgr, 59-65, group vpres, Fairchild Camera & Instrument Corp, 65-68; pres, 68-75, CHMN, INTEL CORP, 75- *Honors & Awards:* Ballentine Medal, Franklin Inst, 66; Harry Goode Award, Am Fedn Info Processing; Cledo Burnetti Award; Medal of Honor, Inst Elec & Electronics Engrs; Faraday Medal, Inst Elec & Electronics Engrs, 79; Nat Medal Sci, 79. *Mem:* Nat Acad Sci; fel Inst Elec & Electronics Engrs; AAAS; Nat Acad Engrs. *Res:* Physical electronics; semiconductor and solid state physics; device technology. *Mailing Add:* Intel Corp 3065 Bowers Ave Santa Clara CA 95051

NOYES, CLAUDIA MARGARET, b Haverhill, NH, Apr 30, 40. ANALYTICAL BIOCHEMISTRY. *Educ:* Univ Vt, BS, 61; Univ Colo, PhD(chem), 66. *Prof Exp:* Res chemist, Armour Grocery Prod Co, 65-67; res assoc med, Sch Med, Univ Chicago, 68-75; RES ASSOC MED, SCH MED, UNIV NC, CHAPEL HILL, 75- *Mem:* AAAS; Am Chem Soc. *Res:* Protein primary structure determination; chromatography; structure and function of blood coagulation proteins. *Mailing Add:* 305-F Bolinwood Apts Chapel Hill NC 27514

NOYES, DAVID HOLBROOK, b Hampton, Va, Feb 5, 35; m 60; c 2. PHYSIOLOGY. *Educ:* Rensselaer Polytech Inst, BEE, 59; Univ Ala, Birmingham, PhD(physiol & biophys), 69. *Prof Exp:* Test engr radar systs, Gen Elec Light Mil Dept, NY, 59; supvr electronic model shop & biomed engr, Univ Ala, Birmingham, 62-66, biomed engr & eng design consult, Res Model Shop, 66-69; asst prof, 69-75, ASSOC PROF PHYSIOL, COL MED, 75-, ASST PROF, DEPT ELEC ENG, OHIO STATE UNIV, 69- *Concurrent Pos:* NIH grants, Col Med, Ohio State Univ, 72-75, NSF grant, 73-75. *Mem:* Am Physiol Soc; Int Asn Dent Res. *Res:* Gastrointestinal physiology; stomatology, periodontology and muscle physiology. *Mailing Add:* Dept of Physiol Ohio State Univ Col of Med Columbus OH 43210

NOYES, H PIERRE, b Paris, France, Dec 10, 23; US citizen; m 47; c 3. THEORETICAL PHYSICS. *Educ:* Harvard Univ, BA, 43; Univ Calif, Berkeley, PhD(physics), 50. *Prof Exp:* Mem staff, Radiation Lab, Mass Inst Technol, 43-44; physicist, Radiation Lab, Univ Calif, 50; Fulbright grantee math physics, Univ Birmingham, 50-51; asst prof physics, Univ Rochester, 51-55; physicist & group leader, Lawrence Livermore Lab, Univ Calif, 55-62; assoc prof theoret physics, 62-67, admin head sect, 62-69, PROF THEORET PHYSICS, STANFORD LINEAR ACCELERATOR CTR, 67- *Concurrent Pos:* Leverhulme lectr, Univ Liverpool, 57-58; Avco vis prof, Cornell Univ, 61; vis scholar, Ctr Advan Studies Behav Sci, Stanford Univ, 68-69; consult, Gen Atomic Div, Gen Dynamics Corp, 59-62, Lockheed Aircraft Corp, 62-63, Lawrence Radiation Lab, Livermore, 62-67 & Physics Int, 65-67; chmn comt for a dir attack on the legality of the Vietnam War, 69-72; mem policy comt, US People's Comt Iran, 77-; Alexander von Humboldt US sr scientist award, 79. *Mem:* AAAS; fel Am Phys Soc; Sigma Xi; Philos Sci Asn; Alternative Natural Philos Asn (pres, 79-). *Res:* Nucleon-nucleon and meson-nucleon interaction; quantum mechanical 3-body problem; applied hydrodynamics and neutronics; computational techniques; foundations of quantum mechanics. *Mailing Add:* Stanford Linear Accelerator Ctr Stanford CA 94305

NOYES, HOWARD ELLIS, b Memphis, Tenn, Apr 5, 22; m 47; c 3. BACTERIOLOGY. *Educ:* Univ Tenn, BS, 47; Ohio State Univ, MS, 49; George Washington Univ, PhD(bact), 55; Am Bd Microbiol, dipl. *Prof Exp:* US Dept Army, bacteriologist, Ft Detrick, Md, 49-51, chief bact sect, Div Surg, Inst Res, Walter Reed Army Med Ctr, 61-63, chief dept bact & mycol, US Army Med Component, SEATO Med Res Lab, 63-66, dep chief dept lab serv, Div Surg, Walter Reed Army Inst Res, 66, chief dept surg microbiol, 66-67, chief dept bact & mycol, Med Res Lab, US Army Med Component, SEATO, 67-70, asst for res mgt, Walter Reed Army Inst Res, 70-74, ASSOC DIR RES MGT, WALTER REED ARMY INST RES, 74- *Mem:* AAAS; Am Soc Microbiol; Soc Exp Biol & Med; NY Acad Sci. *Res:* Medical microbiology as it relates to surgery with emphasis on creation and therapy of experimental wounds, the mechanism of action of bacterial toxins and the evaluation of new antimicrobial agents. *Mailing Add:* Inst of Res Walter Reed Army Med Ctr Washington DC 20012

NOYES, JOHN CHANNING, b Portland, Ore, Dec 23, 20; m 43; c 3. PHYSICS. *Educ:* Univ Portland, BS, 47; Univ Notre Dame, PhD(physics), 52. *Prof Exp:* Res engr, Boeing Airplane Co, 51-54, res specialist nuclear physics, 54-56, sr group engr, 56-58, mgr space physics, Syst Mgt Off, 58-59, mem staff, Geo-Astrophys Lab, Boeing Sci Res Lab, 59-61, lab head, 61-69, dir, 69-71, mgr environ physics, 71, space prog scientist. 71-74; proj scientist large space telescope prog, 74-77, space proj scientist, 77-80, PRIN

SCIENTIST, BOEING AEROSPACE CO, BOEING CO, 80- *Concurrent Pos:* Mem tech comt space physics & astron, Am Inst Aeronaut & Astronaut, 74-80. *Mem:* AAAS; Am Astron Soc; Am Geophys Union. *Res:* Solar-terrestrial relationships; solar activity; upper atmosphere, planetary and space physics; astronomy from space. *Mailing Add:* Boeing Aerospace Co Boeing Co PO Box 3999 Seattle WA 98124

NOYES, PAUL R, b Shreveport, La, Oct 3, 28; m 61; c 2. ORGANIC CHEMISTRY, POLYMER CHEMISTRY. *Educ:* Centenary Col, BS, 49; Univ Tex, MS, 54, PhD(chem), 55. *Prof Exp:* Res chemist, 54-63, STAFF CHEMIST, E I DU PONT DE NEMOURS & CO, INC, 63- *Mem:* Am Chem Soc; Tech Asn Pulp & Paper Indust. *Res:* Adhesives; adhesion; paper coatings. *Mailing Add:* E I Du Pont de Nemours & Co Inc Marshall Lab 3500 Grays Ferry Philadelphia PA 19146

NOYES, RICHARD MACY, b Champaign, Ill, Apr 6, 19; m 46, 73. PHYSICAL CHEMISTRY, CHEMICAL KINETICS. *Educ:* Harvard Univ, AB, 39; Calif Inst Technol, PhD(phys chem), 42. *Prof Exp:* Instr, Calif Inst Technol, 42-44, res fel, Nat Defense Res Comt Proj, 42-46; from instr to assoc prof chem, Columbia Univ, 46-58; head dept, 66-68 & 75-78, PROF CHEM, UNIV ORE, 58- *Concurrent Pos:* Vis prof, Univ Leeds, 55-56 & Oxford Univ, 71-72; mem subcomt kinetics chem reactions, Nat Res Coun, 60-, mem-at-large, Div Chem & Chem Tech, 63-66; Fulbright fel, Univ Victoria, NZ, 64; NSF sr fel, Max Planck Inst Phys Chem, Gottingen, 65; mem chem adv panel, NSF, 69-71; Alexander von Humboldt fel, Max Planck Inst Biophys Chem, Gottingen, 78-79. *Mem:* Nat Acad Sci; Am Chem Soc; Am Phys Soc. *Res:* Thermodynamic properties of ions in solution; mechanisms of chemical reactions including reactions of diatomic molecules, diffusion controlled reactions, isotopic exchange reactions of organic iodides, and reactions oscillating in time and space. *Mailing Add:* Dept Chem Univ Oregon Eugene OR 97403

NOYES, ROBERT WILSON, b Winchester, Mass, Dec 27, 34; m 60; c 2. ASTROPHYSICS. *Educ:* Haverford Col, BA, 57; Calif Inst Technol, PhD(physics), 63. *Prof Exp:* Lectr astron, 62-73, assoc dir, Ctr Astrophys, 73-80, PROF ASTRON, HARVARD UNIV, 73-; PHYSICIST, SMITHSONIAN ASTROPHYS OBSERV, 62- *Mem:* Am Astron Soc; Int Astron Union. *Res:* Aerodynamics and spectroscopy of the solar atmosphere; ultraviolet observations of solar and stellar spectra from space vehicles; infrared solar and stellar spectroscopy. *Mailing Add:* Ctr for Astrophys 60 Garden St Cambridge MA 02138

NOYES, RUSSELL, JR, b Indianapolis, Ind, Dec 25, 34; m 60; c 3. PSYCHIATRY. *Educ:* DePauw Univ, BA, 56; Ind Univ, MD, 59; Am Bd Psychiat & Neurol, dipl, 66. *Prof Exp:* Rotating intern, Philadelphia Gen Hosp, 59-60; resident psychiat, Inst Living, Conn, 60-61 & Univ Iowa, 61-63; mem staff, US Naval Hosp, Great Lakes, Ill, 63-65; asst prof, 65-71, PROF PSYCHIAT, UNIV IOWA, 78- staff psychiatrist, Lake County Ment Health Clin, Waukegan, Ill, 63-65. *Mem:* Fel Am Psychiat Asn; AMA; Am Psychopath Asn. *Res:* Psychosomatic medicine. *Mailing Add:* 326 MacBride Rd Iowa City IA 52240

NOYES, WARD DAVID, b Schenectady, NY, Aug 25, 27; m 50; c 4. INTERNAL MEDICINE, HEMATOLOGY. *Educ:* Univ Rochester, BA, 49, MD, 53. *Prof Exp:* From intern to asst resident med, King County Hosp, Seattle, Wash, 53-56; instr, Univ Wash, 59-61; from asst prof to assoc prof, 61-70, prof med, 70-77, PROF COL MED, UNIV FLA & CHIEF HEMAT, 77- *Concurrent Pos:* Res fel hemat, Univ Wash, 56-59; USPHS res fel, Oxford & Malmo Gen Hosp, Sweden, 58. *Mem:* Am Fedn Clin Res; Int Soc Hemat; Am Soc Hemat; Am Soc Clin Oncol. *Res:* Problems in erythrokinetics and red cell metabolism. *Mailing Add:* Dept of Med Univ of Fla Col of Med Gainesville FL 32601

NOYES, WILLIAM ALBERT, JR, physical chemistry, deceased

NOZ, MARILYN E, b New York, NY, June 17, 39. THEORETICAL PHYSICS. *Educ:* Marymount Col, NY, BA, 61; Fordham Univ, MS, 63, PhD(physics), 69. *Prof Exp:* From instr to asst prof physics, Marymount Col, 64-69; assoc prof physics, Ind Univ Pa, 69-74; ASSOC PROF RADIOL, NY UNIV, 74- *Mem:* Am Phys Soc. *Res:* High energy theoretical physics; covariant harmonic oscillators; quark and parton theory; symmetry schemes for classifying elementary particles; projection operator techniques for calculating generalized vector coupling coefficients. *Mailing Add:* Dept of Radiol 550 First Ave New York NY 10016

NOZAKI, KENZIE, b Los Angeles, Calif, June 1, 16; m 44; c 2. CHEMISTRY, PHYSICAL CHEMISTRY. *Educ:* Univ Calif, Los Angeles, BA, 37, MA, 38; Stanford Univ, PhD(chem), 40. *Prof Exp:* Asst chem, Univ Calif, Los Angeles, 37-38; Franklin fel, Stanford Univ, 38-40; instr Univ Calif, 41-42; dir res, War Relocation Authority, Calif, 43; Pittsburgh Plate Glass fel, Harvard Univ, 43-45, res assoc, 43-45; res chemist, Shell Develop Co, 46-72, sr staff res chemist, Shell Oil Co, 72, CONSULT RES CHEMIST, SHELL DEVELOP CO, 72- *Mem:* Am Chem Soc. *Res:* High polymers; free radicals; reaction mechanisms; molecular rearrangements; organic peroxides; kinetics; homogeneous and heterogeneous catalysis; organic nitrogen compounds; carbonylation; coordination chemistry; automotive fuels. *Mailing Add:* Shell Develop Co Westhollow Res Ctr PO Box 1380 Houston TX 77001

NOZAKI, YASUHIKO, b Yamagata, Japan, June 14, 13; m; c 2. BIOPHYSICAL CHEMISTRY. *Educ:* Univ Tokyo, BS, 37, PhD(pharm), 45. *Prof Exp:* Asst pharm, Univ Tokyo, 37-39, instr, 39-45; prof chem, Nihon Women's Col, 46-48; prof, Kyoritsu Col Pharm, 48-51; tech off microanal, Nat Inst Hyg Sci, Tokyo, 51-60, sect chief vitamin chem, 60-62; ASSOC BIOCHEM, MED CTR, DUKE UNIV, 62- *Concurrent Pos:* Res assoc, Harvard Univ, 54-55 & Univ Iowa, 57-59. *Mem:* Am Chem Soc; Am Soc Biol Chemists. *Res:* Naphthoresorcinol reaction of glucuronic acid; interaction of copper and zinc ions with imidazoles; titration of native and denatured proteins; solubility of amino acids in relation to configuration of proteins; structure and function of biological membranes. *Mailing Add:* Dept of Biochem Duke Univ Med Ctr Durham NC 27710

NOZIK, ARTHUR JACK, b Springfield, Mass, Jan 10, 36; m 58; c 2. PHYSICAL CHEMISTRY, ENERGY CONVERSION. *Educ:* Cornell Univ, BChE, 59; Yale Univ, MS, 62, PhD(phys chem), 67. *Prof Exp:* Res engr chem eng, Douglas Aircraft Co, Santa Monica, Ca, 59-60; res engr, Cent Res Div, Am Cyanamid Co, 61-64, res chemist, 67-74, sr staff chemist, Mat Res Ctr, Allied Chem Co, 74-78; sr scientist, 78-79, BR CHIEF, PHOTOCONVERSION RES BR, SOLAR ENERGY RES INST, 79- *Concurrent Pos:* Instr, Southern Conn State Col, 62-64, lectr, 68-74; NATO lectr, 80; US rep, Prog on Photocatalytic H2 Prod, Int Energy Agency, 80-; prin investr, US-Yugoslavia Coop Res Prog, 82- *Mem:* Am Phys Soc; Am Chem Soc; Int Solar Energy Soc; AAAS; Electrochem Soc. *Res:* Chemical and physical applications of Mossbauer spectroscopy; optical, magnetic and transport properties of solids and thin films; heterogeneous catalysis; solar energy conversion; hydrogen energy systems; photoelectrochemistry. *Mailing Add:* 1662 Bear Mountain Dr Boulder CO 80304

NOZZOLILLO, CONSTANCE, b Spencerville, Ont, July 18, 26; m 52. PLANT BIOCHEMISTRY. *Educ:* Queen's Univ (Ont), BA, 49, MA, 50; Univ Ottawa, PhD(plant biochem), 63. *Prof Exp:* Res off plant physiol, Can Dept Agr, 50-53, microbiol, 58-60; asst prof, 63-74, ASSOC PROF BOT, UNIV OTTAWA, 74- *Mem:* AAAS; Am Soc Plant Physiol; Bot Soc Am; Can Soc Plant Physiol; Phytochem Soc NAm (pres, 81-82). *Res:* Physiology of seedling development; chemotaxonomic aspects of anthocyanins. *Mailing Add:* Dept Biol Univ Ottawa Ottawa ON K1N 6W5 Can

NRIAGU, JEROME OKONKWO, b Oreri Town, Nigeria, Oct 24, 42; Can citizen. GEOENVIRONMENTAL SCIENCE, GEOCHEMISTRY. *Educ:* Univ Ibadan, Nigeria, BS, 65; Univ Wis-Madison, MS, 67; Univ Toronto, PhD(geol & geochem), 70. *Prof Exp:* RES SCIENTIST, ENVIRON CAN, CAN CTR INLAND WATERS, 70- *Concurrent Pos:* Mem, comt on lead in human environ, Nat Acad Sci, 79-80 & comt global biogeochem cycle sulfur, Spec Comt on Probs Environ, Int Coun Sci Unions, 78-81. *Mem:* Geochem Soc; AAAS; Am Soc Limnol & Oceanog. *Res:* Biogeochemistry of the elements in the environment; stable isotopes as pollutant source and behavior indicators; environmental cycling of trace metals. *Mailing Add:* Can Ctr Inland Waters Box 5050 Burlington ON L7S 1A1 Can

NUCCITELLI, RICHARD LEE, b San Francisco, Calif, Feb 18, 48; m 70; c 2. DEVELOPMENTAL BIOLOGY. *Educ:* Univ Santa Clara, BS, 70; Purdue Univ, MS, 72, PhD(biol), 75. *Prof Exp:* NIH fel physiol, Los Angeles, 76-78, ASST PROF ZOOL, UNIV CALIF, DAVIS, 78- *Mem:* Am Soc Cell Biol; Soc Develop Biol; Biophys Soc; AAAS. *Res:* Mechanism of ooplamsic segergation in early development; role of the plasma membrane in pattern formation; bioelectric aspects of development. *Mailing Add:* Dept Zool Univ Calif Davis CA 95616

NUCKLES, DOUGLAS BOYD, b Hampton, Va, Mar 7, 31; m 57; c 2. DENTISTRY. *Educ:* Med Col Va, BS, 59, DDS, 60; The Citadel, MAT, 73. *Prof Exp:* Instr oper, Crown & Bridge & Dent Mat, Sch Dent, Med Col Va, 60-64, asst prof oper & dent mat, 64-68, assoc prof restorative dent, 68-71; assoc prof crown & bridge, 71-72, assoc prof, 72-73, PROF OPER DENT, COL DENT MED, MED UNIV SC, 73- *Concurrent Pos:* Johnson & Johnson res grant, Med Univ SC, 73-75; consult dept mat sci, Sch Eng, Univ Va, 64-71; mem subcomts dent instruments & hand pieces, Am Nat Standards Comt, 70; dir, Dent Auxiliary Utilization Prog, Med Univ SC, 76- *Mem:* Am Dent Asn; Am Asn Dent Schs; Int Asn Dent Res. *Res:* Properties of dental materials; clinical evaluation of dental restorations. *Mailing Add:* Dept of Oper Dent Col Dent Med 171 Ashley Ave Charleston SC 29425

NUCKOLLS, JOHN HOPKINS, b Chicago, Ill, Nov 17, 30; m 52; c 2. APPLIED PHYSICS. *Educ:* Wheaton Col, BS, 53; Columbia Univ, MA, 55. *Prof Exp:* Physicist, 55-65, assoc div leader, 65-80, DIV LEADER, LAWRENCE LIVERMORE NAT LAB, UNIV CALIF, 80- *Concurrent Pos:* Mem vulnerability task force, Defense Sci Bd, 69-72. *Honors & Awards:* E O Lawrence Award, USAEC, 69; James Clark Maxwell Prize, Am Phys Soc, 81. *Mem:* Fel Am Phys Soc. *Res:* Nuclear explosives; inertial confinement; underground nuclear explosions. *Mailing Add:* Lawrence Livermore Nat Lab Univ of Calif PO Box 808 Livermore CA 94550

NUDELMAN, SOL, b Brooklyn, NY, Aug 14, 22; m 50; c 2. PHYSICS. *Educ:* Union Col, NY, BS, 45; Ind Univ, MS, 48; Univ Md, PhD(physics), 55. *Prof Exp:* Asst physics, Ind Univ, 46-48; instr, Union Col, NY, 48-49; instr, Knox Col, 49-51; physicist, US Naval Ord Lab, 51-56; res physicist, Univ Mich, 56-61; mgr solid state res, IIT Res Inst, 61-64; prof elec eng, Univ RI, 65-73; PROF RADIOL & OPTICAL SCI, UNIV ARIZ, 73- *Mem:* AAAS; Am Phys Soc; Am Asn Physics Teachers; Inst Elec & Electronics Eng; Soc Photo-Optical Instrumentation Engrs. *Res:* Influence of electric fields on phosphors; electroluminescent phosphors; luminescent displays; electrical and optical properties of semiconductors; infrared sensitive photodetectors; photoelectronic imaging devices; imaging for diagnostic medicine. *Mailing Add:* Ariz Health Sci Ctr Univ of Ariz Tucson AZ 85724

NUENKE, RICHARD HAROLD, b Bay City, Mich, Sept 3, 32; div; c 2. BIOCHEMISTRY. *Educ:* Univ Mich, BS, 53; Vanderbilt Univ, PhD(biochem), 61. *Prof Exp:* Res assoc biochem, Univ Ill, 60-62; asst prof physiol chem, 62-66, lab coord, 67-71, ASSOC PROF PHYSIOL CHEM, OHIO STATE UNIV, 67- *Concurrent Pos:* Powelson Prof Med, Ohio State Univ, 78- *Mem:* AAAS; Am Chem Soc. *Res:* Protein structure. *Mailing Add:* Ohio State Univ 2078 Graves Hall 333 W 10th Ave Columbus OH 43210

NUESE, CHARLES J, b Endicott, NY, July 39; m 61; c 3. ELECTRICAL ENGINEERING. *Educ:* Univ Conn, BS, 61; Univ Ill, MS, 62, PhD(elec eng), 66. *Prof Exp:* Mem tech staff, 66-77, HEAD SEMICONDUCTOR DEVICE RES, SARNOFF RES CTR, RCA LABS, 77- *Mem:* Am Phys Soc; Inst Elec & Electronics Engrs. *Res:* Semiconductor injection lasers and light-emitting diodes in III-V compounds; GaAs bipolar transistors; defects and device degradation; Zn-diffusion; direct-indirect effects; semiconductor contacts and electrolytic etching; heterojunction lasers; vapor-phase epitaxy. *Mailing Add:* RCA Labs Sarnoff Res Ctr Princeton NJ 08540

NUESSLE, ALBERT CHRISTIAN, b Philadelphia, Pa, Feb 24, 15; m 40; c 4. TEXTILE CHEMISTRY. *Educ:* Univ Pa, BS, 36. *Prof Exp:* Textile res chemist, Joseph Bancroft & Sons Co, 37, asst supt finishing, 38-42, textile res chemist, 43-46; head, Textile Appl Lab, Rohm and Haas Co, 47-64, sr chemist, 65-76; RETIRED. *Mem:* Am Asn Textile Chemists & Colorists. *Res:* Textile finishing agents and auxiliaries, including surfactants; textile application processes and methods, including bleaching, dyeing and finishing; fiber, yarn, fabric properties. *Mailing Add:* W Cnty Li Rd Hatboro PA 19040

NUESSLE, NOEL OLIVER, b St Louis, Mo, June 20, 28; m 56; c 5. PHARMACEUTICS. *Educ:* St Louis Col Pharm, BS, 49; Univ Fla, MS, 55, PhD(pharmaceut chem), 58. *Prof Exp:* Asst, Univ Fla, 54-57; from asst prof to assoc prof, 58-75, PROF PHARM & COODR EXTERNSHIPS, UNIV MO-KANSAS CITY, 75- *Mem:* Am Pharmaceut Asn; Acad Pharmaceut Sci; Sigma Xi. *Res:* Pharmaceutical formulation; biopharmaceutics; sterilization by irradiation. *Mailing Add:* Dept of Pharm Univ of Mo 5100 Rockhill Rd Kansas City MO 64110

NUETZEL, JOHN ARLINGTON, b East St Louis, Ill, Feb 16, 25; m 46; c 6. INTERNAL MEDICINE. *Educ:* Wash Univ, MD, 47; Am Bd Internal Med, dipl, 54. *Prof Exp:* Intern, Univ Mich, 47-48; resident, US Vet Admin, Mo, 49-51; ASSOC PROF CLIN MED, ST LOUIS UNIV, 64- *Concurrent Pos:* Fel hypertension, Wash Univ & Barnes Hosp, 48-49; med dir, St Mary's Health Ctr; mem courtesy staff, St John's Hosp. *Mem:* AMA; Am Heart Asn; fel Am Col Cardiol; fel Am Col Physicians. *Res:* Hypertension; cardiology. *Mailing Add:* 911 S Brentwood Blvd Clayton MO 63105

NUFFIELD, EDWARD WILFRID, b Gretna, Man, Apr 13, 14; m 39; c 3. MINERALOGY. *Educ:* Univ BC, BA, 40; Univ Toronto, PhD(mineral), 44. *Prof Exp:* Asst, Geol Surv Can, 40-42; lectr, 43-49, from asst prof to assoc prof geol, 49-62, assoc dean, Fac Arts & Sci, 62-64, chmn dept geol, 64-72, prof, 62-79, EMER PROF GEOL, UNIV TORONTO, 79- *Concurrent Pos:* Asst, Ont Dept Mines, 43-44 & 48, geologist, 49-51. *Honors & Awards:* Sr Award, Royal Soc Can, 63; Can Silver Jubilee Medal, 77. *Mem:* Fel Mineral Soc Am; Am Crystallog Asn; fel Royal Soc Can; Mineral Asn Can (pres, 56-58). *Res:* X-ray crystallography; crystal chemistry; determination of the crystal structures* of sulphosalt minerals. *Mailing Add:* 401-1649 Comox St Vancouver BC V6G 1P4 Can

NUGENT, CHARLES ARTER, JR, b Denver, Colo, Nov 18, 24; m 50; c 3. INTERNAL MEDICINE, ENDOCRINOLOGY. *Educ:* Yale Univ, MD, 51. *Prof Exp:* From intern to asst resident, New Haven Hosp, 51-53; resident, Col Med, Univ Utah, 54-56, from instr to assoc prof, 56-67; prof, Col Med, Univ Hawaii, 67-70; PROF MED, COL MED, UNIV ARIZ, 70- *Concurrent Pos:* Res fel, Col Med, Univ Utah, 54. *Mem:* Am Soc Clin Invest; Endocrine Soc; Western Asn Physicians. *Res:* Hypertension; radioimmunoassay of steroid; control of adrenal steroid secretion. *Mailing Add:* Dept of Internal Med Ariz Med Ctr Tucson AZ 85724

NUGENT, GEORGE ROBERT, b Yonkers, NY, Feb 6, 21; m 47; c 5. NEUROSURGERY. *Educ:* Kenyon Col, AB, 50; Univ Cincinnati, MD, 53. *Prof Exp:* Instr neurosurg, Med Ctr, Duke Univ, 57-58; asst dir div neurosurg, Col Med, Univ Cincinnati, 58-61; from asst prof to assoc prof surg, 61-69, PROF SURG, DIV NEUROSURG, MED CTR, WVA UNIV, 69-, CHMN DIV, 70- *Concurrent Pos:* Chief neurosurg, Cincinnati Vet Admin Hosp, 58-61. *Mem:* Am Asn Neurol Surg; Soc Neurol Surg; Cong Neurol Surgeons; Int Soc Res Stereoencephalotomy. *Res:* Treatment of trigeminal neuralgia; sterotaxic brain surgery; teaching methods; microneurosurgery; treatment of pain. *Mailing Add:* Dept Neurosurg Univ Hosp Morgantown WV 26506

NUGENT, LEONARD JAMES, b Chicago, Ill, Oct 1, 30; m 52; c 4. CHEMICAL PHYSICS. *Educ:* Ill Inst Technol, BS, 54, MS, 57; Univ Wis, PhD(phys chem), 59. *Prof Exp:* Res assoc, Nat Res Coun, Nat Bur Standards, 58-59, physicist, 59-61; sr physicist, Gen Dynamics Corp, 61-62; sr physicist, Electro-Optical Systs, Inc, 62-66; sr staff scientist, Chem Div, Oak Ridge Nat Lab, 66-76; mem tech staff, Corp Technol, Inc, 76-79; PRES, ALLWEST TECHNOL, 79- *Mem:* Fel Am Phys Soc; Am Chem Soc; Am Asn Phys Teachers. *Res:* Molecular and atomic spectra; atmospheric, chemical and plasma physics; microwave components and subsystems and systems. *Mailing Add:* 450 N Mathilda J101 Sunnyvale CA 94086

NUGENT, MAURICE JOSEPH, JR, b Salt Lake City, Utah, Dec 22, 37. ORGANIC CHEMISTRY. *Educ:* Univ Colo, BA, 61; Calif Inst Technol, PhD(chem), 65. *Prof Exp:* NIH res fel chem, Harvard Univ, 65-66; asst prof, 66-73, ASSOC PROF CHEM, TULANE UNIV, 73- *Concurrent Pos:* Vis assoc chem, Calif Inst Technol, 75-76. *Mem:* Am Chem Soc. *Res:* Mechanisms of enzymatic reactions; antibiotics and metabolic control reagents. *Mailing Add:* Dept of Chem Tulane Univ New Orleans LA 70118

NUGENT, ROBERT CHARLES, b Jersey City, NJ, Sept 22, 36; m 58; c 3. GEOLOGY. *Educ:* Hofstra Univ, BA, 58; Univ Rochester, MS, 60; Northwestern Univ, PhD(geol), 67. *Prof Exp:* Develop geologist, Chevron Oil Co, Standard Oil Co Calif, La, 65-68; asst prof, State Univ NY, 68-70, chmn dept earth sci, 72-76, assoc prof geol, 70-80; SR RES SPECIALIST, SEISMIC STRATIGRAPHY, EXXON PROD RES CO, 80- *Mem:* Geol Soc Am; Soc Econ Paleont & Mineral; Am Asn Petrol Geologists. *Res:* Erosion and deposition along shores of Lake Ontario and the St Lawrence River; bottom sediments of Chaumont Bay, New York; spit and gravel bar formation at mouth of Salmon River, New York. *Mailing Add:* Velocity Interpretation Group Exxon Prod Res Co Houston TX 77084

NUGENT, SHERWIN THOMAS, b St John's, Nfld, Sept 25, 38; m 62; c 2. ENGINEERING, PHYSICS. *Educ:* Mem Univ Nfld, BSc, 59; Tech Univ NS, BEng, 61; Univ Toronto, MASc, 63; Univ NB, PhD(elec eng), 67. *Prof Exp:* Engr, Maritime Tel & Tel Co Ltd, 61-62; lectr physics, Univ NB, 66-67; Nat Res Coun Can fel, Univ BC, 67-68; asst prof eng physics, 68-77, ASSOC PROF ENG PHYSICS, DALHOUSIE UNIV, 77- *Mem:* Am Asn Physics Teachers; Inst Elec & Electronics Engrs. *Res:* Nonlinear optics; control systems; signal processing. *Mailing Add:* Dept Eng Physics Dalhousie Univ Halifax NS B3H 3J5 Can

NUITE, JO ANN, b Albany, NY, Oct 30, 45; m 80. PHARMACOLOGY, NEUROBIOLOGY. *Educ:* Col St Rose, BA, 67; Univ NC, Chapel Hill, PhD(pharmacol), 71. *Prof Exp:* PHARMACOLOGIST, DRUG ABUSE CTR, NIMH/Nat Inst Drug Abuse, 71-74; ASST PROF PHARMACOL, SCHS MED & DENT, GEORGETOWN UNIV, 74- *Concurrent Pos:* Res assoc cent nerv syst pharmacol, Univ NC, Chapel Hill, 71-72; mem, Drug Abuse Adv Comt. *Mem:* AAAS; NY Acad Sci; Int Narcotic Addiction Res Club. *Res:* Central nervous system pharmacology and neurobiology; pharmacological and toxicological effects of drugs on adult and developing organism, particularly psychoactive drugs methods of characterizing novel drugs and relating changes in biogenic amine, amine metabolism to possible mechanism of action. *Mailing Add:* Dept Pharmacol Sch Med & Dent Georgetown Univ Washington DC 20007

NUKI, KLAUS, b Vienna, Austria, May 5, 31; m 63; c 3. HISTOCHEMISTRY, PERIODONTOLOGY. *Educ:* Univ London, BDS, 55, PhD(histochem), 67; Univ Ill, Chicago, MS, 60. *Prof Exp:* House surgeon, Queen Victoria Hosp, East Grinstead, Eng, 55-56; res asst oral path, Univ Ill, Chicago, 57-60; lectr path & periodont, London Hosp Med Col, 60-67; res assoc periodont, Royal Dent Col, Denmark, 63-64; assoc prof dent, 67-71, prof dent & head dept oral biol & div histol & histochem, Col Dent, Univ Iowa, 71-75; PROF PERIDONT & ASSOC DEAN GRAD DENT EDUC, SCH DENT MED, UNIV CONN, 75- *Mem:* Am Asn Dent Schs; Int Asn Dent Res; Royal Soc Med. *Res:* Bone resorption mechanisms; pathology; micro-chemistry of inflammation; microcirculation of gingiva; investigations of periodontium. *Mailing Add:* Univ Conn Health Ctr Farmington CT 06032

NULL, HAROLD R, b Memphis, Tenn, May 16, 29; m 50; c 3. CHEMICAL ENGINEERING. *Educ:* Univ Tenn, BS, 50, MS, 51, PhD(chem eng), 55. *Prof Exp:* Res engr chem eng, E I du Pont de Nemours & Co, 56-57; asst prof, Univ Dayton, 57-59; res chem engr, 59-64, group leader, Eng Res, 64, eng supt, 64-69, eng fel, 69-77, SR ENG FEL, MONSANTO CO, 77- *Concurrent Pos:* Consult, 57-59; affil prof, Washington Univ, 68- *Mem:* Am Inst Chem Engrs; Sigma Xi. *Res:* Thermodynamics; phase equilibrium; separations technology; liquid-liquid extraction; energy conservation. *Mailing Add:* Monsanto Co 800 N Lindbergh Blvd St Louis MO 63166

NUMMY, WILLIAM RALPH, b Brooklyn, NY, Oct 2, 21; m 49; c 4. ORGANIC CHEMISTRY. *Educ:* Univ of the South, BS, 47; Univ Rochester, PhD(chem), 50. *Prof Exp:* Anal chemist, Magnus, Mabee & Reynard, Inc, 39-42; res chemist, Arnold, Hoffman & Co, 50-53; res chemist, Dow Chem Co, 53, group leader, 53-56, div leader, 56, asst dir phys res lab, 56-60, asst dir polymer res lab, 60-61, dir plastics dept, res labs, 61-64, mgr plastics develop & serv, 64-67, mgr plant sci bus, 67-68, mgr agr prod dept, 68-69, mgr life sci res, 69-70, dir cent res labs, 70-74, dir res & develop, Dow Lepetit Co, 74-76; DIR PHARMACEUT RES & DEVELOP, DOW CHEM CO, 76- *Mem:* Am Chem Soc. *Res:* Claisen rearrangement mechanism; high polymer synthesis; polyamides; polysulfides and plastic foams. *Mailing Add:* 711 W Meadowbrook Dr Midland MI 48642

NUNAMAKER, RICHARD ALLAN, b Youngstown, Ohio, Aug 4, 51; m 78. APICULTURE, TOXICOLOGY. *Educ:* Miami Univ, BA, 74; Univ Northern Colo, MA, 76; Univ Wyo, PhD(entom), 80. *Prof Exp:* ENTOMOLOGIST, HONEY BEE PESTICIDES/DIS RES UNIT, AGR RES SERV, USDA, 77- *Concurrent Pos:* Asst adj prof plant sci, Univ Wyo, 82- *Mem:* Entom Soc Am; Int Bee Res Asn; Apimondia; Am Honey Producers Asn; NAm Benthological Soc. *Res:* Biochemical and physiological modifications in honey bees that have been exposed to pesticides, with particular emphasis to enzyme systems and cell ultrastructure. *Mailing Add:* Honey Bee Pesticides/Dis Res Unit Agr Res Serv USDA Univ Sta Box 3168 Laramie WY 82071

NUNAN, CRAIG S(PENCER), b Medford, Ore, Dec 22, 18; m 48; c 4. ELECTRICAL ENGINEERING. *Educ:* Univ Calif, BS, 40, MS, 49. *Prof Exp:* Engr, Pac Gas & Elec Co, 40-41; engr, Elec Sect, Bur Ships, US Dept Navy, DC, 41-46; proj engr, Lawrence Radiation Lab, Univ Calif, 46-53; dir res, Chromatic TV Corp, 53-55; gen mgr, Radiation Div, 55-68, SYSTS SPECIALIST, VARIAN ASSOCS, 68- *Res:* Development and application of medical-electronic equipment for cancer therapy and medical diagnostics. *Mailing Add:* 26665 St Francis Dr Los Altos Hills CA 94022

NUNEMACHER, JEFFREY LYNN, mathematical analysis, see previous edition

NUNES, ANTHONY CHARLES, b New Bedford, Mass, Nov 1, 42; m 72; c 3. SOLID STATE PHYSICS. *Educ:* Mass Inst Technol, BSc, 64, PhD(physics), 69. *Prof Exp:* Res assoc physics, Brookhaven Nat Lab, 69-71, res assoc biol, 71-74; physicist, Inst Laue-Langevin, Grenoble, France, 74-76; ASSOC PROF PHYSICS, UNIV RI, 76- *Concurrent Pos:* Consult small angle neutron scattering, Mass Inst Technol, 76-77; Res Corp grant, 77-; NSF grant, 78-80. *Mem:* Sigma Xi; Am Phys Soc; AAAS. *Res:* Thermal neutron and x-ray scattering applied to problems in solid state physics, magnetic colloids and protein structure; development of instrumentation for neutron scattering. *Mailing Add:* Dept of Physics Univ of RI Kingston RI 02881

NUNES, MATHEWS ANTHONY, medicinal chemistry, see previous edition

NUNES, PAUL DONALD, b New Bedford, Mass, Aug 29, 44. GEOCHRONOLOGY. *Educ:* Tufts Univ, BS, 66; Univ Calif, Santa Barbara, PhD(geol), 70. *Prof Exp:* Asst I geochronology res, Swiss Fed Inst Technol, 70-72; geologist, US Geol Surv, 73-75; res assoc geol, Royal Ont Mus, 75-80. *Concurrent Pos:* Nat Res Coun assoc, US Geol Surv, Denver, 72-73. *Mem:* Geochem Soc; Am Geophys Union. *Res:* Use of uranium-thorium-lead and rubidium-strontium natural decay systems to probe and further clarify our understanding of the evolution of the earth and moon. *Mailing Add:* 28 Jenny Lind St New Bedford MA 02740

NUNES, THOMAS LESTER, chemical instrumentation, see previous edition

NUNEZ, LOYS JOSEPH, b New Orleans, La, Mar 18, 26. CHEMISTRY, TOXICOLOGY. *Educ:* Tulane Univ, BS, 47; La State Univ, Baton Rouge, MS, 55, PhD(chem), 60. *Prof Exp:* Chemist, Cities Serv Refining Corp & Res & Develop Corp, 47-53, res chemist, 59-60; supvr phys res sect, Austin Labs, Jefferson Chem Co, Inc, Tex, 60-71; HEAD BIOMAT SECT, MAT SCI TOXICOL LABS, UNIV TENN CTR FOR HEALTH SCI, 71-, ASSOC PROF DENT & PHARM, 72- *Mem:* Am Chem Soc. *Res:* Dental biomaterials; toxicity of thermodegradation products of fabrics and plastics; chemical and polymer carcinogenesis; drug-plastic sorption diffusion. *Mailing Add:* Mat Sci Toxicol Labs Univ of Tenn Ctr for Health Sci Memphis TN 38163

NUNEZ, WILLIAM J, III, b New Orleans, La, Jan 17, 44; m 65; c 2. IMMUNOLOGY, MICROBIOLOGY. *Educ:* La State Univ, Baton Rouge, BS, 65, MS, 67; NTex State Univ, PhD(immunol), 70. *Prof Exp:* asst prof, 70-73, ASSOC PROF BIOL & CHMN DEPT, UNIV DETROIT, 73- *Concurrent Pos:* Tuberc & Health Soc Wayne County fel, 71-73, Univ Detroit, 71-, Nat Multiple Sclerosis Soc, Environ Protection Agency & Scholl Found res grants, 75. *Mem:* AAAS; Am Soc Microbiol; Am Thoracic Soc. *Res:* Allergy, particularly cellular mechanisms of delayed hypersensitivity involved in tuberculin hypersensitivity and experimental autoallergic encephalomyelitis; delayed hypersensitivity; particularly passive transfer mechanisms of tuberculin, chemical contact dermatitis and experimental allergic encephalomyelitis; fluorescent antibody techniques for rapid and specific detection of human pollution indicators in water. *Mailing Add:* Dept of Biol Univ of Detroit 2001 W McNichols Detroit MI 48221

NUNKE, RONALD JOHN, b Kenosha, Wis, Mar 9, 26; m 53; c 3. MATHEMATICS. *Educ:* Univ Chicago, SB, 50, SM, 51, PhD(math), 55. *Prof Exp:* Instr math, Northwestern Univ, 53-54 & Yale Univ, 55-58; from asst prof to assoc prof, 58-69, PROF MATH, UNIV WASH, 69- *Mem:* Am Math Soc; Math Asn Am. *Res:* Abelian groups; homological algebra. *Mailing Add:* Dept of Math Univ of Wash Seattle WA 98195

NUNLEY, ROBERT GRAY, b Quinwood, WVa, Feb 5, 30; m 52; c 4. PHYCOLOGY. *Educ:* Marshall Col, AB, 52, MA, 53; WVa Univ, PhD(bot), 66. *Prof Exp:* Teacher pub schs, WVa, 53-54, teacher & prin, 57-61; teacher, Ohio, 56-57; instr biol, WVa Univ, 63-65; assoc prof, 65-68, PROF BIOL & HEAD DEPT, MORRIS HARVEY COL, 68- *Mem:* AAAS; Am Inst Biol Sci. *Res:* Ecology of freshwater benthic algae; taxonomy of the genus Trachelomonas in West Virginia. *Mailing Add:* Dept of Biol Morris Harvey Col Charleston WV 25304

NUNN, ARTHUR SHERMAN, JR, b Independence, Mo, Nov 9, 22; m 50; c 5. PHYSIOLOGY. *Educ:* Kans State Univ, BS, 55; Univ Iowa, MS, 59, PhD(physiol), 60. *Prof Exp:* Instr physiol, Sch Med, St Louis Univ, 60-62; from asst prof to assoc prof, Sch Med, Univ Miami, 62-67; assoc prof, 67-72, PROF PHYSIOL, SCH MED, IND UNIV, INDIANAPOLIS, 72- *Concurrent Pos:* US Army res & develop fel, Univ Miami, 62-67. *Mem:* AAAS; Am Physiol Soc. *Res:* Membrane transport of sugars; the role of cations in the transmembrane movement of organic compounds; gastro-intestinal physiology. *Mailing Add:* Dept of Physiol Ind Univ Sch of Med Indianapolis IN 46202

NUNN, DOROTHY MAE, b Cincinnati, Ohio. MICROBIOLOGY. *Educ:* Univ Cincinnati, BS, 55, PhD(microbiol), 62. *Prof Exp:* Asst prof microbiol, Univ Dayton, 62-65; assoc prof, E Tenn State Univ, 65-67; ASSOC PROF BIOL, UNIV AKRON, 67- *Mem:* AAAS; Am Soc Microbiol; Brit Soc Gen Microbiol. *Res:* Bacterial physiology and bioenergetics; mechanism of action of bacterial toxins. *Mailing Add:* Dept of Biol Univ of Akron Akron OH 44325

NUNN, LESLIE GREY, JR, b Uvalde, Tex, May 16, 17. ORGANIC CHEMISTRY. *Educ:* Univ Tex, BA, 38, MA, 41; PhD(org chem), 43; Seton Hall Univ, LLB, 63. *Prof Exp:* Tutor chem, Univ Tex, 39-41, instr, 41; res & develop chemist, Am Cyanamid Co, Conn, 43-46; res chemist, Carter Oil Co, Okla, 46-50; applns chemist, Cent Res Lab, Gen Aniline & Film Corp, Pa, 50-52, asst tech mgr indust chems, Antara Chem Div, NY, 52-56, process develop chemist, 56-64; attorney, Nopco Chem Co, 65-66, asst patent counsel, 66-69; patent counsel, 69-80, SR PATENT COUNSEL, DIAMOND SHAMROCK CORP, 80- *Res:* Manufacture of synthetic organic compounds; nitrogen heterocyclics; petroleum production and drilling practices; surfactants. *Mailing Add:* Diamond Shamrock Corp PO Box 2386-R Morristown NJ 07960

NUNN, ROBERT HARRY, b Tacoma, Wash, Nov 9, 33; m 55; c 3. FLUID MECHANICS, POWER SYSTEMS. *Educ:* Univ Calif, Los Angeles, BS, 55, MS, 64; Univ Calif, Davis, PhD(mech eng), 67. *Prof Exp:* Res aerospace engr, US Naval Weapons Ctr, 60-68; asst prof, 68-71, assoc prof, 71-80, chmn dept, 71-75, PROF MECH ENG, NAVAL POSTGRAD SCH, 80- *Concurrent Pos:* Dep sci dir, Off Naval Res, London, 75-77. *Mem:* Assoc fel Am Inst Aeronaut & Astronaut; Am Soc Mech Engrs; Sigma Xi; Soc Naval Architects & Marine Engrs. *Res:* Internal ballistics; mechanics of intersecting flows; reaction propulsion systems; power systems; design optimization. *Mailing Add:* 1115 Melton Pl Pacific Grove CA 93950

NUNN, ROLAND CICERO, b Miami, Fla, July 24, 30; m 51; c 4. FUEL TECHNOLOGY, PHYSICAL CHEMISTRY. *Educ:* Duke Univ, BS, 52; Pa State Univ, PhD(fuel technol), 55. *Prof Exp:* Chemist, Esso Res & Eng Co, NJ, 55-59; mgr, 59-77, MGR SPEC PROD, CHEVRON RES CO, 77- *Mem:* Am Chem Soc; Sigma Xi; Tech Asn Pulp & Paper Indust; Am Soc Testing & Mat; Soc Coatings Technol. *Res:* Railroad and marine diesel fuels and lubricants; distillate burner fuels; liquified petroleum gas uses; special products. *Mailing Add:* Chevron Res Co 576 Standard Ave Richmond CA 94802

NUNN, WALTER M(ELROSE), JR, b New Orleans, La, Sept 16, 25; m 49. PHYSICS, MATHEMATICS. *Educ:* Tulane Univ, BS, 50; Okla State Univ, MS, 52; Univ Mich, PhD(elec eng), 61; Univ Ill, Urbana, MS, 69. *Prof Exp:* Instr elec eng, Okla State Univ, 50-52 & Rensselaer Polytech Inst, 52-54; res engr, Hughes Aircraft Co, Calif, 54-56; res assoc elec eng, Univ Mich, 56-60; asst prof, Univ Minn, Minneapolis, 60-63; prof, Tulane Univ, 63-65, res prof physics, Sch Med, 66-69, consult appln lasers to cancer res, 65-66; prof elec eng, 69-77, PROF ELEC ENG, FLA INST TECHNOL, 77- *Concurrent Pos:* Consult, Minneapolis-Honeywell Co, Minn, 60-63, Nat Res Coun-Nat Acad Sci, 63-64, US Dept Navy, 65-66, Harris Corp, Melbourne, Fla, 71, Redstone Arsenal, US Army Missle Comnd & DBA Systs, Inc, 78; prin investr, NASA contract, 81. *Mem:* Sr mem Inst Elec & Electronics Engrs; Am Phys Soc. *Res:* Electromagnetic theory; microwave and quantum electronics; lasers; plasma physics. *Mailing Add:* Dept of Elec Eng Fla Inst of Technol Melbourne FL 32901

NUNNALLY, DAVID AMBROSE, b Memphis, Tenn, Sept 13, 34; m 56; c 5. ZOOLOGY, BIOLOGY. *Educ:* Univ of the South, BS, 56; Wash Univ, PhD(zool), 61. *Prof Exp:* From instr to asst prof, 60-65, ASSOC PROF BIOL, VANDERBILT UNIV, 65- *Mem:* AAAS; Am Soc Zool. *Res:* Physiological embryology; physiology of parasitic flatworms. *Mailing Add:* Dept Gen Biol Box 1533 Substa B Vanderbilt Univ Nashville TN 37235

NUNNALLY, HUEY NEAL, b Atlanta, Ga, Dec 28, 44; m 68; c 2. BIOMEDICAL ENGINEERING, ELECTRICAL ENGINEERING. *Educ:* Ga Inst Technol, BEE, 66, MSEE, 68, PhD(elec eng), 71. *Prof Exp:* Assoc aircraft engr, Lockheed-Ga Co, 65-66; res consult biomed eng, US Army Edgewood Arsenal, 71; asst prof, 71-78, ASSOC PROF ELEC ENG, GA INST TECHNOL, 78- *Concurrent Pos:* Asst res prof, Sch Med, Emory Univ, 71-74; res engr, Philip Morris Res Ctr, 78- *Mem:* Inst Elec & Electronics Eng. *Res:* Auditory physiology; electrical stimulation of nervous system; electrical stimulation of muscular system; power systems; robotics. *Mailing Add:* Philip Morris Res Ctr PO Box 26583 Richmond VA 23261

NUNNALLY, NELSON RUDOLPH, b Monroe, Ga, Dec 24, 35; m 58; c 4. PHYSICAL GEOGRAPHY. *Educ:* Univ Ga, BS, 58, MA, 61; Univ Ill, PhD(geog), 65. *Prof Exp:* From instr to assoc prof geog, E Tenn State Univ, 60-67; assoc prof, Fla Atlantic Univ, 67-68; asst prof, Univ Ill, 68-71; assoc prof, Univ Okla, 71-74; assoc prof geog, 74-81, ASSOC PROF GEOG & EARTH SCI, UNIV NC, CHARLOTTE, 81- *Mem:* Asn Am Geog; Am Soc Photogram. *Res:* Physical geography; remote sensing. *Mailing Add:* Dept of Geog Univ of NC UNCC Sta Charlotte NC 28223

NUNNALLY, STEPHENS WATSON, b Gadsden, Ala, Nov 30, 27; m 57; c 3. CONSTRUCTION ENGINEERING, CIVIL ENGINEERING. *Educ:* US Mil Acad, BS, 49; Northwestern Univ, MS, 58, PhD(civil eng), 66. *Prof Exp:* Officer, US Army Corps Engrs, 49-70; asst prof construct eng, Univ Fla, 71-75; assoc prof, 75-80, PROF CONSTRUCT ENG, NC STATE UNIV, 80- *Concurrent Pos:* Consult, Res Triangle Inst, 77-; vis lectr, Univ Stellenbosch, SAfrica, 80; dir training prog, M Binladin Orgn, Saudi Arabia, 81. *Mem:* Am Soc Civil Engrs; Am Soc Eng Educ; Soc Am Mil Engrs; Am Rd & Transp Builders Asn. *Res:* Construction equipment management; project planning and control; construction productivity improvement. *Mailing Add:* Dept Civil Eng NC State Univ Raleigh NC 27650

NUNNEMACHER, RUDOLPH FINK, b Milwaukee, Wis, Mar 21, 12; m 38, 75; c 4. HISTOLOGY. *Educ:* Kenyon Col, BS, 34; Harvard Univ, MA, 35, PhD(histol), 38. *Prof Exp:* Instr histol & embryol, Med Sch, Univ Okla, 38-39; from asst prof to assoc prof, 39-55, dir eve col, 53-54, chmn dept, 59-76, PROF BIOL, CLARK UNIV, 55- *Concurrent Pos:* Instr, Worcester City & Clinton Hosps, 42-45; trustee, Bermuda Biol Sta. *Mem:* AAAS; Am Soc Zoologists; Explorers Club. *Res:* Structure, function of arthropod eyes; nervous system by electron microscopy. *Mailing Add:* Dept of Biol Clark Univ Worcester MA 01610

NUR, AMOS M, b Haifa, Israel, Feb 9, 38; m 68. EXPLORATION GEOPHYSICS, TECTONOPHYSICS. *Educ:* Hebrew Univ Jerusalem, BS, 62; Mass Inst Technol, PhD(geophys), 69. *Prof Exp:* Res assoc geophys, Mass Inst Technol, 69-70; asst prof, 70-75, assoc prof, 75-79, PROF GEOPHYS, STANFORD UNIV, 79- *Concurrent Pos:* Sloan fel, Stanford Univ, 72-74; mem earth sci adv bd, NSF, 74-77; vis prof, Weizmann Inst Sci, 75. *Honors & Awards:* Maclwane Award, Am Geophys Union, 74; Newcomb Cleveland Prize, AAAS, 75. *Mem:* Fel Am Geophys Union; Seismol Soc Am; Soc Petrol Engrs; fel Geol Soc Am. *Res:* Tectonophysics; rock mechanics; physical hydrology; earthquake mechanics; exploration geophysics. *Mailing Add:* Dept of Geophysics Stanford Univ Stanford CA 94305

NUR, HUSSAIN SAYID, b Mahmoudia, Iraq, July 1, 39; m 69. MATHEMATICAL ANALYSIS. *Educ:* Univ Baghdad, BSc, 61; Univ Calif, Berkeley, MA, 64, PhD(math), 67. *Prof Exp:* Teaching asst math, Univ Baghdad, 61-62; from asst prof to assoc prof, 67-73, PROF MATH, FRESNO STATE UNIV, 73- *Mem:* Am Math Soc. *Res:* Singular perturbation of linear partial differential equations. *Mailing Add:* Dept Math Fresno State Univ Fresno CA 93740

NUR, UZI, b Ein Harod, Israel, June 28, 28; m 52; c 2. CYTOGENETICS. *Educ:* Hebrew Univ, Israel, MSc, 58; Univ Calif, Berkeley, PhD(genetics), 62. *Prof Exp:* USPHS trainee, 62-63, asst prof, 63-67, assoc prof, 67-78, PROF BIOL, UNIV ROCHESTEr, 78- *Mem:* Genetics Soc Am; Am Soc Naturalists; Soc Study Evolution. *Res:* Control of facultative heterochromatinization; evolution and population genetics of sexual and parthenogenetic scale insects; maintenance of parasitic B chromosomes. *Mailing Add:* Dept Biol/Hutchison Univ Rochester Rochester NY 14627

NURMIA, MATTI JUHANI, b Rauma, Finland, Aug 26, 30. NUCLEAR PHYSICS, SEISMOLOGY. *Educ:* Univ Helsinki, MA, 52, PhD(physics), 58. *Prof Exp:* Asst prof physics, Univ Ark, 57-58; assoc prof, Univ Helsinki, 58-62; vis prof, Okla State Univ, 62-63; assoc prof, Univ Helsinki, 63-66;

scientist nuclear chem, Lawrence Radiation Lab, 66-78; SR SCIENTIST NUCLEAR SCI, LAWRENCE BERKELEY LAB, 78- *Concurrent Pos:* Seismologist, Univ Helsinki, 58-62; consult, Finnish Atomic Energy Co, 58-62; vis scientist, Lawrence Radiation Lab, 65-66. *Res:* Synthesis and study of new chemical elements; natural radioactivities. *Mailing Add:* Dept Nuclear Sci Lawrence Berkeley Lab Berkeley CA 94720

NURNBERGER, JOHN IGNATIUS, b Chicago, Ill, Apr 9, 16; m 43; c 4. CYTOLOGY, CHEMISTRY. *Educ:* Loyola Univ, Ill, BS, 38; Northwestern Univ, MS, 42, MD, 43. *Prof Exp:* Res neurologist, Neurol Inst, NY, 46-48; res fel, Med Nobel Inst Cell Res & Genetics, Stockholm, Sweden, 49-50; asst prof med & psychiat, Sch Med, Yale Univ, 53-56; actg dean, Sch Med, 63-64, prof psychiat & chmn dept & dir, Inst Psychiat Res, 56-74, DISTINGUISHED PROF PSYCHIAT & CHMN EXEC BD, INST PSYCHIAT RES, MED CTR, IND UNIV, INDIANAPOLIS, 74- *Concurrent Pos:* Psychiatrist, Inst Living, 48-49, res assoc, 50-56, dir residency training, 50-56; mem, Ment Health Study Sect, NIMH, 59-63, mem exp psychol study sect, USPHS, 60-63; mem bd dir, Found Fund Res Psychiat, 72- *Mem:* Soc Biol Psychiat; Histochem Soc; fel Am Psychiat Asn; Asn Res Nerv & Ment Dis; Am Neurol Asn. *Res:* Cytochemical and biochemical studies in nitrogen metabolism; pastoral and clinical psychiatry. *Mailing Add:* Dept of Psychiat Ind Univ Med Ctr Indianapolis IN 46207

NURSALL, JOHN RALPH, b Regina, Sask, Dec 25, 25; m 53; c 3. ZOOLOGY. *Educ:* Univ Sask, BA, 47, MA, 49; Univ Wis, PhD(zool), 53. *Prof Exp:* Instr biol, Univ Sask, 48-49; asst zool, Univ Wis, 49-53; lectr, 53-55, from asst prof to assoc prof, 55-64, chmn dept, 64-69, 74-78, PROF ZOOL, UNIV ALTA, 64- *Concurrent Pos:* Nuffield travel grant, Gt Brit, 54, Nuffield fel, 62-63. *Mem:* AAAS; Am Soc Ichthyol & Herpet; Soc Study Evolution; Can Soc Zool; Am Soc Zoologists. *Res:* Morphology of fish; paleontology; fish behavior. *Mailing Add:* Dept Zool Univ Alta Edmonton AB T6G 2E7 Can

NUSIM, STANLEY HERBERT, b New York, NY, Oct 2, 35; m 60; c 2. CHEMICAL ENGINEERING. *Educ:* City Col New York, BChE, 57; NY Univ, MChE, 60, PhD(chem eng), 67. *Prof Exp:* Asst res engr, Chem Eng, Battelle Mem Inst, Ohio, 56; res chem engr, Chem Eng Res & Develop Dept, Merck Sharp & Dohme Res Labs, 57-60, sr chem engr, 60-64, eng assoc, 66-68, sect mgr, 68-70, mgr tech serv dept, Merck Chem Div, 70-73, mgr mfg, Merk Chem Mfg Div, 73-81, dir subsid projs, 81-82, EXEC DIR TECH OPERS, LATIN AM, FAR EAST & NEAR EAST, MERCK SHARP & DOHME INT DIV, MERCK & CO, INC, 82- *Mem:* Am Chem Soc; Am Inst Chem Engrs; NY Acad Sci. *Res:* Synthetic organic process research and development with emphasis in the areas of kinetics, catalysis and diffusional operations. *Mailing Add:* Merck & Co Inc PO Box 2000 Rahway NJ 07065

NUSS, DONALD LEE, b Murfreesboro, Tenn, May 15, 47; m 65; c 1. BIOCHEMISTRY, VIROLOGY. *Educ:* Edinboro State Col, BA, 69; Univ NH, PhD(biochem), 73. *Prof Exp:* Fel, Roche Inst Molecular Biol, 73-75, res assoc virol, 75-76; RES SCIENTIST VIROL, NY STATE DEPT HEALTH, 76- *Mem:* Am Soc Microbiol. *Res:* Translational control mechanism in virus infected and uninfected animal and plant cells; mechanism of virus replication and assembly. *Mailing Add:* Div of Labs & Res Empire State Plaza Albany NY 12201

NUSSBAUM, ADOLF EDWARD, b Rheydt, Ger, Jan 10, 25; nat US; m 57; c 2. MATHEMATICS. *Educ:* Columbia Univ, MA, 50, PhD(math), 57. *Prof Exp:* Lectr, Columbia Col, 51-52; staff mem, Electronic Comput Proj, Inst Advan Study, 52-53; instr math, Univ Conn, 53-55; from instr to asst prof, Rensselaer Polytech Inst, 55-58; from asst prof to assoc prof, 58-66, PROF MATH, WASHINGTON UNIV, 66- *Concurrent Pos:* Mem, Inst Advan Study & NSF fel, 62-63; vis scholar, Stanford Univ, 67-68. *Mem:* AAAS; Am Math Soc. *Res:* Analysis and functional analysis. *Mailing Add:* Dept of Math Washington Univ St Louis MO 63130

NUSSBAUM, ALEXANDER LEOPOLD, b Leipzig, Ger, Dec 30, 25; nat US; m 57; c 3. ORGANIC CHEMISTRY, BIOCHEMISTRY. *Educ:* City Col New York, BS, 48; Purdue Univ, MS, 50; Wayne State Univ, PhD(chem), 54. *Prof Exp:* Vis investr, Inst Chem, Nat Univ Mex, 50; chemist, Syntex, SAm, 50-51 & Worcester Found Exp Biol, 54-55; sr chemist, Schering Corp, 55-65; group chief, Hoffmann-La Roche, Inc, 65-76; DIR DEPT BIOORG CHEM, BOSTON BIOMED RES INST, 76- *Concurrent Pos:* Res assoc, Med Sch, Stanford Univ, 61-63; vis lectr, Stevens Inst Technol, 64-65; assoc res prof, Sch Med, Univ Md; vis lectr, Fairleigh Dickenson Univ, 74-75; vis prof, Dept Biol Chem, Harvard Med Sch, 75, assoc prof, 77- *Mem:* AAAS; Am Chem Soc; NY Acad Sci; Am Soc Biol Chemists; fel Am Inst Chem. *Res:* Chemistry of natural products, especially steroids and nucleotides; photochemistry; nucleic acid biochemistry; virology; molecular biology of cancer viruses. *Mailing Add:* Boston Biomed Res Inst 20 Staniford St Boston MA 02114

NUSSBAUM, ALLEN, b Phila, Pa, Aug 22, 19; m 45; c 4. SOLID STATE PHYSICS. *Educ:* Univ Pa, BA, 39, MA, 40, PhD(physics), 54. *Prof Exp:* Physicist, Honeywell Inc, 54-62; PROF ELEC ENG & DIR GRAD STUDY, UNIV MINN, MINNEAPOLIS, 62- *Mem:* Am Phys Soc; Inst Elec & Electronics Eng; Brit Inst Physics. *Res:* Geometrical optics; semiconducting materials device development; theory of junction diodes; electromagnetic and quantum properties of materials. *Mailing Add:* Dept of Elec Eng Univ of Minn Minneapolis MN 55455

NUSSBAUM, ELMER, b Monroe, Ind, Sept 2, 20; m 49; c 4. BIOPHYSICS. *Educ:* Taylor Univ, BA, 49; Ball State Univ, MA, 52; Univ Rochester, PhD(radiation biol), 57. *Prof Exp:* instr physics, Taylor Univ, 49-52, asst prof, 53; res assoc biophys, Univ Rochester, 53-57; assoc prof, 57-59, PROF PHYSICS, TAYLOR UNIV, 59-, DIR RES, 61-, CHMN, SCI DIV, 68- *Concurrent Pos:* Consult, Oak Ridge Assoc Univs, 60-, sr scientist, 62-63; sabbatical leave, Oak Ridge Nat Lab, 79. *Mem:* AAAS; Am Asn Physics Teachers; Solar Energy Soc; Health Physics Soc. *Res:* Solubility of radon in fatty acids and body tissues; diffusion of radon through semipermeable materials; radionuclides in the biosphere; physics; environmental radioactivity; radiation detectors; solar energy; health physics. *Mailing Add:* Dept of Physics Taylor Univ Upland IN 46989

NUSSBAUM, MIRKO, b Belgrade, Yugoslavia, July 24, 30; US citizen; m. EXPERIMENTAL HIGH ENERGY PHYSICS. *Educ:* Rutgers Univ, AB, 54; Univ Chicago, SM, 56; Johns Hopkins Univ, PhD(physics), 62. *Prof Exp:* Sr physicist, Martin Co, Md, 56-60; instr physics, Johns Hopkins Univ, 61-62; res assoc, Columbia Univ, 62-64; asst prof, Univ Pa, 64-69; assoc prof, 69-71, PROF PHYSICS, UNIV CINCINNATI, 71- *Mem:* Fel Am Phys Soc. *Res:* Fundamental particle research through use of bubble chambers and spark chamber counter techniques. *Mailing Add:* Dept of Physics Univ of Cincinnati Cincinnati OH 45221

NUSSBAUM, MURRAY, b Brooklyn, NY, May 19, 27; m 55; c 2. MEDICINE, HEMATOLOGY. *Educ:* Univ Vt, BS, 49, MD, 52; Am Bd Int Med, cert hemat, 74. *Prof Exp:* From instr to assoc prof, 57-69, dir lab med course, 57-71, PROF MED, HEMAT DIV, COL MED & DENT NJ, 69- *Concurrent Pos:* USPHS res fel hemat, 54-55; res assoc, Mt Sinai Hosp, New York, 59-62; chief hemat, Jersey City Med Ctr, 63-66; dir hemat med serv, Martland Hosp, 66-; mem med adv comt, Metrop Chap, Hemophilia Found, 66-69. *Mem:* Am Soc Hemat; Am Fedn Clin Res; fel Int Soc Hemat; fel Am Col Physicians. *Res:* Blood coagulation and fibrinolysis; medical education. *Mailing Add:* Div of Hemat Col of Med & Dent of NJ Newark NJ 07107

NUSSBAUM, NOEL SIDNEY, b Brooklyn, NY, Jan 26, 35; m 57; c 3. PHYSIOLOGY, ENDOCRINOLOGY. *Educ:* Brooklyn Col, BA, 56; Williams Col, MA, 58; Yale Univ, PhD(biol), 64. *Prof Exp:* From instr to asst prof biol, Bowdoin Col, 63-65; from asst prof to assoc prof biol, 65-75, ASSOC PROF PHYSIOL, SCH MED, WRIGHT STATE UNIV, 75- *Concurrent Pos:* Consult, Aerospace Med Res Lab, US Air Force, Wright-Patterson AFB, 74- *Mem:* Am Soc Zool; Am Soc Cell Biol; Orthopaedic Res Soc. *Res:* Vertebrate physiology and morphogenesis; mineral metabolism; ultrastructure of calcified tissue; biochemical and biomechanical response of dense connective tissue to endocrine therapy. *Mailing Add:* Dept of Physiol Sch of Med Wright State Univ Dayton OH 45435

NUSSBAUM, ROGER DAVID, b Philadelphia, Pa, Jan 29, 44; m 66; c 2. MATHEMATICAL ANALYSIS. *Educ:* Harvard Univ, AB, 65; Univ Chicago, PhD(math), 69. *Prof Exp:* Asst prof, 69-73, assoc prof, 73-77, PROF MATH, RUTGERS UNIV, NEW BRUNSWICK, 77- *Mem:* Am Math Soc. *Res:* Nonlinear functional analysis, particularly fixed point theorems and their applications to nonlinear problems. *Mailing Add:* Dept of Math Rutgers Univ New Brunswick NJ 08903

NUSSBAUM, RONALD ARCHIE, b Rupert, Idaho, Feb 9, 42. HERPETOLOGY. *Educ:* Univ Idaho, BS, 67; Cent Wash State Col, MS, 68; Ore State Univ, PhD(zool), 72. *Prof Exp:* Res assoc ecosyst anal, Sch Forestry, Ore State Univ, 72-73; asst prof & asst cur, 74-80, ASSOC PROF & ASSOC CUR, DIV BIOL SCI & MUS ZOOL, UNIV MICH, ANN ARBOR, 80- *Concurrent Pos:* Assoc ed, Systematic Zoology & J Morphology. *Mem:* Soc Syst Zoologists; Am Soc Naturalists; Am Soc Ichthyologists & Herpetologists; Ecol Soc Am; Soc Study Evolution. *Res:* Evolution, systematics, life history and ecology of amphibians and reptiles; evolution of life history strategies; island biogeography; vertebrate morphology; cytotaxonomy. *Mailing Add:* Mus Zool Univ Mich Ann Arbor MI 48104

NUSSBAUM, RUDI HANS, b Furth, Ger, Mar 21, 22; nat US; m 47; c 3. SOLID STATE PHYSICS. *Educ:* Univ Amsterdam, PhD(exp physics), 54. *Prof Exp:* Res assoc nuclear physics, Inst Nuclear Res, Univ Amsterdam, 52-54; UNESCO fel, Nuclear Physics Lab, Liverpool, Eng, 54-55; res assoc, Ind Univ, 55-56; European Orgn Nuclear Res sr fel, Geneva, 56-57; asst prof physics, Univ Calif, 57-59; assoc prof, 59-65, PROF PHYSICS, PORTLAND STATE UNIV, 65- *Concurrent Pos:* Vis prof, Univ Wash, 65-66; consult, Tektronix Inc; exchange prof, Univ Canterbury, NZ, 71-72; vis prof, Univ Wash, 74, Univ Groningen. *Mem:* Am Phys Soc; Am Asn Physics Teachers; Netherlands Phys Soc; Am Fedn Scientists; Union Concerned Scientists. *Res:* Mossbauer effect applied to impurity lattice dynamics; study of adsorbed monolayers of molecules on graphite surfaces. *Mailing Add:* Dept of Physics Portland State Univ PO Box 751 Portland OR 97207

NUSSENBAUM, SIEGFRIED, b Vienna, Austria, Nov 21, 19; nat US; m 51; c 2. BIOCHEMISTRY, ORGANIC CHEMISTRY. *Educ:* Univ Calif, BS, 41, MA, 48, PhD(biochem), 51. *Prof Exp:* Anal chemist, Manganese Ore Co & Pan Am Eng Co, 42-43, asst chief chemist, 43-45; chemist, Nat Lead Co, 45; asst, Univ Calif, 48-51, fel, 51-52; from instr to assoc prof, 52-62, PROF CHEM, SACRAMENTO STATE UNIV, 62- *Concurrent Pos:* Consult biochemist, Sacramento County Hosp, 58-; lectr clin path, Univ Calif, 69- *Mem:* AAAS; Am Chem Soc. *Res:* Polysaccharide metabolism and chemistry; enzyme, analytical and clinical chemistry. *Mailing Add:* Dept of Chem Sacramento State Univ 6000 J St Sacramento CA 95819

NUSSENZVEIG, HERCH MOYSES, b Sao Paulo, Brazil, Jan 16, 33; m 62; c 3. SCATTERING THEORY, QUANTUM OPTICS. *Educ:* Univ Sao Paulo, BSc, 54, PhD(physics), 57. *Prof Exp:* Asst prof theoret physics, Univ Sao Paulo, 56-57; from asst prof to prof, Brazilian Ctr Physics Res, 57-68; vis prof, Univ Rochester, 65-68, sr res assoc & prof physics, 68-75; dir Inst Physics, 78-82, PROF PHYSICS, UNIV SAO PAULO, 75- *Concurrent Pos:* Nat Res Coun Brazil res fels, Theoret Physics Inst, State Univ Utrecht, 60-61, Dept Math Physics, Univ Birmingham, 61 & Inst Theoret Physics, Swiss Fed Inst Technol, 61; vis mem, Courant Inst Math Sci, NY Univ, 63-64 & Inst Adv Study, 64-65; vis prof, Univ Paris, Orsay, 73; vis scientist, Nat Ctr Atmospheric Res, 79-80. *Mem:* Am Phys Soc; Asn Math Physics; NY Acad Sci; Brazilian Phys Soc (pres, 81-); Brazilian Acad Sci. *Res:* Quantum optics; scattering theory; dispersion relations. *Mailing Add:* Inst Physics Univ Sao Paulo Sao Paulo Brazil

NUSSENZWEIG, VICTOR, b Sao Paulo, Brazil, Nov 2, 28; m 54; c 3. IMMUNOPARASITOLOGY. *Educ:* Univ Sao Paulo, MD, 53, PhD(parasitol), 57. *Prof Exp:* Asst prof parasitol, Univ Sao Paulo, 53-63; res fel immunochem, Pasteur Inst, Paris, 58-60; res assoc microbiol & immunol,

Escola Paulista de Med, Sao Paulo, 61-62; res assoc, 63-65, asst prof, 65-67, assoc prof, 67-71, PROF PATH & IMMUNOL, SCH MED, NEW YORK UNIV, 71- *Concurrent Pos:* Chmn, Chagas Dis Steering Comt, WHO, 75-; prin investr grants, NIH, World Health Orgn & Rockefeller Found, 65-; appointee, Comt Immunodiagnosis Cancer, NIH, 70-73, Organizing Comt, Int Complement Workshop, 79-; ed, J Immunol Methods & Contemp Top Immunol, 78. *Mem:* Am Asn Immunologists; Harvey Soc; Brazilian Soc Immunologists. *Res:* Immunology especially regulatory mechanisms of activation of the complement system and membrane receptors for complement; parasitology especially immune response and protective immunity to parasites, in particular malaria antigens. *Mailing Add:* 599 MSB Dept Path Med Ctr New York Univ 550 First Ave New York NY 10016

NUSSER, WILFORD LEE, b Sylvia, Kans, Oct 6, 24; m 43; c 5. PARASITOLOGY, PHYSIOLOGY. *Educ:* Bethel Col, Kans, BA, 49; Kans State Univ, MS, 50; Iowa State Univ, PhD(parasitol), 58. *Prof Exp:* Instr microbiol, Col Osteop Med & Surg, 54-57, asst prof physiol, 57-60, actg head dept, 58-60; res fel neuroanat, Emory Univ, 60-63; prof physiol & head dept, Col Osteop Med & Surg, 63-66; grants assoc, 66-67, dir arthritis & orthop prog, Nat Inst Arthritis, Metab & Digestive Dis, 67-74; chief scientist, Prog Br, Nat Eye Inst, NIH, 74-77; ASSOC DIR, EXTRAMURAL PROGS, NAT INST ENVIRON HEALTH SCI, 77- *Res:* Electro Electron microscopy; Wallerian degeneration and regeneration of peripheral nerves; endocrinology; site of production of the erythropoietic hormone; neuroanatomy. *Mailing Add:* Extramural Prog Nat Inst Environ Health Sci Res Triangle Park NC 20014

NUSSMANN, DAVID GEORGE, b Burlington, Iowa, May 8, 37. GEOLOGY, STRATIGRAPHIC GEOPHYSICS. *Educ:* Harvard Univ, AB, 59; Univ Mich, MA, 61, PhD(geol, geochem), 65. *Prof Exp:* Geologist, Explor & Prod Res Div, Shell Develop Co, Tex, 64-70, staff geologist, Shell Oil Co, La, 70-74, geol engr, 74-76, SR STAFF GEOL ENGR, EXPLOR & PROD RES DIV, SHELL DEVELOP CO, 76- *Mem:* Am Asn Petrol Geologists; Geol Soc Am; Soc Petrol Eng; Geochem Soc. *Res:* Sediment geochemistry; geostatistics; petroleum geology. *Mailing Add:* Shell Develop Co PO Box 481 Houston TX 77001

NUSYNOWITZ, MARTIN LAWRENCE, b New York, NY, July 21, 33; m 55; c 3. NUCLEAR MEDICINE, ENDOCRINOLOGY. *Educ:* NY Univ, BA, 54; State Univ NY, MD, 58. *Prof Exp:* Intern med, Letterman Gen Hosp, San Francisco, Med Corps, US Army, 58-59, resident internal med, Tripler Gen Hosp, Honolulu, Hawaii, 59-62, chief radioisotope-endocrine serv, 62-63, chief nuclear-med endocrine serv & dept med res & develop, William Beaumont Gen Hosp, 65-77; PROF NUCLEAR MED & HEAD DIV, UNIV TEX HEALTH SCI CTR, 77- *Concurrent Pos:* Fel mil med & allied sci, Walter Reed Army Inst Res, Washington, DC, 63-64; fel endocrinol & metab, Sch Med, Univ Calif, San Francisco, 64-65; Dorothy Hutton scholar endocrinol, 68; consult, Surgeon Gen, US Army, 71-77. *Mem:* Soc Nuclear Med; Endocrine Soc; fel Am Col Physicians; fel Am Col Nuclear Physicians; Am Fedn Clin Res. *Res:* In vitro thyroid function tests; clinical aspects of thyroid disease; computer applications in nuclear medicine; diagnostic nuclear medical techniques in clinical problems. *Mailing Add:* Div of Nuclear Med Univ of Tex Health Sci Ctr San Antonio TX 78284

NUTAKKI, DHARMA RAO, b Vizayawada, Andhra Pradesh, India, July 18, 37; m 58; c 3. ELECTRICAL ENGINEERING. *Educ:* Andhra Univ, India, BE, 59; Indian Inst Sci, ME, 61, PhD(elec eng), 65. *Prof Exp:* Lectr elec eng, Indian Inst Sci, 62-67; from asst prof to assoc prof, 67-76, PROF ELEC ENG, UNIV CALGARY, 76- *Mem:* Inst Elec & Electronics Engrs. *Res:* Power system stability and analysis; sensitivity analysis; optimal control; network diakoptics; switching surges; state estimation. *Mailing Add:* Dept of Elec Eng Univ of Calgary Calgary AB T2N 1N4 Can

NUTE, C THOMAS, b Troy, Pa, Dec 12, 45; m 68; c 3. COMPUTER ENGINEERING. *Educ:* Univ Calif, San Diego, BA, 68; Tex A&M Univ, MS, 70, PhD(comput sci), 77. *Prof Exp:* Systs analyst space tracking officer, US Air Force, 68-75; instr comput sci, Tex A&M Univ, 75-77; asst prof comput eng, Case Western Reserve Univ, 77- *Concurrent Pos:* Consult, Bailey Control Co, 78-, Nordson Corp, 78- & Data Basics, Inc, 78- *Mem:* Asn Comput Mach; Inst Elec & Electronic Engrs. *Res:* Computer program behavior; performance measurement and evaluation. *Mailing Add:* General Dynamics Mail Zone 5943 PO Box 748 Fort Worth TX 76101

NUTE, PETER ERIC, b Manchester, NH, Nov 20, 38; m 61; c 1. PHYSICAL ANTHROPOLOGY, BIOCHEMICAL GENETICS. *Educ:* Yale Univ, BS, 60; Duke Univ, PhD(anat), 69. *Prof Exp:* NIH fel med genetics, 69-71, spec fel med & hemat, 71-72, lectr anthrop, 72-74, actg asst prof, 75, asst prof, 75-77, ASSOC PROF ANTHROP, UNIV WASH, 77- *Concurrent Pos:* Res affil, Regional Primate Res Ctr, Univ Wash, 72-, sr fel med, 72-73, res asst prof, 73-77, adj assoc prof, 77-; co-prin investr, USPHS contract, 74-76, prin investr, USPHS grant, 77-80. *Mem:* AAAS; Am Asn Phys Anthropologists; NY Acad Sci; Genetics Soc Am; Pop Ref Bur. *Res:* Molecular genetics and evolution, especially as related to medicine and primate evolution. *Mailing Add:* Dept of Anthrop DH-05 Univ of Wash Seattle WA 98195

NUTLEY, HUGH, b Tacoma, Wash, Jan 30, 32; m 55; c 6. NUCLEAR PHYSICS. *Educ:* Mass Inst Technol, SB, 54; Univ Wash, PhD(physics), 60, BA, 73, MA, 74, MS, 76. *Prof Exp:* Res specialist, Radiation Effects Lab, Boeing Co, 62-66; from asst prof to assoc prof, 66-75, PROF PHYSICS, SEATTLE PAC UNIV, 75- *Mem:* Am Asn Physics Teachers; Am Inst Chem Engrs; Am Sci Affil. *Res:* Beta ray spectroscopy; vapor explosions; radiation damage to electronic components. *Mailing Add:* Dept of Physics Seattle Pac Univ Seattle WA 98119

NUTT, RUTH FOELSCHE, b Flensburg, Ger, July 12, 40; US citizen; m 58; c 1. MEDICINAL CHEMISTRY, NATURAL PRODUCT CHEMISTRY. *Educ:* Univ NMex, BS, 62; Univ Pa, PhD, 81. *Prof Exp:* Asst chemist indole & pyridine anticancer agts, 62-65, res chemist nucleoside & carbohydrate chem, 65-67, sr res chemist peptide synthesis, 67-76, res fel, 76-81, SR RES FEL PEPTIDE SYNTHESIS, MERCK SHARP & DOHME RES LABS, 81- *Mem:* Am Chem Soc. *Res:* Organic synthesis; nucleosides; central nervous system-active peptides; design and synthesis of releasing hormone agonists and antagonists; mechanisms of amino acid racemization; amino acid. *Mailing Add:* Merck Sharp & Dohme Res Labs West Point PA 19486

NUTTALL, ALBERT HAROLD, b New Bedford, Mass, May 29, 33; m 55; c 4. SPECTRAL ANALYSIS, PERFORMANCE ANALYSIS. *Educ:* Mass Inst Technol, SB, 54, SM, 55, ScD, 58. *Prof Exp:* Asst prof elec eng, Mass Inst Technol, 58-59; res engr, Melpar Inc, 57-60; res engr, Litton Indust, 60-68; RES ENGR, NAVAL UNDERWATER SYST CTR, 68- *Concurrent Pos:* Assoc ed, Trans Info Theory, Inst Elec & Electronics Engrs, 60-67. *Res:* Analysis of signal processing techniques; derivation of performance of detection and communication schemes; derivation of new spectral analysis techniques and their performance. *Mailing Add:* Code 3302 Naval Underwater Systs Ctr New London CT 06320

NUTTALL, FRANK Q, b May 8, 29; US citizen; c 4. INTERNAL MEDICINE. *Educ:* Univ Utah, MD, 55; Univ Minn, PhD(biochem), 70. *Prof Exp:* Chief admin sect, Vet Admin Hosp, 61-63, chief clin chem, 63-69, assoc prof, Univ, 71-75, PROF INTERNAL MED, SCH MED, UNIV MINN, MINNEAPOLIS, 75-, CHIEF METAB-ENDOCRINE SECT, VET ADMIN HOSP, 70- *Mem:* Am Diabetes Asn; Am Soc Biol Chemists; fel Am Col Physicians; Endocrine Soc. *Res:* Diabetes mellitus; control of glycogen metabolism; glycogen synthetase system. *Mailing Add:* Metab-Endocrine Sect Vet Admin Hosp Minneapolis MN 55417

NUTTALL, HERBERT ERICKSEN, JR, b Salt Lake City, Utah, Apr 10, 44; m 67; c 3. CHEMICAL ENGINEERING. *Educ:* Univ Utah, BS, 66; Univ Ariz, MS, 68, PhD(chem eng), 71. *Prof Exp:* Chem engr, Garrett Res & Develop Co, Inc, 71-72; vis asst prof, Univ Tex, Austin, 72-73; asst prof, 74-76, ASSOC PROF, UNIV N MEX, 77- *Concurrent Pos:* Joint fac/staff appointment, Sandia Labs, Albuquerque, 74-; consult, Sci Applns Inc, 77-, Los Alamos Nat Lab, 80- & Synfuels Eng & Develop, Inc, 81- *Mem:* Am Inst Chem Engrs; AAAS; Rocky Mountain Fuel Soc (pres elect, 79-80); Am Chem Soc. *Res:* Process simulation by digital computer; fossil energy, particularly coal, oil shale and tar sands; disposal of radioactive wastes. *Mailing Add:* Dept of Chem & Nuclear Eng Univ of NMex Albuquerque NM 87131

NUTTALL, JOHN, b Haslingden, Eng, Oct 8, 36; m 62; c 2. THEORETICAL PHYSICS. *Educ:* Cambridge Univ, BA, 57, PhD(theoret physics), 61. *Prof Exp:* Res fel, St John's Col, Cambridge, 61-62; scientist, RCA Victor Co Ltd, Can, 62-64; NSF sr scientist, Tex A&M Univ, 64-65, assoc prof physics, 65-69, prof physics, 69-72; vis prof, 72, PROF PHYSICS, UNIV WESTERN ONT, 72- *Res:* Quantum scattering theory in atomic physics; approximation theory. *Mailing Add:* Dept of Physics Univ of Western Ont London ON N6A 5B8 Can

NUTTALL, KEITH, metallurgy, materials science, see previous edition

NUTTALL, WESLEY FORD, b Regina, Sask, Oct 24, 30. SOIL FERTILITY. *Educ:* Univ Sask, BSA, 58, MSc, 60; McGill Univ, PhD(soil chem), 65. *Prof Exp:* RES SCIENTIST, RES BR, CAN DEPT AGR, 65- *Mem:* Can Soc Soil Sci; Am Soc Agron. *Res:* Plant nutrition; statistics; agrometeorology. *Mailing Add:* Res Sta Can Dept of Agr Box 1901 Melfort SK S0E 1A0 Can

NUTTER, GENE DOUGLAS, b Columbus, Tex, June 9, 29; m 56; c 2. PHYSICS. *Educ:* Univ Nebr, BS, 51, MS, 56. *Prof Exp:* Physicist, Nat Bur Standards, 52-54; eng supvr, Atomics Int, NAm Rockwell, Inc, 56-67; ASST DIR MEASUREMENT SCI LAB, INSTRUMENTATION SYSTS CTR, UNIV WIS-MADISON, 67- *Concurrent Pos:* UN Ed, Sci & Cult Orgn consult & lectr, Repub Korea, 68. *Mem:* Sr mem Instrument Soc Am; sr mem Inst Elec & Electronic Engrs; Am Inst Physics; Am Soc Mech Eng; Am Soc Test & Mat; Optical Soc Am. *Res:* Methodology and instrumentation for high accuracy measurements, especially measurement of temperature and thermal properties by radiometric methods; radiation thermometry from 100 degrees celsius to 4000 degrees celsius. *Mailing Add:* Instrumentation Systs Ctr Univ of Wis-Madison 1500 Johnson Dr Madison WI 53706

NUTTER, JAMES I(RVING), b Lawrence, Mass, Sept 4, 35; m 59; c 4. CHEMICAL ENGINEERING, PHYSICAL CHEMISTRY. *Educ:* Northeastern Univ, BS, 59; Iowa State Univ, MS, 61, PhD(chem eng), 63. *Prof Exp:* Teaching asst chem eng, Iowa State Univ, 59-63; res engr polymers, Wash Res Ctr, W R Grace & Co, 63, 64-66 & process res & develop, 66-68; supvr kinetics group, NASA Marshall Space Flight Ctr, 63-64; supvr process develop, Lord Mfg Co, Lord Corp, 68-70; tech dir design & develop, Robin Industs, Inc, Cleveland, 70-75; mgr res & develop, Scandura, Inc, 75-81; MGR PROCESS ENG, REEVES BROS, INC, 81- *Mem:* Am Chem Soc; Am Soc Testing & Mat; Soc Plastic Engrs; Sigma Xi; NY Acad Sci. *Res:* Adsorption, permeation and diffusion processes; polymers. *Mailing Add:* 8033 Rising Meadow Matthews NC 28105

NUTTER, ROBERT LELAND, b Boston, Mass, Jan 20, 22; m 46; c 2. BIOPHYSICS, VIROLOGY. *Educ:* Andrews Univ, BA, 44; Univ Colo, MS, 49; Iowa State Univ, PhD(biophys), 57. *Prof Exp:* Physicist, Nat Bur Standards, 44-45; asst physics, Univ Colo, 45-46; from instr to asst prof, Pac Union Col, 46-52; asst, Iowa State Univ, 52-53, instr, 53-56; asst prof, Pac Union Col, 56-57; from instr to assoc prof, 57-68, PROF MICROBIOL, SCH MED, LOMA LINDA UNIV, 68- *Concurrent Pos:* Instr, Univ Colo, 48-49; Am Cancer Soc Scholar, Col Med, Hershey Med Ctr & vis prof microbiol, Pa State Univ, 71-72. *Mem:* AAAS; Am Soc Microbiol. *Res:* Bacteriophages; animal viruses; virus nucleic acids; herpesviruses and other oncogenic viruses. *Mailing Add:* Dept of Microbiol Loma Linda Univ Sch of Med Loma Linda CA 92354

NUTTER, ROY STERLING, JR, b Kingwood, WVa, Apr 28, 44; m 66; c 2. ELECTRICAL ENGINEERING, COMPUTER ENGINEERING. *Educ:* WVa Univ, BSEE, 66, MSEE, 68, PhD(elec eng), 71. *Prof Exp:* Lectr elec eng, WVa Univ, 72; prof engr comput design, NCR Corp, 72-74; asst prof, 74-80, ASSOC PROF ELEC ENG, WEST VA UNIV, 80- *Concurrent Pos:* consult coal mine monitoring & control systems. *Mem:* sr mem Inst Elec & Electronics Engrs; Nat Soc Prof Engrs. *Res:* Microprocessor applications to coal mine monitoring and control; computer architecture; multivalued logic. *Mailing Add:* Dept of Elec Eng 833 Elec Engr Morgantown WV 26506

NUTTER, WILLIAM ERMAL, b Boomer, WVa, Sept 26, 27; m 52; c 3. BIOCHEMISTRY. *Educ:* WVa Inst Technol, BS, 53; Univ WVa, MS, 57, PhD(biochem), 59. *Prof Exp:* Res assoc biochem, Univ Iowa, 59-61; from asst ed to assoc ed, 61-65, asst head dept biochem ed, 65-71, head dept biochem ed anal, 71-73, ASST MGR, BIOCHEM DEPT, CHEM ABSTR SERV, OHIO STATE UNIV, 73- *Mem:* Am Chem Soc; AAAS; Sigma Xi. *Res:* Bacterial utilization of amino acids and peptides; mammalian metabolism of tryptophan; synthesis of kynurenine; kinetics of d-amino acid oxidase with d-kynurenine; chemical information and documentation. *Mailing Add:* Chem Abstr Serv Ohio State Univ Columbus OH 43210

NUTTING, ALBERT DEANE, b Otisfield, Maine, Sept 6, 05; m 40. FORESTRY. *Educ:* Univ Maine, BS, 27. *Prof Exp:* Forester, Finch, Pruyn & Co, 27-31; exten forester, Univ Maine, 31-48; forest comnr, State of Maine, 48-58; dir, Sch Forestry, 58-71, dir sch forest res, 70-71, EMER DIR SCH FOREST RESOURCES, UNIV MAINE, ORONO, 71- *Concurrent Pos:* Chmn, Nat Coop Forestry Res Bd. *Honors & Awards:* New Eng Coun Award, 58; Maine Forest Industs Award, 59; Northern Loggers Asn Award, 63. *Mem:* Fel Soc Am Foresters; Am Forestry Asn. *Res:* Forest management and products. *Mailing Add:* RFD 1 Otisfield Oxford ME 04270

NUTTING, EHARD FORREST, b Milwaukee, Wis, Oct 4, 29; m 51; c 6. ENDOCRINOLOGY, PHARMACOLOGY. *Educ:* Utah State Univ, BS, 51; Univ Wis, MS, 56, PhD(endocrinol), 62. *Prof Exp:* Res fel genetics, Univ Wis, 54-56 & res fel zool, 58-60; res investr endocrinol testing, 60-64, reprod endocrinol, 65-69, sr res investr reprod physiol, 69-70, res group leader fertility control, 70-71, res dir endocrinol dept, 71-73, dir, Dept Biol Res, Searle Labs Div, 73-75, sr res scientist, Dept Sci, 75-78, dir contraception res, 78-79, DIR CELLULAR & ENDOCRINE DIS, SEARLE LABS DIV, G D SEARLE & CO, 80- *Concurrent Pos:* Consult, Nat Inst Child Health & Human Develop, 71-78. *Mem:* Endocrine Soc; Soc Exp Biol & Med; Soc Study Reprod; Brit Soc Study Fertil; Am Soc Pharmacol & Exp Therapeut. *Res:* Physiology of the female reproductive tract; pharmacological control of fertility; gamete transport; physiology and pharmacology of factors involved in inflammation and cellular growth processes. *Mailing Add:* Searle Labs Div G D Searle & Co PO Box 5110 Chicago IL 60680

NUTTING, WILLIAM BROWN, b Worcester, Mass, Apr 15, 18; m 68; c 4. ACAROLOGY, INVERTEBRATE ZOOLOGY. *Educ:* Univ Mass, BS, 40, MS, 48; Cornell Univ, PhD(zool), 50. *Prof Exp:* From instr to assoc prof, 50-64, PROF ZOOL, UNIV MASS, AMHERST, 64- *Concurrent Pos:* Fel, Univ Queensland, 58; vis prof, Wallaceville Res Ctr, NZ, 72; vis prof, Stanford Univ Med Sch, 75 & Univ Greenland, 79. *Mem:* Sigma Xi. *Res:* Biology; ecology; pathogenesis and systematics of mites, especially Demodicidae; natural history. *Mailing Add:* Dept Zool Univ Mass Amherst MA 01003

NUTTING, WILLIAM LEROY, b Pepperell, Mass, July 26, 22; m 44; c 3. ENTOMOLOGY. *Educ:* Harvard Univ, AB, 43, PhD(biol), 50. *Prof Exp:* Res fel biol, Harvard Univ, 50-55; assoc entomologist, 55-62, assoc prof, 58-62, PROF ENTOM & ENTOMOLOGIST, UNIV ARIZ, 62- *Concurrent Pos:* Prin res scientist & prog leader, Grassland Termites Res Prog, Int Ctr Insect Physiol & Ecol, Nairobi, Kenya, 79-81. *Mem:* AAAS; Am Soc Zool; Entom Soc Am; Am Inst Biol Sci; Int Union Study Social Insects. *Res:* Insect morphology, behavior and ecology, especially Orthoptera, Isoptera and other social insects; symbiosis. *Mailing Add:* Dept Entom Univ Ariz Tucson AZ 85721

NUTTLI, OTTO WILLIAM, b St Louis, Mo, Dec 11, 26. GEOPHYSICS. *Educ:* St Louis Univ, BS, 48, MS, 50, PhD(geophys), 53. *Prof Exp:* From instr to assoc prof, 52-62, PROF GEOPHYS & GEOPHYS ENG, ST LOUIS UNIV, 62- *Concurrent Pos:* Ed bull, Seismol Soc Am, 71-75. *Mem:* AAAS; Seismol Soc Am (pres, 75-76); Soc Explor Geophys; fel Am Geophys Union; fel Royal Astron Soc. *Res:* Attenuation of elastic waves; earthquake shear waves; seismicity of Eastern North America; qualification of earthquakes; engineering seismology. *Mailing Add:* Earth & Atmos Sci St Louis Univ PO Box 8099 Laclede Sta St Louis MO 63156

NUZZI, ROBERT, b New York, NY, July 7, 42; m 68. ESTUARINE ECOLOGY, PHYTOPLANKTON. *Educ:* Fordham Univ, BS, 63, MS, 65, PhD(microbiol), 69. *Prof Exp:* Teaching asst biol, Fordham Univ, 64-68; instr, St Francis Col, NY, 68-70; assoc res scientist microbiol, NY Ocean Sci Lab, Affil Cols & Univs, Inc, 70-74, res scientist, 74-75; marine biologist, Dept Eviron Control, 75-78, MARINE BIOLOGIST, DEPT HEALTH SERV, SUFFOLK COUNTY, 78- *Concurrent Pos:* Res assoc, NY Ocean Sci Lab, Affil Cols & Univs, Inc, 75- *Mem:* AAAS; Am Inst Biol Sci; Am Soc Limnol & Oceanog; NY Acad Sci; Estuarine Res Fedn. *Res:* Phytoplankton systematics; estuarine ecology; wetland ecology. *Mailing Add:* Suffolk Co Dept Health Serv PO Box G 841 Central Islip NY 11722

NYBAKKEN, JAMES W, b Warren, Minn, Sept 16, 36; m 60; c 2. MARINE ECOLOGY. *Educ:* St Olaf Col, BA, 58; Univ Wis, MS, 61, PhD(zool), 65. *Prof Exp:* Teaching asst marine biol, Univ Miami, 58-59; cur, Zool Mus, Univ Wis, 61, 62 & 64-65; from asst prof to assoc prof, 65-72, PROF BIOL, CALIF STATE UNIV, HAYWARD, 73-, STAFF MEM, MOSS LANDING MARINE LAB, 66- *Concurrent Pos:* Off Naval Res vis investr, Marine Lab, Univ Ariz, 66; res assoc, Univ Wash, 68-69, 72 & 73. *Mem:* AAAS; Ecol Soc Am; Am Soc Zool; Marine Biol Asn UK. *Res:* Ecology and systematics of gastropod mollusks of the genus Conus; ecology of nudibranch mollusks; benthic invertebrate ecology. *Mailing Add:* Moss Landing Marine Labs Box 223 Moss Landing CA 95039

NYBERG, DAVID DOLPH, b Vancouver, Wash, June 10, 28; m 51; c 2. POLYMER CHEMISTRY. *Educ:* Ore State Univ, BS, 52, PhD(org chem), 56. *Prof Exp:* Group leader, Shell Chem Co, 56-66; staff mem, 66-72, mgr explor develop, thermofit tech dept, 72-76, MGR ADVAN MAT DEVELOP, ENERGY DIV, RAYCHEM CORP, 76- *Mem:* Am Chem Soc. *Res:* Polymer synthesis; plastics and rubber technology; radiation crosslinking; adhesion; specialty formulating. *Mailing Add:* Raychem Corp 300 Constitution Dr Menlo Park CA 94025

NYBERG, DENNIS WAYNE, b Oklahoma City, Okla, Feb 11, 44; m 67; c 5. GENETICS, EVOLUTION. *Educ:* Mass Inst Technol, SB, 65; Univ Ill, Urbana-Champaign, MS, 69, PhD(zool), 71. *Prof Exp:* Fel biol, Univ Sussex, 71-72; res assoc, Ind Univ, 72-73; asst prof, 73-77, ASSOC PROF BIOL, UNIV ILL, CHICAGO CIRCLE, 77- *Concurrent Pos:* NSF grant, Univ Ill, Chicago Circle, 76-78; NIH grant, Univ Ill, Chicago, 79-82; fac res leave, Argonne Nat Lab, 80-81. *Mem:* Genetics Soc Am; Am Genetic Asn; Soc Study Evolution; Soc Protozoologists; AAAS. *Res:* Evolutionary role of breeding systems; genetics of metal tolerance in protozoa; aging processes in ciliates. *Mailing Add:* Dept of Biol Sci Univ of Ill at Chicago Circle Chicago IL 60648

NYBOER, JAN, b Holland, Mich, Apr 21, 06; m 39; c 4. INTERNAL MEDICINE. *Educ:* Univ Mich, AB, 26, MS, 29, ScD(med physiol), 32, MD, 35. *Prof Exp:* Asst biol, Hope Col, 25-27; asst mammal, Univ Mich, 28, asst & demonstr physiol, 28-34, asst electrocardiol, Univ Hosp, 34-35; intern, St Louis Maternity Hosp & Barnes Hosp, Wash Univ, 35-36 & Harvard Med Serv, Boston City Hosp, 36-37; fel med, NY Post-Grad Med Sch, Columbia Univ, 37-41; asst med dir, Conn Mutual Life Ins Co, 41-47; asst prof pharmacol, Dartmouth Med Sch, 47-55; chief cardiovasc physiol & assoc physician, Harper Hosp, 55-65; assoc physiol res, 73-76, DIR RES, REHAB INST, WAYNE STATE UNIV, 65-, PROF PHYSIOL & PHARMACOL, SCH MED, 59-, EMER PROF PHYSIOL, 76- *Concurrent Pos:* Asst attend physician, NY Postgrad Hosp & Clin, 37-47; clin instr, Sch Med, Yale Univ, 42-47; consult, US Vet Admin Hosp, Vt, 48-55; consult, Hitchcock Clin, 48-55, res assoc, Hitchcock Found, 54-55; exchange scientist, Czech Acad Sci, 71 & All India Inst Med Sci 78. *Mem:* Am Physiol Soc; Am Heart Asn; fel Am Col Cardiol; Am Fedn Clin Res. *Res:* Physiology of the heart and respiration; electrocardiography; electrical impedance plethysmography; development of direct writing electrocardiography; displacement and counterforce ballistocardiography; bioelectrical impedance for total body water during renal dialysis and congestive heart failure; leanness and fatness. *Mailing Add:* 570 Cadieux Grosse Pointe MI 48201

NYBORG, WESLEY LEMARS, b Ruthven, Iowa, May 15, 17; m 45; c 1. BIOPHYSICS, ACOUSTICS. *Educ:* Luther Col, AB, 41; Pa State Univ, MS, 44, PhD(physics), 47. *Prof Exp:* Asst physics, Pa State Univ, 41-43, instr, 43-44 & 47-49, asst, 44-47, asst prof, 49-50; from asst prof to assoc prof, Brown Univ, 50-60; PROF PHYSICS, UNIV VT, 60- *Concurrent Pos:* USPHS fel, Sch Adv Study, Mass Inst Technol, 56-57; vis scientist, Oxford Univ, 60-61; mem adv comt radiation bio-effects, Food & Drug Admin, 72-76. *Mem:* AAAS; Acoust Soc Am; Am Phys Soc; Biophys Soc; Am Asn Physics Teachers. *Res:* Acoustics; ultrasonics; biophysical ultrasound; environmental biophysics; physical mechanisms for biological effects of ultrasound. *Mailing Add:* Dept of Physics Cook Phys Sci Bldg Univ of Vt Burlington VT 05401

NYBURG, STANLEY CECIL, b London, Eng, Dec 15, 24; m 49; c 2. CRYSTALLOGRAPHY. *Educ:* King's Col, Univ London, BSc, 45, DSc(crystallog, thermodynamics), 73; Univ Leeds, PhD(crystallog), 49. *Prof Exp:* Crystallographer, Brit Rubber PProducers' Res Asn, 49-52; from asst lectr to sr lectr chem, Univ Keele, 52-64; PROF CHEM, UNIV TORONTO, 64- *Concurrent Pos:* Vis prof crystallog, Univ Pittsburgh, 62-63; vis prof, Univ Sydney, Australia. *Mem:* Fel The Chem Soc; assoc Brit Inst Physics & Phys Soc. *Res:* Crystal structure analysis; thermodynamics. *Mailing Add:* 133 Belsize Dr Toronto ON M4S 1L3 Can

NYCE, JACK LELAND, polymer chemistry, rubber chemistry, see previous edition

NYCZEPIR, ANDREW PETER, b Englewood, NJ, Feb 25, 52. NEMATOLOGY. *Educ:* Univ Ga, BSA, 74; Clemson Univ, MS, 76, PhD(plant pathol-nematol), 80. *Prof Exp:* Grad res asst, Clemson Univ, 74-76, 77-80; NEMATOLOGIST, RES, WASH STATE UNIV, AGR RES SERV, USDA, 80- *Mem:* Soc Nematologist; Orgn Trop Am Nematologists; Sigma Xi; NY Acad Sci. *Res:* Host-parasite relationships and control of plant parasitic nematodes. *Mailing Add:* 1801 Benson Ave Elwood Apts 1 Prosser WA 99350

NYDEGGER, CORINNE NEMETZ, b Milwaukee, Wis. MEDICAL ANTHROPOLOGY, GERONTOLOGY. *Educ:* Univ Wis, Madison, BA, 51; Cornell Univ, MA, 70; Pa State Univ, PhD(human develop), 73. *Prof Exp:* Res field-team mem, Six Cultures Proj, Harvard-Yale-Cornell Proj, 54-56; asst dir res geriatrics, Pa State Univ, 72-73; NIMH fel, Dept Sociol & Inst Human Develop, Univ Calif, Berkeley, 73-74; lectr med anthrop prog, 75-77, ADJ ASSOC PROF MED ANTHROP PROG, UNIV CALIF, SAN FRANCISCO, 77- *Concurrent Pos:* USPHS res fel, Human Develop & Med Anthrop Prog, Univ Calif, San Francisco, 74-76; lectr adult develop, Sch Soc Welfare, Univ Calif, Berkeley, 76; mem, P I Timing Fatherhood Proj, 77-82, life course rev comt, NIMH; assoc ed, Res Aging. *Mem:* Fel Geront Soc; fel Soc Appl Anthrop; Soc Cross Cult Res; Soc Study Social Probs; Med Anthrop Asn. *Res:* Timing--effects of chronological age on events and roles; responses to timing deviance; deviance and medical models; group responses to negative labeling; fatherhood, especially deviant patterns. *Mailing Add:* Med Anthrop Prog Univ Calif 1320 Third Ave San Francisco CA 94143

NYE, EDWIN (PACKARD), b Atkinson, NH, Jan 29, 20; m 44; c 3. MECHANICAL ENGINEERING. *Educ:* Univ NH, BS, 41; Harvard Univ, MS, 47. *Prof Exp:* Serv engr controls, Bailey Meter Co, 41-42; instr mech eng, Univ NH, 42-44; proj engr fluid flow, Nat Adv Comt Aeronaut, 44-46; from instr to assoc prof mech eng, Pa State Univ, 47-59; prof eng, 58-60, chmn dept, 60-70, dean fac, 70-81, HALLDEN PROF ENG, TRINITY COL, CONN, 60- *Concurrent Pos:* Chmn bd dir, Univ Res Inst Conn, Inc, 70- *Mem:* Soc Hist Technol; Am Soc Mech Engrs. *Res:* Conversion of stored energies to mechanical and electrical form. *Mailing Add:* Off of the Dean of Fac Trinity Col Hartford CT 06106

NYE, PATRICK WILLIAM, biophysics, psychophysics, see previous edition

NYE, ROBERT EUGENE, JR, b Cincinnati, Ohio, Feb 6, 22; m 48; c 3. PHYSIOLOGY. *Educ:* Ohio Univ, AB, 43; Univ Rochester, MD, 47. *Prof Exp:* Intern med, Strong Mem Hosp, Rochester, NY, 47-48, asst resident, 48-49; house physician, Hammersmith Hosp, London, Eng, 51; instr, Univ Rochester, 54-56; from instr to assoc prof, 56-73, PROF PHYSIOL, DARTMOUTH MED SCH, 73- *Concurrent Pos:* Buswell fel, Univ Rochester, 49-50, univ fel, 51-54; assoc staff, Mary Hitchcock Mem Hosp, 56-65, consult staff, 65- *Mem:* Am Fedn Clin Res; Am Physiol Soc. *Res:* Cardiovascular and pulmonary physiology, especially the relations between perfusion and ventilation in the lung. *Mailing Add:* Dept of Physiol Dartmouth Med Sch Hanover NH 03755

NYE, SYLVANUS WILLIAM, b Buffalo, NY, Mar 28, 30; m 56; c 2. PATHOLOGY. *Educ:* Hamilton Col, AB, 52; Univ Rochester, MD, 57; Am Bd Path, cert. *Prof Exp:* From intern to chief resident path, Sch Med, Univ NC, Chapel Hill, 57-60, instr path & trainee clin microbiol & path, 60-62; from asst prof to prof path, Sch Med, ECarolina Univ, 69-74, chmn dept, 71-74; MEM STAFF, LENOIR MEM HOSP, 74- *Concurrent Pos:* Pathologist, SEATO Med Res Lab, US Army Component, Bangkok, Thailand, 63-65. *Mem:* AAAS; Col Am Path; Int Acad Path; Am Soc Trop Med & Hyg; Am Soc Clin Path. *Res:* Geographic pathology. *Mailing Add:* Lenoir Mem Hosp Kinston NC 28501

NYE, WARREN EDWARD, b Madison, Wis, Aug 19, 12. BIOLOGY. *Educ:* Columbia Col, AB, 34; Univ Wis, MA, 39, PhD(zool), 45. *Prof Exp:* Chmn Dept, 50-67, PROF BIOL, LORAS COL, 41- *Concurrent Pos:* Mem Bd Exam in the Basic Sci, State of Iowa, 57- *Mem:* AAAS; Nat Asn Biol Teachers. *Res:* Cytology; spermiogenesis; field ecology of pheasant and fox studies; spermiogenesis in Necturus maculosus. *Mailing Add:* Dept of Biol Loras Col Dubuque IA 52001

NYGAARD, KAARE JOHANN, b Notodden, Norway, July 10, 34; m 59; c 2. ATOMIC PHYSICS, QUANTUM OPTICS. *Educ:* Norweg Inst Technol, MS, 59, PhD(physics), 63. *Prof Exp:* Res asst gas discharge physics, Norweg Inst Technol, 59-60, res fel, 61-63; vis res assoc, Univ Hamburg, 60; mem res staff, Princeton Univ, 64 & Sperry Rand Res Ctr, 65-68; assoc prof, 68-75, PROF PHYSICS, UNIV MO-ROLLA, 75- *Concurrent Pos:* Vis prof, FOM Inst Atomic & Molecular Physics, Amsterdam, Neth, 74-75. *Mem:* AAAS; Am Geophys Union; Am Phys Soc; Norweg Phys Soc; sr mem Inst Elec & Electronics Engrs. *Res:* Electron impact ionization in metal vapors; photo-ionization of excited cesium atoms as source of polarized electrons; plasma diagnostics; dissociation of HCL. *Mailing Add:* Dept of Physics Univ of Mo Rolla MO 65401

NYGAARD, ODDVAR FRITHJOF, b Oslo, Norway, Oct 30, 22; nat US; m 46; c 2. RADIOBIOLOGY, CHEMISTRY. *Educ:* Norweg Tech Univ, Sivilingenior, 47; Univ Minn, PhD(physiol chem), 51. *Prof Exp:* Asst tech org chem, Tech Univ Norway, 47; asst physiol chem, Univ Minn, 48-51; fel oncol, McArdle Mem Lab, Univ Wis, 51-52, res assoc, 54-57; res biochemist, Norsk Hydro's Inst Cancer Res, Norweg Radium Hosp, 52-54; Norweg Cancer Soc fel, 54; res chemist, AEC biol effects of irradiation lab, Univ Mich, 57-59; sr inst radiol, 59-62, res assoc, 59-63, asst prof biochem, 59-68, asst prof radiol, 62-65, assoc prof radiol, 65-68, assoc prof biochem & radiol, 68-75, assoc dir div radiation biol, 63-76, PROF RADIOL, CASE WESTERN RESERVE UNIV, 75-, DIR DIV RADIOTION BIOL, 76- *Concurrent Pos:* Ed-in-chief, Radiation Research, Radiation Res Soc, 72-79; special asst to the dir, Low-Level Radiation Effects, Nat Cancer Inst, 79- *Mem:* Environ Mutagen Soc; Am Chem Soc; Soc Develop Biol; Radiation Res Soc; Coun Biol Ed. *Res:* Nucleic acid metabolism and control; biological effects of radiation; biochemistry of hypoxic cell radiosensitizers and carcinogens; modification of radiation response in hypoxic and anoxic cells. *Mailing Add:* Div Radia Biol Dept Radiol Case Western Reserve Univ Cleveland OH 44106

NYGREEN, PAUL W, b Bellingham, Wash, May 15, 25. GEOLOGY, OCEANOGRAPHY. *Educ:* Univ Wash, BS, 53; Univ Nebr, MSc, 55. *Prof Exp:* Geologist, Standard Oil Co Tex, 55-62, biostratigrapher, 62-64; biostratigrapher, Calif Oil Co, Okla, 64-65, sr biostratigrapher, Chevron Oil Co, 65-69, staff biostratigrapher, 69-71, STAFF BIOSTRATIGRAPHER, CHEVRON OVERSEAS PETROL INC, CHEVRON OIL CO, 71- *Concurrent Pos:* Supvry paleontologist, West Australian Petrol Proprietary Ltd, 71-74; supvr biostratigraphy, Arabian Am Oil Co, Saudi Arabia, 78-80, asst chief geologist, 80- *Mem:* AAAS; Geol Soc Am; Paleont Soc; Am Asn Petrol Geol; Am Asn Stratig Palynologists. *Mailing Add:* Aramco Explor Dept Chevron Oil Co Dhaharan Saudia Arabia

NYGREN, STEPHEN FREDRICK, b Evanston, Ill, Mar 3, 42; m 64. ELECTRICAL ENGINEERING. *Educ:* Carnegie Inst Technol, BS, 64; Stanford Univ, MS, 65, PhD(elec eng), 69. *Prof Exp:* MEM TECH STAFF, BELL TEL LABS, INC, 68- *Mem:* Am Phys Soc. *Res:* III-V compound semiconductor materials, including crystal growth, epitaxial layer growth and diffusion. *Mailing Add:* Bell Tel Labs Inc 2525 N 11th St Reading PA 19604

NYHAN, WILLIAM LEO, b Boston, Mass, Mar 13, 26; m 48; c 3. PEDIATRICS, BIOCHEMISTRY. *Educ:* Columbia Univ, MD, 49; Univ Ill, MS, 56, PhD(pharmacol), 58. *Prof Exp:* From asst prof to assoc prof pediat, Sch Med, Johns Hopkins Univ, 58-63; prof pediat & biochem & chmn dept pediat, Univ Miami, 63-69; PROF PEDIAT & CHMN DEPT, SCH MED, UNIV CALIF, SAN DIEGO, 69- *Concurrent Pos:* Fel, Nat Found, 55-58; Am Cancer Soc fac res assoc, 61-63. *Mem:* AAAS; Am Chem Soc; Soc Pediat Res; Am Asn Cancer Res; Am Pediat Soc. *Res:* Amino acid metabolism; biochemical genetics; metabolism of tumors; developmental pharmacology. *Mailing Add:* Dept of Pediat Univ of Calif San Diego Sch Med La Jolla CA 92093

NYHUS, LLOYD MILTON, b Mt Vernon, Wash, June 24, 23; m 49; c 2. SURGERY, PHYSIOLOGY. *Educ:* Pac Lutheran Col, BA, 45; Univ Ala, MD, 47; Am Bd Surg, dipl, 57. *Hon Degrees:* Dr, Univ Thessoloniki, 69, Univ Uppsala, 74 & Chihuahua Univ, 75. *Prof Exp:* From intern to asst resident surg, King County Hosp, Seattle, 47-50; res assoc, Univ Wash, 52-53; resident, King County Hosp, 54; from instr to prof surg, Sch Med, Univ Wash, 54-67; PROF SURG & HEAD DEPT, ABRAHAM LINCOLN SCH MED, UNIV ILL MED CTR, CHICAGO & SURGEON-IN-CHIEF, UNIV HOSP, 67- *Concurrent Pos:* USPHS res fel, 52-54; Guggenheim fel, Sweden & Scotland, 55-56; sr consult, West Side Vet Admin Hosp, Chicago, 67-; sr attend, Cook County Hosp, Chicago, 68- *Mem:* Soc Univ Surg; Am Gastroenterol Asn; fel Am Col Surgeons; Am Surg Asn; Int Soc Surg. *Res:* Gastric physiology and surgery; peptic ulcer; hernia; esophageal physiology. *Mailing Add:* Dept of Surg Univ of Ill Hosp Chicago IL 60612

NYI, KAYSON, b Chungking, China, Apr 11, 45; m 70. ORGANIC CHEMISTRY. *Educ:* Mass Inst Technol, SB, 65; Univ Chicago, PhD(org chem), 71. *Prof Exp:* SR CHEMIST, RES DIV, ROHM AND HAAS CO, 71- *Mem:* Am Chem Soc. *Res:* Synthetic organic chemistry; photochemistry. *Mailing Add:* 121 Tower Rd Sellersville PA 18960

NYIKOS, PETER JOSEPH, b Salzburg, Austria, Mar 8, 46; US citizen. TOPOLOGY. *Educ:* Washington & Jefferson Col, BA, 67; Carnegie-Mellon Univ, MS, 68, PhD(topology), 71. *Prof Exp:* Mathematician, Biomed Lab, Edgewood Arsenal, US Army, 72-73; NSF fel, Univ Chicago, 73-74; vis lectr math, Univ Ill, Urbana, 74-76; vis asst prof, Auburn Univ, 76-79; mem staff, Inst Med & Math, Ohio Univ, 79; ASSOC PROF, UNIV SC, 79- *Mem:* Am Math Soc. *Res:* Set-theoretic topology, especially theory of nonmetrizable manifolds, countably compact spaces, zero-dimensional spaces, and Stone-Cech compactification of discrete spaces; theory of partially ordered sets and Boolean algebras. *Mailing Add:* Dept Math Univ SC Columbia SC 29208

NYIRADY, STEPHEN ARNOLD, microbiology, see previous edition

NYLAND, GEORGE, b Eastburg, Alta, Apr 3, 19; US citizen; m 41; c 3. PLANT PATHOLOGY. *Educ:* State Col Wash, BS, 40, PhD(plant path), 48; La State Univ, MS, 42. *Prof Exp:* Asst, State Col Washington, 39-40, from instr to asst prof plant path, 46-48; asst, La State Univ, 40-42; instr & jr plant pathologist, 48-50, asst prof & plant pathologist, 50-56, assoc prof & assoc plant pathologist, 56-62, PROF PLANT PATH & PLANT PATHOLOGIST, COL AGR, UNIV CALIF, DAVIS, 62- *Concurrent Pos:* Jr plant pathologist, Exp Sta, State Col Washington, 46-48, asst plant pathologist, 47-48. *Honors & Awards:* Calif Asn Nursery Men spec Res Award, 67. *Mem:* AAAS; Am Phytopath Soc; Sigma Xi. *Res:* Stone, pome fruit and ornamental plants virus and mycoplasma diseases; chemotherapy; thermotherapy. *Mailing Add:* Dept of Plant Path Col of Agr Univ of Calif Davis CA 95616

NYLEN, MARIE USSING, b Copenhagen, Denmark, Apr 13, 24; US citizen; m 56; c 3. DENTAL RESEARCH, ELECTRON MICROSCOPY. *Educ:* Royal Dent Col, Denmark, DDS, 47. *Hon Degrees:* DrOdont, Royal Dent Col, Denmark, 73. *Prof Exp:* Pvt pract, 47-48; instr oper dent, Royal Dent Col, Denmark, 48-49; guest worker dent histol, Nat Inst Dent Res, 49-50, asst prof oral diag & res assoc electron micros, Royal Dent Col, Denmark, 51-55; vis assoc biophys, 55-60, biologist, 60-65, actg chief lab histol & path, 65-69, mem dent study sect, 70-74, chief lab biol struct, 69-76, DIR INTRAMURAL RES, NAT INST DENT RES, 76- *Concurrent Pos:* USPHS fel, Nat Inst Dent Res, 50-51; vis investr, Marine Biol Lab, Woods Hole, 69-72; prof lectr, Schs Med & Dent, Georgetown Univ, 70- *Honors & Awards:* Dept Health, Educ & Welfare Super Serv Honor Award, 69; Int Asn Dent Res Award, 70; Federal Woman's Award, 75; Isaac Scheur Mem Award, 77. *Mem:* Fel AAAS; Electron Micros Soc; Am Dent Asn; Am Soc Cell Biol; fel Am Col Dent. *Res:* Biophysical studies of developing and mature mineralized tissues and associated cells in normal and pathologic states. *Mailing Add:* Nat Inst of Dent Res Bldg 30 Rm132 Bethesda MD 20014

NYLUND, ROBERT E, b Lowell, Mass, May 12, 37; m 62; c 1. PHYSICAL CHEMISTRY. *Educ:* Northeastern Univ, BS, 60; Univ Iowa, PhD(phys chem), 64. *Prof Exp:* Asst prof, 64-69, ASSOC PROF CHEM, SUSQUEHANNA UNIV, 69-, CHMN DEPT, 75- *Mem:* Am Chem Soc. *Res:* Physical chemistry of biologically important polymers and proteins. *Mailing Add:* Dept of Chem Susquehanna Univ Selinsgrove PA 17870

NYLUND, ROBERT EINAR, b Ely, Minn, Jan 22, 16; m 40; c 2. HORTICULTURE. *Educ:* Univ Minn, BS, 38, MS, 42, PhD(hort), 45. *Prof Exp:* Asst, Univ Minn, St Paul, 38, horticulturist, Northwest Exp Sta, 39-41, from instr to assoc prof, 39-59, actg head dept hort sci & landscape archit, 75-76, prof hort, 59-78; RETIRED. *Concurrent Pos:* Fulbright lectr, Univ Helsinki, 59-60 & 72; Univ Minn Off Int Prog grant, 65. *Mem:* Fel AAAS; Am Soc Hort Sci; Weed Sci Soc Am; European Potato Asn; Potato Asn Am. *Res:* Physiology of vegetable crops and potatoes; weed control. *Mailing Add:* 1480 Raymond St Paul MN 55108

NYMAN, CARL JOHN, b New Orleans, La, Oct 21, 24; m 50; c 3. INORGANIC CHEMISTRY. *Educ:* Tulane Univ, BS, 44, MS, 45; Univ Ill, PhD(inorg chem), 48. *Prof Exp:* Jr technologist, Shell Oil Co, Inc, Calif, 44; asst chem, Univ Ill, 45-47, instr, 48; from instr to assoc prof, 48-61, PROF CHEM, WASH STATE UNIV, 61-, DEAN, GRAD SCH, 68-, ASSOC PROVOST RES, 81. *Concurrent Pos:* Vis fel, Cornell Univ, 59-60; vis fel, Imp Col Sci & Technol, London, 66-67. *Mem:* AAAS; Am Chem Soc. *Res:* Catalytic reduction of sodium sulfate; polarography in liquid ammonia; stability of complex ions; solutions of complex and polynuclear inorganic ions; organometallic complexes; peroxo-complexes of metals; catalytic oxygenation reactions. *Mailing Add:* Grad Sch Wash State Univ Pullman WA 99164

NYMAN, DALE JAMES, b Bancroft, Iowa, June 4, 31; m 60; c 2. GROUNDWATER GEOLOGY. *Educ:* Iowa State Univ, BS, 53, MS, 58. *Prof Exp:* GEOLOGIST, US GEOL SURV, 58-, HYDROLOGIST, 58- *Mem:* Am Geophys Union; Geol Soc Am; Soc Prof Well Log Analysts; Nat Water Well Asn. *Res:* Application of geology to hydrologic problems; ground-water surface-water relationships; ground-water management and modeling; application of remote sensing to ground water problems. *Mailing Add:* 3168 Sherry Dr Baton Rouge LA 70816

NYMAN, MELVIN ANDREW, b Big Rapids, Mich, Aug 19, 44. MATHEMATICS. *Educ:* Ferris State Col, BS, 65; Mich State Univ, MS, 67, PhD(math), 72. *Prof Exp:* Instr math, Ferris State Col, 67-69; from asst prof to assoc prof math, Manchester Col, 72-81; ASSOC PROF & CHMN MATH & COMPUT STUDIES, ALMA COL, 81- *Concurrent Pos:* Analyst & mathematician, Solar Energy Res Inst, Golden, Colo, 80-81. *Mem:* Am Math Soc; Math Asn Am. *Mailing Add:* Dept Math & Comput Studies Alma Col Alma MI 48801

NYMAN, THOMAS HARRY, b Seattle, Wash, Feb 11, 42. ELECTRONICS, SYSTEMS ENGINEERING. *Educ:* Univ Wash, BS, 64; Mass Inst Technol, SM, 66. *Prof Exp:* Staff mem data transmission, Bell Telephone Labs, 64-66; officer, USS Enterprise Engr Dept, US Navy, 66-67, prog mgr sensor syst develop, Defense Comn Planning Group, 67-69; group leader sensor syst, Mitre Corp, 69-75; staff specialist electronics, Off Dir, Defense Res & Eng, Dept Defense, 75-78; dept dir, Gen Res Corp, 78-80; ASSOC & DEPT MGR SYSTS INTEGRATION, MITRE CORP, 81- *Concurrent Pos:* Mem navig & commun/positioning/identification working group, Dept Defense, 75-77, mem steering comt embedded comput software, 76-78; mem steering comt avionics, Am Defense Prepardness Asn, 77-78; mem adv comt guid, control & info processing, NASA, 77-78. *Mem:* Inst Elec & Electronics Engrs; Am Inst Navig. *Res:* Systems issues of controlling and stabiliing networks of communications and command and control systems; structuring issues of interoperability by hierarchial layers; dynamic reallocation of computer and communications resources for land battle applications. *Mailing Add:* Mitre Corp 1820 Dolly Madison Blvd McLean VA 22102

NYMANN, DEWAYNE STANLEY, b Cedar Falls, Iowa, June 27, 35; m 56; c 1. MATHEMATICS. *Educ:* Univ Northern Iowa, BA, 57; Univ Kans, MA, 59, PhD(math), 64. *Prof Exp:* Asst prof math, Tex Christian Univ, 64-65 & Univ Tex, 65-70; ASSOC PROF MATH, UNIV TENN, CHATTANOOGA, 70- *Mem:* Am Math Soc; Sigma Xi; Math Asn Am. *Res:* Algebra group theory; generalized nilpotent and solvable groups. *Mailing Add:* Dept of Math Univ of Tenn Chattanooga TN 37403

NYMANN, JAMES EUGENE, b Cedar Falls, Iowa, Nov 24, 38; m 58; c 3. MATHEMATICS. *Educ:* Univ Northern Iowa, BA, 61; Univ Ariz, MS, 63, PhD(math), 65. *Prof Exp:* Asst prof, Univ Hawaii, 65-67; assoc prof, 67-74, PROF MATH, UNIV TEX, EL PASO, 74- *Concurrent Pos:* Fulbright-Hays lectr, Univ Liberia, 72-73 & Univ Malawi, 77-79. *Mem:* Am Math Soc; Math Asn Am. *Res:* Number theory and analysis. *Mailing Add:* Dept of Math Univ of Tex El Paso TX 79968

NYPAN, LESTER JENS, b Minneapolis, Minn, Oct 30, 29; m 54. MECHANICAL ENGINEERING. *Educ:* Univ Minn, Minneapolis, BS, 51, MSME, 52, PhD(mech eng), 60. *Prof Exp:* Instr mech eng, Univ Minn, Minneapolis, 54-58; sr engr, Mech Div, Gen Mills, Inc, 56-60 & Lockheed-Calif Co, 60-62; PROF ENG, CALIF STATE UNIV, NORTHRIDGE, 62- *Mem:* Am Soc Mech Engrs; Soc Lubrication Engrs; Am Soc Eng Educ; Nat Soc Prof Engrs. *Res:* Hydrodynamic lubrication; journal bearings; rolling element bearings; measurement; instruments; vibration dynamics; material fatigue. *Mailing Add:* Sch Eng Calif State Univ Northridge CA 91330

NYQUIST, DENNIS PAUL, b Detroit, Mich, Aug 18, 39. ELECTRICAL ENGINEERING. *Educ:* Lawrence Inst Technol, BS, 61; Wayne State Univ, MS, 64; Mich State Univ, PhD(elec eng), 66. *Prof Exp:* Prod engr, Ford Motor Co, 61-63, res engr, Res Lab, 65; from instr to asst prof elec eng, 66-70, sr investr res grant, US Air Force, 67-71, assoc prof elec eng & systs sci, 70-81, PROF ELEC ENG, MICH STATE UNIV, 81- *Mem:* AAAS; Inst Elec & Electronics Engrs. *Res:* Applied electromagnetics; radiation and scattering of electromagnetic waves; interaction of electromagnetic waves with plasma; application of electromagnetic theory to electric theory of nerves. *Mailing Add:* Dept of Elec Eng Mich State Univ East Lansing MI 48824

NYQUIST, HARLAN LEROY, b Scobey, Mont, Aug 12, 29; m 55; c 3. ORGANIC CHEMISTRY. *Educ:* Mont State Col, BS, 51; Univ Calif, Los Angeles, PhD(chem), 56. *Prof Exp:* From instr to asst prof chem, Univ Calif, Santa Barbara, 56-62; from asst prof to assoc prof, 62-68, PROF CHEM, CALIF STATE UNIV, NORTHRIDGE, 68- *Concurrent Pos:* Distinguished vis prof, Dept Chem, Air Force Acad, Colo, 82-83. *Mem:* Am Chem Soc; Sigma Xi. *Res:* Mechanisms of organic reactions; synthesis and reactions of s-triazines; stereochemistry. *Mailing Add:* Dept Chem Calif State Univ Northridge CA 91330

NYQUIST, JUDITH KAY, b Gary, Ind, June 22, 41. NEUROPHYSIOLOGY. *Educ:* St Olaf Col, BA, 63; Univ Wash, PhD(physiol, biophys), 69. *Prof Exp:* Asst prof neurosurg, Med Col Va, 70-71; asst adj prof, Dept Surg, Univ Calif, 71-76; res physiologist, div neurosurg, Vet Admin Hosp, San Diego, 72-76; asst res neuroscientist, Dept Surg, Univ Calif, San Diego, 76-80; MEM STAFF, DEPT CLIN RES, SCRIPPS CLIN & RES FOUND, 80- *Concurrent Pos:* Ment Health Training Prog fel, Brain Res Inst, Univ Calif, Los Angeles, 69-70; asst adj prof surg, Sch Med, Univ Calif, San Diego, 72- *Mem:* Soc Neurosci; Int Asn Study Pain; Am Pain Soc. *Res:* Neurophysiology of mammalian somatosensory systems, particularly pain, and motor systems; utilizing evoked potential and single neuron recording techniques. *Mailing Add:* Scripps Clin & Res Found 10666 N Torrey Pines Rd La Jolla CA 92037

NYQUIST, LAURENCE ELWOOD, b Tracy, Minn, July 28, 39; m 63; c 2. GEOCHEMISTRY, MASS SPECTROMETRY. *Educ:* Macalester Col, BA, 61; Univ Minn, MS, 63, PhD(physics), 69. *Prof Exp:* Sci asst mass spectrometry, Swiss Fed Inst Technol, 65-68; res assoc physics, Univ Minn, 69-71; AEROSPACE TECHNICIAN GEOCHEM, NASA JOHNSON SPACE CTR, 71- *Concurrent Pos:* Mem, Lunar Sample Anal Planning Team, 75-76 & Lunar Sci Rev Panel, 76-77. *Honors & Awards:* Exceptional Sci Serv, NASA, 76. *Mem:* Am Geophys Union; Meteoritical Soc. *Res:* Chronological and geochemical evolution of the moon and other solid bodies in the solar system; radiometric ages by Rb-Sr and Sm-Nd techniques; use of strontium and neodymium isotopes as petrogenetic tracers. *Mailing Add:* Code SN-7 NASA Johnson Space Ctr Houston TX 77058

NYQUIST, RICHARD ALLEN, b Rockford, Ill, May 3, 28; m 56; c 4. MOLECULAR SPECTROSCOPY. *Educ:* Augustana Col, Ill, BA, 51; Okla State Univ, MS, 53. *Prof Exp:* Proj leader infrared spectros, Chem Physics Res Lab, 53-71, ASSOC SCIENTIST INFRARED & RAMAN SPECTROS, ANAL LABS, DOW CHEM CO, 71- *Mem:* Am Chem Soc; Coblentz Soc; Am Soc Test Mat; Soc Appl Spectrosc. *Res:* Vibrational spectroscopy; elucidation of chemical structure. *Mailing Add:* 3707 Westbrier Terr Midland MI 48640

NYQUIST, SALLY ELIZABETH, b Hutchinson, Minn, Nov 8, 41. CELL BIOLOGY. *Educ:* Wheaton Col, BS, 63; Purdue Univ, Lafayette, PhD(biol), 70. *Prof Exp:* Volunteer, Peace Corps, 63-65; Kettering Found res fel, Charles F Kettering Res Lab, 70-72; ASST PROF BIOL, BUCKNELL UNIV, 72- *Mem:* Am Soc Cell Biol. *Res:* Golgi apparatus membranes, enzymatic activities and composition. *Mailing Add:* Dept of Biol Bucknell Univ Lewisburg PA 17837

NYQUIST, WYMAN ELLSWORTH, b Scobey, Mont, June 13, 28; m 52; c 2. STATISTICAL ANALYSIS, QUANTITATIVE GENETICS. *Educ:* Mont State Univ, BS, 50; Univ Calif, PhD(genetics), 53. *Prof Exp:* Asst agron, Univ Calif, 50-52, instr, 53-57, lectr, 57-58, asst prof, 58-63; assoc prof, 63-68, PROF AGRON, PURDUE UNIV, 68- *Concurrent Pos:* Jr agronomist, Exp Sta, Univ Calif, 53-57, asst agronomist, 57-63; NIH spec res fel, 69-70. *Mem:* Am Soc Agron; Genetics Soc Am; Biomet Soc; Coun Agr Sci & Technol; Crop Sci Soc Am. *Res:* Development of statistical models relating to quantitative genetic variation, particularly in plant populations and their utilization in evaluating alternative breeding systems. *Mailing Add:* Dept of Agron Purdue Univ West Lafayette IN 47907

NYQUIST-BATTIE, CYNTHIA, b Burbank, Calif, Dec 19, 47; m 81; c 1. NEUROBIOLOGY. *Educ:* Univ Calif, Irvine, BS, 71; Univ Calif, Los Angeles, PhD(anat), 77. *Prof Exp:* Fel biochem, Mt Sinai Med Sch, 77-79; res assoc neurobiol, Vet Admin, Kansas City, 79-80; ASST PROF BIOL SCI, NORTHERN ILL UNIV, 80- *Concurrent Pos:* Instr, Univ Calif, Irvine, 76. *Mem:* Soc Neurosci; Am Asn Anatomists. *Res:* Developmental neurobiology including effects of alcohol and radiation on adrenergic receptors, and neuron development. *Mailing Add:* Dept Biol Sci Northern Ill Univ De Kalb IL 60115

NYSTED, LEONARD NORMAN, b Marshfield, Wis, May 17, 27; m 47; c 2. PHARMACEUTICAL CHEMISTRY. *Educ:* St Olaf Col, BS, 51. *Prof Exp:* Preparations & res chemist, G D Searle & Co, 51-56; dir chem res, Duraclean Co, 56-58; res chemist, 58-64, SR RES INVESTR, G D SEARLE & CO, 64- *Mem:* Am Chem Soc. *Res:* Medicinal chemistry particularly steroids and prostaglandins, insecticides and detergents. *Mailing Add:* 617 Rice St Highland Park IL 60035

NYSTROM, ROBERT FORREST, b Chicago, Ill, May 30, 20; m 44; c 3. ORGANIC CHEMISTRY, RADIOCHEMISTRY. *Educ:* Univ Chicago, BS, 42, PhD(org chem), 47. *Prof Exp:* Asst, Off Sci Res & Develop Proj, Univ Chicago, 43-45; res chemist, Monsanto Chem Co, Tenn, 47-48; asst prof chem & animal sci, 48-53, assoc prof chem, 53-61, prof, 61-80, dir radioisotope lab, 53-80, EMER PROF, UNIV ILL, URBANA, 80- *Honors & Awards:* Radiation Indust Award, Am Nuclear Soc, 68. *Mem:* Am Chem Soc. *Res:* Reduction of organic compounds by lithium aluminum hydride, lithium borohydride and complex hydrides; radiation-induced reactions; organic reactions and mechanisms with carbon 14; tritium. *Mailing Add:* PO Box 309 Lake Hamilton FL 33851

NYVALL, ROBERT FREDERICK, b Thief River Falls, Minn, Aug 23, 39; m 62; c 2. PLANT PATHOLOGY. *Educ:* Univ Minn, BS, 65, MS, 66, PhD(plant path), 69. *Prof Exp:* Asst prof, 70-73, assoc prof, 73-81, PROF PLANT PATH, IOWA STATE UNIV, 81-, EXTEN PLANT PATHOLOGIST, 70- *Mem:* Am Inst Biol Sci; Am Phytopath Soc. *Res:* Ecology of soil; root rot and wilt fungi. *Mailing Add:* Dept of Bot & Plant Path Iowa State Univ Ames IA 50010

NYYSSONEN, DIANA, b Cambridge, Mass. OPTICS. *Educ:* Boston Univ, BA, 65; Univ Rochester, PhD(optics), 75. *Prof Exp:* Staff scientist optics, Tech Oper, Inc, 64-68; PHYSICIST OPTICS, NAT BUR STANDARDS, 69-, GROUP LEADER, 80- *Mem:* Optical Soc Am; Soc Photo-Optical Instrumentation Engrs. *Res:* Densitometry, microdensitometry, optical systems evaluation and application of the theory of partial coherence to measurement problems on optical imagery and diffracted fields, integrated-circuit metrology. *Mailing Add:* A331 Tech Nat Bur Standards Washington DC 20234

O

OACE, SUSAN M, b St Paul, Minn, Nov 10, 41. NUTRITION. *Educ:* Univ Minn, St Paul, BS, 63; Univ Calif, Berkeley, PhD(nutrit), 67. *Prof Exp:* Res nutritionist, Univ Calif, Berkeley, 67-68; asst prof nutrit, Univ Calif, Davis, 68-73; asst prof, 73-75, dir, Coord Dietetics Prog, 76-80, ASSOC PROF NUTRIT, UNIV CALIF, BERKELEY, 75- *Concurrent Pos:* Ed, J Nutrut Educ, 79-82; mem joint coun, Foods & Agr Sci, 79-82. *Mem:* Am Inst Nutrit; Am Dietetic Asn; NY Acad Sci; Soc Nutrit Educ; Soc Exp Biol & Med. *Res:* Metabolic interrelationships among folic acid, vitamin B12 and methionine; interaction of intestinal microflora with nutritional and health status of host; dietary fiber. *Mailing Add:* Dept of Nutrit Sci Univ of Calif Berkeley CA 94720

OAKBERG, EUGENE FRANKLIN, b Moline, Ill, Oct 4, 16; m 43, 64; c 4. GENETICS. *Educ:* Monmouth Col, BS, 40; Kans State Col, MS, 42; Iowa State Col, PhD(genetics), 45. *Prof Exp:* Asst zool, Kans State Col, 40-42; instr & res assoc genetics, Iowa State Col, 44-45; med bacteriologist, Off Sci Res & Develop, Genetics Dept, Carnegie Inst, 45, res assoc, Cold Spring Harbor, NY, 46; histologist, Mich State Col, 47-50; asst prof genetics, Iowa State Col, 51; SR BIOLOGIST, OAK RIDGE NAT LAB, 52- *Mem:* AAAS; Genetics Soc Am; Radiation Res Soc; Environ Mutagen Soc. *Res:* Mouse genetics; mammalian gametogenesis; radiobiology. *Mailing Add:* Biol Div Oak Ridge Nat Lab PO Box Y Oak Ridge TN 37830

OAKES, BILLY DEAN, b Tulsa, Okla, Sept 5, 28; m 50; c 2. ORGANIC CHEMISTRY. *Educ:* Okla State Univ, BS, 50; Univ Wichita, MS, 52. *Prof Exp:* AEC asst, Univ Wichita, 52 & Ga Inst Technol, 52-53; res chemist, Dowell Div, 53-62 & Chem Dept Res Lab, Mich, 62-64, proj leader, 64-69, res specialist, Resources Res Dept, 69-76, RES LEADER, PROCESS RES & ENG DEP, TEX DIV, DOW CHEM CO, 76- *Mem:* Am Chem Soc; Nat Asn Corrosion Eng. *Res:* Corrosion studies; corrosion inhibitors for aqueous solutions, primarily acids, amine gas processing solvents and automotive engine coolants; environmental modifications designed to allow the use of low cost construction materials in sea water desalination plants. *Mailing Add:* Process Res & Eng Dept B-2008 Bldg Dow Chem Co US Am Freeport TX 77541

OAKES, MELVIN ERVIN LOUIS, b Vicksburg, Miss, May 11, 36; m 63; c 3. PLASMA PHYSICS. *Educ:* Fla State Univ, PhD(plasma physics), 64. *Prof Exp:* Asst physics, Fla State Univ, 58-60 & 60-64; physicist, Army Res Guided Missile Agency, Redstone Arsenal, 60; asst prof physics, Univ Ga, 64; res assoc, 64-65, from asst prof to assoc prof, 65-75, PROF PHYSICS, UNIV TEX, AUSTIN, 75- *Mem:* Am Phys Soc; Am Asn Physics Teachers. *Res:* Electromagnetic interaction with plasmas; plasma waves and radio frequency heating. *Mailing Add:* Dept of Physics Univ of Tex Austin TX 78712

OAKES, ROBERT JAMES, b Minneapolis, Minn, Jan 21, 36; m 55; c 2. THEORETICAL HIGH ENERGY PHYSICS. *Educ:* Univ Minn, BS, 57, MS, 59, PhD(physics), 62. *Prof Exp:* NSF fel physics, Stanford Univ, 62-64, lectr, 64, asst prof, 64-68; assoc prof, 68-70, PROF PHYSICS, NORTHWESTERN UNIV, 70-, PROF PHYSICS & ASTRON, 76- *Concurrent Pos:* A P Sloan Found res fel, 65-67; vis scientist, Europ Orgn Nuclear Res, 66-67; mem, Inst Advan Study, 67-68; vis scientist, Deutsches Elektron-Synchrotron, 71-72 & Los Alamos Sci Lab, 71-; mem, Deep Underwater Muon & Neutrino Detection steering comt, 78- *Mem:* Fel Am Phys Soc; NY Acad Sci. *Res:* Strong interactions; theoretical, high energy and nuclear physics; field theory; weak interactions. *Mailing Add:* Dept of Physics Northwestern Univ Evanston IL 60201

OAKES, THOMAS WYATT, b Danville, Va, June 14, 50; m 74. ENVIRONMENTAL ENGINEERING, HEALTH PHYSICS. *Educ:* Va Polytech Inst & State Univ, BS, 73, MS, 75; Univ Tenn, MS, 80. *Prof Exp:* Health physicist, Va Polytech Inst & State Univ, 73-74; engr radiation, Nuclear Div, Babcock & Wilcox, 74-75; health physics supvr monitoring group, 75-76, group leader environ monitoring, 76-77, sect head, Environ Surveillance Sect, 77-79, ENVIRON COORDR, OAK RIDGE NAT LAB, 78-, DEPT HEAD, 79- *Mem:* AAAS; Health Physics Soc; Am Nuclear Soc; NY Acad Sci; Am Indust Hyg Asn. *Res:* Environmental surveillance; quality assurance; determinations of pollutant assessment of environments impact of energy system; biological monitoring neutron activation; health physics; environment health; cost-benefit analysis. *Mailing Add:* Environ Surveillance Sect PO Box X Oak Ridge TN 37830

OAKESHOTT, GORDON B, b Oakland, Calif, Dec 24, 04; m 29; c 3. GEOLOGY. *Educ:* Univ Calif, BS, 28, MS, 29; Univ Southern Calif, PhD(geol), 36. *Prof Exp:* Asst field geologist, Shell Oil Co, 29-30; instr earth sci, Compton Dist Jr Col, 30-48; supv mining geologist, Calif State Div Mines & Geol, 48-56, dep chief, 56-57 & 59-72, actg chief, 58; CONSULT GEOLOGIST, 73- *Concurrent Pos:* Instr geol, Calif State Univ, Sacramento, 73 & Calif State Univ, San Francisco, 75. *Mem:* Fel AAAS; fel & hon mem Geol Soc Am; Asn Prof Geol Scientists; Seismol Soc Am; Nat Asn Geol Teachers (pres, 71). *Res:* Geology of the San Gabriel Mountains; stratigraphy of California Coast and transverse ranges; surface faulting and associated earthquakes; geology of California. *Mailing Add:* 3040 Totterdell St Oakland CA 94611

OAKFORD, ROBERT VERNON, b Winfield, Kans, Nov 3, 17; m 48; c 3. INDUSTRIAL ENGINEERING. *Educ:* Stanford Univ, BA, 40, MS, 56. *Prof Exp:* Engr, Northrop Aircraft, Inc, 41-45; secy-treas, Oakford Gas & Appliance Corp, 45-49; engr, US Govt, 51-53; lectr, 55-57, assoc prof, 57-62, prof, 62-77, EMER PROF INDUST ENG, STANFORD UNIV, 77- *Concurrent Pos:* Consult, McKinsey & Co, 57-62 & Res Div, State Dept Correction, Calif, 59-62. *Mem:* AAAS; Am Soc Eng Educ. *Res:* Theory and practice of school scheduling; engineering economy and capital budgeting. *Mailing Add:* Dept of Indust Eng Stanford Univ Stanford CA 94305

OAKLEY, BRUCE, b Philadelphia, Pa, Oct 22, 36; m 58; c 2. NEUROBIOLOGY. *Educ:* Swarthmore Col, BA, 58; Brown Univ, MSc, 60, PhD(psychol), 62. *Prof Exp:* Asst prof psychol, Brown Univ, 62-63; Nat Acad Sci-Nat Res Coun sr fel physiol, Royal Vet Col Sweden, 63-64; USPHS fel zool, Univ Calif, Los Angeles, 64-65, asst res zoologist, 65-66; asst prof, 66-71, assoc prof zool, 71-76, PROF BIOL SCI, UNIV MICH, ANN ARBOR, 76- *Mem:* AAAS; Am Soc Zool; NY Acad Sci; Soc Neurosci. *Res:* Physiology and behavior of taste; neural mechanism of preference and aversion; sensory receptors and coding; trophic functions of neurons; developmental neurobiology. *Mailing Add:* Neurosci Bldg Univ of Mich Ann Arbor MI 48104

OAKLEY, BURKS, II, bioengineering, see previous edition

OAKLEY, DAVID CHARLES, b Marysville, Calif, July 4, 29; m 52; c 3. SCIENCE ADMINISTRATION, NUCLEAR SCIENCE. *Educ:* Calif Inst Technol, BS, 50, MS, 52, PhD(physics & math), 55. *Prof Exp:* Physicist nuclear sci, Lawrence Livermore Lab, 54-73; asst dept dir for testing, Nuclear Sci Admin, Defense Nuclear Agency, 73-76; PHYSICIST NUCLEAR SCI, LAWRENCE LIVERMORE LAB, 76- *Mem:* Am Phys Soc; Sigma Xi. *Res:* Administration of underground nuclear testing of nuclear weapons effects on materials and systems of military interest. *Mailing Add:* Lawrence Livermore Lab PO Box 808 Livermore CA 94550

OAKS, B ANN, b Winnipeg, Man, June 4, 29. PLANT PHYSIOLOGY. *Educ:* Univ Toronto, BA, 51; Univ Sask, MA, 54, PhD(plant physiol), 58. *Prof Exp:* Res asst plant physiol, Univ Man, 53-54; Von Humboldt grant, Bact Inst, Feising, Ger, 58-60; res assoc biol sci, Purdue Univ, 60-64; from asst prof to assoc prof, 64-74, PROF BIOL, McMASTER UNIV, 74- *Mem:* Am Soc Plant Physiol; Can Soc Plant Physiol. *Res:* Intermediary metabolism in plants; processes regulating development in seedlings. *Mailing Add:* Dept of Biol McMaster Univ Hamilton ON L8S 4L8 Can

OAKS, EMILY CAYWOOD JORDAN, b Pittsburgh, Pa, Feb 15, 39; m 61; c 2. VERTEBRATE ZOOLOGY. *Educ:* Rice Univ, BA, 61; Yale Univ, MS, 64, PhD(biol), 67. *Prof Exp:* asst prof zool, 67-81, ASST PROF BIOL, UTAH STATE UNIV, 81- *Mem:* Am Soc Mammal; Soc Study Evolution. *Res:* Anatomy and adaptive function of the middle ear in mammals. *Mailing Add:* Dept of Biol Utah State Univ Logan UT 84322

OAKS, J HOWARD, b Camden, NJ, Mar 3, 30; m 57; c 5. DENTISTRY. *Educ:* Wesleyan Univ, BA, 52; Harvard Univ, DMD, 56. *Prof Exp:* Instr oper dent, Sch Dent Med, Harvard Univ, 56-64, lectr oper dent & assoc dean, 64-68, actg dean, 67-68; prof dent med & dean, Sch Dent Med, 68-74, VPRES HEALTH SCI, STATE UNIV NY STONY BROOK, 74- *Concurrent Pos:* Mem dent educ rev comt, Bur Health Manpower Educ, NIH, 67-70, consult, div physician & health professions educ, 70-; vpres for Deans, Am Asn Dent Schs, 72-73. *Mailing Add:* Off VPres Health Sci Ctr State Univ NY Stony Brook NY 11794

OAKS, JOHN ADAMS, b Alma, Mich, Apr 8, 42; m 65; c 2. CELL BIOLOGY, PARASITOLOGY. *Educ:* Colby Col, BA, 64; Tulane Univ, MS, 68, PhD(cell biol), 70. *Prof Exp:* Asst prof parasitol, Tulane Univ, 70-73; asst prof, 73-79, ASSOC PROF, DEPT ANAT, COL MED, UNIV IOWA, 79- *Mem:* AAAS; Am Soc Cell Biol; Histochem Soc; Am Soc Parasitol; Am Soc Trop Med Hyg. *Res:* Mechanisms of plasma membrane synthesis; structural and functional aspects of helminth surfaces; mechanism of host cellular reactions to Toxocara canis; comparative aspects of free-living and parasitic helminth epithelia. *Mailing Add:* Dept Anat Col Med Univ Iowa Iowa City IA 52240

OAKS, ROBERT QUINCY, JR, b Houston, Tex, Aug 29, 38; m 61; c 2. GEOLOGY. *Educ:* Rice Univ, BA, 60; Yale Univ, PhD(geol), 65. *Prof Exp:* Res geologist, Jersey Prod Res Co, 64 & Esso Prod Res Co, 65-66; from asst prof to assoc prof, 66-79, PROF GEOL, UTAH STATE UNIV, 79- *Mem:* AAAS; Soc Econ Paleont & Mineral; Geol Soc Am; Am Asn Petrol Geol; Int Asn Sedimentol. *Res:* Ordovician quartzites in northern Utah and southen Idaho; the role of fine-grained sediments in promoting erosion in mountain lands; regolith classification for land-management needs; Cambrian carbonates and sandstones in northern Utah and southern Idaho; mudflows and debrisflows on alluvial fans in Death Valley and Eureka Valley, Calif; structure and stratigraphy of northeastern Amadeus basin, Central Australia. *Mailing Add:* Dept of Geol Utah State Univ Logan UT 84322

OAKS, WILBUR W, b Philadelphia, Pa, Oct 12, 28; m 54; c 3. INTERNAL MEDICINE. *Educ:* Lafayette Col, BS, 51; Hahnemann Med Col, MD, 55. *Prof Exp:* From instr to assoc prof med, 61-69, teaching coordr & dir postgrad educ, 62-70, PROF MED & DIR DIV GEN INTERNAL MED, HAHNEMANN MED COL, 69-, CHMN DEPT MED, 73- *Concurrent Pos:* Staff physician, Hahnemann Hosp, 61- *Honors & Awards:* Christian R & Mary F Lindback Found Award. *Mem:* Am Fedn Clin Res; AMA; Am Col Chest Physicians; Asn Am Med Cols. *Res:* Hypertension. *Mailing Add:* Div of Gen Internal Med Hahnemann Med Col Philadelphia PA 19102

OALMANN, MARGARET CLAIRE, b Covington, La, Aug 16, 29; m 62; c 3. EPIDEMIOLOGY. *Educ:* La State Univ, BSNEd, 56; Tulane Univ, MPH, 58, DPH(chronic dis, epidemiol), 60. *Prof Exp:* From actg head nurse to head nurse, Charity Hosp La, New Orleans, 49-53, clin instr, 53-57; res assoc, Tulane Univ, 60-62; from instr to asst prof path, 62-70, asst prof, 70-72, ASSOC PROF PATH, PUB HEALTH & PREV MED, MED CTR, LA STATE UNIV, NEW ORLEANS, 72- *Concurrent Pos:* Vis scientist, Charity Hosp, La, 60-; epidemiol consult mortality in nuns, Am Cancer Soc Grant, 63- *Mem:* AAAS; fel Am Heart Asn; Am Pub Health Asn; Asn Teachers Prev Med; Royal Soc Health. *Res:* Epidemiology of cardiovascular disease and cancer. *Mailing Add:* Dept of Path La State Univ Med Ctr New Orleans LA 70112

OATES, GORDON CEDRIC, b Vancouver, BC, Feb 28, 32; m 61; c 4. AERONAUTICAL ENGINEERING. *Educ:* Univ BC, BASc, 54; Univ Birmingham, MSc, 56; Calif Inst Technol, PhD(mech eng), 59. *Prof Exp:* From asst prof to assoc prof aeronaut eng, Mass Inst Technol, 59-67; assoc prof, 67-70, PROF AERONAUT ENG, UNIV WASH, 70- *Concurrent Pos:* Guest prof, Royal Inst Technol, Stockholm, 70; distinguished vis prof, US Air Force Acad, 75-76. *Mem:* Am Inst Aeronaut & Astronaut; Am Soc Eng Educ; Am Soc Mech Engrs. *Res:* Propulsion and energy conversion; bio-fluid mechanics. *Mailing Add:* Dept of Aeronaut & Astronaut FS-10 Univ of Wash Seattle WA 98105

OATES, JIMMIE C, b Memphis, Tenn, Apr 14, 33; m 54; c 2. PHYSICS. *Educ:* Memphis State Univ, BS, 58; Vanderbilt Univ, MS, 60, PhD(physics), 63. *Prof Exp:* Assoc prof, 62-70, PROF PHYSICS, QUEENS COL, NC, 70- *Res:* Bioacoustics. *Mailing Add:* Dept of Physics Queens Col Charlotte NC 28207

OATES, JOHN ALEXANDER, b Fayetteville, NC, Apr 23, 32; m 56; c 3. CLINICAL PHARMACOLOGY, INTERNAL MEDICINE. *Educ:* Wake Forest Col, BS, 53; Bowman Gray Sch Med, MD, 56. *Prof Exp:* Intern internal med, New York Hosp, 56-57, asst resident, 57-58; clin assoc exp therapeut, Nat Heart Inst, 58-61; asst resident med, New York Hosp, 61-62; sr investr, 62-63; from asst prof to assoc prof pharmacol & med, 63-69, PROF PHARMACOL & MED, SCH MED, VANDERBILT UNIV, 69- *Concurrent Pos:* Burroughs Wellcome scholar clin pharmacol, 65-70; counr, Asn Am Physicians, 75- *Honors & Awards:* Am Soc PHarmacol & Exp Therapeut Award Exp Therapeut, 69. *Mem:* Am Soc Clin Invest; Asn Am Physicians (secy, 70-75); Am Soc Pharmacol & Exp Therapeut. *Res:* Vasoactive amines and peptides; prostaglandins; antihypertensive agents; autonomic pharmacology. *Mailing Add:* Vanderbilt Univ Sch of Med Nashville TN 37232

OATES, RICHARD PATRICK, b Gary, Ind, Mar 17, 37. BIOSTATISTICS. *Educ:* Purdue Univ, BS, 58; Iowa State Univ, MS, 60, PhD(bact), 64. *Prof Exp:* Asst prof, 65-75, ASSOC PROF BIOSTATIST, STATE UNIV NY UPSTATE MED CTR, 75- *Concurrent Pos:* NIH fel, Iowa State Univ, 64-65. *Mem:* Biomet Soc; Sigma Xi; NY Acad Sci. *Res:* Medical research; epidemiology. *Mailing Add:* Dept Prev Med State Univ NY Upstate Med Ctr Syracuse NY 13210

OATMAN, EARL R, b Sylvester, Tex, Oct 21, 20; m 53; c 3. ENTOMOLOGY. *Educ:* Asst instr entom, Univ Mo, 51-52; res asst entom & parasitol, Univ Calif, Berkeley, 53-56; from asst prof to assoc prof entom, Univ Wis, 56-62; from asst entomlogist to assoc entomologist, 62-72, ENTOMOLOGIST, DIV BIOL CONTROL, UNIV CALIF, RIVERSIDE, 72-, PROF ENTOM, 75- *Mem:* Entom Soc Am. *Res:* Population ecology and biological control of insects and mites associated with agronomic and horticultural crops. *Mailing Add:* Div of Biol Control Univ of Calif Riverside CA 92502

O'BANNON, JOHN HORATIO, b West Palm Beach, Fla, Sept 23, 26; m 52; c 3. NEMATOLOGY. *Educ:* Univ Ariz, BS & MS, 57; Ariz State Univ, PhD(bot), 65. *Prof Exp:* Nematologist, Cotton Res Ctr, Ariz, 57-65, nematologist, nematol invests, Agr Res Serv, USDA, Orlando, 65-78; NEMATOLOGIST, IRRIG AGR RES & EXT CTR, WASH STATE UNIV, 78- *Mem:* Am Phytopath Soc; Soc Nematologists (pres, 74-75). *Res:* Nematology concerned with the biology, ecology and control of plant parasitic nematodes. *Mailing Add:* Irrig Agr Res & Ext Ctr Wash State Univ Box 30 Prosser WA 99350

O'BARR, RICHARD DALE, b Thorsby, Ala, Apr 26, 32; m 59; c 3. PLANT NUTRITION, PLANT ANALYSIS. *Educ:* Ala Polytech Inst, BS, 52; Univ Ga, MS, 71, PhD(plant sci), 74. *Prof Exp:* Asst prof hort, 74-79, ASSOC PROF & SUPT HORT & ADMIN, PECAN RES & EXTENSION STA, LA STATE UNIV, 79- *Mem:* Am Soc Hort Sci. *Res:* Physiology of bearing pecan trees; germination and seed sources for rootstocks, toxicity studies and colchicine; new varieties are studied for geographical adaptability and possible release; tissue analysis of leaves, shucks, shells and kernels to determine nutritional status of trees. *Mailing Add:* Pecan Sta La State Univ PO Box 5519 Shreveport LA 71105

O'BARR, WILLIAM MCALSTON, b Sylvania, Ga, Dec 1, 42; m 65; c 2. ANTHROPOLOGY. *Educ:* Emory Univ, BA, 64; Northwestern Univ, MA, 66, PhD(anthrop), 69. *Prof Exp:* Res assoc med sociol, Communicable Dis Ctr, USPHS, 64-67; res assoc social anthrop, Univ Dar es Salaam, 67-68; asst prof, 69-74, ASSOC PROF ANTHROP, DUKE UNIV, 74- *Concurrent Pos:* Vis assoc prof, Dalhousie Univ, Can, 76, Northwestern Univ, 78. *Mem:* Am Anthrop Asn; African Studies Asn; Am Ethnol Soc; Royal Anthrop Inst Gt Brit. *Res:* Language of politics and law; advertising language; bilingualism; African ethnology; political anthropology. *Mailing Add:* Dept of Anthrop Duke Univ Durham NC 27706

OBBINK, RUSSELL C, b Omaha, Nebr, Sept 29, 24; m 46; c 5. ANALYTICAL CHEMISTRY, ORGANIC CHEMISTRY. *Educ:* Univ Portland, BSc, 53. *Prof Exp:* Analyst, Alcoa, Aluminum Co Am, Wash, 49-53, anal chemist, 53-57, sr chemist, 57-65, res chemist, Alcoa Res Labs, Aluminum Co Am, 65-67, group leader, 67-70, sect head, 73-78, sci assoc, Anal Chem Div, Alcoa Tech Ctr, 78-81; RES ASSOC, AM SOC TESTING & MAT, 80- *Mem:* Sigma Xi; Fine Particle Soc; Am Soc Testing & Mat. *Res:* Development of analytical methods for use in aluminum industry. *Mailing Add:* 636 Vance Dr Lower Burrell PA 15068

OBEAR, FREDERICK W, b Malden, Mass, June 9, 35; m 59; c 3. INORGANIC CHEMISTRY. *Educ:* Lowell Tech Inst, BS, 56; Univ NH, PhD(chem), 61. *Prof Exp:* Asst chem, Univ NH, 56-58, fel, 58-60; asst prof, Oakland Univ, 60-66, dean freshmen, 64-66, asst provost, 65-68, vprovost, 68-70, assoc prof chem, 66-78, vpres acad affairs & provost, 70-81; PROF CHEM, UNIV TENN, 78-, CHANCELLOR, 81- *Mem:* Am Chem Soc; AAAS. *Res:* Transition metal inorganic chemistry structure and mechanisms; academic administration. *Mailing Add:* Off Chancellor Univ Tenn Chattanooga TN 37402

OBENCHAIN, CARL F(RANKLIN), b Hailey, Idaho, Apr 25, 35; m 61; c 2. NUCLEAR ENGINEERING. *Educ:* Ore State Univ, BS, 58; Univ Mich, MSE, 59 & 61, PhD(chem eng), 64; Univ Idaho, MBA, 77. *Prof Exp:* Reactor analyst-physicist, Atomic Energy Div, Phillips Petrol Co, 64-67, group leader, 67-69; power reactor safety anal group, Idaho Nuclear Corp, 69-71; group supvr, Nuclear Safety Prog Div, Aerojet Nuclear Corp, 71-74; proj mgr, Reactor Behav Div, Aerojet Nuclear & EG&G, Idaho, 74-77; MGR, REGULATORY SUPPORT BR, EG&G, IDAHO, 77- *Concurrent Pos:* Adj prof, Univ Idaho, 65- *Mem:* AAAS; Am Inst Chem Engrs; Am Nuclear Soc. *Res:* Solute interactions in dilute liquid metal systems; thermal-hydraulic analysis of nuclear reactors; water reactor safety. *Mailing Add:* EG&G Idaho Inc PO Box 1625 Idaho Falls ID 83415

OBENCHAIN, FREDERICK DECROES, acarology, insect physiology, see previous edition

OBENCHAIN, ROBERT LINCOLN, b Indianapolis, Ind, Apr 2, 41; m 69, 76; c 1. STATISTICS, OPERATIONS RESEARCH. *Educ:* Northwestern Univ, BS, 64; Univ NC, Chapel Hill, PhD(statist), 69. *Prof Exp:* MEM TECH STAFF STATIST, BELL TELEPHONE LABS, 69- *Concurrent Pos:* Vis assoc prof statist, Univ Wis-Madison, 79-80; assoc ed, J Am Statist Asn, 80- *Mem:* Am Statist Asn; Inst Math Statist. *Res:* Biased linear regression techniques; multivariate analysis. *Mailing Add:* Bell Telephone Labs WB-1D312 Holmdel NJ 07733

OBENDORF, RALPH LOUIS, b Milan, Ind, July 11, 38. PLANT PHYSIOLOGY, AGRONOMY. *Educ:* Purdue Univ, BS, 60; Univ California, Davis, MS, 62, PhD(plant physiol), 66. *Prof Exp:* Asst prof field crop sci, 66-71, assoc prof, 71-77, mem fac crop sci, 77-81, PROF AGRON, CORNELL UNIV, 81- *Concurrent Pos:* Vis scientist, Inst Cancer Res, Philadelphia, Pa, 72-73. *Mem:* AAAS; Am Soc Plant Physiol; Am Inst Biol Sci; Crop Sci Soc Am; Am Soc Agron. *Res:* Physiology and biochemistry of cold sensitivity during grain formation, germination and seedling growth, greening and photosynthetic development. *Mailing Add:* Dept of Agron Cornell Univ Ithaca NY 14853

OBENLAND, CLAYTON O, b Kansas City, Mo, Dec 22, 12; m 41; c 1. INDUSTRIAL CHEMISTRY. *Educ:* Kans State Univ, BS, 35, MS, 50. *Prof Exp:* Asst chemist, Monsanto Chem Co, Ill, 39-41, tech asst plant develop, 41-42 & 46-47, asst supvr chem prod, 47-49; scheduler prod control, Gen Aniline Works, NY, 50-51; chemist, Olin-Mathieson Chem Corp, NY, 52-56, group leader pre-pilot lab, 56-59, sr chemist, Conn, 59-69; patent agent, Carborundum Co, Niagara Falls, 69-75; LAB SUPVR, NIAGARA UNIV, 67- *Mem:* Am Chem Soc. *Res:* Synthetic organic and inorganic chemistry, especially boron chemistry. *Mailing Add:* 62 Culpepper Rd Williamsville NY 14221

OBENSHAIN, FELIX EDWARD, b Pikeville, Ky, Mar 31, 28; m 50; c 4. NUCLEAR PHYSICS, SOLID STATE PHYSICS. *Educ:* Va Polytech Inst, BS, 52; Univ Pittsburgh, PhD(physics), 60. *Prof Exp:* Physicist, Atomic Power Div, Westinghouse Elec Corp, 52-56; PHYSICIST, OAK RIDGE NAT LAB, 59-; PROF PHYSICS, UNIV TENN, KNOXVILLE, 68- *Concurrent Pos:* Partic, AEC Int Sci Exchange Prog, Cent Inst Nuclear Res, Karlsruhe, Ger, 65-66. *Mem:* Fel Am Phys Soc. *Res:* Heavy-ion nuclear reactions, fusion and fission studies; applications of Mossbauer effect in nuclear and solid state physics; positron polarization as related to C and P violation in weak interactions. *Mailing Add:* Oak Ridge Nat Lab PO Box X Oak Ridge TN 37830

OBER, DAVID RAY, b Garrett, Ind, Dec 6, 39; m 63; c 2. NUCLEAR PHYSICS. *Educ:* Manchester Col, BA, 62; Purdue Univ, MS, 64, PhD(physics), 68. *Prof Exp:* Teaching asst physics, Purdue Univ, 62-66, res asst, 66-68; asst prof, 68-72, assoc prof, 72-76, PROF PHYSICS, BALL STATE UNIV, 76- *Mem:* Am Asn Physics Teachers; Am Phys Soc. *Res:* Low energy nuclear physics. *Mailing Add:* Dept of Physics Ball State Univ Muncie IN 47306

OBER, ROBERT ELWOOD, b Springfield, Ohio, Nov 13, 31; m 55; c 3. DRUG METABOLISM, NEW DRUG DEVELOPMENT. *Educ:* Ohio State Univ, BS, 53, MS, 55; Univ Ill, PhD(biochem), 58. *Prof Exp:* From assoc res biochemist to res biochemist, Res Div, Parke, Davis & Co, 58-66; assoc prof, Col Pharm, Ohio State Univ, 66-69; head biochem pharmacol group, 69-70, supvr drug metab, 70-73, MGR DRUG METAB, RIKER LABS, 3M CO, 73-; ASSOC PROF PHARM, UNIV MINN, MINNEAPOLIS, 70- *Mem:* Am Chem Soc; Acad Pharmaceut Sci; AAAS; Sigma Xi. *Res:* Laboratory and clinical drug metabolism and pharmacokinetics; biochemistry of fatty acids; steroids; radiotracer methodology; synthesis of radioisotopically labelled compounds. *Mailing Add:* 3M Co Riker Labs Bldg 270-35-05 3M Ctr St Paul MN 55144

OBER, WILLIAM B, b Boston, Mass, May 15, 20; m 52; c 2. PATHOLOGY. *Educ:* Harvard Col, AB, 41; Boston Univ, MD, 46. *Prof Exp:* Pathologist, Boston Lying-in Hosp, 53-55; assoc prof & clin prof path, NY Med Col, 60-72; prof path, Mt Sinai Sch Med, 72-78; pathologist, Beth Israel Hosp, 70-78; DIR LABS, HACKENSACK HOSP, HACKENSACK, NJ, 78- *Concurrent Pos:* Instr path, Harvard Med Sch, 53-55; dir labs path, Knickerbocker Hosp, 56-70; consult pathologist, First US Army Med Lab, 58-68, Margaret Sanger Res Bur, 60-73, Lutheran Hosp, Brooklyn, 65-, St Barnabas Hosp, Bronx, 66- & Roger Williams Hosp, Providence, RI, 68-; vis prof path, NJ Col Med, Univ Med & Dent NJ, 78- *Mem:* Royal Micros Soc; Am Asn Pathologists; NY Acad Med; Int Acad Path; Am Asn Path & Bact. *Res:* Experimental production of toxaemia of pregnancy; medical analysis of literary problems. *Mailing Add:* 10 Nathan D Perlman Pl New York NY 10003

OBERDING, DENNIS GEORGE, b Plum City, Wis, Dec 4, 35; m 56; c 5. ANALYTICAL CHEMISTRY, SPECTROSCOPY. *Educ:* Univ Wis-River Falls, BS, 60. *Prof Exp:* Chemist, 60-73, sr anal chemist, 73-77, SUPVR INSTRUMENT ANAL, ETHYL CORP RES LABS, 77- *Mem:* Am Chem Soc. *Res:* Spectroscopy and chromatography specifically, infrared; nuclear magnetic resonance and high pressure liquid chromatography. *Mailing Add:* Ethyl Corp Res Labs 1600 W 8 Michigan Rd Ferndale MI 48220

OBERDORFER, MICHAEL DOUGLAS, b Athens, Ohio, Aug 29, 42; m 68; c 1. DEVELOPMENTAL NEUROBIOLOGY. *Educ:* Rockford Col, BA, 66; Univ Wis-Madison, PhD(zool), 75. *Prof Exp:* NIH fel neurosci, Dept Anat, Univ Wis, 75-77; asst prof, Dept Neurobiol, Univ Tex Med Sch Houston, 77-82; PANEL DIR DEVELOP NEUROSCI, NSF, 82- *Mem:* AAAS; Am Soc Cell Biol; Soc Neurosci. *Res:* Anatomical development of mammalian visual systems. *Mailing Add:* Dept Neurobiol & Anat Health Sci Ctr Univ Tex PO Box 20708 Houston TX 77025

OBERDÖRSTER, GÜNTER, b Cologne, Ger, Feb 27, 39; m 68; c 2. INHALATION TOXICOLOGY. *Educ:* Univ Giessen, Dr med vet, 66. *Prof Exp:* Sci staff mem, Lab Pharmacol, Tropon Co, 66-67; asst prof physiol, Inst Normal & Pathol Physiol, Univ Cologne, 68-71; sci staff mem toxicol, Inst Toxicol & Aerosol Res, 71-79; ASSOC PROF INHALATION TOXICOL, UNIV ROCHESTER, 79- *Concurrent Pos:* Vis asst prof, Univ Rochester, 75-76; appointee, Contact Group Heavy Metals, European Commission, 77-79. *Mem:* Ger Physiol Soc; Asn Aerosol Res; Am Thoracic Soc; Am Col Vet Toxicol. *Res:* Effects of air pollutants (fibers, heavy metals, oxidants, particles of combustion processes); lung clearance mechanisms (lymphatics, macrophages); effects of air contaminants on lung permeability; effects of chelating agents after inhalation of heavy metal aerosols. *Mailing Add:* Dept RBB Med Ctr Univ Rochester Rochester NY 14642

OBERENDER, FREDERICK G, b Cambridge, Mass, Feb 6, 33; m 57; c 4. ORGANIC CHEMISTRY, PETROLEUM CHEMISTRY. *Educ:* Trinity Col, Conn, BS, 54, MS, 56; Pa State Univ, PhD(org chem), 60. *Prof Exp:* Chemist, 59-60, sr chemist, 60-64, res chemist, 64-69, group leader, 69-73, asst supvr, 73-77, SUPVR, TEXACO, INC, 77- *Mem:* Sigma Xi; Am Chem Soc. *Res:* Synthetic lubricants; lubricant additives; polynuclear aromatic hydrocarbons; chelate polymers; nitrogen containing heterocyclics; fuel technology. *Mailing Add:* RD 4 Hopewell Rd Wappingers Falls NY 12590

OBERHARDT, BRUCE J, biophysics, see previous edition

OBERHELMAN, HARRY ALVIN, JR, b Chicago, Ill, Nov 15, 23; m 46; c 5. SURGERY. *Educ:* Univ Chicago, BS, 46, MD, 47. *Prof Exp:* From instr to assoc prof, Sch Med, Univ Chicago, 56-60; assoc prof, 60-64, PROF SURG, SCH MED, STANFORD UNIV, 64- *Concurrent Pos:* USPHS grant, Stanford Univ, 60-68; dir, Am Bd Surg, 72-78. *Mem:* Soc Univ Surg; Am Surg Asn; Am Gastroenterol Asn. *Res:* Gastrointestinal physiology, with emphasis on gastric motility and inflammatory diseases of the pancreas and colon. *Mailing Add:* 300 Pasteur Dr Stanford CA 94305

OBERHOFER, EDWARD SAMUEL, b Elizabeth, NJ, May 11, 39; m 67; c 2. NUCLEAR PHYSICS. *Educ:* NC State Univ, BS, 61, MS, 64, PhD(physics), 67. *Prof Exp:* Asst prof, 67-74, ASSOC PROF PHYSICS, UNIV NC, CHARLOTTE, 74-, CHMN PHYSICS DEPT, 77- *Mem:* Am Phys Soc; Am Asn Physics Teachers. *Res:* Low energy nuclear physics; nuclear spectroscopy. *Mailing Add:* Dept of Physics Univ of NC Charlotte NC 28223

OBERHOLTZER, JAMES EDWARD, b Elizabethtown, Pa, June 18, 42; m 67. ANALYTICAL CHEMISTRY. *Educ:* Elizabethtown Col, BS, 64; Purdue Univ, PhD(anal chem), 69. *Prof Exp:* RES CHEMIST, ARTHUR D LITTLE, INC, 68- *Mem:* AAAS; Am Chem Soc. *Res:* Instrumentation and methodology for chemical analyses, especially gas chromatography and mass spectrometry; application of digital computers to scientific research; analytical techniques for monitoring environmental pollution. *Mailing Add:* Res & Develop Arthur Little Inc 15 Acorn Park Cambridge MA 02140

OBERLANDER, HERBERT, b Manchester, NH, Oct 2, 39; m 62. BIOLOGY. *Educ:* Univ Conn, BA, 61; Western Reserve Univ, PhD(biol), 65. *Prof Exp:* NIH fel, Inst Zool, Zurich, 65-66; asst prof biol, Brandeis Univ, 66-71; RES PHYSIOLOGIST, INSECT ATTRACTANTS, BEHAV & BASIC BIOL RES LAB, AGR RES SERV, USDA, 71- *Concurrent Pos:* Mem grad fac, Dept Entom, Univ Fla, 71- *Mem:* Entom Soc Am; Soc Develop Biol; Tissue Cult Asn; Int Soc Develop Biol. *Res:* Insect physiology; endocrine control of post-embryonic development in insects and other arthropods. *Mailing Add:* Behav & Basic Biol Res Lab Agr Res Serv USDA PO Box 14565 Gainesville FL 32604

OBERLE, RICHARD ALAN, mathematical analysis, see previous edition

OBERLE, THOMAS M, b Mankato, Minn, Mar 10, 30; m 53; c 6. INORGANIC CHEMISTRY. *Educ:* Col St Thomas, BSc, 52. *Prof Exp:* Jr chemist, Ames Lab, Atomic Energy Comn, Iowa State Univ, 52-54; chemist, 56-60, group leader prod develop, 60-64, mgr, 64-69, dir instnl & consumer res & develop, 69-72, asst vpres res & develop, 72-75, VPRES RES & DEVELOP, US ECONS LAB, INC, 75- *Mem:* Am Inst Chem. *Res:* Product development of detergent compounds for institutional and consumer needs. *Mailing Add:* Res & Develop Ctr Econs Lab Inc 840 Sibley Memorial Hwy Mendota Heights MN 55118

OBERLEAS, DONALD, b Sheridan, Ind, Feb 14, 33. NUTRITIONAL BIOCHEMISTRY. *Educ:* Purdue Univ, BS, 55; Univ Ky, MS, 59; Univ Mo, PhD(agr chem), 64. *Prof Exp:* Res chemist nutrit biochem, Vet Admin Hosp, Allen Park, Mich, 64-76; from instr to assoc prof biochem med, Wayne State Univ, 64-76; PROF NUTRIT & FOOD SCI & CHMN DEPT, UNIV KY, 76- *Concurrent Pos:* Actg assoc chief staff res, Vet Admin Hosp, Allen Park, Mich, 73-76. *Mem:* Am Inst Nutrit; Soc Exp Biol & Med; Sigma Xi; Int Asn Bioinorg Scientists; Soc Nutrit Educ. *Res:* Trace element metabolism; trace element availability. *Mailing Add:* Dept of Nutrit Univ of Ky Lexington KY 40506

OBERLIN, DANIEL MALCOLM, b Tulsa, Okla, Sept 16, 48; m 67; c 1. MATHEMATICAL ANALYSIS. *Educ:* Univ Tulsa, BS, 70; Univ Md, MA, 72, PhD(math), 74. *Prof Exp:* Asst prof, 74-81, ASSOC PROF MATH, FLA STATE UNIV, 81- *Mem:* Am Math Soc. *Res:* Harmonic analysis on locally compact groups. *Mailing Add:* Dept of Math Fla State Univ Tallahassee FL 32306

OBERLY, GENE HERMAN, b Palisade, Colo, Apr 27, 25; m 47; c 1. POMOLOGY. *Educ:* Utah State Univ, BS, 49, MS, 50; Mich State Univ, PhD(hort, plant nutrit), 59. *Prof Exp:* Salesman agr chem, C D Smith Drug Co, Colo, 50-51; exten horticulturist, Utah State Univ, 51-54; farm dir & assoc prof hort, Am Univ, Beirut, 54-57; asst hort, Mich State Univ, 57-59; Assoc prof pomol, Univ Conn, 59-62; ASSOC PROF POMOL, CORNELL UNIV, 62- *Mem:* Am Soc Hort Sci. *Res:* Plant nutrition on horticultural crops. *Mailing Add:* Dept of Pomol Cornell Univ Ithaca NY 14853

OBERLY, RALPH EDWIN, b Columbus, Ohio, Feb 13, 41; m 64. PHYSICS. *Educ:* Ohio State Univ, BS, 63, PhD(physics), 70. *Prof Exp:* Res engr, NAm Aviation, Ohio, 63-64; ASSOC PROF PHYSICS, CHMN PHYSICS & PHYS SCI, MARSHALL UNIV, 70- *Mem:* Am Asn Physics Teachers; Optical Soc Am. *Res:* Infrared molecular spectroscopy of small molecules; optical instruments. *Mailing Add:* Dept of Physics Marshall Univ Huntington WV 25701

OBERMAN, ALBERT, b St Louis, Mo, Feb 9, 34; m 54; c 3. PREVENTIVE MEDICINE, EPIDEMIOLOGY. *Educ:* Wash Univ, AB, 55, MD, 59; Univ Mich, MPH, 66. *Prof Exp:* Investr thousand aviation study, US Naval Base, Pensacola, Fla, 62-65; Nat Heart Inst spec res assoc epidemiol, Sch Pub Health, Univ Mich, 66-67; prof pub health & epidemiol & assoc prof med, 66-81, PROF & CHMN DEPT PREV MED, SCH MED, UNIV ALA, BIRMINGHAM, 81-, DIR, DIV PREV MED, MED CTR, 66- *Concurrent Pos:* Mem med adv bd, Naval Aerospace Med Inst Fla, 65-; mem policy & data monitoring comn, Nat Heart, Lung & Blood Inst, 78-; clin trials review comt, NIH, HEW; Mosby scholar award, Univ Mo; vchmn gen prev med, Am Bd Prev Med, 79-; mem adv panel, Am Inst Biol Sci Oper Med, NASA, 80- *Mem:* Am Pub Health Asn; fel Am Col Physicians; fel Am Col Prev Med; fel Am Heart Asn; Int Soc Cardiol. *Res:* Epidemiology of chronic diseases, especially cardiovascular; exercise and cardiovascular rehabilitation. *Mailing Add:* Dept Prev Med Univ of Ala Med Ctr Univ Sta Birmingham AL 35294

OBERMAN, HAROLD A, b Chicago, Ill, Oct 21, 32; m 59; c 3. MEDICINE, PATHOLOGY. *Educ:* Univ Omaha, AB, 53; Univ Nebr, MD, 56. *Prof Exp:* Asst chief dept path, Walter Reed Gen Hosp, 61-63; from asst prof to assoc prof path, 63-69, PROF PATH, SCH MED, UNIV MICH, ANN ARBOR, 69-, HEAD SECT CLIN PATH, 80-, DIR, CLIN LAB, UNIV HOSP, 80- *Concurrent Pos:* Consult, Vet Admin Hosp, Ann Arbor, 63- & Wayne County Gen Hosp, 66- *Mem:* Am Soc Clin Path; Col Am Path; Int Acad Path; Am Asn Path; Am Asn Blood Banks. *Res:* Blood banking and blood transfusion; surgical pathology; pathology of breast disease, lymph node disease and neoplasms of head and neck. *Mailing Add:* M5246 Med Sci Bldg Univ of Mich Med Sch Ann Arbor MI 48104

OBERMAYER, ARTHUR S, b Philadelphia, Pa, July 17, 31; m 63; c 3. ORGANIC CHEMISTRY, PHYSICS. *Educ:* Swarthmore Col, BA, 52; Mass Inst Technol, PhD(chem), 56. *Prof Exp:* Group leader, Tracerlab, Inc, Mass, 56-59; mgr div phys sci, Allied Res Assocs, Inc, 59-61; PRES & & CHMN BD, MOLECULON RES CORP, Mass, 61- *Concurrent Pos:* Dir, Strem Chem, Inc, Mass; adv coun exp res & develop incentives prog, NSF, 73-75; dir govt mgt task force, 75-78; cong assessment panel appln sci & technol, 76-; adv coun, NSF, 80-; mem, US Senate Small Business Comt, Nat Adv Coun, 81- *Mem:* Sigma Xi; Fed Am Scientists (treas, 71-73); Am Chem Soc; Asn Tech Professionals. *Res:* Polymer membrane research for controlled release pharmaceuticals, toxic vapor monitoring, and chemical separation processes; science policy options relative to small business innovation. *Mailing Add:* Moleculon Res Corp 139 Main St Cambridge MA 02142

O'BERRY, PHILLIP AARON, b Tampa, Fla, Feb 1, 33; m 60; c 6. VETERINARY MICROBIOLOGY. *Educ:* Univ Fla, BS, 55; Auburn Univ, DVM, 60; Iowa State Univ, PhD(vet microbiol), 67. *Prof Exp:* Res vet, Nat Animal Dis Lab, 61-67; res adminr cattle dis, Vet Sci Res Div, 67-72, asst dir, 72-73, actg dir, 73-74, DIR, NAT ANIMAL DIS CTR, AGR RES SERV, USDA, 74- *Concurrent Pos:* Mem, Food & Agr Orgn Expert Panel on Livestock Infertility, 66-70; mem, Comt Fed Labs, Fed Coun Sci & Technol, 74-, Steering Comt, World Food Conf of 76, 74-76, Comt Animal Health, World Food & Nutrit Study, Nat Acad Sci, 75-77, Sci Adv Comt, Pan Am Ctr Zoonotic Dis, Buenos Aires, Arg, Pan Am Health Orgn, 76- & sci adv, Italian govt, 79. *Honors & Awards:* Cert of Merit, Agr Res Serv, 72. *Mem:* AAAS; Am Vet Med Asn; Am Soc Microbiol; Am Asn Bovine Practitioners; Conf Res Workers Animal Dis. *Res:* Microbiological aspects of Vibrio fetus and Mycoplasma species and their relationship to diseases of livestock. *Mailing Add:* Nat Animal Dis Ctr PO Box 70 Ames IA 50010

OBERSTAR, HELEN ELIZABETH, b Ottawa, Ill, Aug 29, 23; m 45. COSMETIC CHEMISTRY. *Educ:* Monmouth Col, BS, 43. *Prof Exp:* Asst food technol, Standard Brands, Inc, NY, 43-45; chemist, Miner Labs, Midwest Div, Arthur D Little, Inc, 46-50; res chemist & supvr, Toni Co Div, Gillette Co, 51-65; group leader, Shulton Inc, 65-71; sect mgr consumer prod div, Am Cyanamid Co, NJ, 72-75; mgr res & develop, Clairol Int, Int Div, 75-80, DIR RES & DEVELOP, CONSUMER PROD, INT DIV, BRISTOL-MYERS CO, NEW YORK, 80- *Mem:* Soc Cosmetic Chem. *Res:* Product development and exploratory research in hair coloring, lightening, hair care products, cosmetics and toiletries; mechanical device developments for cosmetics. *Mailing Add:* 512 Belden Hill Rd Wilton CT 06897

OBERSTER, ARTHUR EUGENE, b Canton, Ohio, July 6, 29; m 55; c 6. ORGANIC CHEMISTRY. *Educ:* Mt Union Col, BS, 51; Univ Notre Dame, PhD(org chem), 57. *Prof Exp:* Sr chemist, Merck & Co, Inc, NJ, 55-59; res specialist, 59-67, sr group leader polymerization, 67-75, RES ASSOC,

FIRESTONE TIRE & RUBBER CO, 75- *Honors & Awards:* Am Chem Soc Award, 50. *Mem:* Am Chem Soc. *Res:* Organic synthesis, particularly steroids, alkaloids, heterocyclics, rubber chemicals, antioxidants, antiozonants and monomers; polymer synthesis, particularly anionic polymerization; elastomer compounding; foam processing. *Mailing Add:* Cent Res Labs Firestone Tire & Rubber Co Akron OH 44317

OBERT, EDWARD FREDRIC, b Detroit, Mich, Jan 18, 10; m 35. MECHANICAL ENGINEERING. *Educ:* Northwestern Univ, BS, 33, ME, 34; Univ Mich, MS, 40. *Prof Exp:* Mfg engr, Western Elec Co, Ill, 29-30; inspector eng mat, Naval Inspection, 35-37; from assoc prof to prof mech eng, Northwestern Univ, 37-59; chmn dept, 63-67, PROF MECH ENG, UNIV WIS-MADISON, 59- *Concurrent Pos:* Consult, US Air Force Acad & Air Force Arctic Medic Lab, 58. *Honors & Awards:* Westinghouse Award, Am Soc Eng Educ, 53, G Edwin Burks Award, 71. *Mem:* Am Soc Mech Engrs; Soc Automotive Engrs. *Res:* Thermodynamics; properties of gases; internal combustion engines. *Mailing Add:* Dept of Mech Eng Univ of Wis Madison WI 53705

OBERT, JESSIE C, b Port Byron, Ill, Mar 26, 11; m 35. NUTRITION. *Educ:* Park Col, AB, 31; Univ Chicago, MS, 42; Ohio State Univ, PhD(nutrit), 51. *Prof Exp:* Nutritionist, Chicago Welfare Dept, 37-42; dir nutrit serv, Maricopa County Chapter, Am Red Cross, 43-47; asst prof home econ, Ohio State Univ, 47-51; instr, Univ Calif, Los Angeles, 52-53; chief nutrit div, Los Angeles Co Health Dept, 53-76; NUTRIT CONSULT, 76- *Mem:* Nutrit Today Soc; Am Dietetic Asn; Soc Nutrit Educ; Am Pub Health Asn; Am Home Econ Asn. *Res:* Activity and weight control; nutritional surveillance; community nutrition. *Mailing Add:* 5122 Bomer Dr Los Angeles CA 90042

OBERTEUFFER, JOHN AMIARD, b Boston, Mass, May 31, 40; m 62; c 2. BIOENGINEERING, ACOUSTICS. *Educ:* Williams Col, BA, 62, MA, 64; Northwestern Univ, PhD(physics), 69. *Prof Exp:* Asst, Northwestern Univ, Ill, 64-69; res assoc neutron physics, Mass Inst Technol, 69-71, mem staff, Francis Bitter Nat Magnet Lab, 71-74; asst dir develop, Sala Magnetics, 74-75, tech dir, 75-76, vpres mkt, 76-80; EXEC VPRES, SONTEK INDUSTS, INC, 80- *Mem:* Inst Elec & Electronics Engrs; Am Phys Soc; Sigma Xi. *Res:* High gradient magnetic separation; basic and applied magnetism in liquids, solids, gases and mixed systems; solid state physics; x-ray and neutron diffraction; acoustics. *Mailing Add:* Sontek Industs Inc 31 Fletcher Ave Lexington MA 02173

OBEY, JAMES H(OWARD), b Detroit, Mich, Aug 29, 16; m 39; c 3. CHEMICAL ENGINEERING. *Educ:* Lawrence Inst Technol, BChE, 43. *Prof Exp:* Proj leader, Ford Motor Co, 39-43; consult, Boeckeler, Assocs, 43; sr fel, Mellon Inst, 43-56; coordr mkt develop, Consol Coal Co, 56-62; pres, Danville Prod, Inc, 62-64; mgr northeast dist, Blaw-Knox Chem Plants, Inc, 64-73; regional sales mgr, Jacobs Eng, 73-74; PRES & GEN MGR, BLAW-KNOX FOOD & CHEM EQUIP, INC, 74-; PRES, WIRZ Y MACHUCA, SOUTH AM, 74- *Mem:* Am Inst Chem Engrs; Am Chem Soc. *Res:* Industrial utilization of proteins; solvent extraction of vegetable oils; pilot plant design and operation; commercialization of new chemical products. *Mailing Add:* Blaw-Knox Food & Chem Equip Inc PO Box 1041 Buffalo NY 14240

OBIJESKI, JOHN FRANCIS, b Bridgeport, Conn, Apr 11, 41; m 62; c 2. MICROBIOLOGY, VIROLOGY. *Educ:* Univ Conn, BA, 65; Rutgers Univ, MS & PhD(virol), 71. *Prof Exp:* RES VIROLOGIST, VIROL SECT, CTR DIS CONTROL, 71- *Mem:* Am Soc Microbiol; Brit Soc Gen Microbiol. *Res:* Molecular and biochemical properties of animal viruses. *Mailing Add:* Virology Sect Ctr for Dis Control Atlanta GA 30333

OBLAD, ALEX GOLDEN, b Salt Lake City, Utah, Nov 26, 09; m 33; c 6. PETROLEUM CHEMISTRY. *Educ:* Univ Utah, BA, 33, MA, 34; Purdue Univ, PhD(phys chem), 37. *Hon Degrees:* DSc, Purdue Univ, 59. *Prof Exp:* Asst, Purdue Univ, 34-37; res chemist, Standard Oil Co, Ind, 37-42; group leader, Magnolia Petrol Co, Tex, 42-44, sect leader, 44-46, chief chem res, 46; head indust res, Tex Res Found, 46-47; dir chem res, Houdry Process Corp, Pa, 47-52, assoc mgr res & develop, 52-55, vpres res & develop & dir, 55-57; vpres res & develop, M W Kellogg Co, NY, 57-66, vpres res & eng develop, 66-69; vpres, Ireco Chem Co, Utah, 69-70; assoc dean col mines & mineral industs, 70-72, actg dean, 72-75, prof metall & fuels, 70-75, DISTINGUISHED PROF FUELS ENG, PROF CHEM, UNIV UTAH, 75- *Concurrent Pos:* Consult, Atomic Energy Projs, 50-57; managing ed publ, Div Petrol Chem, Am Chem Soc, 54-69; dir, Int Cong Catalysis, 55-64; vpres & dir, Nat Inst Catalysis, 65-69. *Honors & Awards:* E V. Murphree Award, Am Chem Soc, 69; Chem Pioneer Award, Am Inst Chemists, 72. Mem: Nat Acad Eng; Sigma Xi; Am Chem Soc; AAAS; Am Inst Chem Engrs. *Mem:* Honors &. *Res:* Catalysis; reaction mechanisms; kinetics and thermodynamics of hydrocarbon reactions; heat capacity of glasses; optical methods of analysis; uranium chemistry and processing; petroleum chemistry; petrochemicals; administration and management of research and development; process engineering and patent licensing. *Mailing Add:* Mineral Sci Bldg Col of Mines & Mineral Indust Univ Utah Salt Lake City UT 84112

OBLINGER, JAMES LESLIE, b Ashland, Ohio, Nov 3, 45; m 68; c 2. FOOD MICROBIOLOGY, FOOD SCIENCE. *Educ:* DePauw Univ, BA, 67; Iowa State Univ, MS, 70, PhD(food technol), 72. *Prof Exp:* Asst prof, 72-77, ASSOC PROF FOOD MICROBIOL, UNIV FLA, 77- *Mem:* Inst Food Technologists; Int Asn Milk Food & Environ Sanitarians; Am Soc Microbiol; Sigma Xi; Am Meat Sci Asn. *Res:* Sources and analysis of microbiological aspects of the food supply; food-borne diseases; red meat and poultry microbiology. *Mailing Add:* 459 Food Sci Bldg Univ of Fla Gainesville FL 32611

O'BOYLE, DENNIS ROBERT, metallurgy, see previous edition

OBRADOVICH, JOHN DINKO, b Fresno, Calif, May 2, 30. GEOPHYSICS. *Educ:* Univ Calif, Berkeley, BA, 57, MA, 59, PhD(geophys), 64. *Prof Exp:* GEOPHYSICIST, US GEOL SURV, 61- *Mem:* AAAS; Am Geophys Union; Geol Soc Am. *Res:* Isotope geology; K-Ar and Rb-Sr geochronology, particularly K-Ar dating of the late Cenozoic. *Mailing Add:* US Geol Surv Fed Ctr Denver CO 80225

OBREMSKI, HENRY J(OHN), b Elmont, NY, Oct 24, 31; m 58; c 2. FLUID DYNAMICS. *Educ:* Polytech Inst Brooklyn, BS, 58; Ill Inst Technol, MS, 62, PhD(mech eng), 66. *Prof Exp:* Engr, United Aircraft Res Lab, 58-60; assoc engr, IIT Res Inst, 60-65; SR RES SCIENTIST, MARTIN MARIETTA LABS, 65- *Mem:* Am Inst Aeronaut & Astronaut; Am Phys Soc. *Res:* Transition in non-steady boundary layers; cavity flows and instabilities; thermal pollution; heat and mass transfer in aluminum cells; ventilation; brine field modelling. *Mailing Add:* 5113 Avoca Ave Ellicot City MD 21043

OBREMSKI, ROBERT JOHN, b Brooklyn, NY, Aug 19, 41; m 64; c 2. COMPUTERIZED SPECTROSCOPY, MOLECULAR SPECTROSCOPY. *Educ:* St John's Univ, NY, BS, 62, MS, 64; Univ Md, College Park, PhD(phys chem), 68. *Prof Exp:* Chemist, Uniroyal, Inc, 68-69 & Spectra-Physics, Inc, 69-71; sr appln chemist, 71-77, PRIN CHEMIST, BECKMAN INSTRUMENTS, INC, 77- *Mem:* Am Chem Soc; Soc Appl Spectros; Coblentz Soc. *Res:* Application of computers to molecular spectroscopy; design of computerized instrumentation; nuclear counting techniques. *Mailing Add:* 19792 LaTierra Lane Yorba Linda CA 92686

O'BRIAN, DENNIS MARTIN, b New York, NY, Mar 28, 31; m 58; c 2. DECISION SUPPORT SYSTEMS. *Educ:* St Anselm's Col, BA, 52; Univ Notre Dame, MS, 55; Fordham Univ, PhD, 60, Univ Conn, MBA, 80. *Prof Exp:* From instr to assoc prof biol, Seton Hall Univ, 59-67; sr res scientist, Dept Toxicol, Squibb Inst Med Res, 67-68, sr res investr, Dept Res Admin, 68-71, sr info res scientist, Div Med Affairs, 71-73; mgr clin info, Johnson & Johnson Res, 73-74; asst dir med support, Vick Div Res & Develop, Richardson-Merrell, Inc, 74-80; DIR INFO SCI & DEVELOP PLANNING, KALIPHARMA, INC, 80- *Mailing Add:* Kalipharma Inc 200 Elmora Ave Elizabeth NJ 07207

O'BRIEN, ANNE T, b New York, NY, Apr 11, 36. ORGANIC CHEMISTRY. *Educ:* Marymount Col, NY, BS, 57; Fordham Univ, PhD(org chem), 64. *Prof Exp:* Fac mem parochial sch, 57-59; from instr to assoc prof chem, Marymount Col, NY, 62-73; assoc prof, 73-76, ADJ ASSOC PROF, DEPT MAN-ENVIRON STUDIES, UNIV WATERLOO, 76-, SR RES LIT CHEMIST, MED RES DIV, AM CYANAMID, 76- *Mem:* Am Chem Soc; Am Inst Chem; Sigma Xi; Am Asn Univ Prof; AAAS. *Res:* Halogen-catalyzed autoxidation; porphyrin synthesis; drug syntheses, resolutions and absolute configurations; futuristics; environmental chemistry; alkaloids; literature science. *Mailing Add:* 15 Crest Dr Tarrytown NY 10591

O'BRIEN, BENEDICT BUTLER, JR, b New Britain, Conn, July 11, 34; m; c 2. PHYSICS. *Educ:* Mass Inst Technol, BS, 55; Univ Munich, PhD(physics), 65. *Prof Exp:* Mem staff elec eng, Ramo Wooldridge Corp & Space Tech Lab, 56-60; scientist plasma physics, Max Planck Inst for Plasma Physics, 60-67; asst prof elec eng, Univ Southern Calif, 67-71; mgr high power laser, 71-77, MGR MILLIMETER WAVE TECHNOL, NORTHROP RES & TECHNOL CTR, 78- *Concurrent Pos:* Instr physics, Univ Md, 62-67; consult, Northrop Res & Tech Ctr, 70-71. *Mem:* Am Phys Soc; Inst Elec & Electronics Engrs. *Res:* Millimeter wave; high power laser; plasma physics. *Mailing Add:* Northrop Res & Technol Ctr One Research Park Palos Verdes Peninsula CA 90274

O'BRIEN, BRIAN, b Denver, Colo, Jan 2, 98; m 22, 56; c 1. ELECTROOPTICS. *Educ:* Yale Univ, PhB, 18, PhD(physics), 22. *Prof Exp:* Res engr, Westinghouse Elec & Mfg Co, 22-23; res physicist, Buffalo Tuberc Asn, 23-30; prof physiol optics, Univ Rochester, 30-46, dir Inst Optics, 38-53, res prof physics & optics, 46-53; vpres res & trustee, Am Optical Co, 53-58; CONSULT PHYSICIST, 58- *Concurrent Pos:* Mem comt pilot selection & training & vision comt, Nat Res Coun, 39-46, chmn div phys sci, 53-61; mem, Nat Defense Res Comt, 40-46; chmn space prog adv coun, NASA, 70-74; mem sci adv bd, US Air Force, 59-70; chmn, Nat Acad Sci Comt, Adv to Air Force Systs Command, 62-74. *Honors & Awards:* President's Medal for Merit, 48; Ives Medal, 51; Exceptional Civilian Serv Medal, US Air Force, 69, Exceptional Serv Medal, 73; Distinguished Pub Serv Medal, NASA, 71. *Mem:* Nat Acad Sci; Nat Acad Eng; fel Optical Soc Am (pres, 51-53); fel Am Phys Soc; fel Am Inst Elec & Electronics Engrs. *Res:* Optical properties of metals and thin films; solar ultraviolet and atmospheric ozone; photographic processes; motion picture systems; very high speed photography; photobiochemical effects; flicker phenomena in vision; retinal structure and visual processes; fiber optics. *Mailing Add:* Box 166 Woodstock CT 06281

O'BRIEN, DANIEL H, b Berkeley, Calif, Oct 26, 32; m 59; c 6. ORGANIC CHEMISTRY. *Educ:* Univ Va, BS, 54, PhD(chem), 61. *Prof Exp:* From instr to asst prof chem, Univ Dayton, 60-66; fel, Case Western Reserve Univ, 66-67; ASSOC PROF CHEM, TEX A&M UNIV, 67- *Concurrent Pos:* Res assoc, Chem Br, Aeronaut Res Lab, Wright-Patterson Air Force Base, 62-66. *Mem:* Am Chem Soc. *Res:* Organometallic chemistry; organic synthesis and characterization of organosilicon compounds. *Mailing Add:* Dept of Chem Tex A&M Univ College Station TX 77843

O'BRIEN, DAVID F, b Litchfield, Ill, Nov 18, 36; m 59; c 3. BIOPHYSICAL CHEMISTRY. *Educ:* Wabash Col, AB, 58; Univ Ill, PhD(org chem), 62. *Prof Exp:* Res chemist, 62-64, sr res chemist, 64-68, RES ASSOC, RES LABS, EASTMAN KODAK CO, 68- *Mem:* Biophys Soc; Am Chem Soc; Asn Res Vision & Ophthal. *Res:* visual transduction; rhodopsin containing synthetic membranes; properties of synthetic membranes; photopolymerization of lipid bilager membranes; polymerized vesicles. *Mailing Add:* Res Labs Eastman Kodak Co Rochester NY 14604

O'BRIEN, DENNIS CRAIG, b Great Bend, Kans, July 20, 38; m 60; c 2. GEOLOGY. *Educ:* Cornell Col, AB, 60; Miami Univ, MS, 64; Univ Mass, Amherst, PhD(geol), 71. *Prof Exp:* Instr, 68-71, ASSOC PROF GEOL, DRAKE UNIV, 76- *Mem:* Geol Soc Am; Sigma Xi; Nat Asn Geol Teachers; Soc Econ Paleontologists & Mineralogists. *Res:* Sedimentary petrography and petrology; Precambrian sedimentary rocks; environmental geology. *Mailing Add:* Dept of Geog & Geol Drake Univ Des Moines IA 50311

O'BRIEN, DONOUGH, b Edinburgh, Scotland, May 9, 23; m 50; c 2. PEDIATRICS. *Educ:* Cambridge Univ, BA, 44, MB, BCh, 46, MA, 47, MD, 52; FRCP, 72. *Prof Exp:* House physician, St Thomas' Hosp, Univ London, 47-48, registr, Inst Child Health, 50-52 & Hosp Sick Children & Guy's Hosp, 53-57; from asst prof to assoc prof pediat, Sch Med, 57-64, PROF PEDIAT, UNIV COLO MED CTR, DENVER, 64- *Mem:* Am Diabetes Asn; Am Fedn Clin Res. *Res:* Biochemical applications to pediatrics. *Mailing Add:* Univ Colo Med Ctr 4200 E Ninth Ave Denver CO 80220

O'BRIEN, EDWARD E, b Toowoomba, Australia, May 16, 33; m 59; c 6. FLUID MECHANICS. *Educ:* Univ Queensland, BS, 55; Purdue Univ, MSME, 57; Johns Hopkins Univ, PhD(mech), 60. *Prof Exp:* Asst thermodyn, Univ Queensland, 54-55; thermodynamicist, Canadair Aircraft Co, Can, 55; asst heat power, Purdue Univ, 55-57; instr mech, Johns Hopkins Univ, 57-60, fel, 60-61; from asst prof to assoc prof eng, 61-67, PROF ENG, STATE UNIV NY, STONY BROOK, 67- *Concurrent Pos:* NSF grants, 62-72; mem meteorol group, Brookhaven Nat Lab, 64; US Pub Health Serv grant, 64-66. *Mem:* Am Phys Soc. *Res:* Turbulent diffusion and mixing; chemically reacting turbulent flows; classical incompressible fluid mechanics; geophysical fluid mechanics. *Mailing Add:* Col of Eng State Univ of NY Stony Brook NY 11794

O'BRIEN, FRANCIS XAVIER, b Quincy, Mass, Sept 6, 35; m 65; c 3. MARINE BIOLOGY. *Educ:* Suffolk Univ, BS, 63; Univ NH, MS, 65, PhD(zool), 72. *Prof Exp:* PROF BIOL & CHMN DEPT, SOUTHEASTERN MASS UNIV, 68- *Concurrent Pos:* Biol consult, US Environ Protection Agency, 75-77. *Mem:* Sigma Xi; AAAS; Nat Shellfish Asn. *Res:* Ecology of marine benthic invertebrates. *Mailing Add:* Dept Biol Southeastern Mass Univ North Dartmouth MA 02747

O'BRIEN, GEORGE SIVESIND, neurology, physiology, deceased

O'BRIEN, HAROLD ALOYSIOUS, JR, b Dallas, Tex, May 17, 36; m 58; c 3. NUCLEAR CHEMISTRY, NUCLEAR MEDICINE. *Educ:* Univ Tex, Austin, BA, 59; NMex State Univ, MS, 61; Univ Tenn, Knoxville, PhD(phys chem), 68. *Prof Exp:* Res assoc nuclear chem, Isotopes Develop Ctr, Oak Ridge Nat Lab, 62-68; mem staff, 68-74, assoc group leader, 74-80, GROUP LEADER, LOS ALAMOS NAT LAB, 74- *Concurrent Pos:* Adj asst prof, 70-78, adj assoc prof, Sch Med, Univ NMex, 78-; Am Cancer Soc grant, 72-74; mem subcomt radiochem, Nat Acad Sci-Nat Res Coun, 74-, mem subcomt nuclear & radiochem, 78-81; chmn, State NMex Radiation Tech Adv Coun, 75- *Mem:* Am Bd Sci in Nuclear Med; AAAS; Am Chem Soc; Soc Nuclear Med. *Res:* Nuclear reactions; cross section studies; radioisotope production and applications; nuclear medicine; high temperature thermodynamics. *Mailing Add:* CNC-3 MS-514 Los Alamos Nat Lab Los Alamos NM 87545

O'BRIEN, JAMES EDWARD, b Loogootee, Ind, June 2, 25. ASTRONOMY, SOLAR PHYSICS. *Educ:* Georgetown Univ, PhD(astron), 69. *Prof Exp:* Instr astron, Georgetown Univ, 65-66; asst prof, 69-81, ASSOC PROF PHYSICS, XAVIER UNIV, 81- *Res:* Lunar-terrestrial relations. *Mailing Add:* Dept of Physics Xavier Univ Cincinnati OH 45207

O'BRIEN, JAMES FRANCIS, b Philadelphia, Pa, July 4, 41; m 70; c 2. PHYSICAL CHEMISTRY, INORGANIC CHEMISTRY. *Educ:* Villanova Univ, BS, 64; Univ Minn, Minneapolis, PhD(chem), 68. *Prof Exp:* Fel, Los Alamos Sci Lab, 68-69; from asst prof to assoc prof, 69-79, PROF CHEM, SOUTHWEST MO STATE COL, 79- *Concurrent Pos:* Vis assoc prof, Univ of Del, 75-76. *Mem:* Am Chem Soc; AAAS. *Res:* Magnetic resonance of inorganic compounds in nonaqueous solvents; electrical conductivity of nonaqueous solutions; kinetics; nuclear quadrupole resonance. *Mailing Add:* Dept of Chem Southwest Mo State Univ Springfield MO 65802

O'BRIEN, JAMES FRANCIS, b Rochester, NY, Aug 23, 34. CYTOLOGY, MICROBIOLOGY. *Educ:* Spring Hill Col, BS, 60; Fordham Univ, MS, 62, PhD(biol), 65. *Prof Exp:* Res assoc biol, Cancer Res Inst, Boston Col, 69; asst prof, 69-73, ASSOC PROF BIOL, LE MOYNE COL, NY, 73- *Concurrent Pos:* Postdoc fel, St Thomas Inst, Cincinnati, 78-79. *Mem:* AAAS; Nat Asn Biol Teachers; NY Acad Sci; Am Asn Jesuit Sci Rs: Cytological investigation of the development of intestinal tract of mosquitoes; electrophoretic study of tissues of rats infected with shaychloroma tumors. *Mailing Add:* Dept of Biol Le Moyne Col Le Moyne Heights Syracuse NY 13214

O'BRIEN, JAMES J, b New York, NY, Aug 10, 35; m 58; c 3. METEOROLOGY, OCEANOGRAPHY. *Educ:* Rutgers Univ, BS, 57; Tex A&M Univ, MS, 64, PhD(meteorol), 66. *Prof Exp:* Chemist, Elchem Dept, E I du Pont de Nemours & Co, 57-58, tech rep, 60-62; fel, Adv Study Group, Nat Ctr Atmospheric Res, 66-67, staff scientist, 67-69; assoc prof, 69-74, PROF METEOROL & OCEANOGR, FLA STATE UNIV, 69- *Concurrent Pos:* Co-dir coastal upwelling exp, Int Decade Ocean Explor-NSF; co ed, Progess Oceanogr, 79-, assoc ed, J Physical Oceanogr, 71- *Mem:* Fel Am Meteorol Soc; Am Geophys Union; Am Chem Soc; Royal Meteorol Soc; Japan Oceanogr Soc. *Res:* Micrometeorology; air-sea interactions; numerical analysis; applied statistics; numerical modeling of ocean circulation; ecological modeling. *Mailing Add:* Dept of Meteorol Fla State Univ Tallahassee FL 32306

O'BRIEN, JOAN A, b Philadelphia, Pa; m 51; c 3. VETERINARY MEDICINE, LARYNGOLOGY. *Educ:* Chestnut Hill Col, AB, 50; Univ Pa, VMD, 63. *Prof Exp:* Intern, 63-64, Dorothy Harrison Eustis Seeing Eye fel, 64-66, instr med, 64-67, asst prof, 67-73, ASST PROF COMP BRONCHOLOGY, ESOPHAGOLOGY & LARYNGEAL SURG, SCH VET MED, UNIV PA, 71-, PROF MED, DEPT CLIN STUDIES, 75-, CHIEF MED, 78- *Concurrent Pos:* Assoc prof med, Dept Otolaryngol, Sch Vet Med, Univ Pa & res assoc prof, Dept Otorhinolaryngol, Hahnemann Med Col & Hosp & Laryngeal Inst, 73- *Honors & Awards:* Gaines Award, Am Vet Med Asn, 78. *Mem:* Am Col Vet Internists; Am Vet Med Asn; Am Broncho-Esophagological Asn. *Res:* Applications of laryngology and bronchoesophagology in naturally occurring disease of animals. *Mailing Add:* Sch Vet Med Univ Pa 3800 Spruce St Philadelphia PA 19174

O'BRIEN, JOHN ALOYSIUS, cell biology, deceased

O'BRIEN, JOHN S, b Rochester, NY, July 14, 34; m 57; c 6. PATHOLOGY, MEDICINE. *Educ:* Creighton Univ, MS, 58, MD, 60. *Prof Exp:* From instr to assoc prof path & med, Sch Med, Univ Southern Calif, 62-68, lectr biochem, 62-67, coordr set clin lects & chief div chem path, 64-68; assoc prof neurosci, 68-70, PROF NEUROSCI & CHMN DEPT, SCH MED, UNIV CALIF, SAN DIEGO, 70-, CHIEF DIV NEUROMETAB DISORDERS, 69- *Concurrent Pos:* USPHS grants, 63-79; Nat Inst Child Health & Human Develop grant, 66-68; Nat Multiple Sclerosis Soc grant, 66-70; Nat Genet Found grant, 70-72; Nat Cyctic Fibrosis Res Found grant, 70-72; Nat Found March of Dimes grant, 70-73; Nat Inst Gen Med Sci grant, 70-75; vis scientist, Univ Calif, Los Angeles, 62 & Scripps Inst, Univ Calif, 63; consult, Childrens Hosp Los Angeles, Pac State Hosp, Pomona, Childrens Hosp San Diego, Fairview State Hosp, Costa Mesa, Pasadena Found Med Res & Dept Neurol, Univ Southern Calif, 64-68. *Mem:* AAAS; Am Fedn Clin Res; Am Soc Exp Path; Am Soc Human Genet; NY Acad Sci. *Res:* Relationships between the molecular structure and disease states; role of lipid molecules in membrane structure and stability; brain lipids; myelination and demyelination. *Mailing Add:* Dept of Neurosci Univ of Calif San Diego Sch Med La Jolla CA 92093

O'BRIEN, KERAN, b Brooklyn, NY, Nov 5, 31; m 61; c 2. RADIATION PHYSICS. *Educ:* Fordham Univ, BS, 53. *Prof Exp:* PHYSICIST, ENVIRON MEASUREMENTS LAB, US DEPT OF ENERGY, 53- *Concurrent Pos:* Mem adv panel accelerator safety, AEC, 65-70 & 77-; mem reference nuclear data panel, Nat Nuclear Data Ctr, 81- *Honors & Awards:* Shielding & Dosimetry Div Award Outstanding Serv, Am Nuclear Soc, 76. *Mem:* Am Nuclear Soc; Radiation Res Soc; Am Phys Soc; Archeol Inst Am. *Res:* Radiation dosimetry associated with particle accelerator shielding with naturally occurring radiation sources; high energy radiation theory and the propagation of atmospheric cosmic rays. *Mailing Add:* Radia Physic Div Dept of Energy 376 Hudson St New York NY 10014

O'BRIEN, LARRY JOE, b Big Spring, Tex, Sept 14, 29; m 53; c 3. PHYSIOLOGY. *Educ:* Hardin-Simmons Univ, BA, 49; NTex State Col, MA, 54; Univ Tex, PhD(physiol), 57; Med Col Ga, MD, 71. *Prof Exp:* Asst physiol, Univ Tex Med Br, 55-56, instr, 56-57; from instr to asst prof, Albany Med Col, 57-60; assoc prof res physiol, Sch Med, Univ Okla, 60-62; from asst prof to assoc prof physiol, Med Col Ga, 62-72, actg chmn dept, 71-72; prof physiol & chmn dept, 72-75, CLIN PROF PHYSIOL & MED, SCH MED, TEX TECH UNIV, 75- *Concurrent Pos:* Chief circulation sect, Civil Aeromed Res Inst, 60-62; attend physician internal med, Methodist Hosp, Lubbock, Tex. *Mem:* AAAS; Am Physiol Soc; Am Heart Asn; NY Acad Sci; Soc Exp Biol & Med. *Res:* Cardiac and peripheral vascular function. *Mailing Add:* Suite 401 Med-Prof Bldg 3801 19th St Lubbock TX 79410

O'BRIEN, LEO J, chemical engineering, see previous edition

O'BRIEN, MICHAEL, b Melrose, Iowa, Oct 1, 18; m 44; c 3. AGRICULTURAL ENGINEERING, BIOLOGICAL ENGINEERING. *Educ:* Iowa State Univ, BS, 48, MS, 49, PhD(agr eng, biol sci), 51. *Prof Exp:* From instr to assoc prof, 50-70, PROF MAT HANDLING, DEPT AGR ENG, UNIV CALIF, DAVIS, 70- *Concurrent Pos:* Grants, Nat Canners Asn, 58, Cling Peach Adv Bd, 61-64, Canners League, 66-68, Tomato Indust, 59-82 & NSF, 70; consult educ & training, Int Harvester Co, Ill, 50, mat handling, US Steel Co, Pa, 65-66 & mat handling & mech harvesting, Dole Co, Hawaii, 68; consult, Neuman, Williams & Anderson Assocs, 79-82. *Mem:* Fel Am Soc Agr Engrs; Am Soc Eng Educ. *Res:* Automation of materials handling and physical properties and quality control of biological materials. *Mailing Add:* Dept of Agr Eng Univ of Calif Davis CA 95616

O'BRIEN, MICHAEL HARVEY, b Soperton, Ga, Mar 22, 42; m 63; c 1. ORGANIC CHEMISTRY. *Educ:* Berry Col, BA, 63; NC State Univ, PhD(chem), 69. *Prof Exp:* NASA training grant, 63-67; RES CHEMIST, E I DU PONT DE NEMOURS & CO, INC, 68- *Mem:* Am Chem Soc. *Res:* Synthesis, structure and reactions of pentavalent organoarsenic compounds. *Mailing Add:* 416 S Ellison Ln Waynesboro VA 22980

O'BRIEN, MORROUGH P, US citizen. ENGINEERING. *Prof Exp:* Emer prof eng & emer dean, Col Eng, Univ Calif, Berkeley. *Concurrent Pos:* Mem coastal eng res bd corps engrs, Nat Acad Eng; consult engr, Gen Elec Co. *Honors & Awards:* Lamme Medal, Am Soc Eng Educ. *Mem:* Nat Acad Eng; Am Soc Civil Engrs. *Mailing Add:* 412 O'Brein Hall Univ Calif Berkeley CA 94720

O'BRIEN, NEAL RAY, b Newark, Ohio, May 25, 37; m 62; c 3. GEOLOGY. *Educ:* DePauw Univ, BA, 59; Univ Ill, MS, 61, PhD(geol), 63. *Prof Exp:* PROF GEOL, STATE UNIV NY COL, POTSDAM, 63- *Concurrent Pos:* Researcher, Kyoto Univ, 69-70 & 77-78. *Mem:* Geol Soc Am; Soc Econ Paleont & Mineral; Clay Mineral Soc. *Res:* Sedimentation; clay mineralogy; electron microscope and x-ray study of clay sediment. *Mailing Add:* Dept Geol Col Arts & Sci State Univ NY Potsdam NY 13676

O'BRIEN, PAUL J, b Haddonfield, NJ, Feb 11, 33; m 61; c 3. BIOCHEMISTRY. *Educ:* Mt St Mary's Col, Md, BS, 54; St John's Univ, NY, MS, 56; Univ Pa, PhD(biochem), 60. *Prof Exp:* Res chemist, Sect Intermediary Metab, Lab Biochem & Metab, Nat Inst Arthritis & Metab Dis, 60-64; res chemist, Sect Cell Biol, Ophthal Br, Nat Inst Neurol Dis & Blindness, 64-65, from actg chief to chief, 65-71; res chemist, 71-81, CHIEF SECT CELL BIOL, LAB VISION RES, NAT EYE INST, 81- *Concurrent Pos:* Ed, Exp Eye Res, 75- *Mem:* AAAS; Asn Res Vision & Ophthal (pres, 81); Am Soc Biol Chemists. *Res:* Carbohydrate metabolism; biosynthesis of glycoproteins; control mechanisms; visual pigment biosynthesis and photoreceptor renewal. *Mailing Add:* Bldg 6 Rm B1A02 Lab Vision Res Nat Eye Inst NIH Bethesda MD 20014

O'BRIEN, PETER J, b London, Eng, July 6, 37. BIOCHEMISTRY. *Educ:* Univ London, BSc, 59; Univ Birmingham, PhD, 63. *Prof Exp:* Res fel med biochem, Univ Birmingham, 63-64, sr res assoc, 64-67; assoc prof, 67-74, PROF BIOCHEM, MEM UNIV NFLD, 74-, MEM CAN RES UNIT, 76- *Concurrent Pos:* Assoc ed, Can J Biochem, 71-75. *Mem:* Brit Biochem Soc; Can Soc Cell Biol; Can Biochem Soc; Am Soc Biol Chemists. *Res:* Intracellular formation, molecular effects and function of lipid peroxides, steroid hydroperoxides and hydrogen peroxide; drug and steroid metabolism; functional organization of electron transport in intracellular membranes. *Mailing Add:* Dept of Biochem Mem Univ of Nfld St John's NF A1C 5S7 Can

O'BRIEN, REDMOND R, b Quincy, Mass, Oct 27, 31; m 59; c 2. MATHEMATICS. *Educ:* Mass Inst Technol, SB, 53, SM, 54, PhD(math), 57. *Prof Exp:* Adv res engr, Sylvania Elec Prod, 57-60; ADV MATHEMATICIAN, IBM CORP, 60- *Mem:* Am Statist Asn; Soc Indust & Appl Math. *Res:* Mathematical analysis of semiconductor devices. *Mailing Add:* IBM Corp Bldg 300-94 East Fishkill NY 12533

O'BRIEN, RICHARD DESMOND, b Sydenham, Eng, May 29, 29; m 81; c 1. NEUROCHEMISTRY. *Educ:* Univ Reading, BSc, 50; Univ Western Ontario, PhD(chem), 54, BA, 56. *Prof Exp:* Chemist, Pesticide Res Inst, Can, 54-60; from assoc prof to prof entom, Cornell Univ, 60-65, chmn sect biochem, 64-65 & sect neurobiol & behav, 65-70, prof neurobiol, 65-79, dir div biol sci, 70-78; PROVOST, UNIV ROCHESTER, 78- *Concurrent Pos:* Nat Res Coun Can fel, Inst Animal Physiol, Cambridge, 56-57; vis assoc prof, Univ Wis, 58-59; Guggenheim fel, Int Lab Genetics & Biophys, Naples, 67-68; ed & founder, Pesticide Biochem & Physiol, 70-78. *Honors & Awards:* Int Award, Am Chem Soc, 71. *Mem:* Fel AAAS; Am Chem Soc; Am Soc Biol Chem. *Res:* Selective toxicity; modes of toxic action; comparative biochemistry; neuropharmacology. *Mailing Add:* Off Provost Univ Rochester Rochester NY 14627

O'BRIEN, RICHARD LEE, b Shenandoah, Iowa, Aug 30, 34; m 57; c 4. ONCOLOGY, CELL BIOLOGY. *Educ:* Creighton Univ, MS, 58, MD, 60. *Prof Exp:* From intern to asst resident med, First Med Div, Bellevue Hosp, Columbia Univ, 60-62; from asst prof to assoc prof, 66-76, dep dir, Cancer Ctr, 75-81, PROF PATH, SCH MED, UNIV SOUTHERN CALIF, 76-, DIR, CANCER CTR, 81- *Concurrent Pos:* Fel biochem, Inst Enzyme Res, Univ Wis-Madison, 62-64; spec fel, Nat Cancer Inst, 67-69; grants, Am Cancer Soc, 67-68 & 75-, Nat Cancer Inst, 67-70 & 74-84, John A Hartford Found, 69-74 & Wright Found, 76-81; vis prof molecular biol, Univ Geneva, 73-74. *Mem:* AAAS; Am Asn Path; Am Asn Cancer Res. *Res:* Mechanisms of oncogenesis; environmental carcinogenesis; control of cell proliferation; molecular biology. *Mailing Add:* Kenneth Norris Jr Cancer Res Inst Sch Med Univ Southern Calif Los Angeles CA 90033

O'BRIEN, ROBERT JOHN, physical chemistry, atmospheric chemistry, see previous edition

O'BRIEN, ROBERT L, b New Bedford, Mass, July 29, 36; m 56, 82; c 5. FLUID MECHANICS, THERMODYNAMICS. *Educ:* Carnegie Inst Technol, BS & MS, 57. *Prof Exp:* Res engr, 55-65, supvr air-breathing propulsion, 65-67, chief, 67-77, mgr eng res, United Aircraft Res Labs, 77-81, MGR DIV COORDR UNITED TECHNOL RES CTR, 81- *Concurrent Pos:* Lectr, Rensselaer Polytech Inst, 64-65; mem, Air Augmented Propulsion Working Group, Joint Army-Navy-NASA-Air Force Interagency Propulsion Comt, 68-, Naval Aeroballistics Adv Comt, 70 & 71 & US Gas Turbine Sci Deleg to People's Repub China, 79. *Mem:* Am Soc Mech Engrs; Am Inst Aeronaut & Astronaut. *Res:* Supersonic inlet technology; gas dynamics; turbulent flow; supersonic boundary layers and heat transfer; turbulent mixing; supersonic compressors; advanced air-breathing propulsion concepts. *Mailing Add:* United Technol Res Ctr East Hartford CT 06108

O'BRIEN, ROBERT NEVILLE, b Nanaimo, BC, June 14, 21; m 52; c 5. PHYSICAL CHEMISTRY. *Educ:* Univ BC, BASc, 51, MASc, 52; Univ Manchester, PhD(metall), 55. *Prof Exp:* Asst physics, Univ BC, 52; fel pure chem, Can Nat Res Coun, 55-57; from asst prof to assoc prof chem, Univ Alta, 57-66; assoc prof, 66-68, PROF CHEM, UNIV VICTORIA, 68- *Concurrent Pos:* Vis scholar, Univ Calif, Berkeley, 64-65; consult, UniRoyal Res Labs & Bapco Paint; mem bd mgt, BC Res Coun; pres & chief consult, ReTech Ltd. *Mem:* Am Chem Soc; Electrochem Soc; fel Chem Inst Can; fel Royal Soc Arts; AAAS. *Res:* Electrode processes; optical studies of working electrodes in metal electrodeposition cells; surface chemistry; electrets; gas-liquid interface. *Mailing Add:* Dept of Chem Univ of Victoria Victoria BC V8W 2Y2 Can

O'BRIEN, ROBERT THOMAS, b Bismarck, NDak, Dec 20, 25; m 48; c 5. BACTERIAL PHYSIOLOGY, BIOCHEMISTRY. *Educ:* Univ NDak, BS, 50, MS, 52; Wash State Univ, PhD(bact), 56. *Prof Exp:* Asst bact, Univ NDak, 50-52, instr, 52; asst, Wash State Univ, 52-53, actg instr, 53-54, asst, 54-56; biol scientist, Gen Elec Co, 56-64, consult microbiologist, 64-66; PROF BIOL, NMEX STATE UNIV, 66-, CHMN DEPT, 78- *Concurrent Pos:* Consult, Azar Bros, Inc, 67- *Mem:* AAAS; Am Soc Microbiol; Brit Soc Gen Microbiol. *Res:* Survival of animal viruses in aquatic environments; mechanisms of hulogen inactivation of animal viruses. *Mailing Add:* Dept of Biol NMex State Univ Las Cruces NM 88003

O'BRIEN, STEPHEN JAMES, b Rochester, NY, Sept 30, 44; m 68. GENETICS. *Educ:* St Francis Col, BS, 66; Cornell Univ, PhD(genetics), 71. *Prof Exp:* NIH fel biochem, 71-73, GENETICIST, NAT CANCER INST, 73-, CHIEF, SECT GENETICS, LAB VIROL CARCINOGENESIS, 80- *Concurrent Pos:* NIH fel, Geront Res Ctr, 71-72; NIH fel, Nat Cancer Inst, 72-73. *Mem:* Am Soc Naturalists; Genetics Soc Am; Tissue Cult Asn; Am Genetics Asn. *Res:* Human biochemical genetics; somatic cell genetics; virol oncology. *Mailing Add:* Viral Biol Br Bldg 37 NCI-NIH Bethesda MD 20014

O'BRIEN, THOMAS DORAN, b Washington, DC, Mar 31, 10; m 35; c 2. INORGANIC CHEMISTRY. *Educ:* George Washington Univ, BS, 35, MS, 38; Univ Ill, PhD(inorg chem), 40. *Prof Exp:* Res chemist, Naval Res Lab, 40-42 & Barrett Div, Allied Chem & Dye Corp, NJ, 42-43; asst prof chem, Tulane Univ, 43-45; from asst prof to assoc prof, Univ Minn, 45-55; prof & head dept, Kans State Univ, 55-60; prof & dean grad sch, 60-77, res coordr, 70-77, EMER PROF CHEM, UNIV NEV, RENO, 77- *Concurrent Pos:* Prog dir & actg dep div dir, NSF, 67-68. *Mem:* Am Chem Soc. *Res:* Inorganic coordination compounds; heterogeneous catalysis. *Mailing Add:* PO Box 832 Bonita CA 92002

O'BRIEN, THOMAS JOSEPH, physical chemistry, theoretical chemistry, see previous edition

O'BRIEN, THOMAS V, b Cincinnati, Ohio, Apr 30, 37; m 62; c 4. TOPOLOGY. *Educ:* Xavier Univ, BS, 59, MS, 60; Syracuse Univ, PhD(math), 65. *Prof Exp:* Asst prof math, Marquette Univ, 64-69; asst prof, 69-71, ASSOC PROF MATH, BOWLING GREEN STATE UNIV, 71- *Mem:* Am Math Soc; Math Asn Am. *Res:* Dynamical systems; study of continuous flows on manifolds. *Mailing Add:* Dept of Math Bowling Green State Univ Bowling Green OH 43403

O'BRIEN, THOMAS W, b Rochester, Minn, Sept 17, 38; m 64. PHYSIOLOGY, BIOCHEMISTRY. *Educ:* St Thomas Col, BS, 62; Marquette Univ, MS, 63, PhD(physiol), 65. *Prof Exp:* Fel biochem, NJ Col Med, 64-65, instr, 65-66; asst prof, 66-74, assoc prof, 74-81, PROF BIOCHEM & MOLECULAR BIOL, COL MED, UNIV FLA, 81- *Mem:* Am Chem Soc; Am Soc Biol Chemists; Am Soc Cell Biol. *Res:* Structure and function of ribosomes; mitochondrial biogenesis; mitochondrial protein synthesis. *Mailing Add:* Dept of Biochem Univ of Fla Gainesville FL 32601

O'BRIEN, TIMOTHY LANE, cell biology, electron microscopy, see previous edition

O'BRIEN, VIVIAN, b Baltimore, Md, Feb 1, 24. FLUID DYNAMICS. *Educ:* Goucher Col, AB, 45; Johns Hopkins Univ, MA, 50, MS, 54, PhD, 60. *Prof Exp:* Jr aerodynamicist, Martin Co, 45-47; asst aeronaut, 47-55, assoc physicist fluid dynamics, Appl Physics Lab, 55-58, PHYSICIST FLUID DYNAMICS, APPL PHYSICS LAB, JOHNS HOPKINS UNIV, 58-, LECTR, DEPT CHEM ENG, 79- *Mem:* Fel Am Phys Soc; Am Inst Aeronaut & Astronaut; Soc Women Engrs. *Res:* Theoretical transonic and supersonic aerodynamics; turbulent flow; viscous vortex flow; viscous biological flows; drops and bubbles; porous media flows; rheology of liquids. *Mailing Add:* Appl Physics Lab J Hopkins Univ Johns Hopkins Rd Laurel MD 20707

O'BRIEN, WALTER J, civil engineering, see previous edition

O'BRIEN, WILLIAM DANIEL, JR, b Chicago, Ill, July 19, 42. BIOACOUSTICS, BIOENGINEERING. *Educ:* Univ Ill, Urbana, BS, 66, MS, 68, PhD(elec eng), 70. *Prof Exp:* Res assoc ultrasonic biophys, Univ Ill, Urbana, 70-71; res scientist, Bur Radiol Health, Food & Drug Admin, 71-75; asst prof, 75-80, ASSOC PROF ELEC ENG & BIOENG, UNIV ILL, URBANA, 80- *Concurrent Pos:* Assoc ed, Trans Sonics Ultrasonics, Inst Elec & Electronics Engrs. *Mem:* Inst Elec & Electronics Engrs; Acoust Soc Am; Am Inst Ultrasound Med; AAAS; Sigma Xi. *Res:* Examination of the mechanisms by which ultrasonic energy interacts with biological materials including ultrasonic biophysics, bioengineering, dosimetry and bioeffects along with selected ultrasonic instrument development. *Mailing Add:* Dept Elec Eng Bioacoust Res Lab Univ Ill 1406 W Green St Urbana IL 61801

O'BRIEN, WILLIAM JOHN, b Summit, NJ, Nov 30, 42; m 64; c 1. AQUATIC ECOLOGY, LIMNOLOGY. *Educ:* Gettysburg Col, BA, 65; Mich State Univ, PhD(aquatic ecol), 70. *Prof Exp:* Coherent Areas Prog fel aquatic ecol & res assoc, W K Kellogg Biol Sta, Mich State Univ, 70-71; asst prof limnol, 71-76, ASSOC PROF SYSTS & ECOL, UNIV KANS, 76- *Concurrent Pos:* Res grant, NSF, 75 & Kans Water Resources Inst, 74. *Mem:* AAAS; Am Soc Limnol & Oceanog; Ecol Soc Am; Int Asn Theoret & Appl Limnol. *Res:* Mathematical models of aquatic systems; primary productivity of aquatic systems; theory of limiting factors; zooplankton ecology; phytozooplankton physiological ecology; ecology of fish seeding. *Mailing Add:* Snow Hall Dept of Systs & Ecol Univ of Kans Lawrence KS 66044

O'BRIEN, WILLIAM JOSEPH, b New York, NY, July 25, 35; m 63; c 2. DENTAL MATERIALS, SURFACE CHEMISTRY. *Educ:* City Col New York, BS, 58; NY Univ, MS, 62; Univ Mich, PhD(metall eng), 67. *Prof Exp:* Assoc dir res, J F Jelenko Co, 58-61; from instr to assoc prof mat sci, Marquette Univ, 61-70; assoc prof, 70-73, PROF & DIR, SURV SCI LAB, DENT RES INST, UNIV MICH, ANN ARBOR, 73- *Concurrent Pos:* Consult, WHO, 67-68 & Am Dent Asn, 67-; chmn dept dent mat, Marquette Univ, 67-70; prin investr, USPHS grant; res assoc, Vet Admin Hosp, Wood, Wis, 67-; secy, Dent Mat Group, 69-73, pres, 75-76. *Honors & Awards:* UN Cert, UN, 67. *Mem:* Gen Systs Res; Int Asn Dent Res. *Res:* Biomaterials; noble metals; surface phenomena; capillary phenomena; ceramics-mechanical and optical properties. *Mailing Add:* Dent Res Inst Univ Mich Ann Arbor MI 48104

O'BRIEN, WILLIAM M, b Bethel, Maine, Feb 26, 31; m 57; c 3. EPIDEMIOLOGY, GENETICS. *Educ:* Tufts Univ, BS, 52; Yale Univ, MD, 56. *Prof Exp:* Clin assoc, Nat Inst Arthritis & Metab Dis, 58-60; sr registr, Manchester Royal Infirmary, Eng, 60-61; sr clin investr, Nat Inst Arthritis & Metab Dis, 61-64; asst prof, Sch Med, Yale Univ, 64-67; assoc prof internal med, 67-72, PROF INTERNAL MED, SCH MED, UNIV VA, 72- *Mem:* AAAS; Am Epidemiol Soc; Am Rheumatism Asn; Asn Comput Mach; Heberden Soc. *Res:* Rheumatic diseases; drug testing. *Mailing Add:* Dept of Internal Med Univ of Va Sch of Med Charlottesville VA 22903

OBRINSKY, WILLIAM, b May 15, 13; US citizen; m 46; c 4. MEDICINE, PEDIATRICS. *Educ:* NY Univ, BS, 34, MD, 38. *Prof Exp:* From intern to resident, Morrisania Hosp, 38-41; resident, Queens Gen Hosp, 41-42 & Mt Sinai Hosp, 46-47; from instr to assoc prof pediat, Sch Med, La State Univ, 48-53; pediatrician, Staten Island Med Ctr, 54-64; from asst clin prof to assoc clin prof pediat, 55-67, assoc prof, 67-68, PROF PEDIAT, ALBERT EINSTEIN COL MED, 68- *Concurrent Pos:* Attend, Montefiore Hosp, 64-; attend, Morrisania Hosp, 64-75, dir pediat, 68-75. *Mem:* AAAS; Am Acad Pediat; Am Pediat Soc; Soc Pediat Res; NY Acad Sci. *Mailing Add:* Dept of Pediat 111 E 210th St Bronx NY 10467

O'BRYANT, DAVID CLAUDE, b Canton, Ill, Mar 18, 35; m 60; c 1. MECHANICAL ENGINEERING. *Educ:* Univ Ill, Urbana, BS, 58, MS, 61, EdD(voc & tech educ), 70. *Prof Exp:* Teaching asst gen eng, Univ Ill, Urbana, 59-60; designer, Carroll Henneman & Assoc, 60-61; instr gen eng, 60-70, ASST PROF GEN ENG, UNIV ILL, URBANA, 70- *Concurrent Pos:* Tech skills coordr, Peace Corps, Kenya, 71-72. *Mem:* Am Tech Educ Asn; Nat Soc Prof Engrs. *Res:* Vocational and technical education; engineering education and evaluation; teaching improvement. *Mailing Add:* 35 Sherwin Dr Urbana IL 61801

OBST, ANDREW WESLEY, b Lwow, Poland, Aug 3, 42; US citizen; m 68. PHYSICS. *Educ:* Univ Alta, BSc, 63, MSc, 66; Univ Ky, PhD(exp nuclear physics), 70. *Prof Exp:* Fel nuclear physics, Fla State Univ, 71-73, Univ Tex, Austin, 73-75 & Northwestern Univ, 75-78; STAFF MEM NUCLEAR PHYSICS, LOS ALAMOS SCI LAB, 78- *Res:* Experimental low and medium energy nuclear physics. *Mailing Add:* MS 674 Los Alamos Sci Lab Los Alamos NM 87545

O'CALLAGHAN, DENNIS JOHN, b New Orleans, La, July 26, 40; m 67; c 1. ANIMAL VIROLOGY, MEDICAL MICROBIOLOGY. *Educ:* Loyola Univ, New Orleans, BS, 62; Univ Miss, PhD(microbiol), 68. *Prof Exp:* Fel virol, Dept Biochem, Med Ctr, Univ Alta, 68-70, asst prof biochem, 70-71; from asst prof to assoc prof, 71-77, PROF MICROBIOL, MED CTR, UNIV MISS, 77- *Concurrent Pos:* Res grant, Brown-Hazen Fund Res Corp, 72; NIH & NSF res grants, 73-; assoc ed, J Miss Acad Sci, 75-; ad hoc grant reviewer, Am Cancer Soc & NIH. *Mem:* Am Soc Biol Chemists; Am Asn Cancer Res; Brit Soc Gen Microbiol; Soc Exp Med & Biol; Am Soc Exp Path. *Res:* Biochemistry of herpes virus replication, concerning control of viral DNA replication of defective interfering particles; tumor virology; role of herpes viruses in human cancer. *Mailing Add:* Dept Microbiol Univ Miss Med Ctr Jackson MS 39216

O'CALLAGHAN, RICHARD J, b New Orleans, La, Jan 17, 44; m 65; c 2. MICROBIOLOGY, MOLECULAR BIOLOGY. *Educ:* La State Univ, BS, 65; Univ Miss, MS, 66, PhD(med microbiol), 70. *Prof Exp:* Fel biochem, Univ Alta, 70-71, instr, 71; asst prof, 72-77, ASSOC PROF MICROBIOL, MED CTR, LA STATE UNIV, 77- *Concurrent Pos:* E G Schleider Educ Fo nd res grants, 64-81; La Heart Asn res grants, 76-79; sci adv, Southern Univ, New Orleans, 76- *Mem:* Am Soc Microbiol. *Res:* Mechanisms and epidemiology of antibiotic resistance; characterization of influeza C virus. *Mailing Add:* Dept of Microbiol La State Univ Sch of Med New Orleans LA 70112

OCAMPO-FRIEDMANN, ROSELI C, b Manila, Philippines, Nov 23, 37. ECOLOGY, PHYCOLOGY. *Educ:* Univ Philippines, BSc, 58; Hebrew Univ Jerusalem, MSc, 66; Fla State Univ, PhD(biol), 73. *Prof Exp:* Res assoc limnol & phycol, Nat Inst Sci & Technol Philippines, 58-67; teaching asst bot & lab technologist phycol, 67-73, RES ASSOC PHYCOL, FLA STATE UNIV, 73- *Concurrent Pos:* Asst prof biol, Fla A&M Univ, 74- *Mem:* Int Phycol Soc; Phycol Soc Am; Bot Soc Am; Indian Phycol Soc; Sigma Xi. *Res:* Culture and taxonomy of unicellular blue-green algae; microbiology; biology of microorganisms in extreme habitats. *Mailing Add:* Dept of Biol Sci Fla State Univ Tallahassee FL 32306

OCCELLI, MARIO LORENZO, b Luino, Italy, Dec 16, 42; US citizen; m 70; c 3. CHEMISTRY. *Educ:* Iowa State Univ, BS, 67, PhD(phys chem), 73. *Prof Exp:* Chemist, Air Prod & Chem, Inc, 73-76; sr res chemist, Davison Div, W R Grace Co, 76-79; SR RES CHEMIST, GULF OIL CORP, 79- *Mem:* Am Chem Soc. *Res:* Zeolites synthesis and characterization; preparation and testing of zeolite based catalysts for the upgrading of heavy oils, shale oils and raffinates from coal; synthesis of chemicals from zeolite catalyzed reactions. *Mailing Add:* 4131 Northampton Dr Allison Park PA 15101

OCCOLOWITZ, JOHN LEWIS, b Melbourne, Australia, July 30, 31; m 62; c 2. MASS SPECTROMETRY. *Educ:* Univ Melbourne, BSc, 52, DipED, 53, MSc, 65. *Prof Exp:* Instr sci, Victoria, Australia Educ Dept, 53-55; res scientist chem, Dept Supply Defense Stands Labs, Australian Govt, 55-67; RES SCIENTIST CHEM, LILLY RES LABS, ELI LILLY & CO, 67- *Mem:* Am Soc Mass Spectrometry. *Res:* Determination of organic structures using mass spectrometry; elucidation of the structure of ions formed in the mass spectrometer, by labelling and measurement of energetics of formation. *Mailing Add:* Dept MC 525 Lilly Res Labs PO Box 618 Indianapolis IN 46206

OCHIAI, EI-ICHIRO, b Tokyo, Japan, Sept 15, 36; m; c 2. BIOINORGANIC CHEMISTRY, CHEMICAL EVOLUTION. *Educ:* Univ Tokyo, BSc, 59, MSc, 61, PhD(chem), 64. *Prof Exp:* Instr indust chem, Univ Tokyo, 64-69; fel chem, Ohio State Univ, 66-68; fel, Univ BC, 69-71, instr, 71-80; sr res assoc, Univ Md, 80-81; ASSOC PROF, DEPT CHEM, JUNIATA COL, 81- *Mem:* Am Chem Soc; AAAS; Japanese Chem Soc. *Res:* Bioinorganic chemistry, especially B12 coenzyme dependent enzyme mechanism, oxygen activation, photosynthetic water decomposition mechanism; bioinorganic aspects of chemical evolution and biological evolution. *Mailing Add:* Dept Chem Juniata Col Huntington PA 16652

OCHOA, SEVERO, b Luarca, Spain, Sept 24, 05; nat; m 31. MOLECULAR BIOLOGY. *Educ:* Malaga Col, Spain, BA, 21; Univ Madrid, MD, 29. *Hon Degrees:* Many from var Am & foreign cols & univs. *Prof Exp:* Lectr physiol & biochem, Sch Med, Univ Madrid, 31-35, head physiol div, Inst Med Res, 35-36; guest res asst physiol, Kaiser-Wilhelm Inst Med Res, 36-37; Lankester investr, Marine Biol Lab, Plymouth, Eng, 37; demonstr biochem & Nuffield res asst, Oxford Univ, 38-40; instr pharmacol & res assoc, Sch Med, Wash Univ, 41-42; res assoc med, Sch Med, NY Univ, 42-45, asst prof biochem, 45-46, prof pharmacol & chmn dept, 46-54, prof biochem & chmn dept, 54-74; DISTINGUISHED MEM, ROCHE INST MOLECULAR BIOL, 74- *Concurrent Pos:* Fel from Univ Madrid, Kaiser-Wilhelm Inst, Berlin & Heidelberg, 29-31 & Nat Inst Med Res, London, 32-33; mem physiol study sect, USPHS, 47-50, biochem study sect, 52-55; mem biochem panel, US Off Naval Res, 53-55, chmn, 55-57; US rep, Int Union Biochem, 55-61; hon prof, San Marcos Univ, Lima, 57; hon mem fac, Univ Chile, 57; mem sci adv comt, Mass Gen Hosp, 57-60; mem dept biol, Brookhaven Nat Lab, 59-62; mem staff, Jane Coffin Childs Fund Med Res, 61-63, Merck Inst Ther Res, 65-74 & Am Cancer Soc, 69-70. *Honors & Awards:* Nobel Prize in Med, 59; Neuberg Medal Biochem, 51; Price Award, Fr Soc Biol Chem, 55; Borden Award, Asn Am Med Cols, 58; NY Univ Medal, 60; Order of the Rising Sun 2nd Class & Gold Medal, Japan, 67; Carlos Jimenez Diaz Lectr Award, Univ Madrid, 69; Quevedo Gold Medal Award, Spain, 69; Albert Gallatin Medal, NY Univ, 70; Nat Medal Sci, 79. *Mem:* Nat Acad Sci; Am Soc Biol Chemists (pres, 58); Harvey Soc (vpres, 52-53, pres, 53-54); fel Am Acad Arts & Sci; fel NY Acad Sci. *Res:* Biochemistry of muscle and fermentation; respiratory enzymes; enzymatic mechanisms of carbon dioxide assimilation, citric and fatty acid cycles; synthesis of nucleic acid and proteins, genetic code and translation of the genetic message. *Mailing Add:* Roche Inst Molecular Biol Nutley NJ 07110

OCHRYMOWYCZ, LEO ARTHUR, b Shaok, Ukraine, May 20, 43; US citizen; m 70. ORGANIC CHEMISTRY. *Educ:* St Mary's Col, Minn, BA, 65; Iowa State Univ, PhD(org chem), 69. *Prof Exp:* Asst prof, 69-74, ASSOC PROF CHEM, UNIV WIS-EAU CLAIRE, 74- *Concurrent Pos:* Res fel, Iowa State Univ, 70-71. *Mem:* Am Chem Soc. *Res:* Chemistry of macrocyclic polythioethers; coordination chemistry of post-transitional metals; general organo-sulfur chemistry, especially beta-keto sulfoxides and lipids; development of carbonyl synthesis reagents. *Mailing Add:* Dept of Chem Univ of Wis Eau Claire WI 54701

OCHS, SIDNEY, b Fall River, Mass, June 30, 24; m 49; c 3. NEUROPHYSIOLOGY, MEDICAL BIOPHYSICS. *Educ:* Univ Chicago, PhD, 52. *Prof Exp:* Res assoc, Ill Neuropsychiat Inst, 53-54; asst prof, Med Ctr, Univ Tex, 56-58; from assoc prof to prof physiol, 58-70, PROF PHYSIOL, SCH MED, IND UNIV, INDIANAPOLIS, 70-, DIR MED BIOPHYS PROG, 68- *Concurrent Pos:* Res fel, Calif Inst Technol, 54-56; NSF sr fel, Dept Biophys, Univ Col, Univ London, 63-64; ed, J Neurobiol, 68-77, assoc ed, 77- *Res:* Functions of cerebral cortex; axoplasmic transport in nerve; muscle membrane properties. *Mailing Add:* 912 Forest Blvd N Dr Indianapolis IN 46240

OCHS, STEFAN A(LBERT), b Frankfurt, Ger, Sept 16, 22; nat US; m 48; c 3. ENGINEERING PHYSICS. *Educ:* Columbia Univ, BS, 43, MA, 49, PhD(physics), 53. *Prof Exp:* Asst, Columbia Univ, 47-50; tutor, City Col New York, 50-51; res engr, RCA Corp, 52-65, sr engr, 65-75; SR MECH ENGR, INT SIGNAL & CONTROL CORP, 75- *Mem:* AAAS. *Res:* Mechanical design of electronic equipment. *Mailing Add:* Int Signal & Control Corp 3050 Hempland Rd Lancaster PA 17601

OCHSNER, (EDWARD WILLIAM) ALTON, thoracic & vascular surgery, deceased

OCHSNER, JOHN LOCKWOOD, b Madison, Wis, Feb 10, 27; m 54; c 4. SURGERY. *Educ:* Tulane Univ La, MD, 52; Am Bd Surg, dipl, 60; Am Bd Thoracic Surg, dipl, 60. *Prof Exp:* From intern to asst resident, Univ Mich Hosp, Ann Arbor, 52-54; resident, Baylor Univ Affil Hosp, Houston, Tex, 56-60; instr, Sch Med, Baylor Univ, 60-61; instr surg, 61-65, clin assoc prof, 65-69, CLIN PROF SURG, SCH MED, TULANE UNIV, 69-, CHMN DEPT SURG, OCHSNER CLIN, 66- *Concurrent Pos:* Chief surg res, Jefferson Davis Hosp, Houston, 58-59 & Tex Children's Hosp, Houston, 59-60; mem staff, Ochsner Clin, 61-66; chief surg, Ochsner Found Hosp, New Orleans; vis surgeon, Charity Hosp La & E A Conway Mem Hosp, Monroe; mem courtesy staff, Sara Mayo Hosp & Flint Goodridge Hosp, New Orleans; consult cardiovasc surgeon, Lafayette Mem Hosp; consult thoracic surgeon, USPHS Hosp, New Orleans; consult heart surgeon, La Dept Health. *Mem:* Soc Vascular Surg; Soc Thoracic Surg; Am Col Surgeons; Am Col Chest Physicians; Int Cardiovasc Soc (secy-gen). *Mailing Add:* Ochsner Clin 1514 Jefferson Hwy New Orleans LA 70121

OCHSNER, SEYMOUR FISKE, b Chicago, Ill, Nov 29, 15; m 45; c 3. RADIOLOGY. *Educ:* Dartmouth Col, AB, 37; Univ Pa, MD, 47. *Prof Exp:* Staff physician, Stony Wold Sanatorium, 47-49; intern, Johnston-Willis Hosp, 49-50; fel radiol, Ochsner Found Hosp, 50-53; assoc prof, 62-67, PROF CLIN RADIOL, SCH MED, TULANE UNIV, 67-; CONSULT, OCHSNER CLIN, 53- *Honors & Awards:* Distinguished Serv Award, Southern Med Asn, 71; Gold Medal, Am Col Radiol, 81. *Mem:* Radiol Soc NAm (vpres, 65); Roentgen Ray Soc (vpres, 66, pres, 76); Am Col Radiol (pres, 72); AMA. *Res:* Clinical radiology and radiation therapy. *Mailing Add:* Ochsner Clin 1514 Jefferson Hwy New Orleans LA 70121

OCKEN, PAUL ROBERT, b New York, NY, July 11, 39; m 65; c 2. BIOCHEMISTRY, ORGANIC CHEMISTRY. *Educ:* Springfield Col, BS, 61; NY Univ, PhD(biochem), 67. *Prof Exp:* Res assoc carcinogenesis & intern environ med, Sch Med, NY Univ, 66-67; instr biochem, 67-68, ASST PROF BIOCHEM, UNIV MED & DENT NJ, 68- *Mem:* AAAS. *Res:* Mechanisms of enzyme catalysis; environmental agents as inducers of cancer; hormone regulation and endogenous factors that influence host-tumor relationship. *Mailing Add:* Dept of Biochem Univ Med & Dent NJ Newark NJ 07103

OCKERMAN, HERBERT W, b Chaplin, Ky, Jan 16, 32; m 55. FOOD CHEMISTRY, STATISTICS. *Educ:* Univ Ky, BS, 54, MS, 58; NC State Col, PhD(animal husb, statist), 62. *Prof Exp:* PROF ANIMAL SCI, OHIO STATE UNIV, 61- *Mem:* Am Meat Sci Asn; Am Soc Animal Sci; Inst Food Technol; Europ Meat Res Workers; Am Soc Testing & Mat. *Res:* Lipids and antioxidants; food flavor and analysis; sterile tissue; tissue biochemistry and microbiology. *Mailing Add:* Dept Animal Sci Ohio State Univ Columbus OH 43210

OCKERSE, RALPH, b Brussels, Belg, May 17, 33; US citizen; m 56, 78; c 4. PLANT PHYSIOLOGY, BIOCHEMISTRY. *Educ:* State Teachers Col Neth, BA, 56; Baldwin Wallace Col, BS, 62; Yale Univ, PhD(plant physiol, biochem), 66. *Prof Exp:* Lab asst photosynthesis, Philips Res Labs, Neth, 53-55; res asst tissue culture, Chas Pfizer Co, NY, 57-58; biochemist, Union Carbide Co, Ohio, 62; from asst prof to prof biol, Hope Col, 66-76; PROF BIOL & CHMN DEPT, SCH SCI, PURDUE UNIV, INDIANAPOLIS, 76- *Concurrent Pos:* NSF res grant, Hope Col, 69-70, dir NSF undergrad res partic grant, 71, 72, 73 & 75; res grant, Res Corp, 74-76. *Mem:* AAAS; Am Chem Soc; Am Soc Plant Physiol; Royal Neth Bot Soc; Japanese Soc Plant Physiologists. *Res:* Physiology and biochemistry of plant growth regulation; mechanism of hormone action and interactions with macromolecules; plant tissue culture and development. *Mailing Add:* Dept Biol Sch Sci Purdue Univ 1201 E 38th St PO Box 647 Indianapolis IN 46223

OCKMAN, NATHAN, b New York, NY, Dec 29, 26. MOLECULAR BIOPHYSICS. *Educ:* Purdue Univ, BS, 49; Univ Calif, Berkeley, MA, 50; Univ Mich, PhD(physics), 57. *Prof Exp:* Fel chem, Harvard Univ, 57-58; mem tech staff, RCA Labs, Inc, 59-65; mem tech staff, Gen Tel & Electronics Labs, 65-69; fel physiol, Albert Einstein Col Med, 70-81; VIS ASSOC PROF PHYSICS, CITY COL NEW YORK, 81- *Mem:* Am Phys Soc. *Res:* Ultraviolet and visible absorption and reflection spectroscopy applied to the study of phospholipid dispersions, monolayers and bilayers; infrared spectroscopy applied to study of monolayers and films of phospholipids and proteins; picosecond laser spectroscopy applied to study of vibrational relaxation of biological molecules. *Mailing Add:* 137 Riverside Dr New York NY 10024

OCONE, LUKE RALPH, b Bridgeport, Conn, Mar 10, 25; m 53; c 4. INORGANIC CHEMISTRY. *Educ:* Brooklyn Polytech Inst, BS, 51; Pa State Univ, PhD(chem), 56. *Prof Exp:* Res chemist photoprod dept, E I du Pont de Nemours & Co, 55-58; group leader explor chem, 58-70, GROUP LEADER COM DEVELOP, PENWALT CORP, 71- *Mem:* Am Chem Soc. *Res:* Metal complexes and metallorganics; photographic science and technology. *Mailing Add:* Penwalt 3 Parkway Philadelphia PA 19102

O'CONNELL, EDMOND J, JR, b Providence, RI, Apr 26, 39; m 65; c 5. ORGANIC CHEMISTRY, PHOTOCHEMISTRY. *Educ:* Providence Col, BS, 60; Yale Univ, PhD(chem), 64. *Prof Exp:* Res chemist radiation physics lab, E I du Pont de Nemours & Co, 64-67; from asst prof to assoc prof chem, 67-75, PROF CHEM, FAIRFIELD UNIV, 75-, CHMN DEPT CHEM, 81- *Concurrent Pos:* Petrol Res Fund grant, 68-70 & 72-74; Res Corp grant, 72-73. *Mem:* Am Chem Soc. *Res:* Organic photochemistry, especially reaction mechanisms and the relation of photo-reactivity to molecular structure. *Mailing Add:* Dept of Chem Fairfield Univ Fairfield CT 06430

O'CONNELL, FRANK DENNIS, b Lynn, Mass, July 21, 27; m 48; c 3. PHARMACOGNOSY. *Educ:* Mass Col Pharm, BS, 51, MS, 53; Purdue Univ, PhD(pharmacog), 57. *Prof Exp:* Asst prof pharm, 57-58, from asst prof to assoc prof pharmacog, 58-69, actg dean, Sch Pharm, 72-73, asst dean, Sch Pharm, 74-81, PROF PHARMACOG, WVA UNIV, 69-, ACTG DEAN, 81- *Mem:* Am Soc Pharmacog (treas, 73-76); Am Pharmaceut Asn. *Res:* Isolation and biosynthesis of natural medicinal products; biochemistry; plant tissue cultures; biochemical transformations. *Mailing Add:* Sch of Pharm WVa Univ Morgantown WV 26506

O'CONNELL, HARRY E(DWARD), b Glens Falls, NY, Mar 17, 16; m 39. CHEMICAL ENGINEERING. *Educ:* Univ Mich, BS, 38, MS 39, PhD, 42. *Prof Exp:* Chem engr, Ethyl Corp, 41-47, head process design, 47-51, group head process eng, 51, assoc dir process develop, 51-54, staff asst to vpres, 54, proj mgr, 54-60; mgr proj develop, Tenneco Chem Co, Tenn Gas Transmission Co, 60-63, vpres, Tenneco Mfg Co, 63-71, vpres & gen mgr Newport Div, Tenneco Chem, Inc, 71-76; exec vpres, 76-78, PRES, PETRO-TEX CHEM CORP, 78- *Mem:* Am Chem Soc; Am Inst Chem Engrs. *Res:* Distillation; heat transfer; thermodynamics. *Mailing Add:* 163 Litchfield Lane Houston TX 77024

O'CONNELL, JESSE ELBERT, b Sanford, NC, July 21, 26. BOTANY. *Educ:* Wake Forest Col, BS, 48, MS, 49; Univ NC, PhD, 55. *Prof Exp:* Instr sci, Chowan Col, 49-50; instr bot, NC State Col, 50-52; asst prof, Univ Idaho, 55-59; sci educ specialist, 59-62, head, Tokyo Off, 62-66, prog dir, US-Japan & US-Repub China Coop Sci Progs, 66-71, prog mgr, E Asia & Pac Progs, 71-77, SECT HEAD, LATIN AM & PAC SECT, DIV INT PROGS, NSF, 77- *Mem:* AAAS; Bot Soc Am. *Res:* Plant geography. *Mailing Add:* Div Int Prog 1800 G St NW Washington DC 20550

O'CONNELL, JOHN JOSEPH, SR, b Natick, Mass, July 1, 29; m 58; c 4. MATERIALS SCIENCE. *Educ:* Clark Univ, BS, 52, MA, 58. *Prof Exp:* Res chemist, Monsanto Chem Co, WVa, 52-55, res chemist, Spec Projs Dept, Mass, 58-61, sr res chemist, Monsanto Res Corp, 61-64, res group leader inorg chem, 64-69; res group leader mat res, Am Hosp Supply Corp, Mass, 69-70, mgr mat res, Corp Technol Ctr, Calif, 70-75, dir res & develop, Oratec/Am Hosp Supply, 75-78, prog mgr dent, Group Technol Ctr, 78-79, PROG DIR DENT MED SPECIALITIES BUS, AM HOSP SUPPLY CORP, 79- *Mem:* Am Chem Soc. *Res:* Biomaterials research, metal coordination compounds as applied to catalyst and materials; dental materials. *Mailing Add:* Am Hosp Supply Corp Med Spec Bus 2132 Michelson Dr Irvine CA 92715

O'CONNELL, JOHN P, b Morristown, NJ, Sept 19, 38; m 59; c 3. CHEMICAL ENGINEERING. *Educ:* Pomona Col, BA, 61; Mass Inst Technol, SB, 61, SM, 62; Univ Calif, Berkeley, PhD(chem eng), 67. *Prof Exp:* Actg instr chem eng, Univ Calif, Berkeley, 65-66; from asst prof to assoc prof, 66-74, actg chmn, 81-82, PROF CHEM ENG, UNIV FLA, 74- *Concurrent Pos:* Vis prof, Univ Calif, Los Angeles, 73; vis scholar, Stanford Univ, 73-74 & Calif Tech, 73. *Mem:* AAAS; Am Chem Soc; Am Soc Eng Educ; Am Inst Chem Engrs. *Res:* Statistical mechanics; molecular thermodynamics; phase equilibria; surfactant systems; micellization and solubilization. *Mailing Add:* Dept Chem Eng Univ Fla Gainesville FL 32601

O'CONNELL, PAUL WILLIAM, b Newark, NY, Aug 5, 22; m 49; c 7. BIOCHEMISTRY. *Educ:* Univ Notre Dame, BS, 43; Univ Rochester, PhD(biochem), 49. *Prof Exp:* Fel chem, Univ Pittsburgh, 49-51; res assoc, 51-64, res sect head, 64-79, RES MGR, UPJOHN CO, 79- *Mem:* AAAS; Am Chem Soc. *Res:* Biochemistry of lipids; enzymes; information handling. *Mailing Add:* 2509 Russet Dr Kalamazoo MI 49008

OCONNELL, RICHARD JOHN, b Helena, Mont, Aug 27, 41; c 1. TECTONOPHYSICS, SOLID EARTH GEOPHYSICS. *Educ:* Calif Inst Technol, BS, 63, MS, 66, PhD(geophysics), 69. *Prof Exp:* Res fel geophysics, Calif Inst Technol, 69-70; res geophysicist, Univ Calif, Los Angeles, 70-71; asst prof geol, 71-74, assoc prof, 74-77, PROF GEOPHYSICS, HARVARD UNIV, 77- *Concurrent Pos:* Consult, Los Alamos Nat Lab, 78-; mem, Lunar & Planetary Coun, Univs Space Res Asn, 82- *Mem:* Am Geophys Union; AAAS. *Res:* Dynamics and evolution of planetary interiors; plate tectonics; rheology of solids; mechanical properties of rocks and minerals. *Mailing Add:* Hoffman Lab Harvard Univ 20 Oxford St Cambridge MA 02138

O'CONNELL, ROBERT F, b Athlone, Ireland, Apr 22, 33; m 63; c 3. SOLID STATE PHYSICS, THEORETICAL PHYSICS. *Educ:* Nat Univ Ireland, BSc, 53, DSc, 75; Univ Notre Dame, PhD(physics), 62. *Prof Exp:* Asst lectr physics, Univ Col, Galway, 53-54; with telecommun br, Dept Posts & Tel, Ireland, 54-58; res assoc theoretic physics, Inst Advan Studies, Dublin, 62-64; from asst prof to assoc prof, 64-69, PROF PHYSICS, LA STATE UNIV, BATON ROUGE, 69- *Concurrent Pos:* Syst analyst, Int Bus Mach Corp, Ireland, 63-64; Nat Acad Sci-Nat Res Coun res assoc, NASA Inst Space Studies, NY, 66-67, sr res assoc, 67-; consult, Theoret Phys Div, Lawrence Livermore Lab, Univ Calif, Livermore, 73-75; sr res fel, Sci Res Coun, Eng, 76. *Honors & Awards:* Sir J J Larmor Prize, Univ Col, Galway, 54; Distinguished Res Master, La State Univ, 75. *Mem:* Fel Am Phys Soc; Am Astron Soc; Int Astron Union; Int Soc Gen Relativity & Gravitation. *Res:* High-energy astrophysics; gravitation; atomic physics; solid state physics. *Mailing Add:* Dept Phys & Astron La State Univ Baton Rouge LA 70803

O'CONNELL, ROBERT JAMES, b Syracuse, NY, July 9, 37; m 60; c 2. NEUROPHYSIOLOGY. *Educ:* LeMoyne Col, NY, BS, 63; State Univ NY, PhD(physiol), 67. *Prof Exp:* USPHS res assoc sensory neurophysiol, Fla State Univ, 67-68; asst prof, 68-74, SR RES ASSOC SENSORY NEUROPHYSIOL, ROCKEFELLER UNIV, 74- *Mem:* AAAS; NY Acad Sci. *Res:* Electrophysiological studies of olfactory receptors; isolation and identification of various mammalian pheromones. *Mailing Add:* 1322 2nd Ave New York NY 10021

O'CONNELL, ROBERT WEST, b San Francisco, Calif, Mar 22, 43. EXTRAGALACTIC ASTRONOMY. *Educ:* Univ Calif, Berkeley, AB, 64; Calif Inst Technol, PhD(astron & physics), 70. *Prof Exp:* Res astronomer, Lick Observ, Univ Calif, 69-71; asst prof, 71-76, ASSOC PROF ASTRON, UNIV VA, 76-, CHMN DEPT & DIR, LEANDER MCCORMICK OBSERV, 79- *Concurrent Pos:* Chmn, Int Joint Sci Working Group Starlab, 80- *Mem:* Am Astron Soc; Royal Astron Soc; Int Astron Union; Sigma Xi. *Res:* Extragalactic astronomy (stellar content of normal galaxies, active galaxy nuclei, radio galaxies); ultraviolet and space astronomy; stellar photometry; properties of low mass stars. *Mailing Add:* Dept Astron Univ Va PO Box 3818 Univ Sta Charlottesville VA 22903

O'CONNOR, BRIAN LEE, b Lennox, Calif, Sept 17, 44; m 64; c 2. HUMAN BIOLOGY, PHYSICAL ANTHROPOLOGY. *Educ:* Univ Calif, Berkeley, AB, 69, PhD(anthrop), 74. *Prof Exp:* Asst prof, 74-81, ASSOC PROF ANAT, SCH MED, IND UNIV, INDIANAPOLIS, 81- *Mem:* Am Asn Anatomists. *Res:* Articular neurology and its functional, evolutionary and pathological significance. *Mailing Add:* Dept of Anat Ind Univ Sch of Med Indianapolis IN 46202

O'CONNOR, CAROL ALF, b Hamilton, Ohio, Nov 7, 48. STATISTICS, BIOSTATISTICS. *Educ:* Bowling Green State Univ, BS, 70, MA, 72, PhD(math), 75. *Prof Exp:* Asst prof math statist, Wright State Univ, 75-76; ASST PROF APPL MATH & COMPUT SCI, UNIV LOUISVILLE, 76- *Mem:* Am Math Soc; Inst Math Statist; Am Statist Asn; Asn Women in Math. *Res:* Probability in abstract spaces; engineering statistics. *Mailing Add:* Dept of Math Appl Math & Comput Sci Univ of Louisville Louisville KY 40208

O'CONNOR, CECILIAN LEONARD, b Philadelphia, Pa, Oct 23, 22. PHYSICS. *Educ:* Catholic Univ, BS, 45, MS, 51, PhD(physics), 54. *Prof Exp:* Instr physics, De La Salle Col, Catholic Univ, 50-54; assoc prof, 54-67, chmn dept, 60-74, PROF PHYSICS, MANHATTAN COL, 67-, CHMN DEPT RADIOL & HEALTH SCI, 77- *Mem:* AAAS; Acoust Soc Am; Am Asn Physics Teachers; NY Acad Sci. *Res:* Thermodynamic properties of gases and liquids at ultrasonic and hypersonic frequencies. *Mailing Add:* Dept of Physics Manhattan Col Bronx NY 10471

O'CONNOR, CHARLES TIMOTHY, b Atlantic City, NJ, Aug 1, 30. MEDICAL ENTOMOLOGY. *Educ:* Rutgers Univ, BS, 53, MS, 55; Ohio State Univ, PhD, 58; Tulane Univ, MPH, 61. *Prof Exp:* Asst dept entom, NJ Agr Exp Sta, 53-55; asst, Ohio Agr Exp Sta, 55-58; med entomologist, USPHS, Tex, 59-60; malaria specialist, US AID, Vietnam, 61-63, Ethiopia, 64-66; specialist malaria eradication br, Ctr Dis Control, USPHS, Haiti, 66-70, Brazil, 70-71; MALARIA SPECIALIST, WHO, 71- *Mem:* Entom Soc

Am; Am Mosquito Control Asn; Sigma Xi. *Res:* Control of livestock pests and of vectors of human diseases; study of the entomological aspects of a large-scale malathion trail in Central Java; cytogenetic studies of several anopheline vectors of malaria. *Mailing Add:* 470-B West Shore Dr Brigantine NJ 08203

O'CONNOR, DAVID EVANS, b Ft Ogden, Fla, Apr 16, 32; m 53; c 2. FATS & FATTY ACID CHEMISTRY. *Educ:* Univ Fla, BS, 54, PhD(chem), 61. *Prof Exp:* Res asst fluorine chem, Univ Fla, 57-58; res chemist, Procter & Gamble Co, 61-66; res chemist, Geigy Chem Corp, 66-67, group leader polymer chem, 67-68; res chemist, 68-73, SECT HEAD, PROCTER & GAMBLE CO, 73- *Mem:* Am Chem Soc; Am Oil Chemists Soc. *Res:* Oxidation of unsaturated fats and fatty acids. *Mailing Add:* Procter & Gamble Co Miami Valley Labs PO Box 39175 Cincinnati OH 45247

O'CONNOR, DONALD J, b New York, NY, Nov 7, 22; m 48; c 3. CIVIL ENGINEERING. *Educ:* Manhattan Col, BCE, 44; Polytech Inst Brooklyn, MCE, 47; NY Univ, EngScD, 56. *Prof Exp:* Instr sanit eng, Manhattan Col, 46-47; mem staff, Polytech Inst, Brooklyn, 48-50; from asst prof to assoc prof, 52-64, PROF, CIVIL ENG, MANHATTAN COL, 64- *Concurrent Pos:* Nat Sci Found res grants, 60-64, mem undergrad res participation prog, 60-65; USPHS res grants, 62-66; New York Health Res Coun res grants, 62-65; Environ Protection Agency res grant, 68-72. *Honors & Awards:* Am Soc Civil Engrs, Rudolph Hering Award, 58. *Mem:* Nat Acad Eng; Am Geophys Union; Am Soc Limnol & Oceanog; Am Soc Civil Engrs. *Res:* Mathematical analysis of water pollution in all natural bodies of water. *Mailing Add:* Dept Civil Eng Manhattan Col Parkway Bronx NY 10471

O'CONNOR, GEORGE ALBERT, b Seymour, Ind, Mar 30, 44; m 68. SOIL CHEMISTRY. *Educ:* Univ Mass, Amherst, BS, 66; Colo State Univ, MS, 68, PhD(agron), 70. *Prof Exp:* Asst agron, Colo State Univ, 66-70; asst prof, 70-75, assoc prof, 75-81, PROF AGRON, NMEX STATE UNIV, 81- *Mem:* Am Soc Agron; Soil Sci Soc Am. *Res:* Salinity; pesticides; heavy metals; hazardous wastes. *Mailing Add:* Dept of Agron NMex State Univ Box 3Q Las Cruces NM 88001

O'CONNOR, GEORGE RICHARD, b Cincinnati, Ohio, Oct 8, 28. OPHTHALMOLOGY. *Educ:* Harvard Univ, AB, 50; Columbia Univ, MD, 54. *Prof Exp:* Asst clin prof ophthal, Univ, 62-66, consult ophthal clin, 62-70, from asst dir to assoc dir, Proctor Found, 62-70, assoc prof, 70-75, PROF OPHTHAMOL, UNIV CALIF, SAN FRANCISCO, 75-, DIR, FRANCIS I PROCTOR FOUND RES OPHTHAL, MED CTR, 70- *Concurrent Pos:* NIH spec trainee biochem, Inst biochem, Univ Uppsala, 60-61 & immunol, State Serum Inst, Copenhagen, Denmark, 61-62. *Mem:* Asn Res Vision & Ophthal; AMA. *Res:* Microbic immunology; immunologic response of human subjects to toxoplasma infections; antibody formation in the toxoplasma infected eye. *Mailing Add:* 95 Kirkham St San Francisco CA 94122

O'CONNOR, JEREMIAH JOSEPH, animal nutrition, see previous edition

O'CONNOR, JOEL STURGES, b Auburn, NY, Mar 6, 37; m 78; c 2. ECOLOGY, FISHERIES. *Educ:* Cornell Univ, BS, 58; Univ RI, PhD(oceanog), 65. *Prof Exp:* Chief comput opers br, Div Tech Info Exten, US AEC, 65-68; sr res assoc marine ecol, Biol Dept, Brookhaven Nat Lab, 68-71; res assoc marine sci res ctr, State Univ NY Stony Brook, 71-73; ECOLOGIST, NE OFF, OFF MARINE POLLUTION ASSESSMENT, NAT OCEANIC & ATMOSPHERIC ADMIN, 73- *Mem:* AAAS; Am Fisheries Soc; Am Inst Biol Sci; Am Soc Limnol & Oceanog; Ecol Soc Am. *Res:* Sampling statistics and computer science; ecology of estuarine and coastal environments, with emphasis on effects of contaminants; marine resource management. *Mailing Add:* NE Off Marine Pollution Assessment Old Biol Bldg State Univ NY Stony Brook NY 11790

O'CONNOR, JOHN DENNIS, b Chicago, Ill, Mar 20, 42; m 64; c 3. ZOOLOGY, BIOCHEMISTRY. *Educ:* Loyola Univ, Chicago, BS, 63; DePaul Univ, MS, 66; Northwestern Univ, Ill, PhD(biol), 68. *Prof Exp:* NIH fel, Mich State Univ, 68-70; asst prof zool, 70-74, assoc prof zool, 74-77, assoc prof develop biol, 77-81, PROF BIOL, UNIV CALIF, LOS ANGELES, 81- *Concurrent Pos:* Vis prof, Roman Cath Univ Nijmegen, Neth, 75-76. *Mem:* AAAS; Am Soc Zool; Soc Develop Biol. *Res:* Regulation of metabolism during crustacean molt cycle. *Mailing Add:* Dept of Biol Univ of Calif 405 Hilgard Ave Los Angeles CA 90024

O'CONNOR, JOHN FRANCIS, b Waterloo, NY, May 24, 35. BIOCHEMISTRY, ENDOCRINOLOGY. *Educ:* St John Fisher Col, BS, 60; Univ Rochester, PhD(org chem), 71. *Prof Exp:* Res fel, Inst Steroid Res, Montefiore Hosp, 69-74, investr, 74-80; ASST PROF, ALBERT EINSTEIN COL MED, 80- *Concurrent Pos:* Instr, Albert Einstein Col Med, 71- *Mem:* AAAS; Am Chem Soc; The Chem Soc; Endocrine Soc; AAAS. *Res:* Natural products; thyroid physiology; radioimmunoassay techniques; immunology. *Mailing Add:* 781 Pelham Rd 1A New Rochelle NY 10805

O'CONNOR, JOHN JOSEPH, b Bowling Green, Ky, May 7, 16; m 46; c 4. PHYSICS. *Educ:* Western Ky State Univ, BS, 39; Vanderbilt Univ, MS, 40. *Prof Exp:* Asst physics, Western Ky State Univ, 38-39; asst, Vanderbilt Univ, 39-40; asst, Ohio State Univ, 40-42; res physicist, Remington Arms Co, Inc, Conn, 42-44, res physicist, E I du Pont de Nemours & Co, Tenn, 44, Wash, 44-46, res physicist, Remington Arms Co, Inc, Div, 46-51, sr physicist, 51-61, res assoc, 61; PROJ ENGR, RCA SERV CO, 61- *Mem:* Am Phys Soc; Am Astronaut Soc; Am Astron Soc. *Res:* Artificial radioactivity; Faraday effect; exterior ballistics and accuracy of projectiles; missile trajectory analysis; orbital mechanics. *Mailing Add:* Mail Unit 645 RCA Serv Co Patrick AFB FL 32925

O'CONNOR, JOHN THOMAS, b New York, NY, Feb 11, 33; m 66; c 2. CIVIL & SANITARY ENGINEERING. *Educ:* Cooper Union, BCE, 55; NJ Inst Technol, MSCE, 58; Johns Hopkins Univ, EngD, 61. *Prof Exp:* Sanit engr, Elson T Killam Sanit & Hydraul Consult Engrs, 55-56; civil engr, George A Fuller Construct Co, NY, 56-57; sanit engr, Parsons, Brinckerhoff, Quade & Douglas, 57; from asst prof to assoc prof sanit eng, Univ Ill, Urbana, 61-69, prof civil eng, 69-75; PROF CIVIL ENG & CHMN DEPT, UNIV MO-COLUMBIA, 75- *Mem:* Am Chem Soc; Am Soc Civil Engrs; Am Water Works Asn; Water Pollution Control Fedn; Am Soc Limnol & Oceanog. *Res:* Fate of radionuclides in natural waters; removal of iron and trace metals from ground waters; water and wastewater treatment; ozonation. *Mailing Add:* Dept of Civil Eng Univ of Mo Columbia MO 65201

O'CONNOR, JOSEPH MICHAEL, b Newark, NJ, Oct 31, 25; m 49; c 2. ORGANIC CHEMISTRY. *Educ:* Seton Hall Univ, BS, 50; Stevens Inst Technol, MS, 55. *Prof Exp:* Jr chemist, Ciba Pharmaceut Co Div, 50-56, from asst chemist to chemist, 57-61, sr chemist, 61-72, sr scientist, 73-81, SR RES SCIENTIST, PHARMACEUT DIV, CIBA-GEIGY CORP, 82- *Mem:* Am Chem Soc; Am Soc Testing & Mat; Am Inst Chemtists; Chromatograph Discussion Group, UK; fel NY Acad Sci. *Res:* Analytical chemistry; chromatography; gas chromatogarphy; synthetic organic chemistry; high pressure reactions; catalytic hydrogenation. *Mailing Add:* 1096 Overlook Terrace Union NJ 07083

O'CONNOR, MATTHEW JAMES, b New York, NY, July 31, 40; m 67; c 2. ANALYTICAL CHEMISTRY, PHYSICAL CHEMISTRY. *Educ:* Univ Calif, Long Beach, BS, 70, MS, 72. *Prof Exp:* Mgr anal & qual assurance labs, 72-74, dir, 74-76, asst vpres pollution, 76-79, VPRES MKT, TECH SERV DIV, APOLLO CHEM CORP, 79- *Mem:* Am Chem Soc; Am Soc Testing & Mat; Air Pollution Control Asn. *Res:* Air pollution. *Mailing Add:* 157 Ironia Rd Mednham NJ 07945

O'CONNOR, MICHAEL L, b South Bend, Ind, Dec 4, 38; m 65. PATHOLOGY. *Educ:* Rockhurst Col, BS, 58; Univ Wis-Madison, MS, 60; Univ Kans, MD, 64. *Prof Exp:* Asst prof path, Case Western Reserve Univ, 69-71; asst prof path, Univ Iowa, 72-76, dir clin labs, Univ Hosps, 72-76; ASSOC PROF PATH, BOWMAN GRAY SCH MED, 76- *Mem:* AMA; Col Am Path; Am Soc Clin Path; Am Asn Clin Chem. *Res:* Computer applications in pathology. *Mailing Add:* Dept Path Bowman Gray Sch Med Winston-Salem NC 27103

O'CONNOR, ROD, b Cape Girardeau, Mo, July 4, 34; m 55; c 4. ORGANIC BIOCHEMISTRY. *Educ:* Southeast Mo State Col, BS, 55; Univ Calif, PhD, 58. *Prof Exp:* Asst prof chem, Univ Omaha, 58-60; assoc prof, Mont State Univ, 60-66; assoc prof chem & dir gen chem, Kent State Univ, 66-67; staff assoc, Adv Coun Col Chem, Stanford Univ, 67-68; prof chem, Univ Ariz, 68-72; vis prof, Wash State Univ, 72-73; PROF CHEM, TEX A&M UNIV, 73- *Concurrent Pos:* NIH res grants, 61-66; consult, Hollister-Stier Labs, 64-66; Am Chem Soc vis scientist & tour speaker; mem, Col Chem Consult Serv; educ consult, Tucara-4 Media Resources, Inc; mem nat adv comt, Individualized Sci Instructional Syst, 72-77; vpres, Romec Envrion Res & Develop, Inc, 80- *Honors & Awards:* Award, Am Chem Soc, 71; Nat Teaching Award, Mfg Chemists Asn, 78. *Mem:* Fel AAAS; Am Chem Soc. *Res:* Multi-media instruction; auto-tutorial systems; chemistry of insect venoms. *Mailing Add:* Dept of Chem Tex A&M Univ College Station TX 77843

O'CONNOR, TIMOTHY EDMOND, b Cork, Ireland, Dec 5, 25; nat US; m 52; c 6. ORGANIC CHEMISTRY, BIOCHEMISTRY. *Educ:* Nat Univ Ireland, BSc, 47, MSc, 48, PhD(chem), 51. *Prof Exp:* Chemist, E I du Pont de Nemours & Co, Del, 52-60, res scientist, 60-61; chemist, Nat Cancer Inst, 63-67, head molecular virol sect, 66-72, assoc chief viral leukemia & lymphoma br, 67-72, dir molecular control prog, 72-75; dir div biol & med res, Argonne Nat Lab, 75-77; interim dir, Div Educ Progs, 80-81, ASSOC DIR EDUC PROGS, ROSWELL PARK MEM INST, 81- *Concurrent Pos:* Fel, Mayo Found, Univ Minn, 50-51 & Univ Wis, 51-52; USPHS spec res fel, NIH, 61-63. *Mem:* AAAS; Am Chem Soc; Am Asn Cancer Res. *Res:* Organic nitrogen compounds; steroids; polymers; refractories; virology; oncology; biophysical characterization of viruses; biochemistry and immunology of chromatins. *Mailing Add:* Roswell Park Mem Inst 666 Elm St Buffalo NY 14263

O'CONNOR, WILLIAM BRIAN, b Brattleboro, Vt, Feb 24, 40; m 64; c 3. REPRODUCTIVE PHYSIOLOGY. *Educ:* St Michael's Col, Vt, BS, 62; Purdue Univ, MS, 66, PhD(zool), 68. *Prof Exp:* Asst prof zool, 67-73, ASSOC PROF ZOOL, UNIV MASS, AMHERST, 73- *Mem:* AAAS; Am Soc Zool. *Res:* Physiology and immunology of relaxin and other protein hormones. *Mailing Add:* Dept of Zool Univ of Mass Amherst MA 01002

O'CONNORS, HAROLD BLANE, JR, b Klamath Falls, Ore, Dec 31, 38. BIOLOGICAL OCEANOGRAPHY. *Educ:* Southern Ore State Col, BS, 66; Ore State Univ, MS, 69, PhD(biol oceanog), 73. *Prof Exp:* ASST PROF BIOL OCEANOG, MARINE SCI RES CTR, STATE UNIV NY, STONY BROOK, 73- *Mem:* Am Soc Limnol & Oceanog. *Res:* Marine primary and secondary productivity; dynamics of marine food webs. *Mailing Add:* Marine Sci Res Ctr State Univ of NY Stony Brook NY 11794

O'CONOR, GREGORY THOMAS, b Cincinnati, Ohio, June 23, 24; m 44; c 7. PATHOLOGY, RESEARCH ADMINISTRATION. *Educ:* Cornell Univ, MD, 48. *Prof Exp:* Asst pathologist, St Francis Hosp, Hartford, Conn, 52-58; sr lectr path, Med Sch, Makerere Univ Col, Uganda, 58-60; sr investr, 60-68, res pathologist, assoc dir, 73-78, dir div cancer cause & prev, 78-80, ASSOC DIR, NAT CANCER INST, 80- *Concurrent Pos:* Mem staff, Int Agency Res Cancer, WHO, Geneva, Switz, 66-67 & Lyons, France, 67-68. *Mem:* Am Soc Clin Path; Col Am Path; Int Acad Path; Am Asn Cancer Res. *Res:* Etiology and pathogenesis of cancer; role of environmental factors; viruses. *Mailing Add:* 5217 Cammack Dr Bethesda MD 20816

O'CONOR, VINCENT JOHN, JR, b Chicago, Ill, Jan 10, 27; m 52; c 4. UROLOGY. *Educ:* Yale Univ, AB, 49; Northwestern Univ, MD, 53; Am Bd Urol, dipl, 62. *Prof Exp:* From intern to resident, Peter Bent Brigham Hosp, Boston, Mass, 53-58; chief resident, Chicago Wesley Mem Hosp, 58-59; from instr to assoc prof, 59-70, PROF UROL, SCH MED, NORTHWESTERN

UNIV, 70-; CHMN DEPT UROL, CHICAGO WESLEY MEM HOSP, 63- *Concurrent Pos:* William Quinby fel urol, Harvard Med Sch, 57-68; attend urologist, Vet Admin Res Hosp & Rehab Inst, Chicago, 59- & Cook County Hosp, 66-; lectr, US Naval Hosp, 65- *Mem:* Fel Am Col Surg; Am Urol Asn; Soc Pelvic Surg; Am Asn Genito-Urinary Surg; Int Soc Urol Endocrinosurg. *Res:* Surgery of the kidney; renal hypertension and transplantation. *Mailing Add:* Dept Urol Northwestern Univ Med Sch Chicago IL 60611

ODAR, FUAT, b Harbin, China, May 8, 34; US citizen; m 59; c 2. FLUID DYNAMICS. *Educ:* Tech Univ Istanbul, Dipl, 56; Northwestern Univ, MS, 58, PhD, 62. *Prof Exp:* Civil engr, Corps Eng, US Army, 58-60, res civil engr, Cold Regions Res Eng Lab, 60-67; sr engr, Bettis Atomic Power Lab, 67-77; MEM STAFF, NUCLEAR REGULATORY COMN, 77- *Mem:* Am Soc Civil Engrs. *Res:* Flow instabilities in nuclear reactors; emergency cooling and safeguards systems in nuclear reactors; forces exerted on bodies moving arbitrarily in fluid; similitude of drifting snow; motion of particles in fluid; reactor safety analysis code program; advanced thermal and hydrodynamics reactor safety code assessment programs; evaluation of reactor safety analysis. *Mailing Add:* Nuclear Regulatory Comn 1717 H St NW Washington DC 20006

ODASZ, F(RANCIS) B(ERNARD), JR, b Richmond Hill, NY, Oct 8, 22; m 56; c 5. ENGINEERING. *Educ:* Polytech Inst Brooklyn, BChE, 44, MChE, 47. *Prof Exp:* Res engr, Parmelee Motor Fuel Co, 45-47; asphalt res engr, Husky Refining Co, 47-52, asst dir tech serv, Husky Oil Co, 52-56, mgr develop & control, Husky Hi-Power, Inc, 56-60; chief process engr, Southwestern Eng Co, 60-62; asst chief planning engr, Bechtel Corp, San Francisco, 62-74; V PRES, ENERGY TRANSP SYSTS, INC, 74- *Concurrent Pos:* Environ planning comnr, City of Mountain View. *Mem:* Am Chem Soc; Am Inst Chem Engrs. *Res:* Asphalt; statistics; rubberized asphalt; refinery and chemical plant design and project management; environmental control; coal slurry pipelines. *Mailing Add:* 1035 Squaw Creek Rd Casper WY 82601

O'DAY, DANTON HARRY, b Vancouver, BC, Jan 31, 46; m 66; c 1. DEVELOPMENTAL BIOLOGY. *Educ:* Univ BC, BS, 67, MS, 69; Univ Del, PhD(develop biol), 72. *Prof Exp:* Asst prof, 71-77, ASSOC PROF ZOOL, ERINDALE COL, UNIV TORONTO, 77- *Mem:* Can Soc Zoologists; Soc Protozoologists; Can Soc Cell Biol. *Res:* The regulation and importance of intracellular and extracellular enzyme accumulation in eucaryotic development; characterization and mode of action of sexual pheromones in cellular slime molds; regulation of cell fusion. *Mailing Add:* Erindale Col Univ Toronto Mississauga ON L5L 1C6 Can

ODDIE, THOMAS HAROLD, b Ballarat, Australia, July 19, 11; div; c 3. RADIOLOGICAL PHYSICS, BIOMETRICS-BIOSTATISTICS. *Educ:* Melbourne Univ, BSc, 32, MSc, 33, DSc(physics), 44. *Prof Exp:* Physicist, Commonwealth X-ray & Radium Lab, Univ Melbourne, 33-40; res engr, Philips Elec Indust, Australia, 40-47; officer chg radioisotopes res, Tracer Elements Invests, Commonwealth Sci & Indust Res Orgn, 47-52; asst prof radiol, Sch Med, Univ Ark, 53-55; assoc prof physics, Bowman Gray Sch Med, 55-56; res physicist, Unit Clin Invest, Royal NShore Hosp, Sydney, Australia, 56-60; from assoc prof to prof radiol, Med Ctr, Univ Ark, Little Rock, 64-74; PROF RADIOL & RES FEL, HARBOR GEN HOSP, UNIV CALIF, 74- *Concurrent Pos:* NIH grants, 61-; consult med div, Oak Ridge Inst Nuclear Studies, 52-56 & 61-71. *Mem:* Soc Nuclear Med; Am Thyroid Asn; Am Asn Physicists Med; fel Brit Inst Physics; fel Australian Inst Physics. *Res:* X-ray and gamma ray measurements; clinical applications of radioisotopes; thyroid kinetics and metabolism; whole-body counting in clinical applications; computer diagnosis; neonatology (biophysics). *Mailing Add:* Univ Calif Harbor Gen Hosp 1000 W Carson St Torrance CA 90509

ODDIS, JOSEPH ANTHONY, b Greensburg, Pa, Nov 5, 28; m 54; c 2. PHARMACY. *Educ:* Duquesne Univ, BS, 50. *Hon Degrees:* DSc, Mass Col Pharm, 75, Philadelphia Col Pharm & Sci, 75 & Union Univ, 76. *Prof Exp:* Staff pharmacist, Mercy Hosp, Pittsburgh, Pa, 50-51, asst chief pharmacist, 53-54; chief pharmacist, Western Pa Hosp, 54-56; staff rep hosp pharm, Am Hosp Asn, Chicago, 56-60; EXEC VPRES, AM SOC HOSP PHARMACISTS, 60-, SECY, RES & EDUC FOUND, 69- *Concurrent Pos:* Consult health facil planning & construct serv, Health Serv & Ment Health Admin, Dept Health, Educ & Welfare, 67-; mem vis comt, Col Pharm, Wayne State Univ, 70-; mem, Nat Adv Comt Allied Health Professions Projs, 69- *Honors & Awards:* Cert of Honor Award, Duquesne Univ Sch Pharm, 69; Whitney Award, Am Soc Hosp Pharmacists, 70; Julius Sturmer Mem Lectr, Philadelphia Col Pharm & Sci, 71. *Mem:* AAAS; Am Pharmaceut Asn; Am Soc Hosp Pharmacists; Int Pharmaceut Fedn; hon mem Can Soc Hosp Pharmacists. *Res:* Hospital pharmacy. *Mailing Add:* Am Soc of Hosp Pharmacists 4630 Montgomery Ave Bethesda MD 20014

ODDIS, LEROY, b Export, Pa, Aug 30, 31; m 54; c 3. ENDOCRINOLOGY. *Educ:* Utica Col, BA, 59; Rutgers Univ, MS, 63, PhD(zool), 64. *Prof Exp:* USPHS fel, 64; asst prof biol, 64-70, ASSOC PROF BIOL, RIDER COL, 70- *Mem:* AAAS; Brit Soc Endocrinol. *Res:* Skin-pigment cell interaction; hormonal control of pigmentation. *Mailing Add:* Dept of Biol Rider Col Trenton NJ 08602

ODDONE, PIERMARIA JORGE, b Arequipa, Peru, Mar 26, 44. HIGH ENERGY PHYSICS. *Educ:* Mass Inst Technol, BS, 65; Princeton Univ, PhD(physics), 70. *Prof Exp:* Res fel physics, Calif Inst Technol, 69-72; PHYSICIST, LAWRENCE BERKELEY LAB, 72- *Concurrent Pos:* Exp facil coordr, Positron-Electron Proj, Lawrence Berkeley Lab, 75- *Mem:* Am Phys Soc. *Res:* Elementary particle research in electron-positron annihilation. *Mailing Add:* 50B-6243 Lawrence Berkeley Lab Univ of Calif Berkeley CA 94720

ODDSON, JOHN KEITH, b Selkirk, Man, Nov 30, 35; m 60; c 3. MATHEMATICS. *Educ:* Univ Toronto, BASc, 57; Mass Inst Technol, SM, 60; Univ Md, PhD(appl math), 65. *Prof Exp:* Lectr math, Univ Waterloo, 57-58 & 60-62; Can NATO res fel partial differential equations, Univ Genoa, 65-66; res asst prof math, Inst Fluid Dynamics & Appl Math, Univ Md, 66-67; asst prof, 67-69, ASSOC PROF MATH, UNIV CALIF, RIVERSIDE, 69- *Concurrent Pos:* Vis prof, Inst Math, Univ Firenze, Florence, Italy, 73-74. *Mem:* Am Math Soc; Sigma Xi. *Res:* Partial differential equations. *Mailing Add:* Dept of Math Univ of Calif Riverside CA 92502

ODE, PHILIP E, b Decorah, Iowa, Mar 10, 35; m 61; c 3. POPULATION BIOLOGY, ENTOMOLOGY. *Educ:* Luther Col, BA, 57; Cornell Univ, MS, 63, PhD(entom), 65. *Prof Exp:* From asst prof to assoc prof, 65-75, chmn dept, 68-74, coordr environ prog, 73-79, PROF BIOL, THIEL COL, 75-, CHMN DEPT, 79-, COORDR HONS PROG, 81- *Mem:* AAAS; Entom Soc Am; Soc Study Evolution; Am Inst Biol Sci; Sigma Xi. *Res:* Biology of Diptera; dispersal of insects and other organisms; animal behavior; population biology; evolution studies. *Mailing Add:* Dept of Biol Thiel Col Greenville PA 16125

ODE, RICHARD HERMAN, b Glendale, Calif, Oct 14, 41; m 69. ENVIRONMENTAL SCIENCES. *Educ:* Univ Notre Dame, Bs, 63, MS, 65; WVa Univ, PhD(org chem), 68. *Prof Exp:* Vis lectr chem, Duquesne Univ, 68-69; Fel natural prod, Ariz State Univ, 69-71, sr res chemist marine natural prod, Cancer Res Inst, 71-73, asst to dir, 73-77; sr res chemist, 77-80, GROUP LEADER ENVIRON RES, MOBAY CHEM CORP, 80- *Mem:* Am Chem Soc; Sigma Xi; Int Ozone Inst. *Res:* Environmental research associated with water, air and solid wastes; carbon analysis and application; biological treatment of waste waters. *Mailing Add:* Mobay Chem Corp New Martinsville WV 26155

ODEGARD, MARK ERIE, b Plentywood, Mont, Nov 1, 40; m 67. SEISMOLOGY, MARINE GEOPHYSICS. *Educ:* Univ Mont, BA, 62; Ore State Univ, MS, 65; Univ Hawaii, PhD(geol & geophys), 75. *Prof Exp:* Geophysicist, Alpine Geophys Assoc Inc, 65-67; res asst, Hawaii Inst Geophys, 69-70, jr geophysicist, 70-74, asst geophysicist, 74-78; SCI OFFICER, OFF NAVAL RES, 78- *Mem:* Seismol Soc Am; Soc Explor Geophysicists; Am Geophys Union; Sigma Xi. *Res:* Structure of the upper mantle, seismic and ocean acoustic sound propagation, marine geophysics, seismic signal processing, geophysical instrumentation. *Mailing Add:* Off of Naval Res Code 483 800 N Quincy St Arlington VA 22217

ODEH, A(ZIZ) S(ALIM), b Nazareth, Palestine, Dec 10, 25; US citizen; m 56; c 2. ENGINEERING. *Educ:* Univ Calif, Berkeley, BS, 51; Univ Calif, Los Angeles, MS, 53, PhD(eng), 59. *Prof Exp:* Res technologist petrol prod, Field Res Lab, Socony Mobil Oil Co, 53-56; assoc eng, Univ Calif, Los Angeles, 58-59; sr res technologist petrol prod, Field Res Lab, 59-63, res assoc, 63-76, sr res assoc, 76-80, SR SCIENTIST, MOBIL RES & DEVELOP CORP, 80-, MGR RESERVOIR ENG RES GROUP, 76- *Concurrent Pos:* Mem bd dirs, Abu Dhabi Nat Reservoir Res Found, 80- *Mem:* Am Inst Mining, Metall & Petrol Engrs; Sigma Xi. *Res:* Petroleum production and reservoir engineering; methods and means to produce oil and natural gas efficiently. *Mailing Add:* Field Res Lab Mobil R&D Corp PO Box 900 Dallas TX 75221

ODEH, FAROUK M, b Nablus, Palestine; US citizen. APPLIED MATHEMATICS. *Educ:* Cairo Univ, BS, 55; Univ Calif, Berkeley, PhD(appl math), 61. *Prof Exp:* RES STAFF MATH, WATSON RES CTR, IBM CORP, 61- *Concurrent Pos:* Temp mem math, Courant Inst Math Sci, NY Univ, 62-63; assoc prof, Am Univ Beirut, 67-68. *Mem:* Am Math Soc; Soc Indust & Appl Math; Math Asn Am. *Res:* Stability theory of difference schemes; bifurcation theory in mechanics. *Mailing Add:* IBM Watson Res Ctr Box 218 Yorktown Heights NY 10598

ODEH, ROBERT EUGENE, b Akron, Ohio, Dec 21, 30; m 58; c 3. MATHEMATICAL STATISTICS, COMPUTER SCIENCE. *Educ:* Carnegie Inst Technol, BS, 52, MS, 54, PhD(math), 62. *Prof Exp:* Programmer analogue comput, Goodyear Aircraft Corp, Ohio, 52-53; instr math, Carnegie Inst Technol, 58-59; from instr to asst prof, Univ Ore, 59-64; assoc prof, 64-71, PROF MATH, UNIV VICTORIA, 71- *Concurrent Pos:* Sr investr, Air Force Off Sci Res grant, 61-62; consult, Ore Res Inst, 62-64 & Attorney Gen Dept, 65-68. *Mem:* AAAS; Am Statist Asn; Inst Math Statist; fel Royal Statist Soc; Math Asn Am. *Res:* Computing; non-parametric c-sample rank-sum tests; transformations used in analysis of variance. *Mailing Add:* Dept of Math Univ of Victoria Victoria BC V8W 2Y2 Can

ODELL, ANDREW PAUL, b Galesburg, Ill, May 6, 49. ASTRONOMY. *Educ:* Univ Iowa, BA, 70; Univ Wis-Madison, PhD(astron), 73. *Prof Exp:* Fel meteorol, Univ Wis, 73-74; asst prof astron, Univ Northern Iowa, 74-79; res assoc, Steward Observ, Univ Ariz, 79-81; ASST PROF ASTRON, NORTHERN ARIZ UNIV, 81- *Mem:* Am Astron Soc. *Res:* Stellar evolution and pulsation; radiation transfer in planetary atmospheres. *Mailing Add:* Dept Physics & Astron Northern Ariz Univ Flagstaff AZ 86011

O'DELL, AUSTIN ALMOND, JR, b Houston, Tex, Nov 28, 33; m 53; c 2. PHYSICS, NUCLEAR RADIATION. *Educ:* Univ Tex, Austin, BS, 54, MA, 55; Mass Inst Technol, PhD(physics), 61. *Prof Exp:* Physicist, Northrop Corp, 61-65; prof physics, Calif Lutheran Col, 65-68; physicist, EG&G, Inc, 68-72; physicist, Mission Res Corp, 72-74; PHYSICIST, LAWRENCE LIVERMORE NAT LAB, 74- *Mem:* Am Phys Soc; Am Nuclear Soc; Sigma Xi. *Res:* Nuclear radiation interactions, transport and detection; statistical data analysis; computer-based instrumentation and applications; nuclear criticality analysis and monitoring systems. *Mailing Add:* L-303 Criticality Safety Off Lawrence Livermore Nat Lab PO Box 808 Livermore CA 94550

O'DELL, BOYD LEE, b Hale, Mo, Oct 14, 16; m 44; c 2. BIOCHEMISTRY, NUTRITION. *Educ:* Univ Mo, AB, 40, PhD(biochem), 43. *Prof Exp:* Sr chemist, Parke, Davis & Co, 43-46; from asst prof to assoc prof, 46-55, PROF NUTRIT BIOCHEM, UNIV MO-COLUMBIA, 55- *Concurrent Pos:* NIH spec fel, Cambridge Univ, 64-65 & Harvard Med Sch, 72; Fulbright scholar, Commonwealth Sci & Indust Res Orgn, Australia, 73. *Honors & Awards:* Borden Award, Am Inst Nutrit. *Mem:* Am Soc Biol Chemists; Am Chem Soc; Soc Exp Biol & Med; Am Inst Nutrit. *Res:* Biochemical and physiological functions of micronutrients; vitamins and trace elements; role of trace elements in reproduction and connective tissue metabolism; bioavailability of zinc. *Mailing Add:* 322 Chem Bldg Univ of Mo Columbia MO 65201

O'DELL, CHARLES ROBERT, b Hamilton Co, Ill, Mar 16, 37; div; c 2. ASTRONOMY. *Educ:* Ill State Univ, BSEd, 59; Univ Wis, PhD(astron), 62. *Prof Exp:* Carnegie fel, Hale Observs, Calif, 62-63; asst prof astron, Univ Calif, Berkeley, 63-64; from asst prof to assoc prof astron, Univ Chicago, 64-67, prof & chmn dept, 67-72, dir, Yerkes Observ, 66-72; assoc dir astron, Sci & Eng Directorate, 72-80, PROJ SCIENTIST SPACE TELESCOPE, NAT AERONAUT & SPACE ADMIN, 72-, ASSOC DIR SCI, 76- *Concurrent Pos:* Guest lectr, Univ Col London, 70 & Univ Moscow, 71; US scientist, Capernrcus Astron Ctr, 73-78 & Int Halley Watch, 81- *Mem:* Am Astron Soc; Int Astron Union; AAAS; Am Inst Aeronaut & Astronaut. *Res:* Physical processes in and evolution of planetary nebulae; diffuse nebulae; comets; characteristics of interstellar grains. *Mailing Add:* TA OZ Marshall Space Flight Ctr AL 35812

ODELL, DANIEL KEITH, b Auburn, NY, Nov 16, 45; m 69; c 3. VERTEBRATE ZOOLOGY. *Educ:* Cornell Univ, BS, 67; Univ Calif, Los Angeles, MA, 70, PhD(biol), 72. *Prof Exp:* Asst prof, 73-79, ASSOC PROF MARINE BIOL, ROSENSTIEL SCH MARINE & ATMOSPHERIC SCI, UNIV MIAMI, 79- *Concurrent Pos:* Sci adv, US Marine Mammal Comn, 78- *Mem:* AAAS; Am Soc Mammalogists; Am Soc Zoologists; Wildlife Soc. *Res:* Biology of marine mammals; cetacean stranding phenomena; biology of the Bottle-Nosed Dolphin, Pygmy Sperm Whale and West Indian Manatee. *Mailing Add:* Rosenstiel Sch Marine & 4600 Rickenbacker Causeway Miami FL 33149

O'DELL, JEAN MARLAND, b Independence, Mo, June 10, 31; m 56; c 5. NUCLEAR SCIENCE, OPERATIONS RESEARCH. *Educ:* Univ Kans, BSEP, 54, MS, 61, PhD(physics), 65. *Prof Exp:* Asst physics, Univ Kans, 58-62, asst nuclear physics, 62-65; exp physicist, 65-73, SR SCIENTIST, LAWRENCE LIVERMORE NAT LAB, UNIV CALIF, 73- *Concurrent Pos:* staff mem, Sci & Technol Div, 79-81, actg asst dep proj mgr, Survivability, 81- *Res:* Nuclear explosives for defense and peaceful uses; compound nucleus formation versus direct interaction investigations bombarding sulphur 32 with deuterons; evaluation of requirements for nuclear weapons for strategic and naval tactical weapon systems. *Mailing Add:* Lawrence Livermore Lab PO Box 808 L-11 Livermore CA 94551

ODELL, LOIS DOROTHEA, b Watertown, NY, Sept 25, 15. BIOLOGY, SCIENCE EDUCATION. *Educ:* State Univ NY Albany, AB, 40; Cornell Univ, MA, 45, PhD(sci educ), 51. *Prof Exp:* Teacher pub sch, NY, 41-43; instr biol, 47-62, PROF BIOL, TOWSON STATE UNIV, 62- *Mem:* AAAS; Am Nature Study Soc. *Res:* Field natural science; botany; science education in the elementary and high school; science education in environmental concepts. *Mailing Add:* Dept of Biol Towson State Univ Baltimore MD 21204

ODELL, NORMAN RAYMOND, b Rochester, NY, Aug 4, 27; m 50; c 3. ORGANIC CHEMISTRY. *Educ:* Whittier Col, BA, 50; Ore State Col, MS, 52, PhD(chem), 55. *Prof Exp:* Chemist, Taylor Instrument Co, 52; chemist grease res, 54-59, group leader, 59-60, asst supvr, Lubricants Res Sect, 60-65, res technologist-managerial, 65-67, supvr, Lubricants Field Serv, Port Arthur Res Lab, 67-81, ASST MGR FUELS & LUBRICANTS, BEACON RES LABS, TEXACO, INC, 81- *Concurrent Pos:* Instr, Dutchess Community Col, 59-60. *Mem:* AAAS; Am Chem Soc; fel Am Inst Chemists; Sigma Xi. *Res:* Synthesis of tracer compounds; tracer studies; exploratory research in grease thickening agents; synthetic lubricants; petroleum additives; mechanisms of petroleum additive behavior; additive processing; automotive and industrial lubricants; lubricant application; lubricating oil processing. *Mailing Add:* Beacon Res Labs Texaco Inc PO Box 509 Beacon NY 12508

ODELL, PATRICK L, b Watonga, Okla, Nov 29, 30; m 58; c 4. MATHEMATICAL STATISTICS. *Educ:* Univ Tex, BS, 52; Okla State Univ, MS, 58, PhD(math statist), 62. *Prof Exp:* Mathematician, Flight Determination Lab, White Sands Missile Range, NMex, 52-53; res scientist, Kaman Nuclear, Inc, 58-59; mathematician, US Navy Nuclear Ord Eval Unit, 59-60, consult mathematician, US Weapons Eval Facility, 60-62; asst prof math, Univ Tex, 62-66; prof, Tex Tech Univ, 66-72; exec dean grad studies & res, 72-75, PROF MATH SCI, UNIV TEX, DALLAS, 72- *Concurrent Pos:* Consult mathematician, Ling-Tempco-Vought, Inc, Tex, 62-64; NSF grants, 63-65 & 77-79; assoc dir, Tex Ctr Res Appl Math & Mech, 64-72; Tex Hwy Res Ctr grant; NASA grant, 70-71, res grant, 72-76; training grant, Environ Protection Agency, 75-76. *Mem:* Soc Indust & Appl Math; fel Am Statist Asn. *Res:* Statistical problems associated with remote sensing from space; statistical problems; statistical analysis of sensitivity data; general theory of matrix inversion; mathematical modelling of the environment. *Mailing Add:* 3105 Canyon Creek Dr Richardson TX 75080

O'DELL, RALPH DOUGLAS, b Leavenworth, Ind, June 11, 38; m 59; c 4. TECHNICAL MANAGEMENT, NUCLEAR ENGINEERING. *Educ:* Univ Tex, BS, 61, PhD(mech eng), 65. *Prof Exp:* From asst prof to assoc prof nuclear eng, Univ NMex, 64-73, dir, Los Alamos Grad Div, 69-73; staff mem, Group TD-5, 73-74, sect leader, Group T-1, 74-76, assoc group leader, Group T-1, 76-79, alternate group leader, Group T-1, 79-80, DEP GROUP LEADER, GROUP T-1, LOS ALAMOS NAT LAB, 80- *Concurrent Pos:* Long term vis staff mem, Los Alamos Sci Lab, 68-69; consult, US Geol Surv, TRIGA Reactor Facility, 69- & US Air Force Nuclear Safety Div, Kirtland AFB, 69-72; mem reactor safeguards adv comt, Univ NMex, 73- *Mem:* Am Nuclear Soc. *Res:* Nuclear transport and reactor theory; numerical methods for nuclear analysis; fast breeder reactors. *Mailing Add:* Group T-1 MS 269 Los Alamos Nat Lab Los Alamos NM 87545

ODELL, THEODORE TELLEFSEN, JR, b Geneva, NY, May 5, 23; m 48, 72; c 3. CELL BIOLOGY, PHYSIOLOGY. *Educ:* Hobart Col, BS, 45; Ind Univ, MA, 50, PhD(zool), 52. *Prof Exp:* Asst zool, Ind Univ, 48-52; assoc biologist, 52-58, biologist, 58-75, assoc mgr, cancer & toxicol prog, 75-77, ASSOC DIR BIOL DIV, OAK RIDGE NAT LAB, 77- *Concurrent Pos:* Lectr, Dept Zool & Biomed Grad Sch, Univ Tenn. *Mem:* AAAS; Radiation Res Soc; Am Physiol Soc; Soc Exp Biol & Med; Am Soc Hemat. *Res:* Physiology of blood platelets; hemopoietic cell kinetics and regulation; radiobiology. *Mailing Add:* Biol Div Oak Ridge Nat Lab Oak Ridge TN 37830

O'DELL, THOMAS BENIAH, b Cassopolis, Mich, June 19, 20; m 43; c 3. PHARMACOLOGY. *Educ:* Wabash Col, AB, 42; Univ Minn, PhD(pharmacol), 50. *Prof Exp:* Chemist coated fabrics, US Rubber Co, 42-44; anal chemist nutrit, Upjohn Co, 44; asst prof pharmacol, Sch Med, Univ Minn, 49-51; sr res pharmacologist, Irwin, Neisler Labs, Ill, 51-60, dir biol res, 60-64; assoc dir med & sci coordr, William S Merrell Co, 64-68, dir drug regulatory affairs, Merrell-Nat Labs, 68-81; SR DIR REGULATORY AFFAIRS, MERRELL DOW PHARMACEUTICALS, DOW CHEM CO, 81- *Mem:* AAAS; Am Soc Pharmacol & Exp Therapeut; Soc Toxicol; NY Acad Sci. *Res:* Virus chemotherapy; hypertension; atherosclerosis; antispasmodics; analgesics; central nervous system. *Mailing Add:* Merrell Dow Pharmaceuticals Dow Chem Co Cincinnati OH 45215

O'DELL, WAYNE TALMAGE, dairy science, see previous edition

ODELL, WILLIAM DOUGLAS, endocrinology, physiology, see previous edition

ODEN, JOHN TINSLEY, b Alexandria, La, Dec 25, 36; m 65; c 2. ENGINEERING MECHANICS. *Educ:* La State, BS, 59; Okla State Univ, MS & PhD(struct mech), 62. *Prof Exp:* Asst prof struct eng, Okla State Univ, 62-63; sr struct engr, Gen Dynamics, Ft Worth, 63-64; assoc prof eng mech, Univ Ala, Huntsville, 64-67, prof, 67-77, chmn dept, 70-77; PROF AEROSPACE ENG & ENG MECH, ENG MECH DEPT, UNIV TEX, 77-, CAROL & HENRY GROPPE PROF ENG, 79- *Concurrent Pos:* Dir, Tex Inst Comput Mech, 74-; vis prof, Fed Univ Rio, Rio de Janiero, 74; vis sci res fel, Brunel Univ, Uxbridge, Eng, 81; distinguished vis mathematician, Univ Md, 81. *Mem:* Am Soc Mech Engrs; Soc Indust & Appl Math; Soc Eng Sci (pres, 79); Am Soc Eng Sci; fel Am Acad Mech. *Res:* Nonlinear continuum mechanics; approximation theory; numerical analysis of nonlinear problems in continuum mechanics. *Mailing Add:* Univ of Tex WRW 305 ASE/EM Dept Austin TX 78712

ODEN, PETER HOWLAND, b Stuttgart, Ger, July 3, 33; US citizen; m 61; c 1. ELECTRICAL ENGINEERING, COMPUTER SCIENCE. *Educ:* Columbia Col, AB, 55; Columbia Univ, BS, 56, MS, 58, PhD(elec eng), 66. *Prof Exp:* Instr elec eng, Columbia Univ, 59-63; MEM RES STAFF, T J WATSON RES CTR, IBM CORP, 63- *Mem:* Asn Comput Mach; Inst Elec & Electronics Engrs. *Res:* Circuit and system theory; automated computer design; stochastic models of computing systems; programming languages; optimizing compilers. *Mailing Add:* IBM Corp T J Watson Res Ctr PO Box 218 Yorktown Heights NY 10598

ODENCRANTZ, FREDERICK KIRK, b New York, NY, Oct 6, 21; m 59; c 3. PHYSICS. *Educ:* Muhlenberg Col, BS, 43; Rutgers Univ, MS, 49; Univ Utah, PhD(physics), 58. *Prof Exp:* Physicist, New Brunswick Lab, US Atomic Energy Comn, 49-50; physicist, US Naval Weapons Ctr, 50-79. *Mem:* Am Phys Soc; Am Geophys Union. *Res:* Physical optics; atmospheric physics. *Mailing Add:* 3780 St Andrews Dr Reno NV 89502

ODENHEIMER, KURT JOHN SIGMUND, b Regensburg, Ger, May 9, 11; US citizen; m 39; c 4. CLINICAL PATHOLOGY, EXPERIMENTAL PATHOLOGY. *Educ:* Univ Munich, MedDent, 35; Univ Pittsburgh, DDS, 40, MEd, 54; Univ Heidelberg, Ger, DMD, 58; Western Reserve Univ, PhD(path), 64. *Prof Exp:* Asst prof gen path, Univ Pittsburgh, 49-53, head dept, 53-55; assoc prof oral diag & clin path, State Univ NY Buffalo, 61-66; prof path & chief exp path, Loyola Univ, 66-69, chmn diag & roentgenol, 67-69; prof path, 69-80, prof dent, 71-80, prof oral path, 77-80, EMER PROF PATH, GEN DENT & EAR, NOSE & THROAT, LA STATE UNIV MED CTR, NEW ORLEANS, 80- *Concurrent Pos:* Res fel path & fed teachers training grant, Western Reserve Univ, 59-61; res grant viral studies primates, Loyola Univ, 67-; consult, Presby Hosp Tumor Bd, Pittsburgh, 51-55, temporomandibular joint disturbances, NIH, 61, oral diag & path, Meyer Mem Hosp, Buffalo, 63-66, new ed Oral Path by K Thomas, 66 & Gulf South Res Inst, La, 67-; vis res assoc, Tulane Delta Primate Res Ctr, 66-; consult dent med, Touro Infirmary, New Orleans, 68-, stomatologist, 81; dent coordr oncol, Charity Hosp; lectr, Loyala Univ, 80- *Mem:* AAAS; Am Dent Asn; AMA; fel Am Acad Oral Path; fel Am Col Dent. *Res:* Peridontal and temporomandibular joint therapy with myotatic splint; effects of enteric viruses upon embryo, child and adult, in acute or chronic, clinical or subclinical forms, using primates as experimental models; radioactive gold and oral cancers; viral infections in genetics. *Mailing Add:* 4123 Vixen St New Orleans LA 70114

ODENSE, PAUL HOLGER, b Winnipeg, Man, Dec 12, 26; m 54; c 3. BIOCHEMISTRY. *Educ:* Univ Toronto, BA, 50, MA, 54; Univ Okla, PhD(biochem), 59. *Prof Exp:* Asst scientist & biochemist, 54-56, assoc scientist, 59-62, SR SCIENTIST, FISHERIES RES BD CAN, 62-, BIOCHEMIST, 59-; SR RES OFFICER, NAT RES COUN CAN, 82- *Mem:* Can Biochem Soc; Chem Inst Can; NY Acad Sci. *Res:* Marine comparative biochemistry and histology; isoenzymes; electrophoretic separations; light and electron microscope histochemistry. *Mailing Add:* Nat Res Coun Can Atlantic Res Lab 1411 Oxford St Halifax NS B3H 3Z1 Can

ODER, FREDERIC CARL EMIL, b Los Angeles, Calif, Oct 23, 19; m 41; c 3. AEROSPACE SCIENCES. *Educ:* Calif Inst Technol, BS, 40, MS, 41; Univ Calif, Los Angeles, PhD(atmospheric physics), 52. *Prof Exp:* Dir geophys res, Air Force Cambridge Res Labs, 49-52, dir weapons syst ballistic missiles div, Air Res & Develop Command, 56-59, dep comdr space systs, 59-60; asst to dir res & eng, Apparatus & Optical Div, Eastman Kodak Co, NY, 60-61, prog mgr, 61-66; vpres & asst gen mgr, Lockheed Missiles & Space Co, 66-73, VPRES & GEN MGR, SPACE SYSTS DIV, LOCKHEED MISSILES & SPACE CO, INC, LOCKHEED AIRCRAFT CORP, 73- *Concurrent Pos:* Consult, Air Force Studies Bd, Nat Acad Sci, 75-; mem, Defense Intel Agency, Sci Adv Comt, 72- *Mem:* Soc Photog Sci & Eng; Sigma Xi; fel Am Inst Aeronaut & Astronaut. *Res:* Specialized optical and photographic systems; atmospheric geophysics. *Mailing Add:* Space Systs Div PO Box 504 Lockheed Missiles & Space Co Inc Sunnyvale CA 94088

ODER, ROBIN ROY, b Jefferson City, Tenn, Sept 26, 34; m 71; c 2. SOLID STATE PHYSICS, ENGINEERING PHYSICS. *Educ:* Mass Inst Technol, BS, 59, PhD(physics), 65. *Prof Exp:* Res physicist magnetism, Francis Bitter Nat Magnet Lab, Mass Inst Technol, 65-70; group leader minerals beneficiation, Clay Div, J M Huber Corp, 70-74; eng specialist process technol, Bechtel Corp, 74-77; res assoc coal & minerals beneficiation, 77-79, DIR, COAL TECHNOL, CHEM & MINERALS DIV, GULF SCI & TECHNOL CO, 79- *Concurrent Pos:* Solid state physics consult, Elec Power Res Inst, 75-77; mem tech adv comts, Prog Coal Gasification, Gulf-TRW Inc, 77-80, Coal Cleaning Test Facil, Elec Power Res Inst, 81- & Eriez Mfg Co, Erie, Pa, 81- *Mem:* AAAS; Am Phys Soc. *Res:* Magnetism; calormetry; thermoelectricity; heat transport; superconductivity; De Haas Van Alphen effect; magnetic separation; clay mineralogy; coal structure; coal desulfurization; economics of coal cleaning; minerals beneficiation. *Mailing Add:* RD 3 Box 229-A Export PA 15630

ODETTE, G(EORGE) ROBERT, b Detroit, Mich, Aug 22, 43. NUCLEAR ENGINEERING, MATERIALS SCIENCE. *Educ:* Rensselaer Polytech Inst, BS, 65; Mass Inst Technol, MS, 68, PhD(nuclear eng), 70. *Prof Exp:* Res asst nuclear eng, Mass Inst Technol, 68-70; assoc prof, 70-81, PROF CHEM & NUCLEAR ENG, UNIV CALIF, SANTA BARBARA, 81- *Concurrent Pos:* Consult, Am Sci & Eng Co, 69-70, Hanford Eng Develop Lab, 70- & Argonne Nat Lab, 74- *Mem:* Am Nuclear Soc; Am Soc Testing & Mat. *Res:* Nuclear metallurgy; radiation effects modeling and data correlation; fundamental microstructure and mechanical behavior; test development; fission, fusion; energy related materials technology. *Mailing Add:* Dept of Chem & Nuclear Eng Univ of Calif Santa Barbara CA 93106

ODIAN, GEORGE G, b New York, NY, July 19, 33. POLYMER CHEMISTRY. *Educ:* City Col New York, BS, 55; Columbia Univ, MA, 56, PhD, 59. *Prof Exp:* Asst, Columbia Univ, 55-57; sr chemist, Thiokol Chem Corp, 58-59; res dir, Radiation Applns, Inc, 59-68; assoc prof, 68-72, PROF CHEM, COL STATEN ISLAND, NY, 72- *Concurrent Pos:* Asst prof, Columbia Univ, 63-68. *Mem:* AAAS; Am Chem Soc. *Res:* Polymer science; radiation chemistry. *Mailing Add:* Col of Staten Island 130 Stuyvesant Pl Staten Island NY 10301

ODIORNE, TRUMAN J, b Johnson City, Tex, Aug 9, 44; m 70. PHYSICAL CHEMISTRY. *Educ:* Southwestern Univ, Tex, BS, 66; Rice Univ, MA & PhD(chem), 71. *Prof Exp:* NIH trainee, Inst Lipid Res, Baylor Col Med, 71-73; staff chemist, Res Triangle Inst, 73-74; chemist, Monrovia, Calif, 74-77, SR DEVELOP CHEMIST, INSTRUMENT PROD, GLASGOW SITE, E I DU PONT DE NEMOURS & CO, INC, 77- *Mem:* AAAS; Am Chem Soc; Am Phys Soc. *Res:* Chemical reaction kinetics; organic mass spectrometry; electron spectroscopy chemical analysis; analytical instrumentation. *Mailing Add:* Instrument Prod Div Glasgow Site Wilmington DE 19898

ODIOSO, RAYMOND C, b Pittsburgh, Pa, Apr 17, 23; m 53; c 6. ORGANIC CHEMISTRY. *Educ:* Duquesne Univ, BS, 47; Carnegie Inst Technol, MS, 50, DSc(chem), 51. *Prof Exp:* Asst, Carnegie Inst Technol, 47-49; fel, Mellon Inst, 51-54; res supvr, Gulf Res & Develop Co, 54-61; res mgr, Colgate-Palmolive Co, NJ, 61-67, assoc dir res lab opers, 67-68; VPRES RES & DEVELOP, DRACKETT CO, BRISTOL-MYERS CO, 68- *Concurrent Pos:* Instr, Carnegie Inst Technol, 52-53. *Mem:* AAAS; Am Chem Soc. *Res:* Kinetics of the benzidine rearrangement; monomer synthesis; alkylation; isomerization; dealkylation; dehydrocyclization; olefin reactions; product development, laundry and dishwashing detergents, bleaches, toilet soap, aerosols, paper products; process research, petrochemicals, and detergents. *Mailing Add:* Drackett Res & Develop Labs 5020 Spring Grove Ave Cincinnati OH 45232

ODISHAW, HUGH, b North Battleford, Sask, Oct 13, 16; nat US; m 58. GEOPHYSICS. *Educ:* Northwestern Univ, AB, 39, MA, 41; Ill Inst Technol, BS, 44. *Hon Degrees:* ScD, Carleton Col, 58. *Prof Exp:* Instr eng, Ill Inst Technol, 41-44, instr math, 44; tech ed & instr radar, Westinghouse Elec Corp, 44-46; asst to dir, Nat Bur Standards, 46-54; exec dir US Comt, Int Geophys Year, Nat Acad Sci-Nat Res Coun, 54-63, dir int geophys year world data ctr, Nat Acad Sci, 57-66, exec dir, Space Sci Bd, 58-72, exec secy, Div Phys Sci, 66-72; DEAN COL EARTH SCI, UNIV ARIZ, 72- *Concurrent Pos:* Consult, Nat Bur Standards, 54-57 & Electronics Div, ACF Co, 54-56; mem, Geophys Res Bd, Nat Acad Sci, chmn, Geophys Study Comt, Geophys Film Comt. *Mem:* AAAS; Am Phys Soc; fel Am Geophys Union; Royal Soc Arts. *Res:* Electronics. *Mailing Add:* Col of Earth Sci Univ of Ariz Tucson AZ 85721

ODLAND, GEORGE FISHER, b Minneapolis, Minn, Aug 27, 22; m 45; c 3. ANATOMY, DERMATOLOGY. *Educ:* Harvard Med Sch, MD, 46. *Prof Exp:* From intern to resident med, Mass Gen Hosp, Boston, 46-55; asst dermat, Harvard Med Sch, 53-55; clin instr anat, 55-60, clin instr med, 56-60, clin asst prof anat & med, 60-62, from asst prof to assoc prof biol struct & med, 62-69, PROF BIOL STRUCT & MED, SCH MED, UNIV WASH, 69-, HEAD DIV DERMAT, 62- *Concurrent Pos:* Res fel anat, Harvard Med Sch, 49-51, res fel dermat, 51-53; attend staff, Univ Hosp, Harborview Med Ctr, Vet Admin Hosp, & USPHS Hosp, Seattle; mem adv coun, Nat Inst Athritis, Metabolic & Digestive Dis, NIH, 73-76, chmn comt, Nat Inst Arthritis, Digestive Dis & Kidney. *Honors & Awards:* Rothman Award, Soc Invest Dermat. *Mem:* Am Acad Dermat; Soc Invest Dermat; Asn Professors Dermat; Am Dermat Asn. *Res:* Electron microscopy; biosynthesis of epidermal keratins; structure/physiologic correlation in microcirculation. *Mailing Add:* Dept of Med Univ of Wash Sch of Med Seattle WA 98195

ODLAND, LURA, b Morgantown, WVa, Nov 2, 21. NUTRITION. *Educ:* Univ RI, BS, 43, DSc, 68; Univ Conn, MS, 45; Univ Wis, PhD(biochem, nutrit), 50. *Prof Exp:* Instr foods & nutrit, Univ Conn, 45; nutritionist comt food composition, Food & Nutrit Bd, Nat Res Coun, 45-47; asst, Univ Wis, 47-50; assoc prof home econ, Exp Sta, Mont State Col, 50-55; exp stas adminr, State Exp Stas Div, USDA, 55-59; dean, 59-79, EMER PROF & EMER DEAN, UNIV TENN, KNOXVILLE, 79- *Concurrent Pos:* Mem comn home econ, Nat Asn State Univ & Land-Grant Cols, 74-77. *Honors & Awards:* Borden Res Award, 77. *Mem:* AAAS; Am Chem Soc; Am Pub Health Asn; Inst Food Technol. *Res:* Conservation of nutritive values of food and food composition; human nutrition; vitamin metabolism and nutritive assessment; bone density and dietary intake relationships in human subjects; surveillence and public policy. *Mailing Add:* Dept Nutrit Univ Tenn Knoxville TN 37916

ODLAND, RUSSELL KENT, b Washington, DC, June 29, 41; m 65; c 2. TECHNICAL MANAGEMENT. *Educ:* Univ Richmond, BS, 64, MS, 71. *Prof Exp:* Res chemist combustion prod anal, Am Tobacco Co, Subsid Am Brands, 64-71; sr res chemist, methods develop, Jim Walter Res Corp, Subsid Jim Walter Corp, 71-80; VPRES TECH OPERS, MGT RMAX, INC, 80- *Concurrent Pos:* Chem consult, K O Labs, 73- *Mem:* Am Chem Soc; Am Inst Chemists. *Res:* Analytical development of new test methods for solving practical problems found in industry. *Mailing Add:* 4540 Fargo Dr Plano TX 75075

ODLE, JOHN WILLIAM, b Tipton, Ind, July 23, 14; m 37; c 3. MILITARY WEAPON SYSTEMS ANALYSIS. *Educ:* Univ Mich, BS, 37, MS, 38, PhD(math), 40. *Prof Exp:* Instr math, Univ Wis, 40-42; asst prof, Pa State Univ, 42-44; opers analyst, US Army Air Force, 44-45; head math div, US Naval Ord Test Sta, 46-55; opers analyst, US Air Force, 55-57; res mathematician eng res inst, Univ Mich, 57-58; dir adv develop dept, Crosley Div, Avco Corp, 58-60; mem staff opers res sect, Arthur D Little, Inc, 60-71; opers res analyst, Naval Ord Lab, 72-79; CONSULT MATH & OPERS RES, 79- *Mem:* Oper Res Soc Am. *Res:* Applied mathematics; operations research. *Mailing Add:* 9208 Friars Rd Bethesda MD 20817

O'DOHERTY, DESMOND SYLVESTER, b Dublin, Ireland, July 27, 20; m 51; c 2. NEUROLOGY. *Educ:* LaSalle Col, AB, 42; Jefferson Med Col, MD, 45. *Prof Exp:* Adj instr, DC Gen Hosp, 50-51; res fel, Med Ctr, 51-52, from instr to assoc prof, 52-61, PROF NEUROL, GEORGETOWN UNIV, 61-, CHMN DEPT, 59- *Concurrent Pos:* Dir, Muscular Dystrophy Clin, 54-; med dir, Georgetown Hosp, 66-67; consult, US Army, US Navy & Vet Admin. *Mem:* Asn Res Nerv & Ment Dis; AMA; fel Am Acad Neurol; Am Neurol Asn; Am Epilepsy Soc. *Res:* Parkinsonism; temporal lobe suppression; syncope; muscular dystrophy; cerebrovascular disease; multiple sclerosis; Huntington's chorea. *Mailing Add:* Dept Neurol Georgetown Univ Hosp Washington DC 22207

O'DOHERTY, PATRICK JOSEPH, b Enniskillen, Northern Ireland, Mar 8, 44; Brit citizen; m 70. BIOCHEMISTRY. *Educ:* Univ Col, Dublin, BSc, 67; Mem Univ Nfld, MSc, 70; Univ Toronto, PhD(biochem), 74. *Prof Exp:* Muscular Dystrophy Asn Can fel biochem, Univ Wis-Madison, 74-77; ASST PROF BIOCHEM, UNIV BC, 77- *Concurrent Pos:* Career develop award & grant, Med Res Coun Can, 77- *Mem:* Biochem Soc, London; Can Biochem Soc; AAAS; Sigma Xi. *Res:* Lipid metabolism. *Mailing Add:* G F Strong Lab Dept of Med Univ of BC Vancouver BC V7R 449 Can

ODOM, DANIEL GWIN, b Mercedes, Tex, Sept 30, 48. BIOCHEMISTRY. *Educ:* Tarleton State Univ, BS, 69; Univ Houston, MS, 72, PhD(biophysics), 73. *Prof Exp:* Res chemist blood preserv, Med Res Lab, US Army, Ft Knox, 73-74 & Letterman Army Inst Res, 74-77; res assoc chem evolution, Ames Res Ctr, 76; fel, Univ Houston, 77-78; asst prof biol & chem, Cornell Col, 78-81; assoc scientist, Univ Houston, 81-82. *Mem:* Am Chem Soc; Sigma Xi; Int Soc Study Origin Life. *Res:* Chemical evolution; prebiotic chemistry. *Mailing Add:* Med Students Off Col Med Univ Iowa Iowa City IA 52242

ODOM, GUY LEARY, b Harvey, La, May 20, 11; m 33; c 3. NEUROSURGERY. *Educ:* Tulane Univ, MD, 33; Am Bd Neurol Surg, dipl. *Prof Exp:* Prof, 50-74, JAMES B DUKE PROF NEUROSURG, SCH MED, DUKE UNIV, 74- *Concurrent Pos:* Consult to Surgeon Gen, USPHS Neurol Prog Proj Comt, 60-65; mem, Int Cong Neurol Surg; secy-treas, Am Bd Neurol Surg, 64-70, chmn, 70-; mem, Nat Adv Neurol Dis & Stroke Coun, 69-71. *Mem:* AMA; Am Asn Neurol Surg (pres, 71-72); Am Acad Neurol Surg (pres, 67); hon mem Cong Neurol Surg; Soc Neurol Surg (secy-treas, 60-65, pres, 70-71). *Res:* Cerebral circulation and intracranial neoplasms. *Mailing Add:* 2812 Chelsea Circle Durham NC 27707

ODOM, HOMER CLYDE, JR, b Hattiesburg, Miss, Dec 9, 42; m 63; c 1. ORGANIC CHEMISTRY. *Educ:* Univ Southern Miss, BA, 63, MS, 66; Clemson Univ, PhD(chem), 70. *Prof Exp:* Chemist, Pan Am Tung Res, 64-66; PROF CHEM & HEAD DEPT, BAPTIST COL CHARLESTON, 70- *Mem:* Am Chem Soc; Royal Soc Chem. *Res:* Natural products; organic residues in nature. *Mailing Add:* Dept of Chem Baptist Col PO Box 10087 Charleston SC 29411

ODOM, IRA EDGAR, b Dover, Tenn, June 12, 32; m 57; c 3. MINERALOGY, PETROLOGY. *Educ:* Southern Ill Univ, BA, 56; Univ Ill, MS, 58, PhD(geol), 63. *Prof Exp:* Assoc geologist, Ill State Geol Surv, 57-64; asst prof, 64-67, PROF GEOL, NORTHERN ILL UNIV, 75- *Mem:* Geol Soc Am; Mineral Soc Am; Clay Minerals Soc. *Res:* Mineralogy, petrology of sedimentary rocks. *Mailing Add:* Dept of Geol Northern Ill Univ De Kalb IL 60115

ODOM, JEROME DAVID, b Greensboro, NC, Apr 27, 42; m 65; c 2. INORGANIC CHEMISTRY. *Educ:* Univ NC, Chapel Hill, BS, 64; Ind Univ, PhD(chem), 68. *Prof Exp:* NSF fel, Bristol Univ, 68-69; from asst prof to assoc prof, 69-77, PROF CHEM, UNIV SC, 77- *Concurrent Pos:* Alexander von Humboldt fel, Univ of Stuttgart, 75-76. *Mem:* Am Chem Soc; Sigma Xi. *Res:* Chemistry of nonmetals; nuclear magnetic resonance spectroscopy; structure and bonding investigations. *Mailing Add:* Dept of Chem Univ of SC Columbia SC 29208

O'DONNELL, ASHTON JAY, b Los Angeles, Calif, Apr 7, 21; m 43; c 4. PHYSICS. *Educ:* Whitman Col, AB, 43. *Prof Exp:* Res physicist radiation lab, Univ Calif & Tenn Eastman Corp, 43-44; res physicist, Tenn Eastman Corp, 44-47; chief spec projs br, Hanford Opers Off, US AEC, Wash, 47-51, dir tech opers div, San Francisco Opers Off, 51-54; mgr nuclear econ res, Stanford Res Inst, 55-56, mgr nuclear develops, 56-57, mgr prog develop, 57-61; Dept State sr sci adv, US Mission to Int Atomic Energy Agency, Vienna, Austria, 61-64; mgr develop, 64-67, mgr, Sci Develop Dept, 67-69, mgr bus develop, 69-72, mgr, Uranium Enrichment Prog, 72-74, gen mgr uranium enrichment assocs, 74-76, vpres & mgr, San Francisco Off, Refinery & Chem Div, Bechtel, Inc, 76-78, VPRES & MGR, NUCLEAR FUEL OPER, BECHTEL CIVIL & MINERALS, INC, 78- *Concurrent Pos:* Adv to US rep sci adv comts, UN & Int Atomic Energy Agency, 61-64; mem adv comt nuclear mat safeguards, US AEC, 70-72; chmn, US Nat Comt Natural Resources, Pac Basin Econ Coun, 70-73; mem, Atomic Indust Forum. *Mem:* Am Nuclear Soc. *Res:* Research planning, administration; international nuclear development; industrial applications of technology. *Mailing Add:* Bechtel Civil & Minerals Inc 50 Beale St PO Box 3965 San Francisco CA 94119

O'DONNELL, BRIAN DESMOND, cosmic ray physics, see previous edition

O'DONNELL, C(EDRIC) F(INTON), b Durham Bridge, NB, June 16, 20; nat US; m 44; c 3. ENGINEERING PHYSICS. *Educ:* McGill Univ, BEng, 49; Mass Inst Technol, MS, 51. *Prof Exp:* Supvr digital comput circuitry, Res Div, Burroughs Corp, 51-52; res engr, Autonetics Div, NAm Aviation, Inc, 52-57, group leader guid anal, 57-58, chief systs anal, 58-59, sect chief comput, 59-60, chief engr, Comput & Data Systs Div, 60-62, VPRES RES & TECHNOL, ROCKWELL INT, 63- *Mem:* Sigma Xi. *Res:* Solid state physics as it applies to digital computers; control and stability of sampled data systems; mass data processing; microelectronics. *Mailing Add:* 1301 N Riedel Fullerton CA 92631

O'DONNELL, EDWARD, b New York, NY, Oct 13, 38; m 68; c 3. GEOLOGY. *Educ:* Queens Col, NY, BS, 61; Univ Cincinnati, MS, 63, PhD(geol), 67. *Prof Exp:* Lectr geol, Queens Col, NY, 60-61; hydrologist, US Geol Surv, 61-62; res asst zooplankton ecol, Lamont Geol Observ, 63; lectr geol, Queens Col, NY, 63-65; geologist, Pan Am Petrol Corp, 67-68; asst prof geol, Univ SFla, 68-76; GEOLOGIST, US NUCLEAR REGULATORY COMN, 76- *Mem:* AAAS; Geol Soc Am; Soc Econ Paleont & Mineral; Am Asn Petrol Geologists; Soc Econ Mineralogists & Paleontologists. *Res:* Sedimentation; stratigraphy; structural geology; petroleum geology; tectonics of the Gulf Coast; tectonics of the Caribbean; nuclear reactor siting; high-level radioactive waste disposal; low-level radioactive waste disposal. *Mailing Add:* US Nuclear Regulatory Comn Washington DC 20555

O'DONNELL, JAMES FRANCIS, b Cleveland, Ohio, July 22, 28; m 55; c 3. BIOCHEMISTRY. *Educ:* St Louis Univ, BS, 49; Univ Chicago, PhD(biochem), 57. *Prof Exp:* Asst prof biol chem & res biochemist, Univ Cincinnati, 57-65, asst prof biol chem & assoc prof exp med, 65-66; grants assoc, Div Res Grants, NIH, 68-69, prog dir, Pop & Reprod Grants Br, Ctr Pop Res, Nat Inst Child Health & Human Develop, 69-71, asst dir, 71-77, DEP DIR DIV RES RESOURCES, NIH, 77-, ACTG DIR, 81- *Mem:* NY Acad Sci. *Res:* Nucleic acid metabolism, particularly liver disease in humans and laboratory animals. *Mailing Add:* Div of Res Resources NIH Bldg 31 Rm 5B-03 Bethesda MD 20014

O'DONNELL, MARTIN JAMES, b Iowa Fall, Iowa, July 8, 46; m 72; c 2. ORGANIC CHEMISTRY. *Educ:* Univ Iowa, BS, 68; Yale Univ, PhD(org chem), 73. *Prof Exp:* Fel, Cath Univ Louvain, Belg, 73-75; ASST PROF CHEM, IND UNIV-PURDUE UNIV, 75- *Concurrent Pos:* Res grants, Petrol Res Fund, Am Chem Soc, 77-79, Res Corp, 78-80 & NIH, 80-83. *Mem:* Am Chem Soc; Royal Soc Chem; Belg Chem Soc. *Res:* Development of new synthetic methods for the preparation of amino acid derivatives, especially methods involving the use of phase-transfer reactions. *Mailing Add:* Dept Chem Ind Univ-Purdue Univ PO Box 647 Indianapolis IN 46223

O'DONNELL, RAYMOND THOMAS, b Baltimore, Md, July 14, 31; m 57; c 5. ANALYTICAL CHEMISTRY, PHYSICAL CHEMISTRY. *Educ:* Loyola Col, Md, BS, 54; Mich State Univ, PhD(anal & phys chem), 67. *Prof Exp:* Instr chem, Col St Thomas, 57-59; asst prof, 64-65, ASSOC PROF ANAL CHEM, STATE UNIV NY COL OSWEGO, 65- *Mem:* AAAS; Am Chem Soc. *Res:* Theoretical studies, development and extension of instrumental methods of analysis, especially polarography, high frequency titrations, chronopotentiometry, spectrofluorometry and radiochemistry. *Mailing Add:* Dept of Chem State Univ of NY Oswego NY 13126

O'DONNELL, VINCENT JOSEPH, b Montreal, Que, Nov 30, 30. BIOCHEMISTRY. *Educ:* McGill Univ, BSc, 51, PhD(biochem), 54. *Prof Exp:* Asst biochem, McGill Univ, 51-54, res assoc & demonstr, 54-56; lectr, Glasgow Univ, 56-59; from asst prof to assoc prof, 59-67, PROF BIOCHEM, UNIV BC, 67- *Mem:* AAAS; Endocrine Soc; NY Acad Sci; Am Chem Soc; Am Soc Biol Chem. *Res:* Metabolism of steroid hormones; metabolism of androgens and estrogens. *Mailing Add:* Dept of Biochem Fac of Med Univ of BC Vancouver BC V6T 1W5 Can

O'DONOGHUE, JOHN LIPOMI, b Lowell, Mass, Apr 12, 47; m 67; c 2. PATHOLOGY, VETERINARY MEDICINE. *Educ:* Univ Pa, VMD, 70, PhD, 79. *Prof Exp:* USPHS trainee & fel path, Univ Pa, 70-74; PATHOLOGIST, EASTMAN KODAK CO, 74- *Concurrent Pos:* Instr lab animal med, Univ Rochester, 74- *Mem:* AAAS; Am Vet Med Asn; Soc Toxicol; Electron Micros Soc Am; Wildlife Dis Asn. *Res:* Toxicological pathology, expecially in neurotoxic diseases and in spontaneous neurological disorders. *Mailing Add:* B-320 Toxicol Sect Eastman Kodak Co Rochester NY 14650

O'DONOHUE, CYNTHIA H, b Washington, DC, Oct 3, 36; div; c 1. ORGANIC CHEMISTRY. *Educ:* Randolph-Macon Woman's Col, AB, 57; Univ Richmond, MS, 67, MBA, 79. *Prof Exp:* Res asst, Am Brands, Inc, 57-61; chemist endocrinol lab dept med, Med Col Va, 61-63; asst scientist, 65-66, assoc scientist & group leader lit processings, Tech Info Facil, 66-70, res scientist, 70-73, head tech info facil, 73-77, sr scientist & leader planning & econ group, 78-79, mgr biomat sci div, 79-81, SR STAFF PROCESS ANALYST, TOBACCO PROD STANDARDS, PHILIP MORRIS, 81- *Concurrent Pos:* Abstr, Chem Abstracts Serv, 63-68 & 75-77. *Mem:* Am Chem Soc; Am Mkt Asn. *Res:* Information storage, retrieval and processing; steroid and synthetic organic chemistry; technical forecasting; acquisition analysis; economic planning; implementation of new technology into manufacturing environment. *Mailing Add:* 9519 Ground Hog Dr Richmond VA 23235

O'DONOHUE, WALTER JOHN, JR, b Washington, DC, Sept 23, 34; m 57; c 1. PULMONARY DISEASES, INTERNAL MEDICINE. *Educ:* Va Mil Inst, BA, 57; Med Col Va, MD, 61. *Prof Exp:* NIH fel & instr med, Med Col Va, 67-69, from asst prof to assoc prof, 69-75, dir clin serv pulmonary dis, 75-77; PROF MED, CHMN PULMONARY MED DIV & ASSOC CHMN MED, CREIGHTON UNIV, 77- Consult pulmonary dis, McGuire Vet Admin Hosp, 69-77, Univ Va, 75-77 & Omaha Vet Admin Hosp, 77-; mem coun cardiopulmonary dis, Am Heart Asn, 72-77; bd trustees, Nat Bd Respiratory Ther, 73-75, vpres, 75, pres, 77-; med dir, Sch Respiratory Ther, J Sargent Reynolds Col, 74-77. *Mem:* Fel Am Col Physicians; fel Am Col Chest Physicians; Am Thoracic Soc. *Res:* Clinical investigation in acute respiratory failure and respiratory intensive care; investigation in pulmonary mechanics and early detection of lung disease. *Mailing Add:* Pulmonary Med Div 601 N 30th St Omaha NE 23298

O'DONOVAN, CORNELIUS JOSEPH, b Bridgeport, Conn, Nov 3, 20; m 43; c 5. PATHOLOGY, INTERNAL MEDICINE. *Educ:* Dartmouth Col, AB, 42; NY Univ, MD, 45. *Prof Exp:* Asst med dir, Armour Labs, Ill, 51-53; sr staff physician, Upjohn Co, Mich, 53-60; dir med res, Merck Sharp & Dohme Res Labs, Pa, 60-63; vpres res & med affairs, Ames Co Div, 63-68, VPRES MED AFFAIRS, MILES LABS, INC, 68- *Concurrent Pos:* Asst clin prof, Col Med, Univ Ill, 52-53. *Mem:* AAAS; AMA; Am Diabetes Asn; NY Acad Sci. *Res:* Clinical evaluation and development of steroid hormones; oral antidiabetic agents; development of diagnostic reagent test systems. *Mailing Add:* Miles Labs Inc PO Box 40 Elkhart IN 46515

ODOR, DOROTHY LOUISE, b Washington, DC, May 25, 22. ANATOMY. *Educ:* Am Univ, BA, 45; Univ Rochester, MS, 48, PhD(anat), 50. *Prof Exp:* Instr, Univ Wash, 50-56; from asst prof to assoc prof, Univ Fla, 56-61; from asst prof to assoc prof, Bowman Gray Sch Med, 61-69; assoc prof anat, Med Col Va, Va Commonwealth Univ, 69-73, prof anat, 73-77; PROF ANAT, SCH MED, UNIV SC, 77- *Mem:* AAAS; Am Asn Anat; Am Soc Cell Biol; Soc Study Reprod; Southern Soc Anatomists. *Res:* Light microscopy and ultrastructure (TEM and SEM) of oviductal and cervical epithelium under normal and experimental conditions; ciliogenesis; histogenesis of ovary; ultrastructure of ovarian follicles; fertilization and meiotic divisions; changes in oviductal and uterine cytology after hormonal administration; mesothelium. *Mailing Add:* Dept Anat Sch Med Univ SC Columbia SC 29208

ODOROFF, CHARLES LAZAR, b Minneapolis, Minn, July 4, 38; m 61; c 2. BIOSTATISTICS. *Educ:* Carleton Col, BA, 60; Harvard Univ, AM, 62, PhD(statist), 66. *Prof Exp:* Asst prof statist & psychiat, 64-70, actg dir div biostatist, 70-74, ASSOC PROF BIOSTATIST & STATIST, SCH MED & DENT, UNIV ROCHESTER, 70-, DIR DIV BIOSTATIST, 74- *Concurrent Pos:* Vis scientist, Radiation Effects Res Found, Hiroshima, Japan, 76-77. *Mem:* AAAS; Am Statist Asn; Biomet Soc; Inst Math Statist. *Res:* Statistical methodology; epidemiology, biometry. *Mailing Add:* Div Biostatist Box 630 Univ Rochester Med Ctr Rochester NY 14642

O'DRISCOLL, KENNETH F(RANCIS), b Staten Island, NY, July 22, 31; m 54; c 5. POLYMER CHEMISTRY, CHEMICAL ENGINEERING. *Educ:* Pratt Inst, BChE, 52; Princeton Univ, MA, 57, PhD(chem), 58. *Prof Exp:* Develop engr, E I du Pont de Nemours & Co, 52-53; from asst prof to prof chem, Villanova Univ, 58-66; from assoc prof to prof chem eng, State Univ NY, Buffalo, 66-70; PROF CHEM ENG, UNIV WATERLOO, 70- *Concurrent Pos:* Vis prof, Kyoto Univ, 64-65; vis prof, Univ Mainz, 76-77 & Univ Lund, 77. *Honors & Awards:* Petrol Res Fund Int Award, 64. *Mem:* Am Chem Soc; Can Inst Chem; Can Soc Chem Engrs. *Res:* Kinetics and thermodynamics of polymerization; immobilization of enzymes and other catalysts. *Mailing Add:* Dept of Chem Eng Univ of Waterloo Waterloo ON N2L 3G1 Can

ODUM, EUGENE PLEASANTS, b Lake Sunapee, NH, Sept 17, 13; m 39; c 1. ECOSYSTEM ECOLOGY, ORNITHOLOGY. *Educ:* Univ NC, AB, 34; Univ Ill, PhD(ecol, ornith), 39. *Prof Exp:* Asst zool, Univ NC, 34-36; instr biol & ornith, Western Reserve Univ, 36-37; asst, Univ Ill, 37-39; res biologist, Edmund Niles Huyck Preserve, NY, 39-40; from instr to prof, 40-57, ALUMNI FOUND DISTINGUISHED PROF ZOOL, UNIV GA, 57-, DIR INST ECOL, 61-, FULLER E CALLAWAY PROF ECOL, 76- *Concurrent Pos:* NSF sr fel, 57-58; instr, Marine Biol Lab, Woods Hole, 57-61. *Honors & Awards:* Mercer Award, Ecol Soc Am, 56. *Mem:* Nat Acad Sci; AAAS; Ecol Soc Am (pres, 64-65); Am Soc Limnol & Oceanog; Am Soc Nat. *Res:* General principles of ecology; vertebrate populations; productivity and ecosystem energetics; ecology of birds; radiation estuarine and wetland ecology. *Mailing Add:* Inst Ecol Univ Ga Athens GA 30601

ODUM, HOWARD THOMAS, b Durham, NC, Sept 1, 24; m 47; c 2. ECOLOGY, SYSTEMS ECOLOGY. *Educ:* Univ NC, AB, 47; Yale Univ, PhD(zool), 51. *Prof Exp:* Asst, Univ NC, 46 & Yale Univ, 47-48; asst prof biol, Univ Fla, 50-54; asst prof zool, Duke Univ, 54-56; dir & res scientist, Inst Marine Sci, Univ Tex, 56-63; chief scientist, Rain Forest Proj, P R Nuclear Ctr, 63-66; prof ecol, Univ NC, Chapel Hill, 66-70; GRAD RES PROF ENVIRON ENG SCI, UNIV FLA, 70-, DIR CTR WETLANDS, 72- *Concurrent Pos:* Instr, Trop Weather Sch, CZ, 45; prin investr, Off Naval Res grant, Univ Fla, 52-54; instr, Marine Biol Lab, Woods Hole, 53, 58; grants, NSF, 55-60, Rockefeller Found, 57-58 & 73-77, Off Naval Res, 58-60, Atomic Energy Comn, 58, 63-76 & USPHS, 59-63; mem comn herbicide in Viet Nam, Nat Acad Sci. *Honors & Awards:* George Mercer Award, Ecol Soc, 57; Merit Award, Asn Tech Writers, 71; Cert of Achievement, Soc Tech Commun; Distinguished Serv Award, Indust Develop Res Coun; Prize, Inst la Vie, Paris, 76. *Mem:* AAAS; Am Soc Limnol & Oceanog; Am Meteorol Soc; Ecol Soc Am; Geochem Soc. *Res:* Energy analysis; biological oceanography; biogeochemistry; ecological engineering; tropical meteorology. *Mailing Add:* Dept of Environ Eng Sci Univ of Fla Gainesville FL 32611

ODUM, WILLIAM EUGENE, b Athens, Ga, Oct 1, 42. ECOLOGY. *Educ:* Univ Ga, BS, 64; Univ Miami, MS, 66, PhD(marine sci), 70. *Prof Exp:* Can Govt res fel, Univ BC, 70-71; asst prof, 71-75, ASSOC PROF ECOL, UNIV VA, 75-, PROF ENVIRON SCI, 80- *Concurrent Pos:* Bd trustees, Nat Parks & Conservation Asn. *Mem:* Am Soc Limnol & Oceanog; Ecol Soc Am; Am Fisheries Soc; Inst Fisheries Biologists. *Res:* Estuarine food webs; plant detritus production; ecology of resource management; ecology of fishes; cycling of heavy metals in ecosystems. *Mailing Add:* Dept of Environ Sci Univ of Va Charlottesville VA 22903

O'DWYER, JOHN J, b Grafton, NSW, Australia, Nov 9, 25; m 55; c 5. THEORETICAL SOLID STATE PHYSICS. *Educ:* Univ Sydney, BSc, 45, BE, 47; Univ Liverpool, PhD(physics), 51. *Prof Exp:* Lectr math, Sydney Tech Col, 47-48; sr res officer physics, Commonwealth Sci & Indust Res Orgn, Australia, 51-57; assoc prof, Univ New South Wales, 57-64; sr scientist, Westinghouse Res Labs, 65; prof physics, Univ Southern Ill, 66-70; PROF PHYSICS, STATE UNIV NY COL OSWEGO, 70- *Concurrent Pos:* Vchmn digest comt, Dielectrics Conf, 67, secy, 70-71, chmn, 74-75. *Mem:* Am Phys Soc; Am Asn Physics Teachers; Brit Inst Physics. *Res:* Theory of dielectrics, especially phenomena occurring at high field strengths. *Mailing Add:* Dept of Physics State Univ of NY Col Oswego NY 13126

OEGERLE, WILLIAM RANDOLPH, astrophysics, see previous edition

OEHLSCHLAGER, ALLAN CAMERON, b Hartford, Conn, Sept 8, 40; m 60; c 3. BIO-ORGANIC CHEMISTRY. *Educ:* Okla State Univ, PhD(org chem), 65. *Prof Exp:* NATO fel org chem, Univ Strasbourg, 65-66; asst prof, 66-69, assoc prof, 69-78, PROF CHEM, SIMON FRASER UNIV, 78- *Mem:* Am Chem Soc; Royal Soc Chem; Chem Soc France; fel Chem Inst Can. *Res:* Membrane active antibiotics; bio-organic chemistry of terpenes; insect attractants. *Mailing Add:* Dept Chem Simon Fraser Univ Burnaby BC V5A 1S6 Can

OEHME, FREDERICK WOLFGANG, b Leipzig, Ger, Oct 14, 33; US citizen; m 60, 81; c 5. TOXICOLOGY, COMPARATIVE MEDICINE. *Educ:* Cornell Univ, BS, 57, DVM, 58; Kans State Univ, MS, 62; Univ Geissen, Dr med vet, 64; Am Bd Vet Toxicol, dipl, 67; Univ Mo-Columbia, PhD(toxicol), 69; Am Bd Toxicol, dipl, 80. *Prof Exp:* Veterinarian, Md, 58-59; instr surg & med col vet med, Kans State Univ, 59-64, from asst prof to assoc prof, 64-66; instr physiol pharm, Univ Mo-Columbia, 66-67, NIH spec res fel toxicol, 67-69; assoc prof toxicol & med, 69-73, PROF TOXICOL, MED & PHYSIOL, COL VET MED, KANS STATE UNIV, 73-, DIR COMP TOXICOL LAB, 69- *Concurrent Pos:* Vis prof col vet med, Univ Giessen, 63-64; consult, private indust gen public, 69-, Food & Drug Admin, Washington, DC, 70-, Univ Kans, 71-, Nat Acad Sci, 71, various state & nat govts, 75-, Nat Inst Environ Health Sci, 74- & World Health Org, 79-; ed & publ, Vet & Human Toxicol, 70- *Mem:* Fel Am Col Vet Toxicol (secy-treas, 70-78); Soc Toxicol; Am Acad Clin Toxicol (pres-elect, 76-78, pres, 78-80). *Res:* Biotransformation and biochemical action of toxicants; clinical and diagnostic toxicology; public health aspects of toxicants; comparative toxicology as a research and diagnostic tool; teaching and communication techniques for standards of excellence in science. *Mailing Add:* Comp Toxicol Lab Kans State Univ Manhattan KS 66506

OEHME, REINHARD, b Wiesbaden, Ger, Jan 26, 28; m 52. THEORETICAL PHYSICS. *Educ:* Univ Göttingen, PhD, 51. *Prof Exp:* Res assoc, Max Planck Inst Physics, Göttingen, Ger, 50-53; res assoc, Enrico Fermi Inst Nuclear Studies, Univ Chicago, 54-56; mem, Inst Adv Study, 56-58; from asst prof to assoc prof dept physics & Enrico Fermi Inst, 58-60, PROF DEPT PHYSICS & ENRICO FERMI INST, UNIV CHICAGO, 64- *Concurrent Pos:* Vis prof, Inst Theoret Physics, Sao Paulo, Brazil, 52-53 & Univ Md, 57; vis scientist, Brookhaven Nat Lab, 57, 60, 62, vis sr scientist, 65 & 67; visitor, Europ Orgn Nuclear Res, Switz, 61, 64, 71 & 73; vis prof, Univ Vienna, 61, Imp Col, Lond, 63-64, Guggenheim fel, 63-64; vis prof, Int Ctr Theoret Physics, 66, 68, 69, 70 & 72; vis prof, Univ Karlsruhe, Ger, 74, 75 & 77, Univ Tokyo, 76, & Max Planck Inst, Munchen, 78. *Honors & Awards:* Sr US Scientist Award, Alexander Von Humboldt Found, 74. *Mem:* Fel Am Phys Soc. *Res:* Elementary particle physics; quantum field theory. *Mailing Add:* Enrico Fermi Inst Univ Chicago Chicago IL 60637

OEHMKE, RICHARD WALLACE, b St Clair, Mich, Dec 19, 35; m 61; c 6. APPLIED CHEMISTRY, RESEARCH ADMINISTRATION. *Educ:* St Joseph's Col, Ind, BS, 58; Univ Ill, Urbana, PhD(inorg chem), 64. *Prof Exp:* Sr chemist, 64-73, supvr com tape div, 73-74, mgr prod develop, 74-78, MGR APPL TECHNOL, COM TAPE DIV, 3M CO, 78- *Res:* High temperature polymers; polymer composites; organometallic catalysis; bio-and biologically reactive polymers; chemical reactions of natural polymers; polymer coatings; chromatography; polymer adhesives; polymer films; technical management. *Mailing Add:* Com Tape Div Bldg 230 3M Ctr St Paul MN 55101

OEHMKE, ROBERT H, b Detroit, Mich, Aug 6, 27; m 50; c 1. MATHEMATICS. *Educ:* Univ Mich, BS, 48; Univ Detroit, MA, 50; Univ Chicago, PhD(math), 54. *Prof Exp:* Instr math, Ill Inst Technol, 53-54; asst prof, Butler Univ, 54-56; instr, Mich State Univ, 52-62; instr, Inst Defense Anal, 62-64; PROF MATH, UNIV IOWA, 64-, CHMN DEPT, 79- *Mem:* Am Math Soc; Math Asn Am; Asn Comput Mach. *Res:* Nonassociative algebra, semigroups and automata. *Mailing Add:* Dept Math Univ Iowa Iowa City IA 52242

OEHSER, PAUL HENRY, b Cherry Creek, NY, Mar 27, 04; m 27; c 2. SCIENCE WRITING. *Educ:* Greenville Col, AB, 25. *Prof Exp:* Asst ed bur biol surv, USDA, 25-31; ed, US Nat Mus, 31-50, asst chief ed div, Smithsonian Inst, 46-50, chief ed & pub div, 50-66, ed Sci Pub, Nat Geog Soc, 66-78; RES ASSOC, SMITHSONIAN INST, 66- *Concurrent Pos:* Ed proc, Am Sci Cong, 40-43; gen ed, US Encycl Hist, 67-68. *Mem:* Wilderness Soc; Thoreau Soc Am (pres, 60); Am Ornithologists' Union. *Res:* Science editing; biological editing and bibliography; American naturalists; conservation; Smithsonian history. *Mailing Add:* 9012 Old Dominion Dr McLean VA 22102

OEI, DJONG-GIE, b Solo, Indonesia, Apr 18, 31; US citizen; m 63; c 4. PHYSICAL CHEMISTRY, INORGANIC CHEMISTRY. *Educ:* Univ Indonesia, Drs, 58; Univ Ky, PhD(phys chem), 61. *Prof Exp:* Lectr phys & inorg chem, Bandung Inst Tech, Indonesia, 61-63; fel dept chem, Univ Ky, 63-64; staff chemist off prod div, Int Bus Mach Corp, Ky, 64-67; sr res engr, Sci Res Staff, 67-69, ASSOC PRIN RES SCIENTIST, RES STAFF, FORD MOTOR CO, 69- *Mem:* Am Chem Soc; Electrochem Soc. *Res:* Chemistry of non-aqueous solvents; coordination compounds; inorganic and organic photoconductors; electrochemistry; inorganic sulfur chemistry. *Mailing Add:* Ford Motor Co PO Box 2053 Rm S-3079 Sci Res Lab Dearborn MI 48121

OEKBER, NORMAN FRED, b Avon, Ohio, Mar 3, 27; m 63; c 6. HORTICULTURE. *Educ:* Ohio State Univ, BS, 49; Cornell Univ, MS, 51, PhD(veg crops), 53. *Prof Exp:* Exten specialist veg crops, Univ Ill, 53-60; EXTEN SPECIALIST VEG CROPS, UNIV ARIZ, 60-, PROF HORT, 71-, RES SCIENTIST HORT, AGR EXP STA, 76- *Concurrent Pos:* Pres, Nat Agr Plastics Cong, 66. *Mem:* Am Soc Hort Sci. *Res:* Crop ecology and environmental control; arid lands production; post-harvest handling. *Mailing Add:* Dept of Plant Sci Univ of Ariz Tucson AZ 85721

OELFKE, WILLIAM C, b Kansas City, Mo, May 28, 41; m 64. GRAVITATIONAL RESEARCH, PHYSICS OF MEASUREMENTS. *Educ:* Stanford Univ, BS, 63; Duke Univ, PhD(physics), 69. *Prof Exp:* Res assoc microwave spectros, Duke Univ, summer 69; asst prof physics, Fla Technol Univ, 69-72, assoc prof, 72-80; PROF PHYSICS, UNIV CENT FLA, 80- *Concurrent Pos:* Sr res assoc, La State Univ, 75-76. *Honors & Awards:* Fac Develop Award, Fla Technol Univ, 75. *Mem:* Sigma Xi; Am Asn Physics Teachers; Am Phys Soc; AAAS. *Res:* Detection of gravitational radiation, superconducting, accelerometry, quantum-limited measurements, measurement of universal gravitational constant. *Mailing Add:* Dept Physics Univ Cent Fla Orlando FL 32816

OELKE, ERVIN ALBERT, b Green Lake, Wis, Dec 14, 33; m 58; c 2. AGRONOMY, PLANT PHYSIOLOGY. *Educ:* Univ Wis, BS, 60, MS, 62, PhD(agron), 64. *Prof Exp:* Agronomist, Rice Exp Sta, Univ Calif, 64-68; assoc prof, 68-80, PROF AGRON & EXTEN AGRONOMIST, UNIV MINN, ST PAUL, 80- *Mem:* Am Soc Agron. *Res:* Ecological factors influencing the seedling development and growth of rice; influence of environment and breeding on chlorophyll and other plant constituents in corn; culture and physiology of wild rice. *Mailing Add:* Dept of Agron & Plant Genetics Univ of Minn St Paul MN 55101

OELRICH, THOMAS MANN, b Cincinnati, Ohio, May 27, 24. MORPHOLOGY. *Educ:* Centre Col, AB, 48; Univ Mich, MS, 50, PhD, 54. *Prof Exp:* From instr to assoc prof, 52-74, PROF ANAT, MED SCH, UNIV MICH, ANN ARBOR, 74- *Mem:* Soc Vert Paleont; Am Asn Anat. *Res:* Human and comparative morphology; vertebrate fossils. *Mailing Add:* Dept of Anat Med Sci II Univ of Mich Ann Arbor MI 48104

OELS, HELEN C, b Philadelphia, Pa, Apr 13, 31. PATHOLOGY, CYTOLOGY. *Educ:* Chestnut Hill Col, BS, 53; Woman's Med Col Pa, MD, 57; Univ Minn, PhD(path), 69; Am Bd Path, dipl & cert anat path, 65, cert clin path, 67. *Prof Exp:* NIH fel, Sch Med, Temple Univ, 58-60; physician, Whitesburg Mem Hosp, Ky, 60-61; mem staff, Mayo Clin, 61-69; asst prof microbiol, 69-71, ASSOC PROF MICROBIOL & IMMUNOL, SCH MED, TEMPLE UNIV, 71-; DIR ANAT PATH, LAB PROCEDURES, INC, 75- *Mem:* Am Soc Clin Path; Am Soc Cytology; AMA; Col Am Pathologists. *Res:* Immunopathology; autoimmune diseases; lymphomas; antigens of histoplasma capsulatim; delayed hypersensitivity; virology; viral oncolysis. *Mailing Add:* Labs Procedures East 600 Allendale Rd King of Prussia PA 19406

OEN, ORDEAN SILAS, b Grafton, NDak, June 29, 27; m 53; c 3. PHYSICS. *Educ:* Concordia Col, BA, 49; Univ NDak, MS, 53; Univ Mo, PhD(physics), 58. *Prof Exp:* Instr physics, Univ Mo, 53-55; summer physicist solid state theory, 57, PHYSICIST, SOLID STATE DIV, OAK RIDGE NAT LAB, 58- *Mem:* Am Phys Soc; Sigma Xi. *Res:* Atomic collisions in solids; theoretical study of radiation effects on solids. *Mailing Add:* Oak Ridge Nat Lab PO Box X Oak Ridge TN 37830

OENE, HENK VAN, physical chemistry, see previous edition

OERTEL, DONATA (MRS BILL M SUGDEN), b Bonn, Ger, Aug 13, 47; US citizen; m 76. NEUROBIOLOGY. *Educ:* Univ Calif, Los Angeles, BA, 69, Santa Barbara, PhD(biol), 75. *Prof Exp:* Res asst neurobiol, Marine Biol Lab, Woods Hole, Mass & Univ Calif, Santa Barbara, 72-75; res assoc, Univ Wis-Madison, 75-77; NIH fel, Harvard Med Sch, 77-78; proj assoc, 78-80, asst scientist, 80-81, ASST PROF NEUROPHYSIOL, UNIV WIS-MADISON, 81- *Mem:* Soc Neurosci. *Res:* Neurophysiology, in particular, physiology of the auditory and visual systems; membrane biophysics. *Mailing Add:* 283 Med Sci Bldg Univ Wis Madison WI 53706

OERTEL, GEORGE FREDERICK, marine geology, see previous edition

OERTEL, GERHARD FRIEDRICH, b Leipzig, Ger, Apr 22, 20; m 46; c 3. STRUCTURAL GEOLOGY. *Educ:* Univ Bonn, Dr rer nat(geol), 45. *Prof Exp:* Asst geol, Univ Bonn, 46-50, Privatdozent, 50; geologist, Co Petrol Portugal, 51-53; geologist, Portuguese State Overseas Ministry, 53-56; assoc prof geol, Pomona Col, 56-60; assoc prof, 60-66, PROF GEOL, UNIV CALIF, LOS ANGELES, 66- *Concurrent Pos:* John Simon Guggenheim Mem Found fel, Univ Edinburgh, 66-67. *Mem:* Am Geophys Union; Geol Soc Am. *Res:* Structural geology of plutonic, volcanic, metamorphic and sedimentary rocks; deformation and fracture of rocks; slaty cleavage; preferred orientation of phyllosilicate mineral grains in rocks. *Mailing Add:* Dept of Earth & Space Sci Univ of Calif Los Angeles CA 90024

OERTEL, GOETZ KUNO HEINRICH, b Stuhm, Ger, Aug 24, 34; m 60; c 2. SOLAR PHYSICS. *Educ:* Univ Kiel, Vordiplom, 56; Univ Md, PhD(physics), 64. *Prof Exp:* Res asst physics, Univ Md, 57-62; aerospace engr, Langley Res Ctr, NASA, 63-68, staff scientist, Solar Prog Mgt, 68-69, dep chief solar physics prog, 69-71, chief, 71-75; head astron sect, NSF, 75; dir communications & mgt support, Off Asst Adminr Nuclear Energy, ERDA, 75-77, actg dir, Div Waste Prod, Nuclear Waste Mgt, 77-81, ACTG DIR, OFF DEFENSE NUCLEAR WASTE & PROD, US DEPT ENERGY, 81- *Concurrent Pos:* On leave, Dept Physics & Astron, Univ Md, 67-68; Partic, Fed Exec Develop Prog, Off Mgt & Budget & Civil Serv Comn, 74-75, spec analyst, Sci & Technol Policy Off, NSF, 74 & Exec Off of the President, 74-75; Fulbright grant. *Mem:* Am Astron Soc; Am Phys Soc; Sigma Xi. *Res:* Plasma spectroscopy; solar physics and astrophysics; program management; science policy; federal budget analysis and formulation; federal management and administration; communications; radioactive waste management. *Mailing Add:* Dept Energy Mail Stop B-107 Washington DC 20545

OERTEL, RICHARD PAUL, b New York, NY, Jan 12, 44; m 67. SPECTROCHEMISTRY. *Educ:* Oberlin Col, BA, 64; Cornell Univ, PhD(chem), 68. *Prof Exp:* Asst prof chem, Cornell Univ, 68-69; RES CHEMIST, PROCTER & GAMBLE CO, 69- *Mem:* Am Chem Soc. *Res:* Application of spectroscopy, chiefly infrared and Raman, to the elucidation of molecular structure in chemical and biochemical systems. *Mailing Add:* Procter & Gamble Co PO Box 39175 Cincinnati OH 45247

OERTLI, JOHANN JAKOB, b Ossingen, Switz, July 16, 27; US citizen; m 61; c 4. SOIL SCIENCE, PLANT NUTRITION. *Educ:* Swiss Fed Inst Technol, FEng, 51; Univ Calif, MS, 53, PhD(soils), 56. *Prof Exp:* From instr to asst prof soil sci, Univ Calif, Los Angeles, 57-63; from assoc prof to prof, Univ Calif, Riverside, 63-74; head, Inst Bot, Univ Basel, Switz, 74-79; PROF CROP SCI, SWISS FED INST TECHNOL, ZURICH, 79- *Concurrent Pos:* Fulbright fel, Ger, 70-71. *Mem:* Soil Conserv Soc of Am; Scand Soc Plant Physiol; Swiss Soc Plant Physiol; Soil Sci Soc Am; Am Soc Agron. *Res:* Mineral nutrition and water relations in plants. *Mailing Add:* Inst Crop Sci Swiss Fed Inst Technol CH 8092 Zurich Switzerland

OESPER, PETER, b Cincinnati, Ohio, Sept 25, 17; m 43; c 1. BIOLOGICAL CHEMISTRY. *Educ:* Swarthmore Col, AB, 38; Princeton Univ, MS, 40, PhD(chem), 41. *Prof Exp:* Instr phys chem, Univ Md, 41-42, asst prof, 42-45; res assoc sch med, Univ Pa, 45-51; asst prof, Hahnemann Med Col, 51-56, from assoc prof to prof, 56-68; chmn, 68-77, PROF CHEM DEPT, ST LAWRENCE UNIV, 68- *Mem:* Am Chem Soc; Am Soc Biol Chem. *Res:* Dipole moments; kinetics and thermodynamics of enzyme reactions. *Mailing Add:* Dept of Chem St Lawrence Univ Canton NY 13617

OESTERLING, MYRNA JANE, b Butler, Pa, Oct 24, 17. BIOCHEMISTRY. *Educ:* Univ Ill, AB, 39, MS, 41; George Washington Univ, PhD(biochem), 44. *Prof Exp:* Asst chem, Sch Med, Yale Univ, 46-47& Univ Ill, 47-50; asst prof physiol chem, 51-67, res assoc prof obstet & gynec (biochem), 67-71, RES ASSOC PROF, PEDIAT, OBSTET & GYNEC (BIOCHEM), MED COL PA, 71- *Concurrent Pos:* Talbot fel, Yale Univ, 44, Coxe fel, 45; Berquist fel, Karolinska Inst, Sweden, 50-51. *Mem:* AAAS; Am Asn Clin Chem; Am Soc Biol Chemists. *Res:* Amino acid nutrition; ascorbic acid method; stability and determination of epinephrine and norepinephrine; excretion of catecholamines in relation to stress; fetoplacental function; perinatology. *Mailing Add:* Dept of Obstet & Gynec Med Col of Pa Philadelphia PA 19129

OESTERLING, THOMAS O, b Butler, Pa, Mar 6, 38; m 60; c 3. PHARMACY, CHEMISTRY. *Educ:* Ohio State Univ, BS, 62, MS, 64, PhD(pharmaceut chem), 66. *Prof Exp:* Sr res assoc, Upjohn Co, 66-70, res head, 70-76; dir dermat res & develop, Johnson & Johnson, 76-78, dir pharmaceut res & develop, 78-80; MEM STAFF, MALLINCKRODT INC RES & DEVELOP, 80- *Mem:* Acad Pharmaceut Sci; Am Chem Soc; AAAS; Am Acad Dermat. *Res:* Rates and mechanisms of chemical degradation of drugs; physically programmed release of drugs from drug delivery systems. *Mailing Add:* Mallinkrodt Inc Res & Develop 675 Brown Rd PO Box 5840 St Louis MO 63134

OESTERREICH, ROGER EDWARD, b Chicago, Ill, Feb 7, 30. PHYSIOLOGICAL PSYCHOLOGY. *Educ:* Univ Mo, AB, 52; Univ Chicago, PhD(biopsychol), 60. *Prof Exp:* Asst psychol, Univ Chicago, 55-59; res assoc, Ill State Psychiat Inst, 60-64; vis asst prof, Ill Inst Technol, 64; asst prof, 64-66, ASSOC PROF PSYCHOL, STATE UNIV NY ALBANY, 66- *Mem:* Soc Neurosci. *Res:* Neural bases of perception; audition; sound localization. *Mailing Add:* Dept of Psychol State Univ of NY Albany NY 12222

OESTERREICHER, HANS, b Innsbruck, Austria, May 16, 39; US citizen; m 69; c 1. SOLID STATE CHEMISTRY. *Educ:* Univ Vienna, PhD(chem), 65. *Prof Exp:* Res assoc solid state chem, Univ Pittsburgh, 65-66 & Brookhaven Nat Lab, 66-67; instr, Cornell Univ, 67-69; asst prof, Grad Ctr, Univ Ore, 68-73, assoc prof, 73; ASSOC PROF SOLID STATE CHEM, UNIV CALIF, SAN DIEGO, 73- *Concurrent Pos:* Guest prof, Univ Konstanz, WGer, 78, 79, 80 & 81; prin investr grants, NSF, NASA, Off Naval Res & Dept Energy. *Mem:* Am Phys Soc. *Res:* Structural, magnetic, electric and thermal properties of solids ,superconductivity; intermetallic compounds and hydrides thereof. *Mailing Add:* Dept of Chem Univ of Calif at San Diego La Jolla CA 92093

OESTERWINTER, CLAUS, b Hamburg, Ger, Jan 18, 28; US citizen; m 53; c 2. ASTRONOMY, CELESTIAL MECHANICS. *Educ:* Yale Univ, MS, 64, PhD(astron), 65. *Prof Exp:* Chief comput, Western Geophys Co Am, 54-59; res astronr, Naval Weapons Lab, 59-75, RES ASTRONR, NAVAL SURFACE WEAPONS CTR, 75- *Mem:* Am Astron Soc; Int Astron Union; Cospar. *Res:* Determination of artificial satellite orbits in support of satellite geodesy; global solution for orbits of moon and major planets; improving orbits of natural satellites. *Mailing Add:* Astronaut Div Naval Surface Weapons Ctr Dahlgren VA 22448

OESTREICH, ALAN EMIL, b New York, NY, Dec 4, 39; m 73. RADIOLOGY, PEDIATRIC RADIOLOGY. *Educ:* Princeton Univ, AB, 61; Johns Hopkins Univ, MD, 65. *Prof Exp:* Asst prof radiol, Univ Mo, Columbia, 71-75, asst prof child health, 72-74, assoc prof radiol & child health, 74-79; ASSOC PROF RADIOL & PEDIAT, COL MED, UNIV CINCINNATI, 80-; PEDIAT RADIOL, CINCINNATI CHILDREN'S HOSP, 80- *Concurrent Pos:* Vis prof, Meharry Med Col, 72-77. *Mem:* Nat Med Asn; Soc Pediat Radiol; Am Col Radiol; Radiol Soc NAm; Am Roentgen Ray Soc. *Res:* Pediatric radiology, especially orthopedics, and including ultrasound and mathematics applications; applications of computers in bone dysplasias, vertebral column, chest, gastrointestinal. *Mailing Add:* XRay Dept Children's Hosp Med Ctr Elland & Bethesda Aves Cincinnati OH 45229

OESTREICHER, HANS LAURENZ, b Vienna, Austria, Apr 22, 12; m 43; c 1. MATHEMATICS. *Educ:* Univ Vienna, PhD(math), 34. *Prof Exp:* Res mathematician, Helmholtz Inst, Ger, 43-47; RES MATHEMATICIAN & CHIEF MATH & ANAL BR, AEROSPACE MED RES LAB, WRIGHT-PATTERSON AFB, 47- *Mem:* Fel Acoust Soc Am; Am Math Soc; NY Acad Sci; Inst Elec & Electronics Eng. *Res:* Applied mathematics; wave propagation; partial differential equations; theory of sound; information processing. *Mailing Add:* 2923 Green Vista Dr Brook Hollow Fairborn OH 45324

OETINGER, DAVID FREDERICK, b Buffalo, NY, Apr 25, 45; m 70; c 2. HELMINTHOLOGY, PARASITOLOGY. *Educ:* Houghton Col, BA, 67; Univ Nebr-Lincoln, MS, 69, PhD(zool), 77. *Prof Exp:* Asst prof, 77-81, ASSOC PROF BIOL, HOUGHTON COL, 81- *Mem:* Am Soc Parasit; Am Micros Soc; Am Soc Microbiol; Am Soc Trop Med & Hyg. *Res:* Helminth biology, in particular, taxonomy; morphology and physiology of the Acanthocephala. *Mailing Add:* Dept of Biol Houghton Col Houghton NY 14744

OETKING, PHILIP, b Madison, Wis, Mar 27, 22; m 45; c 2. MARINE GEOLOGY. *Educ:* Univ Wis, PhB, 46, MS, 48, PhD, 52. *Prof Exp:* Asst geol, Univ Wis, 46-50; res geologist, Sun Oil Co, 51-57; geological consult, 57-61; explor geologist, Scott Hammonds, oil producer, 61-62; sr scientist lunar geol, Chance Vought Corp, 62-63; res scientist, Grad Res Ctr, Southwest, 63-67; dir, Ocean Sci & Eng Lab, Southwest Res Inst, 67-76; DIR PLANNING & ENVIRON AFFAIRS, PORT OF CORPUS CHRISTI, 76- *Mem:* AAAS; Am Asn Petrol Geol; Am Asn Port Authorities. *Res:* Lunar and planetary geological research; light reflectivity measurements; preparation of regional geological highway maps of the United States; Gulf Coast stratigraphic, structural and sedimentation problems; coastal zone, estuarine and Gulf of Mexico environmental geology. *Mailing Add:* Port Corpus Christi Authority PO Box 1541 Corpus Christi TX 78403

OETTGEN, HERBERT FRIEDRICH, b Cologne, Ger, Nov 22, 23; m 57; c 3. MEDICINE, IMMUNOLOGY. *Educ:* Univ Cologne, MD, 51. *Prof Exp:* Intern, Red Cross Hosp, Neuwied, Ger, 51; resident path, Munic Hosp, Cologne, 52-54, resident med, 55-58; res assoc, 60-62, consult, 62-63, assoc, 63-67, assoc mem, 67-69, MEM, SLOAN-KETTERING INST CANCER RES, 70-; ASSOC PROF BIOL, SLOAN- KETTERING DIV, CORNELL UNIV, 73-, PROF MED, COL MED, 73- *Concurrent Pos:* Vis res fel, Sloan-Kettering Inst Cancer Res, 58-60; fel med, Mem Hosp Cancer & Allied Dis, 58-62; res gynec & obstet, Sch Med, Univ Marburg, 54-55; pvt docent, Univ Cologne, 62-69, vis prof, 69-; clin asst, Mem Hosp Cancer & Allied Dis, 65-67, asst attend physician, 67-69, assoc attend physician, 69-70, attend physician, 70-; asst prof med, Col Med, Cornell Univ, 67-70; mem cancer res ctr rev comt, NIH. *Honors & Awards:* Wilhelm Warner Award for Cancer Res, 70. *Mem:* Am Asn Cancer Res; Am Fedn Clin Res; Am Soc Hemat; NY Acad Sci; Am Soc Clin Oncol. *Res:* Cancer immunology; clinical oncology. *Mailing Add:* Sloan-Kettering Inst 410 E 68th St New York NY 10021

OETTING, FRANKLIN LEE, b Pueblo, Colo, June 21, 30; m 56; c 4. PHYSICAL CHEMISTRY, THERMODYNAMICS. *Educ:* Univ Colo, BS, 52, MS, 54; Univ Wash, Seattle, PhD(phys chem), 60. *Prof Exp:* Instr chem, Regis Col, 54-56; phys chemist, Dow Chem Co, Mich, 60-63, from res chemist to sr res chemist, Rocky Flats Div, Golden, 63-68, assoc scientist, 68-74; mem dept chem, Int Atomic Energy Agency, Vienna, Austria, 74-76; MEM STAFF, ATOMICS INT DIV, ROCKY FLATS PLANT, ROCKWELL INT, 76- *Concurrent Pos:* Mem, Calorimetry Conf, 61- *Mem:* AAAS; Am Chem Soc; Sigma Xi. *Res:* High temperature and isothermal calorimetry; compilation of thermodynamic data. *Mailing Add:* Atomics Int Div Rocky Flats Plant Rockwell Int Golden CO 80401

OETTING, ROBERT B(ENFIELD), b Lee's Summit, Mo, Aug 5, 33; m 60; c 2. AEROSPACE ENGINEERING, MECHANICAL ENGINEERING. *Educ:* Mo Sch Mines, BS, 55; Purdue Univ, MS, 57; Univ Md, PhD(mech eng), 64. *Prof Exp:* Asst aeronaut eng, Purdue Univ, 55-57; instr mech eng, Mo Sch Mines, 58-59 & Univ Md, 59-64; assoc prof, 64-69, PROF MECH & AEROSPACE ENG, UNIV MO-ROLLA, 69- *Mem:* Am Inst Aeronaut & Astronaut; Am Soc Eng Educ; Soc Automotive Engrs; Am Soc Aerospace

Educ. *Res:* Dynamic properties of structural materials; gas dynamics, including boundary layer flows and wake studies; airplane performance, including stability and control; wind energy conversion systems, analysis and design. *Mailing Add:* Mech & Aerospace Eng Univ of Mo Rolla MO 65401

OETTINGER, ANTHONY GERVIN, b Nuremberg, Ger, Mar 29, 29; nat US; m 54; c 2. APPLIED MATHEMATICS, LINGUISTICS. *Educ:* Harvard Univ, AB, 51, PhD(appl math), 54. *Prof Exp:* NSF fel & res fel appl math, 54-55, instr, 55-56, from asst prof to assoc prof appl math & ling, 57-63, prof ling, 63-75, GORDON MCKAY PROF APPL MATH, HARVARD UNIV, 63-, PROF INFO RESOURCES POLICY, 75-, DIR, PROG INFO TECHNOL & PUB POLICY, 73- *Concurrent Pos:* Consult, Arthur D Little, Inc, Cambridge, Mass, 56-80; consult off sci & technol, Exec Off of President of US, 61-73; consult, Bellcomm, Inc, Washington, DC, 63-67; mem adv bd, Chem Abstr Serv, Columbus, Ohio, 64-66; mem adv comt automatic lang processing, Nat Acad Sci-Nat Res Coun, Washington, DC, 64-66, chmn comput sci & eng bd, 67-73; mem res adv comt, Syst Develop Corp, Santa Monica, Calif, 65-68; res assoc prog technol & soc, Harvard Univ, 66-72; chmn bd trustees, Lang Res Found, Cambridge, Mass, 70-75; consult comt automation opportunities serv areas, Fed Coun Sci & Technol, 71-72; mem CATV comn, Commonwealth Mass, 72-75, chmn, 75-79, chmn comt regulation, 72- assoc univ sem comput & relation to man & soc, Columbia Univ, 73-; adv subcomt econ & soc impact of new broadcast media, Comt Econ Develop, New York, 73-75. *Mem:* Fel AAAS; Asn Comput Mach; fel Am Acad Arts & Sci; fel Inst Elec & Electronics Engrs; Sigma Xi. *Res:* Automatic information processing systems, design and applications, educational technology and policy, programming theory and information sciences. *Mailing Add:* Aiken Comput Lab Harvard Univ Cambridge MA 02138

OETTINGER, FRANK FREDERIC, b New York, NY, Aug 6, 40; m 63; c 3. SEMICONDUCTOR ELECTRONICS, PHYSICAL ELECTRONICS. *Educ:* Pratt Inst, BEE, 63; NY Univ, MSEE, 66. *Prof Exp:* Electronics engr semiconductor measurement develop, Appl Sci Lab, US Navy, 63-67; group leader, Electron Devices Sect, 67-73, actg chief, 73-75, chief, 75-78, chief, semiconductor devices sect, 78-81, DEP CHIEF, SEMICONDUCTOR DEVICES & CIRCUITS DIV, NAT BUR STANDARDS, 81- *Honors & Awards:* Silver Medal, US Dept Com, 76. *Mem:* Sr Inst Elec & Electronics Engrs. *Res:* Development of improved measurement methods and associated technology to enhance the performance, interchangeability, and reliability of semiconductor devices. *Mailing Add:* Semiconductor Devices & Circuits Div Nat Bur of Standards Washington DC 20234

O'FALLON, JOHN ROBERT, b Princeton, Minn, Aug 20, 37; m 62; c 3. PHYSICS. *Educ:* St John's Univ, BS, 59; Univ Ill, Urbana, MS, 61, PhD(physics), 65. *Prof Exp:* Res assoc high energy physics, Univ Mich, 65-67; from asst prof to prof physics, St Louis Univ, 67-78; asst to the pres, 76-77, admin dir, 77-79, VPRES ADMIN, ARGONNE UNIV ASN, 79- *Concurrent Pos:* Guest scientist, Argonne Nat Lab, 65-81 & Lawrence Berkeley Lab, 70-71; vis scientist, Brookhaven Nat Lab, 66-68 & 80- *Mem:* Am Phys Soc; Sigma Xi. *Res:* Experimental high energy physics; proton proton and proton neutron scattering with polarized beams and polarized targets. *Mailing Add:* Argonne Univ Asn PO Box 307 Argonne IL 60439

O'FALLON, NANCY MCCUMBER, b Jackson, Miss, Oct 25, 38; m 62; c 3. INSTRUMENTATION. *Educ:* St Louis Univ, BS, 60; Univ Ill, Urbana, MS, 61, PhD(physics), 66. *Prof Exp:* Vis asst prof physics, Univ Mo, St Louis, 72-74; asst physicist, 74-76, PHYSICIST, APPL PHYSICS DIV, ARGONNE NAT LAB, 76-, PROG MGR INSTRUMENTATION & CONTROL FOSSIL ENERGY, 78- *Mem:* Instrument Soc Am; Asn Women Sci; Am Phys Soc; AAAS. *Res:* Development of instruments based on nuclear, acoustic, optical and other advanced techniques for process control in large-scale coal gasification, liquefaction, and fluidized-bed combustion. *Mailing Add:* Appl Physics Div Bldg 316 Argonne Nat Lab Argonne IL 60439

O'FALLON, WILLIAM M, b Princeton, Minn, Mar 7, 34; m 61; c 2. BIOSTATISTICS, MATHEMATICAL STATISTICS. *Educ:* St John's Univ, Minn, BA, 56; Vanderbilt Univ, MAT, 57; Univ NC, PhD(statist), 67. Educ: Instr math, St John's Univ, Minn, 57-60; res assoc biostatist, Univ NC, Chapel Hill, 63-67; from asst prof to assoc prof community health sci, Med Ctr, Duke Univ, 66-74, asst prof math, 66-74; Nat Cancer Inst fel, 74-75, CONSULT BIOSTATIST & HEAD SECT MED RES STATIST, MAYO CLIN, 75-, ASSOC PROF BIOSTATIST, MAYO GRAD SCH MED, UNIV MINN, 78- *Mem:* AAAS; Math Asn Am; Am Statist Asn; Biomet Soc. *Res:* Mathematical and stochastic models of biological phenomena; multivariate analysis of biomedical data; statistical analysis of epidemiological data. *Mailing Add:* Sect of Med Res Statist Mayo Clin Rochester MN 55901

O'FARRELL, CHARLES PATRICK, b Elizabeth, NJ, Oct 30, 37; m 61; c 1. RUBBER CHEMISTRY. *Educ:* St Peter's Col, NJ, BS, 60; Rutgers Univ, PhD(phys & org chem), 65. *Prof Exp:* Res chemist, Esso Res & Eng Co, 64-66; head group mkt tech serv & tire applications, 77-78, RES ASSOC RUBBER CHEM, EXXON CHEM CO, 68- *Concurrent Pos:* Planning assoc, Elastomers Dept, Exxon Chem Americas, 79-82. *Mem:* Am Chem Soc. *Res:* Artificial latices produced from elastomeric polymers. *Mailing Add:* Exxon Chem Americas PO Box 3272 Houston TX 77001

O'FARRELL, MICHAEL JOHN, b Los Angeles, Calif, July 4, 44; m 65; c 3. MAMMALIAN ECOLOGY, BEHAVIORAL BIOLOGY. *Educ:* Univ Nev, Las Vegas, BS, 68; NMex Highlands Univ, MS, 71; Univ Nev, Reno, PhD(zool), 73. *Prof Exp:* Fel & res assoc mammal, Savannah River Ecol Lab, Univ Ga, 73-74; res assoc desert ecol, Univ Nev, Las Vegas, 74-75, asst prof biol, 75-76; CUR RES, ZOOL SOC NEV, LAS VEGAS, 76- *Mem:* Am Soc Mammalogists; Ecol Soc Am; Animal Behav Soc; Sigma Xi. *Res:* Small mammal community ecology; coexistence and social structure in natural populations, temperature regulation and body composition; behavioral ecology. *Mailing Add:* 4241 S Ridgeview Dr Las Vegas NV 89103

O'FARRELL, THOMAS PAUL, mammalian ecology, see previous edition

OFELT, GEORGE STERLING, b Washington, DC, Jan 22, 37; m 62; c 2. SPECTROSCOPY. *Educ:* Col William & Mary, BS, 57; Johns Hopkins Univ, PhD(physics), 62. *Prof Exp:* Instr physics, Johns Hopkins Univ, 62-63; asst prof, Col William & Mary, 63-67; ASSOC PROF OCEANOG, OLD DOM UNIV, 67- *Concurrent Pos:* Consult & lectr, NASA, 63- *Mem:* Optical Soc Am. *Res:* Ultraviolet and visible spectroscopy; optical oceanography. *Mailing Add:* 824 St Clement Rd Virginia Beach VA 23455

OFENGAND, EDWARD JAMES, b Taunton, Mass, Aug 15, 32; m 63; c 3. PROTEIN SYNTHESIS, TRANSFER RNA. *Educ:* Mass Inst Technol, BS & MS, 55; Wash Univ, St Louis, PhD(microbiol), 59. *Prof Exp:* NSF fel, Med Res Coun, Cambridge, Eng, 59-61; Rockefeller Inst fel, 61-62, NIH fel, 62; lectr biochem sch med, Univ Calif, San Francisco, 62-67, asst prof, 67-69; assoc mem, 69-77, MEM, ROCHE INST MOLECULAR BIOL, 78- *Mem:* AAAS; Am Soc Biol Chem; Am Chem Soc; Am Soc Microbiol; NY Acad Sci. *Res:* Structure and function of transfer RNA; structure and function of the ribosome; photoaffinity labelling of macromolecules. *Mailing Add:* Dept of Biochem Roche Inst of Molecular Biol Nutley NJ 07110

OFFEN, GEORGE RICHARD, US citizen. MECHANICAL ENGINEERING, ENVIRONMENTAL ENGINEERING. *Educ:* Stanford Univ, BS, 61, PhD(mech eng), 73; Mass Inst Technol, MS, 62. *Prof Exp:* Test engr conv bombs, Air Proving Ground Command, Eglin AFB, 62-65; res engr oil field reservoir eng, Chevron Res Co, Standard Oil Calif, 65-66 & Inst Francais du Petrole, 66-67; teaching & res asst mech eng, Stanford Univ, 68-73; actg asst prof, Santa Clara Univ, 73-74; STAFF ENGR, SECT LEADER & DEP MGR ENG, ENERGY & ENVIRON DIV, ACUREX CORP, 74- *Mem:* Am Soc Mech Engrs; AAAS. *Res:* Air pollution control technologies; multimedia environmental control of synfuel plants; alternative energy conversion systems for industrial and institutional facilities; management systems for environmental programs; turbulent boundary layers and multiphase flow in porous media. *Mailing Add:* Energy & Environ Div 485 Clyde Ave Mountain View CA 94042

OFFEN, HENRY WILLIAM, b Uelzen, Ger, Apr 28, 37; US citizen; m 61; c 2. PHYSICAL CHEMISTRY. *Educ:* St Olaf Col, BA, 58; Univ Calif, Los Angeles, PhD(chem), 63. *Prof Exp:* Instr chem, Occidental Col, 62-63; from asst prof to assoc prof, 63-73, dean, Off Res Develop, 72-78, PROF PHYS CHEM, UNIV CALIF, SANTA BARBARA, 73- *Mem:* AAAS; Am Phys Soc; Am Chem Soc. *Res:* High pressure spectroscopy; aqueous solutions; organic solids; charge-transfer interaction. *Mailing Add:* Dept of Chem Univ of Calif Santa Barbara CA 93106

OFFENBACHER, ELMER LAZARD, b Frankfurt am Main, Ger, Sept 29, 23; US citizen; m 52; c 3. PHYSICS. *Educ:* Brooklyn Col, AB, 43; Univ Pa, MS, 49, PhD(physics), 51. *Prof Exp:* Asst instr physics, Amherst Col, 43-44; physicist, Nat Adv Comt Aeronaut, Va, 44; asst instr physics, Univ Pa, 47-51; from asst prof to assoc prof, 51-65, PROF PHYSICS, TEMPLE UNIV, 65- *Concurrent Pos:* Physicist, Frankford Arsenal, US Dept Army, 53-54, consult, 54- *Mem:* Am Phys Soc; Am Asn Physics Teachers. *Res:* Solid state physics; ice physics; biomechanics; electron spin resonance. *Mailing Add:* Dept of Physics Temple Univ Philadelphia PA 19122

OFFENBERGER, ALLAN ANTHONY, b Lintlaw, Sask, Aug 11, 38; m 63; c 2. PLASMA PHYSICS, LASERS. *Educ:* Univ BC, BASc, 62, MASc, 63; Mass Inst Technol, PhD(nuclear eng), 68. *Prof Exp:* From asst prof to assoc prof elec eng, 68-75, PROF ELEC ENG, UNIV ALTA, 75- *Concurrent Pos:* Killam res fel, 80-82. *Mem:* Can Asn Physicists; Am Phys Soc; Sigma Xi. *Res:* Laser-plasma interactions; plasma production, heating, nonlinear interaction; scattering, absorption, interferometry diagnostics. *Mailing Add:* Dept of Elec Eng Univ of Alta Edmonton AB T6G 2G7 Can

OFFENHARTZ, EDWARD, b Brooklyn, NY, Mar 1, 28; m 51; c 5. MECHANICAL ENGINEERING, AERONAUTICAL ENGINEERING. *Educ:* Polytech Inst Brooklyn, BSME, 48; Harvard, PMD, 70. *Prof Exp:* Aeronaut res scientist, Nat Adv Comt Aeronaut, 48-56; res engr, Res & Adv Develop Div, Avco Corp, 56, group leader exp aerodyn, 56-59, prof engr, 59-60, sr proj engr, 60-62, proj mgr Apollo res & develop, 62-64, proj dir manned space systs, 64-65, dep dir oper space systs, 65-66, dir Apollo prog off & mfg, 66-67; dep dir oper & mgr proj eng, Perkin-Elmer Corp, 67-68, asst gen mgr opers, Optical Technol Div, 68-70; prog dir spec projs, 70-73, dir earth limb measurements satellite prog, 73-75, PROG DIR INT OFFSET MGT, GRUMMAN AEROSPACE CORP, 75- *Concurrent Pos:* Lectr, Univ Calif, Los Angeles, 65 & 66; mem defense sci bd, Shuttle Utilization Comt, US Dept Defense, 74-76; consult, New York City Dept Investigations, 76-77. *Mem:* Am Inst Aeronaut & Astronaut; Sigma Xi; Am Mgt Asn. *Res:* Applied research in supersonic and hypersonic aerodynamics; static and dynamic stability; heat transfer; ablation phenomena and detailed reentry vehicle design and development; aerothermodynamic and thermostructural analysis concerned with high temperature materials. *Mailing Add:* Grumman Aerospace Corp Plant 5 MS C33-05 Bethpage NY 11714

OFFENHAUER, ROBERT DWIGHT, b Sandusky, Ohio, June 24, 18; m 42; c 3. ORGANIC CHEMISTRY. *Educ:* DePauw Univ, AB, 40; Univ Wis, PhD(org chem), 44. *Prof Exp:* Res chemist, Allied Chem & Dye Corp, 44-48; chemist, 48-59, RES ASSOC LABS, MOBIL OIL CORP, 59- *Mem:* Am Chem Soc. *Res:* Petrochemicals; microbiology; petroleum chemistry; high polymers; textiles and organic synthesis; cyclohexanoic acid and derivatives; homogeneous catalysis. *Mailing Add:* Mobil Labs Princeton NJ 08540

OFFENKRANTZ, WILLIAM CHARLES, b Newark, NJ, Sept 2, 24; m 53; c 2. PSYCHIATRY, PSYCHOANALYSIS. *Educ:* Rutgers Univ, BS, 45; Columbia Univ, MD, 47; William Alanson White Inst, NY, dipl psychoanal, 57; Chicago Inst Psychoanal, dipl, 66. *Prof Exp:* Prof psychiat, Univ Chicago, 57-79; PROF PSYCHIAT & MENT HEALTH SCI, MED COL WISCONSIN, 79- *Mem:* Am Psychoanal Asn; Am Psychiat Asn; Group Advan Psychiat. *Res:* Clinical research in psychoanalysis; investigating relationships among dreams of the night. *Mailing Add:* Dept Psychiat Med Col Wis 2015 E Newport Ave Suite 201 Milwaukee WI 53211

OFFER, DANIEL, b Berlin, Ger, Dec 24, 29; US citizen; m 71; c 2. PSYCHIATRY. *Educ:* Univ Rochester, BA, 53; Univ Chicago, MD, 57. *Prof Exp:* Dir residency prog & assoc dir hosp, 66-73, co-chmn, Dept Psychiat, 74-77, DIR, LAB STUDY ADOLESCENTS, MICHAEL REESE HOSP, 68-, CHMN, DEPT PSYCHIAT, 77-; PROF PSYCHIAT, PRITZKER SCH MED, UNIV CHICAGO, 73- *Concurrent Pos:* Consult, Dept Ment Health, State of Ill, 64-; mem exec comt, Nicholas Pritzker Ctr & Hosp, 68-73; mem prof adv comt, Family Inst Chicago, 69-73; ed in chief, J Youth & Adolescence, 70-; mem prof adv coun, Ment Health Div, Chicago Bd Health, 70-73; fel, Ctr Advan Study Behav Sci, Stanford, Calif, 73-74. *Mem:* AAAS; fel Am Psychiat Asn; AMA; Int Cong Child Psychiat & Allied Profs; Am Soc Adolescent Psychiat (pres, 72-73). *Res:* Study of normal adolescent boys from teenage to young manhood; analysis of data collected over the past few years on juvenile delinquents. *Mailing Add:* Dept Psychiat Michael Reese Hosp 29th St & Ellis Ave Chicago IL 60616

OFFIELD, TERRY WATSON, b Amarillo, Tex, May 27, 33; m 57; c 2. GEOLOGY. *Educ:* Va Polytech Inst, BS, 53; Univ Ill, MS, 55; Yale Univ, PhD(geol), 62. *Prof Exp:* Geologist, Aluminum Co Am, 55; geologist, NY State Geol Surv, 57-59; geologist, Ariz, 61-69, coordr uranium geophys prog, 74-77, chief br uranium & thorium resources, 77-81, asst chief, Br Petrophys & Remote Sensing, 75-77, GEOLOGIST, US GEOL SURV, COLO, 69- *Mem:* AAAS; Geol Soc Am; Am Geophys Union. *Res:* Structural geology; Himalayan structure; lunar geology; terrestrial impact structures; remote sensing techniques for geologic mapping and uranium exploration; thermal-infrared studies; uranium geology. *Mailing Add:* Br Petrophysics & Remote Sensing US Geol Surv Denver Fed Ctr Denver CO 80225

OFFNER, FRANKLIN FALLER, b Chicago, Ill, Apr 8, 11; m 56; c 4. BIOPHYSICS. *Educ:* Cornell Univ, BChem, 33; Calif Inst Technol, MS, 34; Univ Chicago, PhD(physics), 38. *Prof Exp:* Asst, Univ Chicago, 35-38; pres, Offner Electronics, Inc, Ill, 39-63; PROF BIOPHYS, NORTHWESTERN UNIV, ILL, 63- *Mem:* Biophys Soc; fel Inst Elec & Electronics Engrs; Am Phys Soc; Am Electroencephalog Soc. *Res:* Theory of the excitable membrane. *Mailing Add:* Biomed Eng Ctr Northwestern Univ Evanston IL 60201

OFFORD, DAVID ROBERT, b Ottawa, Ont, Nov 13, 33; m 62; c 3. CHILD PSYCHIATRY. *Educ:* Queens Univ, Ont, MDCM, 57; CRCP(C), 65. *Prof Exp:* Jr rotating intern, Montreal Gen Hosp, 57-58, resident staff psychiat, 58-59 & 59-60; fel child psychiat, Children's Serv Ctr Wyo Valley, Wilkes-Barre, Pa, 60-62; from instr to asst prof psychiat, Div Child Psychiat, Univ Fla, 62-67; assoc prof behav sci, Col Med, Pa State Univ, 67-72; PROF PSYCHIAT, UNIV OTTAWA, 72-; STAFF PSYCHIATRIST, ROYAL OTTAWA HOSP, 72-, DIR RES & TRAINING CHILDREN'S SERV, 75-; ASSOC PROF BEHAV SCI, MILTON S HERSHEY MED CTR, PA STATE UNIV, 76- *Concurrent Pos:* Examr psychiat, Royal Col Physicians & Surgeons Can, 75- *Mem:* AMA; Am Psychiat Asn; Am Acad Child Psychiat; Am Orthopsychiat Asn; Am Pub Health asn. *Res:* The study of the natural histories, including childhood antecedents of the severe psychosocial diseases of adulthood, especially schizophrenia, sociopathy, alcoholism, affective disorder and retardation. *Mailing Add:* Royal Ottawa Hosp 1145 Carling Ave Ottawa ON K1N 6N5 Can

OFFUTT, MARION SAMUEL, b Mexico, Mo, Dec 22, 18; m 45; c 1. AGRONOMY. *Educ:* Univ Mo, BS, 48, MS, 52, PhD(plant breeding, genetics), 54. *Prof Exp:* County agent agr exten, Univ Mo, 48-50, from instr to assoc prof field crops, 52-56; PROF AGRON, UNIV ARK, FAYETTEVILLE, 56- *Mem:* Fel Am Soc Agron; Crop Sci Soc Am. *Res:* Plant breeding; genetics; management of forage legumes. *Mailing Add:* Dept Agron Plant Sci Bldg Rm 115 Univ Ark Fayetteville AR 72701

OFFUTT, WILLIAM FRANKLIN, b Slippery Rock, Pa, Feb 24, 19; m 53; c 3. OPERATIONS RESEARCH. *Educ:* Grove City Col, BSc, 40; Univ Pittsburgh, PhD(phys chem), 48. *Prof Exp:* Physicist div war res, Columbia Univ, 42-43; mem staff opers eval group, Off Chief Naval Opers, US Dept Navy, 48-54; sr scientist, E H Smith & Co, 54-56; mem staff weapons systs eval div, Inst Defense Anal, 56-60; mgr mkt res fed systs div, Int Bus Mach Corp, 60-81; sr res assoc, Inst Defense Anal, 65-66; mgr opers res, Fed Systs Div, IBM Corp, 67-80; RETIRED. *Mem:* Fel AAAS; Opers Res Soc Am (treas, 56-59). *Res:* Thermodynamics of solutions; operations analysis. *Mailing Add:* 11009 Rosemont Dr Rockville MD 20852

O'FLAHERTY, LARRANCE MICHAEL ARTHUR, b Wynyard, Sask, June 14, 41; US citizen; m 64. ALGOLOGY. *Educ:* Western Wash State Col, BA, 63; Ore State Univ, MA, 66, PhD(bot, phycol), 68. *Prof Exp:* From asst prof to assoc prof, 69-79, PROF BIOL, WESTERN ILL UNIV, 79- *Mem:* Am Bryol & Lichenological Soc; Phycol Soc Am; Int Phycol Soc; Am Soc Limnol & Oceanog. *Res:* Blue-green algae in culture; phytoplankton ecology. *Mailing Add:* Dept of Biol Sci Western Ill Univ Macomb IL 61455

OFNER, PETER, b Berlin, Ger, June 21, 23; US citizen. ORGANIC CHEMISTRY, ANDROLOGY. *Educ:* Univ London, BSc, 45, PhD(org chem), 50. *Prof Exp:* Res chemist, Wellcome Found, Burroughs Wellcome & Co, Eng, 46-50; asst res chemist, Courtauld Inst Biochem, Middlesex Hosp, London, 52-53; res biochemist, Nat Inst Med Res, 53-54 & Hormone Res Lab, Sch Med, Boston Univ, 55-57; CHIEF STEROID LAB, LEMUEL SHATTUCK HOSP, 57- *Concurrent Pos:* Econ Coop Admin fel enzymol, Univ Chicago, Sloan-Kettering Inst Cancer Res & Univ Utah, 50-52; res fel med, Harvard Univ, 58-60; res assoc med, Harvard Univ, 60-62 & Sch Dent Med, 63-, asst prof, 69-73, lectr pharm, 73-79, lectr toxicol, Sch Pub Health, 79-; lectr, Sch Med, Tufts Univ, 69-73, assoc prof urol, 73- *Mem:* Am Chem Soc; The Chem Soc; Brit Biochem Soc; Royal Inst Chem. *Res:* Effects and disposition of androgens and estrogens in male accessory sex organs; tissue culture. *Mailing Add:* Steroid Lab Lemuel Shattuck Hosp 170 Morton St Jamaica Plain MA 02130

O'FOGHLUDHA, FEARGHUS TADHG, b Dublin, Ireland, Jan 8, 27; m 56; c 2. MEDICAL PHYSICS. *Educ:* Nat Univ Ireland, BSc, 48, MSc, 49, PhD(physics), 61; Am Bd Radiol, cert, 65. *Prof Exp:* Asst physics, Univ Col, Dublin, 50-54; sr physicist, St Luke's Hosp, Dublin, 54-63; assoc prof radiation physics, Med Col Va, 63-65, prof & chmn div, 65-70; PROF RADIATION PHYSICS & DIR DIV, MED CTR, DUKE UNIV, 70- *Concurrent Pos:* Vis scientist, Oak Ridge Assoc Univs, 56, counr, 64-; res assoc, Univ Mich, 57; vis lectr, Univ Col Dublin, 58-63; adj prof physics, Duke Univ, 75-; US ed, Physics Med & Biol, 76- *Mem:* Am Phys Soc; Am Asn Physicists in Med (pres, 71); Am Col Radiol; Brit Inst Physics (fel Phys Soc). *Res:* Gamma ray spectrometry. *Mailing Add:* Dept of Radiol Duke Univ Med Ctr Durham NC 27710

OFSTEAD, EILERT A, b Minneapolis, Minn, Dec 15, 34; m 62; c 3. POLYMER CHEMISTRY. *Educ:* St Thomas Col, BS, 56; Univ Md, PhD(org chem), 63. *Prof Exp:* Am Dent Asn res asst dent, Nat Bur Standards, 57-58; RES SCIENTIST, GOODYEAR TIRE & RUBBER CO, 62- *Mem:* Am Chem Soc. *Res:* Reaction mechanisms; ring-opening polymerizations; synthetic elastomers. *Mailing Add:* Res Div Goodyear Tire & Rubber Co Akron OH 44316

OFTEDAHL, MARVIN LOREN, b Chicago, Ill, June 21, 31; m 58; c 1. ORGANIC CHEMISTRY. *Educ:* Northwestern Univ, BA, 56; Wash Univ, St Louis, PhD(carbohydrate chem), 60. *Prof Exp:* Sr res chemist org chem div, 60-67, res specialist, Indust Chem Co, 67-77, sr res specialist, Indust Chem Co, 77-80, RES GROUP LEADER, CORP RES & DEVELOP STAFF, MONSANTO CO, 80- *Mem:* Am Chem Soc; Sigma Xi. *Res:* Chemistry of carbyhydrates; organosulfur chemistry; oxygen and nitrogen heterocyclics; food and flavor chemistry; pharmaceuticals; pharmaceutical process development. *Mailing Add:* Monsanto Co 800 N Lindbergh Blvd St Louis MO 63166

O'GALLAGHER, JOSEPH JAMES, b Chicago, Ill, Oct 23, 39; m 63; c 2. PHYSICS. *Educ:* Mass Inst Technol, SB, 61; Univ Chicago, SM, 62, PhD(physics), 67. *Prof Exp:* Res assoc physics, Enrico Fermi Inst, Univ Chicago, 67-70; asst prof physics, Univ Md, College Park, 71-76; SR RES ASSOC, ENRICO FERMI INST, UNIV CHICAGO, 76- *Concurrent Pos:* Vis fel, Max Planck Inst Physics, 75-76; fel, Alexander Von Humboldt Found, 75. *Mem:* Am Phys Soc; Int Solar Energy Soc. *Res:* Solar energy; photo-thermal and photovoltaic conversion utilizing non-imaging and non-tracking optical concentrators; technical aspects of alternate and renewable energy sources; space physics; cosmic ray modulation; interplanetary propagation of solar cosmic radiation; detection techniques for energetic charged particles. *Mailing Add:* Enrico Fermi Inst 5630 S Ellis Chicago IL 60637

OGAR, GEORGE W(ILLIAM), b Dorchester, Mass, Nov 24, 18; m 54; c 4. SYSTEMS ANALYSIS, COMPUTER SIMULATION. *Educ:* Col Holy Cross, AB, 40; Boston Col, MA, 41; Harvard Univ, MEngSc, 49. *Prof Exp:* Electronics scientist, Air Force Cambridge Res Ctr, 50-52; electronics engr, Boston Naval Shipyard, 52-54; electronics scientist, Air Force Cambridge Res Ctr, 55; from asst prof to assoc prof elec eng, Air Force Inst Technol, 55-62; sr engr, AC Spark Plug Electronics Div, Gen Motors Corp, 62-64; systs analyst, Dynamics Res Corp, 64-66; PRIN ENGR, RAYTHEON MISSILE SYSTS DIV, 66- *Mem:* Inst Elec & Electronics Engrs. *Res:* Communications; electronic systems; applied mathematics; avionics; radar systems. *Mailing Add:* Raytheon Missile Systs Div Hartwell Rd Bedford MA 01730

O'GARA, BARTHOLOMEW WILLIS, b Laurel, Nebr, Mar 21, 23; m 49. ZOOLOGY, FISH & GAME MANAGEMENT. *Educ:* Mont State Univ, BS, 64; Univ Mont, PhD(zool), 68. *Prof Exp:* Asst leader, 68-78, RES BIOLOGIST, US FISH & WILDLIFE SERV, MONT COOP WILDLIFE RES UNIT, UNIV MONT, 68-, LEADER, 78- *Concurrent Pos:* Affil prof zool, forestry & wildlife biol, Univ Mont, 70-; US Fish & Wildlife Refuge Div grant, Red Rocks Nat Wildlife Refuge, Mont, 71; US Forest Serv grant elk migrations, 73-; res grants coyote-domestic sheep interactions, 74-, coyote-pronghorn interactions, 77, Sheldon Game Range, Nev, 78 & C M Russell Game Range, Mont, 78- *Mem:* Soc Study Reproduction; Am Soc Mammalogists; Wildlife Soc. *Res:* Mammalian reproduction, particularly of game species. *Mailing Add:* Mont Coop Wildlife Res Unit Univ of Mont Missoula MT 59812

OGARD, ALLEN E, b Ada, Minn, Dec 9, 31; m 56; c 2. GEOCHEMISTRY AND NUCLEAR WASTE. *Educ:* St Olaf Col, BA, 53; Univ Chicago, PhD(chem), 57. *Prof Exp:* Res chemist, Westinghouse Res Labs, 57; staff mem chem, Los Alamos Sci Lab, 57-70; guest scientist, Swiss Inst Reactor Res, 70-72; CHEMIST, LOS ALAMOS NAT LAB, 72- *Concurrent Pos:* Res fel, Inst Transurane, Karlsruhe, Ger, 64-65. *Mem:* Am Chem Soc. *Res:* Preparation and properties of high temperature plutonium reactor fuel materials; on-site and laboratory research pertaining to the geochemistry and hydrology of nuclear waste repository areas. *Mailing Add:* CNC-11 MS-514 Los Alamos Nat Lab Los Alamos NM 87545

OGASAWARA, FRANK X, b San Diego, Calif, Nov 10, 13; m 45; c 3. COMPARATIVE PHYSIOLOGY. *Educ:* Univ Calif, BS, 50, PhD, 57. *Prof Exp:* Res physiologist reprod, 55-58, asst prof poultry reprod, 58-66, assoc prof poultry reprod & animal physiol, 66-73, assoc physiologist, Exp Sta, 69-74, prof animal physiol, 73-76, PROF AVIAN SCI, UNIV CALIF, DAVIS, 73-, PHYSIOLOGIST EXP STA, 74- *Mem:* Am Poultry Sci Asn; Am Fertil Soc; World Poultry Sci Asn. *Res:* Poultry reproductive physiology. *Mailing Add:* Dept of Avian Sci Univ of Calif Davis CA 95616

OGATA, AKIO, b Puunene, Hawaii, July 20, 27; m 54; c 2. HYDRAULIC ENGINEERING. *Educ:* Utah Univ, BS, 51; Northwestern Univ, MS, 56, PhD(civil eng), 58. *Prof Exp:* Jr indust engr, Hawaiian Com & Sugar Co, 51-53; hydraul engr, East Maui Irrig Co, 53-55; res assoc fluid mech, Northwestern Univ, 57-58; hydraul engr, 58-63, res hydraul engr, 63-72, res hydrologist, Hawaii, 72-77, MEM STAFF, US GEOL SURV, 77- *Mem:* AAAS; Am Water Resources Asn; Am Geophys Union. *Res:* Transport mechanism in flow of fluids through porous media; flow dynamics of lakes and tidal estuaries. *Mailing Add:* US Geol Surv 345 Middlefield Rd Menlo Park CA 94025

OGATA, HISASHI, b Tokyo, Japan, June 10, 26; m 58; c 2. NUCLEAR PHYSICS. *Educ:* Tokyo Col Sci, BSc, 55; Tokyo Univ Educ, MSc, 57; Case Western Reserve Univ, PhD(physics), 63. *Prof Exp:* Res assoc nuclear physics nuclear data proj, Nat Acad Sci-Nat Res Coun, 62-63; res assoc nuclear data proj physics div, Oak Ridge Nat Lab, 64-65; asst prof, 65-68, ASSOC PROF NUCLEAR PHYSICS, UNIV WINDSOR, 68- *Concurrent Pos:* Nat Res Coun Can grant, 65-; Ont Dept Univ Affairs res grant, 67-70; vis scientist, Univ Tokyo, 74-75. *Mem:* Am Phys Soc; Can Asn Physicists. *Res:* Theoretical nuclear physics, particularly nuclear structure and low energy nuclear properties. *Mailing Add:* Dept Physics Univ Windsor Windsor ON N9B 3P4 Can

OGATA, KATSUHIKO, b Tokyo, Japan, Jan 6, 25; m 61; c 1. MECHANICAL ENGINEERING, INSTRUMENTATION. *Educ:* Univ Tokyo, BS, 47; Univ Ill, MS, 53; Univ Calif, PhD(eng sci), 56. *Prof Exp:* Asst combustion, Sci Res Inst, Tokyo, 48-51; fuel engr, Nippon Steel Tube Co, 51-52; from asst prof to assoc prof mech eng, Univ Minn, Minneapolis, 56-60; prof elec eng, Yokohama Nat Univ, 60-61; PROF MECH ENG, UNIV MINN, MINNEAPOLIS, 61- *Concurrent Pos:* Consult, Univac Div, Remington Rand Corp, Minn, 56. *Mem:* Am Soc Mech Engrs; Sigma Xi. *Res:* Automatic controls; nonlinear system analysis; operations research. *Mailing Add:* Dept of Mech Eng Univ of Minn Minneapolis MN 55455

OGAWA, HAJIMU, b Pasadena, Calif, June 18, 31; m 58; c 2. MATHEMATICS. *Educ:* Calif Inst Technol, BS, 53; Univ Calif, Berkeley, PhD(appl math), 61. *Prof Exp:* Lectr math, Univ Calif, Riverside, 60-61, from asst prof to assoc prof, 61-68; PROF MATH, STATE UNIV NY ALBANY, 68- *Concurrent Pos:* NSF grants, 62-68 & 69-71; vis asst prof, Univ Calif, Berkeley, 63-64; vis mem, Courant Inst Math Sci, NY Univ, 66-67. *Mem:* Am Math Soc; Math Asn Am; Soc Indust & Appl Math. *Res:* Partial differential equations. *Mailing Add:* Dept of Math State Univ of NY Albany NY 12222

OGAWA, JOSEPH MINORU, b Sanger, Calif, Apr 24, 25; m 54; c 3. PLANT PATHOLOGY. *Educ:* Univ Calif, BS, 50, PhD(plant path), 54. *Prof Exp:* Asst specialist plant path, 53-55, lectr, 55-62, from asst prof to assoc prof, 62-68, jr plant pathologist, 55-57, from asst plant pathologist to assoc plant pathologist, 57-58, PROF PLANT PATH & PLANT PATHOLOGIST, UNIV CALIF, DAVIS, 68- *Concurrent Pos:* Mem staff, UN Food & Agr Orgn, 67-68. *Mem:* AAAS; Am Phytopath Soc. *Res:* Diseases of deciduous fruit and nut crops; hop diseases; postharvest diseases; fungicides. *Mailing Add:* Dept Plant Path Univ Calif Davis CA 95616

OGBORN, LAWRENCE L, b Richmond, Ind, May 2, 32; m 54. POWER ELECTRONICS, INSTRUMENTATION. *Educ:* Rose Polytech Inst, BSEE, 54; Purdue Univ, MSEE, 57, PhD(elec eng), 61. *Prof Exp:* Mem tech staff elec eng, Bell Tel Labs, Inc, 54-56; asst, 56-57, from instr to asst prof elec eng, 57-63, assoc prof, 63-78, DIR, ELEC & HYBRID VEHICLE SYSTS DEVELOP LAB, PURDUE UNIV, WEST LAFAYETTE, 78- *Mem:* AAAS; Inst Elec & Electronics Engrs; Nat Soc Prof Engrs; Am Soc Eng Educ. *Res:* Electrical properties of materials; electronic circuit analysis and design; information processing in living systems. *Mailing Add:* Dept Elec Eng Purdue Univ West Lafayette IN 47907

OGBURN, CLIFTON ALFRED, b Philadelphia, Pa, Apr 27, 30. IMMUNOLOGY. *Educ:* Univ Pa, PhD(bact), 57. *Prof Exp:* From instr immunol in pediat to asst prof pediat, Sch Med, Univ Pa, 57-69; assoc prof, 69-75, PROF MICROBIOL, MED COL PA, 75-, MEM MED STAFF, 69-, ASSOC DEAN GRAD STUDIES, 76-, ACTG CHMN, 80- *Mem:* Transplantation Soc; Am Asn Immunologists; Am Soc Microbiol; NY Acad Sci. *Res:* Genesis of antibody; serology; transplantation immunity; purification; characterization of interferon tumor immunology. *Mailing Add:* Dept of Microbiol Med Col of Pa Philadelphia PA 19129

OGBURN, PHILLIP NASH, b Klamath Falls, Ore, Aug 18, 40; m 61; c 2. CARDIOVASCULAR PHYSIOLOGY. *Educ:* Wash State Univ, DVM, 65; Ohio State Univ, PhD(cardiovasc physiol), 71. *Prof Exp:* Intern med & surg, Animal Med Ctr, 65-66; vet pvt pract, 66-67; asst prof, 71-75, ASSOC PROF CARDIOL, COL VET MED, UNIV MINN, ST PAUL, 75- *Concurrent Pos:* Consult, 3M & Daig & Raltech Corp. *Mem:* Am Vet Med Asn; Acad Vet Cardiol; Am Animal Hosp Asn. *Res:* Effects of myocardial hypertrophy on excitation of ventricular myocardium and conduction system; comparative electrophysiology; comparative electrocardiography. *Mailing Add:* C336 Vet Hosp Univ of Minn St Paul MN 55108

OGDEN, DAVID ANDERSON, b Westfield, NJ, June 25, 31; m 54; c 4. NEPHROLOGY, INTERNAL MEDICINE. *Educ:* Cornell Univ, BA, 53, MD, 57. *Prof Exp:* From asst prof to assoc prof, Univ Colo, Denver, 63-69; assoc prof, 69-74, PROF MED, MED CTR, UNIV ARIZ, 74-, CHIEF RENAL SECT, 69- *Concurrent Pos:* Am Col Physicians fel, 2nd Med Div, Bellevue Hosp, New York, 59-60, NY Heart Asn fel, 60-61; clin investr, Vet Admin Hosp & Med Ctr, Univ Colo, Denver, 63-66; chief renal sect, Vet Admin Hosps, Denver, Colo, 65-69 & Tucson, Ariz, 69-; mem, Nat Renal Transplant Adv Group, US Vet Admin, 71-77; vpres, Nat Kidney Found, 80-82. *Mem:* Int Soc Nephrology; Am Soc Nephrology; Am Soc Artificial Internal Organs; Am Fedn Clin Res. *Res:* Function of the transplanted human kidney; divalent ion metabolism in uremia; problems in chronic hemodialysis. *Mailing Add:* Renal Sect Univ of Ariz Med Ctr Tucson AZ 85724

OGDEN, H(ORACE) R(USSELL), b Houghton, Mich, Feb 9, 20; m 47. PHYSICAL METALLURGY. *Educ:* Mich Col Mining & Technol, BS, 41; Ohio State Univ, MS, 53. *Prof Exp:* Res metallurgist, 45-50, asst chief nonferrous phys metall div, 50-55, consult, 55-60, chief nonferrous metall div, 60-77, MGR, MAGNESIUM RES CTR, BATTELLE MEM INST, 77- *Mem:* Am Soc Metals; Am Inst Mining, Metall & Petrol Engrs. *Res:* Physical metallurgy of titanium alloys and refractory metals; titanium alloy development; general physical metallurgy. *Mailing Add:* 452 Overbrook Dr Columbus OH 43214

OGDEN, INGRAM WESLEY, b Henryetta, Okla, Apr 29, 20; m 47; c 3. DENTISTRY. *Educ:* Univ Okla, BS, 41; Univ Mo, DDS, 44; Columbia Univ, cert oral biol, 55. *Prof Exp:* PROF ORAL DIAG, COL DENT, HOWARD UNIV, 66-; MEM STAFF DENT AUXILIARIES, MONTGOMERY COL, 70- *Concurrent Pos:* Ed consult, J Am Dent Asn, 66-; USPHS grant cancer training, Col Dent, Howard Univ, 70-73, USPHS grant dent therapist training, 71-72. *Mem:* Am Acad Oral Path. *Res:* Clinical recognition of oral cancer; improved health care delivery. *Mailing Add:* 9904 Holmhurst Rd Bethesda MD 20034

OGDEN, JAMES GORDON, III, b Martha's Vineyard, Mass, July 6, 28; m 56; c 4. ECOLOGY. *Educ:* Fla Southern Col, BS, 51, BA, 52; Univ Tenn, MS, 54; Yale Univ, PhD(biol), 58. *Prof Exp:* Asst biol, Fla Southern Col, 48-52; lab asst bot, Univ Tenn, 52-54; asst biol, Yale Univ, 54-57; climatologist, Conn Agr Exp Sta, 56; from asst prof to assoc prof bot, Ohio Wesleyan Univ, 58-63, prof & dir radiocarbon dating lab, 63-69; PROF BIOL & DIR RADIOCARBON DATING LAB, DALHOUSIE UNIV, 69- *Concurrent Pos:* Mem comt, NS Environ Control Coun, 73-77; fel, J S Guggenheim Found, 63. *Mem:* Am Soc Limnol & Oceanog; Am Quaternary Asn. *Res:* Precipitation chemistry; biogeochemistry; biogeography; pollen stratigraphy; paleoecology; climatology; microclimatic ecology; instrumentation for environmental studies; post-glacial history of vegetation and climate. *Mailing Add:* Dept Biol Dalhousie Univ Halifax NS B3H 3J5 Can

OGDEN, JOAN MARY, b New York, NY, July 21, 50. PLASMA PHYSICS, APPLIED MATHEMATICS. *Educ:* Univ Ill, BS, 70; Univ Md, PhD(physics), 77. *Prof Exp:* Teaching asst physics, Univ Md, 71-73, res asst plasma physics, 73-77; res assoc, Plasma Physics Lab, Princeton Univ, 77-79; CONSULT PHYSICS. *Concurrent Pos:* Comput prog. *Mem:* Am Phys Soc. *Res:* Computer simulation; nuclear fusion; electromagnetism. *Mailing Add:* R D S Box 620 Princeton NJ 08540

OGDEN, JOHN CONRAD, b Morristown, NJ, Nov 27, 40; m 69. MARINE ECOLOGY. *Educ:* Princeton Univ, AB, 62; Stanford Univ, PhD(biol), 68. *Prof Exp:* NIH trainee genetics, Univ Calif, Berkeley, 68-69; Smithsonian Inst fel, Smithsonian Trop Res Inst, CZ, 69-71, Am Philos Soc fel, 71; asst prof marine biol, 71-77, WI Lab, St Croix, VI, 74-77, assoc prof, Rutherford, 77-80, PROF MARINE BIOL, WINDIES LAB, VI, FAIRLEIGH DICKINSON UNIV, RUTHERFORD, 80- *Mem:* Am Soc Naturalists; Ecol Soc Am; AAAS; Sigma Xi; Western Soc Naturalists. *Res:* Ecology and behavior of animals and plants in shallow water marine communities; coastal zone development and management. *Mailing Add:* West Indies Lab PO Box 4010 Christiansted St Croix VI 00820

OGDEN, LAWRENCE, b Maryville, Mo, Nov 9, 19; m 48; c 2. GEOLOGY. *Educ:* Univ Tulsa, BS, 48; Univ Wis, MS, 50; Northwest Mo State Col, BS, 51; Colo Sch Mines, DSc(geol), 58. *Prof Exp:* Instr geol, Colo Sch Mines, 52-58, asst prof, 58-63; assoc prof, 63-66, PROF GEOL, EASTERN MICH UNIV, 66- *Mem:* Geol Soc Am; Nat Asn Geol Teachers. *Res:* Engineering geology; ground water; earth science education. *Mailing Add:* Dept of Geog & Geol Eastern Mich Univ Ypsilanti MI 48197

OGDEN, PHILIP MYRON, b Nampa, Idaho, Feb 3, 38; m 62; c 2. PHYSICS. *Educ:* Seattle Pac Col, BS, 59; Univ Calif, PhD(physics), 64. *Prof Exp:* From asst prof to assoc prof physics, Seattle Pac Col, 64-69; asst prof, 69-76, PROF PHYSICS, ROBERTS WESLEYAN COL, 76-, CHMN DIV NATURAL SCI & MATH, 74- *Mem:* Am Phys Soc; Am Sci Affiliation; Am Asn Physics Teachers. *Res:* High energy or elementary particle physics; cosmic ray physics. *Mailing Add:* Div of Natural Sci & Math Roberts Wesleyan Col Rochester NY 14624

OGDEN, ROBERT DAVID, mathematics, see previous edition

OGDEN, THOMAS E, b Lincoln, Nebr, Mar 23, 29; m 75; c 3. PHYSIOLOGY. *Educ:* Univ Calif, BA, 50, MD, 54, PhD(physiol), 62. *Prof Exp:* From res instr to res assoc prof physiol & neurol, Col Med, Univ Utah, 69-72, prof neurol, 72-75; prof physiol, Doheny Eye Found, 75-76, PROF PHYSIOL, UNIV SOUTHERN CALIF, 75- *Mem:* Asn Res Vision Ophthal. *Res:* Retinal neurophysiology and anatomy. *Mailing Add:* Dept of Physiol Sch of Med Los Angeles CA 90033

OGDEN, WILLIAM FREDERICK, b Randolph Field, Tex, Sept 11, 42. MATHEMATICS, COMPUTER SCIENCE. *Educ:* Univ Ark, Fayetteville, BS, 64; Stanford Univ, MS, 66, PhD(math), 69. *Prof Exp:* asst prof, 68-76, ASSOC PROF MATH & COMPUT SCI, CASE WESTERN RESERVE UNIV, 76- *Concurrent Pos:* NSF res grant, 71-72. *Mem:* Am Math Soc; Asn Comput Math. *Res:* Automata theory and programming languages. *Mailing Add:* Dept of Systs Eng Case Western Reserve Univ Cleveland OH 44106

OGDIN, CAROL ANNE, b Columbus, Ohio, Jan 12, 41. ELECTRICAL ENGINEERING, COMPUTER SCIENCE. *Prof Exp:* Sr analyst software comput, C-E-I-R Div, Control Data Corp, 67-70; TECH DIR ENG, SOFTWARE TECH INC, 70- *Concurrent Pos:* Engr-in-residence, NC State Univ, Raleigh, 74; tech dir eng, Teledyne-Geotech Inc, 76-77. *Honors & Awards:* Neale Award, 77. *Mem:* Sr Inst Elec & Electronic Engrs; Asn Comput Mach; Am Mensa Soc. *Res:* Computer hardware and software design, with particular emphasis on interdisciplinary techniques, projject management and behavioral changes. *Mailing Add:* Software Tech Inc 114 Harvard St Alexandria VA 22314

OGG, ALEX GRANT, JR, b Worland, Wyo, May 3, 41; m 62; c 2. PLANT PHYSIOLOGY, AGRONOMY. *Educ:* Univ Wyo, BS, 63; Ore State Univ, MS, 66, PhD(bot), 70. *Prof Exp:* Aide weed res, Univ Wyo, 59-63; res technician, Wash, 63-66, plant physiologist, Ore, 66-69, PLANT PHYSIOLOGIST, USDA, 69- *Concurrent Pos:* Mem, Coun Agr Sci & Technol. *Mem:* Weed Sci Soc Am. *Res:* Weed control research in horticultural crops in the Pacific Northwest. *Mailing Add:* Irrigated Agr Res & Exten Ctr Prosser WA 99350

OGG, FRANK CHAPPELL, JR, b Champaign, Ill, Jan 22, 30. APPLIED MATHEMATICS. *Educ:* Bowling Green State Univ, BA, 51; Johns Hopkins Univ, MA & PhD(math), 55. *Prof Exp:* Jr instr math, Johns Hopkins Univ, 51-55; res engr, Bendix Corp, 55-57, prin res engr, 57-60; res scientist, Carlyle Barton Lab, Johns Hopkins Univ, 60-68, lectr elec eng, 61-67; ASSOC PROF MATH, UNIV TOLEDO, 68- *Concurrent Pos:* Indust consult. *Mem:* Am Math Soc; sr mem Inst Elec & Electronics Engrs. *Res:* Mathematical physics and engineering. *Mailing Add:* Dept of Math Univ of Toledo Toledo OH 43606

OGG, JAMES ELVIS, b Centralia, Ill, Dec 24, 24; m 48; c 2. MICROBIAL GENETICS. *Educ:* Univ Ill, BS, 49; Cornell Univ, PhD(bact), 56. *Prof Exp:* With US Army Biol Labs, Md, 50-53 & 56-58; head dept, 67-77, PROF MICROBIOL, COLO STATE UNIV, 58- *Concurrent Pos:* Consult-evaluator, NCent Asn Cols & Schs, 74- *Mem:* AAAS; Soc Indust Microbiol; Am Soc Microbiol. *Res:* Microbial and molecular genetics; genetic and biochemical aspects of pathogenicity in bacteria. *Mailing Add:* Dept of Microbiology Colo State Univ Ft Collins CO 80523

OGIER, WALTER THOMAS, b Pasadena, Calif, June 18, 25; m 54; c 4. EXPERIMENTAL PHYSICS. *Educ:* Calif Inst Technol, BS, 47, PhD(physics), 53. *Prof Exp:* From instr to asst prof physics, Univ Calif, 54-60; from asst prof to assoc prof, 60-67, PROF PHYSICS, POMONA COL, 67-, CHMN, DEPT PHYSICS & ASTRON, 72- *Mem:* Am Phys Soc; Am Asn Physics Teachers. *Res:* X-ray scattering from deformed metals; proton produced x-rays. *Mailing Add:* Dept of Physics Pomona Col Claremont CA 91711

OGILVIE, ALFRED LIVINGSTON, b Vancouver, BC, Jan 20, 21; m 54; c 4. PERIODONTICS. *Educ:* Univ Toronto, DDS, 44; Univ Calif, MS, 48; Am Bd Periodont, dipl. *Prof Exp:* From instr periodont & endodontics to asst prof, Sch Dent, Univ Wash, 48-50; instr periodont & oral histol, Col Dent, Univ Calif, 50-51; from asst prof periodont & endodont to assoc prof, Sch Dent, Univ Wash, 51-65, prof periodont, 65-75; PROF ORAL MED, FAC DENT, UNIV BC, 76-, DIR, GRAD PERIODONT, 78- *Mem:* Can Dent Asn; Can Acad Periodont; Am Acad Periodont; Am Col Dentists; hon fel Royal Col Dent Can. *Res:* Endodontics; oral microanatomy. *Mailing Add:* Univ of BC Fac Dent Vancouver BC V6T 1S7 Can

OGILVIE, JAMES LOUIS, b Houston, Tex, Sept 20, 29; m 51; c 2. ANALYTICAL CHEMISTRY. *Educ:* Univ Tex, Austin, BS, 50, MA, 52, PhD(chem), 55. *Prof Exp:* Res chemist, Shell Oil Co, Tex, 54-61; sr res chemist, 61-69, res specialist, 69-74, sr res specialist, 74-79, SR GROUP LEADER, MONSANTO CO, 79- *Mem:* Am Chem Soc; Soc Appl Spectros. *Res:* X-ray photoelectron spectroscopy applied to catalyst structure; x-ray emission spectroscopy; x-ray diffraction. *Mailing Add:* Monsanto Co 800 N Lindbergh Blvd St Louis MO 63167

OGILVIE, JAMES WILLIAM, JR, b Orlando, Fla, Oct 20, 25; m 50; c 3. BIOCHEMISTRY, ORGANIC CHEMISTRY. *Educ:* Rollins Col, BS, 50; Johns Hopkins Univ, MA, 52, PhD(chem), 55. *Prof Exp:* USPHS fel biochem, Sch Med, Johns Hopkins Univ, 55-57, from instr to asst prof, 57-67; ASSOC PROF BIOCHEM, SCH MED, UNIV VA, 67- *Mem:* AAAS; Am Soc Biol Chemists; Am Chem Soc; Biophys Soc. *Res:* Mechanisms of enzyme action; biochemical control mechanisms; organic and bioorganic reaction mechanisms. *Mailing Add:* Dept of Biochem Univ of Va Sch of Med Charlottesville VA 22901

OGILVIE, JOHN FRANKLIN, chemical physics, see previous edition

OGILVIE, KEITH W, b Solihull, Eng, Feb 20, 26; m 76; c 2. PHYSICS, SPACE SCIENCE. *Educ:* Univ Edinburgh, BSc, 49, PhD(physics), 54. *Prof Exp:* Physicist, Brit Elec & Appl Indust Res Asn, 54; fel physics, Nat Res Coun Can, 55-57; lectr, Univ Sydney, 57-60; Nat Acad Sci fel, 60-63; physicist, NASA, 63-67, sect head, Goddard Space Flight Ctr, 67-71, BR HEAD, GODDARD SPACE FLIGHT CTR, NASA, GREENBELT, MD, 71- *Mem:* Am Geophys Union; fel Brit Inst Physics. *Res:* Composition and properties of the interplanetary plasma; cosmic rays and solar produced high energy particles. *Mailing Add:* Code 692 Goddard Space Flight Ctr Greenbelt MD 20771

OGILVIE, KELVIN KENNETH, b Windsor, NS, Nov 6, 42; m 64; c 1. BIO-ORGANIC CHEMISTRY. *Educ:* Acadia Univ, BSc, 63, Hons, 64; Northwestern Univ, PhD(chem), 68. *Prof Exp:* From asst prof to assoc prof chem, Univ Man, 68-74; assoc prof, 74-78, PROF CHEM, McGILL UNIV, 78- *Concurrent Pos:* Upjohn Chem Co fel, 74-76 & Steacie Mem fel, Nat Sci & Educ Res Coun Can, 82-84. *Mem:* Am Chem Soc; fel Chem Inst Can. *Res:* Synthesis of nucleotides; photochemistry of biological systems; phosphate chemistry. *Mailing Add:* Dept of Chem McGill Univ Montreal PQ H3A 2K6 Can

OGILVIE, MARILYN BAILEY, b Duncan, Okla, Mar 22, 36; div; c 3. HISTORY OF SCIENCE, BIOLOGY. *Educ:* Baker Univ, BA, 57; Univ Kans, MA, 59; Univ Okla, PhD(hist sci), 73. *Prof Exp:* Teacher biol, Phoenix Union High Sch, 59-61; teacher biol & chem, St Andrew's Col, Tanzania, E Africa, 61-62; adj asst prof hist sci, Portland State Univ, Ore, 71-75; prof hist, Oscar Rose Jr Col, Midwest City, Okla, 75-76; vis asst prof hist sci, Univ Okla, 77, adj asst prof hist sci, 77-79; specialist natural sci, 79-80, ASST PROF NATURAL SCI, OKLA BAPTIST UNIV, 80- *Concurrent Pos:* NSF resident pub serv sci, Omniplex Mus, Univ Okla, 77-78. *Mem:* Sigma Xi; Hist Sci Soc. *Res:* Women in science; Robert Chambers and pre-Darwinian evolutionary biology. *Mailing Add:* Hist of Sci Collections Univ of Okla Norman OK 73019

OGILVIE, MARVIN LEE, b Pontiac, Mich, May 3, 35; m 65; c 2. PHYSIOLOGICAL CHEMISTRY. *Educ:* Mich State Univ, BS, 57; Univ Wis-Madison, MS, 59, PhD(biochem), 62. *Prof Exp:* Babcock fel biochem, Univ Wis, 62-63; asst prof biochem & soil sci, Univ Nev, Reno, 63-64; SR RES SCIENTIST BIOCHEM & PHYSIOL, UPJOHN CO, 64- *Mem:* AAAS; Soc Study Reproduction; Am Soc Animal Sci. *Res:* Physiological chemistry relating to the mechanism of drug action; development of growth promotants for ruminants and non-ruminants; rumen function and physiology. *Mailing Add:* 1915 Holliday Kalamazoo MI 49001

OGILVIE, RICHARD IAN, b Sudbury, Ont, Oct 9, 36; m 65. CLINICAL PHARMACOLOGY. *Educ:* Univ Toronto, MD, 60; FRCP, 66, FACP, 79. *Prof Exp:* Lectr pharmacol, 67-68, from asst prof to assoc prof, 68-78, PROF PHARMACOL & MED & CHMN, DEPT PHARMACOL & THERAPEUT, McGILL UNIV, 78-; SR PHYSICIAN & DIR, CLIN PHARMACOL DIV, MONTREAL GEN HOSP, 76- *Concurrent Pos:* Fel, Can Found Adv Therapeut, 67-69; res grants, Que Med Res Coun, Med Res Coun Can, Que Heart Found & Can Found Adv Therapeut, 68-; res asst, Royal Victoria Hosp, Montreal, 68. *Mem:* Can Soc Clin Invest; Pharmacol Soc Can; Am Soc Clin Pharmacol; Am Soc Pharmacol & Exp Therapeut; Can Soc Clin Pharmacol (pres, 79-). *Res:* Clinical pharmacology of drugs affecting the cardiovascular system and metabolism; correlation of dry disposition with effect; clinical trials. *Mailing Add:* Dept of Pharmacol McGill Univ Montreal PQ H3A 1Y6 Can

OGILVIE, ROBERT EDWARD, b Wallace, Idaho, Sept 25, 23; div; c 3. ELECTRON OPTICS, MATERIALS SCIENCE. *Educ:* Univ Wash, BS, 50; Mass Inst Technol, SM, 52, MetE, 54, ScD, 55. *Prof Exp:* From asst prof to assoc prof, 55-66, PROF METALL, MASS INST TECHNOL, 66- *Concurrent Pos:* Vpres & dir res, Adv Metals Res, Burlington, 63-; vis res lab, Boston Mus Fine Arts, 68- *Mem:* Am Soc Metals; Mat Anal Soc (pres, 70). *Res:* Crystallography and x-ray diffraction; electron optics; phase diagrams, diffusion and phase transformations; metallic meteorites. *Mailing Add:* Rm 13-5069 Mass Inst of Technol Cambridge MA 02139

OGILVIE, T(HOMAS) FRANCIS, b Atlantic City, NJ, Sept 26, 29; m 50; c 3. SHIP HYDRODYNAMICS, PERTURBATION METHODS. *Educ:* Cornell Univ, AB, 50; Univ Md, MS, 57; Univ Calif, Berkeley, PhD(eng sci), 60. *Prof Exp:* Physicist, Underwater Explosions Br, David Taylor Model Basin, Dept Navy, 51-55, ship-wave anal sect, 55-60, head, 60-62, head free surface phenomena br, 62, liaison scientist, Off Naval Res, London Br Off, 62-64, head free surface phenomena br, David Taylor Model Basin, Washington, DC, 64-67; prof fluid mech, Univ Mich, Ann Arbor, 67-81, chmn, Dept Naval Archit & Marine Eng, 73-81; HEAD, DEPT OCEAN ENG, MASS INST TECHNOL, 82- *Concurrent Pos:* Prof lectr, Am Univ, 61-62 & 65-66. *Mem:* Soc Naval Archit & Marine Engrs; Soc Naval Architects of Japan. *Res:* Free surface phenomena, especially interactions between waves, ships or other structures; boundary value problems and perturbation theory in fluid mechanics. *Mailing Add:* Dept Ocean Eng Mass Inst Technol 5-230 Cambridge MA 02139

OGILVY, WINSTON STOWELL, b Le Mars, Iowa, Dec 3, 18; m 46; c 3. FOOD SCIENCE. *Educ:* Iowa State Univ, BS, 41, PhD(food technol), 50. *Prof Exp:* Bacteriologist, Armour & Co, 50-52, head bact sect, 52-56, assoc tech dir, 56-57; dir nutrit prod develop, Mead Johnson & Co, 57-66, VPRES FOOD PROD RES & DEVELOP, MEAD JOHNSON & CO DIV, BRISTOL-MYERS CO, 66- *Mem:* Am Oil Chem Soc; Am Chem Soc; Inst Food Technol. *Res:* Development of infant formulas, therapeutic foods; nutrition; food microbiology; research and development administration. *Mailing Add:* Mead Johnson Nutritionals 2404 Pennsylvania Ave Evansville IN 47721

OGIMACHI, NAOMI NEIL, b Los Angeles, Calif, Oct 10, 25; m 53; c 4. FLUORINE CHEMISTRY, HIGH ENERGY COMPOUNDS. *Educ:* Univ Calif, Los Angeles, BS, 50; Univ Calif, Berkeley, PhD(org chem), 55. *Prof Exp:* Chemist, Naval Weapons Test Sta, 50-52; asst chem, Univ Calif, Davis, 52-55; res chemist, E I du Pont de Nemours & Co, 55-57; res chemist, Naval Weapons Test Sta, 57-59; res specialist, Rocketdyne Div, Rockwell Int, 59-69; res chemist, Halocarbon Prod Corp, NJ, 70-75; staff scientist, Fluorochem Inc, 75; SR RES SCIENTIST, TELEDYNE McCORMICK SELPH, 75- *Mem:* AAAS; Am Chem Soc; The Chem Soc; Sigma Xi; Int Pyrotech Soc. *Res:* Chemistry of inorganic fluorine compounds; hydrazine and ammonia chemistry; organic synthesis; aromatic molecular complexes; characterization of liquid rocket propellants; analysis of solid propellants and explosives; fluorocarbon chemistry; synthesis of high energy compounds. *Mailing Add:* Teledyne McCormick Selph PO Box 6 Hollister CA 95023

OGINSKY, EVELYN LENORE, b New York, NY, Apr 6, 19. MICROBIAL PHYSIOLOGY. *Educ:* Cornell Univ, BA, 38; Univ Chicago, MS, 39; Univ Md, PhD(bact), 46. *Prof Exp:* Instr bact, Univ Md, 42-46; res assoc, Merck Inst Therapeut Res, 48-56; assoc prof, 57-63, prof bact, Med Sch, Univ Ore, 63-73; PROF MICROBIOL & ASSOC DEAN, GRAD SCH BIOMED SCI, UNIV TEX HEALTH SCI CTR, SAN ANTONIO, 74- *Concurrent Pos:* Donner Found fel, Harvard Med Sch, 46-47. *Mem:* AAAS; Am Soc Microbiol; Am Soc Biol Chemists; Am Acad Microbiol; Brit Soc Gen Microbiol. *Res:* Physiology and metabolism of microorganisms. *Mailing Add:* Grad Sch of Biomed Sci Univ of Tex Health Sci Ctr San Antonio TX 78284

OGLE, JAMES D, b Cleveland, Ohio, Feb 16, 20; m 42. BIOCHEMISTRY. *Educ:* Miami Univ, BS, 42; Univ Cincinnati, MS, 49, PhD(biochem), 52. *Prof Exp:* Asst prof, 53-65, ASSOC PROF BIOL CHEM, COL MED, UNIV CINCINNATI, 65- *Mem:* Am Chem Soc. *Res:* Proteolytic enzymes; complement proteins. *Mailing Add:* 945 Sutton Ave Cincinnati OH 45230

OGLE, PEARL REXFORD, JR, b Columbus, Ohio, June 27, 28; m 53; c 6. INORGANIC CHEMISTRY, PHYSICAL CHEMISTRY. *Educ:* Capital Univ, BS, 50; Ohio State Univ, MS, 52; Mich State Univ, PhD(chem), 55. *Prof Exp:* Prin scientist, Goodyear Atomic Corp, 55-64; asst prof, 64-70, ASSOC PROF CHEM, OTTERBEIN COL, 70-, CHMN DEPT, 74- *Concurrent Pos:* Res Corp grant, 65-; Air Force Off Sci Res grant, 66-70. *Mem:* AAAS; Chem Soc. *Res:* Mixed solvents; nitrogen dioxide-hydrogen fluoride; nitrosyl fluoride-hydrogen fluoride; nitryl fluoride-hydrogen fluoride; chemical isotope separation; uranium-molybdenum; nitrogen oxide-transition metal fluoride chemistry; selective ion electrodes. *Mailing Add:* Dept of Chem Otterbein Col Westerville OH 43081

OGLE, THOMAS FRANK, b St Paul, Minn, Oct 10, 42; div; c 2. REPRODUCTIVE ENDOCRINOLOGY. *Educ:* Purdue Univ, BS, 66; Wash State Univ, MS, 69, PhD(wildlife biol & zool), 73. *Prof Exp:* Fel endocrinol, Sch Med, Univ Va, 72-74; asst prof, 74-80, ASSOC PROF PHYSIOL, MED COL GA, 80- *Concurrent Pos:* NIH fel, 74. *Honors & Awards:* Nat Wildlife Fedn Fel Award, 70. *Mem:* Sigma Xi; Endocrine Soc; Soc Study Reproduction; Am Physiol Soc; Soc Exp Biol & Med. *Res:* Influence of ACTH and hyperadrenocorticoidism on ovarian function and maintenance of pregnancy with particular reference to natural regulation of population density. *Mailing Add:* Dept Physiol Med Col Ga Augusta GA 30912

OGLE, WAYNE LEROY, b Knoxville, Tenn, Dec 23, 22; m 48; c 2. HORTICULTURE. *Educ:* Univ Tenn, BS, 48; Univ Del, MS, 50; Univ Md, PhD(hort), 52. *Prof Exp:* Asst hort, Univ Del, 49-50; from asst to asst prof, Univ Md, 50-54; asst prof, Univ RI, 54-57; assoc prof, 57-66, PROF HORT, CLEMSON UNIV, 66- *Mem:* Am Soc Hort Sci; Inst Food Technologists. *Res:* Mineral nutrition of plants; herbicides and breeding of vegetable crops. *Mailing Add:* Dept of Hort Clemson Univ Clemson SC 29631

OGLE, WILLIAM ELWOOD, b Los Angeles, Calif, Aug 30, 17; m 72; c 5. PHYSICS. *Educ:* Univ Nev, AB, 40; Univ Ill, MS, 42, PhD(physics), 44. *Hon Degrees:* ScD, Univ Nev, 63. *Prof Exp:* Instr physics, Univ Ill, 43-44; exp physicist, Los Alamos Sci Lab, NMex, 44-52, alternate J div leader, 52-65, J div leader, 65-72; consult, 72-77; PRES, ENERGY SYST INC, 77- *Concurrent Pos:* Consult, Energy Res & Develop Agency, 72- & Defense Nuclear Agency, 73-77; contractor, Dept Energy & Defense Nuclear Agency, 77- *Honors & Awards:* Dept of Defense Award, 56, Distinguished Pub Serv Medal, 66; Dept Navy Distinguished Serv Medal, 63; AEC Citation, 71. *Mem:* Fel Am Phys Soc; Am Nuclear Soc; Am Geophys Union. *Res:* Gamma ray energies; gamma-proton processes; nuclear weapons testing; environmental effects; nuclear weapons effects and testing; geothermal energy development. *Mailing Add:* 4528 Delong Dr Anchorage AK 99502

OGLESBY, CLARKSON HILL, b Clarksville, Mo, Nov 9, 08; m 38; c 3. CIVIL ENGINEERING. *Educ:* Stanford Univ, AB, 32, Engr, 36. *Prof Exp:* Draftsman & computer, State Hwy Dept, Ariz, 28-30, off engr & inspector, 32-34, bridge designer, 36-38, from field engr to resident engr, 38-41; from construct engr to chief engr, Vinson & Pringle Construct Co, 41-43; from actg asst prof to prof civil eng, Stanford Univ, 43-74; RETIRED. *Concurrent Pos:* Consult engr, Stanford Res Inst, 58-77 & Systan, Info in Costa Rica, 78; engr, State Div, Bay Toll Crossings, Calif; Fulbright lectr, Imp Col, Univ London, 65-66; lectr at univs in Colombia, Chile, Australia & SAfrica, 74-78; sci writer, 82. *Honors & Awards:* Golden Beaver Award, 64; Hwy Res Bd Award, 69 & 71. *Mem:* Fel Am Soc Civil Engrs; Am Rd Builders Asn. *Res:* Highway and public works economics; construction management technology. *Mailing Add:* 850 Cedro Way Stanford CA 94305

OGLESBY, DAVID BERGER, b Charlottesville, Va, Mar 3, 41. ENGINEERING SCIENCE. *Educ:* Va Mil Inst, BS, 63; Univ Va, MAM, 65, DSc, 69. *Prof Exp:* Res engr, Univ Va, 67-68; ASST PROF ENG MECH, UNIV MO, 68- *Concurrent Pos:* Res assoc, D K Eng Assoc Inc, 72-74. *Mem:* Am Soc Civil Engrs. *Res:* Stress analysis of engineering structures with primary emphasis on plates and shells. *Mailing Add:* Dept of Eng Mech Univ of Mo Rolla MO 65401

OGLESBY, GAYLE ARDEN, b McGehee, Ark, Mar 11, 25; m 46; c 2. PETROLEUM GEOLOGY, MINERALOGY. *Educ:* Univ Ark, BS, 51, MS, 52. *Prof Exp:* Staff geologist, Ark State Geol Surv, 52-55 & Ohio Oil Co, 55-56; dist geologist, Oil & Gas Div, Reynolds Mining Corp, 56-57; wellsite geologist, Petrobras Exploracao, Brazil, 57-58; regional geologist, Br Mineral Classification, Gulf Coast Region, 58-73, chief br marine eval, 73-77, supvry geologist, New Energy Off, US Gen Acct Off, 77-81, JOINT INTEREST SPECIALIST, OFFSHORE DIV, SUPERIOR OIL, US GEOL SURV, 81- *Mem:* Am Asn Petrol Geologists; Am Inst Prof Geologists. *Res:* Petroleum geology exploration and development; geochemical and mineralogical analysis to determine stratigraphic correlations; oil, gas, sulfur and salt reservoir and deposit studies and evaluations in the outer continental shelf. *Mailing Add:* Gen Acct Off One Allen Center-Suite 955 Houston TX 77002

OGLESBY, LARRY CALMER, b Corvallis, Ore, Mar 26, 36; m 64; c 2. INVERTEBRATE ZOOLOGY, COMPARATIVE PHYSIOLOGY. *Educ:* Ore State Col, BA & BS, 58; Fla State Univ, MS, 60; Univ Calif, Berkeley, PhD(zool), 64. *Prof Exp:* Asst prof biol, Reed Col, 64-67; NATO fel, Univ Newcastle, 67-68; asst prof, 68-71, assoc prof, 71-79, chmn, Dept Zool, 75-78, instr, Marine Biol Lab, 75, PROF ZOOL, BIOL DEPT, POMONA COL, 79- *Concurrent Pos:* NSF res grant, 65-67; vis prof, Marine Biol Inst, Univ Ore, 69, 70, 73, & 79 & Col William & Mary, 74-75; res grant, Energy Res & Develop Admin, 76-77. *Mem:* Brit Soc Exp Biol; Am Soc Zoologists; Marine Biol Asn UK; fel AAAS. *Res:* Physiology of osmotic and ionic regulation in polychaete annelids and sipunculans; annelid parasites and other symbionts; ecological physiology of brackish water invertebrates; life cycles of trematodes; ecology of Salton Sea. *Mailing Add:* Dept Biol Pomona Col Claremont CA 91711

OGLESBY, RAY THURMOND, b Lynchburg, Va, Apr 16, 32; m 56; c 3. AQUATIC BIOLOGY. *Educ:* Univ Richmond, BS, 53; Col William & Mary, MA, 55; Univ NC, PhD(environ biol), 62. *Prof Exp:* Res biologist, Bur Com Fisheries, US Fish & Wildlife Serv, 58-59; res asst prof sanit biol, Univ Wash, 62-66, from res asst prof to assoc prof appl biol, 66-68; task group leader aquatic sci, Col Agr & Life Sci, 71-74; assoc prof dept conserv, 68-77, PROF DEPT NATURAL RESOURCES, CORNELL UNIV, 77- *Concurrent Pos:* Consult, Mobil Oil Co, Wash, 65, Rockefeller Found, 70-71 & Village of Lake Placid, 71-77; co-prin investr, Pac Northwest Pulp & Paper Asn grant, 65-67; prin investr, USPHS grant, 65-68, res contract, 66-68; prin investr, NSF res grant, 67-68; Int Aluminum Corp res contract, 67-68; Off Water Resources Res res grant, 68-71; Cayuga County res grant, 71-73; co-prin investr, Rockefeller Found res grant, 71-76; sci adv, NY State Assembly Comn on Environ Conserv; mem, Am Inst Biol Sci Life Sci Team Assessment Biol Impacts, 74-; prin investr res grant, Monsanto Chem, 77-78; vis scientist, Water Res Ctr, Stevenace, Eng, 75-76. *Mem:* Am Soc Limnol & Oceanog; Ecol Soc Am; Freshwater Biol Asn UK. *Res:* Lake and estuarine eutrophication; effects of pollutants on the biota of receiving waters; ecology of aquatic microbial communities. *Mailing Add:* Fernow Hall Cornell Univ Ithaca NY 14850

OGLESBY, SABERT, JR, b Birmingham, Ala, May 14, 21; m 44; c 1. ELECTRICAL ENGINEERING. *Educ:* Auburn Univ, BS, 43; Purdue Univ, MS, 50. *Prof Exp:* Res engr, Southern Res Inst, 46-48; instr elec eng, Purdue Univ, 48-50; head spec eng proj sect, 50-57, head eng div, 57-64, dir eng res, 64-74, vpres, 74-80, PRES, SOUTHERN RES INST, 80- *Mem:* Inst Elec & Electronics Engrs. *Res:* Air conditioning; servomechanisms; general engineering; environmental engineering. *Mailing Add:* Southern Res Inst Eng Res 2000 Ninth Ave S Birmingham AL 35205

OGLIARUSO, MICHAEL ANTHONY, b Brooklyn, NY, Aug 10, 38; m 61; c 1. PHYSICAL ORGANIC CHEMISTRY. *Educ:* Polytech Inst Brooklyn, BS, 60, PhD(chem), 65. *Prof Exp:* Teaching fel chem, Polytech Inst Brooklyn, 61-62, instr phys chem, 64; actg asst prof org chem, Univ Calif, Los Angeles, 65-66, res asst phys org chem, 66-67; asst prof, 67-72, assoc prof, 72-78, PROF ORG CHEM, VA POLYTECH INST & STATE UNIV, 78- *Mem:* Sigma Xi. *Res:* Electron-paramagnetic resonance spectroscopy; observations and reactions of organic radical ions; non-benzenoid aromatic molecules, stable organic anions; dianions and carbonium ions. *Mailing Add:* Dept of Chem Va Polytech Inst & State Univ Blacksburg VA 24061

O'GRADY, LAWRENCE J, b Montreal, Que, Dec 20, 17; m 51; c 3. SOIL FERTILITY. *Educ:* St Laurent Col, BA, 40; Okla Agr Inst, BSA, 44; Mich State Univ, PhD(soil sci), 48. *Prof Exp:* Asst prof soil sci, Okla Agr Inst, 48-50, prof, 50-54, head dept, 54-62; head dept, 62-72, PROF SOIL SCI, LAVAL UNIV, 72- *Res:* Soil fertility and chemistry. *Mailing Add:* Dept Soil Sci Laval Univ Ste-Foy PQ G1K 7P4 Can

O'GRADY, WILLIAM EDWARD, b Longmont, Colo, Oct 8, 39; m 66; c 3. PHYSICAL CHEMISTRY, SURFACE SCIENCE. *Educ:* Colo Sch Mines, BS, 64; Univ Pa, PhD(chem), 73. *Prof Exp:* Chemist anal chem, Shell Chem Co, 64-66; sr res assoc electrochem, Case Western Reserve Univ, 72-77; ASSOC CHEMIST ELECTROCHEM, DEPT ENRRGY & ENVIRON, BROOKHAVEN NAT LAB, 77- *Mem:* Am Electrochem Soc; Am Vacuum Soc. *Res:* Electrocatalysis and electrode kinetics; applications of surface science to electrochemistry; structure and properties of small particles; single crystal studies; quantum mechanical calculations on small particles. *Mailing Add:* Dept of Energy & Environ 801 Brookhaven Nat Lab Upton NY 11973

OGREN, DAVID ERNEST, b Wichita, Kans, Aug 4, 30. GEOLOGY. *Educ:* Ore State Col, BS, 57, MS, 58; Northwestern Univ, PhD(geol), 61. *Prof Exp:* Instr geol, Univ Wis, 61-62; asst prof, 62-70, ASSOC PROF GEOL, GA STATE UNIV, 70- *Mem:* AAAS; Soc Econ Paleont & Mineral; Geol Soc Am; Am Asn Petrol Geol. *Res:* Stratigraphy; paleontology. *Mailing Add:* Dept of Geol Ga State Univ Atlanta GA 30303

OGREN, HAROLD OLOF, b Grayling, Mich, Apr 24, 43; m 68; c 2. EXPERIMENTAL HIGH ENERGY PHYSICS. *Educ:* Univ Mich, BS, 65; Cornell Univ, MS, 67, PhD(physics), 70. *Prof Exp:* Vis scientist high energy physics, Nat Lab Frascati, 70-73; fel, Europ Asn Nuclear Res, 73-75; asst prof, 75-78, ASSOC PROF PHYSICS, IND UNIV, BLOOMINGTON, 78- *Mem:* Am Phys Soc. *Res:* Strong interaction physics of fundamental particles. *Mailing Add:* Dept of Physics Ind Univ Bloomington IN 47401

OGREN, HERMAN AUGUST, b Kenosha, Wis, Mar 31, 25; m 51; c 6. ECOLOGY. *Educ:* Univ Wis, BS, 50; Univ Mont, MS, 54; Univ Southern Calif, PhD(zool), 60. *Prof Exp:* State biologist, Mont Fish & Game Comn, 52-54; lab assoc zool, Univ Southern Calif, 54-56; instr, Exten Div, Univ NC, 56-57; state biologist, Dept Game & Fish, NMex, 57-60; asst prof zool, Elmhurst Col, 60-63; assoc prof, 63-70, bd trustees fac res grant, 64-65, PROF ZOOL, CARTHAGE COL, 70- *Concurrent Pos:* NSF grant, 62. *Honors & Awards:* Ann Honorarium, Am Soc Mammal, 55. *Mem:* Am Soc Mammal; Wildlife Soc. *Res:* Fish and wildlife technology; wild sheep of United States, Canada and Mexico, and of Essox Maskinonge in northern Wisconsin; presence of radioactivity in animals. *Mailing Add:* Dept of Zool Carthage Col Kenosha WI 53140

OGREN, MARILEE P, b Hessville, Ind, Aug 16, 51. NEUROANATOMY, VISON. *Educ:* Ind Univ, BA, 73; Univ Wash, PhD(psychol, biol struct), 78. *Prof Exp:* Res trainee visual neuroanat, Dept Ophthal, Univ Wash, 74-78; fel develop visual neuroanat & res assoc, Sch Med, Yale Univ, 78-79; RES ASSOC, SCH MED, UNIV WASH, 81- *Res:* Development of the primate visual system, particularly the pulvinar nucleus of the thalamus and the related areas of visual cortex; methods of study include Golgi impregnation; tritiated thymadine autoradiography; electron microscopy; immunocytochemical localization of visual system neurotransmitters in primates. *Mailing Add:* Dept Ophthalmol RJ-10 Univ Wash Sch Med Seattle WA 98195

OGREN, PAUL JOSEPH, b Madrid, Iowa, July 3, 41; m 63; c 2. PHYSICAL CHEMISTRY. *Educ:* Earlham Col, BA, 63; Univ Wis, PhD(chem), 68. *Prof Exp:* From asst prof to assoc prof chem, Maryville Col, 67-72; assoc prof chem, Cent Col, Iowa, 72-79; ASSOC PROF CHEM, EARLHAM COL, RICHMOND, IND, 79- *Concurrent Pos:* Advan Study Prog fel, Nat Ctr Atmospheric Res, 71-72. *Mem:* Am Chem Soc. *Res:* Solid state radiation chemistry; pulse radiolysis; photochemistry. *Mailing Add:* Dept Chem Earlham Col Richmond IN 47374

OGREN, ROBERT EDWARD, b Jamestown, NY, Feb 9, 22; m 48; c 2. ZOOLOGY, ANATOMY. *Educ:* Wheaton Col, BA, 47; Northwestern Univ, MS, 48; Univ Ill, PhD(zool, physiol), 53. *Prof Exp:* Asst zool, Univ Ill, 48-53; asst prof physiol & zool, Ursinus Col, 53-57; asst prof histol & anat, Dickinson Col, 57-63, actg chmn dept biol, 59-60; assoc prof embryol, histol & cell biol, 63-81, PROF BIOL, ANAT & PHYSIOL, WILKES COL, 81- *Mem:* Fel AAAS; Am Soc Zoologists; Am Soc Parasitologists; Am Micros Soc; Soc Protozoologists. *Res:* Comparative morphology; cytology; development and physiology of tapeworm hexacanth embryos; biology of land planarians; invertebrates; parasitology; histology; embryology. *Mailing Add:* Dept Biol Wilkes Col Wilkes-Barre PA 18703

OGREN, WILLIAM LEWIS, b Ashland, Wis, Oct 8, 38; m 67; c 3. PLANT PHYSIOLOGY. *Educ:* Univ Wis-Madison, BS, 61; Wayne State Univ, PhD(biochem), 65. *Prof Exp:* Res chemist, Parker Div, Hooker Chem Corp, 61-62; from asst prof to assoc prof plant physiol, 66-77, PROF PHYSIOL, UNIV ILL, URBANA, 77- *Concurrent Pos:* Plant physiologist, USDA, 65-79, res leader, 79- *Honors & Awards:* Crop Sci Award, 79. *Mem:* Am Soc Biol Chemists; Am Soc Plant Physiologists; fel Am Soc Agron; Crop Sci Soc Am. *Res:* Biochemistry, physiology and genetics of photosynthesis in soybeans and other crops; photorespiration. *Mailing Add:* Dept of Agron Univ of Ill Urbana IL 61801

OGRYZLO, ELMER ALEXANDER, b Dauphin, Man, Aug 18, 33; m 59; c 4. PHYSICAL CHEMISTRY. *Educ:* Univ Man, BSc, 55, MSc, 56; McGill Univ, PhD(phys chem), 59. *Prof Exp:* Exhibition of 1851 overseas fel, Univ Sheffield, 58-59; from instr to assoc prof chem, 59-71, PROF CHEM, UNIV BC, 71- *Concurrent Pos:* Nat Res Coun Can sr res fel, Univ Amsterdam, 66-67. *Mem:* Am Chem Soc; Chem Inst Can; Royal Soc Chem. *Res:* Kinetics of halogen atom reactions; reactions of electronically excited oxygen molecules; spectroscopy of small molecules; chemiluminescence. *Mailing Add:* Dept of Chem Univ of BC Vancouver BC V6T 1W5 Can

OGURA, JOSEPH H, b San Francisco, Calif, May 25, 15; m 42; c 3. OTOLARYNGOLOGY. *Educ:* Univ Calif, BA, 37, MD, 41; Am Bd Otolaryngol, dipl. *Prof Exp:* Intern, San Francisco County Hosp, 40-41; asst resident med & path, Univ Calif Hosp, 41-42; resident path, Cincinnati Gen Hosp, 42-43, resident & instr med, 43-45; resident otolaryngol, Barnes Hosp, St Louis, 45-48; from instr to prof, 48-66, LINDBURG PROF OTOLARYNGOL & HEAD DEPT, SCH MED, WASH UNIV, 66- *Concurrent Pos:* Attend otolaryngologist, Barnes, Children's & McMillan Hosps; consult otolaryngologist, Jewish, Vet Admin & St Louis City Hosps; mem bd dir, Am Bd Otolaryngol; mem, Nat Cancer Adv Bd. *Mem:* Am Soc Ophthal & Otolaryngol Allergy; Am Col Surgeons; Am Acad Ophthal & Otolaryngol; Am Laryngol Asn (pres); Am Acad Facial Plastic & Reconstruct Surg. *Res:* Head and neck surgery; transplantation of larynx; naso-pulmonary mechanics. *Mailing Add:* 1038 Winwood Dr St Louis MO 63124

OH, CHAN SOO, b Kwangju, Korea, July 4, 38; m 68; c 2. ORGANIC CHEMISTRY. *Educ:* Seoul Nat Univ, BS, 61; St John's Univ, MS, 67; PhD(org chem), 70. *Prof Exp:* Sr chemist, Columbia Pharmaceut Corp, 65-70; mem tech staff, David Sarnoff Res Ctr, 70-72; sr chemist, Helipot Div, Beckman Instruments, 72-74; mem tech staff, David Sarnoff Res Ctr, RCA Labs, 74; SR CHEMIST, HELIPOT DIV, BECKMAN INSTRUMENTS, 75- *Mem:* Am Chem Soc. *Res:* Organic synthesis; liquid crystal materials; liquid crystal display devices; immunochemistry. *Mailing Add:* Beckman Instruments Inc 2500 Harbor Blvd Fullerton CA 92634

OH, HILARIO LIM, b Cagayan de Oro, Philippines, Jan 14, 36; m 68; c 4. MECHANICAL ENGINEERING. *Educ:* Univ Philippines, BS, 60; Purdue Univ, MS, 63, Univ Calif, Berkeley, PhD(mech eng), 67. *Prof Exp:* Mech engr, Calif Packing Corp, 60-62; res asst, Univ Calif, Berkeley, 64-67, NSF res grant, 67-68; sr res scientist, 68-80, STAFF RES SCIENTIST, GEN MOTORS RES LABS, 80- *Mem:* Am Soc Mech Engrs. *Res:* Fracture of brittle and polymeric solids; mechanical behavior of materials; digital signal processing. *Mailing Add:* Gen Motors Res Labs Math Dept 12 Mile & Mound Rd Warren MI 48090

OH, JANG OK, b Seoul, Korea, Jan 15, 27; m 55; c 1. VIROLOGY, PATHOLOGY. *Educ:* Severance Union Med Col, MD, 48; Univ Wash, PhD(microbiol), 60. *Prof Exp:* Instr microbiol, Severance Union Med Col, 49-51; resident path, Hamot Hosp, Erie, Pa, 53-55; teaching & res asst, Sch Med, Univ Wash, 57-59, res assoc, 59-60, res instr, 60-61; res assoc path, Fac Med, Univ BC, 61-63, asst prof, 63-66; from asst to assoc res microbiologist, 66-71, RES MICROBIOLOGIST, FRANCIS I PROCTOR FOUND, MED CTR, UNIV CALIF, SAN FRANCISCO, 71- *Concurrent Pos:* Res fel microbiol, Commun Dis Lab, Med Ctr, Ind Univ, 55-56; Lederle med fac award, 63-66; Consult, NIH, 79-83. *Mem:* Asn Res Vision & Ophthamol; Am Soc Microbiol; Am Soc Exp Path; Soc Exp Biol & Med. *Res:* Ocular virology, pathogenesis and treatment; nonspecific resistance to viral infection, its mechanism and application to experimental infection; chemotherapy of ocular viral infection. *Mailing Add:* Proctor Found Univ of Calif Med Ctr San Francisco CA 94143

OH, SE JEUNG, b Kimhae, Korea, June 17, 35; US citizen; m 64. ELECTRICAL ENGINEERING, COMPUTER SCIENCES. *Educ:* Univ Colo, BS, 59; Columbia Univ, MS, 63, PhD(elec eng), 66. *Prof Exp:* Instr elec eng, Southern Colo State Col, 59-60; engr, Develop Lab, Data Systs Div, Int Bus Mach Corp, 60-61; lectr elec eng, City Col New York, 61-64; res asst, Columbia Univ, 63-66; mem tech staff, Bell Tel Labs, 66-68; from asst prof to assoc prof, 68-76, chmn dept, 74-78, PROF ELEC ENG, CITY COL NEW YORK, 77-, CHMN DEPT, 81- *Concurrent Pos:* Electronics consult, UNESCO, 69; consult, Bell Labs, 72- *Mem:* Inst Elec & Electronics Engrs. *Res:* Computer architecture and software engineering. *Mailing Add:* Dept Elec Eng City Col New York New York NY 10031

OH, SHIN JOONG, b Seoul, Korea, Nov 16, 36; US citizen; m 66; c 3. NEUROLOGY. *Educ:* Seoul Nat Univ, Korea, MD, 60, Master Med, 62. *Prof Exp:* Asst prof neurol, Meharry Med Col, 68-70; asst prof, 70-72, assoc prof, 72-80, PROF, DEPT NEUROMUSCULAR DIS, SCH MED, UNIV ALA, BIRMINGHAM, 80- *Concurrent Pos:* Res fel, Inst Endemic Dis, Seoul Nat Univ Hosp, 64-66 & Epidemiol & Genetic Unit, Univ Minn Med Ctr, 68; consult, Brookwood Hosp, Birmingham, 75; chief, Neurol Serv, Vet Admin Hosp & dir, Electromyogram Lab, Univ Hosp, Birmingham, 70- *Mem:* Am Acad Neurol; Am Asn Electromyography & Electrodiagnosis. *Res:* Neuromuscular disease; electromyography and electrodiagnosis. *Mailing Add:* Dept of Neurol Univ of Ala Univ Sta Birmingham AL 35294

OH, WILLIAM, b Philippines, May 22, 31; m 60; c 2. PEDIATRICS. *Educ:* Xavier Univ, Philippines, BA, 53; Univ Santo Tomas, Manila, MD, 58. *Prof Exp:* Res assoc, Karolinska Inst, Sweden, 64-66; asst prof pediat, Chicago Med Sch, 66-68; assoc prof, Univ Calif, Los Angeles, 69-72, prof, 72-74; PROF PEDIAT & OBSTET, BROWN UNIV, 74- *Concurrent Pos:* Fel neonatology, Michael Reese Hosp, Chicago, 62-64; pediatrician-in-chief, Women & Infants Hosp, RI, 74. *Mem:* Soc Pediat Res; Am Pediat Soc; Am Soc Clin Res; Perinatal Res Soc (pres, 81). *Res:* Perinatal biology with specific interest on carbohydrate metabolism, fluid and electrolyte balance and respiratory distress syndrome in the newborn. *Mailing Add:* Dept of Perinatal Med Women & Infants Hosp Providence RI 02908

O'HALLORAN, THOMAS A, b New York, NY, Apr 13, 31; m 54; c 4. PHYSICS. *Educ:* Ore State Col, BS, 53, MS, 54; Univ Calif, Berkeley, PhD(elem particle physics), 63. *Prof Exp:* Res assoc elem particle physics, Univ Calif, Berkeley, 63-64; res fel, Harvard Univ, 64-66; from asst prof to assoc prof, 66-70, PROF PHYSICS, UNIV ILL, URBANA, 70- *Concurrent Pos:* J S Guggenheim fel, 79. *Mem:* Am Phys Soc. *Res:* Elementary particles. *Mailing Add:* Dept of Physics Univ of Ill Urbana IL 61801

OHAN, WILLIAM J(OSEPH), JR, b Chicago, Ill, Feb 9, 17; m 41; c 2. CHEMICAL ENGINEERING. *Educ:* Purdue Univ, BS, 48. *Prof Exp:* Chem technologist, 49-50, proj leader food irradiation, 50-57, sr develop engr, 57-68, SAFETY COORDR, GEN FOODS TECH CTR, GEN FOODS CORP, 68- *Res:* Paper and column chromatography to determine food constituents and additives and the effect of digestive process; irradiation for preservation, processing and deinfestation; protein isolation processes; spray drying. *Mailing Add:* 19 Rosewood Dr New City NY 10956

OHANIAN, HANS C, b Leipzig, Ger, Apr 29, 41; m 66. PHYSICS. *Educ:* Univ Calif, Berkeley, BA, 64; Princeton Univ, PhD(physics), 68. *Prof Exp:* asst prof physics, Rensselaer Polytech Inst, 68-76; ASSOC PROF PHYSICS, UNION COL, 76- *Concurrent Pos:* Vis fel physics, Princeton Univ, 75-76. *Mem:* Am Phys Soc. *Res:* Gravitation and field theory. *Mailing Add:* Dept of Physics Rensselaer Polytech Inst Troy NY 12181

OHANIAN, SARKIS HAROUTUN, b Everett, Mass, Nov 2, 36; m 59; c 1. IMMUNOLOGY, BIOCHEMISTRY. *Educ:* Univ Calif, Los Angeles, BA, 60; Univ NC, Chapel Hill, PhD(microbiol), 67. *Prof Exp:* NIH fel, Med Ctr, NY Univ, 67-68 & Duke Univ, 68-69; asst prof immunol dept surg, Med Col Va, 69-71; RES MICROBIOLOGIST IMMUNOL, NAT CANCER INST, NIH, 71- *Mem:* AAAS; Am Asn Cancer Res; Am Asn Immunologists; Am Asn Microbiologists; Sigma Xi. *Res:* immunochemistry of cell biology. *Mailing Add:* Lab of Immunobiol Nat Cancer Inst NIH Bethesda MD 20014

O'HARA, JAMES B(ERNARD), b Kirby, Wyo, Sept 20, 22; m 46; c 5. CHEMICAL ENGINEERING. *Educ:* Univ Ill, BS, 44; Mich Univ, MS, 45; Case Univ, PhD(chem eng), 49. *Prof Exp:* Asst eng res, Mich Univ, 45; chem engr, Sherwin-Williams Co, 45-46; asst prof chem eng, Mo Sch Mines, 48-50; asst prof chem eng, Lehigh Univ, 50-51; asst mgr eng, Mathieson Chem Corp, 51-56; sr process engr, Escambia Chem Corp, 56-58; group leader, Eng Res Dept, A E Staley Mfg Corp, 58-65; mgr process licensing & develop, Los Angeles, 65-77, mgr, Energy Dept, 77-80, DIR, MKT COAL CONVERSION, RALPH M PARSONS CO, 80- *Concurrent Pos:* M Van Winkle distinguished lectr, Univ Tex, 81. *Mem:* Am Inst Chem Engrs; NY Acad Sci; Sigma Xi. *Mailing Add:* Ralph M Parsons Co 100 Walnut St Pasadena CA 91124

O'HARA, JAMES CARLOSS, mechanical engineering, see previous edition

O'HARA, NORBERT WILHELM, b Youngstown, Ohio, Oct 7, 30; m 67; c 7. BASEMENT GEOLOGY, GEOLOGICAL OCEANOGRAPHY. *Educ:* Mich State Col, BS, 52;; Mich State Univ, MS, 54, PhD(geophysics), 67. *Prof Exp:* Asst prof geol, Eastern Mich Univ, 60-63; asst prof, Mich State Univ, 63-65; asst prof, Grand Valley State Col, 65-67; res assoc, Mich State Univ, 67-68; assoc prof oceanog, World Campus Afloat, Chapman Col, 68-69; res assoc, Univ Mich, 69-71; res geophysicist, Naval Res Ctr, 71-75; PROF OCEANOG & DEPT HEAD, FLA INST TECHNOL, 75- *Concurrent Pos:* Geosci consult, N W O'Hara & Assocs, 75-82; chmn, Fla Intercollegiate Comt Oceanog, 78-80; mem exec comt, Sea Grant Asn, 78-81; geophysicist, NSF Antarctic Field Expedition, 65-66; prin investr, Western Great Lakes Aeromagnetic Surv, 63-67. *Mem:* Soc Explor Geophysicists; Geol Soc Am; Am Geophys Union. *Res:* Basement geology through the use of gravity and magnetic methods; regional tectonics; geopotential mapping; geothermal areas. *Mailing Add:* 1300 S Ramona Ave Indialantic FL 32903

O'HARE, JOHN MICHAEL, b Des Moines, Iowa, Oct 2, 38; m 64; c 4. SOLID STATE PHYSICS, OPTICS. *Educ:* Loras Col, BS, 60; Purdue Univ, MS, 62; State Univ NY Buffalo, PhD(physics), 66. *Prof Exp:* Instr physics, State Univ NY Buffalo, 65-66; from asst prof to assoc prof, 66-77, PROF PHYSICS, UNIV DAYTON, 77- *Mem:* Am Phys Soc. *Res:* Theoretical atomic and molecular physics; crystal field theory; optical properties of solids, experimental and theoretical. *Mailing Add:* Dept Physics Univ Dayton Dayton OH 45409

O'HARE, PATRICK, b Dundalk, Ireland, Aug 6, 36; m 64; c 3. PHYSICAL CHEMISTRY. *Educ:* Nat Univ Ireland, BS, 57, MS, 58; Queen's Univ Belfast, PhD(phys chem), 61, DSc(phys chem), 71. *Prof Exp:* Demonstr chem, Queen's Univ Belfast, 58-61, Imp Chem Indust fel, 61-63; resident res assoc, 64-66, ASSOC CHEMIST, ARGONNE NAT LAB, 66- *Concurrent Pos:* Vis prof, Univ Toronto, & Int Atomic Energy Agency, Vienna, 76-78. *Mem:* Am Chem Soc; assoc mem Int Union Pure & Appl Chem. *Res:* Thermochemistry of nuclear materials; bond energies in inorganic molecules. *Mailing Add:* Argonne Nat Lab Argonne IL 60439

OHASHI, YOSHIKAZU, b Tokyo, Japan, June 30, 41; m 70; c 3. MINERALOGY, CRYSTALLOGRAPHY. *Educ:* Tokyo Univ, BS, 66, MS, 68; Harvard Univ, PhD(geol), 73. *Prof Exp:* Fel, Geophys Lab, Carnegie Inst Washington, 72-76; ASST PROF GEOL, UNIV PA, 76- *Mem:* Mineral Soc Am; Mineral Asn Can; Am Crystallog Asn; Mineral Soc Great Brit; Inst Elec & Electronics Engrs Comput Soc. *Res:* Crystal structure analysis of rock-forming silicate minerals; crystallographic computing. *Mailing Add:* Dept Geol Univ Pa Philadelphia PA 19105

OHATA, CARL ANDREWS, b Pearl City, Hawaii, Sept 22, 47; m 71; c 2. NEUROPHYSIOLOGY, THERMOPHYSIOLOGY. *Educ:* Univ Hawaii, BA, 69, MS, 72; Univ Alaska, PhD(zoophysiol), 76. *Prof Exp:* Res asst dept physiol, Sch Med, Univ Hawaii, 70-72; res asst zoophysiol, Inst Artic Biol, Univ Alaska, 72-76; res assoc physiol, Cardiovascular Control Sect, Marine Biomed Inst, Univ Tex Med Br, Galveston, 76-77; Nat Heart, Lung & Blood Inst NIH fel, Dept Physiol & Biophys, Sch Med, Health Sci Ctr, Univ Okla, 77-79; RES PHYSIOLOGIST ENVIRON MED, US ARMY RES INST, NATICK, MASS, 79- *Concurrent Pos:* Consult, Sea Otter Oiling Working Group, US Fish & Wildlife Serv, 77-78; mem animal use comt, US Army Res Inst Environ Med, 80- *Mem:* Am Physiol Soc; AAAS; Soc Exp Biol & Med; Soc Neurosci; Sigma Xi. *Res:* Neural control of circulation; temperature regulation; physiology of marine mammals. *Mailing Add:* Exp Pathol Div US Army Res Inst Environ Med Natick MA 01760

O'HAVER, THOMAS CALVIN, b Atlanta, Ga, Oct 13, 41; m 68. ANALYTICAL CHEMISTRY. *Educ:* Spring Hill Col, BS, 63; Univ Fla, PhD(chem), 68. *Prof Exp:* From asst prof to assoc prof, 68-78, PROF CHEM, UNIV MD, 78- *Concurrent Pos:* Advan Res Proj Agency, Dept Defense fel, Ctr Mat Res, 68-71, NSF Instnl Sci Equip Prog fel, 69-72 & Petrol Res Found-Am Chem Soc fel, 69-72; NSF res grants, 74-80; res grant, US Dept Agr, Agr Res Serv, 76- *Mem:* Am Chem Soc; Soc Appl Spectros. *Res:* Multielement atomic spectrometry; analytical instrumentation; automation; computer applications. *Mailing Add:* Dept Chem Univ Md College Park MD 20742

O'HAYRE, ARTHUR PAUL, forest hydrology, see previous edition

O'HEA, EUGENE KEVIN, b Cork, Ireland, Mar 27, 41. PHYSIOLOGY. *Educ:* Univ Col, Dublin, BAgr Sc, 64, MAgrSc, 66; Univ Ill, PhD(nutrit biochem), 69, Univ Western Ont, MD, 76. *Prof Exp:* Asst prof, 70-80, ASSOC PROF PHYSIOL, UNIV WESTERN ONT, 80- *Mem:* Can Physiol Soc; Nutrit Soc Can; Am Physiol Soc. *Res:* Endocrinology; fat synthesis and its regulations; energy balance. *Mailing Add:* Dept of Physiol Univ of Western Ont London ON N6A 5B8 Can

O'HEARN, GEORGE THOMAS, b Manitowoc, Wis, Sept 26, 34; m 59; c 3. SCIENCE EDUCATION. *Educ:* Univ Wis-Madison, BS, 57, MS, 59, PhD(sci educ), 64. *Prof Exp:* Asst prof sci educ, Univ & prin investr, Res & Develop Ctr Cognitive Learning, Univ Wis-Madison, 64-68, US Off Educ grant sci literacy, 64-66; assoc prof, 68-70, PROF SCI EDUC, UNIV WIS-GREEN BAY, 70-, DIR OFF EDUC RES & DEVELOP & CO-DIR STATE ASSESSMENT CTR NONTRADITIONAL LEARNING, 75- *Mem:* Fel AAAS; Nat Asn Res Sci Teaching; Nat Sci Teachers Asn. *Res:* Research design, social implications of science, science learning. *Mailing Add:* Univ of Wis Green Bay WI 54302

O'HERN, ELIZABETH MOOT, b Richmondville, NY, Sept 1, 13; m 52. MEDICAL MICROBIOLOGY. *Educ:* Univ Calif, BA, 45, MA, 47; Univ Wash, PhD(microbiol, mycol), 56. *Prof Exp:* Asst parasitol & mycol, Univ Calif, 45-48; instr microbiol, Univ Wash, 56-57 & State Univ NY Downstate Med Ctr, 57-62; asst prof, Sch Med, George Washington Univ, 62-65; sr scientist, Bionetics Res Labs, 65-66, prin investr, 66-68; prog adminr microbiol training prog, 68-75, prog adminr genetics res grants, 74-75, spec asst to dir, 75-76, ADMIN SPEC PROG, NAT INST GEN MED SCI, 77- *Mem:* Am Pub Health Asn; AAAS; Am Soc Cell Biologists; Am Soc Trop Med & Hyg; Am Soc Microbiol; Mycol Soc Am. *Res:* Medical mycology; host-parasite relationships; malaria chemotherapy. *Mailing Add:* Westwood Bldg Rm 955 Nat Inst Gen Med Sci Bethesda MD 20014

O'HERN, EUGENE A, b Flint, Mich, Jan 20, 27; m 51; c 4. MECHANICAL ENGINEERING. *Educ:* Purdue Univ, BS & BNS, 48, MS, 49, PhD(mech eng), 51. *Prof Exp:* Res engr, Missile & Control Equip Div, N Am Rockwell Corp, 51-54, proj engr, 54-55, anal supvr, 55-57, proj engr autonetics, 57-60, sect chief, 60-62, asst mgr, 62-64, chief scientist, 65-70, mgr syst eng space div, 70-72, MEM TECH STAFF, SPACE DIV, ROCKWELL INT, 72- *Concurrent Pos:* Lectr, Univ Southern Calif, 59-65. *Mem:* Am Inst Aeronaut & Astronaut; Soc Automotive Engrs. *Res:* Control system analysis; aircraft dynamics; flight control system synthesis; avionics system analysis; risk analysis. *Mailing Add:* 1233 Longview Dr Fullerton CA 92631

OHKI, KENNETH, b Livingston, Calif, June 13, 22; m 45; c 2. PLANT PHYSIOLOGY. *Educ:* Univ Calif, Berkeley, BS, 49, MS, 51, PhD(plant physiol), 63. *Prof Exp:* Supvr & specialist plant physiol res, Int Minerals & Chem Corp, Ill, 64-70; from asst prof to assoc prof, 71-79, PROF AGRON, GA EXP STA, UNIV GA, 79- *Concurrent Pos:* Res asst, Calif Inst Technol, 50-53. *Mem:* Am Soc Plant Physiologists; Am Soc Agron; Crop Sci Soc Am; Soil Sci Soc Am. *Res:* Plant nutrition and analysis; growth and development of sugar beets; ion absorption in relation to antecedent nutrition; plant growth regulator; micronutrient nutrition of plants. *Mailing Add:* Dept of Agron Ga Exp Sta Univ of Ga Experiment GA 30212

OHKI, SHINPEI, b Japan, Jan 1, 33; m 71. BIOPHYSICS. *Educ:* Kyoto Univ, BS, 56, MS, 58, PhD(physics), 65. *Prof Exp:* Instr physics, Tokyo Metrop Univ, 61-65; res assoc theoret biol, 65-66, asst prof biophys, 66-73, ASSOC PROF BIOPHYS, STATE UNIV NY BUFFALO, 73- *Concurrent Pos:* Grants, Damon Runyon Mem Fund, 68-71, Nat Inst Neurol Dis & Stroke, 69-75 & Nat Inst Gen Med, 78-; fel, Japan Soc Prom Sci. *Mem:* Biophys Soc; NY Acad Sci. *Res:* Investigation of a mechanism of excitatory and inhibitory phenomena of membranes; adhesion and fusion of model and biological membranes. *Mailing Add:* Dept of Biophys 224 Cary Hall NY Buffalo NY 14214

OHL, DONALD GORDON, b Milton, Pa, Apr 13, 15; m 46; c 1. MATHEMATICS. *Educ:* Ursinus Col, BS, 36; Bucknell Univ, MS, 47. *Prof Exp:* High sch teacher, Pa, 37-41; instr math, Univ & chmn dept, Olney Undergrad Ctr, Temple Univ, 46; from instr to asst prof, 46-60, assoc prof, 60-81, EMER PROF MATH, BUCKNELL UNIV, 81-; CONSULT, 81- *Mem:* Am Math Soc; Math Asn Am; Nat Coun Teachers Math. *Res:* Mathematics education; general mathematics. *Mailing Add:* Dept of Mathematics Bucknell Univ Lewisburg PA 17837

OHLBERG, STANLEY MILES, b Brooklyn, NY, June 20, 21; m 54; c 3. PHYSICAL CHEMISTRY. *Educ:* Univ Mich, BS, 43; Rutgers Univ, MS, 50, PhD(phys chem), 51. *Prof Exp:* Anal & indust chemist, Manhattan Proj, Linde Air Prod Co, 43-46; asst inorg chem, Rutgers Univ, 46-51; fel x-ray diffraction anal, Dept Res Chem Physics, Mellon Inst, 51-56; res scientist, Verona Res Ctr, Koppers Co, 56-58; scientist, 58-71, staff scientist, 71-73, SR SCIENTIST, GLASS RES CTR, PPG INDUSTS, INC, 73- *Honors & Awards:* Frank Forest Award, Am Ceramic Soc, 66. *Mem:* Am Chem Soc; fel Am Ceramic Soc. *Res:* Structures of materials; physics and chemistry of glass. *Mailing Add:* Glass Res Ctr PPG Industs Inc Box 11472 Pittsburgh PA 15238

OHLE, ERNEST LINWOOD, b St Louis, Mo, Dec 17, 17; m 43; c 4. ECONOMIC GEOLOGY. *Educ:* Washington Univ, AB, 38, MS, 40; Harvard Univ, MA, 41, PhD, 50. *Prof Exp:* Geologist, Am Zinc Co, Tenn, 41-42, Ark, 42-43 & Tenn, 44-46, asst mine supt, 46-47; geologist, St Joseph Lead Co, Mo, 48-57; chief geologist, White Pine Copper Co, 57-61; vpres explor, Copper Range Co, 60-61; staff geologist, 61-65, asst chief geologist, 65-68, eval mgr, 68-71, consult geologist, Hanna Mining Co, 71-78; RETIRED, 78- *Concurrent Pos:* Mem bd mineral resources, NSF, 74-77; adj prof, Univ Utah, 73; pres, Doc Econ Geol Found, 78- *Mem:* Geol Soc Am; Soc Econ Geologists (pres, 75); Am Inst Prof Geologists; Am Asn Petrol Geologists; Am Inst Mining, Metall & Petrol Engrs. *Res:* Ore deposition; structural control of ore deposits; limestone permeability as related to ore deposition. *Mailing Add:* 5293 Blue Spruce Circle Salt Lake City UT 84117

OHLENBUSCH, ROBERT EUGENE, b Edinburg, Tex, Oct 18, 30; m 63; c 2. DENTISTRY, MICROBIOLOGY. *Educ:* Tex Lutheran Col, BS, 52; Univ Tex, DDS, 56. *Prof Exp:* Dent Corps, US Army, 56-, dentist, 56-58, res asst dent, Walter Reed Army Inst Res, 58-61, res dent officer oral microbiol, US Army Inst Dent Res, 63-67, comdr, 137th Med Detachment, Repub Vietnam, 67-68, exec officer, 102nd Med Detachment, Munich, Ger, 70-71, exec officer prev dent & dir dent educ, Dent Co, Ft Jackson, SC, 71-74, spec projs officer, Hq, Health Serv Command, Ft Sam Houston, Tex, 74-75, CHIEF GARRISON DENT CLIN, DEPT DENT, FT SAM HOUSTON, 75- *Concurrent Pos:* Lectr, Georgetown Univ, 63-67. *Mem:* Am Dent Asn; Am Soc Microbiol; Int Asn Dent Res. *Res:* Preventive dentistry. *Mailing Add:* 11511 Whisper Dew San Antonio TX 78230

OHLENDORF, HARRY MAX, b Lockhart, Tex, Oct 12, 40. WILDLIFE RESEARCH. *Educ:* Tex A&M Univ, BS, 62, MS, 69, PhD(wildlife ecol), 71. *Prof Exp:* Wildlife res biologist, 71-73, asst dir ecol res admin, Laurel, Md, 73-80, WILDLIFE RES BIOLOGIST, PATUXENT WILDLIFE RES CTR, FISH & WILDLIFE SERV, US DEPT INTERIOR, UNIV CALIF, DAVIS, 80- *Mem:* Wilson Ornith Soc; Pac Seabird Group. *Res:* Effects of environmental pollutants on fish-eating birds and their habitat. *Mailing Add:* US Fish & Wildlife Serv Univ Calif Wildlife & Fisheries Biol Davis CA 95616

OHLINE, ROBERT WAYNE, b St Louis, Mo, Mar 9, 34; m 66; c 2. ANALYTICAL CHEMISTRY. *Educ:* Grinnel Col, AB, 56; Northwestern Univ, MS, 58, PhD, 60. *Prof Exp:* Anal chemist, Mallinckrodt Chem Works, 60-61; from asst prof to assoc prof, 61-72, chmn, Dept Chem, 77-81, PROF CHEM, NMEX INST MINING & TECHNOL, 72- *Mem:* Am Chem Soc; The Chem Soc. *Res:* Instrumental methods; wet analytical methods; gas chromatography; ion production in flames; combustion kinetics of cellulosic fuels. *Mailing Add:* Dept of Chem NMex Inst of Mining & Technol Socorro NM 87801

OHLROGGE, ALVIN JOHN, b Chilton, Wis, Sept 19, 15; m 44; c 2. SOILS. *Educ:* Univ Wis, BS, 37; Purdue Univ, PhD(soils), 43. *Prof Exp:* Asst, 42-45, from asst prof to assoc prof, 45-58, PROF AGRON, PURDUE UNIV, WEST LAFAYETTE, 58- *Concurrent Pos:* Soil fertil adv, Pakistan Govt, Food & Agr Orgn, UN, 52; NSF fel, Univ Calif, 58-59; vchmn, Nat Joint Comt Fertilizer Appln, 60, chmn, 61; consult, FDA & indust. *Honors & Awards:* Soil Sci Award, Am Soc Agron, 61, Agron Res Award, 76. *Mem:* Fel AAAS; Soil Sci Soc Am; fel Am Soc Agron; hon mem Am Soybean Asn. *Res:* Soil fertility; plant physiology; nutrient uptake from fertilizer bands; growth regulators. *Mailing Add:* Dept of Agron Purdue Univ West Lafayette IN 47906

OHLROGGE, JOHN BEYER, biochemistry, plant physiology, see previous edition

OHLSEN, GERALD G, b Eugene, Ore, May 1, 33; m 58; c 3. NUCLEAR PHYSICS. *Educ:* Univ Ore, BA, 55; Stanford Univ, MS, 57, PhD(physics), 60. *Prof Exp:* Asst prof physics, Univ Tex, 60-61; res fel nuclear physics, Australian Nat Univ, 61-64, fel, 64-65; staff mem, Los Alamos Sci Lab, 65-80. *Mem:* AAAS; Am Phys Soc. *Res:* Low energy nuclear physics; polarized ion sources. *Mailing Add:* 1068 San Idlefonso Los Alamos NM 87544

OHLSEN, WILLIAM DAVID, b Evanston, Ill, June 8, 32; m 56; c 3. SOLID STATE PHYSICS. *Educ:* Iowa State Univ, BS, 54; Cornell Univ, PhD(physics), 62. *Prof Exp:* From asst prof to assoc prof, 61-74, PROF PHYSICS, UNIV UTAH, 74- *Concurrent Pos:* Vis prof, Munich Tech Univ, 69. *Mem:* Am Phys Soc; Am Asn Phys Teachers; Am Asn Univ Professors. *Res:* Magnetic resonance and optical studies of defects in solids. *Mailing Add:* Dept Physics Univ Utah Salt Lake City UT 84112

OHLSON, JOHN E, b Seattle, Wash, May 29, 40; m 62; c 3. SATELLITE COMMUNICATIONS. *Educ:* Mass Inst Technol, BS, 62; Stanford Univ, MS, 63, PhD(elec eng), 67. *Prof Exp:* Asst prof elec eng, Univ Southern Calif, 67-71; assoc prof elec eng, Naval Postgrad Sch, 71-78, prof, 78-81; VPRES, STANFORD TELECOMMUNICATIONS, INC, 81- *Concurrent Pos:* Consult, Jet Propulsion Lab, 68-81; Sigma Xi Mennneken res award, Naval Postgrad Sch, 79. *Mem:* Inst Elec & Electronics Engrs; Sigma Xi. *Res:* Communication and radar theory and applications; satellite communications; radioscience. *Mailing Add:* Dept Elec Eng Naval Postgrad Sch Monterey CA 93940

OHLSSON, ROBERT LOUIS, b St Paul, Minn, Jan 10, 15. ELECTRICAL ENGINEERING. *Educ:* Univ Mich, BSE, 39, MS, 40. *Prof Exp:* Spec res assoc, Radio Res Lab, Harvard Univ, 43-45; engr, Eng Res Inst, 46-58, asst dir, 58-60, ASSOC DIR INST SCI & TECHNOL, WILLOW RUN LABS, UNIV MICH, ANN ARBOR, 60- *Mem:* Inst Elec & Electronics Engrs. *Res:* Guided missile systems; air defense problems; countermeasures; combat surveillance. *Mailing Add:* Willow Run Labs Univ Mich Ann Arbor MI 48109

OHLSSON-WILHELM, BETSY MAE, b Boston, Mass, July 17, 42; m 69. GENETICS, MOLECULAR BIOLOGY. *Educ:* Radcliffe Col, AB, 63; Harvard Univ, PhD(bact), 69. *Prof Exp:* Am Cancer Soc fel biophys, Univ Chicago, 68-70; res assoc, Inst Cancer Res, 70-73; ASST PROF MICROBIOL, SCH MFD & DENT, UNIV ROCHESTER, 73- *Concurrent Pos:* NIH grant. *Res:* Somatic cell genetics; regulation and control mechanisms in somatic cells; cell biology. *Mailing Add:* Dept of Microbiol Sch Med & Dent Univ of Rochester Rochester NY 14642

OHM, E(DWARD) A(LLEN), b Milwaukee, Wis, July 4, 26. ELECTRICAL ENGINEERING. *Educ:* Univ Wis, BS, 50, MS, 51, PhD(elec eng), 53. *Prof Exp:* MEM TECH STAFF, BELL TEL LABS, INC, 53- *Mem:* Inst Elec & Electronics Engrs. *Res:* Waveguide components; low noise receiving systems; space communications; optical modulators. *Mailing Add:* 4 Stonehenge Dr Holmdel NJ 07733

OHM, HERBERT WILLIS, b Albert Lea, Minn, Jan 28, 45. AGRONOMY, GENETICS. *Educ:* Univ Minn, BS, 67; NDak State Univ, MSc, 69; Purdue Univ, PhD(genetics, plant breeding), 72. *Prof Exp:* Asst prof, 72-76, ASSOC PROF AGRON, PURDUE UNIV, 77- *Mem:* Am Soc Agron; Crop Sci Soc Am; Sigma Xi; Coun Agr Sci & Technol. *Res:* Plant disease and insect (pest) resistance; wheat; oats; plant physiological traits; cereal protein; Yellow Dwarf virus; plant breeding systems. *Mailing Add:* Dept of Agron Purdue Univ West Lafayette IN 47907

OHM, JACK ELTON, b Milwaukee, Wis, Sept 23, 32. MATHEMATICS. *Educ:* Univ Chicago, BS, 54; Univ Calif, Berkeley, PhD(math), 59. *Prof Exp:* Teaching asst math, Univ Calif, Berkeley, 54-57, teaching assoc, 57-59; NSF fel, Johns Hopkins Univ, 59-60; asst prof, Univ Wis, 60-65; assoc prof, 65-69, PROF MATH, LA STATE UNIV, BATON ROUGE, 69- *Concurrent Pos:* Wis Alumni Res Found fel & res assoc math, Univ Calif, Berkeley, 64-65; vis prof, Purdue Univ, 71-72 & Univ Wis, Milwakee, 78-79. *Mem:* Am Math Soc. *Res:* Algebraic geometry; commutative algebra. *Mailing Add:* Dept of Math La State Univ Baton Rouge LA 70803

OHMAN, GUNNAR P(ETER), b Sweden, Dec 15, 18; nat US; m 48; c 3. ELECTRICAL ENGINEERING. *Educ:* Ill Inst Technol, BS, 43; Univ Md, MS, 48, PhD(elec eng), 59. *Prof Exp:* Elec engr, 43-45, electronics engr & group leader, 45-47, electronic scientist & sect head, 47-67, consult, 67-69, res & develop prog coord, 69-76, ASSOC SUPT TACT ELECTRONIC WARFARE DIV, NAVAL RES LAB, 76- *Concurrent Pos:* Lectr, grad sch, Univ Md, 50- *Mem:* Sci Res Soc Am; sr mem Inst Elec & Electronics Engrs. *Res:* Electronics; radar; navigational aids; microwave radiometry; pulse and microwave circuitry; circuit theory; applied mathematics. *Mailing Add:* 5717 Blackhawk Dr Forest Heights MD 20021

OHMAN, JOHN HAMILTON, research administration, forestry, see previous edition

OHMART, ROBERT DALE, b Tatum, NMex, Jan 2, 38; m 58; c 4. ZOOLOGY. *Educ:* NMex State Univ, BS, 61, MS, 63; Univ Ariz, PhD(vert zool), 68. *Prof Exp:* NIH fel, Univ Calif, Davis, 68-70; asst prof, 70-74, assoc prof, 74-81, PROF ZOOL, ARIZ STATE UNIV, 81-, ASSOC DIR, CTR ENVIRON STUDIES, 80- *Mem:* Am Ornith Union; Wildlife Soc; Cooper Ornith Soc; Am Inst Biol Sci. *Res:* Wildlife ecology; avian environmental physiology. *Mailing Add:* Dept of Zool Ariz State Univ Tempe AZ 85287

OHME, PAUL ADOLPH, b Montgomery, Ala, Nov 4, 40; m 64; c 2. MATHEMATICS. *Educ:* Huntingdon Col, BA, 63; Univ Ala, MA, 64; Fla State Univ, PhD(math), 71. *Prof Exp:* Asst prof math, Franklin & Marshall Col, 71-73; assoc prof math, Miss Col, 73-80; MEM FAC, DEPT MATH, NORTHEAST LA UNIV, 80- *Mem:* Sigma Xi; Math Asn Am; Nat Coun Teachers Math; Am Math Soc. *Res:* Application of differential equations to biological problems. *Mailing Add:* Dept Math Northeast La Univ Monroe LA 71209

OHMER, MERLIN MAURICE, b Napoleonville, La, Mar 15, 23; m 47; c 3. MATHEMATICS. *Educ:* Tulane Univ, BS, 44, MS, 48; Univ Pittsburgh, PhD(math). *Prof Exp:* Asst physics, Tulane Univ, 42-43, asst math, 47-48; from asst prof to prof, Univ Southwestern La, 48-66; prof & head dept, 66-69, DEAN COL SCI, NICHOLLS STATE UNIV, 69- *Concurrent Pos:* Vis instr, Tulane Univ, 49-50; vis assoc prof, Univ Pittsburgh, 53-54; vis lectr, Math Asn Am, 64-73; consult, La State Dept Educ; mem, Nat Metric Speakers Bur. *Mem:* Math Asn Am; Am Math Soc; Nat Coun Teachers Math. *Res:* Teacher training and innovations; game theory; symbolic logic; geometry; promotion of the metric system in the United States. *Mailing Add:* 106 Acadia Lane Thibodaux LA 70301

OHMOTO, HIROSHI, b Heijo, Japan, Nov 7, 41; m 65; c 2. GEOCHEMISTRY. *Educ:* Hokkaido Univ, BS, 64; Princeton Univ, AM, 67, PhD(geol), 69. *Prof Exp:* Fel geochem, Univ Alta, 68-69, fel, 68-70, lectr, 69-70; from asst prof to assoc prof, 70-78, PROF GEOCHEM, PA STATE UNIV, UNIVERSITY PARK, 78- *Concurrent Pos:* NSF RES GRANT, 72-; Humboldt fel, 81. *Honors & Awards:* Lindgren Award, Soc Econ Geologists, 70; Clark Medal, Geochem Soc, 73. *Mem:* Soc Econ Geologists; Geochem Soc. *Res:* Causes of variation of stable isotopes in geologic processes; geological, geochemical and hydrological processes of the formation of metallic ore deposits. *Mailing Add:* Dept of Geosci Pa State Univ University Park PA 16802

OHMS, JACK IVAN, b Walnut, Iowa, Jan 1, 30; m 54; c 3. ANALYTICAL BIOCHEMISTRY. *Educ:* Iowa State Univ, BS, 53; Mich State Univ, PhD(dairy husb), 61. *Prof Exp:* Res asst, Am Found Biol Res, Wis, 53-57; NIH fel, 61-62; appln specialist, 62-66, SR SCIENTIST, SPINCO DIV, BECKMAN INSTRUMENTS INC, 66- *Mem:* AAAS; NY Acad Sci. *Res:* Physiology of reproduction of domestic animals; endocrine immunochemistry; biomedical instrumentation; biochemical calorimetry; liquid chromatography of biochemicals; automated sequence determination of proteins and peptides. *Mailing Add:* 877 Aspen Way Palo Alto CA 94303

OHMS, RICHARD EARL, b Payette, Idaho, June 13, 27; m 56; c 2. PLANT PATHOLOGY. *Educ:* Univ Idaho, BS, 50, MS, 52; Univ Ill, PhD(plant path), 55. *Prof Exp:* Asst plant path, Univ Idaho, 52-55; asst plant pathologist, SDak State Col, 55-57; assoc horticulturist & exten specialist hort, 57-74, exten & res prof, 73-74, EXTEN PROF & EXTEN CROP SPECIALIST, EXTEN SERV, UNIV IDAHO, 74- *Concurrent Pos:* Seed potato consult, Jordan & Int Potato Ctr, Lima, Peru. *Mem:* Am Soc Hort Sci; Am Phytopath Soc; Potato Asn Am. *Res:* Cereal. *Mailing Add:* Univ of Idaho Dept of Plant & Soil Sci Moscow ID 83843

OHNESORGE, WILLIAM EDWARD, b Acushnet, Mass, Sept 11, 31; m 60. ANALYTICAL CHEMISTRY. *Educ:* Brown Univ, ScB, 53; Mass Inst Technol, PhD(chem), 56. *Prof Exp:* From instr to assoc prof chem, Univ RI, 56-65; assoc prof, 65-71, asst chmn dept, 69-77, PROF CHEM, LEHIGH UNIV, 71- *Concurrent Pos:* Vis asst prof, Mass Inst Technol, 64-65; vis prof clin biochem, Univ Toronto, 74; prog dir chem anal, Nat Sci Found, 80-81. *Mem:* Am Chem Soc. *Res:* Fluorescence spectroscopy; electroanalytical chemistry; clinical chemistry; complex ions; luminescence analysis. *Mailing Add:* Dept of Chem Lehigh Univ Bethlehem PA 18015

OHNISHI, TOMOKO, b Kobe, Japan, June 8, 41; m 58; c 2. BIOCHEMISTRY, BIOPHYSICS. *Educ:* Nat Kyoto Univ, BS, 56, MS, 58; Nat Nagoya Univ, PhD(biochem), 62. *Prof Exp:* Johnson Res Found vis asst prof, 67-71, asst prof, 71-77, RES ASSOC PROF BIOCHEM & BIOPHYS, UNIV PA, 77- *Mem:* Am Soc Biol Chemists; Biophys Soc; AAAS. *Res:* Electron transfer and energy conservation in mitochondria; membrane structure and function; bacterial and yeast electron transfer; metabolism. *Mailing Add:* Dept of Biochem & Biophys BB505 Univ of Pa Sch of Med Philadelphia PA 19104

OHNISHI, TSUYOSHI, b Otsu, Japan, Dec 17, 31; m 58; c 2. BIOPHYSICS, BIOCHEMISTRY. *Educ:* Kyoto Univ, BS, 54, MS, 56; Nagoya Univ, PhD(biophys), 60. *Prof Exp:* Japanese Soc Prom Sci fel, Nagoya Univ, 60-62 & res fel physiol, Med Sch, 62-63, res fel physics, Univ, 64-65; assoc prof biophys, Waseda Univ, Japan, 65-67; vis assoc prof, Johnson Found, Univ Pa, 67-68; asst prof biophys, Med Col Pa, 69-72; ASSOC PROF BIOCHEM & ANESTHESIA, HAHNEMANN MED COL, 73- *Concurrent Pos:* Vis res fel, Univ Tokyo, 63-65. *Mem:* Biophys Soc; Am Soc Anesthesiol. *Res:* Calcium transport in sarcoplasmic reticulum and erythrocyte; characterization of non-muscular membrane action; effect of anesthetics on cardiac muscle; effect of anesthetics on sickle cells; development of the Murexide method for calcium and other dual-wavelength spectrophotometry for biophysics and biochemistry. *Mailing Add:* Biophys Lab Dept of Anesthesiol Hahnemann Med Col Philadelphia PA 19102

OHNO, SUSUMU, b Tokyo, Japan, Feb 2, 28; m 52; c 3. CYTOGENETICS. *Educ:* Tokyo Univ Agr & Technol, DVM, 49; Hokkaido Univ, PhD(path), 56, DSc, 61. *Prof Exp:* Res assoc, Dept Exp Path, 52-62, sr res scientist, Dept Biol, 62-66, CHMN DEPT BIOL, CITY OF HOPE MED CTR, 66- *Mem:* Int Soc Hemat; Genetics Soc Am; Am Asn Cancer Res. *Res:* Clinical genetics. *Mailing Add:* Dept of Biol City of Hope Med Ctr Duarte CA 91010

OHNUKI, YASUSHI, b Kawasaki City, Japan, July 30, 26; c 2. CYTOGENETICS. *Educ:* Hokkaido Univ, BSc, 54, MSc, 56, DSc(cytogenetics), 61. *Prof Exp:* Tobacco Indust Res Comt fel, Dept Anat, Univ Tex Med Br, Galveston, 59-60 & Dept Cellular Biol, Pasadena Found Med Res, 60-61; res assoc, Makino Lab, Fac Sci, Hokkaido Univ, 61-64; chief cytogenetics sect, 64-66, dir dept cytogenetics, 66-72, PROJ DIR CYTOGENETICS STUDIES STRUCTURE & FUNCTION

CHROMOSOMES, PASADENA FOUND MED RES, 72-, HEAD DEPT CYTOGENETICS, 77- *Mem:* Am Soc Cell Biol; Tissue Cult Asn; Genetics Soc Japan. *Res:* Studies on structure and function of chromosomes; cytogenetic studies of cellular aging and development of prostatic cancer. *Mailing Add:* Dept of Cytogenetics 99 N El Molino Ave Pasadena CA 91101

OHNUMA, SHOROKU, b Akita, Japan, Apr 19, 28; m 56; c 2. ACCELERATOR PHYSICS. *Educ:* Univ Tokyo, BSc, 50; Univ Rochester, PhD(physics), 57. *Prof Exp:* Res assoc physics, Yale Univ, 56-59; asst prof, Waseda Univ, Japan, 59-62; res assoc, Yale Univ, 62-66, sr res assoc, 67-70; PHYSICIST II, FERMI NAT ACCELERATOR LAB, 70- *Concurrent Pos:* Consult, Brookhaven Nat Lab, 64-69. *Mem:* Am Phys Soc. *Res:* Accelerator physics theory. *Mailing Add:* Fermi Nat Accelerator Lab PO Box 500 Batavia IL 60510

OHNUMA, TAKAO, b Sendai, Japan, May 16, 32; m 66; c 3. INTERNAL MEDICINE, CANCER. *Educ:* Tohoku Univ, Japan, MD, 57; Univ London, PhD(biochem), 65. *Prof Exp:* Intern, Naval Hosp, Yokosuka, Japan, 57-58; intern, Lincoln Hosp, Bronx, NY, 58-59; asst resident, Bird S Coler Mem Hosp, Welfare Island, 59-60; resident, Roswell Park Mem Inst, 60-61; vis scientist chem, Chester Beatty Res Inst, London, 63-65; asst med, Tohoku Univ Hosp, Sendai, Japan, 68; cancer res clinician, Dept Med, Roswell Park Mem Inst, 68-73; ASSOC PROF, DEPT NEOPLASTIC DIS, MT SINAI SCH MED, 73- *Concurrent Pos:* Res fel med, Roswell Park Mem Inst, 61-63; res asst prof med, State Univ NY Buffalo, 70-73; assoc attend physician, Dept Neoplastic Dis, Mt Sinai Hosp, New York, 73- *Mem:* Am Chem Soc; Am Asn Cancer Res; Am Soc Clin Oncol. *Res:* Cancer chemotherapy; preclinical and clinical pharmacology. *Mailing Add:* Dept of Neoplastic Dis Mt Sinai Sch of Med New York NY 10029

OHR, ELEONORE A, b New York, NY, Jan 28, 32. CELL PHYSIOLOGY. *Educ:* Univ Rochester, AB, 54, MS, 58, PhD(physiol), 62. *Prof Exp:* Asst prof, 63-68, ASSOC PROF PHYSIOL, SCH MED, STATE UNIV NY BUFFALO, 68- *Concurrent Pos:* NIH Fel biophys, Univ Buffalo, 60-61; Am Heart Asn career investr fel muscle proteins, Cardiovasc Res Inst, Med Ctr, Univ Calif, San Francisco, 62-63; gen res support grant, Sch Med, State Univ NY Buffalo, 65-66; Heart Asn Western NY, Inc res support grant, 67-68; United Health Found Western NY, Inc res support grant, 69-74. *Mem:* AAAS; assoc Am Physiol Soc. *Res:* Chemistry of tricainemethanesulfonate and its effects on epithelial transport systems; inulin space in skeletal muscle in vitro; transport of organic bases by renal cortical slices; active transport; electrophysiology. *Mailing Add:* Dept of Physiol State Univ of NY Sch of Med Buffalo NY 14214

OHR, S(EKYU) MICHAEL, b Haiju, Korea, Nov 12, 32; US citizen; m 55; c 2. PHYSICAL METALLURGY, PHYSICS. *Educ:* Ore State Univ, BS & MS, 56; Columbia Univ, PhD(metall), 63. *Prof Exp:* Physicist, Res Lab, Int Nickel Co, Inc, 58-60; PHYSICIST, SOLID STATE DIV, OAK RIDGE NAT LAB, 63- *Mem:* Am Phys Soc; Am Inst Mining, Metall & Petrol Engrs; Electron Micros Soc Am. *Res:* Dislocations and plastic deformation in solids; electron microscopy and diffraction fracture; radiation damage in solids; numerical methods. *Mailing Add:* Solid State Div Oak Ridge Nat Lab PO Box X Oak Ridge TN 37830

OHRING, GEORGE, b New York, NY, June 20, 31; m 53; c 3. METEOROLOGY. *Educ:* City Col New York, BS, 52; NY Univ, MS, 54, PhD(meteorol), 57. *Prof Exp:* Atmospheric physicist, Air Force Cambridge Res Labs, 57-60; mgr meteorol physics dept, GCA Corp, 60-65, dir meteorol lab, 65-71; ASSOC PROF METEOROL TEL-AVIV UNIV, 71- *Concurrent Pos:* Vis prof, Tel-Aviv Univ, 69-70; consult, Master Plan, Israel Meteorol Serv, 72-74; vis scientist, Environ Res & Technol, 74 & Nat Oceanic & Atmospheric Admin, 77-81; vis prof, Univ Md, 76; mem, Int Radiation Comn, 75- *Mem:* AAAS; Am Meteorol Soc; Am Geophys Union; Sigma Xi; Israel Meteorol Soc. *Res:* Atmospheric radiation; climate models; atmospheric soundings from satellites; meteorology of planetary atmospheres. *Mailing Add:* Dept of Geophys & Planetary Sci Tel-Aviv Univ Ramat Aviv Israel

OHRING, MILTON, b Stryj, Poland, Apr 6, 36; US citizen; m 60; c 1. METALLURGY, MATERIALS SCIENCE. *Educ:* Queen's Col, NY, BS, 58; Columbia Univ, BS, 58, MS, 61, DSc(metall), 65. *Prof Exp:* From instr to asst prof metall, Cooper Union, 59-64; from asst prof to assoc prof metall, 64-77, PROF MAT & METALL, STEVENS INST TECHNOL, 77- *Res:* Imperfection in ionic crystals; Mossbauer effect application in metals and nonmetals; thim film technology; electromigration in metal films. *Mailing Add:* Dept Metall Castle Point Hoboken NJ 07030

OHSOL, ERNEST O(SBORNE), b Washington, DC, May 28, 16; m 40, 77; c 4. CHEMICAL ENGINEERING. *Educ:* City Col New York, BS, 36; Mass Inst Technol, ScD(chem eng), 39. *Prof Exp:* Chem engr, Standard Oil Develop Co, NJ, 39-50; mgr process develop, Chem Div, Gen Elec Co, 50-51, mgr new prod develop, 52; dir chem eng, Pittsburgh Coke & Chem Co, 52-54, dir res & develop, 54-60; vpres chem opers, Haveg Industs, 60-64; vpres tech develop, Chem Construct Corp, 65-67; dir chem eng dept, Cent Res Div, Am Cyanamid Co, 67-72; chief process engr, Eastern Div, Jacobs Eng Co, 73-75; corp mgr, Europ fluid processing, Selas Corp Am, Munich, Ger, 75-78; ccordr, C H Dexter Div, The Dexter Corp, 78-80; CONSULT, SHELL-NIGERIAN TRAINING PROJ, KING-WILKINSON, INC, 80- *Concurrent Pos:* Mem process develop comt, Off Rubber Reserve, 46-49; adj prof, Stevens Inst Technol, 47-49. *Mem:* Am Chem Soc; fel Am Inst Chem Engrs; Tech Asn Pulp & Paper Indust. *Res:* Design of synthetic rubber plants; new processes for petrochemicals, especially ethylene phthalic anhydride, maleic anhydride, phenolic resins, silicones, melamine, coal chemicals and plastics; activated carbon; paper and protective coatings; industrial kinetics; fluidization; oil and gas production. *Mailing Add:* 711 Hyannis Port N Crosby TX 77532

OHTA, MASAO, b Kobe, Japan, May 4, 19; m 49. PHYSICAL CHEMISTRY. *Educ:* Kyoto Univ, BS, 43; Univ Calif, MS, 56; Univ Akron, PhD(chem), 59. *Prof Exp:* Res chemist polymer chem, Mitsui Chem Co, Japan, 43-52 & Monsanto Co, 59-71; sr assoc ed, 71-80, SR ED, CHEM ABSTR SERV, 80- *Mem:* Am Chem Soc. *Res:* Physical chemistry of polymers. *Mailing Add:* Chem Abstr Serv Columbus OH 43210

OHTAKE, TAKESHI, b Chiba, Japan, Jan 22, 26; m 53; c 3. CLOUD PHYSICS, CLIMATOLOGY. *Educ:* Tohoku Univ, Japan, BSc, 52, DSc(meteorol), 61. *Prof Exp:* Technician meteorol, Cent Meteorol Observ, Tokyo, Japan, 43-44; res assoc, Meteorol Res Inst, 47-49; sr res assoc, Geophys Inst, Tohoku Univ, Japan, 52-64; assoc prof, 64-75, PROF GEOPHYS, GEOPHYS INST, UNIV ALASKA, FAIRBANKS, 75- *Concurrent Pos:* USPHS res fel, 65-69; NSF res fels, 65-82; vis assoc prof, Dept Atmospheric Sci, Colo State Univ, 69-71. *Mem:* Am Geophys Union; Am Meteorol Soc; foreign mem Royal Meteorol Soc; Meteorol Soc Japan. *Res:* Electron microscopic studies for fog, cloud, ice crystal and ice fog nuclei and cloud condensation nuclei; physical and chemical explanation of fog, cloud, snowfall and rainfall formation mechanisms; ice crystal nucleation; weather modification. *Mailing Add:* Geophys Inst Univ Alaska Fairbanks AK 99701

OICKLE, CHARLES, b Worcester, Mass, July 11, 23; m 46; c 2. MECHANICAL ENGINEERING, AERONAUTICAL ENGINEERING. *Educ:* Worcester Polytech Inst, BS, 44. *Prof Exp:* Res engr, Res Labs, United Aircraft Corp, 46-52, supvr compressor aerodyn, 52-54, supvr subsonic aerodyn, 54-55, head fluid mech sect, 55-59, head eval sect, 59-62, mgr res engr, 62-67, mgr eng res labs, 67-77; ASST DIR RES FOR DIV COORD, UNITED TECHNOL RES CTR, 77- *Mem:* Am Inst Aeronaut & Astronaut; assoc fel Sigma Xi. *Res:* Applied research in aircraft, missile and space propulsion; advanced materials; aerophysics; mathematics; high-power laser systems. *Mailing Add:* 224 Clearfield Rd Wethersfield CT 06109

OIEN, HELEN GROSSBECK, b Paterson, NJ, July 11, 40; m 68. BIOCHEMISTRY, NUTRITION. *Educ:* Rutgers Univ, New Brunswick, AB, 62; Cornell Univ, MS, 64, PhD(biochem), 68. *Prof Exp:* Sr scientist biochem, Shulton, Inc, NJ, 68-69; sr res biochemist, 69-75, res fel, 75-77, SR PROJ COORDR, DEPT PROJ PLANNING & MGT, MERCK & CO, INC, 77- *Mem:* AAAS; Am Chem Soc. *Res:* Prostaglandins, especially mechanisms of action; cyclic adenosinemonophosphate; collagen biosynthesis; mechanisms of skin penetration by drugs; intermediary metab-lism of nitrogen bases. *Mailing Add:* Merck & Co Inc Rahway NJ 07065

OISHI, NOBORU, b Kapaa, Hawaii, Nov 11, 28; m 57; c 1. ONCOLOGY, IMMUNOHEMATOLOGY. *Educ:* Wash Univ, AB, 49, MD, 53. *Prof Exp:* assoc prof, 65-80, PROF MED, SCH MED, UNIV HAWAII, MANOA, 80-; DIR CLIN SCI, CANCER CTR HAWAII, 74- *Concurrent Pos:* USPHS fel hemat, Univ Rochester, 58-59; consult, Queen's Med Ctr, Kuakini Hosp & Home, Inc & St Francis Hosp, 58-; dir clin lab, Annex Lab, Inc, 67-; vpres, Blood Bank Hawaii. *Mem:* Fel Am Col Physicians; Am Soc Hemat; Am Soc Clin Oncol; NY Acad Sci; Asn Advan Med Instrumentation. *Res:* Study of the immune capacity of patients with malignant disorders; tumor markers, invitro growth of tumor cells. *Mailing Add:* 1010 S King St Honolulu HI 96814

OJA, TONIS, b Tallin, Estonia, Aug 22, 37; US citizen; m 61; c 2. PHYSICS, CHEMISTRY. *Educ:* McGill Univ, BSc, 59; Rensselaer Polytech Inst, PhD(physics), 66. *Prof Exp:* Res asst, RCA Victor Res Labs, Can, 59-61; res assoc physics, Brown Univ, 66-68, asst prof, 68-69; asst prof, Univ Denver, 69-73; assoc prof, Ohio Univ, 73-74; ASSOC PROF PHYSICS, HUNTER COL, NY, 74- *Concurrent Pos:* Consult, Matec Inc, RI, 72- *Mem:* Am Phys Soc. *Res:* Nuclear magnetic and nuclear quadrupole resonance; glasses and material of biological interest; phase transitions; critical phenomena. *Mailing Add:* Hunter Col New York NY 10021

OJAKAAR, LEO, b Valga, Estonia, Apr 26, 26; US citizen; m 59; c 2. ORGANIC CHEMISTRY. *Educ:* Millikin Univ, BS, 53; Va Polytech Inst, MS, 61, PhD(org chem), 64. *Prof Exp:* Res asst chem, Rutgers Univ, 56-59; RES CHEMIST, E I DU PONT DE NEMOURS & CO, INC, 64- *Mem:* Am Chem Soc; Sigma Xi. *Res:* New high molecular weight aromatic hydrocarbons; new isocyanates and urethanes with industrial importance; synthetic rubbers; new neoprene compounds; elastomer chemistry; flurocarbon chemistry. *Mailing Add:* Exp Sta Bldg 353 E I du Pont de Nemours & Co Inc Wilmington DE 19898

OJALVO, IRVING U(LYSSES), b New York, NY, Jan 16, 36; m 64; c 2. APPLIED MECHANICS. *Educ:* City Col New York, BME, 56; Mass Inst Technol, SM, 57; NY Univ, ScD(mech eng), 62. *Prof Exp:* Instr eng mech, NY Univ, 57-60; specialist res & develop, Repub Aviation Corp, 61-66; consult, Harry Belock Assoc, 66-68; group leader, 68-80, SUPVR, PERKIN-ELMER, GRUMMAN AEROSPACE CORP, 80- *Concurrent Pos:* Adj assoc prof, Hofstra Univ, 64-; adj prof, NY Univ, 68-72. *Mem:* Am Soc Mech Engrs; Nat Soc Prof Engrs; Am Acad Mech. *Res:* Structural analysis; dynamics; bonded and bolted joints; thermal stress; numerical methods; applied mathematics. *Mailing Add:* Grumman Aerospace Corp 460|35 Bethpage NY 11714

OJALVO, MORRIS, b New York, NY, Mar 4, 24; m 48; c 4. CIVIL ENGINEERING. *Educ:* Rensselaer Polytech Inst, BCE, 44, MCE, 52; Lehigh Univ, PhD(civil eng), 60; Ohio State Univ, JD, 78. *Prof Exp:* Tutor civil eng, City Col New York, 47-49; instr, Rensselaer Polytech Inst, 49-51; asst prof, Princeton Univ, 51-58; res instr, Lehigh Univ, 58-60; assoc prof, 60-64, PROF CIVIL ENG, OHIO STATE UNIV, 64- *Mem:* Am Soc Civil Engrs; Struct Stability Res Coun. *Res:* Structural mechanics and stability; plasticity; elasticity; limit analysis; thin-walled structural members. *Mailing Add:* Dept of Civil Eng Ohio State Univ Columbus OH 43210

OJALVO, MORRIS S(OLOMON), b New York, NY, July 6, 23; m 49; c 3. MECHANICAL ENGINEERING. *Educ:* Cooper Union, BME, 44; Univ Del, MME, 49; Purdue Univ, PhD(mech eng), 62. *Prof Exp:* Asst, Eng Exp Sta, Pa State Univ, 46-47; instr physics, Univ Ill, 47-48; asst & instr mech eng, Univ Del, 48-50; from asst prof to assoc prof, Univ Md, 50-55; assoc prof, Univ Del, 55-56; asst & instr, Purdue Univ, 56-60; assoc prof, George 14 Washington Univ, 60-62, prof eng & appl sci, 62-66; PROG DIR, ENG DIV, NSF, 65- *Concurrent Pos:* Prof lectr, George Washington Univ, 66-; UNESCO mech eng, Nat Polytech Inst, Mex, 67-69. *Mem:* Fel Am Soc Mech Engrs; Soc Automotive Engrs; Am Soc Eng Educ; Fine Particle Soc (vpres, 77-78, pres, 78-79). *Res:* Combined forced and free convection heat transfer; thermodynamics; fluid mechanics; energy conversion; particulate technology. *Mailing Add:* 8502 Barron St Takoma Park MD 20012

OJEDA, SERGIO RAUL, b Valdivia, Chile, Apr 19, 46; m 68; c 3. NEUROENDOCRINOLOGY, ENDOCRINOLOGY. *Educ:* Univ Chile, DVM, 68. *Prof Exp:* Instr physiol, Univ Austral, Chile, 68, asst prof, 68-71; Ford Found res fel, 72-74, asst prof, 74-78, ASSOC PROF PHYSIOL, HEALTH SCI CTR, UNIV TEX, 78- *Concurrent Pos:* Prin investr, Univ Tex grant, 74-75 & NIH grant, 77-81 & 81-85. *Mem:* Endocrine Soc; Am Physiol Soc; Int Soc Neuroendocrinol; Soc Exp Biol Med; Soc Study Reproduction. *Res:* Neuroendocrinology of sexual development; neural and hormonal control of anterior pituitary function. *Mailing Add:* Dept of Physiol Univ Tex Health Sci Ctr Dallas TX 75235

OKA, SEISHI WILLIAM, b Salinas, Calif, Feb 11, 36. HUMAN GENETICS, DENTISTRY. *Educ:* Univ Calif, Berkeley, BS, 59; Univ Pac, DDS, 63; Univ Pittsburgh, PhD(human genetics), 78. *Prof Exp:* Res fel anthrop, Cowell Mem Hosp, Univ Calif, Berkeley, 64-66; res assoc dent anthrop, Cleft Palate Res Ctr, Univ Pittsburgh, 66-69, trainee human genetics dept biostatist, 69-74; CHIEF GEN SERV GENETICS, LANCASTER CLEFT PALATE CLIN, 74-, EXEC DIR, 79- *Concurrent Pos:* Pvt pract dent, 64-65; lectr dent anthrop, Univ Pittsburgh, 67-70, clin instr dept oper dent, Sch Dent Med, 69-74, clin staff, Cleft Palate Res Ctr, 72-74; clin instr div human genetics, Dept Pediat, Milton S Hershey Med Ctr, Pa State Univ, 75-; consult prog develop, Lancaster Cleft Palate Clin, 78- *Mem:* Am Soc Human Genetics; Am Genetic Asn; Int Soc Elec & Electronic Engrs; Am Cleft Palate Asn; Soc Cranio-facial Genetics. *Mailing Add:* Lancaster Cleft Palate Clin 24 N Lime St Lancaster PA 17602

OKA, TAKAMI, b Tokyo, Japan, Jan 1, 40; m 69; c 1. DEVELOPMENTAL BIOLOGY, PHARMACOLOGY. *Educ:* Univ Tokyo, BS, 63; Stanford Univ, PhD(pharmacol), 69. *Prof Exp:* Vis scientist, Nat Inst Radiol Sci, Japan, 63-64; res fel muscle protein & actin, Med Sch, Stanford Univ, 64-65; vis fel mammary gland, 69-71, staff fel, 71-73, SR INVESTR MAMMARY GLAND, NAT INST ARTHRITIS, METAB & DIGESTIVE DIS, 74- *Res:* Hormonal regulation of cellular function and development; biochemistry. *Mailing Add:* Nat Inst Arthritis Metab & Digestive Dis NIH Bldg 10 Rm 9B-15 Bethesda MD 20205

OKABAYASHI, MICHIO, b Tokyo, Japan, Dec 10, 39; m 68; c 2. PLASMA PHYSICS. *Educ:* Univ Tokyo, BS, 63, MS, 65, PhD(physics), 68. *Prof Exp:* Fel, 68-71, res staff, 71-75, RES PHYSICIST, PRINCETON UNIV, 75- *Mem:* Am Phys Soc. *Res:* Thermonuclear fusion research. *Mailing Add:* Plasma Physics Lab Princeton Univ Princeton NJ 08540

OKABE, HIDEO, b Naganoken, Japan, Dec 13, 23; m 59; c 3. PHYSICAL CHEMISTRY. *Educ:* Univ Tokyo, BS, 47; Univ Rochester, PhD(chem), 57. *Prof Exp:* Nat Res Coun Can fel, 56-58; phys chemist, 59-71, div consult, 71-74, sr scientist, Div Phys Chem, 74-78, SR SCIENTIST, DIV MOLECULAR SPECTROS, NAT BUR STANDARDS, 78- *Concurrent Pos:* Guest prof, Inst Phys Chem, Univ Bonn, 63-65; vis prof, Dept Chem, Tokyo Inst Technol, Japan, 78; NASA sr res assoc, Goddard Space Flight Ctr NASA, Greenbelt, Md, 82- *Honors & Awards:* Gold Medal, Dept of Com, 73. *Mem:* Am Chem Soc; Sigma Xi. *Res:* Vacuum ultraviolet photochemistry in the gas phase; fluorescence; air pollution; planetary atmospheres. *Mailing Add:* Div of Molecular Spectros Nat Bur of Standards Washington DC 20234

OKADA, R(OBERT) H(ARRY), b New York, NY, Nov 13, 25; m 56; c 4. ELECTRICAL ENGINEERING. *Educ:* Drexel Inst, BS, 48; Univ Pa, MS, 49, PhD(elec eng), 57. *Prof Exp:* Assoc res engr, Burroughs Corp, 49-52; chief engr, Polyphase Instrument Co, 52-54; from asst prof to assoc prof elec eng, Moore Sch, Univ Pa, 54-61, asst prof elec eng in med, Med Sch, 57-61; sr staff mem, Arthur D Little, Inc, 61-62; tech dir, Epsco Pac, 62-63; PRES & FOUNDER, R O ASSOCS, INC, 63- *Concurrent Pos:* Consult, Providential Mutual Life Ins Co, 56-59, Burroughs Corp, 57- & Air Design, Inc. *Mem:* Sigma Xi; Biophys Soc; Inst Elec & Electronics Engrs. *Res:* Networks; circuits; fields; electrocardiography; instrumentation. *Mailing Add:* R O Assocs Inc 246 Caspian Dr Sunnyvale CA 94086

OKADA, TADASHI A, b Numazu, Japan, Mar 31, 28; m 56. CYTOGENETICS, MOLECULAR BIOLOGY. *Educ:* Hokkaido Univ, BS, 53, MS, 55, DS(cytogenetics), 59. *Prof Exp:* Asst res scientist, Dept Biochem, City of Hope Med Ctr, Duarte, Calif, 56-62; asst res scientist, DNA denaturation, Univ Edinburgh, 62-63; res scientist, Biol Div, Ciba Ltd, Switz, 63-65; asst res scientist, Dept Biochem, 65-69, ASSOC RES SCIENTIST, DEPT MED GENETICS, CITY OF HOPE MED CTR, 69-; ASSOC RES SCIENTIST, UNIV CALIF, SAN DIEGO, 79- *Mem:* Am Soc Cell Biol; Electron Micros Soc Am; Biophys Soc. *Res:* Ultrastructure of meiosis and mitosis; initiation of DNA synthesis; structure of chromatin and DNA; protein complexes. *Mailing Add:* Dept of Med Genetics City of Hope Med Ctr Duarte CA 91010

OKAL, EMILE ANDRE, b Paris, France, Aug 7, 50; m 78; c 1. SEISMOLOGY, GEOPHYSICS. *Educ:* Univ Paris, Agrege, 71; Ecole Normale Superiere, Univ Paris, MS, 72; Calif Inst Technol, PhD(geophys), 78. *Prof Exp:* Res fel geophys, Calif Inst Technol, 78; asst prof, 78-81, ASSOC PROF GEOPHYS, YALE UNIV, 81- *Mem:* Am Geophys Union; Seismol Soc Am. *Res:* Plate tectonics; planetology. *Mailing Add:* Dept Geophys PO Box 6666 New Haven CT 06511

OKAMOTO, K KEITH, b Upland, Calif, Sept 15, 20; m 55; c 3. CHEMICAL ENGINEERING. *Educ:* Univ Tulsa, BS, 57; Univ Tex, MS, 49, PhD(chem eng), 52. *Prof Exp:* Res engr, Calif Res Corp, 52-59; sr res engr, plastics div, 59-62, group leader, hydrocarbon div, 62-65, group supvr, 65-66, SR GROUP SUPVR, HYDROCARBON & POLYMER DIV, MONSANTO CO, 66- *Mem:* Am Chem Soc; Am Inst Chem Engrs. *Res:* Hydrocarbon process research; hydrocarbon phase equilibria; ethylene; reforming; methanol process technology. *Mailing Add:* Monsanto Co 201 Bay St Texas City TX 77590

OKAMOTO, MICHIKO, b Tokyo, Japan, Mar 3, 32; m 59; c 1. PHARMACOLOGY. *Educ:* Tokyo Col Pharm, BS, 54; Purdue Univ, MS, 57; Cornell Univ, PhD(pharmacol), 64. *Prof Exp:* Assoc prof, 71-77, PROF PHARMACOL, MED COL, CORNELL UNIV, 77- *Concurrent Pos:* Res fel pharmacol, Med Col, Cornell Univ, 64-66, USPHS training fel, 64-67. *Mem:* AAAS; Am Soc Pharmacol & Exp Therapeut; Harvey Soc; NY Acad Sci; Soc Neurosci. *Res:* Neuropharmacology of synaptic transmission and nerves; pharmacology of drugs of abuse; sedative-hypnotics and alcohol. *Mailing Add:* Dept of Pharmacol Cornell Univ Med Col New York NY 10021

OKAMURA, JUDY PAULETTE, b Glendale, Calif, Oct 12, 42; m 70; c 2. ANALYTICAL CHEMISTRY. *Educ:* Calif State Univ, Fresno, BS, 64; Calif State Univ, San Diego, MS, 69; Univ Calif, Riverside, PhD(chem), 72. *Prof Exp:* Sr chemist, Anal Res Labs Inc, 72-73; ASST PROF CHEM, SNA BERNARDINO VALLEY COL, 73- *Mem:* Am Chem Soc. *Res:* Physical basis for separations in all areas of chromatography. *Mailing Add:* Dept of Chem San Bernardino Valley Col San Bernardino CA 92403

OKAMURA, KIYOHISA, b Chuseinan-do, Korea, Feb 8, 35. SYSTEMS & MECHANICAL ENGINEERING. *Educ:* Kyushu Univ, BS, 57; Univ Tokyo, MSME, 59; Purdue Univ, PhD(automatic control), 63. *Prof Exp:* Mem res staff, Japan Atomic Energy Res Inst, 59-60; sr proj engr, Allison Div, Gen Motors Corp, 63-66; asst prof systs eng, Rensselaer Polytech Inst, 66-68; ASSOC PROF MECH ENG, N DAK STATE UNIV, 68- *Mem:* Am Soc Mech Engrs; Am Soc Eng Educ; Japan Soc Mech Eng. *Res:* Automatic control; bioengineering; microprocessor applied. *Mailing Add:* Dept of Mech Eng NDak State Univ Fargo ND 58102

OKAMURA, WILLIAM H, b Los Angeles, Calif, Feb 19, 41; m 70. SYNTHETIC ORGANIC CHEMISTRY, MEDICINAL CHEMISTRY. *Educ:* Univ Calif, Los Angeles, BS, 62; Columbia Univ, PhD(org chem), 66. *Prof Exp:* Nat Acad Sci-Nat Res Coun-Air Force Off Sci Res fel, Cambridge Univ, 66-67; asst prof org chem, 67-74, assoc prof, 74-76, PROF CHEM, UNIV CALIF, RIVERSIDE, 76- *Mem:* Am Chem Soc; Am Soc Photobiol. *Res:* Natural products; vitamin D analogs and metabolites; retinoids; chemistry of vision; aromatic molecules; heterocycles; organometallics; allene chemistry. *Mailing Add:* Dept of Chem Univ of Calif Riverside CA 92521

OKAMURA, YOSHINOBU, b Nara, Japan, Nov 14, 50; m 82. SOLID STATE PHYSICS. *Educ:* Kobe Univ, BSc, 73, MSc, 75; State Univ NY Buffalo, PhD(physics), 81. *Prof Exp:* Fel kinetics theory, Dept Chem, McGill Univ, 79-81; FEL DIFFUSION SOLIDS, DEPT CHEM, UNIV WESTERN ONT, 81- *Res:* Noneguilibrium phenomena; diffusion in solids; polymer conformation; lorentz gas in terms of correlated walks; kinetic theory and irreversible thermodynamics. *Mailing Add:* Dept Chem Univ Western Ont London PQ N6A 5B7 Can

O'KANE, DANIEL JOSEPH, b Jackson Heights, NY, June 20, 19; m 46; c 3. BACTERIOLOGY. *Educ:* Cornell Univ, BS, 40, PhD(bact), 47; Univ Wis, MS, 41. *Hon Degrees:* MA, Univ Pa, 71. *Prof Exp:* From asst prof to assoc prof microbiol, 47-56, from vdean to actg dean grad sch arts & sci, 66-74, dep assoc provost, 74-78, chmn dept biol, 78-80, PROF MICROBIOL, UNIV PA, 56-, ASSOC CHMN, 80- *Concurrent Pos:* Fulbright & Guggenheim fel, Oxford Univ, 55-56; Wis Alumni Res Found scholar & Abbott Labs fel; mem microbiol training comt, Nat Inst Gen Med Sci, chmn microbiol training panel, 68-69. *Mem:* AAAS; Am Soc Microbiol; fel Am Acad Microbiol; NY Acad Sci; Brit Soc Gen Microbiol. *Res:* Microbial metabolism and physiology; control of carbohydrate metabolism. *Mailing Add:* Dept of Biol Univ of Pa Philadelphia PA 19104

OKASHIMO, KATSUMI, b Vancouver, BC, Mar 18, 29; m 54; c 4. MATHEMATICS, ACADEMIC ADMINISTRATION. *Educ:* McMaster Univ, BA, 52; Univ Toronto, MA, 53, PhD(math), 55. *Prof Exp:* Rep sci comput, Defence Res Bd, 55-59; mgr math & eng comput, Ontario Hydro, 60-67; from assoc prof to prof math & statist, dir, Inst Comput Sci, 67-77, PROF COMPUT & INFO SCI, UNIV GUELPH, 71- *Mem:* Asn Comput Mach; Math Asn Am. *Res:* Management and administration of data processing; educational techniques in computer science; system analysis and design. *Mailing Add:* Dept of Comput & Info Sci Univ of Guelph Guelph ON N1H 2M6 Can

OKAYA, YOSHI HARU, b Osaka, Japan, Feb 11, 27; m 50; c 4. CRYSTALLOGRAPHY. *Educ:* Osaka Univ, BS, 47, PhD(crystallog), 56. *Prof Exp:* Res assoc physics, Pa State Univ, 53-56, from asst prof to assoc prof, 56-61; res physicist, Res Ctr, IBM Corp, 61-67; PROF CHEM, STATE UNIV NY STONY BROOK, 67- *Concurrent Pos:* Mem staff, Brookhaven Nat Lab, 58 & Nat Lab High Energy Physics, Tsukuba, Japan, 81. *Mem:* Am Crystallog Asn; Crystallog Soc Japan; Chem Soc Japan. *Res:* Crystal chemistry; crystal structure determination in organic and inorganic compounds; disorder and diffuse scattering; structural basis for physical behaviors; computer controlled experiments, design and concept; solid state chemistry; use of synchrotron radiation. *Mailing Add:* Dept Chem State Univ NY Stony Brook NY 11794

OKAZAKI, HARUO, b Kochi, Japan, Apr 11, 26; US citizen; m 57; c 3. PATHOLOGY, NEUROPATHOLOGY. *Educ:* Kochi Col, BS, 47; Osaka Univ, MD, 51. *Prof Exp:* Asst instr psychiat, Keio Univ Med Sch, 52-53; resident neurol, Kings County Hosp, Brooklyn, 54-56, resident neuropath,

56-57; assoc, Col Physicians & Surgeons, Columbia Univ, 58-59; from instr to asst prof, State Univ NY Downstate Med Ctr, 59-63; spec appointee, 65, asst prof, 67-73, ASSOC PROF PATH, MAYO MED SCH, UNIV MINN, 73-, MEM STAFF, MAYO CLIN, 66- *Concurrent Pos:* Res fel, Rockland State Hosp, NY, 53-54; vis fel path, Columbia-Presby Med Ctr, New York, 64; Nat Inst Neurol Dis & Blindness spec fel, 65; mem stroke coun, Am Heart Asn. *Mem:* Am Asn Neuropath; Asn Res Nerv & Ment Dis; Am Acad Neurol; Japanese Soc Neurol & Psychiat. *Res:* Human pathology with particular reference to neurologic and psychiatric diseases; anatomic pathology. *Mailing Add:* 1339 NW 20th St Rochester MN 55901

OKE, JOHN BEVERLEY, b Sault Ste Marie, Ont, Mar 23, 28; m 55; c 3. ASTRONOMY. *Educ:* Univ Toronto, BA, 49, MA, 50; Princeton Univ, PhD(astron), 53. *Prof Exp:* Lectr astron, Univ Toronto, 53-56, asst prof, 56-58; from asst prof to assoc prof, 58-64, assoc dir, Observ, 70-78, PROF ASTRON, CALIF INST TECHNOL, 64-, STAFF MEM, HALE OBSERV, 58- *Mem:* Am Astron Soc. *Res:* Photoelectric spectrophotometry of stars, galaxies and quasars; astronomical instrumentation. *Mailing Add:* Hale Observ Calif Inst of Technol Pasadena CA 91125

OKE, TIMOTHY RICHARD, b Devon, Eng, Nov 22, 41; m 67; c 2. MICROCLIMATOLOGY. *Educ:* Bristol Univ, BSc, 63; McMaster Univ, MA, 64, PhD(geog), 67. *Prof Exp:* Res asst microclimat, McMaster Univ, 64-66, lectr, 66-67; asst prof geog, McGill Univ, 67-70; asst prof, 70-71, assoc prof, 71-78, PROF GEOG, UNIV BC, 78- *Concurrent Pos:* Res grants, Nat Res Coun Can, 67-68, 68- & Atmospheric Environ Serv, 68-; rapporteur urban climate, World Meteorol Orgn, 71-; vis scientist, Uppsala Univ, 75; vis prof, Bristol Univ, 76; ed, Atmosphere-Ocean, 77-80; mem, Can Nat Comt, World Climate Res Prog. *Mem:* Am Meteorol Soc; fel Royal Meteorol Soc; Can Meteorol & Ocean Soc; Can Asn Geog. *Res:* Micrometeorology of the lowest layers of the atmosphere; urban climatology; energy balance; air pollution. *Mailing Add:* Dept of Geog Univ of BC Vancouver BC V6T 1W5 Can

O'KEEFE, DAVID PATRICK, metallurgy, see previous edition

O'KEEFE, DENNIS ROBERT, b Ottawa, Ont, Nov 15, 39; m 65; c 2. PHYSICS. *Educ:* Univ Ottawa, BSc, 62; Univ Toronto, MASc, 64, PhD(appl sci & eng), 68. *Prof Exp:* STAFF SCIENTIST EXP PHYSICS & CHEM, GEN ATOMIC CO, 68- *Concurrent Pos:* Nat Res Coun scholar, Can. *Mem:* Am Phys Soc. *Res:* Surface physics and chemistry; rarefied gas dynamics; gas-surface interactions; molecular and atomic beam techniques; ultrahigh vacuum technology; advanced energy concepts; nuclear reactor engineering; thermochemical water splitting for hydrogen production. *Mailing Add:* Gen Atomic Co PO Box 81608 San Diego CA 92138

O'KEEFE, J GEORGE, b Averill Park, NY, Feb 6, 31; m 64; c 2. PHYSICS. *Educ:* St Bernardine of Siena Col, BS, 52; Rensselaer Polytech Inst, MS, 56; Brown Univ, PhD(physics), 61. *Prof Exp:* Res assoc physics, Brown Univ, 61-62; from asst prof to assoc prof, 62-71, PROF PHYSICS, RI COL, 71- *Mem:* Fel AAAS; Am Asn Physics Teachers; Am Inst Physics; Nat Sci Teachers Asn; Sigma Xi. *Res:* Nuclear magnetic resonance. *Mailing Add:* 20 Maple Crest Dr Greenville RI 02828

O'KEEFE, JOHN ALOYSIUS, b Lynn, Mass, Oct 13, 16; m 41; c 9. ASTRONOMY, GEOPHYSICS. *Educ:* Harvard Univ, AB, 37; Univ Chicago, PhD(astron), 41. *Prof Exp:* Prof math & physics, Brenau Col, 41-42; mathematician, Army Map Serv, 45-58; ASTRONR, GODDARD SPACE FLIGHT CTR, NASA, 58- *Mem:* Am Astron Soc; Am Geophys Union; Int Astron Union; Int Union Geod & Geophys; Am Astronaut Soc. *Res:* Origin of the moon; tektites; geodesy, especially isostasy; solid particles in space; planetary rings; ancient climates. *Mailing Add:* Code 681 NASA Goddard Space Flight Ctr Greenbelt MD 20771

O'KEEFE, JOHN DUGAN, b Analonda, Mont, Nov 7, 37; m 68; c 2. PLANITARY IMPACT, LASER PHYSICS. *Educ:* Calif State Univ, Long Beach, BS, 62; Univ Southern Calif, MS, 65; Univ Calif, Los Angeles, PhD(planetary physics), 76. *Prof Exp:* Res physicist, Space Div, Rockwell Int, 62-69; SR SCIENTIST & PROG MGR, TRW INC, 69- *Concurrent Pos:* Vis res assoc, Calif Inst Technol, 76- *Mem:* Optical Soc Am; Am Geophys Union. *Res:* Role of hypervelocity impact on the evolution of the solar system, including the effect on extinction of biota on earth; high energy lasers and phenomenology. *Mailing Add:* Calif Inst Technol 1201 E Calif Blvd Pasadena CA 91125

O'KEEFE, JOHN JOSEPH, b Philadelphia, Pa, Dec 30, 09; m 44; c 5. MEDICINE. *Educ:* St Joseph's Col, BS, 33; Jefferson Med Col, MD, 37; Am Bd Otolaryngol, dipl, 46. *Prof Exp:* Intern, Jefferson Hosp, 37-39, asst, 39-42, prof clin otolaryngol & bronchoesophagol, 47-72, PROF OTOLARYNGOL & CHMN DEPT, THOMAS JEFFERSON UNIV, 72- *Concurrent Pos:* Ross V Patterson fel broncho-esophagol, Jefferson Hosp, 39-41; consult, Vet Admin Hosps, 72; hon prof otolaryngol, Grad Sch Med, Univ Pa; attend physician, Jefferson Hosp; chief bronchoesophagol & laryngeal surg, Our Lady of Lourdes & St Joseph's Hosps; hon attend physician, Pa Hosp. *Mem:* Fel Am Acad Ophthal & Otolaryngol; fel Am Laryngol Asn; fel Am Col Surgeons; fel Am Laryngol, Rhinol & Otol Soc; fel Am Col Chest Physicians. *Mailing Add:* 111 S Eleventh St Philadelphia PA 19107

O'KEEFE, KELLY RAY, analytical chemistry, see previous edition

O'KEEFE, MICHAEL ADRIAN, b Melbourne, Australia, Sept 8, 42. SOLID STATE PHYSICS, ELECTRON MICROSCOPY. *Educ:* Univ Melbourne, BSc, 70, PhD(physics), 75. *Prof Exp:* Sci officer catalysis, Commonwealth Sci & Indust, 61-68; exp officer, Res Orgn, 68-69, exp officer electron micros, 69-75; FEL ELECTRON MICROS, ARIZ STATE UNIV, 76- *Mem:* AAAS; Electron Micros Soc Am. *Res:* High resolution; computation of electron microscope lattice images of minerals and defect structures for comparison with experimental images as an aid to structure determination. *Mailing Add:* Ctr for Solid State Sci Ariz State Univ Tempe AZ 85281

O'KEEFE, ROBERT BERNARD, horticulture, forestry, see previous edition

O'KEEFE, THOMAS JOSEPH, b St Louis, Mo, Oct 2, 35; m 57; c 5. METALLURGICAL ENGINEERING. *Educ:* Mo Sch Mines, BS, 58; Univ Mo-Rolla, PhD(metall eng), 65. *Prof Exp:* Process control metallurgist metall eng, Dow Metal Prod, 59-61; res dir, Metal System Div, Air Prod & Chem, 77-78; PROF METALL ENG, MAT RES CTR, UNIV MO-ROLLA, 78- *Concurrent Pos:* Prof metall eng, Univ Mo-Rolla, 65-77; comt mem, Electrolytic Technol Adv Comt, Dept Energy, 77-80; comt mem, Int Metals Rev Comt, 78-81. *Mem:* Am Inst Mining & Metall Engrs; Sigma Xi. *Res:* Electrodeposition processes of nonferrous metals and dental materials. *Mailing Add:* 5 Crestview Dr Rolla MO 65401

O'KEEFFE, DAVID JOHN, b New York, NY, July 5, 30; m 56; c 6. PHYSICS. *Educ:* St Peter's Col, NJ, BS, 53; Univ Md, MS, 62; Cath Univ Am, PhD(physics), 69. *Prof Exp:* PHYSICIST, NAVAL SURFACE WEAPONS CTR, WHITE OAK LAB, 55- *Mem:* Am Phys Soc. *Res:* Theoretical investigations of the behavior of solids under high pressure utilizing the methodologies of statistical mechanics, lattice dynamics and the nature of the cohesive energy of the solid in question. *Mailing Add:* 18 Lakeside Dr Greenbelt MD 20770

O'KEEFFE, LAWRENCE EUGENE, b Walhalla, NDak, May 12, 34; m 54; c 6. AGRICULTURAL ENTOMOLOGY, INTEGRATED PEST MANAGEMENT. *Educ:* NDak State Univ, BS, 56, MS, 58; Iowa State Univ, PhD(econ entom), 65. *Prof Exp:* Port entomologist, Wis Dept Agr, 60-62; asst state entomologist, Iowa Dept Agr, 62-65; exten entomologist, 65-69, asst prof entom & asst entomologist, 69-73, assoc prof entom & assoc entomologist, 73-81, PROF ENTOM & ENTOMOLOGIST, UNIV IDAHO, 81- *Mem:* Entom Soc Am; Sigma Xi. *Res:* Host-plant resistance to insects and host-plant selection; applied and regulatory entomology; control of insects of grain legumes and soil arthropods, especially wireworms. *Mailing Add:* Dept of Entom Univ of Idaho Moscow ID 83843

O'KEEFFE, MICHAEL, b Bury St Edmunds, Eng, Apr 3, 34. SOLID STATE CHEMISTRY. *Educ:* Bristol Univ, BSc, 54, PhD(chem), 58, DSc, 77. *Prof Exp:* Chemist, Mullard Res Labs, 58-59; res assoc chem, Ind Univ, 60-62; from asst prof to assoc prof, 63-69, PROF CHEM, ARIZ STATE UNIV, 69- *Concurrent Pos:* Fel, Ind Univ, 60-62. *Res:* Chemistry of solids. *Mailing Add:* Dept of Chem Ariz State Univ Tempe AZ 82587

O'KELLEY, GROVER DAVIS, b Birmingham, Ala, Nov 23, 28; m 50; c 2. TRANSURANIUM ELEMENT CHEMISTRY, NUCLEAR WASTE CHEMISTRY. *Educ:* Howard Col, AB, 48; Univ Calif, Berkeley, PhD(chem), 51. *Prof Exp:* Chemist nuclear chem res, Radiation Lab, 49-51; lead chemist, Calif Res & Develop Co, 51-54; sr chemist, 54-59, group leader, 59-74, SR RES STAFF MEM, CHEM DIV, OAK RIDGE NAT LAB, 74- *Concurrent Pos:* Prof chem, Univ Tenn, Knoxville, 64-; chmn, Gordon Res Conf on Nuclear Chem, 67; mem, Lunar Sample Preliminary Exam Team, 69-70; mem comt on nuclear sci & chmn subcomt on radiochem, Nat Res Coun, 74-78. *Honors & Awards:* Apollo Achievement Award, NASA, 70 & Group Achievement Award, 73. *Mem:* AAAS; fel Am Phys Soc; Am Geophys Union; Am Chem Soc; Sigma Xi. *Res:* Chemical behavior of transuranium elements in aqueous solution as related to nuclide migration in geologic media; electrochemistry; radiochemistry and nuclear chemistry. *Mailing Add:* Chem Div Oak Ridge Nat Lab PO Box X Oak Ridge TN 37830

O'KELLEY, JOSEPH CHARLES, b Unadilla, Ga, May 9, 22; m 51; c 4. PLANT PHYSIOLOGY. *Educ:* Univ NC, AB, 43, MA, 48; Iowa State Col, PhD(plant physiol), 50. *Prof Exp:* From asst prof to assoc prof, 51-61, chmn dept, 70-73, PROF BIOL, UNIV ALA, 61- *Concurrent Pos:* NSF fel, Univ Wis, 54-55; NIH fel, Johns Hopkins Univ, 65-66. *Mem:* AAAS; Am Soc Photobiol; Phycol Soc Am; Bot Soc Am; Am Soc Plant Physiologists. *Res:* Algal and cell physiology; photobiology. *Mailing Add:* Dept of Biol Univ of Ala University AL 35486

OKEN, DONALD, b New York, NY, Jan 21, 28; m 66; c 2. PSYCHIATRY. *Educ:* Syracuse Univ, 44-45; Harvard Univ, MD, 49; Am Bd Psychiat & Neurol, dipl psychiat, 58. *Prof Exp:* Res assoc, Psychosomatic & Psychiat Inst, Michael Reese Hosp, Chicago, 56-58, from asst dir to assoc dir, 58-65; chief clin res br, NIMH, 66-68, actg dir div extramural res progs, 66-67; chmn dept, 68-80, PROF PSYCHIAT, STATE UNIV NY UPSTATE MED CTR, 68- *Concurrent Pos:* Buswell fel med & psychiat, Sch Med, Univ Rochester, 51-52; NIMH training fel, Neuropsychiat & Psychiat Inst, Univ Ill, 55-56; Found Fund Res in Psychiat fel, Psychosom & Psychiat Inst, Michael Reese Hosp, 57-59; examr, Am Bd Psychiat & Neurol, 61-; mem, Ment Health Bd, Onondaga County, NY, 69-76; vis prof psychiat, Col Med, Univ NC, 77-78; Ed-in-chief, Psychosomatic Med, 82- *Mem:* AAAS; Am Psychiat Asn; Am Psychosom Soc. *Res:* Psychosomatic medicine. *Mailing Add:* Dept of Psychiat State Univ of NY Upstate Med Ctr Syracuse NY 13210

OKERHOLM, RICHARD ARTHUR, b Woburn, Mass, Nov 10, 41; m 65; c 2. BIOCHEMISTRY. *Educ:* Lowell Technol Inst, BS, 64; Boston Univ, PhD(biochem), 70. *Prof Exp:* NIH fel, Boston Univ, 69-70; res biochemist, Parke-Davis & Co, 70-73, sr res biochemist, 73-77; sect head, 77-79, DEPT HEAD DRUG METAB, MERRELL NAT LABS, 79- *Mem:* Am Chem Soc; Am Soc Mass Spectrometry; NY Acad Sci; Am Soc Pharmacol & Exp Therapeut; Sigma Xi. *Res:* Analysis, pharmacokinetics and metabolism of drugs; application of mass spectrometry to the analysis of drugs in biological fluids. *Mailing Add:* Drug Metab Dept 2110 E Galbraith Cincinnati OH 45215

OKEY, ALLAN BERNHARDT, endocrinology, cancer, see previous edition

OKIISHI, THEODORE HISAO, b Honolulu, Hawaii, Jan 15, 39; m 63; c 4. TURBOMACHINE FLUID DYNAMICS. *Educ:* Iowa State Univ, BS, 60, MS, 63, PhD(mech eng & eng mech), 65. *Prof Exp:* From asst prof to assoc prof, 67-77, PROF MECH ENG, IOWA STATE UNIV, 77- *Honors & Awards:* Cert of Recognition, NASA, 75; Ralph R Teetor Award, Soc Automotive Engrs, 76. *Mem:* Am Soc Mech Engrs; Am Inst Aeronaut & Astronaut. *Res:* Turbomachinery fluid mechanics. *Mailing Add:* Dept of Mech Eng Iowa State Univ Ames IA 50011

OKINAKA, YUTAKA, b Osaka, Japan, Jan 22, 26; m 50; c 2. ELECTROCHEMISTRY, ANALYTICAL CHEMISTRY. *Educ:* Tohoku Univ, Japan, BS, 48, DSc, 59; Univ Minn, MS, 57. *Prof Exp:* Assoc anal chem, Tohoku Univ, Japan, 48-54, asst prof electrochem, 60-63; fel, Univ Minn, 56-60; MEM TECH STAFF BELL TEL LABS, INC, 63- *Honors & Awards:* Res Award, Electrochem Soc. *Mem:* Am Chem Soc; Electrochem Soc; Am Electroplater's Soc. *Res:* Electrochemical and chemical metal deposition process research and development. *Mailing Add:* Bell Tel Labs Inc Murray Hill NJ 07974

OKITA, GEROGE TORAO, b Seattle, Wash, Jan 18, 22; m 58; c 3. PHARMACOLOGY. *Educ:* Ohio State Univ, BA, 48; Univ Chicago, PhD(pharmacol), 51. *Prof Exp:* From instr to asst prof pharmacol, Univ Chicago, 53-63; assoc prof, 63-66, actg chmn, 68-70 & 76-77, PROF PHARMACOL, MED SCH, NORTHWESTERN UNIV, 66- *Concurrent Pos:* USPHS fel, Univ Chicago, 52. *Mem:* Cardiac Muscle Soc; AAAS; Am Soc Pharmacol & Exp Therapeut; Int Soc Biochem Pharmacol; Am Heart Asn. *Res:* Metabolism and mechanism of action of digitalis; metabolic effect and mode of action of environmental toxicants. *Mailing Add:* Dept of Pharmacol Northwestern Univ Med Sch Chicago IL 60611

O'KONSKI, CHESTER THOMAS, b Kewaunee, Wis, May 12, 21; m 48; c 4. CHEMISTRY, BIOPHYSICS. *Educ:* Univ Wis, BS, 42; Northwestern Univ Ill, MS, 46, PhD(phys chem), 49. *Prof Exp:* From instr to assoc prof, 48-60, PROF CHEM, UNIV CALIF, BERKELEY, 60- *Concurrent Pos:* Guggenheim fel, 55; Knapp Mem lectr, Univ Wis, 58; Miller Sci Found res prof, Univ Calif, Berkeley, 60; NIH fel, Princeton Univ & Harvard Univ, 62-63; Nobel guest prof, Univ Uppsala, 70; Wis Alumni Res Found fel; Nat Res Coun fel. *Mem:* AAAS; Am Chem Soc; Am Phys Soc; Biophys Soc. *Res:* Physical chemistry of macromolecules; electro-optics; electronic structure of molecules; proteins and mechanisms of muscle and membranes; nucleic acids. *Mailing Add:* Dept of Chem Univ of Calif Berkeley CA 94720

OKOS, MARTIN ROBERT, b Toledo, Ohio, Sept 30, 45; m 70; c 2. CHEMICAL ENGINEERING, FOOD SCIENCE. *Educ:* Ohio State Univ, BS, 67, MS, 72, PhD(chem eng), 75. *Prof Exp:* Res assoc food sci, Ohio State Univ, 67-68; lab instr dept mech, US Military Acad, 69-70; teaching & res assoc chem eng, Ohio State Univ, 70-75; ASST PROF AGR ENG, PURDUE UNIV, 75- *Mem:* Am Soc Agr Eng; Am Inst Chem Eng; Am Soc Cereal Chem; Am Soc Dairy Sci; Am Chem Soc. *Res:* Food process design; heat and mass transfer in food; energy conservation in food processing; immobilized enzymes for food processing; protein diffusion and adsorption. *Mailing Add:* Dept of Agr Eng Purdue Univ West Lafayette IN 47906

OKRASINSKI, STANLEY JOHN, b Wilkes-Barre, Pa, Oct 29, 52; m 79. KINETICS AND MECHANISM, HOMOGENEOUS CATALYSIS. *Educ:* Kings Col (Pa), BS, 74; Princeton Univ, MA, 76, PhD(chem), 78. *Prof Exp:* Fel, Univ Chicago, 79-81; ASST PROF ORGANOMETALLIC CHEM, UNIV NEBR-LINCOLN, 81- *Mem:* Am Chem Soc. *Res:* Organometallic reaction mechanisms; synthesis of organometallics; organometallics applied to organic synthesis; metal cluster chemistry; homogeneous catalysis; electrochemistry of organometallic compounds. *Mailing Add:* Chem Dept Univ Nebr Lincoln NE 68588

OKREND, HAROLD, microbiology, see previous edition

OKRENT, DAVID, b Passaic, NJ, Apr 19, 22; m 48; c 3. NUCLEAR PHYSICS. *Educ:* Stevens Inst Technol, ME, 43; Harvard Univ, MA, 48, PhD(physics), 51. *Prof Exp:* Mech engr, Nat Adv Comt Aeronaut, 43-46; from assoc physicist to sr physicist, Argonne Nat Lab, 51-71; PROF ENG & APPL SCI, UNIV CALIF, LOS ANGELES, 71- *Concurrent Pos:* US deleg, Int Conf Peaceful Uses Atomic Energy, Geneva, 55, 58, 64 & 71; consult adv comt reactor safeguards & reactor hazards eval br, AEC, 59-, mem adv comt reactor safeguards, 63-, vchmn, 65, chmn, 66; Guggenheim fel, 61-62 & 67-68; vis prof, Univ Wash, 63 & Univ Ariz, 70-71; Argonne Univs Asn distinguished appt award, 70-71. *Honors & Awards:* Tommy Thompson Award, Am Nuclear Soc, 80. *Mem:* Nat Acad Eng; fel Am Phys Soc; fel Am Nuclear Soc. *Res:* Nuclear reactor physics, safety and fuels; neutron cross sections; high temperature materials; fast reactor technology; fusion reactor technology; risk-benefit. *Mailing Add:* 5532 Boelter Hall Univ of Calif Los Angeles CA 90024

OKRESS, ERNEST CARL, b Hamtramck, Mich, Mar 9, 10. PHYSICS, ELECTRONIC ENGINEERING. *Educ:* Univ Detroit, BEE, 35; Univ Mich, MS, 40; Sussex Col Technol, Eng, ScD, 74. *Prof Exp:* Mgr microwave ctr, Westinghouse Elec Corp, 40-59; sr res engr, Sperry Rand Corp, 59-62; mgr plasma physics, Res Div, Am Standard, Inc, 62-68; sr consult eng, S-F-D Lab Div, Varian Assocs, Inc, 68; mem sci staff & sr physicist, Brookhaven Nat Lab, 68-70; sr res physicist, EMR Photoelec Div, Weston Instruments, Inc, 70-72; consult engr, Westinghouse Elec Corp, 72 & EMR Photoelec Div, Schlumberger Co, 72-74; sr physicist, Space Sci Lab, Gen Elec Co, 74-75; consult physicist, Gen Elec Co, 75-77 & Univ City Sci Ctr, 77-78; CONSULT, PRIN SCIENTIST & PRIN INVESTR, FRANKLIN RES CTR DIV, FRANKLIN INST, 78- *Concurrent Pos:* Lectr, US Off Educ, 43; consult physicist, USDA, 70-74. *Mem:* Fel Am Phys Soc; fel Inst Elec & Electronics Engrs. *Res:* Plasma physics; electromagnetic levitation of liquid electrial conductors, including tungsten, beryllium, etc; high energy/power nanosecond periodic pulse technology; electromagnetic radiation thermonuclear plasma confinement physics; spherical phased array antenna theory; suppressed electric discharge physics. *Mailing Add:* 2601 Pennsylvania Ave Philadelphia PA 19130

OKTAY, EROL, b Safranbolu, Turkey, Aug 3, 38; m 65; c 1. NUCLEAR ENGINEERING, PLASMA PHYSICS. *Educ:* Univ Mich, BS, 63, MS, 64, PhD(nuclear eng), 69. *Prof Exp:* Asst res eng, Gas Dynamics Lab, Univ Mich, 63-68, teaching fel nuclear radiation, 69, asst res engr, 69-70; asst prof nuclear eng, Mass Inst Technol, 70-71; asst prof physics & astron, Univ Md, College Park, 71-74; PHYSICIST, US ENERGY RES & DEVELOP ADMIN, 74- *Mem:* AAAS; Am Phys Soc; Am Nuclear Soc; NY Acad Sci. *Res:* Exploding wires; plasma physics and spectroscopy; gas dynamics. *Mailing Add:* 5233 Windmill Lane Columbia MD 21044

OKUBO, AKIRA, b Tokyo, Japan, Feb 5, 25. PHYSICAL OCEANOGRAPHY, MATHEMATICAL BIOLOGY. *Educ:* Tokyo Inst Technol, BE, 47, MA, 49; Johns Hopkins Univ, PhD(oceanog), 63. *Prof Exp:* Lab asst, Japan Meteorol Agency, Tokyo, 50-54, chief chem sub-sect, 54-58; res asst oceanog, Johns Hopkins Univ, 58-63, res assoc, Chesapeake Bay Inst, 63-68, res scientist, 68-74; PROF PHYS ECOL, MARINE SCI RES CTR, STATE UNIV NY STONY BROOK, 74- *Concurrent Pos:* Vis prof, Kyoto Univ, 78-79. *Mem:* AAAS; Am Soc Naturalists; Ecol Soc Am; Ecol Soc Japan; Am Soc Limnol & Oceanog. *Res:* Mathematical ecology; turbulent diffusion in the sea; mathematical modeling for animal dispersal. *Mailing Add:* Marine Sci Res Ctr State Univ of NY Stony Brook NY 11794

OKUBO, SUSUMU, b Tokyo, Japan, Mar 2, 30; US citizen; m 65. PARTICLE PHYSICS. *Educ:* Univ Tokyo, MS, 52; Univ Rochester, PhD(physics), 68. *Prof Exp:* Res assoc physics, Univ Rochester, 67-69; res assoc, Univ Napoli, Italy, 69-70; vis physicist, CERN, Geneve, Switz, 70-71; sr res assoc, 72-74, PROF PHYSICS, UNIV ROCHESTER, 74- *Honors & Awards:* Nishina Mem Award, Nishina Found, Japan, 76. *Mem:* Am Physics Soc. *Res:* Particle physics, mostly on symmetry principle. *Mailing Add:* Dept of Physics Univ of Rochester Rochester NY 14627

OKUDO, CHUZO, b Hokkaido, Japan, Mar 5, 48. MATHEMATICS, COMPUTER SCIENCE. *Educ:* Gallaudet Col, BA, 70; Pa State Univ, PhD(math), 75. *Prof Exp:* Teacher, Am Sch Deaf, 75-76; asst prof, Nat Tech Inst Deaf, 76-78; ASST PROF, GALLAUDET COL, 78- *Mem:* AAAS. *Mailing Add:* Dept of Math Galludet Col Washington DC 20002

OKULITCH, ANDREW VLADIMIR, b Toronto, Ont, Dec 1, 41; m 65; c 2. GEOLOGY, STRUCTURAL GEOLOGY. *Educ:* Univ BC, BSc, 64, PhD(geol), 69. *Prof Exp:* RES SCIENTIST GEOL, GEOL SURV CAN, 74- *Mem:* Geol Asn Can; Geol Soc Am. *Res:* Structure and stratigraphy of southern Cordillera, British Columbia; tectonics; metamorphism and evolution; proterozoic fold belts of the Canadian shield; structure and stratigraphy of Canadian arctic archipelago. *Mailing Add:* Geol Surv of Can 3303 - 33rd St Northwest Calgary AB T2L 2A7 Can

OKULITCH, VLADIMIR JOSEPH, b St Petersburg, Russia, June 18, 06; nat Can; m 34; c 2. GEOLOGY, INVERTEBRATE PALEONTOLOGY. *Educ:* Univ BC, BASc, 31, MASc, 32; McGill Univ, PhD(geol, paleont), 34. *Hon Degrees:* DSc, Univ BC, 72. *Prof Exp:* Surveyor, Atlin Ruffner Mines, 29, geologist, 30-31; asst geol, Univ BC, 31-32 & Univ McGill, 33-34; Royal Soc Can fel, Mus Comp Zool, Harvard Univ, 34-36; instr, Univ Toronto, 36-69, lectr gen & hist geol, 39-42; from asst prof to assoc prof geol, 42-49, prof paleont & stratig, 49-53, chmn div geol, 53-59, R W Brock prof geol & head dept, 59-63, dean fac sci, 63-71, EMER DEAN SCI, UNIV BC, 71- *Concurrent Pos:* Vis prof, Univ Southern Calif, Univ Calif, Los Angeles & Univ Hawaii; sr asst, Que Geol Surv, 33-34; geologist, Shawinigan Chem, Ltd, 37; consult geologist, Calif Standard Co, Shell Oil Co & Sproule & Assocs; mem, Nat Adv Comt Astron. *Mem:* Fel Geol Soc Am; fel Paleont Soc; fel Royal Soc Can; Royal Astron Soc Can. *Res:* Lower Cambrian fauna; Archaeocyatha; corals and sponges of the Paleozoic era; lower Cambrian fossils; Paleozoic stratigraphy; Cordilleran geology. *Mailing Add:* 1843 Knox Rd Vancouver BC V6T 1S4 Can

OKULSKI, THOMAS ALEXANDER, b New Brunswick, NJ, 1943. RADIOLOGY. *Educ:* Jefferson Med Col, MD, 69; Am Bd Radiol, dipl, cert diag radiol, 75. *Prof Exp:* Intern, Temple Hosp, 69-70, resident diag radiol, 70-71 & 73-75, fel angiography & ultrasound, 75-76; asst prof, 76-81, CLIN ASST PROF RADIOL, UNIV SOUTH FLA, 81-; MEM STAFF, VET ADMIN HOSP, TAMPA, 76- *Mem:* Am Inst Ultrasound Med. *Mailing Add:* Vet Admin Hosp 13000 N 30th St Tampa FL 33612

OKUN, D(ANIEL) A(LEXANDER), b New York, NY, June 19, 17; m 46; c 2. ENVIRONMENTAL ENGINEERING. *Educ:* Cooper Union, BS, 37; Calif Inst Technol, MS, 38; Harvard Univ, ScD(sanit eng), 48. *Prof Exp:* Asst sanit engr, USPHS, DC, Ohio, NJ & NY, 40-42; from asst to assoc, Malcolm Pirnie Engrs, NY, Conn, Fla, Va & Venezuela, 48-52; assoc prof, 52-55, prof, 55-73, chmn dept, 55-73, dir int prog sanit eng design, 62-70, chmn fac, 70-73, KENAN PROF ENVIRON ENG, SCH PUB HEALTH, UNIV NC, CHAPEL HILL, 73- *Concurrent Pos:* Consult, WHO, AID & Environ Protection Agency, 52-; NSF sr fel, 60; vis prof, Int Course Sanit Eng, Delft Technol Univ, 60-61; Fed Water Pollution Control Admin fel, Univ Col, Univ London, 66-67 & 73-74, Fulbright award, 73-74; dir, US Dept Com Environ Control Sem, Bangkok, 70, Rotterdam, Warsaw, Prague & Bucharest, 71; dir, Wapora, Inc, 70-; chmn, Comt Metrop Wash Water Supply Studies, Nat Res Coun, 76-80; vis lectr, Duke Univ & Asian Inst Technol, Thailand; mem, Bd Sci & Technol for Int Develop, Nat Res Coun, 79- & vchmn, Environ Studies Bd, 80- *Honors & Awards:* Eddy Medal, Water Pollution Control Fedn, 50; Gordon Maskew Fair Award, Am Acad Environ Engrs, 72; Thomas Jefferson Award, Univ NC, Chapel Hill, 73; Gordon Y Billard Award, NY Acad Scis, 75; Simon W Freese Award, Am Soc Civil Engrs, 77; Gordon M Fair Medal, Water Pollution Control Fedn, 78. *Mem:* Nat Acad Eng; Inst Med-Nat Acad Sci; fel Am Soc Civil Engrs; Water Pollution Control Fedn; Am Acad Environ Engrs (pres, 69-70). *Res:* Water quality management. *Mailing Add:* Dept Environ Sci & Eng Univ NC Chapel Hill NC 27514

OKUN, LAWRENCE M, b Toledo, Ohio, Apr 12, 40; m 70. NEUROBIOLOGY. *Educ:* Wesleyan Univ, BA, 62; Stanford Univ, PhD(genetics), 68. *Prof Exp:* Nat Res Coun fel biol chem, Harvard Med Sch, 69-70, USPHS fel, 70-71; asst prof, 71-74, ASSOC PROF BIOL, UNIV UTAH, 74- *Concurrent Pos:* Estab investr, Am Heart Asn, 75-80. *Res:* Development, physiology, and biochemistry of neurons cultured in vitro. *Mailing Add:* Dept of Biol Univ of Utah Salt Lake City UT 84112

OKUN, RONALD, b Los Angeles, Calif, Aug 7, 32; m 58; c 2. CLINICAL PHARMACOLOGY. *Educ:* Univ Calif, Los Angeles, BA, 54; Univ Calif, San Francisco, MD & MS, 58. *Prof Exp:* Teaching asst, Univ Calif, San Francisco, 58; intern & resident, Vet Admin, 58-61; asst prof med & pharmacol, Univ

Calif, Los Angeles, 63-72, ASSOC PROF MED, MED PHARMACOL & THERAPEUT, UNIV CALIF, IRVINE-CALIF COL MED, 72- *Concurrent Pos:* Fel clin pharmacol, Johns Hopkins Hosp, 61-63; res pharmacologist, Vet Admin, 64- *Res:* Toxicology; internal medicine. *Mailing Add:* Cedars-Sinai Med Ctr 8700 Beverly Blvd Los Angeles CA 90048

OKUNEWICK, JAMES PHILIP, b Chicago, Ill, Apr 30, 34; m 57; c 4. HEMATOLOGY, CANCER. *Educ:* Loyola Univ, Calif, BS, 51; Univ Calif, Los Angeles, MS, 62, PhD(biophys, nuclear med), 65. *Prof Exp:* Mem res staff radiobiol div, Atomic Energy Proj, Univ Calif, Los Angeles, 55-57, radiobiologist, Labs Nuclear Med & Radiation Biol, 59-65; phys scientist, Rand Corp, Calif, 65-66; sr proj leader, Armed Forces Radiobiol Res Inst, Md, 66-68; assoc biologist, Cellular & Radiation Biol Labs, 68-72, sr biologist & head viral oncogenesis, Cancer Res Unit, 72-77, HEAD, EXP HEMAT SECT, CANCER RES LABS, ALLEGHENY-SINGER RES CORP, ALLEGHENY GEN HOSP, 77- *Concurrent Pos:* Consult, Oak Ridge Inst Nuclear Studies, 66-68; lectr, Dept Biol, Am Univ, 67; adj assoc prof radiation health, Univ Pittsburgh, 70-; assoc ed, Exp Hemat, 73 & Radiation Res, 77- *Mem:* AAAS; Radiation Res Soc; Soc Exp Biol Med; Am Soc Hemat; Int Soc Exp Hemat (pres, 73-74). *Res:* Radiobiology; hematopoietic system; oncogenic virus; bone marrow transplantation. *Mailing Add:* Allegheny Gen Hosp 320 E North Ave Pittsburgh PA 15212

OLAFSON, BARRY DUANE, b Valley City, NDak, Oct 12, 49. THEORETICAL CHEMISTRY. *Educ:* Univ NDak, BS, 71; Calif Inst Technol, PhD(chem), 78. *Prof Exp:* Res fel chem, Harvard Univ, 78-81; RES FEL CHEM, CALIF INST TECHNOL, 81- *Mem:* Am Chem Soc. *Res:* Electronic structure of molecules; macromolecular dynamics; protein-substrate interactions; theoretical studies of biological reaction mechanisms. *Mailing Add:* Arthur Amos Noyes Lab Chem Physics Calif Inst Technol Pasadena CA 91125

OLAFSSON, PATRICK GORDON, b Winnipeg, Man, Aug 21, 20; m 58. ORGANIC CHEMISTRY. *Educ:* McGill Univ, BS, 46; Univ Man, MS, 50; Ore State Univ, PhD(org chem), 59. *Prof Exp:* Metall chemist, Vulcan Iron & Steel Works, Can, 39-44; res chemist, E I du Pont de Nemours & Co, 59-60; assoc prof, 60-64, PROF CHEM, STATE UNIV NY ALBANY, 64- *Mem:* Am Chem Soc. *Res:* Thermal hydrogen shifts across conjugated pi-electron systems; differential thermal analysis of nucleic acids; reactions of singlet oxygen; atmospheric chemistry. *Mailing Add:* Dept of Chem State Univ of NY Albany NY 12222

OLAH, ARTHUR FRANK, b Bridgeport, Conn, May 28, 41; m 65; c 2. PLANT PHYSIOLOGY, PHYTOPATHOLOGY. *Educ:* Miami Univ, BA, 63, MA, 65; NC State Univ, PhD, 70. *Prof Exp:* Instr biol, NC Cent Univ, 67; from asst prof to assoc prof, Frostburg State Col, 70-74; asst, Off of Pub Lands Coordr, Town of Fairfield, 75-76, wetlands compliance officer, 76-78; RES ASSOC, UNIV R I, 78- *Mem:* AAAS; Bot Soc Am; Am Soc Plant Physiologists; Am Phytopath Soc; Phytochem Soc NAm. *Res:* Phenolic compounds in diseased plants; epiphtic algae; acid tolerant plants. *Mailing Add:* Dept Plant Path/Entom Univ RI Kingston RI 02881

OLAH, GEORGE ANDREW, b Budapest, Hungary, May 22, 27; m 49; c 2. ORGANIC CHEMISTRY. *Educ:* Budapest Tech Univ, PhD(org chem), 49. *Prof Exp:* Asst & assoc prof chem, Budapest Tech Univ, 49-54; assoc dir & head org chem dept, Cent Res Inst, Hungarian Acad Sci, 54-56; res scientist, Dow Chem Co Can, 57-64 & Dow Chem Co, 64-65; prof chem, 65-69, C F Mabery prof res chem, Case Western Reserve Univ, 69-77; DISTINGUISHED PROF CHEM, UNIV SOUTHERN CALIF, 77-, DIR, HYDROCARBON RES INST, 80- *Honors & Awards:* Petrol Chem Award, Am Chem Soc, 64, Baekeland Award, 67, Morley Medal, 70 & Synthetic Chem Award, 79. *Mem:* Nat Acad Sci; Am Chem Soc; fel Chem Inst Can; The Chem Soc; Swiss Chem Soc. *Res:* Organic reaction mechanism; hydrocarbon chemistry; carbocations; Friedel-Crafts reactions; intermediate complexes; chemical carcinogenesis; biological alkylating agents; organic fluorine and phosphorus compounds. *Mailing Add:* Dept of Chem Univ of Southern Calif Los Angeles CA 90007

OLAH, JUDITH AGNES, b Budapest, Hungary, Jan 21, 29; m 49; c 2. ORGANIC CHEMISTRY. *Educ:* Tech Univ, Budapest, MS, 55. *Prof Exp:* Res chemist, Cent Res Inst Chem, Hungarian Acad Sci, 55-56; sr res assoc chem, Case Western Reserve Univ, 66-77; ADJ ASSOC PROF CHEM, UNIV SOUTHERN CALIF, 77- *Res:* Synthetic and mechanistic organic chemistry, electrophilic reactions. *Mailing Add:* Dept of Chem Univ of Southern Calif Los Angeles CA 90007

OLANDER, D(ONALD) R(AYMOND), b Duluth, Minn, Nov 6, 31; m 56; c 3. NUCLEAR ENGINEERING. *Educ:* Columbia Univ, AB, 53, BS, 54; Mass Inst Technol, ScD(chem eng), 58. *Prof Exp:* Asst prof chem eng, 58-61, from asst prof to assoc prof nuclear eng, 61-70, PROF NUCLEAR ENG, UNIV CALIF, BERKELEY, 70- *Concurrent Pos:* Europ Atomic Energy Comn sr fel, 65-66. *Mem:* Am Nuclear Soc. *Res:* Nuclear materials and chemistry; high temperature reactions and properties. *Mailing Add:* Dept of Nuclear Eng Univ of Calif Berkeley CA 94720

OLANDER, DONALD PAUL, b Boulder, Colo, June 24, 40; m 66. ANALYTICAL CHEMISTRY. *Educ:* Washburn Univ, Topeka, BSc, 64; Univ Nebr-Lincoln, MSc, 67, PhD(chem), 70. *Prof Exp:* Asst prof, 69-74, ASSOC PROF CHEM, APPALACHIAN STATE UNIV, 74- *Mem:* Sigma Xi. Am Chem Soc. *Res:* Ion-solvent interactions; nonaqueous solvents; analyses of natural waters and soils. *Mailing Add:* Dept of Chem Appalachian State Univ Boone NC 28607

OLANDER, HARVEY JOHAN, b San Francisco, Calif, Nov 19, 32; m 69; c 2. VETERINARY PATHOLOGY. *Educ:* Univ Calif, Davis, BS, 56, DVM, 58, PhD(comp path), 63. *Prof Exp:* Asst prof vet path, Purdue Univ, 62-65; asst prof, Univ Calif, Davis, 65; assoc prof, State Univ NY Vet Col, Cornell Univ, 65-68; PROF VET PATH, ANIMAL DIS DIAG LAB, PURDUE UNIV, WEST LAFAYETTE, 68- *Concurrent Pos:* Vis prof path, Ontario Vet Col, Univ Guelph, 78. *Mem:* Am Vet Med Asn; Am Col Vet Path; Conf Res Workers Animal Dis; Comp Gastroenterol Soc (pres 73-74); NY Acad Sci. *Res:* Pathology of infectious diseases of domestic animals; comparative gastroenterology; swine dysentary; salmonellosis. *Mailing Add:* Dept Vet Microbiol Path & Health Purdue Univ West Lafayette IN 47906

OLANDER, JAMES ALTON, b Boulder, Colo, Oct 9, 44. INORGANIC CHEMISTRY, HYDROMETALLURGY. *Educ:* Washburn Univ, Topeka, BS, 65; La State Univ, Baton Rouge, PhD, 70. *Prof Exp:* Asst chem, La State Univ, Baton Rouge, 68-70; res chemist, Deepsea Ventures, Inc, 70-74, res dir, 74-76; res chemist, US Bur Mines, Salt Lake City, 76-78; SR METALLURGIST, AMOCO MINERALS, 78- *Mem:* Am Chem Soc; Am Inst Mining, Metall & Petrol Engrs. *Res:* Ion-ion and ion-solvent interactions; electrolytic solutions; nonaqueous solvents; liquid ion exchange. *Mailing Add:* 17847 Lunmuhaus Dr No 4 Golden CO 80401

OLBRICH, STEVEN EMIL, b Chicago, Ill, Nov 24, 38; m 68; c 2. DIARY SCIENCE. *Educ:* Univ Wis-Madison, BS, 65; Univ Hawaii, MS, 68; Univ Mo-Columbia, PhD(nutrit), 71. *Prof Exp:* From res asst to res assoc nutrit, Univ Mo-Columbia, 68-72; res assoc, 72-74, DAIRY SPECIALIST, DEPT ANIMAL SCI, UNIV HAWAII, 75-, ASST PROF ANIMAL SCI, 76- *Mem:* Am Dairy Sci Asn; Am Soc Animal Sci. *Res:* Animal nutrition, dairy science and environmental physiology. *Mailing Add:* Dept of Animal Sci Univ of Hawaii Honolulu HI 96822

OLCOTT, EUGENE L, b St Louis, Mo, Apr 18, 18; m 49; c 3. REFRACTORY MATERIALS, GRAPHITE COMPOSITES. *Educ:* Univ Mo, BS, 40. *Prof Exp:* Metall observer, Bethlehem Steel Corp, NY, 40-41; jr metallurgist, J H Williams Co, 41; head high temperature sect, Gen Elec Co, 41-46; metall engr, Mat Sect, Bur Aeronaut, US Dept Navy, Washington, DC, 46-51, head high temperature mat sect, Bur Ships, 51-56; metall engr missile eng group, Atlantic Res Corp, 56-57, dir mat div, 57-75; CONSULT, 75- *Mem:* Am Soc Metals; Am Ceramic Soc. *Res:* High temperature, graphite composite and propulsion materials. *Mailing Add:* Rte 1 Box 44 Shepherdstown WV 25443

OLD, BRUCE S(COTT), b Norfolk, Va, Oct 21, 13; m 39; c 5. METALLURGY. *Educ:* Univ NC, BS, 35; Mass Inst Technol, ScD(metall), 38. *Prof Exp:* Consult, Dewey & Almy Chem Co, Mass, 37-38; res engr, Bethlehem Steel Co, Pa, 38-41; metallurgist, Arthur D Little, Inc, 46-51, dir, 49-51, vpres, 51-60, sr vpres, 60-78; PRES, BRUCE S OLD ASSOCS INC, 79- *Concurrent Pos:* Chief metall & mat br, AEC, 47-49, consult, 49-55; pres, Cambridge Corp, 51-53, chmn bd, 53-55; consult, Sci Adv Comt, Exec Off of the President, 53-56; pres, Nuclear Metals, Inc, 54-57; chmn, Nat Conf Admin Res, 66. *Mem:* Nat Acad Eng; NY Acad Sci; fel AAAS; fel Am Soc Metals; Am Inst Mining, Metall & Petrol Engrs. *Res:* Direct reduction; research on research; age hardening; physical chemistry of steel making; blast furnace; metallurgy as related to atomic energy; cryogenic engineering; radioactive waste disposal. *Mailing Add:* Bruce S Old Assocs Inc PO Box 706 Concord MA 01742

OLD, LLOYD JOHN, b San Francisco, Calif, Sept 23, 33. CANCER, IMMUNOLOGY. *Educ:* Univ Calif, BA, 55, MD, 58. *Prof Exp:* Res fellow, Sloan-Kettering Inst Cancer Res, 58-59, res assoc, 59-60, assoc, 60-64, assoc mem, 64-67; res assoc, 60-62, from asst prof to assoc prof, 62-69, PROF BIOL, GRAD SCH MED SCI, CORNELL UNIV, 69-; MEM, SLOAN-KETTERING INST CANCER RES, 67-, VPRES & ASSOC DIR SCI DEVELOP, 73- *Concurrent Pos:* Consult, Nat Cancer Inst, 67, mem develop res working group, 69, mem spec virus cancer prog, Immunol Group, 70; assoc med dir, New York Cancer Res Inst, Inc, 70, med dir, 71-; mem med & sci adv bd & bd trustee, Leukemia Soc Am, 70-73; mem sci adv bd, Jane Coffin Childs Mem Fund Med Res, 70-; adv ed, J Exp Med, 71; Louis Gross Mem lectr, 72; assoc ed, Virology, 72-74; Harvey Soc lectr, 73. *Honors & Awards:* Roche Award, Roche Inst, 57; Award, Alfred P Sloan Found, 62; Lucy Wortham James Award, James Ewing Soc, 70. *Mem:* Inst of Med of Nat Acad Sci; AAAS; Am Asn Cancer Res; Soc Exp Biol & Med; Am Asn Immunol. *Res:* Tumor immunobiology; immunogenetics; viral oncology. *Mailing Add:* Sloan-Kettering Inst Cancer Res 1275 York Ave New York NY 10021

OLD, THOMAS EUGENE, b Spokane, Wash, Aug 2, 43; m 63; c 1. ATMOSPHERIC PHYSICS. *Educ:* Gonzaga Univ, BS, 66; Univ Idaho, MS, 69; State Univ NY Albany, PhD(physics), 71. *Prof Exp:* Res assoc physics, State Univ NY Albany, 71-72; TECH STAFF ATMOSPHERIC PHYSICS, MISSION RES CORP, 72- *Mem:* Am Geophys Union. *Res:* Atmospheric nuclear effects; magnetohydrodynamics. *Mailing Add:* Mission Res Corp PO Drawer 719 Santa Barbara CA 93101

OLDALE, ROBERT NICHOLAS, b North Attleboro, Mass. GEOLOGY. *Educ:* St Lawrence Univ, BS, 53. *Prof Exp:* GEOLOGIST, US GEOL SURV, 55- *Mem:* Fel Geol Soc Am; Am Quaternary Asn. *Res:* Glacial and marine geology, with emphasis on the advance and retreat of the late Wisconsin ice and the postglacial marine transgression in the northeastern United States. *Mailing Add:* US Geol Surv Woods Hole MA 02543

OLDEMEYER, DONALD LEROY, b Brush, Colo, Nov 7, 24; m 48; c 3. PLANT BREEDING. *Educ:* Colo Agr & Mech Col, BS, 48; Pa State Univ, PhD(agron), 52. *Prof Exp:* Asst agronomist, State Col Wash, 52-54; plant breeder, 54-69, mgr agr res, 69-72, MGR SEED PROD & DEVELOP, AMALGAMATED SUGAR CO, 72- *Mem:* Am Soc Agron; Am Soc Sugar Beet Technologists. *Res:* Variety improvement and seed production of sugarbeets. *Mailing Add:* 109 N Sixth St Nyssa OR 97913

OLDEMEYER, JOHN LEE, b Ft Collins, Colo, Mar 12, 41; m 63; c 3. UNGULATE HABITAT ECOLOGY. *Educ:* Colo State Univ, BS, 63, MS, 66; Pa State Univ, PhD(forest resources), 81. *Prof Exp:* Biometrician, 66-71, MEM STAFF, DENVER WILDLIFE RES CTR, US FISH & WILDLIFE SERV, 71- *Concurrent Pos:* Affil fac, Colo State Univ, 79- *Mem:* Biomet Soc; Wildlife Soc; Soc Range Mgt. *Res:* Effects of forest and range management on wildlife and their habitat; dealing with ungulate habitat on National Wildlife Refuges. *Mailing Add:* Denver Wildlife Res Ctr US Fish & Wildlife Serv 1300 Blue Spruce Dr Ft Collins CO 80524

OLDEMEYER, ROBERT KING, b Brush, Colo, Sept 23, 22; m 44; c 2. PLANT BREEDING, AGRONOMY. *Educ:* Colo State Univ, BS, 47; Univ Wis, MS, 48, PhD(genetics), 50. *Prof Exp:* Plant breeder, 50-60, dir seed develop, 60-68, agr res, 68-71, mgr seed processing & prod, 71-73, MGR VARIETY DEVELOP, GREAT WESTERN SUGAR CO, 73- *Concurrent Pos:* Staff affil, Colo State Univ, 73- *Mem:* Am Soc Agron; Am Soc Sugar Beet Technologists; Am Inst Biol Sci; Int Inst Beet Sugar Res. *Res:* Breeding of sugar beets, dry beans and vegetables; sugar beet diseases. *Mailing Add:* Great Western Sugar Co 11939 Sugarmill Rd Longmont CO 80501

OLDENBURG, C(HARLES) C(LIFFORD), b Blue Island, Ill, Feb 1, 29; m 53; c 3. CHEMICAL ENGINEERING. *Educ:* Ill Inst Technol, BS, 50; Purdue Univ, MS, 51; Univ Tex, PhD(chem eng), 57. *Prof Exp:* Res chem engr, Jefferson Chem Co, 51-57; Calif Res Co, 57-64; sect head, Stauffer Chem Co, 64-65; sr res assoc, Chevron Res Co, 65-70, MEM TECH STAFF, STANDARD OIL CO CALIF, 70- *Mem:* Am Chem Soc; Am Inst Chem Engrs. *Res:* Catalysis; kinetics; dialysis; crystallization. *Mailing Add:* Standard Oil Co of Calif PO Box 3495 San Francisco CA 94119

OLDENBURG, DOUGLAS WILLIAM, b Edmonton, Alta, Mar 9, 46; m 67; c 2. GEOPHYSICS. *Educ:* Univ Alta, BSc, 67, MSc, 69; Univ Calif, San Diego, PhD(earth Sci), 74. *Prof Exp:* Fel geophysics, Dept Physics, Univ Alta, 74-75, Isaac W Killam fel, 75-76, res assoc, 76-77; asst prof, 77-81, ASSOC PROF DEPT GEOPHYS & ASTRON, UNIV BC, 81- *Concurrent Pos:* Assoc ed, Geophys J, Royal Astron Soc, 79-81. *Honors & Awards:* Ekhart Prize, Scripps Inst Oceanog, 75. *Mem:* Royal Astron Soc; Soc Explor Geophysicists. *Res:* Application of inversion theory to geophysics. *Mailing Add:* Dept Geophys & Astron Univ BC Vancouver BC V6T 1W5 Can

OLDENBURG, THEODORE RICHARD, b Muskegon, Mich, Apr 8, 32; m 59; c 2. PEDODONTICS. *Educ:* Univ NC, DDS, 57, MS, 62. *Prof Exp:* From asst prof to assoc prof dent, 62-69, PROF PEDODONT & CHMN DEPT, SCH DENT, UNIV NC, CHAPEL HILL, 69- *Concurrent Pos:* United Cerebral Palsy clin fel, 60-62; mem USAF sr dent prog, 56-57; consult accreditation comt, Am Dent Asn, 67-77, coun dent educ & US Army Dent Corps; examr, Am Bd Pedodont, 72-79. *Mem:* Am Dent Asn; Am Acad Pedodont (pres, 79-80); Am Soc Dent for Children; Int Asn Dent Res. *Res:* Educational research in clinical restorative pedodontics. *Mailing Add:* Dept Pedodont Univ NC Chapel Hill NC 27515

OLDENDORF, WILLIAM HENRY, b Schenectady, NY, Mar 27, 25; m 45; c 3. NEUROLOGY, PSYCHIATRY. *Educ:* Albany Med Col, MD, 47; Am Bd Psychiat & Neurol, dipl, cert psychiat, 53, cert neurol, 55. *Prof Exp:* Intern med, Ellis Hosp, Schenectady, NY, 47-48; resident psychiat, Binghamton State Hosp, 48-50 & Letchworth Village State Sch, Thiells, 50-52; resident neurol, Univ Minn Hosps, Minneapolis, 54-55; assoc chief neurol, 55-69, med investr, Wadsworth Hosp, 69-75, SR MED INVESTR, BRENTWOOD HOSP, VET ADMIN CTR, 75-; PROF NEUROL, SCH MED, UNIV CALIF, LOS ANGELES, 70-, PROF PSYCHIAT, 76- *Concurrent Pos:* Clin fel, Univ Minn, Minneapolis, 55; from clin instr to asst clin prof, Sch Med, Univ Calif, Los Angeles, 56-65, assoc prof, 65-70, USPHS res grants, 59-82; NIH spec fel physiol, Univ Col, Univ London, 65-66; mem coun stroke, Am Heart Asn, 69. *Honors & Awards:* Silver Medal Award, Soc Nuclear Med, 69; Ziedses des Plantes Gold Medal, Med Physics Soc, Würzburg, 74. *Mem:* Soc Nuclear Med; fel Am Acad Neurol; fel Am Acad Arts & Sci; AMA; fel Am Neurol Asn. *Res:* Nuclear medicine applied in clinical neurological research, including studies related to human brain isotope uptake studies, cerebral blood flow in man, cerebrospinal fluid, central nervous system instrumentation and development of photographic techniques relating to brain isotope scanning and cerebral angiography in man. *Mailing Add:* Wadsworth Hosp Vet Admin Ctr Los Angeles CA 90073

OLDENKAMP, RICHARD D(OUGLAS), b Conrad, Mont, Aug 23, 31; m 53; c 5. CHEMICAL ENGINEERING. *Educ:* Mont State Col, BS, 56; Univ Pittsburgh, MS, 59, PhD(chem eng), 62. *Prof Exp:* Engr, Bettis Atomic Power Lab, Westinghouse Elec Corp, 56-63; res specialist, Atomics Int Div, 63-67, proj engr, 67-71, proj mgr, 71-75, prog mgr, 75-78, DIR APPLN & PRELIMINARY ENG, ENVIRON & ENERGY SYSTS DIV, ENERGY SYSTS GROUP, ROCKWELL INT CORP, 78- *Mem:* Am Chem Soc; Sigma Xi. *Res:* Air pollution control process development. *Mailing Add:* Environ & Energy Systs Div 8900 DeSoto Ave Canoga Park CA 91304

OLDERMAN, GERALD M, physical chemistry, see previous edition

OLDFIELD, DANIEL G, b New York, NY, July 24, 25; m 50; c 2. CELL BIOLOGY, BIOPHYSICS. *Educ:* Columbia Univ, BS, 50; Univ Chicago, MS, 58, PhD(math biol), 65. *Prof Exp:* Jr scientist, Argonne Cancer Res Hosp, Univ Chicago, 53-55, assoc scientist, 55-62, sr biophysicist, Univ Chicago, Toxicity Lab, 62-64, asst prof, Lab Cytol, 65-68; asst prof, 68-70, ASSOC PROF BIOL SCI, DEPAUL UNIV, 70- *Mem:* Histochem Soc; Am Phys Soc; Radiation Res Soc; Soc Math Biol; Int Soc Stereology. *Res:* Analysis of cell cycle and organelle interactions by cytofluorometry; cytopathology. *Mailing Add:* Dept of Biol Sci DePaul Univ 1036 WBelden Ave Chicago IL 60614

OLDFIELD, ERIC, b London, Eng, May 23, 48. MOLECULAR BIOLOGY, BIOPHYSICAL CHEMISTRY. *Educ:* Bristol Univ, BS, 69; Sheffield Univ, PhD(chem), 72. *Prof Exp:* Europ Molecular Biol Org fel chem, Ind Univ, 72-74; vis scientist, Mass Inst Technol, 74-75; asst prof, 75-80, ASSOC PROF CHEM, UNIV ILL, URBANA, 80- *Concurrent Pos:* Dir, NSF Regional Instrumentation Fac, Nuclear Magnetic Reconane Spectroscopy. *Honors & Awards:* Meldola Medal, Royal Inst Chem. *Mem:* Fel Royal Soc Chem. *Res:* Nuclear magnetic resonance spectroscopy; biological membrane structure; lipid-protein interactions; catalyst structure. *Mailing Add:* 76 Noyes Lab Sch of Chem Sci Univ of Ill Urbana IL 61801

OLDFIELD, GEORGE NEWTON, b San Jose, Calif, Sept 6, 36; m 59; c 3. ENTOMOLOGY, ACAROLOGY. *Educ:* Fresno State Col, BA, 62; Univ Calif, Riverside, MS, 66, PhD(entom), 71. *Prof Exp:* Agr res technician, 62-65, entomologist, 65-68, RES ENTOMOLOGIST, SCI & EDUC ADMIN-AGR RES, USDA, 68- *Mem:* Am Phytopath Soc; Entom Soc Am; Acarological Soc Am; Sigma Xi. *Res:* Arthropod vectors of fruit tree pathogens; reproductive biology and virus vector capabilities of Eriophyoidea. *Mailing Add:* Boyden Entom Lab USDA Univ of Calif Riverside CA 92521

OLDFIELD, JAMES EDMUND, b Victoria, BC, Aug 30, 21; nat US; m 42; c 5. ANIMAL NUTRITION. *Educ:* Univ BC, BS, 41, MS, 49; Ore State Col, PhD(animal nutrit, biochem), 51. *Prof Exp:* Instr animal husb, Univ BC, 48-49; from asst prof to assoc prof, 51-59, PROF ANIMAL NUTRIT, ORE STATE UNIV, 59-, HEAD DEPT ANIMAL SCI, 67- *Concurrent Pos:* Basic res award, Ore Agr Exp Sta, 61, Sigma Xi res award, Ore State Univ, 64; res travel award, Nat Feed Ingredients Asn, 69; Fulbright scholar, Massey Univ, NZ, 74, Rosenfeld distinguished prof agr sci, 81. *Honors & Awards:* Morrison Award, Am Soc Animal Sci, 72, Distinguished Serv Award, 74. *Mem:* Am Chem Soc; Am Inst Nutrit; hon fel Am Soc Animal Sci (secy-treas, 62-65, vpres, 65, pres, 66); NY Acad Sci; Agr Inst Can. *Res:* Vitamins, minerals, and antibiotics as feed supplements in animal nutrition; nutritional diseases; metabolic diseases; alternate feed sources; relative efficiencies of domestic animal species as human food producers. *Mailing Add:* Dept Animal Sci Ore State Univ Corvallis OR 97331

OLDFIELD, THOMAS EDWARD, b Fond du Lac, Wis, Oct 11, 47; m 70; c 2. PHYSIOLOGICAL ECOLOGY. *Educ:* Mich Technol Univ, BS, 70; Utah State Univ, MS, 73, PhD(physiol), 75. *Prof Exp:* Asst prof physiol, Ferris State Col, 75-76; asst prof physiol, Millikin Univ, 76-78; ASST PROF PHYSIOL, FERRIS STATE COL, 78- *Concurrent Pos:* Sigma Xi res grant, 74. *Mem:* AAAS; Am Soc Zoologists; Sigma Xi. *Res:* Development of reliable methods to be used in the determination of energy utilization of free-living animals. *Mailing Add:* Dept of Biol Sci Ferris State Col Big Rapids MI 49307

OLDFIELD, WILLIAM, b Manchester, Eng, Dec 10, 31; m 57; c 3. MATERIALS SCIENCE, METALLURGY. *Educ:* Univ Manchester, BSc, 54, MSc, 61; Stanford Univ, PhD(mat sci), 69. *Prof Exp:* Sr sci officer, Brit Cast Iron Res Asn, 56-61; prin sci officer, UK Atomic Energy Authority, 61-64; metallurgist, Tech Ctr, Owens-Ill, Inc, 64-65; res assoc solidification, Stanford Univ, 65-68; fel mat res, Columbus Labs, Battelle Mem Inst, 68-69; proj mgr, Res & Develop Lab, Wiltron Co, 69-70; PRES, MAT RES & COMPUT SIMULATION CORP, 70- *Honors & Awards:* Grossman Award, Am Soc Metals, 66. *Mem:* Am Soc Metals; Am Soc Testing & Mat; Sigma Xi. *Res:* Solidification and crystal growth; computer applications in materials research; nuclear fuel materials; nuclear pressure vessel steels; hydrogen damage in pressure vessels; statistics of materials behaviour. *Mailing Add:* 4561 Camino Molinero Santa Barbara CA 93110

OLDHAM, BILL WAYNE, b Paris, Tex, Oct 30, 34; m; c 3. MATHEMATICS. *Educ:* Abilene Christian Univ, BA, 56; Okla State Univ, MS, 63; Univ Northern Colo, EdD(math educ), 72. *Prof Exp:* Teacher math, Ft Sumner Sch, NMex, 56-59; teacher sci, Yale City Sch, Okla, 60-61; PROF MATH, HARDING COL, 61- *Mem:* Nat Coun Teachers Math; Am Math Soc. *Res:* Mathematics learning theory; mathematics applications in business and industry. *Mailing Add:* Dept of Math Harding Col Searcy AL 72143

OLDHAM, KEITH BENTLEY, b Ashton-under-Lyne, Eng, Feb 4, 29; m 53; c 5. ELECTROCHEMISTRY, PHYSICAL CHEMISTRY. *Educ:* Univ Manchester, BSc, 49, PhD(phys chem), 52, DSc, 70. *Prof Exp:* Res assoc anal chem, Univ Ill, Urbana, 52-55; vis scientist, Rensselaer Polytech Inst, 55; asst lectr phys chem, Imp Col, Univ London, 55-57; lectr chem, Univ Newcastle, 57-64; vis assoc anal chem, Calif Inst Technol, 64-65; lectr chem, Univ Newcastle, 65-66; mem tech staff, Sci Ctr, NAm Rockwell Corp, Calif, 66-70; chmn dept, 72-79, PROF CHEM, TRENT UNIV, 70- *Concurrent Pos:* Consult, Consumers' Asn, 56-66; mem schs exam bd, Univ Durham, 58-64; mem, Int Comt Electrochem Thermodyn & Kinetics, 61-; consult, Royal Aircraft Estab, 63-66; vis scientist, Sci Ctr, NAm Aviation, Inc, 64-65; fac mem, Calif Lutheran Col, 67-69; div ed, J Electrochem Soc, 78-81; mem, Chem Grant Selection Comt, Nat Sci & Eng Res Coun Can, 78-81; adj prof, Queen's Univ, 80-; vis prof, Deakin Univ, Australia, 81-82. *Mem:* Electrochem Soc; Royal Inst Chem; Chem Inst Can. *Res:* Transport processes; various aspects of physical and analytical chemistry; practical and theoretical aspects of electrochemistry; applied mathematics-properties of functions, fractional calculus. *Mailing Add:* Dept Chem Trent Univ Peterborough ON K9J 7B8 Can

OLDHAM, ROBERT KENNETH, b Pocatello, Idaho, Sept 16, 41; c 5. INTERNAL MEDICINE, MEDICAL ONCOLOGY. *Educ:* Univ Mo, BS, 64, MD, 68. *Prof Exp:* Clin assoc radiation, Nat Cancer Inst, 70-71, clin assoc immunol, 71-72; res assoc, ICIG-Hosp Paul Brousse, Villejuif, France, 72-73; sr invest immunodiag, Nat Cancer Inst, 73-75; DIR DIV ONCOL & ASSOC DIR CANCER RES CTR, VANDERBILT UNIV HOSP, 75- *Mem:* Am Asn Cancer Res; Am Fedn Clin Res; Am Soc Clin Oncol; fel Am Col Physicians. *Res:* In vitro assays in tumor immunology; stimulation of immunoreactivity of host defense systems with adjuvants; culture of human tumors in vitro. *Mailing Add:* Div of Oncol Dept of Med Vanderbilt Univ Med Ctr Nashville TN 37232

OLDHAM, SUSAN BANKS, b San Francisco, Calif, Aug 6, 42. ENDOCRINOLOGY. *Educ:* Univ Calif, Los Angeles, BS, 64; Univ Southern Calif, PhD(biochem), 68. *Prof Exp:* Fel endocrine res, Mayo Clin, 68-72; res assoc endocrinol, 72-73, ASST PROF MED & BIOCHEM, SCH MED, UNIV SOUTHERN CALIF, 73- *Mem:* Am Soc Bone & Mineral Res; Endocrine Soc; Am Fedn Clin Res; Sigma Xi; AAAS. *Res:* The regulation of the parathyroid gland and the metabolism of parathyroid hormone; the role of calcium-binding proteins in tissue metabolism; the mechanisms by which hypomagnesemia causes hypocalcemia; the regulation of vitamin D metabolism; causes of hypercalcemia in cancer. *Mailing Add:* Sch of Med Univ of Southern Calif 2025 Zonal Ave Hoffman Bldg Los Angeles CA 90033

OLDHAM, WILLIAM G, b Detroit, Mich, May 5, 38; m 60. ELECTRICAL ENGINEERING. *Educ:* Carnegie Inst Technol, BS, 60, MS, 61, PhD(elec eng), 63. *Prof Exp:* Mem staff physics, Siemens-Schuckertwerke, Erlangen, Ger, 63-64; asst prof elec eng, 64-76, PROF ELEC ENG, UNIV CALIF, BERKELEY, 76- *Mem:* Am Phys Soc; Electrochem Soc; fel Inst Elec & Electronics Engrs. *Res:* Semiconductor electronics; electrical properties of III-V compounds. *Mailing Add:* Dept of Elec Eng Univ of Calif Berkeley CA 94720

OLDS, CARL DOUGLAS, mathematics, deceased

OLDS, DANIEL WAYNE, b Richland Co, Ill, Mar 27, 35; m 60; c 2. PHYSICS. *Educ:* Wabash Col, AB, 56; Duke Univ, PhD, 64. *Prof Exp:* Asst prof, 63-66, actg chmn dept, 63-71, assoc prof, 66-76, mgr comput terminal, 68-75, dir, Acad Comput Ctr, 75-80, PROF PHYSICS, WOFFORD COL, 76-, CHMN DEPT, 71-, DIR, COMPUT SERV, 80- *Mem:* Am Asn Physics Teachers. *Mailing Add:* Dept Physics Wofford Col Spartanburg SC 29301

OLDS, DURWARD, b Conneaut, Ohio, Apr 12, 21; m 47; c 2. DAIRY SCIENCE, VETERINARY MEDICINE. *Educ:* Ohio State Univ, DVM, 43; Univ Ill, MS, 54, PhD(dairy sci), 56. *Prof Exp:* Artificial insemination technician, Clark County Breeder's Coop, Wis, 44-46; asst dairying, 46-51, assoc prof, 51-56, PROF DAIRYING, UNIV KY, 56- *Mem:* Am Soc Animal Sci; Am Dairy Sci Asn; Am Vet Med Asn; Soc Stud Reprod. *Res:* Physiology of reproduction; artificial insemination; causes of infertility in dairy cattle. *Mailing Add:* Dept of Animal Sci Univ of Ky Lexington KY 40506

OLDS, GRANVILLE M(ORRISON), b Galena, Kans, Aug 6, 22; m 47; c 4. CHEMICAL ENGINEERING. *Educ:* Univ Okla, BChE, 50, MChE, 51. *Prof Exp:* Opers supvr, Hanford Reactor Oper, Gen Elec Co, 51-56; sr serv engr, Boiler Div, Southwest Serv Dist, Atomic Energy Div, 57, guest scientist, LMFRE Proj, Brookhaven Nat Lab, 57-59, opers supvr, NS Savannah Proj, 59-63, mgr eng, 63-67, proj mgr, Nuclear Power Generation Dept, Boiler Div, 67-71, sr proj mgr, Power Generation Div, Nuclear Power Generation Dept, 71-74, mgr, Nuclear Serv Dept, 75-79, mgr field serv & eng, 79-81, MGR CUSTOMER SERV, BABCOCK & WILCOX CO, 82- *Res:* Application of nuclear energy to ship propulsion and electrical generation, particularly field and conceptual engineering, safeguards, licensing and fuel management. *Mailing Add:* Res Ctr Babcock & Wilcox Co PO Box 1260 Lynchburg VA 24501

OLDS-CLARKE, PATRICIA JEAN, b Waseca, Minn, Aug 15, 43; m 75. ANDROGENETICS, DEVELOPMENTAL BIOLOGY. *Educ:* Macalester Col, BA, 65; Wash Univ, PhD(biol), 70. *Prof Exp:* Fel, Johns Hopkins Univ, 70-71; res fel, Harvard Med Sch, 71-72, res assoc anat, 72-73, instr, 73-74; asst prof biol, Bryn Mawr Col, 74-80; ASST PROF ANAT, SCH MED, TEMPLE UNIV, 80- *Mem:* AAAS; Am Soc Cell Biol; Soc Develop Biol; Soc Study Reprod; Sigma Xi. *Res:* Analysis of fertile and sterile sperm with abnormal motility and surface characteristics, from mice with one or two T haplotypes. *Mailing Add:* Dept Anat Sch Med Temple Univ 3420 N Broad St Philadelphia PA 19140

OLDSHUE, J(AMES) Y(OUNG), b Chicago, Ill, Apr 18, 25; m 47; c 3. CHEMICAL ENGINEERING. *Educ:* Ill Inst Technol, BS, 47, MS, 49, PhD, 51. *Prof Exp:* Chem engr, Los Alamos Sci Lab, 45-46; head develop eng, 50-54, dir res, 54-64, tech dir, 64-71, V PRES MIXING TECHNOL, MIXING EQUIP CO, INC, 71- *Concurrent Pos:* Lectr, Univ Rochester, 54 & 57; continuing educ lectr, Am Inst Chem Engrs & for Prof Advan. *Mem:* Nat Acad Eng; Am Inst Chem Engrs (pres, 79-); Am Chem Soc. *Res:* Fluid mixing; author or coauthor of over 100 publications. *Mailing Add:* 141 Tyringham Rd Rochester NY 14617

OLDSTONE, MICHAEL BEAUREGUARD ALAN, b New York, NY, Feb 9, 34; m 60; c 3. EXPERIMENTAL BIOLOGY, NEUROBIOLOGY. *Educ:* Univ Ala, BS, 54; Univ Md, MD, 61. *Prof Exp:* USPHS fel rickettsiol & virol, Sch Med, Univ Md, 58, intern med, Univ Hosp, 61, resident, 62-63, resident neurol, 63-64, chief resident, 64-66; fel, Dept Exp Path, 66-69, assoc, 69-71, ASSOC MEM, DEPT IMMUNOPATH & DIV NEUROL, SCRIPPS CLIN & RES FOUND, 71-, HEAD NEUROL RES, FOUND, 69- *Concurrent Pos:* NIH-AID career develop award, 69; adj prof path, Univ Calif, San Diego, 71- & adj prof neurosci, 72-; mem ad hoc sci adv comt, Multiple Sclerosis. *Mem:* Am Acad Neurol; Am Asn Immunol; Am Asn Neuropath; Am Soc Exp Path; Am Soc Microbiol. *Res:* Viral immunopathology; viruses and immunity. *Mailing Add:* Dept of Immunopath Scripps Clin & Res Found La Jolla CA 92037

O'LEARY, BRIAN TODD, b Boston, Mass, Jan 27, 40; m 64; c 2. ASTRONOMY. *Educ:* Williams Col, BA, 61; Georgetown Univ, MA, 64; Univ Calif, Berkeley, PhD(astron), 67. *Prof Exp:* Physicist, Goddard Space Flight Ctr, NASA, 61-62; high sch teacher, Washington, DC, 64; scientist-astronaut, Manned Spacecraft Ctr, NASA, 67-68; asst prof astron & space sci, Cornell Univ, 68-71; vis assoc, Calif Inst Technol, 71; assoc prof interdisciplinary sci, San Francisco State Univ, 71-72; asst prof astron & sci policy assessment, Hampshire Col, 72-75; spec consult on energy, Subcomt on Energy & Environ, US House Interior Comt, 75; res fac mem & lectr, Physics Dept, Princeton Univ, 75-80; WRITER & LECTR, 80- *Concurrent Pos:* Consult, NASA Ames Res Ctr, 71-72; vis assoc prof, Sch Law, Univ Calif, Berkeley, 72; lectr astron, Univ Pa, 78-80. *Mem:* Fel AAAS; Am Astron Soc; Am Geophys Union. *Res:* Technology assessment. *Mailing Add:* 31272 Flying Cloud Dr Laguna Niguel CA 92677

O'LEARY, DENNIS PATRICK, b Dec 24, 39; US citizen; m 64; c 2. BIOPHYSICS, NEUROPHYSIOLOGY. *Educ:* Univ Chicago, SB, 62; Univ Iowa, PhD(physiol, biophys), 69. *Prof Exp:* Asst prof surg & anat, Univ Calif, Los Angeles, 71-74; res assoc prof otolaryngol & pharmacol, ASSOC PROF OTOLARYNGOL & PHYSIOL, 74-78, UNIV PITTSBURGH, 78- *Concurrent Pos:* USPHS res fel, Univ Calif, Los Angeles, 69-70. *Mem:* Am Physiol Soc; AAAS; Biophys Soc; Soc Neurosci; Int Brain Res Orgn. *Res:* Biophysical mechanisms of sensory transduction; stability and control in the vestibular system; applications of time series analysis, stochastic processes and filtering theory to investigations of neuronal information processing. *Mailing Add:* Dept of Otolaryngol Univ of Pittsburgh Pittsburgh PA 15213

O'LEARY, GERARD PAUL, JR, b Bridgeport, Conn, Oct 16, 40. MICROBIOLOGY, BIOCHEMISTRY. *Educ:* Mt St Mary's Col, Md, BS, 62; NMex State Univ, MS, 64; Univ NH, PhD(microbiol), 67. *Prof Exp:* Nat Res Coun Can fel, Macdonald Col, McGill Univ, 67-69; ASSOC PROF BIOL, PROVIDENCE COL, 69- *Mem:* AAAS; Am Soc Microbiol; Am Inst Biol Sci; Can Soc Microbiol; NAm Apiotherapy Soc. *Res:* Isolation and chemical characterization of marine bacterial lipopolysaccharides; effects of bacterial endotoxins on fresh water fish; characterization of an actomyosin-like protein complex from a procaryotic system; the effects of bee venom in adjuvant induced arthritis; high pressure liquid chromatography of steroids and venoms; elemental analysis of body fluids and tissues by DC plasma emission spectroscopy; isoelectric focusing of animal and bacterial proteins. *Mailing Add:* Dept of Biol Providence Col Providence RI 02918

O'LEARY, JAMES WILLIAM, b Painesville, Ohio, Aug 10, 38; m 63; c 3. PLANT PHYSIOLOGY. *Educ:* Ohio State Univ, BS, 60, MS, 61; Duke Univ, PhD(bot), 64. *Prof Exp:* Asst prof bot, Univ Ariz, 63-66; asst prof biol, Bowling Green State Univ, 66-67; assoc prof biol sci, Univ, 67-71, plant physiologist, Environ Res Lab, 68-74, PROF BIOL SCI, UNIV ARIZ, 71-, RES PROF BIOL SCI, ENVIRON RES LAB, 74- *Mem:* AAAS; Am Soc Plant Physiol; Am Inst Biol Sci. *Res:* Plant water relations; physiological ecology of desert plants; controlled environments; salinity effects on plants. *Mailing Add:* 2012 E Le Madera Dr Tucson AZ 85719

O'LEARY, KEVIN JOSEPH, b Winthrop, Mass, Aug 8, 32; m 54; c 5. POLYMER CHEMISTRY. *Educ:* Boston Col, BS, 55; Case Western Reserve Univ, MS, 62, PhD(eng), 67. *Prof Exp:* Anal chemist, US Army Chem Ctr, Md, 55-57; sr res chemist & anal area supvr, Diamond Alkali Res Ctr, Ohio, 57-64, res assoc, Res Ctr, Diamond Shamrock Corp, 67-69, mgr anal & electrochem res, 69-71, assoc dir res, T R Evans Res Ctr, 71-, assoc dir res electrochem/anal, 71-75, asst dir res phys sci, 75-76, dir technol, Electrolytic Systs Div, 76-78, dir corp res, T R Evans Res Ctr, 78-80; MEM STAFF, OLIN CORP, 80- *Concurrent Pos:* Vis prof, Lake Erie Col, 67-68. *Mem:* Am Phys Soc; Am Chem Soc; Soc Appl Spectros; Am Crystallog Asn; Electrochem Soc. *Res:* Polymer morphology, deformation of crystalline polymers; small and wide angle x-ray diffraction; electron microscopy; thermodynamics and analytical chemistry; electrochemistry. *Mailing Add:* Olin Corp 120 Long Ridge Rd Stamford CT 06904

O'LEARY, MARION HUGH, b Quincy, Ill, Mar 24, 41; m 81; c 3. ORGANIC CHEMISTRY, BIOCHEMISTRY. *Educ:* Univ Ill, BS, 63; Mass Inst Technol, PhD(org chem), 66. *Prof Exp:* NIH res fel biochem, Harvard Univ, 66-67; from asst prof to assoc prof, 67-78, prof chem, 78-80, PROF CHEM & BIOCHEM, UNIV WIS-MADISON, 80- *Concurrent Pos:* NIH & Res Corp res grants, 67-; Sloan Found fel, 72-74; NSF res grant; USDA res grant, 79-80. *Mem:* AAAS; Am Chem Soc; Am Soc Biol Chemists. *Res:* Mechanisms of action of enzymes; bio-organic chemistry; plant biochemistry; isotope effects. *Mailing Add:* Dept of Chem Univ of Wis Madison WI 53706

O'LEARY, W(ILLIAM) J(OSEPH), chemistry, metallurgy, deceased

O'LEARY, WILLIAM MICHAEL, microbiology, biochemistry, see previous edition

OLECHOWSKI, JEROME ROBERT, b Buffalo, NY, Jan 10, 31; m 56; c 5. PHYSICAL CHEMISTRY, ORGANIC CHEMISTRY. *Educ:* Canisius Col, BS, 52; Pa State Univ, MS, 55; La State Univ, PhD(chem), 58. *Prof Exp:* Asst chem, Pa State Univ, 52-54 & La State Univ, 54-57; res chemist, Copolymer Rubber & Chem Corp, 57-61 & Cities Serv Res & Develop Co, 61-63; prin res chemist, Columbian Carbon Co, 63-70; res assoc, Petrochem Group, Cities Serv Co, NJ, 70-77, int tech liaison, 71-77; GROUP LEADER, CHEM PROD RES, UNION CAMP CORP, 77- *Concurrent Pos:* Prof, McNeese State Col, 63. *Mem:* Am Chem Soc. *Res:* Reactions of ozone with organic substances; Ziegler-Natta type catalysts for polymerization of unsaturated substances; metal-ion olefin complexes and oxidation; rearrangement of trihaloalkenes; organometallic chemistry of transition elements; chemistry of medium ring compounds; chemistry of terpenes, rosin and other silvichemicals. *Mailing Add:* Chem Prod Res Union Camp Corp Princeton NJ 08540

OLECKNO, WILLIAM ANTON, b St Charles, Ill, Dec 16, 48; m 75. PUBLIC HEALTH. *Educ:* Ind Univ, BS, 71, PhD(health & safety educ), 80; Univ Pittsburgh, MPH, 73. *Prof Exp:* Sanitarian, DuPage County Health Dept, 70-71; sanitarian II, Ill Dept Pub Health, 72; res assoc, Consad Res Corp, 73; coordr & asst prof environ health, Ind Univ Med Sch, 73-80; COORDR & ASSOC PROF COMMUNITY HEALTH, NORTHERN ILL UNIV, 80- *Concurrent Pos:* Pub health consult, Nat Automatic Merchandising Asn, 75-80; vis lectr, Ind Univ, 77-80; ed, Hoosier Sanitarian, 79-80; tech consult, Nat Educ Comt, Nat Environ Health Asn, 81-82. *Mem:* Nat Environ Health Asn; Am Pub Health Asn. *Res:* Environmental health, primarily water quality; development of an index of the water pollution potential of sanitary landfills; impact analysis of national drinking water regulations; development of learning modules on water quality. *Mailing Add:* 310 W Alden Pl #3 DeKalb IL 60115

OLEESKY, SAMUEL S(IMON), b New York, NY, June 16, 13; m 39; c 5. ELECTRONIC ENGINEERING, PLASTICS. *Educ:* Univ Iowa, BSEE, 35. *Prof Exp:* Sect head antennas & radomes, US Naval Air Develop Ctr, Pa, 45-51; vpres & chief scientist, Zenith Plastics Co, Calif, 51-56, chief scientist, Zenith Plastics Div, Minn Mining & Mfg Co, 56-60; electronics consult, 60-64; pres & gen mgr, Nasol Corp, 64-65; design eng specialist, Northrop Ventura, 65-66; sr engr & scientist, Missile & Space Systs Div, Douglas Aircraft Co, Calif, 66-70. *Concurrent Pos:* Consult, Stanford Res Inst, 57,

Arnold Eng Ctr, US Air Force, 62, Telecomput Corp, Calif, 62-64 & Flexible Tubing Corp, Conn, 63-64; lectr, Univ Calif, Los Angeles, 63-64; consult ed, Microwave J, 65- *Mem:* Sr mem Soc Plastics Engrs. *Res:* Radome and antenna design; reinforced plastics; ceramics; inventor multilayer broadband microwave radome. *Mailing Add:* 5438 Saloma Ave Van Nuys CA 91411

OLEINICK, NANCY LANDY, b Pittsburgh, Pa, Feb 26, 41; m 62; c 2. BIOCHEMISTRY. *Educ:* Chatham Col, BS, 62; Univ Pittsburgh, PhD(biochem), 66. *Prof Exp:* from instr to asst prof, Sch Med, 68-76, asst prof, Sch Dent, 71-76, ASSOC PROF RADIATION BIOL & BIOCHEM, SCH MED & SCH DENT, CASE WESTERN RESERVE UNIV, 76- *Concurrent Pos:* Fel biochem, Sch Med, Case Western Reserve Univ, 66-68; Nat Inst Allergy & Infectious Dis fel, 67-69; Nat Cancer Inst res grant, 73-; assoc ed, Radiation Res. *Mem:* Am Soc Biol Chemists; Am Soc Cell Biol; Radiation Res Soc. *Res:* Protein synthesis in vivo and in vitro; interrelationships between ionizing radiation, protein synthesis and the biological expressions of radiation damage; radiosensitivity of ribosomal RNA genes and transcriptionally active chromatin; mechanism of radiation-induced mitotic delay. *Mailing Add:* Wearn Res Bldg Case Western Reserve Univ Cleveland OH 44106

OLEKSIUK, LESLIE WILLIAM, engineering physics, see previous edition

OLEM, HARVEY, b Boston, Mass, Aug 23, 51; m 76. ENVIRONMENTAL ENGINEERING, CIVIL ENGINEERING. *Educ:* Tufts Univ, BS, 73; Pa State Univ, MS, 75, PhD(civil eng), 78. *Prof Exp:* Res asst environ eng, Pa State Univ, 76-78; ENVIRON ENGR, TENN VALLEY AUTH, 78- *Concurrent Pos:* Instr, Munic Training Div dept community affairs, Commonwealth Pa, 77-78. *Mem:* Water Pollution Control Fedn; Am Water Works Asn; Nat Soc Prof Engrs; Sigma Xi. *Res:* Water pollution control; water quality management; wastewater microbiology; water and wastewater disinfection; industrial wastewater treatment; acid mine drainage pollution control. *Mailing Add:* 248 401 Bldg Tenn Valley Auth Chattanooga TN 37401

OLENICK, JOHN GEORGE, b Throop, Pa, Oct 31, 35; m 59; c 5. BIOCHEMISTRY, MOLECULAR BIOLOGY. *Educ:* Univ Scranton, BS, 58; Albany Med Col, MS, 61; Univ Md, College Park, PhD(microbiol), 71. *Prof Exp:* Biochemist, Sect Kidney & Electrolyte Metab, Nat Heart Inst, 61-62; chief chem sect, Dept Cell & Media Prod, Microbiol Assocs, Inc, 62-63; biochemist, 63-71, asst chief, Dept Molecular Biol, 71-76, res biochemist, Dept Biol Che, 76-79, asst chief, 79-81, CHIEF, DEPT APPL BIOCHEM, WALTER REED ARMY INST RES, 81- *Concurrent Pos:* Consult, Bio-Medium Corp, 73-75. *Res:* Biochemistry and molecular biology of parasitic protozoa; biosynthesis of proteins and nucleic acids; membrane structure and function. *Mailing Add:* Dept of Biol Chem Walter Reed Army Inst of Res Washington DC 20012

OLENICK, RICHARD PETER, b Chicago, Ill, Dec 22, 51. WEAK INTERACTIONS, MAGNETIC COOPERATIVE PHENOMENA. *Educ:* Ill Inst Technol, BS, 73; Purdue Univ, MS, 75, PhD(physics), 79. *Prof Exp:* ASST PROF PHYSICS, UNIV DALLAS, 79- *Mem:* Am Phys Soc; Sigma Xi; NY Acad Sci. *Res:* Time reversal violation within the framework of grand unified theories; synergistic hysteresis. *Mailing Add:* Dept Physics Univ Dallas Irving TX 75061

OLER, NORMAN, b Sheffield, Eng, July 12, 29; US citizen; m 57; c 2. MATHEMATICS. *Educ:* McGill Univ, BS, 51, MS, 53, PhD(math), 57. *Prof Exp:* Asst prof math, McGill Univ, 57-60; res assoc, Columbia Univ, 60-61, asst prof, 61-63; assoc prof, 63-67, PROF MATH, UNIV PA, 67- *Concurrent Pos:* Nat Res Coun Can overseas fel, 58-59; NSF sci fac fel, 65-66. *Mem:* Am Math Soc; Can Math Soc. *Res:* Geometry of numbers with particular interest in packing and covering problems. *Mailing Add:* Dept of Math Univ of Pa Philadelphia PA 19174

OLES, KEITH FLOYD, b Seattle, Wash, June 9, 21; m 46; c 2. GEOLOGY. *Educ:* Univ Wash, BS, 43, MS, 52, PhD, 56. *Prof Exp:* Instr geol, Univ Wash, 47-52; asst prof, Washington & Lee Univ, 52-53; mem spec explor group, Union Oil Co, Calif, 53-58, dist geologist, Wyo Dist, 58-61; assoc prof, 61-72, PROF GEOL, ORE STATE UNIV, 72- *Concurrent Pos:* Mem prof develop panel, Coun Educ in Geol Sci, Am Geol Inst, 68-73, visitor, Vis Geol Sci Prog, 69-70; consult & chief party, North Slope, Alaska, Union Oil Co Calif-Gulf Oil Corp, 69; geol consult; vis prof fel, Univ Wales, 76. *Mem:* Am Asn Petrol Geologists; Am Inst Prof Geologists; Int Asn Sedimentologists. *Res:* Paleoenvironments of Cretaceous rocks of Pacific Northwest and British Columbia; stratigraphy and structure of fold belts. *Mailing Add:* 3815 NW Hayes Ave Corvallis OR 97330

OLESEN, DOUGLAS EUGENE, b Tonasket, Wash, Jan 12, 39; m 64; c 2. WATER POLLUTION. *Educ:* Univ Wash, BS, 62, MS, 63, PhD(civil eng), 72. *Prof Exp:* Res engr, Space Res Div, Boeing Aircraft Corp, 63-64; res engr, Water & Waste Mgt Sect, Water & Land Resources Dept, Pac Northwest Labs, Pac Northwest Div, Battelle Mem Inst, 67-68, mgr, 68-70, mgr, Water Resources Systs Sect, 70-71, mgr, 71-75, dep dir res, 75, dir res, 75-79, dir, Pac Northwest Div, 79, VPRES, BATTELLE MEM INST, 79- *Concurrent Pos:* Affiliate assoc prof, Univ Wash, 73-; mem, Study Adv Comt, Joint Ctr Grad Study, 79-; mem, Interagency Comt Acid Rain, Fed Interagency Task Force, 80- *Mem:* Fed Water Pollution Control Fedn. *Res:* Development of combined biological and physical/chemical processes for municipal and industrial wastewater treatment. *Mailing Add:* PO Box 999 Richland WA 99352

OLESKE, JAMES MATTHEW, b Hoboken, NJ, Mar 16, 45; m 71; c 2. MEDICINE, IMMUNOLOGY. *Educ:* Univ Detroit, BS, 67; NJ Col Med, MD, 71; Columbia Univ, MPH, 74. *Prof Exp:* Intern, Martland Hosp, 71-74; fel immunol, Emory Univ, 74-76; ASST PROF PEDIAT & PREV MED, COL MED & DENT NJ, 76-, DIR, DIV ALLERGY, IMMUNOL & INFECTIOUS DIS, DEPT PEDIAT, 81- *Concurrent Pos:* Dir immunol & attend, St Michael's Med Ctr, 76- *Mem:* Am Acad Pediat; Am Acad Allergy & Immunol; Am Pub Health Asn; Am Soc Microbiol. *Res:* Clinical human immunology; infectious diseases and allergy. *Mailing Add:* St Michael's Med Ctr 306 High St Newark NJ 07102

OLESON, NORMAN LEE, b Detroit, Mich, Aug 19, 12; m 39; c 3. PHYSICS. *Educ:* Univ Mich, BS, 35, MS, 37, PhD(physics), 40. *Prof Exp:* Asst, Univ Mich, 36-40; instr physics, US Coast Guard Acad, 40-46; res physicist, Gen Elec Co, 46-48; prof physics, Naval Postgrad Sch, 48-69; chmn dept, 69-78, PROF PHYSICS, UNIV S FLA, 78- *Concurrent Pos:* Vis prof, Queen's Univ, Belfast, 55-56 & Mass Inst Technol, 67-68; consult, Lawrence Radiation Lab, Univ Calif, 58-69. *Mem:* AAAS; Sigma Xi; fel Am Phys Soc. *Res:* Gamma ray studies of light radioactive elements; multiple scattering of fast electrons; electrical and optical studies of positive column of gas mixtures; plasmas in magnetic fields; non-linear plasma waves; plasma heating. *Mailing Add:* Dept of Physics Univ of S Fla Tampa FL 33620

OLEWINE, DONALD AUSTIN, b Harrisburg, Pa, May 4, 28; m 57; c 3. PHYSIOLOGY. *Educ:* Dickinson Col, BS, 50; Univ NC, PhD, 57. *Prof Exp:* Instr physiol, Col Med, Univ Vt, 57-58; physiologist, Geront Sect, Nat Heart Inst, Baltimore City Hosps, 58-62; asst prof biol, Bucknell Univ, 62-65; from asst prof to assoc prof, 65-71, actg head dept, 67-71, PROF BIOL, GA SOUTHERN COL, 71- *Mem:* Am Soc Zoologists; NY Acad Sci; Am Col Sports Med; Nat Sci Teachers Asn. *Res:* Endocrine, renal and exercise physiology; gerontology. *Mailing Add:* Dept of Biol Ga Southern Col Statesboro GA 30458

OLEXIA, PAUL DALE, b McKeesport, Pa, July 31, 31; m 68; c 2. MYCOLOGY, TAXONOMY. *Educ:* Wabash Col, BA, 61; State Univ NY Buffalo, MA, 65; Univ Tenn, Knoxville, PhD(bot), 68. *Prof Exp:* Vis asst prof biol, Colgate Univ, 67-68; asst prof, 68-74, ASSOC PROF BIOL, KALAMAZOO COL, 74- *Mem:* Mycol Soc Am; Int Asn Plant Taxon. *Res:* Morphological and physiological taxonomy of the basidiomycetous fungi, Clavariaceae. *Mailing Add:* Dept of Biol Kalamazoo Col Kalamazoo MI 49001

OLF, HEINZ GUNTHER, b Wetzlar, Ger, Nov 1, 34. POLYMER PHYSICS. *Educ:* Munich Tech Univ, Vordiplom, 57, Diplom, 60, Dr rer nat(physics), 69. *Prof Exp:* Physicist, Res Triangle Inst, 61-78; ASSOC PROF, DEPT WOOD & PAPER SCI, SCH FOREST RESOURCES, NC STATE UNIV, 78- *Mem:* AAAS; Am Phys Soc; Am Chem Soc; Ger Phys Soc. *Res:* Solid state physics of high polymers; application of nuclear magnetic resonance techniques, x-ray scattering, infrared and Raman spectroscopy to polymers; mechanical properties of polymers. *Mailing Add:* Dept Wood & Paper Sci NC State Univ Raleigh NC 27607

OLFE, D(ANIEL), b St Louis, Mo, Feb 4, 35; m 64; c 2. ENGINEERING SCIENCE. *Educ:* Princeton Univ, BSE, 57; Calif Inst Technol, PhD(eng sci), 60. *Prof Exp:* Assoc prof aeronaut, NY Univ, 60-64; assoc prof, 64-69, PROF ENG PHYSICS, UNIV CALIF, SAN DIEGO, 69- *Mem:* Am Inst Aeronaut & Astronaut; Am Meteorol Soc. *Res:* Gas dynamics; radiative transfer; geophysical fluid mechanics. *Mailing Add:* Dept of Appl Mech & Eng Sci Mail Code B-010 La Jolla CA 92093

OLIET, SEYMOUR, b Perth Amboy, NJ, July 12, 27; m 49; c 2. DENTISTRY. *Educ:* Univ Pa, DDS, 53; Am Bd Endodontics, dipl, 65. *Prof Exp:* Instr oral med, 53-56, assoc, 56-61, from asst prof to assoc prof clin oral med, 61-71, chmn dept, 71-80, PROF ENDODONT, SCH DENT, UNIV PA, 71- *Concurrent Pos:* Clin asst, Southern Div, Albert Einstein Med Ctr, 53-55, chief endodontics, 55-, adj, 55-60, sr attend, 60-; consult endodontics, US Army, Ft Dix, NJ, 61 & Vet Admin Hosp, Philadelphia, Pa, 67-; dir & pres, Am Bd Endodont. *Honors & Awards:* Am Acad Dent Med Award, 53. *Mem:* Fel AAAS; Am Dent Asn; Int Asn Dent Res; Am Acad Dent Med; hon mem Brazilian Endodontic Asn. *Res:* Use of salt and glass beads for rapid resterilization of root canal instruments and armamentarium; development of a torsional tester for root canal instruments and detailed studies on physical properties of root canal instruments; Gutia Percha; clinical research on one-visit endodontics. *Mailing Add:* 625 Medical Arts Bldg Philadelphia PA 19102

OLIGER, JOSEPH EMMERT, b Greensburg, Ind, Sept 3, 41; m 66; c 2. NUMERICAL ANALYSIS, APPLIED MATHEMATICS. *Educ:* Univ Colo, BA, 66, MA, 71; Univ Uppsala, PhD(comput sci), 73. *Prof Exp:* Prog, Nat Ctr Atmospheric Res, 65-73, mgr appl prog, 73-74; asst prof comput sci, 74-80, ASSOC PROF COMPUT SCI, STANFORD UNIV, 80- *Concurrent Pos:* Vis prof, Univ Stockholm, 71-72; vis staff mem, Los Alamos Sci Lab, 75-; consult, Lawrence Livermore Lab, 76-; ed J Numerical Anal, Soc Indust & Appl Math, 76; vis asst prof, Math Res Ctr, Univ Wis-Madison, 78-79; vis prof, Univ Paris-Sud, 79. *Mem:* Am Math Soc; Soc Indust & Appl Math; Math Asn Am. *Res:* Numerical methods for partial differential equations; computational fluid dynamics and numerical weather prediction, ordinary and partial differential equations. *Mailing Add:* Dept of Comput Sci Stanford Univ Stanford CA 94305

OLIN, ARTHUR DAVID, b New York, NY, July 5, 28; m 54; c 3. ORGANIC CHEMISTRY. *Educ:* St Peter's Col, NJ, BS, 49; Rutgers Univ, PhD(org chem), 56. *Prof Exp:* Asst chem, Rutgers Univ, 50-54; res chemist polymer chem, Nat Starch & Chem Corp, 55; res chemist org chem, Toms River Chem Corp, 56-81, SR CHEMIST, CIBA-GEIGY CORP, 81- *Concurrent Pos:* Asst res specialist, Rutgers Univ, 55-56; coadj assoc prof, Ocean County Col, 70-71. *Mem:* Am Chem Soc. *Res:* Process development and synthesis of vat and anthraquinone dyes and organic intermediates. *Mailing Add:* Ciba-Geigy Corp State Hwy 37 Toms River NJ 08753

OLIN, JACQUELINE S, b Lansford, Pa, Nov 27, 32; m 55; c 2. ORGANIC CHEMISTRY, ANALYTICAL CHEMISTRY. *Educ:* Dickinson Col, BS, 54; Harvard Univ, MA, 55. *Prof Exp:* Teaching fel chem, Univ Pa, 55-56; res chemist, NIH, 56-57; instr chem, Dickinson Col, 59-60; res chemist, Cornell

Univ, 60-61; RES CHEMIST, SMITHSONIAN INST, 62- *Concurrent Pos:* Res collabr, Brookhaven Nat Lab, 66-; guest worker, Nat Bur Standards, 68- *Mem:* Fel Int Inst Conserv Hist & Artistic Works; fel Am Inst Conver Hist & Artistic Works. *Res:* Analysis of ceramic artifacts using neutron activation analysis for determination of provenance on basis of trace element constituents, extended to glasses with special attention to medieval stained glass. *Mailing Add:* 9506 Watts Rd Great Falls VA 22066

OLIN, PHILIP, b Winnipeg, Man, Nov 21, 41; m 66. MATHEMATICAL LOGIC. *Educ:* Univ Man, BS, 63; Cornell Univ, PhD(math logic), 67. *Prof Exp:* Res assoc & lectr math, Cornell Univ, 67-69; asst prof, McGill Univ, 69-70; asst prof, 70-74, ASSOC PROF MATH, YORK UNIV, 74- *Mem:* Am Math Soc. *Res:* Model theory; recursion theory. *Mailing Add:* Dept of Math York Univ Toronto ON M3J 1P3 Can

OLIN, WILLIAM (HAROLD), b Menominee, Mich, Mar 7, 24; m 50; c 3. ORTHODONTICS. *Educ:* Marquette Univ, DDS, 47; Univ Iowa, MS, 48. *Prof Exp:* From asst prof to assoc prof, 48-64, PROF OTOLARYNGOL & MAXILLOFACIAL SURG, COL MED, UNIV IOWA, 64- *Mem:* Am Dent Asn; Am Cleft Palate Asn (past pres); Int Dent Fedn; Am Asn Orthod. *Res:* Clefts of lip and palate; growth of the facial bones in cleft lip and palate patients, orofacial deformities. *Mailing Add:* Univ of Iowa Hosps Iowa City IA 52240

OLINE, LARRY WARD, b Stafford, Kans, July 8, 37; m 59; c 3. ENGINEERING MECHANICS. *Educ:* Sterling Col, BA, 59; Univ Kans, BS, 61; Univ NMex, MS, 63; Ga Inst Technol, PhD(eng mech), 68. *Prof Exp:* Mech engr, Sandia Corp, 61-63; res asst, Ga Inst Technol, 63-67; assoc prof solid mech, 67-77, PROF ENG, UNIV S FLA, 77- *Concurrent Pos:* NSF grant strain-rate behav particulate filled epoxy, 70; NASA grnat elastic plate spallation, 71 & 72. *Mem:* Soc Exp Stress Anal. *Res:* Stress wave propagation in solids; particulate-filled composites. *Mailing Add:* Dept of Solid Mech Univ of S Fla Tampa FL 33620

OLINER, ARTHUR A(ARON), b Shanghai, China, Mar 5, 21; US citizen; m 46; c 2. MICROWAVES, ANTENNAS. *Educ:* Brooklyn Col, BA, 41; Cornell Univ, PhD(physics), 46. *Prof Exp:* Asst physics, Cornell Univ, 41-45; res assoc elec eng, 46-53, assoc prof, 53-57, head dept electrophys, 66-71, head dept elec eng & electrophys, 71-74, PROF ELECTROPHYS, 57-, & DIR, MICROWAVE RES INST, POLYTECH INST NEW YORK, 67- *Concurrent Pos:* Chmn adv panel, Nat Bur Standards, 60-64; dir, Merrimac Industs, NJ, 61-; tech consult to indust, Inst Premium, Brit Inst Elec Engrs, 63; Guggenheim fel, 65-66; vis res scholar, Tokyo Inst Technol, Japan, 78; vis prof, Cent China Inst Technol, Wuhan, China, 80. *Honors & Awards:* Microwave Prize, Inst Elec & Electronics Engrs, 67; Sigma Xi Citation for Distinguished Res, 74. *Mem:* Fel AAAS; fel British Inst Elec & Electronics Engrs; hon mem Inst Elec & Electronics Engrs; Int Union Radio Sci; Optical Soc Am. *Res:* Microwave theory and techniques; surface and leaky wave antennas; phased array antennas; periodic structures; plasmas; microwave networks and structures; electromagnetic radiation and diffraction; microwave acoustics; integrated optics. *Mailing Add:* Dept of Elec Eng & Electrophys Polytech Inst of New York Brooklyn NY 11201

OLINGER, BART, b Gettysburg, Pa, Feb 11, 43; m 67; c 2. HIGH PRESSURE PHYSICS. *Educ:* Gettysburg Col, BA, 64; Univ Chicago, MA, 66, PhD(geophys), 70. *Prof Exp:* RES STAFF SHOCK WAVE PHYSICS, LOS ALAMOS SCI LAB, 70- *Mem:* Sigma Xi. *Res:* Study of the physical properties of materials under both shock and static compression. *Mailing Add:* Los Alamos Sci Lab Group M6 Mail Stop 970 Los Alamos NM 87544

OLINICK, MICHAEL, b Detroit, Mich, May 29, 41; m 63; c 3. MATHEMATICS. *Educ:* Univ Mich, Ann Arbor, BA, 63; Univ Wis-Madison, MA, 64, PhD(math), 70. *Prof Exp:* Asst lectr math, Univ Col Nairobi, Kenya, 65-66; instr, Univ Wis-Madison, 69-70; from asst prof to assoc prof, 70-81, PROF MATH, MIDDLEBURY COL, 81- *Concurrent Pos:* Res assoc, Univ Calif, Berkeley, 75-76; vis assoc prof, San Diego State Univ, 79; vis prof, Wesleyan Univ, 81. *Mem:* Am Math Soc; Soc Indust & Appl Math; Math Asn Am; Opers Res Soc Am. *Res:* Topology of manifolds; monotone and compact mappings on euclidean spaces; mathematical modeling in social sciences. *Mailing Add:* Dept of Math Middlebury Col Middlebury VT 05753

OLINS, ADA LEVY, b Tel Aviv, Israel, Mar 5, 38; US citizen; m 61; c 2. BIOCHEMISTRY, ELECTRON MICROSCOPY. *Educ:* City Col New York, BS, 60; Radcliffe Col, MA, 62; NY Univ, PhD(biochem), 65. *Prof Exp:* Fel biochem, Dartmouth Col, 65-67; consult, Biol Div, Oak Ridge Nat Lab, Univ Tenn, 67-77, res asst prof biol, Oak Ridge Grad Sch Biomed Sci, 77-80, res assoc prof, 80-82. *Concurrent Pos:* USPHS spec fel cell biol, King's Col, Univ London, 70-71; res assoc, Oak Ridge Grad Sch Biomed Sci, Univ Tenn, 72-75, res assoc & lectr, 75-77; NSF res grant, 76-81; vis prof, German Cancer Res Ctr, Heidelberg, 79-80; res grant, Am Cancer Soc, 81-83. *Mem:* Am Soc Cell Biologists; Biophys Soc. *Res:* DNA-protein interaction; chromosomal organization; nuclear ultrastructure; 3-dimensional image reconstruction. *Mailing Add:* Biol Div PO Box Y Oak Ridge TN 37830

OLINS, DONALD EDWARD, b New York, NY, Jan 11, 37; m 61; c 2. BIOCHEMISTRY. *Educ:* Univ Rochester, AB, 58; Rockefeller Univ, PhD(biochem), 64. *Prof Exp:* Instr microbiol, Dartmouth Med Sch, 66-67, res fel moleculear biol, 64-65, Whitney fel, 65-67; from asst prof to assoc prof, 67-76, PROF, OAK RIDGE GRAD SCH BIOMED SCI, UNIV TENN, 76- *Concurrent Pos:* Vis scientist, King's Col, Univ London, 70-71 & German Cancer Res Ctr, Heidelberg, 79-80; Humboldt US sr scientist award, 79-80. *Mem:* Biophys Soc; Am Soc Biol Chem. *Res:* Chemical structure of chromosomes and DNA-nucleoproteins. *Mailing Add:* Grad Sch of Biomed Sci Oak Ridge Nat Lab Oak Ridge TN 37830

OLIPHANT, CHARLES WINFIELD, b Oklahoma City, Okla, Mar 13, 20; m 42; c 2. GEOLOGY. *Educ:* Harvard Univ, BS, 41, MA, 47, PhD(geophys), 48. *Prof Exp:* Res assoc & asst to dir, Radio Res Lab, Harvard Univ, 42-46; PRES, OLIPHANT LABS, INC, 48-; CHMN, CEJA CORP, 66- *Mem:* AAAS; Soc Explor Geophysicists; Seismol Soc Am; Opers Res Soc Am; Am Asn Petrol Geologists. *Res:* Petroleum exploration; elastic properties of rocks; stratigraphy; seismic signal processing. *Mailing Add:* CEJA Corp 4400 One Williams Ctr Tulsa OK 74172

OLIPHANT, EDWARD EUGENE, b San Francisco, Calif, May 31, 42; m 66. REPRODUCTIVE BIOLOGY, BIOLOGICAL CHEMISTRY. *Educ:* Univ Redlands, BS, 64; Calif State Col, Long Beach, MS, 66; Univ Calif, Davis, PhD(biochem), 70. *Prof Exp:* Fel biochem, Univ Calif, Davis, 70-71; fel reprod biol, Univ Pa, 71-73; asst prof, 73-79, ASSOC PROF, DEPT OBSTET & GYNEC, SCH MED, UNIV VA, 79- *Mem:* Soc Study Reprod; Am Soc Cell Biol; Am Asn Anat. *Res:* The biochemistry of sperm penetration into ova and early embryo development. *Mailing Add:* Dept Obstet & Gynec Univ Va Sch Med Charlottesville VA 22903

OLIPHANT, MALCOLM WILLIAM, b Chicago, Ill, Apr 15, 20; m 43; c 2. MATHEMATICS. *Educ:* Georgetown Univ, BS, 47; Johns Hopkins Univ, MA, 48; Cath Univ Am, PhD(math), 57. *Prof Exp:* Instr math, Johns Hopkins Univ, 47-48; mathematician, Nat Bur Standards, 48-50; prof math & chmn dept, Georgetown Univ, 49-66; dean acad affairs, 66-80, PROF MATH, HAWAII LOA COL, 66-, VPRES, RESPONSE OF HAWAII, 79- *Concurrent Pos:* Mem, Int Cong Mathematicians, Edinburgh, 58. *Mem:* AAAS; Am Math Soc; Math Asn Am. *Res:* Mathematical analysis; modern measure theory. *Mailing Add:* 1606 Ulupii St Kailua HI 96734

OLIVE, AULSEY THOMAS, b Mount Gilead, NC, May 23, 31; m 53; c 2. ENTOMOLOGY. *Educ:* Wake Forest Col, BS, 53; NC State Univ, MS, 55, PhD(entom), 61. *Prof Exp:* Asst prof, 61-66, ASSOC PROF BIOL, WAKE FOREST UNIV, 66- *Concurrent Pos:* NSF grant, 65-67. *Mem:* Entom Soc Am. *Res:* Taxonomic and biosystematic study of aphids of the eastern United States; cytogenetic approach to the species problem in the aphid genus Dactynotus Rafinesque. *Mailing Add:* Dept Biol Box 7327 Wake Forest Univ Winston-Salem NC 27109

OLIVE, DAVID WOLPH, b Weeping Water, Nebr, Nov 6, 27; m 56; c 1. ELECTRICAL ENGINEERING. *Educ:* Univ Nebr, BS, 50; Ill Inst Technol, MS, 54; Univ Wis, PhD(elec eng), 60. *Prof Exp:* Electronics engr, naval ord div, Eastman Kodak Co, NY, 51-52; power engr, switchgear div, Gen Elec Co, Pa, 54-55; instr elec eng, Univ Nebr, 55-58, asst prof, 60-63; sr engr, elec utility eng, Westinghouse Elec Corp, Pa, 63-65; assoc prof elec eng, Univ Nebr, 65-69; L F Hunt Prof elec power eng, Univ Southern Calif, 69-76; PROF ELEC ENG, UNIV NEBR, 76- *Res:* Electromechanical energy conversion; control systems; power system analysis and operations. *Mailing Add:* Dept of Elec Eng Univ of Nebr Lincoln NB 68558

OLIVE, GLORIA, b New York, NY, June 8, 23. MATHEMATICS. *Educ:* Brooklyn Col, BA, 44; Univ Wis, MA, 46; Ore State Univ, PhD(math), 63. *Prof Exp:* Asst math, Univ Wis, 44-46; instr, Univ Ariz, 46-48 & Idaho State Col, 48-50; asst, Ore State Col, 50-51; from asst prof to prof & head dept, Anderson Col, Ind, 52-68; prof, Univ Wis-Superior, 68-71; SR LECTR PURE MATH, UNIV OTAGO, NZ, 72- *Concurrent Pos:* Mathematician, US Dept Defense, 51; Wis Bd Regents res grant, Univ Wis-Superior, 70-71. *Mem:* Am Math Soc; Math Asn Am; NZ Math Soc. *Res:* Generalized powers; b-transform. *Mailing Add:* Dept of Math Univ of Otago Dunedin New Zealand

OLIVE, JOHN H, b Glenford, Ohio, Apr 16, 29; m 58; c 4. CELL PHYSIOLOGY, AQUATIC BIOLOGY. *Educ:* Ohio State Univ, BS, 53; Kent State Univ, MA, 61, PhD(biol), 64. *Prof Exp:* From assoc prof to prof biol, Ashland Col, 64-70; ASSOC PROF BIOL, UNIV AKRON, 70- *Concurrent Pos:* AEC res grant, 65- *Mem:* AAAS; Am Inst Biol Sci; Phycol Soc Am; Am Soc Limnol & Oceanog; Sigma Xi. *Res:* Phytoplankton photosynthesis; nutrition of blue-green algae. *Mailing Add:* Dept of Biol Univ of Akron Akron OH 44325

OLIVE, JOSEPH P, b Israel, Mar 14, 41; US citizen; m 65; c 1. COMMUNICATIONS SCIENCE. *Educ:* Univ Chicago, BS & MS, 64, MA & PhD(physics), 69. *Prof Exp:* MEM TECH STAFF, BELL LABS, NJ, 69- *Concurrent Pos:* Nat Endowment Arts grant, 74. *Mem:* Acoust Soc Am; Am Composers Alliance. *Res:* Production of speech and music by computers. *Mailing Add:* Bell Labs Inc 2D529 600 Mountain View Murray Hill NJ 07940

OLIVE, LINDSAY SHEPHERD, b Florence, SC, Apr 30, 17; m 42. BOTANY. *Educ:* Univ NC, AB, 38, MA, 40, PhD(bot), 42. *Prof Exp:* Lab asst bot, Univ NC, 38-42, instr, 42-44; mycologist & consult diagnostician, Emergency Plant Dis Proj, USDA, 44-45; asst prof bot, Univ Ga, 45-46; assoc prof, La State Univ, 46-49; from assoc prof to prof, Columbia Univ, 49-68; UNIV DISTINGUISHED PROF, UNIV NC, CHAPEL HILL, 68- *Concurrent Pos:* Guggenheim fel, 56. *Mem:* Fel AAAS; Mycol Soc Am (vpres, 59, pres, 66); Bot Soc Am; Torrey Bot Soc (vpres, 61, pres, 62); Soc Protozool. *Res:* Cytology, genetics, morphology and taxonomy of fungi and mycetozoans. *Mailing Add:* Dept of Bot Univ of NC Chapel Hill NC 27514

OLIVE, PEGGY LOUISE, b Montreal, Que, May 30, 48; m 74. RADIATION BIOLOGY, BIOCHEMISTRY. *Educ:* Bishop's Univ, BSc, 69; Univ Western Ont, MSc, 72; McMaster Univ, PhD(biochem), 76. *Prof Exp:* Res asst, Ont Cancer Found, 69-72 & Dept Biochem, McMaster Univ, 72-76; res assoc dept human oncol, Univ Wis, 76-77; instr, 77-78, ASST PROF ONCOL, ENVIRON HEALTH SCI, ONCOL CTR, JOHNS HOPKINS UNIV, 78- *Mem:* Biophys Soc; Radiation Res Soc; Am Asn Cancer Res; Environ Mutagen Soc. *Res:* Interactions of chemical modifiers of radiation damage with mammalian cells; correlation between biological endpoints of damage and biochemical reactivity. *Mailing Add:* Sect of Radiobiol 600 N Wolfe Baltimore MD 21205

OLIVE, WILDS WILLIAMSON, physical geology, see previous edition

OLIVER, ABE D, JR, b Castleberry, Ala, Dec 3, 25; m 50; c 2. ENTOMOLOGY, FORESTRY. *Educ:* Auburn Univ, BS, 53, MS, 54; La State Univ, PhD(entom), 63. *Prof Exp:* Asst entomologist, Miss State Univ, 54-55; asst entomologist, 55-58, from asst prof to assoc prof, 58-68, PROF ENTOM, LA STATE UNIV, BATON ROUGE, 68- *Mem:* Entom Soc Am. *Res:* Forest insect research, especially ecology and economics; floriculture insect research, especially economics and systematics; biological control of aquatic weeds with insects. *Mailing Add:* Dept of Entom Life Sci Bldg La State Univ Baton Rouge LA 70803

OLIVER, BARRY GORDON, b Winnipeg, Man, Feb 21, 42; m 64; c 2. ENVIRONMENTAL CHEMISTRY. *Educ:* Univ Man, BSc, 63, MSc, 65, PhD(phys chem), 69. *Prof Exp:* Res assoc, Rensselaer Polytech Inst, 68-69, asst prof chem, 69-70; Nat Res Coun Can fel phys chem, Inland Waters Br, Can Dept Environ, 70-72, RES SCIENTIST, CAN CENTRE INLAND WATERS, 73- *Mem:* Chem Inst Can; Spectros Soc Can. *Res:* Vibrational spectroscopy; analysis of trace metals in sediments and natural waters; water chemistry; water and wastewater treatment methods; chlorination byproducts, sources and pathways of organic pollutants in the aqueous environment. *Mailing Add:* Environ Contaminats Div Can Ctr Inland Waters Burlington ON L7R 4A6 Can

OLIVER, BENNIE F(RANK), b Monessen, Pa, Oct 19, 27; m 52; c 3. METALLURGY. *Educ:* Pa State Univ, BS, 52, MS, 54, PhD(metall, physics), 59. *Prof Exp:* Instr metall, Pa State Univ, 54-59, asst prof, 59-60; res scientist, E C Bain Lab Fundamental Res, US Steel Corp, 60-67; assoc prog dir eng mat, NSF, 67-68; PROF IN CHG METALL, UNIV TENN, KNOXVILLE, 68- *Mem:* Am Soc Metals; Am Inst Mining, Metall & Petrol Engrs. *Res:* Process metallurgy; refining; high purity materials; trace elements; solidification and crystal growth. *Mailing Add:* Dept of Chem & Metall Eng Univ of Tenn Knoxville TN 37916

OLIVER, BERNARD M(ORE), b Santa Cruz, Calif, May 27, 16; m; c 3. DESIGN ENGINEERING, RADIO ASTRONOMY. *Educ:* Stanford Univ, BA, 35; Calif Inst Technol, MS, 36, PhD(elec eng & phys), 39. *Prof Exp:* Mem tech staff, Bell Tel Labs, Inc, 39-52; dir res, 52-57, VPRES, HEWLETT-PACKARD CO, 57- *Honors & Awards:* Lamme Medal, Inst Elec & Electronics Engrs, 76. *Mem:* Nat Acad Sci; Nat Acad Eng; Am Astron Soc; Astron Soc Pac; Inst Elec & Electronics Engrs (pres, 65-66). *Res:* Electronic circuits and system design; electronic instrumentation; information theory; search for extra-terrestrial intelligence. *Mailing Add:* Hewlett-Packard Co 1501 Page Mill Rd Palo Alto CA 94304

OLIVER, CALVIN C(LEEK), b Castleberry, Ala, Apr 5, 32; m 54; c 3. MECHANICAL ENGINEERING. *Educ:* Ga Inst Technol, BME, 57, MSME, 58; Purdue Univ, PhD(mech eng), 63. *Prof Exp:* Instr thermodyn, Ga Inst Technol, 57-59, asst prof heat transfer, 59-61; asst prof fluid mech, Purdue Univ, 63-65, assoc prof heat transfer, 65-67; prof, 67-76, PROF MECH ENG & ENG SCI, UNIV FLA, 76- *Concurrent Pos:* Assoc, Ga Tech Exp Sta, 58-61; consult, Midwest Appl Sci Corp, 64- & Controlled Acoust, Inc, 71- *Mem:* Am Soc Mech Engrs; Am Soc Eng Educ. *Res:* Thermal phenomena; nuclear technology; acoustics; thermophysical properties; heat transfer; thermal radiation; hypersonic flow with chemical reactions; electric arcs. *Mailing Add:* Dept of Mech Eng Univ of Fla Gainesville FL 32601

OLIVER, CARL EDWARD, b Anniston, Ala, Feb 26, 43; m 65. MATHEMATICS. *Educ:* Univ Ala, Tuscaloosa, BS, 65, MA, 67, PhD(math), 69. *Prof Exp:* Asst prof math, US Air Force Inst Technol, 69-74, mathematician, Weapons Lab, 74-78, PROG MGR COMPUT MATH, US AIR FORCE OFF SCI RES, 78- *Concurrent Pos:* Lectr, Ohio State Univ, 70-71, Wright State Univ, 71-74, NMex Highlands Univ, 74-78, George Mason Univ, 79- *Mem:* Am Math Soc; Math Asn Am; Soc Indust & Appl Math. *Res:* Interrelations and applications of the concepts within integration theory; numerical linear algebra, especially sparse matrix theory. *Mailing Add:* 7305 Fathom Ct Burke VA 22015

OLIVER, CONSTANCE, b Whittier, Calif, Nov 23, 42. CELL BIOLOGY, CYTOCHEMISTRY. *Educ:* Northwestern Univ, BA, 64; Univ Utah, MS, 67; Univ Tex, Austin, PhD(zool), 71. *Prof Exp:* Fel, Sloan Kettering Inst, 71-72, res assoc, 72-74; staff fel, 74-76, sr staff fel, 76-79, RES BIOLOGIST, NAT INST DENT RES, 79- *Concurrent Pos:* Asst attend cytochemist path, Mem Sloan Kettering Cancer Ctr, 73-74. *Mem:* Am Soc Cell Biol; Histochem Soc; Sigma Xi. *Res:* Electron microscopy; structure and function of Golgi apparatus, GERL, and lysosomes; mechanisms of cellular secretion. *Mailing Add:* Nat Inst Dent Res Bldg 30 Rm 211 NIH Bethesda MD 20205

OLIVER, DAPHNA R, b Tel Aviv, Israel, Aug 10, 45; US & Israeli citizen; c 2. BIOLOGY. *Educ:* Bar Ilan Univ, BSc, 66; Univ Calif, Los Angeles, PhD(med microbiol), 73. *Prof Exp:* Fel biol chem, Univ Mich, Ann Arbor, 72-74, res assoc microbiol, 74-76; vis asst prof, 77-78, ASST PROF BIOL SCI, OAKLAND UNIV, 78- *Mem:* Am Soc Microbiol; AAAS; Am Asn Univ Prof; Am Soc Med Technol; Sigma Xi. *Res:* Relationship between plasmids and pathogenicity in streptococci. *Mailing Add:* Dept of Biol Sci Oakland Univ Rochester MI 48063

OLIVER, DAVID JOHN, b Marcellus, NY, Sept 13, 49; m 71; c 2. PLANT PHYSIOLOGY, BIOCHEMISTRY. *Educ:* State Univ NY, BS & BForestry, 71, MS & MF, 73; Cornell Univ, PhD(bot), 75. *Prof Exp:* Res & teaching asst plant physiol & genetics, Col Forestry, State Univ NY, 71-73; res & teaching asst plant physiol, Cornell Univ, 73-75; NSF fel, 75-76, agr scientist biochem, Conn Agr Exp Sta, 76-80; ASST PROF, UNIV IDAHO, 80- *Mem:* Am Soc Plant Physiol. *Res:* Mechanism of photosynthetic carbon dioxide fixation by green plants including electron transport, photophorylation, photorespiration and oxidative phosphorylation; also application of plant tissue culture to crop improvement. *Mailing Add:* Dept Bact & Biochem Univ Idaho Moscow ID 83843

OLIVER, DAVID W, b Fairfax Co, Va, Dec 21, 32; m 58; c 4. SOLID STATE PHYSICS, CONTROL THEORY. *Educ:* Va Polytech Inst, BS, 55, MS, 56; Mass Inst Technol, PhD(physics), 61. *Prof Exp:* Physicist, 61-73, LIAISON SCIENTIST, AIRCRAFT ENGINE BUS GROUP, GEN ELEC CO, 73-, ACTG MGR, LIAISON BR, 75-, MGR AUTOMATION & CONTROL LAB, 78-, ACTG MGR, SOLID STATE COMMUN BR, 79- *Concurrent Pos:* Consult electronics technol & mat. *Mem:* Am Phys Soc; Inst Elec & Electronics Engrs. *Res:* Microwave spectroscopy with application to chemical reaction rates for diatomic gases; acoustics at microwave frequencies and above; growth of inorganic single crystals and their characterization; ultrasonic nondestructive evaluation. *Mailing Add:* Corp Res & Develop Ctr Gen Elec Co PO Box 8 Schenectady NY 12301

OLIVER, DENIS RICHARD, b Santa Barbara, Calif, Nov 12, 41. BIOCHEMISTRY. *Educ:* Calif State Univ, Long Beach, BS, 65; Univ Iowa, PhD(zool), 71. *Prof Exp:* NSF Ctr Excellence res fel biochem, 71-72, res assoc, 72-73, instr biochem & assoc dir, 73-77, assoc, 77-80, ASSOC PROF BIOCHEM, UNIV IOWA, 80-, DIR, PHYSICIAN'S ASST PROG, 77- *Mem:* Sigma Xi; Am Soc Allied Health Prof. *Res:* Structure and organization of nucleohistone in terms of the spatial relationship between histone chromosomal proteins and DNA in chromatin and the mechanism by which newly synthesized histone is deposited. *Mailing Add:* Physician's Asst Prog Col of Med Univ of Iowa Iowa City IA 52242

OLIVER, DONALD RAYMOND, b Saskatoon, Sask, Aug 20, 30. ENTOMOLOGY, FRESHWATER BIOLOGY. *Educ:* Univ Sask, BA, 53, MA, 55; McGill Univ, PhD(limnol & entom), 61. *Prof Exp:* RES SCIENTIST ENTOM, BIOSYSTS RES INST, AGR CAN, 62- *Concurrent Pos:* Adj prof biol dept, Carleton Univ, 70- *Mem:* Entom Soc Can; fel Arctic Inst NAm. *Res:* Biosystematics of Chironomidae such as Diptera. *Mailing Add:* 10 Barnes Court Nepean ON K2H 7C2 Can

OLIVER, EARL DAVIS, b Douglas, Ariz, Aug 10, 23; m 60; c 3. CHEMICAL ENGINEERING, ECONOMICS. *Educ:* Univ Wash, BS, 44, MS, 47; Univ Wis, PhD(chem eng), 52. *Prof Exp:* Engr, Arabian Am Oil Co, 47-50 & Shell Develop Co, 52-60; assoc prof chem eng, Univ NMex, 60-65; engr, Colony Develop Co, 65-67; sr chem engr, SRI Int, 67-75, sr engr & economist, 75-80; MGR PROCESS EVALUATION, SYNTHETIC FUELS ASSOC, INC, 80- *Concurrent Pos:* Exten teacher, Univ Calif, 55-60; sr res scientist, McAllister & Assocs, 61-62; vis prof, Univ Tex, 64. *Mem:* Am Inst Chem Engrs. *Res:* Perform engineering, economic and market studies for industrial and governmental clients; write reports; plan experimental programs; develop, design and evaluate economics of processes for energy, environment and petrochemicals. *Mailing Add:* 2049 Kent Dr Los Altos CA 94022

OLIVER, EUGENE JOSEPH, b Pawtucket, RI, Jan 28, 41; m 70. MICROBIOLOGY, BIOCHEMISTRY. *Educ:* RI Col, BEd, 62; Univ Mass, PhD(microbiol), 69. *Prof Exp:* Teacher, Scituate Jr-Sr High Sch, 62-64; res assoc biochem, Univ Mass, 69-71; health scientist adminr, Nat Inst Gen Med Sci, 74-80, HEALTH SCIENTIST ADMINR, NAT INST NEUROL COMMUN DISORDRS & STROKE, NIH, 80- *Concurrent Pos:* NIH fel biochem, Nat Heart & Lung Inst, 71- *Mem:* AAAS; Am Soc Microbiol. *Res:* Enzymology of bacteria and higher organisms; carbohydrate and amino acid metabolism; molecular mechanisms of cryobiological adaptation. *Mailing Add:* Dept of Biochem Neurol Commun Disorders & Stroke Bethesda MD 20014

OLIVER, G CHARLES, b Gainesville, Fla, Sept 30, 31; m 79; c 1. CARDIOVASCULAR DISEASE. *Educ:* Harvard Univ, AB, 53; Harvard Med Sch, MD, 57; Am Bd Internal Med, dipl, 65; Am Bd Cardiovasc Dis, dipl, 70. *Prof Exp:* Chief, Cardiovasc Div, Jewish Hosp, St Louis, 71-81; from instr to prof med, 66-81, co-dir, Cardiovasc Div, 75-81, CLIN PROF MED, SCH MED, WASHINGTON UNIV, 81-; CHIEF CARDIOL, FAITH HOSP, ST LOUIS, 81- *Concurrent Pos:* Fel cardiol, Med Ctr, Stanford Univ, 60-61; USPHS fel, Guy's Hosp, London, Eng, 63-65; mem policy bd, Clin Trials Thrombolytic Agents, NIH, 73-; mem electrocardiography comt, Am Heart Asn, 74- *Mem:* AAAS; fel Am Col Cardiol; NY Acad Sci; Am Heart Asn. *Res:* Computer applications to cardiology; pharmacology of digitalis. *Mailing Add:* 4 Creekside Lane St Louis MO 63141

OLIVER, GENE LEECH, b Rockford, Ill, June 7, 29; m 55, 80; c 3. PHOTOGRAPHIC CHEMISTRY, ORGANIC CHEMISTRY. *Educ:* Beloit Col, BS, 50; Northwestern Univ, PhD, 55. *Prof Exp:* Res chemist, 54-65, res assoc, 65-74, TECH STAFF ASSOC, EASTMAN KODAK CO, 74- *Mem:* Am Chem Soc (counr, 74-); Soc Photog Scientists & Engrs; Sigma Xi. *Res:* Photographic sensitizing and image dyes; silver halide emulsion technology; organic heterocyclic chemistry; photographic patents. *Mailing Add:* Eastman Kodak Res Labs Rochester NY 14650

OLIVER, GEORGE JOSEPH, health physics, see previous edition

OLIVER, JACK ERTLE, b Massillon, Ohio, Sept 26, 23; m 64; c 2. GEOPHYSICS. *Educ:* Columbia Univ, BA, 47, MA, 50, PhD(geophys), 53. *Prof Exp:* Scientist's aide, US Naval Res Lab, 47; physicist, Air Force Cambridge Res Lab, 51; res assoc, Lamont-Doherty Geol Observ, Columbia Univ, 53-55; from instr to prof geol, Columbia Univ, 55-71; chmn, Dept Geol Sci, 71-81, IRVING PORTER CHURCH PROF ENG, CORNELL UNIV, 71- *Concurrent Pos:* Consult, President's Sci Adv Comt Panel Seismic Improv, 58-59, Air Force Tech Appln Ctr, 58-65, Advan Res Projs Agency, 59-63, US Arms Control & Disarmament Agency, 62-73, Comt Seismol & Earthquake Eng, UNESCO, 65 & AEC, 69-74; chmn dept geol, Columbia Univ, 69-71, adj prof, 71-73; mem, Comt Polar Res, Nat Acad Sci, mem Comt Seismol, 60-72, chmn, 66-70; chmn, Geodesy Comt, 75-76; mem, Sci Adv Bd, US Air Force, 60-63 & 64-69; mem, Off Sci Res Contractor's Res & Eval Panel, 61-74, chmn, 66-68; mem, Adv Comt, US Coast & Geod Surv, 62-66, Panel Solid Earth Probs, 62-; mem, Nat Comt Upper Mantle Prog, 63-71, Site Selection Comt, 65, Carnegie Inst Adv Comt Awards, Gilbert & Wood Fund, 64-68 & Geophys Res Bd, 69-70; chmn exec comt, Off Earth Sci, Nat Res

Coun, 76-79, chmn, Geol Sci Bd, Assembly Math & Appli Sci, 81-84; mem, US Geodynamics Comt, 79-82. *Honors & Awards:* Walter Bucher Medal, Am Geophys Union, 81. *Mem:* AAAS; fel Seismol Soc Am (vpres, 62-64, pres, 64-65); fel Am Geophys Union; fel Geol Soc Am. *Res:* Seismology; geotectonics. *Mailing Add:* Dept of Geol Sci Kimball Hall Cornell Univ Ithaca NY 14853

OLIVER, JACK WALLACE, b Ellettsville, Ind, Jan 6, 38; m 60; c 2. VETERINARY PHARMACOLOGY. *Educ:* Purdue Univ, BS, 60, MS, 63, DVM, 66, PhD(vet physiol), 69. *Prof Exp:* Nat Inst Arthritis & Metab Dis fel, 67-69; asst prof vet pharmacol, Sch Vet Med, Purdue Univ, 69-70; asst prof vet endocrinol & pharmacol, Col Vet Med, Tex A&M Univ, 70-71; pvt pract, Ind, 71-72; asst prof vet pharmacol, Col Vet Med, Ohio State Univ, 72-75; assoc prof, 75-81, PROF VET PHARMACOL, COL VET MED, UNIV TENN, KNOXVILLE, 81- *Mem:* Am Soc Vet Physiol & Pharmacol; Am Vet Med Asn; Asn Am Vet Med Cols; Am Col Vet Pharm & Therapeut. *Res:* Thyroid function as affected by dietary factors, infection organisms and altered physiological states; thyroid/structural tissue interrelationships; diagnostic procedures for hormones by radioimmunoassay and high performance liquid chromatography. *Mailing Add:* Dept Environ Practice Col Vet Med Univ Tenn Knoxville TN 37996

OLIVER, JAMES HENRY, JR, b Augusta, Ga, Mar 10, 31; m 57; c 2. ACAROLOGY, CYTOGENETICS. *Educ:* Ga Southern Col, BS, 52; Fla State Univ, MS, 54; Univ Kans, PhD(entom), 62. *Prof Exp:* NATO fel, Univ Melbourne, 62-63; from asst prof entom & parasitol to assoc prof entom, Univ Calif, Berkeley, 63-68; assoc prof, Univ Ga, 68-69; CALLAWAY PROF BIOL, GA SOUTHERN COL, 69- *Concurrent Pos:* Consult, US Naval Med Res Unit 3, 63-, US Agency Int Develop & Trop Med & Parasitol Study Sect, NIH, 79-83. *Mem:* AAAS; Entom Soc Am; Sigma Xi; Acarological Soc Am; Int Soc Invert Reproduction. *Res:* Cytology, genetics, reproduction and bionomics of arthropods. *Mailing Add:* Dept of Biol Ga Southern Col Statesboro GA 30458

OLIVER, JAMES RUSSELL, b Egan, La, Sept 12, 24; m 45; c 3. PHYSICAL CHEMISTRY, NUCLEAR CHEMISTRY. *Educ:* Univ Southwestern La, BS, 50; Tulane Univ, MS, 51, PhD(chem), 55. *Prof Exp:* From assoc prof to prof chem, 54-70, dir comput ctr, 60-70, dean grad sch, 61-73, PROF COMPUT SCI, UNIV SOUTHWESTERN LA, 70-, DEAN ACAD & FINANCIAL PLANNING & V PRES ADMIN AFFAIRS, 73- *Concurrent Pos:* Consult, Electro-Acid Corp & Silverloy Int Corp, Nev; asst state supt educ for mgt, res & finance, 72-73; exec dir, State Bd Educ, 73; mem data processing corrd & adv coun, State La, 78-; pres, Phoenix Comput Systs, Inc, 77-; mem bd dirs, Southwest Educ Res Lab, 78- *Mem:* AAAS; Am Chem Soc; Am Nuclear Soc; Asn Comput Mach; Soc Indust & Appl Math. *Res:* Coordination compounds; radioactive tracers; reactor fuel processing; radioactive waste disposal; reaction kinetics; radiation chemistry; digital computers; science eduation; science talent search and writing; design of computer languages. *Mailing Add:* 324 Charlotte St Lafayette LA 70506

OLIVER, JANET MARY, b Adelaide, South Australia, Nov 14, 45. CELL PHYSIOLOGY. *Educ:* Univ Adelaide, BSc, 66; Flinders Univ South Australia, BScHons, 67; Univ Alta, MSc, 69; Univ London, PhD(biochem), 72. *Prof Exp:* Asst prof physiol, 73-78, ASSOC PROF PHYSIOL & PATH, HEALTH CTR, UNIV CONN, 78- *Concurrent Pos:* Leukemia Soc Am fel, Harvard Med Sch, 72-73. *Mem:* Am Asn Path; Am Soc Cell Biol; Brit Biochem Soc. *Res:* Role of microtubules and microfilaments in regulation of cell surface functions; control of microtubule assembly in leukocytes and cultured cells; inherited and acquired defects in cytoskeleton and cell surface properties. *Mailing Add:* Dept of Physiol Univ of Conn Health Ctr Farmington CT 06032

OLIVER, JEANETTE CLEMENTS, plant anatomy, plant taxonomy, see previous edition

OLIVER, JOEL DAY, b Amarillo, Tex, Dec 27, 45; m 66; c 3. STRUCTURAL CHEMISTRY. *Educ:* WTex State Univ, BS, 68; Univ Tex, Austin, PhD(phys chem), 71. *Prof Exp:* asst prof phys chem, West Tex State Univ, 71-79; X-RAY LAB MGR, PROCTER & GAMBLE CO, 79- *Mem:* Am Chem Soc; Am Crystallog Asn; The Chem Soc. *Res:* X-ray diffraction studies of organic and organometallic compounds; laboratory automation; minicomputer applications to chemistry; variable-temperature x-ray powder diffraction studies; phase transitions. *Mailing Add:* 11967 E Elkwood Ave Cincinnati OH 45240

OLIVER, JOHN EOFF, JR, b Stephenville, Tex, June 22, 33; m 57; c 3. COMPARATIVE NEUROLOGY. *Educ:* Tex A&M Univ, DVM, 57; Auburn Univ, MS, 66; Univ Minn, St Paul, PhD(neuroanat), 69; Am Col Vet Internal Med, dipl. *Prof Exp:* Instr vet surg, Col Vet Med, Colo State Univ, 57-58; veterinarian, Houston, Tex, 60-63; res asst vet neurol, Sch Vet Med, Auburn Univ, 63-66; USPHS fel neuroanat, Col Vet Med, Univ Minn, St Paul, 66-67, spec fel, 67-68; assoc prof comp neurol, Col Vet Med, Univ Ga, 68-72; prof small animal clin & head dept, Sch Vet Sci & Med, Purdue Univ, Lafayette, 72-75; PROF SMALL ANIMAL MED & HEAD DEPT, COL VET MED, UNIV GA, 75- *Mem:* AAAS; Am Vet Med Asn; Am Vet Radiol Soc; Am Asn Vet Neurol; Am Col Vet Internal Med (vpres, 74-75, pres, 76-77). *Res:* Neural control of micturition; pathophysiology of neurogenic bladder; models of neural diseases; hydrocephalus. *Mailing Add:* Dept of Small Animal Med Col of Vet Med Univ of Ga Athens GA 30602

OLIVER, JOHN PARKER, b New Rochelle, NY, Nov 24, 39; m 63; c 3. ASTRONOMY. *Educ:* Rensselaer Polytech Inst, BS, 62; Univ Calif, Los Angeles, MA, 68, PhD(astron), 74. *Prof Exp:* Mem tech staff astron, Aerospace Corp, 65-67; asst prof, 70-76, ASSOC PROF ASTRON, UNIV FLA, 76-, DIR, ROSEMARY HILL OBSERV, 81- *Mem:* AAAS; Am Astron Soc; Int Astron Union. *Res:* Astronomical photoelectric photometry; lunar occultations of stars; eclipsing binary stars; astronomical instrumentation; spectroscopy. *Mailing Add:* Dept Astron 211 SSRB Univ of Fla Gainesville FL 32611

OLIVER, JOHN PRESTON, b Klamath Falls, Ore, Aug 7, 34; m 56; c 3. INORGANIC CHEMISTRY. *Educ:* Univ Ore, BA, 56, PhD(chem), 59. *Prof Exp:* From asst prof to assoc prof, 59-67, PROF CHEM, WAYNE STATE UNIV, 67-, CHMN DEPT, 71- *Mem:* Am Chem Soc; The Chem Soc. *Res:* Synthesis of organometallic compounds of Groups II, III and IV; alkyl-metal exchange reactions; nuclear magnetic resonance spectra of organometallic compounds. *Mailing Add:* 135 Chem Bldg Wayne State Univ Detroit MI 48202

OLIVER, KELLY HOYET, JR, b Roseboro, Ark, June 22, 23; m 47; c 3. AQUATIC BIOLOGY. *Educ:* Southern Methodist Univ, BS, 52, MS, 53; Okla State Univ, PhD(zool), 63. *Prof Exp:* Aquatic biologist, Anderson Fish Farms, 53; teacher pub schs, Ark, 53-61; from asst prof to assoc prof biol, Ark State Col, 62-64; chief biologist, Chem Biol Lab, Vitro Serv, Eglin AFB, 64-68; assoc prof, 68-73, PROF BIOL, HENDERSON STATE COL, 73-; PRES, KOCOMORO, INC, 73- *Concurrent Pos:* Res biologist, Crossett Co, 56-61; mem, Int Cong Limnol, 62; NSF vis scientist, Ark high schs, 63-64. *Mem:* AAAS; Ecol Soc Am. *Res:* Fishery management; pollution biology; effect of industrial waste, especially paper and petroleum, on aquatic organisms and bacterial ecology; ecology of Lake De Gray, Arkansas, especially change in fauna and flora and physiochemical conditions during river/lake transition; toxicity of contaminants on bluegills and annelids. *Mailing Add:* Dept of Biol Henderson State Col Arkadelphia AR 71923

OLIVER, MONTAGUE, b Antigua, BWI, Feb 24, 19; US citizen; m 52; c 4. GENETICS, PHYSIOLOGY. *Educ:* Tuskegee Inst, BS, 51, MS, 52; Purdue Univ, MSA, 54, PhD(biol), 61. *Prof Exp:* Teacher, High Sch, Ala, 54-55; res dir genetics, Gunn Bros Quail Farm, Tex, 55-56; teacher, High Sch, Ill, 56-57 & Ind, 57-62; assoc prof biol, 62-72, PROF BIOL, CALUMET COL, 72- *Concurrent Pos:* Sub-consult, Argonne Nat Lab,Ill, 65-66. *Mem:* AAAS; Am Asn Biol Teachersl Nat Sci Teachers Asn; Am Inst Biol Sci. *Res:* Heritability and selection of egg production in the fowl; relative efficiency of methods of teaching biological science; general zoology and botany. *Mailing Add:* 1111 E 19th Ave Gary IN 46407

OLIVER, MORRIS ALBERT, b Milford-Haven, Wales, Feb 12, 18; nat US; m 48; c 3. ENGINEERING STATISTICS. *Educ:* Oxford Univ, BA, 48, MA, 52. *Prof Exp:* Head sci dept, Eaglebrook Sch, Mass, 48-50; prof math, Bennington Col, 50-55; mathematician, AMP, Inc, 55-65, mgr, Precision Artwork Lab, 73-77, SR MATHEMATICIAN & MGR ENG COMPUT SERV, AMP, INC, 66- *Concurrent Pos:* Consult, AMP, Inc, 53-55; mem, Grad Fac, Pa State Univ, 58. *Mem:* Am Math Soc; NY Acad Sci; fel Royal Statist Soc; Am Statist Asn. *Res:* Statistical engineering. *Mailing Add:* Precision Artwork Lab AMP Inc Harrisburg PA 17105

OLIVER, PAUL ALFRED, b Tripoli, Libya, Feb 4, 40; US citizen; m 63. COMPUTER SCIENCE, MATHEMATICS. *Educ:* Univ Md, BS, 62; Ohio State Univ, MS, 64; Univ NC, Chapel Hill, PhD(comput sci), 69. *Prof Exp:* Mathematician, Res & Tech Div, Air Force Syst Command, 65-66; dir comput ctr, Univ NC, Chapel Hill, 68-70; sr staff scientist, Sperry-UNIVAC Div, 70-73; dir, FCCTS, US Govt, 73-79; PRES, EDS WORLD CORP,79- *Mem:* AAAS; Inst Elec & Electronics Engrs; Asn Systs Mgt; Am Mgt Asn; Asn Comput Mach. *Res:* Software engineering; systems performance and management. *Mailing Add:* 8380 Greensboro Dr # 5-401 McLean VA 22102

OLIVER, RICHARD CHARLES, b Minneapolis, Minn, Mar 16, 30; m 53; c 4. PERIODONTOLOGY. *Educ:* Univ Minn, BS, 52, DDS, 53; Loma Linda Univ, MS, 62. *Prof Exp:* From assoc prof to prof periodont, Sch Dent, Loma Linda Univ, 62-75; dean, Sch Dent, Univ Southern Calif, 75-77; DEAN, SCH DENT, UNIV MINN, 77- *Concurrent Pos:* Fulbright-Hays res scholar, Denmark, 67-68. *Mem:* Am Dent Asn; Am Acad Periodont; Int Asn Dent Res; Am Asn Dent Sch. *Res:* Vascularization following periodontal surgery; epidemiology of periodontal disease and therapy. *Mailing Add:* Sch of Dent 515 SE Delware St Minneapolis MN 55455

OLIVER, RICHARD CLARKE, mechanical engineering, aeronautical engineering, see previous edition

OLIVER, ROBERT C(ARL), b Bisbee, Ariz, Aug 20, 25; m 53; c 3. CHEMICAL ENGINEERING. *Educ:* Univ Wash, BS, 48, MS, 49; Mass Inst Technol, ScD(chem eng), 53. *Prof Exp:* Asst, Univ Wash, 47-49; asst, Mass Inst Technol, 49-50, res assoc, 51-53; res engr, Union Oil Co, Calif, 53-55; sr res engr, Res Div, Fluor Corp, Ltd, 55-59, prin res engr, 59-60; res scientist, Aeronutronic Div, Ford Motor Co, 60-62, supvr, Thermochem, 62-63; asst dir, Sci & Technol Div, 76-78, MEM SR TECH STAFF, INST DEFENSE ANAL, 63-, ASST DIR, SCI & TECHNOL DIV, 80- *Mem:* Am Inst Aeronaut & Astronaut; Am Inst Chem Engrs; Air Pollution Control Asn; Am Geophys Union. *Res:* Missile propulsion; aircraft and rocket vehicle atmospheric effects such as contrails, ozone and climate; materials; fuels. *Mailing Add:* Inst Defense Anal 1801 N Beauregard Alexandria VA 22311

OLIVER, ROBERT M(ILLER), b Swissvale, Pa, Jan 18, 16; m 43; c 1. MECHANICAL ENGINEERING. *Educ:* Univ Calif, BS, 38, MS, 40. *Prof Exp:* Engr mech, Westinghouse Air Brake Co, 40-41; asst prof mech eng, Univ Nev, 41-44 & 45-46; proj engr, Div War Res, Univ Calif, 44-45; asst prof, Colo Sch Mines, 46-47; from asst prof to prof, 47-78, EMER PROF ENG DESIGN & ECON EVAL, UNIV COLO, BOULDER, 78- *Concurrent Pos:* Design consult, 54- *Res:* Machine design and graphics; graphical analysis; design; electromechanical control circuitry; servomechanisms; electronic acoustic systems. *Mailing Add:* 5893 Baseline Boulder CO 80303

OLIVER, ROBERT MARQUAM, b Seattle, Wash, May 5, 31; m 60; c 3. OPERATIONS RESEARCH, APPLIED MATHEMATICS. *Educ:* Mass Inst Technol, BSc, 52, PhD(opers res), 57. *Prof Exp:* Sr engr, Goodyear Aircraft Corp, 53; lectr, Mass Inst Technol, 57; div dir & mem bd dir, Broadview Res Corp, 57-60; assoc prof indust eng, 61-65, chmn dept, 64-68, PROF INDUST ENG & OPERS RES, UNIV CALIF, BERKELEY, 65-, ASST TO VPRES, 68- *Concurrent Pos:* Mem, Nat Conf Solid Waste Mgt; mem comt transp systs, Nat Acad Sci. *Mem:* Opers Res Soc Am; Inst Mgt Sci; Oper Res Soc UK. *Res:* Traffic flow; transportation. *Mailing Add:* Dept of Indust Eng Univ of Calif Berkeley CA 94720

OLIVER, THOMAS ALBERT, b Winnipeg, Man, Dec 16, 24. GEOLOGY. *Educ:* Univ Man, MSc, 49; Univ Calif, Los Angeles, PhD(geol), 52. *Prof Exp:* Geologist, Man Mines Br, Dept Mines & Nat Resources, Can, 50-52 & Calif Standard Co, 52-59; from asst prof to assoc prof, 59-67, PROF GEOL, UNIV CALGARY, 67-, DEAN SCI, 78- *Mem:* Geol Soc Am. *Res:* Stratigraphy; sedimentation. *Mailing Add:* Dept of Geol Univ of Calgary Calgary AB T2N 1N4 Can

OLIVER, THOMAS K, JR, b Hobart Mills, Calif, Dec 21, 25; m 49; c 2. PEDIATRICS. *Educ:* Univ Calif, Berkeley, 43-45; Harvard Med Sch, MD, 49. *Prof Exp:* Instr pediat, Med Col, Cornell Univ, 53-55; from asst prof to assoc prof, Ohio State Univ, 55-63; from assoc prof to prof pediat, Univ Wash, 63-70; PROF PEDIAT & CHMN DEPT, SCH MED, UNIV PITTSBURGH, 70-; MED DIR, CHILDREN'S HOSP PITTSBURGH, 70- *Concurrent Pos:* Spec fel neonatal physiol, Karolinska Inst, Sweden, 60-61; consult ed, Monographs Neonatology, 75-; co-ed, Seminars Perinatology, 75- *Mem:* Soc Pediat Res; Am Pediat Soc; Asn Am Med Cols; Am Acad Pediat. *Res:* Neonatal biology; pulmonary physiology in childhood; acid-base physiology. *Mailing Add:* Children's Hosp of Pittsburgh 125 DeSoto St Pittsburgh PA 15213

OLIVER, THOMAS KILBURY, b St Louis, Mo, Sept 24, 22; m 63; c 4. INSTRUMENTATION, CONTROL SYSTEMS. *Educ:* US Mil Acad, BS, 43; Mass Inst Technol, MS, 48, DSc(instrumentation), 53. *Prof Exp:* Proj engr, Off Air Res, US Air Force, 48-51, assoc prof elec eng, Air Force Inst Technol, 53-56, US Air Force Acad, 56-60, chief guidance systs testing, Guidance & Control Div, Holloman AFB, 60-63; aerospace scientist, NAm Aviation, Inc, 63-64; prin staff engr, Honeywell, Inc, 64-67; assoc prof elec eng, 67-74, SR RES ENGR, S DAK SCH MINES & TECHNOL, 74- *Mem:* Am Inst Aeronaut & Astronaut; Am Soc Eng Educ; Inst Elec & Electronics Engrs. *Res:* Dynamics of complex feedback systems; energy from humid air. *Mailing Add:* Dept of Elec Eng SDak Sch of Mines & Technol Rapid City SD 57701

OLIVER, VICTOR L, zoology, parasitology, see previous edition

OLIVER, WALLACE LEE, b Chicago, Ill, Apr 8, 44; m 71; c 1. PHYSICAL ORGANIC CHEMISTRY. *Educ:* Calif Inst Technol, BS, 66; Northwestern Univ, PhD(chem), 70, JD, 74. *Prof Exp:* Fel, Liverpool Univ, 70-71; patent attorney, 74-77, SR PATENT ATTORNEY, STANDARD OIL CO, 77- *Mem:* Sigma Xi. *Res:* Conformational analysis of heterocyclic compounds; nuclear magnetic resonance spectroscopy. *Mailing Add:* Standard Oil Co 200 E Randolph Dr Chicago IL 60601

OLIVER, WILLIAM ALBERT, JR, b Columbus, Ohio, June 26, 26; m 48; c 2. PALEONTOLOGY. *Educ:* Univ Ill, BS, 48; Cornell Univ, MA, 50, PhD, 52. *Prof Exp:* From instr to asst prof geol, Brown Univ, 52-57; RES GEOLOGIST-PALEONTOLOGIST, US GEOL SURV, 57- *Concurrent Pos:* Trustee, Paleont Res Inst, 77-79; ed, Paleont Soc, 64-69; res prof, George Washington Univ, 69-70; mem, US Nat Comt Geol, 75-79, chmn, 78-79. *Mem:* Geol Soc Am; Paleont Soc (pres, 75); Palaeont Asn; Am Geol Inst (pres, 77). *Res:* Devonian corals and stratigraphy, paleoecology, and biogeography. *Mailing Add:* US Geol Surv E305 Nat Mus Bldg Washington DC 20560

OLIVER, WILLIAM J, b Blackshear, Ga, Mar 30, 25; m 49; c 3. PEDIATRICS. *Educ:* Univ Mich, MDO, 48; Am Bd Pediat, Cert, 54; Sub-Bd Pediat Nephrol, cert, 74. *Prof Exp:* From instr to assoc prof pediat, 53-65, dir pediat lab, Med Ctr, 59-67, PROF PEDIAT, SCH MED, UNIV MICH, ANN ARBOR, 65-, CHMN DEPT PEDIAT & COMMUN DIS, 67- *Concurrent Pos:* Chief pediat serv, Wayne County Gen Hosp, 58-61. *Mem:* Am Pediat Soc; Am Soc Nephrology; Am Acad Pediat; Soc Pediat Res. *Res:* Renal physiology and pathology; fluid and electrolyte metabolism; adaptation of primitive peoples with their environment, disease patterns, mineral metabolism and growth patterns of Yanomama Indians of South America. *Mailing Add:* Dept of Pediat & Commun Dis Univ of Mich Ann Arbor MI 48109

OLIVER, WILLIAM PARKER, b Philadelphia, Pa, Dec 23, 40; m 74. HIGH ENERGY PHYSICS. *Educ:* Univ Calif, Berkeley, BS, 62, PhD(physics), 69. *Prof Exp:* Res assoc, Lawrence Berkeley Lab, Univ Calif, 69-71; res assoc, Univ Wash, 71-76; ASST PROF PHYSICS, TUFTS UNIV, 77- *Res:* Experimental high energy physics. *Mailing Add:* Dept of Physics Tufts Univ Medford MA 02155

OLIVER-GONZALES, JOSE, b Lares, PR, Aug 21, 12; US citizen; m 35; c 3. PARASITOLOGY. *Educ:* Univ PR, BA, 38; Univ Chicago, MS, 39, PhD(parasitol, bact), 41. *Prof Exp:* Instr parasitol, Sch Trop Med, Univ PR, 40; res assoc, Univ Chicago, 42; from asst prof to assoc prof, 43-54, PROF PARASITOL, SCH MED, UNIV PR, SAN JUAN, 54-, HEAD DEPT, 60- *Concurrent Pos:* Res assoc, Western Reserve Univ, 47-48; consult, Parasitol & Trop Med Study Sect, NIH, 53-56, mem, US-Japan Coop Med Sci Prog, 65-70, Nat Adv Allergy & Infectious Dis Coun, 66-70; consult, Vet Admin Hosp, San Juan, Presby Hosp, Auxilio Mutuo Hosp & Doctor's Hosp, San Juan, La State Univ Med Ctr & Inst Int Med, New Orleans; Guggenheim fel, 62-63. *Honors & Awards:* Purdue Frederick Prize, PR Med Asn, 57; Martinez Award, PR Comt Bilharzia Control, 59; Perez Award, Personnel Off, Govt PR, 60; Ashford Award, Am Soc Trop Med & Hyg, 47. *Mem:* AAAS; fel Am Soc Trop Med & Hyg; Am Soc Parasitol; Soc Exp Biol & Med. *Res:* Immunity to infections with helminth parasites; prevention and control of infections with Schistosoma mansoni; metabolism of Schistosoma mansoni and Trichinella spiralis; chemotherapy, immunology and immunochemistry related to parasitic infections. *Mailing Add:* Bucare 13 Santurce PR 00913

OLIVERIO, VINCENT THOMAS, b Cleveland, Ohio, Dec 7, 28; m 53; c 11. PHARMACOLOGY, ORGANIC CHEMISTRY. *Educ:* Xavier Univ, Cincinnati, Ohio, BS, 51, MS, 53; Univ Fla, Gainesville, PhD(oncol), 55. *Prof Exp:* USPHS fel cancer res, Univ Fla, 54-55; proj assoc oncol, McArdle Mem Lab, 55-59; sr investr lab chem pharmacol, NIH, Nat Cancer Inst, 59-67, head biochem pharmacol sect, 67-73, chief lab chem pharmacol, 69-73, assoc dir exp ther, 73-77, ASSOC DIR DEVELOP THERAPEUT PROG, DIV CANCER TREATMENT, NAT CANCER INST, 76- *Concurrent Pos:* Mem med technologist, Bd US Civil Serv, 63-64; mem study group III, Bur Drugs, Food & Drug Admin, 74; cancer res emphasis grant, Div Cancer Treat, Nat Cancer Inst, 75-76. *Honors & Awards:* Superior Service Honor Award, NIH, Nat Cancer Inst, 74. *Mem:* Am Soc Pharmacol & Exp Therapeut; Am Asn Cancer Res; AAAS; Sigma Xi. *Res:* Physiological disposition of antitumor agents and other drugs in animals and man; influence of combination drug eherapy in man and animals on protein binding, renal clearance, metabolism, and therapeutic activity of individual agents. *Mailing Add:* Nat Cancer Inst 8300 Colesville Rd Silver Spring MD 20910

OLIVERO, JOHN JOSEPH, JR, b Yonkers, NY, Jan 18, 41; m 61; c 4. AERONOMY, METEOROLOGY. *Educ:* Fla State Univ, BS, 62; Col William & Mary, MS, 66; Univ Mich, Ann Arbor, PhD(aeronomy), 70. *Prof Exp:* Aerospace technologist appl res & develop, Langley Res Ctr, NASA, Va, 62-70; res assoc fel, Physics & Astron, Univ Fla, 70-72; asst prof meterol & ionospheric res lab, 72-77, ASSOC PROF METEROL, PA STATE UNIV, 77- *Mem:* AAAS; Am Meteorol Soc; Sigma Xi; Am Geophys Union. *Res:* Minor constituent photochemistry and transport; microwave radiometry; upper atmospheric composition, structure, energetics, circulation and thermal processes; atmospheric measurements; aerosol physics; climatic change, environmental impact. *Mailing Add:* 509 Walker Pa State Univ University Park PA 16802

OLIVER-PADILLA, FERNANDO LUIS, b Mayaguez, PR, Apr 9, 22; US citizen; m 45; c 3. DAIRY SCIENCE, ANIMAL BREEDING. *Educ:* Univ PR, BS, 42; Kans State Univ, MS, 58, PhD(animal breeding), 61. *Prof Exp:* Agr exten agent, Agr Exten Serv, Univ PR, 42-53, livestock specialist, 53-56, 58-59 & 61-63; assoc prof natural sci & head dept, 63-66, PROF GENETICS & PHYSIOL, INTER-AM UNIV PR, HATO REY, 66- *Concurrent Pos:* Sire analyst, PR Artificial Breeding Coop, 58-; consult, PR Agr Coun, Dept Agr, 61-63 & PR Dairy Farmers Asn, 63-; sen, Inter-Am Univ Fac Sen, 66-69, 71-74 & 77-80. *Mem:* AAAS; Am Dairy Sci Asn; NY Acad Sci; PR Col Agriculturists; Latin Am Asn Animal Prod. *Res:* Genetic parameters in the dairy population of Puerto Rico; the genotypic and phenotypic frequencies of ABO and Rh groups in the Puerto Rican population; studies on possible mode of inheritance of diabetes mellitus; psycho-physiological effects of the contraceptive pill on a sample of Puerto Rican women; effects of rectally absorbed insulin on the glycemic levels of alloxan induced diabetes in rats. *Mailing Add:* Dept of Natural Sci Inter-Am Univ of PR Hato Rey PR 00919

OLIVETO, EUGENE PAUL, b New York, NY, Mar 15, 24; m 48; c 2. ORGANIC CHEMISTRY. *Educ:* City Col New York, BS, 43; Purdue Univ, PhD(org chem), 48. *Prof Exp:* Res chemist, Schenley Res Inst, 43-44; asst chem, Purdue Univ, 44-48; res chemist, Schering Corp, 48-50, group leader, 50-58, mgr, Natural Prod Res Dept, 58-64; sr group chief, 64, sect chief, 64-66, dir animal health & fine chem res, 66-68, DIR FINE CHEM RES, HOFFMANN-LA ROCHE, INC, 68- *Mem:* AAAS; fel Am Inst Chemists; Am Chem Soc; fel NY Acad Sci; The Chem Soc. *Res:* Nitroparaffins; synthesis, photolysis and pyrolysis of organic nitrites; organic medicinals; partial and total synthesis of steroidal sex and adrenal hormones; analogs; food additives; vitamins. *Mailing Add:* Res Div Hoffmann-La Roche Inc Nutley NJ 07110

OLIVIER, KENNETH LEO, b Los Angeles, Calif, May 19, 32; m 54; c 6. ORGANIC CHEMISTRY. *Educ:* Loyola Univ, Calif, BS, 54; Univ Calif, Los Angeles, PhD(chem), 58. *Prof Exp:* Res chemist, Plastics Dept, E I du Pont de Nemours & Co, 57-60; res chemist, 60-65, sr res chemist, 65-69, SUPVR INDUST CHEM, UNION OIL CO CALIF, 69- *Mem:* Am Chem Soc. *Res:* Petrochemicals; emulsion polymerization; hot melt adhesives. *Mailing Add:* Res Dept Union Oil Co of Calif Brea CA 92621

OLIVO, RICHARD FRANCIS, b New York, NY, Sept 26, 42; m 71. NEUROBIOLOGY. *Educ:* Columbia Univ, AB, 63; Harvard Univ, AM, 65, PhD(biol), 69. *Prof Exp:* Tutor biol, Harvard Univ, 66-68; vis asst prof, State Univ NY Stony Brook, 70-71; asst prof, Williams Col, 71-73; asst prof, 73-79, ASSOC PROF BIOL, SMITH COL, 79- *Concurrent Pos:* Consult, Harper & Row, Inc, 69-71. *Mem:* AAAS; Am Soc Zoologists; Soc Neurosci. *Res:* Sensory physiology; invertebrate nervous systems; laboratory microcomputing. *Mailing Add:* Dept of Biol Sci Smith Col Northampton MA 01063

OLKIN, INGRAM, b Waterbury, Conn, July 23, 24; m 45; c 3. MATHEMATICAL STATISTICS. *Educ:* City Col New York, BS, 47; Columbia Univ, MA, 49; Univ NC, PhD(math statist), 51. *Prof Exp:* Asst prof statist, Mich State Univ, 51-55; vis assoc prof, Univ Chicago, 55-56; assoc prof, Mich State Univ, 56-60; prof, Univ Minn, 60-61; chmn dept statist, 74-77, PROF STATIST & EDUC, STANFORD UNIV, 61- *Concurrent Pos:* Assoc ed, J Am Statist Asn, 60-70, J Educ Statist, 77- & J Psychomet, 80-; overseas fel, Churchill Col, Cambridge Univ, 67-68; fel psychomet, Educ Testing Serv, 71-72; ed, Ann Math Statist, 71-74; vis prof, Univ British Col, 77; Fulbright fel, Univ Copenhagen, 79. *Mem:* Fel Inst Math Statist; fel Am Statist Asn; Am Math Soc; fel Int Statist Inst; Psychomet Soc. *Res:* Multivariate analysis; mathematical models in the behavioral sciences. *Mailing Add:* Dept of Statist Stanford Univ Stanford CA 94305

OLLA, BORI LIBORIO, b Jersey City, NJ, Jan 22, 37; m 58; c 2. ANIMAL BEHAVIOR, FISH BIOLOGY. *Educ:* Fairleigh Dickinson Univ, BS, 59; Univ Hawaii, MS, 62. *Prof Exp:* Res asst shark behav, Hawaii Marine Lab, Honolulu, 61-62; instr biol, Chaminade Col Hawaii, 62; asst zool, Univ Md, 62-63; asst fish neurol, NIH, 63; asst neurol, Col Med, Seton Hall Univ, 63; asst prof marine sci, C W Post Col, Long Island Univ, 75-79, CHIEF BEHAV INVEST, NAT MARINE FISHERIES SERV, NAT OCEANIC & ATMOSPHERIC ADMIN, 63- *Concurrent Pos:* Vis lectr, Boston Univ-Marine Biol Lab, Woods Hole, 76-78; vis adj prof marine biol, Cook Col,

Rutgers Univ, 77-; adj mem, Sch Oceanog, Ore State Univ, 78- & Zool Dept, Rutgers Univ, 79- *Honors & Awards:* Bronze Medal, US Dept Com, 75. *Res:* Field and laboratory studies on marine fishes and invertebrates; behavioral ecology in relation to fishery biology and social behavior, including schooling, territoriality, aggression; biorhythms, feeding, home ranges; chemosensory responses; effects of environmental stress, including temperature and petroleum on behavior norms. *Mailing Add:* Sandy Hook Lab Nat Marine Fisheries Serv NOAA Highlands NJ 07732

OLLEMAN, ROGER D(EAN), b Cornelia, Ga, Nov 25, 23; m 47; c 3. METALLURGY. *Educ:* Univ Wash, BS, 48; Carnegie Inst Technol, MS, 50; Univ Pittsburgh, PhD, 55. *Prof Exp:* Group leader, Westinghouse Res Lab, 50-55; asst br head, Dept Metall Res, Kaiser Aluminum & Chem Corp, 55-59; from assoc prof to prof mech eng, Ore State Univ, 59-76, head dept metall eng, 69-72; PRES, ACCIDENT & FAILURE INVESTS, INC, 74- *Concurrent Pos:* Consult, Kaiser Aluminum & Chem Corp, 59-60, Albany Metall Res Ctr, US Bur Mines, 62-72 & Lawrence Radiation Lab, 65-66; courtesy prof, Ore State Univ, 76- *Honors & Awards:* Templin Award, Am Soc Testing & Mat, 53. *Mem:* Am Soc Metals; Am Soc Mech Engrs; Am Inst Mining, Metall & Petrol Engrs; Am Soc Eng Educ. *Res:* Physical and mechanical metallurgy; mechanisms of flow and fracture; crystallography and phase transformations; cryogenic properties. *Mailing Add:* Accident & Failure Invests Inc 2107 NW Fillmore Ave Corvallis OR 97330

OLLERENSHAW, NEIL CAMPBELL, b Matlock, Eng, Sept 12, 33; Can citizen; m 60; c 3. GEOLOGY. *Educ:* Univ Wales, BSc, 57; Univ Toronto, MA, 59, PhD(geol), 63. *Prof Exp:* RES SCIENTIST, GEOL SURV CAN, 62- *Mem:* Can Soc Petrol Geologists; Soc Econ Paleont & Mineral. *Res:* Structural geology; stratigraphy and facies-tectonics relationships of the Rocky Mountain foothills and Eastern Cordillera. *Mailing Add:* Geol Surv of Can 3303 33rd St NW Calgary AB T2L 2A7 Can

OLLERHEAD, ROBIN WEMP, b Simcoe, Ont, Mar 12, 37; m 59; c 3. ION-SOLID INTERACTIONS. *Educ:* Univ Western Ont, BSc, 59; Yale Univ, MS, 60, PhD(physics), 64. *Prof Exp:* Asst res officer nuclear physics, Atomic Energy Can Ltd, 64-66, assoc res officer, 66-68; assoc prof physics, 68-71, PROF PHYSICS, UNIV GUELPH, 71- *Concurrent Pos:* NATO sci fel & Rutherford Mem fel, Oxford Univ, 63-64. *Mem:* Am Phys Soc; Can Asn Physicists. *Res:* Ion-solid interactions; materials analysis using ion beams and nuclear physics techniques; sputtering. *Mailing Add:* Dept of Physics Univ of Guelph Guelph ON N1G 2W1 Can

OLLERICH, DWAYNE A, b Sioux Falls, SDak, June 30, 34. ANATOMY, NEUROANATOMY. *Educ:* Augustana Col, SDak, BA, 60; Univ NDak, MS, 62, PhD(anat), 64. *Prof Exp:* Asst prof neuroanat & histol, Univ Alta, 65-66; from asst prof to assoc prof, 66-77, chmn dept anat, 72-79, PROF NEUROANAT, SCH MED, UNIV NORTH DAK, 77-, ASSOC DEAN ACAD AFFAIRS, 79- *Concurrent Pos:* Fel anat, Univ Alta, 64-65, Med Res Coun Can fel, 65-66. *Mem:* Am Asn Anat; Am Soc Cell Biol. *Res:* Electron microscopy; cytology; drug toxicity. *Mailing Add:* Dept of Anat Univ of NDak Sch of Med Grand Forks ND 58201

OLLINGER, JANET, organic chemistry, see previous edition

OLLIS, DAVID F(REDERICK), b San Francisco, Calif, Sept 28, 41; m 64; c 2. CHEMICAL ENGINEERING. *Educ:* Calif Inst Technol, BS, 63; Northwestern Univ, MS, 64; Stanford Univ, PhD(chem eng), 69. *Prof Exp:* Res engr, Montebello Res Lab, Texaco Inc, Calif, 64-65; asst prof chem eng, Princeton Univ, 69-77, assoc prof, 77-80; MEM FAC, CHEM ENG DEPT, UNIV CALIF, DAVIS, 80- *Concurrent Pos:* Nat Ctr Sci Res fel, Ctr Phys & Chem Kinetics, Univ Nancy, France, 69. *Mem:* Am Inst Chem Engrs; Am Chem Soc. *Res:* Surface chemistry, especially adsorption, catalysis and corrosion; solid state chemistry; biochemical engineering; kinetics of living systems. *Mailing Add:* Dept Chem Eng Univ Calif Davis CA 95616

OLLOM, JOHN FREDERICK, b Ward, WVa, Dec 28, 22; m 54; c 3. PHYSICS. *Educ:* Harvard Univ, PhD, 52. *Prof Exp:* Asst prof physics, Univ WVa, 51-56; PROF PHYSICS, DREW UNIV, 56- *Concurrent Pos:* Mem tech staff, Bell Labs, Inc. *Mem:* Am Phys Soc; Am Asn Physics Teachers. *Res:* Magnetism; microwave spectroscopy. *Mailing Add:* Dept of Physics Drew Univ Madison NJ 07940

OLMER, JANE CHASNOFF, b St Louis, Mo; wid. MATHEMATICS, COMPUTER SCIENCE. *Educ:* Wellesley Col, BA, 34; Washington Univ, MS, 37; Univ Chicago, cert, 61. *Prof Exp:* Teacher, Am Sch Paris, 37-39; ed & broadcaster, Paris Letter, 39-41; statistician, Drop Forging Asn, 42-43 & Fed Pub Housing Authority, 43-44; consult, May Co, 45; anal statistician, US Navy Electronics Supply Off, 54-55, supvr anal statistician, 55-56, digital comput syst specialist trainee, 56, mathematician, 56-59, tech head adv logistics res & develop, 59-61; sr mathematician, Appl Physics Lab, Johns Hopkins Univ, 61-77; GROUP MGR, PRICE, WILLIAMS & ASSOCS INC, 78- *Concurrent Pos:* Permanent deleg, Univac Users Asn, 57-61; cert, Data Processing Mgt Asn, 65, mem, Data Processing Testing Comt & dir educ, Washington, DC chap, 65-67; mgr, Text & Info Processing & Retrieval Proj, SHARE. *Honors & Awards:* US Navy Superior Accomplishment Award, 61. *Mem:* Asn Comput Mach; Sigma Xi. *Res:* Operations research in inventory control; mathematical programming on business computers; information handling and retrieval and high level computer languages in research and development environment using business and scientific computers; design and implementation of integrated data processing and word processing systems. *Mailing Add:* 2510 Virginia Ave NW Washington DC 20037

OLMSTEAD, JOHN AARON, b Buffalo, NY, Feb 21, 30; m 60. ELECTRICAL ENGINEERING. *Educ:* Univ Buffalo, BS, 52; Newark Col Eng, MS, 57. *Prof Exp:* Engr electron tube div, Radio Corp Am, 52-55, group leader, 55-57; asst prof elec eng, Univ Buffalo, 57-60; engr, Electron Components & Devices Div, Radio Corp Am, 59-61, LEADER TECH STAFF, ELECTRON COMPONENTS & DEVICES DIV, RCA CORP, 61- *Mem:* Sr mem Inst Elec & Electronics Engrs. *Res:* Gaseous electronic conduction phenomena; solid state physics; device characterization and associated physical phenomena; device fabrication techniques. *Mailing Add:* RCA Corp Rte 202 Somerville NJ 08876

OLMSTEAD, WILLIAM EDWARD, b San Antonio, Tex, June 2, 36; m 57; c 2. APPLIED MATHEMATICS. *Educ:* Rice Univ, BS, 59; Northwestern Univ, MS, 62, PhD(eng sci), 63. *Prof Exp:* Res engr, Southwest Res Inst, 59-60; fel, Johns Hopkins Univ, 63-64; from asst prof to assoc prof, 64-71, PROF APPL MATH, NORTHWESTERN UNIV, 71-, DIR APPL MATH, 78- *Concurrent Pos:* Vis mem, Courant Inst Math Sci, NY Univ, 67-68; chmn, Comt Appl Math, Northwestern Univ, 72-76, mem, Exec Comt, Coun Theoret & Appl Mech, 74-; regional lectr, Soc Indust & Appl Math, 72-73 & 78-79; vis prof, Univ Col, London, 73. *Mem:* Soc Indust & Appl Math; Am Math Soc; Am Phys Soc. *Res:* Nonlinear boundary value problems; diffusion-dissipation processes; viscous flow theory. *Mailing Add:* Technol Inst Northwestern Univ Evanston IL 60201

OLMSTEAD, WILLIAM NEERGAARD, b Bryn Mawr, Pa, Mar 4, 50; m 81. PHYSICAL ORGANIC CHEMISTRY. *Educ:* Yale Univ, BS, 72; Stanford Univ, PhD(chem), 77. *Prof Exp:* Fel org chem, Northwestern Univ, 76-78; SR CHEMIST ORG CHEM, EXXON RES & ENG CO, 78- *Mem:* Am Chem Soc. *Res:* Gas phase and solution chemistry of ions; nonaqueous solvents and electrolyte solutions; solvent effects on organic reactions; shale and coal chemistry; pyrolysis of organic compounds. *Mailing Add:* Exxon Res & Eng Co PO 45 Linden NJ 07036

OLMSTED, CLINTON ALBERT, b Chicago, Ill, Oct 27, 25; m 52; c 4. PHYSIOLOGY. *Educ:* Univ Calif, AB, 48, MA, 54, PhD(comp physiol), 56. *Prof Exp:* Asst, Univ Calif, 49-51 & 54-56; radiobiologist, US Naval Radiol Defense Lab, 51-54; res neurologist, Med Ctr, Univ Calif, Los Angeles, 57-59; asst prof zool, Univ Wis, 59-63; sr res physiologist, Battelle Mem Inst, 63-64; head, Cell Biol Div, Inst Lipid Res, Berkeley, Calif, 65; ASSOC PROF BIOL SCI, UNIV NEW ORLEANS, 65- *Concurrent Pos:* Mem & head, Lipid Biochem Sect, Div Nutrit Biochem, Commonwealth Sci & Indust Res Orgn, Adelaide, SAustralia, 70-72; sr lectr physiol, Godfrey Huggins Sch Med, Univ Zimbabwe, 77- *Mem:* AAAS; Am Soc Cell Biol; Am Physiol Soc; NY Acad Sci; Australian Biochem Soc. *Res:* Comparative physiology; cellular physiology with emphasis on general mechanisms in neurophysiology; lipid metabolism, lipid transport, and the role of phospholipids in drug transport and sodium transport affected by lipid soluble drugs. *Mailing Add:* Dept Biol Univ New Orleans New Orleans LA 70148

OLMSTED, FRANKLIN HOWARD, b Los Angeles, Calif, Nov 23, 21; m 55; c 2. GEOLOGY. *Educ:* Pomona Col, BA, 42; Claremont Cols, MA, 48; Bryn Mawr Col, PhD, 61. *Prof Exp:* Lectr & instr geol, Claremont Cols, 48-49; geologist, 49-69, STAFF HYDROLOGIST, WATER RESOURCES DIV, US GEOL SURV, 69- *Mem:* AAAS; Geol Soc Am; Am Geophys Union. *Res:* Ground-water geology; petrology; development of methods of hydrogeologic exploration of geothermal areas. *Mailing Add:* Water Resources Div US Geol Surv Menlo Park CA 94025

OLMSTED, JOANNA BELLE, b Chicago, Ill, Mar 8, 47. CELL BIOLOGY. *Educ:* Earlham Col, BA, 67; Yale Univ, PhD(biol), 71. *Prof Exp:* Fel biochem, Lab Molecular Biol, Univ Wis-Madison, 71-74; asst prof, 75-81, ASSOC PROF BIOL, UNIV ROCHESTER, 81- *Concurrent Pos:* NIH fel, 71-73. *Mem:* Am Soc Cell Biol. *Res:* Control of cell division and differentiation; regulation of synthesis, assembly and organization of cytoskeletal proteins for cellular functions. *Mailing Add:* Dept of Biol Univ of Rochester Rochester NY 14627

OLMSTED, RICHARD DALE, b Bismarck, NDak, Nov 1, 47; m 69; c 1. THEORETICAL CHEMISTRY. *Educ:* Augsburg Col, BA, 69; Univ Wis-Madison, PhD(chem), 74. *Prof Exp:* Fel chem, Univ BC, 74-76; instr, 76-80, ASST PROF CHEM, AUGSBURG COL, 80- *Concurrent Pos:* Vis asst prof, Univ Wis, 77 & 78 & Univ BC, 81 & 82; consult polymer physics, 3M Co, St Paul, 81- *Mem:* Am Chem Soc; Sigma Xi. *Res:* Nonequilibrium statistical mechanics; kinetic theory and transport properties of gaseous systems. *Mailing Add:* Dept Chem Augsburg Col 731 21st Ave S Minneapolis MN 55454

OLMSTED, RICHARD W, b Darien, Conn, June 27, 20; m 43; c 4. PEDIATRICS. *Educ:* Dartmouth Col, BA, 41; Harvard Med Sch, MD, 44. *Prof Exp:* Clin instr pediat, Sch Med, Yale Univ, 49-53; asst prof, Sch Med, Temple Univ, 55-62; prof pediat & chmn dept, Med Sch, Univ Ore, 62-74; assoc exec dir, Am Acad Pediat, Evanston, Ill, 74-78; MED DIR, CHILDREN'S HOSP, DENVER, 78- *Mem:* Am Acad Pediat; Am Pediat Soc. *Res:* Hearing disorders in children. *Mailing Add:* Children's Hosp 1056 E Nineteenth Ave Denver CO 80218

OLNESS, ALAN, b Kenyon, Minn, Sept 22, 41; m 63; c 4. SOIL BIOCHEM, SOIL SCIENCE. *Educ:* Univ Minn, BS, 63, MS, 67, PhD(soil sci), 73. *Prof Exp:* Res asst soil sci, Univ Minn, 63-67; soil scientist, Soil Struct Group, 67-70, Nat Agr Water Qual Mgt Lab, 70-77 & Food Crops Res Team, Regional Develop Off EAfrica, 77-78, SOIL SCIENTIST, NORTH CENT SOIL CONSERV RES CTR, AGR RES SERV, USDA, 78- *Mem:* Am Soc Agron; Soil Sci Soc Am; Int Soc Soil Sci; Am Chem Soc. *Res:* Influence of agricultural management practices on crop residue nutrient use efficiency with particular emphasis on nitrogen fertilizer applications, transport, and transformations within the agricultural environment. *Mailing Add:* N Cent Soil Conserv Res Ctr North Iowa Ave Morris MN 56267

OLNESS, DOLORES URQUIZA, b Kingsport, Tenn, Mar 20, 35; m 57; c 3. SOLID STATE PHYSICS. *Educ:* Duke Univ, AB, 57, PhD(physics), 61. *Prof Exp:* Res assoc molecular physics, Duke Univ, 61 & Univ NC, 61-63; SR PHYSICIST, LAWRENCE LIVERMORE LAB, UNIV CALIF, 63- *Mem:* Am Phys Soc. *Res:* Organic low temperature molecular spectroscopy; organic photoconductors; lasers, damage to transparent solids; in-situ coal gasification. *Mailing Add:* 4345 Guilford Ave Livermore CA 94550

OLNESS, JOHN WILLIAM, b Broderick, Sask, Sept 4, 29; US citizen; m 58; c 5. NUCLEAR PHYSICS. *Educ:* St Olaf Col, BA, 51; Duke Univ, PhD(physics), 57. *Prof Exp:* Res assoc nuclear physics, Duke Univ, 57-58; res physicist, Aeronaut Res Labs, Wright-Patterson AFB, Ohio, 58-63; assoc physicist, 63-68, PHYSICIST, BROOKHAVEN NAT LAB, 68- *Res:* Nuclear spectroscopy. *Mailing Add:* Physics Dept Bldg 901-A Brookhaven Nat Lab Upton NY 11973

OLNESS, ROBERT JAMES, b Milaca, Minn, Jan 22, 33; m 57; c 3. STATISTICAL PHYSICS, THERMODYNAMICS. *Educ:* Mass Inst Technol, BS, 56; Duke Univ, PhD(nuclear physics), 62. *Prof Exp:* Res assoc physics, Univ NC, 61-63; sr physicist, Lawrence Radiation Lab, Univ Calif, 63-68; assoc prof physics, Northern Mich Univ, 68-69; SR PHYSICIST, LAWRENCE LIVERMORE LAB, UNIV CALIF, 69- *Mem:* Am Phys Soc. *Res:* Thermodynamics and statistical mechanics; atomic and molecular physics. *Mailing Add:* 4345 Guilford Ave Livermore CA 94550

OLNEY, CHARLES EDWARD, b Assam, India, Nov 7, 24; US citizen; m 45; c 4. AGRICULTURAL CHEMISTRY. *Educ:* Tufts Col, BS, 45; Univ RI, MS, 53; Univ Conn, PhD(biochem), 67. *Prof Exp:* Teacher, R W Traip Acad, 46-48; agr chemist, Agr Exp Sta, 48-70, PROF FOOD & RESOURCE CHEM, UNIV RI, 70- *Res:* Pesticide residues; lipids. *Mailing Add:* Dept of Food Sci & Technol Univ of RI Kingston RI 02881

OLNEY, JOHN WILLIAM, b Marathon, Iowa, Oct 23, 31; m 57; c 3. PSYCHIATRY, NEUROPATHOLOGY. *Educ:* Univ Iowa, BA, 57, MD, 63; Am Bd Psychiat & Neurol, dipl, 70. *Prof Exp:* Intern, Kaiser Permanente Found, San Francisco, Calif, 63-64; resident, 64-68, from instr to assoc prof psychiat, 68-77, PROF PSYCHIAT & NEUROPATH, SCH MED, WASH UNIV, 77- *Concurrent Pos:* NIMH biol sci trainee, Wash Univ, 66-68 & career invest award, 68-; asst psychiatrist, Barnes Hosp, 68-; consult psychiatrist, Malcolm Bliss Ment Health Ctr, 68- *Mem:* Psychiat Res Soc; Am Psychiat Asn; Am Asn Neuropath; Soc Neurosci; Asn Res Nervous & Ment Dis. *Res:* Adverse influences on the development of the immature central nervous system and neuropsychiatric disturbances resulting therefrom. *Mailing Add:* Dept Psychiat Sch Med Wash Univ St Louis MO 63110

O'LOANE, JAMES KENNETH, b Walla Walla, Wash, Dec 12, 13; m 43; c 4. CHEMICAL PHYSICS. *Educ:* St Benedict's Col, BSc, 35; Univ Wash, MSc, 44; Harvard Univ, MA, 47, PhD(chem physics), 50. *Prof Exp:* Instr, St Martin's Acad & Jr Col, 37-38; jr chemist, Shell Develop Co, 43-45; from asst prof to assoc prof chem, Univ NH, 48-54; sr anal chemist, Indust Lab, 54-58, proj physicist, Apparatus & Optical Div, Lincoln Plant, 58-59, sr res chemist, Res Labs, 59-62, RES ASSOC, EASTMAN KODAK CO RES LABS, 63- *Mem:* Am Chem Soc; Optical Soc Am; Am Phys Soc. *Res:* Polymer physical chemistry; fourier transform spectroscopy of polymer films; polymer thermodynamics; optical activity. *Mailing Add:* 331 Seneca Pkwy Rochester NY 14613

OLOFFS, PETER CHRISTIAN, b Rügen, Ger, July 18, 29; Can citizen; m 58; c 2. PESTICIDE CHEMISTRY. *Educ:* Ernst-August Univ, Ger, dipl agr, 56; Univ BC, MSA, 64; Univ Wis-Madison, PhD(pesticide chem & biochem), 68. *Prof Exp:* Chemist, Later Chem Ltd, BC, 58-63; sessional lectr zool, Univ BC, 63-64; asst prof, 68-74, assoc prof, 74-80, PROF BIOL SCI, SIMON FRASER UNIV, 80- *Mem:* AAAS; Entom Soc Am; Am Chem Soc. *Res:* Persistence of pesticides in soils, plants, natural waters; pesticide-related aspects of public and occupational health; interrelationships between hepatic dysfunction and exposure to pesticide residues. *Mailing Add:* Dept of Biol Sci Simon Fraser Univ Burnaby BC V5A 1S6 Can

OLOFSON, ROY ARNE, b Chicago, Ill, Feb 26, 36. ORGANIC CHEMISTRY. *Educ:* Univ Chicago, BS & MS, 57; Harvard Univ, PhD(org chem), 61. *Prof Exp:* Instr org chem, Harvard Univ, 61-64, asst prof, 64-65; assoc prof, 65-71, PROF ORG CHEM, PA STATE UNIV, 71- *Concurrent Pos:* Consult, FMC Corp, 62-73, Armour Pharmaceut Co, 65-70 & McNeil Labs, 74-; mem, Adv Bd, J Org Chem, 73-77. *Mem:* Am Chem Soc; The Chem Soc; Sigma Xi. *Res:* Synthetic organic, heterocyclic and peptide chemistry; reaction mechanisms. *Mailing Add:* Dept of Chem Pa State Univ University Park PA 16802

O'LOUGHLIN, BERNARD JAMES, b Beaudette, Minn, Oct 30, 14; m 42; c 8. RADIOLOGY. *Educ:* Col St Thomas, BS, 37; Creighton Univ, MS, 41, MD, 42; Southwestern Univ, cert, 48; Univ Minn, PhD(radiol), 50; Am Bd Radiol, dipl, 48. *Prof Exp:* Resident radiol, Southwestern Univ & McKinney Vet Admin Hosp, Dallas, 46-48; from instr to assoc prof, Univ Minn, 48-52; from asst prof to prof, Sch Med, Univ Calif, Los Angeles, 52-64, prof radiol sci & chmn dept, 64-69; chmn fac med, Calif Col Med, Univ Calif, Irvine, 71-72, chmn dept, 69-74, prof radiol sci, 69-77; PROF RADIOL SCI, SCH MED, UNIV CALIF, LOS ANGELES, 77- *Concurrent Pos:* Consult radiologist, St Joseph's Holy Family Hosps, 48-49 & 50-52; radiologist, Vet Admin Hosp, Minneapolis, 48-49, chief dept, 49-52; chief diag div, Ctr Health Sci, Univ Calif, Los Angeles, 52-62, chief pediat diag div, 62-64; vis prof, Oxford Univ, 60-62; chief physician radiol Unit II, Los Angeles County Hosp, 64-68; vis prof, Univ London, 72-73; counr, Univ Calif, Irvine. *Mem:* Radiol Soc NAm; Roentgen Ray Soc; fel Am Col Chest Physicians; fel Am Col Radiol; fel Am Acad Pediat. *Res:* Inferior vena cava; cancer of the lung; disturbances in cardiovascular function. *Mailing Add:* Dept of Radiol Sci 7533 Van Nuys Blvd Van Nuys CA 91405

O'LOUGHLIN, WALTER K(LEIN), b Chicago, Ill, Dec 9, 10; m 37; c 1. CHEMICAL ENGINEERING. *Educ:* Catholic Univ, BS, 33, MS, 35. *Prof Exp:* Mem staff, res dept, Com Solvents Corp, 35-42, 46, tech develop dept, 46-49; directorate of intel, US Dept Air Force, 49-50; from mgr develop, Davison Div, to dir, new prod develop, res div, W R Grace & Co, 51-63, dir contract opers, 63-64, vpres, 64-77; RETIRED. *Concurrent Pos:* Consult, directorate of intel, US Dept Air Force, 51-53. *Mem:* Am Chem Soc; Am Ord Asn; Com Develop Asn; Am Inst Chem Engrs. *Res:* Technical and economic evaluation of processes; research administration. *Mailing Add:* 501 Wilton Rd Towson MD 21204

OLSEN, ARTHUR MARTIN, b Chicago, Ill, Aug 27, 09; m 36; c 4. INTERNAL MEDICINE. *Educ:* Dartmouth Col, AB, 30; Rush Med Col, MD, 35; Univ Minn, MS, 38. *Prof Exp:* First asst med, Mayo Grad Sch Med, Univ Minn, 38-39, from asst prof to prof med, 40-76; DIR INT ACTIV, INT ACAD CHEST PHYSICIANS & SURGEONS, AM COL CHEST PHYSICIANS, 76- *Concurrent Pos:* Consult, Mayo Clin, 38-, head sect med, 49-68, chmn div thoracic dis, 68-71; trustee, Mayo Found, 61-68; mem nat heart & lung adv coun, NIH, 70-71. *Mem:* Am Soc Gastrointestinal Endoscopy (secy-treas, Am Gastroscopic Soc, 58-61, pres, 62-63); Am Col Chest Physicians (pres, 70); Am Broncho-Esophagol Asn (pres, 69-70); Am Thoracic Soc; Am Asn Thoracic Surg. *Res:* Esophageal motility; broncho-esophagology. *Mailing Add:* Mayo Clin 200 First St NW Rochester MN 55901

OLSEN, CARL JOHN, b Oakland, Calif, May 18, 28; m 64; c 2. ORGANIC CHEMISTRY. *Educ:* Univ San Francisco, BS, 50, MS, 52; Univ Southern Calif, PhD(chem), 62. *Prof Exp:* Asst chem, Walter Reed Army Med Ctr, 53-54; instr, Los Angeles Valley Col, 60-61; from asst prof to assoc prof, 61-71, PROF CHEM, CALIF STATE UNIV, NORTHRIDGE, 71- *Concurrent Pos:* Res Corp Cottrell grant, 63-64; NSF inst grants, 65-66. *Mem:* Am Chem Soc. *Res:* Organic reaction mechanisms; thermal and photochemical studies on reactions and reactivities of organic free radicals; free radicals in the field of environmental health; synthesis and properties of metalocenes. *Mailing Add:* Dept of Chem Calif State Univ Northridge CA 91330

OLSEN, CHARLES EDWARD, b Dover, NJ, May 17, 43; m 73. IMMMUNOLOGY. *Educ:* Rensselaer Polytech Inst, BS, 65; Univ Calif, Berkeley, PhD(biochem), 76. *Prof Exp:* Fel, Nat Inst Dental Res, NIH, 76-79; SR RES SCIENTIST, JOHNSON & JOHNSON RES, 80- *Mem:* AAAS; Sigma Xi. *Res:* Investigation of the molecular and cellular processes involved in the healing of normal and infected wounds. *Mailing Add:* Johnson & Johnson Res Rte 1 North Brunswick NJ 08902

OLSEN, CLARENCE WILMOTT, b Indianapolis, Ind, Dec 1, 03; m 29; c 2. NEUROLOGY. *Educ:* Ohio State Univ, BA, 23; Univ Mich, MA, 25, MD, 27. *Prof Exp:* Instr med, 30-34, from asst prof to assoc prof nerv dis, 34-52, clin prof, 52-64, PROF NEUROL, SCH MED, LOMA LINDA UNIV, 64- *Concurrent Pos:* Consult, US Vet Admin Hosps, Loma Linda, 78- *Mem:* Fel AMA; Am Psychiat Asn; fel Am Col Physicians. *Res:* Vascular diseases of the brain; respiratory rhythm in nervous diseases. *Mailing Add:* Dept of Neurol Loma Linda Univ Sch of Med Loma Linda CA 92354

OLSEN, DONNA MAE, b Wooster, Ohio, Sept 14, 40; m 70. HEALTH SERVICES RESEARCH, COMMUNITY MEDICINE. *Educ:* Hiram Col, BA, 62; Utah State Univ, MS, 65, PhD(pop ecol), 72. *Prof Exp:* Res assoc, 71-77, instr, 74-77, ASST PROF COMMUNITY MED, SCH MED, UNIV UTAH, 77- *Mem:* Asn Teachers Prev Med; Am Pub Health Asn. *Res:* Evaluation of non-physician providers; solution of rural health problems; use of mini-computers in small medical practices. *Mailing Add:* Dept of Family & Community Med Univ of Utah 50 N Medical Dr Salt Lake City UT 84132

OLSEN, DOUGLAS ALFRED, b Minneapolis, Minn, Oct 10, 30; m 58; c 3. PHYSICAL CHEMISTRY. *Educ:* Gustavus Adolphus Col, BA, 53; Univ Iowa, MS, 55, PhD(phys chem), 60. *Prof Exp:* Teaching asst, Univ Iowa, 53-55; develop chemist, Bemis, Inc, 55-57; sr res scientist, Honeywell, Inc, 59-63; proj leader phys chem, Archer Daniels Midland Co, 63-67; sect mgr chem, Appl Sci Div, Litton Systs, Inc, 67-70; vpres, Bio-Medicus Inc, 70-75; PRES, PMD INC, 75- *Concurrent Pos:* Res assoc, Univ Minn, 73-76; vis prof, Tech Univ Denmark, 74. *Honors & Awards:* IR-100 Award, Indust Res Inst, 72. *Mem:* AAAS; Am Chem Soc; Am Soc Artificial Internal Organs. *Res:* Surface chemistry; electrochemistry; chemical kinetics; radiochemistry; artificial organs; biomedical materials; operations analysis. *Mailing Add:* 4106 Linden Hills Blvd Minneapolis MN 55410

OLSEN, EDWARD JOHN, b Chicago, Ill, Nov 23, 27; m 54; c 2. GEOLOGY. *Educ:* Univ Chicago, BA, 51, MS, 55, PhD, 59. *Hon Degrees:* LHD, Augustana Col, 79. *Prof Exp:* Geologist, Geol Surv Can, 53, US Geol Surv, 54 & Can Johns-Manville Co, Ltd, 56-59; asst prof mineral & petrol, Western Reserve Univ & Case Inst, 59-60; chmn dept geol, 74-78, CUR MINERAL, DEPT GEOL, FIELD MUS NATURAL HIST, 60- *Concurrent Pos:* Guest researcher, Argonne Nat Lab, 67-80; adj prof, Univ Ill, Chicago Circle, 70-, res assoc prof, 77- *Mem:* Fel Mineral Soc Am; Geochem Soc; Mineral Asn Can; fel Meteoretical Soc. *Res:* Thermodynamics of mineral systems; phase equilibria in meteorites; optical and x-ray spectroscopy; electron microprobe. *Mailing Add:* Dept of Geol Field Mus of Natural Hist Chicago IL 60605

OLSEN, EDWARD TAIT, b Brooklyn, NY, June 12, 42; m 68. RADIO ASTRONOMY, PLANETARY ATMOSPHERES. *Educ:* Mass Inst Technol, BS, 64; Calif Inst Technol, MS, 67; Univ Mich, PhD(astron), 72. *Prof Exp:* Resident res assoc radio astron, Nat Res Coun, 72-74, sr scientist radio astron & planetary atmospheres, 74-78, MEM TECH STAFF, JET PROPULSION LAB, 78- *Mem:* Am Astron Soc; Sigma Xi; Planetary Soc; AAAS. *Res:* Microwave studies of the Jovian synchrotron emission and of the atmospheres of the major planets; the search for extraterrestrial intelligence. *Mailing Add:* T1106 Jet Propulsion Lab 4800 Oak Grove Dr Pasadena CA 91103

OLSEN, EDWIN CARL, III, b Salt Lake City, Utah, Dec 20, 32; m 57; c 3. IRRIGATION ENGINEERING, SOIL CONSERVATION. *Educ:* Utah State Univ, BS, 59, PhD(irrig eng), 65. *Prof Exp:* Engr, Tipton & Kalmbach, Inc, Pakistan, 64-66; water resources engr, USAID, Laos, 66-68; ASSOC PROF AGR & IRRIG ENG, UTAH STATE UNIV, 68-, DIR, INT IRRIG CTR, 80- *Mem:* Am Soc Civil Engrs; Am Soc Agr Engrs; Am Geophys Union; Int Asn Sci Hydrol. *Res:* On farm water management in sub-humid and arid areas of developing countries, especially drainage, soil salinity control, irrigation system management, evapotranspiration and hydrologic balance. *Mailing Add:* Dept Agr & Irrig Eng Utah State Univ Logan UT 84321

OLSEN, EUGENE DONALD, b La Crosse, Wis, Dec 10, 33; wid; c 3. ANALYTICAL CHEMISTRY, CLINICAL CHEMISTRY. *Educ:* Univ Wis, BS, 55, PhD(anal chem), 60. *Prof Exp:* Instr chem, Univ Wis, 60; asst prof, Franklin & Marshall Col, 60-64; from asst prof to assoc prof, 64-73, PROF CHEM, UNIV S FLA, 73- *Concurrent Pos:* Supvr undergrad res participation, NSF, 60-70, res grants, 64-66; NIH spec fel, Med Sch, 71-72. *Mem:* Am Chem Soc; Royal Soc Chem; Asn Clin Scientists. *Res:* Teaching films; ion exchange separation of radioelements; instrumental methods of analysis; chelometric titrations; electrochemical analysis; automation in analysis; reactions in nonaqueous and mixed solvents; clinical and medicinal chemistry. *Mailing Add:* Dept of Chem Univ of SFla Tampa FL 33620

OLSEN, FARREL JOHN, b Salt Lake City, Utah, Mar 2, 29; m 55; c 3. AGRONOMY. *Educ:* Utah State Univ, BS, 54, MS, 58; Rutgers Univ, New Brunswick, PhD(crop prod), 61. *Prof Exp:* Exten agronomist, WVa Univ, 61-66; plant scientist, Sci Info Exchange, Smithsonian Inst, 66-67, pasture agronomist, WVa Univ, 67-71; assoc prof, 74-78, PROF PLANT & SOIL SCI, SCH AGR, SOUTHERN ILL UNIV, CARBONDALE, 78-, PASTURE AGRONOMIST, 71- *Mem:* Am Soc Agron. *Res:* Planted pastures, their establishment, management and utilization; nutritive value. *Mailing Add:* Dept of Plant & Soil Sci Southern Ill Univ Carbondale IL 62901

OLSEN, GEORGE DUANE, b DeKalb, Ill, Jan 5, 40; m 65; c 2. CLINICAL PHARMACOLOGY. *Educ:* Dartmouth Col, AB, 62; Dartmouth Med Sch, BMS, 64; Harvard Med Sch, MD, 66. *Prof Exp:* Intern med, Univ Hosps Cleveland, 66-67; med dir, Indian Health Ctr, USPHS, 67-69; asst prof, 70-78, ASSOC PROF PHARMACOL, MED SCH, ORE HEALTH SCI UNIV, 78-, INSTR MED, 72- *Concurrent Pos:* NIH training grant pharmacol, Med Sch, Univ Ore, 69-70; Fogarty sr int fel & NATO sr scientist fel, 81-82. *Mem:* AAAS; Am Fedn Clin Res; Am Soc Pharmacol & Exp Therapeut; Am Soc Clin Pharmacol & Therapeut; Perinatal Res Soc. *Res:* Perinatal pharmacology; respiratory pharmacology. *Mailing Add:* Dept Pharmacol Sch Med Ore Health Sci Univ Portland OR 92701

OLSEN, GERNER A(KTANDER), b Lister, Norway, Sept 30, 09; US citizen; m 37; c 3. CIVIL ENGINEERING. *Educ:* Polytech Inst Brooklyn, CE, 31; Mass Inst Technol, SM, 32. *Prof Exp:* Draftsman, John Olsen Flooring Co, NY, 32-33; jr engr, US Engrs, 33; designer & draftsman, Gibbs & Hill, 34; off mgr, Haakonsen Towing & Transp Co, 34-36; instr civil eng, Norwich Univ, 36-38; assoc prof, Rutgers Univ, 38-45; res dir, Santee Mills, SC, 45; develop engr, Bakelite Corp, NJ, 45-49; from asst prof to prof, 49-74, EMER PROF CIVIL ENG, CITY COL NEW YORK, 74-, SECY GEN FAC & BIOMED ENG COORDR, 67- *Concurrent Pos:* Lectr, Stevens Inst Technol, 47-; Fier med fel, Hosp Joint Dis, 63; NIH fel biomed eng, Univ Va, 65 & 72, consult, 51-70; vis clin prof, Ohio State Univ, 73- *Mem:* Am Soc Testing & Mat; Am Soc Eng Educ; Am Soc Civil Engrs; Soc Exp Stress Anal; assoc mem Scoliosis Res Soc. *Res:* Physical properties of engineering materials; stress analysis; structures; orthopedic engineering and research; correction of scoliotic spinal curves by electrical muscle stimulation. *Mailing Add:* 50 James St Westwood NJ 07675

OLSEN, GLENN W, b North Lima, Ohio, Sept 7, 31; m 57; c 2. MATHEMATICS EDUCATION. *Educ:* Edinboro State Col, BSEd, 53; Pa State Univ, MEd, 58; Cornell Univ, PhD(math, math educ), 68. *Prof Exp:* Teacher, Randolph East Mead High Sch, 53-59; assoc prof math, Indiana Univ Pa, 60-65; head dept, 68-74, PROF MATH, EDINBORO STATE COL, 68- *Mem:* Math Asn Am. *Res:* Number theory; set theory; analysis; problems in the teaching of mathematics. *Mailing Add:* Dept of Math Edinboro State Col Edinboro PA 16444

OLSEN, GREGORY HAMMOND, b Brooklyn, NY, Apr 20, 45; div; c 2. SOLID STATE PHYSICS. *Educ:* Fairleigh Dickinson Univ, BS, 66, BS & MS, 68; Univ Va, PhD(mat sci), 71. *Prof Exp:* Teaching asst physics, Fairleigh Dickinson Univ, 66-68; vis scientist electron micros, Univ Port Elizabeth, Repub S Africa, 71-72; mem tech staff crystal growth, 72-79, RES LEADER, RCA LABS, 80- *Mem:* AAAS; Inst Elec & Electronic Engrs; Electrochem Soc; Am Phys Soc; Sigma Xi. *Res:* Study of crystal growth and structural defects in semiconductors for electro-optical devices; synthesized the first vapor phase epitaxy gallium arsenic continuous wave laser and the first vapor phase epitaxy indium gallium arsenic phosphorus 1.25, 1.55 and 1.65 micron continuous wave laser; vapor phase epitaxy 1.0-1.7 unit of measure Indium Gallium Arsenic photodetector. *Mailing Add:* RCA Labs Princeton NJ 08540

OLSEN, JAMES CALVIN, b San Diego, Calif, May 17, 39; m 64; c 2. FISHERIES, BIOMETRICS. *Educ:* Ore State Univ, BS, 61; Univ Wash, MS, 64, PhD(fisheries), 69. *Prof Exp:* Res asst salmon res, Fisheries Res Inst, Univ Wash, 61-63, res asst fisheries res, Col Fisheries, 63-68; math statistician fisheries pop dynamics, 68-77, DEP LAB DIR, AUKE BAY LAB, NAT MARINE FISHERIES SERV, 77- *Mem:* Am Fisheries Soc. *Res:* Development of analytic methods for estimating abundance and production of marine populations. *Mailing Add:* Auke Bay Lab PO Box 155 Auke Bay AK 99821

OLSEN, JAMES LEROY, b Minneapolis, Minn, June 8, 30; m 55; c 4. INDUSTRIAL PHARMACY. *Educ:* Univ Minn, Minneapolis, BS, 54, PhD(pharm), 64. *Prof Exp:* Pharmacist supvr, Sch Pharm, Univ Minn, 58-63; asst vpres, Clark-Cleveland Div, Richardson-Merrell Corp, 63-69; asst prof pharmaceut, 69-74, ASSOC PROF PHARM & CHMN DIV PHARMACEUT, SCH PHARM, UNIV NC, CHAPEL HILL, 74- *Concurrent Pos:* Food & Drug Admin fel, Sch Pharm, Univ NC, Chapel Hill, 71- *Mem:* Am Pharmaceut Asn; Acad Pharmaceut Sci. *Res:* Pharmaceutical dosage forms; tablets; long-acting dosage forms; dissolution. *Mailing Add:* Sch of Pharm Univ of NC Chapel Hill NC 27514

OLSEN, JOHN HENRY, b Detroit, Mich, Aug 18, 39; m 64; c 4. FLUID MECHANICS. *Educ:* Mass Inst Technol, BS, 61, MS, 63, PhD(mech eng), 66. *Prof Exp:* Res assoc fluid mech, Mass Inst Technol, 66; staff mem, Boeing Sci Res Labs, 66-72; VPRES, FLOW RES INC, 72- *Mem:* AAAS; Am Soc Mech Engrs; Am Meteorol Soc. *Res:* Incompressible flow; unsteady flow; vortex motion; wakes; high pressure jets; electrokinetics. *Mailing Add:* Box 788 Rte 1 Vashon WA 98070

OLSEN, KATHIE LYNN, b Portland, Ore, Aug 3, 52. NEUROENDOCRINOLOGY, PSYCHOBIOLOGY. *Educ:* Chatham Col, BS, 74; Univ Calif, Irvine, PhD(psychobiol), 79. *Prof Exp:* Fel neurobiol, Dept Neuropath, Harvard Med Sch, 79-80; RES SCIENTIST, LONG ISLAND RES INST, STATE UNIV NY, STONY BROOK, 80- *Concurrent Pos:* NIH prin investr, 81-84. *Mem:* Asn Women Sci; Soc Neurosci. *Res:* Developmental and regulatory mechanisms underlying the expression of behaviors; developmental psychoeuroendocrinology; hormone-genome interaction. *Mailing Add:* Long Island Res Inst HSC 10T State Univ NY Stony Brook NY 11777

OLSEN, KENNETH HAROLD, b Ogden, Utah, Feb 20, 30; m 55; c 4. GEOPHYSICS, ASTROPHYSICS. *Educ:* Idaho State Col, BS, 52; Calif Inst Technol, MS, 54, PhD(physics), 57. *Prof Exp:* Staff mem, 57-71, alt group leader, 71-74, GROUP LEADER, LOS ALAMOS NAT LAB, 74- *Concurrent Pos:* Grad asst, Mt Wilson Observ, Calif Inst Technol, 52-57. *Mem:* Royal Astron Soc; Seismol Soc Am; Soc Explor Geophysicists; Int Astron Union; AAAS. *Res:* Measurement of transition probabilities for atomic spectra; computer calculations of astrophysical problems; underground explosion phenomenology; water waves, tsunamis; seismology; infrared Fourier transform spectroscopy; solar eclipse observations; crustal structure, seismic refraction profiling, geophysics and tectonics of Rio Grande rift; synthetic seismogram modeling. *Mailing Add:* 226 Venado Los Alamos NM 87544

OLSEN, KENNETH LAURENCE, b Enumclaw, Wash, July 25, 21; m 46, 73; c 2. PLANT PHYSIOLOGY. *Educ:* Wash State Univ, BS, 45, MS, 50; Univ Calif, PhD(plant physiol), 50. *Prof Exp:* Asst bot, Wash State Univ, 44-46; instr gen bot & plant physiol, Ore State Col, 46-47; asst plant physiol & weed control, Univ Calif, 47-50, plant physiologist, Inter-Am Inst Agr Sci, 50-54; plant physiologist, Rice Invests, Field Crops Res Br, Agr Res Serv, 54-57, plant physiologist, Agr Mkt Serv, 57-64, PLANT PHYSIOLOGIST, SCI & EDUC ADMIN-AGR RES, USDA, 64- *Mem:* AAAS; Am Soc Hort Sci; Am Soc Plant Physiol; Am Chem Soc. *Res:* Biochemical changes during maturation and ripening of fruits; effect of modified atmospheres during storage. *Mailing Add:* Sci & Educ Admin-Agr Res USDA 1104 N Western Ave Wenatchee WA 98801

OLSEN, KENNETH WAYNE, b Chicago, Ill, Dec 19, 44; m 66; c 3. PROTEIN CHEMISTRY, BIOCHEMISTRY. *Educ:* Iowa State Univ, BS, 67; Duke Univ, PhD(biochem), 72. *Prof Exp:* Res assoc protein crystallog, Purdue Univ, 72-75; ASST PROF BIOCHEM, MED CTR, UNIV MISS, 75- *Concurrent Pos:* Fel, Am Cancer Soc, 72-74. *Mem:* Am Crystallog Asn. *Res:* Protein chemistry and crystallog; enzymology; heme transport proteins; affinity chromatography. *Mailing Add:* Dept of Biochem Med Ctr Univ of Miss Jackson MS 39216

OLSEN, LARRY CARROL, b St Joseph, Mo, July 25, 37; m 60; c 3. SOLID STATE SCIENCE. *Educ:* Univ Kans, BS, 60, PhD(physics), 65. *Prof Exp:* Asst prof physics, Univ Kans, 65; sr scientist, McDonnell Douglas Corp, 65-74; assoc prof eng, 74-80, PROF MAT SCI & ENG, JOINT CTR GRAD STUDY, 81- *Concurrent Pos:* Lectr, Joint Ctr Grad Study, 67-74. *Mem:* Am Phys Soc; Sigma Xi. *Res:* Photovoltaic research and development; solar cell studies based on silicon, cuprous-oxide and other materials; transport properties of solids; radiation effects in materials; electron-voltaic, thermoelectric and other forms of energy conversion. *Mailing Add:* 1837 Norwood Ct Richland WA 99352

OLSEN, ORVIL ALVA, b Biggar, Sask, July 22, 17; m 45; c 3. BOTANY. *Educ:* Univ Sask, BSA, 41; Univ Man, MSc, 48; McGill Univ, PhD(plant path), 61. *Prof Exp:* Res asst potato breeding, Man Dept Agr, 46-49; asst prof plant path, McGill Univ, 51-57; res officer, Can Dept Agr, 57-65, res scientist, 65-68; ASSOC PROF BOT, MEM UNIV NFLD, 68- *Mem:* Agr Inst Can; Can Phytopath Soc; Can Bot Asn. *Res:* Ecology of vegetation of spray zones created by waterfalls; floristics of Newfoundland. *Mailing Add:* Dept of Biol Mem Univ of Nfld Regional Col Corner Brook NF A1C 5S7 Can

OLSEN, PETER FREDRIC, b Red Bank, NJ, Apr 7, 35; m 70. ECOLOGY. *Educ:* Univ Mich, BS, 56, MS, 57; Auburn Univ, PhD(zool), 65. *Prof Exp:* Res fel muskrat pop dynamics, Wildlife Mgt Inst, Delta Waterfowl Res Sta, 55-56; game biologist, Mich Dept Conserv, 57-58; res assoc dis ecol, Auburn Univ, 60-62; sr res ecologist, head ecol sect & asst res prof wildlife dis ecol, Univ Utah, 63-70; sr res ecologist & vpres, EcoDynamics, Inc, 70-73; SR ECOLOGIST, DAMES & MOORE CONSULT ENGRS, 74- *Mem:* AAAS; Wildlife Soc; Am Soc Mammal; Ecol Soc Am; Am Inst Biol Sci. *Res:* Analysis and evaluation of ecological and other impacts upon the environment which may result from proposed development activities. *Mailing Add:* Dames & Moore 250 E Broadway Salt Lake City UT 84111

OLSEN, RALPH A, b Moroni, Utah, Jan 30, 25; m 49; c 7. SOIL CHEMISTRY. *Educ:* Brigham Young Univ, BS, 49; Cornell Univ, MS, 51, PhD(agron), 53. *Prof Exp:* Soil scientist, USDA, 53-56; assoc prof, 56-64, PROF CHEM, MONT STATE UNIV, 64- *Concurrent Pos:* Fel, Mineral Nutrit Pioneering Res Lab, Md, 61-62; Inst Biol Chem fel, Univ Copenhagen, 65-66. *Mem:* Soil Sci Soc Am; Am Chem Soc; Sigma Xi. *Res:* Potentiometric measurements in colloidal suspensions; mechanisms involved in the movement of ions from soils to plant roots; inorganic nutrition of green plants; ion movement through living membranes. *Mailing Add:* Dept of Chem Mont State Univ Bozeman MT 59715

OLSEN, RICHARD DENNIS, b LaCrosse, Wis, Jan 9, 43. AQUATIC ECOLOGY. *Educ:* Univ Wis, LaCrosse, BS, 69; Ariz State Univ, PhD(bot & microbiol), 75. *Prof Exp:* STAFF SCIENTIST ENVIRON SCI, ARGONNE NAT LAB, 74- *Mem:* Am Soc Limnol & Oceanog; Phycol Soc Am. *Res:* Environmental research and assessment projects; aquatic edology and water quality; including ecology of primary producers, effects of environmental perturbations on aquatic systems, and water quality analysis and monitoring. *Mailing Add:* EIS Div Bldg 10 9700 S Cass Ave Argonne IL 60439

OLSEN, RICHARD GEORGE, b Independence, Mo, June 25, 37; m 57; c 4. VIROLOGY. *Educ:* Univ Mo-Kansas City, BA, 59; Atlanta Univ, MS, 64; State Univ NY Buffalo, PhD(virol), 69. *Prof Exp:* Instr microbiol, Metrop Jr Col, 63-67; from asst prof to assoc prof, 69-77, PROF VIROL, COL VET MED, OHIO STATE UNIV, 77- *Mem:* Am Soc Microbiol; Am Asn Cancer Res; Tissue Cult Asn; Int Asn Comp Res Leukemia. *Res:* Immunology of the cat and man to oncogenic viruses, including tumor poxviruses and RNA oncornaviruses. *Mailing Add:* Dept of Vet Path Col of Vet Med Ohio State Univ Columbus OH 43210

OLSEN, RICHARD KENNETH, b Provo, Utah, Sept 3, 35; m 54; c 5. ORGANIC CHEMISTRY. *Educ:* Brigham Young Univ, AB, 60; Univ Ill, PhD(org chem), 64. *Prof Exp:* Fel org chem, Stanford Res Inst, 64-65; res assoc, Univ Utah, 65-67; from asst prof to assoc prof chem, 67-77, PROF CHEM & BIOCHEM, UTAH STATE UNIV, 77- *Mem:* Am Chem Soc. *Res:* Synthetic organic chemistry; natural products; peptide antibiotics. *Mailing Add:* Dept of Chem Utah State Univ Logan UT 84321

OLSEN, RICHARD STANDAL, b Lansing, Mich, Nov 13, 36; m 65; c 2. CHEMICAL ENGINEERING. *Educ:* Pac Lutheran Univ, BA, 59; Ore State Univ, PhD(chem eng), 67. *Prof Exp:* chem res engr, 66-80, PROJ SUPVR, ALBANY METALL RES CTR, FED BUR MINES, 80- *Mem:* Sigam Xi. *Res:* Chemical processes involved in extractive metallurgy; chlorination processes; chlorination of base metal sulfides. *Mailing Add:* 732 Broadalbin Albany OR 97321

OLSEN, RICHARD WILLIAM, b Marshfield, Wis, Aug 13, 44; m 67; c 2. BIOCHEMISTRY. *Educ:* Dartmouth Col, AB, 66; Univ Calif, Berkeley, PhD(biochem), 71. *Prof Exp:* USPHS fel, Inst Pasteur, Paris, 71-72; asst prof biochem, 72-78, PROF BIOMED SCI & BIOCHEM, UNIV CALIF, RIVERSIDE, 78- *Mem:* Soc Neurosci; Int Soc Neurochem; Am Soc Biol Chemists. *Res:* Biochemistry of the nervous system; excitable membrane constituents, receptor proteins; gamma-amino-bityric acid; mode of action of neurotransmitters, drugs, and insecticides; microtubules and their role in cellular response to regulatory stimuli. *Mailing Add:* Dept of Biochem Univ of Calif Riverside CA 92502

OLSEN, ROBERT GERNER, b Brooklyn, NY, Apr 9, 46; m 74; c 2. ELECTROMAGNETISM, ELECTRICAL ENGINEERING. *Educ:* Rutgers Univ, BS, 68; Univ Colo, MS, 70, PhD(elec eng), 74. *Prof Exp:* Sr scientist elec eng, Westinghouse Geores Lab, 71-73; asst prof, 73-78, ASSOC PROF ELEC ENG, WASH STATE UNIV, 78- *Concurrent Pos:* Assoc mem, Comn B, US Nat Comt, Int Union Radio Sci, 76-; consult, Westinghouse Geophys Instrumentation Syst, Boulder, Colo, 78- & Gen Tel & Electron Corp Labs, Waltham, Mass, 80- *Mem:* Inst Elec & Electronics Engrs; Sigma Xi. *Res:* Antenna theory; underground electromagnetic wave propagation; numerical solution of electrostatics problems. *Mailing Add:* Dept of Elec Eng Wash State Univ Pullman WA 99164

OLSEN, ROBERT JAMES, soil science, see previous edition

OLSEN, ROBERT THORVALD, b Brookfield, Ill, Mar 10, 15; m 41; c 2. SYNTHETIC ORGANIC CHEMISTRY. *Educ:* Newark Col Eng, BSChE, 36; Columbia Univ, MSChE, 37; Mass Inst Technol, PhD(org chem), 42. *Prof Exp:* Chem engr, Eastman Kodak Co, NY, 37-39; sr res chemist, Gen Aniline & Film Corp, 42-48, Plymouth Cordage Co, 48-54 & Celotex Corp, 54-56; res mgr, Standard Register Co, 56-61; dir res & develop, Gamma Chem Corp, Great Meadows, 61-68; tech dir fine chem, Ashland Chem Co, 68-76; CONSULT, 76- *Mem:* AAAS; Am Chem Soc; Am Wine Soc; Am Soc Enol; Soc Wine Educrs. *Res:* Chemical engineering; research management. *Mailing Add:* 1 Country Lane Eastham MA 02642

OLSEN, RODNEY L, b Duluth, Minn, July 10, 36; m 58; c 2. ANALYTICAL CHEMISTRY. *Educ:* Univ Minn, Duluth, BA, 58; Iowa State Univ, MS, 60, PhD(anal chem), 62. *Prof Exp:* From asst prof to assoc prof, 62-73, PROF CHEM, HAMLINE UNIV, 73- *Mem:* Am Chem Soc. *Res:* Fluorometric methods; radiochemistry; analytical separations. *Mailing Add:* Dept of Chem Hamline Univ St Paul MN 55104

OLSEN, RONALD G, b Duluth, Minn, Oct 22, 37; m 62; c 2. CHEMISTRY PHOTOGRAPHY, ORGANIC CHEMISTRY. *Educ:* Univ Minn, Duluth, BA, 59; Ind Univ, PhD(org chem), 65. *Prof Exp:* RES ASSOC, EASTMAN KODAK CO, 65- *Mem:* Soc Photographic Scientists & Engrs. *Res:* Synthetic organic chemistry; photographic systems. *Mailing Add:* 9 Ambleside Fairport NY 14450

OLSEN, RONALD H, b New Ulm, Minn, June 26, 32; m 58; c 6. MICROBIOLOGY. *Educ:* Univ Minn, BA, 57, MS, 59, PhD(microbiol), 62. *Prof Exp:* Asst prof microbiol, Colo State Univ, 62-63; vpres res & develop, Dairy Technics Inc, 63-65; assoc prof, 65-74, PROF MICROBIOL, UNIV MICH, ANN ARBOR, 74- *Mem:* AAAS; Am Soc Microbiol. *Res:* Bacterial physiology; physiological basis for the minimum temperature of growth. *Mailing Add:* Dept of Microbiol Univ of Mich Ann Arbor MI 48109

OLSEN, SIGURD, limnology, deceased

OLSEN, STANLEY JOHN, b Akron, Ohio, June 24, 19; m 42; c 1. BIOLOGICAL ANTHROPOLOGY, ARCHAEOLOGY. *Prof Exp:* Lab technician vert paleont, Harvard Univ, 45-56; vert paleontologist, Fla Geol Surv, 56-58; from assoc prof to prof zooarchaeol, Fla State Univ, 68-73; PROF ANTHROP, UNIV ARIZ, 73-; ZOOARCHAEOLOGIST, ARIZ STATE MUS, 73- *Concurrent Pos:* Res assoc, Mus Northern Ariz, 66-; NSF grant, Fla Geol Surv, 64-66, Harvard Univ Guide Found grant, 66; NSF grant, Fla State Univ, 67-69 & 69-70, Am Philos Soc grant, 70 & Nat Geog Soc grant, 82. *Mem:* Soc Vert Paleont (pres, 65-66); Am Soc Mammal; Soc Am Archaeol; Am Soc Ichthyol & Herpet; Soc Syst Zool. *Res:* Analysis of vertebrates from archaeological sites in the Western Hemisphere; beginnings of animal domestication in China; origins of domestic dog. *Mailing Add:* Dept of Anthrop Univ of Ariz Tucson AZ 85721

OLSEN, STEPHEN LARS, PARTICLE PHYSICS. *Educ:* City Col New York, BS, 63; Univ Wis, MS, 65, PhD(physics), 70. *Prof Exp:* Res assoc physics, Univ Wis, 70 & Rockefeller Univ, 70-72; asst prof, 72-75, ASSOC PROF PHYSICS, UNIV ROCHESTER, 75- *Concurrent Pos:* Fel, Alfred P Sloan Found, 73-77; mem prog adv comt, Fermi Nat Accelerator Lab, 75-78. *Res:* Experimental studies of the interactions between elementary particles at high energies. *Mailing Add:* Dept Physics Univ Rochester Rochester NY 14627

OLSEN, STEPHEN LARS, b Mar 22, 42; US citizen. PARTICLE PHYSICS. *Educ:* City Col NY, BS, 63; Univ Wis, MS, 65, PhD(physics), 70. *Prof Exp:* Res assoc physics, Univ Wis, 70 & Rockefeller Univ, 70-72; asst prof, 72-75, ASSOC PROF PHYSICS, UNIV ROCHESTER, 75- *Concurrent Pos:* Fel, Alfred P Sloan Found, 73-77; mem prog adv comt, Ferni Nat Accelerator Lab, 75-78. *Res:* Experimental studies of the interactions between elementary particles at high energies. *Mailing Add:* Dept Physics Univ Rochester Rochester NY 14627

OLSEN, WARD ALAN, b Holmen, Wis, Sept 13, 34; m 61; c 3. INTERNAL MEDICINE, GASTROENTEROLOGY. *Educ:* Univ Wis-Madison, BS, 56, MD, 59. *Prof Exp:* From intern to resident, Harvard Med Serv, Boston City Hosp, 59-62 & 64-65; instr med, Harvard Med Sch, 67-68; from asst prof to assoc prof, 68-78, PROF MED, UNIV WIS-MADISON, 78- *Concurrent Pos:* Fel gastroenterol, Boston Univ, 65-67; chief gastroenterol, Vet Admin Hosp, Madison, Wis, 68- *Mem:* Am Fedn Clin Res; Cent Soc Clin Res; Am Soc Clin Invest; Am Gastroenterol Asn. *Res:* Intestinal absorption. *Mailing Add:* Vet Admin Hosp 2500 Overlook Terr Madison WI 53705

OLSEN, WILLIAM CHARLES, b Edmonton, Alta, Mar 25, 33; m 57; c 2. NUCLEAR PHYSICS. *Educ:* Univ BC, BASc, 56, MASc, 59; Univ Alta, PhD(nuclear physics), 64. *Prof Exp:* Res officer, Atomic Energy Can Ltd, Ont, 58-60; res assoc, 64, from asst prof to assoc prof, 64-74, PROF NUCLEAR PHYSICS, UNIV ALTA, 74- *Res:* Low and intermediate energy nuclear physics leading to information on the nuclear structure of low and medium mass nuclei. *Mailing Add:* 12415 52nd Ave Edmonton AB T6H 0P5 Can

OLSHANSKY, ROBERT, theoretical physics, see previous edition

OLSHEN, RICHARD ALLEN, b Portland, Ore, May 17, 42; m 63; c 1. STATISTICS, MATHEMATICS. *Educ:* Univ Calif, Berkeley, AB, 63; Yale Univ, MS, 65, PhD(statist), 66. *Prof Exp:* Lectr statist & res staff statistician, Yale Univ, 66-67; asst prof statist, Stanford Univ, 67-72; assoc prof, Univ Mich, Ann Arbor, 72-75; assoc prof, 75-77, PROF MATH, UNIV CALIF, SAN DIEGO, 77-, DIR BIOSTATIST-EPIDEMIOL UNIT, CANCER CTR, 78- *Concurrent Pos:* Vis asst prof, Columbia Univ, 70-71; vis assoc prof, Stanford Univ, 73-75. *Mem:* Fel Inst Math Statist; Am Statist Asn. *Mailing Add:* Dept of Math Univ of Calif at San Diego La Jolla CA 92093

OLSON, ALBERT LLOYD, b Mountain View, Calif, Dec 14, 24; m 48; c 3. PATHOLOGY. *Educ:* Col Med Evangelists, MD, 49; Am Bd Path, dipl, 58, cert clin path, 60. *Prof Exp:* From instr to asst prof, 58-64, ASSOC PROF PATH, LOMA LINDA UNIV, 64- *Res:* Medicine. *Mailing Add:* Clin Lab White Mem Med Ctr 1720 Brooklyn Ave Los Angeles CA 90033

OLSON, ALFRED C, b Chicago, Ill, July 18, 26; m 66; c 1. BIOCHEMISTRY. *Educ:* Northwestern Univ, BS, 49; Univ Wis, PhD(phys & org chem), 54. *Prof Exp:* Chemist, Calif Res Corp Div, Standard Oil Co Calif, 54-60; RES CHEMIST, WESTERN REGIONAL RES CTR, AGR RES SERV USDA, 60- *Concurrent Pos:* Res fel, Div Biol, Calif Inst Technol, 60-63. *Mem:* Am Chem Soc; Am Soc Plant Physiol; Tissue Cult Asn; Inst Food Sci & Technol; AAAS. *Res:* Bioavailability of nutrients; nutritional problems of dry beans; plant tissue culture; immobilized enzymes. *Mailing Add:* Western Regional Res Ctr Agr Res Serv USDA 800 Buchanan Albany CA 94710

OLSON, ALLAN THEODORE, b Cochrane, Ont, July 10, 30; m 64. THERMODYNAMICS, MECHANICS. *Educ:* Queen's Univ, Ont, BSc, 53; Univ Birmingham, MSc, 55. *Prof Exp:* Res officer mech eng, Nat Res Coun Can, 55-57; ASSOC PROF THERMODYN & MECH, UNIV WESTERN ONT, 57- *Mailing Add:* 230 Wychwood Pk London ON N6G 1S2 Can

OLSON, ANDREW CLARENCE, JR, b San Diego, Calif, Nov 10, 17; m 45; c 2. PARASITOLOGY. *Educ:* San Diego State Univ, BA, 39; Univ Idaho, MS, 42; Ore State Univ, PhD, 55. *Prof Exp:* From instr to assoc prof, 46-58, chmn dept, 57-60, PROF ZOOL, SAN DIEGO STATE UNIV, 58- *Mem:* AAAS; Am Soc Parasitol; Am Soc Mammal; Wildlife Dis Asn. *Res:* Ecology of fish parasites. *Mailing Add:* Dept of Zool San Diego State Univ San Diego CA 92182

OLSON, ANITA CORA, biochemistry, immunochemistry, see previous edition

OLSON, ARTHUR OLAF, b Lethbridge, Alta, May 11, 42; m 63; c 2. BIOCHEMISTRY, HORTICULTURE. *Educ:* Univ Alta, BSc, 64, PhD(plant biochem), 67. *Prof Exp:* Exten horticulturist, Alta Dept Agr, 64; res fel biochem, McMaster Univ, 67-68; res biochemist, Atomic Energy Can, Ltd, 68-69; dir, Alta Hort Res Ctr, 70-74, dir, Plant Indust Div, 74-79, ASST DEP MINISTER RES & OPER, ALTA DEPT AGR, 79- *Concurrent Pos:* Ed, Can Soc Hort Sci, 71- *Mem:* Agr Inst Can; Can Soc Hort Sci. *Res:* Aging effects of ethylene in plants and animals; mutation damage and its repair in algae and yeast; post harvest physiology and storage biochemistry. *Mailing Add:* Plant Indust Div Alta Dept of Agr Edmonton AB T5K 2C8 Can

OLSON, ARTHUR RUSSELL, b Lawrence, Mass, Jan 22, 19; m 42; c 4. TEXTILE CHEMISTRY. *Educ:* Mass Inst Technol, BS, 39. *Prof Exp:* Develop chemist, Hunt-Rankin Leather Co, Mass, 39-42; plastics chemist, United Shoe Mach Corp, 46-50; dir & chemist, McMillan Lab, Inc, 50-52; res chemist, Finishing Div, 52-60, Fiber Prod Div, 60-64, res mgr, Fiber Prod Div, 64-77, RES ASSOC, KENDALL CO, 77- *Mem:* AAAS; Am Chem Soc. *Res:* Plastics technology; synthetic resins and plastics; textiles and textiles materials. *Mailing Add:* 6 Eastover Rd Walpole MA 02081

OLSON, AUSTIN C(ARLEN), b Missoula, Mont, Feb 4, 18; m 45; c 2. CHEMICAL ENGINEERING. *Educ:* Mont State Univ, BS, 39; Univ Minn, MS, 41, PhD(chem eng), 48. *Prof Exp:* Asst chem eng, Univ Minn, 39-41, instr, 41-42; assoc res engr, Chevron Res Co Div, 48-51, res engr, 51-59, group supvr, 59-62, supv engr, 62-66, sect supvr, 66-73, CHMN PROJ MGR, CHEVRON RES CO, STANDARD OIL CO CALIF, 73- *Mem:* Am Chem Soc; Am Inst Chem Engrs. *Res:* Petroleum and petrochemical plant and process design and economic evaluation; environmental engineering. *Mailing Add:* Chevron Res Co 576 Standard Ave Richmond CA 94802

OLSON, CARL, b Sac City, Iowa, Sept 15, 10; m 34; c 4. COMPARATIVE PATHOLOGY. *Educ:* Iowa State Univ, DVM, 31; Univ Minn, MS, 34, PhD(comp path), 35. *Prof Exp:* Asst prof path, State Univ NY Vet Col, Cornell Univ, 35-37; res prof, Univ Mass, 37-45; prof animal path & hyg & chmn dept, Univ Nebr, 45-56; chmn dept, 62-63, VET SCI, UNIV WIS-MADISON, 56- *Mem:* Am Col Vet Path; Am Vet Med Asn; Am Asn Pathologists; Am Asn Avian Path; Conf Res Workers Animal Dis (pres, 58). *Res:* Pathogenesis of animal diseases, especially neoplastic particularly pepillomatosis and bovine leukosis. *Mailing Add:* Dept of Vet Sci Univ of Wis-Madison Madison WI 53706

OLSON, CARTER LEROY, b Iola, Wis, Jan 13, 35; m 60; c 1. ANALYTICAL CHEMISTRY. *Educ:* Wis State Col, Stevens Point, BS, 56; Univ Kans, PhD(chem), 62. *Prof Exp:* Res assoc & fel anal chem, Univ Wis, 61-63; from asst prof to assoc prof pharmaceut anal, 63-73, ASSOC PROF MED CHEM, COL PHARM, OHIO STATE UNIV, 73- *Mem:* Am Chem Soc. *Res:* Continuous methods of analysis; electroanalytical chemistry; analysis based on the rates of chemical reactions including the rates of enzyme catalyzed reactions. *Mailing Add:* Col of Pharm Ohio State Univ Columbus OH 43210

OLSON, CLIFFORD GERALD, b Osakis, Minn, July 6, 42; m 65. SOLID STATE PHYSICS. *Educ:* Hamline Univ, BS, 64; Iowa State Univ, PhD(physics), 70. *Prof Exp:* Fel, 70-71, PHYSICIST, AMES LAB, US DEPT ENERGY, IOWA STATE UNIV, 71- *Mem:* Am Phys Soc; Optical Soc Am. *Res:* Photo emission and optical properties of solids using synchrotron radiation. *Mailing Add:* Synchrotron Radiation Ctr Ames Lab US Dept Energy 3725 Schneider Dr Rte 4 Stoughton WI 53589

OLSON, DALE WILSON, b Mountain Lake, Minn, July 27, 41. MAGNETISM. *Educ:* Carleton Col, BA, 62; Univ Rochester, PhD(physics), 70. *Prof Exp:* Asst prof, 68-73, ASSOC PROF PHYSICS, UNIV NORTHERN IOWA, 73- *Mem:* Am Phys Soc; Am Asn Physics Teachers. *Res:* Electron paramagnetic resonance; phase transitions. *Mailing Add:* Dept of Physics Univ of Northern Iowa Cedar Falls IA 50613

OLSON, DANFORD HAROLD, b Minneapolis, Minn, Jan 17, 35; m 55; c 4. ORGANIC CHEMISTRY. *Educ:* Univ Minn, BS, 56; Kans State Univ, PhD(chem), 62. *Prof Exp:* Res scientist petrochem, Denver Res Ctr, Marathon Oil Co, 62-66; res scientist, Shell Oil Co Res Ctr, Wood River, 66-70, supvr, Eng Lubricants, 70-75, SUPVR ENG LUBRICANTS, SHELL DEVELOP RES CTR, HOUSTON, 75- *Mem:* Am Chem Soc; Soc Automotive Engrs; Sigma Xi. *Res:* Synthesis of small ring heterocyclics; use of nitrogen oxides in organic synthesis; liquid and gas phase oxidation reactions; dehydrogenation; computer applications; product development. *Mailing Add:* 12622 Campsite Trail Cypress TX 77429

OLSON, DAVID GARDELS, b Melrose Park, Ill, Jan 25, 40; m 73. OPERATIONS RESEARCH, SYSTEMS ANALYSIS. *Educ:* Purdue Univ, BS, 61; Mass Inst Technol, SM, 63; Northwestern Univ, Evanston, PhD(indust eng), 71. *Prof Exp:* Mem prof staff, Ctr Naval Anal, Inst Naval Studies, 62-64; physicist, US Naval Undersea Res & Develop Ctr, 64-68; sr opers res analyst, Opers Res Task Force, Chicago Police Dept, 68-69; asst prof indust eng, Ctr Large Scale Systs, Purdue Univ, 71-74; opers res analyst, Naval Underwater Systs Ctr, Newport, RI, 74-78; assoc prof indust eng, Univ RI, 78-80; OPERS RES ANALYST, NAVAL UNDERWATER RES SYSTS CTR, 80- *Concurrent Pos:* Lectr, Traffic Inst, Northwestern Univ, Evanston, 70-78; consult, US Naval Underwater Systs Ctr, RI, 72-74; mem panel, Comt Undersea Warfare, Nat Res Coun-Nat Acad Sci, 72-74; adj prof indust eng, Univ RI, 81- *Mem:* AAAS; Opers Res Soc Am; sr mem Am Inst Indust Engrs. *Res:* Applications of search theory and Markov processes to problems of surveillance in the areas of pollution and police operations; applications of mathematical programming; military operations research. *Mailing Add:* Code 601 Naval Underwater Syst Ctr Newport RI 02840

OLSON, DAVID HAROLD, b Stoughton, Wis, Apr 27, 37; m 59; c 2. PHYSICAL CHEMISTRY. *Educ:* Univ Wis, BS, 59; Iowa State Univ, PhD(phys chem), 63. *Prof Exp:* Sr res chemist, 63-74, RES ASSOC, RES DEPT, MOBIL RES & DEVELOP CORP, 74- *Mem:* Am Chem Soc; Am Crystallog Asn. *Res:* Chemical crystallography; zeolite crystal chemistry and catalysis. *Mailing Add:* Cent Res Div Mobil Res & Develop Corp Princeton NJ 08540

OLSON, DAVID LEROY, b Oakland, Calif, Mar 17, 42; m 63; c 4. METALLURGY, CORROSION. *Educ:* Wash State Univ, BS, 65; Cornell Univ, PhD(mat sci), 70. *Prof Exp:* Mem tech staff, Semiconductor Res & Develop Lab, Tex Instruments, Inc, 69-70; res assoc metall eng, Ohio State Univ, 70-72; from asst prof to assoc prof, 72-78, PROF PHYS METALL, COLO SCH MINES, 78-, DIR, CTR WELDING RES, 81- *Concurrent Pos:* Consult, Govt & Indust, 72-; vis sr scientist, Norweg Inst Technol, Troudheim, Norway, 79. *Honors & Awards:* Bradley Stoughton Award, Am Soc Metals, 76; Adams Mem Award, Am Welding Soc, 78. *Mem:* Am Soc Metals; Am Inst Mining, Metall & Petrol Engrs; Am Phys Soc; Am Welding Soc; Am Ceramic Soc. *Res:* Welding metallurgy; reactive metals; pyrometallurgical reactions in welding; weld metal microstructure-property relationships; phase transformations during welding and the behavior of welding consumables and processes. *Mailing Add:* Dept Metall Eng Colo Sch Mines Golden CO 80401

OLSON, DON A, b Racine, Wis, Apr 5, 30; m 57; c 1. REHABILITATION MEDICINE, SPEECH PATHOLOGY. *Educ:* Univ Wis-Madison, BS, 52; Northwestern Univ, MS, 55, PhD(speech path, audiol), 65. *Prof Exp:* Dir speech path, Hearing & Speech Clin, Med Col Ala, 59-65; assoc prof communicative disorders, 65-69, DIR TRAINING REHAB MED, REHAB INST CHICAGO, NORTHWESTERN UNIV, 69-, ASSOC PROF NEUROL & REHAB MED, MED SCH, 69- *Concurrent Pos:* Consult, Vis Nurse Asns Evanston & Skokie Valley, Chicago Metrop Nursing Asn, Home Health Care NSuburban Chicago & adv comt, Med Sch Allied Health; pres, Nat Paraplegia Found, 74- *Mem:* Am Cong Rehab Med; Am Speech & Hearing Asn; Acad Aphasia; Coun Except Children. *Res:* Expressive aphasia and psychology of the brain damaged. *Mailing Add:* Rehab Inst Chicago 345 E Superior St Chicago IL 60611

OLSON, DONALD B, b Greybull, Wyo, May 28, 52; m 74; c 1. PHYSICAL OCEANOGRAPHY. *Educ:* Univ Wyo, BS, 74; Tex A&M Univ, MS & PhD(phys ocean), 76. *Prof Exp:* Res asst, Tex A&M Univ, 75-79; ASST PROF, ROSENSTIEL SCH MARINE & ATMOSPHERIC SCI, UNIV MIAMI, 79- *Concurrent Pos:* Asst res scientist, Tex A&M Univ, 79. *Mem:* Am Meteorol Soc; Am Geophys Union. *Res:* General ocean circulation, particularly mesoscale eddies, rings and fronts and their relationship to the mean flow. *Mailing Add:* Div Meteorol & Phys Oceanog Univ Miami 4600 Rickenbacker Causeway Miami FL 33149

OLSON, DONALD LEE, dentistry, oral pathology, see previous edition

OLSON, DONALD RICHARD, b Sargent, Nebr, Dec 26, 17; m 44; c 3. MECHANICAL ENGINEERING. *Educ:* Ore State Univ, BS, 42; Yale Univ, MEng, 44, DEng, 51. *Prof Exp:* Asst prof mech eng, Yale Univ, 51-57, assoc prof, 57-62; head powerplants, Ord Res Lab, 62-72, PROF MECH ENG, PA STATE UNIV, 62-, HEAD DEPT, 72- *Mem:* Am Soc Mech Engrs; Soc Automotive Engrs. *Res:* Thermodynamics and combustion as related to power systems. *Mailing Add:* Dept of Mech Eng 206 Pa State Univ University Park PA 16802

OLSON, DOUGLAS BERNARD, b Beeville, Tex, May 14, 45. PHYSICAL CHEMISTRY. *Educ:* Southwest Tex State Col, BS, 67; Univ Tex, MA, 69, PhD(chem), 77. *Prof Exp:* RES CHEMIST PHYSICAL CHEM, AERO CHEM RES LABS, 77- *Mem:* Combustion Inst; Am Chem Soc. *Res:* Gas kinetics of combustion reactions; soot formation. *Mailing Add:* Aero Chem Res Lab PO Box 12 Princeton NJ 08540

OLSON, EDWARD COOPER, b US, June 7, 30; m 59; c 2. ASTROPHYSICS. *Educ:* Worcester Polytech Inst, BS, 52; Ind Univ, PhD(astron), 61. *Prof Exp:* Instr physics, Worcester Polytech Inst, 52; asst prof astron, Smith Col, 60-63 & Rensselaer Polytech Inst, 64-65; from asst prof to assoc prof, 66-81, PROF ASTRON, UNIV ILL, URBANA, 81- *Concurrent Pos:* Adj prof, San Diego State Univ. *Mem:* Am Astron Soc; Royal Astron Soc; Int Astron Union. *Res:* Spectrophotometry and mass exchange in eclipsing binary systems. *Mailing Add:* Dept Astron Univ Ill 1011 W Springfield Urbana IL 61801

OLSON, EDWIN ANDREW, b Gary, Ind, May 21, 25; m 54; c 3. GEOLOGY, GEOCHEMISTRY. *Educ:* Univ Pittsburgh, BS, 47, MS, 49; Columbia Univ, PhD(geochem), 63. *Prof Exp:* Lectr math, Univ Pittsburgh, 47-49; develop engr, E I du Pont de Nemours & Co, 49-53; asst prof phys sci, Northwestern Col, Minn, 53-56; asst geochem, Lamont Geol Observ, Columbia Univ, 56-60; from asst prof to assoc prof geol, 60-69, PROF GEOL, WHITWORTH COL, WASH, 69- *Concurrent Pos:* NSF res grant, 61- *Mem:* Geochem Soc; Am Sci Affil. *Res:* Theoretical geochemical aspects relating to the accuracy of radiocarbon dating. *Mailing Add:* Dept of Earth Sci Whitworth Col Spokane WA 99251

OLSON, EDWIN S, b Red Wing, Minn, Oct 23, 37; m 63; c 3. ORGANIC CHEMISTRY. *Educ:* St Olaf Col, BA, 59; Calif Inst Technol, PhD(org chem), 64. *Prof Exp:* Asst prof org chem, Idaho State Univ, 64-68; from asst prof to assoc prof org chem, SDak State Univ, 68-77, prof chem, 77-80; RES CHEMIST, GRAND FORKS ENERGY TECHNOL CTR, 80- *Mem:* Am Chem Soc; Royal Soc Chem. *Res:* Organic analytical; high performance liquid chromatography; gas chromatography; mass spectrometry; nuclear magnetic resonance; coal chemistry; transition metal catalysis. *Mailing Add:* Grand Forks Energy Technol Ctr Box 8213 Univ Station Grand Forks ND 58202

OLSON, EMANUEL A, b Holdredge, Nebr, Feb 19, 16; m 39; c 2. AGRICULTURAL ENGINEERING. *Educ:* Univ Nebr, BS, 39. *Prof Exp:* Asst exten engr, Univ Nebr-Lincoln, 39-42, proj leader exten eng, 46-78, from assoc prof to prof agr eng, 52-78; RETIRED. *Concurrent Pos:* Consult, Behlen Mfg Co, Nebr, 64-65, Hart Carter, Ill, 68, Centron Corp, Kans, 69, Farmland Industs, Inc, 70 & Hubbard Milling Co, Minn, 71. *Honors & Awards:* Awards, Am Soc Agr Engrs, 48, 53, 62, 66, 70, 71, 74, 75 & 79. *Mem:* Fel Am Soc Agr Engrs; Nat Soc Prof Engrs. *Res:* Livestock waste management; rural water systems; livestock production facilities; crop conditioning, storage and processing; farmstead mechanization and concrete tilt-up construction. *Mailing Add:* 925 S 52nd St Lincoln NE 68510

OLSON, ERIK JOSEPH, b New York, NY, Aug 17, 32; m 61; c 3. PHARMACOLOGY. *Educ:* Cornell Univ, BS, 54; Purdue Univ, PhD(biochem), 61. *Prof Exp:* Instr physiol, Sch Med, Vanderbilt Univ, 61-63; res assoc med, Sch Med, Western Reserve Univ, 63-64; ASST PROF PHARMACOL, MEHARRY MED COL, 64- *Concurrent Pos:* Fel muscular dystrophy, Vanderbilt Univ, 62-63; NIH career develop award, Meharry Med Col, 66-71. *Mem:* Am Chem Soc; Am Phys Soc. *Res:* Active calcium transport; carbamyl phosphate synthesis. *Mailing Add:* Dept of Pharmacol Meharry Med Col Nashville TN 37208

OLSON, EVERETT CLAIRE, b Waupaca, Wis, Nov 6, 10; m 39; c 3. VERTEBRATE PALEONTOLOGY. *Educ:* Univ Chicago, BS, 32, MS, 33, PhD(geol, vert paleont), 35. *Prof Exp:* From instr to prof vert paleont, Univ Chicago, 35-69; prof, 69-78, chmn dept, 70-72, EMER PROF ZOOL, UNIV CALIF, LOS ANGELES, 78- *Concurrent Pos:* Secy dept vert paleont, Univ Chicago, 45-57, chmn, 57-61, assoc dean, Div Phys Sci, 48-60, chmn, Interdiv Comt Paleozool, 48-69; ed, Evolution, 53-58 & J Geol, 62-68. *Mem:* Nat Acad Sci; fel Geol Soc Am; Soc Vert Paleont (secy-treas, 48, pres, 50); Soc Study Evolution (pres, 65); Soc Syst Zool (pres, 79). *Res:* Permian reptiles and amphibians; biometry of fossils. *Mailing Add:* Dept of Biol Univ of Calif Los Angeles CA 90024

OLSON, FERRON ALLRED, b Tooele, Utah, July 2, 21; m 44; c 5. METALLURGICAL ENGINEERING, PHYSICAL CHEMISTRY. *Educ:* Univ Utah, BS, 53, PhD(fuel technol), 56. *Prof Exp:* Chemist, Shell Develop Co Div, Shell Oil Co, 56-61; assoc res prof, 61-63, assoc prof metall, 63-69, prof mineral eng, 69-75, chmn dept mining, metall & fuel eng, 66-74, PROF METALL, UNIV UTAH, 75- *Concurrent Pos:* Fulbright prof, Univ Belgrade, Bor Campus, 74-75; bd dir, Accreditation Bd, eng & technol, 75-82; consult hydrometall copper, Chilean Res Ctr, 78-; guest lectr, Univ Belgrade, 80. *Mem:* Am Inst Mining, Metall & Petrol Engrs; Am Chem Soc; Am Soc Metals; Am Soc Eng Educ; Sigma Xi. *Res:* Physics and chemistry of surfaces; hydrometallurgy explosives; interfacial phenomena, hydrometallurgy, kinetics and mechanism of solid state decomposition. *Mailing Add:* 412 W C Browning Bldg Univ of Utah Salt Lake City UT 84112

OLSON, FRANK R, b Uddevalla, Sweden, May 25, 22; nat US; m 50; c 1. MATHEMATICS. *Educ:* Alfred Univ, BA, 47; Kent State Univ, MA, 50; Duke Univ, PhD(math), 54. *Prof Exp:* Instr math, Hamilton Col, 47-48, Kent State Univ, 49-50 & Duke Univ, 53-54; from asst prof to assoc prof, State Univ NY Buffalo, 54-67; PROF MATH & CHMN DEPT, STATE UNIV NY COL FREDONIA, 67- *Mem:* Am Math Soc; Math Asn Am. *Res:* Algebra, especially arithmetic properties of Bernoulli numbers and determinants. *Mailing Add:* Dept of Math State Univ of NY Col Fredonia NY 14063

OLSON, FRANKLYN C W, b Waukegan, Ill, Mar 15, 10; m 39; c 3. PHYSICAL OCEANOGRAPHY. *Educ:* Univ Chicago, SB, 33; Ohio State Univ, PhD(physics), 50. *Prof Exp:* Physicist, Am Can Co, Ill, 34-42; design engr, Stewart-Warner Corp, 42-43; res assoc, Northwestern Technol Inst, 43-46; asst prof physics & in-chg dept, Univ Ill, 46-47; res assoc, Franz Stone Inst Hydrobiol, Ohio State Univ, 47-50; assoc prof oceanog, Oceanog Inst, Fla State Univ, 50-57; head, Oceanog Br, US Naval Mine Defense Lab, Fla, 57-60; mem tech staff adv mil systs, Radio Corp Am, 60-63; mem consult staff, US Naval Coastal Systs Lab, 63-76; OPERS RES ANALYST, POTOMAC RES INC, 76- *Res:* Lake currents; inshore oceanography; theory of water waves. *Mailing Add:* 119 Pearl Ave Panama City Beach FL 32407

OLSON, GEORGE GILBERT, b Omaha, Nebr, Nov 6, 24; m 47; c 4. PHYSICAL CHEMISTRY, METALLURGY. *Educ:* Univ Colo, BA, 47, PhD(phys chem), 51. *Prof Exp:* Res dir, Builders Supply Corp, Ariz, 51-53; Ariz Res Consults, Inc, 53-61; assoc dir, Colo State Univ Res Found, 61-63, dir, 63-68; vpres res, Farad Corp, 68-71; PROF CHEM ENG & VPRES RES, COLO STATE UNIV, 71- *Concurrent Pos:* Consult, Webb & Knapp, Inc, NY, 58-64 & Henry J Kaiser, Hawaii, 60-63; consult & dir, Malleable Iron Fitting Co, Conn, 62-69 & Bigelow Mfg Co, 63-73; dir, Chemsearch Corp, Colo, 63-; dir, Assoc Western Univs, 71-; pres, Colo State Univ Res Found, 71- *Mem:* AAAS; Inst Mining, Metall & Petrol Engrs; Am Inst Chem Engrs; Am Chem Soc. *Res:* Hydrometallurgy; solvent extraction; biomass processing, coatings and sealants, synthetic fuels. *Mailing Add:* Admin Bldg Colo State Univ Ft Collins CO 80523

OLSON, GERALD ALLEN, b Iowa City, Iowa, Dec 14, 44; m 70; c 3. VETERINARY MEDICINE, MICROBIOLOGY. *Educ:* Auburn Univ, DVM, 68; Univ Fla, MS, 71. *Prof Exp:* NIH fel, Univ Fla, 68-71, from asst prof to assoc prof vet med & microbiol, 71-77, ASSOC PROF VET MED & MICROBIOL, UNIV TENN, 77- *Concurrent Pos:* Consult, Am Asn Accreditation Lab Animal Care, 74-78 & St Judes Children's Res Hosp, 78- *Honors & Awards:* Pres Award, Am Soc Microbiol, 71. *Mem:* Am Vet Med Asn; Am Asn Lab Animal Sci; Am Col Lab Animal Med. *Res:* Oral microbiology and immunology; diseases and pathology of animals. *Mailing Add:* 956 Court Box 17 Coleman Bldg Univ of Tenn Memphis TN 38163

OLSON, GERALD WALTER, b Gothenburg, Nebr, Mar 22, 32; m 61; c 3. SOIL MORPHOLOGY, AGRONOMY. *Educ:* Univ Nebr, BSc, 54, MSc, 59; Univ Wis, PhD(soil genesis & classification), 62. *Prof Exp:* Asst soils, Agr Res Serv & Univ Nebr, 56-57; jr officer, Int Coop Admin, India, 57-58; party chief soil surv, Univ Wis, 59-62; soil technologist, 62-66, asst prof, 66-71, ASSOC PROF SOIL SCI RESOURCE DEVELOP, CORNELL UNIV, 71- *Concurrent Pos:* Mem, Nat Comt Environ Soil Sci, Soil Conserv Serv; consult, Archaeol Expeds, Tikal, El Peten, Guatemala, Cent Am, Sardis, Turkey, San Antonio, Brit Honduras, 74 & Valle de Naco & La Conteada, Honduras, 75; sr consult land classification, Food & Agr Orgn, UN, Rome, 72 & soil surv interpretations, Soil Inst Iran & Food & Agr Orgn, UN, Tehran, Iran, 72; vis soil scientist, Kans Geol Surv, Univ Kans, 73; consult, Ministerio de Obras Publicas, Venezuela & Empresa Brasileira de Pesquisa Agropecuaria, Brazil & AID, Washington, DC, 75; vis prof soil surv interpretations, Inter-Am Ctr Integral Develop Water & Lands, Univ Andes, Venezuela, 75; guest lectr, Univ Simon Bolivar & Ministerio de Obras Publicas, Venezuela, 75. *Mem:* Fel AAAS; Am Soc Agron; Soil Sci Soc Am; Soil Conserv Soc Am; Asn Am Geogrs. *Res:* Interpretation of soil survey for urban development in New York; soil survey inventory for resource utilization for economic development; planning and development through use of soil information; waste disposal in soils; ecological implications of soils. *Mailing Add:* Dept of Agron Cornell Univ Ithaca NY 14853

OLSON, GORDON LEE, b Clinton, Minn, Oct 1, 51. STELLAR WINDS, STELLAR EVOLUTION. *Educ:* Univ Minn, Minneapolis, BS, 73; Univ Wis-Madison, MS, 75, PhD(astrophys), 77. *Prof Exp:* Scientific collabr, Astrophys Inst, Free Univ, Brussels, 77-79; res assoc, Joint Inst for Lab Astrophys, Univ Colo, Boulder, 79-81; STAFF MEM, LOS ALAMOS NAT LAB, 81- *Mem:* Am Astron Soc. *Mailing Add:* 470 Aragon White Rock NM 87544

OLSON, H(ILDING) M, b Crystal Lake, Ill, Dec 14, 23; m 48; c 2. ELECTRICAL ENGINEERING. *Educ:* Northwestern Univ, BSEE, 48; Stevens Inst Technol, MS, 54; Polytech Inst Brooklyn, DEE, 59. *Prof Exp:* Engr, Radio Corp Am, 48-53; mem tech staff, 53-60, supvr magnetron develop, 60-63, supvr semiconductor device develop, 63-68, supvr traveling wave-tube & avalanche-diode develop, 68-73, MEM TECH STAFF MICROWAVE INTEGRATED CIRCUITS, BELL LABS, 73- *Res:* Microwave electron tubes; microwave semiconductor devices and circuits employing them; computer modeling of semiconductor devices. *Mailing Add:* Apt B 1940 Alsace Rd Reading PA 19604

OLSON, HAROLD CECIL, b Brookings, SDak, Nov 18, 05; m 32; c 1. DAIRY BACTERIOLOGY. *Educ:* SDak State Col, BS, 28; Univ WVa, MS, 30; Iowa State Univ, PhD(dairy bact), 32. *Prof Exp:* Asst, Exp Sta, Iowa State Univ, 32-34, instr dairy bact, 34-37, asst prof, 37-40; prof, 40-71, actg head dept, 48-50, EMER PROF DAIRY SCI, OKLA STATE UNIV, 71- *Concurrent Pos:* Consult, Cult Dairy Prod, 71- ed, Am Cult Dairy Prod Inst J, 69-74. *Honors & Awards:* Pfizer Award; Nordica Award. *Mem:* Am Dairy Sci Asn; Int Asn Milk, Food & Environ Sanit. *Res:* Bacteriology of butter, milk, cheese and sweetened condensed milk; feed flavors in milk; cheese manufacturing; cheese cultures; marketing of dairy products. *Mailing Add:* 802 S Ridge Rd Stillwater OK 74074

OLSON, HARRY FERDINAND, b Mt Pleasant, Iowa, Dec 28, 02; m 35. ELECTROACOUSTICS. *Educ:* Univ Iowa, BE, 24, MS, 25, PhD(acoust), 28, EE, 34. *Hon Degrees:* DSc, Iowa Wesleyan Univ, 59. *Prof Exp:* Asst physics, Univ Iowa, 26-28; asst, Res Lab, RCA Corp, 28-30, Eng Dept, Photophone, NY, 30-32, dir acoust res, RCA Mfg Co, 32-42, dir, Acoust & Electromech Lab, 42-66, staff vpres acoust & electromech res, 66-68; CONSULT, 68- *Concurrent Pos:* Lectr, Columbia Univ. *Honors & Awards:* Silver Medal, Am Acoust Soc, 74, Gold Medal, 81; Mod Pioneer Award, Nat Mfrs Asn; Warner Medal, Soc Motion Picture & TV Engrs; Potts Medal, Audio Eng Soc; Consumer Electronics Award, Inst Elec & Electronics Engrs, Kelly Medal, Lamme Medal; John Ericsson Medal, Am Soc Swedish Engrs. *Mem:* Nat Acad Sci; fel Acoust Soc Am (pres, 52); fel Am Phys Soc; fel Audio Eng Soc (past pres); fel Inst Elec & Electronics Engrs. *Res:* General acoustics; electronics. *Mailing Add:* 71 Palmer Sq Princeton NJ 08540

OLSON, HOWARD H, b Chicago, Ill May 23, 27; m 51; c 4. DAIRY SCIENCE, PHYSIOLOGY. *Educ:* Univ Wis, BS, 48; Univ Minn, MS, 50, PhD(dairy physiol), 52. *Prof Exp:* Mem res staff, Curtiss Breeding Serv, 52-54; from asst prof to assoc prof, 54-68, PROF DAIRY SCI, UNIV SOUTHERN ILL, CARBONDALE, 68-, DIR INT AGR, 79- *Concurrent Pos:* Physiol teaching workshop grant, 60; Fulbright-Hays lectr, Ain Shams Univ, Cairo, 66-67; res grant, Population Dynamics, 74 & 75; Fulbright lectr, Univ Peradeniya, Srilanka, 81-82; consult, US Feed Grains Coun, Japan & People's Rep China, 81. *Mem:* Am Dairy Sci Asn; Am Soc Animal Sci; World Pop Soc; Soc Study Reproduction. *Res:* Artificial insemination of dairy cattle; physiology of reproduction; dairy cattle nutrition studies on ad libitum grain feeding; development of complete feeds. *Mailing Add:* 30 Hillcrest Dr Carbondale IL 62901

OLSON, J(ERRY) S, b Chicago, Ill, Mar 22, 28; m 50; c 2. ECOLOGY. *Educ:* Univ Chicago, PhB, 47, BS, 48, MS, 49, PhD(bot), 51. *Prof Exp:* Asst geol Univ Chicago, 47-49; fel statist, 51-52; asst forest ecologist, Conn Agr Exp Sta, 52-57, assoc forest ecologist, 57-58; PROF BOT, UNIV TENN, KNOXVILLE, 64-; SYSTEMS ECOLOGIST, OAK RIDGE NAT LAB, 68-, SR ECOLOGIST, ENVIRON SCI DIV, 75- *Concurrent Pos:* Geobotanist, Health Physics Div, Oak Ridge Nat Lab, 58-70, plant ecol, group leader, 64-67; lectr, Univ Tenn, Knoxville, 60-64; Oak Ridge Assoc Univs traveling lectr, 60-; Guggenheim fel, 62-64; univ lectr, Univ London, 63; sr res adviser ecol sci div, 70-73; environ analyst biomed environ res, AEC/ERDA Div, 73-75. *Honors & Awards:* Ecol Soc Am Mercer Award, 58. *Mem:* Am Meteorol Soc; Bot Soc Am; AAAS; Ecol Soc Am; Am Geophys Union. *Res:* Geomorphology; Pleistocene; sedimentology; statistic pedology; sand dunes; eastern hemlock forests; biogeochemistry; radiation; productivity; regulation of ecosystems; computers and systems biology. *Mailing Add:* Oak Ridge Nat Lab Bldg 1505 Oak Ridge TN 37830

OLSON, JAMES ALLEN, b Minneapolis, Minn, Oct 10, 24; m 53; c 3. NUTRITIONAL BIOCHEMISTRY. *Educ:* Gustavus Adolphus Col, BS, 46; Harvard Univ, PhD(biochem), 52. *Prof Exp:* Fel biochem, Int Ctr Chem & Microbiol, Rome, 52-54, Ital Govt spec fel, 54; res assoc, Harvard Univ, 54-56; from asst prof to prof biochem, Col Med, Univ Fla, 56-66; actg prof & chmn dept, Mahidol Univ, Thailand, 66-72, grad res prof biochem & nutrit, 72-74; prof biomed sci, Fed Univ Bahia, Brazil, 74-75; PROF BIOCHEM & CHMN DEPT BIOCHEM & BIOPHYS, IOWA STATE UNIV, 75- *Concurrent Pos:* Consult, NSF, 62-65; mem, Comt Spec Caroten, Nat Res Coun, 64-68; guest prof, Kyoto Univ, 65; staff mem, Rockefeller Found, 66-75; ed for Asia, J Lipid Res, 66-72; consult, WHO, 69 & 75; mem, Comt Grad Educ Nutrit, Int Union Nutrit Sci, 70-72; guest prof, Univ London, 71; mem comt int nutrit prog, Nat Acad Sci, 76-; mem US nat comt, Int Union Nutrit Sci, 77-; consult, NIH, 78-82. *Mem:* Fel AAAS; Am Chem Soc; Am Soc Biol Chem; Am Inst Nutrit; Soc Exp Biol & Med. *Res:* Metabolism and function of vitamin A; absorption and storage of fat soluble vitamins; biological pattern formation; evaluation of human nutritional status; physiological and chemical factors influencing appetite. *Mailing Add:* Dept of Biochem & Biophys Iowa State Univ Ames IA 50011

OLSON, JAMES GORDON, b Palo Alto, Calif, Dec 16, 40; m 64; c 2. EPIDEMIOLOGY, VIROLOGY. *Educ:* Univ Calif, Santa Barabra, BA, 64; San Jose State Col, MA, 66; Univ Calif, Berkeley, MPH, 72, PhD(epidemiol), 77. *Prof Exp:* Virologist, US Navy Med Res Unit 2, 75-78, virologist, Jakarta Detachment, 78-80; VIROLOGIST, YALE ARBORVIRUS RES UNIT, SCH MED, YALE UNIV, 80- *Mem:* Am Soc Trop Med & Hyg; Soc Epidemiol Res; Am Pub Health Asn; Roy Soc Trop Med & Hyg; Am Soc Rickettsiology. *Res:* Epidemiology of arboviral diseases of man, the association of vector bionomics with incidence rates of arthropod-borne diseases and prediction of and control of epidemics. *Mailing Add:* Yale Arborvirus Res Unit Sch Med Yale Univ 60 College St New Haven CT 06510

OLSON, JAMES PAUL, b Quincy, Mass, Feb 10, 41; m 61; c 2. CIVIL ENGINEERING. *Educ:* Tufts Univ, BSCE, 62, MS, 66; NC State Univ, PhD, 69. *Prof Exp:* Engr, Sikorsky Aircraft, United Aircraft Corp, 62-63 & Sylvania Electronic Systs, Gen Tel & Electronics Corp, 63-64; asst prof civil eng, 69-77, ASSOC PROF CIVIL ENG, UNIV VT, 77- *Mem:* Assoc mem Am Soc Civil Engrs; Am Soc Photogram. *Res:* Soil behavior; foundation engineering; engineering applications of remote sensing and photo interpretation. *Mailing Add:* Dept of Civil Eng Univ of Vt Burlington VT 05401

OLSON, JAMES ROBERT, b Whittier, Calif, July 26, 43; m 64; c 4. WOOD SCIENCE & TECHNOLOGY, FOREST PRODUCTS. *Educ:* Univ Calif, Berkeley, BS, 71, MS, 74, PhD(wood sci technol), 79. *Prof Exp:* Asst specialist timber physics, Forest Prod Lab, Univ Calif, Berkeley, 71-79; ASST PROF WOOD SCI & TECHNOL, DEPT FORESTRY, UNIV KY, 79- *Concurrent Pos:* Lectr, Dept Forestry & Resource Mgt, Univ Calif, 75. *Mem:* Forest Prod Res Soc; Soc Wood Sci & Technol; Soc Am Foresters. *Res:* Methods for better utilization of low grade hardwoods; improved procedures for hardwood drying; effect of tree improvement practices on wood quality. *Mailing Add:* Dept Forestry 00731 Univ Ky Lexington KY 40546

OLSON, JERRY CHIPMAN, b Los Angeles, Calif, Dec 25, 17; m; c 3. GEOLOGY. *Educ:* Univ Calif, Los Angeles, AB, 39, MA, 47, PhD(geol), 53. *Prof Exp:* Geologist, US Geol Surv, 39-60, chief, Radioactive Mat Br, 60-69, geologist, 69-79. *Mem:* Mineral Soc Am; fel Geol Soc Am; Soc Econ Geol. *Res:* Economic geology; metamorphic rocks; geology of pegmatites, alkalic rocks, thorium, uranium and rare-earth mineral deposits and resources, geology of southwestern Colorado. *Mailing Add:* 13556 W Park Dr Magalia CA 95954

OLSON, JIMMY KARL, b Twin Falls, Idaho, Feb 18, 42; m 64; c 2. MEDICAL ENTOMOLOGY. *Educ:* Univ Idaho, BS, 65; Univ Ill, Urbana, PhD(entom), 71. *Prof Exp:* Asst prof med entom, 71-75, ASSOC PROF ENTOM, TEX A&M UNIV, 75- *Mem:* AAAS; Am Soc Trop Med & Hyg; Am Mosquito Control Asn; Entom Soc Am. *Res:* Mosquito bionomics and control; role of hematophagous arthropods in the transmission of disease agents affecting man and his domestic animals. *Mailing Add:* Dept of Entom Tex A&M Univ College Station TX 77843

OLSON, JOHN BENNET, b Minneapolis, Minn, Feb 13, 17; m 41; c 4. ZOOLOGY, SCIENCE EDUCATION. *Educ:* Beloit Col, BS, 38; Univ Calif, Los Angeles, MA, 41, PhD(zool), 50. *Prof Exp:* Instr biol, Brooklyn Col, 48-50; asst prof, San Jose State Col, 50-53; sr res assoc cardiol, Childrens Hosp, Los Angeles, 53-57; res fel chem, Calif Inst Technol, 57-58; chmn, Div Natural Sci, Shimer Col, 58-64; assoc prof, 64-81, EMER PROF BIOL EDUC, PURDUE UNIV, WEST LAFAYETTE, 81- *Concurrent Pos:* Vis lectr, Univ Calif, Santa Barbara, 50, Berkeley, 51, 52 & 53; sci consult pub schs, Calif, 52-53; dir summer inst, NSF, Purdue, 64-73. *Mem:* AAAS; Nat Asn Res Sci Teaching; Nat Asn Biol Teachers; NY Acad Sci; Am Inst Biol Sci. *Res:* Marine copepods; congenital heart defects in mammals; science teaching. *Mailing Add:* Dept of Biol Sci Purdue Univ West Lafayette IN 47907

OLSON, JOHN BERNARD, b Chicago, Ill, Aug 20, 31; m 61; c 3. ECOLOGY, GENETICS. *Educ:* Univ Ill, Urbana, BS, 58, PhD(zool), 65. *Prof Exp:* From asst prof to prof biol, 63-72, dean, Col Arts & Sci, 72-75, PROF BIOL, WINTHROP COL, 75- *Mem:* AAAS; Cooper Ornith Soc. *Res:* Bioenergetic requirements during the annual cycle of migratory and nonmigratory birds. *Mailing Add:* Dept of Biol Winthrop Col Rock Hill SC 29733

OLSON, JOHN MELVIN, b Niagara Falls, NY, Sept 18, 29; m 53; c 3. PHOTOBIOLOGY. *Educ:* Wesleyan Univ, BA, 51; Univ Pa, PhD(biophys), 57. *Prof Exp:* USPHS res fel, Biophys Lab, Univ Utrecht & Univ Leiden, 57-58; instr physics & biochem, Brandeis Univ, 58-59, asst prof, 59-61; from asst biophysicist to assoc biophysicist, 61-65, BIOPHYSICIST, BROOKHAVEN NAT LAB, 65- *Concurrent Pos:* USPHS res fel, Lab Chem Biodynamics, Lawrence Berkeley Lab, 70-71; lectr, Univ Calif, Berkeley, 71; adj prof, State Univ NY Stony Brook, 72; Lady Davis vis scholar, Israel Inst Technol, Haifa, 81. *Mem:* AAAS; Biophys Soc; Am Soc Biol Chem; Am Soc Photobiol; Int Solar Energy Soc. *Res:* Energy conversion in photosynthesis; structure and function of photosynthetic membranes in green bacteria; photoproduction of hydrogen; evolution of photosynthesis. *Mailing Add:* Dept of Biol Brookhaven Nat Lab Upton NY 11973

OLSON, JOHN RICHARD, b Ferryville, Wis, Sept 14, 32. PHYSICS. *Educ:* Luther Col, BA, 54; Iowa State Univ, PhD(physics), 63. *Prof Exp:* Instr physics, Iowa State Univ, 63; mem tech staff, Bell Tel Labs, 63-65; lectr physics, Bryn Mawr Col, 65-66, asst prof, 66-72; MEM FAC, DEPT PHYSICS, UNIV DENVER, 72- *Concurrent Pos:* Vis asst prof, Univ Denver, 70-71. *Mem:* Am Asn Physics Teachers. *Res:* Atomic and molecular physics, especially molecular energy transfer; quadrupole mass spectrometry; ultra-high vacuum systems; balloon-borne experimentation techniques; sound propagation in deep water. *Mailing Add:* Dept of Physics Univ of Denver Denver CO 80208

OLSON, JOHN VICTOR, b Kibbie, Mich, June 24, 13; m 40; c 1. DENTISTRY. *Educ:* Univ Mich, DDS, 36, MS, 38. *Prof Exp:* Asst prof prosthetics, Sch Dent, St Louis Univ, 47-49, assoc prof, 49-50, dir postgrad dent educ, 48-50; dean, Dent Sch, Univ Tex Health Sci Ctr, San Antonio, 69-72; PROF RESTORATIVE DENT, UNIV TEX DENT BR, HOUSTON, 50-, DEAN, 52- *Concurrent Pos:* Consult, Vet Admin Hosp, Houston, Tex, 52, Univ Tex Med Br & M D Anderson Hosp & Tumor Inst, 52- *Mem:* AAAS. *Res:* Prosthetic dentistry; dental education. *Mailing Add:* Univ Tex Dent Br PO Box 20068 Houston TX 77025

OLSON, JON H, b Akron, Ohio, Jan 31, 34; m 57; c 3. CHEMICAL ENGINEERING. *Educ:* Princeton Univ, BS, 55; Yale Univ, DEng(chem eng), 60. *Prof Exp:* Engr, Eng Res Lab, E I du Pont de Nemours & Co, Del, 59-62 & Radiation Physics Lab, 62-63; from asst prof to assoc prof chem eng, 63-68, PROF CHEM ENG, UNIV DEL, 68-, ASSOC DEAN ENG, 77- *Concurrent Pos:* Consult, Houdry Process & Chem Co, 66- *Mem:* AAAS; Am Inst Chem Engrs; Am Chem Soc. *Res:* Chemical reactor engineering; mixing; photochemistry. *Mailing Add:* Dept of Chem Eng Univ of Del Newark DE 19711

OLSON, KARL WILLIAM, b Canton, Ohio, Mar 27, 36; m 59; c 3. ELECTRICAL ENGINEERING. *Educ:* Ohio State Univ, BSc & MSc, 59, PhD(elec eng), 65. *Prof Exp:* Res assoc, 60-64, res assoc, Commun & Control Systs Lab, 64-65, asst supvr, 65-67, ASST PROF ELEC ENG, UNIV & ASSOC SUPVR COMMUN & CONTROL SYSTS LAB, OHIO STATE UNIV, 67- *Mem:* Inst Elec & Electronics Engrs. *Res:* Automatic highways; designing and testing automatic lateral and longitudinal control systems for automobiles. *Mailing Add:* Dept of Elec Eng 2024 Neil Ave Columbus OH 43210

OLSON, KENNETH B, b Seattle, Wash, Jan 21, 08; m 37; c 2. MEDICINE, ONCOLOGY. *Educ:* Univ Wash, BS, 29; Harvard Med Sch, MD, 33. *Prof Exp:* Resident path, Boston City Hosp, Mass, 33-34; intern & asst resident & resident surgeon, Presby Hosp, New York, 34-40; instr, Col Physicians & Surgeons, Columbia Univ, 40-41; dir, Firland Sanatorium, Seattle, Wash, 43-45; from instr to prof med, Albany Med Col, 50-71, dir div oncol, 51-72, prof med & actg head med oncol, Div Hematol, J Hillis Miller Health Ctr, Univ Fla, 76, EMER PROF MED, ALBANY MED COL, 72-; EMER PROF MED ONCOL, DIV HEMATOL, J HILLIS MILLER HEALTH CTR, UNIV FLA, 76- *Concurrent Pos:* Mem cancer clin invest rev comt, Nat Cancer Inst, 68-72, mem breast cancer task force, 71-, chief, Diag Br, Div Cancer Biol & Diag, 72-73; consult, 73-81; consult, Fla Cancer Coun, Halifax Med Ctr Hosp. *Mem:* Am Soc Cancer Res; AMA; Soc Surg Oncol; Am Soc Clin Oncol (pres, 71-72). *Res:* Lung and breast cancer; liver function; chemotherapy of cancer; biological effects of irradiation; estrogen receptors; blood clotting. *Mailing Add:* 810 Oakview Dr New Smyrna Beach FL 32069

OLSON, KENNETH E(ARL), chemical engineering, see previous edition

OLSON, KENNETH JEAN, b Saginaw Co, Mich, July 8, 16; m 43; c 2. TOXICOLOGY. *Educ:* Kalamazoo Col, AB, 42; Mich State Col, MS, 44, PhD(biochem), 47; Am Bd Indust Hyg, dipl. *Prof Exp:* Res pharmacologist, Upjohn Co, 47-54, sect head endocrinol, 54; toxicologist, Dept Biochem, Dow Chem Co, 54-68, mgr toxicol dept, Dow Corning Corp, 68-73, sr res specialist, Toxicol Res Lab, 73-75, group leader acute toxicol & info serv, 75-81, assoc scientist, 79; RETIRED. *Mem:* Soc Toxicol. *Res:* Industrial toxicology; dental caries in white rats; method for absorption and elimination of thiouracil; pharmacology of spasmolytics, antihistaminics and local anesthetics. *Mailing Add:* 608 Crescent Dr Midland MI 48640

OLSON, LEE CHARLES, b Austin, Minn, June 2, 36; m 61; c 4. PLANT BIOCHEMISTRY, PLANT PHYSIOLOGY. *Educ:* SDak State Univ, BS, 58; Univ Wis, MS, 62, PhD(biochem), 64. *Prof Exp:* Asst prof plant physiol, Univ Minn, St Paul, 65-67, agron, 67-70; MEM FAC, DEPT BIOL, CHRISTOPHER NEWPORT COL, 71- *Mem:* Am Chem Soc; Sigma Xi; Am Soc Plant Physiologists. *Res:* Amino acid metabolism; plant cell culture. *Mailing Add:* Dept of Biol Christopher Newport Col Newport News VA 23606

OLSON, LEONARD CARL, b Marietta, Ohio, July 17, 45; m 69. LABORATORY ANIMAL MEDICINE, PRIMATE MEDICINE. *Educ:* St Olaf Col, BA, 67; Purdue Univ, DVM, 75. *Prof Exp:* Fel, Lab Animal Med, Med Sch, Univ Mich, 77-79; HEAD ANIMAL SCI DEPT PRIMATE MED, ORE REGIONAL PRIMATE RES CTR, 79- *Mem:* Am Col Lab Animal Med; Am Asn Lab Animal Sci; Asn Primate Vet Clinicians; Am Vet Med Asn; Am Soc Vet Clin Path. *Res:* Documenting or investigating diseases of laboratory animals with an emphasis on diseases of non-human primates; establishinng normative data for a wide variety of non-human primate species. *Mailing Add:* Ore Regional Primate Res Ctr 505 NW 185th Ave Beaverton OR 97006

OLSON, LEROY DAVID, b East Chain, Minn, July 22, 29; m 56; c 1. VETERINARY PATHOLOGY, VETERINARY VIROLOGY. *Educ:* Univ Minn, BS, 54, DVM, 58; Purdue Univ, MS, 62, PhD(vet path), 65. *Prof Exp:* Instr vet path, Purdue Univ, 60-65; assoc prof, 65-81, PROF VET PATH, UNIV MO-COLUMBIA, 81- *Mem:* AAAS; Am Vet Med Asn; Am Soc Microbiol; Am Soc Vet Parasitol. *Res:* Immunopathology, especially experimental allergic encephalomyelitis; avian cancer viruses; viral enteric diseases of swine; Pasteurella multocida infections in turkeys. *Mailing Add:* 116 W Burnam Columbia MO 65201

OLSON, LEROY JUSTIN, b Fargo, NDak, May 28, 26; m 53; c 2. MICROBIOLOGY. *Educ:* Concordia Col, BA, 50; Kans State Univ, MS, 53; Univ Tex, PhD(parasitol), 57. *Prof Exp:* Instr biol, Concordia Col, 50-51; asst vet parasitol & zool, Kans State Univ, 51-53; asst prev med & pub health, 53, instr bact & parasitol, 54-56, from asst prof to assoc prof microbiol, 57-66, PROF MICROBIOL, UNIV TEX MED BR, GALVESTON, 66- *Mem:* Am Soc Parasitol; Am Soc Microbiol; AAAS. *Res:* Host-parasite relationships; immunology; gut allergy and pathology. *Mailing Add:* Dept of Microbiol Univ of Tex Med Br Galveston TX 77551

OLSON, LLOYD CLARENCE, b Spokane, Wash, Jan 30, 35; m 58; c 3. MICROBIOLOGY, PEDIATRICS. *Educ:* Reed Col, AB, 57; Harvard Med Sch, MD, 61. *Prof Exp:* From intern to resident pediat, Univ Rochester, 61-63, resident, 63-64; virologist, Walter Reed Army Inst Res, 64-67; vis assoc prof microbiol, Mahidol Univ, Thailand, 67-70, vis lectr, 68-70, vis prof microbiol, 70-73; assoc prof microbiol, Sch Med, Ind Univ, 73-76; PROF PEDIAT, SCH MED, UNIV MO, 76-, ASSOC CHMN DEPT, 78-; MEM

STAFF, CHILDREN'S MERCY HOSP, 76-, MEM STAFF INFECTIOUS DIS, 76- *Concurrent Pos:* Virologist, SEATO Med Res Lab, Thailand, 67-70; mem staff, Rockefeller Found, Thailand, 70-73. *Mem:* AAAS; Soc Pediat Res; Soc Exp Biol Med; Am Soc Microbiol; Infectious Dis Soc Am. *Res:* Clinical and epidemiologic aspects of virus diseases; host defense mechanisms to virus infections. *Mailing Add:* Children's Mercy Hosp Kansas City MO 64108

OLSON, MAGNUS, b South Fron, Norway, June 29, 09; US citizen; m 38; c 2. ZOOLOGY. *Educ:* St Olaf Col, AB, 32; Univ Minn, AM, 34, PhD(histol), 36. *Prof Exp:* Asst zool, 32-36, asst, Comt Educ Res, 36-37, instr educ & zool, 37-38, from instr to to prof zool, 38-77, chmn dept, 66-77, EMER PROF ZOOL, UNIV MINN, MINNEAPOLIS, 77- *Mem:* AAAS; assoc Am Soc Zool. *Res:* Histology of invertebrate muscle; ovogenesis in Mammalia; myeloid metaplasia in mammalian thymus; wound healing in rabbits. *Mailing Add:* Dept of Zool Univ of Minn Minneapolis MN 55455

OLSON, MARK OBED JEROME, b Clarkfield, Minn, Aug 20, 40; m 66. BIOCHEMISTRY, PHARMACOLOGY. *Educ:* St Olaf Col, BA, 62; Univ Minn, Minneapolis, PhD(biochem), 67. *Prof Exp:* Asst prof pharmacol, Baylor Col Med, 69-74, assoc prof, 74-79; ASSOC PROF BIOCHEM, UNIV MISS MED CTR, 79- *Concurrent Pos:* Med Res Coun Can fel, Univ Alta, 67-69; Am Cancer Soc grant pharmacol, Baylor Col Med, 69-70; NSF grant, 73-74; Nat Cancer Inst proj grant, 77-79; vis scientist, Nat Inst Arthritis, Metab & Digestive Dis, NIH, 78; NIH grant, 80- *Mem:* AAAS; Am Asn Cancer Res; Am Chem Soc; Biophys Soc; Am Soc Biol Chemists. *Res:* Functional and evolutionary aspects of protein structure; phytohemagglutinins; proteolytic enzymes; structure and role of nuclear proteins in genetic regulation; mechanism of enzyme action. *Mailing Add:* Dept Biochem Univ Miss Med Ctr 2500 N State St Jackson MS 39216

OLSON, MAYNARD VICTOR, b Washington, DC, Oct 2, 43; m 68; c 2. MOLECULAR GENETICS. *Educ:* Calif Inst Technol, BS, 65; Stanford Univ, PhD(chem), 70. *Prof Exp:* Asst prof chem, Dartmouth Col, 70-76; res assoc, Univ Wash, 76-79; ASST PROF GENETICS, WASHINGTON UNIV, 79- *Mem:* AAAS. *Res:* Structure and function of eukaryotic genes. *Mailing Add:* Dept of Genetics Washington Univ Sch of Med St Louis MO 63110

OLSON, MELVIN MARTIN, b Bangor, Wis, Aug 30, 15; m 41; c 3. ORGANIC CHEMISTRY. *Educ:* Wis State Teachers Col, La Crosse, BS, 38; Univ Wis, PhM, 39, PhD(chem), 50. *Prof Exp:* Instr high sch, Wis, 39-41; instr high sch & Maquoketa Jr Col, Iowa, 41-43; asst chem, Univ Wis, 46-50, prof, Exten Div, 50-51; res chemist, Paint Div, Pittsburgh Plate Glass Co, 51-54; res chemist, Tape Div, Minn Mining & Mfg Co, 54-59, res specialist, 56-69, SR RES SPECIALIST, INDUST TAPE DIV, 3M CO, 69- *Mem:* Am Chem Soc. *Res:* Modification of paint vehicles with silicon compounds; synthesis of silicon compounds; formulation of organic structural adhesives; water dispersible pressure-sensitive adhesives, water-dispersible hot-melt adhesives; ethylene oxide detection. *Mailing Add:* 7609 Portland Ave S Minneapolis MN 55423

OLSON, MERLE STRATTE, b Northfield, Minn, Aug 22, 40; m 64. BIOCHEMISTRY. *Educ:* St Olaf Col, BA, 62; Univ Minn, Minneapolis, PhD(biochem), 66. *Prof Exp:* Asst biochem, Univ Minn, Minneapolis, 62-66; assoc prof biochem, Col Med, Univ Ariz, 68-76; PROF BIOCHEM, UNIV TEX, HEALTH SCI CTR SAN ANTONIO, 76- *Concurrent Pos:* Johnson Res Found res fel biochem, Univ Pa, 66-68. *Mem:* Am Soc Biol Chem; Am Soc Cell Biol. *Res:* Regulation of nultienzyme complexes in complex metabolic systems; complement receptors on cellular membranes. *Mailing Add:* Dept of Biochem Univ of Tex Health Sci Ctr San Antonio TX 78284

OLSON, NORMAN FREDRICK, b Edmund, Wis, Feb 8, 31; m 57; c 2. FOOD TECHNOLOGY. *Educ:* Univ Wis, BS, 53, MS, 57, PhD(dairy & food industs), 59. *Prof Exp:* Asst prof, 58-63, assoc prof, 63-71, PROF FOOD SCI, UNIV WIS-MADISON, 71- *Honors & Awards:* Pfizer Award in Cheese Res. *Mem:* Am Dairy Sci Asn; Inst Food Technol; Am Soc Microbiol. *Res:* Chemistry, microbiologyand enzymology of cheese manufacture and maturation; mechanization of cheese manufacture; rheology of cheese; bacteriological problems of natural cheese; food fermentations, particularly cheese technology; technology of encapsulated and immobilized enzymes. *Mailing Add:* Dept Food Sci Univ Wis Madison WI 53706

OLSON, NORMAN O, b Regan, NDak, June 1, 14; m 40; c 3. VETERINARY MEDICINE. *Educ:* Wash State Univ, DVM, 38. *Prof Exp:* Vet disease control res, USDA, 38-44, res vet, Food & Drug Admin, 44-48; prof animal path, WVa Univ, 48-81; RETIRED. *Honors & Awards:* Am Feed Mfrs Award, Am Vet Med Asn, 72. *Mem:* Am Vet Med Asn; Poultry Sci Asn. *Res:* Virus and bacterial diseases of farm animals; mycoplasma and virology. *Mailing Add:* Div of Animal & Vet Sci WVa Univ Morgantown WV 26506

OLSON, OSCAR EDWARD, b Sioux Falls, SDak, Jan 19, 14; m 43; c 2. AGRICULTURAL BIOCHEMISTRY. *Educ:* SDak State Col, BS, 36, MS, 37; Univ Wis, PhD(biochem), 48. *Prof Exp:* Sta analyst, Agr Exp Sta, SDak State Col, 37-42; chemist, Fruit & Veg Prod Lab, USDA, 48-49; biochemist, Div Labs, Mich State Dept Health, 49-51; head, Exp Sta Biochem, 51-73, dean, grad div, 58-65, prof, 75-79, EMER PROF CHEM, SDAK STATE UNIV, 79- *Concurrent Pos:* Vis prof, Inst Enzyme Res, Univ Wis-Madison, 62-63; vis scientist, US Plant, Soil & Nutrit Lab, NY, 73-74. *Mem:* Poultry Sci Asn; Am Chem Soc; Am Inst Nutrit; Am Soc Biol Chem. *Res:* Selenium and nitrate poisoning; calcium metabolism in poultry. *Mailing Add:* Dept Chem Animal Sci Bldg SDak State Univ Brookings SD 57006

OLSON, PAUL B, b Tea, SDak, Mar 5, 24; m 47; c 2. ANALYTICAL CHEMISTRY. *Educ:* Augustana Col, BA, 44; Univ Minn, Minneapolis, MS, 48. *Prof Exp:* Chemist, Minn Mining & Mfg Co, 48-67, res specialist, 67-76, SR RES SPECIALIST CHEM, 3M CO, 76- *Mem:* Am Chem Soc; Am Microchem Soc; Catalysis Soc. *Res:* Organic microanalysis. *Mailing Add:* 3M Ctr PO Box 33221 St Paul MN 55133

OLSON, PETER LEE, b Lincoln, Nebr, Aug 8, 50; m 77. GEOPHYSICS, GEOPHYSICAL FLUID DYNAMICS. *Educ:* Univ Colo, BA, 72; Univ Calif, MA, 74, PhD(geophys), 77. *Prof Exp:* ASST PROF GEOPHYSICS, JOHNS HOPKINS UNIV, 77- *Mem:* Am Geophys Union. *Res:* Dynamics of the earths interior; geomagnetism. *Mailing Add:* Dept of Earth & Planetary Sci Johns Hopkins Univ Baltimore MD 21218

OLSON, RAYMOND VERLIN, b Pembina Co, NDak, Oct 4, 19; m 43; c 3. AGRONOMY. *Educ:* NDak Agr Col, BS, 41; Univ Wis, MS, 42, PhD(soils), 47. *Prof Exp:* Chemist, Hercules Powder Co, Del; 42-45; from assoc prof to prof soils, 47-52, head dept, 52-70, dir, Int Agr Progs, 70-72, PROF AGRON, KANS STATE UNIV, 52- *Concurrent Pos:* Party chief, Ahmadu Bello Univ Proj, Nigeria, 64-66, 72-74, dean, Fac Agr, 64-65, provost agr, vet med, 71-74 & Int Atomic Energy Agency, Vienna, 79; consult, Ministry Agr, Iran, 68, IRI Inst Brazil, 69, US Agency Int Develop, West Africa, 76 & Philippine Dept Agr, 77. *Honors & Awards:* Gamma Sigma Delta Int Award, Distinguished Serv to Agr, 68. *Mem:* Fel Am Soc Agron; Soil Sci Soc Am; Int Soc Soil Sci. *Res:* Soil chemistry; plant nutrient availability; soil nitrogen; iron chlorosis. *Mailing Add:* Dept of Agron Kans State Univ Manhattan KS 66506

OLSON, REUBEN MAGNUS, b Ferryville, Wis, Feb 12, 19; m 43; c 4. FLUID MECHANICS, HEAT TRANSFER. *Educ:* Univ Minn, Minneapolis, BME, 39, MSME, 41, PhD(mech eng), 64. *Prof Exp:* Res asst mech eng, Eng Exp Sta, Univ Minn, Minneapolis, 39-40, instr, 40-42; ord engr, US Naval Ord Lab, Md, 42-50; res assoc hydraul, St Anthony Falls Hydraul Lab, Univ Minn, Minneapolis, 50-55, lectr hydromech, Univ, 55-62 & 63-64; assoc prof fluid mech, 64-67, PROF FLUID MECH, OHIO UNIV, 67-, CHMN DEPT CIVIL ENG, 75- *Concurrent Pos:* Vis prof, Tech Univ Norway, 70-71. *Mem:* Am Soc Eng Educ; Am Soc Mech Engrs; Int Asn Hydraul Res. *Res:* Revetment hydraulics; cavitation testing; flow development in ducts; mass transfer as related to heat transfer; shear layers; vortex flows. *Mailing Add:* Col of Eng Ohio Univ Athens OH 45701

OLSON, RICHARD DAVID, b Reading, Pa, Oct 10, 44. NEUROSCIENCES. *Educ:* Univ Redlands, BA, 66; St Louis Univ, MS, 68, PhD(psychol), 70. *Prof Exp:* Asst prof psychol, La State Univ, 70-74, assoc prof anat, Sch Med, 76-77; assoc prof, 74-80, chmn psychol, 74-81, PROF PSYCHOL, UNIV NEW ORLEANS, 80-, ASSOC DEAN GRAD SCH, 82- *Concurrent Pos:* Prin investr, New Orleans Parent-Child Develop Ctr, 75-79. *Mem:* Am Psychol Asn; Am Statist Asn; Animal Behav Soc; Soc Neurosci; Sigma Xi. *Res:* Studying the effects of neuropeptides, especially the endogenous opiates, on behavior using animal models to evaluate the clinical potential of effective peptides. *Mailing Add:* Dept of Psychol Univ of New Orleans New Orleans LA 70148

OLSON, RICHARD HUBBELL, b Meriden, Conn, Nov 25, 28; m 54; c 4. ECONOMIC GEOLOGY. *Educ:* Tufts Univ, BS, 50; Univ Utah, PhD(geol), 60. *Prof Exp:* Field geologist, US AEC, 51-53; geologist & draftsman, Gulf Oil Corp, 55-56; econ geologist, Union Carbide Corp, 57-59; asst prof econ geol, Univ Nev, 59-64; econ geologist, Chas Pfizer & Co, Inc, 65-69; dir, Mineral Resources Dept, Monsanto Co, 69-71; CONSULT GEOLOGIST, 72- *Mem:* Geol Soc Am; Am Inst Mining, Metall & Petrol Engrs; Soc Econ Geol; Explorers Club. *Res:* Industrial mineral deposits; economic geology of mineral deposits. *Mailing Add:* 14618 W 6th Ave Suite 202 Golden CO 80401

OLSON, RICHARD LOUIS, b El Paso, Tex, Aug 14, 32; m 55; c 2. BOTANY, GENETICS. *Educ:* Univ Utah, BS, 54, MS, 55; Univ Calif, Berkeley, PhD(genetics), 64. *Prof Exp:* Preliminary design engr, AiResearch Mfg Co Div, Garrett Corp, Calif, 62-64; mgr biosci, 64-74, gen mgr, Best Prog, Resources Conserv Co Div, 74-77, TECHNOL MGR, LARGE SPACE SYSTS, BOEING CO, 78- *Concurrent Pos:* Chmn scientist comt, Northwest Pollution Control Asn. *Mem:* AAAS; Am Inst Aeronaut & Astronaut. *Res:* Technology advancement for large space systems; sludge drying equipment development; waste management and water management problems related to manned space flight; toxicology; space craft eterilization and exobiology; urban development; waste and water management; urban and agricultural pollution abatement. *Mailing Add:* Boeing Aerospace Co PO Box 3999 MS 8F-03 Seattle WA 98124

OLSON, ROBERT AUGUST, b Nebr, Apr 14, 17; m 39; c 3. SOILS. *Educ:* Univ Nebr, MSc, 49. *Prof Exp:* Soil surveyor & technologist, Soil Conserv Serv, USDA, 38-43; asst exten agronomist, 46-48, from asst prof to assoc prof, 48-57, PROF AGRON, UNIV NEBR, LINCOLN, 57- *Concurrent Pos:* Consult, Orgn Europ Econ Coop, Paris, 58; sr off, Int Atomic Energy Agency, Austria, 62; mgr, Int Fertilizer Prog, Food & Agr Orgn, Rome, 67-69; actg dir, Joint Div Atomic Energy in Food & Agr, Food & Agr Orgn-Int Atomic Energy Agency, Vienna, 74-75; mem, Comt Trop Soils, Nat Acad Sci-Nat Res Coun, 69-72; mem, Nat Acad Sci Wheat Deleg to People's Repub China, 76. *Honors & Awards:* Int Serv Agron Award, Am Soc Agron, 71. *Mem:* Fel Soil Sci Soc Am; fel Am Soc Agron; Int Soil Sci Soc. *Res:* Plant nutrition studies with radioisotope tracers; improving validity of soil testing; abatement of agricultural pollution. *Mailing Add:* Dept of Agron Univ of Nebr Lincoln NE 68503

OLSON, ROBERT ELDON, b Thief River Falls, Minn, May 4, 40; m 65; c 2. ZOOLOGY, PARASITOLOGY. *Educ:* Concordia Col, Moorhead, Minn, BA, 62; Mont State Univ, MS, 64, PhD(zool), 68. *Prof Exp:* Res assoc, 68-75, asst prof zool, 75-79, asst prof, 79-81, ASSOC PROF FISHERIES & WILDLIFE, MARINE SCI CTR, ORE STATE UNIV, 81- *Mem:* Am Soc Parasitol; Am Fisheries Soc; Am Micros Soc; Wildlife Dis Asn. *Res:* Ecology of protozoans and helminths parasitizing marine fishes and shell fishes. *Mailing Add:* Marine Sci Ctr Ore State Univ Newport OR 97365

OLSON, ROBERT EUGENE, b Minneapolis, Minn, Jan 23, 19; m 44; c 5. BIOCHEMISTRY, MEDICINE. *Educ:* Gustavus Adolphus Col, AB, 38; St Louis Univ, PhD(biochem), 44; MD, 51; Am Bd Nutrit, dipl. *Prof Exp:* Asst biochem, Sch Med, St Louis Univ, 38-43; instr biochem & nutrit, Sch Pub

Health, Harvard Univ, 46-47, estab investr, Am Heart Asn, 51-52; prof biochem & nutrit, Grad Sch Pub Health & lectr med, Sch Med, Univ Pittsburgh, 52-65; assoc prof med, 65-72, ALICE A DOISY PROF BIOCHEM & CHMN DEPT, SCH MED, ST LOUIS UNIV, 65-, PROF MED, 72- *Concurrent Pos:* Harvard Med Sch, Nutrit Found fel, 47-49, Am Heart Asn fel, 49-51; Guggenheim & Fulbright fel, Oxford Univ, 61-62 & Univ Freiburg, 70-71; house physician, Peter Bent Brigham Hosp, Boston, Mass, 51-52; dir nutrit clin, Falk Clin, Univ Pittsburg Med Ctr, 53-65; consult metab & nutrit study sect, Res Grants Div, USPHS, 53-57, 58-59, biochem training comt, 59-63, training comt, Nat Heart Inst, 64-68; clin assoc, St Margaret Mem Hosp, 54-60, consult, 55-65; mem panel biochem & nutrit, Comt Growth, Nat Res Coun, 54-56; sci adv comt, Nat Vitamin Found, 55-58; from vpres to pres, Am Bd Nutrit, 60-63; consult & dir metab unit, Presby Hosp, 60-65; dir, Anemia Malnutrition Res Ctr, Thailand, 65-77; Atwater Lectureship, USDA, 78. *Honors & Awards:* McCollum Award, Am Soc CLin Nutrit, 65; Goldberger Award, AMA, 74; Noyes Lectureship, Univ Ill, Urbana, 80. *Mem:* Asn Chmn Biochem Med Schs (pres, 79-80); Am Chem Soc; Am Soc Biol Chem; Am Inst Nutrit (pres, 80-81); fel Am Pub Health Asn. *Res:* Cardiac metabolism; role of the fat-soluble vitamins; experimental and clinical nutrition. *Mailing Add:* Dept Biochem Sch Med St Louis Univ St Louis MO 63104

OLSON, ROBERT LEROY, b Portland, Ore, Apr 24, 32; m 57; c 2. PHYSIOLOGY, MEDICINE. *Educ:* Ore State Univ, BS, 54; Univ Ore, MD, 58. *Prof Exp:* Resident, 62-64, from instr to assoc prof, 64-74, PROF DERMAT, SCH MED, UNIV OKLA, 74- *Mem:* Soc Invest Dermat; Am Acad Dermat; Am Dermat Asn. *Res:* Cutaneous physiology; ultraviolet light physiology; electron microscopy. *Mailing Add:* 3400 NW Expressway Suite 707 Oklahoma City OK 73112

OLSON, ROY E, b Aberdeen, Wash, May 24, 29; m 62; c 3. SOLID STATE PHYSICS. *Educ:* Univ Calif, Berkeley, PhD(physics), 58. *Prof Exp:* PROF PHYSICS, CALIF STATE UNIV, NORTHRIDGE, 62- *Mailing Add:* Dept of Physics & Astron Calif State Univ Northridge CA 91324

OLSON, ROY EDWIN, b Richmond, Ind, Sept 13, 31; m 67; c 3. GEOTECHNICAL ENGINEERING, CIVIL ENGINEERING. *Educ:* Univ Minn, BS, 53, MS, 55; Univ Ill, Urbana, PhD(civil eng), 60. *Prof Exp:* From instr to prof, Univ Ill, Urbana, 58-70; PROF CIVIL ENG, UNIV TEX, AUSTIN, 70- *Concurrent Pos:* NSF res grants; Air Force Weapons Lab grant; Off Naval Res res grant; mem hwy res bd, Nat Acad Sci-Nat Res Coun. *Honors & Awards:* Huber Prize, Am Soc Civil Engrs, 72; Hogentogler Award, Am Soc Testing & Mat, 73; Norman Medal, Am Soc Civil Engrs, 75. *Mem:* AAAS; Am Soc Civil Engrs; Am Soc Testing & Mat; Clay Minerals Soc; US Nat Soc Soil Mech & Found Eng (chmn, 73-74). *Res:* Foundation engineering; physico-chemical properties of clays; numerical analysis of consolidation of clays; apparatus development; marine foundation engineering; research in consolidation of soft clays, water flow around radioactive waste disposal sites, physicochemical phenomena and soil mechanics. *Mailing Add:* Dept Civil Eng Univ Tex Austin TX 78712

OLSON, STANLEY WILLIAM, b Chicago, Ill, Feb 10, 14; m 36; c 3. MEDICINE. *Educ:* Wheaton Col, Ill, BS, 34; Univ Ill, MD, 38; Univ Minn, MS, 43; Am Bd Internal Med, dipl. *Hon Degrees:* LLD, Wheaton Col, Ill, 53; DSc, Univ Akron, 79. *Prof Exp:* Asst to dir, Mayo Found, Univ Minn, 46-47, asst dir, 47-50; prof med & dean col med, Univ Ill, 50-53 & Baylor Univ, 53-66; dir regional med progs serv, Health Serv & Ment Health Admin, 68-70; pres, Southwest Found Res & Educ, 70-73; provost, 73-79, EMER PROVOST & PROF MED, COL MED, NORTHEASTERN OHIO UNIV, 79- *Concurrent Pos:* Consult, State Univ NY, 49 & Comn, 54; mem med adv panel, US Off Voc Rehab Admin, 60-65; mem comt med sch-vet admin rels, 62-66; mem nat adv coun health res facil, NIH, 63-67; mem rev panel construct schs med, USPHS, 64-66; mem, Nat Adv Comn Health Manpower, 66; prof med, Vanderbilt Univ, 67-68; clin prof med, Meharry Med Col, 67-68; dir, Tenn Mid-South Regional Med Prof, 67-68; consult med educ, 79- *Mem:* Am Asn Med Cols (vpres, 60-61); fel Am Col Physicians. *Res:* Medical administration; medical education for national defense. *Mailing Add:* Northeastern Ohio Univ Col Med 4209 State Rte 44 Rootstown OH 44272

OLSON, STORRS LOVEJOY, b Chicago, Ill, Apr 3, 44. ORNITHOLOGY. *Educ:* Fla State Univ, BS, 66, MS, 68; Johns Hopkins Univ, ScD(biol), 72. *Prof Exp:* CUR ORNITH, SMITHSONIAN INST, 72- *Honors & Awards:* A B Howell Award, Cooper Ornith Soc, 72; Ernest P Edwards Award, Wilson Ornith Soc, 73. *Mem:* Am Ornithologists Union; Soc Vert Paleont; Royal Australasian Ornithologists Union. *Res:* Higher systematics, evolution and paleontology of birds. *Mailing Add:* Div of Birds Nat Mus of Natural Hist Smithsonian Inst Washington DC 20560

OLSON, TAMLIN CURTIS, b Colton, SDak, Feb 21, 32; m 55; c 4. SOIL PHYSICS. *Educ:* Univ Md, BS, 57, MS, 59; Purdue Univ, PhD, 66. *Prof Exp:* Res soil scientist, 60-63, supvy soil scientist, 63-73, res leader, 73-76, asst area dir, 76-80, ASSOC AREA DIR, MICH-MINN-WIS AREA, AGR RES SERV, USDA, 80- *Concurrent Pos:* Assoc prof plant sci, SDak State Univ, 63-73; res assoc soil sci, Univ Minn, 73-76, adj prof, 76- *Mem:* Am Soc Agron; Soil Sci Soc Am; fel Soil Conserv Soc Am. *Res:* Flow of fluids through porous media; water use by agronomic crops. *Mailing Add:* Rm 266 North Hall Univ of Minn St Paul MN 55108

OLSON, WALTER HAROLD, b New Haven, Conn, May 12, 45; m 70; c 2. BIOMEDICAL ENGINEERING. *Educ:* Pa State Univ, BS, 67; Univ Mich, MS, 68, PhD(bioeng), 73. *Prof Exp:* Teaching fel elec eng, Univ Mich, 69-73; asst prof elec eng, Univ Ill, Urbana, 73-77; ASSOC PROF HEALTH SCI TECHNOL, MASS INST TECHNOL, 77- *Concurrent Pos:* Consult, Regional Health Resources Ctr, 74-; actg prog dir, NIH Bioeng Training, Univ Ill, 75-76. *Mem:* Inst Elec & Electronics Engrs; Asn Advan Med Instrumentation. *Res:* Biomedical instrumentation including transducers, electronics and digital signal processing; ambulatory ECG monitoring with portable microprocessor; ophthalmology instrumentation; methods for altering corneal curvature. *Mailing Add:* Mass Inst Technol Rm 20A-121 Cambridge MA 02139

OLSON, WALTER T, b Royal Oak, Mich, July 4, 17; m 43. CHEMISTRY. *Educ:* DePauw Univ, AB, 39; Case Inst Technol, BS, 40, PhD(chem), 42. *Prof Exp:* Instr chem, Case Inst Technol, 40-42; res chemist, Nat Adv Comt Aeronaut, Lewis Res Ctr, NASA, 42-45, chief, Combustion Br, 45-50, Fuels & Combustion Res Div, 50-58, Propulsion Chem Div, NASA-Lewis, 58-60, Chem & Energy Conversion Div, 60-62, asst dir pub affairs, 62-72, dir tech utilization & pub affairs, 72-81; DIR COMMUNITY CAPITAL INVEST STRATEGY, GREATER CLEVELAND GROWTH ASN, 81- *Concurrent Pos:* Consult, Dept Defense; chmn adv com, Fenn Col Eng, Cleveland State Univ. *Mem:* Fel AAAS; fel Am Inst Aeronaut & Astronaut; Am Chem Soc; Sigma Xi; Combustion Inst. *Res:* High speed combustion for aircraft engines; high energy fuels; organic synthesis; local anesthetics; rocket engines and propulsion and power for space flight; energy conversion systems. *Mailing Add:* Lewis Research Ctr Cleveland OH 44135

OLSON, WILLARD ORVIN, b Polk Co, Wis, May 9, 33; m 61; c 2. NUCLEAR ENGINEERING, PHYSICS. *Educ:* Univ Wis-River Falls, BS, 56; Vanderbilt Univ, MS, 58; Ore State Univ, PhD(nuclear eng), 74. *Prof Exp:* Instr physics, Mankato State Col, 58-62, asst prof, 64-67; instr nuclear eng, Ore State Univ, 72-73; SR PHYSICIST REACTOR PHYSICS, IDAHO NAT ENG LAB-ERDA, 75- *Mem:* Am Nuclear Soc. *Res:* Reactor physics; numerical and computer methods. *Mailing Add:* Idaho Nat Eng Lab-ERDA PO Box 1625 Idaho Falls ID 83401

OLSON, WILLARD PAUL, b Detroit, Mich, Aug 6, 39; m 64; c 2. ENVIRONMENTAL PHYSICS. *Educ:* Univ Calif, Los Angeles, BS, 62, MS, 64, PhD(physics), 68. *Prof Exp:* Res scientist, Astrophysics Res Corp, 64-65; consult, Rand Corp, 65-66; sr scientist, 68-74, chief environ effects br, 74-77, CHIEF, THERMODYN & ENVIRON DEPT, McDONNELL DOUGLAS ASTRONAUT CO, 77- *Concurrent Pos:* Mem Air Force Sci Adv Bd Comt on Aeronomy, 76-78. *Mem:* Int Asn Geomagnetism & Aeronomy; AAAS; Am Geophys Union; Am Phys Soc; Int Acad Astronaut. *Res:* Magnetospheric electric and magnetic fields and their interactions with charged particles; quantitative modelling and prediction of environmental effects and associated computer software development. *Mailing Add:* McDonnell Douglas Astronaut Co 5301 Bolsa Ave Huntington Beach CA 92647

OLSON, WILLIAM ARTHUR, b Minneapolis, Minn, Oct 19, 32; m 56; c 3. TOXICOLOGY, BIOCHEMISTRY. *Educ:* Univ Minn, BS, 54, MS, 60, PhD(nutrit), 62. *Prof Exp:* Res supvr nutrit, Chas Pfizer & Co, 62-65; dir animal health res, Smith Kline & French Labs, 65-69; staff scientist, Hazelton Labs, 69-73; OWNER-MGR, CFR SERV, 73- *Mem:* AAAS; Am Soc Animal Sci; Am Dairy Sci Asn; Animal Nutrit Res Coun. *Res:* Determination of the safe use of chemicals as drugs, veterinary drugs, food additives, pesticides or household articles; toxicology; product development. *Mailing Add:* Ctr for Regulatory Serv 2347 Paddock Lane Reston VA 22091

OLSON, WILLIAM BRUCE, b Omaha, Nebr, Dec 28, 30; m 59; c 3. PHYSICAL CHEMISTRY. *Educ:* Univ Wash, BS, 53, PhD(phys chem), 60. *Prof Exp:* Res assoc phys chem, Princeton Univ, 60-61; PHYSICIST, NAT BUR STANDARDS, 61- *Honors & Awards:* Silver Medal, US Dept Com, 73. *Mem:* Optical Soc Am. *Res:* Molecular Structure and vibrational-rotational level structure of polyatomic molecules in gasphase via high resolution infrared spectroscopy; high precesion infrared spectrophotomatric instrumentation; precision infrared wavelength standards. *Mailing Add:* Ctr Chem Phys Nat Bur of Standards Washington DC 20234

OLSON, WILLIAM MARVIN, b Rock Island, Ill, June 15, 29; m 55; c 3. HIGH TEMPERATURE CHEMISTRY. *Educ:* Augustana Col, Ill, BA, 51; Univ Iowa, PhD(inorg chem), 59. *Prof Exp:* MEM STAFF, LOS ALAMOS NAT LAB, 56- *Concurrent Pos:* Fel, Europ Inst Transuranium Elements, EURATOM, Karlsruhe, Ger, 68-69. *Mem:* Am Vacuum Soc. *Res:* Thermodynamics, especially of actinides and their compounds. *Mailing Add:* CMB-11 Group MS-505 Los Alamos Nat Lab Los Alamos NM 87545

OLSON, WILMA KING, b Philadelphia, Pa, Dec 1, 45; m 69; c 1. BIOPHYSICAL CHEMISTRY, POLYMER CHEMISTRY. *Educ:* Univ Del, BS, 67; Stanford Univ, PhD(chem), 71. *Prof Exp:* Fel chem, Stanford Univ, 70-71; Damon Runyon Fund fel, Columbia Univ, 71-72; from asst prof to assoc prof, 72-79, PROF CHEM, DOUGLASS COL, RUTGERS UNIV, NEW BRUNSWICK, 79- *Concurrent Pos:* Sloan Found fel, 75; USPHS career develop award, 75; J S Guggenheim Found fel, 78-79; guest prof, Univ Basel, 78-79 & Jilin Univ, China, 81. *Mem:* Am Chem Soc; Biophys Soc. *Res:* Relationship of structure, conformation and function in biological macromolecules, particularly nucleic acids. *Mailing Add:* Dept of Chem Wright/Rieman Labs Rutgers Univ New Brunswick NJ 08903

OLSSON, CARL ALFRED, b Boston, Mass, Nov 29, 38; m; c 2. UROLOGY. *Educ:* Bowdoin Col, 59; Sch Med, Boston Univ, MD, 63; Am Bd Urol, cert, 72. *Prof Exp:* Intern surg, Mass Mem Hosp, 63-64; resident, Univ Hosp, 64-66; resident urol, Boston Vet Admin & Boston City Hosps, 66-69; from asst prof to assoc prof urol, 71-74, PROF UROL & CHMN DEPT, SCH MED, BOSTON UNIV, 74-; CHIEF UROL DEPT, UNIV HOSP, 71- *Concurrent Pos:* Fel urol, Cleveland Clin Found, 67-68; fel, Nat Kidney Found, 69 & NIH Spec Res, 69; consult urol, US Naval Hosp, 72-74; lectr surg, Sch Med, Tufts Univ, 72-; consult urol, US Pub Health Hosp, 72-; delegate res comt, Am Urol Asn, 74-77; mem exam comt, Am Bd Urol, 74-; urol consult chief surg serv, Vet Admin, 76-; trustee, Boston Interhospital Organ Bank, 76-; ed bd, Invest Urol, 77-; chief urol dept, Boston City Hosp, 74-77; asst chief urol sect, Boston Vet Admin Hosp, 75- *Mem:* AMA; Am Fertil Soc; Am Soc Artificial Internal Organs; Am Urol Asn; Soc Univ Urol. *Res:* Urologic cancer. *Mailing Add:* Univ Hosp 75 E Newton St Boston MA 02118

OLSSON, CARL NIELS, radio astronomy, see previous edition

OLSSON, RAY ANDREW, b Livermore, Calif, Nov 30, 31; m 54; c 3. PHYSIOLOGY. *Educ:* George Washington Univ, MD, 56. *Prof Exp:* With US Army, 55-76, resident internal med, George Washington Univ, 58-60, res internist, Dept Cardiorespiratory Dis, Walter Reed Army Inst Res, 61-63, dir div clin res, SEATO Med Res Lab, Bangkok, 63-66, asst chief dept cardiorespiratory dis, Walter Reed Army Inst Res, 67-70, dep dir div med, 70-71, dir div med, 71-76; PROF MED, UNIV SOUTH FLA COL MED, 76- *Concurrent Pos:* Assoc ed, Am J Physiol. *Honors & Awards:* Order of the White Elephant, Royal Thai Govt, 66. *Mem:* AAAS; Am Physiol Soc; Am Fedn Clin Res; Am Col Physicians; AMA. *Res:* Cardiovascular physiology; coronary circulation; cardiac metabolism. *Mailing Add:* Div Internal Med Univ South Fla Col Med Tampa FL 33620

OLSSON, RICHARD KEITH, b Newark, NJ, Mar 23, 31; m 57; c 3. GEOLOGY. *Educ:* Rutgers Univ, BS, 53, MS, 54; Princeton Univ, MA, 56, PhD(geol), 58. *Prof Exp:* Asst field geologist, Mobil Oil Co Div, Socony Mobil Oil Co, Inc, 53; explor geologist, Pinon Uranium Co, 55; asst geol, Rutgers Univ, 53-54 & Princeton Univ, 54-56; from instr to assoc prof, 57-71, prof geol, 71-77, CHMN GEOL SCI DEPT, RUTGERS UNIV, 77- *Concurrent Pos:* Consult, Humble Oil Co, 63-66. *Mem:* Geol Soc Am; Soc Econ Paleontologists & Mineralogists; Am Asn Petrol Geol; Paleont Soc. *Res:* Stratigraphy; micropaleontology, sedimentalogy; paleoecology; Late Cretaceous and Tertiary section of the geologic rock column; evolution and biostratigraphy of planktonic foraminifera. *Mailing Add:* Dept of Geol Rutgers Univ New Brunswick NJ 08903

OLSTAD, ROGER GALE, b Minneapolis, Minn, Jan 16, 34; m 55; c 2. SCIENCE EDUCATION. *Educ:* Univ Minn, BS, 55, MA, 59, PhD(educ), 63. *Prof Exp:* Instr high sch, Minn, 55-56; instr biol educ, Univ Minn, 56-63; asst prof sci educ, Univ Ill, 63-64; from asst prof to assoc prof, 64-71, PROF SCI EDUC, UNIV WASH, 71-, ASSOC DEAN GRAD STUDIES, 68- *Concurrent Pos:* Bd trustees, Pac Sci Ctr Found, 77- *Mem:* Fel AAAS; Nat Asn Res Sci Teaching (pres, 76-79); Nat Sci Teachers Asn; Nat Asn Biol Teachers. *Res:* Science curriculum development, organization and evaluation; science testo and testing. *Mailing Add:* Col Educ DQ-12 Univ of Wash Seattle WA 98195

OLSTER, ELLIOT FREDERICK, b New York, NY, Nov 23, 42; m 64; c 3. MATERIALS ENGINEERING, STRUCTURAL ENGINEERING. *Educ:* Drexel Inst Technol, BS, 65; Mass Inst Technol, MS, 67, ScD, 71. *Prof Exp:* Staff engr mat res, Systs Div, Avco Corp, 71-73; res engr, Plastics Develop Ctr, Ford Motor Corp, 73-75; ROTOR SYSTS ENGR AEROSPACE DEVELOP, SIKORSKY AIRCRAFT DIV, UNITED TECHNOL CORP, 75- *Mem:* Sigma Xi. *Res:* Crack propagation; fatigue and failure mechanisms in composite materials. *Mailing Add:* Sikorsky Aircraft Div N Main St Stratford CT 06602

OLSTOWSKI, FRANCISZEK, b New York, NY, Apr 23, 27; m 52; c 5. POLYMER CHEMISTRY. *Educ:* Tex A&M Univ, BS, 54. *Prof Exp:* Res & develop engr, magnesium technol, 54-56, proj engr fluorine res, 56-62, proj engr graphite technol, 62-65, sr res engr, 65-72, RES SPECIALIST, DOW CHEM CO, 72- *Mem:* AAAS; Am Chem Soc; Electrochem Soc; NY Acad Sci; fel Am Inst Chemists. *Res:* Electrolytic production of magnesium metal and fluorocarbons; synthesis of fluoro-olefins; inorganic fluoride synthesis; natural graphite technology; catalytic oxidation of olefins; polyurethane technology; reaction molding systems; plastic composite processes. *Mailing Add:* 912 North Ave A Freeport TX 77541

OLSZANSKI, DENNIS JOHN, b Rossford, Ohio, Feb 27, 48; m 68; c 3. CATALYSIS. *Educ:* Univ Dayton, BS, 70; Mich State Univ, PhD(inorg chem), 75. *Prof Exp:* Res assoc inorg chem, Ohio State Univ, 75-77; res chemist, Engelhard Minerals & Chem Corp, 77-79; SR RES CHEMIST, CALSICAT DIV, MALLINCKRODT, INC, 79- *Mem:* Am Chem Soc. *Res:* Coordination chemistry of scandium; bioinorganic chemistry, especially activation of molecular oxygen and nitrogen by transition metal complexes; catalysis by transition metals and zeolites. *Mailing Add:* Calsicat Div Mallinckrodt Inc 1707 Gaskell Ave Erie PA 16503

OLT, R(ICHARD) G(REVE), b Dayton, Ohio, Aug 12, 09; m 38; c 2. MECHANICAL ENGINEERING. *Educ:* Univ Cincinnati, ME, 33. *Prof Exp:* Test engr, Delco Prod Div, Gen Motors Corp, Ohio, 33-36, mech engr & asst head res, Moraine Prod Div, 38-44, proj engr, Optron Lab, 44-47; mech engr, Infilco, Inc, Ill, 36-37; physicist & group leader, Mound Lab, Monsanto Co, Ohio, 47-54; mgr mach develop, Mobay Chem Co, Mo, 54-55; mech engr, Atomic Proj, Monsanto Co, 55, mech engr, Res Dept, 55-57, group leader, 57-61, group leader, Monsanto Res Corp, 61-65, eng specialist, 65-75; CONSULT, 75- *Mem:* Fel Am Soc Mech Engrs; Optical Soc Am. *Res:* Design and development of physical and chemical research equipment; ultramicrobalances; quartz fibers and microtubes and microopenings; calorimeters; highly porous metals. *Mailing Add:* 3403 N 21st St Tacoma WA 98406

OLTE, ANDREJS, b Skujene, Latvia, Nov 17, 27; nat US; m 63; c 2. ENGINEERING. *Educ:* Univ Calif, BS, 54, MS, 57, PhD(elec eng), 59. *Prof Exp:* Asst elec eng, Univ Calif, 54-59; from asst prof to assoc prof, 59-66, PROF ELEC ENG, UNIV MICH, ANN ARBOR, 66- *Mem:* Inst Elec & Electronics Engrs. *Res:* Electromagnetic diffraction theory; propagation of radio waves; ionized gases. *Mailing Add:* 314 Hilldale Dr Ann Arbor MI 48105

OLTENACU, ELIZABETH ALLISON BRANFORD, b Pontefract, Eng, Sept 5, 47; m 73. ANIMAL SCIENCE. *Educ:* Univ Edinburgh, BSc, 70; Univ Minn, St Paul, MS, 72, PhD(animal sci), 74. *Prof Exp:* Res assoc, 74-79, lectr, 78-79, ASST PROF ANIMAL SCI, CORNELL UNIV, 79- *Mem:* Brit Soc Animal Prod; Inst Biol; Am Genetic Asn. *Res:* Computer studies of genetic and non-genetic influences affecting physiological and behavioral traits in domestic livestock; development of adjustment factors for environmental sources of variation and determination of potential results of selection programs for such traits. *Mailing Add:* Dept of Animal Sci 132 Morrison Hall Cornell Univ Ithaca NY 14853

OLTHOF, THEODORUS HENDRIKUS ANTONIUS, b Deventer, Netherlands, July 15, 34; Can citizen. NEMATOLOGY, PLANT PATHOLOGY. *Educ:* State Col Trop Agr, Netherlands, dipl, 55; McGill Univ, BSc, 58, PhD(plant path), 63. *Prof Exp:* Res officer potatoes, 62-64, res officer nematol, 64-73, RES SCIENTIST, RES STA, CAN DEPT AGR, 73- *Mem:* Am Phytopath Soc; Can Phytopath Soc; Soc Nematol; Soc Europ Nematol. *Res:* Nematode-fungus interactions; field-ecology of root-lesion nematodes in tobacco; crop loss assessment; population dynamics. *Mailing Add:* Res Sta Agr Can Vineland Station ON L0R 2E0 Can

OLTJEN, ROBERT RAYMOND, b Robinson, Kans, Jan 13, 32; m 56; c 3. RUMINANT NUTRITION. *Educ:* Kans State Univ, BS, 50, MS, 58; Okla State Univ, PhD(animal nutrit), 61. *Prof Exp:* Res animal husbandman, Beef Cattle Res Br, Animal Sci Res Div, 62-69, leader nutrit invest, 69-72, chief, Ruminant Nutrit Lab, Agr Res Serv, USDA, 72-77; DIR, ROMAN L HRUSKA US MEAT ANIMAL RES CTR, CLAY CENTER, NEBR, 77- *Concurrent Pos:* Mem comt animal nutrit, Nat Acad Sci-Nat Res Coun, 72-76, chmn comt animal nutrit, 77-79. *Honors & Awards:* Nutrit Res Award, Am Feed Mfrs Asn, 71; Presidential Citation, 72; Cert Animal Scientist, Am Soc Animal Sci, 75; Moorman Mfg Travel Award, 77. *Mem:* Am Inst Nutrit; Am Soc Animal Sci; Am Dairy Sci Asn. *Res:* Digestion and metabolism of various nitrogen and energy sources by ruminants; finishing diets for beef cattle; research on cellulose wastes and non-protein nitrogen for ruminants. *Mailing Add:* Sci & Educ Serv-Agr Res USDA PO Box 166 Clay Center NE 68933

OLTZ, DONALD FREDERICK, palynology, see previous edition

OLUM, PAUL, b Binghamton, NY, Aug 16, 18; m 42; c 3. MATHEMATICS. *Educ:* Harvard Univ, AB, 40; Princeton Univ, AM, 42; Harvard Univ, PhD(math), 47. *Prof Exp:* Theoret physicist, Manhattan Proj, Princeton Univ, 41-42 & Los Alamos Sci Lab, 43-45; Jewett fel, Harvard Univ, 47-48 & Inst Advan Study, 48-49; from asst prof to prof math, Cornell Univ, 49-74, chmn dept, 63-66; dean, Col Natural Sci, Univ Tex, Austin, 74-76; vpres acad affairs & provost, 76-80, actg pres, 80-81, PRES, UNIV ORE, 81- *Concurrent Pos:* Mem, Inst Advan Study, 55-56 & Nat Res Coun adv comt, Off Ordn Res, 58-61; vis prof, Univ Paris & Hebrew Univ, Israel, 62-63; NSF sr res fel, Stanford Univ, 66-67; vis prof, Univ Wash, 70-71; mem bd trustees, Cornell Univ, 71-75. *Mem:* Am Math Soc; Math Asn Am; Sigma Xi. *Res:* Algebraic topology. *Mailing Add:* Pres Univ of Ore Eugene OR 97403

OLVER, ELWOOD FORREST, b Connelsville, Pa, Apr 10, 22; m 44; c 3. AGRICULTURAL ENGINEERING. *Educ:* Pa State Univ, BS, 43, MS, 49; Iowa State Univ, PhD(agr eng), 57. *Prof Exp:* Rural engr rural elec, Pa Power & Light Co, 46-48; asst prof agr eng, Pa State Univ, 48-50, assoc prof, 52-57, dir dept security, 57-60; educ dir rural elec, Iowa Rural Elec Coop Asn, 50-52; PROF DEPT AGR ENG, UNIV ILL, 60-, HEAD PROCESSING DIV, 70- *Concurrent Pos:* Group leader sci team, J Nehru Agr Univ, India, 67-69; consult, Coop Res Sci & Educ Admin, USDA, 77-78 & 80-82; exec secy, Ill Electrification Coun, 70- *Mem:* Fel Am Soc Agr Engrs; Sigma Xi; Am Soc Eng Educ. *Res:* Automation in dairy farming; studying the principle of management by exception. *Mailing Add:* Dept of Agr Eng Univ of Ill Urbana IL 61808

OLVER, FRANK WILLIAM JOHN, b Croydon, Eng, Dec 15, 24; m 48; c 3. APPLIED MATHEMATICS. *Educ:* Univ London, BSc, 45, MSc, 48, DSc(math anal), 61. *Prof Exp:* Exp officer numerical anal, Nautical Almanac Off, Eng, 44-45; sr prin sci officer, Nat Phys Lab, 45-61, head numerical methods sect, 53-61; mathematician, Nat Bur Stand, DC, 61-69; RES PROF, INST PHYS SCI & TECHNOL, UNIV MD, 69- *Concurrent Pos:* Mathematician, Nat Bur Stand, Washington, DC, 69-; ed, J Math Anal, Soc Indust & Anal Math, 69- Appl Math, 64-; assoc ed, J Res, Nat Bur Standards, 66-78. *Mem:* Am Math Soc; Soc Indust & Appl Math; Math Asn Am; fel Inst Math & Applns UK. *Res:* Asymptotics; numerical analysis; special functions. *Mailing Add:* Inst Phys Sci & Technol Univ Md College Park MD 20742

OLVER, JOHN WALTER, b Honesdale, Pa, Sept 3, 36; m 59. ANALYTICAL CHEMISTRY. *Educ:* Rensselaer Polytech Inst, BS, 55; Tufts Univ, MS, 56; Mass Inst Technol, PhD(voltametric studies), 61. *Prof Exp:* Actg head dept chem, Franklin Inst, 56-58; instr chem, Mass Inst Technol, 61-62; ASST PROF CHEM, UNIV MASS, AMHERST, 62- *Mem:* Am Chem Soc. *Res:* Electrochemical methods of analysis; chemical separations. *Mailing Add:* 1333 West Amherst MA 01002

OLVER, PETER JOHN, b Twickenham, Eng, Jan 11, 52; m 76; c 1. LIE GROUPS, DIFFERENTIAL EQUATIONS. *Educ:* Brown Univ, ScB, 73; Harvard Univ, PhD(math), 76. *Prof Exp:* L E Dickson instr math, Univ Chicago, 76-78; res assoc math, Univ Oxford, Eng, 78-80; ASST PROF MATH, UNIV MINN, 80- *Mem:* Am Math Soc; Soc Indust & Appl Math. *Res:* Applications of lie groups to differential equations in fluid dynamics and elasticity, especially in conservation laws and Hamiltonian structures. *Mailing Add:* Sch Math Univ Minn Minneapolis MN 55455

OLYMPIA, PEDRO LIM, JR, b Mindoro, Philippines, June 29, 41. CHEMISTRY, CHEMICAL PHYSICS. *Educ:* Univ Philippines, BS, 60; Villanova Univ, MS, 65; Univ Fla, PhD(chem physics), 68. *Prof Exp:* Res & develop chemist, San Miguel Corp, 61-63; NSF fel, Tufts Univ, 68-69, AEC fel, 69-70; US Air Force fel, Univ Ga, 70-71; ASSOC PROF CHEM, WASH TECH INST, 71- *Res:* Quantum chemistry and physics; atomic and molecular structure; density matrix theory; computers in chemistry and physics. *Mailing Add:* 308 Gruenther Ave Rockville MD 20851

OLYNYK, PAUL, b Ymir, BC, Aug 5, 18; m 71; c 4. CHEMISTRY. *Educ:* McGill Univ, BSc, 39; Univ Toronto, PhD(chem), 44. *Prof Exp:* Qual control supvr radar parts, Res Enterprises Ltd, 44-45; res chemist biol mat, Fine Chem of Can Ltd, 45-46; instr chem, Univ Rochester, 46-48; res assoc antibiotic plants, Babies & Children's Hosp, 48-50, res assoc fats & fat metab, 50-52; res chemist paint formulation, Sherwin-Williams Co, 52-57 & Glidden

Co, 57-59; assoc dir inst urban studies & dir div environ sci, 69-71, ASSOC PROF CHEM, CLEVELAND STATE UNIV, 59- *Mem:* Am Chem Soc; Fedn Am Scientists; Int Asn Great Lakes Res. *Res:* Antibiotics from plant; radiocarbon C-14 in proteins and fats; fat metabolism; water and air pollution; sediment and environmental chemistry; toxic organics. *Mailing Add:* Dept of Chem Cleveland State Univ Cleveland OH 44115

OLYPHANT, MURRAY, JR, b New York, NY, May 2, 23; m 47; c 3. ELECTRICAL ENGINEERING. *Educ:* Princeton Univ, BS, 44, MSE, 47. *Prof Exp:* Instr plastics & dielec, Princeton Univ, 47-51, res assoc, 51-52; res engr elec prod, Minn Mining & Mfg Co, 52-65, group leader elec prod lab, 65-67, supvr, dielec mat & syst lab, 67-70, sr res specialist, 70-76; sr res specialist electronic prod, 76-80, DIV SCIENTIST, 3M CO, 80- *Concurrent Pos:* Bd mem, Conf Elec Insulation & Dielec Phenomena, Nat Res Coun. *Mem:* AAAS; fel Inst Elec & Electronics Engrs. *Res:* Electrical properties of plastics; breakdown and corona resistance of electrical insulation; microwave dielectric measurements; computer connecting systems. *Mailing Add:* 3M Co 3M Bldg Ctr St Paul MN 55109

OMACHI, AKIRA, b Sacramento, Calif, Sept 10, 22; m 51; c 2. PHYSIOLOGY. *Educ:* Univ Buffalo, BA, 44; Univ Minn, MS, 48, PhD(physiol), 50. *Prof Exp:* Instr physiol, Univ Minn, 48-49; from instr to asst prof, Med SCh, Loyola Univ, Ill, 49-57; from asst prof to assoc prof, 57-69, PROF PHYSIOL, COL MED, UNIV ILL MED CTR, 69- *Mem:* AAAS; Am Physiol Soc; Am Asn Univ Profs; Biophys Soc; Sigma Xi. *Res:* Electrolyte metabolism; cell physiology and metabolism; membrane transport. *Mailing Add:* Dept of Physiol & Biophys Univ of Ill Med Ctr Box 6998 Chicago IL 60680

O'MAHONY, JOHN SEAN, food science, see previous edition

O'MALLEY, BENEDICT BERNARD, biochemistry, pharmacology, deceased

O'MALLEY, BERT W, b Pittsburgh, Pa, Dec 19, 36; m 60; c 4. ENDOCRINOLOGY, MOLECULAR BIOLOGY. *Educ:* Univ Pittsburgh, BS, 59, MD, 63. *Prof Exp:* From intern to resident, Med Ctr, Duke Univ, 63-65; clin assoc, Endocrinol Br, Nat Cancer Inst, 65-67, sr investr, 67-68, head molecular biol sect, 68-69; prof reproductive physiol, Vanderbilt Chair, Sch Med, Vanderbilt Univ, 69-72; PROF CELL BIOL & CHMN DEPT, BAYLOR COL MED, 72- *Mem:* Endocrine Soc; Soc Study Reproduction. *Res:* Reproductive physiology; mechanism of hormone action; hormone-mediated cell differentiation; molecular biology of the animal cell. *Mailing Add:* Dept of Cell Biol Baylor Col of Med Houston TX 77030

O'MALLEY, EDWARD PAUL, b Hudson, NY, May 30, 26. PSYCHIATRY, PHARMACOLOGY. *Educ:* St John's Univ, NY, BS, 49; Loyola Univ, Ill, MS, 53, PhD(pharmacol), 54; State Univ NY Downstate Med Ctr, MD, 58; Am Bd Psychiat & Neurol, dipl, 65. *Prof Exp:* Intern, St Vincent's Hosp, New York, 58-59; resident psychiat, Bronx Vet Admin Hosp & NY State Psychiat Inst, New York, 59-62; sch psychiatrist, Bur Child Guid, NY Bd Educ, 63-67; med dir, West Nassau Ment Health Ctr, 67-68; dir, Community Ment Health Serv Suffolk County, 68-72; comnr, Orange County Ment Health Serv, NY, 72-74; asst clin prof psychiat, NJ Med Sch, 74-80; ASSOC CLIN PROF PSYCHIAT, UNIV CALIF, SAN DIEGO, 80- *Concurrent Pos:* Asst clin prof, State Univ NY Stony Brook; consult psychiatrist, Riverside Hosp, Bronx, NY, 62-63; visitor, New York Dept Corrections, 62-66; consult, Cath Charities Guid Inst, 62-; assoc attend, St Vincent's Hosp, 62-; clin attend, St Francis Hosp, Bronx, 63-; courtesy attend psychiatrist, Arden Hill Hosp, Goshen, NY; assoc attend psychiatrist, Bronx Lebanon Hosp & St Luke's Hosp; clin instr, NY Med Col, 76- *Mem:* AMA; fel Am Psychiat Asn. *Res:* Psychopharmacological and psychiatric research; pharmacological, biochemical and physiological studies at the basic science level. *Mailing Add:* Univ Calif San Diego La Jolla CA 92037

O'MALLEY, JAMES JOSEPH, b Philadelphia, Pa, Sept 17, 40; m 64; c 3. POLYMER CHEMISTRY, POLYMER PHYSICS. *Educ:* Villanova Univ, BS, 62; State Univ NY Col Forestry, Syracuse Univ, MS, 64, PhD(phys chem), 67. *Prof Exp:* From assoc scientist, to sr scientist, 67-74, MGR POLYMER RES, XEROX CORP, 74- *Mem:* AAAS; Am Chem Soc; Am Phys Soc. *Res:* Synthesis and characterization of block and graft copolymers; interactions of synthetic and bio-polymers; surface and electrical properties of polymers. *Mailing Add:* Res Lab Xerox Corp Webster NY 14580

O'MALLEY, JOHN RICHARD, b Huntington, Ind, May 17, 28; m 53; c 6. ELECTRICAL ENGINEERING. *Educ:* Purdue Univ, BS, 51, MS, 52; Georgetown Univ, LLB, 56; Univ Fla, PhD(elec eng), 64. *Prof Exp:* Patent examr, US Patent Off, 52-56; patent atty, Gen Elec Co, 56-59; assoc prof, 59-81, PROF ELEC ENG, UNIV FLA, 81- *Mem:* Inst Elec & Electronics Engrs; Am Soc Eng Educ. *Res:* Patent law; network synthesis; switching circuits. *Mailing Add:* Dept of Elec Eng Univ of Fla Gainesville FL 32601

O'MALLEY, JOSEPH PAUL, b Boston, Mass, Mar 22, 30; m 53; c 6. MEDICINE. *Educ:* Col of the Holy Cross, BS, 51; Harvard Univ, MD, 56. *Prof Exp:* Intern, USPHS Hosp, Brighton, Mass, 56-57; res investr, NIH, 57-66, asst to dir invest new drugs, Div Biol Stand, 67-72, DIR INVEST NEW DRUGS STAFF, BUR BIOLOGICS, FOOD & DRUG ADMIN, 72- *Res:* Cultivating the etiologic agent of human hepatitis. *Mailing Add:* Bur of Biologics Food & Drug Admin Bethesda MD 20014

O'MALLEY, MARY THERESE, b Chicago, Ill. MATHEMATICS. *Educ:* Univ Nebr, BA, 55; Cath Univ Am, MA, 63; Columbia Univ, PhD(math), 71. *Prof Exp:* Asst prof, 68-80, ASSOC PROF MATH, ROSARY COL, RIVER FOREST, ILL, 80- *Mem:* Math Asn Am; Am Math Soc; Sigma Xi. *Res:* Algebra. *Mailing Add:* Dept of Math Rosary Col River Forest IL 60305

O'MALLEY, MATTHEW JOSEPH, b Miami, Fla, Oct 21, 40; m 64; c 2. ALGEBRA. *Educ:* Spring Hill Col, BS, 62; Fla State Univ, MS, 64, PhD(math), 67. *Prof Exp:* Mathematician, Manned Spacecraft Ctr, NASA, 67-71; asst prof, 71-74, assoc prof, 74-81, PROF MATH, UNIV HOUSTON, 81- *Mem:* Am Math Soc. *Res:* Cummutative ring theory; pattern recognition. *Mailing Add:* Dept of Math Univ of Houston Houston TX 77004

O'MALLEY, RICHARD JOHN, b Jersey City, NJ, Dec 20, 45; m 70. MATHEMATICAL ANALYSIS. *Educ:* Seton Hall Univ, BS, 67; Purdue Univ, MS, 69, PhD(math), 72. *Prof Exp:* ASST PROF MATH, UNIV WIS-MILWAUKEE, 72- *Concurrent Pos:* Univ Wis-Milwaukee res grant, 75. *Mem:* Am Math Soc. *Res:* Analysis of functions of a real variable, particularly approximate continuity and density properties. *Mailing Add:* Dept of Math Univ of Wis Milwaukee WI 53201

O'MALLEY, ROBERT EDMUND, JR, b Rochester, NH, May 23, 39; m 68; c 3. APPLIED MATHEMATICS. *Educ:* Univ NH, BS, 60, MS, 61; Stanford Univ, PhD(math), 66. *Prof Exp:* Asst prof math, Univ NC, Chapel Hill, 66-68; assoc prof, NY Univ, 68-73; prof math, Univ Ariz, 73-76, chmn appl math, 76-81; PROF & CHMN MATH SCI, RENSSELAER POLYTECH INST, 81- *Concurrent Pos:* Vis mem, Courant Inst Math Sci, NY Univ, 66-67; vis asst prof, Math Res Ctr, Univ Wis, 67-68; sr vis fel, Univ Edinburgh, 71-72. *Mem:* Am Math Soc; Soc Indust & Appl Math. *Res:* Singular perturbation problems; asymptotic expansions; differential equations. *Mailing Add:* Dept Math Sci Rensselaer Polytech Inst Troy NY 12181

O'MALLEY, ROBERT FRANCIS, b Framingham, Mass, Apr 2, 18; m 44; c 5. FLUORINE CHEMISTRY. *Educ:* Boston Col, BS, 40, MS, 48; Mass Inst Technol, PhD(inorg chem), 61. *Prof Exp:* From instr to asst prof, 47-65, admin asst, 52-56, chmn dept chem, 56-66, 71-74, assoc prof, 65-81, PROF INORG CHEM, BOSTON COL, 81- *Concurrent Pos:* Vis prof, Harvard Univ, 65. *Mem:* AAAS; Am Chem Soc; Electrochem Soc. *Res:* Electrochemical and oxidative fluorination of aromatic compounds. *Mailing Add:* Dept of Chem Boston Col Chestnut Hill MA 02167

OMAN, CARL HENRY, b Camden, NJ, April 21, 38; m 62, 81; c 3. EXPLORATORY GEOLOGY. *Educ:* Rutgers Univ, BA, 59, MS, 60; Fla State Univ, PhD(geol), 65. *Prof Exp:* Exp & prod geologist oil, gas & minerals & district geol, Exxon Corp, 65-78; CHIEF GEOLOGIST, EVEREST MINERALS CORP, 78- *Mem:* Am Asn Petrol Geologists. *Res:* Locating commercial quantities of oil, gas and uranium using techniques of biostratigraphy, physical stratigraphy, structural geology, geochemistry and geophysics. *Mailing Add:* Everest Minerals Corp PO Box 1339 Corpus Christi TX 78403

OMAN, CHARLES MCMASTER, b Brooklyn, NY, Feb 22, 44; m 74; c 1. AERONAUTICAL ENGINEERING, BIOMEDICAL ENGINEERING. *Educ:* Princeton Univ, BSE, 66; Mass Inst Technol, SM, 68, PhD(instrumentation, automatic control), 72. *Prof Exp:* From asst prof to assoc prof aeronaut & astronaut, 72-79, Hermann von Helmholtz assoc prof, Div Health Sci & Technol, 77-79, prin res scientist, 79-81, SR RES ENGR, MASS INST TECHNOL, 81-, ASSOC DIR, MANNED VEHICLE LAB, 81, HERMANN VON HELMHOLTZ ASSOC PROF DIV HEALTH SCI & TECHNOL, 77- *Mem:* Soc Neurosci; Baronay Soc; Aerospace Med Asn. *Res:* Vestibular function; human spatial orientation and disorientation, motion sickness; control of posture and movement; biomedical instrumentation; automatic control and signal processing. *Mailing Add:* Manned Vehicle Lab Rm 37-219 Mass Inst Technol Cambridge MA 02139

OMAN, PAUL WILSON, b Garnett, Kans, Feb 22, 08; m 31; c 6. ENTOMOLOGY. *Educ:* Univ Kans, AB, 30, AM, 35; George Washington Univ, PhD(entom), 41. *Prof Exp:* Jr entomologist bur entom & plant quarantine, USDA, 30-34, from asst entomologist to prin entomologist, 34-59, chief insect identification & parasite introd res br, 59-60, dir res & tech progs div, Far East Regional Res Off, Agr Res Serv, 60-63, asst dir entom res div, 63-67; actg head dept, 73-74, prof entom, 67-75, EMER PROF ENTOM, ORE STATE UNIV, 75- *Mem:* Fel Entom Soc Am (2nd vpres, 48, pres-elect, 58, pres, 59); fel Royal Entom Soc London. *Res:* Insect systematics; biological control of insects and weeds; medical entomology. *Mailing Add:* Dept of Entom Ore State Univ Corvallis OR 97331

OMAN, RICHARD A(RTHUR), fluid mechanics, see previous edition

OMAN, ROBERT MILTON, b Easton, Mass, Aug 12, 34; m 62; c 1. ELECTRON PHYSICS. *Educ:* Northeastern Univ, BS, 57; Brown Univ, ScM, 60, PhD(physics), 63. *Prof Exp:* From res asst to res assoc physics, Brown Univ, 58-63; res scientist, United Aircraft Corp, Conn, 63-64; tech specialist, Litton Systs, Inc, Minn, 64-66; sr res scientist, Norton Res Corp, Mass, 66-70; ASSOC PROF PHYSICS, N SHORE COMMUNITY COL, 71- *Mem:* Am Vacuum Soc. *Res:* Theoretical physical electronics; solid state and experimental solid state physics; electron mirror microscopy; magnetron gauges; electron transport in semiconductors; applied mathematics. *Mailing Add:* 204 Fair Oaks Park Needham MA 02192

O'MARA, JAMES HERBERT, b St Clair, Mich, Oct 11, 36. PHYSICAL CHEMISTRY. *Educ:* George Washington Univ, BS, 57, MS, 61; Duke Univ, PhD(phys chem), 68. *Prof Exp:* Chemist, Polymers Div, Nat Bur Standards, 57-63; SR CHEMIST, ROHM AND HAAS CO, 67- *Mem:* AAAS; Am Chem Soc; Am Soc Testing & Mat; Soc Automotive Engrs. *Res:* Physical chemistry of polymers in dilute solution and bulk; chemistry of oil additives. *Mailing Add:* Rohm and Haas Co Spring House PA 19477

O'MARA, JOSEPH GEORGE, b Boston, Mass, Sept 7, 11; m 38. GENETICS. *Educ:* Univ Mass, BS, 33; Harvard Univ, MS, 34, PhD(biol), 36. *Prof Exp:* Geneticist, Univ Mo, 36-42, Emergency Rubber Proj, 43-44 & Univ Mo, 44-50; prof genetics, Iowa State Univ, 50-65, chmn dept, 59-65; prof bot & head dept, 65-67, prof biol & head dept, 67-77, EMER PROF BIOL, PA STATE UNIV, 77- *Mem:* Soc Study Evolution. *Res:* Theoretical and applied genetics; human heredity; mathematical genetics; cytology; cytogenetics. *Mailing Add:* Dept of Biol Pa Sta Univ University Park PA 16802

O'MARA, MICHAEL MARTIN, b Lackawanna, NY, Jan 24, 42; c 1. ORGANIC ANALYTICAL CHEMISTRY. *Educ:* Canisius Col, BS, 64; Univ Cincinnati, PhD(chem), 68. *Prof Exp:* Develop scientist, B F Goodrich Co, 68-72, sr develop scientist, 72-75, res & develop group leader, 75-77, develop mgr estane thermoplastic polyurethane, 75-78, gen mgr, 78-81, VPRES RES & DEVELOP, B F GOODRICH CHEM GROUP, 81- *Mem:* Am Chem Soc. *Res:* Thermal degradation of polymers; flammability, smoke and toxic gas generation characteristics of polymers; gas chromatographic-mass spectrometric analyses. *Mailing Add:* B F Goodrich Chem Group 6100 Oak Tree Blvd Cleveland OH 44131

O'MARA, ROBERT E, b Flushing, NY, Dec 8, 33; m 64; c 3. RADIOLOGY, NUCLEAR MEDICINE. *Educ:* Univ Rochester, BA, 55; Albany Med Col, MD, 59; Am Bd Radiol, dipl, 67; Am Bd Nuclear Med, dipl, 72. *Prof Exp:* Intern, St Louis Hosp, Wash Univ, 59-60, resident radiol, St Vincent's Hosp, New York, 63-66; dir nuclear med, Sch Med, Univ Ariz, 71-75; chief nuclear med serv, Vet Admin Hosp, Tucson, 71-75; PROF RADIOL & CHIEF DIV NUCLEAR MED, DEPT RADIOL, UNIV ROCHESTER, SCH OF MED & DENT, 75- *Concurrent Pos:* NIH fel nuclear med, State Univ NY Upstate Med Ctr, 66-67 & clin nuclear med, 67-71. *Mem:* Am Col Nuclear Physicians; Soc Nuclear Med; Radiol Soc NAm; Am Col Radiol; Am Bd Nuclear Med. *Res:* Diagnostic applications of radionuclides and development of radiopharmaceuticals. *Mailing Add:* Div of Nuclear Med 601 Elmwood Ave Univ of Rochester Med Ctr Rochester NY 14642

OMATA, ROBERT ROKURO, b Hanford, Calif, Nov 3, 20; m 48; c 3. BACTERIOLOGY. *Educ:* Univ Calif, AB, 44; Univ Minn, MS, 46, PhD(bact), 49. *Prof Exp:* Asst bact & immunol, Univ Minn, 45-47; from asst bacteriologist to bacteriologist, Nat Inst Dent Res, 53-60, mem staff div res grants, 60-63, scientist adminr, Off Int Res, 63-68, scientist adminr, Off Int Res, Pac Off, Tokyo, 64-67, head int fels sect, Scholars & Fels Prog Br, Fogarty Int Ctr, NIH, 68-74, INT PROG SPECIALIST, OFF INT AFFAIRS, NAT CANCER INST, 74- *Concurrent Pos:* Am Dent Asn res fel, Nat Inst Dent Res, 49-53 & USPHS, 53- *Mem:* AAAS; Am Soc Microbiol; Sigma Xi. *Res:* Oral microbiology; bacterial physiology and biochemistry; physiology of oral fusobacteria, spirochetes and clostridia; biochemistry and nutrition; science administration; general medical sciences. *Mailing Add:* Off of Int Affairs Nat Cancer Inst Bethesda MD 20014

O'MATHUNA, DIARMUID, b Corcaigh, Ireland, Mar 22, 34. APPLIED MATHEMATICS. *Educ:* Nat Univ Ireland, BSc, 55, MSc, 57; Mass Inst Technol, PhD(math), 62. *Prof Exp:* Temp mem math & mech, Courant Inst Math Sci, NY Univ, 62-64; instr math biol, Harvard Med Sch, 64-66; aerospace engr, Electronics Res Ctr, NASA, 66-70; MATHEMATICIAN, TRANSP SYSTS CTR, DEPT TRANSP, 70- *Concurrent Pos:* Vis scientist, Dublin Inst Advan Studies, 75. *Res:* Continuum mechanics; celestial mechanics; immunogenetics; biochemical kinetics; singular perturbation theory; transportation systems. *Mailing Add:* Transp Systs Ctr Kendall Sq Cambridge MA 02142

OMAYE, STANLEY TERUO, biochemical nutrition, see previous edition

OMDAHL, JOHN L, b Des Moines, Iowa, July 29, 40; m 63; c 4. ENDOCRINOLOGY. *Educ:* Colo State Univ, BS, 63, MS, 65; Univ Ky, PhD(physiol & biophys), 69. *Prof Exp:* Res chemist physiol, Vet Admin, 66-69; fel biochem, Univ Wis, 69-72; asst prof, 72-79, ASSOC PROF BIOCHEM, UNIV NMEX, 79- *Concurrent Pos:* Vis staff mem, Los Alamos Nat Lab, 80-81; vis assoc prof, Univ Tex Health Sci Ctr, Dallas, 81. *Mem:* Am Soc Biol Chemists; Sigma Xi; Am Soc Bone & Mineral Res. *Res:* Molecular mechanisms of enzyme regulation; cytochrome p-450 hydroxglase enzymes and the bioactivation of vitamin D; calcium homostasis and the mode-of-actions for vitamin D and parathyroid hormone. *Mailing Add:* Dept Biochem Sch Med Univ NMex Albuquerque NM 87131

O'MEARA, ANN RITA, b Boston, Mass, Dec 11, 42; m 71; c 1. BIOCHEMISTRY. *Educ:* Regis Col, BA, 64; Boston Col, MA, 67, PhD(biochem), 69. *Prof Exp:* Fel geront, 69-70, fel reprod biochem, 70-72, asst res prof, 72-74, ASST PROF BIOCHEM, SCH MED, BOSTON UNIV, 74- *Concurrent Pos:* Prin investr, NIH grant, 74-78; admis comt mem, Sch Med, Boston Univ, 76-78. *Mem:* AAAS. *Res:* Regulation of gene expression in eukaryotes as mediated through changes in the interaction of proteins and DNA in chromatin, with particular emphasis on protein modification. *Mailing Add:* Dept of Biochem Boston Univ Sch of Med Boston MA 02118

O'MEARA, DESMOND, b Daingean, Ireland, Oct 12, 26; m 53; c 6. ORGANIC CHEMISTRY, STATISTICS. *Educ:* Univ Dublin, BA & BSc, 49, MSc, 52; St Andrews Univ, PhD(chem), 57. *Prof Exp:* Asst, Queen's Col, St Andrews Univ, 52-55; org chemist, Brit Rayon Res Asn, Eng, 55-58; actg group leader pulping, Res Div, Columbia Cellulose Co Ltd, BC, 58, group leader, 58-59, group leader bleaching, 59-62; group leader chem, Res & Develop Dept, Consol Paper Corp Ltd, Que, 62-67, group leader, Statist Serv, 63-67; dir opers res, 67-74, DIR MGT SCI, CONSOL-BATHURST LTD, 74- *Mem:* Tech Asn Pulp & Paper Indust; Can Pulp & Paper Asn; Can Oper Res Soc. *Res:* Sugar nitrates; mechanism of degradation of cellulose and oxycellulose; wood pulp cooking and bleaching; statistical experimental design; operations research; computer applications. *Mailing Add:* Consol-Bathurst Ltd PO Box 69 800 Dorchester Blvd W Montreal PQ H3B 1X9 Can

O'MEARA, FRANCIS EDMUND, b New York, NY, Aug 8, 23; m 44; c 6. EXPERIMENTAL PHYSICS. *Educ:* Univ Mich, BS, 47. *Prof Exp:* Asst observer, US Weather Bur, 42-43; mass spectrometer technician, Oak Ridge Nat Lab, 47-48, physicist, NEPA Proj, 48-51; sr physicist, Res Lab, Bendix Aviation Corp, 51-54; div chief opers anal, US Air Force, 54-57, mem staff weapons systs eval group, 57-58; chief reactor eng sect, US AEC, 58-59; proj scientist, Booz-Allen Appl Res, 59-61; div chief opers anal, US Air Force, 61-63; mgr eval, Douglas Aircraft Co, Inc, 63-71; DIR PROGS & BUDGET, NAT OCEANIC & ATMOSPHERIC ADMIN, 72- *Mem:* Fel AAAS; assoc fel Am Inst Aeronaut & Astronaut; Am Phys Soc; NY Acad Sci. *Res:* Nuclear weapons and reactors; operations research. *Mailing Add:* 203 Mannakee St Rockville MD 20850

O'MEARA, GEORGE FRANCIS, b Lowell, Mass, Sept 9, 41; m 64; c 4. MEDICAL ENTOMOLOGY, GENETICS. *Educ:* Univ Notre Dame, BS, 64, MS, 67, PhD(biol), 69. *Prof Exp:* RES ENTOMOLOGIST, FLA MED ENTOM LAB, UNIV FLA, 69- *Concurrent Pos:* Adj assoc prof zool, Fla Atlantic Univ, 77- *Mem:* AAAS; Entom Soc Am; Am Mosquito Control Asn; Am Genetic Asn. *Res:* Reproductive and population biology of mosquitoes. *Mailing Add:* Fla Med Entom Lab PO Box 520 Vero Beach FL 32961

O'MEARA, O TIMOTHY, b Cape Town, SAfrica, Jan 29, 28; m 53; c 5. MATHEMATICS. *Educ:* Univ Cape Town, BSc, 47, MSc, 48; Princeton Univ, PhD(math), 53. *Prof Exp:* Lectr math, Univ Otago, NZ, 53-56; lectr math, Princeton Univ, 57, asst prof, 58-62; mem, Inst Advan Study, 57-58; head dept, 65-66, chmn dept, 68-72, prof math, 62-76, KENNA PROF MATH, UNIV NOTRE DAME, 76-, PROVOST, 78- *Concurrent Pos:* Sloan fel, 60-63; vis prof, Calif Inst Technol, 67-68; mem adv panel math sci, NSF, 74-77; Gauss prof, Gottingen Acad Sci, 78. *Mem:* Am Math Soc. *Res:* Algebra; linear groups; number theory; quadratic forms. *Mailing Add:* Dept of Math Univ of Notre Dame Notre Dame IN 46556

O'MELIA, ANNE FRANCES, developmental biology, biochemistry, see previous edition

O'MELIA, CHARLES R(ICHARD), b New York, NY, Nov 1, 34; m 56; c 6. ENVIRONMENTAL ENGINEERING, ENVIRONMENTAL CHEMISTRY. *Educ:* Manhattan Col, BCE, 55; Univ Mich, Ann Arbor, MSE, 56, PhD(sanit eng), 63. *Prof Exp:* Asst engr, Hazen & Sawyer, Engrs, 56-57; asst sanit eng, Univ Mich, 57-60; asst prof, Ga Inst Technol, 61-64; fel appl chem, Harvard Univ, 64-66, lectr, 65-66; assoc prof environ sci & eng, Univ NC, Chapel Hill, 66-70, prof, 70-80, dep chmn, 77-80; PROF ENVIRON ENG, JOHNS HOPKINS UNIV, 80- *Concurrent Pos:* Consult, Eng & Urban Health Sci Study Sect, NIH, 70-; Swiss Fed Inst Technol, 71; eng & urban health sci study sect, Environ Protection Agency, 71-; assoc ed, Environ Sci & Technol, J Am Chem Soc, 75- *Honors & Awards:* Publ Award, Am Water Works Asn, 66; Distinguished Fac Award, 72, Environ Sci Award, 75, Asn Environ Eng Prof. *Mem:* Am Chem Soc; Am Soc Civil Engrs; Am Water Works Asn; Water Pollution Control Fedn; Am Soc Limnol & Oceanog. *Res:* Aquatic chemistry; predictive modeling of natural systems; theory of water and wastewater treatment. *Mailing Add:* Dept Geog & Environ Eng Johns Hopkins Univ Baltimore MD 21218

OMENN, GILBERT STANLEY, b Chester, Pa, Aug 30, 41; m 67; c 2. MEDICAL GENETICS, HUMAN GENETICS. *Educ:* Princeton Univ, AB, 61; Harvard Med Sch, MD, 65; Univ Wash, PhD, 72. *Prof Exp:* Intern & asst resident, Mass Gen Hosp, 65-67; res assoc protein chem, Nat Inst Arthritis & Metab Dis, 67-69; asst prof, 71-73, ASSOC PROF MED, UNIV WASH, 73- *Concurrent Pos:* Teaching fel internal med, Mass Gen Hosp, Harvard Univ, 65-67; USPHS spec fel & univ sr fel med genetics, Univ Wash, 69-71, Nat Genetics Found fel, 61-72, Nat Inst Gen Med Sci res career develop award, 72-; White House fel, AEC, 73-74; attend physician, Univ Hosp, Harborview Med Ctr & Children's Orthop Hosp, Seattle, Wash, 71-; dir, Robert Wood Johnson Found Clin Scholars Prog, 74-77; consult, AEC & Fed Energy Admin, 74-76; asst dir, Off Sci & Technol Policy, Executive Off of the President, 77-; Am J Med Genetics, Behav Genetics, Forum in Med; Investr, Howard Hughes Med Inst. assoc ed, Am J Human Genetics. *Mem:* Nat Inst Med (Nat Acad Sci); Am Soc Human Genetics; Am Soc Neurochem; Soc Study Social Biol; Am Fedn Clin Res; Soc Biol Psychiat. *Res:* Enzyme variation in human brain; genetics of behavioral traits and disorders; prenatal diagnosis; pharmacogenetics. *Mailing Add:* Off Sci & Technol Policy Exec Off of President Washington DC 20500

OMER, GEORGE ELBERT, JR, b Kansas City, Kans, Dec 23, 22; m 49; c 2. ORTHOPEDIC SURGERY. *Educ:* Ft Hays Kans State Col, BA, 44; Univ Kans, MD, 50; Baylor Univ, MS, 55; Am Bd Orthop Surg, dipl. *Prof Exp:* Chief surg serv, Irwin Army Hosp, Ft Riley, Kans, 57-59, consult orthop surg, Eighth US Army, Korea, 59-60, chief hand surg, Fitzsimons Army Hosp, Denver, Colo, 62-64, dir orthop path, Armed Forces Inst Path, Washington, DC, 64-65, chief hand surg ctr, Brooke Army Med Ctr, Ft Sam Houston, Tex, 66-70, chief orthop, 67-70; PROF ORTHOP, CHMN DEPT & CHMN DIV HAND SURG, SCH MED, UNIV N MEX, 70- *Concurrent Pos:* Instr, Univ Kans, 46-47; asst clin prof, Sch Med, Univ Colo, 61-63; assoc clin prof, Georgetown Univ, 64-65, Univ Tex Med Sch San Antonio, 66-70 & Univ Tex Med Br Galveston, 68-70; consult orthop & hand surg, numerous civilian and mil hosps, 62- Indian Health, USPHS, 66- & orthop, Surgeon Gen, US Army, 69- *Mem:* Am Acad Orthop Surg; Am Asn Surg of Trauma; Am Col Surg; Am Orthop Asn; Am Soc Surg of Hand. *Res:* Hand surgery; peripheral nerve repair and sensibility; tendon transfers for reconstruction of nerve loss; evacuation of injuries and emergency room care; burn injuries. *Mailing Add:* Dept of Orthop Univ of NMex Health Sci Ctr Albuquerque NM 87131

OMER, GUY CLIFTON, JR, b Mankato, Kans, Mar 20, 12; m 42; c 2. PHYSICS. *Educ:* Univ Kans, BS, 36, MS, 37; Calif Inst Technol, PhD(physics), 47. *Prof Exp:* Instr, Univ Hawaii, 41-43; asst prof, Occidental Col, 47-48 & Univ Ore, 48-49; asst prof phys sci, physics & astron, Univ Chicago, 49-55; chmn dept phys sci, 67-72, PROF PHYSICS & ASTRON, UNIV FLA, 55- *Concurrent Pos:* Res fel, Calif Inst Technol, 47-48; vis prof, Univ Calif, Los Angeles, 64-65; sr vis fel, Inst Astron, Cambridge, Eng, 72; prof, Fla at Utrecht, Univ Utrecht, Holland, 73; sr vis fel, Dept Astrophys, Univ Oxford, 73. *Mem:* Am Phys Soc; Int Astron Union; Seismol Soc Am; Am Asn Physics Teachers; fel Royal Astron Soc. *Res:* Relativity; cosmology; general education. *Mailing Add:* Dept of Physics & Astron 217A SSRB Univ of Fla Gainesville FL 32601

OMID, AHMAD, b Abadeh, Iran, May 6, 31; m 57; c 2. AGRONOMY, PHYSIOLOGY. *Educ:* Calif State Polytech Col, BS, 55 & 57; Ore State Univ, MS, 62, PhD(farm crops), 64. *Prof Exp:* PLANT PHYSIOL GROUP LEADER, CHEVRON CHEM CO, 62-, SR PLANT PHYSIOLOGIST, 70- *Mem:* Weed Sci Soc Am. *Res:* Use of herbicides and growth regulators for control and modification of plant growth, including studies of mode of action and movement of these chemicals in plants and soils. *Mailing Add:* Plant Physiol Dept 940 Hensley Richmond CA 94804

OMIDVAR, KAZEM, b Mashad, Iran, Dec 6, 26. ATOMIC PHYSICS, ASTROPHYSICS. *Educ:* Univ Teheran, BS, 51; NY Univ, MS, 54, PhD(physics), 59. *Prof Exp:* Instr physics, Cooper Union, 54-56 & NY Univ, 56-57; lectr, Rutgers Univ, 57-58; instr, City Col New York, 58-59; assoc prof, Univ Teheran, 59-60; sr scientist, Theoret Studies Group, 60-77, SR SCIENTIST STRATOSPHERE PHYS & CHEM BRANCH, NASA/GODDARD SPACE FLIGHT CTR, 77- *Concurrent Pos:* Lectr, Univ Md, 61-64. *Mem:* Fel Am Phys Soc; Am Astron Soc. *Res:* Development of reliable formula for calculating ionization, excitation and charge exchange cross sections in electron-atom and ion-atom collisions; calculation of multiphotom absorption of radiation in atoms; calculations of absorption of radiation by ozone. *Mailing Add:* Stratosphere Physics & Chem Br NASA/Goddard Space Flight Ctr Greenbelt MD 20771

OMODT, GARY WILSON, b LaCrosse, Wis, July 30, 29; m 57; c 6. PHARMACEUTICAL CHEMISTRY. *Educ:* Univ Minn, BS, 53, PhD(pharmaceut chem), 59. *Prof Exp:* assoc prof 58-80, PROF PHARMACEUT CHEM & HEAD DEPT, COL PHARM, SDAK STATE UNIV, 80- *Mem:* Am Pharmaceut Asn; Am Asn Cols Pharm; Sigma Xi. *Res:* Synthesis of organic medicinal agents. *Mailing Add:* Dept Pharmaceut Chem Col Pharm SDak State Univ Brookings SD 57007

O'MORCHOE, CHARLES CHRISTOPHER C, b Quetta, India, May 7, 31; m 55; c 2. ANATOMY, PHYSIOLOGY. *Educ:* Univ Dublin, BA, 53, MB, BCh & BA Obstet, 55, MA, 59, MD, 61, PhD(physiol), 69. *Prof Exp:* Intern med, surg, gynec & obstet, Halifax Gen Hosp, Eng, 55-57; lectr anat, Sch Med, Univ Dublin, 57-61; vis lectr physiol, Sch Med, Univ Md, 61-62; instr anat, Harvard Med Sch, 62-63; lectr, Sch Med, Univ Dublin, 63-65, assoc prof physiol, 66-68; from assoc prof to prof anat, Sch Med, Univ Md, Baltimore City, 68-73, actg chmn dept, 71-73; PROF ANAT & CHMN DEPT, STRITCH SCH MED, LOYOLA UNIV CHICAGO, 74- *Concurrent Pos:* Chmn, Anat Bd Med, 71-73. *Mem:* Am Soc Nephrology; Brit Physiol Soc; Int Soc Nephrology; Am Asn Anat; Int Soc Lymphology. *Res:* Anatomy and physiology of renal vascular circulation and renal lymphatic system; urinary cytology in reproductive endocrinology; medical education; histology; lymphology; nephrology. *Mailing Add:* Dept of Anat Loyola Univ Stritch Sch of Med Maywood IL 60153

O'MORCHOE, PATRICIA JEAN, b Halifax, Eng, Sept 15, 30; m 55; c 2. HISTOLOGY, CYTOLOGY. *Educ:* Univ Dublin, BA, 53, MB, BCh & BAO, 55, MA & MD, 66. *Prof Exp:* House officer obstet & gynec, surg & med, Brit Nat Health Serv, Halifax Gen Hosp, Eng, 55-57; jr lectr physiol & histol, Univ Dublin, 59-61; instr cytopath, Johns Hopkins Univ, 61-62; res assoc path & surg, Harvard Univ, 62-63; lectr physiol & histol, Univ Dublin, 63-68; instr cytopath, Johns Hopkins Univ, 68-70; asst prof anat & histol, Univ Md, Baltimore City, 70-74; assoc prof, 74-80, PROF PATH & ANAT, STRITCH SCH MED, LOYOLA UNIV CHICAGO, 80- *Concurrent Pos:* Frank C Bressler Reserve Fund grant anat, Univ Md, Baltimore City, 71-72; NIH grants, 74-77, 78-80 & 81-83; vis lectr, Johns Hopkins Hosp & Med Sch, Johns Hopkins Univ, 70-73, asst prof path, 73-74. *Mem:* Am Soc Cytol; Am Asn Anat. *Res:* Function and morphology of the cells in renal lymph in unstimulated and phagocytically and antigenically stimulated dogs; structure and function of renal lympharic system. *Mailing Add:* Dept of Anat 2160 S First Ave Maywood IL 60153

OMRAN, ABDEL RAHIM, b Cairo, Egypt, Mar 29, 25; m 53; c 3. EPIDEMIOLOGY. *Educ:* Minufia Sch, Egypt, BS, 45; Cairo Univ, MD, 52, DPH, 54; Columbia Univ, MPH, 56, DrPH, 59; Trudeau Sch Tuberc, Nat Tuberc & Respiratory Dis Asn, cert, 59. *Prof Exp:* Lectr, Cairo Univ, 59-63; res scientist & clin assoc prof environ med, NY Univ, 63-66; assoc prof epidemiol, 66-71, PROF EPIDEMIOL, UNIV NC, CHAPEL HILL, 71- *Concurrent Pos:* WHO study fel health serv eastern & western Europe, 63; clin assoc prof, Univ Ky, 64-66; Ford Found consult, India, 69; coordr epidemiol studies in Asian countries, WHO, 69-, dir, Int Reference Ctr on Epidemiol of Human Reproduction, 71-; assoc dir pop epidemiol, Carolina Pop Ctr, 70- *Honors & Awards:* Sci Achievement Medal, Egyptian Govt. *Mem:* Royal Soc Health; Asn Teachers Prev Med; Soc Epidemiol Res; Am Thoracic Soc; fel Am Pub Health Asn. *Res:* Epidemiological studies of human reproduction in Asia and the Middle East; population problems and prospects in the Middle East; development of manual on community medicine for developing countries; health and disease patterns associated with demographic change; Muslim fertility. *Mailing Add:* Carolina Pop Ctr Chapel Hill NC 27514

OMTVEDT, IRVIN T, b Wis, June 12, 35; m 59; c 2. ANIMAL SCIENCE. *Educ:* Univ Wis, BS, 57; Okla State Univ, MS, 59, PhD(animal breeding), 61. *Prof Exp:* Performance testing field man, Univ Wis, 56-57; res asst animal sci, Okla State Univ, 58-61; from asst prof to assoc prof, Univ Minn, 62-64, exten specialist, 62-64; from assoc prof to prof animal sci, Okla State Univ, 64-73; assoc dir agr exp sta & asst dean agr, Auburn Univ, 73-75; PROF ANIMAL SCI & HEAD DEPT, UNIV NEBR, 75- *Mem:* Am Soc Animal Sci; Am Dairy Sci Asn; AAAS; Coun Agr Sci & Technol. *Res:* Swine breeding investigations involving crossbreeding and combining ability; effects of high ambient temperature on reproductive performance of swine. *Mailing Add:* Dept Animal Sci Univ Nebr Lincoln NE 68588

OMURA, JIMMY KAZUHIRO, b San Jose, Calif, Sept 8, 40. SYSTEMS SCIENCE. *Educ:* Mass Inst Technol, BS & MS, 63; Stanford Univ, PhD(elec eng), 66. *Prof Exp:* Sci adv commun eng, Stanford Res Inst, 66-69; from asst prof to assoc prof, 59-78, PROF SYSTS SCI, UNIV CALIF, LOS ANGELES, 78- *Concurrent Pos:* Consult, indust & govt. *Mem:* Fel Inst Elec & Electronics Engrs. *Res:* Feedback communication systems; statistical analysis of systems; coding techniques; mathematical programming applications; data compression systems; laser and spread spectrum communication systems; satellite communication systems; rate distortion theory. *Mailing Add:* Dept Systs Sci Univ Calif Los Angeles CA 90024

OMURA, YOSHIAKI, b Tomari, Japan, Mar 28, 34; m 62; c 3. CARDIOLOGY, ELECTROPHYSIOLOGY. *Educ:* Waseda Univ, Japan, BSc, 57; Yokohama City Univ, MD, 58; Columbia Univ, MedScD(surg, pharmacol), 65. *Prof Exp:* From intern to resident physician, Tokyo Univ Hosp, 58-59; intern, Norwalk Hosp, Conn, 59-60; resident physician, Francis Delafield Hosp, Columbia Univ, 61-64; instr surg & asst prof pharmacol, NY Med Col, 66-71; DIR MED RES, HEART DIS RES FOUND, 71-; ATTEND PHYSICIAN, LONG ISLAND COL HOSP, 81- *Concurrent Pos:* John Polacheck Found res support grant, 67-70; Heart Dis Found res grant, 70-; vis res prof elec eng, Manhattan Col, 62-; consult, Columbia Univ, 65-66; part-time emergency room physician, Englewood Hosp, NJ, 65-66; consult, State Univ NY Downstate Med Ctr, 66; chmn sci dept, Children's Art & Sci Workshop, New York, 71-; dir res & bd trustees, Acupuncture Res Found & Am Found Acupuncture, 73-; consult & vis prof, Univ Paris, 73-74; ed-in-chief, Acupuncture & Electrotherapeut Res, Int J Pergamon Press, 74-; consult, Lincoln Hosp, New York, 74; chmn, Columbia Univ Affil & Community Med Comt Community Bd, Francis Delafield Hosp, 74-75; chmn int stand comt, Int Kirlian Res Asn, 75-; Maitre de Recherche of the Nat Inst Health & Med Res of the French Govt, Res Unit 95, Nancy, 77; ed consult, J Electrocardiology, 79-; vpres, Int Kirlian Res Asn, 81-; adj prof pharmacol, Univ Health Sci, Chicago Med Sch, 81- *Mem:* Fel Am Soc Chinese Med; fel Am Col Angiol; fel NY Cardiol Soc; fel Am Acad Acupuncture; fel Int Col Acupuncture & Electrotherapeutics. *Res:* Biophysics and pharmaco-electro-physiology of single cardiac cells in vivo and in vitro; shock, fibrillation, burn and electrolytes; surgery and medical electronics; inorganic and organic semiconductors with negative resistance characteristics; electrophysiology of nerve and muscle; rapidly changing electric and magnetic fields for pain control and neuromuscular rehabilitation; effects of acupuncture and electrotherapeutics on cardiovascular and nervous systems; pharmacology; electronics. *Mailing Add:* Apt 8-I 800 Riverside Dr New York NY 10032

ONAK, THOMAS PHILIP, b Omaha, Nebr, July 30, 32; m 54. METALLIC CHEMISTRY, ORGANIC CHEMISTRY. *Educ:* San Diego State Univ, AB, 54; Univ Calif, Berkeley, PhD(chem), 58. *Prof Exp:* Res chemist, Olin Mathieson Chem Corp, 57-59; from asst prof to assoc prof, 59-66, PROF CHEM, CALIF STATE UNIV, LOS ANGELES, 66- *Concurrent Pos:* Fulbright res fel, Cambridge Univ, 65-66; res career develop award, NIH, 73-77. *Mem:* Am Chem Soc; Royal Soc Chem. *Res:* Synthetic, structure and isotope studies on organoboron hydrides and carboranes; natural products. *Mailing Add:* Dept of Chem Calif State Univ Los Angeles CA 90032

O'NAN, MICHAEL ERNEST, b Ft Knox, Ky, Aug 9, 43. ALGEBRA. *Educ:* Stanford Univ, BS, 65; Princeton Univ, PhD(math), 69. *Prof Exp:* Asst prof, 70-73, assoc prof, 73-77, PROF MATH, RUTGERS UNIV, NEW BRUNSWICK, 77- *Concurrent Pos:* Vis asst prof math, Univ Chicago, 71-72; Sloan fel, 74. *Mem:* Am Math Soc. *Res:* Classification problems in the study of finite simple groups, those associated with doubly-transitive permutation groups. *Mailing Add:* Dept of Math Rutgers Univ New Brunswick NJ 08903

ONAT, E(MIN) T(URAN), b Istanbul, Turkey, Jan 28, 25; m 59. MECHANICS. *Educ:* Tech Univ Istanbul, Dipl, 48, DSc, 51. *Prof Exp:* Res fel appl math, Brown Univ, 51-52, Jewett fel, 52-53, res assoc, 53-57, assoc prof eng, 57-60, prof, 60-65; PROF ENG, YALE UNIV, 65- *Concurrent Pos:* Consult, Turkish Elec Authority, 56-57; Guggenheim fel, 63-64. *Mem:* Am Math Soc; Opers Res Soc Am; assoc Am Soc Mech Engrs. *Res:* Applied mechanics of solids; plasticity and viscoelasticity. *Mailing Add:* Dept of Eng & Appl Sci Yale Univ New Haven CT 06520

ONCLEY, JOHN LAWRENCE, b Wheaton, Ill, Feb 14, 10; m 33, 72; c 2. MOLECULAR BIOPHYSICS. *Educ:* Southwestern Col, Kans, AB, 29; Univ Wis, PhD, 33. *Hon Degrees:* MA, Harvard Univ, 46; DSc, Southwestern Col, Kans, 54. *Prof Exp:* Asst chem, Univ Wis, 29-31; Nat Res Coun fel, Mass Inst Technol, 32-34; instr, Univ Wis, 34-35 & Mass Inst Technol, 35-43; from asst prof to prof biol chem, Harvard Med Sch, 43-62; prof, 62-80, dir, Biophys Res Div, Inst Sci & Technol, 72-76, EMER PROF CHEM & BIOL CHEM, UNIV MICH, ANN ARBOR, 80- *Concurrent Pos:* Res assoc, Harvard Med Sch, 39-41, assoc, 41-43; Guggenheim & Fulbright fels, King's Col, Univ London, 53; mem comn plasma fractionation, Ctr Blood Res, 53-; fel, Coun High Blood Pressure Res, Am Heart Asn. *Honors & Awards:* Award, Am Chem Soc, 43; Stouffer Prize, 72. *Mem:* Nat Acad Sci; Am Chem Soc; Biophys Soc; Am Acad Arts & Sci; NY Acad Sci. *Res:* Dielectric properties of gases, liquids and proteins; biophysical chemistry of protein systems; fractionation and interactions of proteins and lipoproteins. *Mailing Add:* Inst of Sci & Technol Univ of Mich Ann Arbor MI 48109

ONCLEY, PAUL BENNETT, b Chicago, Ill, June 22, 11; m 33; c 2. ACOUSTICS. *Educ:* Southwestern Col Kans, AB, 31; Univ Rochester, BMusic, 32, MMusic, 33; Columbia Univ, PhD(music acoustics), 52. *Prof Exp:* Asst prof vocal music, Univ NC, Greensboro, 37-42; electronics engr, Div Phys War Res, Duke Univ, 42-45; mem tech staff, Bell Tel Labs, Inc, 45-49; assoc prof vocal music, Westminster Choir Col, 49-53; asst to dir eng, Gulton Indust, 53-58; res specialist, Aerospace Div, Boeing Co, 58-63, Space Div, 63-67 & Com Airplane Div, 67-74; sr res scientist, Man, Acoustics & Noise, Inc, 74-80. *Concurrent Pos:* Res Corp res grant acoustics of singing, 49-51; design consult, Rangertone, Inc, 49-51 & Kay Elec Co, 53; lectr, Columbia Univ, 50-52; guest prof, Highline Col, 62-63; conductor, Tacoma Youth Symphony, 63-66; guest prof, Pa Lutheran Univ, 75-76. *Mem:* Acoust Soc Am; Am Inst Aeronaut & Astronaut. *Res:* Music; acoustics of speech and music, particularly physics and physiology of singing; electronic music; ultrasonics and underwater sound; systems engineering for aerospace and physics of space exploration; airplane noise propagation; acoustic impedance measurements. *Mailing Add:* 6533 Seaview Dr NW 311-B Seattle WA 98117

ONDETTI, MIGUEL ANGEL, b Buenos Aires, Arg, May 14, 30; m 58; c 2. ORGANIC CHEMISTRY. *Educ:* Univ Buenos Aires, Dr Chem, 57. *Prof Exp:* Sr res chemist, Squibb Inst Med Res, Buenos Aires, 56-60, NJ, 60-66, res supvr, Dept Org Chem, 66-73, sect head, 73-76, dir, Biol Chem Dept, 76-79, assoc dir, 79-81, VPRES BASIC RES, SQUIBB INST MED RES, 81-

Concurrent Pos: Instr, Univ Buenos Aires, 57-60. *Honors & Awards:* Alfred Burger Award, Am Chem Soc. *Mem:* Am Chem Soc; Arg Chem Soc; Swiss Chem Soc; Am Soc Biol Chemists. *Res:* Isolation, structure determination and synthesis of natural products; peptide isolation and synthesis; synthesis and study of enzyme inhibitors. *Mailing Add:* Squibb Inst for Med Res PO Box 4000 Princeton NJ 08540

ONDIK, HELEN MARGARET, b New York, NY, Dec 25, 30. CRYSTALLOGRAPHY. *Educ:* Hunter Col, AB, 52; Johns Hopkins Univ, MA, 54, PhD(chem), 57. *Prof Exp:* Fulbright grant, Univ Amsterdam, 57-58; PHYS CHEMIST, NAT BUR STANDARDS, 58- *Honors & Awards:* Silver Medal, Dept Commerce, 71. *Mem:* AAAS; Am Chem Soc; Am Crystallog Asn. *Res:* Solution and crystal chemistry of condensed phosphates; crystallographic data compilation; inorganic structures. *Mailing Add:* Nat Bur of Standards Washington DC 20234

ONDO, JEROME G, b Homestead, Pa, July 25, 39; m 67; c 2. NEUROENDOCRINOLOGY, CANCER. *Educ:* Univ Pittsburgh, BS, 62; John Carroll Univ, MS, 64; Univ Va, PhD(physiol), 70. *Prof Exp:* Asst prof, 72-77, ASSOC PROF PHYSIOL, MED UNIV SC, 77- *Concurrent Pos:* NIH grant, Univ Tex Southwestern Med Sch Dallas, 70-72. *Mem:* Am Physiol Soc. *Res:* Reproduction; mammary cancer. *Mailing Add:* Dept of Physiol Med Univ SC Charleston SC 29401

ONDOV, JOHN MICHAEL, b Somerville, NJ, Jan 22, 48. AEROSOL CHEMISTRY, NUCLEAR ANALYTICAL CHEMISTRY. *Educ:* Muhlenberg Col, BS, 70; Univ Md, PhD(chem), 74. *Prof Exp:* SR SCIENTIST AEROSOL CHEM, LAWRENCE LIVERMORE LAB, UNIV CALIF, 75- *Mem:* Am Chem Soc; AAAS. *Res:* Physical and chemical properties of aerosols; studies of formation distribution and transport and transformation of physical and chemical anthropogenic atmospheric aerosol; nuclear activation techniques for elemental analysis. *Mailing Add:* Lawrence Livermore Lab PO Box 5507 Livermore CA 94550

ONDRAKO, JOANNE MARIE, microbial physiology, see previous edition

ONDREJKA, ARTHUR RICHARD, b New York, NY, Mar 20, 34; m 59; c 3. ELECTRICAL ENGINEERING, PHYSICS. *Educ:* Univ Colo, AB, 62, MS, 73. *Prof Exp:* Technician, 59-63, PHYSICIST & ENGR ELECTRONICS, NAT BUR STANDARDS, 64- *Mem:* Sigma Xi. *Res:* Measurement of time domain characteristics of systems, in particular antennas and microwave systems and lasers and optical components. *Mailing Add:* Sect 724.04 325 Broadway Boulder CO 80302

ONDRUSEK, MICHAEL GENE, b Sweetwater, Tex, June 14, 50. PSYCHOPHARMACOLOGY, NEUROCHEMISTRY. *Educ:* Univ Calif, Riverside, BS, 72; Univ Tex, Austin, BFA & PhD(psychopharmacol), 77. *Prof Exp:* Teaching & res asst psychol & pharmacol, Univ Tex, 73-76; RES ASSOC NEUROPHARMACOL & PSYCHIAT, SCH MED, UNIV NC, CHAPEL HILL, 76- *Concurrent Pos:* Learning-exp trainee, NIH, 72-74, behav-genetics trainee, 75, res assoc, 77-78; fels, Nat Inst Drug Abuse, 76-77 & 79- *Mem:* AAAS; Soc Neurosci; Sigma Xi. *Res:* Psychopharmacology of drugs of abuse; mechanisms of action of various psychotropic agents; etiology of physical dependence and withdrawal involvement of psychological variables on drug action. *Mailing Add:* Dept Psychiat Univ NC Sch Med Chapel Hill NC 27514

O'NEAL, CHARLES HAROLD, b Miami, Fla, Feb 18, 36; m 60; c 3. BIOCHEMISTRY. *Educ:* Ga Inst Technol, BS, 57; Emory Univ, PhD(biochem), 63. *Prof Exp:* Asst chem, Ga Inst Technol, 54-56 & Eng Exp Sta, 56-57; asst biochem, Emory Univ, 57-59; scientist, Nat Heart Inst, 63-65; res assoc biochem, Rockefeller Univ, 65-68, asst prof, 68; ASSOC PROF BIOPHYS, MED COL VA, 68- *Concurrent Pos:* vis scientist, Lab Molecular Biol, Med Res Coun, Cambridge, Eng, 71-72; comnr Sci Manpower Comn & Pres Va Commonwealth Univ Fac Senate, 77-78. *Mem:* AAAS; Am Inst Chem; Biochem Soc; Biophys Soc; Am Chem Soc. *Res:* Biochemical genetics; cytology. *Mailing Add:* Dept of Biophys Med Col of Va Box 877 Richmond VA 23298

O'NEAL, FLOYD BRELAND, b Fairfax, SC, May 4, 28; m 54; c 5. ANALYTICAL CHEMISTRY. *Educ:* The Citadel, BS, 48; Tulane Univ, MS, 50; Ga Inst Technol, PhD(chem), 59. *Prof Exp:* From instr to prof chem, Univ Tex, El Paso, 54-66; prof chem & head dept, 66-76, PROF CHEM, AUGUSTA COL, 76- *Mem:* Fel AAAS; Am Chem Soc; Sigma Xi. *Res:* chelate formation; solvent extraction. *Mailing Add:* Dept Chem Augusta Col Augusta GA 30910

ONEAL, GLEN, JR, b Great Falls, Mont, Feb 2, 17; m 41; c 1. APPLIED PHYSICS, ELECTRONICS. *Educ:* Mont State Univ, BS, 40; Univ Pa, MS, 47. *Prof Exp:* Assoc physicist, US Naval Ord Lab, 41-45; physicist, Sun Oil Co, 47-55; res physicist, Am Viscose Corp, 55-63; res physicist, FMC Corp Chem Group, Princeton, NJ, 63-; SR PHYSICIST, CORP ENG & CONSTRUCT, PRINCETON, NJ, 81- *Concurrent Pos:* Res assoc, Nat Bur Standards, 68-70. *Honors & Awards:* Citation, Nat Bur Standards, 70. *Mem:* Am Phys Soc; Am Soc Testing & Mat; Sigma Xi; Inst Elec & Electronics Engrs. *Res:* Application of electronic instrumentation to problems in material testing, polymer research and pharmaceutical applications; materials research. *Mailing Add:* 128 Yale Ave Swarthmore PA 19081

O'NEAL, HARRY E, b Cincinnati, Ohio, Apr 2, 31; div; c 2. PHYSICAL CHEMISTRY. *Educ:* Harvard Univ, BA, 53; Univ Wash, PhD(chem), 57. *Prof Exp:* Res chemist, Shell Oil Co, 57-59; res assoc, Univ Southern Calif, 59-60; from asst prof to assoc prof, 61-70, PROF CHEM, SAN DIEGO STATE UNIV, 70- *Concurrent Pos:* Alexander von Humboldt Found sr scientist res award, 75. *Mem:* Am Phys Soc. *Res:* Thermodynamics; chemical kinetics. *Mailing Add:* Dept of Chem San Diego State Univ 5402 College Ave San Diego CA 92115

O'NEAL, HARRY ROGER, b Kansas City, Kans, Jan 2, 35. PHYSICAL CHEMISTRY. *Educ:* Univ Kansas City, BS, 58; Univ Calif, Berkeley, PhD(chem), 63. *Prof Exp:* Res chemist, Du Pont Co, 62-65 & Douglas Aircraft Co, 65-66; fel chem, Pa State Univ, 66-67; asst prof, Lowell Tech Inst, 67-70; ASST PROF CHEM, PA STATE UNIV, OGONTZ CAMPUS, 70- *Mem:* Am Chem Soc. *Res:* Thermodynamic and transport properties of solids at low temperatures; thermodynamics and kinetics of phase transitions. *Mailing Add:* Dept of Chem Pa State Univ Abington PA 19001

O'NEAL, HUBERT RONALD, b Rotan, Tex, Apr 27, 37; m 60; c 4. ORGANIC CHEMISTRY. *Educ:* Tex Tech Col, BS, 59; NTex State Univ, MS, 64, PhD(chem), 67. *Prof Exp:* Chemist, Sherwin-Williams Co, Tex, 59-61; res chemist, W R Grace & Co, Md, 67-68; from res chemist to sr res chemist, 68-74, res group leader, Petro-Tex Chem Corp, 74-77; supt process res, Denka Chem Corp, 77-80; TECH DIR, KOCIDE CHEM CORP, 80- *Mem:* Am Chem Soc; NY Acad Sci; Sigma Xi. *Res:* Polymer research on elastomeric materials; ketene chemistry and aldehyde polymerizations; synthetic rubber chemistry; polymerization kinetics; agricultural fungicides. *Mailing Add:* 11202 Pecan Creek Dr Houston TX 77043

O'NEAL, JOHN BENJAMIN, JR, b Macon, Ga, Oct 15, 34; m 60; c 1. ELECTRICAL ENGINEERING. *Educ:* Ga Inst Technol, BEE, 57; Univ SC, MEE, 60; Univ Fla, PhD(elec eng), 63. *Prof Exp:* Engr, Southern Bell Tel & Tel Co, 57 & Martin Co, Fla, 59-60; mem tech staff, Bell Tel Labs, Inc, 64-66, supv eng, 66-67; asst prof elec eng, 67-76, PROF ELEC ENG, NC STATE UNIV, 76- *Mem:* Inst Elec & Electronics Engrs. *Res:* Studies of communications theory to determine efficient use of bandwidth for television transmission; information theory. *Mailing Add:* Dept of Elec Eng NC State Univ Raleigh NC 27607

O'NEAL, LYMAN HENRY, b Princeton, Ind, Jan 18, 42; m 64; c 2. ENTOMOLOGY, ZOOLOGY. *Educ:* Oakland City Col, AB, 63; Univ Minn, MS, 70, PhD(entom), 73. *Prof Exp:* Teacher, Francisco High Sch, 63-66; res asst entom, Univ Minn, 67-73; teaching assoc biol, Macalester Col, 67-68; asst prof, 73-76, chmn, Div Arts & Sci, 76-78, ASSOC PROF BIOL, OAKLAND CITY COL, 76- *Mem:* Entom Soc Am; Nat Asn Biol Teachers. *Res:* Insect photoreceptors and photobehavior; insects injurious to crops; insect pollinators. *Mailing Add:* Dept of Biol Oakland City Col Oakland City IN 47660

O'NEAL, PATRICIA L, b St Louis, Mo, June 14, 23. PSYCHIATRY. *Educ:* Wash Univ, AB, 44, MD, 48. *Prof Exp:* Intern, Univ Iowa Hosps, 48-49; resident psychiat, Barnes & Allied Hosps, St Louis, Mo, 49-51; from instr to asst prof, 52-61, ASSOC PROF PSYCHIAT, SCH MED, WASH UNIV, 61- *Concurrent Pos:* Fel psychosom med, Sch Med, Wash Univ, 52. *Res:* Clinical psychiatry, especially social psychiatry. *Mailing Add:* 4989 Barnes Hosp Plaza St Louis MO 63110

O'NEAL, ROBERT MUNGER, b Wiggins, Miss, Oct 7, 22; m 47; c 4. PATHOLOGY. *Educ:* Univ Miss, BS, 43; Univ Tenn, MD, 45. *Prof Exp:* Resident chest dis, State Sanatorium, Miss, 49-52; from instr to assoc prof path, Sch Med, Wash Univ, 54-61; prof & chmn dept, Col Med, Baylor Univ, 61-69; prof, Albany Med Col, 69-73; prof path & chmn dept, Cols Med & Dent, Univ Okla, 73-78; PROF & CHMN, DEPT PATH, UNIV MISS, 78- *Concurrent Pos:* Fel path, Mass Gen Hosp, 52-54; dir, Bender Hyg Lab, 69-73. *Mem:* Am Soc Exp Path; Am Soc Clin Path; Am Thoracic Soc; Am Asn Path & Bact; Col Am Path. *Res:* Cardiovascular and pulmonary diseases; atherosclerosis. *Mailing Add:* Dept of Path Miss Med Ctr Jackson MS 39216

O'NEAL, RUSSELL D, b Columbus, Ind, Feb 15, 14; m 48; c 2. PHYSICS. *Educ:* DePauw Univ, AB, 36; Univ Ill, PhD(physics), 41. *Prof Exp:* Asst physics, Univ Ill, 36-41, instr, 41-42; mem staff, Radiation Lab, Mass Inst Technol, 42-43, sect head, 43-45, group leader, 45; proj physicist, Eastman Kodak Co, 45-48; head aerophysics group, Willow Run Res Ctr, Univ Mich, 49, from asst dir to dir, 50-52; asst div mgr, Consol Vultee Aircraft Corp, 52-53, prog dir, 53-55; dir systs planning, Bendix Corp, 55-57, gen mgr, Systs Div, 57-60, vpres eng & res, 60-63, vpres & group exec aerospace systs, 63-66; asst secy, Army Res & Develop, Washington, 66-68; exec vpres aerospace, Bendix Corp, 68-69, pres, Bendix Aerospace-Electronics Group, 69-72, pres, Group Opers, 72-73; exec vpres, KMS Fusion, Inc, 74-75, chmn & chief exec officer, 75-76, CONSULT, KMS INDUSTS, INC & KMS FUSION, INC, 76- *Concurrent Pos:* Mem, Study Group Guided Missiles, Dept Defense, 58-59; consult, Sci Adv Panel, US Army, 69-; mem, Nat Sci Bd, 72-; trustee, Asian Inst Technol. *Mem:* Fel Am Phys Soc; fel Inst Elec & Electronics Engrs; assoc Am Inst Aeronaut & Astron. *Res:* Nuclear physics; guided missiles; systems analysis; laser fusion. *Mailing Add:* KMS Industs Inc Box 1778 Ann Arbor MI 48106

O'NEAL, STEVEN GEORGE, b Peru, Ind, Oct 28, 47; m 70; c 1. MEMBRANE BIOCHEMISTRY, ENZYMOLOGY. *Educ:* Wabash Col, BA, 70; Univ SC, PhD(chem & biochem), 77. *Prof Exp:* Instr biol, Wabash Col, 70-72; NIH fel, Cornell Univ, 77-79, assoc fel, 79-80; ASST PROF CHEM, UNIV OKLA, 80- *Mem:* AAAS; Am Chem Soc; NY Acad Sci; Sigma Xi. *Res:* Determining the reaction mechanisms, membrane biogenesis, and physiological significance of memrane-bound ion translocases and other receptors. *Mailing Add:* Dept Chem Univ Okla 620 Parrington Oval Norman OK 73019

O'NEAL, THOMAS DENNY, b Vandalia, Ill, June 5, 41; div; c 1. PLANT PHYSIOLOGY, AGRONOMY. *Educ:* Southern Ill Univ, Carbondale, BS, 63; Duke Univ, PhD(plant physiol), 68. *Prof Exp:* Res assoc plant physiol, Univ Ky, 68-69 & Carleton Univ, 71-73; fel, Brandeis Univ, 69-71; asst prof, Rensselaer Polytech Inst, 73-75; group leader plant growth regulator discovery, Am Cyanamid Co, 75-79; GROWTH REGULATOR SPECIALIST, BASF WYANDOTTE, 80- *Mem:* Am Soc Plant Physiologists; Sigma Xi; AAAS. *Res:* Discovery of new plant growth regulants to enhance yield, quality or harvestability of key agronomic crops; enzymatic regulation of N and C metabolism in plants. *Mailing Add:* BASF Wyandotte 100 Cherry Hill Rd Parsippany NJ 07054

O'NEAL, THOMAS NORMAN, b Ft Smith, Ark, Sept 17, 38; m 63; c 2. EXPERIMENTAL SOLID STATE PHYSICS. *Educ:* Miss Col, BS, 60; Univ Fla, MS, 62; Clemson Univ, PhD(physics), 70. *Prof Exp:* From asst prof to assoc prof, 63-75, PROF PHYSICS, CARSON-NEWMAN COL, 75- *Mem:* Am Asn Physics Teachers. *Res:* Electron irradiation damage in metals. *Mailing Add:* Dept of Physics Carson-Newman Col Jefferson City TN 37760

ONEDA, SADAO, b Akita, Japan, June 30, 23; m 50; c 2. THEORETICAL PHYSICS. *Educ:* Tohoku Univ, Japan, BSc, 46, MSc, 48; Nagoya Univ, DrSci(theoret physics), 53. *Prof Exp:* Res assoc theoret physics, Tohoku Univ, Japan, 48-50; from asst prof to prof, Kanazawa Univ, 50-63; from asst prof to assoc prof, 63-67, PROF PHYSICS, UNIV MD, COLLEGE PARK, 67- *Concurrent Pos:* Mem staff, Res Inst Fundamental Physics, Kyoto Univ, 53-55 & 60-63; Imp Chem Industs fel, Univ Manchester, 55-57; mem, Inst Advan Study, 57-58; res assoc, Univ Md, 58-60; vis prof physics, Univ Wis-Milwaukee, 69-70; vis scientist, Int Ctr Theoret Physics, Trieste, 70; vis res mem, Res Inst Fundamental Physics, Kyoto Univ, 77. *Mem:* Fel Am Phys Soc; Phys Soc Japan. *Res:* Physics; theoretical elementary particle physics; field theory. *Mailing Add:* 1 Lakeside Dr Greenbelt MD 20770

ONEGA, RONALD JOSEPH, b Latrobe, Pa, May 11, 35; m 59; c 2. NUCLEAR PHYSICS. *Educ:* Pa State Univ, BS, 61, PhD(physics), 64. *Prof Exp:* Asst prof physics, 64-71, asst prof nuclear eng, 71-73, ASSOC PROF NUCLEAR ENG, VA POLYTECH INST & STATE UNIV, 73- *Mem:* Am Phys Soc; Am Nuclear Soc. *Res:* Reactor physics and analysis; nuclear reactor dynamics; fusion. *Mailing Add:* Nuclear Eng Group Dept Mech Eng Va Polytech Inst & State Univ Blacksburg VA 24061

O'NEIL, ELIZABETH JEAN, b Palo Alto, Calif, Jan 29, 42; m 65; c 2. APPLIED MATHEMATICS. *Educ:* Mass Inst Technol, SB, 63; Harvard Univ, MA, 64, PhD(appl math), 68. *Prof Exp:* Vis mem appl math, Courant Inst Math Sci, NY Univ, 66-67, asst prof, 67-68; lectr, Mass Inst Technol, 68-70; ASSOC PROF MATH, UNIV MASS, BOSTON, 70- *Mem:* Soc Indust & Appl Math. *Res:* Computer operating systems analysis; numerical algorithms; asymptotic techniques. *Mailing Add:* 201 Waltham St Lexington MA 02173

O'NEIL, ELIZABETH JEAN, b Palo Alto, Calif, Jan 29, 42; m 65; c 2. APPLIED MATHEMATICS. *Educ:* Mass Inst Technol, SB, 63; Harvard Univ, MA, 64, PhD(appl math), 68. *Prof Exp:* Vis mem appl math, Courant Inst Math Sci, Ny Univ, 66-67, asst prof, 67-68; lectr, Mass Inst Technol, 68-70; ASSOC PROF MATH, UNIV MASS, BOSTON, 70- *Mem:* Soc Indust & Appl Math. *Res:* Computer operating systems analysis; numerical algorithms; asymptotic techniques. *Mailing Add:* 201 Waltham St Lexington MA 02173

O'NEIL, JAMES R, b Chicago, Ill, July 16, 34. GEOCHEMISTRY, PHYSICAL CHEMISTRY. *Educ:* Loyola Univ Ill, BS, 56; Carnegie-Mellon Univ, MS, 59; Univ Chicago, PhD(chem), 63. *Prof Exp:* Res fel geochem, Univ Chicago, 63 & Calif Inst Technol, 63-65; CHEMIST, BR ISOTOPE GEOL, US GEOL SURV, 65- *Concurrent Pos:* Exchange scientist to USSR, 72; consult prof, Stanford Univ, 75-; vis prof, Australian Nat Univ, 76; vis scientist, Univ Paris, 80. *Mem:* AAAS; Am Chem Soc; Am Geophys Union; Geochem Soc. *Res:* Studies of stable isotope variations in natural materials; laboratory determination of equilibrium constants for isotope exchange reactions of geologic significance; solute-water interactions; structure of water; mantle geochemistry. *Mailing Add:* Br Isotope Geol US Geol Surv 345 Middlefield Rd Menlo Park CA 94025

O'NEIL, LOUIS-C, b Sherbrooke, Que, Jan 20, 30; m 55; c 5. ENTOMOLOGY, ZOOLOGY. *Educ:* Univ Montreal, BA, 50; Laval Univ, BSCApp, 54; State Univ NY Col Forestry, Syracuse Univ, MSc, 56, PhD(forest entom), 61. *Prof Exp:* Res off forest entom & path br, Can Dept Forestry, 55-62; assoc prof, 62-72, secy Fac Sci, 67-70, chmn dept biol, 70-72, dean, Fac Sci, 72-78, prof invert zool & entom, 72-78, DIR PERSONNEL, UNIV SHERBROOKE, 78- *Concurrent Pos:* Res assoc, Sch Forestry, Yale Univ, 65, 66, 67. *Mem:* Entom Soc Can; Can Soc Zool. *Res:* Ecology of land slug introduced in eastern Canada; relationships between sawflies and their host trees; forest sawfly outbreaks and tree growth. *Mailing Add:* Personnel Serv Univ of Sherbrooke Sherbrooke PQ J1K 2R1 Can

O'NEIL, PATRICK EUGENE, b Mineola, NY, July 19, 42; m 65; c 2. MATHEMATICS, COMPUTER SCIENCE. *Educ:* Mass Inst Technol, BS, 63; Univ Chicago, MS, 64; Rockefeller Univ, PhD(math), 69. *Prof Exp:* Systs programmer, Cambridge Sci Ctr, Int Bus Mach Corp, 64-66, mem staff opers res, 68-69; Off Naval Res fel & res assoc combinatorics, Mass Inst Technol, 69-70, asst prof comput sci, 70-72; consult comput sci, 72-74; asst prof comput sci, Univ Mass, Boston, 74-77; sr systs programmer, Keydata Corp, Watertown, 77-80; PRIN SOFTWARE ENG, PRIME COMPUT INC, FRAMINGHAM, MASS, 80- *Concurrent Pos:* Mem, Artificial Intel Lab, Mass, 70-72. *Mem:* Math Asn Am; Asn Comput Mach. *Res:* Combinatorial structures; asymptotic counting; algorithmic complexity; data retrieval; operating systems; discrete algorithms in graphs and networks; software systems. *Mailing Add:* 201 Waltham St Lexington MA 02173

O'NEIL, PETER VINCENT, mathematics, see previous edition

ONEIL, STEPHEN VINCENT, b Pawtucket, RI, May 3, 47. MOLECULAR PHYSICS, APPLIED MATHEMATICS. *Educ:* Providence Col, BS, 69; Univ Calif, Berkeley, PhD(chem), 73. *Prof Exp:* Res fel chem, Harvard Univ, 73-74; res assoc chem, Joint Inst Lab Astrophys, 74-76; res assoc comput chem, Inst Comput Appln Sci & Eng, 77; MEM APPL MATH, JOINT INST LAB ASTROPHYS, UNIV COLO, BOULDER, 77- *Res:* Ab initio calculation of electronic continuum processes and bound electronic states of molecules. *Mailing Add:* Joint Inst for Lab Astrophys Univ of Colo Boulder CO 80309

O'NEILL, BRIAN, b Bristol, Eng, Sept 20, 40; m 69; c 2. STATISTICS. *Educ:* Bath Univ, BSc, 65. *Prof Exp:* Statist consult, Unilever, London, Eng, 65-66; statistician, Wolf Res & Develop Corp, 67-69; VPRES RES, INS INST HWY SAFETY, 69-; SR VPRES RES, HWY LOSS DATA INST, 77- *Concurrent Pos:* Mem exec bd, Comt Alcohol & Drugs, Nat Safety Coun, 73-; mem adv panel, Nat Accident Sampling Syst, Dept Transp, 78 & 81. *Mem:* Am Statist Asn; Inst Math & Appl, UK; Royal Statist Soc. *Res:* Highway crash loss reduction, including human behavior, vehicle performance and design and highway design. *Mailing Add:* Ins Inst for Hwy Safety Watergate 600 Washington DC 20037

O'NEILL, EDWARD JOHN, b Washington, DC, Feb 15, 42. TOPOLOGY, OPERATIONS RESEARCH. *Educ:* Cath Univ Am, AB, 63; Yale Univ, MA, 65, PhD(math), 76. *Prof Exp:* Instr, 67-69, ASST PROF MATH, FAIRFIELD UNIV, 69- *Mem:* Am Math Soc; Opers Res Soc Am. *Res:* Algebraic topology; cohomology operations. *Mailing Add:* Dept of Math Fairfield Univ Fairfield CT 06430

O'NEILL, EDWARD LEO, b Boston, Mass, Nov 29, 27; m 51; c 3. PHYSICS. *Educ:* Boston Col, AB, 49; Boston Univ, MA, 51, PhD(physics), 54. *Prof Exp:* Res assoc physics, Res Lab, Boston Univ, 54-56, from asst prof to assoc prof, 56-66; VIS PROF PHYSICS, WORCESTER POLYTECH INST, 66- *Concurrent Pos:* Mem staff, Itek Corp, 58-60; vis prof, Mass Inst Technol, 61-62 & Univ Calif, Berkeley, 64-65. *Honors & Awards:* Lomb Medal, Optical Soc Am, 58. *Mem:* AAAS; Optical Soc Am; Am Asn Physics Teachers. *Res:* Communication theory; quantum and statistical optics. *Mailing Add:* Dept of Physics Worcester Polytech Inst Worcester MA 01609

O'NEILL, EDWARD TRUE, b Charlevoix, Mich, July 20, 40; m 76; c 2. INFORMATION SCIENCE, OPERATIONS RESEARCH. *Educ:* Albion Col, BA, 62; Purdue Univ, BSIE, 63, MSIE, 66, PhD(opers res), 70. *Prof Exp:* Asst prof, 68-71, asst dean, 70-75, ASSOC PROF INFO SCI, SCH INFO & LIBR STUDIES, STATE UNIV NY BUFFALO, 71- *Concurrent Pos:* Vis distinguished scholar, OCLC, Inc, 78-79. *Mem:* Am Soc Info Sci; Am Libr Asn; Opers Res Soc Am. *Res:* Bibliometrics; subject cataloging; information retrieval; rank frequency modeling. *Mailing Add:* Sch of Info & Libr Studies State Univ of NY Buffalo NY 14260

O'NEILL, EUGENE F, b Brooklyn, NY, July 2, 18; m 42; c 4. COMMUNICATIONS ENGINEERING. *Educ:* Columbia Univ, BS, 40, MS, 41. *Hon Degrees:* DrSci, Bates Col, 63 & St John's Univ, NY, 65; Milan Polytech Inst, DrEng, 64. *Prof Exp:* Mem tech staff, Bell Tel Labs, 41-56, proj head speech interpolation, 56-60, dir, Telstar Satellite Proj, 60-65, exec dir, Transmission Div, 66-78, EXEC DIR PROJ PLANNING, BELL LABS, 78- *Honors & Awards:* Int Commun Award, Inst Elec & Electronics Engrs, 72. *Mem:* Fel Inst Elec & Electronics Engrs. *Res:* Development of long haul toll transmission systems. *Mailing Add:* Bell Tel Labs Holmdel NJ 07733

O'NEILL, FRANK JOHN, b New York, NY, Apr 26, 40; c 2. CELL BIOLOGY, VIROLOGY. *Educ:* Long Island Univ, BA, 63; Hunter Col, MA, 67; Univ Utah, PhD(molecular biol, genetic biol), 69. *Prof Exp:* asst prof, 71-79, PROF MICROBIOL & PATH, UNIV UTAH MED CTR, 79- *Concurrent Pos:* NIH fel microbiol, Milton S Hershey Med Ctr, Pa State Univ, 69-71; Eleanor Roosevelt-Am Cancer Soc Int Cancer fel, Freiburg, WGer, 77-78. *Mem:* Am Soc Human Genetics; Environ Mutagen Soc; Am Soc Microbiol; Am Asn Cancer Res. *Res:* Elucidation and establishment of mechanisms of viral oncogenesis and viral latency in vitro and in vivo; cytogenetics, especially chromosomal changes occurring during and following viral oncogenesis. *Mailing Add:* Res Serv Vet Admin Med Ctr Salt Lake City UT 84113

O'NEILL, GEORGE FRANCIS, b Yonkers, NY, Sept 27, 22; m 43; c 2. NUCLEAR PHYSICS. *Educ:* Mt St Mary's Col Md, BS, 43; Fordham Univ, MS, 47, PhD(physics), 51. *Prof Exp:* Physicist, Argonne Nat Lab, 50-53; sr res supvr, exp reactor physics div, Savannah Lab, E I du Pont de Nemours & Co, Inc, 53-68; with AEC Combined Opers Planning, Oak Ridge, 69-70; sr physicist, Advan Oper Planning, 70-74, RES STAFF PHYSICIST, SAVANNAH RIVER LAB, E I DU PONT DE NEMOURS & CO, INC, 74- *Concurrent Pos:* Guest lectr, Dept Nuclear Eng, Univ SC, 67-68; US rep, Can-Am D20 Reactor Comt, 67-68. *Mem:* AAAS; Am Nuclear Soc; Am Phys Soc. *Res:* Cosmic rays; heavy water nuclear reactors; exponential pile assemblies; critical pile assemblies; nuclear reactor fuel cycle. *Mailing Add:* Savannah River Lab E I du Pont de Nemours & Co Inc Aiken SC 29801

O'NEILL, GEORGE JOSEPH, polymer chemistry, see previous edition

O'NEILL, GERARD KITCHEN, b Brooklyn, NY, Feb 6, 27; m 50, 73; c 3. PHYSICS. *Educ:* Swarthmore Col, BA, 50; Cornell Univ, PhD(physics), 54. *Prof Exp:* From instr to assoc prof, 54-65, PROF PHYSICS, PRINCETON UNIV, 65- *Mem:* Fel Am Phys Soc. *Res:* Experimental elementary particle and nuclear physics; orbital astronomy techniques; space utilization. *Mailing Add:* Dept Physics Princeton Univ Princeton NJ 08540

O'NEILL, JAMES A, JR, b New York, NY, Dec 7, 33; m 59; c 3. PEDIATRIC SURGERY. *Educ:* Georgetown Univ, BS, 55; Yale Univ, MD, 59. *Prof Exp:* Instr surg, Sch Med, Vanderbilt Univ, 64-65; instr pediat surg, Sch Med, Ohio State Univ, 67-69; from asst prof to assoc prof, Sch Med, La State Univ, 69-71; prof pediat surg, Sch Med, Vanderbilt Univ, 71-81; PROF PEDIAT SURG, SCH MED, UNIV PA, 81- *Concurrent Pos:* USPHS fel pediat oncol, Ohio State Univ, 67-68; consult, US Army Hosp, Ft Campbell, Ky, 71- & US Army Inst Surg Res, 71-; surgeon-in-chief, Children's Hosp Philadelphia, 81- *Mem:* Am Col Surg; Am Burn Asn; Am Acad Pediat; Am Surg Asn; Am Pediat Surg Asn. *Res:* General and thoracic pediatric surgery; various aspects of burn injury; stress ulceration; gastrointestinal effects of injury. *Mailing Add:* Children's Hosp Philadelphia 34th & Civic Ctr Blvd Philadelphia PA 19104

O'NEILL, JOHN CORNELIUS, b Philadelphia, Pa, July 3, 29. APPLIED MATHEMATICS. *Educ:* Cath Univ, BA, 52; Villanova Univ, MA, 59; Univ Pittsburgh, PhD, 67. *Prof Exp:* Teacher high schs, Pa, 52-53 & Md, 53-64; asst prof, 67-71, chmn, Dept Math Sci, 74-82, ASSOC PROF MATH, LA SALLE COL, 71- *Mem:* Inst Elec & Electronics Eng; Math Asn Am. *Res:* Computer software systems; computer architecture; computer communications. *Mailing Add:* Dept of Math Sci La Salle Col Philadelphia PA 19141

O'NEILL, JOHN DACEY, b Detroit, Mich, July 9, 30. MATHEMATICS. *Educ:* Xavier Univ, Ohio, AB, 54; Loyola Univ, Ill, MA, PhL, STL & MS, 60; Wayne State Univ, PhD(math), 67. *Prof Exp:* Instr math & theol, high sch, 56-59; PROF MATH, DETROIT UNIV, 61- *Mem:* Math Asn Am; Am Math Soc. *Res:* Abelian groups; Ring theory. *Mailing Add:* Dept Math Univ Detroit Detroit MI 48221

O'NEILL, JOHN FRANCIS, b Peoria, Ill, Feb 9, 37; m 61; c 1. ELECTRICAL ENGINEERING. *Educ:* St Louis Univ, BSEE, 59; NY Univ, MEE, 61, PhD(elec eng), 67. *Prof Exp:* Mem tech staff data systs, 59-65 & SWITCHING SYSTS, BELL TEL LABS, INC, 67- *Mem:* Inst Elec & Electronics Engrs. *Res:* Active network theory; switching control; switching networks. *Mailing Add:* Bell Tel Labs 1200 W 120 Ave Denver CO 80234

O'NEILL, JOHN H(ENRY), JR, b New Orleans, La, Mar 25, 22; m 50; c 3. CHEMICAL ENGINEERING, RESEARCH & DEVELOPMENT MANAGEMENT. *Educ:* La State Univ, BS, 43; Mass Inst Technol, ScD(chem eng), 51. *Prof Exp:* Res assoc soil solidification, Mass Inst Technol, 49-50; res engr process develop, E I du Pont de Nemours & Co, 50-52, tech investr, Res Div, Film Dept, 52-56, res supvr, 56-64; dir eng, 65-71, RES DIR, MILLIKEN RES CORP, 71- *Mem:* Am Chem Soc; Am Inst Chem Engrs. *Res:* Product and process research and development of polymers, polymeric films, chemical manufacturing; textile fabric product research, manufacturing, dyeing and finishing; design and development of textile machinery. *Mailing Add:* 113 Eastwood Circle Spartanburg SC 29302

O'NEILL, JOHN JOSEPH, b Queens, NY, Aug 26, 19; m 43; c 3. BIOCHEMISTRY. *Educ:* St Francis Col, NY, BS, 42; Univ Md, MS, 53, PhD(biochem), 55. *Prof Exp:* Res assoc physiol, Sch Med, Cornell Univ, 46-47; biochemist, Physiol Div, Med Lab, US Army Chem Res & Develop Lab, 47-50, org chemist, Biochem Div, Res Directorate, 50-54, biochemist, 54-56, br chief, 56-60; assoc prof biochem pharmacol, Sch Med, Univ Md, Baltimore City, 60-70; prof biochem pharmacol, Col Med, Ohio State Univ, 70-75; PROF & CHMN DEPT PHARMACOL, MED SCH, TEMPLE UNIV, 75- *Concurrent Pos:* NIMH fel pharmacol, Sch Med, Wash Univ, 63-64; res collab, Biochem Dept, Brookhaven Nat Lab, 61-; consult, US Army Chem Res & Develop Lab, Md, 61-, Melpar Div, Westinghouse Elec Co, Va, 62-, NSF, 72-, Environ Protection Agency, 76-, Nat Res Coun Comt, 80- & Ad Hoc Comt, Nat Inst Neurol Disease & Stroke. *Mem:* Am Chem Soc; Am Soc Neurochem; Int Soc Neurochem; Am Soc Pharmacol & Exp Therapeut; Fedn Am Soc Exp Biol. *Res:* Neurochemistry; biochemistry of the central nervous system; glycolysis; enzyme kinetics and control mechanisms; isotopes in intermediary metabolism; neurotoxins and organophosphorous anticholinesterases; neurohumoral substances and drug action. *Mailing Add:* Dept Pharmacol Sch Med Temple Univ 3420 N Broad St Philadelphia PA 19140

ONEILL, JOSEPH LAWRENCE, b Philadelphia, Pa, Jan 2, 31. PHARMACY. *Educ:* Philadelphia Col Pharm & Sci, BS, 55, MS, 56. *Prof Exp:* Res assoc, 56-61, pharmacist, 61-62, sr res pharmacist, 64-73, RES FEL, RES LABS, MERCK SHARP & DOHME, 73- *Mem:* Am Pharmaceut Asn; Acad Pharmaceut Sci. *Res:* Steoride, topical and oral liquid dosage forms; sterilization of solids for injections; topical gel system. *Mailing Add:* Crown Park Apts D 26 Oak Blvd & W Main St Lansdale PA 19446

O'NEILL, MALCOLM ROSS, atomic physics, see previous edition

O'NEILL, MICHAEL WAYNE, b San Antonio, Tex, Feb 17, 40; m 72; c 1. CIVIL ENGINEERING. *Educ:* Univ Tex, Austin, BS, 63, MS, 64, PhD(civil eng), 70. *Prof Exp:* Proj mgr civil eng, Southwestern Labs Inc, 71-74; asst prof, 74-78, ASSOC PROF CIVIL ENG, UNIV HOUSTON, 78- *Concurrent Pos:* Fel, Univ Tex, 70-71; spec consult, Southwestern Labs, Inc, 74- *Honors & Awards:* John Hawley Award, Am Soc Civil Engrs, 76. *Mem:* Am Soc Civil Engrs; Int Soc Soil Mech & Found Eng; Transp Res Bd. *Res:* Behavior of deep foundations, expansive clays and machine foundations. *Mailing Add:* Dept of Civil Eng Univ of Houston Houston TX 77004

ONEILL, PATRICIA LYNN TIMKO, b Chicago, Ill, April 19, 49; m 77; c 1. BIOMECHANICS, BENTHIC ECOLOGY. *Educ:* Univ Urbana, BS, 71; Univ Calif, Los Angeles, PhD(biol), 75. *Prof Exp:* Lectr biol, Univ Calif, Los Angeles, 76-77; fel, Cocos Found, Duke Univ, 78-79; ASST PROF BIOL, PORTLAND STATE UNIV, 79- *Concurrent Pos:* Hon fel, Dept Zool, Univ Cape Town, 77-78; sr marine biologist, VTN Oregon, Inc, 79-80. *Res:* Mechanical properties and structure of invertebrate collagenous tissues; structure of echinoderm calcite; torsional stress analysis of ratite bird limbs; age structure and density regulation of benthic invertebrate populations. *Mailing Add:* Dept Biol Portland State Univ Box 751 Portland OR 97207

O'NEILL, PATRICK JOSEPH, b Columbus, Ohio, July 12, 49; m 73; c 2. PHARMACOLOGY. *Educ:* Ohio State Univ, BS, 72, PhD(pharmacol), 76. *Prof Exp:* Res assoc, Ohio State Univ, 72-76; res scientist, McNeil Labs Inc, 76-77, sr scientist, 77-79, GROUP LEADER, MCNEIL PHARMACEUT, JOHNSON & JOHNSON, 79- *Mem:* AAAS; Sigma Xi; Am Soc Pharmacol & Exp Therapeut. *Res:* Drug metabolism. *Mailing Add:* McNeil Pharmaceut Welsh & McKean Rd Springhouse PA 19477

O'NEILL, R(USSELL) R(ICHARD), b Chicago, Ill, June 6, 16; m 39, 67; c 2. ENGINEERING. *Educ:* Univ Calif, Berkeley, BS, 38; Univ Calif, Los Angeles, MS, 40, PhD, 56. *Prof Exp:* Engr, Dowell, Inc, 40-41; design & develop engr, Dow Chem Co, 41-44; design engr, AiRes Mfg Co, 44-46; lectr eng & asst head eng exten, 46-56, from asst dean to dean, Sch Eng & Appl Sci, 56-78, PROF ENG, UNIV CALIF, LOS ANGELES, 56-, DEAN, SCH ENG & APPL SCI, 78- *Concurrent Pos:* Staff engr, Nat Res Coun, 54; chmn, Maritime Transp Res Bd, Nat Acad Sci-Nat Res Coun, 77-81; bd adv, Naval Post Grad Sch, 75-; trustee, West Coast Univ, 80- *Mem:* Nat Acad Eng; Am Soc Eng Educ; Sigma Xi; Soc Naval Architects & Marine Engrs. *Res:* Cargo handling. *Mailing Add:* Sch Eng & Appl Sci Univ Calif Los Angeles CA 90024

O'NEILL, RICHARD DELOS, b Cohocton, NY, Oct 6, 20; m 48; c 4. BACTERIOLOGY. *Educ:* Canisius Col, BS, 42; Syracuse Univ, MS, 48, PhD, 51. *Prof Exp:* Asst bact, NY Univ Syracuse, 47-49, from instr to asst prof, 49-57, from assoc dir to dir microbiol & biochem, Res Ctr, Univ Res Corp, NY, 57-65; mgr biochem res, Glidden Co, 65-70, DIR FOODS RES & DEVELOP, GLIDDEN-DURKEE DIV, SCM CORP, 70- *Mem:* Inst Food Technol; Am Oil Chem Soc; Indust Res Inst; Soc Indust Microbiol. *Res:* Microbial decomposition of cellulose; microbiology of paper and paper board; vitamin nutrition of bacteria and fungi; effects of surface active agents on bacteria; migration of food packaging components; food and food additives. *Mailing Add:* Glidden-Durkee Div SCM Corp 16651 Sprague Rd Strongsville OH 44136

O'NEILL, RICHARD THOMAS, b Winnetka, Ill, Dec 7, 33; m 59; c 2. PHYSICAL INORGANIC CHEMISTRY. *Educ:* Loyola Univ Ill, BS, 55; Carnegie Inst Technol, MS, 59, PhD(chem), 60. *Prof Exp:* From asst prof to assoc prof, 59-70, PROF CHEM, XAVIER UNIV OHIO, 70-, COORDR ACAD COMPUT, 73- *Mem:* Am Chem Soc; Soc Appl Spectros; Coblentz Soc; Sigma Xi. *Res:* Chemical spectroscopy; molecular association; charge transfer complexes; hydrogen bonding; educational use of computers. *Mailing Add:* Comput Ctr Xavier Univ Cincinnati OH 45207

O'NEILL, ROBERT VINCENT, b Pittsburgh, Pa, Apr 13, 40; m 67. ECOLOGY. *Educ:* Cathedral Col, BA, 61; Univ Ill, PhD(zool), 67. *Prof Exp:* Fel systs ecol, NSF, 67-68; assoc health physicist, 68-69, SYSTS ECOLOGIST, OAK RIDGE NAT LAB, 69- *Mem:* Ecol Soc Am. *Res:* Systems ecology. *Mailing Add:* Environ Sci Div Bldg 1505 Oak Ridge Nat Lab Oak Ridge TN 37830

O'NEILL, RONALD C, b Beverly, Mass, July 20, 29; m 53; c 2. TOPOLOGY. *Educ:* Columbia Univ, AB, 51, MA, 52; Purdue Univ, PhD(math), 62. *Prof Exp:* From instr to asst prof math, Univ Mich, 61-66; asst prof, 66-67, ASSOC PROF MATH, MICH STATE UNIV, 67- *Mem:* Am Math Soc; Math Asn Am. *Mailing Add:* Dept of Math Col Natural Sci Mich State Univ East Lansing MI 48824

O'NEILL, THOMAS BRENDAN, b Boston, Mass, Oct 16, 23; m 47; c 5. MICROBIOLOGY, BOTANY. *Educ:* Univ Notre Dame, BS, 50, MS, 51; Univ Calif, PhD(bot), 56. *Prof Exp:* Machinists apprentice, Bethlehem Steel Co, Mass, 41-43; asst, Univ Notre Dame, 50-51 & Univ Calif, 51-54, assoc bot, 54-55; INSTR BOT & MICROBIOL, VENTURA COL, 55- *Concurrent Pos:* Res biologist, US Naval Civil Eng Lab, 57-; NSF fel, Scripps Inst, Calif, 62-63; lectr, Univ Calif, Santa Barbara. *Mem:* AAAS; Bot Soc Am; Sigma Xi. *Res:* Marine microbiology; teaching methods; biodegradation of hydrocarbons. *Mailing Add:* Dept of Biol Ventura Col Ventura CA 93003

O'NEILL, THOMAS HALL ROBINSON, b Bel Air, Md, Feb 21, 23; m 50; c 5. METEOROLOGY. *Educ:* Mt St Mary's Col, BA, 43; US Naval Postgrad Sch, MS, 54; Fla State Univ, PhD(meteorol), 64. *Prof Exp:* Meteorologist & oceanogr, USS Midway, US Navy, 54-55, instr meteorol & oceanog, US Naval Postgrad Sch, 55-57, staff meteorologist & oceanogr, Commander Amphibious Forces Atlantic, 57-59, exec off, Navy Weather Res Facil, 59-61, head satellite meteorol br, Astronaut Div, Chief Naval Opers, 64-67, chief environ sci div, Off Dir Defense Res & Eng, Va, 67-70, sr mgr, Nat Ctr Atmospheric Res, 70-74; global atmospheric res prog mgr, NASA, 74-77; consult, 77-78; EXEC SECY, US COMN GLOBAL ATMOSPHERIC RES PROG, 78- *Concurrent Pos:* Dir tech serv, Naval Weather Serv Command, 64-67; mem, US-Can Mil Coop Comt Oceanog, 64-67; alt mem, Interagency Comt Atmospheric Sci, 64-70; mem, Interagency Comt Appl Meteorol Res, 64-70; assoc mem, Meteorol Working Group-Interrange Instrument Group, 64-70; mem oceanog forecasting panel, Interdept Comn Oceanog, 66-67; liaison mem, US Comt Global Atmospheric Res Prog, 68-74; mem, Interagency Comt 1970 Solar Eclipse, 68-70. *Mem:* Am Meteorol Soc; Sigma Xi. *Res:* Diagnostic studies of atmospheric vertical motion and precipitation; synoptic meteorology; numerical weather prediction; weather modification; tropical meteorology. *Mailing Add:* 5926 Merritt Pl Falls Church VA 22041

O'NEILL, WILLIAM D(ENNIS), b Chicago, Ill, Apr 3, 38; m 61; c 4. SYSTEMS ANALYSIS. *Educ:* Col St Thomas, BA, 60; Univ Notre Dame, BS, 61, MS, 63, PhD(elec eng), 65. *Prof Exp:* Instr elec eng, Univ Notre Dame, 60-61; res assoc, Particle Accelerator Div, Argonne Nat Lab, 61-62; from asst prof to assoc prof, 65-73, PROF SYSTS ENG, UNIV ILL, CHICAGO CIRCLE, 73-, RES ASSOC PHYSIOL, UNIV ILL COL MED, 71- *Concurrent Pos:* Consult, Argonne Nat Lab, 61- & Biosysts, Inc, Mass, 65-; res assoc, Presby St Luke's Hosp, 65-71; res grants, Dept Defense, 67-68, Univ Ill, 68-69 & NIH, 68-77. *Mem:* Inst Elec & Electronics Engrs; Tensor Soc. *Res:* Automatic control; socio-economic system modeling; demographic control systems; statistics, estimation. *Mailing Add:* 1035 Sci & Eng Off Bldg Univ of Ill at Chicago Circle Chicago IL 60680

ONG, CHUNG-JIAN JERRY, b China, June 19, 44; US citizen; m 71. POLYMER PHYSICS. *Educ:* Nat Taiwan Univ, BS, 68; Univ Mass, MS, 72, PhD(polymer sci, eng), 73. *Prof Exp:* Res scientist, 73-80, SR RES SCIENTIST POLYMER PHYSICS, AM CYANAMID CO, 80- *Mem:* Am Chem Soc; Am Soc Testing & Mat. *Res:* Physical chemistry of polymers, especially in physical, mechanical and rheological studies of polymer blends and elastomers. *Mailing Add:* Chem Res Div Am Cyanamid Co Bound Brook NJ 08805

ONG, ENG-BEE, b Seremban, Malaysia, Aug 9, 33; m. PROTEIN CHEMISTRY, FIBRINOLYSIS. *Educ:* Univ Miami, BS, 58; Tulane Univ, PhD(biochem), 64. *Prof Exp:* Instr biochem, Med Ctr, Tulane Univ, 64-65; res assoc, Rockefeller Univ, 65-68, asst prof, 68; clin biochemist, Ochsner Clin, 68-70; ASST PROF CLIN PATH, MED CTR, NY UNIV, 70- *Mem:* Am Chem Soc; Sigma Xi. *Res:* Chemistry of amino acids, peptides and proteins; chromatography of amino acids and peptides; structure and function of proteases; fractionation and characterization of blood coagulation factors; protein sequence. *Mailing Add:* Dept of Path NY Univ Med Ctr New York NY 10016

ONG, JOHN NATHAN, JR, b Rio Tinto, Spain, May 27, 27; wid; c 4. GENERAL ENGINEERING, METALLURGY. *Educ:* Univ Utah, BSChE, 52, PhD(metall), 55. *Prof Exp:* Res metallurgist, Uranium Corp Am, 55-56 & Howe Sound Co, 56; asst prof mech eng, Washington Univ, 56-61; res scientist, Aeronutronic, 61-63; res scientist, Aeronaut Div, Ford Motor Co, Calif, 63-66; assoc prof mat, 66-68, chmn dept, 67-71, prof, 68-73, PROF INDUST & SYSTS ENG, UNIV WIS-MILWAUKEE, 73- *Concurrent Pos:* Consult, McDonnell Aircraft Corp, 56-60, Mallinckrodt Chem Works, 57-60 & Cutler-Hammer Corp, 67. *Honors & Awards:* Gold Medal Award, Am Inst Mining, Metall & Petrol Engrs, 57. *Mem:* AAAS; Am Inst Mining, Metall & Petrol Engrs; Soc Gen Systs Res; Am Soc Eng Educ. *Res:* Design; problem solving; general systems theory; oncology; science of creative intelligence; solid state chemistry and kinetics; thermodynamics. *Mailing Add:* Univ Wis PO Box 784 Milwaukee WI 53201

ONG, JOHN TJOAN HO, b Jakarta, Indonesia, Sept 5, 37; m 61; c 2. PHARMACEUTICS. *Educ:* Bandung Inst Technol, CPharm, 60, Drs(pharm), 65; Univ Ky, PhD(pharmaceut), 74. *Prof Exp:* Teaching asst pharmaceut, Sch Pharm, Bandung Inst Technol, 63-65; lectr, Sch Pharm, Univ Indonesia, 65-69; pharmacist, Sanitas Pharm, Jakarta, 69-70; res staff pharmaceut chem, Univ Ky, 70-71, teaching asst pharmaceut, 71-74; sr scientist pharmaceut, Lilly Res Labs, Div Eli Lilly & Co, 74-81; STAFF RES PHARMACEUT, SYNTEX RES, 81- *Mem:* Am Pharmaceut Asn. *Res:* Stability kinetics of drugs; development of dosage forms; physical and chemical factors influencing the bioavailability of drugs from their dosage forms; synthesis of prodrugs. *Mailing Add:* Syntex Res 3401 Hillview Ave Palo Alto CA 94304

ONG, KWOK MAW, physics, see previous edition

ONG, POEN SING, b Semarang, Indonesia, Mar 13, 27; m 61; c 1. ELECTRICAL ENGINEERING. *Educ:* Technol Univ Delft, Engr, 56, ScD, 59. *Prof Exp:* Prin scientist electron & x-ray beam, Philips Electronic Instruments, 61-71; assoc prof biophysics, M D Anderson Hosp, 71-76; ASSOC PROF ELEC ENG, UNIV HOUSTON, 76- *Mem:* Inst Elec & Electronic Engrs. *Res:* Electron and x-ray microbeam technology; x-ray microscopy; electron microscopy; x-ray microanalysis. *Mailing Add:* Elec Eng Dept Univ Houston Houston TX 77004

ONG, RUDI S(IONG) B(WEE), b Malang, Indonesia, Mar 7, 28; nat US; m 51; c 2. PLASMA PHYSICS. *Educ:* Univ Mich, PhD(mech eng), 56. *Prof Exp:* Asst hydrodyn, Eng Res Inst, 53-56, from asst prof to prof aeronaut eng, 57-64, PROF AEROSPACE ENG, UNIV MICH, 64- *Mem:* Am Phys Soc. *Res:* Applied mathematics; plasma physics; space plasma physics; plasma astrophysics. *Mailing Add:* Dept of Aerospace Eng Univ of Mich Ann Arbor MI 48109

ONG, TONG-MAN, b Tainan, Taiwan, June 9, 35; US citizen; m 66; c 2. GENETIC TOXICOLOGY, MYCOLOGY. *Educ:* Taiwan Normal Univ, BSc, 60; Ill State Univ, MS, 67, PhD(genetics), 70. *Prof Exp:* Fel genetics, Oak Ridge Nat Lab, 70-72; staff fel genetics, Nat Inst Environ Health Sci, 72-77, geneticist, 77-78; SECT CHIEF MICROBIOL, NAT INST OCCUP SAFETY & HEALTH, 78- *Concurrent Pos:* Adj assoc prof, WVa Univ, 79. *Mem:* Genetics Soc Am; AAAS; Environ Mutagen Soc. *Res:* Development, improvement and validation of short-term assays to study the mutagenic activity of complex mixtures from workplace environments and to monitor mutagens in occupational settings. *Mailing Add:* Nat Inst Occup Safety & Health 944 Chestnut Ridge Rd Morgantown WV 26505

ONGERTH, HENRY J, b San Francisco, Calif, 1913. SANITARY ENGINEERING. *Educ:* Univ Calif, BS, 32; Univ Mich, MA, 34. *Prof Exp:* Sanit engr, Calif Dept Health, 38-42; sanit engr-in-chg sewerage design, San Francisco Dist Corps Engrs, 42-43; sanit engr, Calif Dept Health, 43-47; consult engr, W J O'Connell & Assocs, 47-48; sanit engr, Calif Dept Health, 48-80, chief, Bur Sanit Eng, 68-80. *Concurrent Pos:* Mem, Adv Comt Revision USPHS Drinking Water Standards, 59-61, Water Supply Panel & Comt Water Qual Criteria, 71-72; chmn, Pub Adv Comt Revision Fed Drinking Water Standards, 76-; mem environ studies bd, Nat Acad Sci; mem, Environ Eng Intersoc Bd. *Mem:* Nat Acad Eng; hon mem Am Water Works Asn; Conf State Sanit Engrs. *Mailing Add:* 905 Contra Costa Ave Berkeley CA 94707

ONISCHAK, MICHAEL, b Chicago, Ill, June 23, 43; m 67; c 2. CHEMICAL ENGINEERING. *Educ:* Ill Inst Technol, BS, 65, MS, 68, PhD(gas technol), 72. *Prof Exp:* Proj mgr chem reactors, Energy Res Corp, 72-77; res supvr coal gasification, 77-80, MGR GASIFICATION DEVELOP, INST GAS TECHNOL, 80- *Mem:* Am Inst Chem Engrs; Am Chem Soc. *Res:* Gas-solid reaction engineering; heat and mass transfer; specific application to energy conversion devices and coal and biomass gasification plants. *Mailing Add:* Inst of Gas Technol 3424 S State St Chicago IL 60616

ONKEN, ARTHUR BLAKE, b Alice Tex, Aug 13, 35; m 56; c 2. SOIL CHEMISTRY, SOIL FERTILITY. *Educ:* Tex A&I Univ, BS, 59; Okla State Univ, MS, 63, PhD(soil chem), 64. *Prof Exp:* PROF SOIL CHEM, AGR EXP STA, TEX A&M UNIV, 64- *Mem:* Am Soc Agron; Soil Sci Soc Am. *Res:* Plant nutrient reactions in soil; plant response to nutrient level; movement of applied plant nutrients and solutes through soil profiles. *Mailing Add:* Agr Res & Exten Ctr Tex A&M Univ Lubbock TX 79401

ONLEY, DAVID S, b London, Eng, July 4, 34; m 57; c 2. THEORETICAL PHYSICS. *Educ:* Oxford Univ, BA, 56, DPhil(theoret physics), 60. *Prof Exp:* Res assoc physics, Duke Univ, 60-61, asst prof, 61-65; assoc prof, 65-69, chmn dept, 73-78, PROF PHYSICS, OHIO UNIV, 69- *Concurrent Pos:* US Army Res Off res grant, 66-73; sabbatical leave, Univ Melbourne, 71-72; US Dept Energy res grant, 79-82. *Mem:* AAAS; Am Phys Soc. *Res:* Nuclear structure; photonuclear theory and analysis of electron scattering from atomic nuclei; nuclear fission. *Mailing Add:* Dept Physics Clippinger Res Labs Ohio Univ Athens OH 45701

ONLEY, JOHN HENRY, organic chemistry, analytical chemistry, see previous edition

ONN, DAVID GOODWIN, b Newark, Eng, Feb 18, 37; m 67; c 1. SOLID STATE PHYSICS, MATERIALS SCIENCE. *Educ:* Bristol Univ, BSc, 58; Oxford Univ, dipl educ, 60; Duke Univ, PhD(physics), 67. *Prof Exp:* Second physics master, Dean Close Sch, Cheltenham, Eng, 59-61; res assoc physics, Univ NC, Chapel Hill, 66-68, instr, 68-69, vis asst prof, 69-70; asst prof physics, 70-73, from asst prof to assoc prof physics & health sci, 73-76, ASSOC PROF PHYSICS, UNIV DEL, 76- *Mem:* Am Inst Physics; Sigma Xi; Am Asn Physics Teachers; Mat Res Soc; Am Carbon Soc. *Res:* Thermal and magnetic properties of metallic glasses; graphite intercalation compounds; electronic states in cryogenic fluids. *Mailing Add:* Dept Physics Univ Del Newark DE 19711

ONO, JOYCE KAZUYO, b Honolulu, Hawaii, Apr 18, 46. INVERTEBRATE ZOOLOGY, NEUROPHYSIOLOGY. *Educ:* Univ Hawaii, BA, 68; Univ Ill, MS, 70; PhD(zool), 75. *Prof Exp:* Asst instr biol & zool, Univ Ill, 68-75; res fel, Pub Health Serv, 75-79, ASST RES SCIENTIST, DIV NEUROSCI, CITY HOPE RES INST, 79- *Concurrent Pos:* Teaching assoc, Univ Wash, Fri Harbor Marine Sta, 76, Stanford Univ, Hopkins Marine Sta, 78, 79, 80. *Mem:* AAAS; Soc Neurosci; Asn Women Sci. *Res:* Processes which underly how nerve cells communicate with each other and other effector cells; identifying and measuring neurotransmitters utilized by identifiable neurons, characterizing the responses evoked by neruotransmitters, and delineating mechanisms of how pharmacological agents affect transmission properties. *Mailing Add:* Div Neurosci City Hope Res Inst 1450 E Duarte Rd Duarte CA 91010

ONO, KANJI, b Tokyo, Japan, Jan 2, 38; m 62; c 3. MATERIALS SCIENCE. *Educ:* Tokyo Inst Technol, BEng, 60; Northwestern Univ, PhD(mat sci), 64. *Prof Exp:* Res asst mat sci, Northwestern Univ, 60-61 & 64-65; from asst prof to assoc prof, 65-76, PROF ENG, UNIV CALIF, LOS ANGELES, 76- *Honors & Awards:* H M Howe Award, Am Soc Metals, 68. *Mem:* Am Inst Mining, Metall & Petrol Engrs; Am Soc Metals; Am Soc Nondestruct Test. *Res:* Dislocations and mechanical properties of solids; physical metallurgy; nondestructive testing of materials. *Mailing Add:* Dept of Mat Univ of Calif Los Angeles CA 90024

ONODA, GEORGE Y, JR, b Suisun, Calif, Oct 5, 38; m 62; c 2. CERAMICS, SURFACE CHEMISTRY. *Educ:* Univ Calif, Berkeley, BS, 61, MS, 62; Mass Inst Technol, PhD(ceramics), 66. *Prof Exp:* Metall engr, Aerojet-Gen Corp, 62-63; sr res engr, NAm Rockwell Corp, 65-68; res scientist, IIT Res Inst, 68-72; PROF, UNIV FLA, 72- *Mem:* Am Ceramic Soc; Nat Inst Ceramic Engrs. *Res:* Ceramic processing; fine particle technology; mineral processing. *Mailing Add:* MTL 157 Dept of Mat Sci & Eng Univ of Fla Gainesville FL 32611

ONOPCHENKO, ANATOLI T, b Lvov, Poland, Feb 12, 37; US citizen; m 63; c 2. ORGANIC CHEMISTRY. *Educ:* Pa State Univ, BS, 60, MS, 62; Univ Md, PhD(chem), 66. *Prof Exp:* Res asst, Pa State Univ, 60-62; asst, Univ Md, 63-66; res chemist, 66-72, sr res chemist, 72-80, RES ASSOC, GULF RES & DEVELOP CO, 80- *Mem:* Am Chem Soc; Am Inst Chemists. *Res:* General organic and petroleum chemistry. *Mailing Add:* 180 Kelvington Dr Monroeville PA 15146

ONSAGER, JEROME ANDREW, b Northwood, NDak, Apr 8, 36; m 58; c 2. ENTOMOLOGY. *Educ:* NDak State Univ, BS, 58, MS, 60, PhD(entom), 63. *Prof Exp:* Res entomologist, Vegetable Insects Invests, Agr Res Serv, USDA, 63-75; RES SERV LEADER, RANGELAND INSECT LAB, AGR RES, USDA, 75- *Mem:* Entom Soc Am. *Res:* Biology and ecology of insects that affect rangeland, with emphasis on development and integration of selective methods for biological chemical and cultural control. *Mailing Add:* Rangeland Insect Lab USDA Bozeman MT 59715

ONSTAD, CHARLES ARNOLD, b Spring Grove, Minn, Oct 30, 41; m 61; c 3. AGRICULTURAL ENGINEERING, HYDROLOGY. *Educ:* Univ Minn, BAE, 64, MSAE, 66; SDak State Univ, PhD(agr eng), 72. *Prof Exp:* AGR ENGR HYDROL, NORTH CENT SOIL CONSERV RES CTR, FOOD RES, AGR RES SERV, USDA, 66- *Concurrent Pos:* Asst prof, Univ Minn, St Paul, 72- *Mem:* Am Soc Agr Engrs; Soil Conserv Soc Am. *Res:* Hydrological and erosional modeling for the purpose of assessing non-point pollution potential on agricultural watersheds. *Mailing Add:* NCent Soil Conserv Res Ctr USDA Sci & Educ Admin Food Res Morris MN 56267

ONSTOTT, EDWARD IRVIN, b Moreland, Ky, Nov 12, 22; m 45; c 4. INORGANIC CHEMISTRY, PHYSICAL CHEMISTRY. *Educ:* Univ Ill, BS, 44, MS, 48, PhD(chem), 50. *Prof Exp:* Chem engr, Firestone Tire & Rubber Co, 44 & 46; RES CHEMIST, LOS ALAMOS NAT LAB, 50- *Mem:* Fel AAAS; fel Am Inst Chem; NY Acad Sci; Am Chem Soc; Electrochem Soc. *Res:* Complex ion and rare earth chemistry; electrochemistry. *Mailing Add:* Los Alamos Nat Lab MS 734 Los Alamos NM 87544

ONTELL, MARCIA, b New York, NY, June 28, 37. ANATOMY, ELECTRON MICROSCOPY. *Educ:* Temple Univ, BA, 58; Fairleigh Dickinson Univ, MS, 68; NJ Col Med & Dent, PhD(anat), 72. *Prof Exp:* Assoc anat, Mt Sinai Med Sch, 72-76; asst prof, 76-80, ASSOC PROF ANAT, SCH MED, UNIV PITTSBURGH, 80- *Concurrent Pos:* Prin investr,

Muscular Dystrophy Asn, 74-76 & 81, NIH Nat Inst Neurol & Commun Disorders & Stroke, 75-84 & NSF Develop Biol, 78-81. *Mem:* Am Asn Anatomists; Am Soc Cell Biol; Tissue Cult Asn; NY Acad Sci. *Res:* Cell maturation; myogenesis and growth of striated muscle; muscle satellite cells; muscle disorders, including muscular dystrophy, denervation atrophy; response of muscle to various pharmacological agents. *Mailing Add:* Dept Anat & Cell Biol Univ Pittsburgh Sch Med Pittsburgh PA 15261

ONTJES, DAVID A, b Lyons, Kans, July 19, 37; m 60; c 4. ENDOCRINOLOGY. *Educ:* Univ Kans, BA, 59; Oxford Univ, MA, 61; Harvard Med Sch, MD, 64. *Prof Exp:* From intern to resident internal med, Harvard Med Serv, Boston City Hosp, 64-66; from asst prof to assoc prof med & pharmacol, 69-76, PROF MED & PHARMACOL, MED SCH, UNIV NC, CHAPEL HILL, 76-, CHIEF, DIV ENDOCRINOL, 72- *Concurrent Pos:* NIH spec res fel, 71; attend physician, NC Mem Hosp, Chapel Hill, 69- *Mem:* Am Soc Pharmacol & Exp Therapeut; Am Soc Clin Invest; fel Am Col Physicians; Endocrine Soc; Am Fedn Clin Res. *Res:* Chemistry and physiology of peptide hormones; peptide hormone receptors; control of adrenal function. *Mailing Add:* Dept of Med Univ of NC Med Sch Chapel Hill NC 27514

ONTKO, JOSEPH ANDREW, b Syracuse, NY, July 30, 32; m 55; c 4. BIOCHEMISTRY. *Educ:* Syracuse Univ, AB, 53; Univ Wis, MS, 55, PhD(biochem), 57. *Prof Exp:* From instr to asst prof biochem, Med Units, Univ Tenn, 59-64, asst prof physiol & biophys, 65-66; assoc prof, 68-74, PROF RES BIOCHEM, SCH MED, UNIV OKLA, 74-; ASSOC MEM, OKLA MED RES FOUND, 68- *Concurrent Pos:* Am Heart Asn res fel, Med Sch, Bristol Univ, 66-67 & Max Planck Inst Cell Chem, Munich, 67-68; consult, Oak Ridge Inst Nuclear Studies, 61-66. *Mem:* AAAS; Biochem Soc; Am Soc Biol Chemists. *Res:* Lipid metabolism; fatty acid oxidation; regulation of cell metabolism; isolation of liver cells. *Mailing Add:* Okla Med Res Found 825 NE 13th St Oklahoma City OK 73104

ONTON, AARE, b Tartu, Estonia, Dec 10, 39; US citizen; m 65; c 3. PHYSICS, ELECTRICAL ENGINEERING. *Educ:* Mass Inst Technol, SB & SM, 62; Purdue Univ, PhD(physics), 67. *Prof Exp:* Res staff mem, Thomas J Watson Res Ctr, IBM Corp, NY, 67-73; RES STAFF MEM, IBM RES LAB, 73- *Concurrent Pos:* Alexander von Humboldt scholar, Max Planck Inst Solid State Res, 72-73. *Mem:* Am Phys Soc. *Res:* Optical properties of solids, particularly electronics bandstructure, electronic impurity states, lattice dynamics, and luminescence; structural, electronic, and magnetic properties of amorphous thin films. *Mailing Add:* IBM Res Lab 5600 Cottle Rd San Jose CA 95193

ONUSKA, FRANCIS IVAN, b Humenne, Slovak, Mar 28, 35; Can citizen; m 61; c 2. ANALYTICAL CHEMISTRY, ORGANIC CHEMISTRY. *Educ:* Slovak Tech Univ, Bratislava, dipl eng, 58; Tech Univ, Prague, MSc, 66; Purkyne Univ, Brno, PhD(anal chem), 67. *Prof Exp:* Res chemist, Dept Tech Develop, Chemko Strazske, 58-66, scientist, Res Base, 66-68; res chemist, Uniroyal Res Labs, 69-73; SCIENTIST TRACE ANAL, NAT WATER RES INST, 73- *Concurrent Pos:* Fel, Lomonosoff State Univ, Moscow, 67. *Mem:* Fel Chem Inst Can; Am Soc Mass Spectrometry. *Res:* Modern separation methods; glass capillary gas and liquid chromatography; mass spectrometry and their tandem; trace organic analysis; environmental analytical chemistry and toxicology. *Mailing Add:* Nat Water Res Inst AMRS PO Box 5050 Burlington ON L7R 4A5 Can

ONWOOD, DAVID P, b London, Eng, Sept 13, 36. PHYSICAL CHEMISTRY. *Educ:* Oxford Univ, BA, 60, DPhil(chem), 66. *Prof Exp:* Res assoc chem, Ill Inst Technol, 63-65, instr 65-66; asst prof, 66-69, ASSOC PROF CHEM, PURDUE UNIV, FT WAYNE, 69- *Concurrent Pos:* NSF partic award, 67-69; vis assoc prof, Univ Toronto, 77-80. *Mem:* AAAS; Am Chem Soc; The Chem Soc. *Res:* Physical chemistry in aqueous solutions; isotope effects; catalytic effects. *Mailing Add:* Dept of Chem Purdue Univ Ft Wayne IN 46815

ONYSHKEVYCH, LUBOMYR S, b Ukraine, Feb 3, 33; US citizen; m 61; c 3. ELECTRONICS ENGINEERING. *Educ:* City Col New York, BEE, 55; Mass Inst Technol, MS, 57, EE, 61. *Prof Exp:* Res asst res lab electronics, Mass Inst Technol, 55-56; staff mem comput memories, RCA Labs, 57-59; mem tech staff comput magnets, Lincoln Labs, Mass Inst Technol, 60-63; mem tech staff comput res, 63-78, GROUP HEAD, ELECTRONIC PACKAGING RES, DAVID SARNOFF RES CTR, RCA LABS, 78- *Honors & Awards:* Indust Res 100 Award. *Mem:* Inst Elec & Electronics Eng; Int Soc Hybrid Microelectronics. *Res:* Electronic packaging; computer memories; transfluxors; twistors; magnetic logic; thin magnetic films; thin film memories; magnetostriction; magnetoresistance; magnetosonic film memories; memory hierarchies; magnetic bubble domains; thick films; microelectronics; encapsulation; microsonics; hybrids. *Mailing Add:* RCA Labs David Sarnoff Res Ctr Princeton NJ 08540

ONYSZCHUK, MARIO, b Wolkow, Poland, July 21, 30; nat Can; m 59; c 3. INORGANIC CHEMISTRY. *Educ:* McGill Univ, BSc, 51; Univ Western Ont, MSc, 52; McGill Univ, PhD(phys chem), 54; Cambridge Univ, PhD(inorg chem), 56. *Prof Exp:* Lectr chem, 56-57, from asst prof to assoc prof, 57-68, PROF CHEM, McGILL UNIV, 68- *Mem:* Am Chem Soc; fel Chem Inst Can; The Chem Soc. *Res:* Coordination compounds of group III and IV halides. *Mailing Add:* Dept of Chem McGill Univ Montreal PQ H3A 2K6 Can

OOI, BOON SENG, b Kuala Lumpur, Malaysia, Apr 21, 40; US citizen; m 66; c 2. MEDICINE, IMMUNOLOGY. *Educ:* Univ Singapore, MB, BS, 64; FRACP, 76. *Prof Exp:* Asst prof, Pritzker Sch Med, Univ Chicago, 73; asst prof, 73-76, ASSOC PROF MED, COL MED, UNIV CINCINNATI, 76- *Mem:* Am Soc Nephrology; Am Fedn Clin Res. *Res:* Immunology of kidney diseases. *Mailing Add:* Univ of Cincinnati Med Ctr 234 Bethesda Ave Cincinnati OH 45267

OOKA, JERI JEAN, b Olaa, Hawaii, Jan 22, 45. PHYTOPATHOLOGY. *Educ:* Univ Hawaii, BA, 66, MS, 69; Univ Minn, PhD(plant path), 75. *Prof Exp:* ASST PLANT PATHOLOGIST, UNIV HAWAII, 75- *Mem:* Am Phytopath Soc; AAAS. *Res:* Diseases of maize, especially epidemiology of Northern Corn Leaf Blight in tropical regions of the world; Fusarium moniliforme kernel and ear rot; aerobiology of Fusarium species; diseases of taro, especially Colocasia esculenta, and other edible Araceae with emphasis on fungal root and corm diseases; fungal root diseases of alfalfa in tropical and subtropical regions. *Mailing Add:* Kauai Br Sta Univ of Hawaii RR 1 Box 278-A Kapaa HI 96746

OONO, YOSHITSUGU, b Fukuoka, Japan, Jan 21, 48. STATISTICAL PHYSICS. *Educ:* Kyushu Univ, Japan, BEng, 70, MEng, 73, PhD(chem physics), 76. *Prof Exp:* Asst prof phys chem, Res Inst Indust Sci, Kyushu Univ, Japan, 76-81; ASST PROF THEORET PHYSICS, UNIV ILL, URBANA-CHAMPAIGN, 81- *Concurrent Pos:* Res assoc polymer physics, James Franck Inst, Univ Chicago, 79-81. *Mem:* Phys Soc Japan. *Res:* Statistical physics; dynamical system; nonequilibruim statistical mechanics; polymer physics. *Mailing Add:* Dept Physics Univ Ill 1110 W Green Urbana IL 61801

OORT, ABRAHAM H, b Leiden, Neth, Sept 2, 34; m 59; c 3. DYNAMIC METEOROLOGY. *Educ:* Univ Leiden, Drs, 59; Mass Inst Technol, SM, 63; State Univ Utrecht, PhD(meteorol), 64. *Prof Exp:* Res asst energy-cycle lower stratosphere, Mass Inst Technol, 63-64; res scientist, Royal Neth Meteorol Inst, 64-66; RES SCIENTIST, GEOPHYS FLUID DYNAMICS LAB, NAT OCEANIC & ATMOSPHERIC ADMIN, 66- *Concurrent Pos:* Vis prof, Princeton Univ. *Honors & Awards:* Gold Medal, US Dept Com, 79. *Mem:* Am Meteorol Soc; Am Geophys Union; Royal Meteorol Soc; NY Acad Sci. *Res:* Dynamic climatology atmosphere and oceans; angular momentum cycle of the earth; energy cycle atmospheric and oceanic motions; dynamics lower stratosphere; energetics Gulf Stream meanders. *Mailing Add:* Nat Ocean & Atmospheric Admin Box 308 Princeton Univ Princeton NJ 08540

OOSTERHOUT, KENNETH CHRISTIAN, b Port Arthur, Tex, Jan 16, 34; m 59; c 3. CHEMICAL ENGINEERING. *Educ:* Lamar State Col, BS, 56; Univ Ill, MS, 58; Pa State Univ, PhD, 67. *Prof Exp:* Engr, Bellaire Labs, Texaco, Inc, 57-58; instr chem eng, Lamar State Col, 58-60; res asst, Pa State Univ, 60-66; ASSOC PROF ENG, TEX A&I UNIV, 66- *Mem:* Am Soc Eng Educ; Am Inst Chem Engrs. *Res:* Ion-exchange resin catalysis in stirred reactors. *Mailing Add:* Box 2046 Tex A&I Univ Kingsville TX 78363

OOSTERHUIS, WILLIAM TENLEY, b Mt Vernon, NY, Mar 28, 40; m 64; c 2. CHEMICAL PHYSICS. *Educ:* Wis State Univ-Platteville, BS, 62; Carnegie Inst Technol, MS, 64, PhD(physics), 67. *Prof Exp:* NSF grant, Atomic Energy Res Estab, Eng, 67-68; res physicist, Carnegie-Mellon Univ, 68-69, asst prof chem & solid state physics, 69-74; solid state chem prog dir, 74-75, assoc prog dir solid state physics, 78-79, STAFF ASSOC, MAT RES LAB SECT, NAT SCI FOUND, 74- *Mem:* Am Phys Soc; Biophys Soc. *Res:* Paramagnetic hyperfine interactions in transition metal complexes, including biological molecules; magnetic critical point phenomena; crystalline electric fields; Mossbauer effect. *Mailing Add:* Div Mat Res Nat Sci Found Washington DC 20550

OOSTERVELD, MARTIN, hydrology, water resources engineering, see previous edition

OPAL, CHET BRIAN, b Chicago, Ill, Nov 30, 42; m 64. AERONOMY, ASTROPHYSICS. *Educ:* Johns Hopkins Univ, BA, 64, PhD(physics), 69. *Prof Exp:* Fel & res assoc physics, Joint Inst Lab Astrophys, Univ Colo, Boulder, 69-71; RES PHYSICIST, E O HULBURT CTR SPACE RES, NAVAL RES LAB, 71- *Concurrent Pos:* E O Hulburt fel, Naval Res Lab, 71-72; vis scholar, McDonald Observ, Univ Tex, 80-81. *Mem:* Am Phys Soc; Am Astron Soc; Am Geophys Union. *Res:* Electron-atom scattering; far-ultraviolet spectroscopy of astrophysical and geophysical phenomena from rockets and satellites; aurora and airglow; electronic imaging devices. *Mailing Add:* Code 4140 Naval Res Lab Washington DC 20375

OPAVA-STITZER, SUSAN C, b New York City, NY, Mar 14, 47; m 73; c 2. RENAL PHYSIOLOGY, ENDOCRINOLOGY. *Educ:* Col Mt St Vincent, BS, 68; Univ Mich, Ann Arbor, PhD(physiol), 72. *Prof Exp:* Fel, Darmouth Med Sch, 72-74; asst prof, 74-80, ASSOC PROF PHYSIOL, UNIV PR MED SCH, 80- *Mem:* Am Physiol Soc; Am Soc Nephrology; Int Soc Nephrology; AAAS. *Res:* Renal physiology, specifically mechanisms of concentration and dilution of urine; electrolyte balance; renin-angiotensin system; control of aldosterone secretion. *Mailing Add:* Dept Physiol Univ PR Med Sch GPO Box 5067 San Juan PR 00936

OPDYKE, NEIL, b Frenchtown, NJ, Feb 7, 33; m 58; c 3. GEOLOGY, GEOPHYSICS. *Educ:* Columbia Col, BA, 55; Univ Durham, PhD(geol), 58. *Prof Exp:* Fel, Rice Univ, 58-59; res fel, Australian Nat Univ, 59-60 & Univ Col Rhodesia & Nyasaland, 61-64; res assoc, Columbia Univ, 65-66, res scientist, Lamont-Doherty Geol Observ, 64-81, sr res assoc, Univ, 66-81; PROF & CHMN, DEPT GEOL, UNIV FLA, 81- *Concurrent Pos:* Fulbright travel grant, Australia, 59-60; adj prof, Columbia Univ, 74-81. *Mem:* AAAS; Geol Soc Am; Am Geophys Union. *Res:* Paleomagnetism; paleoclimatology. *Mailing Add:* Dept Geol Univ Fla 1112 GPA Gainesville FL 32611

OPECHOWSKI, WLADYSLAW, b Warsaw, Poland, Mar 10, 11; nat Can citizen; m 33; c 1. THEORETICAL PHYSICS. *Educ:* Univ Warsaw, MPhil, 35. *Hon Degrees:* DSc, Univ Wroclaw, Poland, 73. *Prof Exp:* Lorentz-Fonds fel, Leiden & physicist, Teylers Stichting, 39-45; physicist, Philips Res Lab, Eindhoven, 45-48; from assoc prof to prof, 58-76, HON PROF PHYSICS, UNIV BC, 76- *Concurrent Pos:* Lorentz prof, State Univ Leiden, 64-65; vis prof, Roman Cath Univ Nijmegen, 68-69. *Mem:* Am Phys Soc; fel Royal Soc Can; Can Asn Physicists; Neth Phys Soc. *Res:* Quantum theory of magnetism; applications of group theory. *Mailing Add:* Dept of Physics Univ of BC Vancouver BC V6T 1W5 Can

OPEL, HOWARD, b Baltimore, Md, June 7, 28; m 64. REPRODUCTIVE PHYSIOLOGY, ENDOCRINOLOGY. *Educ:* Univ Md, BS, 50, MS, 59; Univ Ill, PhD(animal sci), 60. *Prof Exp:* RES SCIENTIST, ANIMAL SCI RES DIV, SCI & EDUC ADMIN-AGR RES, USDA, 60- *Mem:* Soc Study Reproduction; Am Asn Anat; Am Soc Zoologists; Poultry Sci Asn; Endocrine Soc. *Res:* Neuroendocrine control of ovulation and oviposition in birds. *Mailing Add:* Rm 39 Bldg 262 Agr Res Ctr Beltsville MD 20705

OPELL, BRENT DOUGLAS, b Washington, Ind, June 12, 49. ZOOLOGY. *Educ:* Butler Univ, BA, 71; Southern Ill Univ, MA, 74; Harvard Univ, PhD(biol), 78. *Prof Exp:* ASST PROF ZOOL, VA POLYTECH INST & STATE UNIV, 78- *Mem:* Am Arachnological Soc; Am Micros Soc; Am Soc Zoologists; Brit Arachnological Soc; Soc Syst Zoologists. *Res:* Morphology; systematics; natural history; behavior of cribellate orb-weaving spiders. *Mailing Add:* Dept of Biol Va Polytech Inst & State Univ Blacksburg VA 24061

OPELLA, STANLEY JOSEPH, b Summit, NJ, Sept 29, 47. PHYSICAL CHEMISTRY, BIOLOGICAL CHEMISTRY. *Educ:* Univ Ky, BS, 69; Stanford Univ, PhD(chem), 74. *Prof Exp:* Fel chem, Mass Inst Technol, 75-76; asst prof, 76-81, ASSOC PROF CHEM, UNIV PA, 81- *Mem:* Am Chem Soc; Am Phys Soc. *Res:* Nuclear magnetic resonance spectroscopy of biological molecules; high resolution solid state and solution nuclear magnetic resonance spectroscopy. *Mailing Add:* Dept of Chem Univ of Pa Philadelphia PA 19104

OPENSHAW, MARTIN DAVID, b Mesa, Ariz, Oct 10, 40; m 64; c 5. SOIL FERTILITY, PLANT PHYSIOLOGY. *Educ:* Ariz State Univ, BS, 65, Iowa State Univ, MS, 68, PhD(soils), 70. *Prof Exp:* Teaching asst soil sci, Iowa State Univ, 65-67, instr, 67-70; asst prof soil sci, Univ Ariz, 70-76, assoc prof, 76-77, exten soil specialist, 70-77; DIR, AM REGISTRY CERTIFIED PROFESSORS AGRON, CROPS & SOILS, LTD, MADISON, WIS, 77- *Mem:* Am Soc Agron; Soil Sci Soc Am; Soil Conserv Soc Am. *Res:* Soil fertility work with field crops and the effect of fertilizers on the environment. *Mailing Add:* 677 South Segoe Rd Madison WI 53711

OPHEL, IVAN LINDSAY, b Adelaide, South Australia, July 20, 24; m 51; c 4. RADIATION ECOLOGY. *Educ:* Univ Okla, BS, 49, MS, 50. *Prof Exp:* Apprentice, Govt Eng & Water Supply Dept, South Australia, 40-41, asst chemist, 42-47, biologist, 51-52; asst limnol, Univ Okla, 48-50; sr biologist environ res, 53-73, HEAD, ENVIRON RES BR, CHALK RIVER NUCLEAR LABS, ATOMIC ENERGY CAN, LTD, 73- *Concurrent Pos:* Chmn adv group methodology radiation effects exp aquatic organisms & ecosysts, Int Atomic Energy Agency, 77; mem, Can Adv Comt Environ Monitoring. *Res:* Biological problems of radioactive waste disposal; radioecology research. *Mailing Add:* Environ Res Br C R Nuclear Labs Atomic Energy of Can Ltd Chalk River ON K0J 1P0 Can

OPHER, REUVEN, astrophysics, solid state physics, see previous edition

OPIE, JOSEPH WENDELL, b Wilmot, SDak, Sept 27, 13; m 40; c 3. ORGANIC CHEMISTRY, FOOD TECHNOLOGY. *Educ:* Univ Minn, ChB, 35, PhD(org chem), 40. *Prof Exp:* Microanalyst, Univ Minn, 35-39; res chemist, Merck & Co, Inc, NJ, 40-42; res assoc, Nat Defense Res Comt, Univ Minn, 42; res chemist, Tex Co, NY, 42-44 & Wyeth, Inc, 44-46; head develop res sect, 46-48, org develop sect, 48-62, formulation concept dept, 62-67, concept develop dept, 67-69 & res & develop, Sperry Div, 69-71, mgr, 71-74, mgr develop, Dept Corp Res, Gen Mills, Inc, 74-78; RETIRED. *Mem:* Inst Food Technol; Am Chem Soc; AAAS. *Res:* Polyalkylgenzenes; polyalkyl-quinones; substituted coumarins; vitamin E; plastics; antibiotics; medicinals; fatty acids product and processes development; mineral flotation starch; plant gums; corrosion; phospholipids; food products. *Mailing Add:* 2515 W52nd St Minneapolis MN 55410

OPIE, THOMAS RANSON, b Staunton, Va, Dec 19, 48; m 80. ORGANIC CHEMISTRY, ORGANOMETALLIC CHEMISTRY. *Educ:* Davidson Col, BS, 71; Cornell Univ, MS, 74, PhD(org chem), 76. *Prof Exp:* RES CHEMIST, ROHM & HAAS CO, 75- *Mem:* Am Chem Soc; Am Sci Affil. *Res:* Synthetic reactions involving completely fluorinated organometallic compounds, chemical process research for agricultural chemicals. *Mailing Add:* Rohm & Haas Co Bristol Res Lab PO Box 219 Bristol PA 19007

OPIE, WILLIAM R(OBERT), b Butte, Mont, Apr 3, 20; m 44; c 2. PHYSICAL METALLURGY. *Educ:* Mont Sch Mines, BS, 42; Mass Inst Technol, ScD, 49. *Hon Degrees:* MetE, Mont Sch Mines, 65; ScD, Mont Tech, 80. *Prof Exp:* Foundry metallurgist, Wright Aeronaut Corp, 42-45; design metallurgist, Anaconda Copper Mining Co, 46; asst, Mass Inst Technol, 47-48; res metallurgist, Am Smelting & Refining Co, 48-50; res supvr, Titanium Div, Nat Lead Co, 50-60; dir res & develop, US Metals Refining Div, 60-68, vpres & tech dir, Amax-Basemetals, 68-71, PRES, AMAX BASE-METALS RES & DEVELOP, INC, AMAX, INC, 71- *Concurrent Pos:* Chmn tech comt, Int Copper Res Asn, 64-66 & Int Germanium Res Comt, 64-66. *Mem:* Fel Am Soc Metals; Am Inst Mining, Metall & Petrol Engrs; Brit Inst Metals; fel Metall Soc. *Res:* Nonferrous extractive metallurgy; copper alloy development; powder metallurgy. *Mailing Add:* 119 Crawfords Corner Rd Holmdel NJ 07008

OPIELA, ALEXANDER DAVID, JR, b Falls City, Tex, Dec 26, 29; m 61; c 5. ELECTRICAL & ENVIRONMENTAL HEALTH ENGINEERING. *Educ:* Univ Tex, Austin, BSc, 52, MSc, 55 & 72. *Prof Exp:* Res engr, Defense Res Lab, Univ Tex, 52-56, systs develop specialist, 56-61; sr engr, Textran Corp, 61-62; sr engr, Tracor, Inc, 62-64; mfg engr, 64-65, asst vpres eng & mfg, 65-69, prod line mgr, 69-70; engr, Air Pollution Control Serv, Tex Dept Health, 72-73, Tex Air Control Bd, 73-81. *Mem:* Inst Elec & Electronics Engrs; Air Pollution Control Asn. *Res:* Cathode ray tube indicators and film data recorders; direction finding and field strength measuring equipment; engineering and manufacturing management; air pollution sources, effects and abatement technology; air pollution control. *Mailing Add:* 6105 Hylawn Austin TX 78723

OPITZ, HERMAN ERNEST, b Kingston, NY, Sept 28, 29; m 54; c 2. INORGANIC CHEMISTRY. *Educ:* Union Col NY, BS, 51; Ind Univ, PhD(chem), 56. *Prof Exp:* Res chemist, Armstrong Cork Co, Pa, 55-69; MGR GLASS RES PACKAGING PROD DIV, KERR GLASS MFG CORP, 69- *Mem:* Am Ceramic Soc. *Res:* Silicon chemistry; inorganic polymers and foams; glass technology. *Mailing Add:* Kerr Glass Mfg Corp PO Box 3900 Lancaster PA 17604

OPITZ, JOHN MARIUS, b Hamburg, Ger, Aug 15, 35; US citizen; m 61; c 5. PEDIATRICS, MEDICAL GENETICS. *Educ:* Univ Iowa, BA, 56, MD, 59; Am Bd Pediat, dipl, 64. *Prof Exp:* From intern to resident pediat, Univ Iowa Hosp, 59-61; resident, Univ Wis-Madison, 61-62, from asst prof to assoc prof pediat & med genetics, 64-72, prof & dir, Wis Clin Genetics Ctr, 72-79; COORDR SHODAIR-MONT REGIONAL GENETICS PROG, SHODAIR CHILDREN'S HOSP, 79- *Concurrent Pos:* NIH fels pediat & med genetics, Univ Wis-Madison, 62-64; adj clin prof, Univ Wash, Seattle, Mont State Univ, Bozeman & Univ Wis-Madison, 79-; ed-in-chief, Am J Med Genetics. *Mem:* AAAS; Am Soc Human Genetics; Am Soc Zool; Am Inst Biol Sci; Int Soc Cranio-Facial Biol. *Res:* Hereditary diseases; single and multiple congenital anomalies; cytogenetics; genetic counseling; errors of sex determination and differentiation; clinical and developmental genetics; mental retardation. *Mailing Add:* Shodair Children's Hospital Box 5539 Helena MT 59604

OPLINGER, EDWARD SCOTT, b Jewell, Kans, Apr 25, 43; m 64; c 3. AGRONOMY. *Educ:* Kans State Univ, BS, 65; Purdue Univ, Lafayette, MS, 69, PhD(agron), 70. *Prof Exp:* Asst prof, 70-75, assoc prof, 75-78, PROF AGRON, UNIV WIS-MADISON, 78- *Mem:* Am Soc Agron; Crop Sci Soc Am; Plant Growth Regulator Working Group. *Res:* Crop production; plant growth regulators; plant physiology. *Mailing Add:* 139 Moore Hall Dept of Agron Univ of Wis Madison WI 53706

OPP, ALBERT GEELMUYDEN, b Fargo, NDak, July 29, 31; m 60; c 2. ASTROPHYSICS. *Educ:* Univ NDak, BS, 53; St Louis Univ, MS, 55; Univ Gottingen, Dr rer nat(geophys), 61. *Prof Exp:* Terrestrial scientist, Air Tech Intel Ctr, US Air Force, 55-57, space systs specialist, Europ Hq, 59-62, instr physics, US Air Force Acad, 62-63; staff scientist, 63-66, dep chief particles & fields prog, 66-70, CHIEF HIGH ENERGY ASTROPHYS, NASA HQ, 70- *Concurrent Pos:* Consult, Kaman Nuclear Div, 62-63; fel pub affairs, Princeton Univ, 70-71. *Mem:* Am Phys Soc; Am Astron Soc; AAAS. *Res:* Cosmic rays; gamma ray astronomy; x-ray astronomy; magnetic fields and plasmas in space; trapped radiation; planetary magnetospheres. *Mailing Add:* Off of Space Sci NASA Washington DC 20546

OPPELT, JOHN ANDREW, b Baltimore, Md, Feb 4, 37; m 60; c 1. MATHEMATICS. *Educ:* Loyola Col, Md, AB, 59; Univ Notre Dame, MS, 61, PhD(math), 65. *Prof Exp:* Instr math, Univ Notre Dame, 65; actg asst prof, Univ Va, 65, asst prof, 65-70; assoc prof, 70-74, chmn dept math, 70-80, actg dean, 80-81, PROF MATH, GEORGE MASON UNIV, 74-; VPRES, BELLARMINE COL, 81- *Concurrent Pos:* Sesquicentennial scholar & vis asst prof, Univ Wash, 69-70. *Mem:* Am Math Soc. *Res:* Modern algebra; Abelian p-mixed groups. *Mailing Add:* Dept of Math George Mason Univ Fairfax VA 22030

OPPELT, JOHN CHRISTIAN, b Baltimore, Md, Dec 11, 31; m 56; c 5. ORGANIC CHEMISTRY. *Educ:* Loyola Col Md, BS, 53; Univ Md, College Park, MS, 58; Rutgers Univ, PhD(org chem), 67. *Prof Exp:* From chemist to res chemist, 58-74, SR RES CHEMIST, AM CYANAMID CO, 74- *Mem:* Am Chem Soc. *Res:* Synthesis of plastics additives, especially antioxidants, stabilizers, ultraviolet and near infrared absorbers; synthesis of alkyl phosphines and derivatives. *Mailing Add:* Discovery Res Dept Am Cyanamid Co Bound Brook NJ 08805

OPPENHEIM, A(NTONI) K(AZIMIERZ), b Warsaw, Poland, Aug 11, 15; nat US; m 45; c 1. MECHANICAL ENGINEERING. *Educ:* Warsaw Inst Technol, dipl, 39; Polish Univ, Eng, dipl, 45; Univ London, DIC & PhD(eng), 45. *Hon Degrees:* DSc, Univ London, 76; Dr, Univ Poitiers, 81. *Prof Exp:* Asst lectr, City & Guilds Col, Eng, 45-48; actg asst prof mech eng, Stanford Univ, 48-50; from asst prof to assoc prof, 50-58, PROF MECH ENG, UNIV CALIF, BERKELEY, 58- *Concurrent Pos:* Lectr, Polish Univ, Eng, 42-48; consult, Shell Develop Co, 52-60; NSF sr fel, 60; assoc prof, Univ Poitiers, 73 & 80. *Honors & Awards:* Water Arbit Prize, Brit Inst Mech Engrs, 49. *Mem:* Nat Acad Eng; fel Am Soc Mech Engrs; fel Am Inst Aeronaut & Astronaut; Am Soc Eng Educ; Am Phys Soc. *Res:* Gas dynamics; wave propagation and unsteady flow phenomena; detonation; radiation; heat transfer, thermodynamics, combustion; internal combustion engines. *Mailing Add:* Univ of Calif Col of Eng Berkeley CA 94720

OPPENHEIM, ALAN VICTOR, b New York, NY, Nov 11, 37; m 64; c 2. ELECTRICAL ENGINEERING. *Educ:* Mass Inst Technol, SB & SM, 61, ScD(elec eng), 64. *Prof Exp:* Asst prof, 64-69, assoc prof, 69-76, assoc div head, Mass Inst Technol Lincoln Lab, 78-80, PROF ELEC ENG, MASS INST TECHNOL, 76- *Concurrent Pos:* Consult, MIT Lincoln Lab, 66-, Comput Signal Processors, Inc, 71-, Schlumberger-Doll Res Lab, 77- & Sanders Assocs, Inc, 79-; ed, Prentice-Hall, Inc, 75-; Guggenheim fel, 72; consult, Stein Assoc, 74-, Chevron Oil Res Co, 75-, Acoust Res, Inc, 76-77, Schlumberger-Doll Res Lab, 77-, EG&G, Inc, Arthur D Little, Inc, Navy Underwater Sound Lab, Nat Acad Sci & Lincoln Lab. *Honors & Awards:* Sr Award, Inst Elec & Electronics Engrs, 69. *Mem:* Fel Inst Elec & Electronics Engrs; Acoust Soc Am. *Res:* Digital signal processing, speech, image and seismic data processing; system theory. *Mailing Add:* Dept of Elec Eng & Comput Sci Mass Inst Technol Rm 36-625 Cambridge MA 02139

OPPENHEIM, BERNARD EDWARD, b Chicago, Ill, July 5, 37; m 63; c 4. NUCLEAR MEDICINE, RADIOLOGY. *Educ:* Univ Ariz, BS, 59; Univ Chicago, MD, 63. *Prof Exp:* Intern, Michael Univ Chicago, Reese Hosp, Chicago, 63-64; resident radiol, 64-67, instr nuclear med, 70-71, from asst prof to assoc prof radiol, 71-76; assoc prof, 76-81, PROF RADIOL, IND

UNIV, 81- *Concurrent Pos:* James Picker Found scholar radiol res, 72-73; consult, Nat Cancer Inst, Nat Acad Sci. *Mem:* AAAS; Radiation Res Soc; AMA; Radiol Soc NAm; Soc Nuclear Med. *Res:* Application of computers to imaging in nuclear medicine; long term effects of low dose in utero-irradiation. *Mailing Add:* Dept of Radiol Sch Med Ind Univ Indianapolis IN 46223

OPPENHEIM, IRWIN, b Boston, Mass, June 30, 29. CHEMICAL PHYSICS. *Educ:* Harvard Univ, AB, 49; Yale Univ, PhD(chem), 56. *Prof Exp:* Asst chem, Calif Inst Technol, 49-51; statist mech, Yale Univ, 51-53; physicist, Nat Bur Stand, 53-60; chief theoret physics, Gen Dynamics/Convair, 60-61; assoc prof, 61-65, PROF CHEM, MASS INST TECHNOL, 65- *Concurrent Pos:* Lectr, Univ Md, 54-60; res assoc, State Univ Leiden, 55-56; vis prof, Weizmann Inst, 58-59 & Univ Calif, San Diego, 66-67; Van Der Waals prof, Univ Amsterdam, 67. *Mem:* Fel Am Phys Soc; fel Am Acad Arts & Sci. *Res:* Statistical mechanics of irreversible processes; isotope effects; nuclear magnetic resonance. *Mailing Add:* Dept Chem Rm 6-221 Mass Inst Technol Cambridge MA 02139

OPPENHEIM, JOSEPH HAROLD, b Connellsville, Pa, Oct 10, 26. ALGEBRA. *Educ:* Univ Chicago, PhB, 48, BS, 54; Univ Ill, MS, 56, PhD(math, algebra), 62. *Prof Exp:* Asst prof math, Rutgers Univ, 60-65; asst prof, 66-71, ASSOC PROF MATH, SAN FRANCISCO STATE UNIV, 71- *Mem:* Math Asn Am; Am Math Soc. *Res:* Representation theory of groups. *Mailing Add:* Dept of Math San Francisco State Univ San Francisco CA 94132

OPPENHEIM, RONALD WILLIAM, b Des Moines, Iowa, Nov 2, 38; m 68; c 1. PSYCHOBIOLOGY. *Educ:* Drake Univ, BA, 62; Wash Univ, PhD(biopsychol), 67. *Prof Exp:* Res biologist, Sch Med, Wash Univ, 67-68; RES SCIENTIST, RES DIV, NC DEPT OF MENT HEALTH, 68- *Concurrent Pos:* Adj prof, Neurobiol Prog, Univ NC, Chapel Hill, 71- *Mem:* AAAS; Am Inst Biol Sci; Animal Behav Soc; Neurosci Soc. *Res:* Neuroembryology; ontogeny of avian embryonic behavior; early posthatching sensory-motor behavior in Aves; neuroanatomical and neuropharmacological development of the spinal cord. *Mailing Add:* Res Div Dept Mental Health Dorothea Dix Hosp Raleigh NC 27602

OPPENHEIMER, CARL HENRY, JR, b Los Angeles, Calif, Nov 13, 21; m 71; c 3. OCEANOGRAPHY, ECOLOGY. *Educ:* Univ Southern Calif, BA, 47, MA, 49; Univ Calif, PhD(marine microbiol), 51. *Prof Exp:* Asst marine biologist, Scripps Inst Calif, 51-55; sr res scientist, Res Ctr, Pan Am Petrol Corp, Okla, 55-57; res scientist & lectr marine microbiol, Univ Tex, 57-61; assoc prof, Inst Marine Sci, Univ Miami, 61-64; prof biol, Fla State Univ, 64-66, chmn dept oceanog, 66-69, prof oceanog & dir, Edward Ball Marine Lab, 66-71; prof microbiol & dir, Marine Sci Inst, 71-73, PROF MARINE SCI, UNIV TEX, PORT ARANSAS, 73- *Concurrent Pos:* Fulbright fel, Univ Oslo, 52-53; res fel, Sea Fish Hatchery, Arendal, Norway, 55; chmn, Int Symposium Marine Microbiol, 61; mem subcomt marine biol, President's Sci Adv Comt, 65-66; chmn, Conf Unresolved Probs Marine Microbiol, 66; mem, Japan-US Cultural Exchange Prog, 66 & President's Panel Oil Pollution, 68-71; vpres, Gulf Univ Res Corp, 66-70, mem prog planning coun, 70-; mem, Governor's Comn Marine Sci & Technol, Fla, 67-71 & sci comn, NSF, 69-72; panel chmn, Am Assembly-Uses of the Sea, 69; US rep adv panel eco-sci, NATO, 71-74; Univ Tex Rep, Univ Coun Water Resources, 71-; mem, Tex Senate Interim Coastal Zone Study Comn, 71- & adv coun, Southern Interstate Nuclear Bd, 71-; Fulbright fel, Univ Naples, 78. *Mem:* Am Soc Microbiol; Am Soc Limnol & Oceanog; Geochem Soc; Brit Soc Gen Microbiol. *Res:* Distribution and function of marine microorganisms; diseases of marine fishes; biological corrosion; marine productivity cycles; effect of detergents in the oceans; marine microbiology; origin and ecology of oil; biological criteria for coastal zone management. *Mailing Add:* Marine Sci Inst Univ of Tex Port Aransas TX 78373

OPPENHEIMER, FRANK, b New York, NY, Aug 14, 12; m 37; c 2. PHYSICS. *Educ:* Johns Hopkins Univ, BA, 33; Calif Inst Technol, PhD(physics), 39. *Prof Exp:* Asst physics, Stanford Univ, 39-41; res assoc, Univ Calif, Berkeley, 41-47; asst prof, Univ Minn, Minneapolis, 47-49; teacher pub sch, Colo, 57-59; res assoc, 59-61, from assoc prof to prof, 61-80, EMER PROF PHYSICS, UNIV COLO, BOULDER, 80- *Concurrent Pos:* Consult high & elem sch sci teaching develop progs, Educ Serv, Inc, Mass, 60-; Guggenheim fel, 65; hon res assoc, Univ Col, Univ London, 65; on leave as dir, The Exploratorium, San Francisco, 69- *Honors & Awards:* Robert A Millikan Award, Am Asn Physics Teachers & Prentice Hall, 73. *Mem:* AAAS; fel Am Phys Soc. *Res:* Beta ray spectroscopy of radioactive elements; electromagnetic uranium isotope separations; cosmic radiation; high energy particle physics; history of contemporary physics; physics pedagogy; social effects of science. *Mailing Add:* The Exploratorium 3601 Lyon St San Francisco CA 94123

OPPENHEIMER, JACK HANS, b Eglesbach, Ger, Sept 14, 27; US citizen; m 53; c 3. ENDOCRINOLOGY, INTERNAL MEDICINE. *Educ:* Princeton Univ, AB, 49; Columbia Univ, MD, 53; Am Bd Internal Med, dipl, 61. *Prof Exp:* Intern med, Boston City Hosp, 53-54; resident med, Duke Univ Hosp, 57-59; asst clin prof neurol, Sch Med, NY Univ, 62-65; from asst prof to assoc prof, 66-73, PROF MED, ALBERT EINSTEIN COL MED, YESHIVA UNIV, 73-; HEAD ENDOCRINE SERV, MONTEFIORE HOSP & MED CTR, 68- *Concurrent Pos:* Fel med, Mem Ctr & Thyroid-Pituitary Study Group, Sloan-Kettering Inst, 54-55; vis fel, Col Physicians & Surgeons, Columbia Univ, 59-60; asst physician, Endocrinol Lab, Presby Hosp, New York, 59-60; from asst attend physician to attend physician, Div Med, Montefiore Hosp & Med Ctr, 60-68; prin investr USPHS grant, 61-; career scientist, Health Res Coun, New York, 62-72; mem bd trustees, Windward Sch, White Plains, NY, 69-71. *Honors & Awards:* Van Meter Award, Am Thyroid Asn, 65. *Mem:* Am Asn Physicians; Am Soc Clin Invest; fel Am Col Physicians; Am Physiol Soc; Am Thyroid Asn (1st vpres, 74). *Res:* Peripheral metabolism and action of the thyroid hormones. *Mailing Add:* Albert Einstein Col of Med Yeshiva Univ New York NY 10033

OPPENHEIMER, JANE MARION, b Philadelphia, Pa, Sept 19, 11. BIOLOGY. *Educ:* Bryn Mawr Col, BA, 32; Yale Univ, PhD(zool), 35. *Hon Degrees:* ScD, Brown Univ, 76. *Prof Exp:* Sterling fel biol, Yale Univ, 35-36, Am Asn Univ Women Berliner res fel, 36-37; res fel embryol, Univ Rochester, 37-38; instr biol, 38-42, Guggenheim fel, 42-43, actg dean grad sch, 46-47, from asst prof to prof biol, 43-74, prof, 74-80, EMER PROF HIST OF SCI, BRYN MAWR COL, 80- *Concurrent Pos:* Rockefeller Found fel, 50-51; Guggenheim fel, 52-53; sr fel, NSF, 59-60; vis prof biol, Johns Hopkins Univ, 66-67; mem, NIH Hist Life Sci Study Sect, 66-70; exchange prof fac sci, Univ Paris, 69. *Honors & Awards:* Wilbur Lucius Cross Medal, Yale Grad Alumni Asn. *Mem:* Soc Develop Biol; Am Soc Zoologists (treas, 57-59, pres, 74); Hist Sci Soc; Am Asn Anat; Am Asn Hist Med. *Res:* Developmental biology; experimental analysis of teleost development; history of embryology. *Mailing Add:* Biol Bldg Bryn Mawr Col Bryn Mawr PA 19010

OPPENHEIMER, LARRY ERIC, b New York, NY, Aug 18, 42; m 64; c 2. COLLOID CHEMISTRY, PARTICLE SIZE ANALYSIS. *Educ:* Clarkson Col Technol, BS, 63, MS, 65, PhD(phys chem), 67. *Prof Exp:* Sr res chemist, 66-80, RES ASSOC, RES LABS, EASTMAN KODAK CO, 80- *Mem:* AAAS; Am Chem Soc; Sigma Xi. *Res:* Light scattering by liquids and solutions; colloid and surface chemistry; growth of colloidal particles; liquid chromatography; unconventional imaging systems. *Mailing Add:* 93 Carverdale Dr Rochester NY 14618

OPPENHEIMER, MICHAEL, b New York, NY, Feb 28, 46. ATMOSPHERIC CHEMISTRY, PHYSICS. *Educ:* Mass Inst Technol, SB, 66; Univ Chicago, PhD(chem physics), 70. *Prof Exp:* Res fel, Smithsonian Ctr Astrophys, Harvard Col Observ, 71-73, physicist, 73-81, lectr, Dept Astron, Harvard Univ, 71-81; SR SCIENTIST, ENVIRON DEFENSE FUND, 81- *Mem:* Am Phys Soc; AAAS; Am Geophys Union; Am Meteorol Soc; Air Pollution Control Asn. *Mailing Add:* Environ Defense Fund 444 Park Ave South New York NY 10016

OPPENHEIMER, MORTON JOSEPH, b Philadelphia, Pa, June 9, 05; m 34; c 2. PHYSIOLOGY. *Educ:* Ursinus Col, AB, 27; Temple Univ, MD, 32, EdM, 38. *Hon Degrees:* ScD, Ursinus Col, 57. *Prof Exp:* From instr to prof, 33-73, chmn dept, 44-70, EMER PROF PHYSIOL, SCH MED, TEMPLE UNIV, 73- *Concurrent Pos:* China Med Bd fel, Manila & Bangkok, 66, 70; with Inst Exp Med, Mayo Clin, 40, 42, 44, 46; consult, US Naval Hosp, Philadelphia & US Vet Admin Hosp, Philadelphia, Nat Heart Inst, Cardiovasc Training Comt & Nat Libr Med, Nat Med AV Ctr & Allied Chem Corp, NJ, 80-81; adj prof, biomed group, Drexel Inst. *Res:* Circulation; heart; radiopaque media. *Mailing Add:* Dept of Physiol Temple Univ Sch of Med Philadelphia PA 19140

OPPENHEIMER, NORMAN JOSEPH, b Summit, NJ, Aug 20, 46; m 69; c 1. BIOCHEMISTRY. *Educ:* Brown Univ, BS, 68; Univ Calif, San Diego, PhD(chem), 73. *Prof Exp:* Res assoc biochem, Ind Univ, 73-75; asst prof, 75-80, ASSOC PROF PHARMACEUT CHEM, UNIV CALIF, SAN FRANCISCO, 80- *Concurrent Pos:* NIH career develop award, 79-84. *Mem:* Am Chem Soc; AAAS; Am Soc Biol Chemists. *Res:* Small molecule/macromolecule interactions; redox and nonredox chemistry and metabolic roles of pyridine coenzymes; mechanism of anticancer drugs. *Mailing Add:* Dept of Pharmaceut Chem Univ of Calif San Francisco CA 94143

OPPENHEIMER, PHILLIP R, b San Francisco, Calif, July 9, 48; m 72; c 1. CLINICAL PHARMACY. *Educ:* Univ Calif, PharmD, 72. *Prof Exp:* Residency, Sch Pharm, Univ Calif Med Ctr, 73; instr, 73-75, ASST PROF PHARM, UNIV SOUTHERN CALIF, 75- *Concurrent Pos:* Chmn comt pharm educ, Calif Pharm Asn, 76-78; consult, Wadsworth Med Ctr, Vet Admin, 77- *Mem:* Am Soc Hosp Pharmacists; Am Asn Col Pharm; Am Pharmaceut Asn. *Res:* Clinical therapeutics of drugs, with emphasis on pediatric pharmacology. *Mailing Add:* Dept of Pharm 1985 Zonal Ave Los Angeles CA 90033

OPPENHEIMER, STEVEN BERNARD, b Brooklyn, NY, Mar 23, 44; m 71. DEVELOPMENTAL BIOLOGY, CANCER. *Educ:* City Univ New York, BS, 65; Johns Hopkins Univ, PhD(biol), 69. *Prof Exp:* Am Cancer Soc fel biol, Univ Calif, San Diego, 69-71; from asst prof to assoc prof, 71-77, PROF BIOL, CALIF STATE UNIV, NORTHRIDGE, 77- *Concurrent Pos:* Trustee, Calif State Univ Found, Northridge, 74-; res grants, Nat Cancer Inst Res, 72- & Nat Sci Found, 81- *Mem:* AAAS; Soc Develop Biol; Am Soc Cell Biol; Am Soc Zoologists; NY Acad Sci. *Res:* Molecular basis of intercellular adhesion and the role of cell surface carbohydrates in morphogenesis and malignancy. *Mailing Add:* Dept of Biol Calif State Univ Northridge CA 91330

OPPENLANDER, JOSEPH CLARENCE, b Bucyrus, Ohio, Apr 6, 31; m 54; c 3. CIVIL ENGINEERING. *Educ:* Case Inst Technol, BSCE, 53; Purdue Univ, Lafayette, MSCE, 57; Univ Ill, Urbana, PhD(civil eng), 62. *Prof Exp:* Instr civil eng, Purdue Univ, 55-57; traffic planner, Allegheny County Planning Dept, 57-58; res assoc, Univ Ill, 58-62; assoc prof, Purdue Univ, 62-69; chmn dept, 69-79, PROF CIVIL ENG, UNIV VT, 69- *Concurrent Pos:* VPres, Trans/Op Inc, 70- *Mem:* Am Soc Civil Engrs; Inst Transp Eng; Sigma Xi. *Res:* Transportation planning, design and operations; urban planning; optimization of civil engineering systems; traffic accident reconstruction. *Mailing Add:* Dept of Civil Eng Univ of Vt Burlington VT 05405

OPPERMANN, JAMES ALEX, b Milwaukee, Wis, Nov 18, 42; m 66; c 2. PHARMACOLOGY, BIOCHEMISTRY. *Educ:* Univ Wis-Madison, BS, 65, MS, 67, PhD(pharmacol), 70. *Prof Exp:* Sr res investr, 70-75, group leader drug metab, 75-81, SECT HEAD DRUG METAB, DEPT DRUG METAB, G D SEARLE & CO, 81- *Res:* Drug metabolism. *Mailing Add:* G D Searle & Co PO Box 5110 Chicago IL 60680

OPPERMANN, ROBERT ARTHUR, microbiology, biochemistry, see previous edition

OPPOLD, W(ILLIAM) A, b Ft Dodge, Iowa, Dec 28, 20; m 43; c 2. CHEMICAL ENGINEERING. *Educ:* Iowa State Col, BChE, 43. *Prof Exp:* Chem engr, Mallinckrodt Chem Works, 43-52; chief opers br, US Atomic Energy Comn, 52-54; works mgr, North Works, Wyandotte Chem Corp, 54-56 & Geismar Works, 56-60; vpres mfg, Jack's Cookie Corp, 60-64; vpres oper serv div, Olin Corp, 64-66, vpres mfg & eng, 66-70, vpres mfg, Chem Group, 70-73; managing dir, Anode Serv (Bermuda) Ltd, 73-76; vpres mfg, 76-78, vpres mfg & eng, 78-80, SR VPRES MFG & ENG, CHEM GROUP, OLIN CORP, 80- *Mem:* Am Inst Chem Engrs. *Res:* Chemical plant management. *Mailing Add:* Olin Corp 120 Long Ridge Rd Stamford CT 06904

OPTRNY, JAROSLAV, b Plzen, Czechoslovakia, Sept 5, 46; Can citizen; c 2. FORMAL LANGUAGES, ALGORITHMIC COMPLEXITY. *Educ:* Charles Univ, Praque, MSc, 68; Univ Waterloo, PhD(comput sci), 75. *Prof Exp:* Lectr math & comput sci, Tech Univ, Plzen, 68-70; asst prof comput sci, Univ Alta, Can, 75-77; ASST PROF COMPUT SCI, CONCORDIA UNIV, MONTREAL, 77- *Concurrent Pos:* Fel, Univ Waterloo, 75. *Mem:* Asn Comput Mach; Europ Asn Theoret Comput Sci. *Res:* Parallel rewriting systems (L-languages); error recovery for compilers; bandwidth problem for graphs. *Mailing Add:* 1455 de Maisonneuve Blvd W Montreal PQ H3G 1M8 Can

ORAHOVATS, PETER DIMITER, b Sofia, Bulgaria, Apr 22, 22; nat US; m 45; c 1. PHYSIOLOGY, PHARMACOLOGY. *Educ:* St Klement Univ, Bulgaria, MD, 45. *Prof Exp:* Instr clin physiol, St Clement Univ, Bulgaria, 45-46; mem staff physiol, Col Physicians & Surgeons, Columbia Univ, 46-51; res assoc physiol & pharmacol, Merck Inst Therapeut Res, 51-59; med dir, 59-60, med & sci dir, 61-62, vpres & dir res & develop div, 62-66, VPRES & DIR SCI DIV, BRISTOL-MYERS PROD DIV, BRISTOL-MYERS CO, 66- *Concurrent Pos:* USPHS fel, Col Physicians & Surgeons, Columbia Univ, 49-51; adj prof pharmacol, Div Biol Sci, Univ Calif, Santa Barbara, 80- *Mem:* Am Soc Pharmacol & Exp Therapeut; Harvey Soc; Royal Soc Med; Pan Am Med Asn. *Res:* Medicine; cardiovascular physiology; blood volume and formation; essential hypertension; pharmacology of analgesics and narcotics. *Mailing Add:* Bristol-Myers Co 345 Park Ave New York NY 10154

O'RAND, MICHAEL GENE, b Carlisle, Eng, Sept 24, 45; US citizen; m 67; c 1. REPRODUCTIVE BIOLOGY, DEVELOPMENTAL BIOLOGY. *Educ:* Univ Calif, Berkeley, AB, 67; Ore State Univ, MS, 69; Temple Univ, PhD(biol), 72. *Prof Exp:* NIH fel, Inst Molecular & Cellular Evolution, Univ Miami, 72-75; asst prof anat, Col Med, Univ Fla, 75-79; ASST PROF ANAT, UNIV NC, 79- *Concurrent Pos:* NIH res grant, Univ Fla, 77-79 & Univ NC, 80-82. *Mem:* AAAS; Am Soc Cell Biol; Soc Study Reproduction. *Res:* Fertilization; immunoreproductive biology; sperm antigens. *Mailing Add:* Dept Anat Lab Cell Biol Univ NC Chapel Hill NC 27514

O'RANGERS, JOHN JOSEPH, b Philadelphia, Pa, June 11, 36; m 65; c 2. IMMUNOCHEMISTRY. *Educ:* St Joseph's Univ, BS, 58; Hahnemann Med Col, PhD(biochem), 72. *Prof Exp:* Instr biochem, Hahnemann Med Col, 72-74; asst prof biochem, Philadelphia Col Osteop Med, 74-75; sr scientist immunochem, Carter Wallace Co, Princeton, NJ, 75-76; SR RES BIOCHEMIST IMMUNOCHEM, FOOD & DRUG ADMIN, 76- *Concurrent Pos:* Lectr, St Joseph's Univ, 73-75. *Mem:* Asn Off Anal Chemists; NY Acad Sci; Sigma Xi; Nat Immunoassay Soc; Nat Comt Clin Lab Standards. *Res:* Effect of hormones on the immune response; immunochemical methods of analysis for antibiotics; hormones and metabolites in tissues. *Mailing Add:* 19212 Walters Ave Poolesville MD 20837

ORATZ, MURRAY, b New York, NY, Apr 17, 27; m 52; c 2. BIOCHEMISTRY. *Educ:* Long Island Univ, BS, 48; Clarkson Col Technol, MS, 50; NY Univ, PhD(biochem), 57. *Prof Exp:* ASST CHIEF NUCLEAR MED SERV, VET ADMIN HOSP, 55- *Concurrent Pos:* Adj prof biochem, Brookdale Ctr NY Univ, Col of Dent, 67- *Mem:* Sigma Xi; NY Acad Sci; Soc Nuclear Med; Am Asn Study Liver Dis; Am Chem Soc. *Res:* Regulation and stimuli for the production of plasma proteins; dynamics of cardiac metabolism. *Mailing Add:* Nuclear Med Serv Vet Admin Hosp 1st Ave at E 24th New York NY 10010

ORAVA, R(AIMO) NORMAN, b Toronto, Ont, Sept 22, 35; m 59; c 2. PHYSICAL METALLURGY. *Educ:* Univ Toronto, BASc, 57; Univ BC, MASc, 59; Univ London, DIC & PhD(phys metall), 63. *Prof Exp:* Sci officer, Eng Physics Sect, Phys Metall Res Labs, Can Dept Mines & Tech Surv, 57; lectr math, Univ Waterloo, 59, lectr appl physics, 59-60; sr scientist, Nonferrous Metall Div, Battelle Mem Inst, Ohio, 63-64; res metallurgist, Mat Sci & Eng Div, Franklin Inst, Pa, 64-65, sr res metallurgist, 65-66; res metallurgist, Metall & Mat Sci Div, Denver Res Inst, Univ Denver, 66-74, lectr, 70-74; actg vpres & dean eng, 75-77, PROF METALL ENG, S DAK SCH MINES & TECHNOL, 74-, DEAN GRAD DIV & DIR RES, 77- *Concurrent Pos:* NSF, Army, Navy and Dept Energy grants; dir, Mining, Mineral Resources & Res Inst, 80-; dir, Masec Corp, 77-, chmn bd, 80- *Mem:* Am Soc Metals; Am Inst Mining, Metall & Petrol Engrs; Sigma Xi; Nat Coun Univ Res Adminr; Coun Grad Schs. *Res:* Mechanical metallurgy; thermomechanics processing; shock effects; explosive forming. *Mailing Add:* SDak Sch of Mines & Technol Rapid City SD 57701

ORBACH, RAYMOND LEE, b Los Angeles, Calif, July 12, 34; m 56; c 3. SOLID STATE PHYSICS. *Educ:* Calif Inst Technol, BS, 56; Univ Calif, Berkeley, PhD(physics), 60. *Prof Exp:* NSF fels, Oxford Univ, 60-61, asst prof appl physics, Harvard Univ, 61-63; assoc prof, 63-66, PROF PHYSICS, UNIV CALIF, LOS ANGELES, 66- *Concurrent Pos:* Alfred P Sloan Found fels, 63-67; asst vchancellor acad change & curric develop, Univ Calif, Los Angeles, 70-72; Guggenheim Found fel, 73-74; mem, Nat Comn Res, 78-80; assoc div ed, Phys Review Letters, 80- *Mem:* Am Phys Soc; Sigma Xi. *Res:* Paramagnetic resonance and spin-lattice relaxation; collective properties of ordered magnetic systems; lattice vibrations and their interactions; optical properties of solids; thermal conductivity of paramagnetic salts; magnetic resonance properties of dilute magnetic alloys; non-equilibrium superconductivity; transport in random systems. *Mailing Add:* Dept of Physics Univ of Calif Los Angeles CA 90024

ORBAN, EDWARD, b Youngstown, Ohio, Mar 5, 15; m 41; c 2. APPLIED CHEMISTRY. *Educ:* Univ Buffalo, BS, 40; Univ Md, PhD(phys chem), 44. *Prof Exp:* Anal chemist, E I du Pont de Nemours & Co, NY, 40-41; asst, Univ Md, 41-44; res chemist, Socony-Mobil Co, Inc, NJ, 44-46; res chemist, Monsanto Co, 46-48, group leader, 48-52, chief tech sect, 52-53 & chem sect, 53-54, sr develop investr, 54-57, mgr develop, Cent Res Dept, 57-69, planning mgr, New Enterprises Div, 69-71, PLANNING MGR INDUST CHEMS, MONSANTO CO, 71- *Mem:* Am Chem Soc; Electrochem Soc; Instrument Soc Am. *Res:* Electrochemistry; metals; instrumentation; electronic materials; single crystal semiconductor materials preparation. *Mailing Add:* 90 Thorncliff Lane Kirkwood MO 63122

ORBAN, JOHN EDWARD, b Cleveland, Ohio, Jan 22, 52; m 78. STATISTICS. *Educ:* Univ Dayton, BS, 74; Ohio State Univ, MS, 76, PhD(statist), 78. *Prof Exp:* Res assoc statist, Nat Bur Standards, 78-80; MEM FAC, DEPT MATH SCI, STATE UNIV NY BINGHAMTON, 80- *Mem:* Am Statist Asn; Inst Math Statist. *Res:* Non-parametric statistics. *Mailing Add:* Dept Math Sci State Univ NY Binghamton NY 13901

ORBIN, DAVID PAUL, nematology, botany, see previous edition

ORCHARD, HENRY JOHN, b Oldbury, Eng, May 7, 22; m 47; c 1. ELECTRICAL ENGINEERING. *Educ:* Univ London, BSc, 46, MSc, 51. *Prof Exp:* Sr sci off, eng res dept, Brit Post Off, 51-56, prin sci off, 56-61; consult network design, Lenkurt Elec Co, Calif, 61-70; PROF ENG & APPL SCI, UNIV CALIF, LOS ANGELES, 70- *Concurrent Pos:* Lectr, Stanford Univ, 67-70; consult, GTE Lenkurt Inc, 70- *Mem:* Fel Brit Inst Elec Engrs; fel Inst Elec & Electronics Engrs. *Res:* Circuit theory; network design; passive, active and digital filters. *Mailing Add:* Dept Elec Eng Univ of Calif Los Angeles CA 90024

ORCHIN, MILTON, b Barnesboro, Pa, June 4, 14; m 41; c 2. ORGANIC CHEMISTRY. *Educ:* Ohio State Univ, BA, 36, MA, 37, PhD(org chem), 39. *Prof Exp:* Chemist, Food & Drug Admin, USDA, 39-42, org res chemist, Bur Animal Indust, 42-43; chief org chem sect synthetic liquid fuels, US Bur Mines, 43-53; assoc prof appl sci, 53-56, head dept chem, 56-62, dir basic sci lab, 62-71, prof chem, 56-81, EMER PROF CHEM & DISTINGUISHED SERV PROF, UNIV CINCINNATI, 81-, DIR, HOKE S GREENE LAB CATALYSIS, 71- *Concurrent Pos:* Guggenheim fel, Sieff Inst, 47-48; vis prof, Ohio State Univ, 66, Israel Inst Technol, 68 & Univ Calif, Berkeley, 69; mem bd gov, Ben Gurion Univ of the Negev, Beersheva, Israel, 75-79. *Honors & Awards:* E V Murphree Award, Am Chem Soc, 80; Morley Medal, 80. *Mem:* AAAS. *Res:* chemistry of carbon monoxide; ultraviolet absorption spectroscopy; catalysis. *Mailing Add:* Dept of Chem Univ of Cincinnati Cincinnati OH 45221

ORCUTT, BRUCE CALL, b New York, NY. DATABASE SYSTEMS, BIOLOGY. *Educ:* Cornell Univ, AB, 61; Purdue Univ, MS, 64; Univ Va, PhD(math), 69. *Prof Exp:* Asst prof math & statist, Georgetown Univ, 69-75; SR RES SCIENTIST, NAT BIOMED RES FOUND, GEORGETOWN MED CTR, 75- *Concurrent Pos:* Lectr, comput sci, Georgetown Univ. *Mem:* Asn Comput Mach. *Res:* Applications of computers in molecular biology. *Mailing Add:* Nat Biomed Res Found Georgetown Univ Med Ctr Washington DC 20007

ORCUTT, DAVID MICHAEL, b Oklahoma City, Okla, June 10, 43; m 67; c 1. PLANT PHYSIOLOGY. *Educ:* Univ Okla, BS, 66; Incarnate Word Col, MS, 70; Univ Md, PhD(plant physiol), 73. *Prof Exp:* Technician plant physiol, US Air Force Sch Aerospace Med, 67-70; asst prof, 73-81, ASSOC PROF PLANT PHYSIOL, VA POLYTECH INST & STATE UNIV, 81- *Mem:* Am Soc Plant Physiologists; Phycol Soc Am. *Res:* The role of plant steroids in growth regulation, host parasite interactions and physiology in higher plants and aquatic plants. *Mailing Add:* Dept of Plant Path & Physiol Va Polytech Inst & State Univ Blacksburg VA 24061

ORCUTT, DONALD ADELBERT, b Traverse City, Mich, June 25, 26; m 50; c 4. BIOCHEMISTRY, INDUSTRIAL PHARMACY. *Educ:* Purdue Univ, Lafayette, BS, 50. *Prof Exp:* Chemist, Armour Pharmaceut, 51-52 & Whitehall Pharmacal Co, 52-58; supvr chem, Miles Labs, Inc, 58-60, asst to dir pharm res & develop, 60-65; vpres & dir labs, Standard Pharmacal Corp, 65-77; mgr, Tablet Tech Serv, Parke-Davis, 78-81; MGR PHARMACEUT RES & DEVELOP, L PERRIGO CO, 81- *Mem:* Am Pharmaceut Asn; Am Chem Soc; Acad Pharmaceut Sci. *Res:* Pharmaceutical formulation, chemistry and instrumentation; food and drug law. *Mailing Add:* 1322 34th St Allegan MI 49010

ORCUTT, FREDERIC SCOTT, JR, b Roanoke, Va, Nov 29, 40; m 65; c 2. ETHOLOGY, ORNITHOLOGY. *Educ:* Cornell Univ, BS, 63, MS, 65, PhD(ethology), 69. *Prof Exp:* Lectr biol, Univ Sask, 69-70; sr res assoc avian reproductive physiol, Univ Wash, 70-71; asst prof, 71-78, ASSOC PROF BIOL, UNIV AKRON, 78- *Mem:* Animal Behav Soc; Am Ornith Union; Cooper Ornith Soc; AAAS; Sigma Xi. *Res:* Avian vocalizations and reproductive isolating mechanisms; hormonal determinants of behavior; avian reproductive physiology; evolution of behavior. *Mailing Add:* Dept of Biol Univ of Akron Akron OH 44325

ORCUTT, HAROLD GEORGE, b Washington, DC, May 6, 18; m 44; c 2. FISH BIOLOGY. *Educ:* Wilson Teachers Col, BS, 41; Stanford Univ, PhD(fisheries biol), 49. *Prof Exp:* Asst biol, Wilson Teachers Col, 38-39; teacher high sch, DC, 40-41; marine investr, State Fish Comn, NH, 41-42; marine biologist, Hopkins Marine Sta, Calif Dept Fish & Game, 48-49 & mus natural hist, Stanford Univ, 49-58, dir marine biol res lab, Stanford Univ, 58-61, dir marine resources res lab, 61-67, LAB SUPVR, OPERS RES BR, MARINE RESOURCES REGION, CALIF DEPT FISH & GAME, 67- *Mem:* Am Inst Fishery Res Biol; Sigma Xi. *Res:* Research conservation and administration of marine fish and shellfish. *Mailing Add:* 2368 Santa Ana Palo Alto CA 94303

ORCUTT, JOHN ARTHUR, b Holyoke, Colo, Aug 29, 43; m 67; c 2. SEISMOLOGY, INVERSE THEORY. *Educ:* US Naval Acad, BS, 66; Univ Liverpool, MSc, 68; Univ Calif, San Diego, PhD(earth sci), 76. *Prof Exp:* Fel, 76-77, RES GEOPHYSICIST, SCRIPPS INST OCEANOG, 77-, ASSOC PROF GEOPHYSICS, 82- *Concurrent Pos:* Vis res assoc, Calif Inst Technol, 78-; assoc ed, J Geophys Res, 81-; mem, Int Crustal Res Drilling Group, Geophysics Planning Adv Comt, Ocean Margin Drilling Prog, 79- *Honors & Awards:* Newcomb Cleveland Prize, AAAS, 80. *Mem:* Am Geophys Union; Soc Explor Geophysicists. *Res:* Interaction of acoustic and seismic waves at the sea floor; computation of synthetic seismograms and use in inverse problems; ocean bottom seismology. *Mailing Add:* Geol Res Div A-015 Scripps Inst Oceanog La Jolla CA 92093

ORCUTT, JOHN C, b Monson, Mass, Oct 10, 27; m 53; c 2. CHEMICAL ENGINEERING. *Educ:* Worcester Polytech Inst, BS, 50, MS, 51; Univ Del, PhD(chem eng), 60. *Prof Exp:* Res engr, Atlantic Refining Co, 51-57, supvr petrol process develop, 60-61; res engr rate processes group, Res Triangle Inst, 61-65, dir measurement & controls lab, 65-68, mgr environ eng dept, 71-72; MGR DEVELOP PROCESS ENG, STAUFFER CHEM CO, 72- *Concurrent Pos:* Adj prof, Univ NC, 70 & Duke Univ, 71. *Mem:* Assoc Am Inst Chem Engrs. *Res:* Behavior of fluidized bed systems; applied mathematics to chemical engineering problems; process optimization and control; chemical reaction kinetics; advanced waste treatment research and development. *Mailing Add:* Eng Dept Stauffer Chem Co Dobbs Ferry NY 10522

ORCUTT, RICHARD G(ATTON), b Wellington, Colo, Mar 9, 24; m 51; c 3. SANITARY & CIVIL ENGINEERING. *Educ:* Univ NMex, BS, 45; Univ Calif, MS, 51, PhD, 56. *Prof Exp:* Jr construct engr, Creole Petrol Corp, Venezuela, 46-48; asst sanit engr, State Dept Pub Health, Calif, 51-52; sr asst sanit engr, USPHS, 52-53; jr res engr, Sanit Eng Res Ctr, Univ Calif, 55-56; PROF CIVIL ENG, UNIV NEV, RENO, 56- *Concurrent Pos:* Fel, Univ Fla, 68. *Mem:* Am Soc Civil Engrs; Am Soc Eng Educ. *Res:* Water resources engineering; economics of water quality management; systems analysis; water resources; waste removal. *Mailing Add:* Dept Civil Eng Univ Nev Reno NV 89507

ORD, JOHN ALLYN, b West Elizabeth, Pa, Mar 9, 12; m 37; c 2. PHYSICS, MATHEMATICS. *Educ:* Carnegie Inst Technol, BS, 34, MS, 35, DSc(physics), 39. *Prof Exp:* Instr physics, Carnegie Inst Technol, 37-38; asst prof, NDak State Col, 38-40; dept dir, Southern Signal Corps Sch, US Army, 42-43, asst commandant, 43-44, exec off signal sect, Southwest Pac Area, 45, dir training, Sandia Base, NMex, 46-48, from exec off to dir, Evans Signal Lab, 49-52, tech liaison off & dep theater signal off, US Army Forces, Far East, 52-55, chief res div & dir Army Res Off, Off Chief Res & Develop, 55-58, mem staff & fac, Army War Col, 59-62, chief res div, Army Materiel Command, 62-65; mgr adv concept sect, Systs Tech Ctr, Philco Corp, 65-66; chief scientist, US Army Foreign Sci & Tech Ctr, 66-67, dep for tech opers, 67-71, dep dir, 71-81; RETIRED. *Concurrent Pos:* Res physicist, Flannery Bolt Co, 46. *Mem:* Sigma Xi. *Res:* Infrared spectroscopy; communications electronics; military research administration. *Mailing Add:* RD 9 Box 511-E Carlisle PA 17013

ORDAHL, CHARLES PHILIP, b Chatahoochie County, Ga, Aug 8, 45. MOLECULAR BIOLOGY, DEVELOPMENTAL BIOLOGY. *Educ:* Univ Colo, Boulder, BA, 67, MA, 70; Univ Colo, Denver, PhD(molecular biol), 74. *Prof Exp:* Fel molecular & develop biol, Case Western Reserve Univ, 74-77; ASST PROF MOLECULAR & DEVELOP BIOL, DEPT ANAT, SCH MED, TEMPLE UNIV, 77- *Mem:* Soc Develop Biol; Soc Cell Biol. *Res:* Gene transcription changes involved in embryonic differentiation of muscle. *Mailing Add:* Dept of Anat Temple Univ Sch of Med Philadelphia PA 19140

ORDAL, ERLING JOSEPH, b Paint Creek, Iowa, Aug 20, 06; m 37; c 3. MICROBIOLOGY. *Educ:* Luther Col, Iowa, BA, 27; Univ Minn, PhD(microbiol, bact), 36. *Prof Exp:* Instr bact, Univ Minn, 36-37; from instr to assoc prof, 37-57, prof, 57-77, EMER PROF BACT, UNIV WASH, 77- *Mem:* Am Soc Microbiol; Am Acad Microbiol; Am Soc Limnol & Oceanog; Am Fisheries Soc; Soc Exp Biol & Med. *Res:* Trace elements in enzymes; myxobacteria; fish pathogens; aquatic and marine microbiology. *Mailing Add:* 3883 44th St NE Seattle WA 98105

ORDAL, GEORGE WINFORD, b Seattle, Wash, Aug 5, 43; m 69; c 3. BIOCHEMISTRY, MOLECULAR BIOLOGY. *Educ:* Harvard Col, AB, 65; Stanford Univ, PhD(biochem), 71. *Prof Exp:* Res assoc biochem, Univ Wis, 71-73; asst prof, 73-79, ASSOC PROF BIOCHEM, UNIV ILL, URBANA, 79- *Concurrent Pos:* Am Cancer Soc fel, Univ Wis, 71-72, USPHS fel, 73; NIH prin investr, Inst Gen Med Sci, 73-; res career develop award, NIH, 76-81. *Mem:* Am Soc Microbiol; Am Soc Biol Chemists. *Res:* Biochemistry and genetics of bacterial chemotaxis; cloning of bacillus subtilis DNA; calcium-binding proteins; enzymatic methylation of membrane proteins; methyl transferases and methylestrases; chemoreceptors; adaptation; phototaxis. *Mailing Add:* 190 Med Sci Bldg Univ of Ill Dept of Biochem Urbana IL 61801

ORDEN, ALEX, b Rochester, NY, Aug 9, 16; m 46; c 3. OPERATIONS RESEARCH. *Educ:* Univ Rochester, BS, 37; Univ Mich, MS, 38; Mass Inst Technol, PhD(math), 50. *Prof Exp:* Alternate chief anal sect, Nat Bur Stand, 42-47; instr math, Mass Inst Technol, 48-49; head comput theory sect, Linear Prog, US Dept Air Force, 50-52; mgr, Comput Lab, Burroughs Corp, 52-58; PROF APPL MATH, INST COMPUT RES, GRAD SCH BUS, UNIV CHICAGO, 58- *Concurrent Pos:* Vis prof, London Sch Econ, 64 & Ga Inst Technol, 66, 67 & 71; prog chmn, Nat Comput Conf, 81- *Mem:* Inst Mgt Sci; Asn Comput Mach; Opers Res Soc Am; Math Prog Soc. *Res:* Linear and nonlinear programming; digital computers; models of business organizations. *Mailing Add:* Grad Sch Bus Univ Chicago Chicago IL 60637

ORDER, STANLEY ELIAS, b Vienna, Austria, Nov 1, 34; US citizen; m 58; c 3. RADIOTHERAPY, IMMUNOLOGY. *Educ:* Albright Col, BS, 56; Tufts Univ, MD, 61; Am Bd Radiol, cert therapeut radiol, 70. *Hon Degrees:* ScD, Albright Col, 78 & Elizabethtown Col, 80. *Prof Exp:* Intern, Ind Univ Hosp, 61-62; resident path, Peter Bent Brigham Hosp, 62-63; chief exp studies, US Army Surg Res Unit, 63-65; from instr to asst prof, Harvard Univ, 69-73, assoc prof radiation ther, 73-78; prof, 78-81, WILLARD & LILLIAN HACKERMAN PROF RADIATION ONCOL, JOHNS HOPKINS UNIV, 81- *Concurrent Pos:* Fel radiation ther, Yale Univ, 65-69. *Mem:* Am Radium Soc; Am Soc Therapeut Radiol; Am Soc Clin Oncol; Am Soc Clin Oncol. *Res:* Hodgkins tumor associated antigens; ovarian carcinoma antigens and immunotherapy; radiolabeled antibody therapy in liver cancer. *Mailing Add:* Johns Hopkins Oncol Ctr 601 N Broadway Baltimore MD 21205

ORDILLE, CAROL MARIA, US citizen. BIOSTATISTICS. *Educ:* Temple Univ, BS, 65; Villanova Univ, MS, 67; Ohio State Univ, PhD(biostatist), 75. *Prof Exp:* Statistician, Merck Sharp & Dohme, 67-68; statist consult, 70-72; res statistician, Schering Corp, 72-75; dir statist & data systs, Delbay Res Corp, 75-80; MGR BIOSTATIST, E I DU PONT DE NEMOURS & CO, 80- *Mem:* Am Statist Asn; Biomet Soc; Soc Clin Trials. *Res:* Development of mathematical models to describe biological phenomena and statistical inference based on such models; data retrieval systems interfaced with statistical programs for clinical and laboratory data. *Mailing Add:* 18 S New Haven Ave Ventnor NJ 08406

ORDMAN, ALFRED BRAM, b Washington, DC, Oct 25, 48; m 71; c 3. BIOCHEMISTRY. *Educ:* Carleton Col, BA, 70; Univ Wis-Madison, PhD(biochem), 74. *Prof Exp:* Res assoc biochem, Univ Minn, 74-77; ASST PROF CHEM, BELOIT COL, 77- *Mem:* Am Chem Soc; AAAS; Sigma Xi. *Res:* Enzyme mechanisms of four electron dehydrogenases; microbial predation; co-metabolism; continuous fermentation. *Mailing Add:* Dept of Chem Beloit Col Beloit WI 53511

ORDMAN, EDWARD THORNE, b Norfolk, Va, Sept 10, 44; m 71. MICROCOMPUTERS, TOPOLOGICAL GROUPS. *Educ:* Kenyon Col, AB, 64; Princeton Univ, MA, 66, PhD(math), 69. *Prof Exp:* Mathematician, Nat Bur Stand, 62-69; asst prof, Univ Ky, 69-74, res assoc & dir comput serv, Bur Govt Serv, 74-76; vis asst prof, Memphis State Univ, 76-77 & 81-82; asst prof, 77-81, ASSOC PROF, NEW ENG COL, 81- *Concurrent Pos:* NSF res grant, 70-71; Fulbright-Hays grant, Univ New South Wales, Sydney, Australia, 73; vis assoc prof, Dept Math Sci, Memphis State Univ, 81-82. *Mem:* Asn Comput Mach; Am Math Soc; Math Asn Am; Australian Math Soc. *Res:* Large topological groups; microcomputers. *Mailing Add:* New Eng Col Henniker NH 03242

ORDUNG, PHILIP F(RANKLIN), b Luverne, Minn, Aug 12, 19; m 45; c 2. ELECTRICAL ENGINEERING. *Educ:* SDak State Col, BS, 40; Yale Univ, ME, 42, DEng, 49. *Prof Exp:* Lab asst, Yale Univ, 40-42, from instr to prof elec eng, 42-62; chmn dept, 62-68, PROF ELEC ENG, UNIV CALIF, SANTA BARBARA, 62- *Concurrent Pos:* Consult, Rand Corp, 60; vis prof, Tech Univ Norway, 68 & 69. *Mem:* Fel AAAS; fel Inst Elec & Electronics Engrs; NY Acad Sci. *Res:* Network and solid-state theories. *Mailing Add:* Dept of Elec Eng Univ of Calif Santa Barbara CA 93106

ORDWAY, ELLEN, b New York, NY, Nov 8, 27. ENTOMOLOGY, POLLINATION. *Educ:* Wheaton Col Mass, BA, 50; Cornell Univ, MS, 55; Univ Kans, PhD(entom), 65. *Prof Exp:* Asst field biol, Dept Trop Res, NY Zool Soc, 50-52; asst zool, Southwestern Res Sta, Am Mus Natural Hist, New York, 55-57; ASSOC PROF BIOL, UNIV MINN, MORRIS, 65- *Mem:* Ecol Soc Am; Entom Soc Am; Soc Study Evolution; Soc Syst Zool; Int Union Study Social Insects. *Res:* Insect biology and behavior as related to intraspecific and interspecific associations and development of social behavior; biology of native prairies, especially insect-plant relationships and pollination; prairie ecology. *Mailing Add:* Div of Sci & Math Univ of Minn Morris MN 56267

ORDWAY, NELSON KNEELAND, b New Brunswick, NJ, Oct 26, 12; wid; c 4. PEDIATRICS, PUBLIC HEALTH. *Educ:* Yale Univ, MD, 38. *Prof Exp:* Intern pediat, New Haven Hosp, Conn, 38-39 & Hosp Univ Pa, Philadelphia, 39-41; asst path, Sch Med, Yale Univ, 41-45, instr pediat, 45-47; from asst prof to assoc prof, Sch Med, La State Univ, 47-52, prof & head dept, 52-54; prof, Schs Med, Univ NC, 54-57 & Yale Univ, 58-67; prof pediat & pub health, Schs Med & Health, Univ Okla, 67-74; chief pediat, Gallup Indian Med Ctr, 74-78; CHILD HEALTH CONSULT, PHOENIX AREA INDIAN HEALTH SERV, 78- *Concurrent Pos:* Prof, Sch Med, Univ Valle, Colombia, 64-65; consult diarrheal dis, WHO; consult med educ, Pan-Am Health Orgn; clin prof pediat, Sch Med, Univ NMex, 75-78; bd sci coun, Children's Nutrit Res Ctr, US Dept Agr & Baylor Col Med. *Mem:* Am Pub Health Asn; Soc Pediat Res; Am Pediat Soc; Am Acad Pediat. *Res:* Diarrhea; acid-base and electrolyte disturbances. *Mailing Add:* Phoenix Area Indian Health Serv 3738 N 16th St suite A Phoenix AZ 85016

ORE, FERNANDO, b Trujillo, Peru, Apr 26, 26; US citizen; m 57; c 2. CHEMICAL ENGINEERING. *Educ:* San Marcos Univ, Lima, BS, 49; Univ Wash, MS, 54, PhD(chem eng), 59. *Prof Exp:* Sr res engr, Am Potash & Chem Corp, 59-65, res proj engr, Whittier Res Lab, 65-68, head Crystallization & Math Modeling Sect, 68-70; mgr, Process Develop, Garrett Res & Develop Co, Div Occidental Petrol Corp, 70-76; RES DIR PHOSPHATES, OCCIDENTAL RES CORP, DIV OCCIDENTAL PETROL CORP, 76- *Mem:* Assoc Am Inst Chem Engrs; Am Chem Soc. *Res:* Mathematical modeling and process optimization, computer applications; solvent extraction; crystallization; phosphate technology. *Mailing Add:* PO Box 19601 Irvine CA 92713

ORE, HENRY THOMAS, b Chicago, Ill, Oct 30, 34; m 54; c 2. SEDIMENTOLOGY. *Educ:* Cornell Col, BA, 57; Wash State Univ, MS, 59; Univ Wyo, PhD(geol), 63. *Prof Exp:* From instr to assoc prof, 63-73, chmn dept, 67-70, PROF GEOL, IDAHO STATE UNIV, 73- *Mem:* Geol Soc Am;

Nat Asn Geol Teachers; Int Asn Sedimentol; Am Asn Univ Profs; Sigma Xi. *Res:* Modern depositional environments; braided streams; sedimentary petrography; mechanics of sediment transport. *Mailing Add:* Dept of Geol Idaho State Univ Pocatello ID 83201

OREAR, DENNIS JOHN, b Harrisburg, Pa, Nov 21, 50; m 77. CATALYSIS. *Educ:* Pa State Univ, BS, 72; Stanford Univ, MS, 75, PhD(chem eng), 80. *Prof Exp:* Res engr, Mobil Res & Develop Co, 72-74; res engr, 77-79, SR RES ENGR, CHEVRON RES CO, 79- *Mem:* Am Inst Chem Engrs; Am Chem Soc. *Res:* Development of refining routes for synthetic fuels from coal and shale oil; developing applications for novel zeolites for use in refineries. *Mailing Add:* Chevron Res Co PO Box 1627 Richmond CA 94802

OREAR, JAY, b Chicago, Ill, Nov 6, 25. PARTICLE PHYSICS. *Educ:* Univ Chicago, PhB, 43, SM, 50, PhD(physics), 53. *Prof Exp:* Res assoc physics, Inst Nuclear Studies, Univ Chicago, 53-54; from instr to asst prof, Columbia Univ, 54-58; assoc prof, 58-64, PROF PHYSICS, CORNELL UNIV, 64- *Concurrent Pos:* NSF sr fel, Europ Orgn Nuclear Res, 64-65; ed, Forum on Physics & Soc, Am Phys Soc, 71-74. *Mem:* Am Phys Soc; Fedn Am Scientists (chmn, 67-68). *Res:* Large-angle, high energy proton-proton and pion-proton scattering. *Mailing Add:* Dept of Physics Cornell Univ Ithaca NY 14853

O'REAR, STEWARD WILLIAM, b Winchester, Va, Jan 13, 19; m 41; c 4. CHEMICAL ENGINEERING, CHEMISTRY. *Educ:* Univ Va, BChE, 40. *Prof Exp:* Chem engr, Joseph E Seagram & Son's, Inc, 40-44; chemist, 46-51, asst supvr, 51-59, supvr, 59-76, CHIEF SUPVR, TECH INFO SERV, SAVANNAH RIVER LAB, E I DU PONT DE NEMOURS & CO, INC, 76- *Mem:* AAAS; Am Chem Soc; Am Soc Testing & Mat. *Res:* Technical communication and documentation; atomic energy literature; science communications. *Mailing Add:* 116 Westwood Dr Aiken SC 29801

OREBAUGH, ERROL GLEN, b Bradenton, Fla, Sept 28, 37; m 61; c 3. PHYSICAL INORGANIC CHEMISTRY. *Educ:* Univ Fla, BSCh, 59; Fla State Univ, PhD(inorg chem), 72. *Prof Exp:* Chemist, 60-67, RES CHEMIST, SAVANNAH RIVER LAB, E I DU PONT DE NEMOURS & CO, INC, 72- *Mem:* Fel Am Inst Chemists; Am Chem Soc. *Res:* Research and development problems of the nuclear fuel cycle, including actinide chemistry, nuclear waste management and environmental chemistry; instrumentation and complexation thermodynamics. *Mailing Add:* Savannah River Lab E I du Pont de Nemours & Co Inc Aiken SC 29801

OREHOTSKY, JOHN LEWIS, b Hartford, Conn, July 24, 34; m 59; c 3. METALLURGY, SOLID STATE PHYSICS. *Educ:* Mass Inst Technol, BS, 56; Polytech Inst Brooklyn, MS, 61; Syracuse Univ, PhD(solid state sci), 71. *Prof Exp:* Res scientist, Sylvania Elec Prod, 56-61; staff scientist, Int Bus Mach Corp, 61-69; asst prof solid state, 71-77, ASSOC PROF ENG, WILKES COL, 77- *Mem:* Am Inst Mining, Metall & Petrol Engrs. *Res:* Transformations; critical point phenomena; transport properties; theory of metals and alloys; magnetism, electrochemistry. *Mailing Add:* Dept of Eng Wilkes Col Wilkes-Barre PA 18703

O'REILLY, DONALD EUGENE, b Chicago, Ill, Mar 22, 30; m 52; c 7. CHEMICAL PHYSICS. *Educ:* Purdue Univ, BS, 51; Univ Chicago, PhD(chem physics), 55. *Prof Exp:* Chem physicist, Gulf Res & Develop Co Div, Gulf Oil Corp, 55-60; chemical physicist, 60-70, SR SCIENTIST, ARGONNE NAT LAB, 70- *Mem:* Am Phys Soc; Am Chem Soc. *Res:* Structure and properties of molecules and solids by nuclear and electron magnetic resonance; phase transitions and ferroelectricity; liquid state physics; catalysis and surface chemistry. *Mailing Add:* Argonne Nat Lab 9700 S Cass Ave Argonne IL 60439

O'REILLY, JAMES EMIL, b Cleveland, Ohio, Jan 14, 45; m 68; c 2. ANALYTICAL CHEMISTRY. *Educ:* Univ Notre Dame, BS, 67; Univ Mich, PhD(chem), 71. *Prof Exp:* Assoc chem, Univ Ill, Urbana, 71-73; asst prof, 73-79, ASSOC PROF CHEM, UNIV KY, 79- *Concurrent Pos:* Vis scientist, Food & Drug Admin, 80-81. *Mem:* Am Chem Soc; Sigma Xi. *Res:* Electrochemistry; gas chromatography; analytical methods development; ion selective electrodes; atomic absorption. *Mailing Add:* Dept of Chem Univ of Ky Lexington KY 40506

O'REILLY, JAMES MICHAEL, b Dayton, Ohio, Nov 25, 34; m 54; c 5. POLYMER PHYSICS, POLYMER CHEMISTRY. *Educ:* Univ Dayton, BS, 56; Univ Notre Dame, PhD(phys chem), 60. *Prof Exp:* Develop chemist, Nat Cash Register Co, 54-56; res assoc polymer physics, Gen Elec Res & Develop Ctr, 60-67; mgr polymer physics & phys chem, Res Labs, Xerox Corp, 67-73, technol mgr, 73-75, prin scientist, 75-80; RES ASSOC, RESEARCH LABS, EASTMAN KODAK CO, 80- *Concurrent Pos:* Part-time assoc prof, Univ Rochester, 71-78. *Mem:* AAAS; Soc Rheol; Am Chem Soc; fel Am Phys Soc. *Res:* Microwave spectroscopy; structure and properties of polymers, electrical, mechanical, thermodynamic and rheological properties; biopolymers; electrophotographic and imaging materials. *Mailing Add:* 44 Bromley Rd Pittsford NY 14534

O'REILLY, LEONARD FRANCIS, b Brooklyn, NY, Aug 31, 38. ENVIRONMENTAL ENGINEERING, ALTERNATIVE ENERGY ENGINEERING. *Educ:* City Col New York, BME, 64. *Prof Exp:* Mech engr water pollution, Dept Water Res, City of New York, 61-65; proj engr cryogenics, Grumman Aircraft, Bethpage, NY, 65-66; proj mgr water pollution, Dept Water Res, City of New York, 67-74 & dir solid waste, Environ Protection Admin, 74-76; PRIN ENVIRON & ENERGY, O'REILLY ASSOCS, 76- *Concurrent Pos:* Energy consult, John Ben Snow Found, 77-; hydropower consult, Polytechnic Inst Brooklyn, 77-; panelist, Nat Acad Sci, 77-; adj prof, Sch Health Sci, Hunter Col, 78-; reviewer, NSF, 80- *Mem:* Am Soc Mech Engrs; Water Pollution Control Fedn; Am Soc Hosp Eng; Asn Energy Engrs; Air Pollution Control Asn. *Res:* Development of wind, solar, hydropower, sewage-generated methane as replacement energy for fossil fuels; resource recovery from solid waste and sludge, particularly methane recovery from landfills. *Mailing Add:* 437 Third St Brooklyn NY 11215

O'REILLY, SEAN, b Killarney, Ireland, Feb 19, 22; US citizen; m 51; c 7. NEUROLOGY. *Educ:* Nat Univ Ireland, MB, 49, MD, 52; FRCP. *Prof Exp:* Registr med, Hosp Infectious Dis, Bradford, Eng, 52; registr dermat, Radcliffe Infirmary, Oxford Univ, 52-54; from intern to resident med, St Mary's Hosp, San Francisco, Calif, 54-56; asst resident neurol, Med Ctr, Univ Calif, San Francisco, 56-59; trainee neurochem & neurol, Nat Hosp Nerv Dis, London, Eng, 59-60; clin instr neurol, Med Ctr, Univ Calif, San Francisco, 60-61, asst prof, 61-69; chmn dept, 69-75, PROF NEUROL, GEORGE WASHINGTON UNIV, 69-, CHMN NEUROBIOL RES TRAINING PROG, 71- *Concurrent Pos:* Consult, Clin Ctr, NIH, Walter Reed Gen Hosp & Vet Admin Cent Off Ctr. *Mem:* Fel Am Acad Neurol; Am Neurol Asn; Asn Res Nerv & Ment Dis; Soc Neurosci. *Res:* Biochemistry of basal ganglia disorders; Huntington's chorea; Parkinson's disease; Wilson's disease; physiology of copper and zinc. *Mailing Add:* Dept Neurol George Washington Univ Washington DC 20037

OREJAS-MIRANDA, BRAULIO, b Montevideo, Uruguay, Feb 18, 33; m 59; c 2. HERPETOLOGY. *Educ:* Univ of the Repub, Uruguay, Lic, 59; Cent Univ Venezuela, cert herpet, 61. *Prof Exp:* Cur herpet, Nat Mus Natural Hist, Uruguay, 57-66; prof zool, Cent Univ, Venezuela, 59-61; chief labs, Nat Mus Natural Hist, Uruguay, 67-70; SPECIALIST BIOL, SCI AFFAIRS DEPT, ORGN AM STATES, WASHINGTON, DC, 70- *Concurrent Pos:* Assoc res, Div Reptiles & Amphibians, Smithsonian Inst, 68; fel, Guggenheim Mem Fund, 69; adv, Nat Zoo, Dominican Repub, 72-75. *Mem:* Am Soc Ichthyologists & Herpetologists; Soc Study Amphibians & Reptiles. *Res:* Snakes, particularly the family Leptotyphlopidae, in several fields--taxonomy, geographical distribution, ecology and evolution. *Mailing Add:* 7522 Sweet Briar Dr College Park MD 20740

O'RELL, DENNIS DEE, b Sacramento, Calif, Nov 28, 41; m 65; c 2. CHEMISTRY, POLYMER CHEMISTRY. *Educ:* Sacramento State Col, BA, 64; Univ Ore, PhD(org chem), 70. *Prof Exp:* Sr res chemist, Ciba-Geigy Corp, 70-72, supvr, Polymer Additives Dept, 72-75; res mgr, Polyfibron Div, 75-77, tech mgr, 77-79, oper mgr cellulose & new prod, 79-81, MGR MKT & TECH ACTIV, W R GRACE & CO, 81- *Mem:* Am Chem Soc. *Res:* Synthetic organic chemistry; alkaloids; heterocyclic chemistry; monomer synthesis. *Mailing Add:* W R Grace & Co 55 Hayden Ave Lexington MA 02173

OREM, MICHAEL WILLIAM, b Sturgis, SDak, Nov 30, 42; m 66; c 2. INTERFACIAL PHYSICAL CHEMISTRY, APPLIED SURFACE SCIENCE. *Educ:* Colo Col, BS, 64; Univ Southern Calif, PhD(surface chem), 69. *Prof Exp:* sr res chemist, Res Labs, 69-76, GROUP LEADER & DEVELOP COORDR, MFG TECHNOL DIV, EASTMAN KODAK CO, 76- *Mem:* Am Chem Soc; Soc Photog Scientists & Engrs. *Res:* Applied surface science: Experimental studies of surfactant properties and interfacial phenomena in continuous-web coating technology and liquid-liquid emulsification technology, particularly in the manufacture of photographic film and paper products. *Mailing Add:* 406 Brookview Dr Rochester NY 14617

OREN, SHMUEL SHIMON, b Bucharest, Romania, Feb 20, 44; US & Israeli citizen; m 68; c 1. OPERATIONS RESEARCH. *Educ:* Israel Inst Technol, BSc, 65, MS, 69; Stanford Univ, MS & PhD(eng econ systs), 72. *Prof Exp:* Tech officer mech eng, Israel Defence Force, 65-69; asst optimization, Stanford Univ, 70-71; res scientist opers res, Palo Alto Res Ctr, Xerox Corp, 72-80; ASSOC PROF ENG ECON SYSTS, TERMAN ENG CTR, STANFORD UNIV, 80- *Concurrent Pos:* Consult assoc prof, Stanford Univ, 72-80 & Xerox Corp, 80-81. *Mem:* Psychomet Soc; Inst Elec & Electronics Engrs; Opers Res Soc Am; Inst Mgt Sci; Math Programming Soc. *Res:* Mathematical modelling optimization techniques; market analysis; pricing strategies; economics of telecommunication; use of quantitative techniques for problem solving and policy analysis. *Mailing Add:* Dept Eng Econ Systs Terman Eng Ctr Stanford Univ Stanford CA 94305

ORENSTEIN, ALBERT, b New York, NY; m 62. PHYSICS. *Educ:* NY Univ, PhD(physics), 63. *Prof Exp:* ASST PROF PHYSICS, QUEENS COL, NY, 58- *Concurrent Pos:* Res assoc, NY Univ, 62- *Res:* Solid state physics. *Mailing Add:* Dept of Physics Queens Col Flushing NY 11367

ORENSTEIN, JAN MARK, b Boston, Mass, Jan 24, 42; m 65; c 2. ULTRASTRUCTURAL MORPHOLOGY. *Educ:* Johns Hopkins Univ, BA, 63; Downstate Med Ctr, State Univ NY, PhD(path), 69, MD, 71. *Prof Exp:* Intern resident path, Presby Hosp New York, 71-73; res assoc cell biol, Lab Biochem, Nat Cancer Inst, NIH, 73-76, resident path, Lab Path, 76-77; asst prof, 77-80, ASSOC PROF PATH, MED CTR, GEORGE WASHINGTON UNIV, 80- *Mem:* Am Soc Cell Biologists; Am Asn Pathologists; Electron Miros Soc Am; Int Soc Heart Res; NY Acad Sci. *Res:* Ultrastructural morphology of myocardial cells and its correlation with physiologic function. *Mailing Add:* Dept Path George Washington Univ Med Ctr 2300 Eye St NW Washington DC 20037

ORESKES, IRWIN, biochemistry, immunology, see previous edition

OREY, STEVEN, b Berlin, Ger, July 17, 28; nat US; m 50; c 1. MATHEMATICS. *Educ:* Cornell Univ, BA, 49, MA, 51, PhD, 53. *Prof Exp:* Instr math, Cornell Univ, 53-54; instr, Univ Minn, 54-56; vis asst prof, Univ Calif, 57-58; vis asst prof, 58-59, assoc prof, 59-65, PROF MATH, UNIV MINN, MINNEAPOLIS, 65- *Mem:* Am Math Soc; Asn Symbolic Logic. *Res:* Mathematical logic; probability theory. *Mailing Add:* Dept of Math Univ of Minn Minneapolis MN 55455

ORGAN, JAMES ALBERT, b Newark, NJ, Mar 29, 31; m 56; c 2. ZOOLOGY. *Educ:* Rutgers Univ, AB, 56; Univ Mich, MS, 58, PhD(zool), 60. *Prof Exp:* Instr zool, Univ Mich, 60-61; from instr to assoc prof biol, 61-71, PROF BIOL, CITY COL NEW YROK, 71- *Mem:* Ecol Soc Am; Am Soc Ichthyol & Herpet; Soc Study Evolution; Am Soc Zool; NY Acad Sci. *Res:* Population ecology; animal behavior; herpetology. *Mailing Add:* Dept of Biol City Col of New York New York NY 10031

ORGANICK, ELLIOTT I(RVING), b Brooklyn, NY, Feb 25, 25; m 53; c 2. COMPUTER SCIENCE. *Educ:* Univ Mich, BS, 44, MS, 47, PhD(chem eng), 50. *Prof Exp:* Chemist, Manhattan Proj, Ill, 44-45; chem engr, M W Kellogg Co, 45-46; sr engr, United Gas Corp, 50-53, sr res engr, 53-55; assoc prof chem eng & dir comput ctr, Houston, 55-63, prof comput sci & chem eng, 63-71, chmn dept comput sci, 67-69; prof comput sci, Univ Utah, 71-80; MEM STAFF, INFERNO MFG CORP, 80- *Concurrent Pos:* Asst dir, Ford Found Prof Comput in Eng Educ, Univ Mich, 60; vis prof, Mass Inst Technol, 68-69; ed-in-chief, ACM Comput Surveys, 72-76; vis prof elec engr, Stanford Univ, 77-78; consult, Burroughs Corp. *Mem:* AAAS; Am Chem Soc; Asn Comput Mach; Am Inst Chem Eng; Soc Indust & Appl Math. *Res:* Computer languages, organization and programming. *Mailing Add:* Inferno Mfg Corp 115 Ricor St Shreveport LA 71107

ORGEBIN-CRIST, MARIE-CLAIRE, b Vannes, France, Mar 20, 36. BIOLOGY, ENDOCRINOLOGY. *Educ:* Sorbonne, Lic Natural Sci & Lic Biol, 57; Univ Lyons, DSc, 61. *Prof Exp:* Res assoc, Med Div, Pop Coun, 62-63; res assoc, 63-64, res instr, 64-66, from asst prof to assoc prof, 66-73, PROF OBSTET & GYNEC & LUCIUS E BURCH CHAIR REPRODUCTIVE BIOL, SCH MED, VANDERBILT UNIV, 73-, DIR CTR FOR POP & REPRODUCTIVE BIOL RES, 73- *Concurrent Pos:* NIH career develop award, 68-73; mem contract rev comt, Ctr Pop Res, NIH, 68-72; mem pop res & training comt, Nat Inst Child Health & Human Develop, 70-74, chmn, 72-74; mem, Int Comt Andrology, 74-, reproductive biol study sect, Nat Inst Child Health & Human Develop, 78- *Mem:* Brit Soc Study Fertil; Am Asn Anat; Soc Study Reproduction. *Res:* Male reproductive physiology. *Mailing Add:* Dept of Obstet & Gynec Vanderbilt Univ Sch Med Nashville TN 37232

ORGEL, LESLIE E, b London, Eng, Jan 12, 27; m 50; c 3. CHEMISTRY. *Educ:* Oxford Univ, BA, 48, PhD(chem), 51. *Prof Exp:* Reader chem, Cambridge Univ, 51-64; SR FEL, SALK INST BIOL STUDIES, 65- *Concurrent Pos:* Adj prof, Univ Calif, San Diego, 65- *Mem:* Fel Royal Soc Chem. *Res:* Prebiotic chemistry; the chemistry of the origins of life. *Mailing Add:* Salk Inst for Biol Studies PO Box 85800 San Diego CA 92138

ORGELL, WALLACE HERMAN, b Eldora, Iowa, Dec 28, 28; m 60. PLANT PHYSIOLOGY. *Educ:* Iowa State Univ, BS, 50; Pa State Univ, MS, 52; Univ Calif, PhD(plant physiol), 54. *Prof Exp:* Asst plant physiol, USDA, Pa State Univ, 50-52; asst bot, Univ Calif, 52-54; NSF fel org chem, Univ Ill, 54-55; plant biochemist, US Chem Corps, Ft Detrick, 55-57 & dept zool & entom, Iowa State Univ, 57-63; assoc prof biol sci, Fla Atlantic Univ, 63-66; prof biol, Hiram Scott Col, 66-67; assoc prof, 67-73, PROF BIOL, MIAMI-DADE COMMUNITY COL, 73- *Mem:* Nat Sci Teachers Asn; Nat Asn Biol Teachers. *Res:* Biochemical aspects of ecology. *Mailing Add:* Miami-Dade Community Col Dept Biol South Campus Miami FL 33176

ORGILL, MONTIE M, b Mammoth, Utah, Feb 25, 29; m 56; c 5. ATMOSPHERIC PHYSICS, AIR POLLUTION. *Educ:* Brigham Young Univ, BS, 51; Univ Utah, MS, 57; Colo State Univ, PhD, 71. *Prof Exp:* Consult & forecaster, Intermt Weather, Inc, Utah, 56-58; asst prof meteorol, Univ Hawaii, 58-62; meteorologist, Colo State Univ, 62-72; sr res scientist, 72-80, PROJ MGR, PAC NORTHWEST LABS, BATELLE MEM INST, 80- *Mem:* Am Meteorol Soc; Am Geophys Union; AAAS; Am Pollution Control Asn. *Res:* Synoptic meteorology; fluid mechanics; micrometeorology and mesometeorology; weather modification; atmospheric resuspension and diffusion research; aircraft sampling research; environmental assessment; applied meteorology; complex terrain meteorology. *Mailing Add:* 1824 Wright Ave Richland WA 99352

ORIANI, RICHARD ANTHONY, b El Salvador, Cent Am, July 19, 20; nat US; m 49; c 4. PHYSICAL CHEMISTRY. *Educ:* City Col New York, BChE, 43; Stevens Inst Technol, MS, 46; Princeton Univ, MA & PhD(phys chem), 48. *Prof Exp:* Lab asst chem eng, City Col New York, 43; res chemist, Bakelite Corp Div Union Carbide & Carbon Corp, 43-46; asst, Princeton Univ, 46-48; res assoc, Gen Elec Co, 48-59; mgr phys chem, Res Lab, US Steel Corp, 59-75, sr res consult, 75-80; PROF & DIR CORROSION RES CTR, UNIV MINN, 80- *Concurrent Pos:* Vis instr, Rensselaer Polytech Inst, 53-54; mem Nat Acad Sci adv panel, Nat Bur Stand, 67-73; consult, 80- *Mem:* Am Phys Soc; Am Chem Soc; fel Am Inst Chem; fel NY Acad Sci. *Res:* Thermodynamics of alloys; electronic structure of alloys; structure and binding in solids; kinetics; surface reactions; hydrogen embrittlement. *Mailing Add:* Dept Chem Eng & Mat Sci Univ Minnesota Minneapolis MN 55455

ORIANS, GORDON HOWELL, b Eau Claire, Wis, July 10, 32; m 55; c 3. ECOLOGY, EVOLUTION. *Educ:* Univ Wis, BS, 54; Univ Calif, Berkeley, PhD(zool), 60. *Prof Exp:* From asst prof to assoc prof, 60-68, PROF ZOOL, UNIV WASH, 68- *Mem:* Cooper Ornith Soc; Ecol Soc Am; Soc Study Evolution; Animal Behav Soc; Am Ornith Union. *Res:* Evolution of vertebrate social systems; factors determining the number of species an environment will support on a sustained basis; plant-herbivore interactions. *Mailing Add:* Dept of Zool Univ of Wash Seattle WA 98195

ORIEL, PATRICK JOHN, physical chemistry, see previous edition

ORIEL, STEVEN S, b New York, NY, Feb 9, 23; m 50; c 3. STRUCTURAL GEOLOGY, STRATIGRAPHY. *Educ:* Columbia Univ, BA, 45; Yale Univ, MS, 47, PhD(geol), 49. *Prof Exp:* Geologist, US Geol Surv, 47-50; res engr geol, Stanolind Oil & Gas Co, 50-53; GEOLOGIST, US GEOL SURV, 53- *Concurrent Pos:* Mem, Am Comn Stratig Nomenclature, chmn, 73-74. *Mem:* AAAS; Geol Soc Am; Am Asn Petrol Geol; Am Geophys Union; Am Inst Prof Geologists. *Res:* Geology of sedimentary rocks; synthesis of stratigraphic information; areal mapping, tectonic analyses and resource appraisals of deformed rocks and Cenozoic sediments in western Wyoming and southeastern Idaho thrust belt; coordinator of Snake River Plain Region studies, including geothermal and earthquake hazard assessments. *Mailing Add:* US Geol Surv Stop 913 Box 25046 Denver Fed Ctr Denver CO 80225

ORIHEL, THOMAS CHARLES, b Akron, Ohio, Feb 10, 29; m 52; c 4. MEDICAL PARASITOLOGY. *Educ:* Univ Akron, BS, 50; Univ Wash, MS, 52; Tulane Univ, PhD(parasitol), 59. *Prof Exp:* NIH fel, Tulane Univ & Univ Miami, 59-61; vector-borne dis specialist, Dept of State, AID Mission to Brit Guiana, 61-63; assoc dir, 75-76, DIR, INT CTR MED RES, 76- RES SCIENTIST & HEAD PARASITOL, DELTA PRIMATE CTR, TULANE UNIV, 63-, PROF PARASITOL, SCH PUB HEALTH & TROP MED, 72-, WILLIAM G VINCENT PROF TROPICAL DIS, 82- *Concurrent Pos:* Mem study sect trop med & parasitol, Nat Inst Allergy & Infectious Dis, NIH, 73-77, chmn study sect trop med & parasitol, Nat Inst Allergy & Infectious Dis, 75-77; mem expert panel parasitic dis, WHO, 73-78; mem panel parasitic dis, US-Japan Coop Med Sci Prog, 74-; dir, Int Col Inf Dis Res, 80. *Mem:* Am Soc Parasitol; Am Soc Trop Med & Hyg; Royal Soc Trop Med & Hyg; Am Soc Microbiol. *Res:* Human and zoonotic filariasis; host-parasite interactions; primate parasites; nematology; parasite morphology and taxonomy. *Mailing Add:* Sch Pub Health & Trop Med Tulane Univ Med Ctr New Orleans LA 70112

ORING, LEWIS WARREN, b New York, NY, Apr 18, 38; m 60; c 2. ECOLOGY, ETHOLOGY. *Educ:* Univ Idaho, BS, 60; Univ Okla, MS, 62, PhD(zool), 66. *Prof Exp:* NSF fel ethology, Univ Copenhagen, 66-67; NIH trainee, Univ Minn, Minneapolis, 67-68; from asst prof to assoc prof, 68-77, PROF BIOL, UNIV N DAK, 77- *Mem:* Animal Behav Soc; Ecol Soc Am; Am Ornith Union; Wilson Ornith Soc; Cooper Ornith Soc. *Res:* Ecological and evolutionary aspects of animal behavior, especially the ways in which environment effects mating systems, spacing patterns and communication. *Mailing Add:* Dept of Biol Univ of NDak Grand Forks ND 58201

ORKAND, RICHARD K, b New York, NY, Apr 23, 36; m 60. PHYSIOLOGY, NEUROBIOLOGY. *Educ:* Columbia Univ, BS, 56; Univ Utah, PhD(pharmacol), 61. *Hon Degrees:* MS, Univ Pa, 74. *Prof Exp:* USPHS fel biophys, Univ Col, Univ London, 61-64; USPHS spec fel neurophysiol, Harvard Med Sch, 64-66; asst prof physiol, Med Ctr, Univ Utah, 66-68; assoc prof zool, Univ Calif, Los Angeles, 68-72, prof biol, 72-74; PROF PHYSIOL & CHMN DEPT PHYSIOL & PHARMACOL, SCH DENT MED, UNIV PA, 74- *Concurrent Pos:* Prof invite, Univ Geneva, 81-82; res assoc, Marine Sci, Univ Calif, Santa Cruz, 81-; assoc ed, J Neurosci, 80-, Neurosci Letters, 81- *Mem:* Soc Neurosci; AAAS; assoc mem Am Physiol Soc. *Res:* Synaptic neurophysiology; skeletal and cardiac muscle excitation-contraction coupling; physiology of neuroglia. *Mailing Add:* Dept Physiol & Pharmacol Univ of Pa Sch Dent Med Philadelphia PA 19104

ORKIN, LAZARUS ALLERTON, b New York, NY, Feb 2, 10; m 41; c 2. MEDICINE, SURGERY. *Educ:* NY Univ, BS, 30, MS, 31, MD, 35; Am Bd Urol, dipl, 44. *Prof Exp:* Intern, Bellevue Hosp, New York, 35-37, asst resident obstet & gynec, 37-38, resident urol, 40-42; resident urol, Royal Victoria Hosp, Montreal, Que, 38-40; dir, 43-78, EMER DIR UROL, BETH ISRAEL MED CTR, 78- *Concurrent Pos:* Consult urologist, Peninsula Gen & St Joseph's Hosps, Long Island, 58-; clin prof, Mt Sinai Sch Med, 68-78, emer prof, 78-; consult urologist, Gracie Square Hosp; consult, Beekman Downtown Hosp, New York & Cath Med Ctr Brooklyn; mem, NY & Brooklyn Comt Trauma. *Mem:* Am Col Legal Med; Am Urol Asn; fel Am Med Writers Asn; fel Am Surg of Trauma; fel Am Col Surg. *Res:* Urological trauma; urinary tract infections. *Mailing Add:* 235 E 57th St New York NY 10022

ORKIN, LOUIS R, b New York, NY, Dec 23, 15; m 38; c 1. ANESTHESIOLOGY. *Educ:* Univ Wis, BA, 37; NY Univ, MD, 41. *Prof Exp:* Dir anesthesia, W W Backus Hosp, Conn, 48-49; asst prof anesthesiol, Postgrad MEd Sch, NY Univ, 50-55; PROF ANESTHESIOL & CHMN DEPT, ALBERT EINSTEIN COL MED, 55- *Concurrent Pos:* Consult, Norwich State Hosp, Conn, 48-49 & Uncas on Thames, 48-49; anesthesiologist, Bellevue Hosp, 50-55; asst attend anesthetist, NY Univ Hosp, 50-54, assoc attend anesthetist, 54-55; consult, US Naval Hosp, St Albans, 54, USPHS Hosp, Staten Island, 54, Triboro Hosp, 55-65 & Montefiore Hosp, New York, 65-; titular prof, Univ Venezuela, 67; vis prof, Univ Calif, San Diego, 71; mem nat res coun, Nat Acad Med, 65-70; sr consult, Bronx Vet Admin Hosp, 55- *Mem:* Am Soc Anesthesiol; AMA; fel NY Acad Sci; fel Am Col Chest Physicians; fel NY Acad Med. *Res:* Physiology and pharmacology related to anesthesiology. *Mailing Add:* Dept of Anesthesiol Albert Einstein Col of Med Bronx NY 10461

ORLAND, FRANK J, b Little Falls, NY, Jan 23, 17; m 43; c 4. HISTORY OF DENTISTRY, ORAL MICROBIOLOGY. *Educ:* Univ Ill, BS, 39, DDS, 41; Univ Chicago, SM, 45, PhD(bact), 49; Am Bd Med Microbiol, dipl. *Prof Exp:* Intern, Zoller Mem Dent Clin, 41-42, asst dent surg, 42-49, from instr to asst prof bact, 49-54, dir, Zoller Clin, 54-66, assoc prof microbiol, 54-58, res assoc prof, 58-64, from instr to assoc prof dent surg, 49-58, PROF DENT SURG, UNIV CHICAGO, 58- *Concurrent Pos:* Fel, Inst Med, Univ Chicago; consult & mem dent study sect & prog planning comt, Nat Inst Dent Res, 55-59; Darnell mem lectr, US Naval Dent Sch, 56; chmn comt info & pub, Inst Med, Univ Chicago; mem panel, Nat Formulary; chmn dent adv bd, Med Heritage Soc; ed, J Dent Res, 58-69. *Mem:* AAAS; Am Soc Microbiol; Electron Micros Soc Am; Am Dent Asn; fel Am Acad Microbiol. *Res:* Experimental dental caries; caries and periodontal disease in germfree and germfree inoculated animals; antigenic analysis of lactobacilli; mechanism of fluoride inhibition in oral bacteria and in tooth decay; morphology and physiology of oral protozoa; historical research in dentistry. *Mailing Add:* Box 418 Zoller Clin Univ of Chicago Chicago IL 60637

ORLAND, GEORGE H, b Los Angeles, Calif, Oct 8, 24; m 44; c 3. MATHEMATICS. *Educ:* City Col New York, BEE, 45; Univ Chicago, MS, 56; Univ Calif, Berkeley, PhD(math), 62. *Prof Exp:* Instr elec eng, Polytech Inst Brooklyn, 46-47; tutor, City Col New York, 48-49; electronics engr, Dept Otolaryngol, Univ Chicago, 50-57, mathematician, Inst Systs Res, 57-59; instr math, Univ Ill, 62-65; asst prof, Wesleyan Univ, 65-67; ASSOC PROF MATH, HARVEY MUDD COL, 67- *Mem:* Am Math Soc. *Res:* Classical and functional analysis; measure theory; convexity; the bending of polyhedra. *Mailing Add:* Dept of Math Harvey Mudd Col Claremont CA 91711

ORLANDO, ANTHONY MICHAEL, b Brooklyn, NY, Jan 27, 42; m 66; c 2. BIOSTATISTICS. *Educ:* City Univ New York, BBA, 63; Columbia Univ, MS, 67; Yale Univ, MPhil, 69, PhD(biostatist), 70. *Prof Exp:* Sr sales analyst, Am-Standard, Inc, 64-65; statistician, Monsanto Chem Co, 65; prin biostatistician, 70-75, dept head statist sci, 75-79, DIR CLIN INFO & STATIST, MEAD JOHNSON & CO, EVANSVILLE, 79- *Mem:* AAAS; Am Statist Asn; Biomet Soc; Sigma Xi; Am Inst Decision Sci. *Res:* Analyzing clinical parameter distributions under a mixture of normal densities; drug comparison hyothesis testing. *Mailing Add:* RR 2 Box 76-C Mt Vernon IN 47620

ORLANDO, CHARLES M, b Tappan, NY, Sept 30, 35; m 64; c 3. ORGANIC CHEMISTRY. *Educ:* Fordham Univ, BS, 57; NY Univ, PhD(org chem), 61. *Prof Exp:* Res chemist, Esso Res & Eng Co, 61-64 & Kay-Fries Chem Co, 64-66; res chemist, 66-72, MGR PROCESS BR, GEN ELEC CORP RES & DEVELOP CTR, 72- *Mem:* Am Chem Soc; Brit Chem Soc. *Res:* Organic photochemistry; organic synthesis; heterocyclic chemistry; chemistry of quinones; polymer synthesis; phenol chemistry; bromination chemistry and flame retardants. *Mailing Add:* PO Box 8 Schenectady NY 12301

ORLANDO, JOSEPH ALEXANDER, b Methuen, Mass, July 16, 29; m 58; c 5. BIOLOGICAL CHEMISTRY. *Educ:* Merrimack Col, BS, 53; NC State Col, MS, 56; Univ Calif, PhD(biochem), 58. *Prof Exp:* Nat Cancer Inst fel biochem, Brandeis Univ, 58-61; ASSOC PROF BIOCHEM, BOSTON COL, 61- *Res:* Photobiology; isolation and characterization of enzymes and enzyme systems associated with light mediated reactions in photosynthetic bacteria. *Mailing Add:* Dept of Biol Boston Col Chestnut Hill MA 02167

ORLANDO, TERRY PHILIP, b Baton Rouge, La, June 3, 52; m 76; c 1. ELECTRICAL ENGINEERING. *Educ:* La State Univ, BS, 74; Stanford Univ, MS, 75, PhD(physics), 81. *Prof Exp:* ASST PROF, DEPT ELEC ENG & COMPUT SCI, MASS INST TECHNOL, 81- *Mem:* Am Phys Soc. *Res:* Superconductors in high magnetic fields; fabrication of thin films of superconductors, superconducting tunneling; phase transitions in two-dimensional superconductors. *Mailing Add:* Mass Inst Technol 13-2122 77 Mass Ave Cambridge MA 02139

ORLANS, F BARBARA, b Jan 14, 28; US citizen; m 59; c 2. PHYSIOLOGY. *Educ:* Birmingham Univ, BSc, 49; London Univ, MSc, 52, PhD(physiol), 54. *Prof Exp:* Res physiologist hormonal control autonomic nervous syst, Nat Heart & Lung Inst, NIH, 56-60; writer free-lance, 67-73; sr staff scientist pop biol, Med Ctr, George Washington Univ, 73-74; grants assoc, Admin Training, 74-75, health sci adminr cardiovasc dis, 75-77, exec secy, 77-79, HEALTH SCIENTIST ADMINR, ADV COUN, CARDIAC DIS BR, NAT HEART, LUNG & BLOOD INST, NIH, 79- *Concurrent Pos:* Fel, Asthma Res Coun Great Brit, 54; fel, Riker Pharmaceut, 58; pres, Scientists Ctr for Animal Welfare, 78- *Mem:* Am Soc Pharmacol & Exp Therapeut; Nat Sci Teachers Asn; Nat Asn Biol Teachers. *Mailing Add:* Nat Heart Lung & Blood Inst Fed 3C-06 Nat Inst Health Bethesda MD 20205

ORLANSKI, ISIDORO, b Buenos Aires, Arg, June 6, 39; m 62; c 3. GEOPHYSICS. *Educ:* Univ Buenos Aires, Lic Physics, 65; Mass Inst Technol, PhD(geophys), 67. *Prof Exp:* SR RES SCIENTIST, GEOPHYS FLUID DYNAMICS LAB, NAT OCEANIC & ATMOSPHERIC ADMIN, 67- *Concurrent Pos:* Res assoc, Mass Inst Technol, 67-68; lectr, Princeton Univ, 71-, vis prof. *Mem:* Am Meteorol Soc; Am Geophys Union. *Res:* Turbulence in stratified flows; dynamics of rotating stratified fluids. *Mailing Add:* Geophys Fluid Dynamics Lab Princeton Univ PO Box 308 Princeton NJ 08540

ORLEMAN, EDWIN FRANKLIN, b Livingstone, Mont, July 19, 15; m 39; c 4. PHYSICAL CHEMISTRY. *Educ:* St Thomas Col, BS, 36; Univ Minn, PhD(phys chem), 41. *Prof Exp:* Instr chem, Unic Calif, 41-43; chemist, Metall Lab, Univ Chicago, 43-44; supt anal res, Tenn Eastman Corp, 44-45; asst prof chem, 45-47, assoc prof chem & chem eng, 47-54, prof, 54-77, EMER PROF CHEM & CHEM ENG, UNIV CALIF, BERKELEY, 77- *Concurrent Pos:* Consult, Radiation Lab, Univ Calif; consult, AEC, 46- *Mem:* Am Chem Soc. *Res:* Inorganic analysis; mechanism of electrode reactions. *Mailing Add:* 19 Anson Way Berkeley CA 94707

ORLIC, DONALD, b Universal, Pa, Dec 11, 32; m 61; c 3. CELL BIOLOGY. *Educ:* Fordham Univ, BS, 59; NY Univ, MS, 63, PhD(biol), 66. *Prof Exp:* Instr anat, Harvard Med Sch, 68-69; asst prof, 69-73, actg chmn dept, 74-76, assoc prof, 73-79, PROF ANAT, NEW YORK MED COL, 79- *Concurrent Pos:* NIH fel, Inst Cellular Path, France, 66-67; NIH fel anat, Harvard Med Sch, 67-68. *Honors & Awards:* A Cressy Morrison Award, NY Acad Sci, 66. *Mem:* Am Soc Cell Biol; Soc Study Blood; Am Soc Hemat; Am Asn Anat. *Res:* Effects of erythropoietin on stem cell differentiation and red cell maturation; development of human fetal gastrointestinal tract. *Mailing Add:* Dept Anat New York Med Col Valhalla NY 10595

ORLICK, CHARLES ALEX, b Milltown, NJ, Sept 30, 27. PHYSICAL CHEMISTRY. *Educ:* Rutgers Univ, BSc, 47, MSc, 50, PhD(chem), 52. *Prof Exp:* Res assoc chem, 51-59, sr res chemist, 59-60, supvr propellant res group, 60-65, supvr appl res group, 65-68, mkt specialist, 68-76, MGR, PROPULSION TECH MKT, ALLEGANY BALLISTICS LAB, HERCULES INC, CUMBERLAND, 76- *Mem:* Am Chem Soc; Combustion Inst. *Mailing Add:* Hercules Inc Allegany Ballistics Lab Cumberland MD 21502

ORLIK, PETER PAUL, b Budapest, Hungary, Nov 12, 38; US citizen; m 64; c 2. MATHEMATICS. *Educ:* Norweg Inst Technol, BS, 61; Univ Mich, Ann Arbor, PhD(math), 66. *Prof Exp:* From asst prof to assoc prof, 66-73, PROF MATH, UNIV WIS-MADISON, 73- *Concurrent Pos:* Mem & NSF fel, Inst Advan Study, 67-69; vis prof, Univ Oslo, 71-72. *Mem:* Am Math Soc. *Res:* Topology; transformation groups. *Mailing Add:* Dept of Math Univ of Wis Madison WI 53706

ORLIN, HYMAN, b New York, NY, July 16, 20; m 43; c 2. GEOPHYSICS, GEODESY. *Educ:* City Col New York, BBA, 42; George Wash Univ, AB, 48, AM, 52; Ohio State Univ, PhD, 62. *Prof Exp:* Mathematician, Coast & Geod Surv, 47-58, supvry geodesist, 58-59, asst chief gravity & astron br, 59-66, tech asst geod div, 66-69, spec asst to dir, Nat Ocean Surv Earth Sci Activities, 69-71; chief scientist, Nat Oceanic & Atmospheric Admin, Nat Ocean Surv, US Dept Commerce, 71-75; EXEC SECY, COMT GEOD, NAT ACAD SCI, 75- *Concurrent Pos:* Lectr, George Wash Univ, 54-61, asst prof lectr, 62-63, assoc prof lectr, 64-65, prof lectr & fac adv, 66- *Mem:* Fel Am Geophys Union. *Res:* Physical and geometric geodesy; geophysics. *Mailing Add:* Nat Acad Sci 2101 Constitution Ave NW Washington DC 20418

ORLOFF, DAVID IRA, b Brooklyn, NY, Mar 14, 44; m 72; c 3. COMBUSTION ENGINEERING, HEAT & MASS TRANSFER. *Educ:* Drexel Univ, BSME, 66, MSME, 68, PhD(thermal sci), 74. *Prof Exp:* Proj engr, Eng Div, Ford Motor Co, 73-74; asst prof, 74-79, ASSOC PROF MECH ENG, UNIV SC, 79- *Concurrent Pos:* Fac researcher, Savannah River Lab, Reactor Eng Group, 75-76 & 77. *Honors & Awards:* Ralph Teetor Award, Soc Automotive Engrs, 77. *Mem:* Am Soc Mech Engrs; Combustion Inst. *Res:* Mathematical models of industrial combustion processes; hazardous and radioactive waste incineration. *Mailing Add:* Col Eng Univ SC Columbia SC 29208

ORLOFF, HAROLD DAVID, b Winnipeg, Man, Nov 24, 15; nat US; m 41; c 3. ORGANIC CHEMISTRY. *Educ:* Univ Man, BSc, 37, MSc, 40. *Prof Exp:* Chemist, Dom Grain Res Labs, Can, 39-40; instr chem, McGill Univ, 40-41; res chemist wood chem, Howard Smith Papers Mills, Ltd, 41-48; res supvr, 48-61, SUPVR RES PLANNING, ETHYL CORP, 61- *Concurrent Pos:* Instr, Univ Detroit, 58. *Honors & Awards:* Weldon Mem Gold Medal, Can Pulp & Paper Asn, 47. *Mem:* AAAS; Am Chem Soc. *Res:* Recovery and utilization of lignin from wood pulping processes; Arborite plastics; alkaline pulping processes; chlorination of benzene; chlorocyclohexane compounds; stereoisomerism of cyclohexane derivatives; phosphorous chemistry; lubricant and fuel additives; antitoxidants; chemistry of phenol, hydrocarbon oxidation; coal combustion in utility boilers; zeolites. *Mailing Add:* 15031 Sutherland Ave Oak Park MI 48237

ORLOFF, JACK, b New York, NY, Dec 22, 21; m 51; c 4. PHYSIOLOGY, MEDICINE. *Educ:* NY Univ, MD, 43. *Prof Exp:* Physiologist, 50-57, chief sect kidney & electrolyte metab, 57-62, chief lab kidney & electrolyte metab, 62-75, DIR INTRAMURAL RES, NAT HEART, LUNG & BLOOD INST, 74- *Concurrent Pos:* Dazian fel med, Med Sch, Yale Univ, 48-49, Life Ins med res fel, 49-50; attend physician, Clin Ctr, Nat Heart Inst, 53-; prof lectr, Med Sch, Georgetown Univ, 64-; fac chmn med physiol grad prog, NIH, 63-67; mem sci adv bd, Nat Kidney Found, 62-71; sect ed, Am J Physiol, 64-68 & J Appl Physiol, 64-68; consult ed, Life Sci; assoc ed, Kidney Int; Am Physiol Soc rep, Div Med Sci, Nat Res Coun, 74-75. *Honors & Awards:* Homer Smith Award, 73; Pub Health Serv Meritorious Serv Award, 74; HEW Distinguished Serv Medal, 77. *Mem:* Inst Med-Nat Acad Sci; Am Physiol Soc; Am Soc Clin Invest; Asn Am Physicians; Fedn Am Sci. *Res:* Kidney and electrolyte physiology; membrane transport; clinical investigation. *Mailing Add:* Dir Intramural Res Nat Heart Lung & Blood Inst Bethesda MD 20205

ORLOFF, JONATHAN H, b New York, NY; m 67; c 2. ELECTRON & ION OPTICS. *Educ:* Mass Inst Technol, BS, 64; Ore Grad Ctr, PhD(physics), 77. *Prof Exp:* Vpres, Elektros, Inc, 71-74; consult, Electron Optics, 74-75; instr, 75-77, asst prof, 77-79, ASSOC PROF PHYSICS, ORE GRAD CTR, 79- *Concurrent Pos:* Consult, Perkin-Elmer Corp, 79-, Hughes Aircraft Corp, 76-78 & Varian Assocs, 78-79. *Mem:* Am Phys Soc; Electron Microscopy Soc Am. *Res:* High brightness electron and ion sources; development and applications of electron and ion optics. *Mailing Add:* Ore Grad Ctr 19600 NW Walker Rd Beaverton OR 97006

ORLOFF, LAWRENCE, b Brooklyn, NY, Feb 12, 41; m 70; c 3. COMBUSTION. *Educ:* Rensselaer Polytech Inst, BS, 63; Georgetown Univ, MA, 71. *Prof Exp:* Patent examr optics, US Patent Off, 64-65; res scientist, 66-78, SR RES SCIENTIST FIRE RES, FACTORY MUTUAL RES CORP, 78- *Honors & Awards:* Silver Medal, Combustion Inst. *Mem:* Combustion Inst; Optical Soc Am. *Res:* Basic experimental research on effects of scale, configuration, and fuel on fire behavior. *Mailing Add:* Factory Mutual Res Corp 1151 Boston-Providence Turnpike Norwood MA 02062

ORLOFF, MALCOLM KENNETH, b Philadelphia, Pa, Feb 26, 39; m 60; c 3. QUANTUM CHEMISTRY. *Educ:* Univ Pa, BA, 60, PhD(phys chem), 64. *Prof Exp:* Fel theoret chem, Yale Univ, 64-65; sr res chemist theoret chem, Am Cyanamid Co, 65-74, group leader, Dyes Tech Serv, 74-75, prod mgr dyes, 75-77, mkt mgr, 77-78; V PRES, RES & DEVELOP, BUFFALO COLOR CORP, 78- *Mem:* Am Asn Textile Colorists & Chemists; Am Chem Soc; Am Phys Soc. *Res:* Quantum mechanics of atomic and molecular systems. *Mailing Add:* Buffalo Color Corp One Garrett Mountain Plaza West Paterson NJ 07424

ORLOFF, MARSHALL JEROME, b Chicago, Ill, Oct 12, 27; m 53; c 6. SURGERY. *Educ:* Univ Ill, BS, 49, MD & MS, 51; Univ Colo, Am Bd Surg, dipl, 59; Am Bd Thoracic Surg, dipl, 60. *Prof Exp:* Asst instr pharmacol, Univ Ill, 49-51; intern, Univ Calif Hosp, San Francisco, 51-52; resident surg, Univ Pa, 52-58, from asst instr to instr, 52-58; from instr to asst prof, Univ Colo, 58-61; prof, Univ Calif, Los Angeles, 61-67; PROF SURG & CHMN DEPT, SCH MED, UNIV CALIF, SAN DIEGO, 67- *Concurrent Pos:* Fel, Harrison Dept Surg, Univ Pa, 52-58, Nat Cancer Inst Inst trainee, 56-58; res grants, Univ Pa, Univ Colo & Univ Calif, 55-74; Markle scholar acad med, 59-64; consult, Vet Admin Hosps, Denver & Grand Junction, Colo & Albuquerque, NMex, 58-61; chief surg, Harbor Gen Hosp, Calif, 61-67; lectr, Univs Chicago, Tex & Boston, 65, Univ Colo, 66 & Albert Einstein Col Med, 68; consult, US Naval Hosp, San Diego, 66- & Nat Bd Med Examr, 67-70; mem clin res training comt, NIH, 66-, surg study sect, 68-; Francis M Smith lectr, Scripps Clin & Res Found, 67; Samuel Lillienthal vis chief surg, Mt Zion Hosp, San Francisco, 68; Michael & Janie Miller vis prof, Univ

Witwatersrand, 70; Edward Pierson Richardson vis prof, Harvard Univ & Mass Gen Hosp, 71; vis prof numerous univs, cols & founds, 67-78; ed-in-chief, World J Surg. *Mem:* AAAS; Am Surg Asn; Am Col Surg; Soc Univ Surg (pres, 71-72); Am Gastroenterol Asn. *Res:* Liver physiology and disease; transplantation; gastrointestinal physiology and surgery; adrenal physiology; metabolism; shock; neuropharmacology; cancer and vascular surgery; diabetes; microsurgery. *Mailing Add:* Dept of Surg Univ of Calif Sch of Med La Jolla CA 92037

ORLOWSKI, JAN ALEXANDER, chemistry, chemical engineering, see previous edition

ORME-JOHNSON, WILLIAM H, b Phoenix, Ariz, Apr 23, 38. ENZYMOLOGY, INORGANIC BIOCHEMISTRY. *Educ:* Univ Tex, Austin, BSc, 59, PhD(chem), 64. *Prof Exp:* Fel, Biochem Inst, Univ Tex, Austin, 64-65; fel, Inst Enzyme Res, Univ Wis, 65-67, asst prof enzyme chem, 67-70, from asst prof to prof biochem, 70-79; PROF CHEM, MASS INST TECHNOL, 79- *Mem:* Am Soc Biol Chemists; Am Chem Soc; Am Soc Microbiologists; fel AAAS. *Res:* Molecular mechanisms of enzyme catalysis, especially electron-transfer reactions, including, nitrogen fixation, steroid hormone synthesis and methanogenesis. *Mailing Add:* Dept Chem (18-407) Mass Inst Technol Cambridge MA 02139

ORMES, JONATHAN FAIRFIELD, b Colorado Springs, Colo; m 64; c 2. ASTROPHYSICS. *Educ:* Stanford Univ, BS, 61; Univ Minn, MS, 66, PhD(physics), 67. *Prof Exp:* Nat Acad Sci-Nat Res Coun resident res assoc & fel cosmic ray astrophys, 66-68, ASTROPHYSICIST & HEAD COSMIC RAY GROUP, GODDARD SPACE FLIGHT CTR, NASA, 68- *Concurrent Pos:* Secy, High Energy Astrophys Mgt Opers Working Group, 74-76; vis assoc prof, Univ Minn, Minneapolis, 77; co-prin investr, Transition Radiation and Ionization Calorimeter for Spacelab, 79- *Mem:* Am Phys Soc; Am Geophys Union; Am Astrophys Soc; AAAS. *Res:* Particle astrophysics, studying composition and energy spectra of high energy cosmic rays to understand acceleration, propagation and nucleosynthesis. *Mailing Add:* Code 661 NASA Greenbelt MD 20771

ORMISTON, EMMETT EZEKIEL, b Oblong, Ill, Nov 21, 09; m 40; c 2. DAIRY SCIENCE. *Educ:* Univ Ill, BS, 35, MS, 37, PhD, 58. *Prof Exp:* From asst to asst prof dairy prod, 38-58, from assoc prof to prof dairy husb, 58-73, EMER PROF DAIRY HUSB, UNIV ILL, URBANA, 73- *Concurrent Pos:* Univ Ill-US Agency Int Develop dairy sci adv & exten adv, Banaras Hindu Univ, 61-63 & dairy sci adv, Uttar Pradesh Agr Univ, India, 68-71. *Mem:* Am Dairy Sci Asn. *Res:* Dairy cattle breeding and management; milking and milk handling at the farm; milk goats. *Mailing Add:* 1101 E Mumford Urbana IL 61801

ORMROD, DOUGLAS PADRAIC, b Langley, BC, May 27, 34; m 57; c 3. PLANT PHYSIOLOGY. *Educ:* Univ BC, BSA, 56; Univ Calif, PhD(plant physiol), 59. *Prof Exp:* Instr agron, Univ Calif, 59-60; from asst prof to prof plant sci, Univ BC, 60-69; PROF HORT SCI, UNIV GUELPH, 69- *Mem:* Am Soc Plant Physiol; Am Soc Hort Sci. *Res:* Growth and development of plants, especially as affected by environmental factors. *Mailing Add:* Dept of Hort Sci Univ of Guelph Guelph ON N1G 2W1 Can

ORMSBEE, ALLEN I(VES), b Reno, Nev, Aug 20, 26; m 46; c 3. AERONAUTICAL ENGINEERING. *Educ:* Univ Ill, BS, 46, MS, 49; Calif Inst Technol, PhD(aeronaut, math), 55. *Prof Exp:* From instr to assoc prof, 46-57, head, Aviation Res Lab, 77-79, PROF AERONAUT & ASTRONAUT ENG, UNIV ILL, 57-, PROF AVIATION, 72- *Concurrent Pos:* Res physicist, Hughes Aircraft Co, 52-54; consult, Gen Dynamics/ Convair, 56-57; design specialist, Douglas Aircraft Co, 57-59, consult, Missiles & Space Systs, 57-78; mem bd aeronaut adv, Ill State Dept Aeronaut, 69-73. *Mem:* Assoc fel Am Inst Aeronaut & Astronaut; Am Soc Eng Educ. *Res:* Aerodynamics and dynamics of guided missiles; spacecraft and aircraft. *Mailing Add:* Dept of Aeronaut & Astronaut Eng Univ of Ill Urbana IL 61801

ORMSBEE, RICHARD ARMSTRONG, b Walla Walla, Wash, Jan 6, 15; m 44; c 2. BIOCHEMISTRY. *Educ:* Mont State Univ, BA, 36; State Col Wash, MS, 38; Brown Univ, PhD(microbiol), 41. *Prof Exp:* Sci aide, USPHS, Mont, 36; jr biologist, US Forest Serv, 38; head lab asst, Brown Univ, 38-41; spec res assoc, Biol Chem Dept, Harvard Med Sch, 41-43; tech aide, Off Sci Res & Develop, DC, 43-45; exec secy, Chem-Biol Coord Ctr, Nat Acad Sci, 45; assoc mem, Sloan-Kettering Inst, 45-47; biochemist, Rocky Mountain Lab, Nat Inst Allergy & Infectious Dis, 47-57, sr scientist, 57-60, sci dir, 60-79; RETIRED. *Concurrent Pos:* Lectr, Mont State Univ. *Mem:* AAAS; Tissue Cult Asn. *Res:* Growth and metabolism of protozoa; rickettsial and viral disease and vaccines; growth, metabolism and structure of rickettsia; antigen, antibody and immune reactions. *Mailing Add:* 803 South 2nd Hamilton MT 59840

ORMSBY, JOSEPH F(RANICS) A(NTHONY), b Troy, NY, Oct 3, 28; m 56; c 5. APPLIED MATHEMATICS, ELECTRICAL ENGINEERING. *Educ:* Rensselaer Polytech Inst, BEE, 50, MEE, 53, MS, 55; Univ Calif, Berkeley, PhD(elec eng), 63. *Prof Exp:* Instr elec eng, Rensselaer Polytech Inst, 50-51, asst proj engr, 51-52, res assoc analog technol, 52-55; asst to prod anal officer, Boston Naval Shipyard, 55-58; mem tech staff, Space Technol Labs, Inc, 58-60; res engr, Univ Calif, Berkeley, 60-63; mem res comt, 66-68, proj leader, 67-68, head theoret studies subdept, 67-71, MEM TECH STAFF, MITRE CORP, BEDFORD, 63- *Mem:* Sci Res Soc Am; Sigma Xi. *Res:* Noise analysis; analog simulation techniques; data processing for industrial engineering; digital techniques; time series analysis; information theory; electromagnetic scattering; space mechanics; radar meteorology; transient field theory; target identification and detection; system analyses. *Mailing Add:* Concord Greene 8-4 Concord MA 01742

ORMSBY, W(ALTER) CLAYTON, b Alfred, NY, Nov 13, 24; m 59; c 2. CERAMICS. *Educ:* Alfred Univ, BS, 48; Pa State Univ, MS, 51, PhD(ceramics), 55. *Prof Exp:* Asst, Pa State Univ, 48-55; ceramic engr & phys chemist, Nat Bur Standards, 55-65; res chemist, 65-76, SUPVRY RES CHEMIST, US DEPT TRANSP, FED HWY ADMIN, 76- *Mem:* Am Ceramic Soc; Mineral Soc Gt Brit & Ireland. *Res:* Stabilization of soils; rheology and mineralogy of clays; surface chemistry of inorganic solids; chemical and mineralogical properties of highway materials. *Mailing Add:* US Dept Transp Fed Hwy Admin HRS-23 Washington DC 20590

ORNA, MARY VIRGINIA, b Newark, NJ, July 4, 34. PHYSICAL CHEMISTRY, ANALYTICAL CHEMISTRY. *Educ:* Chestnut Hill Col, BS, 55; Fordham Univ, MA, 58, PhD(phys chem), 62; Catholic Univ, MA, 67. *Prof Exp:* Jr chemist, Hoffmann-LaRoche, Inc, NJ, 55-56; teacher, Acad Mt St Ursula, 58-61; instr chem, Bronx Community Col, 61-62; PROF & CHMN DEPT INORG & ANAL CHEM, COL NEW ROCHELLE, 66- *Honors & Awards:* Am Cyanamid Co Award, 60-61. *Mem:* Am Chem Soc; Soc Appl Spectros. *Res:* Chelation in mixed solvents; inorganic infrared spectroscopy. *Mailing Add:* Dept of Chem Col of New Rochelle New Rochelle NY 10801

ORNDORFF, ROY LEE, JR, b Washington, DC, Aug 10, 35; m 59; c 5. MECHANICAL ENGINEERING, AUTOMOTIVE ENGINEERING. *Educ:* Va Polytech Inst, BS, 57; Purdue Univ, MS, 58. *Prof Exp:* Lab instr mech eng, Purdue Univ, 57-58; engr, B F Goodrich Res Ctr, 60-63, res engr, 63-66, srresengr,66-72, sr prod engr, Eng Systs Div, 72-78, SECT LEADER, ENG PROD GROUP, B F GOODRICH, 78- *Mem:* Am Soc Mech Engrs; Soc Automotive Engrs. *Res:* Rubber and plastic new products; wet and dry non-metallic bearings; dry dynamic seals; rubber friction and wear; composites; applied thermodynamics; inflatable products. *Mailing Add:* 7827 Birchwood Dr Kent OH 44240

ORNDUFF, ROBERT, b Portland, Ore, June 13, 32. BOTANY. *Educ:* Reed Col, BA, 53; Univ Wash, MSc, 56; Univ Calif, Berkeley, PhD(bot), 61. *Prof Exp:* Asst prof biol, Reed Col, 61-62; asst prof bot, Duke Univ, 62-63; from asst prof to assoc prof, 63-71, assoc dir, Univ Bot Garden, 71-73, PROF BOT, UNIV HERBARIUM, 69-, DIR, JEPSON HERBARIUM & LIBR, 68-, DIR, UNIV BOT GARDEN, 73-, DIR, UNIV HERBARIUM, 75- *Mem:* AAAS; Bot Soc Am; Soc Study Evolution; Am Soc Plant Taxon. *Res:* Biosystematics of angiosperms; Pacific basin phytogeography; reproductive biology of heterostylous plants. *Mailing Add:* Dept of Bot Univ of Calif Berkeley CA 94720

ORNE, DAVID, b Detroit, Mich, Sept 9, 35; m 63; c 2. ENGINEERING MECHANICS, BIOMECHANICS. *Educ:* Univ Mich, Ann Arbor, BSCE, 58, MSCE, 59, PhD(eng mech), 69. *Prof Exp:* Stress analyst spacecraft struct, Lockheed Aircraft Corp, Calif, 59-60; asst prof civil eng & appl mech, San Jose State Col, 61-62; instr theoret & appl mech, Univ Ill, Urbana, 62; res engr, structures, E H Plesset & Assocs, Calif, 62-63; sr struct engr, Systs Ctr, United Aircraft Corp, 63-65; asst prof, 69-74, ASSOC PROF MECH ENG, WAYNE STATE UNIV, 74- *Concurrent Pos:* Sabbatical leave, Mech Eng Design Div, Stanford Univ, 75-76. *Mem:* Orthopedic Res Soc; Biomed Res Soc; Am Soc Mech Engrs. *Res:* Biomechanics; structural dynamics; vibrations; solid mechanics; structures; computer-aided design; optimum design. *Mailing Add:* Dept of Mech Eng Wayne State Univ Detroit MI 48202

ORNE, MARTIN THEODORE, b Vienna, Austria, Oct 16, 27; US citizen; m 62. PSYCHIATRY, PSYCHOLOGY. *Educ:* Harvard Col, BA, 48, Harvard Univ, AM, 51, PhD, 58; Tufts Univ, MD, 55. *Prof Exp:* USPHS fel, Boston Psychopath Hosp, 56-57; lectr social rels, Harvard Univ, 58-59, res assoc, 59-60; instr psychiat, Harvard Med Sch, 59-62, assoc, 62-64; assoc prof, 64-67, PROF PSYCHIAT, MED SCH, UNIV PA, 67-; DIR UNIT EXP PSYCHIAT, INST OF PA HOSP, 64- *Concurrent Pos:* Dir, Studies in Hypnosis & Human Ecol Projs, Mass Ment Health Ctr, 59-64; Fulbright scholar, Univ Sydney, Australia, 60; ed, Int J Clin & Exp Hypnosis, 62; consult, Surg Gen Study Sect, NIMH, 66-74 & Vet Admin Hosp, Philadelphia, 72. *Honors & Awards:* Bernard B Raginsky Award, Soc Clin & Exp Hypnosis, 69. *Mem:* Am Psychiat Asn; Am Psychol Asn; Int Soc Hypnosis (pres, 76-79); Am Psychosomatic Soc; Soc Clin & Exp Hypnosis (pres, 71-73). *Res:* Nature of hypnosis and special states of consciousness, objectification of subjective events, effects of the observational context on data in social and experimental psychology, psychotherapy and psychophysiology. *Mailing Add:* Unit for Exp Psychiat 111 N 49th St Philadelphia PA 19139

ORNER, JOHN WILLIAM, b Binghamton, NY, Aug 24, 15; m 40; c 3. PHYSICS, ELECTRONICS. *Educ:* Univ Natal, BSc, 48, MSc, 53. *Prof Exp:* Asst test engr, Elec Supply Comn SAfrica, 49-56; physicist, US Army Mat Res Agency, Mass, 56-65 & NASA Electronics Res Ctr, 65-66; sr staff engr, Space Systs Div, Avco Corp, 66-71; sr engr, 71-80, CONSULT, STONE & WEBSTER ENG CORP, BOSTON, 80- *Honors & Awards:* Award, SAfrican Cable Makers Asn, 58. *Mem:* Fel Am Soc Nondestructive Testing. *Res:* Generation of high frequency radio interference from power lines and reticulation systems; nondestructive testing and instrumentation. *Mailing Add:* 203 Wildwood St Wilmington MA 01887

ORNSTEIN, DONALD SAMUEL, b New York, NY, July 30, 34; m 65; c 3. PURE MATHEMATICS. *Educ:* Univ Chicago, PhD(math), 56. *Prof Exp:* PROF MATH, STANFORD UNIV, 60- *Honors & Awards:* Bocher Prize, Am Math Soc. *Mem:* Am Math Soc. *Res:* Ergodic theory. *Mailing Add:* Dept of Math Stanford Univ Stanford CA 94305

ORNSTEIN, LEONARD, b New York, NY, Feb 8, 26; m 45; c 4. CELL BIOLOGY, BIOPHYSICS. *Educ:* Columbia Univ, AB, 48, AM, 49, PhD(zool), 57. *Prof Exp:* Asst zool, Columbia Univ, 49-52, asst cytol, 50-52, instr histol, 51-52; res assoc path, 54-67, DIR CELL RES LAB, MT SINAI HOSP, NEW YORK, 54-, PROF PATH, MT SINAI SCH MED, 66- *Concurrent Pos:* Res assoc, Columbia Univ, 52-64; consult, Am Cyanamid Co, 57-58, Canal Indust Corp, 62-69, Space-Gen Corp, 65-66, Airborne

Instrument Corp, 65-67, Farrand Optical Co, 66-67, IBM Watson Labs, 67-68 & Technicon Corp, 69-; vis prof, Harvard Univ, 67-68; mem develop biol panel, NSF, 70-73. *Mem:* Am Soc Cell Biol; Histochem Soc. *Res:* Techniques and instrumentation in microspectrophotometry, phase, interference and electron microscopy; microcinematography; enzyme cytochemistry; microchemistry; fluorescence microscopy; freeze-substitution; microtomy; electrophoresis; information theory and pattern recognition. *Mailing Add:* 5 Biltom Rd White Plains NY 10607

ORNSTEIN, WILHELM, b Jaroslaw, Poland, Nov 9, 05; US citizen; m 46. APPLIED MATHEMATICS, MATHEMATICAL ANALYSIS. *Educ:* Tech Hochsch, Brunn, MS, 29; Tech Univ, Berlin, DrIng, 33. *Prof Exp:* Tech secy to dir, Gen Motors, Poland, 34-39; prof mech, Turkish Mil Acad, Istanbul, 40-42; tech adv, Mid East Hq, US Army, Cairo, 43-46; lectr mech, Univ Pa, 47-48; assoc prof mech eng, Newark Col Eng, 48-50, prof, 50-54; prof, 55-74, EMER PROF APPL MATH, WASH UNIV, 74- *Concurrent Pos:* Vis prof, Stevens Inst Technol, 50-52. *Honors & Awards:* Meritorious Civilian Serv Overseas Award, US Army, 46; Medal of Freedom, War Dept, 48. *Mem:* Am Math Soc. *Mailing Add:* Dept Syst Sci & Math Wash Univ St Louis MO 63130

ORNSTON, LEO NICHOLAS, b Philadelphia, Pa, Jan 7, 40; m 74; c 2. MICROBIAL PHYSIOLOGY, BIOCHEMISTRY. *Educ:* Harvard Univ, BA, 61; Univ Calif, Berkeley, PhD(comp biochem), 65. *Prof Exp:* Res assoc bact, Univ Calif, Berkeley, 65-66; NIH fel biochem, Univ Leicester, 66-68; fel, Univ Ill, Urbana, 68-69; asst prof, 69-74, assoc prof, 74-81, PROF BIOL, YALE UNIV, 81- *Concurrent Pos:* John Simon Guggenheim Found fel, 73-74. *Mem:* Am Soc Biol Chem; Am Soc Microbiol; Brit Soc Gen Microbiol; Am Chem Soc. *Res:* Regulation of convergent and divergent pathways in bacteria; evolution of microbial enzymes. *Mailing Add:* Dept of Biol Yale Univ New Haven CT 06520

ORO, JUAN, b Lerida, Spain, Oct 26, 23; m 49; c 4. BIOCHEMISTRY. *Educ:* Univ Barcelona, Lic, 47; Baylor Univ, PhD(biochem), 56. *Prof Exp:* From instr to assoc prof chem, 55-63, chmn dept biophys sci, 67-69, PROF CHEM, UNIV HOUSTON, 63- *Concurrent Pos:* NASA grants, 62-, partic, Viking Mars Lander Molecular Anal Team, 69-; hon coun, Highest Coun Sci Res, Spain, 69; prof, Univ Barcelona, 71, pres sci coun, Inst Fundamental Biol, 71. *Mem:* AAAS; Am Chem Soc; Am Soc Biol Chem; Geochem Soc; Span Soc Biochem. *Res:* Mechanisms of enzyme action; synthesis of biochemical compounds; neurobiochemistry; application of biological principles for the improvement of the quality of human life; comprehensive study of carbonaceous, organic and organogenic matter in returned lunar samples; biochemical applications of gas chromatography and mass spectrometry; organic cosmochemistry and paleochemistry; molecular and biological evolution; origin of life. *Mailing Add:* Dept of Chem Sci Univ of Houston Houston TX 77004

ORONSKY, ARNOLD LEWIS, biochemistry, physiology, see previous edition

OROS, MARGARET OLAVA (ERICKSON), b Sheyenne, NDak, Oct 5, 12; m 51; c 1. PETROLEUM GEOLOGY. *Educ:* Univ NDak, BA, 39. *Prof Exp:* Lab instr geol, Univ NDak, 38-40; radio assembler, Bendix Aviation Co, Calif, 42-43; lab asst spectrog anal, Aluminum Co Am, 42-48; chem engr, Harvey Aluminum Co, 48-51; geologist, Ill State Geol Surv, 53-62; geologist, State Geol Surv, Kans, 62-78; GEOL CONSULT, 78- *Mem:* Sigma Xi; Am Asn Petrol Geol; Am Inst Prof Geol; fel Geol Soc Am. *Res:* Spectrography; metallurgical control of aluminum alloys; geological cross sections; field studies; petroleum statistical reports; crude oil reserves estimates; pipeline and petroleum industry map. *Mailing Add:* 913 Madeline Lane Lawrence KS 66044

OROSHNIK, JESSE, b New York, NY, May 12, 24; m 55; c 2. PHYSICS. *Educ:* City Col New York, BS, 48; Univ Fla, MS, 50. *Prof Exp:* Aeronaut res scientist, NASA, 54; physicist, Standard Piezo Co, 54-55; sr engr, Gen Tel & Electronics Labs, Inc, 55-61; engr res & develop labs, Westinghouse Elec Corp, 61-66; group leader, Adv Fabrication Tech Sect, Electronics Res Lab, Corning Glass Works, 66-68; physicist, Nat Bur Standards, Washington, DC, 68-71; physicist, Naval Weapons Eng Support Activity, 71-75, PHYSICIST, NAVAL RES LAB, US NAVY, 75- *Concurrent Pos:* NY State Regents War Serv scholar, 57. *Mem:* Am Phys Soc; Sigma Xi. *Res:* Adhesion and adhesive fracture of polymers in polymer-metal bonds. *Mailing Add:* Code 6120 Naval Res Lab Washington DC 20375

OROSZIAN, STEPHEN, immunochemistry, biochemical pharmacology, see previous edition

O'ROURKE, EDMUND NEWTON, JR, b New Orleans, La, Nov 22, 23; m 47; c 1. HORTICULTURE. *Educ:* Southwestern La Inst, BS, 48; Cornell Univ, MS, 53, PhD, 55. *Prof Exp:* Jr horticulturist, USDA, 48-51; asst pomol, Cornell Univ, 51-54; assoc prof, 54-59, PROF HORT, LA STATE UNIV, BATON ROUGE, 59- *Mem:* Am Soc Hort Sci. *Res:* Breeding and improvement of figs, pears, apples and other fruits for the Gulf Coast area; ecology of fruit varieties; commercial floriculture. *Mailing Add:* Dept of Hort La State Univ Baton Rouge LA 70803

O'ROURKE, JAMES, b Trenton, NJ, Mar 2, 25; m 54; c 4. OPHTHALMOLOGY. *Educ:* Georgetown Univ, MD, 49; Univ Pa, MSc, 54. *Prof Exp:* Resident surgeon, 52-54; clin assoc ophthal, NIH, 54-55, chief clin res, 55-57; assoc prof, Sch Med, Georgetown Univ, 57-65, prof ophthal surg, 65-69; PROF SURG & DIR DIV OPHTHAL, HEALTH CTR, UNIV CONN, 69- *Concurrent Pos:* Res fel, Wills Eye Hosp, Pa, 51-52; consult, Oak Ridge Nat Lab, 55-57 & NIH, 57-, mem vision res & training comt, Nat Eye Inst, 71-75; adj prof physics, Trinity Col, Conn, 72-; armed forces vision res comt, Nat Res Coun. *Mem:* Asn Res Vision & Ophthal; Am Acad Ophthal & Otolaryngol; Am Ophthal Soc; Soc Nuclear Med. *Res:* Ocular uptake of radioactive sources; ocular blood flow; tumor detection. *Mailing Add:* Univ of Conn Health Ctr Farmington Ave Farmington CT 06032

O'ROURKE, RICHARD CLAIR, b Minneapolis, Minn, July 8, 30. PHILOSOPHY OF SCIENCE, BOTANY. *Educ:* Col St Thomas, BS, 53; Univ Minn, Minneapolis, MS, 58, PhD(philos sci, bot), 66. *Prof Exp:* PROF BIOL & PHILOS SCI, WINONA STATE UNIV, 65- *Concurrent Pos:* Staff mem, Univ Minn, 71-72. *Mem:* AAAS. *Res:* Logic of the empirical sciences. *Mailing Add:* Dept of Biol Winona State Univ Winona MN 55987

O'ROURKE, THOMAS DENIS, b Pittsburgh, Pa, July 31, 48; m 78. GEOTECHNICAL ENGINEERING, CIVIL ENGINEERING. *Educ:* Cornell Univ, BS, 70; Univ Ill, MS, 73, PhD(civil eng), 75. *Prof Exp:* Engr, Dames & Moore Consult Engrs, 70; res asst eng, Univ Ill, 70-75, asst prof, 75-78; asst prof, 78-81, ASSOC PROF ENG, CORNELL UNIV, 81- *Honors & Awards:* C A Hogentogler Award, Am Soc Testing & Mat, 76. *Mem:* Am Soc Civil Engrs. *Res:* Underground construction with emphasis on construction in urban areas; structural interaction with soil and rock; mining subsidence; buried pipelines; soil and rock instrumentation. *Mailing Add:* 265 Hollister Hall Cornell Univ Ithaca NY 14853

OROWAN, EGON, b Budapest, Hungary, Aug 2, 02; nat US; m 41; c 1. PHYSICS. *Educ:* Tech Univ, Berlin, Dipl, 29, DEng, 32; Cambridge Univ, MA, 48. *Hon Degrees:* DrIng, Tech Univ, Berlin, 65. *Prof Exp:* Asst prof, Tech Univ, Berlin, 28-32; in charge construct proj, United Incandescent Lamp & Elec Co, Hungary, 35-37; res assoc physics, Univ Birmingham, 37-39; res assoc, Cavendish Lab, Cambridge Univ, 39-47, reader physics of metals, 47-50; prof mech eng, 50-51, George Westinghouse prof, 51-62, prof, 58-68, EMER PROF MECH ENG, MASS INST TECHNOL, 68- *Concurrent Pos:* Vis prof, Calif Inst Technol, 58 & Carnegie Inst Technol, 63; res fel & consult, Boeing Sci Res Labs, Wash, 65-66; consult, E I du Pont de Nemours & Co. *Honors & Awards:* Hawksley Gold Medal, Brit Inst Mech Eng, 44; Bingham Medal, Am Soc Rheol, 59. *Mem:* Nat Acad Sci; Am Soc Testing & Mat; Am Inst Mining, Metall & Petrol Eng; fel Am Acad Arts & Sci; Am Geophys Union. *Res:* Physics of strength, plasticity and other mechanical properties of solids; mechanical problems of geology. *Mailing Add:* 44 Payson Terr Belmont MA 02178

ORPHAN, VICTOR JOHN, b Norfolk, Va, Oct 7, 40; m 68. NUCLEAR PHYSICS & ENGINEERING. *Educ:* Univ Va, BME, 62; Mass Inst Technol, SM, 64, ScD(nuclear eng), 67. *Prof Exp:* br mgr, Nuclear Technol Br, Gulf Radiation Technol, San Diego, 67-80; VPRES, INSTRUMENTATION RES DIV, SCI APPL INC, 80- *Mem:* Am Phys Soc; Am Nuclear Soc. *Res:* Neutron capture gamma-ray spectroscopy; inelastic neutron scattering cross sections. *Mailing Add:* Sci Appl Inc Instrumentation Res 4060 Sorrento Valley Blvd San Diego CA 92121

ORPHANIDES, GUS GEORGE, b Kew Gardens, NY, Jan 27, 47; m 68; c 2. ORGANIC POLYMER CHEMISTRY. *Educ:* Hobart Col, BS, 67; Ohio State Univ, PhD(org chem), 72. *Prof Exp:* Org chemist, US Army Foreign Sci & Technol Ctr, 72-74; chemist, Elastomer Chem Dept, E I Du Pont de Nemours & Co, Inc, 74-81; CHEMIST, INDUST CHEM DIV, AIR PROD & CHEM, INC, 81- *Concurrent Pos:* Chemist, US Army Tech Working Group Org Mat, 72-74. *Mem:* Am Chem Soc. *Res:* Structure property relationships in organic polymers; elastomer curing chemistry; general organic synthesis and chemistry of divalent carbon. *Mailing Add:* Indust Chem Div Air Prod & Chem Inc Allentown PA 18104

ORPHANOS, DEMETRIUS GEORGE, b Naxos, Greece, Dec 22, 22; Can citizen; m 61; c 2. ORGANIC CHEMISTRY. *Educ:* Nat Univ Athens, BSc, 55; McGill Univ, PhD(org chem), 63. *Prof Exp:* Anal chemist, Nemea Gen Chem Lab, Greece, 55-56 & Lorado Uranium Mills, Ltd, Can, 57-58; res assoc org res, Mass Inst Technol, 62-64; group leader, Can Tech Tape Ltd, 64-67; sr org chemist, Tracerlab-Lab for Electronics, Inc, 67; group leader org chem, 67-74, SR RES CHEMIST, NEW ENG NUCLEAR CORP, 74- *Mem:* Am Chem Soc. *Res:* Analytical chemistry; synthesis of natural products; heterocyclics; propolymer heterocyclic systems; biologically active compounds; organic peroxides; radiochemicals. *Mailing Add:* 25 Towne Crest Dr Stoneham MA 02180

ORPHANOUDAKIS, STELIOS CONSTANTINE, b Rethymno, Crete, Nov 13, 48; m 74; c 2. MEDICAL IMAGING, DIGITAL IMAGE PROCESSING. *Educ:* Dartmouth Col, BA, 71, PhD(biomed eng), 76; Mass Inst Technol, MS, 73. *Prof Exp:* Med physicist med physics bioeng, Yale-New Haven Hosp, 75-76; asst clin prof diagnostic radiol, Sch Med, 76-77, asst prof, 77-78, asst prof diagnostic radiol, eng & appl sci, 78-81, ASSOC PROF DIAGNOSTIC RADIOL & ELEC ENG, YALE UNIV, 81- *Concurrent Pos:* Mem med staff, Yale-New Haven Hosp, 79- *Mem:* NY Acad Sci; Am Asn Physicists Med; Inst Elec & Electronics Engrs; AAAS. *Res:* Digital signal processing; image processing; image analysis applications in medical imaging: computed tomography, ultrasound, digital radiography. *Mailing Add:* Dept Diagnostic Radiol Sch Med Yale Univ 333 Cedar St New Haven CT 06510

ORPURT, PHILIP ARVID, b Peru, Ind, Aug 9, 21; m 45; c 5. MYCOLOGY. *Educ:* Manchester Col, BA, 48; Univ Wis, MS, 50, PhD(bot), 54. *Prof Exp:* Instr bot & zool, Wausau exten, Univ Wis, 50-51; PROF BIOL, MANCHESTER COL, 54-, CHMN BIOL DEPT, 80- *Concurrent Pos:* NIH fel, Inst Marine Sci, Univ Miami, 62-63. *Mem:* Mycol Soc Am; Am Inst Biol Sci; Int Oceanog Found. *Res:* Soil and marine microfungi; mycotoxins; paleoecology. *Mailing Add:* Dept Biol Manchester Col North Manchester IN 46962

ORR, ALAN R, b Des Moines, Iowa, May 13, 36; div; c 3. BOTANY, CELL BIOLOGY. *Educ:* Simpson Col, BA, 61; Purdue Univ, MS, 64, PhD(bot), 66. *Prof Exp:* From asst prof to assoc prof, 65-78, PROF BIOL, UNIV NORTHERN IOWA, 78- *Mem:* Bot Soc Am; AAAS. *Res:* Developmental botany, morphogenesis of reproductive organs, particularly biochemical events associated with morphological changes in meristematic tissue. *Mailing Add:* Dept of Biol Univ of Northern Iowa Cedar Falls IA 50613

ORR, BEATRICE YEWER, b Milwaukee, Wis, Jan 4, 51; m 77. ANATOMY, TERATOLOGY. *Educ:* Univ Denver, BS, 73; Med Col Wis, PhD(anat), 78. *Prof Exp:* FEL TERATOLOGY, AM DENT ASN RES INST, 78- *Concurrent Pos:* Adj instr histol, Stritch Sch Med, Loyola Univ, 78- *Mem:* Teratology Soc; Am Asn Lab Animal Sci. *Res:* Sirenomelia; craniofacial abnormalities; neural crest; scanning electron microscopy. *Mailing Add:* Am Dent Asn Res Inst 211 E Chicago Ave Chicago IL 60611

ORR, CHARLES HENRY, b Griffin, Ga, May 24, 24; m 52; c 6. COMPUTER SCIENCE. *Educ:* Ohio State Univ, BSc, 48, MSc, 49; Syracuse Univ, PhD(chem), 53. *Prof Exp:* Asst instr, Syracuse Univ, 50-51; res chemist, 53-69, DESIGN SPECIALIST COMPUT LANG, PROCTER & GAMBLE CO, 70- *Mem:* Am Chem Soc; Sigma Xi. *Res:* Introduction of new computer languages; computer application to automatic data reduction; use of Boolean logic in computer languages; decision tables. *Mailing Add:* 1831 Greenpine Dr Cincinnati OH 45231

ORR, CLYDE, JR, b Lewisburg, Tenn, Oct 1, 21; m 44; c 4. CHEMICAL ENGINEERING. *Educ:* Univ Tenn, BS, 44, MS, 48; Ga Inst Technol, PhD(chem eng), 53. *Prof Exp:* Chem engr, Wilson Dam, Tenn Valley Authority, 46-47; asst, Eng Exp Sta, 48-51, res engr, 51-58, assoc prof chem eng, 53-58, res prof, 58-62, prof, 62-66, Regents prof, 66-80, EMER PROF CHEM ENG, GA INST TECHNOL, 80- *Concurrent Pos:* Chmn, Bd Dirs, Micromeritics Instrument Corp, Ga. *Mem:* Am Chem Soc; Am Inst Chem Engrs. *Res:* Surface chemistry; aerosols; heat transfer; instrumentation. *Mailing Add:* 5091 Hidden Branches Circle Dunwoody GA 30338

ORR, DONALD EUGENE, JR, b Kokomo, Ind, Jan 17, 45; m 67; c 2. ANIMAL SCIENCE. *Educ:* Purdue Univ, West Lafayette, BS, 67; Pa State Univ, MS, 69; Mich State Univ, PhD(animal husb, nutrit), 75. *Prof Exp:* Fac res asst animal sci, Pa State Univ, 67-69; swine res specialist, Feed Res Div, Cent Soya Co, 74-75; asst prof, 75-81, ASSOC PROF ANIMAL SCI, TEX TECH UNIV, 81- *Mem:* Am Soc Animal Sci; Sigma Xi. *Res:* Nutrition of the newborn and early-weaned pig; nutrition of the gestating and lactating sow; swine housing and management. *Mailing Add:* Dept of Animal Sci Tex Tech Univ Lubbock TX 79409

ORR, F(RED) A(NDREW), b Newton, Ill, June 16, 20; m 56; c 1. CHEMICAL ENGINEERING. *Educ:* Univ Ill, BS, 44; Washington Univ, St Louis, MS, 60. *Prof Exp:* Jr chemist, Granite City Steel Co, 39-40, sr chemist, 40-41; anal chemist, Dept Appl Chem, Univ Ill, 42-44, asst, Munitions Develop Lab, Nat Defense Res Comt, 44-45; res chemist & engr, Shell Oil Co, 45-61, technologist, Econ & Scheduling Dept, 61-63, process engr, tech comput group, Tech Dept, Wood River Refining, 63-70, process engr, Econ & Scheduling Dept, Wood River Res Lab, 70-78; RETIRED. *Mem:* Am Chem Soc; Opers Res Soc Am; Am Inst Chem Engrs; Inst Mgt Sci. *Res:* Data analysis by regression studies; high speed computer programming to solve problems in chemical analysis; electronic instrumentation analysis and simulation; chemical engineering plant development and design; development of refinery scheduling computer program. *Mailing Add:* 2430 Lynch Ave Granite City IL 62040

ORR, GEOFFREY F, mycology, see previous edition

ORR, HENRY CLAYTON, b Baltimore, Md, Oct 19, 23. BIOLOGY. *Educ:* Howard Univ, BS, 49; George Washington Univ, MS, 61, PhD, 67. *Prof Exp:* Biologist & cytologist, Nat Cancer Inst, 53-65; cell biologist & immunocytochemist, Bionetics Res Labs, Inc, 65-67; chief cell biol sect, Div Biol Standards, NIH, 67-72; DIR, CELLULAR PHYSIOL BR, BUR OF BIOLOGICS, FOOD & DRUG ADMIN, 72- *Mem:* Tissue Cult Asn; Am Soc Cell Biol; Am Soc Microbiol. *Res:* Modulations affecting the safety of in vitro cell substrates used in producing viral vaccines, mechanisms and kinetics of replication of mammalian viruses in cells; immunobiology. *Mailing Add:* Bur of Biologics Food & Drug Admin 8800 Rockville Pike Bethesda MD 20014

ORR, HENRY LLOYD, b Milverton, Ont, Nov 8, 19; m 45; c 3. POULTRY SCIENCE. *Educ:* Ont Agr Col, BSA, 43; Pa State Univ, MS, 52. *Prof Exp:* From lectr to assoc prof, 47-82, PROF DEPT ANIMAL & POULTRY SCI, ONT AGR COL, UNIV GUELPH, 82- *Mem:* Am Poultry Sci Asn; World Poultry Sci Asn; Am Meat Sci Asn. *Res:* Quality control in eggs, poultry meat and products and meat yields. *Mailing Add:* Dept of Animal & Poultry Sci Ont Agr Col Univ of Guelph Guelph ON N1G 2W1 Can

ORR, HENRY PORTER, b Opelika, Ala, Aug 20, 21. FLORICULTURE. *Educ:* Ala Polytech Inst, BS, 42; Ohio State Univ, MS, 47, PhD, 62. *Prof Exp:* From asst prof to assoc prof, 47-62, PROF HORT, AUBURN UNIV, 62- *Mem:* Am Soc Hort Sci. *Res:* Watering methods; leaf abscission of Azaleas; nutrition of woody ornamental plants; marketing of woody ornamentals. *Mailing Add:* Dept of Hort Auburn Univ Auburn AL 36830

ORR, HOWARD DENNIS, b Harmony, Pa, Apr 1, 24; m 47; c 4. ZOOLOGY. *Educ:* Geneva Col, BS, 50; Univ Pittsburgh, MS, 52, PhD, 55. *Prof Exp:* From asst prof to assoc prof, 54-66, PROF BIOL, ST OLAF COL, 66- *Concurrent Pos:* NSF fel, Univ Ga, 63-64. *Mem:* Am Soc Mammal; Ecol Soc Am; Animal Behav Soc. *Res:* Ecology; behavior and physiology of mammals. *Mailing Add:* Dept of Biol St Olaf Col Northfield MN 55057

ORR, JACK EDWARD, b Delphi, Ind, Dec 11, 18; m 42; c 1. PHARMACY. *Educ:* Purdue Univ, BS, 40; Univ Wis, PhD(pharmaceut chem), 43. *Prof Exp:* Instr pharm, Ohio State Univ, 43-44, asst prof, 46-47; prof pharmaceut chem, Univ Utah, 47-52; prof pharmaceut chem & dean sch pharm, Mont State Univ, 52-56; Wash state chemist, 56-78, dean, Sch Pharm, 56-78, PROF PHARM, UNIV WASH, 56- *Mem:* Am Pharmaceut Asn; Am Asn Cols Pharm (pres, 64-65). *Res:* Pharmaceutical education. *Mailing Add:* Sch of Pharm Univ of Wash SB-68 Seattle WA 98195

ORR, JAMES ANTHONY, b Madison, Wis, Sept 9, 48; m 71; c 1. MAMMALIAN PHYSIOLOGY, CARDIOPULMONARY PHYSIOLOGY. *Educ:* Loras Col, BS, 70; Univ Wis-Madison, PhD(vet sci physiol), 74. *Prof Exp:* Asst scientist cardiopulmonary physiol, Univ Wis-Madison, 74-75; ASST PROF PHYSIOL & CELL BIOL, UNIV KANS, 75- *Mem:* Am Soc Vet Physiologists & Pharmacologists. *Res:* Chemical control of ventilation, specifically the role of chemoreceptors in health and disease; cerebral circulation and response of this circulatory bed to hyperoxia and hypoxia. *Mailing Add:* Dept of Physiol & Cell Biol Univ of Kans Lawrence KS 66045

ORR, JAMES CAMERON, b Paisley, Scotland, Aug 10, 30; US citizen; m 59; c 2. BIOCHEMISTRY, ORGANIC CHEMISTRY. *Educ:* Univ London, BSc & ARCS, 54; Univ Glasgow, PhD(chem), 60. *Prof Exp:* Asst lectr chem, Univ Glasgow, 55-57; res chemist, Syntex SA, Mex, 59-63; from assoc to assoc prof biol chem, Harvard Med Sch, 63-75, tutor biochem sci, Harvard Univ, 63-75; PROF BIOCHEM & CHEM & ASSOC DEAN, BASIC MED SCI, MEM UNIV NFLD, 75- *Mem:* AAAS; Am Chem Soc; Am Soc Biol Chem; Endocrine Soc; The Chem Soc. *Res:* Mechanisms of organic chemical reactions, particularly those involving steroids and enzymes. *Mailing Add:* Basic Med Sci Mem Univ Nfld St John's NF A1C 5S7 Can

ORR, LEIGHTON, b Pittsburgh, Pa, Feb 11, 07; m 32; c 2. MECHANICAL ENGINEERING. *Educ:* Univ Pittsburgh, BS, 28. *Prof Exp:* Test engr, Pittsburgh Testing Lab, 30-36; res engr, PPG Industs Inc, 36-50, head phys testing, 50-72; TECH GLASS CONSULT, 72- *Concurrent Pos:* Consult to various industs. *Mem:* Fel Am Soc Mech Engrs; Am Soc Testing & Mat. *Res:* Analysis of fractures and defects, determine type of stress and stress intensity causing failure; safety and impact performance, rating degree of anneal and temper; selection of glass sizes, type and thickness for wind load on single and double windows in buildings and water loads on multiple laminated windows in aquaria. *Mailing Add:* Box 291 RD 4 Tarentum PA 15084

ORR, LOWELL PRESTON, b Ross Co, Ohio, Dec 11, 30; m 64; c 2. VERTEBRATE ECOLOGY, HERPETOLOGY. *Educ:* Miami Univ, BS, 52; Kent State Univ, MEd, 56; Univ Tenn, PhD(zool), 62. *Prof Exp:* Instr biol, Pub Sch, Ohio, 52-55; instr, 56-57 & 61-63, from asst prof to assoc prof, 63-73, PROF BIOL SCI, KENT STATE UNIV, 73- *Mem:* Soc Study Amphibian Reptiles; Herpet League; Sigma Xi; Ecol Soc Am; Am Soc Ichthyol & Herpet. *Res:* Evolutionary ecology of vertebrate populations; competitive interactions and natural history of salamanders. *Mailing Add:* Dept of Biol Sci Kent State Univ Kent OH 44242

ORR, MARSHALL H, b Providence, RI, Dec 7, 42; m 64; c 3. ACOUSTICAL OCEANOGRAPHY, PHYSICS. *Educ:* Univ RI, BS, 65; Univ Maine, MS, 67; Pa State Univ, PhD(physics), 72. *Prof Exp:* Instr physics, Univ Maine, 67-68; asst prof, Pa State Univ, 72-73, res assoc, Appl Res Lab, 73-74; asst scientist underwater acoust & physics, Dept Ocean Eng, Woods Hole Oceanog Inst, 74-78, assoc scientist acoust oceanog physics, 78-81; SR RES GEOPHYSICIST, SEISMOL DEPT, GULF RES & DEVELOP CO, 81- *Concurrent Pos:* Consult to Off Technol Assessment, US Cong. *Mem:* AAAS; Am Geophys Union; Soc Explor Geophysicists; Acoust Soc Am. *Res:* Land and marine hydrocarbon exploration using vertical seismic profiling, horizontal seismic array and well logging techniques; use of high frequency acoustic backscattering systems as remote sensors of physical processes in the ocean environment; mixing processes; internal waves. *Mailing Add:* Gulf Res & Develop Co PO Drawer 2038 Pittsburgh PA 15230

ORR, MARY FAITH, b Ashland, Ala, June 29, 20. ANATOMY. *Educ:* Univ Ala, BA, 41; Vanderbilt Univ, MA, 54, PhD(anat), 61. *Prof Exp:* Asst tissue cult, Univ Tex Med Br, 45-50; instr oncol & dir tissue cult, Vanderbilt Univ, 50-60; from instr to asst prof anat, 60-67, ASSOC PROF ANAT, MED SCH, NORTHWESTERN UNIV, CHICAGO, 67- *Concurrent Pos:* Sr investr on assoc staff & dir tissue cult lab, Chicago Wesley Mem Hosp, Ill, 60-64. *Mem:* AAAS; Soc Neurosci; Am Asn Anat; Tissue Cult Asn; Am Soc Cell Biol. *Res:* Cancer; development of sensory elements of the inner ear in vivo and in organ culture; differentiation of nerve tissue and organ rudiments in tissue culture; spleen cultures. *Mailing Add:* Dept of Anat Northwestern Univ Med Sch Chicago IL 60611

ORR, ORTY EDWIN, b Neodesha, Kans, Aug 18, 20; m 47; c 2. VERTEBRATE ZOOLOGY. *Educ:* Kans State Col, Pittsburgh, BS, 51; Okla State Univ, MS, 52, PhD(zool), 58. *Prof Exp:* Biologist, Nebr Game & Parks Comn, 54-62; from asst prof to assoc prof biol sci, San Antonio Col, 62-66; PROF BIOL SCI, MO SOUTHERN STATE COL, 66-, HEAD DEPT, 68- *Concurrent Pos:* Nat Sci Insts fels, field biol, Colo State Univ, 68, radiation biol, Argonne Nat Lab, 69, math col teachers, Univ Mont, 70 & radiation biol & environ qual, Cornell Univ, 71-72. *Mem:* Am Fisheries Soc; Am Inst Biol Sci. *Res:* Fresh water fishery. *Mailing Add:* Dept of Biol Mo Southern State Col Joplin MO 64801

ORR, RICHARD CLAYTON, b Oakland, Calif, Mar 28, 41; m 64; c 2. MATHEMATICS. *Educ:* Humboldt State Col, AB, 64; Syracuse Univ, MA, 66, PhD(math), 69. *Prof Exp:* Asst prof, 69-72, ASSOC PROF MATH, STATE UNIV NY COL OSWEGO 72-, CHMN DEPT, 74-.*Mem:* Am Math Soc; Math Asn Am. *Res:* Analytic number theory; sieve methods. *Mailing Add:* Dept of Math State Univ NY Col Oswego NY 13126

ORR, ROBERT S, b Philadelphia, Pa, Dec 18, 37. ORGANIC CHEMISTRY. *Educ:* Univ Pa, BA, 59; Univ Del, MS, 62, PhD(chem), 64. *Prof Exp:* From asst prof to assoc prof, 64-72, PROF CHEM, DEL VALLEY COL, 72-, CHMN DEPT, 66-, CHMN, DIV SCI, 80- *Mem:* AAAS; Am Chem Soc. *Res:* Teaching of organic chemistry and biochemistry on undergraduate level. *Mailing Add:* Dept Chem Del Valley Col Doylestown PA 18901

ORR, ROBERT THOMAS, b San Francisco, Calif, Aug 17, 08; m 72. MAMMALOGY, ORNITHOLOGY. *Educ:* Univ San Francisco, BS, 29; Univ Calif, MA, 31, PhD(zool), 37. *Hon Degrees:* DSc, Univ San Francisco, 76. *Prof Exp:* Asst, Mus Vert Zool, Univ Calif, 32-35; wildlife technician, US Nat Park Serv, 35-36; from asst curator to curator, 36-75, assoc dir acad, 64-75, SR SCIENTIST, DEPT BIRDS & MAMMALS, CALIF ACAD SCI, 75- *Concurrent Pos:* From asst prof to prof, Univ San Francisco, 42-64; vis prof, Univ Calif, Berkeley, 62 & 64, prof-in-res, Univ Exten Prog, San Blas, Mex, 62; mem adv comt, Friends Sea Otter & Calif Marine Mammal Ctr. *Honors & Awards:* Fel Medal, Calif Acad Sci, 73. *Mem:* AAAS; hon mem Am Soc Mammal (secy, 38-42, 47-59, vpres, 53-55, pres, 58-60); hon mem Cooper Ornith Soc (vpres, 64-67, pres, 67-70); Soc Syst Zool; fel Am Ornith Union. *Res:* Population, behavioral and taxonomic studies on marine mammals; life history and taxonomy of North American bats and rabbits; distributional and taxonomic studies on Mexican birds and mammals; distribution of fleshy fungi in western North America. *Mailing Add:* Calif Acad Sci Golden Gate Park San Francisco CA 94118

ORR, ROBERT WILLIAM, b Evansville, Ind, Nov 24, 40; div. GEOLOGY. *Educ:* Univ Ill, BS, 62; Univ Tex, MA, 64; Ind Univ, PhD(geol), 67. *Prof Exp:* Res asst geol, Ill Geol Surv, 63-64; from asst prof to assoc prof, 67-75, PROF GEOL, BALL STATE UNIV, 75-, CHMN DEPT, 81- *Concurrent Pos:* Fel Ind Geol Surv Natural Resources. *Mem:* Fel Geol Soc Am; Soc Econ Paleont & Mineral. *Res:* Conodont biostratigraphy of the Devonian system, especially Middle Devonian rocks of North America. *Mailing Add:* Dept Geol Ball State Univ Muncie IN 47306

ORR, ROBIN DENISE MOORE, b Sydney, Australia, Feb 7, 34; US citizen; m 58; c 2. NUTRITION. *Educ:* Sydney Tech Col, ASTC, 54; Iowa State Univ, SM, 59; Harvard Sch Public Health, MSc, 72, DSc, 79. *Prof Exp:* Instr nutrit, East Sydney Tech Col, 55-57; therapeut dietitian, Seiler's Dietary Serv, Watham, Mass, 66-70; lectr, 77-79, ASST PROF COMMUN NUTRIT, FAC MED, MEM UNIV NEWFOUNDLAND, 79- *Concurrent Pos:* Tutor, Quincy House, Harvard Col, 73-76. *Mem:* Nutrit Soc Can; Am Dietetic Asn; Can Dietetic Asn; Can Public Health Asn; Newfoundland Public Health Asn. *Res:* Dietary patterns and nutritional status of population groups; dietary intake methodology; organization of nutrition services; evaluation of nutrition programmes. *Mailing Add:* Fac Med Mem Univ Newfoundland St John's NF A1B 3V6 Can

ORR, WILLIAM CAMPBELL, b St Louis, Mo, Dec 27, 20; m 46; c 3. NUCLEAR CHEMISTRY. *Educ:* Princeton Univ, AB, 42; Univ Calif, PhD(chem), 48. *Hon Degrees:* ScD, MacMurray Col, 68. *Prof Exp:* Chemist, Radiation Lab, Univ Calif, 48-49; from asst prof to prof chem, 49-78, assoc provost, 65-74, assoc vpres acad affairs, 74-78, EMER PROF CHEM, UNIV CONN, 78- *Mem:* Fel AAAS; Am Chem Soc; Am Phys Soc. *Res:* Tracer studies of diffusion in solids and molten salts. *Mailing Add:* 23 Dunham Pond Rd Storrs CT 06268

ORR, WILLIAM H(AROLD), b Buffalo, NY, Nov 3, 30; wid; c 4. TELEPHONE TECHNOLOGY, MATERIALS PROCESS TECHNOLOGY. *Educ:* Cornell Univ, BEngPhys, 53, PhD(eng physics), 62; Cath Univ, MS, 57. *Prof Exp:* Instr, US Naval Acad, 55-57; mem tech staff thin films, Bell Labs, NJ, 62-64, group supvr integrated circuit develop group, Pa, 65-70, head, Process Capability Dept, Ind, 70-73, HEAD, TELEPHONE TECHNOL DEPT, BELL LABS, INDIANAPOLIS, 74- *Mem:* Inst Elec & Electronics Engrs; Components, Hybrids & Mfg Technol Soc. *Res:* Thin films; surface physics; film components and circuits; vacuum technology; solid state physics; integrated circuits; materials and processing technology; acoustic components; telephone cords; computer operations; computer aided design; metals; plastics; molding; electrets; engineering physics. *Mailing Add:* Bell Labs 2525 Shadeland Ave PO Box 1008 Indianapolis IN 46206

ORR, WILLIAM N, b Sioux Falls, SDak, June 13, 39; m 58; c 1. GEOLOGY. *Educ:* Univ Okla, BS, 61; Univ Calif, MA, 63; Mich State Univ, PhD(geol), 67. *Prof Exp:* Asst prof geol, Eastern Wash State Col, 66-67; asst prof, 67-74, ASSOC PROF GEOL, UNIV ORE, 74- *Concurrent Pos:* Prog assoc, Ocean Sediment Coring, NSF, 78- *Res:* Paleontology; biostratigraphy; paleoecology. *Mailing Add:* Dept of Geol Univ of Ore Eugene OR 97403

ORR, WILSON LEE, b Roswell, NMex, Jan 8, 23; m 44; c 2. ORGANIC GEOCHEMISTRY. *Educ:* Bethany-Peniel Col, AB, 45; Purdue Univ, MS, 47; Univ Southern Calif, PhD, 54. *Prof Exp:* Chemist prod control, Wabash Ord Works, US Dept Army, Ind, 45; asst, Purdue Univ, 45-47; vis asst prof, Sch Aeronaut, Univ Southern Calif, 48-49, staff chemist & res assoc geochem, Allan Hancock Found, 49-55, lectr & res assoc dept geol, 55-58, res assoc chem, 58-59; res engr & supvr, Atomiv Int Div, NAm Aviation, Inc, 60-63; RES ASSOC, FIELD RES LAB, MOBIL RES & DEVELOP CORP, 64- *Mem:* AAAS; Am Chem Soc; Geochem Soc; Sigma Xi. *Res:* Marine and petroleum geochemistry; organic geochemistry of sediments and petroleum. *Mailing Add:* Field Res Lab Mobil Res & Develop Corp Box 900 Dallas TX 75221

ORRALL, FRANK QUIMBY, b Somerville, Mass, Oct 15, 25; m 49; c 3. ASTROPHYSICS. *Educ:* Univ Mass, BS, 50; Harvard Univ, AM, 53, PhD(astron), 55. *Prof Exp:* Astrophysicist, Col Observ, Harvard Univ, 55-56; solar physicist, Sacramento Peak Observ, NMex, 56-64; PROF PHYSICS & ASTRON, INST ASTRON & UNIV HAWAII, MANOA, 64- *Concurrent Pos:* Vis scientist, High Altitude Observ, Colo, 70-71. *Mem:* Am Astron Soc; Inst Astron Union. *Res:* Solar physics; observation and theory of phenomena of the sun's atmosphere. *Mailing Add:* Dept of Physics & Astron Univ of Hawaii at Manoa Honolulu HI 96822

ORREGO, HECTOR, b Santiago, Chile, Dec 4, 23; Chilean & Can citizen; m 48; c 4. GASTROENTEROLOGY, PHARMACOLOGY. *Educ:* Univ Chile, MD, 49; FRCPS(C). *Prof Exp:* Asst prof med, Univ Chile, 50-64, prof med & pathophysiol, 64-73; vis prof med physiol & pharmacol, 74-76, PROF PHARMACOL, MED & PHYSIOL, UNIV TORONTO, 76-; HEAD GASTROENTEROL PROG, DEPT MED, ADDICTION RES FOUND CLIN INST, 77- *Concurrent Pos:* W R Kellog Found & Am Col Physicians int fels, 50-52; head sect gastroenterol, Univ Chile Clin Hosp, Santiago, 53-73; prof function pathophysiol & gastroenterol, Cath Univ Chile, Santiago, 56-73; subrogate dean, Univ Chile, 69; Addiction Res Found grant, 77- *Mem:* Am Col Physicians; Int Asn Study Liver; Am Asn Study Liver Dis; Can Soc Clin Invest. *Res:* Alcohol and the liver; intestinal absorption. *Mailing Add:* Dept of Med 33 Russell St Toronto ON M5S 2S1 Can

ORREN, MERLE MORRISON, b Chicago, Ill, Oct 2, 46; m 68; c 2. NEUROPSYCHOLOGY, PHYSIOLOGICAL PSYCHOLOGY. *Educ:* Oberlin Col, BA, 68; Boston Univ, MA, 70, PhD(psychol), 74. *Prof Exp:* RES PSYCHOLOGIST, SCH MED, BOSTON UNIV, 72- *Res:* Electrophysiological and behavioral changes in epilepsy; neural and behavioral plasticities in human visual development. *Mailing Add:* Boston Univ Sch of Med 80 E Concord St Boston MA 02118

ORRINGER, OSCAR, structural mechanics, materials science, see previous edition

ORROK, GEORGE TIMOTHY, b Boston, Mass, Nov 25, 30. PHYSICS. *Educ:* Harvard Univ, BA, 52, MA, 53, PhD(physics), 59. *Prof Exp:* Mem tech staff, Bell Tel Labs, 59-62; mem tech staff, Bellcomm, Inc, 62-64, suprvr environ sci, 64-65, dept head, 65-72; SUPVR SYSTS IDENTIFICATION, BELL TEL LABS, 72- *Mem:* AAAS; Am Phys Soc. *Res:* Solidification of pure metals; semiconductor device application and evaluation; environment and space sciences; quality assurance. *Mailing Add:* Bell Tel Labs Crawfords Corner Rd Holmdel NJ 07733

ORS, JOSE ALBERTO, b Havana, Cuba, June 14, 44; m 67; c 1. PHOTOCHEMISTRY. *Educ:* Univ S Fla, BA, 67, MS, 72, PhD(chem), 74. *Prof Exp:* Chemist air & water pollution, Environ Protection Comn, Fla, 68-69; res staff mem org photochem, T J Watson Res Ctr, IBM Corp, 74-80; MEM RES STAFF POLYMERIC MAT ENG, ENG RES CTR, WESTERN ELEC CO, 80- *Mem:* Am Chem Soc; NY Acad Sci; Inter-Am Photochem Soc. *Res:* Photocycloaddition of aromatic hydrocarbons to olefins; photochemical reactions in terpenes; reactions involving singlet oxygen. *Mailing Add:* Eng Res Ctr Western Elec Co Box 900 Princeton NJ 08540

ORSBORN, JOHN F, b Gary, Ind, Aug 13, 29; m 54; c 4. FLUID MECHANICS, HYDROLOGY. *Educ:* Colo Col, BA, 52; Univ Colo, BSCE, 57; Univ Minn, MSCE, 60; Univ Wis, PhD(civil eng), 64. *Prof Exp:* Eng aid, Soil Conserv Serv, USDA, Colo, 52-55; res fel hydraul models, St Anthony Falls Hydraul Lab, Univ Minn, 57-61, instr civil eng, 58-61; res assoc, Univ Wis, 61-64; asst prof fluid mech & asst hydraul engr, Lab, 64-69, assoc prof civil eng, Univ, 69-77, prof civil eng & chmn dept, 77-81, PROF & HYDRAUL ENGR, WASH STATE UNIV, 81- *Concurrent Pos:* Ford Found fel, Univ Wis, 61-64; assoc hydraul engr & head, R L Albrook Hydraul Lab, 69-74; consult, UN, Environ Protection Agency, Nat Water Comn, US Fish & Wildlife Serv, US Forest Serv & consulting firms. *Mem:* Am Soc Civil Engrs; Am Fish Soc; Am Soc Engr Educ; Nat Soc Prof Engrs. *Res:* Drainage basin influences on hydrologic parameters; dams, appurtenances and hydraulic design; river engineering and mechanics; flood plain management; drainage basin systems and stream flows. *Mailing Add:* Dept Civil Eng Wash State Univ Pullman WA 99163

ORSEN, STEFAN, electronics, see previous edition

ORSENIGO, JOSEPH REUTER, b Barryville, NY, Apr 4, 22; m 52; c 2. WEED SCIENCE. *Educ:* Cornell Univ, BS, 48, PhD(veg crops), 53. *Prof Exp:* Agronomist & mgr, Rice Res Sta, Ibec Res Inst, Venezuela, 53-55; agronomist-horticulturist & mgr cacao ctr, Inter-Am Inst Agr Sci, Costa Rica, 55-57; asst horticulturist, Univ Fla, 57, prof, 57-75, horticulturist, plant physiologist & emer prof herbicide & weed sci res, Agr Res & Educ Ctr, Inst Food & Agr Sci, 57-75; DIR RES, FLA SUGAR CANE LEAGUE, 76- *Concurrent Pos:* Adv, US Agency Int Develop, Costa Rica, 65-67; weed sci consult, Inter-Am Inst Agr Sci, Cent Am, 66; consult, Univ Calif, Multidisciplinary Pest Mgt Surv-Cent Am, 72. *Mem:* Fel AAAS; Am Soc Agron; Am Soc Hort Sci; Plant Growth Regulator Soc Am; Weed Sci Soc Am. *Res:* Weed science and herbicide research in agronomic crops in tropical America; sugarcane, agronomic and vegetable crops on organic soils; cocoa, coffee, corn, rice, sugarcane and general agriculture in Latin America; sucrose enhancement in sugarcane; air and water quality related to sugarcane. *Mailing Add:* FSCL Box 1148 Clewiston FL 33440

ORSI, ERNEST VINICIO, b New York, NY, Aug 10, 22; m 49; c 4. CELL BIOLOGY, VIROLOGY. *Educ:* Queen's Col, NY, BS, 44; Fordham Univ, MS, 48; St Louis Univ, PhD(biol), 55. *Prof Exp:* Sr staff mem, Virus Res Sect, Lederle Labs, Am Cyanamid Co, 54-61; prin res scientist virus diag, New York City Health Dept, 61-65; assoc prof, 65-72, PROF BIOL, SETON HALL UNIV, 72- *Concurrent Pos:* Brown-Hazen Fund grant, 65; contract hyperbaric enhancement of virus infection, Off Naval Res, 68-74; Deborah Hosp Found grant, 77-78, Fannie E Ripple Found grant, 79 & Stony-Wold-Herbert Fund grant, 80-81; exchange prof, Virol Dept, Wuhan Univ, 81. *Mem:* AAAS; Am Soc Microbiologists; Harvey Soc; Sigma Xi; Tissue Cult Asn. *Res:* Cell-virus relationships in normal neoplastic and transplantation systems as influenced either by changes in cell properties following sub-cultivation or induced by environmental factors. *Mailing Add:* Dept Biol Seton Hall Univ South Orange NJ 07079

ORSINI, MARGARET WARD (GIORDANO), b LeRoy, NY, Mar 18, 16; wid. EMBRYOLOGY, PHYSIOLOGY OF REPRODUCTIONS. *Educ:* Mt Holyoke Col, BA, 37; Cornell Univ, PhD(zool), 46. *Prof Exp:* Technician & asst path, Sch Med, St Louis Univ, 37-38; med technologist, Lister Clin Lab, 38-40; asst biol, Manhattanville Col, 40-42; asst histol & embryol, Cornell Univ, 42-46; instr zool, Duke Univ, 46-49; NIH fel, 49-52, res assoc, 52-53, PROF ANAT, MED SCH, UNIV WIS-MADISON, 72- *Concurrent Pos:*

Prin investr NIH grants, 59-76 & 79-82. *Mem:* Fel AAAS; fel NY Acad Sci; Am Asn Anat; Soc Exp Biol & Med; Soc Study Reproduction. *Res:* Physiology of reproduction; estrous cycle of hamster; ovulation; comparative morphogenesis and endocrinology of implantation; giant cells and vascular changes in gestation and post-partum involution; control of decidualization; comparison of pregnancy and pseudopregnancy; immunoreproduction; hormonal and morphology correlates of hamster. *Mailing Add:* Dept Anat Med Sch Univ Wis Madison WI 53706

ORSZAG, STEVEN ALAN, b New York, NY, Feb 27, 43; m 64; c 2. APPLIED MATHEMATICS. *Educ:* Mass Inst Technol, BS, 62; Princeton Univ, PhD(astrophys), 66. *Prof Exp:* Mem, Inst Adv Study, 66-67; from asst prof to assoc prof, 67-75, PROF APPL MATH, MASS INST TECHNOL, 75- *Concurrent Pos:* A P Sloan fel, 70-72; mem staff, Nat Ctr Atmospheric Res, 69-71; consult, Cambridge Hydro, 75-, ONR, 76-, Vector Tech, 78-, Los Alamos Sci Lab, 72- & NASA, 75- *Mem:* Am Phys Soc; Soc Appl & Indust Math. *Res:* Fluid dynamics; numerical methods. *Mailing Add:* Dept of Math Mass Inst Technol Cambridge MA 02139

ORT, CAROL ANN, b Boston, Mass, Sept 14, 47; m 71. NEUROBIOLOGY, CELL BIOLOGY. *Educ:* Mich State Univ, BS, 69; Univ Calif, Berkeley, PhD(molecular biol, neurobiol), 74. *Prof Exp:* Muscular Dystrophy Asn Am Inc fel neurobiol, Univ Calif, San Francisco, 74-76; lectr zool & neurobiol, San Francisco State Univ, 76-77; ASST PROF CELL BIOL & NEUROBIOL, UNIV NEV, 77- *Concurrent Pos:* prin investr, Univ Nev Res Adv Bd, 77-79, NIH, 79-82. *Mem:* Neurosci Soc; AAAS; Asn Women Sci; Am Soc Cell Biol; Am Soc Zoologists. *Res:* Neurogenic and myogenic mechanisms controlling the development of differentiated muscle fiber types in regenerating salamander limbs. *Mailing Add:* Dept Biol Univ Nev Reno NV 89557

ORT, DONALD RICHARD, b Weymouth, Mass, Feb 20, 49; m 71; c 2. BIOCHEMISTRY, PLANT PHYSIOLOGY. *Educ:* Wake Forest Univ, BS, 71; Mich State Univ, PhD(plant biochem), 74. *Prof Exp:* Fel biochem, Purdue Univ, 74-76; sr fel, Univ Wash, 76-78; ASST PROF PLANT BIOCHEM, UNIV ILL, URBANA, 78- *Concurrent Pos:* NIH Nat Serv award, 75-77. *Mem:* Am Soc Plant Physiol; Biophys Soc. *Res:* Photosynthesis; mechanism of energy coupling between photosynthetic electron transport and adenosine triphosphate. *Mailing Add:* Dept Bot 289 Morrill Hall Univ Ill Urbana IL 61801

ORT, MORRIS RICHARD, b Liberty Center, Ohio, Sept 16, 27; m 51; c 3. SYNTHESIS, CATALYSIS. *Educ:* Bowling Green State Univ, BS, 51; Univ Cincinnati, MS, 62. *Prof Exp:* Res chemist, 51-66, res specialist, 66-73, sci fel, 73-80, SR SCI FEL, MONSANTO CO, 80- *Mem:* Am Chem Soc. *Res:* Polymer synthesis; catalysis; gas phase polymerization; solid state polymerization; polyolefins; condensation polymers; organometallics; organic synthesis. *Mailing Add:* 6 Bittersweet Lane Wilbraham MA 01095

ORTEGA, GUSTAVO RAMON, b El Paso, Tex, Dec 6, 45. PHARMACEUTICAL CHEMISTRY. *Educ:* Univ Tex, Austin, BS, 69, PhD(pharmaceut chem), 76. *Prof Exp:* Asst prof, 75-80, ASSOC PROF PHARMACEUT CHEM, SOUTHWESTERN OKLA STATE UNIV, 80- *Mem:* AAAS; Am Chem Soc; Am Asn Col Pharm. *Res:* Application of structure activity relationships to the synthesis of synthetic medicinal agents; analysis of commercially available pharmaceuticals. *Mailing Add:* Sch Pharm Southwestern Okla State Univ Weatherford OK 73096

ORTEGA, JACOBO, b Allende, Mex, Mar 21, 29; m 56; c 3. PLANT PATHOLOGY, PLANT GENETICS. *Educ:* Univ Coah, Mex, BSc, 56; Okla State Univ, MSc, 58; Univ Minn, PhD(plant path & genetics), 60. *Prof Exp:* Asst wheat breeding, Rockefeller Found, Mex, 54-56; head sect, Nat Inst Agr Res SAG, 61-66; chief pathologist & plant breeder, World Seeds, Inc, 66-71; res agronomist, Calif Milling Corp, Los Angeles, 71-73; asst prof, 73-77, ASSOC PROF BIOL, PAN AM UNIV, 77- *Mem:* AAAS. *Res:* Wheat diseases and genetics; agro-economical research of the wheat and milling industries of California. *Mailing Add:* Dept of Biol Pan Am Univ Edinburg TX 78539

ORTEGA, JAMES M, b Madison, Wis, June 15, 32; m 57; c 1. NUMERICAL ANALYSIS. *Educ:* Univ NMex, BS, 54; Stanford Univ, PhD(math), 62. *Prof Exp:* Programmer, Sandia Corp, NMex, 56-58, mathematician, 62-63; mathematician, Bellcomm, Inc, Washington, DC, 63-64; asst prof comput sci, Univ Md, College Park, 64-66, assoc prof prof comput sci & appl math, 66-69; vis prof, Univ Calif, San Diego, 71-72; dir, ICASE, NASA-Langley Res Ctr, 72-77; prof math & head dept, NC State Univ, 77-79; CHARLES HENDERSON PROF & CHMN, APPL MATH & COMPUT SCI, UNIV VA, 79-, ASSOC DEAN, ENG & APPL SCI, 80- *Concurrent Pos:* From assoc ed to ed, SIAM Rev, Soc Indust & Appl Math, 65-68; prof comput sci, math & appl math, Univ Md, College Park, 69-74; adj prof math & physics, Col William & Mary, 73-77; adj prof appl math & comput sci, Univ Va, 73-77; consult & mem COSERs numerical comput panel, NSF, 75-78. *Mem:* Am Math Soc; Asn Comput Mach; Soc Indust & Appl Math. *Res:* Numerical analysis; applied mathematics; computer science. *Mailing Add:* Appl Math & Comput Sci Thornton Hall Univ Va Charlottesville VA 22901

ORTEGO, JAMES DALE, b Washington, La, Sept 23, 41; m 65; c 3. INORGANIC CHEMISTRY. *Educ:* Univ Southwestern La, BS, 63; La State Univ, PhD(chem), 68. *Prof Exp:* Asst prof, 68-75, assoc prof, 75-81, PROF CHEM, LAMAR UNIV, 81- *Concurrent Pos:* Welch Found res grant, Lamar Univ, 69-83. *Mem:* Am Chem Soc; Sigma Xi. *Res:* Coordination chemistry of transition metal and uranium complexes; oxygen complexes of biological interest. *Mailing Add:* Dept Chem Lamar Univ Beaumont TX 77710

ORTEL, WILLIAM CHARLES GORMLEY, b Spokane, Wash, Sept 28, 26; m 51; c 3. DATA COMMUNICATIONS. *Educ:* Yale Univ, BS, 49, MS, 50, PhD(physics), 53. *Prof Exp:* Asst physics, Yale Univ, 53-54; NSF fel, Inst Theoret Physics, Denmark, 54-55; physicist, Missile Div, Lockheed Aircraft Corp, 55-56; PHYSICIST, BELL LABS, 56- *Res:* Assessment of new technologies for computing and communication systems including experiments with components, analysis of performance; proposal, market evaluation and development of data terminals, microprocessor applications, mini and microcomputer software; integrated circuits; data communications; optical transmission. *Mailing Add:* Bell Labs Holmdel NJ 07733

ORTEN, JAMES M, b Farmington, Mo, Nov 29, 04; m 32. BIOCHEMISTRY. *Educ:* Univ Denver, BS, 28, MS, 29; Univ Colo, PhD(physiol chem), 32. *Prof Exp:* Asst pharm, Univ Denver, 27-28; instr biochem, Univ Colo, 31-32; from asst prof to assoc prof, 37-57, prof biochem, 57-75, dir grad affairs, 71-75, EMER PROF BIOCHEM & HON DIR ASST DEAN GRAD PROGS, SCH MED, WAYNE STATE UNIV, 75- *Concurrent Pos:* Coxe fel, Yale Univ, 32-33 & 34-35, Nat Res Coun fel, 33-34, Pfizer & Co fel, 35-37; guest, Int Physiol Cong, Switz, 38. *Mem:* Fel AAAS; Am Chem Soc; Am Soc Biol Chem; Soc Exp Biol & Med; fel Am Inst Nutrit (secy, 52-55). *Res:* Effect of dietary protein and metallic elements on hemopoiesis; metabolism of organic acids, alcohol and the porphyrins; carbohydrate metabolism in experimental diabetes. *Mailing Add:* Dept of Biochem Wayne State Univ Sch of Med Detroit MI 48201

ORTENBURGER, IRENE BEARDSLEY, see Beardsley, Irene Adelaide

ORTENBURGER, LEIGH NATUS, b Norman, Okla, Feb 14, 29; m 56; c 2. APPLIED STATISTICS. *Educ:* Univ Okla, BS, 52; Univ Calif, Berkeley, MA, 53; Stanford Univ, MS, 65. *Prof Exp:* Sr engr, Sylvania Reconnaissance Systs Lab, 57-59, from develop engr to advan develop engr, 60-63, eng specialist, 63-64 & Sylvania Electronic Defense Lab, 64-68, sr eng specialist, Sylvania Electronic Defense Lab, 68-80, SR ENG SPECIALIST, GTE PROD CORP, SYLVANIA SYSTS GROUP, GTE SYLVANIA, 80- *Mem:* Opers Res Soc Am; Inst Math Statist. *Res:* Radio wave propagation; robust estimation methods. *Mailing Add:* 4237 Los Palos Ave Palo Alto CA 94306

ORTH, CHARLES DOUGLAS, b Seattle, Wash, June 1, 42; m 64; c 2. PLASMA PHYSICS, HIGH ENERGY PHYSICS. *Educ:* Univ Wash, BS, 64; Calif Inst Technol, PhD(physics), 70. *Prof Exp:* Res assoc cosmic ray physics, NASA Manned Spacecraft Ctr, 70-72; asst res physicist astrophys & cosmic ray physics, Univ Calif, Berkeley, 72-78; PHYSICIST, LAWRENCE LIVERMORE NAT LAB, 78- *Concurrent Pos:* Consult, Space Sci Steering Comt, NASA, 79- *Mem:* Am Phys Soc; Sigma Xi; Planetary Soc. *Res:* Charge and energy spectra of high energy cosmic rays; age of cosmic rays and abundance of cosmic ray Be-10; anisotropy of microwave blackbody radiation; real time correction of atmospherically degraded telescope images; target design for inertial confinement fusion. *Mailing Add:* L-23 Lawrence Livermore Nat Lab PO Box 808 Livermore CA 94550

ORTH, CHARLES JOSEPH, b Fontana, Calif, Aug 13, 30; m 59; c 1. GEOCHEMISTRY. *Educ:* San Diego State Col, BA, 54; Univ NMex, PhD(chem), 69. *Prof Exp:* STAFF MEM RADIOCHEM, LOS ALAMOS SCI LAB, 56- *Mem:* Am Phys Soc; Am Chem Soc. *Res:* Nuclear structure; pion-nucleus and muon-nucleus reactions; muonic x-rays; trace element abundances in sedimentary rocks. *Mailing Add:* 281 Chamisa Los Alamos NM 87544

ORTH, GEORGE OTTO, JR, b Seattle, Wash, July 14, 13; m 40; c 3. ORGANIC CHEMISTRY. *Educ:* Univ Wash, BS, 36. *Prof Exp:* Plant chemist, Solvents, Inc, 33-35; plant chemist & engr, Preservative Paint Co, 35-41; res chemist, Seattle Gas Co, 41-42; lab mgr, A J Norton, Consult Chemists, 42-51; vpres, Food, Chem & Res Labs, Inc, 53-58; lab dir, Korry Mfg Co, 63-68; CONSULT, 51- *Concurrent Pos:* Mem comt estab synthetic rubber mfg corp, Tokyo, Japan, 53; private res, 58- *Mem:* Fel AAAS; fel life mem Am Inst Chem; emer mem Am Chem Soc; Asn Consult Chem & Chem Eng; emer mem Inst Food Technol. *Res:* High polymers; wood specialities and chemistry; organic nitrogen derivatives; protective coatings; adhesives and plastics; wood fiber specialties; oil adsorbents as related to ecology; wood cellulose animal nutrition technology; agriculture crop utilization. *Mailing Add:* 10807 Roosevelt Way NE Seattle WA 98125

ORTH, JOHN C(ARL), b Sioux City, Iowa, June 20, 31; m 56; c 5. CHEMICAL ENGINEERING. *Educ:* Univ Seattle, BS, 57. *Prof Exp:* Trainee, Allis-Chalmers Mfg Co, Wis, 58-59, appln engr, 59-61, res engr, 61-62, engr-in-charge appl res, 62-64; group leader energy conversion, Monsanto Res Corp, Mass, 64-66; chief advan power sources br, Power Equip Div, US Army Mobility Equip Res & Develop Ctr, 66-69, chief, Advan Develop Div, Electrotechnol Lab, 69-71, chief, Electrotechnol Dept, 71-74; tech dir, Mineral Res Ctr, Butte, Mont, 74-76; dir, Mont Dept Natural Resources, 77-78; dep managing dir, 78-80, VPRES, MONT ENERGY RES & DEVELOP INST, 80- *Mem:* Am Inst Chem Engrs. *Res:* Solids processing and agglomeration; direct reduction of iron ore; electro-chemical energy conversion. *Mailing Add:* Mont Energy Res & Develop Inst Box 3809 Butte MT 59701

ORTH, PAUL GERHARDT, b Chicago, Ill, Apr 18, 29; m 57; c 4. SOIL FERTILITY, IRRIGATION. *Educ:* Univ Ariz, BS, 51; Wash State Univ, MS, 53; Univ Wis, PhD(phosphate availability), 59. *Prof Exp:* Asst soils chemist, 59-77, ASSOC SOILS CHEMIST, AGR RES & EDUC CTR, UNIV FLA, 77- *Mem:* Am Soc Agron; Soil Sci Soc Am; Am Soc Horticultural Sci. *Res:* Slow release fertilizers; irrigation; calcareous soils; climatology; analysis of plant tissue for inorganic plant nutrients; fertilizer efficiency and leaching loss. *Mailing Add:* Agr Res & Educ Ctr Univ of Fla 18905 SW 280th St Homestead FL 33031

ORTH, ROBERT JOSEPH, b Elizabeth, NJ, Nov 16, 47; m 73. BIOLOGICAL OCEANOGRAPHY. *Educ:* Rutgers Univ, BA, 69; Univ Va, MS, 71; Univ Md, College Park, PhD(zool), 75. *Prof Exp:* Asst marine scientist marine biol, Va Inst Marine Sci, 74-77; instr, 75-77, ASST PROF MARINE BIOL, SCH MARINE SCI, COL WILLIAM & MARY & ASSOC MARINE SCIENTIST MARINE BIOL, VA INST MARINE SCI, 77- *Concurrent Pos:* Instr marine biol, Dept Marine Sci, Univ Va, 75-77. *Mem:* Int Asn Aquatic Vascular Plant Biologists; Ecol Soc Am. *Res:* Biology of seagrasses; structional and functional aspects of marine benthos. *Mailing Add:* Va Inst of Marine Sci Gloucester Point VA 23062

ORTH, WILLIAM ALBERT, b Coatesville, Pa, Sept 28, 31; m 58; c 2. CONTINUUM MECHANICS. *Educ:* US Mil Acad, BS, 54; Purdue Univ, MS, 61; Brown Univ, PhD(appl math), 70. *Prof Exp:* Dep chief staff civil eng, Strategic Air Command Hq, 72-74; asst prof mech, 61-63, asst prof math, 68-70, prof physics & head dept, 74-78, DEAN FAC, US AIR FORCE ACAD, 78- *Mem:* Am Soc Eng Educ; Am Asn Physics Teachers; Math Asn Am; Am Inst Aeronaut & Astronaut. *Mailing Add:* USAFA/DF US Air Force Academy CO 80840

ORTHOEFER, FRANK THEODORE, b Columbus, Ohio, Mar 31, 41; m 65; c 2. FOOD SCIENCE, CHEMISTRY. *Educ:* Ohio State Univ, BSc, 63, MS, 65; Mich State Univ, PhD(food sci), 69; Univ Ill, MBA, 82. *Prof Exp:* Food technologist chem, Battelle Mem Inst, 65-66; sr scientist, Glidden Durkee Div, SCM Corp, 69-71, sect head foods foods, 71-72; asst prof food sci, Univ Fla, 72-73; sr scientist food technol, 73-82, SECT HEAD, PROTEIN, OILS & DEVELOP, A E STALEY MFG CO, 82- *Mem:* Inst Food Technologists; Inst Shortening & Edible Oils; Am Oil Chemists. *Res:* Chemistry of fats and oils; protein chemistry; pigment chemistry. *Mailing Add:* 70 Hickory Point Court Decatur IL 62526

ORTHOEFER, JOHN GEORGE, b Columbus, Ohio, Nov 7, 32; m 64; c 3. VETERINARY MEDICINE. *Educ:* Ohio State Univ, BS, 59, DVM, 63; Univ Calif, Davis, MS, 72. *Prof Exp:* Vet div epidemiol, Fla State Bd Health, 63-64 & Commun Dis Ctr, Kans City, Kans, 64-66; toxicologist path, Food & Drug Admin, Washington, DC, 66-69; vet labb animal, Nat Air Pollution Control Admin, USPHS, 69-71; training path, Univ Calif, Davis, 71-74; pathologist, Health Effects Res Lab, US Environ Protection Agency, 74-81; ADJ RES SCIENTIST, DIV COMP PATH, UNIV FLA, 81- *Mem:* Am Vet Med Asn; Int Acad Path; Am Col Toxicol. *Res:* Descriptive pathology of the lung with a goal toward the development of more accurate morphometric techniques in lung pathology. *Mailing Add:* 3525 NW 31st St Gainesville FL 32605

ORTHWEIN, W(ILLIAM) C(OE), b Toledo, Ohio, Jan 27, 24; m 48; c 3. ENGINEERING MECHANICS. *Educ:* Mass Inst Technol, BS, 48; Univ Mich, MS, 50, PhD(eng mech), 59. *Prof Exp:* Aerophysicist, Convair Div, Gen Dynamics Corp, Tex, 51-52; res assoc, Univ Mich, 52-58; adv engr, Int Bus Mach Corp, NY, 58-61; assoc prof Univ Okla, 61-63; res scientist, NASA, 63-65; PROF ENG, SOUTHERN ILL UNIV, 65- *Mem:* Am Soc Mech Engrs; Am Soc Civil Engrs; Soc Exp Stress Anal; Tensor Soc; Nat Soc Prof Engrs. *Res:* Machine design; computer aided design; nonlinear elasticity; vibrations. *Mailing Add:* PO Box 3332 Carbondale IL 62901

ORTIZ, ARACELI, b Culebra, PR, Jan 15, 37; m 76; c 1. DENTISTRY, ORAL PATHOLOGY. *Educ:* Univ PR, BS, 58, DMD, 62; Ind Univ, MSD(oral path), 67; Am Bd Oral Path, dipl; Am Bd Oral Med, dipl; Am Bd Forensic Odontol, dipl. *Prof Exp:* Assoc prof, McGill Univ, 67-73; ASSOC PROF ORAL PATH, ORAL MED & FORENSIC ODONTOL, SCH DENT, UNIV PR, 73- *Concurrent Pos:* Mem clin cancer training comt, NIH, 72-73; attend, Univ Dist Hosp, 73-75 & 78-; consult, Vet Admin Hosp, San Juan, PR, 74-; consult, Criminal Invest Corps, Police Acad, 74-; assoc oral surg, Dr Rafael Lopez Mussa Munic Hosp, 75-; consult, Hosp Auxilio Mutuo, 76- *Mem:* Fel Am Acad Oral Path; Am Acad Oral Med; Am Soc Forensic Odontol; Can Soc Forensic Sci; Am Cancer Soc. *Res:* Herpes virus; cancer education programs. *Mailing Add:* Univ of PR Sch of Dent GPO Box 5067 San Juan PR 00936

ORTIZ, MELCHOR, JR, b Victoria, Tex, Nov 14, 42; m 69; c 3. APPLIED STATISTICS. *Educ:* Tex A&I Univ, BS, 70, MS, 71; Tex A&M Univ, PhD(statist), 75. *Prof Exp:* asst prof, 75-80, ASSOC PROF STATIST, NMEX STATE UNIV, 80- *Concurrent Pos:* Statist consult. *Mem:* Am Statist Asn; Biometric Soc; Sigma Xi. *Res:* Nonconvex mathematical programming. *Mailing Add:* Col of Agr & Home Econ NMex State Univ Las Cruces NM 88001

ORTIZ DE MONTELLANO, PAUL RICHARD, b Mexico City, Mex, Sept 6, 42; US citizen. BIO-ORGANIC CHEMISTRY, PHARMACEUTICAL CHEMISTRY. *Educ:* Mass Inst Technol, BA, 64; Harvard Univ, MA, 66, PhD(chem), 68. *Prof Exp:* NATO fel, Swiss Fed Inst Technol, 68-69; group leader pharmaceut chem, Syntex Res Labs, 69-71; asst prof, 72-78, assoc prof, 78-80, PROF PHARMACEUT CHEM, SCH PHARM, UNIV CALIF, SAN FRANCISCO, 80- *Concurrent Pos:* Consult, Panel Vapor Phase Pollutants, Nat Acad Sci; assoc prof, Inst Chem, Univ Louis Pasteur, 78-79; A P Sloan Found res fel, 78. *Mem:* Am Chem Soc; The Chem Soc; AAAS; Soc Advan Chicanos & Native Am Sci. *Res:* Sterol biosynthesis and regulation; cytochrome P-450; enzyme mechanisms and inhibition; drug metabolism; strained ring biological intermediates; synthetic methods; toxicology. *Mailing Add:* Sch of Pharm Univ of Calif San Francisco CA 94143

ORTMAN, ELDON EMIL, b Marion, SDak, Aug 11, 34; m 57; c 3. ENTOMOLOGY. *Educ:* Tabor Col, AB, 56; Kans State Univ, MS, 57, PhD(entom), 63. *Prof Exp:* Asst entom, Kans State Univ, 56-59, instr, 59-61; res entomologist, Northern Grain Insect Res Lab, Entom Res Div, Agr Res Serv, USDA, 61-68, lab dir & invest leader, 68-72; PROF ENTOM & HEAD DEPT, PURDUE UNIV, WEST LAFAYETTE, 72- *Concurrent Pos:* Prof, Sdak State Univ, 68-72. *Mem:* Entom Soc Am; Sigma Xi; AAAS. *Mailing Add:* Dept of Entom Purdue Univ West Lafayette IN 47906

ORTMAN, HAROLD R, b Buffalo, NY, Dec 19, 17; m 39, 60; c 6. DENTISTRY. *Educ:* Univ Buffalo, DDS, 41; Am Bd Prosthodont, dipl, 56. *Prof Exp:* From instr to assoc prof prosthodont, Univ Buffalo, 42-62; clin prof, 62-64, PROF PROSTHODONT & CHMN DEPT, SCH DENT, STATE UNIV NY BUFFALO, 64- *Mem:* Am Prosthodont Soc (pres, 80); Am Col Prosthodontists; fel Am Col Dent. *Res:* Prosthodontics; bone physiology; occlusion; denture retention; denture resins; refitting denture bases with todays concepts and material. *Mailing Add:* Capen Hall G56E Sch Dent State Univ of NY Buffalo NY 14214

ORTMAN, ROBERT A, b Detroit, Mich, Mar 4, 26; m 53; c 4. ZOOLOGY. *Educ:* Univ Calif, BA, 51, MA, 53, PhD(zool), 55. *Prof Exp:* Asst zool, Univ Calif, 53-55, jr res zoologist, Mus Vet Zool, 56; res officer, Med Res Coun, Otago, NZ, 55-56; instr zool, Tulane Univ, 56-57; assoc prof biol, Mem Univ, 57-59; asst prof, Boston Col, 59-62; asst prof, 62-70, ASSOC PROF BIOL, CITY COL NEW YORK, 70- *Concurrent Pos:* Res grants, Nat Res Coun Can, 58-59, USPHS, 59-66. *Mem:* AAAS; Am Soc Zool; Am Asn Anatomists. *Res:* Pituitary cytology and endocrinology; comparative endocrinology; vertebrate histology; cytochemistry; electron microscopy. *Mailing Add:* Dept of Biol City Col of New York New York NY 10031

ORTNER, DONALD JOHN, b Stoneham, Mass, Aug 23, 38; m 60; c 3. PHYSICAL ANTHROPOLOGY. *Educ:* Columbia Union Col, BA, 60; Syracuse Univ, MA, 67; Univ Kans, PhD(anthrop), 70. *Prof Exp:* Grant, 68-70, assoc curator, 70-80, CURRATOR ANTHROP, SMITHSONIAN INST, 80- *Concurrent Pos:* NIH grants, 69-72 & 72-73; assoc prof, Univ Md, 71-75. *Mem:* Am Asn Phys Anthrop; Paleopath Asn. *Res:* Calcified tissue biology; paleopathology. *Mailing Add:* Dept Anthrop Smithsonian Inst Washington DC 20560

ORTNER, MARY JOANNE, b Windsor, Can, 10, 46; US citizen. PHARMACOLOGY, BIOPHYSICS. *Educ:* Calif State Univ, BS, 68, MS, 71; Univ Hawaii, PhD(pharmacol), 76. *Prof Exp:* Instr biol, Ramona Convent High Sch, 68-69; res asst zool, Calif State Univ, 69-71; res asst pharmacol, Univ Hawaii, 71-76; NRSA fel molecular pharmacol, Nat Heart, Lung & Blood Inst, 76-77; staff fel, 77-80, SR STAFF FEL, NAT INST ENVIRON HEALTH SCI, NIH, 80- *Mem:* AAAS; Am Soc Photobiol; Bioelectromagnetic Soc. *Res:* Effects of drugs on membranes; biophysical techniques, especially ESR, fluorescence spectroscopy and microscopy, circular dichroism; the mechanism of histamine release from mast cells and the molecular mechanism of compound 48/80; influence of microwave radiation on molecular systems; molecular mechanisms of photosensitization. *Mailing Add:* Nat Inst of Environ Health Sci Lab of Environ Biophys Box 12233 Research Triangle Park NC 27709

ORTO, LOUISE A (MRS PATRICK FAMIGHETTI), b New York, NY, Sept 25, 30; m 65. LABORATORY MEDICINE. *Educ:* Col New Rochelle, BA, 52; Columbia Univ, MS, 63. *Prof Exp:* Res assoc human nutrit biochem, Nutrit Res Lab, St Luke's Convalescent Hosp, Greenwich, Conn, 52-60; asst dir res, Geriatric Nutrit Lab, Osborn Mem Home, 52-74; asst dir res, Nutrit & Metab Res Div, 60-74, DIR CLIN LAB, BURKE REHAB CTR, 74- *Concurrent Pos:* Managing ed, Nutrit Reports Int, 69-74, assoc ed, 75-; cert, Nat Registry Clin Chem & Nat Cert Agency for Med Lab Personnel. *Mem:* Fel Am Inst Chem; Am Chem Soc; Am Inst Nutrit; Am Soc Med Technol. *Res:* Proteins; amino acids; nutritional requirements. *Mailing Add:* Clin Lab Burke Rehab Ctr White Plains NY 10605

ORTOLEVA, PETER JOSEPH, b Brooklyn, NY, Nov 5, 42; div; c 1. BIOLOGICAL RHYTHMS, BIOPHYSICS. *Educ:* Rensselaer Polytech Inst, BS, 64; Cornell Univ, PhD(appl physics), 70. *Prof Exp:* Fel chem, Mass Inst Technol, 70-75; asst prof, 75-77, ASSOC PROF CHEM, IND UNIV, 77- *Res:* Onset of spatial and temporal patterns that occur in far from equilibrium reacting systems are studied with the theory of irreversible processes, with applications made to physical, chemical, biological and geological systems; rate of chemical reactions in condensed systems studied using statistical mechanics; growth of chemically complex crystals studied theoretically. *Mailing Add:* Dept of Chem Ind Univ Bloomington IN 47401

ORTON, COLIN GEORGE, b London, Eng, June 4, 38; m 64; c 3. MEDICAL PHYSICS. *Educ:* Bristol Univ, BSc, 59; Univ London, MSc, 61, PhD(radiation physics), 65. *Prof Exp:* Lectr physics, St Bartholomew's Hosp, Univ London, 61-66; from instr to assoc prof physics, Med Ctr, NY Univ, 66-75; chief physicist, RI Hosp, 76-78; assoc prof radiation med, Brown Univ, 76-81; PROF RADIATION ONCOL, MED SCH, WAYNE STATE UNIV, 81-; CHIEF PHYSICIST, HARPER HOSP, 81- *Concurrent Pos:* Consult, Morristown Mem Hosp, NJ, 68-75; lectr, St Vincent's Hosp, New York, 70-71 & Metrop Hosp, New York, 71-75; ed bull, Am Asn Physicists in Med, 71-73; adj prof biol, Fairleigh Dickinson Univ, 73-75; ed, Progress Med Radiation Physics, 78- *Mem:* Am Asn Physicists in Med (pres-elect, 81); Brit Inst Physics; Brit Inst Radiol; Health Physics Soc; Am Inst Physics. *Res:* Radiation; radiobiology; radiation oncology; computers in medicine; radiation dosimetry. *Mailing Add:* Radiation Oncol Ctr Harper Grace Hosp 3990 John Rd Detroit MI 48201

ORTON, GEORGE W, b Hopkinsville, Ky, Oct 31, 19; m 43; c 2. MATERIALS & ENVIRONMENTAL ENGINEERING. *Educ:* Univ Ky, BS, 43; Carnegie Inst Technol, MS, 48; Ohio State Univ, PhD(metall eng), 61. *Prof Exp:* US Air Force, 43-69, sect chief alloy develop, Wright-Patterson AFB, Ohio, 48-52, div chief mfg methods, Ger, 52-55, br chief mech equip, NMex, 55-59, instr metall, US Air Force Acad, 61-62, assoc prof, 62-64, dir res, 64-66, exchange prof, Philippine Mil Acad, 66-68, chief mfg technol div, Air Force Systs Command, Wright-Patterson AFB, Ohio, 68-69; PROF ENG, UNIV PR, MAYAGUEZ, 69- *Concurrent Pos:* Chmn, PR Comt Indust Pollution. *Mem:* Am Soc Eng Educ; Am Soc Metals. *Res:* Development of high-strength, low density alloys for aerospace vehicles; adaption of American manufacturing standards to European plants; design of material handling systems. *Mailing Add:* Col Eng Univ PR Mayaguez PR 00708

ORTON, GLENN SCOTT, b Fall River, Mass, July 24, 48. PLANETARY ATMOSPHERES. *Educ:* Brown Univ, ScB, 70; Calif Inst Technol, PhD(planetary sci), 75. *Prof Exp:* Assoc scientist, Div Geol & Planetary Sci, 75, resident res planetary atmospheres, Space Sci Div, 75-77, sr scientist, Earth & Space Sci Div, 77-79, MEM TECH STAFF, NASA JET PROPULSION LAB, CALIF INST TECHNOL, 79- *Concurrent Pos:* mem adv missions studies team, Jet Propulsion Lab, 78-; Mem NASA infeared telescope comt, Proposal Review Comt, 81- *Mem:* Sigma Xi; Int Astron Union; Am Astron Soc. *Res:* Determination of thermal structure, composition, opacity, energy balance and climatology of planetary atmospheres; remote sensing of thermal radiation and reflected solar radiation from the atmospheres of outer planets. *Mailing Add:* 183-301 Jet Propulsion Lab 4800 Oak Grove Dr Pasadena CA 91109

ORTON, WILLIAM R, JR, b Texarkana, Tex, May 4, 22; m 50; c 4. MATHEMATICS. *Educ:* Univ Ark, BA, 47; Univ Ill, MA, 48, PhD(math), 51. *Prof Exp:* Fulbright fel, Univ Paris, 51-52; instr math, Oberlin Col, 52-53; from asst prof to assoc prof, 53-61, PROF MATH, UNIV ARK, FAYETTEVILLE, 61- *Concurrent Pos:* NSF fac fel, Univ Wash, 65-66; mem NSF staff, India, 67-68; Fulbright lectr, Univ Tehran, Iran, 77-78; dir, Minority Engr Prog, 81-82. *Mem:* Am Math Soc; Math Asn Am. *Res:* Integration; mathematics education. *Mailing Add:* Dept of Math SE 324 Univ of Ark Fayetteville AR 72701

ORTS, FRANK A, b Gonzales, Tex, May 6, 31; m 53; c 2. MEAT SCIENCE. *Educ:* Tex A&M Univ, BS, 53, MS, 59, PhD(animal sci), 68. *Prof Exp:* Instr meats, 59-63, asst prof animal sci, 63-81, EXTEN MEAT SPECIALIST, TEX A&M UNIV, 63- *Honors & Awards:* Distinguished Meats Exten-Indust Award, Am Meat Sci Asn, 75. *Mem:* Am Meat Sci Asn; Am Soc Animal Sci; Sigma Xi. *Res:* Carcass composition. *Mailing Add:* Dept Animal Sci Kleberg Ctr Rm 114 Tex A&M Univ College Station TX 77843

ORTS, RICHARD JOHN, b Moulton, Tex, Oct 13, 41; m 63; c 3. MAMMALIAN PHYSIOLOGY, ENDOCRINOLOGY. *Educ:* Sam Houston State Univ, BS, 64, MA, 65; Tex A&M Univ, PhD(reproductive physiol), 70. *Prof Exp:* Instr biol, San Jacinto Col, 65-67; asst prof physiol, Okla State Univ, 73-80; SR ENDOCRINOLOGIST, 3M CO, 80- *Mem:* Am Physiol Soc; Endocrine Soc; Soc Study Reproduction; Am Soc Zoologists. *Res:* Reproductive endocrinology; neuroendocrinology; pineal physiology. *Mailing Add:* 3M Co 3M Ctr Bldg 218-3 St Paul MN 55144

ORTTUNG, WILLIAM HERBERT, b Philadelphia, Pa, June 16, 34; m 63; c 2. PHYSICAL CHEMISTRY. *Educ:* Mass Inst Technol, SB, 56; Univ Calif, Berkeley, PhD(phys chem), 61. *Prof Exp:* Asst prof chem, Stanford Univ, 60-63; asst prof, 63-69, assoc prof, 69-79, PROF CHEM, UNIV CALIF, RIVERSIDE, 79- *Mem:* AAAS; Am Chem Soc; Am Phys Soc. *Res:* Theory of molecular polarizability; molecular electrostatics; dielectric theory; electro-optical phenomena; crystal and molecular optics; physical biochemistry. *Mailing Add:* Dept of Chem Univ of Calif Riverside CA 92521

ORTWERTH, BERYL JOHN, b St Louis, Mo, Aug 13, 37. BIOCHEMISTRY, OPHTHALMOLOGY. *Educ:* St Louis Univ, BS, 59; Univ Mo, MS, 62, PhD(biochem), 65. *Prof Exp:* Asst prof, 68-73, assoc prof, 73-81, PROF OPHTHAL, UNIV MO-COLUMBIA, 81- *Concurrent Pos:* Am Cancer Soc grant, Oak Ridge Nat Lab, 66-68. *Mem:* AAAS; Am Soc Biol Chem; Asn Res Vision & Ophthal; Am Chem Soc. *Res:* Control of cell division; structure and function of transfer RNA; lens proteinases and inhibitors; cataract biochemistry. *Mailing Add:* Dept Ophthal Med Ctr Univ Mo Columbia MO 65201

ORVIK, JON ANTHONY, physical organic chemistry, see previous edition

ORVILLE, HAROLD DUVALL, b Baltimore, Md, Jan 23, 32; m 54; c 4. METEOROLOGY. *Educ:* Univ Va, BA, 54; Fla State Univ, MS, 59; Univ Ariz, PhD(meteorol), 65. *Prof Exp:* Res asst meteorl, Univ Ariz, 63-65; from asst prof to assoc prof, 65-73, HEAD NUMERICAL MODELS GROUP, INST ATMOSPHERIC SCI, SDAK SCH MINES & TECHNOL, 65-, PROF METEOROL, 73-, HEAD DEPT, 74- *Concurrent Pos:* Mem, Int Comn Cloud Physics, 71-80; consult, Off Environ Modification, Nat Oceanic & Atmospheric Admin, 72-73; ed, J Atmospheric Sci, 78- *Mem:* Am Meteorol Soc; Am Geophys Union. *Res:* Numerical modeling of medium scale atmospheric motions and cloud development; cloud photogrammetry and modification; measurements of cloud characteristics from specially instrumented aircraft; data analysis by computer. *Mailing Add:* Inst of Atmospheric Sci SDak Sch of Mines & Technol Rapid City SD 57701

ORVILLE, PHILIP MOORE, b Ottawa, Ill, Feb 24, 30; m 57; c 3. GEOLOGY. *Educ:* Calif Inst Technol, BS, 52; Yale Univ, MA, 54, PhD(geol), 58. *Prof Exp:* Fel petrol, Geophys Lab, Carnegie Inst Technol, 57-60; asst prof petrol & mineral, Cornell Univ, 60-62; assoc prof, 62-72, PROF PETROL & MINERAL, YALE UNIV, 72- *Concurrent Pos:* Ed, Am J Sci. *Mem:* Geol Soc Am; Am Geophys Union; Geochem Soc; Mineral Soc Am. *Res:* Experimental petrology; feldspars; equilibrium between volatile and silicate phases. *Mailing Add:* Dept of Geol & Geophys Yale Univ New Haven CT 06520

ORVILLE, RICHARD EDMONDS, b Long Beach, Calif, July 28, 36; m 64; c 2. ATMOSPHERIC PHYSICS, SPECTROSCOPY. *Educ:* Princeton Univ, AB, 58; Univ Ariz, MS, 63, PhD(meteorol), 66. *Prof Exp:* Mgr mfg, Procter & Gamble Co, 59-60; res asst physics, Johns Hopkins Univ, 60-61; res asst meteorol, Univ Ariz, 61-64, res assoc, 64-66; sr res scientist, Westinghouse Elec Corp, 66-68; assoc prof, 68-81, PROF ATMOSPHERIC SCI, STATE UNIV NY ALBANY, 81- *Concurrent Pos:* Assoc prog dir, NSF, 70-71; vis prof, Univ Wis-Madison, 79. *Mem:* fel Am Meteorol Soc; Am Geophys Union. *Res:* Cloud physics; atmospheric electricity; spectroscopy. *Mailing Add:* Dept Atmospheric Sci State Univ NY Albany NY 12222

ORVIS, ALAN LEROY, b Cleveland, Ohio, May 2, 21; m 47; c 2. MEDICAL PHYSICS. *Educ:* Westminster Col, BS, 44; Case Western Reserve Univ, MS, 49; Univ Tex, PhD(physics), 52. *Prof Exp:* Instr physics, Univ Tex, 50-52; instr, 56-59, asst prof, 59-66, ASSOC PROF BIOPHYS, MAYO GRAD SCH MED, 66; CONSULT BIOPHYS, MAYO CLIN, 52- *Mem:* AAAS; Am Phys Soc; Meteorol Soc Am; Health Physics Soc; Soc Nulcear Med. *Res:* Radioisotope measurements; radiological physics; health physics. *Mailing Add:* Curie Pavilion Mayo Clin Rochester MN 55901

ORWIG, LARRY EUGENE, b York, Pa, Jan 8, 44; m 78; c 1. SPACE SCIENCES, ASTROPHYSICS. *Educ:* Lebanon Valley Col, BS, 65; Univ NH, PhD(physics), 71. *Prof Exp:* Nat Acad Sci-Nat Res Coun fel, 72-74, ASTROPHYSICIST X-RAY ASTRON, GODDARD SPACE FLIGHT CTR, NASA, 74- *Mem:* Am Phys Soc; Am Astron Soc. *Res:* Experimental x-ray and gamma-ray astronomy; solar flare phenomena; pulsars. *Mailing Add:* Code 684 NASA Greenbelt MD 20771

ORWOLL, RICHARD DAVID, b Minneapolis, Minn, July 25, 45; m 68. PHYSICAL CHEMISTRY. *Educ:* St Olaf Col, BA, 67; Univ Calif, San Diego, PhD(chem), 71. *Prof Exp:* Teacher chem, Govt Sch, Hamburg, Ger, 71-72; fel, Univ Tex, 72-74; CHEMIST, FIBER INDUSTS, INC, 74- *Res:* Development of fibers for industrial end uses and the investigation of liquid-crystalline systems using nuclear magnetic resonance. *Mailing Add:* 6101 Patrick Pl Charlotte NC 28210

ORWOLL, ROBERT ARVID, b Minneapolis, Minn, Aug 28, 40; m 72; c 2. PHYSICAL CHEMISTRY. *Educ:* St Olaf Col, BA, 62; Stanford Univ, PhD(chem), 66. *Prof Exp:* Res instr chem, Dartmouth Col, 66-68; inst mat sci fel chem, Univ Conn, 68-69; asst prof, 69-72, ASSOC PROF CHEM, COL WILLIAM & MARY, 72- *Mem:* AAAS; Am Chem Soc. *Res:* Physical chemistry of macromolecules; thermodynamics of polymer solutions; thermodynamic properties of liquid crystals. *Mailing Add:* Dept of Chem Col of William & Mary Williamsburg VA 23185

ORY, HORACE ANTHONY, b Amite, La, Dec 16, 32; m 58. PHYSICAL CHEMISTRY. *Educ:* Southeastern La Col, BS, 53; La State Univ, PhD(chem), 57. *Prof Exp:* Phys scientist, Monsanto Chem Co, 57-60, E H Plesset Assocs, 60-63, Astrophys Res Corp, 63-64, Heliodyne Corp, 63-64 & Rand Corp, 64-71; PHYS SCIENTIST, R&D ASSOCS, 71- *Mem:* AAAS; Am Chem Soc; Am Phys Soc; fel Am Inst Chem. *Res:* Spectroscopy; reaction kinetics; electrooptics. *Mailing Add:* R&D Assoc PO Box 9695 Marina Del Rey CA 90291

ORY, ROBERT LOUIS, b New Orleans, La, Nov 26, 25; m 48; c 2. BIOCHEMISTRY, NUTRITION. *Educ:* Loyola Univ, La, BS, 48; Univ Detroit, MS, 50; Agr & Mech Col, Tex, PhD(biochem, nutrit), 54. *Prof Exp:* Asst, Univ Detroit, 48-50; chemist, Exp Sta, Agr & Mech Col, Tex, 50-54; chemist, Colloidal Properties Unit, 54, oil seeds sect, 55-57, biochemist, Seed Proteins Pioneering Lab, 58-69, head protein properties res, 69-72, RES LEADER BIOCHEM RES, OILSEED & FOOD LAB, SOUTHERN REGIONAL RES CTR, USDA, 72- *Concurrent Pos:* Fulbright res scholar, Copenhagen Univ, 68-69. *Mem:* AAAS; Am Chem Soc; Sigma Xi; Am Soc Biol Chemists; Inst Food Technologists. *Res:* Biosynthesis of amino acids in microorganisms; isolation and characterization of proteins and enzymes, including lipases, proteases, phosphatases and amylases, from oilseeds and barley seeds; plant lectins; biosynthesis of aflatoxins; rice dietary fiber; peanut proteins for food uses; antigens in cotton dust and bioassay for byssinosis. *Mailing Add:* Southern Regional Res Ctr PO Box 19687 New Orleans LA 70179

ORZECH, CHESTER EUGENE, JR, b Chicago, Ill, Dec 31, 37; m 63; c 4. ANALYTICAL CHEMISTRY, THERMAL ANALYSIS. *Educ:* Ill Inst Technol, BS, 60; Mich State Univ, PhD(org chem), 68. *Prof Exp:* SECT HEAD ANAL CHEM, AYERST LABS, INC, 65- *Mem:* NAm Thermal Anal Soc. *Res:* Analytical chemistry of pharmaceuticals; limited organic synthesis; NMR spectroscopy; thermal analysis of pharmaceuticals. *Mailing Add:* Ayerst Labs Inc Rouses Point NY 12979

ORZECH, GRACE GEIST, algebra, see previous edition

ORZECH, MORRIS, b Arg, Feb 10, 42; US citizen; m 63. MATHEMATICS. *Educ:* Columbia Col, AB, 62; Cornell Univ, PhD(math), 67. *Prof Exp:* Asst prof math, Univ Ill, Urbana, 66-68; asst prof, 68-76, ASSOC MATH, QUEEN'S UNIV, ONT, 76- *Mailing Add:* Dept of Math Queen's Univ Kingston ON K7L 3N6 Can

ORZECHOWSKI, ADAM, b Poland, Mar 8, 16; nat US; m 47; c 1. PHYSICAL CHEMISTRY, MICROSCOPY. *Educ:* Univ Liege, DSc(appl sci), 52. *Prof Exp:* Fel, Nat Res Coun Can, 52-53; res chemist, Allied Chem Corp, NJ, 53-56; sr res chemist, Cabot Corp, 57-67; scientist, 67-72, SR CHEMIST & PROJ LEADER OPTICAL MICROS, XEROX CORP, 72- *Res:* Heterogeneous catalysis; hydrogenation; oxidation; polymerization; surface chemistry of silica and of carbon black; dispersions of pigments; small particle morphology; optical microscopy transmitted and reflected; photomicrography. *Mailing Add:* 64 Clintwood Court Rochester NY 14620

ORZECHOWSKI, RAYMOND FRANK, b Camden, NJ, Feb 28, 38; m 61; c 3. PHARMACOLOGY. *Educ:* Philadelphia Col Pharm, BSc, 59; Temple Univ, MS, 61, PhD(pharmacol), 64. *Prof Exp:* Sr res pharmacologist, Nat Drug Co, Richardson-Merrell, Inc, Philadelphia, 64-70; from asst prof to assoc prof, 70-80, PROF PHARMACOL, PHILADELPHIA COL PHARM & SCI, 80- *Mem:* AAAS; Am Pharmaceut Asn; Sigma Xi; Soc Toxicol; Am Soc Pharmacol. *Res:* cardiovascular and autonomic pharmacology; inflammation and anti-inflammatory agents; peripheral dopamine receptors. *Mailing Add:* Dept Pharmacol Phila Col Pharmacol & Sci Philadelphia PA 19104

OSAWA, YOSHIO, b Tokyo, Japan, May 28, 30; m 55; c 2. ORGANIC CHEMISTRY, ENDOCRINOLOGY. *Educ:* Tokyo Metrop Univ, BS, 53; Univ Tokyo, MS, 55, PhD(org chem), 59. *Prof Exp:* Res scientist, Tsurumi Res Lab Chem, Teikoku Hormone Mfg Co, Japan, 56-58, chief div steroid chem, Div Total Synthesis of steroids, 58-64, prin res scientist, 64-67; assoc scientist, 67-70, head dept steroid biochem, 71-75, PRIN RES SCIENTIST & ASSOC DIR, POST-DOCTORAL TRAINING PROG, MED FOUND BUFFALO, 70-, HEAD DEPT ENDOCRINE BIOCHEM, 75-; ASST RES PROF BIOCHEM, ROSWELL PARK DIV, GRAD SCH, STATE UNIV NY BUFFALO, 74- *Concurrent Pos:* Fel steroid chem, Dept Med, Roswell

Park Mem Inst, 60-63; Am Cancer Soc fac res award, 69-74; consult to clin staff, Roswell Park Mem Inst, 73- 73-; vis prof, Sch Med, Nihon Univ, Tokyo, 77, 78. *Mem:* Am Chem Soc; Chem Soc Japan; Endocrine Soc; NY Acad Sci. *Res:* Synthesis and structure-function relationships of estrogens; total synthesis of steroids; steroid reactions; polymer-iron preparation for anemia; estrogen metabolites; stereochemistry and mechanism of steroid biosynthesis; clinical assay of estrogen conjugates; steroid biochemistry and endocrinology. *Mailing Add:* Med Found of Buffalo 73 High St Buffalo NY 14203

OSBAHR, ALBERT J, JR, b Nov 4, 31; US citizen; m 57; c 3. PHYSICAL BIOCHEMISTRY, PHYSICAL ORGANIC CHEMISTRY. *Educ:* Fordham Univ, BS, 52, MS, 53; Georgetown Univ, PhD(phys biochem), 59. *Prof Exp:* Chemist, Cent Labs, NY, 52-53 & Quaker Maid Labs, 53-54; biochemist, Naval Med Res Inst, 55-58; res biochemist, Geront Inst, NIH, 58-60, RES INVESTR, NAT INST ARTHRITIS, METAB & DIGESTIVE DIS, 60- *Concurrent Pos:* Prof lectr, Georgetown Univ, 58- *Mem:* AAAS; Am Chem Soc. *Res:* Structure of macromolecules and its correlation to function of molecules; relationship of structure to biological activity; protein modification; enzymology and enzyme kinetics; function of metal ions in biological systems; blood clotting mechanism; muscle biochemistry; polymerization of proteins as involved in muscular contraction and blood coagulation. *Mailing Add:* 624 Blossom Dr Woodley Garden Rockville MD 20850

OSBERG, G(USTAV) L(AWRENCE), b Alta, Can, July 9, 17; m 44; c 3. CHEMICAL ENGINEERING. *Educ:* Univ Alta, BSc, 39; Univ Toronto, MA, 47, PhD(phys chem), 49. *Prof Exp:* Jr res officer, Nat Res Coun Can, 40-41, from assoc res officer to sr res officer chem eng & head sect, Appl Chem Div, 49-69, chief, Financial Planning & Budgeting, 67-81; RETIRED. *Concurrent Pos:* Ed, Can J Chem Eng, 62-67. *Res:* Fluidized solids applications and theory; catalytic oxidation. *Mailing Add:* Nat Res Coun of Can Ottawa ON K1A 0K6 Can

OSBERG, PHILIP HENRY, b Melrose, Mass, Oct 23, 24; m 48; c 2. GEOLOGY. *Educ:* Dartmouth Col, AB, 47; Harvard Univ, AM, 49, PhD(geol), 52. *Prof Exp:* Asst prof geol, Pa State Univ, 51-52; from asst prof to assoc prof, Colby Col, 52-57; assoc prof, 57-63, head dept geol sci, 66-71, PROF GEOL, UNIV MAINE, ORONO, 63- *Concurrent Pos:* Fulbright sr res fel, Oslo, Norway, 65-66; geologist, US Geol Surv, var times, 68- *Mem:* Geol Soc Am; Mineral Soc Am; Norweg Geol Soc. *Res:* Metamorphic petrology; structural geology; regional geology of the northern Appalachians. *Mailing Add:* Dept of Geol Sci Univ of Maine Orono ME 04473

OSBORG, HANS, b Halberstadt, Ger, Oct 18, 01; nat US; m 30; c 2. PHYSICAL CHEMISTRY. *Educ:* Univ Braunschweig, Ger, BS, 24, MS, 25, DrIng, 27. *Prof Exp:* Mem staff, Res Inst, Ger Metal Co, Inc, 27-29; dir res prod & eng, Lithium Metal Dept, Maywood Chem Works, 29-34; exec vpres, Del, 58-66, PRES, CHEMIRAD CORP, DEL, 66-, TECH DIR, 58-, PRES, NY, 50- *Concurrent Pos:* Mgt consult, 34-; tech dir, Metalectro Corp, Md, 50-53, pres, 53-55. *Mem:* Am Chem Soc; Am Inst Mining, Metall & Petrol Eng; NY Acad Sci; Tech Asn Pulp & Paper Indust. *Res:* Ethylene imines; aziridines; hydrazines, especially unsymmetrical dimethyl hydrazine; chemistry and metallurgy of lithium; boron hydrides; especially diborane and its compounds. *Mailing Add:* PO Box 152 80 Longview Rd Port Washington NY 11050

OSBORN, CLAIBORN LEE, b Austin, Tex, Sept 15, 33; m 59; c 3. ORGANIC CHEMISTRY, RADIATION CHEMISTRY. *Educ:* Univ Tex, BA, 56, PhD(org chem), 60. *Prof Exp:* Chemist, Celanese Chem Co, 60-62, sr res chemist, 62-63; Robert A Welch Found fel photochem, Univ Tex, 63-65; res chemist, 65-68, proj scientist radiation chem, 68-72, res scientist, 72-75, sr res scientist, 75-78, RES ASSOC, UNION CARBIDE CORP, 79- *Mem:* Am Chem Soc. *Res:* Photochemistry; application of photochemical techniques to polymer processing; electrochemistry; electropolymerization; photoresists; photoelectro chemistry. *Mailing Add:* Chem & Plastics Group Union Carbide Corp PO Box 8361 South Charleston WV 25303

OSBORN, ELBURT FRANKLIN, b Winnebago Co, Ill, Aug 13, 11; m 39; c 2. CERAMICS ENGINEERING, RESEARCH ADMINISTRATION. *Educ:* DePauw Univ, BA, 32; Northwestern Univ, MS, 34; Calif Inst Technol, PhD(geol), 38. *Hon Degrees:* ScD, Alfred Univ, 65, Northwestern Univ, 72, DePauw Univ, 72 & Ohio State Univ, 72. *Prof Exp:* Instr geol, Northwestern Univ, 37; geologist, Val d'Or, Can, 38; petrologist, Geophys Lab, Carnegie Inst, 38-42; phys chemist, Nat Defense Res Comt, 42-45; res chemist, Eastman Kodak Co, NY, 45-46; prof geochem, Col Mineral Industs, 46-70, head dept earth sci, 46-53, dean col, 53-59, vpres res, 59-70, EMER PROF GEOCHEM, COL EARTH & MINERAL SCI, PA STATE UNIV, UNIVERSITY PARK, 70-, EMER PROF RES, 71-; EMER DISTINGUISHED PROF, CARNEGIE INST WASHINGTON, 77- *Concurrent Pos:* Mem adv comt geophys br, Off Naval Res, Nat Acad Sci-Nat Res Coun, 47-50, mem, Mat Adv Bd, 65-69, chmn comt on mineral sci & technol, 66-70, chmn bd mineral resources & mem comn natural resources, Nat Res Coun, 74-77; mem earth sci panel, NSF, 53-55, mem div comt math, phys & eng sci, 55-59, chmn, 57-58, mem adv panels course content improv prog, 60-61, phys sci facil, 60-64; mem bd dirs, Am Geol Inst, 56-59; NSF sr fel, Cambridge Univ, 58; mem adv panel mineral prod div, Nat Bur Standards, 58-62, chmn, 58-59, metall div, 58-64, mem div chem & chem technol, 60-63; mem bd, Univ Corp Atmospheric Res, 59-67; mem adv comt basic res, US Army Res Off Ceramics, 60-63; vchmn, Sirimar Corp, Italy, 61-63; mem bd, Geisinger Med Ctr, 62-, mem bd dirs, Inst Med Educ & Res, 69-; mem, Pa Health Res Inst, 66-70; mem bd dirs, Pa Sci & Eng Found, 68-71, 74-; distinguished prof, Geophys Lab, Carnegie Inst Washington, 73-77; mem earth sci adv bd, Stanford Univ, 69-72; mem bd dirs, Pa Res Corp, 71-, vpres, 74-80, pres, 80-; dir, Bur Mines, Washington, DC, 70-73; mem adv bd, Col Eng, Univ Calif, Berkeley, 74-78; mem mat adv comt, Off Technol Assessment, Cong of US, 74-79; mem geosci adv panel, Los Alamos Sci Lab, 75-79; chmn, US Nat Comt for Geol, Nat Acad Sci, 75-77; chmn adv comt mining & mineral eng res, Secy of Interior, 78-; mem, Continental Sci Drilling Comt, Nat Res Coun, 80-, Panel Geochem Fibrous Mat Related to Health Risks, 79- & chmn, Comt Geol Aspects Indust Waste Disposal, 79-81. *Honors & Awards:* Award, Am Iron & Steel Inst, 54; Roebling Medal, Mineral Soc Am, 72; John Jeppson Award, Am Ceramic Soc, 73; Hal Williams Hardinge Award, Soc Mining Engrs, 74; Albert Victor Bleininger Award, Am Ceramic Soc, 76. *Mem:* Nat Acad Eng; Eng; hon mem Am Ceramic Soc (pres, 65); hon mem Can Ceramic Soc; fel Mineral Soc Am (pres, 60). *Res:* Physicochemical petrology; glass technology; physical chemistry of refractories; blast furnance and open hearth slags; phase equilibira in mineral systems; industrial minerals; mineral synthesis; mineral and energy resources. *Mailing Add:* 330 E Irvin Ave State Col PA 16801

OSBORN, H(ARLAND) JAMES, b Alexandria, Minn, June 24, 32; m 53; c 3. SYNTHETIC ORGANIC CHEMISTRY, PHOTOGRAPHIC CHEMISTRY. *Educ:* Univ Minn, BS, 54, PhD(org chem), 58. *Prof Exp:* RES CHEMIST, EASTMAN KODAK CO, 58- *Mem:* Am Chem Soc. *Res:* Organic synthesis; design of color photographic systems; chemistry and physics of photographic development. *Mailing Add:* 24 Skycrest Dr Rochester NY 14616

OSBORN, HENRY H(OOPER), b Hartford, Conn, Dec 3, 26; m 59; c 2. MECHANICAL ENGINEERING. *Educ:* Tufts Univ, BSME, 50; Purdue Univ, MSME, 56, PhD(mech eng), 58. *Prof Exp:* Anal engr, Pratt & Whitney Aircraft Div, United Aircraft Corp, 50-52; instr mech eng, Bucknell Univ, 52-54; from asst prof to assoc prof, Purdue Univ, 58-64; proj engr, 64-65, mgr appl res, 65-77, CHIEF ENGR, AIR PREHEATER CO, INC, 77- *Mem:* Am Soc Mech Engrs; Am Soc Eng Educ. *Res:* Thermodynamics; heat and mass transfer; air pollution control; water desalination. *Mailing Add:* Air Preheater Co Inc Develop Lab Andover Rd Wellsville NY 14895

OSBORN, HERBERT B, b San Juan, PR, July 9, 29. HYDROLOGY. *Educ:* Stanford Univ, BS, 52, MS, 53, CE, 56; Univ Ariz, PhD, 71. *Prof Exp:* Hydraul engr, Ariz, 56-58, Miss, 58-60, RES HYDRAUL ENGR, SOUTHWEST WATERSHED RES CTR, USDA, 61- *Concurrent Pos:* Staff scientist, Nat Prog Staff, Agr Res Serv, USDA, 74-75; mem steering comt, Bd Agr & Renewable Resources, Nat Res Coun-Nat Acad Sci, 75-76. *Mem:* AAAS; Am Geophys Union; Am Meteorol Soc; Int Asn Statist in Phys Sci. *Res:* Hydrologic research on thunderstorms and thunderstorm runoff on semiarid rangeland watersheds in the southwest. *Mailing Add:* Southwest Watershed Res Ctr USDA 442 E Seventh St Tucson AZ 85705

OSBORN, HOWARD ASHLEY, b Evanston, Ill, May 16, 28; m 51; c 4. MATHEMATICS. *Educ:* Princeton Univ, AB, 49; Stanford Univ, PhD, 55. *Prof Exp:* Instr math, Univ Calif, 54-56; from asst prof to assoc prof, 56-65, PROF MATH, UNIV ILL, URBANA, 65- *Concurrent Pos:* Consult, Rand Corp, 54-65; NSF grants, 58-60, 62- *Mem:* Am Math Soc; Math Asn Am. *Res:* Differentiable manifolds; piecewise linear manifolds. *Mailing Add:* Dept of Math Univ of Ill Urbana IL 61801

OSBORN, J MARSHALL, JR, b New York, NY, Sept 11, 30; m 59, 75; c 2. MATHEMATICS. *Educ:* Princeton Univ, AB, 52; Univ Chicago, PhD(math), 57. *Prof Exp:* Instr math, Univ Conn, 57; res instr, 57-59, from asst prof to assoc prof, 59-67, PROF MATH, UNIV WIS-MADISON, 67- *Mem:* Am Math Soc; Math Asn Am. *Res:* Nonassociative algebra. *Mailing Add:* Dept of Math Univ of Wis Madison WI 53706

OSBORN, J(OHN) R(OBERT), b Kansas City, Mo, Aug 11, 24; m 45; c 3. MECHANICAL ENGINEERING. *Educ:* Purdue Univ, BS, 50, MS, 53, PhD(mech eng), 57. *Prof Exp:* Jr engr, Thiokol Chem Corp, 50-51; asst, 51-57, from asst prof to assoc prof mech eng, 57-61, prof mech eng, 61-70 & 70-79, PROF AERONAUT & ASTRON, PURDUE UNIV, WEST LAFAYETTE, 80- *Concurrent Pos:* Br chief, Ballistics Res Lab, Aberdeen Proving Ground, 70-71. *Mem:* Am Inst Aeronaut & Astronaut; Soc Automotive Engrs. *Res:* Combustion instability in rockets; high frequency response instrumentation; combustion problems in air pollution; combustion in solid rockets and interior ballistics. *Mailing Add:* Sch of Mech Eng Purdue Univ West Lafayette IN 47907

OSBORN, JAMES MAXWELL, b Ypsilanti, Mich, Sept 10, 29; m 55; c 4. ANALYTICAL MATHEMATICS. *Educ:* Univ Mich, BS, 51, MS, 52, PhD(math), 55. *Prof Exp:* Instr math, Ohio State Univ, 54-57; asst prof, 57-60, ASSOC PROF MATH, GA INST TECHNOL, 60- *Mem:* Am Math Soc; Math Asn Am. *Res:* Complex variables. *Mailing Add:* Sch of Math Ga Inst Technol Atlanta GA 30332

OSBORN, JEFFREY WHITAKER, b London, Eng, Jan 2, 30; m 73; c 4. DENTAL ANATOMY, PALEONTOLOGY. *Educ:* Univ London, BDS, 55, PhD(anat), 66; FDSRCS, 60. *Prof Exp:* Registr conserv dent, Guy's Hosp, Univ London, 56-57, demonstr dent anat, 57-64, lectr anat, 64-68, sr lectr, 68-71, reader, 71-75, prof, 75-78; PROF ORAL BIOL, FAC DENT, UNIV ALTA, 78- *Concurrent Pos:* Vis prof vert paleont, Mus Comp Zool, Harvard Univ, 71-72. *Res:* Evolution, comparative anatomy, development and structure of teeth and jaws. *Mailing Add:* 6508 124th St Edmonton AB T6H 3V3 Can

OSBORN, JOHN EDWARD, b Onamia, Minn, July 12, 36; m 59; c 3. NUMERICAL ANALYSIS, PARTIAL DIFFERENTIAL EQUATIONS. *Educ:* Univ Minn, Minneapolis, BS, 58, MS, 63, PhD(math), 65. *Prof Exp:* From asst prof to assoc prof, 65-75, PROF MATH, UNIV MD, COLLEGE PARK, 75- *Concurrent Pos:* NSF res grants, 66-68 & 72- *Mem:* Am Math Soc; Soc Indust & Appl Math. *Res:* Numerical solution of partial differential equations. *Mailing Add:* Dept of Math Univ of Md College Park MD 20742

OSBORN, JUNE ELAINE, b Endicott, NY, May 28, 37; m 66; c 3. VIROLOGY, INFECTIOUS DISEASE. *Educ:* Oberlin Col, BA, 57; Case Western Reserve Univ, MD, 61. *Prof Exp:* Intern & resident pediat, Children's Hosp Med Ctr, Boston, 61-62 & 63-64; resident, Mass Gen Hosp, 62-63; fel infectious dis, Sch Med, Johns Hopkins Univ, 64-65 & Sch Med,

Univ Pittsburgh, 65-66; from instr to assoc prof, 66-75, PROF PEDIAT & MED MICROBIOL, SCH MED, UNIV WIS-MADISON, 75- *Concurrent Pos:* Mem panel viral & rickettsial vaccines, Food & Drug Admin, 73-79, mem exp virol study sect, NIH Div Res Grants, 75-79; assoc dean, Grad Sch Biol Sci, Univ Wis-Madison, 75; mem, Panel Vaccines & Related Immunol Prod, 80-, chair, Life Sci Associateship Review Panel, Nat Res Coun, 80-, mem, Med Affairs Adv Comt, Yale Univ, 81- *Mem:* Am Acad Pediat; Am Asn Immunologists; Soc Pediat Res; Infectious Dis Soc Am; Am Acad Microbiol. *Res:* Pathogenesis of cytomegalovirus infections; nucleic acid homology of human and simian papovaviruses; mechanism of papovavirus oncogenesis; mechanisms of viral persistence and latency. *Mailing Add:* 497 Med Sci Bldg Univ of Wis Sch of Med Madison WI 53706

OSBORN, KENNETH WAKEMAN, b Lansing, Mich, Feb 4, 37. MARINE BIOLOGY, COASTAL ECOLOGY. *Educ:* Mich State Univ, BS, 60. *Prof Exp:* Marine biologist res, Tex Game & Fish Comn, 61-63; fishery biologist res, US Bur Com Fisheries, 63-67; fishery biologist environ impact assessment, US Bur Sport Fish & Wildlife, 67-69; marine biologist, US Army Corps Engrs, 69-72; fisheries biologist coastal zone mgt, Nat Marine Fisheries Serv, 72-78; FISHERIES ADVISOR FISH DEVELOP, USAID, 78- *Mem:* Am Inst Fishery Res Biologists; Gulf Estuarine Res Soc; Coastal Soc. *Res:* Marine, estuarine and coastal fishery biology, ecology, development and management; environmental conservation of living marine resources and the habitats upon which they depend; coastal zone management. *Mailing Add:* 6009 Bush Hill Dr Alexandria VA 22310

OSBORN, MARY JANE, b Colorado Springs, Colo, Sept 24, 27; m 50. MOLECULAR BIOLOGY, BIOCHEMISTRY. *Educ:* Univ Calif, Berkeley, BA, 48; Univ Wash, PHD(biochem), 58. *Prof Exp:* From instr to asst prof microbiol, Sch Med, NY Univ, 61-63; from asst prof to assoc prof molecular biol, Albert Einstein Col Med, 63-68; PROF MICROBIOL, SCH MED, UNIV CONN HEALTH CTR, 68-, HEAD DEPT, 80- *Concurrent Pos:* USPHS fel, Sch Med, NY Univ, 59-61, career develop award & res grants, Sch Med, NY Univ, ALbert Einstein Col Med & Univ Conn Health Ctr, 62-; NSF res grants, Albert Einstein Col Med, 65-68; mem microbial chem study sect, NIH, 68-72; mem res comt, Am Heart Asn, 72-77; mem comt space biol & med, Space Sci Bd, Nat Acad Sci, 74-77; mem bd sci counrs, Nat Heart & Lung Inst, 75-79; assoc ed, J Biol Chem, 78-80; mem, Nat Sci Bd, 80-86. *Mem:* Nat Acad Sci; AAAS; Am Soc Biol Chem (pres, 81-82); Am Chem Soc (pres, Div Biol Chem, 75-76); fel Am Acad Arts & Sci. *Res:* Biosynthesis of bacterial lipopolysaccharides; biogenesis of membranes. *Mailing Add:* Dept Microbiol Univ Conn Health Ctr Farmington CT 06032

OSBORN, RICHARD KENT, b Ft Wayne, Ind, Mar 12, 19; m 45; c 4. PLASMA PHYSICS, PHYSICAL OPTICS. *Educ:* Mich State Univ, BS, 48, MS, 49; Case Western Reserve Univ, PhD(physics), 52. *Prof Exp:* Physicist, Oak Ridge Nat Lab, 52-57; assoc prof, 57-59, PROF NUCLEAR ENG, UNIV MICH, ANN ARBOR, 59-, CONSULT, RES INST, 57- *Concurrent Pos:* Consult, Oak Ridge Nat Lab, 57-65 & KMS-Fusion, Inc, Ann Arbor, 72- *Mem:* Am Phys Soc; Am Nuclear Soc. *Res:* Nuclear, reactor and plasma physics; aspects of theories of liquids. *Mailing Add:* 1330 Ardmoor Dr Ann Arbor MI 48103

OSBORN, ROGER (COOK), b Crystal City, Tex, Mar 14, 20; m 42; c 3. MATHEMATICS. *Educ:* Univ Tex, BA, 40, MA, 42, PhD(math), 54. *Prof Exp:* Teacher high sch, Tex, 40-42; instr appl math, 42-44, 46-53, from instr to assoc prof, 53-67, PROF MATH, UNIV TEX, AUSTIN, 67- *Res:* Number theory; differential equations; mathematics education. *Mailing Add:* Dept of Math Univ of Tex Austin TX 78712

OSBORN, RONALD GEORGE, b Los Angeles, Calif, May 22, 48; m 77. SYSTEMS ECOLOGY, STATISTICS. *Educ:* Calif State Col, Long Beach, BS, 71; San Diego State Univ, MS, 75. *Prof Exp:* Res asst ecol, US Int Biol Prog, 72, 73 & 74; statistician ornith, Patuxent Wildlife Res Ctr, 75-77, WILDLIFE BIOLOGIST ENVIRON MGT, WESTERN ENERGY & LAND USE TEAM, US FISH & WILDLIFE SERV, 77- *Honors & Awards:* Spec Achievement Award, US Fish & Wildlife Serv, 78. *Res:* Development of simulation modeling, geographical analysis and data base structuring to aid understanding and management of ecological processes; geo-processing. *Mailing Add:* US Fish & Wildlife Serv 2625 Redwing Rd Ft Collins CO 80526

OSBORN, TERRY WAYNE, b Roswell, NMex, May 17, 43. BIOCHEMISTRY, PHYSICAL BIOCHEMISTRY. *Educ:* Univ Calif, Riverside, BS, 69, PhD(biochem), 75. *Prof Exp:* Res scientist biochem, 76, res scientist & proj leader, 76, res scientist & proj team leader, 76-77, GROUP LEADER & SR RES SCIENTIST BIOCHEM & CHEM, McGAW LABS, AM HOSP SUPPLY CORP, 78- *Mem:* Sigma Xi; Am Chem Soc; Am Oil Chemists Soc; Inst Food Technologists. *Res:* Development and use of lipids and amino acids solutions for total parenteral nutrition; studies on essential fatty acids; photochemical degradation of tryptophan; vitamin D and steroid binding proteins. *Mailing Add:* McGaw Labs Am Hosp Supply Corp 2525 McGaw Ave Irvine CA 92714

OSBORNE, CARL ANDREW, b Pittsburgh, Pa, Sept 17, 40; m 64; c 3. VETERINARY MEDICINE, PATHOLOGY. *Educ:* Purdue Univ, Lafayette, DVM, 64; Univ Minn, St Paul, PhD(vet med), 70. *Prof Exp:* From instr to assoc prof vet med, 64-75, PROF VET CLIN SCI, COL VET MED, UNIV MINN, ST PAUL, 75-, CHMN DEPT SMALL ANIMAL CLIN SCI, 76- *Concurrent Pos:* Mem, Nat Kidney Found. *Honors & Awards:* Vet of Year, Am Animal Hosp Asn, 74; Gaines Award, Am Vet Med Asn, 77. *Mem:* Am Soc Vet Clin Path; Am Vet Med Asn; Am Soc Nephrology. *Res:* Pathophysiology of congenital and inherited renal diseases; pathophysiology of glomerulonephritis; pathophysiology of neoplasms of the urinary system; relationship of calcium metabolism to renal disease; urolithiasis. *Mailing Add:* Col Vet Med Univ of Minn St Paul MN 55101

OSBORNE, CHARLES EDWARD, b Mt Croghan, SC, Aug 4, 29; m 55; c 2. SYNTHETIC ORGANIC CHEMISTRY. *Educ:* Univ NC, BS, 51; Univ Maine, MS, 53; Northwestern Univ, PhD(chem), 56. *Prof Exp:* Chemist, Eastman Kodak Co, 51-52, chemist, Tenn Eastman Co, 56-59, sr chemist, 59-63, sr chemist, Eastman Chem Prod, Inc, 63-64, sr chemist, Tenn Eastman Co, 64-71, DEVELOP ASSOC, TENN EASTMAN CO, 71- *Mem:* Am Chem Soc. *Res:* Syntheses of organic compounds. *Mailing Add:* 1540 Belmeade Dr Kingsport TN 37664

OSBORNE, DAVID WENDELL, b Brush, Colo, Jan 11, 35; m 55; c 2. ORGANIC CHEMISTRY. *Educ:* Colo Col, BS, 57; Univ Del, PhD(org chem), 60. *Prof Exp:* Spec assignments chemist, Dow Chem Co, 60-61, res chemist, Edgar C Britton Res Lab, 61-65, proj leader, 65-66, group leader, 66-69, div leader, 69-70, res mgr chem biol res, 70-71, res mgr, Agr Org Dept, 71-76, res mgr, Agr Prod Dept, 76-80. *Mem:* Am Chem Soc; Sci Res Soc Am. *Res:* Synthesis and chemical properties of agricultural chemicals. *Mailing Add:* 4400 Partridge Ln Midland MI 48640

OSBORNE, FRANK HAROLD, b San Juan, PR, Dec 20, 44; m 67. MICROBIOLOGY. *Educ:* State Univ NY Albany, BS, 67, MS, 69; Rensselaer Polytech Inst, PhD(biol), 73. *Prof Exp:* ASST PROF BIOL, KEAN COL NJ, 73- *Mem:* AAAS; Am Soc Microbiol; Soc Indust Microbiol. *Res:* Microbiology of arsenic compound oxidation including ecology of arsenite oxidizers and biochemistry and enzymology of arsenite oxidation. *Mailing Add:* Dept of Biol Kean Col Morris Ave Union NJ 07083

OSBORNE, FRANKLIN TALMAGE, b Pewee Valley, Ky, Dec 1, 39; m 61; c 3. CHEMICAL ENGINEERING. *Educ:* Tex A&M Univ, BS, 61; NC State Univ, PhD(chem eng), 69. *Prof Exp:* Res engr synthetic fibers, Chemstrand Res Ctr, Inc, NC, 64-66, sr res engr, 69-70, sr res specialist non-woven fabrics, 70-71, sr group leader, Textile Div, 71-77, SUPVR FIBER INTERMEDIATES, MONSANTO CO, 77- *Mem:* Am Inst Chem Engrs. *Res:* Chemical reactor design; textile chemistry; team innovating new chemical processes. *Mailing Add:* Pensacola Tech Ctr PO Box 12830 Pensacola FL 32575

OSBORNE, GEORGE EDWIN, b Rochester, Ind, Oct 9, 17; m 44; c 5. PHARMACY. *Educ:* Purdue Univ, BS, 39, MS, 41, PhD(pharm), 49. *Prof Exp:* Instr pharm, Univ Kans, 46; instr pharmaceut chem, Purdue Univ, 46-49; from asst prof to assoc prof pharm, Univ Utah, 49-57; head dept, 57-69, PROF PHARM, COL PHARM, UNIV RI, 57- *Concurrent Pos:* Ford Found fac fel advan educ, 54-55. *Mem:* Am Pharmaceut Asn; Am Asn Cols Pharm. *Res:* Pharmaceutical education; historical and cultural aspects of pharmacy; formulation and development of pharmaceutical products. *Mailing Add:* Col of Pharm Univ of RI Kingston RI 02881

OSBORNE, JAMES WILLIAM, b Pana, Ill, Jan 17, 28; m 50; c 2. PHYSIOLOGY, RADIOBIOLOGY. *Educ:* Univ Ill, BS, 49, MS, 51, PhD(physiol), 55. *Prof Exp:* Asst physics, Univ Ill, 50-51, res assoc, Control Systs Lab, 51-55; from asst prof to assoc prof, 55-67, PROF RADIOBIOLOGY, RADIATION RES LAB, UNIV IOWA, 67-, DIR, 78- *Concurrent Pos:* NIH spec fel, Eng, 65-66. *Mem:* Radiation Res Soc; Cell Kinetics Soc; Am Physiol Soc; Soc Exp Biol & Med. *Res:* Effect of x-radiation on mammalian small intestine; means of preventing radiation damage or promoting recovery in irradiated animals; radiation-induced carcinogenesis; identification and characterization of tumor-associated circulating antigens. *Mailing Add:* Radiation Res Lab Univ of Iowa Col of Med Iowa City IA 52242

OSBORNE, JOHN ALAN, b Medicine Hat, Alta, Apr 22, 22; m 58; c 2. MEDICINE, CARDIOLOGY. *Educ:* Univ Alta, BSc, 44, MD, 48; FRCPS(C). *Prof Exp:* Dir cardiovasc labs & asst chief med, Baylor Univ Hosp, Tex, 53-54; asst dir, 56-62, DIR DEPT DIAG CARDIAC SERV, VANCOUVER GEN HOSP, BC, 62-; CLIN ASSOC PROF MED, UNIV BC, 62- *Concurrent Pos:* Nuffield travelling fel med, London, Eng, 51-52; Calif Heart Asn fel, Los Angeles, 52-53; instr, Univ Tex Southwestern Med Sch, 53-54; fel coun clin cardiol, Am Heart Asn, 66- *Mem:* Fel Am Heart Asn; fel Am Col Cardiol (gov, 64-66); Can Cardiovasc Soc. *Res:* Electrophysiology, particularly electrocardiology; clinical studies on cardiovascular drugs. *Mailing Add:* Dept of Cardiol Vancouver Gen Hosp Vancouver BC V5Z 1M9 Can

OSBORNE, JOHN WILLIAM, b Sullivan, Ind, Jan 30, 39. DENTAL RESEARCH. *Educ:* Ind Univ, DDS, 63, MSD, 68. *Prof Exp:* Instr oper & dent mat, State Univ NY Buffalo, 65-68, asst prof oper, 68-71, assoc prof, 71-73; assoc prof dent mat, Ind Univ, Indianapolis, 73-78; PROF RESTORATIVE DENT, STATE UNIV NY STONY BROOK, 78- *Mem:* Int Asn Dent Res; Am Dent Asn; Am Acad Oper Dent. *Res:* Clinical research in dental materials; dental amalgam, cements, composite resins and base metal alloys. *Mailing Add:* Sch of Dent Med State Univ of NY Stony Brook NY 11790

OSBORNE, LANCE SMITH, b Albuquerque, NMex, Nov 8, 49; m 72; c 1. AGRICULTURAL ENTOMOLOGY. *Educ:* Univ Calif, Davis, BS, 74, PhD(entom), 80. *Prof Exp:* Res fel entom, Univ Calif, Davis, 79-80, res entomologist, 80-81; ASST PROF ENTOM, AGR RES CTR APOPKA, UNIV FLA, 81- *Mem:* Entom Soc Am. *Res:* Control of arthropool pests of tropical foliage plants. *Mailing Add:* Inst Food & Agr Sci Agr Res Ctr Rte 3 Box 580 Apopka FL 32703

OSBORNE, LOUIS SHREVE, b Rome, Italy, Sept 8, 23; m 50; c 3. ELEMENTARY PARTICLE PHYSICS. *Educ:* Calif Inst Technol, BS, 44; Mass Inst Technol, PhD(physics), 50. *Prof Exp:* Res assoc physics, 49-50, assoc prof, 59-64, GROUP SUPVR, SYNCHROTRON LAB, MASS INST TECHNOL, 50-, PROF PHYSICS, UNIV, 64- *Concurrent Pos:* Guggenheim & Fulbright fels, 59-60; Minna James Heineman fel, 66-67. *Mem:* Am Phys Soc; Am Acad Arts & Sci. *Res:* High energy nuclear physics. *Mailing Add:* Mass Inst Technol Rm 24-036 Cambridge MA 02139

OSBORNE, MELVILLE, b Carteret, NJ, Apr 21, 22; m 59; c 3. PHARMACOLOGY, PHYSIOLOGY. *Educ:* Drew Univ, BA, 52; Princeton Univ, MA & PhD(biol sci), 59. *Prof Exp:* Jr pharmacologist, Ciba Pharmaceut Co, 52-55; group leader cardiovasc pharmacol, Geigy Chem Co, 59-61 & Warner-Lambert Pharmaceut Co, 61-66; cardiovasc pharmacologist, 66-71, res group chief, Sect Cardiovasc Pharmacol, 71-73, SECT HEAD CARDIOVASC-RENAL PHARMACOL, HOFFMANN LA-ROCHE, INC, 73- *Mem:* Am Soc Pharmacol & Exp Therapeut. *Res:* Adrenergic mechanism relative to the control of the cardiovascular system and development of drugs which alter these mechanisms. *Mailing Add:* Dept of Pharmacol Hoffmann La-Roche Inc Nutley NJ 07110

OSBORNE, MORRIS FLOYD, b Henderson Co, NC, Sept 14, 31; m 55; c 3. NUCLEAR ENGINEERING, CHEMISTRY. *Educ:* Univ NC, BA, 53. *Prof Exp:* Res asst mat properties, Oak Ridge Nat Lab, 54-57, mem res staff, 57-66, mem res staff reactor safety, 66-75, mem res staff, Nuclear Res Ctr, Ger, 75-77, MEM RES STAFF REACTOR SAFETY, OAK RIDGE NAT LAB, 77- *Mem:* Am Nuclear Soc. *Res:* Utilization and application of nuclear energy, especially fission product behavior, nuclear fuel performance; high temperature materials; nuclear reactor safety. *Mailing Add:* Oak Ridge Nat Lab PO Box X Oak Ridge TN 37830

OSBORNE, PAUL JAMES, b Blackwater, Va, Dec 29, 21; m 42; c 2. INVERTEBRATE ZOOLOGY, PHYSIOLOGY. *Educ:* Univ Va, BA, 50, MA, 51; Univ Fla, PhD, 55. *Prof Exp:* Asst biol, Univ Va, 51, technician biochem res, 51-52; asst biol, Univ Fla, 52-54; assoc prof, 55-62, chmn dept, 65-68, PROF BIOL, LYNCHBURG COL, 63 , CHMN DIV LIFE SCI, 71- *Concurrent Pos:* Mem staff, Randolph-Macon Woman's Col, 68-69. *Res:* Morphology and histochemistry of invertebrates, especially enzymes of platyhelminthes; biochemical analysis of invertebrates; human physiology, genetics and history; cell physiology; histochemistry and electron microscopy. *Mailing Add:* Dept of Biol Lynchburg Col Lynchburg VA 24501

OSBORNE, PHILLIP W(ALLACE), b Louisville, Ky, Aug 26, 24; m 49; c 4. METALLURGY. *Educ:* George Washington Univ, BME, 48; Univ Wash, MSME, 51; Univ Calif, Berkeley, PhD(metall), 62. *Prof Exp:* Stress analyst, Boeing Airplane Co, 53-54; asst prof, Ore State Univ, 54-59; assoc prof mech Eng, Univ PR, 64-68; assoc prof, 68-71, PROF MECH ENG, CALIF STATE UNIV, SACRAMENTO, 71- *Concurrent Pos:* NSF fel, Max Planck Inst Metall, Stuttgart, Ger, 62-64. *Mem:* AAAS; Am Soc Metals. *Res:* Mechanics of deformation of metals; fracture. *Mailing Add:* Dept of Mech Eng Calif State Univ Sacramento CA 95819

OSBORNE, RICHARD HAZELET, b Kennecott, Alaska, June 18, 20; m 44; c 3. HUMAN GENETICS, ANTHROPOLOGY. *Educ:* Univ Wash, BS & BA, 49; Columbia Univ, PhD(genetics), 56. *Prof Exp:* Res assoc, Inst Study Human Variation, Columbia Univ, 53-58; from asst prof to assoc prof, Sloan-Kettering Div, Cornell Univ, 58-64; PROF ANTHROP, SCH LETT & SCI & PROF MED, GENETICS, SCH MED, UNIV WIS-MADISON, 64- *Concurrent Pos:* Vis asst prof, Albert Einstein Col Med, 57-58; asst div prev med, Sloan-Kettering Inst Cancer Res, 58-60, assoc, 60-62, assoc mem, 62-64; assoc univ sem genetics & evolution of man, Columbia Univ, 58-64; assoc res geneticist, Dept Prev Med, Mem Hosp, 59-63, clin geneticist, Dept Med, 63-65; career scientist, Health Res Coun New York, 62-64; consult cult anthrop fel rev comt, NIMH, 69-73, perinatal res comt, Nat Inst Neurol Dis & Stroke, 70-73, genetics task force & phys growth task force; mem comt epidemiol & vet follow-up studies, Nat Res Coun, 69-75. *Mem:* Fel AAAS; Am Soc Nat; Am Asn Phys Anthrop; Am Soc Human Genetics; Genetics Soc Am. *Res:* Undergraduate and graduate teaching of human biology and evolutionary theory; twin and sibling studies of quantitative variables and of genetic environmental interaction in health and disease. *Mailing Add:* 1180 Observatory Dr Univ of Wis Madison WI 53706

OSBORNE, RICHARD VINCENT, b Manchester, Eng, Mar 12, 36; m 59; c 3. HEALTH PHYSICS, RADIATION PROTECTION. *Educ:* Cambridge Univ, BA, 59; Univ London, PhD(biophys), 62. *Prof Exp:* Fel radiation detection, Dept Indust Med, NY Univ Med Ctr, 62; res officer, Biol & Health Physics Div, 62-81, RES OFFICER HEALTH PHYSICS BR, CHALK RIVER NUCLEAR LABS, ATOMIC ENERGY CAN, LTD, 81- *Concurrent Pos:* Mem comt 36, Nat Coun Radiation Protection & Measurements, 72-75, mem expert group on effluent releases, Nuclear Energy Agency of Orgn for Econ Coop and Develop, 77-79, mem expert group uranium mgt, 80-; mem Comt 4, Int Comn Radiol Protection, 81- *Honors & Awards:* Elda E Anderson Award, Health Physics Soc, 75. *Mem:* Can Radiation Protection Asn; Health Physics Soc; Radiation Res Soc; Can Asn Physicists. *Res:* High sensitivity alpha particle spectroscopy; transport of radionuclides in the environment; microdosimetry; detection of hazards of and protection against tritium. *Mailing Add:* Atomic Energy Can Ltd Chalk River ON K0J 1J0 Can

OSBORNE, ROBERT HOWARD, b Akron, Ohio, June 29, 39; m 66. STRATIGRAPHY. *Educ:* Kent State Univ, BS, 61; Wash State Univ Univ, MS, 63; Ohio State Univ, PhD(geol), 66. *Prof Exp:* Asst prof, 66-70, assoc prof 70-80, PROF GEOL, UNIV SOUTHERN CALIF, 80- *Concurrent Pos:* Consult, numerous co; expert witness, State Calif. *Mem:* Am Statist Asn; Geol Soc Am; Am Asn Petrol Geol; Soc Econ Paleont & Mineral. *Res:* Quantitative stratigraphy; statistical applications in sedimentary petrology and stratigraphy. *Mailing Add:* Dept of Geol Sci Univ of Southern Calif Los Angeles CA 90007

OSBORNE, ROBERT J(ARVIS), b El Paso, Tex, Oct 26, 27; m 52, 77; c 2. CHEMICAL ENGINEERING. *Educ:* Johns Hopkins Univ, BE, 50; Mass Inst Technol, MS, 52. *Prof Exp:* Res engr friction mat, Johns Manville Corp, 52-55; res engr fiber polymers, Cent Res Labs, Celanese Corp, 55-58; res engr tobacco develop, Res & Develop Div, Am Mach & Foundry Co, 58-60, unit mgr, 60-64, area mgr chem eng, 64-65, asst lab mgr, Chem Develop Lab, 65; mgr process develop, Cloth Div, Malden Mills, Inc, 65-67, mgr eng, 67-71; mgr eng, Sweetheart Plastics Inc, 71-74; mgr mech res, 74-77, DIR RES ENG, CHICOPEE INC, 77- *Mem:* Am Chem Soc; Am Inst Chem Engrs. *Res:* Acetylation and polycondensation kinetics; mixing of non-Newtonian fluids; film casting; dehydration processes; pulp refining processes; textile chemical finishing processes; plastics extrusion and thermoforming processes; non-woven textile processes. *Mailing Add:* 192 Canterbury Ct PO Box 1087 East Windsor NJ 08520

OSBORNE, ROBERT KIDDER, b Kansas City, Mo, Feb 9, 21; m 48; c 1. PHYSICS. *Educ:* Mass Inst Technol, SB, 42, PhD(physics), 47. *Prof Exp:* Instr physics, Mass Inst Technol, 45-49; MEM STAFF, LOS ALAMOS SCI LAB, 49- *Mem:* Am Phys Soc. *Res:* Radioactive disintegration; investigation of nuclear energy levels through study of radioactive disintegration. *Mailing Add:* Los Alamos Sci Lab Univ Calif PO Box 1663 Los Alamos NM 87545

OSBORNE, WEYMAR ZACK, b Pampa, Tex, Nov 6, 32; m 59; c 3. COSMIC RAY PHYSICS, EXPERIMENTAL HIGH ENERGY PHYSICS. *Educ:* Univ Okla, BS, 54, MS, 57, PhD(physics), 61. *Prof Exp:* NSF fel, Dublin Inst Advan Studies, 61; NSF fel, Lawrence Radiation Lab, Univ Calif, 61-62, physicist, 63-65; asst prof physics, Ind Univ, 65-69; nat acad sci sr resident, NASA Manned Spacecraft Ctr, 69-71; RES ASSOC PHYSICS & ADJ PROF, UNIV HOUSTON, 71- *Mem:* Am Phys Soc. *Res:* Transition cosmic ray nuclei; magnetic monopoles; transition radiation; elementary particles; biological effects of energetic heavy ions. *Mailing Add:* Dept of Physics Univ of Houston Houston TX 77004

OSBORNE, WILLIAM WESLEY, b Buhl, Idaho, Apr 29, 20; m 50; c 2. BACTERIOLOGY, PUBLIC HEALTH. *Educ:* State Col Wash, BS, 46. *Prof Exp:* Bacteriologist, Lab Sect, State Dept Health, Wash, 47-48; bacteriologist, Ft Lawton State Hosp, Seattle, 48-49; microbiol res div, Bur Agr & Indust Chem, USDA, Md, 49-50, microbiol sect, Poultry Prod Unit, Western Utilization Res Br, Agr Res Serv, 50-55; process develop div, Biol Warfare Labs, US Army, 55-56; microbiol unit, Res & Develop Sect, Indust Test Lab, Bur Ships, US Navy, 56-58; chief bacteriologist, Lab Serv, Presby Hosp Hosp, Philadelphia, 58-60; MGR, MICROBIOL CONTROL DEPT, WILLIAM H RORER, INC, 60- *Mem:* Am Soc Microbiol. *Res:* Food technology; agriculture bacteriology; clinical, medical and sanitary bacteriology; germicides and disinfectants. *Mailing Add:* 1736 Aidenn Lair Rd Dresher PA 19025

OSBURN, BENNIE IRVE, b Independence, Iowa, Jan 30, 37; m 60; c 3. VETERINARY PATHOLOGY. *Educ:* Kans State Univ, BS, 59, DVM, 61; Univ Calif, Davis, PhD(comp path), 65; Am Col Vet Path, dipl. *Prof Exp:* From asst prof to assoc prof vet path, Col Vet Med, Okla State Univ, 64-68; Nat Inst Child Health & Human Develop spec res fel, Wilmer Inst, Sch Med, Johns Hopkins Univ, 68-70; assoc prof vet path, 70-74, PROF PATH, SCH VET MED, UNIV CALIF, DAVIS, 74-, ASSOC DEAN RES, 76- *Concurrent Pos:* Researcher immunol, Calif Primate Res Ctr, 74- *Mem:* Am Vet Med Asn; Int Acad Path; Am Soc Exp Path; US Animal Health Asn; Am Col Vet Path (pres, 82). *Res:* Host responses and pathogenesis of congenital infections. *Mailing Add:* Dept of Path Univ Calif Sch of Vet Med Davis CA 95616

OSBURN, JAMES O(CTAVIUS), b Black Rock, Ark, June 19, 19; m 42; c 3. CHEMICAL ENGINEERING. *Educ:* Univ Mich, BS, 39, MS, 40, PhD(chem eng), 44. *Prof Exp:* Res chemist, Werner G Smith Co, Mich, 42-45; from instr to assoc prof chem eng, 46-57, chmn chem eng prog, 74-78, PROF CHEM ENG, UNIV IOWA, 57- *Mem:* Am Chem Soc; Am Soc Eng Educ; Am Inst Chem Engrs. *Res:* Solvent extraction; computer applications. *Mailing Add:* Dept Chem Eng Univ Iowa Iowa City IA 52242

OSBURN, RICHARD LEE, b Pensacola, Fla, May 16, 40; m 64; c 1. ENTOMOLOGY, GENETICS. *Educ:* Ga Southern Col, BS, 62, MS, 70; Univ Ga, PhD(entom), 77. *Prof Exp:* Res asst biol, Ga Southern Col, 68-71, instr anat, 71-72, res assoc tick biol, 72-77; RES ENTOMOLOGIST TICK RES, AGR RES, SCI & EDUC ADMIN, USDA, 77- *Concurrent Pos:* NIH fel, Ga Southern Col, 76-77. *Mem:* Entom Soc Am; Acarological Soc Am; AAAS. *Res:* Physiology and genetics of ticks (Ixodidae) with special emphasis on genetic hybridization of Boophilus sp and reproductive biology of Amblyomma americanum (Lone Star Tick). *Mailing Add:* US Livestock Insects Lab PO Box 232 Kerrville TX 78028

OSCAI, LAWRENCE B, b Doylestown, Ohio, July 13, 38; div; c 1. EXERCISE PHYSIOLOGY. *Educ:* La Sierra Col, BS, 61; Univ Colo, MS, 63; Univ Ill, Urbana, PhD(phys educ), 67. *Prof Exp:* Asst prof, 70-72, ASSOC PROF PHYS EDUC, UNIV ILL, CHICAGO CIRCLE, 72- *Concurrent Pos:* USPHS res fel, Sch Med, Wash Univ, 67-70. *Mem:* Am Col Sports Med; Am Inst Nutrit; Am Physiol Soc. *Res:* Effect of exercise on lipid metabolism, including appetite and weight gain, weight reduction, body composition, adipose tissue cellularity and the enzyme lipoprotein lipase. *Mailing Add:* Box 4348 Univ of Ill Chicago Circle Chicago IL 60680

OSCAR, IRVING S, b New York, NY, July 20, 23. ELECTRONIC ENGINEERING. *Educ:* NY Univ, BA, 47, MSEE, 52. *Prof Exp:* Proj dir tech writing, Coastal Pub Inc, NY, 50-54; sr engr, Davies Labs, Md, 54-57, chief engr, Davies Labs Div, Honeywell Inc, 57-60, chief engr, Data Sect, Systs Div, Pa, 60-61; chief engr, Systs Div, Epsco, Inc, Mass, 61-63; prin engr, Booz Allen Appl Res, Inc, 63-65; consult electronic eng & instrumentation, 65; PRES, I S OSCAR ASSOCS, INC, 65- *Mem:* Inst Elec & Electronics Engrs. *Res:* Computer oriented, data acquisition systems; real time analysis and control; magnetic tape recording systems; digital and analog; developmental engineering in electronic instrumentation. *Mailing Add:* I S Oscar Assocs Inc 8811 Colesville Rd Silver Spring MD 20910

OSE, EARL EUGENE, b Pana, Ill, June 18, 25; m 47; c 3. MICROBIOLOGY. *Educ:* Univ Ill, Urbana, BS, 50, MS, 56. *Prof Exp:* Bacteriologist, Ill Dept Pub Health, 50-56; instr, Vet Col, Univ Ill, Urbana, 56-57; bacteriologist, 57-65, sr bacteriologist, 65-69, res scientist, 69-75, RES ASSOC, ELI LILLY & CO, 75- *Concurrent Pos:* Lectr, Eve Div, Ind Cent Col, 61-66. *Mem:* Poultry Sci

Asn; Am Soc Microbiol. *Res:* Mycoplasma infections of poultry and swine; oral erysipelas vaccine; hog cholera and shipping fever vaccines; in vitro and in vivo evaluation of antimicrobials. *Mailing Add:* Eli Lilly & Co Greenfield Labs PO Box 708 Greenfield IN 46140

OSEASOHN, ROBERT, b New York, NY, Jan 23, 24; m 48; c 3. EPIDEMIOLOGY. *Educ:* Tufts Univ, BS, 43; State Univ NY, MD, 47. *Prof Exp:* Demonstr prev med & med, Sch Med, Western Reserve Univ, 51-52; asst med, Sch Med, Boston Univ, 55-57; sr instr prev med & med, Sch Med, Western Reserve Univ, 57-60, from asst prof to assoc prof prev med, 60-67, asst prof med, 61-67; prof epidemiol & community med & chmn dept, Univ NMex, 67-72, prof med, Sch Med, 68-72; prof epidemiol & assoc dean, Sch Pub Health & prof med, Sch Med, Univ Tex, Houston, 72-74; PROF EPIDEMIOL & HEALTH, CHMN DEPT & PROF MED, MCGILL UNIV, 74- *Concurrent Pos:* Attend physician, Vet Admin Hosp, Boston, Mass, 55-57; asst physician, Univ Hosps, Cleveland, 57-67; attend physician, Crile Vet Admin Hosp, 59-67; chief epidemiol sect & dep dir, Pak-SEATO Cholera Res Lab, Dacca. EPakistan, 63-65; attend physician, Vet Admin Hosp, Albuquerque, 67-72 & Bernalillo County Med Ctr, Albuquerque, 67-72; attend staff, Royal Victoria Hosp, Montreal, 74- *Mem:* fel Am Col Epidemiol; Am Epidemiol Soc; Int Epidemiol Asn; Can Soc Clin Res; fel Am Col Physicians. *Res:* Disease control. *Mailing Add:* Dept Epidemiol McGill Univ Montreal PQ H3A 2B4 Can

OSEBOLD, JOHN WILLIAM, b Great Falls, Mont, Jan 9, 21; m 44; c 2. IMMUNOLOGY, MICROBIOLOGY. *Educ:* Wash State Univ, BS, 43, DVM, 44; Ore State Univ, MS, 51; Univ Calif, PhD(comp path), 53. *Prof Exp:* Fed vet in charge brucellosis diag lab, Bur Animal Indust, USDA, 44-46; pvt pract vet med, 46-49; instr vet med & vet microbiol, Ore State Univ, 49-50; lectr vet microbiol, 50-53, asst prof vet med, 53-57, assoc prof immunol, 57-62, PROF IMMUNOL, UNIV CALIF, DAVIS, 62- *Mem:* Am Asn Immunol; Am Col Vet Microbiol; Am Soc Microbiol; Am Vet Med Asn; Am Acad Microbiol. *Res:* Dynamics of infection and resistance; cellular immunity, immunoglobulins serology and immunization. *Mailing Add:* Sch of Vet Med Univ of Calif Davis CA 95616

OSEI-GYIMAH, PETER, b Ghana, March 14, 46. PHARMACY. *Educ:* Univ Wis, Platteville, BSc, 72; Ohio State Univ, Columbus, PhD(pharm), 76. *Prof Exp:* Fel res assoc, Rensselaer Polytech Inst, 76-80; RES SCIENTIST, ROHM AND HAAS CO, 81- *Mem:* Am Chem Soc. *Res:* Design and synthesis of bronchodilator agents bearing the isoquinoline nucleus; morphine-like compounds as irreversible opiate receptor ligandus; synthetic polymers and their fabrication into ultrafiltration and reverse osmosis membranes. *Mailing Add:* 5 Shannon Rd North Wales PA 19454

OSEPCHUK, JOHN M, b Peabody, Mass, Feb 11, 27; m 56; c 3. PHYSICS, MICROWAVE POWER TECHNOLOGY. *Educ:* Harvard Univ, AB, 49, AM, 50, PhD(appl physics), 57. *Prof Exp:* Res & develop engr microwave tubes, Raytheon Co, 50-53, consult, 53-56, tech liaison, Gen Tel Co, France, 56-57, eng sect head, Spencer Lab, 57-60, prin engr, 60-62; chief microwave engr, Sage Labs, Inc, 62-64; prin res scientist, 64-75, CONSULT SCIENTIST, RES DIV, RAYTHEON CO, 75- *Mem:* Fel Inst Elec & Electronics Engrs; Am Phys Soc. *Res:* Crossed field electron devices; interaction of electromagnetic waves with electron beams or plasmas; secondary emission from dielectrics; biological effects of microwaves; microwave ovens; electron beam and semiconductor hydrid devices; microwave power applications. *Mailing Add:* 248 Deacon Haynes Rd Concord MA 07142

OSER, BERNARD LEVUSSOVE, b Philadelphia, Pa, Feb 2, 99; m 23; c 2. NUTRITION: TOXICOLOGY. *Educ:* Univ Pa, BS, 20, MS, 25; Fordham Univ, PhD, 27. *Prof Exp:* Asst physiol chem, Jefferson Med Col, 20-21; biochemist, Philadelphia Gen Hosp, Pa, 22-26; asst dir biol lab, Food & Drug Res Labs, Inc, 26-34, dir, 34-70, from vpres to pres, 39-70, chmn, 70-74; CONSULT, BERNARD L OSER ASSOCS, INC, 74- *Concurrent Pos:* Instr, Grad Sch Med, Univ Pa, 22-26; pres, Am Coun Independent Labs, 48-49; mem expert comt food additives, Food & Agr Orgn, WHO, 58-63; adj prof, Columbia Univ, 59-70; mem food protection comt, Nat Acad Sci-Nat Res Coun, 64-71; sci ed, Food Drug Cosmetic Law J, 57- chmn, Food & Drug Res Labs, Inc, 70-73. *Honors & Awards:* Babcock-Hart Award, Inst Food Technol, 58. *Mem:* Am Chem Soc; Soc Toxicol; NY Acad Med; Am Soc Pharmacol & Exp Therapeut; Am Col Toxicol. *Res:* Technicolegal; physiological chemistry. *Mailing Add:* Bernard L Oser Assocs Inc 108-18 Queens Blvd Forest Hills NY 11375

OSER, HANS JOERG, b Constance, Ger, Dec 7, 29; m 58; c 3. APPLIED MATHEMATICS. *Educ:* Univ Freiburg, Dipl, 54, Dr rer nat(math), 57. *Prof Exp:* Fel, Inst Fluid Dynamics, Univ Md, 57-58; mathematician-analyst, Comput Lab, Nat Bur Standards, 58-62, consult to chief appl math div, 62-66; exec secy commerce tech adv bd, Dept Commerce, 66-67; chief systs dynamics sect, 68-70, chief math anal sect, Appl Math Div, 70-78, SR SCI ADV, NAT BUR STANDARDS, 78- *Concurrent Pos:* Asst prof, Univ Col, Univ Md, 58-62; lectr, Catholic Univ, 62-66. *Mem:* AAAS; Asn Comput Mach; Soc Rheol; Soc Indist & Appl Math. *Res:* Numerical and functional analysis; computer modelling; science administration; science policy. *Mailing Add:* Nat Measurement Lab Nat Bur Standards Washington DC 20234

OSGOOD, CHARLES EDGAR, b Washington, DC, Feb 1, 38; m 64; c 2. ENTOMOLOGY, PHYTOPATHOLOGY. *Educ:* Univ Md, BS, 61; Ore State Univ, MS, 64, PhD(entom), 68. *Prof Exp:* Res scientist, Res Sta, Can Dept Agr, 68-76; TECH REP AGR CHEM DEVELOP, DIAMOND SHAMROCK CORP, 76- *Mem:* Entom Soc Can; Entom Soc Am; Am Phytopath Soc; Sigma Xi. *Res:* Behavior and management of the leaf-cutter bee Megachile rotundata; density dependent behavioral changes affecting reproductive rate in insects; pest management of flea beetles on rape crops. *Mailing Add:* 11134 Chickadee Dr Boise ID 83705

OSGOOD, CHARLES FREEMAN, b New Castle, Pa, Oct 16, 38; m 68; c 1. MATHEMATICS. *Educ:* Haverford Col, BA, 60; Univ Calif, Berkeley, MA, 62, PhD(Diophantine approximation), 64. *Prof Exp:* From instr to assoc prof math, Univ Ill, Urbana, 64-72; RES MATHEMATICIAN, NAVAL RES LAB, 70- *Concurrent Pos:* Res assoc, Nat Bur Standards, DC, 66-68; adj prof math, Univ RI, 80-; lectr math, George Washington Univ, 80- *Mem:* Am Math Soc; AAAS; Inst Elec & Electronics Engrs. *Res:* Diophantine approximation of power series by rational functions; numbical integration of singular integrals; complex variables. *Mailing Add:* Code 77 Naval Res Lab Washington DC 20375

OSGOOD, CHRISTOPHER JAMES, b Winfield, Kans, Jan 3, 49; m 77; c 1. BIOLOGY, GENETICS. *Educ:* Brown Univ, AB, 71, PhD(biol), 77. *Prof Exp:* Res assoc biochem, Dept Genetics, Univ Calif, Davis, 77-80; MEM FAC, T H MORGAN SCH BIOSCI, UNIV KY, 80- *Mem:* Genetics Soc Am; AAAS; Environ Mutagen Soc; Sigma Xi. *Res:* Biochemistry and genetics of DNA-repair in higher organisms. *Mailing Add:* T H Morgan Sch Biosci Univ Ky Lexington KY 40506

OSGOOD, DAVID WILLIAM, b Grant's Pass, Ore, May 19, 40; m 58; c 2. VERTEBRATE ZOOLOGY, ECOLOGY. *Educ:* Portland State Col, BS, 63; Duke Univ, MA, 65, PhD(zool), 68. *Prof Exp:* Instr comp anat, Duke Univ, 67-68; asst prof comp anat, Butler Univ, 68-73, assoc prof, 73-79, prof, 79-82; PRES, MINI-MITTER CO, INC, 82- *Mem:* AAAS; Am Soc Ichthyol & Herpet; Am Soc Mammal. *Res:* Effects of developmental temperature on systematic characters in colubrid snakes; bio-telemetric study of body temperature in reptiles; applications of telemetry to behavioral and ecological problems in small mammals and reptiles. *Mailing Add:* Mini-Mitter Co Inc 56995 Besson Rd Bend OR 97702

OSGOOD, ELMER CLAYTON, b Greenfield, Mass, Aug 4, 06; m 34; c 2. ENGINEERING. *Educ:* Rensselaer Polytech Inst, CE, 28, DEng(struct), 31. *Prof Exp:* Jr civil engr, Civilian Conserv Corps, US Forest Serv, 34-35, asst civil engr, 35-41; design sect, Pub Works Dept, Operating Base, Bur Yards & Docks, US Dept Navy, Va, 41-42, assoc struct engr, 42-44, struct engr, 44-46; from asst prof to prof civil eng, 46-73, EMER PROF CIVIL ENG, UNIV MASS, AMHERST, 73- *Mem:* Am Soc Civil Engrs. *Res:* Structures; civil engineering. *Mailing Add:* Long Hill Rd Leverett MA 01054

OSGOOD, RICHARD MAGEE, JR, b Kansas City, Mo, Dec 28, 43; m 66; c 3. LASERS. *Educ:* US Mil Acad, BS, 65; Ohio State Univ, MS, 68; Mass Inst Technol, PhD(physics), 73. *Prof Exp:* Res assoc physics, Mass Inst Technol, 69-73, mem res staff, Lincoln Lab, 73-81; assoc prof, 81-82, PROF ELEC ENG, COLUMBIA UNIV, 82- *Concurrent Pos:* Vis staff, Los Alamos Nat Lab, 78; mem ad hoc Comt Advan Isotope Separation, Energy Res Adv Bd, Dept Energy, 80; mem adv bd, Spectros Lab, Mass Inst Technol, 81-; consult, Lawrence Livermore Nat Lab & Allied Corp, 82- *Honors & Awards:* Samual Burka Award, US Avionics Lab, 69. *Mem:* Optical Soc Am; sr mem Inst Elec & Electronics Engrs. *Res:* Microelectronic devices and fabrication; laser devices and physics; surface chemistry; atomic and molecular physics. *Mailing Add:* Dept Elec Eng Columbia Univ New York NY 10027

OSGOOD, ROBERT VERNON, b Wilmington, Del, Dec 26, 41; m 64; c 2. WEED SCIENCE, PLANT GROWTH REGULATION. *Educ:* Univ Miami, BS, 64; Univ Hawaii, MS, 67, PhD(hort), 69. *Prof Exp:* Asst agronomist, 69-71, assoc agronomist, 71-77, AGRONOMIST, HAWAIIAN SUGAR PLANTERS ASN, 77- *Mem:* Weed Sci Soc Am; Asian Pac Weed Sci Soc; Plant Growth Regulator Soc. *Res:* Development of new herbicides and growth regulators for sugarcane; studies relating to reasons for varietal differences in tolerance to herbicides. *Mailing Add:* Hawaiin Sugar Planters' Asn 99-193 Aiea Hts Dr Aiea HI 96701

O'SHAUGHNESSY, CHARLES DENNIS, b Moose Jaw, Sask, Oct 11, 41; m 64; c 2. STATISTICS. *Educ:* Univ Sask, BA, 62, PhD(statist), 68; Univ Chicago, MSc, 65. *Prof Exp:* Asst prof, 68-71, ASSOC PROF MATH, UNIV SASK, 71- *Concurrent Pos:* Nat Res Coun Can grant, Univ Sask, 69-72. *Mem:* Inst Math Statist; Can Math Cong; Statist Sci Asn Can. *Res:* Design of statistical experiments, in particular, block designs. *Mailing Add:* Dept of Math Univ of Sask Saskatoon S7N 0W0 Can

O'SHEA, DONALD CHARLES, b Akron, Ohio, Nov 14, 38; m 62; c 4. MOLECULAR SPECTROSCOPY. *Educ:* Univ Akron, BS, 60; Ohio State Univ, MS, 63; Johns Hopkins Univ, PhD(physics), 68. *Prof Exp:* Fel physics, Harvard Univ, 68-70; asst prof, 70-75, ASSOC PROF PHYSICS, GA INST TECHNOL, 75- *Mem:* Am Phys Soc; Sigma Xi; Optical Soc Am; Am Asn Physics Teachers. *Res:* Light scattering spectroscopy of molecular materials, particularly biological materials; applied optics. *Mailing Add:* Sch Physics Ga Inst Technol Atlanta GA 30332

O'SHEA, FRANCIS XAVIER, b New York, NY, May 14, 32; m 54; c 6. ORGANIC POLYMER CHEMISTRY. *Educ:* St John's Univ, NY, BS, 54; Univ Notre Dame, PhD(org chem), 58. *Prof Exp:* Res chemist, Naugatuck Chem Div, US Rubber Co, 57-65, group leader plastics res, 65-68; develop mgr, 68-72, SR RES SCIENTIST CORP RES, UNIROYAL, INC, 72- *Mem:* Am Chem Soc. *Res:* Synthesis of nondiscoloring antioxidants, particularly sterically hindered phenols; stabilization of hydrocarbon polymers; synthesis of new plastics; thermoplastic polyurethane synthesis and morphology; thermoplastic elastomers; polymer blends. *Mailing Add:* 211 Wedgewood Dr Naugatuck CT 06770

O'SHEA, TIMOTHY ALLAN, b Lorain, Ohio, Nov 3, 44; m 68; c 2. ENVIRONMENTAL CHEMISTRY, ANALYTICAL CHEMISTRY. *Educ:* Univ Toledo, BS, 66, MS, 69; Univ Mich, MS, 70, PhD(environ health sci), 72. *Prof Exp:* Asst prof chem, Univ Mich-Dearborn, 72-78; ASSOC PROF CHEM, TEX WESLEYAN COL, 78- *Mem:* AAAS; Am Chem Soc; Sigma Xi. *Res:* Application of electroanalytical techniques to the study of trace metals in natural waters. *Mailing Add:* Dept Chem Tex Wesleyan Col Fort Worth TX 76105

OSHER, JOHN EDWARD, b Estherville, Iowa, Oct 15, 29; m 52; c 3. PLASMA PHYSICS. *Educ:* Iowa State Col, BS, 51; Univ Calif, PhD(physics), 56. *Prof Exp:* Res fel exp nuclear physics, Univ Calif, 56-57; staff mem, Los Alamos Sci Lab, 57-63; plasma physics dept head, Aerojet-Gen Nucleonics Div, Gen Tire & Rubber Co, Calif, 63-65; PHYSICIST, LAWRENCE LIVERMORE LAB, UNIV CALIF, 65- *Mem:* Am Phys Soc. *Res:* High energy nuclear physics. *Mailing Add:* 148 Via Bonita Alamo CA 94507

OSHER, STANLEY JOEL, b Brooklyn, NY, Apr 24, 42. MATHEMATICS. *Educ:* Brooklyn Col, BS, 62; NY Univ, MS, 64, PhD(math), 66. *Prof Exp:* Asst mathematician, Brookhaven Nat Lab, 66-67, assoc mathematician, 67-68; asst prof math, Univ Calif, Berkeley, 68-70; assoc prof math, State Univ NY Stony Brook, 70-76, prof, 76-80; PROF MATH, UNIV CALIF, LOS ANGELES, 80- *Mem:* Am Math Soc. *Res:* Numerical and functional analysis; partial differential equations. *Mailing Add:* Dept Math Univ Calif Los Angeles CA 90024

OSHEROFF, DOUGLAS DEAN, b Aberdeen, Wash, Aug 1, 45; m 70. LOW TEMPERATURE PHYSICS. *Educ:* Calif Inst Technol, BS, 67; Cornell Univ, MS, 69, PhD(physics), 73. *Prof Exp:* MEM TECH STAFF PHYSICS RES, BELL LABS, AM TEL & TEL CO, 72- *Concurrent Pos:* MacArthur Prize fel, MacArthur Found, 81. *Honors & Awards:* Simon Prize, Brit Inst Physics, 76; Oliver E. Buckley Solid-State Physics Prize, Am Phys Soc, 81. *Mem:* Am Phys Soc. *Res:* Ultralow temperature physics; properties of solid and liquid helium-3; superfluidity; nuclear ordering. *Mailing Add:* Bell Labs 600 Mountain Ave Murray Hill NJ 07974

OSHIMA, EUGENE AKIO, b Kaneohe, Hawaii, Jan 2, 34; m 59; c 3. SCIENCE EDUCATION, BIOLOGY. *Educ:* Univ North Col, BA, 55, MA, 56; Okla State Univ, DEd(sci ed), 66. *Prof Exp:* Head sci dept high sch, Kans, 56-64; mem spec staff sci educ, Okla State Univ, 64-66; from asst prof to assoc prof, 66-75, head dept, 67-71, PROF BIOLOGY, CENT MO STATE UNIV, 75- *Concurrent Pos:* Sci consult, Okla State Univ, 65 & E Cent State Col, 66. *Mem:* Nat Sci Teachers Asn. *Res:* Changes in attitudes and confidence in teaching science of prospective elementary school teachers. *Mailing Add:* Dept Biol Cent Mo State Univ Warrensburg MO 64093

OSHIRO, GEORGE, b Kenora, Ont, Nov 17, 38; m 67; c 2. PHARMACOLOGY. *Educ:* Univ Man, BS, 64, PhD(pharmacol), 72. *Prof Exp:* Can Heart Found fel cardiovasc pharmacol, McGill Univ, 72-75; sr pharmacologist, 75-78, RES ASSOC, AYERST RES LABS, 78- *Mem:* AAAS. *Res:* To study the factors giving rise to the various forms of hypertension and to work out the mechanism of action of new anti-hypertensive agents. *Mailing Add:* Ayerst Res Labs PO Box 6115 Montreal PQ H3C 3J1 Can

OSHIRO, LYNDON SATORU, b Hilo, Hawaii, Aug 8, 33; m 61; c 3. VIROLOGY, ELECTRON MICROSCOPY. *Educ:* Univ Utah, BS, 56, PhD(microbiol), 63; Univ Hawaii, MS, 60. *Prof Exp:* ELECTRON MICROSCOPIST, VIRAL & RICKETTSIAL DIS LAB, CALIF STATE DEPT HEALTH SERV, 66- *Concurrent Pos:* NIH trainee virol, Viral & Rickettsial Dis Lab, Calif State Dept Health, 63-65; Nat Inst Allergy & Infectious Dis fel electron micros, Col Physicians & Surgeons, Columbia Univ, 65-66. *Mem:* Am Soc Microbiol; Am Asn Immunol; Soc Gen Microbiol; Soc Exp Biol Med. *Res:* Morphology and development of several selected viral agents. *Mailing Add:* Calif State Dept Health Serv 2151 Berkeley Way Berkeley CA 94704

OSHIRO, YUKI, b Okinawa, Japan, Feb 20, 35; m 71. BIOCHEMISTRY. *Educ:* Univ Calif, Los Angeles, BS, 62; Univ Southern Calif, PhD(biochem), 67. *Prof Exp:* Sr scientist, Frederick Cancer Res Ctr, Nat Cancer Inst, 73-77; RES SCIENTIST, SEARLE LABS, 78- *Concurrent Pos:* Fel biochem, Salk Inst Biol Studies, 67-70, USPHS fel, 68-70; staff fel chem carcinogenesis & etiol, Biol Br, Nat Cancer Inst, 70-72. *Mem:* Am Chem Soc; AAAS; Environ Mutagen Soc; NY Acad Sci. *Res:* Chemical carcinogenesis; toxicology; pharmacology. *Mailing Add:* Searle Lab Box 5110 Chicago IL 60680

OSIFCHIN, NICHOLAS, b Phillipsburg, NJ, June 3, 24; m 61; c 5. ELECTRICAL ENGINEERING. *Educ:* Rutgers Univ, BS, 51; Stevens Inst Technol, MS, 59. *Prof Exp:* Head dept eng mech, 61-63, head dept exploratory develop, 63-68, dir, Electro Mech Lab, 68-71, dir, Loop Transmission Syst, 71-74, DIR, BLDG & ENERGY SYST, BELL LABS, AM TEL & TEL CO, 74- *Concurrent Pos:* Prof mech eng, Stevens Inst Technol, 65-74. *Mem:* Inst Elec & Electronic Engrs; Am Soc Mech Engrs. *Res:* Telecommunications energy systems; systems engineering; electromechanical systems. *Mailing Add:* Bell Labs Whippany NJ 07981

OSINCHAK, JOSEPH, b Fountain Springs, Pa, Sept 20, 37; m 60; c 4. ANATOMY. *Educ:* Susquehanna Univ, AB, 59; Duke Univ, PhD(anat), 63. *Prof Exp:* USPHS fel, Duke Univ, 63-64; instr anat, Albert Einstein Col Med, 64-66, assoc, 66-68; assoc prof, 68-80, PROF BIOL, CITY COL NEW YORK, 80- *Concurrent Pos:* NIH fel, 64-66. *Mem:* Am Soc Cell Biol; Histochem Soc; Am Asn Anat; Electron Micros Soc Am. *Res:* Fine structure of neuroendocrine organs; application of cytochemical techniques to electron microscopy. *Mailing Add:* Dept of Biol City Col of New York New York NY 10031

OSIPOW, LLOYD IRVING, b Brooklyn, NY, Feb 23, 19; m 41. PHYSICAL CHEMISTRY. *Educ:* Columbia Univ, BS, 39. *Prof Exp:* Chemist, Chem Warfare Serv, 41-44; res group dir surface chem, Foster D Snell, Inc, 48-69; pres, Omar Res, Inc, 69-81; PRES, AEROSOL PROD TECH, INC, 81- *Concurrent Pos:* Lectr, Polytech Inst Brooklyn, 55. Mem; Am Chem Soc; Am Oil Chem Soc; Soc Cosmetic Chem; Sci Res Soc Am. *Res:* Surface and cosmetic chemistry; fats and oils; detergents. *Mailing Add:* 2 Fifth Ave New York NY 10011

OSKI, FRANK, b Philadelphia, Pa, June 17, 32; m 57; c 3. MEDICINE, PEDIATRICS. *Educ:* Swarthmore Col, BA, 54; Univ Pa, MD, 58. *Prof Exp:* Assoc pediat, Sch Med, Univ Pa, 63-65, from asst prof to assoc prof, 65-72; PROF PEDIAT & CHMN DEPT, STATE UNIV NY UPSTATE MED CTR, 72- *Concurrent Pos:* Fel pediat hemat, Boston Children's Hosp, Mass, 61-63. *Mem:* AAAS; Soc Pediat Res; Am Soc Hemat; Am Soc Clin Invest; Am Fedn Clin Res. *Res:* Problems in pediatric hematology, specifically red cell metabolism and the consequences of nutritional deficiencies. *Mailing Add:* State Univ Hosp 750 E Adams St Syracuse NY 13210

OSLAND, ROBERT BIRGER, b Ft Collins, Colo, May 19, 34; m 63; c 3. REPRODUCTIVE PHYSIOLOGY, NEUROENDOCRINOLOGY. *Educ:* Calif Polytech State Univ, San Luis Obispo, BS, 62; Ore State Univ, MS, 68; Univ Nebr-Lincoln, PhD(physiol), 72. *Prof Exp:* Res asst physiol, Ore State Univ, 66-68 & Univ Nebr, 68-72; NIH neuroendocrinol trainee, Univ Calif, San Francisco, 72-75, asst res physiologist neuroendocrinol, 75-78; assoc prof, 78-80, PROF DAIRY SCI, CALIF STATE UNIV, FRESNO, 80- *Concurrent Pos:* Consult, Calif Dairymen, 77-; res dir, Calif Milk Adv Bd, 78-79. *Mem:* Am Dairy Sci Asn; Am Soc Animal Sci; Sigma Xi. *Res:* Anti-fertility effects of a non-steroidal compound devoid of many side effects of present birth control pill; milk progesterone radioimmunoassay. *Mailing Add:* Dept of Animal Sci Calif State Univ Fresno CA 93740

OSLER, MARGARET J, b New York, NY, Nov 27, 42. HISTORY & PHILOSOPHY OF SCIENCE. *Educ:* Swarthmore Col, BA, 63; Ind Univ, MA, 66, PhD(hist & philos sci), 68. *Prof Exp:* Asst prof hist sci, Ore State Univ, 68-70; asst prof hist, Harvey Mudd Col, 70-74; asst prof, Wake Forest Univ, 74-75; asst prof, 75-77, ASSOC PROF HIST, UNIV CALGARY, 77- *Mem:* Hist Sci Soc; Can Soc Hist & Philos Sci. *Res:* 17th century science. *Mailing Add:* Dept Hist Univ Calgary Calgary AB T2N 1N4 Can

OSLER, ROBERT DONALD, b Elsie, Nebr, Feb 6, 24; m 47; c 3. CROP BREEDING, AGRONOMY. *Educ:* Univ Nebr, BS, 47; Colo Agr & Mech Col, MS, 49; Univ Minn, PhD(plant breeding), 51. *Prof Exp:* Asst barley breeding, Colo Agr & Mech Col, 47-49; asst oat breeding, Univ Minn, 49-51; asst soybean breeding, US Regional Soybean Lab, 51-54; assoc geneticist corn breeding, Rockefeller Found, 54-56, geneticist, 56-60, asst dir agr sci, 60-65; dep dir resident progs, 67-73, DEP DIR GEN & TREAS, INT CTR CORN & WHEAT IMPROV, 74-; ASSOC DIR, ROCKEFELLER FOUND, 65- *Mem:* AAAS; Am Asn Agron. *Mailing Add:* CIMMYT APDO Postal 6-641 06600 Mexico DF Mexico

OSMAN, ELIZABETH MARY, b Ottawa, Ill, Apr 29, 15. ORGANIC CHEMISTRY, AGRICULTURAL & FOOD CHEMISTRY. *Educ:* Univ Ill, BS, 37, MS, 38; Bryn Mawr, PhD(org chem), 42. *Prof Exp:* Lit searcher, Hercules Powder Co, 41-42, res chemist, 42-44; res chemist, Corn Prod Ref Co, 44-51; from asst prof to assoc prof foods & nutrit, Mich State Univ, 51-56; assoc prof home econ, Univ Ill, 56-63; prof home econ, Univ Iowa, 63-78; PROF FOOD & NUTRIT, IOWA STATE UNIV, 78- *Mem:* Am Chem Soc; Inst Food Technol; Am Asn Cereal Chem; AAAS. *Res:* Starch; carbohydrate chemistry; polymerization; three carbon tautomerism; foods; starch in foods; carbohydrate enzymes. *Mailing Add:* Dept Food & Nutrit Iowa State Univ Ames IA 50011

OSMAN, JACK DOUGLAS, b Philadelphia, Pa, Jan 26, 43; m 66; c 2. HEALTH EDUCATION, NUTRITION. *Educ:* West Chester State Col, Pa, BS, 65; Univ Md, MA, 67; Ohio State Univ, PhD(health & educ), 71. *Prof Exp:* High sch teacher health, Washington, DC, 67-69; instr, Ohio State Univ, 69-71; PROF HEALTH, TOWSON STATE UNIV, 71- *Mem:* Am Sch Health Asn; Am Alliance Health; Nutrit Today Soc; Soc Nutrit Educ; Am Med Joggers Asn. *Res:* Health behaviors focusing on clarifying values and initiating change in the areas of nutrition, weight control and fitness; spiritual aspects of health and counseling. *Mailing Add:* Dept of Health Sci Towson State Univ Baltimore MD 21204

OSMAN, MOHAMED OSMAN MOHAMED, b Cairo, Egypt, Aug 10, 36. MECHANICAL ENGINEERING. *Educ:* Cairo Univ, BSc, 57; Swiss Fed Inst Technol, DrScTechn, 64. *Prof Exp:* Assoc prof, 66-73, PROF ENG, CONCORDIA UNIV, 73- *Concurrent Pos:* Consult, var corp, 68- *Mem:* Am Soc Mech Engrs; Soc Mfg Engrs; Can Soc Mech Engrs; Int Fedn Mach & Mechanisms. *Res:* Design and production engineering; dynamics and stability of machine tools; kinematics and dynamics of mechanisms; surface mechanics; deep-hole machining and metal cutting. *Mailing Add:* Hall Bldg H 929 Concordia Univ 1455 de Maisonneuve Blvd W Montreal PQ H3G 1M8 Can

OSMAN, RICHARD WILLIAM, b Fountain Hill, Pa, Feb 24, 48. MARINE ECOLOGY, EVOLUTIONARY BIOLOGY. *Educ:* Brown Univ, AB, 70; Univ Chicago, PhD(geophys sci), 75. *Prof Exp:* Asst prof geol, Northern Ill Univ, 75-76; ASST RES BIOLOGIST, MARINE SCI INST, UNIV CALIF, SANTA BARBARA, 76- *Mem:* AAAS; Ecol Soc Am; Soc Study Evolution; Am Inst Biol Sci. *Res:* Applications of species equilibrium theory in fluctuating environments; role of disturbance in regulating species diversity; evolution of latitudinal gradients in species richness; symbiotic relationships of sessile marine epifauna. *Mailing Add:* Marine Rev Comt Res Ctr 533 Stevens Ave Solana Beach CA 92075

OSMANSKI, C PAUL, anatomy, pathology, see previous edition

OSMENT, LAMAR SUTTON, b Pascagoula, Miss, Apr 9, 24; m 47. DERMATOLOGY. *Educ:* Birmingham-Southern Col, BS, 45; Univ Ala, MD, 51. *Prof Exp:* Intern, Univ Hosp, 51-52, resident dermat, Med Col, 52-53, from asst prof to assoc prof, 57-70, PROF DERMAT, MED COL, UNIV ALA, BIRMINGHAM, 70- *Concurrent Pos:* Fel dermat, Med Col, Univ Ala, Birmingham, 53-55; mem staff, Univ Hosp, 55-, Vet Admin Hosp, 57-, Baptist Hosps, 58-, St Vincent Hosp, 59- & Children's Hosp, 62- *Mem:* AMA; Am Acad Dermat; Am Dermat Asn. *Res:* Systemic and topical agents used in dermatology; acrodermatitis enteropathica; bacteriology and mycology of the skin. *Mailing Add:* Univ of Ala Med Ctr Birmingham AL 35294

OSMER, PATRICK STEWART, b Jamestown, NY, Dec 17, 43; m 73; c 2. ASTRONOMY. *Educ:* Case Inst Technol, BS, 65; Calif Inst Technol, PhD(astron), 70. *Prof Exp:* Res assoc astron, 69-70, asst astronr, 70-73, assoc astronr, 73-76, ASTRONR, CERRO TOLOLO INTER-AM OBSERV, 77-, DIR, 81- *Mem:* Am Astron Soc; Am Astron Soc Pac; Int Astron Union. *Res:* Spectroscopy and spectrophotometry of galactic and extra galactic objects; quasars. *Mailing Add:* Casilla 603 La Serena Chile

OSMERS, HERMAN REINHARD, b New York, NY, Oct 27, 37; m 58; c 3. CHEMICAL ENGINEERING. *Educ:* Johns Hopkins Univ, BES, 60; Univ Del, MChE, 67, PhD(chem eng), 69. *Prof Exp:* Prod engr, Union Carbide Plastics Corp, 60-61; process engr, Procter & Gamble Co, 62-64; asst prof, 68-78, ASSOC PROF CHEM ENG, UNIV ROCHESTER, 78- *Concurrent Pos:* Indust tech consult, 77- *Mem:* Am Inst Chem Engrs; Am Chem Soc; Soc Rheol; Am Soc Mech Engrs; Soc Plastic Engrs. *Res:* Plastic/polymer processing; environmental and chemical processes. *Mailing Add:* Dept of Chem Eng Univ of Rochester Rochester NY 14627

OSMOND, DENNIS GORDON, b New York, NY, Jan 31, 30; m 55; c 3. ANATOMY, IMMUNOLOGY. *Educ:* Bristol Univ, BSc, 51, MB, ChB, 54, DSc, 75. *Prof Exp:* House surgeon, Royal Gwent Hosp, Newport. Eng, 54; house physician, Bristol Royal Infirmary, 55; demonstr anat, Bristol Univ, 57-59, lectr, 59-60, 61-64; instr, Univ Wash, 60-61; from assoc prof to prof, 65-74, ROBERT REFORD PROF ANAT, McGILL UNIV, 74- *Concurrent Pos:* Vis scientist, Walter & Eliza Hall Inst Med Res, 72-73; vis hon res fel, Univ Birmingham, Eng, 79; vis scientist, Basel Inst Immunol, Switz, 80. *Mem:* Can Asn Anat; Am Asn Anat; Anat Soc Gt Brit & Ireland; Can Soc Immunol; Reticuloendothelial Soc. *Res:* Experimental hematology and cellular immunology; life histories and functional properties of lymphocyte populations, especially in bone marrow; differentiation of surface membrane receptors; lymphocyte cultures; cell separation; kinetics of cellular proliferation; hemopoietic effects of ionizing irradiation; bone marrow circulation; humoral control of hemopoiesis. *Mailing Add:* McGill Univ Dept of Anat 3640 University St Montreal PQ H3A 2B2 Can

OSMOND, JOHN KENNETH, b Janesville, Wis, May 12, 28; m 57; c 2. GEOLOGY. *Educ:* Univ Wis, BA, 50, MA, 52, PhD(geol), 54. *Prof Exp:* Fel geochem, Welch Found, Rice Inst, 57-58 & Petrol Res Fund, Am Chem Soc, 58-59; asst prof geol, 59-65, assoc prof, 65-77, PROF GEOL, FLA STATE UNIV, 77- *Mem:* Geochem Soc. *Res:* Nuclear geology; geochemistry; mineralogy; geology of the radioactive elements; geochronology. *Mailing Add:* Dept of Geol Fla State Univ Tallahassee FL 32306

OSMUN, JOHN VINCENT, b Amherst, Mass, Feb 22, 18; m 42; c 1. ENTOMOLOGY. *Educ:* Univ Mass, BS, 40; Amherst Col, MA, 42; Univ Ill, PhD, 56. *Prof Exp:* Field entomologist, US Dept Army, 42-43; res rep, Merck & Co, Inc, 46-48; asst prof, 48-56, head dept, 56-74, PROF ENTOM, PURDUE UNIV, WEST LAFAYETTE, 56- *Concurrent Pos:* Mem US entom deleg, USSR, 59; mem comt insect pest mgt & control, Nat Acad Sci-Nat Res Coun, 67-68; founder & mem, Govt Interstate Interdist Pesticide Coun, 69-72, chmn, 72; mem, Fed Task Group Training Objectives & Standardization Pesticides, 71-72; mem, Ind Pesticide Rev Bd, 72-76; consult, Coop States Res Serv, 72-73. *Mem:* Entom Soc Am. *Res:* Household and industrial entomology; thermal aerosol insecticide dispersion; pest management; competencies for insecticide use. *Mailing Add:* Dept of Entom Purdue Univ West Lafayette IN 47907

OSOBA, DAVID, b Glendon, Alta, Apr 10, 32; c 2. ONCOLOGY, IMMUNOLOGY. *Educ:* Univ Alta, BSc, 54, MD, 56; FRCP(C), 61. *Prof Exp:* Clin instr med, Univ BC, 63-65, asst prof, 65-66; asst prof, 66-72, ASSOC PROF, UNIV TORONTO, 72-; HEAD, DIV MED ONCOL, SUNNYBROOK MED CTR & ONT CANCER FOUND, TORONTO-BAYVIEW CLIN, 78- *Concurrent Pos:* McEachern fel, Chester Beatty Res Inst, London, Eng, 62-63; fel hemat, Vancouver Gen Hosp, BC, 61-62; assoc hematologist, Vancouver Gen Hosp, 63-65; mem staff, Med Res Coun Can, 65-68, assoc, 68-80. *Honors & Awards:* Medal, Royal Col Physicians & Surgeons, Can. *Mem:* Am Soc Hemat; Can Soc Clin Invest; Am Asn Immunol; Can Soc Immunol; Am Soc Clin Oncol. *Res:* Immunological aspects of malignancy; functions of thymus; immunological deficiency diseases; cellular and humoral immunity. *Mailing Add:* Sunnybrook Med Ctr & Toronto-Bayview Clin 2075 Bayview Ave Toronto ON M4N 3M5 Can

OSOBA, JOSEPH SCHILLER, b Temple, Tex, Dec 5, 19; m 43; c 1. PHYSICS. *Educ:* Univ Tex, BA, 41; Wash Univ, PhD(physics), 49. *Prof Exp:* Res engr, Humble Oil & Refining Co, 49-52, sr res engr, 52-54, res specialist, 54-58, sr res specialist, Esso Prod Res Co, 58-67; PROF PETROL ENG, TEX A&M UNIV, 67- *Mem:* Am Phys Soc; Am Inst Mining, Metall & Petrol Eng. *Res:* Fluid mechanics; electric and radioactive logging; geochemistry; subsurface flow meters; hydrocarbon analysis; new oil recovery techniques. *Mailing Add:* Dept of Petrol Eng Tex A&M Univ College Station TX 77843

OSOFSKY, BARBARA LANGER, b Beacon, NY, Aug 4, 37; m 58; c 3. ALGEBRA. *Educ:* Cornell Univ, BA, 59, MA, 60; Rutgers Univ, PhD(algebra), 64. *Prof Exp:* Assoc mem tech staff, Bell Labs, Inc, NJ, 60; instr math, Douglass Col, 61-63, from asst prof to assoc prof, 64-71, PROF MATH, RUTGERS UNIV, 71- *Concurrent Pos:* NSF res grant, 65-67, 70-79; mem, Sch Math, Inst Adv Study, 67-68; mem-at-large, Coun Conf Bd Math Sci, 72-74, chmn, Bd Trustees, 80-82; proceedings ed comt, Am Math Soc, 74-77, managing ed, 76-77. *Mem:* Am Math Soc; Math Asn Am. *Res:* Associative rings and modules; homological algebra. *Mailing Add:* Dept Math Rutgers Col Rutgers Univ New Brunswick NJ 08903

OSOFSKY, HOWARD J, b Syracuse, NY, May 24, 35; m; c 3. OBSTETRICS & GYNECOLOGY, PSYCHIATRY. *Educ:* Syracuse Univ, BA, 55, PhD(psychol), 74; NY State Col Med, MD, 58. *Prof Exp:* From asst prof to assoc prof obstet & gynec, State Univ NY Upstate Med Ctr, 64-71; prof obstet & gynec, Health Sci Ctr, Temple Univ, 71-76, res psychiatrist, 79-80, PSYCHIATRIST, MENNINGER FOUND, TOPEKA, 80-; CLIN PROF OBSTET & GYNEC, UNIV KANS MED CTR, 80- *Concurrent Pos:* Ed-in-chief, Clin Obstet & Gynec, 72-, adj prof obstet & gynec, Health Sci Ctr, Temple Univ, 76-; ed, Advan Clin Obstet & Gynec, 80- *Mem:* Fel Am Col Obstet & Gynec; fel Am Orthopsychiat Asn. *Res:* Psychological aspects of obstetrics and gynecology with emphasis upon adjustment patterns of couples; pregnancy, the effects of prenatal nutrition upon pregnancy outcome and infant development and psychological effects of abortion and sterilization. *Mailing Add:* Menninger Found Box 829 Topeka KS 66606

OSOL, ARTHUR, b Riga, Latvia, Dec 1, 05; US citizen; m 28. ANALYTICAL CHEMISTRY. *Educ:* Philadelphia Col Pharm, BS, 28, MS, 30; Univ Pa, MS, 31, PhD(chem), 33. *Hon Degrees:* LLD, Eastern Baptist Col, 64; DSc, Thomas Jefferson Univ, 71. *Prof Exp:* From asst to assoc prof chem, 28-37, prof chem & dir sch chem, 37-63, dean sci, 59-63, pres, 63-75, EMER PRES, PHILADELPHIA COL PHARM & SCI, 75- *Concurrent Pos:* Dir, Univ City Sci Ctr Corp, Pa, 63-75, pres, 68-72; tech ed, Am Druggist Magazine, 33-45; ed, Remington's Pharmaceut Sci; ed-in-chief, US Dispensatory, J B Lippincott co, 47-; mem revision comt, US Pharmacopeia, 50-70; mem health comt, League of Nations, 33-37; chmn phys chem comt, Nat Conf Pharmaceut Res, 34-41; mem sci adv comt, Smaller War Plants Corp, 42-46. *Mem:* Fel AAAS; Am Chem Soc; Electrochem Soc; Am Pharmaceut Asn; fel Am Inst Chem. *Res:* Infrared and ultraviolet spectrophotometry; solubility of inorganic and organic compounds; preparation of stable forms of drugs for medicinal use; nonaqueous methods of analysis. *Mailing Add:* Philadelphia Col Pharm & Sci 43rd St & Kingsessing Mall Philadelphia PA 19104

OSPENSON, J NILS, b New York, NY, Jan 28, 24; m 46; c 4. ORGANIC CHEMISTRY. *Educ:* Drew Univ, BA, 48; Royal Inst Technol, Sweden, PhD(chem), 50. *Prof Exp:* Res assoc, Swedish Forest Prod Res Lab, 47-50; sr chemist, Calif Spray Chem Corp, 51-55, lead res chemist, 55-60, supvr chem res, Ortho Div, Calif Chem Co, 60-68, mgr, Cent Res Labs, Chevron Chem Co, 68-73, mgr res & develop, Ortho Div, Chevron Chem Co, 73-79, GEN MGR, CHEVRON ENVIRON HEALTH CTR, STANDARD OIL OF CALIF, 79- *Mem:* Am Chem Soc. *Res:* New organic pesticides; correlations of chemical structure to biological activity; metabolism of pesticides; residue chemical research; synthesis; biological screening; process chemistry; metabolism; residue and analytical functions; toxicology studies and responsible for human and environmental health evaluation for all social products. *Mailing Add:* Chevron Environ Health Ctr PO Box 1272 Richmond CA 94802

OSRI, STANLEY M(AURICE), b Chicago, Ill, July 30, 16; m 44; c 1. CHEMICAL ENGINEERING. *Educ:* Ill Inst Technol, BS, 38. *Prof Exp:* Supt, Qual Plating Co, 38-40; indust engr, Kraft Foods Co, 40-41, res engr, 45-47, prod mgr, Whey Prod, 47-51, mgr eng res, 51-57; res mgr, Res & Develop Div, Nat Dairy Prod Corp, 57-63, dir prod develop, Kraftco Corp, 63-65, dir eng, Res & Develop Div, 65-71, nat prod sales mgr, Kraft Foods Div, 71-78; RETIRED. *Concurrent Pos:* Pres, Bd Educ, high sch dist 207, Cook County, Ill. *Mem:* Am Inst Chem Engrs; Inst Food Technol; Am Inst Chemists. *Res:* Research administration; new product development; application of chemical engineering unit operations to the food industry. *Mailing Add:* 9620 Oak Lane Des Plaines IL 60016

OSSAKOW, SIDNEY LEONARD, b Brooklyn, NY, Dec 14, 38; m 67; c 3. PLASMA PHYSICS. *Educ:* Mass Inst Technol, BS, 60; Univ Calif, Los Angeles, MS, 62, PhD(theoret physics), 66. *Prof Exp:* Asst physics, Univ Calif, Los Angeles, 60-63, asst theoret plasma physics, 63-66; res fel plasma physics lab, Princeton Univ, 66-67; assoc res scientist, Lockheed Palo Alto Res Lab, Lockheed Missiles & Space Co, 67-71; res physicist, 71-77, supvry res physicist, 77-80, HEAD, GEOPHYS & PLASMA DYNAMICS BR, US NAVAL RES LAB, WASHINGTON, DC, 78-, SUPT, PLASMA PHYSICS DIV, 81- *Concurrent Pos:* Mem tech staff, Hughes Res Lab, 63-64; consult, Rand Corp, 65-67. *Mem:* Am Geophys Union; Am Phys Soc. *Res:* Plasma kinetic and fluid theory; instabilities, non-linear effects, computer simulation and electromagnetic wave propagation; space and ionospheric plasmas; magnetospheric phenomena; nuclear weapons effects. *Mailing Add:* 7106 Plandome Ct Springfield VA 22153

OSSERMAN, ELLIOTT FREDERICK, b New York, NY, Aug 1, 25; m 49; c 2. MEDICINE. *Educ:* Columbia Univ, BA, 44, MD, 47. *Prof Exp:* Assoc med, 53-57, from asst prof to assoc prof, 57-68, prof path, 68-69, Am Cancer Soc prof path, 69-71, AM CANCER SOC PROF MED, COL PHYSICIANS & SURGEONS, COLUMBIA UNIV, 71-, ASSOC DIR, INST CANCER RES, 69- *Concurrent Pos:* Attend physician, Presby Hosp, 71- *Mem:* AAAS; Am Asn Immunol; Am Soc Clin Invest; Harvey Soc; Int Soc Hemat. *Res:* Clinical immunology; gamma globulin structure; plasma cell dyscrasias, myeloma, macroglobulinemia, amyloidosis and the associated abnormalities in gamma globulin synthesis; lysozyme, monocytic dyscrasias, macrophage function. *Mailing Add:* Inst Cancer Res 701 W 168th St New York NY 10032

OSSERMAN, ROBERT, b New York, NY, Dec 19, 26; m 76; c 3. GEOMETRY, MATHEMATICAL ANALYSIS. *Educ:* NY Univ, BA, 46; Harvard Univ, MA, 48, PhD, 55. *Prof Exp:* Instr math, Univ Colo, 52-53; actg asst prof, 55-57, from asst prof to assoc prof, 57-66, chmn dept, 73-79, PROF MATH, STANFORD UNIV, 66- *Concurrent Pos:* Mem inst math sci, NY Univ, 57-58; head math br, Off Naval Res, 60-61; vis lectr & res assoc, Harvard Univ, 61-62; Fulbright lectr, Univ Paris, 65-66; Guggenheim fel, Univ Warwick, 76-77. *Mem:* Math Asn Am; Am Math Soc. *Res:* Complex variables; minimal and Riemann surfaces; Riemannian geometry. *Mailing Add:* Dept of Math Stanford Univ Stanford CA 94305

OSSESIA, MICHEL GERMAIN, b Houston, Pa, May 4, 29; m 55; c 3. MATHEMATICS. *Educ:* Univ Pittsburgh, BS, 50, MLitt, 57, PhD(algebra), 61. *Prof Exp:* Asst prof math, Duquesne Univ, 57-61; prof, Slippery Rock State Col, 61-63; assoc prof, Seton Hall Univ, 63-65; prof, Univ Alaska, 65-66; head dept, 66-74, PROF MATH, CLARION STATE COL, 66- *Mem:* Am Math Soc; Math Asn Am. *Res:* Continuous limits. *Mailing Add:* Dept of Math Clarion State Col Clarion PA 16214

OSTAFF, WILLIAM A(LLEN), b Cleveland, Ohio, Nov 29, 14; m 45; c 2. SPACE PHYSICS, ELECTRICAL ENGINEERING. *Educ:* Ohio Univ, BSEE, 40. *Prof Exp:* Elec engr, Parker Appliance Co, 40-41 & Trumbull Elec Mfg Co, 41; electronics engr, Bur Ships, US Dept Navy, 41-52, asst chief engr, Ord Exp Unit, 52-58, lectr, Bur Ord, 56-59, systs engr, Spec Projs Off, 58-63; EXP CONSULT, SPACE PHYSICS OBSERV, GODDARD SPACE FLIGHT CTR, NASA, 63- *Concurrent Pos:* Instr astron, Montgomery Col, 76. *Mem:* AAAS; sr mem Inst Elec & Electronics Eng; NY Acad Sci; Nat Soc Prof Engrs; Acoust Soc Am. *Res:* Remote sensing; automatic control; solar physics. *Mailing Add:* 10208 Drumm Ave Kensington MD 20895

OSTAP, STEPHEN, b Winnipeg, Man, Aug 31, 24; m 52; c 1. INORGANIC CHEMISTRY. *Educ:* Univ Man, BSc, 45. *Prof Exp:* Control chemist asphalt, Can Bitumuls Ltd, 46-47; process develop chemist plutonium, Atomic Energy Can, 48-51; SR CONSULT ALUMINUM, ALUMINUM CO CAN, 51- *Mem:* Chem Inst Can; Metall Soc Am. *Res:* Reactions of the different oxides of iron, titanium, silicon, aluminum and aluminum silicates in sodium hydroxide solutions at 100 degrees-300 degrees centigrade. *Mailing Add:* Alcan Int Ltd Box 8400 Kingston ON K7L 4Z4 Can

OSTAPENKO, A(LEXIS), b Ukraine, Oct 1, 23; nat US; m 58; c 3. CIVIL ENGINEERING. *Educ:* Munich Tech Univ, dipl, 51; Mass Inst Technol, ScD, 57. *Prof Exp:* Draftsman, Fay, Spofford & Thorndike, Mass, 52; struct designer, Thomas Worcester, Inc, 52-55, Jackson & Moreland Int, Inc, 55, Badger Mfg Co, 56 & Erdman, Anthony & Hosley, Inc, 57; from asst prof to assoc prof, 57-65, PROF CIVIL ENG, LEHIGH UNIV, 65- *Mem:* Am Soc Civil Engrs; Am Soc Eng Educ; Int Asn Shell Struct. *Res:* Elastic and inelastic behavior of structures and components; plastic design; ultimate strength of plate structures. *Mailing Add:* Dept Civil Eng Lehigh Univ Bethlehem PA 18015

OSTAZESKI, STANLEY A, b Superior, Wis, Apr 17, 26; m 50; c 5. PLANT PATHOLOGY, MYCOLOGY. *Educ:* Wis State Univ, Superior, BS, 52; Univ Ill, Urbana, MS, 55, PhD(plant path), 57. *Prof Exp:* Plant pathologist, USDA, Fla, 57-60; plant path adv, AID, Ethiopia, 60-62; RES PLANT PATHOLOGIST, USDA, 62- *Mem:* Am Phytopath Soc; Mycol Soc Am. *Res:* Diseases of forage legumes. *Mailing Add:* Plant Genetics & Germplasm Inst Agr Res Ctr-W Agr Res Serv USDA Beltsville MD 20705

OSTBERG, DONALD ROSS, mathematics, deceased

OSTDAHL, HAROLD E(VERETT), b Duluth, Minn, Jan 12, 17; m 41; c 3. MECHANICAL ENGINEERING. *Educ:* Univ Minn, BME, 38, MS, 40. *Prof Exp:* Heating engr, Minneapolis Gas Light Co, 39; res engr, Remington Arms Co, E I du Pont de Nemours & Co, Inc, Conn & NY, 40-43, area engr, Tenn & Wash, 43-46, res engr, NY, 47, res supvr, 48-50, process engr, 50-53, area supt, Savannah River Plant, 53-55, tech & mfg supt, 55-59, asst plant mgr, May Plant, 60, process mgr, Nylon Div, 60-63, asst to dir nylon mfg, 63-71, MECHANIZATION MGR, E I DU PONT DE NEMOURS & CO, INC, 71- *Concurrent Pos:* Professional engr, State Del. *Mem:* Am Soc Mech Engrs. *Res:* Synthetic textile fibers; metallography; atomic energy. *Mailing Add:* PO Box 3932 Greenville DE 19807

OSTDICK, THOMAS, b Elgin, Ill, Aug 18, 28. INORGANIC CHEMISTRY, ACADEMIC ADMINISTRATION. *Educ:* St Meinrad Col, BA, 52; Notre Dame Univ, MS, 57, PhD(chem, math), 58. *Prof Exp:* From asst prof to assoc prof, 58-70, acad dean, 63-75, PROF CHEM & MATH, ST MEINRAD COL, 70-, PRES, 75- *Concurrent Pos:* NASA res fel, 65-71; mem acad comn, Coun Advan Small Col, 72-75; assoc ed, Am Benedictine Review, 67-; mem exec comt, Indian Conf Higher Educ, 80- *Mem:* AAAS; Am Chem Soc; Math Asn Am; Sigma Xi; fel Am Inst Chemists. *Res:* Preparation, reactions and properties of organoboron and organosilicon compounds; heat-resistant polymers. *Mailing Add:* St Meinrad Col St Meinrad IN 47577

O'STEEN, WENDALL KEITH, b Meigs, Ga, July 3, 28; m 51; c 2. ANATOMY, NEUROBIOLOGY. *Educ:* Emory Univ, BA, 48, MS, 50; Duke Univ, PhD(zool), 58. *Prof Exp:* Asst prof biol, Jr Col, Emory Univ, 48-49, asst, Univ, 49-50, instr, 50-51; asst prof, Wofford Col, 51-53; asst zool, Duke Univ, 55-57; from instr to prof anat, Univ Tex Med Br, 58-68; prof anat, Sch Med, Emory Univ, 68-77; PROF & CHMN ANAT DEPT, BOWMAN GRAY SCH MED, WAKE FOREST UNIV, 77- *Concurrent Pos:* Vis lectr, Sch Med, Univ Miami, 63. *Mem:* AAAS; Am Asn Anat; Endocrine Soc; Soc Neurosci; Sigma Xi. *Res:* Neuroendocrinology; biogenic amines; reproduction; visual system; photoneuroendocrinology. *Mailing Add:* Dept Anat Bowman Gray Sch Med Wake Forest Univ Winston-Salem NC 27103

OSTENDORF, DAVID WILLIAM, b Stamford, Conn, Feb 6, 50; m 78; c 1. CIVIL ENGINEERING. *Educ:* Univ Mich, BSE, 72; Mass Inst Technol, SM, 78, ScD, 80. *Prof Exp:* Engr hydrothermal, Stone & Webster Eng Corp, 73-75; res asst civil eng, Mass Inst Technol, 77-80; ASST PROF FLUID MECH, DEPT CIVIL ENG, UNIV MASS, 80- *Mem:* Am Soc Civil Engrs; Am Geophys Union. *Res:* Models of momentum, pollutant and sediment transport processes in the coastal and estuarine environment. *Mailing Add:* Dept Civil Eng Univ Mass Amherst MA 01003

OSTENSO, GRACE LAUDON, b Tomah, Wis, Sept 15, 32; m 63. NUTRITION. *Educ:* Stout State Univ, BS, 54; Univ Wis, MS, 60, PhD(foods, nutrit, indust eng), 63. *Prof Exp:* Dietetic intern, Peter Bent Brigham Hosp, Boston, Mass, 54-55, admin dietitian, 55-57, asst dir dietetics, 57-59; res asst foods & nutrit, Univ Wis-Madison, 59-63, asst prof, 63-67; consult, Food Systs Anal, 69-70; group head, Nutrit & Tech Serv, US Dept Agr, 70-73, dir nutrit & tech serv staff, Food & Nutrit Serv, 73-78; MEM PROF STAFF, COMT SCI & TECHNOL, US HOUSE REPS, 78- *Concurrent Pos:* Consult, Hosp Systs Res Group, Dept Indust Eng, Univ Mich, 64-65, div hosp & med facilities, Res Br, US Dept Health, Educ & Welfare, 64-69 & Off of Surgeon Gen, Army Med Specialist Corp, 69-73; assoc ed technol, Encycl Britannica, 67-69. *Honors & Awards:* Medallion Award, Am Dietetic Asn, 78. *Mem:* Fel AAAS; Am Pub Health Asn; fel Royal Soc Health; Inst Food Technologists; Nutrit Today Soc. *Res:* Nutrition and food systems analysis and management. *Mailing Add:* 2871 Audubon Terrace NW Washington DC 20008

OSTENSO, NED ALLEN, b Fargo, NDak, June 22, 30; m 63. GEOLOGY, MARINE GEOPHYSICS. *Educ:* Univ Wis, BS, 52, MS, 53, PhD(geol, geophys), 62. *Prof Exp:* Geophysicist, Arctic Inst NAm, 56-58; proj assoc geol & geophys, Univ Wis, 58-63, asst prof, 63-66; oceanogr, Off Naval Res, Chicago, 66-68, dir geol & geophys prog, Washington, DC, 68-70; dir, Off Sci & Technol, Exec Off President, 70; dep dir & sr oceanogr ocean sci & technol div, Off Naval Res, 70-76; DIR, NAT SEA GRANT COL PROG, 76-; DEP ASST ADMINR RES & DEVELOP, NAT OCEANIC & ATMOSPHERIC ADMIN, 78- *Concurrent Pos:* Foreign affairs fel, Off Naval Res, 75, Cong fel, 75-76. *Mem:* Am Geophys Union; Geol Soc Am; Soc Explor Geophys; Glaciol Soc; Acad Polit Sci. *Res:* Artic and antarctic research; gravity; magnetism; oceanography. *Mailing Add:* 2871 Audubon Terr NW Washington DC 20008

OSTER, BERND, b Ger, Feb 22, 26; US citizen; m 61; c 3. MATERIALS SCIENCE ENGINEERING. *Educ:* Univ RI, BS, 50; Worcester Polytech Inst, MS, 51; Univ Mass, MS, 71, PhD(polymer chem), 74. *Prof Exp:* Res engr, Monsanto Co, Everett, Mass, 51-57, res specialist, Springfield, Mass, 57-70; RES ASSOC, NORTON CO, WORCESTER, MASS, 76- *Concurrent Pos:* Lectr chem, Western New Eng Col, Mass, 75-76. *Mem:* Am Chem Soc. *Res:* Polymerization mechanism and kinetics; metal removal theory. *Mailing Add:* 111 Malden St Holden MA 01520

OSTER, CARL FREDERICH, b Abington, Pa, Sept 21, 27; m 51; c 3. ELECTRON MICROSCOPY, PHOTOCHEMISTRY. *Educ:* Univ Pa, BS, 54. *Prof Exp:* Res chemist electron micros & res assoc, 68-75, res lab head, 75-81, SR RES LAB HEAD, SURFACE CHARACTERIZATION, RES LABS, EASTMAN KODAK CO, 81- *Mem:* Am Chem Soc; Electron Micros Soc Am; Am Inst Chemists. *Res:* Characterization of both chemical and physical properties of surfaces using analytical instrumentation, photoelectron spectroscopy, light and electron microscopy; elemental analysis using neutron activation and atomic spectroscopy techniques. *Mailing Add:* Eastman Kodak Co Res Labs Rochester NY 14650

OSTER, CLARENCE ALFRED, b Madras, Ore, Apr 3, 33; m 58; c 3. COMPUTER SCIENCE, MATHEMATICS. *Educ:* Univ Ore, BS, 57, MS, 58. *Prof Exp:* Assoc res engr comput sci, Jet Propulsion Lab, Calif Inst Technol, 58-59; electronic data processing analyst, Gen Elec Co, Richland, Wash, 59-64, mathematician, 64-65; SR RES SCIENTIST COMPUT SCI & MATH, PAC NORTHWEST DIV, BATTELLE MEM INST, 65- *Concurrent Pos:* Lectr math, Joint Ctr Grad Study, Univ Wash, Wash State Univ & Ore State Univ, 65- *Mem:* Sigma Xi; Soc Indust & Appl Math; Asn Comput Mach; Math Asn Am; AAAS. *Res:* Error propagation in digital computation; function evaluation. *Mailing Add:* Battelle Pac Northwest Labs Battelle Blvd Richland WA 99352

OSTER, EUGENE ARTHUR, b Cincinnati, Ohio, June 2, 29; m 53; c 2. CHEMICAL ENGINEERING. *Educ:* Mass Inst Technol, BS, 51, MS, 54, DSc(chem eng), 66. *Prof Exp:* Proj engr, Div Sponsor Res, Mass Inst Technol, 52 & 56; sr engr, Small Aircraft Engine Lab, Gen Elec Co, 56-58, supvr, 58-60, mgr, Fuel Cell Lab, 60-65; mgr, Okemos Res Lab, 65-66, DIR ENG RES, TECH CTR, OWENS-ILL, INC, 66- *Mem:* Am Chem Soc; Combustion Inst. *Res:* Fuel cells for space and ground-power; electrophotography and photoelectrets; propulsion and fuels. *Mailing Add:* 5312 Coldstream Toledo OH 43623

OSTER, GEORGE F, b New York, NY, Apr 20, 40. MATHEMATICAL BIOLOGY. *Educ:* US Merchant Marine Acad, BS, 61; Columbia Univ, MS, 63, EngScD, 67. *Prof Exp:* Instr, City Col New York, 64-67; NIH fel biophys, Lawrence Radiation Lab, 68-71, mem fac mech eng, 71-72, mem fac entom, 72-74, assoc prof entom, 74-77, PROF BIOPHYS, ZOOL & ENTOM, UNIV CALIF, BERKELEY, 78- *Concurrent Pos:* Guggenheim fel, J S Guggenheim Found, 75. *Honors & Awards:* Louis E Levy Medal, Franklin Inst, 71 & 74. *Res:* Developmental cell biology; biomechanics; biomathematics; biophysics; embryology. *Mailing Add:* Dept Entom Univ Calif Berkeley CA 94720

OSTER, GERALD, b Providence, RI, Mar 24, 18; m 73; c 2. BIOPHYSICS, PHYSICAL CHEMISTRY. *Educ:* Brown Univ, ScB, 40; Cornell Univ, PhD(phys chem), 43. *Prof Exp:* Mem staff virus res, Rockefeller Inst Med Res, 45-48; vis scientist x-ray scattering, Univ London, 48-50; vis scientist nucleic acids, Univ Paris, 50-51; prof chem, Polytech Inst Brooklyn, 51-69; PROF BIOPHYS, MT SINAI SCH MED, 69- *Concurrent Pos:* Fel, Mass Inst Technol, 43-44; fel, Princeton Univ, 44-45. *Mem:* AAAS. *Res:* Polymer chemistry and biophysical chemistry as applied to reproductive physiology and to muscle physiology. *Mailing Add:* Dept of Biophys Mt Sinai Sch of Med Grad Sch New York NY 10029

OSTER, IRWIN ISAAC, b New York, NY, Jan 12, 30; m 50; c 3. GENETICS. *Educ:* Long Island Univ, BSc, 50; Ind Univ, PhD(genetics), 56. *Prof Exp:* Lab asst gen zool, Ind Univ, 50-52, res asst, 52-53, 54-56, NSF fel, 56-57, res exec zool, 57-59; vis investr & demonstr genetics, Inst Animal Genetics, Univ Edinburgh, 53-54; asst mem, Inst Cancer Res, Philadel- phia, Pa, 59-65; PROF BIOL, BOWLING GREEN STATE UNIV, 66- *Concurrent Pos:* Lectr genetics, Univ Pa, 60-65; vis assoc prof radiobiol & & zool, Rutgers Univ, 61-63; consult zool, Prof H J Muller, Ind Univ, 59-, NASA, 63- & Pure Food & Drug Admin, 63-65. *Honors & Awards:* Sigma Xi Res Award, Ind Univ, 55. *Mem:* AAAS; Am Soc Naturalists; Genetics Soc Am; Radiation Res Soc; NY Acad Sci. *Res:* Modification of radiation and chemical mutagenesis in Drosophila, Bombyx and mammals; synthesis of new genetic strains; developmental analysis of mutations affecting growth and development; carcinogenesis; cytological analysis of spontaneous and induced chromosome aberrations in insects, mammals and humans. *Mailing Add:* Dept of Biol Bowling Green State Univ Bowling Green OH 43403

OSTER, JAMES DONALD, b Hazen, NDak, Nov 24, 37; m 58; c 3. SOIL CHEMISTRY. *Educ:* NDak State Univ, BS, 59; Purdue Univ, MS, 62, PhD(soil chem), 64. *Prof Exp:* Teaching asst soils, Purdue Univ, 59-61, asst soil chem, 61-63; soil scientist, US Salinity Lab, Agr Res Serv, USDA, 65-81;

SOIL & WATER SPECIALIST, COOP EXTEN, UNIV CALIF, RIVERSIDE, 81- *Concurrent Pos:* Vis scientist, Agr Res Org, Volcani Ctr, Bet Dagan, Israel, 75-76. *Mem:* Am Soc Agron; Soil Sci Soc Am. *Res:* Thermodynamics of soil moisture and ion movement; soil-plant-water relationships; remote sensing of soil salinity. *Mailing Add:* Soils & Environ Sci Univ Calif Riverside CA 92521

OSTER, LUDWIG FRIEDRICH, b Konstanz, Ger, Mar 8, 31; US citizen; m 56; c 2. ASTROPHYSICS. *Educ:* Univ Freiburg, Dipl, 54; Univ Kiel, Dr rer nat, 56. *Prof Exp:* Fel, Univ Kiel, 56-58; asst physics, Yale Univ, 58-60; from asst prof to assoc prof, 65-67; assoc prof, 67-70, PROF, JOINT INST LAB ASTROPHYS, UNIV COLO, BOULDER, 70- *Concurrent Pos:* Vis prof, Univ Bonn, 66; vis fel, Joint Inst Lab Astrophys, Univ Colo, 66-67; vis prof, Johns Hopkins Univ, 81; sr res assoc, Goddard Space Flight Ctr, Nat Res Ctr, NASA, 81-82. *Honors & Awards:* Sr US Scientist Award, Alexander von Humboldt Found, 74. *Mem:* Am Phys Soc; Am Astron Soc; Ger Astron Soc; Int Astron Union. *Res:* Solar and plasma physics; theoretical radio astronomy; radiation theory. *Mailing Add:* 7511 Vale St Chevy Chase MD 20815

OSTER, MARK OTHO, b Chicago, Ill, June 2, 37; m 56; c 3. BIOCHEMISTRY, MICROBIOLOGY. *Educ:* Purdue Univ, BS, 59; Agr & Mech Col Tex, MS, 61; Univ Ill, PhD(chem), 65. *Prof Exp:* Res chemist, Univ Calif, Los Angeles, 65-68; ASST PROF LIFE SCI, IND STATE UNIV, TERRE HAUTE, 68- *Mem:* AAAS; Am Chem Soc; Am Soc Microbiol. *Res:* Biosynthesis of diterpenes and gibberellin precursors in plants and microorganisms; regulation of pyruvate breakdown in acetate auxotrophs of Escherichia coli. *Mailing Add:* Dept of Life Sci Ind State Univ Terre Haute IN 47809

OSTERBERG, ARNOLD CURTIS, b Rochester, Minn, Sept 14, 21; m 46; c 4. PHARMACOLOGY. *Educ:* Univ Iowa, BA, 42; Univ Minn, PhD, 53. *Prof Exp:* Asst pharmacol, Univ Minn, 48-53; RES PHARMACOLOGIST, LEDERLE LABS, AM CYANAMID CO, 53- *Mem:* Am Soc Pharmacol & Exp Therapeut. *Res:* Analgesia; anticholinergics; central nervous system. *Mailing Add:* Dept of Pharmacol Lederle Labs Pearl River NY 10965

OSTERBERG, CHARLES LAMAR, b Miami, Ariz, June 15, 20; m 45; c 3. OCEANOGRAPHY. *Educ:* Ariz State Col, BS, 48, MA, 49; Ore State Univ, MS, 60, PhD(oceanog), 63. *Prof Exp:* Res assoc astron, Lowell Observ, Ariz, 49-53; jr scientist, Atmospheric Res Observ, 53-56; teacher high sch, 56-59; from instr to prof oceanog, Ore State Univ, 62-67; marine biologist, Div Biol & Med, 67-72, from actg chief to chief environ sci br, 69-72, 72, asst dir environ sci, US Atomic Energy Comn, 72-73, mgr environ progs, Div Biomed & Environ Res, Energy Res & Develop Admin, 73-76; dir, Lab Marine Radioactiv, Monaco, 76-79; MARINE SCIENTIST, DEPT ENERGY, 79- *Concurrent Pos:* Consult, Int Atomic Energy Agency, Vienna. *Mem:* AAAS; Am Soc Limnol & Oceanog; Ecol Soc Am; Sigma Xi; Am Inst Biol Sci. *Res:* Marine radioecology; biological and chemical oceanography; gamma ray spectrometry; fate of artificial radionuclides in sea and their transport through food chains. *Mailing Add:* Off of Environ Res Dept of Energy Washington DC 20545

OSTERBERG, DONALD MOURETZ, b Teaneck, NJ, Oct 28, 37; m 62; c 2. ICHTHYOLOGY. *Educ:* Montclair State Col, BA, 59; Mich State Univ, MS, 61; Univ Ottawa, PhD(ichthyol), 78. *Prof Exp:* High sch teacher biol, NJ, 61-68; ASST PROF BIOL, STATE UNIV NY COL POTSDAM, 68- *Concurrent Pos:* Consult & resource adv, NY Dept Environ Conserv, 77-; consult, St Lawrence Seaway Develop Corp, 78- *Mem:* Am Fisheries Soc; Sigma Xi; Can Conf Freshwater Fisheries Res. *Res:* Age, growth, food and behavior of the muskellunge and other warmwater fish in Saint Lawrence River & Saint Lawrence County, New York; vertebrates of Saint Lawrence County. *Mailing Add:* Dept of Biol State Univ of NY Col Potsdam NY 13676

OSTERBERG, J(ORJ) O(SCAR), b New York, NY, Jan 18, 15; m 42; c 4. CIVIL ENGINEERING. *Educ:* Columbia Univ, BS, 35, CE, 36; Harvard Univ, MS, 37; Cornell Univ, PhD(civil eng), 40. *Prof Exp:* Asst engr, US Waterways Exp Sta, 40-42; assoc, Univ Ill, 42-43; lectr, 43-45, from asst prof to assoc prof civil eng, 45-52, PROF CIVIL ENG & DIR GEOTECH CTR, NORTHWESTERN UNIV, 52-, WALTER P MURPHY PROF, 81- *Concurrent Pos:* Consult, various firms. *Mem:* Am Soc Civil Engrs; Am Soc Testing & Mat; Am Soc Eng Educ; Int Soc Soil Mech & Found Engrs. *Res:* Soil mechanics and foundations; frost action of soils. *Mailing Add:* Technol Inst Northwestern Univ Evanston IL 60201

OSTERBERG, ROBERT EDWARD, b Brooklyn, NY, July 4, 42. PHARMACOLOGY, TOXICOLOGY. *Educ:* Brooklyn Col Pharm, BS, 65; Georgetown Univ, MS, 69, PhD(pharmacol), 72. *Prof Exp:* Hosp pharmacist, Metrop Hosp, New York, 66, pharmacologist toxicol, US Food & Drug Admin, 72-73; pharmacologist toxicol, US Consumer Prod Safety Comn, 73-78; SUPVRY PHARMACOLOGIST, FOOD & DRUG ADMIN, 78- *Mem:* Soc Toxicol; Am Col Toxicol; Environ Mutagen Soc. *Res:* Petroleum distillates and organic solvents and their toxicological effects; mutagenic, irritant and skin sensitization properties of chemicals in consumer products; cardiovascular and neuropharmacology; inophores. *Mailing Add:* Food & Drug Admin Div of Toxicol HFF-154 Washington DC 20204

OSTERBROCK, CARL H, b Cincinnati, Ohio, Mar 8, 31; m 54; c 2. ELECTRICAL ENGINEERING. *Educ:* Univ Cincinnati, EE, 54; Univ Ill, MS, 55; Mich State Univ, PhD(elec eng), 64. *Prof Exp:* Propagation engr, Crosley Broadcasting Corp, 54; mem tech staff, Bell Tel Labs, 55-56; from instr to assoc prof, 56-71, asst to pres, 72-73, PROF ELEC ENG, UNIV CINCINNATI, 71-, V PROVOST ACAD AFFAIRS, 73- *Mem:* Inst Elec & Electronics Eng; Am Soc Eng Educ. *Res:* Discrete and continuous parameter system theory. *Mailing Add:* Dept of Elec & Comput Eng Univ of Cincinnati Cincinnati OH 45221

OSTERBROCK, DONALD EDWARD, b Cincinnati, Ohio, July 13, 24; m 52; c 3. ASTRONOMY. *Educ:* Univ Chicago, PhB, 48, BS, 48, MS, 49, PhD(astron), 52. *Prof Exp:* Fel astron, Princeton Univ, 52-53; from instr to asst prof, Calif Inst Technol, 53-58; from asst prof to prof, Univ Wis-Madison, 58-73, chmn dept, 69-72; dir astron, 72-81, PROF ASTRON, LICK OBSERV, UNIV CALIF, SANTA CRUZ, 72- *Concurrent Pos:* Guggenheim fel, Inst Advan Study, 60-61; vis prof, Univ Chicago, 63-64, Univ Minn, 77-78 & Ohio State Univ, 80-; NSF sr fel, Univ Col, London, 68-69; chmn sect astron, Nat Acad Sci, 71-74. *Mem:* Nat Acad Sci; Am Acad Arts & Sci; Int Astron Union; Am Astron Soc; assoc Royal Astron Soc. *Res:* Gaseous nebulae; quasars and active nuclei of galaxies; galactic structure; interstellar matter. *Mailing Add:* Lick Observ Univ of Calif Santa Cruz CA 95064

OSTERCAMP, DARYL LEE, b Garner, Iowa, Feb 5, 32; m 58; c 2. ORGANIC CHEMISTRY. *Educ:* St Olaf Col, BA, 53; Univ Wis, MS, 55; Univ Minn, PhD(chem), 59. *Prof Exp:* Instr chem & math, Luther Col, 54-56; res assoc org chem, Pa State Univ, 59-60; from asst prof to assoc prof, 60-72, PROF CHEM, CONCORDIA COL, 72- *Concurrent Pos:* Fulbright prof, Col Sci, Mosul, Iraq, 64-65; NSF sci fac fel, Univ E Anglia, 69-70; vis prof, Univ Petrol & Minerals, Dhahran, Saudi Arabia, 77-80. *Honors & Awards:* Nere Sundet Prof Chem, 73. *Mem:* Am Chem Soc. *Res:* Vinylogues of imides; octahydroquinolines and dacahydroquinolines; conformational analysis of saturated heterocycles; spectroscopic properties of vinylogous systems. *Mailing Add:* Dept of Chem Concordia Col Moorhead MN 56560

OSTERHELD, ROBERT KEITH, b Brooklyn, NY, Apr 19, 25; m 52; c 4. PHYSICAL INORGANIC CHEMISTRY. *Educ:* Polytech Inst Brooklyn, BS, 45; Univ Ill, PhD(chem), 50. *Prof Exp:* Instr chem, Cornell Univ, 50-54; from asst prof to assoc prof, 54-65, PROF CHEM, UNIV MONT, 65-, CHMN DEPT, 73- *Mem:* Am Chem Soc. *Res:* Phosphate chemistry; high temperature inorganic chemistry; mechanism of thermal decomposition of solids. *Mailing Add:* Dept of Chem Univ of Mont Missoula MT 59812

OSTERHOLTZ, FREDERICK DAVID, b Charleston, WVa, July 29, 38; m 60; c 2. ORGANIC CHEMISTRY, POLYMER CHEMISTRY. *Educ:* Univ Pa, BSc, 59; Mass Inst Technol, PhD(org chem), 64. *Prof Exp:* CHEMIST, UNION CARBIDE CORP, 63- *Mem:* Am Chem Soc. *Res:* Radiation chemistry of organic compounds and nitrogen; polymer radiation chemistry; organosilicon chemistry. *Mailing Add:* 81 Oak Dr Pleasantville NY 10570

OSTERHOUDT, HANS WALTER, b Houston, Tex, Feb 29, 36; m 62; c 2. PHYSICAL CHEMISTRY. *Educ:* Colo State Univ, BS, 58; Univ Wis-Madison, PhD(phys chem), 64. *Prof Exp:* Res chemist, Armstrong Cork Co, 64-68; sr res chemist, 68-71, res assoc polymer chem, 71-73, lab head, 73-78, RES ASSOC PHYS CHEM & MAT SCI, EASTMAN KODAK CO, 78- *Mem:* Am Chem Soc; Electrochem Soc. *Res:* Physical chemistry and materials science; electrochemistry of batteries; corrosion; polymer membranes; polymer molecular weight determination; ultrasonics. *Mailing Add:* 4090 Canal Rd Spencerport NY 14559

OSTERHOUT, SUYDAM, b Brooklyn, NY, Nov 13, 25. VIROLOGY. *Educ:* Princeton Univ, BA, 45; Duke Univ, MD, 49; Rockefeller Inst, PhD(microbiol), 59; Am Bd Internal Med, dipl, 59. *Prof Exp:* Intern path, Cleveland City Hosp, 50; intern med, Mass Mem Hosp, 50-51; from jr asst resident to resident, Duke Hosp, 53-56; PROF MICROBIOL & MED, SCH MED, DUKE UNIV, 59-, ASST DEAN ADMIS, 66- *Concurrent Pos:* Markle scholar, Sch Med, Duke Univ, 59- *Mem:* Fel Am Col Physicians. *Res:* Infectious diseases; internal medicine. *Mailing Add:* Box 3007 Sch of Med Duke Univ Durham NC 27706

OSTERKAMP, THOMAS EUGENE, US citizen. GLACIOLOGY. *Educ:* Southern Ill Univ, BA, 62; St Louis Univ, MS, 64, PhD(physics), 68. *Prof Exp:* ASSOC PROF PHYSICS & GEOPHYS, UNIV ALASKA, FAIRBANKS, 68- *Concurrent Pos:* Mem glaciol panel, Comt Polar Res, Nat Acad Sci, 74-77. *Mem:* Glaciol Soc; Am Geophys Union. *Res:* Scientific aspects of engineering problems involving snow, ice and permafrost. *Mailing Add:* Geophys Inst Univ of Alaska Fairbanks AK 99701

OSTERLE, J(OHN) F(LETCHER), b Pittsburgh, Pa, July 31, 25; m 59; c 2. MECHANICAL ENGINEERING. *Educ:* Carnegie Inst Technol, BS, 46, MS, 49, DSc(mech eng), 52. *Prof Exp:* From instr to assoc prof, 46-58, THEODORE AHRENS PROF MECH ENG, CARNEGIE-MELLON UNIV, 58-, CHMN NUCLEAR SCI & ENG, 75- *Concurrent Pos:* Vis prof, Delft Univ Technol, Neth, 57-58 & Oxford Univ, 71. *Honors & Awards:* Walter D Hodson Award, Am Soc Lubrication Engrs, 56. *Mem:* Am Soc Mech Engrs; Am Nuclear Soc. *Res:* Fluid mechanics; thermodynamics. *Mailing Add:* Dept Mech Eng Carnegie-Mellon Univ Pittsburgh PA 15213

OSTERMAN, GEORGE B, b McKeesport, Pa, Oct 17, 10; m 48; c 4. BIOLOGY. *Educ:* Washington & Jefferson Col, AB, 33, MS, 35. *Prof Exp:* Asst biol, NY Univ, 35-39; from instr to asst prof, Washington & Jefferson Col, 39-59; from asst prof to assoc prof, 59-78, EMER PROF BIOL, MT UNION COL, 79- *Res:* Fresh water organisms; orthoptera distribution. *Mailing Add:* 2433 Union Ave NE Minerva OH 44657

OSTERMAN, JOSEPH VINCENT, JR, b Washington, DC, Dec 12, 35; m 58; c 3. RICKETTSIAL DISEASES. *Educ:* Univ Md, College Park, BA, 57, PhD(med microbiol), 69. *Prof Exp:* Fel cell biol, Univ Md, 69-71, asst prof microbiol, Sch Med, 71-74; chief, Rickettsial Dis Sect, 74-79, CHIEF, DEPT RICKETTSIAL DIS, WALTER REED ARMY INST RES, 79- *Mem:* Am Soc Microbiol; Am Soc Trop Med & Hyg. *Res:* Rickettsial diseases of military importance, with particular emphasis on scrub typhus; biochemistry, genetics, immunology and vaccine development. *Mailing Add:* Dept Rickettsial Dis Walter Reed Army Inst Res Washington DC 20012

OSTERMANN, RUSSELL DEAN, b Wichita, Kans, Mar 24, 52; m 80; c 1. CHEMICAL ENGINEERING, FERMENTATION ENGINEERING. *Educ:* Univ Kans, BS, 74, PhD(chem eng), 80. *Prof Exp:* Res asst, NSF, Univ Kans, 72; tech serv engr, Sabine River Works, E I Du Pont de Nemours & Co, 74-75; res asst, chem eng, Univ Kans, 75-79; asst prof chem eng, Tex A&M Univ, 79-81; ASST PROF PETROL ENG, UNIV ALASKA, 81- *Concurrent Pos:* Planning engr, Northern Natural Gas Co, 75; asst adj instr mat & energy balances, Univ Kans, 77. *Mem:* Am Inst Chem Engrs. *Res:* Kinetic studies of cellulose liquefaction; fermentation technology. *Mailing Add:* 718 A Chandalar Univ Alaska Fairbanks AK 99701

OSTERMAYER, FREDERICK WILLIAM, JR, b New York, NY, Aug 12, 37. PHYSICS. *Educ:* Mass Inst Technol, SB & SM, 59; Lehigh Univ, PhD(physics), 68. *Prof Exp:* Mem tech staff solid state devices, 59-65, MEM TECH STAFF ELECTRONIC DEVICES & MAT, BELL LABS, INC, 68- *Mem:* Am Phys Soc. *Res:* Optical fibers and materials; solid state lasers; luminescence of solids; semiconductor electrochemistry. *Mailing Add:* Bell Labs Inc 600 Mountain Ave Murray Hill NJ 07974

OSTERRITTER, JOHN FERDINAND, b Millvale, Pa, Feb 1, 23. OCCUPATIONAL MEDICINE. *Educ:* Univ Pittsburgh, BS, 45, MD, 50, MPH, 52, PhD(occup health), 55. *Prof Exp:* Res assoc chemist, Mellon Inst, 44-46; asst to med dir, Indust Hyg Found, 52-53; assoc physician, Pittsburgh Coke & Chem Co, 53-55; resident chest dis, Bergen Pines Hosp, 56-57; med dir, Celanese Corp Am, 57-65; CONSULT OCCUP HEALTH & INDUST MED, 65- *Mem:* AAAS; AMA; Am Occupational Med Asn; Indust Med Asn; Am Pub Health Asn. *Res:* Occupational health methodologies; environmental and industrial health; preventive medicine; industrial toxicology; toxicity of triaryl phosphates; labelling of industrial chemical containers and hazardous household substances. *Mailing Add:* 300 East 71st New York NY 10021

OSTERUD, HAROLD T, b Richmond, Va, May 1, 23; m 49; c 3. PUBLIC HEALTH, PREVENTIVE MEDICINE. *Educ:* Randolph-Macon Col, BS, 44; Med Col Va, MD, 47; Univ NC, MPH, 51. *Prof Exp:* Health officer, Wasco-Sherman Health Dept, 48-50, Coquille County Health Dept, 53-55 & Lane County Health Dept, 56-61; assoc prof pub health, 61-65, PROF PUB HEALTH, MED SCH, ORE HEALTH SCI UNIV, 65-, CHMN DEPT, 67- *Concurrent Pos:* Mem, Prev Med & Dent Rev Panel, 65-70. *Honors & Awards:* Sippy Award, Am Pub Health Asn, 69. *Mem:* Am Pub Health Asn. *Res:* Health manpower; physician study and health care delivery. *Mailing Add:* Dept Pub Health Ore Health Sci Univ Portland OR 97201

OSTERWALD, FRANK WILLIAM, b Casper, Wyo, Feb 11, 22; m 47; c 4. PHYSICAL GEOLOGY. *Educ:* Univ Wyo, BA, 44, MS, 47; Univ Chicago, PhD(geol), 51. *Prof Exp:* Asst geol, Univ Wyo, 46-47 & Univ Chicago, 47-48; supply instr, Univ Wyo, 48-49, asst prof, 50-52; geologist, 52-64, res geologist, 64-80, CONSULT, US GEOL SURV, 80- *Concurrent Pos:* Asst geologist, State Geol Surv, Wyo, 47, 49-51. *Mem:* Geol Soc Am; Soc Econ Geol; Am Inst Prof Geologists; Am Asn Petrol Geol; Asn Eng Geol. *Res:* Engineering geology, especially geologic features affecting coal mine bumps, stability of underground openings; structure and petrology of the cores of Rocky Mountain ranges; investigations related to coal mine development in western US. *Mailing Add:* 40 S Dover St Lakewood CO 80226

OSTERYOUNG, JANET G, b Pittsburgh, Pa, Mar 1, 39; m 69; c 2. ELECTROANALYTICAL CHEMISTRY. *Educ:* Swarthmore Col, BA, 61; Calif Inst Technol, PhD(chem), 67. *Prof Exp:* Res fel chem, Calif Inst Technol, 66-67; asst prof, Mont State Univ, 67-68; res fel, Colo State Univ, 68-69, assoc prof civil eng, 73-79; ASSOC PROF CHEM, STATE UNIV NY, BUFFALO, 79- *Mem:* Am Chem Soc; Electrochem Soc; AAAS; Sigma Xi. *Res:* Electroanalytical methods development especially for toxic substances; characterization of natural waters; plulse voltammetry; microelectrodes. *Mailing Add:* Dept Chem State Univ NY Buffalo NY 14214

OSTERYOUNG, ROBERT ALLEN, b US, Jan 20, 27; m 69; c 5. ANALYTICAL CHEMISTRY. *Educ:* Ohio Univ, BS, 49; Univ Ill, MS, 51, PhD, 54. *Prof Exp:* Res chemist, Harshaw Chem Co, 51-52; asst, Univ Ill, 52-54; from asst prof to assoc prof chem, Rensselaer Polytech, 54-59; res specialist, Atomics Int Div, NAm Rockwell Corp, 59-62, group leader phys chem, Sci Ctr, 62-67; prof chem, Colo State Univ, 68-79, chmn dept, 68-78; PROF CHEM, STATE UNIV NY AT BUFFALO, 79- *Concurrent Pos:* Vis assoc chem, Calif Inst Technol, 63-68; asst dir phys sci dept, Autonetics Div, NAm Rockwell Corp, 67, dir, Mat & Process Lab & assoc dir, Sci Ctr, 68. *Mem:* Fel AAAS; Am Chem Soc; Electrochem Soc; Int Soc Electrochem. *Res:* Ionic liquid chemistry and electrochemistry; electroanalytical chemistry; pulse voltommetry; on line use of computers in electrochemistry. *Mailing Add:* Dept of Chem State Univ NY Buffalo NY 14214

OSTFELD, ADRIAN MICHAEL, b St Louis, Mo, Sept 2, 26; m 50; c 3. EPIDEMIOLOGY, PUBLIC HEALTH. *Educ:* Wash Univ, MD, 51. *Prof Exp:* Asst resident med, Barnes Hosp, St Louis, Mo, 52-53; instr med, Med Col, Cornell Univ, 55-56; from asst prof to prof prev med, Univ Ill Col Med, 56-66, prof prev med & community health & head dept, 66-68; chem dept epidemiol & pub health, 68-70, LAUDER PROF EPIDEMIOL & PUB HEALTH, YALE UNIV, 68- *Concurrent Pos:* Commonwealth fel, NY Hosp, 53-55; proj dir ecol migrant pop, Int Biol Prog, Nat Acad Sci, 67-; spec consult to Surgeon Gen, USPHS; vpres, Coun Epidemiol, Am Heart Asn, fel, Coun Stroke & chmn, Comt on Hypertension, 70-75; chmn epidemiol & biomet comt, NIH; chmn epidemiol adv comt, Nat Heart & Lung Inst; consult, Coun Regional Med Prog; assoc ed, J Behav Med & Behav Med Ann, 70-75. *Mem:* Am Psychosom Soc; Am Soc Pharmacol & Exp Therapeut; Am Pub Health Asn; Asn Teachers Prev Med; fel Am Col Angiol. *Res:* Epidemiology of hypertension and cerebrovascular diseases; community surveys; geriatrics; human behavior and psychosomatic medicine; epidemiology of cardiovascular disease. *Mailing Add:* Lab of Epidemiol & Pub Health Yale Univ Sch of Med New Haven CT 06510

OSTFIELD, HOWARD G, b Pittsburgh, Pa, Mar 8, 41; m 62; c 2. ORGANIC POLYMER CHEMISTRY. *Educ:* Univ Pittsburgh, BS, 62 & 69. *Prof Exp:* Chemist, Pittsburgh Plate Glass Co, 63-64; res assoc chem, Mellon Inst, 64-66; group leader chem, 66-76, sect mgr, 76-78, mgr flexible urethrene foam, 78-80, MGR URETHRENES FOR AUTOMOTIVE USE, MOBAY CHEM CORP, 80- *Concurrent Pos:* Instr math, Univ Pittsburgh. *Res:* Application development work in the field of polyurethane chemistry, including the development of high molecular weight polyethers for flexible foams and the development of various processing techniques for the various polymers. *Mailing Add:* Mobay Chem Corp Pittsburgh PA 15205

OSTLE, BERNARD, b Vancouver, BC, June 29, 21; nat US; m 53; c 2. STATISTICS. *Educ:* Univ BC, BA, 45, MA, 46; Iowa State Univ, PhD(statist), 49. *Prof Exp:* Instr statist, Univ Minn, 46-47; from instr to asst prof, Iowa State Univ, 47-52; from assoc prof to prof math, Mont State Col, 52-57, dir statist lab & statistician, Agr Exp Sta, 56-57; mem staff, Reliability Dept, Sandia Corp, NMex, 57-58, supvr statist sect, 58-60; prof eng, Ariz State Univ, 60-63; chmn statist test design, Rocketdyne Div, Rockwell Corp, 63-67; dean, Col Natural Sci, 67-80, actg vpres for res & dean grad studies, 80-81, PROF STATIST, UNIV CENT FLA, 81- *Concurrent Pos:* Consult, Humble Oil & Ref Co, 52, Motorola, Inc, 61-63 & AvCir, Flight Safety Found, 62. *Mem:* AAAS; fel Am Statist Asn; Am Soc Qual Control; Sigma Xi; Am Inst Indust Eng. *Res:* Quality control; reliability; statistical design of experiments; statistical analysis of data. *Mailing Add:* Dept Statist Univ Cent Fla PO Box 25000 Orlando FL 32816

OSTLIND, DAN A, b McPherson, Kans, June 19, 36; m 58. PARASITOLOGY, ENTOMOLOGY. *Educ:* Bethany Col, Kans, BS, 58; Kansas State Univ, MS, 62, PhD(parasitol), 66. *Prof Exp:* Parasitologist, Moorman Mfg Co, 66-67; sr res parasitologist, 67-69, res fel, 69-77, SR RES FEL, MERCK INST, 77- *Mem:* Am Soc Parasitol; Am Asn Vet Parasitologists. *Res:* Chemotherapy of parasites; helminthology; radiation. *Mailing Add:* Merck Inst Rahway NJ 07065

OSTLUND, H GOTE, b Stockholm, Sweden, June 26, 23; m 50; c 2. MARINE CHEMISTRY, ATMOSPHERIC CHEMISTRY. *Educ:* Univ Stockholm, Fil Kand, 49, Fil lic, 59. *Prof Exp:* Asst inorg chem, Royal Inst Technol, Sweden, 48-52; head labs, Svenska Salpeterverken Koping, 52-54; dir, Radioactive Dating Lab, Stockholm, 54-63; vis assoc prof, 60-61, assoc prof geochem, Inst Marine Sci, 63-67, PROF MARINE & ATMOSPHERIC CHEM, ROSENSTIEL SCH MARINE & ATMOSPHERIC SCI, UNIV MIAMI, 67- *Concurrent Pos:* Consult, Adv Panel Oceanog, NSF, 70-74, chmn div chem oceanog, 70-74; coordr proj, Geochem Ocean Sect Study, 76-81, Translent Tracers in the ocean, 79- *Mem:* AAAS; Am Geophys Union; Am Meteorol Soc; Swedish Geophys Soc. *Res:* Low level counting techniques; chemical meteorology and air-sea interaction; radioactive isotopes for tracing and dating ocean currents; arctic oceanography. *Mailing Add:* Rosenstiel Sch Univ of Miami 4600 Rickenbacker Causeway Miami FL 33149

OSTLUND, NEIL SINCLAIR, b Calgary, Alta, Nov 18, 42. THEORETICAL CHEMISTRY. *Educ:* Univ Sask, BA, 63; Carnegie-Mellon Univ, MSc, 68, PhD(theoret chem), 69. *Prof Exp:* Res fel theoret chem, Harvard, 69-71; asst prof, Univ Ark, Fayetteville, 71-75, assoc prof, 75-80; ASSOC PROF, CARNEGIE-MELLON UNIV, 80- *Mem:* Am Phys Soc; Am Chem Soc; Inst Elec & Electronics Engrs; Asn Comput Mach. *Res:* Theory; computer architecture. *Mailing Add:* Dept Comput Sci Carnegie-Mellon Univ Pittsburgh PA 15213

OSTMANN, BERNARD GEORGE, b Washington, DC, Aug 14, 27; m 55; c 5. TEXTILE TECHNOLOGY. *Educ:* Cath Univ Am, BS, 50. *Prof Exp:* From chemist to res chemist, 50-67, SR RES CHEMIST, TEXTILE RES LAB, E I DU PONT DE NEMOURS & CO, 67- *Res:* Synthetic fiber chemistry and technology. *Mailing Add:* 2212 Pennington Dr Wilmington DE 19810

OSTRACH, SIMON, b Providence, RI, Dec 26, 23; m 75; c 5. FLUID & THERMAL SCIENCES. *Educ:* Univ RI, BS, 44, ME, 49; Brown Univ, ScM, 49, PhD(appl math), 50. *Prof Exp:* Res scientist aeronaut, Nat Adv Comt Aeronaut, 44-47; res assoc appl math, Brown Univ, 47-50; br chief fluid mech, NASA, 50-60; prof fluid & Thermal sci, Case Inst Technol, 60-70; W J AUSTIN DISTINGUISHED PROF ENG, CASE WESTERN RESERVE UNIV, 70- *Concurrent Pos:* Mem res adv comt, NASA, 63-75; consult, Gen Elec Space Sci Lab, 75-77, Diamond Shamrock Electrode Div, 77- & Gen Motors Res Labs, 79-; lectr, Am Soc Mech Engrs, 78-79; Freeman scholar, 82. *Honors & Awards:* Heat Transfer Mem Award, Am Soc Mech Engrs, 75; Sigma Xi. *Mem:* Nat Acad Eng; fel Am Soc Mech Engrs; fel Am Inst Aeronaut & Astronaut; fel Am Acad Mech. *Res:* Aerospace science; natural convection; reduced-gravity phenomena; materials processing; biological fluid mechanics. *Mailing Add:* Dept of Mech Eng Case Western Reserve Univ Cleveland OH 44106

OSTRAND, PHILLIP ARTHUR, b Chicago, Ill, Nov 2, 36; m 63. MATHEMATICS. *Educ:* Univ Ill, Urbana, BS, 59; Northwestern Univ, Ill, MA, 62, PhD(math), 65. *Prof Exp:* Asst prof math, Rosary Col, 65-66; asst prof, 68-74, ASSOC PROF MATH, UNIV CALIF, SANTA BARBARA, 74- *Mem:* Am Math Soc; Math Asn Am. *Res:* Combinatorial analysis; graph, dimension and approximation theory. *Mailing Add:* Dept of Math Univ of Calif Santa Barbara CA 93106

OSTRANDER, CHARLES EVANS, b Jamestown, NY, Oct 30, 16; m 45; c 2. POULTRY SCIENCE. *Educ:* Cornell Univ, BS, 41; Mich State Univ, MS, 60. *Prof Exp:* Teacher pub schs, 41-45; from asst to assoc county agr agent, Onondaga County, NY, 46-51; asst prof poultry sci, Cornell Univ, 51-52; sales mgr, Marshall Bros Hatchery, 52-56; from asst prof to assoc prof, 56-72, prof, 72-81, EMER PROF POULTRY SCI, CORNELL UNIV, 81- *Honors & Awards:* Pfizer Nat Poultry Exten Award, 80. *Mem:* Poultry Sci Asn; World Poultry Sci Asn; Ctr Appl Sci & Technol. *Res:* Poultry management; waste disposal; lighting regimes to conserve energy. *Mailing Add:* Dept of Poultry Sci Cornell Univ 204 Rice Hall Ithaca NY 14853

OSTRANDER, DARL REED, b Ann Arbor, Mich, Apr 29, 35; m 57; c 2. LIMNOLOGY. *Educ:* Eastern Mich Univ, BS, 61; Univ Mich, MS, 65; Univ Conn, PhD(ecol-fisheries), 74. *Prof Exp:* Asst prof, 65-76, ASSOC PROF BIOL, CENT CONN STATE COL, 76- *Concurrent Pos:* Assoc consult, Environ Mgt Coun, 74- *Mem:* Ecol Soc Am; Am Soc Limnol & Oceanog. *Res:* Analysis of plant and mineral distribution in inland wetlands; recovery of perturbed tidal wetlands. *Mailing Add:* Dept of Biol Cent Conn State Col New Britain CT 06050

OSTRANDER, LEE E, b Glens Falls, NY, Feb 18, 39; m; c 2. ELECTRICAL ENGINEERING, BIOENGINEERING. *Educ:* Hamilton Col, AB, 61; Univ Rochester, MS, 63, PhD(elec eng), 66. *Prof Exp:* Res assoc eng, Case Western Reserve Univ, 65-66, from asst prof to assoc prof, 66-74; bioengr, S C Johnson & Son Inc, 74-75; ASSOC PROF ENG, RENSSELAER POLYTECH INST, 76- *Mem:* Inst Elec & Electronics Engrs. *Res:* Application of control engineering and process identification to problems in the life sciences, clinical medicine and bioinstrumentation. *Mailing Add:* Ctr for Biomed Eng Rensselaer Polytech Inst Troy NY 12181

OSTRANDER, PETER ERLING, b Rahway, NJ, Aug 12, 43; m 70. NUCLEAR PHYSICS. *Educ:* Ill Inst Technol, BS, 65; Pa State Univ, PhD(physics), 70. *Prof Exp:* Asst prof, 69-76, ASSOC PROF PHYSICS, PA STATE UNIV, 76- *Mem:* Am Phys Soc. *Res:* Theoretical calculations of photopion cross-sections including final state interactions. *Mailing Add:* Rm 203 Pa State Univ Fayette Campus Rte 119 N Uniontown PA 15401

OSTRAND-ROSENBERG, SUZANNE T, b New York, NY, July 8, 48; m 71; c 2. IMMUNOLOGY. *Educ:* Barnard Col, Columbia Univ, AB, 70; Calif Inst Technol, PhD(immunol), 75. *Prof Exp:* Fel immunol, Johns Hopkins Univ, 74-77; ASST PROF BIOL SCI, UNIV MD, BALTIMORE COUNTY, 77- *Mem:* Am Asn Immunologists; AAAS. *Res:* Genetic control of tumor rejection in mammals, with emphasis on the regulation and role of the major histocompatibility complexes in cell mediated tumor immunity. *Mailing Add:* Dept Biol Sci Univ Md Baltimore County Catonsville MD 21228

OSTRIKER, JEREMIAH P, b New York, NY, Apr 13, 37; m 58; c 3. ASTROPHYSICS. *Educ:* Harvard Univ, AB, 59; Univ Chicago, PhD(astrophys), 64. *Prof Exp:* NSF fel, 64-65, lectr & res assoc, 65-66, from asst prof to assoc prof, 66-71, PROF ASTROPHYS, PRINCETON UNIV, 71-, CHMN, DEPT ASTROPHYS SCI & DIR, PRINCETON UNIV OBSERV, 79- *Concurrent Pos:* Alfred P Sloan fel, 70-72. *Honors & Awards:* Helen B Warner Prize, Am Astron Soc, 72; Henry Norris Russell Prize, Am Astron Soc, 80. *Mem:* Nat Acad Sci; Am Acad Arts & Sci; Int Astron Union. *Res:* Structure and stability of nonspherical self gravitating bodies; high energy astrophysics; galaxy origin and evolution. *Mailing Add:* Princeton Univ Observ Princeton NJ 08544

OSTRO, MARC JEFFREY, biochemistry, molecular biology, see previous edition

OSTROFF, ANTON G, b Moline, Ill, Nov 6, 25; m 54; c 3. WATER CHEMISTRY. *Educ:* Augustana Col, Ill, BA, 50; Southern Methodist Univ, MS, 52; Univ Iowa, PhD(inorg chem), 57. *Prof Exp:* Res chemist, 52-53, sr res technologist, 56-79, MGR ANALYTICAL SERV, FIELD RES LAB, MOBIL RES & DEVELOP CORP, 79- *Mem:* Am Chem Soc; Am Soc Testing & Mat; Soc Petrol Engrs; Nat Asn Corrosion Engrs. *Res:* Chemistry of subsurface brines; corrosion of oilfield equipment; geochemistry; trace elements in rocks and waters; water pollution; thermal gravimetric analysis and differential thermal analysis of metal sulfates; analysis of phenol carbonation products; analytical chemistry. *Mailing Add:* 619 Misty Glen Lane Dallas TX 75232

OSTROFF, NORMAN, chemical engineering, mathematics, see previous edition

OSTROFSKY, BENJAMIN, b Philadelphia, Pa, July 26, 25; m 56; c 2. INDUSTRIAL ENGINEERING, OPERATIONS RESEARCH. *Educ:* Drexel Univ, BS, 47; Univ Calif, Los Angeles, MEng, 62, PhD(eng), 68. *Prof Exp:* Prod test engr elec & mech test, E G Budd Mfg Co, Red Lion, Pa, 48; proj eng consult, George C Lewis Co, Philadelphia, 40-50; prod mgr mfg, Generator Equip Co, Los Angeles, Calif, 53-54; res engr aircraft testing, Douglas Aircraft Co, Santa Monica, 54-57; sr engr advan design, Norair Div, Northrop Corp, 57-61; mem tech staff opers mgt, Electronics Div, TRW Systs, Calif, 61-64, sr staff engr, 64-69; chmn prod logistics mgt, 71-74, PROF PROD LOGISTICS MGT, COL BUS ADMIN, UNIV HOUSTON, 69-, PROF INDUST & SYSTS ENG, COL ENG, 69- *Concurrent Pos:* Lectr & teaching fel, Ford Found Educ Develop Prog Design, Univ Calif, Los Angeles, 62-65, lectr systs design, 65-69; consult var industs & govt orgn, 70- *Honors & Awards:* Armitage Medal, Soc Logistics Engrs, 78. *Mem:* Fel Soc Logistics Engrs; assoc fel Am Inst Aeronaut & Astronaut; Opers Res Soc Am; Nat Soc Prof Engrs; fel AAAS. *Res:* Methods of systems design; information systems for operational performance; quantitative methods for criteria function synthesis; systems optimization; educational methods for teaching systems design, logistics methods and systems theory; engineering management. *Mailing Add:* Dept Indust Eng Univ of Houston Houston TX 77004

OSTROFSKY, BERNARD, b New York, NY, Jan 14, 22; m 46; c 2. PHYSICS, PHYSICAL CHEMISTRY. *Educ:* City Col New York, BS, 45. *Prof Exp:* Res chemist, Manhattan Proj, Columbia Univ, 42-45; physicist, Res Labs, Nat Lead Indust, 45-53; sr phys chemist, Commonwealth Eng Co Ohio, 53-54; proj supvr mat sci, Eng Res Div, Standard Oil Co, Ind, 54-61; res proj supvr, Res & Develop Dept, Amoco Oil Co, 61-72; sr res assoc & proj mgr, Standard Oil Co, Ind, 72-81; PRES, BERNARD OSTROFSKY ASSOC INC, 81- *Concurrent Pos:* Tech ed, Mat Eval, J Am Soc Nondestructive Testing, 68- *Honors & Awards:* John Vaalor Award, 70. *Mem:* Fel Am Soc Nondestructive Testing; Am Crystallog Asn; Am Chem Soc; Electron Probe Soc Am; Am Soc Testing & Mat. *Res:* X-ray and electron diffraction; x-ray microbeam analysis; materials science; ultrasonics, radiography; leak testing; magnetic inspection; liquid penetrants; electronics; crystallography; scanning electron microscopy; acoustic emission. *Mailing Add:* 23 River Rd Naperville IL 60540

OSTROFSKY, MILTON LEWIS, b Bridgeport, Conn, Sept 9, 47. LIMNOLOGY, ECOLOGY. *Educ:* Univ Vt, BA, 69; Univ Waterloo, MSc, 74, PhD(biol), 76. *Prof Exp:* Environ consult limnol, Sheppard T Powell Assocs, 70-75; res assoc, Dept Biol, McGill Univ, 76-78; ASST PROF BIOL, ALLEGHENY COL, 78- *Mem:* Int Asn Theoret & Appl Limnol; Phycol Soc Am; Am Soc Limnol & Oceanog. *Res:* Trophic changes during the maturation of reservoir ecosystems; effect of various nutrient concentrations on the qualitative and quantitative aspects of the plankton of freshwater lakes. *Mailing Add:* Dept of Biol Allegheny Col Meadville PA 16335

OSTROM, CARL ERIC, b Philadelphia, Pa, May 29, 12; m 41; c 4. FORESTRY. *Educ:* Pa State Univ, BS, 33; Yale Univ, MF, 41, PhD(forestry), 44. *Prof Exp:* Asst technician, Northern Rocky Mt Forest & Range Exp Sta, US Forest Serv, 34-36, silviculturist, Northeastern Forest Exp Sta, 36-44, Southeastern Forest Exp Sta, 44-57, dir, Div Timber Mgt Res, 57-74, assoc dep chief, Biol Res, 74-75; dir sci progs, Soc Am Foresters, 75-77; RETIRED. *Concurrent Pos:* Consult, UN Spec Fund, Thailand, 62. *Mem:* Soc Am Foresters. *Res:* Silviculture; forest management. *Mailing Add:* 2233 Sequoya Lane Prescott AZ 86301

OSTROM, JOHN HAROLD, b New York, NY, Feb 18, 28; m 52; c 2. VERTEBRATE PALEONTOLOGY. *Educ:* Union Col, NY, BS, 51; Columbia Univ, PhD(geol), 60. *Prof Exp:* Res asst vert paleont, Am Mus Natural Hist, 51-56; from instr to asst prof geol, Beloit Col, 56-61; from asst prof to assoc prof geol & asst cur to assoc cur vert paleont, 61-71, PROF GEOL & GEOPHYS, YALE UNIV, 74-, CUR VERT PALEONT, PEABODY MUS NATURAL HIST, 71- *Concurrent Pos:* Guggenheim fel, 66-67; lectr, Brooklyn Col, 55-56; res assoc, Am Mus Natural Hist, 65-; ed, Am J Sci, 67-, Bull, Soc Vert Paleont, 63-73 & Peabody Mus Publ, 70-; Alexander von Humboldt sr scientist award, W Ger, 76-77. *Mem:* AAAS; Soc Study Evolution; Soc Vert Paleont (pres, 69-70); Asn Earth Sci Ed; Sigma Xi (pres, 72-73). *Res:* Vertebrate paleontology, especially ancient reptiles; vertebrate evolution; Mesozoic stratigraphy. *Mailing Add:* Dept of Geol & Geophys Yale Univ New Haven CT 06520

OSTROM, MEREDITH EGGERS, b Rock Island, Ill, Nov 16, 30; m 53; c 3. GEOLOGY. *Educ:* Augustana Col, BS, 52; Univ Ill, MS, 54, PhD, 59. *Prof Exp:* Asst geologist, Univ Ill, 52-54; asst geologist coal sect, State Geol Surv, Ill, 54-55, asst geologist, Indust Minerals Sect, 55-59; asst state geologist, 59-67, assoc state geologist, 67-72, STATE GEOLOGIST & DIR, WIS GEOL & NATURAL HIST SURV, 72-; PROF GEOL & GEOPHYS, UNIV WIS-MADISON, 76- *Concurrent Pos:* Chmn dept environ sci, Univ Wis Exten, 72-76. *Mem:* Geol Soc Am; Soc Econ Paleont & Mineral; Am Asn Petrol Geol; Am Inst Prof Geol; Asn Am State Geol. *Res:* Industrial minerals; nonmetallic mineral deposits; stratigraphy; ground water geology. *Mailing Add:* Wis Geol & Natural Hist Surv 1815 University Ave Madison WI 53706

OSTROM, THEODORE GLEASON, b Nicollet, Minn, Jan 4, 16; m 49; c 4. MATHEMATICS. *Educ:* Univ Minn, BA, 37, MA & BS, 39, PhD(math), 47. *Prof Exp:* Instr math, Univ Minn, 46-47; from asst prof to prof math, Univ Mont, 47-60, chmn dept, 54-60; chmn dept, 69-71, prof, 60-81, EMER PROF MATH, WASH STATE UNIV, 81- *Concurrent Pos:* Vis prof, Univ Frankfurt, 66-67. *Mem:* Am Math Soc; Math Asn Am. *Res:* Finite projective planes. *Mailing Add:* Dept of Math Wash State Univ Pullman WA 99164

OSTROM, THOMAS ROSS, b San Francisco, Calif, May 23, 24; m 49; c 2. SANITARY ENGINEERING, BALLISTICS. *Educ:* Univ Calif, BS, 44; Harvard Univ, MSSE, 48, PhD(sanit eng), 55. *Prof Exp:* US Army, 45-75, mil govt officer, Hq Korea, 45-47, sanit engr, Health Physics Div, Oak Ridge Nat Lab, Tenn, 49-50, engr health physics, Joint Task Force 3, 50-51, sanit engr, Indust Waste Br, Los Alamos Field Off, 51-53, chmn sanit eng div, US Army Environ Health Lab, Army Chem Ctr, Md, 55-58, chmn sanit eng dept, Walter Reed Army Inst Res, Washington, DC, 59-62, sanit engr, Hq 7th Army, 62-64, chief med & biol sci br, Off Chief Res & Develop, Hq, Dept Army, 64-68, commanding officer, Wound Data & Munitions Effectiveness Team, Vietnam, 68-69, mem fac, Indust Col Armed Forces, 69-71, dir res, develop & eng, Munitions Command, 71-72, commanding officer, US Army Ballistics Res Labs, 72-75; RETIRED. *Concurrent Pos:* Consult, US Army Mat Systs Anal Activity, 76- & Gen Elec, TEMPO, 77- *Mem:* Nat Soc Prof Engrs; Am Soc Civil Engrs; Health Physics Soc; Soc Am Mil Engrs; Am Acad Environ Engrs. *Res:* Radio-strontium content of and distribution of radiostronitum in fallout; disposal of low level radioactive wastes; sewage disposal procedures under extreme cold conditions. *Mailing Add:* 102 Duncannon Rd Bel Air MD 21014

OSTROVSKY, DAVID SAUL, b Cleveland, Ohio, Jan 28, 43. ZOOLOGY. *Educ:* Case Western Reserve Univ, BA, 65; Univ Mich, MS, 67, PhD, 70. *Prof Exp:* Asst prof zool, Ohio Wesleyan Univ, 72-73; ASST PROF BIOL, MILLERSVILLE STATE COL, 73- *Mem:* Am Soc Zool. *Res:* The problem of enzyme development in relation to both structural and functional differentiation. *Mailing Add:* Dept of Biol Millersville State Col Millersville PA 17551

OSTROW, JAY DONALD, b New York, NY, Jan 1, 30; m 56; c 3. GASTROENTEROLOGY. *Educ:* Yale Univ, BS, 50; Harvard Med Sch, MD, 54; Univ London, MSc, 70. *Prof Exp:* Intern med, Johns Hopkins Hosp, 54-55; asst resident, Peter Bent Brigham Hosp, 57-58; instr med, Harvard Med Serv, 61-62; sr instr, Western Reserve Univ & Univ Hosps, 62-64, asst prof, 64-69; from asst prof to assoc prof med, Sch Med, Univ Pa, 71-78; OTHO S A SPRAGUE PROF MED, NORTHWESTERN UNIV, CHICAGO, 78-, CHIEF, GASTROENTEROL SECT, 78- *Concurrent Pos:* NIH res fel gastroenterol, Peter Bent Brigham Hosp, 58-59; Nat Inst Arthritis & Metab Dis res fel liver dis & nutrit, Harvard Med Serv & Thorndike Lab,

Boston City Hosp, 59-62; Nat Inst Arthritis & Metab Dis res grant, 63- *Mem:* Am Soc Photobiol; Am Soc Clin Invest; Am Asn Study Liver Dis; Am Gastroenterol Asn; Am Physiol Soc. *Res:* Phototherapy; bilirubin metabolism; gallbladder absorption; gallstones; gastrointestinal bleeding. *Mailing Add:* Northwestern Univ Sch Med 303 E Chicago Ave Chicago IL 60611

OSTROW, SIDNEY MAURICE, b New York, NY, May 14, 16; m 47; c 3. IONOSPHERIC PHYSICS, GENERAL PHYSICS. *Educ:* City Col New York, BS, 37. *Prof Exp:* Physicist, Cent Radio Propagation Lab, Nat Bur Standards, 42-65; asst chief, Prediction Serv Sect, 47-70, physicist, Inst Telecommun Sci & Aeronomy, Environ Sci Serv Admin, 65-71, physicist, Environ Data Serv, Nat Oceanic & Atmospheric Admin, 71-73; RETIRED. *Concurrent Pos:* In charge Adak radio propagation field sta, 46-47, chief, Int Geophys Year World Data Ctr A Airglow & Ionosphere, 47-61; guest res worker, Data Studies Div, Nat Geophys & Solar Terrestrial Data Ctr, Environ Data Serv, Nat Oceanic & Atmospheric Admin, 73-77. *Mem:* Fel AAAS; Am Phys Soc; Am Geophys Union; sr mem, Inst Elec & Electronics Engrs. *Res:* Ionospheric climatology and morphology; ionospheric physics and radio propagation. *Mailing Add:* 100 S 34th St Boulder CO 80303

OSTROWSKI, EDWARD JOSEPH, b Phillipston, Pa, Mar 19, 23; m 50; c 2. METALLURGICAL ENGINEERING. *Educ:* Univ Pittsburgh, BS, 64. *Prof Exp:* mem staff, Follansbee Steel Corp, Ohio, 43-45; mem staff, US Bur Mines, Pa, 45-60, supv prod metallurgist & proj leader, 60; sr res engr, Res Ctr, 60-63, supvr, 63-67, div chief process metall, Res Ctr, 67-77, MGR QUAL CONTROL, MINERAL RESOURCES DIV, NAT STEEL CO, PITTSBURGH, 77- *Concurrent Pos:* Indust rep, Blast Furnace Res, Inc, 62 ; secy, Blast Furnace Comt, Am Iron & Steel Inst, 62- *Honors & Awards:* J E Johnson, Jr Award, Am Inst Mining, Metall & Petrol Engrs, 63, Iron Making Conf Award, 63; James B Austin Award, Am Inst Mining, Metall & Petrol Engrs, Iron & Steel Soc, 78. *Mem:* Asn Iron & Steel Engrs; Am Iron & Steel Inst; Am Soc Testing & Mat; Am Inst Mining, Metall & Petrol Engrs (vpres, 78-). *Res:* Steel making; blast furnaces. *Mailing Add:* Nat Steel Corp Mineral Resources Div 2800 Grant Bldg Weirton WV 26062

OSTROWSKI, HENRY STANLEY, chemical engineering, fluid mechanics, see previous edition

OSTROWSKI, RONALD STEPHEN, b Chicago, Ill, Mar 3, 39; m 68; c 1. GENETICS. *Educ:* Northern Ill Univ, BS, 66, MS, 68; Univ Notre Dame, PhD, 72. *Prof Exp:* Asst prof, 71-77, ASSOC PROF BIOL, UNIV NC, CHARLOTTE, 77-, ASST TO VCHANCELLOR & DIR EVE PROG, 78- *Mem:* AAAS; Genetics Soc Am. *Res:* Developmental genetics. *Mailing Add:* Dept of Biol Univ of NC Charlotte NC 28213

OSTROY, SANFORD EUGENE, b Scranton, Pa, Dec 28, 39; m 62; c 2. NEUROBIOLOGY. *Educ:* Univ Scranton, BS, 61; Case Inst Technol, PhD(chem), 66. *Prof Exp:* NIH fel biophys chem, Cornell Univ, 66-68; asst prof, 68-73, assoc prof, 73-80, PROF BIOL SCI & BIOCHEM, PURDUE UNIV, 80- *Concurrent Pos:* NIH res career develop award & grant, 70-75; hon res assoc biol, Harvard Univ, 74-75. *Mem:* Fedn Biol Chemists; Am Chem Soc; Biophys Soc; Soc Neurosci; Asn Res Vision & Ophthal. *Res:* Sensory physiology; rhodopsin structure and function; membrane biophysics; vision. *Mailing Add:* Dept Biol Sci Purdue Univ West Lafayette IN 47906

OSTWALD, PETER FREDERIC, b Berlin, Ger, Jan 5, 28; US citizen; m 60; c 2. PSYCHIATRY, COMMUNICATION SCIENCES. *Educ:* Univ Calif, Berkeley, AB, 47; Univ Calif, San Francisco, MD, 50. *Prof Exp:* Asst resident psychiat, Sch Med, Cornell Univ, 51-53 & 55-56; chief resident, Langley Porter Neuropsychiat Inst, 56-57; res psychiatrist, 58-63, from asst prof to assoc prof, 60-70, PROF PSYCHIAT, SCH MED, UNIV CALIF, SAN FRANCISCO, 70- *Concurrent Pos:* USPHS grant, Langley Porter Neuropsychiat Inst, 57-60, Found Fund Res Psychiat grant, 60-63; attend psychiatrist, Langley Porter Neuropsychiat Inst, 60-; consult, Dept Rehab, Psychiat; AMA. *Res:* Acoustical communication; speech disorders; hearing and language problems; psychotherapy; psychiatric care; education. *Mailing Add:* Univ of Calif Sch of Med 401 Parnassus Ave San Francisco CA 94122

OSTWALD, PHILLIP F, b Omaha, Nebr, Oct 21, 31; m 56; c 3. INDUSTRIAL ENGINEERING. *Educ:* Univ Nebr, BS, 54; Ohio State Univ, MS, 56; Okla State Univ, PhD(indust eng), 66. *Prof Exp:* Time study engr, Giddings & Lewis Mach Tool Co, Wis, 56-58; proj staff engr & group leader standards sect, Fabrication Div, Collins Radio Co, Iowa, 58-62; asst prof indust eng, Univ Omaha, 62-63; instr, Okla State Univ, 63-66; from asst prof to assoc prof eng design & econ eval, 66-74, PROF MECH AND INDUST ENG, UNIV COLO, BOULDER, 74- *Mem:* Am Soc Eng Educ; Am Inst Indust Engrs; Soc Mfg Eng; Am Asn Cost Eng. *Res:* Manufacturing dynamics in process machining; dynamic chip breaking; memomotion measurement of factory delay allowances; cost engineering analysis of complex engineering systems. *Mailing Add:* Eng Ctr OT 4-6 Univ of Colo Boulder CO 80309

OSTWALD, ROSEMARIE, b Vienna, Austria, June 24, 15; m 36; c 3. NUTRITION, BIOCHEMISTRY. *Educ:* Univ Zurich, PhD(org chem), 39. *Prof Exp:* Res assoc chem, 46-57, assoc nutrit & lectr biochem, 57-63, asst prof nutrit & biochem, 63-68, assoc prof nutrit, 68-74, PROF NUTRIT & BIOCHEMIST IN AGR EXP STA, UNIV CALIF, BERKELEY, 74- *Mem:* AAAS; Am Chem Soc; Am Inst Nutrit; Am Oil Chem Soc. *Res:* Interrelationships of diet, hormones and lipid metabolism. *Mailing Add:* Dept of Nutrit Sci Univ of Calif Berkeley CA 94720

OSUCH, CARL, b Chicago, Ill, Feb 2, 25; m 48; c 4. ORGANIC CHEMISTRY. *Educ:* Antioch Col, BS, 50; Univ Pittsburgh, PhD, 55. *Prof Exp:* Res chemist, Monsanto Co, 55-64; from asst prof to assoc prof, 64-70, PROF CHEM, UNIV DUBUQUE, 70-, CHMN SCI DIV, 74- *Concurrent Pos:* Petrol Res Fund grant, 67-70; consult, Dubuque police dept, 72- *Mem:* Sigma Xi; Soc Appl Spectros; Coblentz Soc; Am Chem Soc. *Res:* Alkyl pyridines; organolithium compounds; bicyclic olefins; organic azides; phosphorus compounds; drug identification. *Mailing Add:* Dept of Chem Univ of Dubuque Dubuque IA 52001

OSUCH, CHRISTOPHER ERION, b Pittsburgh, Pa, Feb 23, 51. MATERIALS RESEARCH, PHOTO RESISTS. *Educ:* Univ Dubuque, BA, 75; Iowa State Univ, PhD(chem), 80. *Prof Exp:* RES CHEMIST, ALLIED CORP, 80- *Res:* Physical and organic chemistry, including work with radical ions and ion pairs; chemistry of sulfur; chemistry of organic materials for photo lithography. *Mailing Add:* 15 Fairfield Ave Mine Hill NJ 07801

OSUCH, MARY ANN V, b Chicago, Ill, Feb 9, 41. BIOCHEMISTRY. *Educ:* DePaul Univ, BS, 62; Northwestern Univ, PhD(biochem), 67. *Prof Exp:* Res biochemist, 67-68, supvr, Mfg Lab, 68-71, tech serv coordr, 71-72, prod mgr, 72-78, MKT MGR, RES PROD DIV, MILES LAB, INC, 78- *Mem:* AAAS; Am Chem Soc; Biomed Mkt; NY Acad Sci. *Res:* Nucleic acids and enzymes; bufadienolides. *Mailing Add:* Res Prod Div Miles Lab Inc 1127 Myrtle St Elkhart IN 46515

O'SULLIVAN, JOHN, b Limerick, Ireland, Oct 30, 42; m 70; c 2. PLANT PHYSIOLOGY, PLANT BREEDING. *Educ:* Univ Col, Dublin, BAgrSc, 68, MAgrSc, 70; Univ Wis, PhD(plant breeding & genetics), 73. *Prof Exp:* RES SCIENTIST AGR, HORT EXP STA, ONT MINISTRY AGR & FOOD, 74- *Mem:* Am Soc Hort Sci; Int Soc Hort Sci; Can Soc Hort Sci; Weed Sci Soc Am. *Res:* Nutrition and irrigation of crops; growth regulators for crop production; weed control. *Mailing Add:* Hort Exp Sta Ont Ministry Agr & Food Simcoe ON N3Y 4N5 Can

OSULLIVAN, JOSEPH, b Ireland, March, 14, 45; m 70; c 2. BIOSYNTHESIS. *Educ:* Nat Univ Ireland, BSc, 66; Univ Dublin, MSc, 67; London Univ, PhD(microbiol), 70. *Prof Exp:* Res asst microbiol, London Univ, 67-72; res fel, Swiss Fed Inst Technol, 72-75, biochem, Univ Oxford, 75-79; SR RES INVESTR MICROBIOL & BIOCHEM, SQUIBB INST MED RES, 79- *Mem:* Am Soc Microbiol; Soc Gen Microbiol; Soc Indust Microbiol; Am Chem Soc. *Res:* Biosynthesis of B-lactam antibiotics, regulation of biosynthesis and characterization of the enqymes involved. *Mailing Add:* Squibb Inst Med Res PO Box 4000 Princeton NJ 08540

O'SULLIVAN, THOMAS DENIS, physical chemistry, electrochemistry, see previous edition

O'SULLIVAN, WILLIAM JOHN, b Springfield, Mass, Apr 21, 31; m 54; c 2. LASERS, FLUID PHYSICS. *Educ:* Univ Pittsburgh, PhD(physics), 58. *Prof Exp:* Res assoc physics, Univ Pittsburgh, 58; asst prof, US Naval Postgrad Sch, 58-59; mem tech staff & consult, Space Tech Labs, Inc, Div Thompson-Ramo-Wooldridge, Inc, 59-65; staff mem, Sandia Corp, 65-68; PROF PHYSICS, UNIV COLO, BOULDER, 68- *Mem:* Am Phys Soc. *Res:* Theory of antiferromagnetism; band structure of solids; nuclear magnetic resonance; behavior of Fermi surfaces under pressure; photo autocorrelation studies of critical fluid behavior. *Mailing Add:* Dept of Physics & Astrophys Univ of Colo Boulder CO 80309

OSVALDS, VALFRIDS, b Dauguli, Latvia, Dec 23, 16; m 42; c 3. ASTRONOMY. *Educ:* Latvia State Univ, Dipl, 43; Univ Hamburg, Dr rer nat, 51. *Prof Exp:* Headmaster, UN Relief & Rehabil Admin Sch, Ger, 46-47; teacher & int asst astron, Univ Va, 51-56, res assoc, 56-57, actg asst prof, 57-58, asst prof, 58-61, actg dir observ & actg chmn dept astron, 60-63, astronomer, McCormick Observ, 57-81, assoc prof astron, 61-81; RETIRED. *Res:* Astrometry; proper motions; parallaxes. *Mailing Add:* Box 3818 Univ Sta Charlottesville VA 22903

OSWALD, EDWARD ODELL, b Newberry, SC, Jan 9, 40; m 61; c 2. BIOCHEMISTRY. *Educ:* Newberry Col, BS, 61; Bowman Gray Med Sch, MS, 63; Univ NC, Chapel Hill, PhD(biochem), 66. *Prof Exp:* NIH res assoc biochem, Univ NC, Chapel Hill, 66-67; dir clin chem, Palms of Pasadena Hosp, 67-68; res biochemist, Nat Inst Environ Health Sci, Environ Protection Agency, 68-80; MEM FAC, DEPT ENVIRON HEALTH SCI, SCH HEALTH, UNIV SC, 80-, CHMN, 79- *Mem:* AAAS; Am Chem Soc; Am Oil Chemists Soc. *Res:* Organic synthesis and metabolism of radioactive labeled lipids and lipid-like natural products. *Mailing Add:* Dept Environ Health Sci Sch Pub Health Univ SC Columbia SC 29208

OSWALD, JOHN WIELAND, b Minneapolis, Minn, Oct 11, 17; m 45; c 3. PLANT PATHOLOGY. *Educ:* DePauw Univ, AB, 38, LLD, 64; Univ Calif, PhD(plant path), 42. *Hon Degrees:* LLD, Cent Col, 66, Univ Louisville, 66 & Univ Calif, Davis, 67; LHD, Juniata Col, 73 & Gettysburg Col, 74; ScD, Temple Univ, 73. *Prof Exp:* From asst prof to prof plant path, Col Agr, Univ Calif, Berkeley, 46-63, vchmn dept, 54-58, from asst vpres to vpres, Univ, 58-63; prof plant path & pres, Univ Ky, 63-68; exec vpres, Univ Calif, Berkeley, 68-70; PROF PLANT PATH & PRES, PA STATE UNIV, 70- *Concurrent Pos:* Fulbright res grant, Neth, 53-54. *Mem:* Am Phytopath Soc. *Res:* Potato diseases; potato scab; viruses; cereal root rots; cereal viruses. *Mailing Add:* Off of the Pres Pa State Univ University Park PA 16802

OSWALD, ROBERT B(ERNARD), JR, b Detroit, Mich, May 25, 32; m 62; c 1. PHYSICS. *Educ:* Univ Mich, BSE(mech eng) & BSE(math), 57, MSE, 58, PhD(nuclear eng), 64. *Prof Exp:* Engr, Aircraft Nuclear Propulsion Div, Gen Elec Co, 58-59; res engr, Eng Sci Div, Am Metal Prod Co, 59-60; res asst radiation effect in semiconductors, Univ Mich, 60-64; res physicist, Harry Diamond Labs, Army Mat Command, 64-73, chief, Lab 300, 73-76, assoc tech dir, 76-79; ASST DEP DIR SCI TECHNOL, DEFENSE NUCLEAR AGENCY, 79- *Concurrent Pos:* Assoc prof, Dept Nuclear Eng, Univ Mich, 69-70. *Honors & Awards:* Award, Inst Elec & Electronics Engrs Conf, 65; Louis J Hamilton Award, Am Nuclear Soc, 76; USA Spec Serv Award, Harry Diamond Labs, 78. *Mem:* Inst Elec & Electronics Engrs. *Res:* Radiation effects in solids; thermal neutron effects in semiconductor materials. *Mailing Add:* Off of the Dir Defense Nuclear Agency Washington DC 20305

OSWALD, TELFORD WILBERT, aerodynamics, engineering mechanics, see previous edition

OSWALD, THOMAS HAROLD, b Chicago, Ill, Apr 16, 44; m 68. BIOENGINEERING, BIOCHEMICAL GENETICS. *Educ:* Univ Mo, BA, 67, MA, 69, PhD(path), 71. *Prof Exp:* Res assoc bot, Purdue Univ, 73-75; res assoc agron, Univ Ga, 75-78; ASSOC PROF GENETICS, TOUGALOO COL, 78- *Mem:* Am Soc Agron; Am Soc Hort Sci; Crop Sci Soc Am. *Res:* Cellular engineering of plants for herbicide resistance; cellular engineering of plants for disease resistance; cyclitol metabolism in plants. *Mailing Add:* Dept of Genetics Tougaloo Col Tougaloo MS 39174

OSWALD, VERNON HARVEY, b Hartville, Ohio, May 11, 25; m 53; c 2. ZOOLOGY. *Educ:* Ohio State Univ, PhD(zool), 56. *Prof Exp:* Prin biologist, Battelle Mem Inst, 51-56; Muellhaupt scholar zool, Ohio State Univ, 56-57; from instr to assoc prof, 57-67, PROF BIOL, CALIF STATE UNIV, CHICO, 67- *Mem:* AAAS; Am Soc Parasitol; Am Micros Soc. *Res:* Helminthology. *Mailing Add:* Dept of Biol Calif State Univ Chico CA 95926

OSWALD, WILLIAM J, b Calif, July 6, 19; m 44; c 4. SANITARY ENGINEERING. *Educ:* Univ Calif, BS, 50, MS, 51, PhD(sanit eng), 57. *Prof Exp:* Eng aid, Sea Water Proj, 49-50, asst sanit eng, 50, jr res engr, 51-52, asst res engr, 53-57, asst prof, Col Eng, 58-59, assoc prof, Col Eng & Sch Pub Health, 59-66, PROF SANIT ENG & PUB HEALTH, UNIV CALIF, BERKELEY, 66- *Concurrent Pos:* Consult to govt & various indust concerns, 53- *Honors & Awards:* Eddy Medal, Water Pollution Control Fedn, 54; Rudolph Hering Medal, 58; James R Croes Medal, Am Soc Civil Engrs, 58, Arthur M Wellington Award, 66. *Mem:* Fel AAAS; Am Soc Civil Engrs; Am Inst Aeronaut & Astronaut; Soc Indust Microbiol. *Res:* Biological engineering, especially development of complex mass ecosystems of microbes such as algae and bacteria for waste disposal and reclamation; environmental control; microbiology; space technology. *Mailing Add:* 633 Davis Hall Univ of Calif Berkeley CA 94720

OSWALT, DALLAS LEON, crop breeding, science education, see previous edition

OSWALT, JESSE HARRELL, b Maben, Miss, May 16, 23; m 51; c 3. INDUSTRIAL ENGINEERING, ACADEMIC ADMINISTRATION. *Educ:* Miss State Univ, BS, 48; Ga Inst Technol, MSIE, 61. *Prof Exp:* Teacher math high sch, Miss, 53-54; process engr, Am Bosch Arma Corp, 54-56; PROF INDUST ENG, MISS STATE UNIV, 56- *Concurrent Pos:* Consult, Voc Rehab Workshop Prog, Miss, 63 & Tech Assistance Prog, Social & Rehab Serv, 66. *Honors & Awards:* President's Citation Meritorious Serv Employ of Handicapped, President's Comt Employ of Handicapped, 72. *Mem:* Am Inst Indust Engrs; Am Soc Eng Educ. *Res:* Hospital management engineering application work methods and training for handicapped workers. *Mailing Add:* Dept of Indust Eng Miss State Univ Drawer U Mississippi State MS 39762

OSWEILER, GARY D, b Sigourney, Iowa, Sept 8, 42; m 66; c 4. VETERINARY TOXICOLOGY. *Educ:* Iowa State Univ, DVM, 66, MS, 68, PhD(vet toxicol), 73. *Prof Exp:* Instr vet path, Iowa Vet Diag Lab, 66-67; instr med, Vet Clin, Iowa State Univ, 68-69, asst prof vet path, 69-70, assoc prof vet toxicol, 71-73; PROF VET TOXICOL, UNIV MO-COLUMBIA, 74- *Concurrent Pos:* Mem exam bd, Am Bd Vet Toxicol, 72-73; consult, Pedco Environ, 73 & Food & Drug Admin, 75; mem task forces, Coun Agr Sci Technol, 74-75. *Mem:* Am Col Vet Toxicologists; Am Vet Med Asn; Coun Res Workers Animal Dis; Soc Toxicol. *Res:* Reproductive and immunologic effects of mycotoxins and heavy metals; residual reproductive effects of lead in rats; bioassay techniques for screening toxins in foods and feeds. *Mailing Add:* Dept Vet Path Col Vet Med Univ Mo Columbia MO 65211

OTA, ASHER KENHACHIRO, b Waianae, Hawaii, Dec 1, 34; m 66; c 1. ENTOMOLOGY. *Educ:* Univ Hawaii, BS, 56, MS, 62; Univ Calif, Berkeley, PhD(entom), 66. *Prof Exp:* Asst entom, Univ Hawaii, 56-61; res entomologist, Entom Res Div, USDA, 66-68; from assoc entomologist to entomologist, 68-74, PRIN ENTOMOLOGIST, EXP STA, HAWAIIAN SUGAR PLANTERS ASN, 74- *Mem:* Sigma Xi; Entom Soc Am. *Res:* Agricultural entomology; insect population ecology; insect resistant varieties; biological control of insects and pests. *Mailing Add:* 46-034 Kumoo Pl Aiea HI 96701

OTAGAKI, KENNETH KENGO, b Laupahoehoe, Hawaii, June 30, 17; m 44; c 5. ANIMAL NUTRITION. *Educ:* Univ Hawaii, BS, 40; Iowa State Col, MS, 46; Univ Calif, PhD(nutrit), 54. *Prof Exp:* Jr animal husbandman, Univ Hawaii, 47-48; sr technician, Nutrit Invest, Univ Calif, Berkeley, 50-53; asst animal scientist, 54-58, assoc animal scientist, 58-64, ANIMAL SCIENTIST, UNIV HAWAII, 64- *Concurrent Pos:* Chmn, State Bd Agr, 63-70; partic, Int Agr Progs, Col Agr, Univ Hawaii, 71-80; mem staff, Bd Int Food & Agr Develop, Washington, DC, 80-81; consult trop agr progs. *Mem:* AAAS; Am Soc Animal Sci; Am Dairy Sci Asn; Am Chem Soc; Am Inst Nutrit. *Res:* Ruminant nutrition. *Mailing Add:* 2653 Huapala St Honolulu HI 96822

OTANI, THEODORE TOSHIRO, b Honolulu, Hawaii, Jan 5, 25; m 47; c 3. BIOCHEMISTRY, SYNTHETIC ORGANIC CHEMISTRY. *Educ:* Univ Hawaii, BS, 47; Univ Denver, MS, 49; Univ Colo, PhD, 53. *Prof Exp:* Fel, Clin Biochem Res Sect, Nat Cancer Inst, 53-55; res assoc chem, Fla State Univ, 55-57; res assoc, Lab Biochem, 57-72, RES BIOCHEMIST, LAB PATHOPHYSIOL, NAT CANCER INST, 72- *Mem:* AAAS. *Res:* Biochemistry of amino acids and peptides; synthesis of amino acids, amino acid analogues and peptides; amino acid antagonists; isolation, characterization and mode of action of antibiotics; isozymes in hepatomas and normal livers; design and chemical synthesis of possible cancer chemotherapeutic compounds. *Mailing Add:* Nat Cancer Inst Bldg 10 Rm BIB-38 NIH 9000 Rockville Pike Bethesda MD 20014

O'TANYI, THEODORE JOHN, JR, neurosciences, see previous edition

OTERO, JOSEPH GUILLERMO, parasitology, bacteriology, see previous edition

OTERO, RAYMOND B, b Rochester, NY, May 8, 38; div; c 3. MICROBIOLOGY, BIOCHEMISTRY. *Educ:* Univ Dayton, BS, 60; Univ Rochester, MS, 63; Univ Md, PhD(microbiol), 68. *Prof Exp:* Control biologist, Lederle Labs Div, Am Cyanamid Co, 63-65; from asst prof to assoc prof microbiol, 68-73, assoc prof biol, 73-76, PROF BIOL, EASTERN KY UNIV, 76- *Concurrent Pos:* Chicago Res Corp grant, 69-; consult path & cytol, Good Samaritan Hosp, 69, St Joseph Hosp, 69- & Cent Baptist Hosp, 80- *Mem:* AAAS; NY Acad Sci; Am Soc Microbiol; Am Thoracic Soc. *Res:* Determination of mode of entry of nucleic acids into whole bacterial cells; bacterial genetics and immunology; clinical microbiology as it applies to patient care. *Mailing Add:* Dept of Biol Sci Eastern Ky Univ Richmond KY 40475

OTEY, FELIX HAROLD, b Melber, Ky, Feb 27, 27; m 50; c 2. ORGANIC CHEMISTRY. *Educ:* Murray State Col, BS, 48; Univ Mo, Columbia, MA, 50. *Prof Exp:* Instr chem, Flat River Jr Col, 50-55 & McMurray Col, 55-56; res chemist, 56-75, RES LEADER CHEM, NORTHERN REGIONAL RES LAB, USDA, 75- *Honors & Awards:* USDA Superior Serv Award, 66. *Mem:* Am Chem Soc. *Res:* The synthesis and characterization of starch derivatives for use as raw materials in surfactants, coatings, rubber, urethane foams, plastics and films. *Mailing Add:* 1128 E Tripp Ave Peoria IL 61603

OTHERSEN, HENRY BIEMANN, JR, b Charleston, SC, Aug 26, 30; c 3. PEDIATRIC SURGERY. *Educ:* Col Charleston, BSM, 50; Med Univ SC, MD, 53; Am Bd Surg, dipl, 63 & 75; Am Bd Thoracic Surg, dipl, 66. *Prof Exp:* Intern, Philadelphia Gen Hosp, 53-54; resident gen surg, Med Col SC, 57-62; demonstr pediat surg, Children's Hosp & Ohio State Univ, 63-64; from asst prof to assoc prof surg, 65-72, PROF SURG & PEDIAT, MED UNIV SC, 72-, CHIEF PEDIAT SURG, 65- *Concurrent Pos:* Fel oncol, Med Col SC, 59-60, teaching fel surg, 61-62; res fel surg, Mass Gen Hosp, 64-65; Am Cancer Soc advan clin fel, Med Col SC, 66-69; resident pediat surg, Children's Hosp, Columbus, 62-64. *Mem:* Asn Acad Surg; Am Burn Asn; Am Col Surg; Am Acad Pediat; Am Pediat Surg Asn. *Res:* Tracheal and esophageal strictures. *Mailing Add:* Dept of Surg 171 Ashley Ave Charleston SC 29403

OTHMER, DONALD F(REDERICK), b Omaha, Nebr, May 11, 04; m 50. CHEMICAL ENGINEERING, INDUSTRIAL CHEMISTRY. *Educ:* Univ Nebr, BChE, 24; Mich Univ, MChE, 25, PhD(chem eng), 27. *Hon Degrees:* Dr Eng, Univ Nebr, 62, Polytech Inst NY, 77, NJ Inst Technol, 78. *Prof Exp:* Chemist, Cudahy Packing Co, 24; chemist & develop engr, Eastman Kodak Co, 27-31; instr, 32-33, asst prof, 33-37, prof & head dept, 37-61, DISTINGUISHED PROF, POLYTECH INST NY, 61- *Concurrent Pos:* Consult to many industs, inst and gov dept in US & foreign countries, 32-; Am Swiss Found Sci exchange lectr, 48-; hon prof, Conception Univ, Chile, 51. *Honors & Awards:* Tyler Award, Am Inst Chem Engrs, 58; Chem Pioneer Award, Am Inst Chemists, 77; Murphy Exxon Award, Am Chem Soc, 78; Perkin Medal, Soc Chem Indust, 78. *Mem:* Am Soc Mech Eng; Am Chem Soc; Am Inst Chem Engrs; Am Inst Chemists; hon life fel Am Soc Mech Eng. *Res:* Synthetic fuels; thermodynamics; author or coauthor of over 330 publications; phase equilibria; data correlation; industrial processes for distillation; desalination; refrigeration; acetylene, acetic acid, methanol; petrochemicals; sugar refining; coal lignite; peat gasification; desulfurization; sewage treatments. *Mailing Add:* Dept Chem Eng Polytech Inst 333 Jay St Brooklyn NY 11201

OTHMER, EKKEHARD, b Koenigsberg, Ger, Oct 15, 33; m 64; c 2. PSYCHIATRY. *Educ:* Univ Hamburg, Diplom, 60, PhD(psychol), 65, MD, 67. *Prof Exp:* Res assoc neurophysiol of sleep, Univ Mo-Columbia, 67-68; asst prof exp psychiat & asst prof psychol, Sch Med, Wash Univ, 68-74, resident psychiat, 71-74; assoc prof psychiat, Med Ctr, Univ Ky, 74-77; PROF PSYCHIAT, MED CTR, UNIV KANS, 77-; MEM STAFF, VET ADMIN HOSP, KANSAS CITY, 77- *Concurrent Pos:* Nat Inst Ment Health fel psychiat, Sch Med, Wash Univ, 70-71; NIH fel, Sch Med, Wash Univ & Med Ctr, Univ Ky, 72-74; chief psychobiol unit, Vet Admin Hosp, Lexington, Ky, 74-76. *Mem:* AMA; Am Psychiat Asn; Soc Neurosci; Asn Psychophysiol Study Sleep; Am Asn Univ Professors. *Res:* Psychobiology and pathology of sleep; biorythms; computer analysis of polygraphic sleep recordings; medical model in psychiatry; diagnostic techniques; neurophysiology of sleep. *Mailing Add:* 10258 Glenwood Overland Park KS 66212

OTHMER, HANS GEORGE, b Hastings, Mich, Oct 15, 43; m 69; c 1. BIOMATHEMATICS. *Educ:* Mich State Univ, BS, 65; Univ Minn, PhD(chem eng), 69. *Prof Exp:* Res engr, Exxon Corp, 69-73; asst prof math, Rutgers Univ, 73-76, assoc prof, 76-79; PROF MATH, UNIV UTAH, 79- *Concurrent Pos:* Assoc ed, Siam J Appl Math, 75-, Math Biosci, 77-; consult, Math Res Ctr, Univ Wis, 79; vis prof, Univ Minn, 80; mem, Spec Study Sect, NIH, 81- *Mem:* Soc Indust & Appl Math; AAAS; Soc Math Biol. *Res:* Theoretical studies of pattern formation in chemically-reacting systems, with application in developmental biology, ecology and chemistry; bifurcation theory and its application in the analysis of nonlinear differential equations. *Mailing Add:* Dept Math Univ Utah Salt Lake City UT 84112

OTHMER, MURRAY E(ADE), b Muscatine, Iowa, Aug 6, 07; m 37; c 1. CHEMICAL ENGINEERING. *Educ:* Grinnell Col, BS, 29; Univ Mich, MSE, 33. *Prof Exp:* Supvr chem, Eastman Kodak Co, 29-32; chem engr, Am Cyanamid Co, 33-36; tech dir, Co Anonima Indust Productora de Grasas, 36-40; assoc prof chem eng, Tufts Univ, 40-47; tech dir, Valores Guatemaltecos, SA, 48-53; prod supvr, Sterling Drug Co, SAm, 53-57; prof chem eng, Univ PR, 57-59; exec head prod & develop & dir, Co Anonima Indust Productora de Grasas, 59-74; CONSULT, 74- *Concurrent Pos:* Consult, Arthur D Little, Inc, 44-47, US State Dept, 45-47 & Valores Guatemaltecos, SAm, 46-48; dir, Co Anonima Indust Tresco, 70-75; mem qual control comt, Nat Inst Oilseed Processors. *Mem:* Fel AAAS; Am Chem Soc; Am Oil Chem Soc; Am Inst Chem Engrs; NY Acad Sci. *Res:* Vegetable oils; pharmaceuticals; aliphatic distillations. *Mailing Add:* 1087 Burning Tree Dr Chapel Hill NC 27514

OTIS, ARTHUR BROOKS, b Grafton, Maine, Sept 11, 13; m 42; c 1. PULMONARY PHYSIOLOGY. *Educ:* Univ Maine, AB, 35; Int YMCA Col, MEd, 37; Brown Univ, MS, 39, PhD(physiol), 41. *Prof Exp:* Res assoc cellular physiol, Univ Iowa, 41-42; from instr to asst prof physiol, Sch Med & Dent, Univ Rochester, 42-51; assoc prof physiol & surg, Sch Med, Johns Hopkins Univ, 52-56; head dept, 56-80, PROF PHYSIOL, COL MED, UNIV FLA, 56- *Concurrent Pos:* Fulbright res scholar, Cambridge Univ, 50-51 & Univ Nijmegen, 64-65; mem physiol training comt, NIH, 58-60, physiol study sect, 60-64; comt eval post doctoral fel applns, NSF, 58-59; respiration sect ed, Am J Physiol & J Appl Physiol, 62-64. *Mem:* Am Physiol Soc; Soc Gen Physiol. *Res:* Respiratory physiology; physiology of hypoxia; comparative physiology. *Mailing Add:* Dept Physiol Univ Fla Col Med Gainesville FL 32610

OTIS, MARSHALL VOIGT, b New London, Wis, Aug 28, 19; m 42; c 3. CHEMISTRY. *Educ:* Univ Wis, BS, 42. *Prof Exp:* Anal chemist, Hercules Powder Co, 42-44; prod supvr, Badger Ord Works, 44-45, develop supvr ultrasonics test method, 45; res chemist, 46-59, SR RES CHEMIST, EASTMAN CHEM DIV, EASTMAN KODAK CO, 59- *Mem:* Am Chem Soc; Soc Appl Spectros; fel Am Inst Chemists. *Res:* Applied spectroscopy; information storage and retrieval by machine methods; high performance liquid chromatography applied densitometry to thin layer chromatograms by computer techniques. *Mailing Add:* Res Labs Bldg 150 Eastman Chem Div Kingsport TN 37662

OTKEN, CHARLES CLAY, b Falfurrias, Tex, Nov 6, 27; m 71; c 5. PHYSICAL ORGANIC CHEMISTRY. *Educ:* Tex A&M Univ, BS, 49; Cornell Univ, PhD(biochem), 54. *Prof Exp:* From instr to assoc prof, 54-67, PROF CHEM, PAN AM UNIV, 67- *Mem:* AAAS; Am Chem Soc; NY Acad Sci. *Res:* Nutritional biochemistry. *Mailing Add:* Dept of Chem Pan Am Univ Edinburg TX 78539

OTOCKA, EDWARD PAUL, b Jersey City, NJ, Mar 11, 40; m 64; c 2. POLYMER CHEMISTRY. *Educ:* Lehigh Univ, BS, 62; Polytech Inst Brooklyn, PhD(polymer chem), 66. *Prof Exp:* Mem tech staff polymer chem, Bell Tel Labs, Inc, 66-73; mem tech staff polymer chem, Pratt & Whitney Aircraft, 73-76; MGR ADVAN MAT MFG TECHNOL, XEROX CORP, 77- *Concurrent Pos:* Adj prof polymer sci & eng, Univ Mass, 75- *Mem:* Am Chem Soc; Am Phys Soc; NY Acad Sci. *Res:* Composite and polymer material science; physical properties of polymers; polymer modification, characterization and stabilization. *Mailing Add:* Xerox Corp Phillips Rd Webster NY 14580

O'TOOLE, JOHN L, b Newark, NJ, Apr 26, 27. PLASTICS ENGINEERING. *Educ:* NJ Inst Technol, BS, 54, MS, 59. *Prof Exp:* Tech staff assoc, Bell Labs, 52-56; res engr plastics, 56-59, supvr, Eng Plastics Lab, 59-64, mgr appln technol, 64-71, tech mgr thermosetting plastics, 71-73, tech mgr, New Prod Res & Develop, 73-76, tech mgr, polyamide appln res & develop, Allied Chem Co, 76-79, INDUST MGR ELEC-ELECTRONICS, ALLIED CORP, FIBERS & PLASTICS CO, 79- *Concurrent Pos:* Mem plastics indust adv bd, Underwriters Labs, 69- *Mem:* Soc Plastics Engrs; Am Soc Testing & Mat; Int Standards Orgn. *Res:* Systematic engineering approach to measuring performance of plastics under engineering stresses which represents a major advance in the state-of-the-art of plastics material selection, material development and part design. *Mailing Add:* PO Box 2332R Allied Corp Fibers & Plastics Co Morristown NJ 07960

OTRHALEK, JOSEPH V, b Czech, Feb 16, 22; nat US; m 47; c 4. CHEMICAL ENGINEERING. *Educ:* Univ Mich, BS, 45. *Prof Exp:* Lab technician, US Rubber Co, 42-44; chem engr, Pilot Plant, Armour & Co, 45-46; res chemist & chem engr, BASF Wyandotte Corp, 46-55, res sect head, 55-59, res supvr & chem engr, 59-63, indust & aircraft prod, 63-71, res mgr process develop, Chem Specialities Div, Consumer Prod Group, 71-79; DIR RES & DEVELOP, INDUST CHEM SPECIALTIES DIV, DETREX CHEM INDUST INC, 79- *Mem:* Am Chem Soc; Am Inst Chem Engrs; Am Soc Testing & Mat; Am Ord Asn; Electroplaters Soc. *Res:* Product and process development for detergents, silicates, minerals, metal finishing, soil amendments; food processing; surfactants; corrosion inhibitors; high temperature reactions; agglomeration; drying; metal working, coolants drawing compounds, cleaners, conversion coatings; industrial liquid waste treatment flocculants; paper mill chemical specialities. *Mailing Add:* 15693 Andover Dr Dearborn MI 48120

OTSU, TAMIO, b Kona, Hawaii, July 25, 23; m 49, 64; c 3. MARINE BIOLOGY. *Educ:* Univ Hawaii, BA, 50. *Prof Exp:* Fishery res biologist, 50-59, supvry fishery biologist, 59-62, chief albacore ecol prog, 62-66, chief tuna ecol prog, 68-70, leader resource monitoring & prediction group, 70-71, LEADER PELAGIC FISH ECOL GROUP, NAT MARINE FISHERIES SERV, 71- *Concurrent Pos:* Chief tuna assessment & develop invests, Nat Marine Fisheries Serv, 72- *Mem:* AAAS; Am Inst Fishery Res Biol; Am Fisheries Soc. *Res:* Ecology and biology of pelagic fishes in the Pacific Ocean. *Mailing Add:* 1106 Lunaai St Kailua HI 96734

OTT, ALETA JO PETRIK, botany, plant taxonomy, see previous edition

OTT, BILLY JOE, b Bearden, Okla, Sept 10, 23; m 43; c 1. SOILS. *Educ:* Okla State Univ, BS, 48, MS, 49, PhD(soil chem), 62. *Prof Exp:* Prof soils, Panhandle Agr & Mech Col, 62-67; PROF SOILS & RESIDENT DIR RES, TEX A&M UNIV, 67- *Mem:* AAAS; Am Soc Agron; Soil Sci Soc Am. *Res:* Dryland and irrigated soils management; soil fertility; soil-plant-water relationships; soil moisture utilization; plant root energy levels and ion absorption. *Mailing Add:* Tex A&M Univ Agr Res & Exten Ctr Rte 3 Lubbock TX 79410

OTT, COBERN ERWIN, b Osyka, Miss, Jan 15, 41; m 67; c 2. MEDICAL PHYSIOLOGY, NEPHROLOGY. *Educ:* Millsaps Col, BS, 64; Univ Miss, PhD(physiol), 71. *Prof Exp:* Res assoc, Sch Med, Univ Miss, 70-71, NIH fel, 71-72; NIH fel, Mayo Grad Sch Med, 72-75; asst prof, 75-80, ASSOC PROF PHYSIOL, UNIV KY MED CTR, 80- *Mem:* Am Fedn Clin Res; Am Soc Nephrology; Am Physiol Soc; Int Soc Nephrology; Soc Exp Biol & Med. *Res:* Basic renal physiology with emphasis on sodium balance and relationship to fluid volumes and blood pressure. *Mailing Add:* Dept of Physiol Univ of Ky Med Ctr Lexington KY 40506

OTT, DONALD GEORGE, b Kinsley, Kans, Aug 13, 26; m 48; c 2. CHEMISTRY, SYNTHETIC ORGANIC CHEMISTRY. *Educ:* Colo State Univ, BS, 50; Wash State Univ, PhD(chem), 53. *Prof Exp:* Org res chemist, Dow Chem Co, 53-54; mem staff, 54-63, alternate group leader biomed res, 63-73, group leader org & biochem synthesis, 73-76, MEM STAFF, LOS ALAMOS SCI LAB, 76- *Concurrent Pos:* USPHS-NIH fel, Cambridge Univ, 60-61. *Mem:* AAAS; Am Chem Soc; Brit Chem Soc. *Res:* Organic and biochemical synthesis of isotopic compounds; organic reaction mechanisms; synthesis and chemistry of explosives; synthesis and characterization of oligonucleotides; applications of stable isotopes of carbon, nitrogen and oxygen; nuclear magnetic resonance. *Mailing Add:* Los Alamos Sci Lab MS 920 Los Alamos NM 87545

OTT, EDWARD, b New York, NY, Dec 22, 41; m 74; c 2. ELECTRICAL ENGINEERING. *Educ:* Cooper Union, BS, 63; Polytech Inst Brooklyn, MS, 65, PhD(electrophys), 67. *Prof Exp:* NSF fel, Dept Appl Math & Theoret Physics, Cambridge Univ, 67-68; prof elec eng, Cornell Univ, 68-79; PROF ELEC ENG & PHYSICS, UNIV MD, COLLEGE PARK, 79- *Mem:* AAAS; Inst Elec & Electronics Engrs; fel Am Physics Soc; Am Geophys Union. *Res:* Plasma physics. *Mailing Add:* Dept Elec Eng Univ MD College Park MD 20740

OTT, GRANVILLE E, b San Angelo, Tex, Nov 8, 35; m 63; c 2. ELECTRICAL ENGINEERING. *Educ:* Univ Tex, Austin, BS, 58, MS, 61, PhD(elec eng), 64. *Prof Exp:* Res engr, defense res lab, Tex, 59-62, sr engr, Tex Instruments, Inc, 64-67, mgr adv planning geophys systs, 67-68; assoc prof elec eng, Univ Mo-Columbia, 68-76; MEM TECH STAFF CONSUMER PROD, TEX INSTRUMENTS, INC, 76- *Concurrent Pos:* Lectr, Univ Houston, 64-66; Nat Sci Found res grants, 70- *Mem:* Inst Elec & Electronics Engrs. *Res:* Design and application of digital systems for data handling, processing and control. *Mailing Add:* Tex Instruments Consumer Prod Lubbock TX 79409

OTT, HENRY C(ARL), b Troy, NY, July 20, 10; m 62; c 2. NUCLEAR ENGINEERING & CHEMICAL ENGINEERING. *Educ:* Rensselaer Polytech Inst, ChE, 32, MChE, 36, PhD(phys chem), 37. *Prof Exp:* From instr to asst prof chem & chem eng, Rensselaer Polytech Inst, 37-48; sect head, Div Res, US Atomic Energy Comn, 48-49, reactor engr, Div Reactor Develop, 49-51, dep chief, Proj Develop Br, 51-52, asst chief eval br, 52-65, asst chief civilian reactors br, 54-56; CONSULT NUCLEAR ENGR, EBASCO SERVS, INC, 56- *Concurrent Pos:* Chief sanit inspector, Lake George Asn, NY, 41-42; chemist, Clinton Labs, Monsanto Chem Co, 46-47. *Mem:* Am Chem Soc; Am Nuclear Soc; Am Inst Chem Engrs. *Res:* Nuclear power plant design; economics of nuclear power; nuclear reactor systems, safety and licensing; nuclear fuel management; thermodynamics; mass and heat transfer; alternate energy systems. *Mailing Add:* Nuclear Eng Ebasco Servs Inc 2 World Trade Ctr New York NY 10048

OTT, J BEVAN, b Cedar City, Utah, July 21, 34; m 53; c 6. PHYSICAL CHEMISTRY. *Educ:* Brigham Young Univ, BS, 55, MS, 56; Univ Calif, PhD, 59. *Prof Exp:* Asst prof chem, Utah State Univ, 59-60; assoc prof, 60-68, PROF CHEM, BRIGHAM YOUNG UNIV, 68- *Concurrent Pos:* Sabbatical leave as res specialist, Atomics Int Div, NAm Rockwell Corp, 66-67. *Mem:* Am Chem Soc. *Res:* Low temperature and solution thermodynamics; phase equilibria. *Mailing Add:* Dept of Chem Brigham Young Univ Provo UT 84601

OTT, JOHN LEWIS, b Sabetha, Kans, Aug 19, 24; m 48; c 2. BACTERIOLOGY. *Educ:* Univ Kans, AB, 45, MA, 51; Iowa State Col, PhD(bact physiol), 56. *Prof Exp:* Bacteriologist, Vet Admin Hosp, 56-59; sr microbiologist, 59-79, RES SCIENTIST, RES LABS, ELI LILLY & CO, 80- *Mem:* AAAS; Am Soc Microbiol; Brit Soc Gen Microbiol; Environ Mutagen Soc; NY Acad Sci. *Res:* Inhibitors of resistance transfer; mutagenesis; biosynthesis of antibiotics; penicillinase and cephlosporinase; mechanisms of antibiotic resistance. *Mailing Add:* 1717 Sherwood Dr Greenfield IN 46140

OTT, KAREN JACOBS, b Atlanta, Ga, Sept 26, 39; m 59; c 2. PARASITOLOGY, INVERTEBRATE ZOOLOGY. *Educ:* Asbury Col, AB, 59; Univ Ky, MS, 61; Rutgers Univ, PhD(zool, parasitol), 65. *Prof Exp:* Instr microbiol & parasitol, Jefferson Med Col, 64-65, grant, 65; asst res specialist, Bur Biol Res, Rutgers Univ, 65-68; asst prof, 69-77, ASSOC PROF BIOL, UNIV EVANSVILLE, 77- *Mem:* AAAS; Am Soc Parasitol; Am Soc Trop Med & Hyg; Nat Asn Biol Teachers; Am Inst Biol Sci. *Res:* Immunological and physiological aspects of host-parasite relationships. *Mailing Add:* Dept of Biol Univ of Evansville Evansville IN 47702

OTT, KARL O, b Klein-Auheim, Ger, Dec 24, 25; m 58; c 2. NUCLEAR ENGINEERING. *Educ:* Univ Frankfurt, BS, 48; Univ Gottingen, 52, PhD(physics), 58. *Prof Exp:* Physicist, Univ Karlsruhe, 55-57; physicist, Gesellschaft Kernforschung, 58-61, asst sect head reactor physics, 61-62, sect head, 63-66; sci asst Univ Karlsruhe, 66-67; PROF NUCLEAR ENG, PURDUE UNIV, 67- *Concurrent Pos:* Exchange scientist, Argonne Nat Lab, 65-66, consult, 67-; consult, Gesellschaft Kernforschung, 66-67; mem, Ger Atomic Forum, 67. *Honors & Awards:* Argonne Univs Asn Award, 73. *Mem:* Fel Am Nuclear Soc; NY Acad Sci. *Res:* Cosmic ray theory; nuclear theory; thermal reactor physics; physics, safety and fuel cycles of fast reactors; risk assessment of large scale technologies. *Mailing Add:* Sch Nuclear Eng Purdue Univ Lafayette IN 47907

OTT, RAY LYMAN, JR, b Kennett Square, Pa, Mar 1, 40; m 64; c 2. STATISTICS. *Educ:* Bucknell Univ, BS, 62, MS, 63; Va Polytech Inst, PhD(statist), 67. *Prof Exp:* Sr statistician, Smith Kline & French Labs, 66-68; from asst prof to assoc prof statist, Univ Fla, 68-75; HEAD DEPT BIOSTATIST, MERRELL RES CTR, 75- *Mem:* Am Statist Asn; Biomet Soc. *Res:* Design of experiments and accompanying estimation procedures. *Mailing Add:* Merrell Res Ctr 2110 E Galbraith Rd Cincinnati OH 45215

OTT, RICHARD L, b Santa Barbara, Calif, June 23; m 48; c 2. VETERINARY MEDICINE. *Educ:* Wash State Univ, BS, 44, DVM, 45. *Prof Exp:* Pvt pract, Wash, 45-46 & 48-49; from asst prof to assoc prof med & surg, 49-59, prof & chmn dept, 59-73, PROF VET CLIN MED & SURG, COL VET MED, WASH STATE UNIV, 73-, ASSOC DEAN, 74- *Concurrent Pos:* NIH grant, 60-65, res grant, 67-74. *Honors & Awards:* Gaines Medal, Am Vet Med Asn, 64. *Mem:* AAAS; Am Vet Med Asn; Conf Res Workers Animal Dis; Am Col Vet Internal Med. *Res:* Immunology, pathogenesis and ecology of virus diseases; small animal medicine and surgery. *Mailing Add:* Dept Vet Clin Med & Surg Col Vet Med Wash State Univ Pullman WA 99163

OTT, TEUNIS JAN, b Zype, Netherlands, Jan 27, 43; m 68; c 2. OPERATIONS RESEARCH, MATHEMATICAL STATISTICS. *Educ:* Univ Amsterdam, BSc, 65, Drs(math statist), 70; Univ Rochester, PhD(opers res), 75. *Prof Exp:* Asst prof opers res, Case Western Reserve Univ, 74-76; asst prof, Univ Tex, 76-78; MEM TECH STAFF & SUPVR, BELL LABS, 78- *Concurrent Pos:* Assoc ed, Mgt Sci. *Mem:* Opers Res Soc Am; Inst Elec & Electronics Engrs; Inst Mgt Sci; Dutch Math Asn; Netherlands Statist Asn. *Res:* Operations research in medical systems; probability theory; computer performance analysis. *Mailing Add:* Rm 1A332 Bell Labs Holmdel NJ 07733

OTT, WALTER RICHARD, b Brooklyn, NY, Jan 20, 43; m 64; c 3. CERAMIC ENGINEERING. *Educ:* Va Polytech Inst, BS, 65; Univ Ill, Urbana, MS, 67; Rutgers Univ, New Brunswick, PhD(ceramic eng), 69. *Prof Exp:* Process engr, Corhart Refractories, 65-66; staff res engr, Ceramic Div, Champion Spark Plug, 69-70; assoc prof ceramic eng, Rutgers Univ, new Brunswick, 70-80; DEAN, NY STATE COL CERAMICS, ALFRED UNIV, ALFRED, NY, 80- *Honors & Awards:* Ralph Teetor Award, Soc Automotive Engrs, 73; Nat Inst Ceramic Engrs Award, 75. *Mem:* Am Ceramic Soc; Brit Soc Glass Technol; Int Confedn Thermal Anal; Am Soc Eng Educ. *Res:* Application of thermal analysis to ceramic systems; kinetics and mechanism of solid state reactions. *Mailing Add:* NY State Col Ceramics Alfred Univ Alfred NY 14802

OTT, WAYNE R, b San Mateo, Calif, Feb 2, 40; m 67. ENVIRONMENTAL STATISTICS, ENVIRONMENTAL MEASUREMENTS. *Educ:* Claremont Mens Col, BA, 63; Stanford Univ, BS, 63, MA, 66, MS, 65, PhD(environ eng), 71. *Prof Exp:* Res engr, Div Air Pollution, US Pub Health Serv, 66-67; sci adv to the dir, Nat Air Pollution Control Admin, 67-68; chief Extramural Labs Br, Lab Opers Div, US Environ Protection Agency, 71-74, sr systs analyst, Quality Assurance Div, 74-79; vis scholar, Dept Statistics, Stanford Univ, 79-81; SR ENVIRON ENGR, OFF RES & DEVELOP, US ENVIRON PROTECTION AGENCY, 81- *Concurrent Pos:* Prin investr, Air Pollution Res, Dept Statist, Stanford Univ, 79-81; mem, Nat Coop Hwy Res Prog, Nat Acad Sci, 75-76; co chmn, Nat Conf Environ Modeling & Simulation, 75-76; consult to Yuguslavia, World Health Orgn, Switz, 81; consult to Mexico City, Pan Am Health Orgn, 77. *Mem:* Air Pollution Control Asn; Am Statist Asn; Am Soc Quality Control. *Res:* Development of mathematical techniques for predicting environmental phenomena, including environmental indices; measurement and modeling of human exposure to air pollution. *Mailing Add:* 1003 N Terrill St Alexandria VA 22304

OTT, WELLAND LEE, b Welland, Ont, Can, Aug 27, 21; m 73. ANALYTICAL CHEMISTRY. *Educ:* Queen's Univ, Ont, BSc, 46. *Prof Exp:* Res asst colloid chem, Queen's Univ, Ont, 46-48, lectr inorg chem, 48-50, chemist, Dept Mineral, 50-51; chemist, 51-53, sect head chem, Metall Labs, 53-73, CHIEF CHEMIST, FALCONBRIDGE NICKEL MINES LTD, 73- *Concurrent Pos:* Chmn Can adv comt, Int Orgn Standardization, 75- *Mem:* Am Soc Testing & Mat; Am Chem Soc. *Res:* Development of instrumental and chemical analytical methods for the analysis and/or determination of nickel, copper, cobalt, ferronickel, gold, silver and the platinum metals; platinum metal chemical metallurgy. *Mailing Add:* Falconbridge Nickel Mines Ltd PO Box 900 Thornhill ON L3T 4A8 Can

OTT, WILLIAM ROGER, b Philadelphia, Pa, Mar 29, 42; m 67; c 3. EXPERIMENTAL ATOMIC PHYSICS, OPTICAL PHYSICS. *Educ:* St Joseph's Col, BS, 63; Univ Pittsburgh, PhD(physics), 68. *Prof Exp:* NSF assoc plasma spectros, 68-70, STAFF PHYSICIST, NAT BUR STAND, 70- *Concurrent Pos:* Alexander von Humboldt fel, Univ Düsseldorf, 77-78. *Honors & Awards:* Superior Performance Award, Nat Bur Stand, 75; Dept Com Silver Medal, 76. *Mem:* Optical Soc Am. *Res:* The application of plasma light sources as intensity standards in the ultraviolet; also, measurements of transition probabilities and line broadening parameters using arc plasmas. *Mailing Add:* Nat Bur Stand Bldg 221 Rm A261 Washington DC 20234

OTTA, JACK DUANE, b Marshaltown, Iowa, Apr 18, 44; m 64; c 2. PLANT PATHOLOGY. *Educ:* Iowa State Univ, BS, 66; Univ Calif, Davis, PhD(plant path), 70. *Prof Exp:* ASST PROF PLANT SCI, SDAK STATE UNIV, 70- *Mem:* Am Phytopath Soc. *Res:* Bacterial diseases of plants; taxonomy of phytopathogenic bacteria; forest pathology. *Mailing Add:* Dept of Plant Sci SDak State Univ Brookings SD 57006

OTTAVIANI, ROBERT AUGUSTINE, organic polymer chemistry, see previous edition

OTTE, CAREL, JR, b Amsterdam, Netherlands, June 29, 22; nat US; m 53; c 4. GEOLOGY. *Educ:* Calif Inst Technol, MS, 50, PhD(geol), 54. *Prof Exp:* Res geologist, Pure Oil Co, 54-55; explor geologist, Shell Oil Co, 55-57; supvr geol res, 57-62, vpres & mgr, Earth Energy, Inc, 62-67, MGR GEOTHERMAL DIV, UNION OIL CO CALIF, 67- *Mem:* Geol Soc Am; Am Asn Petrol Geologists. *Res:* Exploration geology. *Mailing Add:* 4261 Commonwealth Ave La Canada CA 91011

OTTE, DANIEL, b Durban, SAfrica, Mar 14, 39; US citizen; m 63; c 2. ZOOLOGY. *Educ:* Univ Mich, BA & PhD(zool), 68. *Prof Exp:* NSF grant & res assoc zool, Univ Mich, 68-69; asst prof, Univ Tex, Austin, 69-75; assoc cur, 75-80, CUR ENTOM, ACAD NATURAL SCI, PHILADELPHIA, 80- *Res:* Insect behavior; evolution of behavior; systematics of North American grasshoppers; systematics of Australian crickets; communication in grasshoppers. *Mailing Add:* Acad of Natural Sci Philadelphia PA 19103

OTTENBRITE, RAPHAEL MARTIN, b Claybank, Sask, Sept 20, 36; m 63; c 3. ORGANIC CHEMISTRY. *Educ:* Univ Windsor, BSc, 58, MSc, 62, PhD(chem), 67; Univ Toronto, dipl ed, 64. *Prof Exp:* Instr chem, Western Ont Inst Technol, 60-64 & Univ Windsor, 64-66; US Air Force fel, Univ Fla, 66-67; asst prof, Med Col Va & Richmond Prof Inst, 67-71; assoc prof, 71-76, PROF CHEM, VA COMMONWEALTH UNIV, 76- *Mem:* Am Chem Soc; Chem Inst Can; Sigma Xi; Nat Cath Educ Asn. *Res:* Synthesis of exocyclic diene systems and study of their diels-alder reactivity; the correlation of these properties by MO calculations; preparation and characterization of polyamions as anticancer and antivirial agents. *Mailing Add:* 2781 E Brigstock Rd Midlothian VA 23113

OTTER, FRED AUGUST, JR, b West Chester, Pa, Sept 11, 28; m 53; c 2. SOLID STATE PHYSICS. *Educ:* Lehigh Univ, BS, 53; Temple Univ, AM, 55; Univ Ill, PhD(physics), 59. *Prof Exp:* Asst physics, Labs, Franklin Inst, 53-55; asst, Univ Ill, 55-57, instr, 58-59; asst prof, Ohio Univ, 59-63; mem staff, Res Labs, United Aircraft Corp, 63-68, mgr surface & film lab, 68-69; prof physics, Clarkson Col Technol, 69-73; prin scientist physics of solids, 73-81, SR PRIN SCIENTIST, UNITED TECHNOL RES CTR, 81- *Concurrent Pos:* Vis prof, Univ Conn, 77- *Mem:* Am Phys Soc; Sigma Xi. *Res:* Superconductivity; surface science; ion implatation. *Mailing Add:* United Technol Res Ctr East Hartford CT 06108

OTTER, RICHARD ROBERT, b Evanston, Ill, May 17, 20; m 49; c 2. MATHEMATICS. *Educ:* Dartmouth Col, AB, 41; Univ Ind, PhD(org chem), 46. *Prof Exp:* Res chemist, Eastman Kodak Co, NY, 42; mem comt med res, Off Sci Res & Develop, Washington, DC, 44-46; instr math, Princeton Univ, 46-47, fel, Off Naval Res, 47-48, vis asst prof, 53-54; from asst prof to assoc prof, 48-65, PROF MATH, UNIV NOTRE DAME, 65- *Mem:* Am Math Soc; Math Asn Am. *Res:* Theory of probability; combinatorial analysis. *Mailing Add:* Dept Math Univ Notre Dame Notre Dame IN 46556

OTTERBY, DONALD EUGENE, b Sioux Falls, SDak, July 2, 32. NUTRITION. *Educ:* SDak State Col, BS, 54, MS, 58; NC State Col, PhD(nutrit), 62. *Prof Exp:* Fel nutrit, NC State Col, 62-63; asst prof nutrit, 63-67, from assoc prof to prof ruminant nutrit, 67-74, PROF ANIMAL SCI, UNIV MINN, ST PAUL, 74- *Mem:* Am Dairy Sci Asn; Am Soc Animal Sci. *Res:* Nutrition of ruminant animals. *Mailing Add:* Dept of Animal Sci Univ of Minn St Paul MN 55101

OTTERMAN, BERNARD, thermal sciences, mechanical engineering, see previous edition

OTTERMAN, JOSEPH, space physics, see previous edition

OTTESEN, ERIC ALBERT, b Baltimore, Md, Nov 13, 43; m 66; c 3. MEDICINE, IMMUNOLOGY. *Educ:* Princeton Univ, BA, 65; Harvard Univ, MD, 70. *Prof Exp:* Intern & resident pediat, Med Ctr, Duke Univ, 70-72; clin assoc infectious dis immunol, 72-75, SR INVESTR IMMUNOL & PARASITOL, NAT INST ALLERGY & INFECTIOUS DIS, 75- *Honors & Awards:* Clin Trop Med Res Award, Am Soc Trop Med & Hyg, 78 & 79. *Mem:* Am Asn Immunologists; Am Acad Allergy; Am Soc Trop Med & Hyg; Infectious Dis Soc Am; Sigma Xi. *Res:* Immunology of parasitic diseases, filariasis, schistosomiasis, the cosinophil and immediate hypersensitivity responses. *Mailing Add:* Lab of Parasitic Dis NIH Bldg 5 Rm 114 Bethesda MD 20205

OTTESON, OTTO HARRY, b Rexburg, Idaho, June 25, 31; m 57; c 6. NUCLEAR PHYSICS. *Educ:* Utah State Univ, BS, 60, MS, 62, PhD(physics), 66. *Prof Exp:* Teaching asst, 61-62, asst prof, 66-73, ASSOC PROF PHYSICS & ASST DEPT HEAD, UTAH STATE UNIV, 73- *Mem:* Am Phys Soc; Am Asn Physics Teachers. *Res:* Medium energy PI; nuclear interactions. *Mailing Add:* Dept of Physics Utah State Univ Logan UT 84322

OTTING, WILLIAM JOSEPH, JR, b St Paul, Minn, Oct 27, 19; m 40; c 3. PHYSICS. *Educ:* George Washington Univ, BS, 46, MS, 49; Cath Univ Am, PhD(physics), 56. *Prof Exp:* Radio engr, Nat Bur Standards, 45-48; physicist, Off Naval Res, 48-52; dir phys sci, Off Sci Res, US Air Force, 52-60; chief scientist, Defense Atomic Support Agency, US Dept Defense, 60-64; asst dean, 64-70, ASSOC PROF PHYSICS, UNIV ILL, CHICAGO CIRCLE, 64-, ASSOC DEAN GRAD COL, 70- *Mem:* Sigma Xi; fel Am Phys Soc. *Res:* Electrochemistry; electromagnetism; chemical, solid state and nuclear physics. *Mailing Add:* 241 Thornhill Lane LBS Barrington IL 60010

OTTINGER, CAROL BLANCHE, b Batesville, Ark, Dec 25, 33. MATHEMATICS. *Educ:* Ark Col, BSE, 54; Okla State Univ, MS, 60, EdD(math), 69. *Prof Exp:* Teacher math high schs, Ark, 54-58 & Okla, 60-63; from asst prof to assoc prof, 63-71, PROF MATH, MISS UNIV FOR WOMEN, 71-, CHMN DEPT, 74- *Mem:* Math Asn Am; Nat Coun Teachers Math; Asn Women Math. *Res:* Topology of decomposition spaces. *Mailing Add:* Dept of Math Miss Univ for Women Box W-269 Columbus MS 39701

OTTINO, JULIO MARIO, b La Plata, Argentina, May 22, 51; m 76. MIXING, TRANSPORT PROCESSES. *Educ:* Nat Univ La Plata, dipl, 74; Univ Minn, PhD(chem eng), 79. *Prof Exp:* ASST PROF CHEM ENG, UNIV MASS, 79-, ADJ PROF POLYMER SCI & ENG, 79- *Mem:* Soc Natural Philos; Am Inst Chem Engrs; Soc Rheology; Soc Indust & Appl Math; Am Chem Soc. *Res:* Fluid mechanics and transport processes; mechanical mixing of fluids; mixing of diffusing and reacting fluids; diffusion and reaction in complex random interspersions; transport processes in polymer blends. *Mailing Add:* Dept Chem Eng Goessmann Lab Univ Mass Amherst MA 01003

OTTKE, ROBERT CRITTENDEN, b Louisville, Ky, Jan 23, 22; m 43, 58; c 4. ORGANIC CHEMISTRY, BIOCHEMISTRY. *Educ:* Yale Univ, BS, 48, PhD(chem), 50. *Prof Exp:* Nat Cancer Inst fel, Stanford Univ, 50-51; res chemist, Chas Pfizer & Co, Inc, 51-53, prod develop, 53-57; pres, Caribe Chem Corp, 57-58; dir commercial develop, Wallerstein Co Div, Baxter Labs,

Inc, 58-61, tech dir, Baxter Int, 61-63; vpres & managing dir labs, Parke Davis, Madrid, Spain, 63-69; partner, Boyden Assocs, 69-76; dir, Europe & MidE, Allergan Pharmaceut, Inc, 76-78; CONSULT, ROBERT OTTKE ASSOCS, MGT CONSULTS, 78- *Mem:* Am Chem Soc; NY Acad Sci. *Res:* Steroid biosynthesis; natural products; enzymology; pharmaceutical chemistry. *Mailing Add:* 2939 Perla Newport Beach CA 92660

OTTMAN, RUTH, b Houston, Tex, May 29, 52. GENETICS, REPRODUCTIVE ENDOCRINOLOGY. *Educ:* Univ Calif, Berkeley, AB, 75, PhD(genetics), 80. *Prof Exp:* Fel epidemiol, Univ Calif, Berkeley, 80-81; fel, Sergievsky Ctr, 80-81, ASST PROF PUB HEALTH, COLUMBIA UNIV, 81- *Concurrent Pos:* Proj dir, Familial Epilepsy Proj, Sergievsky Ctr, Columbia Univ, 80-, Sergievsky fel, 81- *Mem:* Soc Epidemiol Res; Am Pub Health Asn; World Fedn Neurol. *Res:* Role of genetic factors in the etiology of complex diseases, including breast cancer, epilepsy and coronaryheart disease; assessment of risk to relatives of affected persons; biological hypotheses about genetic and nongenetic mechanisms increasing risk in high-risk families; methodologies for studying familial aggregation. *Mailing Add:* Sergievsky Ctr Columbia Univ 630 W 168th St New York NY 10032

OTTO, ALBERT DEAN, b Marshalltown, Iowa, Nov 5, 39; m 62; c 2. MATHEMATICS. *Educ:* Univ Iowa, BA, 61, MS, 62, PhD(math), 65. *Prof Exp:* Asst prof math, Lehigh Univ, 65-69; assoc prof, 69-75, PROF MATH, ILL STATE UNIV, 75-, CHMN DEPT, 76- *Mem:* Am Math Soc; Math Asn Am. *Res:* Study of the automorphisms of finite groups and of combinatorial objects. *Mailing Add:* Dept of Math Ill State Univ Normal IL 61761

OTTO, DAVID ARTHUR, b Ft Scott, Kans, Feb 19, 34; c 3. MARINE BIOLOGY, PALEOBOTANY. *Educ:* Univ Kans, AB, 56; Kans State Teachers Col, MS, 57; Univ Mo, PhD(bot, geol), 67. *Prof Exp:* PROF BIOL, STEPHENS COL, 57- *Mem:* Am Inst Biol Sci; Bot Soc Am. *Res:* Investigations of Middle Pennsylvanian fossil plants found in coal ball petrifactions; plants fossils; marine mammals and invertebrates. *Mailing Add:* Dept of Natural Sci Stephens Col Columbia MO 65201

OTTO, FRED BISHOP, b Bangor, Maine, Aug 17, 34; m 57; c 4. PHYSICS, ENGINEERING. *Educ:* Univ Maine, Orono, BS, 56; Univ Conn, MA, 60, PhD(physics), 65. *Prof Exp:* Elec engr, Sylvania Elec Co, 56-58; grad asst physics, Univ Conn, 58-64; asst prof, Colby Col, 64-68; asst prof elec eng, Univ Maine, 68-74; design engr, Eaton W Tarbell & Assocs, 74-79; qual control engr, PyrAlarm, 79-80; CONSULT ENGR, 80- *Mem:* Am Phys Soc; Am Asn Physics Teachers; Illuminating Eng Soc; Nat Soc Prof Engrs; Am Soc Heating, Refrig & Air-Conditioning Engrs. *Mailing Add:* 169 Main St Orono ME 04473

OTTO, FRED DOUGLAS, b Hardisty, Alta, Jan 12, 35; m 60; c 3. CHEMICAL ENGINEERING. *Educ:* Univ Alta, BSc, 57, MSc, 59; Univ Mich, Ann Arbor, PhD(chem eng), 63. *Prof Exp:* From asst prof to assoc prof, 62-70, actg chmn dept, 70-72, PROF CHEM ENG, UNIV ALTA, 70-, CHMN DEPT, 75- *Mem:* Can Soc Chem Eng; Am Inst Chem Engrs; Am Soc Eng Educ. *Res:* Heavy water production processes; natural gas processing; mass transfer; gas-liquid reactions. *Mailing Add:* Dept of Chem & Petrol Eng Univ of Alta Edmonton AB T6G 2G7 Can

OTTO, GILBERT FRED, b Chicago, Ill, Dec 16, 01; m 32; c 2. PARASITOLOGY. *Educ:* Kalamazoo Col, AB, 26; Kans State Col, MS, 27; Johns Hopkins Univ, ScD(parasitol), 29. *Prof Exp:* Asst zool, Kans State Col, 26-27; asst helminth, Sch Hyg & Pub Health, Johns Hopkins Univ, 27-29; from instr to assoc prof, 29-42, assoc prof parasitol, 42-53, asst dean sch, 40-47, parasitologist, Johns Hopkins Hosp, 47-53; head dept parasitol, Res Div, Abbott Labs, Ill, 53-60, dir agr & vet res div, Sci Divs, 60-65, asst dir personnel div, 65-66; prof zool, 66-72, adj prof, 72-81, SR RES ASSOC, UNIV MD, 81-. *Concurrent Pos:* Consult, USPHS, 41, 46-53, hookworm & malaria div, State Bd Health, Ga, 42-43 & Surgeon Gen, US Army, 58-66; mem & dir field expeds, Nat Res Coun & Am Child Health Asn, 27-32; expert WHO, UN, 52-74, comt parasitic dis, Armed Forces Epidemiol Bd, 53-57, Lobund adv bd, Univ Notre Dame, 58-66 & adv bd parasitol, Univ Md, 65-66; ed, J Am Heartworm Soc, 74-; consult, Food & Drug Admin, 77- *Mem:* AAAS; Am Soc Parasitol (treas, 37-40, vpres, 55, pres-elect, 56, pres, 57); Am Soc Trop Med & Hyg; Am Heartworm Soc (secy-treas, 74-77, pres, 77-80); Am Epidemiol Soc. *Res:* Epidemiology of parasitic diseases; immunity to animal parasites; chemotherapy of parasitic diseases; pharmacology of arsenic and antimony; ascariasis; trichinosis; hookworm disease; filariasis; amebiasis; trypanosomiasis; malaria; leucocytozoon; coccidiosis; schistosomiasis; canine heartworm disease. *Mailing Add:* 10506 Greenacres Dr Silver Spring MD 20903

OTTO, HARLEY JOHN, b Richfield, Kans, May 5, 28; m 53; c 2. AGRONOMY. *Educ:* Colo State Univ, BSc, 52; Cornell Univ, PhD(plant breeding), 56. *Prof Exp:* Asst prof plant breeding, Cornell Univ, 56-57, asst prof agron, 57-58; asst prof agron, Univ Minn, St Paul, 58-60, assoc prof, 60-63, prof, 63-75; EXEC VPRES, MINN CROP IMPROV ASN, ST PAUL, 75- *Concurrent Pos:* Dir, Asn Off Seed Certifying Agencies, 61- *Mem:* Am Soc Agron; Crop Sci Soc Am; Coun Agr Sci & Technol. *Res:* Extension education and research in production of field crops; quality seed production and distribution. *Mailing Add:* Minn Crop Improv Asn Univ of Minn St Paul MN 55101

OTTO, JOHN B, JR, b Kingsville, Tex, Nov 4, 18; m 50; c 2. CHEMISTRY. *Educ:* Tex Col Arts & Indust, BS, 41; Univ Tex, MA, 43, PhD, 50. *Prof Exp:* Tutor chem, Univ Tex, 41-42, instr, 42-44; jr chemist, Clinton Lab, Oak Ridge, 44-46; res chemist, Mound Lab, Monsanto Chem Co, Ohio, 50-54; SR RES CHEMIST, FIELD RES LAB, MOBIL RES & DEVELOP CORP, 54- *Mem:* AAAS; Am Chem Soc. *Res:* Chemical reactions in liquid ammonia; radio chemistry; chemical separations and analysis for geochronology research; uranium in situ leach mining and leach solution processing research; heavy oil production research and development. *Mailing Add:* Field Res Lab Mobil Res & Develop Corp Box 900 Dallas TX 75221

OTTO, KLAUS, b Friedrichroda, Ger, Sept 18, 29; US citizen; m 62; c 2. ENVIRONMENTAL CHEMISTRY, PHYSICAL CHEMISTRY. *Educ:* Univ Hamburg, Vordiplom, 53, Dipl, 57, Dr rer nat(phys chem), 59. *Prof Exp:* Asst phys chem, Univ Hamburg, 60; res assoc, Argonne Nat Lab, 60-62; SR SCIENTIST, FORD MOTOR CO, DEARBORN, 62-, PRIN RES SCIENTIST ASSOC, 80- *Mem:* AAAS; Am Chem Soc; Catalysis Soc. *Res:* Hydrides of transition metals; low temperature calorimetry; electrical properties and nuclear magnetic resonance of inorganic glasses; catalysis of air pollutants, especially nitric oxide; coal gasification; automotive fuels and lubricants. *Mailing Add:* 35173 W Six Mile Rd Livonia MI 48152

OTTO, NORMAN CHARLES, b Detroit, Mich, Oct 10, 44; m 69; c 1. CHEMICAL ENGINEERING. *Educ:* Univ Mich, BS, 66; Univ Ill, MS, 69, PhD(chem eng), 71. *Prof Exp:* Res engr chem eng, Am Cyanamid Co, 71-73; RES SCIENTIST CATALYST MODELING, SCI RES LABS, FORD MOTOR CO, 73- *Res:* Catalysis with emphasis on mathematical modeling of automotive exhaust catalysts. *Mailing Add:* Sci Res Labs Ford Motor Co PO Box 2053 Dearborn MI 48121

OTTO, ROBERT EMIL, b Irvington, NJ, Jan 30, 32; m 66; c 2. CHEMICAL ENGINEERING. *Educ:* Rensselaer Polytech Inst, BChE, 53; Univ Del, PhD(chem eng), 57. *Prof Exp:* Staff asst res & develop, US Air Force, 56-59; sr chem engr, Monsanto Co, 59-65; eng supvr, 65-69; develop mgr, Fisher Controls Co, 69-77; SR ENG FEL, MONSANTO CO, 77- *Mem:* Am Chem Soc; Am Inst Chem Engrs. *Res:* Process control language development; computer control of industrial processes; non-Newtonian fluid flow. *Mailing Add:* Monsanto Co 800 N Lindbergh Blvd St Louis MO 63166

OTTO, ROBERT GEORGE, aquatic ecology, see previous edition

OTTO, ROLAND JOHN, b Milwaukee, Wis, Aug 29, 46; m 68. NUCLEAR CHEMISTRY, PHYSICAL CHEMISTRY. *Educ:* Valparaiso Univ, BS, 68; Purdue Univ, PhD(chem), 74. *Prof Exp:* Staff mem nuclear chem, 74-78, SCIENTIST PHYS CHEM, LAWRENCE BERKELEY LAB, UNIV CALIF, 78- *Mem:* Am Chem Soc. *Res:* Heavy ion nuclear reaction; thermodynamics of electrolyte solutions. *Mailing Add:* Lawrence Berkeley Lab Univ of Calif Berkeley CA 94720

OTTO, WOLFGANG KARL FERDINAND, b Germany, June 12, 27; US citizen; m 59; c 3. PHYSICAL CHEMISTRY, TEXTILE CHEMISTRY. *Educ:* Textile Eng Sch, Germany, Textile engr, 49; Aachen Tech Univ, dipl chem, 54, Dr rer nat, 57. *Prof Exp:* Sci asst, Inst Fuel Chem, Aachen Tech Univ, 54-57; trainee & group leader, Esso, Inc, 57, coordr, 59; supvr fiber develop, Hoechst Dye Works, Inc, 60; proj chemist res & develop, United Carbon Co, Inc, 60, sr chemist, 63; sr res chemist, 64-74, res assoc, 74-80, SR SCIENTIST, MILLIKEN RES CORP, 80- *Mem:* Am Chem Soc; Am Asn Textile Chem & Colorists; Fiber Soc; Am Inst Chemists. *Res:* Surface phenomena; colloidal systems; textiles; synthetic fibers; polymers; adhesives; coatings; textile finishes. *Mailing Add:* Milliken Res Corp PO Box 1927 Spartanburg SC 29304

OTTOBONI, M(INNA) ALICE, b Perrin, Tex; m 65. TOXICOLOGY, BIOCHEMISTRY. *Educ:* Univ Tex, BA, 54; Univ Calif, Davis, PhD(comp biochem), 59. *Prof Exp:* Res chemist toxicol eval, Dried Fruit Asn, Calif, 59-63; STAFF TOXICOLOGIST, CALIF STATE DEPT HEALTH, 63- *Concurrent Pos:* Nat Inst Environ Health Sci res grant, Calif State Dept Pub Health, 67-72; collabr, Dried Fruit Asn Calif & Western Regional Res Lab, Agr Res Serv, USDA, 59-63. *Mem:* AAAS; Am Inst Biol Sci; NY Acad Sci; Am Conf Govt Indust Hygienists; Am Asn Lab Animal Sci. *Res:* Intermediary metabolism; comparative biochemistry; toxicity and metabolic fate of chemicals; acute and chronic toxicity, mode of action and metabolism of environmental chemicals. *Mailing Add:* Lab Serv Br Calif State Dept Health 2151 Berkeley Way Berkeley CA 94704

OTTOLENGHI, ABRAMO CESARE, b Torino, Italy, Apr 13, 31; US citizen; m 58; c 4. MEDICAL MICROBIOLOGY. *Educ:* Wilmington Col, Ohio, BS, 50; Rutgers Univ, MS, 52; Univ Pa, PhD(med microbiol), 50. *Prof Exp:* Res asst preparation & potency testing of vaccines, Labs Life, Quito, Ecuador, 50-51 & 53-56 & Univ Pa, 56-59; res microbiologist, Sidney Hillman Med Ctr, Pa, 59-64; from asst prof to assoc prof, 64-72, PROF MED MICROBIOL, COL MED, OHIO STATE UNIV, 72- *Concurrent Pos:* Instr, Ogontz Campus, Pa State Univ, 58-59 & 60-64 & Lab Gen Biol, Rutgers Univ, 59-60; consult, South Div, Albert Einstein Med Ctr, 59-63 & Ohio Dept Health Medicare Lab Cert, 66- *Mem:* Am Soc Microbiol; NY Acad Sci; Sigma Xi. *Res:* Membrane antigens; bacterial exocellular products; phospholipids structure and function relating to host parasite relationships; antiphospholipid antibodies; medical education; membrane structure and function; electron microscopy. *Mailing Add:* Dept of Med Microbiol Ohio State Univ Columbus OH 43210

OTTOLENGHI, ATHOS, b Pavia, Italy, May 31, 23; US citizen; m 53; c 2. PHARMACOLOGY. *Educ:* Univ Pavia, MD, 46. *Prof Exp:* Assoc prof pharmacol, Univ Bari, 48-53; res assoc, 53-59, asst prof, 59-65, assoc prof, 65-75, PROF PHARMACOL, DUKE UNIV, 75- *Concurrent Pos:* Fel physiol, Univ Pavia, 46-48. *Mem:* Am Oil Chem Soc; Radiation Res Soc; Am Soc Pharmacol & Exp Therapeut. *Res:* Biochemistry of phospholipids and alteration of phospholipase activity in normal and experimental conditions; biochemistry of whole body irradiation in mammals; eosinophilic leukocytes and kinetics of bone marrow. *Mailing Add:* Dept Pharmacol Duke Univ Med Ctr Durham NC 27710

OTTOSON, HAROLD, b Millston, Wis, Mar 21, 30; m 55; c 4. MATHEMATICS. *Educ:* Wis State Univ, BS, 51; Univ Wis, MS, 54. *Prof Exp:* Instr math, Tri-State Eng Col, 54-55; math analyst, Lockheed Aircraft Corp, 55-56; mathematician, Bendix Pac, Bendix Corp, 56-59; sr staff engr, TRW Comput Co, 59-62; mgr syst design dept, Data & Info Syst Div, Int Tel & Tel Corp, 62-64; sr assoc, Planning Res Corp, 64-66; mem res staff, 66-67, subdept head spec projs, 67-68, assoc mgr nat syst anal dept, 68-69, head data processing systs dept, 69-75, head, Info Systs Dept, 75-78, DEPT HEAD, COMMAND & CONTROL ENG, MITRE CORP, 78- *Mem:* Asn Comput Mach. *Res:* Operations research; computer simulation and systems design; applied probability. *Mailing Add:* Mitre Corp Westgate Res Park McLean VA 22101

OTVOS, ERVIN GEORGE, b Budapest, Hungary, Mar 14, 35; m 66; c 2. SEDIMENTOLOGY, GEOMORPHOLOGY. *Educ:* Eo6tvo6s Lorand Univ, dipl, 58; Yale Univ, MS, 62; Univ Mass, PhD(geol), 64. *Prof Exp:* Co geologist, Matra Mineral Mines Co, Hungary, 58-60; asst phys, hist & eng geol, Univ Mass, 62-64; geologist, Brit Petrol Ltd, Can, 64; explor geologist, New Orleans Explor Div, Mobil Oil Corp, 65-68; asst prof, La State Univ, New Orleans, 68-71; HEAD GEOL DIV, GULF COAST RES LAB, 71- *Concurrent Pos:* Adj prof, Univ Southern Miss Gulf Park Campus, 71-, adj prof, 74-; mem subcomn Americas, Int Asn Quaternary Res Comn on Shorelines, 73- *Mem:* Fel Geol Soc Am. *Res:* Sedimentary, geomorphologic and stratigraphic aspects of coastal processes; Northeast Gulf of Mexico Coastal Plain stratigraphy and geomorphology; barrier island evolution; sedimentation and pollution problems of recent coastal water bodies; Pleistocene stratigraphy of NE Gulf coast. *Mailing Add:* Geol Div Gulf Coast Res Lab Ocean Springs MS 39564 S

OTVOS, JOHN WILLIAM, b Budapest, Hungary, Nov 26, 17; nat US; m 45; c 3. PHYSICAL CHEMISTRY. *Educ:* Harvard Univ, BS, 39; Calif Inst Technol, PhD(phys chem), 43. *Prof Exp:* Asst chem, Calif Inst Technol, 39-41; chemist, Shell Develop Co, 46-52, asst head spectros dept, 52-57, head chem physics dept, 57-71, mgr anal res, 71-76; STAFF SR SCIENTIST, LAWRENCE BERKELEY LAB, 76- *Mem:* Am Chem Soc. *Res:* Kinetics; reaction mechanisms; radioisotopes; spectroscopy; photochemistry. *Mailing Add:* Lawrence Berkeley Lab Univ of Calif Berkeley CA 94720

OTWAY, HARRY JOHN, b Omaha, Nebr, Apr 23, 35; m 68. RISK ASSESSMENT, SCIENCE POLICY. *Educ:* NDak State Univ, BS, 58; Univ NMex, MS, 61; Univ Calif, PhD(nuclear sci), 69. *Prof Exp:* Instr eng, NDak State Univ, 57-58; staff mem, Los Alamos Sci Lab, Univ Calif, 58-61; sect leader, 61-66; pilot & flight instr, Golden West Airline, Calif, 66-69; staff scientist, Los Alamos Sci Lab, Univ Calif, 69-72; first officer div nuclear safety & environ protection, Int Atomic Energy Agency, sr officer & proj leader, Joint Int Atomic Energy Agency/Int Inst Appl Systs Anal res proj, 74-78; PRIN SCI OFFICER & HEAD TECHNOL ASSESSMENT SECT, JOINT RES CENTRE, COMN EUROPEAN COMMUNITIES, 78- *Concurrent Pos:* Mem appl ecol group steering comt, AEC, 70-72; reactor safety consult, A B Atomenergi, Sweden, 71-72; res scholar, Int Inst Appl Systs Anal, 74-; adv, WHO, 78-; risk assessment consult, Asn Reactor Safety, Ger, 78- environmental impact assessment; social and psychological aspects of technological risks; vis prof psychol & eng, Univ Ill, Urbana, 79. *Mailing Add:* Technol Assessment Sect Europ Communities Ispra V2 Italy I-21020

OTWELL, WALTER STEVEN, b Va, Nov 20, 48. FOOD SCIENCE. *Educ:* Va Mil Inst, BS, 71; Univ Va, MS, 73; NC State Univ, PhD(food sci), 78. *Prof Exp:* Res assoc, Dept Food Sci, NC State Univ, 78; ASST PROF, DEPT FOOD SCI & HUMAN NUTRIT, UNIV FLA, 78- *Mem:* Inst Food Technologists. *Res:* Applied food science relative to utilization of seafoods. *Mailing Add:* 325 Food Sci Bldg Univ of Fla Gainesville FL 32611

OU, JONATHAN TSIEN-HSIONG, b Formosa, July 31, 34; m 62; c 2. MICROBIOLOGY, GENETICS. *Educ:* Nat Taiwan Univ, BS, 57; Univ Pa, PhD(biol), 67. *Prof Exp:* Res assoc microbial genetics, Univ Pa, 67-68; res assoc, 68-74, asst mem, 74-78, ASSOC MEM, INST CANCER RES, 78- *Concurrent Pos:* Guest scholar, Inst Virus Res, 81; res fel, Japan Soc Prom Sci. *Mem:* Genetics Soc Am; Am Soc Microbiol. *Res:* The mechanism of bacterial conjugation in Escherichia coli and the interaction between bacteriophage and bacteria. *Mailing Add:* Inst for Cancer Res 7701 Burholme Ave Philadelphia PA 19111

OU, LO-CHANG, b Shanghai, China, Oct 16, 32; m 61; c 4. PHYSIOLOGY, BIOCHEMISTRY. *Educ:* Peking Univ, BSc, 54; Dartmouth Med Sch, PhD(physiol), 71. *Prof Exp:* Teaching asst biochem, Peking Univ, 54-59, lectr, 59-62; demonstr physiol, Univ Hong Kong, 62-64; res asst, 64-71, Nat Heart & Lung Inst res assoc physiol, 71-77, asst prof, 77-80, RES ASSOC PROF PHYSIOL, DARTMOUTH MED SCH, 80- *Res:* Pathophysiology of hypoxia; role of the higher nervous system on the regulation of respiration at high altitude and sea level. *Mailing Add:* Dept Physiol Dartmouth Med Sch Hanover NH 03755

OUANO, AUGUSTUS CENIZA, b Mandawe, Philippines, Mar 2, 36; US citizen; m 64; c 1. CHEMICAL ENGINEERING, POLYMER PHYSICS. *Educ:* Mapua Inst Technol, BSChE, 57; Purdue Univ, MSChE, 61; Stevens Inst Technol, PhD(chem eng), 69. *Prof Exp:* Develop engr, Continental Can Co, 61-64; res chemist, Rexall Chem Co, 64-66; res & develop engr, Packaging Corp Am, 66-67; mem res staff polymer characterization, 70-81, MGR POLYMER PROCESSING & MAT, IBM CORP, 81- *Mem:* Am Chem Soc; Am Inst Physics. *Res:* Determination of molecular weight distribution and molecular weight average of polymers and the relationships between molecular characteristics of polymer to its synthesis and end use properties; diffusion and transport phenomenon in liquid systems. *Mailing Add:* IBM Corp PO Box 218 Yorktown Heights NY 10549

OUDERKIRK, JOHN THOMAS, b Amsterdam, NY, May 21, 31; m 53; c 2. ORGANIC CHEMISTRY, PHYSICAL CHEMISTRY. *Educ:* Hamilton Col, AB, 52; Cornell Univ, PhD(chem), 57. *Prof Exp:* Res chemist, Hooker Chem Corp, 55-58; res chemist, Toms River Chem Corp, 58-61, prod chemist, Chem Specialties Dept, 61-64; asst prod mgr, Ciba Corp, 64-65, sect leader, Textile & Paper Auxiliaries Div, 65-66; tech dir, NY Color & Chem Corp, Belleville, 66-67; res mgr, Chem Div, Sun Chem Corp, 67-71, consult, 71-74; mem staff, Chemetron Corp, 74-80; MEM STAFF, BASF WYANDOTTE CORP, 80- *Mem:* Am Chem Soc; Am Asn Textile Chemists & Colorists; Royal Soc Chem. *Res:* Reaction mechanisms; polyamides; polyesters; dyestuffs; pigments; textile and paper auxiliaries; instrumental analysis; fluorescence. *Mailing Add:* 268 Maple Ave Holland MI 49423

OUELLET, HENRI ROGER, b Riviere-du-Loup, Que, Jan 29, 38; m 64; c 1. ORNITHOLOGY, BIOSYSTEMATICS. *Educ:* Univ NB, BA, 62; McGill Univ, MSc, 67, PhD(biol), 77. *Prof Exp:* Asst cur vert zool, Redpath Mus, McGill Univ, 66-67, assoc cur, 67-70; asst cur, 70-76, CUR ORNITH & CHIEF DIV VERT ZOOL, NAT MUS CAN, 77- *Concurrent Pos:* Res minister cult affairs, Govt Que, 65-67; mem, Endangered Wildlife Can Comt, 78- *Mem:* Am Ornith Union; Sigma Xi. *Res:* Ornithological research, museum oriented, particularly in the fields of zoogeography and systematics; bird fauna of Holarctic Region. *Mailing Add:* Nat Mus of Natural Sci Nat Mus of Can Ottawa ON K1A 0M8 Can

OUELLET, LUDOVIC, b Tingwick, Que, Mar 27, 23; m 50; c 6. PHYSICAL CHEMISTRY. *Educ:* Laval Univ, BSc, 47, DSc(chem), 49. *Prof Exp:* Merck fel, Cath Univ Am, 50-51; USPHS fel, Naval Med Res Inst, 51-52 & trainee, Univ Wis, 52-53; from asst prof to assoc prof chem, Univ Ottawa, 53-58; chmn dept, 67-72, PROF CHEM, LAVAL UNIV, 60-, CHMN DEPT, 81- *Concurrent Pos:* Pres, Res Comn, 71-78; pres, Univ Res Comn, Univ Coun Quebec, 69-72; mem, Coun Sci Policy Quebec, 71-73; pres, Order Chemists Que, 76-78. *Mem:* Am Chem Soc; Chem Inst Can. *Res:* Chemical kinetics; mechanism of reactions; especially enzymatic reactions; science policy. *Mailing Add:* Dept of Chem Laval Univ Quebec PQ G1K 7P4 Can

OUELLETTE, GUILLEMOND BENOIT, b St Hilaire, NB, Jan 16, 32; m 54, 75; c 6. HISTOPATHOLOGY. *Educ:* St Joseph's Col, NB, BA, 52; Cornell Univ, PhD(phytopath), 60. *Prof Exp:* FOREST PATHOLOGIST, CAN DEPT ENVIRON, 58- *Concurrent Pos:* Lectr, Laval Univ, 64- *Mem:* Can Bot Asn; Bot Soc Am; Can Phytopath Soc. *Res:* Host parasite relationships in Dutch elm disease; morphology, physiology and taxonomy of fungi; electron microscope on histopathology of Dutch elm disease. *Mailing Add:* Laurentian Forest Res Ctr PO Box 3800 Ste-Foy PQ G1V 4C7 Can

OUELLETTE, ROBERT J, b St Johnsbury, Vt, Dec 13, 38; m 59; c 3. ORGANIC CHEMISTRY. *Educ:* Univ Vt, BS, 59; Univ Calif, Berkeley, PhD(chem), 62. *Prof Exp:* From asst prof to assoc prof, 62-72, PROF CHEM, OHIO STATE UNIV, 72- *Concurrent Pos:* NSF grants, 65-71; Petrol Res Fund grants, 65-67 & 70-72. *Mem:* Am Chem Soc. *Res:* Organometallic chemistry; conformational analysis; nuclear magnetic resonance. *Mailing Add:* Dept of Chem Ohio State Univ Columbus OH 43210

OUGHSTUN, KURT EDMUND, b New Britain, Conn, Jan 12, 49; m 70; c 2. ELECTROMAGNETIC THEORY, QUANTUM OPTICS. *Educ:* Cent Conn State Col, BA, 72; Inst Optics, Univ Rochester, MS, 74, PhD(optics), 78. *Prof Exp:* RES SCIENTIST, UNITED TECHNOLOGIES CORP, 76- *Mem:* Optical Soc Am; Am Asn Physics Teachers; Nat Geog Soc. *Res:* Linear and nonlinear electromagnetic phenomena; dispersive pulse propagation; semiclassical radiation theory; diffraction and scattering theory; laser physics. *Mailing Add:* 94 Jerry Daniels Rd Marlborough CT 06447

OUIMET, ALFRED J, JR, b Wilmington, NC, Apr 7, 31; m 54; c 3. INFORMATION SCIENCE, SOLID STATE SCIENCE. *Educ:* Univ Conn, BA, 53, PhD(phys chem), 62. *Prof Exp:* Res chemist, Gen Elec Co, 53-54; asst instr chem, Univ Conn, 56-62; chemist, Esso Res & Eng Co, 62-66; ED CHEM LIT, CHEM ABSTR SERV, 66- *Res:* Kinetic study of the thermal decomposition of aluminum trimethyl; basic and products application research on aerospace lubricants. *Mailing Add:* Chem Abstr Serv Ohio State Univ Columbus OH 43210

OUJESKY, HELEN MATUSEVICH, b Ft Worth, Tex, Aug 14, 30; m 51; c 3. MICROBIOLOGY, RADIATION BIOLOGY. *Educ:* Tex Woman's Univ, BA & BS, 51, PhD(radiation biol), 68; Tex Christian Univ, MA, 65. *Prof Exp:* Teacher high sch, 51-63; asst prof biol, Tex Woman's Univ, 68-73; assoc prof, 73-80, PROF EARTH & LIFE SCI & ACTING DIV DIR, ALLIED HEALTH & LIFE SCI, UNIV TEX, SAN ANTONIO, 80- *Mem:* Soc Indust Microbiol; Am Soc Microbiol; Radiation Res Soc. *Res:* Effects of gases on DNA polymerase and microorganisms; incorporation of calcium 45 in fish scales; survey of plankton; effects of environmental pollutants on microbial metabolism. *Mailing Add:* Div Allied Health & Life Sci Univ of Tex San Antonio TX 78285

OULMAN, CHARLES S, b Lake Mills, Iowa, Aug 6, 33; m 61; c 2. SANITARY ENGINEERING. *Educ:* Iowa State Univ, BS, 55, PhD(sanit eng), 63. *Prof Exp:* Assoc civil eng, 56-57, from instr to assoc prof, 57-74, PROF CIVIL ENG, IOWA STATE UNIV, 74- *Honors & Awards:* Co-recipient Gold Medal, Filtration Soc, 70. *Mem:* Am Soc Civil Engrs; Am Water Works Asn; Water Pollution Control Fedn; Filtration Soc. *Res:* Water and waste treatment. *Mailing Add:* Dept of Civil Eng Iowa State Univ Ames IA 50010

OURECKY, DONALD K, genetics, cytology, see previous edition

OURSLER, CLELLIE CURTIS, b Cynthiana, Ind, Nov 26, 15; m 37; c 2. MATHEMATICS. *Educ:* Ind Univ, AB, 37; Univ Chicago, SM, 41; Ill Inst Technol, PhD(math), 58. *Prof Exp:* Teacher pub sch, Ill, 37-38, prin, 38-40; teacher, Ind, 40-49; instr math, Ind Univ, Northwest, 49-59; from asst prof to assoc prof, 59-72, PROF MATH, SOUTHERN ILL UNIV, EDWARDSVILLE, 72- *Mem:* Am Math Soc; Math Asn Am. *Res:* Abstract algebra; theory of numbers; finite geometries; quaternions; matrices with integer elements. *Mailing Add:* Sch of Sci & Eng Southern Ill Univ Edwardsville IL 62026

OUSEPH, PULLOM JOHN, b Kerala, India, Jan 21, 33; m; c 1. NUCLEAR PHYSICS. *Educ:* Univ Kerala, BSc, 53; Univ Saugor, MSc, 55; Fordham Univ, PhD(nuclear physics), 62. *Prof Exp:* Asst physics, Fordham Univ, 57-61; from asst prof to assoc prof, 62-70, PROF PHYSICS, UNIV LOUISVILLE, 70-, CHMN DEPT, 76- *Mem:* Am Phys Soc; Am Asn Physics Teachers. *Res:* Low energy nuclear physics, especially angular correlation of successive radiations and Mossbauer effect. *Mailing Add:* Dept Physics Univ Louisville Louisville KY 40208

OUSTERHOUT, LAWRENCE ELWYN, b Deming, NMex, Jan 20, 22; m 45; c 7. NUTRITION, BIOCHEMISTRY. *Educ:* Ore State Univ, BS, 43; Univ Calif, Davis, PhD(nutrit), 59. *Prof Exp:* Biochemist, Tech Lab, Bur Com Fisheries, US Fish & Wildlife Serv, 59-61; mgr poultry nutrit, Quaker Oats Co, Ill, 61-66; from assoc prof to prof animal nutrit, Univ RI, 66-73; consult poultry nutrit & mgt, 73-78; ASSOC POULTRY SCIENTIST, W WASH RES & EXTEN CTR, WASH STATE UNIV, 78- *Concurrent Pos:* Consult, poultry & feed indust, domestic & foreign. *Mem:* Am Inst Nutrit; Poultry Sci Asn. *Res:* Amino acid availability and protein quality, particularly with industrial fishery products; broiler breederr, laying hen; turkey nutrition and management. *Mailing Add:* W Wash Res & Exten Ctr Wash State Univ Puyallup WA 98371

OUTCALT, DAVID L, b Los Angeles, Calif, Jan 30, 35; m 56; c 4. MATHEMATICS. *Educ:* Pomona Col, BA, 56; Claremont Grad Sch, MA, 58; Ohio State Univ, PhD(math), 63. *Prof Exp:* Asst instr math, Ohio State Univ, 60-62; from instr to asst prof, Claremont Men's Col, 62-64; from lectr to assoc prof, 64-72, chmn dept, 69-72, PROF MATH, UNIV CALIF, SANTA BARBARA, 72- *Concurrent Pos:* Co-investr, US Air Force Off Sci Res grant, 64-71, prin investr, 71-73; vis assoc prof, Univ Hawaii, 67-68 & vis prof 71-72; acad asst instructional develop, Univ Calif, Santa Barbara, 73- *Mem:* AAAS; Am Math Soc; Math Asn Am; Soc Indust & Appl Math; Sigma Xi. *Res:* Non-associative rings and algebras. *Mailing Add:* Dept of Math Univ of Calif Santa Barbara CA 93106

OUTCALT, SAMUEL IRVINE, b Oak Park, Ill, Aug 26, 36; m 59; c 3. PHYSICAL GEOGRAPHY. *Educ:* Univ Cincinnati, BA, 59; Univ Colo, MA, 64; Univ BC, PhD(geog), 70. *Prof Exp:* Actg asst prof environ sci, Univ Va, 68-70; from asst prof to assoc prof, 70-78, PROF GEOG, UNIV MICH, ANN ARBOR, 78- *Concurrent Pos:* Res assoc, Arctic Inst NAm, 70; consult, Geog Applications Prog-US Geol Surv, 70-; res geogr, Infrared & Optics Div, Willow Run Labs, 72; partic, US-Int Biol Prog-Aerobiol Prog, 72- & US-Int Biol Prog-Tundra Biome, 72; mem staff, Activity under US/USSR Environ Protection Agreement, Northern Ecosysts, 76-; mem comt on permafrost, Nat Acad Sci, 76-78; mem staff, US/Yugoslav Smithsonian Limnol Res, 77- *Mem:* Am Geophys Union; Glaciol Soc; Asn Am Geog. *Res:* Interaction between surface climatological conditions and geomorphic evolution in Arctic-Alpine terrain; thermal modeling; computer applications in physical geography. *Mailing Add:* Dept of Geog Univ of Mich Ann Arbor MI 48104

OUTERBRIDGE, JOHN STUART, b Hunan, China, Sept 20, 36; m 63; c 3. PHYSIOLOGY, OTOLOGY. *Educ:* Mt Allison Univ, BS, 57, BA, 58; McGill Univ, MD, CM, 62, PhD(physiol), 69. *Prof Exp:* Intern, Royal Victoria Hosp, Montreal, 62-63, jr asst resident med, 63-64; lectr physiol, Biomed Eng Unit, 67-69, asst prof otolaryngol & biomed eng, 70-73, asst prof physiol, 69-74, ASSOC PROF OTOLARYNGOL & BIOMED ENG, McGILL UNIV, 73-, ASSOC PROF PHYSIOL, 74-, DIR OTOLARYNGOL RES LABS, 70-, ACTG DIR BIOMED ENG UNIT, 75- *Concurrent Pos:* Med Res Coun Can grant, 69- & scholar, 70-; Defense Res Bd Can grant, 68-; asst otolaryngologist, Royal Victoria Hosp, 70- *Mem:* Inst Elec & Electronics Eng; Biomed Eng Soc. *Res:* Vestibular and oculomotor systems; vestibular control of head and eye movements; diagnostic evaluation of vestibular systems; biomedical engineering; mathematical biology. *Mailing Add:* Biomed Eng Unit McGill Univ PO Box 6070 Montreal PQ H3A 2T5 Can

OUTHOUSE, JAMES BURTON, b Canandaigua, NY, Sept 20, 16; m 40; c 3. ANIMAL PHYSIOLOGY, ANIMAL SCIENCE. *Educ:* Cornell Univ, BS, 38; Univ Md, MS, 42; Purdue Univ, PhD, 56. *Prof Exp:* Instr & asst animal husb, Univ Md, 38-41, from asst prof to assoc prof, 41-52; from instr to assoc prof, 52-61, PROF ANIMAL HUSB, PURDUE UNIV, 61- *Concurrent Pos:* Vis prof, Univ Edinburgh, 70-71. *Mem:* AAAS; Am Soc Animal Sci; Brit Soc Animal Prod; Sigma Xi. *Res:* Nutrition studies with sheep and beef cattle; breeding studies with Finn sheep; management studies on accelerated lambing; artificial rearing of lambs and confinement programs; forages and pasture for sheep and lambs; animal nutrition. *Mailing Add:* Dept Animal Sci Purdue Univ West Lafayette IN 47907

OUTKA, DARRYLL E, b Grand Island, Nebr, Feb 25, 29; m 52; c 2. CELL BIOLOGY, PROTOZOOLOGY. *Educ:* San Diego State Col, BS, 51; Univ Calif, Berkeley, MA, 59, PhD(zool), 62. *Prof Exp:* Asst prof biol, Calif State Col Long Beach, 62-66; from asst prof to assoc prof cell biol, Iowa State Univ, 66-78, assoc prof, Univ Nottingham, 78-79, ASSOC PROF, IOWA STATE UNIV, 80- *Concurrent Pos:* NIH res grant, 63-66; NSF res grant, 65-67; USDA res grant, 78-79. *Mem:* Soc Protozool (treas, 69-72); Am Soc Cell Biol. *Res:* Plant cell culture and morphogenesis in plants; electron microscopy of plants; biochemistry of plant cells. *Mailing Add:* Dept Biochem & Biophysics Iowa State Univ Ames IA 50011

OUTLAND, RODERICK HENDERSON, b Hamlin, Ky, Oct 30, 22; m 60. CYTOLOGY. *Educ:* Murray State Col, BS, 47; Vanderbilt Univ, MA, 49, PhD(biol, cytol), 53. *Prof Exp:* Instr biol, Paducah Jr Col, Ky, 47-48 & Gettysburg Col, 49-50; from asst prof to assoc prof, 53-66, PROF BIOL, NORTHWESTERN STATE UNIV, 66- *Concurrent Pos:* Asst prof, Loyola Univ, La, 54-56. *Mem:* Bot Soc Am. *Res:* Cytology and physiology of Louisiana irises. *Mailing Add:* Dept of Biol Northwestern State Univ Natchitoches LA 71457

OUTLAW, HENRY EARL, b Pickwick, Tenn, June 17, 37; m; c 1. BIOCHEMISTRY, MOLECULAR BIOLOGY. *Educ:* Delta State Col, BS, 61; Univ Miss, MS, 64, PhD(pharm), 65. *Prof Exp:* Fel pharmacol, Sch Med, Univ Fla, 65-66; asst prof, 66-74, PROF CHEM, DELTA STATE UNIV, 74-, CHMN DEPT PHYS SCI, 69- *Mem:* Am Chem Soc. *Res:* Chemistry of muscle contraction; isolation and biochemical characterization of subcellular constituents. *Mailing Add:* Dept of Phys Sci Delta State Univ Cleveland MS 38732

OUTLAW, RONALD ALLEN, b Norfolk, Va, June 6, 37; m 65; c 2. VACUUM PHYSICS, MATERIALS SCIENCE. *Educ:* Va Polytech Inst, BS, 60, MS, 69, PhD(mat sci), 72. *Prof Exp:* AERO-SPACE TECHNOLOGIST VACUUM PHYSICS & MAT SCI, LANGLEY RES CTR, NASA, 63- *Concurrent Pos:* Adj assoc prof physics, Old Dominion Univ, 78- *Mem:* Am Vacuum Soc; Am Phys Soc; Am Soc Metals. *Res:* Physical and chemical adsorption of gases on metals; diffusion and solubility of gases in metals; vacuum instrumentation and low pressure physics; purification of metals; thin film nucleation and growth; photovoltaics. *Mailing Add:* MC 160 Langley Res Ctr NASA Hampton VA 23665

OUTTEN, LORA MILTON, b Pocomoke City, Md, Aug 17, 13. ICHTHYOLOGY, VERTEBRATE ECOLOGY. *Educ:* Western Md Col, AB, 34, AM, 37; Cornell Univ, MS, 50, PhD(vert zool, ichthyol, entom, limnol), 56. *Prof Exp:* Lab asst biol, Western Md Col, 33-34 & 36-37; instr high schs, Md & Va, 34-36, 40-41 & 43-46; from asst prof to prof, 46-79, chmn, Dept Biol, 66-71, chair ecol res, 71-79, EMER PROF BIOL, MARS HILL COL, 79- *Mem:* Fel AAAS; Am Soc Zool; Am Inst Biol Sci; Am Soc Ichthyol & Herpet; Ecol Soc Am. *Res:* Life history, ecology, habits, behavior, development, morphology and distribution of fishes and other vertebrates; effects of insecticides on honeybees; aquatic insects; limnology; vertebrate zoology; distribution of fishes in southeastern United States, Bahamas, Caribbean area, Panama, Bermuda, Britain, Hawaii, Australia and New Zealand. *Mailing Add:* Dept of Biol Box 722-C Mars Hill Col Mars Hill NC 28754

OUTWATER, JOHN O(GDEN), b London, Eng, Jan 2, 23; nat US; m 52; c 4. MECHANICAL ENGINEERING. *Educ:* Cambridge Univ, BA, 43, MA, 48, PhD, 76; Mass Inst Technol, ScD(mech eng), 50. *Prof Exp:* Engr, E I du Pont de Nemours & Co, 50-52; proj engr, Universal Moulded Prod Corp, 52-54; indust liaison officer, Mass Inst Technol, 54-55; chmn dept, 55-63, PROF MECH ENG, UNIV VT, 55- *Concurrent Pos:* Dir, Vt Instrument Co; consult, Nat Acad Sci, Monsanto Res Co, Naval Ord Lab, US Dept Navy, Chemstrand Corp, Whiting Corp, Gen Elec Co & Grumman Aircraft Eng Corp; Leader expeds, Wenner-Gren Found. *Mem:* Fel Am Soc Mech Engrs; Am Soc Testing & Mat; Soc Hist Technol. *Res:* Mechanical properties of non-metallic materials; reinforced plastics; mechanics of rigid bodies; pre-Columbian construction techniques; ski accident research. *Mailing Add:* Dept of Mech Eng Univ of Vt Burlington VT 05404

OUTZEN, HENRY CLAIR, JR, anatomy, cancer immunology, see previous edition

OUZTS, JOHNNY DREW, b Indianola, Miss, Nov 29, 34; m 57; c 4. MEDICAL ENTOMOLOGY, AQUATIC WEED CONTROL. *Educ:* Delta State Col, BS, 57; Miss State Univ, MS, 61, PhD(entom), 63. *Prof Exp:* Actg head dept & asst dean, Sch Arts & Sci, 63-74, head dept, 74-79, PROF BIOL SCI, DELTA STATE COL, 63-, ASSOC DEAN, SCH ARTS & SCI, 74-, DIR, CTR ALLUVIAL PLAINS STUDIES, 80- *Mem:* Entom Soc Am; Am Mosquito Asn. *Res:* Chlorinated hydrocarbon resistance in fresh and flood-water; breeding mosquitoes; biological control of cotton insects; practical entomology for student agricultural pilots; plant pathology; weed and biological pest control. *Mailing Add:* Box 3262 Delta State Univ Cleveland MS 38733

OVADIA, JACQUES, b Vienna, Austria, Nov 16, 23; nat US; m 56; c 2. MEDICAL PHYSICS. *Educ:* Brooklyn Col, BA, 44; Univ Ill, MS, 47, PhD(nuclear physics), 51. *Prof Exp:* Instr radiol, Univ Ill, 51-52; res assoc biophys, Sloan-Kettering Inst, 52-56; chief physicist radiation ther, Michael Reese Hosp, Chicago, 56-72; prof radiol, Med Col Wis, 72; CHMN MED PHYSICS, MICHAEL REESE HOSP, 73-; PROF RADIOL, UNIV CHICAGO, 74- *Concurrent Pos:* Adj prof physics, Ill Inst Technol, 72- *Mem:* Health Physics Soc; Am Soc Ther Radiol; Radiation Res Soc; Radiol Soc NAm; Am Asn Physicists in Med. *Res:* High energy electrons and x-rays for therapy; short-lived isotope tracers; mechanism of action of radiation; pulse radiolysis. *Mailing Add:* 1722 East 55th St Chicago IL 60615

OVALLE, WILLIAM KEITH, JR, b Ancon, CZ, Mar 18, 44; US citizen. MEDICAL SCIENCE. *Educ:* St Joseph's Col, Pa, BS, 66; Temple Univ, PhD(anat), 71. *Prof Exp:* Muscular Dystrophy Asn Can fel neurophysiol, Univ Alta, 70-72; asst prof anat, 72-77, ASSOC PROF ANAT, FAC MED, UNIV BC, 77- *Mem:* Am Asn Anatomists; Am Soc Cell Biol; AAAS; Can Asn Anatomists; Sigma Xi. *Res:* Neuromuscular ultrastructure and functional morphology; electron microscopy and histochemistry of the peripheral nervous system system and muscle during development in health and disease. *Mailing Add:* Dept of Anat Fac of Med Univ of BC Vancouver BC V6T 1W5 Can

OVARY, ZOLTAN, b Kolosvar, Hungary, Apr 13, 07. IMMUNOLOGY. *Educ:* Univ Paris, MD, 35, Lic es Sci, 39. *Prof Exp:* Res assoc microbiol, Sch Med, Johns Hopkins Univ, 55-59; from asst prof to assoc prof path, 59-64, PROF PATH, SCH MED, NY UNIV, 64- *Concurrent Pos:* Res fel, Brazilian Super Coun Res, 52; Fulbright fel, 54-55. *Mem:* Am Soc Immunol; Soc Exp Biol & Med; Am Acad Allergy; Harvey Soc; fel NY Acad Sci. *Res:* Hypersensitivity; anaphylaxis; antibody structure; antigenicity; function of the reticuloendothelial system. *Mailing Add:* Dept of Path NY Univ Sch of Med New York NY 10016

OVE, PETER, b Dellstedt, Ger, Aug 31, 30; US citizen; m 56; c 3. CELL BIOLOGY, BIOCHEMISTRY. *Educ:* Univ Pittsburgh, BS, 63, PhD(cell biol), 67. *Prof Exp:* Asst prof clin pharmacol, Med Ctr, Duke Univ, 68-69; asst prof, 69-73, assoc prof, 73-78, PROF CELL BIOL & DIR GRAD STUDIES, SCH MED, UNIV PITTSBURGH, 78- *Mem:* Am Asn Cancer Res; Am Soc Cell Biol; Am Asn Anat. *Res:* Control of growth of mammalian cells; cancer problems; biology of aging. *Mailing Add:* Dept of Anat & Cell Biol Univ of Pittsburgh Sch of Med Pittsburgh PA 15213

OVENALL, DERICK WILLIAM, b Bloxwich, Eng, Sept 26, 30; m 65; c 2. PHYSICAL CHEMISTRY. *Educ:* Univ Manchester, BSc, 52; Univ Birmingham, PhD(chem), 55. *Prof Exp:* Res fel chem, Univ Birmingham, 55-57; res assoc physics, Duke Univ, 57-59; sr sci officer, Nat Phys Lab, Eng, 59-60; physicist, Battelle Mem Inst, Switzerland, 60-61; res chemist, Plastics Dept, 62-71, RES CHEMIST, CENT RES & DEVELOP DEPT, EXP STA, E I DU PONT DE NEMOURS & CO, INC, 71- *Mem:* Am Chem Soc. *Res:* Spectroscopy; high resolution nuclear magnetic resonance; electron spin resonance; radiation damage. *Mailing Add:* Cent Res & Develop Dept Exp Sta E I du Pont de Nemours & Co Inc Wilmington DE 19898

OVENDEN, MICHAEL W, b London, Eng, May 21, 26; m 71. ASTRONOMY, ASTROPHYSICS. *Educ:* Univ London, BSc, 47, PhD(astrophys), 55; Cambridge Univ, MA, 51. *Prof Exp:* Jr observer astron, Cambridge Observ, 48-52; from lectr to sr lectr, Univ Glasgow, 53-66; prof astron, 66-74, PROF GEOPHYS & ASTRON, UNIV BC, 74- *Concurrent Pos:* Tech officer, Dom Astrophys Observ, Victoria, BC, 61; lectr, Emily Carr Col Visual Arts, Vancouver, BC, 81. *Mem:* Am Astron Soc; Brit Astron Soc (secy, 46-51, vpres, 51-53); fel Royal Astron Soc (secy, 57-66, vpres, 66); fel Royal Soc Edinburgh; Am Inst Archeol. *Res:* Dynamics of the solar system; physics of close binary stars; history of astronomy. *Mailing Add:* Dept of Geophys & Astron Univ BC Vancouver BC V6T 1W5 Can

OVENFORS, CARL-OLOF NILS STEN, b Stockholm, Sweden, Sept 26, 23; c 2. RADIOLOGY. *Educ:* Karolinska Inst, Sweden, BS, 44, MD, 51, PhD, 64, Docent, 64. *Prof Exp:* Asst dir thoracic radiol, Univ Hosp of Karolinska, Stockholm, 62-69, dir thoracic radiol, 69-70; assoc prof, 70-73, PROF RADIOL, UNIV CALIF, SAN FRANCISCO, 73- *Concurrent Pos:* James Picker Found scholar, 61-62, grant, Karolinska Inst, Sweden, 66-68; radiol res grants, 62-68; consult radiol, Swedish Armed Forces; mem, Coun for Cardiac Radiol; vis prof, Univ Calif, Los Angeles, 79, Karolinska Inst, Stockholm, Sweden, 79 & Univ Lyon, France, 80. *Mem:* Radiol Soc NAm; Asn Univ Radiol; NAm Soc Cardiac Radiol; Am Thoracic Soc; Fleischner Soc. *Res:* Cardiovascular and pulmonary radiology; author of numerous publications. *Mailing Add:* Dept Radiol Univ Calif Med Ctr San Francisco CA 94143

OVENSHINE, A THOMAS, b New York, NY, Mar 25, 36; m 59; c 3. GEOLOGY. *Educ:* Yale Univ, BS, 58; Va Polytech Univ, MS, 62; Univ Calif, Los Angeles, PhD(geol), 65. *Prof Exp:* Geologist, 65-70, asst chief, 70-72, chief, Br Alaskan Geol, 76-80, CHIEF, OFF MINERAL RESOURCES, US GEOL SURV, 80- *Mem:* Fel Geol Asn Can; Soc Econ Paleontologists & Mineralogists; Arctic Inst NAm; AAAS; fel Geol Soc Am. *Res:* Pre-Pleistocene glacial deposits; sedimentary structures; Silurian-Devonian conodonts; geology of southeastern Alaska. *Mailing Add:* Off Mineral Resources Nat Ctr US Geol Surv Reston VA 22902

OVERALL, JAMES CARNEY, JR, b Nashville, Tenn, Sept 27, 37; m 65; c 4. PEDIATRICS, INFECTIOUS DISEASES. *Educ:* Davidson Col, BS, 59; Vanderbilt Univ, MD, 63; Am Bd Pediat, cert, 68. *Prof Exp:* Intern pediat, Vanderbilt Univ Hosp, 63-64; from jr resident to sr resident, Babies Hosp, Columbia Presby Med Ctr, 64-66; res assoc, Nat Inst Neurol Dis & Blindness, NIH, Bethesda, Md, 66-68; instr & fel pediat & microbiol, Sch Med, Univ Rochester, 68-70; asst prof, 70-74, assoc prof pedist & microbiol, 74-79, HEAD, DIV INFECTIOUS DIS, DEPT PEDIAT & DIR TRAINING PROG PEDIAT INFECTIOUS DIS, COL MED, UNIV UTAH, 70-, PROF PEDIAT, 79-, PROF PATHOL, 81- *Concurrent Pos:* Head, Clin Epidemiol & Develop Immunol Unit, Infectious Dis Sect, Perinatal Res Br, Nat Inst Neurol Dis & Blindness, 67-68; proj officer, Rubella Vaccine Prog, Nat Inst Allergy & Infectious Dis, Parke-Davis Co & Philips-Roxane Co, 67-68; asst pediatrician, Strong Mem Hosp, Rochester, NY, 68-70; pediatrician, Univ Utah Med Ctr, Salt Lake City, 70-; consult infectious dis, Primary Children's Med Ctr, Salt Lake City, 70-, active staff, 76-; consult infectious dis, Vet Admin Hosp, Salt Lake City, 70-; investr, Howard Hughes Med Inst, 74-; vis res assoc neurol & pediat, Dept Neurol, Univ Calif, San Francisco, 78-79. *Mem:* Infect Dis Soc Am; Am Soc Microbiol; Am Fedn Clin Res; Soc Pediat Res; Sigma Xi. *Res:* Virology; herpes simplex virus infections, antiviral chemotherapy; host resistance to viral infections; viral immunology; viral-bacterial or fungal synergism; neonatal infections; hospital acquired infections in a newborn intensive care unit. *Mailing Add:* Div of Infectious Dis Dept of Pediat Univ of Utah Salt Lake City UT 84132

OVERBECK, HENRY WEST, b Chicago, Ill, Oct 29, 30; m 60; c 2. MEDICAL PHYSIOLOGY, INTERNAL MEDICINE. *Educ:* Princeton Univ, BA, 52; Northwestern Univ, MD, 56; Univ Okla, PhD(physiol), 66; Am Bd Internal Med, cert. *Prof Exp:* Intern, Mary Fletcher Hosp, Univ Vt, 56-57; resident physician, Sch Med, Northwestern Univ, 59-62; instr internal med, Sch Med, Univ Okla, 63-66; from asst prof to prof physiol & internal med, Mich State Univ, 66-76; prof physiol & internal med, Uniformed Servs Univ Health Sci, Bethesda, Md, 76-78; PROF MED & PHYSIOL, UNIV ALA MED CTR, BIRMINGHAM, 78- *Concurrent Pos:* USPHS career develop award, 66-71; Vet Admin clin investr, 63-66; consult, Vet Admin Hosp, Saginaw, Mich, 66-73; fel cardiol, Emory Univ Sch Med, Atlanta, 73-74; fel coun high blood pressure & coun circulation, Am Heart Asn, 76-79; mem hypertension task force, Nat Heart Lung & Blood Inst, assoc ed, Hypertension. *Mem:* Cent Soc Clin Res; Soc Exp Biol & Med; Am Soc Clin Pharmacol & Therapeut; Am Physiol Soc; fel Am Col Physicians. *Res:* Cardiovascular physiology and pathophysiology, especially hypertension. *Mailing Add:* Dept Med Univ Ala Med Ctr University Station Birmingham AL 35294

OVERBERG, RICHARD JOSEPH, polymer chemistry, see previous edition

OVERBERGER, CHARLES GILBERT, b Barnesboro, Pa, Oct 12, 20; m 45; c 4. POLYMER CHEMISTRY. *Educ:* Pa State Col, BS, 41; Univ Ill, PhD(org chem), 44. *Hon Degrees:* DSc, Holy Cross Col, 66; DSc, L I Univ, 68. *Prof Exp:* Res chemist, Allied Chem Co, Pa, 41; asst org chem, Univ Ill, 41-43; assoc, Rubber Reserve Corp, 44-46; Du Pont fel, Mass Inst Technol, 46-47; from asst prof to assoc prof chem, Polytech Inst Brooklyn, 47-52, prof org chem, 52-66, assoc dir polymer res inst, 51-64, dir, 64-66, head dept chem, 55-64, vpres res, 64-65, dean sci, 64-66; chmn dept chem, 67-72, DIR MACROMOLECULAR RES CTR, UNIV MICH, 68-, VPRES RES, 72- *Concurrent Pos:* Consult, Armed Forces; ed, J Polymer Sci & Fortschritte der Hochpolymerenforschung; pres macromolecular div, Int Union Pure & Appl Chem, 75-77; mem bur, Int Union Pure & Appl Chem, 78- *Mem:* AAAS; Am Chem Soc (pres, 67); Am Inst Chem; Brit Chem Soc; Brit Soc Chem Indust. *Res:* Organic synthesis; mechanisms of organic reactions; the use of polymers as reactants in organic reactions; synthesis and properties of asymmetric polymers in solution; chemistry of diazines and decomposition of cyclic azo compounds. *Mailing Add:* Dept of Chem Univ of Mich Ann Arbor MI 48109

OVERBERGER, JAMES EDWIN, b Barnesboro, Pa, July 1, 30; m 58; c 2. DENTISTRY. *Educ:* Univ Pittsburgh, BS, 52, DDS, 54; Univ Mich, MS, 57. *Prof Exp:* Clin instr human resources, Univ Mich, 56-57; asst prof dent mat, Sch Dent, WVa Univ, 57-62, assoc prof prosthodont, 62-67; assoc prof, Sch Dent, Univ NC, Chapel Hill, 67-69; actg dean, 79-80, 81-82, PROF DENT MAT & ASSOC DEAN SCH DENT, WEST VA UNIV, 69- *Mem:* Fel Am Col Dent; Am Dent Asn; Int Asn Dent Res. *Res:* Dental materials; restorative dentistry. *Mailing Add:* WVa Univ Sch of Dent Morgantown WV 26506

OVERBURY, STEVEN H, physical chemistry, see previous edition

OVERBY, LACY RASCO, b Model, Tenn, July 27, 20; m 48; c 4. BIOCHEMISTRY, VIROLOGY. *Educ:* Vanderbilt Univ, BA, 41, MS, 48, PhD(chem), 50. *Prof Exp:* Control & prod supvr, E I du Pont de Nemours & Co, 41-43; asst, Vanderbilt Univ, 46-49; sect mgr nucleic acid res, Abbott Labs, 49-62; vis scholar microbiol, Univ Ill, 62-64; mgr dept virol, 69-73, DIR DIV EXP BIOL, ABBOTT LABS, 73-, DIR, GENETIC ENG, 81- *Concurrent Pos:* Assoc res fel, Abbott Labs, 64-69; lectr, Northwestern Univ, 68-; assoc ed, J Malacol Virol, 77-; mem, Int Adv Bd Asian J Clin Sci, 80- *Mem:* AAAS; Am Chem Soc; Am Inst Nutrit; Am Soc Biol Chem; Am Soc Microbiol. *Res:* Amino acids and proteins; chemistry and biochemistry of vitamins and growth factors; viruses and nucleic acids; hepatitis viruses; molecular biology; genetic engineering. *Mailing Add:* Div of Exp Biol Abbott Labs North Chicago IL 60064

OVERCAMP, THOMAS JOSEPH, b Toledo, Ohio, Feb 22, 46; m 69; c 3. AIR POLLUTION METEOROLOGY, ENVIRONMENTAL ENGINEERING. *Educ:* Mich State Univ, BS, 68; Mass Inst Technol, SM, 70, PhD(mech eng), 73. *Prof Exp:* Res assoc, Meteorol Prog, Univ Md, 72-74, vis asst prof, 74-75; asst prof environ systs eng, 75-78, ASSOC PROF ENVIRON SYSTS ENG, CLEMSON UNIV, 78- *Mem:* Air Pollution Control Asn; Am Meteorol Soc; Am Soc Mech Engrs. *Res:* Atmospheric diffusion; plume rise; aerosol science. *Mailing Add:* Dept of Environ Systs Eng Clemson Univ Clemson SC 29631

OVERCASH, JEAN PARKS, b Kannapolis, NC, Aug 15, 17; m 44. HORTICULTURE, AGRICULTURE. *Educ:* NC State Univ, BS, 38; Univ Wis, MS, 39, PhD(hort, plant physiol), 41. *Prof Exp:* Asst res horticulturist, Exp Sta, Univ Tenn, 42-45, assoc res horticulturist, 45; assoc prof & assoc horticulturist, 45-59, PROF & HORTICULTURIST, MISS STATE UNIV, 59- *Mem:* Fel Am Soc Hort Sci; Int Soc Hort Sci; Sigma Xi; Am Pomol Soc. *Res:* Physiology of tree fruits, especially pecans, grapes and peaches; rest period of peaches and grapes. *Mailing Add:* Agr & Forestry Exp Sta Miss State Univ PO Drawer T Mississippi State MS 39762

OVERDAHL, CURTIS J, b Elk Point, SDak, June 24, 17; m 53; c 3. SOILS. *Educ:* Univ Minn, BS, 47, MS, 49; Purdue Univ, PhD(soils), 57. *Prof Exp:* Exten area agronomist, Iowa State Univ, 49-53; exten agronomist, Purdue Univ, 53-54; EXTEN SPECIALIST SOILS, UNIV MINN, ST PAUL, 56- *Mem:* Am Soc Agron. *Res:* Soil management and fertilizers; agricultural extension service. *Mailing Add:* Dept of Soils Exten Div Univ of Minn St Paul MN 55108

OVEREND, JOHN, b Keighley, Eng, Oct 3, 28; m 54; c 3. PHYSICAL CHEMISTRY. *Educ:* Oxford Univ, BA, 52, DPhil(chem), 56. *Hon Degrees:* DSc, Oxford Univ, 78. *Prof Exp:* Res fel, Univ Minn, 55-58; res chemist, Dow Chem Co, 58-60; from asst prof, to assoc prof, 60-67, PROF CHEM, UNIV MINN, MINNEAPOLIS, 67- *Concurrent Pos:* Guggenheim fel, 67-68; vis staff mem, Los Alamos Sci Lab, 74- *Honors & Awards:* Coblentz Mem Prize, Coblentz Soc, 64. *Mem:* Am Phys Soc; Am Chem Soc; Optical Soc Am; Royal Chem Soc. *Res:* Molecular structure and dynamics; molecular spectra; surface chemistry; infrared circular dichroism. *Mailing Add:* Dept of Chem Univ of Minn Minneapolis MN 55455

OVEREND, RALPH PHILLIPS, b Eng, Apr 7, 44; Can citizen. PHYSICAL CHEMISTRY. *Educ:* Univ Salford, MSc, 68; Univ Dundee, PhD(phys chem), 72. *Prof Exp:* Chemist, UKAEA, Winfrith in Dorset, 66-68; fel, Chem div, 72-74, asst res officer, 74-76, biomass energy res & develop prog convenor, 76-80, TASK COORDR, RENEWABLE ENERGY, NAT RES COUN CAN, 80- *Mem:* Royal Soc Chem; Royal Inst Chem; Chem Inst Can; Forest Prod Res Soc. *Res:* Gas kinetics of species important to the atmosphere; the chemical conversion of biomass and biomass productivity. *Mailing Add:* Div Energy Res & Develop M-50 Nat Res Coun of Can Ottawa ON K1A 0R6 Can

OVERHAGE, CARL F J, b London, Eng, Apr 2, 10; nat US; m 40. ELECTRONICS, PHOTOGRAPHY. *Educ:* Calif Inst Technol, BS, 31, MS, 34, PhD(physics), 37. *Prof Exp:* Physicist, Technicolor Motion Picture Corp, 37-40, actg dir res, 40-42; mem staff, Radiation Lab, Mass Inst Technol, 42-45; res supvr, Color Control Dept, Eastman Kodak Co, 46-48, asst dir, Color Tech Div, 49-54; div head, Lincoln Lab, 55-57, dir, 57-64, prof eng, 61-73, EMER PROF ENG, MASS INST TECHNOL, 73- *Concurrent Pos:* Sci consult, US Army Air Force, 45; mem sci adv bd, US Air Force, 51-57, sci adv comt ballistic missiles, Secy Defense, 59-61; mem, Defense Sci Bd, 62-63; tech adv bd, Fed Aviation Agency, 62-65; mem, Nat Adv Comn on Libr,

66-67; exec dir, Univ Info Technol Corp, 68-73. *Honors & Awards:* Presidential Cert Merit, 48; Exceptional Service Award, US Air Force, 58. *Mem:* Fel Am Acad Arts & Sci (vpres, 64-66); fel Am Phys Soc; fel Optical Soc Am. *Res:* Photography; electronics. *Mailing Add:* 1112 Calle Cataline Santa Fe NM 87501

OVERHAUSER, ALBERT WARNER, b San Diego, Calif, Aug 17, 25; m 51; c 8. THEORETICAL SOLID STATE PHYSICS. *Educ:* Univ of Calif, AB, 48, PhD(physics), 51. *Hon Degrees:* DSc, Univ Calif, 79. *Prof Exp:* Res assoc, Univ Ill, 51-53; from asst prof to assoc prof physics, Cornell Univ, 53-58; supvr, Solid State Physics, Ford Motor Co, 58-62, mgr, Theoret Sci, 62-69, asst dir, Phys Sci, 69-72, dir, Phys Sci Lab, 72-73; prof, 73-74, STUART PROF PHYSICS, PURDUE UNIV, 74- *Honors & Awards:* Oliver E Buckley Solid State Physics Prize, Am Phys Soc, 75; Alexander von Humboldt US sr scientist award, 79. *Mem:* Nat Acad Sci; Am Acad Arts & Sci; fel Am Phys Soc. *Res:* Many-electron theory; transport theory; neutron interferometry. *Mailing Add:* Dept of Physics Purdue Univ West Lafayette IN 47907

OVERHOLT, JOHN LOUGH, b Estherville, Iowa, May 28, 09; m 39; c 3. OPERATIONS RESEARCH. *Educ:* Iowa State Col, BS, 32; Lehigh Univ, MS, 35. *Prof Exp:* Res investr, NJ Zinc Co, 34-55; mem Opers Eval Group, Mass Inst Technol, 55-62; mem, Franklin Inst, 62-67, mem, 67-75, CONSULT CTR NAVAL ANAL, UNIV ROCHESTER, 75- *Mem:* Am Chem Soc; Opers Res Soc Am; Am Statist Asn. *Res:* Interior paint formulation; fundamental drying oil research; heavy chemical processes; titanium compounds and processes; statistics and experimental design; Colonial history; military operations research on air, sea and land problems. *Mailing Add:* Rte 1 Box 173 Kilmarnock VA 22482

OVERLAND, JAMES EDWARD, b Portland, Ore, Oct 30, 47. OCEANOGRAPHY. *Educ:* Univ Wash, BS, 70, MS, 71; NY Univ, PhD(oceanog), 73. *Prof Exp:* Phys scientist, Nat Meterol Ctr, 73-76, SUPVRY OCEANOGRAPHER, PAC MARINE ENVIRON LAB, NAT OCEANIC & ATMOSPHERIC ADMIN, 76- *Mem:* Am Meterol Soc. *Res:* Marine prediction activities such as coastal winds, waves and sea ice. *Mailing Add:* Pac Marine Environ Lab 3711 15th Ave NE Seattle WA 98105

OVERLEASE, WILLIAM R, b Elkhart, Ind, Oct 2, 25; m 55. ECOLOGY, BOTANY. *Educ:* Mich State Univ, BS & BSF, 50, MS, 52, PhD(bot), 64. *Prof Exp:* Naturalist, State Park Serv, Ind Dept Conserv, 51-56; educator natural hist, Acad Natural Sci, Philadelphia, 56-59; instr natural sci, Mich State Univ, 60-62; assoc prof sci, 64-65, PROF BIOL, WEST CHESTER STATE COL, 65- *Concurrent Pos:* Consult outdoor ed, Primary & Sec Schs & Local & State Park Systs. *Mem:* AAAS; Ecol Soc Am. *Res:* Flora of Northwestern Michigan, Benzie County; early plant succession on abandoned fields, Southeastern Pennsylvania; bird population studies, Pennsylvania, Michigan, Indiana; the red oak group (Erythrobalanus) in Michigan and nearby states; one hundred and fifty years of vegetation change in Chester County Pennsylvania. *Mailing Add:* Dept of Biol West Chester State Col West Chester PA 19380

OVERLEY, JACK CASTLE, b Kalamazoo, Mich, Aug 23, 32; m 59. NUCLEAR PHYSICS. *Educ:* Mass Inst Technol, BS, 54; Calif Inst Technol, PhD(physics), 61. *Prof Exp:* Res assoc physics, Calif Inst Technol, 60-61 & Univ Wis, 61-63; asst prof, Yale Univ, 63-68; asst dean sci serv, Col Lib Arts, 73-75, ASSOC PROF PHYSICS, UNIV ORE, 68- *Concurrent Pos:* Asst dir, A W Wright Nuclear Structure Lab, Yale Univ, 66-68; vis assoc physics, Calif Inst Technol, 75-76. *Mem:* AAAS; Am Phys Soc; Am Asn Physics Teachers; Sigma Xi. *Res:* Experimental nuclear physics, primarily nuclear spectroscopy and reactions involving charged particles and neutrons. *Mailing Add:* Dept of Physics Univ of Ore Eugene OR 97403

OVERMAN, ALLEN RAY, b Goldsboro, NC, Mar 11, 37; m 64; c 2. AGRICULTURAL ENGINEERING. *Educ:* NC State Univ, BS, 60, MS, 63, PhD(agr eng), 65. *Prof Exp:* Res assoc agron, Univ Ill, Urbana, 65-69; asst prof agr eng & asst agr engr, 69-74, assoc prof, 74-79, PROF AGR & ASSOC AGR ENGR, UNIV FLA, 79- *Mem:* Am Soc Agr Eng; Am Soc Civil Eng; Am Inst Chem Eng; Water Pollution Control Fedn; Am Soc Agron. *Res:* Transport processes in soil and chemical kinetics; wastewater treatment. *Mailing Add:* Dept Agr Eng Univ Fla Gainesville FL 32601

OVERMAN, AMEGDA JACK, b Tampa, Fla, May 17, 20; m 53. PLANT NEMATOLOGY. *Educ:* Univ Tampa, BS, 42; Univ Fla, MS, 51. *Prof Exp:* Asst in soils chem, 51-56, asst soils microbiologist, 56-68, assoc nematologist, 68-73, NEMATOLOGIST, INST FOOD & AGR SCI, AGR RES & EDUC CTR, UNIV FLA, 73- *Mem:* Soc Nematol; Europ Soc Nematol; Orgn Trop Am Nematol. *Res:* Bionomics, pathogenicity and control of nematodes attacking vegetables, ornamentals and agronomic crops. *Mailing Add:* Agr Res & Educ Ctr 5007 60th St E Bradenton FL 33508

OVERMAN, DENNIS ORTON, b Union City, Ind, Oct 16, 43; m 66; c 3. TERATOLOGY. *Educ:* Bowling Green State Univ, BA, 65; Univ Mich, MS, 67, PhD(anat), 70. *Prof Exp:* Res assoc develop biol, Univ Colo, 70-71; from instr to asst prof, 71-76, ASSOC PROF ANAT, W VA UNIV, 76- *Mem:* Teratology Soc; Am Asn Anatomists; Soc Develop Biol. *Res:* Mechanisms and inhibition of teratogenesis in orofacial malformations and limb development. *Mailing Add:* Dept of Anat WVa Univ Morgantown WV 26506

OVERMAN, JOSEPH DEWITT, b Champaign, Ill, Feb 23, 18; m 45; c 4. PHYSICAL CHEMISTRY. *Educ:* Univ Ill, BA, 41; Univ Rochester, PhD(chem), 45. *Prof Exp:* RES CHEMIST, E I DU PONT DE NEMOURS & CO, INC, PARLIN, NJ, 45- *Mem:* Am Chem Soc. *Res:* Reaction kinetics; photochemistry; photographic emulsions; reaction rate of Claisen rearrangement; photochemical decomposition of unsymmetrical dimethylhydrazine. *Mailing Add:* 115 Broadbent Rd Northminster Wilmington DE 19810

OVERMAN, LARRY EUGENE, b Chicago, Ill, Mar 9, 43; m 66. ORGANIC CHEMISTRY. *Educ:* Earlham Col, BA, 65; Univ Wis-Madison, PhD(org chem), 69. *Prof Exp:* NIH fel, Columbia Univ, 69-71; asst prof, 71-76, assoc prof, 76-79, PROF CHEM, UNIV CALIF, IRVINE, 79- *Concurrent Pos:* A P Sloan Found fel, 75-77; Camille & Henry Dreyfus teacher-scholar award, 76-81. *Mem:* AAAS; Am Chem Soc. *Res:* New methods for organic synthesis; natural products synthesis. *Mailing Add:* Dept of Chem Univ of Calif Irvine CA 92717

OVERMAN, RALPH THEODORE, b Clifton, Ariz, Aug 9, 19; m 45, 71; c 2. MEDICAL EDUCATION. *Educ:* Kans State Teachers Col, AB, 39, MS, 40; La State Univ, PhD(phys chem), 43. *Hon Degrees:* DSc, Philadelphia Col Pharm, 59. *Prof Exp:* Plant chemist, Flintkote Co, La, 42; instr chem, La State Univ, 42-43; head dept sci, La Col, 43-44; tech supt, Fercleve Corp, Tenn, 44-45; sr res chemist, Oak Ridge Nat Labs, 45-48, chmn spec training div, Oak Ridge Inst Nuclear Studies, 48-65; consult, Ralph T Overman Consult Serv, 65-68; dir educ, Technicon Corp, 68-69; vpres, Universal Med Servs, 70; planning dir, Bistate Regional Med Prog, 70-74; MEM STAFF REGIONAL MED EDUC CTR, VET ADMIN HOSP, ST LOUIS, 74- *Concurrent Pos:* Assoc prof, Sch Med, St Louis Univ; lectr, Sch Med, Wash Univ; pres, Compuhealth, St Louis, MO. *Mem:* Fel AAAS; fel Am Nuclear Soc; Am Chem Soc; Am Col Nuclear Physicians; Soc Nuclear Med. *Res:* Radiochemistry; nuclear medicine; health care planning. *Mailing Add:* Regional Med Educ Ctr 14B Vet Admin Med Ctr St Louis MO 63125

OVERMAN, TIMOTHY LLOYD, b Cincinnati, Ohio, Dec 9, 43; m 68; c 2. CLINICAL MICROBIOLOGY. *Educ:* Univ Cincinnati, BS, 66, MS, 69, PhD(microbiol), 72; Am Bd Med Microbiol, dipl, 75. *Prof Exp:* Fel pub health & med microbiol, Ctr Dis Control, Atlanta, Ga, 71-73; asst prof path, Col Med, 74-81, asst prof med technol, Col Allied Health Professions, 79-81, ASSOC PROF PATH & MED TECHNOL, UNIV KY, 81-; ASST PROF PATH, COL MED, UNIV KY, 74- *Mem:* Acad Clin Lab Physicians & Scientists; Am Soc Microbiol. *Res:* Diagnostic microbiology, especially oxidase-positive fermentative bacteria, non-fermentative bacteria and parasitology. *Mailing Add:* Path Serv (113CD) Vet Admin Med Ctr Lexington KY 40511

OVERMAN, WILLIAM T, b Santa Monica, Calif, May 11, 51; m 75; c 1. COMPUTER HARDWARE. *Educ:* Univ Calif, Los Angeles, BS, 73, Davis, MS, 75, Los Angeles, PhD(comput sci), 81. *Prof Exp:* Comput scientist, Lawrence Livermore Nat Lab, 73-75; res engr, Comput Sci Dept, Univ Calif, Los Angeles, 76-78; res assoc, Univ Southern Calif, Info Sci Inst, 78-81; MEM TECH STAFF, COMPUT SCI, AEROSPACE CORP, 81- *Mem:* Asn Comput Mach. *Res:* Formal verification of computer programs and hardware, sequential and concurrent systems, including functional and timing verification. *Mailing Add:* Aerospace Corp PO Box 92957 Los Angeles CA 90009

OVERMIRE, THOMAS GORDON, biology, see previous edition

OVERMYER, ROBERT FRANKLIN, b Chicago, Ill, Aug 9, 29; m 59; c 2. ENVIRONMENTAL SCIENCES. *Educ:* DePauw Univ, BA, 50; Ill Inst Technol, MS, 59. *Prof Exp:* Field engr, Schlumberger Well Surv Corp, 54-56; res asst solid state physics, Gen Atomic Div, Gen Dynamics Corp, 58-60, staff assoc, 60-67; mgr radiation effects, Physics Br, Gulf Gen Atomic, Inc, 67-71, mgr spec nuclear effects dept, Gulf Radiation Technol, 71-73; vpres, Intelcom Radiation Technol, 73-76; mgr nuclear prog, 76-80, VPRES, NUCLEAR, ENVIRONMENTAL & GEOTECH PROG, FORD, BACON & DAVIS, UTAH, 80- *Concurrent Pos:* US delegate working group uranium tailings, Orgn Econ Coop & Develop, Nuclear Energy Agency. *Mem:* Am Inst Physics; Am Soc Mining Engrs. *Res:* Semiconductor thermoelectric materials; engineering and environmental assessments of uranium mill tailings; research on radon diffusion; health impact of mill tailings; nuclear waste management; radiation measurement instrumentation; environmental radiation measurements. *Mailing Add:* 1093 Alton Way Salt Lake City UT 84108

OVERPECK, JAMES GENTRY, physiology, see previous edition

OVERSETH, OLIVER ENOCH, JR, b New York, NY, May 11, 28; m 54; c 2. EXPERIMENTAL HIGH ENERGY PHYSICS. *Educ:* Univ Chicago, BS, 53; Brown Univ, PhD(physics), 58. *Prof Exp:* Instr physics, Princeton Univ, 57-60; from asst prof to assoc prof, 61-67, PROF PHYSICS, UNIV MICH, ANN ARBOR, 68- *Concurrent Pos:* Sci assoc, CERN, 74- *Mem:* Am Phys Soc. *Res:* Elementary particles. *Mailing Add:* Dept of Physics Univ of Mich Ann Arbor MI 48109

OVERSKEI, DAVID ORVIN, b Brookings, SDak, Dec 26, 48; m 73. PLASMA PHYSICS. *Educ:* Univ Calif, Berkeley, AB, 71; Mass Inst Technol, PhD(physics), 76. *Prof Exp:* Oper mgr, Plasma Physics Ctr Prog, Francis Bitter Nat Magnet Lab Plasma Fusion Ctr, Mass Inst Technol, 76-81; TOKAMAK PHYSICS PROG MGR, FUSION DIV, GEN ATOMIC CO, 81- *Mem:* Am Phys Soc. *Res:* Controlled thermonuclear fusion research. *Mailing Add:* Gen Atomic Co PO Box 81608 San Diego CA 92138

OVERSTREET, ROBIN MILES, b Eugene, Ore, June 1, 39; m 64; c 2. PARASITOLOGY, MARINE BIOLOGY. *Educ:* Univ Ore, BA, 63; Univ Miami, MS, 66, PhD(marine biol), 68. *Prof Exp:* Nat Inst Allergy & Infectious Dis fel parasitol, Med Sch, Tulane Univ, 68- 69; parasitologist, Gulf Coast Res Lab, 69-70; HEAD SECT PARASITOL, GULF COAST RES LAB, 70- *Concurrent Pos:* Adj prof biol, Univ Southern Miss, 70- & Univ Miss 71- *Mem:* Am Soc Parasitol; Am Fisheries Soc; Soc Invert Path; Am Micros Soc; Helminth Soc Wash. *Res:* Taxonomy and biology of marine and estuarine parasites. *Mailing Add:* Gulf Coast Res Lab Ocean Springs MS 39564

OVERTON, DONALD EDWARD, hydrology, hydraulics, see previous edition

OVERTON, EDWARD BEARDSLEE, b Mobile, Ala, Nov 21, 42. ANALYTICAL CHEMISTRY, INORGANIC CHEMISTRY. *Educ:* Univ Ala, Tuscaloosa, BS, 65, PhD(chem), 70. *Prof Exp:* Asst prof chem, Northeast La Univ, 70-76; PROJ MGR, CTR BIOORG STUDIES, UNIV NEW ORLEANS, 76- *Mem:* Am Chem Soc; AAAS. *Res:* Trace hydrocarbon analysis; data processing high resolution gas chromatographic and gas chromatography/mass spectrometry data. *Mailing Add:* Ctr Bioorg Studies Univ New Orleans New Orleans LA 70148

OVERTON, WILLIAM CALVIN, JR, b Dallas, Tex, Oct 26, 18; m 46; c 3. PHYSICS. *Educ:* NTex State Univ, BS, 41; Rice Univ, MA, 49, PhD(physics), 50. *Prof Exp:* Proj engr, Missile Guid & Control Systs Res, S W Marshall Co, 46-47; sr res physicist acoustic oil well logging theory, Field Res Labs, Magnolia Petrol Co, 50-51; physicist, US Naval Res Lab, 51-62; PHYSICIST, LOS ALAMOS NAT LAB, UNIV CALIF, 62- *Concurrent Pos:* Lectr, Univ Md Grad Exten Sch at Naval Res Lab, 52, 54-56 & 60. *Mem:* Fel Am Phys Soc; Sigma Xi. *Res:* Solid state and low temperature physics; lattice dynamics; thermodynamics. *Mailing Add:* Los Alamos Nat Lab PO Box 1663 Los Alamos NM 87544

OVERTURF, GARY D, b Santa Ana, Calif, Nov 27, 43; m 65; c 1. INFECTIOUS DISEASES, PEDIATRICS. *Educ:* Western NMex Univ, BA, 65; Univ NMex, MD, 69. *Prof Exp:* Fel infectious dis, Univ Southern Calif, 72-74, asst prof pediat, 74-78; DIR, COMMUN DIS SERV, LOS ANGELES COUNTY-UNIV SOUTHERN CALIF MED CTR, 75-; ASSOC PROF PEDIAT, UNIV SOUTHERN CALIF, 78- *Mem:* Soc Pediat Res; Am Soc Microbiol; Am Acad Pediat; Infectious Dis Soc Am. *Res:* Medical microbiology, including antimicrobial susceptibility and mechanisms of action; vaccines and immune responses to infectious agents of humans. *Mailing Add:* Commun Dis Serv Univ of Southern Calif Med Ctr Los Angeles CA 90033

OVERTURF, MERRILL L, b Ottumwa, Iowa, Aug 31, 38; m 73. BIOCHEMISTRY. *Educ:* Univ Iowa, BS, 61, PhD(prev med), 70. *Prof Exp:* Instr med parasitol, Univ Iowa, 70-72; asst prof internal med, 72-78, ASSOC PROF INTERNAL MED, UNIV TEX MED SCH HOUSTON, 78- *Concurrent Pos:* Nat Heart & Lung Inst grant & Iowa Heart Asn grant, Univ Iowa, 71-72; Nat Heart & Lung Inst grant, Univ Tex, 72-81. *Mem:* Am Soc Pharmacol & Exp Therapeut; Am Heart Asn; Am Oil Chemists Soc; Am Fedn Clin Res. *Res:* Biochemistry of renovascular hypertension; renin-angiotensin-aldosterone system; atherosclerosis. *Mailing Add:* Dept of Med Univ of Tex Med Sch Houston TX 77025

OVIATT, CANDACE ANN, b Bennington, Vt, June 17, 39; m 71. ECOLOGY. *Educ:* Bates Col, BS, 61; Univ RI, PhD(biol oceanog), 67. *Prof Exp:* Res assoc, Sch Pub Health, Harvard Univ, 65-69; ASSOC RES PROF & MGR, MARINE ECOSYSTS RES LAB, GRAD SCH OCEANOG, UNIV RI, 69- *Mem:* Am Soc Limnol & Oceanog; AAAS. *Res:* Total systems studies of marine environments; the role of different populations in marine systems; the effects of stress and its role in stability; budgets for marine systems; practical application of the above for understanding and/or management. *Mailing Add:* Box 17 Grad Sch of Oceanog Univ RI Kingston RI 02882

OVIATT, CHARLES DIXON, b Washington, Pa, Dec 24, 24; m 48; c 5. APPLIED STATISTICS. *Educ:* Tarkio Col, AB, 47; Ohio State Univ, MS, 49, PhD, 54. *Prof Exp:* Prof chem, Tarkio Col, 49-57; staff ed phys sci, McGraw Hill Encyclop of Sci & Technol, 57-60; res chemist, E I du Pont de Nemours & Co, 60-61; sr sci ed, Webster Div, McGraw Hill Book Co, 61-69, exec ed, 69-71, ed-in-chief, 71-72; DIR STATEWIDE ASSESSMENT PROJ, MO STATE DEPT ELEM & SEC EDUC, 74- *Mem:* Am Chem Soc; Nat Sci Teachers Asn. *Res:* Technical editing; educational publishing, author; educational research. *Mailing Add:* Rte 1 Box 34 Vienna MO 65582

OVSHINSKY, IRIS M(IROY), b New York, NY, July 13, 27; m 59; c 5. SEMICONDUCTORS, BIOCHEMISTRY. *Educ:* Swarthmore Col, BA, 48; Univ Mich, MS, 50; Boston Univ, PhD(biol), 60. *Prof Exp:* Res assoc biochem, Worcester Found Exp Biol, 56-59; VPRES, ENERGY CONVERSION DEVICES, INC, 60- *Res:* Amorphous and disordered semiconductors; structural characteristics of information bearing material. *Mailing Add:* Energy Conversion Devices Inc 1675 W Maple Rd Troy MI 48084

OVSHINSKY, STANFORD R(OBERT), b Akron, Ohio, Nov 24, 22; m 59; c 5. SEMICONDUCTORS, NEUROPHYSIOLOGY. *Hon Degrees:* DSci, Lawrence Inst Technol, 80, DEng, Bowling Green State Univ, 81. *Prof Exp:* Pres, Stanford-Roberts Mfg, 46-50; mgr, Ctr Drive Dept, New Brit Mach Co, 50-52; dir res, Hupp Corp, 52-55; pres, Gen Automation, Inc, 55-58 & Ovitron Corp, 58-59; chmn bd, 60-78, PRES, ENERGY CONVERSION DEVICES, INC, 60- *Concurrent Pos:* Adj prof eng sci, Col Eng, Wayne State Univ, 78- *Honors & Awards:* Diesel Gold Medal, 68. *Mem:* Electrochem Soc; Soc Automotive Engrs; Am Phys Soc; Inst Elec & Electronics Engrs. *Res:* Amorphous and disordered semiconductors; structural characteristics of information bearing material. *Mailing Add:* Energy Conversion Devices Inc 1675 W Maple Rd Troy MI 48084

OVUNC, BULENT AHMET, b Samsun, Turkey, Oct 14, 27; m 57; c 1. CIVIL ENGINEERING, COMPUTER SCIENCE. *Educ:* Istanbul Tech Univ, MSc, 54, PhD(elasticity), 63. *Prof Exp:* Asst prof civil eng, Istanbul Tech Univ, 54-65; acad res asst, Univ BC, 65-67; assoc prof, 67-70, prof civil eng, 70-81, M EROI GIRARD PROF CIVIL ENG, UNIV SOUTHWESTERN LA, 81- *Concurrent Pos:* Designer struct, 55-65; Orgn Econ Coop & Develop fel, Istanbul Tech Univ, 63-65; consult comput prog to eng firms, 65-68. *Mem:* Am Soc Civil Engrs; Am Soc Mech Engrs; Am Concrete Inst; Int Asn Bridge & Struct Engrs; Sigma Xi. *Res:* Structures; dynamics of structures; finite element methods; plastic design; elasticity and related computer programmings; plates and shells. *Mailing Add:* Dept Civil Eng Univ Southwestern La Box 40172 Lafayette LA 70504

OWADES, JOSEPH LAWRENCE, b New York, NY, July 9, 19; m 69. BIOCHEMISTRY. *Educ:* City Col New York, BS, 39; Polytech Inst Brooklyn, MS, 44, PhD(chem), 50. *Prof Exp:* Chemist, Naval Supply Dept, 40-49 & Fleischmann Labs, 49-53; asst chief chemist & brewing & food consult, Schwarz Labs, 53-56, chief chemist, 56-58, dir labs & brewing res, 59-60; dir res & tech serv, Liebman Breweries, Inc, 60-65; vpres & tech dir, Rheingold Breweries, Inc, 65-68; consult, Karolos Fix Co, Athens, Greece, 69-70; coordr tech ctr, Anheuser-Busch, Inc, 70-71; consult to food & fermentation industs, 75-; DIR, CTR BREWING STUDIES, 77- *Mem:* Am Chem Soc; Am Soc Brewing Chemists; Master Brewers Asn Am; Inst Food Technologists; NY Acad Sci. *Res:* Yeast derivatives; sterols; brewing; foods. *Mailing Add:* 1575 Tremont St Boston MA 02120

OWCZAREK, J(ERZY) A(NTONI), b Piotrkow, Poland, Nov 2, 26; nat US; m 59. MECHANICAL ENGINEERING. *Educ:* Polish Univ Col Eng, Dipl Ing, 50; Univ London, PhD, 54. *Prof Exp:* Asst lectr thermodyn, Polish Univ, Col, 50-52; lectr thermodyn & mech, Battersea Col Technol, 52-53, thermodyn & fluid mech, Queen Mary Col, Univ London, 53-54; develop engr, Gen Elec Co, 55-60; assoc prof, 60-65, PROF MECH ENG, LEHIGH UNIV, 65- *Concurrent Pos:* Consult, De Laval Turbine Inc, 67- & Bell Labs, 74- *Mem:* Am Soc Mech Engrs; Am Inst Aeronaut & Astronaut; Am Soc Eng Educ. *Res:* Gas dynamics; turbine fluid mechanics; thermodynamics. *Mailing Add:* Dept Mech Eng & Mech Lehigh Univ Bethlehem PA 18015

OWCZARSKI, WILLIAM A(NTHONY), b Adams, Mass, June 13, 34; m 58; c 3. PHYSICAL & PROCESS METALLURGY. *Educ:* Univ Mass, BS, 55; Rensselaer Polytech Inst, MS, 58, PhD(phys metall), 62. *Prof Exp:* Welding engr, Sprague Elec Co, 55-57; metallurgist, Knolls Atomic Power Lab, Gen Elec Co, 58-61; sr res assoc metals joining, Adv Mat Res & Develop Lab, Pratt & Whitney Aircraft Div, United Aircraft Corp, 62-69, res supvr alloy processing, 69-71, tech supvr metal joining, 71-72, asst mgr, Mat Eng & Res Lab, Commercial Prod Div, 72-80, MGR TECH PLANNING, PRATT & WHITNEY AIRCRAFT GROUP, UNITED TECHNOL CORP, 80- *Honors & Awards:* William Spraragen Award, Am Welding Soc, 66, 69 & 72, Adams Mem Lectr, 73; George Mead Gold Medal, United Technol Corp, 74. *Mem:* Am Welding Soc; fel Am Soc Metals. *Res:* Welding metallurgy; high temperature nickel alloys; manufacturing technology. *Mailing Add:* Pratt & Whitney Aircraft Group 400 Main St East Hartford CT 06108

OWCZARZAK, ALFRED, b New York, NY, Jan 21, 23; m 50; c 3. CELL BIOLOGY, BIOLOGICAL STRUCTURE. *Educ:* Cornell Univ, BS, 44; Univ Wis, PhD(bot), 53. *Prof Exp:* Proj asst bot, Univ Wis, 48-49, asst, 49-53, proj assoc, 53-54, proj assoc path, Serv Mem Insts, 54-55; res assoc zool, 55-58, from instr to asst prof, 55-61, ASSOC PROF ZOOL, ORE STATE UNIV, 61- *Mem:* AAAS; Am Soc Zool; Am Soc Cell Biol. *Res:* Cytological effects of chemical treatments; tissue culture; microtechnique; cytochemistry; comparative vertebrate histology; cell ultrastructure. *Mailing Add:* Dept of Zool Ore State Univ Corvallis OR 97331

OWELLEN, RICHARD JOHN, b Rochester, NY, Nov 9, 35; m 60; c 2. ONCOLOGY, MEDICINE. *Educ:* Rensselaer Polytech Inst, BS, 57; Carnegie Inst Technol, MS & PhD(org chem), 60; Johns Hopkins Univ, MD, 67. *Prof Exp:* Asst prof med, 68-74, from asst prof to assoc prof oncol, Sch Med, Johns Hopkins Univ, 74-77. *Concurrent Pos:* NIH fel, Stanford Univ, 61-63; consult, Res Inst for Advan Studies, 64-67. *Mem:* AAAS; Am Soc Pharmacog; Am Asn Cancer Res; Am Soc Pharmacol & Exp Therapeut. *Res:* Pharmacology, clinical pharmacology, and metabolism of the Vinca Alkaloids; tubulin-vinca interactions; structure activity relations of Vinca alkaloids, including synthesis of congeners; marine pharmacology. *Mailing Add:* 1823 Dunwoody Rd Baltimore MD 21234

OWEN, ALICE KONING, b Kalamazoo, Mich, Jan 20, 30; m 55; c 2. EMBRYOLOGY. *Educ:* Kalamazoo Col, BA, 51; Iowa State Univ, MS, 53, PhD(embryol), 55. *Prof Exp:* Asst prof anat & physiol, Northeast Mo State Univ, 63-65; ASST PROF BIOL & PHYSIOL, UNIV NDAK, 66- *Mem:* AAAS; Am Soc Zool; Am Inst Biol Sci. *Res:* Development of integument in chicks; effect of vitamin E on development in rats. *Mailing Add:* Dept of Physiol Univ of NDak Grand Forks ND 58201

OWEN, BERNARD LAWTON, b Presidio, Tex, Nov 10, 29; m 52; c 3. ENTOMOLOGY. *Educ:* Agr & Mech Col, Tex, BS, 51, MS, 54; Auburn Univ, PhD(entom), 59. *Prof Exp:* Entomologist, Agr Res Serv, USDA, 58-59; consult, 59; from asst prof to assoc prof, 59-66, chmn, Natural Sci & Math Div, 69-79, PROF ZOOL, KANS WESLEYAN UNIV, 66- *Mem:* AAAS; Int Asn Impact Assessment; Nat Asn Biol Teachers. *Res:* Environmental physiology of arthropods. *Mailing Add:* Dept Biol Kans Wesleyan Univ Salina KS 67401

OWEN, BRUCE DOUGLAS, b Edmonton, Alta, Oct 1, 27; m 51; c 2. ANIMAL NUTRITION, ANIMAL PHYSIOLOGY. *Educ:* Univ Alta, BSc, 50, MSc, 52; Univ Sask, PhD(animal nutrit), 61. *Prof Exp:* Animal nutritionist, Lederle Labs Div, Am Cyanamid Co, NY, 52-54; animal husbandman, Can Dept Agr, 54-57; from lectr to prof animal sci, Univ Sask, 57-77; PROF ANIMAL SCI & CHMN DEPT, UNIV BC, 77- *Mem:* Agr Inst Can; Am Soc Animal Sci; Can Soc Animal Sci; Nutrit Soc Can. *Res:* Passive immunity; fat soluble vitamin transport; vitamin requirements of swine; protein quality evaluation; swine nutrition and physiology, factors influencing composition of feed grains and forages. *Mailing Add:* Dept of Animal Sci Univ of BC Vancouver BC V6T 1W5 Can

OWEN, CHARLES ARCHIBALD, JR, b Assiut, Egypt, Dec 3, 15; US citizen; m 39; c 3. BIOCHEMISTRY. *Educ:* Monmouth Col, AB, 36, Univ Iowa, MD, 41; Univ Minn, PhD, 50. *Hon Degrees:* DSc, Monmouth Col, 58. *Prof Exp:* Asst path, Univ Iowa, 38-39; from instr to assoc prof clin path, Mayo Found, Univ Minn, 50-60, prof med res, 60-81; RETIRED. *Concurrent Pos:* Consult, Mayo Clin, 50-, head sect exp biochem, 59-, head sect clin path, 61-70. *Mem:* AAAS; Am Soc Clin Path; Am Soc Exp Path; Soc Exp Biol & Med; Am Physiol Soc. *Res:* Blood coagulation; biologic aspects of radioisotopes. *Mailing Add:* 9 Skyline Dr Rochester MN 55901

OWEN, CHARLES SCOTT, b Springfield, Mo, July 4, 42. BIOPHYSICS. *Educ:* Univ Rochester, BS, 64; Univ Pa, PhD(physics), 70. *Prof Exp:* Res assoc physics, Wash Univ, 69-71 & Univ Calif, Santa Barbara, 71-72; res assoc biophysics, 72-77, ASST PROF PATH & BIOCHEM-BIOPHYSICS, UNIV PA, 77- *Mem:* Biophys Soc; Am Phys Soc; AAAS. *Res:* Magnetic sorting of cells; physical properties of immunoglobulins and protein-membrane interactions. *Mailing Add:* Dept of Biochem & Biophys Sch of Med G3 Univ of Pa Philadelphia PA 19104

OWEN, DAVID A, b New York, NY, July 13, 37; m; c 3. THEORETICAL PHYSICS. *Educ:* Univ Pa, MS, 61; Johns Hopkins Univ, PhD(physics), 70. *Prof Exp:* Physicist appl magnetohydrodyn, Naval Air Develop Ctr, Johnsville, Pa, 61-64; res fel physics, Univ Surrey, 70-72; res assoc, Ctr Theoret Physics, CNRS, Marseille, France, 72-73; vis prof, Racah Inst, Hebrew Univ, Jerusalem, 73-74; SR LECTR PHYSICS & RES, THE BEN GURION UNIV, ISRAEL, 74- *Concurrent Pos:* Gilman fel, Johns Hopkins Univ, 64-67, NASA fel, 67-69, fel, 69-70. *Mem:* Am Phys Soc; Sigma Xi. *Res:* Quantum field theory and the bound states occurring in such theories; compton scattering from bound electron; hyperfine structure of positronium and muonium, muonis atoms and gauge theories. *Mailing Add:* Dept of Physics Ben Gurion Univ Beer Sheva Israel

OWEN, DAVID ALLAN, b Coronado, Calif, Mar 19, 43; m 77. INORGANIC CHEMISTRY, ORGANIC CHEMISTRY. *Educ:* Univ Ill, Urbana, BS, 65; Univ Calif, Riverside, PhD(inorg chem), 70. *Prof Exp:* Res chemist & proj leader, Union Carbide Res Inst, Tarrytown, NY, 70-73; res assoc & lectr, Southern Ill Univ, Carbondale, 73-75; vis asst prof chem, Univ Okla, Norman, 75-78; ASST PROF ORGANOMETALLIC CHEM, MURRAY STATE UNIV, 78- *Concurrent Pos:* Instr, Shawnee Community Col, Ullin, Ill, 75; consult, micronutrient balance, Compost Corp, Canyon, Tex, 76-78 & Huttrell Corp, Murray, Ky, 79; reviewer chem texts, Holt Rinehart Winston Publ, CBS Inc, NY, 77-78; Col Arts & Sci Res grant, Univ Okla, 77-78; Am Soc Eng Educ vis fac fel, L B Johnson Space Ctr, NASA, 80-81. *Mem:* Am Chem Soc; AAAS; Sigma Xi. *Res:* All aspects of the synthesis, characterization, structural elucidation, electrochemistry and catalytic activity of novel compounds of the transition metals, boron and carbon. *Mailing Add:* Blackburn Sci Hall Murray State Univ Murray KY 42071

OWEN, DAVID R, b San Luis Obispo, Calif, Apr 14, 42; m 68. APPLIED MATHEMATICS. *Educ:* Calif Inst Technol, BSc, 63; Brown Univ, PhD(appl math), 68. *Prof Exp:* From asst prof to assoc prof, 67-77, PROF MATH, CARNEGIE-MELLON UNIV, 77- *Honors & Awards:* Von Humboldt Found Sr US Scientist Award, 74; Bateman lectr, 79. *Mem:* Math Asn Am; Am Math Soc. *Res:* Continuum thermodynamics; rate-independent materials; materials with elastic range. *Mailing Add:* Dept Math Carnegie-Mellon Univ Pittsburgh PA 15213

OWEN, DONALD BRUCE, b Portland, Ore, Jan 24, 22; m 52; c 4. APPLIED STATISTICS. *Educ:* Univ Wash, BS, 45, MS, 46, PhD(math statist), 51. *Prof Exp:* Assoc math, Univ Wash, 46-50, res assoc statist, 50-51, instr math, 51-52; asst prof math & consult statist lab, Purdue Univ, 52-54; staff mem math statist, Sandia Corp, 54-57, supvr statist res div, 57-64; head math & stochastic systs div, Grad Res Ctr & adj prof statist, Univ, 64-66, PROF STATIST, SOUTHERN METHODIST UNIV, 66- *Concurrent Pos:* Consult, Sandia Corp, 64-67; prof, Univ Tex, 65-66; dir, Prog Vis Lectr in Statist, 70-73; coord ed, Marcel Dekker Statist Ser, 70-; ed, Commun in Statist, 71- *Mem:* Fel AAAS; fel Am Statist Asn; Am Soc Qual Control; Int Asn Statist Phys Sci; Am Math Soc. *Res:* Tabulations of statistical functions; bivariate normal probability distribution and associated integrals; applications of statistics to physics and engineering; double sample procedures. *Mailing Add:* 7614 Tophill Lane Dallas TX 75248

OWEN, DONALD EDWARD, b San Antonio, Tex, Nov 29, 36; m 81; c 3. STRATIGRAPHY, GEOLOGY. *Educ:* Lamar Univ, BS, 57; Univ Kans, MS, 59, PhD(geol), 63. *Prof Exp:* Res scientist, Bur Econ Geol, Univ Tex, 62-64; from instr to prof geol, Bowling Green State Univ, 64-78, dir geol field camp, 64-68 & 78, NSF res grant, 65-66; geol assoc, 78-79, tech asst to vpres, Eastern Int Area, 79-81, RES ASSOC, CITIES SERV CO, 81- *Concurrent Pos:* Adj asst prof, State Univ NY Binghamton, 65, 66; sr lectr sch earth sci, Macquarie Univ, Australia, 69-71; consult geologist, Planet Mgt & Res Proprietary Ltd, Australia, 69-71; NMex Bur Mines & Mineral Resources res grants, 74-77; assoc ed, Soc Econ Paleontologists & Mineralogists, 74-; mem, NAm Comn Stratigraphic Nomenclature, 78- *Honors & Awards:* A I Levorsen Mem Award, Am Asn Petrol Geologists, 75. *Mem:* Am Asn Petrol Geologists; Soc Econ Paleontologists & Mineralogists; Geol Soc Australia; Int Asn Sedimentologists. *Res:* Sedimentology; Cretaceous stratigraphy of southwestern United States; Dakota sandstone of San Juan Basin, New Mexico; modern sediments of coastal North Carolina; Devonian of central New South Wales, Australia. *Mailing Add:* Cities Serv Co PO Box 3908 Tulsa OK 74102

OWEN, DONALD EUGENE, b Emporia, Kans, Oct 20, 28; m 55; c 2. GEOLOGY, PETROLEUM GEOLOGY. *Educ:* Univ Kans, BS, 49; Univ Tex, MA, 51; Univ Wis, PhD(geol), 64. *Prof Exp:* Geophysicist, Calif Co, 51-56, area geologist, Mont, 56-58, dist staff geologist, 58-60; asst prof, 63-66, assoc prof, 66-79, PROF GEOL, IND STATE UNIV, 79- *Mem:* AAAS; Geol Soc Am; Am Asn Petrol Geol; Nat Asn Geol Teachers. *Res:* Cretaceous stratigraphy; paleogeologic and onlap maps of North America; Williston Basin stratigraphy and structure. *Mailing Add:* Dept Geog & Geol Ind State Univ Terre Haute IN 47809

OWEN, DONALD ROBERTSON, JR, polymer chemistry, see previous edition

OWEN, FLETCHER BAILEY, b Richmond, Va, Nov 6, 29. PHARMACOLOGY. *Educ:* Univ Richmond, BS, 51; Med Col Va, PhD(pharmacol), 56, MD, 59. *Prof Exp:* Intern, Richmond Mem Hosp, 59-60; clin investr, 60-63, DIR MED SERV, A H ROBINS CO, INC, 63- *Concurrent Pos:* Instr, Med Col Va, 60-64, lectr, 64- *Mem:* AMA; NY Acad Sci. *Res:* Clincial pharmacology; drugs. *Mailing Add:* A H Robins Co Inc 1407 Cummings Dr Richmond VA 23220

OWEN, FOSTER GAMBLE, b Flat Creek, Ala, Jan 24, 26; m 50; c 4. DAIRY NUTRITION. *Educ:* Auburn Univ, BS, 48; Iowa State Univ, MS, 55, PhD, 56. *Prof Exp:* Asst dairy husb, Iowa State Univ, 53-55; asst prof animal husb, Univ Ark, 55-57; assoc prof dairy husb, 57-64, PROF ANIMAL SCI, UNIV NEBR, LINCOLN, 64- *Mem:* Am Soc Animal Sci; Am Dairy Sci Asn; Am Forage & Grassland Coun. *Res:* Dairy cattle nutrition and feeding methods, calf nutrition and feeding programs, forage preservation and nutritional value. *Mailing Add:* Dept of Animal Sci Univ of Nebr Lincoln NE 68583

OWEN, FRANCES LEE, b Hardinsburg, Ky, Apr 7, 49; m 78; c 1. IMMUNOLOGY, CELL BIOLOGY. *Educ:* Univ Ky, BS, 71; Case Western Reserve Univ, PhD(microbiol), 75. *Prof Exp:* Fel immunol, Case Western Reserve Univ, 75 & Brandeis Univ, 75-77; ASST PROF PATH, SCH MED, TUFTS UNIV, 78- *Concurrent Pos:* Prin investr, NIH res grant, 78-84. *Mem:* Fedn Am Socs Exp Biol; NY Acad Sci. *Res:* Studying basic immunogenetics of T cell receptors for defined antigens with emphasis on structural and biological relevance of antigen binding molecules in congenic mice. *Mailing Add:* Dept of Path Sch of Med Tufts Univ Boston MA 02111

OWEN, FRAZER NELSON, b Atlanta, Ga, Feb 4, 47. ASTRONOMY. *Educ:* Duke Univ, BS, 69; Univ Tex, PhD(astron), 74. *Prof Exp:* Res assoc astron, 73-75, asst scientist, 75-77, assoc scientist, 77-79, SCIENTIST, NAT RADIO ASTRON OBSERV, 79- *Mem:* Am Astron Soc; Royal Astron Soc; Int Astron Union. *Res:* Extragalactic radio astronomy; clusters of galaxies; radio galaxies; quasars; radio flare stars. *Mailing Add:* Nat Radio Astron Observ 1000 Bullock Ave PO Box 0 Socorro NM 87801

OWEN, GENE SCOTT, b Roswell, NMex, Oct 25, 43; m 77. BIOPHYSICAL CHEMISTRY, COMPUTER SCIENCE. *Educ:* Harvey Mudd Col, BS, 65; Univ Wash, PhD(chem), 70. *Prof Exp:* Fel chem, Ga Inst Technol, 70-72; asst prof, 72-77, ASSOC PROF CHEM, ATLANTA UNIV, 77- *Concurrent Pos:* Chmn, Asst Chief Staff Task Force Comput Chem Educ. *Mem:* Am Chem Soc; Inst Elec & Electronics Engrs; Asn Comput Mach. *Res:* Conformational studies on enzymes; computers in chemical research and education. *Mailing Add:* Dept of Chem Atlanta Univ Atlanta GA 30314

OWEN, GEORGE ERNEST, b St Louis, Mo, Jan 7, 22; m 59; c 1. NUCLEAR PHYSICS. *Educ:* Wash Univ, BSME, 43, MA, 48, PhD(physics), 50. *Prof Exp:* Asst prof physics, Univ Pittsburgh, 50-51; from asst prof to assoc prof, 51-59, PROF PHYSICS, JOHNS HOPKINS UNIV, 59-, CHMN DEPT, 68-, DEAN ARTS & SCI, 72-, DEAN HOMEWOOD FAC, 78- *Concurrent Pos:* Estab math teaching prog high sch teachers, Esso Educ Found, 58-60. *Mem:* Fel Am Phys Soc. *Res:* Beta ray and gamma ray spectroscopy; special nuclear physics; confirmed Fermi theory of beta decay; proposed heavy particle stripping theory; neutron detectors and medium energy nuclear reactions. *Mailing Add:* 4100 N Charles St Baltimore MD 21218

OWEN, GEORGE MURDOCK, b Alliance, Ohio, Feb 16, 30; m 52; c 3. PEDIATRICS, NUTRITION. *Educ:* Hiram Col, AB, 51; Univ Cincinnati, MD, 55. *Prof Exp:* Rotating intern, Univ Iowa, 55-56, resident pediat, 56-58; clin assoc, Nat Inst Allergy & Infectious Dis, 58-60; from asst prof to assoc prof, Univ Iowa, 66; from assoc prof to prof pediat, Col Med, Ohio State Univ, 66-73; prof pediat & dir clin nutrit prog, Sch Med, Univ NMex, 73-77; prof & dir human nutrit prog & prof pediat & fel, Ctr Human Growth & Develop, Univ Mich, 77-81; MED DIR, INT DIV, BRISTOL-MYERS CO, 81- *Concurrent Pos:* Res fel, Metab Sect, Univ Iowa, 60-62. *Mem:* Am Acad Pediat; Am Soc Clin Nutrit; Soc Pediat Res; Am Inst Nutrit; Am Pediat Soc. *Res:* Nutrition, growth and body composition of normal infants; nutrition status. *Mailing Add:* Bristol-Myers Co Int Div 345 Park Ave New York NY 10154

OWEN, HARRY A(SHTON), JR, b Hawthorn, Fla, Sept 22, 19; m 42; c 2. ELECTRICAL ENGINEERING. *Educ:* Univ Fla, BEE, 48, MSE, 52; NC State Univ, PhD, 63. *Prof Exp:* Instr elec eng, Univ Fla, 48-51; from instr to assoc prof, 51-64, PROF ELEC ENG, DUKE UNIV, 64-, CHMN DEPT, 68- *Concurrent Pos:* NSF fac fel, 58; consult, Ed Dept, Western Elec Co, 58; NASA sr res assoc, Goddard Space Flight Ctr, 67-68; sr res fel, Europ Space Agency, Noordwijk, The Neth, 75-76. *Mem:* Am Soc Eng Educ; Inst Elec & Electronics Engrs. *Res:* Electronic instrumentation; electronic power conditioning circuits; computer aided design and applications; satellite information processing. *Mailing Add:* Dept of Elec Eng Duke Univ Durham NC 27706

OWEN, HERBERT ELMER, JR, plant ecology, plant biochemistry, see previous edition

OWEN, HOWARD MALCOLM, b Richmond, Va, Dec 16, 13; m 39; c 3. ZOOLOGY. *Educ:* Hampden-Sydney Col, AB, 35; Univ Va, MA, 43, PhD(biol), 45. *Prof Exp:* Asst biologist, Va Fisheries Lab, Col William & Mary, 45-46; asst prof biol, Univ SC, 46-47; spec biologist, State Dept Wildlife, La, 47-50; prof biol, 50-78, EMER PROF BIOL, UNIV OF THE SOUTH, 78-; CONSULT BIOL COMPUT, 79- *Mem:* Fel AAAS; Am Micros Soc; Am Genetic Asn; Am Soc Parasitologists; Am Soc Study Evolution. *Res:* Structure of flagella; cytology of marine mollusks; physiology of oysters; marine ecology; radioisotopes genetics; use of computer in undergraduate education. *Mailing Add:* Dept of Biol Univ of the South Sewanee TN 37375

OWEN, JAMES EMMET, b Cleveland, Ohio, May 23, 35; m 61; c 6. INORGANIC CHEMISTRY. *Educ:* John Carroll Univ, BS, 57; Case Inst Technol, PhD(chem), 61. *Prof Exp:* Res scientist, US Rubber Co, 61-63; group leader, 63-66, sr res assoc, 66-67, dir inorg phys res, 67-69, dir cent res, 69-70, DIR INORG & PHYS RES, HARSHAW CHEM CO, 70- *Mem:* AAAS; Am Chem Soc; Am Inst Chemists. *Res:* Fundamental studies of inorganic pigment systems; pigments based on non-stoichiometric metal oxides; pigments based on II-VI type semiconductors; investigation of adsorption phenomena; structural characteristics of adsorbents as related to adsorption performance. *Mailing Add:* 3002 Manchester Rd Shaker Heights OH 44120

OWEN, JAMES ROBERT, b Leake Co, Miss, Mar 26, 14; m 37. PHYSICAL CHEMISTRY. *Educ:* Okla Agr & Mech Col, BS, 35; Univ Wis, PhM, 37. *Prof Exp:* Asst, Exp Sta, Okla Agr & Mech Col, 33-35; asst chem, Univ Wis, 36-37; sect chief, Phillips Petrol Co, 37-58, tech supt, Ambrosia Mill, NMex, 58-62, develop engr, Patent Div, 62-69; CONSULT HETEROGENEOUS CATALYSIS, 69- *Mem:* Catalysis Soc; Am Chem Soc. *Mailing Add:* 2413 Summit Rd Bartlesville OK 74003

OWEN, JOEL, b Boston, Mass, Feb 22, 35. STATISTICS, OPERATIONS RESEARCH. *Educ:* Yeshiva Univ, BA, 56; Boston Univ, MA, 57; Harvard Univ, PhD(statist), 66. *Prof Exp:* Res scientist appl math & statist, Waltham Lab, Sylvania Electronic Systs Div, 57-61, adv res scientist math statist, Appl Res Lab, 61-64; sr mathematician, Info Res Asn, Inc, 65-66; asst prof statist & opers res, 66-70, assoc prof statist, 70-73, PROF STATIST, GRAD SCH BUS, NY UNIV, 73-, CHMN DEPT QUANT ANAL, 76- *Res:* Pattern recognition; discrimination analysis; game and decision theory; mathematical formulation of financial accounting theory and portfolio theory. *Mailing Add:* Grad Sch of Bus NY Univ 100 Trinity Pl New York NY 10006

OWEN, JOHN ATKINSON, JR, b South Boston, Va, Sept 24, 24; m 52; c 2. INTERNAL MEDICINE, METABOLISM. *Educ:* Hampden-Sydney Col, BS, 44; Univ Va, MD, 48. *Prof Exp:* Intern, Cincinnati Gen Hosp, Ohio, 48-49; asst resident internal med, Univ Va Hosp, 50-52; asst prof med, Med Col Ga, 56-58; asst clin prof internal med, Sch Med, George Washington Univ, 58-60; from asst prof to assoc prof internal med, 60-70, dir div clin pharmacol, 64-71, vchmn dept internal med, 72-74, PROF INTERNAL MED, SCH MED, UNIV VA, 70- *Concurrent Pos:* Fel internal med, Univ Va Hosp, 50-52; res fel metab, Duke Univ Hosp, 54-56; Am Diabetes Asn res fel, 55-56; pres, US Pharmacopeial Conv, 75-80; ed-in-chief, Hosp Formulary, 74-; chmn, Nat Coun Drugs, 79-80. *Mem:* Am Fedn Clin Res; Endocrine Soc; Am Diabetes Asn; AMA; fel Am Col Clin Pharmacol. *Res:* Experimental and clinical diabetes; diabetogenic and anti-diabetic drugs; clinical trials and animal research. *Mailing Add:* Dept of Internal Med Univ of Va Hosp Box 242 Charlottesville VA 22908

OWEN, JOHN HARDING, b San Francisco, Calif, Dec 22, 31; m 51; c3. INORGANIC CHEMISTRY, PHYSICAL CHEMISTRY. *Educ:* Hampden-Sydney Col, BS, 53; Fla State Univ, MS, 55. *Prof Exp:* Res chemist, sr res supvr, 68-76, chief supvvr, 76-78, SITE COORDR SAFEGUARDS, SAVANNAH RIVER LAB, E I DU PONT DE NEMOURS & CO, INC, 79- *Concurrent Pos:* Instr, Augusta Col, 59-63 & Univ SC, 63-75; traveling lectr, Oak Ridge Inst Nuclear Studies, 63-66. *Res:* Theory and application of diffusion processes in solids; science administration; technical management. *Mailing Add:* 1319 Williams Dr Aiken SC 29801

OWEN, JOHN REINDEL, b Cleveland, Ohio, July 20, 39; div; c 3. ORGANIC CHEMISTRY. *Educ:* Oberlin Col, AB, 61; Univ Rochester, PhD(org chem), 66. *Prof Exp:* Res chemist, 65-73, sr res chemist, 73-76, LAB HEAD, EASTMAN KODAK CO, 76- *Res:* Physical and chemical interactions of organic compounds with silver halide dispersions in gelatin. *Mailing Add:* Res Labs Bldg 82A Eastman Kodak Co 1669 Lake Ave Rochester NY 14615

OWEN, LAWRENCE BARRY, geochemistry, see previous edition

OWEN, OLIVER ELON, b Roswell, NMex, Dec 24, 34; c 3. MEDICINE, METABOLISM. *Educ:* Cent State Col, Okla, BS, 58; Univ Colo, MD, 62. *Prof Exp:* Asst med, Peter Bent Brigham Hosp, Boston, Mass, 65-68; from asst prof to assoc prof, 68-75, PROF MED, TEMPLE UNIV HOSP, 75-, PROG DIR, GEN CLIN RES CTR, 68- *Concurrent Pos:* Independent investr, Fels Res Inst, Temple Univ Hosp, 68- *Honors & Awards:* George Morris Piersol Award, Am Col Physicians, 68. *Mem:* Am Fedn Clin Res; Am Diabetes Asn; Am Soc Clin Invest; Am Col Physicians; Asn Am Physicians. *Res:* Diabetes. *Mailing Add:* Temple Univ Hosp 3401 N Broad St Philadelphia PA 19140

OWEN, RAY BUCKLIN, JR, b Providence, RI, July 14, 37; m 62; c 2. WILDLIFE ECOLOGY. *Educ:* Bowdoin Col, AB, 59; Univ Ill, MS, 66, PhD(ecol), 68. *Prof Exp:* Instr biol, Univ Ill, 67-68; from asst prof to assoc prof, 68-77, PROF WILDLIFE RESOURCES, UNIV MAINE, ORONO, 77- *Mem:* AAAS; Am Ornith Union; Wildlife Soc; Ecol Soc Am. *Res:* Ecological energetics; wetlands ecology; animal behavior. *Mailing Add:* Sch Forest Resources Forest Resources Bldg Univ Maine Orono ME 04473

OWEN, RAY DAVID, b Genesee, Wis, Oct 30, 15; m 39; c 1. GENETICS, IMMUNOLOGY. *Educ:* Carroll Col, Wis, BS, 37; Univ Wis, PhM, 38, PhD(genetics), 41. *Hon Degrees:* ScD, Carroll Col, Wis, 62, Univ Pac, 66 & Univ Wis, 79. *Prof Exp:* Asst genetics, Univ Wis, 40-41, res fel, 41-43, asst prof genetics & zool, 43-47; assoc prof biol, 47-53, chmn dept, 61-68, vpres student affairs & dean students, 74-80, PROF BIOL, CALIF INST TECHNOL, 53- *Concurrent Pos:* Gosney fel, 46-47; res partic, Oak Ridge Nat Lab, 57-58, consult, 58- *Honors & Awards:* Mendel Medal, Czech Acad Sci. *Mem:* Nat Acad Sci; Am Acad Arts & Sci; Am Soc Human Genetics; Genetics Soc Am (treas, 56-59, vpres, 60-61, pres, 62); Soc Study Evolution. *Res:* Immunogenetics; serology; vertebrate and developmental genetics; genetics and immunology of tissue transplantation. *Mailing Add:* Div of Biol Calif Inst of Technol Pasadena CA 91109

OWEN, ROBERT BARRY, b Chicago, Ill, Oct 16, 43; m 70; c 2. OPTICS. *Educ:* Va Polytech Inst & State Univ, BS, 66, PhD(physics), 72. *Prof Exp:* Teaching asst physics, Va Polytech Inst, 66-69; aerospace technologist, 66-72, AERO TECHNOLOGIST OPTICS, GEORGE C MARSHALL SPACE FLIGHT CTR, NASA, 72- *Concurrent Pos:* Prin investr, optical measurement systs grants, 79-; consult optical measurement systs, 80- *Mem:* Sigma Xi; Optical Soc Am. *Res:* Optical measurement techniques; interferometric, holographic and schlieren/shadowgraph systems for low-gravity use; tracer/opticcal grid and modified schlieren and optical correlation systmes; materials processing (metal-models, electrodeposition, crystal growth, surfaces). *Mailing Add:* ES 74 NASA Marshall Space Flight Center AL 35812

OWEN, ROBERT MICHAEL, b Philadelphia, Pa, Feb 17, 46. CHEMICAL OCEANOGRAPHY, MARINE GEOCHEMISTRY. *Educ:* Drexel Univ, BS, 69; Univ Wis-Madison, MS, 74, PhD(oceanog, limnol), 75. *Prof Exp:* Develop chemist, Rohm & Haas Co, 69-72; res asst oceanog, Univ Wis-Madison, 72-75; ASST PROF OCEANOG, UNIV MICH, 75- *Mem:* AAAS; Int Asn Great Lakes Res; Soc Econ Paleontologists & Mineralogists; Sigma Xi; Am Soc Limnol & Oceanog. *Res:* Chemical and textural partitioning of trace elements in sediments; marine mineral exploration; geochemical and mathematical techniques for determining sediment dispersal patterns; organic associations of trace elements in sediments. *Mailing Add:* Dept of Atmospheric & Oceanic Sci Rm 1215 Space Res Bldg Ann Arbor MI 48109

OWEN, ROBERT W, JR, b Denver, Colo, Jan 29, 35; m. OCEANOGRAPHY. *Educ:* Univ Wash, BSci, 57; Univ Calif, San Diego, MSci, 63, PhD, 72. *Prof Exp:* Asst oceanogr, Univ Wash, 58-59; OCEANOGR, FISHERY OCEANOG CTR, NAT MARINE FISHERIES SERV, 61- *Concurrent Pos:* Consult, Calif Dept Fish & Game, 65- *Mem:* Am Geophys Union; Optical Soc Am; Am Inst Physics; Am Soc Limnol & Oceanog. *Res:* Dynamics of motion in the surface layers of the sea; consequences in plankton ecology. *Mailing Add:* Fishery Oceanog Ctr Nat Marine Fish Serv PO Box 271 La Jolla CA 92037

OWEN, STANLEY PAUL, b Earlie, Alta, Mar 30, 24; US citizen; m 46; c 2. BIOCHEMISTRY. *Educ:* Univ Alta, BSc, 50, MSc, 52; Univ Wis, PhD(biochem), 55. *Prof Exp:* Res assoc, Fermentation Res & Develop Dept, 55-62, biochemist, Biochem Dept, 62-67, head microbial control, 67-69, mgr prod control II, 67-76, GROUP MGR CONTROL LAB OPERS, UPJOHN CO, 76- *Concurrent Pos:* Mem comt revision, US Pharmacopeia. *Mem:* Fedn Int Pharmaceut; Am Pharmaceut Asn; Int Asn Biol Standardization. Am Soc Microbiol; Am Inst Biol Sci. *Res:* Antibiotic, vitamin and biological product assays; pathogen and sterility testing; biological availability of drugs; quality control. *Mailing Add:* Control Lab Opers Upjohn Co 7171 Portage Rd Kalamazoo MI 49001

OWEN, TERENCE CUNLIFFE, b Cannock, Eng, Nov 29, 30; m 53; c 2. ORGANIC CHEMISTRY. *Educ:* Univ Manchester, BSc, 51, PhD(chem), 54. *Prof Exp:* Tech officer chem, Nobel Div, Imp Chem Indust, Scotland, 54-57; from lectr to sr lectr, Liverpool Col Technol, Eng, 57-64; assoc prof, 64-70, chmn dept chem, 74-78, PROF CHEM, UNIV S FLA, 70- *Concurrent Pos:* Res fel, Vanderbilt Univ, 60-61; consult, Summers Steelworks, Eng, 58-60 & Bristol Labs, 68-; fel, Royal Inst Chem, 62. *Mem:* Am Chem Soc; Royal Soc Chem; Sigma Xi. *Res:* Penicillin and cephalosporin synthesis; mechanisms of enzyme catalysis. *Mailing Add:* Dept of Chem Univ of SFla Tampa FL 33620

OWEN, THOMAS E(DWIN), b Alexandria, La, Jan 6, 31; m 53; c 2. ELECTRICAL ENGINEERING. *Educ:* Southwestern La Inst, BSEE, 52; Univ Tex, MSEE, 57, PhD, 64. *Prof Exp:* Res engr, undersea warfare div, defense res lab, Univ Tex, 55-60, asst prof elec eng, 57-60; sr res engr, 60, mgr earth sci appln, 60-71, asst dir, Dept Electronic Systs Res, 71-76, DIR, DEPT GEOSCI, ELECTRONIC SYSTS DIV, SOUTHWEST RES INST, 76- *Mem:* AAAS; Acoust Soc Am; Inst Elec & Electronics Engrs; Am Geophys Union; Sigma Xi. *Res:* Electronic instrumentation, data acquistion and reduction systems; electro-acoustic transducer design and fabrication; underwater acoustics; ultrasonics; atmospheric acoustics; high-resolution electrical and seismic exploration systems and applications. *Mailing Add:* Southwest Res Inst PO Drawer 28510 San Antonio TX 78284

OWEN, TOBIAS CHANT, b Oshkosh, Wis, Mar 20, 36; m 60. ASTROPHYSICS, PLANETARY SCIENCES. *Educ:* Univ Chicago, BA, 55, BS, 59, MS, 60; Univ Ariz, PhD(astron), 65. *Prof Exp:* Res physicist, IIT Res Inst, 64-67, sr scientist, 67-69, sci adv, 69-70; vis assoc prof planetary sci, Calif Inst Technol, 70; assoc prof, 70-72, PROF ASTRON, STATE UNIV NY STONY BROOK, 72- *Concurrent Pos:* Consult, NASA, 72-; vpres comn 16, Int Astron Union, 73-76; pres, Comn 16, 76-79, chmn, Outer Solar Syst Task Group, 75-, mem working group Planetary & Satellite Nomenclature, 75-, res assoc, Int Astron Union, Calif Inst Technol, 76. *Honors & Awards:* Medal Aero-Club Cairo, 77; Newcomb-Cleveland Prize, AAAS, 77. *Mem:* Fel AAAS; Am Astron Soc; Int Astron Union; Int Soc Study Origin Life; Int Asn Geochem & Cosmochem. *Res:* Planetary atmospheres and surfaces; satellites; comets; exploration of the solar system. *Mailing Add:* Dept Earth & Space Sci State Univ of NY Stony Brook NY 11794

OWEN, WALTER S, b Liverpool, Eng, Mar 13, 20; m 53; c 1. MATERIALS SCIENCE, METALLURGY. *Educ:* Univ Liverpool, BEng, 40, MEng, 42, PhD(metall), 50. *Prof Exp:* Metallurgist, Eng Elec Co, Ltd, 40-46; asst lectr metall, Univ Liverpool, 46-48, lectr, 48-54; mem res staff, Mass Inst Technol, 54-57; Thomas R Briggs prof mat sci, Cornell Univ, 66-70; dean technol inst, Northwestern Univ, Evanston, 70-71, vpres sci & res, 71-73; PROF MAT SCI & ENG & HEAD DEPT, MASS INST TECHNOL, 73- *Concurrent Pos:* Commonwealth Fund fel, Mass Inst Technol, 51-52; consult, Int Nickel Ltd, Eng, 61-65, Eng Elec Co, 62-66, Richard Thomas & Baldwin, 63-66 & Manlabs, Mass, 66; Henry Bell Wortley prof metall, Univ Liverpool, 57-66. *Mem:* Nat Acad Eng; Am Soc Metals; Am Inst Mining, Metall & Petrol Engrs; Brit Inst Metall; Brit Iron & Steel Inst. *Res:* Physical metallurgy of steel; deformation and fracture of solids; martensitic transformations. *Mailing Add:* Mass Inst of Technol Rm 8-307 77 Massachusetts Ave Cambridge MA 02139

OWEN, WALTER WYCLIFFE, b Pine Bluff, Ark, Sept 19, 06; m 32; c 2. CHEMISTRY. *Educ:* Univ Ark, BS, 29; Univ NC, PhD(phys chem), 39. *Prof Exp:* Supvr treating, Int Creosoting & Construct Co, Tex, 29-30; exp & sales engr, Sowers Mfg Co, NY, 30-32; res chemist, Rayon Div, E I du Pont de Nemours & Co, 32-36, 39-41, chief chemist, Va, 41-45, tech serv engr, Del, 45-49, tech res tire yarn sales, 49-54, mgr indust tech serv, Textile Fibers Dept, 54-60, tech specialist, 60-68; CONSULT PROCESSING & APPLN SYNTHETIC FIBERS, 68- *Mem:* Am Chem Soc. *Res:* Viscose rayon process; permeability of regenerated cellulose film to carbon dioxide; industrial applications of man-made fibers. *Mailing Add:* 10803 Bonaparte Bend Austin TX 78750

OWEN, WILLIAM BERT, b Gilbertsville, Ky, Oct 28, 03; m 32. ENTOMOLOGY. *Educ:* Univ Ky, BA, 27; Univ Minn, MA, 29, PhD(entom), 36. *Prof Exp:* Instr zool, Hamline Univ, 29-30 & Ore State Col, 30-31; from instr to asst prof, Univ Wyo, 31-34; asst, Univ Minn, 35-36; prof, 46-71, EMER PROF ZOOL, UNIV WYO, 71- *Concurrent Pos:* Researcher, Montpellier & Leyden, 64; fac affil, Colo State Univ, 72- *Mem:* Am Soc Parasitol; Entom Soc Am; Mosquito Control Asn. *Res:* Taxonomy of Culcidae; biology of mosquitoes of western North America; chemical senses of insects; insect morphology. *Mailing Add:* Dept of Zool & Entom Colo State Univ Ft Collins CO 80523

OWENS, AARON JAMES, b Pottsville, Pa, Feb 5, 47; m 70; c 2. STRATOSPHERIC MODELING. *Educ:* Williams Col, BA, 69; Calif Inst Technol, MS, 71, PhD(theoret physics & econ), 73. *Prof Exp:* Asst prof physics, Lake Forest Col, 73-76; physicist, Cent Res Inst Physics, Budapest, 76-77; asst prof, Kenyon Col, 77-78; res physicist, Bartol Res Found, Franklin Inst, 78-80; SR ENGR, E I DU PONT DE NEMOURS & CO, INC, 80- *Concurrent Pos:* Adj assoc prof, Univ Del, 81- *Mem:* Am Phys Soc; Am Geophys Union; Sigma Xi. *Res:* Mathematical modeling of physical systems; stratospheric chemistry and transport modeling; cosmic-ray propagation; analysis of random data. *Mailing Add:* E I Du Pont de Nemours Co Inc E304 Wilmington DE 19898

OWENS, ALBERT HENRY, JR, b Staten Island, NY, Aug 27, 26; m 49; c 4. INTERNAL MEDICINE, PHARMACOLOGY. *Educ:* Johns Hopkins Univ, BA, MD, 49; Am Bd Internal Med, dipl, 56. *Prof Exp:* Mem staff internal med, Univ Hosp, 49-50, 52-53, 55-56, physician, 56-76, from instr to assoc prof med, Sch Med, 56-68, instr pathobiol, Sch Hyg & Pub Health, 57-76, PROF ONCOL & MED, SCH MED, JOHNS HOPKINS UNIV, 68-, DIR ONCOL CTR, 76- *Concurrent Pos:* Fel pharmacol & exp therapeut, Sch Med, Johns Hopkins Univ, 53-55; vis physician, Baltimore City Hosp, 57- *Mem:* Am Soc Pharmacol & Exp Therapeut; fel Am Col Physicians; NY Acad Sci; Am Soc Clin Oncol; Am Asn Cancer Insts. *Res:* Neoplastic diseases. *Mailing Add:* Dept of Internal Med Johns Hopkins Univ Sch of Med Baltimore MD 21205

OWENS, BOONE BAILEY, b Chefoo, China, Dec 13, 32; US citizen; c 4. LITHIUM BATTERY CHEMISTRY, MEDICAL BATTERY RELIABILITY. *Educ:* Whittier Col, BA, 54; Iowa State Univ, PhD(phys & inorg chem, math), 57. *Prof Exp:* Asst chem, Ames Lab, AEC, 54-57; instr, Univ Calif, Santa Barbara, 57-59; sr chemist, Atomics Int Div, NAm Aviation, Inc, 59-63, res specialist, 63-68; mem tech staff, Gen Tel & Electronics Labs, 68-69; prin scientist, Gould Ionics Inc, 69-72 & Energy Technol Dept, Gould Labs, 72-74, mgr battery res & develop sect, Gould Labs-Energy Res, Gould Inc, 74-75; mgr power sources res & develop dept, 75-78, DIR BATTERY DEVELOP, MEDTRONIC, INC, 78- *Concurrent Pos:* Consult, Glass Prod Co, Calif, 58-59; ed, Battery Div, J Electrochem Soc, 73-80 & Progress Batteries & Solar Cells, 78-; chmn/mem sci comt, Int Conference Solid Electrolytes, 76, 78, 80 & 83 & mem sci comt, Int Meeting Lithium Batteries, 82. *Mem:* AAAS; Am Chem Soc; Sigma Xi; Electrochem Soc. *Res:* High energy batteries; solid electrolytes; solid state batteries; lithium pacemaker batteries; batteries for implantable medical devices; author of 65 technical papers. *Mailing Add:* Medtronic Inc 3055 Old Highway Eight Minneapolis MN 55418

OWENS, CHARLES ALLEN, b Bristol, Tenn, Mar 18, 45; m 67; c 2. BOTANY. *Educ:* King Col, AB, 66; Va Polytech Inst & State Univ, MS, 68, PhD(genetics), 71. *Prof Exp:* Asst prof, 70-74, assoc prof, 75-80, PROF BIOL, KING COL, 81- *Mem:* Am Genetic Asn; Am Inst Biol Sci; AAAS; Sigma Xi. *Res:* Development of techniques for studying plant karyotypes to be extended to comprehensive study of the abundant Applachian flora. *Mailing Add:* 335 Meadowcrest Dr Bristol VA 24201

OWENS, CHARLES WESLEY, b Billings, Okla, Oct 27, 35; m 55; c 4. PHYSICAL CHEMISTRY. *Educ:* Colo Col, BS, 57; Univ Kans, PhD(phys chem), 63. *Prof Exp:* Res assoc radiochem, Univ Kans, 63; asst prof, 63-69, assoc prof, 69-78, PROF CHEM, UNIV NH, 78- *Concurrent Pos:* Res fel appl chem, Harvard Univ, 70-71. *Mem:* Am Chem Soc. *Res:* Wood chemistry; hot-atom chemistry; solid state chemistry. *Mailing Add:* Dept of Chem Parsons Hall Univ of NH Durham NH 03824

OWENS, CLARENCE BURGESS, b Smithville, Tex, June 17, 26; m 49; c 5. AGRONOMY, PLANT PHYSIOLOGY. *Educ:* Prairie View Col, BSc, 48; Ohio State Univ, MSc, 51, PhD, 54. *Prof Exp:* Instr agr, US Vet Admin, 48-50; from asst prof to assoc prof, 53-57, PROF AGRON, FLA A&M UNIV, 57- *Concurrent Pos:* Dir summer & in-serv, Earth Sci Insts, NSF, 64-66; campus coordr, US AID-Fla A&M Univ Kenya contract, 72; res agron adv, US ICA, 57-59. *Mem:* AAAS; Am Soc Agron; Weed Sci Soc Am. *Res:* Chemical weed control; crop fertilization; soil fertility. *Mailing Add:* Dept of Agron Fla A&M Univ Box 8 Tallahassee FL 32301

OWENS, CLIFFORD, b Raven, Ky, Jan 5, 31; m 54. PHYSICAL INORGANIC CHEMISTRY. *Educ:* Rutgers Univ, BA, 57; Drexel Univ, MS, 61, PhD(phys chem), 69. *Prof Exp:* Anal chemist petrol, Gulf Oil Corp, 57-60; res chemist org coatings, Campbell Soup Co, 60-63, emission spectroscopist, 63-66; asst chem, Drexel Univ, 66-69; from instr to asst prof, 69-75, ASSOC PROF CHEM, RUTGERS UNIV, 75- *Concurrent Pos:* Consult, Drexel Univ, 74- *Mem:* Soc Appl Spectrog. *Res:* Study of the instability of chloramine compounds; sweat poisoning of activated carbon surfaces; vapor phase equilibria of binary systems where complexation may occur; synthesis and characterization of inorganic complexes involving phosphoryl and nitroxide compounds. *Mailing Add:* Dept Chem Rutgers Univ Camden NJ 08101

OWENS, DANIEL KENYON, agricultural chemistry, see previous edition

OWENS, DAVID KINGSTON, b Milwaukee, Wis, Sept 14, 48; m 69; c 2. PHYSICS. *Educ:* Mass Inst Technol, SM & SB, 71, PhD(physics), 76. *Prof Exp:* RES STAFF PLASMA PHYSICS, PLASMA PHYSICS LAB, PRINCETON UNIV, 76- *Mem:* Am Phys Soc; AAAS. *Res:* Atomic and surface processes in plasmas; studies of high temperature tokamak plasmas. *Mailing Add:* Plasma Physics Lab PO Box 451 Princeton NJ 08544

OWENS, DAVID WILLIAM, b Greensburg, Ind, Nov 24, 46; m 71. COMPARATIVE ENDOCRINOLOGY, MARINE BIOLOGY. *Educ:* William Jewell Col, BA, 68; Univ Ariz, PhD(zool), 76. *Prof Exp:* Marine biologist, Fiji Islands, US Peace Corps, 68-71; fel physiol, Dept Zool, Colo State Univ, 76-78; ASST PROF, DEPT BIOL, TEX A&M UNIV, 78- *Mem:* AAAS; Herpetologists League; Am Soc Zoologists. *Res:* Endocrine control of reproduction in non-mammalian vertebrates; marine turtle and fish behavior. *Mailing Add:* Dept of Biol Tex A&M Univ College Station TX 77843

OWENS, EDWARD HENRY, b Stamford, Eng, Mar 25, 45. GEOMORPHOLOGY, SEDIMENTOLOGY. *Educ:* Univ Col Wales, BSc, 67; McMaster Univ, MSc, 69; Univ SC, PhD(geol), 75. *Prof Exp:* Res scientist, Geol Surv Can, 71-75; asst prof geol, Coastal Studies Inst, La State Univ, 72-79; ASSOC, WOODWARD-CLYDE CONSULTS, 79- *Concurrent Pos:* Chmn, Sable Island Dune Restoration & Terrain Mgt Subcomt, Can, 74-75. *Mem:* Geol Soc Am; Geol Asn Can; Soc Econ Paleontologists & Mineralogists; Sigma Xi; Arctic Inst NAm. *Res:* Barrier beach geomorphology and sediments, particularly the mechanics of sediment transport and deposition; action of ice on beaches in mid- and high-latitudes; effects of oil-spills on coasts. *Mailing Add:* Woodward-Clyde Consults 16 Bastion Square Victoria BC 70803 V8W 1H9 Can

OWENS, FRANK JAMES, b Dublin, Ireland, Oct 24, 39; US citizen; m 72. SOLID STATE PHYSICS, CHEMICAL PHYSICS. *Educ:* Manhattan Col, BS, 62; Univ Conn, MS, 64, PhD(physics), 68. *Prof Exp:* Instr physics, Univ Conn, 62-65, res asst, 65-68; solid state physicist, Feltman Res Lab, 68-77; PRES & SOLID STATE PHYSICIST, ENERGETIC MAT LAB, ARRADCOM, 77- *Concurrent Pos:* Space scientist, Goddard Space Flight Ctr, NASA, 64-65; consult solid state physics, US Army Res Off, 68; lectr, dept physics, Grad Sch Sci & Eng, Fairleigh Dickinson Univ, 78, NJ Inst Technol, 77. *Mem:* Am Phys Soc. *Res:* Paramagnetic resonance and raman spectroscopy studies of dynamics processes involved in solid state phase transitions; also effects of shock and radiation on solids; high pressure physics and lattice stability; initiation of detonation in condensed materials. *Mailing Add:* Energetic Mat Lab Bldg 3022 ARRADCOM Dover NJ 07801

OWENS, FREDERICK HAMMANN, b Royersford, Pa, Dec 29, 28; m 61; c 3. ORGANIC CHEMISTRY. *Educ:* Ursinus Col, BS, 53; Univ Ill, MS, 54, PhD(chem), 58. *Prof Exp:* Res chemist, 57-73, proj leader plastic res, 73-76, MGR INFO SERV, RES DIV LABS, ROHM AND HAAS CO, 76- *Mem:* Am Chem Soc. *Res:* Macrocyclic compounds; synthesis of monomers and polymers; information science. *Mailing Add:* 480 Steamboat Dr Southampton PA 18966

OWENS, FREDRIC NEWELL, b Baldwin, Wis, Sept 1, 41. ANIMAL NUTRITION. *Educ:* Univ Minn, St Paul, BS, 64, PhD(nutrit), 68. *Prof Exp:* Asst prof animal sci, Univ Ill, Urbana, 68-74; assoc prof animal sci, 74-78, PROF, OKLA STATE UNIV, 78- *Honors & Awards:* Tyler Award, Okla State, 80. *Mem:* Am Soc Animal Sci; Am Dairy Sci Asn. *Res:* Amino acid and nitrogen metabolism of the ruminant animal. *Mailing Add:* Animal Sci Dept Okla State Univ Stillwater OK 74078

OWENS, GUY, b Amarillo, Tex, Jan 25, 26; m 49; c 2. NEUROSURGERY, ANATOMY. *Educ:* Tufts Univ, BS, 46; Harvard Univ, MD, 50; Am Bd Neurol Surg, dipl, 60. *Prof Exp:* Intern surg, Vanderbilt Univ Hosp, 50-51, asst, Sch Med, 51-52, asst neurosurg, 54-56, from instr to asst prof, 56-60; chief dept, Roswell Park Mem Inst, 60-68; PROF SURG, SCH MED, UNIV CONN, 68- *Concurrent Pos:* Markle scholar, Sch Med, Vanderbilt Univ, 51-52 & 54-56; Rockefeller fel med sci, Nat Res Coun, 57-58; resident, Vanderbilt Univ, 56-57, chief outpatient dept & vis surgeon, 58-60; attend neurosurgeon, Vet Admin Hosp, Nashville, Tenn, 58-60 & Buffalo, 63-; partic brain tumor workshop, NIH, 66- *Mem:* Am Soc Clin Invest; Am Asn Anat; AMA; Am Fedn Clin Res; Am Physiol Soc. *Res:* Neurophysiology; neuroanatomy. *Mailing Add:* Univ of Conn Med Ctr Farmington CT 06032

OWENS, JAMES CARL, b Saginaw, Mich, May 24, 37; m 61; c 2. OPTICS. *Educ:* Oberlin Col,AB, 59; Harvard Univ, AM, 60, PhD(physics), 65. *Prof Exp:* Asst appl physics, Harvard Univ, 63-64; physicist & proj leader atmospheric physics, Cent Radio Propagation Lab, Nat Bur Standards, 64-65 & Inst Telecommun Sci & Aeronomy, Environ Sci Serv Admin, 65-69; RES ASSOC, PHYSICS DIV, RES LABS, EASTMAN KODAK CO, 69-, HEAD IMAGE PROCESSES LAB, 76- *Concurrent Pos:* Mem comn 1, US Nat Comt Int Sci Radio Union, 65- *Mem:* Am Phys Soc; Optical Soc Am; Inst Elec & Electronics Eng; Soc Photog Sci & Eng. *Res:* Coherent optics and laser applications; photographic science and novel imaging systems; lattice vibrations in crystals; dielectric properties of solids; atmospheric optics. *Mailing Add:* Res Labs Bldg 81 Eastman Kodak Co Rochester NY 14650

OWENS, JAMES SAMUEL, b McKinney, Ky, Mar 27, 08; m 34; c 2. PHYSICS, CERAMIC ENGINEERING. *Educ:* Univ Chattanooga, BS, 28; Univ Mich, MS, 30, PhD(physics), 32. *Prof Exp:* Asst physics, Univ Chattanooga, 26-28 & Univ Wis, 28-29; assoc eng res, Univ Mich, 29-31, asst physics & internal med, 32-33; res physicist, Dow Chem Co, 33-39; mem staff, Cent Tech Lab, Armstrong Cork Co, Pa, 39-40, asst chief chemist, Glass & Closure Div, 40-43; chief tech aide, Nat Defense Res Comt, Univ Mich, 43-46; prof univ & exec dir res found, Ohio State Univ, 46-51; asst to mgr, 51-54, gen mgr, 54-70, vpres & gen mgr ceramic mfg opers, Ceramic Div, Champion Spark Plug Co, 71-73. *Concurrent Pos:* Mem comt spectros as appl to chem, Nat Res Coun, 37-42; mem panel infrared, Comt Electronics, Res & Develop Bd, 47-52, chmn, 49-52, mem panel metals & minerals, Comt Mat,

52-54; mem adv bd, Ceramic Eng Dept, Univ Ill, 68-71. *Honors & Awards:* Presidential Cert Merit, 48; Awards, Am Ceramic Soc, 69 & 78. *Mem:* Am Phys Soc; fel & hon mem Am Ceramic Soc (vpres, 63-64, pres, 67-68); Nat Inst Ceramic Eng. *Res:* Reactions between activated and normal atoms and molecules; quantitative spectrographic analysis of alloys and chemicals; spectrophotometry; photochemistry; physical and chemical properties of glasses; infrared radiation sources, detectors and propagation; refractory, dielectric and high temperature ceramics; spark plug insulators. *Mailing Add:* 21 Radnor Circle Grosse Pointe MI 48236

OWENS, JOHN CHARLES, b Plainview, Tex, May 30, 44; m 65; c 2. ECONOMIC ENTOMOLOGY. *Educ:* WTex State Univ, BA, 66; Tex Tech Univ, MS, 69; Iowa State Univ, PhD(entom), 71. *Prof Exp:* Asst prof entom, Iowa State Univ, 71-75; assoc prof entom & arthropod biol, Tex Tech Univ, 75-76; Mgr entom, Pioneer Hi-Bred Int, 76-77; ASSOC PROF ENTOM, NEW MEX STATE UNIV, 77- *Concurrent Pos:* Consult entomologist, Corn Prod Syst Inc, 75-; mem invert control task group, Am Inst Biol Sci, 75- *Mem:* Entom Soc Am; Am Soc Agron; Am Registry Prof Entomologists; Crop Sci Soc Am. *Res:* Pest management strategies for field crop and rangeland insects. *Mailing Add:* Dept of Entom & Plant Path NMex State Univ Las Cruces NM 88003

OWENS, JOHN N, b Portland, Ore, Apr 18, 36; m 54; c 2. BOTANY. *Educ:* Portland State Col, BS, 59; Ore State Univ, MS, 61, PhD(bot), 63. *Prof Exp:* assoc prof, 63-77, PROF BIOL, UNIV VICTORIA, BC, 77- *Mem:* Bot Soc Am; Can Bot Asn. *Res:* Plant anatomy and morphogenesis; developmental anatomy and morphogenesis of conifers; vegetative and reproductive bud and shoot development; pollen development; pollination mechanisms; ovule, embryo and seed development of conifers. *Mailing Add:* Dept of Biol Univ of Victoria Victoria BC V8W 2Y2 Can

OWENS, JOSEPH FRANCIS, III, b Syracuse, NY, Sept 23, 46; m 70. THEORETICAL ELEMENTARY PARTICLE PHYSICS. *Educ:* Worcester Polytech Inst, BSc, 68; Tufts Univ, PhD(physics), 73. *Prof Exp:* Res assoc physics, Case Western Reserve Univ, 73-76; res assoc physics, 76-79, res asst prof, 79-80, ASST PROF PHYSICS, FLA STATE UNIV, 80- *Mem:* Am Phys Soc. *Res:* Theoretical high energy physics dealing with interactions among various quarks and gluons. *Mailing Add:* Dept of Physics Fla State Univ Tallahassee FL 32306

OWENS, KENNETH, b Cheshire, Eng, Apr 2, 34; m 60; c 3. BIOCHEMISTRY. *Educ:* Liverpool Univ, BS, 57; Manchester Univ, MS, 59; London Univ, PhD(biochem), 64. *Prof Exp:* Lectr biochem, Inst Neurol, London Univ, 64-67, sr lectr, 67-69; res assoc, Mass Inst Technol, 69-70; res assoc, Dept Med, Harvard Univ, 70-73, asst prof, 73-75; assoc prof biophys, Med Col Va, 75-81. *Concurrent Pos:* Consult, Biores Inst, Cambridge, Mass, 74-75. *Mem:* Am Asn Path; Biochem Soc Gt Brit; Biophys Soc; Int Study Group Res Cardiac Metab; Sigma Xi. *Res:* Biochemistry of cell membranes; lysosomes and cell death through ischemia. *Mailing Add:* 809 Arlington Circle Richmond VA 23299

OWENS, KENNETH EUGENE, b Battle Creek, Mich, Apr 16, 26; m 55; c 2. PHYSICAL CHEMISTRY. *Educ:* Univ Calif, BS, 49; Univ Minn, PhD(phys chem), 55. *Prof Exp:* Microchemist, Univ Calif, 49-50; res chemist, 55-64, proj leader, 64-67, res supvr, 67-72, SR RES SPECIALIST, MINN MINING & MFG CO, 72- *Mem:* Am Chem Soc; Soc Rheol; Am Inst Chemists; Am Phys Soc. *Res:* Chemical reaction kinetics; photochemical processes; surface and physical properties of polymeric materials; reactions and properties of ceramic materials; biological and environmental applications. *Mailing Add:* 3M Co 3M Ctr St Paul MN 55144

OWENS, LOWELL DAVIS, b Wayne, Nebr, Apr 19, 31; m 56; c 3. PLANT PHYSIOLOGY. *Educ:* Univ Nebr, BS, 52; Mich State Univ, MS, 55; Univ Ill, PhD(agron), 58. *Prof Exp:* Soil conservationist, Soil Conserv Serv, USDA, 52-53; asst, Mich State Univ, 53-55 & Univ Ill, 55-58; soil scientist, Agr Res Serv, 58-71, USDA liaison, SC State Col, 71-73, soil scientist, 73-80, PLANT PHYSIOLOGIST, AGR RES SERV, USDA, 80- *Mem:* AAAS; Soil Sci Soc Am; Am Inst Biol Sci; Am Soc Plant Physiol; Am Soc Microbiol. *Res:* Plant tissue culture; plant and microbiology; physiology. *Mailing Add:* Plant Physiol Inst USDA Agr Res Ctr-W Beltsville MD 20705

OWENS, PATRICK N, sanitary engineering, see previous edition

OWENS, ROBERT HUNTER, b Philadelphia, Pa, Apr 9, 21; m 48; c 4. MATHEMATICS. *Educ:* Webb Inst Naval Archit, BS, 44; Columbia Univ, MA, 48; Calif Inst Technol, PhD(math), 52. *Prof Exp:* Instr math, Stevens Inst Technol, 46-48; asst, Calif Inst Technol, 49-52; res assoc appl math, Brown Univ, 52-53; Off Naval Res phys sci coordr, Calif, 53-54 & mathematician, DC, 54-56; from asst prof to assoc prof math, Univ NH, 56-62; actg head math sci sect, NSF, 63-64; chmn dept, 64-74, actg chmn dept, 78-79, PROF APPL MATH & COMPUT SCI, UNIV VA, 64- *Concurrent Pos:* Liaison scientist, Off Naval Res, London, 70-71; vis scientist, Dept Health, Educ & Welfare, 74-75. *Mem:* Math Asn Am; Soc Indust & Appl Math. *Res:* Applied mathematics and numerical analysis; numerical methods. *Mailing Add:* Dept of Appl Math & Comput Sci Univ of Va Charlottesville VA 22901

OWENS, ROBERT STEPHEN, b Albany, NY, Dec 21, 29; m 53; c 5. RESEARCH ADMINISTRATION, MECHANICAL ENGINEERING. *Educ:* State Univ NY Maritime Col, BMarSci, 54; Rensselaer Polytech Inst, BME, 60. *Prof Exp:* Mech engr friction wear lubrication, 53-65, proj engr chem systs processes, 65-66, mech engr, Metall & Ceramics Lab, 66-68, mgr liaison & admin, Mat Sci & Eng Dept, 68-70, mgr mat characterization opers, 70-73, mgr uranium enrichment proj, Gen Elec/Exxon, 73-75, MGR PLANNING & RESOURCES, ENERGY SECTOR, GEN ELEC RES & DEVELOP CTR, 75- *Mem:* Am Soc Lubrication Engrs. *Res:* Applied research in the area of friction wear and lubrication. *Mailing Add:* Gen Elec Res & Develop Ctr Box 8 Schenectady NY 12301

OWENS, THOMAS CHARLES, b Fargo, NDak, May 8, 41; m 62; c 3. CHEMICAL ENGINEERING. *Educ:* Univ NDak, BSChE, 63; Iowa State Univ, MS, 65, PhD(chem eng), 67. *Prof Exp:* Sr res engr, Esso Prod Res Co, Tex, 67-68; PROF CHEM ENG, UNIV NDAK, 68- *Mem:* AAAS; Am Inst Chem Engrs; Am Chem Soc. *Res:* Separation and purification; solvent extraction; lignite processing technology; rheology of suspensions; membrane separation techniques; water and waste treatment. *Mailing Add:* 1809 N Third St Grand Forks ND 58201

OWENS, WILLIAM LEO, b Redding, Calif, Jan 13, 30; m 59; c 3. MECHANICAL ENGINEERING. *Educ:* Wash State Univ, BS, 53; Univ Calif, Berkeley, MS, 59; Univ Aberdeen, PhD(mech eng), 61. *Prof Exp:* Res engr, Univ Calif, Berkeley, 57-59; sr res fel, Univ Aberdeen, 59-61; aerothermo specialist, United Technol Ctr, 62-63; STAFF ENGR RES & DEVELOP, LOCKHEED MISSILES & SPACE CO, 63- *Concurrent Pos:* Sr res fel, UK Atomic Energy Auth, 59-61; mem tech adv comt, Heat Transfer Res Inc, 77-81. *Mem:* Am Soc Mech Engrs; Am Inst Aeronaut & Astronaut. *Res:* Heat transfer and fluid dynamics, boiling, condensing and two phase flow; biofouling; ocean thermal energy conversion; chemical and electric propulsion. *Mailing Add:* 455 Grant Ave Palo Alto CA 94306

OWENS, WILLIAM RICHARD, b Philadelphia, Pa, Aug 9, 41; m 69; c 1. TECHNICAL MANAGEMENT. *Educ:* Wesleyan Univ, BA, 63; Case Western Reserve Univ, MS, 65, PhD(physics), 68. *Prof Exp:* Asst physics, Case Western Reserve Univ, 63-68; fel, Tulane Univ, 68-70; assoc prof, Pontificia Univ Catolica, Rio De Janeno, Brazil, 71-77; sr scientist, 78-80, TECH MGR INFRARED ANAL, ANALTICS, 80- *Mem:* Sigma Xi; Am Phys Soc; Brazilian Phys Soc. *Res:* Infrared modeling and analysis; nuclear structure physics; radiation damage; x-ray fluorescence analysis; nuclear instrumentation; software development. *Mailing Add:* 614 Camborne Ave NE Fort Walton Beach FL 32548

OWENSBY, CLENTON EDGAR, b Clovis, NMex, Mar 17, 40; m 59; c 3. RANGE SCIENCE, ECOLOGY. *Educ:* NMex State Univ, BS, 64; Kans State Univ, PhD(range sci), 69. *Prof Exp:* Res asst, 64-67, from instr to asst prof, 67-74, assoc prof, 74-78, PROF RANGE MGR, KANS STATE UNIV, 79- *Mem:* Soc Range Mgt. *Res:* Native range burning; fertilization; management systems; carbohydrate reserves; soil chemical properties and animal performance; photosynthesis; root exudation. *Mailing Add:* Dept of Agron Kans State Univ Manhattan KS 66506

OWERS, NOEL OSCAR, b Nagpur, India, Oct 1, 26; US citizen; m 60; c 4. BIOLOGY, ANATOMY. *Educ:* Nagpur Univ, BSc, 48, PhD(reproduction biol), 57; Argonne Nat Lab, dipl, 58. *Prof Exp:* Asst prof biol, Duquesne Univ, 58-59; res assoc anat, Univ Wis, 61-63; asst prof, Univ Iowa, 63-69; ASSOC PROF ANAT, HEALTH SCI DIV, VA COMMONWEALTH UNIV, 69- *Concurrent Pos:* NSF-AEC fel, Univ Mich, 59; NIH fel, Univ Wis, 59-61; NASA-Am Soc Eng Educ fac fel, Ames Res Ctr, Stanford Univ, 70-71; consult, Univ Wash, 67-68. *Mem:* AAAS; Am Asn Anat; Am Soc Cell Biol; Microcirc Soc. *Res:* Proteolytic activity of normal and reproductive cells, malignant and non-malignant tumor cells, bacteria and fungi and other life forms, in vivo and vitro; methods of detection of proteinases. *Mailing Add:* Dept of Anat Health Sci Div Va Commonwealth Univ Richmond VA 23298

OWINGS, ADDISON DAVIS, b Hattiesburg, Miss, Feb 8, 36; m 64; c 2. AGRONOMY, AGRICULTURAL STATISTICS. *Educ:* Miss State Univ, BS, 57, MS, 62, PhD(agron), 66. *Prof Exp:* Asst agronomist, Miss Agr Exp Sta, 57-59; from instr to assoc prof, 63-70, PROF AGRON, SOUTHEASTERN LA UNIV, 70-, HEAD DEPT, 67- *Honors & Awards:* NDEA fel; Hon State Farmer, FFA, La. *Mem:* Am Soc Agron; Am Quarter Horse Asn; Am Farm Bur Fedn. *Res:* Crops and plant breeding. *Mailing Add:* PO Box 703 Univ Sta Hammond LA 70402

OWINGS, JAMES CLAGGETT, JR, b Baltimore, Md, Feb 8, 40. MATHEMATICAL LOGIC. *Educ:* Dartmouth Col, BA, 62; Cornell Univ, PhD(math), 66. *Prof Exp:* Asst prof, 66-70, ASSOC PROF MATH, UNIV MD, 70- *Mem:* Asn Symbolic Logic; Am Math Soc; Math Asn Am; Soc Exact Philos. *Res:* Metarecursion theory; graph theory; combinatorics; mathematical linguistics. *Mailing Add:* Dept of Math Univ of Md College Park MD 20742

OWNBEY, GERALD BRUCE, b Kirksville, Mo, Oct 10, 16; m 68; c 1. PLANT TAXONOMY. *Educ:* Univ Wyo, BA, 39, MA, 40; Wash Univ, St Louis, PhD(bot), 47. *Prof Exp:* Instr bot, 47-48, asst prof & actg cur herbarium, 48-49, assoc prof, 51-56, chmn dept bot, 60-62, PROF BOT, UNIV MINN, ST PAUL, 56-, CUR HERBARIUM, 49- *Concurrent Pos:* Guggenheim fel, 53-54. *Mem:* Am Inst Biol Sci; Bot Soc Am; Am Soc Plant Taxon; Soc Study Evolution; Am Fern Soc. *Res:* Taxonomy and cytotaxonomy of Corydalis, Argemone and Cirsium. *Mailing Add:* Dept of Bot Univ of Minn St Paul MN 55108

OWNBY, CHARLOTTE LEDBETTER, b Amory, Miss, July 27, 47. VETERINARY ANATOMY. *Educ:* Univ Tenn, Knoxville, BS, 69, MS, 71; Colo State Univ, PhD(anat), 75. *Prof Exp:* Instr, 74-75, asst prof, 75-80, ASSOC PROF HISTOL & ELECTRON MICROS, OKLA STATE UNIV, 80-, DIR, ELECTRON MICROSCOPE LAB, 77- *Mem:* AAAS; Sigma Xi; Am Asn Vet Anatomists; Electrin Micros Soc Am; Am Asn Anatomists. *Res:* Light and electron microscopic study of myonecrosis induced by pure myotoxins of rattlesnake venom. *Mailing Add:* Col of Vet Med Okla State Univ Stillwater OK 74074

OWNBY, DENNIS RANDALL, b Athens, Ohio, July 14, 48; m 70; c 2. IMMUNOLOGY, ALLERGY. *Educ:* Ohio Univ, BS, 69; Med Col Ohio, MD, 72. *Prof Exp:* Intern, Sch Med, Duke Univ, 72-73, resident, 73-74, res fel, 74-77, asst prof pediat immunol, 77-79; STAFF PHYSICIAN, HENRY FORD HOSP, 80- *Concurrent Pos:* Young investr, Nat Inst Allergy & Infectious Dis res grants, 78-81. *Mem:* Am Acad Pediat; Am Acad Allergy. *Res:* Physiology of human lymphocyte function. *Mailing Add:* Henry Ford Hosp 2799 W Grand Blvd Detroit MI 48202

OWNBY, JAMES DONALD, b Sevierville, Tenn, Sept 30, 44; m 69; c 1. PLANT PHYSIOLOGY. *Educ:* Univ Tenn, Knoxville, BS, 66, MA, 71; Colo State Univ, PhD(plant physiol), 74. *Prof Exp:* Res assoc algal physiol, Langston Univ, 74-75; ASST PROF PLANT PHYSIOL, OKLA STATE UNIV, 75- *Mem:* Am Soc Plant Physiologists. *Res:* Control of growth and nitrogen metabolism in blue-green algae; effects of herbicides and growth regulators on nitrogen fixation in blue-green algae. *Mailing Add:* Sch of Biol Sci Okla State Univ Stillwater OK 74074

OWNBY, P(AUL) DARRELL, b Salt Lake City, Utah, Nov 9, 35; m 61; c 7. CERAMIC ENGINEERING, MATERIALS SCIENCE. *Educ:* Univ Utah, BS, 61; Univ Mo-Rolla, MS, 62; Ohio State Univ, PhD(ceramic eng), 67. *Prof Exp:* Ceramic engr, Sprague Elec Co, 61; res ceramist, Battelle Mem Inst, 63-67; from asst prof to assoc prof, 68-74, res assoc, Indust Res Ctr, 68, PROF CERAMIC ENG, UNIV MO-ROLLA, 74-, RES ASSOC, GRAD CTR MAT RES, 68- *Concurrent Pos:* Consult, Battelle Mem Inst, 68-70, Dynasil Corp Am, 69- & Eagle Picher, 70-; vis scientist, Max Planck Inst Mat Sci, Stuttgart, Ger, 74-75. *Mem:* Am Ceramic Soc; Nat Inst Ceramic Engrs; Ceramic Educ Coun. *Res:* Glass ceramics; surface phenomena; field emission; molecular beam; ultra-high vacuum; final sintering; boron compounds; metal-ceramic interfaces; atmosphere control. *Mailing Add:* Dept of Ceramic Eng Univ of Mo Rolla MO 65401

OWRE, OSCAR THEODORE, b Minneapolis, Minn, Oct 10, 17; m 48; c 1. ORNITHOLOGY. *Educ:* Univ Miami, Fla, AB, 41, MS, 49; Univ Mich, PhD, 58. *Prof Exp:* Asst mus zool, Univ Mich, 51-52; instr zool, 48-50 & 52-54, from asst prof to assoc prof, 55-69, MAYTAG PROF ORNITH, 69- *Res.* Functional morphology, biology of introduction, ecology and natural history of South Florida birds. *Mailing Add:* Dept of Biol Univ of Miami Coral Gables FL 33124

OWSLEY, DENNIS CLARK, b Los Angeles, Calif, Mar 26, 43; m 63; c 2. SYNTHETIC ORGANIC CHEMISTRY. *Educ:* Univ Calif, Riverside, AB, 65, PhD(org chem), 69. *Prof Exp:* Sr res chemist, 69-75, res specialist, Cent Res Dept, Monsanto Co, 75-77, RES SPECIALIST, MONSANTO INDUST CHEM CO, 77- *Mem:* Am Chem Soc; AAAS. *Res:* Organic synthesis; photochemistry; metallo-organic chemistry; organo-sulfur chemistry; heterocycles; small rings. *Mailing Add:* Monsanto Co 800 N Lindbergh Blvd St Louis MO 63166

OWSLEY, NORMAN LEE, electrical engineering, see previous edition

OWSTON, PEYTON WOOD, b Pittsburgh, Pa, Feb 13, 38; m 63; c 2. FOREST PHYSIOLOGY. *Educ:* Univ Mich, BSc, 60, MF, 62, PhD(forestry), 66. *Prof Exp:* Res forester, Pac Southwest Forest & Range Exp Sta, 66-69, PLANT PHYSIOLOGIST, PAC NORTHWEST FOREST & RANGE EXP STA, US FOREST SERV, 69- *Mem:* Soc Am Foresters. *Res:* Tree-soil-water relations; growth of forest trees. *Mailing Add:* Pac NW Forest & Range Exp Sta 3200 Jefferson Way Corvallis OR 97331

OWYANG, GILBERT HSIAOPIN, b Tientsin, China; US citizen; m 65; c 2. APPLIED PHYSICS, ELECTRICAL ENGINEERING. *Educ:* Ta Tung Univ, China, BSc, 44; Harvard Univ, SM, 50, PhD(appl physics), 59. *Prof Exp:* Engr elec, Shanghai Power Co, China, 44-49; sr designer power syst, Devenco Inc, 51-53; engr, Frank L Capps Co Inc, 54-55; res asst appl physics, Gordon McKay Lab, Harvard Univ, 55-59; assoc res physicist electromagnetics, Radiation Lab, Univ Mich, 59-61; PROF ELEC ENG, WORCESTER POLYTECH INST, 61- *Mem:* Sigma Xi; Inst Elec & Electronic Engrs. *Res:* Wave propagation in ionized media; energy transmission and radiation in homogeneous media and inhomogeneous media; electromagnetics. *Mailing Add:* Dept of Elec Eng Institute Rd Worcester MA 01609

OXENDER, DALE LAVERN, b Constantine, Mich, Aug 30, 32; m 55; c 2. BIOCHEMISTRY. *Educ:* Manchester Col, BA, 54; Purdue Univ, MS, 56, PhD, 59. *Prof Exp:* Res assoc, 58-59, from instr to assoc prof, 59-75, PROF BIOCHEM, MED SCH, UNIV MICH, ANN ARBOR, 75- *Mem:* Am Chem Soc; Am Soc Biol Chem; Am Micros Soc. *Res:* Cloning and expression of amino acid transport genes in Chinese hamster, human cells and microorganisms. *Mailing Add:* Dept Biol Chem M5319 Univ Mich Ann Arbor MI 48104

OXENREITER, M(AURICE) F(RANK), b Pittsburgh, Pa, Oct 26, 24; m 50; c 5. CHEMICAL ENGINEERING. *Educ:* Univ Pittsburgh, BS, 48, MS, 49, PhD(chem eng), 52; Univ Chicago, MBA, 70. *Prof Exp:* Asst, Univ Pittsburgh, 49-52; proj chem engr, Standard Oil Co of Ind, 52-60, group leader, 60-65, res assoc, Am Oil Co, 65-70, dir process res, 70-75, MGR PROCESS RES, AMOCO OIL CO, 75- *Mem:* Am Inst Chem Engrs. *Res:* Differential latent heats of vaporization; petroleum refining; coal, oil shale and tar sands conversion and refining; process design and economics; process development. *Mailing Add:* Res & Develop Dept PO Box 400 Naperville IL 60540

OXFORD, C(HARLES) W(ILLIAM), b Texarkana, Tex, Nov 16, 21; m 46; c 2. CHEMICAL ENGINEERING. *Educ:* Univ Ark, BSChE, 44; Univ Okla, PhD(chem eng), 52. *Prof Exp:* Jr engr, Ark-La Gas Co, 40; asst chemist, Koppers Co, 41; control foreman, Dickey Clay Mfg Co, 42; asst prof chem eng, Univ Ark, 48-50 & 51-52, assoc prof, 52-55; res engr, Boeing Airplane Co, 55; consult, Humble Oil Co, 56; PROF CHEM ENG & ASSOC DEAN ENG, UNIV ARK, FAYETTEVILLE, 57-, ADMIN VPRES, 68-, VPRES ACAD AFFAIRS, 79- *Concurrent Pos:* Res partic, Carbide & Carbon Chem Co, 52. *Mem:* Am Soc Eng Educ; Am Inst Chem Engrs. *Res:* Revaporization of hydrocarbons; gas flow at low pressure. *Mailing Add:* 1024 Eastwood Fayetteville AR 72701

OXLEY, JAMES EDWARD, electrochemistry, see previous edition

OXLEY, JOSEPH H(UBBARD), b Akron, Ohio, Aug 8, 29; m 51; c 6. CHEMICAL ENGINEERING. *Educ:* Carnegie Inst Technol, BS, 52, PhD(chem eng), 56. *Prof Exp:* Asst div chief, Battelle Mem Inst, 56-66, assoc mgr, Battelle Develop Corp, 66-72, mgr fuels & combustion sect, 72-76, ASST MGR, ENERGY & ENVIRON TECH DEPT, BATTELLE-COLUMBUS LABS, 77- *Mem:* Am Chem Soc; Am Inst Chem Engrs; Electrochem Soc; Am Inst Metall Eng; Licensing Exec Soc. *Res:* Halide metallurgy; coated particle nuclear fuels; mass transfer phenomenon; catalysis; coal conversion; flue gas treatment. *Mailing Add:* Battelle-Columbus Labs 505 King Ave Columbus OH 43201

OXLEY, PHILIP, b Utica, NY, Feb 1, 22; m 46; c 5. PETROLEUM GEOLOGY. *Educ:* Denison Univ, BA, 43; Columbia Univ, MA, 48, PhD, 52. *Prof Exp:* Asst, Geol Dept, Columbia Univ, 46-48; instr geol, Hamilton Col, 48-51, asst prof & chmn dept, 51-53; petrol geologist, Calif Co, La, 53-57; dist & div explor supt, Tenn Gas Transmission Co, 57-61; div explor mgr, Signal Oil & Gas Co, 61-65, vpres & mgr domestic explor, 65-69; exec vpres, Tex Crude Oil, 69-71; geol mgr explor, Tenneco Oil Co, 71-72, mgr foreign explor & prof, 72-76, vpres, 72-74, sr vpres, 74-81, PRES, TENNECO OIL EXPLOR & PROD CO, 81- *Concurrent Pos:* Temporary expert, NY State Mus, 50-51; party chief, Nfld Geol Surv, 52. *Mem:* Fel Geol Soc Am; Am Asn Petrol Geol. *Res:* Ordovician Chazyan stratigraphy of New York and Vermont; Ordovician stratigraphy and areal geology of western Newfoundland; petroleum geology of Texas-Louisiana Gulf Coast and offshore. *Mailing Add:* 153 Hickory Ridge Houston TX 77024

OXLEY, THERON D, JR, b Randlett, Okla, Apr 3, 31; m 57. MATHEMATICS. *Educ:* Tex Christian Univ, BA, 51; Purdue Univ, MS, 53, PhD(math), 56. *Prof Exp:* Asst, Purdue Univ, 51-56; asst prof math, Kans State Univ, 56-60; asst prof, 60-64, ASSOC PROF MATH, DRAKE UNIV, 64- *Mem:* Am Math Soc; Math Asn Am. *Res:* Complex variable; infinite series. *Mailing Add:* Dept of Math Drake Univ Des Moines IA 50310

OXMAN, MICHAEL ALLAN, b Milwaukee, Wis, Nov 7, 35; m 58; c 3. INFORMATION SCIENCE, RESEARCH ADMINISTRATION. *Educ:* Univ Wis, BS, 58, MS, 60, PhD(medicinal chem), 63. *Prof Exp:* Prod chemist, Aldrich Chem Co, Inc, 63; scientist, NIH, 63-65; assoc res chemist, Sterling-Winthrop Res Inst, 65-68, health scientist adminr, Spec Res Resources Br, Div Res Facilities & Resources, NIH, 68-71, prog adminr, Biotechnol Resources Br, Div Res Resources, 71-74, chief tech files implementation br, Spec Info Serv, Nat Libr Med, 74-75, exec secy, review br, Div Extramural affairs, Nat Heart & Lung Inst, 75-78, health scientist adminr, Biomed Res Support Prog, 78-80, ASST DIR REVIEW, DIV RES RESOURCES, NIH, 80- *Mem:* Am Chem Soc. *Res:* Medicinal chemistry; aromatic biogenesis; oxidative phosphorylation; vitamin E; steroids; development of on-line, interactive toxicology data base. *Mailing Add:* Div Res Resources NIH Bethesda MD 20205

OXNARD, CHARLES ERNEST, b Durham, Eng, Sept 9, 33; m 59; c 2. BIOLOGICAL ANTHROPOLOGY, EVOLUTIONARY BIOLOGY. *Educ:* Univ Birmingham, BSc, 55, MB, ChB, 58, PhD(med anat), 62, DSc(sci), 75. *Prof Exp:* House physician, Queen Elizabeth Hosp, Birmingham, 58-59, house surgeon, 59; from lectr to sr lectr anat, Univ Birmingham, 62-66; assoc prof, 66-70, master biol col div & assoc dean col & div biol sci, 72-73, prof anat, Univ Chicago, 70-78, dean col, 73-77; PROF ANAT & BIOL SCI, UNIV SOUTHERN CALIF, 78- DEAN GRAD SCH, 78- *Concurrent Pos:* Res grants, US Dept Health, Educ & Welfare, 63-66, 67-70, Agr Res Coun Gt Brit, 64-66, Louis Block Fund, Univ Chicago, 66-70, USPHS, 67-70, 74-77, NSF, 71-; overseas assoc, Univ Birmingham, 72-; assoc ed, Am J Anat, 72-78 & Am J Phys Anthrop, 74-78; external examr, 75-77, vis prof Univ Hong Kong, 77- *Mem:* AAAS; Am Asn Anat; Am Asn Phys Anthrop; Am Soc Zool; Anat Soc Gt Brit & Ireland. *Res:* Evolution of form in mammals, especially primates, utilizing comparative anatomical, biometric and biomechanical techniques; vitamin B12 deficiency in primates, especially its effects on nervous system, mucous membranes, blood, growth and reproduction. *Mailing Add:* Grad Sch Univ Southern Calif Los Angeles CA 60637

OXTOBY, DAVID W, b Bryn Mawr, Pa, Oct 17, 51; m 77. PHYSICAL CHEMISTRY. *Educ:* Harvard Univ, BA, 72; Univ Calif, Berkeley, PhD(chem), 75. *Prof Exp:* Res assoc chem, Univ Chicago, 75-76 & Univ Paris, 76-77; ASST PROF CHEM, UNIV CHICAGO, 77- *Concurrent Pos:* Alfred P Sloan Found fel, 77- *Mem:* Am Phys Soc; Royal Soc Chem. *Res:* Theoretical physical chemistry; statistical mechanics of fluids; light scattering; relaxation processes in liquids; phase transitions. *Mailing Add:* James Franck Inst Univ of Chicago Chicago IL 60637

OXTOBY, JOHN CORNING, b Saginaw, Mich, Sept 14, 10; m 45; c 3. MATHEMATICS. *Educ:* Univ Calif, AB, 33, AM, 34. *Hon Degrees:* DSc, Widener Univ, 80. *Prof Exp:* From asst prof to assoc prof, 39-54, prof, 54-79, EMER PROF MATH, BRYN MAWR COL, 79- *Concurrent Pos:* Ed, Am Math Soc Bull, 56-60; res assoc, Yale Univ, 60-61. *Mem:* Am Math Soc; Math Asn Am. *Res:* Topology and measure theory. *Mailing Add:* Dept of Math Phys Sci Bldg Bryn Mawr Col Bryn Mawr PA 19010

OYAMA, JIRO, b Los Angeles, Calif, Aug 2, 25; m 66. PHYSIOLOGY, BIOCHEMISTRY. *Educ:* Northwestern Univ, BS, 49; George Washington Univ, MS, 56, PhD(biochem), 60. *Prof Exp:* Biochemist, NIH, 50-56; res biochemist, US Food & Drug Admin, 56-61; RES SCIENTIST, AMES RES CTR, NASA, 61- *Concurrent Pos:* Lectr & spec consult, San Jose State Univ, 69-74; lectr, Stanford Univ, 70-80. *Mem:* Am Chem Soc; Am Physiol Soc; Sigma Xi. *Res:* Gravitational biology; acceleration stress physiology; insulin action; carbohydrate metabolism; thermoregulation; respiratory metabolism; aging; developmental physiology; bone and muscle. *Mailing Add:* Biomed Res Div 239-17 Ames Res Ctr NASA Moffett Field CA 94035

OYAMA, VANCE I, b Los Angeles, Calif, June 6, 22; m 45; c 3. BIOCHEMISTRY, ORGANIC CHEMISTRY. *Educ:* George Washington Univ, BS, 53, MS, 60. *Prof Exp:* Med technologist, USPHS, Johns Hopkins Univ, 45-47; med technologist, NIH, 47, chemist, 47-60; sr scientist, Jet Propulsion Lab, Calif Inst Technol, 60-63; prin scientist, 63-65, chief, Life Detection Systs Br, 65-76, CHIEF, PLANETARY EXPLOR OFF, AMES RES CTR, NASA, 76- *Mem:* AAAS; Soil Sci Soc Am; fel Am Inst Chem; Am Soc Microbiol; Am Chem Soc. *Res:* Viable organisms in lunar samples, gas exchange exploration, Viking Mission, sounder gas chromatograph Pioneer Venus Mission; pyrolysis; gas chromatography; carbon dioxide fixation; metabolic monitors; life detection sciences; lunar sciences; planetary sciences and biology; chemical evolution; origin of life. *Mailing Add:* Mail Stop 239-12 NASA-Ames Res Ctr Moffett Field CA 94035

OYEN, ORDEAN JAMES, b Appleton, Minn, June 27, 44; m 65; c 2. SKELETAL BIOLOGY & HISTOLOGY. *Educ:* Univ Minn, BA, 69, PhD(anthrop & anat), 74. *Prof Exp:* Instr anat & anthrop, Univ Minn, 73-74; asst prof phys anthrop, Tex A&M Univ, 74-79; ASST PROF ANAT, SCH DENT, CASE WESTERN RESERVE UNIV, 79- *Concurrent Pos:* Adj asst prof anthrop, Case Western Univ, 81- *Honors & Awards:* Centennial lectr, Creighton Univ, 78. *Mem:* Am Asn Phys Anthropologists. *Res:* Evolution biology, with emphasis on skeletal biology, histology and functional anatomy; theoretical and experimental aspects of craniofacial morphogenesis. *Mailing Add:* Sch Dent Case Western Reserve Univ Cleveland OH 44106

OYER, ALDEN TREMAINE, b Easton, Pa, July 13, 47; m 69. COMPUTER SCIENCE, ELECTRICAL ENGINEERING. *Educ:* Lafayette Col, BS, 69; Univ Wyo, PhD(physics), 76. *Prof Exp:* MEM STAFF, LOS ALAMOS NAT LAB, 76- *Concurrent Pos:* Consult, Nuclear Regulatory Comn, 77- *Mem:* Asn Comput Mach; Inst Elec & Electronic Engrs. *Res:* Computer Security; computer systems; telecommunications. *Mailing Add:* Los Alamos Sci Lab PO Box 1663 Los Alamos NM 87545

OYER, HERBERT JOSEPH, b Groveland, Ill, Jan 28, 21; m 47; c 1. AUDIOLOGY, PSYCHOLOGY. *Educ:* Bluffton Col, AB, 43; Bowling Green State Univ, MSEd, 49; Ohio State Univ, PhD, 55. *Prof Exp:* Dir, Speech & Hearing Clin, 60-71, prof & chmn, Dept Speech, 64-67, prof & chmn, Dept Audiol & Speech Sci, 67-71, dean, Col Community Arts & Sci, 71-75, dean, Grad Sch, 75-81, PROF AUDIOL & SPEECH SCI, MICH STATE UNIV, 81- *Concurrent Pos:* Am Speech & Hearing Asn fel, 61. *Mem:* Acoust Soc Am; Am Psychol Asn; Acad Rehab Audiol (pres); Am Speech & Hearing Asn (vpres). *Res:* Visual communication; auditory processing; speech intelligibility. *Mailing Add:* 366 Community Arts & Sci Mich State Univ East Lansing MI 48824

OYEWOLE, SAUNDRA HERNDON, b Washington, DC, Apr 26, 43; m 70; c 3. MICROBIOLOGY. *Educ:* Howard Univ, BS, 65; Univ Chicago, MS, 67; Univ Mass, PhD(microbiol), 73. *Prof Exp:* Asst prof, 73-79, ASSOC PROF MICROBIOL, SCH NATURAL SCI, HAMPSHIRE COL, 79- *Concurrent Pos:* Res assoc, Dept Biochem, Univ Mass, 73- *Mem:* Am Soc Microbiol; AAAS. *Res:* Development, structure and function of bacterial photosynthetic membranes; photochemical apparatus of the green photosynthetic bacteria. *Mailing Add:* Sch of Natural Sci Hampshire Col Amherst MA 01002

OYLER, ALAN RICHARD, b Key West, Fla, Oct 13, 47; m 70. ANALYTICAL CHEMISTRY, SYNTHETIC ORGANIC CHEMISTRY. *Educ:* Albright Col, BS, 69; Lehigh Univ, PhD(chem), 73. *Prof Exp:* Res specialist chem, Univ Minn, 73-81; MEM STAFF, MOLECULAR SPECTROS DEPT, ORTHO PHARMACEUT CORP, 81- *Mem:* Am Chem Soc; AAAS. *Res:* Polynuclear aromatic hydrocarbons; analytical techniques and chemistry; trace organic analysis; high performance liquid chromatography. *Mailing Add:* Molecular Spectros Dept Ortho Pharmaceut Corp Raritan NJ 08869

OYLER, GLENN W(ALKER), b Franklin Co, Pa, Sept 28, 23; div; c 3. METALLURGICAL ENGINEERING. *Educ:* Pa State Univ, BS, 49; Univ Pittsburgh, MS, 51; Lehigh Univ, PhD(metall eng), 53; Univ RI, cert mgt, 63. *Prof Exp:* Welder, Fairchild Aircraft Corp, Md, 41-42; welding engr, Aluminum Co Am, Pa, 49-51; head welding div, Linde Co, Union Carbide Corp, NJ, 53-60; chief welding engr & proj mgr, Metals & Controls, Inc Div, Tex Instruments, Inc, Mass, 60-63; dir appl res & develop, ACF Industs, Inc, NMex, 63-67; mfg mgr, Lockheed Missiles & Space Co, Calif, 67-69; chief advan mfg technol, Martin Marietta Corp, 69-77; tech dir, Am Weling Soc, 77-80; EXEC DIR, WELDING RES COUN, NY, 80- *Mem:* Am Welding Soc; fel Am Soc Metals; Am Soc Mech Eng. *Res:* Research, development and production support of metallic and non-metallic materials. *Mailing Add:* Welding Res Coun 345 E 47th St New York NY 10017

OYLER, J MACK, b Sapulpa, Okla, Aug 8, 26; m 52; c 2. PHYSIOLOGY. *Educ:* Okla State Univ, DVM, 53, PhD(physiol), 69. *Prof Exp:* Asst prof vet sci, Univ Ark, 54-55; pvt pract, Grove, Okla, 56-65; asst prof physiol, Okla State Univ, 68-69; from asst prof to assoc prof physiol, Univ Ga, 71-73; assoc prof med & surg, Okla State Univ, 73-75; prof vet med, Va Polytech Inst & State Univ, 75-80; PROF & ASSOC DEAN, COL VET MED, OKLA STATE UNIV, 80- *Mem:* Am Vet Med Asn; Am Soc Vet Physiol & Pharmacol. *Res:* Metabolism with special interest in blood-brain barrier and neonatal studies. *Mailing Add:* Col of Vet Med Okla State Univ Stillwater OK 74078

OYSTER, CLYDE WILLIAM, b Marietta, Ohio, Apr 29, 40; m 67. VISUAL PHYSIOLOGY. *Educ:* Ohio State Univ, BS, 63; Univ Calif, Berkeley, PhD(physiol optics), 67. *Prof Exp:* Asst prof, 70-75, ASSOC PROF PHYSIOL OPTICS, SCH OPTOM, MED CTR, UNIV ALA, BIRMINGHAM, 75- *Concurrent Pos:* Fight for Sight res fel, Australian Nat Univ, 68-70; sr res fel visual physiol, Dept Physiol, Med Fac Rotterdam, 70; Nat Eye Inst grant, Univ Ala, Birmingham, 71- mem vision res prog comt, Nat Eye Inst, 74-77. *Mem:* AAAS; Asn Res Vision & Ophthal; Soc Neurosci; Am Acad Optom. *Res:* Information processing in the visual system; neural interactions in retina and visual pathways. *Mailing Add:* Sch of Optom Univ of Ala Med Ctr Birmingham AL 35294

OYSTER, DALE EUGENE, b Ashland, Ohio, July 31, 20; m 42; c 3. PHYSICS. *Educ:* Marietta Col, BA, 42; Univ Mich, MS, 46. *Prof Exp:* Physicist, Radar Lab, US Air Force, Ohio, 42-45, engr, Eng Div, Wright Air Develop Ctr, 46-48, opers analyst, Hq, 48-51, 54-56, & spec weapons ctr, 51-54, dep for requirements, Off Secy, 56-58; head systs opers dept, Rand Corp, 58-67; mgr advan systs, Aerospace & Systs Group, NAm Rockwell Corp, 67-71; dir technol div, Hq, Environ Protection Agency, 71-73, actg dep asst admin, 73-75, chief, Nuclear Technol Div, 75-77, SR SCIENTIST, INTERNATIONAL NUCLEAR AFFAIRS DIV, US ARMS CONTROL & DISARMAMENT AGENCY, 77- *Mem:* Opers Res Soc Am; Inst Elec & Electronics Engrs. *Res:* Environmental protection technology; systems engineering; operations research; international nuclear energy safeguards; national technical intelligence methods. *Mailing Add:* 6901 Pacific Lane Annandale VA 22003

OZA, KANDARP GOVINDLAL, b Gujarat, India, July 12, 42. ELECTRICAL & SYSTEMS ENGINEERING. *Educ:* Gujarat Univ, India, BEE, 63; Univ Calif, Berkeley, MS, 64, PhD(elec eng), 67. *Prof Exp:* Asst prof elec eng, Univ Okla, 68-69; mem tech staff, Bell Tel Labs, 69-70; asst prof elec eng, Indian Inst Technol, Kanpur, 70; MEM TECH STAFF, BELL TEL LABS, 71- *Concurrent Pos:* Adj prof, Fairleigh-Dickinson Univ, 73-76; Bell Labs vis prof, Tuskegee Inst, Ala, 77-78. *Mem:* Inst Elec & Electronics Engrs. *Res:* Control, communications and computer systems; new telecommunication services; digital switching and transmissions; microprocessor-based systems; engineering economics. *Mailing Add:* Bell Tel Labs Holmdel NJ 07733

OZAKI, HENRY YOSHIO, b Eau Gallie, Fla, Oct 25, 23; m 59. VEGETABLE CROPS. *Educ:* Univ Fla, BSA, 49; Cornell Univ, MS, 51, PhD, 54. *Prof Exp:* Asst veg crops, Cornell Univ, 49-53; asst horticulturist, Plantation Field Lab, Agr Res Sta, 54-68, assoc horticulturist, 68-69, ASSOC PROF HORT, MORIKAMI FARM, AGR RES CTR, UNIV FLA, 69- *Mem:* Am Soc Hort Sci. *Res:* Vegetable research on sandy soils of Florida. *Mailing Add:* Morikami Farm Agr Res Ctr IFAS Univ Fla 6656 167th Pl S Delray Beach FL 33444

OZAKI, SATOSHI, b Osaka, Japan, July 4, 29; m 60; c 2. HIGH ENERGY EXPERIMENTAL PHYSICS. *Educ:* Osaka Univ, BS, 53, MS, 55; Mass Inst Technol, PhD(physics), 59. *Prof Exp:* Res asst physics, Mass Inst Technol, 56-59; res assoc, 59-61, asst physicist, 61-63, assoc physicist, 63-66, physicist, 66-72, GROUP LEADER PHYSICS, BROOKHAVEN NAT LAB, 70-, SR PHYSICIST, 72- *Concurrent Pos:* Vis prof, Osaka Univ, 75-76; vis prof & dir, Dept Physics, Nat Lab High Energy Physics, Japan, 81- *Mem:* Fel Am Phys Soc; Phys Soc Japan. *Res:* Study of high energy particle interactions; particle spectroscopy; high energy physics instrumentation. *Mailing Add:* Dept Physics Brookhaven Nat Lab Upton NY 11973

OZAN, M TURGUT, b Ankara, Turkey, May 8, 19; m 65. INDUSTRIAL ENGINEERING, OPERATIONS RESEARCH. *Educ:* Swiss Fed Inst Technol, BS & MS, 50; Univ Birmingham, MS, 58; Washington Univ, St Louis, DSc, 63. *Prof Exp:* Design engr, Asper Mach Tool Co, Switz, 50; proj engr, MAKKIM, Turkey, 50-52, chief engr, 52-54, dir prod planning, 54-56; asst prof indust eng & chmn dept, 60-63, assoc prof, 63-65, PROF INDUST ENG, ST MARY'S UNIV SAN ANTONIO, TEX, 65-, ASSOC DEAN ENG, 67- *Concurrent Pos:* Consult, 60-; consult, Keuffel & Esser Co, Hoboken, 70-; lectr & consult, Inst Technol Y De Estud Superiores De Monterrey, Mex, 72- *Mem:* Am Inst Indust Engrs; Nat Asn Corrosion Engrs; Opers Res Soc Am; Am Soc Eng Educ; Am Soc Nondestructive Testing. *Res:* Probability, statistics, reliability theory and operations research as applied to the design, operation and control of production systems; search theory; scheduling and flow line balancing problems in production planning; design optimization. *Mailing Add:* 5418 E Rolling Ridge Dr San Antonio TX 78228

OZAROW, VERNON, b New York, NY, Sept 12, 20; m 44; c 3. PHYSICAL CHEMISTRY. *Educ:* City Col New York, BS, 42; Pa State Univ, PhD, 54. *Prof Exp:* Chemist, Carbide & Carbon Chem Corp, 44-45; phys chemist, Electronics Lab, Gen Elec Co, 50-58, consult, Semiconductor Prod Dept, 58-61, mgr semiconductor mat, 61-62, phys chemist, Lamp Res Lab, 62-63 & Res & Develop Ctr, 63-67; sr scientist, Rensselaer Res Corp, 67-68; from assoc dir to dir off sci & technol, NY State Educ Dept, 68-72; assoc provost grad educ & res, State Univ NY, 73-76; dir, off state col, NJ Dept Higher Educ, 76-77; dir, div energy systs, NY Energy Off, 77-79; SR STAFF SCI MGR, NY STATE SCI & TECHNOL FOUND, 80- *Concurrent Pos:* Mem comt educ systs, Nat Acad Eng. *Mem:* Am Chem Soc; Am Phys Soc; Electrochem Soc; AAAS. *Res:* Semiconductor materials and devices; electrophotography. *Mailing Add:* 2069 Lexington Pkwy Schenectady NY 12309

OZAWA, KENNETH SUSUMU, b Tokyo, Japan, Nov 22, 31; US citizen; m 63; c 2. FLUID PHYSICS. *Educ:* John Carroll Univ, BS, 59, MS, 60; Univ Kans, PhD(eng mech), 75. *Prof Exp:* Instr physics, John Carroll Univ, 60-63; asst prof, 63-75, ASSOC PROF PHYSICS, CALIF POLYTECH STATE UNIV, 75- *Mem:* Am Geophys Union; Am Asn Physics Teachers. *Res:* Experimental study of wind-induced waves and currents in lakes of limited fetch and depth. *Mailing Add:* Dept of Physics Calif Polytech State Univ San Luis Obispo CA 93407

OZBUN, JIM L, b Carson, NDak, Sept 3, 36; m 59; c 2. PLANT PHYSIOLOGY. *Educ:* NDak State Univ, BS, 59, MS, 61; NC State Univ, PhD(soils, plant physiol), 64. *Prof Exp:* From asst prof to assoc prof plant physiol, 64-74, from actg chmn to chmn dept veg crops, 71-75, asst dir res, NY Exp Sta & NY State Col Agr, 67-70, assoc dir exten, NY State Col Agr & Live Sci & prof plant physiol, Cornell Univ, 74-76; prof hort sci & landscape archit & head dept, Univ Minn, 76-81; ASSOC DEAN AGR & DIR RES, KANS STATE UNIV, 81- *Concurrent Pos:* Sabbatical leave, Dept Biochem & Biophys, Univ Calif, Davis, 70-71. *Honors & Awards:* Campbell Award, Am Inst Biol Sci, 65. *Mem:* Am Soc Hort Sci. *Res:* Photosynthesis; effect of light and potassium nutrition on photosynthesis and respiration; influence of ammonia nitrogen on potassium and water use efficiency; vernalization and flowering; yield physiology. *Mailing Add:* Dept of Hort Sci & Landscape Archit Univ of Minn St Paul MN 55108

OZBURN, GEORGE W, b Guelph, Ont; m 39; c 4. ENTOMOLOGY, BIOLOGY. *Educ:* McGill Univ, BScAgr, 55, PhD(entom), 62; Univ London, DIC, 56. *Prof Exp:* Sci officer, Nigerian Stored Prod Res Unit, Nigeria, 56-59; asst prof biol, Northern Mich Univ, 62-65; asst prof, 65-71, assoc prof, 71-76, PROF BIOL, LAKEHEAD UNIV, 76- *Concurrent Pos:* Grants, Nat Res Coun, 65-69, USPHS, 66-68, Dept Univ Affairs, 70-71, Environ Protection, 72-75 & Ministry of Environ, 74-76, 77-80 & 81- *Mem:* Entom Soc Am; Can Soc Zool. *Res:* Insecticide resistance; pest control; aquatic entomology and biology related to pollutants and environment changes; aquatic toxicology. *Mailing Add:* Dept of Biol Lakehead Univ Thunder Bay ON P7B 5E1 Can

OZER, HARVEY LEON, b Boston, Mass, July 6, 38; m 60. VIROLOGY, CELL BIOLOGY. *Educ:* Harvard Univ, AB, 60; Stanford Univ, MD, 65. *Prof Exp:* Intern pediat, Children's Hosp Med Ctr, Boston, 65-66; res assoc, Lab Biol of Viruses, Nat Inst Allergy & Infectious Dis, 66-68; sr staff fel, Lab Biochem, Nat Cancer Inst, 69-72; sr scientist, Worcester Found Exp Biol, 72-77; PROF DEPT BIOL SCI, HUNTER COL, CITY UNIV OF NY, 77- *Concurrent Pos:* Vis fel, Inst Tumor Biol, Karolinska Inst, Sweden, 64; USPHS fel, Lab Viral Dis, Nat Inst Allergy & Infectious Dis, 68-69; prof lectr, Med Sch, George Washington Univ, 68-71; vis fac microbiol, Med Sch, Univ Mass, 72-77; virol study sect, NIH, 78- *Honors & Awards:* Borden Award, Med Sch, Stanford Univ, 65. *Mem:* Am Soc Microbiol; Genetics Soc Am. *Res:* Animal virology; genetics; mammalian cell biochemistry and genetics; tumor biology. *Mailing Add:* Hunter Col City Univ of NY New York NY 10021

OZER, MARK NORMAN, b Cambridge, Mass, Jan 17, 32; c 5. NEUROLOGY. *Educ:* Harvard Col, BA, 53; Boston Univ, MD, 57. *Prof Exp:* Instr neurol, 65-67, asst prof, 67-70, ASSOC PROF CHILD HEALTH & DEVELOP, SCH MED, GEORGE WASHINGTON UNIV, 71- *Concurrent Pos:* NIMH Spec fel, Washington Sch Psychiat, DC, 64-65; consult, US Air Force, 65-71; consult neurologist, Nat Childrens Ctr, Washington, DC, 65-71; prog dir learning studies, Childrens Hosp, Nat Med Ctr, Washington, DC, 65-74; multiple grants, 65-74; assoc prof psychiat & pediat, Univ Md, 67-74; consult neurologist, Prince Georges County Health Dept, Md, 67-70 & 77-; lectr, Dept Maternal & Child Health, Univ Mich, 68-70; consult neurologist, Northern Va Training Ctr, Va, 75-77. *Mem:* Am Acad Neurol; Am Soc Cybernetics (pres, 76-77); Am Acad Aphasia; Int Neuropsychol Soc; Soc Neurosci. *Res:* Development of assessment techniques for use with handicapped individuals that illustrate the sampling of the brain as an adaptive system; the design of delivery systems for the implementation of such techniques and the training of professionals in their use. *Mailing Add:* George Washington Univ Sch Med 3000 Connecticut Ave NW Washington DC 20008

OZERE, RUDOLPH L, b Winnipeg, Man, Mar 14, 26; m 59; c 2. PEDIATRICS, MICROBIOLOGY. *Educ:* McGill Univ, BSc, 47; Univ Ottawa, MD, 53; Harvard Univ, SM, 67. *Prof Exp:* Lectr bact, 61-70, asst prof prev med, 63-70, from asst prof to assoc prof pediat, 61-70, PROF PEDIAT, DALHOUSIE UNIV, 70-, LECTR MICROBIOL, 70-, ASST PROF PREV MED, 77- *Concurrent Pos:* Res fel microbiol, Dalhousie Univ, 59-61. *Mem:* Am Fedn Clin Res; Can Soc Clin Invest; Am Pediat Soc. *Res:* Epidemiology; clinical pediatrics. *Mailing Add:* Dept of Pediat Dalhousie Univ Fac of Med Halifax NS B3H 4H6 Can

OZIER, IRVING, b Montreal, Que, Sept 7, 38; m 63; c 3. MOLECULAR SPECTROSCOPY. *Educ:* Univ Toronto, BA, 60; Harvard Univ, AM, 61, PhD(physics), 65. *Prof Exp:* Alfred P Sloan res fel, 72-74; vis res fel, Katholieke Univ, Nijmegen, Netherlands, 76-77. *Mem:* Am Phys Soc; Can Asn Physicists. *Res:* Forbidden rotational transitions, small electric dipole moments; far-infrared and microwave spectroscopy; hindered internal rotation; magnetic resonance in molecules; nuclear hyperfine interactions and rotational magnetic moments; tetrahedral molecules; molecular beams. *Mailing Add:* Dept of Physics Univ of BC Vancouver BC V6T 2A6 Can

OZIMEK, EDWARD JOSEPH, b West Natrona, Pa, Nov 11, 45; m 68; c 3. SOLID STATE PHYSICS. *Educ:* Mt Union Col, BS, 68; Univ Akron, MS, 72; Colo State Univ, DPhil(physics), 77. *Prof Exp:* Asst prof, Univ Wis-Stout, 76-77; staff physicist piezoelec, Allied Chem Corp, 77-79; adj asst prof, Univ Ariz, 79-81; STAFF ENGR, IBM CORP, 81- *Mem:* AAAS; NY Acad Sci; Am Phys Soc; Inst Elec & Electronics Engrs. *Res:* Ultrasonic attenuation and velocity dispersion in materials; electron transport in metals; piezoelectric properties of oxide crystals; heat transfer and predictive thermal dosimetry in materials; magnetic properties of thin films; digital magnetic recording heads. *Mailing Add:* Gen Prod Div IBM Corp 74B-061-2 Tucson AZ 85744

OZIMKOSKI, RAYMOND EDWARD, b New York, NY, July 3, 27. MATHEMATICS. *Educ:* Fordham Univ, BS, 46, MS, 47. *Prof Exp:* From instr to asst prof math, Fordham Univ, 47-59; from asst prof to assoc prof, 59-68, PROF MATH, MERRIMACK COL, 68- *Mem:* Am Math Soc; Math Asn Am. *Mailing Add:* Dept of Math Merrimack Col North Andover MA 01845

OZIOMEK, JAMES, b Akron, Ohio, Feb 17, 41; m 60; c 4. ORGANIC CHEMISTRY, POLYMER CHEMISTRY. *Educ:* Case Inst Technol, BS, 63; Univ Calif, Berkeley, PhD(chem), 68. *Prof Exp:* res scientist, 68-75, sr res scientist, 75-78, ASSOC SCIENTIST, CENT RES LAB, FIRESTONE TIRE & RUBBER CO, 78- *Concurrent Pos:* Vis scientist, Inst Polymer Sci, Univ Akron, 73-74. *Mem:* Am Chem Soc; Sigma Xi. *Res:* Anionic and Ziegler polymerization for preparation of elastomers; cationic polymerization; urethane chemistry; adhesion. *Mailing Add:* Cent Res Lab Firestone Tire & Rubber Co Akron OH 44317

OZISIK, M NECATI, b Istanbul, Turkey, June 17, 23; m 57; c 1. MECHANICAL ENGINEERING. *Educ:* Univ London, BS, 47, PhD(mech eng), 50. *Prof Exp:* Sr res scientist, Am Soc Heating, Refrig & Air Conditioning Engrs Res Lab, 57-59 & Oak Ridge Nat Lab, 59-63; assoc prof, 63-66, PROF MECH ENG, NC STATE UNIV, 66- *Honors & Awards:* F Bernard Hall Prize, Brit Inst Mech Engrs, 52; Western Elec Fund Award, Am Soc Eng Educ, 72; Turkish Sci Award, 80. *Mem:* Am Soc Mech Engrs; Int Asn Hydrogen Energy. *Res:* Heat transfer; fluid mechanics. *Mailing Add:* Dept of Mech & Aerospace Eng NC State Univ Raleigh NC 27650

OZOG, FRANCIS JOSEPH, b Poland, Sept 9, 22; nat US; m 48; c 3. PHYSICAL CHEMISTRY, ORGANIC CHEMISTRY. *Educ:* Univ Detroit, BS, 47; Northwestern Univ, PhD(chem), 50. *Prof Exp:* From instr to assoc prof, 50-63, head dept, 57-69, dir div natural sci & math, 64-66 & 71-75, PROF CHEM, REGIS COL, 64- *Mem:* Am Chem Soc; fel, Asn Off Racing Chemists; fel Am Inst Chemists. *Res:* Toxicology and forensic chemistry. *Mailing Add:* Dept of Chem Regis Col Denver CO 80221

OZOL, MICHAEL ARVID, b New York, NY, Nov 27, 34; m 58; c 2. GEOLOGY. *Educ:* City Col New York,BS, 57; Univ Pittsburgh, MS, 58; Rensselaer Polytech Inst, PhD(geol), 63. *Prof Exp:* Asst petrologic res, Rensselaer Polytech Inst, 60-63; hwy mat res analyst, Va Hwy Res Coun, 63-71; sr res scientist, Res Inst Advan Studies, 71-78, prin scientist, 78-80, DIR, TECH DEVELOP, MARTIN MARIETTA AGGREGATES,, MARTIN MARIETTA CORP, 80- *Mem:* AAAS; Geol Soc Am; Am Soc Testing & Mat. *Res:* Properties of rocks which determine their suitability for use as aggregate; behavior of aggregate materials, including physical and chemical reactions; petrography of concrete and aggregates. *Mailing Add:* Martin Marietta Corp 6801 Rockledge Dr Bethesda MD 20034

OZSVATH, ISTVAN, b Kolesd, Hungary, Sept 10, 28; m 50; c 1. MATHEMATICAL PHYSICS. *Educ:* Eotvos Lorand Univ, Budapest, MS, 51; Univ Hamburg, PhD(astron), 60. *Prof Exp:* Res assoc astron, Konkoly Observ, Hungary, 51-56 & Hamburg Observ, Ger, 56-62; vis lectr math, Univ Tex, 62-63; assoc prof, 63-67, PROF MATH & MATH PHYSICS, UNIV TEX, DALLAS, 67- *Res:* Relativistic cosmology; general relativity. *Mailing Add:* Dept Math Univ Tex at Dallas Box 688 Richardson TX 75080

OZZELLO, LUCIANO, pathology, see previous edition

P

PAABO, MAYA, b Estonia, June 11, 29; US citizen. ANALYTICAL CHEMISTRY. *Educ:* George Washington Univ, BS, 56, MS, 62. *Prof Exp:* RES CHEMIST, NAT BUR STANDARDS, 56- *Mem:* Am Soc Mass Spectrometry; Am Chem Soc. *Res:* Relative strength of acids and bases in aprotic media; development of acidity scales in alcohol-water solvents and in heavy water; analytical chemical studies of polymeric materials and their combustion products as they relate to hazards from fires. *Mailing Add:* Ctr for Fire Res Nat Bur of Standards Washington DC 20234

PAAL, FRANK F, b Budapest, Hungary, Aug 25, 30; US citizen. COMPUTER SCIENCE. *Educ:* McGill Univ, BSc, 59; Stanford Univ, MA, 62; Univ Calif, Los Angeles, MSc, 65, PhD(comput sci), 69. *Prof Exp:* Sr engr, Hoffman Electronics, 61-63; assoc prof, 67-81, PROF ELEC ENG, CALIF STATE UNIV, LONG BEACH, 81- *Mem:* Inst Elec & Electronics Engrs; Am Fedn Info Processing; Int Fedn Info Processing. *Res:* Arithmetic processors; simulation of dynamic systems. *Mailing Add:* Dept of Elec Eng 6101 E Seventh St Long Beach CA 90804

PAASWELL, ROBERT E(MIL), b Red Wing, Minn, Jan 15, 37; m 58; c 2. TRANSPORTATION, CIVIL ENGINEERING. *Educ:* Columbia Univ, BA, 56, BS, 57, MS, 61; Rutgers Univ, PhD(civil eng), 65. *Prof Exp:* Civil engr, Spencer, White & Prentis, Inc, 57-59; teaching asst soil mech, Columbia Univ, 59-62; from asst prof to assoc prof civil eng, State Univ NY Buffalo, 64-76, prof 76-80, dir, Ctr Transp Studies & Res, 78-81, prof, Dept Environ Design & Planning, 80-81; DIR URBAN TRANSP & PROF ENG, UNIV ILL, CHICAGO CIRCLE, 82- *Concurrent Pos:* State Univ NY Res Found fac grant, 66-; mem comt, Nat Acad Sci-Nat Res Coun, 66; Greater London Coun res fel polit & econ planning, Eng, 71-72; fac tech consult; energy consult, US Cong, 73-74; fac fel, US Dept Transp, 76-77. *Honors & Awards:* Award & Medal, US Dept Transp, 77. *Mem:* AAAS; Am Soc Civil Engrs; Sigma Xi. *Res:* Urban transport studies; special service transportation analysis; problems of the carless; urban transportation; urban planning and systems; environmental systems. *Mailing Add:* Urban Transp Ctr Univ Ill Chicago Circle Box 4348 Chicago IL 60680

PAAVOLA, LAURIE GAIL, b LaCrosse, Wis; m 71. CELL BIOLOGY, ANATOMY. *Educ:* San Diego State Univ, AB, 65; Stanford Univ, PhD(anat), 70. *Prof Exp:* ASST PROF ANAT, SCH MED, TEMPLE UNIV, 72- *Concurrent Pos:* NIH fels, Dept Anat, Stanford Univ, 70-71 & Dept Anat, Temple Univ, 71-72; prin investr, Nat Inst Child Health & Human Develop res grant, 78-80. *Mem:* Am Asn Anatomists; Am Soc Cell Biol; AAAS. *Res:* Reproductive biology; ovary; cell biology of granulosa cells and luteal cells; smooth membrane biogenesis during luteinization; mechanisms of ovarian lipid metabolism; role of autophagy and heterophagy in luteolysis; electron microscope cytochemistry; transmission and scanning electron microscopy. *Mailing Add:* Dept of Anat 3420 N Broad St Philadelphia PA 19140

PABST, ADOLF, b Chicago, Ill, Nov 30, 99; m 29. MINERALOGY, CRYSTALLOGRAPHY. *Educ:* Univ Ill, BA, 25; Univ Calif, PhD(geol), 28. *Prof Exp:* Lectr, 27-28, from instr to prof, 29-67, EMER PROF MINERAL, UNIV CALIF, BERKELEY, 67- *Concurrent Pos:* Am-Scand Found fel, Univ Oslo, 28-29; Guggenheim fel, 38-39; Fulbright scholar, Univ Vienna, 55-56; distinguished vis prof, Univ Nev, 67-68; vis prof, Univ Ore, 68-69; Fulbright vis prof, Univ Kiel & Tech Univ, Berlin, 70-71; prin investr, NSF Proj Mineral & Petrol of Green River Formation of Utah, Wyo & Colo, 74-78. *Honors & Awards:* Roebling Medal, Mineral Soc Am, 65; Friedrich Becke Medal, Austrian Mineral Soc, 74; Hon Award, Calif Fedn Mineral Socs, Inc, 78. *Mem:* Fel Geol Soc Am (vpres, 52); fel Mineral Soc Am (vpres, 48, pres, 51); Am Crystallog Asn (vpres, 47, pres, 48) ; Mineral Asn Can; hon mem Ger Mineral Soc. *Res:* Crystallography; crystal structure; Green River mineralogy. *Mailing Add:* Dept Geol & Geophys Univ Calif Berkeley CA 94720

PABST, MICHAEL JOHN, b Washington, DC, Oct 19, 45; m 69; c 2. PHAGOCYTES, IMMUNITY. *Educ:* Boston Col, BS, 67; Purdue Univ, PhD(biochem), 72. *Prof Exp:* Staff fel biochem, NIH, 72-74; asst prof oral biol, Sch Dent, 74-77, ASST PROF BIOCHEM, SCH MED, UNIV COLO, 76- *Concurrent Pos:* Asst prof pediat, Nat Jewish Hosp & Res Ctr, 77- *Mem:* Am Soc Microbiol; Am Soc Biol Chemists. *Res:* Mechanisms of macrophage and neutrophil killing of microorganisms. *Mailing Add:* Dept of Pediat Nat Jewish Hosp & Res Ctr Denver CO 80206

PACAK, MILOS, b Kladno, Czech; US citizen; m 42; c 1. MEDICAL INFORMATION SCIENCE, COMPUTATIONAL LINGUISTICS. *Educ:* Charles Univ, Prague, Czech, LLD, 37, PolScD, 37. *Prof Exp:* Sr ling mach transl, Georgetown Univ, 55-66; sr ling mach transl, Itek Corp, 66-67; HEAD MED INFO SECT, NIH, 67- *Concurrent Pos:* Adj prof, Am Univ, 67-74; reviewer, NSF, 67-; reviewer, Nat Endowment for Humanities, 74- *Mem:* Am Soc Info Sci; Asn Comput Ling. *Res:* Semantic structuring of medical terms; structuring of computer oriented medical dictionaries. *Mailing Add:* Div of Comput Res & Technol NIH Bldg 12-A Bethesda MD 20205

PACANSKY, THOMAS JOHN, b Erie, Pa, Dec 17, 46; m 72. POLYMER CHEMISTRY. *Educ:* Gannon Col, BS, 68; Univ Mich, Ann Arbor, MS, 70, PhD(chem), 72. *Prof Exp:* Assoc scientist, Xerox Corp, 72-74, scientist polymer chem, 74-79; develop chemist, 79-80, MGR, CHEM DEPT, EXXON ENTERPRISES, 80- *Mem:* Am Chem Soc; Sigma Xi. *Res:* Material properties of polymers relating to their imaging by photochemical, thermal and electrical applications. *Mailing Add:* Exxon Enterprises 328 Gibraltar Dr Sunnyvale CA 94086

PACE, CARLOS NICK, b Salt Lake City, Utah, Feb 22, 40; m 59; c 3. PHYSICAL BIOCHEMISTRY. *Educ:* Univ Utah, BS, 62; Duke Univ, PhD(biochem), 66. *Prof Exp:* USPHS fel, Cornell Univ, 66-68; ASSOC PROF BIOCHEM, TEX A&M UNIV, 68- *Mem:* Am Soc Biol Chemists; Am Chem Soc. *Res:* Physical chemical studies of proteins and enzymes; protein turnover. *Mailing Add:* Dept of Biochem Tex A&M Univ College Station TX 77843

PACE, CAROLINE S, b Richmond, Va, May 19, 42; m 61; c 2. PHYSIOLOGY. *Educ:* Va Commonwealth Univ, BS, 67; Med Col Va, PhD(physiol), 73. *Prof Exp:* Teaching asst anat & embryol biol, Va Commonwealth Univ, 65-67, lab instr, 67-68; fel, Wash Univ, 72-74, res asst prof pharmacol, 74-76; asst prof, 76-79, ASSOC PROF PHYSIOL, UNIV ALA, 79- *Mem:* Am Diabetes Asn; Endocrine Soc; Am Physiol Soc; Soc Gen Physiologists; Sigma Xi. *Res:* Stimulus-secretion coupling in pancreatic islets of Langerhans employing electrophysiological, biochemical and functional approaches. *Mailing Add:* Dept Physiol Diabetes Hosp Univ of Ala Sch of Med Birmingham AL 35294

PACE, DANIEL GANNON, b Pittsburgh, Pa, May 1, 45. PHARMACOLOGY. *Educ:* Univ Pittsburgh, BS, 67; Georgetown Univ, PhD(pharmacol), 75. *Prof Exp:* Fel cardiovasc pharmacol, Mt Sinai Hosp, Cleveland, Ohio, 75; asst prof, Case Western Reserve Med Sch, 75-78; SR SCIENTIST CARDIOVASC PHARMACOL, HOFFMANN LA ROCHE, 78- *Res:* Drug action on the cardiovascular system. *Mailing Add:* Dept of Pharmacol Hoffmann La Roche Nutley NJ 07110

PACE, DONALD M, b Wilkes-Barre, Pa, Nov 8, 06; m 36; c 3. CELL PHYSIOLOGY. *Educ:* Susquehanna Univ, BS, 28; Duke Univ, MS, 29, PhD(zool), 31. *Hon Degrees:* DSc, Susquehanna Univ, 61. *Prof Exp:* Res asst, Johns Hopkins Univ, 31-33, instr zool, 33-42; from asst prof to prof physiol, Univ Nebr, 42-67, chmn dept, 46-62, dir inst cellular res, 51-67; actg acad vpres, 71, prof, 67-81, dir cellular res, 67-81, EMER PROF PHYSIOL & PHARMACOL, COL PHARM, UNIV OF THE PAC, 81- *Mem:* Fel AAAS; Am Soc Zool; Am Physiol Soc; Soc Gen Physiol; fel NY Acad Sci. *Res:* Factors involved in normal and abnormal cell growth, metabolism, morphology, cytology and tissue cultures. *Mailing Add:* Dept of Physiol & Pharmacol Univ of the Pac Stockton CA 95207

PACE, GARY LEE, malacology, see previous edition

PACE, HENRY ALEXANDER, b Cleveland, Ohio, Mar 7, 14; m 45; c 2. ORGANIC CHEMISTRY. *Educ:* Univ Ill, BS, 36; Iowa State Univ, PhD(org chem), 40. *Prof Exp:* Asst org chem, Iowa State Univ, 36-40; org res chemist, 40-65, res sci, Goodyear Tire & Rubber Co, 66-79, RETIRED. *Concurrent Pos:* Consult. *Mem:* AAAS; Am Chem Soc; Am Inst Chem. *Res:* Thermosetting and thermoplastic resins; petrochemical by-products; epoxy resins; fabrication of acrylic resins; rigid and elastomeric polyurethane foams and resins; electrophoresis equipment. *Mailing Add:* 1997 Wyndham Rd Akron OH 44313

PACE, HENRY BUFORD, b Thomasville, Tenn, Nov 21, 29; m 54; c 2. PHYSIOLOGY. *Educ:* Univ Tenn, BS, 52, MS, 57; Tex A&M Univ, PhD(physiol), 64. *Prof Exp:* Res asst reproductive physiol, AEC Agr Res Lab, Univ Tenn, 55-60; assoc radiobiologist, Radiation Biol Lab, Tex A&M Univ, 60-65; from asst prof to assoc prof physiol, St Louis Col Pharm, 65-68; assoc prof physiol, 68-74, PROF PHARMACOL & PHYSIOL, SCH PHARM, UNIV MISS, 68- Prof Exp: NIMH grant teratogenesis of marijuana, Univ Miss, 68-72. *Mem:* Am Asn Lab Animal Sci; Soc Study Reprod. *Res:* Pharmacology, toxicology and teratogenesis of drugs and other chemical compounds; male and female reproductive physiology. *Mailing Add:* 418 Longest Rd Oxford MS 38655

PACE, JUDITH G, b Scranton, Pa, Dec 24, 49; m 72. ENZYMOLOGY, INTERMEDIARY METABOLISM. *Educ:* Marywood Col, BS, 71; Hood Col, MS, 77; George Washington Univ, PhD(biochem), 80. *Prof Exp:* Med asst, Pvt Physician, 66-71; res asst chem, Marywood Col, 70-71; chemist, US Naval Ship Res & Develop Ctr, 71-73, RES CHEMIST, US ARMY MED RES INST INFECTIOUS DIS, 77- *Concurrent Pos:* Lectr biochem, Hood Col, 77-78. *Mem:* Am Chem Soc; Am Fed Clin Res; AAAS. *Res:* Effect of infectious diseases on fatty acid metabolism, specifically the hepatic carnitine-acylcarnitine system; effect of mycotoxins on host metabolism; the metabolism and detoxication of mycotoxins. *Mailing Add:* US Army Med Res Inst Infectious Dis Bldg 1425 Fort Detrick Frederick MD 21701

PACE, JUDITH LEE, immunobiology, immunochemistry, see previous edition

PACE, MARSHALL OSTEEN, b Greenville, SC, Sept 10, 41; m 68. ELECTRICAL ENGINEERING. *Educ:* Univ SC, BS, 63; Mass Inst Technol, MS & EE, 65; Ga Inst Technol, PhD(elec eng), 70. *Prof Exp:* Engr, Columbia Prod Co, 65; from asst prof to assoc prof, 70-78, PROF ELEC ENG, UNIV TENN, KNOXVILLE, 78- *Concurrent Pos:* Res assoc, Environ Systs Corp, 72; prin investr govt & indust res, Univ Tenn, 72-; fac fel, NASA, Huntsville, Ala, 73; consult, Oak Ridge Nat Lab, 74- *Mem:* Inst Elec & Electronics Engrs; Conf Int des Grands Reseaux Electriques. *Res:* Gaseous and solid state electronics; direct energy conversion; high voltage phenomena; atomic collisions; statistical communications theory; electromagnetics; power systems. *Mailing Add:* Dept of Elec Eng Ferris Hall Univ of Tenn Knoxville TN 37916

PACE, MARVIN M, b Coalville, Utah, Mar 11, 44; m 63; c 5. REPRODUCTIVE PHYSIOLOGY, ANIMAL SCIENCE. *Educ:* Utah State Univ, BS, 66; Univ Minn, MS, 68, PhD(animal sci), 71. *Prof Exp:* Res asst, Univ Minn, 66-71; ASSOC DIR RES, AM BREEDERS SERV DIV, W R GRACE CO, 71- *Mem:* Am Soc Animal Sci; Soc Study Reproduction. *Res:* Study of biochemical changes that take place in spermatozoa during preservation and how these changes affect fertilization. *Mailing Add:* Am Breeders Serv Rt 1 DeForest WI 53532

PACE, NELLO, b Richmond, Calif, June 20, 16; m 39, 59; c 2. PHYSIOLOGY. *Educ:* Univ Calif, BS, 36, PhD(physiol), 40. *Prof Exp:* Asst physiol, Univ Calif, 36-40; res assoc, Med Col Va, 40-41; head, physiol facil, Naval Med Res Inst, Bethesda, Md, 41-46; res assoc med physics, 46-53, from asst prof to assoc prof physiol, 48-57, chmn dept physiol anat, 64-67, dir White Mountain Res Sta, 50-77, prof, 57-77, EMER PROF PHYSIOL, UNIV CALIF, BERKELEY, 77- *Concurrent Pos:* Officer-in-chg Unit 1, Off Naval Res, 51-53; asst leader & chief scientist, Himalayan Exped to Makalu, 54; leader, Int Physiol Exped to Antarctica, 57-58; consult to adminr, NASA, 63, experimenter on Biosatellite III, 65-70, experimenter on Cosmos 1129, 78-80; chmn panel on gravitational biol, Comt on Space Res, Int Coun Sci Unions, 71-81; mem comn on gravitational physiol, Int Union Physiol Sci, 73- *Mem:* AAAS; Soc Exp Biol & Med; Am Physiol Soc; Aerospace Med Asn; Int Acad Astronaut. *Res:* Gravitational physiology; environmental physiology; in vivo body composition. *Mailing Add:* Environ Physiol Lab T 2251 Univ of Calif Berkeley CA 94720

PACE, NORMAN R, biochemistry, see previous edition

PACE, SALVATORE JOSEPH, b Trieste, Italy, Apr 23, 44; US citizen; m 67; c 2. CHEMISTRY. *Educ:* Syracuse Univ, AB, 65, PhD(chem), 70. *Prof Exp:* Res fel, Univ Mich, 70-71 & Pa State Univ, 71-72; mem staff electrochem, Kettering Res Lab, 72-73; res scientist, Technicon Inst Corp, 73-80; MEM STAFF, EXP STA, E I DU PONT DE NEMOURS & CO, INC, 80- *Mem:* Am Chem Soc. *Res:* Electrochemical kinetics of fast reactions; electron transfer properties of metalloporphyrins and related compounds of biological importance; development of electrochemical sensors for clinical medicine applications. *Mailing Add:* Exp Sta E-325-375 E I du Pont de Nemours & Co Inc Wilmington DE 19898

PACE, WESLEY EMORY, b Esmont, Va, Nov 15, 24; m 46; c 3. MATHEMATICS. *Educ:* Univ Va, BA, 45, MA, 51. *Prof Exp:* Instr math, Univ Va, 48-53; from instr to asst prof, 53-58, ASSOC PROF MATH, VA POLYTECH INST & STATE UNIV, 58- *Mem:* Math Asn Am. *Res:* Topology, mainly transformation theory. *Mailing Add:* Dept of Math Va Polytech Inst & State Univ Blacksburg VA 24060

PACE, WILLIAM GREENVILLE, b Columbus, Ohio, Mar 22, 27; m 49; c 3. SURGERY. *Educ:* Dartmouth Col, AB, 48; Univ Pa, MD, 52; Ohio State Univ, MMSc, 59. *Prof Exp:* From instr to prof surg, Col Med, Ohio State Univ, 60-74, asst dean col med postgrad educ, 63-72, asst dean admin, 72-74. *Concurrent Pos:* Adv clin fel, Am Cancer Soc, 61-64. *Mem:* Am Asn Surg of Trauma; Soc Surg Alimentary Tract; Soc Univ Surg; Am Surg Asn; Am Col Surgeons. *Res:* Parathyroid and pancreas interrelationships; effects of chemotherapy in regional administration; cryotherapy; immunology. *Mailing Add:* Dept Surg Ohio State Univ Hosp Columbus OH 43210

PACE ASCIAK, CECIL, b Malta, Jan 1, 40; Can citizen. ORGANIC CHEMISTRY, BIOCHEMISTRY. *Educ:* Loyola Col, Que, BSc, 62; McGill Univ, PhD(org chem), 66. *Prof Exp:* Med Res Coun fel, fel neurochem, Montreal Neurol Inst, McGill Univ, 66-68, Med Res Coun scholar, 68-72; RES SCIENTIST, HOSP FOR SICK CHILDREN, 72-; asst prof, 72-78, ASSOC PROF PHARMACOL, UNIV TORONTO, 78- *Concurrent Pos:* Josiah Macy Found scholar, 80-81. *Mem:* Am Chem Soc; Am Soc Neurochem; Sigma Xi; Chem Inst Can; NY Acad Sci. *Res:* Natural products; photochemistry; prostaglandins; lipids; prostaglandin biosynthesis and metabolism during animal development. *Mailing Add:* Hosp for Sick Children Res Inst 555 University Ave Toronto ON M5G 1X8 Can

PACER, JOHN CHARLES, b Toledo, Ohio, Apr 23, 47; m 70; c 2. NUCLEAR CHEMISTRY. *Educ:* Univ Toledo, BS, 69; Purdue Univ, PhD(phys chem), 74. *Prof Exp:* Res asst nuclear chem, Purdue Univ, 69-74; fel nuclear chem, Ames Lab, USERDA, 74-76; SR RES SCIENTIST, BENDIX FIELD ENG CORP, 76- *Mem:* Am Chem Soc; Am Phys Soc. *Res:* The use of isotopic techniques for uranium exploration; helium jet transport of fission products; nuclear spectroscopy of neutron rich nuclei; geochemical characterization of nuclear waste sites; field radiation measurements; transport studies of isotopic species. *Mailing Add:* 560 McMullin Dr Grand Junction CO 81501

PACER, RICHARD A, b Toledo, Ohio, Jan 15, 39; m 66; c 2. ANALYTICAL CHEMISTRY, RADIOCHEMISTRY. *Educ:* Univ Toledo, BS, 60, MS, 62; Univ Mich, PhD(anal chem), 65. *Prof Exp:* From asst to assoc prof, 65-78, PROF CHEM, PURDUE UNIV, FT WAYNE, 78- *Mem:* Am Chem Soc; Am Asn Univ Prof. *Res:* liquid seintillation counting; isotope dilution analysis; analytical chemistry of technetium and rhenium. *Mailing Add:* Dept of Chem Purdue Univ Ft Wayne IN 46805

PACHA, ROBERT EDWARD, b Payette, Idaho, Sept 4, 32; m 64. MICROBIOLOGY. *Educ:* Univ Wash, BS, 55, MS, 58, PhD(microbiol), 61. *Prof Exp:* Res instr microbiol, Univ Wash, 61-64; from asst prof to assoc prof, Ore State Univ, 64-70; assoc prof, 70-73, PROF BIOL, CENT WASH UNIV, 73-, DIR, CTR MED TECHNOL, 74- *Mem:* AAAS; Am Soc Microbiol; Brit Soc Gen Microbiol; Am Soc Limnol & Oceanog; Am Fisheries Soc. *Res:* Bacteriology of pure and polluted water; fish diseases; higher bacteria; myxobacteria. *Mailing Add:* Dept Biol Sci Cent Wash Univ Ellensburg WA 98926

PACHCIARZ, JUDITH ANN, immunology, microbiology, see previous edition

PACHECO, ANTHONY LOUIS, b New Bedford, Mass, Sept 12, 32; m 56, 77; c 4. FISH BIOLOGY, FISHERIES. *Educ:* Univ Mass, BS, 54; Col William & Mary, MA, 57. *Prof Exp:* Aquatic res biologist, Va Inst Marine Sci, 56-59; fishery res biologist, Biol Lab, Bur Com Fisheries, US Dept Interior, 59-66 & Sandy Hook Marine Lab, Bur Sport Fisheries & Wildlife, 66-69, FISHERY RES BIOLOGIST, SANDY HOOK LAB, NORTHEAST FISHERIES CTR, NAT MARINE FISHERIES SERV, NAT OCEANIC & ATMOSPHERIC ADMIN, 69- *Mem:* Am Fisheries Soc; Am Inst Fishery Res Biologists; Atlantic Estuarine Res Soc; Am Littoral Soc. *Res:* Ecology of estuarine and coastal marine fishes; distribution, age-growth studies and estimation techniques to assess population abundance; coastal fisheries. *Mailing Add:* Sandy Hook Lab Nat Marine Fisheries Serv Highlands NJ 07732

PACHMAN, DANIEL JAMES, b New York, NY, Dec 20, 11; m 35; c 2. PEDIATRICS. *Educ:* Univ NC, AB, 31; Duke Univ, MD, 34; Am Bd Pediat, dipl, 38. *Prof Exp:* Intern pediat, Univ Chicago, 34-35; intern, Med Ctr, Cornell Univ, 35-36; instr pediat, Duke Univ & resident & attend pediatrician, Duke Hosp, 36-37; instr pediat, Univ Chicago, 37-40 & Northwestern Univ, 40-50; clin asst prof, 50-58, clin assoc prof, 58-67, CLIN PROF PEDIAT, UNIV ILL COL MED, 67-; PROF, RUSH MED COL, 71- *Concurrent Pos:* Attend pediatrician, Clins, Univ Chicago, 37-40; mem courtesy staff, Chicago Lying-In Hosp, 49-; attend pediatrician, Ill Res & Educ Hosp, 50-; consult, South Shore Hosp, 54- & Bd Educ, Chicago, 54-; chmn dept pediat, Ill Cent Hosp, 58-70, consult pediatrician, 70-; chmn, Ill Pediat Coord Coun, 69-; consult pediatrician, Presby-St Luke's Hosp, 70-; attend pediatrician, SChicago Hosp, 71-; Am Acad Pediat liaison rep on Nat Adv Health Coun, Nat Cong Parents & Teachers; pvt pract; assoc attend pediatrician, Children's Mem Hosp, 72- *Honors & Awards:* Archibald Hoyne Award, Chicago Pediat Soc, 77. *Mem:* Fel AMA; Am Heart Asn; fel Am Acad Pediat. *Res:* Carbohydrate metabolism; lipoid diseases; clinical approach. *Mailing Add:* 1212 N Lake Shore Dr Chicago IL 60610

PACHMAN, LAUREN M, b Durham, NC, Mar 16, 37; c 2. PEDIATRICS, IMMUNOLOGY. *Educ:* Wellesley Col, BA, 57; Univ Chicago, MD, 61. *Prof Exp:* Asst physician pediat, Rockefeller Univ & Columbia Univ Col Physicians & Surgeons, 64-66; from instr to asst prof, Med Sch, Univ Chicago, 66-71; assoc prof, 71-78, PROF PEDIAT, MED SCH, NORTHWESTERN UNIV, 78- *Concurrent Pos:* Dr Astrid Fagraeus sponsor, State Bacteriol Lab, Solna, Sweden, 60; NIH fel, 64-66. *Mem:* Am Asn Immunol; Soc Pediat Res; Am Rheumatism Asn; AAAS. *Res:* Pediatric immunology and rheumatology; pharmacokinetics; cell-mediated immunity; immune complex disease. *Mailing Add:* 2300 Children's Plaza Chicago IL 60614

PACHOLCZYK, ANDRZEJ GRZEGORZ, b Warsaw, Poland, Sept 23, 35; m 63; c 3. THEORETICAL ASTROPHYSICS, RADIO ASTRONOMY. *Educ:* Univ Warsaw, MSc, 56 & 57, DSc(math, physics), 61. *Prof Exp:* Asst physics, Univ Warsaw, 55-57; sr asst astron, Polish Acad Sci, 58-61, adj, 61-62; vis scientist, Harvard Col Observ, 62-63, res fel, 63-64; vis fel, Joint Inst Lab Astrophys, Boulder, Colo, 64-65; asst prof, 65-68, ASSOC PROF ASTRON, UNIV ARIZ, 68-, ASSOC ASTRONR, STEWARD OBSERV, 70- *Concurrent Pos:* Polish Acad Sci res fel, Astron Inst, 58-59; lectr, Univ Warsaw, 58-59, 61-62; Ital Foreign Ministry res fel, Univ Turin, 59-60; vis scientist, Inst Earth Physics, USSR Acad Sci, 62 & Astron Inst Czech Acad Sci, 62; sr res fel, Univ Sussex, 73; vis prof, Nat Res Coun, Bologna, 73; vis scientist, Nat Radio Astron Observ, 76. *Mem:* Int Astron Union; Am Astron Soc; fel Royal Astron Soc; Polish Astron Soc (actg secy, 59-61, secy, 61-63); Polish Phys Soc. *Res:* Gravitational instability; magnetohydrodynamics; physics of interstellar medium; theoretical radioastronomy; physics of extragalactic radio sources. *Mailing Add:* Dept of Astron Univ of Ariz Tucson AZ 85721

PACHTER, IRWIN JACOB, b New York, NY, July 15, 25; m 53; c 2. ORGANIC CHEMISTRY. *Educ:* Univ Calif, Los Angeles, BS, 47; Univ NMex, MS, 49; Univ Southern Calif, PhD, 51. *Prof Exp:* Fel, Univ Ill, 51-52 & Harvard Univ, 52-53; res chemist, Ethyl Corp, 53-55; assoc res chemist, Smith Kline & French Labs, 55-62, asst sect head, 62; dir med chem, Endo Labs, Inc, NY, 62-66, dir res, 67-70; VPRES RES & DEVELOP, BRISTOL LABS, 70- *Concurrent Pos:* Lectr, Adelphi Univ, 63-69; chmn conf med chem, Gordon Res Conf, 71, mem selection & scheduling comt, 71-75; chmn task force on drug abuse prev, Pharmaceut Mfrs Asn, 71-73 & Res & Develop Sect, 75-76; mem med chem ad hoc study group, Walter Reed Army Inst Res, 73-75, chmn, 75-77. *Mem:* Am Chem Soc (secy, Div Med Chem, 72-74, chmn, 74-75). *Res:* Heterocyclic relationships of pharmaceuticals; narcotic antagonists; analgetics; psychotherapeutics; diuretics; antibiotics; natural products. *Mailing Add:* Bristol Labs PO Box 657 Syracuse NY 13201

PACHTMAN, ELLIOTT A, b Newark, NJ, Aug 8, 19; m 48; c 5. BIOCHEMISTRY. *Educ:* Univ Colo, AB, 47; Univ Ill, MS, 53; Georgetown Univ, PhD(biochem), 58; Nat Registry Clin Chem, cert. *Prof Exp:* Histopathologist, Maimonides Hosp, 38-40; biochemist, US Vet Admin, New York, 47-48; dir microbiol C F Kirk Pharmaceut Co, NY, 48-51; res microbiologist, Toni Co, Col Med, Univ Ill, 51-53; res immunochemist, Allergen Sect, Utilization Res Br, USDA, 53-55; asst chief technologist, US Fish & Wildlife Serv, 55-56; res assoc biochem, Georgetown Univ, 56-58; dir microbiol, chmn res prog team, Nat Drug Co, 58-61; assoc dir clin lab, Beth-El Hosp, 61-62; dir clin lab sect, Vet Admin Hosp, Philadelphia, Pa, 62-65; assoc dir lab & dir res & develop, Long Island Lab, Flushing, NY, 65-66; dir biochem, Daroff Div Albert Einstein Med Ctr, 66-76; DIR LABS, UNION HEALTH CTR, 76- *Concurrent Pos:* Consult, Lower Bucks Hosp, Bristol, Pa; dir-consult, Med Diagnostics, Inc, Norristown, Pa; consult automated fluorometry, Am Instrument Co, Silver Spring, Md, hemat, Daroff Div, Albert Einstein Med Ctr; asst prof, Dept Path, Jefferson Med Col. *Mem:* AAAS; Am Microbiol Soc; Am Chem Soc; Am Asn Clin Chem. *Res:* Automation of routine and complex procedures; hormones-spectrophotometrically, fluorometrically and gas-liquid chromatography; enzymes and isozymes; electrophoresis; radioimmunoassay; toxicology, drug screen; immunoglobulins, immunohematology and vaccines. *Mailing Add:* 1603 Longshore Ave Philadelphia PA 19149

PACIFICI, JAMES GRADY, b Savannah, Ga, May 20, 39. PHYSICAL ORGANIC CHEMISTRY. *Educ:* Univ Ga, BS, 62, PhD(chem), 66. *Prof Exp:* NSF fel, Mass Inst Technol, 66-67; SR RES CHEMIST, TENN EASTMAN CO DIV, EASTMAN KODAK CO, 67- *Mem:* Am Chem Soc; The Chem Soc. *Res:* Photochemistry of molecular and macromolecular systems; mechanism of free radical reactions. *Mailing Add:* Bldg 150A Tennessee Eastman Co Kingsport TN 37660

PACIOREK, KAZIMIERA J L, b Poland, Feb 18, 31; US citizen; m 57; c 1. POLYMER CHEMISTRY, FLUORINE CHEMISTRY. *Educ:* Univ Western Australia, BSc, 53, hons, 54, PhD(org chem), 57. *Prof Exp:* Fel org chem, Wayne State Univ, 56-57; res chemist, Wyandotte Chem Corp, Mich, 57-61; sr res chemist, US Naval Ordn Lab, Calif, 61-64, MHD Res, Inc, 64-66 & Marquardt Corp, 66-70; sr res chemist, Dynamic Sci Div, Marshall Industs, 70-72; SR SCIENTIST, ULTRASYSTEMS, INC, 72- *Mem:* Am Chem Soc; Royal Australian Chem Inst. *Res:* Natural products, especially triterpenoids and steroids; fluorocarbons; organometallics, particularly the chemistry of phosphorus and silicon; adoption of discharge techniques to various synthetic aspects; oxidative polymer degradation, flammability of materials. *Mailing Add:* Ultrasystems Inc 2400 Michelson Dr Irvine CA 92715

PACIOTTI, MICHAEL ANTHONY, b St Paul, Minn, Aug 18, 42; m 66; c 2. APPLIED PHYSICS, PHYSICS. *Educ:* Univ Calif, Berkeley, BS, 64, PhD(physics), 69. *Prof Exp:* Res asst physics, Lawrence Berkeley Lab, 66-69; MEM STAFF PHYSICS, LOS ALAMOS SCI LAB, 70- *Res:* Practical application of particle accelerators; application of negative pi-mesons to radiation therapy; charged particle beam optics; proton computerized tomography. *Mailing Add:* Los Alamos Sci Lab PO Box 1663 Los Alamos NM 87545

PACK, ALBERT BOYD, b Kamas, Utah, May 10, 19; m 45; c 3. AGRICULTURAL METEOROLOGY. *Educ:* Brigham Young Univ, BS, 40; Univ Mass, MS, 43; NC State Univ, PhD(plant physiol), 50. *Prof Exp:* Asst prof plant physiol, Conn Agr Exp Sta, 46-47 & 50-55; state climatologist, Nat Weather Serv, US Dept Commerce, Conn & RI, 56-59 & SDak, 59-61; state climatologist, Nat Oceanic & Atmospheric Admin, NY, 62-73, sr res assoc, 73-77, sr ext assoc, 77-81, SR LECTR, STATE UNIV NY COL AGR & LIFE SCI, CORNELL UNIV, 81- *Concurrent Pos:* Asst prof, Cornell Univ, 67-73. *Mem:* Am Meteorol Soc. *Res:* Effect of macro-climate and various weather elements on growth, phenology and yield of crops and on vegetation in general; climate of New York State. *Mailing Add:* Div Atmospheric Sci Dept Agron Cornell Univ Ithaca NY 14850

PACK, JOHN LEE, b Silver City, NMex, June 7, 27; m 50; c 5. PHYSICS. *Educ:* Univ NMex, BS, 50, MS, 52. *Prof Exp:* Res asst electronics, Univ NMex, 49-50, res assoc, 51; int res engr, 52-58, res engr, 58-64, SR ENGR, WESTINGHOUSE RES & DEVELOP CTR, 64- *Mem:* Sr mem Inst Elec & Electronics Eng; Am Phys Soc. *Res:* Drift velocity of electrons in gases; attachment and detachment of electrons in molecular oxygen and molecular oxygen mixtures; negative ions in air; oxygen and gas mixtures; hydration of oxygen negative ions; carbon dioxide lasers; copper halide lasers; excimer lasers; glow to arc transitions. *Mailing Add:* Westinghouse Res & Develop Ctr Pittsburgh PA 15235

PACK, MERRILL RAYMOND, b Idaho Falls, Idaho, Apr 15, 23; m 49; c 6. PLANT PHYSIOLOGY. *Educ:* Brigham Young Univ, BS, 49; Rutgers Univ, PhD(soils), 52. *Prof Exp:* Asst prof soils, NMex State Univ, 52-56; plant physiologist, US Steel Corp, Utah, 56-63; PROF & PLANT PHYSIOLOGIST, WASH STATE UNIV, 63- *Mem:* AAAS; Am Soc Plant Physiol; Air Pollution Control Asn. *Res:* Soil fertility; plant nutrition; effect of air pollutants on plants; biogenic sources of air pollution; atmospheric analysis. *Mailing Add:* Air Pollution Res Sect Chem Eng Dept Wash Sta Univ Pullman WA 99163

PACK, RUSSELL T, b Grace, Idaho, Nov 20, 37; m 62; c 7. QUANTUM MECHANICS, STATISTICAL MECHANICS. *Educ:* Brigham Young Univ, BS, 62; Univ Wis-Madison, PhD(phys chem), 67. *Prof Exp:* Res fel chem eng, Univ Minn, 66-67; from asst prof to assoc prof chem, Brigham Young Univ, 67-75; RES SCIENTIST, LOS ALAMOS SCI LAB, 75- *Concurrent Pos:* Vis scientist, Los Alamos Sci Lab, 73-74, consult, 74-75; Alexander von Humbolt Sr Scientist Award, 81. *Mem:* Am Chem Soc; Am Phys Soc. *Res:* Theoretical physical chemistry; molecular quantum mechanics; molecular collisions; statistical mechanics. *Mailing Add:* Theoret Molecular Physics Group Los Alamos Sci Lab Los Alamos NM 87545

PACKARD, DAVID, b Pueblo, Colo, Sept 7, 12; m 38; c 4. ELECTRICAL ENGINEERING. *Educ:* Stanford Univ, BA, 34, EE, 39. *Hon Degrees:* ScD, Colo Col, 64; LLD, Univ Calif, 66 & Cath Univ Am, 70. *Prof Exp:* Engr, Vacuum Tube Eng Dept, Gen Elec Co, 36-38; partner, Hewlett-Packard Co, Calif, 39-46, pres, 47-64, chmn bd & chief exec officer, 64-69; chmn bd & chief exec officer, Dep Secy Defense, Washington, DC, 69-71; CHMN BD, HEWLETT-PACKARD CO, 72- *Concurrent Pos:* Trustee, Stanford Univ, 54-69, dir & chmn exec comt, Stanford Res Inst, 58-69; dir, Standard Oil Calif, mem sr exec coun, Conf Bd, dir, Caterpillar Tractor Co & dir, Trans World Airlines, 72- *Honors & Awards:* James Forrestal Mem Award, Nat Security Indust Asn, 72; Silver Quill Award, Am Business Press, Inc, 72; Benjamin F Fairless Mem Award, US Iron & Steel Inst, 72. *Mem:* Nat Acad Eng; AAAS; Am Mgt Asn (vpres at large, 59); hon mem Instrument Soc Am; fel Inst Elec & Electronics Engrs. *Res:* Design and development of measuring equipment. *Mailing Add:* Hewlett-Packard Co 1501 Page Mill Rd Palo Alto CA 94304

PACKARD, FRED MALLERY, b Rutherford, NJ, Apr 2, 13; m 51; c 1. CONSERVATION. *Educ:* Harvard Univ, BA, 36; Univ Colo, MA, 42. *Prof Exp:* Exec & field investr, Emergency Conserv Comt, NY, 38-39; sr wildlife technician, Nat Park Serv, 40-41; exec & field investr, Emergency Conserv Comt, NY, 42; exec secy, Nat Parks Asn, 46-58; dir parks, Fairfax County Park Authority, 59-61; recreation specialist, Bur Land Mgt, 61-63; int specialist, Nat Park Serv, 63-78. *Concurrent Pos:* Secy, Comn Nat Parks & Protected Areas, Int Union Conserv Nature & Natural Resources, 58-69, 75-78. *Mem:* Nat Parks & Conservation Asn; Sierra Club; hon mem Int Union Conserv Nature & Natural Resources; Defenders of Wildlife. *Res:* Wildlife research in Yellowstone and Rocky Mountain National Parks; national and international activities in natural resource conservation, especially national parks and reserves. *Mailing Add:* 4058 Elizabeth Lane Fairfax VA 22030

PACKARD, GARY CLAIRE, b Los Angeles, Calif, Oct 25, 38; m 68. PHYSIOLOGICAL ECOLOGY, ZOOLOGY. *Educ:* Univ Ill, Urbana, BS, 60; Univ Kans, MA, 63, PhD(zool), 66. *Prof Exp:* USPHS assoc zoophysiol, Wash State Univ, 66-67; asst prof zool, Clemson Univ, 67-68; asst prof zool, 68-72, assoc prof, 72-77, PROF ZOOL & ENTOM, COLO STATE UNIV, 77- *Mem:* Am Ornith Union; Am Soc Zoologists; Cooper Ornith Soc; Ecol Soc Am; Soc Syst Zool. *Res:* Vertebrate systematics and evolution; comparative physiology of vertebrates. *Mailing Add:* Dept of Zool & Entom Colo State Univ Ft Collins CO 80521

PACKARD, KARLE SANBORN, JR, b Boston, Mass, July 15, 21; m 44; c 1. MICROWAVE ELECTRONICS. *Educ:* Columbia Univ, AB, 43; NY Univ, MS, 51; Polytech Inst NY, MS, 78. *Prof Exp:* Engr, Div War Res, Columbia Univ, 43-44; physicist, Nat Carbon Co, 44-46; engr, Cutler-Hammer, Inc, 46-55, consult, 55-58, mgr reliability, 58-61, eng consult, 61-62, dept head, 62-64, dir long range planning, AIL Div, 64-77, DIR PLANNING, INSTRUMENTS & SYSTS GROUP, EATON CORP, 78- *Mem:* Hist Sci Soc; Soc for Hist Technol; Am Phys Soc; sr mem Inst Elec & Electronics Eng; Inst Mgt Sci. *Res:* Microwave electronics; technical and business planning; management science. *Mailing Add:* 18 Homestead Path Huntington NY 11743

PACKARD, MARTIN EVERETT, b Eugene, Ore, Mar 10, 21; m 43; c 2. PHYSICS. *Educ:* Ore State Col, BA, 42; Stanford Univ, PhD(physics), 49. *Prof Exp:* Res engr labs, Westinghouse Elec Co, Pa, 42-45; asst physics, Stanford Univ, 45-46, res assoc, 46-48, instr, 49-51; res physicist, 51-53, dir res, Instrument Div, 53-63, vpres anal, Instrument Div, 63-69, CORP VPRES, VARIAN ASSOCS, 69-, ASST TO BD CHMN, 74- *Honors & Awards:* Morris E Leeds Award, Inst Elec & Electronics Eng, 71. *Mem:* Sigma Xi; Am Phys Soc; Am Geophys Union; Am Inst Aeronaut & Astronaut. *Res:* Microwave tubes; nuclear magnetic resonance; molecular spectroscopy; magnetometers atomic frequency standards; clinical immunoassay. *Mailing Add:* Varian Assocs 611 Hansen Way Palo Alto CA 94303

PACKARD, PATRICIA LOIS, b May 15, 27; US citizen. SYSTEMATIC BOTANY. *Educ:* Col Idaho, BA, 49; Ore State Col, MS, 52; Wash State Univ, PhD(bot), 65. *Prof Exp:* Assoc prof, 55-59, PROF BIOL, COL IDAHO, 59- *Mem:* AAAS; Am Soc Plant Taxon; Torrey Bot Club; Int Asn Plant Taxon. *Res:* Constant fertile hybrid between two heterobasic species of Calochortus; evolution of the flora of the Northern Great Basin. *Mailing Add:* Dept of Biol Col of Idaho Caldwell ID 83605

PACKARD, RICHARD DARRELL, b Livermore Falls, Maine, Apr 21, 28; m 51; c 2. CHEMICAL ENGINEERING. *Educ:* Univ Maine, BS, 50; Mass Inst Technol, SM, 51; Yale Univ, MEng, 55; NY Univ, DEngSci, 60. *Prof Exp:* Paper tester, Int Paper Co, 44-45 & 47-48; instr chem eng, NY Univ, 55-57; asst prof, Northeastern Univ, 57-59; device develop engr, Clevite Transistor Prod Div, Clevite Corp, 59-60; proj engr, Electronics Corp Am, 61-63; prin develop engr, Honeywell Radiation Ctr, Mass, 63-66; chief electro-optical device res, Melpar, Inc, 66-67; staff scientist & sect head infrared detectors, NASA Electronics Res Ctr, Cambridge, 67-70; mgr develop, Infrared Indust, Inc, Waltham, Mass & Santa Barbara, Calif, 70-73; PRES, RDP CONSULTS, 73- *Concurrent Pos:* Consult, Martin Co. *Mem:* Sr mem Am Chem Soc; sr mem Am Soc Mil Engrs; assoc Am Inst Chem Engrs. *Res:* Solid state physics; semiconductor devices; infrared detectors, arrays and systems; nuclear and electromagnetic pulse. *Mailing Add:* 102 River St Cambridge MA 02139

PACKARD, ROBERT GAY, b Regina, NMex, Aug 13, 24; m 54. ACOUSTICS. *Educ:* Univ Tex, BS, 49, MA, 50, PhD(physics), 52. *Prof Exp:* Res mathematician, Univ Tex, 47-49, res scientist, 49, defense res lab, 50-52; assoc prof physics, Baylor Univ, 52-54; prof & chmn dept, Col Pac, 54-55; prof, Miss Col, 55-56; assoc prof, 56-60, PROF PHYSICS, BAYLOR UNIV, 60-, CHMN DEPT, 81- *Concurrent Pos:* Vis prof, Calif field staff, Airlangga Univ, Indonesia, 61-62; lectr, US Army-Baylor Sch Hosp Admin, Brooke Army Hosp, Ft Sam Houston, Tex; leader, Southeast Asia Student Conf, 70; vis prof, Univ Sains Malaysia, Penang, 76. *Mem:* Acoustical Soc Am; Nat Asn Physics Teachers; Brit Inst Physics. *Res:* Underwater sound; electrochemistry; medical physics. *Mailing Add:* Dept of Physics Baylor Univ Waco TX 76703

PACKARD, THEODORE TRAIN, b Glencove, NY, Jan 24, 42; c 2. CHEMICAL OCEANOGRAPHY. *Educ:* Mass Inst Technol, BS, 63; Univ Wash, MS, 67, PhD(chem oceanog), 69. *Prof Exp:* Res assoc chem oceanog, Univ Wash, 69-70, sr res assoc, 70-72, res asst prof, 72-76; RES SCIENTIST, BIGELOW LAB OCEAN SCI, 76- *Mem:* Limnol Oceanog; Marine Biol Asn Eng; Catalan Biol Soc; AAAS; Am Chem soc. *Res:* Deep sea biology and chemistry; plankton respiration. *Mailing Add:* 107 Townsend Ave Boothbay ME 04537

PACKARD, VERNAL SIDNEY, JR, b Auburn, Maine, June 10, 30; m 57; c 2. FOOD SCIENCE. *Educ:* Univ Maine, BS, 54; Univ Minn, MS, 56, PhD(dairy indust), 60. *Prof Exp:* Assoc prof, 60-75, PROF FOOD SCI & NUTRIT, 75-, EXTEN SPECIALIST DAIRY PRODS, UNIV MINN, ST PAUL, 60- *Mem:* Int Asn Milk, Food & Environ Sanitarians; Am Dairy Sci Asn. *Res:* Hydrolytic rancidity; laboratory and process control; dairy products; food product nutritional evaluation. *Mailing Add:* 136 h Meat Sci Lab Dept Food Sci & Nutrit Univ Minn St Paul MN 55101

PACKCHANIAN, ARDZROONY (ARTHUR), b Armenia, Nov 17, 00; nat US. BACTERIOLOGY, PROTOZOOLOGY. *Educ:* Univ Mich, MS, 30, PhD, 33. *Prof Exp:* Asst bact, Med Sch, Univ Mich, 28-32; res bacteriologist & protozoologist, Sch Med, Wash Univ, 33-34 & NY Postgrad Med Sch, Columbia Univ, 34-36; protozoologist, NIH, 36-41; assoc prof bact & trop med, 41-46, prof bact & parasitol, 46-57, dir microbiol lab, 46-57, PROF MICROBIOL, UNIV TEX MED BR GALVESTON, 57- *Concurrent Pos:* Relator, Int Am Cong Med, Rio de Janeiro, 46. *Mem:* AAAS; Am Soc Microbiol; Am Soc Parasitol; Am Soc Mammal; Soc Exp Biol & Med. *Res:* Antiseptics and disinfectants; bacterial variations; micrurgy; tissue culture; electrophoresis; immunochemistry; tropical medicine; altitude tolerance of insects; leishmaniasis; chemotherapy; radioactive isotopes; cultivation of trypanosomes and spirochetes; infections immunity and epidemiology; leprosy. *Mailing Add:* Dept Microbiol Univ Tex Med Br Galveston TX 77550

PACKEL, EDWARD WESLER, b Philadelphia, Pa, July 23, 41; m 68. MATHEMATICS ANALYSIS. *Educ:* Amherst Col, BA, 63; Mass Inst Technol, PhD(math), 67. *Prof Exp:* Asst prof math, Reed Col, 67-70; asst prof, 70-75, ASSOC PROF MATH, LAKE FOREST COL, 75- *Concurrent Pos:* NSF Res Grants, 79- *Mem:* Am Math Soc; Sigma Xi. *Res:* Operator theory; hilbert space and quantum mechanics; game theory; axiomatic social choice theory. *Mailing Add:* Dept of Math Lake Forest Col Lake Forest IL 60045

PACKER, CHARLES M, b Colorado Springs, Colo, Apr 21, 30; m 53, 71; c 5. MATERIALS SCIENCE. *Educ:* Univ Utah, BSChE, 54; Stanford Univ, MS, 63, PhD(mat sci), 68. *Prof Exp:* Assoc engr, 57-59, scientist, 59-63, sr scientist, 63-71, res scientist, 71-76, STAFF SCIENTIST, LOCKHEED MISSILES & SPACE CO, PALO ALTO, 76- *Mem:* Am Soc Metals; Am Ceramic Soc. *Res:* Mechanical behavior of metals, particularly relating to superplasticity effects; x-ray diffraction; measurements and development of techniques; evaluation and development of protective coatings for refractory metals. *Mailing Add:* 3961 Brookline Way Redwood City CA 94062

PACKER, KENNETH FREDERICK, b Grand Rapids, Mich, Aug 12, 24; m 48; c 4. METALLURGICAL & INDUSTRIAL ENGINEERING. *Educ:* Univ Mich, BSE, 48-49, MSE, 52; Purdue Univ, PhD(indust eng), 62. *Prof Exp:* Asst metallurgist, Exp Foundry, Am Brake Shoe Co, 50-52; instr prod eng, Univ Mich, 52-57; chief metallurgist, Danly Mach Specialties, 57-62; PRES, PACKER ENG ASSOCS, INC, 62- *Concurrent Pos:* Faculty rep, Foundry Ed Found; mem Fatigue Welding Joints Comt, Welding Res Coun, 58-62, ord adv comt Welding Armor Res Sub-comt, 62-64. *Mem:* Am Soc Metals; Am Soc Mech Engrs; Am Soc Testing & Mat; Am Inst Indust Engrs; Nat Soc Prof Engrs. *Res:* Materials, developing applications and metals manufacturing processes. *Mailing Add:* Packer Eng Assocs Inc PO Box 353 Naperville IL 60566

PACKER, LEO S, b Roumania, Aug 5, 20; US citizen; m 48; c 3. MECHANICAL ENGINEERING. *Educ:* City Col New York, BME, 41; Harvard Univ, MS, 48; Cornell Univ, PhD, 56. *Prof Exp:* Mech engr res & develop, BG Corp, 41-43; develop engr, Gyroscopics Div, Arma Corp, 47-50; res mech engr, Physics Dept, Cornell Aeronaut Lab, 50-52, head, Instrumentation Sect, Appl Physics Dept, 52-59; dir eng & mgr, Mil Prod Div, Bausch & Lomb, Inc, 59-62; eng mgr & assoc dir, Xerox Corp, 62-66; asst postmaster gen in chg, Bur Res & Eng, Post Off Dept, Washington, DC, 66-69; consult, NASA, 69-70; vpres corp res, Recognition Equip, Inc, 69-73; dir technol policy & space affairs, US Dept State, Washington, DC, 73-76; counr sci & technol affairs, US Mission to OECD, Paris, 76-78; consult technol planning & mgt, Washington, DC, 78-81; RESIDENT DIR, APPL SCI & TECHNOL PROG, NAT ACAD SCI, CAIRO, EGYPT, 81- *Concurrent Pos:* Prof lectr, Univ Buffalo. *Mem:* AAAS; Am Soc Mech Engrs; Inst Elec & Electronics Engrs. *Res:* Mechanics, dynamics and vibrations; aeronautical instrumentation; kinematics; stress analysis; research and development management; technology policy; international science and technology issues. *Mailing Add:* Nat Acad Sci BOSTID/JH-219 2101 Constitution Ave NW Washington DC 20418

PACKER, LESTER, b New York, NY, Aug 28, 29; m 56; c 3. BIOCHEMISTRY. *Educ:* Brooklyn Col, BS, 51, MS, 52; Yale Univ, PhD(microbiol), 56. *Prof Exp:* Assoc biophys, Johnson Found Med Physics, Pa, 57-59; assoc biochem, Dartmouth Med Sch, 59; asst prof microbiol, Southwestern Med Sch, Tex, 60-61; from asst prof to assoc prof, 61-66, assoc prof, Miller Inst Basic Res Sci, 66-68, PROF PHYSIOL, UNIV CALIF, BERKELEY, 68-, DIR MEMBRANE BIOENERGETICS GROUP, LAWRENCE BERKELEY LAB, 75- *Mem:* Am Chem Soc; Biophys Soc; Am Soc Biol Chemists; Royal Soc Chem; NY Acad Sci. *Res:* Membrane bioenergetics; cellular aging. *Mailing Add:* Dept of Physiol & Anat Univ of Calif Berkeley CA 94720

PACKER, RANDALL KENT, b Lock Haven, Pa, Nov 5, 45; m 65. COMPARATIVE PHYSIOLOGY. *Educ:* Lock Haven State Col, BS, 67; Pa State Univ, PhD(zool), 71. *Prof Exp:* Asst, Pa State Univ, 67-70; asst prof, 71-75, assoc prof, 75-80, PROF BIOL SCI, GEORGE WASHINGTON UNIV, 80- *Mem:* AAAS; Am Soc Zoologists. *Res:* Comparative environmental physiology, specifically, extra-renal electrolyte and water balance in fish, reptiles, and amphibians, as well as respiration in fish and amphibians. *Mailing Add:* Dept of Biol Sci George Washington Univ Washington DC 20052

PACKER, RAYMOND ALLEN, b Clemons, Iowa, July 27, 14; m 40; c 5. VETERINARY MICROBIOLOGY. *Educ:* Iowa State Univ, BS & DVM, 40, MS, 42, PhD(vet bact), 47. *Prof Exp:* Asst vet hyg, 40-41, from instr to assoc prof vet hyg, 41-52, head dept, 52-80, PROF VET MICROBIOL & PREV MED, IOWA STATE UNIV, 52- *Mem:* Am Soc Microbiol; Am Vet Med Asn; Am Col Vet Microbiol. *Res:* Veterinary immunology and virology; pathogenic bacteriology. *Mailing Add:* Dept of Vet Microbiol Iowa State Univ Ames IA 50011

PACKETT, LEONARD VASCO, b Concord, Tenn, Feb 22, 32; m 54; c 2. BIOCHEMISTRY. *Educ:* Berea Col, BS, 54; Tex A&M Univ, MS, 56, PhD(biochem, nutrit), 59. *Prof Exp:* Asst animal husb, Tex A&M Univ, 54-56 & biochem & nutrit, 56-58; asst prof biochem, Purdue Univ, 58-66; assoc prof, 66-72, PROF NUTRIT & FOOD SCI, DEPT HOME ECON, UNIV KY, 72-, CHMN DEPT, 66- *Concurrent Pos:* NIH fel, Philadelphia Gen Hosp, 65-66. *Mem:* Am Inst Nutrit; Am Inst Chem; Am Chem Soc; Soc Nutrit Educ. *Res:* Nutrient requirements and metabolism; metabolic disease; parathyroid function; urolithiasis; mucopolysaccharides; radioactive tracers. *Mailing Add:* Dept of Home Econ Univ of Ky Lexington KY 40506

PACKHAM, MARIAN AITCHISON, b Toronto, Ont, Dec 13, 27; m 49; c 2. BIOCHEMISTRY. *Educ:* Univ Toronto, BA, 49, PhD(biochem), 54. *Prof Exp:* Lectr biochem, 66-67, from asst prof to assoc prof, 67-75, PROF BIOCHEM, UNIV TORONTO, 75- *Concurrent Pos:* Mem coun thrombosis, Am Heart Asn. *Mem:* Can Biochem Soc; Can Soc Clin Invest; Am Soc Hemat; Am Asn Path; Int Soc Thrombosis & Hemostasis. *Res:* Biochemical aspects of the functions of blood platelets in hemostasis and thrombosis. *Mailing Add:* Dept of Biochem Univ of Toronto Toronto ON M5S 1A8 Can

PACKMAN, ALBERT M, b Philadelphia, Pa, Jan 18, 30; m 61. MEDICINAL CHEMISTRY. *Educ:* Temple Univ, BS, 51; Philadelphia Col Pharm & Sci, MS, 52, DSc, 56. *Prof Exp:* Org chemist, Nat Drug Co, 56-59; sr org chemist, Int Latex Corp, 59-60; res adminstr, Denver Chem Co, 60-61; sr org chemist, 61-67, actg res dir, 67-68, dir tech serv, 68-77, VPRES TECH & DIR, DERMIK LABS, INC, DIV WILLIAM H RORER, INC, 77- *Concurrent Pos:* Lectr, Philadelphia Col Pharm & Sci, 67-69. *Mem:* Am Chem Soc; Am Pharmaceut Asn; Soc Cosmetic Chemists; Am Acad Dermat; NY Acad Sci. *Res:* Synthesis of medicinal compounds particularly cardiovascular agents, analygesics and antibacterial agents; development and clinical testing of fermatological products. *Mailing Add:* 3223 Lenape Dr Dresher PA 19025

PACKMAN, ELIAS WOLFE, b Philadelphia, Pa, Mar 13, 30; m 51; c 3. PHARMACOLOGY. *Educ:* Philadelphia Col Pharm, BSc, 51, MSc, 52, DSc(pharmacol), 54. *Prof Exp:* Asst, 51-52, from instr to assoc prof, 52-66, PROF PHARMACOL, PHILADELPHIA COL PHARM & SCI, 66- *Concurrent Pos:* Lectr, Philadelphia Col Osteop, 60; mem, Drug Device Cosmetic Bd, Pa. *Mem:* Am Pharmaceut Asn; Am Asn Cols Pharm; NY Acad Sci. *Res:* Reticulo-endothelial-system; histamine and antihistamine pharmacology; fate of white blood cells; techniques involving radioisotopes. *Mailing Add:* Philadelphia Col Pharm & Sci 43rd St & Kingsessing Ave Philadelphia PA 19104

PACKMAN, PAUL F, materials science, see previous edition

PACKMAN, PAUL FREDERICK, b Brooklyn, NY, July 30, 36; m 62; c 2. QUALITY CONTROL. *Educ:* Cooper Union Sch Eng, BSME, 60; Syracuse Univ, MS, 62, PhD(solid state), 64. *Prof Exp:* Team leader mech behav res, Lockheed, Ga, 64-68; assoc prof, Vanderbilt Univ, Tenn, 68-71; resident fel, Nat Acad Sci, 71-72; dir mat sci, Vanderbilt Univ, 72-74, prof eng, 74-77; CHMN & PROF, CIVIL & MECH ENG DEPT, SOUTHERN METHODIST UNIV, 78- *Concurrent Pos:* Adj prof, Dept Eng Mech, Ga Inst Technol, 64-68; consult, Failure Anal, 74-82, Nat Mat Adv Bd, 78, 79 & 81 & Hgy Transp Res Bd, 81-82. *Mem:* Am Soc Testing & Mat; Am Soc Metals; Am Soc Non-Destructive Testing; Am Mining, Metall & Petrol Engrs. *Res:* Fracture and fatigue; analysis of failures in structural components; non-destructive inspection and reliability of inspection procedures. *Mailing Add:* Civil & Mech Eng Dept Southern Methodist Univ Dallas TX 75275

PACKMAN, PAUL MICHAEL, b St Louis, Mo, Aug 5, 38; m 65; c 2. NEUROENDOCRINOLOGY, NEUROCHEMISTRY. *Educ:* Wash Univ, BA, 59, MD, 63. *Prof Exp:* Intern med, Vanderbilt Univ Hosp, 63-64; staff assoc biochem, Nat Inst Arthritic & Metab Dis, 64-67; fel neuroendocrinol, Dept Anat, Oxford Univ, 67-68, Inst Neurobiol, Univ Goteborg, 68-69 & Dept Pharmacol, Med Sch, Wash Univ, 69-70; asst res, Dept Psychiat, 70-73, asst prof, 73-78, ASSOC PROF PSYCHIAT, MED SCH, WASH UNIV, 78- *Honors & Awards:* Res Award Med, Borden Found, 63; Res Scientist Develop Award, NIMH, 74. *Mem:* Am Psychiat Asn; Psychiat Res Soc; Int Soc Neuroendocrinol; Int Soc Psychoneuroendocrinol; Endocrine Soc. *Mailing Add:* Dept of Psychiat Box 8134 St Louis MO 63110

PACKMAN, SEYMOUR, b Mt Vernon, NY, Feb 3, 43. HUMAN GENETICS, PEDIATRICS. *Educ:* Columbia Col, AB, 63; Wash Univ, MD, 68. *Prof Exp:* ASST PROF PEDIAT, UNIV CALIF, SAN FRANCISCO, 77- *Mem:* Am Soc Human Genetics; AAAS; Am Fedn Clin Res. *Res:* Human biochemical genetics. *Mailing Add:* Dept of Pediat Univ of Calif San Francisco CA 94143

PACOFSKY, EDWARD ANTHONY, organic chemistry, polymer science, see previous edition

PADALINO, JOSEPH JOHN, b Newark, NJ, June 26, 22; m 48; c 3. ELECTRICAL ENGINEERING. *Educ:* Newark Col Eng, BSEE, 44; Univ Pa, MSEE, 47; Polytech Inst Brooklyn, PhD(elec eng), 63. *Prof Exp:* Instr elec eng, Newark Col Eng, 47-51; mem staff, Bell Tel Labs, Inc, 51-54; assoc prof, 54-63, PROF ELEC ENG, NJ INST TECHNOL, 63- *Concurrent Pos:* Consult, Bendix, 63, Picatinny Arsenal, 64-65 & Radio Frequency Labs, 66- *Mem:* Am Soc Eng Educ; Inst Elec & Electronics Engrs. *Res:* Servomechanisms; network theory. *Mailing Add:* Dept of Elec Eng NJ Inst Technol Newark NJ 07102

PADAWER, JACQUES, b Liege, Belg, Sept 3, 25; nat US; m 51; c 3. ANATOMY, CELL BIOLOGY. *Educ:* NY Univ, BA, 50, MS, 52, PhD(physiol), 54. *Prof Exp:* From instr to asst prof biochem, 55-60, from asst prof to assoc prof anat, 60-72, PROF ANAT, ALBERT EINSTEIN COL MED, 72- *Concurrent Pos:* Am Heart Asn fel, NY Univ, 54-57; Am Heart Asn estab investr, 57-62. *Mem:* Am Asn Anat; Am Soc Cell Biol; Reticuloendothelial Soc; Soc Exp Biol Med; fel NY Acad Sci. *Res:* Behavior and function of mast cell and basophil leukocyte; cellular effects ultrasound; vitamin A and tumors. *Mailing Add:* Dept Anat Albert Einstein Col Med New York NY 10461

PADBERG, HARRIET A, b St Louis, Mo, Nov 13, 22. MATHEMATICS. *Educ:* Maryville Col, Mo, BA, 43; Univ Cincinnati, MMus, 49; Univ St Louis, MA, 56, PhD(math), 64. *Prof Exp:* Teacher math, Acad Sacred Heart, Cincinnati, 46-47; instr math & music, Acad & Col Sacred Heart, Grand Coteau, 47-48 & 50-55; teacher, Acad Sacred Heart, St Charles, 48-50; from asst prof to assoc prof, 56-68, PROF MATH & MUSIC, MARYVILLE COL, ST LOUIS, 68- *Concurrent Pos:* Organist, 46-; music coordr weekly televised Mass, 65-68; mem, Nat Educ Comt of Nat Asn for Music Therapy. *Mem:* Sigma Xi; Am Math Soc; Math Asn Am. *Res:* Aesthetics; computer music; teacher training. *Mailing Add:* Maryville Col of the Sacred Heart 13550 Conway Rd St Louis MO 63141

PADBURY, JOHN JAMES, b Rockland, Maine, July 24, 16; m 43; c 1. ORGANIC POLYMER CHEMISTRY. *Educ:* Bowdoin Col, BS, 39; NY Univ, PhD(org chem), 44. *Prof Exp:* Instr chem, NY Univ, 42-43; res chemist, 43-49, group leader, 49-54, mgr synthetic fibers res, 54-57, dir polymer res dept, 57-61; tech dir plastics res, 61-71, mgr tech serv, 71-77, asst to dir, 77-79, MGR REGULATORY AFFAIRS, AM CYANAMID CO, 79- *Mem:* Am Chem Soc. *Res:* Plastics; resins; high polymers; synthetic fibers. *Mailing Add:* Am Cyanamid Co 1937 W Main St Stamford CT 06904

PADDACK, STEPHEN J(OSEPH), b Cincinnati, Ohio, Dec 26, 34; m 62; c 4. AERONAUTICAL & AEROSPACE ENGINEERING. *Educ:* Cath Univ Am, BAE, 59, MASE, 64, PhD(eng), 73. *Prof Exp:* Assoc engr, Boeing Co, 59-61; aerospace engr, 61-70, proj opers dir, IMP Proj, 70-74, spacecraft mgr, IMP Proj, 72-74, dep tech mgr, ISEE proj, 74-78 & COBE proj, 78-81, CHIEF, ADVAN MISSIONS ANAL OFF, NASA-GODDARD SPACE FLIGHT CTR, 81- *Mem:* Am Geophys Union. *Res:* Technical management and future planning for all aspects of spaceflight projects; astrodynamics, including applied celestial mechanics, orbit and trajectory analysis and mission analysis of space flights, dynamics and mechanics; planetology related to small celestial bodies; space science. *Mailing Add:* NASA/Goddard Space Flight Ctr Code 701 Greenbelt MD 20771

PADDEN, FRANK JOSEPH, JR, b Scranton, Pa, Sept 21, 28; m 55; c 5. POLYMER PHYSICS. *Educ:* Scranton Univ, BS, 50. *Prof Exp:* Res asst, Mellon Inst Indust Res, 51-52, res assoc, 52-54, jr fel, 54-55; physicist, Am Viscose Corp, 57-60, res physicist, 60; MEM TECH STAFF, BELL LABS, 60- *Honors & Awards:* Polymer Physics Award, Am Phys Soc, 73. *Mem:* Fel Am Phys Soc. *Res:* Physics of high polymers. *Mailing Add:* Bell Labs Rm 1d-201 PO Box 261 Murray Hill NJ 07974

PADDISON, FLETCHER C, b Superior, Ariz, Nov 29, 21; m 46; c 3. SYSTEMS ENGINEERING. *Educ:* Cath Univ, AB, 56. *Prof Exp:* Supvr servomech, Auxiliary Power Systs & Gyroscope Develop Proj, 49-56, mem prin prof staff, 56, proj engr intercontinental ballistic missile defense, 56-58, asst to proj engr long range TYPHON missile, 60-62, proj engr, 62-64, tech adv to assoc dir, 62-66, asst advan res projs agency prog mgr, 66-71, ASST DIR ADVAN RES PROG OFF & PROG MGR, REGIONAL OPERS RES CONTRACT, US DEPT ENERGY, APPL PHYSICS LAB, JOHNS HOPKINS UNIV, 71- *Mem:* Am Soc Mech Engrs. *Res:* Servomechanisms; large system interface management techniques; thin material response to nuclear radiation; radar cross section measurement techniques; special instrumentation and mission analysis US Navy Surface Effect Ships; direct applications of geothermal energy in the eastern US and estimated life cycle costs. *Mailing Add:* Johns Hopkins Univ Appl Physics Lab Johns Hopkins Rd Laurel MD 20707

PADDISON, RICHARD MILTON, b Rochester, NY, Aug 20, 19; m 43, 66; c 8. NEUROLOGY. *Educ:* Duke Univ, AB, 43, MD, 45. *Prof Exp:* Instr neurol & neuroanat, Sch Med, Univ Ga, 48-49; from asst prof to assoc prof neurol, 54-59, head dept, 65-77, PROF NEUROL, LA STATE UNIV SCH MED, NEW ORLEANS, 59- *Concurrent Pos:* Dir Continuing Med Educ & Coordr Alumni Affairs, La State Univ Sch Med, 80-; consult, Hotel Dieu Hosp, Southern Baptist Hosp & Charity Hosp, New Orleans, 80- *Mem:* Asn Res Nerv & Ment Dis; fel Am Psychiat Asn; fel Am Col Physicians; fel Am Acad Neurol; Am Acad Cerebral Palsy. *Res:* Vascular disease; epilepsy. *Mailing Add:* Dept of Neurol La State Univ Sch of Med New Orleans LA 70112

PADDOCK, ARNOLD (DAVID), physical metallurgy, see previous edition

PADDOCK, ELTON FARNHAM, b Worcester, Mass, Dec 11, 13; m 37; c 2. PLANT CYTOGENETICS. *Educ:* Whittier Col, AB, 36; Univ Calif, PhD(genetics), 42. *Prof Exp:* Asst genetics, Univ Calif, 40; Muellhaupt scholar, Ohio State Univ, 41-43; plant pathologist, Exp Sta, Tex A&M Univ, 43-45; from asst prof to assoc prof, 45-68, PROF GENETICS & CYTOL,

OHIO STATE UNIV, 68- *Concurrent Pos:* Am consult, Summer Sci Inst, US Agency Int Develop, India, 65 & 67. *Mem:* AAAS; Am Inst Biol Sci; Genetics Soc Am; Bot Soc Am; Am Genetic Asn. *Res:* Cytology of Hevea brasiliensis; cytogenetics of polyploids and interspecific hybrids of Solanum; disease resistance breeding of tomatoes; chiasma failure and adjacent distribution in Rhoeo spathacea; somatic crossing-over in soybean. *Mailing Add:* Dept of Genetics Ohio State Univ Columbus OH 43210

PADDOCK, GARY VINCENT, b Port Townsend, Wash, July 13, 42; m 66; c 1. MOLECULAR BIOLOGY. *Educ:* Univ Wash, BS, 64; Univ Calif, San Diego, PhD(chem), 73. *Prof Exp:* Officer, Eng Dept, US Navy, 64-69; teaching asst chem, Univ Calif, San Diego, 69-73; fel, Univ Calif, Los Angeles, 73-77; ASST PROF IMMUNOL & MICROBIOL, MED UNIV SC, 77- *Concurrent Pos:* Celeste Durand Rogers fel cancer res, 73-74; Helen Hay Whitney fel, 74-77. *Res:* Eucaryotic gene regulation with emphasis on the hemoglobin genes and the technology involved in recombinant DNA construction and nucleotide sequencing. *Mailing Add:* Dept Basic & Clin Immunol & Microbiol 171 Ashley Ave Charleston SC 29425

PADDOCK, RICHARD ELSOM, b Watsonville, Calif, Dec 14, 41. COMPUTER SCIENCE. *Educ:* Stanford Univ, BS, 63; Duke Univ, MA, 68. *Prof Exp:* Instr physics & astron, NC Wesleyan Col, 66-68; SYSTS ANALYST, RES TRIANGLE INST, 68- *Res:* Computer applications related to air pollution control; modeling of physical processes, data base management. *Mailing Add:* Res Triangle Inst PO Box 12194 Research Triangle Park NC 27709

PADDOCK, ROBERT ALTON, b Port Washington, NY, Dec 10, 42; m 67; c 3. ANALYTICAL PREDICTIONS, DATA ANALYSIS. *Educ:* Washington & Lee Univ, BS, 64; Mich State Univ, MS, 66, PhD(physics), 69. *Prof Exp:* Asst prof physics, Ripon Col, 69-74; MEM STAFF, ENVIRON ENG SCI DIV, ARGONNE NAT LAB, 74- *Mem:* Am Phys Soc. *Res:* Physical environmental effects in water systems due to power production. *Mailing Add:* Environ Eng Sci Div Bldg 12-A Argonne Nat Lab Argonne IL 60439

PADEGS, ANDRIS, b Riga, Latvia, Mar 27, 29; nat US; m 54; c 3. COMPUTER SCIENCE, ELECTRICAL ENGINEERING. *Educ:* Dartmouth Col, AB, 53, Thayer Sch Eng, MS, 54; Carnegie Inst Technol, PhD(elec eng), 58. *Prof Exp:* Asst servomechanisms res, Carnegie Inst Technol, 54-56, proj engr, 56-57; assoc engr data processing mach, 58-60, staff engr, 60-63, adv engr, 63-65, sr engr, 65-68, mgr processor archit, 68-69, mgr archit design & control, 69-71, PROG MGR SYST ARCHIT, IBM CORP, 71- *Mem:* Inst Elec & Electronics Engrs. *Res:* Computer architecture, planning and specification of data processing systems; alternating current servomechanisms. *Mailing Add:* Merry Hill Rd Poughkeepsie NY 12603

PADEN, JOHN WILBURN, b Bakersfield, Calif, Dec 24, 33. MYCOLOGY. *Educ:* Univ Calif, Berkeley, BS, 55; Univ Idaho, MS, 61, PhD(bot), 68. *Prof Exp:* Asst plant pathologist, Col Agr, Univ Idaho, 60-61; agr res technician soil microbiol, USDA, Wash, 62-63; instr biol, 66-67, asst prof, 67-77, ASSOC PROF BIOL, UNIV VICTORIA, 77- *Mem:* Mycol Soc Am; Bot Soc Am; Can Bot Asn; Brit Mycol Soc; NY Acad Sci. *Res:* Systematics of ascomycetes, especially discomycetes; ecology and taxonomy of soil-borne fungi. *Mailing Add:* Dept of Biol Univ of Victoria Victoria BC V8W 2Y2 Can

PADER, MORTON, b New York, NY, June 5, 21; m 45; c 2. INDUSTRIAL CHEMISTRY. *Educ:* City Col New York, BS, 41; NY Univ, MS, 47, PhD(org chem), 49. *Prof Exp:* Chemist, Food Res Labs, Inc, NY, 41-46, chief chemist, 46-47; assoc chemist, Thomas J Lipton, Inc, 50-52; assoc res chemist, Res & Develop Div, 52-60, chief food prod sect, 60-63, MGR PERSONAL PRODS DEVELOP, RES CTR, LEVER BROS CO, 63- *Mem:* AAAS; Am Chem Soc; Sigma Xi; Soc Cosmetic Chem; Int Asn Dent Res. *Res:* Reaction rates and mechanisms; protein chemistry and technology; nutrition; food technology; industrial chemicals and operations; food chemistry and product development; development of products for oral and personal hygiene; mechanism and inhibition of caries and calculus. *Mailing Add:* Lever Bros Res Ctr 45 River Rd Edgewater NJ 07020

PADGETT, ALGIE ROSS, b Morocco, Ind, Apr 20, 11; m 33; c 3. ORGANIC CHEMISTRY. *Educ:* Purdue Univ, BS, 32, MS, 36, PhD(org chem), 37; Am Inst Chemists, cert. *Prof Exp:* Lab asst chem, Purdue Univ, 32-35; res chemist, Humble Oil & Ref Co, 37-40, res sect head, 40-41, chemist, Baytown Ordn Works, 41-45, res sect head, 45-47, res dept head, Res & Develop Div, 47-64, asst dir anal res div, Exxon Res & Eng Co, 64-66, sr staff adv, 66-71, ANNUITANT, EXXON RES & ENG CO, 71- *Concurrent Pos:* Coordr equal employ opportunity prog, 66-71. *Mem:* Fel AAAS; fel Am Inst Chemists; Am Chem Soc; Am Inst Chem Eng. *Res:* Pure aromatics from petroleum; synthetic fuels and lubricants; physical, chemical and instrumental analytical technique. *Mailing Add:* Elkins Lake Box 14 Huntsville TX 77340

PADGETT, ALICE ADAMS, physical chemistry, see previous edition

PADGETT, BILLIE LOU, b South Gate, Calif, May 23, 30. MEDICAL MICROBIOLOGY. *Educ:* Univ Calif, BA, 52; Univ Wis, MS, 55, PhD(med microbiol), 57. *Prof Exp:* PROJ ASSOC MED MICROBIOL, MED SCH, UNIV WIS-MADISON, 57- *Concurrent Pos:* Alumni Res Found fel, Med Sch, Univ Wis-Madison, 58-59; USPHS fel, 65-67. *Mem:* AAAS; Am Soc Microbiol. *Res:* Viral enhancement by fibroma virus; papova virus associated with progressive multifocal leucoencephalopathy. *Mailing Add:* Dept of Med Microbiol Med Sch Univ Wis Madison WI 53706

PADGETT, DAVID EMERSON, b Fayetteville, NC, Jan 27, 45; m 70; c 2. MYCOLOGY, BOTANY. *Educ:* Duke Univ, AB, 67; Ohio State Univ, MS, 73, PhD(bot), 75. *Prof Exp:* Res assoc, Paint Res Inst, 72-75; fel, USAEC, 73-74; ASST PROF BIOL, UNIV NC, WILMINGTON, 75- *Concurrent Pos:* NSF grant, 78-80. *Mem:* Mycol Soc Am; Can Soc Plant Physiol. *Res:* Estuarine distribution and salinity tolerance of saprolegniaceaus fungi. *Mailing Add:* Dept of Biol Univ of NC Wilmington NC 28406

PADGETT, DORAN WILLIAM, b Alexandria, Va, Sept 9, 25; m 46; c 3. NUCLEAR PHYSICS. *Educ:* Am Univ, BS, 52; Cath Univ, PhD(meson theory), 64. *Prof Exp:* Nuclear physicist, Nat Bur Stand, 52-55; proj engr, Eng Res & Develop Lab, US Dept Army, 55-56; res admin, Air Force Off Sci Res, 56-63 & Off Naval Res, 63-65; asst prof, Col William & Mary, 65-66; head, Nuclear Phys Br, 66-74, dir radiation & plasma phys progs, 74-78, PHYS CONSULT, OFF NAVAL RES, 78- *Concurrent Pos:* Vis scientist, Naval Res Lab, 71-72. *Mem:* Am Phys Soc. *Res:* Methods and formalism of quantum field theory; meson, nuclear reaction and atomic and molecular collision theories; experimental nuclear and high energy physics; nuclear structure; transport theory of energetic heavy ion penetration as associated with simulation of fast neutron damage in reactor materials; high energy neutrino beam applications. *Mailing Add:* 3801 N 36th Rd Arlington VA 22207

PADGETT, GEORGE ARNOLD, b East Detroit, Mich, Feb 17, 31; m 51. PATHOLOGY, GENETICS. *Educ:* Mich State Univ, BS, 59, MS, 61, DVM, 61. *Prof Exp:* NIH fel, 61-65; from asst to assoc prof vet path, Wash State Univ, 65-77; PROF PATH, MICH STATE UNIV, 77- *Concurrent Pos:* NIH grant, 65-; res assoc, Rockefeller Univ, 66- *Mem:* AAAS; Am Soc Exp Path. *Res:* Experimental pathology of genetic diseases of animals which also occur in man. *Mailing Add:* Dept of Path Mich State Univ East Lansing MI 48824

PADGETT, WILLIAM JOWAYNE, b Walhalla, SC, May 15, 43; m 65; c 2. STATISTICS, MATHEMATICS. *Educ:* Clemson Univ, BS, 66, MS, 68; Va Polytech Inst & State Univ, PhD(statist), 71. *Prof Exp:* From asst to assoc prof, 71-77, PROF MATH, UNIV SC, 77- *Mem:* Soc Indust & Applied Math; Am Statist Asn; Inst Math Statist. *Res:* Random and stochastic equations and their applications; limit theorems for random elements in abstract spaces; reliability theory. *Mailing Add:* Dept of Math Comput Sci & Stat Univ of SC Columbia SC 29208

PADGITT, DENNIS DARRELL, b Malvern, Iowa, Jan 1, 39; m 61; c 2. DAIRY HUSBANDRY. *Educ:* Iowa State Univ, BS, 62; Univ Mo-Columbia, MS, 64, PhD(dairy sci), 67. *Prof Exp:* PROF ANIMAL & DAIRY SCI, NORTHWEST MO STATE UNIV, 67- *Mem:* Am Dairy Sci Asn; Nat Asn Col Teachers Agr. *Res:* Effect of rumen buffers on milk production and microbial activity. *Mailing Add:* Northwest Mo State Univ Maryville MO 64468

PADHI, SALLY BULPITT, b Darien, Conn, July 12, 44; m 70; c 2. MICROBIOLOGY, INSECT PATHOLOGY. *Educ:* Univ Conn, BS, 67; Univ Mass, MS, 69; Rutgers Univ, PhD(microbiol), 74. *Prof Exp:* Lectr, 77-78, FEL INSECT VIROL, WAKSMAN INST MICROBIOL, RUTGERS UNIV, 74- *Concurrent Pos:* Consult, 80- *Mem:* Am Soc Microbiol; Tissue Culture Asn; Sigma Xi. *Res:* The characterization of insect viruses especially those that have potential use as biological control agents. *Mailing Add:* Waksman Inst Microbiol Rutgers Univ New Brunswick NJ 08903

PADIAN, KEVIN, b Morristown, NJ, Mar 12, 51; m 73; c 1. PALEOBIOLOGY, MACROEVOLUTION. *Educ:* Colgate Univ, BA, 72, MAT, 74; Yale Univ, MPhil, 78, PhD(biol), 80. *Prof Exp:* ASST PROF PALEONT, UNIV CALIF, BERKELEY, 80- *Mem:* Soc Study Evolution; Soc Vert Paleont; Soc Syst Zool; Paleont Soc; Sigma Xi. *Res:* Evolutionary patterns and processes; vertebrate paleontology and zoology; functional morphology; Mesozoic vertebrate faunas. *Mailing Add:* Dept Paleont Univ Calif Berkeley CA 94720

PADILLA, ANDREW, JR, b Honolulu, Hawaii, Apr 21, 37. CHEMICAL ENGINEERING. *Educ:* Col St Thomas, BA, 60; Univ Notre Dame, BS, 60; Univ Mich, Ann Arbor, MS, 62, PhD(chem eng), 66. *Prof Exp:* Sr res engr, Battelle Northwest, Battelle Mem Inst, 66-70, Westinghouse Hanford Co, Westinghouse Elec, 70-71; chem engr, Argonne Nat Lab, 71-73; fel engr, 74-79, adv engr, 79, MGR REACTOR DYNAMICS, WESTINGHOUSE HANFORD CO, WESTINGHOUSE ELEC CORP, 79- *Mem:* Am Nuclear Soc. *Res:* Design (thermal-hydraulic analysis of fuel bundles) and safety (local faults and hypothetical maximum accidents) analyses of fast nuclear reactor cores. *Mailing Add:* 2025 Davison Ave Richland WA 99352

PADILLA, GEORGE M, b Guatemala, May 27, 29; US citizen; m 57; c 3. CELL PHYSIOLOGY, BIOPHYSICS. *Educ:* George Washington Univ, BS, 52, MS, 53; Univ Calif, Los Angeles, PhD(zool), 60. *Prof Exp:* Res fel cell physiol, Nat Cancer Inst, 60-62, biologist, Geront Br, Nat Heart Inst, 62-63; biologist, Biol Div, Oak Ridge Nat Lab, 63-65; asst prof physiol, 65-67, ASSOC PROF PHYSIOL, PHARMACOL, MED CTR, DUKE UNIV, 67- *Concurrent Pos:* Dir, Babies Hosp Res Ctr, Wilmington, NC, 65; actg dir, Wrightsville Marine Biomed Lab, 65-66, consult, Biol Div, Oak Ridge Nat Lab, 65-70. *Mem:* Soc Gen Physiol; Am Soc Cell Biol; Am Physiol Soc. *Res:* Cell division synchrony; physiology and identification of marine algal toxins; cell growth; comparative marine cellular physiology; cellular control systems in cell cycle; oncology. *Mailing Add:* Dept of Physiol Duke Univ Med Ctr Durham NC 27710

PADLAN, EDUARDO AGUSTIN, b Manila, Philippines, Aug 31, 40. BIOPHYSICS. *Educ:* Univ Philippines, BS, 60; Johns Hopkins Univ, PhD(biophysics), 68. *Prof Exp:* Asst prof physics, Univ Philippines, 68-69; vis scientist molecular biol, NIH, 71-78; res assoc, 69-71, RES SCIENTIST BIOPHYSICS, JOHNS HOPKINS UNIV, 78- *Mem:* Biophys Soc; Am Crystallog Asn; Am Soc Biol Chem; Am Asn Immunol. *Res:* Crystallographic investigation of the molecular structure and biological function of proteins. *Mailing Add:* Dept of Biophysics Johns Hopkins Univ Baltimore MD 21218

PADMANABHAN, G R, b Madras, India, July 12, 35; m 64; c 2. ANALYTICAL CHEMISTRY, PHYSICAL CHEMISTRY. *Educ:* Univ Madras, BSc, 56; Univ Pittsburgh, PhD(anal chem), 63. *Prof Exp:* Jr chemist, Atomic Energy Estab, Bombay, India, 57-60; sr chemist, Hooker Chem Corp, NY, 64-66 & Hoffmann-La Roche, Inc, NJ, 66-70; MGR, PHARMA DIV, CIBA-GEIGY CORP, 70- *Mem:* Am Chem Soc; Am Pharmaceut Asn. *Res:* Non-aqueous solvents; electrochemistry; gas, liquid and thin-layer chromatography; thermal methods of analysis microscopy; purification and separation techniques; pharmaceutical analysis with particular emphasis on non-aqueous solvents and chromatographic techniques. *Mailing Add:* Pharma Div Ciba-Geigy Corp Box 100 Suffern NY 10901

PADMORE, JOEL M, b Macy, Nebr, Dec 8, 38; m 60; c 3. ANALYTICAL CHEMISTRY, AGRICULTURAL CHEMISTRY. *Educ:* Munic Univ Omaha, BA, 60; Mont State Univ, PhD(chem), 64. *Prof Exp:* From asst prof to prof chem, Univ SDak, 64-79; STATE CHEMIST, SDAK STATE CHEM LAB, 79- *Mem:* Asn Off Anal Chemists; Am Chem Soc; Asn Am Feed Control Off; Asn Am Fertil Control Off. *Res:* Analytical methods for pesticides; gas chromatography; instrumental analysis; flame spectroscopy. *Mailing Add:* State Chem Lab Vermillion SD 57069

PADNOS, NORMAN, b Brooklyn, NY, Oct 23, 37; m; c 5. PHYSICAL CHEMISTRY. *Educ:* Brooklyn Col, BS, 57; Univ Rochester, PhD(phys chem), 63. *Prof Exp:* Asst prof chem, NC Col Durham, 63-68; CHEMIST, NEW YORK CITY DEPT AIR RESOURCES, 68- *Mem:* Am Chem Soc; NY Acad Sci; Int Solar Energy Soc. *Res:* Photochemistry; theoretical chemistry; analytical chemistry of air pollution. *Mailing Add:* NY City Dept Air Resources 51 Astor Pl New York NY 10003

PADOVANI, ELAINE REEVES, b Kansas City, Mo, Dec 10, 38; m 63; c 2. METAMORPHIC PETROLOGY, GEOPHYSICS. *Educ:* Vassar Col, AB, 61; Stanford Univ, MS, 63; Univ Tex, Dallas, PhD(petrol geochem), 77. *Prof Exp:* Res assoc, Dept Earth & Planetary Sci, Mass Inst Technol, 77-81; PROG DIR PETROGENESIS & MINERAL RESOURCES, EARTH SCI DIV, NSF, 81- *Mem:* Am Geophys Union; Paleontol Soc. *Res:* Chemistry mineralogy and physical properties of the deep crust beneath the continents; evolution of the continents through time and constraints on mechanisms of melt production, fluid transport and chemical equilibration at depth. *Mailing Add:* Petrogenesis & Mineral Resources Earth Sci Div NSF 1800 G St NW Washington DC 20550

PADOVANI, FRANCOIS ANTOINE, b Versailles, France, Aug 22, 37; m 63; c 2. PHYSICS. *Educ:* Advan Sch Elec, France, EE, 59; Stanford Univ, PhD(elec eng), 62. *Prof Exp:* Engr, Nat Ctr Study Telecommun, Paris, France, 63-64; mem tech staff, 64-70, eng mgr, 70-76, MGR, RES & DEVELOP, TEX INSTRUMENTS, INC, 76- *Mem:* Am Phys Soc; Sigma Xi; Electrochem Soc. *Res:* Semiconductor physics; laser research and applications to solid state physics; conduction mechanism in Schottky barriers; crystal growth; polysilicon manufacturing; electromechanical controls; metallurgy. *Mailing Add:* Tex Instruments Inc 34 Forest St MS 12-1-A Attleboro MA 02703

PADRON, JORGE LOUIS, b Havana, Cuba, July 3, 31; m 57; c 2. BIOCHEMISTRY. *Educ:* Okla Baptist Univ, BS, 52; Univ Okla, MS, 54, PhD(biochem, bact), 56. *Prof Exp:* Asst prof chem, Okla Baptist Univ, 54-56; from assoc prof to prof, 57-64, head dept, 60-74, VPRES ACAD AFFAIRS & DEAN COL, DRURY COL, 74- *Concurrent Pos:* Fulbright lectr, Seville, Spain, 62-63 & Quito, Ecuador, 66-67; NATO fel, Oxford Univ. *Mem:* Am Chem Soc; Am Soc Microbiol; NY Acad Sci. *Res:* Bacterial physiology; altered metabolic pathways accompanying chloramphenicol resistance in Staphylococcus aeurus; glucose acetoacetate condensate as an antidiabetogenic factor. *Mailing Add:* Off of Dean Drury Col Springfield MO 65802

PADRTA, FRANK GEORGE, b Chicago, Ill, Apr 29, 30; m 57; c 2. ORGANIC CHEMISTRY, PHYSICAL CHEMISTRY. *Educ:* Elmhurst Col, BS, 56. *Prof Exp:* Lab technician, 52-56, chemist, 56-64, assoc res coordr, 64-68, res coordr, 68-74, group leader, 74-81, RES COORDR, UNIVERSAL OIL PROD CO, 68- *Mem:* Am Chem Soc; Am Soc Mass Spectrometry; Am Soc Testing & Mat. *Res:* Mass spectrometry; gas chromatography; liquid solid chromatography; infrared spectroscopy; catalysis research; new petroleum products; air pollution. *Mailing Add:* Universal Oil Prod Co Ten Universal Oil Prod Plaza Des Plaines IL 60016

PADUANA, JOSEPH A, b Utica, NY, Sept 9, 17; m 44. SOIL MECHANICS, FOUNDATION ENGINEERING. *Educ:* Cooper Union, BCE, 50; Polytech Inst Brooklyn, MCE, 60; Univ Calif, Berkeley, PhD(civil eng), 66. *Prof Exp:* Struct engr, Corbett, Tinghir & Co, NY, 50-54; proj engr, Moran, Proctor, Meuser & Rutledge, 54-59; sr proj engr, Raymond Int, Inc, 60-62; PROF CIVIL ENG & CHMN DEPT, CALIF STATE UNIV, SACRAMENTO, 65- *Concurrent Pos:* NSF grant for instructional sci equip, 67; mem hwy res bd, Nat Acad Sci-Nat Res Coun. *Mem:* Am Soc Civil Engrs. *Res:* Strength of soils; vertical drains in clay soils; soil stabilization; cracking and erosion of earth dams; pile capacities; computer programming. *Mailing Add:* Dept of Civil Eng Calif State Univ Sacramento CA 95819

PADULO, LOUIS, b Athens, Ala, Dec 14, 36; m 63; c 2. ELECTRICAL ENGINEERING, MATHEMATICS. *Educ:* Fairleigh Dickinson Univ, BS, 59; Stanford Univ, MS, 62; Ga Inst Technol, PhD(elec eng), 66. *Prof Exp:* Engr, Radio Corp Am, 59-60; acting instr elec eng, Stanford Univ, 60-62; asst prof San Jose State Col, 62-63; asst prof math, Ga State Col, 66-67; asst prof math, Morehouse Col, 67-68, assoc prof, 68-69, acting chmn dept, 67-68; vis assoc prof elec eng, Stanford Univ, 69-71, assoc prof, 71-76; DEAN COL ENG & PROF ELEC ENG, BOSTON UNIV, 76- *Concurrent Pos:* Consult, math, Eng Exp Sta, Ga Inst Technol, 66-; mathematician, Thomas J Watson Res Ctr, Int Bus Mach Corp, 68; dir dual degree prog, Atlanta Univ Ctr & Ga Inst Technol, 69-; vis assoc prof, Columbia Univ, 69, Harvard Univ, 70 & Stanford Univ, 71; spec asst to pres, Morehouse Col, 70- *Mem:* Math Asn Am; Inst Elec & Electronics Engrs. *Res:* Communication theory and data processing; linear system theory; applied mathematics; automata theory; computation theory; linear algebra; analysis; optimization; discrete mathematics. *Mailing Add:* Col of Eng 110 Cummington St Boston MA 02215

PADWA, ALBERT, b New York, NY, Oct 3, 37; m 60; c 3. ORGANIC CHEMISTRY. *Educ:* Columbia Univ, BA, 59, MA, 60, PhD(chem), 62. *Prof Exp:* NSF fel, Univ Wis, 62-63; asst prof chem, Ohio State Univ, 63-66; assoc prof chem, State Univ NY Buffalo, 66-69, prof, 69-79; PROF CHEM, EMORY UNIV, 79- *Mem:* Am Chem Soc. *Res:* Mechanistic organic photochemistry; chemistry of small strained rings; free radical reactions. *Mailing Add:* Dept Chem Emory Univ Atlanta GA 30322

PADYKULA, HELEN ANN, b Chicopee, Mass, Dec 27, 24. CELL BIOLOGY. *Educ:* Univ Mass, BS, 46; Mt Holyoke Col, MA, 48; Radcliffe Col, PhD(med sci), 54. *Prof Exp:* Asst zool, Mt Holyoke Col, 46-48; instr, Wellesley Col, 48-50; from instr to asst prof anat, Harvard Med Sch, 53-64; vis lectr zool, 61-62, PROF BIOL, LAB ELECTRON MICROS, WELLESLEY COL, 64- *Concurrent Pos:* Teaching asst, Marine Biol Lab, Woods Hole, 48-49; vis investr, Med Col, Cornell Univ, 58-59; USPHS res career develop award, 59-64, spec res fel, 71-72; adv to freshmen, Radcliffe Col, 63-64; dir NSF undergrad res participation prog biol sci, Wellesley Col, 66-70; mem reproductive biol study sect, NIH, 68-72; vis investr, Ian Clunies Ross Res Lab, Commonwealth Sci & Indust Res Orgn, Prospect, Australia, 71; Am ed, Histochemie, 71; vis prof, Dept Anat, McGill Univ, 72; assoc ed, Am J Anat, 71-74; mem sci adv comt, Muscular Dystrophy Asn, 72-75; mem bd sci coun, Nat Eye Inst, 72-76; vis prof, Univ NC, Chapel Hill, 75; assoc ed, Anat Record, 75- *Mem:* Am Asn Anat; Histochem Soc; Am Soc Cell Biol; Soc Develop Biol; Int Soc Develop Biol. *Res:* Histochemistry and electron microscopy; mammalian differentiation, especially uterus, placenta and skeletal muscle. *Mailing Add:* Lab of Electron Micros Wellesley Col Wellesley MA 02181

PAE, K(OOK) D(ONG), b Seoul, Korea. MECHANICS, MATERIALS SCIENCE. *Educ:* Missouri Valley Col, BS, 56; Univ Mo, MS, 58; Pa State Univ, PhD(mech), 62. *Prof Exp:* From asst prof to assoc prof, 62-70, PROF MECH & MAT SCI, RUTGERS UNIV, NEW BRUNSWICK, 70- *Mem:* Am Phys Soc; Am Soc Mech Eng; Am Soc Eng Educ; Am Asn Univ Professors; Sigma Xi. *Res:* Effects of high pressure on mechanical behavior; physical properties of polymers. *Mailing Add:* Dept of Mech & Mat Sci Rutgers Univ New Brunswick NJ 08903

PAEGE, LYNN MERTON, microbiology, see previous edition

PAEGLE, JULIA NOGUES, b Buenos Aires, Argentina, May 13, 43; m 68; c 3. STATISTICAL METEOROLOGY. *Educ:* Univ Buenos Aires, BS, 63; Univ Calif, Los Angeles, MA, 67, PhD(meteorol), 69. *Prof Exp:* Asst prof, 71-76, assoc prof, 76-82, PROF METEOROL, UNIV UTAH, 82- *Concurrent Pos:* Vis prof, Univ Buenos Aires, 71; guest investr, Argentine Weather Serv, 72; vis scientist, Nat Ctr Atmospheric Sci, 75 & 77; vis assoc prof, Univ Calif Los Angeles, 78; vis prof, Univ Veracruz, 79; vis scientist, Nat Meteorol Ctr, 80-81. *Mem:* Am Meteorol Soc; Centro Argentno de Meteorologos; Meteorol Soc Japan. *Res:* Statistical and dynamical analyses of planetary scale atmospheric circulations; deflection and modification of air currents by mountains; interaction of tropical motions with mid-latitude flows. *Mailing Add:* Dept Meteorol Univ Utah Salt Lake City UT 84112

PAESLER, MICHAEL ARTHUR, b Elgin, Ill, Apr 19, 46; m 80. LASER ANNEALING, AMORPHOUS SEMICONDUCTORS. *Educ:* Beloit Col, BA, 68; Univ Chicago, MS, 71, PhD(physics), 75. *Prof Exp:* Guest scientist physics, Max Planck Inst, 75-76; res fel appl sci, Harvard Univ, 77-80; ASST PROF PHYSICS, NC STATE UNIV, 80- *Mem:* Am Phys Soc; Mat Res Soc. *Res:* Interaction of high power lasers with semiconductors; photoluminescance and Raman spectroscopy of semiconductors; electrical and optical properties of amorphous semiconductors; growth and characterization of insulators on crystalline III-V semiconductors. *Mailing Add:* Dept Physics NC State Univ Raleigh NC 27650

PAETKAU, VERNER HENRY, b Rosthern, Sask, July 26, 41; m 65; c 3. BIOCHEMISTRY, IMMUNOLOGY. *Educ:* Univ Alta, BSc, 63; Univ Wis, MSc, 65, PhD(biochem), 67. *Prof Exp:* Fel biochem, Enzyme Inst, Univ Wis, 67-69; from asst prof to assoc prof, 69-78, PROF BIOCHEM, UNIV ALTA, 78- *Concurrent Pos:* Med Res Coun scholar, Univ Alta, 69-73. *Mem:* Am Soc Biol Chemists; Can Biochem Soc. *Res:* Control of immune responses by intercellular signals; biochemistry of lymphokines; structure and organization of immunoglobulin genes. *Mailing Add:* Dept of Biochem Univ of Alta Edmonton AB T6G 2H7 Can

PAFFENBARGER, GEORGE CORBLY, b McArthur, Ohio, Nov 3, 02; m 25; c 3. DENTISTRY. *Educ:* Ohio State Univ, DDS, 24. *Hon Degrees:* DSc, Ohio State Univ, 44, Nihon Univ, Tokyo, 61, Col Med & Dent NJ, 75 & Georgetown Univ, 78; MDS, Nihon Univ, Tokyo, 59. *Prof Exp:* Pvt pract, Ohio, 24-25; mem staff, Palama Settlement Dent Clin, Honolulu, Hawaii, 25-27; instr oper dent, Col Dent, Ohio State Univ, 27-29; res assoc, 29-41 & 46-68, SR RES ASSOC, AM DENT ASN HEALTH FOUND RES DIV, NAT BUR STANDARDS, 68- *Concurrent Pos:* Lectr, Fac Med, Univ St Andrews, 59; vis prof, Nihon Univ, Tokyo, 61. *Honors & Awards:* Spenadel Award, 1st Dist Dent Soc, 57; Callahan Award, Am Acad Plastics Res in Dent, 58; Souder Award, Int Asn Dent Res, 58; William J Gies Award, Am Col Dent, 65; Int Miller Award, Int Dent Fedn, 72. *Mem:* AAAS (vpres, 57); hon mem Am Dent Asn; fel Am Col Dent; Int Asn Dent Res (pres, 54); hon mem Ger Soc Dent. *Res:* Physical and chemical properties of dental materials. *Mailing Add:* Am Dent Asn Health Found Res Div Nat Bur of Standards Washington DC 20234

PAFFENBARGER, RALPH SEAL, JR, b Columbus, Ohio, Oct 21, 22; m 43; c 6. EPIDEMIOLOGY. *Educ:* Ohio State Univ, BA, 44; Northwestern Univ, BM, 46, MD, 47; Johns Hopkins Univ, MPH, 52, DPH, 54. *Prof Exp:* Epidemiologist, USPHS Commun Dis Ctr, Ga, 47-53, Lab Infectious Dis, Nat Microbiol Inst, 53-55, Robert A Taft Sanit Eng Ctr, Ohio, 55-59 & Nat Heart Inst, 59-68; chief bur adult health & chronic dis, Bur Adult Health & Chronic Dis, Calif State Dept Pub Health, 68-70, chief epidemiol sect, 71-78; prof epidemiol, Sch Pub Health, Univ Calif, Berkeley, 69-80; PROF, SCH MED,

STANFORD UNIV, 77- *Concurrent Pos:* Asst, La State Univ, 49-50; res assoc, Sch Hyg & Pub Health, Johns Hopkins Univ, 52-54; asst clin prof, Col Med, Univ Cincinnati, 55-59; clin assoc, Harvard Univ, 60-65, lectr, 65- *Mem:* AAAS; Sigma Xi; Am Pub Health Asn; AMA. *Res:* Epidemiologic studies of acute and chronic diseases, poliomyelitis, diarrheal disease, mental illness, coronary heart disease, stroke and cancer. *Mailing Add:* Dept Epidemiol Stanford Univ Sch Med Stanford CA 94305

PAFFENHOFER, GUSTAV-ADOLF, HERMANN, b Wetzlar, Ger, Aug 19, 38. BIOLOGICAL OCEANOGRAPHY. *Educ:* Justus-Liebig-Universitat, Giessen Ger, Dr rer nat (zool), 68. *Prof Exp:* Res zoologist, Scripps Inst Oceanog, 68-70; marine biologist, Biologische Anstalt Helgoland, 70-74; asst prof, 74-77, ASSOC PROF OCEANOG, SKIDAWAY INST OCEANOG, 77- *Concurrent Pos:* Adj assoc prof, Dept Zool, Univ Ga, Athens, 75-; Dept Energy & NSF grants, 76-81. *Mem:* Am Soc Limnol & Oceanog. *Res:* Marine zooplankton ecology; marine plankton food web dynamics. *Mailing Add:* Skidaway Inst Oceanog PO Box 13687 Savannah GA 31406

PAFFORD, WILLIAM N, b Camden, Tenn, May 21, 29; m 50; c 2. SCIENCE EDUCATION. *Educ:* George Peabody Col, 57, MA, 58, EdS, 63; Univ Ky, EdD, 67. *Prof Exp:* Instr, Montgomery Bell Acad, Tenn, 58-63; asst prof biol, Radford Col, 63-65; coordr student teaching sci area, Univ Ky, 66-67; chmn dept gen sci & sci educ, 73-78, asst dean, Col Educ, 78-81, PROF SCI EDUC, EAST TENN STATE UNIV, 67-, ASSOC DEAN, COL EDUC, 81- *Mem:* Nat Sci Teachers Asn; Asn Educ Teachers Sci. *Res:* Adoption of educational innovations in science; effect of personal characteristics on student performance in science courses. *Mailing Add:* Dept of Sci Educ ETenn State Univ Johnson City TN 37601

PAGANELLI, CHARLES VICTOR, b New York, NY, Feb 13, 29; m 54; c 5. BIOPHYSICS, PHYSIOLOGY. *Educ:* Hamilton Col, AB, 50; Harvard Univ, MA, 53, PhD, 57. *Prof Exp:* From instr to assoc prof, 58-71, assoc chmn, 76-80, actg chmn, 80-81, PROF PHYSIOL, SCH MED, STATE UNIV NY BUFFALO, 71- *Concurrent Pos:* Polio Found fel, Copenhagen, 56-58; vis prof physiol, Univ Hawaii, 74-75. *Honors & Awards:* Elliott Coues Award, Am Ornithol Union, 81. *Mem:* Undersea Med Soc; AAAS; Am Physiol Soc. *Res:* Permeability of biological and artificial membranes; diffusion; active transport. *Mailing Add:* Dept Physiol State Univ NY Buffalo NY 14214

PAGAN-FONT, FRANCISCO ALFREDO, b Mayaguez, PR, June 18, 40; US citizen; m 65; c 5. FISHERIES MANAGEMENT. *Educ:* Univ PR, BS, 63, MS, 67; Auburn Univ, PhD(fisheries mgt), 70. *Prof Exp:* Asst prof, 70-73, asst dir dept, 71-73, ASSOC PROF MARINE & FISHERIES SCI & AQUACULT & DIR, DEPT MARINE SCI, UNIV PR, MAYAGUEZ, 73- *Concurrent Pos:* Mem PR & The Sea Comt, Govt Pr, 72; US Dept Interior res grants, 71-73; PR Dept Agr & US Dept Com res grant, 71-76; Upjohn Co res grant, 75; fishery resources off & aquaculturist, Food & Agr Orgn, UN, 76-79; exec dir develop & admin marine, lacustrine & flurial resources, PR Corp, 79-81; pres bd dirs, Fajardo Drydock, Inc, 79-81. *Mem:* Am Fisheries Soc; World Maricult Soc; Am Inst Fishery Res Biologists; Asn Island Marine Labs Caribbean (1st vpres, 73-74). *Res:* The aquaculture of Tilapia and channel catfish cultures, mono- and polycultures of fishes, hybridization in Tilapias, cage culture of fishes, and mariculture of fishes, shrimp and oysters; artificial reefs; planning aquaculture development and research; training of senior aquaculturist; research administration. *Mailing Add:* PO Box 3547 Mayaguez PR 00708

PAGANO, ALFRED HORTON, b New York, NY, July 14, 30; m 53; c 3. ENVIRONMENTAL REGULATION, DYE CHEMISTRY. *Educ:* Cornell Univ, BA, 52; Columbia Univ, MA, 53; Ohio State Univ, PhD(org chem), 60. *Prof Exp:* Res chemist, 60-73, prod supvr, 73-81, SR SUPVR, E I DU PONT DE NEMOURS & CO INC, 81- *Mem:* Am Chem Soc. *Res:* Hydrogenation of nitrocompounds; amination; action of oxidizing agents on salts of primary nitroalkanes; oxidative dimerization; responsible for production of azo and anthraquinone dyes for textile or carpet use. *Mailing Add:* E I du Pont de Nemours & Co Deepwater NJ 08023

PAGANO, JOSEPH FRANK, b Cleveland, Ohio, July 15, 19; m 42; c 2. MICROBIOLOGY. *Educ:* Univ Ill, BS, 42, MS, 47, PhD(microbiol), 49; Am Bd Med Microbiol, dipl. *Prof Exp:* Bacteriologist, Ill State Water Surv, 46-48; res assoc microbiol, Univ Ill, 49-50; head dept chemother res, Squibb Inst Med Res, 50-61; asst dir biol div, Sterling Winthrop Res Inst, 61-62; sect head microbiol, Smith Kline & French Labs, 62-66, asst dept mgr infectious dis, 66-67, dir microbiol, 67-71, tech dir, 72-78, DIR ENVIRON HEALTH & QUAL CONTROL PROGS, CORP TECH SERV, SMITH KLINE DIAG DIV, SMITH KLINE CORP, 78-, CONSULT, 79- *Concurrent Pos:* Res assoc prof, Grad Sch, Hahnemann Med Col. *Mem:* Fel Am Acad Microbiol; Am Soc Microbiol; Soc Indust Microbiol; Am Indust Hyg Asn; fel NY Acad Sci. *Res:* Antibiotics; chemotherapeutics; fermentations; microbial genetics and biochemistry; diagnostics; environmental health quality assurance. *Mailing Add:* Smith Kline Corp 149 Sheldrake Dr Paoli PA 19301

PAGANO, JOSEPH STEPHEN, b Rochester, NY, Dec 29, 31; c 2. VIROLOGY, INTERNAL MEDICINE. *Educ:* Univ Rochester, AB, 53; Yale Univ, MD, 57. *Prof Exp:* Assoc prof med, bacteriol & immunol, 68-73, dir, Virol Lab, 69-74, dir, Div Infectious Dis, 72-75, DIR CANCER RES CTR, UNIV NC SCH MED, 74-, PROF MED, BACTERIOL & IMMUNOL, 73-; ATTEND PHYSICIAN MED & INFECTIOUS DIS, NC MEM HOSP, 65- *Concurrent Pos:* Mem ed bd, J Virol, 74-, assoc ed, 79-; mem, Virol Study Sect, 75-; bd assoc ed, Cancer Res, 76-80 & J Immunol, 77-80; assoc ed, J Virology, 79- *Honors & Awards:* Sinsheimer Award, Sinsheimer Found, 66; USPHS Res Career Award, NIH, 68. *Mem:* Infectious Dis Soc Am; Am Soc Microbiol; Am Asn Immunol; Am Asn Cancer Res; Am Soc Clin Invest. *Res:* Cancer and virus infections; tumor virology and molecular biology of Herpes viruses, especially Epstein-Barr viruses. *Mailing Add:* 503 Swing Bldg Univ NC Sch of Med Chapel Hill NC 27514

PAGANO, RICHARD EMIL, b New York, NY, June 13, 44; m 66; c 3. BIOPHYSICS. *Educ:* Johns Hopkins Univ, BA, 65; Univ Va, PhD(biophys), 68. *Prof Exp:* Staff assoc membrane biophysics, Lab Phys Biol, NIH, 68-70; sr fel membrane biophys, Polymer Dept, Weizmann Inst Sci, Rehovoth, Israel, 70-72; STAFF MEM, DEPT EMBRYOL, CARNEGIE INST WASHINGTON, 72- *Concurrent Pos:* Sr asst scientist, USPHS, 68-70; assoc prof, Johns Hopkins Univ, 76-; mem cell biol study sect, NSF, 77-79, chmn, Membrane Biophys Subgroup, 78-79. *Mem:* AAAS; Am Soc Cell Biologists; Biophys Soc. *Res:* Organization, dynamics and metabolism of lipids in eukaryotic cells; membrane assembly; membrane fusion; synthetic membranes. *Mailing Add:* Dept Embryol Carnegie Inst Baltimore MD 21210

PAGE, ALAN CAMERON, b Lawrence, Mass, May 16, 42; m 66; c 2. FOREST MANAGEMENT. *Educ:* Cornell Univ, BS, 64; Yale Univ, MF, 66; Univ Mass, Amherst, PhD(forestry), 74. *Prof Exp:* PRES FOREST MGT, GREEN DIAMOND FORESTRY SERV, INC, 71- *Mem:* Soc Am Foresters. *Res:* Computer analysis of forest management options both biological and economic. *Mailing Add:* Blue Meadow Rd Belchertown MA 01007

PAGE, ALBERT LEE, b New Lenox, Ill, Mar 19, 27; m 52; c 2. SOIL CHEMISTRY. *Educ:* Univ Calif, Riverside, BA, 56; Univ Calif, Davis, PhD(soil sci), 60. *Prof Exp:* From asst prof to assoc prof, 60-71, head, Div Soil Sci, 71-75, dir, Kerney Found Soil Sci, 75-80, PROF SOIL SCI, UNIV CALIF, RIVERSIDE, 71- *Concurrent Pos:* Guggenheim Mem Found fel & Fulbright-Hays award, 66-67; comt mem, Nat Acad Sci-Subcomt Geochem & Environ Health, 75-81. *Mem:* AAAS; Soil Sci Soc Am; Am Soc Agron. *Res:* Chemical and mineralogical properties of soils; chemistry of hydrolyzable metals in colloid systems; ion exchange equilibrium; environmental trace metal contamination. *Mailing Add:* Dept of Soil & Environ Sci Univ of Calif Riverside CA 92521

PAGE, ARTHUR R, b Winona, Minn, Mar 22, 30; m 51; c 3. IMMUNOLOGY, PEDIATRICS. *Educ:* Univ Minn, MD, 56. *Prof Exp:* Asst prof, 61-66, assoc prof, 66-76, PROF PEDIAT, MED SCH, UNIV MINN, MINNEAPOLIS, 76- *Concurrent Pos:* USPHS fel, 59-61, career develop award, 61-71. *Mem:* Am Soc Exp Path; Soc Pediat Res. *Res:* Inflammation. *Mailing Add:* Dept of Pediat Univ of Minn Med Sch Minneapolis MN 55455

PAGE, BENJAMIN MARKHAM, b Pasadena, Calif, May 6, 11; m 35; c 2. GEOLOGY. *Educ:* Stanford Univ, AB, 33, MA, 34, PhD(geol), 40. *Prof Exp:* Field geologist, 35-37; from instr to asst prof geol, Univ Southern Calif, 37-41; assoc prof, 43-51, exec head dept, 57-69, prof, 51-76, EMER PROF GEOL, STANFORD UNIV, 76- *Concurrent Pos:* Asst geologist, US Geol Surv, 42-45; sci consult, Nat Resources Sect, Allies Occupation, Japan, 50-51; geol consult, UN Tech Asst Admin, Yugoslavia, 55; Guggenheim fel, Italy, 59-60; consult, Adv Comt Reactor Safeguards, Nuclear Regulatory Comn, 67-; geol res, Mineral Res & Serv Org, Taiwan, 74 & 77. *Mem:* Fel Geol Soc Am; AAAS; Am Geophys Union. *Res:* Structural geology; tectonics; geology of continental margins; plate interactions. *Mailing Add:* Dept of Geol Stanford Univ Stanford CA 94305

PAGE, CALVIN AMES, b Minneapolis, Minn, Nov 8, 22; m 48; c 2. MICROBIOLOGY. *Educ:* Mich State Univ, BS, 49, MS, 50, PhD(virol), 54. *Prof Exp:* Assoc prof biol, Southwestern La Univ, 51-54, prof bact & head dept, 54-59; dir, Microbiol Res & Consult Lab, 59-63; microbiologist, Shell Develop Co, Calif, 63-69; assoc dir res, Animal Health Div, Schering-Plough Corp, Kenilworth, NJ, 69-73, gen mgr, Schering Corp, PR, 73-77; mem staff, Arnar-Stone, Inc, 77-80, PLANT MGR, SEARLE PHARMACEUT, 80- *Res:* Bacterial metabolism; infectious diseases; experimental chemotherapy. *Mailing Add:* Searle Pharmaceut 1735 E Mission Hills Rd Northbrook IL 60062

PAGE, CARL VICTOR, b Flint, Mich, Apr 26, 38; m 62; c 1. COMPUTER SCIENCE. *Educ:* Univ Mich, BSE(sci eng) & BSE(eng math), 60, MS, 61, PhD(commun sci), 65. *Prof Exp:* Lectr elec eng, Univ Mich, 66; asst prof info sci, Univ NC, 66-67; from asst prof to assoc prof comput sci, 67-76, PROF COMPUT SCI, MICH STATE UNIV, 76- *Mem:* Inst Elec & Electronics Engrs; Asn Comput Mach. *Res:* Artificial intelligence; adaptive systems; automata theory; compiler theory; formal languages; pattern recognition. *Mailing Add:* Dept of Comput Sci Mich State Univ East Lansing MI 48824

PAGE, CHARLES HENRY, b East Orange, NJ, Aug 28, 41; m 63; c 1. NEUROPHYSIOLOGY, COMPARATIVE PHYSIOLOGY. *Educ:* Allegheny Col, BS, 63; Univ Ill, Urbana, MS, 66, PhD(physiol), 69. *Prof Exp:* NIH fel biol, Stanford Univ, 68-70; asst prof zool, Ohio Univ, 70-74; asst prof, 74-76, ASSOC PROF PHYSIOL, RUTGERS UNIV, 76- *Concurrent Pos:* NIH grant, Ohio Univ, 72-74; NIH res grant, 74- *Mem:* AAAS; Am Physiol Soc; Soc Exp Biol; Am Soc Zool; Soc Neurosci. *Res:* Arthropod neurophysiology; proprioceptive reflexes; central control of movement; ventilatory reflexes. *Mailing Add:* Dept of Physiol Rutgers Univ New Brunswick NJ 08903

PAGE, CLAYTON R, III, b Austin, Tex, July 18, 43; m 65; c 1. CELL BIOLOGY, PARASITOLOGY. *Educ:* Marshall Univ, BA, 65; Univ Cincinnati, PhD(parasitol), 70. *Prof Exp:* NIH trainee, Univ Calif, Los Angeles, 69-71; ASST PROF CELL BIOL & PARASITOL, TULANE UNIV, 71- *Concurrent Pos:* Am Soc Trop Med & Hyg China travel award, 78. *Mem:* AAAS; Royal Soc Trop Med & Hyg; Am Soc Parasitol (secy-treas, 78-); Am Soc Trop Med & Hyg; Am Soc Cell Biol. *Res:* Host-parasite integration; helminth biochemistry and physiology; pathology of schistosomiasis and trypanosomiasis. *Mailing Add:* Dept of Biol Tulane Univ New Orleans LA 70118

PAGE, D(ERRICK) J(OHN), b London, Eng, Jan 20, 37; m 66. ELECTRICAL ENGINEERING. *Educ:* Univ Birmingham, BSc, 59, PhD(elec eng), 63. *Prof Exp:* Sr engr, 63-68, MGR SEMICONDUCTORS RES, RES LABS, WESTINGHOUSE ELEC CORP, 69- *Mem:* Inst Elec &

Electronics Engrs. *Res:* Space-charge-limited current in insulators and the development of space-charge-limited current devices; II-VI compounds, particularly in thin film form and electroluminescence in thin films and devices; silicon power devices and solar cells. *Mailing Add:* Res & Develop Ctr Churchill Borough Pittsburgh PA 15235

PAGE, DAVID SANBORN, b Suffern, NY, June 1, 43; m 64; c 2. BIO-ORGANIC CHEMISTRY, MARINE CHEMISTRY. *Educ:* Brown Univ, BS, 65; Purdue Univ, PhD(phys chem), 70. *Prof Exp:* Vis asst prof chem, Purdue Univ, 70-71; asst prof chem, Bates Col, 71-74; ASSOC PROF CHEM, BOWDOIN COL, 74- *Concurrent Pos:* Adj asst prof chem, Univ NH, 75- *Mem:* Am Chem Soc. *Res:* Enzyme-substrate and substrate analog interactions; physiologic indicators of pollution stress; trace analysis of hydrocarbons in the marine environment; toxic effects of hydrocarbons on marine organisms. *Mailing Add:* Dept of Chem Bowdoin Col Brunswick ME 04011

PAGE, DEREK HOWARD, b Sheffield, Eng, Nov 22, 29; m 55; c 4. PULP & PAPER TECHNOLOGY. *Educ:* Cambridge Univ, BA, 53, MA, 57, PhD(physics), 68. *Prof Exp:* Scientist, Brit Insulated Callendars Cables, 53-54; head fibre & paper physics sect, Brit Paper & Bd Indust Res Asn, 55-64; DIR MAT SCI DIV, PULP & PAPER RES INST CAN, 64- *Concurrent Pos:* Fel, Tech Asn Pulp & Paper Indust, 75. *Honors & Awards:* Res & Develop Div Award, Tech Asn Pulp & Paper Indust USA, 72. *Mem:* Tech Asn Pulp & Paper Indust; fel Royal Microscopic Soc; Fel Inst Physics. *Res:* Structure and physical properties of wood, wood pulp fibres and paper. *Mailing Add:* 570 St Johns Rd Point Claire PQ H9R 3J9 Can

PAGE, EDWIN HOWARD, b Glasgow, Ky, Feb 3, 20; m 41; c 2. VETERINARY MEDICINE. *Educ:* Western Ky Univ, BS, 40; Ohio State Univ, DVM, 53. *Prof Exp:* Teacher pub sch, Ky, 40-41; instr mach oper, E I du Pont de Nemours & Co, Inc, 41-42; owner-operator dairy farm, Ky, 46-49; pvt pract vet med, Ky, 53-64; from assoc prof to prof vet clin, 64-73, PROF LARGE ANIMAL CLINS, SCH VET SCI & MED, PURDUE UNIV, WEST LAFAYETTE, 73-, HEAD DEPT LARGE ANIMALS, 76- *Mem:* Am Asn Vet Clinicians; Am Vet Med Asn. *Res:* Use of an autogenous vaccine in the treatment of equine sarcoid. *Mailing Add:* Dept of Vet Clins Purdue Univ Sch of Vet Sci & Med West Lafayette IN 47907

PAGE, ERNEST, b Cologne, Ger, May 30, 27; nat US. BIOPHYSICS. *Educ:* Univ Calif, AB, 49, MD, 52. *Prof Exp:* Am Heart Asn estab investr biophys, Biophys Lab, Harvard Med Sch, 59-65; assoc prof, 65-69, PROF MED & PHYSIOL, SCH MED, UNIV CHICAGO, 69- *Mem:* Biophys Soc; Am Physiol Soc; Am Soc Cell Biol; Soc Gen Physiologists; Am Asn Anatomists. *Res:* Membrane transport phenomena and electron microscopy in mammalian heart muscle. *Mailing Add:* Dept of Med 950 E 59th St Hosp Box 137 Chicago IL 60637

PAGE, IRVINE HEINLY, b Indianapolis, Ind, Jan 7, 01; m 30; c 2. CARDIOVASCULAR DISEASES. *Educ:* Cornell Univ, AB & MD, 26. *Hon Degrees:* LLD, John Carroll Univ, 56; DSc, Union Univ, 57, Boston Univ, 57, Ohio State Univ, 60, Univ Brazil, 61, Cleveland State Univ, 70 & Ind Univ, 75; MD, Univ Siena, Italy, 65 & Med Col Ohio, 73. *Prof Exp:* Intern, Presby Hosp, New York, 26-28; chief, Chem Div, Kaiser Wilhelm Inst, Munich, 28-31; assoc mem, Hosp, Rockefeller Inst, 31-37; dir, Lilly Clin & Lab Clin Res, Indianapolis City Hosp, 37-45; dir, 45-66, sr consult, 66-68, EMER CONSULT, RES DIV, CLEVELAND CLIN, 68- *Concurrent Pos:* Ed emer, Modern Med; ed, Coronary Club, Inc, 72; mem, Subcomt Clin Res, Nat Res Coun, Nat Adv Heart Coun, Coun Adv Sci Writing, Expert Adv Bd, WHO & Coun Arteriosclerosis, Am Heart Asn. *Mem:* Sr mem Nat Inst Med-Nat Acad Sci; Am Soc Biol Chem; Soc Exp Biol & Med (pres, 72-); Am Heart Asn (pres). *Res:* Chemistry of the brain; clinical research; hypertension; shock; arteriosclerosis; Bright's disease. *Mailing Add:* Box 516 Hyannis Port MA 02647

PAGE, JOANNA R ZIEGLER, b Gainesville, Fla, Aug 28, 38; m 66; c 2. PHYCOLOGY. *Educ:* Bucknell Univ, BS, 60; Cornell Univ, MS, 63, PhD(bot), 66. *Prof Exp:* NSF fel bot, Yale Univ, 65-66; asst prof, Univ Conn, 66-68, biol, 68-71; lectr bot, Univ Mass, 73-74, 74-75, 75-76, 77-78 & 78-79. *Concurrent Pos:* Vis asst prof bot, Univ Mass, 79-80, 80-81 & 81-82; NSF Coop Grad fel. *Mem:* Phycol Soc Am; Bot Soc Am; Int Phycol Soc; Sigma Xi. *Res:* Biological clocks; algal life cycles and reproduction. *Mailing Add:* 125 Blue Meadow Rd Belchertown MA 01007

PAGE, JOHN ARTHUR, analytical chemistry, see previous edition

PAGE, JOHN BOYD, JR, b Columbus, Ohio, Sept 4, 38; m 66; c 1. THEORETICAL SOLID STATE PHYSICS. *Educ:* Univ Utah, BS, 60, PhD(physics), 66. *Prof Exp:* Res assoc physics, Univ Frankfurt, 66-67 & Cornell Univ, 68-69; asst prof, 69-75, assoc prof, 75-80, PROF PHYSICS, ARIZ STATE UNIV, 80- *Concurrent Pos:* Vis scientist, Max Planck Inst Solid State Physics, Stuttgart, Ger, 75-76. *Mem:* Am Phys Soc; Am Asn Physics Teachers; Sigma Xi. *Res:* Theoretical solid state physics, particularly resonance light scattering, impurity-induced raman scattering and phonon physics in imperfect and perfect crystals; light scattering studies of solids. *Mailing Add:* Dept of Physics Ariz State Univ Tempe AZ 85287

PAGE, JOHN GARDNER, b Milwaukee, Wis, Sept 14, 40; m 62; c 2. PHARMACOLOGY, TOXICOLOGY. *Educ:* Univ Wis-Madison, BS, 64, MS, 66, PhD(pharmacol), 67. *Prof Exp:* Sr toxicologist, Eli Lilly & Co, 69-77; dir toxicol & path, Rhone Poulenc, Inc, 77-80; MEM STAFF, TOXICO DEPT, TOXIGENICS, INC, 80- *Concurrent Pos:* NIH staff fel, Lab Chem Pharmacol, Nat Heart Inst, 67-69. *Mem:* AAAS; Am Soc Pharmacol & Exp Therapeut; Int Soc Biochem Pharmacol; Sigma Xi; Fed Am Soc Exp Biol. *Res:* Biochemical basis and/or mechanism for pharmacological and toxicological activity of potential therapeutic compounds. *Mailing Add:* Toxicol Dept Toxigenics Inc 1800 E Pershing Rd Decatur IL 62526

PAGE, LARRY J, b Brookfield, Mo, Dec 14, 41; m 62. SPACE PHYSICS. *Educ:* Colo State Univ, BS, 64; Univ Utah, PhD(physics), 69. *Prof Exp:* Reactor physicist, Pac Northwest Labs, Battelle Mem Inst, 64-66; SR MEM TECH STAFF PHYSICS, ELECTROMAGNETIC SYSTS LABS, 69- *Mem:* Am Phys Soc; Optical Soc Am; Asn Comput Mach. *Res:* Energy band calculations and defect calculations in alkali halides; systems engineering and system design for high speed digital signal processing systems. *Mailing Add:* Electromagnetic Systs Labs 495 Java Dr Sunnyvale CA 94086

PAGE, LAWRENCE MERLE, b Fairbury, Ill, Apr 17, 44. ICHTYHOLOGY, INVERTEBRATE ZOOLOGY. *Educ:* Ill State Univ, BS, 66; Univ Ill, Urbana, MS, 68, PhD(zool), 72. *Prof Exp:* Res biologist, Ill Natural Hist Surv, 65-72; fish biologist, Sargent & Lundy Engrs, 72; asst taxonomist, 72-77, assoc taxonomist, 77-80, ICHTHYOLOGIST, ILL NATURAL HIST SURV, 80- *Concurrent Pos:* Consult, Mo Bot Garden, 73-76; assoc ichthyol, Mus Natural Hist, Univ Kans, 79- *Mem:* Am Soc Ichthyologists & Herpetologists; Int Asn Astacology; Soc Syst Zool; Ecol Soc Am; Sigma Xi. *Res:* Systematics and life histories of darters (Percidae) and minnows (Cyprinidae), amphipods, isopods and decapods. *Mailing Add:* Ill Natural Hist Surv Natural Resources Bldg 172 Urbana IL 61801

PAGE, LESLIE ANDREW, b Minneapolis, Minn, June 5, 24; m 52; c 4. VETERINARY MICROBIOLOGY, WILDLIFE DISEASES. *Educ:* Univ Minn, BA, 49; Univ Calif, MA, 53, PhD(bact), 56. *Prof Exp:* Asst res microbiologist avian med, Sch Vet Med, Univ Calif, Davis, 56-59, assoc specialist & lectr avian med & microbiol, 60-61; res leader chlamydial infections livestock & poultry & microbiologist, Nat Animal Dis Ctr, USDA, 61-79; CONSULT, 79- *Concurrent Pos:* Ed, Bull Wildlife Dis Asn, 65-67, managing ed, J Wildlife Dis, 67-70. *Mem:* Fel Am Acad Microbiol; Am Soc Microbiol; Wildlife Dis Asn (vpres, 71-72, pres, 72-73); Conf Res Workers Animal Dis; Soc Exp Biol & Med. *Res:* Microbiology of animal diseases, especially Chlamydia infections of birds and mammals; bacterial taxonomy; microbial diseases of chickens, penguins and reptiles. *Mailing Add:* Nat Animal Dis Ctr PO Box 70 N Cent Region USDA Ames IA 50010

PAGE, LORNE ALBERT, b Buffalo, NY, July 28, 21; m 46; c 5. EXPERIMENTAL PHYSICS. *Educ:* Queen's Univ, Ont, BSc, 44; Cornell Univ, PhD(physics), 50. *Prof Exp:* Asst physics, Cornell Univ, 45-46, Lab Nuclear Studies, 46-49; from asst prof to assoc prof, 50-58, PROF PHYSICS, UNIV PITTSBURGH, 58- *Concurrent Pos:* Guggenheim fel, Inst Physics, Univ Uppsala, 57-58; Sloan res fel, Univ Pittsburgh, 61-65. *Mem:* Am Phys Soc; Sigma Xi; NY Acad Sci; Optical Soc Am. *Res:* Electron-photon processes; magnetism; electrodynamics. *Mailing Add:* Dept of Physics & Astron Univ of Pittsburgh Pittsburgh PA 15260

PAGE, LOT BATES, b Tarrytown, NY, Apr 8, 23; m 50; c 3. INTERNAL MEDICINE. *Educ:* Harvard Univ, MD, 49. *Prof Exp:* Intern med, Mass Gen Hosp, 49-50; instr physiol, Sch Med, NY Univ, 50-52; resident med, Mass Gen Hosp, 54-56, instr, 58-59, assoc, 59-66, dir clin lab, 59-61, chief hypertension study unit, 61-66; assoc prof med, 66-70, PROF MED, SCH MED, TUFTS UNIV, 70-; CHIEF MED, NEWTON-WELLESLEY HOSP, 66- *Concurrent Pos:* USPHS fel, Mas Gen Hosp, 56-58; USPHS grants, 61-64 & 64-; mem heart prog proj comt B, Nat Heart Inst, 66-69; mem coun high blood pressure res, Am Heart Asn, 69- *Res:* Development of radioimmunoassay techniques for angiotensins and other small peptide hormones; cardiovascular disease in primitive people; catecholamine metabolism; renal physiology; biochemical methodology. *Mailing Add:* 2000 Washington St Newton Lower Falls MA 02162

PAGE, LOUISE, b Payson, Utah. NUTRITION. *Educ:* Utah State Univ, BS, 45; Univ Wis, MS, 50, PhD(nutrit), 63. *Prof Exp:* Dietitian, foods & nutrit, Women's Med Specialist Corp, US Army, 46-48; home economist foods, Mont Agr Exp Sta, 50-54; NUTRIT ANAL FOODS & NUTRIT, CONSUMER & FOOD ECON INST, SCI & EDUC ADMIN-AGR RES, USDA, 54-, LEADER FOOD & DIET APPRAISAL RES GROUP, 72- *Concurrent Pos:* Mem, Nat Nutrit Adv Comt Head Start, 66-69, USDA Plentiful Foods Comt, 66-72, Nat Comt Diet Ther, Am Dietetic Asn, 70, Secretariat Tech Comt Nutrit, White House Conf on Aging, 71, Yearbook of Agr Comt, 74 & Rural Health Subcomt, Nat Rural Develop Comt, 75- *Mem:* Am Inst Nutrit; Am Home Econ Asn; Am Dietetic Asn. *Res:* Development of research-based dietary guidance materials; nutritional evaluation of food supplies and diets. *Mailing Add:* USDA Sci & Educ Admin Hyattsville MD 20782

PAGE, MALCOLM I, b Lavonia Twp, Mich, Apr 28, 30; m; c 3. INTERNAL MEDICINE, INFECTIOUS DISEASES. *Educ:* Wayne Univ, AB, 52; Univ Chicago, MD, 56; Am Bd Internal Med, dipl, 64. *Prof Exp:* Officer EIS, Nat Commun Dis Ctr, 57-59; epidemiologist, Mary Imogene Bassett Hosp, 59-62; asst chief epidemiol, Nat Commun Dis Ctr, 62-63; asst prof med, Univ Chicago, 63-65; physician-in-chief, Mary Imogene Bassett Hosp, 65-72; PROF MED, MED COL GA, 72- *Concurrent Pos:* Vol instr, Sch Med, Emory Univ, 62-63; assoc clin prof, Col Physicians & Surgeons, Columbia Univ, 65-72. *Mem:* Am Col Physicians; Am Soc Microbiol. *Mailing Add:* Dept Med Med Col Ga Augusta GA 30902

PAGE, NELSON FRANKLIN, b Salisbury, NC, Nov 17, 38; m 64; c 2. MATHEMATICS. *Educ:* Univ NC, Chapel Hill, BA, 61, MA, 65, PhD(math), 67. *Prof Exp:* From instr to asst prof math, Univ NC, Greensboro, 66-74; mem fac, 74-77, assoc prof, 77-81, PROF MATH, HIGH POINT COL, 81- *Mem:* Am Math Soc; Math Asn Am. *Res:* Functional Hilbert spaces; analytic function theory. *Mailing Add:* Dept of Math 933 Montlier Ave High Point NC 27262

PAGE, NORBERT PAUL, b Farmersville, Ohio, Dec 29, 32; m 55; c 4. VETERINARY MEDICINE, RADIATION BIOLOGY. *Educ:* Ohio State Univ, DVM, 56; Univ Rochester, MS, 63; Am Bd Vet Pub Health, dipl, Am Bd Toxicol, dipl. *Prof Exp:* Dir rabies control, Dept Health, Columbus, Ohio, 56; officer vet serv, Selfridge AFB, Mich, 56-58; pvt practr vet med, Ohio,

58-59; chief vet serv, Itazuke AFB, US Air Force, Japan, 59-62; fel radiation biol, Univ Rochester, 62-63; dir, Large Animal Radiobiol Prog, Naval Radiol Defense Lab, 63-67, sci adminr mammalian radiobiol, Hq, US AEC, Washington, DC, 67-70; chief prog & data anal unit, Nat Cancer Inst, 71-73, chief carcinogenic bioassay & prog resources br, 73-76; chief priorities & res anal br, Nat Inst Occup Safety & Health, 76-78, dir health rev div, Off Toxic Substance, 78-79, DIR SCIENTIFIC AFFAIRS, US ENVIRON PROTECTION AGENCY, 79-81; SR TOXICOLOGIST, NAT LIBRARY MED, 81- *Concurrent Pos:* Consult, Off Civil Defense & AEC, 67 & Nat Acad Sci Adv Comt, Inst Lab Animal Resources, 67-70; AEC liaison, Hemat Study Sect, NIH, 69-71. *Honors & Awards:* Navy Commendation Medal, 68. *Mem:* Am Vet Med Asn; Am Col Toxicol; Radiation Res Soc; Am Pub Health Asn; Am Col Vet Toxicol. *Res:* Biological effects of radiation exposure; radiation and chemical carcinogenesis; toxicology; safety assessment; national and international affairs. *Mailing Add:* Nat Library Med Bethesda MD 20209

PAGE, NORMAN J, b Boulder, Colo, Jan 2, 39; m 61; c 2. PETROLOGY. *Educ:* Dartmouth Col, BA, 61; Univ Calif, Berkeley, PhD(geol), 66. *Prof Exp:* Phys sci aide geol, 57-66, GEOLOGIST, US GEOL SURV, 66- *Concurrent Pos:* Teaching asst, Univ Calif, 62-66. *Mem:* Mineral Soc Am; Geol Soc Am; Soc Econ Geol. *Res:* Ultramafic rocks, specificially origin of platinum group and sulfide minerals; serpentization and its relation to emplacement of rocks; details of mineral relations in igneous, metamorphic or ore grade rocks as a means to develop experimental studies to solve geologic problems. *Mailing Add:* US Geol Surv 345 Middlefield Rd Menlo Park CA 94025

PAGE, NORWOOD RUFUS, b Lake View, SC, May 10, 19; m 49; c 4. SOIL CHEMISTRY, PLANT NUTRITION. *Educ:* Clemson Col, BS(chem) & BS(gen sci), 39; NC State Univ, MS, 41; Univ Ga, PhD(plant sci), 59. *Prof Exp:* Asst chemist, Clemson Univ, 46-47, assoc agronomist, 47-60, prof agron, 60-65, head dept, Agr Chem Serv, 65-79; SOIL SCIENTIST, ENVIRON LAB, WATERWAYS EXP STA, US ARMY CORPS ENGRS, 79- *Mem:* Am Soc Agron; Soil Sci Soc Am; Asn Offs Anal Chem. *Res:* Soil chemistry of micronutrients and their availability to plants. *Mailing Add:* 106 Calhoun Clemson SC 29631

PAGE, ORVILLE T, b Burlington, Ont, Feb 13, 21; m 44; c 2. PLANT SCIENCE. *Educ:* Ont Agr Col, BSA, 49; Iowa State Univ, MS, 52, PhD(plant path), 54. *Prof Exp:* Assoc prof, Ont Agr Col, 52-57; plant pathologist, Div Trop Res, United Fruit Co, Honduras, 57-59, Cent Res Labs, 59-61; res off, Can Dept Agr, 61-65; prof biol, Univ NB, 65-73, assoc dean sci, 70-73; DEP DIR, INT POTATO CTR, LIMA PERU, 73- *Mem:* Am Phytopath Soc; Can Phytopath Soc (pres, 71); Can Soc Microbiol. *Res:* All aspects of potato research in developing countries. *Mailing Add:* Int Potato Ctr Apartado 5969 Lima Peru

PAGE, RECTOR LEE, b Wichita, Kans, Feb 4, 44; m 65; c 2. MATHEMATICS, COMPUTER SCIENCE. *Educ:* Stanford Univ, BS, 66; Univ Calif, San Diego, PhD(math), 70. *Prof Exp:* Programmer, IBM Sci Ctr, Calif, 65-66; asst prof, 70-77, ASSOC PROF COMPUT SCI, COLO STATE UNIV, 77- *Mem:* Asn Comput Mach. *Res:* Programming languages; multiprocessor systems; Fourier analysis. *Mailing Add:* Dept of Comput Sci Colo State Univ Ft Collins CO 80523

PAGE, ROBERT ALAN, JR, b New York, NY, Nov 28, 38; m 64. SEISMOLOGY, TECTONICS. *Educ:* Harvard Col, AB, 60; Columbia Univ, PhD(geophys), 67. *Prof Exp:* Res assoc seismol, Lamont Geol Observ, Columbia Univ, 67-70; geophysicist, 70-75, chief, Br Earthquake Hazards, 75-78, coordr, Earthquake Hazards Prog, 78-80, GEOPHYSICIST, US GEOL SURV, 80- *Mem:* Seismol Soc Am; Am Geophys Union; Earthquake Eng Res Inst. *Res:* Seismicity, crustal deformation and tectonics particularly in Alaska; strong-motion seismology; earthquake hazards; earthquake prediction. *Mailing Add:* US Geol Surv 345 Middlefield Rd Menlo Park CA 94025

PAGE, ROBERT GRIFFITH, b Bryn Mawr, Pa, Mar 25, 21; m 47; c 3. MEDICINE. *Educ:* Princeton Univ, AB, 43; Univ Pa, MD, 45. *Prof Exp:* Resident med, Hosp Univ Pa, 48-49, instr pharmacol, 49-51, asst, 51-53; from asst prof to assoc prof med, Sch Med, Univ Chicago, 53-68, asst dean med educ, 57-63, assoc dean div biol sci, 63-68; dean, Med Col Ohio, 68-74, provost, 72-74, prof med & pharmacol, 68-78; ADJ PROF COMMUNITY MED, DARTMOUTH MED SCH, 78-; CO-DIR, MOUNTAIN VALLEY HEALTH CTR, LONDONDERRY, 78- *Concurrent Pos:* Vis prof, Univ Rangoon, 51-53; mem bd gov, Inst Med Chicago, 66-68; adj prof med & pharmacol, Med Col Ohio, 78- *Mem:* AAAS; Am Soc Pharmacol & Exp Therapeut; Asn Am Med Cols; Am Fedn Clin Res; Am Heart Asn. *Res:* Cardiac physiology, pharmacology and clinical investigation. *Mailing Add:* RFD Londonderry VT 05148

PAGE, ROBERT HENRY, b Philadelphia, Pa, Nov 5, 27; m 48; c 5. MECHANICAL ENGINEERING. *Educ:* Univ Ohio, BSME, 49; Univ Ill, MS, 51, PhD(eng), 55. *Prof Exp:* Instr & res assoc mech eng, Univ Ill, 49-55; vis lectr, Stevens Inst Technol, 56-57, prof, 57-61; prof mech & aerospace eng, Rutgers Univ, 61-79, chmn dept, 61-76; DEAN ENG, TEX A&M UNIV, 79- *Concurrent Pos:* Res engr, Esso Res & Eng Co, 55-57, separated flow consult, 60-81; mem, Nat Space Eng Comt, 67-71, chmn, 69-70. *Honors & Awards:* Centennial Medal, Am Soc Mech Engrs, 80. *Mem:* Fel Am Soc Mech Engrs; Am Soc Eng Educ; Am Phys Soc; Am Astronaut Soc; Am Inst Aeronaut & Astronaut. *Res:* Aerothermodynamics; gas dynamics; separated flows. *Mailing Add:* Dean Eng Tex A&M Univ College Station TX 77843

PAGE, ROBERT LEROY, b Belgrade, Maine, Mar 20, 31; m 64; c 1. MATHEMATICS, PHYSICAL SCIENCE. *Educ:* Tufts Col, BS, 53; Univ Maine, Orono, MA, 59; Fla State Univ, PhD(math educ), 70. *Prof Exp:* From asst prof to assoc prof math, Nasson Col, 59-65; asst prof, Bates Col, 65-67; from asst prof to assoc prof, 69-74, PROF MATH & PHYS SCI, UNIV MAINE, AUGUSTA, 74-, CHMN, DIV SCI & MATH, 71- *Concurrent Pos:* Vis lectr, New Eng Acad Sci, 64-67; coordr dept math, Nasson Col, 64-65. *Mem:* Math Asn Am. *Res:* Pure mathematics, especially number theory; mathematical education, particularly curriculum development and use of audio-visual media. *Mailing Add:* Dept of Math Univ of Maine Augusta ME 04330

PAGE, ROY CHRISTOPHER, b Campobello, SC, Feb 7, 32. EXPERIMENTAL PATHOLOGY, PERIODONTOLOGY. *Educ:* Berea Col, AB, 53; Univ Md, Baltimore City, DDS, 57; Univ Wash, cert periodont, 63, PhD(exp path), 67. *Prof Exp:* Asst prof, 67-70, assoc prof, 70-74, affil scientist, Ctr Res Oral Biol, 70-76, PROF PATH & PERIODONT, SCHS MED & DENT, UNIV WASH, 74-, DIR, CTR RES ORAL BIOL, 76- *Concurrent Pos:* Nat Inst Gen Med Sci grant, 67-; NIH res career develop award, Univ Wash, 67-72; Nat Heart Inst grant, 67-; Nat Inst Dent Res grant, 70-; mem bd counrs, Nat Inst Dent Res, 73- *Mem:* AAAS; Am Soc Exp Path; Am Chem Soc; Am Acad Periodont. *Res:* Connective tissue maturation and diseases; immunopathology of periodontal disease; long term chronic inflammatory disease. *Mailing Add:* Dept of Path Univ of Wash Sch of Med Seattle WA 98115

PAGE, SAMUEL WILLIAM, b Williston, SC, Jan 25, 45. ORGANIC CHEMISTRY. *Educ:* The Citadel, BS, 67; Univ Ga, PhD(org chem), 71. *Prof Exp:* RES CHEMIST, DIV CHEM TECHNOL, FOOD & DRUG ADMIN, 74- *Mem:* Am Chem Soc; AAAS; Sigma Xi. *Res:* Isolation, identification and synthesis of food contaminants. *Mailing Add:* Div of Chem Technol HFF-425 Food & Drug Admin 200 C St SW Washington DC 20204

PAGE, THOMAS LEE, b Lima, Ohio, Mar 5, 41; m 63; c 1. LIMNOLOGY. *Educ:* Ohio Northern Univ, AB, 63; Kent State Univ, MA, 66, PhD(ecol), 71. *Prof Exp:* NIH fel ecol, Ctr Biol Natural Systs, Washington Univ, 70-72; assoc sect mgr, 72-80, MGR FRESHWATER SCI SECT, ECCOSYSTS DEPT, NORTHWEST LABS, BATTELLE MEM INST, 80- *Mem:* AAAS; Am Soc Limnol & Oceanog; Ecol Soc Am; Am Inst Biol Sci; Int Limnol Soc. *Res:* Limnology and ecology of freshwater communities; environmental ecology; pollution biology. *Mailing Add:* Ecosysts Dept Battelle NW Labs PO Box 999 Richland WA 99352

PAGE, THORNTON LEIGH, b New Haven, Conn, Aug 13, 13; m 48; c 3. ASTROPHYSICS, SPACE PHYSICS. *Educ:* Yale Univ, BS, 34; Oxford Univ, PhD(astrophys), 38. *Hon Degrees:* ScD, Nat Univ Cordoba, 69. *Prof Exp:* Chief asst, Univ Observ, Oxford Univ, 37-38; instr astrophys, Univ Chicago, 38-41 & 46-47, asst prof, 47-50; dep dir opers res off, Johns Hopkins Univ, 50-58; prof astron, Wesleyan Univ, 58-68; Nat Acad Sci res assoc, Manned Spacecraft Ctr, NASA, 68-71; astrophysicist, US Naval Res Lab, 71-76; CONTRACTOR ASTROPHYS RES, NASA, 77- *Concurrent Pos:* Vis prof, Univ Calif, Los Angeles, 64; Nat Acad Sci res assoc, Smithsonian Astrophys Observ, 65-66; adj prof, Univ Houston, 69-74 & Wesleyan Univ, 71-74; consult, United Aircraft Corp, Conn, 58-71, Grumman Aircraft Eng Corp, 64-69 & Army Officers Sch Rev Bd, 65; astrophysicist, Naval Res Lab, 71-76; mem, Adv Bd, Earth Sci Curriculum Proj; consult, Lockheed Electronics Co, 78-81; prof astron, Univ Houston, 81-82. *Honors & Awards:* Chapman res prize, 37; exceptional sci achievement medal, NASA. *Mem:* AAAS (vpres, 67-70); fel Am Astron Soc; Int Astron Union; fel Royal Astron Soc; Int Statist Inst. *Res:* Spectra of planetary nebulae; comets; twilight sky; spiral nebulae; ultraviolet camera-spectrograph used on the moon; operations research on naval weapons; land warfare; far-ultraviolet photometry of stars, nebulae and galaxies; large magillanic cloud. *Mailing Add:* 18639 Point Lookout Dr Houston TX 77058

PAGE, WALTER, b Sioux City, Iowa, Aug 16, 19; m 48; c 2. ZOOLOGY. *Educ:* Union Col, Nebr, BA, 48; Univ Nebr, MS, 51; Mich State Univ, PhD(zool), 62. *Prof Exp:* From asst instr to assoc prof, 48-63, PROF BIOL, UNION COL, NEBR, 63- *Res:* Esterase activity in developing chick embryos. *Mailing Add:* Dept of Biol Union Col Lincoln NE 68506

PAGELS, HEINZ RUDOLF, b New York, NY, Feb 19, 39; m 69. THEORETICAL PHYSICS. *Educ:* Princeton Univ, AB, 60; Stanford Univ, PhD(physics), 65. *Prof Exp:* Res assoc theoret physics, Univ NC, 65-66; res assoc, 66-67, asst prof, 67-68, ASSOC PROF THEORET PHYSICS, ROCKEFELLER UNIV, 68- *Concurrent Pos:* Sloan Found fel, 67-69; consult, Brookhaven Nat Lab, 67-69 & Los Alamos Nat Labs, 77-; chmn, Phys Sci Div, NY Acad Sci, 72-75, vpres, 76-, mem bd gov, 76-, chmn sect activ comt, 76- & chmn human rights comt, 76-; trustee & treas, Aspen Ctr Physics, 73- *Mem:* Am Phys Soc; NY Acad Sci. *Res:* High energy particle physics; weak, electromagnetic and strong interactions. *Mailing Add:* Dept of Physics Rockefeller Univ New York NY 10021

PAGENKOPF, ANDREA L, b Hamilton, Mont, July 28, 42; m 64. NUTRITION. *Educ:* Univ Mont, BA, 64; Purdue Univ, PhD, 68. *Prof Exp:* Asst prof foods, Purdue Univ, 68 & Univ Ill, 68-69; asst prof, 69-77, ASSOC PROF FOODS & NUTRIT, MONT STATE UNIV, 77-, CONSULT, EXPANDED FOODS & NUTRIT EDUC PROG, 71- *Mem:* Inst Food Technologists; Am Soc Microbiol; Am Dietetic Asn; Soc Nutrit Educ; Am Home Econ Asn. *Res:* Metabolism of salmonellae in food systems; food quality, both keeping quality and safety aspects of present food supply with emphasis on newer processing methods and convenience foods; nutrition and disease; child nutrition. *Mailing Add:* Coop Exten Serv Mont State Univ Bozeman MT 59715

PAGENKOPF, GORDON K, b Hamilton, Mont, May 24, 41; m 64. PHYSICAL INORGANIC CHEMISTRY. *Educ:* Univ Mont, BA, 63, MS, 64; Purdue Univ, PhD(chem), 68. *Prof Exp:* Asst prof, 69-73, assoc prof, 73-78, PROF CHEM, MONT STATE UNIV, 78- *Concurrent Pos:* Nat Cancer Inst res fel, Univ Ill, Urbana, 69. *Mem:* Am Chem Soc. *Res:* Kinetics and mechanisms of reactions in solution; trace analysis of environmental pollutants; equilibrium modeling of environmental systems. *Mailing Add:* Dept of Chem Mont State Univ Bozeman MT 59715

PAGER, DAVID, b East London, SAfrica, Mar 26, 35; m 65; c 3. COMPUTER SCIENCE, MATHEMATICS. *Educ:* Univ Cape Town, BSci, 56; Univ London, PhD(math), 61. *Prof Exp:* Mathematician, Data Electronic Comput Group, EMI Indust, Eng, 57-58; consult math, Govt Can, 61-62; mgr sci systs, IBM Corp, 63-64; mgr software develop, Univac, London, 65-68; PROF INFO & COMPUT SCI, UNIV HAWAII, 68-, NSF RES GRANT, 69- *Mem:*

Am Math Soc; Asn Symbolic Logic; Asn Comput Mach; Inst Elec & Electronics Engrs; Soc Indust & Appl Math. *Res:* Complexity theory, recursive function theory; software science; communication of complex information; artificial intelligence. *Mailing Add:* Dept of Info & Comput Sci Univ of Hawaii 2565 The Mall Honolulu HI 96822

PAGES, ROBERT ALEX, b New York, NY, Oct 10, 41. BIO-ORGANIC CHEMISTRY. *Educ:* Polytech Inst Brooklyn, BS, 62; Univ Va, PhD(chem), 66. *Prof Exp:* Staff fel, Clin Endocrinol Br, Nat Inst Arthritis, Metab & Digestive Dis, 68-73; res scientist, 73-77, SR SCIENTIST, PHILLIP MORRIS RES CTR, 77- *Mem:* AAAS; Am Chem Soc; Environ Mutagen Soc; Tissue Cult Asn. *Res:* Biological effects of cigarette smoke; environmental mutagenesis; in vitro bioassays; chemistry and thyroid hormones; hormone binding proteins; medicinal chemistry. *Mailing Add:* Phillip Morris Res Ctr PO Box 26583 Richmond VA 23261

PAGNAMENTA, ANTONIO, b Zurich, Switz, Jan 13, 34; m 54; c 2. PHYSICS. *Educ:* Swiss Fed Inst Technol, BS, 59, MS, 61; Univ Md, College Park, PhD(physics), 65. *Prof Exp:* Res asst, Univ Md, 61-65; asst prof physics, Rutgers Univ, New Brunswick, 65-70; assoc prof, 70-72, PROF PHYSICS, UNIV ILL, CHICAGO CIRCLE, 72- *Concurrent Pos:* Res fel particle physics, Europ Ctr Nuclear Res, Geneva, 66-67. *Mem:* Am Phys Soc; Swiss Phys Soc; Swiss Math Soc. *Res:* Field and particle physics; theoretical high energy physics. *Mailing Add:* Dept of Physics Univ of Ill at Chicago Circle Chicago IL 60680

PAGNI, PATRICK JOHN, b Chicago, Ill, Nov 28, 42; m 70. MECHANICAL ENGINEERING. *Educ:* Univ Detroit, BAeE, 65; Mass Inst Technol, SM, 67, MechE, 69, PhD(mech eng), 70. *Prof Exp:* Asst prof, 70-76, ASSOC PROF MECH ENG, UNIV CALIF, BERKELEY, 76- *Concurrent Pos:* NSF & Nat Bur Standards grants, particulate pollution & fire spread, Univ Calif, Berkeley, 71-; res fel appl mech, Div Appl Sci, Harvard Univ, 74 & 77. *Mem:* Am Phys Soc; Am Inst Aeronaut & Astronaut; Am Soc Mech Engrs; Am Soc Eng Educ; Combustion Inst. *Res:* Mathematical modeling of fire spread; laser applications to particulate pollution monitoring; theoretical kinetics of gas-surface interactions; combustion generated particulates and mathematical modeling of fire phenomena. *Mailing Add:* Dept of Mech Eng Univ of Calif Berkeley CA 94720

PAGNI, RICHARD, b Chicago, Ill, Dec 14, 41. ORGANIC CHEMISTRY. *Educ:* Northwestern Univ, BA, 63; Univ Wis, PhD(org chem), 68. *Prof Exp:* NIH fel, Columbia Univ, 68-69; asst prof, 69-76, assoc prof, 76-81, PROF CHEM, UNIV TENN, KNOXVILLE, 81- *Mem:* AAAS; Am Chem Soc; Royal Soc Chem. *Res:* Photochemistry of hydrocarbons; physical organic chemistry. *Mailing Add:* Dept of Chem Univ of Tenn Knoxville TN 37916

PAHL, HERBERT BOWEN, b Camden, NJ, Aug 14, 27; m 51; c 2. PUBLIC HEALTH ADMINISTRATION. *Educ:* Swarthmore Col, BA, 50; Univ Mich, MS, 52, PhD(biochem), 55. *Prof Exp:* Fel, Nat Cancer Inst, Sloan-Kettering Inst, 55-57; asst prof biochem, Vanderbilt Univ, 57-60; exec secy, Grad Res Training Grant Prog, NIH, 60-62, asst chief & chief, Spec Res Resources Br, 62-64, chief, Gen Res Support Br, 64-66; exec secy, Comt Res Life Sci, Nat Acad Sci-Nat Res Coun, 66-69; dep assoc dir sci progs, Nat Inst Gen Med Sci, NIH, 69-71; dep dir Regional Med Prog, Health Serv & Ment Health Admin, USPHS, 71-73, dir, Regional Med Progs, Health Resources Admin, 73-75, asst to adminr, 75; STAFF DIR, COMT STUDY NAT NEEDS BIOMED & BEHAV SCI RES PERSONNEL, NAT ACAD SCI-NAT RES COUN, 75- *Concurrent Pos:* Instr, City Col New York, 56-57. *Mem:* AAAS. *Res:* Intermediary metabolism of nucleic acids; fractionation of nucleic acids; protein biosynthesis. *Mailing Add:* 626 Warfield Dr Rockville MD 20850

PAHL, WALTER HENRY, b South Haven, Mich, Dec 6, 17; m 43; c 2. ENGINEERING MANAGEMENT. *Educ:* Univ Ill, Urbana, BS, 40. *Prof Exp:* Develop engr, 40-42, pilot plant supvr, 42-43, tech supt nat synthetic rubber, 43-48, proj mgr eng, 48-49, tech dir midstates subsidiary, 49-56, eng mgr chem div, 56-62, group eng mgr chem & film div, 62-66, dir div eng, 66-69, exec dir eng, 69-73, VPRES INT MFG, 3M CO, 73- *Mem:* Am Inst Chem Engrs; Am Chem Soc. *Res:* Technical management; chemical processing. *Mailing Add:* 2050 Loren Rd St Paul MN 55113

PAHNISH, OTTO FLOYD, b Dillon, Mont, Sept 19, 20; m 45; c 2. ANIMAL BREEDING. *Educ:* Univ Idaho, MS, 49; Ore State Univ, PhD(animal husb), 58. *Prof Exp:* From instr to assoc prof animal husb, Univ Ariz, 48-64; supt, Range Livestock Exp Sta, Mont Agr Exp Sta, 64-76, researcher animal breeding, 76-81; RETIRED. *Mem:* Am Soc Animal Sci. *Res:* Livestock genetics, including hereditary abnormalities and improvement of breeding and selection methods; crossbreeding and linecrossing of beef cattle; genetic-environmental interaction. *Mailing Add:* 1004 S Cale Ave Miles City MT 59301

PAHNKE, ALDEN J(OHN), b Green Bay, Wis, Nov 29, 26; m 47; c 4. MECHANICAL ENGINEERING. *Educ:* Univ Wis, BS, 47, MS, 49, PhD(mech eng), 51. *Prof Exp:* Instr thermodyn, Univ Wis, 47-48; res engr, 51-53, res supvr, 53-60, sr res engr, 60-65, sr supvr, 65-68, asst dir, 68-72, mgr res & develop petrol chem, 72-80, DIR RES & DEVELOP & TECH MGR, PETROL CHEM DIV, E I DU PONT DE NEMOURS & CO, INC, 80- *Mem:* Soc Automotive Engrs; Am Chem Soc; Am Petrol Inst; Am Soc Testing & Mat. *Res:* Combustion; thermodynamics; fuel and lubricant performance; air pollution. *Mailing Add:* Petrol Lab E I du Pont de Nemours & Co Inc Wilmington DE 19898

PAI, ANNA CHAO, b Peking, China, Jan 27, 35; US citizen; m 59; c 2. GENETICS, EMBRYOLOGY. *Educ:* Sweet Briar Col, BA, 57; Bryn Mawr Col, MA, 59; Albert Einstein Col Med, PhD(genetics), 64. *Prof Exp:* Teacher, Moravian Sem for Girls, 59-60; instr genetics, Albert Einstein Col Med, 64-65; asst prof, 69-77, ASSOC PROF BIOL, MONTCLAIR STATE COL, 77-, CHAIRPERSON, DEPT BIOL, 79- *Mem:* AAAS; Am Soc Zoologists; Environ Mutagen Soc; Sigma Xi; Am Inst Biol Teachers. *Res:* Developmental genetics, especially the effects of gene action on mammalian development. *Mailing Add:* Dept Biol Montclair State Col Upper Montclair NJ 07043

PAI, DAMODAR MANGALORE, b Mangalore, India; US citizen; m 65; c 2. MATERIALS SCIENCE, PHYSICS. *Educ:* Indian Inst Sci, DIISc, 57; Univ Minn, MS, 61, PhD(elec eng), 65. *Prof Exp:* Physicist, assoc scientist & scientist physics of solids, 65-73, sr scientist, 73-80, PRIN SCIENTIST ORG & INORG PHOTOCONDUCTORS, XEROX CORP, 80- *Mem:* Am Phys Soc. *Res:* Design and study of new photoconductive systems for xerography, both organic and inorganic; research of fundamental photoconductor physics; photogeneration, transport, phenomena near glass transition, temperature, etc. *Mailing Add:* 72 Shagbark Way Fairport NY 14450

PAI, DAVID H(SIEN)-C(HUNG), b Kweilin, China, Jan 7, 36; US citizen; m 59; c 2. SOLID MECHANICS. *Educ:* Va Mil Inst, BS, 58; Lehigh Univ, MS, 60; NY Univ, ScD(eng sci), 65. *Prof Exp:* Develop engr, Res Div, 60-63, sr engr, 64-65, res assoc creep anal & plasticity theory, 66-68, asst head solid mech dept, 69-73, chief engr nuclear dept, 73-77, MGR ENG TECHNOL DEPT, FOSTER WHEELER ENERGY CORP, 77- *Concurrent Pos:* Mem steering comt high temperature struct design technol, US Atomic Energy Comn, 70- *Mem:* Am Soc Civil Engrs; Am Soc Mech Engrs. *Res:* Creep and plastic behavior of structural and machine components; metal fatigue; pressure vessel design and analysis. *Mailing Add:* Foster Wheeler Energy Corp 9 Peach Tree Hill Rd Livingston NJ 07039

PAI, S(HIH) I, b China, Sept 30, 13; nat US; m 60; c 4. FLUID DYNAMICS, APPLIED MATHEMATICS. *Educ:* Nat Cent Univ, China, BS, 35; Mass Inst Technol, MS, 38; Calif Inst Technol, PhD(aeronaut, math), 40. *Hon Degrees:* Dr Techn, Vienna Tech Univ, 68. *Prof Exp:* Prof aerodyn, Nat Cent Univ, China, 40-47; vis prof aeronaut eng, Cornell Univ, 47-48; tech consult, Cornell Aeronaut Lab, Inc, 48-49, res assoc, 49-51; assoc res prof fluid dynamics, 52-56, RES PROF, INST PHYS SCI & TECHNOL & AEROSPACE, UNIV MD, COLLEGE PARK, 76- *Concurrent Pos:* Guggenheim fel, 57-58; vis prof, Inst Theoret Gasdynamics, Aachen, Ger, 57-58, Univ Tokyo, 66, Univ Karlsruhe 80-81 & Univ Paris VI, 81; NSFxsr consult, Martin Co, 56-57, Gen Elec Co, 59-, NAm Rockwell Corp, 65- & Sandia Corp, 65-; NSF sr fel, 66-67; vis prof, Vienna Tech Univ, 67-; vis scientist, Norwegian Defense Res Estab, 73-74. *Honors & Awards:* Award of Achievement in Eng, Chinese Soc Engrs, NY, 62; Sr US Scientist Award, Humboldt Found, Ger, 78. *Mem:* Am Phys Soc; assoc fel Am Inst Aeronaut & Astronaut; Sigma Xi. *Res:* Turbulence; jet and boundary layer flow; stability of flow; supersonic and hypersonic flow; two phase flows; aeroelasticity; magneto-gas dynamics; plasma dynamics; radiation gas dynamics. *Mailing Add:* Inst Phys Sci & Technol Univ Md Col of Eng College Park MD 20742

PAI, VENKATRAO K, b Coondapoor, India, Jan 7, 39. CHEMICAL ENGINEERING. *Educ:* Univ Bombay, BChE, 61; Northwestern Univ, MS, 63, PhD(chem eng), 65. *Prof Exp:* Res chem engr, Cent Res Labs, 65-80, MGR, PROD DEVELOP, CHEM RES DIV, AM CYANAMID CO, 80- *Mem:* Am Inst Chem Engrs; Am Chem Soc. *Res:* Process development; reactor engineering; heat transfer; rheology of spinning; plant design. *Mailing Add:* Stamford Res Labs 1937 W Main St Stamford CT 06902

PAIDOUSSIS, MICHAEL PANDELI, b Nicosia, Cyprus, Aug 20, 35; m 58. APPLIED MECHANICS, FLUID DYNAMICS. *Educ:* McGill Univ, BEng, 58; Cambridge Univ, PhD(eng), 63. *Prof Exp:* Overseas fel nuclear eng, Gen Elec Co, Eng, 58-60; Nat Res Coun Can spec scholarship, 61-63; asst res officer hydroelasticity, Chalk River Nuclear Labs, Atomic Energy Can Ltd, 63-65, assoc res officer, 65-67; from asst prof to assoc prof mech eng, 67-76, PROF MECH ENG, McGILL UNIV, 76-, CHMN DEPT, 77- *Honors & Awards:* Brit Asn Medal, 58; George Stephenson Prize, Inst Mech Engrs, London, 75. *Mem:* Eng Inst Can; fel Brit Inst Mech Engrs; Can Soc Mech Engrs; Am Acad Mech; Int Asn Hydraulics Res. *Res:* Pressure waves in flexible pipes; vibration of cylinders in flow; dynamics of flexible pipes containing flow and cylinders in axial and cross flow; vibration and stability of shells. *Mailing Add:* Dept Mech Eng 817 Sherbrooke St W Montreal PQ H3A 2K6 Can

PAIGE, DAVID M(ARSH), b Rochester, NY, Aug 4, 18; m 49. CHEMICAL ENGINEERING, MECHANICAL ENGINEERING. *Educ:* BSChE, Univ Rochester, 41. *Prof Exp:* Engr, E I du Pont de Nemours & Co, 41-50; proj engr atomic energy, Am Cyanamid Co, 50-53; engr & group leader, Phillips Petrol Co, 53-55, sect head chem eng develop, 55-60; assoc staff engr, Idaho Div, Nat Reactor Testing Sta, Argonne Nat Lab, 60-72; SR ENGR, ALLIED CHEM CORP IDAHO CHEM PROGS, IDAHO NAT ENG LAB, 72- *Mem:* Sigma Xi; Am Inst Chem Engrs; Am Chem Soc; Am Nuclear Soc. *Res:* Application of polymers to fibers and films; chemical separations as applied to fuel recovery in atomic energy field; remote equipment design for hot cells; numerical tape controlled equipment for remote hot cell equipment. *Mailing Add:* Rte 9 Box 291 Idaho Falls ID 83401

PAIGE, FRANK EATON, JR, b Philadelphia, Pa, Oct 21, 44. ELEMENTARY PARTICLE PHYSICS. *Educ:* Mass Inst Technol, BS, 66, PhD(physics), 70. *Prof Exp:* Res assoc, 70-72, assoc physicist, 72-76, PHYSICIST, BROOKHAVEN NAT LAB, 76- *Concurrent Pos:* Asst res physicist, Univ Calif, San Diego, 75-76. *Res:* Elementary particle theory and phenomenology; theory of hadronic reactions. *Mailing Add:* Dept of Physics Brookhaven Nat Lab Upton NY 11973

PAIGE, HILLIARD W, US citizen. ENGINEERING. *Educ:* Worcester Polytech Inst, BA & ME, 41. *Hon Degrees:* Dr, Worcester Polytech Inst, 71. *Prof Exp:* SR CONSULT DIR, INT ENERGY ASSOCS, LTD, 76- *Concurrent Pos:* Mem defense sci bd, Dept Defense, 67. *Honors & Awards:* Pub Serv Award, NASA & Order of Merit, Repub of Italy, 69. *Mem:* Nat Acad Eng; fel Am Inst Aeronaut & Astronaut; Am Nuclear Soc. *Res:* Orbit control systems. *Mailing Add:* Int Energy Asn Ltd 600 New Hampshire Ave NW Suite 600 Washington DC 20037

PAIGE, RUSSELL ALSTON, b Grand Junction, Colo, May 23, 29; m 53; c 5. ENGINEERING GEOLOGY, GEOMORPHOLOGY. *Educ:* Univ Alaska, BS, 55; Univ Wash, MSc, 59. *Prof Exp:* Eng geologist, US Geol Surv, Alaska, 55-57 & Peter Kiewit Sons Co, Wash, 59-62; mining geologist, 62; eng geologist, Haner, Ross & Sporseen Consult Engrs, Ore, 62-63; eng geologist, US Naval Civil Eng Lab, 63-72; DEPT HEAD, GEOL DIV 170, HARZA ENG CO, 72- *Concurrent Pos:* Proj geologist, Strontia Springs Dam construct, Harza Eng Co. *Mem:* Fel Geol Soc Am; Asn Eng Geologists; Glaciol Soc. *Res:* Engineering and environmental geology of polar regions; engineering geology of large dams. *Mailing Add:* 150 S Wacker Dr Chicago IL 60606

PAIGE, DAVID M, b Brooklyn, NY, Aug 20, 39; m 59; c 2. PEDIATRIC NUTRITION, MATERNAL NUTRITION. *Educ:* Long Island Univ, BS, 60; NY Med Col, MD, 64; Johns Hopkins Univ, MPH, 69. *Prof Exp:* Intern pediat, Univ NY, Downstate, 64-65, resident, 65; pub health officer, USPHS, 65-67; resident, Johns Hopkins Hosp & Univ, 67-69; PROF MATERNAL & CHILD HEALTH, SCH HYGIENE & PUB HEALTH & PROF PEDIATRICS, SCH MED, JOHNS HOPKINS UNIV, 81- *Concurrent Pos:* Consult pediat, John F Kennedy Inst, 69-; attend pediatrician, Johns Hopkins Hosp, 69-; consult nutrit, USDA, 73-, Fed Trade Comn, 73-79, Dept Health & Mental Hyg, 74- & US Cong Off Technol Assessment, 76-78; mem panel, Nat Cancer Inst, NIH, 76-78; prin investr, USDA, 80-; ed, Manual Clin Nutrit, 81- *Mem:* Fed Am Soc Exp Biol; Am Soc Clin Nutrit; Am Inst Nutrit; Am Pub Health Asn; Asn Teachers Maternal & Child Care. *Res:* Maternal, infant and child nutrition, including lactose digestion and milk consumption; evaluation ofnutritional supplementation of high risk pregnant women and school children; infant feeding patterns and practices. *Mailing Add:* Sch Hyg & Pub Health Johns Hopkins Univ 615 N Wolfe St Baltimore MD 21205

PAIGEN, BEVERLY JOYCE, b Chicago, Ill, Aug 14, 38; m 70; c 2. ENVIRONMENTAL HEALTH. *Educ:* Wheaton Col, Ill, BS, 60; State Univ NY, Buffalo, PhD(biol), 67. *Prof Exp:* Res technician, Roswell Park Mem Inst, Buffalo, 60-62; grad student, State Univ NY, Buffalo, 63-67; fel, Roswell Park Mem Inst, 67-70; lectr, Rachel Carson Col, State Univ NY, Buffalo, 71-73, dir, 73-75; sr res scientist, Roswell Park Mem Inst, 75-78, res scientist V, 78-82; RES BIOCHEMIST, CHILDRENS HOSP MED CTR, OAKLAND, CALIF, 82- *Concurrent Pos:* Consult, Sci Adv Bd, Subcomt Coke Oven Emissions, Environ Protection Agency, 78-80 & Subcomt Polycyclic Org Matter, 78-80 & Carcinogen Assessment Group, 78-81; mem, Admin Toxic Substances Adv Comt, Environ Protection Agency, 77-79; speaker, Nat Speakers Bur, Am Inst Chem Engrs 77-79 & Am Chem Soc, 78-79. *Mem:* AAAS; Am Cancer Res; Am Asn Human Genetics; Geochem Environ Health. *Res:* Genetic susceptibility to cancer and atherosclerosis; environmental health, toxicology, health effects of hazardous waste. *Mailing Add:* Childrens Hosp Med Ctr 51st & Grove Sts Oakland CA 94609

PAIGEN, KENNETH, b New York, NY, Nov 14, 27; m 47, 70; c 5. BIOCHEMICAL GENETICS. *Educ:* Johns Hopkins Univ, AB, 46; Calif Inst Technol, PhD(biochem), 50. *Prof Exp:* Carnegie fel genetics, Carnegie Inst, 50-52; assoc med, Peter Bent Brigham Hosp, Boston, Mass, 52-53; USPHS fel, Virus Lab, Univ Calif, 53-55; sr cancer res scientist, 55-58, assoc cancer res scientist, 58-62, prin cancer res scientist, 62-67, assoc chief scientist, 67-72, PROF BIOL & CHMN GRAD PROG & DIR, DEPT MOLECULAR BIOL, ROSWELL PARK MEM INST, 72- *Concurrent Pos:* Vis prof genetics, Univ Calif, Berkeley, 81- *Mem:* AAAS; Genetics Soc; Am Chem Soc; Am Soc Biol Chem; Am Asn Cancer Res. *Res:* Regulation of gene expression in mammals; intracellular location of enzymes; developmental genetics. *Mailing Add:* Roswell Park Mem Inst 666 Elm St Buffalo NY 14203

PAIK, HO JUNG, b Seoul, Korea, Mar 25, 44; m 69; c 2. CRYOGENIC ENGINEERING, GRAVITATION PHYSICS. *Educ:* Seoul Nat Univ, BS, 66; Stanford Univ, MS, 70, PhD(physics), 74. *Prof Exp:* Res assoc physics, Stanford Univ, 74-78; ASST PROF PHYSICS, UNIV MD, COLLEGE PARK, 78- *Concurrent Pos:* Alfred Sloan fel, 81- *Mem:* Korean Sci & Eng Asn; Am Phys Soc. *Res:* Search for gravitational waves using cryogenic technology; new test of Newton's law of gravity, using superconducting gravity gradiometers; theoretical work on interaction of gravitational waves with antennas of various geometries. *Mailing Add:* Dept of Physics & Astron Univ of Md College Park MD 20742

PAIK, S(UNGIK) F(RANCIS), b Seoul, Korea, Nov 12, 35; US citizen; m 57; c 3. ELECTRICAL ENGINEERING. *Educ:* Northwestern Univ, BS, 58; Stanford Univ, MS, 59, PhD(elec eng), 61. *Prof Exp:* Sr scientist, Raytheon Res Div, 61-64; assoc prof elec eng, Northwestern Univ, 64-68; dir tube res, Microwave Assocs, Inc, Burlington, 68-70; ENG MGR SOLID STATE PRODS, RAYTHEON CO, SMDO, WALTHAM, 70- *Mem:* Inst Elec & Electronics Engrs. *Res:* Solid state microwave amplifiers, circuits. *Mailing Add:* Raytheon Co Smdo Bearfoot Rd Northborough MA 01532

PAIK, WOON KI, b Naju, Korea, Mar 2, 25; m 59. BIOCHEMISTRY. *Educ:* Severance Med Col, Korea, MD, 47; Dalhousie Univ, MS, 56. *Prof Exp:* Asst biochem, Severance Med Col, Korea, 47-48; instr, Ewha Women's Univ, 50-53; asst cellular physiol, Dalhousie Univ, 53-56; vis scientist, Nat Cancer Inst, 56-58; res assoc physiol chem, Univ Wis, 58-61; from asst prof to assoc prof biochem, Fac Med, Univ Ottawa, Ont, 61-66; assoc prof, 66-73, SR INVESTR, FELS RES INST, TEMPLE UNIV, 66-, PROF BIOCHEM, 73- *Res:* Enzyme purification; biochemical studies on amphibian metamorphosis; amino acid metabolism; protein modification; gene regulation. *Mailing Add:* Fels Res Inst Temple Univ Philadelphia PA 19140

PAIKOFF, MYRON, b Brooklyn, NY, Jan 31, 32; m 55; c 3. PHARMACEUTICAL CHEMISTRY. *Educ:* Columbia Univ, BS, 52; Purdue Univ, MS, 54, PhD, 56. *Prof Exp:* Asst dir pharmaceut res & develop, 71-75, DIR PROD DEVELOP, STERLING-WINTHROP RES INST, 75- *Mem:* Acad Pharmaceut Sci; Am Pharmaceut Asn; Sigma Xi. *Res:* Pharmaceuticals; liquid and emulsion technology; kinetics; general pharmaceutical research. *Mailing Add:* Sterling-Winthrop Res Inst Rensselaer NY 12144

PAILTHORP, JOHN RAYMOND, b Spokane, Wash, Nov 14, 20; m 42; c 3. ORGANIC CHEMISTRY. *Educ:* Mich State Univ, BS, 42; Univ Wis, MS, 47. *Prof Exp:* Res chemist, Res & Develop Div, E I du Pont De Nemours & Co Inc, 47-53, res supvr, 53-56, res div head, 56-59, mgr, Develop Sect, Res & Develop Div, 60-68, asst dir res & develop, Elastomer Chem Dept, 68-79, tech dir, Polymer Prod Div, 79-81. *Mem:* Am Chem Soc; Am Ord Asn; Am Inst Chemists. *Res:* Elastomers; polymers. *Mailing Add:* 852 Cranbrook Dr Wilmington DE 19803

PAIM, UNO, b June 12, 22; Can citizen; m 50. ENVIRONMENTAL PHYSIOLOGY, FISH BIOLOGY. *Educ:* Univ Toronto, BA, 57, PhD(zool), 62. *Prof Exp:* From asst prof to assoc prof, 62-69, PROF BIOL, UNIV NB, 69- *Mem:* AAAS; Can Soc Zoologists; Entom Soc Can; Am Fisheries Soc. *Res:* Responses of animals to directive factors and feeding stimuli; toxicology of water pollution; biology and productivity of salmonids; aquaculture. *Mailing Add:* Dept Biol Univ NB Fredericton NB E3B 5A3 Can

PAINE, ALAN HENRY, b Biddiford, Maine, May 23, 17; m 47; c 2. MATHEMATICS. *Educ:* Gorham State Col, BS, 40; Columbia Univ, MA, 47, EdD(math educ), 60. *Prof Exp:* Teacher high sch, Vt, 40-41; prof math, Marlboro Col, 47-51; engr, Kearfott Co, NJ, 51-53; PROF MATH, POTOMAC STATE COL, 54- *Mem:* Math Asn Am. *Res:* Teaching of mathematics and mathematics education. *Mailing Add:* 320 Valley View Ave Keyser WV 26726

PAINE, CLAIR MAYNARD, b Westmoreland, NH, Jan 4, 30; m 55; c 2. BIOCHEMISTRY. *Educ:* Univ NH, BS, 51; Rutgers Univ, MS, 57, PhD(agr, biochem), 59. *Prof Exp:* Asst agr biochem, Rutgers Univ, 54-58; Nat Cancer Inst fel, Sch Med, George Washington Univ, 58-59; sr res fel biochem, May Inst Med Res, Jewish Hosp, Cincinnati, 59-61, biochemist, 61-63; Nat Inst Neurol Dis & Blindness fel, Retina Found, Boston, 63-66; from asst prof to assoc prof, 66-70, PROF BIOL, SALEM STATE COL, 71- *Mem:* AAAS; Am Inst Biol Sci. *Res:* Amino acid transport; electrolyte metabolism; muscle contraction; educational methods. *Mailing Add:* 82 South Rd Bedford MA 01730

PAINE, DAVID PHILIP, b Dillon, Mont, Dec 27, 29; m 55; c 2. FOREST MENSURATION, AERIAL PHOTOS. *Educ:* Ore State Univ, BS, 53, MS, 58; Univ Wash, PhD(forest mensuration), 65. *Prof Exp:* Forester, Intermountain Forest & Range Exp Sta, US Forest Serv, 55-57 & 58-59; asst prof mensuration aerial photog, Univ WVa, 62; asst prof, 62-67, ASSOC PROF FOREST MGT, ORE STATE UNIV, 67- *Honors & Awards:* Aufderheide Award, 73. *Mem:* Soc Am Foresters; Am Soc Photogram. *Res:* Aerial photo mensuration, remote sensing, photo volume tables for trees and stands; coniferous regeneration using aerial photos and double sampling. *Mailing Add:* Sch Forestry Ore State Univ Corvallis OR 97331

PAINE, DWIGHT MILTON, b Albion, NY, Oct 11, 31; m 56; c 4. MATHEMATICS. *Educ:* Univ Rochester, BA, 52; McGill Univ, BA, 56; Fuller Theol Sem, MDiv, 59; Univ Wis, MS, 61, PhD(math), 63. *Prof Exp:* From asst prof to assoc prof math, Wells Col, 63-72; assoc prof, 72-79, PROF MATH, MESSIAH COL, 79- *Concurrent Pos:* Vis res assoc, Cornell Univ, 69-70. *Mem:* Math Asn Am. *Res:* Systems of partitions of sets. *Mailing Add:* Dept Math Messiah Col Grantham PA 17027

PAINE, KENNETH WILLIAM, b London, Eng, Oct 16, 21; Can citizen; m 53; c 4. NEUROSURGERY. *Educ:* Univ London, MB, BS, 44; FRCS, 51; FRCS(C), 59. *Prof Exp:* Head dept, 62-74, PROF NEUROSURG, UNIV SASK, 62- *Concurrent Pos:* Med Res Coun grant brain tumor transplants, 62-64 & spinal stenosis, spondylosis & disc degeneration, 71- *Mem:* Am Asn Neurol Surg; Can Neurosurg Soc (vpres); Can Med Asn; Soc Brit Neurosurg. *Res:* Intracranial aneurysms; aqueduct stenosis; thalamic tumors; carpal tunnel syndrome; lumbar disc protrusions; lumbar spinal stenosis. *Mailing Add:* Dept of Neurosurg Univ of Sask Hosp Saskatoon SK S7N 0W0 Can

PAINE, LEE ALFRED, b Kansas City, Kans, Nov 24, 20. FOREST PATHOLOGY. *Educ:* Univ Idaho, MS, 47; Swiss Fed Inst Technol, PhD(path), 51. *Prof Exp:* Res officer forest path, Forest Biol Div, Can Sci Serv, 53-57; FOREST PATHOLOGIST, PAC SOUTHWEST FOREST & RANGE EXP STA, US FOREST SERV, 57- *Mem:* AAAS; Am Phytopath Soc; Soc Am Foresters; Mycol Soc Am; NY Acad Sci. *Res:* Physiology of fungi; trunk rots; abiotic diseases; hazardous trees in recreational areas. *Mailing Add:* Forest Dis Res Pac SW Forest & Range Exp Sta Berkeley CA 94701

PAINE, PHILIP LOWELL, b Orlando, Fla, June 11, 45; m 74; c 2. CELL PHYSIOLOGY, INTRACELLULAR TRANSPORT. *Educ:* Calif Inst Technol, BS, 67; Univ Fla Col Med, PhD(anat), 71. *Prof Exp:* Fel physiol, Dept Physiol & Biophysics, Univ Miami Med Sch, 71-73; res assoc, 73-75, RES SCIENTIST & HEAD INTRACELLULAR TRANSP SECT CELL PHYSIOL, DEPT BIOL, MICH CANCER FOUND, 75- *Concurrent Pos:* Fel, Damon Runyon Mem Fund Cancer Res, 71. *Mem:* Biophys Soc; Am Soc Cell Biol. *Res:* Intra and intercellular movement of molecules, including transport kinetics and equilibrium distributions. *Mailing Add:* Mich Cancer Found 110 E Warren Detroit MI 48201

PAINE, RICHARD BRADFORD, b Hyannis, Mass, July 16, 28; m 51; c 2. COMPUTER SCIENCES. *Educ:* Walla Walla Col, BS, 52; Univ Wash, MS, 57, PhD, 58. *Prof Exp:* Asst prof math, Cent Mich Col, 57-58; assoc prof, Stephen F Austin State Col, 58-60; asst prof, Walla Walla Col, 60-61; asst prof, 61-63, ASSOC PROF MATH, COLO COL, 63- *Mem:* Asn Comput Mach. *Res:* Software engineering; systems programming. *Mailing Add:* Colo Col Colorado Springs CO 80903

PAINE, ROBERT, b Aberdeen, Miss, Mar 31, 21; m 48; c 3. PHYSIOLOGY. *Educ:* Harvard Univ, MD, 44; Am Bd Internal Med, dipl, 52. *Prof Exp:* From intern to resident med, Barnes Hosp, St Louis, Mo, 44-46; from instr to asst prof, 50-71, CLIN PROF MED, WASH UNIV, 72-; CHIEF MED, ST LUKES HOSP, 62- *Concurrent Pos:* Fel cardiol, Wash Univ, 47-48. *Mem:* Fel Am Col Physicians; fel Am Col Cardiol. *Res:* Cardiovascular investigation. *Mailing Add:* 5505 Delmar St Louis MO 63112

PAINE, ROBERT H, b Nunda, NY, Sept 8, 28; m 52; c 2. ORGANIC CHEMISTRY, INORGANIC CHEMISTRY. *Educ:* Univ Rochester, BS, 51, PhD(org chem), 60; Worcester Polytech Inst, MS, 53. *Prof Exp:* Instr chem, Worcester Polytech Inst, 53-54; chemist distillation prod, 60-64, sr engr, Film Tech Serv Div, 64-70, tech assoc, 70-74, supvr develop, 74-80, SR TECH ASSOC, PHOTOCHEM DIV, EASTMAN KODAK CO, 81- *Concurrent Pos:* From asst lectr to lectr, Univ Rochester, 61-68, sr lectr & chem coordr, 68- *Mem:* Am Chem Soc. *Res:* Photographic chemistry; migration aptitudes in neophyl system; alkyl phosphate monomers. *Mailing Add:* Kodak Park Photochem Div Bldg 46 Eastman Kodak Co Rochester NY 14650

PAINE, ROBERT MADISON, b Yonkers, NY, June 24, 25; m 46; c 3. METALLURGICAL CHEMISTRY. *Educ:* Mich State Univ, BS, 48, MS, 49. *Prof Exp:* Asst phys chem, Mich State Univ, 48-49; res chemist inorg & x-ray chem, Mallinckrodt Chem Works, 49-55; SECT SUPVR PHYS CHEM RES & DEVELOP, BRUSH WELLMAN, INC, 55- *Mem:* Metall Soc; Am Soc Lubrication Eng; Am Electroplaters Soc. *Res:* X-ray diffraction and solid gas reactions; intermetallic compounds as high temperature structural materials; corrosion protection and control; wear research; electroplating. *Mailing Add:* Res & Develop Lab Brush Wellman Inc Cleveland OH 44110

PAINE, ROBERT T, b Cambridge, Mass, Apr 13, 33; m 59; c 3. ZOOLOGY, ECOLOGY. *Educ:* Harvard Univ, AB, 54; Univ Mich, MS, 59, PhD(zool), 61. *Prof Exp:* Sverdrup fel, Scripps Inst Oceanog, Univ Calif, San Diego, 61-62; from asst prof to assoc prof, 62-71, PROF ZOOL, UNIV WASH, 71- *Mem:* Ecol Soc Am (vpres, 77-78, pres, 79-80); Soc Study Evolution; Am Soc Naturalists; Am Soc Limnol & Oceanog. *Res:* Algal ecology, prey-predator relationships and invertebrate natural history. *Mailing Add:* Dept of Zool Univ of Wash Seattle WA 98195

PAINE, ROBERT TREAT, JR, b Colorado Springs, Colo, Dec 15, 44; m 67. INORGANIC CHEMISTRY. *Educ:* Univ Calif, Berkeley, BS, 66; Univ Mich, Ann Arbor, PhD(chem), 70. *Prof Exp:* Res assoc chem, Northwestern Univ, 70-72 & Los Alamos Sci Lab, Univ Calif, 72-74; asst prof, 74-78, ASSOC PROF CHEM, UNIV NMEX, 78- *Mem:* Am Chem Soc; NY Acad Sci. *Res:* Inorganic chemistry of phosphorus compounds; organometallic chemistry; hydride and fluoride chemistry; structural studies of inorganic compounds. *Mailing Add:* Dept of Chem Univ of NMex Albuquerque NM 87131

PAINE, T(HOMAS) O(TTEN), b Berkeley, Calif, Nov 9, 21; m 46; c 4. PHYSICAL METALLURGY. *Educ:* Brown Univ, AB, 42; Stanford Univ, MSc, 47, PhD(metall), 49. *Prof Exp:* Res assoc liquid metals, Stanford Univ, 48-49; res assoc ferromagnetism, Res Lab, Gen Elec Co, 49-51, mgr, Measurements Lab, 51-58, mgr tech anal, Res & Develop Ctr, 59-62, mgr, TEMPO-Ctr Adv Studies, 63-68; dep adminr, NASA, 68-70; vpres & group exec power generation, Gen Elec Co, 70-76; PRES & CHIEF OPERATING OFFICER, NORTHROP CORP, 76- *Honors & Awards:* Indust Sci Award, AAAS, 56; Faraday Medal, Inst Elec Eng, London, 76. *Mem:* Nat Acad Eng; AAAS; Am Phys Soc; Am Inst Aeronaut & Astronaut; Inst Elec & Electronics Engrs. *Res:* Magnetic and structural materials; fine particles; instrumentation; interdisciplinary studies; operations research; solid state; government-industrial science; computers; management systems; aerospace. *Mailing Add:* Northrop Corp 1800 Century Park E Los Angeles CA 90067

PAINE, THOMAS FITE, JR, b Aberdeen, Miss, Feb 13, 18; m 41; c 4. MEDICINE. *Educ:* Vanderbilt Univ, BA, 39, MD, 42; Am Bd Internal Med, dipl. *Prof Exp:* From instr to assoc med, Harvard Med Sch, 50-53; assoc prof bact & internal med, Univ Mich, 53-54; prof microbiol & med & chmn dept microbiol, Med Ctr, Univ Ala, 54-61; PROF MED, SCH MED, VANDERBILT UNIV, 61-; CHIEF DEPT MED, NASHVILLE GEN HOSP, 61- *Concurrent Pos:* Am Col Physicians fel, Thorndike Mem Lab, Boston City Hosp, Mass, 46-48; res fel med, Harvard Med Sch, 47-49; Nat Res Coun fel, Mass Gen Hosp, 48-49; Med Res Coun Unit Chem Microbiol res fel, Sch Biochem, Cambridge Univ, 49-50; in chg lab infectious dis res, Mass Gen Hosp, 50-52, chief dept bact & asst physician, 52-53; mem infectious dis & trop med training grant comt, NIH, 60-64; vis res worker, Dept Path, Cambridge Univ, 69-70; mem nat adv allergy & infectious dis coun, NIH, 69-72; Fulbright lectr, Univ Sains, Penang, Malaysia, 75-76. *Mem:* AAAS; Am Soc Microbiol; Soc Exp Biol & Med; AMA; Am Fedn Clin Res. *Res:* Antibiotics; clinical infectious disease. *Mailing Add:* Dept of Med Nashville Gen Hosp Nashville TN 37210

PAINTAL, AMREEK SINGH, b Kanpur, India, Apr 1, 40. HYDRAULICS, HYDROLOGY. *Educ:* Agra Col, BSc, 58; Univ Roorkee, BE, 61, ME, 62; Univ Minn, PhD(fluid mech), 69. *Prof Exp:* Lectr civil eng, Univ Roorkee, 62-65; from asst prof to assoc prof, WVa Inst Technol, 69-73; sr civil engr, 73-79, PRIN CIVIL ENGR, METROP SANIT DIST OF GREATER CHICAGO, 79- *Concurrent Pos:* Instr hydraul, Ill Inst Technol, 74-81, adj asst prof, 81- *Mem:* AAAS; Am Soc Civil Engrs; Am Soc Eng Educ; Am Geophys Union; Int Asn Hydraul Res. *Res:* Hydraulic engineering, especially sediment transport, stochastic processes, sewer design, hydraulic structure design and urban drainage; hydrological precipitation and runoff relationships. *Mailing Add:* Metrop Sanit Dist Greater Chicago 100 E Erie St Chicago IL 60611

PAINTER, GAYLE STANFORD, b Columbia, SC, Feb 27, 41; m 62; c 2. QUANTUM THEORY OF ATOMIC CLUSTERS. *Educ:* Univ SC, BS, 63, PhD(physics), 67. *Prof Exp:* Fel physics, Univ Fla, 67-69; RES PHYSICIST, METALS & CERAMICS DIV, OAK RIDGE NAT LAB, 69- *Concurrent Pos:* Guest scientist, Int Solid State Res, Julich, Ger, 74-75. *Mem:* Fel Am Phys Soc. *Res:* Theory of electronic structure of crystalline compounds, surfaces and atom clusters; theory of chemical phenomena, chemisorption and bonding at surfaces and inhomogeneous systems. *Mailing Add:* Metals & Ceramics Div Oak Ridge Nat Lab Oak Ridge TN 37830

PAINTER, JACK T(IMBERLAKE), b Kincaid, WVa, July 23, 30. CIVIL ENGINEERING. *Educ:* WVa Univ, BSCE, 50, MSCE, 55. *Prof Exp:* Instr civil eng, Univ WVa, 50-51, 53-55; from asst prof to assoc prof, 55-62, PROF CIVIL ENG, LA TECH UNIV, 62- *Mem:* Am Inst Steel Construct; Am Soc Civil Eng; Am Soc Eng Educ. *Res:* Structural analysis; photogrammetry. *Mailing Add:* Dept Civil Eng La Tech Univ Ruston LA 71272

PAINTER, JAMES HOWARD, b Eolia, Mo, Nov 25, 35; m 55; c 2. THERMODYNAMICS. *Educ:* Univ Mo, Rolla, BS, 60. *Prof Exp:* Res scientist, 60-70, sr group engr, Res Labs, 70-80, SR TECH SPECIALIST, MCDONNELL DOUGLAS ASTRONAUT CO, 80- *Mem:* Am Inst Aeronaut & Astronaut. *Res:* Advanced reentry simulation using arc heaters; development of multimegawatt arc heaters for accurate reentry flowfield simulation; development of advanced techniques for reentry simulation using existing advanced reentry arc heater facilities. *Mailing Add:* 1931 Rustic Oak Chesterfield MO 63017

PAINTER, KENT, b Providence, RI, Sept 23, 42; m 64; c 2. BIONUCLEONICS. *Educ:* Univ RI, BS, 65; Colo State Univ, MBA, 77; Purdue Univ, MS, 67, PhD(bionucleonics), 70. *Prof Exp:* Tech mgr anal prod, Amersham Searle Corp, 70-73; mgr opers radioimmunoassay, Micromed Diag, Inc, 73-77; MANAGING DIR, WESTERN CHEM RES CORP, 78- *Concurrent Pos:* Affil prof radiol, Colo State Univ, 74- *Mem:* Am Chem Soc; Health Physics Soc; Am Asn Clin Chemists; AAAS; Sigma Xi. *Res:* Radioimmunoassay; labeled compound synthesis; liquid scintillation counting. *Mailing Add:* 1305 Lakewood Dr Ft Collins CO 80521

PAINTER, LINDA ROBINSON, b Lexington, Ky, May 4, 40; m 67. RADIATION PHYSICS. *Educ:* Univ Louisville, BS, 62; Univ Tenn, MS, 63, PhD(physics), 68. *Prof Exp:* Consult physicist & adj res & develop participant, Health & Safety Res Div, Oak Ridge Nat Lab, 67-; asst prof, 68-75, ASSOC PROF PHYSICS, UNIV TENN, KNOXVILLE, 75- *Mem:* Am Phys Soc; Am Phys Soc Southeastern Sect; Radiation Res Soc; Health Physics Soc. *Res:* Optical and dielectric properties of liquids in the vacuum ultraviolet. *Mailing Add:* Dept of Physics Univ of Tenn Knoxville TN 37916

PAINTER, RICHARD J, b Greensboro, NC, July 20, 31; m 57; c 2. MATHEMATICS. *Educ:* Univ NC, BA, 53, MA, 56, PhD(math), 63. *Prof Exp:* Programmer math, Martin Co, Colo, 57-58; math analyst, Babcock & Wilcox Co, Va, 58-60; assoc prof, 63-74, PROF MATH, COLO STATE UNIV, 74- *Mem:* Am Math Soc; Math Asn Am. *Res:* Matrix analysis. *Mailing Add:* Dept of Math & Comput Sci Colo State Univ Ft Collins CO 80521

PAINTER, ROBERT BLAIR, b Columbus, Ohio, Sept 9, 24; m 48; c 5. RADIOBIOLOGY. *Educ:* Ohio State Univ, BSc, 47, MSc, 49, PhD(bact), 55. *Prof Exp:* Mem staff, Chem Warfare Labs, US Dept Army, 49-52; prin bacteriologist, Battelle Mem Inst, 52-54, proj leader, 59-61; asst microbiologist, Brookhaven Nat Lab, 56-59; br chief, Ames Res Ctr, NASA, 61-65; PROF MICROBIOL, UNIV CALIF, SAN FRANCISCO, 65-, ASSOC DIR LAB RADIOBIOL, 74- *Mem:* Biophys Soc; Radiation Res Soc; Am Soc Cell Biol; Environ Mutagen Soc. *Res:* Radiation effects on nucleic acid metabolism; organization of DNA in mammalian cells. *Mailing Add:* Lab of Radiobiol & Environ Health Univ of Calif San Francisco CA 94143

PAINTER, ROBERT HILTON, b Eng, Nov 27, 32; m 55; c 2. BIOCHEMISTRY. *Educ:* Liverpool Univ, BSc, 53, PhD(biochem), 56. *Prof Exp:* Biochemist, Blood Prod Unit, Lister Inst, London, 56-57; res asst, Connaught Med Res Labs, 57-60, res assoc, 60-68, assoc prof, 68-74, asst dean, Sch Grad Studies, 75-79, PROF BIOCHEM, UNIV TORONTO, 68- *Mem:* Fel Royal Inst Chemists; Am Asn Immunologists; Can Biochem Soc; Can Soc Immunologists; Am Soc Hemat. *Res:* Protein chemistry; plasma proteins and enzymes; immunoglobulins; complement; Fc receptors. *Mailing Add:* Dept of Biochem Univ of Toronto Toronto ON M5S 2R8 Can

PAINTER, RUTH COBURN ROBBINS, b Bethel, Conn, July 21, 10; m 40; c 2. NUTRITIONAL BIOCHEMISTRY, TOXICOLOGY. *Educ:* Univ Hawaii, BS, 31, MS, 34. *Prof Exp:* Asst nutrit invests, Univ Hawaii, 31-37; assoc chemist, Dept Home Econ, USDA, 37; nutrit chemist, Wash State Col, 37-40; instr chem, NDak State Col, 42-43; technician environ toxicol, Univ Calif, Davis, 60-62, from asst specialist to specialist, 62-76; RETIRED. *Mem:* AAAS; Am Chem Soc; Entom Soc Am; Inst Food Technologists. *Res:* Human and insect nutritional biochemistry; toxicology of food additives especially pesticides; data bank of pesticides used in California. *Mailing Add:* 815 Miller Dr Davis CA 95616

PAIR, CLAUDE H(ERMAN), b Tekoa, Wash, July 20, 11; m 36; c 2. IRRIGATION ENGINEERING. *Educ:* Wash State Univ, BS, 32, MS, 33, BA, 34. *Prof Exp:* Agr engr, Soil Conserv Serv, USDA, 35-48, irrig engr, Soil Conserv Res Serv, 48-54, irrig engr, Agr Res Serv, 54-61, res engr irrig, Snake River Conserv Res Ctr, 61-75; RETIRED. *Concurrent Pos:* Mem nat comt, Int Comt Irrig & Drainage; irrig consult, 75- *Honors & Awards:* John Deere Gold Medal Award, Am soc Agr Engrs, 81. *Mem:* Fel Am Soc Agr Engrs; Sigma Xi. *Res:* Sprinkler irrigation; irrigation, especially methods of water application and requirements. *Mailing Add:* 215 Hillview Dr Boise ID 83702

PAIRENT, FREDERICK WILLIAM, b Philadelphia, Pa, Jan 18, 32; m 58; c 1. MEDICAL EDUCATION, BIOCHEMISTRY. *Educ:* St Joseph's Col, Pa, BS, 53; Loyola Univ, Ill, MS, 59, PhD(biochem), 61. *Prof Exp:* Chemist, Smith, Kline & French Labs, 56-57; instr biochem, Loyola Univ, Ill, 61-65; div dir multidiscipline teaching labs, 72-74, PROF BIOL CHEM & MED, HANEMANN MED COL, 65-, ASSOC DEAN MED EDUC & DIR OFF MED EDUC, 75- *Mem:* Am Asn Med Cols; Soc Teachers Family Med. *Res:* Enzymology of proteolytic enzymes of pancreas and blood coagulation; metabolism of exocrine pancreas; pancreatic insufficiency; medical education. *Mailing Add:* Off of Med Educ Hahnemann Med Col Philadelphia PA 19102

PAIS, ABRAHAM, b Amsterdam, Holland, May 19, 18; nat US; m 56, 76; c 1. THEORETICAL PHYSICS. *Educ:* Univ Amsterdam, BSc, 38; Univ Utrecht, MS, 40, PhD(theoret physics), 41. *Prof Exp:* Prof physics, Inst Advan Study, 50-63; prof, 63-81, DETLEV W BRONK PROF PHYSICS, ROCKEFELLER UNIV, 81- *Honors & Awards:* J R Oppenheimer Mem Prize, 79. *Mem:* Nat Acad Sci; Am Acad Arts & Sci; fel Am Phys Soc; Royal Netherlands Acad Sci. *Res:* Physics of fundamental particles; field theory. *Mailing Add:* Dept Physics Rockefeller Univ New York NY 10021

PAISLEY, DAVID M, b Buckhannon, WVa, Feb 26, 35; m 57; c 3. ORGANIC CHEMISTRY. *Educ:* WVa Wesleyan Col, BS, 57; Univ Ill, MS, 59, PhD(org chem), 61. *Prof Exp:* Patent agent, Law Dept, Union Carbide Corp, 61-63, asst to vpres, Develop Dept, 63-65, mgr pharmaceut mkt res, 65-67; dir mkt res, E R Squibb & Sons, Inc, 67-70; drug indust security analyst, Donaldson, Lufkin & Jenrette, Inc, 70-75; VPRES & HEAD HEALTH RES GROUP, MERRILL, LYNCH, PIERCE, FENNER & SMITH, INC, 75- *Mem:* Am Chem Soc. *Res:* New drug research and development; drug marketing and marketing research. *Mailing Add:* Merrill Lynch Pierce 165 Broadway New York NY 10006

PAISLEY, NANCY SANDELIN, b Duluth, Minn, Feb 20, 36; m 57; c 3. BIOCHEMISTRY. *Educ:* Univ Minn, BS, 57; Univ Ill, MA, 59, PhD(biochem), 61. *Prof Exp:* Res scientist, Esso Res & Eng Co, 61-63, econ analyst, Standard Oil Co, NJ, 63-65; ASST PROF CHEM, MONTCLAIR STATE COL, 66- *Concurrent Pos:* Vis asst prof biochem, NJ Col Med & Dent. *Mem:* AAAS; Nutrit Today Soc. *Res:* Purification and characterization of long lipoprotein lipase. *Mailing Add:* 52 Wayside Pl Montclair NJ 07042

PAJARI, GEORGE EDWARD, b Montreal, Que, Mar 24, 36; m 55; c 2. PETROLOGY, GEOCHEMISTRY. *Educ:* McGill Univ, BSc, 58; Cambridge Univ, PhD(petrol), 66. *Prof Exp:* From lectr to assoc prof petrol, 64-74, assoc prof geol, 74-77, PROF GEOL, UNIV NB, 77- *Mem:* Geol Asn Can; Mineral Asn Can. *Res:* Physio-chemical processes operative in igneous differentiation. *Mailing Add:* Dept of Geol Univ of NB Fredericton NB E3B 5A3 Can

PAK, CHARLES Y, b Seoul, Korea, Nov 27, 35; US citizen; m 63. PHYSICAL CHEMISTRY, ENDOCRINOLOGY. *Educ:* Univ Chicago, BS, 58, MD, 61. *Prof Exp:* Intern med, Univ Chicago Clins, 51-62, asst resident, 62-63; vis scientist, Lab Phys Biol, NIH, 63-65, sr investr lab clin endocrinol, Nat Heart Inst, 65-69, head sect mineral metab, Endocrinol Br, 69-71; assoc prof, 72-75, PROF INTERNAL MED & CHIEF SECT MINERAL METAB, UNIV TEX HEALTH SCI CTR DALLAS, 75-, PROG DIR, GEN CLIN RES CTR, 74- *Mem:* Endocrine Soc; Am Soc Nephrology; Am Soc Clin Invest; Biophys Soc; Am Soc Pharmacol & Exp Therapeut. *Res:* Renal stones; calcium and phosphorus metabolism; mechanism and treatment of nephrolithiasis; parathyroid function; calcium absorption; bone disease. *Mailing Add:* Dept of Internal Med Univ of Tex Health Sci Ctr Dallas TX 75235

PAK, WILLIAM LOUIS, b Suwon, Korea, Sept 27, 32; US citizen; m 58; c 2. VISUAL PHYSIOLOGY, NEUROBIOLOGY. *Educ:* Boston Univ, AB, 55; Cornell Univ, PhD(physics), 60. *Prof Exp:* Instr physics, Stevens Inst Technol, 60-61, asst prof, 61-65; from asst prof to assoc prof, 65-72, PROF BIOL, PURDUE UNIV, 72- *Concurrent Pos:* USPHS trainee biophys, Univ Chicago, 63-64, career develop award, 66-71; NSF fel, 64-65; vis scientist, Med Sch, Keio Univ, Japan, 67 & Max Planck Inst Biol Cybernet, 71; mem, Visual Sci Study Sect, NIH, 72-75. *Mem:* AAAS; Am Physiol Soc; Biophys Soc; Asn Res Vision & Ophthal; Soc Neurosci. *Res:* Photoreceptor mechanism; genetic dissection of vision. *Mailing Add:* 3009 Georgeton Rd West Lafayette IN 47906

PAKE, GEORGE EDWARD, b Jeffersonville, Ohio, Apr 1, 24; m 47; c 4. PHYSICS. *Educ:* Carnegie Inst Technol, BS & MS, 45; Harvard Univ, PhD(physics), 48. *Hon Degrees:* DSc, Carnegie Inst Technol, 66 & Univ Mo-Rolla, 66; LLD, Kent State Univ, 67. *Prof Exp:* Mem physics adv panel, NSF, 58-60 & 63-66; chmn physics surv comt, Nat Acad Sci-Nat Res Coun, 64-66; mem, President's Sci Adv Comt, 65-69. *Mem:* Nat Inst Med-Nat Acad Sci; AAAS; fel Am Phys Soc (pres, 77). *Res:* Nuclear magnetic resonance; paramagnetic resonance of free radicals; magnetic properties of solids. *Mailing Add:* Xerox Corp Palo Alto Res Ctr 3333 Coyote Hill Rd Palo Alto CA 94304

PAKES, STEVEN P, b East St Louis, Ill, Jan 19, 34; m 54; c 4. PATHOLOGY, LABORATORY ANIMAL MEDICINE. *Educ:* Ohio State Univ, BSc, 56, DVM, 60, MSc, 64, PhD(vet path), 72. *Prof Exp:* Vet pathologist, US Army, Ft Detrick, Md, 60-62; chief animal colonies, Pine Bluff Arsenal, Ark, 64-66; chief comp path, Naval Aerospace Med Inst, 66-69; dir lab animal med, Col Vet Med, Ohio State Univ, 69-72; assoc prof, 72-80, PROF COMP MED & CHMN DEPT, SOUTHWESTERN MED SCH, UNIV TEX HEALTH SCI CTR, DALLAS, 80- *Concurrent Pos:* Mem exam comt, Am Col Lab Animal Med, 68-69; mem exec comt, Inst Lab Animal Resources, Nat Acad Sci-Nat Res Coun; chmn coun accreditation, Am Asn Accreditation of Animal Care, 74- *Mem:* Am Col Lab Animal Med (pres, 73); Am Vet Med Asn; Am Asn Lab Animal Sci; Sigma Xi. *Res:* Infectious diseases of laboratory animals; effect of spontaneous diseases of laboratory animals on biomedical research. *Mailing Add:* Southwestern Med Sch 5323 Harry Hines Blvd Dallas TX 75235

PAKISER, LOUIS CHARLES, JR, b Denver, Colo, Feb 8, 19; m 39. GEOPHYICS. *Educ:* Colo Sch Mines, GeolE, 42. *Prof Exp:* Geophysicst, Carter Oil Co, 42-49; nat exec dir, Am Vet Comt, 49-52; geophysicist, Geophys Br, 52-60, chief ground surv sect, 54-57, br rep, Denver, 58-60, chief, Crustal Studies Br, 60-66, chief, Off Earthquake Res & Crustal Studies, Nat Ctr Earthquake Res, Calif, 67-71, RES GEOPHYSICIST, US GEOL SURV, DENVER, 71- *Concurrent Pos:* Mem, Ad Hoc Panel Earthquake Prediction, Off Sci & Technol, 64-66; Adv Bd & Steering Comt, Earth Sci Curriculum Proj & Educ Prog, Am Geol Inst, 65-69; chmn, Adv Comt Minority Partic Prog, Am Geol Inst, 73-75; vis scientist, Univ New Orleans, 82. *Honors & Awards:* Distinguished Serv Award, US Dept Interior, 70. *Mem:* AAAS; Am Geophys Union; Geol Soc Am. *Res:* Structural geology; crustal studies; exploration geophysics; tectonics. *Mailing Add:* Perry Pine Rt 1 Sedalia CO 80135

PAKMAN, LEONARD MARVIN, b Philadelphia, Pa, Apr 8, 33; m; c 2. MICROBIOLOGY. *Educ:* Univ Pa, BA, 56, PhD(microbiol), 63. *Prof Exp:* Asst instr microbiol, Univ Pa, 58-63; asst prof med microbiol, Jefferson Med Col, 63-70; asst prof, Schs Dent & Pharm, 70-73, assoc prof, 73-80, PROF MICROBIOL, SCH DENT, TEMPLE UNIV, 80- *Concurrent Pos:* Consult microbiol, Johnson Found Med Physics, Univ Pa, 57-61 & Franklin Inst Res Labs, Philadelphia, 68-72; tech adv serv, Attorneys, Ft Washington, Pa, 78- *Mem:* AAAS; Am Soc Microbiol; Int Asn Dent Res; Sigma Xi. *Res:* Effects of hyperbaric oxygen on microorganisms, drug potentiation, infectious processes and tumor chemotherapy; effects of chemotherapeutic agents on and interactions of oral microbes; identification of anaerobic microorganisms associated with root canal infections. *Mailing Add:* Dept Microbiol Temple Univ Dent Sch Philadelphia PA 19140

PAKSTYS, MICHAEL PETER, b June 7, 35; US citizen. ENGINEERING MECHANICS. *Educ:* Tufts Univ, BS, 57; Northeastern Univ, MS, 62; Univ RI, Phd(ocean eng), 77. *Prof Exp:* Struct engr, Green Eng Assoc, 57-61; Res & develop engr, 61-63, eng supvr, 63-74, PROJ MGR, GEN DYNAMICS CORP, 74- *Concurrent Pos:* Seminar lectr, Pa State Univ, Mass Inst Technol & Polytech Inst NY, 66-; lectr, Grad Sch, Univ Conn, 80-81. *Mem:* Am Soc Mech Engrs; Am Soc Naval Engrs; Am Defense Preparedness Asn. *Res:* Shock and vibration analysis and testing of structures and ocean based systems; computer aided design analysis using finite element method computer codes; numerical analysis methods for fluid-structure dynamic interaction including ship collision. *Mailing Add:* 11 South Ridge Rd Niantic CT 06357

PAKURAR, ALICE SWOPE, b Portsmouth, Ohio, Oct 4, 41; m 71. ANATOMY. *Educ:* Ohio Univ, BS, 63; Univ Mich, Ann Arbor, MS, 65, PhD(anat), 68. *Prof Exp:* ASST PROF ANAT, MED COL VA, VA COMMONWEALTH UNIV, 70- *Concurrent Pos:* USPHS fel, Case Western Reserve Univ, 68-70. *Mem:* Tissue Cult Asn; Am Asn Anat. *Res:* Intrinsic and extrinsic controls of the ovary. *Mailing Add:* Dept of Anat Med Col of Va Richmond VA 23298

PAKVASA, SANDIP, b Bombay, India, Dec 24, 35. PHYSICS. *Educ:* Univ Baroda, BSc, 54, MSc, 57; Purdue Univ, PhD(physics), 65. *Prof Exp:* Lectr elec eng, Univ Baroda, 60-61; asst physics, Purdue Univ, 61-65; res assoc, Syracuse Univ, 65-67; assoc physicist, 67-68, from asst prof to assoc prof, 68-74, PROF PHYSICS, UNIV HAWAII, 74- *Concurrent Pos:* Vis scientist, Tata Inst Fundamental Res, 70; vis mem, Inst Adv Study, Princeton, 75; vis prof, Univ Wis-Madison, 78; fel, Japan Soc Promotion Sci. *Mem:* Fel Am Phys Soc. *Res:* Theoretical physics; clementary particle physics. *Mailing Add:* Dept of Physics & Astron Univ of Hawaii Honolulu HI 96822

PAL, BIMAL CHANDRA, b Kanthegerra, Bangladesh, June 1, 26; m 50; c 2. ORGANIC CHEMISTRY, BIOCHEMISTRY. *Educ:* Univ Calcutta, BSc, 44, MSc, 46, PhD(chem), 62. *Prof Exp:* Chemist, Shalimar Paints, Calcutta, India, 47-48; Sri Durga Oil Mills, Barakar, 48-50; asst chem examr, Med Col Govt WBengal, Calcutta, 50-57; res assoc biochem, Western Mich Univ, 57-58; asst prof chem, Tuskegee Inst, 58-63; fel, Case Western Reserve Univ, 63-64; res assoc, Univ Toronto, 64-67; BIOCHEMIST, OAK RIDGE NAT LAB, 67- *Concurrent Pos:* Res partic, Oak Ridge Nat Lab, 61-62; lectr, Grad Sch Biomed Sci, Univ Tenn, Knoxville, 68- *Mem:* AAAS; Royal Soc Chem; Am Chem Soc. *Res:* Chemistry and biochemistry of purines, pyrimidines, nucleosides, nucleotides, polynucleotides and nucleic acids. *Mailing Add:* Biol Div Oak Ridge Nat Lab Oak Ridge TN 37830

PAL, DHIRAJ, b India. SOIL SCIENCE. *Educ:* Agra Univ, BS, 66; Indian Agr Res Inst, MS, 68; Univ Calif, PhD(soil sci), 73. *Prof Exp:* Fel, Univ Calif, Davis, 73-75, NC State Univ, 76-80; Independent consult & adv, Global Educ Corp, 80-81; MEM STAFF, WESTON, 81- *Concurrent Pos:* Fel, Nat Resources Anal Ctr, New Zealand, 75. *Res:* Terrestrial and aquatic microbiology and biochemistry; agricultural waste management; design of land treatment systems for a variety of industrial effluents; hazardous waste management alternatives; fate of organic and inorganic (metals) chemicals in the environment. *Mailing Add:* Weston Weston Way West Chester PA 09380

PALACAS, JAMES GEORGE, b New York, NY, Nov 12, 30; m 55; c 4. ORGANIC GEOCHEMISTRY. *Educ:* Harvard Univ, BA, 52; Pa State Univ, MS, 57; Univ Minn, PhD(geol, biochem), 59. *Prof Exp:* Geologist, US Geol Surv, 52-53; geologist, Shell Oil Co, 59-63; GEOLOGIST, OIL & GAS RESOURCES BR, US GEOL SURV, 63- *Mem:* AAAS; Geol Soc Am; Am Asn Petrol Geologists; Geochem Soc; Soc Econ Paleontologists & Mineralogists. *Res:* Organic geochemistry of recent and ancient sediments; geochemistry of bitumens and humic acids; petroleum geology; geochemistry and oil source-rock potential of carbonates. *Mailing Add:* US Geol Surv Fed Ctr Denver CO 80225

PALADE, GEORGE E, b Jassy, Romania, Nov 19, 12; US citizen; m; c 2. CELL BIOLOGY, HISTOLOGY. *Educ:* Univ Bucharest, MD, 40. *Hon Degrees:* DSc, Yale Univ, 67 & Univ Chicago, 68; ND, Univ Bern, 68. *Prof Exp:* Intern, Asn Civil Hosps Bucharest, 33-39; prosector asst, Fac Med, Univ Bucharest, 35, from asst prof to assoc prof, Inst Anat, 36-46; from asst prof to prof cell biol, vis investr & head sect cell biol, Rockefeller Univ, 46-73; PROF CELL BIOL & CHMN SECT, SCH MED, YALE UNIV, 73- *Concurrent Pos:* Instr, Queen Mary Sch Nursing, Bucharest, 36-45. *Honors & Awards:* Nobel Prize Physiol or Med, 74; Passano Award, 64; Albert Lasker Basic Med Res Award, 66; T Duckett Jones Award, Helen Hay Whitney Found, 66; Hurwitz Prize, 70. *Mem:* Nat Acad Sci; fel Am Acad Arts & Sci; foreign mem Royal Belg Acad Med; Acad Leopoldina. *Res:* Cell biology; structural-functional correlations at the subcellular level; biology of cellular membranes. *Mailing Add:* Sect of Cell Biol Yale Univ Sch of Med New Haven CT 06510

PALADINO, A(LBERT) E(DWARD), ceramics, materials science, see previous edition

PALAIA, FRANK LINCOLN, JR, medical research, see previous edition

PALAIC, DJURO, b Ruma, Yugoslavia, July 24, 37; Can citizen; m 63; c 2. PHARMACOLOGY. *Educ:* Univ Zagreb, MD, 62; PhD(pharmacol), 65. *Prof Exp:* Asst pharmacol, Inst Rudjer Boskovic, Zagreb, 62-65; asst prof, 67-73, ASSOC PROF PHARMACOL, UNIV MONTREAL, 73- *Concurrent Pos:* Res fel, Cleveland Clin Found, 65-67; lectr, Fac Med, Univ Zagreb, 64-65; affil, Dept Clin Pharmacol, Montreal Gen Hosp. *Res:* Pharmacology of angiotensin and serotonin. *Mailing Add:* Dept of Pharmacol Univ of Montreal Montreal PQ H3L 3J7 Can

PALAIS, JOSEPH C(YRUS), b Portland, Maine, Feb 2, 36; m 61; c 2. ELECTRICAL ENGINEERING. *Educ:* Univ Ariz, BSEE, 59; Univ Mich, MSE, 62, PhD(elec eng), 64. *Prof Exp:* Microwave engr, Motorola, Inc, Ariz, 59-60; asst res engr, Cooley Electronics Lab, Univ Mich, 60-64; from asst prof to assoc prof elec eng, 64-73, PROF ELEC ENG, ARIZ STATE UNIV, 73- *Concurrent Pos:* Consult, Stanford Res Inst, 65-67, Motorola, Inc, Ariz, 71 & 78 & Sperry, Inc, Ariz, 72-75; vis assoc prof, Technion--Israel Inst Technol, 73. *Mem:* AAAS; Inst Elec & Electronics Engrs; Optical Soc Am; Soc Photo-optical Instrumentation Engrs. *Res:* Fiber optical communications; laser; holography. *Mailing Add:* Col of Eng & Appl Sci Ariz State Univ Tempe AZ 85287

PALAIS, RICHARD SHELDON, b Lynn, Mass, May 22, 31; m 54; c 3. MATHEMATICS. *Educ:* Harvard Univ, AB, 52, MA, 54, PhD(math), 56. *Prof Exp:* Instr math, Univ Chicago, 56-58; NSF fel & mem, Inst Advan Study, 58-60; from asst prof to assoc prof, 60-65, PROF MATH, BRANDEIS UNIV, 65- *Concurrent Pos:* NSF sr fel, 62-63; Sloan Found res fel, 65-67; ed, Am Math Soc Trans, 66-70; mem, Inst Advan Study, 63-64, 68-69 & 74-75; guest prof, Univ Bonn, 81-82. *Mem:* Am Math Soc (trustee, 71-); Math Asn Am; Asn Comput Mach. *Res:* Differential geometry and topology; transformation groups; global analysis. *Mailing Add:* Dept of Math Brandeis Univ Waltham MA 02154

PALAITIS, WALDEMAR, b Lithuania, Apr 3, 39; US citizen; m 62; c 2. PHYSICAL ORGANIC CHEMISTRY, BIOPHYSICAL CHEMISTRY. *Educ:* La Salle Col, BS, 65; St Joseph's Col, Pa, MS, 66; Univ Pa, PhD(phys & org chem), 69. *Prof Exp:* Assoc prof chem, Mt St Mary's Col, 69-75; asst prof chem, East Stroudsburg State Col, 75-77, assoc prof, 75-80; group leader anal res, Hoechst-Roussel Pharmaceut Inc, 80-81; SR RES ANALYST, MERCK & CO, INC, RAHWAY, NJ, 81- *Mem:* Am Chem Soc; Sigma Xi; NY Acad Sci. *Res:* Homogeneous reaction kinetics related to enzyme catalysis; synthesis of steroids and heterocyclics; nuclear magnetic resonance spectroscopy. *Mailing Add:* 413 Manor Dr Nazareth PA 18064

PALAS, FRANK JOSEPH, b Libuse, La, Oct 24, 18; m 49. MATHEMATICS. *Educ:* Univ Okla, MEd, 48, PhD(math), 56. *Prof Exp:* Asst math, Univ Okla, 55-56; from asst prof to assoc prof, 56-71, PROF MATH, SOUTHERN METHODIST UNIV, 71- *Mem:* Am Math Soc; Math Asn Am. *Res:* Analysis; special functions; number theory geometry. *Mailing Add:* Dept of Math Southern Methodist Univ Dallas TX 75222

PALASZEK, MARY DE PAUL, b Grand Rapids, Mich, Aug 23, 35. CHEMISTRY. *Educ:* Mercy Col, Mich, AB, 58; Univ Detroit, MS, 60; Mich State Univ, PhD(chem), 65. *Prof Exp:* Instr natural sci, Our Lady of Mercy High Sch, 58; from asst prof to assoc prof chem, Mercy Col, Mich, 60-74, prof, 74-79; MGR & CLIN CHEMIST, SAMARITAN HEALTH CTR, 79- *Concurrent Pos:* Asst to dean, Mercy Col, Mich, 65-66; instr, Our Lady of Mercy High Sch, 65; consortium grant partic, Dept Health, Educ & Welfare, 67-68; Du Pont grant, 69-70; vis assoc, Nat Inst Environ Health Sci, 72-74; chemist, Rex Hosp, Raleigh, NC, 73-74. *Mem:* Am Chem Soc; Am Asn Clin Chemists. *Res:* Thiouronium salts; polythienyls; oxetanes; thiosugars; halogenated pesticides; amniotic fluid; analytes. *Mailing Add:* Samaritan Health Ctr 660 Clinton Detroit MI 48219

PALATNICK, BARTON, b Brooklyn, NY, Oct 29, 40. PHYSICS. *Educ:* Yale Univ, BA, 62; Columbia Univ, MA, 64, PhD(physics), 68. *Prof Exp:* Asst prof physics, 68-74, ASSOC PROF PHYSICS, CALIF STATE POLYTECH UNIV, POMONA, 74- *Concurrent Pos:* Sr physicist, Gen Dynamics, Pomona, 74-75. *Mem:* Sigma Xi; Am Asn Physics Teachers. *Res:* Near ultraviolet magnetic rotation spectrum of carbon disulfide; infrared detectors; holography. *Mailing Add:* Dept of Physics 3801 W Temple Ave Pomona CA 91768

PALATY, VLADIMIR, b Prague, Czech, Oct 12, 33; m 62; c 1. BIOPHYSICS, PHYSIOLOGY. *Educ:* Col Chem Technol, Prague, Ing, 57, PhD(chem), 61. *Prof Exp:* Asst prof chem, Col Chem Technol, Prague, 57-61; res assoc physiol, Inst Physiol, Czech Acad Sci, 61-69; assoc prof, 69-76, PROF BIOPHYS, UNIV BC, 76- *Concurrent Pos:* Med Res Coun Can fel, Univ BC, 68-69. *Mem:* Can Physiol Soc; Biophys Soc. *Res:* Physiology of vascular smooth muscle. *Mailing Add:* Dept of Anat Univ of BC Vancouver BC V6T 1W5 Can

PALAY, SANFORD LOUIS, b Cleveland, Ohio, Sept 23, 18; m 70; c 2. NEUROANATOMY, NEUROCYTOLOGY. *Educ:* Oberlin Col, AB, 40; Western Reserve Univ, MD, 43. *Hon Degrees:* MA, Harvard Univ, 62. *Prof Exp:* Intern, New Haven Hosp, Conn, 44; asst resident, Western Reserve Univ Hosps, 45-46; from instr to assoc prof anat, Sch Med, Yale Univ, 49-56; chief sect neurocytol, Lab Neuroanat Sci, Nat Inst Neurol Dis & Blindness, 56-69, chief lab, 60-61; vis investr, Middlesex Hosp, London, Eng, 61; BULLARD PROF NEUROANAT, HARVARD MED SCH, 61- *Concurrent Pos:* Res fel, Western Reserve Univ Hosp, 45-46; Nat Res Coun fel, Rockefeller Inst, 48; Guggenheim fel, 71-72; vis investr, Rockefeller Inst, 53; mem fel bd, NIH, 58-61, cell biol study sect, 59-61, 62-65, assoc, Neurosci Res Prog, 62-67, hon assoc, 74-; Phillips lectr, Haverford Col, 59; chmn, Gordon Res Conf Cell Struct & Metab, 60; Ramsay Henderson Trust lectr, Univ Edinburgh, 62; mem anat sci training comt, Nat Inst Gen Med Sci, 68-; vis prof, Univ Wash, 69 & Univ Osaka Med Sch, 78; distinguished scientist lectr, Sch Med, Tulane Univ, 69, 75 & Univ Ark, 77; mem adv comt, HVEM Resources, 73-; Rogowski mem lectr, Yale Univ, 73; distinguished lectr biol structure, Univ Miami, 74. *Mem:* Nat Acad Sci; AAAS; fel Am Acad Arts & Sci; Am Asn Anat; Histochem Soc. *Res:* Neurosecretion; electron microscopy of the nervous system. *Mailing Add:* Dept of Anat Harvard Med Sch Boston MA 02115

PALAZOTTO, ANTHONY NICHOLAS, b Brooklyn, NY, Dec 15, 35; m 60; c 8. SOLID MECHANICS, CIVIL ENGINEERING. *Educ:* NY Univ, BCE, 55, PhD(solid mech), 68; Polytech Inst Brooklyn, MCE, 61. *Prof Exp:* Civil engr, private practice, 55-63; struct engr, Severud Assoc, 63-75; assoc prof eng mech, Univ Bridgeport, 68-75; PROF ENG & SCI, AIR FORCE INST TECHNOL, 75- *Concurrent Pos:* Asst prof, Univ Conn, 63-66; Nat Sci Found initiation grant, 69. *Mem:* Am Soc Civil Engrs; Am Inst Aeronaut & Astronaut. *Res:* Plasticity; use of finite elements; composite materials. *Mailing Add:* Air Force Inst Technol 6358 Siena St Dayton OH 45459

PALAZZOLO, MATTHEW JOSEPH, b Detroit, Mich, Aug 19, 45; m 71; c 2. INHALATION TOXICOLOGY, IMMUNOTOXICOLOGY. *Educ:* Wayne State Univ, BS, 67, Sch Med, MS, 71, PhD(physiol), 74; Am Bd Toxicol, dipl, 81. *Prof Exp:* toxicologist, 74-80, SR TOXICOLOGIST, GILETTE MED EVAL LABS, ROCKVILLE, MD, 80- *Concurrent Pos:* Adj fac, Howard Univ, 81-82; mem, Indust Task Force Inhalation Testing Consumer Products, 81-82. *Mem:* Europ Soc Toxicol; Am Indust Hyg Asn; NY Acad Sci. *Res:* Inhalation and dermal toxicology with emphasis on cell mediated immune mechanisms; correlation between severity and/or incidence of pulmonary lesions with immunological status. *Mailing Add:* Gillette Med Eval Labs 1413 Res Blvd Rockville MD 20850

PALCHAK, ROBERT JOSEPH FRANCIS, b Braddock, Pa, May 23, 27; m 53; c 5. ORGANIC CHEMISTRY. *Educ:* Univ Pittsburgh, BSc, 48, MSc, 50; Univ Cincinnati, PhD(chem), 53. *Prof Exp:* Asst prof pharm, Univ Pittsburgh, 53-56; sr res chemist, Olin Mathieson Chem Corp, NY, 56-58 & Allegany Ballistics Lab, Hercules Powder Co, 58-61; sr res chemist, Atlantic Res Corp, Va, 61-63, proj dir propulsion chem & polymers, 63-69; prin scientist, Northrop Corp Labs, Hawthorne, 69-71; INDEPENDENT CONSULT, 71- *Concurrent Pos:* Mem, Comt Foamed Plastics, Adv Bd Mil Personnel Supplies, Nat Acad Sci-Nat Res Coun, 63-; pres, Seminars Health Professionals. *Mem:* NY Acad Sci; Am Pharmaceut Asn; Am Chem Soc; The Chem Soc. *Res:* Chemistry of acetylenes, allenes, thiopenes, boron hydrides, nitrogen-fluorine compounds, polyurethanes, foamed plastics, cationically initiated polymerizations, general organic and organometallic synthesis. *Mailing Add:* 18012 Darmel Pl Santa Ana CA 92705

PALDUS, JOSEF, b Bzi, Czech, Nov 25, 35; m 61; c 1. CORRELATION PROBLEM, QUANTUM CHEMICAL METHODOLOGY. *Educ:* Charles Univ, Prague, MSc, 58; Czech Acad Sci, PhD(chem, physics), 61. *Prof Exp:* Jr sci off quantum chem, Inst Phys Chem, Czech Acad Sci, 61-62 & 64-65, sr sci off, 65-68; assoc prof appl math, 68-75, prof appl math & chem, 75-78, ASSOC DEAN GRAD STUDIES, FAC MATH, UNIV WATERLOO, 78- *Concurrent Pos:* Prof, Guelph-Waterloo Ctr Grad Work Chem, 74-; vis prof, Catholic Univ Nijmegen, Holland, 81. *Honors & Awards:* Annual Prize, Div Chem, Czech Acad Sci, 62 & 67. *Mem:* Am Phys Soc; Can Appl Math Soc. *Res:* Electronic structure of the atomic and molecular systems; correlation problem and the use of the many-body, group theoretical and diagrammatical techniques in theoretical chemistry and physics. *Mailing Add:* Dept Appl Math Univ Waterloo Waterloo ON W2L 3G1 Can

PALDY, LESTER GEORGE, b New York, NY, Mar 19, 34; m 59; c 2. SCIENCE COMMUNICATIONS, SCIENCE POLICY. *Educ:* State Univ NY Stony Brook, BS, 62; Hofstra Univ, MA, 66. *Prof Exp:* Instr physics, Cold Spring Harbor High Sch, 63-67; assoc ed, The Physics Teacher, 67-72; assoc prog dir, NSF, 72-73; ASSOC PROF TECHNOL & SOCIOL, STATE UNIV NY STONY BROOK, 76-, ADJ ASST PROF PHYSICS, 70-, DEAN, CTR CONTINUING EDUC, 76- *Concurrent Pos:* Consult ed, Physics Teacher, 72-; ed, J Col Sci Teaching, 78-; adv bd, Physics Today, 73-76. *Honors & Awards:* Distinguished Serv Citation, Am Asn Physics Teachers, 75. *Mem:* Am Asn Physics Teachers; Nat Sci Teachers Asn; AAAS; Arms Control Asn; Foreign Policy Asn. *Res:* Formulation of US science education policy; arms control. *Mailing Add:* Ctr Continuing Educ State Univ of NY Stony Brook NY 11794

PALEG, LESLIE G, plant physiology, see previous edition

PALEN, JOSEPH W, b Srpingfield, Mo, June 4, 35; m 76; c 3. CHEMICAL ENGINEERING, HEAT TRANSFER. *Educ:* Univ Mo, BS, 57; Univ Ill, MS, 65. *Prof Exp:* Chem engr, Phillips Petrol Co, 57-61, res engr, 61-63; asst tech dir, 65-80, ASSOC TECH DIR, HEAT TRANSFER RES INC, ALHAMBRA, 65- *Mem:* Am Inst Chem Engrs. *Res:* Industrial process heat transfer research, especially design methods for process heat transfer equipment. *Mailing Add:* 1221 Pleasantridge Dr Altadena CA 91001

PALENIK, GUS J, b Chicago, Ill, Mar 29, 33; m 59; c 3. CRYSTALLOGRAPHY. *Educ:* Ill Inst Technol, BSc, 53; Univ Southern Calif, PhD(chem), 60. *Prof Exp:* Res chemist, US Naval Weapons Ctr, 59-66; assoc prof chem, Univ Waterloo, 66-70; assoc prof, 70-74, PROF CHEM, UNIV FLA, 74- *Mem:* AAAS; Am Crystallog Asn; Am Chem Soc; Royal Soc Chem. *Res:* X-ray crystallographic studies of various drugs and metal complexes. *Mailing Add:* Dept of Chem Univ of Fla Gainesville FL 32611

PALERMO, FELICE CHARLES, b New Brunswick, NJ, Nov 8, 31; m 74; c 3. ORGANIC POLYMER CHEMISTRY. *Educ:* Rutgers Univ, BA, 59. *Prof Exp:* Prod develop chemist surg dressings, Johnson & Johnson, New Brunswick, 56-60, group leader nonwoven fabrics, Chicago, 60-63, prod develop engr, 63-65, mgr prod develop, 65-70, dir prod develop, 70-73; dir marketing, 74-75, VPRES RES & DEVELOP, ADHESIVE TAPES, PERMACEL DIV, AVERY INT INC, 73- *Mem:* Am Chem Soc; Soc Chem Indust; Am Soc Testing & Mat; AAAS; Asn Res Dirs. *Res:* Pressure-sensitive, thermoplastic, thermosetting adhesives and coatings for industrial and electrical insulation applications. *Mailing Add:* PO Box 172 Asbury NJ 08802

PALEVITZ, BARRY ALLAN, b Brooklyn, NY, July 25, 44; m 67; c 2. CELL BIOLOGY, PLANT PHYSIOLOGY. *Educ:* Brooklyn Col, BS, 66; Univ Wis, PhD(bot), 71. *Prof Exp:* Fel, Stanford Univ, 71-74, res assoc biol, 73-74; asst prof biol, State Univ NY Stony Brook, 74-78; ASSOC PROF BOT, UNIV GA, 78- *Concurrent Pos:* FEl, NSF, 71-72 & NIH, 72-73; guest lectr, Int Bot Cong, 81; mem, Cell Biol Panel, NSF, 81- *Mem:* Am Soc Cell Biol; AAAS. *Res:* Analysis of the basic mechanisms responsible for motility and morphogenesis in plant cells, using optical, electron microscopic and biochemical techniques; video techniques in microscopy; Golgi-endoplasmic reticulum; vacuole plasmalemma interrelationships. *Mailing Add:* Bot Dept Univ Ga Athens GA 30602

PALEVSKY, GERALD, b New York, NY, Jan 8, 26; m 48; c 3. CIVIL ENGINEERING, ENVIRONMENTAL HEALTH. *Educ:* Va Polytech Inst, BS, 47; Columbia Univ, MS, 49, EngScD, 78; NY Univ, MCE, 51; Environ Eng Intersoc, dipl, 79. *Prof Exp:* Instr civil eng, NC State Col, 47-48; civil & sanit engr, NY Univ, 49-51; design engr, Malcolm Pirnie Engrs, NY, 51-53; utilities engr, Brown & Blauvelt, Consult Engrs, NY, 53-55; asst prof civil eng, 68-74, assoc prof, 74-80, PROF CIVIL ENG, CITY COL NEW YORK, 80-, EVENING DIV SUPVR, 74-; CONSULT ENGR, 55- *Concurrent Pos:* From adj instr to adj assoc prof, NY Univ, 54-62, from res scientist to sr res scientist, 56-62; consult, USPHS, 58-65; spec lectr, Columbia Univ, 59-60; dir sewage treatment plant operators short course, Grad II, NY, 63-66; vis assoc prof, Manhattan Col, 64-67; lectr, City Col New York, 65-68; adj prof & pub health engr, Dept Pub Health, Med Col, Cornell Univ, 77- *Mem:* Am Soc Civil Engrs; Am Water Works Asn; Water Pollution Control Fedn; Nat Soc Prof Engrs. *Res:* Environmental impact assessment and health problems relating to environmental control; water supply, treatment and distribution; wastewater collection, treatment and disposal; solid waste handling and resource recovery; industrial hygiene. *Mailing Add:* 61 Kalda Ave New Hyde Park NY 11040

PALEY, HIRAM, b Rochester, NY, Sept 9, 33; m 61; c 3. ALGEBRA. *Educ:* Univ Rochester, AB, 55; Univ Wis, MS, 56, PhD(math), 59. *Prof Exp:* Teaching asst, Univ Wis, 58-59; asst prof, 59-66, ASSOC PROF MATH, UNIV ILL, URBANA, 66- *Mem:* Am Math Soc; Math Asn Am. *Mailing Add:* 706 W California Urbana IL 61801

PALFREY, THOMAS ROSSMAN, JR, b Champaign, Ill, Dec 20, 25; m 49; c 3. PHYSICS. *Educ:* Cornell Univ, BA, 49, PhD(physics), 53. *Prof Exp:* Asst physics, Cornell Univ, 49-52; from asst prof to assoc prof, 52-60, asst dean grad sch, 66-70, PROF PHYSICS, PURDUE UNIV, WEST LAFAYETTE, 60- *Mem:* Am Phys Soc. *Res:* Photonuclear effects of high energies; high energy experimental physics. *Mailing Add:* Dept of Physics Purdue Univ West Lafayette IN 47906

PALIK, EDWARD DANIEL, b Elyria, Ohio, Sept 21, 28; m 57; c 3. SEMICONDUCTORS. *Educ:* Ohio State Univ, BSc, 50, MSc, 52, PhD, 55. *Prof Exp:* Asst prof, Ohio State Univ, 55-56; fel, Univ Mich, 56-57 & Ohio State Univ, 57-58; RES PHYSICIST, US NAVAL RES LAB, 58- *Mem:* Optical Soc Am; Am Phys Soc. *Res:* Magnetooptical properties of solids; infrared properties of semiconductors; microstructure electronics. *Mailing Add:* 904 Pocahontas Dr Ft Washington MD 20744

PALIK, EMIL SAMUEL, b Elyria, Ohio, Apr 25, 23; m 53; c 2. PHYSICAL CHEMISTRY. *Educ:* Ohio State Univ, BSc, 49, MSc, 51. *Prof Exp:* Res assoc chem, Ohio State Univ Res Found, 51-53; SR PHYS CHEMIST, LAMP DIV, GEN ELEC CO, 53- *Mem:* Am Soc Testing & Mat; Fine Particle Soc. *Res:* Methods for the particle size measurement of fine powders of sub-sieve size and for the specific surface area determination of powders and related topics; scanning electron microscopy and energy-dispersive x-ray microanalysis. *Mailing Add:* 1751 Lyndhurst Rd Cleveland OH 44124

PALILLA, FRANK C, b New York, NY, Feb 10, 25; m 45; c 2. INORGANIC CHEMISTRY. *Educ:* Brooklyn Col, BS, 48; Polytech Inst Brooklyn, MS, 52. *Hon Degrees:* PhD, Brooklyn Col, 74. *Prof Exp:* Res chemist, Sylvania Elec Prod, Inc, 48-59; res engr, Gen Tel & Electronics Labs, Inc, 59-61, eng specialist, 61-64, sr eng specialist, 64-66, mgr luminescent mat, 66-70, mgr optoelectronics mat, GTE Labs, Inc, 70-72, SR SCIENTIST & PRIN INVESTR EXPLOR RES, GTE LABS, 72- *Honors & Awards:* Annual Award, Electrochem Soc, 71. *Mem:* Electrochem Soc; Am Chem Soc; Sigma Xi (pres, 76); Am Inst Chemists; Am Ceramic Soc. *Res:* Electronic and photoconductive luminescent, magnetic and optical materials; research and technical management in high energy lithium bateries and catalytic materials related to energy and pollution problems; development of high temperature ceramics and composites. *Mailing Add:* GTE Labs 40 Sylvan Rd Waltham MA 02154

PALINCSAR, EDWARD EMIL, b Chicago, Ill, May 23, 20; m 57; c 3. BIOLOGY, PHYSIOLOGY. *Educ:* Roosevelt Univ, BS, 52; Northwestern Univ, MS, 54, PhD(biol), 57. *Prof Exp:* Asst, Northwestern Univ, 55-56; from asst prof to prof gen physiol, 57-74, PROF BIOL, LOYOLA UNIV CHICAGO, 74- *Concurrent Pos:* Lalor fel, 59. *Mem:* AAAS; Am Soc Microbiol; Soc Protozool; fel Am Cancer Soc; Am Soc Cell Biol. *Res:* Ageing and nucleic acid metabolism; physiology of cell division; protein synthesis; eutely; metabolic effects of cell division blockage; action of carcinogenic and carcinostatic agents; ageing and lysosomes; aging and philosophy of cnidaria; biological clocks. *Mailing Add:* Dept Biol Loyola Univ 6525 N Sheridan Rd Chicago IL 60626

PALIWAL, BHUDATT R, b Khewra, India, Aug 12, 38; US citizen; m 71; c 3. RADIOLOGICAL PHYSICS. *Educ:* Sri Aurobindo Int Educ Ctr, BSc, 59, MS, 61; Univ Tex, Houston, PhD(biophysics), 73. *Prof Exp:* Asst prof med physics & radiol, 73-77, ASSOC PROF HUMAN ONCOL, UNIV WIS-MADISON, 77- *Concurrent Pos:* Fel Sri Aurobindo Int Educ Ctr, 59-62, WHO, 64-65 & Int Atomic Energy Agency, 70-72. *Mem:* Am Asn Phys Med; Am Col Radiol. *Res:* High energy radiation applications in radiation therapy of cancer patient; hyperthermia treatment of cancer. *Mailing Add:* Univ of Wis 600 Highland Ave K41B100 Madison WI 53792

PALIWAL, YOGESH CHANDRA, b Jodhpur, India, May 3, 42; Can citizen; m 65; c 3. PLANT VIROLOGY, PLANT PATHOLOGY. *Educ:* Agra Univ, BSc, 59; Indian Agr Res Inst, New Delhi, MSc, 61, PhD(virol), 65. *Prof Exp:* Res assoc corn path, Rockefeller Found, 64-65; fel cereal virol, Nat Res Coun, Agr Can, 65-67; RES SCIENTIST PLANT VIROL, CHEM & BIOL RES INST, CAN DEPT AGR, 67- *Concurrent Pos:* Adv, Res Br, Electron Microscope Ctr, Agr Can, Ottawa, 73-75. *Mem:* Am Phytopath Soc; Can Phytopath Soc; Indian Phytopath Soc. *Res:* Virus diseases; vector relations; ultrastructure of infected plants and insects. *Mailing Add:* Chem & Biol Res Inst Res Br Agr Can Ottawa ON K1A 0C6 Can

PALKA, JOHN MILAN, b Paris, France, July 29, 39; US citizen; m 60; c 2. NEUROBIOLOGY. *Educ:* Swarthmore Col, BA, 60; Univ Calif, Los Angeles, PhD(zool), 65. *Prof Exp:* Fulbright vis lectr zool, Sri Venkateswara Univ, India, 65-66; asst prof, Rice Univ, 66-69; from asst prof to assoc prof, 69-78, PROF ZOOL, UNIV WASH, 78- *Concurrent Pos:* Guggenheim fel, Cambridge Univ, Eng, 75-76. *Mem:* Fel AAAS; Am Soc Zool; Soc Neurosci. *Res:* Anatomy and physiology of insect sensory systems; nervous system during development and metamorphosis. *Mailing Add:* Dept Zool Univ Wash Seattle WA 98195

PALKE, WILLIAM ENGLAND, b Youngstown, Ohio, Feb 5, 41; m 62; c 2. CHEMICAL PHYSICS. *Educ:* Calif Inst Technol, BS, 62; Harvard Univ, PhD(chem physics), 66. *Prof Exp:* A A Noyes res fel, Calif Inst Technol, 66-68; asst prof chem, 68-74, assoc prof, 74-80, PROF THEORET PHYS CHEM, UNIV CALIF, SANTA BARBARA, 80- *Concurrent Pos:* Sabbatical leave, prog officer chem physics, NSF, 81-82. *Mem:* Am Phys Soc. *Res:* Theoretical applications of quantum mechanics to problems of chemical interest. *Mailing Add:* Dept Chem Univ Calif Santa Barbara CA 93106

PALL, MARTIN L, b Montreal, Que, Jan 20, 42; m 70. BIOCHEMISTRY, GENETICS. *Educ:* Johns Hopkins Univ, BA, 62; Calif Inst Technol, PhD(biochem, genetics), 68. *Prof Exp:* Asst prof biol, Reed Col, 67-72; asst prof, 72-75, ASSOC PROF GENETICS & BIOCHEM, WASH STATE UNIV, 75- *Mem:* Genetics Soc Am; Am Soc Zoologists. *Res:* Biochemical genetics; biochemistry of regulation; cyclic nucleotides in cell regulation; gene duplication and carcinogenesis. *Mailing Add:* Prog in Genetics Wash State Univ Pullman WA 99164

PALLADINO, NUNZIO J(OSEPH), b Allentown, Pa, Nov 10, 16; m 45; c 3. NUCLEAR ENGINEERING. *Educ:* Lehigh Univ, BS, 38, MS, 39. *Hon Degrees:* DEng, Lehigh Univ, 64. *Prof Exp:* Steam turbine design engr, Westinghouse Elec Corp, 39-42, 45-46, sect mgr core design, Atomic Power Div, 50-51, subdiv mgr, 52-59; nuclear reactor designer, Oak Ridge Nat Lab, 46-48 & Argonne Nat Lab, 48-50; prof nuclear eng & head dept, Pa State Univ, 59-66, dean, Col Eng, 66-81; CHMN, NUCLEAR REGULATORY COMN, 81- *Concurrent Pos:* Past mem US Adv Comt Reactor Safeguards; past chmn, Pa Adv Comt Atomic Energy. *Mem:* Nat Acad Eng; Am Soc Mech Engrs; Am Soc Eng Educ; Am Nuclear Soc (past pres). *Res:* Experimental and analytical thermal and hydraulic problems encountered in the design of nuclear reactor cores; mechanical problems associated with the design of nuclear reactor cores. *Mailing Add:* Nuclear Regulatory Comn 1717 H St Northwest Washington DC 20555

PALLADINO, RICHARD WALTER, b Cleveland, Ohio, Apr 20, 33; m 60; c 3. PLASMA PHYSICS DIAGNOSTICS, LASER APPLICATIONS. *Educ:* Case Inst Technol, BS, 55. *Prof Exp:* prof tech staff, 55-80, PROJ PHYSICIST, PLASMA PHYSICS LAB, PRINCETON UNIV, 81- *Mem:* Am Phys Soc. *Res:* Diagnostics; spectroscopy; optics; laser technology; far infrared techniques; fiber optics; detector calibration; radiometry. *Mailing Add:* Plasma Physics Lab PO Box 451 Princeton Univ Princeton NJ 08544

PALLANSCH, MICHAEL J, b St Joseph, Minn, Nov 17, 18; m 53; c 7. BIOCHEMISTRY. *Educ:* St John's Univ, Minn, BS, 48; Univ Minn, Minneapolis, PhD(biochem), 53. *Prof Exp:* Res asst, Univ Minn, Minneapolis, 49-51, asst scientist surg, 51-53; res fel, Univ Minn, St Paul, 53-55; from chemist to supvry chemist dairy prod, 55-73, staff scientist processing technol, 73-74, asst adminr, 74-77, CHIEF SCIENTIST SCI & EDUC, AGR RES SERV, USDA, 77- *Honors & Awards:* Borden Award, Am Dairy Sci Asn, 63. *Mem:* Am Chem Soc; Sigma Xi; AAAS. *Res:* Food and fiber processing and distribution; nutrition; health and safety. *Mailing Add:* Agr Res Rm 330A Bldg US Dept Agr Washington DC 20250

PALLARDY, STEPHEN GERARD, b St Louis, Mo, Mar 19, 51; m 81. WATER RELATIONS, PHYSIOLOGICAL PLANT ECOLOGY. *Educ:* Univ Ill, BS, 73, MS, 75; Univ Wis, PhD(forestry & bot), 78. *Prof Exp:* Asst prof forestry, Kans State Univ, 79-80; ASST PROF FORESTRY, UNIV MO, 80- *Mem:* Am Soc Plant Physiologists; Ecol Soc Am. *Res:* Physiological and ecological responses of plants to water stress; comparative aspects of inter and intra specific variation in water relations of forest trees. *Mailing Add:* Sch Forestry 1-31 Agr Bldg Univ Mo Columbia MO 65211

PALLAS, JAMES EDWARD, JR, plant physiology, see previous edition

PALLAVICINI, MARIA GEORGINA, b San Francisco, Calif, Sept 20, 52. PHARMACOLOGY, TUMOR BIOLOGY. *Educ:* Univ Calif, Berkeley, BA, 73; Univ Utah, PhD(pharmacol), 77. *Prof Exp:* Fel radiation biol, Ont Cancer Inst & Ont Cancer Treat & Res Found, 77-78, BIOMED SCIENTIST,

TUMOR BIOL PHARMACOL, LAWRENCE LIVERMORE LAB, UNIV CALIF, 78- *Mem:* Cell Kinetics Soc; Radiation Res Soc; Asn Advan Cancer Res. *Res:* Effects of anti-cancer drugs on normal and neoplastic tissue, including basic research in tumor, gastrointestinal and hematopoictic biology, cell kinetics and pharmacology. *Mailing Add:* Biomed & Environ Res Div Univ Calif Livermore CA 94550

PALLEN, ROBERT HARRIS, physical chemistry, polymer chemistry, see previous edition

PALLETT, DAVID STEPHEN, b Watertown, Wis, June 14, 38; m 68; c 3. ACOUSTICS. *Educ:* Ripon Col, AB, 61; Pa State Univ, University Park, MS, 64, PhD(eng acoust), 72. *Prof Exp:* Res asst acoust & vibration, Ord Res Lab, Pa State Univ, 64-73; mem appl acoust staff, 72-76, chief appl acoustics, 76-78, chief, Acoust Eng Div, 78-80, PHYSICAL SCIENTIST, INST COMPUT SCI & TECHNOL, NAT BUR STANDARDS, 80- *Concurrent Pos:* Consult, Reliance Elec Co, 70; Dept Com Sci Fel, 77-78. *Mem:* Acoust Soc Am. *Res:* Acoustic radiation and structural vibration properties of complex structures; noise reduction; speech recognition and synthesis; signal processing. *Mailing Add:* A 216 Technol Bldg Inst Comput Sci & Technol Nat Bur Standards Washington DC 20234

PALLIE, WAZIR, b Colombo, Ceylon, Mar 12, 22; m 55; c 3. HUMAN ANATOMY, MEDICINE. *Educ:* Univ Ceylon, MB, BS, 45; Oxford Univ, DPhil, 55. *Prof Exp:* House surgeon, Gen Hosp, Colombo, 46-47; from med officer health to dist med officer, Colombo, 47-50; tutor & demonstr anat, Oxford Univ, 51-55; lectr anat, Univ Ceylon, 55-56, head dept, 61-62; Found prof & head dept, Fac Med, Univ Malaya, 62-69, PROF ANAT, McMASTER UNIV, 69-, CHMN DEPT, 75- *Concurrent Pos:* Res fel electron microscopy, Univ Calif, Los Angeles, 57-58; mem res comt, World Fedn Neurol & comt for teaching, Univ Biol Sci, 72- *Mem:* Affil Royal Soc Med. *Res:* Neuroanatomy and neurohistology, studies in cerebral asymmetries; medical education, especially the integration of multidiscipline morphological concepts into one program. *Mailing Add:* Dept of Anat McMaster Univ Med Ctr Hamilton ON L8S 4L8 Can

PALLMANN, ALBERT J, b Wiesbaden, Ger, Dec 12, 26; m 58; c 1. ATMOSPHERIC PHYSICS, ENVIRONMENTAL SCIENCES. *Educ:* Univ Cologne, Doktorand, 53, PhD(meteorol, physics, math), 58. *Prof Exp:* Res assoc meteorol, Univ Cologne, 54-58; trop meteorologist, Ministry of Defense, El Salvador, 58-59, head anal ctr, 59-62; from asst prof to assoc prof geophys & meteorol, 63-69, PROF METEOROL, ST LOUIS UNIV, 69- *Concurrent Pos:* Consult, Salvadorean Govt, 58-62; prof, Air Force Hq, Nat Naval Sch, El Salvador, 59-62; consult, Univ Corp Atmospheric Res, Colo, 64-67, St Louis Univ sci rep, 67-80; consult, McDonnell Aircraft Corp, 66-67; prin investr res projs sponsored by govt agencies, 67- *Mem:* Am Meteorol Soc; Am Geophys Union. *Res:* Radiative transfer physics of planetary atmospheres; air pollution thermal energetics and climate; solar energy meteorological research and training project; encounter of science and technology with theology. *Mailing Add:* Dept Earth & Atmospheric Sci St Louis Univ PO Box 8099 St Louis MO 63156

PALLONE, ADRIAN JOSEPH, b Lille, France, Apr 8, 28; US citizen; m 54; c 4. APPLIED MECHANICS, AERONAUTICAL ENGINEERING. *Educ:* Polytech Inst NY, BE, 52, ME, 53, PhD(appl mech), 59. *Prof Exp:* Res scientist, Bell Aerospace Syst, 54-55; res assoc, Polytech Inst NY, 55-59; chief, Exp & Theoret Aerodyn Sect, 59-63, mgr, Aerophysics Dept, Avco Syst Div, 63-66; prof aerospace Eng, NY Univ, 66-67; dir technol, 67-77, CHIEF SCIENTIST, AVCO SYST DIV, 77- *Mem:* Am Inst Aeronaut & Astronaut; Sigma Xi; NY Acad Sci. *Res:* Theoretical and experimental work in gas dynamics; boundary layer theories; reentry physics; plasma chemistry, utilizing electric arc to achieve reaction environment. *Mailing Add:* Avco Syst Div 201 Lowell St Wilmington MA 01887

PALLOS, FERENC M, b Hungary, May 24, 33; m 60; c 2. ORGANIC CHEMISTRY, PESTICIDE CHEMISTRY. *Educ:* Swiss Fed Inst Technol, Dipl Ing Chem, 58, DSc(org chem), 62. *Prof Exp:* Res chemist, Fluka, AG, Switz, 58-60; fel, Swiss Fed Inst Technol, 62-63; res chemist, 63-65, sr res chemist, 65-73, RES ASSOC, WESTERN RES CTR, STAUFFER CHEM CO, 73- *Honors & Awards:* IR-100 Award, Indust Res Inst, 74. *Mem:* Am Chem Soc; Swiss Chem Asn; Soc Ger Chem. *Res:* Herbicide antidotes; insect hormones; herbicides; insecticides; drug research. *Mailing Add:* Western Res Ctr Stauffer Chem Co Richmond CA 94804

PALLOTTA, BARRY S, b Brooklyn, NY, Jan 18, 51. PHYSIOLOGY, BIOPHYSICS. *Educ:* State Univ NY Stony Brook, BS, 73; Univ Vt, PhD(physiol & biophysics), 78. *Prof Exp:* FEL PHYSIOL & BIOPHYSICS, SCH MED, UNIV MIAMI, 78- *Mem:* Soc Neurosci. *Res:* Synaptic transmission, especially neuromuscular junction; acetylcholine-receptor channel kinetics; mechanisms of transmitter release. *Mailing Add:* Dept of Physiol & Biophysics Sch of Med Univ of Miami Miami FL 33101

PALLOTTA, DOMINICK JOHN, b Syracuse, NY, Oct 6, 42; m 67; c 2. BIOLOGY. *Educ:* State Univ NY Col Cortland, BS, 65; State Univ NY Col Buffalo, PhD(biol), 71. *Prof Exp:* Fel biol, Rice Univ, 70-71; asst prof, 71-75, ASSOC PROF BIOL, LAVAL UNIV, 75- *Concurrent Pos:* Nat Res Coun Can fel, 71-73. *Mem:* Am Soc Cell Biol; Can Soc Cell Biol. *Res:* Chromosomal proteins and the regulation of RNA synthesis; developmental biology. *Mailing Add:* Dept of Biol Laval Univ Quebec PQ C1K 7P4 Can

PALLUCONI, FRANK DON, b Iron Mountain, Mich, July 8, 39; m 62; c 2. REMOTE SENSING, PLANETARY SCIENCE. *Educ:* Mich Tech Univ, BS, 61; Pa State Univ, MS, 63. *Prof Exp:* Sr engr planetary sci, 69-73, mem tech staff, 74-78, co-investr, 76-78, team leader Mars IR Mapping, 78-80, asst mgr climate res, NASA HQ, 80-81, MISSION SCIENTIST MARS GEOCHEM ORBITER, JET PROPULSION LAB, 81- *Mem:* Am Astron Soc; AAAS; Am Geophys Union. *Res:* Remote sensing of planetary surfaces and atmospheres at visible, infrared and radio wave lengths; interpretation of these observations and spacecraft instrument development. *Mailing Add:* Jet Propulsion Lab 4800 Oak Grove Dr Pasadena CA 91109

PALM, CHARLES EDMUND, b Austin, Tex, June 24, 11; m 37; c 1. ENTOMOLOGY. *Educ:* Univ Ark, AB, 31; Cornell Univ, PhD(econ entom), 35. *Hon Degrees:* Dr Laws, Univ Ark, 67. *Prof Exp:* Asst bot & entom, Univ Ark, 29-31; asst biol, 32-34, instr entom, 34-35, asst exten entomologist, 35-36, asst prof entom, 36-38, prof entom & limnol & head dept, 38-57, dir res, State Univ NY Cols Agr & Home Econ, 57-59, dean col, 59-73, prof, 59-76, EMER PROF ENTOM, & LIBERTY HYDE BAILEY EMER PROF AGR SCI, NY STATE COL AGR & LIFE SCI, 76- . *Concurrent Pos:* Mem, Second Citizens Comt Study Food & Drug Admin, HEW, 55; chmn comt plant & animal pests, Nat Acad Sci-Nat Res Coun, 63-70, mem agr bd, 65-71, chmn, 65-68 & mem bd agr & renewable resources, 73-76; chmn coun chief admin officers, Nat Asn State Univs & Land Grant Cols, 68-69. *Mem:* Entom Soc Am (pres, 53); Am Asn Econ Entom (pres, 52). *Res:* Insect ecology and photography. *Mailing Add:* 16-B Strawberry Hill Rd Eastwood Common NY 14850

PALM, ELMER THURMAN, b Roseburg, Ore, Mar 24, 27; m 53; c 4. PLANT PATHOLOGY. *Educ:* Ore State Col, BS, 51, MS, 52, PhD(plant path), 58. *Prof Exp:* Asst plant path, Exp Sta, Ore State Col, 49-52 & 56-57 & Boyce Thompson Inst Plant Res, 52-56; sr plant pathologist, Crop Protection Inst, NH, 57-63; mgr, Biol Res Sect, Velsicol Chem Corp, 63-69; res plant physiologist, Growth Sci Ctr, Int Minerals & Chem Corp, 69-73; consult, 73-74; RES & DEVELOP REP, AM HOECHST CORP, 74- *Mem:* Am Soc Phytopath; Weed Sci Soc Am; Entom Soc Am. *Res:* Development of agricultural products for both domestic and international use; agronomy. *Mailing Add:* 212 Spring Prairie Rd Burlington WI 53105

PALM, JOHN DANIEL, b Missoula, Mont, Sept 5, 24; m 47; c 3. HUMAN GENETICS, BIOLOGY. *Educ:* Gustavus Adolphus Col, BA, 48; Univ Minn, MA, 50, PhD(zool, bact), 54. *Prof Exp:* Res assoc, Dight Inst Human Genetics, Univ Minn, 51-53; sr scientist biol res, Gen Mills, Inc, Minn, 53-56; assoc prof biol, Wis State Univ, Oshkosh, 52-62; ASSOC PROF BIOL, ST OLAF COL, 62- *Concurrent Pos:* Resident res assoc, Biomed Div, Argonne Nat Lab, 66-67; sabbatical, Soya Prod & Res Assoc, 75- *Res:* Developmental physiology and physiological genetics of human neuropsychological diseases. *Mailing Add:* Dept of Biol St Olaf Col Northfield MN 55057

PALM, JOHN WILLIAM, chemical engineering, see previous edition

PALM, PAUL EUGENE, toxicology, pathology, see previous edition

PALM, WILLIAM JOHN, b Baltimore, Md, Mar 1, 44; m 68; c 3. ROBOT ENGINEERING, SYSTEMS ANALYSIS. *Educ:* Loyola Col, Md, BS, 66; Northwestern Univ, Evanston, PhD(mech eng & astronaut sci), 71. *Prof Exp:* Asst prof, 71-76, ASSOC PROF MECH ENG & APPL MECH, UNIV RI, 76- *Mem:* Am Soc Mech Engrs; Inst Elec & Electronics Engrs; Sigma Xi. *Res:* Control systems; optimization techniques; robotics. *Mailing Add:* Dept of Mech Eng Univ of RI Kingston RI 02881

PALMADESSO, PETER JOSEPH, b Newark, NJ, Sept 5, 40; m 67; c 2. PHYSICS. *Educ:* St Peter's Col, NJ, BS, 61; Rutgers Univ, New Brunswick, MS, 63; Stevens Inst Technol, PhD(physics), 70. *Prof Exp:* Nat Res Coun resident res assoc, Goddard Space Flight Ctr, NASA, Md, 70-72; fel, Ctr Theoret Physics, Univ Md, College Park, 72-74; MEM STAFF, NAVAL RES LAB, 74- *Mem:* Am Phys Soc; Am Geophys Union. *Res:* Nonlinear wave phenomena in plasmas; space plasma physics; stability theory. *Mailing Add:* Naval Res Lab 4555 Overlook Ave SW Washington DC 20375

PALMATIER, ELMER ARTHUR, b Tacoma, Wash, Sept 23, 12; m 37; c 3. BOTANY. *Educ:* Univ Nebr, BSc, 35, MSc, 37; Cornell Univ, PhD(bot), 43. *Prof Exp:* Asst bot, Univ Nebr, 35-37; from asst to instr bot, Cornell Univ, 37-42; from instr to assoc prof, 42-59, instr geog, Army Specialized Training Prog, 44-45, dir conserv workshop, 58, PROF BOT, UNIV RI, 59- *Concurrent Pos:* Mem staff, Nebr Dept Conserv, 36-37 & RI Dept Agr & Conserv, 48-52; US State Dept exchange prof, Univ Baghdad, 61-62; assoc prog dir, NSF, 65-66; vis prof Duke Univ, 70. *Mem:* AAAS; Bot Soc Am; Ecol Soc Am. *Res:* Floral morphology and anatomy of Saxifragaceae; marine and fresh water algae; aquatic seed plants; duck food plants; development of vegetation; salt marsh ecology. *Mailing Add:* Dept of Bot Univ of RI Kingston RI 02881

PALMATIER, EVERETT DYSON, b Winnipeg, Man, Mar 31, 17; nat US; m 41; c 2. PHYSICS. *Educ:* Univ Man, BSc, 38; Cornell Univ, PhD(physics), 51. *Prof Exp:* Asst physics, Cornell Univ, 38-40 & 46-48; from asst prof to prof, 49-59, chmn dept physics, 56-65, vchancellor advan studies & res, 65-69, KENAN PROF PHYSICS, UNIV NC, CHAPEL HILL, 59-, ALUMNI DISTINGUISHED PROF FRESHMAN INSTR, 69- *Concurrent Pos:* NSF sr fel, Univ Bristol, 60-61. *Mem:* Am Phys Soc. *Res:* Cosmic radiation; nuclear physics. *Mailing Add:* Dept of Physics Univ of NC Chapel Hill NC 27514

PALMBLAD, IVAN G, b Gresham, Ore, May 21, 38. ECOLOGY, EVOLUTION. *Educ:* Portland State Col, BS, 60; Univ Wash, Seattle, PhD(ecol), 66. *Prof Exp:* Instr gen sci, Portland State Col, 60-62; assoc biol, Univ Wash, 65-66; from asst prof to assoc prof bot, 66-73, ASSOC PROF BIOL, UTAH STATE UNIV, 73- *Mem:* Ecol Soc Am; Soc Study Evolution. *Res:* Plant competition; germination polymorphisms; plant-herbivore interaction. *Mailing Add:* Dept of Bot Utah State Univ Logan UT 84322

PALMEDO, PHILIP F, b New York, NY, Mar 11, 34; m 61. NUCLEAR PHYSICS, SYSTEMS ANALYSIS. *Educ:* Williams Col, BA, 56; Mass Inst Technol, MS, 58, PhD(nuclear eng), 62. *Prof Exp:* Instr nuclear eng, Mass Inst Technol, 60-61; vis researcher reactor physics, Saclay Nuclear Res Ctr, France, 62-63; asst physicist, Nuclear Eng Dept, Brookhaven Nat Lab, 64-66, assoc physicist, 66-68, physicist, Dept Appl Sci, 68-79, head, Energy Pol Anal Div, 76-79; CHMN, ENERGY DEVELOP INT, 79- *Concurrent Pos:* Assoc ed, Energy Systs & Policy, 74- *Res:* Reactor physics; energy systems and policy analysis; regional energy planning; environmental assessment; energy in developing countries. *Mailing Add:* Energy Develop Int 100 N Country Rd Setauket NY 11733

PALMEIRA, RICARDO ANTONIO RIBEIRO, b Recife, Brazil, Sept 6, 30; m 61. SPACE SCIENCE, COSMIC RAY PHYSICS. *Educ:* Recife Univ, BS, 53; Mass Inst Technol, PhD(physics), 60. *Prof Exp:* From asst prof to assoc prof cosmic rays, Brazilian Ctr Phys Res, 53-63; Nat Acad Sci-NASA fel, Goddard Space Flight Ctr, 63-66; asst prof cosmic rays, Univ Tex, Dallas, 66-72; prof space sci, Inst Space Sci, Brazil, 72-77; prog supvr, 77-78, RES ASSOC, SEISCOM DELTA, INC, 78- *Concurrent Pos:* Vis prof, Carnegie Inst Dept Terrestial Magnetism, 61. *Mem:* Am Phys Soc; Am Geophys Union; Phys Soc Brazil; Int Astron Union; Astron Soc Brazil. *Res:* Radioastronomy; high energy physics; astrophysics; gamma ray astronomy. *Mailing Add:* 4045 Linkwood Apt 431 Houston TX 77025

PALMER, ALAN, b Newcastle, Eng, May 2, 36; US citizen; m 63; c 3. EPIDEMIOLOGY, HEALTH SURVEILLANCE. *Educ:* San Francisco State Col, BA, 64; Univ Calif, Los Angeles, MPH, 68; Univ Utah, PhD(health sci), 75. *Prof Exp:* Physiologist/epidemiologist, Respiratory Dis Control Prog, Bur State Serv, Med Syst Develop Lab, Heart Dis Control Prog & Nat Ctr for Health Statist, Nat Health Surv, 64-69; epidemologist, Western Area Occup Health Lab, Salt Lake City, 70-74; actg chief morbidity field surv, Med Invest Br, Div Field Studies & Clin Invest, Nat Inst Occup Safety & Health, 74-78; sr epidemiologist & mgr health surveillance group, Ctr Occup & Environ Safety & Health, SRI Int, 78-80; PRES, PALMER ASSOCS, 81- *Concurrent Pos:* Cardio-pulmonary adv, Nat Health Surv, Nat Ctr Health Statist, 64-; consult, Bilateral Occup Health Prog between US, Poland & Yugoslavia, 73-; consult, Emory Univ Respiratory Screening Prog & Stanford Res Inst, Ctr for Occup & Environ Safety & Health on Morbidity Surv, 74-; actg chief, Med Invest Br, Div Field Studies & Clin Invest, Nat Inst Occup Safety & Health, USPHS, Dept Health Educ & Welfare, 74-; asst prof exp med, Pulmonary Div, Univ Cincinnati, 74-; proj dir, Nat Study Prevalence Byssinosis in Cotton Gin & Cotton Warehouse Workers. *Mem:* Am Thoracic Soc. *Res:* Beauty and household aerosols, particularly hairspray and respiratory disease in beauticians; silicosis and respiratory disease in brickworkers; morbidity of workers in a leadsmelter due to exposures to lead, cadmium arsenic and SO2; byssinosis in cotton gin and warehouse workers; mortality study in workers in coal hydrogenation process. *Mailing Add:* PO Box 305 333 Ravenwood Ave Moss Bench CA 94038

PALMER, ALAN BLAKESLEE, b Syracuse, NY, May 23, 34; m 59. PHYSICAL CHEMISTRY. *Educ:* Syracuse Univ, BA, 56, PhD(phys chem), 63. *Prof Exp:* Res chemist, Exp Sta, Indust & Biochem Dept, 63-68, develop & serv rep, Indust Chem Dept, New York, 71-72, prod mgr, Indust Specialty Div, Del, 72-74, res supvr, Indust Chem Dept, 74-77, tech supt, Chem, Dyes & Pigments Dept, 77-78, prod supt, Chem & Pigments Dept, 78-79, mgr occup safety & health, 79-81, GEN SUPT, CHEM & PIGMENTS DEPT, E I DU PONT DE NEMOURS & CO, INC, 81- *Mem:* AAAS; Am Chem Soc; fel Am Inst Chemists. *Res:* Infrared spectroscopy; colloid chemistry; high temperature inorganic chemistry; hydrogen peroxide process chemistry; azo-polymerization initiators. *Mailing Add:* 1207 Greenway Rd Wilmington DE 19803

PALMER, ALLISON RALPH, b Bound Brook, NJ, Jan 9, 27; m 49; c 5. INVERTEBRATE PALEONTOLOGY. *Educ:* Pa State Univ, BS, 46; Univ Minn, PhD(geol), 50. *Prof Exp:* Sci aide, Bur Econ Geol, Tex, 47-48; Cambrian paleontologist & stratigrapher, US Geol Surv, 50-66; prof paleont, State Univ NY Stony Brook, 66-80, chmn, Dept Earth & Space Sci, 74-77; CENTENNIAL SCI PROG COORDR, GEOL SOC AM, 80- *Concurrent Pos:* Pres, Cambrian Subcomn, Int Stratig Comn, 72- *Honors & Awards:* Walcott Medal, Nat Acad Sci, 67. *Mem:* Fel AAAS; Paleont Soc; fel Geol Soc Am; Am Asn Petrol Geologists. *Res:* Cambrian stratigraphy, trilobites and phosphatic brachiopods. *Mailing Add:* Geol Soc Am Box 9140 Boulder CO 80301

PALMER, ARTHUR N, b Pittsfield, Mass, Aug 8, 40; m 66. HYDROLOGY. *Educ:* Williams Col, BA, 62; Ind Univ, MA, 65, PhD(hydrogeol), 69. *Prof Exp:* assoc prof, 67-80, PROF HYDROLOGY, STATE UNIV NY COL ONEONTA, 80- *Concurrent Pos:* Res Found fel & grant-in-aid, State Univ NY, 74; vis prof, Karst Geol, Western Ky Univ, 80-82. *Mem:* AAAS; Cave Res Found; Nat Spelol Soc; Geol Soc Am; Brit Cave Res Asn. *Res:* Karst hydrology; geomorphology; geophysics; Mississippian stratigraphy of midwest United States; weathering of limestones; carbonate petrology. *Mailing Add:* Dept of Earth Sci State Univ of NY Col Oneonta NY 13820

PALMER, BRYAN D, b Logan, Kans, July 5, 36; m 59; c 3. INORGANIC CHEMISTRY. *Educ:* Ft Hays Kans State Col, BS, 58; Univ Ark, MS, 64, PhD(chem), 66. *Prof Exp:* PROF CHEM, HENDERSON STATE UNIV, 66-, CHMN DEPT, 71- *Mem:* AAAS; Am Chem Soc; Am Geophys Union. *Res:* Atmospheric transport of radioactive nuclear weapons debris; environmental radioactivity. *Mailing Add:* Dept of Chem Henderson State Univ Arkadelphia AR 71923

PALMER, BYRON ALLEN, b Dillon, Colo, Aug 27, 49. FOURIER TRANSFORM SPECTROSCOPY. *Educ:* Colo Sch Mines, BS, 71; Purdue Univ, MS, 73, PhD(physics), 77. *Prof Exp:* PHYSICIST, LOS ALAMOS NAT LAB, 77- *Concurrent Pos:* Assoc ed, J Optical Soc Am, 82- *Mem:* Optical Soc Am; Am Phys Soc. *Res:* Study of atomic structure of rare earth and actinide elements using emission spectroscopy; generation of wavelength standards for the visibal, ultraviolet and infrared regions. *Mailing Add:* Los Alamos Nat Lab MS-740 CMB-1 Los Alamos NM 87544

PALMER, CATHERINE GARDELLA, b New York, NY, Apr 28, 24; m 54; c 3. CYTOGENETICS. *Educ:* Hunter Col, AB, 49; Ind Univ, PhD(cytogenetics), 53. *Prof Exp:* From asst prof to assoc prof med, 62-66, assoc prof med genetics, 66-70, PROF MED GENETICS, MED CTR, IND UNIV, INDIANAPOLIS, 70- ASST DEAN GRAD AFFAIRS, SCH MED, 81- *Concurrent Pos:* USPHS career develop award, 63-73. *Mem:* AAAS; Genetics Soc Am; Am Soc Human Genetics; Tissue Cult Asn; Genetics Soc Can. *Res:* Human cytogenetics. *Mailing Add:* Dept of Med Genetics Ind Univ Med Ctr Indianapolis IN 46202

PALMER, DAN F, virology, immunology, see previous edition

PALMER, DARWIN L, b Long Beach, Calif, Dec 20, 30; m 58; c 2. MEDICINE, INFECTIOUS DISEASES. *Educ:* Oberlin Col, BA, 53; Columbia Univ, MA, 54; NY Univ, MD, 60. *Prof Exp:* From intern to resident med, Med Ctr, Univ Colo, 60-64; from instr to assoc prof, 65-76, PROF MED, SCH MED, UNIV NMEX, 76-, CHIEF, DIV INFECTIOUS DIS, DEPT MED, 79-; CHIEF INFECTIOUS DIS, MED SERV, VET ADMIN HOSP, 66- *Concurrent Pos:* NIH fel infectious dis, Univ Colo, 64-65; mem consult staff, Bernalillo County Med Ctr, Vet Admin Hosp, Presby Hosp, St Joseph's Hosp & Bataan Mem Hosp, 65-; vis assoc prof, Johns Hopkins Univ Sch Med, 74-75. *Mem:* AAAS; NY Acad Sci; Am Fedn Clin Res; Infectious Dis Soc Am; Am Soc Microbiol. *Res:* Investigation of host defense mechanisms in the infection prone individual. *Mailing Add:* Vet Admin Hosp Infect Dis Sect 2100 Ridgecrest Dr SE Albuquerque NM 87108

PALMER, DAVID B, agricultural engineering, see previous edition

PALMER, EDDY DAVIS, b NJ, Nov 7, 17; m 43; c 3. GASTROENTEROLOGY. *Educ:* Dartmouth Col, AB, 39; Tulane Univ, MS, 40; Univ Rochester, MD, 43. *Prof Exp:* CLIN PROF MED, COL MED & DENT NJ, 66- *Concurrent Pos:* Chief gastroenterol, Vet Admin Hosp, East Orange, NJ, 66-72. *Mem:* Am Soc Trop Med & Hyg; fel AMA; Am Gastroenterol Asn; fel Am Col Physicians; Am Soc Gastrointestinal Endoscopy. *Res:* Clinical gastroenterology. *Mailing Add:* 43 Flocktown Rd Long Valley NJ 07853

PALMER, EDGAR M, b Hartford, Conn, May 17, 34; m 64; c 2. MATHEMATICS. *Educ:* Wesleyan Univ, BA, 56; Trinity Col, Conn, MS, 60; Univ Mich, PhD(math), 65. *Prof Exp:* Numerical analyst comput, Res Labs, United Aircraft Corp, 56-60; teaching asst math, Univ Mich, 60-65, res assoc, 65-67; asst prof, 67-70, assoc prof, 70-76, PROF MATH, MICH STATE UNIV, 76- *Concurrent Pos:* Res assoc, Univ Col, Univ London, 66-67. *Mem:* Am Math Soc; Math Asn Am. *Res:* Combinatorial and graph theory; numerical analyses. *Mailing Add:* Dept Math Mich State Univ East Lansing MI 48824

PALMER, EDWARD WILKERSON, engineering mechanics, structural engineering, deceased

PALMER, EUGENE CHARLES, b Elmhurst, Ill, Nov 4, 38; m 60; c 1. NEUROCHEMISTRY, PHARMACOLOGY. *Educ:* Tenn Technol Univ, BS, 60; Vanderbilt Univ, PhD(anat), 68. *Prof Exp:* Assoc prof pharmacol, Sch Med, Univ NMex, 70-77; prof pharmacol, Col Med, Univ SAla, 77-82; DIR RES, FIRST-MASSEY NEUROL INST, 82- *Concurrent Pos:* USPHS fel pharmacol, Vanderbilt Univ, 68-70; NIMH & NMex Heart Asn res grants, Univ NMex, 71-; res grants, March Dimes, 74-76, NSF, 77-79, Epilipsy Found Am, 76-77 & Ala Affil, Am Heart Asn, 78-79. *Mem:* Soc Neurosci; Am Soc Neurochem; Am Soc Pharmacol & Exp Therapeut; Neurocirculation Soc. *Res:* Effect of psychotropic drugs on the adenyl cyclase system and other neurochemical processes in the central nervous system. *Mailing Add:* First-Massey Neurol Inst Suite 104 356 24th Ave N Nashville TN 37203

PALMER, FREDERICK B ST CLAIR, b London, Ont, June 5, 38; m 59; c 4. BIOCHEMISTRY. *Educ:* Univ Western Ont, BSc, 60, PhD(biochem), 65. *Prof Exp:* Asst prof, 67-71, ASSOC PROF BIOCHEM, DALHOUSIE UNIV, 71- *Concurrent Pos:* Med Res Coun Can fel, Agr Res Coun Inst Animal Physiol, Babraham, Eng, 65-67. *Mem:* Can Biochem Soc. *Res:* Phospholipid metabolism; lipoprotein structure and metabolism. *Mailing Add:* Dept Biochem Dalhousie Univ Halifax NS B3H 4H7 Can

PALMER, GLENN EARL, b Maple, Ont, Apr 13, 35; m 62; c 2. ORGANIC CHEMISTRY. *Educ:* Univ Toronto, BSc, 61, MA, 62; Imp Col, Univ London, dipl chem, 63; Queen's Univ, Ont, PhD(chem), 67. *Prof Exp:* Lectr chem, Royal Mil Col Can, 63-66 & Univ Toronto, 66-67; assoc prof, 67-81, PROF CHEM, UNIV PRINCE EDWARD ISLAND, 81- *Concurrent Pos:* Fel, Univ Toronto, 66-67; chmn dept chem, Univ Prince Edward Island, 69-72. *Mem:* Chem Inst Can; Am Chem Soc; Royal Soc Chem. *Res:* Organic reaction mechanisms; molecular photochemistry; chemical education. *Mailing Add:* Dept Chem Univ Prince Edward Island Charlottetown PE C1A 4P3 Can

PALMER, GRAHAM, b Tonyrefail, Eng, Sept 30, 35; m 60; c 2. BIOCHEMISTRY. *Educ:* Univ Sheffield, BSc, 57, PhD(biochem), 62. *Prof Exp:* Asst lectr biochem, Univ Sheffield, 60-61; proj assoc, Inst Enzyme Res, 61-64; asst prof biochem & assoc res biophysicist, Univ Mich, Ann Arbor, 64-70, assoc prof biol chem & res biophsicist, 70-72; PROF BIOCHEM, RICE UNIV, 72-; ASSOC, RICHARDSON COL, 77- *Concurrent Pos:* NIH career develop award, 66- *Mem:* Am Soc Biol Chemists. *Res:* Mechanism of biological oxidations, particularly in applications of spectroscopic techniques to the study of flavoproteins and metal emzymes. *Mailing Add:* Dept of Biochem Rice Univ Houston TX 77001

PALMER, GRANT H, b Cleveland, Ohio, Nov 30, 11; m 40. BIOCHEMISTRY, NUTRITION. *Educ:* Univ Redlands, BA, 38. *Prof Exp:* Lab aide, Regional Salinity Labs, 39; lab technician, San Bernardino County Hosp, 39-40; res biochemist, Calif Fruit Growers Exchange, 40-50; res biochemist, Sunkist Growers, Inc, Calif, 50-56, pharmaceut prod develop, 56-63, pharmaceut coordr, 63-69, mgr, Corona Res & Develop Labs, 69-75, asst to div mgr prod res & develop, 75-76; RETIRED. *Mem:* Am Chem Soc. *Res:* Citrus bioflavonoids; pharmaceutical pectin; plasma expanders; toxicity of pesticides; nutritional studies; citrus pharmaceutical products. *Mailing Add:* 817 W Olive St Corona CA 91720

PALMER, H(AROLD) A(RTHUR), b Nampa, Idaho, Dec 22, 19; m 43; c 3. PHYSICAL CHEMISTRY. *Educ:* Col Idaho, BS, 41; Univ Okla, MA, 46, PhD(chem), 50. *Prof Exp:* Physics aide, Nat Bur Standards, 42-43; instr math, Col Idaho, 43-44; chemist, Basic Magnesium, Inc, 44 & Cutter Labs, 44-45; instr math, Univ Okla, 45-49; assoc prof, Midwestern Univ, 50-51; chemist, United Gas Corp, 51-53; chemist, 53-65, supvr prod res, 65-74, SR RES ASSOC, BELLAIRE LAB, TEXACO, INC, 74- *Mem:* AAAS; Am Chem Soc; Am Inst Chem. *Res:* Uranium mining; petroleum production. *Mailing Add:* 5235 Lymbar Houston TX 77096

PALMER, H CURRIES, b Moncton, NB, Oct 25, 35. GEOPHYSICS, GEOLOGY. *Educ:* St Francis Xavier Univ, BSc, 57; Princeton Univ, PhD(geol), 63. *Prof Exp:* Fel, 63-66, asst prof, 66-69, ASSOC PROF GEOPHYS, UNIV WESTERN ONT, 69- *Concurrent Pos:* Nat Res Coun Can fel, 64-66. *Mem:* Geol Soc Am; Soc Econ Geol. *Res:* Paleomagnetism. *Mailing Add:* Dept of Geophysics Univ of Western Ont London ON N6A 5B8 Can

PALMER, HAROLD DEAN, marine geology, see previous edition

PALMER, HARVEY EARL, b Inkom, Idaho, Oct 17, 29; m 54; c 5. RADIOLOGICAL PHYSICS, MEDICAL PHYSICS. *Educ:* Idaho State Univ, BS, 55; Univ Idaho, MS, 61. *Prof Exp:* Chemist, Gen Elec Co, 56-59, sr physicist, 59-65; res assoc, 65-80, STAFF SCIENTIST, PAC NORTHWEST LABS, BATTELLE MEM INST, 80-; ASSOC PROF RADIOL, UNIV WASH, 69- *Mem:* Health Physics Soc; Soc Nuclear Med. *Res:* Studies of radioactivity in people; metabolism of fallout isotopes in humans; whole body counters and other methods of studying internally deposited radioactivity; medical research using radioisotopes. *Mailing Add:* Pac NW Labs Battelle Mem Inst Box 999 Richland WA 99352

PALMER, HARVEY JOHN, b New York, NY, Apr 3, 46. CHEMICAL ENGINEERING. *Educ:* Univ Rochester, BS, 67; Univ Wash, PhD(chem eng), 71. *Prof Exp:* Res engr, Mixing Equip Co, 66-67; asst prof chem eng, 71-78, ASSOC PROF CHEM ENG, UNIV ROCHESTER, 78- *Mem:* Sigma Xi; Am Inst Chem Engrs. *Res:* Interfacial phenomena; reactions at fluid-fluid interfaces; heat and mass transfer; convective instability. *Mailing Add:* Dept of Chem Eng Univ of Rochester Rochester NY 14627

PALMER, HOWARD BENEDICT, b Indianapolis, Ind, July 10, 25; m 51; c 3. PHYSICAL CHEMISTRY, FUEL SCIENCE. *Educ:* Carnegie Inst Technol, BS, 48; Univ Wis, PhD(chem), 52. *Prof Exp:* Res assoc chem, Brown Univ, 52, instr, 53-55; from asst prof to prof fuel technol, 55-66, prof fuel sci, 66-77, PROF ENERGY SCI, & ASSOC DEAN GRAD SCH, PA STATE UNIV, 77- *Concurrent Pos:* Head dept fuel technol, Pa State Univ, 59-65; chmn, fuel sci sect, 69-76; vis scientist, Imp Col, Univ London, 63; vis prof, Univ Pittsburgh, 71; consult, United Technol Res Ctr, 68- & Brookhaven Nat Lab, 75-, Exxon Corp, 80- & Sandia Nat Lab, 78-; ed, Combustion & Flame, 72- *Mem:* Am Chem Soc; AAAS; Combustion Inst; Inst Energy London; Am Phys Soc. *Res:* Gaseous reaction kinetics; combustion processes; chemiluminescent reactions in gases; electronic spectra of small molecules; carbon formation and vaporization. *Mailing Add:* 309 Kern Grad Ctr Pa State Univ University Park PA 16802

PALMER, JAMES D(ANIEL), b Washington, DC, Mar 8, 30; m 52; c 3. ELECTRICAL ENGINEERING. *Educ:* Univ Calif, BSEE, 55, MSEE, 57; Univ Okla, PhD, 63. *Prof Exp:* Res engr, Univ Calif, 55-57; from asst prof to prof elec eng, Univ Okla, 57-66, dir sch elec eng, 63-66, proj engr, High-Speed Computer Proj, 58-60, res assoc & proj dir, Res Inst, 58-66, dir systs res ctr, 64-66; proj elec eng & dean sci & eng, Union Col, NY, 66-71; pres, Metrop State Col, 71-78; adminr res & spec admin, US Dept Transp, 78-80; VPRES & GEN MGR RES, MECH TECH INC, 80- *Concurrent Pos:* Consult, McDonnell Aircraft Corp, Mo, 59-69, Streeter-Amet Div, Goodman Indust, Ill, 61-66 & Univ Okla Res Inst, 66-68; mem & chmn bd trustees, Hudson Mohawk Asn Cols & Univs, 69-71; mem bd dirs, Auraria Higher Educ Ctr; mem, Colo Fulbright-Hays Scholar Comt; mem bd, Rocky Mt Region Inst Int Engrs; consult & mem bd, Systs Mgt Co, Mass. *Mem:* Inst Elec & Electronics Engrs. *Res:* Plasma dynamics; adaptive control in social systems. *Mailing Add:* Mech Tech Inc 968 Albany Shaker Rd Latham NY 12110

PALMER, JAMES E, geology, geophysics, see previous edition

PALMER, JAMES FREDERICK, b Toronto, Ont, Feb 2, 31; m 56; c 3. SAFETY ENGINEERING, ENVIRONMENTAL SCIENCE. *Educ:* Univ BC, BASc, 53; Queen's Univ, Ont, MSc, 55. *Prof Exp:* Nuclear engr reactor res, Atomic Energy Can Ltd, 54-63; liaison officer attached to Phillips Petrol Co, Idaho, 63-65; nuclear safety engr, 65-75, ENVIRON AUTHORITY, ATOMIC ENERGY CAN LTD, 75- *Res:* Reactor safety, particularly development of methods for detecting and locating fuel failures in nuclear reactors; studies of environmental effects due to releases of radioactivity from nuclear facilities. *Mailing Add:* 7 Frontenac Crescent Deep River ON Can

PALMER, JAMES KENNETH, b Camden, NJ, Sept 29, 26; m 49; c 6. FOOD BIOCHEMISTRY. *Educ:* Juniata Col, BS, 48; Pa State Univ, MS, 50, PhD(agr & biochem), 52. *Prof Exp:* Asst biochemist, Conn Agr Exp Sta, 52-56; sr res biochemist, Va Inst Sci Res, 56-59; sr biochemist, United Fruit Co, 59-65; prin res scientist, Div Food Preservation, Commonwealth Sci & Indust Res Orgn, Australia, 65-68; assoc prof food biochem, Mass Inst Technol, 68-73; sr res assoc, US Army Natick Labs, 73-75; ASSOC PROF FOOD BIOCHEM, VA POLYTECH INST & STATE UNIV, 75- *Mem:* AAAS; Am Chem Soc; Am Soc Biol Chem; Am Soc Plant Physiologists; Inst Food Technologists. *Res:* Biochemistry of fruit ripening; biogenesis of flavor components; phenolases; biochemical analysis; carbohydrates in foods. *Mailing Add:* Dept of Food Sci & Tech Va Polytech Inst & State Univ Blacksburg VA 24061

PALMER, JAMES MCLEAN, b Saginaw, Mich, Sept 3, 37; m 63, 81; c 3. OPTICS. *Educ:* Grinnell Col, AB, 59; Univ Ariz, MS, 73, PhD(optics), 75. *Prof Exp:* Sr engr, Hoffman Semiconductor, 59-67, Globe-Union, Centralab Semiconductor, 67-70; res asst, 73-75, res assoc, 76-77, res specialist, 78-80, RES ASSOC, OPTICAL SCI CTR, UNIV ARIZ, 81- *Concurrent Pos:* Pres, Radiometrics, 70-; lectr optical eng, Optical Sci Ctr, Univ Ariz, 81- *Mem:* Optical Soc Am; Inst Elec & Electronic Engrs; Soc Photo-Optical-Instrumentation Engrs; Coun Optical Radiation Measurements. *Res:* Placed Pioneer-Venus solar flux radiometer on venus; measuring ground-based solar radiation stability; design and build various radiometric instruments. *Mailing Add:* Optical Sci Ctr 528 N Martin Tucson AZ 85719

PALMER, JAY, b Moab, Utah, Nov 18, 28; div; c 2. PHYSICAL CHEMISTRY, INORGANIC CHEMISTRY. *Educ:* Utah State Univ, BS, 50, MS, 56; Northwestern Univ, MA, 76, PhD(inorg chem), 60. *Prof Exp:* Chemist, US Gypsum Co, 56-57 & Portland Cement Asn, 58; dir inorg chem res, Morton Chem Co, Ill, 59-70; mgr res & develop, CF Industs, Inc, 70-73; res assoc & mgr phosphate res, US Gypsum Co, 73-76; ASSOC PROF CHEM, UNIV S FLA, 76- *Concurrent Pos:* Lectr, Roosevelt Univ, 61-70; lectr, Northwestern Univ, 62; chem consult, US Gypsum Co, 76- *Mem:* Am Chem Soc. *Res:* Inorganic reactions in solution and the solid state; surface and colloid chemistry. *Mailing Add:* 521 Royal Greens Dr Temple Terrace FL 33617

PALMER, JEFFRESS GARY, b Brooklyn, NY, Oct 7, 21; m 51; c 2. INTERNAL MEDICINE, HEMATOLOGY. *Educ:* Emory Univ, BS, 42, MD, 44. *Prof Exp:* Intern med, NC Baptist Hosp, Winston-Salem, 44-45; asst resident & resident, Lawson Vet Admin Hosp, Ga, 47-49; from asst prof to assoc prof, 52-64, PROF MED, SCH MED, UNIV NC, CHAPEL HILL, 64- *Concurrent Pos:* Fel, Col Med, Univ Utah, 49-52; consult, Vet Admin, Fayetteville, NC. *Mem:* AAAS; AMA; Am Fedn Clin Res; Am Soc Hemat. *Res:* Antibiotics; hematology; chemotherapy; spleen; leukocytes; steroids. *Mailing Add:* Dept Med Univ NC Chapel Hill NC 27514

PALMER, JOHN DAVIS, b Sterling, Ill, Oct 31, 31; m 57; c 2. CLINICAL PHARMACOLOGY. *Educ:* Univ Colo, BS, 54, MS, 55; Univ Minn, PhD(pharmacol), 61, MD, 62. *Prof Exp:* Intern internal med, Univ Minn Hosps, 62-63; asst prof pharmacol, Sch Med, Univ Colo, 63-66; DIR MULTIDISCIPLINE TEACHING LABS, COL MED, UNIV ARIZ, 66-, ASSOC PROF PHARMACOL, 69-, ASST PROF INTERNAL MED, 73- *Concurrent Pos:* Grants, USPHS, 64-66, Am Heart Asn, 66-69 & ARiz Heart Asn, 69-; consult, Denver Vet Admin Hosp, Colo, 64-66 & Tucson Vet Admin Hosp, Ariz, 66-; consult physician educ br, Bur Health Manpower Educ, NIH, 71, mem med educ rev comt, 71-73; consult, Bur Health Resources Develop, 73- *Mem:* AAAS; Am Fedn Clin Res; Am Soc Pharmacol & Exp Therapeut. *Res:* Mechanisms and treatment of septic and cardiogenic shock; medical education; design and development of multidiscipline teaching laboratories. *Mailing Add:* Ariz Med Ctr Univ of Ariz Col of Med Tucson AZ 85724

PALMER, JOHN DERRY, b Chicago, Ill, May 26, 32; m 60; c 1. BIOLOGICAL RHYTHMS. *Educ:* Lake Forest Col, BA, 57; Northwestern Univ, MS, 59, PhD(comp physiol), 62. *Prof Exp:* From instr to asst prof biol, Univ Ill, 61-63; NSF fel, Eng, 63-64; from asst prof to prof, NY Univ, 66-74; PROF ZOOL & CHMN DEPT, UNIV MASS, AMHERST, 74- *Concurrent Pos:* Mem corp, Marine Biol Lab, Woods Hole, 64-; chmn dept biol, NY Univ, 68-73. *Mem:* Fel AAAS; Am Inst Biol Sci; Am Soc Naturalists; Int Soc Chronobiol; Soc Gen Physiologists. *Res:* Biological rhythms in algae, crustaceans and birds. *Mailing Add:* Dept of Zool Univ of Mass Amherst MA 01003

PALMER, JOHN FRANK, JR, b Cedar Rapids, Iowa, Oct 23, 15; m 70; c 5. INDUSTRIAL ORGANIC CHEMISTRY. *Educ:* Coe Col, BA, 37; Iowa State Univ, PhD(phys chem), 41. *Prof Exp:* Res chemist, Monsanto Co, Mo, 41-47, group leader, 47-53, res liaison, 53-54, group leader, 54-61, res specialist, 61-71; process chemist, 71-73, plant process res mgr, 73-79, MGR, PROCESS & ANAL TECHNOL, EDWIN COOPER, INC, DIV ETHLY CORP, 79- *Mem:* Am Chem Soc; Am Soc Testing & Mat. *Res:* Exploratory research on organic chemical processes; resin materials; surface coating; absorption spectroscopy; oil additives for lubricating oils; catalytic hydrogenation and dehydrogenation. *Mailing Add:* Edwin Cooper Inc Div Ethly Corp 125 W Lafayette St Louis MO 63104

PALMER, JOHN GILBERT, plant pathology, see previous edition

PALMER, JOHN LEE, b Los Angeles, Calif, Sept 15, 35; m 58; c 3. MECHANICAL ENGINEERING, COMPUTER AIDED DESIGN. *Educ:* US Mil Acad, BS, 58; Purdue Univ, MS, 63, PhD(mech eng), 73. *Prof Exp:* Sr adv, RVN Rebuild Depot, 66-67; exec officer res mgt, Aberdeen Res & Develop Ctr, Aberdeen Proving Ground, Md, 68-69; assoc prof weapon syst eng, US Mil Acad, 73-78; US MIL ACAD FEL ANAL TECH, US ARMY WAR COL, 78- *Mem:* Am Soc Eng Educ; Am Soc Mech Engrs. *Res:* Use of computers, micro-processors, and computer driven graphic devices to teach engineering design. *Mailing Add:* Dept of Eng US Mil Acad West Point NY 10996

PALMER, JOHN M, b Yakima, Wash, May 8, 22; m 47; c 2. SPEECH PATHOLOGY, AUDIOLOGY. *Educ:* Univ Wash, BA, 46, MA, 50; Univ Mich, PhD(speech), 52. *Prof Exp:* PROF SPEECH & HEARING SCI, UNIV WASH, 52- *Concurrent Pos:* Consult, Children's Orthop & Hosps, Seattle, 52-, Univ Wash Hosp, 57- *Mem:* Fel Am Speech & Hearing Asn. *Res:* Organic speech disorders; cleft palate; speech pathology, science and physiology. *Mailing Add:* Speech and Hearing Clin Univ of Wash Seattle WA 98105

PALMER, JOHN PARKER, b Los Angeles, Calif, July 16, 39; m 60; c 3. ELECTRONICS ENGINEERING. *Educ:* Univ Mich, BSE, 62; Univ Calif, Riverside, PhD(physics), 69. *Prof Exp:* Physicist, Gen Dynamics, Pomana, 62-65; asst prof, 69-72, assoc prof, 72-78, PROF ELEC ENGR, CALIF POLYTECH STATE UNIV, 78-, CHMN DEPT, 81- *Concurrent Pos:* Design specialist, Gen Dynamics, Pomona, 70-80; staff engr, Hughes Aircraft Co, 81- *Mem:* Inst Elec & Electronics Engrs; Optical Soc Am. *Res:* Analog and digital circuit design, electronic noise analysis; management operating system large scale intergration structures; fiber optic devices and communication systems; sampled data signal processing. *Mailing Add:* Elec & Comput Eng Dept Calif Polytech State Univ Pomona CA 91768

PALMER, JOHN WARREN, b Marshalltown, Iowa, July 27, 08; m 31; c 3. BIOCHEMISTRY. *Educ:* Univ Iowa, BA, 28, MS, 29; Columbia Univ, PhD(biochem), 33. *Prof Exp:* Asst chem, Univ Iowa, 28-29; asst biochem, Col Physicians & Surgeons, Columbia Univ, 30-36, instr, 36; biochemist, Biol Lab, E R Squibb & Sons, 36-45, head dept protein fractionation, 45-49, dir biochem develop, 48-49, biol develop, 49-52; dir biol prod, Hyland Div, Travenol Labs, Inc, 52-53, dir labs, 53-78, vpres, 55-78; RETIRED. *Concurrent Pos:* Mem, Rev Comt, US Pharmacopoeia, 60-70. *Mem:* AAAS; Am Chem Soc; Am Asn Immunologists; Am Pub Health Asn; NY Acad Sci. *Res:* Chemistry of the skin and of the eye; mucins and mucoids; bacterial carbohydrates and toxins; toxoids; antitoxins and antibodies; serum proteins; bromide metabolism; development and production of biological pharmaceuticals. *Mailing Add:* 3006 La Ventana San Clemente CA 92672

PALMER, JON (CARL), b Galva, Ill, Jan 20, 40; m 64; c 1. IMMUNOLOGY, MOLECULAR BIOLOGY. *Educ:* Knox Col, AB, 62; Univ Calif, Berkeley, PhD(molecular biol), 68. *Prof Exp:* ASST PROF, WISTAR INST ANAT & BIOL, 70- *Concurrent Pos:* Nat Inst Allergy & Infectious Dis fel, Walter & Eliza Hall Inst Med Res, Melbourne, 68-70. *Res:* Molecular biology of the immune response; cellular cooperation; control of expression of genetic information; tumor-host relationship. *Mailing Add:* Wistar Inst of Anat & Biol 36th & Spruce St Philadelphia PA 19104

PALMER, JUNE WILSON, biochemistry, cell biology, see previous edition

PALMER, KATHERINE VAN WINKLE, b Oakville, Wash, Feb 4, 95; m 21; c 1. PALEONTOLOGY, STRATIGRAPHY. *Educ:* Univ Wash, BS, 18; Cornell Univ, PhD(paleont), 25; ScD, Tulane Univ, 78. *Hon Degrees:* DSc, Tulane Univ, 78. *Prof Exp:* Asst geol, Univ Ore, 18; asst, Cornell Univ, 21 & 25, Hecksher asst paleont, 25-27, lectr, 42-43 & 45; actg asst prof paleont & hist geol, Univ Wash, 22; cur paleont, Oberlin Col, 28-29; tech expert zool, State Mus, NY, 45-46; spec tech expert, McGill Univ, 50-51; dir, 51-78, DIR EMER PALEONT RES INST, 78- *Concurrent Pos:* Secy-treas, Cushman Found, 54-71; grants, Am Philos Soc, Am Geol Soc & NSF, 55-56. *Honors & Awards:* Paleont Soc Award, 72; Western Soc Malacologists Award, 74. *Mem:* AAAS; fel Paleont Soc; fel Geol Soc Am; Am Asn Petrol Geologists; hon mem Am Malacol Union (vpres, 58-59, pres, 60). *Res:* Paleontology; stratigraphy; conchology. *Mailing Add:* 206 Oak Hill Rd Ithaca NY 14850

PALMER, KEITH HENRY, b Retford, Eng, July 3, 28; m 58; c 1. BIOCHEMICAL PHARMACOLOGY. *Educ:* Univ Nottingham, BPharm, 52, MPharm, 54; Univ Paris, Dr Univ, 56. *Prof Exp:* Demonstr, Univ Nottingham, 52-53; from asst prof to assoc prof pharmaceut chem, Univ Alta, 58-64; group leader, Div Chem & Life Sci, Res Triangle Inst, NC, 64-71; assoc prof biochem pharmacol, Brown Univ, 71-74; SECT LEADER DRUG METAB & PHARMACOKINETICS, RES DIV, SCHERING CORP, 74- *Concurrent Pos:* Nat Res Coun Can res fel, 56-58; mem alkaloids comt, Brit Pharmacopoeia Comn, 59-64; head div drug metab, Roger Williams Gen Hosp, Providence, RI, 71-74. *Mem:* Am Soc Pharmacol & Exp Therapeut; Am Chem Soc; Pharmaceut Soc Gt Brit. *Res:* Drug metabolism; analytical biopharmacology; organic chemistry; pharmaceutical chemistry; pharmacognosy. *Mailing Add:* Drug Metab & Pharmacokinetics 60 Orange St Bloomfield NJ 07003

PALMER, KENNETH CHARLES, b Everett, Mass, Oct 23, 44; m 68; c 2. EXPERIMENTAL PATHOLOGY, PULMONARY DISEASES. *Educ:* Merrimack Col, BA, 66; Villanova Univ, MS, 72; Boston Univ, PhD(path), 77. *Prof Exp:* Res asst bioenergetics, Boston Biomedical Res Inst, 66-67; res asst lung path, Sch Med, Boston Univ, 73-76; res instr path, Sch Med, Boston Univ, 77-79, asst prof path, 79-80; ASST PROF PATH & CHIEF, DIV PULMONARY PATHOBIOL, SCH MED, WAYNE STATE UNIV, 80- *Concurrent Pos:* NIH fel, Boston Univ, 76-78; NIH young pulmonary invest award, Mallory Inst Path, 78-81, res assoc, 76-80. *Mem:* AAAS; Am Soc Cell Biol; Am Asn Pathologists; Am Thoracic Soc; NY Acad Sci. *Res:* Pathology; electron microscopy; biochemistry. *Mailing Add:* Dept Path Sch Med Wayne State Univ Detroit MI 48201

PALMER, KENT FRIEDLEY, b Chicago, Ill, Sept 26, 41; m 68; c 2. MOLECULAR PHYSICS, SPECTROSCOPY. *Educ:* Ohio State Univ, BS, 64, PhD(physics), 72. *Prof Exp:* Acad counselor phys sci, Col Arts & Sci, Ohio State Univ, 71-72; res assoc, Dept Physics, Kans State Univ, 72-74; vis asst prof, Dept Physics, Univ Ky, 74-76; ASST PROF PHYSICS & CHMN DEPT, WESTMINSTER COL, 76- *Concurrent Pos:* Summer fac res assoc, US Air Force & Am Soc Eng Educ, 76; subcontractor, ARO Inc Oper Contractor Arnold Eng & Develop Ctr, Arnold Air Force Sta, Tenn, 78-82. *Mem:* Optical Soc Am; Am Asn Physics Teachers. *Res:* High resolution spectroscopy of small molecules; spectroscopy of condensed molecular species found in planetary atmospheres, rocket and jet plumes; time-resolved spectroscopy of rare gas atoms and molecules; optical properties of thin dielectric films. *Mailing Add:* Dept of Physics Westminster Col Fulton MO 65251

PALMER, LARRY ALAN, b Wichita, Kans, Oct 11, 45; m 67; c 1. NEUROPSYCHOLOGY. *Educ:* Drexel Univ, BS, 67; Univ Pa, PhD(physiol), 72. *Prof Exp:* Fel, 72-75, ASST PROF, DEPT ANAT, UNIV PA, 75- *Mem:* Soc Neurosci. *Res:* Physiological and anatomical determination of neuron connectivity in visual cortex of cat. *Mailing Add:* 286 French Creek Rd Phoenixville PA 19151

PALMER, LAURENCE CLIVE, b Washington, DC, Dec 25, 32; m 56; c 2. ELECTRICAL ENGINEERING. *Educ:* Washington & Lee Univ, BS, 55; Rensselaer Polytech Inst, BEE, 55; Univ Md, MS, 63, PhD(elec eng), 70. *Prof Exp:* Prin engr, Emerson Res Lab, Div Emerson Radio, 57-60; sect mgr engr, Wash Technol Assoc, Inc, 60-61, Radcom-Emertron Div, Litton Syst, 61-63; sr scientist, Comput Sci Corp, 63-74; SR SCIENTIST, SYSTS TECH DIV, COMSAT LABS, COMMUN SATELLITE CORP, 74- *Concurrent Pos:* Electron officer, US Army Signal Corps, 55-57; jr engr, Emerson Res Lab, Emerson Radio, 55. *Mem:* Inst Elec & Electronics Engrs. *Res:* Analysis and simulation of the satellite communication systems with emphasis on modulation, multiple-access techniques. *Mailing Add:* 10910 Old Coach Rd Potomac MD 20854

PALMER, LEIGH HUNT, b Altadena, Calif, May 9, 35; m 58; c 4. PHYSICS, ASTRONOMY. *Educ:* Univ Calif, Berkeley, BA, 57, PhD(physics), 66. *Prof Exp:* ASST PROF PHYSICS, SIMON FRASER UNIV, 66- *Mem:* Can Asn Physicists; Am Asn Physics Teachers. *Res:* Astronomy; astrophysics. *Mailing Add:* Rm P8433-Sci Complex Dept Physics Simon Fraser Univ Burnaby BC V5A 1S6 Can

PALMER, LEONARD A, b Seattle, Wash, Aug 8, 31. GEOLOGY. *Educ:* Univ Wash, BS, 53, MS, 60; Univ Calif, Los Angeles, PhD(geol), 67. *Prof Exp:* Asst prof geol, Univ Hawaii, 65-67; asst prof geol, 67-74, ASSOC PROF EARTH SCI, PORTLAND STATE UNIV, 74- *Concurrent Pos:* Consult, var industs & govt agencies. *Mem:* AAAS; Geol Soc Am; Asn Eng Geol; Int Asn Quaternary Res. *Res:* Environmental geology; applied geomorphology. *Mailing Add:* Dept of Earth Sci 17A CH Portland State Univ Portland OR 97207

PALMER, LOUIS THOMAS, plant pathology, see previous edition

PALMER, MICHAEL RULE, b Amarillo, Tex, Sept 29, 50. NEUROPHYSIOLOGY, DEVELOPMENTAL NEUROBIOLOGY. *Educ:* Colo Col, BA, 73; Tex A&M Univ, MS, 76; Univ Colo, PhD(pharmacol), 80. *Prof Exp:* Teaching asst mammalian anat, Tex A&M Univ, 74-75, teaching lab coordr physiol, 75-76, res asst & sr lab tech, 76; res fel, 80-81, ASST PROF NEUROPHARMACOL, SCH MED, UNIV COLO, 82- *Concurrent Pos:* Co-instr, Med Sch, Univ Colo, 79-80; vis scientist, Karolinska Inst, Stockholm, Sweden, 81-82. *Mem:* Soc Neurosci; AAAS; Brit Brain Res Asn; Europ Brain & Behavior Soc. *Res:* Opiates and opioid peptides; psychatropic drugs; alcohol lead neurotoxicity; brain transplants; drug-neurotransmitter interaction; adrenegic and dopanimergic neurotransmitter systems. *Mailing Add:* Box C236 Dept Pharmacol Univ Colo Health Sci Ctr Denver CO 80262

PALMER, PATRICK EDWARD, b St Johns, Mich, Dec 6, 40; m 63; c 3. RADIO ASTRONOMY. *Educ:* Univ Chicago, SB, 63; Harvard Univ, MA, 65, PhD(physics), 68. *Prof Exp:* Radio astronr, Harvard Col Observ, 68; from asst prof to assoc prof, 68-75, PROF ASTRON, UNIV CHICAGO, 75- *Concurrent Pos:* Alfred P Sloan Found fel, 70; vis assoc prof, Calif Inst Technol, 72; vis lectr radio astron, Cambridge Univ, 73; vis res astronomer, Univ Calif, Berkeley, 77, vis astronomer, Nat Radio Astron Observ, 80. *Honors & Awards:* Bart J Bok Prize for res in galactic structure, Harvard Col Observ, 69; Helen B Warner Prize, Am Astron Soc, 75. *Mem:* Royal Astron Soc; Union Scientifique Radio Int; Am Astron Soc; AAAS. *Res:* Observation and analysis of radio frequency molecular emission lines from the interstellar medium. *Mailing Add:* Astron & Astrophysics Ctr 5640 S Ellis Ave Chicago IL 60637

PALMER, RALPH SIMON, b Richmond, Maine, June 13, 14; m; c 3. VERTEBRATE ZOOLOGY. *Educ:* Univ Maine, AB, 37; Cornell Univ, PhD(ornith), 40. *Prof Exp:* Asst ornith, Cornell Univ, 38-39; asst, State Conserv Comn, NY, 42; instr zool, Conserv Div, Vassar Col, 42-47, asst prof, 47-49; state zoologist, NY State Mus, 49-76; FAC ASSOC ZOOL & FOREST RESOURCES, UNIV MAINE, 77- *Concurrent Pos:* Res assoc, Smithsonian, 79- *Mem:* Am Soc Mammal. *Res:* Avian and mammalian ecology and life histories. *Mailing Add:* Box 74 Tenants Harbor ME 04860

PALMER, RAY FREDERICK, b Los Angeles, Calif, July 26, 23; m 46; c 5. RADIATION BIOLOGY. *Educ:* Fresno State Col, AB, 48; Ore State Univ, MS, 50. *Prof Exp:* Chemist, Gen Elec Co, Richland, Wash, 50-53, biologist, 53-60, mgr tech admin, 60-65; mgr tech admin, 65-67, SR RES SCIENTIST, PAC NORTHWEST LABS, BATTELLE MEM INST, 67- *Mem:* Health Physics Soc; Radiation Res Soc. *Res:* Radionuclide metabolism; biophysics; radiation dosimetry and inhalation toxicology. *Mailing Add:* Biol Dept Pac Northwest Labs Battelle Mem Inst PO Box 999 Richland WA 99352

PALMER, REID G, b Pemberville, Ohio, June 21, 41; m 67. PLANT BREEDING, GENETICS. *Educ:* Ont Agr Col, Toronto, BSA, 63; Univ Ill, MS, 65; Ind Univ, Bloomington, PhD(genetics), 70. *Prof Exp:* Res asst agron, Univ Ill, 63-65; teaching asst bot, Ind Univ, Bloomington, 66; RES GENETICIST, PLANT SCI RES DIV, AGR AGR RES, USDA, IOWA STATE UNIV, 70- *Mem:* Am Soc Agron; Crop Sci Soc Am; Genetics Soc Am; Am Genetic Asn. *Res:* Cytogenetics of soybeans. *Mailing Add:* Plant Sci Res Div ARS Dept of Agron Iowa St Univ Ames IA 50011

PALMER, RICHARD ALAN, b Austin, Tex, Nov 13, 35; m 62; c 4. INORGANIC CHEMISTRY. *Educ:* Univ Tex, BS, 57; Univ Ill, MS, 62, PhD(inorg chem), 65. *Prof Exp:* NIH fel inorg chem, Copenhagen Univ, 65-66; asst prof, 66-71, assoc prof, 71-78, PROF INORG CHEM, DUKE UNIV, 78- *Mem:* Royal Soc Chem; Am Chem Soc. *Res:* Transition metal ion complexes; infrared, visible, ultraviolet, nuclear magnetic resonance, electron paramagnetic resonance spectroscopy; single crystal spectroscopy and x-ray diffraction; photoacoustic spectroscopy; complexes of crown ethers. *Mailing Add:* Dept Chem Duke Univ Durham NC 27706

PALMER, RICHARD CARL, b Walls, Miss, Nov 8, 31; m 53; c 3. RADIATION CHEMISTRY, RADIOLOGICAL PHYSICS. *Educ:* Memphis State Col, BS, 54, MA, 55; Vanderbilt Univ, PhD(chem), 58; Am Bd Radiol, dipl. *Prof Exp:* Lab asst physics, Memphis State Col, 52-54; Oak Ridge Inst Nuclear Studies fel health physics, Vanderbilt Univ, 54-55, res asst chem, 55-58; asst prof, Ga Inst Technol, 58-61; sr scientist, E G & G, Inc, 62, sci specialist nucleonics, 63-65 & accelerator physics, 66; assoc prof radiol & physics, 66-70, PROF ALLIED HEALTH PROFESSIONS, EMORY UNIV, 71-, ASSOC PROF RADIOL, 74- *Concurrent Pos:* Consult, E G & G, Inc, 67-69. *Mem:* AAAS; Am Chem Soc; Am Asn Univ Prof; Sigma Xi; Am Asn Physicists Med. *Res:* Radiochemistry; radiation effects; radiological health. *Mailing Add:* Dept of Radiol Emory Univ Sch of Med Atlanta GA 30322

PALMER, RICHARD CLAXTON, b Washington, DC, Oct 9, 22; m 56; c 2. ELECTRICAL ENGINEERING. *Educ:* Univ Va, BEE, 43. *Prof Exp:* Test engr, Gen Elec Co, NY, 43-44; process improv engr, Tenn Eastman Co, 44-46; develop engr, Remington Rand, Inc, Conn, 46; res engr, Allen B DuMont Labs, Inc, NJ, 46-60; MEM TECH STAFF, RCA LABS, 60- *Concurrent Pos:* Mem panel 12, Nat TV Systs Comt, 51-53. *Mem:* Inst Elec & Electronics Engrs. *Res:* Television cameras and systems; television display devices; high density recording systems. *Mailing Add:* David Sarnoff Res Ctr RCA Labs Princeton NJ 08540

PALMER, RICHARD EVERETT, b New York, NY, Apr 26, 44; m 71. PHYSICS. *Educ:* Mass Inst Technol, SB, 66; Princeton Univ, PhD(physics), 71. *Prof Exp:* MEM STAFF PHYSICS, SANDIA LABS, 71- *Mem:* Am Phys Soc. *Res:* Research and development of high power lasers for laser fusion. *Mailing Add:* Sandia Labs Orgn 400 PO Box 5800 Albuquerque NM 87185

PALMER, ROBERT GERALD, b Phillips, Wis, May 25, 36; m 57; c 3. SOIL MANAGEMENT & FERTILITY, CONSULTING. *Educ:* Univ Tenn, Knoxville, BS, 60, MS, 62; Iowa State Univ, PhD(soil mgt), 67. *Prof Exp:* Instr soils, Iowa State Univ, 64-66; asst prof soil mgt & exten specialist, Okla State Univ, 66-68; tech adv soils, Univ Tenn-India Agr Progs, 68-70; assoc prof, Western Ill Univ, 70-78, prof agr, 78-81; vpres & treas, 77-79, PRES, KEYAGR SERV, INC, MACOMB, 79- *Concurrent Pos:* Vis assoc prof, Fed Univ Santa Maria, Brazil with Southern Ill Univ & UN Food & Agr Orgn, 75-76. *Mem:* Am Soc Agron; Soil Sci Soc Am; Soil Conserv Soc Am; Sigma Xi. *Res:* Mine land reclamation; crop production. *Mailing Add:* 30 Steven Ct Macomb IL 61455

PALMER, ROBERT HOWARD, b Chicago, Ill, Nov 3, 31; m 60; c 2. INTERNAL MEDICINE, GASTROENTEROLOGY. *Educ:* Oberlin Col, AB, 53; Harvard Med Sch, MD, 57. *Prof Exp:* Intern, Pa Hosp, Philadelphia, 57-58; resident, 58-61, from instr to assoc prof med, Hosps & Clins, Univ Chicago, 69-73; adj prof & med dir, Ctr Prevention of Premature Arteriosclerosis, Rockefeller Univ, 73-79; PROF CLIN MED, COL PHYS & SURG, COLUMBIA UNIV, 79-; ATTEND PHYSICIAN, PRESBY HOSP, 78- *Concurrent Pos:* Nat Found fel, Karolinska Inst, Sweden, 62-63; Arthritis Found spec investr, Univ Chicago, 66-67; mem gen med A study sect, NIH, 69-73; mem gastroenterol merit rev bd, Vet Admin, 71-; adj prof, Med Sch, Cornell Univ, 73-78; attend physician, New York Hosp, 73-78. *Mem:* Am Asn Study Liver Dis; fel Am Col Physicians; Am Fedn Clin Res; Am Gastroenterol Asn; Am Soc Clin Invest. *Res:* Bile acid biochemistry and pharmacology; arteriosclerosis research; gallstone formation; hepatic metabolism. *Mailing Add:* Dept of Med 630 W 168th St New York NY 10032

PALMER, ROBERT LEWIS, b Portland, Ore, Nov 12, 39; m 68; c 2. SURFACE PHYSICS. *Educ:* San Diego State Univ, AB, 61. *Prof Exp:* Res assoc physics, Gen Atomic, San Diego, 61-72; SR PHYSICIST, IRT CORP, SAN DIEGO, 72- *Mem:* Am Phys Soc; Am Vacuum Soc; AAAS. *Res:* Molecular beam studies of physical and chemical interactions on single crystal surfaces. *Mailing Add:* IRT Corp PO Box 80817 San Diego CA 92138

PALMER, ROGER, b Albany, NY, Sept 23, 31; m 80. PHARMACOLOGY, MEDICINE. *Educ:* St Louis Univ, BS, 53; Univ Fla, MD, 60. *Prof Exp:* From intern to resident med, Johns Hopkins Hosp, 60-62; from instr to assoc prof pharmacol, Col Med, Univ Fla, 62-69; PROF PHARMACOL & CHIEF DIV CLIN PHARMACOL, UNIV MIAMI, 69-, CHMN DEPT PHARMACOL, 70- *Concurrent Pos:* NIH grant, 64-67 & 73-; Markle scholar acad med, 65- *Mem:* Am Soc Pharmacol & Exp Therapeut. *Res:* Cardiovascular pharmacology. *Mailing Add:* Univ Miami Dept Med PO Box 016760 Miami FL 33101

PALMER, RUFUS N(ELSON), b Bath, Maine, Mar 7, 02; m 31. ENGINEERING. *Educ:* Mass Inst Technol, SB, 25, ScD(ceramic eng), 38. *Prof Exp:* Res engr & plant engr, Exolon Co, NY & Can, 25-34; indust fel, Mellon Inst, 37-47; consult engr, 47-66; chief engr, Hall Industs, 66-72; RETIRED. *Mem:* AAAS; Am Chem Soc; Am Ceramic Soc. *Res:* Chemical and mechanical engineering; artificial abrasives and refractories; electromagnetic ore separators; ceramics, pearl button machine design. *Mailing Add:* 476 Broadmoor Ave Pittsburgh PA 15228

PALMER, RUPERT DEWITT, b Winston Co, Miss, Jan 28, 29; m 54; c 2. WEED SCIENCE. *Educ:* Miss State Univ, BS, 52, MS, 54; La State Univ, PhD(bot), 59. *Prof Exp:* Assoc prof weed sci, Agr Exp Sta, Miss State Univ, 54-66; exten agronomist weed control & assoc prof agron, 66-74, assoc prof weed sci, 74-81, PROF WEED SCI, TEX A&M UNIV, 80-, EXTEN WEED SPECIALIST, 74- *Mem:* Weed Sci Soc Am. *Mailing Add:* Dept Soil & Crop Sci Tex A&M Univ College Station TX 77843

PALMER, SUSAN ELAINE, geology, organic geochemistry, see previous edition

PALMER, SUSHMA MAHYERA, b Sirhind, India, Jan 13, 44; US citizen; m 67. NUTRITIONAL BIOCHEMISTRY, CLINICAL NUTRITION. *Educ:* Univ Delhi, BSc, 63, MS, 65; Univ Belgrade, DSc, 77. *Prof Exp:* Asst lectr advan nutrit, Lady Irwin Col, Univ Delhi, 65-66; therapeut dietitian, Washington Hosp Ctr, 66-67; res nutritionist biochem, George Hyman Res Found, George Washington Univ, 68; dir nutrit & asst prof pediat, Sch Med, Georgetown Univ, 71-75; fel nutrit & biochem, Inst Mother & Child Health, Univ Belgrade, 75-78; staff scientist nutrit & biochem, 78-79, PROJ DIR, NAT ACAD SCI, 79- *Concurrent Pos:* Consult, NVa Child Develop Ctr, 71-75; instr nutrit, Univ Md, 72-75; grant, Am Inst Nutrit, 78; mem, Prog Adv Comt, Nat Inst Dent Res, NIH, 79- *Mem:* Soc Nutrit Educ; Am Dietetic Asn; Am Inst Nutrit; NY Acad Sci; AAAS. *Res:* Vitamin A, RBP and immune mechanism; subclinical zinc deficiency and growth; pediatric nutrition and developmental disorders; feeding problems in children; dietary factors in etiology and prevention of cancer. *Mailing Add:* Nat Acad Sci 2101 Constitution Ave NW Washington DC 20418

PALMER, THEODORE W, b Boston, Mass, Oct 19, 35; m 61; c 3. MATHEMATICS. *Educ:* Johns Hopkins Univ, BS & MA, 58; Harvard Univ, AM, 59, PhD(math), 66. *Prof Exp:* Instr math, Tufts Univ, 65-66; vis asst prof, Math Res Ctr, Univ Wis, 66-67; from asst prof to assoc prof, Univ Kans, 67-70; assoc prof, 70-75, PROF MATH, UNIV ORE, 75-, HEAD DEPT, 80- *Concurrent Pos:* Vis assoc prof, Univ Calif, Berkeley, 76 & 77. *Mem:* AAAS; Am Math Soc; Math Asn Am; Sigma Xi. *Res:* Banach algebras; linear operator theory. *Mailing Add:* Dept of Math Univ of Ore Eugene OR 97403

PALMER, THOMAS ADOLPH, b Salt Lake City, Utah, Oct 12, 35; c 2. ANALYTICAL CHEMISTRY. *Educ:* Univ Santa Clara, BS, 57; Iowa State Univ, PhD(anal chem), 61. *Prof Exp:* Sr res analyst, Olin Mathieson Chem Corp, 61-62; sr chemist, Lockheed Propulsion Co, 62-66; staff res chemist, 66-80, SR STAFF RES CHEM, KAISER ALUMINUM & CHEM CORP, 80- *Mem:* Am Chem Soc; Sigma Xi. *Res:* Absorption spectroscopy. *Mailing Add:* Kaiser Aluminum & Chem Corp PO Box 877 Pleasanton CA 94566

PALMER, TIMOTHY TROW, b Evanston, Ill, Mar 22, 38; m 62; c 3. MEDICAL PARASITOLOGY, OCCUPATIONAL HEALTH. *Educ:* Carleton Col, BA, 60; Univ Minn, MS, 64, PhD(zool), 74; Univ Southern Calif, MS, 81. *Prof Exp:* RES PARASITOLOGIST, NAVAL MED RES INST, US NAVY, 64-, RES PARASITOLOGIST, OCCUP HEALTH OFF, 80-, HEAD SAFETY PROG, 81- *Concurrent Pos:* adj asst prof preventive med & biomet, Uniformed Serv Univ Health Sci, 80- *Mem:* Am Soc Trop Med & Hyg; Am Soc Parasitologists; Am Inst Biol Sci; Soc Protozoologists; Wildlife Dis Asn. *Res:* Malaria vaccine development, using sporozoite stage as antigen source, and serologic assessment of recipient's immune status; avian hematozoa and mammalian trypanosomes; lab safety. *Mailing Add:* Naval Med Res Inst Bethesda MD 20814

PALMER, WILLIAM FRANKLIN, b New York, NY, Mar 5, 37; m 63; c 3. PHYSICS. *Educ:* Harvard Univ, AB, 58; Johns Hopkins Univ, PhD(physics), 67. *Prof Exp:* Res assoc physics, Argonne Nat Lab, 67-69; from asst prof to assoc prof, 69-79, PROF PHYSICS, OHIO STATE UNIV, 79- *Mem:* Am Phys Soc. *Res:* High energy physics theory. *Mailing Add:* Dept of Physics Ohio State Univ Columbus OH 43210

PALMER, WINIFRED G, b Brooklyn, NY. BIOCHEMISTRY. *Educ:* Brooklyn Col, BS, 62; Univ Conn, PhD(biochem), 67. *Prof Exp:* Res assoc biochem, Oak Ridge Nat Lab, 67-72; res scientist immunochem, Frederick Cancer Res Ctr, 72-78; sr biologist, Enviro Control, 78-80; PRIN SCIENTIST, TRACOR JITCO, 81- *Mem:* Reticuloendothelial Soc; AAAS; Sigma Xi; Soc Toxicol. *Res:* Co-carcinogenesis and lung cancer; chemical carcinogenesis; industrial toxicology. *Mailing Add:* Tracor Jitco 1776 E Jefferson St Rockville MD 20852

PALMERE, RAYMOND M, b Irvington, NJ, Aug 20, 25; m 49; c 12. AGRICULTURAL CHEMISTRY. *Educ:* Rutgers Univ, BA, 55; Seton Hall Univ, MS, 63, PhD(chem), 66. *Prof Exp:* Asst, Squibb Inst Med Res, 55-59, chemist, 59-63, res chemist, 63-65; res chemist, 65-67, SR RES CHEMIST, FMC CORP, PRINCETON, 67- *Mem:* Am Chem Soc. *Res:* Natural products; synthesis of yohimbine alkaloids, 9-alpha-bromo-11-keto and 11, 12 oxygenated progesterones; enzymatic hydroxylations of beta diketones; insect physiology; juvenile hormone. *Mailing Add:* Chem Res & Develop FMC Corp PO Box 8 Princeton NJ 08540

PALMES, EDWARD DANNELLY, b Mobile, Ala, July 5, 16; m 43; c 3. BIOCHEMISTRY. *Educ:* Springhill Col, BS, 38; Georgetown Univ, MS, 39, PhD(biochem), 47. *Prof Exp:* Jr & asst chemist, NIH, 41-44; biochemist, Med Dept, Field Res Lab, 47-48; from asst prof to assoc prof, 48-60, PROF ENVIRON MED, MED CTR, NY UNIV, 60- *Mem:* AAAS; Am Chem Soc; Am Physiol Soc; Am Indust Hyg Asn; Soc Toxicol. *Res:* Toxicology. *Mailing Add:* Inst Environ Med NY Univ Med Ctr New York NY 10016

PALMIERI, JOSEPH NICHOLAS, b Providence, RI, Aug 24, 32; m 60; c 2. NUCLEAR PHYSICS. *Educ:* Brown Univ, ScB, 54; Harvard Univ, AM, 55, PhD, 59. *Prof Exp:* Instr physics, Harvard Univ, 58-61; from asst prof to assoc prof, 61-67, PROF PHYSICS, OBERLIN COL, 67- *Concurrent Pos:* NSF sci fac fel, 71-72. *Mem:* Am Phys Soc; Am Asn Physics Teachers; Am Inst Physics. *Res:* Nucleon scattering. *Mailing Add:* Dept of Physics Oberlin Col Oberlin OH 44074

PALMISANO, PAUL ANTHONY, b Cincinnati, Ohio, Dec 30, 29. PEDIATRICS, PHARMACOLOGY. *Educ:* Xavier Univ, Ohio, BS, 52; Univ Cincinnati, MD, 56; Am Bd Pediat, dipl, 62; Univ Calif, Berkeley, MPH, 79. *Prof Exp:* Instr pediat, Univ Cincinnati, 61-62; med officer, Food & Drug Admin, 63-66; asst prof pharmacol, 67-68, from asst prof to assoc prof, 68-73, asst dean, Sch Med, 74-80, PROF PEDIAT, UNIV ALA, BIRMINGHAM, 73-, ASSOC DEAN, SCH MED, 80- *Concurrent Pos:* Fel clin pharmacol, Univ Ala, Birmingham, 66-67; mem panel pediat scope subcomt, US Pharmacopoeia, 66- *Mem:* Am Acad Pediat; Am Pub Health Asn. *Res:* Placental transfer of drugs, salicylate toxicology; plumbism; poison control; accident prevention. *Mailing Add:* Dept of Pediat Univ of Ala Med Ctr Birmingham AL 35233

PALMORE, JULIAN IVANHOE, III, b Baltimore, Md, Sept 26, 38; m 67; c 2. MATHEMATICS, CELESTIAL MECHANICS. *Educ:* Cornell Univ, BEP, 61; Univ Ala, MA, 64; Princeton Univ, MSE, 65; Yale Univ, MS, 66, PhD(astron), 67; Univ Calif, Berkeley, PhD(math), 73. *Prof Exp:* Res assoc, Ctr Control Sci, Univ Minn, 67-68; vis fel math, Princeton Univ, 68-69; actg instr & lectr, Univ Calif, Berkeley, 70-73; instr, Mass Inst Technol, 73-75; vis asst prof, Univ Mich, Ann Arbor, 75-77; asst prof, 77-80, ASSOC PROF MATH, UNIV ILL, URBANA, 80- *Concurrent Pos:* Lilly fel, Mass Inst Technol, 74-75; NSF grants, 74-83, prin investr, 78-; Ctr Advan Study fel, Univ Ill, 79; fac judge, Lilly open fels, 79-83. *Mem:* Asn Math Physics; Am Math Soc; fel Royal Astron Soc. *Res:* Algebraic topology and global analysis; the n-body problem; dynamical systems and celestial mechanics; mathematical physics and the study of the motion of vortices; mechanics of spaceflight; probability; differential equations. *Mailing Add:* Dept Math Univ Ill 1409 W Green St Urbana IL 61801

PALMORE, WILLIAM P, b Beatrice, Ala, Dec 13, 34; m 65; c 2. VETERINARY PHYSIOLOGY. *Educ:* Auburn Univ, DVM, 59, MS, 64; Yale Univ, PhD(physiol), 67. *Prof Exp:* NIH res fel, 61-66; Am Vet Med Asn res fel, 66-67; res assoc path, Sch Med, Yale Univ, 67-68; from asst prof to assoc prof physiol, Sch Vet Med, Univ Mo-Columbia, 68-74; ASSOC PROF PHYSIOL, COL VET MED, UNIV FLA, 74- *Mem:* AAAS; Am Vet Med Asn. *Res:* Adrenocortical research. *Mailing Add:* Col of Vet Med Univ of Fla Gainesville FL 32601

PALMOUR, HAYNE, III, b Gainesville, Ga, Feb 27, 25; m 54; c 3. CERAMIC ENGINEERING. *Educ:* Ga Inst Technol, BCerE, 48, MS, 50; NC State Univ, PhD(ceramic eng), 61. *Prof Exp:* Res engr, US Bur Mines, 50-51; mgt trainee, US Dept Interior, 51-52; admin analyst, Nat Capital Parks, US Park Serv, 52-53; from res engr to sr res engr, Am Lava Corp, Tenn, 53-57; instr ceramic eng, 57-58, res engr, 58-61, res assoc prof ceramic eng, 61-65, res prof ceramic engr, 65-81, PROF CERAMIC ENG, NC STATE UNIV, 81- *Concurrent Pos:* Consult, Hygrodynamics, Inc, 61-63, US Air Force, 62-64, Am Instrument Co, Inc, 63-67 & W R Grace & Co, 68-75, Babcock & Wilcox Co, 72-75, 81-, US Army, 76-77, EG&G Idaho Corp, 81-; mem adv comt, Metals & Ceramics Div, Oak Ridge Nat Lab, 75-77, chmn, 77; mem comt dynamic compaction of metal & ceramic powders, Nat Mat Adv Bd, Nat Acad Sci, 80- *Honors & Awards:* Res Award, Sigma Xi, 61. *Mem:* Fel Am Ceramic Soc; Nat Inst Ceramic Engrs. *Res:* Properties and applications of polycrystalline ceramics, glass; ceramic raw materials and processing; densification dynamics and kinetics, rate controlled sintering; energy conservation; microstructural characterization; failure analysis; dynamic compaction of powders, densification of shock conditioned powders; thermal energy storage. *Mailing Add:* Eng Res Serv Div NC State Univ 2140 Burlington Eng Labs Raleigh NC 27650

PALMQUIST, DONALD LEONARD, b Silverton, Ore, July 2, 36; m 62; c 2. ANIMAL NUTRITION. *Educ:* Ore State Col, BS, 58; Univ Calif, Davis, PhD(nutrit), 65. *Prof Exp:* Res assoc dairy sci, Univ Ill, Urbana, 65-67; asst prof, 67-73, ASSOC PROF DAIRY SCI, OHIO AGR RES & DEVELOP CTR & OHIO STATE UNIV, 73- *Concurrent Pos:* Assoc res biochemist, Radioisotope Res Div, Vet Admin, Wadsworth Vet Admin Hosp, Los Angeles, 73-74. *Mem:* Am Soc Animal Sci; Am Oil Chemists Soc; Am Dairy Sci Asn; Am Inst Nutrit. *Res:* Lipid metabolism of the dairy cow; selenium nutrition of humans and domestic animals; intermediary metabolism of rumen microorganisms; essential fatty acid metabolism; lipid kinetics. *Mailing Add:* Dept of Dairy Sci Ohio Agr Res & Develop Ctr Wooster OH 44691

PALMQUIST, JOHN CHARLES, b Omaha, Nebr, Sept 6, 34; m 56; c 3. GEOLOGY. *Educ:* Augustana Col, AB, 56; Univ Iowa, MS, 58, PhD(geol), 61. *Prof Exp:* Asst geol, Univ Iowa, 56-61; geologist, Calif Co, 61-62; from asst prof to assoc prof geol, Monmouth Col, Ill, 62-68; ASSOC GEOL, LAWRENCE UNIV, 68- *Concurrent Pos:* consult petroleum explor, 79- *Mem:* Fel Geol Soc Am; Nat Asn Geol Teachers; Am Asn Petrol Geologists. *Res:* Basement influence on later tectonics; structural analysis of metamorphic tectonites; metamorphic petrology; structural geology. *Mailing Add:* Dept of Geol Lawrence Univ Appleton WI 54911

PALMQUIST, ROBERT CLARENCE, b Chicago, Ill, Aug 8, 38; m 59; c 2. GEOMORPHOLOGY, ENVIRONMENTAL GEOLOGY. *Educ:* Augustana Col, BA, 60; Univ Wis-Madison, PhD(geol), 65. *Prof Exp:* Asst prof, 65-69, ASSOC PROF GEOL, IOWA STATE UNIV, 69- *Mem:* Geol Soc Am; AAAS; Sigma Xi. *Res:* Environmental and temporal influences in the development of mass movements; application of geological data to computerized land use analysis; relationship between depositional landforms and glacial processes. *Mailing Add:* Dept of Earth Sci Iowa State Univ Ames IA 50011

PALMS, JOHN MICHAEL, b Rijswijk, Neth, June 6, 35; US citizen; m 58; c 3. NUCLEAR PHYSICS, APPLIED PHYSICS. *Educ:* The Citadel, BS, 58; Emory Univ, MS, 59; Univ NMex, PhD(physics), 66. *Hon Degrees:* DSc, The Citadel, 80. *Prof Exp:* Instr physics, US Air Force Acad, 61-62 & Univ NMex, 62-63; staff mem nuclear physics, Los Alamos Sci Lab, 63-66, mem grad thesis prog, 64-66; chmn dept, 69-74, dean, Emory Col, 74-79, FAC MEM PHYSICS, EMORY UNIV, 66-, VPRES ARTS & SCI, 79- *Concurrent Pos:* Staff mem nuclear physics, Sandia Corp, NMex, 62-63; mem semiconductor detector panel, Nat Res Coun, 65-; consult var nuclear industs and hosps. *Mem:* AAAS; Fedn Am Scientists; Am Nuclear Soc; Inst Elec & Electronics Engrs; Soc Nuclear Med. *Res:* Neutron inelastic scattering; coulomb excitation; Ge-gamma-ray detectors; semiconductor detectors; medical and radio-environmental physics; x-ray physics, radio-ecology and radiation dose physics. *Mailing Add:* Emory Col Emory Univ Atlanta GA 30322

PALOCHAK, MURIEL E, b Newark, NJ, Dec 5, 19; m 62. INDUSTRIAL MICROBIOLOGY. *Educ:* Univ Chicago, BS, 39; Univ Ill, MS, 40. *Prof Exp:* Bacteriologist, W F Straub & Co, 40-41 & Continental Can Co, 41-43; head bact lab, Pepsodent Div, Lever Bros Co, 43-51; dir microbiol sect labs, AMA, 51-55; bacteriologist, Foster D Snell Co, 55-56, Lehn & Fink Prod Corp, 56-62 & Warner-Lambert Pharmaceut Co, 62-64; mgr microbiol, West Chem Prod Inc, Long Island City, NY, 65-80; CONSULT MICROBIOL, 80- *Mem:* Am Soc Microbiol; Soc Indust Microbiol. *Res:* Pharmaceuticals; good manufacturing practices; lactobacilli; antiseptics; disinfection and sterilization; antibiotics assay. *Mailing Add:* 315 W Grand St 7-H Elizabeth NJ 07202

PALOCZ, ISTVAN, b Budapest, Hungary, Sept 24, 20; US citizen; m 53; c 2. ELECTROPHYSICS. *Educ:* Budapest Tech Univ, dipl eng, 45, docent, 54; Polytech Inst Brooklyn, PhD(electrophys), 62. *Prof Exp:* Res staff mem, Tungsram Univ, Budapest, 45-50; asst prof elec eng & appl math, Budapest Tech Univ, 50-54, assoc prof, 54-56; res staff mem, Watson Lab, Columbia Univ, 57-61 & Res Ctr, Int Bus Mach Corp, 61-66; assoc prof elec eng, 65-67, PROF ELECTROPHYS, DEPT ELEC ENG & ELECTROPHYS, POLYTECH INST NEW YORK, 67- *Concurrent Pos:* Consult, Tungsram Univ, Budapest, 50-56, Gen Precision Inc, 66 & Comput Sci Inc, 67-68. *Honors & Awards:* Hungarian Nat Award for Excellent Teaching. *Mem:* Sr mem Inst Elec & Electronics Engrs. *Res:* Applied mathematics; wave propagation; field theory. *Mailing Add:* Dept of Elec Eng & Electrophys Polytech Inst of NY 333 Jay St Brooklyn NY 11201

PALOHEIMO, JYRI ERKKI, mathematical biology, see previous edition

PALOPOLI, FRANK PATRICK, b Pittsburgh, Pa, Feb 19, 22; m 44; c 5. ORGANIC CHEMISTRY, MEDICINAL CHEMISTRY. *Educ:* Duquesne Univ, BS, 43, MS, 48. *Prof Exp:* Res chemist, Wm S Merrell Co Div, 50-63, dir chem res, Nat Drug Co Div, 63-70, head chem develop, Res Ctr Div, Richardson-Merrell, Inc, 70-81, HEAD CHEM DEVELOP, MERRELL-DOW PHARMACEUT, INC, 81- *Mem:* Am Chem Soc. *Res:* Chemistry of synthetic drugs; medicinal agents; antiinflammatory, fertility-sterility, cardiovascular and hypocholesteremic drugs. *Mailing Add:* Merrell-Dow Pharmaceut Inc 2110 E Galbraith Rd Cincinnati OH 45215

PALOTAY, JAMES LAJOS, b Los Angeles, Calif, Oct 3, 22; m 42; c 2. COMPARATIVE PATHOLOGY. *Educ:* Kans State Univ, DVM, 50; Colo State Univ, MS, 58; Am Col Vet Path, dipl, 59. *Prof Exp:* Asst prof path & bact, Colo State Univ, 50-51; res vet, Monfort Feed Lots, Colo, 51-55; asst prof path, Wash State Univ, 55-63; sr res scientist, Biol Lab, Gen Elec Co, 63-64; mgr comp toxicol sect, Pac Northwest Labs, Battelle Mem Inst, 64-68; sci dir, Ore Zool Ctr, 68-69; ASSOC SCIENTIST, ORE REGIONAL PRIMATE RES CTR, 69- *Mem:* AAAS; Am Vet Med Asn; Am Col Vet Path; Int Acad Path. *Mailing Add:* Ore Regional Primate Res Ctr 505 NW 185th St Beaverton OR 97006

PALOYAN, EDWARD, b Paris, France, Mar 19, 32; US citizen; m; c 4. SURGERY. *Educ:* Univ Chicago, MD, 56; Am Bd Surg, dipl, 65. *Prof Exp:* Intern, Univ Hosp, Univ Chicago, 56-57, jr asst resident & res asst, 57-58 & 60-61, sr asst resident, 61-62, resident, Univ Hosps & Clins, 62-63, instr & chief resident, 64-65, from asst prof to assoc prof, 64-73, secy dept surg, 70-73; PROF SURG, STRITCH SCH MED, LOYOLA UNIV CHICAGO, 73-; ASSOC CHIEF OF STAFF FOR RES, VET ADMIN HOSP, HINES, 73- *Concurrent Pos:* Am Diabetes Asn fel, Univ Chicago Hosps & Clins, 62-63; mem bd dirs, Chicago Inst Med, 74. *Mem:* Fel Am Diabetes Asn; Am Fedn Clin Res; fel Am Col Surg; Soc Univ Surg; Am Surg Asn. *Mailing Add:* Dept of Surg Stritch Sch of Med Loyola Univ of Chicago Maywood IL 60153

PALS, DONALD THEODORE, b Cicero, Ill, Mar 29, 34; m 58; c 2. PHARMACOLOGY. *Educ:* Calvin Col, AB, 56; Univ Ill, MS, 60, PhD(physiol), 63. *Prof Exp:* Sr res pharmacologist, Norwich Pharmacal Co, 63-68, res assoc, 68-74; RES ASSOC, UPJOHN CO, 74- *Mem:* Am Soc Pharmacol & Exp Therapeut. *Res:* Cardiovascular pharmacology; mechanism of action and development of antihypertensive drugs. *Mailing Add:* Cardiovasc Dis Res Div Upjohn Co Kalamazoo MI 49001

PALSER, BARBARA FRANCES, b Worcester, Mass, June 2, 16. BOTANY. *Educ:* Mt Holyoke Col, AB, 38, AM, 40; Univ Chicago, PhD(bot), 42. *Hon Degrees:* DSc, Mount Holyoke Col, 78. *Prof Exp:* From instr to prof bot, Univ Chicago, 42-65, examr biol sci, 45-46 & Div Biol Sequence, 47-49; assoc prof, 65-66, dir grad prog in bot, 72-79, PROF BOT, RUTGERS UNIV, NEW BRUNSWICK, 66- *Concurrent Pos:* Bot adv, Encycl Britannica, 57-59; ed, Bot Gazette, 59-65; vis prof, Duke Univ, 62; Erskine fel, Univ Canterbury, 69. *Mem:* AAAS; Bot Soc Am (secy, 70-74, vpres, 75, pres, 76); Torrey Bot Club (pres, 68); Int Soc Plant Morphol; Am Inst Biol Sci. *Res:* Anatomy and morphology of Pteridophytes; histological responses to growth-regulating substances; floral morphology and anatomy of angiosperms, particularly Ericales; experimental anatomy. *Mailing Add:* Dept of Bot Nelson Biol Lab Rutgers Univ New Brunswick NJ 08903

PALTER, N(ORMAN) H(OWARD), b Brooklyn, NY, May 12, 21; m 44; c 1. ENGINEERING. *Educ:* City Col New York, BEE, 42. *Prof Exp:* Develop engr, Hazeltine Electronics Corp, 45-48; proj engr, Sperry Gyroscope Co Div, 48-50, sr proj engr, 50-52, eng dept head, 52-62, mgr UK Polaris navig prog, 62-64, avionics systs prog mgr, 64-66, chief engr, Info & Commun Div, 66-67, mgr civil & indust systs, Sperry Syst Mgt Div, 68-72, mgr traffic & transp syst, 72-75, MGR OCEAN & MIL SYST, SPERRY SYST MGT DIV, SPERRY RAND CORP, 75- *Mem:* Sr mem Inst Elec & Electronics Engrs. *Res:* Design and development of radar, missiles, countermeasures, navigation and avionics systems, vehicular traffic systems, simulation systems; ship positioning systems. *Mailing Add:* Sperry Systs Mgt Sperry Corp Marcus Ave & Lakeville Rd Great Neck NY 11020

PALUBINSKAS, ALPHONSE J, b Lowell, Mass, Mar 24, 22; m 48; c 2. RADIOLOGY. *Educ:* Oberlin Col, BA, 48; Harvard Med Sch, MD, 52. *Prof Exp:* Intern med, Henry Ford Hosp, Detroit, 52-53; resident radiol, Peter Bent Brigham Hosp, Boston, 53-56, assoc radiologist, 56-57; from asst prof to assoc prof radiol, 59-69, PROF RADIOL, SCH MED, UNIV CALIF, SAN FRANCISCO, 69-, ASSOC RADIOLOGIST, 59- *Concurrent Pos:* Picker fel radiol res, Univ Col Hosp, London, Nat Hosp Nerv Dis, 57-58 & Karolinska Hosp Stockholm, 58-59; Commonwealth fel, 67. *Res:* Clinical diagnostic radiology. *Mailing Add:* Dept of Radiol Univ of Calif Med Ctr San Francisco CA 94143

PALUBINSKAS, FELIX STANLEY, b Lowell, Mass, Jan 16, 20; m 46; c 1. MEDICINE, OPTICS. *Educ:* Mass Inst Technol, BS, 44; Harvard Univ, AM, 47; Iowa State Univ, PhD(physics), 52; Tufts Univ, MD, 60. *Prof Exp:* Asst physics, Mass Inst Technol, 40-42 & Spectros Lab, 42-43, physicist, Confidential Instrument Develop Lab, 44-46; instr high sch, Mass, 46-47; instr physics, Iowa State Univ, 47-50; asst, Univ Ill, 50-52; physicist, Gen Elec Co, 52-53; prof electronic eng & head dept, Lowell Tech Inst, 53-56; intern, USPHS Hosp, Baltimore, Md, 60-61; staff to tech dir, Mitre Corp, Bedford, 61-68; PROF PHYSICS, BRIDGEWATER STATE COL, 68- *Concurrent Pos:* Consult biotechnol, Sch Aerospace Med, US Air Force, 79. *Mem:* AAAS; Am Phys Soc; Optical Soc Am; Aerospace Med Soc; Am Asn Physics Teachers. *Res:* Teaching of medicine, and physics. *Mailing Add:* Dept of Physics Bridgewater State Col Bridgewater MA 02324

PALUCH, ILGA RIEKSTINS, cloud physics, see previous edition

PALUMBO, FRANCIS XAVIER BERNARD, b Scranton, Pa, June 19, 45; m 71; c 1. HEALTH CARE ADMINISTRATION, PHARMACY. *Educ:* Med Col SC, BS, 68; Univ Miss, MS, 73, PhD(health care admin), 74. *Prof Exp:* Pharmacist, US Army Health Clin, Pentagon, 69-71 & Dart Drug Corp, 69-71; teaching & res asst, Pharmaceut & Pharm Admin, Sch Pharm, Univ Miss, 71-74; actg chmn, Dept Pharm Admin, 78-79, asst prof pharm admin, 74-79, ASSOC PROF PHARM PRAC & ADMIN SCI, SCH PHARM, UNIV MD, 79- *Concurrent Pos:* Prin investr, Hoffmann-La Roche grant, 75-77 & Nat Ctr Health Serv res grant, 79-82. *Mem:* Am Asn Col Pharm. *Res:* Social and economic aspects of health, particularly appropriate drug use by the elderly in long-term care institutions; and cost containment in third party payment programs. *Mailing Add:* Sch of Pharm 636 W Lombard St Baltimore MD 21201

PALUMBO, SAMUEL ANTHONY, b Oak Park, Ill, June 4, 39; m 65; c 2. MICROBIOLOGY, FOOD SCIENCE. *Educ:* Loyola Univ, Ill, BS, 61; Univ Ill, Urbana, MS, 63, PhD(food sci), 67. *Prof Exp:* res microbiologist, Meat Lab, Eastern Mkt Nutrit Res Div, 67-80, RES MICROBIOLOGIST, FOOD SAFETY LAB, EASTERN REGIONAL RES CTR, AGR RES SERV, USDA, 80- *Mem:* Am Soc Microbiol; Inst Food Technologists; Am Meat Sci Asn. *Res:* Food microbiology; food safety. *Mailing Add:* 8105 Douglas Rd Wyndmoor Philadelphia PA 19118

PALUSAMY, SAM SUBBU, b Tamil Nadu, India, Nov 14, 39; m 65; c 1. SOLID MECHANICS, NUCLEAR ENGINEERING. *Educ:* Univ Madras, BE, 63; Univ Waterloo, MASc, 66, PhD(solid mech), 70. *Prof Exp:* Jr engr, Tamil Nadu Pub Works Dept, India, 63; lectr civil eng, Annamalai Univ, 63-65; res asst solid mech, Univ Waterloo, 65-69, fel, 70; vis asst prof civil eng, Sir George Williams Univ, 70-71, sr res assoc syst bldg, 71-72; sr engr, 72-77, prin engr, 77-80, FEL ENGR, WESTINGHOUSE NUCLEAR ENERGY SYST, 80- *Concurrent Pos:* Task group chmn, Pressure Vessel Res Comt, 76-; chmn, Working Group Boker Code, Am Soc Mech Engrs. *Mem:* Assoc Am Soc Mech Engrs. *Res:* Pressure vessels; plastic analysis; model testing; system building, structural optimization; safety analysis; fracture mechanics; pipe whip; reactor vessel. *Mailing Add:* Nuclear Technol Div Westinghouse Nuclear Energy Syst Pittsburgh PA 15230

PAMER, TREVA LOUISE, b Doylestown, Ohio, Sept 22, 38; m 78. BIOCHEMISTRY. *Educ:* Kent State Univ, BS, 60; City Col New York, MA, 63; New York Med Col, PhD(biochem), 69. *Prof Exp:* Chemist, Klett Mfg Co, 60-63; res technologist anal chem, Chas Pfizer & Co, Inc, 63-64; res assoc gastroenterol, New York Med Col, 64-71; lectr org chem, Mercy Col, 67-70; from asst prof to assoc prof, 68-80, PROF CHEM, JERSEY CITY STATE COL, 80- *Mem:* AAAS; Am Chem Soc; Int Inst Conserv Hist & Artistic Works; Am Soc Testing & Mat. *Res:* Sulfated glycoproteins; composition of gastric secretion as related to gastric disorders; chemistry of art materials; conservation of art objects. *Mailing Add:* Dept Chem Jersey City State Col Jersey City NJ 07305

PAMIDI, PRABHAKAR RAMARAO, b Bangalore, India, Feb 18, 42; m 74; c 1. STRUCTURAL ANALYSIS, MECHANISMS & KINEMATICS. *Educ:* Univ Mysore, BE, 63; Indian Inst Sci, Bangalore, ME, 65; Okla State Univ, PhD(mech eng), 70. *Prof Exp:* Scientist, Cent Mech Eng Res Inst, Durgapur, India, 65-66; engr, Am Bur Shipping, 70-74; SR PRIN ENGR, COMPUT SCI CORP, 74- *Mem:* Am Soc Mech Engrs. *Res:* Structural analysis using finite element techniques; applied mechanics; mechanisms and kinematics; vibrations; dynamics; engineering mechanics. *Mailing Add:* Syst Sci Div Comput Sci Corp 8728 Colesville Rd Silver Spring MD 20910

PAMNANI, MOTILAL BHAGWANDAS, b Rohri, Pakistan, Oct 5, 33; m 70; c 1. PHYSIOLOGY, CARDIOVASCULAR DISEASES. *Educ:* Univ Bombay, MBBS (MD), 57, MS, 67; Mich State Univ, PhD(physiol), 75. *Prof Exp:* Resident med, G T Hosp & Infectious Dis Hosp, India, 57-58; lectr physiol, M P Shah Med Col, 58-61; lectr, Grant Med Col, India, 61-63, asst prof, 63-71; fel, Mich State Univ, 71-74, asst prof physiol, 75-76; asst prof, 76-80, ASSOC PROF PHYSIOL, UNIFORMED SERV UNIV HEALTH SCI, BETHESDA, 80-, ASST PROF MED, 80- *Concurrent Pos:* Grant in aid res, Mich Heart Asn, 76. *Mem:* Am Physiol Soc; Soc Exp Biol & Med; Am Fedn Clin Res. *Res:* Hypertension; studying role of veins, changes in vessel wall composition, membrane sodium potassium pump activity and vasoactive hormones in experimental and essential hypertension. *Mailing Add:* Dept of Physiol Col of Human Med 4301 Jones Bridge Rd Bethesda MD 20014

PAMPE, WILLIAM R, b Parkersburg, Ill, Dec 5, 23; m 49; c 2. GEOLOGY, PALEONTOLOGY. *Educ:* Univ Ill, AB, 47, MS, 48; Univ Nebr, PhD(geol), 66. *Prof Exp:* Explor geologist, Pure Oil Co, 48-60; from asst prof to assoc prof, 66-78, PROF GEOL, LAMAR UNIV, 78- *Mem:* AAAS; Sigma Xi; Nat Asn Geol Teachers; Paleont Soc. *Res:* Detailed studies of invertebrate fossils especially on brachiopods. *Mailing Add:* Dept of Geol Lamar Univ Beaumont TX 77710

PAN, BINGHAM Y(ING) K(UEI), b China, Feb 11, 23; m 49; c 2. CHEMICAL ENGINEERING. *Educ:* Ord Eng Col, China, BS, 47; Va Polytech Inst, MS, 56, PhD(chem eng), 59. *Prof Exp:* Engr, 23rd Arsenal, China, 47-49; instr chem eng, Ord Sch & Hualien Eng Inst, 49-52; group leader ord design & res, Ord Serv, 52-55; teaching asst & fel instrumentation & unit opers, Va Polytech Inst, 55-59; res engr, Monsanto Co, 59-60, sr res engr, 61-65, sr process engr, 65-66, specialist, 66-74; group head, Occidental Res Corp, 74-80; MEM STAFF, C F BRAUN & CO, 80- *Mem:* Am Chem Soc; Am Inst Chem Engrs. *Res:* Thermodynamics; kinetics; reactor design and process optimization. *Mailing Add:* C F Braun & Co 1000 S Fremont Ave Alhambra CA 91802

PAN, CHUEN YONG, b Miao-li, Taiwan, Feb 6, 40; Can citizen; m 66; c 2. CHEMICAL ENGINEERING, PHYSICAL CHEMISTRY. *Educ:* Nat Taiwan Univ, BSc, 62; Univ Ottawa, MSc, 66; Univ Toronto, PhD(chem eng), 70. *Prof Exp:* RES ENGR, RES COUN ALTA, 70- *Mem:* Chem Inst Can; Can Soc Chem Eng. *Res:* Physical separation techniques; adsorption; permeation; mass transfer. *Mailing Add:* Res Coun Alta 11315-87th Ave Edmonton AB T6G 2C2 Can

PAN, CODA H T, b Shanghai, China, Feb 10, 29; US citizen; m 51; c 2. MECHANICAL ENGINEERING, APPLIED MATHEMATICS. *Educ:* Ill Inst Technol, BS, 50; Rensselaer Polytech Inst, MS, 58, PhD(aeronaut eng, astronaut), 61. *Prof Exp:* Stress analyst combustion eng, Superheater Co, 50; test engr, Gen Elec Co, 50-51, design engr, Meter Instrument Lab, 51-52, rotating assignments, Adv Eng Prog, 52-54, develop engr, Gas Turbine Dept, 54-58, supvr adv eng prog, 58-61, fluid mech engr, 61; mgr res, Mech Technol Inc, 61-70, assoc dir res & technol, 70-73; tech dir, Shaker Res Corp, 73-81; PROF MECH ENGRS, COLOMBIA UNIV, 81- *Concurrent Pos:* Adj prof, Rensselaer Polytech Inst, 61-65, 71-; consult, Army Res Off, 70-74; vis prof, Royal Tech Univ Denmark, 71; NIH spec fel microrheology of erythrocytes, Columbia Univ, 71-72; prin investr, Spacelab I, NASA, 78-; mem coun thrombosis, Am Heart Asn. *Honors & Awards:* Indust Res IR-100 Award, 67. *Mem:* Fel Am Soc Mech Engrs; Am Phys Soc; fel Am Soc Lubrication Engrs. *Res:* Gas lubrication; fluid film bearings; rotor dynamics; friction excited vibrations; elastohydrodynamics; process fluid lubrication, physics of fluids; mechanics and rheology of erythrocytes; hemodynamics; rheology. *Mailing Add:* 17 Alpine Dr Latham NY 12110

PAN, HUO PING, b Foochow, China, Feb 13, 21; US citizen; m 55; c 1. FOOD SCIENCE, BIOCHEMICAL ENGINEERING. *Educ:* Nat Southwest Assoc Univ, China, BS, 46; Univ Ill, PhD(food sci), 54. *Prof Exp:* Teaching asst anal chem, Mining Eng Dept, Nat Yunnan Univ, 46-49; mem staff food chem, Div Indust Corp, Mass Inst Technol, 54-55 & Div Sponsored Res, 55-57, res assoc, Dept Food Technol, 57-58; asst biochemist food chem, Agr Exp Sta, Univ Fla, 58-63, asst res prof, Dept Chem Eng, 63-64; res biochemist drug metab, 64-75, res chemist, Patuxent Wildlife Res Ctr, 75-76, RES CHEMIST, DENVER WILDLIFE RES CTR, US DEPT INTERIOR, 76- *Mem:* AAAS; Am Chem Soc; Int Soc Study Xenobiotics. *Res:* Drug metabolism in birds; toxication-detoxication enzyme systems; chemical effects of high energy radiation. *Mailing Add:* Denver Wildlife Res Ctr Bldg 16 Denver Fed Ctr Denver CO 80225

PAN, HUO-HSI, b Foochow, China, Nov 11, 18; m 60; c 2. APPLIED MECHANICS, MECHANICAL ENGINEERING. *Educ:* Nat Southwest Assoc Univ, China, BS, 43; Agr & Mech Col Tex, MS, 49; Kans State Col, MS, 50; Univ Calif, Berkeley, PhD(mech eng), 54. *Prof Exp:* Asst engr, Yunnan Copper Smelting Plant, China, 42-43; mem tech staff, 21st Arsenal, 43-44, head inspection dept, 44-47; asst prof eng mech, Univ Toledo, 54-55; asst prof gen eng, Univ Ill, 55-57; asst prof eng mech, NY Univ, 57-59, from asst prof to prof appl mech, 59-71, prof mech eng, 71-73; prof appl mech, 73-74, prof mech eng, 74-76, PROF MECH & AEROSPACE ENG, POLYTECH INST NEW YORK, 76- *Concurrent Pos:* Res grants, NSF, 64-67 & NASA, 66-68. *Mem:* Am Inst Aeronaut & Astronaut; Soc Indust & Appl Math; Soc Eng Sci; Am Soc Mech Engrs. *Res:* Elasticity; viscoelasticity; vibrations and dynamics of elastic and viscoelastic systems. *Mailing Add:* Dept of Mech & Aerospace Eng 333 Jay St Brooklyn NY 11201

PAN, IN-CHANG, b Tokyo, Japan, Mar 28, 29; US citizen; m 54; c 2. IMMUNOPATHOLOGY, IMMUNOLOGY. *Educ:* Nat Taiwan Univ, DVM, 51; Univ Calif, Davis, MS, 60; Purdue Univ, PhD(vet path), 66. *Prof Exp:* Vet med officer microbiol, Taiwan Prov Inst Animal Health, 51-54; instr path, Nat Taiwan Univ, 54-63 & Purdue Univ, 63-66; fel, Ont Vet Col, 66-67, asst prof, 67-68; VET MED OFFICER IMMUNOPATH, PLUM ISLAND ANIMAL DIS CTR, AGR RES SERV, USDA, 68- *Mem:* Am Asn Immunologists; Am Asn Pathologists; NY Acad Sci; Conf Res Workers Animal Dis; US Animal Health Asn. *Res:* Elucidation of the immunopathology of African swine fever and its possible role in the pathogenesis of chronic African swine fever; persistent viral infection; development of a vaccine for African swine fever; comparative pathology. *Mailing Add:* Plum Island Animal Dis Ctr Agr Res Serv USDA Greenport NY 11944

PAN, KEE-CHUAN, b China, Aug 13, 41; m 71; c 2. PHYSICAL CHEMISTRY. *Educ:* Nat Taiwan Univ, BS, 63; Nat Tsing Hua Univ, Taiwan, MS, 65; State Univ NY, Buffalo, PhD(phys chem), 70. *Prof Exp:* Prof phys chem & chmn dept, Tamkang Univ, Taiwan, 70-78; res assoc, Brandeis Univ, 75-76 & Pa State Univ, 78; res chemist, 78-80, SR RES CHEMIST, EASTMAN KODAK CO, 80- *Mem:* Am Chem Soc; Am Electrochem Soc. *Res:* Electrochemistry. *Mailing Add:* Eastman Kodak Co 1669 Lake Ave Rochester NY 14650

PAN, KO CHANG, b Kwangsi, China, Jan 13, 39; m 68. ENGINEERING MECHANICS. *Educ:* Nat Taiwan Univ, BS, 61; Tex A&M Univ, ME, 64; Univ Iowa, PhD, 69. *Prof Exp:* Res asst elasticity, Univ Iowa, 64-69; MECH ENGR, US ARMY ARMAMENT RES & DEVELOP COMMAND, 69- *Mem:* Am Soc Mech Engrs; Sigma Xi. *Res:* Elasticity; plate and shell; dynamics; optimization. *Mailing Add:* US Army Armament Res & Develop Command DRDAR-LCW-E Dover NJ 07871

PAN, POH-HSI, b Hangzhou, China, July 15, 22; US citizen; m 55; c 2. GEOPHYSICS. *Educ:* Chekiang Univ, BS, 44; Colo Sch Mines, MSc, 63; Rice Univ, PhD(geophys), 69. *Prof Exp:* Mech engr, Chinese Petrol Corp, 47-54, seismic & gravity party chief, 54-59, chief geophysicist, 60; geophysicist, 63-73, geophys specialist, 73-75, US Atlantic Geophys Team Leader, 76-77, geophys proj coordr, 77-78, GEOPHYS ADV, MOBIL OIL CORP, 79- *Concurrent Pos:* Vis prof, Cheng Kung Univ, Taiwan, 58-60; adj lectr, Rice Univ, 76- *Mem:* Soc Explor Geophysicists; Europ Asn Explor Geophysicists. *Res:* Seismic stratigraphic study and gravimetric analysis in petroleum exploration. *Mailing Add:* Mobil Oil Corp PO Box 900 Dallas TX 75221

PAN, SAMUEL CHENG, b Changshu, China, Apr 12, 12; m 39; c 1. BIOCHEMISTRY. *Educ:* Chekiang Univ, BS, 35; Univ Wis, PhD(biochem), 39. *Prof Exp:* Assoc prof, Southwestern Assoc Univ, China, 39-43; chief chemist, Anshun Distillery, Nat Resources Comn, 43-45; prof, Nat Cent Univ, China, 45-46 & Chungking Univ, 46-47; vis res scientist, Joseph E Seagram & Sons, Inc, 47-51; res assoc, Squibb Inst Med Res, 51-68, sr res fel, 68-74; RETIRED. *Mem:* AAAS; Am Chem Soc; Am Soc Microbiol; Soc

Indust Microbiol; NY Acad Sci. *Res:* Fermentation technology; enzymic synthesis of oligosaccharides; analytical techniques; microbiological transformation of steroids. *Mailing Add:* 28 Beacon Hill Dr Metuchen NJ 08840

PAN, STEVE CHIA-TUNG, b Kaohsiung, Formosa, Mar 20, 22; m 51; c 3. MEDICINE. *Educ:* Tokyo Jikeikai Med Col, Japan, MD, 47; Harvard Univ, MPH, 53. *Prof Exp:* Parasitologist, 406th Med Gen Lab, US Army, 46-52; res assoc, 54-55, instr, 55-59, assoc, 59-63, asst prof trop pub health, 63-69, assoc prof, 69-80, PROF TROP PUB HEALTH, SCH PUB HEALTH, HARVARD UNIV, 80- *Concurrent Pos:* Milton res fel, Sch Pub Health, Harvard Univ, 53-54. *Mem:* Am Soc Trop Med & Hyg; Am Soc Parasitol; fel Royal Soc Trop Med & Hyg; Soc Protozool. *Res:* In vitro cultivation; nuclear division and histochemistry and intestinal protozoa of man; helminths infections; schistosomiasis and ascariasis; histology and histopathology of fresh water snails. *Mailing Add:* Dept of Trop Pub Health Harvard Univ Sch of Pub Health Boston MA 02115

PAN, YUAN-SIANG, b Fuchou, China; US citizen. ENGINEERING. *Educ:* Cheng Kung Univ, Taiwan, BS, 57; Brown Univ, PhD(eng), 64. *Prof Exp:* Res asst fluid mech, Brown Univ, 61-62; mem res staff mech eng, Mass Inst Technol, 62-64, res assoc, 64-65; from res asst prof to res assoc prof aeronaut & astronaut, NY Univ, 65-69; assoc prof aerospace eng, Univ Tenn Space Inst, Tullahoma, 69-73; sr staff scientist, JIFAS, Langley Res Ctr, NASA, 73-75, sr res assoc, Nat Res Coun, 75-78; MECH ENGR, PITTSBURGH ENERGY TECHNOL CTR, US DEPT ENERGY, 78- *Concurrent Pos:* Consult, Northrop Serv Inc, Huntsville, 71-; Nat Res Coun sr res assoc, Nat Res Coun-Nat Acad Sci, 75-77; NASA fel acoust, JIFAS, NASA Langley Res Ctr & George Washington Univ, 75-77. *Mem:* AAAS; Am Inst Aeronaut & Astronaut; Am Soc Mech Engrs; Combustion Inst; Sigma Xi. *Res:* Modern fluid mechanics, particularly aero-acoustics and sonic boom phenomena; supersonic, hypersonic and rarefied flow; wave propagation; shock dynamics; combustion of coal and coal-derived fuels and combustion technology of coal slurry mixtures; supersonic combustion; noise generation and propagation. *Mailing Add:* Pittsburgh Energy Technol Ctr PO Box 10940 Pittsburgh PA 15236

PAN, YUH KANG, b Canton, China, Feb 14, 37; m 64; c 2. THEORETICAL CHEMISTRY. *Educ:* Nat Univ Taiwan, BSc, 59; Mich State Univ, PhD(chem), 66. *Prof Exp:* Fel chem physics, Univ Southern Calif, 66-67; fel theoret chem, Harvard Univ, 67; from asst prof to assoc prof, 67-74, PROF CHEM, BOSTON COL, 74- *Concurrent Pos:* Vis prof, Stuttgart Univ, 74 & Max-Plank Inst Radiation Chem, Mülheim, WGer, 75; ed, J Molecular Sci, 81-; hon prof, Chinese Acad Sci, Lanzhou Univ & Jilin Univ. *Mem:* Am Chem Soc; Am Phys Soc; Royal Soc Chem. *Res:* Theory of spectroscopy; quantum dynamics and biology. *Mailing Add:* Dept Chem Boston Col Chestnut Hill MA 02167

PAN, YU-LI, b Cheng-Tu, China, Aug 20, 39. EXPERIMENTAL HIGH ENERGY PHYSICS, LASERS. *Educ:* Univ Okla, BS, 57; Univ Calif, Berkeley, PhD(physics), 64. *Prof Exp:* Res assoc physics, Lawrence Radiation Lab, Univ Calif, 64-65; instr, Univ Pa, 65-68, asst prof, 68-69; SR RES PHYSICIST, LAWRENCE LIVERMORE LAB, UNIV CALIF, 70- *Mem:* Am Phys Soc. *Res:* High energy physics; gas laser; laser fusion. *Mailing Add:* Lawrence Livermore Lab Univ of Calif PO Box 808 Livermore CA 94550

PANAGIDES, JOHN, b New York, NY, Aug 15, 44; m 67; c 3. BIOCHEMISTRY. *Educ:* City Col New York, BS, 66; Univ NC, MS, 68; State Univ NY Buffalo, PhD(biol), 72. *Prof Exp:* Res assoc biochem cytol, Rockefeller Univ, 72-73; res biologist, 73-80, SR RES BIOLOGIST, LEDERLE LABS, 80- *Concurrent Pos:* Adj asst prof, Pace Univ, 78. *Mem:* NY Acad Sci; AAAS; Am Soc Pharmacol & Exp Therapeut. *Res:* Biochemistry and immunology of the inflammatory response; connective tissue metabolism; biochemical cytology; biochemical and immunopharmacology; cellular immunology. *Mailing Add:* Inflammation & Immunol Res Dept Metab Dis Res Sect Lederle Labs Pearl River NY 10965

PANALAKS, THAVIL, b Bangkok, Thailand, Nov 9, 17; Can citizen; m 58. ANALYTICAL CHEMISTRY, FOOD CHEMISTRY. *Educ:* Univ Hawaii, BS, 43; Univ Toronto, MSA, 48, PhD(chem), 56. *Prof Exp:* Res asst agron, Nebr Agr Exp Sta, 48-50; instr food chem, Univ Toronto, 51-54, sr res asst biochem, Connaught Med Res Labs, 54-56; chemist, Can Dept Nat Health & Welfare, 57-65, res scientist anal chem, 65-79; CONSULT, CAN EXEC SERV OVERSEAS, 80-81. *Concurrent Pos:* NATO scholar, 65. *Mem:* AAAS; Am Chem Soc; Nutrit Soc Can. *Res:* Detection and determination of toxic substances in foods; nitrosamines, polycyclic aromatic hydrocarbons, and mycotoxins. *Mailing Add:* 71 Jacqes Cartier Pointe Gatineau PQ J8T 2W3 Can

PANAR, MANUEL, b Edmonton, Alta, Jan 19, 35; m 64. PHYSICAL ORGANIC CHEMISTRY, POLYMER SCIENCE. *Educ:* Univ Alta, BSc, 57; Calif Inst Technol, PhD(chem), 61. *Prof Exp:* Res fel chem, Harvard Univ, 61-63; res chemist, 64-68, res supvr, 69-80, RES MGR, CENT RES DEPT, E I DU PONT DE NEMOURS & CO, INC, 80- *Mem:* Am Chem Soc. *Res:* Physical organic and polymer physical chemistry; structure of anisotropic liquids; solvent-solute interactions; polymer morphology. *Mailing Add:* Cent Res Dept E I du Pont de Nemours & Co Inc Wilmington DE 19898

PANARELLA, EMILIO, b Ferrandina, Italy, Jan 3, 33; m 63; c 3. PHYSICS. *Educ:* Navig Sch, Camogli, Italy, dipl, 51; Univ Navig, Naples, Italy, Dr, 56. *Prof Exp:* With Malpensa Airport, Milano, 58-60; teacher navig, Navig Sch, Savona, 60-61; NATO fel microwave technol, Polytech Inst Brooklyn, 61-62; res officer, Microwave Res Inst, Florence, Italy, 62-64; RES OFFFICER, NAT RES COUN CAN, 64- *Mem:* Am Phys Soc; Europ Phys Soc; Ital Phys Soc; NY Acad Sci; Inst Elec & Electronics Engrs. *Res:* Plasma and laser physics. *Mailing Add:* Nat Res Coun Ottawa ON K1A 0R6 Can

PANASENKO, SHARON MULDOON, b Oakland, Calif, April 30, 50. BIOCHEMISTRY. *Educ:* Univ Calif, Berkeley, AB, 72; Stanford Univ, PhD(biochem), 77. *Prof Exp:* Fel biochem, Univ Calif, Berkeley, 77-79; ASST PROF BIOCHEM, POMONA COL, 79- *Res:* Modification of proteins and phospholipids during chemotaxis and development in myxococcus xanthus. *Mailing Add:* Dept Chem Pomona Col Claremont CA 91711

PANAYAPPAN, RAMANATHAN, b Madras, India, Sept 21, 36; US citizen; m 60; c 2. POLLUTION CHEMISTRY. *Educ:* Annamalai Univ Madras, BSc, 59, MSc, 67; Howard Univ, PhD(inorg chem), 73. *Prof Exp:* Lectr chem, Annamalai Univ Madras, 60-67; adj prof polymer chem res, NASA Res Proj, Shaw Univ, 74-75; RES CHEMIST HIGH TEMPERATURE CHEM & POLLUTION, US NAVAL RES LAB, 75- *Mem:* Am Chem Soc. *Res:* Water and air pollution; high temperature solution chemistry. *Mailing Add:* Code 6133 4555 Overlook Ave SW Washington DC 20375

PANCAKE, SAMUEL JOSEPH, b McCook, Nebr, Oct 5, 42. CANCER. *Educ:* Ft Hays Kans State Col, BS, 63; Harvard Univ, PhD(biochem), 70. *Prof Exp:* Fel transplantation immunol, Albert Einstein Col Med, 69-72; staff fel tumor immunol, Nat Cancer Inst, NIH, 72-75; ASST PROF TUMOR IMMUNOL & CELL PHYSIOL, DEPT BIOL, GEORGETOWN UNIV, 75- *Concurrent Pos:* Am Cancer Soc fel, 69-71. *Res:* Exploration of those biochemical and immunological changes of the cell surface which are related to the altered cell functions associated with tumorigenic transformation. *Mailing Add:* 1809 12th St NW Washington DC 20009

PANCIERA, ROGER J, b Westerly, RI, Sept 30, 29; m 53; c 2. VETERINARY PATHOLOGY. *Educ:* Okla State Univ, DVM, 53; Cornell Univ, MS, 55, PhD, 60; Am Col Vet Path, dipl, 63. *Prof Exp:* From asst to instr vet path, Cornell Univ, 53-56; asst prof, 56-63, PROF VET PATH, OKLA STATE UNIV, 63- *Mem:* Am Vet Med Asn; NY Acad Sci. *Res:* General veterinary pathology; toxicology. *Mailing Add:* Dept of Vet Path Okla State Univ Stillwater OK 74074

PANCOE, WILLIAM LOUIS, JR, b Chester, Pa, Feb 9, 38; m 61; c 3. ENDOCRINOLOGY. *Educ:* Univ Del, BA, 59, MA, 61; Colo State Univ, PhD(physiol), 65. *Prof Exp:* Asst prof zool & physiol, 64-68, dir inst radiation biol, 67-70, assoc prof, 68-76, PROF ZOOL & PHYSIOL, UNIV WYO, 76-, ASST DEAN FOR STUDENT PROG, COL HUMAN MED, 76- *Concurrent Pos:* NSF vis lectr, 67; Am Inst Biol Sci vis radiation biologist, 68-76. *Mem:* Fel AAAS; Am Soc Zoologists; Am Inst Biol Sci; Soc Exp Biol & Med. *Res:* Thyroidal interactions as applicable to adrenal interactions, atherosclerosis, reproduction and wound healing; basic and therapeutic aspects of sarcoma 37; biotelemetry of intestinal movements as affected by hormones. *Mailing Add:* Dept Zool & Physiol Univ Wyo Laramie WY 82070

PANDE, CHANDRA SHEKHAR, physical metallurgy, physics, see previous edition

PANDE, GYAN SHANKER, b Aug 5, 32; Can citizen; m 72; c 2. CHEMISTRY. *Educ:* Agra Univ, India, BSc, 51; Lucknow Univ, India, MSc, 53, PhD(chem), 58. *Prof Exp:* Lectr chem, Lucknow Univ, 55-58 & Roorkee Univ, India, 59-60; res assoc chem, Univ Saskatoon, Can, 60-65; res chemist, Uniroyal Res Labs, Guelph, Can, 65-72; mgr prod mkt develop, Conap Inc, Olean, NY, 73-74, dir res & develop, 75-77; MEM STAFF, CORDIS CORP, 77- *Mem:* Am Chem Soc; sr mem Chem Inst Can. *Res:* Synthesis and evaluation of polyurethanes; epoxies as adhesives and encapsulants. *Mailing Add:* Cordis Corp Bldg K3 PO Box 370428 Miami FL 33137

PANDE, SHRI VARDHAN, b Kanpur, India, Nov 4, 40; m 65. BIOCHEMISTRY. *Educ:* Univ Lucknow, BSc, 58, MSc, 60; Univ Delhi, PhD(biochem), 65. *Prof Exp:* Jr res officer biochem, V Patel Chest Inst, Delhi, India, 65; res scholar, Lab Nuclear Med & Radiation Biol, Univ Calif, Los Angeles, 66-69; prof res asst, Univ Man, 69-70; sr researcher, 70-72, DIR LAB INTERMEDIARY METAB, CLIN RES INST MONTREAL, 72- *Concurrent Pos:* Tutor, Univ Man, 69-70; asst prof, Univ Montreal, 71-76, assoc prof, 76-; assoc mem McGill Univ, 73- *Mem:* Am Chem Soc; NY Acad Sci. *Res:* Metabolism and functions of carnitine; mitochondrial functions and transports; fatty acid oxidation and ketogenesis; regulation of metabolism. *Mailing Add:* Clin Res Inst Montreal 110 Pine Ave W Montreal PQ H2W 1R7 Can

PANDELL, ALEXANDER JERRY, b San Francisco, Calif, June 19, 42. ORGANIC CHEMISTRY. *Educ:* San Francisco State Col, BS, 64; Stanford Univ, PhD(org chem), 68. *Prof Exp:* Res fel org chem, Harvard Univ, 68-69; asst prof chem, Boston Univ, 69-70; from asst prof to assoc prof, 70-76, chmn dept, 73-79, PROF CHEM, CALIF STATE COL, STANISLAUS, 77- *Concurrent Pos:* Am Chem Soc-Petrol Res Fund grants, 71-74 & 81-83. *Mem:* Am Chem Soc. *Res:* Transition metal catalyzed oxidations of aromatic systems. *Mailing Add:* Dept Chem Calif State Col Stanislaus Turlock CA 95380

PANDEY, JAGDISH NARAYAN, b Varanasi, India, Nov 2, 36; m 54; c 5. MATHEMATICS. *Educ:* Banaras Hindu Univ, BSc, 55, MSc, 57; State Univ NY Stony Brook, PhD(math), 67. *Prof Exp:* Lectr math, Banaras Hindu Univ, 57-58 & 59-64; head dept, SC Col, Ballia, India, 58-59; fel, Univ Alta, 67-68; asst prof, 68-72, assoc prof, 72-81, PROF MATH, CARLETON UNIV, 81- *Concurrent Pos:* Nat Res Coun Can grant, 68- *Mem:* Am Math Soc; Can Math Cong. *Res:* Generalized integral transform and functions; abstract differential equations. *Mailing Add:* Dept Math Carleton Univ Ottawa ON K1S 5B6 Can

PANDEY, RAGHVENDRA KUMAR, b Bath, Bihar, India, Jan 7, 37; m 67. APPLIED PHYSICS, SOLID STATE MATERIALS. *Educ:* Bihar Univ, BSc, 57; Patna Univ, MSc, 59; Cologne Univ, WGer, Dr rer nat, 67. *Prof Exp:* Sr res physicist, NCR Co, Dayton, 68-72 & Cincinnati Electronics Corp, 73-74; prof electronics, Inst Nac de Astrofisica, Optica y Electronica, Puebla, Mex, 74-77; ASSOC PROF ELEC ENG, TEX A&M UNIV, 77- *Mem:* Am

Phys Soc; sr mem Inst Elec & Electronics Engrs; AAAS. *Res:* Crystal growth, magnetism, ferroelectricity, x-ray diffraction and optical properties of solids; electro-optical devices. *Mailing Add:* Dept of Elec Eng Tex A&M Univ College Station TX 77843

PANDEY, RAMESH CHANDRA, b Naugaon, Almora, India, Nov 5, 38. ORGANIC CHEMISTRY. *Educ:* Univ Allahabad, BSc, 58; Univ Gorakhpur, MSc, 60; Univ Poona, PhD(terpenoids), 65. *Prof Exp:* Jr res fel terpenoids, Nat Chem Lab, Poona, 60-64, res officer med plants, 65-67; res assoc polyene antibiotics, Chem Dept, Univ Ill, Urbana, 67-70; scientist appl res, Nat Chem Lab, Poona, 70-72; vis scientist antiobiotics & mass spectros, Chem Dept, Univ Ill, Urbana, 72-77; SR SCIENTIST, ANTITUMOR COMPOUNDS, NCI-FREDERICK CANCER RES FACIL, NAT CANCER INST, 77- *Concurrent Pos:* Consult, Amphotericin B Group, Sch Med, Washington Univ, St Louis, 76- *Mem:* Am Chem Soc; Am Soc Mass Spectrometry; Am Soc Microbiol; NY Acad Sci; Am Soc Pharmacognosy. *Res:* Antibiotics, terpenoids, applied research, PMR, CMR and mass spectral studies. *Mailing Add:* Frederick Cancer Res Facil Nat Cancer Inst PO Box B Frederick MD 21701

PANDEY, SURENDRA NATH, b Mirzapur, India, July 3, 45; US citizen; m 67; c 2. EXPERIMENTAL SOLID STATE PHYSICS. *Educ:* Univ Allahabad, India, BSc, 61, MSc, 63; Howard Univ, Washington, DC, PhD(physics), 73. *Prof Exp:* Spectrogr chem-physics, Qual Control Lab, Hindustan Aluminum Corp, Mirzapur, India, 63-64; res physicist, Phys Res Lab, Fertilizer Corp, India, Sindri, India, 64-67; asst prof, 73-80, ASSOC PROF PHYSICS, ALBANY STATE COL, ALBANY, GA, 80- *Concurrent Pos:* Mem acad adv comt, Univ Syst Ga. *Mem:* Am Asn Physics Teachers; Am Phys Soc. *Res:* Low and high temperature study on thermal expansion by x-ray diffraction of solids; electromagnetic radiation absorption by organic dyes and solutions, especially ultraviolet, visible and infrared. *Mailing Add:* Dept of Chem & Physics Albany State Col Albany GA 31705

PANDIT, HEMCHANDRA M, b Chinchani, India, May 4, 24; m 53; c 3. ANIMAL PHYSIOLOGY. *Educ:* Univ Bombay, BSc, 46, MSc, 50; State Univ NY Buffalo, PhD(biol), 67. *Prof Exp:* Jr lectr biol, Elphinstone Col, Bombay, 46-48 & RR Col, Univ Bombay, 49-52; res asst, Indian Cancer Res Ctr, 50-52 & 55-62 & Haffkine Inst Bombay, 52-55; asst biol, State Univ NY Buffalo, 62-66; assoc prof, Villa Marie Col Buffalo, 66-68; assoc prof, 68-73, PROF BIOL, D'YOUVILLE COL, 73- *Res:* Snake venoms; leprosy; renal physiology and philosophy. *Mailing Add:* Dept of Biol D'Youville Col Buffalo NY 14201

PANDOLF, KENT BARRY, b Needham, Mass, Feb 24, 45; m 68. ENVIRONMENTAL PHYSIOLOGY, EXERCISE PHYSIOLOGY. *Educ:* Boston Univ, BS, 67; Univ Pittsburgh, MA, 68, MPH, 70, PhD(work physiol), 72. *Prof Exp:* Vis asst fel environ physiol, John B Pierce Found Lab, New Haven, Conn, 72-73; res physiologist, 73-78, CHIEF, PHYSIOL BR, US ARMY RES INST ENVIRON MED, 78- *Concurrent Pos:* Fel, Sch Med, Yale Univ, 72-73; adj asst prof, Boston Univ, 76- *Mem:* Am Physiol Soc; Sigma Xi; fel Am Col Sports Med. *Res:* Independent, original research into areas of environmental and work physiology pertaining to human performance with some research involving perceptual and motivational aspects of physical work and heat exposure of men. *Mailing Add:* Mil Ergonomics Div US Army Res Inst of Environ Med Natick MA 01760

PANDOLFE, WILLIAM DAVID, b Hartford, Conn, Nov 5, 45; m 76. PHYSICAL CHEMISTRY. *Educ:* Col Holy Cross, BS, 67; Rutgers Univ, MS, 71, PhD(phys chem), 74. *Prof Exp:* MGR RES & DEVELOP, GAULIN CORP, 74- *Mem:* Am Chem Soc. *Res:* Colloid science and emulsion technology. *Mailing Add:* 91 Partridge Rd Billerica MA 01821

PANDOLFO, JOSEPH P, b New York, NY, Sept 26, 30; m 52; c 6. METEOROLOGY, OCEANOGRAPHY. *Educ:* Fordham Univ, BS, 51; NY Univ, MS, 56, PhD(meteorol, oceanog), 61. *Prof Exp:* Weather officer, US Air Force, 51-55; from instr to asst prof meteorol & oceanog, NY Univ, 57-62; res scientist, Travelers Res Ctr, Inc, 62-69; res fel, 69-71, vpres, 71-76, PRES, CTR ENVIRON & MAN, INC, 76-, MEM BD DIRS, 77- *Concurrent Pos:* Consult, Barbados Oceanog & Meteorol Exp, Environ Sci Serv Admin, 67-69; NSF res grants, Ctr Environ & Man, Inc, 69-; consult, Int Field Year Great Lakes, Nat Oceanog & Atmospheric Agency, 71-74 & Int Decade OceanExplor, NSF, 72-75. *Mem:* AAAS; Am Meteorol Soc. *Res:* Dynamic oceanography; dynamics and physics of planetary boundary layers; computer simulation, atmospheric and oceanic systems; air-land and air-sea interactions; solar energy. *Mailing Add:* Ctr for Environ & Man Inc Hartford CT 06120

PANDORF, ROBERT CLAY, b Cincinnati, Ohio. LOW TEMPERATURE PHYSICS. *Educ:* Miami Univ, Ohio, BA, 57, MA, 59; Ohio State Univ, PhD(physics), 67. *Prof Exp:* Fel physics, Mass Inst Technol, 67-70; PROJ PHYSICIST, CHARLES STARK DRAPER LAB, 70- *Concurrent Pos:* Res asst, Ohio State Univ, 59-66, res assoc, 66-67. *Mem:* Am Phys Soc. *Res:* Study of the viscous and other physical properties of liquid helium at ultra-low temperatures and its application to ultra precision inertial instrumentation. *Mailing Add:* 139 Winchester St Newton Highlands MA 02161

PANDRES, DAVE, JR, b Duncan, Okla, Jan 10, 28; m 53; c 4. THEORETICAL PHYSICS. *Educ:* Univ Tex, BS, 49, MA, 56, PhD(physics), 58. *Prof Exp:* Elec engr, Brown & Root, Inc, 49; systs engr, Chance-Vought Aircraft Co, 51-52; adv res scientist, Ohio Oil Co, 58-60; assoc res scientist, Martin Co, 60-62; sr res & develop scientist, Lockheed-Calif Co, 62-64; res scientist, Douglas Advan Res Lab, 64-66, assoc dir math sci, 66-69, dir math sci, 69-71; asst prof, 71-78, ASSOC PROF MATH, NORTH GA COL, 78- *Mem:* Am Phys Soc. *Res:* General relativity; unified field theory; foundations of quantum theory; possible origins of the internal symmetries. *Mailing Add:* Dept of Math N Ga Col Dahlonega GA 30533

PANDYA, KRISHNAKANT HARIPRASAD, b Mehmedabad, India, Oct 19, 35; m 54; c 1. PHARMACOLOGY, PHARMACOGNOSY. *Educ:* Gujarat Univ, India, BS, 58, MS, 61, PhD(pharmacol), 68. *Prof Exp:* Demonstr, L M Col Pharm, Gujarat Univ, 58-61, tutor, 61-63, jr lectr pharmacol, B J Med Col, 63-69, asst prof, 69-70; from instr to asst prof, 71-77, ASSOC PROF PHARMACOL, KIRKSVILLE COL OSTEOP MED, 77- *Mem:* Am Soc Pharmacol & Exp Therapeut; AAAS; NY Acad Sci. *Res:* Autonomic nervous system; modifications of the responses, release, evolution, etc of the neurohumoral transmitters in vivo; cardiovascular and respiratory systems. *Mailing Add:* Dept of Pharmacol Kirksville Col of Osteop Med Kirksville MO 63501

PANEK, EDWARD JOHN, b Grand Rapids, Minn, Sept 27, 41; m 66; c 2. ENVIROMENTAL CHEMISTRY, ORGANOMETALLIC CHEMISTRY. *Educ:* Univ Wis-Madison, BS, 63; Mass Inst Technol, PhD(org chem), 68. *Prof Exp:* NIH fel chem, Dept Chem, Iowa State Univ, 68-69; asst prof chem, Tulane Univ, 69-75; res staff chem, 75-81, RES SUPVR, BASF WYANDOTTE CORP, 81- *Mem:* Am Chem Soc; AAAS. *Res:* Activation of anions by complexing agents with particular emphasis on carbanions and anionic polymerization catalysts. *Mailing Add:* Org Res BASF Wyandotte Corp Wyandotte MI 48192

PANEK, LOUIS A(NTHONY), b Boston, Mass, Dec 3, 19; m 43; c 2. MINING ENGINEERING, ROCK MECHANICS. *Educ:* Mich Col Mining & Technol, BS, 41; Columbia Univ, MS, 46, PhD(eng), 49. *Prof Exp:* Mining res engr, 49-65, mgr ground control res, 65-78, SR RES SCIENTIST, US BUR MINES, 78- *Concurrent Pos:* Warren lectr, Univ Minn, 55. *Honors & Awards:* Peele Award, Am Inst Mining, Metall & Petrol Engrs, 57. *Mem:* Am Statist Asn; Int Soc Rock Mech; Am Inst Mining, Metall & Petrol Engrs; Sigma Xi. *Res:* Support and control of roof and ground in the vicinity of underground openings based on theoretical and experimental stress analysis; application of these principles to the design of mine openings and methods of mining; in-place testing and measurement of rock mass structural behavior. *Mailing Add:* 8 Hillside Dr Denver CO 80215

PANEM, SANDRA, b Brooklyn, NY, June 25, 46; m 71. ANIMAL VIROLOGY. *Educ:* Univ Chicago, SB, 66, PhD(virol), 70. *Prof Exp:* Fel path, 70-71, res assoc instr, 71-76, ASST PROF PATH, UNIV CHICAGO, 76- *Concurrent Pos:* Fel, Damon Runyan Mem Fund Cancer Res, 70-72; spec fel, Leukemia Soc Am, 75-77, scholar, 78-83; Kellogg Nat fel, 81-83. *Mem:* Am Asn Cancer Res; Am Soc Microbiol; AAAS. *Res:* Control of type C oncornavirus expression in murine and human cells. *Mailing Add:* Kovler Viral Oncol Labs 910 E 58th St Chicago IL 60637

PANESSA-WARREN, BARBARA JEAN, b Yonkers, NY, Feb 21, 47; m. CELL BIOLOGY. *Educ:* NY Univ, BA, 68, MS, 71, PhD(cell biol), 74. *Prof Exp:* Sr res technician, Lab Infectious Dis & Immunol, Med Ctr, Bellevue, 68-69, teaching fel, Grad Sch Arts & Sci & Washington Sq Col Arts & Sci, asst prof physiol & pathophysiol, St Vincent's Hosp & Med Ctr, New York, 74-78; res assoc orthop surg & head, Anal Electron Micros & Cell Biol Lab, 78-80, RES ASST PROF, DEPT ANAT SCI, HEALTH SCI CTR, STATE UNIV NY, STONY BROOK, 80- *Concurrent Pos:* Sr instr, St Vincent's Hosp Sch Nursing, New York, 69-73; consult, Gen Tel & Electronics, NY, 72, Stauffer Chem Co, NY, 73, Esso Res & Eng, NJ, 73 & Latham Publ Co, 74-75; NATO prof, Inst Zool, Univ Siena, Italy, 74 & 75; NIH fel physiol & ophthal, Med Sch, NY Univ, 75-78; guest assoc scientist, Div Instrumentation, Brookhaven Nat Lab, 79- *Honors & Awards:* Wilhelm Bernhard Award, Eur Electon Micros Soc, 80; Burton Medal, Electron Micros Soc Am, 81. *Mem:* Am Soc Cell Biol; Biophys Soc Am; Electron Micros Soc Am; Microbeam Anal Soc Am; NY Acad Sci. *Res:* Elemental content and distribution in vertebrate eyes (retina-choroid); high resolution imaging and composition of biological subcellular components; x-ray microanalysis; x-ray flourescence spectroscopy; proton induced x-ray emission spectroscopy; scanning transmission electron microscopy; routine transmission electron microscopy and scanning electron microscope. *Mailing Add:* Dept Orthop Surg State Univ NY Stony Brook NY 11794

PANETH, NIGEL SEFTON, b London, Eng, Sept 19, 46; m 73; c 1. EPIDEMIOLOGY, PEDIATRICS. *Educ:* Columbia Col, AB, 68, MPH, 78; Dartmouth Col, BMS, 70; Harvard Univ, MD, 72. *Prof Exp:* Asst clin prof pediat, Albert Einstein Col Med, 77-78; ASST PROF PUB HEALTH & PEDIAT, COLUMBIA UNIV, 78- *Mem:* Am Acad Pediat; Soc Epidemiol Res; Int Epidemiol Asn. *Res:* Epidemiology of epilepsy, cerebral palsy and mental retardation, in particular the relationship of these conditions to events in the perinatal period. *Mailing Add:* G H Sergievsky Ctr Fac of Med Columbia Univ New York NY 10032

PANETTA, CHARLES ANTHONY, b Albany, NY, Sept 12, 32; m 59; c 2. ORGANIC CHEMISTRY. *Educ:* Manhattan Col, BS, 54; Rensselaer Polytech Inst, PhD(org chem), 61. *Prof Exp:* Sr chemist, Bristol Labs, Inc, 60-64, proj supvr, 64-65; res assoc chem, Mass Inst Technol, 65-67; asst prof chem & pharmaceut chem, 67-70, assoc prof chem, 70-73, PROF CHEM, UNIV MISS, 73- *Concurrent Pos:* Res grants, Res Corp, Bristol Labs, NSF & NIH. *Mem:* Am Chem Soc. *Res:* Chemistry of penicillin antibiotics; amino acids and peptides; general organic synthesis. *Mailing Add:* Dept of Chem Univ of Miss University MS 38677

PANG, CHAN YUEH, b China, Oct, 47. HIGH ENERGY PHYSICS. *Educ:* Univ Chicago, PhD(physics), 73. *Prof Exp:* Res assoc, Univ Ill, Urbana, 73-75, res asst prof physics, 75-77; mem staff, Lawrence Berkeley Lab, 77-80; PHYSICIST, BECHTEL NAT, 81- *Mem:* Am Phys Soc. *Res:* Neutral currents in weak interactions and other interactions induced by neutrino; nuclear physics. *Mailing Add:* Bechtel Nat PO Box 3965 San Francisco CA 94105

PANG, HENRIANNA YICKSING, b Hong Kong, Dec 23, 52; Brit citizen; m 80; c 1. CHEMISTRY. *Educ:* San Diego State Univ, BSc, 75; Univ Utah, PhD(med chem), 82. *Prof Exp:* ASSOC, MASS INST TECHNOL, 82- *Mem:* Am Chem Soc; Am Soc Mass Spectrometry. *Mailing Add:* Mass Inst Technol 56-012 77 Massachusetts Ave Cambridge MA 02139

PANG, KEVIN DIT KWAN, b China; US citizen; m. SPACE SCIENCES, REMOTE SENSING. *Educ:* Univ Hawaii, BA, 62; Univ Calif, Los Angeles, MS, 63, PhD(space physics), 70. *Prof Exp:* Teaching asst physics, Univ Hawaii, 61-62; geophysicist earth sci, Inst Geophysics, Univ Calif, Los Angeles, 63-70; res assoc atmospheric physics, Lab Atmospheric & Space Physics, Univ Colo, 70-73; res assoc space physics, Jet Propulsion Lab, Calif Inst Technol, 74-76; staff scientist space sci, Planetary Sci Inst, Sci Appln, Inc, 76-80; CONSULT SPACE SCI, JET PROPULSION LAB, CALIF INST TECHNOL, 80- *Concurrent Pos:* Consult, Planetary Sci Dept, Rand Corp, 64-65 & Goddard Inst Space Studies, NASA, 73-74; prin investr, var NASA grants, 76- *Honors & Awards:* Group Achievement Award, NASA, 77; Sigma Xi Award. *Mem:* Sigma Xi; Int Astron Union; Am Astron Soc; Am Meteorol Soc; Am Geophys Union. *Res:* Experimental and theoretical investigations of the atmosphere and surface of the earth, planets and satellites, especially by remote sensing techniques; laboratory simulation studies of physical and chemical processes on solar system bodies. *Mailing Add:* Jet Propulsion Lab 183-901 4800 Oak Grove Dr Pasadena CA 91109

PANG, KIM-CHING SANDY, b Hong Kong. PHARMACOKINETICS, HEPATIC DRUG CLEARANCE. *Educ:* Univ Toronto, BSc, 71; Univ Calif, San Francisco, PhD(pharm chem), 75. *Prof Exp:* Teaching asst pharm dispensing pharmacokinetics, Univ Calif, San Francisco, 71-73, teaching fel pharmacokinetics, 73-74, res asst, 74-75; vis fel metab pharmacokinetics, Lab Chem Pharmacol, NIH, Bethesda, 76-78; ASST PROF PHARMACEUT, UNIV HOUSTON, 78- *Concurrent Pos:* Consult, Nat Inst Drug Abuse, 77-78; adj asst prof, Baylor Col Med, Houston, 78-; mem, Spec Study Sect, NIH, 79-80 & ad hoc mem, Pharm Study Sect, NIH, 81. *Mem:* Am Soc Pharmacol & Exp Therapeut; AAAS; Sigma Xi. *Res:* Hepatic clearance of drugs; pharmacokinetics of drugs and their metabolites; drug metabolism. *Mailing Add:* Dept Pharmaceut Tex Med Ctr Univ Houston 1441 Moursund St Houston TX 77030

PANG, PETER KAI TO, b Hong Kong, Oct 14, 41; m 69. COMPARATIVE PHYSIOLOGY, ENDOCRINOLOGY. *Educ:* Univ Hong Kong, BSc, 63, BSc, 64; Yale Univ, MSc, 67, PhD(biol), 70. *Hon Degrees:* DSc, Univ Hong Kong, 81. *Prof Exp:* Res asst, Bingham Lab, Yale Univ, 64-65, instr biol, 70-71; instr pharmacol, Col Physicians & Surgeons, Columbia Univ, 72-73, assoc, 73-74; assoc prof biol, Brooklyn Col, City Col New York, 74-76; assoc prof, 76-81, PROF PHARMACOL, SCH MED, TEX TECH UNIV, 81- *Mem:* Am Physiol Soc; Am Soc Bone & Mineral Res; Soc Endocrinol; Endocrine Soc; AAAS. *Res:* Hormonal control of calcium regulation and osmoregulation in lower vertebrates; endocrine evolution. *Mailing Add:* Dept of Pharmacol Tex Tech Univ Health Sci Ctrs Lubbock TX 79413

PANGBORN, JACK, b Denver, Colo, Mar 20, 25; m 56. ELECTRON MICROSCOPY. *Educ:* Pac Union Col, BS, 51; Univ Calif, MS, 60. *Prof Exp:* Lab technician, 52-59, dir electron micros lab, 59-69, DIR FACILITY ADVAN INSTRUMENTATION, UNIV CALIF, DAVIS, 69- *Mem:* Electron Micros Soc Am; Am Soc Microbiol. *Res:* Biological electron microscopy. *Mailing Add:* Facility for Advan Instrumentation Univ of Calif Davis CA 95616

PANGBORN, ROBERT NORTHRUP, b New York, NY, May 26, 51; m 76; c 1. X-RAY DIFFRACTION ANALYSIS. *Educ:* Rutgers Univ, BS & BA, 74, MS, 77, PhD(mech & mat sci), 79. *Prof Exp:* Res assoc, Electron Micros Lab, Rutgers Univ, 79; ASST PROF ENG SCI & MECH, PA STATE UNIV, 79- *Concurrent Pos:* Lectr appl x-ray methods, Ctr Prof Advan, 78. *Mem:* Am Soc Metals; Am Crystallographic Asn; Am Soc Eng Educ; Sigma Xi. *Res:* Characterization of microplasticity developed during metal fatigue; defects and fracture in crystalline materials; structure and failure analysis; nondestructive testing and evaluation, x-ray diffraction and stress measurement. *Mailing Add:* 227 Hammond Bldg Pa State Univ University Park PA 16802

PANGBORN, ROSE MARIE VALDES, b Las Cruces, NMex, Aug 19, 32; m 56. FOOD TECHNOLOGY, PSYCHOPHYSICS. *Educ:* NMex State Univ, BS, 53; Iowa State Univ, MS, 55. *Prof Exp:* Res asst foods, Iowa State Univ, 53-55; from jr specialist to assoc prof, 55-71, assoc dean, Col Agr & Environ Sci & actg chmn dept consumer sci, 73-75, PROF FOOD SCI & TECHNOL, UNIV CALIF, DAVIS, 71- *Concurrent Pos:* NIH consult, Univ Chile, 66; vis prof, Swed Inst Food Preservation Res, 70-71; vis scientist, Nestle Res Lab, Switz, 78; invited guest, Polish Acad Sci & invited lectr, Univ Guelph, Can, 79. *Mem:* AAAS; Soc Nutrit Educ; fel Inst Food Technologists; Am Inst Nutrit; Asn Chemoreception Sci. *Res:* Food psychophysics; behavioral responses to gustatory and olfactory stimuli; oral perception; saliva. *Mailing Add:* Dept of Food Sci & Technol Univ of Calif Davis CA 95616

PANG-CHING, GLENN K, b Hilo, Hawaii, Feb 10, 31; m 61; c 2. AUDIOLOGY. *Educ:* Calif State Univ, Los Angeles, BS, 57; Purdue Univ, MS, 58; Univ Southern Calif, PhD(audiol), 66. *Prof Exp:* Audiologist, Vet Admin, Washington, DC, 58-59 & Los Angeles, 59-65; PROF AUDIOL & SPEECH PATH, DIV SPEECH PATH & AUDIOL, SCH MED, UNIV HAWAII, 65- *Mem:* Am Speech & Hearing Asn. *Res:* Clinical research in audiology. *Mailing Add:* Div Speech Path & Audiol 2560 Campus Rd Honolulu HI 96822

PANICCI, RONALD J, b New York, NY, Oct 20, 41. ORGANIC CHEMISTRY. *Educ:* Col Holy Cross, BS, 63; Univ NH, PhD(org chem), 67. *Prof Exp:* Asst prof, 67-74, assoc prof, 74-77, PROF CHEM, SOUTHERN CONN STATE COL, 77-, CHMN DEPT, 76- *Concurrent Pos:* Consult, Kemtrek Co, Conn, 67- & Baron Consult Co, 68- *Mem:* AAAS; Am Chem Soc. *Res:* Organic reaction mechanisms relative to ring chain tautomerism; rearrangement reactions and organometallic chemistry; qualitative and quantitative use of nuclear magnetic resonance in reaction mechanisms; biochemistry of algae. *Mailing Add:* Dept Chem Southern Conn State Col 501 Crescent St New Haven CT 06515

PANISH, MORTON B, b New York, NY, Apr 8, 29; m 51; c 3. PHYSICAL CHEMISTRY, MATERIALS SCIENCE. *Educ:* Denver Univ, BS, 50; Mich State Univ, MS, 52, PhD(phys chem), 54. *Prof Exp:* Chemist molten salt chem, Oak Ridge Nat Lab, 54-57; mem tech staff phys chem, Res & Advan Develop Div, Avco Corp, 57-62, sect head phys chem, 62-64; mem tech staff solid state chem, 64-69, DEPT HEAD MAT SCI, BELL LABS, 69- *Honors & Awards:* Electronics Div Award, Electrochem Soc, 73 & Solid State Sci Award, 79. *Mem:* Electrochem Soc; Fel Am Phys Soc; Inst Elec & Electronic Engrs. *Res:* Chemical thermodynamic studies of semiconductor systems; thermodynamics of impurity incorporation in semiconductors; phase chemistry; epitaxial crystal growth of semiconductors; semiconductor devices, particularly injection lasers. *Mailing Add:* Bell Labs 600 Mountain Ave Murray Hill NJ 07974

PANISSET, JEAN-CLAUDE, b Oka, Que, Apr 27, 35; m 57; c 2. PHARMACOLOGY. *Educ:* Univ Montreal, BA, 54, DVM, 59, MSc, 60, PhD(pharmacol), 62. *Prof Exp:* Res assoc autonomic pharmacol, Cleveland Clin, Ohio, 62-63; pharmacologist, Food & Drug Directorate, Can, 63-64; asst prof autonomic pharmacol, 64-70, assoc prof pharmacol, 70-76, PROF PHARMACOL & CHMN DEPT, FAC VET MED, UNIV MONTREAL, 76-; DIR RES, INST BIO-ENDOCRINOL INC, 70- *Mem:* Fel Am Col Vet Toxicologists; fel Am Col Vet Pharmacologists & Therapeut; Can Vet Med Asn; Pharmacol Soc Can; Am Soc Pharmacol & Therapeut. *Res:* Endocrinology; biopharmacuetics; radioimmunology. *Mailing Add:* 10850 Hamon St Montreal PQ H3C 3J7 Can

PANITZ, ERIC, parasitology, microbiology, see previous edition

PANITZ, JANDA KIRK GRIFFITH, b Mechanicsburg, Pa, Feb 2, 45; m 67. SURFACE PHYSICS, SOLID STATE PHYSICS. *Educ:* Pa State Univ, BS, 66, MS, 69, PhD(physics), 75. *Prof Exp:* Teaching asst physics, Pa State Univ, 66-68; physicist IR optics, Ballistic Res Lab, Aberdeen Proving Ground, 67; res asst physics, Appl Res Lab, Pa State Univ, 69-75; res assoc elec eng, Bur Eng Res, Univ NMex, 76-77; STAFF SCIENTIST PHYSICS, SANDIA LABS, ALBUQUERQUE, 78- *Concurrent Pos:* Consult, Sandia Labs, 71-73. *Mem:* AAAS; Am Vacuum Soc; Sigma Xi. *Res:* Thin film physics and surface physics; also theoretical solid state physics and lattice dynamics; geometrical optics and infrared optical systems. *Mailing Add:* 228 N Star Rte Edgewood NM 87015

PANKAVICH, JOHN ANTHONY, b Long Island City, NY, Jan 25, 29; m 56; c 4. ANIMAL SCIENCE & NUTRITION. *Educ:* St Francis Col, NY, BS, 51; Syracuse Univ, MS, 53; NY Univ, PhD(parasitol), 66. *Prof Exp:* Biol technician, Rockefeller Inst Med Res, 47; RES BIOLOGIST, AGR CTR, AM CYANAMID CO, 56- *Mem:* Am Soc Parasitologists. *Res:* Evaluation and discovery of anthelmintics for parasitisms found in large and small animals; development of anthelmintic screening models for discovering anthelmintics; in vitro growth of parasites; abnormal host-parasite relationships; visceral larva migrans. *Mailing Add:* 20 Sedgwick Rd Hamilton Square NJ 08690

PANKEY, GEORGE ATKINSON, b Shreveport, La, Aug 11, 33; m 72; c 4. INFECTIOUS DISEASES, INTERNAL MEDICINE. *Educ:* Tulane Univ, New Orleans, BS, 54, MD, 57; Univ Minn, Minneapolis, MS, 61; Am Bd Internal Med, cert, 65, cert infectious dis, 72. *Prof Exp:* Intern med, Univ Minn Hosps, Minneapolis, 57-58, resident internal med, 58-60; resident, Vet Admin Hosp & Gen Hosp, Minneapolis, 60-61; instr med, Div Infectious Dis, Sch Med, Tulane Univ, 61-63; mem staff & consult infectious dis, 63-72, HEAD SECT INFECTIOUS DIS, OCHSNER CLIN, 72-, MEM STAFF & CONSULT INFECTIOUS DIS, OCHSNER FOUND HOSP, 63- *Concurrent Pos:* Asst vis physician, Charity Hosp La, New Orleans, 61-62, vis physician, 62-75, sr vis physician, 75-; instr infectious dis, Sch Med, Tulane Univ, 63-65, from clin asst prof to clin assoc prof, 65-73, clin prof med, 73-; clin assoc prof, Dept Oral Diag, Med & Radiol, Sch Dent, La State Univ, New Orleans, 70-, clin prof med, Sch Med, 79-; consult, Instnl Rels Comt, Am Soc Internal Med, 72-73; med consult, World Health Info Serv, 74-; consult physician, Dept Med, Vet Admin Med Ctr, Biloxi, Miss, 78- *Honors & Awards:* Physician Recog Award, AMA, 78-81. *Mem:* Fel Am Col Physicians; fel Am Col Prev Med; fel Infectious Dis Soc Am; fel Am Col Chest Physicians; Am Soc Trop Med & Hyg. *Res:* Antimicrobial evaluation; endocarditis; systemic fungal diseases; mycobacteria, especially in vitro antimicrobial susceptibility and treatment. *Mailing Add:* Ochsner Clin 1514 Jefferson Hwy New Orleans LA 70121

PANKIWSKYJ, KOST ANDRIJ, b Lviv, Ukraine, Dec 20, 36; US citizen. GEOLOGY. *Educ:* Mass Inst Technol, BS, 59; Harvard Univ, PhD(geol), 64. *Prof Exp:* Lectr mineral, Univ Mass, 64; ASST PROF MINERAL & PETROL, UNIV HAWAII, 64-, ASSOC PROF GEOL & GEOPHYS, 72- *Concurrent Pos:* Field geologist, Maine Geol Surv, 60- *Mem:* Mineral Soc Am; Geochem Soc; Mineral Soc Gt Brit & Ireland. *Res:* Structural and stratigraphic mapping in northwestern Maine; chemical and mineralogical composition of Hawaiian basalts. *Mailing Add:* Dept of Geol & Geophys HIG 205 Univ of Hawaii Honolulu HI 96822

PANKOVE, JACQUES I, b Russia, Nov 23, 22; nat US; m 50; c 2. SOLID STATE PHYSICS. *Educ:* Univ Calif, BS, 44, MS, 48; Univ Paris, PhD(physics), 60. *Prof Exp:* Lab asst, Univ Calif, 46-48; solid state physicist, 48-71, FEL TECH STAFF, RCA LABS, 71- *Concurrent Pos:* Vis McKay lectr, Univ Calif, Berkeley, 68-69; assoc ed, J Quantum Electronics, 68-77; vis prof, Univ Campinas, Brazil, 75. *Honors & Awards:* Radio Corp Am Award, 52, 53 & 63; Ebers Award, Inst Elec & Electronics Engrs, 75. *Mem:* AAAS; fel Am Phys Soc; fel Inst Elec & Electronics Engrs. *Res:* Semiconductor devices and semiconductor properties; superconductivity; luminescence; lasers. *Mailing Add:* RCA Labs Princeton NJ 08540

PANKOVICH, ARSEN M, b Banja Luka, Yugoslavia, Aug 3, 30; US citizen. ORTHOPEDIC SURGERY. *Educ:* Univ Belgrade, MD, 54. *Prof Exp:* Instr orthop surg, Med Col, Cornell Univ, 66-67; from asst prof to assoc prof, Sch Med, Univ Chicago, 67-72; PROF ORTHOP SURG, ABRAHAM LINCOLN SCH MED, UNIV ILL MED CTR, 72-, CHMN DEPT ORTHOP SURG, COOK COUNTY HOSP, 72- *Concurrent Pos:* USPHS fel, Univ Chicago, 61-62 & Hosp Spec Surg, New York, 65-67. *Mem:* Am Acad Orthop Surg; Am Col Surg; Orthop Res Soc; Clin Orthopaedic Soc; Sigma Xi. *Res:* Bone physiology, enzymes and calcification; diagnosis and treatment of fractures and dislocations. *Mailing Add:* Cook County Hosp 1825 West Harrison St Chicago IL 60612

PANKOW, JAMES FREDERICK, b Mexico City, Mex, Jan 14, 51; US citizen; m 79. NATURAL WATER CHEMISTRY, ENVIRONMENTAL ORGANIC ANALYSIS. *Educ:* State Univ NY, Bingham, BA, 73; Calif Inst Technol, MS, 76, PhD(environ sci), 78. *Prof Exp:* Instr, 78-80, ASST PROF WATER CHEM, ORE GRAD CTR, 80- *Mem:* Am Chem Soc. *Res:* Behavior of organic chemicals in the environment and their analysis by modern methods including capillary gonococcal/mass spectrometry; natural water chemistry. *Mailing Add:* Dept Envin Sci Ore Grad Ctr 19600 NW Walker Rd Beaverton OR 97006

PANKRATZ, RONALD ERNEST, b Moundridge, Kans, Apr 19, 18; m 43; c 8. ANALYTICAL CHEMISTRY. *Educ:* Bethel Col, Kans, AB, 41. *Prof Exp:* Chemist, Weldon Springs Ord Works, Atlas Powder Co, Mo, 42-43; res chemist, Presstite Eng Co, 43-45 & Cole Chem Co, 45-48; control chemist, Flint Eaton & Co, Ill, 48-57; chief chemist, Ft Dodge Labs Inc, Am Home Prod Co, 57-62, dir pharmaceut control & res assoc, Diamond Labs, Iowa, 62-64; chemist, Chemagro Corp, Mo, 64-65; res chemist, Abbott Labs, Ill, 65-69; dir qual control, Med Chem Corp, 70-71; MGR CHEM DIV, POLYSCI CORP, NILES, 71- *Mem:* Am Chem Soc. *Res:* Analytical research; tissue residue studies. *Mailing Add:* 3528 Winhaven Dr Waukegan IL 60085

PANLILIO, FILADELFO, b Philippines, Feb 5, 18; US citizen; m 40; c 2. ENGINEERING MECHANICS, MECHANICAL ENGINEERING. *Educ:* Univ Philippines, BSME, 38; Univ Mich, MS, 42, PhD(eng mech), 46. *Prof Exp:* Instr mech, Univ Philippines, 38-41; from instr to asst prof, Univ Mich, 45-48; from asst prof to assoc prof, Univ Philippines, 48-53, prof & chmn, 53-55; assoc prof mech eng, 55-57, PROF MECH ENG, UNION COL, 57- *Concurrent Pos:* Consult, Gen Elec Co, 56, ALCO Prod, Inc, 58, Knolls Atomic Power Lab, Gen Elec Co, 60 & Watervliet Arsenal, US Army Weapons Command, 63- *Mem:* Soc Exp Stress Anal; Am Soc Mech Engrs; Am Soc Metals. *Res:* Deformable body mechanics; continuum mechanics; finite elements. *Mailing Add:* Dept of Mech Eng Union Col Schenectady NY 12308

PANNABECKER, RICHARD FLOYD, b Bluffton, Ohio, May 21, 22; m 45; c 5. ZOOLOGY. *Educ:* Roosevelt Univ, BS, 48; Univ Chicago, PhD(zool), 57. *Prof Exp:* Asst zool, Univ Chicago, 50-54; from asst prof to assoc prof biol, Ohio Northern Univ, 54-61; assoc prof, 61-64, PROF BIOL, BLUFFTON COL, 64- *Mem:* AAAS; Am Inst Biol Sci. *Res:* Vertebrate embryology and endocrinology, particularly sex differentiation in vertebrates. *Mailing Add:* Dept of Biol Bluffton Col Bluffton OH 45817

PANNBACKER, RICHARD GEORGE, biochemistry, pharmacology, see previous edition

PANNELL, KEITH HOWARD, b London, Eng Aug 27, 40; c 3. ORGANOMETALLIC CHEMISTRY. *Educ:* Univ Durham, BSc, 62, MSc, 63; Univ Toronto, PhD(organometallic chem), 66. *Prof Exp:* Res assoc, Univ Ga, 66-68; sr res fel, Univ Sussex, 68-70; asst prof, 71-73, assoc prof, 73-80, PROF CHEM, UNIV TEX, EL PASO, 80- *Mem:* The Chem Soc; Am Chem Soc. *Res:* Interactions of metals and metalloids with organic molecules; clay/organometallic interactions. *Mailing Add:* Dept Chem Univ Tex El Paso TX 79968

PANNELL, LOLITA, b Millburn, NJ, May 10, 12. BACTERIOLOGY. *Educ:* Brown Univ, PhB, 34; Univ Kans, MA, 47, PhD(bact), 50. *Prof Exp:* Instr phys educ, Essex County Hosp, NJ, 34-39; bacteriologist, Sch Med & Dent, Univ Rochester, 39-41 & Meadowbrook Hosp, 41-43; lab asst bact, hemat & virol, Univ Kans, 46-50; asst prof bact & immunol, Jefferson Med Col, 50-54; from asst prof to prof bact, 54-75, EMER PROF BACT, MED UNIV SC, 75- *Mem:* AAAS; Am Soc Microbiol; Am Pub Health Asn; NY Acad Sci. *Res:* Glanders; melioidosis; tularemia; rheumatic fever. *Mailing Add:* 224 Molasses Lane Mt Pleasant SC 29464

PANNELL, RICHARD BYRON, b Salt Lake City, Utah, May 1, 52; m 77; c 2. CATALYSIS, PHYSICAL CHEMISTRY. *Educ:* Univ Utah, BS, 74; Brigham Young Univ, PhD(chem eng), 78. *Prof Exp:* RES ENGR CATALYSIS, GULF SCI & TECHNOL CO, 78- *Mem:* Am Chem Soc. *Res:* Synthesis gas conversion to fuels and chemicals and surface properties of heterogeneous catalysts; catalyst preparation, catalyst charcterization and kinetics. *Mailing Add:* Gulf Sci & Technol Co PO Drawer 2038 Pittsburgh PA 15230

PANNER, BERNARD J, b Youngstown, Ohio, Oct 9, 28; m 62; c 3. PATHOLOGY. *Educ:* Western Reserve Univ, AB, 49, MD, 53. *Prof Exp:* PROF PATH, MED CTR, UNIV ROCHESTER, 61- *Mem:* AAAS; Am Soc Exp Path; Electron Micros Soc Am; Am Asn Path & Bact. *Res:* Experimental pathology and clinical renal diseases; ultrastructure of smooth muscle. *Mailing Add:* Univ of Rochester Med Ctr 601 Elmwood Ave Rochester NY 14642

PANNILL, FITZHUGH CARTER, JR, b Rosemont, Pa, July 4, 21; m 46; c 3. INTERNAL MEDICINE. *Educ:* Yale Univ, BS, 42, MD, 45; Am Bd Internal Med, dipl, 53. *Prof Exp:* From instr to asst prof med, Col Med, Baylor Univ, 51-54; clin instr, Univ Tex Southwestern Med Sch, 59-60, asst prof internal med & asst dean grants & sponsored res, 61-64; assoc prof med, Hahnemann Med Col, 60-61; prof med & dean, Univ Tex Med Sch San Antonio, 65-73; PROF MED & VPRES HEALTH SCI, STATE UNIV NY BUFFALO, 73- *Concurrent Pos:* Markle Found award acad med, 62-67; pvt pract, Tex, 54-60. *Mem:* Fel Am Col Physicians; AMA; Asn Am Med Col; Am Fedn Clin Res. *Mailing Add:* Off of VPres of Health Sci State Univ of NY Buffalo NY 14222

PANNU, SARDUL S, b Wadala Banger, Panjab, India, Nov 1, 35; US citizen; m 66; c 2. ANALYTICAL CHEMISTRY. *Educ:* Khalsa Col, BSc, 56, MSc, 58; George Washington Univ, PhD(anal chem), 65. *Prof Exp:* Lectr chem, Khalsa Col, 58-60; prof, Southern Union State Jr Col, 65-66; from asst prof to assoc prof, Randolph-Macon Col, 66-69; assoc prof, 69-71, NASA res grant, 70-71, PROF CHEM, UNIV DC, 71- *Concurrent Pos:* NIH biomed grant, 74-77. *Mem:* Am Chem Soc; Indian Chem Soc. *Res:* Electroanalytical determination of transition elements. *Mailing Add:* Dept of Chem Univ of DC Washington DC 20005

PANOFF, ROBERT, b New York, NY, Aug 16, 21; m 53; c 6. NUCLEAR & MARINE ENGINEERING. *Educ:* Union Col, NY, BS, 42. *Hon Degrees:* ScD, Allegheny Col, 59. *Prof Exp:* Supvry engr submarine propulsion design, Elec Sect, Bur Ships, US Dept Navy, 42-50, dir nuclear & marine eng, Ship Appln Div-Naval Reactors, 50-54, sr submarine proj mgr, Nuclear Propulsion Div, Bur Ships & asst mgr naval reactors, AEC, 54-64; PRIN OFF & DIR, MPR ASSOCS, INC, 64- *Concurrent Pos:* Consult to dir res & eng, US Dept Defense, 66-; mem antisubmarine warfare panel, Defense Sci Bd, 66-; chmn ships bd, Naval Res Adv Comt, 74-78. *Honors & Awards:* Meritorious Serv Award, US Dept Navy, 52, Distinguished Serv Award, 59. *Mem:* Soc Naval Archit & Marine Engrs. *Res:* Development of nuclear propulsion plants for naval vessels, merchant ships and oceanographic vehicles; development of nuclear power plants for generation of electricity. *Mailing Add:* MPR Assocs Inc 1140 Connecticut Ave NW Washington DC 20036

PANOFSKY, HANS ARNOLD, b Cassel, Ger, Sept 18, 17; m 43; c 2. MICROMETEOROLOGY. *Educ:* Princeton Univ, AB, 38; Univ Calif, PhD(astron), 41. *Prof Exp:* Instr astron, Wilson Col, 41-42; instr meteorol, NY, Univ, 42-45, res assoc physics & meteorol, 45-46, from asst prof to assoc prof meteorol, 46-51; assoc prof, 51-53, PROF METEOROL, PA STATE UNIV, UNIVERSITY PARK, 54-, EVAN PUGH RES PROF, 66- *Concurrent Pos:* Guggenheim fel, 60; mem climatic impact comt, Nat Acad Sci, 73- *Honors & Awards:* Meisinger Award, 65; C G Rossby Res Medal, 76. *Mem:* Fel AAAS; fel Am Meteorol Soc; Am Geophys Union; Royal Meteorol Soc. *Res:* Dynamic meteorology; turbulence; satellite meteorology. *Mailing Add:* 1000A Plaza Dr State College PA 16801

PANOFSKY, WOLFGANG K H, b Berlin, Ger, Apr 24, 19; nat US; m 42; c 5. PHYSICS. *Educ:* Princeton Univ, AB, 38; Calif Inst Technol, PhD(physics), 42. *Prof Exp:* From tech proj dir to proj dir, Off Sci Res & Develop, 42-45; from asst prof to assoc prof physics, radiation lab, Univ Calif, 45-51; PROF PHYSICS, STANFORD UNIV, 51-, DIR STANFORD LINEAR ACCELERATOR CTR, 61- *Concurrent Pos:* Dir high energy physics lab, Stanford Univ, 53-61; mem high energy comn, Int Union Pure & Appl Physics, 58-60; guest prof, Europ Orgn Nuclear Res, Geneva, 59; Guggenheim fel, 59; chmn tech working group high altitude detection, US del, Geneva, 59, vchmn tech working group II, 59; mem, President's Sci Adv Comt, 60-63; Richtmyer lectr, 63; consult, Atomic Energy Comn, US Air Force; consult, Radiation Lab, Univ Calif & NSF; mem, Adv Res Proj Agency. *Honors & Awards:* Ernest Orlando Lawrence Award, Atomic Energy Comn, 61; Calif Scientist of Year Award, 67; Nat Medal Sci, 69; Franklin Inst Award, 70. *Mem:* Nat Acad Sci; fel Am Phys Soc (vpres). *Res:* High energy physics; particle accelerators. *Mailing Add:* Stanford Linear Accelerator Ctr PO Box 4349 Stanford CA 94305

PANOPOULOS, NICKOLAS JOHN, b Doliana Kynourias, Greece. PLANT PATHOLOGY, MICROBIAL GENETICS. *Educ:* Agr Col Athens, BS, 66; Univ Calif, Berkeley, PhD(plant path), 71. *Prof Exp:* Asst res fel, 71-75, asst plant pathologist & lectr, 75-80, ASSOC PROF PLANT PATH, UNIV CALIF, BERKELEY, 80- *Mem:* Am Phytopath Soc; Am Soc Microbiol. *Res:* Genetics of bacterial pathogenicity on plants. *Mailing Add:* Dept Plant Path Univ Calif Berkeley CA 94720

PANOS, CHARLES, b Pittsburgh, Pa, July 15, 29; m 57; c 3. BACTERIOLOGY, BIOCHEMISTRY. *Educ:* Univ Pittsburgh, BSc, 52, MS, 53, PhD(bact), 56. *Prof Exp:* Asst prof bact, Univ Fla, 56-57; asst prof biochem, Sch Med, Univ Ill, 57-61; assoc mem res, Albert Einstein Med Ctr, Northern Div, Philadelphia, 61-68, mem, 68-72; PROF MICROBIOL, MED SCH, THOMAS JEFFERSON UNIV, 72- *Concurrent Pos:* Res fel biochem, Sch Med, Univ Ill, 57-61; USPHS career develop award, 60 & 63-; res assoc prof, Sch Med, Temple Univ, 61-72. *Mem:* Am Soc Microbiol; Am Soc Biol Chem; Brit Soc Gen Microbiol; Int Orgn Mycoplasmology; fel Am Acad Microbiol. *Res:* Microbial metabolism; intermediary lipid metabolism; cell wall biosynthesis; biochemistry of bacterial L-forms and mycoplasmas. *Mailing Add:* Dept Microbiol Jefferson Alumni Hall Thomas Jefferson Univ Med Sch Philadelphia PA 19107

PANOS, PETER S, b Chicago, Ill. CHEMICAL ENGINEERING. *Educ:* Northwestern Univ, BS, 61; Univ Chicago, MBA, 64. *Prof Exp:* Training specialist, Procter & Gamble Mfg Co, 61-63; supvr eng econ, Inst Gas Technol, 63-69; GROUP VPRES, DUFF & PHELPS INC, 69- *Mem:* Nat Soc Prof Engrs; Am Inst Chem Engrs; Am Gas Asn; Inst Chartered Financial Analysts. *Res:* Utility engineering; liquefied natural gas; substitute gas supply. *Mailing Add:* Duff & Phelps Inc 55 E Monroe St Chicago IL 60603

PANSKY, BEN, b Milwaukee, Wis, Feb 18, 28; m 53. ANATOMY. *Educ:* Univ Wis, BA, 48, MS, 50, PhD(anat), 54; New York Med Col, MD, 68; Nat Bd Med Examiners, dipl. *Prof Exp:* Instr histol, neuroanat & anat, Univ Wis, 51-53; from instr to assoc prof anat, New York Med Col, 53-68; resident path, Columbia Presby Hosp, Col Physicians & Surgeons, 68-69, path trainee &

supvr autopsy serv, 69-70; PROF ANAT, MED COL OHIO, 70-, DIR BACCALAUREATE, BIOL NURSING, 76- *Mem:* AAAS; Am Asn Anat; Am Heart Asn. *Res:* Hematological studies as related to endocrine variations; immunohistochemistry; immunocytochemistry; pituitary gland and hypothalamus. *Mailing Add:* Med Col of Ohio Dept of Anat C S 10008 Toledo OH 43699

PANSON, GILBERT STEPHEN, b Paterson, NJ, Apr 11, 20; m 44; c 2. PHYSICAL CHEMISTRY, ORGANIC CHEMISTRY. *Educ:* Brown Univ, ScB, 41; Columbia Univ, MA, 50, PhD(chem), 53. *Prof Exp:* From instr to asst prof chem, Hobart Col, 41-44; res chemist, Tenn Eastman Co, 44-46; from asst prof to assoc prof chem, 46-60, actg dean, Newark Col Arts & Sci, 71-73; PROF CHEM, RUTGERS UNIV, NEWARK, 60-, CHMN DEPT, 62-, DEAN, GRAD SCH, 75- *Concurrent Pos:* Vis prof chem, Univ Calif, Berkeley, 73-74. *Mem:* Am Chem Soc. *Res:* Physical organic chemistry; separation of isotopes; reaction kinetics; separation of organic compounds by thermal diffusion. *Mailing Add:* Dept of Chem Rutgers Univ Newark NJ 07102

PANTELIDES, SOKRATES THEODORE, b Limassol, Cyprus, Nov 20, 48; m 72; c 1. THEORETICAL SOLID STATE PHYSICS. *Educ:* Northern Ill Univ, BS, 69; Univ Ill, Urbana, MS, 70, PhD(physics), 73. *Prof Exp:* Res assoc physics, Univ Ill, Urbana, 73 & W W Hansen Labs, Stanford Univ, 73-75; RES STAFF MEM PHYSICS, T J WATSON RES CTR, IBM CORP, 75- *Concurrent Pos:* Vis prof, Dept Theoret Physics, Univ Lund, 75; actg chair prof, Dept Theoret Phys, 78. *Mem:* Fel Am Phys Soc. *Res:* Theory of electronic properties of solids; theory of semiconductor surfaces and interfaces; the systematics of band structures, optical properties and dielectric constants; theory of excitons and photoemission; theory of impurities and defects in semiconductors. *Mailing Add:* T J Watson Res Ctr IBM Corp Yorktown Heights NY 10598

PANTO, JOSEPH SALVATORE, b Lawrence, Mass, Dec 25, 25; m 52; c 2. TEXTILE CHEMISTRY. *Educ:* Lowell Technol Inst, BS, 51, MS, 63. *Prof Exp:* Res assoc textile chem, Burlington Industs Inc, 51-53; ASST DIR TECH SERV, ALBANY INT RES CO, 53- *Mem:* Am Chem Soc; Am Asn Textile Chemists & Colorists (vpres, 72); fel Am Inst Chemists; Brit Soc Dyers & Colourists; Am Arbitration Asn. *Res:* Color measurement and the application of textile colorants to fibrous materials; application, by novel techniques, of resin pre-condensates to cellulosic fibers to impart resistance to creasing. *Mailing Add:* 13 Valley Rd Dover MA 02030

PANTON, R(ONALD) L(EE), b Neodesha, Kans, Feb 14, 33; m 60; c 3. FLUID MECHANICS. *Educ:* Wichita State Univ, AB & BS, 56; Univ Wis, MS, 62; Univ Calif, Berkeley, PhD(mech eng), 66. *Prof Exp:* Engr, NAm Aviation, Inc, 56-58; asst prof mech & aerospace eng, Okla State Univ, 66-71; assoc prof mech eng, 71-76, PROF MECH ENG, UNIV TEX, AUSTIN, 76- *Mem:* Am Inst Aeronaut & Astronaut; Am Soc Mech Engrs; Am Phys Soc. *Res:* Fluid mechanics, combustion, turbulence, incompressible flow. *Mailing Add:* Dept of Mech Eng Univ of Tex Austin TX 78712

PANTUCK, EUGENE JOEL, b Boston, Mass, Feb 8, 38; m 60; c 2. ANESTHESIOLOGY, BIOCHEMICAL PHARMACOLOGY. *Educ:* Tufts Univ, BS, 59, MD, 63. *Prof Exp:* Intern med & surg, Montefiore Hosp, New York, 63-64; resident anesthesiol, Presby Hosp, New York, 64-66; dep chief, USPHS Hosp, Baltimore, 67-68, chief, 68-69; asst prof, 69-77, asst attend anesthesiologist, Presby Hosp, 69-77, ASSOC PROF ANESTHESIOL, COLUMBIA UNIV, 77-, ASSOC ATTEND ANESTHESIOLOGIST, PRESBY HOSP, 77- *Concurrent Pos:* Res trainee anesthesiol, Columbia Univ, 66-67. *Mem:* Am Soc Pharmacol & Exp Therapeut; Am Soc Anesthesiol. *Res:* Drug metabolism; drug interaction; enzyme induction; chemical carcinogenesis. *Mailing Add:* Presby Hosp 622 W 168th St New York NY 10032

PANUSH, RICHARD SHELDON, b Detroit, Mich, Nov 9, 42; m 66; c 3. CLINICAL IMMUNOLOGY, RHEUMATOLOGY. *Educ:* Univ Mich Honors Col, BA, 65, Med Sch, MD, 67. *Prof Exp:* Intern, Duke Univ Med Ctr, 67-68 & jr asst res, 68-69; res fel, Dept Med, Harvard Med Sch, 69-71; chief rheumatology, Dept Med, Silas B Hayes Army Hosp, 71-72 & Fitzsimons Gen Hosp, 72-73; asst prof clin immunol, Col Med, Univ Fla, 73-77; CHIEF RHEUMATOLOGY, GAINESVILLE VET ADMIN MED CTR, 73-; CHIEF CLIN IMMUNOL, COL MED, UNIV FLA, 76-, ASSOC PROF, 77- *Mem:* Am Rheumatism Asn; Am Fed Clin Res; Am Col Physicians; Am Asn Immunologists; Am Acad Allergy. *Res:* Immunologic aspects of rheumatic diseases. *Mailing Add:* Div Clin Immunol Dept Med Box J-277 Univ Fla Gainesville FL 32610

PANUSKA, JOSEPH ALLAN, b Baltimore, Md, July 3, 27. ENVIRONMENTAL PHYSIOLOGY. *Educ:* Loyola Col, Md, BS, 48; St Louis Univ, PhL, 54, PhD(biol), 58; Woodstock Col, STL, 61. *Hon Degrees:* LLD, Scranton Univ, 74. *Prof Exp:* NIH trainee physiol, Sch Med, Emory Univ, 62-63, instr, 63; from asst prof to assoc prof biol, 63-72, spiritual dir, Sch Med, 64-68, assoc chmn dept biol, Georgetown Univ, 70-73, prof biol, 72-79; ACAD V PRES & PROF BIOL, BOSTON COL, 79- *Concurrent Pos:* NSF res grant, 60-61, St Joseph's Univ, Loyola Col, Boston Col Campus Sch Handicapped, 79-; US Army Med Res & Develop Command res contract, 64-68; vis fel & vis scientist, Dept Path & St Edmund's House, Cambridge Univ, 69-70; mem, Am Found Biol Res, 68-, pres bd dirs, 74-79, vpres, 79-; mem bd trustees, Univ Scranton, 70-73 & St Peter's Col, 71-73; pres bd dirs, Jesuit Community Georgetown Univ, Inc, 71-73; ed-in-chief, Cryobiol, 71-74; Off Naval Res med & dent res contract, 71-74; provincial, Md Prov, Soc of Jesus, 73-79; pres bd of trustees, Woodstock Theol Ctr & Corp Roman Cath Clergymen, 73-79; mem bd dirs, Cambridge Ctr Social Studies, 73-79. *Honors & Awards:* Harbison Prize for Distinguished Teaching, Danforth Found, 69. *Mem:* AAAS; Am Physiol Soc; Soc Cryobiol; Soc Exp Biol & Med; Sigma Xi. *Res:* Low temperature effects on mammals, including hypothermia and hibernation; stress on cardiovascular system and animal behavior. *Mailing Add:* Boston Col Chestnut Hill MA 02167

PANUZIO, FRANK L, b Bridgeport, Conn, July 18, 07; m 49; c 1. CIVIL ENGINEERING. *Educ:* Cornell Univ, CE, 30, MCE, 32. *Prof Exp:* Hydraul engr, US Bur Reclamation, Colo, 33-36; struct & hydraul engr, NY Dist Corps Eng, US Army, 36-41, chief airport design sect, 41-44, asst & dept chief eng div, 44-51, chief eng div, Atlantic Dist Corps Eng, 51-53, asst chief eng div, NY Dist Corps Eng, 53-65, dep chief eng div, 65-66, chief, 66-69, sr eng consult, 69-72, chief, Postal Proj Mgt Br, 72-74, chief, Design Br Eng Div, 74; CONSULT CIVIL ENG, 74- *Concurrent Pos:* Adj prof, NY Univ, 40, 46-47, 48 & Polytech Inst Brooklyn, 47-48. *Mem:* Am Soc Civil Engrs; Am Geophys Union; Am Concrete Inst; Sigma Xi. *Res:* Administration and direction of engineering endeavors in connection with water resource planning, civil works construction and military construction activities. *Mailing Add:* 1385 Capitol Ave Bridgeport CT 06604

PANVINI, ROBERT S, b Brooklyn, NY, Apr 22, 37; m 59; c 3. HIGH ENERGY PHYSICS. *Educ:* Rensselaer Polytech Inst, ScB, 58; Brandeis Univ, PhD(physics), 65. *Prof Exp:* Res assoc exp high energy physics, Brookhaven Nat Lab, 65-67, from asst physicist to assoc physicist, 67-71; assoc prof physics, 71-80, PROF PHYSICS & ASTRON, VANDERBILT UNIV, 80- *Res:* Experimental high energy physics, instrumentation, programming and analysis of experimental data. *Mailing Add:* Dept of Physics Vanderbilt Univ Nashville TN 37203

PANZER, HANS PETER, b Ratingen, WGer, July 26, 22; nat US; m 56; c 2. ORGANIC POLYMER CHEMISTRY. *Educ:* Univ Muenster, Ger, Dipl, 54, Dr rer nat, 57. *Prof Exp:* Fel carbohydrate chem, Purdue Univ, 57-58; sr res chemist, Res & Develop Div, Am Machine & Foundry Co, 59-63; res specialist, Technol Ctr, Gen Foods Corp, 63-65; group leader, Indust Chem Div, 66-71, sr res chemist, Indust Chem & Plastics Div, 71-72 & Chem Res Div, 72-74, proj leader polymer res, 74-79, res group leader, 79-81, PRIN RES CHEMIST, CHEM RES DIV, AM CYANAMID CO, 81- *Mem:* Am Chem Soc; German Chem Soc. *Res:* Organic synthesis; synthetic and natural polymers; polyelectrolytes; organic flocculants; water treating and mining chemicals. *Mailing Add:* 150 Old N Stamford Rd Stamford CT 06905

PANZER, JAMES DAVID, clinical pharmacology, see previous edition

PANZER, JEROME, b New York, NY, Apr 5, 31; m 54; c 3. PETROLEUM TECHNOLOGY. *Educ:* NY Univ, BA, 52; Cornell Univ, PhD(org chem), 56. *Prof Exp:* Chemist, Esso Res & Eng Co, 56-65, proj leader lubricants res, 65-70; RES ASSOC, EXXON RES & ENG CO, 70- Mem. *Mem:* Am Chem Soc; Soc Automotive Engrs. *Res:* Gasoline product quality; automotive emissions; non-aqueous colloidal systems; surface chemistry; coal liquids; alcohol fuels. *Mailing Add:* Exxon Res & Eng Co PO Box 51 Linden NJ 07036

PANZER, RICHARD EARL, b Hastings, Nebr, Feb 9, 23; m 48; c 2. PHYSICAL INORGANIC CHEMISTRY. *Educ:* Col of the Pac, BA, 48; Univ Nev, MS, 50; Univ NMex, PhD(chem), 59. *Prof Exp:* Aide phys sci, Indust Lab, US Navy Yard, 43-44; asst, Univ Nev, 48-50; chemist, Titanium Res Unit, US Bur Mines, 51-53; sr chemist, Metall Res Lab, Reynolds Metals Co, 53-55; asst chem, Univ NMex, 55-58; res electrochemist, US Naval Ord Lab, Calif, 58-70 & Mare Island Naval Shipyard, 70-73; res chemist, Naval Ship Res & Develop Ctr, 73-78; CONSULT, 78- *Concurrent Pos:* Naval Ord Lab fel chem, Univ Mich, 66-67. *Mem:* Sigma Xi; Nat Audubon Soc. *Res:* Energy conversion; computer applications to chemistry; physical metallurgy; coatings; corrosion; oceanography; materials science. *Mailing Add:* 158 N Lake Dr Stevensville MD 21666

PAO, CHIA-VEN, b An-Whei, China, Aug 10, 33; US citizen; m 63; c 3. APPLIED MATHEMATICS, APPLIED MECHANICS. *Educ:* Nat Taiwan Univ, BS, 59; Kans State Univ, MS, 62; Univ Pittsburgh, PhD(math), 68. *Prof Exp:* Engr, Westinghouse Elec Corp, 62-67; assoc prof, 69-79, PROF MATH, NC STATE UNIV, 80- *Concurrent Pos:* Fel, NASA, 68-69; Army Res Off grant, 70-73. *Mem:* Am Math Soc; Soc Indust & Appl Math. *Res:* Nonlinear reaction; diffusion systems, neutron transport and radiative transfer problems; biological systems; reactor dynamics; Boltzmann equations; integro-partial differential equations and stability theory; numerical solutions of partial differential equations. *Mailing Add:* Dept of Math NC State Univ Raleigh NC 27650

PAO, HSIEN PING, b Ningpo, China, July 1, 35; US citizen; m 65; c 2. FLUID MECHANICS, ATMOSPHERIC SCIENCES. *Educ:* Nat Taiwan Univ, BS, 56; Johns Hopkins Univ, PhD(fluid mech), 63. *Prof Exp:* Res asst fluid mech, Johns Hopkins Univ, 58-63, res assoc, 63-64; from asst prof to assoc prof, 64-70, PROF FLUID MECH, CATH UNIV AM, 70- *Concurrent Pos:* Consult, Appl Sci Div, Litton Syst, Inc, 67-68, Singer Info Serv Co, 70-, Flow Res, Inc, Kent, Wash, Integrated Syst, Rockville, o Md & MERDOC Res Labs, US Army, Ft Belvoir, Va. *Mem:* Am Meteorol Soc; Am Phys Soc; Am Soc Civil Engrs. *Res:* Stability and boundary layer problems in fluid mechanics; stratified and rotating fluid flows; magnetohydrodynamic flows; dynamics of cable system; water pollution; oceanic fronts; atmospheric dynamics. *Mailing Add:* Dept Civil Eng Cath Univ Am Washington DC 20064

PAO, RICHARD H(SIEN) F(ENG), b China, Apr 22, 26; nat US; m 61. CIVIL ENGINEERING. *Educ:* St John's Univ, China, BSCE, 49; Univ Ill, MS, 51, PhD, 53. *Prof Exp:* Struct designer, J G White Eng Corp, 53-54; from asst prof to prof civil eng, Rose-Hulman Inst Technol, 54-67, chmn dept, 62-67, dir acad develop coun, 66-67; PROF CIVIL ENG & ENG MECH, CLEVELAND STATE UNIV, 67- *Concurrent Pos:* Fel fluid mech, Harvard Univ, 64-65. *Mem:* AAAS; Int Water Resources Asn; Am Acad Mech; Am Soc Civil Engrs; Int Asn Hydraul Res. *Res:* Fluid mechanics; hydrology; hydraulic engineering; engineering systems design. *Mailing Add:* Dept of Civil Eng Cleveland State Univ Cleveland OH 44115

PAO, S(UI-KWONG) PAUL, fluid mechanics, applied mathematics, see previous edition

PAO, Y(EN)-C(HING), b Ninpo, China, Mar 4, 35; US citizen; m 60. ENGINEERING, MATHEMATICS. *Educ:* Nat Taiwan Univ, BS, 56; Univ Utah, MS, 59, MA, 61; Cornell Univ, PhD(mech), 65. *Prof Exp:* Mech engr, Montek Assocs, Inc, 59; design engr, EIMCO Corp, 59-61; assoc res engr, Boeing Co, 61-63; consult, Therm Advan Res Co, 64-65; preliminary design engr, Garrett Corp, 65-66; assoc prof eng mech, 66-71, PROF MECH ENG & ENG MECH, UNIV NEBR, LINCOLN, 71- *Concurrent Pos:* NSF-NIH grants, Univ Nebr, 67-79; collabr, vis scientist & consult, Mayo Clin, 73-82; consult, var industs. *Mem:* Sigma Xi; AAAS; Am Soc Mech Engrs; Soc Biomed Engrs; Am Acad Mech. *Res:* Mechanics; applied mathematics; simulation; computer applications; composite materials; cardiopulmonary mechanics. *Mailing Add:* 311 Bancroft Hall Univ Nebr Lincoln NE 68588

PAO, YIH-HSING, b Nanking, China, Jan 19, 30; m 57; c 3. APPLIED MECHANICS, STRUCTURAL ENGINEERING. *Educ:* Univ Taiwan, BS, 52; Rensselaer Polytech Inst, MS, 55; Columbia Univ, PhD(eng mech), 59. *Prof Exp:* Asst eng mech, Rensselaer Polytech Inst, 53-55 & Columbia Univ, 56-58; from asst prof to assoc prof, 58-68, chmn, Theoret & Appl Mech Dept, 74-80, PROF ENG MECH, CORNELL UNIV, 68- *Concurrent Pos:* Consult, industs; vis prof, Stanford Univ, Princeton Univ & Nat Taiwan Univ; assoc ed, J Thermal Stresses. *Mem:* Soc Eng Sci; Am Soc Mech Engrs; Am Acad Mech; Acoust Soc Am. *Res:* Vibrations; elasticity; visco-elasticity; stress waves in solids; dynamics of structures; non-destructive testing of materials by ultrasound. *Mailing Add:* Dept of Theoret & Appl Mech Thurston Hall Cornell Univ Ithaca NY 14853

PAO, YOH-HAN, b China, July 17, 22; nat US; m 48; c 3. PHYSICS. *Educ:* Lester Inst, China, BS, 45; Syracuse Univ, MS, 49; Pa State Univ, PhD(appl physics), 52. *Prof Exp:* Asst prof eng res, Pa State Univ, 52-53; res physicist, E I du Pont de Nemours & Co, 53-56, res assoc, 56-59, supvr phys res, 59-61; sr res physicist, lab appl sci & res assoc, inst study metals, Univ Chicago, 61-62; mem tech staff, Bell Tel Labs, NJ, 62-67; prof appl physics, 67-76, PROF ELEC ENG & APPL PHYSICS, CASE WESTERN RESERVE UNIV, 76-, HEAD DEPT ELEC ENG & APPL PHYSICS, 69- *Mem:* Am Phys Soc; Optical Soc Am; NY Acad Sci. *Res:* Chemical physics; optics; lasers; polymers. *Mailing Add:* Dept of Elec Eng & Appl Physics Case Western Reserve Univ Cleveland OH 44106

PAO, YOUNG-PING, b Anhwei Prov, China, Oct 14, 35; m 66; c 3. PLASMA PHYSICS, FLUID DYNAMICS. *Educ:* Princeton Univ, PhD(aerospace sci), 65. *Prof Exp:* From asst prof to assoc prof appl math, Brown Univ, 65-73; RES PROF MATH, NY UNIV, 74- *Mem:* Am Phys Soc. *Res:* Theoretical plasma physics; equilibrium, stability and transport properties for magnetic fusion plasmas; kinetic theory of gases. *Mailing Add:* Courant Inst 251 Mercer St New York NY 10012

PAOLETTI, ROBERT ANTHONY, b Greenfield, Mass, Oct 2, 42; m 64; c 2. DEVELOPMENTAL BIOLOGY. *Educ:* Univ Mass, BS, 64; Johns Hopkins Univ, PhD(biol), 68. *Prof Exp:* From asst prof to assoc prof, 68-78, PROF BIOL, KING'S COL, PA, 78-, EDUC COORDR, PHYSICIAN'S ASST PROG, 74- *Concurrent Pos:* Mem, Hastings Ctr, Inst Soc, Ethics & Life Sci. *Mem:* AAAS; Sigma Xi. *Res:* Biology of isolated chromatin; characterization of chromosomal proteins and their interaction with DNA; genetic engineering; bioethics. *Mailing Add:* Dept of Biol King's Col 133 N River St Wilkes-Barre PA 18702

PAOLI, THOMAS LEE, b Springfield, Ill, May 27, 40; m 65. APPLIED PHYSICS, QUANTUM ELECTRONICS. *Educ:* Brown Univ, BSc & BA, 62; Stanford Univ, PhD(appl physics), 67. *Prof Exp:* Mem tech staff, Solid State Device Lab, Bell Labs, Inc, 67-81; MEM RES STAFF, PALO ALTO RES CTR, XEROX CORP, 81- *Mem:* Am Phys Soc; Inst Elec & Electronics Engrs. *Res:* Semiconductor lasers. *Mailing Add:* Stanford Indust Pk 3333 Coyote Hill Rd Palo Alto CA 94306

PAOLILLO, DOMINICK JOSEPH, botany, see previous edition

PAOLINI, FRANCIS RUDOLPH, b Newburgh, NY, July 13, 30; m 56; c 4. X-RAY SPECTROMETRY. *Educ:* Rensselaer Polytech Inst, BS, 51; Mass Inst Technol, PhD(physics, math), 60. *Prof Exp:* Sr scientist, Am Sci Eng Inc, 60-65, proj dir space res syst div, 65-69; tech dir, 69-74, VPRES ENG, PHILIPS ELECTRONIC INSTRUMENTS, INC, 74- *Mem:* AAAS; Am Phys Soc; Fedn Am Scientists; Am Mgt Asn. *Mailing Add:* Philips Electronic Instruments Inc 85 McKee Dr Mahwah NJ 07430

PAOLINI, PAUL JOSEPH, JR, b Newburgh, NY, May 4, 42; m 67; c 2. BIOPHYSICS, PHYSIOLOGY. *Educ:* Rensselaer Polytech Inst, BS, 63, MS, 64; Univ Calif, Davis, PhD(zool), 68. *Prof Exp:* Lab technician muscle physiol, Univ Calif, Davis, 67-68; asst prof biol sci, Univ Ga, 68-70; from asst prof to assoc prof, 70-76, chmn physiol prog, 75-77, PROF BIOL, SAN DIEGO STATE UNIV, 76-; RES PROF, DEPT PHYSIOL, UNIV PAC, SAN FRANCISCO, 77- *Concurrent Pos:* Am Heart Asn res grants, Univ Ga, 69-70, San Diego State Univ, 70-71, San Diego County Heart Asn res grants, 71-73; NSF res grant, 73-75; NIH res grant, 77- *Mem:* AAAS; Biophys Soc; Sigma Xi; Am Soc Cell Biol. *Res:* Physiology and biophysics of skeletal and cardiac vertebrate muscle; computer applications and techniques in biological research. *Mailing Add:* Dept of Biol San Diego State Univ San Diego CA 92182

PAONI, NICHOLAS FRANCIS, b Ilion, NY, May 13, 50; m 70; c 3. PROTEIN CHEMISTRY, MOLECULAR GENETICS. *Educ:* Univ Calif, Davis, BS, 72; Univ Notre Dame, PhD(biochem), 77. *Prof Exp:* Teaching & res asst chem & biochem, Univ Notre Dame, 72-77; fel, Univ Calif, Berkeley, 77-80; PROJ LEADER, BLOOD GROUP DEGRADING ENZYMES PROG, NAVAL BIOSCI LAB, UNIV CALIF, 80- *Res:* Cell surface modification of human erythrocytes-alteration of cellular antigenicity. *Mailing Add:* Univ Calif Naval Biosci Lab Naval Supply Ctr Oakland CA 94625

PAPA, ANTHONY JOSEPH, b New York, NY, Aug 27, 30; m 57; c 5. ORGANIC CHEMISTRY. *Educ:* WVa Univ, BS, 55, MS, 57; Wash State Univ, PhD(org chem), 61. *Prof Exp:* Res assoc, Purdue Univ, 61-62; res chemist org & polymer chem, E I du Pont de Nemours & Co, Del, 62-66; MEM STAFF, UNION CARBIDE CORP, 66- *Mem:* Am Chem Soc. *Res:* Polymer synthesis (relationship between chemical structure and physical properties of polymers) and development of catalytic processes. *Mailing Add:* Plastics Div Union Carbide Corp South Charleston WV 25303

PAPA, KENNETH E, b Octavia, Nebr, July 25, 31; m 59; c 2. GENETICS. *Educ:* Univ Nebr, BS, 57, MS, 59; Cornell Univ, PhD(genetics), 64. *Prof Exp:* From asst prof to assoc prof, 64-78, PROF PLANT GENETICS, UNIV GA, 78- *Mem:* Mycol Soc Am; Genetics Soc Am; Am Genetic Asn. *Res:* Fungal genetics, quantitative inheritance in Neurospora; aflatoxins in Aspergillus. *Mailing Add:* Dept Plant Path Univ of Ga Athens GA 30602

PAPAC, ROSE, b Montesano, Wash, Oct 18, 27. INTERNAL MEDICINE. *Educ:* Univ Seattle, BS, 49; St Louis Univ, MD, 53. *Prof Exp:* Intern internal med, St Louis Univ Hosps, 53-54; asst resident, Stanford Univ Hosps, 54-56; asst cancer res, Chester Beatty Inst Cancer Res, Eng, 56-57; res physician, Cancer Inst, Med Ctr, Univ Calif, San Francisco, 58-59, asst clin prof, 59-63; asst prof internal med, 63-72, ASSOC PROF INTERNAL MED, SCH MED, YALE UNIV, 72- *Concurrent Pos:* Res fel, Sloan-Kettering Inst, NY, 57-58. *Mem:* AMA; Am Soc Hemat; NY Acad Sci. *Res:* Clinical cancer chemotherapy; tissue culture studies of cell cycle. *Mailing Add:* Dept of Internal Med Yale Univ Sch of Med New Haven CT 06510

PAPACHRISTOU, CHRISTOS A, b Chalkis, Greece. FIRMWARE ENGINEERING, MICROPROGRAMMABLE MICROPROCESSING. *Educ:* Nat Polytech Univ, Greece, BS, 64; Philips Technol Inst, Netherlands, MS, 65; Johns Hopkins Univ, Baltimore, PhD(elec eng), 73. *Prof Exp:* Asst prof elec eng, Manhattan Col, 72-73; asst prof elec eng, Drexel Univ, 73-79; J Morrow Res Chair, 80, ASSOC PROF ELEC ENG & COMPUT ENG, UNIV CINCINNATI, 79- *Concurrent Pos:* Consult, Naval Air Develop Ctr, 74-75; prin investr, US Army Res Off, 82. *Mem:* Inst Elec & Electronics Engrs; Asn Comput Mach; Sigma Xi. *Res:* Hardware microprogram control scheme directed by a user-oriented firmware language; associative, table look-up, processing for residue arithmetic and multiple-valued logic; state machine implementation using programmable array logic. *Mailing Add:* Elec & Comput Eng Dept Univ Cincinnati Cincinnati OH 45221

PAPACONSTANTINOU, JOHN, b Philadelphia, Pa, Dec 2, 30; m 67; c 2. BIOCHEMISTRY. *Educ:* Temple Univ, BA, 52, MA, 54; Johns Hopkins Univ, PhD(biochem), 58. *Prof Exp:* Am Cancer Soc res fel embryol, Carnegie Inst, 58-60; instr microbiol, Sch Med, Johns Hopkins Univ, 60-62; asst prof zool & entom, Univ Conn, 62-66; res prof zool, Univ Ga, 66-77; mem sr res staff, Biol Div, Oak Ridge Nat Lab, 77-80; MEM FAC, DEPT HUMAN BIOL, CHEM & GENETICS, UNIV TEX MED BR, GALVESTON, 80- *Concurrent Pos:* Mem cell biol study sect, NIH, 68-71, mem spec study sect estab genetics res ctrs, Nat Inst Gen Med Sci; prof, Oak Ridge Grad Sch Biomed Sci, Univ Tenn; staff mem, Biol Div, Oak Ridge Nat Lab, 66-77. *Honors & Awards:* Newcomb-Cleveland Prize, AAAS. *Mem:* AAAS; Soc Develop Biol (secy-treas, 71-72); Am Chem Soc; Am Inst Biol Sci; Am Soc Biol Chemists. *Res:* Nucleic acid and protein synthesis of cells in tissue culture; chemical embryology; mechanisms of differential gene action in cellular differentiation. *Mailing Add:* Dept Human Biol, Chem & Genetics Univ Tex Med Br Galveston TX 77550

PAPACONSTANTOPOULOS, DIMITRIOS A, b Athens, Greece, Sept 10, 36; m 69; c 1. SOLID STATE PHYSICS. *Educ:* Nat Univ Athens, BS, 61; NATO fel, Univ London, 62-64, Imp Col, dipl, 63, MS, 64, PhD(theoret Physics), 67. *Prof Exp:* Asst lectr physics, Mid-Essex Tech Col, Eng, 64-65 & Hendon Col Technol, 65-66; from asst prof to prof physics, George Mason Univ, 67-77, chmn dept, 74-77; RES PHYSICIST & SR CONSULT, NAVAL RES LAB, 77- *Concurrent Pos:* Consult, Naval Res Lab, 70- *Mem:* Fel Am Phys Soc; Am Asn Physics Teachers. *Res:* Theoretical solid state physics; energy band theory; superconductivity. *Mailing Add:* Naval Res Lab Washington DC 20375

PAPACOSTAS, CHARLES ARTHUR, b Peabody, Mass, Mar 12, 21; m 48; c 4. PHARMACOLOGY. *Educ:* Mass Col Pharm, BS, 42; Boston Univ, AM, 52, PhD(physiol), 56. *Prof Exp:* Retail pharmacist, 45-50; from instr to assoc prof pharmacol, 55-66, PROF PHARMACOL, SCH MED, TEMPLE UNIV, 66-, VCHMN, DEPT PHARMACOL, 75- *Mem:* AAAS; Am Soc Pharmacol & Exp Therapeut; Am Heart Asn. *Res:* Histamine and histamine liberators; vascular response during adrenocortical suppression; adrenal steroids in essential hypertension; cardiovascular and metabolic effects of nicotine and other autonomic agents. *Mailing Add:* Dept of Pharmacol Temple Univ Sch of Med Philadelphia PA 19140

PAPACOSTAS, CONSTANTINOS SYMEON, b Paphos, Cyprus, Sept 26, 46. TRAFFIC & TRANSPORT ENGINEERING. *Educ:* Youngstown State Univ, BE, 69; Carnegie-Mellon Univ, MS, 71, PhD(civil eng), 74. *Prof Exp:* asst prof, 74-80, ASSOC PROF CIVIL ENG, UNIV HAWAII, MANOA, 80- *Concurrent Pos:* Prin investr, var projs; univ rep, Transp Res Bd, Nad Acad Sci, 77- *Mem:* AAAS; Transp Res Bd; Am Soc Eng Educ; Am Asn Univ Professors. *Res:* Transportation demand analysis; population dynamics; environmental impacts; statewide transportation safety data systems; simulation of transportation operations. *Mailing Add:* Dept Civil Eng Univ Hawaii Manoa Honolulu HI 96822

PAPADAKIS, EMMANUEL PHILIPPOS, b New York, NY, Dec 25, 34; m 60; c 4. NONDESTRUCTIVE TESTING, ULTRASONICS. *Educ:* Mass Inst Technol, SB, 56, PhD(physics), 62; Univ Mich, MM, 79. *Prof Exp:* Mem tech staff, Bell Tel Labs, Am Tel & Tel Co, Pa, 62-69; br chief, Panametrics, Inc, Mass, 69-70, dept head, 70-73; PRIN STAFF ENGR, FORD MOTOR CO, 73- *Honors & Awards:* Biennial Award, Acoust Soc Am, 68; Mehl Honor lectr, Am Soc Nondestructive Testing, 79. *Mem:* Am Phys Soc; fel Acoust

Soc Am; Inst Elec & Electronics Engrs; Am Soc Testing & Mat; Am Soc Nondestructive Testing. *Res:* Ultrasonics; research and development; grain scattering; grain size distribution, microstructure, preferred orientation; broadband transducers; velocity, attenuation measurement methods; elevated temperatures; diffraction; propagation; acoustic emission; sonics; eddy currents; acoustic filters; nondestructive testing. *Mailing Add:* Ford Motor Co 24500 Glendale Ave Detroit MI 48239

PAPADOPOULOS, ALEX SPERO, b Roytsi-Arcadia, Greece, Jan 1, 46. APPLIED STATISTICS, OPERATIONS RESEARCH. *Educ:* Univ RI, BS, 68, MS, 69; Va Polytech Inst & State Univ, MS, 70, PhD(statist), 72. *Prof Exp:* Lectr math, Keene State Col, 72-76; asst prof, Col Charleston, 76-78; ASSOC PROF MATH, UNIV NC, CHARLOTTE, 78- *Mem:* Am Statist Asn; Am Math Soc. *Res:* Reliability theory and applications; Bayesian statistics; time series; simulation; water pollution modeling. *Mailing Add:* Dept of Math Univ of NC Charlotte NC 28213

PAPADOPOULOS, ELEFTHERIOS PAUL, b Thessaloniki, Greece, Sept 26, 26; m 68; c 1. ORGANIC CHEMISTRY. *Educ:* Univ Thessaloniki, BSc, 54; Univ Kans, PhD(org chem), 61. *Prof Exp:* From instr to asst prof chem, Am Univ Beirut, 61-65; res fel, Harvard Univ, 65-66; from asst prof to assoc prof, Am Univ Beirut, 66-68; res fel, Univ Ky, 68-69; ASSOC PROF CHEM, UNIV NMEX, 69- *Mem:* AAAS; Am Chem Soc; Am Inst Chemists; NY Acad Sci. *Res:* Chemistry of heterocyclic compounds; reactions of isocyanates and isothiocyanates; oxidation reactions. *Mailing Add:* Dept of Chem Univ of NMex Albuquerque NM 87106

PAPADOPOULOS, NICHOLAS M, b Greece, July 21, 23; nat US; m 56; c 1. BIOCHEMISTRY. *Educ:* Am Univ, BA, 51; George Washington Univ, MS, 53, PhD(biochem), 56. *Prof Exp:* Vis scientist, NIH, 56-57; asst prof biochem, Sch Med, Georgetown Univ, 57-61; assoc prof, Med Col Va, 61-64, vis prof neurol, 64-74; biochemist & chief Protein & Lipid Sect, Div Biochem, Walter Reed Army Inst Res, Walter Reed Med Ctr, 64-74; BIOCHEMIST, NAT CANCER INST, NIH, 74- *Mem:* Am Soc Biol Chemists; fel Soc Exp Biol & Med; Am Asn Clin Chemists; Am Acad Neurol. *Res:* Chemical investigation of nervous diseases; nicotine metabolism; clinical chemistry. *Mailing Add:* Nat Cancer Inst NIH Bethesda MD 20014

PAPADOPULOS, STAVROS STEFANU, b Istanbul, Turkey, Sept 21, 36; US citizen; m 63; c 2. GROUNDWATER HYDROLOGY. *Educ:* Robert Col, Istanbul, BS, 59; NMex Inst Mining & Technol, MS, 62; Princeton Univ, MA, 63, PhD(civil eng), 64. *Prof Exp:* Res hydrologist, US Geol Surv, 63-66; assoc prof groundwater hydrol, Univ Minn, 66-67; head hydrol dept, Harza Eng Co, Ill, 67-69; assoc prof groundwater hydrol, Univ Ill, Chicago Circle, 69-70; res hydrologist, US Geol Surv, 70-79; PRES, S S PAPADOPULOS & ASSOCS, INC, 79- *Concurrent Pos:* Assoc prof lectr, George Washington Univ, 65-66; vis assoc prof, Univ Ill, Chicago Circle, 68-69; chief groundwater hydrologist, Harza Eng Co, 69-70. *Honors & Awards:* Meritorious Serv Award, US Dept Interior, 77; Spec Achievement Award, US Geol Surv, 77. *Mem:* Am Soc Civil Engrs; Am Geophys Union; Int Asn Hydrogeologists; Sigma Xi. Asn; Nat Water Well Asn. *Res:* Analysis of groundwater systems through use of mathematical and digital modeling techniques; development of methods for pumping test analyses and aquifer evaluation. *Mailing Add:* 8216 Scotch Bend Way Potomac MD 20854

PAPAEFTHYMIOU, GEORGIA CHRISTOU, b Athens, Greece. BIOLOGICAL PHYSICS, CHEMICAL PHYSICS. *Educ:* Barnard Col, BA, 68; Columbia Univ, MA, 70, PhD(physics), 74. *Prof Exp:* RES STAFF MOSSBAUER SPECTROS, NAT MAGNET LAB, MASS INST TECHNOL, 74- *Mem:* Am Phys Soc; Sigma Xi. *Res:* Mossbauer spectroscopy of biomolecules and iron containing chemical complexes forming the active sites of proteins and enzymes; electronic structure and hyperfine interactions in solids. *Mailing Add:* 285 Harvard Cambridge MA 02139

PAPAGIANNIS, MICHAEL D, b Athens, Greece, Sept 3, 32; m 61; c 2. ASTROPHYSICS, SPACE PHYSICS. *Educ:* Nat Tech Univ, Athens, MS, 55; Univ Va, MS, 60; Harvard Univ, PhD(physics), 64. *Prof Exp:* Lectr radio astron, Harvard Univ, 64-65; from asst prof to assoc prof astron, 65-70, PROF ASTRON, BOSTON UNIV, 70-, CHMN DEPT, 69- *Concurrent Pos:* Assoc, Harvard Observ, Harvard Univ, 64-; Air Force Geophys Lab grants, 65-; vis prof, Univ Athens, 71-72. *Mem:* Am Astron Soc; Am Geophys Union; Int Union Radio Sci; Int Astron Union. *Res:* Radio astronomy; active sun; solar-terrestrial relations; astrophysical plasmas; search for extratervertrial life. *Mailing Add:* Dept of Astron Boston Univ 725 Commonwealth Ave Boston MA 02215

PAPAHADJOPOULOS, DEMETRIOS PANAYOTIS, b Patras, Greece, Aug 24, 34; m 59; c 3. BIOCHEMISTRY, BIOPHYSICS. *Educ:* Nat Univ Athens, BS, 57; Univ Wash, PhD(biochem), 63. *Prof Exp:* NIH res fel physiol, Inst Animal Physiol, Babraham, Eng, 64-67, Am Heart Asn estab investr, 67-72; from asst res prof to res prof biochem, biophysiol & cell biol, State Univ NY, Buffalo, 72-78, mem ctr theoret biol, 68-78; PROF PHARMACOL, CANCER RES INST, UNIV CALIF MED SCH, SAN FRANCISCO, 78- *Concurrent Pos:* Vis sr cancer res scientist, Roswell Park Mem Inst, 67-68, assoc cancer res scientist, 68-74, prin cancer res scientist, 74-78; estab investr, Am Heart Asn, 67-78, fel coun arteriosclerosis, mem res study comt, 72-75. *Honors & Awards:* K S Cole Award, Biophys Soc, 80. *Mem:* Am Chem Soc; Am Soc Biol Chemists; fel NY Acad Sci; Biophys Soc; Am Soc Cell Biol. *Res:* Membrane structure and function; phospholipid-protein interactions; blood coagulation; surface phenomena; pharmacological use of lipid vesicles; author or coauthor of over 150 publications. *Mailing Add:* Cancer Res Inst Univ of Calif Med Sch San Francisco CA 94143

PAPAHRONIS, B(ASIL) T(RIFON), chemical engineering, see previous edition

PAPAIOANNOU, CHRISTOS GEORGE, b Athens, Greece, Dec 3, 34; US citizen; m 65; c 3. ORGANIC CHEMISTRY. *Educ:* Univ Athens, BS, 58; Mich State Univ, PhD(org chem), 67. *Prof Exp:* Qual control supvr, Fix Corp, Athens, Greece, 61; res chemist, Democritos Nuclear Res Ctr, Athens, 62-63; res assoc org chem, Columbia Univ, 67-68; res chemist, Am Cyanamide Co, 68-71; group leader organometallic chem, Nat Patent Develop Corp, 71-73; SR RES INVESTR PHARMACEUT, E R SQUIBB & SONS, INC, 73- *Mem:* Am Chem Soc; Greek Chem Soc. *Res:* Pharmaceutical research; synthetic methods; organometallic chemistry; process development. *Mailing Add:* E R Squibb & Sons Inc PO Box 4000 Princeton NJ 08540

PAPAIOANNOU, STAMATIOS E, b Athens, Greece, Mar 27, 34; m 68. BIOCHEMISTRY. *Educ:* Nat Univ Athens, BS, 57; Ore State Univ, MS, 62, PhD(biochem), 66. *Prof Exp:* Asst biochem, Ore State Univ, 62-66; fel, Univ Minn, 66-68; res investr, G D Searle & Co, 68-75, res scientist, Dept Biol Res, 75-81. *Mem:* Am Chem Soc; Endocrine Soc; NY Acad Sci; AAAS. *Res:* Biochemical pharmacology, especially molecular endocrinological and enzymological studies in cardiovascular research. *Mailing Add:* G D Searle & Co PO Box 5110 Chicago IL 60680

PAPANASTASSIOU, DIMITRI A, b Athens, Greece, Nov 15, 42; m 64; c 2. MASS SPECTROMETRY. *Educ:* Calif Inst Technol, BS, 65, PhD(physics), 69. *Prof Exp:* Fel physics, 70, Millikan res fel, 71, instr freshmen physics, 71-72 & 79-80, sr res fel planet sci & physics, 72-73 & planetary sci, 73-76, res assoc, 76-81, SR RES ASSOC GEOCHEM, CALIF INST TECHNOL, 81- *Concurrent Pos:* Co-investr lunar samples, NASA, 71-, mem, Comt Post-Viking Explor Mars, 73-74 & Lunar Sample Anal Planning Team, 74-79. *Honors & Awards:* F W Clarke Medal, Geochem Soc, 72. *Mem:* Am Phys Soc; Am Geophys Union; AAAS; fel Meteoritical Soc. *Res:* Formation and evolution of meteorites and planets; establishment of a time sequence of condensation in the solar nebula; search for exotic nuclear matter preserved in meteorites; precision mass spectrometry and its application to physical-chemical problems. *Mailing Add:* Geol 170-25 Calif Inst Technol Pasadena CA 91125

PAPANICOLAOU, GEORGE CONSTANTINE, b Athens, Greece, Jan 23, 43; m 67. MATHEMATICS. *Educ:* Union Col, NY, BEE, 65; NY Univ, MS, 67, PhD(math), 69. *Prof Exp:* From asst prof to assoc prof, 69-76, PROF MATH, COURANT INST, NY UNIV, 76- *Mem:* Am Math Soc; Soc Indust & Appl Math. *Res:* Applied mathematics; mathematical physics. *Mailing Add:* Courant Inst 251 Mercer St New York NY 10012

PAPANIKOLAOU, NICHOLAS E, b Greece, July 2, 37; US citizen; m 67; c 2. ORGANIC CHEMISTRY. *Educ:* St Anselm's Col, BA, 62; Univ NH, PhD(chem), 67. *Prof Exp:* Assoc prof, 67-76, PROF CHEM, SLIPPERY ROCK STATE COL, 76- *Mem:* Am Chem Soc. *Res:* Optically active organosulfur and organophosphorus compounds. *Mailing Add:* Dept of Chem Slippery Rock State Col Slippery Rock PA 16057

PAPANTONOPOULOU, AIGLI HELEN, b Port Said, Egypt; Greek citizen; m 76; c 1. ALGEBRAIC GEOMETRY, COMMUTATIVE ALGEBRA. *Educ:* Columbia Univ, BA, 69; Univ Calif, Berkeley, MA, 71, PhD(math), 75. *Prof Exp:* Instr, Univ Pa, 75-77, Bryn Mawr Col, 77-79; ASST PROF MATH, LEHIGH UNIV, 79- *Concurrent Pos:* Vis prof, Univ Crete, Greece, 80-81; reviewer, Am Math Reviews, 80- *Mem:* Am Math Soc. *Res:* Algebraic intersection theories and applied to Grassmann varieties and flag varieties and problems in enumerative geometry. *Mailing Add:* Dept Math Lehigh Univ Bethlehem PA 18015

PAPARIELLO, GERALD JOSEPH, b New York, NY, Feb 3, 34; m 57; c 4. ANALYTICAL CHEMISTRY, TECHNICAL MANAGEMENT. *Educ:* Fordham Univ, BS, 56; Univ Wis, MS, 58, PhD(pharmaceut chem), 60. *Prof Exp:* Sr chemist anal res, Ciba Pharmaceut Co, 60-63, assoc dir phys chem res, 63-66; mgr anal res dept, 66-76, DIR PHARMACEUT RES & DEVELOP, WYETH LABS, INC, 76- *Concurrent Pos:* Mem comt revision, US Pharmacopoeia, 70-80; mem comt specifications, Nat Formulary, 70-74. *Mem:* Am Chem Soc; Am Crystallog Asn; fel Acad Pharmaceut Sci (vpres, 78-79). *Res:* Organic and functional group analysis; analysis of pharmaceutical systems; x-ray fluorescence and diffraction; analytical separations; automated analysis; chemical kinetics. *Mailing Add:* Wyeth Labs Inc PO Box 8299 Philadelphia PA 19101

PAPAS, CHARLES HERACH, b Troy, NY, Mar 29, 18; m 51; c 1. ELECTRODYNAMICS. *Educ:* Mass Inst Technol, BS, 41; Harvard Univ, MS, 46, PhD(electromagnetic theory), 48. *Prof Exp:* Res fel, Harvard Univ, 48-50; mem staff, Los Alamos Sci Lab & consult, Radiation Lab, Univ Calif, 50-52; assoc prof, 53-59, PROF PHYSICS, CALIF INST TECHNOL, 59- *Mem:* Am Math Soc; Am Phys Soc; Inst Elec & Electronics Engrs; foreign mem Acad Sci Armenian Soviet Socialist Repub. *Res:* Electromagnetic theory; gravitational electrodynamics. *Mailing Add:* Calif Inst Technol Pasadena CA 91109

PAPAS, TAKIS S, b Athens, Greece, June 19, 35; US citizen; m; c 2. BIOCHEMISTRY, VIROLOGY. *Educ:* Univ NH, BS, 63, MS, 66; Marquette Univ, PhD(biochem), 70. *Prof Exp:* Res analyst biochem, Biomolecular Hyg Sect, Univ NH, 62-64, res asst, Univ, 64-66; res asst, Marquette Sch Med, 66-70; staff fel, Nat Heart Inst, NIH, 70-72; sr staff fel molecular virol, 72-75, res chemist molecular biol of tumor viruses, 75-78, HEAD CARCINOGENESIS REGULATION SECT, NAT CANCER INST, 78- *Mem:* Am Chem Soc; Am Soc Biol Chemists; Leukemia Soc Am. *Res:* Enzyme chemistry; enzyme kinetics; protein synthesis; nucleic acid; protein nucleic-acid interactions; lipid metabolism; modification of viral growth and replication by natural and synthetic substances; molecular biochemistry of oncorna virus; molecular cloning of transforming genes of acute leukemia viruses. *Mailing Add:* Rm 1D18 Bldg 37 Nat Cancer Inst Lab Tumor Virus Genetics Bethesda MD 20014

PAPASTAMATIOU, NICOLAS, b Athens, Greece, Nov 18, 39. PHYSICS. *Educ:* Nat Univ Athens, BSc, 61; Oxford Univ, DPhil(theoret physics), 66. *Prof Exp:* Res assoc physics, Syracuse Univ, 66-68; from asst prof to assoc prof, 68-78, PROF PHYSICS, UNIV WIS-MILWAUKEE, 78- *Concurrent Pos:* Vis prof, Nat Univ Athens, 72-73 & Univ Alta, 80-81. *Mem:* Am Phys Soc; AAAS. *Res:* Quantum field theory; high energy physics. *Mailing Add:* Dept Physics Univ Wis Milwaukee WI 53201

PAPASTEPHANOU, CONSTANTIN, b Cairo, Egypt, Dec 30, 45; nat US; m 71; c 1. BIOCHEMISTRY, ANALYTICAL CHEMISTRY. *Educ:* Ain Shams Univ, Cairo, BS, 67; Univ London, MS, 68, DIC, 68; Univ Miami, PhD(biochem), 72. *Prof Exp:* Proj assoc biochem, Univ Wis-Madison, 72-73; res investr anal chem, Squibb Inst Med Res, 73-77; sect head methods develop, E R Squibb & Sons, 77, sect head, mat control, 77-78; mgr quality control, Squibb Puerto Rico, 78-80; dept head, Chemical Control, 80-81, DIR PROD QUALITY CONTROL, E R SQUIBB & SONS, 81- *Concurrent Pos:* Fel, Univ Wis-Madison, 72-73. *Mem:* Am Pharm Assoc; Am Chem Soc; Brit Biochem Soc. *Res:* Biochemistry of terpenes and carotenoids; enzymology; metabolic pathways; analytical biochemistry and chemistry. *Mailing Add:* E R Squibb & Sons Inc PO Box 191 New Brunswick NJ 08903

PAPAVIZAS, GEORGE CONSTANTINE, b Kriminion, Greece, July 10, 22; US citizen; m 54; c 2. PLANT PATHOLOGY. *Educ:* Univ Thessaloniki, dipl, 47; Univ Minn, MS, 53, PhD(mycol, plant path), 57. *Prof Exp:* Plant breeder, Inst Plant Breeding, Greece, 50-51; from asst to instr, Univ Minn, 52-57; exp mycologist, Plant Sci Res Div, 57-64, microbiologist & leader mushroom & microbiol invests, 64-72, CHIEF, SOILBORNE DIS LAB, PLANT PROTECTION INST, SCI & EDUC ADMIN, AGR RES, USDA, 72- *Honors & Awards:* Campbell Award, Am Inst Biol Sci, 63; Superior Serv Award, USDA, 65. *Mem:* Fel Am Phytopath Soc; Mycol Soc Am. *Res:* Microecology of soilborne diseases of plants in relation to biological control; integrated pest management; soil fungi and their activities in soil. *Mailing Add:* Soilborne Dis Lab Agr Res Ctr-West USDA Beltsville MD 20705

PAPAZIAN, HAROLD ARAM, physical chemistry, see previous edition

PAPAZIAN, LOUIS ARTHUR, b Cambridge, Mass, Jan 25, 31. PHYSICAL CHEMISTRY. *Educ:* Northeastern Univ, BS, 54, MS, 56; Wayne State Univ, PhD(phys chem), 61. *Prof Exp:* Sr res chemist, Mobil Chem Co, NJ, 62-70; sr res scientist, Columbian Div, Cities Serv Co, 70-78; RES SCIENTIST, AM CYANAMID CO, 78- *Res:* Polymer characterization; all phases of liquid chromatography; processing of carbon-black-rubber systems. *Mailing Add:* Am Cyanamid Co 1937 W Main St Stamford CT 06904

PAPE, BRIAN EUGENE, b St Louis, Mo, Oct 13, 43; m 71; c 4. TOXICOLOGY, PATHOLOGY. *Educ:* Wash Univ, BA, 66; Mich State Univ, MS, 69, PhD(toxicol), 72; Univ Mo, MBA, 82. *Prof Exp:* Res asst toxicol, Mich State Univ, 66-72; res assoc, 72-74, asst prof, 74-78, ASSOC PROF PATH, MED CTR, UNIV MO-COLUMBIA, 78-, DIR TOXICOL LAB, 72- *Mem:* Am Asn Univ Prof; Int Asn Forensic Toxicol. *Res:* Analytical techniques in biomedical and environmental toxicology; photochemistry of bioactive compounds; fate of xenobiotics and bio-pharmacological mechanisms; clinical and forensic toxicology. *Mailing Add:* RR 1 Rocheport MO 65279

PAPE, LEON, b New York, NY, Feb 8, 25; m 49; c 3. BIOPHYSICS, PHYSICS. *Educ:* Brooklyn Col, AB, 49; Univ Southern Calif, MS, 53, PhD(biophys), 65. *Prof Exp:* Radiol physicist, Cedars Lebanon Hosp, Los Angeles, 55-58 & City Hope Med Ctr, 58-62; prof physics & biophys, Calif State Col, Los Angeles, 61-71; LECTR, ZOOPHYSIOL LAB, UNIV COPENHAGEN, 71- *Concurrent Pos:* Chief investr instnl grant, City Hope Med Ctr, 65-66; vis assoc prof, Univ Southern Calif, 66-67. *Mem:* AAAS; Am Inst Physics; Am Asn Physics Teachers; Biophys Soc; Am Asn Physicists in Med. *Res:* Macromolecular structure and function; cellular membranes; transport phenomena. *Mailing Add:* Zoophysiol Lab B Universitetsparken 13 2100 Copenhagen Denmark

PAPEE, HENRY MICHAEL, b Cracow, Poland, Oct 22, 23; nat Can; m 51; c 2. ATMOSPHERIC CHEMISTRY. *Educ:* Univ Rome, Dr Chem, 51. *Prof Exp:* Res chemist, Metall Res Div, Sherritt-Gordon Mines, Ltd, Can, 51-54; res assoc chem, Univ Ottawa, Ont, 54-58; res officer, Nat Res Coun Can, 58-60; DIR LAB AEROSOL NUCLEATION, NAT RES COUN ITALY, 60- *Mem:* Am Chem Soc; Am Meteorol Soc; Am Geophys Union; Chem Inst Can. *Res:* Atmospheric chemistry; chemistry of atmospheric precipitation phenomena. *Mailing Add:* Via Vettore 4 Monte Sacro 00141 Rome Italy

PAPENDICK, ROBERT I, b Bridgewater, SDak, May 22, 31; m 50; c 5. AGRONOMY. *Educ:* SDak State Univ, BS, 57, PhD(agron), 62. *Prof Exp:* Exten serv soil specialist, SDak State Univ, 58-59; res soil physicist, Tenn Valley Authority, 63-65; res soil scientist, soil & water conserv res div, 65-70, COLLABR AGRON, SCI & EDUC ADMIN-AGR RES, USDA, 70-; ASSOC PROF SOILS, WASH STATE UNIV, 71- *Mem:* Am Soc Agron. *Res:* Soil-plant-fertilizer relationships leading to development of new fertilizer materials; soil water management problems leading to erosion control. *Mailing Add:* Dept of Agron & Soils Wash State Univ Pullman WA 99163

PAPENFUSS, GEORGE FREDERIK, b Harrismith, SAfrica, Nov 4, 03; nat US; m 29; c 1. PHYCOLOGY. *Educ:* NC State Univ, BS, 29; Johns Hopkins Univ, PhD(bot), 33. *Prof Exp:* Asst bot, Johns Hopkins Univ, 29-31, instr, Col Teachers, 33-34; fel, Univs Lund & Uppsala, 34-35; investr, Univ Cape Town, 35-38 & Univ Lund, 39-40; asst prof bot, Univ Hawaii, 40-42; from res assoc to prof, 42-71, cur algal collections, 46-71, EMER PROF BOT, UNIV CALIF, BERKELEY, 71- *Concurrent Pos:* Mem comt for algae, Int Bot Cong, 48-75, chmn, 64-75, Bot Soc Am deleg for algae, 50, mem gen comt sect nomenclature, 54-75, vpres sect phycol, Paris, 54 & Montreal, 59, hon vpres, X Int Cong, Edinburgh, 64; Guggenheim fel, 49-50; ed algae, Index Nominum Genericorum, 54-70; Miller res prof, 60-61. *Honors & Awards:* Cert of Merit, Bot Soc Am; Berkeley Citation, Univ Calif, Berkeley, 71. *Mem:* Fel AAAS; Bot Soc Am; Phycol Soc Am (pres, 56-57); Int Soc Plant Morphol; hon fel Royal Soc SAfrica. *Res:* Structure, reproduction and taxonomy of green, brown and red marine algae; marine algal flora of South Africa. *Mailing Add:* Dept of Bot Univ of Calif Berkeley CA 94720

PAPERNIK, LAZAR, b Moscow, USSR, Feb, 26, 44; US citizen; m; c 2. APPLIED MECHANICS. *Educ:* Moscow State Univ, MS & BC, 66; Mech Eng Res Inst, Moscow, PhD(appl mech), 72. *Prof Exp:* Res fel solid mech, Mech Eng Res Inst, Moscow, 65-74; ASST PROF APPL MECH, UNIV CINCINNATI, 77- *Concurrent Pos:* Scientific ed, Navka Publ House, Moscow, 67-74. *Mem:* Soc Rhology; Soc Eng Sci. *Res:* Solid mechanics; theory viscoelasticity; theory viscoplasticity. *Mailing Add:* ML#70 Dept Aerospace Eng & Appl Mech Univ Cincinnati Cincinnati OH 45221

PAPERT, SEYMOUR A, b Pretoria, SAfrica, Mar 1, 28. MATHEMATICS. *Educ:* Univ Witwatersrand, BA, 49, PhD(math), 52; Cambridge Univ, PhD(math), 59. *Prof Exp:* Royal Comn res scholar, Exhib 1851, St John's Col, Cambridge Univ, 54-56; researcher, Henri Poincare Inst, Univ Paris, 56-57; researcher child develop, int ctr genetic epistemology, Univ Geneva, 58-63; sr fel, Nat Phys Lab, London, 59-61; asst lectr cybernet, Univ Geneva, 62-63; res assoc elec eng, 63-67, PROF APPL MATH & CO-DIR, ARTIFICIAL INTEL LAB, MASS INST TECHNOL, 67-, CECIL & IDA GREEN PROF EDUC, 74- *Concurrent Pos:* Guggenheim mem fel, 80-81; Marconi Int fel, 81. *Res:* Cybernetics; child development; psychology and mathematics; science of cognition. *Mailing Add:* Dept Math Mass Inst of Technol 77 Massachusetts Ave Cambridge MA 02139

PAPEZIK, VLADIMIR STEPHEN, b Brno, Czech, Feb 5, 27; Can citizen; m 61. GEOLOGY. *Educ:* Univ BC, BA, 54, MSc, 57; McGill Univ, PhD(geol), 61. *Prof Exp:* Mine geologist, Deer Horn Mines, Ltd, BC, 55 & Spanish Am Mines, Ont, 55-56; from asst prof to assoc prof, 61-71, PROF MINERAL, MEM UNIV NFLD, 71- *Mem:* Geol Asn Can; Mineral Asn Can; Mineral Soc Am; Can Inst Mining & Metall; Geol Soc Am. *Res:* Volcanic rocks, especially ignimbrites, their mineralogy and petrochemistry; pyrophyllite deposits; low-grade metamorphism; rift volcanism. *Mailing Add:* Dept of Geol Mem Univ Nfld St John's NF A1B 3X5 Can

PAPIAN, WILLIAM NATHANIEL, b New York, NY, July 27, 16; m 46, 66; c 2. ELECTRICAL ENGINEERING. *Educ:* Mass Inst Technol, SB, 48, SM, 50. *Prof Exp:* Res asst, Servo Lab, Mass Inst Technol, 48-50, res engr, Digital Comput Lab, 50-55, group leader, Lincoln Lab, 55-62, asst dir biomed comput proj, 62-64; prof elec eng, Washington Univ, 65-72; vis scientist, Health Servs & Ment Health Admin, HEW, 72-73; CHIEF ENGR, CLAXTON WALKER & ASSOCS POTOMAC, 74- *Concurrent Pos:* Mem, Adv Comt Comput in Res, NIH, 61-63; NIH grant comput technol in biomed res, Mass Inst Technol, 62-64; mem adv panel to Nat Bur Standards, Nat Acad Sci-Nat Res Coun, 63-64; NIH grant, Advan Res Projs Agency contract & dir comput res lab, Washington Univ, 64-67, asst vchancellor res, 66-68, sr fel, Ctr Biol Eng, 66-72. *Mem:* AAAS; fel Inst Elec & Electronics Engrs; Am Arbit Asn; Nat Soc Prof Engrs. *Res:* Energy conservation in residential construction; deterioration of residential buildings and components. *Mailing Add:* 1424 E W Shadyside Rd Shadyside MD 20764

PAPIKE, JAMES JOSEPH, b Virginia, Minn, Feb 11, 37; m 58; c 4. CRYSTALLOGRAPHY, MINERALOGY. *Educ:* SDak Sch Mines & Technol, BS, 59; Univ Minn, PhD(geol), 64. *Prof Exp:* Geologist, US Geol Surv, Washington, DC, 64-69; assoc prof, 69-71, chmn dept earth & space scis, 71-74, PROF CRYSTALLOG, STATE UNIV NY STONY BROOK, 71- *Concurrent Pos:* Vis prof, Bd Earth Scis, Univ Calif, Santa Cruz, 75-76; mem, Lunar Sample Anal Planning Team, 70-73; mem, Lunar & Planetary Sci Coun, 74-76; NASA grant, 75-; US Nat Comt for Geochem, Nat Res Coun, 78-; NSF grant, 78- *Honors & Awards:* NASA Medal for Except Sci Achievement, 73; Mineral Soc Am Award, 74. *Mem:* Geochem Soc; fel Mineral Soc Am; Am Geophys Union; Meteoritical Soc; fel Geol Soc Am. *Res:* Crystal chemistry of rock-forming silicates; intracrystalline equilibria; properties of mineral solid solutions. *Mailing Add:* Dept of Earth & Space Sci State Univ of NY Stony Brook NY 11794

PAPINI, GIORGIO AUGUSTO, b Crenona, Italy, May 8, 34; m 59; c 4. UNIFIED FIELD THEORIES, GRAVITATIONAL EFFECTS. *Educ:* Univ Pavia, Italy, PhD(physics), 58. *Prof Exp:* Researcher theoret physics, Ctr Nuclear Res, Ispra, Italy, 58; scholar theoret physics, Inst Advan Studies, Dublin, 58-60; asst lectr physics, Math Dept, Univ Leeds, 60-61; prof incaricato physics, Univ Catania, 61-64; res assoc physics, Inst Field Physics, Univ NC, Chapel Hill, 64-66; dept head, 69-79, PROF, DEPT PHYSICS & ASTRON, UNIV REGINA, 66- *Concurrent Pos:* Consult, Sicilian Ctr Nuclear Physics, Catania, 62-64, Nat Health Inst, Rome, 64, Hughes Res Labs, 65; vis scientist, Int Ctr Theoret Physics, Trieste, 67, Eur Space Res Inst, Frascati, 70, Astrophysics Labs, Nat Res Coun, Italy, 73, Univ BC, Vancouver, 80-81. *Mem:* Can Asn Physicists; Am Phys Soc; Int Soc Gen Relativity Gravitation. *Res:* The role of gravitation in astrophysics; elementary particle physcis; solid state physics. *Mailing Add:* Dept Physics & Astron Univ Regina Regina SK S4S 0A2 Can

PAPIRMEISTER, BRUNO, biochemistry, see previous edition

PAPKA, RAYMOND EDWARD, b Thermopolis, Wyo, July 11, 45; m 64; c 3. ANATOMY. *Educ:* Univ Wyo, BS, 67; Tulane Univ, PhD(anat), 71. *Prof Exp:* ASSOC PROF ANAT, MED CTR, UNIV KY, 71- *Mem:* AAAS; NY Acad Sci; Am Soc Cell Biol; Am Asn Anatomists; Soc Neurosci. *Res:* Neurobiology; autonomic nervous system; developmental neurobiology. *Mailing Add:* Dept of Anat Univ of Ky Med Ctr Lexington KY 40506

PAPKE, KEITH GEORGE, b Mankato, Minn, Feb 5, 24; m 54; c 2. GEOLOGY. *Educ:* SDak Sch Mines & Technol, BS, 48; Univ Ariz, MS, 52. *Prof Exp:* Mining engr, Phelps Dodge Corp, Ariz, 48-50; geologist, Am Smelting & Refining Co, 52-56 & Southern Pac Co, 56-61; chief geologist, Standard Slag Co, Nev, 61-66; ECON GEOLOGIST, NEV BUR MINES &

GEOL, 66- *Mem:* Am Inst Mining, Metall & Petrol Engrs; Clay Minerals Soc; Soc Econ Geologists. *Res:* Geology, physical and chemical properties, uses and specifications, and economics of industrial minerals, especially those occurring in the western states; talc; saline minerals; fluorspar; clay mineralogy; zeolites; barite. *Mailing Add:* Nev Bur of Mines & Geol Univ of Nev Reno NV 89557

PAPKOFF, HAROLD, b San Jose, Calif, June 11, 25; m 53; c 2. BIOCHEMISTRY. *Educ:* Univ Calif, AB, 50, PhD(biochem), 57. *Prof Exp:* From jr res biochemist to assoc res biochemist, 57-73, from lectr to assoc prof exp endocrinol, 62-72, prof anat, 72-73, PROF EXP ENDOCRINOL & RES BIOCHEMIST, HORMONE RES LAB, MED SCH, UNIV CALIF, SAN FRANCISCO, 73-, PROF OBSTET & GYNEC, 76- *Concurrent Pos:* USPHS spec fel chem path, St Mary's Hosp, London, Eng, 61-62; career develop award, 64. *Honors & Awards:* Ayerst Award, Endocrine Soc, 78. *Mem:* AAAS; Am Soc Biol Chemists; Endocrine Soc; Am Soc Zoologists; Soc Study Reproduction. *Res:* Purification and characterization of pituitary hormones; relation of structure to biological activity of proteins and peptides; comparative endocrinology. *Mailing Add:* 1088 Health Sci W Hormone Res Lab Univ of Calif Med Ctr San Francisco CA 94143

PAPOULIS, ATHANASIOS, b Greece, Jan 18, 21; nat US; m 53; c 5. SYSTEMS ENGINEERING, APPLIED MATHEMATICS. *Educ:* Polytech Inst Greece, MechE, 41, EE, 42; Univ Pa, MS, 47, MA, 48, PhD(math), 50. *Prof Exp:* Instr elec eng, Univ Pa, 48-51; asst prof, Union Col, 51-52; ASST PROF ELEC ENG, POLYTECH INST NY, 52- *Concurrent Pos:* Prof, NSF fac fel, Darmstadt Tech Univ, 59-60; vis prof, Univ Calif, Los Angeles, 64-65. *Mem:* Fel Inst Elec & Electronics Engrs. *Res:* Applied mathematics; systems; communications. *Mailing Add:* Dept Elec Eng Polytech Inst NY Rt 110 Farmington NY 11735

PAPOUTSAKIS, ELEFTHERIOS TERRY, b Alexandroupolis, Greece, May 29, 51. BIOCHEMICAL ENGINEERING, REACTION ENGINEERING. *Educ:* Nat Tech Univ, Athens, dipl, 74; Purdue Univ, MS, 76, PhD(chem eng), 79. *Prof Exp:* ASST PROF CHEM ENG, RICE UNIV, 80- *Mem:* Am Inst Chem Engrs; Am Chem Soc; AAAS; Am Soc Microbiol; NY Acad Sci. *Res:* Biochemical and fermentation engineering; biokinetics; transport and bioenergetics of single and mammalian cells; immobilized whole cells; single cell protein production from one-carbon compounds; applied mathematics in transport and reaction engineering. *Mailing Add:* Dept Chem Eng Rice Univ PO Box 1892 Houston TX 77251

PAPP, FRANCIS JOSEPH, IV, b Chicago, Ill, Aug 30, 42; m 65; c 4. MATHEMATICS. *Educ:* Univ Notre Dame, BS, 64; Univ Del, MS, 66, PhD(math), 69. *Prof Exp:* Asst prof, Dept Math Sci, Univ Lethbridge, 69-74, assoc prof, 74-81, chmn, Dept Math Sci, 78-79; ASSOC PROF, DEPT MATH, UNIV MICH, DEARBORN, 81- *Concurrent Pos:* Vis scholar, Univ Mich, Ann Arbor, 75-76; consult ed, Math Reviews, 78, ed, 79-81. *Mem:* Am Math Soc; Math Asn Am; Res Soc North Am. *Res:* Number theory; functional equations; general topology. *Mailing Add:* Dept Math Univ Mich 4901 Evergreen Rd Dearborn MI 48128

PAPP, KIM ALEXANDER, b Calgary, Alta, Mar 21, 53; m 80. GALAXY DYNAMICS, STELLAR DYNAMICS. *Educ:* Univ Calgary, BSc, 74; York Univ, MSc, 76, PhD(physics), 80. *Prof Exp:* NATO fel, Univ Chicago, 80-81; ASST PROF PHYSICS, UNIV WATERLOO, 81- *Concurrent Pos:* Consult, Algas Eng, 74, KAPTECH, 80- *Mem:* Am Astron Soc; Am Phys Soc; Can Astron Soc; Royal Astron Soc Can. *Res:* Formation of galaxies and their subsequent interaction and evolution. *Mailing Add:* Dept Physics Univ Waterloo Waterloo ON N2L 3G1 Can

PAPPADEMOS, JOHN NICHOLAS, b St Louis, Mo, Mar 12, 25; m 51; c 3. THEORETICAL HIGH ENERGY PHYSICS, PHILOSOPHY OF SCIENCE. *Educ:* Iowa State Univ, BS, 45; Washington Univ, MA, 52; Univ Chicago, PhD(physics), 63. *Prof Exp:* Tech consult, Washington Univ, 54-55; instr physics, Bailey Schs, Inc, 55-57; asst prof, 57-63, ASSOC PROF PHYSICS, UNIV ILL, CHICAGO CIRCLE, 63- *Concurrent Pos:* NSF res grant, 65-66; transl consult, Plenum Press, 71-; assoc ed, Revolutionary World, 75- *Mem:* Am Asn Physics Teachers. *Res:* Theoretical nuclear physics; theory of elementary particle interactions. *Mailing Add:* Dept of Physics Univ of Ill at Chicago Circle Chicago IL 60680

PAPPAGIANIS, DEMOSTHENES, b San Diego, Calif, Mar 31, 28; m 56; c 2. MEDICAL MICROBIOLOGY. *Educ:* Univ Calif, AB, 49, MS, 51; PhD(bact), 56; Stanford Univ, MD, 62. *Prof Exp:* Asst & lab technician, Div Food Technol, Univ Calif, 46-51, from jr res bacteriologist to asst res bacteriologist, Naval Biol Lab, 51-59, consult, 59-61, lectr, Univ, 56-58; intern, Walter Reed Gen Hosp, 62-63; assoc prof med microbiol, Sch Pub Health, Univ Calif, Berkeley, 63-67, PROF MED MICROBIOL, SCH MED, UNIV CALIF, DAVIS, 67-, CHMN DEPT, 68- *Mem:* Am Soc Microbiol; Mycol Soc Am. *Res:* Medical mycology; experimental pathology; physiology and immunology of Coccidioides immitis; human brucellosis; immunology of infectious diseases. *Mailing Add:* Dept of Med Microbiol Univ of Calif Sch of Med Davis CA 95616

PAPPALARDO, LEONARD THOMAS, b New York, NY, Dec 1, 29; m 55; c 4. ORGANIC CHEMISTRY, POLYMER CHEMISTRY. *Educ:* Fordham Col, BS, 51; NY Univ, MS, 59. *Prof Exp:* Chemist, Am Sugar Refining Co, 51-53 & Eng Ctr, Columbia Univ, 55-57; sr res chemist, Tex US Chem Co, 57-67; ASSOC MEM TECH STAFF, ORG MAT RES & DEVELOP DEPT, BELL TEL LABS, MURRAY HILL, 67- *Mem:* AAAS; Am Chem Soc. *Res:* Organic polymer chemistry of elastomers and synthetic resins; synthesis and characterization as well as relating properties to structure; printed circuit materials research, development and consulting. *Mailing Add:* 312 Mountain Way Morris Plains NJ 07950

PAPPALARDO, ROMANO GIUSEPPE, b Genoa, Italy; US citizen. SOLID STATE SCIENCE. *Educ:* Univ Pavia, PhD(solid state physics), 55. *Prof Exp:* Docent physics, Univ Pavia, 55-56; fel cryogenics, Univ Bristol, 56-57; vis res prof spectros, Univ Pittsburgh, 57-59; vis scholar, Bell Tel Labs, 59-61; res scientist chem, Cyanamide Europ Res Inst, Geneva, Switz, 61-66; resident res assoc, Transuranic Lab, Argonne Nat Lab, 66-68; MEM TECH STAFF, GTE LABS, 68- *Concurrent Pos:* Fulbright scholar, 57. *Mem:* Electrochem Soc. *Res:* Spectroscopy of transition-metal and rare-earth ions and its relation to phosphor technology. *Mailing Add:* GTE Labs 40 Sylvan Rd Waltham MA 02254

PAPPANO, ACHILLES JOHN, b Allentown, Pa, Mar 21, 40; m 63; c 4. PHARMACOLOGY. *Educ:* St Joseph's Col, Pa, BS, 62; Univ Pa, PhD(pharmacol), 66. *Prof Exp:* Instr pharmacol, Sch Med, Tulane Univ, 66-67; from asst prof to assoc prof, 68-80, PROF PHARMACOL, SCHS MED & DENT MED, UNIV CONN, 80- *Concurrent Pos:* Nat Heart Inst fel, Sch Med, Univ Va, 67-68. *Mem:* Am Heart Asn; Am Soc Pharmacol & Exp Therapeut. *Res:* Drug action in embryonic heart; cardiac electrophysiology; developmental pharmacology; heart cell culture. *Mailing Add:* Dept of Pharmacol Univ of Conn Health Ctr Farmington CT 06032

PAPPAS, ANTHONY JOHN, b Memphis, Tenn, Jan 21, 40. CHEMISTRY. *Educ:* Univ Miami, BS, 63, MS, 65, PhD(chem), 69. *Prof Exp:* Fel under Dr George W Watt, Univ Tex, Austin, 69-71; asst prof, 71-77, assoc prof, 77-80, SR ASSOC PROF, MIAMI-DADE COMMUNITY COL, SOUTH CAMPUS, 80- *Mem:* AAAS; Am Chem Soc. *Res:* Synthesis, characterization and application of inorganic coordination compounds; new synthetic routes for preparation of inorganic and organic compounds via enhancement by coordination to metals. *Mailing Add:* Dept of Chem Miami-Dade Community Col Miami FL 33176

PAPPAS, BETTY COLLEEN, organic chemistry, see previous edition

PAPPAS, DANIEL SAMUEL, b Northampton, Mass, Dec 18, 42; m 76. PLASMA PHYSICS. *Educ:* Univ Calif, Los Angeles, BS, 69, MS, 71. *Prof Exp:* Res asst plasma physics, Univ Calif, Los Angeles, 70-71; res physicist, Jet Propulsion Lab, Calif Inst Technol, 71-72; res physicist nuclear fusion, Lawrence Livermore Lab, Univ Calif, 72-73; res physicist, Nat Magnet Lab, 74-80, RES PHYSICIST NUCLEAR FUSION, PLASMA FUSION CTR, MASS INST TECHNOL, 80- *Mem:* Am Phys Soc. *Res:* Controlled fusion research-tokamaks, especially measurements of thermonuclear neurt neutron emission, ion temperature by neutrons and charge exchange, scaling laws of fusion devices, particle confinement and recycling and impurity studies; astrons, particle accelerators and III thermionics. *Mailing Add:* Mass Inst of Technol 170 Albany St Cambridge MA 02139

PAPPAS, GEORGE DEMETRIOS, b Portland, Maine, Nov 26, 26; m 52; c 2. NEUROBIOLOGY. *Educ:* Bowdoin Col, AB, 47; Ohio State Univ, MS, 48, PhD(zool), 52. *Prof Exp:* Vis investr cytol, Rockefeller Inst, 52-54; from asst prof to assoc prof anat, Col Physicians & Surgeons, Columbia Univ, 56-66; prof anat, Albert Einstein Col Med, 67-77, prof neurosci, 74-77; PROF ANAT & HEAD DEPT, COL MED, UNIV ILL, 77- *Concurrent Pos:* Fel anat & cytol, NY Univ-Bellevue Med Ctr, 54-56; vis prof neurosci, Albert Einstein Col Med, 77- *Mem:* Fel AAAS; Am Asn Anat; Am Soc Cell Biol (pres, 75); fel NY Acad Sci; Electron Micros Soc Am. *Res:* Electron microscopy; cytochemistry; neurocytology; synapses; ocular tissue; vascular system; biological membranes. *Mailing Add:* Dept Anat Col Med Univ Ill Chicago IL 60680

PAPPAS, GEORGE STEPHEN, b Poughkeepsie, NY, Oct 16, 23; m 46; c 3. PHYSIOLOGY. *Educ:* Fordham Univ, BS, 47, MS, 49; NY Univ, PhD(biol), 60. *Prof Exp:* From instr to assoc prof, 48-63, chmn dept, 60-69, vpres, 69-70, actg pres, 70-71, vpres, 71-76, PROF BIOL, IONA COL, 63-, CHMN DEPT, 77- *Concurrent Pos:* Am Physiol Soc grant, 60; Fulbright fel endocrine physiol, Cairo, Egypt, 66. *Mem:* AAAS; fel NY Acad Sci. *Res:* Antimetabolites and vitamin analogs; endocrine physiology; gonadotrophic effects of adrenalectonized animals; thyroid-adrenal function; developmental biology; history of biology. *Mailing Add:* Dept of Biol Iona Col New Rochelle NY 10801

PAPPAS, JAMES JOHN, b Bridgeport, Conn, July 22, 31; m 60; c 3. ORGANIC CHEMISTRY. *Educ:* Mass Inst Technol, BS, 52, MS, 54; Columbia Univ, PhD(org chem), 59. *Prof Exp:* Jr chemist, Merck & Co, NJ, 54-56; chemist, Esso Res & Eng Co, 59-62; sr chemist, Cent Res Labs, Inmont Corp, 62-67; mgr chem prod, 67-70; sr res chemist, Esso Res & Eng Co, 70-71; SR RES CHEMIST, J M HUBER CORP, 71- *Mem:* Am Chem Soc. *Res:* Reactions of ozone; hydrogenation; phosphorus and sulfur chemistry; synthetic lubricants; lubricant and fuel additives; wax modifiers; polymer synthesis and modification; electrophotography; liquid and solid toners; dyes; pigments; printing inks; coatings. *Mailing Add:* J M Huber Corp Edison NJ 08817

PAPPAS, LARRY GEORGE, b Chadron, Nebr, Nov 16, 46; m 72; c 1. INSECT PHYSIOLOGY. *Educ:* Hiram Scott Col, BS, 69; Univ Wyo, MS, 71; Univ Ill, Urbana, PhD(entom), 75. *Prof Exp:* Res asst zool, Univ Wyo, 69-71; res assoc, Va Polytech Inst & State Univ, 75-77; instr biol, Col St Teresa, Winona, Minn, 77-79; ASST PROF BIOL, PERU STATE COL, NEBR, 79- *Mem:* Sigma Xi; Entom Soc Am; AAAS; Am Mosquito Control Asn. *Res:* Physiological basis of insect behavior. *Mailing Add:* Natural Sci Div Peru State Col Peru NE 68421

PAPPAS, NICHOLAS, b Kearny, NJ, Sept 22, 30; m 53; c 4. ORGANIC CHEMISTRY, POLYMER CHEMISTRY. *Educ:* Yale Univ, BS, 52; Brown Univ, PhD(org chem), 57. *Prof Exp:* Res chemist, 56-62, staff chemist, 62-63, res supvr polymers, 63-65, develop supvr finishes res, 65-66, asst lab mgr, Mich, 66-69, lab mgr, 69-70, asst nat mgr indust finishes, 70-71, nat mgr indust finishes & mkt dir, 71-73, div dir, 73-76, mgr, corp planning activ, 76-78, gen mgr, 78-81, VPRES, FABRICS & FINISHES, E I DU PONT DE NEMOURS & CO, INC, 81- *Res:* Organic synthesis; polymer synthesis and evaluation; development of finishes. *Mailing Add:* Fabrics & Finishes Dept E I du Pont de Nemours & Co Inc Wilmington DE 19898

PAPPAS, PETER WILLIAM, b Pasadena, Calif, Dec 9, 44; m 66; c 2. MEMBRANE BIOLOGY. *Educ:* Humboldt State Col, Calif, BA, 66, MA, 68; Univ Okla, PhD(zool), 71. *Prof Exp:* asst prof, 73-77, ASSOC PROF ZOOL, OHIO STATE UNIV, 77- *Concurrent Pos:* NIH fel, Rice Univ, Houston, 71-73. *Honors & Awards:* Sigma Xi Res Award, Ohio State Univ, 75. *Mem:* Am Soc Parasitologists; Am Soc Trop Med & Hyg; Sigma Xi. *Res:* Biochemical aspects of host-parasite relationships; biochemistry and physiology of parasites; membrane transport in parasitic helminths and protozoa. *Mailing Add:* Dept of Zool 1735 Neil Ave Ohio State Univ Columbus OH 43210

PAPPAS, S PETER, b Hartford, Conn, Feb 3, 36; m 61; c 2. ORGANIC CHEMISTRY. *Educ:* Dartmouth Col, BA, 58; Univ Wis, PhD(chem), 62. *Prof Exp:* Fels, Univ Wis, 62-63 & Brandeis Univ, 63-64; asst prof chem, Emory Univ, 64-68; assoc prof, 68-73, PROF CHEM, NDAK STATE UNIV, 73- *Concurrent Pos:* NIH grant, 64-67; Am Chem Soc Petrol Res Fund grant, 66-69; indust consult var chem co, res assoc, DeSoto, Inc, 73; indust grants, 73-; NASA grant, 73-75; Off Water Res grant, 77-; Paint Res Inst grant, 77-; vis prof, Univ Stuttgart, 77. *Honors & Awards:* First Place Roon Awards, Fedn Socs Coatings Technol, 74, 75 & 76; DAAD Award, 77. *Mem:* Am Chem Soc. *Res:* Photochemistry, synthesis, catalysis and reaction mechanisms as applied to coatings applications. *Mailing Add:* Dept of Chem NDak State Univ Fargo ND 58102

PAPPATHEODOROU, SOFIA, b New York, NY, Feb 15, 40. ORGANOMETALLIC CHEMISTRY. *Educ:* Univ Miami, BS, 62, MS, 65, PhD(chem), 78. *Prof Exp:* Lab instr chem, Univ Miami, 65-68 & 70-71; lab instr chem, Miami-Dade Community Col, 76-78; vis prof chem, Dept Phys Sci, Fla Int Univ, 76, adj instr, 76-78; fel chem, Papanicolaou Cancer Res Inst, 79-81; LECTR, CHEM, CALIF STATE UNIV, FRESNO, 81- *Mem:* Am Chem Soc; Sigma Xi. *Res:* Synthesis and product analysis of olefins form alcohols and platinum salts, and product distributions in the reactions of Grignard reagents with conjugated enones. *Mailing Add:* Chem Dept Calif State Univ Fresno CA 93740

PAPPELIS, ARISTOTEL JOHN, b Cloquet, Minn, May 25, 28; m 51; c 3. PLANT PATHOLOGY. *Educ:* Wis State Col, Superior, BS, 51; Iowa State Univ, PhD(plant physiol), 57. *Prof Exp:* Plant physiologist, Mkt Serv, USDA, 57-58; asst prof biol sci, Western Ill Univ, 58-60; from asst prof to assoc prof, 60-71, PROF BOT, SOUTHERN ILL UNIV, CARBONDALE, 71- *Concurrent Pos:* Shell Merit fel, Stanford Univ, 70. *Mem:* Am Soc Plant Physiologists; Am Phytopath Soc; Am Inst Biol Sci; Mycol Soc Am. *Res:* Senescence and host-parasite interactions in plants. *Mailing Add:* Dept of Bot Southern Ill Univ Carbondale IL 62901

PAPPENHAGEN, JAMES MEREDITH, b Alliance, Ohio, Apr 1, 26; m 48; c 3. ANALYTICAL CHEMISTRY. *Educ:* Mt Union Col, BS, 49; Purdue Univ, MS, 51, PhD(chem), 53. *Prof Exp:* From asst prof to assoc prof, 52-62, chmn dept, 61-64, PROF CHEM, KENYON COL, 62-, CHMN DEPT, 76- *Concurrent Pos:* Vis prof environ systs eng, Clemson Univ, 66-67; consult, Off Water Progs, Environ Protection Agency; mem, Standard Methods Comt, Am Water Works Asn & Water Pollution Control Fedn. *Honors & Awards:* Wendell R LaDue Citation, 77. *Mem:* AAAS; Am Chem Soc; Am Water Works Asn. *Res:* Spectrophotometry and instrumentation; determination of ions in wastes and waters. *Mailing Add:* Dept of Chem Kenyon Col Gambier OH 43022

PAPPENHEIMER, ALWIN MAX, JR, b Cedarhurst, NY, Nov 25, 08; m 38; c 3. BIOCHEMISTRY. *Educ:* Harvard Univ, SB, 29, PhD(org chem), 32. *Prof Exp:* Instr & tutor biochem sci, Harvard Univ, 30-33; Nat Res Coun fel med, Nat Inst Med Res London, 33-34; instr appl immunol, Sch Pub Health, Harvard Univ, 36-39; asst prof biochem & bact, Sch Med, Univ Pa, 39-41; from asst prof to prof microbiol, Col Med, NY Univ, 41-58; chmn bd tutors in biochem, 58-63, prof, 58-79, EMER PROF BIOL, HARVARD UNIV, 79- *Concurrent Pos:* Bradford fel, Harvard Med Sch, 36-37; sr chemist, State Antitoxin & Vaccine Lab, Mass, 36-39; Guggenheim fel, 66-67; consult, Surgeon Gen Mem Comn Immunization, Armed Forces Epidemiol Bd. *Honors & Awards:* Eli Lilly Award, 42. *Mem:* Nat Acad Sci; Am Acad Arts & Sci; Am Chem Soc; Am Soc Biol Chemists; Am Soc Microbiol. *Res:* Chemistry and mode of action of bacterial toxins; immunochemistry; immunization; bacterial metabolism. *Mailing Add:* Harvard Univ Biol Labs 16 Divinity Ave Cambridge MA 02138

PAPPENHEIMER, JOHN RICHARD, b New York, NY, Oct 25, 15; m 49; c 4. PHYSIOLOGY. *Educ:* Harvard Univ, BS, 36; Cambridge Univ, PhD(physiol), 40. *Prof Exp:* Demonstr pharmacol, Univ Col, Univ London, 39-40; instr, Col Physicians & Surgeons, Columbia Univ, 41-42; assoc, 45-49, asst prof, 49-53, vis prof, 53-68, GEORGE HIGGINSON PROF PHYSIOL, HARVARD MED SCH, 68- *Concurrent Pos:* Res fel physiol, Col Physicians & Surgeons, Columbia Univ, 40-41; Johnson Res Found fel, Univ Pa, 41-45; overseas fel, Churchill Col, Cambridge, Eng, 71-72; career investr, Am Heart Asn, 53-; George Eastman Univ prof & fel Balliol Col, Oxford, 75-76. *Mem:* Nat Acad Sci; AAAS; Am Physiol Soc (pres, 64-65); Soc Gen Physiol; Harvey Soc. *Res:* Kidney; respiration; hemodynamics; permeability; cerebrospinal fluid; control of sleep. *Mailing Add:* Dept of Physiol Harvard Med Sch Boston MA 02115

PAPPER, EMANUEL MARTIN, b New York, NY, July 12, 15; m 75; c 2. ANESTHESIOLOGY. *Educ:* Columbia Univ, AB, 35; NY Univ, MD, 38; Am Bd Anesthesiol, dipl, 43. *Hon Degrees:* MD, Univ Uppsala, 64, Univ Turin, 66, Univ Vienna, 77. *Prof Exp:* From intern to resident anesthesiol, Bellevue Hosp, 39-42; from instr to assoc prof, NY Univ, 42-49; prof & chmn dept, Col Physicians & Surgeons, Columbia Univ, 49-69; dean, Sch Med & vpres med affairs, 69-71, PROF ANESTHESIOL, SCH MED, UNIV MIAMI, 69- *Concurrent Pos:* Fel, NY Univ, 40; dir anesthesiol serv, Presby Hosp, 49-69; dir & vis anesthesiologist, Francis Delafield Hosp, 51-69; consult, Huntington Hosp, Div Med Sci, Nat Res Coun, US Navy & First Army; mem surg study sect, NIH, 58-, nat adv heart coun, 62-64; mem, President's Comn Heart Dis, Cancer & Stroke, 64; prin consult, Nat Inst Gen Med Sci, 65-66, chmn gen med res prog-proj comt, 66-67. *Mem:* AAAS; Am Soc Anesthesiol; Am Soc Pharmacol & Exp Therapeut; Am Soc Clin Invest; Am Thoracic Soc. *Res:* Pharmacology of drugs; physiology of circulation. *Mailing Add:* Dept Anesthesiol Sch Med Univ Miami PO Box 016370 Miami FL 33101

PAPPER, SOLOMON, b New York, NY, May 28, 22; m 43; c 3. INTERNAL MEDICINE, METABOLISM. *Educ:* Columbia Univ, AB, 42; NY Univ, MD, 44; Am Bd Internal Med, dipl. *Prof Exp:* Res fel med, Harvard Med Sch & Thorndike Mem Lab, 50-52; instr, Med Sch, Univ Cincinnati & assoc, May Inst Med Res, 52-53; instr, Med Sch, Tufts Univ, 53-54, from asst clin prof to assoc clin prof, 54-59, assoc prof, 59-60; prof, Med Col Va, 60-62; prof & chmn dept, Sch Med, Univ NMex, 62-68; prof med & co-chmn dept, Sch Med, Univ Miami, 68-71; prof, Univ Colo Med Ctr, Denver, 71-73; DISTINGUISHED PROF MED, UNIV OKLA, 74, HEAD COL MED, 77- *Concurrent Pos:* Asst, Boston City Hosp, 50-52; staff physician & chief metab, Boston Vet Admin Hosp, 53-58, asst chief med & dir res, 58-60; instr, Harvard Univ, 53-59; chief med serv, Miami Vet Admin Hosp, Fla, 68-71; chmn dept med, Gen Rose Mem Hosp, 71-73; distinguished physician, Oklahoma City Vet Admin Hosp. *Honors & Awards:* Distinguished serv award, Nat Kidney Found, 70. *Mem:* Endocrine Soc; Am Fedn Clin Res; Am Soc Clin Invest; Asn Am Physicians. *Res:* Diurnal rhythm of renal excretion of fluid and electrolytes; liver disease and electrolyte excretion; fluid and electrolyte metabolism; the kidney in hypertension. *Mailing Add:* 921 NE 13th St Oklahoma City OK 73104

PAPPIS, JAMES, engineering, materials science, see previous edition

PAPPIUS, HANNA M, b Lakocin, Poland, July 26, 25; Can citizen; m 50; c 3. NEUROCHEMISTRY. *Educ:* McGill Univ, BSc, 46, MSc, 48, PhD(biochem), 52. *Prof Exp:* From lectr to assoc prof, 54-79, PROF NEUROL & NEUROSURG, MCGILL UNIV, 79-, ASSOC NEUROCHEMIST, MONTREAL NEUROL INST, 53- *Mem:* Can Physiol Soc; Can Biochem Soc; Can Soc Clin Chem; Am Soc Neurochem; Int Soc Neurochem. *Res:* Cerebral edema and electrolyte metabolism; water and electrolyte distribution in cerebral tissues; functional disturbances in injured brain. *Mailing Add:* Montreal Neurol Inst McGill Univ 3801 University St Montreal PQ H3A 2B4 Can

PAPPO, RAPHAEL, medicinal chemistry, organic chemistry, see previous edition

PAPSIDERO, LAWRENCE D, b Buffalo, NY, Sep 2, 49; m 72; c 1. IMMUNO PATHOLOGY, HYBRIDOMA RESEARCH. *Educ:* Ohio State Univ, MS, 74; State Univ NY, Buffalo, BA, 71, PhD(exp path), 78. *Prof Exp:* Fel, 78-79, cancer res scientist, 79-81, SR CANCER RES SCIENTIST, ROSWELL PARK MEM INST, 81- *Honors & Awards:* Investr Res Award, Nat Cancer Inst, 81. *Res:* Immuno diagnosis of cancer. *Mailing Add:* Diag Immunol Dept Roswell Park Mem Inst Buffalo NY 14263

PAQUE, RONALD E, b Green Bay, Wis, Apr 29, 38. MICROBIOLOGY, IMMUNOLOGY. *Educ:* Wis State Univ-Oshkosh, BS, 60; Univ Wis, MS, 63; Univ Ariz, PhD(microbiol, biochem), 66. *Prof Exp:* Proj asst virol, Univ Wis, 61, asst bact, 61-62, asst virol, 62-63; asst microbiol, Univ Ariz, 63-64, training fel, 65-66; assoc dir immunol div, Cancer Chemother Dept, Microbiol Assocs, 66-68; asst prof microbiol, Univ Ill Col Med, 70-74; ASSOC PROF MICROBIOL, HEALTH SCI CTR, UNIV TEX, SAN ANTONIO, 74- *Concurrent Pos:* USPHS fel cellular immunol, Univ Ill Col Med, 68-70; mem study sect, NIH; reviewer, NSF; invited partic, 2nd RNA Conf, Peking, China. *Mem:* AAAS; Am Asn Immunol; Am Soc Microbiol. *Res:* Tumor, cellular and transplantation immunology; RNA chemistry; transfer of immunity with subcellular fractions; delayed-type hypersensitivity; immunology of viral-induced myocarditis. *Mailing Add:* Dept of Microbiol Univ of Tex Health Sci Ctr San Antonio TX 78284

PAQUET, JEAN GUY, b Montmagny, Que, Jan 5, 38. ELECTRICAL ENGINEERING, AUTOMATIC CONTROL SYSTEMS. *Educ:* Laval Univ, BApplSc, 59, PhD(elec eng), 63; Ecol Nat Sup Aeronautique, Paris, MSc, 60. *Prof Exp:* From assoc prof to prof, Laval Univ, 67-71, head dept elec eng, 67-69, vdean res, Fac Sci, 69-72; spec asst to vpres sci, Nat Res Coun Can, 71-72; vrector acad, 72-77, RECTOR, LAVAL UNIV, 77- *Concurrent Pos:* Fels, French govt, 59, Nat Res Coun of Can, 61, NATO, 62, NSF, 64 & Que govt, 65; grants, Nat Res Coun Can, 64-77 & Defence Res Bd Can, 65-76; mem assoc comt on automatic control, Nat Res Coun Can, 63-70; mem, Coun Que Univs, 73-77; mem, Spec Task Force on Res & Develop, Sci Coun Can, 76- *Mem:* Inst Elec & Electronics Engrs; Am Soc Eng Educ; Can Res Mgt Asn; fel AAAS; Innovation Mgt Inst Can. *Res:* Control systems engineering. *Mailing Add:* Off of the Rector Laval Univ Quebec PQ G1K 7P4 Can

PAQUETTE, DAVID GEORGE, b Annapolis, Md, Apr 21, 45; m 70. MATERIALS SCIENCE ENGINEERING. *Educ:* Univ Calif, Santa Barbara, BA, 67, MA, 69, PhD(physics), 73. *Prof Exp:* Res assoc/assoc instr, Univ Utah, 73-76, res asst prof mat sci & eng, 76-77; SR SCIENTIST, FORD AEROSPACE & COMMUN CORP, 77- *Mem:* Am Phys Soc; Am Ceramic Soc. *Res:* Fabrication and characterization of advanced composite ceramic materials; characterization of beta alumina ceramic materials for sodium-sulfur battery development; design and analysis of data from sodium sulfur electrochemical cells; ceramic composites with increased fracture toughness. *Mailing Add:* 767 Allegheny Ave Costa Mesa CA 92626

PAQUETTE, GERARD ARTHUR, b Winooski, Vt, Aug 5, 26; m 55; c 5. COMPUTER SCIENCE EDUCATION, MATHEMATICS EDUCATION. *Educ:* La Mennais Col, BA, 52; Bridgewater State Col, MEd, 57; Boston Col, MA, 61; Pa State Univ, PhD(math educ), 71. *Prof Exp:* Teacher high sch, Que, 45-49, high sch, Mass, 49-53 & Mt Assumption Inst, 53-54; chmn dept math, Middletown High Sch, RI, 54-67; assoc prof, 67-76, PROF MATH

EDUC, BOSTON STATE COL, 76- *Concurrent Pos:* Lectr, Univ RI, 61-64 & Bridgewater State Col, 61-64; math consult, RI State Dept Educ, 64-67. *Res:* Theory of instruction; instructional strategies; modes of representation in instruction; implementation of computer assisted instruction; mathematics curricular materials. *Mailing Add:* Dept of Math Boston State Col Boston MA 02115

PAQUETTE, GUY, b Montreal, Que, Oct 4, 30; m 59; c 2. THEORETICAL PHYSICS. *Educ:* Univ Montreal, BSc, 51; Univ BC, MA, 53, PhD(physics), 56. *Prof Exp:* From asst prof to assoc prof, 56-69, PROF PHYSICS, UNIV MONTREAL, 69-, CHMN DEPT, 73- *Concurrent Pos:* Nat Res Coun Can res fel, King's Col, Univ London, 57-58 & State Univ Leyden, 58-59; consult, RCA Victor Co, 62-64; vis, Saclay Nuclear Res Ctr, Saclay, France, 66-67. *Mem:* Am Phys Soc; Can Asn Physicists. *Res:* Physics of magnetoplasmas; waves in plasmas. *Mailing Add:* Dept of Physics Univ of Montreal CP 6128 Montreal PQ H3C 3J7 Can

PAQUETTE, LEO ARMAND, b Worcester, Mass, July 15, 34; m 57; c 5. ORGANIC CHEMISTRY. *Educ:* Col of the Holy Cross, BS, 56; Mass Inst Technol, PhD(org chem), 59. *Prof Exp:* Res assoc chem, Upjohn Co, 59-63; from asst prof to assoc prof, 63-69, PROF CHEM, OHIO STATE UNIV, 69- *Concurrent Pos:* Alfred P Sloan Found fel, 65-67. *Mem:* Am Chem Soc; Royal Soc Chem. *Res:* Synthetic organic chemistry; organosilicon reagents; unusual molecules; molecular rearrangements; transition metal catalysis. *Mailing Add:* Dept of Chem Ohio State Univ 88 W 18th Ave Columbus OH 43210

PAQUETTE, ROBERT GEORGE, b Chippewa Falls, Wis, Feb 5, 15; m 41; c 5. PHYSICAL OCEANOGRAPHY, OCEAN ENGINEERING. *Educ:* Univ Wash, BS, 36, PhD(phys chem), 41. *Prof Exp:* Instr math, US Naval Acad, 41-42, instr chem & elec eng, 42-45; res chemist, Plywood Res Found, Wash, 46; res assoc meteorol physics, Univ Wash, 46-49, res oceanogr, 49-55, res assoc prof & lectr oceanog, 55-61; head phys oceanog group, Gen Motors Lab, Santa Barbara, 61-71; assoc prof, 71-75, PROF OCEANOG, NAVAL POSTGRAD SCH, 74- *Mem:* Am Geophys Union. *Res:* Arctic oceanography; oceanographic instrumentation; direct measurement of ocean currents. *Mailing Add:* Code 68 Naval Postgrad Sch Monterey CA 93940

PAQUETTE, THOMAS LEROY, b Seattle, Wash, Mar 25, 48. BIOCHEMISTRY. *Educ:* Univ Calif, Santa Barbara, BS, 70; Univ Ore, PhD(chem), 77. *Prof Exp:* Fel biochem, Washington Univ, 77-80; RES ASST PROF MED, UNIV WASHINGTON, 80- *Mem:* Am Diabetes Asn. *Res:* Pancreatic hormones. *Mailing Add:* Diabetes Res Ctr US Public Health Serv Hosp 1131 14th Ave S Quarters 8 Seattle WA 98144

PAQUIN, ROGER JOSEPH ALFRED, plant physiology, biochemistry, see previous edition

PARACER, SURINDAR MOHAN, b Lyallpur, India, Jan 25, 41; m 68; c 2. SYMBIOLOGY, HISTORY OF SCIENCE. *Educ:* Panjab Univ, BS, 59; SDak State Univ, MS, 61; Univ Calif, Davis, PhD(nematol), 66. *Prof Exp:* Res assoc, Univ Mass, 65-67; asst prof biol, Nichols Col, 67-69 & Assumption Col, Mass, 69-70; from asst to assoc prof, 70-77, PROF BIOL, WORCESTER STATE COL, 77- *Mem:* AAAS; Sigma Xi; Nat Sci Teachers Asn; Hist Sci Soc; Soc Nematologists. *Res:* Biology of the host-parasite relationship; history of symbiology. *Mailing Add:* Dept Biol Worcester State Col Worcester MA 01602

PARADIS, RODOLPHE OMER, agronomy, entomology, see previous edition

PARADISE, LOIS JEAN, b Boston, Mass, Oct 26, 28. MEDICAL MICROBIOLOGY. *Educ:* Brown Univ, AB, 50; Univ Mich, MS, 55, PhD(bact), 60. *Prof Exp:* From res assoc to asst prof microbiol, Univ Mich, Ann Arbor, 60-72; ASSOC PROF MED MICROBIOL, UNIV S FLA, 73- *Mem:* Am Soc Microbiol; Reticuleudothelial Soc. *Res:* Tumor immunology; respiratory carcinogenesis; pathogenesis of respiratory infections. *Mailing Add:* Dept of Med Microbiol Box 10 Univ of S Fla Col of Med Tampa FL 33612

PARADISE, NORMAN FRANCIS, b Minneapolis, Minn, Jan 19, 43; c 2. PHYSIOLOGY. *Educ:* Univ Minn, BA, 66, PhD(physiol), 71. *Prof Exp:* USPHS fel, 71-73, Minn Med Found fel, 73-74, Minn Heart Asn fel, biophys sci unit, Mayo Grad Sch Med, Mayo Found, 75-77; asst prof, 77-81, ASSOC PROF, COL MED, NORTHEASTERN OHIO UNIV, 81- *Concurrent Pos:* Lectr, Am Asn Nurse Anesthetists. *Mem:* AAAS; Am Physiol Soc; Sigma Xi; NY Acad Sci. *Res:* Cardiovascular physiology; cardiac muscle; effects of hypertension on ventricular function; regulation of cardiac contractility. *Mailing Add:* Dept of Physiol Northeastern Ohio Univs Sch of Med Rootstown OH 44272

PARADISE, RAYMOND R, b Holyoke, Mass, Aug 28, 31; m 57; c 4. PHARMACOLOGY. *Educ:* Hampden Col Pharm, BS, 53; Univ Kansas City, MS, 55; Univ Tenn, PhD(pharmacol), 60. *Prof Exp:* From asst prof to assoc prof, 62-73, PROF PHARMACOL & ANESTHESIOL, SCH MED, IND UNIV, INDIANAPOLIS, 73- *Concurrent Pos:* USPHS fel, Univ Southern Calif, 60-62; referee ed proc, Soc Exp Biol & Med, 72-78. *Mem:* Am Soc Pharmacol & Exp Therapeut; Soc Exp Biol & Med. *Res:* Anesthetics on metabolism; neonatal pharmacology. *Mailing Add:* Dept of Pharmacol Sch of Med Ind Univ 1100 W Michigan St Indianapolis IN 46202

PARAKKAL, PAUL FAB, b Alwaye, India, July 21, 31; US citizen; m 60; c 2. BIOLOGY, ELECTRON MICROSCOPY. *Educ:* Kerala Univ, Trivandrum, India, BSc, 52; McGill Univ, MSc, 59; Brown Univ, PhD(biol), 62. *Prof Exp:* Res assoc, Med Sch, Boston Univ, 64-68, asst res prof dermatol, 64-68; assoc scientist biol, Ore Reg Primate Ctr, 68-73; HEALTH SCI ADMINR BIOL, NAT INST DENT RES, NIH, 73- *Mem:* Am Soc Cell Biol. *Res:* Control mechanisms of the hair growth cycle. *Mailing Add:* Westwood Bldg Rm 519 Nat Inst Dent Res Bethesda MD 20014

PARANCHYCH, WILLIAM, b Drumheller, Alta, Feb 4, 33; m 57; c 1. BIOCHEMISTRY, MICROBIOLOGY. *Educ:* Univ Alta, BSc, 54, MSc, 58; McGill Univ, PhD(biochem), 61. *Prof Exp:* Clin biochemist, Misericordia Hosp, Edmonton, Alta, 54-56; res assoc virol, Wistar Inst, 61-63; from asst prof to assoc prof, 63-71, PROF BIOCHEM, UNIV ALTA, 71- *Mem:* Am Soc Biol Chemists; Am Soc Microbiol; AAAS; Can Soc Microbiol; Can Biochem Soc. *Res:* Mechanisms Biochemical and genetic studies on bacterial pili: a comparison of the structure and function of conjugative and nonconjugative systems. *Mailing Add:* Dept of Biochem Univ of Alta Edmonton AB T6G 2H7 Can

PARANJAPE, BHALACHANDRA VISHWANATH, b Gondia, India, Dec 2, 22; m 54; c 3. PHYSICS. *Educ:* Univ Nagpur, BSc, 45; Univ Liverpool, PhD, 57. *Prof Exp:* Asst physics, Univ Liverpool, 56-57; res assoc, Purdue Univ, 58-59; asst prof, La State Univ, 59; from asst prof to assoc prof, 61-70, PROF PHYSICS, UNIV ALTA, 70- *Res:* Theoretical aspects of semiconductor physics; dielectric breakdown; Ettingshausen coefficient. *Mailing Add:* Dept of Physics Univ Alta Edmonton AB T6G 2E1 Can

PARAS, PETER, radiological health, nuclear medicine, see previous edition

PARASCANDOLA, JOHN LOUIS, b New York, NY, July 14, 41; m 63; c 2. HISTORY OF SCIENCE. *Educ:* Brooklyn Col, BS, 63; Univ Wis-Madison, MS, 68, PhD(hist sci), 68. *Prof Exp:* Josiah Macy Jr Found fel hist sci, Harvard Univ, 68-69; asst prof hist pharm, 69-73 & hist sci, 70-73, ASSOC PROF HIST PHARM & HIST SCI, 73- *Mem:* Am Inst Hist Pharm (dir, 73-); Hist Sci Soc; Am Asn Hist Med; Int Acad Hist Pharm. *Res:* History of pharmacology and drug therapy; history of pharmaceutical chemistry and biochemistry. *Mailing Add:* Sch of Pharm Univ of Wis Madison WI 53706

PARASKEVAS, FRIXOS, b Serrai, Greece, Sept 13, 28; Can citizen; m 60; c 2. IMMUNOLOGY. *Educ:* Aristotelian Univ Thessaloniki, MD, 51. *Prof Exp:* Lectr, 64-65, from asst prof to assoc prof, 65-76, PROF MED, UNIV MAN, 76-, PROF IMMUNOL, 78- *Concurrent Pos:* Consult, R H Inst, Winnipeg; dir, Immunoprotein Lab, Health Sci Ctr, Winnipeg. *Mem:* Can Soc Immunol; Am Asn Immunologists; Am Soc Hemat. *Res:* Activation of immune response; regulation of immune response. *Mailing Add:* Dept of Med Univ of Man 100 Olivia St Winnipeg MB R3E 0V9 Can

PARASKEVOPOULOS, DEMETRIS E, b Athens, Greece. PHYSICS, ELECTRICAL ENGINEERING. *Educ:* Nat Univ Athens, dipl sci & physics, 69; Brown Univ, MSc, 72; Boston Univ, MA, 74, PhD(physics), 76. *Prof Exp:* Res staff mem solid state, Nat Magnet Lab, Mass Inst Technol, 76-77; PROJ MGR RES & DEVELOP, XEROX CORP, 77- *Mem:* Am Phys Soc; Inst Elec & Electronics Engrs. *Mailing Add:* Xerox Corp 800 Philips Rd Webster NY 14580

PARASKEVOPOULOS, GEORGE, b Athens, Greece, Apr 25, 29; Can citizen; m 60; c 1. PHYSICAL CHEMISTRY. *Educ:* Nat Tech Univ, Athens, BEng, 54; Univ Toronto, MSc, 60; McGill Univ, PhD(phys chem), 65. *Prof Exp:* Res chemist, Can Industs Ltd, 59-61; fel chem, 65-67, asst res officer, 67-71, assoc res officer, 71-80, SR RES OFFICER CHEM, NAT RES COUN CAN, 80- *Mem:* Chem Inst Can. *Res:* Reaction kinetics in the gas phase, particularly elementary reactions of atoms and free radicals; photochemistry; atmospheric chemistry. *Mailing Add:* Div Chem Nat Res Coun Can Ottawa ON K1A 0R9 Can

PARASURAMAN, RAJA, b New Delhi, India, Aug 2, 50. HUMAN NEUROPHYSIOLOGY, HUMAN FACTORS. *Educ:* Univ London, Eng, BSc, 72; Univ Aston, Eng, MSc, 73, PhD(psychol), 76. *Prof Exp:* Lectr II psychol, Lanchester Polytech, Eng, 76-77; lectr II psychol, Wolverhampton Polytech, Eng, 77-78; RES PSYCHOLOGIST PSYCHOL, UNIV CALIF, LOS ANGELES, 78- *Concurrent Pos:* Consult, Logicon Inc & Vector Res Inc, 81- *Mem:* AAAS; Human Factors Soc; Soc Psychophysiol Res; Psychonomic Soc. *Res:* Human neurophysiology; human performance; attention and vigilance; man-machine systems. *Mailing Add:* Dept Psychol Univ Calif Los Angeles CA 90024

PARASZCZAK, JURIJ ROSTYSLAN, b Rochdale, Eng, May 19, 52; m. ELECTRONICS ENGINEERING. *Educ:* Univ Sheffield, BSc, 73, PhD(phys chem), 76. *Prof Exp:* Res assoc, Univ Wis, Madison, 77-79; RES STAFF MEM, IBM RES, 79- *Mem:* Sigma Xi. *Res:* Design, manufacture, evaluation and modelling of resist materials for microlithography; study of plasma processing on dielectrics and resists. *Mailing Add:* PO Box 218 Yorktown Heights NY 10598

PARCELL, LLOYD JAMISON, b Rocky Mt, Va, May 30, 35; m 58; c 3. WATER CHEMISTRY. *Educ:* Roanoke Col, BS, 57; Univ Va, PhD(chem), 63. *Prof Exp:* Proj chemist, Am Viscose Corp, 57-58; chemist, Texaco Exp Inc, 63-64, sr chemist, 64-67; res chemist, 67-78, SR PROJ CHEMIST, TEXACO, INC, 78- *Mem:* Am Chem Soc; Am Water Works Asn. *Res:* Electrochemistry; waste water treatment; biological oxidation of compounds; radiochemistry; heterogeneous exchange reactions; photochemical reactions; boron chemistry; ortho-para hydrogen conversion; hydrogen diffusion through metals. *Mailing Add:* Port Arthur Res Labs Texaco Inc PO Box 1608 Port Arthur TX 77640

PARCELL, ROBERT FORD, b USA, Sept 1, 22; m 54; c 2. ORGANIC CHEMISTRY. *Educ:* Univ Fla, BS, 44, MS, 48, PhD(chem), 50. *Prof Exp:* Res chemist, Parke, Davis & Co, 50-66, lab dir, 66-71, sect dir, 71-77; CONSULT FINE CHEM & DRUGS OF ABUSE, 77- *Mem:* Am Chem Soc. *Res:* Synthetic organic medicinals. *Mailing Add:* 1538 Mockingbird Lane Lakeland FL 33801

PARCELLS, ALAN JEROME, b Los Angeles, Calif, Jan 29, 29; m 60; c 2. BIOCHEMISTRY. *Educ:* Univ Calif, Berkeley, AB, 54, PhD(biochem), 58. *Prof Exp:* Res fel biochem, Univ Utah, 58-59; RES ASSOC, UPJOHN CO, 59- *Mem:* AAAS; Am Chem Soc. *Res:* Purification and characterization of protein and polypeptide hormones, particularly growth hormones; chromatographic and electrophoretic purification methods; terminal and total amino acid analysis; purification and in vitro characterization of antilymphocyte globulins; modification of immunoglobulins; development of in vitro assays for prediction of immunosuppressive drugs. *Mailing Add:* Dept 7965 91 1 Upjohn Co Kalamazoo MI 49001

PARCHEN, FRANK RAYMOND, JR, b Clinton, Iowa, Nov 29, 23; m 45; c 3. PHYSICAL CHEMISTRY. *Educ:* Iowa State Univ, BS, 49, MS, 51, PhD(phys chem), 55. *Prof Exp:* Res assoc, Vet Med Res Inst, Iowa State Univ, 50-55; res chemist, Iowa, 55-58, develop supvr, Iowa, 58-59 & Tenn, 59-60, area supvr, Tenn, 59-61, tech supt, Iowa, 61-67, prod mgr cellophane, Del, 67-70, process mgr cellophane, 70-77, MFG CONSULT, E I DU PONT DE NEMOURS & CO, INC, 77- *Mem:* AAAS; Am Chem Soc; Am Inst Chem Eng; Tech Asn Pulp & Paper Indust. *Res:* Polymer chemistry. *Mailing Add:* E I du Pont de Nemours & Co Inc FXD PPD D-6070 Wilmington DE 19898

PARCHER, JAMES V(ERNON), b Drumright, Okla, July 21, 20; m 43; c 5. SOIL MECHANICS. *Educ:* Okla State Univ, BS, 41, MS, 48; Harvard Univ, AM, 67; Univ Ark, PhD, 68. *Prof Exp:* Jr engr, Peters Cartridge Div, Remington Arms Co, 41-42; from instr to assoc prof civil eng, 47-68, actg head, 68-69, head sch, 69-80, PROF CIVIL ENG, OKLA STATE UNIV, 68-, HEAD DEPT, 80- *Concurrent Pos:* NSF sci fac fel, 65-66; comt mem, Bldg Res Adv Bd, Nat Acad Sci, 78- *Mem:* Fel Am Soc Civil Engrs; Nat Soc Prof Engrs; Int Soc Soil Mech & Found Engrs. *Res:* Foundation engineering; slope stability; stabilization; behavior of expansive soils. *Mailing Add:* Sch of Civil Eng Okla State Univ Stillwater OK 74078

PARCHMENT, JOHN GERALD, b Cumberland City, Tenn, Aug 13, 23; m 57; c 2. ZOOLOGY, ECOLOGY. *Educ:* Mid Tenn State Univ, BS, 44; George Peabody Col, MA, 47; Vanderbilt Univ, PhD(limnol), 61. *Prof Exp:* From instr to asst prof, 49-63, PROF BIOL, MID TENN STATE UNIV, 63- *Concurrent Pos:* Tenn Acad Natural Sci Found lectr, vis scientists prog, 64-67. *Mem:* Fel AAAS. *Res:* Stream limnology; plankton and bottom organisms. *Mailing Add:* Dept of Biol Mid Tenn State Univ Murfreesboro TN 37130

PARCZEWSKI, KRZYSZTOF I(GNACY), b Wilno, Poland, Sept 23, 26; US citizen. CHEMICAL ENGINEERING. *Educ:* Nat Univ Ireland, BSc, 51; Univ London, dipl chem eng, 52; Univ Nottingham, PhD(psychrometry), 56. *Prof Exp:* Develop engr, Powell Duffryn Carbon Prod Ltd, 52-53; res asst, Sch Eng, Univ Nottingham, 53-58; res engr, Cent Res Lab, Celanese Corp Am, 58-60; res scientist, Res Div, Am Radiator & Standard Sanit Corp, NJ, 60-66; engr, Knolls Atomic Power Lab, Gen Elec Co, 66-74; reactor engr, 74-80, SR CHEM ENGR, US NUCLEAR REGULATORY COMN, 80- *Mem:* Am Chem Soc; Am Inst Chem Engrs; AAAS. *Res:* Psychrometry; heat and mass transfer; thermodynamics; heat transfer in boiling; two-phase flow; nuclear chemical engineering. *Mailing Add:* US Nuclear Regulatory Comn Washington DC 20555

PARDEE, ARTHUR BECK, b Chicago, Ill, July 13, 21; c 4. BIOCHEMISTRY. *Educ:* Univ Calif, Berkeley, BS, 42; Calif Inst Technol, MS, 43, PhD, 47. *Prof Exp:* From instr to assoc prof biol, Univ Calif, Berkeley, 49-61; prof biochem, Princeton Univ, 61-75; PROF PHARMACOL, HARVARD MED SCH, 75- *Concurrent Pos:* Merck fel, Univ Wis, 47-48; NSF sr fel, Pasteur Inst, 57-58; Am Cancer Soc scholar, Imperial Cancer Res Inst, London, 72-73; mem comt sci & pub policy, Nat Acad Sci, 73-76; trustee, Inst Cancer Res, Philadelphia, 73-, Waksman Found, NY, 76- & Friederich Miescher Inst, Basel, 80. *Honors & Awards:* Paul Lewis Award, Am Chem Soc, 60; Krebs Medal, Europ Biochem Soc, 73; Rosensteil Medal, Brandeis Univ, 75; 3R Award, Fedn Am Socs Exp Biol, 80. *Mem:* Nat Inst Med; Am Soc Biol Chemists (pres, 80); hon mem Japanese Biochem Soc; Am Acad Arts & Sci. *Mailing Add:* Sidney Farber Cancer Inst 44 Binney St Boston MA 02115

PARDEE, OTWAY O'MEARA, b Seattle, Wash, June 26, 20; m 46; c 3. COMPUTER SCIENCE, MATHEMATICS. *Educ:* Univ Wash, BS, 41; Stanford Univ, PhD(elec eng), 48. *Prof Exp:* From instr to assoc prof math, 48-69, dir comput ctr, 62-69, PROF COMPUT & INFO SCI, SYRACUSE UNIV, 69- *Mem:* Am Math Soc; Am Phys Soc; Math Asn Am; Inst Elec & Electronics Engrs; Asn Comput Mach. *Res:* Applied mathematics; computing. *Mailing Add:* Dept of Comput & Info Sci 313 Link Hall Syracuse Univ Syracuse NY 13210

PARDEE, WILLIAM A(UGUSTUS), b Valdosta, Ga, Sept 12, 14; m 41; c 2. CHEMICAL ENGINEERING. *Educ:* Emory Univ, BS, 36; Yale Univ, DEng, 41. *Prof Exp:* Chem engr, Gulf Res & Develop Co, 41-63, tech adv, Gulf Oil Corp, 64-67, commercial develop & licensing, Eng Dept, Gulf Res & Develop Co, 67-73; RETIRED; PRES, WILLIAM A PARDEE, INC, 73- *Mem:* Am Chem Soc; Am Inst Chem Engrs. *Res:* Rubber chemicals; alkylation; vapor phase catalytic reactions; catalyst development; petroleum refinery processes; alkylation of benzene; chlorination of metal oxides; petrochemical process development; process licensing. *Mailing Add:* 402 Duke of Kent Dr Gibsonia PA 15044

PARDEE, WILLIAM DURLEY, b New Haven, Conn, July 7, 29; m 55; c 4. PLANT BREEDING, AGRONOMY. *Educ:* Dartmouth Col, AB, 51; Cornell Univ, PhD(plant breeding), 60. *Prof Exp:* Res assoc plant breeding, Cornell Univ, 60-61; from asst prof to assoc prof crops exten, Univ Ill, 61-66; assoc prof, 66-70, PROF PLANT BREEDING EXTEN, CORNELL UNIV, 70-, CHMN, DEPT PLANT BREEDING & BIOMET, 79- *Concurrent Pos:* Vis prof, Ore State Univ, 73; dir, Asn Off Seed Cert Agencies. *Mem:* Am Forage & Grassland Coun; fel Am Soc Agron; Crop Sci Soc Am. *Res:* Seed production; trends in farmer seed usage; factors influencing variety choice by farmers; maximizing forage and grain yields; factors in companion crop competition; seed certification. *Mailing Add:* Dept Plant Breeding Cornell Univ Ithaca NY 14850

PARDEE, WILLIAM JOSEPH, b Davenport, Iowa, Nov 6, 44; div; c 2. THEORETICAL SOLID STATE PHYSICS. *Educ:* Iowa State Univ, BS, 66; Univ Ill, Urbana, PhD(physics), 71. *Prof Exp:* Res assoc physics, Univ Wash, 70-72; vis asst prof, Univ Ore, 72-73; res assoc, Ind Univ, Bloomington, 73-74; mem tech staff theoret physics, 74-80, GROUP MGR, SCI CTR, ROCKWELL INT, 80- *Mem:* Am Phys Soc; Metall Soc. *Res:* Ion transport in solids; acoustic emission; temper embrittlement; ultrasonic non-destructive evaluation; fracture and fatigue including statistical mechanics of crack initiation and early growth. *Mailing Add:* Sci Ctr Rockwell Int 1049 Camino Dos Rios Thousand Oaks CA 91360

PARDEN, ROBERT JAMES, b Mason City, Iowa, Apr 17, 22; m 55; c 4. ENGINEERING. *Educ:* Univ Iowa, BS, 47, MS, 51, PhD(eng), 53. *Prof Exp:* Assoc prof eng, Ill Inst Technol, 53-54; PROF ENG, UNIV SANTA CLARA, 54-, DEAN SCH ENG, 55- *Mem:* Am Soc Eng Educ; Am Soc Mech Engrs; Am Inst Indust Engrs. *Res:* Industrial engineering. *Mailing Add:* Sch of Eng Univ of Santa Clara Santa Clara CA 95053

PARDINI, RONALD SHIELDS, b San Francisco, Calif, Nov 10, 38; m 61; c 2. BIOCHEMISTRY, PHARMACOLOGY. *Educ:* Calif State Polytech Col, BS, 61; Univ Ill, PhD(food sci, biochem), 65. *Prof Exp:* Fel biomed, Stanford Res Inst, 67-68; from asst prof to assoc prof, 68-76, PROF BIOCHEM, UNIV NEV, RENO, 76-, CHMN DEPT, 78-; DIR, ALLIE M LEE LAB CANCER RES, 76-, DIR NATURAL PROD LAB, 81- *Concurrent Pos:* Am Diabetes Asn grant, Univ Nev, Reno, 71-; mem adv comt, State Nev Clin Lab, 71-82 & NSF grant, 76-80. *Mem:* Am Chem Soc; Sigma Xi. *Res:* Pesticide toxicology; biochemical pharmacology; phytochemistry; cancer research. *Mailing Add:* Div of Biochem Univ of Nev Reno NV 89557

PARDO, RICHARD CLAUDE, b Danville, Ky, Apr 26, 47; div; c 1. NUCLEAR PHYSICS, NUCLEAR ASTROPHYSICS. *Educ:* Univ Louisville, BS, 71; Univ Tex, Austin, PhD(physics), 76. *Prof Exp:* Res assoc nuclear physics, Cyclotron Lab, Mich State Univ, 76-78, asst prof nuclear physics & asst dir, Heavy Ion Lab, 78-79; ASST SCIENTIST, ARGONNE NAT LAB, 79- *Mem:* Am Phys Soc. *Res:* Design and construction of superconducting heavy ion linear accelerator for nuclear research; accelerator control, beam diagnostics, and magnet design. *Mailing Add:* Bldg 203 F-153 Argonne Nat Lab Argonne IL 60439

PARDO, WILLIAM BERMUDEZ, b New York, NY, Jan 14, 28; m 53; c 3. PHYSICS. *Educ:* Hunter Col, AB, 49; Northwestern Univ, PhD(physics), 57. *Prof Exp:* Asst physics, Northwestern Univ, 49-53; tech dir nuclear develop group, Westinghouse Air Brake Co, 53-56; res physicist, Reaction Motors, Inc, 56-57; asst prof, 57-63, ASSOC PROF PHYSICS, UNIV MIAMI, 63- *Concurrent Pos:* Consult, thermonuclear div, Oak Ridge Nat Lab. *Mem:* Am Phys Soc. *Res:* Nuclear physics and reactors; space propulsion; plasma physics. *Mailing Add:* Dept of Physics Univ of Miami Coral Gables FL 33124

PARDUE, HARRY L, b Big Creek, WVa, May 3, 34; m 57; c 1. ANALYTICAL CHEMISTRY. *Educ:* Marshall Univ, BS, 56, MS, 57; Univ Ill, PhD(chem), 61. *Prof Exp:* From asst prof to assoc prof, 61-70, PROF CHEM, PURDUE UNIV, WEST LAFAYETTE, 70- *Honors & Awards:* Award, Am Asn Clin Chemists, 79; Chem Instrumentation Award, Anal Chem Div, Am Chem Soc, 82. *Mem:* Am Chem Soc; Am Asn Clin Chemists. *Res:* Instrumentation for chemical research; chemical kinetics. *Mailing Add:* Dept of Chem Purdue Univ West Lafayette IN 47907

PARDUE, MARY LOU, b Lexington, Ky, Sept 15, 33. CELL BIOLOGY, DEVELOPMENTAL BIOLOGY. *Educ:* Col William & Mary, BS, 55; Univ Tenn, MS, 59; Yale Univ, PhD(biol), 70. *Prof Exp:* assoc prof, 72-80, PROF BIOL, MASS INST TECHNOL, 80- *Concurrent Pos:* Instr molecular cytogenetics, Cold Spring Harbor Lab, 71-78; mem, Genetics Study Sect, NIH, 74-78; mem, Wistar Inst Sci Adv Comt, 76-; instr molecular biol, Drosophila Colo Spring Harbor Lab, 79 & 80; mem, Cellular & Molecular Basis Dis Rev Comt, NIH, 80. *Mem:* Am Soc Cell Biol; AAAS; Genetics Soc Am (vpres, 81-); fel AAAS. *Res:* Structure and function of eukaryotic chromosomes; studies of gene activity during development and the role of repeated gene sequences in the organization of the eukaryotic chromosome. *Mailing Add:* Dept Biol Rm 16-717 Mass Inst Technol Cambridge MA 02139

PARDUE, WILLIAM M, b Lexington, Ky, Sept 14, 35; m 57; c 2. METALLURGICAL ENGINEERING. *Educ:* Va Polytech Inst, BS, 57; Ohio State Univ, MSc, 60. *Prof Exp:* Prin metallurgist, 57-62, proj leader nuclear metall, 62-64, asst div chief, 64-66, div cheif nuclear metall, Battelle Mem Inst, 66-71, DEPT MGR, OFF NUCLEAR WASTE ISOLATION, BATTELLE COLUMBUS LABS, 78- *Mem:* Am Soc Metals; Am Ceramic Soc; Am Nuclear Soc; Am Soc Testing & Mat. *Res:* Nuclear fuel cycle; thermodynamic studies of numerous materials and combinations of materials; nuclear waste management. *Mailing Add:* 2591 Henthorn Rd Columbus OH 43221

PARE, VICTOR KENNETH, b Oak Park, Ill, Aug 3, 28; m 50; c 2. PHYSICS. *Educ:* Cornell Univ, BS, 51, PhD(eng physics), 58. *Prof Exp:* Assoc develop engr, 51-54, PHYSICIST, OAK RIDGE NAT LAB, 58- *Mem:* Am Nuclear Soc; Inst Elec & Electronics Engrs; Am Phys Soc. *Res:* Reactor noise analysis; reactor instrumentation; plasma diagnostics; tokamaks; radiation defects in metals. *Mailing Add:* Instrumentation & Controls Div Oak Ridge Nat Lab PO Box X Oak Ridge TN 37830

PAREES, DAVID MARC, b New York, NY, Jan 1, 50; m 71; c 2. ANALYTICAL CHEMISTRTY. *Educ:* State Univ NY, Binghhamton, BA, 71; Univ Mass, Amherst, PhD(anal chem), 76. *Prof Exp:* Res chemist, 76-78, prin res chemist, 78-81, SR PRIN RES CHEMIST, CORP RES SERV ANAL SERV, AIR PROD & CHEMICALS, INC, 82- *Mem:* Am Soc Testing & Mat; Am Soc Mass Spectrometry. *Res:* Chromatographic methods developmennt for trace annalysis and coal liquids characterization utilizing element-selective gas chromatographic detectors and quadruple mass spectrometry. *Mailing Add:* Air Prod & Chemicals Inc Box 538 Allentown PA 18105

PAREJKO, RONALD ANTHONY, b Chicago, Ill, Oct 21, 40; m 63; c 4. ENVIRONMENTAL SCIENCES, MICROBIOLOGY. *Educ:* Wis State Univ-Eau Claire, BS, 63; Univ Wis-Madison, MS, 67, PhD(bact), 69. *Prof Exp:* Asst prof, 69-73, assoc prof microbiol, 74-78, PROF BIOL, NORTHERN MICH UNIV, 79- *Concurrent Pos:* Adj prof, Mich State Univ, 80- *Mem:* Fel Am Soc Microbiol; Am Soc Microbiol; Sigma Xi. *Res:* Regulation and kinetics of Klebsiella pneumoniae nitrogenase and chlorinated hydrocarbon pesticide analysis in higher trophic level animals. *Mailing Add:* Dept of Biol Northern Mich Univ Marquette MI 49855

PARELES, STEPHEN RONALD, food chemistry, chemical instrumentation, see previous edition

PARENCIA, CHARLES R, b Port Lavaca, Tex, Oct 26, 13. ENTOMOLOGY. *Educ:* Tex A&M Univ, BS, 34. *Prof Exp:* Pub sch prin, Tex, 34-42; entomologist, Waco Cotton Insects Lab, 42-53, entomologist-in-chg, 53-62, asst to chief cotton insects res br, 62-72, staff specialist entom, Nat Prog Staff, Plant & Entom Sci, Beltsville, Md, 72-76, supvry res entomologist, Sci & Educ Admin-Agr Res, 76-81, COLLABR, BIOENVIRON INSECT CONTROL LAB, USDA, 81- *Mem:* AAAS; Entom Soc Am; Am Inst Biol Sci. *Res:* Development of more efficient methods of cotton insect control. *Mailing Add:* US Delta States Res Ctr PO Box 225 Stoneville MI 38776

PARENT, ANDRE, b Montreal, Quebec, Oct 3, 44; m 70; c 3. NEUROANATOMY, HISTOCHEMISTRY. *Educ:* Univ Montreal, BSc, 67; Univ Laval, PhD(physiol), 70. *Prof Exp:* Asst prof, 71-76, assoc prof, 76-81, PROF, DEPT ANAT, FAC MED, LAVAL UNIV, 81- *Concurrent Pos:* Vis prof, Dept Psychol, Brain Res Inst, Univ Calif, Los Angeles, 75. *Mem:* Soc Neurosci; AAAS; Am Asn Anatomists; Can Asn Anatomists. *Res:* Anatomy of chemically specified neuronal systems in the brain, particularly the monoanivergic and the cholinergic systems; basal ganglia and the limbic system. *Mailing Add:* Lab De Neurobiol Hopital De L'Enfant Jesus 1401 18th St Quebec PQ G1J 1Z4 Can

PARENT, JOSEPH D(OMINIC), b Boston, Mass, Aug 4, 10; m 41; c 8. CHEMISTRY, CHEMICAL ENGINEERING. *Educ:* Cath Univ, BS, 29; Rensselaer Polytech Inst, MS, 31; Ohio State Univ, PhD(chem eng), 33. *Prof Exp:* Chemist, DC Paper Co, 29-30; asst instr chem eng, Ohio State Univ, 32-33; lithographer, US Coast & Geod Surv, 34-35; from instr to asst prof chem, Loyola Univ, Ill, 35-42; assoc prof chem eng, Kans State Col, 42-43; from chem engr to ed dir, Inst Gas Technol, 43-53; res consult, Peoples Gas Light & Coke Co, Chicago, 53-62; ENERGY CONSULT, INST GAS TECHNOL, 62- *Mem:* Am Chem Soc; Am Gas Asn; Am Inst Chem Engrs. *Res:* Natural gas and energy supply problems. *Mailing Add:* 614 Linden Ave Wilmette IL 60091

PARENT, RICHARD ALFRED, b Lynn, Mass, Jan 1, 35; m 58; c 3. ORGANIC CHEMISTRY. *Educ:* Univ Mass, BS, 57; Northeastern Univ, MS, 59; Rutgers Univ, PhD(org chem), 63. *Prof Exp:* Chemist, Am Cyanamid Co, NJ, 59-61, res chemist, 63-69; res chemist, Xerox Corp, 69-71, mgr explor develop, 71-73, mgr color technol, 73, staff specialist toxicol, 73-80; MEM STAFF, FOOD DRUG RES LABS, INC, 80- *Concurrent Pos:* Mem bd dirs, Delta Labs Inc, 69-, consult toxicol, 75-; consult toxicologist, Independent Union Airline Flight Attend, 77- *Mem:* Am Indust Hyg Asn; Am Chem Soc; NY Acad Sci; AAAS; Am Soc Testing & Mat. *Res:* Acute, sub-acute, chronic toxicology; mutagenesis; carcinogenesis; teratology; inhalation toxicity; intra-tracheal studies; tracer studies; percutaneous absorption; computer readible data bases; ozone; colorants; polymers; smoke toxicity pyrolysis studies; xerographic materials; air sampling and analysis; health hazard evaluation; industrial toxicology. *Mailing Add:* Food Drug Res Labs Inc PO Box 107 Rte 17C Waverly NY 14892

PARETSKY, DAVID, b Brooklyn, NY, Nov 15, 18; m 42; c 5. MICROBIOLOGY. *Educ:* City Col New York, BS, 39; Iowa State Col, PhD(physiol bact), 48. *Prof Exp:* Res assoc bact, Agr Exp Sta, Iowa State Col, 42-43 & 46-48; asst prof biol, Rensselaer Polytech Inst, 48-51; from asst prof to assoc prof, 51-59, chmn dept bact, 57-76, PROF BACT, UNIV KANS, 59-, UNIV DISTINGUISHED PROF, 76- *Concurrent Pos:* Instr, Iowa State Col, 48; mem, Kans Adv Lab Comn, 58-; vis prof, Univ Wis, 64-65 & Hadassah Med Sch, Jerusalem, 76; mem microbiol fel rev panel, NIH, 64-68; NSF Coop Col-Sch Sci Prog panelist, 66; Found Microbiol lectr, 71-72; mem cancer res training panel, Nat Cancer Inst, 71-74. *Mem:* Am Soc Microbiol; Am Soc Biol Chemists; fel AAAS. *Res:* Production of ethanol, 2, 3-butylene glycol and acetoin by corn fermentation; preparation of immune polysaccharides from meningococci; metabolism of amino acids by microorganisms; physiology of rickettsiae; pathobiology; biochemistry of bacteria; regulation of transcription during infection. *Mailing Add:* Dept of Microbiol Univ of Kans Lawrence KS 66044

PARGMAN, DAVID, b New York, NY, July 15, 37; m 63; c 3. EXERCISE PHYSIOLOGY, NUTRITION. *Educ:* City Col New York, BSEd, 59; Columbia Univ, MA, 59; NY Univ, PhD(health, phys educ), 66. *Prof Exp:* Lectr health & phys educ, City Col New York, 59-66; from asst prof to assoc prof educ, Boston Univ, 66-77, chmn dept, 77-79; FULL PROF EDUC, FLA STATE UNIV, 77- *Mem:* Fel Am Col Sports Med; Am Aliance Health, Phys Educ & Recreation; NAm Soc Psychol Sport & Phys Activity; Int Soc Sport Psychol; NAm Soc Social Sport. *Res:* Sport psychology-sociology; obesity; body weight regulation. *Mailing Add:* Dept Movement Sci & Phys Educ Fla State Univ Tallahassee FL 32306

PARHAM, JAMES CROWDER, II, b Salem, Mass, Mar 26, 38; m 69. BIO-ORGANIC CHEMISTRY, MEDICINAL CHEMISTRY. *Educ:* Bates Col, BS, 59; Duke Univ, MA, 61, PhD(chem), 63. *Prof Exp:* Res assoc, 63-66, assoc, 66-72, ASSOC MEM, DONALD S WALKER LAB, SLOAN-KETTERING INST CANCER RES, 72- *Concurrent Pos:* Lectr, Sch Gen Studies, Queens Col, NY, 64-66; asst prof biochem, Grad Sch Med Sci, Sloan Kettering Div, Med Col, Cornell Univ, 66-74, assoc prof, 74- *Mem:* Am Chem Soc; Sigma Xi. *Res:* Synthetic organic chemistry, especially aromatic nitrogen heterocycles; design and synthesis of chemotherapeutic agents; mechanisms of chemical carcinogenesis; photochemistry of heterocyclic n-oxides. *Mailing Add:* Donald S Walker Lab Sloan-Kettering Inst Cancer Res Rye NY 10580

PARHAM, MARC ELLOUS, b Quincy, Mass, Sept 16, 48; m 74. ORGANIC CHEMISTRY. *Educ:* Duke Univ, BS, 70; Cornell Univ, PhD(chem), 77. *Prof Exp:* Fel, Mass Inst Tech, 77-78; mem staff, Ciba-Geigy Corp, 78-82; MEM STAFF, CLIN ASSAYS DIV, TRAVENOL LABS, INC, 82- *Mem:* Am Chem Soc; fel Am Inst Chemists. *Res:* Development of chemical processes to produce new polymers and speciality organic compounds in extreme purity. *Mailing Add:* Travenol Labs Inc One Baxter Parkway Deerfield IL 60015

PARHAM, WALTER EDWARD, b Minneapolis, Minn, Jan 21, 30; m 55; c 5. GEOLOGY, MINERALOGY. *Educ:* Univ Ill, BS, 56, MS, 58, PhD(geol), 62. *Prof Exp:* Asst geologist, Ill State Geol Surv, 58-63; asst prof clay mineral, Minn Geol Serv, Dept Geol & Geophys, Univ Minn, Minneapolis, 63-71; assoc prof geol & geophys, Minn Geol Surv, Dept Geol & Geophys, Univ Minn, St Paul, 71-76; phys sci officer, Off Sci & Technol, Agency Int Develop, US Dept State, 76-78; sr analyst, 78-80, PROG MGR FOOD & RENEWABLE RESOURCES, OFF TECHNOL ASSESSMENT, US CONGRESS, 80- *Concurrent Pos:* Univ grant, Univ Minn, Minneapolis, 65-66, grad sch & off int progs grants rock weathering, Hong Kong, 67 & 69; Am Cancer Soc grant health & rock weathering, Hong Kong, 75; Alfred P Sloan grant, PLATO comput pop dynamics appl to environ geol problems. *Mem:* AAAS; Sigma Xi; Fedn Am Scientists; Asn Int L'Etude Argiles. Clay Minerals Soc. *Res:* Tropical rock weathering; clay mineral formation; environmental geology and developing countries; tropical deforestation. *Mailing Add:* Off Technol Assessment US Congress Washington DC 20510

PARIKH, GOKALDAS CHANDULAL, virology, immunology, see previous edition

PARIKH, INDU, Indian citizen. BIOCHEMISTRY. *Educ:* Univ Zurich, PhD(chem), 65. *Prof Exp:* Asst prof pharmacol & med, Med Sch, Johns Hopkins Univ, 70-75; GROUP LEADER, WELLCOME RES LABS, BURROUGHS WELLCOME CO, 75- *Concurrent Pos:* Fel, Weizmann Inst Sci, 66-68; NIH fel, 68-70. *Res:* Steroidal hormone action; enzyme immunoassay; affinity chromatography. *Mailing Add:* Molecular Biol Dept Wellcome Res Labs Research Triangle Park NC 27709

PARIKH, INDU, Indian citizen. BIOCHEMISTRY. *Educ:* Univ Zurich, PHD(chem), 65. *Prof Exp:* Asst prof pharmacol & med, Med Sch, Johns Hopkins Univ, 70-75; group leader, 75-77, ASST DEPT HEAD, WELLCOME RES LABS, BURROUGHS WELLCOME CO, 77- *Concurrent Pos:* Fel, Weimann Inst Sci, 66-68; NIH fel, 68-70. *Mem:* Am Soc Biol Chemists; Am Soc Pharmacol & Exp Therapeut; AAAS; NY Acad Sci; Am Chem Soc. *Res:* Steroidal hormone action; enzyme immunoassay; affinity chromatogrphy. *Mailing Add:* Molecular Biol Dept Wellcome Res Labs Research Triangle Park NC 27709

PARIKH, JEKISHAN R, b India, Dec 21, 22; m 59; c 3. STEROID CHEMISTRY. *Educ:* Univ Bombay, BSc, 43; Univ Calif, Berkeley, MS, 50, PhD(pharm chem), 53. *Prof Exp:* Prod chemist, Chemo-Pharma Labs, Ltd, India, 43-45, works mgr, 45-48; res assoc, Cobb Chem Labs, Univ Va, 53-55 & Nat Cancer Inst, 55-58; sci officer, Glaxo Labs, Ltd, Eng, 58-60, exec officer, India, 60-63, mgr fine chem factory, 63-64; res scientist chem processing res & develop, 64-75, sr res scientist, 75-79, ADMIN ASST TECH TO THE VPRES, FINE CHEM DIV, UPJOHN CO, 79- *Honors & Awards:* W E Upjohn Award, Upjohn Co, 74. *Mem:* Am Chem Soc. *Mailing Add:* Upjohn Co Unit 1100 Kalamazoo MI 49001

PARIKH, N(IRANJAN) M, b Godhra, India, Jan 14, 29; US citizen; m 54; c 3. METALLURGY, CERAMICS. *Educ:* Univ Bombay, BSc, 48; Alfred Univ, BS, 49, MS, 50; Mass Inst Technol, ScD(ceramics), 54. *Prof Exp:* Res engr, Sci Lab, Ford Motor Co, Mich, 54-57; sr res off, Govt India, Bombay, Atomic Energy Res Estab, 58-59; res metallurgist, Ill Inst Technol Res Inst, 59-61, sr metallurgist, 61-63, res metallurgist, Metal Sci Adv, 63-64, asst dir metal sci, 64-65, dir metals res, 65-75; planning dir res & develop, 75-76, dir metals technol, 76-80, MANAGING DIR MAT TECHNOL, TECH CTR, AM CAN CO, 80- *Mem:* Fel Am Soc Metals; fel Am Ceramic Soc; fel Brit Inst Metals; fel Am Inst Chem; Am Inst Mining, Metall & Petrol Engrs. *Res:* Metal container fabrication and corrosion; electrochemistry; packaging technology; resource recovery; recycling of aluminum, steel, tin, copper, etc; furnace design; mechanical working and forming of metals; tribology; biomaterials; slag processing; deformation and fracture, extractive metallurgy; research management. *Mailing Add:* 835 Humboldt Winnetka IL 60093

PARIKH, SARVABHAUM SOHANLAL, b Tarapur, India, July 31, 35; m 60; c 2. NUCLEAR CHEMISTRY, ANALYTICAL CHEMISTRY. *Educ:* Gujarat Univ, India, BSc, 55; Ohio State Univ, MSc, 60; McGill Univ, PhD(nuclear chem), 66. *Prof Exp:* Apprentice textile chem, Ahmedabad Advance Mills Ltd, Tata Textiles, India, 55-57; res asst, Dept Chem, Ohio State Univ, 58-59; asst ed chem, 60-62, asst ed nuclear chem, 66-68, assoc ed, 68-69, sr assoc indexer, 69-73, SR ED, CHEM ABSTR SERV, AM CHEM SOC, OHIO STATE UNIV, 73- *Concurrent Pos:* Res assoc, Radiochem Lab, McGill Univ, 66. *Mem:* Sr mem Am Chem Soc. *Res:* Qualitative and quantitative chemical analysis; nuclear properties and reactions; fission and spallation; radiochemical separations; chemistry of nuclear reactor fuels; indexing and editing of nuclear phenomena and technology; information and literature chemistry. *Mailing Add:* Chem Abstr Serv Ohio State Univ Columbus OH 43210

PARIS, CLARK DAVIS, b Delaware Co, Iowa, Aug 10, 11; m 72. HORTICULTURE. *Educ:* Univ Iowa, BS, 36; Iowa State Univ, MS, 39; Mich State Univ, PhD(hort), 56. *Prof Exp:* Horticulturist, Iowa Ment Health Hosp, 39-44; asst gardener, San Diego County Hosp, 44-45; plant breeder, W Atlee Burpee Co, 45-52 & Pan-Am Seeds, Inc, 52-54; res instr hort, Mich State Univ, 56-61, ed & proj leader food sci, 61-78; RETIRED. *Concurrent Pos:* Bibliogr, Mich State Univ Libr, 68-78. *Honors & Awards:* Laurie Award, Am Soc Hort Sci, 59. *Res:* Flower color genetics; general genetics; plant breeding; photography; world food problems. *Mailing Add:* Hacienda de Valencia Space 274 201 S Greenfield Rd Mesa AZ 85206

PARIS, DEMETRIUS T, b Stavroupolis, Greece, Sept 27, 28; US citizen; m 52; c 2. ELECTRICAL ENGINEERING. *Educ:* Miss State Univ, BSEE, 51; Ga Inst Technol, MSEE, 58, PhD(elec eng), 62. *Prof Exp:* Design engr, Westinghouse Elec Corp, 52-58; sr engr, Lockheed-Ga Co, 58-59; from asst prof to assoc prof elec eng, 59-66, PROF ELEC ENG, GA INST TECHNOL, 66-, DIR SCH ELEC ENG, 69- *Concurrent Pos:* Consult, Lockheed-Ga Co, 62- & Sci Atlanta, Inc, 65- *Mem:* Fel Inst Elec & Electronics Engrs; Am Soc Eng Educ. *Res:* Electromagnetics. *Mailing Add:* Sch of Elec Eng Ga Inst of Technol Atlanta GA 30332

PARIS, DORIS FORT, b Roanoke, Va, July 3, 24; m 45, 67; c 2. BIOCHEMISTRY, MICROBIOLOGY. *Educ:* Univ Va, BS, 46; Univ Ga, MS, 66. *Prof Exp:* Med technologist toxicol, Univ Va Hosp, Charlottesville, 43-45; RES CHEMIST BIOCHEM, ENVIRON RES LAB, US ENVIRON PROTECTION AGENCY, 66- *Mem:* Am Soc Microbiol; Am Chem Soc. *Res:* Microbial transformation of toxic substances in aquatic systems; biochemistry of algae and bacteria. *Mailing Add:* Environ Res Lab US Environ Protection Agency Athens GA 30605

PARIS, GERARD YVON, medicinal chemistry, organic chemistry, see previous edition

PARIS, JEAN PHILIP, b Buffalo, NY, Dec 2, 35; m 56; c 4. ANALYTICAL CHEMISTRY, PHYSICAL CHEMISTRY. *Educ:* Univ Mich, BS, 57; Purdue Univ, PhD(chem), 60. *Prof Exp:* Res chemist, Polychem Dept, E I du Pont de Nemours & Co, Inc, 60-62; lectr chem, Juniata Col, 62, res chemist, Radiation Physics Lab, E I du Pont de Nemours & Co, Inc, 62-65 & Elastomers Dept, 65-69; PRES, THERMOELEC UNLIMITED, INC, 69- *Concurrent Pos:* Res chemist, Am Cyanamid Co, Conn, 58 & E I du Pont de Nemours & Co, Inc, 59. *Mem:* Am Chem Soc; Soc Appl Spectros. *Res:* Thermoelectric instrumentation; electronic spectroscopy; photochromism; reaction kinetics. *Mailing Add:* 1202 Harrison Ave Holly Oak Terr Wilmington DE 19809

PARIS, OSCAR HALL, b Greensboro, NC, Mar 22, 31; m; c 3. RADIATION ECOLOGY. *Educ:* Univ NC, AB, 53, MA, 56; Univ Calif, PhD(zool), 60. *Prof Exp:* Asst prof zool, Univ NC, 60-62; from asst prof to assoc prof, Univ Calif, Berkeley, 62-71; prof zool & head dept zool & physiol, Univ Wyo, 71-76, dir, Jackson Hole Biol Res Sta, 73-76; ENVIRON SCIENTIST & ADMIN JUDGE ATOMIC SAFETY & LICENSING BD PANEL, US NUCLEAR REGULATORY COMN, 76- *Mem:* Fel AAAS; Ecol Soc Am; Brit Ecol Soc; Am Inst Biol Sci. *Res:* Population ecology; invertebrate ecology. *Mailing Add:* Atomic Safety & Licensing Bd Panel US Nuclear Regulatory Comn Washington DC 20555

PARISEK, CHARLES BRUCE, b Hibernia, NJ, Nov 4, 31; m 64; c 3. ORGANIC CHEMISTRY, POLYMER CHEMISTRY. *Educ:* Rutgers Univ, New Brunswick, BSc, 52; Univ Kans, PhD(org chem), 62. *Prof Exp:* Asst ed, Chem Abstr Serv, Am Chem Soc, 58-59; res chemist, Reaction Motors Div, Thiokol Chem Corp, 62-65; sr res chemist, Tex-US Chem Co, 65-69; sr res scientist latex technol & med prod, Corp Res Ctr, Int Paper Co, Tuxedo, NY, 69-77; sr res scientist, Johnson & Johnson, 78; sr consult, Booz, Allen & Hamilton, 78-80; MGR SUPPLIES & CHEM, MAGNETOGRAPHY, AM INT PRINTER SYSTS, 80- *Concurrent Pos:* Lectr, Ohio State Univ, 58-59; instr, Park Col, 59-60 & Fairleigh Dickinson Univ, 69- *Mem:* Am Chem Soc; The Chem Soc. *Res:* Mechanism of organophosphorus compounds decomposition; synthesis of organic and inorganic polymers; latex technology; electrooptical properties of organic compounds; radiation processing. *Mailing Add:* 27 Sherman Pl Morristown NJ 07960

PARISER, ERNST REINHARD, b Berlin, Ger, Aug 16, 18; US citizen; m 43; c 2. FOOD SCIENCE. *Educ:* Cambridge Univ, BA, 40, MA, 44. *Prof Exp:* Asst to Ch Weizmann, Synthetic Rubber, Grosvenor Lab, London, Eng, 42-46; prod mgr oil seed extraction & processing, TURYAG, AO, Izmir, Turkey, 47-57; res assoc, Dept Nutrit & Food Sci, Mass Inst Technol, 57-61; prog leader, Fish Protein Concentrate Prog, US Dept Interior, 61-67; chief scientist & dir eng, Marine Resources, Avco Corp, 67-69; staff mem, Div Sponsored Res, 69-72, dir, Marine Adv Serv, Sea Grant Col Prog, 73-78, SR RES SCIENTIST, DEPT NUTRIT & FOOD SCI, MASS INST TECHNOL, 72-, ASSOC DIR EDUC COORD, SEA GRANT COL PROG, 78- *Concurrent Pos:* Mem, President's Sci Adv Comt, 67; vpres, Cardinal Proteins Ltd, Halifax, NS, 68-70; mem, Adv Comt Technol Innovation, Nat Acad Sci, 72-; vchmn & chmn, New Eng Adv Serv, 75; mem, Bd Sci & Technol, Int Develop, Nat Acad Sci, 78-81. *Res:* Protein supplementation; nutrition education; fish protein and other protein concentrates; nutrition policy planning; food habits; post harvest food losses; science education for pre-college students; lipid composition of marine animals. *Mailing Add:* Rm E38-320 Mass Inst of Technol Cambridge MA 02139

PARISER, HARRY, b Newark, NJ, Jan 19, 11; m 45; c 2. DERMATOLOGY, SYPHILOLOGY. *Educ:* Univ Pa, BA, 31, MD, 35, DSc(med), 40; Am Bd Dermat, dipl. *Prof Exp:* Instr dermat & syphil, Sch Med, Univ Pa, 37-42; venereal dis control officer, USPHS, 42-46; consult dermat & syphil, 46-73, USPHS; PROF MICROBIOL & CELL BIOL, EASTERN VA MED SCH, 73-, ASSOC PROF MED, 75- *Concurrent Pos:* Consult dermat & syphil, US Naval Hosp, Portsmouth, Va, 46-58, Vet Admin Hosp, Kecoughtan, Va, 46-66, Norfolk Gen Hosp & DePaul Hosp, Norfolk, Va, 46-; pvt pract dermat, 46-; spec consult, USPHS, 60-73; lectr dermat & syphil, Med Col Va, 62-; mem, Nat Comn Venereal Dis; assoc ed, J Am Venereal Dis Asn, 73-78. *Honors & Awards:* Thomas Parras Award, Am Venereal Dis Asn, 80. *Mem:* AMA; Am Acad Dermat; Am Venereal Dis Asn (pres, 70-71); Am Pub Health Asn. *Res:* Author of approximately 40 publications and contributing author in two textbooks on various aspects of sexually transmitted diseases. *Mailing Add:* Medical Tower Norfolk VA 23507

PARISER, RUDOLPH, b Harbin, China, Dec 8, 23; nat US; m 72. PHYSICAL CHEMISTRY. *Educ:* Univ Calif, BS, 44; Univ Minn, PhD(phys chem), 50. *Prof Exp:* Res chemist, Org Chem Dept, 50-53, res supvr, 53-57, res supvr, Elastomer Chem Dept, 57-59, div head, 59-63, asst lab dir, 63-67, lab dir, 67-70, dir explor res & mgr res & develop, 70-72, mgr mkt res & develop, 72-74, dir explor res, 74-76, dir pioneering res, elastomer chem dept, 76-79, res dir, polymer prod dept, 79-81, DIR POLYMER SCI, CENT RES & DEVELOP DEPT, E I DU PONT DE NEMOURS & CO, INC, WILMINGTON, 81- *Concurrent Pos:* Assoc ed, J Chem Sci, Nat Res Coun, 66-79, chem phys letters, 67-70, Du Pont Innovation, 69-75, adv bd, J Polymer Sci, 80-, mem comt chem sci, 79-, co-chmn ad hoc panel polymer sci & eng, 79-81. *Honors & Awards:* Outstanding Achievement Award, Univ Minn, 76. *Mem:* AAAS; Am Chem Soc; Am Phys Soc; Soc Rheol; NY Acad Sci. *Res:* Research administration; rubber chemistry; polymer science; quantum chemistry; over 30 publications. *Mailing Add:* RD 2 Box 106 Old Public Rd Hockessin DE 19707

PARISH, CURTIS LEE, b Ellensburg, Wash, Apr 10, 37; m 72; c 7. PLANT PATHOLOGY, BIOCHEMISTRY. *Educ:* Wash State Univ, BS, 59; Univ Ariz, PhD(plant path), 65. *Prof Exp:* PLANT PATHOLOGIST TREE FRUIT VIROL, SCI & EDUC ADMIN, USDA, 65- *Mem:* Am Phytopath Soc. *Res:* Tree fruit virus diseases; virology; serology; physiology of parasitism. *Mailing Add:* Fruit Res Lab 1104 N Western Wenatchee WA 98801

PARISH, DARRELL JOE, b Beebe, Ark, Dec 20, 34; m 60; c 2. ORGANIC POLYMER CHEMISTRY. *Educ:* Univ Louisville, BS, 56, PhD(chem), 60. *Prof Exp:* Asst, AEC, Louisville, 56-60; res chemist, 60-72, staff scientist, Film Dept, 72-77, SR RES CHEMIST, PLASTIC PROD & RESINS DEPT, E I DU PONT DE NEMOURS & CO, INC, 77- *Res:* Radiation and polymer chemistry; research and development of polyimide and polyester film forming polymers. *Mailing Add:* E I du Pont de Nemours & Co Inc PO Box 89 Circleville OH 43113

PARISH, HARLIE ALBERT, JR, b Great Bend, Kans, Oct 29, 40; m 64; c 1. ORGANIC CHEMISTRY, MEDICINAL CHEMISTRY. *Educ:* Ft Hays State Univ, BS, 62, MS, 65; Univ Mo, PhD(chem), 69. *Prof Exp:* Res chemist, Brown & Williamson Tobacco Corp, 68-73; res assoc biochem, Sch Med, Univ Louisville, 73-77; ASST PROF RES, SOUTHWESTERN AT MEMPHIS, 77- *Concurrent Pos:* Consult, Molecular Design Int, 77- *Mem:* AAAS; Am Chem Soc; Sigma Xi. *Res:* Organic synthesis; medicinal chemistry of diuretics and antineoplastic agents. *Mailing Add:* 4293 Beechcliff Lane Memphis TN 38128

PARISH, JEFFREY LEE, b Sturgis, Mich, May 23, 45; m 71; c 1. SPACE PLASMA PHYSICS. *Educ:* Purdue Univ, BS; Univ Ill, MS, 71; Univ Iowa, PhD(physics), 80. *Prof Exp:* RES ASSOC PROF, UTAH STATE UNIV, 80- *Mem:* Am Math Soc; Am Geophys Union. *Mailing Add:* Ctr Atmospheric & Space Sci Utah State Univ Logan UT 84322

PARISH, RICHARD LEE, b Kansas City, Mo, May 31, 45; m 68; c 2. MACHINE DESIGN, ENGINEERING MANAGEMENT. *Educ:* Univ Mo-Columbia, BS, 67, MS, 68, PhD(agr eng), 70. *Prof Exp:* From asst prof to assoc prof agr eng, Univ Ark, Fayetteville, 69-74; sr proj leader, 74-80, MGR, MECH RES & DEVELOP, O M SCOTT & SONS CO, 80- *Concurrent Pos:* Consult agr mach design, Dickey Mach Works, 74. *Mem:* Am Soc Agr Engrs. *Res:* Farm machinery development and testing; design and development of lawn and garden equipment; engineering management. *Mailing Add:* O M Scott & Sons Co Marysville OH 43040

PARISH, ROGER COOK, b Utica, NY, Jan 20, 40; m 62; c 2. ORGANIC CHEMISTRY, MEDICINAL CHEMISTRY. *Educ:* Utica Col, BA, 60; Univ Chicago, MS, 64, PhD(org chem), 65. *Prof Exp:* Res chemist, E I du Pont de Nemours & Co, Inc, 65-67; sr med chemist, Smith Kline & French Labs, 67-70, assoc dir chem, 71, mgr chem res, 71-78, MGR RES OPERS, ANIMAL HEALTH PROD, SMITH KLINE CORP, 78- *Mem:* Am Chem Soc; NY Acad Sci; Am Soc Microbiol; Sigma Xi; AAAS. *Res:* Synthetic organic chemistry; antiparasitic chemotherapy; animal nutrition. *Mailing Add:* Smith Kline Corp 1600 Paoli Pike West Chester PA 19380

PARISH, TRUEMAN DAVIS, b Cincinnati, Ohio, Mar 15, 39; m 64; c 2. CHEMICAL ENGINEERING. *Educ:* Univ Mich, BSE, 62; Mass Inst Technol, SM, 63; Rice Univ, PhD(chem eng), 67. *Prof Exp:* Chem engr, Procter & Gamble Co, 63-64; chem engr, 67-69, supvry engr, advan eng technol group, 69-71, res assoc, Process Design & Eval Res Lab, 71-76, coordr advan process technol group, 76-78, DIR ENG RES, EASTMAN CHEM DIV, EASTMAN KODAK CO, 78- *Mem:* Am Inst Chem Engrs; Nat Soc Prof Engrs. *Res:* Chemical reactor design, mixing and optimization; venture analysis. *Mailing Add:* 4534 Brookridge Dr Kingsport TN 37664

PARISH, WILLIAM R, b Grinnell, Iowa, Sept 6, 20; m 43; c 2. ELECTRICAL ENGINEERING. *Educ:* Iowa State Col, BS, 44; Univ Idaho, MS, 52. *Prof Exp:* From instr to assoc prof, 47-64, PROF ELEC ENG, UNIV IDAHO, 64- *Concurrent Pos:* Engr, Gen Elec Co, 59-60; sr specialist engr, Boeing Aerospace Co, 77-78. *Mem:* Am Soc Eng Educ; Inst Elec & Electronics Engrs. *Res:* Radio communication systems; radio wave propagation. *Mailing Add:* Dept of Elec Eng Univ of Idaho Moscow ID 83843

PARISI, GEORGE I, b Newark, NJ, Feb 6, 31; m 54; c 3. PHYSICAL CHEMISTRY. *Educ:* Newark Col Eng, BS, 51, MS, 53; Rutgers Univ, PhD(phys chem), 66. *Prof Exp:* Develop engr, Celanese Corp Am, 51-55; MEM TECH STAFF, BELL LABS, INC, 55- *Mem:* Am Chem Soc; Electrochem Soc; Am Inst Chem Eng; fel Am Inst Chem. *Res:* Rheology of polymers; design and development of high reliability electronic components; Mossbauer effect studies; applied research in thin film technology, including sputtering, vapor deposition, photolithography and anodization; silicon integrated circuit processing and quality control. *Mailing Add:* 379 Mountain Ave Murray Hill NJ 07974

PARISI, JOSEPH THOMAS, b Chicago, Ill, Apr 28, 34; m 63; c 1. MICROBIOLOGY. *Educ:* Loyola Univ Chicago, BS, 56; Ohio State Univ, MSc, 58, PhD(microbiol), 62. *Prof Exp:* Asst prof biol, Duquesne Univ, 62-65; from asst prof to assoc prof, 65-75, PROF MICROBIOL, SCH MED, UNIV MO-COLUMBIA, 75- *Concurrent Pos:* NIH res grant microbiol, Univ Mo-Columbia, 67-69. *Mem:* Am Soc Microbiol; Sigma Xi. *Res:* Microbial genetics; epidemiology. *Mailing Add:* Dept of Microbiol Univ Mo Sch of Med Columbia MO 65212

PARISSE, ANTHONY JOHN, b Brooklyn, NY, Oct 25, 36; m 59; c 2. COSMETIC CHEMISTRY, PHARMACEUTICAL CHEMISTRY. *Educ:* St John's Univ, BS, 58; Rutgers Univ, MBA, 73. *Prof Exp:* Res chemist pharmaceut, Whitehall Labs, Am Home Prod, 59-61; sr scientist, Johnson & Johnson, 61-65; ASSOC DIR TOILETRIES RES, CARTER-WALLACE INC, CRANBURY, 65- *Mem:* Soc Cosmetic Chemists; Am Chem Soc; Am Pharmaceut Soc; Acad Pharmaceut Sci. *Res:* Inhibition of perspiration; structure, chemical composition and chemical reactivity of human hair; inhalation of airborne particles. *Mailing Add:* 60 Oliver Ave Edison NJ 08817

PARIZA, MICHAEL WILLARD, b Waukesha, Wis, Mar 10, 43; m 67; c 3. DIET & CANCER, MICROBIAL TOXINS. *Educ:* Univ Wis-Madison, BS, 67; Kans State Univ, MS, 69, PhD(microbiol), 73. *Prof Exp:* Trainee oncol, McArdle Lab Cancer Res, 73-76, asst prof, 76-81, ASSOC PROF FOOD MICROBIOL & TOXICOL & ASSOC CHMN DEPT, UNIV WIS-MADISON, 81- *Concurrent Pos:* Prin investr, NIH grants, 79- *Mem:* Am Asn Cancer Res; Am Soc Microbiol; Inst Food Technologists; AAAS; Genetic Toxicol Asn. *Res:* Role of diet and nutrition in carcinogenesis; mechanism of action of food-borne microbial toxins; mutagenicity versus carcinogenicity. *Mailing Add:* Dept Food Microbiol & Toxicol Univ Wis 1925 Willow Dr Madison WI 53706

PARIZEK, ELDON JOSEPH, b Iowa City, Iowa, Apr 30, 20; m 44; c 4. GEOLOGY. *Educ:* Univ Iowa, BS, 42, MS, 47, PhD(geol), 49. *Prof Exp:* Asst geologist, Iowa Geol Surv, 46-47; instr geol, Univ Iowa, 47-49; from asst prof to assoc prof, Univ Ga, 49-57; from asst prof to assoc prof, 57-63, PROF GEOL, UNIV MO-KANSAS CITY, 63-, CHMN DEPT GEOSCI, 74-, INTERIM DEAN COL ARTS & SCI, 78- *Concurrent Pos:* Asst geologist, State Geol Surv, Mo, 48-49 & 57-, Ga, 51-57. *Mem:* Geol Soc Am; Asn Am Geogrs; Nat Asn Geol Teachers. *Res:* General geology of southeast Missouri; metamorphic and igneous geology of east central Georgia Piedmont; geomorphology of Georgia Piedmont; structural geology; volume changes in shales; stratigraphy of northwest Missouri; geomorphology of northwest Missouri and eastern Kansas. *Mailing Add:* Dept of Geosci Univ of Mo Kansas City MO 64110

PARIZEK, RICHARD RUDOLPH, b Stafford Springs, Conn, Aug 15, 34; m 61; c 1. HYDROGEOLOGY, ENVIRONMENTAL GEOLOGY. *Educ:* Univ Conn, BA, 56; Univ Ill, MS, 60, PhD(geol), 61. *Prof Exp:* Res asst, Ill State Geol Surv, 56-61; assoc prof, 61-71, prof hydrogeol, 71-77, PROF GEOL, PA STATE UNIV, UNIVERSITY PARK, 78-, STAFF GEOLOGIST, 61- *Concurrent Pos:* Consult, Off Water Resources Res, 64-, Pa Coal Res Bd, 65- & Dept Health, Educ & Welfare, 65-; consult, Pa Dept Environ Resources, 68- & Pa Dept Transp, 74-; Pa rep, Pollution from Land Use Activities Ref Group, Int Joint Comn, 73-; examiner, Pa Civil Serv Comn, 74- *Mem:* Geol Soc Am; AAAS; Am Geophys Union. *Res:* Environmental geology with special concern for land use, water supply, waste disposal and coal mining; occurrence and groundwater resource evaluation in carbonate and fractured rock terrains; pleistocene geology. *Mailing Add:* 340 Deike Bldg Pa State Univ University Park PA 16802

PARK, CHAN MO, b Seoul, Korea, Apr 3, 35; m 63; c 3. COMPUTER SCIENCE, CHEMICAL ENGINEERING. *Educ:* Seoul Nat Univ, BS, 58; Univ Md, MS, 64, PhD(chem eng), 69. *Prof Exp:* Res assoc comput sci, Univ Md, College Park, 64, res programmer, 64-68, fel, 68-69, asst prof, 69-72; assoc prof comput sci, Korea Advan Inst Sci, 73-76; sr res scientist, Nat Biomed Res Found, 76-79; ASSOC PROF COMPUT SCI, CATHOLIC UNIV AM, 79- *Concurrent Pos:* Consult, Comput Ctr, Korea Inst Sci & Technol, 73-76; resident prof systs mgt, Korea Ctrs, Univ Southern Calif, 75-76; vis lectr comput sci, Univ Md, 76- *Mem:* Inst Elec & Electronics Comput Soc; Asn Comput Mach; Pattern Recognition Soc; Korean Scientists & Engrs Asn Am (vpres, 77-78). *Res:* Application of computers to engineering and biomedical problems; picture processing; computer systems and digital simulation. *Mailing Add:* 6100 Greentree Rd Bethesda MD 20817

PARK, CHARLES RAWLINSON, b Baltimore, Md, Mar 2, 16; m 53; c 1. PHYSIOLOGY, BIOCHEMISTRY. *Educ:* Harvard Univ, AB, 37; Johns Hopkins Univ, MD, 41. *Prof Exp:* Intern, Johns Hopkins Hosp, 41-42; from med asst resident to resident, Peter Bent Brigham Hosp, 42-44; PROF PHYSIOL & HEAD DEPT, SCH MED, VANDERBILT UNIV, 52-, DIR, HOWARD HUGHES MEDICAL INST, 80- *Concurrent Pos:* USPHS fel biochem, Sch Med, Wash Univ, 47-49, Welch fel internal med, 49-52. *Mem:* AAAS; Am Soc Clin Invest (vpres, 60-61); Am Soc Biol Chem; Asn Chairmen Dept Physiol (pres, 77-78); Asn Am Physicians. *Res:* Hormonal effects on carbohydrate metabolism. *Mailing Add:* Dept of Physiol Vanderbilt Univ Sch of Med Nashville TN 37232

PARK, CHONG EEL, b S Korea, Mar 20, 27; m 52; c 4. FOOD MICROBIOLOGY. *Educ:* Univ Hawaii, PhD(microbiol), 66. *Prof Exp:* Prof microbiol, Western Col, Miami Univ, 66-67; res assoc med res, Univ Toronto, 67-69; res assoc biochem, Univ Ottawa, 69-70; RES SCIENTIST FOOD MICROBIOL, HEALTH PROTECTION BR, HEALTH & WELFARE CAN, 70- *Mem:* Can Fedn Biol Soc; Can Soc Microbiologist; Int Asn Milk Food & Environ Sanitarians; Am Sci Affil. *Res:* Development of methodology for isolation and detection of health hazardous organisms and toxins from food. *Mailing Add:* 1489 Orchard Dr Ottawa ON K1H 7C5 Can

PARK, CHONG JIN, b Korea, Apr 2, 36; m 64; c 3. MATHEMATICAL STATISTICS. *Educ:* Univ Wash, BS, 61, BA, 62; Kans State Univ, MS, 63; Univ Wis-Madison, MS, 64, PhD(statist), 68. *Prof Exp:* Instr statist, Kans State Univ, 66-67; asst prof, Univ Nebr, Lincoln, 67-71; vis asst prof, Univ Wis-Madison, 71-72; assoc prof, 72-78, PROF MATH SCI, SAN DEIGO STATE UNIV, 78- *Concurrent Pos:* Consult, Kelco, San Diego, Calif, 73-; res fel, US Air Force, Edwards, Calif, 80. *Mem:* Inst Math Statist; Am Statist Asn; Int Asn Statist in Phys Sci. *Res:* Nonparametric statistics via combinatorial methods; spectral analysis of time series data. *Mailing Add:* Dept of Math San Diego State Univ San Diego CA 92182

PARK, CHUL, b Taegu, Korea, June 8, 34; US citizen; m 62; c 3. AERONAUTICAL ENGINEERING. *Educ:* Seoul Nat Univ, BS, 57, MS, 60; Univ London, PhD(aeronaut eng), 64. *Prof Exp:* Instr aerodyn, Korean Air Force Acad, 58-61; res assoc magnetohydrodyn, 64-67, RES SCIENTIST FLUID MECH, AMES RES CTR, NASA, 67- *Concurrent Pos:* Vis engr mech eng, Mass Inst Technol, 71-72. *Mem:* Am Inst Aeronaut & Astronaut. *Res:* Fluid mechanics and high temperature thermophysics related to space travel. *Mailing Add:* Mail Stop 229-4 Entry Technol Br Ames Res Ctr NASA Moffett Field CA 94305

PARK, CHULL, b Seoul, Korea, Feb 29, 32; m 64; c 2. MATHEMATICS, AERONAUTICAL ENGINEERING. *Educ:* Seoul Nat Univ, BS, 59; Southern Ill Univ, MS, 64; Univ Minn, PhD(math), 68. *Prof Exp:* Teacher, Sook Myung High Sch, 59-62; asst prof math, Bemidji State Col, 67-68; asst prof math, 68-74, assoc prof, 75-81, PROF MATH & STATIST, MIAMI UNIV, 81- *Mem:* Am Math Soc; Math Asn Am; Inst Math Statist. *Res:* Gaussian stochastic processes including Wiener process (Brownian motion process); absorption probabilities of Wiener process, stochastic intergrals, stochastic differential equations; laws of iterated logarithms. *Mailing Add:* Dept of Math Miami Univ Oxford OH 45056

PARK, CHUNG GUN, b Seoul, Korea, Jan 11, 39; US citizen; m 67. ATMOSPHERIC PHYSICS. *Educ:* Stanford Univ, BS, 61, MS, 64, PhD(elec eng), 70. *Prof Exp:* Engr semiconductor, Hewlett Packard Co, 61-65; res engr, 65-66, res assoc, 70-76, SR RES ASSOC SPACE SCI, STANFORD UNIV, 76- *Concurrent Pos:* Secy, Subcomn Planetary & Space Prob of Atmospheric Elec, 75-; assoc ed, J Geophys Res, 76-; mem, US Nat Comt & Exec Comt, Int Sci Radio Union, 77-; mem, Comt Atmospheric Elec, Am Geophys Union, 77-; mem, US Panel Mid Atmospheric Prog, 78- *Honors & Awards:* Antarctic Serv Medal, NSF, 76. *Mem:* Am Geophys Union; AAAS; Int Asn Geomagnetism & Aeronomy. *Res:* Space science and atmospheric electricity. *Mailing Add:* Radiosci Lab Stanford Univ Stanford CA 94305

PARK, CHUNG HO, b Seoul, Korea, July 4, 36; div; c 2. ORGANIC CHEMISTRY. *Educ:* Univ Ill, Urbana, BS, 60; Mass Inst Technol, PhD(org chem), 62. *Prof Exp:* RES CHEMIST, CENT RES DEPT, E I DU PONT DE NEMOURS & CO, INC, 65- *Mem:* Am Chem Soc. *Res:* Reactions involving medium and large ring compounds and stereochemistry; macrobicyclic diamines, crown ethers and biologically active compounds. *Mailing Add:* Cent Res Dept Exp Sta E I du Pont de Nemours & Co Inc Wilmington DE 19898

PARK, CONRAD B, b Kannapolis, NC, Nov 6, 19; m 43; c 5. CHEMISTRY. *Educ:* Newberry Col, AB, 41; Univ NC, MA, 43, PhD, 52. *Prof Exp:* Asst chem, Clemson Col, 41-42 & Univ NC, 42-43; res chemist, Tex Co, 43-46; prof chem, Carthage Col, 46-48; from assoc prof to prof, Lenoir-Rhyna Col, 48-56; acad dean, 56-74, PROF CHEM, NEWBERRY COL, 56- *Mem:* Am Chem Soc. *Res:* Surface active agents; ultraviolet spectroscopy; low temperature fractional distillation. *Mailing Add:* Dept of Chem Newberry Col Newberry SC 29108

PARK, DAVID ALLEN, b New York, NY, Oct 13, 19; m 45; c 4. THEORETICAL PHYSICS. *Educ:* Harvard Univ, AB, 41; Univ Mich, PhD(physics), 50. *Prof Exp:* Instr physics, Williams Col, 41-44; res assoc, Radio Res Lab, 44-45; mem, Inst Advan Study, 50-51; instr physics, Univ Mich, 50; from asst prof to assoc prof, 51-60, PROF PHYSICS, WILLIAMS COL, 60- *Concurrent Pos:* Lectr, Univ Ceylon, 55-56 & 72; fel, Cambridge Univ, 62-63; prof, Univ NC, 64. *Mem:* Fel Am Phys Soc. *Mailing Add:* Dept of Physics Williams Col Williamstown MA 01267

PARK, DUK-WON, b Kyong-Buk, Korea, Mar 8, 45; m 74; c 2. MINING ENGINEERING, GEOLOGICAL ENGINEERING. *Educ:* Inha Univ, Korea, BS, 67; Univ Mo, Rolla, MS, 71, PhD(geol eng), 75. *Prof Exp:* Asst proj engr, D'Applonia Consult Engrs Inc, 75-76; res assoc, WVa Univ, 76-77, asst prof, 77-81, assoc prof, 81; ASSOC PROF MINING ENG, UNIV ALA, 81- *Concurrent Pos:* Fac res partic, US Dept Energy, 79. *Mem:* Am Soc Mech Engrs; Asn Eng Geologists; Am Soc Testing & Mat. *Res:* Rock mechanics; mine ground control; mine ventilation; applications of rolographic interferometry to geotechnical problems; slope stability; ground water. *Mailing Add:* Dept Mineral Eng Univ Ala PO Box 1460 University AL 35486

PARK, EDWARD C(AHILL), (JR), b Wollaston, Mass, Nov 26, 23; m 51. PHYSICS, ELECTROOPTICS. *Educ:* Harvard Univ, AB, 47; Univ Birmingham, PhD(exp nuclear physics), 56. *Prof Exp:* Res asst, Univ Birmingham, 53-54; teaching intern, Amherst Col, 54-55; staff mem radar technol, Lincoln Lab, Mass Inst Technol, 55-57; staff mem superconductivity, Advan Res Div, Arthur D Little, Inc, Mass, 57, proj engr, Eng Div, 57-60, group leader electronic systs, Santa Monica Opers, Calif, 60-64; sr staff engr, Res & Develop Div, Hughes Aircraft Co, Calif, 64-68; sr mem tech staff, Litton Systs, Inc, Calif, 68-70; sr phys scientist, Eng Sci Dept, Rand Corp, 70-72; SR RESEARCHER, R&D ASSOCS, 72- *Mem:* Sigma Xi; Inst Elec & Electronics Engrs; Optical Soc Am. *Res:* Electrooptic and sensor systems analysis. *Mailing Add:* 932 Ocean Front Santa Monica CA 90403

PARK, EFTON LILBORN, JR, b Ft Morgan, Colo, Mar 15, 36; m 60; c 4. CHEMICAL ENGINEERING. *Educ:* Univ Colo, BS, 58; Rice Univ, MS, 63; Univ Okla, PhD(chem eng), 65. *Prof Exp:* Prof chem eng, Univ Mo-Rolla, 64-78; CHMN DEPT CHEM ENG, UNIV MISS, 78- *Concurrent Pos:* Grants, NSF, 65-68 & 69-72, Petrol Res Fund, 66-69 & NASA, 78- *Mem:* Am Inst Chem Engrs; Am Soc Mech Engrs; Am Soc Eng Educ. *Res:* Heat transfer in cryogenic systems; boiling heat transfer; condensation heat transfer. *Mailing Add:* Dept of Chem Eng Univ of Miss University MS 38677

PARK, GEORGE BENNET, b Port Arthur, Tex, Jan 26, 46; m 70; c 2. ANALYTICAL CHEMISTRY, ELECTROANALYTICAL CHEMISTRY. *Educ:* Newberry Col, BS, 67; Univ NC, Chapel Hill, MA, 69; Univ Kans, PhD(chem), 73. *Prof Exp:* Asst prof chem, Clemson Univ, 73-80; MEM STAFF, DRUG METAB DEPT, STERLING WINTHROP RES INST, 80- *Mem:* Am Chem Soc; Med Electronics & Data Soc. *Res:* HPLC determination of low levels of drugs of abuse; electroanalytical chemistry of drugs of abuse and porphyrins; electroanalytical methods applied to enzyme assays. *Mailing Add:* Drug Metab Dept Sterling Winthrop Res Inst Rensselaer NY 12144

PARK, GERALD L(ESLIE), b Minneapolis, Minn, Feb 7, 33; m 57; c 3. SYSTEMS & ELECTRICAL ENGINEERING. *Educ:* Univ Minn, Minneapolis, BME, 55, PhD(elec eng), 64; Stanford Univ, MS, 58. *Prof Exp:* Instr elec eng, Univ Minn, 58-64; asst prof, 64-67, assoc prof elec eng & systs sci, 67-72, PROF ELEC ENG & SYSTS SCI, MICH STATE UNIV, 72- *Mem:* Sr mem Inst Elec & Electronics Engrs; Simulation Coun; Int Conf Large Elec Systs. *Res:* Electric power systems with emphasis on wind-electric systems, instrumentation and planning; electrical accidents. *Mailing Add:* Dept of Elec Eng & Systs Sci Mich State Univ East Lansing MI 48824

PARK, HEEBOK, b Seoul, Korea, Nov 25, 33; m 62; c 1. STATISTICS. *Educ:* Seoul Nat Univ, BS, 57; Univ Chicago, MS, 61, PhD(statist), 64. *Prof Exp:* Asst prof statist, Purdue Univ, 64-67; assoc prof, 67-73, PROF STATIST, CALIF STATE UNIV, HAYWARD, 73-, CHMN DEPT, 74- *Concurrent Pos:* Am Heart Asn statistician, Coronary Heart Dis Res Proj, Chicago, 61- *Mem:* Inst Math Statist (treas, 78-); Am Statist Asn. *Res:* Inference procedures and data analysis. *Mailing Add:* Dept of Statist Calif State Univ 25800 Hillary St Hayward CA 94545

PARK, HERBERT WILLIAM, III, b Gowanda, NY, May 31, 20; m 47; c 5. REHABILITATION MEDICINE. *Educ:* Univ NC, BS, 44; Duke Univ, MD, 45. *Prof Exp:* Chief phys med & rehab serv, Vet Admin Hosp, Ft Thomas, Ky, 49-50; asst prof phys med, Univ Va, 50-52; prof phys med & rehab, 52-60, med coordr rehab serv, 57-59, CLIN PROF PHYS MED & REHAB, MED COL VA, 60-; med dir, West End Med Rehab Ctr, 69-80; DIR DEPT PHYSICAL MED, MCGUIRE CLIN, 80- *Concurrent Pos:* Baruch fel biol, Mass Inst Technol, 46-47; Baruch fel physiol, Harvard Med Sch, 47; Baruch fel phys med, Mass Gen Hosp, 47-49; med dir, Woodrow Wilson Rehab Ctr, Fishersville, Va, 50-52; med dir, Baruch Ctr Phys Med & Baruch Sch Phys Ther, 52-59, psychiatrist-in-chief, Hosps, 52-59; mem comt prosthetic educ & info, Nat Acad Sci-Nat Res Coun, 58-65; consult, McGuire Vet Admin Hosp, Richmond City Nursing Home; consult med devices related to rehab med, Dept Health, Educ & Welfare, 74-78; dir prosthetics & orthotics clin, Med Col Va, 74-; chmn subcomt on prosthetics & orthotics, Panel on Physical Med Devices, Food & Drug Admin, HEW, 74-78. *Mem:* Am Col Physicians; Am Soc Internal Med; AMA; Am Acad Phys Med & Rehab. *Res:* Body mechanics as it relates to the field of prosthetics and orthotics. *Mailing Add:* McGuire Clin 7702 Parham Rd STEL Richmond VA 23229

PARK, JAE YOUNG, b Chochiwon, Korea, May 4, 30; m 51; c 3. THEORETICAL PHYSICS, NUCLEAR PHYSICS. *Educ:* Seoul Nat Univ, BSc, 52; Rensselaer Polytech Inst, MSc, 56; Univ NC, PhD(physics), 62. *Prof Exp:* Instr physics, Pusan Univ, Korea, 52-53 & Han Yang Inst Tech, Korea, 53-54; from asst prof to assoc prof, 62-74, PROF PHYSICS, NC STATE UNIV, 75- *Concurrent Pos:* NATO sr fel sci, NSF, 73. *Mem:* Am Phys Soc; Sigma Xi; Am Asn Univ Prof; Am Asn Physics Teachers. *Res:* Nuclear reactions; nuclear structure; heavy-ion physics. *Mailing Add:* Dept of Physics NC State Univ Raleigh NC 27650

PARK, JAMES LEMUEL, b Wichita Falls, Tex, Dec 6, 40; m 63; c 2. PHYSICS. *Educ:* Univ Tex, BA, 63; Yale Univ, MS, 64, PhD(physics), 67. *Prof Exp:* From asst prof to assoc prof, 67-77, chmn dept, 77-80, PROF PHYSICS, WASH STATE UNIV, 77- *Mem:* Sigma Xi. *Res:* Mathematical and philosophical foundations of physics, especially quantum theory; quantum theory of measurement; irreversibility. *Mailing Add:* Dept Physics Wash State Univ Pullman WA 99163

PARK, JAMES THEODORE, b Palo Alto, Calif, Aug 3, 22; m 52. MICROBIOLOGY, BIOCHEMISTRY. *Educ:* Cent Mich Univ, AB, 43; Univ Wis, MS, 44, PhD(biochem), 49. *Prof Exp:* Asst biochem, Univ Wis, 43-44 & 46-49; biochemist, US Army Chem Corps, Md, 49-53; res assoc, Walter Reed Army Inst Res, 53-57; assoc prof microbiol, Sch Med, Vanderbilt Univ, 58-62; chmn dept, 62-70, PROF MOLECULAR BIOL & MICROBIOL, SCH MED, TUFTS UNIV, 62- *Concurrent Pos:* NSF sr fel, Cambridge Univ, 57-58; NIH spec fel, Univ Umeå, Sweden, 69-70; mem study sect bact & mycol, NIH, 64-68; mem microbiol training comt, Nat Inst Gen Med Sci, 70-73. *Mem:* Am Acad Arts & Sci; Am Chem Soc; Am Soc Biol Chem; Am Soc Microbiol; Brit Soc Gen Microbiol. *Res:* Mode of action of antibiotics; chemistry of microorganisms; biosynthesis of bacterial cell walls. *Mailing Add:* Dept Molecular Biol & Microbiol Tufts Univ 136 Harrison Ave Boston MA 02111

PARK, JANE HARTING, b St Louis, Mo, Mar 25, 25; m 53; c 1. BIOCHEMISTRY. *Educ:* Wash Univ, BS, 46, PhD(biochem), 52. *Prof Exp:* From instr to assoc prof, 54-69, PROF PHYSIOL, SCH MED, VANDERBILT UNIV, 69- *Concurrent Pos:* Am Cancer Soc scholar, 55-58; NIH sr res fel, 58-; mem physiol chem study sect, NIH. *Mem:* Am Chem Soc; Am Cancer Soc; Am Soc Biol Chemists. *Res:* Mechanism of enzymatic catalysis; oxidative phosphorylation; metabolic pathways in muscle. *Mailing Add:* Dept of Physiol Vanderbilt Univ Sch of Med Nashville TN 37203

PARK, JOHN HOWARD, JR, b Washington, DC, May 16, 32; m 51; c 3. ELECTRICAL ENGINEERING. *Educ:* Univ Md, BS, 54; Johns Hopkins Univ, MS, 57, DE(elec eng), 60. *Prof Exp:* Res asst elec eng, Radiation Lab, Johns Hopkins Univ, 54-57, res staff asst, 57-59; tech specialist, Electronics Div, Gen Mills, Inc, 59-62, lab mgr systs anal, 62-63; lectr elec eng, Univ Minn, Minneapolis, 61-62, assoc prof, 63-79; sr prin engr, 79-81, OPER MGR, COMPUT SCI CORP, 81- *Concurrent Pos:* Consult, Appl Sci Div, Litton Industs, Inc, 63-64, Univac Div, Sperry Rand, Inc, 64-79, Systs & Res Div, Honeywell Inc, 66, Electroprod Div, 3M Co, 70-74 & PKM Corp, 71-74. *Mem:* Inst Elec & Electronics Engrs. *Res:* Statistical theory of communication; estimation of signal parameters; effect of noise in modulation systems; speech compression; satellite communications; adaptive antenna arrays. *Mailing Add:* Comput Sci Corp 6565 Arlington Blvd Falls Church VA 22046

PARK, JOHN THORNTON, b Phillipsburg, NJ, Jan 3, 35; m 56; c 2. ATOMIC PHYSICS. *Educ:* Nebr Wesleyan Univ, BA, 56; Univ Nebr, PhD(physics), 63. *Prof Exp:* NSF fel, Univ Col, London, 63-64; asst prof, 64-71, PROF PHYSICS, UNIV MO-ROLLA, 71-, CHMN DEPT, 77- *Mem:* Fel Am Phys Soc; Am Asn Physics Teachers. *Res:* Ionic and atomic collisional excitation and energy loss processes. *Mailing Add:* Dept of Physics Univ of Mo Rolla MO 65401

PARK, KISOON, US citizen. PHYSICAL CHEMISTRY. *Educ:* Seoul Nat Univ, BS, 61; Univ Utah, MS, 64, PhD(metall), 66. *Prof Exp:* Chemist, 66-73, proj scientist, 73-78, RES SCIENTIST, UNION CARBIDE CORP, 76- *Concurrent Pos:* Guest lectr, NC State Univ, 73-77. *Mem:* Sigma Xi; Electrochem Soc; Nat Asn Corrosion Engrs; Am Chem Soc. *Res:* Surface and colloid chemistry; radiation polymerization; friction and lubrication of textile fibers; corrosion science and technology. *Mailing Add:* Chem & Plastics Tech Ctr Union Carbide Corp PO Box 8361 South Charleston WV 25303

PARK, KWANGJAI, b Wonsan, Korea, Oct 12, 35; m 57; c 3. SOLID STATE PHYSICS, OPTICS. *Educ:* Harvard Univ, BA, 58; Univ Calif, Berkeley, PhD(physics), 65. *Prof Exp:* Res scientist plasma physics, Giannini Sci Corp, 58-61; mem tech staff nonlinear optics, Bell Tel Labs, 65-66; asst prof, 66-71, ASSOC PROF PHYSICS, UNIV ORE, 71- *Concurrent Pos:* Vis prof, Sogang Univ, Seoul, Korea, 72-73. *Mem:* Am Phys Soc; fel Korean Phys Soc. *Res:* Optical properties of solids, including color centers, band structure of crystals, and interaction of matter and high intensity light. *Mailing Add:* Dept of Physics Univ of Ore Eugene OR 97403

PARK, MYUNG KUN, b Suhung, Korea, Sept 30, 34; m 67; c 3. PEDIATRIC CARDIOLOGY, PHARMACOLOGY. *Educ:* Seoul Nat Univ, dipl, 56, MD, 60. *Prof Exp:* Fel pediat cardiol, Sch Med, Univ Wash, 65-68, instr pediat, 66-68, res fel pharmacol, 71-73; asst prof pediat, Univ Kans Med Ctr, Kansas City, 73-76; ASSOC PROF PEDIAT, UNIV TEX HEALTH SCI CTR, SAN ANTONIO, 76- *Mem:* NY Acad Sci; Am Acad Pediat; Soc Pediat Res; Am Soc Pharmacol & Exp Therapeut; Soc Exp Biol & Med. *Res:* Developmental pharmacology; mechanism of hypoxic pulmonary hypertension; digitalis pharmacology. *Mailing Add:* Dept of Pediat Univ of Tex Health Sci Ctr San Antonio TX 78284

PARK, PAUL HEECHUNG, b Seoul, Korea, Mar 15, 41; US citizen; m 70; c 3. CHEMICAL ENGINEERING, MATHEMATICS. *Educ:* Seoul Nat Univ, BS, 65; Mich State Univ, MS, 68, PhD(chem eng), 72. *Prof Exp:* Sr develop engr wet spinning, Monsanto Textiles Co, 73-74; res engr polymer processing & melt spinning, Am Cyanamid Co, 74-77; sr res engr mat res, 77-80, SUPVR NEW PROD & TECHNOL, MOBIL CHEM CO, 80- *Concurrent Pos:* Res assoc, Mich State Univ, 72-73. *Mem:* Am Inst Chem Engrs; Am Chem Soc; Soc Rheology. *Res:* Polymer characterization via solution and melt rheology and its processing; molecular orientation, structural interpretation of polymer processes and structure-property correlation for spun fiber and biaxially oriented film; multi phase polymer blends and multi layer biaxially oriented film technology development. *Mailing Add:* Tech Ctr Mobil Chem Co Macedon NY 14502

PARK, PAUL KILHO, b Kobe, Japan, Feb 4, 31; m; c 2. OCEANOGRAPHY. *Educ:* Pusan Fisheries Col, BS, 53; Tex A&M Univ, MS, 57, PhD(oceanog), 61. *Prof Exp:* From asst prof to prof oceanog, Ore State Univ, 61-76; MGR OCEAN DUMPING PROG, US DEPT COM, NAT OCEANIC & ATMOSPHERIC ADMIN, 77- *Concurrent Pos:* Prog dir phys oceanog, NSF, 69-70, head oceanog sect, 70-71. *Mem:* AAAS; Am Soc Limnol & Oceanog; Am Geophys Union; Am Chem Soc. *Res:* Carbon dioxide system; biogeochemistry of hydrosphere; marine pollution. *Mailing Add:* 7 Fallswood Court Rockville MD 20854

PARK, RICHARD AVERY, IV, b Sedalia, Mo, Dec 20, 38; m 62; c 2. ENVIRONMENTAL SCIENCES. *Educ:* La State Univ, BS, 61; Univ Wis, MS, 65, PhD(paleoecol), 67. *Prof Exp:* Asst prof, 66-71, assoc prof geol, 71-76, PROF GEOL, RENSSELAER POLYTECH INST, 77- *Concurrent Pos:* Chief math ecologist, Rensselaer Fresh Water Inst, 72-; mem sci adv panel, Southwest Ctr Urban Res, Houston, 75- *Mem:* Soc Econ Paleont & Mineral; Geol Soc Am; Int Asn Math Geol; Ecol Soc Am; Brit Freshwater Biol Asn. *Res:* Ecosystem and land-use simulation; multivariate analysis; ecology of American and European lakes; paleoecology. *Mailing Add:* Dept of Geol Rensselaer Polytechnic Inst Troy NY 12181

PARK, ROBERT L, b Kansas City, Mo, Jan 16, 31; m 51; c 2. PHYSICS. *Educ:* Univ Tex, BS, 58, MA, 60; Brown Univ, PhD(physics), 65. *Prof Exp:* Res assoc physics, Brown Univ, 64-65; res physicist, Sandia Corp, 65-69, supvr, Surface Kinetics Div, Sandia Lab, 69-74; dir, Ctr Mat Res, 75-78, assoc chmn dept physics & astron, 77-78, PROF PHYSICS & ASTRON, UNIV MD, COLLEGE PARK, 74-, CHMN DEPT, 78- *Mem:* AAAS; fel Am Phys Soc; Am Vacuum Soc. *Res:* Physics of solid surfaces; surface structure and gas-surface interactions. *Mailing Add:* Dept of Physics & Astron Univ of Md College Park MD 20742

PARK, ROBERT LYNN, b Idaho Falls, Idaho, Sept 1, 32; m 62; c 6. ANIMAL SCIENCE, ANIMAL BREEDING. *Educ:* Brigham Young Univ, BS, 56; Cornell Univ, MS, 58, PhD(animal husb), 62. *Prof Exp:* Spec county agent, Univ Ariz, 59, res animal husb, Agr Res Serv, USDA, 61-65; from asst prof to assoc prof, 65-73, PROF ANIMAL SCI, BRIGHAM YOUNG UNIV, 73- *Concurrent Pos:* Mem pasture & livestock comt, Caribbean Comn, 63-65. *Mem:* Sigma Xi; Am Soc Animal Sci; Am Dairy Sci Asn. *Res:* Population genetics and animal breeding; biomathematics and biostatistics in agriculture; microcomputers. *Mailing Add:* Dept Animal Sci Brigham Young Univ Provo UT 84602

PARK, ROBERT WILLIAM, b Eaton County, Mich, Oct 2, 29; m 49; c 4. PAPER CHEMISTRY. *Educ:* Albion Col, AB, 52; Western Mich Univ, MBA, 68. *Prof Exp:* Staff chemist, Film Div, Am Viscose Corp, 52-55, prod supvr, 55-60, prod admin, 60-62; sr res specialist, Res & Develop Div, Packaging Corp Am, 62-66, res group leader, 66-68, dir res & develop, 68-70; mgr new prod res, Appleton Papers, Inc, 70-71, com prod mgr, 71-81; DIR PROD DEVELOP, SHAWANO PAPER MILLS, 81- *Mem:* Am Chem Soc; Tech Asn Pulp & Paper Indust. *Res:* Development of coated specialty papers for graphic arts, technical specialty papers, and coated plastics; research administration; development of specialty light weight millifarad, milligram, creped papers. *Mailing Add:* Shawano Paper Mills PO Box 437 Shawano WI 54166

PARK, RODERIC BRUCE, b Cannes, France, Jan 7, 32; US citizen; m 53; c 3. PLANT PHYSIOLOGY. *Educ:* Harvard Univ, BA, 53; Calif Inst Technol, PhD(biol), 58. *Prof Exp:* Chemist, Lawrence Radiation Lab, 58-60,from asst prof to assoc prof, 60-66, provost & dean col lett & sci, 72-80, PROF BOT, UNIV CALIF, BERKELEY, 66-, VCHANCELLOR, 80- *Concurrent Pos:* Mem, Harvard Bd Overseers, 81-87. *Honors & Awards:* NY Bot Gardens Award, 62. *Mem:* AAAS; Am Soc Plant Physiol. *Res:* Carbon isotope fractionation in photosynthesis; membrane structure; photosynthesis as related to plant ultrastructure. *Mailing Add:* VChancellor Univ Calif 200 California Hall Berkeley CA 94720

PARK, SAMUEL, b Seoul, Korea, May 26, 36. MATHEMATICAL ANALYSIS. *Educ:* WVa Wesleyan Col, BS, 56; Univ Pittsburgh, MA, 57, PhD(math), 59. *Prof Exp:* Teaching fel math, Univ Pittsburgh, 56-59; res assoc, Columbia Univ, 59-60; asst prof, Rutgers Univ, 60-65; assoc prof, 65-71, PROF MATH, LONG ISLAND UNIV, 71-, CHMN MATH DEPT, 79- *Mem:* Am Math Soc; Math Asn Am. *Res:* Analysis, particularly ordinary differential equations and theory of summability; Fourier analysis. *Mailing Add:* Dept of Math Long Island Univ Brooklyn NY 11201

PARK, SU-MOON, b Korea, Dec 1, 41; m 67; c 3. ELECTROANALYTICAL CHEMISTRY, PHOTOCHEMISTRY. *Educ:* Seoul Nat Univ, Korea, BS, 64; Tex Tech Univ, MS, 72; Univ Tex, Austin, PhD(chem), 75. *Prof Exp:* Anal chemist, Choong-Ju Fertilizer Corp, Korea, 64-67; lab supvr, Yong-Nam Chem Co, Ltd, 67-70; asst prof, 75-81, ASSOC PROF CHEM, UNIV NMEX, 81- *Concurrent Pos:* Fel, Oak Ridge Assoc Univ Fac Res Participation, 80. *Mem:* Am Chem Soc; Electrochem Soc, Inc; Korean Chem Soc. *Res:* Electrogenerated chemiluminescence; chemistry of exciplex; energy transfer of the excited states; organic electrochemistry; donor-acceptor complexes of organic compounds; energy conversion employing semiconductor; liquid junction cells. *Mailing Add:* Dept of Chem Univ of NMex Albuquerque NM 87131

PARK, TAISOO, b Milyang, Korea, July 9, 29; m 76; c 1. INVERTEBRATE ZOOLOGY. *Educ:* Pusan Fisheries Col, Korea, BS, 52, MS, 57; Univ Wash, PhD(zool), 65. *Prof Exp:* Instr, Pusan Fisheries Col, 52-60; res assoc, Univ Wash, 65-66; asst prof, Univ Md, 66-67; asst scientist, Woods Hole Oceanog Inst, 67-69; asst prof oceanog, 69-73, ASSOC PROF BIOL & MARINE SCI, TEX A&M UNIV, 73- *Concurrent Pos:* NSF grants, 67-76; vis prof, Seoul Nat Univ, Korea, 79. *Mem:* Am Soc Zoologists; Ecol Soc Am; Am Soc Limnol & Oceanog; Marine Biol Asn UK; Sigma Xi. *Res:* Systematics and distribution of marine calanoid Copepoda on a world-wide base; general biology of the calanoid Copepoda including functional anatomy, reproduction, and development; community ecology of marine planktonic copepods in the Gulf of Mexico. *Mailing Add:* Dept Marine Biol Tex A&M Univ Galveston TX 77550

PARK, THOMAS, b Danville, Ill, Nov 17, 08; m 28, 69; c 2. POPULATION ECOLOGY. *Educ:* Univ Chicago, BS, 30, PhD(zool), 32. *Hon Degrees:* ScD, Univ Ill, 73. *Prof Exp:* Cur zool, Univ Chicago, 30-31, asst, 31-33; Nat Res Coun fel, Johns Hopkins Univ, 33-35, instr biol, Sch Hyg & Pub Health, 35-36, assoc, 36-37; from instr to prof zool, 37-68, assoc dean div biol sci, 43-46, prof biol, 68-74, EMER PROF BIOL, UNIV CHICAGO, 74- *Concurrent Pos:* Ed, Ecology, Ecol Soc Am, 40-50; Rockefeller Found fel, Oxford Univ, 48; sci attache, Am Embassy, London, 49; vis prof, Univ Calif, 52-; ed, Physiol Zool, 55-75; vis prof, Univ Ill, Chicago Circle, 74- *Honors & Awards:* Eminent Ecologist Citation, Ecol Soc Am, 71. *Mem:* AAAS (pres, 61); Am Soc Zool; Ecol Soc Am (pres, 59); Am Soc Naturalists; Soc Study Evolution. *Res:* Experimental population studies with Tribolium species; experimental biology of populations. *Mailing Add:* 5715 S Blackstone Ave Chicago IL 60637

PARK, VERNON KEE, b Austin, Tex, Sept 27, 28; m 55; c 4. POLYMER CHEMISTRY. *Educ:* Tulane Univ, BS, 48; Univ Tex, MA, 58. *Prof Exp:* From chemist to sr chemist, 57-73, asst dep supt, 73-75, develop assoc, 75-78, RES ASSOC, TEX EASTMAN CO, 79- *Res:* Polyolefin catalysts; application research on adhesives and emulsifiable polymers; polymer research. *Mailing Add:* 204 Ramblewood Ct Longview TX 75601

PARK, WILLIAM H, b Carlisle, Pa, Mar 2, 29; m 54; c 4. MECHANICAL ENGINEERING. *Educ:* Pa State Univ, BS, 52, MS, 59; Cornell Univ, PhD(mach design), 66. *Prof Exp:* Design engr, Sanders & Thomas, Inc, 52-53; from instr to asst prof mech eng, 53-66, ASSOC PROF MECH ENG, PA STATE UNIV, 66- *Concurrent Pos:* Ford Found prin res engr assoc, Ford Motor Co, 68-69; consult, Eriez Magnetics, 57- & Syntron Co, 66- *Mem:* Soc Automotive Engrs; Am Soc Mech Engrs; Simulation Coun; Instrument Soc Am; Am Soc Eng Educ. *Res:* Repetitive impact vibrations; analog-hybrid computer simulation; road roughness-vehicle response; road roughness measurement; biomedical research and design. *Mailing Add:* Dept of Mech Eng Pa State Univ 207 Mech Eng Bldg University Park PA 16802

PARK, WON CHOON, b Hambuk, Korea, Oct 6, 37; m 66; c 2. ECONOMIC GEOLOGY. *Educ:* Seoul Nat Univ, BS, 60; Univ Mo-Rolla, MS, 62; Univ Heidelberg, DSc(mineral), 68. *Prof Exp:* Geologist, Rio Algom Can Inc, 64; asst, Univ Heidelberg, 66-69; from asst prof to assoc prof geol, Boston Univ, 69-75; ore microscopist, Ledgemont Lab, Kennecott Copper Corp, 75-77; PRIN RES GEOLOGIST, OCCIDENTAL RES CORP, 77- *Concurrent Pos:* Swiss Nat Fund fel, 71; consult, Ledgemont Lab, Kennecott Copper Corp, 74-75; adj prof, Univ Calif, Riverside, 78- *Mem:* Geol Soc Am; Geochem Soc; Soc Econ Geol; Am Inst Mining & Metall Engrs; Korean Scientists & Engrs Asn in Am. *Res:* Ore deposits in sedimentary rocks; textures and stability relationships of sulfide minerals; carbonate diagenesis; petrology applied to mineral beneficiation and extraction. *Mailing Add:* Occidental Res Corp PO Box 19601 Irvine CA 92713

PARK, WON JOON, b Sun-Chun, Korea, Sept 18, 35; US citizen; m 66; c 2. MATHEMATICS, STATISTICS. *Educ:* Seoul Nat Univ, BA, 57; Univ Calif, Riverside, MA, 66; Univ Minn, Minneapolis, PhD(math), 69. *Prof Exp:* Asst prof, 69-72, assoc prof, 73-80, PROF MATH, WRIGHT STATE UNIV, 81- *Mem:* Inst Math Statist; Am Statist Asn. *Res:* Stochastic processes and reliability. *Mailing Add:* Dept of Math Wright State Univ Dayton OH 45431

PARK, YOON SOO, b Raichun, Korea, July 4, 29; US citizen; m 60; c 3. SOLID STATE PHYSICS. *Educ:* Seoul Nat Univ, BS, 52; Univ Alta, MS, 55; Univ Cincinnati, PhD(physics), 63. *Prof Exp:* Lectr physics, Pusan Nat Univ, 52; res physicist, D H Baldwin Co, 56-62; res physicist, 63-71, group leader, Aerospace Res Labs, 71-75, TASK MGR AIR FORCE AVIONICS LAB, WRIGHT-PATTERSON AFB, 75- *Concurrent Pos:* Lectr, Univ Dayton, 66; guest lectr, Tech Univ Berlin, 68-69; vis prof, Seoul Nat Univ, 78; consult, UN Indust Develop Orgn, 80. *Honors & Awards:* Air Force Sci Achievement Award, Air Force Systs Command, 71, 72, 73, 77 & 78. *Mem:* Fel Am Phys Soc; Korean Phys Soc; sr mem Inst Elec & Electronics Engrs. *Res:* Optical and electrical properties of semiconductors; ion implantation; radiation damage; crystal growth, cryogenic and optical techniques; photoconductivity and luminescence. *Mailing Add:* Electronic Res Br Air Force Avionics Lab Wright-Patterson AFB OH 45433

PARK, YOUNG D, b Korea, Dec 29, 32; m 65; c 2. SYSTEMS ENGINEERING, CHEMICAL ENGINEERING. *Educ:* Univ Va, BChE, 57. *Prof Exp:* Univ fel, Polytech Inst Brooklyn, 60, NSF fel, 60-61; proj engr, Buyers Lab Inc, 61-66; comput appln engr, Realtime Systs Inc, 66-68; process analyst, Digital Appln, Inc, 68-69; mgr systs eng, Mauchly Assocs, Inc, 69-70; sr engr, Davis Comput Systs, 70-71 & Metromation, Inc, Princeton, 71-73; sr prin engr, Comput Sci Corp, 73-80; PROCESS COMPUT SYSTS MGR, CATALYTIC INC, 80- *Concurrent Pos:* Workshop coordr course on comput prog, Engrs Joint Coun, 68; consult, Oyer Prof Comput Serv, Inc, 68. *Mem:* Am Inst Chem Engrs; Am Chem Soc. *Res:* Computer applications, optimization and simulation of chemical processes; process control. *Mailing Add:* 15 Chateau Dr Cherry Hill NJ 08003

PARKA, STANLEY JOHN, b Holyoke, Mass, May 18, 35; m 56; c 4. WEED SCIENCE. *Educ:* Univ Mass, BS, 56; Purdue Univ, MS, 58, PhD(plant physiol), 60. *Prof Exp:* Plant physiologist, Ferry Morse Seed Co, Calif, 59-60; veg exten specialist, Univ Fla, 60-61; plant physiologist, 61-65, head eastern field res, 65-66, head NAm Field Res, 66-72, head Greenfield plant sci res, 72-73, res assoc, 73-77, RES ADV, GREENFIELD LABS, ELI LILLY & CO, 77- *Mem:* Weed Sci Soc Am; Plant Growth Regulator Working Group; Aquatic Plant Mgt Soc. *Res:* Development of chemicals which regulate plant growth and weed control in agriculture. *Mailing Add:* 2902 Senour Rd Indianapolis IN 46239

PARKANYI, CYRIL, b Prague, Czech, Sept 11, 33; m 60; c 1. PHYSICAL ORGANIC CHEMISTRY. *Educ:* Charles Univ, Prague, MS, 56, Dr rer nat(chem), 66; Czech Acad Sci, PhD(org chem), 62. *Prof Exp:* Phys & anal chemist, Res & Control Inst Food Indust, Prague Czech, 55-56; researcher, Inst Org Chem & Biochem, Czech Acad Sci, 56-59, res scientist, Inst Phys Chem, 60-65; vis scientist, State Univ Leiden, 65; res fel, Calif Inst Technol, 65-67; res scientist, Inst Phys Chem, Czech Acad Sci, 67-68; res assoc, Calif Inst Technol, 68-69; assoc prof, 69-71, PROF CHEM, UNIV TEX, EL PASO, 71- *Concurrent Pos:* Vis res prof, Univ d'Aix-Marseille, Marseille, France, 74 & 77; vis prof, Univ Kuwait, 76, Univ Groningen, Neth, 78 & Univ Sci Techn de Lille, Villeneuve d'Ascq, France, 80, 81 & 82; fac res award, Univ Tex, El Paso, 80. *Honors & Awards:* Czech Acad Sci Award, 63. *Mem:* Inter-Am Photochem Soc; Am Chem Soc; Sigma Xi; Fedn Am Scientists; fel NY Acad Sci. *Res:* Theoretical and quantum organic chemistry; photochemistry; heterocyclic chemistry. *Mailing Add:* 6601 Mariposa Dr El Paso TX 79912

PARKE, EDWARD CHARLES, JR, b Fresno, Calif, Oct 10, 18; m 44; c 3. OPTICS, SCIENCE EDUCATION. *Educ:* Univ Redlands, BA, 47, MA, 49; Univ Colo, PhD(sci educ), 67. *Prof Exp:* Instr physics, Univ Redlands, 47-49; head dept physics, Reedley Col, 49-53; from asst prof to assoc prof, 53-67, chmn dept, 57-74, PROF PHYSICS, HUMBOLDT STATE UNIV, 67- *Mem:* Am Asn Physics Teachers. *Res:* Instructional methods in physics and the physics laboratory. *Mailing Add:* Dept of Physics Humboldt State Univ Arcata CA 95521

PARKE, RUSSELL FRANK, b Kirkland, Ill, Jan 11, 32; m 56; c 2. PHARMACY. *Educ:* Purdue Univ, BS, 54, MS, 56, PhD, 58. *Prof Exp:* Asst prof pharm, Butler Univ, 58-64; SR PHARMACEUT CHEMIST, ELI LILLY & CO, INDIANAPOLIS, 64- *Mem:* Am Chem Soc. *Res:* Drug stability; data storage and retrieval; international product development. *Mailing Add:* Eli Lilly & Co PO Box 61B Indianapolis IN 46206

PARKE, WESLEY WILKIN, b Wallingford, Conn, Sept 30, 26; m 53; c 2. VERTEBRATE ANATOMY, EMBRYOLOGY. *Educ:* Univ Conn, BS, 51, MA, 54, PhD(vert anat), 57. *Prof Exp:* From instr to assoc prof anat, Jefferson Med Col, Thomas Jefferson Univ, 57-74; prof gross anat, Sch Med, Southern Ill Univ, Carbondale, 74-78; PROF & CHMN DEPT ANAT, SCH MED, UNIV S DAK, 78- *Concurrent Pos:* Consult & lectr, US Naval Hosp, Philadelphia, Pa; intern anat, Col Surgeons. *Mem:* AAAS; Am Asn Anat; World Asn Vet Anat; fel Sigma Xi. *Res:* Evolution and development of respiratory system; visceral teratology; vascular anatomy of abdominal and thoracic viscera; lymphangiology and microcirculation; development and anatomy of spine and spinalcord. *Mailing Add:* Dept of Anat Univ of S Dak Sch of Med Vermillion SD 57069

PARKE, WILLIAM C, b Washington, DC, Oct 29, 41; m 69. ELEMENTARY PARTICLE PHYSICS. *Educ:* George Washington Univ, BS, 63, PhD(theoret physics), 67. *Prof Exp:* Nat Acad Sci-Nat Bur Standards res assoc theoret physics, Nat Bur Standards, 67-69; from lectr to asst prof, 66-74, ASSOC PROF PHYSICS, GEORGE WASHINGTON UNIV, 74- *Mem:* Am Phys Soc; Am Inst Physics. *Res:* Field theory; Regge poles; low mass nuclei. *Mailing Add:* Dept of Physics George Washington Univ Washington DC 20052

PARKENING, TERRY ARTHUR, b Omaha, Nebr, Jan 24, 43; m 65; c 1. REPRODUCTIVE BIOLOGY, ENDOCRINOLOGY. *Educ:* Midland Col, BS, 65; Univ SDak, MA, 68; Univ Ore, PhD(biol), 74. *Prof Exp:* asst prof, 76-79, ASSOC PROF ANAT, UNIV TEX MED BR, GALVESTON, 79- *Concurrent Pos:* Res scientist, Worcester Found Exp Biol, NIH, 74-76; NIH grants, Univ Tex, 77-80 & 81. *Mem:* Sigma Xi; Am Asn Anat; Soc Study Reprod; Geront Soc; Am Asn Tissue Banks. *Res:* Reproductive biology and endocrinology, specifically fertilization, implantation and the effects of aging on reproduction. *Mailing Add:* Dept of Anat Univ of Tex Med Br Galveston TX 77550

PARKER, ALAN DOUGLAS, b Wellsville, NY, Sept 21, 45; m 71. MYCOLOGY, BOTANY. *Educ:* Eastern Ill Univ, BS, 69, MS, 71; Univ Ill, PhD(mycol), 76. *Prof Exp:* ASST PROF BOT & MICROBIOL, UNIV WIS CTR-WAUKESHA, 76- *Mem:* Mycol Soc Am; Brit Mycol Soc. *Res:* Taxonomy and ecology of coprophilous ascomycetes. *Mailing Add:* Univ of Wis Ctr 1500 University Dr Waukesha WI 53186

PARKER, ALBERT JOHN, b East St Louis, Ill, July 16, 53. BIOGEOGRAPHY, SYNOPTIC CLIMATOLOGY. *Educ:* Mich State Univ, BS, 75; Univ Wis, Madison, MS, 77, PhD(geog), 80. *Prof Exp:* ASST PROF GEOG, UNIV GA, 80- *Mem:* Asn Am Geographers; Ecol Soc Am; Soil Sci Soc Am. *Res:* Structure and dynamics of conifer forests in western North America with field experience in southeastern Arizona, the Sierra Nevada, and northern Rocky Mountains. *Mailing Add:* Dept Geog Univ Ga Athens GA 30602

PARKER, ALICE CLINE, b Birmingham, Ala, Apr 10, 48; m 80. COMPUTER ENGINEERING. *Educ:* NC State Univ, BS, 70, PhD(elec eng), 75; Stanford Univ, MS, 71. *Prof Exp:* Asst prof elec eng, Carnegie-Mellon Univ, 75-80; ASST PROF ELEC ENG, UNIV SOUTHERN CALIF, 80- *Concurrent Pos:* Prin investr, US Army Res Off grant, 77-; consult, US Army Electronics Command, 78-79, Info Sci Inst, Digital Equip Corp, Hewlett Packard Corp, Nat Inst Educ, 80, Xerox Corp & Aerospace Corp, 81-; nat lectr, Asn Comput Mach, 79-80. *Mem:* Inst Elec & Electronics Engrs; Sigma Xi; Asn Comput Mach. *Res:* Automatic design of digital systems; computer programs which evaluate cost and performance tradeoffs and automatically make design decisions in order to produce an implementation of a digital system from a higher-level specification. *Mailing Add:* Dept Elec Eng Systs Univ Southern Calif Los Angeles CA 90007

PARKER, ARTHUR L (PETE), b Stillwater, Okla, July 29, 50; m 73. PROCESS SIMULATION & OPTIMIZATION. *Educ:* NMex State Univ, BS, 73; Univ Wis, MS, 75, PhD(chem eng), 78. *Prof Exp:* Res engr, Shell Develop Co, 78-81; PROCESS ENGR, SHELL OIL CO, 81- *Mem:* Am Inst Chem Engrs. *Mailing Add:* Shell Oil Co PO Box 3105 Houston TX 77001

PARKER, B(LAINE) F(RANK), b Gaston Co, NC, June 12, 24; m; c 2. AGRICULTURAL ENGINEERING. *Educ:* Va Polytech Inst, BSAE, 50, MSAE, 52; Mich State Univ, PhD(agr eng), 54. *Prof Exp:* Instr agr eng, Va Polytech Inst, 50-52; asst, Mich State Univ, 52-54; asst prof, NC State Col, 54-57; assoc prof, 57-58, chmn agr eng dept, 59-74, PROF AGR ENG, UNIV KY, 59- *Mem:* Fel Am Soc Agr Engrs; Am Soc Eng Educ; Int Solar Energy Soc. *Res:* Environmental design and research on requirements for domestic animals, poultry and animal care facilities; solar thermal energy research, specifically new concepts of solar collectors and development of heat storages. *Mailing Add:* Dept of Agr Eng Univ of Ky Lexington KY 40506

PARKER, BARRY RICHARD, b Penticton, BC, Apr 13, 35; m 62; c 1. THEORETICAL PHYSICS. *Educ:* Univ BC, BA, 59, MSc, 61; Utah State Univ, PhD(physics), 68. *Prof Exp:* Lectr physics, Weber State Col, 63-65, assoc prof, 65-66; assoc prof, 68-71, PROF PHYSICS, IDAHO STATE UNIV, 71- *Mem:* Am Phys Soc. *Res:* Applications of physics to a better understanding of the DNA molecule; gravitational collapse and interactions. *Mailing Add:* Dept of Physics Idaho State Univ Pocatello ID 83201

PARKER, BRENT M, b St Louis, Mo, July 3, 27; m 53; c 3. INTERNAL MEDICINE, CARDIOLOGY. *Educ:* Wash Univ, MD, 52. *Prof Exp:* Sect chief cardiol, Vet Admin Hosp, Portland, Ore, 57-59; from instr to to assoc prof med, Wash Univ, 59-73; PROF MED, UNIV MO, COLUMBIA, 73-, ASSOC DEAN & ASSOC HOSP DIR, SCH MED, 76- *Concurrent Pos:* USPHS res fel, Wash Univ, 55-57, USPHS res grant, 60-66; consult, Ft Leonard Wood, Mo, 63-70; fel coun clin cardiol, Am Heart Asn, 69; chief of staff, Univ Mo Hosp, 76- *Mem:* Fel Am Col Cardiol; Am Fedn Clin Res; Am Col Physicians. *Mailing Add:* Sch of Med Univ Mo W117 807 Stadium Rd Columbia MO 65212

PARKER, BRUCE C, b Rockingham, Vt, June 20, 33; m 61; c 2. PHYCOLOGY. *Educ:* Tufts Univ, BS, 55; Yale Univ, MS, 57; Univ Tex, PhD(bot), 60. *Prof Exp:* NSF fel phycol, Univ Col, London, 60-61; asst prof bot, Univ Calif, Los Angeles, 61-65; assoc prof, Washington Univ, 65-69; PROF BIOL, VA POLYTECH INST & STATE UNIV, 69- *Concurrent Pos:* NSF res grants, 62-82; historian, Phycol Soc Am, 71- *Honors & Awards:* Darbaker Prize, Bot Soc Am, 70. *Mem:* Phycol Soc Am (secy-treas, 65-67, vpres, 68, pres, 69); Am Soc Limnol & Oceanog; Int Phycol Soc; Bot Soc Am. *Res:* Algal ecology and physiology; microbiology; Antarctic freshwater ecosystems; chemical composition of glacial ice and snow. *Mailing Add:* Dept of Biol Va Polytech Inst & State Univ Blacksburg VA 24061

PARKER, CALVIN ALFRED, b Chicago, Ill, Sept 20, 31; m 56; c 3. GEOLOGY. *Educ:* Northwestern Univ, BS, 53; Univ Wis, MS, 56, PhD(geol), 58. *Prof Exp:* Prod geologist, Shell Develop Co, 57-60, staff prod geologist, Shell Oil Co, Tex, 60-67, Royal Dutch Shell Group, Netherlands & Brunei Shell Petrol Co, Borneo, 67-69, staff geol engr, oil co, Tex, 69-70, SR STAFF GEOL ENGR, SHELL OIL CO, LA, 70- *Res:* Production geology; paleoecology; geochemistry; stratigraphy. *Mailing Add:* Prod Dept Shell Oil Co PO Box 61555 New Orleans LA 70160

PARKER, CAROL ELAINE GREENBERG, b Fayetteville, NC, Dec 25, 47; m 72. ANALYTICAL CHEMISTRY, MASS SPECTROMETRY. *Educ:* Cornell Univ, BA, 69; Univ NC, Chapel Hill, MS, 73, PhD(chem), 77. *Prof Exp:* Res technician chem, Div Environ Sci & Eng, Univ NC, Chapel Hill, 73-76; vis assoc, 76-77, RES CHEMIST, NAT INST ENVIRON HEALTH SCI, 77- *Concurrent Pos:* Res assoc, Dept Plant Sci, NC A&T State Univ, 76- *Mem:* Am Soc Mass Spectrometry; Am Chem Soc; Am Soc Agron. *Res:* Application of analytical chemistry, especially gas chromatography; mass spectrometry to problems in the analysis of biological and/or environmental materials. *Mailing Add:* Rte 3 Box 232 Apex NC 27502

PARKER, CHARLES D, b Missoula, Mont, Aug 22, 24; m 49; c 3. AUDIOLOGY. *Educ:* Mont State Univ, BA, 49; Univ Iowa, MA, 52, PhD, 53. *Prof Exp:* Assoc prof, 58-66, PROF SPEECH PATH & AUDIOL & CHMN DEPT, UNIV MONT, 66-, DIR SPEECH & HEARING CLIN, 57- *Concurrent Pos:* Adv, US Dept Army, 53-54. *Mem:* Acoust Soc Am; Am Speech & Hearing Asn. *Res:* Speech pathology; psychoacoustics. *Mailing Add:* Dept of Speech Path & Audiol Univ of Montana Missoula MT 59812

PARKER, CHARLES J, JR, b Tonawanda, NY, Apr 3, 30. BIOCHEMISTRY. *Educ:* Univ Buffalo, BA, 51, MA, 56, PhD, 58. *Prof Exp:* Mem fac, 60-70, ASSOC PROF BIOCHEM, COL MED, WAYNE STATE UNIV, 70- *Concurrent Pos:* Res fel med, Retina Found, Mass Gen Hosp, 58-60. *Mem:* AAAS; Am Chem Soc. *Res:* Muscle biochemistry. *Mailing Add:* Dept of Biochem Wayne State Univ Col of Med Detroit MI 48202

PARKER, CHARLES W, b St Louis, Mo, Mar 23, 30; m 53; c 5. INTERNAL MEDICINE, IMMUNOLOGY. *Educ:* Wash Univ, MD, 53. *Prof Exp:* Instr, 60, from asst prof to assoc prof, 63-66, PROF MED, SCH MED, WASH UNIV, 66- *Concurrent Pos:* Allergy Found fel, Sch Med, Wash Univ, 59-61, USPHS res fel, 61-62; USPHS res & training grants, 62-, assoc prof microbiol, 73-76, dir div immunol, 62-76. *Mem:* Am Soc Clin Invest; Am Acad Allergy; Am Asn Immunol. *Res:* Human penicillin allergy; immunochemistry. *Mailing Add:* Dept of Int Med Sch of Med Wash Univ 660 South Euclid St Louis MO 63130

PARKER, CLEOFUS VARREN, JR, b Houston, Tex, Dec 20, 37; m 61; c 2. RADIATION PHYSICS. *Educ:* Sam Houston State Univ, BA, 61, MS, 62; Univ Tex, Austin, PhD(physics), 69. *Prof Exp:* Instr physics, Sam Houston State Univ, 62-63; res scientist, Tex Nuclear Div, Nuclear-Chicago Corp, 63-68, proj leader, 68-69; assoc prof, 69-74, head dept, 74-76, PROF PHYSICS, ANGELO STATE UNIV, 74- *Mem:* Am Asn Physics Teachers; Sigma Xi. *Res:* Dosimetry techniques for simulated solar proton radiation; thermoluminescent dosimetry; neutron activation analysis; fast neutron cross section measurements; electron spin resonance; computer techniques; microcomputer applications. *Mailing Add:* Dept of Physics Angelo State Univ San Angelo TX 76901

PARKER, CURTIS LLOYD, b Floyd Co, Va, Mar 28, 42; m 64; c 2. CELL BIOLOGY. *Educ:* Knoxville Col, BS, 65; Univ Tenn, PhD(zool), 73. *Prof Exp:* Res assoc biol, Oak Ridge Nat Lab, 65-68, fel develop biochem, Biol Div, 73-75; ASST PROF ANAT, BOWMAN GRAY SCH MED, 75- *Concurrent Pos:* Fel, Univ Tenn, 68-71, Southern Fund fel, 72-73. *Mem:* Tissue Cult Asn. *Res:* Leukemia research, cell biology and developmental biology differentiation; regulation of tissue specific proteins, cell and tissue culture. *Mailing Add:* Bowman Gray Sch Med Wake Forest Univ Winston-Salem NC 27103

PARKER, DAVID GARLAND, b Washington, DC, Nov 6, 40; m 64; c 2. ENVIRONMENTAL & CIVIL ENGINEERING. *Educ:* Va Polytech Inst & State Univ, BS, 65, MS, 68, PhD(civil eng), 71. *Prof Exp:* Instr eng technol, Roanoke Tech Inst, 65-66; asst prof, Wytheville Community Col, 67-69; asst prof civil eng, Lamar Univ, 71-72; asst prof, 72-81, PROF CIVIL ENG, UNIV ARK, FAYETTEVILLE, 81- *Concurrent Pos:* Wastewater consult, Mobil Oil Co, 71-72. *Mem:* Am Soc Civil Engrs; Water Pollution Control Fedn; Am Soc Eng Educ. *Res:* Wastewater treatment; sludge treatment; solid waste disposal; water treatment. *Mailing Add:* Dept of Civil Eng Univ of Ark Fayetteville AR 72701

PARKER, DON EARL, b Gainesville, Tex, Aug 31, 32; m 61; c 2. APPLIED STATISTICS. *Educ:* NTex State Univ, BA, 57, MA, 60; Univ Okla, PhD(biostatist), 70. *Prof Exp:* Asst prof math, Austin Col, 60-64; asst prof, 69-74, assoc prof, 74-77, PROF BIOSTATIST, OKLA HEALTH SCI CTR, 77- *Concurrent Pos:* Statist Consult, Okla Med Res Found, 75- & FAA, 73- *Mem:* Am Statist Asn; Am Public Health Asn. *Res:* Application of statistical techniques to biological and medical research problems & development of computer techniques for these applications. *Mailing Add:* Biostatist Dept Okla Health Sci Ctr 616 NE 15th Oklahoma City OK 73104

PARKER, DON TIMOTHY, bacteriology, see previous edition

PARKER, DONAL C, b Pittsburgh, Pa, Aug 13, 31; m 56; c 1. ENDOCRINOLOGY, INTERNAL MEDICINE. *Educ:* Univ Pittsburgh, BS, 53, MD, 57. *Prof Exp:* Intern, Cleveland Clin Educ Found, 57-58, from resident to sr resident, 61-63, chief resident internal med, 63-64; assoc endocrinol, Scripps Clin & Res Found, 67-72, assoc mem, 72-73; clin investr, 73-76, STAFF PHYSICIAN, SAN DIEGO VET ADMIN MED CTR, 76- *Concurrent Pos:* Spec fel endocrinol & metab, Cleveland Clin, 64-65; res trainee endocrinol, Scripps Clin & Res Found, 65-67; asst adj prof med, Sch Med, Univ Calif, San Diego, 69-72, asst prof med-in-residence, 73-75, assoc adj prof med, 75-79, clin prof med, 79- *Mem:* Asn Psychophysiol Study Sleep; Am Fedn Clin Res; Endocrine Soc; Int Soc Chronobiol. *Res:* Neuroendocrine control mechanisms; pituitary peptide hormone release; hormone release across the sleep-wake cycle; biologic rhythms. *Mailing Add:* San Diego Vet Admin Hosp Rm 6051 3350 La Jolla Village Dr San Diego CA 92161

PARKER, DONALD LESTER, b Mobile, Ala, Dec 19, 44. ELEMENTARY PARTICLE PHYSICS. *Educ:* Spring Hill Col, BS, 66; Mich State Univ, PhD(physics), 71. *Prof Exp:* Res assoc. Mich State Univ, 72-75, instr, 74-75; ASST PROF PHYSICS, IOWA STATE UNIV, 75- *Mem:* Am Phys Soc; AAAS; Fedn Am Scientists. *Res:* Experimental elementary particle research; studies of the strong force and hadronic states of matter. *Mailing Add:* Dept of Physics Iowa State Univ Ames IA 50011

PARKER, DOROTHY LUNDQUIST, b Webster, SDak, Sept 13, 39; m 71. VIROLOGY. *Educ:* Univ SDak, BA, 61; Univ Calif, Berkeley, MA, 64, PhD(molecular biol), 71. *Prof Exp:* Res technician molecular biol, Virus Lab, Univ Calif, Berkeley, 64-66; asst prof, 71-76, ASSOC PROF BIOL, HALSEY SCI CTR, UNIV WIS-OSHKOSH, 77- *Mem:* Sigma Xi; Am Soc Microbiol; AAAS. *Res:* Biology of blue-green algae, cyanobacteria; isolation and characterization of viruses, cyanophages, infecting blue-green algae. *Mailing Add:* Dept Biol Halsey Sci Ctr Univ of Wis Oshkosh WI 54901

PARKER, E(RNEST) T(ILDEN), b Royal Oak, Mich, July 26, 26; m 55; c 1. MATHEMATICS. *Educ:* Northwestern Univ, BA, 47; Ohio State Univ, PhD(math), 57. *Prof Exp:* Res assoc math, Ohio State Univ, 57; instr, Univ Mich, 57-58; prin mathematician, Univac Div, Sperry Rand Corp, Minn, 58-64; assoc prof, 64-68, PROF MATH, UNIV ILL, URBANA, 68- *Concurrent Pos:* Lectr, Univ Minn, 60-62. *Mem:* Am Math Soc. *Res:* Orthogonal Latin squares and finite projective planes; finite groups and graphs; application of digital computers. *Mailing Add:* Dept of Math Univ of Ill Urbana IL 61801

PARKER, EARL ELMER, b Malvern, Ark, Sept 22, 18; m 41; c 2. ORGANIC POLYMER CHEMISTRY. *Educ:* Miss State Col, BS, 40; Ind Univ, PhD(chem), 43. *Prof Exp:* Res chemist, PPG Industs Inc, 43-50, res supvr, 50-54, dept head, 54-58, res assoc, 58-63, sr res assoc, 64-65, scientist, 65-81; RETIRED. *Mem:* AAAS; Am Chem Soc. *Res:* Synthesis of amino acids; polyester resins; oil bodying catalysts; polyurethanes; epoxy resins; surface coatings; unsaturated polyester resins. *Mailing Add:* 411 Stonham Dr Sun City Center FL 33570

PARKER, EARL RANDALL, b Denver, Colo, Nov 22, 12; m 35; c 3. PHYSICAL METALLURGY. *Educ:* Colo Sch Mines, MetE, 35. *Prof Exp:* Res metallurgist, Res Lab, Gen Elec Co, 35-44; assoc prof phys metall, 44-50, chmn div mat sci & engr, 53-57, dir inst eng res, 57-64, PROF PHYS METALL, UNIV CALIF, BERKELEY, 50- *Concurrent Pos:* Guggenheim fel, 60. *Honors & Awards:* Mathewson Gold Medal, Am Inst Mining, Metall & Petrol Engrs, 56; Sauveur Award, Am Soc Metals, 64, Gold Medal, 72; Sch Mines Distinguished Achievement Medal, 66; Bendix Gold Medal, Am Soc Eng Educ, 69. *Mem:* Nat Acad Eng; fel Am Soc Metals (pres, 68); fel Am Inst Mining, Metall & Petrol Engrs; fel Am Phys Soc; Am Soc Eng Educ. *Res:* Mechanical behavior of materials. *Mailing Add:* Dept of Mat Sci & Eng Mining Bldg Univ of Calif Berkeley CA 94720

PARKER, EDWARD MINTER, b West Point, NY, June 19, 09; m 35; c 2. OPERATIONS RESEARCH, ENGINEERING. *Educ:* US Mil Acad, BS, 31; Oxford Univ, BA & MA, 34; Princeton Univ, MS, 37. *Prof Exp:* From asst prof to assoc prof eng, State Univ Iowa, 46-49; sr analyst, Opers Res Off, Johns Hopkins Univ, 49-62 & Inst Defense Analyses, 62-65; independent consult opers res, 65-74; RETIRED. *Mailing Add:* 2610 44th St NW Washington DC 20007

PARKER, EUGENE NEWMAN, b Houghton, Mich, June 10, 27; m 54; c 2. ASTROPHYSICS. *Educ:* Mich State Col, BS, 48; Calif Inst Technol, PhD(physics), 51. *Prof Exp:* Instr math & astron, Univ Utah, 51-53, asst prof physics, 53-55; res assoc, 55-57, from asst prof to assoc prof, 57-62, PROF PHYSICS, ENRICO FERMI INST, UNIV CHICAGO, 62-, PROF ASTRON, 67- *Mem:* Nat Acad Sci; Am Phys Soc; Am Astron Soc; Am Geophys Union. *Res:* Theoretical plasma physics; magnetohydrodynamics; solar and terrestrial physics. *Mailing Add:* Lab Astrophys & Space Res Enrico Fermi Inst Univ Chicago Chicago IL 60637

PARKER, EVERETTE FRANCIS, accelerator physics, see previous edition

PARKER, FRANCES LAWRENCE, b Brookline, Mass, Mar 28, 06. MICROPALEONTOLOGY. *Educ:* Vassar Col, AB, 28; Mass Inst Technol, MS, 30. *Prof Exp:* Res asst, Cushman Lab, 30-40; sr paleontologist, Shell Oil Co, 43-45; mem staff micropaleont, Woods Hole Oceanog Inst, 47-50; from asst res geologist to assoc res geologist, 50-66, res paleontologist, 66-73, RES ASSOC, SCRIPPS INST OCEANOG, UNIV CALIF, SAN DIEGO, 73- *Concurrent Pos:* Fel, Woods Hole Oceanog Inst, 37-40; dir & hon fel, Cushman Found Foraminiferal Res, 64- *Honors & Awards:* Joseph A Cushman Award. *Mem:* Paleont Res Inst. *Res:* Fossil and recent foraminifera; stratigraphic and ecological studies. *Mailing Add:* Scripps Inst of Oceanog Univ of Calif at San Diego La Jolla CA 92093

PARKER, FRANCIS DUNBAR, b Boston, Mass, July 27, 18; m 42; c 4. APPLIED MATHEMATICS. *Educ:* Middlebury Col, AB, 39; Boston Univ, AM, 42; Case Inst Technol, PhD(math), 51. *Prof Exp:* Instr, Cranbrook Sch, 39-40; instr math, Staunton Mil Acad, 40-41 & Montclair Acad, 41-42; mem staff, Radiation Lab, Mass Inst Technol, 42-45; instr math, Case Inst Technol, 45-51; asst prof, St Lawrence Univ, 51-53; from assoc prof to prof, Clarkson Col Technol, 53-57; prof & head dept, Univ Alaska, 57-63, chmn div sci & math, 58-61; prof math & exec off dept, State Univ NY Buffalo, 63-66; PROF MATH, ST LAWRENCE UNIV, 66- *Concurrent Pos:* Vis prof, Univ Aberdeen, Scotland, 73, Univ York, Eng, 74, Calif State Univ, Los Angeles, 75, 77-78 & 81-82 & Plymouth Polytech, Eng, 78-79. *Mem:* Soc Indust & Appl Math; Am Math Soc; Math Asn Am. *Res:* Microwave propagation; radar antenna design; graph theory. *Mailing Add:* Dept Math St Lawrence Univ Canton NY 13617

PARKER, FRANK L, b Somerville, Mass, Mar 23, 26; m 54; c 4. HYDROLOGY & WATER RESOURCES. *Educ:* Mass Inst Technol, SB, 48; Harvard Univ, PhD(civil eng), 55. *Prof Exp:* Engr, US Bur Reclamation, 48; civil engr, Rockland Light & Power Co, NY, 49; res assoc, Harvard Univ, 50-55; consult hydraul engr, Howard M Turner, Mass, 55; eng leader, Oak Ridge Nat Lab, 56-60, sect chief radioactive waste disposal, 62-67; assoc prof environ & water resources eng, 67-68, PROF ENVIRON & WATER RESOURCES ENG, VANDERBILT UNIV, 68- *Concurrent Pos:* Mem, Int Atomic Energy Agency, Austria, 61; assoc prof, Univ Tenn; vis lectr, Vanderbilt Univ; consult, Ital, Pakistan & Israeli AEC; lectr, UK Atomic Energy Authority; chmn comt waste isolation pilot plant, Nat Acad Sci, 69, mem bd radioactive waste mgt, 78-; consult, WHO, 68-; mem panel water qual, UNESCO, 69; mem adv comt reactor safeguards, Nat Res Coun, 75-, Dept Energy, 79-, Battelle Mem Inst, 79- *Mem:* AAAS; Am Soc Civil Engrs; Health Physics Soc; Am Geophys Union; Am Nuclear Soc. *Res:* Geological and environmental radioactive waste disposal; water resources; thermal pollution; environmental effects of energy production; sanitary and environmental engineering. *Mailing Add:* Dept of Environ & Water Resources Eng Vanderbilt Univ Nashville TN 37235

PARKER, FRANK S, b Boston, Mass, Jan 25, 21; m 46; c 2. BIOCHEMISTRY, SPECTROCHEMISTRY. *Educ:* Tufts Col, BS, 42, MS, 44; Johns Hopkins Univ, PhD(chem), 50. *Prof Exp:* Asst chem, Tufts Col, 42-44; jr instr, Johns Hopkins Univ, 46-50; asst prof biol, Bryn Mawr Col, 50-54; from asst prof to assoc prof, State Univ NY Downstate Med Ctr, 54-63; assoc prof, 63-70, PROF BIOCHEM, NEW YORK MED COL, 70- *Concurrent Pos:* Career scientist, Health Res Coun New York, 63-69. *Mem:* AAAS; Am Chem Soc; Am Soc Biol Chemists; Coblentz Soc; Soc Appl Spectros. *Res:* Infrared studies with enzymes, amino acids, peptides and carbohydrates; aqueous solution infrared spectroscopy; attenuated total reflectance spectroscopy; binding studies of drugs with biological materials; hydrogen bonding studies; biophysics; analytical chemistry. *Mailing Add:* New York Med Col Dept of Biochem Basic Sci Bldg Valhalla NY 10595

PARKER, GEORGE ANTHONY, b Tarentum, Pa, June 24, 36. CHEMISTRY. *Educ:* Carnegie-Mellon Univ, BS, 58; Pa State Univ, PhD(org chem), 63. *Prof Exp:* Fel silicones, 63-66, coal chem, 66-67, FEL METAL OXIDES, MELLON INST SCI, 67- *Mem:* AAAS; Am Chem Soc; Am Inst Chemists; Electrochem Soc; Sigma Xi. *Res:* Metal oxides; battery chemistry; organometallics. *Mailing Add:* Mellon Inst of Sci 4400 Fifth Ave Pittsburgh PA 15213

PARKER, GEORGE RALPH, b Tulsa, Okla, Sept 16, 42; m 65; c 2. ECOLOGY, FORESTRY. *Educ:* Okla State Univ, BS, 64, MS, 67; Mich State Univ, PhD(forest ecol), 70. *Prof Exp:* ASST PROF FOREST ECOL, PURDUE UNIV, LAFAYETTE, 70- *Mem:* Ecol Soc Am; Soc Am Foresters. *Res:* Structure and functioning of forested ecosystems. *Mailing Add:* Dept of Forestry & Nat Resource Purdue Univ West Lafayette IN 47907

PARKER, GEORGE W, b Ft Worth, Tex, May 23, 39; m 67; c 1. NUCLEAR MAGNETIC RESONANCE. *Educ:* Univ of the South, BA, 61; Univ SC, PhD(physics), 65. *Prof Exp:* From instr to asst prof, 65-75, ASSOC PROF PHYSICS, NC STATE UNIV, 75- *Mem:* Am Phys Soc; Am Asn Physics Teachers. *Res:* Nuclear magentic resonance lineshapes in solids; calculation of magnetic susceptibilities and chemical shielding constants. *Mailing Add:* Dept of Physics PO Box 5367 NC State Univ Raleigh NC 27607

PARKER, GORDON ARTHUR, b Monroe, Mich, July 6, 36; m 62. ANALYTICAL CHEMISTRY. *Educ:* Univ Mich, BS, 58; Wayne State Univ, MS, 62, PhD(anal chem), 66. *Prof Exp:* From instr to asst prof, 65-73, ASSOC PROF CHEM, UNIV TOLEDO, 73- *Mem:* Am Chem Soc; Soc Appl Spectros; Soc Col Sci Teachers. *Res:* Spectrophotometric and polarographic analysis. *Mailing Add:* Dept of Chem Univ of Toledo Toledo OH 43606

PARKER, H DENNISON, b Lake Wales, Fla, June 20, 41; m 61; c 2. ENVIRONMENTAL PUBLIC RELATIONS. *Educ:* Colo State Univ, BS, 68, PhD(range ecol), 72. *Prof Exp:* Prin scientist ecol remote sensing, Lockheed Electronics Co, NASA, Houston, 72-73; staff ecologist synthetic fuels develop, Cameran Engrs, Denver, 73-74; mgr ecosystems analysis, Western Sci Serv, Colo, 74-76; remote sensing specialist, US Fish & Wildlife Serv, 76-78, leader, Data Systs Group, Western Energy Team, 78-80; PRES, PARKER SCI, INC, 80- *Mem:* Am Soc Photogram; Sigma Xi; AAAS. *Res:* Application of remote sensing to wildlife census; habitat inventory; maping and analysis. *Mailing Add:* Parker Sci Inc 333 W Drake Rd S-30 Ft Collins CO 80526

PARKER, HAROLD R, b Los Angeles, Calif, Jan 10, 20; m 49; c 5. RENAL PHYSIOLOGY, ANESTHESIOLOGY/SURGERY. *Educ:* Univ Calif, Davis, BS, 50, DVM, 52, PhD(comp path), 61. *Prof Exp:* Res assoc radiobiol, 56-58, res assoc physiol, 58-61, asst prof, 61-67, assoc prof physiol, 67-78, PROF SURG, UNIV CALIF, DAVIS, 78- *Concurrent Pos:* Sacramento-Yolo-Sierra Heart Asn fel, 68-69. *Mem:* AAAS; Am Physiol Soc; Am Soc Vet Physiol & Pharmacol; Am Heart Asn. *Res:* Renal function, fluid and electrolyte balance in domestic animals; intensive care medicine, especially renal failure, hemofiltration, hemo and peritoneal dialysis; experimental surgery. *Mailing Add:* Dept of Surg Univ of Calif Sch of Vet Med Davis CA 95616

PARKER, HARRY W(ILLIAM), b Tulia, Tex, June 4, 32; m 54; c 2. CHEMICAL ENGINEERING. *Educ:* Tex Technol Col, BS, 53; Northwestern Univ, MS, 54, PhD(chem eng), 56. *Prof Exp:* Theoret develop engr, Phillips Petrol Co, 56-62, res group leader, 62-70; assoc prof chem eng, Tex Tech Univ, 70-77, prof, 77-79; Engr, Eng Soc Comn Energy, 79-81; PROF CHEM ENG, TEX TECH UNIV, 81- *Mem:* Soc Petrol Engrs; Am Inst Chem Engrs. *Res:* Economics and pilot plant operation regarding thermochemical conversion of biomass to energy and animal feeds; enhanced oil recovery and flow through porous media; in situ oil shale retorting. *Mailing Add:* Dept Chem Eng Tex Tech Univ Lubbock TX 79409

PARKER, HELEN MEISTER, b Chicago, Ill, July 17, 35; m 55; c 1. PHYSICAL BIOCHEMISTRY, NUTRITION. *Educ:* Ohio State Univ, BSc, 56, MSc, 57; Univ Minn, PhD(phys chem), 67. *Prof Exp:* Res assoc biochem, 67-70, RES ASSOC ANIMAL SCI, UNIV ILL, URBANA, 70- *Res:* Protein physical chemistry; enzyme structure and function; mineral metabolism; parathyroid function; mineral bioavailability. *Mailing Add:* 124 Animal Sci Lab Univ Ill 1207 W Gregory Dr Urbana IL 61801

PARKER, HENRY SEABURY, III, b Newport, RI, Apr 19, 44; m 70; c 2. PHYCOLOGY, AQUACULTURE. *Educ:* Harvard Univ, BA, 66; Univ RI, MA, 71, PhD(biol oceanog), 79. *Prof Exp:* Mgr aquaculture, Marine Colloids Div, FMC Corp, 71-73; vis lectr aquaculture, 79-80, ASST PROF AQUACULTURE & BIOL, BIOL DEPT, SOUTHEASTERN MASS UNIV, 80- *Concurrent Pos:* Consult, Nat Alcohol Fuels Comn, 78-80 & Nonquitt Asn, 80-; NSF co-prin investr, Coastal & Estuarine Marine Biol Pre-Col Sch Teachers, 80-; chmn res comt & bd mem, Lloyd Environ Ctr Coastal & Estuarine Studies. *Mem:* Am Soc Limnol & Oceanog; Phycol Soc Am; Nat Shellfisheries Asn; Int Phycol Soc; AAAS. *Res:* Physiological ecology of marine macroalgae, particularly interacting effects of nutrients, light and water motion on growth and nitrogen metabolism; cultivation of macroalgae. *Mailing Add:* Biol Dept Southeastern Mass Univ North Dartmouth MA 02747

PARKER, HENRY WHIPPLE, b Concord, NH, May 31, 24; m 52; c 4. CIVIL ENGINEERING. *Educ:* Dartmouth Col, BS, 45, MS, 47. *Prof Exp:* Estimating engr, Winston Bros & Co, W Coast, 47-50, estimator, Off Engr Supt, Colombia, 52-56, asst proj mgr construct, Calif, 59-60, proj engr, 60-62, proj engr, Atlas-Winston Ltd, Que, 56-69; assoc prof civil eng, 62-72, PROF CIVIL ENG, STANFORD UNIV, 72- *Mem:* Am Soc Civil Engrs; Am Soc Eng Educ. *Res:* Construction management research; methods improvement techniques; human resources management. *Mailing Add:* Dept of Civil Eng Stanford Univ Stanford CA 94305

PARKER, HERBERT EDMUND, b Springville, Tenn, Oct 21, 19; m 45; c 3. BIOCHEMISTRY. *Educ:* Univ Tenn, BSA, 42; Purdue Univ, MS, 48, PhD(biochem), 50. *Prof Exp:* From asst prof to assoc prof, 50-65, PROF BIOCHEM, PURDUE UNIV, LAFAYETTE, 65-, ASST HEAD DEPT, 77- *Mem:* Am Inst Nutrit; Am Soc Biol Chem. *Res:* Mineral metabolism; inorganic nutrition of plants and animals. *Mailing Add:* Dept of Biochem Purdue Univ West Lafayette IN 47907

PARKER, HERBERT MYERS, b Accrington, Eng, Apr 13, 10; m 36; c 4. HEALTH PHYSICS. *Educ:* Univ Manchester, BSc, 30, MSc, 31. *Prof Exp:* Physicist, Christie Hosp & Holt Radium Inst, Manchester, 32-38 & Swedish Hosp, Seattle, Wash, 38-42; health physicist, Metall Lab, Univ Chicago, 42-43; sect chief, Clinton Labs, Tenn, 43-44; chief supvr, Hanford Works, 44-48, supt, Health Instruments, 48-51, dir radiol sci, 51-56, mgr Hanford Labs, 56-65, staff consult, Pac Northwest Labs, Battelle Mem Inst, 65-71; PRES, HMP ASSOCS, 71- *Concurrent Pos:* Asst prof radiol, Univ Wash, 52-62; mem, Nat Coun Radiation Protection & Measurements, 64-; chmn tech electronic prods radiation safety standards cmn, 69-73. *Honors & Awards:* Janeway Medal, 55; W D Cooledge Award, Am Asn Physicists Med, 79. *Mem:* Nat Acad Eng; Am Radium Soc; Am Nuclear Soc; Am Asn Physicists Med; Health Physics Soc. *Res:* Environmental science; development of radiation exposure standards. *Mailing Add:* 2030 Harris Ave Richland WA 99352

PARKER, HOWARD ASHLEY, JR, b Tulsa, Okla, Dec 26, 21; m 50; c 4. CHEMICAL ENGINEERING. *Educ:* Cornell Univ, BChE, 44. *Prof Exp:* Process design engr, 44746, group leader, Process Design Sect, 46-51, tech dir, Destrehan Refining, Pan-Am Southern Corp, 51-56, asst mgr opers, Mfg Dept, Am Oil Co, 56-57, asst to gen mgr mfg, 57-59, mgr coord & supply planning, 59-62, admin mgr, Atlanta Region, Mkt Dept, 62-63, regional mgr, Kansas City Region, 63-65, mgr reseller mkt, Gen Off, 65-68, gen mgr mkt staff serv, 68-70, gen mgr com mkt, Am Oil Co, 70-74, PRES, CED & DIR, AMOCO PIPELINE CO, STANDARD OIL CO, IND, 74- *Concurrent Pos:* Dir, Atlas Supply Co, 65-68; exec vpres, Harvam Corp, 65-68; pres, Tempo Designs, Inc, 68-70, pres, Amoco Enterprises, Inc, 68-70 & Apex Terminals, Inc, 70-74; dir, Asphalt Inst, 70-74, Colonial Pipeline Co, 74- & Chicago Pipeline Co, 76-; pres & dir, Dixie Pipeline Co, 78- & Frontier Pipeline Co, 81- *Mem:* Am Inst Chem Engrs; Am Petrol Inst; Asn Oil Pipelines. *Res:* Plant design. *Mailing Add:* 1017 Rolling Pass Glenview IL 60025

PARKER, JACK LINDSAY, b Springville, Utah, June 15, 30; m; c 8. NUCLEAR PHYSICS, COSMIC RAY PHYSICS. *Educ:* Brigham Young Univ, BS, 55, MS, 56; Univ Utah, PhD(physics), 67. *Prof Exp:* Physicist, Wright Air Develop Ctr, 58-60; STAFF MEM, LOS ALAMOS SCI LAB, UNIV CALIF, 67- *Res:* Low energy nuclear physics; gamma ray spectroscopy. *Mailing Add:* Los Alamos Sci Lab Los Alamos NM 87544

PARKER, JACK STEELE, b Palo Alto, Calif, July 6, 18; m 46; c 1. AERONAUTICAL ENGINEERING. *Educ:* Leland Stanford Jr Univ, BS, 39. *Hon Degrees:* MBA, Southeastern Mass Univ; LLB, Clark Univ. *Prof Exp:* Mech engr, Western Pipe & Steel Co Calif, San Francisco, 39-40; marine survr, Am Bur Shipping, Seattle, 40-42; asst gen supt, Todd Shipyards, Inc, Houston, 42-44, gen supt outfitting, San Pedro, Calif, 44-46; asst chief engr, Am Potash & Chem Co, Trona, Calif, 46-50; asst mgr design & construct, Gen Elec Co, Richland, Wash, 50-52, opers mgr aircraft nuclear propulsion proj, Cincinnati, 52-53, gen mgr small aircraft engine dept, Lynn, Mass, 53-54, gen mgr aircraft gas turbine div, Cincinnati, 55-57, vpres rels serv, Exec Off, 57-61, vpres & group exec aerospace & defense, 61-68, exec vpres, 68, vchmn bd & exec officer, 68-80- *Concurrent Pos:* Trustee, St Louis Univ, 67-69 & Rensselaer Polytech Inst; chmn conf bd, Grand Central Art Galleries, 72-74; chmn bd overseers, Hoover Inst, 73-76; chmn adv coun, Grad Sch Bus, Stanford Univ. *Mem:* Nat Acad Eng; assoc fel Royal Aeronaut Soc; fel Am Inst Aeronaut & Astronaut; Soc Automotive Engrs; Aerospace Industs Asn. *Mailing Add:* Gen Elec Co 3135 Easton Turnpike Fairfield CT 06431

PARKER, JAMES EVANS, b Memphis, Tenn, July 9, 28; m 57; c 2. PHYSICS. *Educ:* Mich State Univ, BS, 56, PhD(physics), 63. *Prof Exp:* Mem staff, Bellcomm, Inc, DC, 62-66; phys scientist, US Govt, 66-73; proj mgr, Systs Consults Inc, DC, 73-81; MEM STAFF, MITRE CORP, 81- *Mem:* Am Inst Aeronaut & Astronaut; Inst Elec & Electronics Engrs. *Res:* High energy nuclear particle physics; systems engineering for Apollo Project. *Mailing Add:* 8205 Hamilton Spring Ct Bethesda MD 20034

PARKER, JAMES HENRY, JR, b Bakersfield, Calif, Dec 4, 26; m 48; c 2. CRYOGENICS. *Educ:* Univ Calif, AB, 48, PhD(physics), 54. *Prof Exp:* Asst, Univ Calif, 49-53; physicist, 53-70, RES ADMIN STAFF, RES LABS, WESTINGHOUSE ELEC CORP, 70- *Mem:* Fel Am Phys Soc; Inst Elec & Electronic Engrs. *Res:* Optical properties solids; electron motion in gases; ultrasonics; low temperature physics. *Mailing Add:* Westinghouse Res & Develop Ctr 1310 Beulah Rd Pittsburgh PA 15235

PARKER, JAMES WILLARD, b Richmond, Ind, Feb 24, 45; m 68; c 2. ORNITHOLOGY, ECOLOGY. *Educ:* Earlham Col, AB, 67; Univ Kans, PhD(biol), 74. *Prof Exp:* Curatorial asst birds, Mus Natural Hist, Univ Kans, 72-73; teaching asst biol, Ohio Wesleyan Univ, 73-74, vis asst prof zool, 74-75; asst prof biol, Wilmington Col, 75-76; asst prof biol, State Univ NY, Fredonia, 76-81; ASST PROF BIOL, UNIV MAINE, FARMINGTON, 81- *Mem:* Am Ornithologists Union; Ecol Soc Am; Am Inst Biol Sci. *Res:* General and vertebrate ecology and evolution with emphasis on the population biology and reproductive strategies of birds. *Mailing Add:* Dept Biol Univ Maine Farmington ME 04938

PARKER, JANET LEA, b Santa Monica, Calif, Aug 27, 47; m 80. CARDIOVASCULAR PHYSIOLOGY, PHARMACOLOGY. *Educ:* NTex State Univ, BS, 69; Mich State Univ, MS, 72, PhD(physiol), 75. *Prof Exp:* Res asst biol, NTex State Univ, 65-70, lab instr, 68-70; res assoc cardiol, Methodist Hosp & Univ Tex Southwestern Med Sch Dallas, 74, fel cardiovasc pharmacol, 77-78, ASST PROF PHARMACOL, UNIV TEX HEALTH SCI CTR, DALLAS, 78- *Concurrent Pos:* NIH fel; mem, Am Heart Asn. *Mem:* Am Fedn Clin Res; Shock Soc. *Res:* Cardiovascular aspects of shock; cerebral circulation, cardiovascular and myocardial depressant activity of anesthetics and antibiotics in control and pathological conditions; cellular mechanisms of myocardial function and dysfunction; cellular mechanisms of action of cardiac drugs and altered drug reactivity. *Mailing Add:* Dept Pharmacol Univ Tex Health Sci Ctr Dallas TX 75235

PARKER, JERALD D, b Ardmore, Okla, Feb 24, 30; m 52; c 4. MECHANICAL ENGINEERING. *Educ:* Okla State Univ, BS, 55, MS, 57; Purdue Univ, PhD(mech eng), 61. *Prof Exp:* From instr to assoc prof, 55-66, PROF MECH ENG, OKLA STATE UNIV, 67- *Honors & Awards:* Year-in-Indust Prof Du Pont Co, 69-70. *Mem:* Am Soc Mech Engrs; Am Soc Heating, Refrig & Air-Conditioning Engrs; Am Nuclear Soc; Nat Soc Prof Engrs. *Res:* Heat transfer and fluid mechanics; solar energy; energy conversion and utilization; heating, ventilating and air-conditioning. *Mailing Add:* Sch Mech & Aerospace Eng Okla State Univ Stillwater OK 74078

PARKER, JERALD VAWER, b Portland, Ore, Mar 3, 39; m 63; c 2. PLASMA PHYSICS. *Educ:* Calif Inst Technol, BS, 60, PhD(physics), 64. *Prof Exp:* Mem staff, Electro-Optical Syst, Pasadena, 64-66, Bell Telephone Labs, 66-69, Hughes Res Lab, 69-75; assoc group leader, 75-78, MEM STAFF, LOS ALAMOS NAT LAB, 78- *Mem:* Am Phys Soc; Sr mem Inst Elec & Electronics Engrs; Sigma Xi. *Res:* Inertial fusion including gas laser development for laser inertial fusion and other novel power sources for heating and compressing plasmas. *Mailing Add:* 60 Loma Del Escolar Los Alamos NM 87544

PARKER, JESSE ELMER, b Wetumpka, Ala, Nov 23, 11; m 38; c 6. POULTRY HUSBANDRY. *Educ:* Univ Tenn, BS, 34; Univ Mo, AM, 36, PhD(animal physiol), 40. *Prof Exp:* Asst poultry husb, Univ Mo, 35-36, instr, 37-39; asst, La State Univ, 36-37; poultry husbandman, Exp Sta & instr animal & poultry husb, Univ Tenn, 39-44; prof poultry husb & head dept, NDak State Col, 44-46; head dept, 46-69, prof, 46-77, EMER PROF POULTRY SCI, ORE STATE UNIV, 77- *Mem:* Poultry Sci Asn; Am Poultry Asn. *Res:* Poultry science; reproduction in poultry; growth of chickens; management of poultry. *Mailing Add:* 642 Northwest 9th St Corvallis OR 97330

PARKER, JOHN ABEL, b Camden, NJ, Sept 1, 23; m 42; c 4. CHEMISTRY. *Educ:* Univ Pa, BA, 48, MS, 49, PhD(org chem), 51. *Prof Exp:* Instr anal chem, Univ Pa, 48-49; group leader org res, Res & Develop Ctr, Armstrong Cork Co, 51-59, mgr chem res unit, 59-62; CHIEF CHEM RES PROJ OFF, AMES RES CTR, NASA, 62- *Concurrent Pos:* Proj engr, Mat Lab, Wright Air Develop Ctr, 54-60 & Air Force Off Sci Res, 60-61. *Honors & Awards:* Outstanding Sci Achievement Medal, NASA, 68. *Mem:* Am Chem Soc; fel Am Inst Chem; NY Acad Sci; assoc fel, Am Inst Aeronaut & Astronaut. *Res:* Structure of colchicine molecule; reactions of polymethyoxy aromatics; polyester polymers; radiation chemistry; condensation polymers; materials science; chemical kinetics; high temperature materials. *Mailing Add:* 1300 McClure Lane Los Altos CA 94022

PARKER, JOHN HILLIARD, b Orlando, Fla, Sept 30, 41; m 67; c 2. PHYSICAL CHEMISTRY, ENVIRONMENTAL SCIENCES. *Educ:* Emory Univ, BS, 63; Univ Calif, Berkeley, PhD(phys chem), 69. *Prof Exp:* Actg instr natural sci, Univ Calif, Berkeley, 66-67; asst prof chem, Univ Col Cape Coast, Ghana, 69-71; asst prof chem, Kans State Univ, 71-72; asst prof, 72-73, assoc dean col arts & sci, 75-76, ASSOC PROF ENVIRON SCI & CHEM, FLA INT UNIV, 73- *Concurrent Pos:* Asst dir, FIU-FAU Joint Ctr Envrion & Urban Probs, 76- *Mem:* Am Chem Soc. *Res:* Molecular energy distribution in the products of exothermic reactions; analysis of indoor air pollution; chemical lasters; energy conservation. *Mailing Add:* Fla Int Univ Miami FL 33199

PARKER, JOHN MASON, III, b Owego, NY, Sept 6, 06; m 41; c 1. GEOLOGY. *Educ:* Cornell Univ, AB, 28, AM, 33, PhD(struct geol), 35. *Prof Exp:* From instr to asst prof geol, NC State Univ, 35-42; from asst geologist to assoc geologist, US Geol Surv, 42-46; from assoc prof to prof, 46-72, EMER PROF GEOL, NC STATE UNIV, 72- *Concurrent Pos:* Geologist, US Geol Surv, 46-61. *Mem:* Geol Soc Am; Am Inst Mining, Metall & Petrol Eng; Am Inst Prof Geol. *Res:* Paleozoic structure in central Appalachians; geology of pegmatites and crystalline rocks; regional systematic jointing in gently dipping sedimentary rocks; structural geology; petrology; economic geology of nonmetallic minerals. *Mailing Add:* 3113 Darien Dr Raleigh NC 27607

PARKER, JOHN ORVAL, b Millington, Mich, Nov 13, 30; Can citizen; m 55; c 4. CARDIOLOGY, CARDIOVASCULAR PHYSIOLOGY. *Educ:* Queen's Univ, Ont, MD & CM, 54, MSc, 58. *Prof Exp:* Lectr, 61-62, from asst prof to assoc prof, 62-71, PROF MED, QUEEN'S UNIV, ONT, 71-, DIR CARDIOPULMONARY LAB, 64-, CHMN DIV CARDIOL, 72- *Concurrent Pos:* Ont Heart Found fel, Queen's Univ, Ont, 61-, Med Res Coun Can med res grant, 68-; attend physician, Kingston Gen Hosp, 61-; consult, Can Forces Hosp, Kingston, 65- *Honors & Awards:* Medal in Med, Royal Col Physicians & Surgeons of Can, 61. *Mem:* Am Soc Clin Invest; Can Soc Clin Invest; Can Cardiovasc Soc; Am Col Cardiol; Am Col Physicians. *Res:* Hemodynamic and metabolic abnormalities in coronary artery disease. *Mailing Add:* Dept Med Queen's Univ Kingston ON K7L 3NG Can

PARKER, JOHN WILLIAM, b Clifton, Ariz, Jan 5, 31; m 57; c 4. EXPERIMENTAL PATHOLOGY. *Educ:* Univ Ariz, BS, 53; Harvard Med Sch, MD, 57; Am Bd Path, dipl anat & clin path, 62. *Prof Exp:* Intern med, Med Ctr, Univ Calif, San Francisco, 57-58, resident path, 58-60; resident, Vet Admin Hosp, San Francisco, 60-62, clin investr, 62, chief clin labs, 62-64; from asst prof to assoc prof, 64-75, PROF PATH, SCH MED, UNIV SOUTHERN CALIF, 75-, DIR CLIN LABS, 74- *Concurrent Pos:* Am Cancer Soc sr Dernham fel, Univ Southern Calif, 64-69, Nat Cancer Inst spec fel, 72-73; clin instr, Sch Med, Univ Calif, San Francisco, 62-64; attend physician, Los Angeles County-Univ Southern Calif Med Ctr, 64-; vis res fel, Walter & Eliza Hall Inst Med Res, Melbourne, Australia, 72-73; co-ed, Hematol Oncol. *Mem:* NY Acad Sci; Am Asn Pathologists; fel Col Am Path; Am Soc Clin Path. Int Acad Path. *Res:* Cellular immunology; mechanisms of lymphocyte transformation; hemopathology. *Mailing Add:* Dept of Path Sch of Med Univ of Southern Calif Los Angeles CA 90033

PARKER, JON IRVING, b Danville, Pa, Jan 1, 44; m 66; c 2. AQUATIC ECOLOGY, BIOLOGY. *Educ:* Bloomsburg State Col, BS, 65; Univ Idaho, MS, 72; Univ NH, PhD(bot), 74. *Prof Exp:* Teacher sci, Union Springs Cent Sch Dist, 65-69; mem staff acquatic res, Radiol & Environ Res Div, Argonne Nat Lab, 74-76, asst ecologist impact assessment, Environ Impact Systs Div, 76-77, asst ecologist aquatic res, Radiol & Environ Res Div, 77-81; ASST PROF, LEHIGH UNIV, 81- *Mem:* Am Soc Limnol & Oceanog; Sigma Xi; Int Asn Theoret & Appl Limnol; Int Asn Great Lakes Res. *Res:* Biogeochemical behavior of pollutants in aquatic ecosystems. *Mailing Add:* Biol Dept 31 Lehigh Univ Bethlehem PA 18015

PARKER, JOSEPH B, JR, b Knox Co, Tenn, July 8, 16; m 46; c 2. PSYCHIATRY. *Educ:* Univ Tenn, BS, 39, MD, 41. *Prof Exp:* Instr psychiat, Duke Univ, 48-49, assoc prof, 53-59; asst prof, Col Med, Univ Tenn, 49-53; prof & chmn dept, Med Ctr, Univ Ky, 59-70; PROF PSYCHIAT & COORDR CONTINUING EDUC, MED CTR, DUKE UNIV, 70- *Concurrent Pos:* Lectr, Sch Social Work, Vanderbilt Univ & Univ Tenn, 50-53; chief psychiat serv, Vet Admin Hosp, 53-59; consult, Vet Admin & USPHS Hosps; mem, Gov Adv Coun Ment Health. *Mem:* Soc Biol Psychiat; AMA; Am Psychopath Asn; Asn Res Nerv & Ment Dis; fel Am Psychiat Asn. *Res:* Affective diorders. *Mailing Add:* Box 3837 Duke Univ Durham NC 27710

PARKER, JOSEPH R(ICHARD), b Grand Island, Nebr, May 8, 16; m 48; c 4. ELECTRO-OPTICS, ELECTRONICS. *Educ:* Univ Nebr, BSc, 43; Univ Pa, MSc, 52. *Prof Exp:* Student engr, Radio Corp Am, 43-44, engr, 44-63; STAFF MEM, LOS ALAMOS SCI LAB, 63- *Mem:* Inst Elec & Electronics Engrs; Optical Soc Am; Laser Inst Am. *Res:* Environment near nuclear burst; rubidium vapor frequency standard; radiation dosimetry; extremely fast solid-state television camera; phonton limited electro-optics. *Mailing Add:* 333 Potrillo Dr Los Alamos NM 87544

PARKER, KATHLYN ANN, b Chicago, Ill, 45. SYNTHETIC ORGANIC CHEMISTRY. *Educ:* Northwestern Univ, BA, 66; Stanford Univ, PhD(org chem), 71. *Prof Exp:* Assoc chem, Columbia Univ, 71-73; ASST PROF CHEM, BROWN UNIV, 73- *Mem:* Am Chem Soc. *Res:* Development of synthetic methods and total synthesis of natural products. *Mailing Add:* Dept of Chem Brown Univ Providence RI 02912

PARKER, KEITH KROM, b Billings, Mont, Jan 24, 50; m 72; c 1. NEUROCHEMISTRY, NEUROPHARMACOLOGY. *Educ:* Mont State Univ, BS, 72; Univ Calif, San Francisco, PhD(pharmacol), 77. *Prof Exp:* Fel pharmacol, Health Sci Ctr, Univ Colo, 77-79; res assoc chem, Univ Denver, 79-81; ASST PROF CHEM, WESTERN MONT COL, 81- *Mem:* AAAS; Sigma Xi. *Res:* Effects of drugs and toxic agents in nerve cell culture and the developing nervous system. *Mailing Add:* Div Math & Sci Western Mont Col Dillon MT 59725

PARKER, KENNETH GARDNER, plant pathology, deceased

PARKER, KITTIE FENLEY, b Fouke, Ark, Dec 3, 10; m 32; c 1. TAXONOMY, BOTANY. *Educ:* Univ Calif, Berkeley, AB, 30, MA, 32; Univ Ariz, PhD(bot), 46. *Prof Exp:* From instr to asst prof bot, Univ Ariz, 47-53; assoc prof lectr taxon, 57-64, assoc prof, 64-73, prof bot, 73-80, EMER PROF BIOL, GEORGE WASHINGTON UNIV, 80- *Concurrent Pos:* Res assoc, Dept Bot, Smithsonian Inst, 62- *Mem:* Int Asn Plant Taxonomists; Am Soc Plant Taxonomists; Asn Trop Biol; Am Inst Biol Sci. *Res:* Compositae of western United States in tribe helenieae, especially genera Hymenoxys and Pectis; flora, particularly weeds of Arizona. *Mailing Add:* Dept Biol Sci George Washington Univ Washington DC 20052

PARKER, LEE WARD, b Fall River, Mass, Sept 28, 23. MATHEMATICAL PHYSICS. *Educ:* NY Univ, BEE, 47; Univ Southern Calif, PhD(physics), 53. *Prof Exp:* Physicist, Calif Res & Develop Co, 53-54, Lawrence Radiation Lab, Univ Calif, 54-61, Allied Res Assocs Inc, Mass, 61-64 & Mt Auburn Res Assocs, Inc, 64-75; PRIN SCIENTIST, LEE W PARKER, INC, 75- *Concurrent Pos:* Asst prof, St Mary's Col, Calif, 59-61. *Mem:* Am Phys Soc; Am Geophys Union; Soc Indust & Appl Math; Inst Elec & Electronics Eng. *Res:* Computational physics; interaction of satellites and probes with plasma; hydrodynamics; focusing of sonic booms; weak shocks; kinetic theory with electric fields; charging of satellite in geomagnetic field. *Mailing Add:* Lee W Parker Inc 252 Lexington Rd Concord MA 01742

PARKER, LEONARD EMANUEL, b New York, NY, May 13, 38; m 61; c 3. THEORETICAL PHYSICS, COSMOLOGY. *Educ:* Univ Rochester, AB, 60; Harvard Univ, AM, 62, PhD(physics), 67. *Prof Exp:* Instr physics, Univ NC, Chapel Hill, 66-68; from asst prof to assoc prof, 68-75, PROF PHYSICS, UNIV WIS-MILWAUKEE, 75- *Concurrent Pos:* NSF res grants, 70- *Honors & Awards:* Gravity Found Award, Gravity Found, 74 & 80. *Mem:* AAAS; Am Phys Soc; Am Asn Physics Teachers; NY Acad Sci. *Res:* Quantum field theory; relativistic astrophysics and cosmology; general relativity. *Mailing Add:* Dept of Physics Univ of Wis Milwaukee WI 53201

PARKER, LEROY A, JR, b Newark, NJ, Feb 12, 30; m 54; c 2. DENTISTRY, NATURAL SCIENCE. *Educ:* Seton Hall Univ, BA, 62; Georgetown Univ, DDS, 54. *Prof Exp:* Instr restorative dent, Col Med & Dent, Seton Hall Univ, 57-60; from asst prof to assoc prof path & oral diag, 60-66, prof oral radiol & treatment planning & chmn dept, 66-69, asst dean clin affairs, 69-70, assoc dean clin affairs, 70-78; PROF ORAL DIAG & RADIOL, COL MED & DENT NJ, 69-, ASSOC DEAN ACAD AFFAIRS, 79- *Concurrent Pos:* Assoc dir dent res, Johnson & Johnson, 65-66. *Mem:* Am Dent Asn; fel Am Col Dent; Int Asn Dent Res. *Res:* Improved methods of oral hygiene; applied radiology; calculus etiology; composition. *Mailing Add:* Sch of Dent Dept of Oral Diag Col of Med & Dent of NJ Newark NJ 07103

PARKER, LESLIE, b Consett, Eng, Apr 28, 39; m 62; c 4. CLINICAL CHEMISTRY. *Educ:* Reading Univ, BSc, 60; Yale Univ, MS, 64 & 66, PhD(molecular biophys), 68. *Prof Exp:* Jr res fel physics, Mass Gen Hosp, 60-62; instr physics & math, Washington & Jefferson Col, 62-63; fel chem, Yale Univ, 68-69; asst prof biochem, Carnegie-Mellon Univ, 69-73; CHIEF BIOCHEMIST, WASHINGTON HOSP, 73- *Mem:* Fel Am Inst Chemists; Am Asn Clin Chem. *Mailing Add:* Dept of Biochem Washington Hosp Washington PA 15301

PARKER, LLOYD ROBINSON, JR, b Rome, Ga, Sept 24, 50. ANALYTICAL CHEMISTRY. *Educ:* Berry Col, BA, 72; Emory Univ, MS, 74; Univ Houston, PhD(chem), 78. *Prof Exp:* ASST PROF CHEM, VASSAR COL, 78- *Mem:* Am Chem Soc; Sigma Xi. *Res:* Optimization and experimental design in analytical chemistry; pattern recognition; computer applications in chemistry; atomic absorption spectroscopy and high-performance liquid chromatography. *Mailing Add:* Dept of Chem Vassar Col Poughkeepsie NY 12601

PARKER, MARILYN ANKENEY, b Chicago, Ill, Dec 13, 40; m 63; c 2. PHYSICAL CHEMISTRY, INORGANIC CHEMISTRY. *Educ:* Univ Wis-Madison, BS, 62; Univ Wash, PhD(phys chem), 67. *Prof Exp:* Asst prof, 67-73, ASSOC PROF CHEM & CHMN DEPT, MONMOUTH COL, 73- *Mem:* Am Chem Soc. *Res:* infrared spectroscopy. *Mailing Add:* Dept of Chem Monmouth Col West Long Branch NJ 07764

PARKER, MARTIN DALE, b Flemingsburg, Ky, Jan 3, 41; m 66; c 2. PHARMACY, PHARMACEUTICS. *Educ:* Univ Ky, BS, 64, PhD(pharmaceut), 72. *Prof Exp:* Pharmacist, Sageser Drugs, Lexington, Ky, 64-66; teaching asst, Purdue Univ, 66-67 & Univ Ky, 67-72; asst prof pharmaceut, Med Univ SC, 72-74; clin instr, Univ Ky, 74-76; CHIEF PHARMACIST & VPRES, ROSEMONT DRUGS, INC, 74- *Mem:* Am Pharmaceut Asn; Am Asn Cols Pharm; Am Col Apothecaries; Sigma Xi. *Res:* New roles for the pharmacist in community practice; clinical orientation models for the pharmacy student; computer application of patient medication records for community practice. *Mailing Add:* Rosemont Drugs Inc 1999 Harrodsburg Rd Lexington KY 40503

PARKER, MARY LANGSTON, b Inverness, Fla, Nov 14, 24; m 53; c 5. MEDICINE, ENDORINCOLOGY. *Educ:* Fla State Univ, BS, 46, MS, 49; Wash Univ, MD, 53. *Prof Exp:* Intern, St Louis Children's Hosp, 53-54; res instr, 62-64, RES ASST PROF MED & PEDIAT, SCH MED, WASH UNIV, 65-, DIR HEALTH SERV, 71- *Mem:* Endocrine Soc. *Res:* Growth and development of children; growth hormone metabolism; physiologic actions; specific immunoassay for measurement of human growth hormone. *Mailing Add:* 307 S Forest Ave St Louis MO 63119

PARKER, MICHAEL, b Detroit, Mich, July 25, 38; m 60. ZOOLOGY, LIMNOLOGY. *Educ:* Univ Mich, BS, 60; Univ Wis, MS, 63, PhD(zool), 66. *Prof Exp:* Res assoc zool, Univ Wash, 66-68; asst prof, 68-72, ASSOC PROF ZOOL, UNIV WYO, 72- *Concurrent Pos:* Asst dir, Jackson Hole Res Sta, 69-71; consult, NSF, 71. *Mem:* AAAS; Am Soc Limnol & Oceanog; Ecol Soc Am; Am Inst Biol Sci; Fedn Am Scientists; Int Soc Theoret & Appl Liminol. *Res:* Phytoplankton and zooplankton ecology; vitamins in aquatic environments; alpine limnology; modeling. *Mailing Add:* Dept of Zool & Physiol Univ of Wyo Laramie WY 82070

PARKER, MILTON MARVIN, psychiatry, deceased

PARKER, MURL WAYNE, b El Dorado, Ark, June 28, 39; m 61; c 3. INDUSTRIAL ENGINEERING. *Educ:* Univ Ark, BSIE, 62, MSIE, 63, PhD(indust eng), 69. *Prof Exp:* Indust engr, E I du Pont de Nemours & Co, 63-66; instr indust eng, Univ Ark, 66-68; from asst prof to assoc prof, 68-75, PROF INDUST ENG, MISS STATE UNIV, 76- *Mem:* Am Inst Indust Engrs; Am Soc Eng Educ; Nat Soc Prof Engrs. *Res:* Engineering economy; systems simulation. *Mailing Add:* PO Drawer U Miss State Univ Mississippi State MS 39762

PARKER, N(ORMAN) F(RANCIS), b Fremont, Nebr, May 14, 23; m 49; c 4. ENGINEERING. *Educ:* Carnegie Inst Technol, BS & MS, 47, DSc(eng), 48. *Prof Exp:* Asst, Carnegie Inst Technol, 46-48; asst sect chief guid, NAm Aviation, Inc, 48-56, asst chief engr, Autonetics Div, 56-59, vpres & gen mgr, Comput & Data Systs, 59-62, exec vpres, 62-66, pres, Autonetics Div & vpres, NAm Aviation, Inc, 66-67; exec vpres, Bendix Corp, 67-68; pres & dir, Varian Assocs, 68-81, chief exec officer, 72-81; DIR US LEASING, INT GAME TECHNOL, 81- *Mem:* Nat Acad Eng; fel Inst Elec & Electronics Engrs; fel Am Inst Aeronaut & Astronaut. *Res:* Servomechanicsms. *Mailing Add:* 1533 Portola Rd 611 Hansen Way Woodside CA 94062

PARKER, NANCY JOHANNE RENTNER, b Kenosha, Wis, June 17, 37; div; c 2. DEVELOPMENTAL BIOLOGY. *Educ:* Lawrence Col, BA, 59; Univ Tex, PhD(zool), 65. *Prof Exp:* NSF fel, Univ Tex, 65; asst prof, 65-73, assoc prof zool, 73-76, ASSOC PROF BIOL SCI, SOUTHERN ILL UNIV, EDWARDSVILLE, 77- *Mem:* Soc Develop Biol. *Res:* Cell death in chick mesonepros. *Mailing Add:* Dept of Biol Sci Southern Ill Univ Edwardsville IL 62025

PARKER, PAMELA J, b Davenport, Iowa, Nov 20, 44. BIOLOGY, ANATOMY. *Educ:* Smith Col, BA, 67; Yale Univ, MFS, 70, PhD(biol), 77. *Prof Exp:* Res assoc biol, Harvard Univ, 74-76; cur mammals, Chicago Zool Soc, 76-79; ASST PROF ECOL & SYSTEMATICS, CORNELL UNIV, 79- *Concurrent Pos:* Lectr, Univ Chicago, 76-78. *Mem:* Am Soc Zool; Am Soc Mammal; Australian Soc Mammal; Soc Vert Paleont. *Res:* Functional morphology, mammalogy, behavior and evolution; mammalian herbivores and plant communities in the semiarid region of Australia. *Mailing Add:* Sect Ecol Syst Cornell Univ Ithaca NY 14853

PARKER, PATRICK LEGRAND, b El Dorado, Ark, Mar 13, 33; m 56; c 3. GEOCHEMISTRY, CHEMISTRY. *Educ:* Univ Ark, BA, 55, MS, 57, PhD(chem), 60. *Prof Exp:* Res scientist, Univ Tex, 59-61; org geochemist, Geophys Lab, Carnegie Inst, 61-63; from asst prof to assoc prof & res asst prof biol, Wilmington Col, 75-76; ASST PROF BIOL, STATE UNIV NY FREDONIA, 76- STUDIES, MARINE SCI INST & DIR, MARINE SCI LAB, UNIV TEX, Am 72-73. *Mem:* Am Chem Soc; Geochem Soc; Am Geophys Union. *Res:* Application of chemistry to geological and near shore marine problems; stable isotope geochemistry of. *Mailing Add:* Marine Sci Inst Univ of Tex at Austin Port Aransas TX 78373

PARKER, PAUL MICHAEL, b Vienna, Austria, June 24, 28; m 58; c 1. MOLECULAR PHYSICS. *Educ:* City Col New York, BS, 53; Ohio State Univ, MS, 55, PhD(physics), 58. *Prof Exp:* Asst physics, Ohio State Univ, 53-56, instr, 57-58; from asst prof to assoc prof, 58-67, PROF PHYSICS, MICH STATE UNIV, 67- *Concurrent Pos:* NIH fel, 62-63. *Mem:* Fel Am Phys Soc; Am Asn Physics Teachers. *Res:* Theory of infrared, microwave and radio frequency spectra. *Mailing Add:* Dept of Physics Mich State Univ East Lansing MI 48824

PARKER, PETER DONALD MACDOUGALL, b New York, NY, Dec 14, 36; m 58; c 3. NUCLEAR PHYSICS. *Educ:* Amherst Col, BA, 58; Calif Inst Technol, PhD(nuclear physics), 63. *Prof Exp:* Res fel nuclear physics, Calif Inst Technol, 63; from asst physicist to assoc physicist, Brookhaven Nat Lab, 63-66; asst prof, 66-70, assoc prof, 70-76, PROF PHYSICS, YALE UNIV, 76- *Concurrent Pos:* Consult, Bell Tel Labs, 65-68 & Brookhaven Nat Lab, 66- *Mem:* Am Phys Soc; Am Astron Soc. *Res:* Structure light nuclei; nuclear astrophysics. *Mailing Add:* Dept of Physics-NSL Yale Univ New Haven CT 06520

PARKER, PETER EDDY, b Flint, Mich, Nov 1, 44; m 67. CHEMICAL ENGINEERING, COMPUTER SCIENCE. *Educ:* Univ Rochester, BS, 66; Univ Pittsburgh, MBA, 67; Univ Mich, PhD(chem eng), 74. *Prof Exp:* Res engr environ sci, Raytheon Co, 74-75; RES ASSOC ENVIRON SCI, INST PAPER CHEM, 75- *Mem:* Am Inst Chem Engrs; Tech Asn Pulp & Paper Indust. *Res:* Computer simulation of processes; environmental system dynamics. *Mailing Add:* Inst of Paper Chem Box 1039 Appleton WI 54912

PARKER, RAYBURN ELLIS, agricultural engineering, environmental engineering, see previous edition

PARKER, RAYMOND LAURENCE, b Roseburg, Ore, Oct 26, 21; m 47; c 2. GEOLOGY. *Educ:* Mont State Univ, BA, 47; Ind Univ, MA, 50; Columbia Univ, PhD, 54. *Prof Exp:* GEOLOGIST, US GEOL SURV, 48- *Concurrent Pos:* Asst, Ind Univ, 49 & Columbia Univ, 51-52. *Mem:* Geol Soc Am. *Res:* Petrology; mineralogy of alunite; regional geology of the Rocky Mountains; mineralogy and geology of niobium and tantalum. *Mailing Add:* US Geol Surv Fed Ctr Denver CO 80225

PARKER, RICHARD ALAN, b Milwaukee, Wis, May 20, 31; m 53; c 7. LIMNOLOGY, COMPUTER SCIENCE. *Educ:* Utah State Univ, BS, 53; Univ Wis, MS, 54, PhD(zool), 56. *Prof Exp:* Asst zool, Univ Wis, 53-56; from instr to assoc prof zool, 56-66, assoc prof info sci, 63-66, actg dir comput ctr & actg chmn info sci, 65-66, chmn dept zool, 65-72, chmn environ sci, 68-71, PROF ZOOL & COMPUT SCI, WASH STATE UNIV, 66- *Concurrent Pos:* NSF sr fel, Oxford Univ, 68-69; Erskine fel, Univ Canterbury, 76; Fulbright scholar, Univ Liege, 80. *Mem:* Am Soc Limnol & Oceanog; Int Asn Theoret & Appl Limnol; Am Soc Naturalists. *Res:* Plankton population dynamics; computer simulation of aquatic ecosystems. *Mailing Add:* Dept of Zool Wash State Univ Pullman WA 99164

PARKER, RICHARD BENNETT, b Ontario, Ore, Sept 19, 25; m 46; c 4. BACTERIOLOGY. *Educ:* Ore State Col, PhD(bact), 55. *Prof Exp:* Instr bact, Ore State Col, 52-54; sr scientist, Res Lab, Carnation Co, 55-59; chmn dept oral biol, 69-71, chmn dept microbiol, 71-78, PROF BACT, DENT SCH, UNIV ORE, 56-, ; VPRES RES & DEVELOP, MICROBIAL GENETICS DIV, PIONEER HI-BRED INT, INC, 73- *Mem:* AAAS; Am Soc Microbiol; Sigma Xi. *Res:* Metabolism of bacteria; lactic acid bacteria; microbial ecology; microorganisms of the mouth and mucous membrane; bioelectrical potentials of microorganisms and hyperbaric studies; studies on periodontal disease and preventive dentistry; studies on (micro)biological control of plant and animal infections. *Mailing Add:* Pioneer Hi-Bred Int Inc Microbial Genetics 3930 SW Macadam Ave Portland OR 97201

PARKER, RICHARD BEWLEY, b Mussoorie, India, July 26, 36; US citizen; m 60; c 2. ECOLOGY, HERPETOLOGY. *Educ:* Hanover Col, BA, 58; Univ Mich, MA, 60; Univ Tex, PhD(zool), 65. *Prof Exp:* Asst prof, 65-69, chmn sci & technol div, 69-70, ASSOC PROF BIOL, SOUTHERN ILL UNIV, EDWARDSVILLE, 69- *Res:* Lizard ecology and physiology; temperature regulation; reproduction. *Mailing Add:* Dept of Biol Sci Southern Ill Univ Edwardsville IL 62025

PARKER, RICHARD C, b Coleman, Tex, July 17, 39; m 63. PHYSICAL CHEMISTRY. *Educ:* Calif State Col Long Beach, BS, 62; Univ Wash, PhD(kinetics), 66. *Prof Exp:* Asst prof, 66-74, assoc prof, 75-80, PROF CHEM, NJ INST TECHNOL, 81- *Mem:* Am Chem Soc; Am Phys Soc; AAAS. *Res:* Kinetics of aminolysis reactions; effect of ultrasound on reaction rates. *Mailing Add:* Dept Chem NJ Inst Technol 323 High St Newark NJ 07102

PARKER, RICHARD GHRIST, b Indianola, Pa, July 17, 41; m 68; c 2. ORGANIC CHEMISTRY. *Educ:* Carnegie-Mellon Univ, BS, 63; Univ Nebr, Lincoln, PhD(chem), 68. *Prof Exp:* Fel, Calif Inst Technol, 68-69; res chemist, 69-70, sr res chemist, 71-76, res assoc, 76-81, RES & DEVELOP ASSOC, RES CTR, B F GOODRICH CO, 81- *Mem:* Am Chem Soc. *Res:* Organic synthesis; plastics stabilization; nuclear magnetic resonance. *Mailing Add:* Res Ctr B F Goodrich Co 9921 Brecksville Rd D 8534 Brecksville OH 44141

PARKER, RICHARD H, b Anaconda, Mont, June 16, 32; c 7. INTERNAL MEDICINE, MICROBIOLOGY. *Educ:* Univ Wash, BS, 54, MD, 58. *Prof Exp:* Intern, Duke Univ, 58-59; resident med, Univ Utah, 59-60, 62-63, instr, 65-66; assoc, Med Sch, Northwestern Univ, Chicago, 66-68, asst prof, 68-72; ASSOC PROF MED, MED SCH, HOWARD UNIV, 72-; CHIEF SECT INFECTIOUS DIS, VET ADMIN HOSP, WASHINGTON, DC, 72- *Concurrent Pos:* Fel infectious dis, Univ Utah, 60-65. *Mem:* Am Soc Microbiol; Am Fedn Clin Res; Am Thoracic Soc; Am Col Physicians; Am Soc Clin Pharmacol. *Res:* Rapid methods for diagnosis of infectious diseases; pharmacologic study of antimicrobial agents. *Mailing Add:* Dept of Med 50 Irving St NW Washington DC 20422

PARKER, RICHARD LANGLEY, b Manhattan, Kans, Apr 5, 29; m 56; c 4. VETERINARY MEDICINE. *Educ:* Kans State Univ, BS, 51, DVM, 55; Univ Minn, MPH, 63. *Prof Exp:* Vet epidemiologist, USPHS, NY State Dept Health, 55-58, chief, Midwest Rabies Sta, Commun Dis Ctr, Wis, 58-61, vet epidemiologist, Minn State Health Dept, 61-62, chief, Commun Dis Ctr Border Rabies Prog, 63-66; rabies adv, Pan-Am Health Orgn, 66-68; asst chief vet pub health sect, Epidemiol Prog, 68-71, chief vet pub health, Ctr Dis Control, 71-75; STATE EPIDEMIOLOGIST, SC DEPT HEALTH & ENVIRON CONTROL, 76- *Mem:* Am Vet Med Asn; Am Pub Health Asn; Conf State & Territorial Epidemiologists. *Res:* Epidemiology and ecology of zoonoses, especially those infecting wildlife. *Mailing Add:* SC Dept Health & Environ Control 2600 Bull St Columbia SC 29201

PARKER, ROBERT ALLAN RIDLEY, b New York, NY, Dec 14, 36; m 58, 81; c 2. ASTRONOMY. *Educ:* Amherst Col, BA, 58; Calif Inst Technol, PhD(astron), 62. *Prof Exp:* NSF fel, Univ Wis-Madison, 62-63, asst prof, 63-67, assoc prof astron, Washburn Observ, 67-72; ASTRONAUT, MANNED SPACECRAFT CTR, NASA, 67- *Concurrent Pos:* Mem support crew, Apollo XV & XVII; prog scientist, Skylab; mission specialist, Spacelab I. *Mem:* Am Astron Soc. *Res:* Interstellar matter; instrumentation. *Mailing Add:* Code CB NASA Manned Spacecraft Ctr Houston TX 77058

PARKER, ROBERT BRUCE, cardiovascular pharmacology, see previous edition

PARKER, ROBERT DAVIS RICKARD, b Honolulu, Hawaii, May 6, 42; US citizen. ENVIRONMENTAL HEALTH, INDUSTRIAL HYGIENE. *Educ:* Univ Hawaii, BA, 64, MSPH, 67; Univ Minn, MS, 70, PhD(environ health), 75. *Prof Exp:* Instr pub health, Univ Hawaii, 67; res asst, Univ Minn, 71; tech scuba diver, Environ Protection Agency, 72; instr environ health, Univ Minn, 72-73; ASST PROF BIOL & PUB HEALTH, UTAH STATE UNIV, 73- *Mem:* Am Pub Health Asn; Nat Environ Health Asn; Am Indust Hyg Asn; Int Asn Great Lakes Res; Sigma Xi. *Res:* heavy metals in atmospheric fallout in intermountain west region; composition and magnituude of periphyton in arrtificial streams. *Mailing Add:* Dept of Biol UMC 55 Utah State Univ Logan UT 84322

PARKER, ROBERT FREDERIC, b St Louis, Mo, Oct 29, 07; m 34; c 2. MEDICINE. *Educ:* Wash Univ, BS, 27, MD, 29. *Prof Exp:* Asst radiol, Wash Univ, 29-30, asst med, 31-32, instr, 32-33; intern, Barnes Hosp, St Louis, 30-31; asst, Rockefeller Inst, 33-36; from instr to asst prof med, 36-40, assoc prof microbiol, 48-54, assoc dean med educ, 64-73, assoc prof med, sch med, 40-77, secy gen fac, 64-76, prof, 54-77, & dean, 73-76, EMER PROF MICROBIOL, CASE WESTERN RESERVE UNIV, 77-, EMER DEAN MED EDUC, 76- *Concurrent Pos:* In-chg microbiol lab & physician, Hosp, Case Western Reserve Univ, 48- *Mem:* Am Soc Clin Invest; Am Soc Microbiol; Soc Exp Biol & Med; Am Asn Immunologists. *Res:* Virus diseases; immunology and quantitative aspects of infection; tissue culture. *Mailing Add:* Univ Hosp Cleveland 2065 Adelbert Rd Cleveland OH 44106

PARKER, ROBERT G, b Detroit, Mich, Jan 29, 25; m 49; c 2. RADIOLOGY. *Educ:* Univ Wis, BS, 46, MD, 48. *Prof Exp:* From asst prof to assoc prof, 59-66, prof radiol, Univ Wash, 68-78; PROF RADIOL, UNIV CALIF LOS ANGELES, 78- *Concurrent Pos:* Consult, USPHS Hosp, Seattle, 57, Vet Admin Hosp, 59-77 & Madigan Army Hosp, Ft Lewis, Wash, 59-77; consult, Wadsworth Vet Admin Hosp & Harbor Gen Hosp, 78- *Mem:* Am Soc Therapeut Radiol; Radiation Res Soc; Am Radium Soc; Radiol Soc NAm. *Res:* Radiation tissue tolerance; fast neutron therapy. *Mailing Add:* Dept Radiation Oncol Univ Calif Los Angeles Ctr Health Sci Los Angeles CA 90024

PARKER, ROBERT HALLETT, b Springfield, Mass, Feb 14, 22; m 45; c 3. ECOLOGY. *Educ:* Univ NMex, BSc, 48, MSc, 49; Copenhagen Univ, Mag Sci & Doctorand, 62. *Prof Exp:* Asst biol, Univ NMex, 48-49; asst zool, Duke Univ, 49-50; marine biologist, State Game & Fish Comn, Tex, 50-51; geophys trainee, Phillips Petrol Co, 51; res biologist, Scripps Inst, Univ Calif, 51-58, jr res ecologist, 58-63; resident ecologist, Systs Ecol Prog, Marine Biol Lab, Woods Hole, 63-66; assoc prof biol & geol, Tex Christian Univ, 66-70; PRES & CHMN BD, COASTAL ECOSYSTS MGT, INC, 70- *Concurrent Pos:* Consult, Am Mus Natural Hist, 57, Standard Oil Co, NJ, 56-58 & Pneumodyn Corp, 60-61; res scientist, Tex Christian Res Found. *Honors & Awards:* Am Asn Petrol Geol Award, 56. *Mem:* Soc Syst Zool; Ecol Soc Am; fel Geol Soc Am; Am Soc Limnol & Oceanog; assoc Am Asn Petrol Geol. *Res:* Using shelled invertebrate ecology to define present day and ancient environments; paleoclimatological and paleoecological problems; terrestrial and aquatic ecology damage assessment; marine population dynamics. *Mailing Add:* 3601 Wren Ave Ft Worth TX 76133

PARKER, ROBERT LOUIS, b Ft Dodge, Iowa, July 4, 29; m 63; c 2. SOLID STATE PHYSICS. *Educ:* Mass Inst Technol, BS, 51; Univ Md, MS, 58, PhD(physics), 60. *Prof Exp:* Physicist, Mech Div, 54-57 & Metal Physics Sect, 57-63, chief crystallization metal sect, 63-74, sr scientist, Metall Div, 74-78, PHYSICIST, METALL DIV, NAT BUR STANDARDS, 78- *Concurrent Pos:* Mem organizing & prog comts, Int Conf Crystal Growth, 65-; dep prin ed, J Crystal Growth, 70- *Mem:* Am Crystallog Asn; Metall Soc; Am Phys Soc; Am Asn Crystal Growth. *Res:* Crystallization; phase transformations; nucleation; interface kinetics and morphology; morphological stability; moving boundary problems; vapor phase growth of crystals; freezing of liquids; whisker growth; convection; origin of imperfections in crystals; ultrasonic measurements of solidification. *Mailing Add:* 9728 Digging Rd Gaithersburg MD 20760

PARKER, ROBERT RAY, zoology, see previous edition

PARKER, ROBERT TARBERT, b Towson, Md, Oct 9, 19; m 42; c 4. INTERNAL MEDICINE. *Educ:* Johns Hopkins Univ, AB, 41, MD, 44; Am Bd Internal Med, dipl, 54. *Prof Exp:* Asst dir div infectious dis, 51-54, dir, 54-57, assoc dean, Sch Med & coordr med educ nat defense prof, 55-59, from instr to asst prof, 51-59, assoc prof med, Sch Med, Univ Md, Baltimore, 59-74, DIR MED, THE GOOD SAMARITAN HOSP, 74-, VPRES MED AFFAIRS, 77- *Concurrent Pos:* Vis physician, Univ Hosp, 51-; consult, USPHS Hosp, 57-; attend physician, St Joseph's Hosp, Baltimore, 59-; dir med, S Baltimore Gen Hosp, 59-74, chief staff, 65-74. *Mem:* Fel Am Col Physicians; Am Fedn Clin Res; NY Acad Sci. *Res:* Infectious diseases. *Mailing Add:* The Good Samaritan Hosp 5601 Loch Raven Blvd Baltimore MD 21239

PARKER, RODGER D, b St Louis, Mo, July 2, 34; m 57; c 2. MATHEMATICS, MATHEMATICAL BIOLOGY. *Educ:* Drury Col, BA, 56; Ind Univ, MA, 60; Johns Hopkins Univ, PhD(oper res), 65. *Prof Exp:* Res assoc, 62-66, from asst prof to assoc prof, 66-74, PROF OPERS RES, SCH HYG & PUB HEALTH, JOHNS HOPKINS UNIV, 74- *Concurrent Pos:* Consult, Food & Drug Admin, 70- & Pan Am Health Orgn, 71- *Res:* Develop methods for computer-aided diagnosis and planning of regional health services. *Mailing Add:* Dept of Opers Res Johns Hopkins Univ Baltimore MD 21205

PARKER, ROGER A, b West Union, Iowa, Jan 31, 43; m 64; c 4. MEDICINAL CHEMISTRY. *Educ:* Univ Iowa, BS, 65; Ohio State Univ, PhD(med chem), 69. *Prof Exp:* org res chemist, Merrell Res Ctr, Richardson-Merrell, Inc, 69-80, ORG RES CHEMIST, MERRELL RES CTR, MERRELL DOW PHARMACEUTICALS, INC, 80- *Mem:* NY Acad Sci; Am Chem Soc. *Res:* Steroid chemistry; heterocyclic medicinal agents; Antifungal agents; antiviral agents; hypocholesterolemic and hypolipidemic agents; antihypertensive agents. *Mailing Add:* Merrell Res Ctr 2110 E Galbraith Rd Cincinnati OH 45215

PARKER, RONALD BRUCE, b Los Angeles, Calif, Mar 21, 32; m 71. MINERALOGY, STRUCTURAL GEOLOGY. *Educ:* Univ Calif, Berkeley, AB, 53, PhD(geol), 59. *Prof Exp:* From asst prof to assoc prof, 59-68, asst cur, geol mus, 74-76, prof geol, 68-76, ADJ PROF, UNIV WYO, 76-, RES AFFIL, UNIV NEBR STATE MUS, 76- *Concurrent Pos:* Sigma Xi-Sci Res Soc Am grant, 61; NSF res grant, 62-66; Univ Wyo fac fel, 65; NATO fel, 66-67; adj prof, Fergus Falls Col, 77- *Mem:* Fel AAAS; fel Geol Soc Am; Mineral Soc Am; Geochem Soc. *Res:* Structural analysis of highly deformed rocks; geochemistry of deformed rocks; x-ray emission analysis of fossils, rocks and minerals; biogeochemistry of vertebrate fossils; chemical study of evolutionary trends in higher organisms; paleobiochemistry; animal nutrition and science. *Mailing Add:* Sammen Sheep Farm Rte 1 Henning MN 56551

PARKER, ROY DENVER, JR, b San Diego, Calif, Jan 18, 43; m 67; c 3. AGRICULTURAL ENTOMOLOGY, EXTENSION ENTOMOLOGY. *Educ:* Kilgore Col, SC, 63; Tex A&M Univ, BS, 66, MS, 68, PhD(entom), 79. *Prof Exp:* Serv mgr, pest control, Hunter Industs,71-72; co exten entom cotton pest mgr, 72-75, EXTEN ENTOMOLOGIST, TEX AGR EXTEN SERV, 78- *Mem:* Entom Soc Am; Am Registry Prof Entomologists. *Res:* Entomology research and educational programs for agricultural producers on corn, sorghum, cotton, pecans, livestock and other insects that are pests of man and his possessions. *Mailing Add:* Rt 2 Box 589 Corpus Christi TX 78410

PARKER, SHERWOOD, b Chicago, Ill, Mar 31, 32. PHYSICS. *Educ:* Univ Ill, BS, 53; Univ Calif, Berkeley, MA, 55, PhD(physics), 59. *Prof Exp:* Physicist, Lawrence Radiation Lab, Calif, 59; from instr to asst prof physics, Univ Chicago, 59-64; asst prof, Lawrence Berkeley Lab, Univ Calif, 64-71; MEM STAFF, UNIV HAWAII, 71- *Mem:* Am Phys Soc; Inst Elec & Electronic Engrs. *Res:* Elementary particle physics. *Mailing Add:* c/o Dept of Physics Lawrence Berkeley Lab 50a Univ Calif Berkeley CA 94720

PARKER, SIDNEY G, b Campbell, Tex, Jan 21, 25. SOLID STATE CHEMISTRY. *Educ:* ETex State Col, BS, 46; Univ Tex, PhD(inorg chem), 51. *Prof Exp:* Res chemist, Mobil Oil Co, 51-53 & E I du Pont de Nemours & Co, Inc, 53-57; MEM TECH STAFF, TEX INSTRUMENTS, INC, 57- *Res:* Study of single crystal growth and epitaxial deposition of infrared detector and laser materials and magnetic bubble materials and silicon. *Mailing Add:* Cent Res Lab Tex Instruments Inc PO Box 225936 MS 145 Dallas TX 75265

PARKER, SIDNEY THOMAS, b Victoria, BC, May 23, 13; nat; m 35; c 2. MATHEMATICS. *Educ:* Univ BC, BA, 31, MA, 34; Univ Cincinnati, PhD(math), 47. *Prof Exp:* Teacher, high sch, BC, 33-37; asst astron, Brown Univ, 37-38; instr math, Hobart Col, 38-42; from instr to asst prof, Univ Louisville, 42-46; Taft fel, Cincinnati, 46-47; from asst prof to assoc prof, 47-51, dir comput ctr, 58-68, PROF MATH, KANS STATE UNIV, 51- *Mem:* Am Math Soc; Soc Indust & Appl Math, Math Asn Am; Asn Comput Mach. *Res:* Continued fractions; recurrence relations; convergence factors and summable integrals; numerical methods; digital computing. *Mailing Add:* Dept of Math Kans State Univ Manhattan KS 66502

PARKER, SYDNEY R(ICHARD), b New York, NY, Apr 18, 23; m 47; c 2. ELECTRICAL ENGINEERING. *Educ:* City Col New York, BEE, 44; Stevens Inst Technol, MS, 48, ScD, 64. *Prof Exp:* Sr engr, Int Resistance Co, 51-52; proj engr, Radio Corp Am, 52-56; assoc prof elec eng, City Col NY, 56-65; prof, Univ Houston, 65-66; prof, Naval Postgrad Sch, 66-75, chmn dept, 70-75; dean, Col Eng, Rutgers Univ, 75-76; PROF ELEC ENG, NAVAL POSTGRAD SCH, 76- *Concurrent Pos:* Consult, United Aircraft Corp, 58, Automation Dynamics Corp, 59-65, NAm Rockwell Corp, 66-75 & Lawrence Livermore Lab, Univ Calif, 78-; mem, Eng Educ Accreditation Bd, 75-; assoc ed, Transactions on Circuits & Systs, 75-77. *Honors & Awards:* Sigma Xi Res Award, Naval Postgrad Sch, 77. *Mem:* AAAS; fel Inst Elec & Electronics Engrs; Am Soc Eng Educ; NY Acad Sci. *Res:* Automatic control systems; circuit theory; computers; sensitivity studies of circuits and systems; computer aided circuit design; digital filter theory and practice. *Mailing Add:* Dept of Elec Eng Naval Postgrad Sch Monterey CA 93940

PARKER, TRAVIS JAY, b Oklahoma City, Okla, Nov 23, 13. GEOLOGY. *Educ:* Tex Tech Col, BS, 33; Univ Tex, MA, 39, PhD(geol), 52. *Prof Exp:* Asst prof geol, NTex Agr Col, 39-40; instr, Univ Tex, 41-42; from asst prof to assoc prof, 47-52, prof, 52-81, EMER PROF GEOL, TEX A&M UNIV, 81- *Mem:* Geol Soc Am; Am Asn Petrol Geol. *Mailing Add:* Dept of Geol Tex A&M Univ College Station TX 77843

PARKER, VINCENT EVELAND, b Kuala Lumpur, Fedn Malay States, Sept 18, 14; US citizen; m 38, 67; c 4. EXPERIMENTAL NUCLEAR PHYSICS. *Educ:* Evansville Col, AB, 36; Ind Univ, PhD(phys chem), 40. *Prof Exp:* Asst, Ind Univ, 36-40; assoc prof phys sci & head dept, Cent Norm Col, 40-41; from instr to asst prof chem, Univ Del, 41-44, from asst prof physics & actg head dept to prof, 44-50, chmn dept, 46-50; prof physics & astron & head dept, La State Univ, 50-62; dep dir, Oak Ridge Assoc Univs, 62-67; dean, sch sci, 67-77, PROF PHYSICS CALIF STATE POLYTECH UNIV, 67- *Concurrent Pos:* Asst microchemist, Biochem Res Found, Franklin Inst, 41-43; mem, Comn Col Physics, 60-64 & gov bd, Am Inst Physics, 63-69; vchmn bd trustees, Col Oak Ridge, 64-66; chmn, Interserv Comt Tech Facilities, Southeastern US, 66; mem ad hoc comt develop, Univ Ala, Huntsville, 66-67 & US Nat Comt, Int Union Pure & Appl Physics, 67-70; chmn judges comt, Inst-US Steel Award Sci Writing, 69-73; for ed, Nuclear Energy Engr. *Honors & Awards:* Distinguished Serv Citation, Am Asn Physics Teachers, 67. *Mem:* Fel AAAS; fel Am Phys Soc; Am Chem Soc; Am Asn Physics Teachers (pres, 63). *Res:* High energy particle accelerators; neutron physics; radioactivity. *Mailing Add:* Dept of Physics Calif State Polytech Univ Pomona CA 91768

PARKER, VIRGIL THOMAS, b Houston, Tex, July 15, 51; m 74. PLANT ECOLOGY, ECOLOGY. *Educ:* Univ Tex, Austin, BA, 73; Univ Calif, Santa Barbara, MA, 75, PhD(biol), 77. *Prof Exp:* Asst prof biol, Rider Col, Lawrenceville, 77-80; ASST PROF BIOL, SAN FRANCISCO STATE UNIV, 80-, DIR, SIERRA NEV FIELD CAMPUS, 80- *Mem:* Ecol Soc Am; Bot Soc Am; Sigma Xi; Am Soc Naturalists. *Res:* Plant-plant interactions (allelopathy competition); wetland ecology; reproductive ecology. *Mailing Add:* Dept of Biol San Francisco State Univ San Francisco CA 94132

PARKER, VIVIAN, physical chemistry, see previous edition

PARKER, WILLARD ALBERT, b Bremerton, Wash, Aug 10, 38; m 62; c 2. MATHEMATICS. *Educ:* Univ Ore, BA, 60, MA, 66, PhD(math), 70; Fuller Theol Sem, BD, 64. *Prof Exp:* Asst prof, 70-80, ASSOC PROF MATH, KANS STATE UNIV, 80- *Mem:* Am Math Soc; Math Asn Am. *Res:* Harmonic analysis on compact groups. *Mailing Add:* Dept Math Kans State Univ Manhattan KS 66502

PARKER, WILLIAM ARTHUR, b Tacoma, Wash, May 23, 49; m 70; c 2. THERAPEUTICS. *Educ:* Univ Minn, BSc, 72, PharmD(clin pharm), 73; Dalhousie Univ, MBA, 79. *Prof Exp:* Res assoc pharmacog, Univ Minn, 71-72, teaching asst clin pharm, 72-73, instr, 73-74; asst prof clin pharm, 74-79, ASSOC PROF PHARM, DALHOUSIE UNIV, 79-, COORDR CLIN PHARM, 74- *Concurrent Pos:* Clin pharmacist consult, Nursing Home Drug Utilization, Minn State Welfare Med Rev Team, 71-73; therapeut consult, Minn State Epilepsy Found, 73-74; clin pharmacist consult & instr, Comprehensive Seizure Ctr & Depts Neurol & Psychiat, St Paul-Ramsey Hosp & Med Ctr, 73-74 & Depts Med & Family Pract, Halifax Infirmary, 75-

Mem: Am Soc Hosp Pharmacists; Can Pharmaceut Asn; Can Soc Hosp Pharmacists; Am Col Clin Pharm; Sigma Xi. *Res:* Assessment and prevention of iatrogenic disease and adverse drug reactions; continuing education and self-learning processes in therapeutics; intravenous compatibility and stability of drugs. *Mailing Add:* Col of Pharm Dalhousie Univ Halifax NS B3H 3J5 Can

PARKER, WILLIAM EVANS, b Newark, NJ, June 7, 40; m 69; c 2. INORGANIC CHEMISTRY, SYMMETRY. *Educ:* Haverford Col, BA, 62; Univ NC, Chapel Hill, MS, 65, PhD(inorg chem), 67. *Prof Exp:* Instr, 67-68, asst prof, 68-78, ASSOC PROF CHEM, GETTYSBURG COL, 78- *Mem:* Am Chem Soc. *Res:* Bonding theories of coordination compounds; kinetic studies of inorganic complexes. *Mailing Add:* Dept of Chem Gettysburg Col Gettysburg PA 17325

PARKER, WILLIAM HENRY, b Greenville, Pa, Oct 3, 41; m 64; c 3. LOW TEMPERATURE PHYSICS, SOLID STATE PHYSICS. *Educ:* Allegheny Col, BS, 63; Univ Pa, MS, 64, PhD, 67. *Prof Exp:* Asst prof, 67-70, assoc prof, 70-76, PROF PHYSICS, UNIV CALIF, IRVINE, 76- *Concurrent Pos:* Alfred P Sloan res fel, 68-70. *Mem:* Am Phys Soc; Am Asn Physics Teachers. *Res:* Superconductivity, tunneling and normal metals. *Mailing Add:* Dept of Physics Univ of Calif Irvine CA 92664

PARKER, WILLIAM JAMES, b Sutherlin, Ore, Dec 11, 26; m 49; c 2. THERMAL SCIENCES. *Educ:* Univ Ore, BS, 52, MS, 53. *Prof Exp:* Physicist, High Temperature Physics Sect, US Naval Radiol Defense Lab, 53-69; PHYSICIST, CTR FIRE RES, NAT BUR STANDARDS, 69- *Res:* Heat transfer; fire research; experimental and theoretical research on the heat release rate, flame spread rate and ignitability of materials. *Mailing Add:* Ctr Fire Res Nat Bur Standards Washington DC 20234

PARKER, WILLIAM LAWRENCE, b Vermillion, SDak, Feb 19, 39; m 69; c 1. ORGANIC CHEMISTRY, ANTIBIOTICS. *Educ:* Columbia Col, BA, 61; Harvard Univ, PhD(chem), 65. *Prof Exp:* Res chemist, Dow Chem Co, 65-69; sr res investr, 69-80, RES GROUP LEADER, SQUIBB INST MED RES, 80- *Mem:* Am Chem Soc; AAAS. *Res:* Structure determination and synthesis of natural products. *Mailing Add:* Squibb Inst for Med Res E R Squibb & Sons PO Box 4000 Princeton NJ 08540

PARKER, WILLIAM SKINKER, b St Louis, Mo, Aug 28, 42; m 79; c 1. VERTEBRATE ECOLOGY. *Educ:* Wabash Col, Ind, BA, 64; Ariz State Univ, MS, 67; Univ Utah, PhD(biol), 74. *Prof Exp:* asst prof, 74-77, ASSOC PROF BIOL, MISS UNIV FOR WOMEN, 77- *Mem:* AAAS; Am Soc Zool; Am Soc Ichthyol & Herpet; Ecol Soc Am; Am Soc Naturalists. *Res:* demography of pond turtles; author or coauthor of 35 publishings on ecology, reptiles and amphibians. *Mailing Add:* Dept of Biol Sci Miss Univ for Women Columbus MS 39701

PARKER, WINFRED EVANS, b Philadelphia, Pa, Aug 29, 25; m 55; c 2. PHYSICAL ORGANIC CHEMISTRY. *Educ:* Univ Pittsburgh, BS, 50; Drexel Inst, MS, 59, PhD(chem), 68. *Prof Exp:* RES CHEMIST, ANIMAL FATS PROD LAB, EASTERN UTILIZATION & RES DEVELOP DIV, USDA, 50- *Concurrent Pos:* Instr, Drexel Univ, 67- *Mem:* Am Chem Soc; fel Am Inst Chem; NY Acad Sci. *Res:* Urea complexes; peracids; thermogravimetric analysis; chemical and physical properties of lubricants from inedible fats and oils. *Mailing Add:* 7201 Sherman St Philadelphia PA 19119

PARKES, ALAN SCHOFIELD, instrumentation, see previous edition

PARKES, KENNETH CARROLL, b Hackensack, NJ, Aug 8, 22; m 53. ORNITHOLOGY. *Educ:* Cornell Univ, BS, 43, MS, 48, PhD(ornith), 52. *Prof Exp:* Cur birds, Cornell Univ, 47-52; from asst cur to assoc cur, Carnegie Mus, 53-61, CUR BIRDS, CARNEGIE MUS NATURAL HIST, 62-, CHIEF CUR LIFE SCI, 75- *Concurrent Pos:* Res fel, Dept Epidemiol & Microbiol, Grad Sch Pub Health, Univ Pittsburgh, 56, adj mem grad fac, 63-; vis lectr, Pymatuning Field Lab, 57; invest assoc, Museo Nat de Hist Nat, Dominican Repub, 80- *Mem:* Wilson Ornith Soc (pres, 73-75); fel Am Ornith Union (2nd vpres, 75-76); Cooper Ornith Soc; Brit Ornith Union; Soc Syst Zool. *Res:* Systematics and distribution of new world and Philippine birds; molt and plumage cycles of birds. *Mailing Add:* Sect Birds Carnegie Mus Nat Hist Pittsburgh PA 15213

PARKHIE, MUKUND RAGHUNATHRAO, US citizen; m 70; c 4. TERATOLOGY, METAL TOXICITY. *Educ:* Univ Jabalpur, DVM, 57; Agra Univ, MVSc, 60; Univ Sask, MSc, 63; Univ Mo-Columbia, PhD(med physiol), 70; Coun for Vet Grad, cert, 72. *Prof Exp:* Vet off vet med & surg, Maharastra Govt Vet Servs, India, 57-58; animal husb exten officer, Rajasthan Govt Animal Husb Servs, India, 58; asst prof Col Vet Med, Osmania Univ, India, 60-61; res assoc hemat, Blood Vascular Dis Res Lab, Univ Toronto Med Sch, 63; res asst pop genetics, Ohio State Univ, 63-65; res asst physiol, Univ Mo-Columbia, 65-70; Nat Acad Sci res assoc, George C Marshall Space Flight Ctr, NASA, Ala, 70-72; staff scientist, URS-Matrix Co, 72-73; vet med officer, Bur Vet Med, 74-79, SPECIAL ASST TO ASSOC DIR, HUMAN FOOD SAFETY, FOOD & DRUG ADMIN, ROCKVILLE, MD, 80- *Concurrent Pos:* Sr vis scientist, Molecular Tox-Div, Med Res Coun Toxicol Lab, Carshalton, Eng, 80-81. *Mem:* AAAS; Soc Toxicol; Am Soc Vet Pharmacol Physiologists; Am Vet Med Asn; Am Col Vet Toxicol. *Res:* Hypothalamic hypophysiotropic neurohormones; drug and chemical induced birth defects; trace element toxicity. *Mailing Add:* 790 W Side Dr Gaithersburg MD 20760

PARKHURST, DAVID FRANK, b Pittsburgh, Pa, Mar 3, 42; div; c 1. ECOLOGY, PLANT PHYSIOLOGY. *Educ:* Univ Colo, Boulder, BS, 65; Univ Wis-Madison, MS, 68, PhD(bot), 70. *Prof Exp:* Lab technician, Inst Arctic & Alpine Res, Colo, 65-66; lectr plant ecol, Univ Wis-Madison, 70, vis asst prof, 70; res scientist, Div Atmospheric Physics, Commonwealth Sci & Indust Res Orgn, 70-73; asst prof, 73-78, asst prof biol, 78-80, ASSOC PROF PUB & ENVIRON AFFAIRS, IND UNIV, BLOOMINGTON, 78-, ASSOC PROF BIOL, 80- *Mem:* AAAS; Ecol Soc Am; Brit Ecol Soc; Am Inst Biol Sci; Am Soc Plant Physiologists. *Res:* Theoretical and experimental studies of adaptive anatomy and physiology of plants, especially as influenced by energy, mass and momentum exchange with the environment. *Mailing Add:* Sch of Pub & Environ Affairs Ind Univ Bloomington IN 47401

PARKHURST, LAWRENCE JOHN, b Kansas City, Mo, Nov 29, 37; m 62; c 2. BIOPHYSICAL CHEMISTRY, BIOCHEMISTRY. *Educ:* Yale Univ, BA, 59, MS, 60, PhD(phys chem), 65. *Prof Exp:* Res assoc biophys, Johnson Found, Univ Pa, 65-66; NIH fel, biophys chem, Cornell Univ, 66-68; from asst prof to assoc prof chem, 69-76, PROF CHEM & LIFE SCI, UNIV NEBR, 76- *Mem:* AAAS; Am Chem Soc; Am Soc Biol Chem; Biophys Soc; Int Photochem Soc. *Res:* Physical chemistry of biological molecules; heme proteins, nucleic acid and ribosome kinetics. *Mailing Add:* Dept of Chem 525 Hamilton Hall Lincoln NE 68588

PARKIN, BLAINE R(APHAEL), b Oakland, Calif, July 25, 22; m 45; c 2. AERODYNAMICS, HYDRODYNAMICS. *Educ:* Calif Inst Technol, BS, 47, MS, 48, PhD(aeronaut), 52. *Prof Exp:* Res engr, Hydrodyn Lab, Calif Inst Technol, 51-54, lectr appl mech, 54-55, res fel eng, 55-56; engr, Rand Corp, 56-62; sr eng specialist, AiResearch Mfg Co, 62-64; mgr aerospace technol & systs anal, Convair Aerospace Div, Gen Dynamics Corp, Calif, 64-67, prog mgr advan aircraft, 67-71; PROF AEROSPACE ENG & DIR GARFIELD THOMAS WATER TUNNEL APPL RES LAB, PA STATE UNIV, UNIVERSITY PARK, 72- *Honors & Awards:* Knapp Award, Am Soc Mech Engrs, 65. *Mem:* Am Inst Aeronaut & Astronaut; fel Am Soc Mech Engrs; Soc Naval Archit & Marine Engrs; Sigma Xi. *Res:* Mechanics of cavitation inception in water flows; cavity flows; wave propagation in solids; applied mechanics; aircraft design. *Mailing Add:* Garfield Thomas Water Tunnel Pa State Univ University Park PA 16802

PARKIN, CURTIS WILLARD, space physics, plasma physics, see previous edition

PARKIN, DON MERRILL, b Salt Lake City, Utah, Nov 7, 43; m 62; c 2. SOLID STATE PHYSICS. *Educ:* Univ Utah, BA, 66, PhD(physics), 70. *Prof Exp:* Fel physics, Brookhaven Nat Lab, 70-72, asst physicist, 72-74; STAFF MEM PHYSICS, LOS ALAMOS SCI LAB, 74- *Mem:* Am Phys Soc; Sigma Xi. *Res:* Defects in solids; radiation effects; neutron sources. *Mailing Add:* Los Alamos Sci Lab MS 734 Los Alamos NM 87545

PARKINS, BOWEN EDWARD, b Omaha, Nebr, Sept 7, 34; m 55; c 4. ACOUSTICS. *Educ:* Univ Kans, BS, 57, MS, 61, PhD(elec eng), 65. *Prof Exp:* Res engr, Electronics Res Labs, Univ Kans, 59-62 & Ctr for Res, 62-65; MEM TECH STAFF, ELEC ENG, BELL TEL LABS, 65- *Mem:* Acoust Soc Am; Sigma Xi. *Res:* Wave propagation; detection and estimation theory and practice. *Mailing Add:* Bell Tel Labs Whippany NJ 07981

PARKINS, CHARLES WARREN, b Pittsburgh, Pa, Feb 4, 37; m 71; c 4. OTORHINOLARYNGOLOGY, SPEECH & HEARING SCIENCE. *Educ:* Bethany Col, BS, 59; Univ Rochester, MD, 63; Am Bd Otorhinolaryngol, dipl, 72. *Prof Exp:* Intern, Wilford Hall, US Air Force Hosp, 63-64; flight surgeon, US Air Force, Ankara, Turkey, 64-67 & Davis-Montham AFB, Ariz, 67-68; resident otolaryngol, Upstate Med Ctr, State Univ NY, 68-72, NIH fel, 72-73, asst prof otorhinolaryngol, 73-81; ASSOC PROF OTORHINOLARYNGOL, MED SCH, UNIV ROCHESTER, 81- *Concurrent Pos:* Fac mem, Self Improv Prog, Am Acad Ophthalmol & Otolaryngol, 73- *Mem:* Fel, Am Acad Ophthalmol & Otolaryngol; Soc Univ Otolaryngologists; assoc Acoust Soc Am; AMA; Am Coun Otolaryngol. *Res:* Auditory neurophysiology involving processing of speech at the eighth nerve single neuron level; electronic prosthetic reproduction. *Mailing Add:* Dept Otolaryngol Box 629 Univ Rochester Sch Med Rochester NY 14642

PARKINS, FREDERICK MILTON, b Princeton, NJ, Sept 8, 35; m 59, 77; c 3. PEDODONTICS, PHYSIOLOGY. *Educ:* Univ Pa, DDS, 60; Univ NC, MSD, 65, PhD(physiol), 69. *Prof Exp:* Instr pedodont, Sch Dent, Univ NC, 65-67; asst prof, Sch Dent Med, Univ Pa, 67-69, dir pedodont & dent auxiliary utilization, 68-69; assoc prof pedodont, Col Dent, Univ Iowa, 69-72, head dept, 69-75, prof, 72-79, asst dean acad affairs, 74-75, assoc dean, 75-79; PROF PEDODONT & DEAN, UNIV LOUISVILLE SCH DENT, 79- *Concurrent Pos:* Dent consult, Dept Pediat, Hahnemann Med Col, 65-69; consult med staff, Children's Hosp of Philadelphia, 67-70 & Vet Admin, 68-70; consult div dent health, USPHS, 69-72, Coun Dent Educ, 74- & Nat Inst Dent Res, 75-, Bur Health Facil, 78-; Robert Wood Johnson Health Policy fel, 77-78; staff, Health & Environ Subcomt, US House Rep, 77-78; mem bd gov, Univ Louisville Hosp, 79- *Mem:* AAAS; Biophys Soc; Sigma Xi; Am Dent Asn; Int Asn Dent Res. *Res:* Fluoride metabolism and therapy; pediatric dentistry; preventive dentistry. *Mailing Add:* Off of Dean Sch Dent Louisville KY 40201

PARKINS, JOHN ALEXANDER, b Warrenton, Va, Apr 18, 16; m 42; c 2. PHYSICAL CHEMISTRY. *Educ:* Washington & Lee Univ, AB, 39; Johns Hopkins Univ, AM, 49, PhD(chem), 51. *Prof Exp:* Res chemist, Geo W Bollman Co, 46-48; res chemist, E I du Pont de Nemours & Co, Inc, 51-60, tech investr, Film Dept, 60-76, patent consult, 76-81; RETIRED. *Concurrent Pos:* Patent agent, 76- *Mem:* Am Chem Soc. *Res:* Polymer chemistry; technical liaison between patents and regulatory affairs and research and development; manufacturing. *Mailing Add:* 14 Vassar Dr Newark DE 19711

PARKINS, WILLIAM EDWARD, b Bozeman, Mont, Mar 1, 16; m 48; c 3. ENERGY CONVERSION. *Educ:* Mont State Univ, BS, 37; Cornell Univ, PhD(physics), 42. *Prof Exp:* Asst physics, Cornell Univ, 39-42; res assoc, Radiation Lab, Univ Calif, 42-46; asst prof physics, Univ Southern Calif, 46-48; group leader exp physics, NAm Aviation, Inc, 49-51 & reactor eng, 52-54, chief engr, Atomics Int Div, 54-59, dir org reactors dept, 59-61, div dir res & tech, 61-69, mgr component eng & technol, NAm Rockwell Corp, 69-72, dir res & technol, Energy Syst Group, Rockwell Int Corp, 72-81;

CONSULT, 81- *Concurrent Pos:* Mem liquid metals comt, AEC & Off Naval Res, 51-54; spec adv US del, Int Conf Peaceful Use Atomic Energy, 55. *Mem:* AAAS; fel Am Phys Soc; fel Am Nuclear Soc; Am Inst Aeronaut & Astronaut. *Res:* Ion and electron physics; mass spectroscopy; particle accelerators; effects of radiation on solids; liquid metal technology; engineering of nuclear reactor plants; energy conversion. *Mailing Add:* 20120 Well Dr Woodland Hills CA 91364

PARKINSON, BRUCE ALAN, b Rochester, Minn, Mar 1, 51. ELECTROCHEMISTRY, INORGANIC CHEMISTRY. *Educ:* Iowa State Univ, BS, 72; Calif Inst Technol, PhD(chem), 77. *Prof Exp:* Fel chem, Bell Labs, 77-78; res chemist, Ames Lab, Dept Energy, 79-81; SR SCIENTIST, SOLAR ENERGY RES INST, 81- *Mem:* Electrochem Soc; Am Chem Soc. *Res:* Semiconductor electrochemistry; solar energy conversion; inorganic electrochemistry; interfacial electrochemistry. *Mailing Add:* Solar Energy Res Inst Golden CO 80401

PARKINSON, CLAIRE LUCILLE, b Bay Shore, NY, March 21, 48. POLAR SCIENCE, CLIMATOLOGY. *Educ:* Wellesley Col, BA, 70; Ohio State Univ, MA, 74, PhD(climat), 77. *Prof Exp:* Res asst, Nat Ctr Atmospheric Res, 76-78; RES SCIENTIST, GOODARD SPACE FLIGHT CTR, NASA, 78- *Res:* Numerical modeling of the annual cycle of Arctic & Antarctic sea ice distributions; analysis of satellite imagery regarding sea ice; examination of sea ice atmosphere and sea ice/ocean interactions. *Mailing Add:* Code 9121 Goddard Space Flight Ctr NASA Greenbelt MD 20771

PARKINSON, DENNIS, b Bolton, Eng, Sept 1, 27. BOTANY, MICROBIOLOGY. *Educ:* Univ London, BSc, 51; Univ Nottingham, PhD(bot), 56. *Prof Exp:* Asst lectr bot, Royal Holloway Col, London, 53-56; lectr, Univ Liverpool, 56-64; prof biol, Univ Waterloo, 64-67; head dept biol, 68-77, prof biol, 67-77 PROF MICROBIOL, UNIV CALGARY, 78- *Concurrent Pos:* Orgn Econ Coop & Develop sr fel, Univ Mich, 63. *Mem:* Brit Mycol Soc; Brit Soc Soil Sci; Can Soc Microbiol. *Res:* Soil microbiology; nature and activity of microbial populations in plant litter; arctic microbiology including effects of oil spillage. *Mailing Add:* Dept of Biol Univ of Calgary Calgary AB T2N 1N4 Can

PARKINSON, G(EOFFREY) VERNON, b Regina, Sask, Dec 13, 24; m 54; c 2. FLUID MECHANICS, DYNAMICS. *Educ:* Univ BC, BASc, 46; Calif Inst Technol, MS, 48, PhD(aeronaut), 51. *Prof Exp:* From asst prof to assoc prof, 51-65, PROF MECH ENG, UNIV BC, 65-, LECTR AERONAUT ENG, 70- *Concurrent Pos:* Nat Res Coun Can grants, 60-; Defence Res Bd Can grant, 61-; Nuffield fel, Nat Phys Lab, UK, 62-63; mem assoc comt aerodyn, Nat Res Coun Can, 65- *Mem:* Fel Can Aeronaut & Space Inst. *Res:* Dynamics and fluid dynamics of flow-induced oscillations of bluff bodies; airfoil and wing theory; unsteady fluid mechanics and gas dynamics theory; biomedical fluid mechanics. *Mailing Add:* Dept of Mech Eng Univ of BC Vancouver BC V6T 1W5 Can

PARKINSON, JOHN STANSFIELD, b Buffalo, NY, Feb 17, 44; m 67; c 3. MOLECULAR GENETICS. *Educ:* Haverford Col, AB, 65; Calif Inst Technol, PhD(genetics, biophys), 70. *Prof Exp:* Vis asst prof microbial genetics, Ore State Univ, 69-70; NSF fel, Univ Wis, 70-71, NIH fel, 71-72; asst prof, 72-76, assoc prof, 76-81, PROF BIOL, UNIV UTAH, 81- *Concurrent Pos:* Prin investr, NIH grant, 73-, Microbiol Genetics Rev Group, NIH, 77-80. *Mem:* Am Soc Microbiol; Am Genetics Soc. *Res:* Genetic and biochemical bases of behavior; transmission and expression of genetic information; mechanism of bacterial chemotaxis and motility. *Mailing Add:* Dept of Biol Univ of Utah Salt Lake City UT 84112

PARKINSON, MICHAEL THADDEUS, high energy physics, see previous edition

PARKINSON, R(OBERT) E(DWARD), b Mt Carmel, Ill, Nov 30, 09; m 36; c 3. CHEMISTRY, METALS. *Educ:* Northwestern Univ, BS, 31; Univ Syracuse, MS, 33. *Prof Exp:* Asst chem, Univ Syracuse, 31-33; metallurgist, Inland Steel Co, 33-35; res engr, Battelle Mem Inst, 35-45; consult, antitrust div, Dept of Justice, 45; coordr tech info, Owens-Ill Glass Co, 45-48; sr testing engr, Sears Roebuck & Co, 49-53; asst to dir res, Kawneer Co, 53-54; asst mgr, Porce- Alume Co, 58; sr res engr, Appl Res Lab, US Steel Corp, 59-71, assoc res consult, 71-74; RETIRED. *Concurrent Pos:* Consult, 74- *Mem:* Am Chem Soc; fel Am Inst Chem. *Res:* Adhesive bonding of metals; special coatings; porcelain enameling of aluminum; metal finishing; materials. *Mailing Add:* PO Box 805 South Well Fleet PA 02663

PARKINSON, THOMAS FRANKLIN, b Tampa, Fla, Feb 22, 25; m 48; c 1. PHYSICS. *Educ:* Auburn Univ, BS, 47; Univ Va, PhD(physics), 53. *Prof Exp:* Physicist, Carbide & Carbon Chem Corp, 48-49; res physicist, Savannah River Lab, E I du Pont de Nemours & Co, 52-60; assoc prof nuclear eng sci, Univ Fla, 60-63, prof, 63-67; prof nuclear eng & chmn dept, Univ Mo-Columbia, 67-75; PROF NUCLEAR ENERGY & DIR NUCLEAR REACTOR LAB, VA POLYTECH INST & STATE UNIV, 75-, CHMN DEPT, 79- *Concurrent Pos:* Fulbright-Hays res fel, Madrid, Spain, 66-67; consult, Nuclear Regulatory Comn, Washington, 74-75 & Int Atomic Energy Agency, Vienna, 79- *Mem:* AAAS; Am Phys Soc; Am Nuclear Soc. *Res:* Nuclear reactor physics; nuclear engineering; activation analysis; neutron spectrometry. *Mailing Add:* Nuclear Reactor Lab Va Polytech Inst & State Univ Blacksburg VA 24061

PARKINSON, TRUMAN DAVID, b East Orange, NJ, May 11, 42; m 66; c 1. APPLIED MECHANICS. *Educ:* Carnegie Inst Technol, BS, 64; Univ Pittsburgh, PhD(physics), 69. *Prof Exp:* Asst physicist, Kitt Peak Nat Observ, 69-74; staff scientist, Gould Labs, Ill, 74-76, proj engr, Gould Labs, 76-80, PROG MGR, FED SYSTS LABS, GOULD INC, OHIO, 80- *Mem:* AAAS. *Res:* Process and product research and development based upon understanding of fundamental physical theory and facility to reduce that understanding to tested and finished hardware; system concept and development through engineering development stage. *Mailing Add:* Gould Labs Gould Inc 540 E 105th St Cleveland OH 44108

PARKINSON, WILLIAM CHARLES, b Jarvis, Ont, Feb 11, 18; US citizen; m 44; c 2. NUCLEAR PHYSICS. *Educ:* Univ Mich, BSE, 40, MS, 41, PhD(physics), 48. *Prof Exp:* Asst nuclear physics, Univ Mich, 36-42; physicist, Appl Physics Lab, Johns Hopkins Univ, 42-46; res assoc, 46-47, from instr to assoc prof, 47-58, dir cyclotron lab, 62-77, PROF PHYSICS, UNIV MICH, ANN ARBOR, 58- *Concurrent Pos:* Fulbright scholar, 52-53; consult, Oak Ridge Nat Lab, 55-60, Los Alamos Nat Lab, 58-60 & Argonne Nat Lab, 59-60; mem subcomt nuclear structure, Nat Acad Sci-Nat Res Coun, 60-72; mem adv panel physics, NSF, 66-69; mem physics rev comn, Argonne Nat Lab, 59-63. *Mem:* Fel Am Phys Soc; NY Acad Sci. *Res:* Nuclear spectroscopy. *Mailing Add:* Dept Physics Univ Mich Ann Arbor MI 48109

PARKINSON, WILLIAM HAMBLETON, b Trenton, NJ, June 26, 32; m 54; c 2. SPECTROSCOPY, ASTROPHYSICS. *Educ:* Western Ont Univ, BSc, 56, MSc, 57, PhD(physics), 59. *Prof Exp:* Nat Res Coun Can fel spectros, Imp Col, London, 59-61; lectr spectros & res physicist, 61-73, LECTR ASTRON, HARVARD UNIV, 73- & ASSOC DIR, CTR ASTROPHYS, 78- *Concurrent Pos:* Consult, Solar Physics Subcomt, NASA, 61-, mem, Space Sci Solar Subcomt, 65-; sr res assoc, Harvard Col Observ, 65-; assoc dir, Ctr Astrophys, Smithsonian Astrophys Observ, 68- & Harvard Col Observ, 73-; physicist, Smithsonian Inst, 73- *Mem:* Int Astron Union; Am Astron Soc; Am Phys Soc. *Res:* Experimental atomic and molecular spectroscopy; astrophysics and upper atmospheric physics from observations with laboratory light sources and from solar pointed rocket and satellite borne experiments. *Mailing Add:* Dept of Astron Harvard Univ Cambridge MA 02138

PARKINSON, WILLIAM WALKER, JR, b White Oak, SC, June 30, 19; m 47; c 1. PHYSICAL CHEMISTRY, POLYMER CHEMISTRY. *Educ:* Erskine Col, AB, 40; Univ NC, PhD, 49. *Prof Exp:* Chemist, Reactor Chem Div, 49-73, chemist, Health Physics Div, 73-79, CHEMIST, GASEOUS DIFFUSION PLANT, OAK RIDGE NAT LAB, 79- *Mem:* Am Chem Soc; fel Am Inst Chem; AAAS. *Res:* Radiation-induced processes in high polymers; the relationship of physical properties of plastics and rubbers to their molecular structure; health physics of internal radioactive isotopes. *Mailing Add:* 834 Nelson Dr Kingston TN 37763

PARKMAN, PAUL DOUGLAS, b Auburn, NY, May 29, 32; m 55. VIROLOGY, PEDIATRICS. *Educ:* St Lawrence Univ, BS, 57; State Univ NY, MD, 57; Am Bd Pediat, dipl, 62. *Hon Degrees:* DSc, St Lawrence Univ, 70. *Prof Exp:* Intern, Mary Imogene Bassett Hosp, Cooperstown, NY, 57-58; resident pediat, State Univ NY Upstate Med Ctr Hosp, 58-60; chief sect gen virol, Lab Viral Immunol, Div Biologics Standards, NIH, 63-72; dir div virol, 72-73, DEP DIR, BUR BIOLOGICS, US FOOD & DRUG ADMIN, 73- *Honors & Awards:* E Mead Johnson Award, Am Acad Pediat, 67; Max Weinstein Award, United Cerebral Palsy, 69; Int Award Distinguished Sci Res, Joseph P Kennedy, Jr Found, 71. *Mem:* Am Asn Immunologists; Soc Pediat Res; Am Epidemiol Soc. *Res:* Laboratory and clinical research in infectious diseases; clinical pediatric investigation. *Mailing Add:* Bur of Biologics US Food & Drug Admin Bethesda MD 20014

PARKMAN, SAMMIE BELL, b Doerun, Ga, Jan 2, 21; m 44; c 4. AGRONOMY. *Educ:* Univ Ga, BS, 42, MS, 47; Miss State Univ, PhD(seed technol), 63. *Prof Exp:* Agronomist, Ga Coastal Plain Exp Sta, 47-55; MGR SEED DIV, GA DEPT AGR, 57- *Mem:* Am Soc Agron. *Res:* Seed technology. *Mailing Add:* 310 Ashton Dr Athens GA 30606

PARKS, ALBERT FIELDING, b Sulphur Rock, Ark, June 27, 09; m 33; c 1. ANALYTICAL CHEMISTRY, INTERNATIONAL TRADE. *Educ:* Ark Col, AB, 29; NY Univ, MSc, 31. *Prof Exp:* Prof, Ark Col, 31-36; chemist, US Customs Lab, La, 36-43, asst chief chemist, 46-49, asst chief, Div Tech Serv Bur Customs, 49-59; asst chief, US Tariff Comn, 60-69, dir off trade & indust, US Tariff Comn, 75; RETIRED. *Mem:* Am Chem Soc; Am Soc Qual Control; Am Inst Chem; NY Acad Sci. *Res:* Analytical methods covering a wide range of imported commodities, such as ores, metals, sugar products, narcotics, drugs, food products and miscellaneous manufactured materials. *Mailing Add:* 1500 Fairway Dr W Memphis AR 72301

PARKS, DONALD E, b Montgomery, WVa, Jan 7, 31; m 53; c 2. PHYSICS. *Educ:* Carnegie Inst Technol, BS, 53, MS, 54, PhD(physics), 58. *Prof Exp:* Instr physics, Carnegie Inst Technol, 58; sr staff mem, John Jay Hopkins Lab Pure & Appl Sci, Gen Atomic Div, Gen Dynamics Corp, 58-65, spec nuclear effects lab, 65-67; physicist, 67-69, SR RES SCIENTIST, SYSTS, SCI & SOFTWARE, 69- *Concurrent Pos:* Consult, Nat Comt Nuclear Energy, Italy, 61, 63-64. *Mem:* Am Phys Soc. *Res:* Atomic physics; plasma physics; slow neutron scattering; neutron thermalization; reactor physics; interaction of electromagnetic radiation with matter; transport theory. *Mailing Add:* Systems, Sci & Software PO Box 1620 La Jolla CA 92037

PARKS, E(DWIN) K(ETCHUM), b Riverbow, Alta, Oct 23, 17; nat US; m 41; c 3. AERONAUTICAL ENGINEERING. *Educ:* Univ Alta, BSc, 49, Univ Toronto, MASc, 50, PhD(aeronaut), 52. *Prof Exp:* Res officer, Nat Res Coun Can, 52-53; assoc prof aeronaut eng, Univ Kans, 53-60; PROF AERONAUT & MECH ENG, UNIV ARIZ, 60- *Mem:* Assoc fel Am Inst Aeronaut & Astronaut. *Res:* Nonstationary and viscous aerodynamics; shock tubes; wind tunnels; airplane dynamics. *Mailing Add:* Dept of Aeronaut & Mech Eng Univ of Ariz Tucson AZ 85721

PARKS, ERIC K, b Meriden, Conn, May 3, 40. PHYSICAL CHEMISTRY. *Educ:* Rensselaer Polytech, BS, 62; Univ Calif, Berkeley, PhD(phys chem), 66. *Prof Exp:* NSF fel chem, Mass Inst Technol, 66-67, res assoc, 67-68; fel, 69-70, PERMANENT STAFF CHEM DIV, ARGONNE NAT LAB, 70- *Mem:* Am Phys Soc. *Res:* Chemical kinetics; molecular beams. *Mailing Add:* Bldg 200 Argonne Nat Lab Argonne IL 60439

PARKS, GEORGE A(LBERT), b Oakland, Calif, May 3, 31; m 56; c 2. GEOCHEMISTRY, MINERAL ENGINEERING. *Educ:* Univ Calif, Berkeley, BS, 53, MS, 54; Mass Inst Technol, PhD(metall), 60. *Prof Exp:* From asst prof to assoc prof, 59-70, PROF MINERAL ENG & GEOCHEM, STANFORD UNIV, 70-, ASSOC CHMN, DEPT APPL EARTH SCI, 74- *Mem:* Am Inst Mining, Metall & Petrol Engrs; Am Chem Soc; Geochem Soc; Soc Geochem & Health. *Res:* Inorganic surface and colloid chemistry of oxides and minerals; applications in extractive metallurgy, geochemistry and environmental pollution abatement; process innovation and interpretation. *Mailing Add:* Dept of Appl Earth Sci Stanford Univ Stanford CA 94305

PARKS, GEORGE KUNG, b Shanghai, China, July 17, 35; US citizen; m 58; c 2. GEOPHYSICS, PHYSICS. *Educ:* Univ Calif, Berkeley, BA, 61, PhD(physics), 66. *Prof Exp:* Res assoc, Univ Minn, Minneapolis, 67-69; assoc prof space physics, Univ Toulouse, 69-71; asst prof, 71-73, assoc prof 73-76, PROF GEOPHYS, UNIV WASH, 76- *Concurrent Pos:* NSF grants, 72- *Honors & Awards:* Hon dipl, Acad Sci, USSR. *Mem:* Am Geophys Union; Am Inst Physics Teachers. *Res:* Space physics; plasma and wave particle interactions; origin of energetic particles in the earth's magnetic field; solar flares. *Mailing Add:* Dept Geophys Univ Wash Seattle WA 98195

PARKS, HAROLD FRANCIS, b Anna, Ill, Sept 28, 20; m 48; c 2. ANATOMY, CYTOLOGY. *Educ:* Southern Ill Univ, BEd, 42; Cornell Univ, PhD(histol, embryol), 50. *Prof Exp:* Asst zool, Cornell Univ, 45-50; from instr to asst prof anat, Univ NC, 50-54; from asst prof to assoc prof, Sch Med & Dent, Univ Rochester, 54-61; prof zool, Cornell Univ, 61-64; PROF ANAT, MED CTR, UNIV KY, 64- *Mem:* AAAS; Am Asn Anatomists; Am Soc Cell Biol; Electro Micros Soc Am; Am Soc Zoologists. *Res:* Cytology and cytochemistry of salivary and cutaneous glands, liver, pancreas, heart and kidney; ultrastructure of tooth and bone; phagocytosis. *Mailing Add:* Dept of Anat Univ of Ky Med Ctr Lexington KY 40506

PARKS, HAROLD GEORGE, b Shelburne Falls, Mass, May 15, 42; m 64; c 3. ELECTRON OPTICS, ELECTRONIC ENGINEERING. *Educ:* Lowell Technol Inst, BS, 64; Syracuse Univ, MS, 69; Rensselaer Polytech Inst, PhD, 80. *Prof Exp:* Elec engr circuit design, Int Bus Mach, 64-66, engr analog & digital design, Xerox Corp, 66-69; ELEC ENGR ELECTRON OPTICS LASER ANNEALING, SEMICONDUTOR PROCESSING, GEN ELEC CO, 69- *Res:* Electron and ion optics, numerical analysis, lens and deflection system designs; beam memory targets and charged partical and target interactions; semiconductor processing. *Mailing Add:* Gen Elec Co PO Box 48 Bldg K1-5C6 Schenectady NY 12301

PARKS, HAROLD RAYMOND, b Wilmington, Del, May 22, 49; m 71; c 2. GEOMETRIC MEASURE THEORY. *Educ:* Dartmouth Col, AB, 71; Princeton Univ, PhD(math), 74. *Prof Exp:* J D Tamarkin instr math, Brown Univ, 74-77; ASST PROF MATH, ORE STATE UNIV, 77- *Mem:* Am Math Soc. *Res:* Methods for computing solutions of the least area problem, particularly those solutions whose existence is guaranteed by results in geometric measure theory. *Mailing Add:* Dept Math Ore State Univ Corvallis OR 97331

PARKS, JAMES C, b Altoona, Pa, Aug 9, 42; m 64; c 1. PLANT SYSTEMATICS. *Educ:* Shippensburg State Col, BS, 64; Vanderbilt Univ, PhD(bot), 68. *Prof Exp:* Asst prof, 68-72, assoc prof, 72-77, PROF BIOL, MILLERSVILLE STATE COL, 77- *Mem:* Int Asn Plant Taxon; Am Soc Plant Taxonomists. *Res:* Plant systematics; floristics; cytotaxonomy; pteridology. *Mailing Add:* Dept of Biol Millersville State Col Millersville PA 17551

PARKS, JAMES EDGAR, b Morganton, NC, Jan 12, 39; m 62; c 4. PHYSICS. *Educ:* Berea Col, BA, 61; Univ Tenn, MS, 65; Univ Ky, PhD(physics), 70. *Prof Exp:* Res assoc health physics, Oak Ridge Nat Lab, 61-64; instr physics, Berea Col, 64-66; res assoc, Univ Ky, 70; asst prof, 70-74, ASSOC PROF PHYSICS, WESTERN KY UNIV, 74- *Concurrent Pos:* Consult, Health Physics Div, Oak Ridge Nat Lab, 74- *Mem:* Am Phys Soc; Am Asn Physics Teachers; Sigma Xi. *Res:* Radiation physics; atomic and molecular physics; atomic collisions; laser physics. *Mailing Add:* Dept of Physics & Astron Western Ky Univ Bowling Green KY 42101

PARKS, JAMES MARSHALL, JR, b Topeka, Kans, Apr 1, 25; m 63; c 3. PALEOECOLOGY, SEDIMENTOLOGY. *Educ:* Univ Kans, AB, 48; Univ Wis, MS, 49, PhD(geol), 51. *Prof Exp:* Asst, Univ Wis, 48-51; Fulbright scholar, Univ Edinburgh, 51-52; res geologist, Shell Develop Co, 52-59; sr res scientist, Pure Oil Co, 59-65, dir, Div Explor Res, 65; supvr geol & geochem res, Union Oil Co Calif, 65-67; PROF GEOL SCI & DIR CTR MARINE & ENVIRON STUDIES, LEHIGH UNIV, 67- *Concurrent Pos:* Res assoc, Wetlands Inst, 72- *Mem:* AAAS; fel Geol Soc Am; Paleont Soc; Soc Econ Paleont & Mineral; Am Asn Petrol Geol. *Res:* Invertebrate paleontology; paleoecology; stratigraphy; sedimentology; carbonate petrography and petrology; computer applications in geology and oceanography; coastal zone geologic processes and oceanography; computer-managed instruction. *Mailing Add:* 4674 Steven Lane Walnutport PA 18088

PARKS, JOEL HARRIS, physics, see previous edition

PARKS, JOHN S, b Washington, DC, Oct 14, 39; m 59; c 3. PEDIATRICS, ENDOCRINOLOGY. *Educ:* Amherst Col, AB, 61; Univ Pa, MD, 66, PhD(biochem), 71. *Prof Exp:* USPHS fel biochem, Univ Pa, 66-67; from intern to resident pediat, Children's Hosp of Philadelphia, 67-69; clin assoc endocrinol, Endocrinol Br, Nat Cancer Inst, 69-70 & Lab Molecular Biol, 70-71; fel, 71-73, assoc dir, div endocrinol, Children's Hosp of Philadelphia, 73-77; ASST PROF PEDIAT, SCH MED, UNIV PA, 73- *Mem:* Endocrine Soc. *Res:* Bacterial gene control; pediatric endocrinology; growth hormone action. *Mailing Add:* Div of Endocrinol 3401 Civic Ctr Blvd Philadelphia PA 19104

PARKS, KENNETH LEE, b Pineville, Ky, Mar 3, 31; m 58. INDUSTRIAL CHEMISTRY. *Educ:* Davidson Col, BS, 54; Univ NC, PhD(anal chem), 59. *Prof Exp:* Chemist, Atlantic Ref Co, 59-60; res chemist, Rohm and Haas Co, 60-61; process chemist, Am Cyanamid Co, 61-64, sr chemist, 64-65; group leader process develop, Fla, 65-67, dir environ & chem control, Tenn, 67-69, coordr, Fla, 69-72, dir res & develop, 72-76; DIR TECH DEVELOP, AGRICO CHEM CO, 76- *Mem:* Am Chem Soc. *Res:* Analytical methods; plant food manufacturing processes and chemistry; pollution control methodology for air and water. *Mailing Add:* Agrico Chem Co Box 1969 Bartow FL 74101

PARKS, LEO WILBURN, b Wetaug, Ill, Nov 21, 30; m 57; c 2. *Educ:* Univ Ill, BS, 52; Ind Univ, MA, 53; Univ Wash, PhD(microbiol), 56. *Prof Exp:* Asst microbiol, Ind Univ, 52-53 & Univ Wash, 53-55; resident res assoc, Argonne Nat Lab, 56-58; from asst prof to assoc prof, 58-66, PROF MICROBIOL, ORE STATE UNIV, 66- *Concurrent Pos:* NSF fel, Univ Copenhagen, 65-66; US Pub Health Serv Fel, Univ Louis Pasteur, Strasbourg, France, 72-73. *Mem:* Am Soc Microbiol; Am Soc Biol Chem; Brit Soc Gen Microbiol; fel AAAS; Am Acad Microbiol. *Res:* Microbial physiology; molecular biology; biochemistry of bacteria. *Mailing Add:* Dept of Microbiol Ore State Univ Corvallis OR 97331

PARKS, LEWIS ARTHUR, b Hutchinson, Kans, Oct 31, 47; m 71; c 2. RADIATION GAUGING. *Educ:* Kans State Teachers Col, BA, 69, MS, 71; Univ Tex, Austin, PhD(physics), 76. *Prof Exp:* Res Assoc, Physics Dept, Fla State Univ, 76-78; STAFF PHYSICIST, IRT CORP, 78- *Mem:* Am Phys Soc. *Res:* radiation guaging, primarily in support of the ordnance industry; experimental heavy ion nuclear research. *Mailing Add:* IRT Corp PO Box 80817 San Diego CA 92138

PARKS, LLOYD MCCLAIN, b Scottsburg, Ind, Mar 21, 12; m 40; c 1. PHARMACEUTICAL CHEMISTRY. *Educ:* Purdue Univ, BS, 33, MS, 36; Univ Wis, PhD(pharmaceut chem), 38. *Hon Degrees:* DSc, Purdue Univ, 62; DPS, Union Col, 71. *Prof Exp:* From instr to prof pharmaceut chem, Univ Wis, 38-56; dean col pharm, Ohio State Univ, 56-77. *Concurrent Pos:* Mem revision comt, US Pharmacopoeia, 50-62, Am Coun Pharmaceut Educ, 62-68. *Honors & Awards:* Ebert Prize, Am Pharmaceut Asn, 52, Res Achievement Award, 66, Remington Honor Medal, 75. *Mem:* AAAS; Am Chem Soc; Am Pharmaceut Asn (pres, 71-72); Am Inst Hist Pharm; Am Soc Pharmacog. *Res:* Organic pharmaceutical chemistry; medicinal chemistry. *Mailing Add:* 5495 Archway Dr Columbus OH 43220

PARKS, NORRIS JIM, b Snyder, Tex, July 5, 43. PHYSICAL CHEMISTRY, NUCLEAR CHEMISTRY. *Educ:* Eastern NMex Univ, BS, 65; Univ Nebr, PhD(phys & nuclear chem), 69. *Prof Exp:* Fel high energy chem dynamics, 69-71, res chemist, Radiobiol Lab, 72-80, RES CHEMIST, LAB FOR ENERGY-RELATED HEALTH RES, UNIV CALIF, DAVIS, 80- *Mem:* Am Chem Soc; Sigma Xi; AAAS. *Res:* Chemical effects of nuclear transformations; high energy gas kinetics; radiation chemistry; radiochemical applications; nuclear applications in medicine; radiobiology; chemical toxicology. *Mailing Add:* Lab Energy-related Health Res Univ of Calif Davis CA 95616

PARKS, PAUL BLAIR, b Erwin, NC, Nov 20, 34; m 55; c 1. EXPERIMENTAL NUCLEAR PHYSICS, REACTOR PHYSICS. *Educ:* Duke Univ, BS, 57, PhD(physics), 63. *Prof Exp:* Res assoc nuclear physics, Duke Univ, 63-64; RES STAFF PHYSICIST, SAVANNAH RIVER LAB, E I DU PONT DE NEMOURS & CO, INC, 64- *Res:* High resolution nuclear structure studies; reactor experiments using pulsed neutron sources; reactor kinetic studies emphasizing space-time effects; reactor safety research using calculated transients reactor charge design; neutron radiography applied to medical or biological problems. *Mailing Add:* Savannah River Lab E I du Pont de Nemours & Co Inc Aiken SC 29801

PARKS, PAUL FRANKLIN, b Opelika, Ala, Nov 9, 33; m 53; c 4. BIOCHEMISTRY, NUTRITION. *Educ:* Auburn Univ, BS, 56, MS, 59; Tex A&M Univ, PhD(biochem), 62. *Prof Exp:* Asst prof biochem, Tex A&M Univ, 62-65; assoc prof, 65-74, asst dean, 68-72, DEAN, GRAD SCH, 72-, PROF ANIMAL SCI, AUBURN UNIV, 74- *Mem:* AAAS; Am Inst Nutrit. *Res:* Relationship between lipid metabolism and certain nutritional diseases. *Mailing Add:* Grad Sch Auburn Univ Auburn AL 36830

PARKS, ROBERT EMMETT, JR, b Glendale, NY, July 29, 21; m 45; c 3. BIOCHEMISTRY, PHARMACOLOGY. *Educ:* Brown Univ, AB, 44; Harvard Univ, MD, 45; Univ Wis, PhD(biochem), 54. *Prof Exp:* Intern, Boston Children's Hosp, 45-46; res assoc biochem, Amherst Col, 48-51; from asst prof to prof pharmacol, Med Sch, Univ Wis, 54-63, actg chmn dept, 62-63; chmn sect biochem pharmacol, 68-76, PROF MED SCI, BROWN UNIV, 63-; ASSOC DIR, ROGER WILLIAMS CANCER CTR, 73- *Concurrent Pos:* Am Cancer Soc fel, Enzyme Inst, Univ Wis, 51-54; John & Mary Markle Found scholar, 56-61. *Mem:* Am Soc Biol Chemists; Am Soc Pharmacol & Exp Therapeut; Am Asn Cancer Res; Am Chem Soc. *Res:* Mechanism of action of antitumor agents; drug metabolism; enzyme mechanisms; regulation of carbohydrate metabolism; drug action. *Mailing Add:* Div of Biol & Med Sci Brown Univ Providence RI 02912

PARKS, ROBERT J, b Los Angeles, Calif, Apr 1, 22; m 47; c 3. ELECTRICAL ENGINEERING. *Educ:* Calif Inst Technol, BSEE, 44. *Prof Exp:* Engr, 47-51, chief, Guid & Control Sect, 51-56, Guid & Control Div, 56-58 & Guid & Control Dept, 58-60, dir, Sergeant Prog, 57-60 & Planetary Prog, 60-62, asst lab dir lunar & planetary projs, 62-65, surveyor proj mgr, 65-67, ASST LAB DIR FLIGHT PROJS, JET PROPULSION LAB, CALIF INST TECHNOL, 67- *Concurrent Pos:* Consult, Tech Adv Panel Aeronaut, Off Secy Defense, 57-58 & Advan Res Projs Agency Ad Hoc Panel Commun Satellite, Inst Defense Anal, 59; mem ad hoc group solid propellants, Bur Naval Weapons, 57-58. *Honors & Awards:* Hill Space Transp Award, 63. *Mem:* Nat Acad Eng; fel Am Inst Aeronaut & Astronaut; fel Inst Elec & Electronics Engrs. *Res:* Automatic guidance and control systems, particularly as applied to ballistic missiles and space vehicles, including the optimization of such systems in the presence of unwanted noise or external distrubances. *Mailing Add:* Jet Propulsion Lab 4800 Oak Grove Dr Pasadena CA 91103

PARKS, RONALD DEE, b Kansas City, Mo, Feb 9, 35; m 57; c 4. EXPERIMENTAL PHYSICS. *Educ:* Kans State Univ, BS, 56; Stanford Univ, MS, 58, PhD(physics), 61. *Prof Exp:* Res assoc physics, Stanford Univ, 61-62; from asst prof to assoc prof, Univ Rochester, 62-68, prof physics, 68-79; PROF PHYSICS, POLYTECH UNIV NY, 79-, DEPT HEAD, 80- *Concurrent Pos:* NSF fel, 61-62; Alfred P Sloan res fel, 63-67. *Mem:* Fel Am Phys Soc. *Res:* Magnetic and thermal properties of paramagnetic metals at low temperatures; order-disorder and magnetic critical phenomena; valence fluctuations and other many body phenomena in Anderson Lattice systems; surface physics; properties of dilute and concentrated spin glasses; photoemission spectroscopy. *Mailing Add:* Dept Physics Polytech Inst 333 Jay St Rochester NY 11201

PARKS, ROSS LOMBARD, b Asheville, NC, Sept 13, 20; m 48; c 3. ANALYTICAL CHEMISTRY. *Educ:* Davidson Col, BS, 43; Univ NC, PhD, 52. *Prof Exp:* Res chemist, Am Enka Corp, 51-54, chief chemist nylon, 54-60, head tire yarn develop, 60-63; head polyester develop, Textiles Div, Monsanto Co, 63-66, tech supvr, Polyester Dept, Monsanto Textiles Co, 66-77, SUPVR ADVAN DEVICES, DEPT ORG MAT RES & DEVELOP, MONSANTO RES CORP, 77- *Mem:* Am Chem Soc. *Res:* Polymer chemistry; polyamides; polyesters. *Mailing Add:* 520 E Rahn Rd Dayton OH 45429

PARKS, TERRY EVERETT, b Satanta, Kans, Feb 20, 41; m 61; c 2. ORGANIC CHEMISTRY, MATHEMATICS EDUCATION. *Educ:* Kans State Teachers Col, BS, 61, MS, 65; Brown Univ, PhD(org chem), 71. *Prof Exp:* Teacher high sch, Kans, 61-66; NIH trainee, Cornell Univ, 70-71; pres, New-Chem Inc, 71-; gen dir, 73-76, supvr fed proj, 71-81, MATH SUPVR, SHAWNEE MISSION PUB SCHS, KANS, 72-, EXEC DIR FED PROJ, 81- *Concurrent Pos:* Consult, Pub Schs, Kans, 71-73; mem, Kans State Metric Educ Task Force, 74-76, adj prof, Kans State Univ, 74-75; instr, Int Grad Sch Educ, 78-79. *Mem:* Nat Coun Teachers Math; Am Chem Soc; US Metric Asn. *Res:* Instructional organic mass spectrometry; fragmentation mechanisms; pseudohalogen isomerizations; instructional design; organic nuclear quadrupole design; finger calculation methods; computers and calculators and their effect on education. *Mailing Add:* 10073 Hemlock Dr Overland Park KS 66212

PARKS, THOMAS WILLIAM, b Buffalo, NY, Mar 16, 39; m 62; c 3. ELECTRICAL ENGINEERING, DIGITAL SIGNAL PROCESSING. *Educ:* Cornell Univ, BEE, 61, MS, 64, PhD(elec eng), 67. *Prof Exp:* Engr, Gen Elec Advan Electronics Ctr, 61-63; from asst prof to assoc prof, 67-77, PROF ELEC ENG, RICE UNIV, 77- *Concurrent Pos:* NSF grants, 70-82; Sr Fulbright Fel, 73. *Honors & Awards:* Sr Scientist Award, Alexander von Humboldt Found, 73. *Mem:* Inst Elec & Electronics Engrs. *Res:* Communication and signal theory; digital signal processing and filtering; geophysical signal analysis. *Mailing Add:* Dept of Elec Eng Rice Univ Houston TX 77001

PARKS, VINCENT JOSEPH, b Chicago, Ill, May 5, 28; m 55; c 7. MECHANICS. *Educ:* Ill Inst Technol, BS, 53; Cath Univ Am, MCE 63, PhD(mech), 68. *Prof Exp:* Proj engr, Andrew Corp, Ill, 53-55; res engr, Armour Res Found, Ill Inst Technol, 55-61; from asst prof to assoc prof, 65-73, PROF CIVIL ENG, CATH UNIV AM, 73- *Concurrent Pos:* Nat Acad Sci resident res associateship, Naval Res Lab, 71-72. *Honors & Awards:* M Hetenyl Award, Soc Exp Stress Anal, 74 & M M Frocth Award, 81. *Mem:* Fel Soc Exp Stress Anal; Am Soc Mech Engrs; Am Acad Mech; Am Asn Univ Professors; Sigma Xi. *Res:* Experimental stress analysis using holography, moire, three dimensional photoelasticity and brittle coatings. *Mailing Add:* Dept of Civil Eng Cath Univ Am Washington DC 20064

PARKS, WILLIAM FRANK, b Pittsburgh, Pa, June 1, 38; m 56. THEORETICAL PHYSICS. *Educ:* Lehigh Univ, BS, 60; Univ Iowa, PhD(physics), 64. *Prof Exp:* Asst prof, 64-73, ASSOC PROF PHYSICS, UNIV MO-ROLLA, 73- *Mem:* Am Phys Soc. *Mailing Add:* Dept of Physics Univ of Mo Rolla MO 65401

PARLEE, NORMAN ALLEN DEVINE, b South Farmington, NS, Can; Mar 23, 15; nat US; m 38; c 2. PHYSICAL CHEMISTRY. *Educ:* Dalhousie Univ, BSc, 35, MSc, 37; McGill Univ, PhD, 39. *Prof Exp:* Lectr, Sir George Williams Col, 38-39; metallogr, Dom Steel & Coal Corp, 39-40, res metallurgist, 42-45, dir res & develop, 45-52; head metal dept, Trenton Steel Works, 41-42; from assoc prof to prof metall, Purdue Univ, 52-62; prof extractive metall, 62-74, PROF APPL EARTH SCI, STANFORD UNIV, 74- *Concurrent Pos:* NSF fel, Cambridge Univ, 59-60. *Honors & Awards:* Murphy Prize, Eng Inst Can, 47. *Mem:* Am Soc Metals; Am Soc Eng Educ; Am Inst Mining, Metall & Petrol Engrs; fel Chem Inst Can. *Res:* Metallography of steel; coke and coke oven by-products; slag utilization; steel making methods for high grade steel; physical chemistry of iron and steel; physical chemistry of metals; reduction and refining processes for metals; reprocessing of spent nuclear fuel; gases in metals; metallurgical thermodynamics. *Mailing Add:* Dept of Appl Earth Sci Stanford Univ Stanford CA 94305

PARLETT, BERESFORD, b London, Eng, July 4, 32; m 60; c 2. MATHEMATICS. *Educ:* Oxford Univ, BA, 55; Stanford Univ, PhD(math), 62. *Prof Exp:* Assoc res scientist, Courant Inst Math Sci, NY Univ, 62-64; asst prof math, Stevens Inst Technol, 64-65; asst prof math, 65-68, assoc prof comput sci, 68-73, chmn dept, 68-71, PROF MATH, ELEC ENG & COMPUT SCI, UNIV CALIF, BERKELEY, 73- *Mem:* Am Math Soc; Asn Comput Mach; Soc Indust & Appl Math. *Res:* Numerical analysis; linear algebra; partial differential equations. *Mailing Add:* Dept Math Univ of Calif Berkeley CA 94720

PARLETT, ROBERT CARLETON, microbiology, medicine, see previous edition

PARLMAN, ROBERT MYLES, organic chemistry, organometallic chemistry, see previous edition

PARLOW, ALBERT FRANCIS, b Boston, Mass, Jan 27, 33. BIOLOGY, PHYSIOLOGY. *Educ:* Harvard Univ, BA, 55; Princeton Univ, PhD(biol), 58. *Prof Exp:* Res fel anat, Harvard Med Sch, 58-59, res fel physiol in obstet & gynec, 59-62; from instr to asst prof physiol, Emory Univ, 62-65; assoc res physiologist, 65-70, RES PROF OBSTET & GYNEC, SCH MED, UNIV CALIF, LOS ANGELES, 70- *Concurrent Pos:* USPHS res career develop award, 66. *Mem:* Endocrine Soc; Am Physiol Soc; Soc Exp Biol & Med; Soc Study Reprod; Soc Gynecol Invest. *Res:* Endocrine regulation of reproduction; bioassay, immunoassay, isolation and structure of protein hormones. *Mailing Add:* Univ Calif Sch Med Harbor Gen Hosp Torrance CA 90509

PARMA, DAVID HOPKINS, b Santa Barbara, Calif, May 10, 40; m 62; c 2. GENETICS. *Educ:* Univ Calif, Davis, BS, 64, MS, 65; Univ Wash, PhD(genetics), 68. *Prof Exp:* NSF fel molecular biol, Carnegie Inst Wash Genetics Res Unit, 68-70; asst prof, 70-76, RES ASSOC PROF BIOL, UNIV UTAH, 76- *Mem:* AAAS. *Res:* Genetics, especially origin and behavior of chromosomal aberrations; bacteriophage genetics; mechanisms of replication and recombination. *Mailing Add:* Dept of Biol Col of Sci 201 S Biol Univ of Utah Salt Lake City UT 84112

PARMALEE, PAUL WOODBURN, b Mansfield, Ohio, Oct 17, 26; m 49; c 2. ZOOLOGY. *Educ:* Ohio Univ, BSEd, 48; Univ Ill, MS, 49; Agr & Mech Col, Tex, PhD(wildlife mgt), 52. *Prof Exp:* Asst prof biol, Stephen F Austin State Col, 52-53; cur zool, Ill State Mus, 53-65, Asst Mus Dir, 65-73; PROF ZOOARCHAEOL, DEPT ANTHROP, UNIV TENN, 73-, DIR McCLUNG MUS, 78- *Mem:* Am Soc Mammal; Cooper Ornith Soc; Soc Am Archaeol; Am Ornith Union; Wilson Ornith Soc. *Res:* Vertebrate zoology; ornithology; mammalogy; osteology; identification of faunal materials from archaeological sites. *Mailing Add:* Dept of Anthrop Univ of Tenn Knoxville TN 37996

PARME, ALFRED L, b 1909. ENGINEERING. *Educ:* Cornell Univ, BSCE, 35. *Prof Exp:* Mem staff, Ebasco, 36-38; mem staff design earth & concrete dams, Corps Engrs, 38-40; struct engr & dir struct bur & advan eng dept, Portland Cement Asn, 40-68; partner, J Fruchtbaum, 69; CONSULT ENGR, 70- *Honors & Awards:* Lindau Award, Am Concrete Inst; Martin Korn Award, Prestressed Concrete Inst. *Mem:* Nat Acad Eng. *Res:* Design reinforced concrete; seismic design; thin shells and arch dams. *Mailing Add:* 6787 Avenida Andorra La Jolla CA 92037

PARMEGIANI, RAULO, b New York, NY, Sept 10, 33; div; c 2. MICROBIAL PHYSIOLOGY. *Educ:* La Salle Col, BA, 55; St John's Univ, NY, MS, 60, PhD, 73. *Prof Exp:* Microbiologist, Pfister Chem Works, Inc, 59-62; res assoc microbiol, Boyce Thompson Inst, 62-76; sr scientist, 76-80, PRIN SCIENTIST, SCHERING CORP, 80- *Mem:* Am Soc Microbiol; Int Soc Human & Animal Mycol. *Res:* Mode of action of antifungal agents; antimicrobial chemotherapy; medical mycology; experimental animal infections; microbial lipid metabolism; agricultural pesticides. *Mailing Add:* Chemother Dept Schering Corp 60 Orange St Bloomfield NJ 07003

PARMELE, JAMES D, chemical engineering, deceased

PARMELEE, ARTHUR H, JR, b Chicago, Ill, Oct 29, 17; m 39; c 4. MEDICINE, PEDIATRICS. *Educ:* Univ Chicago, BS, 40, MD, 43. *Prof Exp:* From instr to assoc prof, 51-67, PROF PEDIAT, SCH MED, UNIV CALIF, LOS ANGELES, 67- *Honors & Awards:* C Anderson Aldrich Award, Child Develop, Am Acad Pediat, 75. *Mem:* Soc Pediat Res; Am Acad Pediat; Am Pediat Soc; Soc Res Child Develop (pres-elect, 81-). *Res:* Child development; behavioral pediatrics; infants at risk. *Mailing Add:* Dept of Pediat Univ of Calif Sch of Med Los Angeles CA 90024

PARMELEE, CARLTON EDWIN, b Hopkins, Mich, Mar 24, 18; m 43; c 2. FOOD SCIENCE. *Educ:* Mich State Univ, BS, 40; Iowa State Univ, MS, 42, PhD(dairy bact), 47. *Prof Exp:* Asst, Iowa State Univ, 40-42; qual control, Kraft Foods Co, Wis, 42-43; res assoc, Iowa State Univ, 43-47, res asst prof dairy bact, 47-50; from asst prof to assoc prof dairy mfg, 50-53, ASSOC PROF ANIMAL SCI, PURDUE UNIV, WEST LAFAYETTE, 53- *Mem:* Am Dairy Sci Asn. *Res:* Dairy and food microbiology; cheese manufacture; quality control of foods. *Mailing Add:* Dept of Animal Sci Purdue Univ West Lafayette IN 47906

PARMELEE, DAVID FREELAND, b Oshkosh, Wis, June 20, 24; m 43; c 1. ORNITHOLOGY. *Educ:* Lawrence Col, BA, 50; Univ Mich, MS, 52; Univ Okla, PhD(zool), 57. *Prof Exp:* Asst zool, Univ Okla, 52-56, instr, 56-58; from asst prof to prof biol, Kans State Teachers Col, 58-70; PROF ECOL & BEHAV BIOL, CHMN FIELD BIOL PROG & PROG DIR CEDAR CREEK NATURAL HIST AREA & LAKE ITASCA FORESTRY & BIOL STA, UNIV MINN, MINNEAPOLIS, 70- *Concurrent Pos:* Dir field opers bird virus-parasite study, Med Ctr, Univ Okla, 63-65. *Mem:* Wilson Ornith Soc; Cooper Ornith Soc; Orgn Biol Field Stas. *Res:* Ornithology, especially the taxonomy, ecology, behavior and breeding biology of arctic and antarctic birds. *Mailing Add:* 349 Bell Mus of Natural Hist Univ of Minn Minneapolis MN 55455

PARMELEE, JOHN AUBREY, b Ottawa, Ont, Oct 14, 24; m 50. MYCOLOGY. *Educ:* McGill Univ, BSc, 49; Univ Toronto, MA, 52, PhD, 61. *Prof Exp:* Asst, 47-48, tech officer, bot & plant path lab, 49-52, agr res officer, 52-60, res officer, 60-66, RES SCIENTIST, BIOSYSTEMATICS RES INST, CAN DEPT AGR, 66-; CUR, NAT MYCOL HERBARIUM, 66- *Mem:* Mycol Soc Am; Can Bot Asn; Can Phytopath Soc. *Res:* Taxonomy of uredinales; general mycology. *Mailing Add:* Biosystematics Res Inst Can Dept Agr Saunders Bldg C&F Ottawa ON K1A 0C6 Can

PARMENTER, CHARLES STEDMAN, b Philadelphia, Pa, Oct 12, 33; m 56; c 3. PHYSICAL CHEMISTRY. *Educ:* Univ Pa, BA, 55; Univ Rochester, PhD(phys chem), 63. *Prof Exp:* Tech rep photo prod, E I du Pont de Nemours & Co, 57-58; NSF res fel chem, Harvard Univ, 62-63, NIH res fel, 63-64; from asst prof to assoc prof, 64-72, PROF CHEM, IND UNIV, BLOOMINGTON, 72- *Concurrent Pos:* Simon H Guggenheim fel, Cambridge Univ, 71-72; vis fel, Joint Inst Lab Astrophys, Nat Bureau Standards & Univ Colo, 77-78; Fulbright sr scholar, Griffith Univ, Australia, 80. *Mem:* AAAS; Am Chem Soc; Am Phys Soc. *Res:* Photochemistry; spectroscopy; energy transfer. *Mailing Add:* Dept of Chem Ind Univ Bloomington IN 47401

PARMENTER, ROBERT HALEY, b Portland, Maine, Sept 19, 25; m 51; c 2. SOLID STATE PHYSICS. *Educ:* Univ Maine, BS, 47; Mass Inst Technol, PhD(physics), 52. *Prof Exp:* Guest mem, Brookhaven Nat Lab, 51-52; mem staff, Lincoln Lab & solid state & molecular group, Mass Inst Technol, 52-54; res physicist, RCA Labs, 54-66; PROF PHYSICS, UNIV ARIZ, 66-, CHMN DEPT, 77- *Concurrent Pos:* Vis lectr, Princeton Univ, 60-61; mem res adv comt electrophys, NASA, 64-68. *Mem:* Fel AAAS; fel Am Phys Soc. *Res:* Electronic energy bands in ordered and disordered solids; group theory of crystals; acoustoelectric effect; superconductivity; space-charge-limited current in insulators. *Mailing Add:* Dept of Physics Univ of Ariz Tucson AZ 85721

PARMENTIER, EDGAR M(ARC), b Waynesburg, Pa, Oct 29, 45. EARTH SCIENCES, FLUID MECHANICS. *Educ:* WVa Univ, BS, 68; Cornell Univ, MEng, 69, PhD(earth sci), 75. *Prof Exp:* Res scientist eng, AVCO-Everett Res Lab, 69-72; res fel geol sci, Oxford Univ, 75-77; asst prof, 77-80, ASSOC PROF GEOL SCI, BROWN UNIV, 80- *Mem:* Am Geophys Union; Sigma Xi. *Res:* Transport processes in the earth; heat and mass transfer. *Mailing Add:* Dept Geol Sci Box 1846 Brown Univ Providence RI 02912

PARMERTER, R REID, b Rochester, NY, June 14, 35. SOLID MECHANICS. *Educ:* Calif Inst Technol, BS, 58, MS, 59, PhD(aeronaut), 64. *Prof Exp:* Stress & vibration engr, AiResearch Mfg Co, Ariz, 56-57; from asst prof to assoc prof aeronaut & astronaut, 63-77, PROF AERONAUT & ASTRONAUT, UNIV WASH, 77- *Concurrent Pos:* Consult, Southwest Engrs, Calif, 57-62, Math Sci Corp, 62-66, Math Sci Northwest, Wash, 66- *Mem:* Soc Exp Stress Anal. *Res:* Nonlinear shell theory; shell stability; photoelasticity; stress analysis of solid propellant rockets; holography; ice mechanics. *Mailing Add:* Dept of Aeronaut & Astronaut Univ of Wash Seattle WA 98195

PARMERTER, STANLEY MARSHALL, b Rochester, NY, Oct 24, 20; m 43; c 3. ORGANIC CHEMISTRY. *Educ:* Greenville Col, 41; Univ Ill, MS, 42, PhD(org chem), 44; John Marshall Law Sch, JD, 80. *Prof Exp:* Asst physics, Greenville Col, 40-41; asst physics & chem, Univ Ill, 42-44, fel, 44-45; res chemist, William S Merrell Co, Ohio, 45-47 & Eastman Kodak Co, 47-52; from instr to prof chem, Wheaton Col, Ill, 52-64, chmn sci div, 59-64; sect leader, Corn Prod Co, 64-69, dir admin serv, 69-75, patent adv, 75-77, patent agent, 78-79, PATENT ATTY, MOFFETT TECH CTR, CPC INT INC, 80- *Concurrent Pos:* Vis res assoc, Argonne Nat Lab, 63-64. *Mem:* Am Chem Soc. *Res:* Organic synthesis; carbohydrate chemistry. *Mailing Add:* Moffett Tech Ctr CPC Int Inc Box 345 Argo IL 60501

PARMETER, JOHN RICHARD, JR, b The Dalles, Ore, Sept 16, 27; m 55; c 3. PLANT PATHOLOGY. *Educ:* Ore State Col, BS, 51; Univ Wis, PhD, 55. *Prof Exp:* Asst plant path, Univ Wis, 51-55; plant pathologist, US Forest Serv, 55-57; from asst prof to assoc prof, 57-69, PROF PLANT PATH, UNIV CALIF, BERKELEY, 69- *Mem:* Am Phytopath Soc; Mycol Soc Am; Brit Mycol Soc; AAAS. *Res:* Diseases of forest trees; soil microbiology; mycology. *Mailing Add:* Dept Plant Path Univ Calif Berkeley CA 94720

PARMLEY, RAY T, b Electra, Tex, Oct 29, 19; m 43; c 4. ANESTHESIOLOGY. *Educ:* Tulane Univ, MD, 44. *Prof Exp:* Intern, Charity Hosp, New Orleans, La, 44-45, resident anesthesiol, 45-46; chief anesthesiol, US Naval Hosp, Philadelphia, Pa, 46-47; dir dept anesthesiol, St Francis Hosp, Wichita, Kans, 54-65; PROF ANESTHESIOL & CHMN DEPT, UNIV KANS MED CTR, KANSAS CITY, 65- *Concurrent Pos:* Consult anesthesiol, Vet Admin Hosp, Wichita, 49-65, McConnell AFB, 55-65 & Vet Admin Hosp, Kansas City, Mo, 65-; asst clin prof surg, Univ Kans Med Ctr, Kansas City, 59-65. *Mem:* Am Soc Anesthesiol; Am Col Anesthesiol; AMA. *Res:* Saddle Block anesthesia. *Mailing Add:* Med Ctr Dept of Anesthesiol Univ of Kans 39th & Rainbow Kansas City KS 66103

PARMLEY, WILLIAM W, b Salt Lake City, Utah, Jan 22, 36; m 61; c 4. CARDIOLOGY. *Educ:* Harvard Univ, AB, 57; Johns Hopkins Univ, MD, 63. *Prof Exp:* Intern, Osler Med Serv, Johns Hopkins Hosp, Baltimore, 63-64, asst resident, 64-65; clin assoc, Cardiol Br, Nat Heart Inst, Bethesda, 65-69; instr med, Harvard Med Sch, 69; assoc prof, Sch Med, Univ Calif, Los Angeles & assoc dir dept cardiol, Cedars-Sinai Med Ctr, 70-74; PROF MED, SCH MED, UNIV CALIF, SAN FRANCISCO & CHIEF, DIV CARDIOL, MOFFITT HOSP, 74- *Concurrent Pos:* Res fel, Cardiovasc Unit, Peter Bent Brigham Hosp, Harvard Med Sch, 67-69, jr assoc med, 69; estab investr, Am Heart Asn, 71-76; chmn, Comt Regulatory Nat Res, 82-83. *Honors & Awards:* Theodore & Susan Cummings Humanitarian Award, Am Col Cardiol, 71. *Mem:* Fel Am Col Cardiol; Am Physiol Soc; Am Fedn Clin Res; Am Soc Clin Invest; Am Asn Physicians. *Res:* Muscle physiology; ventricular function; cardiac pharmacology. *Mailing Add:* Univ Calif Med Ctr 1186 Moffitt Hosp San Francisco CA 94143

PARNELL, DENNIS RICHARD, b Rochester, NY, Dec 30, 39. PLANT SCIENCE. *Educ:* Whittier Col, BA, 61; Univ Calif, Los Angeles, MA, 63, PhD(plant sci), 65. *Prof Exp:* From asst prof to assoc prof, 65-74, PROF BIOL SCI, CALIF STATE UNIV, HAYWARD, 74-, DEAN, SCH SCI, 80- *Mem:* AAAS; Soc Study Evolution; Bot Soc Am; Am Soc Plant Taxonomists; Am Inst Biol Sci. *Res:* Plant systematics, cytogenetics and anatomy. *Mailing Add:* Sch Sci Calif State Univ Hayward CA 94542

PARNELL, JAMES FRANKLIN, b Timmonsville, SC, May 15, 34; m 62. ORNITHOLOGY, ECOLOGY. *Educ:* NC State Univ, BS, 59, MS, 61, PhD(zool), 64. *Prof Exp:* From asst prof to assoc prof, 64-69, chmn dept, 69-71, PROF BIOL, UNIV NC, WILMINGTON, 69- *Mem:* Am Ornith Union; Wildlife Soc; Wilson Ornith Soc; Ecol Soc. *Res:* Ecology and distribution of vertebrates, particularly the habitat relations of birds. *Mailing Add:* Dept of Biol Univ of NC Wilmington NC 28401

PARNELL, JEROME PATRICK, b Brooklyn, NY, Apr 2, 18; m 42; c 5. ANATOMY. *Educ:* Manhattan Col, BS, 41; St Louis Univ, MS, 43; NY Univ, PhD(anat), 49. *Prof Exp:* Instr anat, NY Univ, 44-47 & Tulane Univ, 47-49; from asst prof to assoc prof, 49-65, PROF ANAT, COL MED, STATE UNIV NY DOWNSTATE MED CTR, 65-, ASSOC DEAN, 71-, PROF CELL BIOL, 80- *Mem:* Am Asn Anatomists. *Res:* Physiology of skin, hair and sebaceous gland; skin cycle of the rat; vitamin A and its relation to skin physiology. *Mailing Add:* 1239 Village Ct Baldwin NY 11510

PARNELL, THOMAS ALFRED, b Lumberton, NC, Nov 24, 31; m 55; c 2. PHYSICS, COSMIC RAY PHYSICS. *Educ:* Univ NC, Chapel Hill, BS, 54, MS, 62, PhD(physics), 65. *Prof Exp:* Res adj physics, Univ NC, Chapel Hill, 63-65, opers analyst, 65-66; asst prof physics, Marshall Univ, 66-67; PHYSICIST, MARSHALL SPACE FLIGHT CTR, NASA, 67-, CHIEF ASTROPHYSICS BR, 68- *Mem:* Am Phys Soc. *Res:* Experimental cosmic ray physics, gamma ray astronomy and development of nuclear instrumentation. *Mailing Add:* 907 Corinth Huntsville AL 35801

PARNES, MILTON N, b Detroit, Mich, Nov 13, 39; m 63; c 3. STATISTICS. *Educ:* Wayne State Univ, BS, 60, PhD(math), 68. *Prof Exp:* Asst prof math, State Univ NY, Buffalo, 67-77; ASST PROF MATH, STATIST DEPT, TEMPLE UNIV, 77- *Res:* Complex analysis; mathematical theory of gambling; biometry; mathematical statistics; measure theory; approximation theory. *Mailing Add:* 1927 Juniper Lane Cornwells Heights PA 19020

PARNES, RAYMOND, applied mechanics, engineering, see previous edition

PAROCHETTI, JAMES V, b Spring Valley, Ill, Apr 24, 40; m 80; c 3. AGRICULTURAL SCIENCE, PESTICIDES. *Educ:* Univ Ill, BS, 62; Purdue Univ, MS, 64, PhD(plant physiol), 67. *Prof Exp:* EXTEN SPECIALIST & PESTICIDE COORDR, EXTENSION SERV, USDA, WASHINGTON, DC, 66- *Mem:* Am Soc Agron; Weed Sci Soc Am. *Res:* Behavior of herbicides in plants and soils; control of herbicide resistant weeds. *Mailing Add:* Extension Serv USDA Washington DC 20742

PARODE, L(OWELL) C(ARR), b Los Angeles, Calif, Oct 27, 24; m 46; c 3. ELECTRONIC ENGINEERING. *Educ:* Calif Inst Technol, BS, 45, MS, 47. *Prof Exp:* Mgr, Guid Lab, 47-71, mgr, Missile Eng Labs, 71-73, PROG MGR, NASA SYSTS DIV, HUGHES AIRCRAFT CO, 73- *Mem:* Sigma Xi; sr mem Inst Elec & Electronics Engrs. *Res:* Missile guidance; tracking radar design; communication systems. *Mailing Add:* 1645 Via Lazo Palos Verdes Estates CA 90274

PARONETTO, FIORENZO, b Treviso, Italy, Jan 18, 29; m 61; c 2. PATHOLOGY. *Educ:* Univ Padua, MD, 52. *Prof Exp:* Fel med, County Hosp, Salt Lake City, Utah, 54-55; fel, Mt Sinai Hosp, New York, 55-56, resident, path, 57-59, intern, 59-60, res fel path, 60-61, res assoc, 62-63, asst attend pathologist, 63-65; from asst prof to assoc prof, 65-71, PROF PATH, MT SINAI SCH MED, 71-; CHIEF LAB SERV, VET ADMIN MED CTR, BRONX, 73- *Mem:* Am Asn Path & Bact; Am Fedn Clin Res; Am Soc Exp Path; Am Asn Immunol; Transplantation Soc. *Res:* Immunopathology. *Mailing Add:* Vet Admin Med Ctr 130 West Kingsbridge Rd Bronx NY 10468

PARPIA, JEEVAK MAHMUD, b Bombay, India, July 22, 52; m 74. LOW TEMPERATURE CONDENSED MATTER. *Educ:* Ill Inst Technol, BSLA, 73; Cornell Univ, MS, 77, PhD(physics), 79. *Prof Exp:* Assoc low temperature physics, Cornell Univ, 78-79; ASST PROF PHYSICS, TEX A&M UNIV, 79- *Concurrent Pos:* Alfred P Sloan res fel, Tex A&M Univ, 81- *Mem:* Am Phys Soc. *Res:* Study of hydrodynamic and magnetic properties of liquid helium three at ultra low temperatures. *Mailing Add:* Physics Dept Tex A&M Univ College Station TX 77843

PARR, ALBERT CLARENCE, b Tooele, Utah, June 22, 42; m 65; c 2. PHYSICS. *Educ:* Ore State Univ, BS(physics) & BS(math), 64; Univ Chicago, MS, 65, PhD(physics), 71. *Prof Exp:* Res asst physics, Univ Chicago, 69-70; asst prof physics, Univ Ala, 71-78, assoc prof, 78-80; RES PHYSICIST ULTRAVIOLET PHYSICS, NAT BUR STANDARDS, 80- *Concurrent Pos:* Sabbatical leave, Nat Bur Standards, 78-79. *Mem:* Am Phys Soc; Optical Soc Am. *Res:* Atomic and molecular physics; photoionization processes in gas phase; reactions on surfaces; synchrotron radiation; photoelectron spectroscopy. *Mailing Add:* Bldg 221 Rm A251 Nat Bur Standards Washington DC 20234

PARR, CHRISTOPHER ALAN, b Oakland, Calif, May 6, 41; div; c 1. THEORETICAL CHEMISTRY, COMPUTER SCIENCE. *Educ:* Univ Calif, Berkeley, BS, 62; Calif Inst Technol, PhD(phys chem), 69. *Prof Exp:* Army Res Off fel theory bimolecular reactions, Univ Calif, Irvine, 68-69; Nat Res Coun Can fel, Univ Toronto, 69-71; asst prof, 71-77, ASSOC PROF CHEM, UNIV TEX, DALLAS, 77- *Mem:* Am Chem Soc; Am Phys Soc. *Res:* Theoretical chemical reaction dynamics; unimolecular dynamics and semiclassical quantization; inter-molecular potential energy functions; energy transfer; computer graphics. *Mailing Add:* Univ Tex Box 688 Richardson TX 75080

PARR, JAMES FLOYD, JR, b Seattle, Wash, Feb 20, 29; m 64; c 2. SOIL MICROBIOLOGY, PLANT PHYSIOLOGY. *Educ:* Wash State Univ, BS, 52, Purdue Univ, MS, 57; PhD(soil microbiol), 61. *Prof Exp:* Irrig exten agent, Agr Exten Serv, Wash State Univ, 53-54; agr exten agent, Mont State Col, 54-55; instr agron, Purdue Univ, 55-57; chemist, Calif Dept Water Resources,

57-58; instr agron, Purdue Univ, 58-61; res assoc bot, Univ Mich, 61-63; res chemist & soil microbiologist, Soils & Fertilizer Res Br, Tenn Valley Auth, 63-67; soil microbiologist, 67-75, CHIEF BIOL WASTE MGT & ORG RESOURCES LAB, AGR RES SERV, USDA, 75- *Mem:* Am Soc Agron; Soil Sci Soc Am; Am Soc Microbiol; Am Soc Plant Physiol. *Res:* Water infiltration into soils; soil organic matter decomposition; effects of surfactants on plant growth; ion uptake by plants; sorption and reaction of anhydrous NH-3 in soils; fertilizer evaluation; fate and persistence of pesticides in soil and water; recycling municipal wastes for soil improvement and plant growth. *Mailing Add:* Agr Res Serv US Dept of Agr Nat Agr Res Ctr Beltsville MD 20705

PARR, JAMES THEODORE, b Lebanon, Ind, Oct 29, 34; m 66; c 1. ALGEBRA. *Educ:* Ind Univ, AB, 56, PhD(math), 64. *Prof Exp:* Lectr math, Ind Univ, 64; from instr to asst prof math, Univ Ill, Urbana, 64-70; ASST PROF MATH, ILL STATE UNIV, 70- *Concurrent Pos:* NSF res fel math, 65-66. *Mem:* Am Math Soc; Math Asn Am. *Res:* Homological algebra; abelian groups; cohomology of cyclic groups of prime square order. *Mailing Add:* Dept of Math Ill State Univ Normal IL 61761

PARR, PHYLLIS GRAHAM, b Princeton, Ind, Dec 4, 37; m 66; c 1. COMPUTER PROGRAMMING, ANALYSIS. *Educ:* Oakland City Col, BSE, 59; Ind Univ, Bloomington, MA, 61, PhD(math), 64. *Prof Exp:* Asst prof math, Ind State Univ, Terre Haute, 64-66 & Univ Ill, Urbana, 66-71; assoc prof, Ill Wesleyan Univ, 71-73; asst prof math, Ill State Univ, 74-75; assoc prof, Ill Wesleyan Univ, 76-77; DATA PROCESSING SPECIALIST, STATE FARM INSURANCE, BLOOMINGTON, ILL, 79- *Mem:* Am Math Soc; Math Asn Am. *Res:* Cohomology of finite groups; finite rings. *Mailing Add:* State Farm Mutual Auto Ins Co One State Farm Plaza Bloomington IL 61701

PARR, ROBERT GHORMLEY, b Chicago, Ill, Sept 22, 21; m 44; c 3. THEORETICAL CHEMISTRY. *Educ:* Brown Univ, AB, 42; Univ Minn, PhD(phys chem), 47. *Prof Exp:* Asst prof chem, Univ Minn, 47-48; from asst prof to prof chem, Carnegie Inst Technol, 48-62, chmn gen fac, 60-61; prof, Johns Hopkins Univ, 62-74, chmn dept, 69-72; WILLIAM R KENAN, JR PROF THEORET CHEM, UNIV NC, CHAPEL HILL, 74- *Concurrent Pos:* Fel, Univ Chicago, 49, res assoc, 57; Guggenheim fel & Fulbright scholar, Univ Cambridge, 53-54; Sloan fel, 56-60; assoc ed, J Chem Physics, 56-58, Chem Revs, 61-63, J Phys Chem, 63-67 & 77-79, Am Chem Soc Monographs, 66-71 & Theoretica Chimica Acta, 66-69; mem chem adv panel, Air Force Off Sci Res, 60-65; chmn, Nat Acad Sci-Nat Res Coun Comt Postdoctoral Fels in Chem, 61-63; vis prof chem & mem ctr adv study, Univ Ill, 62; chmn panel theoret chem, Westheimer Comt for the Surv of Chem, Nat Acad Sci, 64; vis prof, State Univ NY, Buffalo & Pa State Univ, 67; NSF sr fel, Oxford Univ & CSIRO, Univ Melbourne, 67-68; vis prof, Japan Soc Promotion Sci, 68 & 79; assoc, Comt on Int Exchange of Persons & mem adv comt for East Asia, 71-; mem, Gordon Res Confs Coun, 74-76; mem, Am Phys Soc panel Pub Affairs, 75-77; Firth prof, Univ Sheffield, 76; vis prof, Israel Inst Technol, 77; mem comn human resources, Nat Res Coun, 79- *Honors & Awards:* Petrol Res Fund Award, Am Chem Soc, 64. *Mem:* Nat Acad Sci; Sigma Xi; Am Chem Soc; fel Am Phys Soc; Int Acad Quantum Molecular Sci (vpres, 73-79, hon pres, 79-). *Res:* Electronic structure of molecules; chemical physics. *Mailing Add:* Dept of Chem Univ of NC Chapel Hill NC 27514

PARR, WILLIAM CHRIS, b Ranger, Tex, Aug 13, 53; m 74; c 1. STATISTICS, MATHEMATICS. *Educ:* Trinity Univ, BA, 74; Southern Methodist Univ, MS, 76, PhD(statist), 78. *Prof Exp:* Teaching asst statist, Southern Methodist Univ, 74-77; asst mgr, Consult Lab, 77-78; ASST PROF STATIST, INST STATIST, TEX A&M UNIV, 78- *Mem:* Am Statist Asn; Inst Math Statist; Am Math Soc; Royal Statist Soc; Psychomet Soc. *Res:* Robust estimation and testing; jackknifing; the foundations of inference. *Mailing Add:* Inst of Statist Tex A&M Univ College Station TX 78743

PARRATT, LYMAN GEORGE, b Salt Lake City, Utah, May 17, 08; m 44; c 2. PHYSICS. *Educ:* Univ Utah, AB, 28; Univ Chicago, PhD(physics), 32. *Prof Exp:* Asst physics, Univ Utah, 28-29 & Univ Chicago, 30-33; Nat Res Coun fel, 33-35, from instr to assoc prof, 35-46, chmn dept, 59-69, prof, 59-77, EMER, PROF DEPT PHYSICS & LAB NUCLEAR STUDIES, 77- LAB ATOMIC & SOLID STATE PHYSICS, 59- *Concurrent Pos:* Physicist & head, Eng Div, Naval Ord Lab, 41-43; group leader, Los Alamos Sci Lab, 43-46. *Mem:* AAAS; fel Am Phys Soc; Fedn Am Sci; Am Asn Physics Teachers. *Res:* X-ray spectroscopy; solid state physics; corrosion of metal surfaces; electronics; underwater ordnance; ship's magnetism; acoustic instruments; torpedoes; submarine detection; probability theory and experimental errors. *Mailing Add:* 513 Wyckoff Rd Ithaca NY 14850

PARRAVANO, CARLO, b Rome, Italy, Dec 28, 45; US citizen; m 70. PHYSICAL CHEMISTRY. *Educ:* Oberlin Col, BA, 67; Univ Calif Santa Cruz, PhD (chem), 74. *Prof Exp:* Instr chem, Eastern Mich Univ, 68-70; ASST PROF CHEM, STATE UNIV NY COL, PURCHASE, 74- *Concurrent Pos:* Assoc, Danforth Found, 78- *Mem:* AAAS; Am Chem Soc; Nat Sci Teachers Asn. *Res:* Gas phase reaction kinetics; application of physical techniques to biochemical and environmental problems. *Mailing Add:* Div Nat Sci State Univ NY Col at Purchase Purchase NY 10577

PARREIRA, HELIO CORREA, b Rio de Janeiro, Brazil, July 12, 26; m 53; c 2. SURFACE CHEMISTRY. *Educ:* Univ Brazil, Bsc, 49; Cambridge Univ, PhD(colloid sci), 58. *Prof Exp:* Asst prof anal chem, Univ Rio de Janeiro, 50-52; phys chemist, Biophys Inst, Univ Brazil, 51-55 & Brazilian Atomic Cmn, 58-60; res assoc surface chem, Sch Mines, Columbia Univ, 60-62, asst prof chem metall, 62-63, asst prof appl chem, 63-65, dir instruction chem, NSF Joint Prog Tech Educ, Sch Eng, 60-65; group leader dept phys & inorg chem, Cent Res Labs, Inmont Corp, NJ, 65-67, prin scientist, 67-69; assoc dir res, 69-70, dir res & develop, 70-72, SR RES ASSOC, JOHNSON & JOHNSON, 72- *Concurrent Pos:* Researcher, Cambridge Univ, 54; ed, Universal Ref Libr, Grosset-Dunlap, Inc, 64; consult, Yeshiva, 64 & Stanley-Thompson Labs, Columbia Univ, 65-66. *Mem:* Am Chem Soc; Sigma Xi; NY Acad Sci. *Res:* Surface phenomena; electrokinetics; electrostatics of interfaces; physical chemistry of colloidal electrolytes; surface infra-red, ESCA, ISS/SIMS; surface chemistry of polymers, metals, silica, adhesives; glass, natural and biological surfaces. *Mailing Add:* Johnson & Johnson Res New Brunswick NJ 08903

PARRENT, GEORGE BURL, JR, theoretical physics, see previous edition

PARRETT, NED ALBERT, b Logansport, Ind, Nov 8, 39; m 63; c 2. MEAT SCIENCE. *Educ:* Purdue Univ, BS, 63; Tex A&M Univ, MS, 68, PhD(animal sci), 72. *Prof Exp:* Instr animal sci, Tex A&M Univ, 65-69; asst prof, 69-77, ASSOC PROF ANIMAL SCI, OHIO STATE UNIV, 77- *Mem:* Am Soc Animal Sci; Inst Food Technologists; Am Meat Sci Asn. *Res:* Carcass evaluation and composition; quality and palatability attributes of carcasses and wholesale cuts; packaging of meat and meat products. *Mailing Add:* Dept Animal Sci Ohio State Univ 2029 Fyffe Rd Columbus OH 43210

PARRILL, IRWIN HOMER, b Kinmundy, Ill, Mar 21, 09; m 32; c 3. PHYSICAL CHEMISTRY, AGRICULTURAL CHEMISTRY. *Educ:* Ill State Norm Univ, BEd, 31; Univ Iowa, MS, PhD(phys chem), 39. *Prof Exp:* Supvr Lake County Dairy Herd Improv Asn, Ill, 28-29; teacher & asst prin high sch, 31-33; asst sci, Univ High Sch, Iowa, 33-34; dean, Eagle Grove Jr Col, 34-36; instr high sch, C Z, 36-39; chemist, Munic Lab, 39-47; assoc prof chem & chmn phys sci div, Farragut Col & Tech Inst, 47-48; instr high sch, Ill, 53-58; lectr, 57-58, from asst prof to prof, 58-74, EMER PROF CHEM, SOUTHERN ILL UNIV, EDWARDSVILLE, 74-, DIR, PARRILL LAB, 52- *Mem:* Am Chem Soc. *Res:* Soils chemistry; chemistry education. *Mailing Add:* RR 2 Box 206 Edwardsville IL 62025

PARRISH, ALVIN EDWARD, b Washington, DC, Sept 6, 22; m 45; c 2. MEDICINE. *Educ:* George Washington Univ, MD, 45. *Prof Exp:* Instr physiol, 47-48, lectr, 48-50, clin instr med, 51-57, assoc prof & assoc dean, 57-64, dir div renal dis, 64-79, PROF MED, SCH MED, GEORGE WASHINGTON UNIV, 64-, DIR CLIN RES, 66-, DIR OFF HUMAN RES, 79- *Concurrent Pos:* Asst chief serv, Vet Admin Hosp, Washington, DC, 51-57, consult, 57- *Mem:* AAAS; AMA; Am Diabetes Asn; fel Am Col Physicians; Am Fedn Clin Res. *Res:* Renal disease. *Mailing Add:* Dept of Med George Washington Univ Med Ctr Washington DC 20037

PARRISH, CLYDE FRANKLIN, b Skillman, Ky, Sept 9, 38; m 58; c 2. PHYSICAL CHEMISTRY, RADIATION CHEMISTRY. *Educ:* Eastern Ky State Col, BS, 59; Univ Louisville, PhD(phys chem), 62. *Prof Exp:* Chemist, Dow Chem Co, Mich, 62-63; asst prof, 63-69, dir, radiation lab, 66-71, ASSOC PROF CHEM, IND STATE UNIV, TERRE HAUTE, 69-; PRES, RPS INDUST & SF LEASING CORP, 71- *Concurrent Pos:* Consult, Dow Chem Co, 63-68 & Nuclear Div, Union Carbide Corp, 65-69. *Mem:* AAAS; Am Soc Testing & Mat; Am Chem Soc. *Res:* Radiation induced solid state polymerization of vinyl monomers; mechanism of particulate adhesion in ten to one hundred micron size range. *Mailing Add:* Dept of Chem Ind State Univ Terre Haute IN 47809

PARRISH, DALE WAYNE, b Franklin Co, Ala, Aug 17, 24. MEDICAL ENTOMOLOGY, BIOMEDICAL SCIENCES. *Educ:* Auburn Univ, BS, 47; Univ Md, MS, 64; Okla State Univ, PhD(med entom), 71; Am Registry Prof Entomologists, cert med entom, 71. *Prof Exp:* Teacher agr, Ala State Dept Educ, 47-48; supvr agr, Farmers Home Admin, USDA, 48-51; med entomologist, US Dept Air Force, 51-67, from sr biomed scientist to chief biomed scientist, US Air Force Med Serv, 67-73, assoc dir biomed sci, US Air Force Biomed Sci Corps, 74; health sci adminr, 74-80, SR SCIENTIST ADMINR, US ENVIRON PROTECTION AGENCY, 81- *Concurrent Pos:* Bd mem, Armed Forces Pest Control Bd, Dept Defense, 56-59 & 71-72; sr med serv consult, Off Surgeon Gen, US Air Force Hq, 71-74; mil joint chiefs-of-staff rep fed working group pest mgt, Pres Coun Environ Qual, 72-73. *Honors & Awards:* Commendation Medal, US Air Force, 67, Cert Achievement, Off Surgeon Gen, 71, Chief Biomed Sci Badge, 71, Meritorious Serv Medal, 72, Cert Achievement, Systs Command Hq, 72; Joint Serv Commendation Medal, Dept Defense, 74. *Mem:* Entom Soc Am; Aerospace Med Asn; Sigma Xi; Am Mosquito Control Asn. *Res:* Epidemiology of arthropod and rodent-borne diseases; wild vertebrate host relationships of ticks; control of arthropod vectors of diseases; toxicology of pesticides, epidemiology of pesticide poisonings, especially effects on human health; aerial dispersal of pesticides-disease vector control. *Mailing Add:* 5105 Acorn Dr Temple Hills MD 20748

PARRISH, DAVID JOE, b Knoxville, Tenn, Dec 23, 43; m 68; c 2. CROP PHYSIOLOGY. *Educ:* E Tenn State Univ, BS, 67; Wake Forest Univ, MA, 70; Cornell Univ, PhD(bot), 76. *Prof Exp:* Lectr biol, Cornell Univ, 75; fel, Univ Nebr, Lincoln, 76-77; ASST PROF CROP PHYSIOL, VA POLYTECH INST & STATE UNIV, 77- *Mem:* Am Soc Plant Physiologists; Am Soc Agron; Crop Sci Soc Am; Plant Growth Regulator Soc Am; Coun Agr Sci & Technol. *Res:* High resolution plant growth measurement; physiology of isolated stem segments; fuel cropping; seed physiology. *Mailing Add:* Dept Agron Va Polytech Inst & State Univ Blacksburg VA 24061

PARRISH, DAVID KEITH, b Clinton, Mo, Sept 29, 44. GEOLOGY. *Educ:* Univ Mo-Columbia, BS, 66, MA, 69; Rice Univ, C Houston, PhD(geol), 72. *Prof Exp:* Res assoc geol, Dept Earth & Space Sci, State Univ NY Stony Brook, 71-74; asst prof geol, Prog & Inst Geosci, Univ Tex, Dallas, 74-75; asst prof geol, Tex A&M Univ, 75-, asst prof geophysics, 77-; MEM STAFF, RE/SPEC, INC, RAPID CITY, 77- *Mem:* Am Geophys Union. *Res:* Theoretical analysis of crustal structures using finite element models; experimental determination of high pressure, temperature mechanical behavior of rocks; analysis of finite strain in rocks. *Mailing Add:* RE/SPEC Inc PO Box 725 Rapid City SD 57709

PARRISH, DONALD BAKER, b Ft Scott, Kans, Sept 24, 13; m 36; c 3. NUTRITION, BIOCHEMISTRY. *Educ:* Kans State Col, BS, 35, MS, 38, PhD(biochem, nutrit), 49. *Prof Exp:* Instr high schs, Kans, 35-43; asst chemist, 43-49, from asst prof to assoc prof chem, 49-62, PROF BIOCHEM, KANS STATE UNIV, 62-, BIOCHEMIST & NUTRITIONIST, AGR EXP STA, 62- *Mem:* Am Chem Soc; Am Soc Animal Sci; Am Dairy Sci Asn; Asn Off Anal Chem; Am Inst Nutrit. *Res:* Vitamin A requirements of farm animals; metabolism and methods of analysis; nutritional requirements of animals; nutritional evaluations of feeds and foods. *Mailing Add:* Dept of Biochem Kans State Univ Manhattan KS 66506

PARRISH, EDWARD ALTON, JR, b Newport News, Va, Jan 7, 37; m 63; c 2. ELECTRONIC ENGINEERING. *Educ:* Univ Va, BEE, 64, MEE, 66, DSc(elec eng), 68. *Prof Exp:* Sr programmer software, Amerad Corp, Va, 61-63; from asst prof to assoc prof, 68-77, PROF ELEC ENG, UNIV VA, 77-, CHMN DEPT, 78- *Mem:* AAAS; Inst Elec & Electronics Engrs; Pattern Recognition Soc. *Res:* Image processing; digital systems; biomedical instrumentation; automation. *Mailing Add:* Dept of Elec Eng Univ of Va Charlottesville VA 22901

PARRISH, FRED KENNETH, b Durham, NC, Oct 17, 27; m 56; c 5. BIOLOGY. *Educ:* Duke Univ, BA, 53; Univ NC, MA, 59; Emory Univ, PhD(biol), 66. *Prof Exp:* Instr biol, Agnes Scott Col, 60-65; asst prof, 65-70, ASSOC PROF BIOL & MEM URBAN LIFE FAC, GA STATE UNIV, 70- *Res:* Aquatic and marine biology; animal behavior. *Mailing Add:* Dept of Biol Ga State Univ Atlanta GA 30303

PARRISH, FREDERICK CHARLES, JR, b Olney, Mo, July 18, 33; m 53; c 4. ANIMAL SCIENCE, BIOCHEMISTRY. *Educ:* Univ Mo, BS, 59, MS, 60, PhD(animal husb), 65. *Prof Exp:* Asst animal husb, Univ Mo, 59-60, instr, 60-65; from asst asst prof to assoc prof, 65-76, PROF ANIMAL SCI & FOOD TECHNOL, 76- *Concurrent Pos:* Food scientist, Coop State Res Serv, USDA, Washington, DC, 72-73. *Mem:* Inst Food Technol; Am Soc Animal Sci; Am Meat Sci Asn. *Res:* Muscle biochemistry and enzymology; relationship of chemistry and structure to meat palatability; postmortem biochemical and biophysical properties of muscle. *Mailing Add:* 150 Food Res Lab Iowa State Univ Ames IA 50010

PARRISH, HERBERT CHARLES, b Jacksboro, Tex, Oct 8, 19; m 41; c 3. MATHEMATICAL ANALYSIS. *Educ:* N Tex State Univ, BS, 39, MS, 41; Ohio State Univ, PhD(math), 55. *Prof Exp:* Instr math, Ohio State Univ, 48-49; from asst prof to assoc prof, 49-58, dir dept, 58-65, PROF MATH, N TEX STATE UNIV, 58- *Mem:* Am Math Soc; Math Asn Am (nat gov, 62-65); Nat Coun Teachers Math. *Res:* Analysis; functions of a real variable; measure and integration. *Mailing Add:* Dept of Math N Tex State Univ Denton TX 76203

PARRISH, JAMES DAVIS, b Bennettsville, SC, Dec 18, 35; m 61; c 2. MARINE ECOLOGY, FISH BIOLOGY. *Educ:* Univ SC, BS, 56; Univ RI, PhD(oceanog), 72. *Prof Exp:* Scientist I & II marine ecol, PR Nuclear Ctr of USAEC, 72-75; asst leader & asst prof fisheries, Mass Coop Fish Res Unit, 75-77, LEADER & ASSOC PROF ZOOL, HAWAII COOP FISH RES UNIT, US FISH & WILDLIFE SERV, 77- *Concurrent Pos:* Mem, Interagency Sci Adv Subcomt Ocean Dredging & Spoiling, 75-77, Sci Statist Comt, West Pac Fish Mgt Coun, 81- *Mem:* AAAS; Am Fisheries Soc; Am Soc Limnol & Oceanog; Ecol Soc Am; Sigma Xi. *Res:* Aquatic population and community ecology; trophic structure; analytical models of ecological systems; species interactions; predation; dynamics of multi-species fish populations; shallow tropical marine systems, coral reef ecology. *Mailing Add:* Hawaii Coop Fish Res Unit 2538 The Mall Univ Hawaii Honolulu HI 96822

PARRISH, ROB GENE, biophysics, anesthesiology, see previous edition

PARRISH, ROBERT A, JR, b Augusta, Ga, Sept 9, 30; m 54; c 2. SURGERY. *Educ:* Mercer Univ, AB, 51; Univ Ga, MS, 53; Med Col Ga, MD, 56; Am Bd Surg, dipl, 63. *Prof Exp:* From instr to assoc prof, 62-70, PROF SURG, MED COL GA, 70-, CHIEF PEDIAT SURG, 72- *Concurrent Pos:* Am Cancer Soc fel, 60-61; NIH fel, 61-62; consult to many hosps in Ga. *Mem:* Am Acad Pediat; Am Col Surgeons; Soc Surg Alimentary Tract; Am Asn Surg of Trauma. *Res:* Pediatric surgery; gastrointestinal tract. *Mailing Add:* Dept Surg Med Col Ga Augusta GA 30902

PARRISH, ROBERT G, b Wis, Apr 4, 24; m 46, 60; c 2. PHYSICAL CHEMISTRY. *Educ:* Univ Wis, BS, 49; Duke Univ, PhD, 52. *Prof Exp:* Merck fel physics, Cambridge Univ, 52-54; res assoc, Royal Inst Gt Brit, 54 & Univ Mich, 54-55; res chemist, 55-59, sr res chemist, 59-61, res assoc, 61-62, supvr res, 62-65, res mgr, 65-78, RES FEL, E I DU PONT DE NEMOURS & CO, INC, 78- *Res:* Protein chemistry; structural biophysics; structure-property relationships in synthetic polymers; cellular plastics; textile fibers. *Mailing Add:* Pioneering Res Lab Du Pont Exp Sta Wilmington DE 19899

PARRISH, WAYNE, b Millersport, Ohio, Dec 18, 20. ZOOLOGY. *Educ:* Ohio State Univ, BS, 48, MS, 55, PhD(radiation biol), 58. *Prof Exp:* Asst biol, Ohio State Univ, 52-56, radiation biol, 56-58, cancer, Univ Hosp, 58-59; res biologist, Miami Valley Hosp, 59-62; asst prof, 62-66, ASSOC PROF ZOOL, OHIO STATE UNIV, 66- *Mem:* AAAS. *Res:* Tissue culture of chloromyeloid leukemia cells; metabolism; radiation; histology; chemotherapy; cytology; electron microscopy. *Mailing Add:* Dept of Zool & Entom Ohio State Univ Columbus OH 43210

PARRISH, WILLIAM, b Philadelphia, Pa, Apr 16, 14; m 41; c 2. X-RAY CRYSTALLOGRAPHY, MATERIALS SCIENCE. *Educ:* Pa State Univ, BS, 35; Mass Inst Technol, PhD(crystallog), 40. *Prof Exp:* Res assoc, Mass Inst Technol, 39-40; instr, Pa State Col, 40-42; chief technologist, Off Chief Signal Officer, NAm Philips Co, Inc, 42-43, head quartz oscillator res & pilot plant, 43-44, chief x-ray & crystallog sect, Philips Labs Div, NY, 44-68; chief mat characterization br, Electronics Res Ctr, NASA, Mass, 68-70; res staff mem, 70-80, MGR, CRYSTALLOG & X-RAY ANALYSIS, RES DIV, IBM CORP, 80- *Concurrent Pos:* Mem nat comt crystallog, 48-57, 65-69, secy-treas, 54-56 & 67-69; mem comn crystallog apparatus, Int Union Crystallog, 51-63, chmn, 57-63; ed, World Dir Crystallographers, 57; mem mat adv bd panel struct, Nat Acad Sci-Nat Res Coun, 65-66. *Honors & Awards:* Citation, US Dept War, 46. *Mem:* Fel Mineral Soc Am; Am Crystallog Asn (secy-treas, 45-49); Mineral Soc Gt Brit & Ireland; Fr Soc Mineral & Crystallog; Microbeam Anal Soc. *Res:* X-ray crystallography; materials science and charcterization; x-ray diffraction and spectroscopy; precision measurements; instrumentation and computers. *Mailing Add:* Dept K41/281 IBM Res Lab 5600 Cottle Rd San Jose CA 95193

PARROTT, EUGENE LEE, b Menasha, Wis, Feb 3, 25; m 48; c 1. PHARMACEUTICS, INDUSTRIAL PHARMACY. *Educ:* Univ Wis, BS, 49, PhD(pharm), 54. *Prof Exp:* Asst prof pharm, Univ Ariz, 54-55, assoc prof, 55-56; pharmaceutical chemist, Chas Pfizer & Co, 56-57; assoc prof pharm, Univ Nebr, 57-62; assoc prof, 62-73, head div pharmaceut, 75-81, PROF INDUST PHARM, COL PHARM, UNIV IOWA, 73- *Mem:* Am Pharmaceut Asn; fel Acad Pharmaceut Sci; NY Acad Sci. *Res:* Applications of physiochemical and physiological principles to formulation, design, production and evaluation of dosage forms. *Mailing Add:* Col of Pharm Univ of Iowa Iowa City IA 52240

PARROTT, MARSHALL WARD, b Roseville, Calif, Nov 28, 27; m 72; c 2. RADIOLOGICAL HEALTH. *Educ:* Univ Calif, Berkeley, AB, 52, MA, 59; Tulane Univ, La, DSc(hyg), 69. *Prof Exp:* Res asst, Lawrence Radiation Lab, Univ Calif, 51-52, physiologist, 52-62; res scientist, Radiobiol Br, NASA Ames Res Ctr, 62-63, biosatellite proj, 63-65; res assoc, Delta Primate Ctr, Tulane Univ, La, 65-69; DIR RADIATION CONTROL, ORE STATE BD HEALTH, 69- *Concurrent Pos:* chmn, Nat Conf Radiation Control Prog Dir, 80-81. *Mem:* AAAS; Radiation Res Soc; Health Physics Soc. *Res:* Effects of internal and external radiation in rats and monkeys; endocrine abnormalities; effects of pesticides; environmental health. *Mailing Add:* Radiation Cont State Health Div State Office Bldg PO Box 231 Portland OR 97207

PARROTT, ROBERT HAROLD, b Jackson Heights, NY, Dec 29, 23; m 50; c 6. VIROLOGY. *Educ:* Fordham Univ, 44; Georgetown Univ, MD, 49. *Prof Exp:* Resident pediat, Children's Hosp, Washington, DC, 50-52; pediatrician, Clin Ctr, Nat Microbiol Inst, 52-56; physician-in-chief & dir, Res Found, 56-62, DIR, CHILDREN'S HOSP NAT MED CTR, WASHINGTON, DC, 62- *Concurrent Pos:* Clin prof, Med Sch, George Washington Univ, 56-65, prof, 69-, chmn, Dept Child Health & Develop, 71-; clin prof, Georgetown Univ, 56-65, prof, 65-69. *Res:* Respiratory viral disease in relation to newly isolated viral agents; general infectious diseases. *Mailing Add:* Children's Hosp Nat Med Ctr 111 Mich Ave NW Washington DC 20010

PARROTT, STEPHEN KINSLEY, b Chicago, Ill, Mar 3, 41. MATHEMATICS. *Educ:* Univ Mich, BS, 61, PhD(math), 65. *Prof Exp:* Instr math, Mass Inst Technol, 65-67; from asst prof to assoc prof, 67-78, PROF MATH, UNIV MASS, BOSTON, 78- *Res:* Functional analysis. *Mailing Add:* Dept of Math Univ of Mass Harbor Campus Boston MA 02125

PARROTT, STEPHEN LAURENT, b East St Louis, Ill, May 3, 49; m 75; c 2. SURFACE CHEMISTRY, PHYSICAL CHEMISTRY. *Educ:* GA Inst Technol, BS, 72, MS, 73, PhD(chem), 77. *Prof Exp:* RES CHEMIST, PHILLIPS PETROL CO, 78- *Concurrent Pos:* Fel Univ Tex Austin, 77-78. *Mem:* Am Chem Soc; Sigma Xi. *Res:* Statistical thermodynamics of solutions; gas-solid interactions; surface spectroscopy; and heterogeneous catalysis. *Mailing Add:* 345 RB-1 Phillips Petrol Co Bartlesville OK 74004

PARROTT, WILLIAM LAMAR, b Fayetteville, Ga, Oct 7, 30; m 53; c 3. ENTOMOLOGY. *Educ:* Purdue Univ, BS, 59, MS, 61; Miss State Univ, PhD, 67. *Prof Exp:* Instr entom, Exp Sta, Purdue Univ, 59-61; ENTOMOLOGIST, AGR RES SERV, USDA, 61- *Mem:* Entom Soc Am. *Res:* Resistance of crop plants to insect attack. *Mailing Add:* Boll Weevil Res Lab Box 5367 Mississippi State MS 39762

PARRY, CHARLES J, b Oneida, NY, Nov 30, 42. ALGEBRA, NUMBER THEORY. *Educ:* State Univ NY, Oswego, BS, 66; Mich State Univ, MS, 67, PhD(math), 70. *Prof Exp:* Asst prof, La State Univ, Baton Rouge, 70-71; asst prof, 71-77, ASSOC PROF MATH, VA POLYTECH INST & STATE UNIV, 77- *Mem:* Am Math Soc; Math Asn Am. *Res:* Algebraic number theory and class field theory; class number problems. *Mailing Add:* Dept of Math Va Polytech Inst & State Univ Blacksburg VA 24061

PARRY, EDWARD PETTERSON, b Ogden, Utah, Nov 5, 22; m 51; c 3. ANALYTICAL CHEMISTRY, ENVIRONMENTAL CHEMISTRY. *Educ:* Univ Utah, BS, 45; Univ Minn, PhD(phys chem), 50. *Prof Exp:* Asst, Univ Minn, 45-48, instr chem, 49-51; instr chem, Univ Conn, 51-54; asst prof, Wash State Col, 54-56; res assoc, Union Oil Co Calif, 56-62; group leader anal chem, NAm Aviation Sci Ctr, 62-68; group leader phys chem, Sci Ctr, 68-71, mgr, 71-76, DIR, AIR MONITORING CTR, ROCKWELL INT CORP, 76- *Mem:* Am Chem Soc; NY Acad Sci; AAAS; Sigma Xi. *Res:* Classical analytical chemistry; electroanalytical chemistry; catalysis; infrared studies of catalytic surfaces; ultraviolet, visible and infrared spectrophotometry; air quality monitoring; air monitoring instrumentation; air quality data validity and quality assurance. *Mailing Add:* Rockwell Int Corp 2421 West Hillcrest Dr Newbury Park CA 91320

PARRY, HUBERT DEAN, b Ogden, Utah, Apr 7, 09; m 36; c 2. METEOROLOGY. *Educ:* Brigham Young Univ, AB, 34; Calif Inst Technol, MS, 37. *Prof Exp:* Supv forecaster, Weather Station, US Weather Bur, Utah, 42-44, supv analyst, Nat Weather Anal Ctr, DC, 44-46, 49-54; from liaison officer to chief meteorol br, US Off Mil Govt, Ger, 46-49; chief airport meteorologist, FORECAST CTR, US Weather Bur, Hawaii, 54-60; res & develop meteorologist for Nat Weather Serv, Nat Oceanic & Atmospheric Admin, 60-73; CONSULT FOR THE ATMOSPHERIC SCI, 73- *Honors &*

Awards: Special Achievement Award, US Dept of Com, 69, Bronze Medal, 73. *Mem:* Am Meteorol Soc. *Res:* Physical meteorology; meteorological instrumentation and observational methods; environmental impact studies; hydrology; studies of effect of weather on energy needs; atmospheric acoustics. *Mailing Add:* 2549 Military Rd Arlington VA 22207

PARRY, MYRON GENE, b Manhattan, Kans, June 20, 33; m 56; c 3. THEORETICAL MECHANICS, APPLIED MECHANICS. *Educ:* Kans State Univ, BS, 59, MS, 61; Univ Ill, PhD(theoret & appl mech), 68. *Prof Exp:* From instr to asst prof eng mech, Univ Mo-Rolla, 61-66; instr, Univ Ill, 66-68; asst prof, 68-71, ASSOC PROF ENG MECH, UNIV MO-ROLLA, 71- *Mem:* Am Soc Eng Educ. *Res:* Post-buckling behavior of thin plates. *Mailing Add:* Dept of Eng Mech Univ of Mo Rolla MO 65401

PARRY, ROBERT WALTER, b Ogden, Utah, Oct 1, 17; m 45; c 2. INORGANIC CHEMISTRY. *Educ:* Utah State Agr Col, BS, 40; Cornell Univ, MS, 42; Univ Ill, PhD(inorg chem), 46. *Prof Exp:* Teaching asst, Cornell Univ, 40-42; asst munitions develop lab, Univ Ill, 42-45; from instr to prof chem, Univ Mich, Ann Arbor, 46-69; PROF CHEM, UNIV UTAH, 69- *Concurrent Pos:* Consult, Callery Chem Co & Stauffer Chem Co; chmn bd trustees, Gordon Res Confs, 69-70; ed, Inorg Chem, 62-64; mem bd dir, Am Chem Soc, 73-, assoc ed, J Am Chem Soc, 70-73 & 75- *Mem:* AAAS; Am Chem Soc (pres, 82); Sigma Xi. *Res:* Coordination chemistry, particularly of fluorophosphines and their derivatives; phosphorus fluorine chemistry boron hydrides; reactions of metalcarbonyl compounds containing one cationic ligand. *Mailing Add:* Dept of Chem Univ of Utah Salt Lake City UT 84112

PARRY, RONALD JOHN, b Los Angeles, Calif, June 9, 42. BIO-ORGANIC CHEMISTRY, NATURAL PRODUCTS CHEMISTRY. *Educ:* Occidental Col, BA, 64; Brandeis Univ, PhD(chem), 68. *Prof Exp:* Fel chem, Univ Liverpool, 68-69, Cambridge Univ, 69-70 & Stanford Univ, 70-71; asst prof, Brandeis Univ, 71-78; ASSOC PROF CHEM, RICE UNIV, 78- *Concurrent Pos:* Res career develop award, NIH, 75-80. *Mem:* Am Chem Soc; Royal Soc Chem; AAAS. *Res:* Investigations of natural product biosynthesis and of stereochemical aspects of enzyme mechanisms. *Mailing Add:* Dept of Chem Rice Univ Houston TX 77001

PARRY, SIDNEY JOHN S, metallurgy, nuclear engineering, see previous edition

PARRY, WILLIAM LOCKHART, b Palatine Bridge, NY, Apr 19, 24; m 52; c 3. UROLOGY. *Educ:* Univ Rochester, MD, 47. *Prof Exp:* Intern surg, Yale Univ Hosps, 47-48; resident surg & urol, Univ Rochester Hosps, 48-52; from asst prof to assoc prof urol, State Univ NY Upstate Med Ctr, 54-62; PROF UROL & HEAD DEPT, MED SCH CTR, UNIV OKLA, 62- *Concurrent Pos:* Fel, Yale Univ Hosps, 47-48; fel, Univ Rochester Hosps, 48-52; mem exec comt & secy urol res group, Cent Off, Vet Admin, Washington, DC, 59-, consult, Cent Off, 61-62. *Mem:* Am Urol Asn; Am Col Surg; AMA. *Res:* Experimental studies of acute renal failure; clinical studies of urologic disease and surgery. *Mailing Add:* Dept of Urol Med Sch Ctr Univ of Okla 800 NE 13th St Oklahoma City OK 73104

PARRY, WILLIAM THOMAS, b Manti, Utah, May 11, 35; m 58; c 2. MINERALOGY, GEOCHEMISTRY. *Educ:* Univ Utah, BS, 57, MS, 59, PhD(geol eng), 61. *Prof Exp:* Exploitation engr, Shell Oil Co, 61-63; assoc prof geosci, Tex Tech Col, 63-67; assoc prof mining & geol eng, 67-69, chmn dept, 69-71, PROF GEOL & GEOPHYS, UNIV UTAH, 71- *Concurrent Pos:* Gulf Oil Corp grant, 64; NSF res grant, 66-68. *Mem:* AAAS; Mineral Soc Am; Geochem Soc. *Mailing Add:* Dept Geol & Geophys Sci Univ of Utah Salt Lake City UT 84112

PARS, HARRY GEORGE, b Pawtucket, RI, Feb 7, 28; m 52; c 2. ORGANIC CHEMISTRY. *Educ:* Harvard Univ, BA, 53; Univ Mich, MS, 55, PhD(org chem), 57. *Prof Exp:* Head med & chem sci drug res & develop, Arthur D Little Co Inc, 57-70; CHMN, CHIEF EXEC OFFICER DRUG RES & DEVELOP & TRUSTEE BASIC RES, SISA INST RES INC, 70-, DIR TOXICOL, 81-; PRES & TRUSTEE BASIC RES, SHEEHAN INST RES INC, 70- *Concurrent Pos:* Consult synthetic substitues, Comt Prob Drug Dependence, Nat Acad Sci. *Mem:* AAAS; Am Chem Soc; NY Acad Sci. *Res:* Pioneered in the design, synthesis, pharmacological and clinical development of new drugs structurally related to the cannabinoids; central nervous system stimulants, depressants, analgesics, anti-glaucoma agents, antihypertensives, anticonvulsants, antidiarrheals, antiinflammatories, and antibiotics. *Mailing Add:* Sisa Inc 763D Concord Ave Cambridge MA 02138

PARSA, ZOHREH, b Iran, Aug 16, 48; m 74; c 1. NUCLEAR PHYSICS, PARTICLE PHYSICS. *Educ:* Del State Col, BS, 69; NY Univ, MS, 71; Polytech Inst NY, PhD(physics), 77. *Prof Exp:* Dir physics & eng lab, Essex County Col, 72-74; instr physics, Hunter Col City Univ NY, 74-76; ASST PROF PHYSICS, NJ INST OF TECHNOL, 77- *Concurrent Pos:* Vis scholar, Northwestern Univ, 80-81; guest assoc physicist, Dept Physics, Brookhaven Nat Lab, 81-83. *Mem:* AAAS; Am Phys Soc; Am Asn Physics Teachers. *Res:* Subnuclear physics and field theories; and nuclear physics. *Mailing Add:* Dept of Physics 323 High St Newark NJ 07102

PARSEGIAN, V(OZCAN) LAWRENCE, b Van, Armenia, Turkey, May 13, 08; nat US; m 38; c 2. NUCLEAR PHYSICS, ENGINEERING. *Educ:* Mass Inst Technol, BS, 33; NY Univ, PhD(physics), 48. *Prof Exp:* Dir res, Tagliabue Mfg Co, 36-47, Physics Dept, Kellex Corp, 47-50 & Res Div, NY Opers Off, US AEC, 50-54; chmn eng group, 54-58, prof nuclear sci & eng, 54-61, dean sch eng, 58-61, distinguished chair of Rensselaer Prof, 61-75, EMER RENSSELAER PROF NUCLEAR SCI & ENG, RENSSELAER POLYTECH INST, 75-, DIR, ARMENIAN ARCHITECT ARCHIVES PROJ, 80- *Concurrent Pos:* Instr, NY Univ, 49; lectr, Columbia Univ; consult, Joint Comt Atomic Energy of US Cong; mem bd dirs, Radiation Applns, Inc, 54- & Cast Tech, Inc, 66-70; consult, State Univ NY & Mass Inst Technol; consult ed, Acad Press, 64-; consult to several cols & univs; mem, NY Gov's Comt Atomic Energy, 58; mem comt com utilization atomic energy, US Chamber Com, 59-65 & comt sci & tech, 65-67; mem, NY State Comt Radiation Utilization, 59-65; consult, World Coun Churches, 76-77. *Mem:* AAAS; Am Nuclear Soc; Am Phys Soc; NY Acad Sci. *Res:* Nuclear science and engineering; nuclear and instrument research; teaching materials and methods that interrelate the physical and life sciences. *Mailing Add:* Rensselaer Polytech Inst Troy NY 12181

PARSEGIAN, VOZKEN ADRIAN, b Boston, Mass, May 28, 39; m 63; c 3. BIOPHYSICS. *Educ:* Dartmouth Col, AB, 60; Harvard Univ, PhD(biophys), 65. *Prof Exp:* NIH fel, Mass Inst Technol, 65-67; res physicist, Nat Insts Health, 67-77; ed, Biophys Jour, 77-80; ED, BIOPHYS DISCUSSIONS, 78- *Mem:* Biophys Soc. *Res:* Theory and measurement of intermolecular forces governing biological structure; cell membrane transport and structure; colloidal systems; computers in scientific publication. *Mailing Add:* Phys Sci Lab DCRT Nat Insts Health Bethesda MD 20014

PARSHALL, CLARENCE MERTON, b Washington, Pa, Apr 19, 14; m 35; c 2. PHYSICS. *Educ:* Washington & Jefferson Col, BS, 35, MS, 37; Purdue Univ, PhD(physics), 41. *Prof Exp:* Lab asst, Yale Univ, 35-36 & Washington & Jefferson Col, 36-37; instr, Purdue Univ, 37-41; res physicist, US Rubber Co, Detroit, 41-53, mgr process develop, Tire Div, 53-72, coordr environ control & energy conserv, 72-78; RETIRED. *Res:* X-ray diffraction of rubber and liquids; fundamentals of breakdown and mixing of natural and synthetic rubbers; extrusion plastometer; structure of amorphous and stretched rubber; properties of crude rubberlike materials; tire processing methods and equipment. *Mailing Add:* 3159 Cheryl Dr Hendersonville NC 28739

PARSHALL, GEORGE WILLIAM, b Hackensack, Minn, Sept 19, 29; m 54; c 3. CHEMISTRY. *Educ:* Univ Ill, PhD(chem), 54. *Prof Exp:* Res chemist, 54-65, res supvr, 65-79, DIR CHEM SCI, E I DU PONT DE NEMOURS & CO, INC, 80- *Concurrent Pos:* Ed-in-chief, Inorg Syntheses, 72-74; ed, J Molecular Catalysis, 77-80. *Mem:* Am Chem Soc. *Res:* Organic and inorganic chemistry; transition metal chemistry; catalysis. *Mailing Add:* Cent Res Dept E I du Pont de Nemours & Co Inc Wilmington DE 19898

PARSIGNAULT, DANIEL RAYMOND, b Paris, France, Feb 5, 37; m 60; c 3. EARTH PARTICLES AND FIELDS. *Educ:* Univ Wis, BS, 60; Southern Ill Univ, MS, 61; Univ Paris, Dr es Sc(nuclear physics), 64. *Prof Exp:* Res physicist, Saclay Nuclear Res Ctr, France, 61-64; res fel nuclear physics, Calif Inst Technol, 64-66; asst prof physics, Ohio State Univ, 66-68; mem res staff, Am Sci & Eng, Inc, 68-76; mem staff, Harvard-Smithsonian Ctr Astrophysics, 76-78; SR SCIENTIST, PHYSICS RES DIV, EMMANUEL COL, 78- *Concurrent Pos:* NATO fel, 64-65. *Mem:* Am Phys Soc; Am Geophys Union. *Res:* Alpha, beta, and gamma ray spectroscopy; nuclear structure and reactions; x-ray astronomy; nuclear physics. *Mailing Add:* Emmanuel College 442 Marrett Rd Lexington MA 02173

PARSLEY, RONALD LEE, b Madison, Wis, July 14, 37; div; c 2. INVERTEBRATE PALEONTOLOGY, GEOLOGY. *Educ:* Univ Calif, Los Angeles, AB, 60; Univ Cincinnati, MS, 63, PhD(geol), 69. *Prof Exp:* Asst prof, 66-71, chmn dept, 71-74, assoc prof, 71-79, PROF GEOL, TULANE UNIV, LA, 79- *Mem:* AAAS; Paleont Soc; Paleont Res Inst; Soc Econ Paleont & Mineral; Geol Soc Am. *Res:* Lower Paleozoic primitive Echinodermata, their systematics, functional morphology and paleoecology. *Mailing Add:* Dept of Earth Sci Tulane Univ New Orleans LA 70118

PARSLY, LEWIS F(ULLER), JR, b Philadelphia, Pa, Jan 27, 18; m 51; c 4. CHEMICAL ENGINEERING. *Educ:* Univ Pa, BS, 40, MS, 47, PhD(chem eng), 48. *Prof Exp:* Jr engr, Am Chem Paint Co, 40 & Elec Storage Battery Co, Pa, 40-41; chem engr, Day & Zimmermann, Inc, 48-51; SR DEVELOP ENGR, NUCLEAR DIV, UNION CARBIDE CORP, 51- *Mem:* Am Chem Soc; Am Nuclear Soc; Am Inst Chem Engrs; Sigma Xi; Nat Soc Prof Engrs. *Res:* Gas absorption; fission product release and transport; thoria slurry handling. *Mailing Add:* Nuclear Div PO Box X Oak Ridge TN 37830

PARSON, JOHN MORRIS, b New Orleans, La, May 29, 46; m 69; c 2. PHYSICAL CHEMISTRY. *Educ:* Harvard Univ, AB, 68; Univ Chicago, PhD(chem), 72. *Prof Exp:* Teacher, chem & physics, Francis Parker High Sch, 68-69; assoc chem, Univ Chicago, 72; asst prof, 72-77, ASSOC PROF CHEMISTRY, OHIO STATE UNIV, 77- *Concurrent Pos:* Fel, Alfred P Sloan Found, 76-80; NSF grant, 76-82; Res Corp grant, 73-75. *Honors & Awards:* E R Norton Prize, Univ Chicago, 72. *Mem:* Am Phys Soc. *Res:* Crossed molecular beams chemistry; transition metal gas phase reactions studied by electronic chemiluminescence and laser excited fluorescence. *Mailing Add:* Dept of Chem 140 W 18th Ave Columbus OH 43210

PARSON, LOUISE ALAYNE, b Boston, Mass, May 29, 47; m 69; c 1. MATHEMATICS. *Educ:* Radcliffe Col, BA, 69; Univ Ill, Chicago Circle, MS, 70, PhD(math), 73. *Prof Exp:* Teaching asst math, Univ Ill, Chicago Circle, 69-72; lectr, 73-75, ASST PROF MATH, OHIO STATE UNIV, 76- *Mem:* Am Math Soc; Math Asn Am; Asn Women Math. *Res:* Automorphic forms and discrete groups. *Mailing Add:* Dept of Math Ohio State Univ Columbus OH 43210

PARSON, WILLIAM WOOD, b Boston, Mass, Dec 1, 39; m 61; c 2. BIOCHEMISTRY. *Educ:* Harvard Col, AB, 61; Case Western Reserve Univ, PhD(biochem), 65. *Prof Exp:* Fel, Univ Pa, 65-67; from asst prof to assoc prof, 67-77, PROF BIOCHEM, UNIV WASH, 77- *Concurrent Pos:* Assoc ed, Biochem, 69- *Res:* Photosynthesis. *Mailing Add:* Dept of Biochem Univ of Wash Seattle WA 98195

PARSONS, CARL MICHAEL, b Salisbury, Md, May 7, 54; m 78. POULTRY NUTRITION. *Educ:* Univ Md, Eastern Shore, BS, 76; Va Polytech Inst & State Univ, MS, 78, PhD(animal sci), 81. *Prof Exp:* Res asst poultry sci, Va Polytech Inst & State Univ, 76-81; ASST PROF ANIMAL SCI, UNIV ILL, URBANA-CHAMPAIGN, 81- *Mem:* Poultry Sci Asn; Animal Nutrit Res Coun; Sigma Xi. *Res:* Poultry production and management with emphasis in the field of nutrition; improved nutritional efficiency for production of poultry meat and eggs, particularly with respect to protein utilization. *Mailing Add:* 1706 W Kirby Ave Champaign IL 61801

PARSONS, DAVID JEROME, b Berkeley, Calif, May 18, 47; m 75. PLANT ECOLOGY, ENVIRONMENTAL MANAGEMENT. *Educ:* Univ Calif, Davis, BS, 69; Stanford Univ, PhD(pop biol), 73. *Prof Exp:* RES SCIENTIST, NAT PARK SERV, US DEPT INTERIOR, 73- *Concurrent Pos:* Assoc, Univ Calif Agr Exp Sta, 74- *Mem:* Ecol Soc Am; AAAS; Bot Soc Am. *Res:* Chaparral ecology; fire ecology of mixed conifer forests; carrying capacities of wilderness areas. *Mailing Add:* Sequoia-Kings Canyon Nat Parks Three Rivers CA 93271

PARSONS, DONALD FREDERICK, b Shoreham-by-Sea, Eng, Nov 28, 28; m 58; c 4. MEDICAL ONCOLOGY, CANCER CELL STRUCTURE. *Educ:* Battersea Col Technol, BSc, 50; Imp Col, dipl, 53; Univ London, PhD(phys chem), 53, MB, BS, 57. *Prof Exp:* Res assoc biophys, Duke Univ, 57-59; biophysicist, Oak Ridge Nat Lab, 59-61; asst prof med biophys, Univ Toronto & mem Staff Ont Cancer Res Inst, 61-66; res prof biophys, State Univ NY Buffalo, 66-76; prin res scientist, Roswell Park Mem Inst, 66-76; RES PHYSICIAN, DIV LAB & RES, NY STATE DEPT HEALTH, 76-, DIR, BIOTECHNOL HIGH VOLTAGE ELECTRON MICROS RESOURCE LAB, 81- *Concurrent Pos:* Res assoc prof biol, State Univ NY, Albany & Rensselaer Polytech Inst, 77. *Mem:* Am Soc Clin Oncol; Am Crystallog Asn; Electron Micros Soc Am; Biophys Soc; Am Asn Cancer Res. *Res:* Characterization of invasive cells by electron microscopy, cytochemistry, immunoflourescense and biochemistry; application of three dimensional image reconstruction and stereoscopy to study structure of cancer cells using the high voltage electron microscopy; electron diffraction of wet protein microcrystals; chemotherapy specific for the motile apparatus of invasive cancer cells. *Mailing Add:* Div of Labs & Res Empire State Plaza Albany NY 12201

PARSONS, JAMES SIDNEY, b Roanoke, Va, Jan 28, 22; m 52; c 2. ANALYTICAL CHEMISTRY. *Educ:* Washington & Lee, BS, 43; Univ Va, MS, 48, PhD(chem), 50. *Prof Exp:* Chemist, Westvaco Chem Div, Food Mach & Chem Corp, 43-46; asst, Univ Va, 47-50; anal chemist, 50-53, res chemist, 54-57, sr res chemist, 58-74, PRIN RES SCI, CHEM RES DIV, AM CYANAMID CO, 74- *Mem:* Am Chem Soc. *Res:* Electroanalytical chemistry; separation techniques; thermal methods of analysis; gas chromatography; environmental analysis. *Mailing Add:* Chem Res Div Am Cyanamid Co Bound Brook NJ 08805

PARSONS, JERRY MONTGOMERY, b Memphis, Tenn, Feb 4, 46; m 66; c 2. HORTICULTURE. *Educ:* Univ Tenn, Martin, BS, 69; Miss State Univ, MS, 71; Kans State Univ, PhD(hort), 74. *Prof Exp:* Res asst hort, Miss State Univ, 69-71 & Kans State Univ, 71-74; VEG SPECIALIST HORT, TEX AGR EXTEN SERV, 74- *Mem:* Am Soc Hort Sci; Am Pomol Soc. *Res:* Educate and inform commercial vegetable growers and home gardeners located in the Texas Agricultural Extension Serv District 13 of new and progressive vegetable culture techniques which might enable a more profitable existence using existing resources. *Mailing Add:* Vegetable Specialist 203 W Nueva Rm 310 San Antonio TX 78207

PARSONS, JESSE LEROY, b Fancie Prairie, Ill, Feb 26, 18; m 42; c 3. BACTERIOLOGY. *Educ:* Ill State Norm Univ, BE, 41; Univ Wis, MS, 48; Purdue Univ, PhD(bact), 58. *Prof Exp:* Asst bact, Univ Wis, 47-49; instr, NDak Agr Col, 49-53; asst, Purdue Univ, 53-55; from asst prof to assoc prof, NDak State Univ, 55-64, prof & chmn dept, 64-69; PROF BIOL, MOORHEAD STATE UNIV, 69-, CHMN DEPT, 78- *Mem:* Am Soc Microbiol; Sigma Xi. *Mailing Add:* Dept of Biol Moorhead State Univ Moorhead MN 56560

PARSONS, JOHN ANDRESEN, b East Orange, NJ, Apr 10, 22; m 45; c 2. RADIOTHERAPY. *Educ:* Bowdoin Col, BS, 43; Syracuse Univ, MD, 46. *Prof Exp:* Assoc chief dept radiation ther, Roswell Park Mem Inst, 53-61; assoc prof, 61-75, PROF RADIOL, UNIV PITTSBURGH, 75-; MED DIR, JOINT RADIATION ONCOL CTR, UNIV HEALTH CTRS, PA, 75- *Concurrent Pos:* Asst prof, Univ Buffalo, 57-62; dir radiation ther, Health Ctr Hosps, Pa, 61-75. *Mem:* Radiol Soc NAm; Am Col Radiol; Am Radium Soc; Am Soc Therapeut Radiol. *Res:* Radiation therapy; radiobiology. *Mailing Add:* Joint Radiation Oncol Ctr Magee-Womens Hosp Div Pittsburgh PA 15213

PARSONS, JOHN ARTHUR, b Pittsburgh, Pa, Dec 8, 32; m 60; c 1. CELL BIOLOGY. *Educ:* Washington & Jefferson Col, BA, 54; Pa State Univ, MS, S6; Fla State Univ, PhD(physiol), 64. *Prof Exp:* Instr biol, Henderson State Teachers Col, 58-59 & Vanderbilt Univ, 59-60; asst prof, Univ Redlands, 63-65; from asst prof to assoc prof, 65-74, PROF BIOL, SAN DIEGO STATE UNIV, 74- *Mem:* AAAS; Am Soc Zoologists; Soc Protozool; Am Soc Cell Biol. *Res:* Mitochondrial origin and DNA. *Mailing Add:* Dept of Biol San Diego State Univ San Diego CA 92182

PARSONS, JOHN DAVID, b Gary, Ind, Nov 22, 25; m 49; c 1. LIMNOLOGY. *Educ:* Southern Illinois Univ, BA, 50, MA, 51; Univ Mo, PhD(zool), 56. *Prof Exp:* From asst prof to assoc prof biol sci, Western Ill Univ, 55-62; assoc prof biol sci & dir Pine Hills Field Sta, Southern Ill Univ, Carbondale, 62-73, prof bot, 73-76; dir environ studies, Parsons & Assocs, 76-79; SR FISH & WILDLIFE BIOLOGIST, OFF SURFACE MINING, DEPT INTERIOR, WASHINGTON, DC, 79- *Concurrent Pos:* Atomic Energy Comn equip grant, 62. *Mem:* Am Fisheries Soc; Int Asn Theoret & Appl Limnol; Am Soc Limnol & Oceanog; Wildlife Soc. *Res:* Aquatic ecology; inorganic pollution of streams; organic and inorganic factors relating to primary production and energy transfer in lakes. *Mailing Add:* Dept of Interior Off of Surface Mining Washington DC 20240

PARSONS, JOHN G, b Man, Can, Dec 3, 39; m 63; c 2. DAIRY CHEMISTRY. *Educ:* Univ Man, BSc, 61, MSc, 63; Pa State Univ, PhD(dairy sci), 68. *Prof Exp:* Asst dairy sci, Univ Man, 62-63; asst, Pa State Univ, 63-65, res asst, 65-68; asst prof, 68-73, assoc prof, 73-79, PROF DAIRY SCI, SDAK STATE UNIV, 79-, HEAD DEPT, 78- *Mem:* Am Dairy Sci Asn; Inst Food Technol. *Res:* Flavor and lipid chemistry of milk products. *Mailing Add:* Dept Dairy Sci SDak State Univ Box 2104 Brookings SD 57007

PARSONS, JOHN LAWRENCE, b Kans, Feb 4, 24; m 45; c 5. AGRONOMY. *Educ:* Kans State Col, BS, 48, MS, 49; Univ Mass, PhD(agron), 53. *Prof Exp:* Asst prof agron, Kans State Col, 48-49; instr, Univ Mass, 49-53; from asst prof to prof, Ohio Agr Res & Develop Ctr, 53-68; asst coordr int affairs, 68-73, PROF AGRON, OHIO STATE UNIV, 73- *Mem:* Am Soc Agron. *Mailing Add:* Dept Agron Ohio State Univ Columbus OH 43210

PARSONS, L CLAIRE, b Flora, La, Aug 1, 33. NEUROPHYSIOLOGY. *Educ:* Northwestern State Col, BS, 54; La State Univ, Baton Rouge, 56-58; Univ Houston, MS, 64; Univ Tex Med Br Galveston, PhD(physiol), 68. *Prof Exp:* Dir res & assoc prof, Sch Nursing, 71-74, ASST PROF PHYSIOL, MED SCH, UNIV VA, 71-, PROF, SCH NURSING, 74- *Concurrent Pos:* NIH spec fel, Surg Neurol Br, Nat Inst Neurol Dis & Stroke, 68-70; lectr, Surg Neurol Br, Nat Inst Neurol Diseases & Stroke, 68-70 & NIH, 68-70; guest lectr, Case Western Reserve Univ, 70-71; prof dir & ed, Human Physiol Ser, 76-80. *Mem:* Sigma Xi; AAAS; Soc Neurosci. *Res:* Sleep and head trauma. *Mailing Add:* 2465 Williston Dr Charlottesville VA 22901

PARSONS, LAWRENCE REED, b Sacramento, Calif, May 22, 44; m 71; c 1. ENVIRONMENTAL PHYSIOLOGY, HORTICULTURE. *Educ:* Univ Calif, Davis, AB, 67, MS, 68; Duke Univ PhD(bot), 72. *Prof Exp:* Res assoc plant physiol, Duke Univ, 72-74; asst prof hort & plant physiol, Univ Minn, St Paul, 74-80; ASST PROF FRUIT CROPS, UNIV FLA, 79- *Mem:* Sigma Xi; Am Soc Hort Sci; Am Soc Plant Physiologists; Crop Sci Soc Am. *Res:* Plant-water relations; effects of cold temperature on plants; plant hardiness. *Mailing Add:* Univ Fla Agr Res & Educ Ctr 700 Experiment Sta Rd Lake Afred FL 33850

PARSONS, MARGARET CRANSTON, insect morphology, see previous edition

PARSONS, MICHAEL L, b Oklahoma City, Okla, Apr 20, 40; m 72; c 2. ANALYTICAL CHEMISTRY. *Educ:* Pittsburg State Univ, BA, 62, MS, 63; Univ Fla, PhD(anal chem), 66. *Prof Exp:* Res chemist, Phillips Petrol Co, 66-67; from asst prof to assoc prof, 67-78, PROF ANAL CHEM, ARIZ STATE UNIV, 78- *Honors & Awards:* W F Meggers Award, Soc Appl Spectros, 67 & 76. *Mem:* Am Chem Soc; Soc Appl Spectros (pres, 79); Optical Soc Am. *Res:* Atomic spectroscopy, including trace metal analysis of environmental, biological, and real world samples; theoretical measurements and calculations; study of excitation sources and spectra; trace organics in environmental samples. *Mailing Add:* Dept of Chem Ariz State Univ Tempe AZ 85281

PARSONS, R(ICHARD) L(EWIS), mechanical engineering, see previous edition

PARSONS, ROBERT HATHAWAY, b Passaic, NJ, May 13, 41. COMPARATIVE PHYSIOLOGY. *Educ:* Del Valley Col, BS, 63; Ore State Univ, MS, 67, PhD(physiol), 69. *Prof Exp:* NIH fel, Case Western Reserve Univ, 69-71, res assoc, 71-72; asst prof, 72-78, ASSOC PROF BIOL, RENSSELAER POLYTECH INST, 78- *Mem:* Am Soc Zool; Soc Gen Physiologists; Am Physiol Soc; Biophys Soc. *Res:* Membrane transport; water transport; non-electrolyte transport. *Mailing Add:* Dept of Biol Rensselaer Polytech Inst Troy NY 12181

PARSONS, ROBERT JEROME, b Syracuse, NY, Mar 27, 07; m 76; c 3. PATHOLOGY. *Educ:* Syracuse Univ, AB, 28, MD, 31. *Prof Exp:* Intern, Peter Bent Brigham Hosp, Boston, Mass, 31-32; intern path, New York Hosp, 33-34, resident, 34-35; asst path & bact, Rockefeller Inst, 35-38; from instr to asst prof path, Med Sch, Univ Mich, 38-46; pathologist & dir labs, Highland Gen Hosp, 46-77. *Concurrent Pos:* Fel med, Harvard Med Sch, 32-33; asst, Med Col, Cornell Univ, 33-35. *Mem:* Am Soc Exp Path; Harvey Soc; AMA; Am Asn Pathologists & Bacteriologists; fel Col Am Pathologists. *Res:* Shope virus; virus of oral papillomatosis in rabbits; histoplasmosis in man and animals; pathology of human pituitary; malaria in man and animals; filariasis; lymphatic physiology; diuretics in dogs. *Mailing Add:* 319 Mountain Ave Piedmont CA 94611

PARSONS, ROBERT W(ESTWOOD), b San Diego, Calif, Sept 13, 32; m 54; c 2. CHEMICAL ENGINEERING. *Educ:* Univ Idaho, BS, 54; Univ Ill, MS, 56, PhD(chem eng), 58. *Prof Exp:* Res engr, Ohio Oil Co, 58-63, adv res engr, 63-69, SR RES ENGR, MARATHON OIL CO, 69- *Concurrent Pos:* Sabbatical leave, Chem Eng Dept, Univ Colo, 76-77. *Mem:* Am Inst Mining, Metall & Petrol Engrs; Am Inst Chem Engrs; Sigma Xi. *Res:* Enhanced oil recovery; use of C02, surfactants, and thermal methods; physical properties of petroleum fluids. *Mailing Add:* 6777 Southridge Lane Littleton CO 80120

PARSONS, RODNEY LAWRENCE, b Southampton, NY, Dec 7, 39; m 61; c 3. PHYSIOLOGY, BIOPHYSICS. *Educ:* Middlebury Col, AB, 62; Stanford Univ, PhD(physiol), 65. *Prof Exp:* From asst prof to assoc prof, 67-73, prof physiol, 73-79, PROF & CHMN ANAT & NEUROBIOL, COL MED, UNIV VT, 79- *Concurrent Pos:* NIH fel physiol, Columbia Univ, 65-67. *Mem:* Am Physiol Soc; Soc Gen Physiol. *Res:* Comparative electrophysiology and pharmacology of synaptic transmission; excitation contraction coupling of skeletal muscle. *Mailing Add:* Dept of Physiol Univ of Vt Col of Med Burlington VT 05401

PARSONS, ROGER BRUCE, b Ft Dodge, Iowa, Dec 19, 32; m 54; c 3. SOIL GENESIS, MORPHOLOGY. *Educ:* Iowa State Univ, BS, 55, PhD(soils), 60; Univ Tenn, MS, 57. *Prof Exp:* Asst agronomist, Univ Tenn, 55-57; teaching asst soil surv, Iowa State Univ, 57-60, res assoc, 60-61; res soil scientist, Soil Surv Invests, Soil Conserv Serv, US Dept Agr, Calif, 61-62, res soil scientist, Ore, 62-74; grad fac mem, Ore State Univ, 64-74, assoc prof soils, 69-74, asst prof, 62-69; soil scientist, 74-80, RES SOIL SCIENTIST, WEST TECH SERV CTR, SOIL CONSERV SERV, US DEPT AGR, ORE, 80- *Mem:* Am Soc Agron; Soil Sci Soc Am; Int Union Quaternary Res. *Res:* Soil genesis and morphology as related to geomorphology, geology, soil classification; soil micromorphology; mineralogy of soil parent materials; soil survey and conservation; archeological uses of soil techniques. *Mailing Add:* WTSC-SCS 511 NW Broadway Portland OR 97209

PARSONS, THERAN DUANE, b St Maries, Idaho, Dec 26, 22; m 45; c 2. INORGANIC CHEMISTRY. *Educ:* Univ Wash, BS, 49, PhD(chem), 53. *Prof Exp:* Res fel, Univ Chicago, 53-55; from asst prof to assoc prof, 55-68, asst dean, Col Sci, 67-70, actg dean, 70-72 & 79-81, assoc dean, 73-81, PROF CHEM, ORE STATE UNIV, 68-, ACTG VPRES ADMIN, 81- *Honors & Awards:* Carter Award, 59; Mosser Award, 66. *Mem:* Am Chem Soc. *Res:* Chemistry of boron; electron-deficient bonding; organometallic chemistry. *Mailing Add:* Dept Chem Ore State Univ Corvallis OR 97331

PARSONS, THOMAS STURGES, b New York, NY, Sept 1, 30; m 57. VERTEBRATE ZOOLOGY. *Educ:* Harvard Univ, AB, 52, AM, 53, PhD(biol), 57. *Prof Exp:* Instr biol, Harvard Univ, 57-60; from asst prof to assoc prof 60-69, PROF ZOOL, UNIV TORONTO, 69- *Mem:* Soc Vert Paleont; Soc Study Evolution; Am Ornith Union; Am Soc Zool; Am Soc Ichthyol & Herpet. *Res:* Anatomy, embryology and paleontology of vertebrates, primarily amphibians and reptiles. *Mailing Add:* Dept of Zool Univ of Toronto Toronto ON M5S 1A1 Can

PARSONS, TIMOTHY F, b Cambridge, Mass, Sept 27, 38; m 60; c 5. ORGANIC CHEMISTRY. *Educ:* Boston Col, BS, 60; Vanderbilt Univ, PhD(org chem), 64. *Prof Exp:* Sr res chemist, Res Labs, 64-68, tech assoc, Paper Sensitizing Div, 69-72, supvr develop, 73-74, supvr develop, Paper Support Div, 74-75, asst dir, Paper Serv Div, 75-77, prog dir photograph prog develop, US & Can Photog Div, 78-80, asst supt, Prod Finishing Div, 80-81, DIR, PAPER SERV DIV, EASTMAN KODAK CO, 81- *Honors & Awards:* Charles Ives Award, Soc Photog & Eng, 80. *Mem:* Am Chem Soc; Soc Photog Sci & Eng. *Res:* Synthesis, structure, and mechanism of antiradiation drugs, especially those capable of thioalkylation; chemistries of photographic systems; photographic process and product development. *Mailing Add:* Eastman Kodak Co Kodak Park B10 Rochester NY 14650

PARSONS, TIMOTHY RICHARD, b Colombo, Ceylon, Nov 1, 32; nat Can; m 58; c 3. OCEANOGRAPHY. *Educ:* McGill Univ, BSc, 53, MSc, 56, PhD(biochem), 59. *Prof Exp:* Sr scientist, Pac Oceanog Group, Fisheries Res Bd Can, 59-62, Off Oceanog, UNESCO, France, 62-64 & Pac Oceanog Group, Fisheries Res Bd Can, 64-71; PROF OCEANOG, INST OCEANOG, UNIV BC, 71- *Concurrent Pos:* Mem, Comt Perfect, Inst Oceanog, Paris. *Mem:* Am Soc Limnol & Oceanog; Int Asn Biol Oceanog; Phycol Soc Am; Plankton Soc Japan; Oceanog Soc Japan. *Res:* Biological and chemical oceanography. *Mailing Add:* Inst of Oceanog Univ of BC Vancouver BC V6T 1W5 Can

PARSONS, TORRENCE DOUGLAS, b Lock Haven, Pa, Mar 7, 41; m 66; c 2. MATHEMATICS. *Educ:* Swarthmore Col, BA, 63; Princeton Univ, MA, 65, PhD(math), 66. *Prof Exp:* Instr math, Princeton Univ, 66-69; asst prof, 69-75, ASSOC PROF MATH, COL SCI, PA STATE UNIV, 75- *Mem:* Am Math Soc; Math Asn Am. *Res:* Combinatorial mathematics; mathematical programming, optimization. *Mailing Add:* Dept Math Col Sci 413 McAllister Bldg Pa State Univ University Park PA 16802

PARSONS, WILLIAM BELLE, JR, b Apollo, Pa, Nov 10, 24; m 45, 73; c 5. MEDICINE. *Educ:* Univ Pittsburgh, BS, 47, MD, 48; Am Bd Internal Med, dipl, 56. *Prof Exp:* Intern med, Western Pa Hosp, Pittsburgh, 48-49; res fel res med, Univ Pittsburgh, 49-50; fel med, Mayo Found, 50-53; first asst, Mayo Clin, 55-56; mem staff, Dept Internal Med, Jackson Clin, 56-73; dir clin res, Armour Pharmaceut Co, 74-78; MEM STAFF, SCOTTSDALE MEM HOSP, 77- *Concurrent Pos:* Dir res med, Jackson Found, 57-73; fel coun arteriosclerosis, Am Heart Asn, 57-; pvt pract internal med, 78- *Mem:* Fel Am Col Physicians; AMA. *Res:* Lipid research; cholesterol-reducing drugs; hypertension; coronary risk factors; hematology; atherosclerosis. *Mailing Add:* 7331 E Osborn Dr Scottsdale AZ 85251

PARTAIN, CLARENCE LEON, b Memphis, Tenn, July 12, 40; m 64; c 3. NUCLEAR MEDICINE. *Educ:* Univ Tenn, BS, 63; Purdue Univ, MS, 65, PhD(nuclear eng), 67; Wash Univ Sch Med, MD, 75. *Prof Exp:* Develop engr, Instrumentation & controls, Oak Ridge Nat Lab, Union Carbide Corp, 66-68; assoc prof nuclear eng, Univ Mo, 68-75; res asst radiol, Mallinckrodt Inst, Sch Med, Wash Univ, 72-75; assoc prof & dir radiol & comput tomography, Univ NC, Chapel Hill, 75-79; ASSOC PROF & DIR RADIOL NUCLEAR MED DIV, SCH MED, VANDERBILT UNIV, 80- *Concurrent Pos:* Deleg, State Tenn, Am Col Nuclear Physicians, 81-82; reviewer & abstractor radiol, Radiol Soc NAm, 77-; consult, Site Vis Nat Cancer Inst & Nat Heart Blood & Lung, NIH, 80-; assoc ed, Comput Tomography, Comput Tomography Soc, 81-; consult, Vet Admin, Dept Med & Surg, 80- & Sci Adv Comn, Am Cancer Soc, 82- *Mem:* Am Roentgen Ray Soc; Asn Univ Radiologists; Inst Elec & Electronics Engrs; Soc Nuclear Med; Radiol Soc NAm. *Res:* Development and evaluation of medical imaging modalities including nuclear medicine, positron emission tomography, center tap, and nuclear magnetic resonance imaging; physiological and mathematical modeling for renal function and cerebrospinal fluid dynamics. *Mailing Add:* Nuclear Med Div Sch Med Vanderbilt Univ Nashville TN 37232

PARTAIN, GERALD LAVERN, b Little Rock, Ark, Feb 18, 25; m 66; c 2. FOREST ECONOMICS. *Educ:* Univ SC, BS, 45; Ore State Univ, BS, 49; NY State Col Forestry, Syracuse Univ, PhD(forestry econ), 72. *Prof Exp:* Design engr, Kaiser Engrs, Calif, 51-53 & Bechtel Engrs, 53-54; assoc prof forestry econ, 54-69, PROF FORESTRY, HUMBOLDT STATE UNIV, 69-, CHMN DEPT, 73- *Concurrent Pos:* Consult land develop; legislative aide & consult, US Senate. *Mem:* Soc Am Foresters; Am Forestry Asn; Int Soc Trop Foresters. *Res:* Forestry in economic development; rural subdivisions and the environment. *Mailing Add:* Dept of Forestry Humboldt State Univ Arcata CA 95521

PARTANEN, CARL RICHARD, b Portland, Ore, Nov 23, 21; m 61; c 3. PLANT CYTOLOGY, PLANT MORPHOGENETICS. *Educ:* Lewis & Clark Col, BA, 50; Harvard Univ, AM, 51, PhD, 54. *Prof Exp:* Am Cancer Soc res fel, Columbia Univ, 54-55 & Harvard Univ, 55-57; res assoc, Children's Cancer Res Found, 57-61; assoc prof, 61-64, chmn dept, 64-70, PROF BIOL, UNIV PITTSBURGH, 64- *Concurrent Pos:* Res fel, Univ Edinburgh, 71-72 & Univ Nottingham, 78-79. *Mem:* Bot Soc Am; Genetics Soc Am; Am Soc Cell Biol; Soc Develop Biol; Tissue Cult Asn. *Res:* Plant development; cell nucleus in relation to growth, differentiation and morphogenesis; radiation-induced tumorization in plants; biology of plants, tissues and cells in culture; plant genetic manipulation. *Mailing Add:* Dept of Biol Sci Univ of Pittsburgh Pittsburgh PA 15260

PARTCH, RICHARD EARL, b Long Beach, Calif, Aug 8, 36; m 57; c 3. ORGANIC CHEMISTRY, MEDICINAL CHEMISTRY. *Educ:* Pomona Col, AB, 58; Univ Rochester, PhD(org chem), 62. *Prof Exp:* Asst prof chem, NMex Highlands Univ, 62-65; asst prof, 65-68, assoc prof & exec off dept, 68-71, ROTARY FOUND FEL, CLARKSON COL TECHNOL, 71- *Concurrent Pos:* Res grants, Res Corp, 63-65, NIH, 63- & Am Heart Asn, 63-; Nat Acad Sci res fel, 67-68. *Mem:* Am Chem Soc; Royal Soc Chem. *Res:* Synthesis of alkaloid materials; model compounds of medicinal interest; synthetic utility and mechanism studies of alcohol-lead tetraacetate reactions; theoretical, synthetic and application studies on tranquilizers and growth hormones. *Mailing Add:* Dept of Chem Clarkson Col of Technol Potsdam NY 13676

PARTENHEIMER, WALTER, b Chicago, Ill, Jan 10, 41; m 67; c 1. INORGANIC CHEMISTRY. *Educ:* Univ Wis-Whitewater, BS, 63; Univ Iowa, PhD(chem), 68. *Prof Exp:* NIH fel, Univ Ill, 68-70; Petrol Res Fund fel, Clarkson Col Technol, 70-73, asst prof inorg chem, 70-75; res chemist, 75-78, sr chemist, 78-80, RES ASSOC, AMOCO CHEM CORP, 81- *Mem:* Am Chem Soc. *Res:* Coordination chemistry; organometallic chemistry; catalysis; catalytic oxidation of organic molecules. *Mailing Add:* Amoco Chem Corp Box 400 Naperville IL 60540

PARTHASARATHI, MANAVASI NARASIMHAN, b Madras, India, Jan 13, 24; m 44; c 3. TECHNICAL MANAGEMENT. *Educ:* Banaras Hindu Univ, BS, 44; Univ Ill, MS, 57, PhD(metall eng), 60. *Prof Exp:* Mem res staff, Univ Ill, 55-60; asst head res dept, Bird & Co, 60-62; gen mgr, Zinc Devlop Asn & Lead Develop Asn, 62-77; MGR, DEVELOP, INT LEAD ZINC RES ORGN, 78- *Concurrent Pos:* Hon secy, Indian Inst Metals, 62-77, ed, Transaction, 63-72; prof, Bengaleng Col, 63-65. *Honors & Awards:* John Taylor Gold Medal, Indian Inst Metals, 72. *Mem:* Fel Am Soc Metals; fel Soc Die Casting Engrs; fel Inst Metallurgists London; fel Indian Standards Inst. *Res:* Metallurgical research; fundamental, applied and industrial; pilot plant; lead zinc and cadmium; product development. *Mailing Add:* 47 Whittier St Hartsdale NY 10530

PARTHASARATHY, RENGACHARY, b Nagari, India, May 3, 36; m 62; c 4. BIOPHYSICS, CRYSTALLOGRAPHY. *Educ:* Univ Madras, MA, 57, Msc, 58, PhD(physics), 62; State Univ NY, PhD(biophys), 66. *Prof Exp:* Sr res asst physics, Univ Madras, 61-62, Coun Sci & Indust Res sr fel, 62-63; from cancer res scientist to sr cancer res scientist, 63-67, assoc cancer res scientist, 67-76, PRIN CANCER RES SCIENTIST, BIOPHYS, ROSWELL PARK MEM INST, 76- *Concurrent Pos:* Asst res prof, Roswell Div, State Univ NY, 66-72, assoc res prof, 72-76, res prof biophys, 76-; NIH grants, 69-72, 74-77, 78-80 & 81-83. *Mem:* Biophys Soc; AAAS; Am Crystallog Asn. *Res:* X-ray optics; protein crystallography; conformational analysis; biological structures; stereochemistry of nucleic acids. *Mailing Add:* Biophys Div Roswell Park Mem Inst Buffalo NY 14203

PARTHASARATHY, SAMPATH, b Madras, India, Dec 27, 47; m 74; c 2. BIOCHEMISTRY. *Educ:* Univ Madras, BSc, 67, MSc, 69; Indian Inst Sci, PhD(biochem), 75. *Prof Exp:* Asst res officer, Ind Counc Med Res, 71-72; sr res fel, Univ Grants Comn, 72-74; Jap Govt Scholar, Kyoto Univ, 75-76; res assoc, Duke Univ Med Ctr, 76-77; fel, 77-78, res assoc, 78-81, ASST PROF, HORMEL INST, UNIV MINN, AUSTIN, 81- *Mem:* AAAS. *Res:* Intestinal absorption of phospholipids; cholesterol metabolism; fatty acid synthesis in S; cerevisiae; regulation of phospholipid synthesis in rat intestine; biosynthesis and metabolism of diol lipids; membrane structure and assembly; lipid dependent enzymes; lipid in normal and neoplastic cells. *Mailing Add:* Hormel Inst Univ Minn 801-16th Ave NE Austin MN 55912

PARTHENIADES, EMMANUEL, b Athens, Greece, Nov 3, 26; US citizen; m 67. HYDRAULIC & COASTAL ENGINEERING. *Educ:* Nat Tech Univ Athens, dipl civil eng, 52; Univ Calif, Berkeley, MS, 55, PhD(hydraul eng), 62. *Prof Exp:* Designer, G Vingos, Greece, 52-53 & A Mahairas, 53-54; sr engr analyst, Dames & More, Calif, 55-59; sr engr, Cooper & Clark, 59-60; teaching asst hydraul, Univ Calif, Berkeley, 59-61, res engr, 61-62; asst prof hydraul & fluid mech, San Jose State Col, 62-63; asst prof hydraul, Mass Inst Technol, 63-66; assoc prof, State Univ NY Buffalo, 66-68; vis assoc prof coastal & oceanog eng, 68-69, PROF COASTAL & OCEANOG ENG, UNIV FLA, 69-, PROF ENG SCI, 80- *Concurrent Pos:* Ford Found fel, Mass Inst Technol, 63-65; co-investr with Dr J F Kennedy, NSF res grant, 65-66; Fed Water Pollution Control Admin res grant, 67-71; NSF res grants, 70-74, 76-79, 78-81; Environ Protection Agency traineeship grant, 70-; Coastal Eng Res Ctr res contract, 70-73; prof chair hydrol structure, Univ Thessaloniki, Greece, 73-; US Army res grants, 80-82. *Mem:* Am Soc Eng Educ; Am Soc Civil Engrs; Int Asn Hydraul Res. *Res:* Erosion and deposition of fine cohesive sediments; stratified flow and salinity intrusions in estuaries; shoaling of estuarial channels; turbulence; sediment transport by waves; thermo-pollution. *Mailing Add:* Dept of Civil & Coastal Eng Univ of Fla Gainesville FL 32601

PARTIDA, GREGORY JOHN, JR, b Pomona, Calif, Sept 14, 42; m 64; c 2. ECONOMIC ENTOMOLOGY. *Educ:* Calif State Polytech Col, Kellogg-Voorhis, BS, 65; Univ Calif, Riverside, MS, 69, PhD(entom), 71. *Prof Exp:* Lab asst agr biol, Calif State Polytech Col, Kellogg-Voorhis, Pomona, 63-65; lab technician entom, Univ Calif, Riverside, 65-66, res asst, 66-70; asst prof entom, Kans State Univ, 71-77; assoc prof, 77-80, PROF PLANT & SOIL SCI, CALIF STATE POLYTECH UNIV, 80- *Mem:* Entom Soc Am. *Res:* Bionomics of insects attacking stored-products; insect ecology. *Mailing Add:* Dept of Plant & Soil Sci Calif State Polytech Univ Pomona CA 91768

PARTIN, DALE LEE, b Toledo, Ohio, Mar 31, 49; m 75; c 2. SOLID STATE PHYSICS, SOLID STATE ELECTRONICS. *Educ:* Carnegie-Mellon Univ, BS, 71, MS, 73, PhD(elec engr), 78. *Prof Exp:* assoc sr res scientist, 78-80, SR RES SCIENTIST PHYSICS, GEN MOTORS RES LAB, 80- *Mem:* Inst Elec & Electronics Engrs; Am Vacuum Soc. *Res:* Lead salt laser diodes grown by molecular beam epitaxy for tuneable, high resolution infra-red spectroscopy. *Mailing Add:* Dept Physics Gen Motors Res Lab Warren MI 48090

PARTIN, JOHN CALVIN, b Ft Lewis, Wash, Mar 21, 33; c 5. MEDICINE, CELL BIOLOGY. *Educ:* Univ Ky, BS, 55; Univ Cincinnati, MD, 59; Am Bd Pediat, dipl, 66. *Prof Exp:* Intern med, Cincinnati Gen Hosp, 59-60; resident pediat, Cincinnati Children's Hosp, 60-62, chief resident, 62-63; from asst prof to assoc prof, 66-74, PROF PEDIAT, UNIV CINCINNATI, 74-, DIR ELECTRON MICROS LAB, CHILDREN'S HOSP RES FOUND, 66-, ASSOC DIR DIV GASTROENTEROL, 68-, DIR MICROBIOL LAB & BACT LAB, 73-, CLIN RES CTR, 76- *Concurrent Pos:* Fel, Med Sch, Johns Hopkins Univ, 65-66; attend pediatrician, Children's & Cincinnati Gen Hosps, 69-; chief pediat, US Trop Res Med Lab, San Juan, 76- *Mem:* AAAS; Am Soc Microbiol; Soc Pediat Res; Am Fedn Clin Res. *Res:* Ultrastructure in childhood gastrointestinal disease affecting lipid metabolism. *Mailing Add:* Children's Hosp Res Found Elland & Bethesda Ave Cincinnati OH 45229

PARTINGTON, MICHAEL W, b Birmingham, Eng, Jan 28, 26; m 47, 66; c 5. PEDIATRICS, MEDICAL GENETICS. *Educ:* Univ London, MB & BS, 48, PhD(physiol), 54; FRCP(E), 65; FRCP(C), 74. *Prof Exp:* Intern med, St Bartholomew's Hosp, London, Eng, 49-50; res asst physiol, London Hosp Med Col, 51-53; resident med, St Bartholomew's Hosp, 53-54, West Norwich Hosp, 54-56 & Jenny Lind Children's Hosp, Norwich, 56-58; lectr child health, Univ Sheffield, 58-59; from asst prof to assoc prof, 61-71, head dept, 71-76, PROF PEDIAT, QUEEN'S UNIV, ONT, 71-, CHMN, DIV MED GENETICS, 81- *Concurrent Pos:* Res fel neurol, Res Inst, Hosp Sick Children, Toronto, Ont, 59-61; Queen Elizabeth II scientist, 61-67. *Mem:* Can Soc Clin Invest; Am Pediat Soc; Can Pediat Soc; Can Col Med Geneticists. *Res:* Effects of ultraviolet light on skin; dysmorphology and medical genetics; mental retardation; phenylketonuria; neonatal amino acid metabolism, especially that of tyrosine; neonatal behavior; serotonin metabolism. *Mailing Add:* Dept of Pediat Queen's Univ Kingston ON K7L 3N6 Can

PARTON, WILLIAM JULIAN, JR, b Palmerton, Pa, Nov 2, 44. BIOMETEOROLOGY, MATHEMATICAL BIOLOGY. *Educ:* Pa State Univ, BS, 66; Univ Okla, MS, 68, PhD(meteorol), 72. *Prof Exp:* Res asst meteorol, Univ Okla, 66-68, spec instr, 68-71; fel math biol, Natural Resource Ecol Lab, Colo State Univ, 71-74; fel biometeorol, Nat Ctr Atmospheric Res, 74-75; RES ASSOC MATH BIOL, COLO STATE UNIV, 75- *Concurrent Pos:* Consult, Nat Park Serv, 75- *Mem:* Am Meteorol Soc; Sigma Xi; Soc Comput Simulation. *Res:* Development of computer models of biological systems; determining impact of weather modification on biological systems and studying interactions between the atmosphere and biosphere. *Mailing Add:* Nat Resource Ecol Lab Colo State Univ Ft Collins CO 80523

PARTRIDGE, ARTHUR DEAN, b Brooklyn, NY, Feb 17, 27; m 52; c 3. PHYTOPATHOLOGY. *Educ:* Univ Maine, BSF, 53; Univ NH, MS, 56, PhD(bot), 57. *Prof Exp:* Pathologist forest & forest prod, US Forest Serv, 57-60; prof forest path, 60-74, prof forestry, 74-77, PROF FOREST RESOURCES, UNIV IDAHO, 77- *Mem:* AAAS; Am Phytopath Soc; Bot Soc Am; Am Forestry Asn. *Res:* Forest and shade tree diseases. *Mailing Add:* Col of Forestry Univ of Idaho Moscow ID 83843

PARTRIDGE, GORDON R(ADFORD), b Denver, Colo, Oct 26, 25; m 48; c 2. ELECTRICAL ENGINEERING. *Educ:* Yale Univ, BEng, 46, MEng, 47, PhD(elec eng), 50. *Prof Exp:* Asst instr elec eng, Yale Univ, 48-50; asst prof, Purdue Univ, 50-53, assoc prof, 53-55; sr engr, Commun & Data Processing Opers, Raytheon Co, 55-62; sr develop engr, 62-81, SR APPLNS ENGR, GENRAD, INC, 81- *Mem:* Inst Elec & Electronics Engrs. *Res:* Transistorized analog-to-digital converters and pulse time multiplex communications equipment; perveance of power triodes; electronic instrumentation; acoustic instrumentation. *Mailing Add:* GenRad Inc 300 Baker Ave Concord MA 01742

PARTRIDGE, JAMES ENOCH, b Riverside, Calif, Nov 24, 42; m 63; c 2. MYROLOGY. *Educ:* Calif State Polytech Univ, BS, 66; Univ Calif, Riverside, PhD(bot), 73. *Prof Exp:* Fel, Dept Biochem, Univ Calif, Riverside, 72-75; fel, 75-78, ASST PROF, DEPT PLANT PATHOL, UNIV NEBR, 78- *Mem:* Am Phytopathol Soc; Sigma Xi. *Res:* Host-parasite interactions primarily involving stalk ruts of corn and sorgham; fungal ribosomes and protoplest culture/regeneration of corn and sorgham. *Mailing Add:* Dept Plant Pathol Univ Nebr Lincoln NE 68583

PARTRIDGE, JERRY ALVIN, b American Falls, Idaho, Oct 24, 39; m 63; c 6. INORGANIC CHEMISTRY. *Educ:* Brigham Young Univ, BS, 61, PhD(inorg chem), 65. *Prof Exp:* Sr res scientist, Pac Northwest Labs, Battelle Mem Inst, 65-76; SR SCIENTIST, WESTINGHOUSE HANFORD CO, 76- *Mem:* Am Chem Soc. *Res:* Metal ion complexes in solution; aqueous phase thermodynamics; solvent extraction of metal ions or compounds; ion exchange; solution calorimetry; nuclear fuel reprocessing; nuclear waste management. *Mailing Add:* 1817 Marshall Ct Richland WA 99352

PARTRIDGE, JOHN JOSEPH, JR, b Atlanta, Ga, Dec 13, 42; m 67. ORGANIC CHEMISTRY. *Educ:* Wheaton Col, Ill, BS, 64; Northwestern Univ, PhD(org chem), 68. *Prof Exp:* NIH fel chem, Columbia Univ, 68-69; RES GROUP CHIEF, DEPT CHEM RES, HOFFMANN-LA ROCHE, INC, 69- *Concurrent Pos:* NIH fel. *Mem:* Am Chem Soc; Chem Soc London; NY Acad Aci; AAAS. *Res:* Synthetic organic chemistry, asymmetric synthesis, natural products, terpenes, terpene glucosides, prostaglandins, vitamin D3 metabolites; steroids; 1, 3-dipolar additions; enzyme inhibitors, antibiotics, pharmaceutical research and development. *Mailing Add:* Dept Chem Res Hoffmann-La Roche Inc Nutley NJ 07110

PARTRIDGE, L DONALD, b Philadelphia, Pa, May 10, 45; m 65; c 2. NEUROPHYSIOLOGY. *Educ:* Mass Inst Technol, BS, 67; Univ Wash, PhD(physiol), 73. *Prof Exp:* Wellcome res fel, Dept physiol, Univ Bristol, Eng, 73-74; fel, Friday Harbor Labs, Univ Wash, 74-76; ASST PROF, DEPT PHYSIOL, UNIV NMEX, 76- *Mem:* Soc Neurosci; Biophys Soc. *Res:* Neuron membrane current processes with particular reference to slow currents underlying the encoding funtions of neurons. *Mailing Add:* Dept Physiol Univ NMex Albuquerque NM 87131

PARTRIDGE, LLOYD DONALD, b Cortland, NY, Dec 18, 22; m 44; c 3. NEUROPHYSIOLOGY, MOTOR CONTROL ANALYSIS. *Educ:* Univ Mich, BS, 48, MS, 49, PhD(physiol), 53. *Prof Exp:* Instr physiol, Univ Mich, 53-56; res asst neurol, Yale Univ, 56-62, from instr to asst prof physiol, 57-62; assoc prof, 62-70, dep chmn dept, 66-73, PROF PHYSIOL & BIOPHYS, UNIV TENN, MEMPHIS, 70- *Concurrent Pos:* Consult, Middletown State Hosp, 56-62; vis prof, Univ Vt, 65 & 66; assoc ed, Trans Biomed Eng, 76-80; vis scientist, Univ Western Ont, 81. *Mem:* Am Acad Neurol; Am Physiol Soc; Bioeng Soc; Soc Neurosci; Int Brain Res Orgn. *Res:* Distributed biological control systems; signal processing by nervous system; unit function in reflexes; reflex regulation and control of movement; muscle dynamics; organization and conversion of neural activity to mechanical response. *Mailing Add:* Dept of Physiol & Biophys Univ of Tenn Med Units Memphis TN 38163

PARTRIDGE, ROBERT BRUCE, b Honolulu, Hawaii, May 16, 40. ASTRONOMY. *Educ:* Princeton Univ, AB, 62; Oxford Univ, DPhil(physics), 65. *Prof Exp:* Instr physics, Princeton Univ, 65-67, asst prof, 67-70; assoc prof, 70-76, PROF ASTRON, HAVERFORD COL, 76- *Concurrent Pos:* Rhodes Scholar fel, Alfred P Sloan Res Found, 71-75; Fulbright Award, Norway, 79. *Mem:* AAAS; Am Astron Soc; Int Astron Union. *Res:* Radio astronomy; astrophysics; cosmology. *Mailing Add:* Dept Astron Haverford Col Haverford PA 19041

PARTYKA, ROBERT EDWARD, b Wakefield, RI, Sept 5, 30; m 57; c 3. PLANT PATHOLOGY. *Educ:* Univ R I, BS, 52; Cornell Univ, PhD(plant path), 58. *Prof Exp:* From asst prof to prof plant path, Ohio State Univ, 57-74, exten plant pathologist, 57-74; PLANT PATHOLOGIST, CHEM-LAWN CORP, 74- *Concurrent Pos:* Adj prof, Ohio State Univ, 74- *Mem:* Am Phytopath Soc; Potato Asn Am; Soc Nematol; Am Inst Biol Sci. *Res:* Turf and urban ornamental disease problems. *Mailing Add:* ChemScape Div ChemLawn 450 W Wilson Bridge Rd Columbus OH 43285

PARUNAK, ANITA NOWLIN, b Washington, DC, Apr 13, 46; m 73. STATISTICS. *Educ:* Univ Pa, Philadelphia, BA, 69; Princeton Univ, MA, 71, PhD(statist), 73. *Prof Exp:* Researcher statist, Dept Statist, Harvard Univ, 75-79; ASST PROF, DEPT BIOSTATIST & RES SCIENTIST, HIGHWAY SAFETY RES INST, UNIV MICH, 79- *Mem:* Am Statist Asn; Biomet Soc; AAAS. *Res:* Data analysis; regression; contingency tables; time series and Fourier analysis. *Mailing Add:* Dept Biostatist Univ Mich Ann Arbor MI 48109

PARUNGO, FARN PWU, b Ann-King Anwhei, China, June 18, 32; US citizen; m 62; c 3. ORGANIC CHEMISTRY, PHYSICAL CHEMISTRY. *Educ:* Nat Taiwan Univ, BS, 55; Univ Colo, PhD(org chem), 61. *Prof Exp:* Res assoc chem, Cornell Univ, 61-62; scientist, Nat Ctr Atmospheric Res, 62-67; res scientist, chem, EG&G, 67-69; RES CHEMIST, ENVIRON SCI LAB, NAT OCEANIC & ATMOSPHERIC ADMIN, 69- *Honors & Awards:* Outstanding Paper Award, Dept Com, NOAA, 75. *Res:* Atmospheric chemistry; natural and anthropogenic chemical reactions in the atmosphere, environmental impact of air pollutions; advertent and inadvertent weather modification. *Mailing Add:* Atmospheric Physics & Chem Lab Dept of Com ERL-NOAA Boulder CO 80303

PARVIN, PHILIP EUGENE, b Manatee, Fla, July 3, 27. FLORICULTURE. *Educ:* Univ Fla, BSAg, 50; Miss State Univ, MS, 52; Mich State Univ, PhD(hort), 65. *Prof Exp:* Instr ornamental hort, Miss State Univ, 52; asst prof floricult, Univ Fla, 53-56; res instr, Floricult Mkt, Mich State Univ, 59-61; exten specialist, Univ Calif, Davis, 63-66; gen mgr, Rod McLellan Co, 66-68; HORTICULTURIST & SUPT, MAUI AGR RES CTR, UNIV HAWAII, 68- *Mem:* Am Soc Hort Sci; Int Soc Hort Sci; Int Plant Propagators Soc. *Res:* Introduction, evaluation, culture, management and marketing of Proteas and foliage plants. *Mailing Add:* Maui Agr Res Ctr Univ of Hawaii PO Box 187 Kula HI 96790

PARVULESCU, ANTARES, b Ploesti, Romania, Nov 15, 23; US citizen; c 1. MATHEMATICAL PHYSICS, ACOUSTICS. *Educ:* Univ Bucharest, Lic math sci, 43. *Prof Exp:* French govt fel, Univ Paris, 46-47; lectr appl math, Univ Witwatersrand, 47-50; lectr math, Univ Calif, Berkeley, 50-51; asst prof physics, Bard Col, 51-54 & Villanova Univ, 54-55; assoc prof & head dept, Gallaudet Col, 55-60; res scientist, Hudson Labs, Columbia Univ, 60-64, sr res assoc physics, 64-68; PROF OCEAN ENG & GEOPHYS, HAWAII INST GEOPHYS, UNIV HAWAII, 68- *Concurrent Pos:* Lectr & actg dir, Vassar Col Observ, 53-54; res physicist, David Taylor Model Basin, US Navy, 59-60; res prof physics, Gallaudet Col, 60-68; consult, Hollerith Comput Mach Ltd SAfrica, 48-50; chief scientist on 19 oceanog exped, 61-; consult, US Navy, 75- *Mem:* Fel Acoust Soc Am; sr mem Inst Elec & Electronics Eng; Audio Eng Soc; NY Acad Sci. *Res:* Mathematical logic; theory of evidence and inference; theory of probability; foundations of quantum theory; ocean acoustics; wave equations; theory of information and signal processing; acoustic radiation; marine bioacoustics. *Mailing Add:* Hawaii Inst of Geophys Univ of Hawaii Honolulu HI 96822

PARZEN, EMANUEL, b New York, NY, Apr 21, 29; m 59; c 2. STATISTICS. *Educ:* Harvard Col, AB, 49; Univ Calif, Berkeley, MA, 51, PhD(math), 53. *Prof Exp:* Asst math, Univ Calif, 49-52; res scientist, Hudson Labs, Columbia Univ, 53-56; from asst prof to prof statist, Stanford Univ, 56-70; prof & chmn statist sci div, State Univ NY, Buffalo, 70-78; DISTINGUISHED PROF STATIST, TEX A&M UNIV, 78- *Concurrent*

Pos: Guest prof, Imp Col, Univ London, 61-62; vis prof, Mass Inst Technol, 64; fel IBM Systs Res Inst, 69-70. *Mem:* fel AAAS; fel Inst Math Statist; fel Am Statist Asn; Am Math Soc; Soc Indust & Appl Math. *Res:* Probability limit theorems; applied probability; statistical inference on stochastic processes; non-parametric statistical data modeling; time series analysis; spectral analysis; statistical communication and control theory; statistical computation; econometrics; systems identification. *Mailing Add:* Inst of Statist Tex A&M Univ College Station TX 77843

PARZEN, GEORGE, b New York, NY, Mar 11, 24. THEORETICAL PHYSICS. *Educ:* City Col New York, BEE, 45; Stanford Univ, PhD(physics), 49. *Prof Exp:* Instr physics, Univ Chicago, 49-51; from asst prof to assoc prof, Notre Dame Univ, 51-56; physicist, Midwestern Univs Res Asn, 56-63; PHYSICIST, ACCELERATOR DEPT, BROOKHAVEN NAT LAB, 63- *Mem:* Am Phys Soc. *Res:* Electron scattering; electrodynamics; energy levels in metals; accelerators; computer physics. *Mailing Add:* Accelerator Dept Brookhaven Nat Lab Upton NY 11973

PARZEN, PHILIP, b Poland; nat US; m 49; c 2. PHYSICAL ELECTRONICS. *Educ:* City Col New York, BS, 39; NY Univ, MS, 46, PhD(math), 53. *Prof Exp:* Develop engr, Fed Telecommun Labs, Int Tel & Tel Corp, 47-53; res scientist radiation lab, Johns Hopkins Univ, 53-56; res assoc prof elec eng, Polytech Inst Brooklyn, 56-58; dir res & develop, Parzen Assocs, 58-60; chief space physics, Repub Aviation, Inc, 60-62; sr mem tech adv staff, Astro- electronics Div, Radio Corp Am, NJ, 62-69; PROF INFO ENG, UNIV ILL, CHICAGO CIRCLE, 69- *Mem:* Am Phys Soc; sr mem Inst Elec & Electronics Engrs. *Res:* Plasmas; gas discharges; microwave tubes; solid state devices. *Mailing Add:* Dept of Info Eng Univ of Ill at Chicago Circle Chicago IL 60680

PAS, ERIC IVAN, b Cape Town, SAfrica, May 12, 48; m 74; c 1. TRANSPORTATION ENGINEERING. *Educ:* Univ Cape Town, BSc, 70, MSc, 74; Northwestern Univ, PhD(transp eng), 80. *Prof Exp:* Engr design, Van Niekeru, Kleyn & Edwards, 71-72; lectr soil mech & transp enng, Univ Cape Town, 72-77; ASST PROF TRANSP ENG, DUKE UNIV, 80- *Mem:* Am Soc Civil Engrs; Am Soc Eng Educ; SAfrica Inst Civil Engrs. *Res:* Modeling and analysis of urban travel behavior; developmennt of tools for simplified analysis of transportation system charges; innovations in transportation engineering education. *Mailing Add:* Dept Civil & Environ Eng Duke Univ Durham NC 27706

PASACHOFF, JAY M(YRON), b New York, NY, July 1, 43; m 74; c 2. ASTRONOMY, ASTROPHYSICS. *Educ:* Harvard Univ, AB, 63, AM, 65, PhD(astron), 69. *Prof Exp:* Res physicist, US Air Force Cambridge Res Labs, 68-69; Menzel Res Fel Astron, Harvard Col Observ, 69-70; res fel astrophys, Calif Inst Technol & Hale Observs, 70-72, asst prof & chmn dept, 72-77, ASSOC PROF, ASTRON DEPT, WILLIAMS COL, 77, DIR, OBSERV & ORBITING SOLAR OBSERVATORY, 72- *Concurrent Pos:* Guest investr, NASA, 73-78; mem, US-Australia Coop Sci Prog, Australian Nat Radio Observ, 74; US nat rep, Comn Teaching Astron, Int Astron Union, 76-; adj assoc prof, Univ Mass, Amherst, 77-; vis colleague & vis assoc prof, Inst Astron, Univ Hawaii, 80-81; with var eclipse expeds, 59-81. *Honors & Awards:* Lockhart lectr, Univ Manitoba, 79. *Mem:* Am Astron Soc; Int Astron Union; NY Acad Sci; Int Union Radio Sci; Am Phys Soc. *Res:* Solar physics, including the structure of the chromosphere and corona; eclipses; stellar spectroscopy; spectral-line radio astronomy; author of textbooks in astronomy and physics and a field guide in astronomy. *Mailing Add:* Hopkins Observ Williams Col Williamstown MA 01267

PASAMANICK, BENJAMIN, b New York, NY, Oct 14, 14; m 42. PSYCHIATRY. *Educ:* Cornell Univ, AB, 36; Univ Md, MD, 41. *Prof Exp:* Resident psychiat, NY State Psychiat Inst, 32; asst child develop, Sch Med, Yale Univ, 43-45; instr psychiat, Med Sch, Univ Mich, 46-47; asst clin prof, Long Island Med Col, 48-49; asst clin prof, Col Med, State Univ NY, 49-50; from asst prof to assoc prof pub health admin, Sch Hyg & Pub Health, Johns Hopkins Univ, 50-55; prof psychiat, Col Med, Ohio State Univ, 55-65; assoc dir res, Ill Dept Ment Health, 65-67; pres & dean, 67-72, SIR AUBREY & LADY HILDA LEWIS PROF SOCIAL PSYCHIAT, NY SCH PSYCHIAT, 72- *Concurrent Pos:* Chief children's serv, Neuropsychiat Inst, Univ Mich, 40-47; chief psychiat div, Kings County Hosp, NY, 47-50; psychiatrist, Johns Hopkins Hosp, 51-55; consult, Baltimore Bd Sch Comnr, 51-55, Nat Inst Neurol Dis & Blindness, 55-58, NIMH, 55-58 & Milbank Fund, 56-58; dir res, Columbus Psychiat Inst & Hosp, Health Ctr, Ohio State Univ, 55-65, consult & chmn comt res, Inst Child Develop & Family Life, 57-59; mem comt ment retardation, Coun State Govt, 57-65; chmn subcomt ment health, US Nat Comt Vital & Health Statist, 58-66 & 70-72; Cutter lectr, Harvard Univ, 60; Bailey lectr, Ill Psychiat Inst, 61; adj prof sociol & anthorp, Ohio State Univ, 63-65; clin prof psychiat, Univ Ill, 65-67 & Chicago Med Sch, 66-67; mem eval unit, Proj Head Start, US Off Econ Opportunity, 65-70; expert comt standardization psychiat diag, WHO, 65-70; Kolb lectr, NIMH, 66-; adj prof epidemiol, Sch Pub Health & admin med, Columbia Univ, 67-76; comnr for res, NY State Dept Ment Hyg, 67-76; adj prof psychol, NY Univ, 68-76; adj prof pediat, Albany Med Col, 72-78, res prof, 78; res prof psychiat & behav sci, State Univ NY, Stonybrook, 77- *Honors & Awards:* Hofheimer Prize, Am Psychiat Asn, 49, 67; Stratton Award, Am Psychopath Asn, 61, Hamilton Medal, 67; La Pouse Gold Medal, Am Pub Health Asn, 77. *Mem:* AAAS; Am Col Psychiatrists; Soc Biol Psychiat; Soc Res Child Develop; Soc Psychol Study Social Issues. *Res:* Child development; ethnic group psychology; epidemiology of neuropsychiatric disorder; measurement and evaluation in psychiatry; sociology; public health. *Mailing Add:* Hayfield Feura Bush Rd Glenmont NY 12208

PASBY, BRIAN, b London, Eng, June 8, 37; m 59; c 2. OCEANOGRAPHY, ECOLOGY. *Educ:* Univ London, BSc, 59, MSc, 60; Tex A&M Univ, PhD(oceanog), 65. *Prof Exp:* Asst prof oceanog, Univ Hawaii, 64-67; assoc prof, 67-78, PROF BIOL, PACE UNIV, WESTCHESTER CAMPUS, 78- *Mem:* Fel Zool Soc London. *Res:* Aquatic ecology. *Mailing Add:* Dept of Biol Pace Univ 861 Bedford Rd Pleasantville NY 10570

PASCAL, THERESA A, b New York, NY, May 23, 23; m 60. IMMUNOBIOLOGY. *Educ:* Hunter Col, BA, 44; NY Univ, MA, 50. *Prof Exp:* Res asst nutrit, NY Univ, 45-51; res asst biochem, Downstate Med Sch, 51-56; res worker immunol, Columbia Univ, 56-63; res assoc immunol, Isaac Albert Res Inst, 63-68; SR RES SCIENTIST IMMUNOL, NY STATE INST RES MENTAL RETARDATION, 68- *Concurrent Pos:* Adj instr, Sch Med, Mt Sinai Hosp, 71- *Mem:* AAAS. *Res:* Investigation of the electrophoretic, biochemical and immunological properties of enzymes of sulfur metabolism, particularly cystathionase and cystathionine synthase. *Mailing Add:* 133 Wooster St New York NY 10012

PASCERI, RALPH EDWARD, b Philadelphia, Pa, Aug 27, 37; m 63; c 1. CHEMICAL ENGINEERING, AIR POLLUTION. *Educ:* Villanova Univ, BChE, 59; Johns Hopkins Univ, DEng(atmospheric aerosols), 64. *Prof Exp:* Sr res engr, Hercules Inc, Md, 64-68; RES SCIENTIST, NJ STATE DEPT ENVIRON PROTECTION, 68- *Res:* Atmospheric aerosols; chemistry; gas dynamics and electromagnetic properties of solid propellant rocket exhausts; motor vehicle air pollution; particulate air pollution. *Mailing Add:* 286 Anderson Rd Morrisville PA 19067

PASCHALL, EUGENE F, b Neosho, Mo, Jan 7, 22; m 46; c 3. CARBOHYDRATE CHEMISTRY. *Educ:* Western State Col Colo, AB, 44; Iowa State Univ, PhD(chem), 51. *Prof Exp:* Sect leader, 56-61, dir prod develop, 61-75, DIR, STARCH & SWEETENER DEPT, MOFFETT TECH CTR, CPC INT, INC, 75- *Mem:* AAAS; Am Chem Soc. *Res:* Synthesis of polysaccharide derivatives for use in food, textile and paper fields; measurement of physical and chemical properties of starch and starch fractions. *Mailing Add:* Moffett Tech Ctr CPC Int Inc Box 345 Argo IL 60501

PASCHALL, HOMER DONALD, b Montgomery Co, Tenn, Aug 29, 26; m 50; c 4. CELL PHYSIOLOGY, ANIMAL PHYSIOLOGY. *Educ:* Trevecca Nazarene Col, AB, 48; Austin Peay State Col, BS, 50; Peabody Col, AM, 50; Iowa State Univ, PhD, 63. *Prof Exp:* Teacher high sch, Tenn, 48-49 & pub sch, Ky, 50-51; instr sci & math, Bethany-Nazarene Col, 51-55; PROF PHYSIOL & HEALTH SCI, BALL STATE UNIV, 55- *Mem:* Sigma Xi; Am Sci Affil. *Mailing Add:* Dept of Physiol & Health Sci Ball State Univ Muncie IN 47306

PASCHER, FRANCES, b New York, NY, June 5, 05; m 31; c 2. DERMATOLOGY. *Educ:* Long Island Col Med, MD, 28. *Prof Exp:* Dir Med Affairs, Almay, Inc, Apex, 76-82; prof clin dermat, 66-72, clin prof dermat, Sch Med, Univ NC, Chapel Hill, 73-78, EMER PROF CLIN DERMAT, SCH MED, NY UNIV, 72-; EMER PROF DERMAT, SCH MED, UNIV NC, CHAPEL HILL, 78- *Concurrent Pos:* Mem dermat panel, US Pharmacoepia Conv, 72-75. *Mem:* Fel, Dermat Found; fel Soc Invest Dermat; fel Am Acad Dermat; Soc Cosmetic Chemists; Pac Dermat Asn. *Res:* Clinical dermatology with special interest in hematologic aspects, relationship to internal medicine; pharmacologic basis of therapeutics of skin disease as therapeutics assays of new drugs to be used in management of skin disease; cosmetics. *Mailing Add:* 1715 Nottingham Rd Raleigh NC 27607

PASCHKE, EDWARD ERNEST, b Evergreen Park, Ill, Feb 22, 43; m 69; c 2. POLYMER CHEMISTRY. *Educ:* Univ Ill, Urbana, BS, 65; Univ Minn, Minneapolis, MS, 67; Univ Iowa, PhD(chem), 71. *Prof Exp:* Res chemist, 70-80, SR RES CHEMIST, STANDARD OIL CO, 80- *Mem:* Am Chem Soc. *Res:* Chemistry; organic chemistry. *Mailing Add:* Naperville Tech Ctr Standard Oil Co Naperville IL 60540

PASCHKE, JOHN DONALD, b Upland, Calif, Nov 6, 25; m 67; c 6. ENTOMOLOGY, VIROLOGY. *Educ:* Univ Calif, PhD(entom), 58. *Prof Exp:* Sr lab technician, Citrus Exp Sta, Univ Calif, 50-53; asst entomologist, Ill Natural Hist Surv, 58-60; from asst prof to assoc prof, 60-68, PROF ENTOM, PURDUE UNIV, LAFAYETTE, 68-, ASST DIR, DIV SPONSORED PROGS, 81- *Concurrent Pos:* Vis fel, St Cross Col, Oxford Univ, 68-69; NIH grants, 61-64, 70-73, 73-76, NSF, 75-77 & USAID, 79-81. *Mem:* AAAS; Entom Soc Am; Soc Invert Path. *Res:* Insect pathology; invertebrate pathology; insect virology; microbial control of pests. *Mailing Add:* Dept Entom Purdue Univ West Lafayette IN 47906

PASCHKE, RICHARD EUGENE, b Chicago, Ill, Mar 13, 37; m 62; c 2. NEUROPSYCHOLOGY. *Educ:* Univ Ill, Urbana, BS, 61; Northern Ill Univ, MA, 64; Purdue Univ, PhD(exp psychol), 69. *Prof Exp:* ASST PROF INTERDISCIPLINARY STUDIES, WILLIAM JAMES COL, 71- *Concurrent Pos:* Fels & grants, Nat Inst Ment Health res fel, Inst Biobehav Sci, Univ Conn, 69-71. *Mem:* AAAS; Am Psychol Asn. *Res:* Relationships between biological determinants of behavior and aspects of the spatio-temporal environment such as social structure, population density, architectural design and general cultural input. *Mailing Add:* Dept Psychol William James Col Allendale MI 49401

PASCHKE, WILLIAM LINDALL, b New York, NY, Aug 19, 46; m 68. MATHEMATICAL ANALYSIS. *Educ:* Dartmouth Col, BA, 67; Univ Ore, MA, 69, PhD(math), 72. *Prof Exp:* Asst prof, 72-78, ASSOC PROF MATH, UNIV KANS, 78- *Mem:* Am Math Soc. *Res:* Functional analysis, in particular algebras of operators on Hilbert space. *Mailing Add:* Dept of Math Univ of Kans Lawrence KS 66045

PASCHOS, EMMANUEL ANTHONY, b Veroia, Greece, July 13, 40; US citizen; m 67; c 2. ELEMENTARY PARTICLE PHYSICS. *Educ:* City Col New York, BS, 62; Cornell Univ, PhD(physics), 67. *Prof Exp:* Res assoc physics, Stanford Linear Accelerator Ctr, 67-69; res assoc, Rockefeller Univ, 69-71; asst physicist, Fermi Nat Accelerator Lab, 71-75; assoc physicist, Brookhaven Nat Lab, 75-80; MEM FAC THEORET PHYS, UNIV DORTMUND, WGER, 80- *Concurrent Pos:* Adj prof, Univ Wis, 74-75; Res Corp grant, 75; prof theoret physics, Univ Dortmund, WGer, 78. *Mem:* Am Phys Soc. *Res:* Elementary particle theory; gauge field theories. *Mailing Add:* Inst Physik Univ Dortmund 4600 Dortmund-50 West Germany

PASCIAK, JOSEPH EDWARD, b Pawtucket, RI, July 3, 50; m 78. APPLIED MATHEMATICS, NUMERICAL ANALYSIS. *Educ:* Northeastern Univ, BA, 73; Cornell Univ, PhD(appl math), 77. *Prof Exp:* Programmer, AVCO Everett Res Lab, 69-73; numerical analyst, Far Field Inc, 74-77; ASST MATH, BROOKHAVEN NAT LAB, 77- *Mem:* Soc Indust & Appl Math; Am Math Soc. *Res:* Numerical analysis of finite element, finite difference and other competing methods, analytical analysis as well as implementation. *Mailing Add:* Brookhaven Nat Lab Upton NY 11973

PASCU, DAN, b Arad, Romania, July 20, 38; US citizen; m 65; c 3. ASTRONOMY, CELESTIAL MECHANICS. *Educ:* Western Reserve Univ, Cleveland, BA, 61; Case Inst Technol, Cleveland, MS, 64; Univ Va, Charlottesville, PhD(astron), 72. *Prof Exp:* ASTRONR, NAUTICAL ALMANAC OFF, NAVY OBSERV, 63- *Mem:* Int Astron Union; Am Astron Soc. *Res:* Astrometric, photometric and dynamical studies of the planetary satellites. *Mailing Add:* Naval Observ Washington DC 20390

PASE, CHARLES PIERCE, b Ellendale, Del, Jan 18, 26. ECOLOGY, FORESTRY. *Educ:* Univ Mont, BS, 50, MS, 58. *Prof Exp:* Forester timber staff, Apache Nat Forest, 50-51; forester range, Cibola Nat Forest, 51; forester wildlife, Kaibah Nat Forest, 52-54; dist ranger, Coconino Nat Forest, 54-55; range conservationist range res, Rocky Mountain Forest & Range Exp Sta, 55-72; habitat ecologist, Food & Agr Orgn, Nairobi, Kenya, 72-75; ecologist, Rocky Mountain Forest & Range Exp Sta, 75-80; MEM STAFF, US FOREST HYDROL LAB, ARIZ STATE UNIV, 80- *Mem:* Soc Range Mgt. *Res:* Vegetation distribution classification and mapping; management of ranges for wildlife and domestic livestock. *Mailing Add:* US Forest Hydrol Lab Ariz State Univ Tempe AZ 85281

PASFIELD, WILLIAM HORTON, b Brooklyn, NY, Dec 28, 24; m 47; c 5. PHYSICAL CHEMISTRY. *Educ:* Mass Inst Technol, BS, 48; Univ Conn, PhD(phys chem), 55. *Prof Exp:* Res chemist, Metal Hydrides, Inc, 49-50; res chemist, E I du Pont de Nemours & Co, 55-58; from asst prof to assoc prof, 58-65, PROF CHEM, ST JOHN'S UNIV, NY, 65- *Mem:* Am Chem Soc. *Res:* Molecular interactions in gases and liquids; volume changes in solutions. *Mailing Add:* Dept of Chem St John's Univ Jamaica NY 11432

PASHLEY, DAVID HENRY, b Seattle, Wash, Apr 24, 39; m 62; c 2. PHYSIOLOGY, DENTIN PERMEABILITY. *Educ:* Univ Portland, BS, 60; Univ Ore, DMD, 64; Univ Rochester, PhD(physiol), 71. *Prof Exp:* From asst prof to assoc prof oral biol, Sch Dent, asst prof physiol, Sch Med, 71-80, PROF BIOL, SCH DENT, MED COL GA, 78-, ASSOC PROF PHYSIOL, SCH MED, 81- *Concurrent Pos:* Prin investr grant, 72-81. *Mem:* AAAS; Am Physiol Soc; Sigma Xi; Int Asn Dent Res. *Res:* Body fluids; renal salivary physiology; renal salivary gland metabolism; permeability characteristics of teeth and oral epithelia; pulp biology. *Mailing Add:* Dept Physiol Sch Med Med Col Ga Augusta GA 30902

PASHLEY, EMIL FREDERICK, JR, b Lakewood, Ohio, Dec 19, 30; m 52; c 4. GEOLOGY, HYDROLOGY. *Educ:* Ohio State Univ, BSc, 52, MSc, 56; Univ Ariz, PhD(geol), 66. *Prof Exp:* Geologist & hydrologist, US Geol Surv, 59-68; assoc prof, 68-74, PROF GEOL, WEBER STATE COL, 74- *Mem:* Geol Soc Am. *Res:* Geohydrology and environmental geology of the Wasatch Front. *Mailing Add:* Dept of Geol Weber State Col Ogden UT 84408

PASIK, PEDRO, b Buenos Aires, Arg, Jan 16, 26; US citizen; m 52; c 3. NEUROANATOMY, NEUROPHYSIOLOGY. *Educ:* Univ Buenos Aires, MD, 51. *Prof Exp:* Asst resident neurol, Bellevue Med Ctr, 53-54; asst resident, Mt Sinai Hosp, 55-56, from res asst to res assoc, 56-66; assoc prof, 66-70, PROF NEUROL, MT SINAI SCH MED, 70- *Concurrent Pos:* Abrahamson fel neurol, 55-56; Nat Inst Neurol Dis & Stroke res career develop award, 63-73; mem fac, City Univ New York, 69-; adj prof, Queens Col, NY, 70- *Mem:* Am Neurol Asn; Soc Neurosci; Harvey Soc; Am Physiol Soc; Am Asn Anat. *Res:* Synaptology of the visual and basal ganglia systems; relationship between brain structure and function and visually guided behavior, through measurement of the effect of experimental cerebral lesions and the description of the anatomic pathways involved. *Mailing Add:* Mt Sinai Sch Med Dept Neurol Fifth Ave & 100th St New York NY 10029

PASIK, TAUBA, b Yasi, Rumania, Mar 18, 27; US citizen; m 52; c 3. NEUROPHYSIOLOGY, NEUROANATOMY. *Educ:* Univ Buenos Aires, MD, 51. *Prof Exp:* Asst resident neurol, Bellevue Med Ctr, 53-54; asst resident, Mt Sinai Hosp, 55-56, res asst, 56-59, res assoc, 59-66; assoc prof, 66-70, PROF NEUROL, MT SINAI SCH MED, 70- *Concurrent Pos:* Sugarmen fel neurol, 55-56; City of New York Health Res Coun career scientist award, 71; mem fac, City Univ New York, 69-; adj prof, Queens Col, NY, 70- *Mem:* AAAS; Am Acad Neurol; Am Neurol Asn; Soc Neurosci; Harvey Soc. *Res:* Relationship between brain structures and function and visually guided behavior, through measurement of the effect of experimental cerebral lesions and the description of the anatomic pathways involved. *Mailing Add:* Mt Sinai Sch of Med Dept Neurol Fifth Ave and 100th St New York NY 10029

PASK, JOSEPH ADAM, b Chicago, Ill, Feb 14, 13; m 38; c 2. CERAMIC ENGINEERING, MATERIALS SCIENCE. *Educ:* Univ Ill, BS, 34, PhD(ceramic eng), 41; Univ Washington, Seattle, MS, 35. *Prof Exp:* Ceramic engr, Willamina Clay Prod Co, Ore, 35-36; asst nonmetallic eng, Northwest Exp Sta, US Bur Mines, 35; asst ceramic eng, Univ Ill, 38, instr, 38-41; asst ceramic engr, Electrotech Lab, US Bur Mines, 41, assoc ceramic engr, Northwest Exp Sta, 42-43; res ceramist lamp div, Westinghouse Elec Corp, NJ, 43-46, res engr ceramic sect, 46-48; assoc prof, 48-53, chmn dept mineral technol, 57-61, assoc dean, Col Eng, 69-80, prof, 53-80, EMER PROF CERAMIC ENG, UNIV CALIF, BERKELEY, 80- *Concurrent Pos:* Asst prof ceramic eng & head dept, Col Mines, Univ Wash, Seattle, 41-43; mem clay mineral comt, Nat Res Coun, 54-64, mat adv bd, 64-68, chmn ad hoc comt ceramic processing, Nat Acad Sci, 64-67; sr scientist, Mat & Molecular Res Div, Lawrence Berkeley Lab, Univ Calif, 68-; pres, Pask Res & Eng, 81- *Honors & Awards:* John Jeppson Medal, Am Ceramic Soc, 67, Ross Coffin Purdy Award, 79. *Mem:* Nat Acad Eng; fel AAAS; hon mem Am Ceramic Soc (vpres, 53); fel Mineral Soc Am; Am Inst Mining, Metall & Petrol Engrs. *Res:* Solid state reactions-diffusion studies; ceramic microstructures; mechanical properties of nonmetallic materials; electrochemistry of glass-metal systems; wetting and bonding. *Mailing Add:* 994 Euclid Ave Berkeley CA 94720

PASKAUSKY, DAVID FRANK, b Waukegan, Ill, Mar 1, 38; m 67; c 3. PHYSICAL OCEANOGRAPHY, PHYSICS. *Educ:* Univ Chicago, SB, 60; DePaul Univ, MS, 64; Tex A&M Univ, PhD(oceanog), 69. *Prof Exp:* Instr physics, Aquinas Col, 62-64; res scientist, Nat Video Corp, 64-65; instr, Milwaukee Sch Eng, 65; asst prof oceanog, Univ Conn, 69-75; sci officer, Off Naval Res, 75-78; HEAD, OCEANOG BR, US COAST GUARD RES & DEVELOP CTR, 78- *Concurrent Pos:* Consult, Sun Oil Co, 70-71, Stone & Webster Eng Corp, 72-73 & Gilbert Assocs, Inc, 72-75; vis assoc prof, Univ Conn, 78- *Mem:* Am Geophys Union; Am Meteorol Soc; Am Asn Physics Teachers; fel Explorers Club; Sigma Xi. *Res:* Real-time data to forecast and to develop numerical models to predict ocean surface circulation for search and rescue, oil spill movement and iceberg drift applications. *Mailing Add:* 9 Laurel Dr Groton CT 06340

PASKE, WILLIAM CHARLES, b Tacoma, Wash, Oct 17, 44. MOLECULAR PHYSICS, SCIENCE EDUCATION. *Educ:* Alaska Methodist Univ, Anchorage, BA, 66; Univ Okla, Norman, MS, 70, PhD(physics), 74. *Prof Exp:* Instr physics, Univ Okla, 74-75; asst prof physics, Kans State Univ, 75-77; asst prof phys, Fort Hays State Univ, 77-78; RES ASSOC, UNIV OKLA, 78- *Mem:* Sigma Xi; Am Asn Physics Teachers; Am Phys Soc. *Res:* Molecular physics, transition probabilities, quenching processes of polyatomic molecules; physics education, non-traditional approach to lab and lecture format, application of Piaget concepts of learning to undergraduate course work. *Mailing Add:* Dept of Physics Kans State Univ Manhattan KS 66506

PASKIEVICI, WLADIMIR, b Bucharest, Rumania, Mar 7, 30; Can citizen; m 57; c 3. NUCLEAR PHYSICS, NUCLEAR ENGINEERING. *Educ:* Univ Strasbourg, LSc, 55, PhD(nuclear physics), 57. *Prof Exp:* Lectr atomic physics, Polytech Sch, Montreal, 58-59, asst prof atomic & nuclear physics, 59-63, assoc prof mod physics, 63-69, assoc prof nuclear eng, 69-77; PROF NUCLEAR ENG, UNIV MONTREAL, 77- *Concurrent Pos:* Nat Res Coun Can fel, 58-59. *Mem:* Am Nuclear Soc; Can Nuclear Asn. *Res:* Nuclear scattering theory; electron spin resonance; nuclear magnetic resonance; radiation effects on materials; reactor kinetics. *Mailing Add:* Dept of Nuclear Eng Univ of Montreal Montreal PQ H3V 1H4 Can

PASKIN, ARTHUR, b Brooklyn, NY, Feb 15, 24; m 53; c 3. PHYSICS. *Educ:* SDak Sch Mines & Technol, BS, 48; Iowa State Univ, PhD(physics), 53. *Prof Exp:* Asst physics, Inst Atomic Res, Iowa State Univ, 48-53; sr physicist, Sylvania Elec Prod Inc, 53-55; solid state physicist, US Army Mat Res Lab, 55-63; physicist, Brookhaven Nat Lab, 63-68; PROF PHYSICS, QUEENS COL NY, 68- *Concurrent Pos:* Secy Army fel, 60-61. *Mem:* Fel Am Phys Soc; Am Soc Metals. *Res:* Theoretical and solid state physics; thermodynamics of magnetic systems; x-ray diffraction diffuse scattering, radiation damage; superconductivity; liquid state of metals; computer simulations and shock waves in solids and fracture. *Mailing Add:* Dept of Physics Queens Col Flushing NY 11367

PASKINS-HURLBURT, ANDREA JEANNE, b Southampton, Eng, Apr 26, 43; US citizen; m 68. TUMOR ANGIOGENESIS, COLLATERAL VESSEL DEVELOPMENT. *Educ:* McGill Univ, BSc, 65, MSc, 70, PhD(exp surg), 74. *Prof Exp:* Res asst, Montreal Gen Hosp, 65-66; technician gastrointestinal res, McGill Univ, 67-74, res assoc, 74-77; RES ASSOC, DEPT RADIOL, HARVARD UNIV, 77- *Res:* Factors which promote the development of a collateral arterial supply to the heart and kidney when the main artery has been occluded; relationship between tumor growth, tumor perfusion and the reactivity of the tumor vasculature. *Mailing Add:* 12 Kenilworth St Newton MA 02158

PASKUSZ, GERHARD F, b Vienna, Austria, Jan 21, 22; US citizen; m 43; c 1. ELECTRICAL ENGINEERING. *Educ:* Univ Calif, Los Angeles, BS, 49, PhD(eng), 61. *Prof Exp:* Teaching asst, Univ Calif, Los Angeles, 50-52, assoc eng, 52-60, res specialist, 60-61; assoc prof elec eng, 61-68, PROF ELEC ENG, UNIV HOUSTON & ASSOC DEAN CULLEN COL ENG, 68-, MEM GRAD FAC, 61- *Concurrent Pos:* Fac consult & lectr, Nat Sci Found Inst Use of Comput Elec Eng, 62-64, Nat Sci Found lectr, 65; vis assoc prof, Baylor Col Med, 65-; consult, Houston Speech & Hearing Ctr, 61-62, SIE-Dresser Electronics, 63 & Inst Bus Mach Corp, Calif, 64. *Mem:* Am Soc Eng Educ; Asn Comput Mach; Inst Elec & Electronics Engrs. *Res:* Bioengineering; circuits and systems; computer applications; linear circuit analysis; teaching methods. *Mailing Add:* 850 Kuhlman Houston TX 77024

PASLAY, PAUL R(OBERT), b New Orleans, La, May 9, 31; m 51; c 2. MECHANICS. *Educ:* La State Univ, BS, 50; Rice Inst, MS, 52; Mass Inst Technol, ScD, 55. *Prof Exp:* Instr, Rice Inst, 50-52; asst prof, Mass Inst Technol, 54-55; vibration & stress analyst, Gen Elec Co, 55-59; from assoc prof to prof mech, Rice Univ, 59-65; vis prof, Brown Univ, 65-66, prof eng, 66-73; dean eng, Oakland Univ, Rochester, Mich, 73-76; dean eng, Univ Ill, Chicago Circle, 76-78; CONSULT MECH ENGR, 78- *Mem:* Am Soc Mech Engrs. *Res:* Deformable body mechanics. *Mailing Add:* 7489 Brompton Blvd Houston TX 77025

PASLEY, JAMES NEVILLE, b Jefferson City, Mo, Sept 19, 39; m 66; c 2. NEUROENDOCRINOLOGY, REPRODUCTION BEHAVIOR. *Educ:* Westminster Col, Mo, AB, 61; Univ Mo, MA, 65; Ore State Univ, PhD(physiol), 69. *Prof Exp:* Asst prof, 70-74, ASSOC PROF PHYSIOL, MED CTR, UNIV ARK, LITTLE ROCK, 74- *Concurrent Pos:* NIH fel pop, endocrines & behav, Albert Einstein Med Ctr, Philadelphia, 69-70. *Mem:* AAAS; Am Physiol Soc; NY Acad Sci; Soc Study Reprod. *Res:* *ffects of environmental and central nervous factors on endocrines and behavior. *Mailing Add:* Dept of Physiol Univ of Ark Med Ctr Little Rock AR 72201

PASQUA, PIETRO F, b Englewood, Colo, May 30, 22; m 45; c 4. NUCLEAR ENGINEERING. *Educ:* Univ Colo, BS, 44; Northwestern Univ, MS, 47, PhD(mech eng), 52. *Prof Exp:* Instr, Univ Colo, 44-45; from asst to instr mech eng, Northwestern Univ, 45-52; assoc prof, 52-56, prof & actg head dept, 56-57, PROF NUCLEAR ENG & HEAD DEPT, UNIV TENN, KNOXVILLE, 57- *Concurrent Pos:* Consult reactor eng exp div, Union Carbide Nuclear Co, Tenn, 54- *Mem:* Am Nuclear Soc; Am Soc Eng Educ. *Res:* Heat transfer. *Mailing Add:* Dept of Nuclear Eng Univ of Tenn Knoxville TN 37916

PASQUINE, DONALD LEO, b New York, NY, Jan 11, 17; m 42; c 1. METALLURGY. *Educ:* NY Univ, BS, 38; Stevens Inst Technol, MS, 49. *Prof Exp:* Heat treater, New Processing Corp, 38-40; asst metallurgist, Carpenter Steel Co, 40-42; eng inspector, US Naval Bur Ord, 42-43; res metallurgist, Gen Cable Corp, 46-48; unit head, Curtiss-Wright Corp, 48-51; mat engr, M W Kellogg Co, 51-53; res metallurgist, Paul D Merica Res Lab, 53-71, tech ed & writer, 71-80, TECH WRITER & COORDR, INT NICKEL CO, INC, 80- *Concurrent Pos:* Vis lectr, Fairleigh Dickinson Univ, 55-; Newark Col Eng, 57-72. *Mem:* Metals Soc; Am Soc Testing & Mat; Am Inst Mining, Metall & Petrol Engrs. *Res:* Physical metallurgy of steels; ultrahigh strength steels; alloying elements in steel; heat treatment and mechanical properties; residual stress; hardenability; fatigue and creep of metals. *Mailing Add:* Int Nickel Co Inc One New York Plaza New York NY 10004

PASS, BOBBY CLIFTON, b Cleveland, Ala, Nov 4, 31; m 53; c 1. INSECT PEST MANAGEMENT. *Educ:* Auburn Univ, BS, 52, MS, 60; Clemson Univ, PhD(entom), 62. *Prof Exp:* Res asst entom, Auburn Univ, 58-60 & Clemson Univ, 60-62; from asst prof to assoc prof, 62-71, PROF ENTOM, UNIV KY, 71-, CHMN DEPT, 68- *Mem:* Entom Soc Am. *Res:* Biology, ecology and control of insect pest of forage crops. *Mailing Add:* Dept of Entom Univ of Ky Lexington KY 40506

PASSANANTI, GAETANO THOMAS, b Wilkes-Barre, Pa, Sept 23, 25; m 50; c 2. ENZYMOLOGY. *Educ:* Pa State Univ, BS, 49, MS, 53, PhD(biochem & org chem), 57. *Prof Exp:* Instr biochem, Univ Mich, 56-60; biochemist, Dept Path, Hurley Hosp, Flint, Mich, 60-63; asst prof biochem, Ohio State Univ, 63-67; biochemist, Inst Path, Harrisburg Hosp, 67-70; res asst biochem, 51-56, ASST PROF PHARMACOL, SCH MED, PA STATE UNIV, 70- *Mem:* Am Soc Pharmacol & Exp Ther. *Res:* Biochemical pharmacology and drug metabolism. *Mailing Add:* Dept of Pharmacol Hershey Med Ctr Pa State Univ Hershey PA 17033

PASSANO, LEONARD MAGRUDER, (III), b Staten Island, NY, Dec 16, 24; m 81; c 1. ZOOLOGY. *Educ:* Harvard Univ, AB, 48; Yale Univ, PhD(zool), 52. *Prof Exp:* NSF fel, Cambridge Univ, 52-53; instr zool, Univ Wash, 53-55; from instr to asst prof, Yale Univ, 55-64; assoc prof, 64-69, PROF ZOOL, UNIV WIS-MADISON, 69- *Concurrent Pos:* Instr, Woods Hole Marine Biol Lab, 54-55; Fulbright res fel, Univ West Indies, 60-61; Guggenheim fel, 63-64; vis prof, French Nat Univ Syst, Univ Lyons, 70. *Mem:* Am Soc Zool; Brit Soc Exp Biol. *Res:* Coelenterate neurophysiology; behavioral physiology; crustacean endocrinology; invertebrate physiology. *Mailing Add:* Dept Zool Univ Wis Madison WI 53706

PASSCHIER, ARIE ANTON, b The Hague, Netherlands, Mar 21, 40; US citizen; m 62. PHYSICAL CHEMISTRY, ANALYTICAL CHEMISTRY. *Educ:* Calif State Col, Long Beach, BS, 61, MA, 63; Univ Wash, PhD(phys chem), 68. *Prof Exp:* Mem tech staff, Rocketdyne Div, 68-69, MEM TECH STAFF AUTONETICS DIV, ROCKWELL INT CORP, 69- *Mem:* AAAS; Am Chem Soc. *Res:* Analysis of gas phase contaminants in inertial instruments; high vacuum systems; mass spectrometry; determination of thermodynamic properties of materials; gas chromatography and gas chromatography/mass spectrometry. *Mailing Add:* Instrument Mat Unit Autonetics Div Rockwell Int Corp 3370 Miraloma Anaheim CA 92804

PASSELL, LAURENCE, b Cleveland, Ohio, Mar 23, 25; m 46; c 2. SOLID STATE PHYSICS. *Educ:* US Merchant Marine Acad, BS, 45; Harvard Univ, AB, 50; Univ Calif, MA, 52, PhD(physics), 55. *Prof Exp:* Port engr, US War Shipping Admin, DC, 45-46; asst, Univ Calif, 50-54, sr scientist, Lawrence Radiation Lab, 55-61; scientist, Danish Atomic Energy Comn Res Estab, Riso, 61-63; SCIENTIST, BROOKHAVEN NAT LAB, 63- *Mem:* Fel Am Phys Soc. *Res:* Neutron physics; low temperature physics; neutron scattering study of condensed phases. *Mailing Add:* Bldg 510 Brookhaven Nat Lab Upton NY 11973

PASSELL, THOMAS OLIVER, b Chicago, Ill, Nov 24, 29; m 52; c 6. NUCLEAR CHEMISTRY. *Educ:* Okla State Univ, BS, 51; Univ Calif, PhD(chem), 54. *Prof Exp:* Asst chem, Univ Calif, 51-52, Radiation Lab, 52-54; nuclear res chemist, Atomic Energy Div, Phillips Petrol Co, 54-55; physicist, Stanford Res Inst, 55-69 & Physics Int Co, 69-71; staff scientist, 71-75, PROJ MGR, ELEC POWER RES INST, LOCKHEED PALO ALTO RES LABS, 75- *Mem:* Am Chem Soc; Am Phys Soc; Am Nuclear Soc; Am Geophys Union; Am Inst Chemists. *Res:* Beta ray spectroscopy; neutron cross sections; levels in light nuclei; nuclear power reactor technology; corrosion technology; controlled thermonuclear research; plasma physics; nuclear detonation effects; x-ray technology. *Mailing Add:* 3825 Louis Rd Palo Alto CA 94303

PASSENHEIM, BURR CHARLES, b St Louis, Mo, Dec 15, 41; div; c 2. EXPERIMENTAL PHYSICS. *Educ:* Univ Calif, Berkeley, AB, 63; Univ Calif, Riverside, MA, 65, PhD(physics), 69. *Prof Exp:* Technician physics, Gen Atomic, 58-63; res asst, Univ Calif, Riverside, 63-68; physicist, Gulf Energy & Environ Systs, 68-71; physicist, IRT Corp, 71-78; MEM STAFF, MISSION RES CORP, 78- *Concurrent Pos:* Instr, San Diego Eve Col, 70-71. *Mem:* Am Phys Soc. *Res:* Experimental physics in atomic and nuclear radiation effects on materials with interests in optics, cryogenics, thermal and mechanical properties and electromagnetic effects. *Mailing Add:* Mission Res Corp 5434 Ruffin Rd San Diego CA 92123

PASSERELLO, CHRIS EDWARD, b New Jersey, Apr 12, 44. ENGINEERING, MECHANICS. *Educ:* Univ Cincinnati, BSASE, 67, MSASE, 68, PhD(mech), 72. *Prof Exp:* Assoc prof aerospace eng & mech, Univ Cincinnati, 76-78; ASSOC PROF ENG MECH, MICH TECHNOL UNIV, 78- *Mem:* Am Inst Aeronaut & Astronaut; Am Acad Mech; Soc Automotive Engrs. *Res:* Continuum mechanics; dynamics and vibrations; structures; finite elements. *Mailing Add:* Dept of Mech Eng & Eng Mech Mich Technol Univ Houghton MI 49931

PASSERI, DAVID, electrical engineering, see previous edition

PASSEY, CHAND ARJUN, b Chawinda, India, Apr 28, 39; Can citizen; m 61; c 4. FOOD SCIENCE, FOOD ENGINEERING. *Educ:* Univ Jabalpur, India, BE Hons, 60; Indian Inst Technol, Kharagpur, ME, 63; Univ Laval, DSc(food sci), 70. *Prof Exp:* From asst prof to assoc prof mech eng, Univ Jabalpur, India, 60-66; fel food sci & eng, Univ Laval, 70-71; res engr & head dept res & develop, Atlantic Bridge Co, 71-76; RES SCIENTIST, HALIFAX LAB, FISHERIES & MARINE SERV, RES & DEVELOP DIRECTORATE, 76- *Concurrent Pos:* Consult to food & chem processors & processing equip mfrs, 76- *Mem:* Am Soc Mech Engrs; Am Inst Chem Engrs; Inst Food Technologists; Am Dairy Sci Asn; Asn Prof Engrs. *Res:* Food products and processes development for enhancing direct utilization of fisheries and agricultural resources; drying, canning, freeze-drying, vacuum drying and heat pumps to ensure energy conservation and product quality improvement in processing of foods and chemicals. *Mailing Add:* Fish & Marine Serv R & D Dir Halifax Lab PO Box 550 Halifax NS Can

PASSEY, RICHARD BOYD, b Mesa, Ariz, Aug 5, 37; m 60; c 6. CLINICAL CHEMISTRY, BIOCHEMISTRY. *Educ:* Utah State Univ, BS, 65; Colo State Univ, PhD(biochem), 69. *Prof Exp:* Asst prof pathol, Sch Med, Univ Tex Med Br, 69-76; asst prof, Sch Med, Univ Ky, 76-77; ASSOC PROF PATHOL, UNIV OKLA HEALTH SCI CTR, 77- *Concurrent Pos:* Dir clin chem & sci dir clin labs, State Okla Teaching Hospshoma City, Okla, 77- *Mem:* Am Asn Clin Chem; AAAS; Am Soc Clin Pathologists. *Res:* Application of clinical chemistry methods to problems in clinical medicine; diagnostic usefulness or urinary LDH isoenzymes in predicting pyelonephritis; evaluation of clinical laboratory instrumentation; fetal monitoring. *Mailing Add:* Sch of Med PO Box 25606 Oklahoma City OK 73125

PASSINO, DORA R MAY, b Portland, Ore, Mar 22, 40; m 74; c 1. FISHERY BIOLOGY, BIOLOGICAL OCEANOGRAPHY. *Educ:* Portland State Univ, BA, 66; Univ Wash, MS, 69, PhD(fisheries), 73. *Prof Exp:* Res assoc oceanog, Nat Acad Sci, 73; PROJ LEADER FISHERIES, US FISH & WILDLIFE SERV, 73- *Concurrent Pos:* Mem, outer continental shelf task force, US Fish & Wildlife Serv, 73 & Lacy act task force, 74. *Honors & Awards:* Cert Fisheries Scientist, Am Fisheries Soc, 78. *Mem:* AAAS; Am Chem Soc; Am Fisheries Soc; Soc Environ Toxicol Chem; Creation Res Soc. *Res:* Effects of environmental stresses and contaminants on metabolism, physiology, reproduction and growth of fish and invertebrates of the Great Lakes and marine ecosystems. *Mailing Add:* Great Lakes Fishery Lab 1451 Green Rd Ann Arbor MI 48105

PASSINO, NICHOLAS ALFRED, b Ft Wayne, Ind, May 24, 40; m 64; c 1. MOLECULAR SPECTROSCOPY, INFRARED PHYSICS. *Educ:* St Procopius Col, BS, 62; Ariz State Univ, MS, 65, PhD(physics), 68. *Prof Exp:* Fac assoc physics, Ariz State Univ, 62-68; res physicist, Brown Eng Co, Inc, 68-69, prin res physicist, 69-71, mgr optics technol br, 71-74, DEP MGR, OPTICS DEPT, TELEDYNE BROWN ENG CO, 74- *Mem:* AAAS; Optical Soc Am. *Res:* Infrared optics and semiconductor detectors; nuclear effects on optical materials and semiconductors; infrared instrumentation and calibration; infrared absorption in gases, vibrational and rotational analysis; military optical systems applications. *Mailing Add:* 104 Tollgate Circle SE Huntsville AL 35801

PASSMAN, DONALD STEVEN, b New York, NY, Mar 28, 40; m 63; c 2. ALGEBRA. *Educ:* Polytech Inst Brooklyn, BS, 60; Harvard Univ, AM, 61, PhD(math), 64. *Prof Exp:* Asst prof math, Univ Calif, Los Angeles, 64-66 & Yale Univ, 66-69; assoc prof, 69-71, PROF MATH, UNIV WIS-MADISON, 72- *Concurrent Pos:* Mathematician, Inst Defense Anal, Princeton, NJ, 69-70. *Mem:* Am Math Soc. *Res:* Infinite group rings; finite groups and group representations. *Mailing Add:* Dept of Math Univ of Wis Madison WI 53706

PASSMAN, FREDERICK JAY, b Philadelphia, Pa, Aug 22, 48; m 68; c 1. ENVIRONMENTAL MICROBIOLOGY. *Educ:* Ind Univ, Bloomington, AB, 70; Univ NH, PhD(microbiol), 77. *Prof Exp:* Microbiologist, Energy Resources Co, Inc, 77-78, dir microbiol lab, 78-80; MEM STAFF, CRCO PETROL SERV INC, 80- *Mem:* Am Soc Microbiol; Am Soc Limnol & Oceanog; Sigma Xi; Oceanic Soc. *Res:* Dynamics of marine microbiol communities of surface films and sediments; elemental composition of marine bacteria; microbiology of municipal and industrial waste recovery, particularly composting. *Mailing Add:* CRCO Petrol Serv Inc 15702 W Hardy Rd Suite 260 Houston TX 77032

PASSMAN, SIDNEY, b Brooklyn, NY, Aug 5, 27; m 51; c 2. PHYSICS, RESEARCH ADMINISTRATION. *Educ:* Columbia Univ, AB, 48, AM, 49, PhD, 52. *Prof Exp:* Asst high energy physics, Nevis Cyclotron Lab, Columbia Univ, 50-52; res physicist guided missile syst anal, Hughes Aircraft Co, 52-55; group leader infrared physics, Rand Corp, 55-63; phys sci off, Sci & Technol Bur, US Arms Control & Disarmament Agency, 63-70; head sci policy res sect, NSF, Washington, DC, 70-73; dir, Div Sci Res & Higher Educ, UNESCO, Paris, 73-81; SPECIAL ASST PLANNING & POLICY ANALYSIS, NAT SCI FOUND, WASHINGTON, DC, 81- *Concurrent Pos:* Optical Soc Am rep, Nat Res Coun, 66-72; mem nat comt, Infrared Info Systs; ed, J Infrared Physics. *Mem:* Fel AAAS; fel Optical Soc Am. *Res:* Scientific research and higher education; science policy; infrared physics and technology; arms control and weapons system research; information retrieval. *Mailing Add:* 1 Carderock Ct Bethesda MD

PASSMAN, STEPHEN LEE, b Suffolk, Va, Sept 3, 42; m 65; c 4. MECHANICS. *Educ:* Ga Inst Technol, BSEM, 64, MSEM, 66, PhD(eng mech), 68. *Prof Exp:* Instr, US Naval Acad, 68-70; res assoc & fel, Johns Hopkins Univ, 70-71; from asst prof to assoc prof eng sci & mech, Ga Inst Technol, 71-78; TECH STAFF, SANDIA NAT LABS, 78- *Concurrent Pos:* Asst prof lectr, George Washington Univ, 69-70. *Mem:* Am Acad Mech; Sigma Xi; Soc Rheol; Soc Natural Philos. *Res:* Continuum mechanics. *Mailing Add:* Div 5531 Sandia Nat Labs Albuquerque NM 87185

PASSMORE, EDMUND M, b Somerville, Mass, July 28, 31; m 54; c 4. METALLURGY, CERAMICS. *Educ:* Mass Inst Tech, SB, 53, SM, 54, ScD(metall), 57. *Prof Exp:* Mem res & develop staff, Avco Space Systs Div, 57-59, ManLabs Inc, 59-63 & Avco Space Systs Div, 63-66; MEM RES & DEVELOP STAFF, GTE SYLVANIA LIGHTING PROD, 67- *Honors & Awards:* Ross-Coffin-Purdy Award, Am Ceramic Soc, 67. *Mem:* Am Inst Mining, Metall & Petrol Engrs; Am Ceramic Soc. *Res:* Publications and patents covering incandescent lamp and evaporation source technology and chemistry; also research and development of materials and components for lighting and other applications; lamps and lighting products. *Mailing Add:* GTE Sylvania Lighting Ctr 100 Endicott St Danvers MA 01923

PASSMORE, HOWARD CLINTON, b Drexel Hill, Pa, Sept 12, 42; m 64; c 2. IMMUNOGENETICS. *Educ:* Franklin & Marshall Col, AB, 64; Rutgers Univ, MS, 66; Univ Mich, PhD(immunogenetics), 70. *Prof Exp:* NSF fel, Univ Calif, San Francisco, 70-71; asst prof, 71-77, ASSOC PROF ZOOL, RUTGERS UNIV, NEW BRUNSWICK, 77- *Mem:* Am Asn Immunologists; AAAS; Genetics Soc Am; Am Soc Human Genetics. *Res:* Immunological and biochemical genetics. *Mailing Add:* Dept of Zool Rutgers Univ New Brunswick NJ 08903

PASSMORE, JACK, b North Devon, UK, Nov 16, 40; Can citizen; m 62; c 3. INORGANIC CHEMISTRY, FLUORINE CHEMISTRY. *Educ:* Bristol Univ, BS, 63; Univ BC, PhD(inorg chem), 67. *Prof Exp:* Fel, McMaster Univ, 68-69; asst prof, 69-74, assoc prof, 74-78, PROF CHEM, UNIV NB, FREDERICTON, 78- *Mem:* Am Chem Soc; Royal Soc Chem; Chem Inst Can. *Res:* Preparation, characterization and chemistry of compounds of interest in terms of current theories of bonding and stereochemistry. *Mailing Add:* Dept Chem Univ New Brunswick Bag Serv 45222 Fredericton NB E3B 6E2 Can

PASSONNEAU, JANET VIVIAN, b Crosby, Minn, June 22, 24; m 48; c 4. BIOCHEMISTRY. *Educ:* Univ Minn, BA, 45; Radcliffe Col, MA, 46, PhD(insect physiol), 49. *Prof Exp:* Assoc biologist, Argonne Nat Lab, 49-52; consult, Oak Ridge Nat Lab, 53-55; res assoc, Vet Admin Hosp, St Louis, 55-56; res assoc, Henry Shaw Sch Bot, Wash Univ, 56-58, res asst prof biochem, Sch Med, 58-64, from asst prof to assoc prof, 64-68; vis assoc prof anesthesia, Med Sch, Northwestern Univ, Chicago, 69-70; HEAD SECT CELLULAR NEUROCHEM, NAT INST NEUROL & COMMUN DISORDERS & STROKE, 70-, CHIEF, LAB NEUROCHEM, 76- *Concurrent Pos:* Mem psychopharmacol res rev comt, NIMH, 69-73, mem clin prog projs res rev comt, 75-77; merit review bd, Vet Admin, 78-82; ed, J Neurochem, 72-, Enzyme, 75- & J Biochem Biophys Methods & Anal Biochem, 79- *Honors & Awards:* Borden Award, Asn Am Med Cols, 66. *Mem:* AAAS; Am Soc Biol Chemists; NY Acad Sci; Am Soc Neurochem; Soc Neurosci. *Res:* Microtechniques for the study of brain metabolism; control mechanisms; enzyme kinetics. *Mailing Add:* Lab Neurochem Bldg 36 Rm 4D20 Nat Inst Neurol & Commun Dis Bethesda MD 20205

PASSOW, ELI (AARON), b Bronx, NY, Sept 4, 39; m 71; c 2. APPROXIMATION THEORY. *Educ:* Mass Inst Technol, BS, 62; Yeshiva Univ, MA, 65, PhD(math), 66. *Prof Exp:* Math analyst, Airborne Instruments Lab, NY, 66-67; instr math, Yeshiva Univ, 67-68; lectr, Bar-Ilan Univ, Israel, 68-70; asst prof, 70-74, assoc prof, 74-80, PROF MATH, TEMPLE UNIV, 80- *Concurrent Pos:* Vis assoc prof, Technion, Israel, 79-80. *Mem:* Am Asn Univ Professors; Math Asn Am. *Res:* Approximation theory; approximation and interpolation with constraints. *Mailing Add:* Dept Math Temple Univ Philadelphia PA 19122

PAST, WALLACE LYLE, b Great Falls, Mont, Feb 15, 24; m 49; c 4. PATHOLOGY. *Educ:* Univ Pa, AB, 44; NY Univ, MD, 48. *Prof Exp:* Resident path, Henry Ford Hosp, Detroit, Mich, 52-55; assoc pathologist, Wilson Mem Hosp, Johnson City, NY, 55-56; PROF PATH, SCH MED, UNIV LOUISVILLE, 56- *Concurrent Pos:* Pathologist, St Edward Hosp, New Albany, Ind, 56-61; consult, Vet Admin Hosp, 56-61. *Mem:* Col Am Path. *Res:* Formation of bone mineral. *Mailing Add:* Dept of Path Univ of Louisville Sch of Med Louisville KY 40201

PASTA, JOHN ROBERT, mathematical physics, computer science, deceased

PASTAN, IRA HARRY, b Winthrop, Mass, June 1, 31; m 53; c 3. MOLECULAR BIOLOGY, CELL BIOLOGY. *Educ:* Tufts Univ, BS, 53, MD, 57. *Prof Exp:* Intern, Grace-New Haven Hosp, Sch Med, Yale Univ, 57-58, asst resident med, 58-59; clin assoc, Nat Inst Arthritis & Metab Dis, 59-61, sr investr endocrine biochem, NIH, 62-69, sr investr, Nat Inst Arthritis & Metab Dis, 62-69, chief sect molecular biol, Endocrinol Br, Nat Cancer Inst, 69-70, CHIEF LAB MOLECULAR BIOL, NAT CANCER INST, 70- *Concurrent Pos:* Fel, Lab Cellular Physiol, NIH, 61-62. *Honors & Awards:* Van Meter Prize, Am Thyroid Asn, 71. *Mem:* AAAS; Am Soc Microbiol; Am Soc Biol Chemists; Am Soc Clin Invest; Am Thyroid Asn. *Res:* Regulation of the expression of genetic information in animal cells and mechanism of malignant transformation. *Mailing Add:* Bldg 37 Rm 4B27 Nat Cancer Inst Bethesda MD 20014

PASTEELNICK, LOUIS ANDRE, b Newark, NJ, June 22, 29; m 63; c 2. QUALITY ASSURANCE, STATISTICS. *Educ:* NJ Inst Technol, BS, 51; Rutgers Univ, MS, 58. *Prof Exp:* Chem engr drug mfg, Merck & Co, 51-53, chem warfare, US Army, 53-55, plastics mfg, M W Kellogg, Minn Mining & Mfg Co, 55-58; quality control statistician, container mfg, Am Can Co, 58-65; QUALITY ASSURANCE, FOOD DRUG & COSMETIC MFG & DIR, QUALITY PLANNING & ENG, PARKE-DAVIS, WARNER-LAMBERT CO, 65- *Honors & Awards:* E R Ott Award, Am Soc Qual Control, 75. *Mem:* Fel Am Soc Qual Control; Am Inst Chem Eng; Am Chem Soc. *Mailing Add:* 201 Tabor Rd Morris Plains NJ 07950

PASTELL, DANIEL L(OUIS), b Seattle, Wash, May 22, 22; m 50; c 2. CHEMICAL ENGINEERING. *Educ:* Univ Wash, Seattle, BS, 44, BS & MS, 47. *Prof Exp:* Group leader combustion res, 50-53, head res div, 53-54, eng div, 54-60, TECH MGR, WESTERN REGION, E I DU PONT DE NEMOURS & CO, INC, 60- *Concurrent Pos:* Chmn motor combustion chamber deposits group, Coord Res Coun USA, 42-43. *Honors & Awards:* Horning Mem Award, Soc Automotive Engrs, 50. *Mem:* Am Chem Soc; Soc Automotive Engrs; Inst Elec & Electronics Engrs; Air Pollution Control Asn. *Res:* Combustion in reciprocating and gas turbine engines. *Mailing Add:* 2904 Via de la Guerra Palos Verdes Estates CA 90274

PASTER, DONALD L(EE), b Providence, RI, June 26, 26; m 47; c 3. HYDRODYNAMICS, ACOUSTICS. *Educ:* Mass Inst Technol, SBAE, 47; Univ RI, MS, 54. *Prof Exp:* Test engr, Aircraft Gas Turbine Div, Gen Elec Co, 47-48, aeronaut engr, 48-50; head internal combustion engines sect & designer of internal combustion engine testing lab, Naval Underwater Ord Sta, 50-51, head hydromech sect, 51-53, head hydroballistics br & dir wind tunnel, 53-56; chief appl res, Fram Corp, 56-59; MGR, SOFTWARE DEVELOP LAB & DIV COORDR SOFTWARE ENG, SUBMARINE SIGNAL DIV, RAYTHEON CO, 59- *Mem:* Acoust Soc Am; Inst Elec & Electronics Engrs. *Res:* Stability and control; body shape design; control surface design; torpedoes; filtration; oceanography; undersea warfare; sonar system analysis; data and narrowband spectrum analysis; digital computer programming and software systems. *Mailing Add:* Submarine Signal Div Raytheon Co PO Box 360 Portsmouth RI 02841

PASTERCZYK, WILLIAM ROBERT, b Chicago, Ill, Feb 4, 17; m 48; c 3. ANALYTICAL CHEMISTRY, BIOCHEMISTRY. *Educ:* DePaul Univ, BS, 40, MS, 43; Loyola Univ Ill, PhD, 54. *Prof Exp:* From instr to assoc prof, 43-58, PROF CHEM, DEPAUL UNIV, 58- *Mem:* Am Chem Soc; Am Asn Univ Professors; Sigma Xi; Soc Appl Spectros. *Mailing Add:* Dept of Chem DePaul Univ 1036 W Belden Ave Chicago IL 60614

PASTERNACK, BERNARD SAMUEL, b Brooklyn, NY, June 18, 32; m 67. EPIDEMIOLOGY, BIOSTATISTICS. *Educ:* Brooklyn Col, BA, 54; NC State Univ, MS, 56, PhD, 59. *Prof Exp:* Asst prof biostatist, Univ NC, 59-61; from asst prof to assoc prof, 61-74, PROF ENVIRON MED, SCH MED, NY UNIV, 74- *Concurrent Pos:* Mem, Epidemiol & Dis Control Study Sect, Nat Inst Health, 80-83; consult task force on res planning in environ health sci, USPHS, 68-69, consult, Polycythemia Vera Study Group, 68- *Mem:* Fel Am Statist Asn; Biomet Soc; fel Am Pub Health Asn; Soc Epidemiol Res; fel Am Col Epidemiol. *Res:* Biomedical statistics; application of statistical methodology to biological, medical and health related sciences. *Mailing Add:* Inst of Environ Med NY Univ Med Ctr New York NY 10016

PASTERNACK, ROBERT FRANCIS, b New York, NY, Sept 20, 36; c 2. PHYSICAL INORGANIC CHEMISTRY, BIOINORGANIC CHEMISTRY. *Educ:* Cornell Univ, BA, 57, PhD(phys inorg chem), 62. *Prof Exp:* Res assoc, Univ Ill, 62-63; from asst prof to prof, 63-76, CHARLES A DANA ENDOWED, PROF CHEM, ITHACA COL, 76- *Concurrent Pos:* Consult, Nat Bur Standards, 63-64 & NY State Dept Educ, 66-67; NSF col teacher res partic grant, 65-68; Petrol Res Fund grant, 67-74; NSF sci fac fel, Univ Rome, 69-70; Sci Course Improv Prog grant, NSF, 69-72; NIH grant, 71-; Res Corp grants, 74-75 & 78-; NSF sci manpower develop grant, Univ London, 77-78; Danforth Assoc, 78-84. *Mem:* AAAS; Am Chem Soc; NY Acad Sci; Sigma Xi. *Res:* Rapid reactions by relaxation spectrometry; porphyrin chemistry; nomenclature of inorganic compounds; kinetics of reactions in solution. *Mailing Add:* Dept Chem Ithaca Col Ithaca NY 14850

PASTERNAK, GAVRIL WILLIAM, b Brooklyn, NY, June 29, 47; m 77; c 1. NEUROLOGY, NEUROPHARMACOLOGY. *Educ:* Johns Hopkins Univ, BA, 69, MD, 73, PhD(pharmacol), 74. *Prof Exp:* ASST PROF NEUROL & PHARMACOL, MED COL, CORNELL UNIV, 79- *Concurrent Pos:* Asst attending neurologist, Mem Sloan Kettering Cancer Ctr, 79- *Honors & Awards:* S Weir Mitchell Award, Am Acad Neurol. *Mem:* Am Acad Neurol; Am Soc Pharmacol & Exp Therapeut; Soc Neurosci. *Res:* Central analgesic mechanisms; opiate receptor heterogeneity and correlating the different subpopulations of binding sites with pharmacological and physiological functions. *Mailing Add:* Dept Neurol & Pharmacol Med Col Cornell Univ New York NY 10021

PASTINE, D JOHN, b Philadelphia, Pa, Jan 31, 36; m 61. THEORETICAL PHYSICS. *Educ:* Cath Univ Am, BA, 57, PhD(physics), 65. *Prof Exp:* Physicist, Nat Bur Stand, 58-61; res physicist, US Naval Ord Lab, 61-75, head, Detonation Physics Br, 75-79, DIR INDEPENDENT RES, WHITE OAK LAB, NAVAL SURFACE WEAPONS CTR, 79- *Concurrent Pos:* Adj prof physics, Wash State Univ, 71- *Mem:* Am Phys Soc. *Res:* Equations of state of solids and high pressures; theory of explosives initiation and detonation; high pressure physics. *Mailing Add:* White Oak Lab Naval Surface Weapons Ctr White Oak MD 20910

PASTO, ARVID ERIC, b Ithaca, NY, Dec 17, 44; m 66; c 2. CERAMIC SCIENCE, NUCLEAR MATERIALS. *Educ:* State Univ NY Col Ceramics, Alfred Univ, BS, 67, MS, 69, PhD(ceramics), 72. *Prof Exp:* Res assoc ceramic mat, Oak Ridge Nat Lab, 72-77, subtask leader, Develop Nuclear Fuels, Metals & Ceramics Div, 77-80; MEM STAFF, GEN TELEPHONE & ELECTRONICS LABS, INC, 80- *Honors & Awards:* Indust Res-100 Award, 79. *Mem:* Am Ceramic Soc; Ceramic Educ Coun. *Res:* Synthesis, characterization and fabrication of refractory ceramic materials and their development into final shapes possessing useful properties; oxides, borides, nitrides and cermets. *Mailing Add:* 9 Wannalancit Trail Littleton MA 01460

PASTO, DANIEL JEROME, b Elmira, NY, Jan 21, 36; m 71; c 2. ORGANIC CHEMISTRY. *Educ:* Rochester Inst Technol, BS, 58; Iowa State Univ, PhD(org chem), 60. *Prof Exp:* NSF fel chem, Harvard Univ, 60-61; from asst prof to assoc prof, 61-69, PROF CHEM, UNIV NOTRE DAME, 69- *Concurrent Pos:* NSF sr fel, Stanford Univ; consult, Miles Labs, Elkhart, Ind, 75-; NATO fel, Univ Louis Pasteur, Strasbourg, France. *Mem:* Am Chem Soc. *Res:* Physical organic reaction mechanisms; electrophilic addition and cycloaddition reactions; reactions and structures of transition metal complexes. *Mailing Add:* Dept of Chem Univ of Notre Dame Notre Dame IN 46556

PASTORE, PETER NICHOLAS, b Bluefield, WVa, Nov 8, 07; m 39; c 5. OTORHINOLARYNGOLOGY. *Educ:* Univ Richmond, AB, 30; Med Col Va, MD, 34; Univ Minn, MS, 39. *Prof Exp:* Intern, Med Col Va, 34-35, resident, 35-36; instr, Mayo Clin, 36-39, staff, 39-42; prof otol, rhinol & laryngol & chmn dept, Med Col, Va, 42-76; chief otolaryngol, 63-76, DIR, CONTINUING MED EDUC, MCGUIRE VET HOSP, 77- *Concurrent Pos:* Fel, Mayo Clin, Minn, 36-39; consult, US Naval Hosp, Portsmouth, Va, 58 & McDonald Army Hosp, Ft Eustis, 64; with Crippled Children's Hosp, Richmond, Richmond Eye, Ear, Nose & Throat Hosp, St Philip Hosp, Ennion G Williams Hosp, Richmond Mem Hosp & Med Col Va Hosp; scholar-in-residence, Med Col Va, Va Commonwealth Univ, 80- *Mem:* Am Otol Soc; Am Laryngol, Rhinol & Otol Soc; fel AMA; Pan-Am Asn Oto-Rhino-Laryngol & Broncho-Esophagol; fel Am Col Surgeons. *Res:* Hearing; speech. *Mailing Add:* 5503 Riverside Dr Richmond VA 23225

PASTOROK, ROBERT ANTHONY, ecology, zoology, see previous edition

PASTUSZYN, ANDRZEJ, b Krakow, Poland, July 31, 40; m 68. BIOCHEMISTRY. *Educ:* Jagiellonian Univ, Poland, MS, 62; Univ Vienna, PhD(biochem), 66. *Prof Exp:* Asst anal chem, Univ Agr, Vienna, 66-68; res assoc, 68-70, sr res assoc biochem, 70-79, RES ASST PROF, UNIV NMEX, ALBUQUERQUE, 79- *Mem:* Am Chem Soc. *Res:* Protein biosynthesis; aminoacyl-transfer ribonucleic acid ligases and role of polyamines in aminoacid activation; cholesterol biosynthesis and regulation. *Mailing Add:* Dept of Biochem Univ of NMex Albuquerque NM 87131

PASZNER, LASZLO, b Koszeg, Hungary, Aug 19, 34; Can citizen; m 60; c 2. WOOD SCIENCE, PULP SCIENCE. *Educ:* Univ BC, BSF, 58, MF, 63, PhD(wood chem), 66. *Prof Exp:* Res technician panel prod, Can Forest Prod Ltd, 58-60; res technician wood technol, Fac Forestry, Univ BC, 60-61; res technician pulping, Harmac Div, MacMillan Bloedell Ltd, 63; fel wood chem, Nat Res Coun Overseas, Ger, Austria, 66-68; res assoc radiation chem, 68-73, asst prof forestry, 73-75, ASSOC PROF FORESTRY, WOOD SCI & INDUST, UNIV BC, 75-, HEAD WOOD SCI & INDUST DIV, 78- *Concurrent Pos:* vchmn wood chem comn, Tech Asn Pulp & Paper Indust, 75- *Mem:* Tech Asn Pulp & Paper Indust; Forest Prod Res Soc; NY Acad Sci; Can Pulp Paper Asn. *Res:* Forest products chemistry; panel products; pulping chemistry; forest industrial pollution and control; polymer chemistry; radiation chemical processing of polymers; chemical conversion of biomass; organosol pulping and saccharification; biochemical technology. *Mailing Add:* Fac Forestry Univ BC Vancouver BC V6T 1W5 Can

PASZTOR, VALERIE MARGARET, b London, Eng, Feb 28, 36; m 62. ZOOLOGY. *Educ:* Univ Birmingham, BSc, 57; McMaster Univ, PhD(zool), 61. *Prof Exp:* Lectr zool, McMaster Univ, 60-61; from lectr to asst prof zool, 61-70, ASSOC PROF BIOL, MCGILL UNIV, 70- *Res:* Neural control of respiration in the lower vertebrates and crustacea. *Mailing Add:* Dept of Zool McGill Univ Montreal PQ H3A 2T5 Can

PASZYC, ALEKSY JERZY, b St Petersburg, Russia, Aug 9, 12; US citizen; m 43; c 3. SYSTEMS ENGINEERING. *Educ:* Warsaw Polytech, MEE, 35, MMechE, 37; Univ London, DIC & PhD(mech eng), 46. *Prof Exp:* Asst prof mech eng, Warsaw Polytech, 37-39; Polish Univ Col, London, Eng, 43-46; tech dir process plant eng & mfg, Hughes & Lancaster, Ltd, Eng, 46-50; chief engr plate & boiler div, John Ingles Co, Ltd, Can, 50-55; proj engr pulp & paper div, H H Simons Ltd, 55-56 & Ralph M Parsons Co, 56-58; chief engr, J H Pomeroy & Co, Inc, 58-60; mgr & chief engr, Pac Automation Prods, Inc, 60-61; div mgr ground systs group, Hughes Aircraft Co, 61-63; HEAD MECH & ELEC ENG DEPT, NAVAL CIVIL ENG LAB, 63- *Mem:* Am Soc Mech Engrs; Inst Elec & Electronics Engrs; Brit Inst Mech Engrs; Brit Inst Elec Engrs; Brit Inst Marine Engrs. *Res:* Scientific management; energy conversion, conservation and recovery; solid state applications to energy control; environmental protection systems; life support systems. *Mailing Add:* 642 Creekmont Ct Ventura CA 93003

PATALAS, KAZIMIERZ, b Rakoniewice, Poland, Aug 24, 25; m 51; c 2. LIMNOLOGY, FISHERIES. *Educ:* Wroclaw Univ, MS, 49, DSc(limnol), 52. *Prof Exp:* Res scientist, Forestry Inst, Poland, 49-50; res scientist, Freshwater Fisheries Inst, Poland, 50-54, head labor, 54-67; RES SCIENTIST, FRESHWATER INST, FISHERIES RES BD CAN, 67- *Concurrent Pos:* Docent habil, Olsztyn Univ, 60; Rockefeller Found fel, Univ BC, Fisheries Res Bd Can & Univ Colo, Boulder, 61; prof, Olsztyn Univ, 67; mem, Int Joint Comn-Int Ref Group on Upper Lakes Pollution, 73-; adj prof zool, Univ Man, 75- *Mem:* Int Asn Theoret & Appl Limnol; Am Soc Limnol & Oceanog; Polish Hydrobiol Asn. *Res:* Crustacean planktonic communities of lakes in relation to eutrophication; eutrophication phenomena in lakes; zoogeographical distribution of planktonic crustaceans. *Mailing Add:* Freshwater Inst 501 University Crescent Winnipeg MB R3T 2N6 Can

PATANELLI, DOLORES J, b Elkhart, Ind, July 20, 32. REPRODUCTIVE PHYSIOLOGY. *Educ:* NY Univ, BA, 55, MS, 58, PhD, 62. *Prof Exp:* Asst to med dir, Pop Coun, Inc, Rockefeller Inst, 56-62; res fel, Merck Inst Therapeut Res, 63-72; REPRODUCTIVE PHYSIOLOGIST, CONTRACEPTIVE DEVELOP BR, CTR POP RES, NAT INST CHILD HEALTH & HUMAN DEVELOP, 72- *Concurrent Pos:* Mem regional health adv comt, Region II, Dept Health, Educ & Welfare. *Mem:* AAAS; Endocrine Soc; Am Fertil Soc; Am Asn Anat; NY Acad Sci. *Res:* Endocrinology; control of fertility; developmental biology. *Mailing Add:* NICHD Ctr Pop Res 7910 Woodmont Ave Bethesda MD 20014

PATCH, RICHARD WALKER, engineering physics, mechanical engineering, see previous edition

PATCHETT, ARTHUR ALLAN, b Middletown, NY, May 28, 29; m 62; c 2. ORGANIC CHEMISTRY. *Educ:* Princeton Univ, AB, 51; Harvard Univ, PhD(org chem), 55. *Prof Exp:* Asst scientist, NIH, 55-57; sr res chemist, Synthetic Chem Dept, Merck & Co, Inc, 57-60, from asst dir to sr dir, 60-71, sr dir lead coord, 71-72, sr dir new lead discovery, Synthetic Chem Dept, 72-76, EXEC DIR NEW LEAD DISCOVERY, MERCK SHARP & DOHME RES LABS, 76- *Mem:* Am Chem Soc; Soc Indust Chem; AAAS. *Res:* Medicinal chemistry. *Mailing Add:* Merck Sharp & Dohme Res Labs PO Box 2000 Rahway NJ 07065

PATCHETT, JOSEPH EDMUND, b Middletown, NY, Oct 9, 30; m 56; c 2. CERAMICS. *Educ:* Rutgers Univ, BSc, 52; Univ Toronto, MA, 54, PhD(geol), 60. *Prof Exp:* Res scientist, Res & Develop Dept, 60-67, ASST DIR RES, NORTON CO, 68-, SECY, NORTON RES CORP, LTD, 70- *Honors & Awards:* Peacock Mem Prize, 60. *Mem:* Mineral Asn Can. *Res:* Abrasive and refractory materials. *Mailing Add:* Norton Res Corp Ltd Niagara Falls ON L2G 6S2 Can

PATCHICK, PAUL FRANCIS, b Los Angeles, Calif, July 22, 29; m 69; c 3. EARTH SCIENCE. *Educ:* Univ Calif, Los Angeles, BA, 52; Univ Southern Calif, MA, 59; Univ Minn, cert mgt concepts, 67; US Army Experimentation Command, cert systs anal, 67. *Prof Exp:* Proj mineralogist, UN Taejon Mineral Lab, Korea, 54-55; staff geologist, Am Potash & Chem Corp, Div Kerr McGee Industs, Inc, 57-59, Collier Carbon & Chem Corp, 60 & Harvey Aluminum Co, 60; asst city geologist, City of Los Angeles, 61; tech adv groundwater develop, Land & Water Resources Div, UN Food & Agr Orgn, El Salvador, 61-63; staff hydrogeologist, Edward E Johnson Div, Universal Oil Prod Co, 64-66; prin scientist, Systs & Res Ctr, Honeywell, Inc, 66-67; sr scientist, Sci Support Lab, Appl Res Dept, Litton Systs, Inc, 67-71; sr partner, Shaw/Patchick & Assocs, 71-76; staff scientist, Atlantic Richfield Hanford Co/Rockwell Hanford Co, 77; PROJ MGR, EXPLOR DEPT, OFF NUCLEAR WASTE ISOLATION, BATTELLE PROJ MGT DIV, 78- *Concurrent Pos:* Guest lectr, Seoul Nat Univ, 53; vis prof, Univ El Salvador, 62-63; Ministry Agr deleg, Govt El Salvador, Third Caribbean Geol Cong, 62; guest lectr AID water develop courses, Univ Minn, 64-65; consult hydrogeologist, UN Develop Prog, Develop & Resources Corp-AID, 66. *Mem:* Fel Geol Soc Am; AAAS; Am Inst Prof Geologists. *Res:* Salt-dome hydrology; water-well perennial yield prediction; water-well specific capacity prediction; development of water from volcanic pyroclastics; geophysics of pyroclastics; terrain analysis by computer; terrain modeling and simulation; hydrogeology of basalt flows. *Mailing Add:* Off Nuclear Waste Isolation 505 King Ave Columbus OH 43201

PATCHING, THOMAS, b Etzikom, Alta, Oct 2, 15; m 40; c 5. MINING ENGINEERING. *Educ:* Univ Alta, BSc, 36. *Prof Exp:* Mining engr, Int Nickel Co Can Ltd, 36-42 & Hudson Bay Mining & Smelting Co, Ltd, 42-47; from asst prof to assoc prof mining eng, 47-72, prof, 72-80, EMER PROF MINING ENG, UNIV ALTA, 80- *Concurrent Pos:* Tech officer, Fuels & Mining Practice Div, Dept Mines & Tech Surv, Can, 56-60. *Mem:* Can Inst Mining & Metall (pres, 71-72). *Res:* Stratastress studies; outbursts of coal and gas. *Mailing Add:* Dept Mineral Eng Univ Alta Edmonton AB T6G 2G7 Can

PATE, BRIAN DAVID, b London, Eng, Feb 11, 28; Can citizen; m 51; c 5. CHEMISTRY. *Educ:* Univ London, BSc, 49, MSc, 51; McGill Univ, PhD(chem), 55. *Prof Exp:* Res assoc chem, McGill Univ, 55-56; from res assoc chem to assoc chemist, Brookhaven Nat Lab, 56-59; assoc prof chem, Wash Univ, 59-64; head dept, Simon Fraser Univ, 64-68, prof chem, 64-77; PROF PHARM CHEM, UNIV BC, 78-, TRIUMF ASSOC DIR, APPL PROG, 77-, DIR PROG POSITRON EMMISSION TOMOGRAPHY, 81- *Mem:* Fel Chem Inst Can. *Res:* Radiopharmaceutical chemistry; positron emission tomography; trace-elements in human hair. *Mailing Add:* TRIUMF Univ of BC Vancouver BC V6T 1W5 Can

PATE, FINDLAY MOYE, b Davisboro, Ga, Jan 24, 41; m 61; c 4. ANIMAL NUTRITION. *Educ:* Univ Ga, BS, 65, PhD(animal nutrit), 70; Ore State Univ, MS, 67. *Prof Exp:* Asst prof & asst animal nutritionist, ASSOC PROF ANIMAL NUTRIT & ASSOC ANIMAL NUTRITIONIST, INST FOOD & AGR SCI, AGR RES & EDUC CTR, UNIV FLA, 77- *Mem:* Am Soc Animal Sci. *Res:* Beef cattle nutrition; mineral metabolism. *Mailing Add:* Agr Res & Educ Ctr Univ of Fla Belle Glade FL 33430

PATE, JAMES WYNFORD, b Wedowee, Ala, Aug 28, 28; m 48; c 3. MEDICINE. *Educ:* Med Col Ga, MD, 50. *Prof Exp:* Resident surgeon, Med Col, Univ Ala, 53-55; resident thoracic surgeon, Vet Admin Hosp, Memphis, Tenn, 55-57, asst chief thoracic surg, 57-59; asst prof surg, 59-65, chmn dept thoracic surg, 65-74, PROF SURG, COL MED, UNIV TENN, MEMPHIS, 65-, CHMN DEPT, 74- *Concurrent Pos:* Dir training, City Hosps, Memphis, 59-; consult, Vet Admin Hosp, Memphis, 59- & Naval Hosp, 61- *Mem:* Am Asn Thoracic Surgeons; Soc Vascular Surg; Am Col Surgeons; Am Col Chest Physicians; Soc Thoracic Surg. *Res:* Thoracic and heart surgery; homografts of tissues and organs. *Mailing Add:* 951 Court Ave Memphis TN 38103

PATEK, ARTHUR JACKSON, JR, b Milwaukee, Wis, May 6, 04; m 32; c 2. MEDICINE. *Educ:* Harvard Univ, BA, 26, MD, 30. *Prof Exp:* Asst med, Harvard Med Sch, 32-34, instr, 34-36; assoc, Col Physicians & Surgeons, Columbia Univ, 36-41, asst prof, 41-46, asst clin prof, 46-50; prof, Western Reserve Univ, 50-52; from assoc clin prof to clin prof, Col Physicians & Surgeons, Columbia Univ, 52-68; chief hepat sect, Med Serv, Vet Admin Hosp, Boston, 68-74; prof med, Sch Med, Tufts Univ, 68-76, emer prof med, 76-81. *Concurrent Pos:* From asst resident physician to resident physician, Thorndike Mem Lab, Boston City Hosp, Mass, 32-36; chief med, Mt Sinai Hosp, Cleveland, Ohio, 50-52, asst attend physician, Presby Hosp; chief med, St Barnabas Hosp, 54-65; attend physician, Goldwater Mem Hosp, 58-68 & med serv, Vet Admin Hosp, 74- *Mem:* Am Soc Clin Invest; Soc Exp Biol & Med; Harvey Soc; fel AMA; Asn Am Physicians. *Res:* Iron deficiency anemia; hemophilia; cirrhosis of the liver; diseases of nutrition. *Mailing Add:* Vet Admin Hosp 150 S Huntington Ave Boston MA 02130

PATEK, DAVID RUSHTON, neuropharmacology, see previous edition

PATEL, ANILBHAI S, b Baroda, India, June 28, 39. BIOMEDICAL ENGINEERING. *Educ:* Univ Baroda, BEE, 60; Purdue Univ, MS, 63; Northwestern Univ, PhD(biomed eng), 66. *Prof Exp:* Jr engr, Koyna Hydro-Elec Proj, 60-61; fel vision res, Biomed Engr Ctr, Northwestern Univ, 66-67; sr res bioengr, Baxter-Travenol Labs Inc, 68-74; prin scientist & biomed engr, Cavitron Corp, 74-80, PRIN SCIENTIST, SYNTEL-CAVITRON CORP, 80- *Mem:* AAAS; Inst Elec & Electronics Engrs; Asn Advan Med Instrumentation. *Res:* Human vision; artificial kidney, heart and valves; cardio-respiratory and neonatal special care devices; pulmonary function testing; application of fluidics, ultrasound, ultraviolet, infrared and laser technologies in medicine and dentistry. *Mailing Add:* 1902 Mcgaw Ave Syntel-Cavitron Corp Irvine CA 92714

PATEL, APPASAHEB RAOJIBHAI, b Baroda, India, Sept 15, 31; m 64; c 5. PHARMACEUTICAL CHEMISTRY. *Educ:* Univ Baroda, BSc, 52, MSc, 55; Univ Calif, PhD(pharmaceut chem), 60. *Prof Exp:* Fel chem, Univ Va, 61-63; res chemist, Leo Pharmaceut Prod, Denmark, 63-64; fel chem, Univ Va, 65-68; sr org chemist, Life Sci Div, Melpar, Inc, Va, 68-70; supvr org & anal chem lab, Life Sci Div, Meloy Labs, Inc, 70-77; prog mgr info & resources segment, 77-78, chemist, Toxicol Br, Carcinogenesis Testing Prog, 78-79, PROG DIR, DIET & NUTRIT, DIV CANCER CAUSE & PREV, NAT CANCER INST, BETHESDA, 79- *Mem:* Am Chem Soc. *Res:* Synthesis of quinoline-methanols as potential therapeutics; cigarette smoke condensate production, fractionation and analysis; tobacco and marijuana analysis; synthesis and analysis of carcinogens. *Mailing Add:* 215 Audrey's Ct Vienna VA 22180

PATEL, ARVINDKUMAR MOTIBHAI, b Isnav, India, Oct 19, 37; m 63; c 3. COMPUTER SCIENCE, SYSTEMS ENGINEERING. *Educ:* Sardar Vallabhbai Vidyapith, India, BE, 59; Univ Ill, Urbana, MS, 61; Univ Colo, Boulder, PhD(elec eng), 69. *Prof Exp:* Lectr elec eng, Birla Eng Col, India, 59-60; sr assoc engr circuit design, 62-65, staff engr systs design, 65-69, adv engr systs reliability, 69-72, SR ENGR, GEN PROD DIV, IBM CORP, 74- *Mem:* Inst Elec & Electronics Engrs. *Res:* Error correcting codes, signal coding, magnetic recording and computer systems reliability. *Mailing Add:* IBM Corp 5600 Cottle Rd San Jose CA 95193

PATEL, CHANDRA KUMAR NARANBHAI, b Baramati, India, July 2, 38; US citizen; m 61; c 2. PHYSICS, ENGINEERING. *Educ:* Univ Poona, BE, 58; Stanford Univ, MS, 59, PhD(elec eng), 61. *Prof Exp:* Mem tech staff, 61-67, head, Infrared Physics & Electronics Res Dept, 67-70, dir, Electronics Res Labs, 70-76, dir, Phys Res Lab, 76-81, EXEC DIR, PHYS RES DIV, BELL LABS, 81- *Concurrent Pos:* Mem bd trustees, Aerospace Corp, Los Angeles, 79- *Honors & Awards:* Adolph Lomb Medal, Optical Soc Am, 66; Ballantine Medal, Franklin Inst, 68; Coblentz Award, Coblentz Soc-Am Am Chem Soc, 74; Honor Award, Assoc Indians in America, 75; Zworykin Award, Nat Acad Eng, 76; Lamme Medal, Inst Elec & Electronics Engrs, 76. *Mem:* Nat Acad Sci; Nat Acad Eng; fel Am Phys Soc; fel Optical Soc Am; fel Am Acad Arts & Sci. *Res:* Gas lasers; molecular lasers in the infrared; high power lasers; nonlinear optics; tunable lasers in the infrared; high resolution spectroscopy; pollution detection in the atmosphere and the stratosphere; use of lasers in surgery. *Mailing Add:* Phys Res Div Bell Labs Murray Hill NJ 07974

PATEL, DALI JEHANGIR, b Agra, India; US citizen; m 57; c 3. MEDICINE, BIOPHYSICS. *Educ:* Grant Med Col, Bombay, MB, BS, 48; Univ Utah, MS, 55; Univ Western Ont, PhD(biophys), 57. *Prof Exp:* Intern, White Mem Hosp, Col Med Evangelists, Los Angeles, 50-51; resident pediat cardiol, Irvington House, NY Univ, 51-52; res asst biophys, Univ Western Ont, 55-57; vis scientist, Nat Heart Inst, 58-62, med officer, Sect Exp Atherosclerosis, 62-79; RES PROF DEPT PHYSIOL & BIOPHYS, COL MED, HOWARD UNIV, 79- *Concurrent Pos:* Fel med, Med Ctr, Univ Calif, San Francisco, 52-53; fel cardiol, Col Med, Univ Utah, 53-55, Am Heart Asn fel, 57-58. *Mem:* Am Physiol Soc. *Res:* Cardiac physiology; circulatory physics; atherosclerosis; preventive cardiology. *Mailing Add:* The Waterford Apt 601 3333 Univ Blvd W Kensington MD 20895

PATEL, GIRISHCHANDRA BABUBHAI, b Mombasa, Kenya, Nov 10, 48; Can citizen; m 74; c 1. FOOD MICROBIOLOGY. *Educ:* Sardar Patel Univ, India, BSc, 69; Univ Sask, Can, MSc, 72, PhD(agr microbiol), 74. *Prof Exp:* Lectr dairy technol, Dairy Sci Col, Sardar Patel Univ, India, 69-70; res asst, Dairy & Food Sci Dept, Univ Sask, Can, 70-71, qual control analyst, 70-72, lab instr, 73-74; fel, 74-75, res assoc food microbiol, 75-76, asst res officer, 76-80, ASSOC RES OFFICER, DIV BIOL SCI, NAT RES COUN CAN, OTTAWA, 80- *Honors & Awards:* Bapuji Desai Gold Medal. *Mem:* Can Soc Microbiologists; Can Inst Food Sci & Technol. *Res:* Isolation, characterization and metabolic studies of the microflora present in anaerobic digestion processes. *Mailing Add:* Div of Biol Sci Nat Res Coun of Can Ottawa ON K1A 0R6 Can

PATEL, GORDHAN, b Lourenco Marques, Mozambique, June 12, 36; US citizen; m 64; c 2. MOLECULAR BIOLOGY. *Educ:* Wash Univ, AB, 59, PhD(zool, nuclear proteins), 64. *Prof Exp:* Res assoc biol, State Univ NY Buffalo, 64-67; from asst prof to assoc prof, 67-81, PROF ZOOL & BIOCHEM, UNIV GA, 81-, HEAD ZOOL, 81- *Mem:* AAAS; Am Soc Cell Biol. *Res:* Role of eukaryotic nuclear proteins in chromatin structure and function, and in regulation of nuclear functions. *Mailing Add:* Dept of Zool Univ of Ga Athens GA 30602

PATEL, GORDHANBHAI NATHALAL, b Manund, Gujarat, India, Feb 2, 42; c 2. PHYSICAL CHEMISTRY, POLYMER SCIENCE. *Educ:* Sardar Patel Univ, India, BS, 64, MS, 66, PhD(polymers), 70. *Prof Exp:* Res asst polymers, Univ Bristol, 70-73; res assoc radiation, Baylor Univ, 73-74; STAFF CHEMIST POLYMERS, ALLIED CHEM CORP, 74- *Mem:* Am Chem Soc. *Res:* Polymer synthesis, characterization and uses; radio chemical changes in polymer; indicators for time, temperature and radiation dosages. *Mailing Add:* Allied Chem Corp Mat Res Ctr Morristown NJ 07960

PATEL, JAMSHED R(UTTONSHAW), b Calcutta, India, Mar 1, 25; US citizen; m 51; c 3. PHYSICAL METALLURGY. *Educ:* Mass Inst Technol, SB, 49, SM, 51, ScD(metall), 54. *Prof Exp:* Asst mech eng, Mass Inst Technol, 49-51, asst phys metall, 51-53; sr engr, Electronics Div, Sylvania Elec Prod, Inc, 53-55; mem res staff, Res Div, Raytheon Co, 55-61; MEM TECH STAFF, BELL TEL LABS, 61- *Mem:* Am Phys Soc. *Res:* Phase transformations; semiconductors; crystal growth; defects in crystals; plastic deformation; dislocations. *Mailing Add:* Bell Tel Labs Murray Hill NJ 07971

PATEL, KALYANJI U, b Kothamdi, India, Dec 23, 25; m 57; c 3. ORGANIC CHEMISTRY, CHEMICAL ENGINEERING. *Educ:* Univ Bombay, BSc, 49; Univ Mich, BS, 51; Mich State Univ, MS, 53, PhD(chem eng), 54. *Prof Exp:* Chemist & chem engr, Micarta Div Eng Lab, Westinghouse Elec Corp, 54-55 & Cent Res Lab, Bordon Chem Co, 56-59; SR CHEM ENGR & CHEMIST, CHEM DIV, 3M CO, 59- *Res:* Surface catalysis; organic synthesis; polymers and plastics; organic coatings; thermoplastics; thermoset polymers; air flotation; synthesis of functional monomers and polymers; fluorochemicals, elastomers and plastics. *Mailing Add:* 3037 Bartelmy Lane St Paul MN 55109

PATEL, MULCHAND SHAMBHUBHAI, b Sipor, India, Sept 9, 39. BIOCHEMISTRY. *Educ:* Gujarat Univ, India, BSc, 61; M S Univ Baroda, MSc, 64; Univ Ill, Urbana, PhD(animal sci), 68. *Prof Exp:* Teacher sci, Ahmedabad, India, 61-62; chemist, Alembic Chem Works, Ltd, Baroda, 62; res asst microbiol, M S Univ Baroda, 64-65; res asst nutrit biochem, Univ Ill, Urbana, 65-68; asst prof res pediat, St Christopher's Hosp Children, 70-72; res asst prof biochem, Temple Univ, 70-75, asst prof res med, 72-75, res assoc prof med & biochem, Sch Med, 75-78; ASSOC PROF BIOCHEM, CASE WESTERN RESERVE UNIV, 78- *Concurrent Pos:* NIH fel biochem, Fels Res Inst, Sch Med, Temple Univ, 68-69; NIH res grants, St Christopher's Hosp Children 71-72, Temple Univ, 72-78 & Case Western Reserve Univ, 78- *Mem:* Brit Biochem Soc; Am Inst Nutrit; Am Soc Biol Chemists; Am Soc Neurochem; Geront Soc. *Res:* Regulation of carbohydrate and lipid metabolism in developing mammalian brain and liver; inborn errors in amino acid and carbohydrate metabolism, diabetes, aging. *Mailing Add:* Dept Biochem Case Western Reserve Univ Cleveland OH 44106

PATEL, NAGIN K, b Navsari, India, June 17, 32; m 62; c 1. PHYSICAL PHARMACY. *Educ:* Gujarat Univ, India, BPharm, 55; Temple Univ, MS, 57; Univ Md, PhD(pharm), 61. *Prof Exp:* Jr instr pharm, Univ Md, 57-61; instr & fel, Temple Univ, 61-62; asst prof, Duquesne Univ, 62-63 & Univ Man, 63-66; from asst prof to assoc prof, Univ Alta, 66-69; res pharmacist, Frank W Horner, Ltd, 69-70, supvr pharm develop, Res Labs, 70-80; group leader explor res, McNeil CPC, 80-81; ASSOC PROF INDUST PHARM, ARNOLD & MARIE SCHWARTZ COL PHARM, LONG ISLAND UNIV, 81- *Concurrent Pos:* Nat Res Coun Can grant, 64-67. *Mem:* Am Pharmaceut Asn; Soc Cosmetic Chem; Indian Pharmaceut Asn. *Res:* Drug-macromolecular proteins, plastics, surfactants, interaction; sustained release dosage and tableting technologies. *Mailing Add:* 15648 du Bosquet Pierrefords Ste Genevieve PQ H9H 1X2 Can

PATEL, NARAYAN GANESH, b Sinaj-na-pura, India, May 5, 28; m 57; c 2. TOXICOLOGY. *Educ:* Univ Bombay, BSc, 50; Univ Poona, MSc, 52; Univ Minn, PhD(toxicol), 59. *Prof Exp:* Entom officer, Bombay Govt, 51-55; res asst entom, Univ Minn, 56-59, res fel toxicol, 59-63, res assoc, 63-64; sr res assoc, Case Western Reserve Univ, 64-69; BIOLOGIST & BIOCHEMIST, CENT RES DEPT, EXP STA, E I DU PONT DE NEMOURS & CO, INC, 69- *Concurrent Pos:* Adj prof, Univ Del, 71- *Mem:* AAAS; Entom Soc Am; Soc Develop Biol; Am Soc Cell Biol; Sigma Xi. *Res:* Physiology, toxicology, endocrinology, developmental biology and biochemistry of insect and invertebrates. *Mailing Add:* Cent Res Dept Exp Sta E I du Pont de Nemours & Co Inc Wilmington DE 19898

PATEL, NUTANKUMAR T, b Cambay, Gujarat State, India. BIOCHEMISTRY, MOLECULAR BIOLOGY. *Educ:* Univ Baroda, BS, 56, MS, 58; Univ Bombay, PhD(biochem), 70. *Prof Exp:* Res asst biochem, Univ Baroda, 58-59, demonstr, 59-61; sci officer biochem, Cancer Res Inst, Bombay, India, 62-71; fel biochem, 71-79, RES SCIENTIST, UNIV TEX MED BR, GALVESTON, 79- *Concurrent Pos:* Prin investr, Am Cancer Soc Institnl Grant Comt, 76-77. *Mem:* AAAS; Sigma Xi. *Res:* Molecular biology of cancer and chemical carcinogenesis, mRNA processing and transport; enzymology; nucleic acids and proteins; chemistry and metabolism. *Mailing Add:* Biochem Div Univ Tex Med Br Galveston TX 77550

PATEL, P(ARBHUBHAI) D(AHYABHAI), b Minkachh, India, Sept 9, 39; c 2. MECHANICAL ENGINEERING, AERONAUTICAL ENGINEERING. *Educ:* Univ Baroda, BE, 62; Columbia Univ, MS, 63, DEngSc(mech & aeronaut eng), 68. *Prof Exp:* Res engr, Foster Wheeler Corp, 64-69; mem tech staff mach aids anal, 69-79, MEM TECH STAFF LIGHTGUIDE CABLE DESIGN & DEVELOP, BELL LABS, 79- *Mem:* Am Soc Mech Engrs. *Res:* Shell theory; thermal stresses; heat conduction with change of phase; electromagnetic theory; lightguide cable design. *Mailing Add:* Bell Labs North Andover MA 01845

PATEL, POPAT-CAL MULJI-BHAI, b Nairobi, Kenya, July 7, US citizen; m 60; c 3. HIGH ENERGY PHYSICS. *Educ:* Manchester Univ, BSc, 55, MSc, 56; Harvard Univ, PhD(physics), 62. *Prof Exp:* Res assoc physics, Mass Inst Technol, 62-65, asst prof, 62-68; assoc prof, 68-81, PROF PHYSICS, MCGILL UNIV, 81- *Mem:* Am Phys Soc; Can Asn Physicists (secy, 71-76); Can Inst Particle Physics. *Res:* Nucleon-nucleon polarization; nucleon Compton effect; pi-zero photoproduction; boson spectroscopy; electromagnetic interactions of nucleons at high energies. *Mailing Add:* Dept Physics McGill Univ Montreal PQ H3A 2T8 Can

PATEL, PRAFULL RAOJIBHAI, b Nadiad, India, Nov 27, 37; m 69; c 1. DENTAL RESEARCH. *Educ:* Univ Baroda, BSc, 58; Univ Bombay, BSc, 60; Columbia Univ, MS, 62; Univ Mich, PhD(pharmaceut chem), 65; Univ Md, DDS, 78. *Prof Exp:* Asst chem, Col Pharm, Columbia Univ, 60-62; asst phys pharm, Univ Mich, 62-63, res asst, 63-65; res assoc, Res Unit, Am Dent Asn Health Found, 65-74 & 79-81. *Mem:* Am Dent Asn. *Res:* Solubility properties of synthetic and biological calcium phosphate minerals; clinical evaluation of biomaterials. *Mailing Add:* 19140 St Johnsbury Lane Germantown MD 20874

PATEL, RUTTON DINSHAW, b Darjeeling, India, June 26, 42; m 70. CHEMICAL ENGINEERING. *Educ:* Indian Inst Technol, Kharagpur, BTech, 63; Purdue Univ, MS, 66, PhD(chem eng), 67. *Prof Exp:* Resident student assoc chem eng, Argonne Nat Lab, 66-67; vis asst prof, Purdue Univ, 67-68; from asst prof to assoc prof, Polytech Inst New York, 68-78; sr eng, 78-81, ENG ASSOC, EXXON RES & ENG CO, 81- *Honors & Awards:* Acharya P C Ray Award, Indian Inst Chem Engrs, 64. *Mem:* Am Inst Chem Engrs; Am Chem Soc; AAAS; Sigma Xi. *Res:* Heat and mass transfer; pulsatile flow and transfer; fluidization; thermal fouling and cooking. *Mailing Add:* Exxon Res & Eng Co PO Box 101 Florham Park NJ 07932

PATEL, SAVINAY S, b Ajarpura, India, Apr 8, 37; m 72; c 1. FOOD SCIENCE. *Educ:* Maharaja Sayajirao Univ, India, BSc, 58; Bombay Univ, BSc, 60; Cornell Univ, MS & PhD(food sci), 68. *Prof Exp:* Mgr res, J H Filbert, Inc, 70-73; res scientist, 73-78, SR SCIENTIST, CENT SOYA, INC, 78- *Mem:* Inst Food Technol; Am Oil Chemist Soc. *Res:* Fats and oils; product and process development. *Mailing Add:* Cent Soya Inc 1300 Fort Wayne Bank Bldg Fort Wayne IN 46802

PATEL, SHARAD A, b Ahmedabad, India, Aug 29, 25; US citizen; m 58; c 3. ELECTRICAL & MECHANICAL ENGINEERING. *Educ:* Benares Hindu Univ, BSc, 49; Polytech Inst Brooklyn, MAeE, 51, PhD(appl mech), 55. *Prof Exp:* Res assoc aerospace eng & appl mech, 54-56, from asst prof to prof appl mech, 56-76, PROF MECH & AEROSPACE ENG, POLYTECH INST NEW YORK, 76- *Mem:* Assoc fel Am Inst Aeronaut & Astronaut. *Res:* Elasticity; plasticity; creep; structural dynamics; applied and solid mechanics. *Mailing Add:* Dept of Appl Mech 333 Jay St Brooklyn NY 11201

PATEL, SIDDHARTH MANILAL, b Santi-Niketan, WBengal, India, Oct 26, 33; m 61; c 3. ANALYTICAL CHEMISTRY, POLLUTION CHEMISTRY. *Educ:* Univ Bombay, BSc, 54, MSc, 57; Ohio State Univ, PhD(anal chem), 66. *Prof Exp:* Teaching asst anal chem, Ohio State Univ, 59-66; sr res chemist, 66-73, GROUP LEADER ENVIRON GROUP, QUANT ANAL SECT, GOODYEAR TIRE & RUBBER CO, 73- *Concurrent Pos:* Lectr, Univ Akron, 67-68 & 70-71. *Mem:* Am Chem Soc. *Res:* Environmental analytical methodology; analytical methods of industrial hygiene; process analysis systems; chromatography; spectroscopy and mass spectrometry. *Mailing Add:* 735 Cliffside Dr Akron OH 44313

PATEL, VIRENDRA C, b Mombasa, Kenya, Nov 9, 38; m 66; c 2. FLUID MECHANICS, HYDRAULICS. *Educ:* Imp Col, Univ London, BSc, 62; Univ Cambridge, PhD(fluid mech), 65. *Prof Exp:* Asst res fluid mech, Univ Cambridge, 65; asst prof aeronaut eng, Indian Inst Technol, Kharagpur, 66-67; sr asst res fluid mech, Univ Cambridge, 67-69; consult aeronaut, Lockheed-Ga Co, 69-70; from asst prof to assoc prof mech & hydraul, 71-75, PROF ENERGY ENG, UNIV IOWA, 75-, CHMN DIV ENERGY ENG, 76-, CHMN MECH ENG DIV, 76- *Concurrent Pos:* Res engr, Iowa Inst Hydraul Res, 71-; consult in field, Iowa Gov's Sci Adv Coun, 77-; mem resistance comt, Int Towing Tank Conf, 78-; vis prof, Univ Fridericiana, Karlsruhe, WGer, 80-81; US sr scientist award, Alexander von Humboldt Found, WGer, 80-81. *Mem:* Am Inst Aeronaut & Astronaut; Am Soc Mech Engrs; Sigma Xi. *Res:* Viscous fluid mechanics; turbulence; industrial aerodynamics. *Mailing Add:* Div Energy Eng Univ of Iowa Iowa City IA 52242

PATEL, VITHALBHAI AMBALAL, b Dec 26, 36; Indian citizen; m 60; c 2. APPLIED MATHEMATICS. *Educ:* VP Col, Vallabh Vidyanagar, India, BSc, 57, MSc, 59; Univ Calif, Berkeley, PhD(eng sci), 70. *Prof Exp:* Tutor math, V P Col, Vallabh Vidyanagar, India, 57-59, lectr, 59; lectr, Sardar Patel Univ, 61-63 & MG Sci Inst, Ahmedabad, 63-65; asst, Univ Calif, Berkeley, 65-69; asst prof, Calif State Univ, Humboldt, 69-73; assoc prof, 73-78, PROF MATH, HUMBOLDT STATE UNIV, 78- *Mem:* Soc Indust & Appl Math; Soc Eng Sci. *Res:* Numerical solutions of the Navier-Stokes equations for the flows around the obstacles; solutions of the simultaneous equations. *Mailing Add:* Dept of Math Humboldt State Univ Arcata CA 95527

PATEL, VITHALBHAI L, b Samathiara, India, Mar 31, 35; US citizen; m 52; c 2. PLASMA PHYSICS, SPACE PHYSICS. *Educ:* Univ Baroda, BSc, 56; Univ Md, MS, 60; Univ NH, PhD(physics), 64. *Prof Exp:* Res asst physics, Phys Res Lab, Ahmedabad, India, 56-58 & Univ Md, 58-61; res asst, Univ NH, 61-63, instr, 64-65; sr res assoc, Rice Univ, 65-66; from asst prof to assoc prof, 66-75, PROF PHYSICS, UNIV DENVER, 75- *Concurrent Pos:* NSF & NASA res grants, 67-; vis assoc prof, Dept Physics & Space Sci Ctr, Univ Minn, Minneapolis, 70-71; mem, Int Asn Geomag & Aeronomy; consult, NASA, 71-; vis scientist, Dept Physics, Mass Inst Technol, 77-78. *Mem:* Univs Space Res Asn; fel Am Phys Soc; Am Geophys Union. *Res:* Interplanetary magnetic field and plasma; plasma physics of the magnetosphere; space and astrophysical problems; geophysics. *Mailing Add:* Dept of Physics Univ of Denver Denver CO 80208

PATEL, YOGENDRA M, toxicology, biochemistry, see previous edition

PATEL-MANDLIK KUSUM J, b India, May 27, 35; US citizen; m 71; c 1. ANIMAL EXPERIMENTS, ELECTRON MICROSCOPY. *Educ:* Univ Bombay, BSc, 56, MSc, 59; Univ Wis-Madison, MS, 62, PhD, 65. *Prof Exp:* ASST PROF, UNIV ILL, 80- *Concurrent Pos:* Prin investr, US Environ Protection Agency projs. *Mem:* Midwest Soc Electron Microscopists. *Res:* Identification of various types of asbestos and its electron diffraction pattern; neurobiology; in vitro respiration and oxidative metabolism; ultrastructural and biochemical correlation of mammalian tissue metabolism; medical entomology; agricultural entomology. *Mailing Add:* 5662 W Sunnyside Chicago IL 60630

PATENAUDE, ROBERT ALAN, algebra, see previous edition

PATENT, GREGORY JOSEPH, b Hong Kong, May 5, 39; US citizen; m 64; c 2. COMPARATIVE ENDOCRINOLOGY. *Educ:* Univ Calif, Berkeley, 61, MA, 65, PhD(zool), 68. *Prof Exp:* Actg asst prof zool, Univ Calif, Berkeley, 68-69; NIH fel, Zool Sta, Naples, Italy, 69-70; asst prof biol, ECarolina Univ, 70-72; from asst prof to assoc prof, 72-82, PROF ZOOL, UNIV MONT, 82- *Concurrent Pos:* NIH trainee, Div Res, Sinai Hosp, Detroit, Mich, 68-69; res grant, NIH, 75; travel grant, NSF, 75. *Mem:* AAAS; Am Soc Zoologists; NY Acad Sci. *Res:* Endocrinology of carbohydrate metabolism in fishes; factors affecting insulin release in vertebrates; cytology and innervation of pancreatic islets; neural regulation of insulin release. *Mailing Add:* Dept of Zool Univ of Mont Missoula MT 59812

PATER, RUTH HSIEH, b Pingtung, China, May 21, 39; US citizen. POLYMER MATRIX COMPOSITES, ADHESIVES. *Educ:* Tamkang Col, BS, 62; Southeastern Mass Univ, MS, 72; Brown Univ, PhD(org chem), 77. *Prof Exp:* Instr gen chem, Tamkang Col, 62-63; vis lectr org & anal chem, Southeastern Mass Univ, 76-77; res assoc, Brown Univ, 77-78; res scientist, United Technol Res Ctr, 78-80; RES CHEMIST, LEWIS RES CTR, NASA, 80- *Mem:* Am Chem Soc; Soc Advan Mat & Process Eng; Adhesion Soc. *Res:* Synthesis and development of high temperature matrix resins and adhesives for aerospace applications; composite fabrication, testing and evaluation; composite surface analysis; interface studies. *Mailing Add:* NASA Lewis Res Ctr MS 49-1 21000 Brookpark Rd Cleveland OH 44135

PATERNO, JOSEPH JOHN, JR, materials science, chemical engineering, see previous edition

PATERSON, ALAN ROBB PHILLIPS, b Nanaimo, BC, Nov 14, 23; m 45; c 2. BIOCHEMISTRY. *Educ:* Univ BC, BA, 50, MA, 52, PhD(biochem), 56. *Prof Exp:* Asst prof biochem, Univ BC, 58-62; PROF BIOCHEM, CANCER RES UNIT, UNIV ALTA, 62-, HON PROF PHARM & DIR McEACHERN LABS, 77- *Mem:* AAAS; Am Asn Cancer Res; Am Soc Biol Chemists; Can Biochem Soc. *Res:* Metabolism of nucleotides and nucleosides. *Mailing Add:* McEachern Lab Univ of Alta Cancer Res Unit Edmonton AB T6G 2E1 Can

PATERSON, ARTHUR RENWICK, b Dumfriesshire, Scotland, June 15, 22; nat US; m 48; c 4. ANALYTICAL CHEMISTRY. *Educ:* Davidson Col, BS, 43; Rutgers Univ, MS, 50, PhD(chem), 52. *Prof Exp:* Sect supvr phys & anal chem sect, 51-71, mgr chem physics dept, 71-78, dir res, Cent Res Lab, 78-80, DIR, ANAL SCI LAB, CORP RES & DEVELOP, ALLIED CHEM CORP, 80- *Mem:* AAAS; Am Chem Soc; Soc Appl Spectros; Am Soc Testing & Mat; Coblentz Soc. *Res:* Mass spectrometry; chromatography; absorption spectroscopy; polymer characterization. *Mailing Add:* 48 Loantaka Lane Morristown NJ 07960

PATERSON, CHRISTOPHER ALEXANDER, b Woking, Eng, Dec 21, 40; m 64; c 2. PHYSIOLOGY. *Educ:* Univ Sheffield, BSc, 63; Univ London, PhD(ocular physiol), 68. *Prof Exp:* Res asst ocular physiol, Inst Ophthal, Univ London, 65-68; assoc prof, 68-81, PROF OPHTHAL & PHYSIOL, UNIV COLO HEALTH SCI CTR, DENVER, 81- *Concurrent Pos:* Nat Eye Inst res grant, Univ Colo Health Sci Ctr, Denver, 69- *Mem:* AAAS; Am Physiol Soc; Asn Res Vision & Ophthal; NY Acad Sci. *Res:* Physiology of the ocular lens, intraocular pressure and cornea. *Mailing Add:* Ophthal Res Univ of Colo Med Ctr Denver CO 80262

PATERSON, DONALD ROBERT, b Burke, NY, Feb 25, 20; m 43; c 3. HORTICULTURE. *Educ:* Cornell Univ, BS, 47; Univ Calif, MS, 50; Mich State Univ, PhD, 52. *Prof Exp:* Asst county agr agent, NY Agr Exten Serv, 47-49; asst horticulturist, 52-56, assoc prof hort, Univ, 70-76, ASSOC HORTICULTURIST, TEX AGR RES & EXTEN CTR, TEX A&M UNIV, 56-, PROF HORT, UNIV, 76- *Mem:* AAAS; Am Soc Hort Sci; Am Soc Plant Physiol. *Res:* Plant growth regulators and mineral nutrition. *Mailing Add:* Drawer E Tex A&M Univ Res & Exten Ctr Overton TX 75684

PATERSON, JAMES LENANDER, b Minneapolis, Minn, Oct 20, 41; m 72; c 2. LOW TEMPERATURE PHYSICS. *Educ:* Yale Univ, BE, 63; Univ Calif, Berkeley, PhD(physics), 73. *Prof Exp:* ASST PROF PHYSICS, UNIV VA, 73- *Mem:* Am Phys Soc. *Res:* Nonequilibrium superconductivity, studying the characteristic response times. *Mailing Add:* Dept of Physics Univ of Va Charlottesville VA 22901

PATERSON, JAMES MCEWAN, b Falkirk, Scotland, Dec 1, 37; m 62. PARTICLE PHYSICS, ACCELERATORS. *Educ:* Univ Glasgow, BSc, 59, PhD(physics), 63. *Prof Exp:* Sr res assoc physics, Cambridge Electron Accelerator, Harvard Univ, 63-72; mem staff physics, Stanford Linear Accelerator Ctr, 72-80, ADJ PROF PHYSICS, STANFORD UNIV, 80- *Res:* Design and development of particle accelerators, in particular electron-positron storage rings and their use in elementary particle physics research. *Mailing Add:* Stanford Linear Accelerator Ctr PO Box 4349 Stanford CA 94305

PATERSON, MALCOLM CYRIL, radiation biophysics, medical biophysics, see previous edition

PATERSON, PHILIP Y, b Minneapolis, Minn, Feb 6, 25; m 47; c 3. INFECTIOUS DISEASES, MICROBIOLOGY. *Educ:* Univ Minn, BS, 46, BM, 47, MD, 48. *Prof Exp:* Instr med, Tulane Univ, 50-51; asst resident & co-resident, Sch Med, Univ Va, 53-55, asst prof microbiol & instr med, 55-57; from asst prof microbiol to assoc prof exp med, Sch Med, NY Univ, 57-65; Sackett prof med & chief infectious dis-hypersensitivity sect, McGaw Med Ctr, 66-75, PROF MICROBIOL & CHMN DEPT MICROBIOL & IMMUNOL, MED & DENT SCHS, NORTHWESTERN UNIV, CHICAGO, 75- *Concurrent Pos:* Am Heart Asn res fel, Sch Med, Tulane Univ, 49-50; Am Heart Asn res fel, 53; estab investr, Am Heart Asn, 55-57; med officer, NIH, 57-60. *Honors & Awards:* Snadel Gold Medal & lectr, Infectious Dis Soc Am, 78. *Mem:* Am Asn Physicians; Am Soc Microbiol; Infectious Dis Soc Am; Am Asn Immunologists; Am Soc Clin Invest. *Res:* Infectious diseases and immunology; experimental tissue damage; autoimmune disease; neuroimmunology. *Mailing Add:* Northwestern Univ 303 E Chicago Ave Chicago IL 60611

PATERSON, ROBERT ANDREW, b Reno, Nev, Jan 23, 26; m 56; c 3. BOTANY. *Educ:* Univ Nev, BA, 49; Stanford Univ, MA, 52; Univ Mich, PhD(bot), 57. *Prof Exp:* From instr to assoc prof bot, Univ Md, 56-67; prof bot & head, Dept Biol, 67-79, ASSOC DEAN, COL ARTS & SCI, VA POLYTECH INST & STATE UNIV, 79- *Concurrent Pos:* NSF grants, 60, 61 & 64 & antarctic fungi, McMurdo Sta, Antarctica, 71 & 72; investr, Mich Biol Sta, 60-67, vis prof, 67; consult, NSF, McMurdo Area, Antarctica, 72; investr Alaskan soil fungi, Dept Energy, 79-81. *Mem:* Bot Soc Am; Mycol Soc Am; Brit Mycol Soc. *Res:* Mycology; limnology; fungal parasites of plankton; lacustrine fungal saprophytes; aquatic Phycomycetes; Antarctic fungi; Antarctic ecosystems; Alaskan soil fungi. *Mailing Add:* Dept Biol Rm 3024 Derring Hall Va Polytech Inst & State Univ Blacksburg VA 24061

PATERSON, ROBERT W, b Jan 19, 39; m 67; c 1. AEROACOUSTICS, GAS DYNAMICS. *Educ:* Princeton Univ, BSE, 60; Harvard Univ, MA, 65, PhD(fluid mech), 69. *Prof Exp:* Nuclear power engr, Atomic Energy Comn, Naval Reactors Br, Washington, DC, 60-62, supvr 62-64; res asst, Div Eng & Appl Physics, Harvard Univ, 66-69; res engr, 69-73, supvr, Aeroacoustics Group, 73-75, MGR, AEROACOUSTICS & EXP GAS DYNAMICS GROUP, GAS DYNAMICS SECT, UNITED TECHNOL RES CTR, 75- *Mem:* Fel Am Inst Aeronaut & Astronaut; Am Soc Mech Engrs; Sigma Xi. *Res:* Aeroacoustics; experimental gas dynamics. *Mailing Add:* Aeroacoustics & Exp Gas Dynamics Group United Technologies Res Ctr East Hartford CT 06108

PATERSON, WILLIAM GORDON, b Montreal, Can. CHEMISTRY. *Educ:* Univ Man, BSc, 56, MSc, 57; McGill Univ, PhD(chem), 60. *Prof Exp:* NATO sci fel & Ramsay Mem fel, Oxford Univ, 60-61, asst prof chem, Univ Alta, 61-63; sr res chemist, 63-68, proj coordr, New Bus Ventures Div, 68-71, prog mgr, 71-73, proj mgr, 73-76, proj mgr, Com Tape Div, 76-77, DIV SALES MKT MGR, CHEM RES DIV, 3M CO, 77- . *Res:* Electrochemistry; synthetic inorganic chemistry; nuclear magnetic resonance; electrophotography; aquatic biology; plant nutrition; encapsulation; insect control. *Mailing Add:* 966 Woodlynn Ave St Paul MN 55113

PATES, ANNE LOUISE, b Monongahela, Pa, Mar 23, 13. BACTERIOLOGY. *Educ:* Fla State Col Women, BS, 36; Univ Mich, MS, 38, PhD(bact), 49. *Prof Exp:* Bacteriologist, Presby Hosp, Philadelphia, Pa, 38-44; instr, Sch 9, Univ Mo, 44-45; from asst prof to assoc prof bact, 49-74, assoc prof biol sci, 74-81, EMER PROF, FLA STATE UNIV, 81- *Mem:* AAAS; Am Soc Microbiol; fel Am Pub Health Asn. *Res:* Antigens of hisoplasma capsulation; avian botulism. *Mailing Add:* Dept of Biol Sci Fla State Univ Tallahassee FL 32306

PATHAK, KESHAV DATTATRAY, biochemistry, see previous edition

PATHAK, MADHUKAR, b Baroda, India, July 29, 27; m 53; c 3. BIOCHEMISTRY, PHOTOBIOLOGY. *Educ:* Univ Baroda, BSc, 48; Univ Bombay, BSc, 50, MB, 53; Univ Ore, MS, 58, PhD, 60. *Prof Exp:* Lectr & biochemist, Med Col, Univ Nagpur, 53-56; res asst biochem & dermat, Med Sch, Univ Ore, 56-60; res fel dermat, Harvard Med Sch, 60-61, from res assoc to assoc, 61-67, asst prof, 67-70, prin assoc dermat, 70-77; res assoc, 61-63, asst biochemist, 63-69, ASSOC BIOCHEMIST, MASS GEN HOSP, 69-; SR ASSOC RES PROF DERMAT, HARVARD MED SCH, 78- *Mem:* AAAS; Soc Invest Dermat; Am Fedn Clin Res; Biophys Soc; NY Acad Sci. *Res:* Skin Cancer; cutaneous photobiology, photochemistry and photosensitization; melanin pigmentation in mammals; porphyrin metabolism; normal and abnormal reactions of man to light; photo medicine. *Mailing Add:* Dept of Dermat Harvard Med Sch Boston MA 02114

PATHAK, SEN, b Azamgarh, India, July 13, 40; m 61; c 4. CYTOGENETICS. *Educ:* Banaras Hindu Univ, BS, 61, MS, 63, dipl Ger lang, 65, PhD(cytogenetics), 67. *Prof Exp:* Jr res fel zool, Coun Sci & Indust Res, New Delhi, 63-67; sr res asst cytogenetics, Banaras Hindu Univ, 68-70; fel path, Baylor Col Med, 70-72; prof investr cell biol, 72-73, res assoc, 73-74, asst prof & asst biologist, 74-78, ASSOC BIOLOGIST, M D ANDERSON HOSP TUMOR INST, 78-, ASSOC PROF, 81- *Concurrent Pos:* Vis prof, Univ de Sao Paulo, Brazil, 81- *Mem:* Am Soc Cell Biol; AAAS; Tissue Cult Asn Am; Genetics Soc Can; Indian Sci Cong Asn. *Res:* Human and mammalian cytogenetics using various chromosomal banding techniques, autoradiography and drug effects on normal and malignant mammalian and human cells; studies on fine structures of mammalian meiotic chromosomes; chromosome analysis in cancer families. *Mailing Add:* Dept of Biol M D Anderson Hosp & Tumor Inst Houston TX 77030

PATHRIA, RAJ KUMAR, b Ramdas, India, Sept 19, 33; m 58; c 3. THEORETICAL PHYSICS, STATISTICAL MECHANICS. *Educ:* Panjab Univ, BSc, 53, MSc, 54; Univ Delhi, PhD(physics), 57. *Prof Exp:* Lectr physics, Univ Delhi, 58-61, reader, 61-64; vis prof, McMaster Univ, 64-65 & Univ Alta, 65-67; prof theoret physics, Panjab Univ, 67-69; vis prof physics, Univ Waterloo, 69-70 & Univ Windsor, 70-71; assoc prof, 71-74, PROF PHYSICS, UNIV WATERLOO, 74- *Concurrent Pos:* Sr res fel, Nat Inst Sci, India, Delhi Univ, 60-61; vis prof fel, Univ Wales, 70. *Mem:* Am Phys Soc; Can Asn Physicists; Indian Physics Asn; Int Astron Union. *Res:* Statistical mechanics of finite systems; lattice sums; low-temperature physics and superfluidity; relativity and cosmology. *Mailing Add:* Dept of Physics Univ of Waterloo Waterloo ON N2L 3G1 Can

PATI, JOGESH CHANDRA, b Baripada, India, Apr 3, 37; m 61; c 4. THEORETICAL PHYSICS. *Educ:* Ravenshaw Col, Utkal, India, BSc, 55; Univ Delhi, MSc, 57; Univ Md, PhD(physics), 60. *Prof Exp:* Tolman fel physics, Calif Inst Technol, 60-62; mem staff, Inst Advan Study, 62-63; from asst prof to assoc prof, 63-72, PROF PHYSICS, UNIV MD, COLLEGE PARK, 72- *Concurrent Pos:* Vis scientist, Tata Inst Fundamental Res, India, Int Ctr Theoret Physics, Trieste, 66-67 & Europ Orgn Nuclear Res, 66-67 & 71; vis prof, Univ Delhi, 71-72, Europ Orgn Nuclear Res, 74 & Int Ctr Theoret Physics, Trieste, 74 & 75; John Simon Guggenheim Mem fel, 79. *Mem:* Am Phys Soc. *Res:* Theoretical elementary particle physics. *Mailing Add:* Dept Physics & Astron Univ Md College Park MD 20742

PATIL, GANAPATI P, b Sunasgaon, India, Feb 2, 34; m 59; c 4. STATISTICS, MATHEMATICS. *Educ:* Univ Poona, BSc, 54, MSc, 55; Univ Mich, MS & PhD(math), 59. *Hon Degrees:* DSc, Indian Statist Inst. *Prof Exp:* Assoc statist, Indian Statist Inst, Calcutta, 55-57; lectr math, Univ Mich, 59-61, res assoc, Res Inst, 59-60; from asst prof to assoc prof, McGill Univ, 61-64; PROF MATH STATIST, PA STATE UNIV, UNIVERSITY PARK, 64- *Concurrent Pos:* Fac consult, Cooley Electronics Lab, Univ Mich, 60-61 & Ord Res Lab, Pa State Univ, 64-66; consult, US Forest Serv, Environ Protection Agency & Nat Marine Fisheries Serv; consult & chmn liaison comn statist ecol, NIH; vis prof, Univ NSW, 67 & Univ Wis, 70. *Mem:* Fel AAAS; fel Am Statist Asn; fel Inst Math Statist; Math Asn Am; Int Statist Inst. *Res:* Discrete statistical models and methods; statistical inference; distribution theory; characterization problems; statistical ecology. *Mailing Add:* Dept of Statist Pa State Univ University Park PA 16802

PATIL, KASHINATH ZIPARU, b Maharashtra, India; m 55; c 3. INDUSTRIAL CATALYSTS, CATALYTIC PROCESSES. *Educ:* Univ Poona, BS, 51, MS, 53; Indian Inst Technol, MTech, 55. *Prof Exp:* Res asst, Indian Inst Sci, 55-56; sr res asst, Sindri Fertilizers & Chem, 57-58; catalyst chemist, W R Grace & Co, 61-67; sr res chemist, Mallinckrodt Chem, 67-73; SR RES CHEMIST, CATALYSIS, RES & DEVELOP CTR, M W KELLOGG CO, 74- *Concurrent Pos:* Abstractor, Chem Abstracts, Am Chem Soc, 65-75. *Mem:* Am Chem Soc; Catalysis Soc; Sigma Xi. *Res:* Catalytic and high pressure reactions; adsorption; catalysis and industrial catalysts; oxidation; hydrogenation; esterification; methanation; steam reforming processes; industrial catalysts. *Mailing Add:* 2914 Kevin Lane Houston TX 77043

PATIL, POPAT N, b Chinchkhede, India, Oct 26, 34; m 64; c 2. PHARMACOLOGY, PHYSIOLOGY. *Educ:* Gujarat Univ, India, BPharm, 56; Ohio State Univ, MS, 60, PhD(pharmacol), 63. *Prof Exp:* From res asst to res assoc, 59-65, asst prof, 65-68, assoc prof, 68-72, PROF PHARMACOL, OHIO STATE UNIV, 72- *Concurrent Pos:* Us sr scientist award, Alexander von Humboldt Found, 80. *Mem:* Am Soc Pharmacol & Exp Therapeut. *Res:* Steric aspects of adrenergic drugs; tachyphylaxis; molecular pharmacology; melanins. *Mailing Add:* Lloyd M Parks Hall Col Pharm 500 West 12th Ave Columbus OH 43210

PATIL, SURESH SIDDHESHWAR, b Sholapur, India, May 2, 35; m 65. PLANT PATHOLOGY. *Educ:* Univ Poona, BSc, 55; Ore State Univ, MS, 59, PhD(plant path), 62. *Prof Exp:* Asst plant path, Ore State Univ, 62-63; asst plant pathologist & Nat Inst Allergy & Infectious Dis res fel, Conn Agr Exp Sta, 63-69; assoc prof, 69-73, PROF PLANT PATH, UNIV HAWAII, 73- *Concurrent Pos:* Vis fel, Dept Biochem, Cambridge Univ, 75-76. *Mem:* AAAS; Am Phytopath Soc; Am Soc Plant Physiol. *Res:* Biochemistry of parasitism and host-pathogen relationships; bacterial phytotoxins; post-harvest pathophysiology; disease resistance. *Mailing Add:* St John Plant Sci Lab 3190 Maile Way Honolulu HI 96822

PATINKIN, SEYMOUR HAROLD, b Chicago, Ill, Mar 25, 26; m 56; c 1. ORGANIC CHEMISTRY. *Educ:* Ill Inst Technol, BS, 49, PhD(chem), 54. *Prof Exp:* Asst US Naval Ord contract, Ill Inst Technol, 50-51 & 52-53; res chemist, Sinclair Res, Inc, 53-66; assoc prof, 66-72, PROF CHEM, ROOSEVELT UNIV, 72- *Mem:* AAAS; Sigma Xi; Am Chem Soc. *Res:* Hydrocarbon chemistry; instrumental analysis; free radical chemistry; nuclear magnetic resonance; free radical reactions of organosilicons with aromatic compounds catalyzed with certain metal salts. *Mailing Add:* 4610 W Dempster St Skokie IL 60076

PATMORE, EDWIN LEE, b Connelsville, Pa, Dec 26, 34; m 58; c 2. ORGANIC CHEMISTRY, INORGANIC CHEMISTRY. *Educ:* Eastern Nazarene Col, BS, 58; Univ Conn, MS, 61, PhD(org chem), 63. *Prof Exp:* Chemist, Chem Res Sect, Beacon Res Labs, 62-63, sr chemist, 63-67, res chemist, Lubricants Res Sect, 67-72, group leader, 72-77, asst supvr, Lubricants Res Sect, 77-80, SUPVR, LUBRICANTS RES SECT, TEXACO, INC, 80- *Mem:* Am Chem Soc; Sigma Xi. *Res:* Organic synthesis; free radical chemistry of coordination compounds; oxidation; petrochemicals; carbanion reactions. *Mailing Add:* PO Box 174 Fishkill NY 12524

PATNAIK, AMIYA KRISHNA, b Orissa, India, Mar 19, 30; m 55; c 4. VETERINARY PATHOLOGY, COMPARATIVE ONCOLOGY. *Educ:* Madras Vet Col, DVM, 51, MS, 62. *Prof Exp:* Res officer salmonellosis, Govt Orissa, India, 62-63, res officer stephanofilariasis, 63-64, vet pathologist, State Vet Labs, 63-64; resident path, Animal Med Ctr, 64-67; pathologist, Food & Drug Res Lab, Inc, 66-68; STAFF PATHOLOGIST, ANIMAL MED CTR, 68- *Res:* Comparative oncology dealing with histology and histologic behavior and veterinary oncology; immunologic and therapeutic aspects of neoplasms; small animal diseases. *Mailing Add:* Animal Med Ctr 510 E 62nd St New York NY 10021

PATNODE, ROBERT ARTHUR, b Mankato, Minn, May 8, 18; m 46; c 3. IMMUNOLOGY. *Educ:* Univ Minn, BA, 44, MS, 46, PhD(bact), 53. *Prof Exp:* Bacteriologist, Tuberc Unit, Commun Dis Ctr, USPHS, Ga, 47-50, actg chief, 50-53; chief tuberc res lab, Vet Admin Hosp, Washington, DC, 53-60; assoc prof, 60-66, PROF MICROBIOL & IMMUNOL, HEALTH SCI CTR, UNIV OKLA, 66- *Concurrent Pos:* Consult grad coun, George Washington Univ, 59-60; vis prof microbiol, Univ Otago, New Zealand, 79. *Mem:* Am Thoracic Soc; Am Soc Microbiol; Am Asn Immunologists; fel Am Acad Microbiol. *Res:* Mechanisms of host resistance in tuberculosis; allergy and immunology in tuberculosis; delayed hypersensitivity. *Mailing Add:* Dept Microbiol & Immunol Univ Okla Health Sci Ctr Oklahoma City OK 73190

PATON, BRUCE CALDER, b Coonoor, India, Aug 28, 25; US citizen; m 55; c 3. CARDIOVASCULAR SURGERY. *Educ:* Univ Edinburgh, BM & ChB, 51; FRCS, 58; Am Bd Surg, dipl, 64. *Prof Exp:* Chief resident surg, Vet Admin Hosp, Denver, Colo, 59-60; dir, Halstead Lab Exp Surg, 60-74, from instr to assoc prof, 60-70, PROF SURG & ACTING DEAN, UNIV COLO MED CTR, DENVER, 70-, CHIEF CARDIAC SURG SERV, 74- *Concurrent Pos:*

Fulbright scholar, 53-55; NIH fel, 60-61; prin investr, USPHS grants, 60-74 & Am Heart Asn grants, 64-69; vis prof, Univ Med Sci, Bangkok, 64; mem exec comt coun cardiovasc surg, Am Heart Asn, 70-74; mem surg study sect, NIH, 71-75. *Honors & Awards:* William Leslie Prize in Med, 56. *Mem:* Am Surg Asn; Am Asn Thoracic Surg; Soc Vascular Surg; Soc Univ Surgeons; Int Cardiovasc Soc. *Res:* Physiology of extracorporeal circulation, hypothermia, prosthetic valves and cardiac valve grafts. *Mailing Add:* Univ of Colo Med Ctr 4200 E Ninth Ave Denver CO 80220

PATON, DAVID, b Baltimore, Md, Aug 16, 30; m; c 1. MEDICINE, OPHTHALMOLOGY. *Educ:* Princeton Univ, BA, 52; Johns Hopkins Univ, MD, 56; Am Bd Ophthal, dipl, 64. *Prof Exp:* Intern med, New York Hosp-Cornell Med Sch, 56-57; sr asst surg, Nat Inst Neurol Dis & Blindness, 57-59; resident ophthal, Wilmer Inst, Johns Hopkins Hosp, 59-62 & 63-64, from asst prof to assoc prof, 64-70; chmn dept, 71-81, PROF OPTHAL, BAYLOR COL MED, 71- *Concurrent Pos:* Markle scholar acad med, 67-; mem, Am Bd Ophthal. *Mem:* Am Acad Ophthal ; fel Am Col Surgeons; Pan-Am Asn Ophthal. *Mailing Add:* Dept of Ophthal Cullen Eye Inst Houston TX 77030

PATON, DAVID MURRAY, b East London, SAfrica, Feb 26, 38; m 62; c 2. PHARMACOLOGY. *Educ:* Univ Cape Town, MB & ChB, 61; Univ Witwatersrand, MD, 74. *Prof Exp:* Intern internal med & surg, Groote Schuur Hosp, Cape Town, 62-63; lectr pharmacol, Univ Cape Town, 63-64; from asst prof to assoc prof, 66-73, actg chmn dept, 74-75, PROF PHARMACOL, UNIV ALTA, 73-, ASST DEAN MED, 77- *Concurrent Pos:* James Hudson Brown fel pharmacol, Yale Univ, 65-66; Can Heart Found res fel, Univ Alta, 66-68, sr res fel, 68-72, scholar, 72-74; vis prof pharmacol, Univ Wurzburg, 71-72. *Mem:* Pharmacol Soc Can; Can Physiol Soc; Brit Pharmacol Soc; Soc Study Reprod. *Res:* Control of contractility of oviducts; mechanisms of transport and release of catecholamines. *Mailing Add:* Dept of Pharmacol Univ of Alta Edmonton AB T6G 2E1 Can

PATON, NEIL (ERIC), b Auckland, New Zealand, Dec 3, 38; m 64; c 2. PHYSICAL METALLURGY, MATERIALS SCIENCE. *Educ:* Univ Auckland, BE, 61, ME, 62; Mass Inst Technol, PhD(metall), 69. *Prof Exp:* Res metallurgist, Atlas Steels, Can, 62-65; group leader struct mat dept, 69-77, actg dir struct mat dept, 77-78, DIR MAT SYNTHESIS & PROCESSING DEPT, ROCKWELL INT SCI CTR, 78- *Concurrent Pos:* Mem, Solid State Sci Comt, Nat Acad Sci, 74-78. *Mem:* Sigma Xi; Am Inst Mining, Metall & Petrol Engrs. *Res:* Materials synthesis and processing; alloy properties; microstructure analysis. *Mailing Add:* Rockwell Int Sci Ctr 1049 Camino Dos Rios Thousand Oaks CA 91360

PATRASCIOIU, ADRIAN NICOLAE, b Romania; US citizen. THEORETICAL PHYSICS. *Educ:* Mass Inst Technol, PhD(physics), 73. *Prof Exp:* Mem physics, Inst Advan Study, Princeton, 73-75; asst res physicist, Univ Calif, San Diego, 75-77; asst prof physics, 77-80, ASSOC PROF PHYSICS, UNIV ARIZ, 80- *Concurrent Pos:* A P Sloan fel, 80. *Res:* Elementary particles. *Mailing Add:* Dept of Physics Univ of Ariz Tucson AZ 85721

PATRIARCHE, MERCER HARDING, b Waltham, Mass, Apr 18, 16; m 46; c 2. FISH BIOLOGY. *Educ:* Mich State Univ, BS, 37, MS, 48. *Prof Exp:* Fisheries biologist, State Conserv Comn, Mo, 48-56; biologist in chg, Rifle River Fisheries Res Sta, State Dept Conserv, Mich, 56-66; fisheris res biologist, Inst Fisheries Res, 66-78, biologist in chg, 78-81; RETIRED. *Concurrent Pos:* Ed, North Am J Fisheries Mgt, 81- *Mem:* Am Fisheries Soc. *Res:* Fish population dynamics; biology and life histories of fish; fish management techniques; basic productivity of lakes and streams. *Mailing Add:* 2677 Esch Ave Ann Arbor MI 48104

PATRIC, JAMES HOLTON, b Rockville, Conn, Dec 24, 22; m 50; c 4. FOREST HYDROLOGY. *Educ:* Univ Conn, BS, 47; Harvard Univ, MF, 57. *Prof Exp:* Work unit conservationist, Soil & Conserv Serv, USDA, 48-55, res forester, San Dimas Exp Forest, US Forest Serv, Calif, 57-60, Coweeta Hydrol Lab, NC, 60-65 & Inst North Forestry, Alaska, 65-67, PROJ LEADER WATERSHED MGT RES, PARSONS TIMBER & WATERSHED LAB, NORTHEASTERN FOREST EXP STA, US FOREST SERV, 67- *Concurrent Pos:* Adj prof, WVa Univ, 68-; Bullard fel advan res, Harvard Univ, 72. *Mem:* Soc Am Foresters; Am Geophys Union. *Res:* Forest hydrology; evaporative losses from forest land; managing forest land to produce more and better water. *Mailing Add:* Parsons Timber & Watershed Lab NEastern Forest Exp Sta Box 445 Parsons WV 26287

PATRICK, CHARLES RUSSELL, b Brookfield, Ga, Mar 30, 40; m 69; c 1. ENTOMOLOGY. *Educ:* Clemson Univ, BS, 63; Auburn Univ, MS, 67; Miss State Univ, PhD(entom), 70. *Prof Exp:* Entomologist, Tenn Dept Agr, 70-80; EXTEN ENTOMOLOGIST, AGR EXTEN SERV, UNIV TENN, 80- *Mem:* Assoc Sigma Xi; Entom Soc Am. *Res:* Field crop insects (corn, soybeans, small grain, stored grain). *Mailing Add:* Agr Exten Serv Univ Tenn 605 Airways Blvd Jackson TN 38301

PATRICK, EDWARD ALFRED, b Wheeling, WVa, Oct 7, 37; m 60; c 4. COMPUTER SCIENCE, MEDICINE. *Educ:* Mass Inst Technol, BS, 60, MS, 62; Purdue Univ, PhD(elec eng), 66; Ind Univ, Indianapolis, MD, 74. *Prof Exp:* From asst prof to assoc prof elec eng, Purdue Univ, 66-74, prof, 74-81; assoc prof community health sci, Sch Med, Ind Univ, Purdue, 70-80; PRES, PATRICK CONSULT INC, WEST LAFAYETTE, 77- *Concurrent Pos:* Staff mem, Instrument Lab, Mass Inst Technol, 59-62, instr, Inst, 60-62; grants, US Air Force, 66-69, Naval Ships Syst Command, 66-70, Naval Air Syst Command, 68-70 & NSF, 68-70 & 74-76; consult, Sylvania Appl Res Lab, 60-63, Tex Instrument Corp, 66-70, Dupont Corp, 67-69, Regenstrief Inst Health Care Delivery, 70-, Univ Ill, 74- & Jewish Hosp, Cincinnati, Ohio, 74-; assoc ed, Computers in Biol & Med, 69- *Mem:* AMA; Pattern Recognition Soc. *Res:* Application of engineering to clinical medicine. *Mailing Add:* Sch Elec Eng Purdue Univ West Lafayette IN 47907

PATRICK, GRAHAM ABNER, b Maysville, NC, Apr 30, 46; m 64; c 2. PHARMACOLOGY, NEUROBIOLOGY. *Educ:* Univ NC, BS, 69, PhD(pharmacol), 73. *Prof Exp:* Instr, 73-74, ASST PROF PHARMACOL, MED COL VA, 74- *Concurrent Pos:* Res grant, Nat Inst Neurol & Commun Dis & Stroke, 76-79, Environ Protection Agency, 79-81. *Mem:* Sigma Xi; Am Soc Pharmacol & Exp Therapeut. *Res:* Drug dependence and tolerance development; central neurotransmitters. *Mailing Add:* Dept of Pharmacol Med Col of Va Box 613 Richmond VA 23298

PATRICK, JAMES BURNS, b Kansas City, Mo, Oct 16, 23; m 44; c 4. ORGANIC CHEMISTRY. *Educ:* Mass Inst Technol, BS, 49; Harvard Univ, MA, 50, PhD(chem), 52. *Prof Exp:* Res chemist, Nat Heart Inst, 52; res chemist, Lederle Labs, Am Cyanamid Co, NY, 53-63, res group leader, 63-67; chmn dept, 67-74, PROF CHEM, MARY BALDWIN COL, 67- *Mem:* Am Chem Soc. *Res:* Chemistry of natural products; structure of alkaloids and antibiotics. *Mailing Add:* Dept of Chem Mary Baldwin Col Staunton VA 24401

PATRICK, JAMES EDWARD, b Westfield, Mass, Oct 25, 44; m 75. DRUG METABOLISM, PHARMACOKINETICS. *Educ:* Marist Col, BA, 66; Pa State Univ, PhD(org chem), 71. *Prof Exp:* Fel steroid biochem, Worcester Found Exp Biol, 71-73; group leader biotransformation, Drug Metab Sect, Ortho Pharmaceut Corp, 73-80; MGR ANAL BIOCHEM/DRUG METAB & PHARMACOKINETICS, SCHERING CORP, 80- *Concurrent Pos:* Adj instr, Somerset County Col, 74-76. *Mem:* Am Chem Soc; Am Pharmaceut Asn. *Res:* Drug disposition and assay development; absorption, distribution, excretion and biotransformation studies of drugs in animals and man; development of analytical methods for drugs in biological fluids. *Mailing Add:* Schering Corp Bloomfield NJ 07003

PATRICK, JAMES R, b Athens, Ohio, Feb 10, 31; m 55; c 3. PEDIATRICS, PATHOLOGY. *Educ:* Ohio Univ, AB, 52; Yale Univ, MD, 56. *Prof Exp:* Intern pediat, Yale-New Haven Med Ctr, 56-57, asst resident, 57-58, chief resident, 58-59; instr pediat, Yale Univ, 58-59; from instr to asst prof path, Univ Southern Calif, 61-65; from asst prof to assoc prof, Georgetown Univ, 65-69; chmn dept path, 69-78, PROF PATH & PEDIAT, MED COL OHIO, 69- *Concurrent Pos:* Fel path, Yale Univ, 59-61; assoc pathologist, Children's Hosp, Los Angeles, 61-65; dir labs & chief pathologist, Children's Hosp, Washington, DC, 65-69. *Mem:* AAAS; Am Asn Path & Bact; Int Acad Path. *Mailing Add:* Dept of Path Med Col of Ohio CS 10008 Toledo OH 43699

PATRICK, MERRELL LEE, b Cynthiana, Ky, July 2, 33; m 59; c 2. APPLIED MATHEMATICS, COMPUTER SCIENCE. *Educ:* Eastern Ky Univ, BS, 55; Univ Ky, MS, 56; Carnegie Inst Technol, PhD(math), 64. *Prof Exp:* Assoc engr, Lockheed Missiles & Space Co, 56-59, sr scientist, 59-62; asst prof math, 64-68, from asst prof to assoc prof comput sci, 68-77, PROF COMPUT SCI, DUKE UNIV, 77-, CHMN COMPUT SCI, 78- *Mem:* Soc Indust & Appl Math; Asn Comput Mach. *Res:* Numerical solution of nonlinear equations; vector and parallel algorithms. *Mailing Add:* Dept of Comput Sci Duke Univ Durham NC 27706

PATRICK, MICHAEL ANDREW, b Wheeling, WVa, Sept 30, 48. MICROBIOLOGY. *Educ:* Fla State Univ, BS, 70; Ohio State Univ, MS, 72, PhD(microbiol), 75. *Prof Exp:* SPEC BIOLOGIST MICROBIOL, US AIR FORCE, 75- *Res:* Hydrocarbon oxidations; effects of heavy metals on microorganisms; pesticide analyses; microbial physiology; electron microscopy; analytical chemistry. *Mailing Add:* AFATL/DLV Eglin AFB FL 32542

PATRICK, MICHAEL HEATH, b Chicago, Ill, Mar 31, 36; m 76; c 3. BIOPHYSICS. *Educ:* Univ Calif, Santa Barbara, AB, 58; Univ Chicago, PhD(biophys), 64. *Prof Exp:* Res assoc biochem, Sch Hyg & Pub Health, Johns Hopkins Univ, 64-66; asst prof, 66-72, assoc prof, 72-80, PROF BIOL, UNIV TEX, DALLAS, 80- *Mem:* AAAS; Biophys Soc; Sigma Xi. *Res:* DNA replication and repair. *Mailing Add:* Univ Tex at Dallas PO Box 688 Richardson TX 75080

PATRICK, RICHARD ALLEN, immunology, biochemistry, see previous edition

PATRICK, RICHARD MONTGOMERY, b Rockford, Ill, Sept 24, 28; m 58; c 3. PHYSICS, PHYSICAL CHEMISTRY. *Educ:* Purdue Univ, BS, 50, MS, 52; Cornell Univ, PhD(aero eng), 56. *Prof Exp:* Scientist plasma physics, 56-69, V PRES PLASMA & ADVAN PROD, AVCO EVERETT RES LAB, 69- *Mem:* Fel Am Phys Soc. *Res:* Atomic and molecular physics; aerodynamics; fluid flows; plasma physics. *Mailing Add:* 99 Arlington St Winchester MA 01890

PATRICK, ROBERT F(RANKLIN), b Helmetta, NJ, Oct 10, 21; m 49; c 3. CERAMICS. *Educ:* Rutgers Univ, BS, 43, MS 47, PhD(ceramics), 49. *Prof Exp:* Asst, Rutgers Univ, 46-47; sr res ceramist, Pemco Corp, 49-52, asst dir res, 52-60; mgr steel refractory res, Corning Glass Works, 60-62; mgr tech serv, 62-64, tech mgr-bonded, 65-66, DIR TECH SERV, CORHART REFRACTORIES CO, 66- *Mem:* Fel Am Ceramic Soc; Am Soc Testing & Mat; Nat Inst Ceramic Engrs; Am Inst Mining, Metall & Petrol Engrs. *Res:* Physical and chemical properties of inorganic glasses and coatings for metals; porcelain enamel technology; color measurement; properties of refractory oxide systems; crystallization from melts; research and development refractories; refract; application engineering. *Mailing Add:* 2222 Village Dr Louisville KY 40205

PATRICK, RUTH (MRS CHARLES HODGE IV), b Topeka, Kans, Nov 26, 07; m 31. BOTANY. *Educ:* Coker Col, BS, 29; Univ Va, MS, 31, PhD(bot), 34. *Hon Degrees:* DSc, Swarthmore Col, Drexel Univ, Univ Mass & Princeton Univ, 80. *Prof Exp:* Asst, Coker Col, 29; asst res, Temple Univ, 34; asst cur micros, 39-48, chmn bd, 73-76, CUR LIMNOL, ACAD NATURAL SCI, 47-, HON CHMN BD, 76- *Concurrent Pos:* Cur, Leidy Micros Soc, 37-47; trustee, Coker Col, 41-; with Am Philos Soc exped, Mex,

47; dir, Henry Found Bot Res, 48-; lectr, Univ Pa, 52-70, prof, 70-; US deleg, Int Cong Limnol, 53; leader, Catherwood Exped, Amazon River, 55; trustee, Chestnut Hill Acad, 57-72; mem bd, E I du Pont de Nemours & Co & Pa Power & Light Co, 72-; adj prof, Univ Pa, 70- *Honors & Awards:* Tyler Ecol Award, 75. *Mem:* Nat Acad Sci; Am Philosophical Soc; Bot Soc Am; Am Soc Limnol & Oceanog; Phycol Soc Am (pres, 54). *Res:* Taxonomy, ecology and physiology of diatoms; limnology; biodynamic cycle of rivers. *Mailing Add:* Limnol Dept Acad Nat Sci 19th & Race St Philadelphia PA 19103

PATRICK, TIMOTHY BENSON, b Huntington, WVa, Dec 25, 41; m 64; c 2. ORGANIC CHEMISTRY. *Educ:* Marshall Univ, BS, 63; WVa Univ, PhD(chem), 67. *Prof Exp:* NASA trainee, WVa Univ, 65-67; fel chem, Ohio State Univ, 67-69; asst prof, 69-72, assoc prof, 72-76, PROF CHEM, SOUTHERN ILL UNIV, 76- *Mem:* Am Chem Soc. *Res:* Organic synthesis; physical organic chemistry; heterocyclic chemistry; organofluorine; carbene chemistry; steroid chemistry. *Mailing Add:* Chem Dept Southern Ill Univ Edwardsville IL 62026

PATRICK, WESLEY CLARE, b North Branch, Mich, Dec 29, 51; m 73; c 2. MINING ENGINEERING. *Educ:* Mich Technol Univ, BS, 74; Univ Mo-Rolla, MS, 75, PhD(mining eng), 78. *Prof Exp:* Staff engr, St Joe Minerals Corp, 74; grad asst rock mech, Univ Mo-Rolla, 74-78; 1st lieutenant, US Army Chem Corps, 78; staff engr, 78-80, PROJ SCIENTIST, LAWRENCE LIVERMORE LAB, 80- *Mem:* Soc Mining Engrs; Soc Exp Stress Anal. *Res:* Deep geologic storage of high level wastes from commercial nuclear reactors; radiation damage, heat transfer, and geomechanical response of the test repository. *Mailing Add:* 1474 Heather Lane Livermore CA 94550

PATRICK, WILLIAM H, JR, b Johns, Miss, Nov 9, 25; m 51; c 4. MARINE SCIENCES. *Educ:* La State Univ, Baton Rouge, BS, 50, MS, 51, PhD(soils), 54. *Hon Degrees:* Ghent Univ, Belgium, Dr. *Prof Exp:* From asst prof to prof agron, 53-76, prof, 77-78, BOYD PROF MARINE SCI, LA STATE UNIV, BATON ROUGE, 78- *Mem:* Fel Soil Sci Soc Am; Am Soc Agron; Int Soc Soil Sci; fel AAAS. *Res:* Physicochemical properties of and reactions in soils, particularly wetland soils. *Mailing Add:* Dept of Marine Sci La State Univ Baton Rouge LA 70803

PATRICK, ZENON ALEXANDER, b Montreal, Que, June 3, 24; m 49; c 3. PLANT PATHOLOGY. *Educ:* McGill Univ, BSc, 48; Univ Toronto, PhD(plant path), 52. *Prof Exp:* Plant pathologist, Can Dept Agr, 52-65; PROF PLANT PATH, UNIV TORONTO, 65- *Concurrent Pos:* Vis prof, Univ Calif, Berkeley, 59-60; mem comt biol control soil borne plant pathogens, NSF, 63-65; consult, Hort Exp Sta, Ont Dept Agr, 65- *Mem:* AAAS; Am Phytopath Soc; Can Phytopath Soc. *Res:* Biology of soil borne pathogens; influence of soil organic matter on root diseases; soil toxins; biological control of plant pathogens. *Mailing Add:* Dept of Bot Univ of Toronto Toronto ON M5S 1A1 Can

PATRONIS, EUGENE THAYER, JR, b Quincy, Fla, Feb 26, 32; m 51; c 2. PHYSICS. *Educ:* Ga Inst Technol, BS, 53, PhD(physics), 61. *Prof Exp:* Instr physics, Ga Inst Technol, 52-58; res assoc, Brookhaven Nat Lab, 57-59; from asst prof to assoc prof, 59-68, PROF PHYSICS, GA INST TECHNOL, 68- *Concurrent Pos:* Consult, McGraw-Hill Bk Co, 59-61. *Mem:* AAAS; Am Phys Soc; Soc Motion Picture & TV Engrs; Audio Eng Soc. *Res:* Nuclear physics; electronics and electronic instruments. *Mailing Add:* Sch of Physics Ga Inst of Technol Atlanta GA 30332

PATSAKOS, GEORGE, b New York, NY, Mar 24, 42. THEORETICAL PHYSICS. *Educ:* Columbia Col, AB, 62; Stanford Univ, PhD(physics), 69. *Prof Exp:* Res assoc physics, Ind Univ, Bloomington, 68-70; vis asst prof, 70-71, asst prof, 71-76, ASSOC PROF PHYSICS, UNIV IDAHO, 76- *Mem:* AAAS; Am Asn Physics Teachers; Am Phys Soc. *Mailing Add:* Dept of Physics Univ of Idaho Moscow ID 83843

PATSCH, WOLFGANG, b Wels, Austria, Aug 10, 46; m 70; c 2. ATHEROSCLEROSIS, METABOLISM. *Educ:* Univ Innsbruck, Austria, MD, 71; Univ Uppsala, Sweden, cert biochem, 78. *Prof Exp:* Resident med, Univ Innsbruck, Austria, 71-74, res intern, 75-77, asst prof, 77-81; vis asst prof prev med, 78-80, ASST PROF PREV MED & MED, WASHINGTON UNIV, MO, 80-, LAB DIR, LIPID LAB, 79- *Concurrent Pos:* mem, Atherosclerosis Coun, Am Heart Asn, 80. *Mem:* Am Fedn Clin Res; Europ Lipoprotein Club; Am Soc Clin Nutrit. *Res:* Structure, function, and metabolism of lipoproteins; synthesis of apoproteins and lipoproteins by hepatocyte cultures. *Mailing Add:* Sch Med Washington Univ Box 8046 4566 Scott Ave St Louis MO 63110

PATSIGA, ROBERT A, b New Brighton, Pa, Sept 8, 34; m 56; c 4. ORGANIC CHEMISTRY, POLYMER CHEMISTRY. *Educ:* Geneva Col, BS, 57; State Univ NY Col Forestry, Syracuse Univ, PhD(org chem), 62. *Prof Exp:* Res chemist, Koppers Co, Inc, 61-63; fel polymer chem, Villanova Univ, 63-64; asst prof org chem, Bethany Col, WVa, 64-68; from asst prof to assoc prof, 68-73, PROF CHEM, IND UNIV PA, 73- *Mem:* Am Chem Soc. *Res:* Synthesis of new polymers, polymerization mechanisms, free radiacal reactions and mechanisms. *Mailing Add:* Dept of Chem Ind Univ of Pa Indiana PA 15705

PATSIS, ANGELOS VLASIOS, b Athens, Greece, May 7, 28; nat US; m 54; c 4. PHYSICAL CHEMISTRY, CHEMICAL ENGINEERING. *Educ:* Athens Univ, BS, 53; Texas A&M Univ, BS, 55; Western Reserve Univ, MS, 58, PhD(chem), 59. *Prof Exp:* Asst anal, Pvt Testing Lab, 47-53; res technologist, Res Lab Agr Tech, Greece, 53-54; exchange vis scientist, Tex Petrol Res Comt, Agr & Mech Univ Tex, 54-55; asst, Off Naval Res, 55 & Western Reserve Univ, 55-59; res chemist, Calif Res Corp, Stand Oil Co Calif, 59-60 & Finishes Dept, E I du Pont de Nemours & Co, Inc, NY, 60-66; assoc prof, 66-70, PROF CHEM, STATE UNIV NY COL NEW PALTZ, 70- *Mem:* Am Chem Soc; NY Acad Sci; Am Asn Univ Professors; Electrochem Soc; AAAS. *Res:* Physical properties of hydrocarbons; oil and gas reservoirs; ultrasonics; colloids; polymers; plastics; coatings; elastomers. *Mailing Add:* Dept of Chem State Univ of NY Col New Paltz NY 12561

PATT, CHARLES RICHARD, mathematics, see previous edition

PATT, HARVEY MILTON, b Chicago, Ill, Aug 2, 18; m 44, 65; c 4. RADIOBIOLOGY, BIOPHYSICS. *Educ:* Univ Chicago, BS, 39, PhD, 42. *Prof Exp:* Res assoc physiol, Univ Chicago, 42-44, instr, 46; from assoc physiologist to sr physiologist, Argonne Nat Lab, 46-64; PROF RADIOBIOL & PHYSIOL & DIR LAB RADIOBIOL, SCH MED, UNIV CALIF, SAN FRANCISCO, 64-, PROF MICROBIOL, 77- *Concurrent Pos:* Mem subcomt radiobiol, Nat Res Coun, 50-64 & radiobiol panel comt growth, 52-56; chmn radiation study sect, NIH, 55-62 & comt radiobiol, Nat Res Coun, 56-58; secy gen, Int Cong Radiation Res, 58; consult, Surgeon Gen, US Army, 59-65; mem biophys sci training comt, NIH, 62-66; sci secy, AEC Adv Comt Biol & Med, 62-70; mem cancer spec prog adv comt, NIH, 73-75. *Honors & Awards:* Ernest Orlando Lawrence Mem Award, USAEC, 64. *Mem:* Fel AAAS; Am Physiol Soc; Soc Exp Biol & Med; Am Asn Cancer Res; Radiation Res Soc (treas, 52-55, vpres, 59, pres, 60). *Res:* Cytokinetics; radiobiology; experimental hematology. *Mailing Add:* Radiobiol Lab Univ Calif Sch of Med San Francisco CA 94143

PATTABHIRAMAN, TAMMANUR R, b Kancheepuram, India, Nov 3, 34. CHEMISTRY, MARINE BIOLOGY. *Educ:* Univ Madras, India, BSc, 56, MA, 57; Univ Hawaii, PhD(chem), 65. *Prof Exp:* Lectr, Univ Madras, India, 58-61; scientist, Coun Sci & Indust Res, India, 65-68; NIH grants & res fel chem, univ Okla, 68-71; NIH GRANT & RES FEL, UNIV SOUTHERN CALIF, 71- *Mem:* Am Chem Soc; Int Soc Toxinol. *Res:* Natural products, plant and marine origin, isolation, structure elucidation and synthesis; chemotaxonomy. *Mailing Add:* Dept Pediat Gen Lab Rm 1G34 Univ Southern Calif/Los Angeles County Med Ctr Los Angeles CA 90033

PATTEE, HAROLD EDWARD, b Phoenix, Ariz, June 27, 34; m 56; c 7. PLANT PHYSIOLOGY, PLANT BIOCHEMISTRY. *Educ:* Brigham Young Univ, BS, 58; Utah State Univ, MS, 60; Purdue Univ PhD(agron), 62. *Prof Exp:* Fel plant biochem, Univ Calif, Los Angeles, 62-63; biochemist, 63-65, RES CHEMIST, MID-ATLANTIC AREA, SOUTHERN REGION, AGR RES SERV, USDA, 65- *Concurrent Pos:* Symposium chmn, Am Chem Soc, 73 & 78; assoc ed, Peanut Sci, 74-76, ed, 76- *Honors & Awards:* Golden Peanut Res Award, Nat Peanut Coun, 77. *Mem:* Am Peanut Res Educ Soc; Sigma Xi; Am Oil Chemists Soc; Am Chem Soc. *Res:* Influence of seed maturation processes on the physiological processes occurring in the seed; isolation and characterization of flavor components from peanut kernels and of seed enzymes. *Mailing Add:* Southern Reg Fed Res NC State Univ Box 5906 Raleigh NC 27607

PATTEE, HOWARD HUNT, JR, b Pasadena, Calif, Oct 5, 26; m 54; c 2. THEORETICAL BIOLOGY, SYSTEMS THEORY. *Educ:* Stanford Univ, BS, 48, PhD(physics), 53. *Prof Exp:* Res assoc physics & biophys, Stanford Univ, 53-60, res biophysicist & lectr biophys, 60-71; vis prof biophys sci, State Univ NY Buffalo, 71-75; PROF, SCH ADVAN TECHNOL, STATE UNIV NY BINGHAMTON, 75- *Concurrent Pos:* Consult, Res Lab, IBM Corp, Calif, 56; NSF sr fel med physics, Karolinska Inst Sweden, 59; consult, Ampex Corp, 60. *Mem:* AAAS; Biophys Soc. *Res:* Origin of life; complex organization theory; linguistic theory; systems theory. *Mailing Add:* Sch of Advan Technol State Univ of NY Binghamton NY 13901

PATTEE, PETER A, b Brooklyn, NY, Nov 15, 32; m 58; c 4. MICROBIAL GENETICS. *Educ:* Univ Maine, BS, 55; Ohio State Univ, MSc, 57, PhD(bact), 61. *Prof Exp:* From asst prof to assoc prof, 61-69, PROF BACT, IOWA STATE UNIV, 69- *Mem:* AAAS; Am Soc Microbiol; Genetics Soc Am. *Res:* Staphylococcus aureus, especially genetic exchange phenomena, genetic analysis, lysogeny, mutagenesis, mechanisms of antibiotic resistance and genetics and biochemistry of biosynthetic pathways and their control. *Mailing Add:* Dept of Bact Iowa State Univ Ames IA 50011

PATTEN, BERNARD CLARENCE, b New York, NY, Jan 28, 31; m 53; c 1. ECOLOGY. *Educ:* Cornell Univ, AB, 52; Rutgers Univ, MS, 54, PhD(bot), 59; Univ Mich, AM, 57. *Prof Exp:* Assoc prof marine sci, Col William & Mary & assoc marine scientist, Va Inst Marine Sci, 59-63; ecologist, Oak Ridge Nat Lab, 63-68; assoc prof bot, Univ Tenn, 64-68; PROF ZOOL, UNIV GA, 68- *Concurrent Pos:* Pres, Ecol Simulations, Inc, 71- *Mem:* AAAS; Soc Gen Syst Res; Am Soc Limnol & Oceanog; Ecol Soc Am; Am Inst Biol Sci. *Res:* Mathematical and theoretical ecology; limnology; oceanography. *Mailing Add:* Dept of Zool Univ of Ga Athens GA 30601

PATTEN, DUNCAN THEUNISSEN, b Detroit, Mich, Oct 13, 34; m 57; c 4. PLANT ECOLOGY, ENVIRONMENTAL BIOLOGY. *Educ:* Amherst Col, BA, 56; Univ Mass, MS, 59; Duke Univ, PhD(bot), 62. *Prof Exp:* Asst prof bot, Va Polytech Inst, 62-65; from asst prof to assoc prof, 65-73, asst acad vpres, 72-76, chmn, Dept Bot/Microbiol, 77-81, PROF BOT, ARIZ STATE UNIV, 73-, DIR, CTR ENVIRON STUDIES, 80- *Concurrent Pos:* Mem comt environ res assessment, Nat Acad Sci-Nat Res Coun Comn Natural Resources, 75-76; mem, Ecol Sci Adv Panel, NSF, 75-78. *Mem:* AAAS; Ecol Soc Am; Bot Soc Am; Brit Ecol Soc; Am Inst Biol Sci. *Res:* Ecology of montane and subalpine zones of Yellowstone National Park and northern Rocky Mountains; autecology of desert succulents and annuals and heat and water flux within the desert ecosystems; man's impact on desert ecosystems. *Mailing Add:* Ctr Environ Studies Ariz State Univ Tempe AZ 85281

PATTEN, GAYLORD PENROD, b Provo, Utah, Nov 30, 38; m 59; c 11. SOIL PHYSICS. *Educ:* Brigham Young Univ, BS, 63; Ohio State Univ, MSc, 65, PhD(soils), 69. *Prof Exp:* From asst prof to assoc prof, 69-77, PROF SOIL SCI, CALIF STATE POLYTECH UNIV, POMONA, 77- *Mem:* Am Soc Agron; Soil Sci Soc Am. *Res:* Soil-water management; practical applications of soil-water-plant physical relationships. *Mailing Add:* Dept of Plant & Soil Sci Calif State Polytech Univ Pomona CA 91768

PATTEN, JIMMY RAY, physiology, see previous edition

PATTEN, RAYMOND ALEX, b Fall River, Mass, Mar 28, 37; m 57; c 2. PHYSICS. *Educ:* Mass Inst Technol, BS, 58; Duke Univ, PhD(physics), 62. *Prof Exp:* Instr & res assoc physics, Duke Univ, 61-62; asst prof, Univ Mass, 62-70; MEM STAFF, NAVAL RES LAB, 70- *Mem:* Am Phys Soc. *Res:* Paramagnetic and cyclotron resonance; electron-nuclear double resonance. *Mailing Add:* Naval Res Lab 4555 Overlook Ave SW Washington DC 20315

PATTENGILL, MERLE DEAN, b McPherson, Kans, Aug 19, 42; m 72; c 2. PHYSICAL CHEMISTRY. *Educ:* Univ Kans, BS, 64; Univ Calif, Irvine, PhD(chem), 69. *Prof Exp:* Proj assoc theoret chem, Univ Wis, 69-71; fel & lectr chem, Univ Toronto, 71-73; asst prof, 73-76, ASSOC PROF CHEM, UNIV KY, 76- *Mem:* Am Chem Soc; Sigma Xi. *Res:* Molecular dynamics; theoretical studies of gas phase rate processes. *Mailing Add:* Dept of Chem Univ of Ky Lexington KY 40506

PATTERSON, ANDREW, JR, b Texarkana, Tex, July 23, 16; m 40; c 4. PHYSICAL CHEMISTRY. *Educ:* Univ Tex, AB, 37, AM, 38, PhD(phys chem), 42. *Hon Degrees:* MA, Yale Univ, 69. *Prof Exp:* Instr chem, Univ Tex, 38-41; asst prof, NTex Agr Col, 41-42; actg assoc prof, Univ NC, 42-43; spec res assoc, Harvard Univ, 43-45; physicist, Underwater Sound Lab, Navy Dept, Conn, 45-46; instr chem & Am Chem Soc fel, 46-48, from asst prof to assoc prof, 48-69, PROF CHEM, YALE UNIV, 69- *Concurrent Pos:* Dir, Edwards St Lab, Yale Univ, 54-56; Master, Morse Col, 61-67; fel, Phys Chem Lab, Oxford, 66-67; mem, consult & chmn mine adv comt, Nat Acad Sci. *Mem:* Am Chem Soc; Sigma Xi. *Res:* Alkali metal-liquid ammonia; ionic association; high field conductance measurements. *Mailing Add:* Sterling Chem Lab Box 1901A Yale Univ Yale Sta New Haven CT 06520

PATTERSON, ARCHIBALD OSCAR, b Monroe, Ga, Dec 26, 08; m 33; c 2. CIVIL ENGINEERING. *Educ:* Ga Sch Technol, BSCivEng, 29. *Prof Exp:* Civil engr, Interstate Com Comn, DC, 29-30; hydraul engr, Water Resources Div, US Geol Surv, Maine & NH, 30-32, WVa & Ky, 32-35, Tenn, Ky & Ala, 35-42, in charge, Knoxville, Tenn, 42-47, dist engr, Surface Water Br, Ocala, Fla, 47-64; dir div water resources, Fla Bd Conserv, 64-67; prof environ eng & dir Fla Water Resources Res Ctr, Univ Fla, 67-70; CONSULT ENGR, 70- *Concurrent Pos:* Chmn comt surface water, Fla Water Resources Study Comn, 57. *Mem:* Am Soc Civil Engrs. *Res:* Investigation of surface water supply; hydrology; water resources planning; water conservation. *Mailing Add:* 1444 S E Eighth St PO Box 1901 Ocala FL 32678

PATTERSON, BRYAN, vertebrate paleontology, deceased

PATTERSON, C(LEO) MAURICE, b Fairfield, Nebr, Dec 24, 13; m 36; c 2. HEALTH PHYSICS, ENVIRONMENTAL ENGINEERING. *Educ:* Univ Nebr, BS(pharm), 30, BS, 34. *Prof Exp:* Sr supvr radiation protection, Hanford Works, E I du Pont de Nemours & Co, Inc, 44-45, chief supvr, 45-46; supt, Hanford Works, Gen Elec Co, 46-51; supt health physics, Savannah River Plant, E I Du Pont de Nemours & Co, Inc, 51-65, res mgr radiol sci, Savannah River Lab, 65-71, supt health physics dept, Savannah River Plant, 71-78; RETIRED. *Concurrent Pos:* Ed, Health Physics J, 66-76; bd mem, So Carolina Dept Health & Environ Control, 77-80. *Mem:* Am Indust Hyg Asn; Health Physics Soc (pres, 62-63); Am Acad Indust Hyg; Am Bd Health Physics. *Res:* Radiological health; planning, development and inauguration of radiation protection programs; fates of radionuclides in the environment. *Mailing Add:* 521 Highland Park Aiken SC 29801

PATTERSON, CHARLES MEADE, b Waynesburg, Pa, June 24, 19; m 67. GEOLOGY. *Educ:* Col Wooster, BA, 40; Columbia Univ, AM, 42, PhD(geol), 47; Calif Inst Technol, MS, 43. *Prof Exp:* Petrographer & geologist, Gulf Res & Develop Co, 47-53 & Nat Rifle Asn, 53-57; commodity specialist, US Bur Mines, 57-63, sci ed, 64-67; geol oceanogr, Ocean Anal Div, Suitland, 67-75, GEOL OCEANOGR, OCEANOG DEPT, US NAVAL OCANOG OFF, WASHINGTON, 75- *Mem:* Geol Soc Am; Sigma Xi. *Res:* Submarine geology; areal geology; alteration in ore deposits; clays; petrography and petrology; weather forecasting and synoptic meteorology; lime; calcium and calcium compounds. *Mailing Add:* US Naval Oceanog Off PO Box 784 Hyattsville MD 20783

PATTERSON, CHRISTOPHER WARREN, b Los Angeles, Calif, Aug 1, 46; m 72; c 1. MOLECULAR SPECTROSCOPY, ATOMIC SPECTROSCOPY. *Educ:* Univ Southern Calif, MS, 68, PhD(physics), 74. *Prof Exp:* Asst prof, Univ Campinas, Brazil, 74-77; MEM STAFF, LOS ALAMOS NAT LAB, UNIV CALIF, 77- *Concurrent Pos:* NSF fel, 68-71; NASA fel, 71-72. *Honors & Awards:* Coblentz Award, 82. *Mem:* Am Phys Soc. *Res:* Theoretical atomic and molecular spectroscopy; quantum optics. *Mailing Add:* T-12 MS 569 Theoret Div Univ Calif Los Alamos NM 87545

PATTERSON, CLAIRE CAMERON, b Des Moines, Iowa, June 2, 22; m 44; c 4. GEOCHEMISTRY, ENVIRONMENTAL CHEMISTRY. *Educ:* Grinnell Col, AB, 43; Univ Iowa, MS, 44; Univ Chicago, PhD(chem), 51. *Hon Degrees:* DSc, Grinnell Col, 72; Dr Honorium Causa, Univ Paris, 75. *Prof Exp:* Spectroscopist emission & mass, Manhattan Proj, 44-46; res assoc geochem & geochronol, Univ Chicago, 51; fel, 52, sr fel, 53-71, res assoc geochem, 71-72, GEOCHEMIST, CALIF INST TECHNOL, 72- *Honors & Awards:* J L Smith Medal, Nat Acad Sci, 73; Goldschmidt Medal, Geochem Soc Am, 80. *Mem:* Geochem Soc Am. *Res:* Esotopic evolution of lead and age on earth; biogeochemistry of lead in marine and terrestrial ecosystems; marine, mammalian and atmospheric lead pollution; archaeology of South American metallurgy; history of ancient metal production. *Mailing Add:* Div Geol & Planetary Sci Calif Inst of Technol Pasadena CA 91125

PATTERSON, DAVID, b Medford, Mass, Aug 24, 44; m 67; c 2. SOMATIC CELL GENETICS, CANCER. *Educ:* Mass Inst Technol, BS, 66; Brandeis Univ, PhD(biol), 71. *Prof Exp:* Fel, 71-73, res assoc, 73, asst prof, 74-78, ASSOC PROF BIOCHEM BIOPHYS & GENETICS & ASSOC DIR, DEPT BIOCHEM, BIOPHYS & GENETICS, ELEANOR ROOSEVELT INST CANCER RES, UNIV COLO HEALTH SCI CTR, 78- *Concurrent Pos:* Mem, Mammalian Genetics Study Sect, NIH, 81- *Mem:* Am Soc Cell Biol; AAAS; Am Soc Human Genetics; Sigma Xi. *Res:* Biochemical genetics of somatic mammalian cells grown in culture with emphasis on the relevance of gene regulation to cancer, aging and birth defects. *Mailing Add:* B129 Roosevelt Inst Cancer Res Univ of Colo Med Ctr Denver CO 80220

PATTERSON, DAVID THOMAS, b Durham, NC, July 18, 46; m 79. ENVIRONMENTAL PHYSIOLOGY, WEED SCIENCE. *Educ:* NC State Univ, BS, 68; Duke Univ, MA, 70, PhD(bot), 73. *Prof Exp:* Res assoc environ physiol, Dept Bot, Duke Univ, 73-76; plant physiologist, USDA, 76-80; MEM STAFF, DUKE UNIV, 80- *Mem:* Ecol Soc Am; Am Soc Agron; Am Soc Plant Physiol; Weed Sci Soc Am; Sigma Xi. *Res:* Physiological plant ecology, chemical and biological plant interactions, ecology and comparative physiology of weeds. *Mailing Add:* Bot Dept Duke Univ Durham NC 27706

PATTERSON, DENNIS BRUCE, b Chicago, Ill, July 20, 41. POLYMER CHEMISTRY, ORGANIC CHEMISTRY. *Educ:* Univ Chicago, BS, 63; Univ Calif, Berkeley, PhD(org chem), 69. *Prof Exp:* Res assoc org chem, Univ Tex, 69-71; mem tech staff, Bell Labs, 71-73; scholar, polymer chem, Pa State Univ, 74-76; sr res chemist, 76-81, RES SCIENTIST, POLYMER CHEM, GOODYEAR TIRE & RUBBER CO, 81- *Mem:* Am Chem Soc; AAAS; Sigma Xi. *Res:* Synthesis and chemical modification of polymers; organic synthesis and physical-organic chemistry; homogenous and heterogenous catalysis; nuclear quadrupole resonance spectroscopy. *Mailing Add:* Goodyear Tire & Rubber Co 1144 E Market St Akron OH 44316

PATTERSON, DENNIS RAY, b Cairo, Ill, Sept 6, 46; m 68; c 3. ORGANIC CHEMISTRY. *Educ:* Univ Mo-St Louis, BS, 68; Univ Chicago, PhD(chem), 74. *Prof Exp:* Fel, Univ Sherbrooke, 73-74; RES CHEMIST, ROHM & HAAS CO, 74- *Mem:* Am Chem Soc. *Res:* Synthesis of agriculturally related chemicals. *Mailing Add:* Rohm & Haas Co Norristown & McKean Rds Springhouse PA 19477

PATTERSON, DONALD DUKE, b Montreal, Que, Oct 13, 27; m 64. POLYMER CHEMISTRY. *Educ:* McGill Univ, BSc, 49, MSc, 51. *Prof Exp:* Nat Res Coun fel, 53-55; asst prof chem, Univ Montreal, 55-64; assoc prof, Univ Strasbourg, 64-66; assoc prof, 66-76, PROF CHEM, MCGILL UNIV, 76- *Res:* Thermodynamics of polymer solutions; statistical thermodynamics; surface chemistry. *Mailing Add:* Dept Chem McGill Univ Montreal PQ H3A 2T6 Can

PATTERSON, DONALD FLOYD, b Maracaibo, Venezuela, Feb 2, 31; US citizen; m 53; c 2. VETERINARY MEDICINE, MEDICAL GENETICS. *Educ:* Okla State Univ, DVM, 54; Univ Pa, DSc, 68. *Prof Exp:* Intern vet med, Angell Mem Animal Hosp, 54-55; instr, Okla State Univ, 55-56; from instr to asst prof cardiol, 58-66, from assoc prof to prof med, 66-73, CHARLOTTE NEWTON SHEPPARD PROF MED, SCH VET MED, UNIV PA & CO-DIR COMP CARDIOVASC STUDIES UNIT, 66-, NIH PROG PROJ GRANT, 71-, CHIEF SECT MED GENETICS, 71-, PROF HUMAN GENETICS, 74- *Concurrent Pos:* NIH spec fel med genetics, Johns Hopkins Univ, 64-66; grant, 67-72; Ralston-Purina Res Award, Am Vet Med Asn, 81. *Honors & Awards:* Gaines Award, Am Vet Med Asn, 72. *Mem:* AAAS; fel Am Col Cardiol; Am Vet Med Asn; Am Soc Vet Physiol & Pharmacol; Am Heart Asn. *Res:* Comparative cardiology and medical genetics, particularly the etiology and pathogenesis of congenital heart disease. *Mailing Add:* Sch of Vet Med Univ of Pa Philadelphia PA 19174

PATTERSON, EARL BYRON, b Reynolds, Nebr, July 21, 23; m 54; c 1. GENETICS. *Educ:* Univ Nebr, BSc, 47; Calif Inst Technol, PhD(genetics), 52. *Prof Exp:* Fel biol, Calif Inst Technol, 52-53; res assoc bot & agron, 53-55, asst prof agron, 55-73, ASSOC PROF AGRON, COL AGR, UNIV ILL, URBANA-CHAMPAIGN, 73- *Mem:* Genetics Soc Am. *Res:* Maize genetics; maize cooperative collection of genetic traits. *Mailing Add:* Dept of Agron Col of Agr 104 Mumford Hall Univ of Ill Urbana IL 61801

PATTERSON, EARL E(DGAR), b Oklahoma City, Okla, Apr 14, 23; m 56; c 2. CHEMICAL ENGINEERING. *Educ:* Univ Okla, BS, 44, MChE, 47; Mass Inst Technol, ScD(chem eng), 50. *Prof Exp:* Asst, Mass Inst Technol, 47-50; chem engr titanium res & develop, E I du Pont de Nemours & Co, Inc, 50-54; lab mgr parts div, 54-57, asst res dir, Metall Res Labs, 57-58, mem staff corporate planning dept, 58-60, dir res eval, 60-64, exec asst to exec vpres res & develop, 64-71, gen dir metall res div, 71-72, spec asst to exec vpres res & develop, 72-78, gen dir spec projs, 78-80, ASST TO GEN MGR, REYNOLDS METALS CO, 80- *Mem:* Am Chem Soc; Am Soc Metals; Am Inst Chem Engrs; Int Transactional Analysis Asn; Int Solar Energy Soc. *Res:* Research administration; economic analysis; titanium metal process metallurgy; high polymers. *Mailing Add:* 8318 Whitewood Rd Richmond VA 23235

PATTERSON, EDWARD MATTHEW, b Savannah, Ga, Dec 11, 43; m 71; c 2. ATMOSPHERIC SCIENCE. *Educ:* Ga Inst Technol, BS, 65, MS, 67, PhD(physics), 74. *Prof Exp:* Fel, Nat Ctr Atmospheric Res, 74-75, scientist, 75-78; RES SCIENTIST, SCH GEOPHYS SCI, GA INST TECHNOL, 78- *Mem:* Am Meterol Soc; Optical Soc Am; Am Geophys Union. *Res:* Atmospheric chemistry; aerosol physics and chemistry; radiative effects of aerosols; visibility studies. *Mailing Add:* Sch of Geophys Sci Ga Inst of Technol Atlanta GA 30332

PATTERSON, ELIZABETH KNIGHT, b Pittsburgh, Pa, Sept 11, 09; m 35. BIOCHEMISTRY, CYTOCHEMISTRY. *Educ:* Wellesley Col, BA, 30; Bryn Mawr Col, MA & PhD(cytol), 40. *Prof Exp:* Tech asst, Rockefeller Inst, 30-34; spec asst, Bur Ord, US Navy Proj, Bryn Mawr Col, 42-43, demonstr biol, 43-44; res assoc, 44-50, assoc mem, 50-77, MEM, INST CANCER RES, 78- *Mem:* Am Asn Cancer Res; Am Chem Soc; NY Acad Sci; Soc Develop Biol; Am Soc Biol Chemists. *Res:* Purification and characterization of dipeptidases. *Mailing Add:* Inst for Cancer Res 7701 Burholme Ave Philadelphia PA 19111

PATTERSON, ERNEST LEONARD, b Crawford, Colo, Nov 18, 18; m 45; c 3. TOXICOLOGY, COMPUTER SCIENCE. *Educ:* Western State Col Colo, AB, 41; Calif Inst Technol, MS, 43; Univ Wis, PhD(biochem), 49. *Prof Exp:* Asst, Western State Col Colo, 39-41 & Calif Inst Technol, 42; explosives chemist, Woods Hole Oceanog Inst, 42-46; asst, Univ Wis, 46-49; RES BIOCHEMIST, LEDERLE LABS, AM CYANAMID CO, 49- *Mem:* Am Chem Soc; Am Soc Biol Chem. *Res:* Isolation, characterization and function of new growth factors; nutrition; antibiotics; fermentation biochemistry. *Mailing Add:* 182 Old Middletown Rd Pearl River NY 10965

PATTERSON, EUGENE B, b Vancouver, BC, Aug 6, 26; nat US; m 53; c 3. ANIMAL NUTRITION. *Educ:* Univ BC, BSA, 50; Wash State Univ, MS, 52, PhD(poultry nutrit), 55. *Prof Exp:* Res asst, Wash State Univ, 52-55; nutritionist, Res Labs, Swift & Co, Ill, 55-57; from nutritionist to regional nutritionist, Agr Res Ctr, Chas Pfizer & Co, Inc, 57-66, mgr, Develop Res Dept, Ind, 66-69, sci dir agr, 69-80, ASSOC DIR AGR RES & DEVELOP, PFIZER INT, INC, 80- *Mem:* Fel AAAS; Poultry Sci Asn; World Poultry Sci Asn; Am Soc Animal Sci; NY Acad Sci. *Res:* Developmental research in animal and poultry health, nutrition, antibiotics, anthelmintics and feed additives. *Mailing Add:* Pfizer Int Inc 235 E 42nd New York NY 10017

PATTERSON, FRED LA VERN, b Reynolds, Nebr, Apr 6, 16; m 43; c 3. PLANT BREEDING, GENETICS. *Educ:* Univ Nebr, BS, 42; Kans State Col, MS, 47; Univ Wis, PhD(plant breeding), 50. *Hon Degrees:* ScD, Univ Nebr, 79. *Prof Exp:* Asst plant breeding, Kans State Col, 46-47 & Univ Wis, 47-50; from asst agronomist to agronomist, 50-76, prof, 70-78, LYNN DISTINGUISHED PROF AGRON, PURDUE UNIV, 78- *Mem:* Am Soc Agron; Genetics Soc Am; Am Phytopath Soc; Genetics Soc Can. *Res:* Plant breeding and genetics of small grains. *Mailing Add:* Dept of Agron Life Sci Bldg Purdue Univ Lafayette IN 47907

PATTERSON, GARY DAVID, b Honolulu, Hawaii, July 31, 46; m 67. POLYMER PHYSICS, CHEMICAL PHYSICS. *Educ:* Harvey Mudd Col, BS, 68; Stanford Univ, PhD(phys chem), 72. *Prof Exp:* MEM TECH STAFF CHEM PHYSICS, BELL LABS, 72- *Mem:* Am Phys Soc; Am Chem Soc; Soc Rheol. *Res:* Rayleigh-Brilloiun and photon correlation spcetroscopy of polymers; dynamics of the glass transition; molecular dynamics of liquids. *Mailing Add:* Bell Labs Murray Hill NJ 07974

PATTERSON, GARY KENT, b Springfield, Mo, Dec 10, 39; m 60; c 3. CHEMICAL ENGINEERING. *Educ:* Mo Sch Mines, BS, 60; Univ Mich, MS, 61; Univ Mo-Rolla, PhD(chem eng), 66. *Prof Exp:* Engr, Esso Res Labs Div, Humble Oil Co, La, 61-63; from asst prof to assoc prof, 66-78, PROF CHEM ENG, UNIV MO-ROLLA, 78- *Concurrent Pos:* Humboldt fel, Max Planck Inst, Gottingen, WGer, 71-72; sect leader, Chem Eng Div, Lawrence Livermore Labs, Livermore, Calif, 77-78. *Mem:* Am Inst Chem Engrs; Am Chem Soc; Soc Rheol. *Res:* Fluid mechanics; turbulence; fluidization; drag reduction; polymer rheology; viscoelasticity; dilute solutions; melts; turbulent mixing in chemical reactors. *Mailing Add:* Dept of Chem Eng Univ of Mo Rolla MO 65401

PATTERSON, GEORGE HAROLD, b Uniontown, Pa, Aug 17, 17; m 41; c 2. ORGANIC CHEMISTRY. *Educ:* Juniata Col, BS, 39; Mass Inst Technol, PhD(org chem), 42. *Prof Exp:* Res chemist, E I Du Pont de Nemours & Co, Inc, 42-51, supvr, 51-53, div head, Jackson Lab, 53-80; RETIRED. *Concurrent Pos:* Ed, Chem Bulletin, Am Chem Soc. *Honors & Awards:* Brumbaugh Sci Prize, 39. *Mem:* AAAS; Am Chem Soc. *Res:* Organic pigments; fluorine and petroleum chemicals; detergents; tanning agents; refrigerants; polymerization of butadiene with organosodium compounds; analytical chemistry. *Mailing Add:* 1501 Woodsdale Rd Wilmington DE 19809

PATTERSON, GLENN WAYNE, b China Grove, NC, Mar 9, 38; m 61; c 3. PLANT PHYSIOLOGY, PLANT BIOCHEMISTRY. *Educ:* NC State Univ, BS, 60; Univ Md, MS, 63, PhD(plant physiol), 64. *Prof Exp:* From asst prof to assoc prof, 64-73, PROF PLANT PHYSIOL, UNIV MD, COLLEGE PARK, 73-, CHMN DEPT, 78- *Mem:* AAAS; Phycol Soc Am; Am Soc Plant Physiol; Am Chem Soc; Am Oil Chem Soc. *Res:* Plant lipid biochemistry, especially lipids of algae. *Mailing Add:* Dept Bot Univ Md College Park MD 20742

PATTERSON, GORDON DERBY, JR, b Columbus, Ohio, May 6, 23. ANALYTICAL CHEMISTRY, POLYMER SCIENCE. *Educ:* Allegheny Col, BS, 44; Purdue Univ, MS, 49, PhD(chem), 52. *Prof Exp:* Asst, Purdue Univ, 46-48, asst instr, 48-50; res chemist, 51-58, anal supvr, Film Dept, 58-73, anal consult, Film Dept, 73-76, res chemist, Plastic Prod & Resins, 76-81, OCCUPATIONAL HEALTH COORDR, POLYMER PRODS DEPT, E I DU PONT DE NEMOURS & CO, INC, 81- *Mem:* AAAS; Am Chem Soc; Am Soc Testing & Mat. *Res:* Physical and mechanical properties of plastics and polymeric films; instrumentation; chemical analysis; development of national and international technical standards for plastics and polymeric films; adoption of SI-metric system by industry and standards organizations; coordination of occupational health safeguards in chemical and physical research facilities. *Mailing Add:* E I du Pont de Nemours & Co Inc Polymer Prod Dept, Exp Sta Wilmington DE 19898

PATTERSON, HARRY ROBERT, b Long Beach, Calif, May 7, 21; m 47; c 4. PHARMACY, BACTERIOLOGY. *Educ:* Univ Southern Calif, BS, 44, MS, 45, PharmD, 51. *Prof Exp:* Retail & hosp pharmacist, 44-48; from instr to assoc prof, 48-61, PROF MICROBIOL, CALIF STATE UNIV, SAN JOSE, 61- *Mem:* AAAS; Am Soc Microbiol. *Res:* Synthesis of vanillin; toxicity of synthetic aromatics; hematology; pathogenic microbiology; immunology; electrophoretic characteristics of fish hemoglobins; antigenic characteristics of salmon erythrocytes; biology curriculum development. *Mailing Add:* San Jose State Univ Dept Microbiol 125 S Seventh St San Jose CA 95192

PATTERSON, HOWARD HUGH, b Los Angeles, Calif, Nov 6, 38; m 69. INORGANIC CHEMISTRY, PHYSICAL CHEMISTRY. *Educ:* Occidental Col, BA, 61; Mass Inst Technol, MS, 64; Brandeis Univ, PhD(phys chem), 68. *Prof Exp:* Asst prof, 68-73, assoc prof, 73-79, PROF CHEM, UNIV MAINE, ORONO, 79- *Concurrent Pos:* Vis scientist, Brookhaven Nat Lab. *Mem:* Am Chem Soc; Am Phys Soc; Sigma Xi. *Res:* Optical spectroscopy of unusual transition metal systems such as mixed valence complexes and platinum blues; application of chemiluminescence and fluorescence to study speciation of chromium plus 3 and chromium plus 3 in environment. *Mailing Add:* Dept of Chem Univ of Maine Orono ME 04473

PATTERSON, IAN D(AVID), b Eckford, Mich, Apr 6, 97; m 22; c 2. CHEMICAL ENGINEERING. *Educ:* Albion Col, AB, 19; Univ Mich, BSE, 20. *Prof Exp:* Chem engr, Goodyear Tire & Rubber Co, Ohio, 20 & Edgewood Arsenal, 21; rubber compounder & res chemist, Goodyear Tire & Rubber Co, 21-27, chief chemist, Eng, 27-36, develop mgr, 36-39, gen supt, St Mary's Mfg Div, 39-42, mil prod engr, process engr & asst mgr, Akron, 42-45, mgr chem prod div, 46-48, synthetic rubber coordr, 48-64; CONSULT CHEM ENGR, 64- *Concurrent Pos:* Mem staff, Int Exec Serv Corps, Korea, 71 & 73. *Mem:* Am Chem Soc; Am Inst Chem Engrs; fel Plastics & Rubber Inst. *Res:* Synthetic rubber; rubber chemistry and compounding resins and plastics. *Mailing Add:* 75 N Portage Path Apt 705 Akron OH 44303

PATTERSON, JAMES DEANE, b Gillette, Wyo, Sept 1, 34. PHYSICS. *Educ:* Univ Mo, AB, 56; Univ Chicago, MS, 57; Univ Kans, PhD(physics), 62. *Prof Exp:* Asst prof physics, Idaho State Univ, 61-63; assoc prof, 63-72, PROF PHYSICS, SDAK SCH MINES & TECHNOL, 72- *Concurrent Pos:* Vis assoc prof, Univ Notre Dame, 69-70; vis prof, Univ Nebr, Lincoln, 75-76. *Mem:* Am Phys Soc; Am Asn Physics Teachers. *Res:* Quantum theory of solids. *Mailing Add:* Dept Physics SDak Sch Mines & Technol Rapid City SD 57701

PATTERSON, JAMES FULTON, b Xenia, Ohio, Apr 11, 18; m 42; c 5. INTERNAL MEDICINE. *Educ:* Antioch Col, BS, 41; Harvard Univ, MD, 44; Am Bd Internal Med, dipl, 52. *Prof Exp:* Intern internal med, Boston City Hosp, 44-45; asst resident, Boston Dispensary, 45-46; resident, New Eng Ctr Hosp, 46-48; from instr to assoc prof, 48-66, PROF INTERNAL MED, MED SCH, TUFTS UNIV, 67- *Concurrent Pos:* Asst physician, New Eng Ctr Hosp, 48-54, physician, 54-, chief gastroenterol, 60-72, chief ambulatory med, 72-; clin & res fel, Mass Gen Hosp & Harvard Univ, 57-58. *Mem:* AAAS; AMA; fel Am Col Physicians. *Res:* Clinical research in gastroenterology and ambulatory medicine. *Mailing Add:* New Eng Med Ctr Hosps 171 Harrison Ave Boston MA 02111

PATTERSON, JAMES HOWARD, b Kansas City, Mo, Jan 22, 21; m 44; c 5. CHEMISTRY. *Educ:* Univ Omaha, BA, 43; Iowa State Col, PhD(chem), 50. *Prof Exp:* Anal chemist, Omaha Test Labs, 43-44; res asst & jr chemist, Inst Atomic Res, Iowa State Col, 44-50; assoc chemist, Argonne Nat Lab, 50-72; STAFF MEM, LOS ALAMOS SCI LAB, 72- *Concurrent Pos:* Testing engr, Metcalf-Hamilton-Kansas City Bridge Co, Can, 43. *Res:* Actinide element chemistry; interaction of actinides and the environment. *Mailing Add:* 2117B 43rd St Los Alamos NM 87544

PATTERSON, JAMES REID, b Charlotte, NC, Jan 15, 18; m 50; c 3. NUCLEAR PHYSICS. *Educ:* Davidson Col, BS, 39; Duke Univ, MA, 41, PhD, 55. *Prof Exp:* Lab instr, Duke Univ, 39-41, asst, 51-52, res assoc, 52-54; instr physics, NC State Col, 46-51; from asst prof to assoc prof, Furman Univ, 54-57; assoc prof, Clemson Col, 57-61; prof & head dept, Rockford Col, 61-67; assoc prof, 67-69, PROF PHYSICS, UNIV WIS-WHITEWATER, 69- *Concurrent Pos:* Researcher, La State Univ, 64, 66 & vis prof, 65. *Res:* Cosmic ray; magnetics; total neutron cross section measurements; beta ray spectrometer. *Mailing Add:* Dept of Physics Univ of Wis Whitewater WI 53190

PATTERSON, JAMES W(ILLIAM), b Montgomery, Ala, Nov 8, 40; m 64; c 2. ENVIRONMENTAL ENGINEERING. *Educ:* Auburn Univ, BS, 64, MS, 67; Univ Fla, PhD(environ eng), 70. *Prof Exp:* Res engr hydraul, Waterways Exp Sta, US Corps Engrs, 64-66; asst prof, 70-72, ASSOC PROF ENVIRON ENG, ILL INST TECHNOL, 72-, CHMN DEPT, 71- *Concurrent Pos:* Dir, Pritzker Environ Studies Ctr, 71-75. *Mem:* AAAS; Water Pollution Control Fedn; Int Asn Water Pollution Res; Am Chem Soc; Am Inst Chem Engrs. *Res:* Chemical and biological processes in polluted environments; biological waste treatment processes, including monitoring and control techniques, chemical processes for water and wastewater purification. *Mailing Add:* Dept of Environ Eng Ill Inst of Technol Chicago IL 60616

PATTERSON, JOHN LEGERWOOD, JR, b Roanoke Rapids, NC, Feb 5, 13. INTERNAL MEDICINE. *Educ:* Princeton Univ, AB, 35; Med Col Va, MD, 39; Univ Va, MS, 43; Am Bd Internal Med, dipl. *Prof Exp:* From instr to asst prof physiol & med, Sch Med, Emory Univ, 47-52; from asst prof to assoc prof, 53-60, chmn div cardiopulmonary labs & res, 60-78, RES PROF MED, MED COL VA, 60- *Mem:* Am Physiol Soc; Am Soc Clin Invest; AMA; Am Heart Asn; Am Fedn Clin Res. *Res:* Mechanisms of control of cerebral circulation and blood flow in the extremities; comparative physiology of the circulation; metabolism of the brain in head inury; determinant mechanisms of breath sounds; metabolism of blood vessels. *Mailing Add:* Dept of Med Med Col of Va Box 282 Richmond VA 23298

PATTERSON, JOHN MILES, b Vineland, NJ, Nov 5, 26; m 48; c 1. ORGANIC CHEMISTRY. *Educ:* Wheaton Col Ill, BS, 49; Northwestern Univ, PhD(chem), 53. *Prof Exp:* Res assoc chem, Northwestern Univ, 52-53; from instr to assoc prof, 53-67, PROF CHEM, UNIV KY, 67- *Mem:* Am Chem Soc. *Res:* Aliphatic nitrogen compounds; heterocyclic chemistry and compounds; free radicals in solution; high temperature reactions; photochemistry. *Mailing Add:* Dept of Chem Univ of Ky Lexington KY 40506

PATTERSON, JOHN W(ILLIAM), b Cleveland, Ohio, Mar 14, 36; m 60; c 2. METALLURGY, CERAMICS. *Educ:* Ohio State Univ, BEM & ME, 62, PhD(metall eng), 66. *Prof Exp:* From asst prof metall to assoc prof, 66-76, PROF MAT SCI & ENG, IOWA STATE UNIV, 76-, PRIN INVESTR SOLID ELECTROCHEM, ENG RES INST, 66- *Mem:* AAAS; Am Soc Metals; Electrochem Soc. *Res:* Mass and charge transport in ceramics at elevated temperatures; thermodynamics. *Mailing Add:* Dept Mat Sci & Eng Iowa State Univ Ames IA 50011

PATTERSON, JOHN WARD, b Baldwin, Kans, Dec 6, 16; m 40; c 4. PHYSIOLOGY, MEDICINE. *Educ:* Ohio Wesleyan Univ, AB, 39; Ohio State Univ, MS, 41, PhD(org chem), 42; Western Reserve Univ, MD, 49. *Hon Degrees:* DSc, Ohio Wesleyan Univ, 65. *Prof Exp:* Asst chem, Ohio State Univ, 39-42; instr, Univ Vt, 42-43; from instr to assoc prof anat, Western Reserve Univ, 47-56, assoc dean, 53-56; prof anat & dean, Univ BC, 56-58; dean sch med, Vanderbilt Univ, 58-62, dir med affairs, 58-59, vchancellor med affairs, 59-62, prof physiol, 62-63; dean, 65-71, exec dir health ctr, 67-75, vpres health affairs, 70-75, PROF PHYSIOL, SCH MED, UNIV CONN, 63- *Mem:* AAAS; Am Chem Soc; Soc Exp Biol & Med; Asn Res Vision & Ophthal; Am Physiol Soc. *Res:* Ultraviolet absorption spectroscopy; stereochemistry; cytochemistry; experimental diabetes; cataracts; medical education. *Mailing Add:* Univ of Conn Health Ctr Farmington CT 06032

PATTERSON, JOSEPH, b Ft Monmouth, NJ, Sept 24, 44. ELECTRICAL ENGINEERING, COMPUTER SCIENCE. *Educ:* Mass Inst Technol, SB, 66, SM, 68; Univ Mich, MS, 74, PhD(elec eng), 73. *Prof Exp:* Res asst quantum electronics, Res Lab Electronics, Mass Inst Technol, 66-68; res asst phys electronics, Electron Physics Lab, Univ Mich, 68-73, programmer behav res, Dept Pharmacol, 73-74; syst analyst health systs, Analytic Serv, Inc, 75-80; MEM TECH STAFF, LIBRA TECHNOL, 80- *Mem:* Sigma Xi; Inst Elec & Electronics Engrs. *Res:* Noise in microwave solid state devices; health information system planning. *Mailing Add:* 1300 Piccard Dr Libra Technol Rockville MD 20850

PATTERSON, JOSEPH GILBERT, b Jackson, Miss, Apr 25, 26; m 57; c 3. GEOLOGY. *Educ:* Miss Col, BA, 46; Southern Baptist Sem, BD, 49; Univ Va, MS, 58. *Prof Exp:* Dist geologist, US Army Engrs, Va, 57-60; dist geologist & asst chief, Mat Testing Lab, Hawaii, 60-62; mat engr, US Bur Pub Rds, Cambodia, 62-64, eng adv soils & geol, USAID, Thailand, 64-70; GEOLOGIST, & REAL ESTATE APPRAISOR, MISS STATE HWY DEPT, JACKSON, 70- *Mem:* Geol Soc Am. *Res:* Materials testing; engineering geology; ground water. *Mailing Add:* 307 E College St Clinton MS 39056

PATTERSON, LARRY K, b Marysville, Kans, Feb 14, 37; m 59; c 2. RADIATION CHEMISTRY, PHOTOCHEMISTRY. *Educ:* Kans State Univ, BS, 59, PhD(chem), 67. *Prof Exp:* Asst prof chem, St Benedicts Col, 65-66; fel photochem, Royal Inst Great Britian, 67-70; fel radiation chem, Carnegie-Mellon Univ, 70-74; res scientist radiobiol, Michael-Reese Hosp, 74-76; ASSOC PROF SPECIALIST RADIATION CHEM, RADIATION LAB, UNIV NOTRE DAME, 76-, FAC FEL, DEPT CHEM, 80- *Concurrent Pos:* Vis scientist, Nat Mus Natural Hist, 81. *Mem:* Radiation Res Soc. *Res:* Photochemicsal and radiation chemical kinetic in homogeneous aquenous sytems and in organiates (micelles, monolayers, vesicles) associated with aqueous media; laboratory automation. *Mailing Add:* Radiation Lab Univ Notre Dame Notre Dame IN 46556

PATTERSON, LOYD THOMAS, b Dekalb Co, Ala, Feb 23, 30; m 47; c 2. IMMUNOLOGY, ANIMAL VIROLOGY. *Educ:* Auburn Univ, BS, 59, MS, 60, PhD(microbiol), 63. *Prof Exp:* James W McLaughlin fel immunol, Med Br, Univ Tex, 63-65; from asst prof to assoc prof, 65-73, PROF MICROBIOL, UNIV ARK, FAYETTEVILLE, 73- *Concurrent Pos:* Consult, Pelfreez Biol & Vet Admin Hosp, Fayetteville. *Mem:* AAAS; Reticuloendothelial Soc; Am Soc Microbiol; Poultry Sci Asn; Sigma Xi. *Res:* C-reactive protein in nonspecific resistance and its occurrence in different species; immune response in tumor induction and in resistance to tumors; ontogeny of immunity; regulation of the immune response. *Mailing Add:* Dept of Animal Sci Univ Ark Fayetteville AR 72701

PATTERSON, MANFORD KENNETH, JR, b Muskogee, Okla, Aug 20, 26; m 53; c 1. BIOCHEMISTRY, CANCER. *Educ:* Univ Okla, BS, 53, MS, 54; Vanderbilt Univ, PhD(biochem), 62. *Prof Exp:* From res chemist to sr res chemist, Biomed Div, 51-65, sect head, 65-73, VPRES, SAMUEL ROBERTS NOBLE FOUND, INC & DIR, BIOMED DIV, 73- *Mem:* Am Chem Soc; Am Soc Biol Chem; Tissue Cult Asn (treas, 72); Am Asn Cancer Res. *Res:* Use of tissue culture techniques to study nutrition of cells; membranes and transport mechanism of metabolites. *Mailing Add:* Samuel Roberts Noble Found Inc Rte 1 Ardmore OK 73401

PATTERSON, MARCEL, b De Leon, Tex, Apr 4, 19; m 47; c 3. MEDICINE. *Educ:* Univ Tex, BA, 39; Tulane Univ, MD, 43; Am Bd Internal Med, dipl. *Prof Exp:* Instr med, Univ Calif, 45; mem staff, Lahey Clin, 49-52; clin instr, Univ Calif, 52-54; from asst prof to assoc prof, 54-63, Piper prof, 63-65, PROF INTERNAL MED, UNIV TEX MED BR GALVESTON, 65- *Concurrent Pos:* Fel gastroenterol, Lahey Clin, 48; consult, John Sealy Hosp, Wilford Hall Hosp, Lackland AFB, San Antonio & USPHS, Galveston; vis prof, Univ Honduras, 70. *Mem:* Am Gastroenterol Asn; Am Fedn Clin Res; fel Am Col Physicians. *Res:* Gastroenterology; chronic ulcerative colitis. *Mailing Add:* 1206 Marine Galveston TX 77550

PATTERSON, MARIA JEVITZ, b Berwyn, Ill, Oct 23, 44; m 70; c 2. INFECTIOUS DISEASES, MICROBIOLOGY. *Educ:* Col St Francis, BS, 66; Registry Med Technologists, cert, 66; Northwestern Univ, PhD(microbiol), 70. *Prof Exp:* asst prof, 72-77, ASSOC PROF MICROBIOL & PUB HEALTH, MICH STATE UNIV, 77- *Concurrent Pos:* NIH trainee clin microbiol, Univ Wash, 70-72; staff microbiologist, Dept Path, Lansing Gen Hosp, Mich, 72-75; fel clin microbiol, Univ Wash, 70-72; staff microbiologist, Clin Labs, Mich State Univ, 78- *Mem:* Am Soc Microbiol; Am Soc Clin Pathologists; SCent Asn Clin Microbiol. *Res:* Host response to infectious disease; viral pathogenesis. *Mailing Add:* Dept of Microbiol & Pub Health Mich State Univ East Lansing MI 48823

PATTERSON, MAX E, b Bourbon, Ind, July 8, 23; m 44; c 2. PLANT PHYSIOLOGY, HORTICULTURE. *Educ:* Purdue Univ, BSA, 49, PhD(plant physiol, biochem, hort), 59; Cornell Univ, MSA, 53. *Prof Exp:* Res assoc plant physiol & hort, NY State Agr Exp Sta, 49-53; instr, Purdue Univ, 53-58; from asst prof to assoc prof, 58-70, PROF PLANT PHYSIOL & HORT, WASH STATE UNIV, 70- *Concurrent Pos:* Vis scientist, East Malling Res Sta, England, 79-80. *Honors & Awards:* Woodbury Award, Am Soc Hort Sci, 63; Dow Chem Co Award, Am Soc Hort Sci, 68; J H Gourley Award, Am Soc Hort Sci, 78. *Mem:* AAAS; Am Soc Hort Sci; Am Soc Plant Physiol. *Res:* Post harvest horticulture. *Mailing Add:* Dept of Hort & Landscape Archit Wash State Univ Pullman WA 99164

PATTERSON, OMAR LEROY, b Seattle, Wash, Apr 7, 18; m 41; c 3. PHYSICS. *Educ:* Univ Minn, BEE, 38, MA, 40. *Prof Exp:* Asst math & mech, Univ Minn, 38-40; test engr, Gen Elec Co, NY, 40-41; physicist, Phys Lab, Sun Oil Co, 46-55; mgr, Strategic Syst Develop Missile & Surface Radar Div, RCA Corp, 55-81; TECH CONSULT, STRATEGIC MILITARY SYSTS, 81- *Res:* Oil reservoir analyzer design; general electronics and mathematics; radar; infrared; analog computer design; advanced weapons systems development. *Mailing Add:* 609 Kings Hwy Moorestown NJ 08057

PATTERSON, RICHARD L, b Brooklyn, NY, Sept 12, 32; m 53; c 2. RESOURCE MANAGEMENT. *Educ:* Univ Mich, BSF, 54, MS, 59, PhD(indust eng), 63. *Prof Exp:* Engr opers anal, Bendix Corp, 60-63; res assoc, Indust Systs Lab, Univ Mich, 63; from asst prof to prof indust & systs eng, Univ Fla, 63-70; PROF NATURAL RESOURCES, UNIV MICH, ANN ARBOR, 70- *Mem:* Opers Res Soc; Soc Am Foresters; Sigma Xi. *Res:* Natural resource management; queuing theory; combinatorial optimization; ecology systems. *Mailing Add:* Sch of Natural Resources Univ of Mich Ann Arbor MI 48104

PATTERSON, RICHARD SHELDON, b Waltham, Mass, Apr 27, 32; m 57; c 2. MEDICAL ENTOMOLOGY. *Educ:* Univ Mass, BS, 54, MS, 55; Cornell Univ, PhD(entom), 62. *Prof Exp:* Entomologist, Midge Res Lab, Fla, 62-64, dir lab, Fla State Bd Health, 64-66; entomologist, 66-78, RES LEADER, INSECTS AFFECTING MAN & ANIMAL BR, GAINESVILLE LAB, USDA, 78- *Concurrent Pos:* Prof, Univ Fla, 68-; WHO scientist genetic control mosquitoes, India, 70-73. *Mem:* Am Mosquito Control Asn; Entom Soc Am. *Res:* Control of insect pests of truck-crops and ornamentals; biology and control of aquatic insects, primarily chironomid midges; biology and control of mosquito; fly biology and control, particularly biocontrol of noxious flies. *Mailing Add:* Agr Res Serv USDA PO Box 14565 Gainesville FL 32604

PATTERSON, ROBERT ALLEN, b Lock Haven, Pa, Nov 23, 27; m 56; c 4. ZOOLOGY. *Educ:* Univ Mich, BSc, 50; Ohio State Univ, MSc, 55, PhD(entom), 57. *Prof Exp:* Asst prof, 57-63, assoc prof, 64-71, PROF ZOOL, ARIZ STATE UNIV, 72- *Concurrent Pos:* NIH res grant, 60-66 & 76-77. *Mem:* Fel AAAS; Int Soc Toxinology. *Res:* Physiology and pharmacology of animal venoms. *Mailing Add:* Dept of Zool Ariz State Univ Tempe AZ 85281

PATTERSON, ROBERT JOE, b Dallas, Tex, Feb 28, 34; m 53; c 3. MATERIALS SCIENCE, PHYSICAL CHEMISTRY. *Educ:* Abilene Christian Univ, BS, 57; Ore State Univ, MS, 63. *Prof Exp:* Tech staff, Mat, Tex Instruments, Inc, 55-67; SR ENGR, TEKTRONIX, INC, 67- *Mem:* Electrochem Soc. *Res:* Thin films for microcircuits; chemical vapor deposition; integrated circuit fabrication. *Mailing Add:* Tektronix Inc PO Box 500 MS 48-269 Beaverton OR 97077

PATTERSON, ROBERT PRESTON, b Statesville, NC, July 13, 39; m 61; c 3. CROP PHYSIOLOGY, CROP PRODUCTION. *Educ:* NC State Univ, BS, 61, MS, 63; Cornell Univ, PhD(agron), 68. *Prof Exp:* Asst prof, 68-72, assoc prof, 72-79, PROF CROP SCI, NC STATE UNIV, 72- *Mem:* Am Soc Agron; Am Soc Plant Physiol. *Res:* Plant nutrition; environmental and physiological aspects of crop production. *Mailing Add:* Dept of Crop Sci NC State Univ Box 5155 Raleigh NC 27650

PATTERSON, RONALD BRINTON, b Wichita, Kans, Apr 20, 41; m 71. ANALYTICAL & ORGANIC CHEMISTRY. *Educ:* Hastings Col, AB, 63; Univ Nebr, Lincoln, PhD(org chem), 70. *Prof Exp:* Res chemist, 69-73, supvr prod develop, 73-80, MGR, PROD DEVELOP, LORILLARD RES CTR, LOEW'S, 80- *Mem:* Am Chem Soc. *Res:* Flavors; high performance liquid chromatography; gas chromatography; tobacco chemistry. *Mailing Add:* Lorillard Res Ctr 420 English St Greensboro NC 27420

PATTERSON, RONALD JAMES, b Pittsburgh, Pa, Apr 16, 43; m 70. IMMUNOBIOLOGY. *Educ:* Washington & Jefferson Col, BA, 65; Northwestern Univ, Evanston, PhD(microbiol), 70. *Prof Exp:* Asst prof, 72-77, ASSOC PROF MICROBIOL, MICH STATE UNIV, 77- *Concurrent Pos:* NIH fel, Univ Wash, 70-72; NIH res grant, Mich State Univ, 72- *Mem:* Am Soc Cell Biol. *Res:* Cell biology. *Mailing Add:* Dept of Microbiol & Pub Health Mich State Univ East Lansing MI 48824

PATTERSON, ROSALYN MITCHELL, b Madison, Ga, Mar 25, 39; m 61; c 3. CYTOGENETICS. *Educ:* Spelman Col, BA, 58; Atlanta Univ, MS, 60; Emory Univ, PhD(biol), 67. *Prof Exp:* From instr to prof biol, Spelman Col, 60-70; consult, Bur Reclamation, Dept Interior, 70-71, coordr nat environ educ develop prog, Nat Park Serv, 71-72; fel cell biol & Nat Inst Gen Med Sci fel, Div Biol Standards, Lab Path, NIH, 72-73; assoc prof biol, Ga State Univ, 74-76; assoc prof, 77-81, PROF BIOL & CHAIRPERSON DEPT, ATLANTA UNIV, 81- *Concurrent Pos:* Southern Fel Fund fel, Ga Inst Technol, 69-70. *Mem:* AAAS; Am Soc Cell Biol; Soc Develop Biol; Sigma Xi. *Res:* Determination of potential free radical activity induced by specific environmental agents in vitro; evaluation of induced free radical activity by electron spin resonance and cytogentic analyses. *Mailing Add:* Dept Biol Atlanta Univ Atlanta GA 30314

PATTERSON, ROY, b Ironwood, Mich, Apr 26, 26; m 48; c 3. INTERNAL MEDICINE. *Educ:* Univ Mich, BS, 50, MD, 53; Am Bd Internal Med, dipl; Am Bd Allergy, dipl. *Prof Exp:* Asst prof internal med, Univ Mich, 59-60; from asst prof to prof internal med, 60-67, assoc chmn dept med, 71-73, ERNEST S BAZLEY PROF ALLERGY & IMMUNOL, MED SCH, NORTHWESTERN UNIV, CHICAGO, 64-, CHMN DEPT MED, 74- *Concurrent Pos:* USPHS res career develop award, 63-; consult, US Vet

Admin Hosps, Ann Arbor, Mich, 58-60 & Chicago, Ill, 60-; attend physician, Vet Admin Res & Passavant Mem Hosps, 61, Cook County Hosp, 63- & Chicago Wesley Mem Hosp, 64- *Mem:* AAAS; fel Am Col Physicians; fel Am Acad Allergy; Am Asn Immunologists; Am Soc Clin Invest. *Res:* Allergy; immunology. *Mailing Add:* Northwestern Univ Med Sch 303 E Chicago Ave Chicago IL 60611

PATTERSON, RUSSEL HUGO, JR, b New York, NY, Apr 1, 29; m 55; c 3. NEUROSURGERY. *Educ:* Stanford Univ, BA, 48; Cornell Univ, MD, 52; Am Bd Neurol Surgeons, cert, 63. *Prof Exp:* Asst, 55-59, instr, 59-61, clin instr, 61-63, from asst prof to assoc prof, 63-71, PROF SURG, MED COL, CORNELL UNIV, 71- *Concurrent Pos:* Mem, Am Bd Neurol Surgeons, 76- *Mem:* AMA; Am Col Surgeons; Am Acad Neurol Surg (secy, 73-); Soc Neurol Surgeons; Am Asn Neurol Surgeons (vpres, 76). *Res:* Cerebrovascular disease. *Mailing Add:* New York Hosp 525 E 68th St New York NY 10021

PATTERSON, SAM H, b Marion, Iowa, Aug 14, 18; m 42; c 2. GEOLOGY. *Educ:* Coe Col, BA, 40; Univ Iowa, MS, 47; Univ Ill, PhD(geol), 55. *Prof Exp:* GEOLOGIST, SCI & EDUC ADMIN-AGR RES, US GEOL SURV, 47- *Mem:* Geol Soc Am; Mineral Soc Am; Clay Minerals Soc; Am Inst Mining, Metall & Petrol Eng; Soc Econ Geologists. *Res:* Bentonite deposits of South Dakota, Wyoming and Montana; refractory clay deposits of eastern Kentucky; bauxite deposits of Hawaii; Fuller's earth deposits of Georgia and Florida; world bauxite. *Mailing Add:* 954 Nat Ctr US Geol Surv Reston VA 22092

PATTERSON, SAMUEL S, b Indianapolis, Ind, Mar 8, 17; m 58, c 2. DENTISTRY. *Educ:* Ind Univ, DDS, 40, MSD, 60; Am Bd Endodont, dipl. *Prof Exp:* From instr to prof oper dent, 49-74, dir grad endodont, 68-74, PROF ENDODONT & CHMN DEPT, SCH DENT, IND UNIV, INDIANAPOLIS, 74- *Concurrent Pos:* Consult, Vet Admin. *Mem:* Am Dent Asn; fel Am Asn Endodontists (past vpres, pres, 68); fel Am Col Dent; fel Int Col Dent; Int Asn Dent Res. *Res:* Effect of therapeutic cobalt 60 radiation on dental structures and investing tissues. *Mailing Add:* 4536 N Meridian St Indianapolis IN 46208

PATTERSON, STEVEN LEROY, b Waco, Tex, Oct 2, 47. PHYSICAL OCEANOGRAPHY. *Educ:* Tex A&M Univ, BS, 70, MS, 72, PhD(oceanog), 78. *Prof Exp:* res assoc, 78-79, ASST RES SCIENTIST, DEPT OCEANOG, TEX A&M UNIV, 81- *Concurrent Pos:* Sr scientist, Sci Applns Inc, McLean, Va, 79-81. *Mem:* Am Geophys Union. *Res:* Descriptive physical oceanography, especially of the Southern Ocean; water mass formation, circulation, and distribution; structure and motion of Southern Ocean frontal zones and cross frontal property fluxes. *Mailing Add:* Dept Oceanog Tex A&M Univ College Station TX 77843

PATTERSON, THOMAS GLOVER, b Spokane, Wash, July 21, 52; m 74. AGRONOMY, PLANT PHYSIOLOGY. *Educ:* Wash State Univ, BS, 74; Univ Minn MS, 77, PhD(agron), 78. *Prof Exp:* Teaching asst agron, Wash State Univ, 74; res asst agron, Univ Minn, 74-78; RES ASSOC PLANT PHYSIOL, BOYCE THOMPSON INST, 78- *Mem:* Am Soc Agron; Am Soc Plant Physiol; AAAS. *Res:* Plant growth and development; biochemical aspects of yield in wheat and soy beans; plant biochemistry; nitrogen fixation and metabolism; photosynthesis; senescence. *Mailing Add:* Boyce Thompson Inst Tower Rd Ithaca NY 14853

PATTERSON, TROY B, b Columbus, Miss, Dec 5, 23; m 48; c 4. ANIMAL BREEDING, ANIMAL GENETICS. *Educ:* Miss State Univ, BS, 47; Tex A&M Univ, MS, 48, PhD(animal breeding), 56. *Prof Exp:* From instr to assoc prof animal husb, Miss State Univ, 48-57; asst genetics, Tex A&M Univ, 53-56; assoc prof animal sci, 57-65, PROF ANIMAL SCI, AUBURN UNIV, 65- *Mem:* Am Soc Animal Sci; Am Genetic Asn. *Res:* Genetic-environment interaction in beef cattle; genetic and environmental parameters of beef cattle; crossbreeding among British breeds. *Mailing Add:* Dept of Animal & Dairy Sci Auburn Univ Auburn AL 36849

PATTERSON, TRUETT CLIFTON, b Greenville, SC, Oct 10, 37; m 59; c 2. INORGANIC CHEMISTRY, ANALYTICAL CHEMISTRY. *Educ:* Furman Univ, BS, 59; Univ Tenn, PhD(chem), 66. *Prof Exp:* Asst prof, 64-66, assoc prof, 67-71, PROF CHEM, CARSON-NEWMAN COL, 72- *Mem:* Sigma Xi; Am Chem Soc. *Res:* Coordination chemistry. *Mailing Add:* Dept of Chem Carson-Newman Col Box 1906 Jefferson City TN 37760

PATTERSON, VERNON HOWE, b Rochester, NY, Feb 5, 10; m 35; c 4. METALLURGY. *Educ:* Univ Rochester, BS, 33. *Prof Exp:* Asst mgr, Personal Finance Co, 33-36; metall asst, Bausch & Lomb Optical Co, 36-37, from asst metallurgist to chief metallurgist, 37-46; sales metallurgist, Am Brake Shoe Co, 46-49; from metall engr to mgr foundry sales, Climax Molybdenum Co, 49-58; mgr distributor sales, Vanadium Corp Am, Ohio, 58-68; mgr, Metall Prod Div, Foote Mineral Co, 68-69, mgr foundry tech serv, 69-75; CONSULT, FOOTE MINERAL CO & MILLER & CO, CHICAGO, 75- *Concurrent Pos:* Gen mgr, Progressive Foundry Works, Inc, 45; instr, Univ Rochester, 45-46; mem teaching staff, Cast Metals Inst, Am Foundrymen's Soc, Des Plaines, Ill. *Honors & Awards:* John H Whiting Gold Medal, Am Foundrymen's Soc, 77; Award, Ductile Iron Soc Award, 77. *Mem:* Am Soc Metals; Am Inst Mining, Metall & Petrol Engrs; Am Foundrymen's Soc; Ductile Iron Soc. *Res:* Metals and finishes for glass molds; stress relief annealing of ferrous and nonferrous metals; photomicrography of metals; identification of aluminum alloys; precious metals for spectacle industry; melting practices for iron and steel; inoculation of cast iron. *Mailing Add:* Foote Mineral Co & Miller & Co 7738 Pleasant Run Scottsdale AZ 85258

PATTERSON, WILLIAM ALEXANDER, b Shankhouse, Eng, July 16, 15; m 46; c 2. PHYSICAL CHEMISTRY. *Educ:* Univ NB, BA, 36; Univ Toronto, 38, PhD(phys chem), 40. *Prof Exp:* Asst chemist, NB Int Paper Co, 36-37; asst chem & demonstr electrochem, Univ Toronto, 37-40; res chemist, Res & Develop Lab, Can Industs, Ltd, 40-51; tech consult instrument applns, Baird Assocs, Inc, 51-55; res group leader, Cryovac Div, W R Grace & Co, Duncan, 55-62, res gr, 62-66, sr scientist for advan technol, 66-70, sr scientist & coordr environ res control, Cryovac Div, 70-80; RETIRED. *Concurrent Pos:* Vis prof, Univ W Indies, 68-70. *Mem:* Am Chem Soc; AAAS. *Res:* Diffusion constants of copper; spectroscopy; process control instrumentation; irradiation chemistry; polymer and film technology; environmental problems. *Mailing Add:* 422 Forest Ave Spartanburg SC 29302

PATTERSON, WILLIAM BRADFORD, b New Rochelle, NY, June 25, 21; m 43; c 4. SURGERY, ONCOLOGY. *Educ:* Harvard Univ, AB, 43, MD, 50. *Prof Exp:* Chemist explosives, E I du Pont de Nemours & Co, Inc, NJ, 42-44; intern & resident surg, Peter Bent Brigham Hosp, 50-55; asst dir, Sears Surg Lab, Boston City Hosp, 56-59; chief prof serv, Pondville Hosp, Walpole, Mass, 59-63; asst clin prof surg, Harvard Med Sch, 61-70; prof oncol in surg, Sch Med & Dent, Univ Rochester, 70-78; DIR CANCER CONTROL, SIDNEY FARBER CANCER INST, 78- *Concurrent Pos:* Nat Cancer Inst trainee, Peter Bent Brigham Hosp, Boston, 51-53; Am Cancer Soc clin fel, New Eng Deaconess Hosp, Boston, 53-54; pvt pract, 63-70; surgeon, Strong Mem Hosp, Rochester, NY, 70-78; consult, Park-Ave Hosp, Rochester, 71-78; chmn surg, Monroe Community Hosp, Rochester, 71-75; mem cancer clin invests rev comt, NIH, 71-75; vis prof surg, Harvard Med Sch, 78-; mem Harvard surg serv, New Eng Deaconess Hosp, Boston, 78- *Mem:* Am Col Surgeons; Am Soc Clin Oncol; Soc Surg Oncol. *Res:* Clinical cancer research, including chemotherapy and surgical technics. *Mailing Add:* Sidney Farber Cancer Inst 44 Binney St Boston MA 02115

PATTERSON, WILLIAM CREIGH, JR, b Royalton, Pa, Mar 26, 21; m 47; c 4. VETERINARY MEDICINE. *Educ:* Pa State Col, BS, 43; Univ Pa, VMD, 49. *Prof Exp:* Vet, Southeast Pa Artificial Breeding Coop, 49-51; asst to dir animal dis & parasite res div, 51-61, dir, Southeast Poultry Res Lab, 61-72, ASST AREA DIR, AGR RES SERV, USDA, 72- *Mem:* Am Vet Med Asn; US Animal Health Asn; Am Asn Avian Path; Poultry Sci Asn; World Vet Poultry Asn. *Res:* Veterinary virology; vesicular stomatitis of horses, cattle and swine; vesicular exanthema of swine; poultry diseases. *Mailing Add:* Russell Res Ctr Agr Res Serv PO Box 5677 Athens GA 30604

PATTERSON, WILLIAM JERRY, b Memphis, Tenn, Aug 8, 39; m 66; c 2. ORGANIC POLYMER CHEMISTRY. *Educ:* Miss State Univ, BS, 61; MS, 63; Univ Ala, PhD(org chem), 74. *Prof Exp:* Chemist, Entom Res Lab, USDA, 61-63; RES CHEMIST, MAT & PROCESSES LAB, MARSHALL SPACE FLIGHT CTR, NASA, 63- *Mem:* Am Chem Soc; Sigma Xi. *Res:* Synthesis, characterization and structure-property correlations of organosilicon and organometallic condensation polymers; reactivity-ratio studies of oxazoline addition copolymers. *Mailing Add:* Mat & Processes Lab Marshall Space Flight Ctr NASA Huntsville AL 35812

PATTIE, DONALD L, b Volt, Mont, Nov 22, 33; m 56; c 2. BIOLOGY, ECOLOGY. *Educ:* Concordia Col, Minn, BA, 55; Mont State Univ, MA, 60; Univ Mont, PhD, 67. *Prof Exp:* From instr to asst prof biol, Pac Lutheran Univ, 63-69; assoc prof, Camrose Lutheran Col, 69-73; INSTR BIOL SCI, NORTHERN ALTA INST TECHNOL, 73- *Concurrent Pos:* NSF study grants, 67-69; Nat Res Coun & Int Biol Prog grant energy flow in avian high Arctic ecosysts, Devon Island, Northwest Territories, Can, 70-72 & 78-81. *Mem:* Am Soc Mammal; Cooper Ornith Soc. *Res:* Ecology of arctic and alpine mammals and birds; mammalian taxonomy. *Mailing Add:* Dept Biol Sci Northern Alta Inst Technol Edmonton AB T5G 2R1 Can

PATTILLO, WALTER HUGH, JR, b Bayboro, NC, Jan 1, 30; m 58; c 2. PARASITOLOGY. *Educ:* Hampton Inst, BS, 52; Iowa State Univ, MS, 54, PhD(parasitol), 56. *Prof Exp:* Asst zool & entom, Iowa State Univ, 53-56; asst prof biol, Tuskegee Inst & res assoc, Carver Found, 58-61; asst undergrad dean, 76-78, PROF BIOL, NC CENT UNIV, 61-, DEAN UNDERGRAD SCH, 78- *Mem:* Sigma Xi; Nat Inst Sci; Soc Protozool. *Res:* Protozoology; Coccidia; Eimeria. *Mailing Add:* Undergrad Sch Arts & Sci NC Cent Univ Durham NC 27707

PATTINSON, CHARLES BYRON, JR, b Collingswood, NJ, Apr 13, 20; m 43; c 3. PETROLEUM CHEMISTRY. *Educ:* Franklin & Marshall Col, BS, 42. *Prof Exp:* Chemist, 42-51, group leader motor oil develop, 51-61, res chemist, 61-68, SR RES CHEMIST, GULF RES & DEVELOP CO, 68- *Mem:* Am Chem Soc; Soc Automotive Eng. *Res:* Standard analytical testing; process research; gasoline and diesel engine crankcase oil development; transmission fluids; gear lubricants; automotive specialties; industrial and government specifications for motor oils world wide; engine fuel and motor oil testing procedures. *Mailing Add:* Gulf Res & Develop Co PO Drawer 2038 Pittsburgh PA 15230

PATTON, ALVA RAE, b Livingston, Mont, Oct 15, 08; m 33; c 1. NUTRITION. *Educ:* Mont State Col, BS, 30; Univ Minn, MS, 33, PhD(biochem), 35. *Prof Exp:* Asst instr biochem, Univ Minn, 30-35; instr, Cornell Univ, 35-36; asst prof animal indust, Univ Ark, 36-38; asst prof poultry nutrit, Colo State Col, 38-39; head chem dept, Exp Sta & prof chem, Mont State Col, 39-43; res chemist, Biol Lab, E I du Pont de Nemours & Co, NJ, 43-45; from assoc prof to prof, 45-72, EMER PROF CHEM, COLO STATE UNIV, 72- *Mem:* AAAS; Am Chem Soc. *Res:* Amino acid nutrition, biochemistry and analysis. *Mailing Add:* 727 Franklin St Port Townsend WA 98368

PATTON, BOBBIE JOE, b Whitt, Tex, Nov 5, 25. PHYSICS. *Educ:* NTex State Univ, BS, 49, MS, 50. *Prof Exp:* Instr physics, NTex State Univ, 50-51; nuclear physicist, Gulf Res & Develop Co, 51-53; res technologist nuclear magnetic resonance, Field Res Lab, Mobil Res & Develp Corp, 53-58, sr res technologist, rock magnetism, 58-66, res assoc rock magnetism, 66-80; TECH PLANNING MGR, MEASUREMENTS WHILE DRILLING, GEARHART INDUST, 81- *Mem:* Sigma Xi; Am Inst Metall Engrs. *Mailing Add:* 1921 W Freeway apt 3 Grand Prairie TX 75051

PATTON, BRUCE RILEY, b Pittsburgh, Pa, May 30, 44. MANY BODY THEORY, PHASE TRANSITIONS. *Educ:* Swarthmore Col, BA, 66; Cornell Univ, PhD(physics), 71. *Prof Exp:* Res assoc physics, Cornell Univ, 71; lectr, Univ Calif, San Diego, 71-73; asst prof, Mass Inst Technol, 73-78; ASSOC PROF PHYSICS, OHIO STATE UNIV, 78- *Concurrent Pos:* Fel, Woodrow Wilson Found, 66-67, NSF, 71-72 & Alfred P Sloan Found, 74-78; Prin investr, NSF; consult, IBM. *Mem:* Am Phys Soc. *Res:* Many-body phenomena in condensed matter, including superconductivity in metals, superfluidity in liquid 3helium, thermodynamics and transport properties of quasi-one-dimensional conductors, and the properties of inhomogeneous and submicron physical systems. *Mailing Add:* Physics Dept Ohio State Univ Columbus OH 43210

PATTON, CARL E, b San Antonio, Tex, Sept 14, 41. SOLID STATE PHYSICS. *Educ:* Mass Inst Technol, SB, 63; Calif Inst Technol, MS, 64, PhD(elec eng), 67. *Prof Exp:* Asst scientist, Jet Propulsion Lab, Calif Inst Technol, 63; sr res scientist, Res Div, Raytheon Corp, 67-69; vis scientist, Inst Solid State Physics, Univ Tokyo, 69-70; sr res scientist, Res Div, Raytheon Corp, 70-71; assoc prof, 71-76, PROF PHYSICS, COLO STATE UNIV, 76- *Concurrent Pos:* Japan Soc Promotion Sci fel, 69-70; Nat Acad Sci exchange fel, Czech Acad Sci, 73 & 79; vis scientist, Inst Fur Angewandte Festkorperphysin, WGer, 77-78; Humbolt Found res fel, 77-78. *Mem:* Am Phys Soc; Inst Elec & Electronics Eng. *Res:* Magnetic thin films; domain wall motion and ferromagnetic resonance; microwave magnetic materials; spin wave instability; relaxation processes; magnetic metals and alloys; induced anisotropy. *Mailing Add:* Dept Physics Colo State Univ Ft Collins CO 80523

PATTON, CHARLES C(LIFFORD), b Cushing, Okla, July 10, 36; m 61; c 2. PETROLEUM ENGINEERING, CORROSION ENGINEERING. *Educ:* Univ Okla, BS, 59; Univ Tex, PhD(petrol eng), 64. *Prof Exp:* Exploitation engr, Shell Oil Co, 59-60; sr res petrol engr, Monsanto Co, 63-64; res scientist corrosion, Continental Oil Co, 64-67, res group leader, 67-69; staff engr, Hudson's Bay Oil & Gas Co, Ltd, 69-70; assoc prof petrol & geol eng, Univ Okla, 70-72, dir sch petrol & geol eng, 72-74; vpres, Petrotech Ltd, 74-80; PRES, C C PATTON & ASSOCS, 80- *Concurrent Pos:* Nat Sci Found res fel sci & pub policy, 71-72. *Mem:* Soc Petrol Engrs; Nat Asn Corrosion Engrs. *Res:* Oilfield corrosion; water treatment for subsurface injection; oilwell stimulation. *Mailing Add:* C C Patton & Assocs Inc 1215 Crossroads Blvd Norman OK 73069

PATTON, CURTIS LEVERNE, b Birmingham, Ala, June 13, 35; m 63; c 1. PARASITOLOGY, CELL BIOLOGY. *Educ:* Fisk Univ, BA, 56; Mich State Univ, MS, 61, PhD(microbiol), 66. *Prof Exp:* Asst microbiol, Mich State Univ, 60-63, from asst instr to instr, 63-67; guest investr, Rockefeller Univ, 67-70; asst prof microbiol, 70-74, dir grad studies, 72-74, asst prof epidemiol, pub health & microbiol, 74-76, ASSOC PROF EPIDEMIOL, PUB HEALTH & MICROBIOL, SCH MED, YALE UNIV, 76- *Concurrent Pos:* Biomed Sci Support grant, 66-67; fel parasitol, Rockefeller Univ, 67-70; USPHS training grant, 67-69, USPHS res grants, 72-77, 78-82 & 82-85; dir, Interdisciplinary Parasitol Training Prog, USPHS grants, 77-80 & 86; mem, Minority Access Res Careers & Nat Inst Gen Med Sci, 78-82; mem, Nat Res Coun Comn Human Resources Eval Panel, 79-81; consult, US Army Med Res & Develop Command, 79-82. *Mem:* AAAS; Am Soc Parasitologists; Soc Protozoologists. *Res:* Cell and molecular biology of trypanosomes; membrane transport in parasitic protozoa; physiology of parasitic protozoa; humoral and cellular responses to parasitic protozoa. *Mailing Add:* Dept of Epidemiol & Pub Health Yale Univ Sch of Med New Haven CT 06510

PATTON, DAVID ROGER, m 52; c 3. WILDLIFE RESEARCH. *Educ:* Univ WVa, BS, 60; Va Polytech Inst, MS, 63; Univ Ariz, PhD(watershed mgt), 74. *Prof Exp:* Forester, Cleveland Nat Forest, US Forest Serv, 60; biologist, US Fish & Wildlife Serv, 60-61 & Santa Fe Nat Forest, US Forest Serv, 63-64, res biologist, Rocky Mt Forest & Range Exp Sta, 64-73, PROJ LEADER, FOREST HYDROL LAB, ARIZ STATE UNIV, ROCKY MT FOREST & RANGE EXP STA, US FOREST SERV, 73- *Concurrent Pos:* Wildlife expert to Govt Repub Zambia, Food & Agr Orgn, UN, 66-67. *Mem:* AAAS; Wildlife Soc; Soc Am Foresters. *Res:* Influence of forest management practices on distribution and abundance of wildlife populations; ecological relationships of animals and their habitat; develop habitat criteria for game, non-game and endangered species on national forests in the Southwest. *Mailing Add:* Forestry Sci Lab RWU Rm 1710 Ariz State Univ Tempe AZ 85281

PATTON, DENNIS DAVID, b Oakland, Calif, Aug 4, 30; m 65; c 2. RADIOLOGY, NUCLEAR MEDICINE. *Educ:* Univ Calif, Berkeley, BA, 53; Univ Calif, Los Angeles, MD, 59. *Prof Exp:* Assoc med physics, Univ Calif, Berkeley, 52-54, sr lab technician, 54-57; mgr biomed group, Planning Res Corp, 58-65; resident radiol, Col Med, Univ Calif, Irvine, 65-68, asst prof, 68-70, chief nuclear med, Orange County Med Ctr, 68-70; assoc prof radiol, Med Ctr, Vanderbilt Univ, 70-75; actg chief nuclear med, Vet Admin Hosp, Tucson, 75-77; DIR, DIV NUCLEAR MED, MED CTR, UNIV ARIZ, 75-, PROF RADIOL, 80- *Concurrent Pos:* Teaching fel, Univ Calif, Irvine, 67-68, grant, 69-70; consult, Long Beach Vet Admin Hosp, Calif, 68-70 & St Joseph's Hosp & Children's Hosp, Orange County, Calif, 69-70. *Mem:* Soc Nuclear Med; Radiol Soc NAm; Am Col Radiol; Am Col Nuclear Med; Asn Univ Radiologists. *Res:* Development of short-life radiopharmaceuticals for diagnostic clinical studies; development of medical imaging systems; operations research and systems analysis in medicine. *Mailing Add:* Div of Nuclear Med Univ of Ariz Med Ctr Tucson AZ 85724

PATTON, ELIZABETH VANDYKE, b Omaha, Nebr, June 24, 44; m 67; c 2. PHYSICAL CHEMISTRY. *Educ:* Univ Mich, BS, 66; Univ Wis, PhD(phys chem), 72. *Prof Exp:* Fel biochem, Sch Med & Dent, Univ Rochester, 71-74; LECTR, ROCHESTER INST TECHNOL, 74- *Mem:* Am Chem Soc. *Res:* Physical properties of biological macromolecules and polypeptides. *Mailing Add:* Dept of Chem Rochester Inst of Technol Rochester NY 14623

PATTON, ERNEST GIBBES, b Greenville, SC, Nov 30, 24; m 50; c 4. ECOLOGY. *Educ:* Yale Univ, BA, 48; Univ NC, MA, 50; Duke Univ, PhD, 55. *Prof Exp:* From asst prof to assoc prof biol, Univ Ala, 53-63, dir arboretum, 58-63; ASSOC PROF BIOL, WOFFORD COL, 63- *Mem:* Ecol Soc Am; Bot Soc Am; Am Inst Biol Sci; Sigma Xi. *Res:* Plant communities; ecology of native shrubs; biological evaluation of land-use. *Mailing Add:* Dept of Biol Wofford Col Spartanburg SC 29301

PATTON, HARRY DICKSON, b Bentonville, Ark, Mar 10, 18; m 43; c 2. PHYSIOLOGY. *Educ:* Univ Ark, BA, 39; Yale Univ, PhD, 43, MD, 46. *Prof Exp:* Res asst physiol, Sch Med, Yale Univ, 43-46; instr psychobiol, Johns Hopkins Univ, 46-47; from asst prof to assoc prof, 47-56, actg chmn dept, 64-66, PROF PHYSIOL & BIOPHYS, SCH MED, UNIV WASH, 56-, CHMN DEPT, 66- *Concurrent Pos:* Mem, Physiol Test Comt, Nat Bd Med Exam, 64-68, chmn, 65-68; mem, Physiol Study Sect, USPHS, 62-66, chmn, 65-66, ad hoc cerebrovasc training rev comt, 66-67, nat adv neurol dis & blindness coun, Nat Inst Neurol Dis & Blindness, 66-70 & chmn Neurol Dis Review Comt B, 75-79. *Mem:* Am Physiol Soc; Soc Neurosci. *Res:* Thalamocortical representation of taste; neuronal organization of sympathetic chain; neural factors in endocrine secretion; cortical activation of pyramidal tract. *Mailing Add:* Univ Wash Sch Med Seattle WA 98195

PATTON, HUGH WILSON, b Lebanon, Tenn, Dec 2, 21; m 50. PHYSICAL CHEMISTRY. *Educ:* Middle Tenn State Col, BS, 45; Vanderbilt Univ, PhD(chem), 52. *Prof Exp:* Prof chem, Ark State Teachers Col, 50-53; from res chemist to sr res chemist, Tenn Eastman Co, 53-62, res assoc, 62-66, res div head, 66-70, asst dir res, 70-73, vpres, Eastman Chem Prod, Inc, 73-78, dir res, 78-79, VPRES & DIR RES, TENN EASTMAN CO, 79- *Mem:* AAAS; Am Chem Soc; Am Phys Soc; Am Soc Textile Technologists; Am Asn Textile Chemists & Colorists. *Res:* Heats of vaporization; gas chromatography; x-ray diffraction; nuclear magnetic resonance. *Mailing Add:* 939 Lookout Dr Kingsport TN 37663

PATTON, JAMES EDWARD, b Detroit, Mich, June 20, 43; m 67; c 2. PHOTOGRAPHIC CHEMISTRY, CHEMICAL ENGINEERING. *Educ:* Univ Mich, BS & BSE, 66; Univ Wis-Madison, PhD(chem eng), 70. *Prof Exp:* RES ASSOC, EASTMAN KODAK CO RES LABS, 70- *Mem:* Am Inst Chem Engrs; Soc Photog Sci & Eng. *Res:* Silver halide chemistry; product development of photographic films. *Mailing Add:* Eastman Kodak Co Res Labs Rochester NY 14650

PATTON, JAMES LLOYD, b St Louis, Mo, June 21, 41; m 66. MAMMALOGY. *Educ:* Univ Ariz, BA, 63, MS, 65, PhD(zool), 69. *Prof Exp:* Asst prof & asst cur, 69-74, assoc prof & assoc cur, 74-79, PROF ZOOL & CUR MAMMALS, MUS VERT ZOOL, UNIV CALIF, BERKELEY, 79- *Mem:* AAAS; Am Soc Mammal; Soc Study Evolution; Genetics Soc Am; Soc Syst Zool. *Res:* Population genetics and historical evolution of heteromyid and geomyid rodents in North America; biosystematics of Neotropical mammals. *Mailing Add:* Mus of Vertebrate Zool Univ of Calif Berkeley CA 94720

PATTON, JAMES WINTON, b Okemah, Okla, Nov 10, 29; m 61; c 3. ORGANIC CHEMISTRY, GEOCHEMISTRY. *Educ:* Univ NMex, BS, 51, MS, 54; Univ Wis-Madison, PhD(chem), 61. *Prof Exp:* Res assoc chem, Univ Southern Calif, 61-62; res chemist, 62-67, advan res chemist, 67-79, SR RES CHEMIST, MARATHON OIL CO, 79- *Concurrent Pos:* Participated in Leg 77 of deep sea drilling proj, Gulf of Mex, 80-81. *Mem:* AAAS; Am Chem Soc; Geochem Soc; Sigma Xi. *Res:* Petrochemicals; organic chemistry; origin and migration of crude oil; autoxidation processes; stable isotopes in geological interpretation. *Mailing Add:* Denver Res Ctr Marathon Oil Co Box 269 Littleton CO 80160

PATTON, JOHN BARRATT, b Marion, Ind, July 1, 15; m 41; c 4. GEOLOGY. *Educ:* Ind Univ, AB, 38, AM, 40, PhD(econ geol), 54. *Prof Exp:* Asst geologist div geol, State Dept Conserv, Ind, 39-40; geologist, Magnolia Petrol Co, Tex, 40-44, Ill, 44-47; head indust minerals sect, Ind Geol Surv, 47-53, prin geologist, 51-59, actg state geologist, 59; from asst prof to assoc prof econ geol, 48-55, actg chmn dept, 59, chmn dept, 59-71, assoc dean res & advan studies, 73-75, PROF ECON GEOL, IND UNIV, BLOOMINGTON, 55-; STATE GEOLOGIST & DIR, IND GEOL SURV, 59- *Mem:* Geol Soc Am; Soc Econ Geol; Am Asn Petrol Geol; Am Inst Mining, Metall & Petrol Eng; Asn Am State Geol (secy-treas, 62-63, vpres, 64, pres elect, 65, pres, 66). *Res:* Industrial minerals; environmental geology; petroleum; stratigraphy; historic masonry materials. *Mailing Add:* Ind Geol Surv 611 N Walnut Grove Bloomington IN 47405

PATTON, JOHN F, b St Louis, Mo, Feb 8, 39; m 68; c 1. PHYSIOLOGY. *Educ:* Wake Forest Univ, BS, 61; Univ Mo, Columbia, Mo, 65, PhD(physiol), 69. *Prof Exp:* Res physiologist, US Army Res Inst Environ Med, Natick, Mass, 69-76; proj leader physiol & toxicol, Patuxent Wildlife Res Ctr, Dept Interior, Laurel, Md, 76-77; RES PHYSIOLOGIST, US ARMY RES INST ENVIRON MED, 77- *Mem:* Am Physiol Soc; Sigma Xi; Am Col Sports Med. *Res:* Environmental physiology; exercise physiology; cold acclimation; hypothermia. *Mailing Add:* US Army Res Inst Environ Med Natick MA 01760

PATTON, JOHN FRANKLIN, b Albany, Mo, Sept 27, 03; m 35; c 2. MEDICINE. *Educ:* Wash Univ, MD, 28; Am Bd Urol, dipl, 41. *Prof Exp:* Intern, St Luke's Hosp, St Louis, Mo, 29; preceptorship, asst & partner to Dr John R Caulk, Sch Med, Wash Univ, 29-38, asst prof, 44-52; chief urol serv, Fitzsimons Army Hosp, 52-54, US Army Hosp, Landstuhl, Ger, 54-57 & Walter Reed Army Hosp, Washington, DC, 57-59, chief dept surg, Walter Reed Gen Hosp, 59-63; assoc prof, 63-69, actg chief dept, 64, PROF SURG, MED CTR, UNIV MO-COLUMBIA, 69- *Concurrent Pos:* Pvt pract, 30-52; chief urol unit I, Wash Univ, St Louis City Hosp, Mo, 33-41; mem staff, Barnard Skin & Cancer Hosp, Barnes Hosp & Deaconess Hosp, 41-51; chief urol sect, St Luke's Hosp, 48-51; asst prof clin urol, Sch Med, Univ Colo, 53-54; consult urol, US Army Europe, 54-57, consult, Surgeon Gen, 57-63, civilian consult, 64- *Honors & Awards:* Legion of Merit & Oak Leaf Cluster. *Mem:* AMA; Am Col Surgeons; Am Urol Asn; Am Asn Genito-Urinary Surgeons; Asn Mil Surgeons US. *Res:* Bladder neck obstruction; ureter; urogenital trauma; polycystic disease; testis tumors. *Mailing Add:* 4006A W Broadway Columbia MO 65201

PATTON, JOHN STUART, b Columbus, Ohio, Sept 9, 46; m 68; c 2. LIPID BIOCHEMISTRY, MARINE BIOLOGY. *Educ:* Pa State Univ, BS, 68; Univ RI, MS, 73; Scripps Inst Oceanog, PhD(marine biol), 76. *Prof Exp:* Swed Med Res Coun fel, Univ Lund, 76-77; Boston Med Found fel, Harvard Med Sch, 77-79; ASST PROF, UNIV GA, 79- *Res:* Lipid digestion; coral-sea anemone physiology; lipid flow and partition in biological systems. *Mailing Add:* Dept Microbiol Univ Ga Athens GA 30602

PATTON, JOHN THOMAS, JR, b Jonesboro, Ark, Jan 30, 17; m 45; c 2. ORGANIC POLYMER CHEMISTRY. *Educ:* Ark State Col, BS, 38; Purdue Univ, PhD(org chem), 47. *Prof Exp:* Teacher high sch, Ark, 38-39; res chemist, Ford Motor Co, Mich, 39-42 & Penick & Ford, Inc, Iowa, 42-43; asst org chem, Purdue Univ, 45; res chemist, Wyandotte Chem Corp, 47-53, from actg sect head to sect head, 53-56, supvr org res, 56-63, mgr org res, 63-64, dir res urethane chem res & develop, 64-79, dir advanced polymer technol, 79-82, ASSOC DIR, BASF-WYANDOTTE CORP, 82- *Honors & Awards:* Thomas Midgley Award, Am Chem Soc, 75; Chem Pioneer Award, Am Inst Chemists, 78. *Mem:* Am Chem Soc; Am Inst Chemists; Sigma Xi; Soc Plastic Engrs; Indust Res Inst. *Res:* Vegetable proteins; starch; textile assistants; detergents; nitroparaffins; alkylene oxides; organic synthesis and plastics; basis for reported optical activity of salts of aliphatic nitro compounds; polyols; polyglycols; heterocyclic nitrogen compounds; halogenation; polyethers; isocyanates; urethanes; cellular plastics; polymers. *Mailing Add:* BASF-Wyandotte Corp 1609 Biddle Ave Wyandotte MI 48192

PATTON, JOHN TINSMAN, b Ft Worth, Tex, May 9, 31; m 53; c 6. CHEMICAL ENGINEERING, PETROLEUM ENGINEERING. *Educ:* Okla State Univ, BS, 53, MS, 58, PhD(chem eng), 59. *Prof Exp:* Chem engr, Tex Eastman Co, 53-56; res engr, Jersey Prod Res Co Div, Standard Oil Co, NJ, 59-61, sect head drilling res, 61-63; petrol engr, Int Petrol Co, 63-64; sect head petrol recovery, Esso Prod Res Co, 64-65; res adv coal processing, Humble Oil & Refining Co, 65-68; prof chem eng, Mich Technol Univ, 68-77; PROF & HEAD CHEM ENG DEPT, N MEX STATE UNIV, 77- *Concurrent Pos:* Consult to oil & chem indust, 67-; pres, Comput/Bioeng Inst Inc, 68-; prin investr enhanced oil recovery by carbon dioxide foam flooding, 77- *Mem:* Soc Petrol Engrs; Am Chem Soc; Am Inst Chem Engrs. *Res:* Biochemical engineering, especially kinetics of biosynthesis; improved methods of oil recovery and drilling techniques; pollution control processes with emphasis on pulp and paper industry. *Mailing Add:* 2855 McDowell Las Cruces NM 88005

PATTON, LEO WESLEY, b Sublette, Kans, July 23, 19; m 49; c 2. ORGANIC CHEMISTRY, ANALYTICAL CHEMISTRY. *Educ:* Southwestern Col, Kans, BA, 41; Univ Kans, MS, 48; Kans State Col Manhattan, PhD(chem), 50. *Prof Exp:* Asst prof chem, McPherson Col, 49; res chemist, 51-72, FEL PETROCHEMICALS, SABINE RIVER LAB, E I DU PONT DE NEMOURS & CO, INC, 72- *Mem:* Am Chem Soc; Am Acad Arts & Sci. *Res:* Analytical methods and processes associated with the production of nylon intermediates. *Mailing Add:* E I du Pont de Nemours & Co Inc Sabine River Lab PO Box 1089 Orange TX 77630

PATTON, NANCY JANE, b Springfield, Ohio, Dec 29, 36. NEUROSCIENCES. *Educ:* Ohio State Univ, BS, 58; Univ Mich, MS, 62; Univ Wis, PhD(anat), 69. *Prof Exp:* Instr anat & physiol, Sargent Col, Boston Univ, 62-65; instr functional neurophysiol, Sch Phys Ther, Univ Wis, 68; assoc prof phys ther & asst prof anat, Col Allied Health Professions, Univ Ky, 69-74, assoc dir curric phys ther, 72-74; assoc prof phys therapeut & asst prof anat, Col Allied Health Sci, Med Univ SC, 74-78, prof phys therapeut & dir phys therapeut prog, 78-81; PROF & CHMN HEALTH SCI, COL ARTS & SCI & DIR PHYS THERAPY, CLEVELAND STATE UNIV, 81- *Mem:* Soc Behav Kinesiology; Am Phys Ther Asn. *Res:* Proprioceptive reflexes; patterns of motor activity in the central nervous system; sensory-motor systems; physical therapy. *Mailing Add:* Health Sci Cleveland State Univ 24th at Euclid Cleveland OH 44115

PATTON, PETER C(LYDE), b Wichita, Kans, June 11, 35; m 57; c 5. COMPUTER SCIENCE, AEROSPACE ENGINEERING. *Educ:* Harvard Univ, AB, 57; Univ Kansas, MA, 59; Univ Stuttgart, PhD(aerospace eng), 66. *Prof Exp:* Jr engr, Wichita Div, Boeing Co, 57; res asst math, Univ Kans, 57-59; assoc engr, Midwest Res Inst, Mo, 59-61; prin programmer, Fed Syst Div, Univac, Minn, 61, sci consult comp appln, Int Div, Lausanne, Switz, 61-63, sci syst mgr, Univac Ltd, London, 63-65; comput group mgr aerospace eng, Univ Stuttgart, 65-67; eng mgr syst design, Data Processing Div, Univac, Minn, 67-68; mgr tech staff, Analysts Inst Corp, 68-71; ASSOC PROF COMPUT SCI & DIR COMPUT CTR, UNIV MINN, MINNEAPOLIS, 71- *Concurrent Pos:* Lectr, Univ Kansas City, 58-59; instr, Kansas City Jr Col, 60-62; res assoc, Univ Stuttgart, 62-65, lectr, 65-67; assoc dir, Ctr Ancient Studies, Univ Minn, 77-78, dir, 78-81. *Mem:* Sr mem Inst Elec & Electronics Engrs; Asn Comput Mach; Am Oriental Soc; fel Brit Inst Math & Appln. *Res:* New applications of computer technology to science and engineering; new computer architectures to meet the needs of advanced applications; computer applications to the study of ancient languages and literature. *Mailing Add:* Comput Ctr Univ of Minn Minneapolis MN 55455

PATTON, PRISCILLA CANDACE, b Worcester, Mass, Apr 14, 27. ECONOMIC GEOLOGY. *Educ:* Wellesley Col, BA, 48. *Prof Exp:* Geologist library res, Mineral Deposits Br, 48-51, ed work, 51-60, geologist, Tech Reports Unit, Geol Div, 60-76, GEOLOGIST CONSERVATION DIV, US GEOL SURV, 76- *Mem:* Geol Soc Am. *Mailing Add:* Conservation Div US Geol Surv Denver Fed Ctr Denver CO 80225

PATTON, ROBERT FRANKLIN, b Albuquerque, NMex, Oct 28, 19; m 46; c 2. FOREST PATHOLOGY. *Educ:* Univ Mich, BS, 40; Univ Idaho, MS, 42; Univ Wis, PhD(plant path), 52. *Prof Exp:* Asst med mycol & antibiotics, Parke, Davis & Co, 46-47; asst plant path, 47-50, from instr to assoc prof forest path, 50-65, PROF FOREST PATH, UNIV WIS-MADISON, 65- *Concurrent Pos:* NATO sr fel sci, Cambridge Univ, 71. *Mem:* Soc Am Foresters; Am Phytopath Soc. *Res:* Resistance to white pine blister rust; forest plantation root diseases; forest tree rusts; fluorescence microscopy; plantation diseases, especially needle infection processes. *Mailing Add:* 125 Frigate Dr Madison WI 53705

PATTON, ROBERT LYLE, b Stockton, Calif, Nov 19, 43; m 72. INORGANIC CHEMISTRY. *Educ:* Univ of the Pac, BS, 64; Univ Calif, Berkeley, PhD(inorg chem), 69. *Prof Exp:* RES SCIENTIST, MOLECULAR SIEVE DEPT, UNION CARBIDE CORP, 69- *Mem:* Am Chem Soc. *Res:* Zeolite molecular sieves, synthesis and properties; ozone chemistry. *Mailing Add:* Linde Div Union Carbide Corp Tarrytown Tech Ctr Tarrytown NY 10591

PATTON, SHARON, b Watertown, Tenn, Sept 14, 47; m 80. PARASITOLOGY. *Educ:* Middle Tenn State Univ, BS, 69; Univ Ky, MS, 71, PhD(parasitol), 75. *Prof Exp:* Scholar Vet Parasitol, Dept Vet Sci, Univ Ky, 75-77; ASST PROF PARASITOL, DEPT PATHOBIOL, UNIV TENN, 77- *Concurrent Pos:* Exec Comt, Asn Southeastern Biologists, 81-84. *Mem:* Sigma Xi; Am Soc Parasitol; Am Soc Trop Med & Hyg; AAAS; Southeastern Soc Parasitol (pres-elect, 80-81, pres, 81-82). *Res:* Veterinary parasitology, helminths. *Mailing Add:* Dept of Pathobiol Col Vet Med Univ Tenn Knoxville TN 37901

PATTON, STUART, b Ebenezer, NY, Nov 2, 20; m 45; c 7. FOOD BIOCHEMISTRY. *Educ:* Pa State Univ, BS, 43; Ohio State Univ, MS, 47, PhD(dairy sci), 48. *Prof Exp:* Chemist, Borden Co, 43-44; from assoc prof to prof food sci, Pa State Univ, 49-66, Evan Pugh res prof agr, 66-80. *Concurrent Pos:* Mem nat adv comt for res vessel Alpha Helix, 71-72; adj prof neurosci, Univ Calif San Diego, 80-; Alexander von Humboldt sr scientist award, 81. *Honors & Awards:* Borden Award, 57; Agr & Food Chem Award, Am Chem Soc, 75. *Mem:* AAAS; Am Chem Soc; Am Dairy Sci Asn; Am Oil Chem Soc; Am Soc Biol Chemists. *Res:* Chemistry and biology of milk; lipid biochemistry; marine biology. *Mailing Add:* Dept Neurosci M-008 Sch Med Univ Calif San Diego La Jolla CA 92093

PATTON, TAD LEMARRE, b Wichita Falls, Tex, June 21, 25; m 52; c 2. ORGANIC CHEMISTRY. *Educ:* Baylor Univ, BS, 46; Univ Notre Dame, MS, 50; Univ Tex, PhD(org chem), 52. *Prof Exp:* Res chemist, Monsanto Chem Co, Ohio, 51-53; res fel, Univ Tex M D Anderson Hosp & Tumor Inst, 53-54, from asst biochemist to assoc biochemist, 54-61; res chemist, Spencer Chem Co, 61-63; res specialist, 63-65, res assoc, 65-70, SR RES ASSOC, EXXON RES & ENG CO, 70- *Mem:* Am Chem Soc; Royal Soc Chem; fel Am Inst Chemists. *Res:* Steroid synthesis, particularly those related to the androgens and estrogens; relationship of molecular structure to physiological activity; organic reaction mechanisms; synthetic polymers and fuels. *Mailing Add:* 5010 Glenhaven Dr Baytown TX 77521

PATTON, THOMAS FLOYD, b McKeesport, Pa, Aug 14, 48; m 70. BIOPHARMACEUTICS. *Educ:* Univ Wis-Madison, BS, 71, MS, 73, PhD(pharmaceut), 75. *Prof Exp:* asst prof, 75-79, ASSOC PROF PHARMACEUT CHEM & PHARM PRACT, SCH PHARM, UNIV KANS, 79- *Mem:* Am Pharmaceut Asn; Acad Pharmaceut Sci; Am Asn Col Pharm; AAAS; Sigma Xi. *Res:* Application of biopharmaceutic-pharmacokinetic concepts to improvement of drug delivery, especially in the areas of ophthalmology and pediatrics. *Mailing Add:* Dept Pharmaceut Chem Sch Pharm Malozz Hall Lawrence KS 66045

PATTON, THOMAS HUDSON, b New Orleans, La, May 24, 34; m 58; c 3. VERTEBRATE PALEONTOLOGY. *Educ:* La State Univ, BS, 60; Univ Tex, MA, 62, PhD(geol), 66. *Prof Exp:* Asst prof zool, Univ Fla, 65-72, asst prof geol, 70-72, assoc prof zool & geol, 72-77; assoc cur, Fla State Mus, 72-77; PRES, PATTON & ASSOCS, INC, 79- *Concurrent Pos:* Assoc cur, Fla State Mus, 64-72; NSF grant, Jamaica, 66-68; Univ Fla & NIH grant & proj leader, Coop Biol Invests, Jamaica, 68-72; consult, local state & fed agencies, private law & eng firms, 79- *Mem:* Soc Vert Paleont; Am Soc Mammal; Am Soc Study Evolution; Geol Soc Am; Am Asn Petrol Geologists. *Res:* Environmental, karst, and historical geology; stratigraphy and geomorphology of Gulf Coast and circum-Caribbean regions; geology of wetlands and associated boundary determinations; environmental law. *Mailing Add:* 4140 NW 27th Lane Ste C Gainesville FL 32606

PATTON, W(ILLARD) T(HOMAS), electrical engineering, see previous edition

PATTON, WENDELL KEELER, b Utica, NY, Sept 29, 32; m 61; c 3. INVERTEBRATE ZOOLOGY. *Educ:* Hamilton Col, AB, 54; Ohio State Univ, MS, 56; Univ Queensland, PhD(zool), 60. *Prof Exp:* Instr zool, Duke Univ, 60-62; from asst prof to assoc prof, 62-71, PROF ZOOL, OHIO WESLEYAN UNIV, 71- *Mem:* AAAS; Am Soc Zoologists; Crustacean Soc; Sigma Xi. *Res:* Commensalism; decapod Crustacea associated with reef corals; ecology of coral reefs. *Mailing Add:* Dept of Zool Ohio Wesleyan Univ Delaware OH 43015

PATTON, WILLIAM HENRY, b Albany, NY, Apr 15, 25; m 63; c 2. VETERINARY MICROBIOLOGY. *Educ:* Mich State Univ, DVM, 50; Univ Wis, MS, 60, PhD(vet sci), 63. *Prof Exp:* Vet diagnostician, Animal Dis Diag Lab, Wis Dept Agr, 50-55; clin trials vet, Am Cyanamid Co, 55-57; res asst vet sci, Univ Wis, 57-62; ASST PROF VET SCI, PA STATE UNIV, 62- *Mem:* AAAS; Am Soc Microbiol; Am Asn Avian Path; Wildlife Dis Asn; Tissue Cult Asn. *Res:* Intracellular parasites of poultry and livestock; host-parasite relationship at level of parasitized cell, relying on systems of animal cells cultured in vitro. *Mailing Add:* Dept of Vet Sci Pa State Univ University Park PA 16802

PATTON, WILLIAM WALLACE, JR, b Vancouver, BC, May 25, 23; US citizen; m 51; c 3. GEOLOGY. *Educ:* Cornell Univ, BA, 45, MS, 48; Stanford Univ, PhD(geol), 59. *Prof Exp:* GEOLOGIST, BR ALASKAN GEOL, US GEOL SURV, 48- *Mem:* Fel AAAS; Geol Soc Am; Am Asn Petrol Geol; Am Geophys Union. *Res:* Geology of western Alaska and the Bering Sea region, particularly stratigraphy and tectonics. *Mailing Add:* Alaskan Mineral Resource Br 345 Middlefield Rd Menlo Park CA 94025

PATTY, CLARENCE WAYNE, b Ringgold, Ga, Oct 7, 32; c 3. TOPOLOGY. *Educ:* Univ Ga, BS, 54, MA, 58, PhD(math), 60. *Prof Exp:* Res instr math, Univ NC, 60-61, from asst prof to assoc prof, 61-67; PROF MATH, VA POLYTECH INST & STATE UNIV, 67-, HEAD DEPT, 70- *Mem:* Am Math Soc; Math Asn Am. *Mailing Add:* Dept Math Va Polytech Inst & State Univ Blacksburg VA 24061

PATTY, RICHARD ROLAND, b Jonesboro, Ark, Sept 28, 33; m 55; c 3. PHOTOACOUSTIC SPECTROSCOPY. *Educ:* Furman Univ, BS, 55; Vanderbilt Univ, MA, 57; Ohio State Univ, PhD(physics), 60. *Prof Exp:* Res assoc physics, Ohio State Univ, 60-61; sr scientist, Philco Res Lab, 63-64; from asst prof to assoc prof, 64-72, PROF PHYSICS, NC STATE UNIV, 72-, HEAD DEPT, 78- *Mem:* AAAS; fel Optical Soc Am; Am Asn Physics Teachers. *Res:* Absorption and emission of infrared radiation by atmospheric gases as related to temperature, optical thickness and total pressure; airglow originating in upper atmosphere; photoacoustic spectroscopy. *Mailing Add:* Dept of Physics NC State Univ Raleigh NC 27607

PATUN, RONALD J(OSEPH), b Chicago, Ill, May 10, 36; m 63; c 4. MANUFACTURING ENGINEERING, SYSTEMS SCIENCE. *Educ:* Univ Ill, BS, 57; Northwestern Univ, MBA, 68. *Prof Exp:* Process engr, Esso Res & Eng Co, NJ, 57-58; process engr plastics div, Diamond Alkali Chem Co, 59-61, res engr cent res div, 61-64; sr chem engr res ctr, 64-70, proj mgr, 70-74, res coordr, York Div, 74-77, MGR MFG SYSTS, BORG-WARNER CORP, 77- *Mem:* Am Inst Chem Engrs; Soc Mfg Engrs; Robot Inst; Comput & Automated Systs Asn. *Res:* Polymer process development; polymerizations, finishing; bech scale, pilot, plant scale-up, continuous and batch; high pressure technology; manufacturing system and cost analysis; equipment and plant design; process simulation; robotics; automated inspection; computer-aided design; computer-aided manufacturing. *Mailing Add:* 831 N Evergreen Ave Arlington Heights IL 60004

PATZ, ARNALL, b Elberton, Ga, June 14, 20; c 4. OPHTHALMOLOGY. *Educ:* Emory Univ, BS, 42, MD, 45. *Prof Exp:* SEEING EYE RES PROF OPHTHAL, JOHNS HOPKINS HOSP, 70-, PROF OPHTHAL, WILMER OPTHAL INST, 69-, CHMN & DIR, DEPT OPHTHAL, 79- *Concurrent Pos:* Prof ophthal, Wilmer Ophthal Inst, Johns Hopkins Hosp, 69- *Honors & Awards:* Albert Lasker Award, Am Pub Health Serv, 56; Mead Johnson Award, Am Acad Pediat, 56; Billings Silver Medal, AMA, 72; Friedenwald Award, Asn Res & Vision Ophthal, 80; Jules Stein Award, Res Prevent Blindness, 81. *Res:* Retinal blood vessel diseases; laser techniques in ophthalmology. *Mailing Add:* Wilmer Ophthal Inst Johns Hopkins Hosp Baltimore MD 21205

PATZERT, WILLIAM CHARLES, b New York, NY, Apr 30, 41; div; c 1. PHYSICAL OCEANOGRAPHY. *Educ:* Purdue Univ, BS, 64; Univ Hawaii, MS, 69, PhD(phys oceanog), 72. *Prof Exp:* Res asst & assoc oceanographer, Univ Hawaii, 65-72; ASST RES OCEANOGRAPHER, SCRIPPS INST OCEANOG, UNIV CALIF, SAN DIEGO, 72- *Concurrent Pos:* Chmn, NORPAX Equatorial Panel, 76-, mem Exec Comt, 76-, Dynamics Plan Comt, 78-; SCOR Panel, 76- *Mem:* Am Meteorol Soc; Am Geophys Union. *Res:* Large-scale, long-term ocean atmosphere variability and its implications for short term environmental forecasting; redistribution of heat in the upper ocean by ocean currents. *Mailing Add:* Univ Calif San Diego Scripps Inst Oceanog A-030 La Jolla CA 92093

PAUCKER, KURT, b Berlin, Ger, Nov 12, 24; nat US; m 49; c 2. VIROLOGY. *Educ:* Pa State Univ, MS, 52; Univ Pa, PhD(virol), 54; Am Bd Med Microbiol, dipl. *Prof Exp:* Asst prof virol, Dept Pub Health & Prev Med, Sch Med, Univ Pa, 59-65, assoc prof, Dept Pediat, 65-70; PROF MICROBIOL & CHMN DEPT, MED COL PA, 71- *Concurrent Pos:* USPHS fel, 54-56, Nat Found fel, Copenhagen, Denmark, 56-58. *Mem:* Am Asn Immunologists; Am Soc Microbiol; fel Am Acad Microbiol. *Res:* Host-virus interactions; viral interference; interferon. *Mailing Add:* Dept of Microbiol Med Col of Pa Philadelphia PA 19129

PAUDLER, WILLIAM W, b Varnsdorf, Czech, Feb 11, 32; US citizen; m 55; c 3. ORGANIC CHEMISTRY. *Educ:* Univ Ill, BS, 54; Ind Univ, PhD(org chem), 59. *Prof Exp:* Res chemist, Procter & Gamble Co, 58-60; res assoc org chem, Princeton Univ, 60-61; distinguished prof chem, Ohio Univ, 61-65, from assoc prof to prof, 65-69, distinguished prof, 69-72; prof chem & chmn dept, Univ Ala, 72-; DEAN, COL SCI, PORTLAND STATE UNIV, 81- *Concurrent Pos:* NSF res grants, 62-69; NIH res grants, 64-69 & 71-74; NSF grants, 71-73 & 75-76. *Mem:* AAAS; Am Chem Soc; Royal Soc Chem. *Res:* Synthetic and theoretical aspects of heterocyclic chemistry; photochemistry; alkaloid chemistry; mass spectroscopy; nuclear magnetic resonance spectroscopy. *Mailing Add:* Col Sci & Dept Chem Portland State Univ Portland OR 97207

PAUERSTEIN, CARL JOSEPH, b New York, NY, May 31, 32; m 55; c 3. OBSTETRICS & GYNECOLOGY. *Educ:* Lehigh Univ, BA, 54; Hahnemann Med Col, MD, 58; Am Bd Obstet & Gynec, dipl, 66. *Prof Exp:* Assoc obstetrician & gynecologist-in-chief, Sinai Hosp, Baltimore, Md, 65-68; assoc prof, 68-72, prof obstet & gynec, 72-79, CHMN OBSTET & GYNEC, UNIV TEX HEALTH SCI CTR, 79- *Concurrent Pos:* Fel gynec path, Sch Med, Johns Hopkins Univ, 65-66, Am Cancer Soc adv clin fel, 66-68; asst prof gynec & obstet, Johns Hopkins Univ, 66-68. *Mem:* Am Col Obstet & Gynec; Am Fertil Soc; Soc Study Reprod; Soc Gynec Invest. *Res:* Gynecological pathology; reproductive physiology. *Mailing Add:* Dept of Obstet Univ Tex Med Sch San Antonio TX 78284

PAUKEN, ROBERT JOHN, b Maumee, Ohio, Aug 30, 39; div; c 2. PETROLEUM GEOCHEMISTRY. *Educ:* Bowling Green State Univ, BSEd, 62, MA, 64, Univ Mo-Columbia, PhD(geol), 69. *Prof Exp:* Lab asst biol, Bowling Green State Univ, 63-64; lab asst geol, Univ Mo-Columbia, 64-65, from asst instr to instr, 65-69; sr res geologist, 69-79, ASSOC & GEOLOGIST, MOBIL EXPLOR & PROD SERV, INC, 79- *Mem:* AAAS; Sigma Xi; Paleont Soc; Geol Soc Am; Am Asn Petrol Geologists. *Res:* Quantitative geology; paleoecology of Middle Devonian ostracodes; population study of the Pleistocene terrestrial gastropod faunas in the loess deposits of Missouri; fracture analysis using remote sensing imagery; uranium exploration. *Mailing Add:* Mobil Res & Develop Corp PO Box 900 Dallas TX 75221

PAUKSTELIS, JOSEPH V, b Linkuva, Lithuania, Nov 25, 39; US citizen. ORGANIC CHEMISTRY. *Educ:* Univ Wis, BS, 60; Univ Ill, Urbana, PhD(org chem), 64. *Prof Exp:* Asst, Univ Ill, Urbana, 60-64; NIH fel, Mass Inst Technol, 64-66; asst prof, 66-74, assoc prof, 74-81, PROF ORG CHEM, KANS STATE UNIV, 81- *Concurrent Pos:* Prog dir, NSF, 79-81. *Mem:* Am Chem Soc; Royal Soc Chem. *Res:* Trans-coplanar rearrangements of glycol monotosylates; synthesis and reactions of N-cyanoammonium salts; synthesis of natural products containing medium sized rings; nuclear magnetic resonance spectroscopy. *Mailing Add:* Dept Chem Kans State Univ Manhattan KS 66506

PAUL, ARA GARO, b New Castle, Pa, Mar 1, 29; m 62; c 2. PHARMACOGNOSY. *Educ:* Idaho State Col, BS, 50; Univ Conn, MS, 53, PhD(pharmacog), 56. *Prof Exp:* Asst prof pharmacog, Butler Univ, 56-57; from asst prof to assoc prof, 57-69, PROF PHARMACOG, COL PHARM, UNIV MICH, ANN ARBOR, 69-, DEAN, 75- *Concurrent Pos:* Vis prof indust microbiol, Tokyo Univ Educ, 65-66; Am Found Pharm Educ Pfeiffer Mem res fel, 65-66; consult, Argonne Nat Lab, 55; vis fac mem, Univ Calif, Berkeley, 72-73; NIH spec fel, 72-73. *Mem:* Sigma Xi; Am Soc Hosp Pharmacists; Am Soc Pharmacog; Am Pharmaceut Asn; fel AAAS. *Res:* Biosynthesis of alkaloids; phytochemistry of fungi; phytochemistry of cacti. *Mailing Add:* Univ Mich Col Pharm Ann Arbor MI 48109

PAUL, ARMINE DEANE, b New Castle, Pa, May 23, 31. INORGANIC CHEMISTRY. *Educ:* Pa State Univ, BS, 52, PhD(chem), 55. *Prof Exp:* Asst chem, Univ Calif, 52-53, chemist, Radiation Lab, 53-55; from asst prof to assoc prof, 55-78, PROF CHEM, WVA UNIV, 78- *Mem:* Am Chem Soc. *Res:* Complex ions; chemistry of tin; qualitative analysis; chemical education. *Mailing Add:* Dept of Chem WVa Univ Morgantown WV 26506

PAUL, B(URTON), b Jersey City, NJ, June 11, 31; m 58; c 2. MECHANICS. *Educ:* Princeton Univ, BSE, 53; Stanford Univ, MS, 54; Polytech Inst Brooklyn, PhD(appl mech, aeronaut eng), 58. *Prof Exp:* Engr, Bulova Res & Develop Labs, Inc, 54-56; res assoc, Polytech Inst Brooklyn, 56-58; asst prof eng, Brown Univ, 58-60; supvr eng mech, Bell Tel Labs, 61-63; head solid mech res, Ingersoll-Rand Res Ctr, 63-69, PROF MECH ENG, UNIV PA, 69- *Mem:* Fel Am Soc Mech Engrs; Am Soc Eng Educ. *Res:* Elasticity; plasticity; dynamics; vibrations; fracture and flow; structural and machine design; vehicle dynamics; mechanical engineering. *Mailing Add:* Dept of Mech Eng & Appl Mech Univ of Pa Philadelphia PA 19104

PAUL, BENOY BHUSHAN, b India, Jan 1, 36; m 67. BIOCHEMISTRY, RADIOBIOLOGY. *Educ:* Comilla Col, Pakistan, BSc, 55; Univ Dacca, MSc, 57; McGill Univ, PhD(biochem), 63. *Prof Exp:* Res asst antibiotics, Univ Dacca, 57-58, lectr phys biochem, 58-60; res biochemist, St Louis Univ, 63-64; res assoc, State Univ NY Downstate Med Ctr, 64-66; biochemist, 66-73, SR BIOCHEMIST & SUPVR MED RES & CLIN CHEM, ST MARGARETS HOSP, 74- *Concurrent Pos:* Res fel obstet & gynec, Sch Med, Tufts Univ, 66-70, asst prof, 70-75, assoc prof, 75- *Mem:* Am Asn Clin Chemists; Am Soc Exp Path; Am Soc Microbiol; Reticuloendothelial Soc. *Res:* Biochemical, antimicrobial and immunological aspects of host-parasite interactions during pregnancy, leukemia and after radiation; biochemical mechanisms of antimicrobial activities of leukocytes. *Mailing Add:* Med Res & Labs St Margarets Hosp Boston MA 02125

PAUL, DAVID I, b New York, NY, Apr 4, 28; m 73; c 3. FERROMAGNETISM, PROPERTIES METALS. *Educ:* Univ Calif, AB, 50, MA, 51, PhD(physics), 56. *Prof Exp:* Res engr mat, NAm Aviation Co, 52-55; res scientist, Hughes Aircraft Co, 56-57; prof mat sci & physics, Univ Calif, 57-62; PROF MAT SCI & METALL, COLUMBIA UNIV, 63- *Concurrent Pos:* Vis prof, Oxford Univ, 70-71 & 77-78 & Hebrew Univ, 73. *Mem:* Fel Am Phys Soc; Am Inst Mining & Metall Engr; Am Inst Elec & Electronics Engrs. *Res:* Magnetic properties of materials. *Mailing Add:* Sch of Eng & Appl Sci Columbia Univ New York NY 10027

PAUL, DEREK (ALEXANDER LEVER), b Brussels, Belg, Oct 1, 29; m 51; c 2. PHYSICS. *Educ:* Cambridge Univ, BA, 50; Queen's Univ, Ont, PhD(physics), 58. *Prof Exp:* Lectr physics, Royal Mil Col, Ont, 53-58, from asst prof to assoc prof, 58-63; assoc prof, 64-75, PROF PHYSICS, UNIV TORONTO, 75- *Mem:* Can Asn Physicists; Brit Inst Physics; Am Phys Soc; Inst Elec & Electronic Engr. *Res:* Electron and positron interactions with atoms and molecules; positronium; neutron physics. *Mailing Add:* Dept of Physics Univ of Toronto Toronto ON M5S 2R5 Can

PAUL, DONALD ROSS, b Yeatesville, NC, Mar 20, 39; m 64. CHEMICAL ENGINEERING, POLYMERS. *Educ:* NC State Col, BS, 61; Univ Wis, MS, 63, PhD(chem eng), 65. *Prof Exp:* Instr chem eng, Univ Wis, 64-65; res chem engr, Chemstrand Res Ctr, Inc, Monsanto Chem Co, 65-67; from asst prof to assoc prof, 67-73, PROF CHEM ENG, UNIV TEX, AUSTIN, 73-, CHMN DEPT, 77- *Concurrent Pos:* Part-time indust consult, 68-; dir, Ctr Polymer Res, 81-; mem bd dirs, Coun Chem Res, 81. *Honors & Awards:* Arthur K Doolittle Award, Am Chem Soc, 73. *Mem:* Am Inst Chem Engrs; Am Chem Soc; Soc Plastics Engrs; NY Acad Sci; Fiber Soc. *Res:* Polymer blends and transport properties of polymers; polymer processing. *Mailing Add:* Dept of Chem Eng Univ of Tex Austin TX 78712

PAUL, EDWARD GRAY, b Salt Lake City, Utah, Jan 3, 31; m 63. ORGANIC CHEMISTRY. *Educ:* Univ Utah, BSc, 58, PhD(org chem), 62. *Prof Exp:* NIH fel chem, Univ Utah, 61-65; assoc prof, 65-69, asst prof, 69-78, PROF CHEM, BRIGHAM YOUNG UNIV, 78- *Mem:* Am Chem Soc. *Res:* Organic synthesis; natural products; nuclear magnetic resonance spectroscopy. *Mailing Add:* Dept of Chem Brigham Young Univ Provo UT 84601

PAUL, ELDOR ALVIN, b Edmonton, Alta, Nov 23, 31; m 55; c 3. SOILS. *Educ:* Univ Alta, BSc, 54, MSc, 56; Univ Minn, PhD, 58. *Prof Exp:* Asst soils, Univ Minn, 56-58; from asst prof to assoc prof soil sci, Univ Sask, 59-70, prof, 70-80; PROF & CHAIR PLANT & SOIL BIOL, UNIV CALIF, BERKELEY, 80- *Mem:* Can Soc Soil Sci; Am Soc Microbiol; Agr Inst Can; Int Soc Soil Sci; Am Soc Agr. *Res:* Microbiology and biochemistry of soil organic matter; effect of microorganisms on soil fertility; microbial ecology. *Mailing Add:* Dept Plant Soil Biol Univ Calif Berkeley CA 94720

PAUL, FRANK W(ATERS), b Jersey Shore, Pa. MECHANICAL ENGINEERING. *Educ:* Pa State Univ, BS, 60, MS, 64; Lehigh Univ, PhD(mech eng), 68. *Prof Exp:* Anal engr thermodyn, Hamilton Stand, United Aircraft Corp, 60, controls, 61-64; instr mech eng, Lehigh Univ, 64-68; from asst prof to assoc prof, Carnegie-Mellon Univ, 68-77; assoc prof, 77-79, PROF MECH ENG, CLEMSON UNIV, 79. *Concurrent Pos:* Mem tech staff, Bell Tel Labs, 65. *Mem:* Am Soc Mech Engrs; Instrument Soc Am; Am Soc Eng Educ; Robots Inst Am; Soc Mfg Eng. *Res:* Dynamic systems modeling; applied control systems; computer aided manufacturing; automated systems; design; robotics. *Mailing Add:* Dept of Mech Eng Clemson Univ Clemson SC 29631

PAUL, GEORGE, (JR), b Houston, Tex, Nov 9, 37; m 69. ELECTRICAL ENGINEERING, MATHEMATICS. *Educ:* Rice Univ, BA, 61, MS, 66, PhD(elec eng), 67. *Prof Exp:* Staff mem, Eng Dept, Houston Sci Ctr, 67-69, mgr eng dept, 69-75, mem staff, Sci Comp Dept, DPD Hq, 75-77, MGR VECTOR ARCHIT, SYST TECHNOL DEPT, T J WATSON RES CTR, IBM CORP, 77- *Mem:* Inst Elec & Electronics Engrs; Soc Indust & Appl Math; Asn Comput Mach; NY Acad Sci. *Res:* Application of computers to large scale scientific problems; computer architecture and design; numerical analysis; Fourier analysis; algebraic coding theory. *Mailing Add:* IBM Corp PO Box 218 Yorktown Heights NY 10598

PAUL, GEORGE T(OMPKINS), b New York, NY, Oct 9, 13; m 41; c 3. MATERIALS SCIENCE ENGINEERING, CHEMICAL ENGINEERING. *Educ:* Columbia Univ, AB, 34, MA, 35, PhD(chem eng), 42. *Prof Exp:* Chemist, Imp Paper & Color Corp, NY, 35-36; demonstration asst, Columbia Univ, 38-39; lab asst, Stuyvesant High Sch, 40-42; from instr to asst prof chem eng, Princeton Univ, 42-52; chem engr, Org Chem Div, Am Cyanamid Co, 52-55; corrosion engr, Int Nickel Co, 55-72; sr mat engr, M W Kellogg, 73-74; mgr mat specif, 74-78, MAT CONSULT, RES-COTTRELL, 78- *Concurrent Pos:* Chem engr, Textile Res Inst, 44-48. *Mem:* Am Chem Soc; Nat Asn Corrosion Engrs. *Res:* Corrosion in chemical environments, by phosphoric and nitric acids and by limestone sulfur dioxide scrubber environments. *Mailing Add:* 131 Walnut St Middlesex NJ 08846

PAUL, GILBERT IVAN, b Ont, May 31, 22; m 45; c 4. STATISTICS. *Educ:* Univ Alta, BSc, 51, MSc, 52; Univ NC, PhD(statist), 56. *Prof Exp:* Asst prof genetics & statist, McGill Univ, 55-59; from asst prof to assoc prof, 59-67, PROF STATIST, UNIV MAN, 67- *Mem:* Biomet Soc. *Res:* Statistics and population genetics. *Mailing Add:* Dept of Statist Univ of Man Winnipeg MB R3T 2N2 Can

PAUL, HARBHAJAN SINGH, b India, June 8, 37; US citizen. NUTRITIONAL BIOCHEMISTRY. *Educ:* Univ Gauhati, India, BVSc, 59; Univ Minn, MS, 66, PhD(nutrit biochem), 69; Am Bd Nutrit, dipl. *Prof Exp:* Fel biochem, State Univ NY Buffalo, 69-70, Univ Hohenheim, Ger, 71-73; res assoc cell biol, 74, res instr nutrit biochem, 74-75, res asst prof, 75-81, res asst prof biochem, 79-81, ASST PROF BIOCHEM, MED SCH, UNIV PITTSBURGH, 81-; ASST PROF MED, MONTEFIORE HOSP, 81- *Mem:* Am Inst Nutrit; AAAS; Sigma Xi. *Res:* Regulation of protein and amino acid metabolism in altered nutritional and hormonal states; metabolic effects of the hypolipidemic drug, clofibrate. *Mailing Add:* Dept Med Montefiore Hosp 3459 5th Ave Pittsburgh PA 15213

PAUL, IAIN C, b Glasgow, Scotland, Oct 1, 38; m 76; c 2. PHYSICAL CHEMISTRY, ORGANIC CHEMISTRY. *Educ:* Glasgow Univ, BSc, 59, PhD(phys chem), 62. *Prof Exp:* Res fel, Harvard Univ, 62-64; asst prof phys chem, 64-68, assoc prof chem, 68-74, PROF CHEM, UNIV ILL, URBANA, 74- *Concurrent Pos:* A P Sloan Found fel, 68-70. *Mem:* Am Crystallog Asn; Am Chem Soc; Royal Soc Chem. *Res:* X-ray crystal structure analysis; three dimensional structure of molecules, particularly those of interest in biological and organic chemistry; structure and function of proteins; solid state chemistry. *Mailing Add:* Dept Chem Univ Ill Urbana IL 61801

PAUL, IGOR, b Kharkov, USSR, Oct 28, 36; US citizen; m 63; c 3. MECHANICAL ENGINEERING. *Educ:* Mass Inst Technol, SB, 60, SM, 61, ME, 62, ScD(mech eng), 64. *Prof Exp:* Res asst mech eng, Mass Inst Technol, 60-61, design engr instrumentation, 61, from instr to asst prof, 61-69, ASSOC PROF MECH ENG, MASS INST TECHNOL, 69- *Concurrent Pos:* Ford fel, 65-67; engineering consult, Mass Gen Hosp & Childrens Hosp Med Ctr. *Honors & Awards:* Ralph R Teetor Award, Soc Automotive Engrs, 66. *Mem:* Assoc Am Soc Mech Engrs; Am Soc Eng Educ; Soc Automotive Engrs; Biomed Eng Soc; Orthopedic Res Soc. *Res:* Design and controls; biomedical engineering and biomechanics; transportation. *Mailing Add:* Dept Mech Eng Mass Inst Technol Cambridge MA 02139

PAUL, JEDDEO, b Georgetown, Guiana, June 2, 29; m 59; c 3. BIOCHEMISTRY, ANALYTICAL CHEMISTRY. *Educ:* Univ London, BS, 53, MS, 55; Unic Birmingham, PhD(biochem), 58. *Prof Exp:* Imp Chem Industs fel, Univ Birmingham, 58-59; analyst, Govt Lab, Guiana, 59-62; head dept chem & soils, Ministry Agr, 62-66; from asst prof to assoc prof, 66-72, PROF CHEM, UNIV BRIDGEPORT, 72- *Concurrent Pos:* Consult, Govt Guiana, 62-66; vis fel, Univ Aberdeen, 64-65. *Mem:* Am Chem Soc; fel Royal Soc Chem. *Res:* Application of selective solvent extraction to simultaneous determination of metals and nonmetals. *Mailing Add:* Dept of Chem Univ of Bridgeport Bridgeport CT 06602

PAUL, JEROME THOMAS, b Chicago, Ill, Sept 22, 12; m 41; c 2. MEDICINE. *Educ:* Loyola Univ, Ill, MD, 37; Univ Ill, MS, 41. *Prof Exp:* Asst, 39-40, from instr to asst prof, 41-52, ASSOC PROF MED, UNIV ILL COL MED, 53- *Concurrent Pos:* Mem assoc staff, St Francis Hosp, Evanston, Ill, 40-47, mem sr staff, 48-, chmn dept med, 58-65; asst attend physician, Ill Res Hosp, 47-, attend physician, Med Clin, 47-; asst attend physician, Presby-St Luke's Hosp, 57-62; asst attend physician, St Joseph Hosp, 62, chief sect metab dis, 64- *Mem:* Am Diabetes Asn; Am Col Physicians; Am Fedn Clin Res; Int Soc Hemat. *Res:* Metabolic diseases; hematology. *Mailing Add:* 3 Woodley Manor Winnetka IL 60093

PAUL, KAMALENDU BIKASH, b Karimganj, India, Apr 1, 37; m 70. HORTICULTURE, PLANT PHYSIOLOGY. *Educ:* Univ Calcutta, BS, 57, BS, 60; Tuskegee Inst, MS, 65; Univ Ottawa, PhD(biol), 71. *Prof Exp:* Res asst biol, Univ Ottawa, 65-70; res scientist plant physiol, Tuskegee Inst, 70-75; asst prof & researcher soybean fertilization, 75-80, ASSOC PROF PLANT & SOIL SCI & PROG LEADER CROP RES, LINCOLN UNIV, 75- *Concurrent Pos:* USDA grant, Tuskegee Inst, 70-, coop state res serv grants, 72-, USDA grant, 75-78 & Sci & Educ Admin-Agr Res grant, 78- *Mem:* Am Soc Hort Sci; Am Soc Agron; Crop Sci Soc Am. *Res:* Seed physiology; various treatments to break seed dormancy; physiological and biochemical changes occurring in seeds during stratification and germination; seed pre-treatment on germination, emergence, growth and yield of vegetable crops; foliar fertilization of soybeans. *Mailing Add:* Dept of Agr Lincoln Univ Jefferson City MO 65101

PAUL, LAWRENCE THOMAS, b Lykens, Pa, June 17, 33. PHYSIOLOGY. *Educ:* Muhlenberg Col, BSc, 55; Ohio State Univ, MSc, 60, PhD(physiol), 63. *Prof Exp:* From instr to asst prof, 63-72, ASSOC PROF PHYSIOL, OHIO STATE UNIV, 72- *Concurrent Pos:* Bremer Found res fel, Ohio State Univ, 63-65. *Mem:* AAAS; Am Physiol Soc. *Res:* Cardiovascular physiology; coronary blood flow; hemodynamics and peripheral circulation. *Mailing Add:* Dept Physiol Ohio State Univ Col Med Columbus OH 43210

PAUL, MILES RICHARD, b Portland, Ore, June 25, 40; m 65. DEVELOPMENTAL BIOLOGY. *Educ:* Harvard Univ, BA, 62; Makerere Univ Col, E Africa, Dip Ed, 63; Stanford Univ, PhD(biol), 70. *Prof Exp:* Educ Off Sci, Mzumbe Sec Sch, Tanzania, 63-65; fel biol, Harvard Univ, 70-72; asst prof, 72-78, ASSOC PROF BIOL, UNIV VICTORIA, BC, 78- *Mem:* Am Soc Cell Biol; Am Soc Zoologists; AAAS. *Res:* Responses of marine invertebrate eggs to fertilization; silkmoth eggshell protein synthesis and eggshell structure. *Mailing Add:* Dept of Biol Univ of Victoria Victoria BC V8W 2Y2 Can

PAUL, MILTON HOLIDAY, b Philadelphia, Pa, Jan 15, 26; m 48; c 3. MEDICINE. *Educ:* Univ Pa, MD, 49; Am Bd Pediat, dipl & cert pediat cardiol, 62. *Prof Exp:* Assoc dir, 58-63, DIR CARDIOL, CHILDREN'S MEM HOSP, 63-; PROF PEDIAT, MED SCH, NORTHWESTERN UNIV, CHICAGO, 67- *Concurrent Pos:* USPHS res fel biochem, Univ Wis, 50-51, USPHS res fel cardiol, Harvard Univ, 53-54, USPHS res fel pediat cardiol, 54-56; mem & examr, Am Bd Pediat, 62-; assoc prof, Med Sch, Northwestern Univ, 63-67. *Mem:* Am Heart Asn; Am Soc Pediat Res. *Res:* Pediatric cardiology; cardiovascular physiology; biomedical engineering; medical information processing. *Mailing Add:* Children's Mem Hosp 707 W Fullerton Ave Chicago IL 60614

PAUL, OGLESBY, b Villanova, Pa, May 3, 16; m 43, 81; c 2. MEDICINE. *Educ:* Harvard Univ, AB, 38; Harvard Med Sch, MD, 42; Am Bd Internal Med, dipl, 54. *Prof Exp:* Asst med, Harvard Med Sch, 46-49; clin assoc prof med, Col Med, Univ Ill, 52-63; prof med, Med Sch, Northwestern Univ, 63-77, vpres health sci, 74-76; PROF MED, HARVARD MED SCH, 78-, DIR ADMISSION, 77- *Concurrent Pos:* Consult, US Naval Hosp, Great Lakes, 59-70; chmn, subspecialty bd cardiovasc dis, Am Bd Internal Med, 62-67; chmn adv comt, Ill Regional Med Prog Heart Dis, Cancer & Stroke, 66-70. *Mem:* Fel AMA; Am Heart Asn (pres, 60-61); Am Clin & Climat Asn; fel Am Col Cardiol; Am Epidemiological Soc. *Res:* Epidemiologic study of coronary heart disease. *Mailing Add:* 25 Shattuck St Boston MA 02115

PAUL, PAULINE CONSTANCE, b McMinnville, Ore, Dec 3, 12. FOOD CHEMISTRY, EDUCATIONAL ADMINISTRATION. *Educ:* Ore State Col, BA, 35; Univ Minn, MS, 37; Iowa State Col, PhD(exp foods), 43. *Prof Exp:* Asst, Univ Minn, 35-37; food technician, Gen Foods Corp, NY, 37-40; asst, Iowa State Col, 40-42; asst res, Swift & Co, Ill, 43-44; from asst res prof to assoc res prof food, Mich State Univ, 44-54; from assoc prof to prof home econ, Univ Calif, Davis, 55-66, chmn dept, 59-61; prof food & nutrit, Univ Nebr, Lincoln, 66-74; dir, Sch Human Resources & Family Studies, Univ Ill, Urbana, 74-79; RETIRED. *Concurrent Pos:* Asst to adminr home econ, Coop State Res Serv, USDA, Washington, DC, 71-72; lectr, Kelvin Grove Col Advan Educ, Brisbane, Australia, 80. *Honors & Awards:* Borden Award Food & Nutrit, Am Home Econ Asn, 74. *Mem:* AAAS; Am Chem Soc; Am Home Econ Asn; Inst Food Technol. *Res:* Tenderness of meat; frozen food; properties of dried milk solids and dried yeast; changes in palatability, microscopic appearance and electrical resistance in beef during the onset and passing of rigor and during subsequent storage; research adminstration. *Mailing Add:* 1317 NW Spring St Corvallis OR 97330

PAUL, PETER, b Dresden, Ger, Nov 24, 32; m 63; c 3. NUCLEAR PHYSICS. *Educ:* Univ Freiburg, BA, 54, PhD(physics), 59; Aachen Tech Inst, MSc, 56. *Prof Exp:* Res assoc nuclear physics, Univ Freiburg, 57-59, asst physics, 62-63; fel, Stanford Univ, 60-62, res assoc physics, 63-64, lectr, 64-65, asst prof, 65-67; from asst prof to prof physics, 67-80, LEADING PROF PHYSICS, STATE UNIV NY STONY BROOK, 80- *Concurrent Pos:* A P Sloan fel, 67-71. *Mem:* Am Phys Soc. *Res:* Level structure of nuclei; research on nuclear structure with tandem accelerator; accelerator design. *Mailing Add:* Dept of Physics State Univ of NY Stony Brook NY 11790

PAUL, PREM SAGAR, b Jullunder, Panjab, India, Oct 5, 47; US citizen; m 73; c 2. VETERINARY MICROBIOLOGY, IMMUNOLOGY. *Educ:* Panjab Agr Univ, BVSc, 69; Univ Minn, PhD(vet microbiol), 75; Am Col Vet Microbiologists, dipl, 77. *Prof Exp:* Res asst vet microbiol, Univ Minn, 69-75, res assoc, 75-78; VET MED OFFICER, VIROL IMMUNOL, NAT ANIMAL DIS CTR, USDA, 78- *Mem:* Sigma Xi; Am Vet Med Asn; Am Asn Vet Immunol; Conf Res Workers in Animal Dis; Am Col Vet Microbiol. *Res:* Leukemia viruses; ontogeny of immune system; cell mediated immunity; biology of porcine pherpesviruses. *Mailing Add:* Nat Animal Dis Ctr USDA-SEA PO Box 70 Ames IA 50010

PAUL, REGINALD, b Lucknow, India, Oct 17, 36; m 65. THEORETICAL CHEMISTRY. *Educ:* Univ Lucknow, BSc, 56, MSc, 57; Univ Alta, MSc, 62; Univ Durham, PhD(chem), 66. *Prof Exp:* Sessional instr, 66-67, asst prof, 67-74, ASSOC PROF CHEM, UNIV CALGARY, 74- *Res:* Applications of methods of second quantization to chemical kinetics and electrolyte transport. *Mailing Add:* Dept of Chem Univ of Calgary Calgary AB T2N 1N4 Can

PAUL, RICHARD JEROME, b Chicago, Ill, Apr 4, 44; m 67; c 2. BIOPHYSICS. *Educ:* St Mary's Col, BA, 66; Harvard Univ, PhD(biophysics). *Prof Exp:* Res fel, Harvard Univ, 72-73, instr, 73-74; angestellter, Univ Heidelberg, Ger, 74-75; hon res asst, Univ Col, London, 75-77; asst prof, 77-79, ASSOC PROF PHYSIOL, COL MED, UNIV CINCINNATI, 79- *Concurrent Pos:* Vis prof, Univ Heidelberg, Ger, 82; res fel, British Am Heart Asn, 75-77; estab investr, Am Heart Asn, 81-86; mem, Hypertension Task Force, NIH & Coun Basic Sci, American Heart Asn. *Mem:* AAAS; Biophys Soc; Am Physiol Soc. *Res:* Muscle energetics and physiology, with particular emphasis on the relations between metabolism and contractility in vascular smooth muscle. *Mailing Add:* Dept Physiol Rm 4259 Univ Cincinnati Col Med 231 Bethesda Ave Cincinnati OH 45267

PAUL, ROBERT E, JR, b Austin, Tex, Oct 14, 27; c 2. RADIOLOGY. *Educ:* Baylor Univ, MD, 50; Temple Univ, MS, 57. *Prof Exp:* Resident radiol, Temple Univ Hosp, 53-56, instr, 56-57; radiologist, New Eng Med Ctr Hosp, 57-65; from asst prof to assoc prof, 57-65, PROF RADIOL & CHMN DEPT, SCH MED, TUFTS UNIV, 65-; RADIOLOGIST-IN-CHIEF, NEW ENG MED CTR HOSP, 65- *Mem:* Fel Am Col Radiol; AMA. *Res:* Gastrointestinal radiology. *Mailing Add:* Dept of Radiol New Eng Med Ctr Hosp Boston MA 02111

PAUL, ROBERT HUGH, b Muskogee, Okla, Apr 21, 27; m 49; c 2. PHYSICS, ELECTRICAL ENGINEERING. *Educ:* Univ Houston, BS, 51; NMex State Univ, MS, 55, PhD(physics), 65. *Prof Exp:* Electronic scientist, Flight Determination Lab, White Sands Missile Range, 51-55, supvry electronics engr, 55-56, electronic scientist, Systs Eng Br, Integrated Range Mission, 56-57, supvry electronic scientist, Electronic Trajectory Br, Range Instrumentation Develop Directorate, 57-60, supvry electronics engr, US Army Res & Develop Activity, 60-62 & Electronic Trajectory Br, Instrumentation Develop Directorate, 62-64, res physicist, Range Eng, 64-73, TECH DIR, INSTRUMENTATION DEVELOP DIRECTORATE, WHITE SANDS MISSILE RANGE, 73- *Mem:* AAAS; Inst Elec & Electronics Engrs; Am Phys Soc. *Res:* Radar signal processing, pattern recognition; propagation of radio waves in the earth's atmosphere; theoretical determination of radar cross section; molecular theories of light scattering by crystals and gases. *Mailing Add:* 2007 Crescent Dr Las Cruces NM 88001

PAUL, ROBERT WILLIAM, JR, b Jersey City, NJ, Nov 27, 46; m 72; c 1. COMMUNITY ECOLOGY, AQUATIC BIOLOGY. *Educ:* Westminster Col, BA, 69; St Louis Univ, MS, 75; VA Polytech Inst & State Univ, PhD(zool), 78. *Prof Exp:* Grad res asst ecol, Va Polytech Inst & State Univ, 75-77; instr, 77-79, ASST PROF BIOL, ST MARY'S COL OF MD, 79- *Concurrent Pos:* Teaching asst, Va Polytech Inst & State Univ, 74-75, St Louis Univ, 72-74; res investr, Biol Sta, Univ Mich, 81-82; Andrew Mellon Found fel, Univ Mich, 81-82; vis prof biol, Evergreen State Col, 81-82. *Mem:* Sigma Xi; Int Asn Appl & Theoret Limnol; Ecol Soc Am; AAAS. *Res:* Decomposition in aquatic ecosystems and the effects of perturbation on decomposition processes; thermal pollution of aquatic communities and its effect; insect ecology. *Mailing Add:* Div Nat Sci & Math St Mary's Col Md St Mary's City MD 20686

PAUL, ROLF, b Neuss, Ger, Oct 31, 30; nat US; m 58; c 2. ORGANIC CHEMISTRY. *Educ:* Purdue Univ, BS, 52, PhD(org chem), 56. *Prof Exp:* ORG CHEMIST, LEDERLE LABS, AM CYANAMID CO, 56- *Mem:* Am Chem Soc. *Res:* Medicinal chemistry. *Mailing Add:* Lederle Labs Am Cyanamid Co Pearl River NY 10965

PAUL, RONALD STANLEY, b Olympia, Wash, Jan 19, 23; m 44; c 3. PHYSICS. *Educ:* Univ Ore, BS, 47, MS, 49, PhD(physics), 51. *Prof Exp:* From physicist to sr physicist, Hanford Atomic Prod Oper, Gen Elec Co, 51-56, mgr testing methods, 56-59, instrument res & develop, 59-62, physics & instruments lab, 62-64; mgr phys & instruments dept, Battelle-Northwest, 65, assoc dir, 66-67, dep dir, 67-68, sr mem corp staff, Battelle Mem Inst, 68-70, dir pac northwest div, 71-73, vpres opers, 73-76, sr vpres, 76-78, exec vpres, 79-81, PRES, BATTELLE MEM INST, 82- *Concurrent Pos:* Lectr, Gen Elec Sch Nuclear Eng, 52-58 & Richland Ctr Grad Studies, Univ Wash, 58-63; Int Atomic Energy Agency consult, Japan, 62. *Mem:* Am Phys Soc; Am Nuclear Soc. *Res:* Nuclear reactor physics and instrumentation; nondestructive testing; general physical, life and environmental sciences; research and development management. *Mailing Add:* Battelle Mem Inst 505 King Ave Columbus OH 43201

PAUL, ROY DENNIS, b Chicago, Ill, July 7, 28; m 54; c 2. PLASTICS, PHYSICAL CHEMISTRY. *Educ:* City Col New York, BS, 50; Rensselaer Polytech Inst, MS, 61. *Prof Exp:* Chemist, Repub Aviation Corp, 53-56; res chemist, Curtiss Wright Corp, 56-58; group leader res chem, Elec Boat Div, Gen Dynamics, 58-62; CHIEF CHEM ENG, HAMILTON STANDARD DIV, UNITED TECHNOLOGIES CORP, 62- *Concurrent Pos:* Instr metall, Univ Conn, 68-70; mem nonmetallic mat comt, Aerospace Mat Soc & Soc Automotive Engrs, 72- *Honors & Awards:* NASA Award, 69 & 81. *Mem:* Am Chem Soc; Metall Soc; Soc Advan Mat & Process Eng; Am Inst Mining, Metall & Petrol Engrs. *Res:* Chemical metallurgical thermodynamics and diffusion; composite materials development and characterization. *Mailing Add:* 44 Ash Dr Windsor CT 06095

PAUL, WILLIAM, b Toronto, Ont, Mar 5, 18; m 45; c 4. BIOPHYSICS. *Educ:* Univ Toronto, BA, 41, PhD(pharmacol), 48. *Prof Exp:* Fel, Cambridge Univ, 48-49; asst prof pharmacol, 49-53, from asst prof to assoc prof path chem, 53-69, prof path chem, 69-80, PROF CLIN BIOCHEM, UNIV TORONTO, 80- *Concurrent Pos:* Commonwealth Med fel, Univ London, 70, dep chmn, Clin Biochem, 71. *Mem:* Can Asn Physicists; Inst Elec & Electronics Eng; Pharmacol Soc Can. *Res:* Oximetry; radioisotope safety; radioimmunoassays. *Mailing Add:* Dept of Clin Biochem Univ of Toronto Toronto ON M5G 1L5 Can

PAUL, WILLIAM, b Scotland, Mar 31, 26; m 52; c 2. SOLID STATE PHYSICS. *Educ:* Aberdeen Univ, MA, 46, PhD(physics), 51. *Hon Degrees:* AM, Harvard Univ, 60. *Prof Exp:* Asst lectr natural philos, Aberdeen Univ, 46-51, lectr, 51-52; Carnegie fel, 52-53, res fel solid state physics, 53-54, from lectr to assoc prof, 54-63, GORDON McKAY PROF APPL PHYSICS, HARVARD UNIV, 63- *Concurrent Pos:* Guggenheim res fel, 59; assoc prof, Univ Paris, 66-67; vis prof, Cavendish Lab, Cambridge Univ, Eng, 74-75. *Mem:* Fel Am Phys Soc; Brit Inst Physics; NY Acad Sci; AAAS; fel Royal Soc Edinburgh. *Res:* Semiconductor physics; optical spectra, especially at infrared wave lengths; high pressure physics; study of properties of amorphous semiconductors and glasses. *Mailing Add:* 229 Pierce Hall Harvard Univ Cambridge MA 02138

PAUL, WILLIAM ERWIN, b Brooklyn, NY, June 12, 36; m 58; c 2. IMMUNOLOGY. *Educ:* Brooklyn Col, AB, 56; State Univ NY Downstate Med Ctr, MD, 60. *Prof Exp:* Intern med, Univ Hosp, Boston Univ, 60-61, asst resident, 61-62; clin assoc, Endocrinol Br, Nat Cancer Inst, 62-64; instr med, NY Univ, 67-68; med officer, 68-70, LAB CHIEF, LAB IMMUNOL, NAT INST ALLERGY & INFECTIOUS DIS, 71- *Concurrent Pos:* USPHS spec res fel path, Sch Med, NY Univ, 64-66, USPHS trainee med, 66-67; clin asst vis physician, Bellevue Hosp, New York, 66-68; mem directing group, Nat Inst Allergy & Infectious Dis Task Force Immunol Dis, 72, mem int fel rev panel, NIH, 74-75, mem transplantation & immunol adv comt, Nat Inst Allergy & Infectious Dis, 74-77; mem fel subcomt, Arthritis Found, 76-81; mem adv group personnel for res, Am Cancer Soc, 78-; co-chmn, Study Group Immunol, Nat Inst Allergy & Infectious Dis, 80; mem sci rev bd, Howard Highes Med Inst, 80-; US chmn, Immunol Bd, Vis Oral Med Res Found, 80-; mem bd dirs, Found Adv Educ Sci, 81- *Mem:* Am Asn Immunologists; Am Fedn Clin Res; Am Soc Clin Invest (pres, 80-81); Am Soc Exp Path; Am Acad Allergy. *Res:* Recognition and regulatory mechanisms in immune responses. *Mailing Add:* Lab of Immunol Nat Inst of Allergy & Infect Dis Bethesda MD 20014

PAUL, WILLIAM LARRY, b Burlington, NC, Aug 8, 42; m 65. PHARMACY. *Educ:* Univ NC, BS, 65; Univ Fla, PhD(pharm sci), 74. *Prof Exp:* DEVELOP SCIENTIST PHARM, BURROUGHS-WELLCOME CO, 74- *Mem:* Am Acad Pharmaceut Sci; Pharmaceut Asn. *Res:* Development of formulations and manufacturing procedures for both sterile and nonsterile liquid and semisolid pharmaceutical dosage forms for human and veterinary use. *Mailing Add:* Burroughs-Wellcome Co Box 1887 Greenville NC 27834

PAULE, ROBERT CHARLES, b St Louis, Mo, Jan 4, 32; m 54; c 2. STATISTICAL CONSULTATION, PHYSICAL CHEMISTRY. *Educ:* Univ Fla, BS, 53, MS, 55; Univ Wis, PhD(phys & high temp chem), 62. *Prof Exp:* Chemist, Esso Res Labs, 62-66; PHYSICAL SCIENTIST, NAT BUR STAND, 66- *Mem:* Am Statist Asn; Am Chem Soc; Am Soc Testing & Mat; Sigma Xi. *Res:* Statistics; development of standard reference materials; high temperature chemistry; Knudsen and Langmuir vapor pressure studies; mass spectrometry; cracking and hydrocracking catalysts. *Mailing Add:* 2 Owens Ct Rockville MD 20850

PAULE, WENDELIN JOSEPH, b Toledo, Ohio, Aug 6, 27; m 59; c 2. ANATOMY. *Educ:* Univ Toledo, BS, 50; Ohio State Univ, MS, 51, PhD, 57. *Prof Exp:* Asst biol, Univ Toledo, 48-50; asst instr anat, Ohio State Univ, 53-56; instr, Univ Buffalo, 56 & 59; asst prof, 59-66, ASSOC PROF ANAT, SCH MED, UNIV SOUTHERN CALIF, 66- *Concurrent Pos:* USPHS fel, Univ Buffalo, 58. *Mem:* Electron Micros Soc Am; Am Asn Anat; AMA; Am Soc Cell Biol. *Res:* Electron microscopy of blood vessels, lipid exocrine glands and endocrines; histochemistry of normal tissues. *Mailing Add:* Dept of Anat Univ of Southern Calif Los Angeles CA 90033

PAULEY, GILBERT BUCKHANNAN, b Klamath Falls, Ore, June 18, 39; m 64; c 1. IMMUNOLOGY, FISHERIES. *Educ:* Univ Wash, BS, 62, MS, 65; Univ Calif, Irvine, PhD(biol), 71. *Prof Exp:* Res asst, Col Fisheries, Univ Wash, 62-65; res scientist, Battelle Mem Inst, 65-68; res asst biol, Univ Calif, Irvine, 70-71; fishery biologist, Nat Marine Fisheries Serv, 71-72; immunologist, Eastern Fish Dis Lab, US Fish & Wildlife Serv, 72-74; ASSOC PROF, COL FISHERIES, UNIV WASH, 74- *Concurrent Pos:* US Fish & Wildlife Serv res grant, Battelle Mem Inst, 66-68, consult, US Fish & Wildlife Serv, 68-69; asst unit leader, Wash Coop Fishery Res Unit, 74- *Honors & Awards:* Thurlow C Nelson Award, Nat Shellfisheries Asn, 64. *Mem:* Am Soc Microbiol; Am Micros Soc; Soc Invert Path; Am Fisheries Soc; Nat Shellfisheries Asn. *Res:* Immunology, pathology and cell biology of invertebrates and fish; recreational fisheries; estuarine pollution. *Mailing Add:* Wash Coop Fishery Res Unit Univ of Wash Seattle WA 98195

PAULEY, JAMES DONALD, b Mason City, Iowa, Nov 15, 41; m 69; c 1. BIOENGINEERING. *Educ:* Iowa State Univ, BS, 63; Univ Colo, MS, 65; Univ Kans, PhD(elec eng), 71. *Prof Exp:* Instr physiol, Univ Colo Med Ctr, Denver, 71-74, bioengr, 70-80, asst prof psychiat, 72-80; MEM STAFF, WYO BIOTELEMETRY, INC, 80- *Mem:* Inst Elec & Electronics Eng; Nat Soc Prof Eng. *Res:* Biotelemetry, especially physiological data from long term implants. *Mailing Add:* 1225 Fla Ave Wyoming Biotelemetry Inc Longmont CO 80501

PAULEY, JAMES L, b Powersville, Mo, Dec 5, 25; m 48; c 4. PHYSICAL CHEMISTRY. *Educ:* Cent Col, Mo, AB, 48; Univ Nebr, MS, 50; Univ Arkansas, PhD(chem), 54. *Prof Exp:* Instr chem, Ft Hays Kans State Col, 49-50; assoc prof, 54-61, PROF CHEM, PITTSBURG STATE UNIV, 61- *Mem:* Am Chem Soc; Sigma Xi. *Res:* Surface and polymer chemistry; ion exchange; solutions of electrolytes. *Mailing Add:* Dept of Chem Pittsburg State Univ Pittsburg KS 66762

PAULEY, THOMAS KYLE, b Ansted, WVa, Oct 26, 40; m 64; c 2. ECOLOGY. *Educ:* Univ Charleston, BS, 62; Marshall Univ, MS, 66; WVa Univ, PhD(ecol), 77. *Prof Exp:* Elem prin, Putnam County Sch, 62-63; jr high teacher sci, Kanawha County Sch, 63-65, high sch teacher biol, 65-66; prof biol, Dept Natural Sci, Salem Col, 66-82; PROF BIOL, DIV NATURAL SCI, UNIV PITTSBURGH AT BRADFORD, 82- *Concurrent Pos:* Prof, WVa Univ, 72-76; consult, US Forest Serv, 76-79, US Off Surface Mining & WVa Hertitage Trust, 80 & Environ Energy, Inc, 81. *Mem:* Soc Study Amphibians & Reptiles. *Res:* Range and distribution of amphibians and reptiles in West Virginia; ecology of the Cheat Mountain salamander; range and distribution of the Mountain earth snake, smallmouth salamander, and jefferson salamander. *Mailing Add:* Div Natural Sci Univ Pittsburgh Bradford PA 16701

PAULI, ARLAND WALTER, plant physiology, see previous edition

PAULIE, M CATHERINE THERESE, b Greenbush, Kans. MATHEMATICS, STATISTICS. *Educ:* Marquette Univ, BS, 67; Univ Ill, MS, 68; St Louis Univ, PhD(math), 71. *Prof Exp:* Elem teacher, Our Lady Lourdes, Pittsburg, 59-64, St Paul Sch, Lyons, 64-66 & St Theresa Sch, Hutchison, 66-67; from asst prof to assoc prof math, 71-75, acad dean, 75-80, ASSOC PROF MATH, ST MARY OF THE PLAINS COL, 81- *Mem:* Math Asn Am; Nat Coun Teachers Math. *Mailing Add:* St Mary of the Plains Col Dodge City KS 67801

PAULIK, FRANK EDWARD, b Chicago, Ill, Sept 11, 35; m 70. ORGANOMETALLIC CHEMISTRY. *Educ:* Univ Ill, BS, 57; Purdue Univ, MS, 60; Univ Cincinnati, PhD(chem), 64. *Prof Exp:* Res assoc, Univ Chicago, 64-65; sr res chemist, Monsanto Polymers & Petrochem Co, 65-75, res specialist, 75-81, SR RES SPECIALIST, MONSANTO INDUST CHEMS CO, 81- *Concurrent Pos:* Ed, Tech Community Monsanto Newsletter, 79, chmn-elect, 80, chmn, 81. *Mem:* Am Chem Soc; Sigma Xi. *Res:* Physical organometallic chemistry; synthesis; transition metal complexes; homogeneous catalysis; process research. *Mailing Add:* Monsanto Indust Chem Co 800 N Lindbergh Blvd St Louis MO 63166

PAULIKAS, GEORGE A, b Pagegiai, Lithuania, May 14, 36; US citizen; m 57; c 1. SPACE PHYSICS. *Educ:* Univ Ill, Urbana, BS, 57, MS, 58; Univ Calif, Berkeley, PhD(physics), 61. *Prof Exp:* Mem tech staff, 61-68, dir, Space Sci Lab, 68-81, VPRES, AEROSPACE CORP, 81- *Concurrent Pos:* Consult, Lawrence Radiation Lab, Univ Calif, 61-66; assoc ed, J Geophys Res, 72-74; mem, Univ Calif Adv Coun Geophys, 74-75, US Air Force Sci Adv Bd, 75-, comt space physics, Nat Acad Sci, 77-80 & adv coun, Space Sci Lab, Univ Calif, Berkeley, 77-; consult, NASA, 75-; mem ad hoc comts, Nat Acad Sci, 70, 73, 79 & 80. *Mem:* Fel Am Phys Soc; Am Geophys Union; Am Inst Aeronaut & Astronaut; Am Astron Soc; Sigma Xi. *Res:* Space and radiation belt physics; space science; plasma physics; atomic physics; solar cosmic rays; effects of space environment on space systems. *Mailing Add:* Lab Opers Aerospace Corp PO Box 92957 Los Angeles CA 90009

PAULIN, GASTON (LUDGER), b Ste-Anne de Beaupre, Que, Feb 19, 34; m 55; c 4. DYNAMIC METEOROLOGY. *Educ:* Laval Univ, BA, 53; Can Govt, Forecasting Dipl, 57; Univ Montreal, BSc, 60; Univ Toronto, MA, 61; McGill Univ, PhD(meteorol), 68. *Prof Exp:* Res asst ballistics, Can Armament Res Defense, 55-56; forecaster meteorol, Can Meteorol Serv, 57-59, meteorologist, 61-64, res scientist meteorol, 68-72; dir, Sch Meteorol, Univ Que, Montreal, 72-74; dir, Que Meteorol Serv, 74-80; DIR RES, QUE MINISTRY ENVIRON, 80- *Concurrent Pos:* Lectr math, Armed Serv Educ Exten, Univ Md, 61-65 & Sir George Williams Univ, 67-72; lectr, Univ Montreal, 72. *Honors & Awards:* Prize, Que Meteorol Soc, 81. *Mem:* Can Meteorol Soc; Meteorol Soc Japan; Am Meteorol Soc. *Res:* Numerical weather prediction models; parameterization of physical effects in atmospheric simulation models; simulation of solar energy at the ground level; climatology of solar energy in the Province of Quebec; climate simulation modelling; long range transport of atmospheric pollution (acid rain). *Mailing Add:* Ministere de l'Environ du Quebec 2360 Chemin Sainte-Foy Quebec PQ G1V 4H2 Can

PAULIN, JEROME JOHN, b Milwaukee, Wis, Jan 18, 36; m 61; c 2. PROTOZOOLOGY, ELECTRON MICROSCOPY. *Educ:* Univ Wis, Whitewater, BE, 62; Univ Ill, Urbana, MS, 63, PhD(zool), 67. *Prof Exp:* Res asst phycol, Univ Ill, Urbana, 64-66; res assoc, protozool, Univ Ill, 66-67; from asst prof to assoc prof, 68-77, PROF ZOOL, UNIV GA, 77- *Concurrent Pos:* Fel dept zool, Univ Ga 67-68; NIH res fel, Univ Wis, 73-74; Nat Acad Sci Exchange Scientist, Prague, Czech, & Leningrad, USSR, 78. *Mem:* Soc Protozool; Am Microscop Soc. *Res:* Ultrastructure of the trypanosomatid flagellates and three-dimensional reconstructions of their chondrion. *Mailing Add:* Dept of Zool Univ Ga Athens GA 30602

PAULING, EDWARD CRELLIN, b Pasadena, Calif, June 4, 37; m 56, 70; c 4. MOLECULAR BIOLOGY. *Educ:* Reed Col, BA, 59; Univ Wash, PhD(genetics), 64. *Prof Exp:* USPHS fel biophys, Stanford Univ, 64-66; from asst prof to assoc prof, 66-77, PROF BIOL, UNIV CALIF, RIVERSIDE, 77- *Mem:* AAAS; Genetics Soc Am; Biophys Soc; Am Soc Microbiol. *Res:* Mechanisms and metabolic significance of repair of radiation induced damage to DNA of bacteria. *Mailing Add:* Dept of Biol Univ of Calif Riverside CA 92502

PAULING, LINUS CARL, b Portland, Ore, Feb 28, 01; m 23; c 4. CHEMISTRY, PHYSICS. *Educ:* Ore State Col, BS, 22; Calif Inst Technol, PhD(chem), 25. *Hon Degrees:* Thirty from US & foreign univs. *Prof Exp:* Nat Res Coun fel quant anal, 25-26; Guggenheim fel, Univs Munich, Zurich & Copenhagen, 26-27; from asst prof to assoc prof theoret chem, Calif Inst Technol, 27-31, prof chem, 31-63, head div chem & chem eng & dir, Gates & Crellin Chem Labs, 37-58; res prof phys & biol sci, Ctr Study Dem Insts, 63-67; prof chem, Univ Calif, San Diego, 67-69; prof chem, 69-74, EMER PROF CHEM, STANFORD UNIV, 74-; FEL, LINUS PAULING INST SCI & MED, 73- *Concurrent Pos:* George Eastman prof, Oxford Univ, 48; vis prof, Univ Calif, Cornell Univ, Univ Ill, Mass Inst Technol, Harvard Univ, Princeton Univ, plus other univs & cols. *Honors & Awards:* Nobel Prize in Chem, 54; Nobel Peace Prize, 63; Langmuir Prize, Am Chem Soc, 31, Nichols Medal, 41 & Linus Pauling Medal, 66; Davy Medal, Royal Soc, 47; Medal for Merit, 48; Pasteur Medal, Biochem Soc France, 52; Addis Medal, Nat Nephrosis Fedn, 55; Phillips Mem Award, Am Col Physicians, 56; Avogadro Medal, Ital Acad Sci, 56; Fermat Medal, Sabatier Medal & Int Grotius Medal, 57; Order of Merit, Repub Italy; Medal, Acad Rumanian People's Repub, 65; Pres of Hon, Int Soc Res Nutrit & Vital Substances, 65-; Silver Medal, Inst France, 66; Supreme Peace Sponsor, World Fel of Relig, 66. *Mem:* Nat Acad Sci; AAAS; Am Phys Soc; Am Philos Soc (vpres, 51-54); Harvey Soc. *Res:* Determination of structure of crystals and molecules; application of quantum mechanics to chemistry; rotation of molecules in crystals; sizes of ions; theory of stability of complex crystals; chemical bond; line spectra; immunochemistry; structure of proteins; molecular abnormality in relation to disease; sickle cell anemia; orthomolecular medicine; vitamin C and cancer; metals and alloys; ferromagnetism. *Mailing Add:* Deer Flat Ranch Big Sur CA 93920

PAULISSEN, LEO JOHN, b Kankakee, Ill, Nov 8, 15; m 56; c 4. MEDICAL MICROBIOLOGY, IMMUNOLOGY. *Educ:* Bradley Polytech Inst, BS, 41; Univ Chicago, SM, 49; Wash Univ, PhD(bact, immunol), 54. *Prof Exp:* Bacteriologist, State Dept Pub Health, Ill, 46-48, serologist, 49-50; asst radiation biol & bact, Sch Med, Wash Univ, 50-54, res assoc, 54-55; res specialist, 55-56, from asst prof to assoc prof, 56-68, PROF BACT, UNIV ARK, FAYETTEVILLE, 68- *Mem:* Fel AAAS; Am Soc Microbiol; Sigma Xi. *Res:* Study of various microbiological and immunological aspects of mouse response to experimental infection with Salmonella enteritidis. *Mailing Add:* Dept of Bot &Bact Univ of Ark Fayetteville AR 72701

PAULK, JOHN IRVINE, b Bufords, Tenn, July 27, 28; m 52; c 2. NUCLEAR ENGINEERING. *Educ:* US Naval Acad, BS, 52; NC State Univ, PhD(nuclear eng), 62. *Prof Exp:* Assoc serv engr, E I du Pont de Nemours & Co, 56-57; reactor physicist, Tenn Valley Authority, 61-63; assoc prof nuclear eng, 63-64, PROF NUCLEAR ENG & HEAD DEPT, MISS STATE UNIV, 64- *Mem:* Am Nuclear Soc. *Res:* Reactor core analysis; radioactive tracer techniques. *Mailing Add:* Dept of Nuclear Eng Drawer NE Miss State Univ State College MS 39762

PAULL, ALLAN E, b Regina, Sask, Mar 5, 18; m 53; c 2. STATISTICS. *Educ:* Univ Man, BA, 38; Univ NC, PhD(exp statist), 48. *Prof Exp:* Staff consult statist & math, Grain Res Lab, Bd Grain Comnrs, Can, 39-41, 48-50; chief statistician, Abitibi Power & Paper Co, Ltd, 50-61; dir opers res, Kimberly-Clark Corp, 61-65; prof statist, Dept Math, Fac Arts & Sci & Sch Bus, 65-71, PROF STATIST, FAC MGT STUDIES, UNIV TORONTO, 71- *Mem:* Am Statist Asn; Opers Res Soc Am; Can Opers Res Soc; Royal Statist Soc; Statist Soc Can. *Res:* Statistical methodology in marketing and business. *Mailing Add:* Fac Mgt Studies Univ Toronto Toronto ON M5S 1V4 Can

PAULL, BARRY RICHARD, b Chicago, Ill, June 1, 47; m 73; c 2. ALLERGY, IMMUNOLOGY. *Educ:* Univ Wis, BSc, 69; Univ Miami, MD, 73; Univ Minn, MS, 78. *Prof Exp:* Intern, Mayo Grad Sch Med, 73-74, resident, 74-75, fel pediat allergy, 75-77, allergy & immunol res fel, 77-78; lectr, 78-80, ASST PROF ALLERGY & IMMUNOL, TEX A&M UNIV, 80- *Concurrent Pos:* Assoc consult, Mayo Clin, 77-; instr, Mayo Med Sch, 77-78. *Mem:* Am Acad Pediat; Am Acad Allergy. *Res:* Insect venoms of the class hymenoptera; identification of allergens in honeybee venom and fire ant venom; identification of allergenic components of the major allergen of ragweed pollen, antigen E and fire ant allergy. *Mailing Add:* 2706 Osler Blvd Bryan TX 77801

PAULL, KENNETH DYWAIN, b Winslow, Ariz, Aug 22, 42; m 68; c 2. MEDICINAL CHEMISTRY. *Educ:* Fresno State Univ, BS, 65; Ariz State Univ, PhD(org chem), 69. *Prof Exp:* Fel, NIH, 69-71; sr scientist, Midwest Res Inst, 71-74; vpres, Starks C P Inc, Subsid Starks Assocs, Inc, 74-78; fac res assoc, Dept Chem, Cancer Res Inst, Ariz State Univ, 78-79; HEAD ACQUISITION SECT, DRUG SYNTHESIS & CHEM BR, DEVELOP THERAPEUT PROG, DIV CANCER TREAT, NAT CANCER INST, 79- *Concurrent Pos:* Prin investr, Midwest Res Inst, 73-74; prin investr, Starks C P Inc, Subsid Starks Assocs, Inc, 75-78 & proj coordr, 76-78. *Mem:* Am Chem Soc. *Res:* Antitumor evaluation of new substances. *Mailing Add:* Blair Bldg Rm 4A01A 8300 Colesville Rd Silver Spring MD 20910

PAULL, RICHARD ALLEN, b Madison, Wis, May 20, 30; m 54; c 3. GEOLOGY. *Educ:* Univ Wis, BS, 52, MS, 53. PhD(geol), 57. *Prof Exp:* Geologist, Pan Am Petrol, Standard Oil Ind, 55-57, res geologist, Jersey Prod Res Co, NJ, 57-60, res group leader, 60-62; assoc prof, 62-65, chmn dept, 62-66, PROF GEOL, UNIV WIS-MILWAUKEE, 65- *Concurrent Pos:* Hon curator, Milwaukee Pub Mus, 62-; dir, NSF Inst & short courses, 65-68; partic, NSF Conf, 65 & 68; consult. *Mem:* Fel Geol Soc Am; Am Asn Petrol Geol; Soc Econ Paleont & Mineral; Nat Asn Geol Teachers (pres, 77-78). *Res:* Classification and techniques for describing clastic rocks; depositional environments of sedimentary rocks; Cretaceous stratigraphy of the western United States; Paleozoic stratigraphy of Idaho. *Mailing Add:* Dept Geol Sci Univ Wis Milwaukee WI 53201

PAULL, WILLIS K, JR, b Butte, Mont, Dec 25, 44; c 3. ANATOMY, NEUROENDOCRINOLOGY. *Educ:* Mont State Univ, BS, 66, MS, 67; Univ Southern Calif, PhD(anat), 73. *Prof Exp:* Asst prof anat, Univ Vt Sch Med, 72-76; ASSOC PROF ANAT, MED COL GA, 76- *Mem:* Am Asn Anat. *Res:* Development of neuroendocrine mechanisms; electron microscopy and immunocytochemistry of neurosecretory systems. *Mailing Add:* Dept of Anat Med Col Ga Augusta GA 30902

PAULLING, J(OHN) R(ANDOLPH), JR, engineering, see previous edition

PAULOS, JOHN ALLEN, b Denver, Colo, July 4, 45; m 72; c 2. LOGIC. *Educ:* Univ Wis, PhD(math), 74. *Prof Exp:* ASSOC PROF MATH, TEMPLE UNIV, 74- *Mem:* Am Asn Advan Sci; Asn Symbolic Logic; Am Philos Asn. *Res:* Philosophy of math; mathematical model theory. *Mailing Add:* Math Dept Temple Univ Philadelphia PA 19122

PAULS, ALLEN C(HARLES), chemical engineering, see previous edition

PAULSEN, CHARLES ALVIN, b Portland, Ore, May 3, 24; m 49; c 5. INTERNAL MEDICINE, ENDOCRINOLOGY. *Educ:* Univ Ore, BA, 47, MD, 52. *Prof Exp:* Instr med, Col Med, Wayne State Univ, 57-58; clin instr, 58-61, from asst prof to assoc prof, 61-70, PROF MED, SCH MED, UNIV WASH, 70- *Concurrent Pos:* USPHS fel med, Col Med, Wayne State Univ, 53-55; consult, US Marine Hosp, Windmill Point, Mich, 57-58; dir labs, Pac Northwest Res Found, 58-61; consult, Vet Admin Hosp, Seattle, Wash, 58- & USPHS Hosp, 61- *Mem:* AAAS; Am Fedn Clin Res; Am Fertil Soc; NY Acad Sci; fel Am Col Physicians. *Mailing Add:* USPHS Hosp PO Box 3145 Seattle WA 98114

PAULSEN, DOUGLAS F, b Baltimore, Md, Oct 7, 52. EXPERIMENTAL EMBRYOLOGY. *Educ:* Western Md Col, BA, 74; Bowman Gray Sch Med, Wake Forest Univ, PhD(anat), 79. *Prof Exp:* Instr anat, Nurse Anesthesia Dept, Bowman Gray Sch Med, 79; fel cell adhesion, Nat Cancer Inst, Calif State Univ, Northridge, 79-80; ASST PROF ANAT, MOREHOUSE SCH MED, 80- *Concurrent Pos:* Prin investr, Am Heart Asn grant, 81-83. *Mem:* Sigma Xi; Soc Develop Biol; Am Asn Anatomists; NY Acad Sci. *Res:* Experimental embryology using the developing chick limb as a model system, study of the role of extracellular matrix/cell membrane interactions in embryonic induction and cytodifferentiation. *Mailing Add:* Dept Anat Morehouse Sch Med 720 Westview Dr Southwest Atlanta GA 30314

PAULSEN, DUANE E, b Fargo, NDak, May 4, 37; m 58; c 1. PHYSICAL CHEMISTRY. *Educ:* NDak State Univ, BS, 58, MS, 59; Mass Inst Technol, PhD(phys chem), 65. *Prof Exp:* Wentworth Inst res chemist, 64-68, RES CHEMIST, AERONOMY LAB, SPECTROS STUDIES BR, AIR FORCE GEOPHYS LAB, 68- *Mem:* AAAS; Am Phys Soc. *Res:* Intermolecular potentials; spectroscopy and spectrophotometry of atmospheric species; gaseous kinetics. *Mailing Add:* PO Box 202 Tyngsborough MA 01879

PAULSEN, ELIZABETH CHARLOTTE, b Danville, Vt, Feb 19, 22. BIOCHEMISTRY. *Educ:* Skidmore Col, AB, 44; Univ Vt, MS, 46; Rutgers Univ, PhD(serol), 53. *Prof Exp:* Asst biochem, Univ Vt, 44-46, instr zool, 46-50; asst, Rutgers Univ, 50-52; asst, Univ Vt, 52-53, asst prof, 53-57; asst res specialist, Rutgers Univ, 57-64, asst prof biochem & microbiol, 64-66; res scientist, Squibb Inst Med Res, 66-70; COORD SCI PROG, MT ANTHONY UNION HIGH SCH, 71- *Mem:* AAAS; NY Acad Sci. *Res:* Immunology; catecholamines; phenylalanine metabolism. *Mailing Add:* Mt Anthony Union High Sch Bennington VT 05201

PAULSEN, ELSA PROEHL, b Clinton, Iowa, Oct 10, 23; m 55; c 2. PEDIATRICS, ENDOCRINOLOGY. *Educ:* Univ Ill, AB, 43; Ind Univ, MA, 45; Univ Minn, MD, 54. *Prof Exp:* From instr to assoc prof pediat, Albert Einstein Col Med, 58-69; ASSOC PROF PEDIAT, MED SCH, UNIV VA, 69- *Concurrent Pos:* USPHS fel, 57-59; Nathan Hofheimer fel, 59-64; career scientist, Health Res Coun, NY, 66-71; guest investr, Rockefeller Univ, 68-69. *Mem:* Lawson Wilkins Pediat Endocrine Soc; Soc Pediat Res; Am Diabetes Asn. *Res:* Pediatric endocrinology; diabetes mellitus occurring in childhood. *Mailing Add:* Dept of Pediat Univ of Va Med Sch Charlottesville VA 22901

PAULSEN, GARY MELVIN, b Frederic, Wis, Mar 23, 39; m 66; c 2. PHYSIOLOGY. *Educ:* Univ Wis, BS, 61, MS, 63, PhD(agron, biochem), 65. *Prof Exp:* From asst prof to assoc prof, 65-75, PROF AGRON, KANS STATE UNIV, 75- *Concurrent Pos:* Rockefeller Found grant & vis scientist, Int Rice Res Inst, Philippines, 71-72. *Mem:* AAAS; Am Soc Plant Physiol; Japanese Soc Plant Physiol; Am Soc Agron; Crop Sci Soc Am. *Res:* Physiology of grain plants, primarily nitrogen and protein metabolism and crop hardiness. *Mailing Add:* Dept of Agron Kans State Univ Manhattan KS 66506

PAULSEN, MARVIN RUSSELL, b Minden, Nebr, July 17, 46; m 70; c 2. AGRICULTURAL ENGINEERING. *Educ:* Univ Nebr, BS, 69, MS, 72; Okla State Univ, PhD(agr eng), 75. *Prof Exp:* Engr, Chevrolet Div, Gen Motors Corp, 69; res asst, Agr Eng Dept, Univ Nebr, 71-72; res & teaching asst, Okla State Univ, 72-75; res asoc, 75-77, asst prof, 77-81, ASSOC PROF, AGR ENG DEPT, UNIV ILL, 81- *Concurrent Pos:* Mem, NC-151 Regional Comt Grain Quality, 78-82, Ill-Iowa Moisture Meter Task Force, 81-82. *Mem:* Am Soc Agr Engrs; Sigma Xi. *Res:* Determination of grain quality of corn and soybeans in export shipment, and from rotary and conventional combine harvesting; determination of corn varietal effects on breakage susceptibility; testing of the calibrations of electronic moisture meters. *Mailing Add:* 230 Agr Bldg Univ Ill 1208 W Peabody Urbana IL 61801

PAULSEN, PAUL, b Denison, Iowa, June 21, 35; m 60; c 4. ANALYTICAL CHEMISTRY. *Educ:* Univ Calif, Riverside, BA, 57; Cornell Univ, PhD(anal chem), 62. *Prof Exp:* ANAL CHEMIST, NAT BUR STAND, 62- *Mem:* Am Chem Soc; Am Soc Mass Spectrometry. *Res:* Trace element determinations in biological matrices, with isotope-dilution spark source mass spectrometry; analysis of high purity materials with spark source mass spectrograph. *Mailing Add:* 17612 Parkridge Dr Gaithersburg MD 20760

PAULSEN, R(EX) E(DWARD), urban systems engineering, see previous edition

PAULSHOCK, MARVIN, b Springfield, Ill, Jan 11, 23; m 51; c 3. ORGANIC CHEMISTRY. *Educ:* Univ Ill, BS, 43; Harvard Univ, AM, 47, PhD(org chem), 48. *Prof Exp:* Res chemist, Grasselli Div, 48-57, res scientist, Indust & Biochem Dept, 57-62, clin res assoc, Pharmaceut Div, Biochem Dept, 63-74, ASSOC DIR CLIN RES, PHARMACEUT DIV, BIOCHEM DEPT, E I DU PONT DE NEMOURS & CO, INC, 74- *Mem:* Am Chem Soc. *Res:* Naphthoquinones; phosphorous chemistry; chemotherapy; clinical evaluation of new drugs. *Mailing Add:* Pharmaceut Div Biochem Dept E I du Pont de Nemours & Co Inc Wilmington DE 19898

PAULSON, BOYD COLTON, JR, b Providence, RI, Mar 1, 46; m 70; c 2. CONSTRUCTION ENGINEERING, CONSTRUCTION MANAGEMENT. *Educ:* Stanford Univ, BS, 67, MS, 69, PhD(civil eng), 71. *Prof Exp:* Asst prof civil eng, Univ Ill, Urbana-Champaign, 72-73; asst prof, 74-77, ASSOC PROF CIVIL ENG, STANFORD UNIV, 77-, ASSOC CHMN DEPT, 80- *Concurrent Pos:* Secy, Proj Mgt Inst, 74-77; prin investr, NSF projs, US Dept Transp & Bus Roundtable, 74-; vis prof, Univ Tokyo, 78; Huber res prize, Am Soc Civil Engrs, 80. *Mem:* Am Soc Civil Engrs; Am Soc Eng Educ. *Res:* Computer applications in construction engineering and management; urban tunneling and deep excavations for transportation and wastewater projects; research and technology in Japanese construction engineering. *Mailing Add:* Dept Civil Eng Stanford Univ Stanford CA 94305

PAULSON, CARLTON, b Barrett, Minn, Dec 9, 34; m 56; c 4. PARASITOLOGY. *Educ:* Concordia Col, Moorhead, Minn, BA, 56; Kans State Univ, MS, 58, PhD(parasitol), 61. *Prof Exp:* From asst prof to assoc prof, 61-73, PROF BIOL, CONCORDIA COL, MOORHEAD, MINN, 73- *Mem:* AAAS; Am Soc Parasitol. *Res:* Metabolism of animal parasites; adenosine triphosphatases of helminth mitochondria. *Mailing Add:* Dept of Biol Concordia Col Moorhead MN 56560

PAULSON, CHARLES MAZWELL, JR, b Camden, NJ, Sept 15, 36; m 75; c 4. PHYSICAL CHEMISTRY, POLYMER SCIENCE. *Educ:* Drexel Univ, BS, 59; Univ Calif, Berkeley, PhD(chem), 65. *Prof Exp:* RES ASSOC PHYS CHEM, E I DU PONT DE NEMOURS & CO INC, 65- *Mem:* Am Chem Soc; Am Phys Soc. *Res:* Molecular electro optics; molecular orientation in polymers; optics of yarns. *Mailing Add:* Exp Sta Bldg 357 E I du Pont de Nemours & Co Inc Wilmington DE 19898

PAULSON, CLAYTON ARVID, b Fergus Falls, Minn, Oct 10, 38; m 63; c 2. OCEANOGRAPHY, METEOROLOGY. *Educ:* Augsburg Col, BA, 60; Univ Wash, PhD(atmospheric sci), 67. *Prof Exp:* From res assoc to res asst prof atmospheric sci, Univ Wash, 67-70; asst prof, 71-74, assoc prof, 74-79, PROF PHYS OCEANOG, ORE STATE UNIV, 79- *Concurrent Pos:* NATO assoc meteorol, Danish Atomic Energy Comn, Riso, Denmark, 70-71. *Mem:* AAAS; Am Geophys Union; Am Meteorol Soc; Royal Meteorol Soc. *Res:* Air-sea interaction; mechanics of turbulence; dynamics of the upper ocean. *Mailing Add:* Dept of Oceanog Ore State Univ Corvallis OR 97331

PAULSON, DAVID F, b Washington, DC, Apr 29, 38; m 61; c 3. UROLOGY, ONCOLOGY. *Educ:* Duke Univ, AB, 60, MD, 64. *Prof Exp:* Assoc prof, 75-80, PROF & CHMN, DEPT UROL, MED CTR, DUKE UNIV, 80- *Concurrent Pos:* Consult urol, Vet Admin Med Ctr, Oteen, NC & Cabarrus Mem Hosp, Concord, NC, 72-; dir urol res, Med Ctr, Duke Univ, 72-; nat chmn, Urol-Oncol Res Group, 73-; consult urol, Durham Count Gen Hosp, 77- *Mem:* Am Asn Genito-Urinary Surgeons; Am Urol Asn; Europ Soc Exp Surg; Am Col Surgeons; Soc Univ Surgeons. *Res:* Genitourinary oncology, etiology, diagnosis and treatment; identification of multimodality programs for control of genitourinary malignancy; tumor-specific androgens. *Mailing Add:* Med Ctr Duke Univ PO Box 2977 Durham NC 27710

PAULSON, DENNIS ROY, b Chicago, Ill, Nov 29, 37; m 63. EVOLUTIONARY BIOLOGY, ECOLOGY. *Educ:* Univ Miami, BS, 58, PhD(zool), 66. *Prof Exp:* Instr zool, Univ NC, Chapel Hill, 64-65, USPHS fel, 66; res assoc, 66-69, asst prof, 69-74, RES ASSOC ZOOL, UNIV WASH, 74- *Concurrent Pos:* NIH res grants, 71-74. *Mem:* Ecol Soc Am; Soc Syst Zool; Am Ornith Union; Soc Study Evolution; AAAS. *Res:* Isolating and releasing mechanisms in Odonata; seasonal regulation in Odonata; systematics of Neotropical Odonata; territoriality in Odonata. *Mailing Add:* 3833 Meridian N Seattle WA 98103

PAULSON, DONALD LOWELL, b St Paul, Minn, Sept 14, 12; m 38; c 3. THORACIC SURGERY. *Educ:* Univ Minn, BS & MB, 35, MD, 36, MS, 37, PhD(surg), 42; Am Bd Surg, dipl; Am Bd Thoracic Surg, dipl. *Prof Exp:* Instr anat, Univ Minn, 36-37; clin instr thoracic surg, 46-48, from clin asst prof to clin assoc prof surg, 48-56, clin assoc prof thoracic surg, 56-62, CLIN PROF THORACIC SURG, UNIV TEX HEALTH SCI CTR, DALLAS, 62- *Concurrent Pos:* Consult, Parkland Mem, Presby Hosps & Children's Med Ctr; mem, Am Bd Thoracic Surg, 64-73, chmn, 71-73; chief sect thoracic surg, Baylor Univ Med Ctr, 62-77, chmn med bd, 76-77. *Mem:* Fel Am Col Surgeons; fel Am Surg Asn; Am Asn Thoracic Surg; Soc Thoracic Surgeons. *Res:* Bronchogenic carcinoma; hiatal hernia. *Mailing Add:* 3600 Gaston Ave Dallas TX 75246

PAULSON, DONALD ROBERT, b Oak Park, Ill, Sept 6, 43; m 66; c 2. ORGANIC CHEMISTRY. *Educ:* Monmouth Col, BA, 65; Ind Univ Univ, PhD(chem), 68. *Prof Exp:* NIH fel, Univ Chicago, 68-70; from asst prof to assoc prof, 70-79, PROF CHEM, CALIF STATE UNIV, LOS ANGELES, 79- *Concurrent Pos:* Vis prof, Univ BC, 77-78. *Mem:* AAAS; Am Chem Soc; The Chem Soc; Int Photochem Soc; Sigma Xi. *Res:* Organic photochemistry; model systems for biological oxygenation; small-ring chemistry. *Mailing Add:* Dept of Chem Calif State Univ Los Angeles CA 90032

PAULSON, EDWARD, b Grantwood, NJ, July 21, 15; m 58; c 1. MATHEMATICAL STATISTICS. *Educ:* Brooklyn Col, BA, 36; Columbia Univ, MA, 38, PhD(math statist), 48. *Prof Exp:* Statist clerk, M R Scharff, Consult Engr, NY, 39; statist clerk, US Bur Census, Washington, DC, 40; Carnegie asst, Columbia Univ, 41, math statistician, Div War Res, 42-45; instr math statist, Univ NC, 47; asst prof math, Univ Wash, 47-53; from asst prof to assoc prof, 53-64, PROF MATH, QUEENS COL, NY, 64- *Concurrent Pos:* Vis mem, Courant Inst Math Sci, NY Univ, 65-66, Guggenheim fel, 68. *Mem:* Am Math Soc; Inst Math Statist. *Res:* Testing of statistical hypotheses; multiple decision problems; sequential analysis. *Mailing Add:* Dept of Math Queens Col Flushing NY 11367

PAULSON, GAYLORD D, b Castlewood, SDak, June 23, 37; m 60; c 2. BIOCHEMISTRY. *Educ:* SDak State Univ, BS, 63; Univ Wis, MS, 65, PhD(biochem), 67. *Prof Exp:* RES CHEMIST, RADIATION & METAB LAB, SCI & EDUC ADMIN-AGR RES, USDA, 67- *Mem:* Am Chem Soc. *Res:* Animal nutrition; metabolism of natural feed stuffs and pesticides. *Mailing Add:* USDA College Station Fargo ND 58102

PAULSON, JACK CHARLES, pulp chemistry, see previous edition

PAULSON, JAMES CARSTEN, b Ashland, Wis, Feb 28, 48; m 70. BIOCHEMISTRY. *Educ:* MacMurray Col, AB, 70; Univ Ill, Urbana, MS, 72, PhD(biochem), 74. *Prof Exp:* NIH fel biochem, Med Ctr, Duke Univ, 74-78; ASST PROF BIOL CHEM, UNIV CALIF, LOS ANGELES, 78- *Mem:* AAAS; Fedn Am Scientists; Sigma Xi. *Res:* Purification and characterization of glycosyl transferases; biosynthesis of carbohydrate prosthetic groups of glycoproteins and glycolipids and biological function of same. *Mailing Add:* Dept of Biol Chem Sch of Med Univ of Calif Los Angeles CA 90024

PAULSON, JAMES M(ARVIN), b Wausau, Wis, Jan 1, 23; m 46; c 2. CIVIL ENGINEERING. *Educ:* The Citadel, BS, 47; Ill Inst Technol, MSCE, 49; Univ Mich, PhD(civil eng), 58. *Prof Exp:* Draftsman, Wausau Iron Works, 46; asst instr eng, Ill Inst Technol, 47-48; engr, C S Whitney, 48-49; from instr to assoc prof, 49-60, chmn dept, 67-72, PROF CIVIL ENG, WAYNE STATE UNIV, 60-, ASSOC DEAN, 73- *Mem:* Am Soc Civil Engrs; Am Concrete Inst. *Res:* Structural engineering. *Mailing Add:* 14711 Rutland Detroit MI 48227

PAULSON, JOHN FREDERICK, b Providence, RI, Oct 29, 29; m 55; c 2. PHYSICAL CHEMISTRY. *Educ:* Haverford Col, AB, 51; Univ Rochester, PhD(chem), 58. *Prof Exp:* Proj assoc chem, Univ Wis, 58-59; RES CHEMIST, AIR FORCE GEOPHYS LAB, 59- *Mem:* Am Chem Soc; Am Phys Soc; Sigma Xi; Am Soc Mass Spectrometry. *Res:* Chemical kinetics; photochemistry; ion-neutral reactions; aeronomy. *Mailing Add:* Air Force Geophys Lab Hanscom AFB MA 01731

PAULSON, LARRY JEROME, b Willmar, Minn, Nov 1, 45; m 66. LIMNOLOGY, FISH BIOLOGY. *Educ:* Univ Nev, Las Vegas, BS, 72; Univ Calif, Davis, MS, 75, PhD(ecol), 77. *Prof Exp:* Res asst fisheries, Univ Nev, Las Vegas, 69-71, res assoc limnol, 71-73; res asst, Univ Calif, Davis, 74-77; RES ASST PROF LIMNOL, UNIV NEV, LAS VEGAS, 77- *Concurrent Pos:* Limnol consult, Ecol Res Assoc, 74-77. *Mem:* Am Fisheries Soc; Am Inst Biol Sci; Am Soc Limnol & Oceanog; Int Asn Theoret & Appl Limnol; Sigma Xi. *Res:* Factors regulating phytoplankton productivity; nutrient cycling and trophic interactions in lakes and reservoirs. *Mailing Add:* Dept of Biol Sci Univ Nev Las Vegas NV 89154

PAULSON, MARK CLEMENTS, b Rossville, Ill, Oct 29, 13; m 40; c 2. ORGANIC CHEMISTRY. *Educ:* Univ Ill, BS, 40; Univ Rochester, PhD(org chem), 43. *Prof Exp:* Instr chem, Univ Rochester, 43-44; res chemist, E I du Pont de Nemours & Co, 44-49; from asst prof to prof chem, Bradley Univ, 49-65, head dept, 64 & 65; prof chem, Chatham Col, 65-79, chmn dept, 65-75; RETIRED. *Mem:* Am Chem Soc; AAAS. *Res:* Attempted assymetric syntheses in the Grignard reaction; synthesis of some substituted thiocarbazones. *Mailing Add:* 616 Tenth St Oakmont PA 15139

PAULSON, OSCAR LAWRENCE, b El Dorado, Ark, Oct 2, 30; m 68. PETROLEUM GEOLOGY, ENVIRONMENTAL GEOLOGY. *Educ:* Miss State Col, BS, 54, MS, 55; La State Univ, PhD(geol), 60. *Prof Exp:* Instr geol, Miss State Univ, 55; computer, United Geophys Corp, 55; instr geol, La State Univ, 59-60; res geologist, La Geol Surv, 60-61; petrol geologist, Gulf Coast Venture, 61-64; independent geologist, 64-66; from asst prof to assoc prof, 66-76, chmn dept, 73-81, PROF GEOL, UNIV SOUTHERN MISS, 76- *Concurrent Pos:* NSF grant, 69-70; consult, NSF In-Serv Inst in Earth Sci, 68-69; fac res award, Gulf Oil Found, 80. *Mem:* Am Inst Prof Geol; Am Asn Petrol Geol. *Res:* Stratigraphy; salt tectonics; research and teaching environmental geology; environmental effects of dead-end canals in coastal zones. *Mailing Add:* Dept Geol Univ Southern Miss Box 8174 Hattiesburg MS 39401

PAULSON, RONALD FREDERICK, plasma physics, mechanical engineering, see previous edition

PAULSON, STUART R, endocrinology, see previous edition

PAULSON, WAYNE LEE, b LaCrosse, Wis, Sept 5, 34; m 57; c 3. ENVIRONMENTAL ENGINEERING. *Educ:* Univ Wis-Madison, BS, 59, MS, 60; Univ Iowa, PhD(sanit eng), 65. *Prof Exp:* From instr to assoc prof, 60-72, PROF CIVIL ENG, UNIV IOWA, 72- *Concurrent Pos:* Consult, Can-Tex Industs, Tex, 66, Penberthy Div, Houdaille Industs, Inc, 67-70; Environ Protection Agency process consult, 69-, Norton, 71 & Dravo, 71- *Mem:* Water Pollution Control Fedn; Am Water Works Asn; Am Soc Eng Educ; Am Soc Civil Engrs; Am Asn Prof Sanit Engrs. *Res:* Biochemical aspects of wastewater treatment processes, oxygen transfer; stream quality, activated sludge process applications. *Mailing Add:* 4110 Eng Bldg Univ of Iowa Iowa City IA 52242

PAULSRUD, JOHN REYNOLD, biochemistry, see previous edition

PAULUS, ALBERT, b Glendo, Wyo, Feb 28, 27. PLANT PATHOLOGY. *Educ:* Univ Wyo, MS, 51; Univ Wis, PhD(plant path), 54. *Prof Exp:* PLANT PATHOLOGIST, UNIV CALIF, RIVERSIDE, 54-, LECTR PLANT PATH, 70- *Mem:* Am Phytopath Soc; Neth Soc Plant Path. *Res:* Disease of vegetable, field and ornamental crops; subtropical diseases; fungicides. *Mailing Add:* Dept of Plant Path Univ of Calif Riverside CA 92521

PAULUS, HAROLD JOHN, b Iowa City, Iowa, Dec 25, 14; m 41; c 2. ENVIRONMENTAL HEALTH, AIR POLLUTION. *Educ:* State Univ Iowa, BS, 37, MS, 39, PhD(sanit chem, sanit eng), 41. *Prof Exp:* Comn officer occup health, USPHS, 47-57; prof, 57-80, EMER PROF AIR POLLUTION, SCH PUB HEALTH, UNIV MINN, MINNEAPOLIS, 80- *Concurrent Pos:* NIH res grants, Univ Minn, 59-72; consult, Minn Pollution Control Agency, 58-60 & Northern States Power Co, 65-73. *Mem:* Air Pollution Control Asn (dir, 73-); Am Indust Hyg Asn (dir, 62-65). *Res:* Relationship of allergic respiratory diseases to air pollutants from the grain industry; design and application of air sampling devices. *Mailing Add:* Dept of Environ Health Univ of Minn Sch of Pub Health Minneapolis MN 55455

PAULY, JOHN EDWARD, b Elgin, Ill, Sept 17, 27; m 49; c 4. ANATOMY. *Educ:* Northwestern Univ, BS, 50; Loyola Univ, Ill, MS, 52, PhD(anat), 55. *Prof Exp:* Res asst anat, Chicago Med Sch, 52-54, res instr, 54-55, instr gross anat, 55-57, assoc, 57-59, asst prof anat, 59-63, asst to pres, 60-62; assoc prof anat, Sch Med, Tulane Univ, 63-67; prof physiol & biophys & head dept, 78-80, PROF ANAT & HEAD DEPT, COL MED, UNIV ARK, LITTLE ROCK, 67- *Concurrent Pos:* Tech adv, Encyclop Britannica Films; mem safety & occup health study sect, Nat Inst Occup Safety & Health, 75-79; ed, Anat News, 72-80, ed, Am J Anat, 80- & co-managing ed, Advances Anat, Embryol & Cell Biol. *Honors & Awards:* Cert of Merit, AMA, 53 & 59; Bronze Award, Ill State Med Soc, 59; Lederle Med Fac Award, 66. *Mem:* Asn Anat Chmn (secy-treas, 69-71); Int Soc Chronobiol; Asn Am Med Cols; Am Soc Cancer Res; Am Physiol Soc. *Res:* Electromyography, histology and comparative anatomy of adrenals; structural change in human adrenal cortex associated with systemic diseases; chronobiology. *Mailing Add:* Dept of Anat Univ of Ark Col of Med Little Rock AR 72205

PAUR, SANDRA ORLEY, b Bismarck, NDak, Nov 4, 46; m 67; c 1. MATHEMATICS. *Educ:* Univ NDak, BS, 68; Ind Univ, MA, 70, PhD(math), 73. *Prof Exp:* ASST PROF MATH, NC STATE UNIV, 73- *Mem:* Am Math Soc; Math Asn Am; Sigma Xi; Asn Women Math. *Res:* Geometric analysis; approximation theory. *Mailing Add:* Dept of Math NC State Univ Raleigh NC 27650

PAUSCH, JERRY BLISS, b Leesburg, Ohio, Jan 21, 39; m 63; c 2. ANALYTICAL CHEMISTRY. *Educ:* Ohio State Univ, BE, 61; Purdue Univ, PhD(anal chem), 69. *Prof Exp:* Chem engr glass fiber res, Hercules, Inc, 61-63; res chemist, gas chromatog, 69-73, sect leader anal res, 73-75, MGR, ANAL RES, B F GOODRICH, 75- *Mem:* Am Chem Soc. *Res:* Gas chromatography; inverse gas chromatography and carbon-13 NMR of specific interactions; polymer blends; trace analysis. *Mailing Add:* 9921 Brecksville Rd Brecksville OH 44141

PAUSCH, ROBERT DALE, economic entomology, insect physiology, see previous edition

PAUSTIAN, FREDERICK FRANZ, b Grand Island, Nebr, Nov 24, 26; m 53; c 4. INTERNAL MEDICINE, GASTROENTEROLOGY. *Educ:* Univ Nebr, BSc, 52, MD, 53. *Prof Exp:* Intern, Grad Hosp, Univ Pa, 53-54, resident internal med, 54-56, resident gastroenterol, 56-57, asst instr, Div Grad Med, 57-58; instr, 58-60, assoc, 60-61, from asst prof to assoc prof, 61-67, PROF INTERNAL MED & PHYSIOL, COL MED, UNIV NEBR, OMAHA, 67-, MEM GRAD FAC, 65-, ASSOC DEAN CONTINUING & GRAD MED EDUC, 80- *Concurrent Pos:* Fel gastroenterol, Grad Hosp, Univ Pa, 57-58; fel trop med & parasitol, Cent Am, Panama, Mex & Sch Med, La State Univ, 60; mem, Residency Rev Comt Internal Med, 71-, vchmn, 75, chmn, 77, mem, Residency Rev Comt Allergy-Immunol, 74- *Mem:* AMA; fel Am Col Physicians; Am Gastroenterol Asn; NY Acad Sci; Bockus Int Soc Gastroenterol. *Res:* Gastrointestinal physiology, specifically secretory and motility research; clinical investigation regarding gastric ulcer, regional enteritis, ulcerative colitis and obscure gastrointestinal blood loss. *Mailing Add:* Dept of Internal Med Univ of Nebr Col of Med Omaha NE 68105

PAUSTIAN, JOHN EARLE, b Grand Island, Nebr, Mar 19, 28; m 51; c 3. ORGANIC CHEMISTRY. *Educ:* Univ Nebr, BSc, 50; Stevens Inst Technol, MSc, 57. *Prof Exp:* Chemist, US Naval Ord Test Sta, 51-53; chemist, Reaction Motors, Inc, 53-57, group leader, Reaction Motors Div, Thiokol Chem Corp, 57-67; sr process res specialist, 67-77, sr res chemist, 77-80, PRIN RES CHEMIST, LUMMUS CO, 80- *Mem:* Catalysis Soc; Am Chem Soc; NY Acad Sci. *Res:* Photochemistry; process development and scale-up; organo-metallic and polymer research and development; petrochemicals. *Mailing Add:* Lummus Co 1515 Broad St Bloomfield NJ 07003

PAUTLER, EUGENE L, b Alden, NY, Aug 10, 31; m 66; c 1. PHYSIOLOGY, BIOPHYSICS. *Educ:* Univ Buffalo, BA, 56, PhD(physiol psychol), 60. *Prof Exp:* Nat Acad Sci fel neuropharmacol, Aerospace Med Lab, Wright-Patterson Air Force Base, Ohio, 60-61; lab dir life sci res, Goodyear Aerospace Corp, 61-65; NIH spec fel electrophysiol, Keio Sch Med, Japan, 65-67; ASSOC PROF PHYSIOL & BIOPHYS, COL VET MED & BIOMED SCI, COLO STATE UNIV, 67- *Mem:* Am Physiol Soc. *Res:* Electrophysiological and ultrastructural cytochemistry studies of the retina. *Mailing Add:* Dept of Physiol & Biophysics Colo State Univ Ft Collins CO 80523

PAVAN, CRODOWALDO, b Campinas, Sao Paulo, Brazil, Nov 29, 19; m 46; c 3. GENETICS. *Educ:* Univ Sao Paulo, BA, 41, PhD(biol), 44. *Prof Exp:* Monitor biol, Univ Sao Paulo, 40-41, asst, 41-52, prof, 52-69; prof zool & dir cytogenetics, pop & theoret genetics proj, Univ Tex Austin, 69-75; prof biol, Univ Sao Paulo, 76-77; PROF GENETICS, UNIV CAMPINAS, BRAZIL,

78- *Concurrent Pos:* Brazilian del sci comt effects atomic radiation, UN, 56-68. *Mem:* Brazilian Acad Sci; Brazilian Soc Advan Sci (vpres, 75-77, pres, 81-82); Brazilian Biol Soc; Brazilian Genetics Soc (pres, 58-59); Papal Acad Sci. *Res:* Population genetics; cytogenetics and chromosomal physiology. *Mailing Add:* Dept of Evolutionary Genetics Univ Campinas Sao Paulo Brazil

PAVEK, JOSEPH JOHN, b Waubun, Minn, Oct 3, 27; m 57; c 7. PLANT BREEDING, PLANT GENETICS. *Educ:* Univ Minn, BS, 55, MS, 63; Univ Wis, PhD(cytogenetics of oats), 65. *Prof Exp:* RES GENETICIST, SCI & EDUC ADMIN-AGR RES, USDA, 65- *Mem:* AAAS; Crop Sci Soc Am; Potato Asn Am. *Res:* Genetics of economically important characteristics of potato; genetics of reaction in oats to rust; cytogenetics of oat aneuploids. *Mailing Add:* Sci & Educ Admin-Agr Res USDA Br Exp Sta Aberdeen ID 83210

PAVELIC, VJEKOSLAV, b Sisak, Yugoslavia, June 20, 29; US citizen; m 54; c 2. MECHANICAL ENGINEERING. *Educ:* Univ Zagreb, Dipl Eng, 55; Univ Wis, MS, 61, PhD(mech eng), 68. *Prof Exp:* Design engr, Badger Meter Corp, 55-56; proj engr, Neodyne Corp, Consult Engrs, 56-57; staff engr, Aqua-Chem Co, 57-60; sr res & develop engr cent res, A O Smith Corp, 60-64; res asst educ, Univ Wis, Madison, 64-68; from asst prof to assoc prof, 68-78, PROF SYSTS DESIGN, UNIV WIS, MILWAUKEE, 78- *Concurrent Pos:* NSF fel, Univ Wis, Milwaukee, 69-71, Am Welding Soc fel, 71-73; indust consult. *Honors & Awards:* Western Elec Fund Award, Am Soc Eng Educ, 77-78. *Mem:* Am Soc Mech Engrs; Am Welding Soc; Am Soc Eng Educ; Sigma Xi. *Res:* Machine design; mechanical system analysis; statistical experiment design; welding and plasma arc; mechanical reliability and probabilistic design. *Mailing Add:* Col of Eng & Appl Sci Univ of Wis Milwaukee WI 53201

PAVEY, ROBERT LOUIS, b Rising Sun, Ind, Apr 4, 33; m 61; c 3. FOOD SCIENCE. *Educ:* Purdue Univ, BS, 56; Univ Mo, MS, 59; Cornell Univ, PhD(animal sci & nutrit), 63. *Prof Exp:* Res scientist animal husb, Res & Develop Ctr, Swift & Co, 56-57; asst animal sci, Univ Mo, 58-59 & Cornell Univ, 59-63; res scientist animal husb, 63-64, res scientist, fresh meats, 64-65, div head dehydrated & aerospace foods, 65-75, res scientist, New Prod, 75-78, fresh meats res, 78-80, POULTRY RES, RES & DEVELOP CTR, SWIFT & CO, 80- *Mem:* Inst Food Technol. *Res:* Food preservation techniques; food processing techniques; dehydration and reconstitution techniques; foods for space feeding; new products food research; health nutrition in foods. *Mailing Add:* Swift & Co Res & Develop Ctr 1919 Swift Dr Oak Brook IL 60521

PAVIA, DONALD LEE, b Portland, Ore, Jan 25, 41. ORGANIC CHEMISTRY, PHOTOCHEMISTRY. *Educ:* Reed Col, AB, 62; Yale Univ, MS, 64, PhD(chem), 68. *Prof Exp:* NIH fel, Univ Wis-Madison, 68-70; asst prof, 70-75, ASSOC PROF CHEM, WESTERN WASH UNIV, 75- *Mem:* Am Chem Soc; Royal Soc Chem. *Res:* Autoxidation reactions; organic photochemistry. *Mailing Add:* Dept of Chem Western Wash Univ Bellingham WA 98225

PAVILANIS, VYTAUTAS, b Kaunas, Lithuania, June 7, 20; Can citizen; m 47; c 4. MEDICINE, VIROLOGY. *Educ:* Univ Kaunas, Lithuania, MD, 42. *Prof Exp:* Asst prof path, Univ Kaunas, Lithuania, 42-44; asst virol, Pasteur Inst, Paris, 45-48; assoc prof virol, Univ, 48-65, head virus dept, 48-71, sci dir, Inst Armand-Frappier, 71-75, res coordr, 75-78, PROF VIROL, UNIV MONTREAL, 65-, ASST DIR, INST ARMAND-FRAPPIER, 78- *Concurrent Pos:* Mem, Can Nat Tech Adv Comt Live Poliovirus Vaccine, 61-64. *Mem:* NY Acad Sci; Royal Soc Can; Can Soc Microbiol; Can Med Asn. *Res:* Quality control of viral, bacterial vaccine and culture media. *Mailing Add:* Inst Armand-Frappier 531 Blvd des Prairies Laval-des-Rapides PQ H7V 1B7 Can

PAVKOVIC, STEPHEN F, b Highland Park, Mich, Oct 29, 32; m 61; c 4. INORGANIC CHEMISTRY. *Educ:* Wayne State Univ, BS, 55, MS, 61; Ohio State Univ, PhD, 64. *Prof Exp:* asst prof, 65-70, ASSOC PROF INORG CHEM, LOYOLA UNIV, CHICAGO, 70- *Mem:* Am Crystallog Asn; Am Chem Soc. *Res:* X-ray crystallographic structural investigations of transition metal coordination complexes. *Mailing Add:* 8021 N Overhill Ave Niles IL 60648

PAVLASEK, TOMAS J(AN) F(RANTISEK), b London, Eng, July 15, 23; Can citizen; m 54; c 3. ELECTRICAL ENGINEERING. *Educ:* McGill Univ, BE, 44, MEng, 48, PhD(elec eng), 58. *Prof Exp:* Res assoc, 48-52, from asst prof to assoc prof, 52-62, secy of fac, 66-67, PROF, MCGILL UNIV, 62-, ASSOC DEAN PLANNING & DEVELOP, FAC ENG, 67- *Mem:* Inst Elec & Electronics Engrs; Am Soc Eng Educ; Eng Inst Can. *Res:* Microwave measurements; automatic control; antennas and electromagnetic wave propagation. *Mailing Add:* McGill Univ Dept Elec Eng 3480 University St Montreal PQ H3A 2T5 Can

PAVLATH, ATTILA ENDRE, b Budapest, Hungary, Mar 11, 30; US citizen; m 51; c 2. FLUORINE CHEMISTRY, GLOW DISCHARGE CHEMISTRY. *Educ:* Budapest Tech Univ, PhD(org fluorine chem), 52. *Hon Degrees:* DSc, Hungarian Acad Sci, 56. *Prof Exp:* Res assoc fluorine chem, Org Chem Inst, Budapest Tech Univ, Hungary, 51-52, asst prof, 52-54; sr group leader, Chem Cent Res Inst, Hungarian Acad Sci, 54-56; res chemist, Dept Chem, McGill Univ, 57-58; sr group leader, Res Dept, Stauffer Chem Co, Calif, 58-67; sr res scientist, 67-72, proj leader, 72-80, RES LEADER, WESTERN REGIONAL RES LAB, USDA, 80- *Concurrent Pos:* Vis prof, Budapest Tech Univ, 54-56. *Honors & Awards:* Award, Hungarian Acad Sci, 52-54; Merit Award, USDA, 71; Outstanding Contrib Chem, Am Chem Soc, 76. *Mem:* Am Chem Soc; Royal Soc Chem. *Res:* Organic and inorganic fluorine chemistry; theoretical organic chemistry; aromatic substitution; high energy oxidizers; low temperature plasma chemistry; natural fibers; biomass gasification and liquefaction. *Mailing Add:* Western Regional Res Lab USDA 800 Buchanan St Berkeley CA 94710

PAVLIDES, LOUIS, b Annapolis, Md, May 11, 21; m 50; c 1. GEOLOGY. *Educ:* Brooklyn Col, AB, 43; Columbia Univ, AM, 48. *Prof Exp:* Geologist, NC, 47-48, NJ, 48, Fla, 48-49, Maine, 49-68, Va, 68-70, Atlantic Environ Geol Br, 70-80, GEOLOGIST, EASTERN REGIONAL GEOL BR, US GEOL SURV, 80- *Mem:* Geol Soc Am; Soc Econ Geol. *Res:* Resources of manganese deposits; structure, stratigraphy and petrology of rocks of northeast Maine; geology of the outer Piedmont and northeast Virginia; geology of New England and the southeast Piedmont. *Mailing Add:* 7518 Creighton Dr College Park MD 20740

PAVLIK, EDWARD JOHN, b Cleveland, Ohio, Dec 16, 46; m 75. BIOCHEMISTRY, CELL BIOLOGY. *Educ:* Univ Denver, BS, 69, MS, 73; Univ Tenn Knoxville, PhD(cell biol), 75. *Prof Exp:* Teaching asst biol sci, Univ Denver, 69-71; biol, zool, Univ Tenn, Knoxville, 74-75; trainee reprod, Univ Ill, Urbana, 76-77, Nat Cancer Inst fel cancer res, 77-78, vis asst prof physiol, 78-80; DIR RES GYNEC/ONCOL, UNIV KY, LEXINGTON, 80-, ASST PROF BIOCHEM, 80- *Mem:* Am Soc Cell Biol; Endocrine Soc. *Res:* Mechanisms of gene activation in eukaryotes; mechanism of steroid hormone action; identification of hormone dependent neoplasias and the endocrinology of these neoplasias; identification of biological control proteins; ovarian cancer treatment. *Mailing Add:* 524 Burrill Univ Ill Urbana IL 61801

PAVLIN, EDWARD GEORGE, b Dauphin, Man, June 17, 40. ANESTHESIOLOGY. *Educ:* Univ Man, BSc, 61, BSc & MD, 68. *Prof Exp:* Res fel, 72-73, instr, 73-75, asst prof, 75-80, ASSOC PROF ANESTHESIOL, SCH MED, UNIV WASH, 80- *Concurrent Pos:* Med dir, Highline Col Sch Respiratory Ther, Midway, Wash, 74-; asst dir respiratory ther, Harborview Med Ctr, Seattle, 74- *Mem:* Am Soc Anesthesiol. *Res:* Control of respiration and determinants of brain extracellular fluid hydrogen ion concentration; effects of anesthesia on physiologic function, pulmonary respiration, respiratory physiology. *Mailing Add:* Dept of Anesthesiol Univ of Wash Sch of Med Seattle WA 98195

PAVLIN, MARK STANLEY, b Wilmington, Del, Nov 6, 51; m 73; c 3. ORGANIC CHEMISTRY. *Educ:* Lehigh Univ, BS, 72; Univ Ill, Urbana, PhD(org chem), 77. *Prof Exp:* Res scientist, 77-81, GROUP LEADER TERPENES, UNION CAMP CORP, 81- *Mem:* Am Chem Soc. *Res:* Process research in terpene synthesis and turpentine conversion. *Mailing Add:* Union Camp Corp Box 412 Princeton NJ 08540

PAVLISKO, JOSEPH ANTHONY, b Bethesda, Md, April 10, 53. BIOMIMETICS, BIOMATERIALS. *Educ:* Rensselaer Polytech Inst, 75; Univ Conn, PhD(polymer chem), 78. *Prof Exp:* Fel polymer chem, Macromolecular Res Inst, Univ Mich, 78-79; SR CHEMIST POLYMER CHEM, RES TRIANGLE INST, 79- *Mem:* Sigma Xi; NY Acad Sci; Am Chem Soc; AAAS. *Res:* Polymer synthetic chemistry; biomimetic systems; catalysis; thermotropic polymer liquid crystals; modifications of polymers. *Mailing Add:* Res Triangle Inst Chem & Life Sci Group Research Triangle Park NC 27709

PAVLOPOULOS, THEODORE G, b Thouria-Kalamata, Greece, Aug 20, 25. OPTICAL PHYSICS. *Educ:* Univ Gottingen, dipl, 51, Dr rer nat(phys chem), 53. *Prof Exp:* Res fel, Max-Planck Inst for Phys Chem, 53; fel physics, Univ Toronto, 53-54; fel phys chem, BC Res Coun, 54-55; lectr physics, Univ BC, 55-56; res assoc, Biophys Prog, Tulane Univ, 56-58; sr res engr, Electronics Dept, Convair Div, Gen Dynamics Corp, 58-62; fel chem, Univ Calif, Los Angeles, 62-65; PHYSICIST, NAVAL OCEAN SYSTS CTR, 65- *Mem:* NY Acad Sci. *Res:* Spectroscopy; solid state physics; optics; electrochemistry; integrated optics. *Mailing Add:* Naval Ocean Systs Ctr San Diego CA 92152

PAVLOS, JOHN, b Cleveland, Ohio, Dec 29, 27; m 53; c 1. ORGANIC CHEMISTRY, BIOCHEMISTRY. *Educ:* Western Reserve Univ, BS, 53, MS, 54, PhD(org chem), 60. *Prof Exp:* Fel biochem, Albert Einstein Col Med, 59-63, res asst prof, 63; from asst prof to assoc prof chem, Davis & Elkins Col, 63-67; ASSOC PROF CHEM, MANHATTANVILLE COL, 67- *Mem:* AAAS; Am Chem Soc. *Res:* Steroid and peptide synthesis; free radical aromatic substitution. *Mailing Add:* Dept of Chem Manhattanville Col Purchase NY 10577

PAVLOVA, MARIA T, b Plovdiv, Bulgaria, Oct 25, 33; US citizen; m 57; c 1. MEDICINE, MICROBIOLOGY. *Educ:* Inst Med, Plovdiv, Bulgaria, MD, 57; Charles Univ, Prague, PhD(microbiol), 69. *Prof Exp:* Attend physician, Pernik City Hosp, Bulgaria, 58-59; chief microbiol, State Dept Health, Pernik, Bulgaria, 59-62; chief microbiol sect prev med, Ministry Pub Health, Sofia, Bulgaria, 62-65; res assoc environ microbiol, Univ Mass, 69-72; SCIENTIST & DIR CLIN MICROBIOL LAB, BROOKHAVEN NAT LAB, 72- *Concurrent Pos:* Ministry Pub Health fel, Bulgaria, 65-69; collabr, Environ Protection Agency grant, 69-72; asst prof med microbiol, State Univ NY, Stony Brook, 76-80, assoc prof, 80- *Mem:* Am Soc Microbiol; Am Registry Microbiologists; Sigma Xi. *Res:* Interaction between chemicals and oncogenic viruses in carcinogenesis; methods for rapid identification of group D streptococci. *Mailing Add:* Med Res Ctr Brookhaven Nat Lab Upton NY 11973

PAVLOVIC, ARTHUR STEPHEN, b Bedford, Ohio, Dec 2, 25; m 47; c 4. SOLID STATE PHYSICS. *Educ:* Yale Univ, BE, 46; Case Inst Technol, MS, 49; Pa State Univ, PhD(physics), 56. *Prof Exp:* Prin physicist, Battelle Mem Inst, 51-52; jr engr, Goodyear Aircraft Corp, 52; jr physicist, Union Carbide Metals Co, 56-58, res physicist, 58-59; from asst prof to assoc prof, 59-66, chmn dept, 68-75, PROF PHYSICS, WVA UNIV, 66- *Mem:* Am Phys Soc; Am Asn Physics Teachers. *Res:* Ferromagnetics; paramagnetism; dielectric materials. *Mailing Add:* Dept of Physics WVa Univ Morgantown WV 26506

PAVLOVIC, DUSAN M(ILOS), b Dobric, Yugoslavia, July 9, 21; nat US; m 59; c 1. METALLURGY. *Educ:* Sch Mines Freiberg, MetE, 45; Stuttgart Tech Univ, DrEng, 49. *Prof Exp:* Res asst, Univ Pittsburgh, 49-50 & Carnegie Inst Technol, 50; res engr, Gibson Elec Co, 50-52; metall engr, Mat Eng Dept,

52-58, resident eng rep in Ger, 59-63, adv scientist, Aerospace Elec Div, Ohio, 63-69, FEL ENGR, BETTIS ATOMIC POWER LAB, WESTINGHOUSE ELEC CO, WEST MIFFLIN, 69- *Mem:* Am Soc Metals; Am Inst Mining, Metall & Petrol Engrs; Inst Elec & Electronics Engrs. *Res:* Physical and mechanical metallurgy of nuclear, composite, magnetic and high-temperature materials; fracture mechanics; powder metallurgy; arc welding; magnetic phenomena; international liaison in electrical technology. *Mailing Add:* 413 Cheri Dr Bridgeville PA 15017

PAVLOVICH, RAYMOND DORAN, b Rocky Point, Wyo, July 14, 34; m 55; c 3. MATERIALS ENGINEERING, CIVIL ENGINEERING. *Educ:* Univ Wyo, BS, 59, MS, 65; Purdue Univ, PhD(civil eng), 75. *Prof Exp:* Off mgr munic eng, Holder Eng Serv, 59-60; engr design & construct, J T Banner & Assoc, Inc, 60-65; res assoc, Wyo Hwy Dept, Univ Wyo, 65-67; grad instr res, Purdue Univ, 67-75; engr-analyst, Asphalt Inst, 75-77; hwy res eng waste utilization, Fed Hwy Admin, Eng Testing Lab Inc, 77, mgr res & develop, 77-81; ASSOC PROF CIVIL ENG, ARIZ STATE UNIV, 81- *Mem:* Nat Acad Sci; Asn Asphalt Paving Technol; Am Soc Testing & Mat; Am Soc Civil Eng; Nat Soc Prof Eng. *Res:* Construction materials developed from recovered resources such as fly ash, reclaimed tire rubber, incinerator residue and mine wastes. *Mailing Add:* Dept Civil Eng Ariz State Univ Tempe AZ 85287

PAVLOVSKIS, OLGERTS RAIMONDS, b Riga, Latvia, Apr 29, 34; m 67; c 2. MICROBIOLOGY. *Educ:* Ore State Univ, Corvallis, BS, 58; Univ Wash, BS, 61, MS, 64; Northwestern Univ, Chicago, PhD(microbiol), 70. *Prof Exp:* Sr lab technician genetics, Dept Med, Sch Med, Univ Wash, 58-61; qual control chem & bact, Western Farmers Asn, Seattle, 64-66; res assoc microbiol, Evanston Hosp, Evanston, Ill, 66-68; MICROBIOLOGIST, NAVAL MED RES INST, BETHESDA, MD, 70- *Concurrent Pos:* Res assoc, Nat Res Coun & Bur Med & surg res associateship, Naval Med Res Inst, Bethesda, Md, 70-72. *Mem:* Am Soc Microbiol. *Res:* Microbial toxins; Pseudomonas aeruginosa exotoxin; kinetics of exotoxin synthesis in vitro and in patients, its mode of action, role in clinical infections; prophylaxis and treatment of Pseudomonas infections; antibody production; vaccine; mechanisms of pathogenesis. *Mailing Add:* Dept of Microbiol Naval Med Res Inst Bethesda MD 20014

PAVONE, BEN W, b Berkeley, Calif, June 11, 16; m 63; c 4. DENTISTRY. *Educ:* Univ Calif, AB, 39, MA, 41, BS & DDS, 45. *Prof Exp:* Chmn div crown & bridge prosthodontics, 65-66, coordr postgrad educ, 55-81, dean sch dent, 65-81, PROF DENT, UNIV CALIF, 65- *Concurrent Pos:* Dir occlusion & oral rehab study groups, Sch Dent, Univ Calif, San Francisco, 56-65, dir temporomandibular joint study group, 60-65; consult prosthodontia plastic & reconstruct surg clin, St Francis Hosp, San Francisco, 56-65; mem continuing educ coun, Calif Dent Asn, 73. *Mem:* Int Acad Dent Res; Am Prosthodontics Soc; Am Acad Restorative Dent; Am Dent Asn. *Mailing Add:* Sch of Dent Univ of Calif San Francisco CA 94143

PAWEL, RICHARD E, b Glens Falls, NY, Mar 12, 32; m 55; c 2. PHYSICAL METALLURGY. *Educ:* Univ Tenn, BS, 53, MS, 54, PhD(metall), 56. *Prof Exp:* METALLURGIST, OAK RIDGE NAT LAB, NUCLEAR DIV, UNION CARBIDE CORP, 59- *Mem:* Am Soc Metals; Electrochem Soc; Sigma Xi. *Res:* Reaction mechanisms in metals; thermal properties and measurements; thermoelectric materials; electron microscopy; gas-metal reactions; surface phenomena; diffusion in refractory metals and oxides; properties of thin films; high-temperature gas corrosion; zirconium and zirconium alloy oxidation. *Mailing Add:* Metals & Ceramics Div Oak Ridge Nat Lab PO Box X Oak Ridge TN 37830

PAWELEK, JOHN MASON, b Baltimore, Md, Apr 15, 42; m 64; c 3. BIOCHEMISTRY, GENETICS. *Educ:* Gettysburg Col, AB, 63; Brown Univ, PhD(develop biol), 67. *Prof Exp:* Asst prof, 70-77, ASSOC PROF DERMATOL, SCH MED, YALE UNIV, 77- *Concurrent Pos:* Am Cancer Soc fel biochem, 67-70, NIH fel genetics, 70-71. *Mem:* Soc Develop Biol; Soc Invest Dermat. *Res:* Biochemical and genetic controls of cell division and the expression of differentiated functions. *Mailing Add:* Dept of Dermat Yale Univ Sch of Med New Haven CT 06510

PAWLICKI, ANTHONY JOSEPH, b Detroit, Mich, Mar 21, 44. EXPERIMENTAL HIGH ENERGY PHYSICS. *Educ:* Univ Detroit, BS, 65; Cornell Univ, MS, 68, PhD(physics), 70. *Prof Exp:* Res assoc physics, Physics Dept, Ind Univ, 70-72; appointee physics, High Energy Physics Div, Argonne Nat Lab, 72-76; res assoc, Univ Toronto, 76-77; WRITER, 77- *Mem:* Am Phys Soc. *Mailing Add:* Box 878 Woodland CO

PAWLISCH, PAUL E, b Madison, Wis, Jan 9, 31; c 2. AGRONOMY. *Educ:* Univ Wis-Madison, BS, 55, MS, 57, PhD(agron, plant path), 59. *Prof Exp:* Res asst cereal breeding, Univ Wis-Madison, 55-59; asst prof, Tex A&M Univ, 59-64; res agronomist, 64-69, exec dir, 69-80, PRES, MALTING BARLEY IMPROV ASN, 80- *Mem:* Am Soc Agron; Am Soc Brewing Chemists; Am Soc Asn Exec. *Mailing Add:* Malting Barley Improv Asn 2040 W Wisconsin Ave Milwaukee WI 53233

PAWLOWICZ, EDMUND F, b Toledo, Ohio, Apr 2, 41; div; c 3. GEOPHYSICS. *Educ:* Ohio State Univ, BEE, 64, MSc, 65, PhD(geophys), 69. *Prof Exp:* Sr proj scientist, Marine Geophys, Naval Civil Eng Lab, Calif, 68-70; assoc prof geophys & dir, Seismol Observ, Bowling Green State Univ, 70-81; STAFF GEOPHYSICIST, AMOCO PROD CO, DENVER, COLO, 81- *Mem:* Am Geophys Union; Soc Explor Geophys; Can Soc Explor Geophysicist; Europ Asn Explor Geophysicists. *Res:* Exploration geophysics; reflection seismology; vertical seismic profiling; potential fields. *Mailing Add:* Amoco Prod Co Amoco Bldg 1670 Broadway Denver CO 80202

PAWLOWSKI, ANTHONY T, b North Abington, Mass, Nov 11, 22; m 49; c 4. PHYSICAL CHEMISTRY. *Educ:* Gannon Col, BS, 51; Boston Col, MS, 56; Rutgers Univ, PhD(thermal diffusion), 56, PhD(phys chem), 65. *Prof Exp:* Instr chem, Calumet Ctr, Purdue Univ, 58-60; instr, Rutgers Univ, 60-65; asst prof phys chem, Providence Col, 65-69; PROF CHEM & CHMN DEPT, ALLEGANY COMMUNITY COL, 69- *Concurrent Pos:* NIH res grant, 65-; consult, Precious Metals Inc, Mass, 65- & Basic Sci Inc, Conn, 70; pres, Theotron Co, Cumberland, Md, 74- *Mem:* Am Chem Soc; Am Phys Soc. *Res:* Thermal diffusion; transport phenomena; electrochemistry, especially electrode processes; Faraday effect; combustion processes. *Mailing Add:* Dept of Chem Allegany Community Col Cumberland MD 21502

PAWLOWSKI, NORMAN E, b Lynnwood, Calif, Aug 22, 38; c 3. ORGANIC CHEMISTRY. *Educ:* Southern Ore Col, BS, 61; Ore State Univ, PhD(chem), 65. *Prof Exp:* Res assoc chem, Univ Mich, 65-66; asst prof, Ill State Univ, 66-68; asst prof food protection, 68-74, sr res asst prof, 74-77, ASSOC PROF FOOD SCI & TECHNOL, ORE STATE UNIV, 77- *Mem:* Am Chem Soc. *Res:* Kinetics; toxicology; free-radicals; spectroscopic identification of metabolites; cyclopropene chemistry. *Mailing Add:* Dept Food Sci & Technol Ore State Univ Corvallis OR 97331

PAWLOWSKI, PHILIP JOHN, b Dunkirk, NY, July 15, 43; m 68; c 1. CELL BIOLOGY. *Educ:* St Bonaventure Univ, BS, 65; State Univ NY Buffalo, MS & PhD(biol), 69. *Prof Exp:* Fel biochem, Univ Pittsburgh, 70-73; res assoc cell biol, 73-80, VIS ASST PROF, DEPT BIOL, WESLEYAN UNIV, 80- *Mem:* Soc Develop Biol. *Res:* Regulation of cell growth and development, specifically the regulation of nucleic acid and protein synthesis and degradation. *Mailing Add:* Dept of Biol Wesleyan Univ Middletown CT 06457

PAWLUK, STEVE, b Egremont, Alta, Sept 21, 30; m 60; c 3. SOIL SCIENCE. *Educ:* Univ Alta, BSc, 53, MSc, 55; Univ Minn, PhD, 57. *Prof Exp:* Asst res officer soil surv, Res Coun Alta, 57-59; from asst prof to assoc prof soil sci, 59-69, assoc chmn dept forest sci, 71-73, chmn dept, 74-79, PROF SOIL SCI, UNIV ALTA, 69- *Honors & Awards:* Gold Medal, Am Inst Chem, 53. *Mem:* Am Soc Agron; fel Can Soc Soil Sci; Int Soc Soil Sci. *Res:* Soil pedology, especially soil mineralogy and chemistry; forest soils; soil micromorphology. *Mailing Add:* Dept Soil Sci Univ Alta Edmonton AB T6G 2G7 Can

PAWSON, BEVERLY ANN, b East Orange, NJ, June 20, 34. ORGANIC CHEMISTRY. *Educ:* Smith Col, BA, 56; Mass Inst Technol, PhD(org chem), 66. *Prof Exp:* Res asst, Mellon Inst, 56-57; res chemist, Esso Res & Eng Co, 57-62; sr chemist, 66-73, res fel, 74, res group chief, 75-80, asst dir med chem, 81, ASSOC DIR CHEM RES, HOFFMANN-LA ROCHE INC, 81- *Mem:* Am Chem Soc. *Res:* Synthetic organic chemistry; natural products; medicinal chemistry, retinoids and chemotherapeutic agents. *Mailing Add:* Hoffmann-LaRoche Inc Nutley NJ 07110

PAWSON, DAVID LEO, b Napier, NZ, Oct 5, 38; m 62; c 2. MARINE ZOOLOGY. *Educ:* Victoria Univ, NZ, BSc, 60, MSc, 61, PhD(zool), 64. *Prof Exp:* Demonstr zool, Victoria Univ, NZ, 59-62, teaching fel, 62-64, lectr, 64; assoc curator, Div Marine Invert, 64-65, curator-in-charge, Div Echinoderms, 65-71, chmn dept invert zool, 71-75, CUR ECHINODERMS, NAT MUS NATURAL HIST, SMITHSONIAN INST, 75- *Concurrent Pos:* Adj lectr, George Washington Univ, 65-; assoc invert, Harvard Univ, 74- *Mem:* AAAS; Soc Syst Zool; Royal Soc NZ; NZ Marine Sci Soc (secy-treas, 63). *Res:* Systematics; zoogeography and evolution of echinoderms, especially echinozoans of southern oceans; higher classification of echinoderms. *Mailing Add:* Nat Mus Natural Hist Smithsonian Inst Washington DC 20560

PAWULA, ROBERT FRANCIS, b Chicago, Ill, May 17, 36. COMMUNICATIONS. *Educ:* Ill Inst Technol, BS, 60; Mass Inst Technol, SM, 61; Calif Inst Technol, PhD(elec eng), 65. *Prof Exp:* Teaching asst elec eng, Calif Inst Technol, 61-62; mem tech staff, Hughes Aircraft Co, 62-65; from asst prof to assoc prof aerospace eng, Univ Calif, San Diego, 65- 75; PRES, RANDOM APPLICATIONS, INC, 75- *Concurrent Pos:* Commun & radar consult, 65- *Mem:* Inst Elec & Electronics Engrs; Am Orthotic & Prosthetic Asn; Eng & Archit Asn. *Res:* Applications of probability theory and stochastic processes to problems in communication theory; information theory and statistical control theory. *Mailing Add:* Random Applns Inc 4611 Chateau Dr San Diego CA 92117

PAX, RALPH A, b Celina, Ohio, May 9, 34; m 61; c 3. PHYSIOLOGY. *Educ:* Univ Dayton, BS, 60; Purdue Univ, MS, 62, PhD(physiol), 64. *Prof Exp:* From asst prof to assoc prof, 64-72, PROF ZOOL, MICH STATE UNIV, 72- *Mem:* AAAS; Am Soc Zool. *Res:* Comparative physiology; neurophysiology; electrophysiology. *Mailing Add:* Dept of Zool Mich State Univ East Lansing MI 48823

PAXSON, JOHN RALPH, b Waco, Tex, Sept 22, 42; m 73. ANALYTICAL CHEMISTRY, INORGANIC CHEMISTRY. *Educ:* ST Mary's Univ, San Antonio, BS, 65; Iowa State Univ, Ames, PhD(inorg chem), 70. *Prof Exp:* Instr chem, North Tex State Univ, Denton, 70-72, supvr instrumentation, 72; res assoc chem, Univ Tex, Austin, 72-74; SUPVR MOLECULAR STRUCTURE, PHILLIPS PETROL CO, BARTLESVILLE, OK, 74- *Concurrent Pos:* Res assoc, Ames Lab USAEC, Ames, Iowa, 67-70; teaching fel, NTex State Univ Fac grant, 70-72; res fel, Robert A Welch Found, Tex, 72-74. *Mem:* Am Chem Soc; The Chem Soc; Coblentz Soc; Soc Appl Spectros. *Res:* Fourier transform infrared spectroscopy; analysis, molecular structure and interactions of petroleum and petroleum products, of polymers and heterogeneous catalytic surfaces. *Mailing Add:* Phillips Res Ctr Res Bldg 1 Phillips Petrol Co Bartlesville OK 74004

PAXTON, H(AROLD) W(ILLIAM), b Eng, Feb 6, 27; nat US; m; c 4. PHYSICAL METALLURGY. *Educ:* Univ Manchester, BSc, 47, MSc, 48; Univ Birmingham, PhD(metall), 52. *Prof Exp:* Prof & head dept metall & mat sci & dir metals res lab, Carnegie-Mellon Univ, 53-74; V PRES RES, US STEEL CORP. *Concurrent Pos:* NSF sr fel, Imp Col, Univ London, 62-63; adj sr fel, Mellon Inst; dir div mat res, NSF, 71-73; vis prof, Mass Inst Technol, 70. *Mem:* Nat Acad Eng; fel Am Soc Metals; Am Inst Mining, Metall & Petrol Engrs; fel Metall Soc; fel AAAS. *Res:* Plastic deformation of solids; phase transformations; corrosion. *Mailing Add:* 115 Eton Dr Pittsburgh PA 15215

PAXTON, HUGH CAMPBELL, b Los Angeles, Calif, Apr 29, 09; m 37; c 2. NUCLEAR PHYSICS. *Educ:* Univ Calif, Los Angeles, AB, 30; Univ Calif, PhD(physics), 37. *Prof Exp:* Mem tech staff, Bell Tel Labs, 30-32; res assoc, Lab Nuclear Chem, Col France, 37-38; instr physics, Columbia Univ, 38-41; physicist, SAM Labs, Manhattan Dist, 42-44; sr admin physicist, Carbide & Carbon Chem Corp, Tenn, 44-45; physicist, Res labs, Sharples Corp, 45-48; mem staff, 48-76, CONSULT, LOS ALAMOS SCI LAB, 76- *Concurrent Pos:* Consult, Nuclear Regulatory Comn Atomic Safety & Licensing Bd Panel, 63- *Mem:* Fel Am Phys Soc; fel Am Nuclear Soc. *Res:* Critical assemblies; criticality and reactor safety; reactor physics. *Mailing Add:* 1229 41st St Los Alamos NM 87544

PAXTON, JACK DUNMIRE, b Oakland, Calif, Feb 17, 36; m 60; c 2. PLANT PATHOLOGY, BIOCHEMISTRY. *Educ:* Univ Calif, Berkeley, BS, 58; Univ Calif, Davis, PhD(plant path), 64. *Prof Exp:* Res assoc, 64-65, asst prof, 65-70, ASSOC PROF PLANT PATH, UNIV ILL, URBANA, 70- *Concurrent Pos:* Mem, Advan Study Insts, NATO, 70, 75 & 80. *Honors & Awards:* Fulbright Award, 72. *Mem:* Am Phytopath Soc; Am Soc Plant Physiol. *Res:* Physiology and biochemistry of host-parasite interactions. *Mailing Add:* Dept of Plant Path Univ of Ill 1102 S Goodwin Urbana IL 61801

PAXTON, K BRADLEY, b Norwich, NY, Dec 31, 38; m 62; c 2. APPLIED MATHEMATICS, ELECTRICAL ENGINEERING. *Educ:* Rensselaer Polytech Inst, BEE, 60; Univ Rochester, MS, 65, PhD(elec eng), 71. *Prof Exp:* Develop engr, Apparatus Div, 60-64, sr develop engr, 64-67, proj engr, 67-69, proj physicist, 69-72, res supvr, 72-75, mgr math modeling & anal, Spec Projs Develop, 75-78, SUPVR SUBSYST EQUIP DEVELOP, EASTMAN KODAK CO, 78- *Concurrent Pos:* Eastman Kodak award, Univ Rochester, 69-71. *Mem:* Soc Indust & Appl Math; Math Asn Am; Soc Photog Scientists & Engrs. *Res:* Analysis of novel imaging systems; electrophotography. *Mailing Add:* Copy Prod Develop B951 KP Eastman Kodak Co Rochester NY 14650

PAXTON, LARRY DANE, medical microbiology, chemotherapy, see previous edition

PAXTON, R(ALPH R(OBERT), b Zion, Ill, Mar 4, 20; m 43; c 2. CHEMICAL ENGINEERING. *Educ:* Univ Ill, BS, 43; Mass Inst Technol, ScD, 49. *Prof Exp:* Jr Chem engr, Res Dept, Standard Oil Co, Ind, 43-46; instr chem eng, Univ Colo, 46-47; asst, Mass Inst Technol, 47-49; asst prof, Stanford Univ, 49-55; engr advan process develop, Gen Elec Co, 55-58; chief engr, Pure Carbon Co, 58-81; DIR ENG & PLANNING, PURE INDUST, INC, 81- *Mem:* Am Chem Soc; Electrochem Soc; Am Soc Lubrication Eng; Am Inst Chem Engrs. *Res:* Reaction kinetics; research management; friction and wear. *Mailing Add:* Pure Carbon Co Hall Ave St Mary's PA 15857

PAXTON, THOMAS RICE, physical chemistry, see previous edition

PAYER, ANDREW FRANCIS, b Pittsburgh, Pa, Aug 20, 43; m 69. HUMAN ANATOMY. *Educ:* Edinboro State Col, BS, 65; Loyola Univ, PhD(anat), 73. *Prof Exp:* ASST PROF ANAT, UNIV TEX MED BR GALVESTON, 73- *Mem:* Am Asn Anat; Sigma Xi. *Res:* Electron microscopy of human and animal gonads. *Mailing Add:* Dept of Anat Univ Tex Med Br Galveston TX 77550

PAYET, CHARLES ROBERT, b Poughkeepsie, NY, Mar 21, 45; m 67; c 2. POLYMER CHEMISTRY, ORGANIC CHEMISTRY. *Educ:* Univ NC, Chapel Hill, BS, 66; Univ Ill, Urbana, PhD(org chem), 70. *Prof Exp:* Clin lab officer, clin chem, US Air Force Sch Aerospace Med, 71-73; res chemist, 74-77, res supvr polymer chem, Pioneering Res Lab, Du Pont Exp Sta, 77-79, res supvr, Nomex End Use Res, 79-81, SUPVR, NYLON RES & DEVELOP, TEXTILE FIBERS DEPT, E I DU PONT DE NEMOURS & CO, INC, 81- *Mem:* Am Chem Soc. *Mailing Add:* Du Pont Co Textile Fibers Dept Martinsville VA 24112

PAYET, MARCEL DANIEL, b Meursac, France, Jan 30, 47; m 73; c 2. CARDIAC ELECTROPHYSIOLOGY, BIOPHYSICS. *Educ:* Univ Poitiers, France, MSc, 70, DrPhysiol, 73; Univ Montreal, PhD(biol), 77. *Prof Exp:* fel, 77-80, ASST PROF, DEPT BIOPHYS, FAC MED, UNIV SHERBROOKE, 80- *Concurrent Pos:* Fel, Can Heart Found, 77-80, res scholarship, 80- *Mem:* NY Acad Sci; Biophys Soc. *Res:* Electrical properties of myocardium; voltage clamp; slow inward current of rat heart; antiarhythmic drugs; molecular pharmacology; automatic activity of cultured cells. *Mailing Add:* Dept Biophys Univ Sherbrooke Sherbrooke PQ J1K 2R1 Can

PAYLORE, PATRICIA PAQUITA, b Roswell, NMex, Sept 27, 09. SCIENTIFIC BIBLIOGRAPHY, SCIENTIFIC DOCUMENTATION. *Educ:* Univ Ariz, BA, 29, MA, 30. *Prof Exp:* Accession asst, Libr, Univ Ariz, 31-37, serials librn, 37-42, acquisition librn, 42-46, asst librn, 46-64, actg librn, Univ, 46, 47-48, 52 & 63-64, res assoc, Off Arid Lands Studies, 65-68, bibliographer, 68-70, asst dir, Off Arid Lands Studies, 71-79. *Concurrent Pos:* Mem, Am Libr Asn Coun, 56-65; ed, Arid Lands Newsletter, Univ Ariz, 75- *Honors & Awards:* Award for Distinguished Contributions Arid Zone Research, AAAS, 74. *Mem:* AAAS. *Res:* Natural resources of deserts; arid lands. *Mailing Add:* Off of Arid Land Studies Univ of Ariz 845 N Park Ave Tucson AZ 85719

PAYMENT, PIERRE, virology, see previous edition

PAYNE, ANITA H, b Karlsruhe, Ger, Nov 24, 26; US citizen; m 49; c 2. BIOCHEMISTRY, ENDOCRINOLOGY. *Educ:* Univ Calif, Berkeley, AB, 49, PhD(physiol), 52. *Prof Exp:* Lab technician med physics, Donner Lab, Univ Calif, 49-52, res physiologist, 52-53, res assoc biochem, 61-69, assoc res biochemist, 69-71, asst prof, 71-76, ASSOC PROF BIOCHEM, STEROID RES UNIT, REPROD ENDOCRINOL PROG, MED CTR, UNIV MICH, ANN ARBOR, 76- *Concurrent Pos:* Nat Cancer Inst fel, 54-55. *Mem:* Am Soc Biol Chemists; Soc Study Reprod; Endocrine Soc; Am Soc Andrology. *Res:* Regulation and metabolism of steroid hormones in gonads. *Mailing Add:* Steroid Res Unit Dept Obstet Gyn Univ of Mich Med Ctr Ann Arbor MI 48109

PAYNE, ANTHONY LUKE, b Delta, Utah, Dec 25, 27. ECONOMIC GEOLOGY. *Educ:* Univ Utah, BS, 49, MS, 50; Stanford Univ, PhD(geol), 59. *Prof Exp:* Resident geologist, Northern Peru Mining & Smelting Co, 50-51; explor geologist, Am Smelting & Ref Co, Ariz, 51-52; geologist, Minas de Matahambre, Cuba, 52-54; consult mining geologist, Shenon & Full, Utah, 54-59; assoc prof mining, 59-68, PROF GEOL, UNIV NEV, 68- *Mem:* Soc Econ Geol; Am Inst Mining, Metall & Petrol Eng. *Res:* Ore deposits; metallogeny; regional geology. *Mailing Add:* 99 Brownstone Dr Reno NV 89512

PAYNE, BERTRAM R, Brit citizen. SENSORY PHYSIOLOGY. *Educ:* Univ Durham, BSc, 74, PhD(zool), 78. *Prof Exp:* Fel, Univ Kassel, WGer, 77-78; res assoc, 78-80, INSTR MED COL, PA, 80- *Concurrent Pos:* Vis prof, Med Col Pa, 81-82. *Mem:* Soc Exp Biol; Soc Neurosci; Asn Res Vision and Ophthalmol. *Res:* Use of electrophysiological and anatomical techniques to study the normal organization, development, plasticity and cell death within the visual system. *Mailing Add:* Dept Physiol & Biochem Med Col Pa Philadelphia PA 19129

PAYNE, DAVID GLENN, b Ont, Can, July 26, 50. HIGH-ENERGY ASTROPHYSICS. *Educ:* Univ Waterloo, BSc, 74; Yale Univ, MPhil, 79, PhD(astrophysics), 79. *Prof Exp:* Res fel, Calif Inst Technol, 79-81; RES FEL ASTROPHYSICS, CTR ASTROPHYSICS, HARVARD UNIV, 81- *Res:* Dynamical and stochastic problems in high-energy and relativistic astrophysics. *Mailing Add:* Ctr Astrophysics Harvard Univ 60 Garden St Cambridge MA 02138

PAYNE, DEWITT ALLEN, b Pasadena, Calif, Mar 1, 44; m 68. ELECTROCHEMISTRY. *Educ:* Calif Inst Technol, BS, 65; Univ Tex, Austin, PhD(chem), 70. *Prof Exp:* RES CHEMIST, TENN EASTMAN CO, 71- *Mem:* Am Chem Soc. *Res:* Electroanalytical chemistry; electroorganic synthesis. *Mailing Add:* 813 Kendricks Creek Rd Kingsport TN 37663

PAYNE, DONALD HUGHEL, b Indianapolis, Ind, June 22, 28; m 50; c 4. PHYSICAL CHEMISTRY. *Educ:* Purdue Univ, BS, 49; Univ Mich, MS, 51, PhD(chem), 54. *Prof Exp:* Res chemist, Exp Sta, 53-59, res supvr, 59-61, new prod develop specialist, 61-65, sr res supvr, 65-70, planning mgr, 70-71, res mgr, Polyolefins Div, 71-73, lab dir, Polymer Intermediates Dept, 73-75, TECH DIR, PETROLEUM CHEMS DIV, E I DU PONT DE NEMOURS & CO, INC, 75- *Mem:* Am Chem Soc; Am Petrol Inst. *Res:* Polymer chemistry; organic reactions; thermodynamics; catalysis; polymerization catalysts. *Mailing Add:* Petrol Lab Org Chem Dept E I du Pont de Nemours & Co Inc Deepwater NJ 08023

PAYNE, DONNA WEST, pharmacology, endocrinology, see previous edition

PAYNE, DWIGHT ARTHUR, inorganic chemistry, see previous edition

PAYNE, ELMER CURRY, b West Lebanon, Ind, July 3, 00; m. CHEMISTRY. *Educ:* Butler Univ, AB, 22; Univ Cincinnati, PhD(chem), 31. *Prof Exp:* Chemist & bacteriologist, Indianapolis Water Co, 23-24; anal & develop chemist, Koppers Co, Ill, 25-28; asst chem, Purdue Univ, 28-29; asst prof, Butler Univ, 32-35; chemist, Food & Drug Admin, USDA, 35-40, insecticide div, Agr Mkt Serv, 40-43; develop chemist, Sylvania Elec Prod, Inc, 43-52; res chemist, AEC, 52-66; CONSULT PHYSICOCHEM RES, 66- *Mem:* Am Chem Soc; Asn Off Anal Chem; AAAS; Sigma Xi. *Res:* Oxide coated cathodes for electronic devices; development of luminescent materials; surface coating processes; electroluminescence; semiconductors; evaluation of methods for detection of size of small particles; continuous process for production of uranium metal; production of free boron in the electric arc; the nature of the oxides of uranium; recovery of anhydrous hydrogen fluoride from aqueous solution by extractive distillation. *Mailing Add:* 440 River Rd Chatham NJ 07928

PAYNE, FRANCIS EUGENE, b Calif, May 4, 26; m 49; c 2. VIROLOGY. *Educ:* Univ Calif, AB, 47, MA, 48; Stanford Univ, MD, 53. *Prof Exp:* Res assoc, 57-60, from asst prof to assoc prof, 60-73, PROF EPIDEMIOL, UNIV MICH, ANN ARBOR, 73- *Concurrent Pos:* Nat Found Infantile Paralysis fel, 56-57. *Mem:* Am Soc Microbiol; Am Soc Cell Biol; Am Asn Immunologists; Soc Exp Biol & Med; Tissue Cult Asn. *Res:* Oncology; tissue culture; subacute and chronic nervous system disease. *Mailing Add:* Dept of Epidemiol Univ of Mich Sch of Pub Health Ann Arbor MI 48109

PAYNE, FRED J, epidemiology, see previous edition

PAYNE, FRED R(AY), b Mayfield, Ky, Jan 26, 31; m 58; c 3. AERONAUTICAL ENGINEERING. *Educ:* Univ Ky, BS, 52; Pa State Univ, MS, 64, PhD(aeronaut eng), 66. *Prof Exp:* Vis res assoc aeronaut eng, Pa State Univ, 66, asst prof, 67; design specialist, Gen Dynamics Corp, Tex, 68-69; from asst prof to assoc prof, 69-75, PROF AEROSPACE ENG, UNIV TEX, ARLINGTON, 75- *Mem:* Am Phys Soc; NY Acad Sci; Am Acad Mech. *Res:* Atmospheric turbulence; large eddy structure of turbulence; hybrid propulsion systems; boundary layer internal methods. *Mailing Add:* Dept Aerospace Eng 306 Eng Bldg Univ of Tex Arlington TX 76019

PAYNE, GEORGE BERNSON, b Salt Lake City, Utah, Nov 21, 22; m 43; c 4. ORGANIC CHEMISTRY. *Educ:* Univ Calif, BS, 47, PhD(chem), 50. *Prof Exp:* Res chemist, Merck & Co, Inc, 50-51; CHEMIST, SHELL DEVELOP CO, 51- *Mem:* Am Chem Soc; NY Acad Sci. *Res:* Organic synthesis; epoxidation; carbanions; sulfur ylids. *Mailing Add:* 308 Harrow Ct Modesto CA 95350

PAYNE, GERALD LEW, b Columbus, Ohio, Mar 11, 38; m 63; c 3. THEORETICAL NUCLEAR PHYSICS, THEORETICAL PLASMA PHYSICS. *Educ:* Ohio State Univ, BS & MS, 61; Univ Calif, San Diego, PhD(physics), 67. *Prof Exp:* Res assoc nuclear physics, Univ Md, 67-69; asst prof, 69-74, assoc prof, 74-80, PROF PHYSICS, UNIV IOWA, 80- *Mem:* Am

Phys Soc; Am Asn Physics Teachers; Am Asn Univ Profs; Sigma Xi; AAAS. *Res:* Theoretical descriptions of nuclear scattering processes andfew body systems. *Mailing Add:* Dept of Physics & Astron Univ of Iowa Iowa City IA 52242

PAYNE, HARRISON H, b Palmer, Mass, Apr 14, 25; m 44. ZOOLOGY, WILDLIFE CONSERVATION. *Educ:* State Univ NY Col Forestry, Syracuse, BS, 50; St Lawrence Univ, MEd, 55; Cornell Univ, EdD(conserv ed), 63. *Prof Exp:* Teacher, Pawling Cent Sch, NY, 52-63; assoc prof zool, 64-69, PROF WILDLIFE CONSERV, COL ENVIRON SCI & FORESTRY, STATE UNIV NY SYRACUSE, 69- *Concurrent Pos:* Ed consult. *Mem:* Soc Am Foresters; Wildlife Soc; Asn Interpretive Naturalists; Am Asn Univ Prof; Nat Asn Student Personnel Admin. *Res:* Conservation education; field biology; natural history. *Mailing Add:* Dept of Environ & Forest Biol State Univ NY Syracuse NY 13210

PAYNE, HOLLAND I, b Johnstown, Ohio, Sept 29, 18; m 42; c 4. RESEARCH ADMINISTRATION, NATURAL SCIENCE. *Educ:* Colo State Col, BA, 49, MA, 52; Okla State Univ, MS, 59, EdD(sci educ), 63. *Prof Exp:* Teacher, Swayne Indian Sch, Nev, 47-50; teacher, Cassia Schs, Idaho, 50-51; teacher pub schs, Nebr, 51-56, prin, 56-58, supvr, 59-62; staff asst math & consult to elem sch teachers, Okla State Univ, 62-63; prog specialist math, 63-69, dir develop serv, 69-74, DIR EDUC EVAL & QUAL CONTROL DEPT, SACRAMENTO CITY UNIFIED SCH DIST, 74- *Concurrent Pos:* Mem, Calif Statewide Math Adv Comt, 67-72 & 76-; mem, Math Assessment Comt, Calif State Dept of Educ, 73- *Res:* Comparative analysis in the achievement of students studying a modern program of mathematics when compared to the achievement of students studying a traditional program; factual history of the Civilian Conservation Corps; US government program for youth from 1933 to 1942. *Mailing Add:* 4985 Helen Way Sacramento CA 95822

PAYNE, HOUSTON KELLEAM, chemical engineering, see previous edition

PAYNE, IRENE R, b Ft Morgan, Colo, Oct 30, 21; c 2. NUTRITION. *Educ:* Colo State Univ, BS, 48, MS, 51; Cornell Univ, PhD(animal nutrit), 60. *Prof Exp:* Res asst agr biochem, Univ Wyo, 51-55, nutrit, 55-57, asst prof, 59-60; asst prof biochem, Pa State Univ, 60-65; assoc prof, 65-74, PROF NUTRIT, SOUTHERN ILL UNIV, CARBONDALE, 74-, ACTG DIR HUMAN DEVELOP DEPT, COL HUMAN RESOURCES, 80- *Mem:* Am Dietetic Asn. *Res:* Metabolic lesions caused by nutritional deficiencies; metabolic and nutritional bases of mental illnesses. *Mailing Add:* 303 Orchard Lane Carbondale IL 62901

PAYNE, IRVING JOHN, microbiology, see previous edition

PAYNE, JAMES EDWARD, b Lynchburg, Va, Feb 10, 44; m 69. EXPERIMENTAL SOLID STATE PHYSICS. *Educ:* Hampden-Sydney Col, BS, 66; Clemson Univ, MS, 69, PhD(physics), 71. *Prof Exp:* Asst prof physics, Clemson Univ, 71-72; asst prof, 72-80, ASSOC PROF PHYSICS, SC STATE COL, 80- *Mem:* Am Phys Soc. *Res:* Low temperature solid state physics; superconductivity. *Mailing Add:* Box 2007 South Carolina State Col Orangeburg SC 29115

PAYNE, JEREMIAH FREDERICK, environmental physiology, see previous edition

PAYNE, JERRY ALLEN, b Winchester, Va, Dec 19, 37; m 81; c 3. ENTOMOLOGY, ECOLOGY. *Educ:* Univ Tenn, BS, 61; Clemson Univ, MS, 63, PhD(entom), 67. *Prof Exp:* Assoc health physicist, Radiation Ecol Sect, Health Physics Div, Oak Ridge Nat Lab, 63-65; res entomologist, Coastal Plain Exp Sta, Mkt Qual Res Div, 67-69, RES ENTOMOLOGIST, SOUTHEASTERN FRUIT & TREE NUT RES LAB, SCI & EDUC ADMIN-AGR RES, USDA, 69- *Concurrent Pos:* Adj prof, Dept Hort, Univ Ga, Athens. *Mem:* Am Soc Mammal; Ecol Soc Am; Entom Soc Am; NAm Fruit Explorers. *Res:* Entomology, particularly those of biological and ecological nature; ecology of carrion; medical-legal entomology; biology and ecology of stored-products insects; fruit and tree nut insects; edible, native fruits and nuts. *Mailing Add:* Southeastern Fruit & Tree Nut Res Lab Sci & Educ Admin-Agr Res USDA PO Box 87 Byron GA 31008

PAYNE, JIMMIE STURGIS, JR, analytical chemistry, air pollution, see previous edition

PAYNE, KENYON THOMAS, b Amherst, Mass, Jan 3, 18; m 42; c 3. AGRONOMY. *Educ:* Kans State Col, BSc, 39; Univ Nebr, MSc, 41; Univ Minn, PhD(plant breeding), 48. *Prof Exp:* Agent, Bur Plant Indust, USDA, Nebr, 39-41; asst prof agron, Purdue Univ, 48-52, assoc prof, 52; prof crop sci & chmn dept, 52-68, PROF CROP & SOIL SCI, MICH STATE UNIV, 68- *Concurrent Pos:* Dean fac agr, Univ Nigeria, 64-66. *Mem:* Fel AAAS; fel Am Soc Agron; Crop Sci Soc Am. *Res:* Plant breeding; turf grasses; turf grass breeding. *Mailing Add:* Dept of Crop & Soil Sci Mich State Univ East Lansing MI 48824

PAYNE, LAWRENCE EDWARD, b Enfield, Ill, Oct 2, 23; m 48; c 5. APPLIED MATHEMATICS. *Educ:* Iowa State Col, BS, 46, MS, 48, PhD(applied math), 50. *Prof Exp:* Jr engr res & develop, Linde Air Prod, 46-47; instr math, Iowa State Col, 48-50; asst prof, Univ Ariz, 50-51; res assoc, Inst Fluid Dynamics & Appl Math, Univ Md, 51-52, from asst res prof to res prof, 52-65; dir, Ctr Appl Math, 67-71, PROF MATH, CORNELL UNIV, 65- *Concurrent Pos:* NSF sr fel, King's Col, Univ Newcastle, 58-59; consult, Nat Bur Stand, 58, 59-65; vis prof, Swiss Fed Inst Technol, 68-69 & 79-80 & Univ Newcastle, 72. *Honors & Awards:* Steele Prize, Am Math Soc, 72. *Mem:* Am Math Soc; Math Asn Am; Sigma Xi; Soc Eng Sci; Am Acad Mech. *Res:* Elasticity; isoperimetric inequalities; approximation methods; partial differential equations. *Mailing Add:* Dept Math Cornell Univ Ithaca NY 14850

PAYNE, LINDA LAWSON, b Spartanburg, SC, Oct 12, 46; m 69; c 2. SOLID STATE PHYSICS. *Educ:* Converse Col, SC, AB, 68; Clemson Univ, SC, MS, 70, PhD(physics), 74. *Prof Exp:* asst prof, 72-80, ASSOC PROF PHYSICS, SC STATE COL, ORANGEBURG, 80- *Concurrent Pos:* NASA/Am Soc Elec Engrs fac fel, 81. *Mem:* Am Asn Physics Teachers; AAAS. *Res:* Study of quantum size effects in thin films of bismuth as the bismuth films are electrically charged. *Mailing Add:* Rte 4 Box 1280 Orangeburg SC 29115

PAYNE, MARVIN GAY, b Barnardsville, NC, Apr 25, 36; m 61; c 2. THEORETICAL PHYSICS. *Educ:* Berea Col, BA, 58; Univ Ky, PhD(theoret physics), 65. *Prof Exp:* From instr to assoc prof physics, Berea Col, 60-69; THEORET PHYSICIST, OAK RIDGE NAT LAB, 71- *Concurrent Pos:* Fel, Yale Univ, 69-70; adj prof, Univ Ky, 73- *Mem:* Am Asn Physics Teachers. *Res:* Radiative transport in planetary atmospheres; Landau damping of ion-acoustic waves; plasma stability theory; atom-atom collision theory; interaction of laser beams with matter-multiphoton processes; theory of spectral line shapes; many body theory; radiation transport theory; biological modeling; theory of superconductivity. *Mailing Add:* Oak Ridge Nat Lab Oak Ridge TN 37830

PAYNE, MARY HEWLETT, b Greensboro, NC, July 7, 19; m 42; c 1. MATHEMATICS. *Educ:* Cornell Univ, AB, 40; Univ Wis, MA, 42; Brown Univ, PhD(physics), 43. *Prof Exp:* Instr physics, Joplin Jr Col, 44-45; instr math, Univ Detroit, 46-48; asst prof, Mich State Col, 48-54; res asst, Columbia Univ, 54-56; sr res engr, Guided Missiles Div, Fairchild Engine & Airplane Corp, 56-58; staff engr, Repub Aviation Corp, 58-65; scientist, NASA Electronics Res Ctr, 65-70; sr analyst, Anal Mech Assocs, 70-73; sr software engr, 73-76, prin software engr, 76-79, CONSULT ENGR, DIGITAL EQUIP CORP, 79- *Mem:* Soc Indust & Appl Math; Comput Soc; Inst Elec & Electronics Engrs; Asn Comput Mach. *Res:* Numerical analysis; information science; applied mathematics; astrodynamics. *Mailing Add:* Digital Equip Corp 146 Main St Maynard MA 01754

PAYNE, MYRON WILLIAM, b Red Wing, Minn, June 10, 45; m 68. SEDIMENTOLOGY, PETROLEUM GEOLOGY. *Educ:* Clemson Univ, BS, 68; Univ SC, MS, 70; Tex A&M Univ, PhD(geol), 73. *Prof Exp:* Geologist, Tenneco Oil Co, 73-74; asst prof geol, Univ Alaska, 75-81; EXPLOR STRATEGIST, SABINE CORP, 82- *Honors & Awards:* J C Sproule Award. *Mem:* Soc Econ Paleontologists & Mineralogists; Geol Soc Am; Am Asn Petrol Geologists. *Res:* Long range exploration strategy for western United States, Alaska and Canada; stratigraphic hydrocarbon traps; paleoenvironments of deposition; tectono-stratigraphic setting of east-central Alaska. *Mailing Add:* PO Box 898 Dallas TX 75221

PAYNE, NICHOLAS CHARLES, b Wrotham, Eng, Apr 16, 42. CHEMISTRY. *Educ:* Imp Col, Univ London, BSc, 64; Univ Sheffield, PhD(chem), 67. *Prof Exp:* Res asst, Northwestern Univ, Evanston, 67-69; from asst prof to assoc prof, 69-79, PROF INORG CHEM, UNIV WESTERN ONT, 79- *Mem:* Chem Inst Can; Royal Soc Chem; Am Chem Soc; Am Crystallog Asn. *Res:* Determinations of absolute configurations by the anomalous dispersion of x-rays; x-ray and optical diffraction studies of plant viruses; crystal structures of catalytically important transition metal complexes; organometallic and phosphine chemistry. *Mailing Add:* Dept Chem Univ Western Ont London ON N6A 5B7 Can

PAYNE, PHILIP WARREN, b New Castle, Ind, Feb 26, 50; m 78. COMPUTATIONAL METHODS. *Educ:* Pomona Col, BA, 71; Princeton Univ, MA, 73, PhD(chem), 76. *Prof Exp:* Res assoc chem, Univ NC, Chapel Hill, 76-77; ASST PROF CHEM, UNIV HAWAII, MANOA, 77- *Concurrent Pos:* NSF fel Univ NC, Chapel Hill, 76. *Mem:* Am Chem Soc; Am Phys Soc. *Res:* Electronic structure of molecules and solids; formal quantum chemistry and development of computational methods; understanding electronic structure and dynamics in larger molecules and defective solids, including surface chemistry; reaction mechanisms in condensed phases. *Mailing Add:* Dept of Chem Univ Hawaii Honolulu HI 96822

PAYNE, RICHARD EARL, b Holyoke, Mass, Apr 2, 36; m 58; c 2. SEA SURFACE METEROGICAL MEASUREMENTS. *Educ:* Bowdoin Col, BS, 58; Univ Md, MS; Univ RI, PhD(phys oceanog). *Prof Exp:* NATO fel, Univ Southampton, Eng, 72-73; fel, 71-72, RES ASSOC, WOODS HOLE OCEANOG INST, 73- *Mem:* Am Geophys Union; Am Meterol Soc. *Res:* Techniques of measuring meteorological parameters in the surface boundary layer over the ocean and methods of deteming air-sea heat fluxes; time series data processing systems and techniques. *Mailing Add:* Woods Hole Oceanog Inst Woods Hole MA 02543

PAYNE, RICHARD N, b Abilene, Tex, Jan 12, 29; m 66. HORTICULTURE. *Educ:* Okla State Univ, BS, 50, PhD, 70; Ohio State Univ, MS, 55. *Prof Exp:* Instr floricult, Okla State Univ, 53-54; asst grower, Furrow & Co, Wholesale Florist, 55-57; asst prof floricult, 57-70, assoc prof, 70-75, PROF HORT, OKLA STATE UNIV, 75- *Mem:* Am Soc Hort Sci. *Res:* Cultural research with ornamental horticultural crops, especially greenhouse crops. *Mailing Add:* Dept of Hort Okla State Univ Stillwater OK 74074

PAYNE, RICHARD STEVEN, b Worcester, Mass, Mar 8, 43; m 65; c 3. PHYSICS, ELECTRICAL ENGINEERING. *Educ:* Dartmouth Col, AB, 64; Yale Univ, PhD(physics), 70. *Prof Exp:* Mem tech staff, 70-74, SUPVR, IC PROCESS DEVELOP, BELL TEL LABS, 74- *Mem:* Int Elec & Electronic Engrs. *Res:* Applications of ion implantation to silicon ICs and devices; development of new complimentary mos IC technology; bipolar process development for ICs and discrete devices. *Mailing Add:* Bell Tel Labs 600 Mountain Ave Murray Hill NJ 07974

PAYNE, ROBERT B, b Niles, Mich, July 24, 38; m 65; c 1. ZOOLOGY. *Educ:* Univ Mich, BS, 60; Univ Calif, Berkeley, PhD(zool), 65. *Prof Exp:* Res assoc zool, Inst African Ornith, Univ Cape Town, 65-67; asst prof, Univ Okla, 67-70; asst prof, 70-74, ASSOC PROF ZOOL, UNIV MICH, ANN ARBOR, 74-, ASSOC CUR BIRDS, BIRD DIV, MUS ZOOL, 74- *Concurrent Pos:*

NSF fel, 65-67 & res grant, 68-73. *Mem:* Soc Study Evolution; Ecol Soc Am; Am Ornith Union; Brit Ornith Union; Animal Behav Soc. *Res:* Reproductive physiology; mechanisms of speciation in vertebrates; behavioral aspects of evolution. *Mailing Add:* Bird Div Mus of Zool Univ of Mich 1109 Washtenow Ann Arbor MI 48104

PAYNE, ROSE MARISE, b Lake Bay, Wash, Aug 5, 09; m 42. IMMUNOLOGY, HEMATOLOGY. *Educ:* Univ Wash, BS, 32, MS, 33, PhD(bact), 37. *Prof Exp:* Asst prof bact, Okla Agr & Mech Col, 37-38; lectr, Seattle Col, 39-42; res asst & assoc, 48-64, sr scientist, 64-72, PROF MED, MED SCH, STANFORD UNIV, 72- *Concurrent Pos:* McDermott Found Tuberc res fel, Univ Wash, 38-39; mem adv comt leukocyte antigen terminology, WHO, 67-, mem expert adv panel immunol, 69-74; counr, I-VII Int Histocompatability Workshop Conf, 69-; mem comt organ transplantation & tissue typing, Am Asn Blood Banks, 70- *Mem:* Am Fedn Clin Res; Am Soc Hemat; Transplantation Soc; Int Soc Hemat; Int Soc Blood Transfusion. *Res:* Immunohematology; leukocytes; serology; genetics. *Mailing Add:* Dept Med S135 Stanford Univ Med Sch Stanford CA 94305

PAYNE, STANLEY E, b Chicago, Ill, Sept 26, 39; m 61; c 4. MATHEMATICS. *Educ:* Hastings Col, BS, 61; Fla State Univ, MS, 63, PhD(math), 66. *Prof Exp:* From asst to instr math, Fla State Univ, 61-66; from asst prof to assoc prof, 66-74, PROF MATH, MIAMI UNIV, 74- *Mem:* Am Math Soc; Math Asn Am. *Res:* Existence, uniqueness and combinatorial properties of finite geometries, graphs and designs; number theory; finite groups. *Mailing Add:* Dept of Math Miami Univ Oxford OH 45056

PAYNE, THOMAS GIBSON, b Rochester, NY, June 30, 15; m 42; c 3. GEOLOGY. *Educ:* Rochester Univ, AB, 37, MS, 39; Univ Chicago, PhD(geol), 42. *Prof Exp:* Geologist & cur, Rochester Mus Arts & Sci, NY, 36-39; asst geol, Univ Chicago, 39-41; instr, Univ Kans, 41-42; geologist, Alaskan Sect, US Geol Surv, 42-53; res geologist, Texaco, Inc, 53-75; EXPLOR CONSULT, 75- *Concurrent Pos:* Subsurface petrol geologist & ed, Kans State Geol Surv, 41-42. *Mem:* Am Petrol Inst; Soc Econ Paleont & Mineral; Geol Soc Am; Am Asn Petrol Geol. *Res:* Stratigraphy, sedimentation and petroleum geology; statistical methods including prediction, surface fitting, correlation and classification. *Mailing Add:* 2801 Dundee Ct Ft Collins CO 80525

PAYNE, THOMAS LEE, b Bakersfield, Calif, Oct 17, 41; m 63. ENTOMOLOGY. *Educ:* Univ Calif, Santa Barbara, BA, 65; Univ Calif, Riverside, MS, 67, PhD(entom), 69. *Prof Exp:* From asst prof to assoc prof, 69-77, PROF ENTOM, TEX A&M UNIV, 78- *Mem:* Sigma Xi; AAAS; Entom Soc Am. *Res:* Insect behavior; pest management; pheromones; antennal olfactory electrophysiological response. *Mailing Add:* Dept of Entom Tex A&M Univ College Station TX 77843

PAYNE, WILBUR BOSWELL, theoretical physics, see previous edition

PAYNE, WILLARD WILLIAM, b Hastings, Mich, Jan 1, 34; m 53. PLANT TAXONOMY. *Educ:* Alma Col, Mich, AB, 55; Ohio Univ, MS, 57; Univ Mich, PhD(bot), 62. *Prof Exp:* Assoc res botanist, Univ Mich, 62-64; from asst prof to assoc prof bot, Univ Ill, Urbana, 64-73, from assoc cur to cur, Herbarium, 65-73; prof taxon & chairperson dept bot, Univ Fla, 73-77, dir, Div Biol Sci, 75-77; V PRES, NEW YORK BOT GARDENS & DIR, CARY ARBORETUM, 77- *Concurrent Pos:* Assoc prog dir syst bot, NSF, 69-70; trustee, Fairchild Trop Garden, 77-80. *Honors & Awards:* George R Cooley Award plant taxon, 64. *Mem:* Int Orgn Biosyst; Am Soc Plant Taxonomists (pres, 77-79); Bot Soc Am; Int Asn Plant Taxon. *Res:* Biosystematics, taxonomy, morphology and evolution of genus Ambrosia; the tribe Ambrosieae and the family Asteraceae; use of stomatal data for taxonomy and evolution of embryophytes; indument evolution; pollen wall evolution. *Mailing Add:* Box AB Cary Arboretum Millbrook NY 12545

PAYNE, WILLIAM JACKSON, b Chattanooga, Tenn, Aug 30, 25; m 49; c 3. MICROBIOLOGY. *Educ:* Col William & Mary, BS, 50; Univ Tenn, MS, 52, PhD(bact), 55. *Prof Exp:* Instr bact, Univ Tenn, 53-54; from asst prof to prof, 55-67, head dept bact, 58-67, prof microbiol & head dept, 67-77, actg dean, Col Arts & Sci, 77-78, DEAN COL ARTS & SCI, UNIV GA, 78- *Concurrent Pos:* Consult, Univ Ala, 59, 68 & 70; chmn, Nat Registry Microbiol, 67-71; consult, Water Qual Prog, Environ Protection Agency, 71-72; lectr, Am Soc for Microbiol Found, 72-73; biol oceanog panel mem, Nat Sci Found, 76-77; vis prof fel biochem, Univ Wales, Cardiff, 75, hon prof fel, 77-82. *Honors & Awards:* M G Michael Res Award, 60; P R Edwards Award, Am Soc Microbiol, 72. *Mem:* Am Soc Microbiol; Am Acad Microbiol; Brit Soc Gen Microbiol; Am Soc Biol Chemists. *Res:* Physiology and biochemistry of denitrification; growth yields. *Mailing Add:* Franklin Col of Arts & Sci Univ of Ga Athens GA 30602

PAYNE, WILLIAM WALKER, b Calverton, Va, June 1, 13; m 36; c 3. PUBLIC HEALTH. *Educ:* Univ Va, BSE, 35; Univ Mich, MSE, 47; Univ Pittsburgh, MPH, 56, ScD(hyg), 59; Am Asn Environ Eng, dipl, 59. *Prof Exp:* Engr, County Comnrs for Montgomery County, Md, 35-43; sanit engr, USPHS, 43-60, sanit eng dir, 60-63; dep sci dir, Nat Cancer Inst, 63-67, dep dir, Nat Inst Environ Health Sci, 67-73, sci coordr, Frederick Cancer Res Ctr, 73-81. *Mem:* Am Indust Hyg Asn; Am Asn Cancer Res. *Res:* Sanitary and public health engineering; environmental cancer research and investigations. *Mailing Add:* 8623 Pinecliff Dr Frederick MD 21701

PAYNTER, CAMEN RUSSELL, b Plankinton, SDak, Dec 23, 16; m 49; c 7. INTERNAL MEDICINE, GASTROENTEROLOGY. *Educ:* Univ Ill, BS, 44, MD, 46; Univ Chicago, MBA, 69; Am Bd Internal Med, dipl, 54, recert, 77, Bd Gastroenterol, dipl, 56; Bd Life Ins Med, dipl, 75. *Prof Exp:* Asst, SDak Exp Sta, 41-43; intern, Harper Hosp, 46-47; asst med, Univ Chicago, 53-54, instr gastroenterol, 54-55; pvt pract, 55-63; assoc med dir, 63-80, MED DIR, WESTERN REGION, CONTINENTAL INS CO, 80- *Concurrent Pos:* Fel x-ray, Harper Hosp, Detroit, Mich, 49; fel internal med, Mayo Found, Minn, 50-53; asst clin prof, Stritch Sch Med, Loyola Univ Chicago, 63-71, assoc clin prof, 71-; attend physician gastroenterol, Vet Admin Hosp, Hines, Ill, 65- *Mem:* Fel Am Col Prev Med; fel Am Pub Health Asn; fel Am Acad Occup Med; fel Am Occup Med Asn; fel Am Col Physicians. *Res:* Selenium toxicity; liver disease; nutrition. *Mailing Add:* 222 S Fernandez Ave Arlington Heights IL 60005

PAYNTER, GERALD C(LYDE), b Savanna, Ill, Oct 24, 38; m 65; c 2. MECHANICAL ENGINEERING, FLUID MECHANICS. *Educ:* Univ Wash, BS, 60, PhD(fluid mech), 65. *Prof Exp:* Actg asst prof mech eng, Univ Wash, 65-66; res engr, 66-67, lead engr, 67-71, sr engr, 71-75, RES ENGR, MIL AIRPLANE DEVELOP, BOEING CO, 75- *Mem:* Am Inst Aeronaut & Astronaut. *Res:* Boundary layer theory; shock-boundary layer interactions. *Mailing Add:* Mil Airplane Develop PO Box 3999 Seattle WA 98124

PAYNTER, HENRY M(ARTYN), b Evanston, Ill, Aug 11, 23; m 44; c 6. SYSTEMS ENGINEERING. *Educ:* Mass Inst Technol, SB, 44, SM, 49, ScD, 51. *Prof Exp:* Jr engr, Puget Sound Power & Light Co, Wash, 44-46; asst civil eng, 46-48, from instr to asst prof civil eng, 48-54, from asst prof to assoc prof mech eng, 54-64, PROF MECH ENG, MASS INST TECHNOL, 64-, HEAD SYSTS DYNAMICS & CONTROL DIV, 63- *Concurrent Pos:* Consult, Stone & Webster Eng Corp, 51-, Chas A Maguire & Assocs, 52-, Foxboro Co, 54-, Jackson & Moreland, 58- & A D Little, 64-; pres, Pi-Square Eng Co, Inc, 54-59; bd chmn, Telos Corp, 71- & Dynacycle Corp, 72-; dir, UST Capital Corp, 71- & HyComp, Inc, 72- *Honors & Awards:* Noble Prize, Joint Eng Socs, 53. *Mem:* Am Soc Civil Engrs; Am Soc Mech Engrs; Inst Elec & Electronics Engrs. *Res:* Systems engineering with emphasis on system dynamics, modelling and simulation, machine computation and automatic control. *Mailing Add:* Dept of Mech Eng Mass Inst of Technol Cambridge MA 02139

PAYNTER, HOWARD L, b West Allis, Wis, Jan 3, 31; m 49; c 3. MECHANICAL ENGINEERING, FLUID MECHANICS. *Educ:* Univ Wis, BS, 55; Univ Calif, San Diego, 56-60; Univ Denver, MS, 65. *Prof Exp:* Jr engr, Gen Dynamics/Convair, 55, sr engr, 55-60; design specialist gas dynamics, Martin Marietta Corp, 60-66, staff engr, 66-69, chief subsysts technol, propulsion res lab, 69-72, chief thermodynamics & fluid mech, propulsion eng, res & develop dept, 71-74; chmn dept, 77-80, ASSOC PROF MECH ENG, TECHNOL DEPT, METROP STATE COL, 75- *Honors & Awards:* Sci Achievement Award, Martin Co, 65, Invention Award, 68. *Mem:* Am Soc Mech Engrs; Nat Soc Prof Engrs; Am Soc Eng Educ. *Res:* Fluid mechanics, including low-graVity behavior associated with aerospace vehicles; technical writing; thermodynamics. *Mailing Add:* Mech Eng Technol Dept 1006 11th St Denver CO 80204

PAYNTER, JOHN, JR, b Brooklyn, NY, Oct 3, 36; m 59; c 6. LUMINESCENT MATERIALS. *Educ:* Queens Col, NY, BS, 58; Columbia Univ, MA, 59, PhD(electrochem), 64. *Prof Exp:* Phys chemist, Gen Elec Res & Develop Ctr, NY, 64-68; tech ldr mat develop, 75, mgr phosphors eng, 78, PHYS CHEMIST, GEN ELEC CO, OHIO, 68- *Mem:* Electrochem Soc. *Res:* Low pressure mercury discharge lamps; phosphors; phosphor coatings. *Mailing Add:* Gen ELec Co 1099 Ivanhoe Rd Cleveland OH 44110

PAYNTER, KENNETH JACK, b Kingston, Ont, Feb 17, 18; m 45; c 3. ANATOMY. *Educ:* Univ Toronto, DDS, 44; Columbia Univ, PhD, 52; FRCD(C), 69. *Prof Exp:* Prof dent anat & head dept, Univ Toronto, 52-67, dir div postgrad dent educ, Fac Dent, 55-67; dean, Col Dent, Univ Sask, 67-73; DIR, MED RES COUN CAN, 73- *Mem:* Am Asn Anatomists; Int Asn Dent Res; Can Dent Asn; Can Fedn Biol Soc. *Res:* Academic administration; dental research. *Mailing Add:* 1811-211 Wurtemburg St Ottawa ON K1N 8R4 Can

PAYNTER, MALCOLM JAMES BENJAMIN, b Dudley, Eng, Oct 9, 37; m 61. MICROBIOLOGY, BIOCHEMISTRY. *Educ:* Univ Sheffield, BSc, 59, MSc, 62, PhD(microbiol), 64. *Prof Exp:* Fel bact, Univ Calif, Davis, 64-66; asst prof environ systs eng, 66-68, bot & bact, 68-69, from asst prof to assoc prof, 69-74, sect chmn, 69-71, PROF MICROBIOL, CLEMSON UNIV, 74-, HEAD DEPT, 71- *Mem:* AAAS; Am Soc Microbiol; Sigma Xi; Brit Soc Gen Microbiol; fel Explorers Club. *Res:* Intermediary metabolism of strict anaerobes; rumen microbiology; methane bacteria; mixed culture systems; microbial ecology; bacteriophage ecology. *Mailing Add:* Dept Microbiol Long Hall Clemson Univ Clemson SC 29631

PAYNTER, ORVILLE EUGENE, toxicology, see previous edition

PAYNTER, RAYMOND ANDREW, JR, b New York, NY, Nov 29, 25; m 60; c 2. ZOOLOGY. *Educ:* Bowdoin Col, BS, 46; Yale Univ, MS, 48, PhD, 54. *Prof Exp:* Field dir sci sta, Bowdoin Col, 46-48; leader, Yale Peabody Mus expeds, Yucatan, 48-49, 50-51, 52; from asst curator to assoc curator birds, Mus Comp Zool, 53-60, lectr biol, Harvard Univ, 63-75, CURATOR BIRDS, MUS COMP ZOOL, HARVARD UNIV, 61-, SR LECTR BIOL, 75- *Concurrent Pos:* Leader, Mus Comp Zool exped, Chiapas, Mex, 54; leader, Harvard-Yale exped, Nepal, Pakistan & India, 57-59 & mus comp zool exped, Ecuador, 65. *Mem:* Soc Syst Zool; Ecol Soc Am; fel Am Ornith Union; Brit Ornith Union. *Res:* Avian biology and systematics. *Mailing Add:* Mus of Comp Zool Harvard Univ Cambridge MA 02138

PAYSON, HENRY EDWARDS, b New York, NY, May 12, 25; m 58; c 4. FORENSIC PSYCHIATRY. *Educ:* Harvard Univ, BS, 48; Columbia Univ, MD, 52; Yale Univ Law Sch, MSL, 78; Darmouth Col, AM, 81; Am Bd Psychiat & Neurol, dipl, 61; Am Bd Forensic Psychiat, dipl, 80. *Prof Exp:* From instr to asst prof psychiat & med, Sch Med, Yale Univ, 58-63; from asst prof to assoc prof, 63-78, PROF PSYCHIAT, DARTMOUTH MED SCH, 78- *Mem:* Fel Am Psychiat Asn. *Res:* Legal abuse of medical systems to avoid legal irrationality. *Mailing Add:* Dept of Psychiat Dartmouth Med Sch Hanover NH 03755

PAYTON, ALBERT LEVERN, b Hattiesburg, Miss, Feb 8, 44; m 65; c 2. ORGANIC CHEMISTRY. *Educ:* Alcorn State Univ, BS, 65; Southern Univ, Baton Rouge, MS, 69; Univ Southern Miss, PhD(chem), 76. *Prof Exp:* Teacher chem, phys & math, Hattiesburg Pub High Sch, 65-67; teaching asst chem, Southern Univ, 67-69; instr chem & math, Dillard Univ, 69-71; teaching asst chem, Univ Southern Miss, 71-74; ASSOC PROF CHEM, MISS VALLEY STATE UNIV, 74- *Concurrent Pos:* Southern fel Fund, Atlanta, 72-73; adv coun mem, Brookhaven Lab, 77-, NSF Grant, 78-81. *Mem:* Am Chem Soc; Nat Inst Sci. *Res:* Lithium-amine reductions of carboxamides, carboxylic acids, and heterocyclic aromatics; synthesis of long-chain aldynoic acids and alkyn-1-ols via coupling of 1-alkynes and dioc acid anhydrides or lactones. *Mailing Add:* Miss Valley State Univ PO Box 131 Itta Bena MS 38941

PAYTON, ARTHUR DAVID, b Chicago, Ill, Sept 19, 35; m 74. ELECTROCHEMISTRY. *Educ:* Ill Inst Technol, BS, 56; Yale Univ, MS, 57, PhD(phys chem), 60. *Prof Exp:* Assoc prof, 62-77, RES PROF CHEM, WILLAMETTE UNIV, 77- *Concurrent Pos:* NIH fel, Bethesda, Md, 60-61; Alexander Von Humboldt Found fel, Bad Godesberg, WGer, 61-62. *Mem:* Am Chem Soc; Royal Soc Chem; Am Asn Physics Teachers; Ger Bunsen Soc Phys Chem; Electrochem Soc. *Res:* Thermoelectric powers and transported entropies in aqueous acids. *Mailing Add:* Dept of Chem Willamette Univ Salem OR 97301

PAYTON, BRIAN WALLACE, b London, Eng. PHYSIOLOGY. *Educ:* Univ London, MB & BS, 57, PhD(pharmacol), 65. *Prof Exp:* Jr lectr, St Bartholomews Hosp Med Sch, Univ London, 58-65; vis asst prof physiol, Col Physicians & Surgeons, Columbia Univ, 65-67; NIH res fel anat, Albert Einstein Med Col, 67-69; PROF PHYSIOL & DIR MED AUDIO-VISUAL SERV, MED SCH, MEM UNIV NFLD, 69- *Concurrent Pos:* Med Res Coun Can res grant, Mem Univ Nfld, 69-72. *Mem:* Biophys Soc; Can Physiol Soc; Asn Biomed Commun Dirs; Inst Med & Biol Illus; Health Sci Commun Asn. *Res:* Synaptic transmission and neural mechanisms; leech neurophysiology. *Mailing Add:* Fac of Med Health Sci Ctr Mem Univ of Nfld St John's NF A1C 5S7 Can

PAYTON, CECIL WARREN, b Orangeburg, SC, Mar 9, 42; m 67; c 1. MICROBIOLOGY. *Educ:* Morris Col, BS, 65; Atlanta Univ, MS, 70; Univ Md, Baltimore, PhD(microbiol), 78. *Prof Exp:* Med lab specialist bact, US Army, 65-68; ASST PROF MICROBIOL & BIOL, MORGAN STATE UNIV, 72- *Concurrent Pos:* Instr microbiol, Community Col Baltimore, 73- *Mem:* AAAS; Am Soc Microbiol. *Res:* Microbial physiology and biochemistry. *Mailing Add:* Dept of Biol Morgan State Univ Baltimore MD 21239

PAYTON, DANIEL N, III, b Lamar, Mo, July 2, 40; m 60; c 1. PHYSICS. *Educ:* Mo Sch Mines & Metall, BS, 62, MS, 64; Univ Mo, PhD(physics), 66. *Prof Exp:* Instr physics, Univ Mo-Rolla, 64; US Atomic Energy Comn fel & staff mem physics, Los Alamos Sci Lab, 65-67; physicist, 67-71, sci adv plasma physics, 71-74, TECH DIR NUCLEAR TECH, AIR FORCE WEAPONS LAB, US AIR FORCE, 74- *Concurrent Pos:* Consult, Sci Applns Inc, 72-74; adj prof nuclear eng, Univ NMex, 74- *Mem:* Sigma Xi; Am Phys Soc; AAAS. *Res:* Analysis of systems survivability; applications of plasma physics research; statistical mechanics of traffic flow and modeling; nonstandard fusion techniques; applications of emerging technologies. *Mailing Add:* 4516 Andrew NE Albuquerque NM 87109

PAYTON, OTTO D, b Elk City, Okla, Dec 30, 29; m 55; c 1. REHABILITATION, EDUCATION. *Educ:* Univ Kans, BS, 56; Ind Univ, MS, 64; Univ Md, PhD(higher educ), 71. *Prof Exp:* Chief phys therapist, Dixon State Sch, Ill, 56-58; chief phys therapist, Rehab Ctr, Elkhart, Ind, 58-66, asst dir, 62-66; instr rehab, Sch Med, Univ Md, 66-70, asst prof phys ther & actg chmn dept, 70-71; assoc prof, 71-76, PROF PHYS THER, MED COL VA, VA COMMONWEALTH UNIV, 76-, DIR GRAD DIV, DEPT PHYS THER, SCH ALLIED HEALTH PROFESSIONS, 71- *Concurrent Pos:* A D Williams res grant, Med Col Va, 72, Med Col Va Found res grant, 73-74; consult, Div Phys Ther, Md State Dept Health, 69-71; chmn grad educ comt, Am Phys Ther Asn, 74 & 77; res fel, Am Phys Ther Asn, 80. *Mem:* Am Phys Ther Asn; Am Cong Rehab Med; Asn Schs Allied Health Professions. *Res:* Gerintalogy; therapeutic kinesiology. *Mailing Add:* Sch Allied Health Professions Dept Phys Ther Box 224 Richmond VA 23298

PAYTON, PATRICK HERBERT, b New Eagle, Pa, June 28, 41. PHYSICAL CHEMISTRY, NUCLEAR CHEMISTRY. *Educ:* Waynesburg Col, BS, 64; Univ Calif, Los Angeles, PhD(phys chem), 74. *Prof Exp:* Fel nuclear & lunar chem, Univ Calif, Los Angeles, 74-75, fel stable isotope geochem, 75; Robert A Welch fel nuclear chem, Marine Biomed Inst, Univ Tex Med Br, Galveston, 75-76; fel geochem, Univ Calif, Los Angeles, 76-77; res scientist, Teledyne Wah Chang Albany, 77-81; SR RES CHEMIST, OCCIDENTAL RES CORP, 81- *Mem:* Am Chem Soc; Am Inst Chem Engrs; Assoc Inst Mech Engrs; Am Vacuum Soc. *Res:* Planetary and lunar geochemistry; stable isotope geochemistry; radioactive fallout; analytical methods; neutron and photon activation analysis. *Mailing Add:* Occidental Res Corp 2100 SE Main St PO Box 19601 Irvine CA 92713

PAYTON, ROBERT GILBERT, b Louisville, Ky, Jan 1, 29; m 71. APPLIED MATHEMATICS. *Educ:* Univ Louisville, BEE, 52; Yale Univ, ME, 53; Harvard Univ, PhD(appl math), 59. *Prof Exp:* Staff scientist appl mech, Avco Corp, 59-61, res group leader, 62-64; from asst prof to assoc prof, 64-73, PROF MATH, ADELPHI UNIV, 73- *Concurrent Pos:* Temporary mem, Courant Inst Math Sci, 61-62; vis prof, Univ Strathclyde, 71-72; sabbatical leave, Imperial Col, London, 80. *Mem:* Am Math Soc. *Res:* Linear elastic wave propagation. *Mailing Add:* Dept of Math Adelphi Univ Garden City NY 11530

PAZ, MARIO MEIR, b Quezaltenango, Guatemala, Mar 21, 24; m 51; c 4. CIVIL ENGINEERING, STRUCTURAL DYNAMICS. *Educ:* Univ Chile, Civil Eng, 54; Iowa State Univ, MS, 57, PhD(theoret & appl mech), 60. *Prof Exp:* Head dept statist, Chilean Serv Statist, 54-58; instr eng, Iowa State Univ, 58-60; from asst prof to assoc prof civil eng, 60-69, PROF CIVIL ENG, UNIV LOUISVILLE, 69-, CHMN DEPT, 80- *Concurrent Pos:* Instr, Univ Chile, 54-57; consult, Rex Chain Belt Co, Ky, 62-; fallout shelter analyst & blast designer, George Washington Univ, 65. *Mem:* Am Soc Eng Educ; Seismol Soc Am; Am Soc Civil Engrs. *Res:* Mechanical vibrations. *Mailing Add:* Dept of Civil Eng Univ of Louisville Louisville KY 40208

PAZ, MERCEDES AURORA, b Buenos Aires, Arg, Apr 7, 28. BIOCHEMISTRY. *Educ:* Univ Buenos Aires, BPharm, 50, MBiochem, 52, PhD(biochem), 55. *Prof Exp:* Chief lab clin anal, Ctr Rheumatic Dis, Univ Buenos Aires, 52-60, instr biol chem, Sch Pharm & Biochem, 57-61, res assoc, Nat Coun Res, 64-65, asst prof, Sch Pharm & Biochem, 65-66; asst prof biochem, Albert Einstein Col Med, 67-72; asst prof, 72-77, ASSOC PROF ORAL BIOL & PATHOPHYSIOL, SCH DENT MED, HARVARD UNIV, 77-; RES ASSOC, CHILDREN'S HOSP MED CTR, 72- *Concurrent Pos:* Arg Nat Coun Res grants, Univ Buenos Aires, 60-61 & Albert Einstein Col Med, 62-63. *Res:* Cellular aging protein chemistry; collagen and elastin. *Mailing Add:* Dept of Orthop Surg Children's Hosp Med Ctr Boston MA 02115

PAZICH, PHILIP MICHAEL, b Sewickly, Pa, Jan 12, 47; m 73. SPACE PHYSICS. *Educ:* Va Mil Inst, BS, 68; Rice Univ, MS, 71, PhD(space physics), 73. *Prof Exp:* Res physicist, US Air Force Geophys Lab, 73-76; proj mgr, US Air Force Space & Missile Systs Orgn, 76-79; MEM TECH STAFF, GEN RES CORP, 79- *Mem:* Am Geophys Union. *Res:* Ionospheric effects of magnetospheric substorms and the properties of the solar wind and its interaction with the earth's magnetosphere. *Mailing Add:* Gen Res Corp PO Box 6770 Santa Barbara CA 93111

PAZIENZA, JOSEPH PETER, b Albany, NY, Oct 15, 25; m 57; c 4. PHARMACY. *Educ:* Union Univ, NY, BS, 47; State Univ NY Teachers Col, Albany, MS, 53. *Prof Exp:* Instr pharm, Albany Col Pharm, Union Univ, NY, 48-49, 50-52; res pharmacist, 55-69, GROUP LEADER, STERLING-WINTHROP RES INST, 69- *Res:* Pharmaceutical dosage forms. *Mailing Add:* Sterling-Winthrop Res Inst Rensselaer NY 12144

PAZOLES, CHRISTOPHER JAMES, b Chicago, Ill, Jan 17, 50; m 72. MOLECULAR BIOLOGY, NEUROBIOLOGY. *Educ:* Oberlin Col, AB, 71; Univ Notre Dame, PhD(microbiol), 75. *Prof Exp:* Staff fel membrane molecular biol, Nat Inst Child Health & Human develop, 75-77, sr staff fel, Clin Hemat Br, Nat Inst Arthritis, Metab & Digestive Dis, NIH, 77-81; RES SCIENTIST BIOCHEM, PHARMACOL DEPT, PFIZER CENT RES, PFIZER INC, GROTON, CONN, 81- *Mem:* Soc Neurosci; AAAS. *Res:* Investigation of peptides in the central nervous system and in peripheral tissues as regulators of physiological processes and disease states; development of novel therapeutic agents based on peptide approaches. *Mailing Add:* Biochem Pharmacol Dept Pfizer Cent Res Groton CT 06340

PAZUR, JOHN HOWARD, b Czech, Jan 17, 22; US citizen; m 50; c 4. BIOCHEMISTRY. *Educ:* Univ Guelph, BSA, 44; McGill Univ, MSc, 46; Iowa State Univ, PhD(chem), 50. *Prof Exp:* Instr chem, Iowa State Univ, 50-51; asst prof biol chem, Univ Ill, 51-52; from asst prof to prof biochem & nutrit, Univ Nebr, 52-66; PROF BIOCHEM, PA STATE UNIV, UNIVERSITY PARK, 66- *Mem:* Am Chem Soc; Am Soc Biol Chem. *Res:* Biochemistry of carbohydrates; mechanism of enzyme action; structure of enzymes; immunochemistry. *Mailing Add:* Dept of Biochem Pa State Univ University Park PA 16802

PE, MAUNG HLA, b Mandalay, Burma, Nov 14, 20; m 57. PHYSICS. *Educ:* Univ Rangoon, BSc, 46; Lehigh Univ, MS, 51, PhD(elec eng), 57; Polytech Inst Brooklyn, MS, 52; NY Univ, MNuclearEng, 57. *Prof Exp:* Lectr elec eng, City Col New York, 57-61; ASSOC PROF PHYSICS, MANHATTAN COL, 61- *Mem:* Assoc mem Physicists in Med; NY Acad Sci; AAAS. *Res:* Magnetohydrodynamics; plasma physics; biophysics. *Mailing Add:* Dept of Physics Manhattan Col Bronx NY 10471

PEABODY, DWIGHT VAN DORN, JR, b Elyria, Ohio, July 19, 24; m 74; c 4. WEED SCIENCE. *Educ:* Ohio State Univ, BS, 49; Wash State Univ, MS, 51. *Prof Exp:* Asst, Wash State Univ, 50-51; asst agronomist, Northwestern Wash Res & Exten Unit, 51-66, ASSOC AGRONOMIST & EXTEN WEED SCIENTIST, NORTHWESTERN WASH RES & EXTEN UNIT, WASH STATE UNIV, 66- *Concurrent Pos:* Consult, Reichhold Chem Inc, 71- *Mem:* Weed Sci Soc Am; Int Weed Sci Soc; Coun Agr Sci & Technol. *Res:* Weed control in agronomic and horticultural crops. *Mailing Add:* Northwestern Wash Res & Exten Unit Wash State Univ Mt Vernon WA 98273

PEABODY, FRANK ROBERT, b Birmingham, Mich, Oct 13, 20; m 47; c 2. MICROBIOLOGY, ENVIRONMENTAL HEALTH. *Educ:* Mich State Univ, BS, 42, MS, 48, PhD(microbiol), 52. *Prof Exp:* From instr to assoc prof, 48-75, PROF MICROBIOL, MICH STATE UNIV, 75-, ASSOC CHMN DEPT, 78- *Concurrent Pos:* Consult, Nat Automatic Merchandising Asn, 57-; adv to Repub SKorea, Int Coop Admin, US Dept State, Washington, DC, 59-60. *Mem:* Am Soc Microbiol; Am Inst Biol Sci; Int Asn Milk, Food & Environ Sanitarians. *Res:* Antiseptics and disinfectants; hospital environment; microbial indicators of water pollution. *Mailing Add:* Dept of Microbiol & Pub Health Mich State Univ East Lansing MI 48824

PEABODY, RICHARD ARTHUR, biochemistry, see previous edition

PEACE, GEORGE EARL, JR, b Norfolk, Va, Feb 4, 45; m 71. ANALYTICAL CHEMISTRY. *Educ:* Lafayette Col, BS, 66; Univ Ill, Urbana, MS, 68, PhD(anal chem), 71. *Prof Exp:* Res asst anal chem, Univ Ill, Urbana, 68-71; asst prof, Lafayette Col, 71-78, assoc prof anal chem, 78-79, chief adv health professions, 75-79; ASSOC PROF ANAL CHEM, COL OF

THE HOLY CROSS, 79- *Concurrent Pos:* Fac fel res grant, 71-72, 74-75; environ sci & eng fel, AAAS & Environ Protection Agency, 79- *Mem:* Soc Appl Spectros; AAAS. *Res:* Teaching analytical chemistry; trace metal analysis; nuclear magnetic resonance. *Mailing Add:* Dept of Chem Col of the Holy Cross Worcester MA 01610

PEACEMAN, DONALD W(ILLIAM), b Miami, Fla, June 1, 26; m 52; c 2. CHEMICAL ENGINEERING, MATHEMATICS. *Educ:* City Col New York, BChE, 47; Mass Inst Technol, ScD, 52. *Prof Exp:* Instr chem eng, Mass Inst Technol, 50; SR RES ADV, EXXON PROD RES CO, 51- *Honors & Awards:* Robert Earll McConnell Award, Am Inst Mining, Metall & Petrol Engrs, 79. *Mem:* Asn Comput Mach; Am Inst Mining, Metall & Petrol Engrs; Am Inst Chem Engrs; Soc Indust & Appl Math. *Res:* Liquid-side resistance in gas absorption; petroleum production; numerical analysis; petroleum reservoir simulation. *Mailing Add:* Exxon Prod Res Co PO 2189 Houston TX 77001

PEACH, MICHAEL EDWIN, b Nottingham, Eng, May 7, 37; m 64; c 2. INORGANIC CHEMISTRY. *Educ:* Cambridge Univ, BA, 59, PhD(chem), 62, MA, 64. *Prof Exp:* NATO fel, Graz Tech Univ, 62-63; fel, Univ Gottingen, 63-64, res assoc chem, 64-65; asst prof, Dalhousie Univ, 65-66; lectr, Loughborough Univ Technol, 66-67; from asst prof to assoc prof, 67-76, PROF CHEM & DIR GRAD STUDIES & RES, ACADIA UNIV, 76- *Concurrent Pos:* Guest prof, Univ Wurzburg, 74-75 & 80-81; Alexander Von Humboldt Found fel, 74-75 & 80-81. *Mem:* Chem Inst Can. *Res:* Chemistry of divalent sulfur compounds, particularly derivative of halogenated thiols and the chemistry of non-aqueous solvent systems. *Mailing Add:* Dept Chem Acadia Univ Wolfville NS B0P 1X0 Can

PEACH, MICHAEL JOE, b Morgantown, WVa, Aug 22, 40; m 66; c 1. PHARMACOLOGY, PHYSIOLOGY. *Educ:* Shepherd Col, BS, 63; WVa Univ, MS, 65, PhD(pharmacol), 68. *Prof Exp:* Instr pharmacol, WVa Univ, 67; from asst prof to assoc prof, 68-76, PROF PHARMACOL, SCH MED, UNIV VA, 76- *Concurrent Pos:* Nat Heart & Lung Inst fel, Res Div, Cleveland Clin, 67-68. *Mem:* AAAS; Am Soc Pharmacol & Exp Therapeut; Soc Neurosci. *Res:* Physiology and pharmacology of the reninangiotensin system and interaction with the sympathoadrenal system; angiotensin and control of aldosterone; arterial hypertension. *Mailing Add:* Dept of Pharmacol Box 448 Univ of Va Sch of Med Charlottesville VA 22908

PEACH, PETER ANGUS, b Scotland, Aug 17, 20; Can citizen; m 46; c 3. GEOLOGY. *Educ:* Univ Edinburgh, BSc, 41; Univ Toronto, MA, 47, PhD(geol), 50. *Prof Exp:* Lectr geol, Univ Toronto, 50-55, from asst prof to assoc prof, 55-68; assoc prof, 68-71, PROF GEOL, BROCK UNIV, 71- *Mem:* Geol Asn Can. *Res:* Petrology. *Mailing Add:* Dept of Geol Sci Brock Univ St Catharines ON L2T 1X2 Can

PEACH, ROY, b Runcorn, Eng. HISTOLOGY. *Educ:* Manchester Univ, Eng, BS, 56, MS, 57, PhD(biophys), 60. *Prof Exp:* Spec fel rheumatism res, Manchester Univ, 59-61, asst lectr biophys, Dept Anat, 61-64, lectr, 64-67; asst prof oral biol, Sch Dent, 67-69, asst prof anat, Sch Med, 68-74, ASSOC PROF ANAT, SCH MED, UNIV NC, CHAPEL HILL, 74-, ORAL BIOL, SCH DENT, 69- *Mem:* Am Asn Anatomists; Anat Soc Gt Brit & Ireland; Electron Micros Soc Am; Int Asn Dent Res; Royal Micros Soc. *Res:* Development and growth, particularly of facial region, in vitro and in vivo, using mainly microscopic techniques, light and electron. *Mailing Add:* Dent Res Ctr & Dept Anat Univ NC Chapel Hill NC 27514

PEACHEY, LEE DEBORDE, b Rochester, NY, Apr 14, 32; m 58; c 3. CELL BIOLOGY, PHYSIOLOGY. *Educ:* Lehigh Univ, BS, 53; Rockefeller Univ, PhD(biophys), 59. *Prof Exp:* From asst prof to assoc prof zool, Columbia Univ, 59-65; assoc prof biochem & biophys, 65-71, PROF BIOL, UNIV PA, 70- *Concurrent Pos:* NSF grants, Columbia Univ, 60-65 & Univ Pa, 65-72; Muscular Dystrophy Asn grant, Univ Pa, 73- & NIH grant, 73-; Guggenheim & Fulbright-Hayes fels, Cambridge Univ, 67-68; mem molecular biol study sect, NIH, 69-73; adj prof molecular, cellular & develop biol, Univ Colo, 69-; mem, Mayor's Sci & Technol Adv Coun, Philadelphia, 72-; Fogarty sr int fel, Univ Col London, 79-80. *Mem:* AAAS; Am Soc Cell Biol; Biophys Soc (pres, 80-81); Electron Micros Soc Am (pres, 82); Int Union Pure & Appl Biophysics. *Res:* Structure and function of muscle cells; electron microscopy; muscle physiology. *Mailing Add:* Dept of Biol Univ of Pa Philadelphia PA 19174

PEACOCK, ANDREW CLINTON, b Boston, Mass, Dec 2, 21; m 43; c 3. BIOCHEMISTRY. *Educ:* Mass Inst Technol, SB, 43, PhD(biochem), 49. *Prof Exp:* Asst nutrit biochem, Mass Inst Technol, 47-49; CHEMIST, NAT CANCER INST, 49- *Mem:* Am Asn Cancer Res; Am Soc Biol Chemists. *Res:* Enzymes and proteins in blood; carcinogenesis and differentiation. *Mailing Add:* Chem Br Nat Cancer Inst Bethesda MD 20205

PEACOCK, ERLE EWART, b Durham, NC, Sept 10, 26; m 54; c 2. SURGERY. *Educ:* Univ NC, cert, 47; Harvard Univ, MD, 49; Am Bd Surg, dipl. *Prof Exp:* Lab asst zool, Univ NC, 44-45; assoc plastic surg, Sch Med, Wash Univ, 55-56; from instr to prof surg, Sch Med, Univ NC, 56-69; prof & chmn surg fac, Col Med, Univ Ariz, 69-74; PROF SURG, TULANE UNIV, 77- *Concurrent Pos:* Dir hand rehab ctr, Univ NC, Chapel Hill, 65-69; mem surg study sect, NIH, mem surg training grants study sect; chmn, Plastic Surg Res Coun, 67; consult, Watts Hosp, Durham, NC, Vet Admin Hosp, Fayetteville & Womack Army Hosp, Ft Bragg, NC; chmn, Am Bd Plastic Surg, 75-76; US Army Surgeon Gen's adv panel consult in trauma. *Mem:* Soc Plastic & Reconstruct Surg; Soc Surg of Hand; Am Col Surgeons; Am Surg Asn; Soc Univ Surgeons. *Res:* Tissue transplantation and wound healing; connective tissue research; plastic and reconstructive surgery. *Mailing Add:* 5115 Baronne New Orleans LA 70115

PEACOCK, HUGH ANTHONY, b Cairo, Ga, May 30, 28; m 49; c 3. AGRONOMY. *Educ:* Univ Fla, BSA, 52, MSA, 53; Iowa State Univ, PhD(plant breeding), 56. *Prof Exp:* Asst breeding, Iowa State Univ, 55-56; asst agronomist, Univ Fla, 57-58; res agronomist, Exp Sta, Univ Ga & USDA, 59-73; AGRONOMIST & DIR AGR RES CTR, AGR EXP STA, UNIV FLA, 73- *Mem:* Am Soc Agron; Am Genetics Asn; Am Soybean Asn; Crop Sci Soc Am. *Res:* Cotton, soybean, corn, grain sorghum and peanut culture and management. *Mailing Add:* Agr Res Ctr Rt 3 Box 575 Jay FL 32565

PEACOCK, JOHN TALMER, b Madison, Ga, Aug 5, 31; m 57; c 2. PLANT ECOLOGY. *Educ:* Maryville Col, BS, 53; Univ Ala, MS, 55; Univ Tex, PhD(bot), 63. *Prof Exp:* Asst bot, Univ Ala, 54-55; instr biol, Tex Col Arts & Indust, 55-60; res assoc plant ecol, Univ Tex, 61-62; from asst prof to assoc prof, 62-66, chmn dept, 68-76, PROF BIOL, TEX A&I UNIV, 66-, DEAN, COL ARTS & SCI, 76- *Mem:* AAAS; Am Inst Biol Sci; Bot Soc Am; Ecol Soc Am; Nat Asn Biol Teachers. *Res:* Physiological ecology of southwestern shrubs, particularly mesquite. *Mailing Add:* Dept of Biol Tex A&I Univ Kingsville TX 78363

PEACOCK, JOHN WILLIAM, b Marion, Ohio, Apr 6, 39; m 61; c 2. ENTOMOLOGY. *Educ:* Ohio State Univ, BS, 61, PhD(entom), 67. *Prof Exp:* RES ENTOMOLOGIST, FOREST SERV, USDA, 61- *Mem:* Entom Soc Am; Lepidop Soc. *Res:* Physiology and behavior in shade tree insect host selection; behavioral responses of insects to chemical constituents of plants; insect pheromones. *Mailing Add:* US Forest Serv Forest Insect & Dis Lab Box 365 Delaware OH 43015

PEACOCK, KEITH, astronomy, physics, see previous edition

PEACOCK, LELON JAMES, b Brevard, NC, May 25, 28; m 45; c 3. PHYSIOLOGICAL PSYCHOLOGY, COMPARATIVE PSYCHOLOGY. *Educ:* Berea Col, AB, 50; Univ Ky, MS, 52, PhD(psychol), 56. *Prof Exp:* Psychophysiologist, US Army Med Res Lab, 54-56; res assoc psychol, Yerkes Labs Primate Biol, 56-58, actg dir, 58-59; from asst prof to assoc prof, 59-65, PROF PSYCHOL, UNIV GA, 66- *Mem:* AAAS; Am Psychol Asn; Int Primatol Soc; Soc Psychophysiol Res; Soc Neurosci. *Res:* Psychophysiology of learning; radiation effects on behavior; measurement of general activity; instrumentation; neuropsychology. *Mailing Add:* Dept of Psychol Univ of Ga Athens GA 30601

PEACOCK, MILTON O, b West Monroe, La, Aug 31, 16; m 56; c 4. BIOCHEMISTRY, NUTRITION. *Educ:* La State Univ, BS, 43, MS, 45; Univ Miss, BS, 52; Univ Ala, PhD(biochem), 63. *Prof Exp:* Mathematician, Ballistics Res Lab, Md, 45-47; asst prof math & physics, Evansville Col, 47-49; assoc prof biol, Miss Southern Col, 49-51; prof pharmacol & chmn, Sch Pharm, Northeast La State Col, 54-57; prof chem & head dept, Ark A&M Col, 63-67; prof chem & pharmacol & chmn, Div Sci & Math, Whitworth Col, Miss, 67-72 & 75-76; assoc prof pharmacol, La Tech Univ, 76-78; PRES & DIR RES & INSTR MATH & SCI, INST SCI & MATH, LA, 72-, SCI HEALTH COUNSELING, 75- *Mem:* Fel Am Inst Chemists; Sigma Xi; Am Chem Soc; Am Pharmaceut Asn. *Res:* Mathematical analysis of interferometer of n plates; mathematical description and correlation of physical phenomena; chromogenic reactions of divalent S compounds with ammonia, amines, amides, and others; magnetotropism of germinating plant embryos; mathematical models of serial dilution; gradient change in concentration, extraction and countercurrent exchange phenomena; mathematical models for natural phenomena and analytical chemical processes; nutritional therapy. *Mailing Add:* Inst Sci & Math Rte 3 Box 198 West Monroe LA 71291

PEACOCK, PETER N B, b Nairobi, Kenya, Nov 3, 21; m 49; c 3. EPIDEMIOLOGY. *Educ:* Univ Cape Town, MB, ChB, 45, dipl pub health, 47; Royal Col Physicians & Surgeons, dipl indust health, 53; Univ Witwatersrand, DTM&H, 57, MD, 69; Samford Univ, MA, 70. *Prof Exp:* Med inspector, Dept Health, Union SAfrica, 47-49, asst chief health officer, 49-52; regional med health officer, Govt Sask, 53-55; prof pub health, Univ Witwatersrand, 56-61; asst prof pub health, Univ Sask, 61-65; prof pub health & epidemiol, Med Ctr, Univ Ala, Birmingham, 65-76, PROF EPIDEMIOL & PREVENATIVE MED, MCNEESE CLIN, UNIV ALA, FAYETTE, 77- *Concurrent Pos:* Med officer health, City of Germiston, 56-61; regional med health officer, Govt Sask, 61-65; mem, Nat Adv Comt Stoke Epidemiology, Cancer Epidemiol & Bioradiation; clin prof pub health, Med Col, Cornell Univ, 72-; chief epidemiol, Am Health Found, New York, 72- *Mem:* Am Pub Health Asn; Can Med Asn; Can Pub Health Asn; fel Royal Soc Trop Med & Hyg; SAfrican Pub Health Asn (pres, 60-61). *Res:* Medical epidemiology; rheumatic fever; bilharzia; typhoid; occupational health; tick paralysis; poliomyelitis; physical fitness; mercury poisoning; the distribution of health services; statistical epidemiology relating to community health; air pollution; stroke. *Mailing Add:* Sch of Med McNeese Clin Univ of Ala Fayette AL 35555

PEACOCK, RICHARD WESLEY, b Scottsburg, Ind, Sept 24, 39. PHYSICS. *Educ:* Tulane Univ, BS, 61, MS, 66, PhD(physics), 70. *Prof Exp:* Instr & head dept math, Fishburne Mil Sch, 73-76; physicist, US Navy Eastern Standards Lab, 76-77; TECH INFO SPECIALIST, LANGLEY RES CTR, NASA, 77- *Mem:* Am Phys Soc; AAAS. *Res:* Three particle system theory; neutron-deutron scattering as a three particle system; weak interactions and basic nuclear systems. *Mailing Add:* 1583 Malibu Pl Newport News VA 22602

PEACOCK, ROY NORMAN, b Sandpoint, Idaho, Mar 19, 30; m 57; c 2. INSTRUMENTATION. *Educ:* Univ Ore, BA, 52, MA, 53; Univ Ill, PhD(physics), 58. *Prof Exp:* From asst prof to assoc prof physics, Univ Ill, Urbana, 62-71; scientist, Granville-Phillips Co, 71-72, vpres res & eng, 72-76; CO-FOUNDER & VPRES RES & ENG, HPS CORP, 76- *Mem:* Am Vacuum Soc; Am Phys Soc. *Res:* Vacuum techniques; solid surfaces; thin films. *Mailing Add:* 8845 Elgin Dr Lafayette CO 80026

PEACOCK, SAMUEL MOORE, JR, b Philadelphia, Pa, May 8, 22. NEUROPHYSIOLOGY. *Educ:* Princeton Univ, AB, 44; Univ Pa, MD, 48. *Prof Exp:* Intern, Bryn Mawr Hosp, Pa, 48-49; from instr to asst prof neurol, Tulane Univ, 49-57; ASST PROF PSYCHIAT, UNIV PA, 59-; sr med res scientist neurophysiol, Dept Clin Res, Eastern Pa Psychiat Inst, 57-80; ASSOC PROF PSYCHIAT, JEFFERSON MED COL, 75- *Concurrent Pos:* Am Col Physicians fel, Tulane Univ, 49-50; USPHS fel, 50-51, USPHS fel, Nat Found Infantile Paralysis, 51-53; Grass Trust fel, Marine Biol Lab, Woods Hole, 51; res assoc, Dept Neurosurg, Pa Hosp, Philadelphia, 61-63. *Mem:* AAAS; Am Physiol Soc; Am Acad Neurol; Soc Biol Psychiat; Am Med EEG Asn. *Res:* Physiology of motor system; neurophysiology of behavior; electroencephalography and evoked response averaging. *Mailing Add:* Lower Pine Creek Rd Chester Springs PA 19425

PEACOCK, VAL EDWARD, b Sioux City, Iowa, Oct 25, 51; m 78. ORGANIC CHEMISTRY. *Educ:* Iowa State Univ, BS, 73; Univ Wis-Madison, PhD (org chem), 78. *Prof Exp:* res assoc org chem, Dept Agr chem, Ore State Univ, 78-80; MEM STAFF, PHILLIP MORRIS RES CTR, 80- *Mem:* Am Chem Soc. *Res:* Physical organic chemistry. *Mailing Add:* PO Box 26853 Philip Morris Res Ctr Richmond VA 23261

PEACOR, DONALD RALPH, b Somerville, Mass, Feb 15, 37; m 60; c 3. MINERALOGY. *Educ:* Tufts Univ, BS, 58; Mass Inst Technol, SM, 60, PhD(crystallog), 62. *Prof Exp:* From instr to assoc prof geol, 62-71, PROF GEOL, UNIV MICH, 71- *Mem:* Mineral Soc Am; Am Crystallog Asn. *Res:* X-ray crystallography of minerals; general mineralogy; high temperature x-ray diffraction. *Mailing Add:* Dept of Geol & Mineral Univ of Mich Ann Arbor MI 48104

PEAK, DAVID, b Brooklyn, NY, Nov 28, 41; m 66. THEORETICAL PHYSICS. *Educ:* State Univ NY Col New Paltz, BS, 65; State Univ NY Albany, PhD(physics), 69. *Prof Exp:* Res assoc physics, State Univ NY Albany, 69-71, instr, 71-75; asst prof, 75-78, ASSOC PROF PHYSICS, UNION COL, 78- *Concurrent Pos:* Res fel, Inst Study Defects in Solids, Albany, NY, 75-; vis fel, Princeton Univ, 78-79; NSF prof develop award, 78-79. *Mem:* Am Phys Soc; Am Asn Physics Teachers. *Res:* Generally, problems in irreversible thermodynamics; in particular, the theory of diffusion-reaction systems, the theory of nucleation and the theory of interacting populations. *Mailing Add:* Dept of Physics Union Col Schenectady NY 12308

PEAK, MEYRICK JAMES, b Southend, Eng, June 29, 37; m 61; c 2. RADIATION BIOLOGY, MICROBIAL MUTAGENESIS. *Educ:* Univ Cape Town, SAfrica, BSc, 60; Univ Calif, PhD(biol), 72. *Prof Exp:* Lectr biol, Univ Cape Town, SAfrica, 63-70; sr lectr biochem, Rhodes Univ, SAfrica, 73-79; SCIENTIST, DIV BIOL & MED RES, ARGONNE NAT LAB, 80- *Concurrent Pos:* Vis prof, Univ Rio de Janeiro, 76; fel, 70-72, vis scientist, Div Biol Med Res, Argonne Nat Lab, 78. *Mem:* Am Soc Photobiol; Environ Mutagenesis Soc. *Res:* Photobiology; algal biochemistry; environmental mutagenesis. *Mailing Add:* Div Biol & Med Res Argonne Nat Lab 9700 S Cass Ave Argonne IL 60439

PEAK, WILFERD WARNER, b Los Angeles, Calif, Jan 17, 24; m 51; c 4. GEOLOGY, ENGINEERING GEOLOGY. *Educ:* Univ Calif, Los Angeles, BA, 48. *Prof Exp:* From jr geologist to assoc geologist, Planning Div, 48-56, assoc to sr geologist, Design & Construct Div, 56-64, chief geologist, Div Safety of Dams, 64-77, CHIEF ENG GEOLOGIST, CALIF STATE DEPT WATER RESOURCES, 77- *Concurrent Pos:* Mem, Calif State Bd Registrn Geologists, 69-76, pres, 69-72. *Mem:* Fel Geol Soc Am; Asn Eng Geologists (secy, 64). *Res:* Methods of utilization of new techniques and tools to investigate foundations of dams and appurtenant hydraulic structures so as to ensure competency of those structures. *Mailing Add:* Calif State Dept Water Resources PO Box 388 Sacramento CA 95802

PEAKALL, DAVID B, b Purley, Eng, Mar 17, 31; m 59; c 4. ENVIRONMENTAL SCIENCES. *Educ:* Univ London, BSc, 52, MSc, 54, PhD(chem), 56, DSc, 79. *Prof Exp:* Sci officer, Ministry Supply, Eng, 56-57; Cabot fel surface chem, State Univ NY Agr & Tech Col, Alfred Univ, 57-59; chemist, Distillers Co, Ltd, Eng, 59-60; res assoc protein chem, State Univ NY Upstate Med Ctr, 60-62, asst prof pharmacol, 62-66; Am Heart Asn estab investr, 66-71; sr res assoc, Langmuir Lab, Div Ecol & Systs, Cornell Univ, 68-75; CHIEF WILDLIFE TOXICOL DIV, CAN WILDLIFE SERV, 75- *Concurrent Pos:* Consult, US-USSR Environ Health Prog, Nat Insts Environ Health Sci, 72-76; mem expert group, Orgn Econ Coop & Develop Ecotoxicol, 78- *Mem:* Am Ornithologists Union; Am Physiol Soc; Ornithologists Union; Soc Environ Toxicol & Chem. *Res:* Effect of pollutants on avian physiology and reproduction; regulation of protein synthesis in spiders. *Mailing Add:* Can Wildlife Serv Ottawa ON K1A 0H3 Can

PEAKE, CLINTON J, b Hancock, NY, Sept 11, 32; m 55; c 3. ORGANIC CHEMISTRY, BIOLOGICAL CHEMISTRY. *Educ:* Harpur Col, AB, 58; Univ Notre Dame, PhD(org chem), 62. *Prof Exp:* Res chemist, FMC Corp, 62-63, res chemist, Niagara Chem Div, 63-68, sr res chemist, 68-80, SR RES CHEMIST, AGR CHEM GROUP, 80- *Mem:* Am Chem Soc; Soc Nematol. *Res:* Pesticide research in the nematicides area; blood chemistry, especially hemostasis. *Mailing Add:* Res Dept Niagara Chem Div FMC Corp 100 Niagara St Middleport NY 14105

PEAKE, EDMUND JAMES, JR, b Omaha, Nebr, July 5, 38; m 64; c 2. ALGEBRA. *Educ:* NMex State Univ, BS, 60, MS, 62, PhD(math), 63. *Prof Exp:* ASST PROF MATH, IOWA STATE UNIV, 63- *Mem:* Math Asn Am. *Res:* Abelian groups; homological and universal algebra; applications to computer science. *Mailing Add:* Dept of Math Iowa State Univ Ames IA 50011

PEAKE, HAROLD J(ACKSON), b Norton, Va, Dec 7, 20; m 42; c 1. ELECTRONICS. *Educ:* Va Polytech Inst, BS, 42; Univ Md, MEA, 53; George Washington Univ, MS, 69. *Prof Exp:* Radio engr, Radio Div, US Naval Res Lab, Washington, DC, 42-49, electronics scientist, Solid State Div, 49-58; res engr & head, Flight Systs Br, Goddard Space Flight Ctr, NASA, Greenbelt, Md, 58-65, assoc chief, Spacecraft Technol Div, 65-69, chief, Electronics Div, 69-74, chief, Off Nat Needs, 74-80; RETIRED. *Concurrent Pos:* Lectr, George Washington Univ, 43-44, 57-; lectr mgt, Am Univ, 75- *Mem:* Sci Res Soc Am; fel Inst Elec & Electronics Engrs; Sigma Xi. *Res:* Radio communications systems radio wave propagation; circuit analysis; cathode-ray oscillography; satellite and space probe instrumentation and telemetry; space electronics; management and supervision. *Mailing Add:* 2213 Sherwood Hall Lane Alexandria VA 22306

PEAKE, ROBERT LEE, b Evansville, Ind, July 6, 35; m 57; c 2. INTERNAL MEDICINE, ENDOCRINOLOGY. *Educ:* Ind Univ, AB, 57, MD, 60. *Prof Exp:* Intern med, Sch Med, Ind Univ, 60-61; resident internal med, 61-62 & 64-65; asst prof, 68-73, ASSOC PROF INTERNAL MED, UNIV TEX MED BR, GALVESTON, 73- *Concurrent Pos:* NIH trainee fel endocrinol & metab, Med Ctr, Ind Univ, 65-68. *Mem:* Am Fedn Clin Res; Endocrine Soc; Am Col Physicians; Am Thyroid Asn. *Res:* Thyroglobulin proteolysis; thyroid hormone release. *Mailing Add:* Dept of Internal Med Univ of Tex Med Br Galveston TX 77550

PEAKE, WILLIAM TOWER, b Oak Park, Ill, Nov 26, 29; m 52; c 2. ELECTRICAL ENGINEERING. *Educ:* Mass Inst Technol, SB, 51, SM, 53, ScD, 60. *Prof Exp:* Asst elec eng, Mass Inst Technol, 51-53; proj engr, Wright Air Develop Ctr, US Air Force, 53-56; from instr to assoc prof, 56-76, PROF ELEC ENG, MASS INST TECHNOL, 76- *Concurrent Pos:* Res assoc otol, Mass Eye & Ear Infirmary, 63- *Mem:* Inst Elec & Electronics Eng; Acoust Soc Am. *Res:* Sensory communication, particularly signal transmission in the ear. *Mailing Add:* Rm 36-825 Mass Inst of Technol Cambridge MA 02139

PEALE, STANTON JERROLD, b Indianapolis, Ind, Jan 23, 37; m 60; c 2. SOLAR SYSTEM PHYSICS, ASTROPHYSICS. *Educ:* Purdue Univ, BS, 59; Cornell Univ, MS, 62, PhD(eng physics), 65. *Prof Exp:* Res assoc space res, Cornell Univ, 64-65; asst prof astron & geophys, Univ Calif, Los Angeles, 65-68; from asst prof to assoc prof, 68-76, PROF PHYSICS, UNIV CALIF, SANTA BARBARA, 76- *Concurrent Pos:* Res Corp Cottrell res grant, 69-; NASA res grant planetary geophys, 70-; consult sci adv group explor outer solar syst, Jet Propulsion Lab, 71-72; vis fel, Joint Inst for Lab Astrophys, Univ Colo, 72-73, 79-80; NASA-Ames Univ Consortium grant, 76-81; mem, NASA Lunar & Planetary Rev Panel, 79-81 & Nat Acad Sci Space Sci Bd Comt on Planetary & Lunar Exp, 80- *Honors & Awards:* Newcomb Cleveland Prize, AAAS, 80. *Mem:* Fel AAAS; Am Astron Soc; Am Geophys Union; Int Astron Union. *Res:* Zodiacal light; small particles in space; dynamics of planetary spins; tidal evolution; nature of the planetary interiors; star formation and origin of the solar system. *Mailing Add:* Dept of Physics Univ of Calif Santa Barbara CA 93106

PEANASKY, ROBERT JOSEPH, b Menominee, Mich, Oct 18, 27; m 53; c 5. BIOCHEMISTRY, ENZYMOLOGY. *Educ:* Marquette Univ, BS, 51, MS, 53; Univ Wis, PhD(biochem), 57. *Prof Exp:* NSF fel & trainee, Sch Med, Marquette Univ, 57-60, asst prof biochem, 60, assoc prof, 64-67; assoc prof, 67-70, PROF BIOCHEM, SCH MED, UNIV SDAK, 70- *Concurrent Pos:* USPHS career develop award, 60-67. *Mem:* Am Chem Soc; Am Soc Biol Chemists; Soc Exp Biol & Med. *Res:* Purification and properties of proteins; mechanism of interaction between protein inhibitors and proteolytic enzymes; biochemistry of protease inhibitors from Ascaris. *Mailing Add:* Dept of Biochem Univ of SDak Sch of Med Vermillion SD 57069

PEARCE, CHARLES WALTER, b Philadelphia, Pa, May 22, 47; m 66; c 3. ELECTRICAL ENGINEERING. *Educ:* Univ Nebr, BS, 69; Lehigh Univ, MS, 74. *Prof Exp:* SR STAFF ENGR SILICON MAT, WESTERN ELEC CO, 69- *Mem:* Electrochem Soc; Am Soc Test & Mat. *Res:* Measurement of electrical, optical and microperfection properties of silicon. *Mailing Add:* Western Elec Co 555 Union Blvd Allentown PA 18103

PEARCE, DAVID ARCHIBALD, b Montreal, Que, Nov 12, 20; US citizen; m 50; c 2. AGRICULTURAL CHEMISTRY. *Educ:* Sir George Williams Univ, BS, 52. *Prof Exp:* Chief chemist, Green Cross Div, Sherwin-Williams Co Can, 52-56; res chemist, Chemagro Corp, Mo, 57-65; formulation res chemist, 65-67, SR RES CHEMIST, RES, DEVELOP & ENG DIV, MOBIL CHEM CO, 67- *Mem:* Am Chem Soc; fel Am Inst Chemists. *Res:* Apparatus for comparing emulsions; pesticide preparation and formulation; formulation research, insecticides, fungicides, herbicides; product development. *Mailing Add:* 22 Finley Rd Edison NJ 08817

PEARCE, DAVID HARRY, b Newport News, Va, July 20, 43; m. BIOMEDICAL ENGINEERING, ELECTRICAL ENGINEERING. *Educ:* Va Polytech Inst & State Univ, BS, 66; Univ Va, PhD(biomed eng), 72; Reg Prof Engr. *Prof Exp:* NIH cardiovasc training grant, 72-74, NIH young investr pulmonary award, 74-76, instr physiol, 73-74, ASST PROF PHYSIOL, MED CTR, UNIV MISS, 74-, BIOMED ENGR, MISS METHODIST REHAB CTR, 76- *Mem:* Biomed Eng Soc; Inst Elec & Electronics Engrs; Sigma Xi. *Res:* Biomedical engineering as applied to medical instrumentation, respiratory and exercise physiology, mathematical modeling and simulation, biological control theory; real time data processing of physiological signals; rehabilitation engineering. *Mailing Add:* Miss Methodist Rehab Ctr PO Box 4878 Fondren Sta Jackson MS 39216

PEARCE, ELI M, b Brooklyn, NY, May 1, 29; m 51; c 2. POLYMER CHEMISTRY. *Educ:* Brooklyn Col, BS, 49; NY Univ, MS, 51; Polytech Inst NY, PhD(polymer chem), 58. *Prof Exp:* Res chemist biochem, NY Univ, Bellevue Med Ctr, 49-53, Army Med Res Lab, 53-55 & E I du Pont de Nemours & Co, Carothers Res Lab, 58-62; sect head, polymer chem, J T Baker Chem Co, 62-68; mgr tech supvr consult, polymer chem, Allied Chem Corp, 68-73; dir polymer sci, Camille Dryfus Lab, 73-74; PROF POLYMER

CHEM & CHEM ENG, 74-, HEAD DEPT CHEM & DIR, POLYMER RES INST, POLYTECH INST NY, 76- *Concurrent Pos:* Assoc ed, J Polymer Sci, 66-, co-ed, Macromolecular Reviews, 75-; adv bd, Macromolecular Synthesis, 70; mem, Nat Mat Adv Bd, 75-78; mem, Comt Polymer Sci & Eng, Nat Res Coun, Nat Acad Sci, 80-81; adv bd, Petrol Res Fund, 82- *Mem:* AAAS; Am Chem Soc (chmn polymer div, 80); Am Inst Chem; Fel NY Acad Sci; Soc Plastics Eng. *Res:* Polymer synthesis; structure property relationships; polymer degradation; polymer flammability; polymers as chemical reagents; polyamides, polyesters, epoxy resins; polymer compatibility. *Mailing Add:* Polytech Inst NY 333 Jay St Brooklyn NY 11201

PEARCE, FRANK G, b Terre Haute, Ind, Sept 17, 18; m 42; c 3. CHEMICAL ENGINEERING. *Educ:* Rose Polytech Inst, BS, 40; Mass Inst Technol, 46. *Prof Exp:* Chem engr, Am Mach & Foundry Co, 46-47; supvr, Res Sect, Pan Am Petrol Corp Div, Standard Oil Co, Inc, 47-58, dir proj eng, Amoco Chem Corp Div, 58-60, div dir res, 60-62, coordr res & develop, 62-64, dir data systs planning, Ill, 64-67, dir info serv & comput sci, 67-70, gen mgr, Info Serv & mgt sci, 70-79; RETIRED. *Mem:* Am Chem Soc; Am Inst Chem Engrs. *Res:* Process design and economics; economics in petrochemicals; industrial and information services management. *Mailing Add:* 3701 Cherry Hills Dr Flossmoor IL 60422

PEARCE, GEORGE WILLIAM, b St John's, Nfld, Dec 27, 42; m 69; c 1. GEOPHYSICS, GEOLOGY. *Educ:* Mem Univ Nfld, BSc, 65, MSc, 67; Univ Toronto, PhD(geophys), 71. *Prof Exp:* Sci officer geophys, Geol Surv Can, 67-69; fel, Lunar Sci Inst, Houston, 70-73; lectr, 73-74, asst prof, 74-77, ASSOC PROF GEOL, ERINDALE COL, UNIV TORONTO, 77- *Mem:* Am Geophys Union; Geol Asn Can; Can Geophys Union. *Res:* Paleomagnetism; at present concentration on sedimentary deposits of Paleozoic age; space geophysics; magnetic properties of natural materials, terrestrial and extraterrestrial. *Mailing Add:* Erindale Col Univ of Toronto Mississauga ON L5L 1C6 Can

PEARCE, JACK B, b Dearborn, Mich, Sept 20, 30; m 53; c 2. MARINE ECOLOGY, ZOOLOGY. *Educ:* Humboldt State Col, BA, 57; Univ Wash, MS, 60, PhD(zool), 62. *Prof Exp:* NIH fel, Marine Lab, Denmark & Marine Sta, Scotland, 62-63; res assoc, Systs Ecol Prog, Marine Biol Lab, Woods Hole Oceanog Inst, 63-65; asst prof biol, Humboldt State Col, 65-67; marine ecologist, Sandy Hook Lab, 67; DIR ENVIRON INVESTS, NORTHEAST FISHERIES CTR, NAT OCEANIC & ATMOSPHERIC ADMIN, 67- *Concurrent Pos:* US mem & chmn environ qual comt, Int Coun Explor Sea; adj assoc prof, Livingston Col, Rutgers Univ & Lehigh Univ. *Honors & Awards:* US Dept Commerce Gold Medal. *Mem:* Marine Biol Asn UK; Scottish Marine Biol Asn. *Res:* Biology of symbiotic crabs of the family Pinnotheridae; synecological study of epibenthic mytilid communities; the effect of man's activities on the marine environment; the effects of contaminants. *Mailing Add:* Northeast Fisheries Ctr Sandy Hook Lab Highlands NJ 07732

PEARCE, KEITH IAN, b London, Eng, Nov 7, 27; Can citizen; m 54; c 4. PSYCHIATRY, MEDICINE. *Educ:* Univ London, MBBS, 54; Univ Sask, MD, 64; FRCPS(C), 61. *Prof Exp:* Resident med officer, Univ Col Hosp, Univ London, 54, casualty surg officer, 55; registr surg, Royal Cancer Hosp, 55-56; registr surg, Whip's Cross Hosp, 56-57; resident psychiat, Univ Sask, 57-61, consult hosp, 61-62, clin dir hosp, 64-66; DIR DEPT PSYCHIAT, FOOTHILLS HOSP, CALGARY, 66-; PROF PSYCHIAT & HEAD DIV, FAC MED, UNIV CALGARY, 69- *Concurrent Pos:* McLaughlin fel, Med Res Coun, Eng, 62-64; chmn Calgary & Region Ment Health Planning Coun, 70- *Mem:* Can Psychiat Asn; Royal Col Psychiat; Int Fedn Med Electronics & Biol Eng. *Res:* Application of computers to medicine, specifically to psychiatric records with in turn its relevance to the delivery of health care. *Mailing Add:* Dept of Psychiat Foothills Hosp Calgary AB T2L 1B7 Can

PEARCE, MORTON LEE, b Chicago, Ill, Aug 22, 20; m 44; c 3. CARDIOLOGY. *Educ:* Univ Chicago, BS, 41, MD, 44. *Prof Exp:* Intern & resident med, Los Angeles County Hosp, 45-48; res assoc hemat, Atomic Energy Proj, Univ Calif, Los Angeles, 48-51; res fel cardiol, Johns Hopkins Univ, 51-52; res fel & instr, Vanderbilt Univ, 52-53; from asst prof to assoc prof med, 53-63, PROF MED, SCH MED, UNIV CALIF, LOS ANGELES, 63- *Concurrent Pos:* Fel coun atherosclerosis & fel coun clin cardiol, Am Heart Asn; vis investr, Cardiovasc Res Inst, Univ Calif, San Francisco, 62-63; consult cardiol, Vet Admin Hosp, Los Angeles; consult, Rand Corp, Santa Monica. *Mem:* Am Fedn Clin; Am Physiol Soc; fel Am Col Cardiol; Asn Univ Cardiologists. *Res:* Cardiology, including hemodynamics, atherosclerosis and electrocardiography. *Mailing Add:* Dept Med Univ Calif Sch Med Los Angeles CA 90024

PEARCE, R MICHAEL, nuclear physics, deceased

PEARCE, RICHARD HUGH, b London, Ont, Apr 30, 24; c 3. EXPERIMENTAL PATHOLOGY. *Educ:* Univ Western Ont, BSc, 46, MSc, 48, PhD(path chem), 51; Am Bd Clin Chem, cert. *Prof Exp:* Res assoc bact, Sch Med, Yale Univ, 49-50; lectr path chem, Univ Western Ont, 50-52, from asst prof to assoc prof, 52-61; assoc prof, 61-76, PROF PATH, FAC MED, UNIV BC, 76- *Concurrent Pos:* Assoc dir dept clin path, Meek Mem Labs, Victoria Hosp, Ont, 52-61; consult, St Thomas-Elgin Gen Hosp, St Thomas; St Paul's Hosp, Vancouver, BC. *Honors & Awards:* Cert & Ames Award, Can Soc Clin Chem. *Mem:* Fel AAAS; Am Chem Soc; fel Am Asn Clin Chemists; Can Biochem Soc; fel Chem Inst Can. *Res:* Connective tissue. *Mailing Add:* Dept Path Univ BC 2045 Wesbrook Pl Vancouver BC V6T 1W5 Can

PEARCE, ROBERT BRENT, b Pendleton, Ore, June 5, 36; m 58; c 4. AGRONOMY, PLANT PHYSIOLOGY. *Educ:* Univ Calif, Davis, BS, 63; Va Polytech Polytech Inst, MS, 65, PhD(agron), 67. *Prof Exp:* Plant physiologist, Forest & Range Br, Plant Indust Sta, USDA, Md, 66-69; CROP PHYSIOLOGIST, DEPT AGRON, IOWA STATE UNIV, 69-, PROF AGRON, 80- *Mem:* Am Soc Agron; Crop Sci Soc Am. *Res:* Increasing crop production through understanding crop growth and its relationship to photosynthesis, plant morphogenesis and the environment of the crop community. *Mailing Add:* Dept of Agron Iowa State Univ Ames IA 50011

PEARCE, THOMAS HULME, b Ottawa, Ont, Mar 20, 38. PETROLOGY, GEOCHEMISTRY. *Educ:* Carleton Univ, BSc, 61; Univ Western Ont, MSc, 63; Queen's Univ, Ont, PhD(geol), 67. *Prof Exp:* Nat Res Coun Can fel, Univ Manchester, 67-69 & Univ Western Ont, 69-70; asst prof geol, Univ Ga, 70-72; asst prof, 72-76, ASSOC PROF GEOL, DEPT GEOL SCI, QUEEN'S UNIV, ONT, 76- *Mem:* AAAS; Geol Asn Can; Mineral Asn Can; fel Geol Soc Am; Mineral Soc Am. *Res:* Petrogenesis; major element igneous geochemistry; variation diagrams; mechanisms of differentiation; experimental petrology; field problems; scale model theory; computer simulation; liquid lines of descent. *Mailing Add:* Dept Geol Sci Queen's Univ Kingston ON K7L 3N6 Can

PEARCY, CARL MARK, JR, b Beaumont, Tex, Aug 23, 35. MATHEMATICS. *Educ:* Tex A&M Univ, BA, 54, MS, 56; Rice Univ, PhD(math), 60. *Prof Exp:* Fel math, Rice Univ, 60-61; res engr, Humble Oil & Refining Co, 61-63; Hildebrant res instr math, Univ Mich, 63-64, asst prof, 64-65; vis assoc prof, Univ Miami, 65-66; assoc prof, 66-68, PROF MATH, UNIV MICH, ANN ARBOR, 68- *Concurrent Pos:* Sloan Found res fel math, 66-68; distinguished vis prof, Bucknell Univ, 72-; ed, Am Math Soc Surv Vol 13, 74. *Mem:* Am Math Soc. *Res:* Theory of linear operators on Hilbert space; numerical solution of partial differential equations. *Mailing Add:* Dept of Math Univ of Mich Ann Arbor MI 48104

PEARCY, ROBERT WOODWELL, b Boston, Mass, Aug 28, 41; m 65. PLANT ECOLOGY, PLANT PHYSIOLOGY. *Educ:* Univ Mont, BS, 63, MS, 65; Colo State Univ, PhD(bot), 69. *Prof Exp:* Fel plant physiol, Dept Plant Biol, Carnegie Inst, 69-71; asst prof biol sci, State Univ NY Albany, 71-75; asst prof, 76-78, ASSOC PROF BOT, UNIV CALIF, DAVIS, 78- *Mem:* AAAS; Ecol Soc Am; Am Soc Plant Physiologists. *Res:* Physiological and biochemical basis for adaptation to environment in plants; comparative physiology of photosynthesis and respiration in ecospecies and ecotypes. *Mailing Add:* Dept of Bot Univ of Calif Davis CA 95616

PEARCY, WILLIAM GORDON, b Evanston, Ill, Oct 14, 29; m 57; c 3. ANIMAL ECOLOGY, BIOLOGICAL OCEANOGRAPHY. *Educ:* Iowa State Univ, BS, 51, MS, 52; Yale Univ, PhD(ecol, oceanog), 60. *Prof Exp:* From asst prof to assoc prof, 60-70, PROF BIOL OCEANOG, ORE STATE UNIV, 70- *Mem:* AAAS; Am Soc Limnol & Oceanog; Am Soc Zoologists; Am Soc Naturalists. *Res:* Ecology, behavior and distribution of marine nekton; estuarine ecology; marine biology. *Mailing Add:* Dept of Oceanog Ore State Univ Corvallis OR 97331

PEARD, WILLIAM JOHN, b Chicago, Ill, Nov 28, 28; m 51; c 4. INORGANIC CHEMISTRY, ANALYTICAL CHEMISTRY. *Educ:* Northwestern Univ, BS, 51; Univ Iowa, MS, 55, PhD(anal chem), 57. *Prof Exp:* Anal chemist, US Steel Corp, 51; res chemist, Dow Chem Co, 56; res chemist, 57-60, group leader inorg res, 61-64, anal supvr res & develop, 64-67, asst dir res, 67-73, lab mgr, 73-77, MGR, ENVIRON AFFAIRS, PPG INDUSTS, 77- *Mem:* Am Chem Soc. *Res:* Inorganic solution chemistry; coordination compounds; transition metal chemistry. *Mailing Add:* 5009 W St Charles Pl Lake Charles LA 70605

PEARDON, DAVID LEE, b Eagle, Wis, Mar 26, 32; m 63; c 2. VETERINARY SCIENCE. *Educ:* Univ Wis, BS, 58, MS, 60, PhD(vet sci), 62. *Prof Exp:* Res parasitologist, Ralston Purina Co, 62-66; res assoc, Whitmoyer Labs, Inc, Pa, 66-69; lab head, 69-73, proj leader, 73-78, sr res assoc, 78-79, SR SCIENTIST, RES LABS, ROHM AND HAAS CO, 79- *Mem:* Am Soc Parasitologists; Am Asn Vet Parasitologists. *Res:* Development of veterinary parasiticides and experimental application of such products. *Mailing Add:* Res Labs Rohm and Haas Co Norristown & McKean Rds Spring House PA 19477

PEARINCOTT, JOSEPH V, b Travancore, India, May 26, 29; US citizen; m 58; c 1. PHYSIOLOGY, ZOOLOGY. *Educ:* Univ Travancore, India, BSc, 49; Aligarh Muslim Univ, MSc, 51; Fordham Univ, PhD(physiol), 59. *Prof Exp:* Instr biol, Fordham Univ, 52-56; fel physiol, Col Physicians & Surgeons, Columbia Univ, 59-61; res assoc physiol & pharmacol, NY Med Col, 61-62; asst prof, 62-68, ASSOC PROF PHYSIOL, NORTHEASTERN UNIV, 68- *Mem:* AAAS; Am Soc Zool; Entom Soc Am; NY Acad Sci. *Res:* Lipid metabolism; neurophysiology; cardiovascular physiology; experimental production and prevention of arteriosclerosis and atherosclerosis; carbohydrate, protein and fat metabolism during insect metamorphosis. *Mailing Add:* 61 Webb St Lexington MA 02173

PEARL, GARY STEVEN, b New York, NY, Dec 4, 49; m 74; c 2. NEUROSCIENCES, NEOPLASIA. *Educ:* Oberlin Col, BA & MA, 71; Emory Univ, PhD(anat), 76, MD, 77, Am Bd Path, dipl. *Prof Exp:* Fel neurosci, Dept Anat, 71-77, resident, 77-81, ASSOC DEPT PATH, EMORY UNIV, 81- *Mem:* NY Acad Sci. *Res:* Mechanisms of glial neoplasia, using experimental tumors and transplantation of human tumors in nude mice; evaluation of gonadal steroids and receptors in tumors, with emphasis on their role in proliferation and differentiation. *Mailing Add:* Dept Path Emory Univ Atlanta GA 30322

PEARL, HARRY AARON, b New York, NY, Aug 10, 14; m 44. MATERIALS SCIENCES, PHYSICAL CHEMISTRY. *Educ:* Brooklyn Col, BS, 34; Polytech Inst Brooklyn, MS, 38. *Prof Exp:* Res chemist, org, biol & phys chem, Harry Caplin Res Labs, 34-36; teacher chem, Brooklyn Tech High Sch, 37-38; chief technician labs, Welfare Hosp, New York, 38-40; chemist, Phys & Chem Test Labs, 40-42; prin electrician radar, 42-43, chemist, fuels & lubricants, Mat Labs, 43-44, phys chemist, rocket propulsion, Rocket Propulsion Labs, 44-45, chief dielec mat, Wright Air Develop Ctr, US Air Force, 45-53; engr, semiconductors, Motorola, 53-54; chief, Mat Eng & Res Labs, Bell Aircraft Corp, 54-60; supvr engr mat & chem, 60-61, chief, Appl Res & Develop Ctr, 61-65; res engr mat, 66-69, chief, Mat Div, Weapons Res & Eng Sta, 69-74, SR RES ENGR MATS & CHEM, NAVAL UNDERWATER SYST CTR, 74- *Concurrent Pos:* US Air Forces Rep, Dept of Defense, Nat Res & Develop Bd, 47-52, alt rep, Radome Panel, 48-51;

consult, Nat Acad Sci, Mat Adv Bd, 63-66; US Rep Int Res & Develop Torpedo Comt, US & France, 72-77, US & Fed Repub Ger, 69-77. *Res:* Metals, plastics, liquids, composites, coatings, structures; thermal, acoustic, electronic, hydrodynamic, chemical, mechanical behavior; propulsion, detection, guidance control, communication; supersonic aircraft; manned, unmanned aerospace and underwater missiles, vehicles, stations; medical-chemistry. *Mailing Add:* US Naval Underwater Syst Ctr Newport Labs Code 3662 Newport RI 02840

PEARL, IRWIN ALBERT, b Seattle, Wash, Dec 25, 13; m 38; c 2. WOOD CHEMISTRY. *Educ:* Univ Wash, BS, 34, MS, 35, PhD(org chem), 37. *Prof Exp:* Res assoc org chem, Univ Wash, 37-41; res assoc, 41-55, sr res assoc org chem, Inst Paper Chem, 55-76; CHEM CONSULT TO FOREST PROD INDUST, 77- *Concurrent Pos:* Anal chemist, NCent Labs, Wash, 37; supvr lab, State Dept Conserv & Develop, Wash, 38-40; consult, Environ Protection Agency. *Mem:* Am Chem Soc; Tech Asn Pulp & Paper Indust; Electrochem Soc; fel NY Acad Sci; Phytochem Soc NAm. *Res:* Utilization of sulfite waste liquor; chemistry of vanillin and its derivatives; pulp mill pollution; chemicals from wood; chemistry of hardwoods; hardwood extractives and bark; pulp and paper mill effluent analysis. *Mailing Add:* 2115 N Linwood Appleton WI 54911

PEARL, JOHN CHRISTOPHER, b Ann Arbor, Mich, Dec 31, 38; m 63; c 2. PLANETARY SATELLITES. *Educ:* Univ Mich, BSE, 61, MS, 63, PhD(physics), 70. *Prof Exp:* Asst res physicist, Space Physics Res Lab, Univ Mich, Ann Arbor, 59-61 & 62-70; AEROSPACE TECHNOLOGIST SPACE SCI, GODDARD SPACE FLIGHT CTR, NASA, 70- *Mem:* Am Phys Soc; Am Geophys Union; Am Astron Soc. *Res:* Determination of thermal and reflective characteristics; chemical composition; evolution of planets and satellites. *Mailing Add:* Mail Code 693 2 Goddard Space Flight Ctr NASA Greenbelt MD 20771

PEARL, JUDEA, b Tel-Aviv, Israel, Sept 4, 36; US citizen; m 60; c 3. HEURISTIC PROGRAMMING, COMPUTER-BASED DECISION-AIDS. *Educ:* Israel Inst Technol, BSc, 60; Newark Col Eng, MSc, 61; Rutgers Univ, MSc, 65; Polytech Inst Brooklyn, PhD(elec eng), 65. *Prof Exp:* Res engr, Dent Sch, NY Univ, 60-61; mem tech staff, RCA Res Labs, 61-65; dir advan memory devices, Electronic Memories, Inc, Calif, 66-69; PROF ENG SYSTS & COMPUT SCI, UNIV CALIF, LOS ANGELES, 69- *Concurrent Pos:* Instr, Newark Col Eng, 61; consult, Ranch Corp, 72 & Integrated Sci Corp, 75. *Mem:* Inst Elec & Electronics Engrs. *Res:* Superconductivity; computer memories; artificial intelligence; simulation of perceptual, cognitive and decision making processes; pattern recognition; complexity of computations. *Mailing Add:* 3545 Ballina Canyon Rd Encino CA 91436

PEARL, MARTIN HERBERT, b New York, NY, June 19, 28. MATHEMATICS. *Educ:* Brooklyn Col, BA, 50; Univ Mich, MA, 51; Univ Wis, PhD(math), 55. *Prof Exp:* Analyst, Nat Security Agency, 55-56; instr math, Univ Rochester, 56-57; res assoc, Nat Res Coun-Nat Bur Standards, 57-58; from asst prof to assoc prof, 58-67, PROF MATH, UNIV MD, COLLEGE PARK, 67- *Concurrent Pos:* Consult, Gen Res & Develop, Inc, 60-61 & Walter Reed Army Med Ctr, 64-67; vis lectr, Imp Col, Univ London, 64-65; mathematician, Nat Bur Standards, 67- *Mem:* Am Math Soc; Soc Indust & Appl Math. *Res:* Algebra; statistics; matrix theory; game theory and linear programming; applications of matrix theory; generalized inverses; applications to statistics. *Mailing Add:* Dept of Math Univ of Md College Park MD 20742

PEARL, W(ESLEY) L(LOYD), b Seattle, Wash, July 10, 21; m 42; c 4. CHEMICAL ENGINEERING. *Educ:* Univ Wash, BS, 42; Inst Paper Chem, Lawrence Col, MS, 48, PhD(paper chem), 51. *Prof Exp:* Proj engr, Longview Fibre Co, Wash, 51-52; chem engr, Hanford Works, Gen Elec Co, 52-55, mgr chem eng develop subsect, Atomic Power Equip Dept, 55-74; PRES, NWT CORP, 74- *Concurrent Pos:* Consult. *Mem:* Am Soc Mech Engrs; Am Nuclear Soc; Nat Asn Corrosion Engrs; Am Inst Chem Engrs. *Res:* Research and development in corrosion, water chemistry, water treatment and liquid, solid and gaseous radioactive wastes. *Mailing Add:* NWT Corp 7015 Realm Dr San Jose CA 95119

PEARL, WILLIAM, b Hungary, Apr 15, 20; nat US; m 49; c 2. PHYSIOLOGY, PHARMACOLOGY. *Educ:* NY Univ, PhD(biol), 60. *Prof Exp:* Res scientist physiol, Warner-Lambert Res Inst Div, Warner-Hudnut, Inc, 59-61; Nat Heart Inst res fel path, Sch Med, NY Univ, 61-63; res scientist, 63-76, MED ED, DEPT MED COMMUN, LEDERLE LABS, AM CYANAMID CO, PEARL RIVER, 76- *Mem:* AAAS; Am Physiol Soc; Histochem Soc; NY Acad Sci. *Res:* Cellular physiology; homogenization techniques; fractionation of subcellular particles by differential centrifugation; cytochemical analysis; distribution and interaction of nucleoprotein particles; biochemical pathology and pharmacology; enzyme parameters of disease; metabolic regulators. *Mailing Add:* 38 Lyncrest Dr Monsey NY 10952

PEARLE, PHILIP MARK, b Bronx, NY, Sept 24, 36; m 59; c 2. THEORETICAL PHYSICS. *Educ:* Mass Inst Technol, BS, 57, MS, 58, PhD(physics), 63. *Prof Exp:* Instr physics, Harvard Univ, 64-66; asst prof physics, Case Western Reserve Univ, 66-69; assoc prof, 69-77, PROF PHYSICS, HAMILTON COL, 77- *Concurrent Pos:* Fel, Univ Geneva, 73-74. *Mem:* Am Phys Soc. *Res:* Foundations of quantum mechanics; classical mechanics, classical electromagnetism, and general relativity. *Mailing Add:* Dept of Physics Hamilton Col Clinton NY 13323

PEARLMAN, ALAN L, b Des Moines, Iowa, June 30, 36; m 57; c 3. NEUROBIOLOGY, NEUROLOGY. *Educ:* State Univ Iowa, AB, 58; Washington Univ, MD, 61. *Prof Exp:* USPHS physiologist neurophysiol, NIMH, Bethesda, 62-64; resident neurol, Harvard Med Sch & Mass Gen Hosp, 64-67; asst prof, 69-73, asst neurologist, Barnes Hosp, St Louis, 69-73, assoc prof neurol & physiol, 73-79, assoc neurologist, 73-79; assoc prof neurol & physiol, 73-79, PROF NEUROL & PHYSIOL, SCH MED, WASHINGTON UNIV, 79-; NEUROLOGIST, BARNES HOSP, ST LOUIS, 79- *Concurrent Pos:* USPHS & Nat Inst Neurol Dis & Stroke res fel neurobiol, Harvard Med Sch, 67-69; USPHS & Nat Eye Inst res grant neurol & physiol, Sch Med, Washington Univ, 70- *Mem:* Am Neurol Asn; Soc Neurosci; Am Acad Neurologists; Asn Res Vision & Ophthal; Am Physiol Soc. *Res:* Neural organization and development of the visual system. *Mailing Add:* Dept of Neurol Washington Univ Sch of Med St Louis MO 63110

PEARLMAN, BRUCE A, b Feb 18, 49. SYNTHETIC ORGANIC CHEMISTRY. *Educ:* Harvard Univ, AB, 71; Columbia Univ, PhD(chem), 76. *Prof Exp:* NIH res fel, Dept Chem, Harvard Univ, 76-79; RES SCIENTIST CHEM PROCESS RES & DEVELOP UNIT, UPJOHN CO, 79- *Mem:* Am Chem Soc. *Res:* New methods for synthesis of pharmaceuticals. *Mailing Add:* 1500-91-1 Upjohn Co Kalamazoo MI 49001

PEARLMAN, MICHAEL R, b Boston, Mass, Aug 21, 41; m 64; c 2. INSTRUMENTATION, ELECTRONICS. *Educ:* Mass Inst Technol, SB, 63, SM, 80; Tufts Univ, PhD(physics) 63. *Prof Exp:* SCIENTIST, SMITHSONIAN ASTROPHYS OBSERV, CAMBRIDGE, 68-; RES ASSOC, HARVARD COL OBSERV, 69- *Concurrent Pos:* Vis scientist, Off Geod Satellites, NASA, 71-72. *Mem:* Inst Elec & Electronics Engrs; Am Phys Soc; Am Geophys Union. *Res:* Optics and electronics; applications to satellite tracking for geodesy and geophysics; atmospheric effects on optical and radio wave propagation; solid state physics and lasers. *Mailing Add:* Smithsonian Astron Observ Mass Inst Technol 60 Garden St Cambridge MA 02138

PEARLMAN, NORMAN, b New York, NY, Aug 2, 22; m 46; c 3. SOLID STATE PHYSICS. *Educ:* City Col New York, BS, 42; Univ Chicago, SM, 49; Purdue Univ, PhD(physics), 52. *Prof Exp:* Jr mathematician, Signal Corps Radar Labs, NJ, 42-43; assoc mathematician, Metall Lab, Univ Chicago, 44-46, asst physics, 47-52; from asst to assoc prof, 54-69, PROF PHYSICS, PURDUE UNIV, WEST LAFAYETTE, 69- *Mem:* AAAS; Am Phys Soc; Am Asn Physics Teachers. *Res:* Low temperature calorimetry; electrical and thermal transport phenomena. *Mailing Add:* Dept of Physics Purdue Univ West Lafayette IN 47907

PEARLMAN, RODNEY, b Melbourne, Australia, May 29, 51. PHARMACEUTICAL CHEMISTRY. *Educ:* Victorian Col Pharm, Melbourne, BPharm, 73; Univ Kans, MS, 76, PhD(pharmaceut chem), 79. *Prof Exp:* Sr pharmaceut chemist, Eli Lilly & Co, 78-81; ASST PROF PHARMACEUT, COL PHARM, UNIV TEX, AUSTIN, 81- *Mem:* Acad Pharmaceut Sci. *Res:* Synthesis and evaluation of drugs; molecular orbital analysis of pharmaceutical agents; physical and organic chemistry of drug degradation; lymphatic absorption of drugs; pharmaceut formulation; peptide stability. *Mailing Add:* Col Pharm Univ Tex Austin TX 78712

PEARLMAN, RONALD C, b Brooklyn, NY, Aug 8, 44; c 2. AUDIOLOGY, SPEECH PATHOLOGY. *Educ:* L I Univ, BA, 67, MS, 70; Univ Mo-Columbia, PhD(audiol), 74. *Prof Exp:* Speech pathologist, West Islip Sch Syst, 67-71; teaching asst speech path & audiol, Univ Mo, 71-73; trainee audiol, Vet Admin Hosp, Columbia, Mo, 73-74; asst prof speech path & audiol, 77-78, ASSOC PROF AUDIOL, HOWARD UNIV, 78- *Mem:* Am Speech & Hearing Asn; Am Audiol Soc; Soc Med Audiol. *Res:* Acoustic impedance of the tympanic membrane; clinical audiology; hearing aids. *Mailing Add:* Dept Commun Arts & Sci Lock Hall Rm 230 Howard Univ Washington DC 20059

PEARLMAN, RONALD E, b Calgary, Alta, Dec 22, 41. MOLECULAR BIOLOGY. *Educ:* McGill Univ, BSc, 61; Harvard Univ, MSc & PhD(biochem), 66. *Prof Exp:* Nat Res Coun Can res fel biochem, Biol Inst, Carlsberg Found, Copenhagen, Denmark, 66-68; asst prof, 68-72, assoc prof, 72-82, PROF BIOL, YORK UNIV, 82- *Concurrent Pos:* Vis prof, Biochem Inst B, Univ Copenhagen, 75-76. *Res:* Enzymology of nucleic acid metabolism; replication, transcription and translation of genetic information and its control; structure, function and organization of eukaryotic genes. *Mailing Add:* Dept of Biol York Univ Toronto ON M3J 1P3 Can

PEARLMAN, SHOLOM, b Ottawa, Ont, July 3, 19; nat US; m 45; c 7. DENTISTRY. *Educ:* Univ Toronto, DDS, 45; Western Reserve Univ, MS, 51. *Prof Exp:* Res asst biochem, Sch Med, Western Reserve Univ, 48-51, asst prof, 51, instr, Sch Dent, 49-51; asst secy, Coun Dent Therapeut, Am Dent Asn, 51-59, secy, Coun Dent Res, 59-68; dir prog develop, 68-75, PROF DENT, SCH DENT, UNIV COLO MED CTR, DENVER, 68- *Concurrent Pos:* mem div med sci, Nat Res Coun, 59-68; spec adv, White House Conf on Aging, 61; mem adv comt sci publ, USPHS, 62-67; mem comt res manpower, Nat Inst Dent Res, 64-65; spec adv dent res, WHO, 65; mem adv bd, Oral Res Abstr, 65-; consult adv screening comt med sci, Comt Int Exchange of Persons, 71-; consult prof adv bd, Colo Migrant Coun, 72-75; mem, Biomed Libr Rev Comt, Nat Libr Med, USPHS, 75-79; vis prof, Pahlavi Univ, Shiraz, Iran, 77-78; assoc ed, Community Dent & Oral Epidemiol, 80- *Mem:* Fel AAAS; fel Am Col Dent; Am Dent Asn; Int Asn Dent Res; Int Dent Fedn. *Res:* Academic and research administration; experimental design; social aspects of health care; health education; public and community health. *Mailing Add:* Sch of Dent Univ of Colo Med Ctr Denver CO 80220

PEARLMAN, WILLIAM HENRY, b New York, NY, Mar 2, 14; m 43. BIOCHEMISTRY. *Educ:* Brooklyn Col, BS, 34; Columbia Univ, PhD(biochem), 40. *Prof Exp:* Res assoc biochem, Clark Univ, 40-44; asst prof, Princeton Univ, 44-45; res assoc, Jefferson Med Col, 45-46, from asst prof to assoc prof, 46-53; res assoc biochem, Harvard Med Sch, 59-61, asst prof biol chem, 61-68; mem staff, Lab Reproductive Biol, 70-81, prof, 69-81, EMER PROF PHARMACOL, SCH MED, UNIV NC, CHAPEL HILL, 81- *Concurrent Pos:* Brit Med Res Coun grant chem & biochem, Guy's Hosp Med Sch, London, 54-57; assoc, Peter Bent Brigham Hosp, 59-68; mem adv panel rev contraceptives & other vaginal prod, Food & Drug Admin, 73-78. *Mem:* AAAS; Am Soc Biol Chemists; Endocrine Soc; Brit Biochem Soc; Brit Soc Endocrinol. *Res:* Cancer; steroid-protein interactions; biochemistry of steroid hormones. *Mailing Add:* Dept Pharmacol 1128 FLOB 231H Univ NC Sch Med Chapel Hill NC 27514

PEARLMUTTER, ANNE FRANCES, b Chelsea, Mass, Oct 28, 40; m 60; c 2. BIOCHEMISTRY. *Educ:* Tulane Univ La, BS, 62; Case Western Reserve Univ, MA, 67, PhD(chem), 69. *Prof Exp:* Teaching assoc, 69-72, instr, 72-74, asst prof, 74-79, ASSOC PROF BIOCHEM, MED COL OHIO, 80- *Mem:* Endocrine Soc; Am Soc Biol Chemists; AAAS; Am Chem Soc. *Res:* Endocrinology; mechanism of steroidogenesis; fast kinetic processes in biochemistry; role of metal ions in biological systems; hormone-protein and hormone-receptor interactions; brain hormone mechanisms of action. *Mailing Add:* Dept of Biochem Med Col of Ohio CS 10008 Toledo OH 43699

PEARLSON, WILBUR H, b Los Angeles, Calif, Oct 19, 15; m 44; c 4. CHEMISTRY. *Educ:* Univ Calif, BS, 38; Pa State Col, PhD(org chem), 43. *Prof Exp:* Res assoc, USDA, Univ Calif, 38-40; from instr to asst prof chem, Pa State Col, 43-47; CHEMIST, MINN MINING & MFG CO, 47- *Mem:* AAAS; Am Chem Soc. *Res:* Organofluorine compounds; mechanism of alkylation reaction; epoxy and phenolic resins; aziridine; urethane resins; patent liaison; regulatory affairs. *Mailing Add:* 3M Ctr 223-6SE 2501 Hudson Rd St Paul MN 55101

PEARLSTEIN, EDGAR AARON, b Pittsburgh, Pa, Mar 19, 27; div; c 1. SOLID STATE PHYSICS. *Educ:* Carnegie Inst Technol, BSc, 47, DSc(physics), 50. *Prof Exp:* Res assoc, Univ Ill, 50-52; res physicist, Carnegie Inst Technol, 52-56; from asst prof to assoc prof, 56-63, PROF PHYSICS, UNIV NEBR-LINCOLN, 63- *Concurrent Pos:* Consult, Westinghouse Elec Corp, 56-57. *Mem:* AAAS; fel Am Phys Soc; Am Asn Physics Teachers; Fedn Am Scientists. *Res:* Radiation effects in solids; electrical and optical properties of insulating crystals. *Mailing Add:* Dept of Physics Univ of Nebr Lincoln NE 68588

PEARLSTEIN, LEON DONALD, b Los Angeles, Calif, Dec 10, 32; m 59; c 2. THEORETICAL PHYSICS. *Educ:* City Col New York, BS, 53; Univ Pa, PhD(physics), 59. *Prof Exp:* Instr physics, Fla State Univ, 58-60; staff mem, Gen Atomic Div, Gen Dynamics Corp, Calif, 60-70; MEM STAFF, LAWRENCE LIVERMORE LAB, 70- *Mem:* Am Phys Soc. *Res:* Theoretical plasma physics applied to controlled thermonuclear research and space physics. *Mailing Add:* Lawrence Livermore Lab 388 PO Box 808 Livermore CA 94550

PEARLSTEIN, ROBERT DAVID, b Gary, Ind, July 20, 49; m 78. INSTRUMENTATION DESIGN. *Educ:* Univ Mo, BA, 71; Univ NC, MS, 77, PhD(bioeng), 82. *Prof Exp:* Lab instr, Dept Elec Eng, Univ Mo, 71-72; res asst physiol, 75-78, RES ASSOC MED, DEPT SURG, DUKE MED CTR & RES ASSOC BIOPHYSICS, SPETNAGEL LAB, DUKE UNIV, 78- *Mem:* AAAS. *Res:* Thermodynamics of energy transduction in mitochondria, with special reference to respiratory chain behavior at low oxygen tension; development of clinical monitoring instrumentation. *Mailing Add:* Duke Med Ctr Box 3807 Durham NC 27710

PEARLSTEIN, ROBERT MILTON, b New York, NY, Oct 16, 37; m 60; c 2. BIOPHYSICS, CHEMICAL PHYSICS. *Educ:* Harvard Univ, BA, 60; Univ Md, PhD(physics), 66. *Prof Exp:* Physicist, Marine Biol Lab, Woods Hole, Mass, 62-63; NSF fel photosynthesis, Biol Div, 66-67, res staff mem, 67-75, group leader photosynthesis, 72-75, res staff mem chem div, 75-78, coordr solar energy res, Oak Ridge Nat Lab, 75-76, prin res scientist, 78-79, SR RES SCIENTIST, CHEM DEPT, BATTELLE COLUMBUS LABS, 79- *Concurrent Pos:* Lectr, Oak Ridge Biomed Grad Sch, Univ Tenn, 69-78; mem hon ed bd, Photochem & Photobiol, 71-73; assoc ed, Biophys J, 81- *Mem:* Fel Am Phys Soc; Biophys Soc; AAAS; Am Soc Photobiol; Sigma Xi. *Res:* Natural and artificial photosynthesis, photochemical conversion of solar energy, chlorophyll chemistry, electronic excited-state energy transfer and exciton transport in bio-organic systems. *Mailing Add:* Chem Dept Battelle Columbus Labs 505 King Ave Columbus OH 43201

PEARLSTEIN, SOL, b Brooklyn, NY, Feb 21, 30; m 51; c 3. NUCLEAR PHYSICS. *Educ:* Polytech Inst Brooklyn, BS, 51; NY Univ, MS, 53; Rensselaer Polytech Inst, PhD(physics), 64. *Prof Exp:* Physicist, Knolls Atomic Power Lab, Gen Elec Co, 52-64; physicist, 64-68, DIR NAT NUCLEAR DATA CTR, BROOKHAVEN NAT LAB, 68- *Concurrent Pos:* Chmn, Cross Sect Eval Working Group, 66-; mem adv comt reactor physics, US Dept Energy, 70-, mem nuclear data comt, 74- *Mem:* Am Nuclear Soc; Am Phys Soc. *Res:* Nuclear data; shielding; reactor theory; critical experiments; data management. *Mailing Add:* Nat Nuclear Data Ctr Brookhaven Nat Lab Upton NY 11973

PEARMAN, G TIMOTHY, b Cape Giradeau, Mo, June 27, 40; m 62; c 1. ACOUSTICS. *Educ:* Cent Methodist Col, BA, 62; Univ Mo, MS, 64, PhD(physics), 67. *Prof Exp:* MEM TECH STAFF, BELL LABS, 67- *Mem:* Inst Elec & Electronics Engrs; Am Phys Soc; Sigma Xi. *Res:* Piezoelectric devices. *Mailing Add:* Bell Labs 555 Union Blvd Allentown PA 18193

PEARRE, SIFFORD, JR, b Baltimore, Md, July 21, 34; m 70; c 2. ZOOPLANKTON ECOLOGY. *Educ:* Univ Va, BS, 57; Dalhousie Univ, Can, MSc, 64, PhD(oceanog), 70. *Prof Exp:* Asst prof zool, Univ NC, 71-73; consult, Marine ecol, Environ Concern, Inc, 73-75 & Plankton Lab, Normandeau Assoc, Inc, 75-76; RES ASSOC OCEANOG, DALHOUSIE UNIV, 76- *Mem:* Am Soc Limnol & Oceanog. *Res:* Food selection, energetics, predation and the influence of various factors on diel vertical migration of zooplankton; chaetognatha, planktonic carnivores. *Mailing Add:* Dept Oceanog Dalhousie Univ Halifax NS B3H 4J1 Can

PEARS, COULTAS D, b Clarksburg, WVa, Feb 7, 25; m 49; c 3. MECHANICAL ENGINEERING. *Educ:* Tulane Univ, BEngMech, 46. *Prof Exp:* Asst head eng, Appalachian Exp Sta, US Bur Mines, 47-57, supt underground gasification, Gorgas Exp Sta, 57; HEAD, DEPT MECH ENG, SOUTHERN RES INST, 57- *Concurrent Pos:* Spec consult, Ala Power Co, 58-63. *Res:* Analysis and evaluation of materials for special application under extreme environments of temperature, vacuum, pressure and chemistry; thermal and stress analysis of systems. *Mailing Add:* Southern Res Inst 2000 Ninth Ave S Birmingham AL 35205

PEARSALL, GEORGE W(ILBUR), b Brentwood, NY, July 13, 33; m 62. MATERIALS SCIENCE, METALLURGY. *Educ:* Rensselaer Polytech Inst, BMetE, 55; Mass Inst Technol, ScD(metall), 61. *Prof Exp:* Res engr metall, Dow Chem Co, Mich, 55-57; asst prof, Mass Inst Technol, 60-64; assoc prof, 64-66, actg dean, 69-71, dean, Sch Eng, 71-74, PROF MECH ENG, DUKE UNIV, 66-, PROF MAT SCI, 80- *Mem:* AAAS; Am Inst Mining, Metall & Petrol Engrs; Am Soc Metals; Am Soc Mech Engrs; Am Soc Testing & Mat. *Res:* Development of materials and processes; deformation behavior of materials; microstructural mechanics; nonlinear properties of alloys and polymers; failure analysis; biomechanics; resource conservation; product design. *Mailing Add:* Sch of Eng Duke Univ Durham NC 27706

PEARSALL, MARION, b Brooklyn, NY, Apr 27, 23. MEDICAL ANTHROPOLOGY, APPLIED ANTHROPOLOGY. *Educ:* Univ NMex, AB, 44; Univ Calif, Berkeley, PhD(anthrop), 50. *Prof Exp:* Asst prof anthrop, Univ Ala, 52-56; Russell Sage Found Social Sci Residency grant, Boston Area Hosps, 56-58; assoc prof rural sociol, 58-60, assoc prof behav sci, Med Ctr, 60-64, PROF BEHAV SCI, MED CTR, UNIV KY, 64- *Mem:* Fel AAAS; fel Am Anthrop Asn; fel Soc Appl Anthrop; fel Royal Anthrop Inst Gt Brit & Ireland; Soc Med Anthrop (pres, 73-74). *Res:* Study of cultures of the American South, especially Appalachia, and of health professions with emphasis on behavioral factors in the organizations, delivery of health services under changing conditions, that is, applied medical behavioral science; cultural bases of health and health care systems, especially in southeastern United States. *Mailing Add:* Dept of Behav Sci Univ of Ky Lexington KY 40506

PEARSALL, S(AMUEL) H(AFF), b Guthrie, Ky, July 17, 23; m 46; c 4. ELECTRICAL ENGINEERING. *Educ:* Vanderbilt Univ, BE, 48, MS, 58. *Prof Exp:* Engr, WSM, Inc, 48-56; assoc prof elec eng, Vanderbilt Univ, 56-64; vpres, R W Benson & Assoc, 64-71; vpres, Bonitron, Inc, 66-71; V PRES, CUTTERS EXCHANGE & CUTTERS ELECTRONICS INT, 71- *Concurrent Pos:* Consult, Temco Corp, Avco Corp, E I du Pont de Nemours & Co, Inc, Army Ballistic Missile Agency & NASA; pres, White Owl Systs, Inc. *Mem:* Sr mem Inst Elec & Electronics Engrs; sr mem Soc Mfg Engrs. *Res:* Industrial control systems. *Mailing Add:* Cutters Electronic Int 706 19th Ave N Nashville TN 37203

PEARSE, GEORGE ANCELL, JR, b Stoneham, Mass, May 18, 30; m 53; c 5. ANALYTICAL CHEMISTRY. *Educ:* Univ Mass, BS, 52; Purdue Univ, MS, 56; Univ Iowa, PhD(chem), 59. *Prof Exp:* Sr chemist, E I du Pont de Nemours & Co, Inc, 59-60; from asst prof to assoc prof, 60-70, actg chmn dept chem, 65-66, chmn dept, 66-72, PROF CHEM, LE MOYNE COL, NY, 70- *Concurrent Pos:* Vis res prof, Stockholm Univ, Sweden, 78-79. *Mem:* Am Chem Soc. *Res:* Coordination chemistry; absorption spectrophotometry; synthesis of analytic-organic reagents and ligands; use of nonaqueous solvents; instrumental methods of analysis. *Mailing Add:* Dept of Chem Le Moyne Col Syracuse NY 13214

PEARSE, JOHN STUART, b Boise, Idaho, May 28, 36; m 70; c 1. MARINE BIOLOGY. *Educ:* Univ Chicago, BS, 58; Stanford Univ, PhD(biol), 65. *Prof Exp:* Asst, Antarctic Deep Freeze, 60-62; asst prof biol, Am Univ Cairo, 65-68; res fel, Calif Inst Technol, 68-71; asst prof, 71-74, assoc prof, 74-78, PROF BIOL, UNIV CALIF, SANTA CRUZ, 78- *Concurrent Pos:* Jr scientist, Te Vega Exped, 65, sr scientist, 68; ed, Marine Biol, 74-76; course dir, Bermuda Biol Sta, 80-81. *Honors & Awards:* Antarctic Serv Award. *Mem:* AAAS; Ecol Soc Am; Am Soc Zoologists; Am Inst Biol Sci; Western Soc Naturalists. *Res:* Reproduction of marine invertebrates; photoperiodism; echinoderm biology; ecology of kelp forests. *Mailing Add:* Ctr for Coastal Marine Studies Univ of Calif Santa Cruz CA 95064

PEARSE, VICKI BUCHSBAUM, b Dec 17, 42; US citizen; m 70; c 1. INVERTEBRATE ZOOLOGY, PHYCOLOGY. *Educ:* Stanford Univ, AB, 63, PhD(biol), 68. *Prof Exp:* NIH res fel zool, Univ Calif, Los Angeles, 68-69; instr, Univ Calif, Irvine, 69-70; res fel, Calif Inst Technol, 70; RES ASSOC BIOL, UNIV CALIF, SANTA CRUZ, 72- *Mem:* Am Soc Zoologists; Western Soc Naturalists. *Res:* Development, maintenance and physiology of symbiotic relationships; calcification; reproduction of marine invertebrates; photoperiodism. *Mailing Add:* Ctr for Coastal Marine Studies Univ of Calif Santa Cruz CA 95064

PEARSE, WARREN HARLAND, b Detroit, Mich, Sept 28, 27; m 50; c 4. OBSTETRICS & GYNECOLOGY. *Educ:* Mich State Univ, BS, 48; Northwestern Univ, MB, 50, MD, 51; Am Bd Obstet & Gynec, dipl, 60. *Prof Exp:* Resident obstet & gynec, Univ Mich, 50-53, 55-56; instr, Col Med, Univ Nebr, Omaha, 59-61, from asst prof to prof, 61-71, chmn dept, 62-71, asst dean, 63-71; dean, Med Col Va, 71-75; EXEC DIR, AM COL OBSTETRICIANS & GYNECOLOGISTS, 75- *Concurrent Pos:* Examr, Am Bd Obstet & Gynec, 60- *Mem:* Am Col Obstetricians & Gynecologists. *Res:* Obstetric manpower; physiology of labor. *Mailing Add:* Am Col of Obstet & Gynec 600 Md Ave Southwest Washington DC 20020

PEARSON, ALBERT MARCHANT, b Oakley, Utah, Sept 3, 16; m 46; c 5. FOOD SCIENCE. *Educ:* Utah State Univ, BS, 40; Iowa State Univ, MS, 41; Cornell Univ, PhD(animal husb), 49. *Prof Exp:* Asst, Iowa State Univ, 40-41 & Cornell Univ, 46-49; from asst prof to assoc prof animal husb, Univ Fla, 49-54; assoc prof, 54-59, PROF FOOD SCI, MICH STATE UNIV, 59- *Concurrent Pos:* Fulbright fel, Meat Indust Res Inst NZ, 71-72. *Honors & Awards:* Morrison Award, Am Soc Animal Sci, 72. *Mem:* Am Soc Animal Sci; Inst Food Technol; Am Inst Nutrit; Am Meat Sci Asn. *Res:* Methods of measuring body composition; isolation and identification of meat flavor components; chemical changes in pre- and post-rigor muscle. *Mailing Add:* 2525 Forest Rd Lansing MI 48910

PEARSON, ALLAN EINAR, b Minneapolis, Minn, June 18, 36; m 61. ENGINEERING. *Educ:* Univ Minn, BS, 58, MS, 59; Columbia Univ, PhD(control systs), 63. *Hon Degrees:* MA, Brown Univ, 66. *Prof Exp:* From asst prof to assoc prof, 63-66, PROF ENG, BROWN UNIV, 70- *Concurrent*

Pos: Fulbright grant, 78. *Mem:* Am Soc Mech Engrs; Inst Elec & Electronics Engrs. *Res:* Automatic control systems theory, particularly the mathematical aspects of adaptive optimal control and system identification. *Mailing Add:* Div of Eng Brown Univ Providence RI 02912

PEARSON, ALLEN MOBLEY, b Mobile, Ala, Jan 14, 09; m 38; c 1. BIOLOGY. *Educ:* Ala Polytech Inst, BS, 31; Iowa State Col, MS, 32, PhD(entom), 36. *Prof Exp:* Asst biologist, Soil Conserv Serv, USDA, 35-37; assoc biologist, US Fish & Wildlife Serv, 37-43; exten specialist, Auburn Univ, 43-47; from assoc prof to prof, 47-71, EMER PROF ZOOL & ENTOM, AUBURN UNIV, 72- *Mem:* Wildlife Soc; assoc Am Soc Mammal; assoc Am Ornithologists Union. *Res:* Entomology; game management. *Mailing Add:* Rte 3 Box 246F Opelika AL 36801

PEARSON, ANTHONY AUGUSTUS, anatomy, deceased

PEARSON, ARTHUR DAVID, b Darlington, Eng, Apr 19, 32; nat US; m 55; c 3. CHEMISTRY. *Educ:* Univ Durham, BSc, 53; Mass Inst Technol, PhD(mat sci), 57. *Prof Exp:* SUPVR, BELL LABS, INC, 57- *Honors & Awards:* Forrest Award, Am Ceramic Soc, 61. *Mem:* Fel Am Ceramic Soc; Optical Soc Am. *Res:* Chemistry and physics of glasses, including chemical, physical, electrical and optical properties; properties of materials for optical waveguide applications. *Mailing Add:* Bell Labs Inc Murray Hill NJ 07974

PEARSON, BENNIE JAKE, b Austin, Tex, Aug 28, 29; m 59. MATHEMATICS. *Educ:* Univ Tex, BA, 50, PhD(math), 55. *Prof Exp:* Instr math, Ill Inst Technol, 55-57; asst prof, Kans State Univ, 57-59; from asst prof to assoc prof, 59-66, PROF MATH, UNIV MO-KANSAS CITY, 66- *Mem:* Am Math Soc; Math Asn Am; Asn Symbolic Logic. *Res:* Ordered topological spaces; continua; curves; dendrites. *Mailing Add:* 5000 Oak Kansas City MO 64112

PEARSON, CARL E, b Vitaby, Sweden, Mar 17, 22; nat US; m 53; c 3. ENGINEERING SCIENCE. *Educ:* Univ BC, BASc, 44; Brown Univ, PhD(appl math), 49. *Prof Exp:* Res assoc mech eng, Harvard Univ, 49-50, from instr to asst prof, 51-57; staff scientist, Arthur D Little, Inc, 57-62; vis prof appl math, Tech Univ Denmark, 62-63; head eng sci group, Sperry Rand Res Ctr, 63-65; chief math anal unit, Airplane Div, Boeing Co, Wash, 65-68; PROF AERONAUT & ASTRONAUT & MATH, UNIV WASH, 68- *Mem:* Am Phys Soc; Am Math Soc; Soc Indust & Appl Math. *Res:* Applied mathematics and mechanics; numerical analysis; thermodynamics; acoustics; electromagnetism; fluid mechanics; elasticity. *Mailing Add:* Guggenheim Hall Univ of Wash Seattle WA 98105

PEARSON, CARL M, b Seattle, Wash, Nov 19, 19; m 49; c 3. MEDICINE. *Educ:* Univ Calif, Los Angeles, AB, 43; Boston Univ, MD, 46. *Prof Exp:* From asst prof to assoc prof, 55-65, PROF MED, SCH MED, UNIV CALIF, LOS ANGELES, 65-, PROF RHEUMATOLOGY & CHIEF DIV, CTR HEALTH SCI, 80- *Mem:* Am Asn Physicians; Am Rheumatism Asn (pres, 77-78); Am Col Physicians; Am Fedn Clin Res; Am Soc Clin Invest. *Res:* Arthritis and rheumatic diseases; diseases and pathology of muscle. *Mailing Add:* Dept of Med Univ of Calif Sch of Med Los Angeles CA 90024

PEARSON, COLIN ARTHUR, b Armidale, Australia, Sept 1, 35; m; c 2. PHYSICS. *Educ:* Univ Sydney, BS, 56, PhD, 61. *Prof Exp:* Res assoc, Univ Sydney, 61-62; group leader nuclear physics, Australian AEC, 62-64; vis prof physics, Mass Inst Technol, 64-65; vis prof, Niels Bohr Inst, Copenhagen, 65-67; vis lectr, Univ Ariz, 67-69; assoc prof, 69-71, CLIN ASSOC PROF RADIATION ONCOL, UNIV ALA, BIRMINGHAM, 71- *Res:* Neutron physics; cosmic rays; high energy photonuclear reactions; relativistic deuteron production; neutron absorption in reactors; nuclear stripping reactions; three-body break-up and scattering; nuclear fission. *Mailing Add:* Dept of Physics Univ of Ala Birmingham AL 35299

PEARSON, DALE SHELDON, b Omaha, Nebr, Oct 4, 42; m 64; c 2. POLYMER SCIENCE, MATERIALS SCIENCE. *Educ:* Iowa State Univ, BS, 64; Univ Akron, MS, 70; Northwestern Univ, PhD(mat sci & eng), 78. *Prof Exp:* Res scientist & group leader, polymer sci & radiation res, Firestone Tire & Rubber Co, 65-74; res asst, polymer sci, Northwestern Univ, 74-78; MEM TECH STAFF, POLYMER PHYSICS, BELL LABS, 78- *Mem:* Am Chem Soc; Am Phys Soc; Soc Rheology. *Res:* Polymer physics, particularly molecular structure and mechanical properties of rubber networks and polymer melts. *Mailing Add:* 165 Blackburn Rd Summit NJ 07901

PEARSON, DANIEL BESTER, III, b Perryton, Tex, May 25, 49. PETROLEUM GEOLOGY, ORGANIC GEOCHEMISTRY. *Educ:* Rice Univ, BA, 71, MA, 73, Calif Inst Technol, MS, 74. *Prof Exp:* Petrol geochemist, source rock geochem, Superior Oil Co, 74-78; res geologist org geochem, Oil & Gas Resources Br, US Geol Surv, 78-80; mem staff, Mobil Oil Co, 80-81; CONSULT, 81- *Mem:* AAAS; Am Asn Petrol Geol; Soc Econ Paleont & Mineral; Geochem Soc; Geol Soc Am. *Res:* Mechanism of origin of petroleum and applications to predicting character of oil and gas in petroleum exploration; sour cerock geology. *Mailing Add:* 902 Clearview San Antonio TX 78228

PEARSON, DAVID D, b Norwich, Conn, Aug 3, 38; m 57; c 4. IMMUNOBIOLOGY, BIOCHEMISTRY. *Educ:* Univ Conn, BA, 60, MS, 63; Univ Kans, PhD(zool), 66. *Prof Exp:* Asst prof zool, Univ Kans, 65-66; Herbert L Spencer assoc prof, 71-77, asst prof, 66-80, ASSOC PROF BIOL, BUCKNELL UNIV, 80- *Concurrent Pos:* USPHS fel immunol, 65-66; consult res, Geisinger Med Ctr, actg dir res, 73-77. *Mem:* AAAS; Am Soc Zoologists; NY Acad Sci. *Res:* Molecular taxonomy; immunobiology; protein biochemistry; serology; autoimmune diseases. *Mailing Add:* Dept of Biol Bucknell Univ Lewisburg PA 17837

PEARSON, DAVID LEANDER, b Fargo, NDak, Nov 11, 43; m 69. ECOLOGY, ORNITHOLOGY. *Educ:* Pac Lutheran Univ, BS, 67; La State Univ, Baton Rouge, MS, 69; Univ Wash, PhD(zool), 73. *Prof Exp:* ASST PROF BIOL, PA STATE UNIV, 74- *Mem:* Am Ornithol Union; Cooper Ornith Soc; Ecol Soc Am; Soc Study Evolution; Sigma Xi. *Res:* Comparative study of bird community structure in tropical lowland forests of the world and ecology and community structure of tiger beetles of the family Cicindelidae. *Mailing Add:* Dept of Biol 208 Mueller Lab Pa State Univ University Park PA 16802

PEARSON, DONALD A, b Los Angeles, Calif, Oct 16, 21; m 45; c 3. CHEMICAL ENGINEERING. *Educ:* Univ Wash, BS, 44, MS, 48. *Prof Exp:* Chem engr, Puget Sound Pulp & Timber Co, 48-51; process engr, Ketchikan Pulp Co, 51-53, tech dir, 53-62, gen supt, 62-66, vpres mfg, Alaska, 66-68, vpres, Wash, 68-70, pres, 70-74; pres & managing prin, Rubens & Pratt, 74-75, pres & managing prin, Rubens, McClure, Pearson Co, Consult Engrs, 75-79, PRES, PEARSON, PAPE, ALLEN, HUGGINS, INC, 80- *Mem:* Am Chem Soc; Tech Asn Pulp & Paper Indust. *Res:* Sulfite pulping of wood to produce wood pulps for use as regenerated cellulose fibers and films. *Mailing Add:* Pearson, Pape, Allen, Huggins, Inc 221 First Ave W Seattle WA 98119

PEARSON, DONALD A, b Boone Co, Ind, Oct 7, 31; m 52; c 2. METALLURGY. *Educ:* Purdue Univ, BS, 58. *Prof Exp:* Res metallurgist, FMC Corp, 59-69, chief mat engr, 69-72, mgr qual control, 72-81, MGR QUAL ASSURANCE, LINK-BELT CHAIN DIV, AUTOMOTIVE PRODS DIV, PT COMPONENTS, INC, 81- *Mem:* Am Inst Mining, Metall & Petrol Engrs; Am Foundrymen's Soc; Am Soc Qual Control; affil Am Soc Testing & Mat; affil Soc Automotive Engrs. *Res:* Ferrous and semiconductor metallurgy. *Mailing Add:* PT Components Inc Automotive Prods Div PO Box 346B Indianapolis IN 46206

PEARSON, DONALD EMANUAL, b Madison, Wis, June 21, 14; m 50; c 3. CHEMISTRY. *Educ:* Univ Wis, BS, 36; Univ Ill, PhD(org chem), 40. *Prof Exp:* Res chemist, Pittsburgh Plate Glass Co, Wis, 40-42; tech aide, Nat Defense Res Comt Contract, Univ Chicago, 44-45; res assoc, Mass Inst Technol, 45-46; from asst prof to assoc prof, 46-57, PROF CHEM, VANDERBILT UNIV, 57- *Mem:* Am Chem Soc. *Res:* Organic chemistry, synthesis and analysis; Beckmann rearrangement; anti-malarial synthesis; drugs. *Mailing Add:* Dept of Chem Vanderbilt Univ Nashville TN 37235

PEARSON, EARL FREEMAN, b Scottsville, Ky, Oct 12, 41; m 62; c 2. PHYSICAL CHEMISTRY, SPECTROSCOPY. *Educ:* Western Ky Univ, BS, 63, MA, 64; Vanderbilt Univ, PhD(chem), 69. *Prof Exp:* NIH grant res assoc, Univ Southern Calif, 68-69; chemist, Shell Develop Co, 69-70; ASSOC PROF CHEM, WESTERN KY UNIV, 70- *Mem:* Am Chem Soc; Sigma Xi. *Res:* Circular dichroism; inorganic electronic spectroscopy. *Mailing Add:* Dept of Chem Western Ky Univ Bowling Green KY 42101

PEARSON, EDWIN FORREST, b St Louis, Mo, June 3, 38; m 63; c 2. MOLECULAR SPECTROSCOPY, CHEMICAL PHYSICS. *Educ:* Yale Univ, BA, 60; Duke Univ, PhD(physics), 68. *Prof Exp:* Asst prof physics, Southern Ill Univ, 68-73; vis scientist, chem, Univ Ill, 73-74; asst prof physics, Univ Mo-Rolla, 76-78; STAFF SCIENTIST, PHYSICS, LASER ANAL, INC, 78- *Concurrent Pos:* Consult Univ Ill, 72-73; Humboldt fel, Alexander von Humboldt Stiftung, Justis Liebig Univ, Ger, 74-76. *Mem:* AAAS; Am Phys Soc; Am Asn Physics Teachers; NY Acad Sci; Optical Soc Am. *Res:* Infrared, millimeter wave and microwave molecular spectroscopy; molecues of interstellar and atmospheric interest; chemical physics. *Mailing Add:* 25 Washington Dr Acton MA 01720

PEARSON, ERMAN A, b Bothell, Wash, July 13, 20; m 46; c 1. SANITARY ENGINEERING. *Educ:* Univ Wash, BS, 46; Mass Inst Technol, SM, 47, ScD(sanit eng), 49; Environ Eng Intersoc Bd, dipl. *Prof Exp:* Maj engr, Boeing Aircraft Co, 41-45; res assoc, Mass Inst Technol, 47-49; from asst prof to assoc prof, 49-60, PROF SANIT ENG, UNIV CALIF, BERKELEY, 60- *Concurrent Pos:* USPHS consult, Rio de Janeiro, Brazil, 58- & Accra, Ghana, 60-61; consult, Pan Am Health Orgn, WHO, 61-63; Fulbright res scholar, Univ Oslo, 62-63; mem, Governor's Comn Ocean Resources, 65-66, Calif Adv Comn Marine & Coastal Resources, 68- & marine bd, Nat Acad Eng, 70-; guest prof, Royal Inst Technol, Sweden, 70-71; res adv, Swed Environ Protection Bd, 70-71. *Mem:* Am Chem Soc; Am Soc Civil Engrs; Am Geophys Union; Int Asn Water Pollution Res (pres, 64-69). *Res:* Water and waste treatment; biological kinetics; pollution analysis; industrial problems; water quality; applied ecology. *Mailing Add:* Rm 635 Davis Hall Univ of Calif Berkeley CA 94720

PEARSON, FREDERICK JOSEPH, b Bethlehem, Pa, July 4, 35. GEOCHEMISTRY, GROUNDWATER GEOLOGY. *Educ:* Harvard Univ, AB, 58; Univ Tex, Austin, MA, 62, PhD(geol), 66. *Prof Exp:* Res sci assoc carbon 14 dating & geochem, Carbon 14 Lab, Univ Tex, Austin, 62-66; hydrologist, NY, 66-69, RES HYDROLOGIST, US GEOL SURV, 69- *Mem:* AAAS; Geochem Soc; Geol Soc Am; Am Geophys Union. *Res:* Carbon 14; tritium; light stable isotopes to indicate sources and rates of movement of groundwater; geochemistry of water-rock interactions. *Mailing Add:* MS 432 US Geol Surv Reston VA 22092

PEARSON, GARY RICHARD, b Livingston, Mon, May 3, 38; m 66; c 3. VIROLOGY, IMMUNOLOGY. *Educ:* Univ Chicago, BS, 60, MS, 63; Stanford Univ, PhD(med microbiol), 67. *Prof Exp:* Fel pub health serv virol, Karolinska Inst, Sweden, 67-69; res assoc, Children's Hosp Philadelphia, 69-70; sr staff fel, 70-72, microbiologist, 72-74, head, microbiol sect, Nat Cancer Inst, NIH, Bethesda, 74-75; consult & assoc prof microbiol, 75-78, CONSULT & PROF MICROBIOL & VIROLOGY, UNIV MINN, MAYO CLIN & MED SCH, 78-, HEAD SECT MICROBIOL, 79- *Concurrent Pos:* Asst prof pediat, Univ Pa, 69-70; vchmn Nat Cancer Prog, 73-75; mem, Sci Rev Comt, Virus Cancer Prog, 76-80. *Mem:* Am Soc Microbiol; AAAS; Am Asn Cancer Res; Am Asn Immunol; Int Asn Comp Res Leukemia & Related Dis. *Res:* Role of herpesviruses in the etiology of human cancers;

immunoprevention of herpesvirus-induced diseases; association of herpesviruses with neurological diseases; definition of immune responses patterns to viruses and associated diseases. *Mailing Add:* Dept Cell Biol Mayo Clinic Rochester MN 55901

PEARSON, GEORGE DENTON, b Oakland, Calif, May 10, 41; m 66; c 3. ANIMAL VIROLOGY. *Educ:* Stanford Univ, BS, 64, PhD(pharmacol), 69. *Prof Exp:* Calif Div, Am Cancer Soc Dernham jr fel, Stanford Univ, 68-71; asst prof biochem, 71-77, ASSOC PROF BIOCHEM & BIOPHYS, ORE STATE UNIV, 77- *Concurrent Pos:* Am Cancer Soc grants, 72-74, 75-; Nat Cancer Inst res grant, 75-; NATO sr fel, NSF, 75- *Mem:* Biophys Soc; Am Soc Microbiol. *Res:* Structure and function of eukaryotic DNA; viral carcinogenesis; mechanism of anticancer and antiviral agents; developmental biochemistry. *Mailing Add:* Dept of Biochem & Biophys Ore State Univ Corvallis OR 97331

PEARSON, GEORGE JOHN, b Burlington, Iowa, June 16, 28; m 52, 81; c 4. APPLIED PHYSICS, PHOTOGRAPHIC SCIENCE. *Educ:* Grinnell Col, AB, 50; Iowa State Univ, MS, 52; Univ Conn, PhD(physics), 63. *Prof Exp:* Jr res assoc thermal measurement, Inst Atomic Res, Iowa State Univ, 52-55; asst instr physics, Univ Conn, 57-58; sr proj engr superconductivity, Westinghouse Res Lab, 63-64; sr proj engr instrumentation, Res Labs, J & L Steel Co, 64; proj mgr & head appl physics, Fisher Sci Co, 65-66; proj & develop engr, Apparatus & Optical Div, 66-69, sr photog engr, Photo Technol Div, 69-74, TECH ASSOC, PHOTO TECHNOL DIV, EASTMAN KODAK CO, 75- *Mem:* AAAS; Am Phys Soc; Am Asn Physics Teachers; Soc Photog Scientists & Engrs. *Res:* Photographic instrumentation and systems. *Mailing Add:* Photo Technol Div Eastman Kodak Co Rochester NY 14650

PEARSON, GERALD LEONDUS, b Salem, Ore, Mar 31, 05; m 29; c 2. SOLID STATE ELECTRONICS. *Educ:* Willamette Univ, AB, 26; Stanford Univ, AM, 29. *Hon Degrees:* ScD, Willamette Univ, 56. *Prof Exp:* Res physicist, Bell Tel Labs, 29-60, head dept appl solid state physics, 57-60; prof elec eng, 60-71, dir ctr mat res, 65-66, EMER PROF ELEC ENG & DIR SOLID-STATE ELECTRONICS LABS, STANFORD UNIV, 71- *Concurrent Pos:* Vis prof elec eng, Stanford Univ, 58 & Univ Tokyo, 66-67; mem ad hoc comt mat & processes electron devices, Nat Mat Adv Bd, 70-72. *Honors & Awards:* Inst Elec & Electronics Engrs Prize, 46; John Scott Award, City of Philadelphia, 56; John Price Wetherill Medal, Franklin Inst, 63; Golden Plate Award, Am Acad Achievement, 64; Marian Smoluchowski Medal, Polish Phys Soc, 76; Solid State Sci & Technol Award, Electrochem Soc, 81; Alfried Krupp von Bohlen & Halbach Prize, 81. *Mem:* Nat Acad Sci; Nat Acad Eng; fel Am Phys Soc; fel Inst Elec & Electronics Engrs; Franklin Inst. *Res:* Physics of semiconductors; transistors; diodes; photocells; noise in resistors and vacuum tubes; contact erosion. *Mailing Add:* Solid-State Electronics Labs Stanford Univ Stanford CA 94305

PEARSON, GLEN HAMILTON, b Seattle, Wash, June 8, 48; m 71. CHEMICAL ENGINEERING, POLYMER RHEOLOGY. *Educ:* Va Polytech Inst & State Univ, BS, 71; Univ Mass, PhD(chem eng), 76. *Prof Exp:* res chemist, Polymer Phys Chem, 75-81, LAB HEAD & CHEM PROCESS ENGR, RES LAB, EASTMAN KODAK CO, 81- *Mem:* Soc Rheology; Am Inst Chem Eng; Am Chem Soc. *Res:* Fluid mechanics; polymer rheology; polymer processing; transport properties of polymers. *Mailing Add:* Res Labs Eastman Kodak Co Rochester NY 14650

PEARSON, HANS LENNART, b Vancouver, BC, Mar 6, 27; US citizen; m 61; c 1. MATHEMATICS. *Educ:* Univ BC, BASc, 49, MA, 51; Ill Inst Technol, PhD(math), 57. *Prof Exp:* From instr to asst prof, 54-63, actg dean grad sch, 75-77, ASSOC PROF MATH, ILL INST TECHNOL, 63- *Mem:* Math Asn Am. *Res:* Special functions; partial differential equations. *Mailing Add:* Dept of Math Ill Inst of Technol Chicago IL 60616

PEARSON, HENRY ALEXANDER, b Heidenheimer, Tex, Oct 26, 33; m 58; c 3. RANGE SCIENCE. *Educ:* Blinn Col, AA, 54, Tex A&M Univ, BS, 58, MS, 59; Utah State Univ, PhD(range sci), 68. *Prof Exp:* Asst range mgt, Tex A&M Univ, 58-59; asst range sci, Utah State Univ, 59-62; range scientist, Rocky Mountain Forest & Range Exp Sta, Ariz, 62-69, proj leader range res, Southern Forest Exp Sta, La, 69-75, prin range/wildlife scientist forest environ res, US Forest Serv, Washington, DC, 75-77; PROJ LEADER RANGE RES, SOUTHERN FOREST EXP STA, 77- *Concurrent Pos:* US Forest Serv rep, Range Livestock Nutrit Tech Comt, 64-69. *Mem:* Soc Range Mgt; Wildlife Soc. *Res:* Nutrition; ruminology. *Mailing Add:* 2500 Shreveport Hwy US Forest Serv Pineville LA 71360

PEARSON, HOWARD ALLEN, b Ancon, CZ, Nov 4, 29; US citizen; m; c 5. PEDIATRICS, HEMATOLOGY. *Educ:* Dartmouth Col, AB, 51, dipl, 52; Harvard Med Sch, MD, 54; Am Bd Pediat, dipl, cert pediat hemat-oncol. *Prof Exp:* Res fel hemat, Children's Med Ctr, Harvard Med Sch, 57-58; asst head clin hemat & asst chief pediat, US Naval Hosp, Bethesda, Md, 58-62; from asst prof to prof pediat, Col Med, Univ Fla, 62-68; PROF PEDIAT, SCH MED, YALE UNIV, 68-, CHMN DEPT, 74- *Concurrent Pos:* Clin instr, Sch Med, Georgetown Univ, 59-62; clin asst prof, Col Med, Howard Univ, 61-62. *Mem:* Am Fedn Clin Res; Am Soc Hemat; Soc Pediat Res; Am Acad Pediat. *Res:* Pediatric hematology. *Mailing Add:* Dept of Pediat Yale Univ Sch of Med New Haven CT 06511

PEARSON, J(OHN) RAYMOND, b Providence, RI, Dec 6, 12; m 43; c 2. MECHANICAL ENGINEERING. *Educ:* Univ RI, BSc, 35; Mass Inst Technol, MSc, 46. *Prof Exp:* Trainee eng, Brown & Sharpe Mfg Co, RI, 35-37; instr sci vocations, Am Bd Comnr Foreign Missions, Turkey, 38-41, from asst prof to assoc prof mech eng, Robert Col, Istanbul, 41-45, prof & chmn dept, 46-54, assoc dean eng, 47-56, actg dean fac, 55-56; vis prof, 56-57, chmn mech eng dept, 75-78, PROF MECH ENG, COL ENG, UNIV MICH, ANN ARBOR, 57-, PROF, DEPT PHYS MED & REHAB, SCH MED, 64-, ASSOC CHMN MECH ENG DEPT, 66- *Concurrent Pos:* Vis prof, Univ Uppsala, 70-71. *Mem:* Fel Am Soc Mech Engrs; Am Soc Eng Educ; Biomed Eng Soc. *Res:* Mechanisms, dynamics of machinery, mechanical vibrations, automatic control; mechanical design; biomechanics; research, design and development of orthotic devices; bioengineering. *Mailing Add:* Dept of Mech Eng Univ of Mich WE 225 Ann Arbor MI 48104

PEARSON, JAMES B, JR, b McGehee, Ark, June 3, 30; m 57; c 6. ELECTRICAL ENGINEERING. *Educ:* Univ Ark, BS, 58, MS, 59; Purdue Univ, PhD(elec eng), 62. *Prof Exp:* Instr elec eng, Univ Ark, 58-59; from instr to asst prof, Purdue Univ, 59-65; assoc prof, 65-70, chmn, Elec Eng Dept, 74-79, PROF ELEC ENG, RICE UNIV, 70-, J S ABERCROMIE PROF ENG, 79- *Mem:* Fel Inst Elec & Electronics Engrs. *Res:* Analysis and design of control systems; control and circuit theories. *Mailing Add:* Dept of Elec Eng Rice Univ Houston TX 77001

PEARSON, JAMES ELDON, b Newton, Mass, Oct 8, 26; m 53; c 5. NEPHROLOGY, PHARMACOLOGY. *Educ:* Loyola Univ, La, BS, 56, MS, 58. *Prof Exp:* Prof asst angiol, Touro Res Inst, 64-68; res assoc pharmacol, LSU Med Ctr, 68-71; res assoc ecol, Pac Biomed Res, Univ Hawaii, 71-72; res assoc nephrol, LSU Med Ctr, 72-74 & Univ Miss Med Ctr, 74-76; RES ASSOC NEPHROL, LSU MED CTR, 76- *Honors & Awards:* Honor Achievement Award, Angiol Res Found, 68. *Mem:* Am Soc Pharmacol & Exp Therapeut; Am Soc Nephrol; Int Soc Nephrol; Am Soc Artificial Internal Organs. *Res:* Nephrology, as it concerns the artificial kidney and drug effects on kidney. *Mailing Add:* Dept of Med 1542 Tulane Ave New Orleans LA 70112

PEARSON, JAMES GORDON, b Cleckheaton, Eng, Apr 18, 22; m 47; c 3. MEDICINE, RADIOTHERAPY. *Educ:* Univ Leeds, MB, ChB, 44; Univ Edinburgh, DMRT, 53; FRCS, 51; FRCR, 57; FRCS(E), 69; FRCP(C), 74. *Prof Exp:* Intern med & surg, Dewsbury Infirmary & Carlisle Infirmary, Eng, 44-45; lectr anat, Univ Leeds, 48-49; house surgeon, Royal Postgrad Med Sch London, 49-50; Hammersmith Hosp, London, Eng, 50-51; sr house officer radiother, Royal Infirmary, Edinburgh, Scotland, 51-53, sr registr, 53-54; fel, Mt Sinai Hosp, New York, 54-55; sr registr, Royal Infirmary, Edinburgh, 55-56; mem clin teaching staff radiother, Univ Edinburgh, 56-70; PROF RADIOTHER & ONCOL, UNIV & DIR RADIOTHER, DR W W CROSS CANCER INST, UNIV ALTA, 70-, DIR DIV RADIOTHER, UNIV ALTA HOSP, 71- *Concurrent Pos:* Consult radiotherapist, Royal Infirmary & Western Gen Hosp, Edinburgh, Scotland, 56-70. *Honors & Awards:* Gordon Richards lectr, Can Asn Radiologists, 81. *Mem:* Am Soc Therapeut Radiol; Can Asn Radiol; Brit Inst Radiol. *Res:* Oesophageal cancer; breast cancer; lung cancer; immunological rejection of tumors. *Mailing Add:* Dept Radiother Cross Cancer Inst 11560 University Ave Edmonton AB T6G 1Z2 Can

PEARSON, JAMES JOSEPH, b Kansas City, Mo, Sept 23, 34; m 57, 69; c 2. SOLID STATE PHYSICS. *Educ:* Yale Univ, BS, 56; Stanford Univ, MS, 57; Univ Pittsburgh, PhD(physics), 61. *Prof Exp:* Res assoc physics, Univ Pittsburgh, 61; jr res physicist, Univ Calif, San Diego, 61-62; res scientist, 63-71, staff scientist, 71-74, MGR SIGNAL PROCESSING LAB, LOCKHEED PALO ALTO RES LAB, 74- *Concurrent Pos:* NSF fel, Saclay Nuclear Res Ctr, France, 62-63. *Mem:* Soc Photo Optical Instrumentation Engrs; Am Phys Soc; Inst Elec & Electronics Engrs. *Res:* Theory of ferromagnetism and antiferromagnetism; spin waves; super-exchange; magnetic anisotropy; crystal field theory; electromagnetic scattering; image data processing. *Mailing Add:* Lockheed Palo Alto Res Lab 3251 Hanover St Palo Alto CA 94304

PEARSON, JAMES MURRAY, b Aberdeen, Scotland, Nov 22, 37; m 62; c 2. PHYSICAL CHEMISTRY, POLYMER CHEMISTRY. *Educ:* Aberdeen Univ, PhD(polymer chem), 62. *Prof Exp:* NSF fel, State Univ NY Col Forestry, Syracuse Univ, 62-64; lectr, Aberdeen Univ, 64-66; asst prof chem, State Univ NY Col Forestry, Syracuse Univ, 66-68; res chemist, 68-72, MGR POLYMER PHYSICS & CHEM, RES LABS, XEROX CORP, 72- *Mem:* Am Chem Soc; NY Acad Sci. *Res:* Kinetics; mechanism polymerization; ionic polymerization; electrical and photochemical properties of polymers. *Mailing Add:* Res Labs Xerox Corp 800 Philips Rd Webster NY 14580

PEARSON, JOHN, b Leyburn, Eng, Apr 24, 23; nat US; m 44; c 3. MECHANICS. *Educ:* Northwestern Univ, BS, 49, MS, 51. *Prof Exp:* Res engr, 51-55, head warhead res br, 55-58, head solid dynamics br, 58-59, head detonation physics group, 59-67, HEAD DETONATION PHYSICS DIV, US NAVAL WEAPONS CTR, 67- *Concurrent Pos:* Lectr, Univ Calif, Los Angeles, 57-67 & Univ Calif, Santa Barbara, 71-72; consult, Lockheed Aircraft Corp, 58-62 & US Air Force, Ohio, 58-62. *Honors & Awards:* L T E Thompson Medal, 65; William B McLean Medal, 79. *Mem:* Fel Am Soc Mech Engrs; Am Soc Metals; Am Phys Soc; Sigma Xi; Am Inst Mining, Metall & Petrol Engrs. *Res:* Elasticity; plasticity; fracture dynamics; behavior of metal-explosive systems; high velocity impact; explosive ordnance; high energy rate forming of materials; high speed photography. *Mailing Add:* Detonation Physics Div Code 383 US Naval Weapons Ctr China Lake CA 93555

PEARSON, JOHN MICHAEL, b Halifax, Eng, Aug 27, 33; m 59; c 2. THEORETICAL PHYSICS. *Educ:* Univ London, BSc, 54; McMaster Univ, PhD(physics), 59. *Prof Exp:* Instr physics, Western Reserve Univ, 59-60; mem res staff, 60-61, from asst prof to assoc prof, 61-70, PROF PHYSICS, UNIV MONTREAL, 70- *Concurrent Pos:* Nat Res Coun fel, Univ Paris, 65-66. *Mem:* Am Phys Soc; Can Asn Physicists. *Res:* Low energy nuclear physics. *Mailing Add:* Dept of Physics Univ of Montreal PO 6128 Montreal PQ H3C 3J7 Can

PEARSON, JOHN RICHARD, b Colorado Springs, Colo, Oct 5, 38; m 61; c 2. CLINICAL CHEMISTRY, BIOCHEMISTRY. *Educ:* Colo State Univ, BS, 60, PhD(chem), 66. *Prof Exp:* Sr res assoc chem, Colo State Dept Pub Health, 66-67, prin res assoc, 67-68; instr, 68-69, ASST PROF CLIN CHEM, UNIV COLO HEALTH SCI CTR, DENVER, 69-, ASST MGR, LAB INFO SYST, 80- *Mem:* Am Asn Clin Chemists; Int Soc Clin Enzym; Am Chem Soc;

Asn Comput Mach. *Res:* Endocrinology, especially steroid chemistry; construction of mathematical models to represent biological systems; automation and effective use of computers in clinical chemistry laboratories. *Mailing Add:* Dept Med Univ Colo Health Sci Ctr Denver CO 80262

PEARSON, JOHN W(ILLIAM), b St Paul, Minn, June 2, 18; m 40; c 2. CHEMICAL ENGINEERING. *Educ:* Univ Minn, BChE, 39. *Prof Exp:* Chem engr, Minn Mining & Mfg Co, 39-44 & Manhattan Dist, Los Alamos, NMex, 45-46; develop engr, 46-53, exec engr eng res, 53-55, mgr, New Prod Di ·, 55-62 & Indust Finishing Dept, 62-68, group eng mgr photographic prod, 68-74, dir div eng, 74-80, EXEC DIR DIV ENG, MINN MINING & MFG CO, 80-, VPRES DEVELOP, 80- *Mem:* Am Chem Soc; Am Inst Chem Engrs. *Res:* Construction of magnetic sound recording media; non-woven textiles; pressure sensitive tape coating; producing pressure sensitive tapes; metal plating. *Mailing Add:* 201 Crestway Lane St Paul MN 55118

PEARSON, JOHN WILLIAM, b Livingston, Mont, June 29, 35; m 64; c 2. MICROBIOLOGY, ONCOLOGY. *Educ:* Mont State Col, BS, 58; George Washington Univ, MS, 63; Rutgers Univ, PhD(microbiol), 68. *Prof Exp:* Microbiologist, Ft Detrick, Md, 63-64; staff fel viral oncol, 68-75, RES MICROBIOLOGIST, NAT CANCER INST, 75- *Mem:* Am Asn Cancer Res; Am Soc Microbiol. *Res:* Viral oncology; design of experiments toward therapy on oncogenic viruses; chemotherapeutic approach through the use of drugs used singly or in combination; immunotherapy and the use of interferon inducers. *Mailing Add:* Bldg 560 RM 11-85 Nat Cancer Inst Frederick Cancer Res Ctr Frederick MD 21701

PEARSON, JOSEPH T(ATEM), b Portsmouth, Va, Dec 7, 33; m 56; c 3. HEAT TRANSFER, FLUID MECHANICS. *Educ:* NC State Univ, BSME, 56, MS, 61; State Univ NY Stony Brook, PhD(eng), 67. *Prof Exp:* Assoc engr, Douglas Aircraft Co, 56-57; mgr, J T Pearson & Co, 57-59; teaching asst mech eng, NC State Univ, 59-61; instr eng, State Univ NY Stony Brook, 61-67; asst prof, 67-72, ASSOC PROF MECH ENG, PURDUE UNIV, LAFAYETTE, 72- *Concurrent Pos:* Heat transfer res grants, Purdue Univ, 68-; consult heat transfer appln, serveral co, 61-; Am Soc Heating, Refrig & Air-Conditioning Engrs grant, Purdue Univ, 71-72. *Mem:* AAAS; Am Soc Mech Engrs; Am Soc Heating, Refrig & Air-Conditioning Engrs. *Res:* Experimental and analytical studies on heat transfer equipment and its effect on the environment. *Mailing Add:* Sch of Mech Eng Purdue Univ Lafayette IN 47907

PEARSON, KEIR GORDON, b Geeveston, Tasmania, Feb 19, 42; m 76; c 3. NEUROPHYSIOLOGY. *Educ:* Univ Tasmania, BE, 64; Oxford Univ, DPhil(physiol), 69. *Prof Exp:* Jr res fel, Merton Col, Oxford Univ, 67-69; from asst prof to assoc prof, 69-78, PROF PHYSIOL, UNIV ALTA, 78- *Mem:* Soc Exp Biol; Neurosci Soc. *Res:* Control of movements in invertebrates; structure of neurons in insects. *Mailing Add:* Dept Physiol Univ Alta Edmonton AB T6G 2H7 Can

PEARSON, LONNIE WILSON, b Jackson, Miss, March 15, 46; m 75; c 2. ELECTROMAGNETIC THEORY, MICROWAVE ENGINEERING. *Educ:* Univ Miss, BSEE, 68, MS, 73; Univ Ill, PhD(elec eng), 76. *Prof Exp:* Instr elec eng, Univ Miss, 68-71; elec engr, US Naval Surface Weapons Ctr, 71-73; res assoc, Electromagnetics Lab, Univ Ill, 74-76; asst prof, Univ Ky, 76-80; ASSOC PROF ELEC ENG, UNIV MISS, 81- *Concurrent Pos:* Consult, US Naval Res Lab, 76-78, Battelle Corp, 77-78, Phys Sci Lab, NMex State Univ, 80-81 & Nat Microtech, Inc, 82- *Mem:* Inst Elec & Electronics Engrs Antennas & Propagation Soc; Inst Elec & Electronics Engrs Microwave Theory & Techniques Soc; Inst Elec & Electronics Engrs Group Electromagnetic Compatibility; Electromagnetics Soc. *Res:* Research in engineering electromagnetics; complex resonance in electromagnetic scattering; computer augmented measurement and parameter recovery, analytical solution methods. *Mailing Add:* Dept Elec Eng Univ Miss University MS 38677

PEARSON, MARK LANDELL, b Toronto, Ont, June 2, 40; m 62; c 2. MOLECULAR GENETICS. *Educ:* Univ Toronto, BA, 62, MA, 64, PhD(med biophys), 66. *Prof Exp:* Asst prof med genetis, Univ Toronto, 69-74, asst prof med biophys, 69-75, assoc prof med genetics, fac med, 74-80, assoc prof med biophys, 75-80; MEM STAFF, CANCER BIOL PROG, FREDERICK CANCER RES CTR, 80- *Concurrent Pos:* Helen Hay Whitney Found fel biochem, Sch Med, Stanford Univ, 66-69; mem fel panel, Nat Cancer Inst Can, 76-77. *Mem:* AAAS; Biophys Soc; Can Soc Cell Biol; Can Biochem Soc. *Res:* Molecular basis of genetic regulation in bacteriophage lambda; molecular genetics of myogenesis in cultured rat myoblast cells. *Mailing Add:* PO Box B Frederick Cancer Res Ctr Frederick MD 21701

PEARSON, MICHAEL J, b Eng, Sep 25, 38; US citizen; m 62; c 2. ALUMINA CHEMISTRY, ALUMINA CATALYSTS. *Educ:* Univ Leeds, BSc, 59, PhD(chem), 62. *Prof Exp:* Fel chem, Univ Wash, 62-64; chemist, Chevron Chem Co, 64-67; STAFF RES CHEMIST, KAISER ALUMINUM & CHEM CORP, 67- *Mem:* Am Chem Soc. *Res:* Reaction mechanisms for the catalytic decomposition of hydrogen sulfide and carbon sulfur compounds. *Mailing Add:* Kaiser Aluminum & Chem Corp PO Box 877 Pleasanton CA 94566

PEARSON, MYRNA SCHMIDT, b Philadelphia, Pa, July 7, 36; m 61; c 2. ORGANIC CHEMISTRY. *Educ:* Univ Pa, AB, 58; Columbia Univ, AM, 59, PhD(chem), 63. *Prof Exp:* Asst prof chem, Clark Univ, 63-64; asst prof, 64-70, ASSOC PROF CHEM, WHEATON COL, MASS, 70- *Mem:* Am Chem Soc. *Res:* Reactions and mechanisms of organophosphorus compounds; free radical chemistry; keto-enol tautomerism; environmental chemistry. *Mailing Add:* Dept of Chem Wheaton Col Norton MA 02766

PEARSON, OLIVER PAYNE, b Philadelphia, Pa, Oct 21, 15; m 44; c 4. ZOOLOGY. *Educ:* Swarthmore Col, AB, 37; Harvard Univ, MA, 40, PhD(biol), 47. *Prof Exp:* Asst prof zool & asst cur mammals, Mus Vert Zool, 47-59, lectr zool, Univ & res assoc, Mus, 59-66, prof zool, Univ, 66-71, actg dir mus, 66-67, dir, 67-71, EMER PROF ZOOL, UNIV & EMER DIR MUS VERT ZOOL, UNIV CALIF, BERKELEY, 71- *Res:* Natural history of Peruvian Andes; reproduction of various mammals; comparative physiology; mammalogy; ecology. *Mailing Add:* Mus Vert Zool Univ Calif Berkeley CA 94720

PEARSON, OLOF HJALMER, b Boston, Mass, Feb 7, 13; m 42; c 4. MEDICINE. *Educ:* Harvard Univ, AB, 34, MD, 39. *Prof Exp:* Intern, Mass Gen Hosp, Boston, 39-41, asst med resident, 41-42; flight surgeon, Pan Am Airways, Africa, 42, med dir, 42-45; from asst prof to assoc prof med, Med Col, Cornell Univ, 48-60; assoc prof, 60-68, PROF MED, SCH MED, CASE WESTERN UNIV, 68-, AM CANCER SOC PROF CLIN ONCOL, 73- *Concurrent Pos:* Fel, Mass Gen Hosp, Boston, 46-48; assoc mem, Sloan-Kettering Inst Cancer Res, 48-60; assoc attend physician, Mem Hosp, New York; assoc attend physician, Univ Hosps, Cleveland, 60- *Mem:* AAAS; Am Soc Clin Invest; Am Soc Biol Chem; Asn Am Physicians; Am Fedn Clin Res. *Res:* Clinical endocrinology; endocrine treatment of cancer. *Mailing Add:* Sch of Med Case Western Univ Cleveland OH 44106

PEARSON, PAUL (HAMMOND), b Bolenge, Belgian Congo, Feb 18, 21; US citizen; m 68; c 4. PEDIATRICS, PUBLIC HEALTH. *Educ:* Northwestern Univ, Chicago, BS, BMed & MD, 47; Univ Calif, Los Angeles, MPH, 63. *Prof Exp:* Fels & pediatrician, Johns Hopkins Hosp, 51-53; from clin instr to asst clin prof pediat, Univ Southern Calif, 53-62; from actg chief to chief ment retardation br, Div Chronic Dis, USPHS, 63-65, asst prog dir, Nat Inst Child Health & Human Develop, 65-66, spec asst child health to Surgeon Gen, 66-67; C LOUIS MEYER PROF CHILD HEALTH & PEDIAT & MED DIR MEYER THER CTR HANDICAPPED CHILDREN, COL MED, UNIV NEBR MED CTR, OMAHA, 67-, PROF PREV MED & DIR MEYER CHILDREN'S REHAB INST, 68- *Concurrent Pos:* Attend physician, Los Angeles Children's Hosp, 53-62; attend staff, Valley Presby Hosp, 58-62, chmn pediat comt, 58-59, mem exec comt, 60-61; neurol consult pub sch dist, San Fernando Valley, 60-62; from clin assoc prof to clin prof pediat, Sch Med, Georgetown Univ, 64-67; consult, United Cerebral Palsy Asns, Inc, 69; consult div develop disabilities, Dept Health, Educ & Welfare, 70, mem nat adv comt, 71-75; mem spec adv comt accessible environ for disabled, Nat Acad Sci; resident child psychiat, Dept Psychiat, Univ BC, 76-77; vis lectr pediat & adolescent med, Harvard Univ & Childrens Hosp Med Ctr, Boston, 81. *Mem:* Am Acad Pediat; Am Pub Health Asn; Am Acad Ment Deficiency; Am Acad Cerebral Palsy (secy, 74-76, pres, 81-82); Am Asn Univ Affil Progs for Develop Disabled (pres, 76-77). *Res:* Development of children with handicaps; anticonvulsive medication; delivery of health services. *Mailing Add:* Meyer Children's Rehab Inst Univ of Nebr Med Ctr Omaha NE 68131

PEARSON, PAUL BROWN, b Oakley, Utah, Nov 28, 05; m 33; c 2. NUTRITION. *Educ:* Brigham Young Univ, BS, 28; Mont State Col, MS, 30; Univ Wis, PhD(biochem, nutrit), 37. *Prof Exp:* Asst prof, Mont State Col, 30-31; res assoc, Univ Calif, 32-35; prof animal nutrit, Agr & Mech Col, Tex, 37-41, distinguished prof, 41-47, dean grad sch & head dept biochem & nutrit, 47-49; chief biol br, AEC, 49-58; with Ford Found Prog Sci & Eng, 58-63; pres & sci dir, Nutrit Found, Inc, NY, 63-72; chmn dept nutrit & food, Drexel Univ, 72-74; PROF, DEPT NUTRIT & FOOD SCI & DEPT FAMILY & COMMUNITY MED, UNIV ARIZ, 74-; CHIEF DEPT NUTRIT, SCH MED, UNIV AUTONOMA DE GUADALAJARA, 74- *Concurrent Pos:* Collabr, Bur Animal Indust, 49-57; prof, Johns Hopkins Univ, 51-58; consult, Energy Res & Develop Admin, 58- & Off Sci & Technol, AID; trustee, Food, Law & Drug Law Inst; mem exec comt, Div Biol & Agr, Nat Res Coun, 50-52; prog comt, Int Cong Nutrit, 60; liaison, Food & Nutrit Bd; adv comt, PR Nuclear Ctr, McCollum-Pratt Inst & Secy of Agr; mem, Agr Res Inst; vis prof, Thomas Jefferson Univ. *Mem:* Fel AAAS; fel Am Soc Animal Sci; Am Chem Soc; Am Inst Nutrit; Am Soc Biol Chemists. *Res:* Mineral metabolism and micronutrients; B vitamins; metabolism of sulfur and enzymes; utilization of proteins and amino acids malnutrition and taste. *Mailing Add:* 401 Agr Sci Bldg Univ of Ariz Tucson AZ 85721

PEARSON, PAUL GUY, b Lake Worth, Fla, Dec 5, 26; m; c 3. ECOLOGY. *Educ:* Univ Fla, BS, 49, MS, 51, PhD, 54. *Prof Exp:* Asst, Univ Fla, 49-54; asst prof zool, Univ Tulsa, 54-55; from asst prof to assoc prof, 55-64, chmn dept, 67-72, assoc provost, 72-77, actg pres, 78, PROF ZOOL, RUTGERS UNIV, NEW BRUNSWICK, 64-, EXEC VPRES, 77- *Concurrent Pos:* Chmn, NJ Noise Control Coun, 75-76. *Mem:* Am Soc Mammal; Ecol Soc Am (secy, 61-64, vpres, 70, treas, 75-); Am Inst Biol Sci (pres, 78). *Res:* Population dynamics; vertebrate natural history; ecosystem analysis; impacts of pesticides and other pollutants. *Mailing Add:* Dept Zool Rutgers Univ New Brunswick NJ 08903

PEARSON, PHILIP RICHARDSON, JR, b Newburyport, Mass, Apr 15, 27; m 57; c 2. PLANT ECOLOGY. *Educ:* Dartmouth Col, AB, 50; Univ Mass, MS, 56; Rutgers Univ, PhD(ecol), 60. *Prof Exp:* Instr bot, Rutgers Univ, 60-61; asst prof biol, Temple Univ, 61-67; assoc prof, 67-71, PROF BIOL, RI COL, 71- *Mem:* AAAS; Ecol Soc Am; Torrey Bot Club; Am Inst Biol Sci. *Res:* Woodland and forest communities of eastern United States. *Mailing Add:* Dept of Biol RI Col Providence RI 02908

PEARSON, PHILLIP T, b Story Co, Iowa, Nov 21, 32; m 54; c 4. VETERINARY SURGERY, BIOMEDICAL ENGINEERING. *Educ:* Iowa State Univ, DVM, 56, PhD(path, surg), 62. *Prof Exp:* Intern vet med, Angell Mem Animal Hosp, Boston, Mass, 56-57; from instr to assoc prof vet med & surg, Iowa State Univ, 57-64; prof & assoc clin dir, Univ Mo, 64-65; chmn, Small Animal Clin, 67-72, PROF VET CLIN SCI, IOWA STATE UNIV, 64-, DEAN, COL VET MED, 72- *Honors & Awards:* Gaines Award, 66. *Mem:* Am Vet Med Asn; Am Asn Vet Clinicians; Am Col Vet Surg. *Res:* Canine nephritis, orthopedics and hyperparathyroidism; surgical and pathological aspects of artificial heart work. *Mailing Add:* Off of the Dean 2506 Vet Admin Col of Vet Med Iowa State Univ Ames IA 50011

PEARSON, R(AY) L(EON), b New York, NY, Mar 31, 30; m 54; c 5. MATERIALS SCIENCE, PHYSICAL CHEMISTRY. *Educ:* Willamette Univ, BS, 51; Univ Utah, MA, 54; PhD(metall), 56. *Prof Exp:* Sr scientist, Oak Ridge Nat Lab, 56-59; prin metallurgist, Aerojet-Gen Nucleonics Div, Gen Tire & Rubber Co, 59-65; PRIN SCIENTIST, OAK RIDGE NAT LAB, 65- *Mem:* Am Ceramic Soc. *Res:* Nuclear fuel development. *Mailing Add:* Oak Ridge Nat Lab PO Box X Oak Ridge TN 37831

PEARSON, RALPH GOTTFRID, b Chicago, Ill, Jan 12, 19; m 41; c 3. CHEMISTRY. *Educ:* Ill Inst Technol, BS, 40; Northwestern Univ, PhD(chem), 43. *Prof Exp:* From instr to prof chem, Northwestern Univ, 43-76; PROF CHEM, UNIV CALIF, SANTA BARBARA, 76- *Concurrent Pos:* Guggenheim fel, 51-52. *Honors & Awards:* Midwest Award, Am Chem Soc, 66 & Inorg Award, 70. *Mem:* Nat Acad Sci; Am Chem Soc. *Res:* Kinetics of organic reactions; theories of organic chemistry; mechanisms of inorganic reactions; theories of inorganic chemistry. *Mailing Add:* Dept of Chem Univ of Calif Santa Barbara CA 93106

PEARSON, ROBERT EDWARD, organic chemistry, science education, see previous edition

PEARSON, ROBERT MELVIN, b Klamath Falls, Ore, Feb 17, 30; m 59; c 3. PHYSICAL CHEMISTRY, ANALYTICAL CHEMISTRY. *Educ:* Univ Nev, Reno, BS, 57, MS, 59; Univ Calif, Davis, PhD(chem), 65. *Prof Exp:* Chemist, Aerojet-Gen Corp, 59-61 & 64-67; CHEMIST, KAISER ALUMINUM & CHEM CORP, 67- *Mem:* Am Chem Soc. *Res:* High resolution nuclear magnetic resonance; wide line nuclear magnetic resonance of solids. *Mailing Add:* Kaiser Aluminum & Chem Corp PO Box 877 Pleasanton CA 94566

PEARSON, ROBERT STANLEY, b Lawrence, Kans, Aug 12, 27; m 51; c 2. INORGANIC CHEMISTRY. *Educ:* Kans State Teachers Col Pittsburg, BS, 50; Kans State Univ, MS, 53, PhD(chem), 64. *Prof Exp:* Chemist, Midwest Solvents Co, Kans, 50-51; instr gen chem, Colo Sch Mines, 55-61; asst prof chem, Idaho State Univ, 61-68; assoc prof chem, 68-70, chmn dept, 71-78, PROF CHEM, UNIV ARK, MONTICELLO, 70- *Mem:* Sigma Xi; Am Chem Soc. *Res:* Application of trace element analysis in geochemistry and geochemical prospecting; ceramic glaze design. *Mailing Add:* Dept Chem Univ Ark Monticello AR 71655

PEARSON, RONALD EARL, b Worcester, Mass, Dec 21, 44; m 65. DAIRY SCIENCE, ANIMAL BREEDING. *Educ:* Univ Mass, Amherst, BS, 66; Iowa State Univ, MS, 70, PhD(animal breeding), 71. *Prof Exp:* Res geneticist, Genetics & Mgt Lab, Beltsville Agr Ctr, Sci & Educ Admin-Agr Res, 71-79, ASSOC PROF, DEPT DAIRY SCI, VA POLYTECH INST & STATE UNIV, BLACKSBURG, VA, 79- *Mem:* Am Dairy Sci Asn; Biomet Soc. *Res:* Dairy cattle breeding and management, including economic evaluation of various breeding and management systems. *Mailing Add:* 2100 Animal Sci Bldg Dept Dairy Sci Va Tech Blacksburg VA 24061

PEARSON, SONNY WAYNE, mechanical engineering, see previous edition

PEARSON, TERRANCE LAVERNE, b Berwick, NS, Dec 19, 37; m 61; c 1. PURE MATHEMATICS. *Educ:* Acadia Univ, BSc, 60; Univ Sask, MSc, 63, PhD(math), 65. *Prof Exp:* Lectr, 60-61, from asst prof to assoc prof, 65-78, PROF MATH, ACADIA UNIV, 78- *Concurrent Pos:* NATO fel, Univ Calif, Santa Barbara, 66-67; fel, Birkbeck Col, Univ London, 73-74. *Mem:* Am Math Soc; London Math Soc. *Res:* General topology; real analysis. *Mailing Add:* Dept of Math Acadia Univ Wolfville NS B0P 1X0 Can

PEARSON, TILLMON HENRY, b Waco, Tex, Sept 23, 21; m 47; c 3. ORGANIC CHEMISTRY. *Educ:* Univ Miami, BS, 46; Univ Wis, PhD(chem), 51. *Prof Exp:* Asst prof chem, Va Mil Inst, 51-52; prof, Hampden-Sydney Col, 52-54, head dept, 53-54; chemist, 54-57, RES ASSOC, ETHYL CORP, 57- *Mem:* Am Chem Soc. *Res:* Organic synthesis; organometallics; petrochemicals; drug synthesis; tissue culture. *Mailing Add:* Ethyl Corp PO Box 341 Baton Rouge LA 70821

PEARSON, WALTER HOWARD, b Troy, NY, Mar 25, 46; m 72; c 1. MARINE BIOLOGY, ANIMAL BEHAVIOR. *Educ:* Bates Col, BS, 67; Univ Alaska, MS, 70; Ore State Univ, PhD(oceanog), 77. *Prof Exp:* Fisheries biol, behav ecol, Nat Marine Fish Serv, Sandy Hook Lab, 75-77; RES SCIENTIST, BEHAV ECOL, BATTELLE PAC NORTHWEST LAB, MARINE RES LAB, 77- *Mem:* AAAS; Animal Behav Soc; NY Acad Sci. *Res:* Behavioral ecology of marine invertebrates; chemoreception in crustaceans and fish, estuarine and intertidal ecology; tidal marsh ecology; fisheries biology of crabs; ecological and behavioral effects of pollution; food habits; predator-prey relationships. *Mailing Add:* Battelle Pac Northwest Lab 439 W Sequim Bay Sequim WA 98382

PEARSON, WESLEY A, b Red Wing, Minn, July 19, 32; m 71; c 2. ORGANIC CHEMISTRY. *Educ:* St Olaf Col, BA, 54; Univ Minn, PhD(org chem), 58. *Prof Exp:* Assoc prof, 58-75, PROF CHEM, ST OLAF COL, 75- *Concurrent Pos:* NSF fac sci fel, Mass Inst Technol, 64-65. *Mem:* Am Chem Soc. *Res:* Organic reaction mechanisms; stereochemistry of cyclic compounds. *Mailing Add:* Dept of Chem St Olaf Col Northfield MN 55057

PEARSON, WILLIAM DEAN, b Moline, Ill, Dec 6, 41; m 66. FISHERIES. *Educ:* Iowa State Univ, BS, 63; Utah State Univ, MS, 67, PhD(fisheries, biol), 70. *Prof Exp:* Biologist aid, Iowa State Conserv Comn, 61; fishery aid, US Fish & Wildlife Serv, Yankton, 62-63, fishery biologist, Logan, 64-66; res asst fisheries, Utah State Univ, 67-70; asst prof aquatic ecol, NTex State Univ, 70-75; asst prof, 75-78, ASSOC PROF RES, WATER RESOURCES LAB, UNIV LOUISVILLE, 78- *Mem:* AAAS; Ecol Soc Am; Am Fisheries Soc; Am Soc Limnol & Oceanog; Brit Freshwater Biol Asn. *Res:* Drift of stream invertebrates; effects of heated waters on aquatic life; population dynamics and production of fish and invertebrates; reservoir fisheries management. *Mailing Add:* Water Resources Lab Univ of Louisville Louisville KY 40208

PEASCOE, WARREN JOSEPH, b San Pedro, Calif, Jan 15, 43; m 70. ORGANIC CHEMISTRY, POLYMER CHEMISTRY. *Educ:* Calif Inst Technol, BS, 65; Univ Ill, Urbana, PhD(chem), 70. *Prof Exp:* RES CHEMIST, OXFORD MGT & RES CTR, UNIROYAL INC, 70- *Mem:* Am Chem Soc. *Res:* Polymerization chemistry; organometallic chemistry. *Mailing Add:* 6 Orchard Rd Woodbridge CT 06525

PEASE, BURTON FRANK, b Reliance, SDak, Jan 25, 28; m 53; c 5. ANALYTICAL CHEMISTRY. *Educ:* Pac Univ, BS, 50; Ore State Univ, PhD(anal chem), 57. *Prof Exp:* Chemist, Surg Res Team & Med Serv, Grad Sch, Walter Reed Inst Med Res, 51-53; instr chem, Ore State Col, 56-57; res technologist, Shell Oil Co Calif, 57-59; from asst prof to assoc prof, 59-67, head dept, 67-70, PROF CHEM, CALIF STATE UNIV, CHICO, 67- *Mem:* Am Chem Soc; Sigma Xi. *Res:* Chemical microscopy; spectrophotometry. *Mailing Add:* Dept Chem Calif State Univ Chico CA 95926

PEASE, DANIEL CHAPIN, b New York, NY, Aug 7, 14; m; c 2. ELECTRON MICROSCOPY. *Educ:* Yale Univ, AB, 36; Calif Inst Technol, MS, 38; Princeton Univ, PhD(cell physiol), 40. *Prof Exp:* Nat Res Coun fel, Stanford Univ, 40-41; instr zool, Columbia Univ, 42; res assoc, Off Sci Res & Develop, Princeton Univ, 43; res assoc, Stanford Univ, 44; instr anat, Sch Med, Univ Southern Calif, 45-46, asst prof neuroanat & histol, 47-49, assoc prof anat, 49-50; assoc prof, 51-54, chmn dept, 73-81, PROF ANAT, MED SCH, UNIV CALIF, LOS ANGELES, 55- *Mem:* Electron Micros Soc Am (pres, 72); Am Asn Anatomists (pres, 79); Am Soc Cell Biologists. *Res:* Electron microscopy of cells and tissues. *Mailing Add:* Dept of Anat Univ of Calif Sch of Med Los Angeles CA 90024

PEASE, JAMES ROBERT, b Halifax, Vt, June 5, 37; c 1. RESOURCE MANAGEMENT. *Educ:* Univ Mass, BA, 60, MS, 70, PhD(resource planning), 72. *Prof Exp:* Consult & prin partner, Terra Planning Assocs, 71-73; ASSOC PROF RESOURCE PLANNING, DEPT GEOG & EXTEN SERV, ORE STATE UNIV, 73- *Mem:* Asn Am Geographers; Am Soc Planning Officials. *Res:* Methodology for environmental impact analysis and for land use planning; ecological criteria for planning policy; land use and land tenure in Latin America. *Mailing Add:* Dept Geog Ore State Univ Corvallis OR 97331

PEASE, LILA GIERASCH, see Gierasch, Lila Mary

PEASE, MARSHALL CARLETON, III, b New York, NY, July 30, 20; div; c 3. PHYSICS, MATHEMATICS. *Educ:* Yale Univ, BS, 40; Princeton Univ, MA, 43. *Prof Exp:* Res assoc, Radio Res Lab, Harvard Univ, 43-45; from sr engr to eng specialist & mgr tube develop, Sylvania Elec Prod, Inc, 46-60; sr engr, 60-64, STAFF SCIENTIST, STANFORD RES INST, 64- *Concurrent Pos:* Lectr, Stanford Univ, 60-70. *Mem:* Fel Inst Elec & Electronics Engrs. *Res:* Computer design; theory of information storage and processing; application of modern algebra to system problems. *Mailing Add:* 151 Carmel Way Portola Valley Menlo Park CA 94025

PEASE, PAUL LORIN, b New Britain, Conn, Aug 6, 43; m 74; c 2. PHYSIOLOGICAL OPTICS. *Educ:* Pa Col Optom, BS, 65, OD, 67; Univ Calif, Berkeley, PhD(physiol optics), 75. *Prof Exp:* dir vision sci, 76-80, ASSOC PROF VISION, NEW ENGLAND COL OPTOM, 73- *Concurrent Pos:* Vis scientist, Univ Calif, Berkeley, 79; consult, Nat Bd Examr Optom, 80- *Mem:* Asn Res Vision & Ophthal; Optical Soc Am; AAAS; Am Acad Optom. *Res:* Neurophysiology and psychophysiology of color vision, color testing and spatial aspects of vision. *Mailing Add:* New England Col Optom 424 Beacon St Boston MA 02115

PEASE, ROBERT LOUIS, b Fitchburg, Mass, July 13, 25; m 70; c 1. PHYSICS. *Educ:* Miami Univ, AB, 43; Mass Inst Technol, PhD(physics), 50. *Prof Exp:* Asst prof math, Univ NH, 50-51; asst phys scientist, Rand Corp, 51-53; asst prof physics, Tufts Univ, 53-56; res physicist, Hughes Aircraft Co, 56-57; staff mem, Lincoln Lab, Mass Inst Technol, 57-60; assoc prof physics, Brooklyn Col, 60-64; vis res physicist, Princeton Univ, 64-65; physicist, Brookhaven Nat Lab, 65-67; PROF PHYSICS, STATE UNIV NY COL NEW PALTZ, 67- *Concurrent Pos:* Consult, Lincoln Lab, Mass Inst Technol, 60-63 & Princeton-Pa Accelerator, 64. *Mem:* Am Phys Soc; Inst Elec & Electronics Engrs. *Res:* Nuclear and elementary particle theory; electromagnetic theory; electrodynamics and particle accelerator theory. *Mailing Add:* Dept of Physics State Univ of New York New Paltz NY 12562

PEASE, ROBERT WRIGHT, b Evanston, Ill, Mar 30, 17; m 38; c 2. PHYSICAL GEOGRAPHY. *Educ:* Univ Calif, Los Angeles, BA, 38, MA, 46, PhD(geog), 60. *Prof Exp:* Tool engr, Douglas Aircraft Co, 40-45; teacher, Los Angeles City Sch Dist, 44-63; lectr geog, Univ Calif, Los Angeles, 63-64; instr, Los Angeles Jr Col Dist, 66-67; assoc prof, 67-77, PROF GEOG, UNIV CALIF, RIVERSIDE, 77- *Concurrent Pos:* Consult, Calif State Dept Educ, 63 & Geog Prog, US Geol Surv, 73- *Mem:* Sigma Xi; Asn Am Geog; Am Soc Photogram. *Res:* Remote sensing, radiation and crop climatology; utilization of remotely acquired data to measure surface energy-exchange phenomena; systems of filters and application for use with color infrared film for earth resources purposes. *Mailing Add:* Dept of Earth Sci Univ of Calif Riverside CA 92521

PEASE, ROGER FABIAN WEDGWOOD, b Cambridge, Eng, Oct 24, 36; m 60; c 3. ELECTRICAL ENGINEERING. *Educ:* Cambridge Univ, BA, 60, MA & PhD(elec eng), 64. *Prof Exp:* Res fel, Trinity Col, Cambridge Univ, 63-67; mem tech staff, Bell Tel Labs, Inc, 67-78; PROF ELEC ENG, STANFORD UNIV, 78- *Concurrent Pos:* Consult, IBM Corp, 64-67; from asst prof to assoc prof, Univ Calif, Berkeley, 64-69. *Mem:* Inst Elec & Electronics Engrs. *Res:* Electron microscopy and electron beam technology; digital encoding of television signals; microstructures and their applications; high density electronic circuitry. *Mailing Add:* Dept of Elec Eng Stanford Univ Stanford CA 94305

PEASLEE, ALFRED TREDWAY, JR, b Dubuque, Iowa, June 25, 30; m 59; c 3. THEORETICAL PHYSICS. *Educ:* Harvard Univ, AB, 52, AM, 53, PhD(physics), 55. *Prof Exp:* STAFF MEM, LOS ALAMOS SCI LAB, 55- *Mem:* AAAS; Am Phys Soc. *Res:* Quantum electrodynamics; classical theoretical physics. *Mailing Add:* 114 El Viento Los Alamos NM 87544

PEASLEE, DAVID CHASE, b White Plains, NY, July 23, 22; m 47, 73; c 3. THEORETICAL PHYSICS, NUCLEAR PHYSICS. *Educ:* Princeton Univ, AB, 43; Mass Inst Technol, PhD(physics), 48. *Prof Exp:* Analyst, Opers Res Group, Washington, DC, 44-46; res assoc physics, Mass Inst Technol, 46-48; assoc physicist, Kellex Corp, 48-49; fel, AEC, Zurich, 49-50; asst prof physics, Wash Univ, 50-51; res assoc, Columbia Univ, 51-54; from assoc prof to prof, Purdue Univ, 54-59; Fulbright fel, Australian Nat Univ, 58, reader theoret physics, 59-61, prof theoret physics, 61-76; vis prof physics, Brown Univ, 76-77, adj prof physics, 77-81; PROF PHYSICS, UNIV MD, 81- *Concurrent Pos:* Mem staff, Dept Energy, Washington, DC. *Mem:* fel Am Phys Soc. *Res:* Structure and interactions of nuclei and elementary particles. *Mailing Add:* Dept Physics Univ Maryland College Park MD 20742

PEASLEE, DOYLE E, b Stockton, Kans, Feb 24, 30; m 53; c 2. SOIL FERTILITY. *Educ:* Kans State Univ, BS, 52, MS, 56; Iowa State Univ, PhD(soil fertil), 60. *Prof Exp:* From asst soil scientist to assoc soil scientist, Conn Agr Exp Sta, 60-66; assoc prof, 66-71, PROF AGRON, UNIV KY, 71-, DIR, DIV REGULATORY SCI, RES & TECHNOL, 80- *Mem:* Am Soc Agron; Soil Sci Soc Am; Crop Sci Soc Am; Int Soil Sci Soc. *Res:* Fertilizer reactions in soils; availability of fertilizer and soil nutrients to plants; analytical methods for elements in soils; effects of nutrients on photosynthesis. *Mailing Add:* Dept Agron Univ Ky Lexington KY 40506

PEASLEE, MARGARET H, b Chicago, Ill, June 15, 35; m 57; c 1. ENDOCRINOLOGY. *Educ:* Fla Southern Col, BS, 59; Northwestern Univ, MS, 64, PhD, 66. *Prof Exp:* From asst prof to prof biol, Univ SDak, Vermillion, 68-76; PROF & HEAD, DEPT ZOOL, LA TECH UNIV, 76- *Concurrent Pos:* Acad opportunity liaison officer, Univ SDak, Vermillion, 74-76. *Mem:* Fel AAAS; Am Inst Biol Sci; Am Soc Zoologists; Sigma Xi. *Res:* Vertebrate endocrinology; melanocyte-stimulating hormone; pigment cell physiology; hormonal relationships in development. *Mailing Add:* Dept of Zool La Tech Univ Ruston LA 71272

PEATMAN, JOHN B(URLING), b Port Chester, NY, Nov 28, 34; m 56; c 3. ELECTRICAL ENGINEERING. *Educ:* Swarthmore Col, BSEE, 56; Case Inst Technol, MSEE, 60, PhD(digital systs), 65. *Prof Exp:* Assoc eval engr, Minneapolis-Honeywell Regulator Co, 56-59; asst prof elec eng, Univ Mo-Rolla, 60-62; from asst prof to assoc prof, 64-77, PROF ELEC ENG, GA INST TECHNOL, 77- *Mem:* Inst Elec & Electronics Engrs. *Res:* Digital systems engineering; algorithmic processes; time-oriented digital systems design techniques. *Mailing Add:* Sch of Elec Eng Ga Inst of Technol Atlanta GA 30332

PEATMAN, WILLIAM BURLING, b Port Chester, NY, July 15, 39; m 60; c 3. PHYSICAL CHEMISTRY. *Educ:* Harvard Univ, BA, 61; Northwestern Univ, MS, 63, PhD(chem), 69. *Prof Exp:* Instr chem, Elmhurst Col, 63-65; NSF grant, Univ Chicago, 69-70; asst prof chem, Vanderbilt Univ, 70-73, assoc prof, 73-79; DEP DIR RES, BERLINER ELEKTRONENSPEICHERRING GES FUER SYNCHROTRONSTRAHLUNG MBH, 79- *Mem:* Am Phys Soc; Am Inst Physics. *Res:* Molecular dynamics; energy transfer processes in plasmas; unimolecular decomposition of metastable molecular ions; photoionization studies. *Mailing Add:* Berliner Elektronenspeicherring GMBH Takustr 3 1 Berlin 33 West Germany

PEATTIE, CHARLES GORDON, b Beacon, NY, Oct 23, 16; m 47; c 2. ELECTROCHEMISTRY. *Educ:* State Univ NY, AB, 40; Univ Okla, MS, 49; Mass Inst Technol, PhD(anal chem), 52. *Prof Exp:* Anal chemist, Res Labs, Tex Co, 40-47; asst physics, Univ Okla, 48-49; asst chem, Mass Inst Technol, 49-50, asst anal chem, 50-52; chemist, Shell Develop Co, 53-56; chemist, Cent Res Labs, Tex Instruments, Inc, 56-66, mgr group qual & reliability assurance, Semiconductor Group, 66-81. *Res:* Semiconductor device and microelectronic circuit reliability; emission spectroscopy; absorption, Raman fluorescence and mass spectrometry; polarography; chemistry and physics of semiconductor surfaces; electrochemistry of molten-carbonate fuel cells. *Mailing Add:* 7707 Midbury Dallas TX 75230

PEAVLER, ROBERT JEAN, b Whittington, Ill, Feb 15, 24; m 57; c 3. INORGANIC CHEMISTRY. *Educ:* Univ Southern Ill, BA, 47; Univ Ill, MS, 48; Purdue Univ, PhD(chem), 53. *Prof Exp:* Engr, Mat Eng Labs, Westinghouse Elec Corp, Pa, 52-59; assoc prof chem & head dept, Ottawa Univ, 59-62; assoc physicist, Midwest Res Inst, 62-64; PROF PHYSICS, NORTHEAST MO STATE UNIV, 64- *Concurrent Pos:* Instr, Carnegie Inst Technol, 57-59. *Mem:* Am Chem Soc; Am Crystallog Asn. *Res:* High temperature chemistry; metallic systems; x-ray spectra. *Mailing Add:* Div of Sci Northeast Mo State Univ Kirksville MO 63501

PEBLY, HARRY E, b Sharpsville, Pa, Feb 1, 23; m 49; c 1. MATERIALS ENGINEERING, INFORMATION TECHNOLOGY. *Educ:* Pa State Univ, BS, 44; Stevens Inst Technol, MS, 57. *Prof Exp:* Mat engr, Westinghouse Elec Corp, 44-46; army ord, Picatinny Arsenal, 47-60, DIR PLASTICS TECH EVAL CTR, ARMY ARMAMENT RES & DEVELOP COMMAND, 60- *Concurrent Pos:* Trustee, Plastics Inst Am, 71-77 & Eng Index, 70-80, ed, adv bd, Int Plastics Selector, 78-, mem, Fed Coun Sci Technol, Panel Info Anal Ctr, 67-72. *Honors & Awards:* Cert achievement, Picatinny Arsenal, US Army, 72; Outstanding Serv Award, Soc Plastics Indust, 65. *Mem:* Am Chem Soc; Soc Plastics Eng; Soc Advan Mat & Process Eng. *Mailing Add:* 198 Center Grove Rd Randolph NJ 07869

PECCI, JOSEPH, b Boston, Mass, Nov 20, 30; m 56; c 5. CLINICAL CHEMISTRY, BIOCHEMISTRY. *Educ:* Mass Col Pharm, BS, 56, MS, 58. *Prof Exp:* Biol chemist, City of Boston Police Dept, 58-59; res chemist, Air Force Cambridge Res Labs, 59-69; res chemist, Vet Admin Hosp, Boston, 69-76, SUPVRY CHEMIST, VET ADMIN MED CTR, BOSTON, 76- *Mem:* AAAS; Am Asn Clin Chemists; Am Chem Soc; AMA. *Res:* Drug detection in biological fluids; clinical chemistry. *Mailing Add:* 56 Pine Ridge Rd Arlington MA 02174

PECHENIK, JAN A, b Jamaica, NY, May 5, 50. INVERTEBRATE ZOOLOGY, PHYSIOLOGICAL ECOLOGY. *Educ:* Duke Univ, BA, 71; Mass Inst Technol, MS, 75; Univ RI, PhD(biol oceanog), 78. *Prof Exp:* Marine biologist, Environ Res Lab, 76-78; lectr biol, 78-79, ASST PROF, TUFTS UNIV, 79- *Mem:* Am Soc Zool; Am Inst Biol Sci; Sigma Xi. *Res:* Reproduction and development of marine invertebrates. *Mailing Add:* Dept Biol Tufts Univ Medford MA 02155

PECHET, LIBERTO, b Braila, Rumania, July 6, 26; m 50; c 3. MEDICINE. *Educ:* Hebrew Univ, MD, 52. *Prof Exp:* Intern, Hadassah Hosp, Jerusalem, Israel, 51-52; village physician, Civil Serv, Ministry of Health, 52-53; res fel med, Harvard Med Sch, 57-59, instr med, 59-61, assoc, 61-66; asst prof path, Sch Med, Univ Colo, 66-69; asst chief, Lab Serv, Vet Admin Hosp, Boston, 69-70; assoc prof, 70-74, PROF MED & PATH & CHIEF SECT HEMAT, MED SCH, UNIV MASS, 74- *Concurrent Pos:* Res fel med, Beth Israel Hosp, 57-60, resident, 60-61, assoc, 61-65, asst vis physician, 65-66; attend hemat, Denver Vet Admin Hosp, 66-69. *Mem:* Am Soc Hemat; Am Fedn Clin Res; Soc Exp Biol & Med; Int Soc Hemat; Am Col Physicians. *Res:* Clinical, physiological and biochemical aspects of blood coagulation. *Mailing Add:* Univ of Mass Med Sch Worcester MA 01610

PECHUKAS, PHILIP, b Akron, Ohio, Oct 30, 42; m 63; c 5. THEORETICAL CHEMISTRY. *Educ:* Yale Univ, BS, 63; Univ Chicago, PhD(chem physics), 66. *Prof Exp:* Nat Acad Sci-Nat Res Coun fel theoret chem, Nat Bur Standards, Washington, DC, 66-67; from asst prof to assoc prof, 67-78, PROF CHEM, COLUMBIA UNIV, 78- *Concurrent Pos:* Sloan Found fel, 70-74; Guggenheim fel, 75. *Res:* Chemical kinetics; semiclassical approximation. *Mailing Add:* Dept of Chem Columbia Univ New York NY 10027

PECHUMAN, LAVERNE LEROY, b Lockport, NY, Oct 18, 13; m 39; c 2. ENTOMOLOGY. *Educ:* Cornell Univ, BS, 35, MS, 37, PhD(entom), 39. *Prof Exp:* Asst entom, Cornell Univ, 35-39; entomologist, Ortho Div, Chevron Chem Co, 39-46, dist mgr, 46-61, sr res scientist, 61-62; assoc prof, 62-73, PROF ENTOM, CORNELL UNIV, 73-, CUR, 62- *Mem:* Fel AAAS; Entom Soc Am; Entom Soc Can. *Res:* Biogeography and insect distribution patterns; taxonomy and biology of Diptera, especially Tabanidae; archeology of New York State. *Mailing Add:* 16 Lakeview Dr Lansing NY 14882

PECINA, RICHARD W, b Cedar Rapids, Iowa, Mar 2, 35; m 56; c 3. CHEMICAL & INDUSTRIAL ENGINEERING. *Educ:* Univ Iowa, BS, 56, MS, 57, PhD(indust & mgt eng), 62. *Prof Exp:* Res engr, Abbott Labs, 59-61; fel recovery potable water from urine, Univ Iowa, 62; res engr, Abbott Labs, North Chicago, 62-63, mgr mat & packaging res, 63-66, mgr plastics prods res & develop, 66-68, opers mgr plastics prods mfg, 68-69, plant mgr hosp prods opers, 69-71, mgr int hosp prod res & develop, 71-72; vpres sci affairs, Respiratory Care, Inc, Ill, 72-75; PRES, RICHARD W PECINA & ASSOC, INC, 75- *Mem:* Soc Plastics Engrs; Sigma Xi. *Res:* Packaging and materials research; water vapor permeability of plastic packaging films; research and development of plastic disposable devices for intravenous feeding solutions. *Mailing Add:* 2348 N Lewis Ave Waukegan IL 60087

PECK, ALAN S, metallurgy, mineralogy, see previous edition

PECK, CARL CURTIS, b Emporia, Kans, Mar 28, 42; m 72; c 1. EXPERIMENTAL BIOLOGY, MEDICINE. *Educ:* Univ Kans, BA, 63, MD, 68. *Prof Exp:* Intern med, Tripl Army Hosp, & resident phys int med, Letterman Army Hosp, 68-72; res fel clin pharmacol, Univ Calif Med Ctr, 72-74; res clin pharmacol, Div Blood Res, Letterman Army Inst Res, 74-77, chief res & develop, 77-80; ASSOC PROF MED & PHARMACOL & DIR, DIV CLIN PHARMACOL, UNIFORMED SERV UNIV HEALTH SCI, 80- *Concurrent Pos:* Asst prof med, Univ Calif Med Ctr, 75- *Honors & Awards:* Res Achievement Award, US Army Med Res & Develop Command, 78. *Mem:* AAAS; Am Soc Clin Pharmacol & Therapeut; Am Col Phys; Am Fedn Clin Res. *Res:* Medicine; biomathematics; biostatistics; experimental design; kinetics; modeling; clinical pharmacology. *Mailing Add:* 4301 Jones Bridge Rd Bethesda MD 20014

PECK, CHARLES FRANKLIN, JR, civil engineering, see previous edition

PECK, CHARLES WILLIAM, b Freer, Tex, Nov 29, 34; m 80; c 4. EXPERIMENTAL HIGH ENERGY PHYSICS. *Educ:* NMex Col Agr & Mech Arts, BS, 56; Calif Inst Technol, PhD(physics), 64. *Prof Exp:* Res fel, 64-65, from asst prof to assoc prof, 65-77, PROF PHYSICS, CALIF INST TECHNOL, 77- *Mem:* Am Inst Physics. *Res:* Meson photoproduction; bubble chamber physics; e-plus, e-minus storage ring experiments. *Mailing Add:* 356-48 Calif Inst Technol Pasadena CA 91125

PECK, DALLAS LYNN, b Cheney, Wash, Mar 28, 29; m 51; c 3. GEOLOGY. *Educ:* Calif Inst Technol, BS, 51, MS, 53; Harvard Univ, PhD, 60. *Prof Exp:* Asst field geol, Calif Inst Technol, 51-52; asst struct geol, Harvard Univ, 52-53; geologist, 51-66, asst chief geologist, Off Geochem & Geophys, 67-72, res geologist, 72-77, chief geologist, 77-81, DIR, US GEOL SURV, 81- *Concurrent Pos:* Mem vis comt, Dept Geol Sci, Harvard Univ, 71-75; mem geosci adv comt, Los Alamos Sci Labs, 75-77. *Mem:* Fel Geol Soc Am; Am Geophys Union; Soc Econ Geologists; Mineral Soc Am; fel AAAS. *Res:* Igneous petrology; Hawaiian lava lakes; Sierra Nevada Batholith. *Mailing Add:* US Geol Surv Nat Ctr Reston VA 22092

PECK, DAVID W, b Whitwell, Tenn, Sept 17, 25; m 52; c 3. PHYSICAL ORGANIC CHEMISTRY. *Educ:* Emory & Henry Col, BS, 49; Univ Va, MS, 51, PhD, 52. *Prof Exp:* Res chemist, 52-62, res proj leader org chem, 62-67, group leader, 67-70, develop scientist, 70-78, SR DEVELOP SCIENTIST ORG CHEM, UNION CARBIDE CORP, 78- *Mem:* Am Chem Soc. *Res:* Synthetic organic chemistry; pesticides. *Mailing Add:* 5277 Walnut Valley Dr Charleston WV 25312

PECK, EDSON RUTHER, b Evanston, Ill, Oct 29, 15; m 46; c 5. PHYSICS. *Educ:* Northwestern Univ, BA, 36, MS, 37; Univ Chicago, PhD(physics), 45. *Prof Exp:* Res physicist, Nat Defense Res Comt, Northwestern Univ, 42, instr physics, 42-46, asst prof, 46-49, assoc prof, 49-62; prof, 62-78, EMER PROF PHYSICS, UNIV IDAHO, 78- *Concurrent Pos:* Am Asn Physics Teachers-Am Inst Physics regional counr, 63-66. *Mem:* AAAS; Am Math Soc; Am Phys Soc; Optical Soc Am; NY Acad Sci. *Res:* Spectroscopy; interferometry; optical dispersion of gases. *Mailing Add:* Dept of Physics Univ of Idaho Moscow ID 83843

PECK, EMILY MANN, b Ft Myers, Fla, Sept 5, 46; m 73. MATHEMATICS, FUNCTIONAL ANALYSIS. *Educ:* NC State Univ, Raleigh, BS, 67; Univ Ill, MS, 68, PhD(math), 72. *Prof Exp:* Asst prof math, Vassar Col, 72-73; asst dean math, 73-80, ASST PROF MATH, UNIV ILL, 73-, ASST DEAN, COL LIBERAL ARTS & SCI, 80- *Mem:* Am Math Soc; Math Asn Am. *Res:* Spaces of continuous functions; Banach lattices. *Mailing Add:* Dept Math Univ Ill Urbana IL 61801

PECK, ERNEST JAMES, JR, b Port Arthur, Tex, July 26, 41; m 65; c 2. BIOCHEMISTRY, NEUROCHEMISTRY. *Educ:* Rice Univ, BA, 63, PhD(biochem), 66. *Prof Exp:* Res assoc biol sci, Purdue Univ, 66-68, Am Cancer Soc fel, 67-69, asst prof, 68-73; asst prof, 73-74, assoc prof, 74-80, prof cell biol, Baylor Col med, 81-82, PROF & CHMN BIOCHEM, UNIV ARK MED SCI, 82- *Mem:* Am Chem Soc; Am Soc Biol Chemists; Am Soc Neurochem; Biophys Soc; Soc Neurosci. *Res:* Chemical processes of cell communication, including steroids, peptide hormones and neurotransmitters; detection and mechanism of action. *Mailing Add:* Biochem Univ Ark Med Sci Little Rock AR 72205

PECK, EUGENE LINCOLN, b Kansas City, Kans, June 2, 22; m 46; c 4. HYDROLOGY, METEOROLOGY. *Educ:* Univ Utah, BS, 47, MS, 51; Utah State Univ, PhD(civil eng), 67. *Prof Exp:* Res hydrologist, Western Region, US Weather Bur, Nat Oceanic & Atmospheric Admin, 48-67, chief res br, Hydrol Res & Develop Lab, 67-72, asst dir, Hydrol Res Lab, 73, dir, 74-80; PRES, HYDEX CORP, FAIRFAX, VA, 80- *Concurrent Pos:* Lectr, Univ Utah, 56- *Honors & Awards:* Silver Medal, US Dept Com, 59 & 75. *Mem:* Am Meteorol Soc; Am Geophys Union. *Res:* Hydrometeorology; precipitation; snow. *Mailing Add:* Hydex Corp 11150 Main St Fairfax VA 22039

PECK, GARNET E, b Windsor, Ont, Feb 4, 30; US citizen; m 57; c 4. PHARMACY. *Educ:* Ohio Northern Univ, BS, 57; Purdue Univ, MS, 59, PhD(indust pharm), 62. *Prof Exp:* Pharmaceut technician, Strong Cobb & Co, Ohio, 47-51 & 53; instr pharmaceut chem, Purdue Univ, 59-62; sr scientist, Mead Johnson Res Ctr, 62-65, group leader, 65-67; assoc prof, 67-73, PROF INDUST PHARM, PURDUE UNIV, WEST LAFAYETTE, 73-, DIR INDUST PHARM LABS, 75- *Mem:* fel AAAS; Am Chem Soc; Am Pharmaceut Asn; fel Am Inst Chemists; NY Acad Sci. *Res:* Pharmaceutical product development; drug analysis; application of radioisotopes to pharmaceutical processing and analysis; flow of solids; solid surface studies. *Mailing Add:* Purdue Univ Sch of Pharm West Lafayette IN 47906

PECK, HARRY DOWD, JR, b Middletown, Conn, May 18, 27; m 75; c 5. MICROBIAL PHYSIOLOGY, ENZYMOLOGY. *Educ:* Wesleyan Univ, BA, 50, MA, 52; Western Reserve Univ, PhD(microbiol), 56. *Prof Exp:* res fel biochem, Mass Gen Hosp, 56-57; vis investr, Rockefeller Inst, 57-58; assoc biochemist, Oak Ridge Nat Lab, 58-64; NSF sr fel, Nat Ctr Sci Res, Ministry Educ, France, 64-65; PROF BIOCHEM & CHMN DEPT, UNIV GA, 65- *Concurrent Pos:* Mem adv panel metabolic biol, NSF & adv panel fels in microbiol, NIH, 67-70; found lectr, Am Soc Microbiol, 73-74, 81-82. *Mem:* Am Soc Biol Chemists; Am Soc Microbiol; Soc Gen Microbiol. *Res:* Enzymology of respiratory sulfate reduction and electron transfer in the sulfate reducing bacteria; oxidative phosphorlylation in anaerobic bacteria; metabolism of inorganic sulfur compounds in autotrophic bacteria. *Mailing Add:* Dept of Biochem Univ of Ga Athens GA 30602

PECK, JOHN F, metallurgy, see previous edition

PECK, JOHN HUBERT, b Rochester, NY, Oct 4, 42; m 64; c 4. MEDICAL ENTOMOLOGY, ENVIRONMENTAL SCIENCE. *Educ:* Clark Univ, BA, 64; Univ Calif, Berkeley, PhD(parasitol), 68. *Prof Exp:* Assoc prof, 68-80, PROF BIOL, ST CLOUD STATE UNIV, 80- *Res:* Ecology and natural control of filth flies; impact of camping on wilderness ecology. *Mailing Add:* Dept of Biol St Cloud State Univ St Cloud MN 56301

PECK, JOSEPH HOWARD, b Salina, Utah, Aug 16, 18; m 47. PALEONTOLOGY. *Educ:* Univ Mo, AB, 40, MA, 41. *Prof Exp:* Mus paleontologist, Univ Calif, Berkeley, 50-55, sr mus paleontologist, 55-77, prin mus scientist, 77-80; RETIRED. *Concurrent Pos:* Ed J Paleont Soc, 71-76. *Mem:* AAAS; Paleont Soc; Geol Soc Am; Am Asn Petrol Geologists. *Res:* Coelenterata, tetracorals and hexacorals; Mollusca, Cephalopoda; history of geology and paleontology. *Mailing Add:* 131 Fiesta Circle Orinda CA 94563

PECK, LYMAN COLT, b Lebanon, Ohio, Dec 10, 20; m 42; c 2. MATHEMATICS. *Educ:* Yale Univ, BS, 42; Univ Chicago, SM, 47; Ohio State Univ, PhD(math educ), 53. *Prof Exp:* Instr math, Ohio Univ, 47-49; asst prof educ, Fla State Univ, 51-52; asst prof math, Iowa State Teachers Col, 52-56; assoc prof, Ohio Wesleyan Univ, 56-61; chmn dept, 71-73, PROF MATH, MIAMI UNIV, 61- *Mem:* Math Asn Am. *Res:* College and high school mathematics curriculum. *Mailing Add:* Dept of Math & Statist Miami Univ Oxford OH 45056

PECK, MERLIN LARRY, b Boise, Idaho, Mar 1, 40; m 63; c 2. BIO-ORGANIC CHEMISTRY. *Educ:* Col of Idaho, BS, 62; Mont State Univ, PhD(chem), 71. *Prof Exp:* Asst prof chem, Lake Superior State Col, 66-69; lectr, Univ Ariz, 69-72; asst dept head educ activity, Am Chem Soc, 72-74; asst prof, 74-78, ASSOC PROF CHEM, TEX A&M UNIV, 78- *Mem:* Am Chem Soc; AAAS; Nat Sci Teachers Asn. *Res:* Development of interactive instructional programs and instructional aids; identification and synthesis of small, naturally occurring amines. *Mailing Add:* Dept of Chem Tex A&M Univ College Station TX 77843

PECK, NATHAN HIRAM, b Phelps, NY, Feb 21, 23; m 52; c 6. HORTICULTURE. *Educ:* Cornell Univ, BS, 51, PhD(soils), 56. *Prof Exp:* Soil scientist, Agr Res Serv, USDA, 56-57; res agronomist, Bird's Eye Div, Gen Foods Corp, 57-59; from asst prof to assoc prof, 59-74, PROF VEG CROPS, NY STATE COL AGR, CORNELL UNIV, 74- *Concurrent Pos:* Assoc prof, Ore State Univ, 65-66; sabbatical, Univ Calif, Davis, 76. *Mem:* Am Soc Agron; Soil Sci Soc Am; Int Soc Soil Sci; Am Soc Hort Sci. *Res:* Soil fertility, cultural practices and evapo-transpiration for vegetable crops. *Mailing Add:* Dept of Seed & Veg Sci NY State Agr Exp Sta Geneva NY 14456

PECK, NEWTON TENNEY, b Honolulu, Hawaii, Feb 3, 37. FUNCTIONAL ANALYSIS. *Educ:* Haverford Col, BA, 59; Univ Wash, PhD(math), 64. *Prof Exp:* Instr math, Yale Univ, 64-66; lectr, Univ Warwick, 67-68; asst prof, 68-70, ASSOC PROF MATH, UNIV ILL, URBANA, 70- *Concurrent Pos:* Alexander von Humboldt Found res fel, Univ Frankfurt, 66-67. *Mem:* Am Math Soc; Math Asn Am; London Math Soc; Sigma Xi. *Res:* Functional analysis, especially non locally convex topological linear spaces. *Mailing Add:* Dept of Math Univ of Ill Urbana IL 61801

PECK, RALPH B(RAZELTON), b Winnipeg, Man, June 23, 12; US citizen; m 37; c 2. CIVIL ENGINEERING. *Educ:* Rensselaer Polytech Inst, CE, 34, DCE, 37. *Prof Exp:* Detailer, Am Bridge Co, Pa, 37-38; lab asst, Arthur Casagrande, Mass, 38-39; lectr, Armour Inst Technol, 39-41; chief testing engr, Holabird & Root, Scioto Ord Plant, Ohio, 41; prof, 41-74, EMER PROF FOUND ENG, UNIV ILL, URBANA, 74- *Concurrent Pos:* Asst subway engr, Chicago, Ill, 39-42. *Honors & Awards:* Norman Medal, Am Soc Civil Engrs, 43, Wellington Prize, 65, Karl Terzaghi Award, 69; Nat Soc Prof Engrs Award, 72, Nat Medal Sci, 74, Washington Award, 76. *Mem:* Nat Acad Eng; hon mem Am Soc Civil Engrs; Nat Soc Prof Engrs; Geol Soc Am; Int Soc Soil Mech & Found Eng (pres, 69-73). *Res:* Behavior of soil masses under stress; foundations; dams; tunnels. *Mailing Add:* 1101 Warm Sands Dr SE Albuquerque NM 87123

PECK, RAYMOND ELLIOTT, b Hamilton, Mo, May 3, 04; m 29. GEOLOGY. *Educ:* Park Col, AB, 26; Univ Mo, AM, 28, PhD(geol), 32. *Prof Exp:* Asst geologist, State Hwy Comn, Mo, 29-30; from instr to prof geol & paleont, 30-71, chmn dept geol, 50-59, actg dean grad sch, 59-60, assoc dean, 61-63, dean res admin, 63-65, vpres res, 65-67, vpres res & grad studies, 67-69, spec asst to chancellor, 69-70, EMER PROF GEOL, UNIV MO-COLUMBIA, 71- *Concurrent Pos:* Fulbright fel, France, 50-51; geologist, US Geol Surv, 58-; co-ed, J Paleont, 69-73. *Mem:* Fel Geol Soc Am; fel Paleont Soc; Soc Econ Paleontologists & Mineralogists (secy-treas, 58-59); Am Asn Petrol Geologists. *Res:* Micropaleontology and stratigraphy of continental Mesozoic and Cenozoic formations; micropaleontology of charophytes, crinoids and ostracods. *Mailing Add:* 10 Lemmon Dr Columbia MO 65201

PECK, RICHARD MERLE, b Cleveland, Ohio, Mar 1, 21; m 50, 63; c 3. ORGANIC CHEMISTRY. *Educ:* Univ Md, BS, 43, PhD(org chem), 47. *Prof Exp:* Asst chem, Univ Md, 43-45, res chemist, 45-47; res assoc, Res Found, Ohio State Univ, 47-49; res assoc, 49-56, ASSOC MEM, INST CANCER RES, 56- *Concurrent Pos:* Am Cancer Soc fel, Royal Cancer Hosp, London, 55-56. *Mem:* Am Chem Soc; Am Asn Cancer Res. *Res:* Antimalarial synthesis; sulfonamides; quinolines; carcinogen-protein conjugates; alkylating antitumor, mutagenic, and carcinogenic agents with mixed bifunctionality; immunization as protection against chemical carcinogenesis in the rat. *Mailing Add:* Inst for Cancer Res Philadelphia PA 19111

PECK, ROBERT E, b Pasadena, Calif, Oct 16, 47; m 70; c 2. COMBUSTION, THERMAL SCIENCES. *Educ:* Univ Calif, Berkeley, BS, 69; Univ Calif, Irvine, MS, 72, PhD(eng), 76. *Prof Exp:* Assoc engr & scientist, McDonnell Douglas Astro Co, 69-71; res asst, Univ Calif, Irvine, 71-76, teaching asst eng, 72-74; ASST PROF MECH ENG, UNIV KY, 76- *Honors & Awards:* Ralph R Teetor Award, Soc Automotive Engrs, 77. *Mem:* Combustion Inst; Am Soc Mech Engrs; Air Pollution Control Asn; Am Soc Eng Educ; Sigma Xi. *Res:* Combustion processes; air pollution control; thermodynamics; kinetic and transport processes affecting pollutant production in pulverized-coal combustion. *Mailing Add:* Dept Mech Eng Univ Ky Lexington KY 40506

PECK, RUSSELL ALLEN, JR, b New Haven, Conn, May 31, 24; m 52. PHYSICS. *Educ:* Yale Univ, BS, 44, MS, 45, PhD(physics), 47. *Prof Exp:* Asst, Yale Univ, 47-48; from instr to assoc prof, 48-59, PROF PHYSICS, BROWN UNIV, 59- *Concurrent Pos:* Guggenheim fel, Univ Birmingham, 56-57; consult, Los Alamos Sci Lab, 63-64; NIH fel radiol, Univ Pa Hosp, 70-71. *Mem:* Fel Am Phys Soc; Am Asn Physics Teachers; Am Asn Physicists in Med. *Res:* Nuclear physics; fast neutron reactions with low energy Cockcroft-Walton accelerator; biomedical applications of neutrons. *Mailing Add:* Dept of Physics Brown Univ Providence RI 02912

• **PECK, STEWART BLAINE,** b Davenport, Iowa, Aug 14, 42; m 70; c 2. ENTOMOLOGY, EVOLUTIONARY BIOLOGY. *Educ:* Univ Ky, BS, 64; Northwestern Univ, Evanston, MS, 66; Harvard Univ, PhD(biol), 71. *Prof Exp:* Lectr biol, 70-71, asst prof, 71-76, ASSOC PROF BIOL, CARLETON UNIV, 76- *Concurrent Pos:* Fel, Carleton Univ, 70-71. *Mem:* Fel Nat Speleol Soc; Soc Syst Zool; Soc Study Evolution; Ecol Soc Am; Am Soc Naturalists. *Res:* Evolutionary biology of cave-inhabiting arthropods and silphoid beetles. *Mailing Add:* Dept of Biol Carleton Univ Ottawa ON K1S 5B6 Can

PECK, THEODORE RICHARD, b Spring Green, Wis, June 16, 31; m 70; c 2. SOIL FERTILITY, SOIL CHEMISTRY. *Educ:* Univ Wis, BS, 57, MS, 58, PhD(soils), 62. *Prof Exp:* From asst prof to assoc prof, 62-74, PROF SOIL CHEM, UNIV ILL, URBANA, 74- *Concurrent Pos:* Sabbatical, Univ Rio Grande do Sul, Brazil, 70-71. *Mem:* AAAS; Soil Sci Soc Am; Am Soc Agron; Coun Soil Testing & Plant Anal (chmn, 75-76); Coun Agr Sci & Technol. *Res:* Soil testing and plant analysis methods, correlation and calibration; soil fertility and pedology; availability of chemical elements in the soil for plants; chemical composition of plants. *Mailing Add:* Dept Agron N-121 Turner Hall Univ Ill Urbana IL 61801

PECK, WILLIAM ARNO, b New Britain, Conn, Sept 28, 33; m 61; c 3. ENDOCRINOLOGY. *Educ:* Harvard Univ, AB, 55; Univ Rochester, MD, 60. *Prof Exp:* Intern ward med, Barnes Hosp, St Louis, 60-61, asst resident, 61-62; fel med metab, Sch Med, Washington Univ, 62-63; clin assoc metab dis, NIH, Bethesda, 63-65; chief resident & instr med, Sch Med, Univ Rochester, 65-66, sr instr, 66-67, from asst prof to assoc prof, 67-73, prof med & biochem, 73-76; JOHN E & ADALINE SIMON PROF MED & CO-CHMN DEPT, SCH MED, WASHINGTON UNIV, PHYSICIAN-IN-CHIEF, JEWISH HOSP ST LOUIS, 76- *Concurrent Pos:* Fel, Univ Rochester, 66-67; assoc physician, Strong Mem Hosp, Rochester, 67-69, head endocrine unit & sr assoc physician, 69-73, physician, 73-76; gen med study sect, NIH, 77-81; res career prog award, Food & Drug Admin, 71, mem adv comt, 74-78, chmn, 76-78. *Honors & Awards:* Doran J Stephens Award, 60; Lederle Med Fac Award, 67. *Mem:* Endocrine Soc; Am Physiol Soc; Asn Am Physicians; Am Soc Clin Invest; Am Soc Biol Chemists. *Res:* Mechanisms of hormone action; regulation of bone and mineral metabolism. *Mailing Add:* 216 S Kingshighway PO Box 14109 St Louis MO 63178

PECK, WILLIAM B, b Neosho, Mo, Apr 27, 20; m 52. ARACHNOLOGY. *Educ:* Iowa State Univ, BS, 42; Cent Mo State Col, MA, 63; Univ Ark, PhD(zool), 68. *Prof Exp:* Mem staff, US Civil Serv, 53-65; from asst prof to assoc prof, 67-75, PROF BIOL, CENT MO STATE UNIV, 75- *Concurrent Pos:* Collabr Arachnida, Entom Res Div, Agr Res Serv, USDA, 69- *Mem:* AAAS; Centre Int de Doc Arachnologique (vpres, 77-80); Am Arachnol Soc (pres, 75-77); Brit Arachnological Soc. *Res:* Biology and systematics of arachnids; human population and behavioral mores. *Mailing Add:* Dept of Biol Cent Mo State Univ Warrensburg MO 64093

PECKA, JAMES THOMAS, b Binghamton, NY, May 19, 32; m 55; c 4. INDUSTRIAL CHEMISTRY. *Educ:* St Bonaventure Univ, BS, 54; Univ Buffalo, MA, 58, PhD(chem), 61. *Prof Exp:* STAFF SCIENTIST, FILM DEPT & SR CHEMIST, PLASTIC PROD & RESINS DEPT, E I DU PONT DE NEMOURS & CO, INC, 60- *Mem:* Am Chem Soc. *Res:* Reactions of cyanogen with amines, aminophenols and aminothiophenols; weatherable films applications; polymeric nonlubricated bearings; high temperature film application; polyester film development and applications. *Mailing Add:* E I du Pont de Nemours & Co Inc PO Box 3000 Florence SC 29501

PECKARSKY, BARBARA LYNN, b Milwaukee, Wis, Aug 18, 47; m 78. STREAM ECOLOGY, COMMUNITY ECOLOGY. *Educ:* Univ Wis-Madison, BS, 69, MS, 71, PhD(zool), 79. *Prof Exp:* ASST PROF ENTOM, CORNELL UNIV, 79- *Concurrent Pos:* Fel, NSF, 80-81; instr, Rocky Mountain Biol Lab, 79, 81. *Mem:* Ecol Soc Am; NAm Benthological Soc; Entom Soc Am; Am Soc Limnol & Oceanog. *Res:* Experimental analysis of the biological factors that influence the distribution and abundance of benthic invertebrates in streams; effects of invertebrate predation and competition among invertebrates on their community structure; behavioral interactions among predators and prey, and among competitors in situ, as well as the results on enclosure experiments. *Mailing Add:* Dept Entom Cornell Univ Ithaca NY 14853

PECKHAM, ALAN EMBREE, b Boise, Idaho, Aug 11, 31. HYDROLOGY. *Educ:* Earlham Col, BA, 53; Univ Nebr, MS, 55. *Prof Exp:* Geologist, US Geol Surv, 55-63; hydrogeologist, Int Atomic Energy Agency, 63-65; staff geologist, US Geol Surv, 65-66; res assoc, Ctr Water Resources Res, Desert Res Inst, 66-72, asst dir, Inst, 68-71, asst dir, Ctr, 71-72; HYDROLOGIST, US ENVIRON PROTECTION AGENCY, 72- *Concurrent Pos:* Leader task force indust waste injection of working group on protection of underground sources of drinking water, US Environ Protection Agency, 75- *Mem:* AAAS; Am Asn Petrol Geologists; Geol Soc Am; Am Geophys Union; Int Asn Sci Hydrol. *Res:* Groundwater geology and hydrology; ground disposal of radioactive wastes; stable and radioactive isotope techniques in hydrogeological studies; protection of underground water sources; water supply and ground disposed of wastes; impacts of waste disposed on groundwater quality; hazardous waste site investigations; underground waste injection control guidance. *Mailing Add:* 8985 W Jefferson Denver CO 80235

PECKHAM, DONALD CHARLES, b Bainbridge, NY, Sept 11, 22; m 49; c 6. PHYSICS. *Educ:* Oberlin Col, AB, 48; Univ Mich, MA, 49; Pa State Univ, PhD(physics), 54. *Prof Exp:* Instr physics, Norwich Univ, 49-51; from asst prof to prof, 54-71, ALVINZA HAYWARD PROF PHYSICS, ST LAWRENCE UNIV, 71- *Concurrent Pos:* NSF sci fac fel, Colo State Univ, 66-67; vis physics fac mem, Ga Inst Technol, 79-80. *Mem:* AAAS; Am Phys Soc; Am Asn Physics Teachers; Optical Soc Am. *Res:* Optics. *Mailing Add:* Dept of Physics St Lawrence Univ Canton NY 13617

PECKHAM, JOHN CECIL, b Enid, Okla, Nov 6, 34; m 58, 73; c 4. PATHOLOGY, ONCOLOGY. *Educ:* Okla State Univ, DVM, 58; Iowa State Univ, MS, 61; Wash State Univ, PhD, 67. *Prof Exp:* Instr vet path, Iowa State Univ, 58-61; asst prof, Wash State Univ, 63-65; pathologist, Dept Path & Toxicol, Pitman-Moore Div, Dow Chem Co, 65-67; sr pathologist, Univ Ga, 67-72; sr pathologist & head, Path Sect, 72-76, HEAD, PATH DIV, SOUTHERN RES INST, 76- *Concurrent Pos:* vis assoc prof, Univ Ala, Birmingham, 72- *Mem:* Am Vet Med Asn; Am Col Vet Path; Int Acad Path. *Res:* Veterinary and comparative pathology; neuropathology; virology and parasitology; toxicology; oncology. *Mailing Add:* 5320 Eighth Ave Birmingham AL 35212

PECKHAM, P HUNTER, b Elmira, NY, June 23, 44; m 66; c 2. REHABILITATION ENGINEERING. *Educ:* Clarkson Col Technol, BS, 66; Case Western Reserve Univ, MS, 68, PhD(biomed eng), 72. *Prof Exp:* Res assoc, Case Western Reserve Univ, 72-74, instr, Div Orthapedic Surg, 74-78; RES BIOMED ENGR, MED CTR, CLEVELAND VET ADMIN, 76-; ASST PROF ORTHOPEDICS, CASE WESTERN RESERVE UNIV, 78-, ASSOC PROF BIOMED ENG, 79- *Concurrent Pos:* Res Career Develop Award, NIH, 78; mem staff, Cryahoga Coun Hosp, 81- *Mem:* Rehab Eng Soc NAm. *Res:* Technology for rehabilitation of the severely disabled; restoration of movement of the arm and hand using functional neuromuscular stimulation. *Mailing Add:* Highland View Hosp 3395 Scranton Rd Cleveland OH 44109

PECKHAM, RICHARD STARK, b Concord, NH; Mar 1, 24; m 50; c 9. ZOOLOGY. *Educ:* Univ NH, BS, 48; Univ Notre Dame, MS, 52, PhD(zool), 55. *Prof Exp:* USPHS jr asst sanitarian, Pan Am Sanit Bur, Guatemala, 48-50; instr biol sci, Holy Cross Cent Sch Nursing, Ind, 54-55, Del Mar Col, 55-59 & Dutchess Community Col, 59-63; PROF BIOL SCI, MT ST MARY COL, NY, 63- *Concurrent Pos:* Mem Int Audio-Tutorial Cong. *Mem:* Am Inst Biol Sci; Sigma Xi. *Res:* Plankton studies; ichthyology. *Mailing Add:* Dept of Biol Mt St Mary Col Newburgh NY 12550

PECKHAM, WILLIAM DIEROLF, b Wichita Falls, Tex, Sept 18, 22; m 50; c 4. BIOCHEMISTRY, ENDOCRINOLOGY. *Educ:* Colo Col, AB, 46; Univ Pittsburgh, PhD(biochem), 55. *Prof Exp:* Res biochemist, Schering Corp, 55-59, sr res biochemist, 59-60, head dept biochem, 60-61; RES ASSOC PHYSIOL, SCH MED, UNIV PITTSBURGH, 61- *Mem:* AAAS; Am Chem Soc; Endocrine Soc; NY Acad Sci. *Res:* Peptide synthesis; regulation of pituitary hormone secretion; mechanisms of hormone action; isolation and purification of primate protein hormones; immunoassay of primate protein hormones. *Mailing Add:* Dept of Physiol Univ of Pittsburgh Sch of Med Pittsburgh PA 15213

PECKINPAUGH, ROBERT OWEN, b Mishawaka, Ind, Jan 1, 22; m 47, 81; c 3. PREVENTIVE MEDICINE, INTERNAL MEDICINE. *Educ:* Ind Univ, BS, 44, MD, 47; Univ Mich, MPH, 64; Am Bd Prev Med, dipl 68. *Prof Exp:* US Navy, 42-72, intern, Naval Hosp, Long Beach, Calif, 47-48, med officer, Long Beach Naval Shipyard, 48-50, resident internal med, Naval Hosp, Bethesda, Md, 50-51, med officer, Hosp Ship Consolation, 51-52, resident, Naval Hosp, Bethesda, 53-54, med officer, Bur Med & Surg, 55-56, Naval Sta Hosp, Naples, Italy, 56-58 & Naval Hosp, Great Lakes, Ill, 58-62, dir sci dept, Naval Med Res Unit 4, 62-63, cmndg officer, Naval Med Res Unit 4, 64-72; DIR CLIN RES, ABBOTT LABS, 72- *Concurrent Pos:* Assoc mem comn influenza, Armed Forces Epidemiol Bd, 64-72, assoc mem comn acute respiratory dist, 68-72; consult, Naval Med Res Unit 4, 72-74; comt training & educ, Pharmaceut Mfg Asn, 75- *Mem:* Am Soc Microbiol; Am Pub Health Asn; Asn Mil Surg US; Soc Epidemiol Res; Int Health Soc. *Res:* Epidemiology, prevention and control of acute respiratory disease, meningococcal disease and related illnesses, including sequelae and complications. *Mailing Add:* 816 Fair Way Libertyville IL 60085

PECKNOLD, PAUL CARSON, b Brandon, Man, Dec 21, 42; US citizen; m 68; c 2. PLANT PATHOLOGY. *Educ:* Calif State Col, Hayward, BS, 67; Univ Calif, Davis, PhD(plant path), 72. *Prof Exp:* Plant pathologist, Calif State Dept Food & Agr, 72-73; ASSOC PROF EXTEN, PURDUE UNIV, WEST LAFAYETTE, 73- *Mem:* Am Phytopath Soc; Apple & Pear Dis Workers. *Res:* Fungicide testing for control of fruit and ornamental diseases. *Mailing Add:* Dept of Bot & Plant Path Lilly Hall Life Sci Purdue Univ West Lafayette IN 47907

PECORA, ROBERT, b New York, NY, Aug 6, 38. PHYSICAL CHEMISTRY. *Educ:* Columbia Univ, AB, 59, AM, 60, PhD(chem), 62. *Prof Exp:* Nat Acad Sci-Nat Res Coun fel, Brussels, 63; res physicist, Columbia Univ, 64; asst prof, 64-70, assoc prof chem, 71-77, PROF CHEM, STANFORD UNIV, 77- *Concurrent Pos:* Vis prof, Victoria Univ Manchester, 70-71; vis prof Univ Nice, 78. *Mem:* AAAS; Am Chem Soc; Am Phys Soc. *Res:* Statistical mechanics of equilibrium and non-equilibrium processes especially applications to liquids and polymers; inelastic scattering of neutrons and light from condensed systems. *Mailing Add:* Dept of Chem Stanford Univ Stanford CA 94305

PECORINI, HECTOR A(NDREW), b New York, NY, Oct 26, 24; m 49; c 3. CHEMICAL ENGINEERING. *Educ:* Cooper Union, BChE, 44; Univ Mich, MS, 50, PhD(chem eng), 54. *Prof Exp:* Chemist, US Indust Chem Co, 46-49; chem engr, 53-70, PROCESS ENGR, E I DU PONT DE NEMOURS & CO, INC, 70- *Mem:* Am Chem Soc; Am Inst Chem Engrs. *Res:* Kinetics of the homogeneous liquid-phase reaction between propylene oxide and methyl alcohol. *Mailing Add:* 2426 Owen Dr Wilmington DE 19808

PECSAR, RAYMOND E(RNEST), b Cleveland, Ohio, Nov 29, 37; m 58; c 4. ENGINEERING, ANALYTICAL CHEMISTRY. *Educ:* Univ Calif, Berkeley, BS, 59; Univ Mich, MSChE, 60, MS, 63, ScD(chem eng), 64. *Prof Exp:* Engr, Beckman Instruments, Inc, 60-61; mem adv tech staff rocket propulsion, Marquardt Corp, 65-67; mgr gas chromatography instrumentation, Varian Aerograph, 67-73; mkt mgr liquid chromatography, Varian Assoc, 73-78; MGR INSTRUMENTATION, BIO-RAD LABS, 78- *Mem:* Am Chem Soc; Instrument Soc Am; Am Soc Testing & Mat. *Res:* Thermodynamics; chemical instrumentation; applied mathematics; rocket propulsion; chemical process design; heat transfer; materials technology; physical chemistry. *Mailing Add:* Bio-Rad Labs 2200 Wright Ave Richmond CA 94804

PECSOK, ROBERT LOUIS, b Cleveland, Ohio, Dec 18, 18; m 40; c 7. ANALYTICAL CHEMISTRY. *Educ:* Harvard Univ, BS, 40, PhD(chem), 48. *Prof Exp:* Prod foreman, Procter & Gamble Co, 40-43; instr chem, Harvard Univ, 48; from asst prof to prof, Univ Calif, Los Angeles, 48-71; prof chem & chmn dept, 71-80, DEAN NATURAL SCI, UNIV HAWAII, HONOLULU, 81- *Concurrent Pos:* Guggenheim fel, 56-57; Am Chem Soc-Petrol Res Fund int fel, 63-64; sci adv, US Food & Drug Admin, 66-69, dir chem technician curric proj, 69-72. *Honors & Awards:* Tolman Medal, Am Chem Soc, 71. *Mem:* Am Chem Soc. *Res:* Polarography; complex ions; chemistry of transition metals; gas chromatography; principles and practice of chromatographic separations. *Mailing Add:* Dept of Chem Univ of Hawaii Honolulu HI 96822

PECZON, BENIGNO DAVID, b Mexico, Pampanga, Philippines, Dec 17, 41; m 64; c 2. BIOCHEMISTRY, PHYSICAL CHEMISTRY. *Educ:* Univ Philippines, BS, 64; Purdue Univ, PhD(chem), 70. *Prof Exp:* Instr chem, Univ Philippines, 63-64; res assoc biochem, Okla State Univ, 69-74; asst scientist, 74-77, ASSOC SCIENTIST BIOCHEM, EYE RES INST RETINA FOUND, 78- *Concurrent Pos:* Instr opthal, Harvard Med Sch, 77- *Mem:* Am Chem Soc; Soc Complex Carbohydrates; Asn Res Vision & Ophthal; AAAS. *Res:* Nature of basement membranes; enzymes. *Mailing Add:* Eye Res Inst of Retina Found 20 Staniford St Boston MA 02114

PEDDICORD, RICHARD G, b Ft Monroe, Va, Feb 17, 39; m 61; c 1. COMPUTER SCIENCE. *Educ:* Univ Calif, Davis, BA, 62, PhD(math), 65; Univ Calif, Berkeley, MA, 64. *Prof Exp:* Asst res systs analyst, Univ Calif, Davis, 66-67; asst prof comput sci, Univ Alta, 68-69; ASST PROF COMPUT SCI, UNIV SAN FRANCISCO, 69- *Mem:* Am Math Soc. *Res:* Linear regression; instability of linear systems; combinatorics; application of computers in medicine and biology; computer hardwear; artificial intelligence. *Mailing Add:* Dept Comput Sci Univ San Francisco San Francisco CA 94117

PEDEN, IRENE C(ARSWELL), b Topeka, Kans, Sept 25, 25; m 62; c 2. ELECTRICAL ENGINEERING, RADIO SCIENCE. *Educ:* Univ Colo, BS, 47; Stanford Univ, MS, 58, PhD(elec eng), 62. *Prof Exp:* Jr engr, Del Power & Light Co, 47-49; jr engr, Aircraft Radio Systs Lab, Stanford Res Inst, 49-50, res engr, 50-52, antenna res group, 54-57; res engr, Midwest Res Inst, Mo, 53-54; res asst, Hansen Lab, Stanford Univ, 58-61, actg instr elec eng, 59-61; from asst prof to assoc prof, 61-71, assoc dean eng, 73-77, PROF ELEC ENG, UNIV WASH, 71- *Concurrent Pos:* Mem, Policy Adv Comt Eng & Appl Sci, NSF, 76-81; mem adv bd, Alaska Geophys Inst, Univ Alaska, 77-80; mem, Army Sci Bd, 78-; mem adv bd, US Merchant Marine Acad, 78- *Honors & Awards:* Acheivement Award, Soc Women Engrs, 73. *Mem:* AAAS; fel Inst Elec & Electronics Engrs; Am Geophys Union; Int Union Radio Sci; Soc Women Engrs. *Res:* Microwave measurements, networks and periodic circuits; radio science with applications to the polar regions. *Mailing Add:* 407 Elec Eng Bldg FT-10 Univ of Wash Seattle WA 98195

PEDERSEN, FRANKLIN D, b St Paul, Nebr, Feb 22, 33; m 61; c 2. MATHEMATICS. *Educ:* Peru State Col, BA, 59; Tulane Univ, MS, 62, PhD(math), 67. *Prof Exp:* Asst prof, 65-76, ASSOC PROF MATH, SOUTHERN ILL UNIV, CARBONDALE, 76- *Concurrent Pos:* Vis lectr, Univ Natal, 70. *Mem:* Am Math Soc; Math Asn Am. *Res:* Algebra; ordered structures. *Mailing Add:* Dept Math Southern Ill Univ Carbondale IL 62901

PEDERSEN, KATHERINE L, b Connersville, Ind, Oct 14, 37; m 61; c 2. TOPOLOGY. *Educ:* St Louis Univ, BS, 59; Tulane Univ, MS, 62, PhD(math), 69. *Prof Exp:* Asst math, Tulane Univ, 60-61; instr math, Newcomb Col, 61-65; instr, 65-69, ASST PROF MATH, SOUTHERN ILL UNIV, CARBONDALE, 69- *Mem:* Am Math Soc; Math Asn Am; Nat Coun Teachers Math. *Res:* Preparing materials for pre-service education of elementary and secondary mathematics teachers. *Mailing Add:* Dept of Math Southern Ill Univ Carbondale IL 62901

PEDERSEN, KNUD B(ORGE), b Odense, Denmark, Nov 26, 32; US citizen; m 53; c 3. NUCLEAR & MECHANICAL ENGINEERING. *Educ:* Iowa State Univ, BS, 58, MS, 64, PhD(nuclear eng), 67. *Prof Exp:* Develop engr, Outboard Marine Corp, 58-60; jr engr, Ames Lab, Atomic Energy Comn, Iowa State Univ, 60-64, instr nuclear eng, univ, 64-67; from asst prof to assoc prof nuclear eng, 67-76, assoc scientist, 67-70, scientist II, 70-76, sr scientist, Ctr Energy & Environ Res, Atomic Energy Comn, 76-80, head, Nuclear Tech Div, 77-80, PROF MECH & NUCLEAR ENG, UNIV PR, 76- *Concurrent Pos:* Consult energy & accident invest. *Mem:* Am Nuclear Soc; Colegiode Ingenieros de PR. *Res:* Reactor safety and kinetics; energy conversion and conservation; methods and policies. *Mailing Add:* Ctr Energy & Environ Res Col Sta Mayaguez PR 00708

PEDERSEN, LEE G, b Oklahoma City, Okla, June 15, 38; m 64; c 2. PHYSICAL CHEMISTRY, CHEMICAL PHYSICS. *Educ:* Univ Tulsa, BCh, 61; Univ Ark, PhD(phys chem), 65. *Prof Exp:* NSF res assoc theoret chem, Columbia Univ, 65-66; NIH res fel, Harvard Univ, 66-67; from asst prof to assoc prof, 67-76, PROF PHYS CHEM, UNIV NC, CHAPEL HILL, 76- *Mem:* Sigma Xi; Am Asn Univ Professors; Am Phys Soc. *Res:* Theoretical chemistry and biology; rotational barriers; H-bond; free radicals; molecular dynamics; photochemistry. *Mailing Add:* Rte 1 Box 201F Durham NC 27705

PEDERSEN, PEDER CHRISTIAN, b Kalundborg, Denmark, Sept 28, 43. PHYSICAL ACOUSTICS. *Educ:* Aalborg Eng Col, Denmark, BS, 71; Univ Utah, ME, 74, PhD(bioeng), 76. *Prof Exp:* ASST PROF ELEC ENG, DEPT ELEC & COMPUT ENG, DREXEL UNIV, 76- *Concurrent Pos:* Proj leader, Sandoz Hosp Supplies Res, Salt Lake City, Utah, 76; Coordr, Clin Eng Prog, Biomed Eng & Sci Inst, Drexel Univ, 80- *Mem:* Inst Elec & Electronics Engrs; Acoustical Soc Am; Am Inst Ultrasound Med; AAAS. *Res:* Study of diagnostic use of low-intensity microwaves for detecting changes in lung water; development of techniques for ultrasonic characterization of lung tissue. *Mailing Add:* Dept Elec & Comput Eng Drexel Univ Philadelphia PA 19104

PEDERSEN, PETER L, b Muskogee, Okla, Oct 31, 39; m 65; c 3. BIOCHEMISTRY, MOLECULAR BIOLOGY. *Educ:* Univ Tulsa, BA, 61; Univ Ark, PhD(chem), 64. *Prof Exp:* From instr to asst prof, 67-72, PROF BIOCHEM, SCH MED, JOHNS HOPKINS UNIV, 72- *Concurrent Pos:* USPHS fel biochem, Sch Med, Johns Hopkins Univ, 64-67; USPHS res grant, 68-; Nat Cancer Inst res award, 69- *Mem:* Am Chem Soc; Am Soc Biol Chemists. *Res:* Bioenergetics mechanism of action, allosteric properties, membrane association and physiological function of those enzyme systems that participate in high energy phosphate bond transfer reactions in normal and pathological tissue, specifically mitochondrial AT Pase and hexokinase; transport of Pi across the plasma and mitochondrial membranes. *Mailing Add:* Dept of Physiol Chem Johns Hopkins Univ Sch of Med Baltimore MD 21205

PEDERSEN, ROGER ARNOLD, b San Bernadino, Calif, Aug 1, 44; m 76; c 2. DEVELOPMENTAL GENETICS, TERATOGENESIS. *Educ:* Stanford Univ, AB, 65; Yale Univ, PhD(biol), 70. *Prof Exp:* USPHS fel, Sch Hyg & Pub Health, Johns Hopkins Univ, 70-71; asst prof radiol, 71-79, asst prof anat, 75-79, ASSOC PROF RADIOL & ANAT, UNIV CALIF, SAN FRANCISCO, 79- *Mem:* AAAS; Am Soc Cell Biol; Soc Develop Biol; Radiation Res Soc. *Res:* Mammalian embryology; mechanisms of cell differentiation and commitment; induction and repair of genetic damage. *Mailing Add:* Lab of Radiobiol Univ of Calif San Francisco CA 94143

PEDERSON, DARRYLL THORALF, b Valley City, NDak, Aug 12, 39; m 61; c 2. HYDROGEOLOGY. *Educ:* Valley City State Col, BSEd, 61; Univ NDak, MST, 66, PhD(geol), 71. *Prof Exp:* Asst prof geol, Minot State Col, 71-73; asst prof geol, Appalachian State Univ, 73-75; ASSOC PROF HYDROGEOL, UNIV NEBR, LINCOLN, 75- *Mem:* Am Inst Prof Geologists; Geol Soc Am; Am Geophys Union; Nat Water Well Asn; AAAS. *Res:* Delineation of the aquifiers of Nebraska and the movement of water from the surface into these aquifiers; surface geophysical techniques, electrical. *Mailing Add:* Conserv & Surv Div 113 Nebr Hall Univ of Nebr Lincoln NE 68588

PEDERSON, DONALD O(SCAR), b Hallock, Minn, Sept 30, 25; m 50, 78; c 4. ELECTRICAL ENGINEERING. *Educ:* NDak Agr Col, BS, 48; Stanford Univ, MS, 49, PhD(elec eng), 51. *Hon Degrees:* DSc, Kathielke Univ, Belgium, 79. *Prof Exp:* Res assoc, Electronic Res Lab, Stanford Univ, 51-53; mem tech staff, Bell Tel Labs, Inc, 53-55; dir, Electronic Res Lab, 60-64, PROF ELEC ENG, UNIV CALIF, BERKELEY, 55- *Concurrent Pos:* Lectr, Newark Col Eng, 53-55; Guggenheim fel, 64. *Honors & Awards:* Educ Medal, Inst Elec & Electronics Engrs, 69. *Mem:* Nat Acad Eng; fel Inst Elec & Electronics Engrs. *Res:* Electronic circuits. *Mailing Add:* Dept of Elec Eng & Comput Sci Univ of Calif Berkeley CA 94720

PEDERSON, LYLE P(ERRY), b Kinbrae, Minn, Apr 23, 29; m 55, 76; c 8. GEOTECHNICAL ENGINEERING, DAM ENGINEERING. *Educ:* Univ Minn, Minneapolis, 52, MS, 56, PhD(civil eng), 64. *Prof Exp:* Instr, Univ Minn, Minneapolis, 56-64, asst prof civil eng, 64-78; vpres, Subterranean Eng, Inc, 78-80; mem staff, Lyle Pederson & Assocs, 80-81; BR MGR, MEAD & HUNT INC, 81- *Concurrent Pos:* Lectr dam safety inspection. *Mem:* Am Soc Civil Engrs; Nat Soc Prof Engrs; Asn Soil & Found Engrs; Am Consult Engrs Coun. *Res:* Soils engineering; shear strength; slope stability; foundation engineering; solid wastes disposal. *Mailing Add:* 3437 Nancy Pl St Paul MN 55112

PEDERSON, ROGER NOEL, b Minneapolis, Minn, Dec 28, 30; m 57; c 2. MATHEMATICS. *Educ:* Univ Minn, BS, 52, MS, 53, PhD(math), 57. *Prof Exp:* Temporary mem, Inst Math Sci, NY Univ, 57-58; Moore instr math, Mass Inst Technol, 58-60; from asst prof to assoc prof, 60-70, PROF MATH, CARNEGIE-MELLON UNIV, 70- *Concurrent Pos:* NSF fel, 61-; vis assoc prof, Stanford Univ, 68-69. *Res:* Partial differential equations; real and complex analysis. *Mailing Add:* Dept of Math 5000 Forbes Ave Pittsburgh PA 15213

PEDERSON, THORU JUDD, b Syracuse, NY, Oct 10, 41; m 66; c 2. CELL BIOLOGY, MOLECULAR BIOLOGY. *Educ:* Syracuse Univ, BS, 63, PhD(zool), 68. *Prof Exp:* Res fel cell biol, Albert Einstein Col Med, 68-71; staff scientist, Worcester Found, 71-73, co-dir, Cancer Ctr, 75-81, SR SCIENTIST, CELL BIOL, WORCESTER FOUND EXP BIOL, 73-, DIR, CANCER CTR, 81- *Concurrent Pos:* Nat scholar, Leukemia Soc Am, 72; mem, Cell Biol Study Sect, NIH, 75-79; ed, J Cell Biol, 78-80 & 81-83; fac physiol course, Marine Biol Lab, Woods Hole, 81-85. *Mem:* Am Soc Biol Chemists; Am Soc Cell Biol; Am Chem Soc; Am Cancer Soc. *Res:* Structure and function of the cell nucleus; molecular biology of gene transcription; cell growth; cell motility; cytoskeleton. *Mailing Add:* Cell Biol Group Worcester Found for Exp Biol Shrewsbury MA 01545

PEDERSON, VERNON CLAYTON, b Nashua, Minn, Dec 26, 29; m 52; c 3. PHYSIOLOGY, ENDOCRINOLOGY. *Educ:* Southwest Mo State Col, BS, 55; Univ Mo, MA, 60, PhD(zool), 63. *Prof Exp:* Instr biol, Southwest Mo State Col, 56-58; asst zool, Univ Mo, 58-61, asst instr, 61-63; asst prof biol, 63-74, ASSOC PROF BIOL SCI, WESTERN ILL UNIV, 74- *Mem:* AAAS; Am Soc Zool. *Res:* Reproductive physiology and endocrinology of wild animal populations. *Mailing Add:* Dept of Biol Sci Western Ill Univ Macomb IL 61455

PEDIGO, LARRY PRESTON, b Great Bend, Kans, Oct 8, 38; m 61; c 2. ENTOMOLOGY. *Educ:* Ft Hays Kans State Col, BS, 63; Purdue Univ, MS, 65, PhD(entom), 67. *Prof Exp:* From asst prof to assoc prof, 67-75, PROF ENTOM, IOWA STATE UNIV, 75- *Mem:* Entom Soc Am. *Res:* Population ecology and management of insect pests with emphasis on sampling procedure; population characteristics; modeling and bioeconomics. *Mailing Add:* Dept of Entom Iowa State Univ Ames IA 50011

PEDLOSKY, JOSEPH, oceanography, dynamic meteorology, see previous edition

PEDOE, DANIEL, b London, Eng, Oct 29, 10; m 33, 66; c 2. MATHEMATICS. *Educ:* Univ London, BSc, 30; Magdalene Col, BA, 33, PhD(math), 37. *Prof Exp:* Lectr math, Univ Southampton, 36-42 & Univ Birmingham, 42-47; reader, Univ London, 47-52; prof, Khartoum Univ, 52-59, Singapore Univ, 59-62 & Purdue Univ, 62-64; prof, 64-80, EMER PROF MATH, UNIV MINN, MINNEAPOLIS, 80- *Concurrent Pos:* Leverhulme res fel, 46-48; sr math consult, Minn Sch Geom Proj, 64-66. *Mem:* Math Asn Am. *Res:* Algebraic geometry; mathematics education. *Mailing Add:* 1956 E River Terrace Minneapolis MN 55414

PEDRAJA, RAFAEL RODOBALDO, b Sagua La Grande, Cuba, Oct 21, 29; US citizen; m 53; c 2. FOOD SCIENCE, MICROBIOLOGY. *Educ:* Super Sch Arts & Trades, Havana, BS, 47; Univ Havana, MS, 50, Dr(agr eng), 52. *Prof Exp:* Auditor chem, Chas Martin Co, Cuba, 53; chemist & bacteriologist spec prod div, Borden Co, 53-56; res chemist, Griffith Labs, Inc, Ill, 56-62; tech dir, Am Dry Milk Inst, 62-65; tech dir food prod div, Super Tea & Coffee Co, 65-67; VPRES RES & DEVELOP & QUAL ASSURANCE, BOOTH FISHERIES DIV, CONSOL FOODS CORP, 67- *Honors & Awards:* Cert Appreciation, La State Univ, 75; Dipl Recognition, Govt Ecuador, 75. *Mem:* AAAS; Am Chem Soc; Am Dairy Sci Asn; Am Asn Cereal Chem; Inst Food Technol. *Res:* Industrial sanitation; oxidative rancidity of fats and oils; mechanisms of the curing of meats; microbiology and composition of dry milks; microbiology and biochemistry of fish and seafoods; development of convenience foods. *Mailing Add:* Booth Fisheries Div Consol Foods 2 N Riverside Plaza Chicago IL 60606

PEDROTTI, LENO STEPHANO, b Zeigler, Ill, May 21, 27; m 51; c 8. LASERS, OPTICAL PHYSICS. *Educ:* Ill State Univ, BS, 49; Univ Ill, MS, 51; Univ Cincinnati, PhD, 61. *Prof Exp:* From instr to assoc prof, 51-64, PROF PHYSICS & CHMN DEPT, US AIR FORCE INST TECHNOL, 64-; tech ed, Tech Educ Res Ctrs Southwest, US Off Educ, 72-80; CHIEF TECH ED, AUTHOR & CONSULT, CTR OCCUPATIONAL RES & DEVELOP, 80- *Concurrent Pos:* Mem, Bd Dirs, Laser Inst Am, 75-82; author/lectr, Laser Inst Am, 75-; pres, Lasop, Inc. *Honors & Awards:* Exceptional Civilian Serv Award, US Air Force, 67, Meritorious Civilian Serv Award, 74. *Mem:* Am Soc Eng Educ; Am Nuclear Soc; Am Asn Physics Teachers; Optical Soc Am; Am Asn Univ Profs. *Res:* Electrical and optical properties of semiconductor crystals at low temperatures; development of laser scalpels for corneal surgery; physics for two-year technical institute students. *Mailing Add:* Dept Physics USAF Inst Technol Wright-Patterson AFB Dayton OH 45433

PEDROZA, GREGORIO CRUZ, b Pearson, Tex, May 3, 41; m 62; c 3. INDUSTRIAL ORGANIC CHEMISTRY. *Educ:* St Mary's Univ, Tex, BS, 63; WVa Univ, PhD(org chem), 68. *Prof Exp:* MGR INDUST ORG CHEM, IBM CORP, 69- *Mem:* Am Chem Soc. *Mailing Add:* 4 Deborah Dr Apalachin NY 13732

PEEBLES, CHARLES ROBERT, b Oak Park, Ill, May 31, 29; m; c 2. PARASITOLOGY. *Educ:* Cornell Univ, AB, 51; Univ Ill, MS, 52, PhD(zool), 57. *Prof Exp:* Asst, Univ Ill, 52-57; assoc parasitologist, Agr Exp Sta, Univ PR, 57-63; asst prof biol, Oberlin Col, 63-65; from asst prof to assoc prof, 65-77, dir student sci training prog, 69-81, PROF NATURAL SCI, MICH STATE UNIV, 77- *Mem:* AAAS; Am Micros Soc; Sigma Xi; Wilderness Soc. *Res:* Ultrastructure of nematodes; biology gastrointestinal parasites of ruminants. *Mailing Add:* Dept of Natural Sci Mich State Univ East Lansing MI 48824

PEEBLES, EDWARD MCCRADY, b Greenwood, Miss, June 26, 24; m 49; c 7. ANATOMY. *Educ:* Univ of the South, BS, 49; Tulane Univ, PhD(anat), 54. *Prof Exp:* Jr instr biol, Johns Hopkins Univ, 49-50; asst, 52-54, from instr to assoc prof, 54-68, PROF ANAT, TULANE UNIV, 68-, ASST DEAN SCH MED, 67- *Mem:* AAAS; Am Asn Anat. *Res:* Experimental neurology; nerve regeneration; gross anatomy; mast cells. *Mailing Add:* Dept of Anat Tulane Univ New Orleans LA 70112

PEEBLES, F(RED) N(EAL), chemical engineering, deceased

PEEBLES, HUGH OSCAR, JR, b Kountze, Tex, May 4, 33; m 55; c 4. PHYSICS. *Educ:* Univ Tex, Austin, BS, 55; Okla State Univ, MS, 60, PhD(physics), 64. *Prof Exp:* Teacher pub schs, Tex, 55-59; asst prof, 63-65, ASSOC PROF PHYSICS, LAMAR UNIV, 65- *Mem:* Am Astron Soc. *Res:* Stellar atmospheres. *Mailing Add:* Box 10046 Lamar Univ Sta Beaumont TX 77710

PEEK, FRANK WILLARD, b South Dayton, NY, Nov 4, 35. ANIMAL BEHAVIOR, NEUROBIOLOGY. *Educ:* State Univ NY Col Fredonia, BS, 63; Univ Ark, Fayetteville, MS, 65; Pa State Univ, PhD(zool), 69. *Prof Exp:* NIH fel, Univ Minn, St Paul, 69-71, res assoc neurobiol, 71-75; INDEPENDENT RES, 75- *Mem:* AAAS; Animal Behav Soc. *Res:* Neural basis of vertebrate behavior, specifically vocalization in birds; auditory and visual communication in birds; conceptual basis of living systems. *Mailing Add:* 215 Scholfield Rd Rochester NY 14617

PEEK, H(ARRY) MILTON, b Blackwell, Okla, Feb 8, 28; m 53; c 2. PHYSICAL CHEMISTRY, ATMOSPHERIC PHYSICS. *Educ:* Univ Okla, BA, 47; Univ Rochester, PhD(chem), 50. *Prof Exp:* Asst chem, Univ Rochester, 47-48; mem staff phys chem, Los Alamos Sci Lab, Univ Calif, 50-62, assoc group leader optical physics, 63-71, alt group leader, 71-72, group leader, 72-76, mem staff field test div, 76-77; asst dep dir testing, Defense Nuclear Agency, 77-78; MEM STAFF FIELD TEST, LOS ALAMOS SCI LAB, UNIV CALIF, 79- *Mem:* Am Phys Soc; Sigma Xi; Am Geophys Union. *Res:* Time resolved absorption spectroscopy of hot gases; radiometric optical studies of nuclear tests; rocket spectroscopy of aurora; ionospheric and magnetospheric plasma injections. *Mailing Add:* 282 Connie Ave Los Alamos NM 87545

PEEK, JAMES MACK, b Unionville, Mo, Sept 5, 33; m 62; c 2. THEORETICAL CHEMISTRY. *Educ:* Western Ill State Col, BSEd, 55; Ohio State Univ, MS, 58, PhD(chem), 62. *Prof Exp:* MEM TECH STAFF THEORET PHYSICS, SANDIA NAT LABS, 62- *Concurrent Pos:* Vis fel, Joint Inst Lab Astrophys, Univ Colo, 71-72. *Mem:* Fel Am Phys Soc; Am Math Soc; AAAS. *Res:* Theory of collisions involving electrons, atoms and molecules with emphasis on molecule formation and dissociation; theoretical study of the structure of simple atoms and molecules. *Mailing Add:* Org 4211 Sandia Nat Labs Albuquerque NM 87185

PEEK, JAMES MERRELL, b Helena, Mont, Sept 18, 36; m 64; c 3. WILDLIFE ECOLOGY. *Educ:* Mont State Univ, BS, 58, MS, 61; Univ Minn, St Paul, PhD(wildlife), 71. *Prof Exp:* Mgt biologist, Mont Fish & Game Dept, 61-63; res biologist, Bur Sport Fisheries & Wildlife, 64; res biologist, Mont Fish & Game Dept, 65-67; res fel wildlife, Univ Minn, St Paul, 67-70; from instr to assoc prof, 70-75, PROF WILDLIFE, UNIV IDAHO, 76- *Mem:* Am Soc Range Mgt; Wildlife Soc; Am Soc Mammal; Ecol Soc Am. *Res:* Ecology and behavior of ungulates. *Mailing Add:* Col Forest Wildlife & Range Sci Univ of Idaho Moscow ID 83843

PEEK, NEAL FRAZIER, b Chico, Calif, Jan 28, 29; m 51; c 4. EXPERIMENTAL NUCLEAR PHYSICS. *Educ:* Univ Calif, Berkeley, BA, 51; Univ Calif, Davis, MA, 59, PhD(exp nuclear physics), 66. *Prof Exp:* Lab technician, Univ Calif, Berkeley, 51-53; sr lab technician, Univ Calif, Davis, 53-55; chemist, US Army, 55-57; lectr physics & res physicist, 59-71, asst prof physics, 71-78, SR LECTR, UNIV CALIF, DAVIS, 78- *Concurrent Pos:* Fel, Assoc Western Univs, 73; vis scientist, Swiss Inst Nuclear Res, Würenlingen, Switzerland, 76. *Mem:* Sigma Xi; Am Phys Soc. *Res:* Applied nuclear experimental physics, including isotope production and in vivo studies with short lived isotopes; spallation isotope production. *Mailing Add:* Dept of Physics Univ of Calif Davis CA 95616

PEEL, JAMES EDWIN, b Lonaconing, Md, Dec 26, 24; m 55; c 2. CHEMICAL ENGINEERING, MARINE ENGINEERING. *Educ:* Carnegie Inst Technol, BS, 53. *Prof Exp:* Develop engr, Pittsburgh Coke & Chem Co, 53-59; proj mgr, Pittsburgh Plate Glass Co, 59-67; div engr, US Chem Co, 67-69; res engr, US Steel Corp, 69-71; PROCESS ENGR, PPG INDUST, INC, 77- & MANAGING DIR, PEEL ENG & CONSTRUCT CO, 65- *Res:* Methods of floatation of sunken vessels by in-situ polyurethane foaming and underwater habitation for mamals by silicone membrane osmosis of carbon dioxide and oxygen. *Mailing Add:* Peel Eng & Construct Co 357 Chadwick St Sewickley PA 15143

PEELER, DUDLEY F, JR, b Boonesville, Miss, June 17, 31; m 59; c 3. NEUROPSYCHOLOGY. *Educ:* Vanderbilt Univ, AB, 53, AM, 62, PhD(psychol), 63. *Prof Exp:* Asst psychol, Vanderbilt Univ, 57-59, res assoc, 60-61; trainee, Vet Admin Hosp, Murfreesboro, Tenn, 61-62; from instr to asst prof, 62-73, chief, Exp Behav Lab, 65-80, ASSOC RES PROF NEUROSURG, MED CTR, UNIV MISS, 73-, CHIEF, NEUROSURG LAB, 80- *Concurrent Pos:* Assoc psychol, Univ Miss, 65-76. *Mem:* AAAS; Int Neuropsychol Soc; Soc Neurosci; Int Soc Develop Psychobiol. *Res:* Neuropsychology of development; behavioral genetics; neuropsychology of motivation and emotion. *Mailing Add:* Dept of Neurosurg Univ of Miss Med Ctr Jackson MS 39216

PEELLE, ROBERT W, b Toledo, Ohio, Jan 13, 29; m 55; c 2. NUCLEAR PHYSICS. *Educ:* Univ Rochester, BS, 49; Princeton Univ, MA, 51, PhD(physics), 58. *Prof Exp:* PHYSICIST, ENG PHYSICS DIV, OAK RIDGE NAT LAB, 54-, SECT HEAD, 76- *Mem:* AAAS; Am Phys Soc; fel Am Nuclear Soc. *Res:* Spectra associated with fission by thermal neutrons; techniques of scintillation and semiconductor spectrometry; space and reactor shielding; continuum reactions in 100 region; fast neutron cross sections of materials important to fusion and fission reactors. *Mailing Add:* Eng Physics Div Oak Ridge Nat Lab PO Box X Oak Ridge TN 37830

PEEPLES, EARLE EDWARD, b West Palm Beach, Fla, Aug 23, 29; m 65; c 2. HUMAN GENETICS EDUCATION. *Educ:* Univ Fla, BS, 51; Southeastern Baptist Sem, BD, 54; Stetson Univ, MS, 62; Univ Tex, Austin, PhD(genetics, zool), 66. *Prof Exp:* Asst prof biol, Mary Hardin-Baylor Col, 60-63; res scientist assoc IV, Univ Tex, Austin, 66-69; assoc prof genetics, Southwestern State Univ, 69-73; assoc prof, 73-80, PROF BIOL SCI, UNIV NORTHERN COLO, 80- *Concurrent Pos:* Consult, Int Found Rat Genetics & Rodent Pest Control, 69-71. *Mem:* AAAS; Am Soc Human Genetics; Sigma Xi. *Res:* Genetic control of enzymes in development of reproductive organs of Drosophila, rat and man; phenol oxidases and adenyl cyclases; role of cyclic AMP in regulating testicular development. *Mailing Add:* Dept of Biol Sci Univ of Northern Colo Greeley CO 80639

PEEPLES, JOHN LEE, JR, plant pathology, microbiology, see previous edition

PEEPLES, JOHNSTON WILLIAM, b Estill, SC, July 30, 48; m 70; c 2. ELECTRICAL ENGINEERING. *Educ:* The Citadel, BS, 70; Univ SC, MS, 76, PhD(eng), 78. *Prof Exp:* Elec engr, tech serv, Westvaco Corp, 70- & commun, US Air Force, 70-73; res asst elec mat, Univ SC, 73-76; elec engr, 76-78, PROJ ENGR, NCR CORP, 78- *Concurrent Pos:* Indust prof, Univ SC, 78- *Mem:* Int Soc Hybrid Microelectron; Inst Elec & Electronics Engrs. *Res:* Microelectronic failure analysis and reliability; environmental testing of microelectronic packaging; silicon crystal growth for photovoltaic power production. *Mailing Add:* 3325 Platt Springs Rd West Columbia SC 29169

PEEPLES, WAYNE JACOBSON, b Corder, Mo, Dec 18, 40; m 65. GEOPHYSICS. *Educ:* William Jewell Col, BA, 63; Wichita State Univ, MSc, 65; Univ Alta, PhD(physics), 69. *Prof Exp:* Fel, Univ Alta, 69-70; res geophysicist, Kennecott Explor, Inc, 70-71; asst res prof geophysics, Univ Utah, 71-76; ASST PROF GEOL SCI, SOUTHERN METHODIST UNIV, 76- *Mem:* Am Geophys Union; Soc Explor Geophys. *Res:* Electromagnetic scattering in geophysics; mathematical inversion of geophysical data; data processing and analysis; solid earth geophysics; lunar geophysics. *Mailing Add:* Dept of Geol Sci Southern Methodist Univ Dallas TX 75275

PEEPLES, WILLIAM DEWEY, JR, b Bessemer, Ala, Apr 19, 28; m 56; c 4. MATHEMATICS. *Educ:* Samford Univ, BS, 48; Univ Wis, MS, 49; Univ Ga, PhD(math), 51. *Prof Exp:* Asst math, Samford Univ, 46-47, Univ Wis, 47-49 & Univ Ga, 49-51; from asst prof to assoc prof, Samford Univ, 51-56; asst prof, Auburn Univ, 56-59; PROF MATH, SAMFORD UNIV, 59-, HEAD DEPT, 67- *Concurrent Pos:* Consult, Hayes Inst Corp. *Mem:* AAAS; Am Math Soc; Math Asn Am; Soc Indust & Appl Math; Edinburgh Math Soc. *Res:* Valuation theory, elliptic curves; algebraic geometry. *Mailing Add:* Dept Math Samford Univ Birmingham AL 35209

PEERCY, PAUL S, b Monticello, Ky, Nov 26, 40. SOLID STATE PHYSICS. *Educ:* Berea Col, BA, 61; Univ Wis-Madison, MS, 63, PhD(physics), 66. *Prof Exp:* Mem tech staff, Bell Labs, 66-68; mem tech staff solid state physics res, 68-76, SUPVR, ION IMPLANTATION PHYSICS DIV, SANDIA LABS, 76- *Mem:* Am Phys Soc. *Res:* Solid state physics with primary emphasis on structural phase transitions in solids; ion implantation and ion beam analysis of solids. *Mailing Add:* Div 5112 Sandia Labs Albuquerque NM 87185

PEERMAN, DWIGHT ELLSWORTH, b Minneapolis, Minn, June 17, 20; m 47; c 2. POLYMER CHEMISTRY. *Educ:* Augsburg Col, BA, 45. *Prof Exp:* Analyst, Minn Bd Indust Health, 43-45; chemist, Gen Mills Chem, Inc, 45-50, sr scientist, 50-62, group leader polymer chem, 62-68, sect leader, Corp Chem Res Dept, 68-69, head, Polymer Applications Dept, 69-81, res assoc, 73-81; PRIN SCIENTIST, HENKEL CORP, 81- *Mem:* Am Chem Soc; Soc Plastics Engrs. *Res:* Development of industrial applications for polymers; polymer reaction kinetics and rheology; structure-property relationships; polymers for fabric bonding and textile improvement; urethane chemistry. *Mailing Add:* 2010 E Hennepin Ave Minneapolis MN 55413

PEERY, CLIFFORD YOUNG, b Coeburn, Va, Sept 24, 34; m 55; c 2. INDUSTRIAL ORGANIC CHEMISTRY. *Educ:* Univ Va, BS, 55; Ohio State Univ, PhD(org chem), 62. *Prof Exp:* Chemist, Merck & Co, Ltd, 55-59; teaching asst, Ohio State Univ, 59-62; chemist, Wyeth Labs, 62-63; res chemist, 63-71, staff chemist, Chem Div, 71-73, PROD MGR, FERMENTATION PROD, UPJOHN CO, 73- *Mem:* Am Chem Soc; Am Inst Chem Engrs. *Res:* Separation and purification of antibiotics and chemicals produced by fermentation processes. *Mailing Add:* Fermentation Prod 1200-38-1 Upjohn Co Kalamazoo MI 49002

PEERY, LARRY JOE, b Moberly, Mo, Dec 24, 41; m 64; c 2. PHYSICS. *Educ:* Univ Mo-Rolla, BS, 64; Okla State Univ, MS, 67, PhD(physics), 70. *Prof Exp:* Coop trainee physics & eng, McDonnell-Douglas Corp, 59-64; res asst physics, Okla State Univ, 64-67; asst prof, 67-69, PROF PHYSICS & CHMN DEPT, CENT METHODIST COL, 69- *Mem:* Am Asn Physics Teachers; Am Phys Soc. *Res:* Plasma physics; lasers; mathematical modeling; innovation in instruction. *Mailing Add:* Dept Physics Cen Methodist Col Fayette MO 65248

PEERY, THOMAS MARTIN, b Lynchburg, Va, Aug 24, 09; m 36; c 3. PATHOLOGY. *Educ:* Newberry Col, AB, 28, DMS, 66; Med Col SC, MD, 32. *Prof Exp:* Intern, Metrop Hosp, NY, 32-33, res physician, 33-34; instr path, Med Col SC, 34-38; from asst prof to prof path, 38-74, EMER PROF PATH, GEORGE WASHINGTON UNIV, 74- *Concurrent Pos:* Dir labs, Alexandria Hosp, 41-46; mem bd dirs, Technicon Corp; consult, Armed Forces Inst Path, Vet Admin Hosp, Washington, DC & Nat Cancer Inst. *Honors & Awards:* Ward Burdick Award, 74. *Mem:* Am Soc Clin Pathologists (vpres, 61, 66-68, pres, 68-69); fel AMA; Am Asn Pathologists & Bacteriologists; fel Col Am Pathologists; Int Acad Path. *Res:* Brucellosis and heart disease; clinical pathology tests in health evaluation; mortality trends in United States; curriculum planning. *Mailing Add:* 2115 Belle Haven Rd Alexandria VA 22307

PEET, MARY MONNIG, b Washington, DC, Aug 4, 47; m 71. PLANT PHYSIOLOGY. *Educ:* Hiram Col, AB, 69; Univ Wis-Madison, MS, 72; Cornell Univ, PhD(bot), 75. *Prof Exp:* Teaching asst bot, Univ Wis-Madison, 69-71; res asst, Cornell Univ, 72-75; res assoc environ physiol, Duke Univ, 75-80; ASST PROF, NC STATE UNIV, 80- *Concurrent Pos:* Adapter sci papers, Biol Sci Curric Study, 73-74. *Mem:* Am Asn Plant Physiologists; Crop Sci Soc Am; Am Soc Hort Sci. *Res:* Production and physiology of greenhouse-grown vegetables, especially as related to carbon dioxide enrichment, nutrition and temperature. *Mailing Add:* Dept Hort Sci Duke Univ Raleigh NC 27650

PEET, NICK PETER, b Houston, Tex, Dec 11, 17; m 42; c 3. CHEMICAL ENGINEERING. *Educ:* Rice Inst, BS, 41. *Prof Exp:* Asst, Tech Serv Div, Exxon Co, USA, 41, from jr chem engr to sr chem engr, 41-50, actg sect head, 50-51, from tech specialist to sr tech specialist, 51-56, sr res specialist, Res & Develop Div, 56-61, sr planning specialist coop planning, 62-65, res coordr, Prod Dept, 65-67, sr planning specialist, 67-77; engr, Tex Air Control Bd, 77-81. *Mem:* Am Inst Chem Engrs. *Res:* Fuel products and processes, particularly fluid catalytic cracking, residuum deasphalting, catalytic hydrogenation and distillation. *Mailing Add:* 5346 Rutherglenn Houston TX 77035

PEET, NORTON PAUL, b Fargo, NDak, June 14, 44; m 67. ORGANIC CHEMISTRY, MEDICINAL CHEMISTRY. *Educ:* Univ Minn, Minneapolis, BA, 66; Univ Nebr, Lincoln, PhD(org chem), 70. *Prof Exp:* Instr chem, Concordia Col, 67; res assoc org chem, Mass Inst Technol, 70-71; res assoc & instr, Univ SC, 71-72; RES CHEMIST, DOW CHEM CO, 72- *Mem:* Am Chem Soc. *Res:* Natural products synthesis; photochemistry and acid-catalyzed rearrangements of beta, gamma-unsaturated ketones; cyclo-addition reactions of 2-ene-1, 3-diones; synthesis of heterocycles; synthesis of 1,2,3-thiadiazoles; synthesis and reactions of benzotriazepine systems. *Mailing Add:* 219 Bldg 9550 Zionsville Rd Indianapolis IN 46268

PEET, ROBERT G(UTHRIE), b Bristol, Pa, Apr 16, 33; m 60; c 2. CHEMICAL ENGINEERING. *Educ:* Pa State Univ, BS, 54; Purdue Univ, PhD(chem eng), 63. *Prof Exp:* Process engr, Am Cyanamid Co, 54-57; res engr, Marathon Oil Co, 62-65; staff engr, E I du Pont de Nemours & Co, Inc, 65-69, res supvr, 69-72, develop supvr, 72-75; MEM STAFF, MOBILE CHEM CO, 75- *Mem:* Am Chem Soc; Am Inst Chem Engrs. *Res:* Mass transfer; polymer processing relationships; petrochemical processing; radiation induced reactions. *Mailing Add:* Films Dept Res & Develop Tech Ctr Macedon NY 14502

PEET, ROBERT KRUG, b Beloit, Wis, Feb 14, 47; m 71. ECOLOGY. *Educ:* Univ Wis-Madison, BA, 70, MS, 71; Cornell Univ, PhD(ecol), 75. *Prof Exp:* asst prof, 75-80, ASSOC PROF BOT, UNIV NC, CHAPEL HILL, 80- *Mem:* Ecol Soc Am; Brit Ecol Soc; Int Asn Ecol; Int Soc Veg Sci. *Res:* Plant succession; diversity of ecological communities; composition and structure of forest vegetation; population dynamics of forest trees; plant geography. *Mailing Add:* Dept of Bot 010A Univ of NC Chapel Hill NC 27514

PEETE, CHARLES HENRY, JR, b Warrenton, NC, Apr 30, 24; m 54; c 3. MEDICINE. *Educ:* Harvard Med Sch, MD, 47; Am Bd Obstet & Gynec, dipl, 57. *Prof Exp:* Asst prof, 56-68, PROF OBSTET & GYNEC, MED CTR, DUKE UNIV, 68- *Mem:* Am Fertil Soc; AMA; Am Col Obstetricians & Gynecologists. *Res:* Obstetrics and gynecology. *Mailing Add:* Dept Obstet & Gynec Duke Univ Med Ctr Durham NC 27710

PEETE, WILLIAM P J, b Warrenton, NC, Mar 29, 21; m 60; c 1. SURGERY. *Educ:* Univ NC, AB, 42; Harvard Univ, MD, 47. *Prof Exp:* Intern & resident surg, Mass Gen Hosp, 47-54; asst prof surg & asst to dean, 55-66, prof surg, 66-70, PROF GEN & THORACIC SURG & DIR SCH MED, DUKE UNIV, 70- *Concurrent Pos:* Fel surg, Harvard Univ, 53-55, Moseley fel, 54-55; consult, US Army. *Mailing Add:* Dept of Surg Duke Univ Sch of Med Durham NC 27706

PEETS, EDWIN ARNOLD, b New York, NY, June 26, 29; m 61; c 1. DERMATOPHARMACOLOGY, BIOCHEMISTRY. *Educ:* St John's Univ, NY, BS, 50; Brooklyn Col, MA, 54; NY Univ, PhD(biol), 66. *Prof Exp:* Anal chemist, Ledoux & Co, NJ, 50-55; res assoc geochem, Lamont Observ, Columbia Univ, 55-58; res biochemist, Lederle Labs, Am Cyanamid Co, NY, 58-66; HEAD DEPT BIOCHEM, SCHERING CORP, 66-, ASSOC DIR BIOL RES, 75-, DIR CLIN RES DERMAT, 80- *Concurrent Pos:* Guest lectr, 71-77, adj assoc prof, Fairleigh Dickinson Univ, 77- *Mem:* AAAS; Am Chem Soc; Am Soc Pharmacol & Exp Therapeut; fel Am Inst Chemists. *Res:* Molecular biology; dermatopharmacology; metabolic diseases; control processes of intracellular metabolism and macromolecules biosynthesis; metabolic and dermatologic diseases and their control by pharmaceutical agents. *Mailing Add:* Schering Corp 86 Orange St Bloomfield NJ 07003

PEEVY, WALTER JACKSON, b Jonesboro, La, Jan 22, 14; m 36; c 4. SOILS. *Educ:* La State Univ, BS, 36; Iowa State Col, MS, 37, PhD(soils), 41. *Prof Exp:* Instr & asst agron, La State Univ, 38-41; assoc, Tex A&M Univ & USDA, 41-43; assoc, 43-47, prof agron & agronomist, 47-81, EMER PROF AGRON, AGR EXP STA, LA STATE UNIV, BATON ROUGE, 81- *Mem:* Am Soc Agron; Soil Sci Soc Am. *Res:* Soil fertility and soil and crop management; soil and water conservation. *Mailing Add:* Dept of Agron La State Univ Baton Rouge LA 70803

PEFFER, JOHN ROSCOE, b Natrona Heights, Pa, Aug 13, 28; m 51; c 3. POLYMER CHEMISTRY. *Educ:* Allegheny Col, BS, 50; Mich State Univ, MS, 52; Carnegie Inst Technol, PhD(org chem), 58. *Prof Exp:* Sr res chemist, Coatings & Resins Div, 58-65, proj leader resin develop, 65-72, res assoc 72-79, SR RES ASSOC, PPG INDUSTS, INC, 72- *Mem:* Am Chem Soc. *Res:* Development of coatings resins; polymer synthesis, including addition, condensation, ring-opening and urethane polymers; polyether polyols; cross linked acetals; epoxy curing agents; unsaturated polyester resins. *Mailing Add:* 151 Glenfield Dr Pittsburgh PA 15235

PEFLEY, RICHARD K, b Sacramento, Calif, June 17, 21; m 47; c 3. MECHANICAL ENGINEERING. *Educ:* Stanford Univ, BA, 44, MS, 51, ME, 60. *Prof Exp:* Testing engr, Pac Mfg Co, 46-47; res engr, Babcock & Wilcox Co, 47-49; chmn dept, 51-81, PROF MECH ENG, UNIV SANTA CLARA, 81- *Concurrent Pos:* Consult, Enterprise Diesel Eng Co, 53-58, Broadview Res Corp, 57-59, Int Bus Mach Corp & Stanford Res Inst. *Mem:* Am Soc Mech Engrs; Am Soc Eng Educ; Am Soc Heat, Refrig & Air-Conditioning Engrs. *Res:* Heat transfer; fluid mechanics; thermodynamics. *Mailing Add:* Dept of Mech Eng Univ of Santa Clara Santa Clara CA 95053

PEGG, ANTHONY EDWARD, b Derbyshire, Eng, Apr 13, 42; m 65; c 2. BIOCHEMISTRY, PHYSIOLOGY. *Educ:* Univ Cambridge, BA, 63, MA, 65, PhD(biochem), 66. *Prof Exp:* Fel pharmacol, Med Sch, Johns Hopkins Univ, 66-69; lectr biochem, Middlesex Hosp Med Sch, Univ London, 69-74; assoc prof physiol, 75-77, PROF PHYSIOL, MED SCH, HERSHEY MED CTR, PA STATE UNIV, 77- *Concurrent Pos:* Michael Sobell fel cancer res, Brit Empire Cancer Res Campaign, 69-74; estab investr, Am Heart Asn, 76-81, mem, Pathobiol Chem Study Sect; dir res grants, NIH, Bethesda, 77-81, chmn, 79-81; assoc ed, Cancer Res, 80- & Am J Physiol, 81- *Mem:* Biochem Soc; Am Asn Cancer Res; Am Physiol Soc; Am Soc Biol Chemists; Am Heart Asn. *Res:* Synthesis and function of polyamines in mammaliam cells; mechanism of carcinogenesis by nitrosamines; nucleic acid methylation. *Mailing Add:* Dept of Physiol Med Sch Pa State Univ Hershey PA 17033

PEGG, DAVID JOHN, b London, Eng, Sept 2, 40; US citizen; m 65; c 2. LASER SPECTROSCOPY, BEAM-FOIL SPECTROSCOPY. *Educ:* Univ Manchester, BSc, 63; Univ NH, MS, 68, PhD(physics), 70. *Prof Exp:* Asst prof, 70-75, assoc prof, 75-80, PROF PHYSICS, UNIV TENN, 80- *Concurrent Pos:* Co-ed, Beam-Foil Spectroscopy, 75-76; vis prof, Univ Lund, Sweden, 78, Univ Lyons, France, 78-79; prin invest, NSF res grants, 73-; consult, Oak Ridge Nat Lab, 70- *Mem:* Am Phys Soc. *Res:* Accelerator-based studies of the structure of atoms and ions using spectroscopic techniques--ions of the beam are excited collisionally or selectively by lasers directed perpendicular or collinear to the beam axis. *Mailing Add:* Dept Physics Univ Tenn Knoxville TN 37996

PEGG, PHILIP JOHN, b Chester, Eng, Mar 14, 36; m 61; c 3. CLINICAL PATHOLOGY. *Educ:* Univ London, MB, BS, 60; FRCPath, 80. *Prof Exp:* Registr hemat, St George's Hosp, London, 63-64; registr chem path, Westminster Med Sch, 64-65; lectr, Univ West Indies, 65-69; ASST PROF PATH, UNIV PA, 69- *Concurrent Pos:* Dir clin chem, Dept Path, Wilmington Med Ctr, 73- *Mem:* Col Am Pathologists; Royal Col Path; Am Asn Clin Chemists; Am Soc Clin Pathologists; Acad Clin Lab Physicians & Scientists. *Res:* Radioimmunoassay, interactions of plasma binding proteins and hormones and effect of drugs on binding proteins; concepts of biochemical normality. *Mailing Add:* Wilmington Med Ctr PO Box 1668 Wilmington DE 19810

PEGLAR, GEORGE W, b Independence, Mo, Sept 2, 22; m 47; c 3. MATHEMATICS. *Educ:* Cent Mo State Col, BS, 42; Univ Chicago, SM, 49; Univ Iowa, PhD(math), 53. *Prof Exp:* From instr to assoc prof, 52-70, PROF MATH, IOWA STATE UNIV, 70- *Concurrent Pos:* Opers analyst, US Air Force, 56-66. *Mem:* Fel AAAS; Am Math Soc; Math Asn Am. *Res:* Algebra; number theory. *Mailing Add:* Dept of Math Iowa State Univ Ames IA 50010

PEGLER, ALWYNNE VERNON, b Perth, Western Australia, Dec 14, 22; Can citizen; m 49; c 4. MINING ENGINEERING, ROCK MECHANICS. *Educ:* Western Australia Sch Mines, AWASM, 52; Queen's Univ, Ont, MSc, 62, PhD(mining), 66. *Prof Exp:* Sr mine surveyor, S Kalgurli Cons Ltd, Western Australia, 48-52; mine tech officer & mine supvr, Roan Antelope Copper Mines Ltd, Northern Rhodesia, 52-58; ventilation & safety engr & mine supvr, Can-Metal Explor Ltd, Ont, Can, 58-60; mine consult, 60-62; from asst prof to assoc prof mining eng, Queen's Univ, Ont, 65-69; prin, Western Australian Sch Mines, 70-75; PRIN EDUC OFFICER, WESTERN AUSTRALIAN INST TECHNOL, 75- *Concurrent Pos:* Consult, Consol

Mining & Smelting Co, BC, 65-69, Haliburton Co, Okla, 65-67 & Metro Ctr Develop Ltd, Ont, 68-69, prin lectr, Div Eng & Sci, 80- *Mem:* fel Australian Inst Eng. *Res:* Rock mechanics, involving mine development and research; measurement of field stresses; hydraulic fracturing; thermal conductivity in rocks; photoelasticity; mine surveying and photogrammetry; mineral technology education research; scientific photography. *Mailing Add:* Western Australian Inst of Technol Bentley Australia

PEGOLOTTI, JAMES ALFRED, b Arcata, Calif, Dec 17, 33. ORGANIC CHEMISTRY. *Educ:* St Mary's Col, Calif, BS, 55; Univ Calif, Los Angeles, PhD(org chem), 59. *Prof Exp:* From instr to assoc prof chem, St Peter's Col, NJ, 59-73, prof chem, 73-81; DEAN, SCH ARTS & SCI, WESTERN CONN STATE COL, DANBURY, 81- *Mem:* Am Chem Soc. *Res:* Chemistry of allylic compounds. *Mailing Add:* Western Conn State Col 181 White St Danbury CT 06810

PEGRAM, GEORGE VERNON, JR, b Nashville, Tenn, Feb 7, 37; m 74; c 4. NEUROSCIENCE, PSYCHOPHYSIOLOGY. *Educ:* Univ of the South, BS, 59; Univ NMex, PhD(psychol), 67. *Prof Exp:* Chief, Bioeffects Div, Holloman AFB, NMex, 68-70; assoc dir, 73-77, DIR NEUROSCI, UNIV ALA MED CTR, 77- *Concurrent Pos:* Fel, Nat Res Coun, 67-68; intern, clin psychol, Univ Ala Med Ctr, 76-77; clin polysomnographer, Asn Sleep Dis Ctrs, 78- *Mem:* AAAS; Asn Psychophysiol Study Sleep; Soc Neurosci; Biofeedback Soc Am; Int Soc Chronobiol. *Res:* Sleep research particularly, effects of protein synthesis inhibition, neurochemistry of sleep, the effects of hypnotics on sleep patterns; biofeedback research into headaches, chronic pain and neuromuscular re-education. *Mailing Add:* Neurosci Prog Univ Sta Birmingham AL 35274

PEHLKE, ROBERT DONALD, b Feb 11, 33; m 56; c 3. METALLURGICAL ENGINEERING. *Educ:* Univ Mich, BSE, 55; Mass Inst Technol, SM, 58, ScD(metall), 60. *Prof Exp:* From asst prof to assoc prof, 60-68, PROF METALL ENG, UNIV MICH, ANN ARBOR, 68-, CHMN DEPT, 73- *Concurrent Pos:* Res engr, Gen Motors Res Labs, 52-54 & Ford Sci Lab, 55-57. *Mem:* Am Inst Mining, Metall & Petrol Engrs; Am Soc Metals; Am Foundrymen's Soc; Am Soc Eng Educ. *Res:* Iron and steelmaking; chemical and extractive metallurgy; melting; computer control of metallurgical processes. *Mailing Add:* Dept Mat & Metall Eng Univ Mich Ann Arbor MI 48104

PEI, DAVID CHUNG-TZE, b Shanghai, China, June 16, 29; Can citizen; m 60; c 2. HEAT TRANSFER, CHEMICAL ENGINEERING. *Educ:* McGill Univ, BEng, 55, PhD(chem eng), 61; Queen's Univ, Ont, MSc, 57. *Prof Exp:* Lectr chem eng, Royal Mil Col, 56-57; from asst prof to assoc prof, 61-70, PROF CHEM ENG, UNIV WATERLOO, 70- *Concurrent Pos:* Nutfield Found travel grant, 65-66. *Mem:* Am Inst Chem Engrs; Chem Inst Can. *Res:* Effects of mass transfer on the rate of heat transfer under combined convection; particle dynamics in a solid-gas conveyer system; high temperature metallurgical reaction initiated by microwaves; investigation of heat transfer rates from a continuous moving surface. *Mailing Add:* Dept of Chem Eng Univ of Waterloo Waterloo ON N2L 3G1 Can

PEI, MING L(UNG), civil engineering, see previous edition

PEI, SHIN-SHEM, b Kweilin, China, Jan 28, 49; m 74; c 1. MICROELECTRONICS, SUPERCONDUCTIVITY. *Educ:* Nat Taiwan Univ, BS, 70; State Univ NY, Stony Brook, PhD(solid state physics), 77. *Prof Exp:* Fel, State Univ NY, Stony Brook, 77; MEM TECH STAFF, BELL LABS, 78- *Mem:* Am Phys Soc. *Res:* Physics of Josephson tunnel; junction and weak links, superconducting material, superconducting microelectronics for high performance memory and logic applications. *Mailing Add:* Bell Labs 600 Mountain Ave Murray Hill NJ 07974

PEIERLS, RONALD F, b Manchester, Eng, Sept 8, 35; m 59; c 2. NUMERICAL METHODS, THEORETICAL HIGH ENERGY PHYSICS. *Educ:* Cambridge Univ, BA, 56; Cornell Univ, PhD(physics), 59. *Prof Exp:* NATO fel physics, Univ Birmingham, 59-61; mem, Inst Advan Study, 61-62; vis asst prof, Cornell Univ, 62-63; assoc physicist, 63-66, physicist, 66-72, SR PHYSICIST, BROOKHAVEN NAT LAB, 72-, CHMN APPL MATH DEPT, 79- *Concurrent Pos:* Adj prof, Stevens Inst Technol, 67-74; vis lectr, Harvard Univ, 69. *Mem:* Fel Am Phys Soc; Soc Indust & Appl Math; AAAS; Fedn Am Scientists. *Res:* Computational techniques; Monte Carlo methods; phenomenology of elementary particle interactions. *Mailing Add:* Brookhaven Nat Lab Upton NY 11973

PEIFER, JAMES J, b Nanticoke, Pa, Apr 29, 24; m 48; c 3. BIOCHEMISTRY. *Educ:* Ursinus Col, BS, 48; Rutgers Univ, PhD(biochem), 54. *Prof Exp:* Asst biochem, Sharp & Dohme Pharm Co, Merck & Co, Inc, 48-49; instr biochem & physiol, Rutgers Univ, 53-54; fel chem & metab of essential fatty acids, Hormel Inst, Minn, 54-56, div leader & res assoc chem, 56-67; actg head dept foods & nutrit, 71-74, ASSOC PROF NUTRIT & BIOCHEM, UNIV GA, 67- *Concurrent Pos:* Am Heart Asn fel, 59-60. *Mem:* AAAS; Am Chem Soc; Am Oil Chem Soc; Soc Exp Biol & Med; fel NY Acad Sci. *Res:* Chemistry and metabolism of lipides; interrelationships in the metabolism of essential fatty acids; protein-lipid interrelationships related to brain development. *Mailing Add:* Dept Foods & Nutrit Univ Ga Athens GA 30601

PEIFFER, HOWARD R, b Reading, Pa, Feb 8, 31. METALLURGY, PHYSICS. *Educ:* Albright Col, BS, 52; Pa State Univ, MS, 54, PhD(metall), 56. *Prof Exp:* Sr scientist metal physics, Res Inst Advan Study, Martin Co, 56-64; RES ASSOC, AMP INC, HARRISBURG, 64- *Concurrent Pos:* Lectr, Loyola Col, Md, 58-64. *Mem:* Am Soc Metals; Am Inst Mining, Metall & Petrol Engrs; Am Phys Soc. *Res:* Defect solid state; composite materials; intermetallic compounds; electrical alloys; interconnection systems; electrical resistivity measurements; explosive deformation. *Mailing Add:* 120 Parkview Rd New Cumberland PA 17070

PEIFFER, ROBER LOUIS, JR, b Chester, Pa, Dec 5, 47; m 77. COMPARATIVE OPHTHALMOLOGY. *Educ:* Univ Minn, BS, 69, DVM, 71, PhD(comp ophthal), 80. *Prof Exp:* Intern, small animal med, Iowa State Univ, 71-72; practr, Blue Cross Animal Hosp, 72-73; resident, small animal surg, Purdue Univ, 73-74; comp ophthal, NIH, Univ Minn, 74-76; asst prof comp ophthal, Univ Fla, 76-78; asst prof, 78-81, ASSOC PROF OPHTHAL & PATH, UNIV NC, CHAPEL HILL, 82-; PROF VET & OPTHAL, NC STATE UNIV, 82- *Concurrent Pos:* Burroughs-Wellcome, 78. *Mem:* Am Col Vet Ophthal; Am Acad Ophthal; Asn Res Vision & Ophthal; Am Vet Med Asn; Am Animal Hosp Asn. *Res:* Glaucoma; Cataractogenesis; ocular immunology; experimental ophthalmic pathology. *Mailing Add:* 617 Bldg 229 H Univ NC Chapel Hill NC 27514

PEIGHTEL, WILLIAM EDGAR, b Huntingdon, Pa, July 27, 27; m 49; c 3. BIOLOGY. *Educ:* Juniata Col, BS, 49; Univ Va, MA, 54, PhD(biol), 61. *Prof Exp:* Assoc prof, 56-62, PROF BIOL, SHIPPENSBURG STATE COL, 62-, CHMN DEPT, 64- *Mem:* Sigma Xi. *Res:* Shell regeneration in mollusks. *Mailing Add:* Dept of Biol Shippensburg State Col Shippensburg PA 17257

PEIKARI, BEHROUZ, b Hamadan, Iran, Mar 16, 38; m 65; c 3. ELECTRICAL ENGINEERING. *Educ:* Univ Tehran, BEng, 61; Univ Ill, Urbana, MS, 64; Univ Calif, Berkeley, PhD(elec eng), 69. *Prof Exp:* Instr elec eng, Univ Tehran, 61-62; res asst, Univ Ill, Urbana, 64-65; asst, Univ Calif, Berkeley, 66-69; asst prof, 69-71, assoc prof, 72-79, PROF ELEC ENG, INFO & CONTROL SCI CTR, SOUTHERN METHODIST UNIV, 80- *Concurrent Pos:* Consult, Arj Mfg Co & Mepsal Mfg Co, Tehran, 61-62; NASA multidisciplinary grant, Southern Methodist Univ, 71. *Mem:* Inst Elec & Electronics Engrs; Sigma Xi. *Res:* Analysis and design of nonlinear electronic circuits and communication networks; digital signal processing. *Mailing Add:* Info & Control Sci Ctr Southern Methodist Univ Dallas TX 75222

PEIL, KELLY M, US citizen. ENGINEERING. *Educ:* Okla State Univ, BA, 68, MS, 69, PhD(environ eng), 72. *Prof Exp:* With US Army Med Bioeng Res & Develop Lab, 72-75; PROJ ENG & MGR, WESTON, 75- *Mem:* Am Soc Civil Eng; Water Pollution Control Fedn; Sigma Xi. *Res:* Wastewater treatment conceptual process development and design; treatment plant evaluations; advanced wastewater treatment process evaluation; facilities and regional planning; sewer system evaluation studies. *Mailing Add:* Weston Weston Way West Chester PA 19380

PEINADO, ROLANDO E, b Colombia, SAm, Nov 17, 38; US citizen; div; c 2. ALGEBRA, BIOMATHEMATICS. *Educ:* Union Col, BA, 58; Univ Nebr, MA, 60, PhD(math), 63. *Prof Exp:* Asst math, Univ Nebr, 59-60; instr, San Diego State Col, 60-61 & Univ Nebr, 61-63; asst prof, Univ Iowa, 63-66; vis prof, Univ PR, Mayaguez, 65-66, from assoc prof to prof, 66-73, RES FEL, MED CAMPUS, UNIV PR, 73- *Mem:* Am Math Soc; Math Asn Am; London Math Soc; Edinburgh Math Soc; NY Acad Sci. *Res:* Ring theory; group theory; semigroup theory; applications of semigroup to biology, especially to neurobiology; brain research and application; mathematical linguistics to biomedicine research; computer science. *Mailing Add:* Dept of Math Univ of PR Mayaguez PR 00708

PEIRCE, EDMUND CONVERSE, II, b Montclair, NJ, Oct 9, 17; m 66; c 8. PHYSIOLOGY, SURGERY. *Educ:* Harvard Univ, SB, 40, MD, 43. *Prof Exp:* Res fel surg, Harvard Med Sch, 47-48; asst prof anat, Sch Med, Johns Hopkins Univ, 48; trainee surg, Nat Heart Inst, 50, staff mem, 53-54, instr, Sch Med, Georgetown Univ, 54; chief, Acuff Clin, Knoxville, Tenn, 54-61; fel surg & vis assoc prof physiol, Emory Univ, 62-64, assoc prof physiol & surg, 64-70; HENRY KAUFMAN PROF HYPERBARIC SURG, MT SINAI SCH MED, 70- *Concurrent Pos:* Attend, Mt Sinai Hosp, 70-; mem, Mt Desert Island Biol Lab, chief dept surg, Bronx Vet Admin Hosp, 71-74. *Mem:* Am Soc Artificial Internal Organs (secy-treas, 60-62, pres, 63); Am Asn Anatomists; Am Physiol Soc; Undersea Med Soc. *Res:* Artificial organs; especially lung and kidney; hypothermia: acid base balance; tissue transplantation. *Mailing Add:* Mt Sinai Sch of Med New York NY 10029

PEIRCE, JAMES JEFFREY, b Easton, Md, Mar 27, 49; m 71; c 2. SANITARY ENGINEERING. *Educ:* Johns Hopkins Univ, BES, 71; Univ Wis, Madison, MSCE, 73, PhD(environ eng & econ), 77. *Prof Exp:* Proj engr elec eng, Airphx Electronics Inc, 69-71; res asst civil eng, Inst Environ Studies, Univ Wis, Madison, 71-73, res asst environ eng, 73-77; sr scientist energy & environ eng, Booz, Allen & Hamilton, 77-79; ASST PROF CIVIL & ENVIRON ENG, DEPT CIVIL & ENVIRON ENG, DUKE UNIV, 79- *Concurrent Pos:* Instr chem, Chesapeake Col, 73; spec consult, Solid & Hazardous Waste, US Environ Protection Agency, 79-; prin investr, Solid Waste Planning, Triangle J Coun, NC Govt, 80-81 & Waste-to-Energy Basic Res, US Dept Energy, 82- *Mem:* Sigma Xi; Asn Environ Eng Prof; Am Soc Eng Educ. *Res:* Solid and hazardous waste management; wastewater treatment sludge processing and disposal; waste-to-energy technologies; support for solid and hazardous waste nationwide regulations. *Mailing Add:* 910 Coker Dr Chapel Hill NC 27514

PEIRCE, JOHN WENTWORTH, b Boston, Mass, Oct 17, 46; m 77; c 2. MARINE GEOPHYSICS, EXPLORATION GEOPHYSICS. *Educ:* Dartmouth Col, AB, 68; Mass Inst Technol, PhD(oceanog), 77. *Prof Exp:* Asst prof geol, Dalhousie Univ, 76-78; GEOPHYS SPECIALIST, EXPLOR GEOPHYSICS, PETROCAN, 78- *Concurrent Pos:* Vis res assoc, marine geophysics, Mass Inst Technol, 78. *Mem:* Am Geophys Union; Geol Asn Can; Geol Soc Am; Soc Explor Geophys. *Res:* Non-seismic exploration geophysics, especially in frontier international areas; plate tectonics as applied to continental margins; basin modelling; evolution of arctic ocean basin and margins. *Mailing Add:* Petro Can PO Box 2844 Calgary AB T2P 3E3 Can

PEIRCE, LINCOLN CARRET, b Newburyport, Mass, May 10, 30; m 53; c 2. PLANT BREEDING. *Educ:* Cornell Univ, BS, 52; Univ Minn, PhD, 58. *Prof Exp:* From asst prof to assoc prof veg breeding, Iowa State Univ, 58-64; actg dean, Col Life Sci & Agr, Univ NH, 78-79, prof plant sci & chmn dept, 64-78. *Mem:* Am Soc Hort Sci; Sigma Xi; fel Am Soc Hort Sci. *Res:* Basic and applied genetic research of vegetable crops. *Mailing Add:* Dept of Plant Sci Univ of NH Durham NH 03824

PEIRENT, ROBERT JOHN, b Lowell, Mass, Apr 12, 21; m 55; c 6. CHEMISTRY, COLOR SCIENCE. *Educ:* Lowell Tech Inst, BS, 49, MS, 53. *Prof Exp:* From instr to prof textile chem, Lowell Technol Inst, 49-75; PROF CHEM, UNIV LOWELL, 75- *Mem:* Am Asn Textile Chemists & Colorists (vpres, 66-67); Am Chem Soc; Brit Soc Dyers & Colourists. *Res:* Mechanisms of chemical dyeing of textile fibers; dyeing reactions in nonaqueous liquids; rate study and acceleration of the dyeing of hydrophobic synthetic fibers; diffusion of dyes in synthetic polymeric fibers via non aqueous liquids and color science measurements. *Mailing Add:* Dept Chem Univ Lowell Lowell MA 01854

PEIRSON, DAVID ROBERT, b Hamilton, Ont, Can, Sept 23, 39; c 2. PLANT PHYSIOLOGY. *Educ:* Univ Waterloo, BSc, 63, MSc, 69; Univ BC, PhD(plant physiol), 72. *Prof Exp:* Teacher sec sch, Baden, Ont, 63-65; teacher biol, Galt Col Inst, 65-67; vis asst prof, Simon Fraser Univ, 72-74; asst prof, 74-80, ASSOC PROF BIOL, WILFRID LAURIER UNIV, 80- *Mem:* Can Soc Plant Physiologists; Am Soc Plant Physiologists. *Res:* Chemical regulation of plant growth; nitrogen metabolism. *Mailing Add:* Dept of Biol Wilfrid Laurier Univ Waterloo ON N2L 3C5 Can

PEIRSON, ROBERT CHARLES, b Grand Island, Nebr, Sept 25, 43. ELECTRICAL ENGINEERING. *Educ:* Univ Mo-Rolla, BS, 65, MS, 66, PhD(elec eng), 68. *Prof Exp:* Asst prof elec eng, Univ Mo-Rolla, 68-76, assoc prof, 76-80; MEM STAFF, ALCOA TECH CTR, ALUMINUM CO AM, 80- *Concurrent Pos:* Sr engr, Braddock Dunn & McDonald, Inc, Tex, 68- *Mem:* Inst Elec & Electronics Engrs. *Res:* Circuit theory; computer-aided network analysis and design. *Mailing Add:* Alcoa Tech Ctr Aluminum Co Am Alcoa Center PA 15069

PEISACH, JACK, b New York, NY, Aug 23, 32; m 64. BIOCHEMISTRY. *Educ:* City Col New York, BS, 53; Columbia Univ, AM, 54, PhD(chem), 58. *Prof Exp:* Instr chem, Manhattan Col, 58-59; sr res asst biochem, 59-62, res asst prof pharmacol, 62-65, asst prof, 65-69, PROF MOLECULAR PHARMACOL & MOLECULAR BIOL, ALBERT EINSTEIN COL MED, 69- *Concurrent Pos:* USPHS fel, Albert Einstein Col Med, 59-61; asst prof chem, Yeshiva Col Med, 61-62; vis scientist, Bell Tel Labs, 64- *Mem:* Biophys Soc; Am Chem Soc; Am Soc Biol Chemists; NY Acad Sci. *Res:* Role of transition metals in biological systems, especially biological oxidation; biochemistry and biophysics of copper- and iron-containing proteins and porphyrins; electron paramagnetic resonance spectroscopy of transition metals. *Mailing Add:* Dept of Molecular Pharmacol Albert Einstein Col of Med Bronx NY 10461

PEISER, HERBERT STEFFEN, b Grunewald, Ger, Aug 19, 17; nat US; m 49; c 3. METROLOGY, INTERNATIONAL RELATIONS. *Educ:* Cambridge Univ, BA, 39, MA, 43. *Prof Exp:* Tech officer, Imp Chem Indust, Eng, 40-47; sr lectr physics, Univ London, 47-48; asst res mgr, Hadfields, 48-57; phys chemist, Nat Bur Standards, 57-69, chief, Mass & Scale, 58-62, chief, Crystal Chem Sect, 64-69, chief, Off Int Rels, 69-79; CONSULT, METROL & INT STANDARDIZATION, 79- *Concurrent Pos:* Res fel & lectr appl physics, Harvard Univ, 65-66; mem, Comn Atomic Weights, Int Union Pure & Appl Chem, 69- *Res:* X-ray crystallography; nondestructive testing; precision mass determinations; physical measurement standards; crystal growth. *Mailing Add:* Nat Bur of Stand Washington DC 20234

PEISS, CLARENCE NORMAN, b Ansonia, Conn, Jan 3, 22; m 49; c 2. PHYSIOLOGY. *Educ:* Stanford Univ, AB, 47, AM, 48, PhD(physiol), 49. *Prof Exp:* Asst, Stanford Univ, 47-48, res assoc, 48-49; fel, Johns Hopkins Univ, 49-50; sr instr, Sch Med, St Louis Univ, 50-52, asst prof, 52-54; from asst prof to assoc prof, 54-58, PROF PHYSIOL, SCH MED, LOYOLA UNIV, CHICAGO, 58-, DEAN, SCH MED, 78- *Concurrent Pos:* Markle Found scholar, Loyola Univ Chicago, 53-58, Lederle med fac award, 58-61; vis lectr, Blackburn Col, 53-54; liaison scientist, Off Naval Res, London, 65-66; mem physiol study sect, NIH, 66-70, consult, artificial heart prog, prog proj comt & cardiovasc training comt; assoc dean, Grad Sch Med Ctr, Loyola Univ, 72-78, Acad Affairs, Sch Med, 75-78. *Mem:* Soc Neurosci; Am Heart Asn; Am Physiol Soc. *Res:* Brain metabolism; environmental physiology; temperature regulation; circulation; neurophysiology. *Mailing Add:* Dept of Physiol Loyola Univ Med Ctr Maywood IL 60153

PEISSNER, LORRAINE C, b Philadelphia, Pa, Jan 15, 19. PHYSIOLOGY. *Educ:* Pa State Univ, BS, 52; Univ Okla, MS, 54, PhD(zool & biochem), 61. *Prof Exp:* Res asst gastroenterol, Okla Med Res Found, 58-62; assoc prof biol, Cent State Univ, Okla, 62-67; ASST PROF PHYSIOL, KIRKSVILLE COL OSTEOP MED, 67-, ASST TO DEAN STUDENTS, 80- *Mem:* AAAS; Shock Soc; Am Physiol Soc; Am Inst Biol Sci. *Res:* Influence of gonadal hormones on anatomy and function of rodent submaxillary gland; mechanisms in regulation of blood flow in peripheral vasculature; search for gastric secretion inhibitor in human saliva and gastric juice; effect of estrogens on parathyroid hormone metabolism. *Mailing Add:* Dept of Physiol Kirksville Col of Osteop Med Kirksville MO 63501

PEITHMAN, ROSCOE EDWARD, b Hoyleton, Ill, Feb 26, 13; m 36; c 2. PHYSICS. *Educ:* Southern Ill Univ, BEd, 35; Univ Ill, MS, 39; Ore State Univ, EdD(educ, physics), 55. *Prof Exp:* Teacher high schs, Ill, 35-42; from asst prof to assoc prof, 46-55, prof, 55-77, EMER PROF PHYSICS, HUMBOLDT STATE UNIV, 77- *Concurrent Pos:* Actg chmn, Div Natural Sci, Humboldt State Univ, 57-58, chmn, Div Phys Sci, 60-69, Dean, Sch Sci, 69-70. *Mem:* Am Asn Physics Teachers. *Res:* Electrical measurments and electronics; air navigation. *Mailing Add:* 2704 Sunny Grove Ave Arcata CA 95521

PEITZ, BETSY, b Pittsburgh, Pa, Dec 11, 48. REPRODUCTIVE PHYSIOLOGY. *Educ:* Carlow Col, BA, 70; Case Western Reserve Univ, PhD(biol), 75. *Prof Exp:* NIH fel reproductive physiol, Med Col, Cornell Univ, 75-77; asst prof, 77-81, ASSOC PROF BIOL, CALIF STATE UNIV, LOS ANGELES, 81- *Mem:* Am Soc Zoologists; AAAS; Soc Study Reproduction. *Res:* Physiology of the male reproductive tract and the adaptive and evolutionary significance of different reproductive patterns. *Mailing Add:* Dept of biol Calif State Univ Los Angeles CA 90032

PEKAREK, ROBERT SIDNEY, b Berwyn, Ill, May 1, 40; c 2. MICROBIOLOGY, BIOCHEMISTRY. *Educ:* Knox Col, Ill, BA, 62; Loyola Univ Chicago, MS, 64, PhD(microbiol), 67. *Prof Exp:* Res microbiologist, US Army Med Res Inst Infectious Dis, 69-74; staff mem, Human Nutrit Lab, USDA, 74-77; RES SCIENTIST, LILLY RES LABS, 77- *Mem:* Am Soc Microbiol; Am Inst Nutrit; Am Soc Clin Nutrit; Fedn Am Socs Exp Biol; Soc Exp Biol & Med. *Res:* Study of alterations in host metabolism during infection and stress, including trace metals, amino acids, serum proteins and endogenous humoral mediating factors; nutritional biochemistry; development of analytical technique for measuring trace element in biological materials; study of pathophysiologic mechanisms during acute and chronic infections; design models for testing antibiotic efficacy; effect of immunostimulating defense mechanisms; effect of nutritional deficiencies on the immune response; antibiotic evaluation in infectious disease models; antibiotic pharmacokinetics. *Mailing Add:* Lilly Res Labs Eli Lilly & Co Indianapolis IN 46285

PEKAS, JEROME CHARLES, b Mott, NDak, Aug 13, 36; m 57; c 5. ANIMAL PHYSIOLOGY, ANIMAL NUTRITION. *Educ:* NDak State Univ, BS, 57; Univ Fla, MS, 58; Iowa State Univ, PhD(animal physiol & nutrit), 61. *Prof Exp:* Asst prof metab, UT-AEC Agr Res Lab, Univ Tenn, 61-64; res scientist, Pac Northwest Labs, Battelle Mem Inst, 64-66; res physiologist, Agr Res Serv, 66-80, GASTROINTESTINAL PHYSIOLOGIST, US MEAT ANIMAL RES CTR, USDA, 80- *Concurrent Pos:* Nat Acad Sci travel grant, Int Cong Physiol, Tokyo, 65; partic, Int Cong Physiol, Munich, 71. *Mem:* Am Physiol Soc; Am Soc Animal Sci; Am Gastroenterol Asn; NY Acad Sci. *Res:* Function and regulation of the exocrine pancreas; interaction between the dietary and functions of the gastrointestinal glands, particularly the pancreas and small intestine. *Mailing Add:* USDA US Meat Anim Res Ctr Box 166 Clay Center NE 68933

PEKAU, OSCAR A, b Can, Feb 15, 41. EARTHQUAKE ENGINEERING, STRUCTURAL DYNAMICS. *Educ:* Univ Toronto, BASc, 64; Univ London, MSc, 65; Univ Waterloo, PhD(structural eng), 71. *Prof Exp:* Structural engr, Morrison, Hershfield, Millman & Huggins, Toronto, 65-67; res asst, Univ Waterloo, 67-70; ASSOC PROF STRUCTURAL ENG, CONCORDIA UNIV, 71- *Concurrent Pos:* Vis scholar, Univ Calif, Berkeley, 78-79. *Mem:* Am Soc Civil Engrs; Can Soc Civil Engrs; Am Soc Eng Educ; Asn Prof Engrs. *Res:* Analysis of building structures under static and dynamic loading; non-linear behaviour of coupled shear walls, precast panal structures, steel frames, and lateral-torsional coupling of the response of buildings during earthquakes. *Mailing Add:* Dept Civil Eng Concordia Univ 1455 Maisonneuve Blvd W Montreal PQ H3G 1M8 Can

PEKERIS, CHAIM LEIB, b Alytus, Lithuania, June 15, 08; nat US; m 33. GEOPHYSICS. *Educ:* Mass Inst Technol, BS, 29, DSc(meteorol), 33. *Prof Exp:* Fel, Rockefeller Found, 34-35 & Cambridge Univ, 35-36; assoc geophys, Mass Inst Technol, 36-41; mem sci staff, Div War Res, Columbia Univ, 41-45, dir math physics group, 45-50; prof appl math, 50-73, DISTINGUISHED INST PROF, WEIZMANN INST SCI, 73- *Concurrent Pos:* Guggenheim fel, 47. *Honors & Awards:* Rothschild Prize, 66; Vetlesen Prize, C Unger Vetlesen Found, 74; Gold Medal, Royal Astron Soc, 80. *Mem:* Nat Acad Sci; fel Royal Astron Soc; Israel Nat Acad Sci; Ital Nat Acad Sci; Am Philos Soc. *Res:* Seismology; underwater sound; atomic spectroscopy; hydrodynamics; electromagnetic wave propagation; applied mathematics; stellar hydrodynamics. *Mailing Add:* Dept of Appl Math Weizmann Inst of Sci Rehovoth Israel

PEKOZ, TEOMAN, b Apr 16, 37; US citizen; m 63; c 2. STRUCTURAL ENGINEERING, CIVIL ENGINEERING. *Educ:* Robert Col, Istanbul, BS, 58; Harvard Univ, MS, 59; Cornell Univ, PhD(civil eng), 67. *Prof Exp:* Engr, struct eng, various eng co, 59-69; ASSOC PROF & MGR STRUCT RES, STRUCT ENG, CORNELL UNIV, 69- *Concurrent Pos:* Consult, Am Iron & Steel Inst, 69- & Mat Handling Inst, 71-; vis prof, Royal Inst Technol, Sweden, 76-77; Gordon McKay fel, Harvard Univ, 58-59. *Mem:* Struct Stability Res Coun; Am Soc Civil Eng; Int Asn Bridge & Struct Eng. *Mailing Add:* Hollister Hall Cornell Univ Ithaca NY 14850

PELAN, BYRON J, b New York, NY, June 5, 21; m 50; c 2. MECHANICAL DESIGN, MECHANICAL ENGINEERING EDUCATION. *Educ:* Rutgers Univ, BSc, 49; Lehigh Univ, MS, 51. *Prof Exp:* Instr mach design, Lafayette Col, 49-51; proj engr, Johns-Manville Corp, 51-56; assoc prof mech eng, 56-80, PROF MECH ENG, RUTGERS UNIV, 80- *Mem:* Am Soc Mech Engrs; Am Soc Eng Educ (secy, 70-72); Soc Exp Stress Anal; AAUP; Nat Soc Prof Engrs. *Res:* Mechanical design; stress analysis; vibration; innovative methods of instruction of engineering students. *Mailing Add:* Col of Eng Rutgers Univ New Brunswick NJ 08903

PELAVIN, LAWRENCE, b Richmond, Va, Sept 17, 42; m 65; c 1. SYNTHETIC ORGANIC CHEMISTRY. *Educ:* NY Univ, BA, 64; Univ Ga, PhD(org chem), 73. *Prof Exp:* From instr to asst prof org chem, Mich State Univ, 73-74; instr org chem, Princeton Univ, 74-75; sr chemist, Synthetic Org Chem Div, Dept Radiochem, New Eng Nuclear Corp, 75-76; SUPVR, ANAL SERV, FINE PARTICLES DIV, CABOT CORP, 76- *Mem:* Am Soc Testing & Mat; Am Chem Soc. *Res:* Carbon black and black filled polymeric materials; thermal analysis of polymers. *Mailing Add:* Cabot Corp Res Ctr Concord Rd Billerica MA 01821

PELCOVITS, ROBERT ALAN, b New York, NY, Jan 25, 54; m 78. PHASE TRANSITIONS. *Educ:* Univ Pa, BA & MS, 74; Harvard Univ, PhD(physics), 78. *Prof Exp:* Res assoc, Univ Ill, Urbana-Champaign, 78-79, Brookhaven Nat Lab, 79-80; ASST PROF PHYSICS, BROWN UNIV, 79- *Mem:* Am Phys Soc. *Res:* Condensed matter theoretical physics including studies of phase transitions in liquid crystals, amorphous systems and liquid helium. *Mailing Add:* Dept Physics Brown Univ Providence RI 02912

PELCZAR, FRANCIS A, b Lawrence, Mass, June 13, 39; m 64; c 2. ORGANIC CHEMISTRY. *Educ:* Merrimack Col, BS, 60; Univ Conn, MS, 63; Univ NH, PhD(org chem), 68. *Prof Exp:* Asst chem, Univ Conn, 60-63; asst, Univ NH, 64-65; from asst prof to assoc prof, 67-77, PROF ORG CHEM, GANNON COL, 77- *Mem:* Am Chem Soc. *Res:* Organometallic and heterocyclic chemistry. *Mailing Add:* Dept Chem Gannon Col On Perry Sq Erie PA 16501

PELIKAN, EDWARD WARREN, b Chicago, Ill, June 15, 26; m 55; c 2. PHARMACOLOGY. *Educ:* Univ Ill, BS, 48, MS, 50, MD, 51. *Prof Exp:* From instr to asst prof pharmacol, Col Med, Univ Ill, 51-53; asst prof, Grad Sch Med, Univ Pa, 55-57; assoc prof, 57-62, PROF PHARMACOL & CHMN DEPT, SCH MED, BOSTON UNIV, 62- *Concurrent Pos:* House officer, Presby Hosp, Chicago, Ill, 51-53. *Mem:* AAAS; Am Soc Pharmacol & Exp Therapeut; NY Acad Sci. *Res:* Methodology; biometrics, autonomic drugs; neuromuscular blocking agents; central nervous system depressants; drugs affecting behavior. *Mailing Add:* Dept of Pharmacol Boston Univ Sch of Med Boston MA 02118

PELKA, DAVID GERARD, b San Diego, Calif, Apr 25, 43; m 69; c 2. PHYSICS, ENERGY SCIENCE. *Educ:* Calif State Univ, Los Angeles, BS, 65; Univ Calif, Riverside, MA, 68, PhD(physics), 71. *Prof Exp:* Res assoc superconductivity, Univ Calif, Riverside, 68-70; PROF PHYSICS, 71- & DIR ENERGY RES CTR, NORTHROP UNIV, 79- *Concurrent Pos:* Energy consult, various govt & pvt co, 75-; mem, Calif Post Second Comt, HEW grant, 76-78 & Los Angeles Solar City Comt, 77- *Honors & Awards:* Distinguished Res Award, Northrop Univ, 76. *Mem:* Int Solar Energy Soc; Am Phys Soc; Am Soc Heating Refrig & Air Conditioning Engrs; Sigma Xi. *Res:* Current research concerned with developing a new optical concentrator which can be used in applications to medium-high temperature thermal energy generation, its characteristics exceed those of fresnel or parabolic concentrators. *Mailing Add:* Dept Physics 1155 W Arbor Vitae St Inglewood CA 90306

PELL, ERIK MAURITZ, b Rattvik, Sweden, Sept 22, 23; nat US; m 51; c 3. SOLID STATE PHYSICS. *Educ:* Marquette Univ, BEE, 44; Cornell Univ, PhD(physics), 51. *Prof Exp:* Asst, Cornell Univ, 47-51; res assoc, Gen Elec Res Lab, NY, 51-61; res mgr, 61-71, staff consult, 71-74, dir res planning, 74-81, DIR, WEBSTER SCI LABS, XEROX CORP, 81- *Mem:* Fel Am Phys Soc; Inst Elec & Electronics Engrs; Electrochem Soc (pres, 80-81); Soc Photog Sci & Eng; NY Acad Sci. *Res:* Semiconducting properties of germanium, silicon, and selenium; photoconductivity; electrophotography. *Mailing Add:* Xerox Corp Xerox Sq Rochester NY 14644

PELL, EVA JOY, b New York, NY, Mar 11, 48; m 69; c 2. PLANT PATHOLOGY. *Educ:* City Col New York, BS, 68; Rutgers Univ, PhD(plant biol), 72. *Prof Exp:* Adj asst prof plant biol, Rutgers Univ, 72-73; asst prof plant path, 73-78, ASSOC PROF PLANT PATH, PA STATE UNIV, UNIVERSITY PARK, 78- *Concurrent Pos:* Mem sci adv bd, Environ Protection Agency, 78-; mem ed staff, Air Pollution Control Asn. *Mem:* Am phytopath Soc; Am Soc Plant Physiol; Air Pollution Control Asn; Potato Asn Am. *Res:* Air pollution effects on vegetation. *Mailing Add:* 211 Buckhout Lab University Park PA 16802

PELL, KYNRIC M(ARTIN), b Toronto, Ont, Apr 5, 38; US citizen; m 62; c 3. MECHANICAL ENGINEERING. *Educ:* Univ Fla, BAsE, 62, MS, 63, PhD(aerospace), 67. *Prof Exp:* Design engr, United Aircraft Corp, 62; res assoc aerospace eng, Univ Fla, 63-67, asst prof, 67-68; asst prof, Auburn Univ, 68-71; asst prof, 71-77, assoc prof, 77-79, PROF MECH ENG, UNIV WYO, 79- *Concurrent Pos:* Consult, Northrop Corp, 70-71 & US Army Missile Command, 77-; pres, SETA Corp, 79- *Honors & Awards:* Transp Res Bd Award, 75. *Mem:* Am Inst Aeronaut & Astronaut; Am Soc Mech Engrs; Sigma Xi. *Res:* Inclement weather engineering including: heat pipes for snow and ice control on highways, snow transport, atmospheric boundry layers; heat transfer; fluid dynamics, laser instrumentation of flight vehicles. *Mailing Add:* Dept Mech Eng Univ Wyo PO Box 3295 Laramie WY 82070

PELL, SIDNEY, b New York, NY, Dec 13, 22; m 50. BIOSTATISTICS, EPIDEMIOLOGY. *Educ:* City Col New York, BBA, 47, MBA, 52; Univ Pittsburgh, PhD(biostatist), 56. *Prof Exp:* Statistician, NY Univ-Bellevue Med Ctr, 51-52; MGR EPIDEMIOL SECT, MED DIV, E I DU PONT DE NEMOURS & CO, 55- *Mem:* fel Am Col Epidemiol; Biomet Soc; fel Am Pub Health Asn; fel Am Heart Asn. *Res:* Epidemiological studies of cardiovascular disease, diabetes, alcoholism and occupational disease. *Mailing Add:* Med Div E I du Pont de Nemours & Co Wilmington DE 19898

PELL, WILLIAM HICKS, b Lewisport, Ky, Oct 15, 14; m 39. APPLIED MATHEMATICS. *Educ:* Univ Ky, BS, 36, MS, 38; Univ Wis, PhD(math), 43. *Prof Exp:* Asst math, Univ Ky, 36-38, prof & head dept, 52-53, prof appl mech, 59-60; asst math, Univ Wis, 38-42; aerodynamicist, Bell Aircraft Corp, NY, 43-47; res assoc appl math, Brown Univ, 47-48, asst prof, 48-51, assoc prof, 51-52 & 53-55; fel, Inst Fluid Dynamics & Appl Math, Univ Md, 55-56; mathematician, Nat Bur Standards, 56-58, actg chief, Math Physics Sect, 58-59, chief, 60-65; prog dir appl math, statist & probability, 65-67, head math sci sect, 67-79, PROG DIR SPEC PROJ, NSF, 79- *Concurrent Pos:* Lectr, Int Bus Mach Corp, 59-60. *Mem:* AAAS; Am Math Soc; Math Asn Am; Am Soc Mech Engrs; Soc Indust & Appl Math. *Res:* Fluid mechanics, especially viscous; theory of elastic and rheological materials. *Mailing Add:* Math Sci Sect Nat Sci Found 1800 G St NW Washington DC 20550

PELLA, JEROME JACOB, b Pierz, Minn, Mar 13, 39. FISHERIES. *Educ:* Univ Minn, BS, 61; Univ Washington, MS, 64, PhD(fisheries), 67. *Prof Exp:* Scientist, Inter-Am Trop Tuna Comn, 65-69; MATH STATISTICIAN, NAT MARINE FISHERIES SERV, 69- *Res:* Applications of stochastic process models in fisheries; development of theory and analytic methods for estimation of potential production from animal populations. *Mailing Add:* Biol Lab Nat Mar Fish Serv PO Box 155 Auke Bay AK 99821

PELLA, MILTON ORVILLE, b Wilmot, Wis, Feb 13, 14; m 44. SCIENCE EDUCATION. *Educ:* Milwaukee State Teachers Col, BE, 36; Univ Wis, MS, 40, PhD(educ, bot), 48. *Prof Exp:* Teacher, Wyler Mil Acad, Wis, 37-38; teacher grade sch, 38-39; teacher, Wis High Sch & Univ Wis-Madison, 39-42 & 46-50; from asst prof to assoc prof, 49-57, PROF SCI EDUC, SCH EDUC, UNIV WIS-MADISON, 57- *Concurrent Pos:* Consult, Ministries Educ, Turkey, 59, Iran, 62 & Jordan, 63; consult, Am Univ Beirut, 62 & 64, Univs Jordan, 65 & 66, Aleppo, Syria, 66, Egypt, 72-80, Univ Damascus Syria, 80 & Yormook Univ Jordan, 80-81. *Mem:* Fel AAAS; Nat Sci Teachers Asn; Nat Asn Res Sci Teaching (pres, 65). *Res:* Teaching of science in elementary schools, its status and development; science concepts and their relationships to factors of educational achievement, culture and experience. *Mailing Add:* 5518 Varsity Hill Madison WI 53705

PELLEGRINI, FRANK C, b Brooklyn, NY, July 10, 40; m 67; c 2. ORGANIC CHEMISTRY. *Educ:* St John's Univ, NY, BS, 62, MS, 64, PhD(org chem), 70. *Prof Exp:* Teaching asst chem, St John's Univ, NY, 62-66, lectr pharmaceut chem, Col Pharm, 66-69; from asst prof to assoc prof, 69-79, chmn dept, 74-77, PROF CHEM, STATE UNIV NY AGR & TECH COL FARMINGDALE, 79- *Mem:* Am Chem Soc. *Res:* Heterocyclic chemistry; synthesis of non-benzenoid aromatic ring systems; complex metal hydride reductions. *Mailing Add:* Dept of Chem State Univ of NY Agr & Tech Col Farmingdale NY 11735

PELLEGRINI, JOHN P, JR, b New Haven, Conn, Jan 23, 26; m 53; c 2. ORGANIC CHEMISTRY. *Educ:* Yale Univ, BS, 46; Univ Ill, MS, 47, PhD(chem), 49; Univ Pittsburgh, MBA, 78. *Prof Exp:* Asst gen chem, Univ Ill, 46-49; res chemist, 49-50, group leader explor res, 50-54, sect head prod res, 54-61, RES ASSOC, GULF RES & DEVELOP CO, 61- *Mem:* AAAS; Am Chem Soc; fel Am Inst Chemists; NY Acad Sci. *Res:* Chemical control and clean up of oil spills; additives for petroleum products; metallocene chemistry; polymer coatings; chemical properties of long-chain olefins. *Mailing Add:* 617 Orchard Hill Dr Pittsburgh PA 15238

PELLEGRINO, EDMUND DANIEL, b Newark, NJ, June 22, 20; m 45; c 7. MEDICAL & HEALTH SCIENCES. *Educ:* St John's Univ, NY, BS, 41; NY Univ, MD, 44. *Hon Degrees:* DSc, St John's Univ, 71; LHD, St Benedict's Col, 71, Loyola Univ Chicago, 71; DSc, Hahnemann Med Col, 71. *Prof Exp:* Intern med, Bellevue Hosp, New York, 44-45; resident, Goldwater Mem Hosp, 45-46; fel, NY Univ, 48, fel & asst, 49-50; asst prof clin med, 53-59; supv tuberc physician, Homer Folks Tuberc Hosp, Oneonta, NY, 51-53; prof med & chmn dept, Med Ctr, Univ Ky, 59-66; prof med, chmn dept & dir ctr, State Univ NY Stony Brook, 66-73, dean sch med, 68-72, vpres health sci & dir ctr, 68-73; prof med & med humanities & chancellor, Univ Tenn Ctr Health Sci, 73-75; prof med, chmn bd & dir, Yale-New Haven Med Ctr, Yale Univ, 75-78; PRES, CATH UNIV AM, 78- *Concurrent Pos:* Asst clin vis physician, Bellevue Hosp, NY, 49-50, from asst vis physician to assoc vis physician, 53-59; dir internal med, Hunterdon Med Ctr, Flemington, NJ, 53-59; consult, Vet Admin Hosp, Lexington, Ky, 59-66, USPHS Hosp, 60-66, Dept Med, Div Internal Med & Nephrol, Nassau County Med Ctr, NY, 68-73 & St Charles Hosp, Port Jefferson, NY, 69-73; sr vis scientist & vis attend physician, Brookhaven Nat Lab, 66-73. *Mem:* Nat Inst Med; Asn Am Med Cols; Am Soc Nephrol; Soc Exp Biol & Med; fel Am Col Chest Physicians. *Res:* Cardiovascular-renal diseases; electrolyte metabolism; bone physiology; medical education; medical humanities. *Mailing Add:* Cath Univ of Am Washington DC 20064

PELLENBARG, ROBERT ERNEST, b Charleston, WVa, Feb 5, 49; m 73; c 2. CHEMICAL OCEANOGRAPHY, CHEMISTRY. *Educ:* George Washington Univ, BS, 71; Univ Miami, MS, 73; Univ Del, PhD(marine sci), 76. *Prof Exp:* Head chem lab, US Naval Oceanog Off, 76-77; fel, 77-79, RES CHEMIST, US NAVAL RES LAB, 79- *Res:* Geochemistry of trace metals; marine chemistry and biochemistry of trace elements and organics; analytical methods development as used for saline waters; trace substances as markers for materials movement in geochemical context. *Mailing Add:* Code 4330 Naval Res Lab Washington DC 20375

PELLER, LEONARD, b New York, NY, July 22, 28. PHYSICAL CHEMISTRY. *Educ:* Univ Calif, BS, 51; Princeton Univ, MA, 53, PhD, 58. *Prof Exp:* Jr res phys chemist, Calif Res Corp, 51; teaching asst, Princeton Univ, 51-53 & 55-57; proj assoc phys chem, Univ Wis, 57-60, instr, 60, lectr, 61; res chemist, Nat Inst Arthritis & Metab Dis, 62-63; vis lectr chem, Univ Calif, Berkeley, 63; ASSOC RES BIOPHYSICIST, MED CTR, UNIV CALIF, SAN FRANCISCO, 63-, ASSOC PROF BIOPHYS, 73- *Mem:* Am Chem Soc. *Res:* Physical chemistry of biological macro-molecules; enzyme kinetics. *Mailing Add:* Cardiovasc Res Inst Univ Calif Med Ctr San Francisco CA 94143

PELLERIN, CHARLES JAMES, JR, b Shreveport, La, Dec 11, 44; m 68; c 2. ASTROPHYSICS. *Educ:* Drexel Univ, BS, 67; Cath Univ Am, MS, 70, PhD(physics), 74. *Prof Exp:* Physicist, Sounding Rocket Br, 67-70, astrophysicist, Lab High Energy Astrophys, Goddard Space Flight Ctr, 70-75, DEP DIR, SPACELAB FLIGHT DIV, NASA, 75- *Mem:* Am Phys Soc. *Res:* Astrophysical problems through measurements of cosmic rays, including solar cosmic rays, galactic positrons and negatrons and gamma rays. *Mailing Add:* Spacelab Flight Div Off Space Sci & Appln NASA Washington DC 20546

PELLETIER, BERNARD RODERICK, marine geology, see previous edition

PELLETIER, CHARLES A, b New Britain, Conn, Jan 10, 32; m 61; c 2. HEALTH PHYSICS, ENVIRONMENTAL HEALTH. *Educ:* Rensselaer Polytech Inst, BCE, 56; Univ Mich, PhD(environ health), 66. *Prof Exp:* Consult health physics, Astra, Inc, 57-58; radiation control engr, Bethlehem Steel Co, 58-60; lectr radiol health, Univ Mich, 60-66, asst prof environ health, 66; chief, Environ Br, Health Serv Lab, US AEC, 67-71, chief environ radiation sect, Div Compliance, 71-73; DEPT MGR, SCIENCE

APPLICATIONS INC, 73- *Mem:* Health Physics Soc; Am Nuclear Soc. *Res:* Evaluation of waste management and effluent and environmental monitoring practices of US Atomic Energy Commission licensed facilities; contract research, occupational and environmental health and safety for nuclear power plants; research and development and services in power plant air and water leak detection. *Mailing Add:* 5803 Greenlawn Dr Bethesda MD 20814

PELLETIER, EUGENE NEIL, plant pathology, see previous edition

PELLETIER, GEORGES H, b June 18, 39; Can citizen; m 68; c 3. ENDOCRINOLOGY. *Educ:* Laval Univ, BA, 60, MD, 65, PhD(endocrinol), 68. *Prof Exp:* Med Res Coun Can fel endocrinol, McGill Univ, 68-69, electron micros, Univ Paris, 69-70 & cytochem, Albert Einstein Col Med, 70-71; asst prof, 71-74, assoc prof, 74-78, PROF PHYSIOL, LAVAL UNIV, 78- *Concurrent Pos:* Mem, Group Med Res Coun Can Molecular Endocrinol, 75- *Mem:* Am Soc Cell Biol; Endocrine Soc; Can Physiol Soc; Can Micros Soc; Can Soc Endocrinol & Metab. *Res:* Ultrastructural identification of the structures which produce the hypothalamic regulatory hormones involved in the regulation of anterior pituitary secretion. *Mailing Add:* Lab of Molecular Endocrinol Univ Laval 2705 Boul Laurier Ste-Foy PQ G1V 4G2 Can

PELLETIER, GERARD EUGENE, b Ottawa, Ont, June 18, 30; m 61; c 2. CHEMISTRY. *Educ:* Univ Ottawa, BSc, 53, MSc, 55; Laval Univ, PhD(chem), 60. *Prof Exp:* Chemist, OPW Paints, Ltd, 53-54 & Imperial Oil Res Labs, 60-62; vdean fac sci, 64-67, dir dept, 67-76, PROF CHEM, UNIV SHERBROOKE, 62- *Mem:* Chem Inst Can. *Res:* Physical chemistry; enzyme kinetics. *Mailing Add:* Dept Chem Univ Sherbrooke Sherbrooke PQ J1K 2R1 Can

PELLETIER, JOAN WICK, b Northampton, Mass, Nov 13, 42; c 2. PURE MATHEMATICS. *Educ:* Smith Col, BA, 64; McGill Univ, MS, 67, PhD(math), 70. *Prof Exp:* Asst prof math, Concordia Univ, 70-72; assoc prof, 72-80, PROF MATH, YORK UNIV, 80- *Mem:* Am Math Soc; Can Math Soc; Asn Women Math. *Res:* Applications of the theory of categories to analysis. *Mailing Add:* Dept of Math York Univ 4700 Keele St Downsview ON M3J 2R3 Can

PELLETIER, OMER, b May 31, 29; Can citizen; m 58; c 4. ANALYTICAL BIOCHEMISTRY, NUTRITIONAL BIOCHEMISTRY. *Educ:* Univ Montreal, BSc, 53; Univ Ottawa, BSc, 64, PhD(biochem), 70. *Prof Exp:* Technologist, 55-64, RES SCIENTIST, HEALTH PROTECTION BR, BUR MED BIOCHEM, CAN, 64-, MGR, 70- *Mem:* Chem Inst Can; Nutrit Soc Can; NY Acad Sci; Am Soc Clin Nutrit; Am Soc Clin Chem. *Res:* Analytical, biochemical nutrition and metabolism and clinical chemistry: vitamins, sugars and lipids; automated, high performance liquid chromatography and global environmental monitoring system reference methods and materials for vitamins, sugars and lipids; metabolism of ascorbic and isoascorbic acid; vitamin C metabolism of smokers. *Mailing Add:* Bur of Med Biochem Tunney's Pasture Ottawa ON K1A 0L2 Can

PELLETIER, REAL LUCIEN, b Montreal, Que, May 17, 19; m 51. PLANT PATHOLOGY. *Educ:* Univ Montreal, BS, 41; McGill Univ, MSc, 44; Univ Wis, PhD(plant path), 53. *Prof Exp:* Asst plant path, MacDonald Col, McGill Univ, 41-46; agr technician sci serv, Can Dept Agr, 46-47; asst bot, Univ Wis, 47-48, asst plant path, 48-53; from asst prof to assoc prof, 53-65, chmn dept, 69-70, PROF PLANT PATH, MACDONALD COL, McGILL UNIV, 65- *Concurrent Pos:* Can Int Develop Agency sr lectr bot, Univ Ghana, 66-67, tech asst dept veg prod, Inst Agron, Hassan, Morocco, 70-72. *Mem:* Am Phytopath Soc; Can Phytopath Soc. *Res:* Disease physiology and epidemiology. *Mailing Add:* Dept Plant Sci Macdonald Col McGill Univ Ste-Anne-de-Bellevue PQ H9X 1C0 Can

PELLETIER, S WILLIAM, b Kankakee, Ill, July 3, 24; m 49; c 6. ORGANIC CHEMISTRY. *Educ:* Univ Ill, BS, 47; Cornell Univ, PhD(org chem), 50. *Prof Exp:* Asst org chem, Cornell Univ, 47-50; instr, Univ Ill, 50-51; res asst chem pharmacol, Rockefeller Inst, 51-54, res assoc, 54-57, from asst prof to assoc prof, 57-62; prof & head dept, 62-69, provost, 69-76, ALUMNI FOUND DISTINGUISHED PROF CHEM, UNIV GA, 69-, UNIV PROF & DIR INST NATURAL PROD RES, 76- *Concurrent Pos:* Radio broadcast engr, Sta WKAN, 47; Gordon lectr, 55, 59 & 69; lectr, Ger Acad Agr Sci, Berlin, 59 & Am-Swiss Found Sci Exchange, 60; commemorative dedication lectr, Shionogi Res Lab, Osaka, Japan, 61; session chmn, Natural Prod Symp, Int Union Pure & Appl Chem, Kyoto, Japan, 64, Riga, Latvia, 70 & Varna, Bulgaria, 78. mem, Undergrad Equip Panel, NSF, 65-67, Med Chem Study Sect, NIH, 68-72 & Adv Bd, Ga Mus Art, 68-; Victor A Coulter lectrs, Univ Miss, 65; mem, Bd Dirs, Story Chem Corp, 69-73 & Ctr Res Libraries, 75-81. *Honors & Awards:* Herty Medalist, Am Chem Soc, 71, Southern Chemists' Award, 72. *Mem:* AAAS; Am Chem Soc; The Chem Soc; fel Royal Soc Arts. *Res:* Synthetic organic chemistry; structure and stereochemistry of diterpenoid alkaloids; diterpenes; triterpenes; application of carbon-13 nuclear magnetic resonance to structure elucidation; X-ray crystallographic structures of natural products. *Mailing Add:* Dept of Chem Univ of Ga Athens GA 30602

PELLETT, DAVID EARL, b Topeka, Kans, July 2, 38; m 67. PHYSICS. *Educ:* Univ Kans, AB, 60, MA, 62; Univ Mich, Ann Arbor, PhD(physics), 66. *Prof Exp:* Res assoc particle physics, Univ Mich, Ann Arbor, 66-67; asst prof, 67-74, ASSOC PROF PHYSICS, UNIV CALIF, DAVIS, 74- *Mem:* Am Phys Soc. *Res:* Experimental high energy particle physics. *Mailing Add:* Dept Physics 225 Physics I Univ Calif Davis CA 95616

PELLETT, HAROLD M, b Atlantic, Iowa, Feb 17, 38; m 60; c 6. HORTICULTURE. *Educ:* Iowa State Univ, BS, 60, MS, 61, PhD(hort), 64. *Prof Exp:* Asst prof hort, Univ Nebr, 64-66; asst prof, 66-73, assoc prof, 73-80, PROF HORT, UNIV MINN, ST PAUL, 80-, SUPT HORT RES CTR, 74- *Mem:* Am Soc Hort Sci; Int Plant Propagators Soc. *Res:* Nursery and landscape management. *Mailing Add:* Dept Hort Sci Univ Minn Col Agr St Paul MN 55101

PELLETT, NORMAN EUGENE, b Atlantic, Iowa, June 26, 34; m 56; c 3. ORNAMENTAL HORTICULTURE. *Educ:* Iowa State Univ, BS, 58; Univ Minn, MS, 64, PhD(hort), 65. *Prof Exp:* Mgr, Pellett Gardens, 58-61; res asst hort, Univ Minn, 61-64; asst prof, State Univ NY Agr & Tech Col Cobleskill, 64-67; asst prof hort, 67-72, ASSOC PROF PLANT & SOIL SCI, COL AGR, UNIV VT, 72- *Mem:* Am Soc Hort Sci; Int Plant Propagators Soc. *Res:* Winter hardiness of ornamental plants. *Mailing Add:* Dept Plant & Soil Sci Col Agr Univ Vt Burlington VT 05405

PELLEY, RALPH L, b Montreal, Que, Feb 3, 23; US citizen; m 46; c 1. ORGANIC CHEMISTRY. *Educ:* Sir George Williams Univ, BSc, 45; Univ NB, MSc, 49; Ohio State Univ, PhD(org chem), 51. *Prof Exp:* Res chemist, E I du Pont de Nemours & Co, 50-54; mgr, Caribou Chem, 54-60; proj leader, FMC Corp, Baltimore, 60-63, supvr, 63-65, res mgr, 65-68, asst dir res, 68-72; DIR RES & DEVELOP, DIXIE CHEM CO, 72- *Mem:* AAAS; Am Chem Soc; Am Inst Chem. *Res:* Industrial process development of large volume organic chemicals; oxidations; halogenation; condensation and polymerization. *Mailing Add:* Dixie Chem Co PO Box 13410 Houston TX 77019

PELLICCIARO, EDWARD JOSEPH, b Beaver Falls, Pa, Mar 20, 21; m 46; c 3. MATHEMATICS. *Educ:* Wagner Col, BS, 49; Univ NC, PhD(math), 53. *Prof Exp:* Instr math, Univ Del, 53-54; res fel, Duke Univ, 54-56; from asst prof to assoc prof, 56-70, PROF MATH, UNIV DEL, 70- *Mem:* Am Math Soc; Math Asn Am; Soc Indust & Appl Math; AAAS. *Res:* Ordinary differential equations. *Mailing Add:* Dept Math Univ Del Newark DE 19711

PELLICER, ANGEL, b Tarragona, Spain, Aug 5, 48; m 80. GENETIC ENGINEERING. *Educ:* Univ Valencia, Spain, MD, 71; Univ Madrid, Spain, PhD(biochem), 76. *Prof Exp:* Fel res assoc, Columbia Univ, 76-80; ASST PROF PATH, NY UNIV MED CTR, 80- *Honors & Awards:* Irma Hirschl Award, Irma Hirschl Trust, 82. *Mem:* Am Soc Microbiol; AAAS. *Res:* Study of eukaryotic gene expression with emphasis in the role of gene transfer and recombinant DNA as approaches for gene isolation and regulation analysis. *Mailing Add:* Dept Path NY Univ Med Ctr 550 1st Ave New York NY 10016

PELLIER, LAURENCE (DELISLE), b Paris, France, US citizen; m. METALLURGY. *Educ:* City Col New York, BChE, 39; Stevens Inst Technol, MS, 42. *Prof Exp:* Metallurgist, Sylvania Elec Prod, Inc, 46-51, Am Cyanamid Co, 51-57 & Int Nickel Co, 58-61; metallurgist, Burndy Corp, 62-64, consult, 64-67; OWNER, PELLIER-DELISLE METALL LAB, 67- *Honors & Awards:* Micrography Prize, Am Soc Metals, 49; Micrography Prize, Am Soc Testing & Mat, 52. *Mem:* Electron Micros Soc Am; Am Inst Mining, Metall & Petrol Engrs; Fr Soc Metall. *Res:* Powder metallurgy; electron microscopy; corrosion. *Mailing Add:* Pellier-Delisle Metall Lab 45 Clapboard Hill Rd Westport CT 06880

PELLIN, MICHAEL JOSEPH, physical chemistry, see previous edition

PELLINI, WILLIAM S, b Bristol, Conn, May 4, 17; m 45; c 3. METALLURGY. *Educ:* Carnegie Inst Technol, BS, 40. *Prof Exp:* Metallurgist, Metals Res Lab, Carnegie Inst Technol, 40-42; metallurgist, Oak Ridge Nat Lab, 47-48; head foundry & welding res, US Naval Res Lab, 48-54, supt metall div, 54-66, assoc dir res mat, 66-67, supt metall div, 67-74; RETIRED. *Concurrent Pos:* Consult, Mat Adv Bd, Nat Acad Sci; sr lectr, Dept Civil & Marine Eng, Mass Inst Technol, 69-; consult, Asn Am Railroads, 74- *Honors & Awards:* Distinguished Civilian Serv Award, US Navy, 61, Dept Defense, 63; Penton Gold Medal, Am Foundrymen's Soc, 61; Gold Medal, Am Soc Naval Eng, 61; Adams Lectr, Am Inst Mining, Metall & Petrol Engrs, 71; Sauveur Achievement Award, Am Soc Metals, 72. *Mem:* Nat Acad Eng; Am Soc Naval Eng; fel Am Soc Metals; Am Inst Mining, Metall & Petrol Engrs; Am Welding Soc. *Res:* Transformation and properties of steels; brittle fracture; weldability; solidification of metals; metals processing; railroad technology. *Mailing Add:* PO Box 68 Carver MA 02330

PELLIS, NEAL ROBERT, b Greensburg, Pa, Mar 24, 44; m 67; c 2. IMMUNOLOGY. *Educ:* Washington & Jefferson Col, BA, 66; Miami Univ, MS, 68, PhD(microbiol), 72. *Prof Exp:* From instr to asst prof immunol, Med Sch, Northwestern Univ, 73-77; asst prof, 77-80, ASSOC PROF IMMUNOL, MED SCH, UNIV TEX, HOUSTON, 80- *Concurrent Pos:* Fel, Med Sch, Stanford Univ; mem staff, Exp Tumor Immunol Lab, Vet Admin, Lake Side Hosp, Chicago, Ill, 73-77. *Mem:* Am Asn Immunologists; Am Asn Cancer Res; Soc Exp Biol & Med. *Res:* Immunity to neoplastic disease; chemical characterization of tumor-associated antigens; immunity to allografts; potentiation of the immune response. *Mailing Add:* Rm 6244 Dept of Surg Univ of Tex Med Sch Houston TX 77030

PELLISSIER, G(EORGE) E(DWARD), JR, b Springfield, Mass, Mar 15, 15; m 41; c 1. METALLURGY. *Educ:* Cornell Univ, BChem, 36, MChem, 38. *Prof Exp:* Group leader, Manhattan Proj, SAM Labs, Columbia Univ, 42-45; res assoc, Res & Develop Lab, US Steel Corp, 45-60, mgr spec proj, Appl Res Lab, 60-66, sr res consult phys metall, 66-68; lab mgr, Ernest F Fullam, Inc, 68-72; mgr mech & mat dept, RRC Int, Inc, 72-77; sr metallurgist, Mech Technol, Inc, 77-81; CONSULT, 81- *Mem:* Fel Am Inst Chem; Electrochem Soc; fel Am Soc Metals; Am Soc Testing & Mat; Electron Micros Soc Am. *Res:* Physical metallurgy of high strength steels; fracture and oxidation of metals; metal composites; electron microscopy; microstructure of materials; materials failure analysis. *Mailing Add:* Mech Technol Inc 968 Albany-Shaker Rd Latham NY 12110

PELLIZZARI, EDO DOMENICO, b Orland, Calif, Mar 17, 42; m 71; c 5. ANALYTICAL CHEMISTRY, ANALYTICAL BIOCHEMISTRY. *Educ:* Calif State Univ, Chico, AB, 63; Purdue Univ, West Lafayette, PhD(anal biochem), 69. *Prof Exp:* Res asst biochem, Mich State Univ, 63-65; res asst biochem, Purdue Univ, West Lafayette, 65-67, teaching asst anal biochem, 67-68; fel anal chem, Tex Res Inst Ment Sci, 69-71; DIV DIR, RES TRIANGLE INST, 71- *Concurrent Pos:* Fulbright-Hayes fel, Univ of Repub, Uruguay, 67; USPHS fel, Tex Res Inst Ment Sci, 69-71. *Mem:* Am Chem Soc;

AAAS; Sigma Xi; Soc Appl Spectros; Air Pollution Control Asn. *Res:* Development and application of techniques and instrumental methods of analysis for biomedical and environmental problems. *Mailing Add:* Res Triangle Inst PO Box 12194 Research Triangle Park NC 27709

PELLON, JOSEPH, b Barre, Vt, Mar 9, 28; m 50; c 2. ORGANIC CHEMISTRY. *Educ:* Univ Vt, BS, 50; Columbia Univ, PhD(chem), 57. *Prof Exp:* Mem staff, Am Cyanamid Co, 50-53; asst chem, Columbia Univ, 53-54; res chemist, Cent Res Div, 57-59, res leader, 59-60, group leader, 60-65, Fibers Res, 66-69, mgr, Fibers Res, 69-78, mgr prod liaison polyacrylamide and explosive ord reconnaissance polymers, 78-81. *Mem:* Am Chem Soc. *Res:* Polymer synthesis and reaction mechanism; free radical chemistry; polymer structure versus polymer properties; acrylic polymers and fibers; polyacrylamide and explosive ordinance reconnaissance polymers. *Mailing Add:* Am Cyanamid Co 1937 W Main St Stamford CT 06902

PELLOUX, REGIS M N, metallurgy, see previous edition

PELOQUIN, ROBERT ALFRED, b Ware, Mass, Sept 10, 33; m 63; c 3. PHYSICAL OCEANOGRAPHY, GEOLOGY. *Educ:* Univ NH, BA, 57; Tex A&M Univ, MS, 70. *Prof Exp:* Oceanogr phys oceanog, US Naval Oceanog Off, 61-72; proj officer, Scripps Inst Oceanog, 72-74; proj & br head, US Naval Oceanog Off, 74-78, div dir phys oceanog, geol & geophhys, 78-79; PROG MGR GEN ENG, NAVAL FACIL ENG COMMAND, 79- *Mem:* Am Geophys Union; Am Meteorol Asn; Marine Technol Soc. *Res:* Oceanographic applications as they relate to Navy environmental problems, including measurement and analysis of ocean currents, vertical distribution of density structure, bottom topography and sediment thickness and properties. *Mailing Add:* Naval Facil Eng Command 200 Stovall St Alex VA 20744

PELOSI, EVELYN TYMINSKI, b Dec 6, 38; US citizen; m 65; c 2. ORGANIC CHEMISTRY. *Educ:* Univ Mass, BS, 60; Univ NH, MS, 63, PhD(org chem), 65. *Prof Exp:* Asst prof chem, State Univ NY Col Oneonta, 67-68; TEACHER CHEM, NORWICH SR HIGH SCH, 77- *Mem:* Sigma Xi. *Res:* Synthetic and stereo chemistry. *Mailing Add:* 111 Hillview Ct Norwich NY 13815

PELOSI, LORENZO FRED, b San Michele di Serino, Italy, Sept 11, 44; US citizen. ORGANIC POLYMER CHEMISTRY, FLUORINE CHEMISTRY. *Educ:* Montclair State Col, BA, 67; Cornell Univ, PhD(org chem), 73. *Prof Exp:* Jr anal chemist, Hoffmann-La Roche, Inc, 67; teaching asst org chem, Cornell Univ, 67-70; fel synthetic org chem, Syntex Res, Inc, 72-74; res chemist, 74-80, SR RES CHEMIST, E I DU PONT DE NEMOURS & CO, INC, 80- *Mem:* Sigma Xi; Am Chem Soc. *Res:* Elastomer characterization and vulcanization; process development. *Mailing Add:* Chem Works Bldg 1155 E I du Pont de Nemours & Co Deep Water NJ 08023

PELOSI, STANFORD SALVATORE, JR, b Revere, Mass, Oct 3, 38; m 65; c 2. ORGANIC CHEMISTRY. *Educ:* Boston Col, BS, 60; Univ NH, PhD(org chem), 65. *Prof Exp:* Org chemist, US Army Aviation Mat Labs, Va, 65-67; sr res chemist, 67-79, UNIT LEADER, NORWICH-EATON PHARMACEUT, 79- *Mem:* Am Chem Soc; Sigma Xi. *Res:* Synthetic organic chemistry; heterocyclic compounds; medicinal chemistry; peptide chemistry. *Mailing Add:* Norwich-Eaton Pahrmaceut PO Box 191 Norwich NY 13815

PELT, ROLAND, JR, b Marianna, Fla, July 10, 31; m 54. CHEMICAL ENGINEERING, MATHEMATICS. *Educ:* Troy State Univ, BS, 52; Univ Miss, BS & MS, 60; Univ Pittsburgh, PhD(chem eng), 64. *Prof Exp:* Engr, Westinghouse Atomic Power Labs, 60-62; process engr, Mobay Chem Co, 62-64, sr process engr, 64-65, tech asst to dir eng, 65-66; develop group leader, 66-67, proj mgr eng, 67-68, proj eng supvr, 68-69, prod mgr, 69-70, asst plant mgr, 70-74, PLANT MGR, CIBA-GEIGY CHEM CORP, MCINTOSH, 74- *Concurrent Pos:* Pres, Delvan Develop Corp, 76- *Mem:* Am Chem Soc; Am Inst Chem Engrs. *Res:* Chemical process design; chemical plant construction; project and production management. *Mailing Add:* Ciba-Geigy Corp PO Box 113 Mobile AL 36553

PELTIER, CHARLES FRANCIS, b Boston, Mass, Oct 6, 45; m 69; c 1. TOPOLOGY. *Educ:* Col of the Holy Cross, BS, 67; Univ Notre Dame, MS, 70, PhD(math), 73. *Prof Exp:* Vis asst prof math, Univ Notre Dame, 73-74; ASST PROF MATH, ST MARY'S COL, 74- *Mem:* Am Math Soc. *Res:* Fiber bundles and classifying spaces, especially with reference to problems in embedding and immersion of manifolds. *Mailing Add:* Dept Math St Mary's Col Notre Dame IN 46556

PELTIER, HUBERT CONRAD, b New York, NY, Apr 6, 25; m 52; c 6. MEDICINE. *Educ:* Ind Univ, Bloomington, MD, 48; Am Bd Pediat, dipl, 54. *Prof Exp:* Intern, Ind Univ Med Ctr, 49; resident pediat, James Whitcomb Riley Hosp Children, 52; pvt pract, 52-56; res physician, Clin Res, Upjohn Co, Kalamazoo, 56-59; chief clin develop, 59-62, mgr, 62-64; vpres & med dir, Bristol Labs, Syracuse, 64-68; sr dir med res & med affairs, 68-70, exec dir domestic med affairs, 70, vpres med affairs, 71-78, vpres res, 78-79, sr vpres develop, 79-81, PRES, MERCK SHARP & DOHME RES LABS, 81- *Mem:* Fel Am Acad Pediat; Am Diabetes Asn; AMA; Pharmaceut Mfrs Asn. *Res:* Clinical pharmacology. *Mailing Add:* Merck Sharp & Dohme Res Labs West Point PA 19486

PELTIER, LEONARD FRANCIS, b Wisconsin Rapids, Wis, Jan 8, 20; m 43; c 2. ORTHOPEDIC SURGERY. *Educ:* Univ Nebr, AB, 41; Univ Minn, MD, 44, PhD(surg), 51. *Prof Exp:* Intern, Sect Orthop Surg, Univ Hosps, Univ Minn, 44-45, resident, 45-46, 48-50, clin instr, 51-53, clin asst prof, 53-56, clin assoc prof surg, 56-57; prof surg & head sect orthop surg, Med Ctr, Univ Kans, 57-71; PROF SURG & HEAD SECT ORTHOP SURG, MED CTR, UNIV ARIZ, 71- *Concurrent Pos:* Markle scholar, 52-56. *Mem:* Soc Univ Surgeons; Am Col Surgeons; Am Acad Orthop Surgeons. *Res:* Orthopedics; traumatology. *Mailing Add:* Dept Surg Univ Ariz Med Ctr Tucson AZ 85721

PELTIER, WILLIAM RICHARD, b Vancouver, BC, Can, Dec 31, 43. DYNAMIC METEOROLOGY, GEOPHYSICS. *Educ:* Univ BC, BSc, 67; Univ Toronto, MSc, 69, PhD(physics), 71. *Prof Exp:* Vis scientist fluid dynamics & geophys, Coop Inst Res Environ Sci, 72-73; vis prof, 73-77, from asst prof to assoc prof, 74-79, PROF PHYSICS, UNIV TORONTO, 79- *Concurrent Pos:* Consult, Coop Inst Res Environ Sci & Inst Arctic & Alpine Res, 74-; Sloan fel, 77-79; Steacie fel, 78; Killam fel, 80-82. *Honors & Awards:* Kirtz Bryan Award, Geol Soc Am, 80. *Mem:* Can Asn Physicists; Can Meteorol Soc. *Res:* Mesoscale atmospheric dynamics; thermal convection and atmospheric waves; visco-elastic structure of the planetary interior; mantle convection; glacio-isostatic rebound; numerical modeling. *Mailing Add:* Dept of Physics Univ of Toronto Toronto ON M5S 1A7 Can

PELTON, FRANK M(URRAY), electronic engineering, see previous edition

PELTON, JOHN FORRESTER, b Los Angeles, Calif, Mar 15, 24; m 48; c 1. PLANT ECOLOGY. *Educ:* Univ Calif, Los Angeles, BS, 45; Univ Minn, MS, 48, PhD(bot), 51. *Prof Exp:* Asst bot, Univ Minn, 46-48, instr, 48-49; instr forestry, Univ Calif, 51-52 & bot, Oberlin Col, 52-53; from asst prof to assoc prof, 53-62, actg head dept, 55-56, PROF BOT & HEAD DEPT, BUTLER UNIV, 62- *Concurrent Pos:* Treas, Rocky Mountain Biol Lab, 57. *Mem:* Bot Soc Am; Ecol Soc Am. *Res:* Ecological life history of seed plants. *Mailing Add:* Dept of Bot Butler Univ Indianapolis IN 46208

PELTON, MICHAEL RAMSAY, b Trion, Ga, July 25, 40; m 62; c 2. WILDLIFE BIOLOGY, MAMMALOGY. *Educ:* Univ Tenn, BS, 62; Univ Ga, MS, 65, PhD(wildlife biol), 69. *Prof Exp:* Asst prof, 68-76, ASSOC PROF FORESTRY, UNIV TENN, KNOXVILLE, 76- *Honors & Awards:* Stoddard-Sutton Award, 69. *Mem:* Am Soc Mammal; Wildlife Soc. *Res:* Game mammal ecology; physiological response of small mammals to environmental conditions; reproductive aspects of game mammal biology. *Mailing Add:* Dept Forestry Univ Tenn 1505 W Cumberland Ave Knoxville TN 37916

PELTZMAN, ALAN, b New York, NY, Dec 25, 37; m 63. CHEMICAL ENGINEERING. *Educ:* City Col New York, BChE, 60; NY Univ, MChE, 64; City Univ New York, PhD(chem eng), 67. *Prof Exp:* Air Force Off Sci Res res asst chem eng, Eng Res Div, NY Univ, 60-62; res asst chem eng, City Col New York, 62-63, Nat Sci Found asst, 63-66, instr, 64; chem engr, Halcon Int, Inc, 66-68, sr chem engr, 68-75; proc mgr res & develop, Halcon Int, Inc & Halcon Rand D Corp, 75-78; TECH DIR, HALCON RAND D CORP, 78- *Mem:* Am Inst Chem Engrs; Am Chem Soc. *Res:* Chemical kinetics; process development; mass transfer operations; chemical economics; heat transfer; unit processes of chemical engineering. *Mailing Add:* Halcon Int Inc 2 Park Ave New York NY 10016

PELUS, LOUIS MARTIN, b Queens, NY, Oct 18, 51; m 74; c 1. IMMUNOBIOLOGY, EXPERIMENTAL HEMATOLOGY. *Educ:* Queens Col, NY, BA, 73; Rutgers Univ, MS, 73, PhD(zool), 73. *Prof Exp:* assoc researcher immunobiol, 77-80, RES ASSOC EXP HEMAT, MEM SLOAN KETTERING CANCER CTR, 80- *Concurrent Pos:* Nat Cancer Inst fel, HEW, 77- *Honors & Awards:* Nat Res Serv Award, Nat Cancer Inst, HEW, 77. *Mem:* Sigma Xi; NY Acad Sci; Int Soc Hemat. *Res:* Investigation of the roles of macrophage derived regulatory molecules in the direction and control of myelopoiesis, particularly subpopulation heterogeneity of stimulator and responder cell populations. *Mailing Add:* Dept of Develop Hematopoiesis Mem Sloan Kettering Cancer Ctr New York NY 10021

PELUSO, ADA, b Antwerp, Belg, Feb 8, 41; US citizen. MATHEMATICS. *Educ:* Hunter Col, BA, 60; NY Univ, ScM, 63, PhD(math), 66. *Prof Exp:* Asst prof, 66-70, ASSOC PROF MATH, HUNTER COL, 71- *Mem:* Am Math Soc; Math Asn Am; AAAS. *Res:* Group theory. *Mailing Add:* Dept Math Hunter Col 695 Park Ave New York NY 10021

PELZ, ROBERT W(ALTER), b Chicago, Ill, Jan 4, 19; m 42; c 3. CERAMICS. *Educ:* Univ Ill, BSc, 46, MSc, 47. *Prof Exp:* Res ceramist, Glass & Porcelain Enamels, 47-52, admin asst, 53-57, sr res engr, 58-61, TECH COORDR, FERRO CORP, 62- *Mem:* Am Ceramic Soc; Soc Aerospace Mat & Process Eng. *Res:* Ceramic research in glass, porcelain enamels and colors. *Mailing Add:* 3971 Humphrey Rd Richfield OH 44286

PELZER, CHARLES FRANCIS, b Detroit, Mich, June 5, 35; m 72; c 1. HUMAN GENETICS, ZOOLOGY. *Educ:* Univ Detroit, BS, 57; Univ Mich, PhD(human genetics), 65. *Prof Exp:* Kettering Found fel, Wabash Col, 65-66; instr biol, Univ Detroit, 66-68; asst prof, 69-74, assoc prof, 74-79, PROF BIOL, SAGINAW VALLEY STATE COL, 79- *Concurrent Pos:* Res assoc, Mich State Univ, 76-77; vis scientist, Am Inst Biol Sci/Energy Res & Develop Admin, 75-78. *Mem:* AAAS; Am Inst Biol Sci; NY Acad Sci; Soc Human Genetics; Genetics Soc Am. *Res:* Genetic screening for blood proteins, especially alpha-1 antitrypsin as related to human diseases as emphysema; genetic control of isozymes; biochemical genetics; genetic counseling; isoelectric focusing; inherited diseases of man. *Mailing Add:* Dept of Biol Saginaw Valley State Col University Center MI 48710

PEMBLE, RICHARD HOPPE, b Indianola, Iowa, Aug 16, 41; m 65; c 1. ECOLOGY, PHYTOGEOGRAPHY. *Educ:* Simpson Col, BA, 63; Univ Mont, MA, 65; Univ Calif, Davis, PhD(bot), 70. *Prof Exp:* Teaching asst biol, Univ Mont, 63-65; res asst bot, Univ Calif, Davis, 65-68, teaching asst, 68-69; from asst prof to assoc prof, 69-80, PROF BIOL, MOORHEAD STATE UNIV, 80- *Mem:* Ecol Soc Am; Am Inst Biol Sci. *Res:* Phytogeography and ecology of the Red River drainage basin in North Dakota and Minnesota. *Mailing Add:* Dept Biol Moorhead State Univ Moorhead MN 56560

PEMENT, FREDRIC WILLIAM, chemistry, chemical engineering, see previous edition

PEMRICK, RAYMOND EDWARD, b Troy, NY, Jan 6, 20; m 48. TEXTILE CHEMISTRY. *Educ:* Siena Col, BS, 43; Rensselaer Polytech Inst, MS, 52. *Prof Exp:* Res chemist, Cluett, Peabody Co, Inc, 46-50; res chemist, Behr-Manning Co div, Norton Co, NY, 51-54, asst to res dir, 54-59, dir lab serv, Tech Dept, 59-62, mgr lab serv, Res Dept, 62-63, asst dir res, 63-70, lab mgr, Coated Abrasives Div, 70-71, mgr res & develop serv & group leader cloth finishing res, 71-75, mgr tech serv, Tech Dept, Coated Abrasives Div, 75-76, mgr tech serv & proj mgr, Synthetics Backings, 76-77, mgr tech serv, 78-81, RES ASSOC, NORTON CO, NY, 81- *Mem:* AAAS; Am Chem Soc; Am Asn Textile Chemists & Colorists; Sigma Xi. *Res:* Coated abrasives; synthetic resins; textiles, including application and fabric design; patents and patent liaison. *Mailing Add:* Norton Co Coated Abrasive Div 10 Ave & 25th St Watervliet NY 12189

PEMSLER, J(OSEPH) PAUL, b New York, NY, July 9, 29; m 54; c 3. PHYSICAL CHEMISTRY, METALLURGY. *Educ:* NY Univ, BS, 49, PhD(phys chem), 54. *Prof Exp:* Teaching fel chem, NY Univ, 50-53; phys chemist, Goodyear Atomic Corp, 53-56; phys chemist, Nuclear Metals, Inc, 56-59, group leader chem metall, 59-62; chem metallurgist, Ledgemont Lab, Kennecott Copper Corp, 62-66, staff scientist, 67-74, group leader chem, 74-75, mgr exploratory res, 75-77; dir new technol, EIC Corp, 77-79; PRES, CASTLE TECHNOL CORP, 79- *Concurrent Pos:* Chmn, Gordon Conf Corrosion, 73. *Honors & Awards:* Francis Mills Turner Award, Electrochem Soc, 58; Extractive Metall Sci Award, Am Inst Mining, Metall & Petrol Engrs, 78. *Mem:* Am Chem Soc; Electrochem Soc; Am Inst Mining, & Petrol Engrs; Am Inst Chemists. *Res:* Electrochemistry; extractive metallurgy; materials science; energy related research and development. *Mailing Add:* 6 Castle Rd Lexington MA 02173

PENA, HUGO GABRIEL, b Tarma, Peru, Mar 24, 28; m 57; c 5. RADIOBIOLOGY, NUCLEAR MEDICINE. *Educ:* Agr Univ, Lima, Peru, BS, 51; Purdue Univ, MS, 66, PhD(bionucleonics), 69. *Prof Exp:* Gen mgr point four prog, Exp Ranch, Int Coop Admin, Lima, Peru, 52-55; lab technician, Gen Hosp, Indianapolis, Ind, 57-60; chief technician, Metab Res Lab, Radioisotope Serv, Vet Admin Hosp, Indianapolis, 60-64; res asst bionucleonics dept, Pharm Sch, Purdue Univ, 64-68; ASSOC CHIEF NUCLEAR MED SERV, VET ADMIN HOSP, 68- *Concurrent Pos:* Lectr, Med Sch, Univ NMex, 69-, asst prof radiopharm, Pharm Sch, 77- *Mem:* AAAS; Health Physics Soc; Am Soc Animal Sci; Int Radiation Protection Asn; Nat Asn Agr Eng, Peru. *Res:* Thyroid physiology, especially radioiodinated compounds metabolism; fallout pollutants in the food chain, particularly their metabolism and translocation in farm animals; radioactive lipid dyes in the assay of atherosclerosis; whole-body counting and nuclear medicine research. *Mailing Add:* Nuclear Med Serv Vet Admin Hosp Albuquerque NM 87108

PENA, JORGE AUGUSTO, b Buenos Aires, Arg, May 6, 19; m 46; c 2. AIR POLLUTION, ATMOSPHERIC CHEMISTRY. *Educ:* Univ Buenos Aires, PhD(chem), 46. *Prof Exp:* Chemist at several factories & labs, Arg, 45-56; instr phys chem, Univ Buenos Aires, 56-59, instr meteorol, 59-67, adj prof, 67; from res asst to res assoc, 67-74, res meteorologist, 74-77, RES ASSOC METEOROL, PA STATE UNIV, 77- *Mem:* Am Meteorol Soc. *Res:* Aerosol particle generation by gas reactions in atmospheric conditions. *Mailing Add:* Dept of Meteorol Pa State Univ University Park PA 16802

PENCE, HARRY EDMOND, b Martins Ferry, Ohio, Feb 4, 37; m 59; c 3. INORGANIC CHEMISTRY. *Educ:* Bethany Col, WVa, BS, 58; Univ WVa, MS, 62; La State Univ, PhD(chem), 68. *Prof Exp:* Instr chem, Washington & Jefferson Col, 61-65, asst prof, 65-66; assoc prof, 67-69, PROF CHEM, STATE UNIV NY COL ONEONTA, 69- *Concurrent Pos:* Pres, Fac Senate, State Univ NY, 75-77. *Mem:* Am Chem Soc; Royal Soc Chem. *Res:* Preparation and spectral studies of transition metal complexes, especially those involving molybdenum and tungsten. *Mailing Add:* Dept of Chem State Univ NY Oneonta NY 13820

PENCE, LELAND HADLEY, b Kearney, Mo, Oct 1, 11; m 38; c 3. BIOORGANIC CHEMISTRY. *Educ:* Univ Fla, BS, 32; Univ Mich, MS, 33, PhD(org chem), 37. *Prof Exp:* Lectr, demonstr & asst, Univ Mich, 33-34; org res chemist, Biochem Res Found, Franklin Inst, 37-39; instr org chem, Reed Col, 39-42, asst prof, 42-45; org res chemist, Ore, 40-45, SR SCIENTIST, DIFCO LABS, INC, DETROIT, 45- *Concurrent Pos:* Org res chemist, Mayo Clin, 40; fel Calif Inst Technol, 43. *Mem:* Fel AAAS; Am Soc Microbiol; Am Chem Soc; Tissue Cult Asn; Sigma Xi. *Res:* Preparation of fluorescent antibodies; isolation and purification of bile acids, phospholipids, lectins, mitogens, phytohemagglutinin, and concanavalin A; synthesis of diagnostic reagents; cytogenetics of human and animal chromosomes; tissue culture reagents. *Mailing Add:* 972 Alberta Ave Ferndale MI 48220

PENCHINA, CLAUDE MICHEL, b Paris, France, Jan 25, 39; US citizen; m 64; c 2. SOLID STATE PHYSICS. *Educ:* Cooper Union Univ, BEE, 59; Syracuse Univ, MS, 61, PhD(physics), 64. *Prof Exp:* Res assoc physics & elec eng, Univ Ill, 63-65; from asst prof to assoc prof, 65-76, PROF PHYSICS, UNIV MASS, AMHERST, 76- *Concurrent Pos:* Vis scientist, Kings Col, Univ London, 71, 77, 78 & Max Planck Inst Solid State Res, 72; consult, Naval Res Lab, PEC Res Corp, Qantix Corp. *Mem:* Am Phys Soc; Sigma Xi; Optical Soc Am; NY Acad Sci. *Res:* Photoconductivity; optical and electronic properties of crystalline and amorphous solids. *Mailing Add:* Hasbrouck Lab Dept Phys & Astron Univ Mass Amherst MA 01003

PENDERGRASS, LEVESTER, b Columbia, SC, May 30, 46; m 68; c 2. PLANT TAXONOMY. *Educ:* Morris Col, BS, 69; Atlanta Univ, MS, 72, PhD(biol & bot), 76. *Prof Exp:* Range aid, 73-75, biol technician, 75-76, botanist, 76-77, REGIONAL BOTANIST, US FOREST SERV, USDA, 77- *Res:* Management of lesser vegetation endangered and sensitive plant species. *Mailing Add:* US Forest Serv 1720 Peachtree Rd NW Atlanta GA 30367

PENDERGRASS, ROBERT NIXON, b Ark, Dec 22, 18; m 44; c 3. STATISTICS. *Educ:* Southwest Mo State Col, BS, 46; Univ Mo, MEd, 51, AM, 52; Va Polytech Inst & State Univ, PhD(statist), 58. *Prof Exp:* Instr math, Univ Mo, 51-53; from assoc prof to prof, Radford Col, 53-62; PROF MATH, SOUTHERN ILL UNIV, EDWARDSVILLE, 62- *Mem:* Math Asn Am; Inst Math Statist; Am Statist Assoc; Nat Coun Teachers Math. *Res:* Statistical inferencel rank analysis. *Mailing Add:* 837 Troy Rd Edwardsville IL 62025

PENDERGRASS, THOMAS WAYNE, b Kansas City, Mo, Sept 23, 45; m 73; c 1. PEDIATRICS, HEMATOLOGY. *Educ:* Univ Ariz, BA, 67; Univ Tenn, MD, 71. *Prof Exp:* Pediat resident, Children's Mem Hosp, Northwestern Univ, 71-73; staff assoc epidemiol, Nat Cancer Inst, 73-75; sr fel pediat hemat & oncol, Univ Wash & Children's Orthop Hosp & Med Ctr, 77-78; sr fel epidemiol, 77-78, ASST PROF PEDIAT, UNIV WASH, 79-, ADJ ASST PROF EPIDEMIOL, 79-; ASST MEM PEDIAT ONCOL & EPIDEMIOL, FRED HUTCHINSON CANCER RES CTR, 78- *Mem:* Soc Epidemiol Res; Am Asn Cancer Educ; Am Soc Clin Oncol. *Res:* Etiology and epidemiology of cancer, especially of childhood cancer; educational methods for dealing with stress; oncology. *Mailing Add:* Childrens Ortho Hosp & Med Ctr PO Box C-5371 Seattle WA 98105

PENDLETON, HUGH NELSON, III, b Gallipolis, Ohio, Aug 14, 35; m 58; c 2. THEORETICAL PHYSICS. *Educ:* Carnegie Inst Technol, BS, 56, MS, 58, PhD(physics), 61. *Prof Exp:* From instr to asst prof, 60-67, assoc prof, 67-78, PROF PHYSICS, BRANDEIS UNIV, 78- *Mem:* AAAS; Am Phys Soc. *Res:* Quantization of fields on curved space-times; supersymmetry; quantum electrodynamics. *Mailing Add:* Dept of Physics Brandeis Univ Waltham MA 02154

PENDLETON, JOHN DAVIS, b Elizabeth City, NC, Sept 20, 12; m 46; c 4. SOIL CHEMISTRY. *Educ:* NC State Col, BS, 35; Rutgers Univ, MS, 39; Cornell Univ, PhD(soil chem), 51. *Prof Exp:* Ed mgr, Chilean Nitrate Co, NJ, 39-41; asst prof, 46-47, assoc prof, 50-81, EMER ASSOC PROF AGRON, VA POLYTECH INST & STATE UNIV, 81- *Concurrent Pos:* Asst prof, Tenn Valley Auth, 46-47. *Mem:* Am Soc Agron. *Res:* Soils; soil physics. *Mailing Add:* Dept of Agron Va Polytech Inst & State Univ Blacksburg VA 24061

PENDLETON, JOHNNY WRYAS, b Hillsboro, Tenn, Jan 1, 22; m 48; c 5. AGRONOMY. *Educ:* Univ Tenn, BS, 48; Univ Ill, MS, 51, PhD, 55. *Prof Exp:* Prof agron, Univ Ill, Urbana, 61-71; PROF AGRON & CHMN DEPT, UNIV WIS-MADISON, 71- *Mem:* Am Soc Agron; Crop Sci Soc Am; Soil Sci Soc Am; Soil Conserv Soc Am. *Res:* Crop ecology and physiology. *Mailing Add:* Dept Agron Univ Wis Madison WI 53706

PENDLETON, ROBERT CECIL, b Torrey, Utah, Nov 5, 18; m 41; c 3. RADIATION ECOLOGY. *Educ:* Univ Utah, BS, 46, MS, 47, PhD(radiation ecol), 52. *Prof Exp:* Instr biol & bot, Weber State Col, 47-50; chief biol br test design & anal, Biol Warfare Labs, Chem Corps, US Army, 52-54; biol scientist, Gen Elec Co, 54-59; res assoc prof & radiol health officer, 60-63, ASSOC PROF BIOL, UNIV UTAH, 66-, DIR DEPT RADIOL HEALTH, 64- *Concurrent Pos:* Consult, Utah State Fish & Game Dept, 60; sci adv nuclear energy, Gov of Utah, 68; consult, Gov of Colo, 69; comnr & vchmn, Utah Nuclear Energy Comn, 71; mem, Adv Coun Sci & Technol, State of Utah, 73-76; chmn, Radiol Health Adv Comt of Utah, 75; mem comt on Radioactive Waste Mgt, Nat Acad Sci Res Coun, 76. *Mem:* Fel AAAS; Ecol Soc Am; Am Soc Limnol & Oceanog; Health Physics Soc; Radiation Res Soc. *Res:* Radiation ecology; accumulation and transfer of radioactive nuclides through food webs; effects of environmental factors on levels and rates of accumulation of radioactive materials in the foods of man; effects of low-level radioactivity on populations. *Mailing Add:* Dept Radiol Health Univ Utah Salt Lake City UT 84112

PENDLETON, ROBERT GRUBB, b Kansas City, Mo, Apr 24, 39; m 64; c 3. PHARMACOLOGY. *Educ:* Univ Mo, AB, 61; Univ Kans, PhD(pharmacol), 66. *Prof Exp:* Sr scientist, Dept Pharmacol, 66-69, sr investr, 69-74, asst dir, 74-77, ASSOC DIR, PHARMACOL, SMITH KLINE & FRENCH LABS, 77- *Concurrent Pos:* Captain, MSC, USAR. *Mem:* Am Soc Pharmacol & Exp Therapeut; Am Col Cardiol; Am Chem Soc; AAAS; NY Acad Sci. *Res:* General pharmacology, including biochemical pharmacology and drug receptor interactions; present research is concerned with epinephrine biosynthesis and catecholaminergic receptors. *Mailing Add:* Smith Kline & French Labs 1500 Spring Garden St Philadelphia PA 19101

PENDLETON, WESLEY WILLIAM, b Providence, RI, Apr 2, 14; m 39; c 4. ELECTRICAL ENGINEERING. *Educ:* Univ RI, BS, 36; Mass Inst Technol, MS, 40. *Prof Exp:* Student engr, Gen Elec Co, 36-38; mem staff, Mass Inst Technol, 38-41; res engr, Westinghouse Elec Corp, 41-49; res engr, Gen Cable Corp, NJ, 49-50; res engr, Anaconda Wire & Cable Co, 50-65, mgr elec sect, Magnet Wire Res Lab, 65-70, mgr res & develop, 70-77, sr engr, 77-80; CONSULT ELEC INSULATION, 80- *Mem:* Sigma Xi; fel Inst Elec & Electronics Engrs. *Res:* Insulation development for high voltage; viscometry; semiconductors; corona studies; magnet wire development; thermal stability of insulation; high temperature and inorganic insulation; electrical-thermal testing of magnet wire enamels; electrical insulation; thermal degradation; magnet wire evaluation test equipment. *Mailing Add:* 1542 Clinton St Muskegon MI 49442

PENDSE, PRATAPSINHA C, b Poona, India, June 9; US citizen. CYTOGENETICS, BOTANY. *Educ:* Univ Bombay, BS, 47; Univ Poona, MS, 51; Utah State Univ, MS, 59, PhD(plant sci), 65. *Prof Exp:* Instr agron, Univ Bombay, 47-50; lectr, Univ Poona, 50-56; asst prof biol, Colgate Univ, 65-66; asst prof biol, 66-74, assoc prof biol sci, 74-76, MEM FAC BIOL SCI, CALIF POLYTECH STATE UNIV, 76- *Mem:* Am Soc Hort Sci; Asn Trop Biol. *Res:* Developmental biology; androgenesis. *Mailing Add:* Dept Biol Sci Calif Polytech State Univ San Luis Obispo CA 94301

PENE, JACQUES JEAN, b Algiers, Algeria, July 19, 37; US citizen; c 1. MICROBIOLOGY, MICROBIAL GENETICS. *Educ:* Univ Calif, Los Angeles, BA, 59, PhD(microbiol), 63. *Prof Exp:* NIH res fel biochem, Albert Einstein Col Med, 63-66; asst prof develop biol, Univ Colo, Boulder, 67-73; ASSOC PROF BIOL SCI, COL ARTS & SCI, UNIV DEL, 73- *Concurrent Pos:* Mem, Microbial Physiol Study Sec, NIH, 80-83. *Mem:* Am Soc Microbiol. *Res:* Genetic control mechanisms in bacteriophage infected bacteria; DNA structure and function; enzymology of RNA synthesis; DNA: membrane interactions; cloning in bacillus. *Mailing Add:* Cell & Molecular Biol Sect Col Arts & Sci Univ Del Newark DE 19711

PENFIELD, MARJORIE PORTER, b Mt Pleasant, Pa, May 28, 42; m 72. FOOD SCIENCE. *Educ:* Pa State Univ, BS, 64, MS, 66; Univ Tenn, PhD(food sci), 73. *Prof Exp:* Exten specialist food & nutrit, Va Polytech Inst & State Univ, 66-71; asst prof food sci, Univ Ky, 74; asst prof, 74-78, ASSOC PROF FOOD SCI, UNIV TENN, KNOXVILLE, 78- *Mem:* Inst Food Technologists; Am Meat Sci Asn; Am Diet Asn; Am Home Econ Asn; Soc Nutrit Educ. *Res:* Sensory evaluation of foods; evaluation of textural qualities of foods by objective methods; influence of heat on properties of meat; factors affecting food-related behavior of individuals. *Mailing Add:* Dept Nutrit & Food Sci Univ of Tenn Knoxville TN 37996

PENFIELD, PAUL, JR, b Detroit, Mich, May 28, 33; m 56; c 3. ELECTRICAL ENGINEERING, PHYSICS. *Educ:* Amherst Col, BA, 55; Mass Inst Technol, ScD(elec eng), 60. *Prof Exp:* From asst prof to assoc prof, 60-69, PROF ELEC ENG, MASS INST TECHNOL, 69- *Concurrent Pos:* Ford Found fel, 60-62; NSF sr fel, 66-67. *Mem:* Fel Inst Elec & Electronics Engrs; Am Phys Soc. *Res:* Varactors; solid-state microwave devices and circuits; noise theory; theory of noise and frequency conversion; electrodynamics of moving media; computer-aided circuit theory. *Mailing Add:* 17 Bradford Rd Weston MA 02193

PENFIELD, ROBERT HARRISON, b Oswego, NY, Nov 25, 21; m 45; c 7. PHYSICS. *Educ:* Syracuse Univ, PhD(physics), 50. *Prof Exp:* Asst physics, Syracuse Univ, 48-50; from asst prof to assoc prof, 50-60, PROF PHYSICS, HARPUR COL, STATE UNIV NY BINGHAMTON, 60- *Concurrent Pos:* NSF grants, 64-68. *Mem:* Am Phys Soc. *Res:* Classical field theory; quantum field theory; quantum theory of the gravitational field. *Mailing Add:* Dept Physics Harpur Col State Univ NY Binghamton NY 13901

PENG, ANDREW CHUNG YEN, b Peiping, China, Feb 14, 24. FOOD CHEMISTRY. *Educ:* Wash State Univ, BS, 61; Mich State Univ, MS, 62, PhD(lipid chem), 65. *Prof Exp:* Food scientist, Res & Develop Ctr, Swift & Co, 65-67; asst prof, 68-72, assoc prof, 72-78, PROF FOOD TECHNOL, DEPT HORT, OHIO STATE UNIV, 78- *Honors & Awards:* MacGee Award, Am Oil Chem Soc, 65. *Mem:* Inst Food Technologists; Am Oil Chem Soc; Am Asn Cereal Chemists. *Res:* Lipids and soybean proteins. *Mailing Add:* Dept of Hort Ohio State Univ Columbus OH 43210

PENG, FRED MING-SHENG, b Taiwan, China, July 15, 36; US citizen; m 64; c 2. POLYMER CHEMISTRY. *Educ:* Tunghai Univ, BS, 59; Syracuse Univ, MS, 64, PhD(chem eng), 67. *Prof Exp:* Sr res engr, 66-74, res specialist polymer sci, 75-79, SR TECHNOL SPECIALIST, MONSANTO CO, 79- *Mem:* Am Inst Chem Engrs. *Res:* Polymerization kinetics and processes, specifically of mass and emulsion; one phase and two phase polymer systems. *Mailing Add:* 132 Brookwood Dr Longmeadow MA 01106

PENG, SHI-KAUNG, b Taiwan, China, Aug 3, 41; m 68; c 2. PATHOLOGY. *Educ:* Nat Taiwan Univ, MD, 66; Northwestern Univ, PhD(path), 71. *Prof Exp:* Intern, St Francis Hosp, Wichita, Kans, 67-68; resident path, Northwestern Univ, 68-71; from instr to asst prof path, 72-77, ASSOC PROF PATH, ALBANY MED COL, 77-, STAFF PATHOLOGIST, 73- *Honors & Awards:* Res Prize, Evanston Hosp, 70. *Mem:* Int Acad Path; Am Soc Clin Path; Am Heart Asn; Electron Micros Soc Am. *Res:* Cholesterol metabolism and atherosclerosis. *Mailing Add:* Dept of Path Albany Med Col Albany NY 12208

PENG, SYD SYH-DENG, b Miaoli, Taiwan, Jan 27, 39; US citizen; m 68; c 2. MINING ENGINEERING, GROUND CONTROL. *Educ:* SDak Sch Mines & Technol, MS, 67; Stanford Univ, PhD(mining eng), 70. *Prof Exp:* Asst mine supt mining eng, Chinese Coal Develop Corp, Taiwan, 59-65; head, Rock Physics Labs, US Bur Mines, Minneapolis, Minn, 70-74; assoc prof mining eng, 74-78, CHMN & PROF MINING ENG DEPT, WEST VA UNIV, 78- *Concurrent Pos:* Pres, Penfel Co, Morgantown, WVa, 74-; mining engr, US Bur Mines, 74-; prin investr, US Bur Mines & US Dept Energy, 74- *Mem:* Am Inst Mining & Metall Engrs; Am Soc Testing & Mat; Int Soc Rock Mech. *Res:* Ground control in coal mining. *Mailing Add:* WVa Univ Col of Mineral & Energy Resources Morgantown WV 26506

PENG, TAI-CHAN, b Vietry, Vietnam, Feb 28, 28; m 54; c 2. PHARMACOLOGY. *Educ:* Univ Geneva, BMedSc, 56, MD, 59. *Prof Exp:* Intern, Hartford City Hosp, Conn, 60; res fel pharmacol, Sch Dent Med, Harvard Univ, 61-63; res assoc pathophysiol, Sch Med, Univ Geneva, 63-64, resident internal med, 64-65; instr pharmacol, Sch Dent Med, Harvard Univ, 65; from instr to asst prof, 65-72, ASSOC PROF PHARMACOL, SCH MED, UNIV NC, CHAPEL HILL, 72- *Concurrent Pos:* Mem rev panel drug interactions proj, Am Pharmaceut Asn, 71-75. *Mem:* AAAS; Endocrine Soc; Am Soc Pharmacol & Exp Therapeut. *Res:* Hormonal and nonhormonal agents affecting calcium homeostasis; endocrine pharmacology and morphology. *Mailing Add:* Dept of Pharmacol Univ of NC Sch of Med Chapel Hill NC 27514

PENG, YEH-SHAN, b Taipei, Taiwan, Feb 11, 36; m 69; c 2. NUTRITION. *Educ:* Nat Taiwan Univ, BS, 61; Univ Calif, Los Angeles, MS, 65; Univ Wis, PhD(biochem & nutrit), 71. *Prof Exp:* RES ASSOC NUTRIT, UNIV ARIZ, 71- *Mem:* Am Inst Nutrit. *Res:* Effects of dietary amino acid patterns and vitamin A on amino acid, metabolisms and food intake. *Mailing Add:* Dept of Nutrit & Food Sci Univ of Ariz Tucson AZ 85719

PENGELLEY, DAVID JOHN, b Toronto, Ont, Aug 30, 52; m 78. ALGEBRAIC TOPOLOGY, HOMOTOPY THEORY. *Educ:* Univ Calif, Santa Cruz, BA, 73; Univ Wash, PhD(math), 80. *Prof Exp:* C L E Moore instr math, Mass Inst Technol, 80-82; ASST PROF, NMEX STATE UNIV, 82- *Res:* Cobordism Thom spectra. *Mailing Add:* NMex State Univ Las Cruces NM 88003

PENGELLEY, ERIC T, b Toronto, Ont, July 18, 19; US citizen; m 48; c 2. PHYSIOLOGY. *Educ:* Univ Toronto, BA, 54, PhD(physiol), 59. *Prof Exp:* Asst prof zool, Univ Calif, Davis, 59-60, lectr biol, Santa Barbara, 60-61; asst prof, Col William & Mary, 61-62; ASST PROF BIOL, UNIV CALIF, RIVERSIDE, 62- *Res:* Hibernation and estivation of small mammals; biological rhythms; history of biology. *Mailing Add:* Dept Biol Univ Calif Riverside CA 92502

PENGRA, JAMES G, b Eugene, Ore, Apr 27, 33; m 56; c 4. NUCLEAR PHYSICS. *Educ:* Univ Ore, BS, 55, MS, 57, PhD(nucleus-electron interaction), 63. *Prof Exp:* From asst prof to assoc prof, 62-76, PROF PHYSICS, WHITMAN COL, 76-, GARRETT FEL, 74- *Mem:* Am Phys Soc; Am Asn Physics Teachers. *Res:* Interaction of the atomic electrons with the nucleus and their behavior following beta decay of the nucleus. *Mailing Add:* Dept Physics Whitman Col Walla Walla WA 99362

PENGRA, ROBERT MONROE, b Rapid City, SDak, Jan 20, 26; m 51; c 3. MICROBIAL PHYSIOLOGY, SOIL MICROBIOLOGY. *Educ:* SDak State Univ, BS, 51, MS, 53; Univ Wis, PhD(bact, biochem), 59. *Prof Exp:* Res asst biochem, SDak Exp Sta, 51-52, 53; from asst prof to assoc prof, 57-68, PROF MICROBIOL, DEPT S DAK STATE UNIV, 68- *Mem:* Am Soc Microbiol; Can Soc Microbiol; Soil Sci Soc Am. *Res:* Mechanism of biological nitrogen fixation and ecology and distribution of nitrogen fixing bacteria in soil as related to nutrient availability and toxic materials. *Mailing Add:* 1117 Western Ave Brookings SD 57006

PENHALE, POLLY ANN, b St Louis, Mo, Dec 18, 47. MARINE BIOLOGY, AQUATIC BOTANY. *Educ:* Earlham Col, BA, 70; NC State Univ, MS, 72, PhD(zool), 76. *Prof Exp:* Res assoc marine bot, Rosenstiel Sch Marine & Atmospheric Sci, Univ Miami, 75-76; aquatic bot, W K Kellogg Biol Sta, Mich State Univ, Hickory Corners, 77-79; MARINE SCIENTIST BIOL, VA INST MARINE SCI, GLOUCESTER POINT, 79- *Mem:* Am Soc Limnol & Oceanog; Int Asn Theoret & Appl Limnol; Int Asn Aquatic Vascular Plant Biologists. *Res:* Macrophyte-epiphyte productivity in seagrass communities; gas transport in marine vascular plants; macrophyte-epiphyte interactions; seagrass ecosystems. *Mailing Add:* Va Inst Marine Sci Gloucester Point VA 23062

PENHOET, EDWARD ETIENNE, b Oakland, Calif, Dec 11, 40; m 62; c 2. BIOCHEMISTRY, VIROLOGY. *Educ:* Stanford Univ, BA, 63; Univ Wash, PhD(biochem), 68. *Prof Exp:* Actg asst prof biol, Univ Calif, San Diego, 70-71; asst prof, 71-77, ASSOC PROF BIOCHEM, UNIV CALIF, BERKELEY, 77- *Concurrent Pos:* Nat Inst Child Health & Human Develop fel, Univ Calif, San Diego, 69-72. *Mem:* AAAS; Am Chem Soc; Am Soc Biol Chemists. *Res:* Control of macromolecular synthesis in normal and virus-infected animal cells. *Mailing Add:* Dept Biochem Univ Calif Berkeley CA 94720

PENHOLLOW, JOHN ORIN, b Tama, Iowa, Aug 26, 34; m 59; c 2. COMPUTER SCIENCE, GEOPHYSICS. *Educ:* State Univ Iowa, BS, 56; Univ Ill, MS, 59, PhD(elec eng), 62. *Prof Exp:* Mem tech staff comput design, Bell Tel Lab, 56-58; teaching asst commun elec eng, Univ Ill, 58-59; res asst comput design, Univ Ill Comput Lab, 59-63; res eng, Exxon Prod Res Co, 63-67, res supvr, 67-68, res mgr, 68-71, asst div geophys mgr, Exxon Co USA, 71-73; geophys mgr, Esso Explor Inc, London & Singapore, 73-77; sr technol & serv, Dept Sci & Technol, 77-79, mgr technol & serv, 79-81, MGR APPL DEVELOP & COORD, DEPT COMMUN & COMPUT SCI, EXXON CORP, 81- *Mem:* Inst Elec & Electronics Engrs; Soc Explor Geophys. *Res:* Computer design, data processing software systems, geophysical (seismic) data enhancement, information storage and retrieval systems, communication and computer networks, business and technical computer applications. *Mailing Add:* Exxon Corp PO Box 153 Florham Park NJ 07932

PENHOS, JUAN CARLOS, b Buenos Aires, Arg, Feb 12, 18; m 44; c 1. PHYSIOLOGY, ENDOCRINOLOGY. *Educ:* Univ Buenos Aires, BA, 35, MD, 42. *Prof Exp:* Asst biochem res, Inst Physiol, Med Sch, Univ Buenos Aires, 45-47; chief instr med, Modelo Inst, 46-52; chief res exp diabetes & lipid metab, Inst Biol & Exp Med, Univ Buenos Aires, 52-64; assoc prof med, NY Med Col, 64-67, dir exp diabetes unit, 65-67; assoc prof med, George Washington Univ, 65-70, PROF PHYSIOL & BIOPHYS, GEORGETOWN UNIV, 70- *Concurrent Pos:* Arg Asn Advan Sci fel, 53-54; Lederle Labs fel, 56-58; Lederle Int, Chicago, 60-62; Nat Coun Sci & Tech Res, Toronto, 62-63; carrier scientist, Nat Coun Sci & Tech Res, 62-64; NIH grants, 65-75; Vet Admin grants, 68-71; chief endocrine res, Vet Admin Hosp, Washington, DC, 68-71, consult diabetes res, 72- *Mem:* AAAS; Am Diabetes Asn; Endocrine Soc; Am Physiol Soc; Am Fedn Clin Res. *Res:* Experimental diabetes; hormones and diabetes; mechanism of insulin and glucagon release; lipid metabolism and hormones in the liver; prostaglandins. *Mailing Add:* Dept Physiol & Biophys Georgetown Univ Med Sch Washington DC 20007

PENICK, GEORGE DIAL, b Columbia, SC, Sept 4, 22; m 47; c 4. VASCULAR PATHOLOGY, DERMATOPATHOLOGY. *Educ:* Univ NC, 44; Harvard Med Sch, MD, 46. *Prof Exp:* Intern path, Presby Hosp, Chicago, 46-47; from instr to prof path, Sch Med, Univ NC, 49-70; head dept, 70-81, PROF PATH, UNIV IOWA, 70- *Concurrent Pos:* Consult pathologist, Watts Hosp, 49-70; asst attend pathologist, NC Mem Hosp, 52-56, assoc attend pathologist, 56-63, attend pathologist, 63-70; Markle scholar, 53-58; pathologist, Rex Hosp, 60-62; dir NIH prog-proj on thrombosis & hemorrhage, Univ NC, 61-70; consult pathologist, Vet Admin Hosp, Iowa City, 70-72, chief lab serv, 72-75. *Mem:* AMA; Am Asn Pathologists; Soc Exp Biol & Med; Col Am Pathologists; Am Soc Clin Pathologists. *Res:* Vascular diseases. *Mailing Add:* Dept of Path Univ of Iowa Iowa City IA 52242

PENICO, ANTHONY JOSEPH, b Philadelphia, Pa, June 11, 23; m 48; c 2. MATHEMATICAL PHYSICS. *Educ:* Univ Pa, AB, 45, PhD(math), 50. *Prof Exp:* Asst instr math, Univ Pa, 44-50, asst, 47-48; from instr to assoc prof, Tufts Univ, 50-56; adv res engr, Microwave Physics Lab, Sylvania Elec Prod, Inc, 56-59, specialist, Labs, Gen Tel & Electronics Corp, 59-62; sr res mathematician, Stanford Res Inst, 62-66; PROF MATH, UNIV MO-ROLLA, 66- *Concurrent Pos:* Consult, Lab Phys Electronics, Tufts Univ, 50-56; mathematician, Air Force Cambridge Res Labs, 52-53; lectr, Eve Grad Eng Sch, Northeastern Univ, 54-56. *Mem:* AAAS; Am Math Soc; Am Phys Soc; Soc Indust & Appl Math; Math Asn Am. *Res:* Equations of mathematical physics; wave theory; abstract algebra. *Mailing Add:* Dept Math Univ Mo Rolla MO 65401

PENISTON, FRANCIS L, b Chillicothe, Mo, Dec 28, 23; m 53; c 2. BACTERIOLOGY. *Educ:* Univ Wichita, BA, 49; Kans State Univ, MS, 50, PhD(bact), 53. *Prof Exp:* Mem staff pharmaceut, Res Lab, Cudahy Packing Co, 53-54; mgr, Tissue Cult Dept, Pitman Moore Co, 54-61; assoc prof bact, Univ Kansas City, 61-62; DIR BIOL PROD, PHILIPS ROXANE, INC, 62- *Res:* Biological products; production and development. *Mailing Add:* Philips Roxane Inc 2621 N Belt Hwy St Joseph MO 64502

PENK, ANNA MICHAELIDES, b Thessaloniki, Greece, May 4, 28; US citizen; m 50; c 4. MATHEMATICAL LOGIC. *Educ:* Whitman Col, BA, 50; Reed Col, MAT, 64; Univ Ore, PhD(math), 73. *Prof Exp:* Instr, Pub Schs, Ore, 63-66; asst prof, 73-77, ASSOC PROF MATH, ORE COL EDUC, 77- *Res:* Elementary topos theory, in particular notions of infinity and axioms of choice; relationships of two set-theoretic equivalents of the choice axiom. *Mailing Add:* 309 19th St NE Salem OR 97301

PENMAN, PAUL D, b Williston, NDak, Sept 25, 37; m 60; c 3. NUCLEAR ENGINEERING, COMPUTER SCIENCE. *Educ:* Univ Colo, BS, 59; Univ Louisville, MS, 65. *Prof Exp:* Group mgr, Process Control & Anal, Advan Naval Reactor Cores, 72-77; dept mgr, Core Mfg Develop, 77; proj mgr, Develop Shops, 77-81, PROJ MGR, DEVELOP LABS OPER, BETTIS ATOMIC POWER LAB, WESTINGHOUSE ELEC CORP, 78- *Mem:* US Naval Inst. *Res:* Nuclear reactor manufacturing development; computer scanning systems; irradiation behavior of fuel and poison materials. *Mailing Add:* Bettis Atomic Power Lab PO Box 79 West Mifflin PA 15122

PENN, THOMAS CLIFTON, b Placid, Tex, Jan 17, 29; m 50; c 1. ELECTRONIC ENGINEERING. *Educ:* Tex Technol Univ, BS, 50; Southern Methodist Univ, MS, 57. *Prof Exp:* Lead systs engr, Chance Vought Aircraft, 54-57; SR MEM TECH STAFF, TEX INSTRUMENTS, INC, 57- *Mem:* Inst Elec & Electronics Engrs; Electrochem Soc. *Res:* Computer memories, electronic circuits, semiconductor fabrication techniques; magnetic bubble memories and plasma fabrication of semiconductor devices. *Mailing Add:* Tex Instruments Inc MS 145 Box 225936 Dallas TX 75265

PENNA, MICHAEL ANTHONY, b Buffalo, NY, June 5, 45; m 68; c 2. MATHEMATICS. *Educ:* Union Col, BS, 67; Univ Ill, Urbana, MS, 68, PhD(math), 74. *Prof Exp:* Asst prof, 73-80, ASSOC PROF MATH, IND UNIV-PURDUE UNIV, INDIANAPOLIS, 80- *Mem:* Am Math Soc; Math Asn Am. *Res:* Geometry and topology. *Mailing Add:* Dept Math Sci 1201 E 38th St Indianapolis IN 46205

PENNA, RICHARD PAUL, b Palo Alto, Calif, Sept 7, 35; m 58; c 3. PHARMACY. *Educ:* Univ Calif, BS, 58, PharmD, 59. *Prof Exp:* Pharmacist, Ryan Pharm, 58-66; asst clin prof pharm, Univ Calif, 61-66; PROF STAFF PHARM, AM PHARMACEUT ASN, 66- *Mem:* AAAS; Am Pub Health Asn; Am Pharmaceut Asn. *Mailing Add:* 2215 Constitution Ave NW Washington DC 20037

PENNAK, ROBERT WILLIAM, b Milwaukee, Wis, June 13, 12; m 35; c 2. ZOOLOGY. *Educ:* Univ Wis, BS, 34, MS, 35, PhD(zool), 38. *Prof Exp:* Asst limnol, Univ Wis, 34-36, zool, 36-38; from instr to prof, 38-74, EMER PROF BIOL, UNIV COLO, BOULDER, 74- *Concurrent Pos:* Stream & lake consult, ecology, mining & land develop firms. *Mem:* Ecol Soc Am; Am Soc Limnol & Oceanog (pres, 63); Am Soc Zoologists; Soc Syst Zool (pres, 64); hon mem Am Micros Soc (vpres, 55, pres, 56). *Res:* Limnology; stream biology; freshwater invertebrates; animal ecology at high altitudes; interstitial microscopic Metazoa of sandy beaches. *Mailing Add:* EPO Biol Univ Colo Boulder CO 80309

PENNDORF, RUDOLF, b Chemnitz, Ger, Nov 29, 11; nat US; m 42; c 3. ATMOSPHERIC PHYSICS. *Educ:* Univ Leipzig, PhD(geophys), 36, PhD(habilitation), 44. *Prof Exp:* Asst meteorol, Univ Leipzig, 34-36, asst prof, 36-42; assoc prof, Univ Strassburg, 42-45; chief forecaster, US Weather Cent, Wiesbaden, 46-47; asst chief, Atmospheric Physics Lab, Air Force Cambridge Res Ctr, 47-56; prin scientist, Res & Advan Develop Div, Avco Corp, Wilmington, 56-61, sect chief geophys, Space Systs Div, 61-73; CONSULT, 73- *Concurrent Pos:* Mem, Armed Forces Vision Comt, Nat Res Coun, 52-57; mem, US Nat Comt, Int Sci Radio Union, 59-78. *Mem:* fel Optical Soc Am; Am Geophys Union. *Res:* physics of the ionosphere; radio wave propagation and communication; atmospheric optics; light scattering; antarctic ionosphere; prediction of high frequency communication conditions; ozone and water vapor. *Mailing Add:* 148 Oakland St Wellesley Hills MA 02181

PENNEBAKER, WILLIAM B, JR, b New Rochelle, NY, Oct 23, 35. PHYSICS. *Educ:* Lehigh Univ, BS, 57; Rutgers Univ, PhD(physics), 62. *Prof Exp:* MEM STAFF, T J WATSON RES CTR, IBM CORP, 62- *Mem:* AAAS; Am Phys Soc; Soc Info Display. *Res:* Solid state physics; thin film physics; display and printing technology. *Mailing Add:* T J Watson Res Ctr IBM Corp PO Box 218 Yorktown Heights NY 10598

PENNELL, MAYNARD L, b Skowhegan, Maine, 1910. AERONAUTICAL ENGINEERING. *Prof Exp:* Aeronaut struct engr, Douglas Aircraft Co, 33-40; from asst proj engr to proj engr B-29, B-50 & C-97, Boeing Co, 40-70, vpres prod develop, 70-74; RETIRED. *Honors & Awards:* Elmer A Sperry Award, 65. *Mem:* Nat Acad Eng; fel Am Inst Aeronaut & Astronaut. *Res:* Design and development of 707, 720 and 727 transports. *Mailing Add:* 1545 NE 143rd St Seattle WA 98125

PENNELL, TIMOTHY CLINARD, b Asheville, NC, Oct 31, 33; m 53; c 3. SURGERY, THORACIC SURGERY. *Educ:* Wake Forest Univ, BS, 55; Bowman Gray Sch Med, MD, 60; Am Bd Surg, dipl, 67. *Prof Exp:* Intern, 60-61, resident, 61-66, asst prof, 68-72, assoc prof, 73-80, PROF SURG, BOWMAN GRAY SCH MED, WAKE FOREST UNIV, 80- *Concurrent Pos:* Am Thoracic Soc teaching fel, Wake Forest Univ, 67-68; vis prof, For Mission Bd, Southern Baptist Conv, Africa & MidE, 68, SAm, 73 & EAfrica & India, 74. *Mem:* Fel Am Col Surg; Am Thoracic Soc; Am Acad Surg. *Res:* Pulmonary lymphatic system of the lung and tissue transplantation, particularly of the pancreas; clinical surgery. *Mailing Add:* Dept of Surg Bowman Gray Sch of Med Winston-Salem NC 27103

PENNEMAN, ROBERT ALLEN, b Springfield, Ill, Feb 5, 19; m 42; c 3. INORGANIC CHEMISTRY. *Educ:* Millikin Univ, AB, 41; Univ Ill, MS, 42, PhD(inorg chem), 47. *Hon Degrees:* ScD, Univ Ill, 61. *Prof Exp:* Res assoc, Metall Lab, Univ Chicago, 42-45 & Clinton Labs, Tenn, 45-46; sect leader, 47-50, alt group leader, 50-74, ASSOC DIV LEADER, LOS ALAMOS SCI LAB, UNIV CALIF, 74- *Mem:* Am Chem Soc; Sigma Xi. *Res:* Sulfurdioxide and laser chemistry; chemistry of hydrazine; radiochemistry; chemistry of americium and curium; infrared spectroscopy of inorganic solution complexes; structural inorganic chemistry; complex fluorides. *Mailing Add:* Los Alamos Sci Lab Los Alamos NM 87545

PENNER, ALVIN PAUL, b Arnaud, Man, Dec 1, 47. THEORETICAL CHEMISTRY, OPERATIONS RESEARCH. *Educ:* Univ Man, BSc, 68, MSc, 70, PhD(chem), 74. *Prof Exp:* Fel chem, Univ Laval, 74-75; res assoc chem, Nat Res Coun Can, 76-77; ANALYST OPERS RES, FRASER CO, LTD, 78- *Concurrent Pos:* Fel, Nat Res Coun Can, 74-75. *Mem:* Chem Inst Can. *Res:* Molecular collision theory; stochastic theories of chemical kinetics; operations research. *Mailing Add:* Cent Tech Dept Fraser Co Ltd Edmundston NB E3V 1S9 Can

PENNER, DONALD, b Mt Lake, Minn, Dec 28, 36; m 63. WEED SCIENCE. *Educ:* Univ Minn, BS, 57, MS, 60; Univ Calif, Davis, PhD(plant physiol), 66. *Prof Exp:* Res botanist, Univ Calif, Davis, 66-67; from asst prof to assoc prof plant physiol & herbicide action, 67-76, PROF CROP & SOIL SCI, MICH STATE UNIV, 76- *Mem:* AAAS; Weed Sci Soc Am; Am Inst Biol Sci; Am Soc Plant Physiologists; Soc Environ Toxicol & Chem. *Res:* Herbicide action and metabolism; environmental toxicology. *Mailing Add:* Dept of Crop & Soil Sci Mich State Univ East Lansing MI 48823

PENNER, DONALD WILLS, b Rosthern, Sask, June 8, 18; m 43; c 3. MEDICINE. *Educ:* Univ Sask, BA, 39; Univ Man, MD, 42; Royal Col Physicians & Surgeons Can, cert specialist path, 45; Am Bd Path, dipl, 50. *Prof Exp:* Lectr, 43-51, from asst prof to assoc prof, 51-77, PATH, UNIV MAN, 77- *Concurrent Pos:* Asst pathologist, Winnipeg Gen Hosp, 44-54, chief pathologist, 55-; consult, Med Legal Dept, Man Govt, 44- & Man Cancer Diag Serv, 45-; pathologist, Shriner's Hosp, 57-67; chief pathologist, Victoria Hosp, 58-67, consult, 67-; consult, Nat Cancer Inst, 58-68 & Selkirk Gen Hosp, 58- *Mem:* Am Soc Clin Pathologists; fel Col Am Pathologists; Can Asn Pathologists (secy-treas, 52-73, vpres, 73, pres, 75-76); cor mem Int Soc Clin Path; World Asn Socs Path (treas, 66-72). *Res:* Cancer; pathology. *Mailing Add:* Health Sci Ctr 700 William Ave Winnipeg MB R3T 2N2 Can

PENNER, HELLMUT PHILIP, b Mountain Lake, Minn, Feb 15, 25. CHEMISTRY. *Educ:* Mass Inst Technol, SB, 45, PhD(org chem), 50. *Prof Exp:* Res assoc polymer chem, Mass Inst Technol, 49-56; asst prof chem, Carleton Col, 51-55; vis asst prof, Univ Ky, 56-57; mem res staff, Ocean Spray Cranberries, Inc, 57; asst prof, 62-67, ASSOC PROF CHEM, FISK UNIV, 67- *Mem:* Am Chem Soc. *Res:* Synthesis of heterocyclic compounds of medicinal potential; organometallic chemistry. *Mailing Add:* Dept Chem Fisk Univ Nashville TN 37203

PENNER, JOYCE ELAINE, b Fresno, Calif, Oct 3, 48. ATMOSPHERIC PHYSICS, APPLIED MATHEMATICS. *Educ:* Univ Calif, Santa Barbara, BA, 70; Harvard Univ, MA, 72, PhD(appl math), 77. *Prof Exp:* PHYSICIST ATMOSPHERIC PHYSICS, LAWRENCE LIVERMORE LAB, UNIV CALIF, 77- *Mem:* Am Geophys Union. *Res:* Chemistry of stratosphere and troposphere; the exosphere and upper atmosphere of Venus. *Mailing Add:* Lawrence Livermore Lab PO Box 808 Livermore CA 94550

PENNER, LAWRENCE RAYMOND, b Lawrence, Kans, Mar 29, 13; m 37; c 6. PARASITOLOGY. *Educ:* Univ Kans, AB, 34, AM, 36; Univ Minn, PhD(zool), 40. *Prof Exp:* Asst zool, Univ Minn, 36-40; Scripps scholar parasitol, Biol Res Inst, Calif, 40-41; instr zool, 41-44, from asst prof to assoc prof zool & entom, 44-57, PROF BIOL, UNIV CONN, 58- *Concurrent Pos:* Am Acad Arts & Sci grant, Harvard Med Sch, 40, vis lectr, Harvard Univ, 45; asst, Sch Pub Health, Univ Mich, 45; entomologist, Poliomyelitis Res Unit, Yale Univ, 46-47 & 48-49; res fel, Biol Res Inst, Calif, 50, Scripps fel, 60; vis prof, Univ Calif, Los Angeles, 60; res assoc, Cape Haze Marine Lab, Fla, 64- *Mem:* Am Soc Trop Med & Hyg; Am Soc Parasitol; Am Micros Soc; Entom Soc Am; Soc Protozool. *Res:* Schistosomiasis; biology of helminth worms of animals; transmission and causation of disease by the diptera; parasites of wildlife. *Mailing Add:* Biol Sci Group U-43 Univ of Conn Storrs CT 06268

PENNER, PETER EDWIN, molecular biology, biochemistry, see previous edition

PENNER, S(TANFORD) S(OLOMON), b Unna, Ger, July 5, 21; nat US; m 42; c 2. ENGINEERING PHYSICS. *Educ:* Union Col, BS, 42; Univ Wis, MS, 43, PhD(phys chem), 46. *Hon Degrees:* Dr, Hochschule Aachen, 81. *Prof Exp:* Res assoc, Allegany Ballistics Lab, Md, 44-45; res assoc, Esso Res Lab, Standard Oil Develop Co, NJ, 46; sr res engr, Jet Propulsion Lab, Calif Inst Technol, 47-50, from asst prof to prof jet propulsion, 50-64; chmn dept aerospace & mech eng sci, 64-68, vchancellor acad affairs, 68-69, dir inst pure & appl phys sci, 68-71, PROF ENG PHYSICS, UNIV CALIF, SAN DIEGO, 64-, DIR, ENERGY CTR, 72- *Concurrent Pos:* US mem propulsion &

energetics panel, NATO Adv Group Aeronaut Res & Develop, 52-68, chmn combustion & propulsion panel, 58-60; ed, J Quant Spectros & Radiative Transfer, 60-; res adv comt eng sci, Off Sci Res, US Air Force, 61-66; comt high-temperature phenomena, Div Chem & Chem Technol, Nat Acad Sci-Nat Res Coun, 61-71; res adv comt air breathing engines, NASA, 62-64; dir res & eng support div, Inst Defense Anal, 62-64; Guggenheim fel, England & Australia, 71-72; ed, Energy, 76-; Nat Sigma Xi lectr, 77-79; chmn, US Comt, Int Inst Appl Systs Anal, 78- *Honors & Awards:* Off Sci Res & Develop Award, 45; People-to-People Award, 57; Spec Citation, Adv Group Aerospace Res & Develop, NATO, 69; Pub Serv Award, Univ Calif, 75; G Edward Pendray Award, Am Inst Aeronaut & Astronaut, 75; Numa Manson Medal, Int Colloquia Gasdynamics Explosions & Reactive Systems,79; Int Columbus Prize, Int Inst Commun Res, 81. *Mem:* Nat Acad Eng; fel AAAS; fel Am Phys Soc; fel Am Inst Aeronaut & Astronaut; fel NY Acad Sci. *Res:* Applied spectroscopy, combustion and propulsion research; energy. *Mailing Add:* Dept Appl Mech & Eng Sci Univ Calif La Jolla CA 92037

PENNER, SAMUEL, b Buffalo, NY, Oct 3, 30; m 52; c 2. EXPERIMENTAL NUCLEAR PHYSICS. *Educ:* Univ Buffalo, BA, 52; Univ Ill, MS & PhD(physics), 56. *Prof Exp:* Asst physics, Univ Ill, 52-55; NSF fel, 56-57; physicist nuclear physics, 57-66, chief electronuclear physics sect, 66-72, actg chief linac radiation div, dep chief nuclear sci div, 72-76, chief nuclear res sect, 76-78, CHIEF, RADIATION SOURCE & INSTRUMENTATION DIV, NAT BUR STANDARDS, 78- *Concurrent Pos:* Guggenheim Found fel, 63-64. *Mem:* Am Phys Soc. *Res:* Electron scattering; photonuclear physics; instrumentation for nuclear physics. *Mailing Add:* Radiation Source Nat Bur Standards Washington DC 20234

PENNER, SIEGFRIED EDMUND, b Mt Lake, Minn, Oct 2, 23. ORGANIC CHEMISTRY. *Educ:* Mass Inst Technol, SB, 45, PhD(org chem), 48. *Prof Exp:* Res chemist, Pan Am Petrol Corp, 48-60, group leader, Chem Div, 60-68, sect head org chem, 68-73, ASST MGR RES & DEVELOP, CHEM DIV, VULCAN MAT CO, 73- *Mem:* Am Chem Soc. *Res:* Synthetic organic chemistry; partial oxidation of hydrocarbons; olefin polymerization; chlorinated hydrocarbons; oxychlorination. *Mailing Add:* Chem Div Vulcan Mat Co PO Box 12283 Wichita KS 67277

PENNEY, CARL MURRAY, b Newport News, Va, Nov 15, 37. OPTICAL PHYSICS. *Educ:* NC State Univ, BS, 59; Univ Mich, MS, 62, PhD(nuclear eng), 65. *Prof Exp:* PHYSICIST, GEN ELEC CORP RES & DEVELOP, 65- *Mem:* Am Phys Soc; Inst Elec & Electronics Engrs; Optical Soc Am. *Res:* Laser development and application of lasers to measurements in the atmosphere and combustion gases. *Mailing Add:* Gen Elec Corp Res & Develop K1-5B33 Schenectady NY 12301

PENNEY, DAVID EMORY, b Decatur, Ga, Jan 26, 38; m 63; c 1. TOPOLOGY. *Educ:* Tulane Univ, BS, 58, PhD(math), 65. *Prof Exp:* Res assoc biophys, Tulane Univ, 55-59; res assoc, Vet Admin Hosp, New Orleans, La, 59-63; instr math, La State Univ, New Orleans, 63-65, asst prof, 65-66; asst prof, 66-71, ASSOC PROF MATH, UNIV GA, 71- *Mem:* Am Soc Ichthyol & Herpet; Am Math Soc; Math Asn Am. *Res:* Number theory; computer utilization; applied mathematics; convexity; geometric topology; knot theory; active transport in biological membranes. *Mailing Add:* Dept Math Univ Ga Athens GA 30601

PENNEY, DAVID GEORGE, b Detroit, Mich, Jan 11, 40; m 63; c 2. CARDIOVASCULAR PHYSIOLOGY. *Educ:* Wayne State Univ, BS, 63; Univ Calif, Los Angeles, MA, 67, PhD(zool), 69. *Prof Exp:* Asst prof physiol, Univ Ill, Chicago Circle, 69-75, assoc prof, 75-77; ASSOC PROF PHYSIOL, WAYNE STATE UNIV, 77- *Mem:* Int Soc Heart Res; Am Physiol Soc; Soc Exp Biol & Med; AAAS. *Res:* Carbon monoxide induced cardiomegaly; cardiovascular stress; exercise physiology. *Mailing Add:* Dept Physiol Wayne State Univ 540 E Canfield Ave Detroit MI 48201

PENNEY, DAVID P, b Waltham, Mass, Dec 11, 33; m 56; c 2. HISTOLOGY, ELECTRON MICROSCOPY. *Educ:* Eastern Nazarene Col, AB, 56; Boston Univ, AM, 57, PhD(biol), 62. *Prof Exp:* Instr anat, Sch Med, Yale Univ, 62-64; asst prof, 64-69, assoc prof anat, 69-77, ASSOC PROF ONCOL IN ANAT, SCH MED & DENT, UNIV ROCHESTER, 77- *Mem:* AAAS; Am Asn Anatomists; Am Soc Cell Biol; Histochem Soc; Electron Micros Soc Am. *Res:* Electron histochemistry; endocrine transplantation and regeneration; neoplasia; radiation toxicology; drug toxicity; cell biology. *Mailing Add:* Dept of Anat Univ of Rochester Sch Med & Dent Rochester NY 14642

PENNEY, WILLIAM HARRY, b Rochester, Minn, June 16, 29; m 55; c 4. CHEMICAL ENGINEERING, PHYSICAL CHEMISTRY. *Educ:* Colo Sch Mines, PRE, 51; Univ Minn, PhD(chem eng, phys chem), 57. *Prof Exp:* Chem engr & res supvr, Cent Res Div, 57-63, res supvr, New Prod Div, 63-65, lab mgr, 65-67, recreation prod tech mgr, 67-73, MEM STAFF COM CHEM DIV, 3M CO, 73- *Mem:* Am Inst Chem Engrs; Am Chem Soc. *Res:* Chemical engineering aspects of compound separations; particle research; process design and polymer and synthetic grass design. *Mailing Add:* 3M Co 3M Ctr Bldg 236-1 St Paul MN 55144

PENNEY, WILLIAM ROY, b Lockesburg, Ark, Jan 24, 37; m 61; c 2. CHEMICAL ENGINEERING. *Educ:* Univ Ark, BS, 59, MS, 62; Okla State Univ, PhD(chem eng), 68. *Prof Exp:* Test engr, McDonnell Aircraft Co, Mo, 59-60; res engr, Phillips Petrol Co, Okla, 62-65; sr engr, 68-71, prin engr specialist, 71-75, MGR & ENGR, MONSANTO CO, 75- *Mem:* Am Inst Chem Engrs. *Res:* Heat transfer; field of transport phenomena, especially mixing. *Mailing Add:* 539 Chalet Ct St Louis MO 63141

PENNEYS, NEAL STUART, biochemistry, see previous edition

PENNEYS, RAYMOND, b Philadelphia, Pa, Oct 15, 19; m 46; c 3. MEDICINE. *Educ:* Temple Univ, 40, MD, 43. *Prof Exp:* Intern, Philadelphia Gen Hosp, Pa, 43-44; instr, Vascular Sect, Dept Med, Univ Pa, 50-58, assoc, 58-62, asst prof, 62-70; ASSOC PROF MED, HAHNEMANN MED COL & HOSP, 70- *Concurrent Pos:* Fel pharm & physiol, Grad Sch Med, Univ Pa, 46-47 & med & prev med, Sch Med, Johns Hopkins Univ, 47-50; chief peripheral vascular sect, Philadelphia Gen Hosp, 58-; pvt pract. *Mem:* AAAS; Am Heart Asn; Am Fedn Clin Res; NY Acad Sci. *Res:* Oxygen tension; peripheral circulation and cardiovascular effects of induced hypoxemia in man. *Mailing Add:* Philadelphia Gen Hosp 1930 Chestnut St Philadelphia PA 19103

PENNIALL, RALPH, b Southampton, Eng, Dec 25, 22; nat US; m 44; c 2. BIOCHEMISTRY. *Educ:* Knox Col, BA, 47; Univ Iowa, MS, 50, PhD(biochem), 53. *Prof Exp:* Asst prof biochem, Col Med, Baylor Univ, 54-56; res assoc, Inst Enzyme Res, Univ Wis, 56-58; from asst prof to assoc prof, 58-68, PROF BIOCHEM, SCH MED, UNIV NC, CHAPEL HILL, 68- *Concurrent Pos:* Am Heart Asn advan res fel, 58-60. *Mem:* AAAS; Am Soc Biol Chemists; Brit Biochem Soc; Am Chem Soc. *Res:* Mitochondrial biogenesis; biochemistry of polymorphonuclear leukocytes; metabolism and function of inorganic polyphosphates; biochemistry of aging. *Mailing Add:* Dept of Biochem Univ of NC Sch of Med Chapel Hill NC 27514

PENNING, JOHN RUSSELL, JR, b Spokane, Wash, Dec 13, 22; m 75. APPLIED PHYSICS. *Educ:* Univ Wash, BS, 48, PhD(physics), 56. *Prof Exp:* Res assoc physics, Cyclotron-Univ Wash, 55-56; res scientist, Space Tech Labs, Calif, 56-59, Boeing Co, Wash, 59-63 & Northrop Corp, Calif, 63-65; RES SCIENTIST, BOEING CO, SEATTLE, 65- *Mem:* Am Phys Soc. *Res:* Radioactive decay; scintillation detectors; exploding foils; plasma physics; shock propagation; dynamic high pressure properties of solids. *Mailing Add:* 32544 36th Ave SW Federal Way WA 98003

PENNINGTON, ANTHONY JAMES, b Newark, NJ, Dec 19, 32; div; c 2. ELECTRICAL ENGINEERING. *Educ:* Princeton Univ, BSE, 57; Univ Mich, MSE, 58, PhD(elec eng), 63. *Prof Exp:* Res engr, Dodco, Inc, NJ, 58-59; appl mathematician, E I du Pont de Nemours & Co, Del, 59-60; from instr to assoc prof elec eng, Univ Mich, 60-68; assoc prof, Drexel Inst Technol, 68-71; v pres for planning systs, Decision Sci Corp, 71-73; pres, A J Pennington, Inc, Consults, 73-79; prin engr, Franklin Inst, 79-80; SR PRIN ENGR, COMPUT SCI CORP, 80- *Concurrent Pos:* mem subcomt use of comput in power syst oper, Fed Power Comn, 66- *Honors & Awards:* Henry Russel Award, Univ Mich, 65. *Mem:* Inst Elec & Electronics Engrs. *Res:* Space vehicle performance analysis and control; chemical process optimization and control; electrical power system planning, analysis and control; digital computer control systems; project economic analysis and financial planning; energy resource analysis modeling; urban and regional systems analysis. *Mailing Add:* Comput Sci Corp 204 W Rte 38 PO Box N Moorestown NJ 08057

PENNINGTON, DAVID EUGENE, b Bryan, Tex, Nov 3, 39; m 62; c 2. INORGANIC CHEMISTRY. *Educ:* NTex State Univ, BA, 62, MS, 63; Pa State Univ, PhD, 67. *Prof Exp:* Fel, State Univ NY Stony Brook, 67; asst prof, 67-74, ASSOC PROF INORG CHEM, BAYLOR UNIV, 74- *Mem:* Am Chem Soc. *Res:* Mechanisms of inorganic reactions involving coordination compounds, particularly electron transfer reactions. *Mailing Add:* 3003 Novice Rd Waco TX 76710

PENNINGTON, EDWIN MCFARLANE, reactor physics, see previous edition

PENNINGTON, FRANK COOK, b Seattle, Wash, Apr 4, 24; m 47; c 2. ORGANIC CHEMISTRY. *Educ:* Reed Col, BA, 48; Univ Rochester, PhD(chem), 51. *Prof Exp:* Res chemist antibiotic chem, Chas Pfizer & Co, 51-55; prof chem, Coe Col, 55-69, chmn dept, 58-69; dean, Sch Nat Sci, 69-78, PROF CHEM, CALIF STATE UNIV, CHICO, 69- *Concurrent Pos:* Res assoc, Argonne Nat Lab, 62-63. *Mem:* Fel AAAS; Am Chem Soc. *Res:* Chemistry of antibiotics and chlorophyll; synthesis of colchicine analogs; synthesis of heterocycles. *Mailing Add:* Dept Chem Calif State Univ Chico CA 95926

PENNINGTON, JOHN VIRGIL, physics, mechanical engineering, deceased

PENNINGTON, KEITH SAMUEL, b West Bromwich, Eng, June 14, 36; m 60; c 3. PHYSICS. *Educ:* Univ Birmingham, BSc, 57; McMaster Univ, PhD(physics), 61. *Prof Exp:* Mem tech staff, Bell Tel Labs, Inc, 61-67; mem prof staff, Info Sci Lab, Gen Elec Res & Develop Ctr, 67; res staff mem, 67-72, mgr explor displays, 72-73, mgr explor terminal technol, 73-78, mem & dir res staff, I/O & Com, T J Watson Res Ctr, 78-79, MGR IMAGE TECHNOLOGIES DEPT, IBM CORP, 79- *Concurrent Pos:* Group leader, Undersea Warfare Comt, Nat Acad Sci, 71. *Mem:* Am Phys Soc; Optical Soc Am; Inst Elec & Electronics Engrs. *Res:* Holography: optical information processing; exploratory terminal technologies. *Mailing Add:* T J Watson Res Ctr IBM Corp PO Box 218 Yorktown Heights NY 10598

PENNINGTON, RALPH HUGH, b Wichita, Kans, Oct 4, 24; m 73; c 2. COMPUTER SCIENCE. *Educ:* US Mil Acad, BS, 46; Stanford Univ, MS, 50, PhD(math), 54. *Prof Exp:* Staff scientist, Proj Matterhorn, US Army, Princeton, 51-52, Radiation Lab, Univ Calif, 53-54, atomic energy specialist, Off Spec Weapons Develop, 55-58, nuclear effects engr, Defense Atomic Support Agency, DC, 58-61, spec asst to dir, Defense Res & Eng, 61-63, chief, Theoret Br, Air Force Weapons Lab, Kirtland AFB, 63-67; chief advan systs studies, Advan Ballistic Missile Defense Agency, 69-71, chief scientist, Defense & Space Div, Syst Develop Corp, 71-75; DIR DATA PROCESSING & SOFTWARE, GEN RES CORP, 75- *Concurrent Pos:* Lectr, George Washington Univ, 58-63. *Mem:* Am Math Soc; Asn Comput Mach. *Res:* Nuclear phenomenology; systems analysis; simulation and modelling; numerical analysis; computer system software; computer programming languages; computer architecture. *Mailing Add:* 506 Yankee Farm Rd Santa Barbara CA 93109

PENNINGTON, RAYMOND CARROLL, b Ft Monroe, Va, Dec 23, 27; m 52; c 2. ANATOMY. *Educ:* Univ Va, BA, 49, MS, 51; Med Col SC, PhD(anat), 67. *Prof Exp:* Asst prof biol, Converse Col, 55-61, res asst, 61-67, asst prof, 67-73, ASSOC PROF ANAT, MED UNIV SC, 73- *Concurrent Pos:* USPHS res grant microcirculatory pathophysiol of alcoholism, 68 & small vessel pathophysiol in diabetes, 73. *Res:* Sludged blood and tissue damage in alcoholism and diabetes. *Mailing Add:* Dept of Anat Med Univ of SC Charleston SC 29401

PENNINGTON, ROBERT ELIJA, b Brenham, Tex, Nov 22, 26; m 46; c 2. CHEMICAL ENGINEERING. *Educ:* Univ Tex, BS, 48, MS, 50, PhD(chem eng), 56. *Prof Exp:* Res chem engr, Humble Oil & Ref Co, Baytown, 56-58, sr res chem engr, 58-61, res specialist, 62, planning specialist, Houston, 62, sr planning specialist, 63-64, res coordr, 64-65; head, Petrol Dept, Esso Res & Eng Co, 65-66, mgr, Baytown Petrol Res Lab, 66-67, lab mgr, Synthetics Fuels Res Lab, Exxon Res & Eng, 67-82; PRES, PENNINGTON CONSULT & ENG CO, 82- *Mem:* Am Chem Soc; Inst Chem Engrs. *Mailing Add:* Rt 5 Box 220 Brenham TX 77833

PENNINGTON, SAMMY NOEL, b Dumas, Tex, Mar 19, 41; m; c 2. ANALYTICAL BIOCHEMISTRY. *Educ:* Kans State Col Pittsburg, BS, 64; Kans State Univ, PhD(chem), 66. *Prof Exp:* Instr biochem, Univ Tex Med Br Galveston, 67-68; asst prof chem, Cent Mo State Col, 68-69; asst scientist biochem, Cancer Res Ctr, Columbia, Mo, 69-70; assoc prof, 70-80, PROF BIOCHEM, ECAROLINA UNIV, 70- *Concurrent Pos:* Consult, Cancer Res Ctr, Columbia, Mo, 68-69; Am Cancer Soc grant, ECarolina Univ, 72-73, NSF res grant, 72-74, alcoholism grant, 76-81 & NIH grant, 79-81. *Mem:* Am Soc Biol Chemists; Sigma Xi. *Res:* Fetal alcohol syndrome; growth and development; molecular mechanism of ethanol induced growth suppression; the role of ethanol-prostaglandin interactions in the pathophysiology of chronic alcoholism. *Mailing Add:* 1909 E Fifth Greenville NC 27834

PENNINGTON, TULLY SANFORD, b Irwinton, Ga, Oct 2, 13. INVERTEBRATE ZOOLOGY, ORNITHOLOGY. *Educ:* Ga Southern Col, BSEd, 36; Cornell Univ, MS, 48; Fla State Univ, EdD, 60. *Prof Exp:* Teacher high sch, Ga, 36-37; teacher & counsr, Bethesda Orphanage, Ga, 37-41; interviewer, US Employ Serv, 45-47; from asst prof to prof, 48-74, EMER PROF BIOL, GA SOUTHERN COL, 74- *Mem:* AAAS; Am Ornithol Union; Nat Asn Biol Teachers; Am Nature Study Soc. *Res:* Factors which influence high school seniors' selection of science courses; development of science courses in elementary grades. *Mailing Add:* 1210 Fair Rd Rte 7 Statesboro GA 30458

PENNINGTON, WAYNE DAVID, b Rochester, Minn, Dec 19, 50; m 78; c 1. SEISMOLOGY. *Educ:* Princeton Univ, AB, 72; Cornell Univ, MS, 76; Univ Wis, Madison, PhD(geophysics), 79. *Prof Exp:* Res asst, Lamont-Doherty Geol Observ, Columbia Univ, 74-76; ASST PROF GEOPHYSICS, DEPT GEOL SCI, UNIV TEX, AUSTIN, 79- *Mem:* Am Geophys Union; Seismol Soc Am; Geol Soc Am; Soc Explor Geophysicists; Sigma Xi. *Res:* Earthquakes of Texas; deep-focus earthquakes; circum-caribbean seismicity and tectonics. *Mailing Add:* Dept Geol Sci Univ Tex Austin TX 78712

PENNISTON, JOHN THOMAS, b St Louis, Mo, Sept 10, 35; m 60; c 2. BIOLOGICAL CHEMISTRY. *Educ:* Harvard Univ, AB, 57, AM, 59, PhD(chem), 62. *Prof Exp:* NIH res fel chem, Harvard Univ, 62; vis asst prof, Pomona Col, 63-64; fel biochem, Inst Enzyme Res, Univ Wis-Madison, 64-66, asst prof, 66-71; assoc prof chem, Univ NC, Chapel Hill, 71-76; assoc prof biochem, 76-79, PROF BIOCHEM, MAYO GRAD SCH MED, UNIV MINN, 79-, CONSULT BIOCHEM, MAYO CLIN, 76- *Concurrent Pos:* Estab investr, Am Heart Asn, 69-74. *Mem:* AAAS; Am Chem Soc; Am Soc Biol Chemists. *Res:* Membrane structure and biological transducing systems; intracellular calcium metabolism; plasma membrane calcium pumps; erythrocyte metabolism and morphology. *Mailing Add:* Biochem Sect Mayo Clin Rochester MN 55905

PENNOCK, BERNARD EUGENE, b Philadelphia, Pa, Jan 30, 38; m 69; c 2. BIOMEDICAL ENGINEERING, PULMONARY PHYSIOLOGY. *Educ:* Drexel Inst, BS, 60, MS, 61; Univ Pa, PhD(biomed eng), 67. *Prof Exp:* Res assoc biomed eng, Presby Hosp, Univ Pa, 67-68; asst prof biophys, Med Col Pa, 68-73; assoc prof med, Univ Okla Health Sci Ctr, 73-80; MEM FAC, UNIV PITTSBURGH, 80- *Concurrent Pos:* Vis lectr, Hosp Univ Pa, 69-73. *Mem:* Biomed Eng Soc; Asn Advan Med Instrumentation; Am Tech Soc. *Res:* Electrical properties of biologic materials; pulmonary physiology; excitable membranes. *Mailing Add:* Univ Pittsburgh Pittsburgh PA 15260

PENNY, JOE EDWARD, neuroanatomy, human anatomy, see previous edition

PENNY, JOHN SLOYAN, b Philadelphia, Pa, Aug 3, 14; m 47; c 5. PALEOBOTANY. *Educ:* La Salle Col, AB, 37; Univ Pa, MS, 39, PhD(bot), 42. *Prof Exp:* Herbarium asst & asst instr bot, Univ Pa, 39-42; geologist, US War Dept, 46-47; paleobotanist, Creole Petrol Corp, Venezuela, 47-50; from asst prof to assoc prof, 50-60, prof & chmn dept, 60-79, EMER PROF BIOL, LA SALLE COL, 79- *Concurrent Pos:* Mem teaching fac, Arboretum of the Barnes Found, 65-80; bot consult, So Co Servs, 73- *Honors & Awards:* Lindback Found Award, 62. *Mem:* AAAS; Geol Soc Am; Bot Soc Am; Int Assoc Plant Taxon. *Res:* Mesozoic paleobotany; stratigraphy; palynology. *Mailing Add:* Dept Biol La Salle Col Philadelphia PA 19141

PENNY, KEITH, b Oklahoma City, Okla, Aug 25, 32; m 55; c 4. NUCLEAR PHYSICS. *Educ:* Univ Okla, BS, 54; Univ Tenn, PhD(physics), 66. *Prof Exp:* Physicist, Oak Ridge Nat Lab, 54-62, dir, Radiation Shielding Info Ctr, 63-66; res scientist, Space Sci & Eng Lab, Defense & Space Systs Dept, Union Carbide Corp, NY, 67-68; PHYSICIST, OAK RIDGE NAT LAB, 68- *Res:* Radiation shielding; nuclear structure; computer technology; information handling. *Mailing Add:* Oak Ridge Nat Lab PO Box X Oak Ridge TN 37830

PENROD, KENNETH EARL, b Blanchester, Ohio, Mar 30, 16; m 42; c 2. PHYSIOLOGY. *Educ:* Miami Univ, BS, 38; Iowa State Univ, PhD(physiol), 42. *Prof Exp:* Instr physiol, Miami Univ, 40-41; res physiologist, Aero Med Lab, Wright Field, Ohio, 41-42; asst prof physiol, Iowa State Univ, 46; asst prof, Sch Med, Boston Univ, 46-50; from assoc prof to prof, Duke Univ, 50-59, asst dean sch med, 52-59; prof physiol & vpres med affairs, WVa Univ, 59-65; provost, Med Ctr, Ind Univ, Indianapolis, 65-69; vchancellor med & health sci, 69-75, dir, 69-80, EXEC DIR COMMUNITY HOSP EDUC PROG, STATE DEPT EDUC, FLA BD REGENTS, 80- *Mem:* AAAS; fel Am Physiol Soc. *Res:* Physiology of altitude; respiration; hypothermia; oxygen toxicity; medical administration. *Mailing Add:* Fla Bd of Regents 107 W Gaines St Tallahassee FL 32301

PENROSE, WILLIAM ROY, b Hamilton, Ont, Jan 20, 43; m 65; c 3. POLLUTION CHEMISTRY. *Educ:* McMaster Univ, BSc, 65; Univ Mich, Ann Arbor, MS, 67, PhD(biol chem), 69. *Prof Exp:* Fel enzym, McMaster Univ, 69-70; fel molecular biol, Univ Toronto, 70-72; res scientist pollution chem, Fisheries & Marine Serv, Environ Can, 72-80; BIOCHEMIST & HEAD, ECOL SECT, RADIOL & ENVIRON RES DIV, ARGONNE NAT LAB, 80- *Mem:* Sigma Xi. *Res:* Effect of pollutants on survival of aquatic and marine animals; analytical chemistry of pollutants; biochemical transformations of pollutants. *Mailing Add:* Radiol & Environ Res Div Argonne Nat Lab Argonne IL 60439

PENSACK, JOSEPH MICHAEL, b Scranton, Pa, Dec 2, 16; m 41; c 6. ANIMAL NUTRITION, ANIMAL PHYSIOLOGY. *Educ:* Pa State Col, BS, 38; Univ NH, MS, 40; Ohio State Univ, PhD(biochem), 48. *Prof Exp:* Asst zool, Univ NH, 38-40, endocrinol, Northwestern Univ, 40-41 & animal sci, Exp Sta, Ohio State Univ, 46-48; res biochemist, Com Solvents Corp, 48-51, dir nutrit res, 51-59; sr biochemist, Am Cyanamid Co, 59-73, chief nutritionist, 73-78, PRIN SCIENTIST, CYANAMID INT, AM CYANAMID CO, 78- *Mem:* AAAS; Am Soc Animal Sci; Poultry Sci Asn. *Res:* Antibiotics; vitamins; non-protein nitrogen; enzymes; marine biology; biology; anabolics. *Mailing Add:* Box 400 Am Cyanamid Co Princeton NJ 08540

PENSAK, DAVID ALAN, b Princeton, NJ, Feb 16, 48; m 75. CHEMISTRY, COMPUTER SCIENCE. *Educ:* Princeton Univ, AB, 69; Harvard Univ, MA, 71, PhD(chem), 73. *Prof Exp:* Fel chem, Harvard Univ, 73-74; res chemist, 74-80, RES SUPRV, CENT RES DEPT, E I DU PONT DE NEMOURS & CO, INC, 80- *Concurrent Pos:* Hon res assoc, Ctr Res Comput Technol, Harvard Univ, 74- *Mem:* Am Chem Soc; Asn Comput Mach; Sigma Xi. *Res:* Application of computer science techniques to chemical problems, especially drug design, molecular modeling and computer-aided synthetic design. *Mailing Add:* Cent Res & Develop Dept Exp Sta E I du Pont de Nemours & Co Inc Wilmington DE 19898

PENSE, ALAN WIGGINS, b Sharon, Conn, Feb 3, 34; m 58; c 3. PHYSICAL METALLURGY, WELDING. *Educ:* Cornell Univ, BMetE, 57; Lehigh Univ, MS, 59, PhD(metall), 62. *Prof Exp:* From instr to assoc prof, 60-71, PROF METALL, LEHIGH UNIV, 71-, CHMN, DEPT METALL & MAT ENG, 77- *Concurrent Pos:* Robinson award, 65; mem, Pressure Vessel Res Comt; consult, Adv Comt Reactor Safeguards, Nuclear Regulatory Comn, 69-; welding handbk comt, Am Welding Soc, 72- *Honors & Awards:* Sparagan Award, Am Welding Soc, 64; Comfort Adams Mem lectr, Am Weld Soc, 80; Western Elec Award, Am Soc Eng Educ, 73; Charles H Jennings Award, 70. *Mem:* Am Soc Metals; Am Welding Soc; Int Inst Welding; Am Soc Testing & Mat. *Res:* Mechanical metallurgy and properties of alloys, particularly low alloy high strength steels; weldability of metals; failure analysis. *Mailing Add:* Whitaker Lab 5 Lehigh Univ Packer & Webster St Bethlehem PA 18015

PENSKY, JACK, b Canton, Ohio, Aug 25, 24; m 56; c 4. BIOCHEMISTRY. *Educ:* Ohio State Univ, BS, 45; Purdue Univ, MS, 49; Western Reserve Univ, PhD(biochem), 54. *Prof Exp:* Res assoc sulfur metab leucocytes, 54-57, sr instr biochem, Inst Path, 57-60, asst prof exp path, 60-71, ASST PROF BIOCHEM, CASE WESTERN RESERVE UNIV, 71- *Concurrent Pos:* USPHS res career develop award, 64; mem staff, Cleveland Vet Admin Hosp, Ohio. *Mem:* AAAS; Endocrine Soc; NY Acad Sci. *Res:* Protein purification; human complement and hormones; immunochemistry. *Mailing Add:* Cleveland Vet Admin Med Ctr 10701 East Blvd Cleveland OH 44106

PENSTONE, S(IDNEY) ROBERT, b Winnipeg, Man, Aug 29, 30; m 53; c 2. ELECTRICAL ENGINEERING. *Educ:* Queen's Univ, BSc, 55, MSc, 57. *Prof Exp:* Defence sci serv officer, Defence Res Telecommun Estab, Defence Res Bd, Can, 57-63; from asst prof to assoc prof, 63-73, PROF ELEC ENG, QUEEN'S UNIV, 73-, ASSOC DEAN, FAC APPL SCI, 81- *Mem:* Can Soc Elec Eng; Inst Elec & Electronics Engrs. *Res:* Electronic instrumentation; electronic circuit theory and design; digital computer displays and interfaces. *Mailing Add:* Dept of Elec Eng Queen's Univ Kingston ON K7L 3N0 Can

PENTECOST, JOSEPH L(UTHER), b Winder, Ga, Apr 23, 30; m 49, 69; c 5. CERAMIC ENGINEERING. *Educ:* Ga Inst Technol, BCerE, 51; Univ Ill, Urbana, MS, 54, PhD(ceramic eng), 56. *Prof Exp:* Sr engr, Melpar, Inc, 56-59; chief res engr, Aeronca Mfg Corp, 59-60; assoc prof ceramic eng, Miss State Univ, 60-61; assoc dir res, Res & Develop, Melpar, Inc, 61-68; mgr, Wash Res Ctr, W R Grace & Co, 68-72; PROF CERAMIC ENG, GA INST TECHNOL, 72- *Concurrent Pos:* Proprietor, Matcos Co, 61- *Honors & Awards:* Prof Achievement Ceramic Eng Award, Nat Inst Ceramic Engrs, 67. *Mem:* Am Ceramic Soc (vpres, 82-83); Am Soc Metals; Nat Inst Ceramic Engrs (pres, 76-77). *Res:* Electrical ceramics; fine particle raw materials; crystal growth; glass fracture. *Mailing Add:* Sch of Ceramic Eng Ga Inst of Technol Atlanta GA 30332

PENTNEY, ROBERTA PIERSON, b Van Nuys, Calif, Jan 11, 36. BIOLOGY, NEUROANATOMY. *Educ:* Col Notre Dame, Calif, BA, 60; Univ Notre Dame, PhD(biol), 65. *Prof Exp:* Res assoc, Univ Notre Dame, 65; from instr to assoc prof biol, Col Notre Dame, Calif, 65-74; ASST PROF BIOL, STATE UNIV NY BUFFALO, 74- *Concurrent Pos:* NIH fel, Col

Physicians & Surgeons, Columbia Univ, 71-74. *Mem:* AAAS; NY Acad Sci; Am Asn Anatomists. *Res:* Physiology and radiation biology; ethanol effects on central nervous system; visual pathways in central nervous system. *Mailing Add:* Dept of Anat Sci State Univ NY Buffalo NY 14214

PENTO, JOSEPH THOMAS, b Masontown, Pa, Sept 1, 43; m 69; c 2. ENDOCRINOLOGY, PHARMACOLOGY. *Educ:* WVa Univ, BA, 65, MS, 67; Univ Mo, PhD(pharmacol), 70. *Prof Exp:* NIH fel, Maimonides Med Ctr, 70-71; asst prof pharmacol, 71-76, assoc prof, 76-80, PROF PHARMACODYNAMICS & TOXICOL, UNIV OKLA HEALTH CTR, 81-, SECT CHIEF, 79- *Concurrent Pos:* Exec comt grant, Univ Okla Res Inst, 71-72; NSF grant, 74-76. *Mem:* AAAS; Sigma Xi; Am Soc Pharmacol Exp Therapeut; Am Soc Animal Sci; Endocrine Soc. *Res:* Calcium metabolism; calcitonin; parathyroid hormone; radio immunoassay. *Mailing Add:* Univ Okla 644 NE 14th St Oklahoma City OK 73190

PENTON, HAROLD ROY, JR, b New Orleans, La, Apr 17, 47; m 69; c 1. POLYMER CHEMISTRY, ORGANIC CHEMISTRY. *Educ:* Fla State Univ, BS, 69; Ga Inst Technol, PhD(org chem), 73. *Prof Exp:* Res chemist polymer chem, Am Enka Co, 73-74, AKZO Res Lab, 74-75; sr res chemist, Am Enka Co, 75-77; sr res chemist polymer chem, 77-81, GROUP LEADER, ETHYL CORP, 81- *Concurrent Pos:* Adj prof, Univ NC, Asheville, 76-77. *Mem:* Am Chem Soc; Soc Plastic Engrs. *Res:* Anionic and ring opening polymerizations; inorganic polymer synthesis; mechanism of polycondensation catalysis; mechanism of polymer degradation; hydrophilic polymer synthesis; polymer blends; polymer grafting; high temperature resistant polymers, engineering thermoplastics. *Mailing Add:* Plastics Appln & Polymer Res 8000 GSRI Ave Baton Rouge LA 70808

PENTON, ZELDA EVE, b New York, NY, Jan 15, 39; m 61; c 2. ANALYTICAL CHEMISTRY. *Educ:* City Col New York, BS, 59; Columbia Univ, MA, 60, PhD(chem), 64. *Prof Exp:* Res assoc biochem, Rockefeller Univ, 64-68; chemist, Signetics Corp, Sunnyvale, 72-74; chemist, Calif State Dept Health, 74-78; SR CHEMIST, INSTRUMENT DIV, VARIAN ASSOCS, 78- *Mem:* Am Chem Soc; Am Soc Testing & Mat. *Res:* Analysis of trace metals in biologicals; biological role of trace metals; gas chromatography of biological and environmental samples; capillary gas chromatography. *Mailing Add:* 5649 Greenridge Rd Castro Valley CA 94546

PENTONEY, RICHARD ELLIS, b Riverside, Calif, Aug 24, 22; m 49; c 3. FORESTRY. *Educ:* Univ Calif, BS, 49; State Univ NY, MS, 52, PhD, 56. *Prof Exp:* Asst wood technol, 53-56, from assoc prof to prof, 56-66, res coordr, 66-67, assoc dean phys sci & res, 67-70, vpres, 70-79, EMER VPRES PROG AFFAIRS, STATE UNIV NY COL ENVIRON SCI & FORESTRY, 79- *Mem:* AAAS; Acoust Soc Am; Soc Exp Stress Anal; NY Acad Sci. *Res:* Viscoelastic, sonic and ultrasonic and fracture properties of wood. *Mailing Add:* State Univ of NY Col of Env Sci & For Syracuse NY 13210

PENWELL, RICHARD CARLTON, b Columbus, Ohio, Apr 2, 42; m 64; c 2. POLYMER SCIENCE, ENGINEERING. *Educ:* Toledo Univ, BSME, 64; Princeton Univ, MSChE, 65; Univ Mass, MSE, 69, PhD(polymer sci), 70. *Prof Exp:* Proj eng polymer processing, Owens Ill Glass Co, 65-67; scientist, 72-78, sr scientist polymer sci, 78-79, MGR SPEC MAT ENG, XEROX CORP, 79- *Concurrent Pos:* NSF fel, Strasbourg, France, 70-71; Mat Sci Fel, Northwestern Univ, 71-72. *Mem:* Soc Rheology; Am Chem Soc. *Res:* Polymer physics, rheology and processing; mechanical and thermal properties of polymers and composites; structure-property relations of polymers. *Mailing Add:* Xerox Corp Xerox Sq W147 Rochester NY 14644

PENZ, P ANDREW, b Detroit, Mich, July 19, 39; m 61; c 2. ELECTROOPTICS. *Educ:* Brown Univ, ScB, 61; Cornell Univ, PhD(physics), 67. *Prof Exp:* Res scientist sci lab, Ford Motor Co, Mich, 66-72; res scientist, 72-77, MGR ADVAN DISPLAYS BR, TEX INSTRUMENTS INC, 77- *Mem:* Am Phys Soc; Sigma Xi; Inst Elec & Electronics Eng; Soc Info Display. *Res:* Solid state physics; transport properties and Fermi surface studies of pure metals; liquid crystals, especially electrohydrodynamic properties; display technology development. *Mailing Add:* Tex Instruments Inc PO Box 5936 MS 147 Dallas TX 75222

PENZIAS, ARNO A, b Munich, Ger, Apr 26, 33; US citizen; m 54; c 3. RADIO ASTRONOMY, PHYSICS. *Educ:* City Col New York, BS, 54; Columbia Univ, MA, 58, PhD(physics), 62. *Hon Degrees:* Dr, Observ Paris, 76. *Prof Exp:* Mem staff radio res, 61-72, head radio tech res dept, 72-74, head radio physics res dept, 74-76, DIR RADIO RES LAB, BELL LABS, INC, 76- *Concurrent Pos:* Lectr, Dept Astrophys Sci, Princeton Univ, 67-72, vis prof, 72-; assoc, Harvard Col Observ, 68-; adj prof, State Univ NY Stony Brook, 75-; trustee, Trenton State Col, 76-; mem astron adv panel, NSF, 77-; assoc lett ed, Astrophys J, 78- *Honors & Awards:* Nobel Prize physics, 78; Henry Draper Medal, Nat Acad Sci, 77; Herschel Medal, Royal Astron Soc, 77. *Mem:* Nat Acad Sci; fel Am Phys Soc; Am Astron Soc; Int Astron Union; Am Acad Arts & Sci. *Res:* Microwave physics; satellite communication; atmospheric physics; millimeter wave instrumentation; radio astronomy techniques; cosmology; interstellar matter. *Mailing Add:* Res Commun Sci Div Bell Telephone Lab Holmdel NJ 07733

PENZIEN, JOSEPH, b Philip, SDak, Nov 27, 24; m 50; c 4. STRUCTURAL ENGINEERING. *Educ:* Univ Wash, Seattle, BS, 45; Mass Inst Technol, ScD, 50. *Prof Exp:* Jr engr, Corps Engrs, 45-46; instr eng, Univ Wash, Seattle, 46-47; res assoc, Mass Inst Technol, 48-50; mem staff, Sandia Corp, NMex, 50-52; sr struct engr, Consol Vultee Aircraft Corp, 52-53; consult, Lawrence Radiation Lab, 57-67, dir, Earthquake Eng Res Ctr, 67-73 & 77-80, assoc prof, 53-67, PROF STRUCTURAL ENG, UNIV CALIF, BERKELEY, 67- *Concurrent Pos:* Nat Sci Found sr fel, 59-60; Inst Advan Study fel, Mass Inst Technol, 59-60; chief tech adv to UNESCO & expert earthquake engr, Int Inst Seismol & Earthquake Eng, Japan, 64-65; mem, Governor's Earthquake Coun, Calif, 72. *Mem:* Nat Acad Eng; Am Soc Civil Engrs; Seismol Soc Am; Soc Exp Stress Anal; Am Concrete Inst. *Res:* Structural mechanics. *Mailing Add:* Earthquake Eng Res Ctr Univ of Calif 1301 S 46th St Richmond CA 94804

PENZOTTI, STANLEY CLARE, JR, pharmacy, see previous edition

PEO, ERNEST RAMY, JR, b Watertown, NY, Apr 21, 25; m 43; c 1. ANIMAL NUTRITION. *Educ:* Okla State Univ, BS, 52, MS, 53; Iowa State Univ, PhD(animal nutrition), 56. *Prof Exp:* Res assoc, Iowa State Univ, 53-54, asst, 54-56; from asst prof to assoc prof animal sci, 56-66, PROF ANIMAL SCI, UNIV NEBR, LINCOLN, 66- *Mem:* Am Soc Animal Sci; Am Inst Nutrit. *Res:* Monogastric nutrition. *Mailing Add:* Dept of Animal Sci Univ of Nebr Col of Agr Lincoln NE 68583

PEOPLES, JOHN, JR, b Staten Island, NY, Jan 22, 33; m 56; c 2. HIGH ENERGY PHYSICS. *Educ:* Carnegie-Mellon Univ, BSEE, 55; Columbia Univ, MA, 61, PhD(physics), 66. *Prof Exp:* Engr, Martin-Marietta Corp, 55-59; instr physics, Columbia Univ, 64-66, asst prof, 66-69; from asst prof to assoc prof, Cornell Univ, 69-72; head, Res Div, 75-80, HEAD ANTIPROTON SOURCE PROJ, FERMI NAT ACCELERRATOR LAB, 81- *Concurrent Pos:* Sloan fel, 70-72. *Mem:* Am Phys Soc; AAAS. *Res:* High energy particle physics; accelerator technology. *Mailing Add:* Res Div Fermilab PO Box 500 Batavia IL 60150

PEOPLES, JOHN RICHARD, b Detroit, Mich, Dec 9, 37; m 61; c 3. AERODYNAMICS, CONTROL ENGINEERING. *Educ:* Univ Detroit, BS, 60; Univ Mich, MS, 62; Univ Southern Calif, MS, 74. *Prof Exp:* Jr eng controls, Bendix Res Ctr, 62-64; design eng shock tubes, NAm Aviation, 64-65; RES ENG MISSILE DESIGN, US NAVAL WEAPONS CTR, 65- *Concurrent Pos:* Fel, Naval Weapons Ctr, 74. *Mem:* Am Inst Aeronaut & Astronaut; Am Soc Mech Engrs. *Res:* Theoretical and applied aerodynamics; missile trajectory simulation; missile stability and control. *Mailing Add:* 813 Vicki Ridgecrest CA 93555

PEOPLES, STUART ANDERSON, b Petaluma, Calif, Nov 3, 07; m 32; c 1. PHARMACOLOGY. *Educ:* Univ Calif, AB, 30, MD, 34. *Prof Exp:* Intern, Univ Hosp, Univ Calif, 33-34, Merck fel, Univ, 34-35; Commonwealth Fund fel, Maudsley Hosp, London, Eng, 35-36; asst prof pharmacol, Univ Louisville, 36-38; assoc prof physiol & pharmacol, Sch Med, Univ Ala, 38-43; prof pharmacol, Col Med, Baylor Univ, 43-47; prof comp pharmacol, Sch Vet Med, lectr pharmacol & exp therapeut, Sch Med & pharmacologist, Exp Sta, 47-74, EMER PROF PHYSIOL SCI, UNIV CALIF, DAVIS, 74-; MED CONSULT, CALIF DEPT FOOD & AGR, 75- *Mem:* AAAS; Am Soc Pharmacol & Exp Therapeut; Soc Exp Biol & Med; AMA; Am Chem Soc. *Res:* Drug metabolism; toxicology; chemotherapy of tuberculosis. *Mailing Add:* Rte 1 Box 2350 Davis CA 95616

PEPE, FRANK ALBERT, b Schenectady, NY, May 22, 31. ANATOMY. *Educ:* Union Col, NY, BS, 53; Yale Univ, PhD(phys chem), 57. *Prof Exp:* Instr, 57-60, assoc, 60-63, from asst prof to assoc prof, 63-70, PROF ANAT, SCH MED, UNIV PA, 70-, CHMN DEPT, 77- *Mem:* AAAS; Am Chem Soc; Biophys Soc; Am Asn Anatomists; NY Acad Sci. *Res:* Molecular anatomy; studies of the molecular organization of the myofibril of striated muscle using immunochemical and electron microscopy techniques. *Mailing Add:* Dept of Anat Univ of Pa Sch of Med Philadelphia PA 19104

PEPE, JOSEPH PHILIP, b Connellsville, Pa, Nov 10, 47; m 69; c 2. ORGANIC CHEMISTRY, PHOTOGRAPHIC SCIENCE. *Educ:* Univ Pittsburgh, BS, 69; Pa State Univ, PhD(chem), 76. *Prof Exp:* Res chemist, 76-80, SR RES CHEMIST PHOTOG SCI, RES LAB, EASTMAN KODAK CO, 80- *Mem:* Am Chem Soc. Res. *Res:* Synthesis of organic components for conventional color-sensitized products; investigation of factors affecting dye stability in color print papers. *Mailing Add:* Res Lab Eastman Kodak Co 1999 Lake Ave Rochester NY 14650

PEPERMASTER, BENJAMIN W, immunology, genetics, see previous edition

PEPIN, HERBERT SPENCER, b Birtle, Man, Jan 28, 28; m 62; c 2. PLANT PATHOLOGY. *Educ:* Univ BC, BSA, 54, MA, 56; Univ Ill, PhD(plant path, bact), 59. *Prof Exp:* Asst plant path, Univ Ill, 56-59; res officer, 59-67, RES SCIENTIST, RES BR, CAN DEPT AGR, 67- *Mem:* Am Phytopath Soc; Can Phytopath Soc; Am Mycol Soc. *Res:* Physiology and biochemistry of disease resistance; root rot diseases. *Mailing Add:* Agr Can Res Sta 6660 NW Marine Dr Vancouver BC B6T 1X2 Can

PEPIN, ROBERT OSBORNE, b Wellesley Hills, Mass, Apr 12, 33; m 60. PHYSICS, SPACE SCIENCES. *Educ:* Harvard Univ, AB, 56; Univ Calif, Berkeley, PhD(physics), 64. *Prof Exp:* Res physicist, Univ Calif, Berkeley, 64; res assoc, 65, from asst prof to assoc prof, 66-74, PROF PHYSICS & ASTRON, INST TECHNOL, UNIV MINN, MINNEAPOLIS, 74- *Mem:* AAAS; Am Geophys Union. *Res:* History of meteoritic and terrestrial matter by mass spectrometry of rare gases. *Mailing Add:* Dept Physics Inst Technol Univ Minn Minneapolis MN 55455

PEPIN, THEODORE JOHN, b St Paul, Minn, Feb 7, 39; m 60; c 2. PHYSICS. *Educ:* Univ Minn, BS, 62, MS, 68, PhD(physics), 70. *Prof Exp:* Grant, Univ Minn, 70; asst prof, 71-75, ASSOC PROF PHYSICS, UNIV WYO, 75- *Mem:* AAAS; Am Geophys Union; Am Optical Soc. *Res:* Remote sensing of atmosphere from earth orbiting satellites to determine ozone and aerosol content of stratosphere; atmospheric and astrophysics research. *Mailing Add:* Dept Physics & Astron Univ Wyo Laramie WY 82071

PEPINSKY, RAYMOND, b St Paul, Minn, Jan 17, 12; m 42; c 2. PHYSICS, BIOLOGY. *Educ:* Univ Minn, BA, 33, MA, 34; Univ Chicago, PhD(physics), 40. *Hon Degrees:* Dr, Univ Giessen, 65. *Prof Exp:* Asst physics, Univ Chicago, 36-39, res assoc, 39; res physicist, US Rubber Co, 40-41; from instr to asst prof physics, Ala Polytech Inst, 41-45, from res assoc prof to res prof, 45-49; dir, Crystallog Res Lab, Pa State Univ, 49-63; distinguished prof chem & physics & chmn dept physics, Fla Atlantic Univ, 63-65; Robert O Law prof physics & chem, Nova Univ Advan Technol, 65-68, chmn dept physics, 67-68; vis prof, 68-70, PROF PHYSICS, METALL & MAT ENG, UNIV FLA, 70-, BIOPHYS, 72- *Concurrent Pos:* Res assoc & mem staff, Radiation Lab, Mass Inst Technol, 42-45; travel grants, Rockefeller Found, Europe, 54

& NSF, Gt Brit, 60; Smith-Mundt fel, Univ Mex, 55; Guggenheim & Smith-Mundt fel, Europe, 58-59; vis prof, Swiss Fed Inst Technol, Zurich, 58-59 & Kyoto Univ, 72; dir Goth Inst, Pa State Univ, 58-63; vis prof & dir instr crystallog, Univ Marburg, Ger, 66; lectr, Japan, 69; consult, Brookhaven Nat Lab, 51-66; mem, Solid State Adv Panel, Off Naval Res, 51-60, Blood Plasma Substitutes Panel, 51-53, Comn Crystallog Apparatus, Int Union Crystallog, 57-66, Crystal Data, 60-63, Gov Bd, Am Inst Physics, 59-62, Adv Comt Data Processing, Nat Bur Standards, 59-61, Comt Use Electronic Comput in Life Sci, 61-63 & Adv Comt Solid State Physics, 60- & Comt Tech Distrib Nuclear Data, Nat Acad Sci, 63-68; secy, Nat Comt Crystallog, Nat Res Coun, 52-54. *Mem:* AAAS; fel Am Phys Soc; Biophys Soc; Am Crystallog Asn; NY Acad Sci. *Res:* Physical, chemical and surface crystallography; theory of x-ray, neutron and slow electron diffraction; structural mechanisms of crystal transitions and melting; biophysics; intermolecular interactions and assembly of biosystems. *Mailing Add:* Dept of Physics Univ of Fla Gainesville FL 32611

PEPKOWITZ, LEONARD PAUL, b Paterson, NJ, Mar 23, 15; m 41, 69; c 5. CHEMISTRY. *Educ:* Univ Minn, BS, 39; Rutgers Univ, PhD(biochem), 43. *Prof Exp:* Asst plant physiol, Rutgers Univ, 40-43; asst chemist, Exp Sta, RI State Col, 42-43; chemist, Los Alamos Sci Lab, Univ Calif, 43-45, group leader, 45-46; res assoc, Res Lab, Gen Elec Co, 46-47, supvr gen anal unit, Knolls Atomic Power Lab, 47-53, mgr chem & metall sect, 53-56; vpres res, develop & serv, Nuclear Mat & Equip Corp, 57-64, vpres & gen mgr, Boron Isotope Separation Facility, 64-71; from asst prof to assoc prof, 71-75, PROF BIOL, ERIE COMMUNITY COL, CITY CAMPUS, 75- *Mem:* AAAS; Am Chem Soc; Sigma Xi. *Res:* Isotope and chemical separations; chemistry of nuclear materials; analytical chemistry; radiochemistry; biochemistry; plant metabolism. *Mailing Add:* Dept of Biol Erie Community Col City Campus Buffalo NY 14209

PEPOY, LOUIS JOHN, b Cleveland, Ohio, Feb 8, 38; m 68; c 2. ORGANIC CHEMISTRY. *Educ:* John Carroll Univ, BS, 61, MS, 65; Wayne State Univ, PhD(org chem), 70. *Prof Exp:* Chemist analyst, Repub Steel Res Ctr, 62-65; chemist, E I du Pont de Nemours & Co, Inc, 69-71; electrocoating chemist, Glidden-Durkee Res Ctr, SCM Corp, 71-75; sr res chemist, 75-76, group leader, 76-80, RES MGR, CHEMETRON CORP, 80- *Mem:* Am Chem Soc. *Res:* Organic pigment synthesis and development; relationships between physical properties, chemical structure, and physical forms of pigments; colloid science; electrodeposition of paints; low energy curing of coatings. *Mailing Add:* Chemetron Corp 491 Columbia Ave Holland MI 49423

PEPPER, EVAN HAROLD, b Windsor, Ont, Aug 14, 27; m 55; c 6. ENVIRONMENTAL BIOLOGY. *Educ:* Univ Detroit, BS, 54; Mich State Univ, MS, 58, PhD(plant path), 61. *Prof Exp:* Tech coordr, Ladish Malting Co, Wis, 60-62; asst prof plant path & plant pathologist, NDak State Univ, 62-67; assoc prof, 67-71, PROF BOT, BRANDON UNIV, 71- *Concurrent Pos:* Vchmn, Man Res Coun, 71-; mem bd dirs, Biomass Energy Inst, Inc, 72; vis prof, Univ Reading, Eng, 73-74. *Mem:* Solar Energy Soc; AAAS; Sigma Xi. *Res:* Energy flows and balances; renewable energy sources; history and philosophy of science. *Mailing Add:* Dept Bot Brandon Univ Brandon MB R7A 6A9 Can

PEPPER, JAMES MORLEY, b Morse, Sask, Mar 30, 20; m 45; c 4. ORGANIC CHEMISTRY. *Educ:* Univ BC, BA, 39, MA, 41; McGill Univ, PhD(chem), 43. *Prof Exp:* Res fel chem McGill Univ, 43-44, lectr, 44-45; res chemist, Dominion Rubber Co, 45-47; assoc prof chem, 47-55, head dept chem & chem eng, 70-76, PROF CHEM, UNIV SASK, 55- *Mem:* Am Chem Soc; Can Pulp & Paper 55-; Chem Inst Can; Nat Am Phytochem Soc. *Res:* Natural products; lignin chemistry; chemistry of phenolic substances. *Mailing Add:* Dept of Chem & Chem Eng Univ of Sask Saskatoon SK S7H 0W0 Can

PEPPER, PAUL MILTON, b Kendallville, Ind, May 16, 09; m 34; c 1. MATHEMATICS. *Educ:* Ind Univ, AB, 31, AM, 32; Univ Cincinnati, PhD(math), 37. *Prof Exp:* Instr math, Univ Cincinnati, 37-38; from instr to assoc prof, Univ Notre Dame, 38-49; assoc prof indust eng, 49-51, asst to dir res found, 51-53, dir mapping & chart res lab, 53-57, assoc prof math, 53-59, from assoc prof to prof indust eng, 56-74, asst to dir res found, 57-67, assoc dir develop, 67-74, EMER PROF INDUST ENG, OHIO STATE UNIV, 74- *Concurrent Pos:* Fel, Harvard Univ, 47; res scientist, Autometics Corp, 59-63; consult, Tech Inc & Chem Abstr, 64-69 & DBA Systs, Inc, 67-70. *Mem:* Fel AAAS; Am Math Soc; Soc Indust & Appl Math; Am Astron Soc; Soc Mfg Engrs. *Res:* Geometry of numbers; abstract metric geometry; potential theory; design of slide rules and nomographs; applied mathematics; photogrammetry; celestial mechanics; geodesy; finite projective planes, by high speed computers. *Mailing Add:* 517 E Schreyer Pl Columbus OH 43214

PEPPER, ROLLIN E, b Glens Falls, NY, June 8, 24; m 53; c 3. MICROBIOLOGY. *Educ:* Earlham Col, BA, 50; Syracuse Univ, MS, 53; Mich State Univ, PhD(microbiol), 63. *Prof Exp:* Assoc scientist, Ethicon, Inc, 51-60; res asst, Mich State Univ, 60-63, res assoc, 63-64; from asst prof to assoc prof, 64-68, chmn dept, 67-77, PROF BIOL, ELIZABETHTOWN COL, 68- *Concurrent Pos:* Vis prof, Univ Zambia, 72-73; indust consult microbiol. *Mem:* Am Soc Microbiol; Am Asn Univ Professors; NY Acad Sci. *Res:* Radiation and chemical sterilization; bacterial metabolism. *Mailing Add:* Dept of Biol Elizabethtown Col Elizabethtown PA 17022

PEPPER, THOMAS PETER, b London, Eng, Jan 26, 18; nat Can; m 53; c 3. NUCLEAR PHYSICS. *Educ:* Univ BC, BA, 39, MA, 41; McGill Univ, PhD(nuclear physics), 48. *Prof Exp:* Sr res asst, Nat Res Coun Can, 41-45, asst res officer, 47-52; with Isotope Prod, Ltd & pres, Isotope Prod, Inc, Curtiss-Wright Corp, 52-57; head physics div, 58-67, asst dir, 67-72, dir, 72-80, EXT DIR, SASK RES COUN, 80- *Mem:* Can Asn Physicists; Can Res Mgt Asn. *Res:* Application of radioactivity; operations research. *Mailing Add:* Sask Res Coun Saskatoon SK S7N 0X1 Can

PEPPER, WILLIAM DONALD, b Dadeville, Ala, Apr 29, 35; m 68; c 1. FOREST BIOMETRY. *Educ:* Auburn Univ, BS, 59; NC State Univ, MF, 65, PhD(forestry), 75. *Prof Exp:* Res forester, Southeastern Forest Exp Sta, 65-66, BIOMETRICIAN, SOUTHERN FOREST EXP STA, US FOREST SERV, 77- *Mem:* Am Statist Asn; Biomet Soc. *Res:* Design and analysis of studies on biological topics, particularly forest resources; forecasting timber growth and yield. *Mailing Add:* Southern Forest Exp Sta Rm T-10210 701 Loyola Ave New Orleans LA 70113

PEPPERBERG, DAVID ROY, b Chicago, Ill, Nov 10, 44; m 70. NEUROBIOLOGY, BIOPHYSICS. *Educ:* Mass Inst Technol, SB, 66, PhD(biophys), 73. *Prof Exp:* Res fel biol, Harvard Univ, 73-76; ASST PROF BIOL SCI, PURDUE UNIV, 77- *Concurrent Pos:* Res fel, NIH, 74-76, Fight for Sight, Inc res fel, 76. *Mem:* Asn Res Vision & Ophthal; Am Chem Soc; Soc Gen Physiologists; Biophys Soc. *Res:* Light and dark adaptation of vertebrate photoreceptors; relationship of adaptational processes to the bleaching and regeneration of visual pigment; interconversion of retinoids in the vertebrate eye. *Mailing Add:* Dept of Biol Sci Purdue Univ West Lafayette IN 47907

PEPPERMAN, ARMAND BENNETT, JR, b New Orleans, La, May 30, 41; m 61; c 3. ORGANIC CHEMISTRY. *Educ:* La State Univ, New Orleans, BS, 63, PhD(org chem), 73. *Prof Exp:* Chemist, Oilseed Crops Lab, 63-68, res chemist, Spec Finishes Invests, 68-72 & Polymer Finishes Res, 72-74, RES CHEMIST, COTTON TEXTILE CHEM LAB, POLYMER FINISHES RES, SOUTHERN REGIONAL RES CTR, SCI & EDUC ADMIN-AGR RES, USDA, 74- *Mem:* Am Chem Soc; Sigma Xi; Weed Sci Soc Am; Controlled Release Soc Am. *Res:* Organophosphorus chemistry; flame retardants for cellulosic textiles; nuclear magnetic resonance spectroscopy; synthesis of plant growth regulators; controlled release formulations. *Mailing Add:* Cotton Textile Chem Lab 1100 Robert E Lee Blvd New Orleans LA 70179

PEPPERS, RUSSEL A, b Belleville, Ill, Feb 23, 32. GEOLOGY, PALYNOLOGY. *Educ:* Univ Ill, BS, 57, MS, 59, PhD(geol, bot), 61. *Prof Exp:* Geologist, Shell Oil Co, 61-63; asst geologist, 63-65, assoc geologist, 65-78, GEOLOGIST, ILL STATE GEOL SURV, 78- *Mem:* AAAS; Geol Soc Am; Bot Soc Am. *Res:* Palynology of Paleozoic strata; coal geology; stratigraphy. *Mailing Add:* Coal Sect Ill State Geol Surv Champaign IL 61820

PEPPLER, HENRY JAMES, b Hussenbach, Russia, Nov 29, 11; nat US; m 39; c 2. MICROBIOLOGY. *Educ:* Univ Wis, BS, 36, MS, 38, PhD(bact), 39. *Prof Exp:* Asst, Univ Wis, 36-39; instr bact, Kans State Col, 39-42; lab officer, US War Dept, 42-46; res microbiologist, Res Lab, Carnation Co, 46-51; dir biochem res, Red Star Yeast & Prod Co, 51-54, mgr res, 54-60; mgr res, Universal Foods Corp, 60-66, dir res & develop, 66-72, dir sci affairs, 72-76; CONSULT, 76- *Honors & Awards:* Award, Am Chem Soc, 66 & Distinguished Serv Award, 72. *Mem:* Am Chem Soc; Am Soc Microbiol; Inst Food Technologists. *Res:* Microbial physiology; zymology; yeast products; food and dairy products. *Mailing Add:* 5157 N Shoreland Ave Whitefish Bay WI 53217

PEPPLER, RICHARD BOND, b Wilmerding, Pa, Mar 2, 22; m 49; c 2. INDUSTRIAL CHEMISTRY. *Educ:* Ohio Wesleyan Univ, BA, 43. *Prof Exp:* Anal chemist, Nat Bur Standards, 44-49, phys chemist, 49-56; asst dir res, 56-64, dir res, 64-79, SR RES ADV, RES LABS, MASTER BUILDERS CO, 80- *Mem:* Am Chem Soc; Am Soc Testing & Mat. *Res:* Physical chemical research in field of ceramics and cementitious systems; phase equilibria; ad mixtures for cementitious systems. *Mailing Add:* Master Builders 23700 Chagrin Blvd Cleveland OH 44122

PEPPLER, RICHARD DOUGLAS, b Trenton, NJ, Sept 24, 43; m 68. ANATOMY. *Educ:* Gettysburg Col, BA, 65; Univ Kans, PhD(anat), 69. *Prof Exp:* Asst prof anat & obstet-gynec, La State Univ, New Orleans, 70-74, assoc prof, 74-78; assoc prof, 78-80, PROF ANAT & OBSTET-GYNEC, COL MED, EAST TENN STATE UNIV, 80-, ASSOC CHMN ANAT, 80- *Mem:* AAAS; Am Asn Anatomists; Soc Study Reproduction; Endocrine Soc; Soc Study Fertility; Sigma Xi. *Res:* Pituitary-ovarian relationships to include specifically follicular development and control of ovulation; ovarian dynamics in mammals; reproductive physiology. *Mailing Add:* Dept of Anat POB 19960A ETenn State Univ Col of Med Johnson City TN 37614

PEQUEGNAT, LINDA LEE HAITHCOCK, b Bedford, Ind, Oct 27, 31; m 57; c 2. BIOLOGICAL OCEANOGRAPHY, TAXONOMY. *Educ:* Pomona Col, BA, 53; Univ Calif, San Diego, MS, 57; Tex A&M Univ, PhD(oceanog), 70. *Prof Exp:* Lab asst zool, Pomona Col, 51-53; lab technician, Univ Tex, 53-54; res asst biol oceanog, Scripps Inst Oceanog, 54-58; res scientist oceanog, Tex A&M Univ, 64-81; RES SCIENTIST, TERECO CORP, 70- *Concurrent Pos:* Cur systematic collection marine organisms, 73-81. *Mem:* AAAS; Am Inst Biol Sci; Am Soc Limnol & Oceanog; Soc Syst Zool; Am Soc Zoologists. *Res:* Taxonomy and systematics of deep-sea crustacea (Mysidacea and Decapoda); coral reef Decapoda; bio-fouling studies. *Mailing Add:* PO Box 2848 College Station TX 77841

PEQUEGNAT, WILLIS EUGENE, b Riverside, Calif, Sept 18, 14; m 37, 57; c 4. OCEANOGRAPHY. *Educ:* Univ Calif, BA, 36; Univ Calif, Los Angeles, MA, 38, PhD(zool), 42. *Prof Exp:* From instr to prof zool, Pomona Col, 40-59; assoc prog dir, NSF, 60-61, prog dir, 61-63; head dept, Tex A&M Univ, 64-66, prof oceanog, 63-80; MEM STAFF, TERECO CORP, 80- *Concurrent Pos:* Ranger naturalist, Nat Park Serv, US Dept Interior, 39; vis asst prof, Univ Chicago, 47; vis assoc prof, Univ Calif, 51, res assoc, Scripps Inst, 54-55; Ford fel, 54; NSF sci fac fel, 58-59; consult, NSF, 63-; pres, TerEco Corp, 69-; vis prof, Univ Aberdeen, 81- *Mem:* Fel AAAS; Am Soc Limnol & Oceanog; Ecol Soc Am; Marine Biol Asn UK. *Res:* Biological oceanography; ecology of the deep sea; ecology of epifauna of the continental shelf; taxonomy of Brachyura and Galatheidae. *Mailing Add:* Tereco Corp PO Box GF College Station TX 77841

PERA, JOHN DOMINIC, b Memphis, Tenn, Oct 5, 22; m 44; c 3. ORGANIC CHEMISTRY. *Educ:* Southwestern at Memphis, BS, 49; Ind Univ, PhD(org chem), 60. *Prof Exp:* Chemist, Cent Labs, Inc, 42-43; chemist, 46-52, prod mgr, 52-53, chief chemist, 53-58, vpres res, 58-71, VPRES RES & DEVELOP, BUCKMAN LABS, INC, 71- *Mem:* Am Chem Soc; Am Inst Chemists; Tech Asn Pulp & Paper Indust; Royal Soc Chem. *Res:* Non pressure preservation of wood with pentachlorophenol; formulation of chemical specialty products; synthesis of organic and barium compounds used in industrial microorganism control; organic sulfur chemistry; organic bromine chemistry. *Mailing Add:* 5187 Cole Rd Memphis TN 38117

PERACCHIO, ALDO ANTHONY, b Brooklyn, NY, Feb 25, 35; m 59; c 2. ENGINEERING, SPACE SCIENCES. *Educ:* City Col NY, BME, 56; Rensselaer Polytech Inst, MME, 59, PhD(mech eng), 68. *Prof Exp:* Anal engr, Hamilton Standard Div, United Aircraft Corp, 56-61, sr anal engr, 61-69; supvr aeroacoust group, United Technol Res Lab, 69-73; HEAD ACOUST TECHNOL, PRATT & WHITNEY AIRCRAFT, 73- *Concurrent Pos:* Adj assoc prof, Rensselaer Polytech Inst. *Mem:* Am Inst Aeronaut & Astronaut. *Res:* Fluid mechanics of turbomachinery and nozzles; kinetics theory of gases applied to fluid mechanics problems; prediction of propeller flow field and aerodynamic performance; experimental and theoretical acoustics research on rotating machinery. *Mailing Add:* Pratt & Whitney Aircraft 400 Main East Hartford CT 06118

PERAINO, CARL, b Passaic, NJ, Mar 10, 35; m 58; c 2. BIOCHEMISTRY, ONCOLOGY. *Educ:* Lebanon Valley Col, BS, 57; Univ Wis, MS, 59, PhD(biochem), 61. *Prof Exp:* Nat Cancer Inst fel oncol, 61-64; instr, McArdle Lab, Univ Wis, 64-65; asst biochemist, 65-70, biochemist, 70-78, SR BIOCHEMIST, ARGONNE NAT LAB, 78- *Mem:* AAAS; Am Soc Biol Chemists; Am Asn Cancer Res. *Res:* Enzyme regulation; hepatocarcinogenesis; enzymology. *Mailing Add:* Biol Div Bldg 202 Argonne Nat Lab Argonne IL 60439

PERALTA, PAULINE HUNTINGTON, b Portland, Ore, June 15, 26; m 50; c 2. VIROLOGY. *Educ:* Stanford Univ, BS, 48; Yale Univ, PhD(physiol chem), 52. *Prof Exp:* Res scientist virol, Mid Am Res Unit, NIH, 58-72; res scientist, Mid Am Res Unit, 72-76, RES SCIENTIST VIROL, GORGAS MEM LAB, 76- *Mem:* Sigma Xi. *Res:* Arbovirology; clinical virology; virus epidemiology. *Mailing Add:* Gorgas Mem Lab Box 6991 Panama 5 Panama

PERCARPIO, EDWARD P(ETER), b Paterson, NJ, Mar 8, 34; m 56; c 3. MECHANICAL ENGINEERING, RUBBER TECHNOLOGY. *Educ:* Newark Col Eng, BS, 55, MS, 58. *Prof Exp:* Engr, Curtiss-Wright Res Div, 55-58; mech engr, Picatinny Arsenal, 58-60; res engr rubber technol, Uniroyal Res Ctr, Middlebury, Conn, 60-74; res engr, 74-80, SR RES ASSOC & DEPT MGR, BECTON-DICKINSON, 80- *Concurrent Pos:* Adj fac, Community Col Morris, 74- *Mem:* Am Soc Mech Engrs; Am Chem Soc. *Res:* Automobile tire research; skid resistance of tires; rubber friction; rubber technology; sealing; medical product design. *Mailing Add:* 36 Boat St North Haledon NJ 07508

PERCHONOCK, CARL DAVID, b Philadelphia, Pa, Mar 30, 46; m 73; c 1. ORGANIC CHEMISTRY, MEDICINAL CHEMISTRY. *Educ:* Univ Pa, BA, 67; Univ Wis, PhD(org chem), 72. *Prof Exp:* Assoc sr investr, 72-79, SR INVESTR MED CHEM, SMITH KLINE & FRENCH LABS, 79- *Concurrent Pos:* NIH fel, Columbia Univ, 72. *Mem:* Am Chem Soc; AAAS. *Res:* Synthesis of biologically active compounds; total synthesis of beta-lactam antibiotics; analogs of arachidonic and metabolites. *Mailing Add:* Smith Kline & French Labs 1500 Spring Garden St Philadelphia PA 19101

PERCICH, JAMES ANGELO, b Detroit, Mich, Sept 14, 44; m 82. CROP PEST MANAGEMENT, CHEMICAL CONTROL. *Educ:* Mich State Univ, BS, 67, MS, 71, PhD(plant path), 75. *Prof Exp:* Fel, Univ Wis, 74-76; fel, 76-77, ASST PROF CHEM CONTROL PLANT DIS, DEPT PLANT PATH, UNIV MINN, 77- *Mem:* Am Soc Agron; AAAS; Can Phytopath Soc; Am Phytopath Soc. *Res:* Plant disease control of fungal pathagens of wild rice (zizania aquatica) and sugar beet; various fungicides and adjudcent materials to increase disease control at lower dosages and numbers of applications. *Mailing Add:* Dept Plant Path 304 Stakman Hall Univ Minn St Paul MN 55108

PERCIVAL, DOUGLAS FRANKLIN, b Ridgetown, Ont, Jan 8, 26; nat US; m 48; c 5. ORGANIC POLYMER CHEMISTRY. *Educ:* Pomona Col, BA, 50; Mich State Univ, MS, 52, PhD, 55. *Prof Exp:* Res chemist natural prod, Mich State Univ, 52-54; res chemist petrochem, Calif Res Corp, Standard Oil Co, Calif, 55-64; res chemist petrochem, Flexible Packaging Div, 64-75, DIR PACKAGING RES & DEVELOP, CROWN ZELLERBACH CORP, 75- *Mem:* Am Chem Soc. *Res:* Polyolefins and copolymers; extrusion coating and laminating. *Mailing Add:* 2475 Harborview Dr San Leandro CA 94577

PERCIVAL, FRANK WILLIAM, b Los Angeles, Calif, June 10, 48; m 69; c 2. PLANT PHYSIOLOGY. *Educ:* Occidental Col, BA, 69; Univ Calif, Santa Barbara, PhD(biol sci), 73. *Prof Exp:* Fel plant physiol, Dept Bot & Plant Path, Mich State Univ, 73-75; asst prof, 75-81, ASSOC PROF BIOL, WESTMONT COL, 81- *Mem:* Am Soc Plant Physiologists; Sigma Xi. *Res:* Regulation of hormone levels in higher plants, focusing on the control of indole-3-acetic acid metabolism. *Mailing Add:* Dept of Biol Westmont Col 955 La Paz Rd Santa Barbara CA 93108

PERCIVAL, WILLIAM COLONY, b Greencastle, Ind, Sept 26, 24; m 50; c 2. ORGANIC CHEMISTRY. *Educ:* Middlebury Col, BA, 46; Pa State Col, MS, 49, PhD(chem), 51. *Prof Exp:* Chemist, NJ, 45-47 & Del, 51-59, qual control supvr, Elastomers Area, Chambers Works, 59-69, div head, 69-80, SR SUPVR, E I DU PONT DE NEMOURS & CO, INC, 80- *Mem:* Am Chem Soc. *Res:* Addition reactions of Grignard reagents; formaldehyde chemistry; organic analytical chemistry; gas chromatography; spectrophotometric methods. *Mailing Add:* 216 Wellington Rd Fairfax Wilmington DE 19803

PERCUS, JEROME K, b New York, NY, June 21, 26; m 65. THEORETICAL PHYSICS. *Educ:* Columbia Univ, BS, 47, MA, 48, PhD(physics), 54. *Prof Exp:* Instr elec eng, Columbia Univ, 52-54; res assoc physics, Courant Inst Math Sci, NY Univ, 54-55; asst prof, Stevens Inst Technol, 55-58; assoc prof, 58-66, PROF PHYSICS, COURANT INST MATH SCI, NY UNIV, 66- *Mem:* Am Math Soc; Am Phys Soc. *Res:* Theory of many-body systems. *Mailing Add:* Courant Inst Math Sci NY Univ 251 Mercer St New York NY 10012

PERCY, JOHN REES, b Windsor, Eng, July 10, 41; Can citizen; m 62; c 1. ASTRONOMY, SCIENCE EDUCATION. *Educ:* Univ Toronto, BSc, 62, MA, 63, PhD(astron), 68. *Prof Exp:* Asst prof, 67-73, assoc prof, 73-78, PROF ASTRON, ERINDALE COL, UNIV TORONTO, 78- *Concurrent Pos:* Leverhulme fel, Cambridge Univ, 72-73. *Mem:* Int Astron Union; Am Astron Soc; Can Astron Soc; Royal Astron Soc Can (vpres, 74-78, pres, 78-79). *Res:* Theory and observation of variable stars; astronomy education. *Mailing Add:* Dept of Astron Erindale Col Univ of Toronto Toronto ON M5S 1A7 Can

PERCY, JOHN SMITH, b South Shields, Eng, Aug 8, 38; m 61; c 3. MEDICINE. *Educ:* Univ Durham, MB & BS, 61; Univ Newcastle, Eng, MD, 66; FRCP(C), 68; FRCP(E), 73, FRCP, 79. *Prof Exp:* Fel med, Med Ctr, Univ Colo, 66-68; asst prof, 68-70, assoc prof, 70-77, PROF MED, UNIV ALTA, 77-, DIR, RHEUMATIC DIS UNIT, 68- *Concurrent Pos:* Can Arthritis & Rheumatism Soc fel, Univ Alta, 68-; examr, Royal Col Physicians & Surgeons Can, 71- *Mem:* Am Rheumatism Asn; Can Rheumatism Asn; Can Soc Immunologists. *Res:* Immunopathology of connective tissue diseases. *Mailing Add:* 9-112 Clin Sci Bldg Univ of Alta Edmonton AB T6G 2G7 Can

PERCY, JONATHAN ARTHUR, b Penrootyn, Wales, Jan 14, 43; Can citizen; m 68; c 2. ENVIRONMENTAL PHYSIOLOGY. *Educ:* Carleton Univ, BSc, 65; Mem Univ Nfld, MSc, 68, PhD(marine biol), 71. *Prof Exp:* Fel, Inst Arctic Biol, Univ Alaska, 71-72; RES SCIENTIST PHYSIOL, ARTIC BIOL STA, FISHERIES & OCEANS, CAN, 72- *Mem:* Arctic Inst NAm; Can Soc Zoologists; Am Soc Limnol & Oceanog. *Res:* Environmental physiology of Arctic marine invertebrates, particularly physiological effects of natural stresses and sublethal physiological effects of oil pollution. *Mailing Add:* Arctic Biol Sta Fisheries & Oceans Can PO Box 400 Ste Anne de Bellevue PQ H9X 3R4 Can

PERDEW, JOHN PAUL, b Cumberland, Md, Aug 30, 43. DENSITY FUNCTIONAL THEORY. *Educ:* Gettysburg Col, AB, 65; Cornell Univ, PhD(physics), 71. *Prof Exp:* Fel physics, Univ Toronto, 71-74 & Rutgers Univ, 74-77; asst prof, 77-79, ASSOC PROF PHYSICS, TULANE UNIV, 79- *Concurrent Pos:* NSF grants, 78-80 & 80- *Mem:* Am Phys Soc. *Res:* Theoretical condensed matter physics; density functional theory of atoms, metals and metal surfaces. *Mailing Add:* Dept of Physics Tulane Univ New Orleans LA 70118

PERDRISAT, CHARLES F, b Geneva, Switz, July 1, 32; m 62. NUCLEAR PHYSICS, HIGH ENERGY PHYSICS. *Educ:* Univ Geneva, MSc, 56; Swiss Fed Inst Technol, PhD(physics), 61. *Prof Exp:* Res asst, Swiss Fed Inst Technol, 61-62 & Inst Theoret Nuclear Physics, Univ Bonn, 62-63; res asst, Univ Ill, 63-65, res asst prof physics, 65-66; asst prof, 66-69, assoc prof, 69-76, PROF PHYSICS, COL WILLIAM & MARY, 76- *Mem:* Swiss Phys Soc; Am Phys Soc; Europ Phys Soc. *Res:* Nuclear spectroscopy; properties of elementary particles; nuclear reactions induced by intermediate energy particles. *Mailing Add:* Dept of Physics Col of William & Mary Williamsburg VA 23685

PERDUE, EDWARD MICHAEL, b Atlanta, Ga, May 21, 47; m 67; c 2. PHYSICAL ORGANIC CHEMISTRY, ORGANIC GEOCHEMISTRY. *Educ:* Ga Inst Technol, BS, 69, PhD(chem), 73. *Prof Exp:* Asst prof, 73-77, ASSOC PROF ENVIRON SCI & CHEM, PORTLAND STATE UNIV, 77- *Mem:* Am Chem Soc; Geochem Soc. *Res:* Thermodynamics of acid-base equilibria; chemical characterization of naturally-occurring polyelectrolytes, such as fulvic and humic acids, in soils and waters. *Mailing Add:* Dept Chem Box 751 Portland State Univ Portland OR 97207

PERDUE, JAMES F, b Chicago, Ill, May 5, 33; m 57; c 3. BIOCHEMISTRY. *Educ:* Wis State Univ, Oshkosh, BS, 58; Univ Wis-Madison, MS, 61, PhD(zool), 63. *Prof Exp:* Trainee, Inst Enzyme Res, Med Sch, Univ Wis-Madison, 63-65, asst prof oncol, 66-75; STAFF SCIENTIST, LADY DAVIS INST, JEWISH GEN HOSP, 75- *Concurrent Pos:* Assoc mem, Depts Exp Med & Biochem & Molecular Cytol Study Sect, McGill Univ, 77-81. *Mem:* Am Soc Biol Chem; Can Biochem Soc; AAAS; Am Asn Cancer Res; Am Soc Cell Biol. *Res:* Isolation and characterization of receptors which bind insulin-like growth factors; regulation of normal and transformed cell replication by growth factors and proteases. *Mailing Add:* Lady Davis Inst Jewish Gen Hosp 3755 Cote St Catherine Montreal PQ H3T 1E2 Can

PERDUE, ROBERT EDWARD, JR, b Norfolk, Va, Oct 18, 24. ECONOMIC BOTANY. *Educ:* Univ Md, BS, 49; Harvard Univ, MA, 51, PhD, 57. *Prof Exp:* Botanist, US Geol Surv, 51-53 & Tex Res Found, 53-56; botanist, 57-73, chief, Med Plant Resources Lab, 73-78, CHIEF, PLANT TAXON LAB, BELTSVILLE AGR RES CTR, AGR RES SERV, USDA, 78- *Mem:* AAAS; Soc Econ Bot; Am Soc Pharmacognosy; Am Inst Biol Sci. *Res:* Natural products from higher plants, especially anti-tumor agents. *Mailing Add:* 11000 Waycroft Way Rockville MD 20705

PEREIRA, CARLOS MARTIN, b Elizabeth, NJ, Oct 9, 40. THEORETICAL PHYSICS, ASTROPHYSICS. *Educ:* Case Western Reserve Univ, AB, 61, PhD(physics), 67. *Prof Exp:* Fel, Case Western Reserve Univ, 67-68; res assoc physics, Syracuse Univ, 68-69 & Aerospace Res Labs, Wright-Patterson AFB, 69-70; fel theoret physics, Univ Md, College Park, 70-72, vis asst prof, 72-74. *Mem:* Am Phys Soc; NY Acad Sci; Sigma Xi. *Res:* Conservation laws in physics; existence theorems for systems of partial differential equations with applications to general relativity; classical field theory; astrophysics; differential geometry; exact solutions of Einstein's field equations; rotating stars; analysis and functional analysis; topology. *Mailing Add:* Apt 604 9737 Mount Pisgah Rd Silver Spring MD 20903

PEREIRA, GERARD P, b Port-au-Prince, Haiti, Mar 22, 37; Can citizen; m 61; c 2. ANATOMY, HISTOLOGY. *Educ:* Columbia Univ, BS, 61; McGill Univ, MS, 65, PhD(anat), 68. *Prof Exp:* Asst prof anat, Fac Med, Laval Univ, 68-70, Col Physicians & Surgeons, Columbia Univ, 70-77; MEM STAFF, DEPT ANAT, UNIV NEBR MED CTR, OMAHA, 77- *Concurrent Pos:* Lectr, Fac Med, Sherbrooke Univ, 66-68; Que Med Res Coun grant, Fac Med, Laval Univ, 69-70; NIH res grant, Col Physicians & Surgeons, Columbia Univ, 71- *Mem:* Can Soc Immunologists; Am Asn Anatomists; Am Soc Cell Biol; Electron Micros Soc Am; NY Acad Sci. *Res:* Immunocytology in germ-free animals; cytology in dietary deficiencies; transmission and scanning electron microscopy coupled with x-ray analysis of cellular components. *Mailing Add:* Dept Anat 42nd & Dewey Ave Omaha NE 68105

PEREIRA, JOSEPH, b Brooklyn, NY, Nov 1, 28; m 55; c 3. BIOCHEMISTRY. *Educ:* City Col New York, BS, 51; Univ Conn, MS, 55, PhD(bact, biochem), 58. *Prof Exp:* Res assoc bact, Univ Conn, 53-57; microbiologist & biochemist, 58-68, proj leader metab dis, 68-71, mgr biochem pharmacol, 71-75, MGR GASTROINTESTINAL, IMMUNOL & VIROL RES, PFIZER, INC, 75- *Res:* Microbial metabolism; drugs affecting gastric secretion; biochemistry of drugs influencing lipid and carbohydrate metabolism. *Mailing Add:* Pfizer Cent Res Pfizer Inc Groton CT 06340

PEREIRA, MARTIN RODRIGUES, b Hilversum, Neth, June 7, 20; US citizen; m 60; c 3. ENVIRONMENTAL PHYSIOLOGY. *Educ:* Fla State Univ, BSc, 60; Rutgers Univ, MSc, 61; St Thomas Inst, PhD(biol, exp med), 66. *Prof Exp:* Biologist, Foreign Technol Div, US Air Force Systs Command, Ohio, 66-67; res scientist, Travelers Res Ctr, Inc, 67-69; physiologist, Grumman Aerospace Corp, 69-70; sr microbiologist, New York City Dept Air Resources, 70-74; environ scientist, 74-80, SR ENVIRON SCIENTIST, GIBBS & HILL, INC, 80- *Concurrent Pos:* Res scientist, Murry & Leonie Guggenheim Inst Dent Res, NY Univ, 71- *Mem:* AAAS. *Res:* Influence of physical environment on man; aeromicrobiology; bioclimatology; microclimatology; synoptic meteorology; magnetobiology; environmental/occupational health. *Mailing Add:* 19 Michael Rd Syosset NY 11791

PEREIRA, MICHAEL ALAN, b New York, NY, May 3, 44; m 67; c 2. BIOCHEMICAL PHARMACOLOGY. *Educ:* Ohio State Univ, BA, 67, PhD(pharmacol), 71. *Prof Exp:* Damon Runyon Mem Fund Cancer Res fel cellular physiol, Nat Heart & Lung Inst, 71-73; res assoc, Gtr New York Blood Ctr, 73-74; res scientist, Dept Environ Med, Med Ctr, NY Univ, 74-78; PHARMACOLOGIST, HEALTH EFFECTS RES LAB, US ENVIRON PROTECTION AGENCY, 78- *Res:* Mechanism of action of coumarin anticoagulants and vitamin K in affecting prothrombin biosynthesis; DNA replication in Escherichia coli; chemical carcinogenesis and mutagenesis; tumor promotion and co-carcinogenesis. *Mailing Add:* 12165 Brookston Dr Cincinnati OH 46240

PEREL, JAMES MAURICE, b Arg, Mar 30, 33; US citizen. CLINICAL PHARMACOLOGY, PSYCHOPHARMACOLOGY. *Educ:* City Col New York, BS, 56; NY Univ, MS, 61, PhD(chem), 64. *Prof Exp:* Assoc res scientist, Dept Med, Med Sch, NY Univ, 63-67; asst prof med, Emory Univ Sch Med, 67-70; assoc res scientist, NY State Psychiat Inst, 70-80; asst prof psychiat, Col Physicians & Surgeons, Columbia Univ, 70-76, assoc prof clin pharmacol, 76-80; PROF PSYCHIAT & PHARMACOL, SCH MED & DIR CLIN PHARMACOL, WESTERN PSYCHIAT INST, UNIV PITTSBURGH, 80- *Concurrent Pos:* Fel pharmacol, NY Univ, 62-64; lectr chem, City Univ New York, 63-67; asst prof chem, Sch Arts & Sci, Emory Univ, 67-70, vis assoc prof med, Sch Med, 70-; USPHS grants psychopharmacol, Col Physicians & Surgeons, Columbia Univ & NY State Psychiat Inst, 70-80; consult, Food & Drug Admin & NIMH. *Mem:* Am Soc Pharmacol & Exp Therapeut; NY Acad Sci; Soc Biol Psychiat; Am Fedn Clin Res; fel Am Inst Chemists. *Res:* Clinical pharmacology of psychoactive agents; drug metabolism; enzymatic mechanisms of drug action; molecular pharmacology of anesthetic agents. *Mailing Add:* Western Psychiat Inst Univ Pittsburgh 3811 O'Hara St Pittsburgh PA 15241

PEREL, JULIUS, b New York, NY, Sept 10, 27; m 50; c 4. ATOMIC PHYSICS. *Educ:* City Col New York, BS, 51; NY Univ, MS, 52, PhD(physics), 62. *Prof Exp:* Physicist, Anton Electronic Lab, NY, 52 & Electronic Prod Co, NY, 52-54; grad asst & instr physics, NY Univ, 55-62; sr physicist, ElectroOptical Systs, Xerox Corp, 62-65, mgr particle physics dept, 65-74; PARTNER/SCIENTIST, PHRASOR SCI, INC, 74- *Concurrent Pos:* Lectr, City Col New York, 54-60. *Mem:* Am Phys Soc; Am Inst Aeronaut & Astronaut. *Res:* Atomic collisions-charge transfer; ionic and molecular beams; surface ionization; electric propulsion-colloid propulsion; electrohydrodynamics; spectroscopy; application of EHD to metallurgy and energy; fast atom beams. *Mailing Add:* Phrasor Sci Inc 1536 Highland Ave Duarte CA 91010

PEREL, WILLIAM MORRIS, b Chicago, Ill, Oct 17, 27. MATHEMATICS. *Educ:* Ind Univ, AB, 49, AM, 50, PhD, 55. *Prof Exp:* Assoc math, Ind Univ, 49-54; asst prof, Ga Inst Technol, 54-56 & Tex Tech Col, 56-59; assoc prof, La State Univ, New Orleans, 59-62; vis prof, Randolph-Macon Woman's Col, 62-63; prof, Univ NC, Chatlotte, 63-66; PROF MATH, WICHITA STATE UNIV, 66-, CHMN DEPT, 67- *Mem:* Am Math Soc; Math Asn Am; Sigma Xi; Edinburgh Math Soc. *Res:* Semigroup and ring ideal theory; number theory; urban society and education. *Mailing Add:* 4400 E 25th St N Wichita KS 67208

PERELSON, ALAN STUART, b Brooklyn, NY, Apr 11, 47; m 68; c 1. BIOPHYSICS, IMMUNOLOGY. *Educ:* Mass Inst Technol, BS(life sci) & BS(elec eng), 67; Univ Calif, Berkeley, PhD(biophys), 72. *Prof Exp:* Actg asst prof med physics, Univ Calif, Berkeley, 73; NIH fel & res assoc chem eng, Univ Minn, 73-74; staff mem theoret biol & biophys, Los Alamos Sci Lab, Univ Calif, 74-78; asst prof med sci, Brown Univ, 78-80; MEM STAFF, LOS ALAMOS NAT LAB, 80- *Concurrent Pos:* Adv ed, J Math Biol, 78-, assoc ed, Bull Math Biol, 78- & book review ed, Math Biosci, 82-; career res develop award, NIH, 79-84. *Mem:* Inst Elec & Electronics Engrs; Am Asn Immunologists; Soc Indust & Appl Math; Soc Gen Physiologists; Soc Math Biol. *Res:* Application of mathematics to chemical and biophysical problems, with particular emphasis on problems in immunology. *Mailing Add:* Theoret Div Los Alamos Nat Lab Los Alamos NM 87545

PERESS, NANCY E, b New York, NY, Feb 2, 43; m 64; c 2. NEUROPATHOLOGY. *Educ:* Hunter Col, MA, 63; State Univ NY, MD, 67. *Prof Exp:* From intern to resident path, Kings County Hosp, New York, 67-69, neuropath, 69-71; asst prof & attend physician path, State Univ NY Downstate Med Ctr & Kings County Hosp, 71-73; asst prof path, 73-80, ASSOC PROF PATH, STATE UNIV NY STONY BROOK & NORTHPORT VET HOSP, 80-, CHIEF NEUROPATH, 73- *Concurrent Pos:* Consult neuropathologist, Nassau County Med Ctr, 74- *Mem:* Am Asn Neuropathologists. *Res:* Pathophysiology of immune disease of the choroid plexus and ciliary body; neuropathology of experimental fetal hypoxia and acidosis. *Mailing Add:* Dept of Path S Campus State Univ of NY Stony Brook NY 11790

PERESSINI, ANTHONY L, b Great Falls, Mont, May 30, 34; m 55; c 5. ANALYTICAL MATHEMATICS. *Educ:* Col Great Falls, BS, 56; Wash State Univ, MA, 58, PhD(math), 61. *Prof Exp:* From instr to assoc prof math, 61-73, PROF MATH, UNIV ILL, URBANA, 73- *Mem:* Am Math Soc. *Res:* Functional analysis; ordered topological vector spaces. *Mailing Add:* Dept Math 273 Allgeld Hall Univ Ill Urbana IL 61803

PERETTI, ETTORE A(LEX), b Butte, Mont, Apr 5, 13; m 37; c 2. METALLURGY. *Educ:* Mont Col Mineral Sci & Technol, BS, 34, MS, 35; Germany, DSc(metall eng), 36. *Hon Degrees:* MetE, Univ Mont, 63. *Prof Exp:* From Instr to asst prof metall eng, Mont Col Mineral Sci & Technol, 36-40; asst prof, Sch Mines, Univ Columbia, 40-46; assoc prof, 46-49, head dept metall eng, 51-69, prof metall eng, 49-78, asst dean col eng, 70-78, EMER PROF, UNIV NOTRE DAME, 78-, ASST DIR NAT CONSORT GRAD DEGREES, MINORITIES ENG, 78- *Concurrent Pos:* Consult, 40-46, 59- *Mem:* Fel Am Soc Metals; Am Soc Testing & Mat; Am Inst Mining, Metall & Petrol Engrs; Brit Inst Metals. *Res:* Metallurgical extractive processes and phase relationships. *Mailing Add:* Box 537 Univ of Notre Dame Notre Dame IN 46556

PERETTIE, DONALD JOSEPH, physical organic chemistry, see previous edition

PEREY, BERNARD JEAN FRANCOIS, b Paris, France, Apr 28, 30; Can citizen; m 57; c 3. SURGERY. *Educ:* Univ Paris, PCB, 49; McGill Univ, MD, CM, 56, MSc, 60, Dipl Surg, 62. *Prof Exp:* Asst prof surg, McGill Univ, 64-67; dir clin sci, 68-70, PROF SURG & CHMN DEPT, UNIV SHERBROOKE, 67-, SURGEON-IN-CHIEF, HOSP, 67-, V DEAN, 73- *Concurrent Pos:* Surgeon, Royal Victoria Hosp, Montreal, 62-67; vpres, Royal Col Physicians & Surgeons Can, 74-76. *Mem:* Am Col Surgeons; Soc Surg Alimentary Tract; Can Asn Gastroenterol (pres); Can Asn Clin Surgeons (pres); Am Surg Asn. *Res:* Gastrointestinal physiology; vascular physiology; wound healing. *Mailing Add:* Univ Hosp Ctr Room 8501 Sherbrooke PQ J1H 5N4 Can

PEREY, FRANCIS GEORGE, b Paris, France, Oct 7, 32; US citizen; c 2. NUCLEAR PHYSICS, PROBABILITY THEORY. *Educ:* McGill Univ, BSc, 56, MSc, 57; Univ Montreal, PhD(physics), 60. *Prof Exp:* PHYSICIST NUCLEAR PHYSICS, OAK RIDGE NAT LAB, 60- *Concurrent Pos:* Mem nuclear data comt, Dept Energy, 70-; US rep nuclear data comt, Nuclear Europ Agency, 78-; corp res fel, Union Carbide Corp, 79. *Mem:* Fel Am Phys Soc. *Res:* Neutron physics. *Mailing Add:* Oak Ridge Nat Lab Oak Ridge TN 37830

PEREYRA, WALTER T, fisheries, ecology, see previous edition

PEREZ, AGRIPINO, agriculture, biology, see previous edition

PEREZ, CARLOS A, b Colombia, Nov 10, 34; US citizen; m 61; c 3. RADIOTHERAPY. *Educ:* Univ Antioquia, Colombia, BS, 52, MD, 60. *Prof Exp:* From instr to assoc prof, 64-72, PROF RADIOL, MALLINCKRODT INST RADIOL, SCH MED, WASH UNIV, 72- *Concurrent Pos:* Fel radiother, M D Anderson Hosp, Houston, 63-64; consult, Vet Admin Hosp, St Louis, 67-, Ellis Fischel State Hosp, Columbia, 67-, Jewish Hosp, St Louis, 70- *Mem:* AAAS; Asn Univ Radiol; Radiol Soc NAm; Am Soc Therapeut Radiol; Am Radium Soc. *Res:* Radiation therapy in combination with surgery or chemotherapy or both in the management of cancer; immunological aspects of malignant tumors and relationship to therapy. *Mailing Add:* Mallinckrodt Inst of Radiol 510 S Kingshighway St Louis MO 63110

PEREZ, JOHN CARLOS, b Park City, Utah, Apr 29, 41; m 73; c 5. VIROLOGY. *Educ:* Univ Utah, BS, 67; Mankato State Col, MA, 69; Utah State Univ, PhD(virol), 73. *Prof Exp:* Res assoc virol, Utah State Univ, 71-72; asst prof, 72-77, ASSOC PROF BIOL, TEX A&I UNIV, 77- *Concurrent Pos:* Am Soc Microbiol Pres fel, 71. *Mem:* Am Soc Microbiol; Sigma Xi. *Res:* Development of a radioimmunoassay for viral antigens. *Mailing Add:* Dept Biol Tex A&I Univ Kingsville TX 78363

PEREZ, JOSEPH DOMINIQUE, b New Orleans, La, Oct 17, 42; m 72; c 2. THEORETICAL PHYSICS. *Educ:* Loyola Univ, La, BS, 64; Univ Md, College Park, PhD(nuclear physics), 68. *Prof Exp:* Res asst physicist, Inst Pure & Appl Phys Sci, Univ Calif, San Diego, 69-71; asst prof physics, Univ Southern Calif, 71-74; RES SCIENTIST, LOCKHEED PALO ALTO RES LAB, 74- *Mem:* Am Phys Soc. *Res:* Many-body theory as applied to nuclear structure, shell model and nuclear and atomic scattering; laser plasmas and laser induced fusion. *Mailing Add:* Orgn 52-11 Bldg 203 Lockheed Palo Alto Res Lab Palo Alto CA 94304

PEREZ-ALBUERNE, EVELIO A, b Ranchuelo, Cuba, July 22, 39; US citizen; m 61; c 3. PHYSICAL CHEMISTRY. *Educ:* Villanova Univ, BChE, 61; Univ Ill, Urbana, MS, 63, PhD(chem eng), 65. *Prof Exp:* Sr res chemist, 65-69, res assoc, 69-79, sr res assoc, 79-80, SR LAB HEAD, RES LABS, EASTMAN KODAK CO, 80- *Mem:* Am Phys Soc; AAAS; Inst Elec & Electronics Engrs. *Res:* Organic semiconductors; solid state physics; solid state chemistry; energy conversion; catalysis. *Mailing Add:* Res Labs Eastman Kodak Co 1669 Laek Ave Rochester NY 14650

PEREZ-FARFANTE, ISABEL CRISTINA, b Havana, Cuba, July 24, 16; US citizen; m 41; c 2. ZOOLOGY. *Educ:* Univ Havana, BS, 38; Radcliffe Col, MS, 44, PhD(biol), 48. *Prof Exp:* Prof invert zool, Univ Havana, 48-60; biologist, Ctr Fisheries Res, 52-55, dir, 59-60; SYST ZOOLOGIST, SYSTS LAB, NAT MARINE FISHERIES SERV, 66- *Concurrent Pos:* Fel, John Simon Guggenheim Mem Found, 42-44; Alexander Agassiz fel oceanog & zool, 44-45; scholar, Radcliffe Inst Independent Study, 63-65; fel, Am Inst Fishery, Res Inst, 77- *Mem:* AAAS; Soc Syst Zool; Crustacean Soc. *Res:* Systematics, morphology and distribution of decapod Crustacea, with special reference to western Atlantic and eastern Pacific regions. *Mailing Add:* Systs Lab Nat Marine Fisheries Sv Nat Mus of Natural Hist Washington DC 20560

PEREZ-MENDEZ, VICTOR, b Guatemala, Aug 8, 23; nat US; m 49; c 2. EXPERIMENTAL HEAVY ION PHYSICS. *Educ:* Hebrew Univ, Israel, MS, 47; Columbia Univ, PhD, 51. *Prof Exp:* Res assoc, Columbia Univ, 51-53; staff physicist, 53-61, SR SCIENTIST, LAWRENCE BERKELEY LAB, UNIV CALIF, 60- *Concurrent Pos:* Vis lectr, Hebrew Univ, 59-60; prof physics, Dept Radiol, Univ Calif, San Francisco, 68- *Mem:* Fel Am Phys Soc; fel NY Acad Sci; sr mem Inst Elec & Electronics Engrs. *Res:* Physics of heavy ions, instrumentation and medical applications. *Mailing Add:* Lawrence Berkeley Lab Univ of Calif Berkeley CA 94720

PEREZ-TAMAYO, RUHERI, b Tampico, Mex, Dec 2, 26; US citizen; m 63; c 5. RADIOTHERAPY. *Educ:* Nat Univ Mex, BS, 45, MD, 52. *Prof Exp:* Rotating intern, Huron Rd Hosp, Cleveland, Ohio, 52-53, resident radiol, 53-55; resident radiother, Penrose Cancer Hosp, Colorado Springs, Colo, 55-56; instr radiother & radiotherapist, Univ Mich Hosp, 56-57; chief of dept radiother, French Hosp, Mexico City, Mex, 57-61; asst prof radiol & head dept radiother, Med Ctr, Univ Colo, 61-63; assoc radiother, Jefferson Med Col Hosp, 63-64; assoc radiother, Penrose Cancer Hosp, 64-66; chief dept radiother, Ellis Fishchel State Cancer Hosp, Columbia, Mo, 66-70; PROF RADIOL & DIR RADIATION THER, LOYOLA UNIV HOSP, 70- *Concurrent Pos:* Cordell Hull fel, 56-57; fel, Armed Forces Inst Path, 57; grants, AEC Mex, 58, USPHS, 61, 62, 65, 66 & 67-70, Milheim Found Cancer Res, 62-63, 65 & 67, Bent Co Cancer Fund, Fluid Res Fund Comt & Am Cancer Soc, 62 & Alpha Phi Omega & Jefferson Med Col, 63; prof, Nat Univ Mex, 58-61; assoc prof, Jefferson Med Col, 63-64; prof, Sch Med, Univ Mo-Columbia, 66-70; consult, Sch Med, Washington Univ, 68-; dir radiation ther, St Joseph's Hosp, 70-71; Gen Res Support grant, Loyola Univ Hosp, Ill, 70-71, 72; consult, Vet Admin Hosp, Hines, Ill, 72-; comt mem cancer educ prog, Nat Cancer Inst, NIH. *Mem:* Am Soc Therapeut Radiol; Radiol Soc NAm; fel Am Col Radiol; Am Asn Cancer Educ; Am Asn Cancer Res. *Res:* Time-dose relationships; mathematical models in radiation therapy; radiation therapy oncology group clinical studies. *Mailing Add:* Loyola Univ Hosp Maywood IL 60153

PERFETTI, RANDOLPH B, b Greensburg, Pa, Sept 11, 49; m 71. ORGANIC CHEMISTRY, BIOCHEMISTRY. *Educ:* Ind Univ Pa, BS, 71; Va Polytech Inst & State Univ, PhD(chem), 75. *Prof Exp:* Fel organic chem, Johns Hopkins Univ, 75-76; CHEMIST PESTICIDES, US ENVIRON PROTECTION AGENCY, 76- *Concurrent Pos:* NSF grant, 71-75. *Mem:* Am Chem Soc; Sigma Xi. *Res:* Mechanisms of enzyme catalyzed reactions; elucidation of via chemical modification and kinetics; synthetic organic chemistry; development of new synthetic techniques; redox reactions. *Mailing Add:* US Environ Protection Agency TS-769 401 M St NW Washington DC 20460

PERFETTI, THOMAS ALBERT, b Jeannette, Pa, Mar 22, 52; m 75. ORGANIC CHEMISTRY, ANALYTICAL CHEMISTRY. *Educ:* Ind Univ Pa, BS, 74; Va Polytech Inst & State Univ, PhD(org chem), 78. *Prof Exp:* Teaching asst org chem, Va Polytech Inst & State Univ, 74-77; RES CHEMIST TOBACCO CHEM, R J REYNOLDS TOBACCO CO, 77- *Concurrent Pos:* Res fel, NASA, Langley, 75, 76. *Mem:* Sigma Xi; Am Chem Soc (treas, 80-81); AAAS; NY Acad Sci. *Res:* Organic synthesis of polyaromatic hydrocarbons; electronic effects associated with sigmatropic rearrangements; structure elucidations; pyrolytic glass capillary chromatography, tobacco chemistry. *Mailing Add:* R J Reynolds Tobacco Co Res Ctr Winston-Salem NC 27102

PERHAC, RALPH MATTHEW, b Brooklyn, NY, July 29, 28; m 50; c 2. GEOCHEMISTRY. *Educ:* Columbia Univ, AB, 49; Cornell Univ, AM, 52; Univ Mich, Ann Arbor, PhD(geol), 61. *Prof Exp:* Mining engr, Anaconda Co, 52-53; dist geologist, AEC, 53-55; explor geologist, Caltex Oil, Australia, 55-57; sr res scientist, Humble Oil & Refining Co, 60-67; from assoc prof to prof geochem, Univ Tenn, Knoxville, 67-74; prog mgr, NSF, Washington, DC, 74-76; prog mgr, 76-80, DEPT DIR, ELEC POWER RES INST, 80- *Concurrent Pos:* Consult, Oak Ridge Nat Lab, 72-75. *Mem:* Mex Geol Soc; Geol Soc Am; Geochem Soc; Am Asn Petrol Geologists; Int Asn Geochem & Cosmochem. *Res:* Hydrogeochemistry; geochemical prospecting; lunar soils; environmental chemistry. *Mailing Add:* Elec Power Res Inst Box 10412 Palo Alto CA 94303

PERHACH, JAMES LAWRENCE, JR, b Pittsburgh, Pa, Oct 26, 43; m 67; c 2. PHARMACOLOGY, MEDICAL SCIENCES. *Educ:* Univ Dayton, BS, 66; Univ Pittsburgh, MS, 69, PhD(pharmacol), 71. *Prof Exp:* Sr scientist, Mead Johnson Pharmaceut Div, Mead Johnson & Co, Bristol Myers Corp, 71-74, sr investr, 74-76, sr res assoc, 76-78, prin res assoc, 78-80; dir pharmacol, 80, EXEC DIR BIOL RES, WALLACE LABS DIV, CARTER-WALLACE, INC, 80- *Concurrent Pos:* Assoc fac mem & consult, Addiction Med Educ Prog, Evansville Ctr, Sch Med, Ind Univ, 72-80; lectr, Grad Sch Nursing, Univ Evansville, 72-80, instr, Col Arts & Sci, 75-77; adj prof toxicol, Philadelphia Col Pharm & Sci, 81- *Mem:* Sigma Xi; Soc Neurosci; AAAS; Am Soc Pharmacol & Exp Therapeut; Am Heart Asn. *Res:* Investigating the alterations in the cardiovascular, autonomic and central nervous systems induced by environmental factors, and the role of these changes in the etiology of hypertension. *Mailing Add:* Wallace Labs Div Carter-Wallace Inc Cranbury NJ 08512

PERI, BARBARA ANNE, b Richmond, Calif, May 15, 25; m 46; c 3. IMMUNOLOGY. *Educ:* Univ Calif, Berkeley, BA, 46; Univ Wis-Madison, MS, 48; Univ Notre Dame, PhD(microbiol), 70. *Prof Exp:* Lab asst bact, Hooper Res Found, Univ Calif, Berkeley, 46; from asst prof to assoc prof biol, Valparaiso Univ, 64-74; res assoc, Pritzker Sch Med, Dept Pediat, LaRabida Res Inst, Univ Chicago, 74-79; RES ASSOC & ASST PROF, DEPT PEDIAT, WYLER CHILDREN'S HOSP, 79- *Mem:* Am Asn Dent Res; Am Soc Microbiol; Am Asn Immunologists; Sigma Xi. *Res:* Secretory antibody; immune response to environmental antigens; diphtheria toxin; maternal regulation of immune response. *Mailing Add:* 221 Ravine Rd Hinsdale IL 60521

PERI, JOHN BAYARD, b Stockton, Calif, May 5, 23; m 46; c 3. PHYSICAL CHEMISTRY. *Educ:* Univ Calif, BS, 43; Univ Wis, PhD(chem), 49. *Prof Exp:* Res asst, Univ Wis, 47-49; res chemist, Calif Res Corp, 49-57; proj chemist, 57-58, sr proj chemist, 58-60, sr res scientist, 60-62, res assoc, 62-79, SR RES ASSOC, AM OIL CO-STANDARDS OIL CO IND, 79- *Mem:* AAAS; Am Chem Soc; Catalysis Soc. *Res:* Catalysis; surface and colloid chemistry; chemical kinetics. *Mailing Add:* 221 Ravine Rd Hinsdale IL 60521

PERILLIE, PASQUALE E, b Bridgeport, Conn, Sept 2, 26; m 52; c 5. MEDICINE. *Educ:* Univ Conn, BA, 51; NY Med Col, MD, 55. *Prof Exp:* USPHS res fel, 59-61; instr, 62-64, asst prof, 64-77, CLIN PROF MED, SCH MED, YALE UNIV, 77- *Concurrent Pos:* Vet Admin clin investr, 62-65; USPHS career res award, 65-; chmn dept med, Bridgeport Hosp, 69- *Mem:* Am Fedn Clin Res; Am Soc Hemat; NY Acad Sci; Sigma Xi; Int Soc Hemat. *Res:* Resistance to infection in leukemia; abnormal hemoglobins; histochemistry of blood cells. *Mailing Add:* Bridgeport Hosp 267 Grant St Bridgeport CT 06602

PERIMAN, PHILLIP, b Memphis, Tex, Dec 5, 38; m 65; c 3. INTERNAL MEDICINE, IMMUNOLOGY. *Educ:* Yale Univ, BA, 61; Wash Univ, MD, 65. *Prof Exp:* From intern to asst resident internal med, Sch Med, NY Univ, 65-67; res assoc, Nat Cancer Inst, 67-69, sr staff fel, Lab Path, 71; asst prof med, Sch Med, George Washington Univ, 71-76; assoc prof & assoc chmn med, Sch Med, Tex Tech Univ, 76-81; MED DIR, DON & SYBIL HARRINGTON CANCER CTR, 81- *Concurrent Pos:* USPHS fel, Sir William Dunn Sch Path, Oxford Univ, 70. *Res:* Tumor immunology; cell biology; delayed hypersensitivity; hematology; oncology; cell differentiation; virus carcinogenesis. *Mailing Add:* Harrington Cancer Ctr 1500 Wallace Blvd Amarillo TX 79106

PERINI, JOSE, b Sao Paulo, Brazil, Mar 1, 28; m 55; c 6. ELECTRICAL ENGINEERING. *Educ:* Polytech Sch, Sao Paulo, BS, 52; Syracuse Univ, PhD(elec eng), 61. *Prof Exp:* Mgr radio maintenance, Real Trasportes Aereos, Brazil, 51-54; asst prof elec eng, Polytech Sch, Sao Paulo, 54-58, assoc prof, 61-62; from asst prof to assoc prof, 62-71, PROF ELEC ENG, SYRACUSE UNIV, 71- *Concurrent Pos:* Consult, Gen Elec Co, Syracuse & Sao Paulo, Brazil, 59- *Mem:* Inst Elec & Electronics Engrs; Brazilian Inst Eng. *Res:* Antennas; transmission lines; radio navigation and communication systems; digital signal processing; computers. *Mailing Add:* Dept of Elec & Comput Eng Syracuse Univ Syracuse NY 13210

PERINO, JANICE VINYARD, b Oklahoma City, Okla, Sept 3, 46; m 68. PLANT ECOLOGY, APPLIED ECOLOGY. *Educ:* Univ Okla, BS, 68; MS, 71; NC State Univ, PhD(bot), 75. *Prof Exp:* Teacher pub schs, Okla, 68-69; ecol res technician bot, NC State Univ, 71-73; asst prof bot, Miami Univ, Ohio, 75-79; STAFF ECOLOGIST, RADIAN CORP, 79- *Mem:* Ecol Soc Am; AAAS; Torrey Bot Club; Sigma Xi. *Res:* Descriptive and applied plant ecology; strategies controlling plant distribution, including reproductive mechanical anisms, resource allocation, and plant-plant interactions; old-field succession and the tall grass prairies; forests, marshes and wetland studies. *Mailing Add:* Environ Analysis Dept Radian Corp Austin TX 78745

PERISHO, CLARENCE H(OWARD), b Granite City, Ill, Dec 23, 24; m 46; c 3. APPLIED MATHEMATICS, AERODYNAMICS. *Educ:* Purdue Univ, BS, 47; St Louis Univ, MS, 58. *Prof Exp:* Res engr, McDonnell Aircraft Corp, St Louis, 47-51, proj dynamics engr, 51-59, chief dynamics engr, 59-61, sect mgr struct dynamics, 61-64, chief struct dynamics engr, Eng Technol Div, 64-71, mgr, 71-81, CHIEF TECHNOL ENGR, STRUCT DYNAMICS, ENG TECH DIV, MCDONNELL AIRCRAFT CO, ST LOUIS, 81- *Mem:* Assoc fel Am Inst Aeronaut & Astronaut. *Res:* Influence of dynamic response, flutter, vibration and acoustics on the design, reliability and performance of aircraft; vertical takeoff vehicles. *Mailing Add:* 270 Greentails Dr Chesterfield MO 63017

PERISHO, CLARENCE R, b Newberg, Ore, Apr 29, 17; m 41; c 3. BIOCHEMISTRY. *Educ:* William Penn Col, BS, 38; Haverford Col, MA, 39; NY Univ, PhD(sci educ), 63. *Prof Exp:* Instr math & sci, Friendsville Acad, 39-40; prof phys sci, Nebr Cent Col, 40-44; instr physics, chem & math, McCook Jr Col, 44-47; from asst prof to assoc prof chem & math, Nebr Wesleyan Univ, 47-54; from instr to asst prof sci, Mankato State Univ, 54-63, assoc prof chem, 63-66, prof, 66-82; RETIRED. *Concurrent Pos:* Acad Year Exten Res Partic Col Teachers, Mankato State Col, 64-66. *Mem:* AAAS; Math Asn Eng; Nat Educ Asn. *Mailing Add:* 804 Belgrade Ave North Mankato MN 56001

PERKEL, DONALD HOWARD, b Jersey City, NJ, Apr 18, 30; m 61; c 2. THEORETICAL BIOLOGY, NEUROSCIENCES. *Educ:* Univ Calif, Berkeley, AB, 53; Stanford Univ, PhD(neurosci), 77. *Prof Exp:* Chemist, Western Div, Tracerlab, Inc, 53-55, physicist, 55-56; mathematician, Aerojet-Gen Nucleonics Div, Gen Tire & Rubber Co, 57-58; physicist, Advan Res Div, Aerojet-Gen Corp Div, 61-63 & Gen Atomic Div, Gen Dynamics Corp, 58-61; resident consult biomath, Rand Corp, 63-65, mathematician, 66-70; sr res assoc biol sci, 70-74, ADJ PROF BIOL SCI, STANFORD UNIV, 74- *Concurrent Pos:* Res assoc med, Sch Med, Univ Southern Calif, 66-70; consult mem, Brain Res Inst, Univ Calif, Los Angeles, 66-70; mem neurol A study sect, NIH, 71-75. *Mem:* AAAS; Biophys Soc; Soc Neurosci; NY Acad Sci. *Res:* Theoretical neurobiology; cable theory; dynamics of synaptic function; functional reconstruction of neuronal circuits; pattern generation in neural systems; statistical analysis of neuroelectric signals; neuronal control of thermoregulation. *Mailing Add:* Dept of Biol Sci Stanford Univ Stanford CA 94305

PERKEL, ROBERT JULES, b New York, NY, Feb 23, 26; m 50; c 3. POLYMER CHEMISTRY, ORGANIC CHEMISTRY. *Educ:* City Col New York, BS, 48; Polytech Inst Brooklyn, MS, PhD(polymer chem), 59. *Prof Exp:* Chemist, Lehman Bros Corp, NJ, 48-56; PRES, JEMA-AM, INC, DUNELLEN, 56- *Mem:* NY Acad Sci; fel Am Inst Chemists; Am Chem Soc; Soc Vacuum Coaters (past pres). *Res:* Organic finishes and inorganic solutions related to electroless spray deposition of metals and vacuum deposition of metals on a variety of substrates. *Mailing Add:* 19 Lamington Rd Somerville NJ 08876

PERKEY, DONALD JOSEPH, meteorology, see previous edition

PERKINS, A THOMAS, b Youngstown, Ohio, Dec 20, 42; m 62; c 3. AGRONOMY. *Educ:* Pa State Univ, BS, 64, PhD(agron), 69. *Prof Exp:* From instr to asst prof agron, Pa State Univ, 66-70; sr plant physiologist, 70-75, MGR SPECIALTY PROD RES, ELI LILLY & CO, 75- *Mem:* Am Soc Agron. *Res:* Research and development of pesticides for uses on turfgrass ornamental species and general noncropland usage; general turfgrass management. *Mailing Add:* Box 708 Greenfield Labs Eli Lilly & Co Greenfield IN 46140

PERKINS, BEN HARRISON, chemistry, deceased

PERKINS, BOBBY FRANK, b Greenville, Tex, Dec 9, 29; m 54; c 3. INVERTEBRATE PALEONTOLOGY. *Educ:* Southern Methodist Univ, BS, 49, MS, 50; Univ Mich, PhD(geol), 56. *Prof Exp:* Instr geol, Southern Methodist Univ, 50-51 & 53-55; asst prof, Univ Houston, 55-56; res paleontologist, Shell Develop Co, 56-66; prof geol, La State Univ, Baton Rouge, 66-75, dir mus geosci, 69-75, chmn dept geol & dir sch geosci, 73-75; PROF GEOL & DEAN GRAD SCH, UNIV TEX, ARLINGTON, 75- *Mem:* Geol Soc Am; Paleont Soc; Soc Econ Paleontologists & Mineralogists; Am Asn Petrol Geologists; Brit Paleont Soc. *Res:* Cretaceous invertebrate paleontology, biostratigraphy and paleoecology; Cretaceous corals and rudistid pelecypods; Cretaceous stratigraphy in Texas and northern Mexico; trace fossils; reef organisms, sediments, and petrography. *Mailing Add:* Grad Sch Univ of Tex Arlington TX 76019

PERKINS, COURTLAND D(AVIS), b Philadelphia, Pa, Dec 27, 12; m 41; c 2. AERONAUTICAL ENGINEERING. *Educ:* Swarthmore Col, BS, 35; Mass Inst Technol, MS, 41. *Prof Exp:* Prof aeronaut eng, Princeton Univ, 45-75, chmn dept, 51-75, assoc dean sch eng, 65-71; PRES, NAT ACAD ENG, 75- *Concurrent Pos:* Chief scientist, US Air Force, 56-57, asst, Sect Res & Develop, 60-61, mem, Sci Adv Bd, 46-, vchmn, 61-68, chmn 68-; chmn adv group aerospace res & develop, NATO, 63-67, US nat deleg, 63-69; mem space sci bd, Nat Acad Sci, 65-70; mem space prog adv coun, NASA, 71-, chmn space systs command, 71- *Mem:* Nat Acad Eng; fel Am Inst Aeronaut & Astronaut (pres, 64); fel Royal Aeronaut Soc. *Res:* Airplane stability and control; airplane dynamics. *Mailing Add:* Nat Acad of Eng 2101 Constitution Ave NW Washington DC 20418

PERKINS, DAVID DEXTER, b Watertown, NY, May 2, 19; m 52. GENETICS, CYTOLOGY. *Educ:* Univ Rochester, AB, 41; Columbia Univ, PhD(zool), 49. *Prof Exp:* Mem fac biol, 48-61, PROF BIOL, STANFORD UNIV, 61- *Concurrent Pos:* Res fels, Univ Glasgow, 54-55, Columbia Univ, 61-62 & Australian Nat Univ, 68-69; mem genetics training comt, NIH, 61-65; ed, Genetics, 63-67; USPHS res career award, 64-; exec bd, Int Genetics Fedn, 78-83. *Mem:* Nat Acad Sci; Genetics Soc Am (pres, 77). *Res:* Genetics. *Mailing Add:* Dept Biol Sci Stanford Univ Stanford CA 94305

PERKINS, DONALD YOUNG, b Ponchatoula, La, June 27, 23; m 56; c 4. HORTICULTURE. *Educ:* La State Univ, BS, 50, MS, 51; Cornell Univ, PhD(veg crops), 54. *Prof Exp:* Instr & jr olericulturist, Univ Calif, 54; assoc horticulturist, La State Univ, 54-57; prin horticulturist, Coop State Res Serv, USDA, 57-66; HEAD DEPT HORT, AUBURN UNIV, 66- *Mem:* AAAS; Am Soc Hort Sci; Am Genetic Asn; Am Inst Biol Sci. *Res:* Vegetable breeding; mineral nutrition of vegetable crops; chemical weed control; horticultural research administration. *Mailing Add:* Dept of Hort Auburn Univ Auburn AL 36830

PERKINS, EDWARD GEORGE, b Canton, Ill, Nov 1, 34; m 57; c 4. ORGANIC CHEMISTRY. *Educ:* Univ Ill, BS, 56, MS & PhD(food chem), 58. *Prof Exp:* Res chemist, Res Div, Armour & Co, 58-62; PROF FOOD SCI, BURNSIDES RES LAB, UNIV ILL, URBANA, 62- *Mem:* AAAS; Am Chem Soc; Am Oil Chemists Soc; Am Inst Nutrit. *Res:* Organic and biochemistry of lipids; lipid methodology; mass spectrometry; organic synthesis. *Mailing Add:* Burnsides Res Lab Dept Food Sci Univ Ill Urbana IL 61801

PERKINS, EDWARD H(OWARD), JR, b Flint, Mich, May 2, 27; m 55; c 2. METALLURGY. *Educ:* Univ Mich, AB, 48, BSE, 50. *Prof Exp:* Div mgr, 53-58, vpres mfg, 58-59, vpres & gen mgr, 59-61, pres, 61-81, CHMN, BROOKS & PERKINS, INC, 81- *Mem:* Am Soc Metals; Am Ord Asn. *Res:* Design, development and manufacture of air cargo equipment; industrial materials handling equipment; aerospace components. *Mailing Add:* Brooks & Perkins Inc 17515 W Nine Mile Rd Suite 750 Southfield MI 48075

PERKINS, EUGENE HAFEN, b St George, Utah, Feb 28, 26; m 48; c 10. IMMUNOLOGY. *Educ:* Brigham Young Univ, BA, 51; Univ Utah, PhD(bact), 58. *Prof Exp:* Res assoc bact, Col Med, Univ Utah, 57-58; BIOLOGIST, OAK RIDGE NAT LAB, 58- *Mem:* AAAS; Radiation Res Soc; Soc Exp Biol & Med; Geront Soc; Am Asn Immunologists. *Res:* Phagocytosis and host defense mechanisms; cellular immunology; senesence of immune response; cellular and kinetic aspects of antibody formation. *Mailing Add:* Oak Ridge Nat Lab PO Box Y Oak Ridge TN 37830

PERKINS, FRANK OVERTON, b Fork Union, Va, Feb 14, 38; m 61. MARINE BIOLOGY. *Educ:* Univ Va, BA, 60; Fla State Univ, MS, 62, PhD(exp biol), 66. *Prof Exp:* Assoc marine scientist, 66-69, sr marine scientist & head dept microbiol & path, 69-77, head, Div Biol Oceanog & asst dir, 77-81, ACTG DIR, VA INST MARINE SCI, 81- *Mem:* Soc Invertebrate Path; Soc Protozoologists; Mycol Soc Am. *Res:* Marine invertebrate pathology; ultrastructure taxonomy and ecology of estuarine Protozoa and microalgae. *Mailing Add:* Va Inst of Marine Sci Gloucester Point VA 23062

PERKINS, HAROLD JACKSON, b London, Ont, July 6, 30; m 54; c 4. BIOCHEMISTRY. *Educ:* Univ BC, BA, 51, MSc, 53; Iowa State Col, PhD(plant biochem), 57. *Prof Exp:* Fel plant physiol, Div Appl Biol, Nat Res Coun Can, 57-58; plant biochemist, Res Sta, Can Dept Agr, 58-63; assoc prof biochem, State Univ NY Col Plattsburgh, 63-64, chmn div, 64-66, prof biochem, 64-77, dean fac sci & math, 66-75, dean grad studies & res, 75-77; PRES, BRANDON UNIV, CAN, 77-, PROF BIOCHEM, 77- *Concurrent Pos:* Consult, Teacher Training Prog Univs, State NY Dept Educ, 66-77, accreditation of col & univ sci & math progs; consult, Design Sci Facilities, State of NJ; mem patent policy bd, State Univ NY, mem grad coun, 65-69 & 75-77; mem, Nat Coun Univ Res Adminr, 75-77; mem, Coun Tissue Cult Asn, 76- *Mem:* AAAS; Sigma Xi. *Res:* Biosynthesis of chlorophylls a and b; analytical chemistry of chlorophylls and their degradation products with particular reference to isotopically labelled compounds. *Mailing Add:* Brandon Univ Brandon MB R7A 6A9 Can

PERKINS, HAROLYN KING, b Six Mile, SC, Jan 24, 37; m 59; c 3. PHYSICAL CHEMISTRY. *Educ:* Wake Forest Col, BS, 57; Cornell Univ, PhD(phys chem), 65. *Prof Exp:* Res assoc phys chem, Cornell Univ, 65-66 & Princeton Univ, 66-67; lit chemist, FMC Corp, NJ, 67-69; Sloan fel, 69-73, res staff & lectr chem eng, Princeton Univ, 73-77; SR RES SCIENTIST, AM CAN CO, RES & DEVELOP CTR, PRINCETON, NJ, 78- *Mem:* Am Chem Soc; Am Phys Soc; Am Inst Chem Eng; Am Vacuum Soc; Adhesion Soc. *Res:* Surface characterization of metals and polymers; adhesion of metals to polymers and polymers to polymers; solid state chemistry; rheology of aqueous foams; mechanical properties of polymers; thermonuclear fusion technology. *Mailing Add:* Am Can Co PO Box 50 Princeton NJ 08540

PERKINS, HENRY CRAWFORD, JR, b Miami, Fla, Nov 23, 35; m 60; c 4. MECHANICAL ENGINEERING. *Educ:* Stanford Univ, BS, 57, MS, 60, PhD(mech eng), 63. *Prof Exp:* Res assoc mech eng, Stanford Univ, 62-63, acting asst prof, 63-64; assoc prof, 64-67, PROF MECH ENG, UNIV ARIZ, 67- *Concurrent Pos:* Vis prof, Tech Univ Denmark, 71-72, US Mil Acad, 78-79 & Stanford Univ, 81-82. *Honors & Awards:* Teetor Award, Soc Automotive Engrs, 76. *Mem:* Am Soc Mech Engrs; Air Pollution Control Asn. *Res:* Thermoscience; air pollution. *Mailing Add:* Dept of Aerospace & Mech Eng Univ of Ariz Tucson AZ 85721

PERKINS, HENRY FRANK, b Quitman Co, Ga, June 19, 21; m 45; c 2. SOIL CHEMISTRY. *Educ:* Univ Ga, BS, 45, MS, 51; Rutgers Univ, PhD(soils), 54. *Prof Exp:* Asst soil surveyor, Soil Conserv Serv, USDA, 45-47; soils analyst, 47-50, asst agronomist, Exp Sta, 50-52, from asst prof to assoc prof, Univ, 54-64, PROF AGRON, UNIV GA, 64- *Concurrent Pos:* Tech ed, Agron Jour. *Mem:* Fel Am Soc Agron; Soil Conserv Soc Am; Int Soc Soil Sci; fel Soil Sci Soc Am. *Res:* Soil fertility, classification and genesis. *Mailing Add:* Dept Agron Univ Ga Athens GA 30602

PERKINS, HENRY THOMAS, physical oceanography, see previous edition

PERKINS, HERBERT ASA, b Boston, Mass, Oct 5, 18; m 42; c 5. HEMATOLOGY. *Educ:* Harvard Univ, AB, 40; Tufts Univ, MD, 43. *Prof Exp:* Asst prof med, Sch Med, Stanford Univ, 53-58; asst prof, Sch Med, Washington Univ, 58-59; dir hemat, Jewish Hosp, St Louis, Mo, 58-59; dir res, 59-80, SCIENTIFIC DIR, IRWIN MEM BLOOD BANK, 80- *Concurrent Pos:* Clin prof med, Univ Calif, San Francisco, 59-; consult, Vet Admin Hosp, San Francisco, Calif & USPHS Hosp. *Honors & Awards:* John Elliott Mem Award, Am Asn Blood Banks. *Mem:* Am Soc Hemat; Int Soc Blood Transfusion; Transplantation Soc; Am Asn Blood Banks; Am Asn Clin Histocompatibility Testing. *Res:* Tissue typing and organ transplantation; immunohematology; blood coagulation; blood banking. *Mailing Add:* Irwin Mem Blood Bank 270 Masonic Ave San Francisco CA 94118

PERKINS, JAMES, b Midland, Pa, Dec 28, 43; m; c 1. CHEMISTRY. *Educ:* Slippery Rock State Col, BS, 65; Univ Pittsburgh, PhD(phys chem), 71. *Prof Exp:* Teacher, Pub Sch, Pa, 65-67; from teaching asst to res asst, Univ Pittsburgh, 67-71; assoc prof, 71-76, PROF CHEM, JACKSON STATE UNIV, 76-, CHMN DEPT, 74- *Concurrent Pos:* Instnl res grant, Jackson State Univ, 71-73; res grants, NASA, 72-74 & NIH, 74; consult, Inst Serv Educ, 73-74; NSF equip grant, 74-76. *Mem:* Am Chem Soc; Soc Appl Spectros; Soc Advan Black Chemists & Chem Engrs. *Res:* Infrared and Raman spectroscopy. *Mailing Add:* Dept of Chem Jackson State Univ Jackson MS 39217

PERKINS, JAMES FRANCIS, b Hillsdale, Tenn, Jan 3, 24; m 49; c 1. QUANTUM PHYSICS. *Educ:* Vanderbilt Univ, AB, 48, MA, 49, PhD(physics), 53. *Prof Exp:* Sr nuclear engr, Convair Div, Gen Dynamics Corp, 53-54; staff scientist, Lockheed Aircraft Corp, 54-59, mgr nuclear proj support dept, 59-60, scientist, 60-61; physicist, 61-63, RES PHYSICIST, PHYS SCI LAB, ARMY MISSILE COMMAND, 63- *Mem:* Am Phys Soc; Sigma Xi. *Res:* Atomic structure; autoionization states; scattering theory; numerical techniques. *Mailing Add:* 102 Mountainwood Dr Huntsville AL 35810

PERKINS, JANET SANFORD, b Chicago, Ill, Oct 27, 13; m 54. LASER ACTION ON MATERIALS, HIGH TEMPERATURE CARBON CHEMISTRY. *Educ:* Wellesley Col, BA, 36; Smith Col, AM, 38; Mass Inst Technol, PhD(chem), 52. *Prof Exp:* Instr chem, Wilson Col, 38-39 & Kendall Hall, 39-40; res chemist, Arthur D Little, Inc, 40-48; res asst chem, Mass Inst Technol, 48-49; res chemist spectros, Barrett Div, Allied Chem & Dye Corp, 51-54; res assoc chem, Wellesley Col, 55-56; spec instr, Simmons Col, 55, asst prof, 56-61; sr staff scientist, Res & Advan Develop Div, Avco Corp, 62-65; consult chemist, 65-66; res chemist, Cabot Corp, 66-68; RES CHEMIST, ARMY MAT & MECH RES CTR, 69- *Mem:* Am Chem Soc; Am Carbon Soc; Plastics Inst London. *Res:* Structure-reactivity relationships; nature of aromaticity; polymer degradation, charring and ablation mechanisms; laser/materials interactions; carbon fiber morphology; surface and solid state chemistry; composites; polymer chemistry. *Mailing Add:* Army Mat & Mech Res Ctr Arsenal St Watertown MA 02172

PERKINS, JOHN PHILLIP, b Phoenix, Ariz, June 27, 37; m 61; c 3. PHARMACOLOGY, BIOCHEMISTRY. *Educ:* Ariz State Univ, BS, 60, MS, 62; Yale Univ, PhD(pharmacol), 66. *Prof Exp:* USPHS fel, Univ Wash, 66-68; asst prof, 68-73, assoc prof pharmacol, Sch Med, Univ Colo, Denver, 74-77; PROF & CHMN PHARMACOL, SCH MED, UNIV NC, CHAPEL HILL, 77- *Res:* Role of cyclic nucleotides in brain function and in the regulation of growth and differentiation of mammalian cells in culture. *Mailing Add:* Dept Pharmacol Univ NC Med Sch Chapel Hill NC 27514

PERKINS, KENDALL, b St Louis, Mo, Feb 23, 08; m 34, 81; c 2. ELECTRICAL ENGINEERING. *Educ:* Washington Univ, St Louis, BSEE, 28. *Hon Degrees:* DEng, Tri-State Col, 66. *Prof Exp:* Engr, Curtiss Robertson Airplane Mfg Co, 28-36, proj engr, 36-40; res engr, Am Airlines, 40-41; proj engr, McDonnell Co, 42, asst chief engr, 43-48, asst to vpres, 48-49, mgr eng, 49-51, vpres eng, 51-67, corp vpres eng & res, McDonnell Douglas Corp, 67-73 & 75-78, CONSULT, McDONNELL DOUGLAS CORP, 78- *Concurrent Pos:* Trustee Emer, Washington Univ. *Honors & Awards:* Aircraft Design Award, Am Inst Aeronaut & Astronaut, 76. *Mem:* Nat Acad Eng; fel Am Inst Aeronaut & Astronaut. *Res:* Engineering management for aircraft missile and spacecraft. *Mailing Add:* 7742 Wise Ave St Louis MO 63117

PERKINS, KENNETH L(EE), b St Charles, Mo, Sept 7, 24; m 48; c 4. APPLIED PHYSICS, PHYSICAL CHEMISTRY. *Educ:* St Louis Univ, BSEE, 50, MS, 52, PhD(physics), 56. *Prof Exp:* Instr elec eng, St Louis Univ, 56; sr res engr, Autonetics Div, NAm Aviation, Inc, 56-60; chief scientist solid state physics, Orbitec Corp, 60; res specialist, 60-61, eng supvr, 61-66, electromech eng specialist, 66-68, MEM TECH STAFF, ROCKWELL INT, ANAHEIM, 68- *Res:* Adhesive systems and organic coating materials for microcircuit applications; methods of determining the hermeticity and analyzing the moisture contents of hybrid microcircuit packages; low cost methods of packaging hybrid microcircuits. *Mailing Add:* 5162 Wendover Rd Yorba Linda CA 92686

PERKINS, KENNETH ROY, b Woburn, Mass, Dec 10, 42; m 72; c 3. MECHANICAL ENGINEERING, NUCLEAR ENGINEERING. *Educ:* Tufts Univ, BS, 66; Univ Ariz, PhD(mech eng), 75. *Prof Exp:* Engr reactor safety, Aerojet Nuclear Co, Gen Tire & Rubber, 73-76; NUCLEAR ENGR REACTOR SAFETY, BROOKHAVEN NAT LAB, 76- *Mem:* Am Nuclear Soc; Am Soc Mech Engrs. *Res:* Liquid metal fast breeder reactor safety and accident analysis; thermal reactor fuels behavior; reactor safety applications of heat transfer and fluid dynamics. *Mailing Add:* Bldg 130 Brookhaven Nat Lab Upton NY 11973

PERKINS, KENNETH WARREN, b Pittsfield, Mass, Mar 3, 27; m 47; c 3. PARASITOLOGY. *Educ:* Berea Col, AB, 48; Purdue Univ, MS, 50, PhD(invert zool), 53. *Prof Exp:* Instr invert zool, Purdue Univ, 51-52; assoc prof biol & chem, High Point Col, 53-55; HEAD DEPT PARASITOL & GENETICS, CAROLINA BIOL SUPPLY CO, 54-, HEAD DEPT GRAPHIC ARTS, 64- *Mem:* AAAS; Am Soc Parasitologists; Am Asn Lab Animal Sci. *Res:* Development of teaching aids in parasitology and genetics; visual aids for zoology and botany. *Mailing Add:* Box 396 Elon College NC 27244

PERKINS, LOIS CLAIRE, b East Aurora, NY, June 29, 26. ANATOMY. *Educ:* Univ Mich, BS, 48; Duke Univ, MA, 58, PhD(anat), 61. *Prof Exp:* High sch teacher, Mich, 48-49; phys therapist, Univ Hosp, Ohio State Univ, 51-54; phys therapist, Rehab Ctr, Inc, Ky, 54-57; instr, 61-63, asst prof, 63-67, ASSOC PROF ANAT, SCH MED, IND UNIV, INDIANAPOLIS, 67- *Mem:* Am Phys Ther Asn; Am Asn Anatomists; Sigma Xi. *Res:* Problems related to sexuality following injury to the spinal cord. *Mailing Add:* Dept of Anat Ind Univ Sch of Med Indianapolis IN 46202

PERKINS, PETER, b Rutland, Vt, Oct 19, 35; m 57; c 3. MATHEMATICS. *Educ:* Univ Vt, BA, 57; Dartmouth Col, MA, 59; Univ Calif, Berkeley, PhD(math), 66. *Prof Exp:* From instr to assoc prof, 62-77, PROF MATH, COL OF THE HOLY CROSS, 77-, WARD GRANTS & RES, 77- *Concurrent Pos:* Mathematician, Itek Labs, 62-64. *Mem:* Am Math Soc; Math Asn Am; Asn Symbolic Logic. *Res:* Automata theory; mathematical linguistics; equational theories. *Mailing Add:* Dept Math Col of the Holy Cross Worcester MA 01610

PERKINS, RICHARD SCOTT, b Hammond, La, June 21, 40; m 64; c 1. ELECTROCHEMISTRY. *Educ:* La State Univ, BS, 62; Univ Utah, PhD(chem) 66. *Prof Exp:* Fel chem, Univ Ottawa, Ont, 66-68 & Univ Utah, 68-69; asst prof, 69-74, ASSOC PROF CHEM, UNIV SOUTHWESTERN LA, 74- *Mem:* Am Chem Soc. *Res:* Photoelectrochemistry; electrochemical double layer and electrode kinetics. *Mailing Add:* Dept Chem Univ Southwestern La Lafayette LA 70504

PERKINS, RICHARD W, b Smithfield, Utah, Oct 5, 26; m 49; c 7. CHEMISTRY, PHYSICS. *Educ:* Utah State Univ, BS, 50, MS, 53. *Prof Exp:* Scientist, Hanford Atomic Prod Oper, Gen Elec Co, 52-58, sr scientist, 58-65; MGR RADIOL CHEM RES, BATTELLE-NORTHWEST, 65- *Mem:* AAAS; Am Chem Soc. *Res:* Chemical, physical and biological behavior of radionuclides in the environment and their use as tracers of geophysical and environmental processes; ultrasensitive and selective radionuclide measuring techniques; cosmic radiation and radioactivity on the lunar surface; lunar history; oceanographic and atmospheric chemical research programs. *Mailing Add:* Pac Northwest Lab Battelle Mem Inst Richland WA 99352

PERKINS, RICHARD W, JR, b Poughkeepsie, NY, Apr 28, 32; m 54; c 4. MECHANICAL ENGINEERING, APPLIED MECHANICS. *Educ:* Dartmouth Col, BA, 54; State Univ NY Col Forestry, Syracuse, MS, 59, PhD(forestry), 63. *Prof Exp:* From instr to asst prof wood prod eng, State Univ NY Col Forestry, Syracuse, 58-64; from asst prof to assoc prof, 64-75, PROF MECH & AEROSPACE ENG, SYRACUSE UNIV, 75-, CHMN DEPT, 81- *Concurrent Pos:* Maitre de Conference, Univ de Poitiers, 73-74. *Mem:* Am Soc Mech Engrs; Am Acad Mech. *Res:* Mechanical behavior of heterogeneous media, solid wood, and paper. *Mailing Add:* Dept of Mech & Aerospace Eng Syracuse Univ Syracuse NY 13210

PERKINS, ROBERT LOUIS, b Bradford, Pa, Feb 20, 31; m 52; c 2. INFECTIOUS DISEASES, INTERNAL MEDICINE. *Educ:* WVa Univ, AB, 53; MS, 54; Johns Hopkins Univ, MD, 56; Ohio State Univ, MMedSci, 62. *Prof Exp:* Resident med, Univ, 56-58, NIH clin res fel med, Div Infectious Dis, 60-62, resident, 62-63, clin instr, Col Med, 61-62, from instr to assoc prof, 63-73, assoc prof med microbiol, 71-74, PROF MED, COL MED, OHIO STATE UNIV, 73-, PROF MED MICROBIOL, 74-, DIR DIV INFECTIOUS DIS, 71- *Concurrent Pos:* Attend physician, Univ Hosps, Columbus, Ohio, 63-; consult infectious dis, Dayton Vet Admin Ctr, Ohio, 65 & Wright-Patterson AFB Hosp, Fairborn, 65- *Mem:* Fel Am Col Physicians; Infectious Dis Soc Am; Am Fedn Clin Res; Am Soc Microbiol; AMA. *Res:* Clinical pharmacology, efficacy and tolerance of antimicrobial agents; in vitro activity and mechanisms of action of antibiotics; scanning electron microscopy. *Mailing Add:* Div Infectious Dis N-1148 Univ Hosp 410 W 10th Ave Columbus OH 43210

PERKINS, ROGER A(LLAN), b Milwaukee, Wis, May 28, 26; m 53; c 3. METALLURGICAL ENGINEERING, MATERIALS SCIENCE. *Educ:* Purdue Univ, BS, 49, MS, 51. *Prof Exp:* Asst, Purdue Univ, 49-50; sr res asst, Metals Res Labs, Electro Metall Co, Union Carbide & Carbon Corp, 51-58; metall engr, Aerojet Gen Corp, Gen Tire & Rubber Co, 58-59, asst sr engr, 59-60; SR MEM RES LAB, LOCKHEED PALO ALTO RES LABS, 60- *Mem:* Fel Am Soc Metals. *Res:* High temperature materials; gas-metal reactions; protective coatings; refractory metals; materials for coal conversion systems. *Mailing Add:* Lockheed Palo Alto Res Labs Dept 52-31 B-204 3251 Hanover St Palo Alto CA 94304

PERKINS, ROGER BRUCE, b Hammond, Ind, Nov 8, 35; m 57; c 3. NUCLEAR PHYSICS. *Educ:* Univ Wis, BS, 55; Princeton Univ, PhD(physics), 59. *Prof Exp:* Res asst physics, Princeton Univ, 59; staff mem, Los Alamos Sci Lab, Univ Calif, 59-64; physicist, Div Res, AEC, 64-65; staff mem, 65-70, alternate div leader physics div, 71-76, div leader, Laser Res & Technol Div, 76-79, dep assoc dir inertial fusion, 79-80, DEP ASSOC DIR ENG SCI, LOS ALAMOS NAT LAB, 81- *Concurrent Pos:* Vis prof, Univ Colo, Boulder, 69-70. *Mem:* AAAS; fel Am Phys Soc; Inst Elec & Electronics Engrs; Am Nuclear Soc. *Res:* Experimental nuclear physics; inertial confinement fusion. *Mailing Add:* Eng Sci Los Alamos Nat Lab Los Alamos NM 87545

PERKINS, RONALD DEE, b Covington, Ky, May 18, 35; m 57; c 2. PETROLOGY, MARINE GEOLOGY. *Educ:* Univ Cincinnati, BS, 57; Univ NMex, MS, 59; Ind Univ, PhD(geol), 62. *Prof Exp:* Geologist, Shell Develop Co, 62-63, res geologist, 63-68; PROF GEOL, DUKE UNIV, 68- *Mem:* Geol Soc Am; Am Asn Petrol Geologists; Soc Econ Paleontologists & Mineralogists; Int Asn Sedimentologists. *Res:* Carbonate petrology; stratigraphy; role of microboring organisms in alteration of marine sediments. *Mailing Add:* Dept of Geol Duke Univ Box 6665 Col Sta Durham NC 27708

PERKINS, STERRETT THEODORE, b Oakland, Calif, July 25, 32; m 70; c 6. NUCLEAR PHYSICS, PLASMA PHYSICS. *Educ:* Univ Calif, Berkeley, BS, 56, MS, 57, PhD(nuclear eng), 65. *Prof Exp:* Mech engr, Lawrence Radiation Lab, Univ Calif, 56-57, nuclear engr, 59-60; nuclear engr, Nucleonics Div, Aerojet-Gen Corp, 57-59, from sr engr to prin nuclear engr, 60-65; PHYSICIST, LAWRENCE LIVERMORE NAT LAB, UNIV CALIF, 65- *Concurrent Pos:* Consult, Nucleonics Div, Aerojet-Gen Corp, 59-60. *Mem:* Am Nuclear Soc; Am Physical Soc. *Res:* Transport theory analysis and cross section evaluation, pertaining to neutrons, charged particles and photons. *Mailing Add:* Lawrence Livermore Nat Lab PO Box 808 Livermore CA 94550

PERKINS, THOMAS K(EEBLE), b Dallas, Tex, Jan 31, 32; m 63; c 2. PETROLEUM PRODUCTION. *Educ:* Agr & Mech Col, Tex, BS, 52, MS, 53; Univ Tex, PhD(chem eng), 57. *Prof Exp:* Res engr, Dow Chem Co, 52; from instr to asst prof chem eng, Univ Tex, 55-57; res engr, Atlantic Ref Co, Atlantic Richfield Co, 57-71, dir process develop res, 71-76, dir well mech res, 76-81; MGR MAT & ARCTIC RES, ARCO OIL & GAS CO, 81- *Concurrent Pos:* Distinguished lectr, Soc Petrol Engrs, 77-78. *Honors & Awards:* Lester C Uren Award, Soc Petrol Engrs, 78. *Mem:* Am Inst Mining, Metall & Petrol Engrs. *Res:* Oil production technology. *Mailing Add:* 6816 Stichter Dallas TX 75230

PERKINS, WALTER GEORGE, physical chemistry, see previous edition

PERKINS, WALTON A, III, b Aurora, Ill, Nov 24, 33; m 54; c 2. COMPUTER SCIENCE. *Educ:* Purdue Univ, BS, 55; Univ Calif, Berkeley, MA, 57, PhD(physics), 59. *Prof Exp:* Physicist, Lawrence Livermore Lab, 59-68, Lawrence Berkeley Lab, 68-73 & Stanford Artificial Intel Lab, 73-74; comput scientist, Gen Motors Res Labs, Warren, Mich, 74-81; COMPUT SCIENTIST, LOCKHEED PALO ALTO RES LAB, 81- *Mem:* Asn Comput Mach; Inst Elec & Electronics Engrs; Am Asn Artificial Intel. *Res:* Instabilities of plasmas contained in magnetic fields; diagnostic equipment used in plasma physics; internal structure of photons and pions; computer vision and knowledge representation. *Mailing Add:* Lockheed Palo Alto Res Lab 3251 Hanover St Palo Alto CA 94304

PERKINS, WILLIAM CLOPTON, b Lynchburg, Va, Jan 6, 34; m 55; c 5. NUCLEAR CHEMISTRY. *Educ:* Duke Univ, BS, 55; Johns Hopkins Univ, 57, PhD(chem), 60. *Prof Exp:* RES CHEMIST, SAVANNAH RIVER LAB, E I DU PONT DE NEMOURS & CO, INC, 60- *Mem:* Am Chem Soc. *Res:* Peaceful uses of nuclear explosions; recovery of actinides from debris; nuclear fuel processing; chemical effects of nuclear reactions; process safety; systems analysis; solvent extraction. *Mailing Add:* Savannah River Lab E I du Pont de Nemours & Co Inc Aiken SC 29801

PERKINS, WILLIAM ELDREDGE, b Paterson, NJ, Mar 16, 38; m 63; c 4. PHYSIOLOGY, PHARMACOLOGY. *Educ:* Lawrence Univ, BA, 60; Univ Ill, Urbana, MS, 62, PhD(physiol), 67. *Prof Exp:* Sr pharmacologist, Pfizer, Inc, 67-71; sr scientist, Warren-Teed Pharmaceut Inc, Rohm and Haas Co, 71-75, group leader, Preclin Res, Rohm and Haas Co, 75-77; SR RES SCIENTIST, ADRIA LABS, INC, 77- *Concurrent Pos:* Adj asst prof, Div Pharm, Col Pharm, Ohio State Univ, 81- *Mem:* Sigma Xi. *Res:* Gastrointestinal physiology and pharmacology; general pharmacology. *Mailing Add:* Adria Labs Inc PO Box 16529 Columbus OH 43216

PERKINS, WILLIAM HUGHES, b Kansas City, Mo, Feb 21, 23; m 52; c 4. SPEECH PATHOLOGY. *Educ:* Southwest Mo State Col, BS, 43; Univ Mo, MA, 49, PhD(speech path), 52. *Prof Exp:* From asst prof to assoc prof, 52-60, PROF SPEECH PATH, UNIV SOUTHERN CALIF, 60- *Honors & Awards:* Dart Award, Univ Southern Calif, 73- *Mem:* AAAS; Am Speech & Hearing Asn; Acoust Soc Am; Am Psychol Asn. *Res:* Behavior and physiology of stuttering; clinical treatment of stuttering; onset of stuttering; vocal behavior; laryngeal physiology. *Mailing Add:* Ctr for Study Commun Disorders Univ of Southern Calif Los Angeles CA 90007

PERKINS, WILLIAM RANDOLPH, b Council Bluffs, Iowa, Sept 1, 34; m 57; c 3. ELECTRICAL ENGINEERING. *Educ:* Harvard Univ, AB, 56; Stanford Univ, MS, 57, PhD(elec eng), 61. *Prof Exp:* Instr elec eng, Stanford Univ, 59-60; from asst prof to assoc prof, 61-69, assoc, Ctr Advan Study, 71-72, PROF ELEC ENG & RES PROF, COORD SCI LAB, UNIV ILL, URBANA, 69- *Mem:* AAAS; fel Inst Elec & Electronics Engrs. *Res:* Control systems, especially parameter sensitivity effects, feedback theory and large scale systems. *Mailing Add:* Coord Sci Lab Univ of Ill Urbana IL 61801

PERKINS, WILLIS DRUMMOND, b Porterville, Calif, Dec 20, 26; m 54. CHEMICAL PHYSICS, SPECTROSCOPY. *Educ:* Mass Inst Technol, SB, 48; Harvard Univ, AM, 50, PhD(chem physics), 52. *Prof Exp:* Res technologist anal chem, Shell Oil Co, 51-60; prod specialist, 60-69, ASST PROD MGR INFRARED, PERKIN-ELMER CORP, 69- *Concurrent Pos:* Lectr appl molecular spectros, Ariz State Univ, 75- *Mem:* Am Chem Soc; Am Phys Soc; Optical Soc Am. *Res:* Spectroscopic instrumentation; infrared and Raman spectroscopy; molecular structure. *Mailing Add:* 21 Half Mile Common Westport CT 06880

PERKO, LAWRENCE MARION, b Pueblo, Colo, May 5, 36; m 62; c 5. APPLIED MATHEMATICS. *Educ:* Univ Colo, BS, 58, MS, 59; Stanford Univ, PhD(math), 65. *Prof Exp:* Res engr, Martin Marietta Co, 59-60; res scientist, Lockheed Res Labs, 63-68; asst prof math, San Jose State Univ, 65-68; assoc prof, 68-80, PROF MATH, NORTHERN ARIZ UNIV, 80- *Res:* Periodic orbits in the restricted three body problem, especially existence, approximation, bifurcation and stability; bifurcation of limit cycles for quadratic systems of ordinary differential equations; singular perturbation theory; nonlinear dynamical systems. *Mailing Add:* Dept of Math Northern Ariz Univ Flagstaff AZ 86001

PERKOFF, GERALD THOMAS, b St Louis, Mo, Sept 22, 26; m; c 3. INTERNAL MEDICINE. *Educ:* Washington Univ, MD, 48. *Prof Exp:* Res fel med, Salt Lake County Gen Hosp, 49-50; from res instr to res asst prof med, Univ Utah, 54-62, assoc prof, 62-63; chief, Washington Univ Med Serv, St Louis City Hosp, 63-68, from assoc prof to prof med, Sch Med, Washington Univ, 63-68, prof med, Prev Med & Pub Health & dir, Div Health Care Res, 68-79, CUR PROF & ASSOC CHMN, DEPT FAMILY & COMMUNITY MED & PROF MED, UNIV MO, COLUMBIA, 79- *Concurrent Pos:* Clin instr, Sch Med, Georgetown Univ, 53-54; Markle scholar med sci, 55-60; career res prof, Found Neuromuscular Dis, 61; chief med serv, Vet Admin Hosp, Salt Lake City, Utah, 61-63; mem, Inst Med, Nat Acad Sci, 78-; Henry J Kaiser sr fel, Ctr Advan Study Behav Sci, Palo Alto, Calif, 76-77. *Mem:* Fel Am Col Physicians; Am Fedn Clin Res; Asn Am Physicians; Am Soc Clin Invest; Am Diabetes Asn. *Res:* Health care research. *Mailing Add:* Div of Health Care Res Washington Univ Sch of Med St Louis MO 63110

PERKOWITZ, SIDNEY, b Brooklyn, NY, May 1, 39; m 67; c 1. SOLID STATE PHYSICS, INFRARED SPECTROSCOPY. *Educ:* Polytech Inst Brooklyn, BS, 60; Univ Pa, MS, 62, PhD(physics), 67. *Prof Exp:* Physicist, Gen Tel & Electronics Labs, Inc, 66-69; asst prof, 69-74, assoc prof, 74-79, PROF PHYSICS, EMORY UNIV, 79-, CHMN DEPT, 80- *Mem:* AAAS; Am Phys Soc; Optical Soc Am. *Res:* Optical properties of semiconductors and superconductors; far infrared and laser spectroscopy; spectroscopy of biological materials; semiconductor transport properties. *Mailing Add:* Dept of Physics Emory Univ Atlanta GA 30322

PERKS, ANTHONY MANNING, b Gloucester, Eng. PHYSIOLOGY, PHARMACOLOGY. *Educ:* Cambridge Univ, BA, 54, MA, 58; Univ St Andrews, PhD(physiol), 59; Oxford Univ, MA, 64. *Prof Exp:* Fel, Col Med, Univ Fla, 59-61; instr pharmacol, Col Physicians & Surgeons, Columbia Univ, 61-63; res officer med res, Nuffield Inst Med Res, Oxford Univ, 63-65; assoc prof biol sci, 65-72, PROF ZOOL, UNIV BC, 72- *Concurrent Pos:* Mem staff, New Eng Inst Med Res, 67-68; hon fac res scholar, Col Med, Univ Fla, Gainesville, 77- *Mem:* Am Physiol Soc; Am Zool Soc; European Soc Comput Endocrinol. *Res:* Endocrinology; studies of the neurohypophysis, particularly elasmobranchs and in mammalian foetuses. *Mailing Add:* Dept Zool Univ BC Vancouver BC V6T 1W5 Can

PERKS, NORMAN WILLIAM, b Aug 25, 32; US citizen; m 55; c 2. ELECTRICAL ENGINEERING, OPERATIONS RESEARCH. *Educ:* Drexel Inst, BS, 58; Pa State Univ, MS, 63, PhD(elec eng, math), 67. *Prof Exp:* From jr engr to sr engr, HRB-Singer, Inc, 58-63; from instr to asst prof elec eng, Pa State Univ, 63-67; STAFF ENGR, HRB-SINGER, INC, 67- *Res:* System analysis of information collection systems; queueing theory; mathematical programming; digital signal processing. *Mailing Add:* Systs Eng Dept HRB-Singer Inc State College PA 16801

PERL, EDWARD ROY, b Chicago, Ill, Oct 6, 26; m 53; c 3. PHYSIOLOGY. *Educ:* Univ Ill, BS, 47, MD, 49, MS, 50. *Prof Exp:* Asst physiol, Univ Ill, 48-49; intern med, Harvard Med Serv, Boston City Hosp, 49-50; fel physiol, Sch Med, Johns Hopkins Univ, 50-52; from asst prof to assoc prof med, State Univ NY Upstate Med Ctr, 54-57; from assoc prof to prof, Col Med, Univ Utah, 57-71, actg head dept, 64-65; PROF PHYSIOL & CHMN DEPT, SCH MED, UNIV NC, CHAPEL HILL, 71-, DIR NEUROBIOL PROG, 73-, PROF NEUROBIOL & CHMN DEPT, 77- *Concurrent Pos:* USPHS fel neurophysiol, 51-52; NSF sr fel, 62-63; vis fel, Lab Physiol, Fac Med, Univ Toulouse, 62-63; vis prof, fac sci, Univ Paris, 65; mem study sect, USPHS, 66-70; vis prof, Univ Milan, 67; vis lectr, Sch Med, Univ Calif, Los Angeles, 68; mem physiol test comt, Nat Bd Med Examrs, 68-71; vis prof, Fac Sci, Univ Aix Marseille, 70. *Mem:* AAAS; Soc Neurosci; Am Physiol Soc; Int Brain Res Orgn. *Res:* Neurophysiology; sensory systems; reflex function; autonomic function. *Mailing Add:* Dept Physiol Univ NC Sch Med Chapel Hill NC 27514

PERL, MARTIN LEWIS, b Brooklyn, NY, June 24, 27; m 48; c 4. PHYSICS. *Educ:* Polytech Inst Brooklyn, BChemEng, 48; Columbia Univ, PhD, 55. *Prof Exp:* Engr, Gen Elec Co, 48-50; asst physics, Columbia Univ, 50-55; from instr to assoc prof, Univ Mich, 55-63; assoc prof, 63-64, PROF PHYSICS, STANFORD UNIV, 64- *Mem:* Nat Acad Sci. *Res:* High energy physics. *Mailing Add:* Stanford Linear Accelerator Ctr Stanford Univ Stanford CA 94305

PER-LEE, JOHN H, b Detroit, Mich, June 30, 29; m 57; c 4. MEDICINE. *Educ:* Dartmouth Col, AB, 51; Cornell Univ, MD, 55. *Prof Exp:* Instr surg, Med Col, Cornell Univ, 58-59; NIH fel otol, 61-62; assoc surg, 62-65, asst prof, 65-69, ASSOC PROF OTOLARYNGOL, SCH MED, EMORY UNIV, 69- *Mem:* Am Laryngol, Rhinol & Otol Soc; Am Acad Otolaryngol & Head & Neck Surg; AMA; Soc Univ Otolaryngol. *Res:* Otology; otolaryngology. *Mailing Add:* Dept Otolaryngol Emory Univ Sch Med Atlanta GA 30322

PERLEY, JAMES E, b Hornell, NY, Jan 21, 39; m 60. PLANT PHYSIOLOGY. *Educ:* Univ Mich, AB, 60; Yale Univ, MS, 61, PhD(biol), 65. *Prof Exp:* Asst prof biol, Wayne State Univ, 65-68; ASSOC PROF BIOL, COL WOOSTER, 68- *Mem:* AAAS; Am Soc Plant Physiologists; Scand Soc Plant Physiologists. *Res:* Microbial biochemistry; plant hormone production in bacteria, fungi and higher plants. *Mailing Add:* Dept Biol Col Wooster Wooster OH 44691

PERLGUT, LOUIS E, b New York, NY, Apr 7, 15; m 40; c 2. BIOCHEMISTRY. *Educ:* Rutgers Univ, BSc, 37, MS, 38, PhD(biochem), 64. *Prof Exp:* Asst res specialist, Rutgers Univ, 64-65; from asst prof to assoc prof, 65-74, chmn dept, 70-71, PROF BIOCHEM, CALIF STATE UNIV, LONG BEACH, 74- *Concurrent Pos:* USPHS grant, 65-67. *Mem:* AAAS; Am Chem Soc. *Res:* Magnesium DNA multistrand complexes; phosphorylated high energy intermediates of oxidative phosphorylation and reverse electron transport. *Mailing Add:* Dept of Chem Calif State Univ Long Beach CA 90801

PERLICH, ROBERT WILLARD, b Minneapolis, Minn, Dec 6, 15; m 39; c 3. ANALYTICAL CHEMISTRY. *Educ:* Univ Minn, BCh, 37, MS, 38. *Prof Exp:* Chemist, Rock Anal Lab, Univ Minn, 39 & Mines Exp Sta, 39-42; chemist, Minn Mining & Mfg Co, 42-46, chief chemist, 46-54, tech supvr atomic energy prog, 54-58, proj supvr, 58-60, supvr photog processing chem, 60-73; RETIRED. *Concurrent Pos:* Pres & chmn bd dirs, Fedn Pharmacy Serv, 74-78. *Mem:* Am Chem Soc; Sigma Xi. *Res:* Micro, trace and industrial analysis. *Mailing Add:* 126 Littrell Dr Medford OR 97501

PERLIN, ARTHUR SAUL, b Sydney, NS, July 7, 23; m 50; c 5. ORGANIC CHEMISTRY. *Educ:* McGill Univ, BSc, 44, MSc, 46, PhD(chem), 49. *Prof Exp:* Res chemist, Nat Res Coun Can, 49-67; PROF CHEM, McGILL UNIV, 67- *Concurrent Pos:* Res fel, Univ Edinburgh, 51-52; sessional lectr, Univ Sask; Merck lectr, Chem Inst Can, 61; prin scientist, Pulp & Paper Res Inst Can, 68- *Honors & Awards:* C S Hudson Award, Am Chem Soc, 79. *Res:* Chemistry and biochemistry of carbohydrates and natural products; nuclear magnetic resonance spectroscopy. *Mailing Add:* Dept of Chem McGill Univ Montreal PQ H3A 2A7 Can

PERLIN, SEYMOUR, b Passaic, NJ, Sept 27, 25; m 58; c 3. PSYCHIATRY. *Educ:* Princeton Univ, BA, 46; Columbia Univ, MD, 50; Am Bd Psychiat & Neurol, dipl. *Prof Exp:* Resident, NY Psychiat Inst, 50-51; intern, Univ Mich Hosp, 51-52; resident, Manhattan Hosp, 52; resident, NY Psychiat Inst, 53-54; asst physician, Presby Hosp, NY, 54; asst psychiatrist, Col Physicians & Surgeons, Columbia Univ, 54; chief sect psychiat, Lab Clin Sci, NIMH,

55-59; chief div psychiat, Montefiore Hosp, NY, 60-63; lectr, Columbia Univ, 63-64; prof psychiat, Sch Med, Johns Hopkins Univ, 65-73, dir clin care & training, Henry Phipps Psychiat Clin Hosp, 65-73, dep dir dept psychiat & behav sci, 70-73; clin prof, 74-77, PROF PSYCHIAT & BEHAV SCI, SCH MED & DIR GRAD EDUC DEPT PSYCHIAT, MED CTR, GEORGE WASHINGTON UNIV, 77- *Concurrent Pos:* USPHS fel, 52-53; fel, Ctr Advan Study Behav Sci, Calif, 59; neuropsychiatrist, Home Aged & Infirm Hebrews, NY, 54; consult, State Dept Ment Hyg, Md, 64-70; chmn ment health study sect B, Div Res Grants, NIH, 64-66; mem clin prog-projs res rev comt, NIMH, 67-; vis fel, Princeton Univ, 73 & Oxford Univ, 74; Joseph P Kennedy Jr fel med, law & ethics, Kennedy Inst Ctr Bioethics, 74-75, sr res scholar, 74-77. *Mem:* Fel Am Psychiat Asn; Am Psychosom Soc; Am Asn Suicidology (pres, 69-); Am Psychopath Asn. *Res:* Clinical studies of psychiatric patients; clinical and ethical issues in suicide, death and dying. *Mailing Add:* George Washington Univ Med Ctr 2150 Pennsylvania Ave NW Washington DC 20037

PERLIS, ALAN JAY, b Pittsburgh, Pa, Apr 1, 22; m 51; c 3. MATHEMATICS. *Educ:* Carnegie Inst Technol, BS, 42; Mass Inst Technol, MS, 47, PhD(math), 49. *Prof Exp:* Res mathematician, Digital Comput Lab, Mass Inst Technol, 48-49, 52; res mathematician comput lab, Aberdeen Proving Ground, 51; asst prof math, Purdue Univ, 52-56; assoc prof, Carnegie Inst Technol, 56-60, prof, 60-71, head dept comput sci, 65-71, dir comput ctr, 56-60, head dept math, 60-64; EUGENE HIGGONS PROF COMPUT SCI, YALE UNIV, 71- *Concurrent Pos:* Exten lectr, Univ Md & Univ Del, 51; ed-in-chief, Communications, Asn Comput Mach. *Mem:* Soc Indust & Appl Math; Asn Comput Mach (pres, 60-62). *Res:* Automatic programming; numerical analysis. *Mailing Add:* Dept Comput Sci Rm 308 10 Hillhouse Ave New Haven CT 06520

PERLIS, HARLAN JAY, electrical engineering, environmental science, see previous edition

PERLIS, IRWIN BERNARD, b Detroit, Mich, Feb 26, 25; m 47; c 4. PLANT CHEMISTRY. *Educ:* Univ Calif, AB, 50; Univ Ill, MS, 52, PhD(bot, chem), 54. *Prof Exp:* Asst plant physiol, Univ Ill, 50-54; res fel plant biochem, Calif Inst Technol, 54-55; biochemist & develop supvr, 55-69, asst dir develop prod & res, 69-73, ASST DIR RES & DEVELOP, RES LABS, GEN CIGAR & TOBACCO CO, INC, DIV CULBRO CORP, 73- *Mem:* Sigma Xi. *Res:* Auxin effects on enzymes, cell wall substances and organic acids during normal growth; chemistry of tobacco; chemistry and technology of tobacco sheets. *Mailing Add:* Res & Develop Ctr Div Culbro Corp 602 N Charlotte St Lancaster PA 17603

PERLIS, SAM, b Maywood, Ill, Apr 18, 13; m 39; c 2. ALGEBRA. *Educ:* Univ Chicago, BS, 34, MS, 36, PhD(math), 38. *Prof Exp:* Asst math, Univ Chicago, 38-39; instr, Ill Inst Technol, 38-41, Univ Mich, 41 & Ill Inst Technol, 41-42; sr res asst, Lockheed Aircraft Corp, Calif, 42-46; from instr to asst prof, 46-51, from assoc prof to prof, 51-79, EMER PROF MATH, PURDUE UNIV, WEST LAFAYETTE, 79- *Mem:* Am Math Soc; Math Asn Am. *Res:* Algebras; radicals; rings; fields; matrices. *Mailing Add:* Dept of Math Purdue Univ West Lafayette IN 47907

PERLISH, JEROME SEYMOUR, biochemistry, see previous edition

PERLMAN, DAVID, b Madison, Wis, Feb 6, 20; m 68. BIOCHEMISTRY. *Educ:* Univ Wis, BA, 41, MSc, 43, PhD(biochem), 45. *Prof Exp:* Biochemist, Hoffmann-La Roche, Inc, NJ, 45; microbiologist, Merck & Co, 45-47; biochemist, E R Squibb & Sons, 47-52 & Squibb Inst Med Div, Olin Mathieson Chem Corp, 52-67; dean sch pharm, 68-75, PROF PHARMACEUT BIOCHEM, SCH PHARM, UNIV WIS-MADISON, 67- *Concurrent Pos:* Knapp vis prof, Sch Pharm, Univ Wis, 58; mem exec comt, Intersci Conf Antimicrobial Agents & Chemother, 63-66, chmn, 66-67; Guggenheim Found fel, 66; chmn vitamins & metab pathways, Gordon Conf, 67; ed, Advan Appl Microbiol, 67-; chmn, Third Int Symp Genetics Indust Microorganisms, 78. *Honors & Awards:* James M Van Lanen Distinguished Serv Award, Am Chem Soc, 77, Marvin J Johnson Award, 78. *Mem:* Am Chem Soc; Am Soc Microbiol; Brit Biochem Soc; fel Am Acad Microbiol; fel Acad Pharmaceut Sci. *Res:* Physiology of microorganisms; intermediary metabolism of molds; production of antibiotics by microorganisms; microbial transformation of organic compounds; tissue culture; industrial fermentations; microbial metabolites; antibiotics. *Mailing Add:* Sch of Pharm Univ of Wis Madison WI 53706

PERLMAN, ELY, b New York, NY, Nov 11, 13; m 40; c 2. ALLERGY, IMMUNOLOGY. *Educ:* Columbia Univ, AB, 34; NY Univ, MD, 38. *Prof Exp:* Littauer pneumonia res fel, Harlem Hosp, 38-40, intern, 40-42; res fel, Dept Allergy New York Hosp & Med Col, Cornell Univ, 42 & Rockefeller Inst Hosp, 42-46; res assoc, 46-48, ASSOC ATTEND PHYSICIAN, MT SINAI HOSP, NEW YORK, 48-; CHIEF ALLERGY SERV, LONG ISLAND JEWISH HOSP, 54- *Concurrent Pos:* Clin asst prof pediat, State Univ NY Downstate Med Ctr, 59-; assoc prof microbiol, Mt Sinai Sch Med, 66-; assoc prof, Sch Med, Health Sci Ctr, State Univ NY Stony Brook, 71- *Mem:* AAAS; Harvey Soc; Am Asn Immunologists; fel Am Col Allergists; fel Am Acad Allergy. *Res:* Nature of cross reactions; theoretical studies on rates of antigen-antibody reactions; purification and electrophoretic analysis of ragweed fractions with immunological studies; C-protein and C-antibody; cold-agglutinins; chemistry and pharmacology of antihistaminics; pollen counting and air pollution; staphycococcal antigens. *Mailing Add:* 118 Crescent Lane Roslyn Heights NY 11577

PERLMAN, ISADORE, b Milwaukee, Wis, Apr 12, 15; m 37; c 3. NUCLEAR CHEMISTRY. *Educ:* Univ Calif, BS, 36, PhD(physiol), 40. *Prof Exp:* Control chemist, Paraffin Co, Inc, Calif, 36-37; Upjohn fel, Univ Calif, 40-41; chemist, Nat Defense Res Comt Proj, 42; res assoc, Metall Lab, Univ Chicago, 42-43; sr chemist, Clinton Labs, Oak Ridge, 43-44; sr chemist, Hanford Eng Works, Gen Elec Co, Wash, 44-45; from assoc prof to prof chem, Univ Calif, Berkeley, 45-74, chmn dept, 57-58, mem lab staff, 45-58, head Nuclear Chem Div & assoc dir, Lawrence Berkeley Lab, 58-74; WITH DEPT PHYSICS, INST ARCHAEOL, HEBREW UNIV JERUSALEM, 74- *Concurrent Pos:* Guggenheim fel, 55, 63; consult, E I du Pont de Nemours & Co, Inc; mem Hist Adv Comt, US Atomic Energy Comn. *Honors & Awards:* Lawrence Mem Award, Atomic Energy Comn, 60; Am Chem Soc Award, 64. *Mem:* Nat Acad Sci; AAAS; Am Chem Soc; Am Phys Soc. *Res:* Nuclear spectroscopy; heavy element chemistry. *Mailing Add:* 2515 Hikgard Ave Berkeley CA 94709

PERLMAN, KATO (KATHERINE) LENARD, b Budapest, Hungary, July 18, 28; m 68. ORGANIC CHEMISTRY. *Educ:* Eotvos Lorand Univ, Budapest, dipl, 50, Dr rer nat(org chem), 61. *Prof Exp:* Res chemist, Chinoin Pharmaceut, Budapest, 50-54; res assoc, Res Inst Pharmaceut Indust, 54-62; res assoc & fel, Princeton Univ, 63-68; ASSOC SCIENTIST, SCH PHARM, UNIV WIS-MADISON, 68- *Mem:* Am Chem Soc; The Chem Soc. *Res:* Synthesis of organic chemicals of medicinal interest, including barbiturates, alkaloids, steroids, peptides, hallucinogenic drugs, tetrahydro- cannabinol and pteridines; antibiotics; vitamin antagonists. *Mailing Add:* Sch Pharm Univ Wis Madison WI 53706

PERLMAN, MARTIN MELVIN, b Montreal, Que, Feb 6, 30; m 51; c 2. SOLID STATE PHYSICS. *Educ:* McGill Univ, BSc, 50, MSc, 51, PhD(physics), 55. *Prof Exp:* Lectr physics, Royal Mil Col, 54-56, asst prof, 56-57; res assoc, RCA Whirlpool Corp, Mich, 57-59; assoc prof, 59-64, PROF PHYSICS, ROYAL MIL COL, QUE, 64- *Concurrent Pos:* Consult, Northern Elec Co, Can, 64-71. *Mem:* fel Am Phys Soc; fel Brit Inst Physics; Inst Elec & Electronics Engrs; Electrochem Soc; Am Asn Physics Teachers. *Res:* Dielectrics; solid state; thermally stimulated currents from corona electron and x-ray irradiated, and field polarized, polymers and crystals; xerographic discharge; transient photocurrents; charge transport; conduction. *Mailing Add:* 7494 Briar Rd Cote St Luc Montreal PQ H4W 1K4 Can

PERLMAN, MICHAEL DAVID, b Chicago, Ill, Dec 1, 42. MATHEMATICAL STATISTICS. *Educ:* Calif Inst Technol, BSc, 63; Stanford Univ, MSc, 65, PhD(statist), 67. *Prof Exp:* From asst prof to assoc prof statist, Univ Minn, 68-73; assoc prof & chmn dept, Univ Chicago, 73-77; PROF STATIST & CHMN DEPT, UNIV WASH, 79- *Concurrent Pos:* Assoc ed, Ann Statist, 74-77, ed, 83-86. *Mem:* Fel Inst Math Statist; fel Am Statist Asn; Math Asn Am. *Res:* Exact small sample properties of multivariate tests and estimates; probability inequalities for convex regions; monotonicity properties of multivariate power functions. *Mailing Add:* State Dept Univ Wash Seattle WA 98195

PERLMAN, MORRIS LEONARD, b Detroit, Mich, Aug 10, 16; m 41; c 2. SOLID STATE CHEMISTRY. *Educ:* La State Univ, BS, 37; Univ Calif, PhD(phys chem), 40. *Prof Exp:* Asst chemist, US Bur Mines, 40-41; res assoc, Radiation Lab, Univ Calif, 41-43, scientist, Los Alamos Sci Lab, 43-46; res assoc, Res Lab, Gen Elec Co, NY, 46-48; asst prof chem, Univ Wyo, 48-49; scientist, 49-57, SR SCIENTIST, BROOKHAVEN NAT LAB, 57- *Concurrent Pos:* Guggenheim fel, 63-64; vis prof, Ore State Univ, 72. *Mem:* AAAS; fel Am Phys Soc; Am Chem Soc. *Res:* Interrelations between chemistry and nuclear transitions; photoelectron spectroscopy; study of solid state and ionic structure with synchrotron radiation. *Mailing Add:* Dept Chem Brookhaven Nat Lab Upton NY 11973

PERLMAN, PHILIP STEWART, b Baltimore, Md, July 27, 45; m 80. GENETICS, MOLECULAR BIOLOGY. *Educ:* Johns Hopkins Univ, BA, 66; Ind Univ, Bloomington, PhD(biochem), 71. *Prof Exp:* Fel biochem with Prof H R Mahler, Ind Univ, Bloomington, 71; asst prof, 71-76, ASSOC PROF GENETICS, OHIO STATE UNIV, 76- *Concurrent Pos:* Vis prof, Universite de Paris Sud, 79-80. *Mem:* AAAS; Sigma Xi; Genetics Soc Am; Am Genetic Asn. *Res:* Molecular mechanisms of mitochondrial genetics; mitochondrial gene structure and regulation; RNA splicing. *Mailing Add:* 621 Biol Sci Bldg Dept Genetics Ohio State Univ 484 W 12th Ave Columbus OH 43210

PERLMAN, ROBERT, b Chicago, Ill, Aug 15, 38; m 64; c 2. BIOCHEMISTRY, MEDICINE. *Educ:* Univ Chicago, AB, 57, SB, 58, MD, 61, PhD(biochem), 63. *Prof Exp:* From intern to resident pediat, Bellevue Hosp, New York, 63-65; staff assoc, Nat Inst Arthritis & Metab Dis, 65-67, med officer, 67-71; assoc prof physiol, Harvard Med Sch, 71-81; PROF & HEAD PHYSIOL & BIOPHYS, UNIV ILL COL MED, 81- *Concurrent Pos:* USPHS fel biochem, Univ Chicago, 61-63. *Res:* Synthesis and secretion of catecholamines; regulation of cell metabolism; physiology. *Mailing Add:* Dept Physiol & Biophys Univ Ill Col Med PO Box 6998 Chicago IL 60680

PERLMAN, T(HEODORE), b New Orleans, La, Sept 30, 23; m 51; c 3. MECHANICAL ENGINEERING. *Educ:* La State Univ, BS, 44. *Prof Exp:* Jr engr, Tex Co, 44; mech engr, Los Alamos Sci Lab, NMex, 44-46 & Cyclotron Lab, Univ Rochester, 46-50; sect supvr, Standards Eng Div, Sandia Corp, 50-56; proj engr, Lawrence Livermore Nat Lab, 56-68, div leader, Weapons Eng Div, 68-73, div leader, Res Eng Div, 73-81. *Concurrent Pos:* Asst, Marianna Islands Base, Atomic Energy Comn, 45, Bikini, 46. *Res:* Cyclotron construction; drafting and design in oil refinery; atomic weapons development; energy research and development. *Mailing Add:* PO Box 808 Mail Drop L123 Lawrence Livermore Lab Livermore CA 94550

PERLMUTT, JOSEPH HERTZ, b Savannah, Ga, Dec 8, 18; m 48; c 3. PHYSIOLOGY. *Educ:* Col Charleston, BS, 39; Univ NC, MA, 42; Princeton Univ, PhD(biol), 50. *Prof Exp:* Asst, Princeton Univ, 47-49; asst prof physiol, Sch Med, Univ Okla, 50; res assoc surg, Sch Med, Univ Pa, 51-53; from asst prof to assoc prof, 53-74, PROF PHYSIOL, SCH MED, UNIV NC, CHAPEL HILL, 74- *Mem:* AAAS; Am Physiol Soc; Soc Exp Biol & Med; Am Soc Nephrology. *Res:* Endocrinology; renal physiology. *Mailing Add:* Morgan Creek Rd Chapel Hill NC 27514

PERLMUTTER, ALFRED, b New York, NY, Dec 7, 14; m 39; c 3. ICHTHYOLOGY. *Educ:* NY Univ, BS, 34; Univ Mich, MS, 36, ScD(zool), 41. *Prof Exp:* Aquatic biologist, US Fish & Wildlife Serv, 40-49; sr aquatic biologist, State Conserv Dept, NY, 50-60; assoc prof, 60-65, PROF BIOL, WASH SQ COL, NY UNIV, 65-, ADJ ASST PROF, GRAD SCH, 52- *Concurrent Pos:* Sea fisheries specialist, State Univ NY-US Opers Mission, Israel, 55-56. *Mem:* AAAS; Am Fisheries Soc; Am Soc Ichthyol & Herpet; Am Soc Limnol & Oceanog; Nat Shellfisheries Asn. *Res:* Aquatic biology; sea fisheries and pond fish culture. *Mailing Add:* Dept of Biol Wash Square Col NY Univ New York NY 10003

PERLMUTTER, ARNOLD, b Brooklyn, NY, Nov 4, 28; m 49; c 2. PHYSICS. *Educ:* Univ Calif, Los Angeles, BA, 49; NY Univ, MS, 51, PhD(physics), 55. *Prof Exp:* Asst physics, NY Univ, 51-54; instr, Cooper Union, 54-55 & Brooklyn Col, 55-56; from asst prof to assoc prof, 56-68, PROF PHYSICS, UNIV MIAMI, 68-, SECY, CTR THEORET STUDIES, 65- *Concurrent Pos:* Res assoc, Midway Lab, Univ Chicago, 56 & Univ Calif, Los Angeles, 60; Fulbright travel grant, Nat Inst Nuclear Physics, Univ Trieste, 61-62; Israel Atomic Energy Comn fel, Weizmann Inst, 62-63; vis physicist, Argonne Nat Lab, 65, consult, 66-; vis prof, Imp Col Sci & Technol, Univ London, 73-74 & Univ Mich, 78- *Mem:* Am Phys Soc; Fedn Am Scientists. *Res:* Photoconductivity of phosphors; optical properties of gallium arsenide; nuclear emulsions; elementary particles; potential scattering computations; electromagnetic radiation; polarized nucleon scattering; global energy problems. *Mailing Add:* Ctr for Theoret Studies Univ of Miami Coral Gables FL 33124

PERLMUTTER, ARTHUR, b Lodz, Poland, Feb 26, 30; US citizen; m 57; c 2. CHEMICAL ENGINEERING. *Educ:* Univ Havana, BS, 55; Columbia Univ, MS, 65. *Prof Exp:* Jr chem engr, Rayon Co, Cuba, 56-57, chem engr, 57-59; chem engr, Goodyear Tire Co Cuba, 59-60; chem engr & pilot plant supvr, Rheingold Breweries, Inc, 61-67; res chem engr, Cent Res Div, Am Cyanamid Co, 68-75, sr process engr, Eng & Construct Div, 75-80; SR TECH ASSOC, CORP ENG DEPT, GAF CORP, 80- *Mem:* Am Chem Soc; Am Inst Chem Engrs. *Res:* Development of high tenacity rayon tire cord; development of low-carbohydrate beer; design of shellfish culture plant; development of fuel tank inerting system; development of solid waste disposal system; disposal of thermoplastic materials. *Mailing Add:* Corp Eng Dept GAF Corp 1361 Alps Rd Wayne NJ 07470

PERLMUTTER, DANIEL D, b Brooklyn, NY, May 24, 31; m 54; c 3. CHEMICAL ENGINEERING. *Educ:* NY Univ, BChE, 52; Yale Univ, DEng, 56. *Prof Exp:* Res & develop engr, Esso Res & Eng Co, 55-58; instr, Newark Col Eng, 56-58; asst prof chem eng, Univ Ill, 58-64; assoc prof, 64-66, chmn grad group chem eng, 69-77, PROF CHEM ENG, UNIV PA, 67- *Concurrent Pos:* Guggenheim fel, 64-65; Fulbright fel, Eng, 68-69 & Yugoslavia, 72. *Honors & Awards:* Lectureship Award, Am Soc Eng Educ, 79. *Mem:* Am Inst Chem Engrs. *Res:* Automatic process control; reactor design. *Mailing Add:* Sch of Chem Eng Univ of Pa Philadelphia PA 19174

PERLMUTTER, FRANK, b NJ, June 2, 12; m 42; c 2. HORTICULTURE. *Educ:* NC State Col, BS, 34; Univ Md, MS, 39. *Prof Exp:* Student aide hort, NC State Col, 34; dist supvr plant dis, USDA, NC, 34, inspector, 36, horticulturist, Plant Indust Sta, Md, 38-41, soil conservationist, NC, 41-46; horticulturist, Caswell Training Sch, 35-36, DC Training Sch, MD, 37-38 & US Vet Admin, NY, 46-48; inspector plant quarantine, USDA, 48-60, supvr, 60-68; TEACHER BIOL, DE WITT CLINTON HIGH SCH, 68-, TEACHER HORTICULT, 77- *Concurrent Pos:* Consult horticult greenhouse gardening, Time Life Encycl Gardening, 77. *Mem:* Fel AAAS; Am Soc Hort Sci; NY Acad Sci; Am Inst Biol Sci. *Res:* Biology, botany; plant quarantine, plant breeding and pathology; entomology; genetics. *Mailing Add:* 3965 Sedgwick Ave Bronx NY 10463

PERLMUTTER, HENRY IRWIN, b Penns Grove, NJ, Mar 20, 19; m 47; c 2. RADIOLOGY. *Educ:* Univ Pa, BA, 48, MA, 50, PhD(anat), 55. *Prof Exp:* From instr to asst prof anat, Hahnemann Med Col, 55-66, res assoc prof, 66-67; asst prof, 67-71, ASSOC PROF RADIOL & ANAT, SCH MED, CASE WESTERN RESERVE UNIV, 71- *Mem:* AAAS; Sigma Xi. *Res:* Cardiovascular research; adrenocortical structure and physiology; neurocytology; gross anatomy; neuroanatomy; histology. *Mailing Add:* Dept of Radiol & Anat Case Western Reserve Univ Cleveland OH 44106

PERLMUTTER, HOWARD D, b Brooklyn, NY, May 27, 38; c 1. ORGANIC CHEMISTRY. *Educ:* Lehigh Univ, BS, 59; NY Univ, MS, 62, PhD(org chem), 63. *Prof Exp:* Fel org chem, Univ Wis, 63-65; asst prof, 65-71, ASSOC PROF CHEM ENG & CHEM, NJ INST TECHNOL, 71- *Concurrent Pos:* NIH fel, 63-65. *Mem:* Am Chem Soc. *Res:* Physical organic chemistry; stereochemistry and mechanism of organic reactions; thermal reorganization reactions; cyclooctatetraenes; novel aromatic and heterocyclic compounds; solid state photochemistry; diazocines. *Mailing Add:* Dept of Chem Eng & Chem NJ Inst of Technol 323 High St Newark NJ 07102

PERLMUTTER, ISAAC, b Russia, Nov 23, 12; nat US; m 47; c 2. METALLURGY. *Educ:* Mass Inst Technol, SB, 34. *Prof Exp:* Metallurgist, Carnegie-Ill Steel Corp, 36-40 & US Bur Mines, 40; proj engr, Metals & Ceramics Div, US Air Force Mat Lab, Wright-Patterson AFB, 41-46, chief high temperature mat sect, 46-59, chief phys metall br, 59-73; CONSULT AIRCRAFT STRUCT METALS, 73- *Mem:* Fel Am Soc Metals. *Res:* Gas turbine materials; beryllium; heat resistant coatings; refractory metals; high strength steels; bearing materials; aircraft structural alloys of titanium and aluminum. *Mailing Add:* 150 Trailwoods Dr Dayton OH 45415

PERLOFF, ALVIN, b Philadelphia, Pa, Feb 9, 30; m 55; c 2. PHYSICAL CHEMISTRY. *Educ:* Univ Pa, BS, 51; Georgetown Univ, PhD(chem), 66. *Prof Exp:* Chemist, 51-54, PHYS CHEMIST, NAT BUR STANDARDS, 56- *Mem:* AAAS; Am Chem Soc; Am Crystallog Asn; Int Union Crystallog. *Res:* Inorganic structure analysis by x-ray diffraction; magnetohydrodynamic materials research. *Mailing Add:* Nat Bur of Standards Washington DC 20234

PERLOFF, DAVID STEVEN, b Philadelphia, Pa, Mar 31, 42; m 65; c 3. PHYSICS, MATERIALS SCIENCE. *Educ:* Univ Pa, BA, 63; Brown Univ, PhD(physics), 69. *Prof Exp:* Res physicist, Corning Glass Works, 68-71, sr mem tech staff, Res & Develop Lab, 72-77, mgr device & process characterization, Advan Technol Ctr, 78-81, MGR CHARACTERIZATION TECHNOL, PHILIPS RES LAB, SIGNETICS CORP, 81- *Mem:* Am Phys Soc; Electrochem Soc. *Res:* Applications of ion implantation to silicon device and integrated circuit fabrication; process modeling and characterization. *Mailing Add:* Philips Res Lab c/o Signetics Corp 811 E Arques Ave Sunnyvale CA 94086

PERLOFF, WILLIAM H(ARRY), JR, b Philadelphia, Pa, May 2, 36; m 59; c 3. PEDIATRICS, INTENSIVE CARE. *Educ:* Swarthmore Col, BS, 57; Northwestern Univ, MS, 58, PhD(civil eng), 62; Case Western Reserve Univ, MD, 77. *Prof Exp:* Asst prof civil eng, Ohio State Univ, 62-65; from assoc prof to prof soil mech, Purdue Univ, 65-73; resident pediat, Cleveland Clinic Found, 77-79; fel clin pharmacol & pediat intensive care, Univ Hosps Cleveland, 79-81; asst prof, Case Western Reserve Univ, 81-82; ASST PROF PEDIAT, SCH MED & DIR, PEDIAT INTENSIVE CARE UNIT, UNIV WIS HOSPS, MADISON, 82- *Mem:* AMA; Soc Critical Care Med; Am Acad Pediat. *Res:* Cardiorespiratory function in pediatric intensive care. *Mailing Add:* Univ Wis Hosp 600 Highland Ave Madison WI 53706

PERLOW, GILBERT JEROME, b New York, NY, Feb 10, 16; m 41. EXPERIMENTAL PHYSICS. *Educ:* Cornell Univ, AB, 36, AM, 37; Univ Chicago, PhD(physics), 40. *Prof Exp:* Instr physics, Univ Minn, 40-41; physicist, Naval Ord Lab, 41-42 & Naval Res Lab, 42-52; res assoc, Univ Minn, 52-53; physicist, 53-58, SR PHYSICIST, ARGONNE NAT LAB, 58- *Concurrent Pos:* Vis assoc prof, Univ Wash, 57; vis physicist, Atomic Energy Res Estab, Eng, 61; vis prof, Univ Ill, Chicago, 65, Munich Tech Univ, 68 & 79 & Free Univ Berlin, 69; ed, J Appl Physics, 70-73 & Appl Physics Lett, 70-; sr Humboldt award, Munich Tech Univ, 74-75. *Mem:* Fel Am Phys Soc. *Res:* X-rays; radio; cosmic rays; nuclear physics; Mossbauer effect. *Mailing Add:* 4919 Northcott Ave Downers Grove IL 60515

PERLOW, MINA REA JONES, b Harrodsburg, Ky; m 41. INORGANIC CHEMISTRY, RADIOCHEMISTRY. *Educ:* Centre Col, AB, 31; Pa State Col, MS, 33; Univ Chicago, PhD(inorg chem), 41. *Prof Exp:* Chemist, WVa Pulp & Paper Co, 33-38; commodity specialist, Inorg Chem Sect, War Prod Bd, 42-45, Civilian Prod Admin, 45-47 & Off Domestic Commerce Chem & Drugs Div, US Dept Commerce, 48-50; consult, USDA, 51; CONSULT CHEMIST, 51- *Concurrent Pos:* Consult, Argonne Nat Lab, 60- *Res:* Lithium-lithium hydride-hydrogen equilibrium; radiochemistry; Mossbauer effect. *Mailing Add:* 4919 Northcott Ave Downers Grove IL 60515

PERLSTEIN, JEROME HOWARD, b New York, NY, Mar 25, 41; m 66; c 2. SOLID STATE CHEMISTRY. *Educ:* Brandeis Univ, AB, 61; Cornell Univ, PhD(chem), 67. *Prof Exp:* Asst prof solid state chem, Johns Hopkins Univ, 67-73; SR RES CHEMIST, EASTMAN KODAK CO, 73- *Mem:* Am Chem Soc. *Res:* Electron transport in transition metal complexes; solid state properties of non-stoichiometric inorganic and organic compounds; low temperature electrical properties and magnetic properties of the solid state; photoconductivity of amorphous organic films. *Mailing Add:* Res Labs Eastman Kodak Co Rochester NY 14650

PERMAN, VICTOR, b Greenwood, Wis, Jan 28, 26; m; c 5. VETERINARY PATHOLOGY. *Educ:* Univ Minn, BS, 53, DVM, 55, PhD(vet path), 62. *Prof Exp:* Instr, 55-58 & 59-62, from asst prof to assoc prof, 62-68, PROF VET PATH, UNIV MINN, ST PAUL, 68- *Concurrent Pos:* Med scientist, Brookhaven Nat Lab, 58-59, res collab, 59-62 & 67- *Mem:* Am Col Vet Path; Am Soc Vet Clin Path; Am Vet Med Asn. *Res:* Comparative hematology; hypoplastic and proliferative diseases of hemic system; veterinary clinical pathology. *Mailing Add:* Col Vet Univ Minnesota St Paul MN 55108

PERMAR, PHILIP H(OWARD), b Pittsburgh, Pa, Feb 3, 20; m 44; c 3. CHEMICAL ENGINEERING. *Educ:* Cornell Univ, BChE, 43. *Prof Exp:* Metall observer, Carnegie-Ill Steel Corp, Ind, 42; asst metall, Cornell Univ, 42-43; metall engr, Exp Sta, 43-50, res mgr nuclear mat div, Savannah River Lab, 50-68, RES METALLURGIST, RADIOL SCI, SAVANNAH RIVER LAB, E I DU PONT DE NEMOURS & CO, INC, 68- *Mem:* Am Soc Metals; Am Nuclear Soc. *Res:* Metallurgy of titanium; stainless steels and uranium; fabrication of nuclear fuel elements; applications of californium-252; nuclear waste management. *Mailing Add:* Savannah River Lab E I du Pont de Nemours & Co Inc Aiken SC 29801

PERMODA, ARTHUR J, b Bay City, Mich, July 24, 12; m 47; c 1. CHEMICAL ENGINEERING. *Educ:* Univ Mich, BS, 38, MS, 48, PhD(chem eng), 55. *Prof Exp:* Eng aide hwy mat testing, Mich State Hwy Dept, 39-42, chief chemist, 46-48; develop engr, Minn Mining & Mfg Co, 48-50; chem engr, Mich State Hwy Dept, 55-78; RETIRED. *Concurrent Pos:* Mem comt, Hwy Res Bd, Nat Acad Sci-Nat Res Coun, 63-79. *Mem:* Am Chem Soc; Nat Soc Prof Engrs. *Res:* Protective coatings; causative factors of deterioration of coatings on highway structural steel; research and development of more durable coatings for highway uses. *Mailing Add:* 2101 Roberts Lane Lansing MI 48910

PERMUTT, SOLBERT, b Birmingham, Ala, Mar 6, 25; m 52; c 3. MEDICINE. *Educ:* Univ Southern Calif, MD, 50. *Prof Exp:* Intern, Univ Chicago Clins, 49-50, asst resident med, 52-53, res assoc anat, Univ, 50-52; chief resident pulmonary div, Montefiore Hosp, New York, 54-55, chief resident med div, 55-56; Nat Found fel med & environ med, Johns Hopkins Univ, 56-58; chief cardiopulmonary physiol div, Nat Jewish Hosp at Denver, Colo, 58-61; asst prof physiol, Sch Med, Univ Colo, 60-61; assoc prof environ med, 61-65, PROF ENVIRON HEALTH SCI, SCH HYG & PUB HEALTH, JOHNS HOPKINS UNIV, 65-, PROF MED, SCH MED, 71-, PROF ANESTHESIOL, 78- *Concurrent Pos:* Mem, Am Heart Asn. *Mem:* AAAS; Am Thoracic Soc; Am Fedn Clin; Am Physiol Soc. *Res:* Am Heart Asn; Am Physiol Soc. Res: Respiratory and circulatory physiology; pulmonary medicine; mechanical interactions of circulatory and respiratory systems. *Mailing Add:* Johns Hopkins Med Insts Baltimore MD 21205

PERO, JANICE GAY, b Lowell, Mass, June 11, 43; m 70; c 2. MOLECULAR BIOLOGY. *Educ:* Oberlin Col, BA, 65; Harvard Univ, PhD(biochem, molecular biol), 71. *Prof Exp:* Res fel biol, 71-75, res assoc, 75, asst prof, 75-78, ASSOC PROF BIOL, HARVARD UNIV, 78- *Concurrent Pos:* Am Cancer Soc fel, 71-73; tutor biochem sci, Harvard Univ, 73-77. *Mem:* Am Soc Microbiol. *Res:* Regulation of gene expression; control of transcription of bacteriophage DNA by regulatory subunits of bacterial RNA polymerase. *Mailing Add:* Harvard Univ Biol Labs 16 Divinity Ave Cambridge MA 02138

PERONA, JOSEPH JAMES, b Blanford, Ind, May 28, 30; m 55; c 4. CHEMICAL ENGINEERING. *Educ:* Rose Polytech Inst, BS, 52; Northwestern Univ, PhD(chem eng), 56. *Prof Exp:* Sr chem engr, Oak Ridge Nat Lab, 56-68; PROF CHEM ENG, UNIV TENN, KNOXVILLE, 68- *Concurrent Pos:* Consult, Oak Ridge Nat Lab, 68- & Dept Energy Hq, 75- *Mem:* Am Inst Chem Engrs. *Res:* Heat transfer; mass transfer and reaction; geothermal energy. *Mailing Add:* Dept of Chem Eng Univ of Tenn Knoxville TN 37996

PERONE, SAMUEL PATRICK, b Rockford, Ill, Oct 1, 38; m 56; c 3. ANALYTICAL CHEMISTRY. *Educ:* Rockford Col, BA, 59; Univ Wis, PhD(anal chem), 63. *Prof Exp:* From asst prof to assoc prof, 62-71, PROF ANAL CHEM, PURDUE UNIV, WEST LAFAYETTE, 71- *Mem:* Am Chem Soc. *Res:* Photoelectrochemistry; lab computer applications to pattern recognition and instrumental analysis. *Mailing Add:* Dept Chem Purdue Univ West Lafayette IN 47907

PEROT, PHANOR L, JR, b Monroe, La, July 19, 28; m 54; c 5. NEUROSURGERY. *Educ:* Tulane Univ, BS, 49, MD, 52; McGill Univ, dipl neurosurg, 61, PhD(neurol, neurosurg), 63; Am Bd Neurol Surg, dipl, 63. *Prof Exp:* Intern, Philadelphia Gen Hosp, Pa, 52-53; asst resident gen surg, Hosp Univ Pa, 53-54; resident neurol serv, Montreal Neurol Inst, 56-57, asst res neurosurg, 57-59; sr neurosurg res & demonstr neurol & neurosurg, Fac Med, McGill Univ, 60-61, from lectr to asst prof neurosurg, 62-68; PROF NEUROL SURG & CHMN DEPT, MED UNIV SC, 68- *Concurrent Pos:* Fel neurosurg path, Montreal Neurol Inst, 57, fel neurophysiol, 59-60; Nat Inst Neurol Dis & Blindness Spec fels, 59-62; asst neurosurgeon, Montreal Neurol Inst & Hosp, 61-68; clin asst neurosurgeon, Royal Victoria Hosp, 61-65, asst neurosurgeon, 65-68. *Mem:* Fel Am Col Surgeons; Am Epilepsy Soc; Soc Univ Neurosurgeons; Soc Neurol Surgeons; Am Acad Neurol Surgeons. *Res:* Basic neurophysiological studies in epilepsy in animals and man; auditory and visual memory in the human brain; clinical neurosurgery; clinical and experimental studies in spinal cord injury. *Mailing Add:* Dept Neurol Surg Med Univ SC Charleston SC 29403

PEROUTKA, STEPHEN JOSEPH, b Baltimore, Md, Feb 21, 54; m 79. NEUROLOGY. *Educ:* Cornell Univ, AB, 75; Johns Hopkins Univ, MD, 79, PhD(pharmacol), 80. *Prof Exp:* Intern med, Stanford Univ, 80-81; RESIDENT FEL NEUROL, JOHNS HOPKINS UNIV, 81- *Res:* Molecular pharmacology of the central nervous system. *Mailing Add:* Dept Neurol Blalock 1415 Johns Hopkins Hosp Baltimore MD 21205

PEROZZI, EDMUND FRANK, b Camden, NJ, Feb 16, 46; m 72. ORGANIC CHEMISTRY. *Educ:* Drexel Univ, BS, 69; Univ Ill, Urbana, PhD(org chem), 74. *Prof Exp:* Fel org chem, Univ Mich, Ann Arbor, 73-74; teacher chem & phys sci, Southeastern Christian Col, 74-77, assoc prof chem, 77-80; MEM STAFF, LITHYL CORP, 80- *Concurrent Pos:* Res assoc, Univ Ill, Urbana, 75-78. *Mem:* Am Chem Soc. *Res:* New organic synthetic reagents; chemistry of hypervalent compounds; x-ray crystallography; organic photochemistry. *Mailing Add:* 1600 W Right Mill Rd Lithyl Corp Ferndale MI 48220

PERPER, ROBERT J, b New York, NY, Mar 6, 33; m 58; c 3. IMMUNOPATHOLOGY. *Educ:* Cornell Univ, DVM, 56; Univ Calif, San Francisco, MS, 65, PhD(comp path), 67. *Prof Exp:* Pvt pract vet med, 56-64; lectr pharmacol, Univ of the Pac, 62-67; sr res scientist, Upjohn Co, Mich, 67-69; sect head anti-inflammatory immunol res, Geigy Pharmaceut, 69-71, mgr anti-inflammatory immunol res, Ciba-Geigy Corp, 71-74; sr dir, Dept Inflammation & Arthritis, Merck Inst Therapeut Res, 74-76; MED DIR, FELINE HEALTH, 78- *Concurrent Pos:* Nat Heart Inst fel, Med Ctr, Univ Calif, San Francisco, 65-68, lectr, Dept Surg, Med Ctr, Univ, 66-67; adj prof, New York Med Col, 71-73, adj prof path, 73-; adj prof path, New York Hosp Med Col, Cornell Univ, 78- *Mem:* Transplantation Soc; Am Asn Immunologists; Am Soc Exp Pathologists; Am Acad Allergy; Am Vet Med Asn. *Res:* Transplantation immunology; anti-inflammatory research. *Mailing Add:* Feline Health 212 E 70th St New York NY 10021

PERR, IRWIN NORMAN, b Newark, NJ, Mar 4, 28; m 52; c 4. PSYCHIATRY, FORENSIC MEDICINE. *Educ:* Franklin & Marshall Col, BS, 46; Jefferson Med Col, MD, 50; Cleveland State Univ, JD, 61. *Prof Exp:* Resident psychiat, Bellevue Hosp-NY Univ, 51-52; resident, Philadelphia Psychiat Hosp, 52; resident, Med Ctr, Univ Calif, San Francisco, 54-56; asst supt, clin dir & dir educ, Fairhill Psychiat Hosp, 56-61; pvt pract, Cleveland, 61-72; PROF PSYCHIAT & PROF COMMUNITY MED, RUTGERS MED SCH, COL MED & DENT NJ, 72- *Concurrent Pos:* Lectr, Sch Law, Cleveland State Univ, 62-65; lectr psychiat & law, Fairhill Psychiat Hosp & Cleveland Psychiat Inst, 62-72; consult psychiat, Juv Court Cuyahoga County, Cleveland, 62-70; clin prof legal med, Sch Law, Case Western Reserve Univ, 71-72; mem, Civil Serv Med Rev Bd, State NJ, 73-; counr, Am Acad Psychiat & Law, 74-77, pres, 77-79; adj prof law, Rutgers Univ, Newark, 77- *Mem:* Am Psychiat Asn; Am Acad Forensic Sci (vpres, 75-76); Am Acad Psychiat Law; Am Soc Law Med; Am Col Legal Med. *Res:* Legal medicine; legal psychiatry. *Mailing Add:* Dept of Psychiat Rutgers Med Sch Piscataway NJ 08854

PERRAULT, GUY, b Amos, Que, Sept 25, 27; m 57; c 3. EARTH SCIENCES. *Educ:* Polytech Sch, Montreal, BSc, 49; Univ Toronto, MSc, 51, PhD(geol sci), 55. *Prof Exp:* Field engr mineral explor, Iron Ore Co, Can, 49-55 & Moneta Porcupine Mines, Ltd, 55-56; prof mineral eng, Polytech Sch, Montreal, 56-75, chmn dept geol eng, 66-72, chmn dept mineral eng, 74-75; vpres res, Quebec Mining Explor Co, 75-77; PROF MINERAL ENG, POLYTECH SCH, MONTREAL, 77- *Concurrent Pos:* Consult engr, St-Lawrence Columbium & Metals, 56-66; mem bd, Mineral Explor Inst, 73-77 & Dighem Ltd, 75-77. *Honors & Awards:* Prix Scientifique, Govt Quebec, 70. *Mem:* Mineral Asn Can (pres, 67-68); fel Mineral Soc Am; Can Inst Mining & Metall; Soc Francaise Mineralogie & Cristallographie; Royal Soc Can. *Res:* Crystal structure of minerals; mineralogy applied to exploration and ore dressing; analytical geochemistry. *Mailing Add:* Polytech Sch PO Box 6079 Sta A Montreal PQ H3C 3A7 Can

PERRAULT, JACQUES, b Montreal, Que, June 25, 44. VIROLOGY, GENE EXPRESSION. *Educ:* McGill Univ, BSc, 64; Univ Calif, San Diego, PhD(virol cell biol), 72. *Prof Exp:* Fel virol, McGill Univ, 72, Univ Calif, Irvine, 72-74, Scripps Clin & Res Found, 74-76; asst res biologist, Univ Calif, San Diego, 76-77; ASST PROF MICROBIOL & IMMUNOL, WASHINGTON UNIV SCH MED, 77- *Concurrent Pos:* Actg instr, Univ Calif, Irvine, 72-74; course master, virol, Washington Univ Sch Med, 78-; Res Career Develop Award, NIH, 80. *Mem:* AAAS; Am Soc Microbiol; Soc Gen Microbiol London. *Res:* Molecular biology of defective interfering particles of RNA viruses and their role in controlling virus growth and maintaining persistent infectious of host cells. *Mailing Add:* Dept Microbiol & Immunol Box 8093 Washington Univ Sch Med St Louis MO 63110

PERRAULT, MARCEL JOSEPH, b St Anaclet, Can, Apr 24, 14. ANIMAL PHYSIOLOGY, ENDOCRINOLOGY. *Educ:* Univ Ottawa, Ont, BA, 35, PhD(physiol), 64; Laval Univ, MA, 49; Cornell Univ, MS, 51. *Prof Exp:* Lectr biol, Univ Ottawa, 46-54, res fel anat, 53-54, asst prof physiol, 54-55, assoc vdean fac sci & eng, 69-76, assoc prof, 55-79; RETIRED. *Concurrent Pos:* Ont Res Found & Nat Res Coun Can res grants. *Mem:* AAAS; Fr-Can Asn Advan Sci; Can Physiol Soc; Am Physiol Soc; Am Inst Biol Sci. *Res:* Physiological and biochemical evaluation of the androgenic function of the testis; action of stress and endocrine relationships. *Mailing Add:* 400 64th Ave (704 W) St Petersburg Beach FL 33706

PERREAULT, DAVID ALFRED, b Pawtucket, RI, Oct 25, 42; m 65; c 3. ELECTRICAL ENGINEERING. *Educ:* Purdue Univ, Lafayette, BSEE & MSEE, 68, PhD(elec eng), 70. *Prof Exp:* Asst prof elec eng, Clarkson Col Technol, 70-75; ASSOC PROF ELEC ENG, BOSTON UNIV, 75- *Concurrent Pos:* Consult, Magnavox Co, 70-; Nat Sci Found res grant, Clarkson Col Technol, 72-73. *Mem:* Inst Elec & Electronics Engrs; Am Soc Eng Educ. *Res:* Nonlinear networks and computer aided design. *Mailing Add:* Dept of Elec Eng Boston Univ Boston MA 02215

PERRENOD, STEPHEN CHARLES, b Natchez, Miss, Jan 31, 51. ASTRONOMY, ASTROPHYSICS. *Educ:* Mass Inst Technol, BS, 72; Harvard Univ, MA, 73, PhD(astron), 77. *Prof Exp:* Res assoc astrophysics, Univ Ill, 77-78; res assoc astron, Kitt Peak Nat Observ, 78-80; SCI SYSTS DESIGNER, SOHIO PETROL CO, 80- *Concurrent Pos:* Scientist, Am Sci & Eng, 73; vis scientist, NASA, 73; teaching fel, Harvard Univ, 73-77; res asst, Smithsonian Astrophys Observ, 74. *Mem:* Am Astron Soc; Am Phys Soc; Soc Petrol Engrs. *Res:* Extragalactic astronomy and cosmology; x-ray sources. *Mailing Add:* Sohio Petrol Co 100 Pine St San Francisco CA 94111

PERRET, GEORGE (EDWARD), b Neuchatel, Switz, Feb 7, 10; nat US; m 40; c 6. NEUROPHYSIOLOGY. *Educ:* Univ Berlin, MD, 38; Northwestern Univ, ScM, 44, PhD(surg), 48. *Prof Exp:* Asst, Kaiser-Wilhelm Inst Brain Res, Ger, 36-40; instr surg, Northwestern Univ, 41-46; assoc, Emory Univ, 46-49; from asst prof to assoc prof, 49-58, chmn div surg, 63-76, prof, 58-78, EMER PROF NEUROSURG, UNIV IOWA, 78- *Concurrent Pos:* Chief neurosurg serv, Lawson Vet Admin Hosp, Ga, 46-49; Fulbright lectr, Univ Salonika, Greece, 51-52; prof neurosurg, Univ Shiraz, Iran, 72. *Mem:* Soc Exp Biol & Med; Am Asn Neurol Surg; Am Asn Neuropath; Am Col Surgeons; Am Acad Neurol. *Res:* Peripheral and central regulation of gastric motility; regeneration in peripheral nerves and muscles; hydrocephalus; increased intracranial pressure and cerebral edema; subarachnoid hemorrhage; cerebral arteriovenous malformations; cerebral aneurysms. *Mailing Add:* Univ of Iowa Hosp Iowa City IA 52241

PERRET, WILLIAM RIKER, b Newark, NJ, Feb 29, 08; m 38; c 2. GEOPHYSICS. *Educ:* Mass Inst Technol, SB, 30, SM, 56. *Prof Exp:* Proj engr, Waterways Exp Sta, US Corps Engrs, Miss, 35-36; asst observer, Schlumberger Well Surv Corp, Tex, 36-37; chief geophys sect, Waterways Exp Sta, US Corps Engrs, 38-43; asst chief vacuum group, Process Improv, Y-12, Clinton Eng Works, Tenn Eastman Corp, 43-46; chief geophys sect, Waterways Exp Sta, US Corps Engrs, 46-51; physicist, Underground Physics Div, 51-73, CONSULT, SANDIA LABS, 73-; CONSULT, DEFENSE NUCLEAR AGENCY, 75-; CONSULT EXPLOSION GEOPHYS, R&D ASSOCS, 77- *Concurrent Pos:* Consult, Boeing Co; vis scientist & lectr, NMex Acad Sci. *Mem:* AAAS; emer fel Am Phys Soc; Soc Explor Geophys; Seismol Soc Am; life mem Am Geophys Union. *Res:* Vacuum gauging; soil corrosion; electrical and seismic exploration; static and dynamic earth stress instrumentation and analysis; underground effects of nuclear explosions. *Mailing Add:* 6116 Natalie Ave NE Albuquerque NM 87110

PERRETTA, MARCO A, b Antofagasta, Chile, Feb 4, 28; m 58; c 2. BIOCHEMISTRY, MOLECULAR BIOLOGY. *Educ:* Univ Chile, Chemist-Pharmacist, 52, Professor Extraordinary, 66, Full Professor, 67. *Prof Exp:* Asst prof anal chem, 51-59, assoc prof biochem, Sch Chem & Pharm, 60-64, prof biochem, Vet Sch, 63-72 & Dept Chem Physiol Sci, 73-75, PROF BIOCHEM & MOLECULAR BIOL, NUTRIT & FOOD TECHNOL INST, UNIV CHILE, 76- *Concurrent Pos:* Fel, Isotope Sch Harwell, Eng, 58 & Dept Biochem, Glasgow Univ, 58-59; consult, Fac Sci, Univ Chile, 70- & Nat Comn Res, Chile, 70-72; Rockefeller Found grant, 60-61; Nat Comn Res, Chile grant, 68-70; Univ Chile Comn Res grant, 70-81. *Mem:* Biol Soc Chile; Biochem Soc Chile; Chem Soc Chile; Endocrinol Soc Chile. *Res:* Molecular mechanism of hormone action; hormonal regulation of erythropoiesis; effects of erythropoietin and testosterone of RNA polymerases activities on rat bone marrow; some aspects in experimental malnutrition in rats. *Mailing Add:* El Toqui 1900 Santiago Chile

PERRI, JOSEPH MARK, b Philadelphia, Pa, June 3, 17; m 43; c 5. COLLOID CHEMISTRY, SYNTHETIC FIBER SCIENCE. *Educ:* Philadelphia Col Pharm, BS, 38; Univ Pa, MS, 39, PhD(chem), 43. *Prof Exp:* Plant chemist, Evanson Soap Co, 39-41; chief chemist, Nat Foam Syst, Inc, 43-49, chem dir, 49-56; RES ASSOC, TEXTILE FIBERS DEPT, E I DU PONT DE NEMOURS & CO, INC, 56- *Mem:* Am Chem Soc; Am Asn Textile Chemists & Colorists. *Res:* Surface active materials; fire fighting foams; fiber science; apparel (automated manufacturers; reinforced composites. *Mailing Add:* Textile Fibers Dept E I du Pont de Nemours & Co Inc Wilmington DE 19898

PERRIGO, LYLE DONOVAN, b San Antonio, Tex, Sept 28, 30; m 59; c 4. CHEMICAL ENGINEERING, PHYSICAL CHEMISTRY. *Educ:* Rice Inst, BA & BS, 53; Univ Idaho, MS, 61. *Prof Exp:* Engr, Gen Elec Co, 56-65; res engr, 65-66, res mgr corrosion, 66-69, res mgr chem eng, 69-73, res mgr food & agr, 73-75, proj mgr ocean thermal energy biofouling & corrosion, 76-78, res mgr technol transfer, Battelle Mem Inst, 78-81, MGR, ALASKA OPERS, BATTELLE MEM INST, 81- *Concurrent Pos:* Mem reactor decontamination info exchange group, US Atomic Energy Comn, 60-69; mem, UN-Washington State Trade Mission, Southeast Asia, 75. *Mem:* Inst Food Technol; Nat Asn Corrosion Eng. *Res:* Decontamination of nuclear reactors and equipment; effects of design on corrosion prevention; cold regions technology; isotope applications. *Mailing Add:* SRA Box 766 Anchorage AK 99507

PERRILL, STEPHEN ARTHUR, b Dayton, Ohio, Mar 13, 41; m 67; c 2. HERPETOLOGY. *Educ:* Ohio Wesleyan Univ, BA, 63; Southern Conn State Col, MS, 68; NC State Univ, PhD(zool), 73. *Prof Exp:* Teacher high schs, Conn, 64-66 & 68-70; asst prof, 73-80, ASSOC PROF ZOOL, BUTLER UNIV, 80- *Mem:* Am Soc Ichthyologists & Herpetologists; Soc Study Amphibians & Reptiles; Herpetologists League; Animal Behav Soc; AAAS. *Res:* Biology of the lizard genus Eumeces. *Mailing Add:* Dept of Zool Butler Univ Indianapolis IN 46208

PERRIN, CARROL HOLLINGSWORTH, b Peterborough, Ont, Dec 21, 12; m 44; c 3. ANALYTICAL CHEMISTRY. *Educ:* Univ Toronto, BA, 37. *Prof Exp:* Analyst chem, Can Packers, Ltd, 37-40, res investr gen chem, 40-41, plastics adhesives, 41-45, anal methods, 45-47, group leader anal methods, 47-77; RETIRED. *Mem:* Fel Asn Off Anal Chem. *Res:* Development of analytical methodology. *Mailing Add:* 8 Hardwood Gate Toronto ON M9W 4G1 Can

PERRIN, CHARLES LEE, b Pittsburgh, Pa, July 22, 38; m 64; c 2. ORGANIC CHEMISTRY. *Educ:* Harvard Univ, AB, 59, PhD(chem), 63. *Prof Exp:* NSF fel, Univ Calif, Berkeley, 63; asst prof, 64-71, assoc prof, 71-80, PROF CHEM, UNIV CALIF, SAN DIEGO, 80- *Concurrent Pos:* Nat Inst Neurol Dis & Stroke spec res fel, Gothenburg Univ, 72-73. *Mem:* AAAS; Am Chem Soc. *Res:* Kinetics and mechanism of organic reactions. *Mailing Add:* Dept Chem Univ Calif San Diego La Jolla CA 92093

PERRIN, EDWARD BURTON, b Greensboro, Vt, Sept 19, 31; m 56; c 2. BIOSTATISTICS. *Educ:* Middlebury Col, AB, 53; Columbia Univ, MA, 56; Stanford Univ, PhD(biostatist), 60. *Prof Exp:* Asst prof biostatist, Grad Sch Pub Health, Univ Pittsburgh, 59-62; from asst prof to prof prev med, Sch Med, Univ Wash, 62-70, head div biostatist, 65-69, prof biostatist & chmn dept, Sch Pub Health & Community Med, 70-72; dep dir, Nat Ctr Health Statist, Dept Health, Educ & Welfare, 72-73, dir, 73-75; res scientist, Human Affairs Res Ctr, 75-77, DIR HEALTH & POP STUDY CTR, BATTELLE MEM INST, 77- *Concurrent Pos:* Fulbright scholar, Edinburgh Univ, 53-54; Milbank Mem Fund fac fel, 64-69; clin prof, Dept Community Med & Int Health, Georgetown Univ, 72-75; prof, Dept Health Serv, Univ Wash, 75- *Honors & Awards:* Spiegelman Gold Medal, Am Pub Health Asn, 70. *Mem:* Inst Med-Nat Acad Sci; fel AAAS; fel Am Pub Health Asn; fel Am Statist Asn; Biomet Soc. *Res:* Health data, its collection, analysis and utilization. *Mailing Add:* 4900 NE 39th St Seattle WA 98105

PERRIN, EUGENE VICTOR, b Detroit, Mich, Mar 7, 27; m 56; c 4. PEDIATRICS, PATHOLOGY. *Educ:* Wayne State Univ, AB, 48; Univ Mich, MD, 53. *Prof Exp:* Intern, Sinai Hosp, Detroit, Mich, 53-54; asst resident path, Children's Med Ctr, Boston, Mass, 55-56; resident, Boston Lying-In & Free Hosp Women, 56-57; resident, New Eng Deaconess Hosp, 57-58; instr, Col Physicians & Surgeons, 58-59; sr res assoc path & pediat, Col Med, Univ Cincinnati, 59-61, from instr to assoc prof, 59-66; assoc pathologist, Inst Path, Case Western Reserve Univ, 66-72, pathologist, 72-74, assoc prof path, pediat & reproductive biol, Sch Med, 66-74, assoc develop biol, 72-74; assoc prof path, 75-77, PROF PATH & ASSOC PEDIAT, OBSTET & ANAT, WAYNE STATE UNIV, 77-; DIR ANAT PATH, CHILD HOSP MICH, 77- *Concurrent Pos:* Pvt pract, Mich, 54-55; teaching fel, Harvard Med Sch, 56-57; resident, Babies Hosp, Presby Hosp, New York, 58-59; asst pathologist, Children's Hosp, Cincinnati, Ohio, 59-61, assoc pathologist, 63-66, pathologist-in-chg, Babies' & Children's Hosp, 66-74; dir labs, Health Hill Hosp, Cleveland, Ohio, 68-74; pathologist-in-chg, Rainbow Hosp, Cleveland; adj assoc prof path, Case Western Reserve Univ, 74-; pathologist, Sinai Hosp, Detroit, 74-75; assoc attend pathologist, Sinai Hosp, 75- & Hutzel Hosp, 76- *Mem:* AAAS; Am Asn Pathologists & Bacteriologists; Soc Occup Environ Health; Am Soc Cell Biol; Tissue Cult Asn. *Res:* Biology of disease in fetus and newborn; placental pathology; metabolic diseases studied in vitro; pediatric oncology; comparative teratology; cytoskeleton in teratology; occupational fetopathy; Great Lakes water quality. *Mailing Add:* Lab Med Child Hosp of Mich 3901 Beaubien Detroit MI 48201

PERRIN, JAMES STUART, b Superior, Wis, June 19, 36. MATERIALS SCIENCE. *Educ:* Mass Inst Technol, BS, 58; Univ Ill, Urbana, MS, 60; Stanford Univ, PhD(mat sci), 69. *Prof Exp:* fel, Columbus Labs, Battelle Mem Inst, 66-74, res leader, 74-81; PRES, FRACTURE CONTROL CORP, 81- *Mem:* Fel Am Soc Testing & Mat; Am Inst Mining, Metall & Petrol Engrs; Am Nuclear Soc; Am Soc Metals; Am Soc Mech Engrs. *Res:* Mechanical and physical properties of unirradiated and irradiated nuclear materials; failure studies and development of new materials for nuclear pressure vessels, piping and fuel rod materials. *Mailing Add:* Fracture Control Corp 340 S Kellog Ave Suite G Goleta CA 93117

PERRIN, WILLIAM FERGUS, b Oconto Falls, Wis, Aug 20, 38; c 2. MAMMALOGY. *Educ:* San Diego State Univ, BS, 66; Univ Calif, Los Angeles, PhD(zool), 72. *Prof Exp:* FISHERY BIOLOGIST, SOUTHWEST FISHERIES CTR, NAT MARINE FISHERIES SERV, 68- *Concurrent Pos:* Res assoc, Smithsonian Inst, 72- & Los Angeles County Mus, 73-; mem, Small Cetaceans Subcomt, Sci Comt, Int Whaling Comn, 74-, chmn, 79-; mem, Ad Hoc Consult Group II, Adv Comt Marine Resources Res, Food & Agr Orgn, UN, 74-76, convenor, 75-76; mem, Whales Adv Group, Survival Serv Comn, Int Union Conserv Nature & Natural Resources, 75-80, comt sci adv, US Marine Mammal Comn, 80-, bd dirs, Mex Soc Study Marine Mammal, 80-; affiliate prof, Col Fisheries, Univ Washington, 81- *Mem:* Am Soc Mammalogists; Am Inst Fishery Res Biologists. *Res:* Systematics, growth and reproduction, and community ecology of pelagic delphinid cetaceans, with emphasis on the eastern tropical Pacific Ocean. *Mailing Add:* Southwest Fisheries Ctr 8604 La Jolla Shores Dr La Jolla CA 92038

PERRINE, JOHN W, JR, b Hightstown, NJ, Feb 26, 27; m 55; c 3. BIOLOGY. *Educ:* Brown Univ, BA, 50; NY Univ, MS, 57, PhD(biol), 64. *Prof Exp:* Res scientist biol, Am Cyanamid Co, 54-66; res scientist, 66-72, group leader, 72-77, RES SCIENTIST, PHARMACEUT DIV, SANDOZ, INC, 77- *Mem:* Am Soc Pharmacol & Exp Therapeut; NY Acad Sci; Reticuloendothelial Soc; Tissue Cult Asn. *Res:* Cell culture, atherosclerosis, inflammation; application of cell culture to the development of anti-atherosclerotic drugs. *Mailing Add:* Biol Res Pharmaceut Div Sandoz Inc Rte 10 East Hanover NJ 07936

PERRINE, R(ICHARD) L(EROY), b Mountain View, Calif, May 15, 24; m 45; c 2. ENVIRONMENTAL SCIENCE & ENGINEERING. *Educ:* San Jose State Col, AB, 49; Stanford Univ, MS, 50, PhD(phys chem), 53. *Prof Exp:* Asst chem res, Stanford Univ, 50-53; res chemist, Calif Res Corp, Div, Standard Oil Co Calif, 53-59; assoc prof eng, 59-63, PROF ENG & APPL SCI, UNIV CALIF, LOS ANGELES, 63-, CHMN DEPT ENVIRON SCI & ENG, 73- *Concurrent Pos:* Lectr, Univ Southern Calif, 57-59; mem, Los Angeles County Energy Comn, 74-81; chmn qual assessment comt, Adv Coun South Coast Air Qual Mgt Dist, 77- *Honors & Awards:* Outstanding Engr Merit Award, Inst Advan Eng, 75. *Mem:* Am Chem Soc; Am Inst Chem Engrs; Soc Petrol Engrs; Air Pollution Control Asn; Am Water Resources Asn. *Res:* Energy resources; physics of flow through porous media. *Mailing Add:* Eng Systs Dept 2066 Eng I Univ Calif Los Angeles CA 90024

PERRINO, CHARLES T, b Vandergrift, Pa, Jan 27, 38; m 64; c 2. SOLID STATE CHEMISTRY. *Educ:* Indiana Univ Pa, BS, 62; Ariz State Univ, PhD(chem), 66. *Prof Exp:* From asst prof to assoc prof, 66-75, PROF CHEM & ASSOC DEAN SCH SCI, CALIF STATE UNIV, HAYWARD, 75- *Concurrent Pos:* Res Found grant, 66-68; NSF acad year exten grant, 67-69. *Honors & Awards:* Fulbright lectr, Univ Ceylon, 69-70. *Mem:* Am Chem Soc. *Res:* Defects and electrical properties in hydrogen bonded solids, namely potassium dihydrogen phosphate and potassium dihydrogen arsenate. *Mailing Add:* Dept of Chem Calif State Univ Hayward CA 94542

PERRITT, ALEXANDER M, b Kearny, NJ, Nov 28, 28; m 55; c 4. MICROBIOLOGY. *Educ:* Syracuse Univ, AB, 51, MS, 57, PhD(microbiol), 61. *Prof Exp:* Bacteriologist, Nat Yeast Corp, NJ, 52-53, 55; jr chemist, Hoffman LaRoche, Inc, 57-58; bacteriologist, Carter-Wallace, Inc, 61-66; dir microbiol, Worthington Biochem Corp, 66-68; res dir microbiol, Foster D Snell, Inc, 68-70; dir microbiol, Affil Med Res, 70-73; proj mgr chemother fermentation, Frederick Cancer Res Ctr, Litton Bionetics, Inc, Md, 74; PRES & DIR RES, PERRITT LABS, INC, 73- *Concurrent Pos:* Mem tech adv comt poison prev packaging, Consumer Prod Safety Comn. *Mem:* AAAS; Am Soc Microbiol; Soc Indust Microbiol; Am Soc Testing & Mat. *Res:* Applied microbiology; fermentation technology; evaluation of poison prevention packaging. *Mailing Add:* Perritt Labs Inc PO Box 147 Hightstown NJ 08520

PERRON, PIERRE OMER, b Louiseville, Que, Aug 19, 39. METALLURGICAL ENGINEERING, NUCLEAR ENGINEERING. *Educ:* Laval Univ, BA, 59, BSc, 63; Univ Strathclyde, Glasgow, PhD(metall), 66. *Prof Exp:* Res officer nuclear mat, Atomic Energy Can, Ltd, 66-68; mgr, radiation protection, Hydro-Quebec, 68-71; dir, mat sci, 71-75, DIR RES & DEVELOP, INDUST RES CENTRE, QUEBEC, 75- *Concurrent Pos:* Kennecott Copper fel, 61-62; Alcan Award, 62-63; Athlone fel, 63-65; NATO fel, 65-66. *Mem:* Am Soc Metals; Can Inst Mining & Metall; Health Physics Soc. *Res:* Director responsible for all research and development activities in materials science, mechanical engineering, electronics and production engineering. *Mailing Add:* 333 Franquet Ste-Foy PQ G1V 4C7 Can

PERRON, YVON G, b Montreal, Que, Feb 14, 25; m 51; c 5. ORGANIC CHEMISTRY, MEDICINAL CHEMISTRY. *Educ:* Univ Montreal, BSc, 48, MSc, 49, PhD(org chem), 51. *Prof Exp:* Nat Res Coun Can fel, 51; asst prof, Univ Montreal, 51-54; fel, Univ Rochester, 54-55; res scientist, Bristol Labs, NY, 55-62, asst dir chem res, 62-63; asst dir res, 63-66, dir labs, 66-71, dir res, 71-74, VPRES RES, BRISTOL LABS CAN, 74- *Mem:* Am Chem Soc; fel Chem Inst Can. *Res:* Chemistry of natural products; synthesis of heterocyclic compounds of potential medicinal interest; determination of structure and synthesis of antibiotics. *Mailing Add:* Bristol Labs of Can 100 Industrial Blvd Candiac PQ J5R 1J1 Can

PERRONE, NICHOLAS, b New York, NY, Apr 30, 30; m 57; c 5. APPLIED MECHANICS, BIOMECHANICS. *Educ:* Polytech Inst Brooklyn, BAeroEng, 51, MS, 53, PhD(appl mech), 58. *Prof Exp:* Res asst aeronaut eng & appl mech, Polytech Inst Brooklyn, 51-54, res assoc, 55-58; asst prof eng sci, Pratt Inst, 58-59, assoc prof, 60-62; sr scientist, Off Naval Res, 62-68, dir struct mech prog, 68; NIH spec res fel biomech, Georgetown Univ, 69-70; DIR STRUCT MECH, OFF NAVAL RES, 70- *Concurrent Pos:* Adj prof mech, Catholic Univ, 64-; consult, US Govt & Nat Acad Sci. *Honors & Awards:* Commendation on Hwy Safety Design, Dept Transp, Fed Hwy Admin, 75; John Curtis Lect Award, Am Soc Eng Educ, 76. *Mem:* Fel AAAS; Am Inst Aeronaut & Astronaut; NY Acad Sci; fel Am Acad Mech; Am Soc Civil Engrs. *Res:* Dynamic plastic, rate-sensitive response of structures;

reactor technology; biodynamics and crashworthiness of vehicle impact; finite difference techniques with arbitrary grids; nonlinear relaxation methods to solve problems with geometric and material nonlinearities. *Mailing Add:* 12207 Valerie Lane Laurel MD 20708

PERROS, THEODORE PETER, b Cumberland, Md, Aug 16, 22; m 73. FLUORINE CHEMISTRY, FORENSIC SCIENCES. *Educ:* George Washington Univ, BS, 46, MS, 47, PhD(chem), 52. *Prof Exp:* Analyst, Res Div, US Naval Ord Lab, 43-46; from asst to assoc prof chem, 46-60, chmn dept forensic sci, 71-73, PROF CHEM, GEORGE WASHINGTON UNIV, 60-, CHMN DEPT, 80- *Concurrent Pos:* Res Corp grant, 53-54; consult, US Naval Ord Lab, 53-56; pres, South Intercollegiate Athletic Conf, 68; secy, Ahepa Educ Found, 70- *Mem:* Am Chem Soc; Sigma Xi; Soc Appl Spectros; fel Am Inst Chemists; fel Am Acad Forensic Sci. *Res:* Coordination chemistry; preparation and characterization of fluorine complexes of platinum; stabilities of inorganic coordination polymers; chemical education. *Mailing Add:* Dept of Chem George Washington Univ Washington DC 20052

PERROTT, GEORGE ST JOHN, medical statistics, deceased

PERROTTA, ANTHONY JOSEPH, b Erie, Pa, Aug 27, 37; m 61; c 2. MINERALOGY, CRYSTALLOGRAPHY. *Educ:* Pa State Univ, BS, 60; Univ Chicago, MS & PhD(mineral, crystallog), 65. *Prof Exp:* Phys scientist ceramics, mineral & crystallog, Union Carbide Corp Res Inst, NY, 67-69; SR RES SCIENTIST, GULF RES & DEVELOP CO, 69- *Mem:* Mineral Soc Am; Am Ceramic Soc; Sigma Xi. *Res:* Crystal structure, phase equilibria, thermal and catalytic properties of mineralogical and ceramic materials. *Mailing Add:* Gulf Res & Develop Co PO Drawer 2038 Pittsburgh PA 15230

PERROTTA, JAMES, b Trenton, NJ, May 19, 19; m 47; c 1. CHEMISTRY. *Educ:* Univ NC, BS, 40. *Prof Exp:* Field rep, Venereal Dis Div, USPHS, 45-46; technician toxoid vaccine mfg, E R Squibb & Sons, Inc, 46-47, tech supvr, 47-50, tech supvr bio-control dept, 50, sect head endocrine mfg, 50-56, asst dept head biochem mfg, 56-61, dept head, 61-64, dept head packaging, 64-65, prod mgr, NY, 65-68, plant mgr, NJ, 68-70, bulk mfg dir, 70-75; asst to pres food div, 75-79, VPRES OPERS, INGREDIENT TECHNOL CORP, 79- *Mem:* Am Pharmaceut Asn; NY Acad Sci; Am Inst Chemists. *Res:* Isolation and crystallization of natural products; insulin; thyroxin; vitamin B12; human blood products; estrogens; development and manufacture of toxoids and vaccines; manufacturing of creams, ointments, liquids, tablets and capsules; fermentation and isolation of antibiotics; manufacture of radiopharmaceuticals; manufacture of tabletting excipients. *Mailing Add:* Ingredient Technol Corp Plaza Nine Rte 9 Woodbridge NJ 07095

PERRY, ALBERT SOLOMON, b Salonika, Greece, Apr 15, 15; nat US; m 46; c 3. INSECT TOXICOLOGY, ENVIRONMENTAL SCIENCES. *Educ:* Univ Calif, BS, 41, PhD(entom), 50. *Prof Exp:* Res entomologist, Calif Spray-Chem Co Div, Stand Oil Co Calif, 50-51; res scientist, Tech Develop Lab, USPHS, 51-74; PROF ENTOM, INST NATURE CONSERV RES, TEL AVIV UNIV, 74- *Concurrent Pos:* Consult, Malaria Eradication Div, WHO, 58. *Mem:* AAAS; Am Chem Soc; Entom Soc Am; Sigma Xi; Israel Entom Soc. *Res:* Insect toxicology and biochemistry; mechanisms of resistance to insecticides; toxicity of pesticides to nontarget organisms; bioaccumulation, magnification, and metabolic fate of pesticides in aquatic food-chain organisms; pesticide monitoring. *Mailing Add:* Inst for Nature Conserv Res 202 Argentina Bldg Ramat Aviv Israel

PERRY, ALFRED EUGENE, b Pendleton, Ore, Jan 12, 31; m 54; c 3. ZOOLOGY, ECOLOGY. *Educ:* Walla Walla Col, BA, 53, MA, 58; Okla State Univ, PhD(zool), 65. *Prof Exp:* Instr biol, Union Col, Nebr, 60-62; res asst zool, Okla State Univ, 62-65; asst prof, Memphis State Univ, 65-69; assoc develop, 78-80, ASSOC PROF BIOL, WALLA WALLA COL, 69-, PROF INDUST TECH, 80- *Concurrent Pos:* Consult, Memphis & Shelby County Health Dept, 65-69. *Mem:* Am Soc Mammal; Am Ornith Union; Soc Study Amphibians & Reptiles; Soc Syst Zool. *Res:* Taxonomy and ecology of pocket mice and pocket gophers. *Mailing Add:* Off of Develop Walla Walla Col College Place WA 99324

PERRY, ALFRED MORRIS, physics, nuclear engineering, see previous edition

PERRY, BILLY WAYNE, b Portland, Tenn, Sept 15, 37. BIOCHEMISTRY, CLINICAL CHEMISTRY. *Educ:* Tenn Technol Univ, BS, 59, MA, 61; Univ Tenn, Memphis, PhD(biochem), 67. *Prof Exp:* From instr to asst prof clin chem, Med Col Ala, 67-70; ASST PROF PATH, MED COL WIS, 70-; ALLIED PROF STAFF, MILWAUKEE COUNTY MED COMPLEX, 70-; ALLIED HEALTH STAFF MEM, FROEDTERT MEM LUTHERAN HOSP, 80- *Concurrent Pos:* Consult scientist, Univ Ala Hosps & Clins, 67-70; consult, Vet Admin Hosp, Birmingham, Ala, 69-70. *Mem:* AAAS; Am Asn Clin Chemists; Am Chem Soc; Am Soc Med Technol; NY Acad Sci. *Res:* Protein structure and function relationship; research and development of methods and instrumentation in clinical chemistry. *Mailing Add:* Dept of Path B700 W Wisconsin Ave Milwaukee WI 53226

PERRY, CHARLES HAMPTON, ceramics science, electrical engineering, see previous edition

PERRY, CHARLES LEWIS, b Culver, Ind, Dec 9, 33; m 64; c 1. ASTRONOMY. *Educ:* Ind Univ, Bloomington, BA, 55; Univ Calif, Berkeley, PhD(astron), 65. *Prof Exp:* Res assoc astron, Kitt Peak Nat Observ, 63-65; res fel, Mt Stromlo Observ, 65-66; asst prof, 66-71, assoc prof, 71-79, PROF PHYSICS & ASTRON, LA STATE UNIV, 79- *Concurrent Pos:* NSF res grants, 67, 69 & 77. *Mem:* Am Astron Soc; Int Astron Union. *Res:* Photoelectric photometry with applications to galactic structure. *Mailing Add:* Dept of Physics & Astron La State Univ Baton Rouge LA 70803

PERRY, CHARLES RUFUS, JR, b Throckmorton, Tex, Oct 1, 36. MATHEMATICS, STATISTICS. *Educ:* Tex Tech Univ, BS, 67, MS, 69, PhD(math), 71. *Prof Exp:* assoc prof math, Tex Lutheran Col, 71-82; MATH STATISTICIAN, STATIST REPORTING SERV, US DEPT AGR, 81- *Concurrent Pos:* Nat Res Coun sr res assoc, Earth Observ Div, Johnson Space Ctr, NASA, 78-80. *Mem:* Math Asn Am; Am Statist Asn. *Res:* Linear algebra; probability and statistics; sample theory. *Mailing Add:* 15923 Mill Point Dr Houston TX 77059

PERRY, CHARLES WILLIAM, b Taunton, Mass, Oct 1, 10; m 43. CHEMICAL ENGINEERING, PETROLEUM ENGINEERING. *Educ:* Northeastern Univ, BS, 34; Mass Inst Technol, MS, 35; Johns Hopkins Univ, DrEng, 40. *Prof Exp:* Jr technologist, Shell Oil Co, 35-37; develop engr, US Indust Chem, Inc, 37-40; design engr, Merck & Co, Inc, 41-42; div chief, Rubber Div, War Prod Bd, 43-44; mgr chem process div, Phillips Petrol Co, 44-51; chief process engr, Phillips Chem Co, 51-52; asst mgr cent eng, Olin Corp, 52-59, assoc dir plant develop, Energy Div, 59-60; vpres mfg, Witco Chem Co, 60-71, sr vpres planning, 71-73; staff petrol engr, Fed Energy Admin, 74; sect head planning, Off Coal Res, 75; sect head enhanced oil recovery, Energy Res & Develop Admin, 76-77; SR STAFF ENGR, FOSSIL FUELS EXTRACTION DIV, DEPT ENERGY, 78- *Mem:* AAAS; Am Inst Mining, Metall & Petrol Engrs; Am Petrol Inst; Am Inst Chem Engrs. *Res:* Continuous distillation; petroleum refining; operation of synthetic rubber plants; chemicals from petroleum; electrolytic caustic soda and chlorine; chemical fertilizers; ammonia; rocket fuels; fuels and lubricants. *Mailing Add:* 19724 Greenside Terr Gaithersburg MD 20760

PERRY, CLARK WILLIAM, b Jersey City, NJ, May 14, 36; m 62; c 3. SYNTHETIC ORGANIC CHEMISTRY. *Educ:* Univ Rochester, BS, 58; Mass Inst Technol, PhD(org chem), 62. *Prof Exp:* Res chemist, Maywood Div, Stepan Chem Co, 62-64, dir res, 64-66; sr chemist, 66-76, ASST GROUP CHIEF, HOFFMAN-LA ROCHE, INC, 77- *Mem:* Am Chem Soc. *Res:* Organic synthesis; labelling of drugs and metabolites with radioisotopes. *Mailing Add:* Hoffmann-La Roche Inc Nutley NJ 07110

PERRY, CLIVE HOWE, b Merton, Eng, May 9, 36; m 60; c 2. SOLID STATE PHYSICS. *Educ:* Univ London, BSc, 57, PhD(low temperature physics), 60. *Prof Exp:* Sloan foreign fel infrared spectros & low temperature physics, Sch Advan Study, Mass Inst Technol, 60-61, res assoc, 61-62, asst prof solid state physics, 62-68; assoc prof, 68-72, PROF SOLID STATE PHYSICS, NORTHEASTERN UNIV, 72- *Concurrent Pos:* Consult, Arthur D Little Corp, 63-64, Air Force Cambridge Res Labs, 65-, Borders Electronics Res Corp, 66-, Melpar Space Sci Labs, 66-, PTR Optics, 70-, Norcon Instruments, 72- & Gilford Instruments, 80; vis guest prof, Max Planck Inst Solid State Physics, 72-73; Nat Ctr Sci Res res assoc, Lab Solid State Physics, Univ Paris, 75; Humboldt Found sr Am scientist award, Max Planck Inst High Magnetic Fields, Grenoble, France, 76. *Honors & Awards:* Coblentz Soc Award Molecular Spectros, 71. *Mem:* Am Phys Soc; fel Brit Inst Physics. *Res:* Low temperature physics; far infrared and Raman spectroscopy; high-pressure physics; phase transitions; internal molecular and lattice vibrations; antiferromagnetic resonances; ferroelectrics; semiconductors; inelastic neutron scattering; high magnetic fields; two demensional electronic systems; supersonic conductors. *Mailing Add:* Solid State Spectros Lab Northeastern Univ Boston MA 02115

PERRY, DAVID ANTHONY, b Kansas City, Kans, Sept 19, 38; wid; c 2. ECOLOGY. *Educ:* Univ Fla, BS, 61; MS, 66; Mont State Univ, MS, 71, PhD(ecol), 74. *Prof Exp:* Res assoc, Dept Biol, Mont State Univ, 74; range ecologist, Mont Dept Natural Resources, 74-75; res forester, Intermountain Forest & Range Exp Sta, US Forest Serv, 75-77; ASST PROF, DEPT FOREST SCI, ORE STATE UNIV, 77- *Mem:* Ecol Soc Am; Sigma Xi. *Res:* Ecology and genetics of coniferous forests; silviculture; nutrient cycling; host-pest relations. *Mailing Add:* Dept Forest Sci Ore State Univ Corvallis OR 97331

PERRY, DENNIS, b West Point, Miss, Dec 25, 32; m 58; c 4. MICROBIOLOGY, BACTERIAL PHYSIOLOGY. *Educ:* Southern Ill Univ, BA, 57, MA, 58; Northwestern Univ, PhD(microbiol), 62. *Prof Exp:* From instr to asst prof, 62-69, ASSOC PROF MICROBIOL, NORTHWESTERN UNIV, CHICAGO, 69- *Mem:* Am Soc Microbiol. *Res:* Genetic transformation of streptococci. *Mailing Add:* Dept of Microbiol Northwestern Univ Med Sch Chicago IL 60611

PERRY, DENNIS GORDON, b Bakersfield, Calif, July 8, 42; m 64; c 2. COMPUTER NETWORKS. *Educ:* Westmont Col, AB, 64; Univ Wash, PhD(chem), 70; Univ NMex, MBA, 81. *Prof Exp:* Fel, Brookhaven Nat Lab, 70-72; mem staff, 72-78, asst group leader, 78-81, DEP GROUP LEADER, LOS ALAMOS NAT LAB, 81- *Mem:* Am Chem Soc; Inst Elec & Electronics Engrs; Am Sci Affil; Asn Comput Mach. *Res:* Fission; charged particle reactions; meson induced reactions; medium and high energy interactions; neutron reactions; cosmic ray interactions; on-line computer applications; network engineering. *Mailing Add:* C-5 MS-255 Los Alamos Sci Lab Los Alamos NM 87545

PERRY, DONALD DUNHAM, b New York, NY, June 9, 22; m 58; c 3. ORGANIC CHEMISTRY, POLYMER CHEMISTRY. *Educ:* Harvard Univ, AB, 43, AM, 48, PhD(org chem), 51. *Prof Exp:* Fel, Ohio State Univ, 50-52; res chemist, Polychem Dept, Exp Sta, E I du Pont de Nemours & Co, Del, 52-55; res chemist, Reaction Motors Inc, NJ, 55-58, unit & sect supvr, Reaction Motors Div, Thiokol Chem Corp, 58-66; mgr cent res, Riegel Paper Corp, 66-70; mgr appl res, Personal Prod Co, 70-72; supvr polymer lab, Polychrome Corp, 72-75; MGR MAT SCI, ELASTIMOLD DIV, AMERACE CORP, 77- *Mem:* Am Chem Soc. *Res:* Synthesis of high energy materials; synthesis and application of polymers for coatings, films, adhesives and fiber systems; radiation-curable polymers; application of plastics and elastomers in electrical insulation. *Mailing Add:* RD 1 Box 414 Milford NJ 08848

PERRY, E L, JR, mathematics, see previous edition

PERRY, EDMOND S, b New York, NY; m 39. PHYSICAL CHEMISTRY. *Educ:* Univ Ill, BS, 35; Univ Wis, PhD(phys chem), 38. *Prof Exp:* Res chemist, Nat Aniline Div, Allied Chem & Dye Corp, 38; res chemist, Eastman Kodak Co, NY, 38-42; res chemist, Distillation Prod, Inc, 42-54; res assoc, Eastman Kodak Co, 54-62, sr res assoc, 62-65, asst head, Photomat Div, 65-73, tech asst to dir, Kodak Res Labs, 73-77; RETIRED. *Concurrent Pos:* Chmn Gordon res conf separations & purifications, 59. *Res:* Electrochemistry; colloids; high vacuum engineering and distillation; physical and chemical separations; tall oil chemistry; chemical engineering; science of image formation and signal recording in chemical and physical systems. *Mailing Add:* 310 Oakridge Rochester NY 14617

PERRY, EDWARD BELK, b Oxford, Mich, Sept 29, 39; m 66; c 3. SOIL MECHANICS, FOUNDATION ENGINEERING. *Educ:* Univ Miss, BS, 62; Miss State Univ, MS, 68; Tex A&M Univ, PhD(civil eng), 73. *Prof Exp:* RES CIVIL ENGR, SOIL MECH, WATERWAYS EXP STA, US ARMY CORP ENGRS, 63- *Mem:* Am Soc Civil Engrs; Am Soc Testing & Mats; Am Soc Eng Educ. *Res:* Reinforced earth; dispersive clays; erosion of soils; streambank protection. *Mailing Add:* US Army Corp Engrs Waterways Exp Sta PO Box 631 Vicksburg MS 39180

PERRY, EDWARD MAHLON, b Providence, RI, Aug 9, 28; m 52; c 5. ORGANIC CHEMISTRY. *Educ:* Brown Univ, ScB, 50; Univ Conn, MS, 55, PhD(org chem), 56. *Prof Exp:* Chemist, ICI Organics, Inc, 55-68; sr develop engr, Owens-Corning Fiberglas Corp, 68-73; LAB DIR, SOLUOL CHEM CO, WEST WARWICK, 73- *Mem:* Am Asn Textile Chemists & Colorists; Am Chem Soc. *Res:* Textiles; fiber. *Mailing Add:* 54 Clark Rd Barrington RI 02806

PERRY, ELI, b Philadelphia, Pa, Dec 28, 20. CHEMICAL ENGINEERING. *Educ:* Univ Pa, BS, 42; Mass Inst Technol, SM, 47. *Prof Exp:* Res engr, 42-46, group leader, 47-50, asst dir res, 50-57, res assoc, 57-79, SR TECHNOL ASSOC, MONSANTO CO, 80- *Concurrent Pos:* Am Chem Soc tour lectr & NSF vis scientist & acad year lectr. *Mem:* AAAS; Am Chem Soc; Am Inst Chem Engrs; Soc Plastics Engrs; Royal Soc Chemists. *Res:* Polymers and plastics; catalysis and kinetics; reaction mechanisms; fibers and permeation. *Mailing Add:* Corp Res & Develop Staff Monsanto Co 800 N Lindbergh Blvd St Louis MO 63166

PERRY, ERIK DAVID, b Dallas, Tex, Oct 17, 52; m 74; c 1. MECHANICAL ENGINEERING, STRUCTURAL ENGINEERING. *Educ:* Cornell Univ, BSME, 74; Univ Mich, MSE, 75. *Prof Exp:* Teaching asst aerospace eng, Univ Mich, 74-75; engr mech-struct design, Antenna Lab, Lockheed Missiles & Space Co, 75-76; engr prof tech staff, Design Fusion Reactors, Plasma Physics Lab, 77-79, HEAD GEN FABRICATION & DESIGN SECT, PLASMA PHYSICS LAB, PRINCETON UNIV, 79- *Mem:* Am Inst Aeronaut & Astronaut; Am Soc Mech Engrs. *Mailing Add:* Plasma Physics Lab PO Box 451 Princeton NJ 08544

PERRY, ERNEST JOHN, b Vienna, Austria, Feb 12, 19; nat US; m 50. PHYSICAL CHEMISTRY. *Educ:* McGill Univ, BSc, 42, PhD(chem), 51. *Prof Exp:* Chemist, Dept Nat Health & Welfare, Ottawa, Can, 51-52; res chemist, 52-60, res assoc, 61-79, SR RES ASSOC, EASTMAN KODAK CO, 80- *Mem:* Am Chem Soc. *Res:* Polymer and colloid chemistry; chemistry related to photography. *Mailing Add:* 236 Frankland Rd Rochester NY 14617

PERRY, EUGENE ARTHUR, b Baraboo, Wis, Mar 14, 38. MICROBIOLOGY, MYCOLOGY. *Educ:* Northland Col, BA, 60; Ind Univ, PhD(mycol), 67. *Prof Exp:* Asst prof, 67-76, ASSOC PROF BIOL, KNOX COL, ILL, 76- *Mem:* AAAS; Bot Soc Am. *Res:* Morphology and physiology of fungi, particularly differentiation of fungal reproductive structures and the physiology of host-parasite relationships in fungi. *Mailing Add:* Dept of Biol Knox Col Galesburg IL 61401

PERRY, EUGENE CARLETON, JR, b Mar 23, 33; US citizen; m 62; c 2. GEOCHEMISTRY. *Educ:* Ga Inst Technol, BS, 54; Mass Inst Technol, PhD(geol), 63. *Prof Exp:* Res assoc geochem, Minn Geol Surv, Univ Minn, Minneapolis, 64-65, asst prof, 65-72; actg chmn dept, 72-77, ASSOC PROF GEOL, NORTHERN ILL UNIV, 72- *Mem:* AAAS; Geochem Soc; Geol Soc Am; Mineral Soc Am. *Res:* Stable isotope chemistry of metamorphic rocks and ancient sediments. *Mailing Add:* Dept of Geol Northern Ill Univ De Kalb IL 60115

PERRY, FRANK ANTHONY, b Lake Charles, La, Dec 16, 21; m 48; c 2. SURGERY. *Educ:* Meharry Med Col, MD, 45; Am Bd Surg, dipl, 53. *Prof Exp:* Intern, Meharry Med Col, 45-46, resident surg, 47-51; fel & resident cancer surg, Mem Ctr Cancer & Allied Dis, 51-54; surg consult, Sloan-Kettering Inst, 55-56; assoc prof, 56, 58-68, coordr regional med prog, 67-72, dir learning resources ctr prog, 73-81, PROF SURG, MEHARRY MED COL, 68-, DIR SURG RES, 58- *Mem:* Am Soc Head & Neck Surg; Am Col Surgeons. *Res:* Fluids and electrolytes. *Mailing Add:* Dept Surg Meharry Med Col Nashville TN 37208

PERRY, FREDERICK G(ARDINER), JR, b Newton, Mass, Oct 24, 21; m 43; c 4. CHEMICAL ENGINEERING. *Educ:* Mass Inst Technol, SB, 43, SM, 47. *Prof Exp:* Group leader, 47-60, SR STAFF ASSOC, RES & DEVELOP DIV, ARTHUR D LITTLE, INC, 60- *Mem:* Forest Prod Res Soc; Tech Asn Pulp & Paper Indust; Am Inst Chem Engrs. *Res:* Technical economic evaluations of processes and projects of the pulp and paper industry. *Mailing Add:* Arthur D Little Inc 15 Acorn Park Cambridge MA 02140

PERRY, HAROLD, b Hamtramck, Mich, June 26, 24; m 48; c 3. RADIOTHERAPY. *Educ:* Howard Univ, MD, 48. *Prof Exp:* Intern, Freedmens Hosp, Washington, DC, 48-49, resident radiol, 49-52; resident radiation ther, Mem Hosp Cancer & Allied Dis, New York, 52 & 55; from asst prof to assoc prof radiol, Univ Cincinnati, 57-66; CLIN ASSOC PROF RADIOL, WAYNE STATE UNIV, 66-; DIR ABRAHAM & ANNA SRERE RADIATION THER CTR, SINAI HOSP OF DETROIT, 66- *Concurrent Pos:* Kress fel, Mem Hosp & Dept Biophys, Sloan-Kettering Inst Cancer Res, 56-57; attend physician, Cincinnati Gen & Daniel Drake Mem Hosps, 57-; Nat Cancer Inst grant, 63-68; consult, Vet Admin Ctr, Dayton, 65-; radiotherapist, Vet Admin Hosp, Allen Park, Mich, 68-72, consult, 72-; mem exec comt, Mich Cancer Found, 70-; attend physician, Sinai Hosp Detroit; vchmn, Mich Cancer Found, 76-79; chmn, Dept Radiation Ther, Sinai Hosp, Detroit, 81; chairperson, Radiation Ther Adv Panel, Mich Cancer Found, 76-; chmn, Radiation Ther Tech Adv Panel, Comprehensive Health Planning Coun Southeastern Mich, 78-; spec lect, 7th Int Conf on Use of Comput in Radiation Ther, Japan, 80. *Honors & Awards:* William E Allen Jr lectr, Nat Med Asn, 79. *Mem:* Nat Med Asn; NY Acad Sci; Am Soc Clin Oncol; Am Asn Physicists Med; Am Soc Prev Oncol. *Res:* Radiation therapy for cancer; computer utilization in radiation treatment planning; combination radiation and chemotherapy in Hodgkin's lymphoma; carcinoma of pancreas; pre-operative adjuvant therapy in rectal carcinoma and combination adjuvant therapy in carcinoma of the lung; dosimetry of high-energy electrons and x-rays. *Mailing Add:* Sinai Hosp of Detroit 6767 W Outer Dr Detroit MI 48235

PERRY, HAROLD OTTO, b Rochester, Minn, Nov 18, 21; m 44; c 4. DERMATOLOGY. *Educ:* Univ Minn, BSc, 44, MB, 46, MD, 47, MS, 53. *Prof Exp:* Consult staff dermat, St Mary's & Rochester Methodist Hosps, 53; from instr to asst prof, 54-69, PROF DERMAT, MAYO GRAD SCH MED, UNIV MINN, 69- *Concurrent Pos:* Chmn & head, Dept Dermat, Mayo Clin, 53- *Mem:* Soc Invest Dermat; Am Dermat Asn; AMA; Am Acad Dermat; Sigma Xi. *Mailing Add:* Dept of Dermat Mayo Clin 200 First St SW Rochester MN 55901

PERRY, HAROLD TYNER, JR, b Bismarck, NDak, Jan 26, 26; m 52; c 2. PHYSIOLOGY. *Educ:* Northwestern Univ, DDS, 52, MS, 54, PhD, 61. *Prof Exp:* Res assoc, 52-54, instr orthod, 54-61, assoc prof, 61-65, PROF ORTHOD, SCH DENT, NORTHWESTERN UNIV, CHICAGO, 65-, CHMN DEPT, 61- *Concurrent Pos:* USPHS fel, Nat Inst Dent Res, 52-54; consult, Vet Admin Hosp, 71. *Mem:* AAAS; Am Dent Asn; Am Asn Orthod; Int Asn Dent Res. *Res:* Electromyography of the head and neck musculature; crania; cranial, facial and dental development. *Mailing Add:* Sch of Dent Northwestern Univ Chicago IL 60611

PERRY, HORACE MITCHELL, JR, b Reading, Pa, June 11, 23; m 45; c 4. MEDICINE. *Educ:* Wash Univ, MD, 46. *Prof Exp:* From intern to asst resident med, Barnes Hosp, 46-48, asst, 47-48; res fel med, 50-51, from instr to assoc prof, 51-72, PROF MED, WASHINGTON UNIV, 72-, DIR, HYPERTENSION DIV, 57-, DIR, HYPERTENSION CLIN, 64- *Concurrent Pos:* Life Ins Med Res fel, 51-53; Am Heart Asn estab investr, 56-61; sr physician, St Louis Vet Admin Hosp, 71-, chief med serv, 63-75; assoc physician, Barnes Hosp, 72-; physician coordr hypertension, Vet Admin, Washington, DC, 77-; consult, Hypertension & Kidney Dis Br, Nat Heart, Lung & Blood Inst, 79- *Mem:* Am Soc Clin Invest; Am Physiol Soc; fel Am Col Physicians; fel Am Col Cardiol. *Res:* Hypertension. *Mailing Add:* 1983 Karlin St Louis MO 63131

PERRY, JACQUELIN, b Denver, Colo, May 31, 18. ORTHOPEDIC SURGERY, KINESIOLOGY. *Educ:* Univ Calif, Los Angeles, BEd, 40; Univ Calif, San Francisco, MS, 50. *Prof Exp:* CHIEF PATHOKINESIOLOGY, RANCHO LOS AMIGOS HOSP, 55-; PROF ORTHOP SURG, UNIV SOUTHERN CALIF, 72- *Concurrent Pos:* Assoc chief surg serv, Rancho Los Amigos Hosp, 55-75; assoc clin prof, Univ Calif, San Francisco, 66-73, clin prof, 73-; consult, Surgeon Gen, US Air Force, 69-80. *Honors & Awards:* Woman of Year in Med, Los Angeles Times, 59; Golden Pen Award, J Am Phys Ther Asn, 65; Award for Orthop Res, Am Acad Orthop Surg, 77; Isabelle R Lenard Goldensen Award, United Cerebral Palsy Asn, 81. *Mem:* Hon mem Am Phys Ther Asn; Am Orthop Asn; Am Acad Orthop Surgeons. *Res:* Rehabilitation; objective measurement of gait; upper extremity function; stroke rehabilitation. *Mailing Add:* Rancho Los Amigos Hosp 7601 Imperial Downey CA 90242

PERRY, JAMES ERNEST, b Washington, DC, Jan 30, 23; m 56; c 3. ELECTROOPTICS. *Prof Exp:* Elec engr res infrared, Optics Div, Naval Res Lab, 47-64; elec engr res & develop infrared systs, Night Vision & Electrooptics Lab, US Army, 64-80; CONSULT, 80- *Concurrent Pos:* US deleg to study group 7, NATO Panel IV (Infrared), 72-73, US Army rep to NATO AC/243, 72-73. *Honors & Awards:* Award for Achievement in Res & Develop, Dept Army, 71; Award for Invention of Thermal Imaging Systs, Night Vision & Electro Optics Lab, 72. *Mem:* Sr mem Inst Elec & Electronics Engrs; AAAS; Infrared Info Symp. *Res:* Infrared, including radiometry and thermal imaging; radiometry associated with nuclear research; development of systems for tactical applications for Army. *Mailing Add:* 10036 Clue Dr Bethesda MD 20034

PERRY, JAMES TILDEN, computer science, see previous edition

PERRY, JEROME JOHN, b Wilkes Barre, Pa, Oct 15, 29; m 56; c 2. MICROBIOLOGY. *Educ:* Pa State Univ, BS, 51; Univ Tex, PhD(microbiol), 56. *Prof Exp:* Asst microbiol, Merck & Co, 51-52; res assoc, Upjohn Co, 56-58; bacteriologist, Am Meat Inst Found, Chicago, 58-59; res scientist, Kitchawan Res Lab, Brooklyn Bot Garden, 59-61 & Univ Tex, 61-64; from asst prof to assoc prof, 64-71, PROF MICROBIOL, NC STATE UNIV, 71- *Mem:* AAAS; Am Chem Soc; Am Soc Microbiol; Am Acad Microbiol; Brit Soc Gen Microbiol. *Res:* Degradation of hydrocarbons by microorganisms; lipid synthesis; biodegradation in marine areas; thermophilic bacteria. *Mailing Add:* Dept of Microbiol NC State Univ Raleigh NC 27607

PERRY, JOHN ARTHUR, b Ridgefield, Conn, Nov 11, 21; m 42, 64; c 1. ANALYTICAL CHEMISTRY. *Educ:* Univ Rochester, BS, 42; La State Univ, MS, 52, PhD(chem), 54. *Prof Exp:* Jr chemist, Shell Develop Corp, 43; chemist, Vallejo Naval Yard, 44-45, Interchem Res Labs, 45 & Monsanto

Chem Corp, 47-50; proj chemist, Stand Oil Co Ind, 54-57; sr res chemist, Sinclair Res Inc, 57-66; lab mgr instrumental anal, Perkin-Elmer Corp, Downers Grove, 66-69; dir instrument div, McCrone Assocs, 69-70; consult, 71-78; TECH DIR CHROMATOGRAPHY, REGIS CHEM, 79- *Mem:* Am Chem Soc. *Res:* Instrumental analysis; gas chromatography; infrared spectrophotometry; emission spectrography; mass spectrometry; distillation control; dielectrophoresis; instrument design; new forms for chromatography. *Mailing Add:* 601 E 32nd St Chicago IL 60616

PERRY, JOHN E(DWARD), b Roanoke Rapids, NC, Mar 2, 24; m 45; c 3. CHEMICAL ENGINEERING. *Educ:* High Point Col, BS, 44; Purdue Univ, MS, 53. *Prof Exp:* Asst engr, Oak Ridge Plant, Tenn Eastman Co, 44-47; engr, Nat Lab, Monsanto Chem Co, 47-48 & Argonne Nat Lab, 48-51; supv engr, Pilot Plant, Union Carbide Nuclear Co, 53-62, mgr, Electroclad Dept, Parma Tech Ctr, Stellite Div, Union Carbide Corp, Ohio, 62-69; chief chem eng, Metals Universal, Inc, 69-70; proj dir fused salt process, 70-72, PRES, GEN METALS TECHNOL CORP, 72- *Res:* Design and development of equipment for fused salts processes, particularly electrodeposition of refractory metals nobium, molybdenum, tungsten and tantalum. *Mailing Add:* Gen Metals Technol Corp 8800 Metro Ct Richmond VA 23234

PERRY, JOHN FOEX, chemical engineering, see previous edition

PERRY, JOHN FRANCIS, JR, b Lubbock, Tex, Aug 6, 23; m 58. SURGERY. *Educ:* Univ Tex, BA, 44, MD, 47; Univ Minn, PhD(surg), 58. *Prof Exp:* From instr to assoc prof, 58-65, PROF SURG, MED SCH, UNIV MINN, ST PAUL, 65- *Mem:* Am Surg Asn; Soc Univ Surgeons; Cent Surg Asn; Am Asn Throacic Surg; Am Asn Surg Trauma. *Res:* Gastrointestinal physiology; envenomation; interstitial irradiation of tumors; trauma. *Mailing Add:* St Paul-Ramsey Hosp 640 Jackson St St Paul MN 55101

PERRY, JOHN MURRAY, b Springfield, Vt, July 19, 25; m 49; c 4. MATHEMATICS. *Educ:* Middlebury Col, AB, 45; Harvard Univ, AM, 51; Univ Rochester, PhD, 60. *Prof Exp:* From instr to prof math, Clarkson Tech Univ, 46-65, chmn dept, 56-63, dir comput ctr, 61-64; NSF fac sci fel, Univ Md, 64-65; prof math & chmn dept, 65-69, dean, 69-75, chmn div phys & math sci, Wells Col, 75-77; ASSOC PROVOST, VA POLYTECH INST & STATE UNIV, 77- *Mem:* AAAS; Am Math Soc; Math Asn Am; Asn Comput Mach; Soc Indust & Appl Math. *Res:* Partial differential equations; numerical analysis. *Mailing Add:* 201 Burruss Hall VA Polytech Inst & State Univ Blacksburg VA 24061

PERRY, JOHN STEPHEN, b Lynbrook, NY, Oct 18, 31; m 53; c 2. METEOROLOGY, COMPUTER SCIENCE. *Educ:* Queens Col, NY, BS, 53; Univ Wash, BS, 54, MS, 60, PhD(meteorol), 66. *Prof Exp:* Forecaster, Air Weather Serv, US Air Force, Korea, 54-55 & La, 55-58, systs analyst, Global Weather Cent, 60-63, Hq, Scott AFB, 66-70 & Air War Col, 70-71, prog mgr, Advan Res Projs Agency, 71-74; exec scientist, US Comt Global Atmospheric Res Prog, 74-76, sci officer, World Meteorol Orgn, 76-78, EXEC DIR CLIMATE BD, NAT ACAD SCI, 78- *Honors & Awards:* Commendation Medal, 63. *Mem:* Am Meteorol Soc. *Res:* Science policy; atmospheric sciences, general; computer sciences, general; environmental, earth and marine science. *Mailing Add:* Nat Acad Sci JH426C 2101 Constitution Ave NW Washington DC 20418

PERRY, JOHN VIVIAN, JR, b Danville, Va, July 10, 24; m 46; c 3. MACHINE DESIGN. *Educ:* Va Polytech Inst, BS, 48; Tex A&M Univ, MS, 54, PhD, 63. *Prof Exp:* From asst prof to assoc prof, 48-74, PROF MECH ENG, TEX A&M UNIV, 74- *Concurrent Pos:* Propulsion & struct engr, Gen Dynamics, 51-53; vis prof, US Mil Acad, West Point, NY, 79-80. *Mem:* Am Soc Mech Engrs; Am Gear Mfrs Asn. *Res:* Applied mechanics; vibrations of foundations in soils; soil mechanics. *Mailing Add:* Dept Mech Eng Tex A&M Univ College Station TX 77840

PERRY, JOSEPH EARL, JR, b Belmont, Mass, Oct 29, 17; m 44; c 2. PHYSICS. *Educ:* Mass Inst Technol, BS, 39; Univ Rochester, PhD(physics), 48. *Prof Exp:* Asst physics, Univ Rochester, 40-42, instr, 45-46; physicist, Radiation Lab, Univ Calif, 42-45; physicist, Appl Physics Lab, Johns Hopkins Univ, 45; res fel, Calif Inst Technol, 47-50; group leader, 59-75, PHYSICIST STAFF MEM, LOS ALAMOS SCI LAB, UNIV CALIF, 50- *Mem:* Fel Am Phys Soc. *Res:* Photoelectricity of semiconductors; spectroscopy of light nuclei; absolute differential cross sections for scattering of protons by protons; van de Graaff studies of interactions of hydrogen nuclides; monoenergetic neutron flux measurement; controls for nuclear reactor rocket engines; weapon location by sound ranging; solar heating and cooling of buildings; passive solar heating of buildings; construction of and experimentation with large neodymium/glass laser system. *Mailing Add:* Los Alamos Scientific Lab Box 1663 MS 571 Los Alamos NM 87545

PERRY, JUDITH JOANNA, astrophysics, see previous edition

PERRY, KENNETH W, b Somerville, NJ, June 13, 36; m 59; c 3. CELL PHYSIOLOGY, MOLECULAR BIOLOGY. *Educ:* Drew Univ, AB, 58; Univ Kans, MA, 60; Syracuse Univ, PhD(zool), 65. *Prof Exp:* NIH fel biochem, NJ Col Med, 65-66, instr, 66-67; sr scientist, Res Inst, Warner-Lambert Pharmaceut Co, 67-77; SR RES PHARMACOLOGIST, BIOMED RES, ICI AMERICAS, INC, 77- *Mem:* Am Rheumatism Asn; Am Physiol Soc; NY Acad Sci; Endocrine Soc; Soc Study Reproduction. *Res:* Steroids and hormone receptor interactions; effects of steroids on metabolism of nucleic acids and proteins; biochemistry of inflammation and the effects of drugs on these biochemical mechanisms. *Mailing Add:* Biomed Res Labs ICI Americas Inc Wilmington DE 19897

PERRY, LLOYD HOLDEN, b Nashua, NH, Mar 8, 16; m 43; c 3. CHEMISTRY. *Educ:* Wesleyan Univ, BA, 38; Univ NH, MS, 40; Mass Inst Technol, PhD(org chem), 46. *Prof Exp:* Instr chem, Univ NH, 39-40; asst, Mass Inst Technol, 42-46; res dir, Union Bay State Chem Co, Fla, 46-48; tech dir, Union Bay State Labs, Inc, 48-59; vpres & tech dir, UBS Chem Co, A E Staley Mfg Co, 59-67; mgr, Chattanooga-Dalton Plants, GAF Corp, 67-81; RETIRED. *Mem:* Am Chem Soc. *Res:* Polymerizations; peroxides; rubber compounding and applications. *Mailing Add:* 609 Marr Dr Signal Mountain TN 37377

PERRY, LORIN EDWARD, b Twin Falls, Idaho, July 24, 14; m 38; c 4. FISHERIES. *Educ:* Utah State Univ, BS, 39; Univ Mich, PhD, 43. *Prof Exp:* Fishery res biologist, US Fish & Wildlife Serv, 38-41 & State Inst Fisheries Res, Mich, 41-43; entomologist & limnologist, USPHS, Ga, 43-46; res biologist, US Fish & Wildlife Serv, Ore, 46-47, biologist & supvr river basins studies, 48-50, chief biologist, Columbia River Fishery Develop Prog, 50-59; prog dir, Columbia Fisheries Prog, US Bur Commercial Fisheries, 59-67; fisheries staff asst, Bur Sport Fisheries & Wildlife, 67-71, dep regional dir Pac region, 71-74; PRES, BIOL SERV, INC, 75- *Concurrent Pos:* Consult, Pac Northwest Regional Comn on Columbia River salmon, 75-78, Pac Fishery Mgt Coun on Pac Salmon, 78-81. *Mem:* Am Fisheries Soc; Am Inst Fishery Res Biol. *Res:* Impounded waters and water development projects, especially salmon and steelhead; life history of fresh water fish salmon management. *Mailing Add:* 6350 SW Spruce Beaverton OR 97005

PERRY, MALCOLM BLYTHE, b Birkenhead, Eng, Apr 26, 30; m 56; c 2. BIOCHEMISTRY. *Educ:* Bristol Univ, BSc, 53, PhD(org chem), 57, DSc, 70. *Prof Exp:* Asst prof chem, Queen's Univ, Ont, 56-62, McLaughlin res prof, 62-63; RES OFFICER BIOL SCI, NAT RES COUN CAN, 63- *Concurrent Pos:* Mem biol comt, Nat Acad Sci-Nat Res Coun. *Mem:* Can Biochem Soc; fel The Chem Soc; Can Soc Immunol; Am Soc Microbiol. *Res:* Natural products; structural investigation of carbohydrates, bacterial and fungal glycans, glycoproteins; biosynthesis; gas-liquid chromatography; synthetic organic chemistry; immunochemistry. *Mailing Add:* 769 Hemlock Rd Ottawa ON K1K 0J9 Can

PERRY, MARGARET NUTT, b Waynesboro, Tenn, Apr 23, 40; m 65; c 2. ACADEMIC ADMINISTRATION, FOOD SCIENCE. *Educ:* Univ Tenn, Martin, BS, 61; Univ Tenn, Knoxville, MS, 63, PhD(nutrit, food sci), 65. *Prof Exp:* Instr food sci, Univ Tenn, Knoxville, 63-64, asst prof, Col Home Econ, 66-68, asst to dean, 67, from asst to assoc dean, 68-73, dean grad studies, 73-79; ASSOC VPRES ACAD AFFAIRS, TENN TECHNOL UNIV, COOKEVILLE, 79- *Concurrent Pos:* Exec Comn, Coun Grad Sch US & Conf Southern Grad Sch, 74-77; Mem, Am Coun Educ, Comn Women, 79-81. *Mem:* Inst Food Technologists; Am Home Econ Asn. *Res:* Development of interdisciplinary graduate programs and research; application of food science and nutrition research to societal needs. *Mailing Add:* Tenn Technol Univ Box 5136 Cookeville TN 38501

PERRY, MARY HERTZOG, b Bethlehem, Pa, Oct 24, 22; m 47; c 3. ANALYTICAL CHEMISTRY, ORGANIC CHEMISTRY. *Educ:* Russell Sage Col, BA, 44; Lehigh Univ, MS, 46, PhD(chem), 49. *Prof Exp:* Instr chem, Cedar Crest Col, 47-48 & Muhlenberg Col, 65-68; from asst prof to assoc prof, 68-75, chmn dept, 70-72, PROF CHEM, CEDAR CRES COL, 75- *Concurrent Pos:* Tech ed, Chemist-Analyst, J T Baker Chem Co, 58-69. *Mem:* Am Chem Soc. *Res:* Use of organic reagents in analytical chemistry. *Mailing Add:* Dept of Chem Cedar Crest Col Allentown PA 18104

PERRY, MARY JANE, b New York, NY, Mar 30, 48. BIOLOGICAL OCEANOGRAPHY. *Educ:* Col New Rochelle, BA, 69; Univ Calif, San Diego, PhD(oceanog), 74. *Prof Exp:* Res asst oceanog, Scripps Inst Oceanog, Univ Calif, San Diego, 69-74; asst prof marine ecol, Univ Ga, 75; res instr marine chem, Dept of Pharmacol, Sch Med, Washington Univ, 75-76; RES ASST PROF OCEANOG, DEPT OF OCEANOG, UNIV WASH, 76- *Concurrent Pos:* Assoc prog dir oceanic biol, Nat Sci Found, 80-82. *Mem:* AAAS; Am Soc Limnol & Oceanog; Phycol Soc Am; Am Geophys Union. *Res:* Marine phytoplankton and bacteria, with emphasis on nutrient dynamics, autotrophy and physiological response to environmental variables and physical water circulation in the ocean. *Mailing Add:* Sch Oceanog Univ of Wash Seattle WA 98195

PERRY, MICHAEL PAUL, b Crystal Falls, Mich, Aug 24, 47. ELECTRICAL ENGINEERING. *Educ:* Mass Inst Technol, ScB, 69; Colo State Univ, MS, 73, PhD(elec eng), 76. *Prof Exp:* Programmer, Inforex Inc, Burlington, 70-71; ELEC ENG, CORP RES & DEVELOP CTR, GEN ELEC CO, 76- *Concurrent Pos:* Instr elec eng, Colo State Univ, 75-76; asst prof elec eng, Union Col, NY, 77- *Mem:* Inst Elec & Electronics Engrs. *Res:* Measurement and calculation of electric and magnetic fields; electromechanical coupling to continuous media and associated heat transfer; design and instrumentation of high voltage and high current devices. *Mailing Add:* Gen Elec Co PO Box 8 Schenectady NY 12301

PERRY, PAUL, b New York, NY, May 12, 26; m 48; c 2. FLAVOR CHEMISTRY, ORGANIC CHEMISTRY. *Educ:* Long Island Univ, BS, 49; Polytech Inst Brooklyn, BS & MS, 52, PhD(chem), 56. *Prof Exp:* Flavor chemist, Reiss & Bernhart, 50-53; flavor chemist, Globe Extracts, 53-56, asst dir res & develop flavor chem, 57-60; vpres res & develop, V & E Kohnstamm, 60-65; dir flavor res & develop, Fries & Fries-Mallinkrodt, 65-70; dir flavor chem develop, Warner-Jenkinson, 70-81, SR SCIENTIST, SEVEN-UP CO/PHILIP MORRIS, 81- *Concurrent Pos:* Flavor consult, NASA, Brookhaven, Long Island, NY, 60-65, Presidential Comn, Food & Drug Admin, 71-74 & Flavor & Extract Mfr, Assoc US, 74- *Honors & Awards:* Awards, Chem Sources Asn, 76 & Cereal Chemists Asn, 77. *Mem:* Inst of Food Technol; Flavor Chemists Soc; Cereal Chemists Asn; Am Soc Enologists; Candy Technologists Asn. *Res:* Flavor and botanical extractions; creation of new flavors; creation of new pilot plant processing systems; creation of new carrier systems for flavoring materials. *Mailing Add:* 731 Wayfield Dr Olivette MO 63132

PERRY, RANDOLPH, JR, b Needham, Mass, Aug 1, 23; m 53; c 2. INDUSTRIAL CHEMISTRY. *Educ:* Harvard Univ, BS, 48; Univ Mich, MS, 49, PhD(chem), 53. *Prof Exp:* RES GROUP LEADER, MONSANTO CO, 52- *Mem:* AAAS; Am Chem Soc. *Res:* Industrial chemicals of phosphorus, nitrogen and sulfur; process development. *Mailing Add:* 18 Thorncliff Ave Kirkwood MO 63122

PERRY, RANDY L, b Ashland City, Tenn, Apr 15, 40; m 65; c 2. ENGINEERING ADMINSTRATION. *Educ:* Univ Tenn, Knoxville, BS, 64, MS, 71, PhD(civil eng), 79. *Prof Exp:* Tests engr, Dept Transportation, State of Tenn, 66-74; asst dir, Transportation Ctr, Univ Tenn, 74-79; assoc prof transportation eng, 79-81, ASST DEAN, COL ENG, TENN TECHNOL UNIV, 81- *Concurrent Pos:* Consult, Flatt & Jared, Attorneys, 81- *Mem:* Am Soc Eng Educ; Am Soc Civil Engrs; Inst Transportation Engrs. *Res:* Transportation safety; student retention in engineering. *Mailing Add:* 881 Hillside Rd Cookeville TN 38501

PERRY, REEVES BALDWIN, b Greenville, Tex, Feb 12, 35; m 64; c 2. PHYSICAL CHEMISTRY. *Educ:* E Tex State Univ, BS, 54; N Tex State Univ, MS, 56; Univ Tex, PhD(phys chem), 66. *Prof Exp:* Chemist, Texaco Inc, 56-59, sr chemist, 65-66; asst prof chem, 66-69, assoc prof, 69-79, PROF CHEM, SOUTHWEST TEX STATE UNIV, 79- *Mem:* Am Chem Soc; Am Inst Chemists. *Res:* Properties of surfactants in aqueous solution. *Mailing Add:* Dept of Chem Southwest Tex State Univ San Marcos TX 78666

PERRY, RICHARD LEE, b Portland, Ore, Jan 22, 30; m 52; c 4. ELECTRON PHYSICS. *Educ:* Linfield Col, BA, 52; Ore State Univ, MS, 55, PhD(physics), 61. *Prof Exp:* Assoc physicist, Linfield Res Inst, 56-61; from asst prof to assoc prof physics, 61-71, actg chmn dept, 67-68, 78, PROF PHYSICS, UNIV OF THE PAC, 71- *Concurrent Pos:* Consult, Thompson-Ramo-Wooldridge, Inc, 62-63, Tektronix, Inc, 63-64; consult, US Army Nuclear Defense Lab, 68, res physicist, 69; res assoc, Ames Res Ctr, NASA, 78- *Mem:* Am Phys Soc; Am Asn Physics Teachers. *Res:* Field emission from silicon; electron tunneling through thin insulating films; photoelectric effect; holographic interferometry. *Mailing Add:* Dept of Physics Univ of the Pac Stockton CA 95211

PERRY, ROBERT DONALD, b Ft Wayne, Ind, Sept 22, 50; m 77. MICROBIOLOGY. *Educ:* Ind Univ, AB, 72; Mich State Univ, MS, 75, PhD(microbiol), 78. *Prof Exp:* RES ASSOC MICROBIOL, DEPT BIOL, WASH UNIV, 77- *Mem:* Am Soc Microbiol; Sigma Xi. *Res:* Microbial inorganic ion transport systems; membrane structure and function; microbial energy transduction. *Mailing Add:* Dept of Biol Wash Univ St Louis MO 63130

PERRY, ROBERT HOOD, JR, b Temple, Tex, Apr 5, 28; m 51. ORGANIC CHEMISTRY, RESEARCH ADMINISTRATION. *Educ:* Baylor Col Med, BS, 48; Univ Tex, PhD(chem), 52. *Prof Exp:* Res chemist, Humble Oil & Ref Co, 52-57, sr res chemist, 57-61, sect head, Exxon Res & Eng Co, NJ, 61-64, asst dir cent basic res lab, 66-67; mgr chem develop, Polaroid Corp, Mass, 67-69; mgr, 69-70, DIR ADVAN DEVELOP, MAGNETIC TAPE LAB, AMPEX CORP, 70- *Mem:* Am Chem Soc; AAAS; NY Acad Sci; Tech Asn Pulp & Paper Indust. *Res:* Chemistry of petroleum hydrocarbons; carbene chemistry; polymerization; autoxidation; synthetic reactions of ozone; photographic chemicals; magnetic materials; synthetic high polymers; magnetic recording; surface coatings; analytical chemistry. *Mailing Add:* 3324 Melendy Dr San Carlos CA 94070

PERRY, ROBERT LEONARD, b New York, NY, Dec 23, 41; m 64; c 2. APPLIED STATISTICS. *Educ:* State Univ NY, Binghamton, BA, 63; Mich State Univ, MS, 65; Rutgers Univ, PhD(statist), 70. *Prof Exp:* Statistician, Ctr Dis Control, USPHS, 67-69; statist consult, Comput Ctr, Rutgers Univ, 69-71; GROUP LEADER & STATISTICIAN, PROCTER & GAMBLE CO, 71- *Mem:* Am Statist Asn; Am Soc Qual Control; Biomet Soc; Sigma Xi. *Res:* Acceptance sampling, particularly lot acceptance and skip-lots; applied statistical methodology pertaining to real problems in industry. *Mailing Add:* 791 Exmoor Dr Cincinnati OH 45240

PERRY, ROBERT PALESE, b Chicago, Ill, Jan 10, 31; m 57; c 3. BIOPHYSICS. *Educ:* Northwestern Univ, BS, 52; Univ Chicago, PhD(biophys), 56. *Prof Exp:* Res assoc, Oak Ridge Nat Lab, 56-57; from res assoc to sr mem, Inst Cancer Res, 60-69, assoc dir, 71-74; assoc prof, 66-73, PROF BIOPHYS, UNIV PA, 73-, MEM GRAD GROUP MOLECULAR BIOL, 61-, MEM GRAD GROUP MICROBIOL, 73- *Concurrent Pos:* Fel biophys, Univ Pa, 57-58; Am Cancer Soc fel, Univ Brussels, 59-60; assoc med physics, Johnson Found & instr molecular biol, Univ Pa, 60-65; UN tech assistance expert & vis lectr, Univ Belgrade, 65; ed, J Cellular Physiol, 67-73; mem adv panel molecular biol, Div Res Grants, NSF, 68-71; mem sci adv comt, Damon Runyon Mem Fund Cancer Res, 70-74; mem vis comt, Dept Embryol, Carnegie Inst Wash, 73-; ed, J Cell Biol, 70-73; ed, Cell, 74-; Guggenheim Found fel, Univ Paris & Univ Zurich, 74-75. *Mem:* Nat Acad Sci; Am Soc Cell Biol; AAAS; Int Cell Res Orgn. *Res:* Synthesis and processing of RNA; biosynthesis and function of ribosomes; control mechanisms of growth and division; interrelationships between macromolecular biosyntheses. *Mailing Add:* Inst for Cancer Res 7701 Burholme Ave Fox Chase Philadelphia PA 19111

PERRY, ROBERT RILEY, b Temple, Tex, Dec 7, 34; m 59; c 2. NUCLEAR PHYSICS, COMPUTER SCIENCES. *Educ:* Rice Inst, BA, 57, MA, 58, PhD(physics), 60; Am Bd Radiol, cert radiol physics. *Prof Exp:* Sr res assoc physics, Rice Univ, 60-63; sr physicist, Texaco Inc, Tex, 63-67; asst prof radiol, 67-77, RADIOL PHYSICIST, UNIV TEX MED BR GALVESTON, 77- *Mem:* Inst Elec & Electronics Engrs; Am Asn Physicists in Med; Soc Nuclear Med. *Res:* Application of physics to medicine; use of computers in medicine; data processing of static and dynamic images of radionuclide distributions in patients. *Mailing Add:* Physics Div Dept of Radiol Univ of Tex Med Br Galveston TX 77550

PERRY, ROBERT W(ILLIAM), b Niagara Falls, NY, Apr 2, 21; m 45; c 1. ENGINEERING. *Educ:* Cornell Univ, BME, 43, MME, 47, PhD(eng), 51. *Prof Exp:* With Pioneering Res Lab, E I du Pont de Nemours & Co, 50-53; mgr hypervelocity & res brs, Arnold Eng Develop Ctr, 53-59; chief re-entry simulation lab, Repub Aviation Corp, 59-65; prof aerospace eng, Polytech Inst Brooklyn, 65-67; sr staff consult, Liquid Metal Eng Ctr, 68-70; Henry Vogt distinguished prof, 71-80, DISTINGUISHED PROF MECH ENG, UNIV LOUISVILLE, 80- *Concurrent Pos:* Mem res adv comt fluid mech, NASA, 59-60. *Mem:* Am Soc Mech Engrs; Am Phys Soc; assoc fel Am Inst Aeronaut & Astronaut; Nat Soc Prof Engrs. *Res:* High temperature gasdynamics; robotics. *Mailing Add:* Dept Mech Eng Speed Sci Sch Univ Louisville Louisville KY 40292

PERRY, RUFUS PATTERSON, b Brunswick, Ga, June 4, 03; m 45; c 2. ORGANIC CHEMISTRY. *Educ:* J C Smith Univ, BA, 25; Univ Iowa, MS, 27, PhD(org chem), 39. *Hon Degrees:* LLD, J C Smith Univ, 56. *Prof Exp:* Prof chem, head dept & chmn dept nat sci, Prairie View State Col, 27-43, dir div arts & sci, 39-43; prof chem, vpres & admin dean, Langston Univ, 43-57; pres, J C Smith Univ, 57-69; prof chem, Washington Tech Inst, 69-70, emer prof, 70-71; CONSULT, 71- *Mem:* AAAS; Am Chem Soc; Nat Inst Sci; Am Inst Chem; Sigma Xi. *Res:* Synthesis of local anesthetics and analgesics; steric hindrance; molecular structures; chemotherapeutic agents; medicinal chemistry. *Mailing Add:* 1725 T St NW Washington DC 20009

PERRY, SEYMOUR MONROE, b New York, NY, May 26, 21; m 52; c 3. HEALTH ADMINISTRATION. *Educ:* Univ Calif, Los Angeles, BA, 43; Am Bd Internal Med, dipl, 55. *Prof Exp:* Intern, Los Angeles County Hosp, 46-48, resident med, 48-51; sr asst surgeon, Indian Gen Hosp, Phoenix, Ariz, USPHS, 52; in chg internal med, Outpatient Clin, USPHS, 52-54; fel hemat, Med Ctr, Univ Calif, Los Angeles, 54-55, asst prof med, 56-60, asst res physician, Atomic Energy Proj, 55-57, in chg hemat training, 57-60, asst clin prof med, Univ, 60-61; sr investr med br, Nat Cancer Inst, 61-65, chief med br, 65-68, assoc sci dir clin trials, 66-71, chief human tumor cell biol br, 68-71, assoc sci dir prog, Div Cancer Treatment, 71-73, dep dir, 73-74, actg dir, 74, spec asst to dir, 74-78, assoc dir med appl res, NIH, actg dep asst secy, health & actg dir, 78-80, DIR, NAT CTR HEALTH CARE TECHNOL, OCCUP SAFETY & HEALTH ADMIN, 80-, ASST SURGEON, GEN PUB HEALTH SERV, 80- *Concurrent Pos:* Instr, Col Med Evangelists, 51-57; attend specialist, Wadsworth Vet Admin Hosp, 58-61. *Mem:* Inst Med-Nat Acad Sci; Am Soc Clin Oncol; Am Soc Hemat; Am Asn Cancer Res; Am Fedn Clin Res. *Res:* Health care technology assessment. *Mailing Add:* Nat Ctr Health Care Technol Parklawn Bldg 17A29 5600 Fishers Lane Rockville MD 20857

PERRY, THOMAS LOCKWOOD, b Asheville, NC, Aug 10, 16; m 41; c 4. BIOCHEMISTRY, PEDIATRICS. *Educ:* Harvard Univ, AB, 37, MD, 42; Oxford Univ, BA, 39. *Prof Exp:* Pvt pediat pract, 47-57; res assoc chem, Calif Inst Technol, 57-62; assoc prof, 62-66, PROF PHARMACOL, UNIV BC, 66- *Res:* Biochemical basis of mental and neurological disease; metabolic disorders of childhood; prevention of mental deficiency; development of methods for diagnosis of heterozygosity and for treatment of genetically determined diseases. *Mailing Add:* Dept of Pharmacol Univ of BC Vancouver BC V6T 1W5 Can

PERRY, THOMAS OLIVER, b Cleveland, Ohio, May 31, 25; m 49; c 3. FOREST GENETICS. *Educ:* Harvard Univ, BS, 49, MA, 50, PhD, 52. *Prof Exp:* From asst prof to assoc prof forestry, Univ Fla, 52-58; NSF res fel, Calif Inst Technol, 59-60; assoc prof, 60-69, PROF FORESTRY, NC STATE UNIV, 69- *Concurrent Pos:* Charles Bullard fel, Harvard Univ, 68-69; consult nat resource mgt. *Mem:* AAAS; Genetics Soc Am; Soc Am Foresters. *Res:* Plant physiology; genetics and physiology of trees; competition. *Mailing Add:* Sch of Forest Resources Box 5488 NC State Univ Raleigh NC 27607

PERRY, TILDEN WAYNE, b Timewell, Ill, June 21, 19; m 43; c 2. ANIMAL NUTRITION. *Educ:* Western Ill Univ, BEd, 40; Iowa State Univ, BS, 42; Purdue Univ, MS, 48, PhD(animal nutrit), 50. *Prof Exp:* Teacher high sch, 40-41; res chemist, E I du Pont de Nemours & Co, 42-46; PROF ANIMAL SCI, PURDUE UNIV, WEST LAFAYETTE, 46- *Honors & Awards:* Am Feed Mfgs Asn Award, Am Soc Animal Sci, 80. *Mem:* Am Soc Animal Sci. *Res:* Animal nutrition, especially with beef cattle, swine and sheep. *Mailing Add:* Dept Animal Sci Purdue Univ West Lafayette IN 47907

PERRY, VERNON G, b Boaz, Ala, May 8, 21; m 48; c 2. PLANT NEMATOLOGY. *Educ:* Ala Polytech Inst, BS, 43, MS, 49; Univ Wis, PhD(plant path), 58. *Prof Exp:* Asst nematologist, Agr Res Serv, USDA, Fla, 49-54, nematologist, Wis, 55-58; actg chmn dept entomo & nematol, 75-76, PROF NEMATOL & ASST CHMN DEPT ENTOM & NEMATOL, AGR EXP STA, UNIV FLA, 59-, ASST DEAN RES, 76- *Mem:* AAAS; fel Soc Nematol; Orgn Trop Am Nematol. *Res:* Feeding habits and pathogenicity to plants of nematology; taxonomy of nematodes and control of soil nematodes; nematode parasites of insects. *Mailing Add:* 1052 McCarty Hall Univ Fla Gainesville FL 32611

PERRY, VERNON P, b Euclid, Ohio, Feb 27, 27; m 50; c 5. BIOLOGY. *Prof Exp:* Technician tissue bank, Nat Naval Med Ctr, US Navy, Bethesda, Md, 50-58, head tissue cult div, Tissue Bank Dept, 58-68; EXEC DIR ADMIN, AM FOUND BIOL RES, 68-, DIR ADMIN & RES, BIOMED RES INST, 71- *Concurrent Pos:* Actg dir, W Alton Jones Cell Sci Ctr, 73-74; guest scientist, Naval Med Res Inst, 77- *Mem:* AAAS; Tissue Cult Asn (vpres, 72-74); Soc Cryobiol (vpres, 70-72); Am Asn Tissue Banks; Am Inst Biol Sci. *Mailing Add:* Biomed Res Inst 12111 Parklawn Dr Rockville MD 20852

PERRY, WILLIAM DANIEL, b Bradenton, Fla, Oct 8, 44; m 65; c 1. INORGANIC CHEMISTRY. *Educ:* Fla State Univ, BS, 65; Univ Ill, Urbana, PhD(inorg chem), 70. *Prof Exp:* Res assoc chem, Fla State Univ, 70-71; asst prof, 71-78, ASSOC PROF CHEM, AUBURN UNIV, 78- *Mem:* Am Chem Soc. *Res:* Study of the structure, properties and kinetics of transition metal complexes. *Mailing Add:* Dept of Chem Auburn Univ Auburn AL 36830

PERRY, WILLIAM JAMES, b Vandergrift, Pa, Oct 11, 27; m 47; c 5. MATHEMATICS. *Educ:* Stanford Univ, BS, 49, MS, 50; Pa State Univ, PhD(math), 57. *Prof Exp:* Instr math, Univ Idaho, 50-51 & Pa State Univ, 51-54; eng mgr, Sylvania Elec Prod, Inc, 54-64, dir electronic defense lab, 61-64; pres, ESL, Inc & dir, Electromagnetic Systs Lab, Sunnyvale, 64-77, dir defense res & eng, 77; under secy defense, Res & Eng, Off Secy Defense,

77-81; PARTNER, HAMBRECHT & QUIST, INVESTMENT BANKERS, 81- *Concurrent Pos:* Sci consult, US Dept Defense, 63-; lectr, Santa Clara Univ, 69-77. *Mem:* Nat Acad Eng; Am Math Soc; Sigma Xi. *Res:* Electromagnetic systems analysis; partial differential equations. *Mailing Add:* 10707 Mora Dr Arlington CA 94022

PERRY, WILLIAM LEON, b Trenton, Mo, Dec 3, 45; m 67; c 1. NONLINEAR DIFFERENTIAL EQUATIONS. *Educ:* Park Col, BA, 67; Univ Ill, MA, 68, PhD(math), 72. *Prof Exp:* Asst prof, 71-77, ASSOC PROF MATH, TEX A&M UNIV, 77- *Mem:* Am Math soc; Math Asn Am. *Res:* Nonlinear differential equations; integral equations and transforms. *Mailing Add:* Dept Math Tex A&M Univ College Station TX 77843

PERRYMAN, CHARLES RICHARD, b Elliot, Iowa, Sept 21, 16; m 40; c 2. RADIOLOGY. *Educ:* Dartmouth Col, BA, 38; Cornell Univ, MD, 42; Univ Pa, DSc, 47. *Prof Exp:* Intern, Bellevue Hosp, NY, 42-43; instr radiol, Sch Med, Univ Pa, 46-47, from assoc to asst prof, 47-49; asst prof, 51-59, assoc prof, 59-78, EMER PROF RADIOL, SCH MED, UNIV PITTSBURGH, 78- *Concurrent Pos:* Mem staff, Dept Radiol, Hosp Univ Pa, 46-51; pres, M D O'Donnell Diag Clin, 75- *Mem:* Am Radium Soc; Am Roentgen Ray Soc; Radiol Soc NAm; Am Nuclear Soc; fel Royal Soc Health. *Res:* Fundamental biological effects of radiation and their modification; roentgen diagnostic aspects of head and nervous system. *Mailing Add:* MD Bldg 1501 Locust St Pittsburgh PA 15219

PERRYMAN, ELIZABETH KAY, b Greenwood, Miss, Apr 11, 40. ENDOCRINOLOGY, CYTOLOGY. *Educ:* Memphis State Univ, BS, 64; Tex Tech Univ, MS, 67; Univ Ariz, PhD(zool), 72. *Prof Exp:* Instr biol, Victoria Col, 67-69; asst prof, 72-77, assoc prof, 77-81, PROF BIOL, CALIF POLYTECH STATE UNIV, SAN LUIS OBISPO, 81- *Concurrent Pos:* Sigma Xi res grant-in-aid, 72; NSF grants, 76-77. *Mem:* Am Soc Zoologists; Am Inst Biol Sci; fel AAAS. *Res:* Ultrastructure of the pituitary gland in relation to the control of pigmentation; study of the nongranulated (stellate) cells of the pituitary gland. *Mailing Add:* Dept of Biol Sci Calif Polytech State Univ San Luis Obispo CA 93407

PERRYMAN, ERIC CHARLES WILLIAM, b Stanwell, Eng, Feb 7, 22; Can citizen; m 45; c 4. METALLURGY. *Educ:* Cambridge Univ, MA, 43. *Prof Exp:* Mem staff metall, Royal Aircraft Estab, Eng, 43-46, Brit Non-Ferrous Metals Res Asn, 46-51 & Aluminium Labs Ltd, Kingston, Ont, 51-54; on attachment, Atomic Energy Can Ltd, 54-57, asst dir chem & metall, 57-60; dep head, Reactor Mat Lab, UK Atomic Energy Authority, 60-63; asst dir chem & metall, 63-65, dir, 65-67, dir fuels & mat, 67-70, dir appl res & develop, 70-78, GEN MGR, COM OPERS, CHALK RIVER NUCLEAR LABS, ATOMIC ENERGY CAN, LTD, 78- *Concurrent Pos:* Mem exec comn & coun, Can Welding Develop Inst, 73-; mem adv comt, Indust Mat Res Inst, 78- *Honors & Awards:* Dofasco Award, 80. *Mem:* Can Inst Mining & Metall; Can Nuclear Asn; fel Royal Soc Can; Brit Nuclear Energy Soc. *Res:* Stress corrosion cracking; recrystallization and recovery processes; irradiation damage; nondestructive testing; creep of materials; corrosion. *Mailing Add:* Atomic Energy of Can Ltd Chalk River Nuclear Labs Chalk River ON K1A 0S4 Can

PERRYMAN, JAMES HARVEY, b Kansas City, Mo, Aug 18, 18; m 50. NEUROPHYSIOLOGY, BIOLOGY. *Educ:* Stanford Univ, AB, 41; Univ Calif, MA, 43, PhD(physiol), 55. *Prof Exp:* Mem biomech group, Univ Calif, 50-52, mem pain study group, 52-53, asst physiol, 53-54; asst prof biol, Univ San Francisco, 54-56; from asst prof physiol & biophys to assoc prof physiol & pharmacol, Col Dent, NY Univ, 56-72; prof oral biol, 74-80, PROF BIODENT SCI, COL MED & DENT NJ, 80-, CHMN OCCLUSION & RES DIR, 72- *Concurrent Pos:* Res physiologist, Univ Calif, 55-56; USPHS res grant, NY Univ, 57-67; res assoc ophthal, NY Univ, 57-67, consult med & periodontia, 64-, consult grad fac, 58-, vis prof neuroanat, 70 & 71; consult med & pain, Bellevue Hosp, New York, 66-68; res prof psychol, Queens Col, 66-70; consult neurosurg, Brooklyn Hosp, 68-69; NSF inst award, Col Med & Dent NJ, 73- *Mem:* Fel AAAS; Am Physiol Soc; Am Psychol Asn; Am Asn Anatomists; Soc Neurosci. *Res:* Nonspecific reflex reactions of tactile, pain and stress stimulation; microelectrode recording spinal and brain stem respiratory potentials; extraocular muscle physiology, neural differentiation and coordination. *Mailing Add:* Dept Biodent Sci Col Med & Dent NJ Newark NJ 07304

PERRYMAN, JOHN KEITH, b Midland, Tex, Oct 16, 35; m 55; c 3. APPLIED MATHEMATICS. *Educ:* Union Col, Nebr, BA, 58; Univ Tex, MA, 60, PhD(math), 63. *Prof Exp:* Spec instr math, Univ Tex, 60-63; asst prof, 63-65, ASSOC PROF MATH, UNIV TEX, ARLINGTON, 65- *Mem:* Am Math Soc; Math Asn Am. *Res:* Mathematical analysis; development of integral transforms; mathematical modeling of medically oriented problems. *Mailing Add:* Univ of Tex Arlington TX 76013

PERSAUD, TRIVEDI VIDHYA NANDAN, b Port Mourant, Guyana, Feb 19, 40; Can citizen; m 66; c 3. ANATOMY, PATHOLOGY. *Educ:* Univ Rostock, MD, 65, DSc, 74; Univ West Indies, Jamaica, PhD(anat), 70; Royal Col Pathologists, London, MRCPath, 72. *Prof Exp:* Intern, Kleinmachnow Hosp, 65-66; govt med officer, Guyana, 66-67; lectr anat, 67-70, sr lectr, Univ West Indies, 70-72; from asst prof to prof anat, 72-77, PROF ANAT & HEAD DEPT, UNIV MAN, 77-, DIR, TERATOLOGY RES LAB, 75-, ASSOC PROF OBSTET, GYNEC & REPROD SCI, 79- *Concurrent Pos:* Ed, West Indian Med Jour, 70-73; consult teratology, Children's Ctr, Winnipeg, 73- & path, Health Sci Ctr, Winnipeg, 73- *Honors & Awards:* Carveth Jr Scientific Award, Can Asn Pathologists, 74; Rh Inst Award, Univ Man, 75; Albert Einstein Centennial Medal, Ger, 81. *Mem:* Royal Soc Med; Am Col Obstet & Gynec; Am Asn Anat; Can Asn Anatomists (pres, 81-83); Teratology Soc. *Res:* Teratology; fetal physiology and reproduction. *Mailing Add:* Dept Anat Fac Med & Dent Basic Med Sci Bldg Univ Man 730 William Ave Winnipeg MB R3E 0W3 Can

PERSELL, RALPH M(OUNTJOY), b New Iberia, La, Sept 17, 08; c 1. CHEMICAL ENGINEERING. *Educ:* Tulane Univ, BEChE, 32. *Prof Exp:* Chemist, State Hyg Dept, Miss, 34-37; field engr, Bristol Co, 37-38; inspector, USFDA, 38-39; chem engr southern regional lab, USDA, 46-59, asst dir prog appraisal, southern utilization res & develop div, Sci & Educ Admin-Agr Res, 59-72, dir Ala & northern Miss res area, 72-75; RETIRED. *Mem:* Am Chem Soc; Am Inst Chem Engrs. *Res:* Improved production of farm crops. *Mailing Add:* 801 Myrtle Ave Natchez MS 39120

PERSHAN, PETER SILAS, b Brooklyn, NY, Nov 9, 34; m 57; c 2. SOLID STATE PHYSICS. *Educ:* Polytech Inst Brooklyn, BS, 56; Harvard Univ, AM, 57, PhD(physics), 60. *Prof Exp:* Res assoc, 60-61, from asst prof to assoc prof, 61-68, GORDON McKAY PROF SOLID STATE PHYSICS, HARVARD UNIV, 68- *Concurrent Pos:* Sloan Found res grant, 63-67; NSF sr fel, Univ Paris, 71-72. *Mem:* Am Phys Soc. *Res:* Cross-relaxation phenomena in magnetic resonance; microwave modulation of light; applications of electron spin resonance; basic theory of nonlinear optics; physical properties of liquid crystals; x-ray scattering using synchrotron radiation. *Mailing Add:* 205 Pierce Hall Harvard Univ Cambridge MA 02138

PERSHE, EDWARD R(ICHARD), b Omaha, Nebr, July 30, 24; m 54; c 2. SANITARY ENGINEERING. *Educ:* Univ Ill, BS, 49, PhD, 66; Mass Inst Technol, MS, 50. *Prof Exp:* Design engr, Gannett Fleming Corddry & Carpenter, Inc, 53-56; proj engr, Black & Veatch Consult Engrs, 56-58; asst prof civil eng, Univ Nebr, 58-62; assoc prof, Northeastern Univ, 66-70; DIR RES, WHITMAN & HOWARD, INC, 70- *Mem:* Am Soc Civil Engrs. *Res:* Municipal and industrial waste treatment. *Mailing Add:* Whitman & Howard Inc 45 William St Wellesley MA 02181

PERSIANI, PAUL J, b Brooklyn, NY, Oct 24, 21; m 52; c 2. PHYSICS. *Educ:* Clarkson Col Technol, BME, 48; St Louis Univ, PhD(physics), 56. *Prof Exp:* Assoc mech engr, 49-52, PHYSICIST, ARGONNE NAT LAB, 56- *Concurrent Pos:* Asst prof, Sch Technol, Northwestern Univ. *Mem:* Sigma Xi. Am Phys Soc; Am Nuclear Soc; AAAS; NY Acad Sci. *Res:* Fission and fusion reactor; neutron, nuclear and plasma physics; physics engineering. *Mailing Add:* Appl Physics Div 9700 S Cass Ave Argonne IL 60439

PERSICO, FRANCIS J, immunopharmacology, biochemistry, see previous edition

PERSKY, GEORGE, b Brooklyn, NY, Apr 26, 38; m 64; c 2. SOLID STATE PHYSICS, ELECTRICAL ENGINEERING. *Educ:* Rensselaer Polytech Inst, BSEE, 59; Polytech Inst Brooklyn, MSEE, 61, PhD(physics), 68. *Prof Exp:* Mem tech staff, Bell Labs, Murray Hill, 67-78; sr prof engr, 78-80, sect head, 80-81, ASST DEPT MGR, NEWPORT BEACH RES CR, HUGHES AIRCRAFT CO, 82- *Mem:* Am Phys Soc; Inst Elec & Electronics Eng. *Res:* High field transport properties of semiconductors; propagation and attenuation of ultrasound and helicon waves in metals; computer aided design. *Mailing Add:* 24751 Doria Way Mission Viejo CA 92691

PERSKY, HAROLD, b Chicago, Ill, Aug 11, 17; m 41, 76; c 1. PSYCHOENDOCRINOLOGY, ENDOCRINOLOGY. *Educ:* Univ Chicago, BS, 36, PhD(chem), 41. *Prof Exp:* Asst, Univ Chicago, 41-42; res assoc metab paralyzed muscle, Res Inst, Michael Reese Hosp, 42-44, asst dir res, Div Neuropsychiat, 46-51, dir biochem lab, Inst Psychosom & Psychiat Res & Training, 51-56; from asst prof to assoc prof biochem, Sch Med, Ind Univ, 56-62; adj res assoc prof, 63-71, PROF PSYCHIAT, SCH MED, UNIV PA, 71- *Concurrent Pos:* Lalor Found fel, Marine Biol Lab, Woods Hole, 48; USPHS res scientist awards, 62-81; assoc mem & mem div encocrinol & reproduction res labs, Albert Einstein Med Ctr, 62-71. *Mem:* AAAS; Am Psychosom Soc; Endocrine Soc. *Res:* Psychoendocrinology of human sexual behavior. *Mailing Add:* Dept of Psychiat Univ of Pa Sch of Med Philadelphia PA 19104

PERSKY, LESTER, b Cleveland, Ohio, Mar 4, 19; m 49; c 3. SURGERY, UROLOGY. *Educ:* Univ Mich, BS, 41; Johns Hopkins Univ, MD, 44. *Prof Exp:* From instr to assoc prof, 53-63, PROF UROL, SCH MED, CASE WESTERN RESERVE UNIV, 63- *Concurrent Pos:* Teaching fel surg, Harvard Univ, 49-50; teach fel, Tufts Univ, 49-50. *Mem:* AAAS; AMA; Am Urol Asn; Am Col Surg; Am Soc Clin Invest. *Res:* Physiology of obstruction to kidney; homotransplantation of organs. *Mailing Add:* Dept of Urol Sch of Med Cleveland OH 44106

PERSON, CLAYTON OSCAR, b Can, May 16, 22; m 47; c 3. GENETICS. *Educ:* Univ Sask, BA, 49 & 50, MA, 51; Univ Alta, PhD(cytogenetics), 53. *Prof Exp:* Asst prof cytol, Univ Alta, 53-54; Nat Res Coun Can fel, Univ Lund, 54-55 & John Innes Inst, 55-56; res off, Can Dept Agr, 56-61; hon res prof, Univ Man, 58-61; prof genetics & head dept, Univ Alta, 61-66; PROF BOT, UNIV BC, 66- *Concurrent Pos:* Consult, Food & Agr Orgn, 75- *Mem:* Am Soc Bot; Am Genetics Soc; Can Genetics Soc; fel, Royal Soc Can; fel Am Phytopath Soc. *Res:* Genetics of parasitism; chromosome behaviour. *Mailing Add:* Dept of Bot Univ of BC Vancouver BC V6T 1W5 Can

PERSON, JAMES CARL, b Portland, Ore, Sept 22, 36; m 60; c 3. CHEMICAL PHYSICS. *Educ:* Willamette Univ, BA, 58; Univ Calif, Berkeley, PhD(phys chem), 64. *Prof Exp:* Asst chemist, Argonne Nat Lab, 63-68, chemist, 68-81; ASST PROF, ST XAVIER COL, 81- *Mem:* Am Phys Soc; Radiation Res Soc. *Res:* Photo absorption and photo-ionization cross section measurements; microcomputer control of laboratory experiments; computer analysis of data; ion-ion recombination kinetics; use of optical data to predict initial yields in radiation chemistry. *Mailing Add:* 424 57th St Downers Grove IL 60516

PERSON, LUCY WU, b Kiangsu, China, Nov 7, 34; m 60; c 3. NUCLEAR CHEMISTRY, PHYSICS. *Educ:* Taiwan Normal Univ, BS, 56; Tsinghua, China, 56-58; Univ Calif, Berkeley, PhD(nuclear chem), 61. *Prof Exp:* Fel, Lawrence Radiation Lab, Univ Calif, 61-63; resident res assoc nuclear chem, Argonne Nat Lab, 63-65, consult, 65-66, resident res assoc, 66, consult, 66-

73, comput scientist, Reactor Anal & Safety Div, 73-81; MEM TECH STAFF, BELL LABS, 81- *Mem:* Am Nuclear Soc (nat prog comt, 77). *Res:* Theoretical study of high energy nuclear reactions, nuclear spectroscopy and nuclear structure; safety analysis of Liquid Metal Facts Breeder Reactor; image reconstruction and computer simulation; software development and management of electronic switch system. *Mailing Add:* 424 57th St Downers Grove IL 60516

PERSON, STANLEY R, b US, Apr 14, 28; m 53; c 3. BIOPHYSICS. *Educ:* Lafayette Col, BS, 51; Yale Univ, PhD(biophys), 57. *Prof Exp:* Asst res biophysicist, Univ Calif, Los Angeles, 57-65; assoc prof, 66-70, PROF BIOPHYS, PA STATE UNIV, 70- *Mem:* AAAS; Biophys Soc. *Res:* Radiation on bacterial viruses; bacterial spores and vegetative cells and mammalian cells in tissue culture; effects of tritiated compounds on Escherichia coli. *Mailing Add:* Dept of Biophys 211 Whitmore Lab Pa State Univ University Park PA 16802

PERSON, STEVEN JOHN, b Albert Lea, Minn, Mar 14, 44; m 65; c 3. MAMMALIAN PHYSIOLOGY. *Educ:* Iowa State Univ, BS, 66, MS, 68; Univ Alaska, PhD(zoophysiol), 75. *Prof Exp:* Instr anat & physiol, Lake Superior State Col, 73-74; pipeline surveillance biologist fish & wildlife mgt, Alaska Dept Fish & Game, 74-75; asst prof anat & physiol, 75-80, ASST PROF BIOL SCI, LAKE SUPERIOR STATE COL, 80- *Res:* Digestibility of forages consumed by Rangifer tarandus with emphasis on the inhibition of rumen microbes caused by dietary lichens. *Mailing Add:* Dept of Biol Lake Superior State Col Sault Ste Marie MI 49783

PERSON, WILLIS BAGLEY, b Salem, Ore, Apr 23, 28; m 49; c 2. PHYSICAL CHEMISTRY. *Educ:* Willamette Univ, BS, 47; Ore State Col, MS, 49; Univ Calif, PhD(chem), 53. *Prof Exp:* Asst, Ore State Col, 47-49 & Univ Calif, 49-52; Du Pont instr phys chem, Univ Minn, 52-53, res fel, 53-54; instr, Harvard Univ, 54-55; from asst prof to assoc prof, Univ Iowa, 55-66; PROF PHYS CHEM, UNIV FLA, 66- *Concurrent Pos:* Guggenheim fel, Univ Chicago, 60-61, vis assoc prof & NSF sr fel, 65-66; vis sr fel, Royal Hon Col, Univ London, 78; UNESCO consult, State Univ Campinas, Brazil, 80. *Mem:* AAAS; Am Chem Soc; Optical Soc Am; Royal Soc Chem; Coblentz Soc. *Res:* Molecular spectroscopy and structure; vibrational spectroscopy, emphasizing infrared intensities and laser applications; theoretical and experimental studies of molecular complexes. *Mailing Add:* Dept Chem Univ Fla Gainesville FL 32611

PERSONEUS, GORDON ROWLAND, b Grand Gorge, NY, Mar 10, 22; m 48; c 3. ORGANIC CHEMISTRY. *Educ:* Union Col, BS, 48. *Prof Exp:* Asst penicillin res, 40-42, cancer res, 48-52, vet bact, 52-55, head bact & pharmacol test dept qual control, 55-73, DIR TECH SERV REGULARTORY AFFAIRS, LEDERLE LABS DIV, AM CYANAMID CO, 73- *Mem:* Soc Indust Microbiol; Parenteral Drug Asn. *Res:* Biological and bacteriological sciences; immunology; test development; quality control; drug regulatory. *Mailing Add:* Lederle Labs Am Cyanamid Co Pearl River NY 10965

PERSSON, JOHN (AXEL), b Copenhagen, Denmark, Sept 4, 19; nat US; m 42; c 1. ELECTRICAL ENGINEERING. *Educ:* Columbia Univ, BSEE, 42. *Prof Exp:* Asst res engr, Res Labs, Union Carbide & Carbon Corp, 45-52, sect leader, Res Labs, Union Carbide Metals Co, NY, 52-60, sr develop engr, 60-69; mgr smelting furnaces, Lectromelt Div, Pa Eng Corp, 69-71; MGR SMELTING FURNACES, LECTROMELT CORP, 71- *Mem:* Inst Elec & Electronics Engrs; Am Inst Mining, Metall & Petrol Engrs. *Res:* Electrothermic and electrometallurgical processes characteristics; industrial electric furnaces. *Mailing Add:* Lectromelt Corp 32nd at AVRR Pittsburgh PA 15201

PERSSON, SVEN ERIC, b Lethbridge, Alta, Oct 16, 45; m 68; c 2. ASTRONOMY. *Educ:* McGill Univ, BS, 66; Calif Inst Technol, PhD(astron), 72. *Prof Exp:* Lectr & res fel astron, Harvard Col Observ & Harvard Univ, 72-75; STAFF MEM ASTRON, HALE OBSERV, CALIF INST TECHNOL, 75- *Mem:* Am Astron Soc. *Res:* Stellar populations of elliptical galaxies from infrared photometry; infrared observations of H II regions. *Mailing Add:* Hale Observ 813 Santa Barbara St Pasadena CA 91101

PERSSON, SVERKER, b Karlshamn, Sweden, Aug 3, 21; m 50; c 4. POWER MACHINERY. *Educ:* Chalmers Technol Univ, Sweden, MS, 45; Mich State Univ, PhD(agr eng), 60. *Prof Exp:* Engr, Bolinder-Munktell, Eskilstuna, 45-47; res engr, Swed Inst Agr Eng, 47-49; assoc prof agr eng, Royal Agr Col Sweden, 47-62, acting head dept, 62-63; assoc prof, Mich State Univ, 63-68; assoc prof, 68-73, PROF AGR ENG, PA STATE UNIV, UNIVERSITY PARK, 73- *Honors & Awards:* John Ericson Medal, 45. *Mem:* Am Soc Agr Engrs; Max Eyth Ges; Int Soc Terrain Vehicles Systs. *Res:* Mushroom and greenhouse production systems; tractors; soil-machine systems; methane from agricultural residue; basic principles of harvesting machines. *Mailing Add:* Dept of Agr Eng Pa State Univ University Park PA 16802

PERT, CANDACE B, b Manhattan, NY, June 26, 46; c 3. NEUROSCIENCE. *Educ:* Bryn Mawr Col, AB, 70; Sch Med, Johns Hopkins Univ, PhD(pharmacol), 74. *Prof Exp:* NIH fel, Johns Hopkins Univ, 74-75; staff fel, 75-77, sr staff fel, 77-78, res pharmacologist, 78-82, CHIEF, SECT BRAIN CHEM, NAT INST MENT HEALTH, 82- *Honors & Awards:* Arthur S Fleming Award, 79. *Mem:* Am Soc Pharmacol & Exp Therapeut; Am Soc Biol Chemists; Soc Neurosci; Int Narcotics Res Conf. *Res:* Brain peptides and their receptors: chemical characteristics, brain distribution and function. *Mailing Add:* Nat Inst Ment Health NIH Bldg 10 Rm 3N256 9000 Rockville Pike Bethesda MD 20205

PERTEL, RICHARD, b Tallinn, Estonia, Mar 22, 28; nat US; m 55; c 3. PHYSICAL CHEMISTRY. *Educ:* Univ Wash, BS, 52; Ill Inst Technol, PhD(chem), 60. *Prof Exp:* From asst prof to assoc prof chem, Univ Houston, 59-65; vis prof, Univ Alta, 65-68; phys chemist, 68-69, SR SCIENTIST, INST GAS TECHNOL, IIT CTR, 69- *Mem:* Am Chem Soc; Am Phys Soc. *Res:* Photochemistry; gas-phase kinetics; combustion and flames; mass spectrometry; optical spectroscopy. *Mailing Add:* 1210 S Salem Lane Arlington Heights IL 60005

PERUMAREDDI, JAYARAMA REDDI, b Gudur, India, Oct 15, 36; m 63. INORGANIC CHEMISTRY, PHYSICAL CHEMISTRY. *Educ:* Andhra Univ, India, BS, 56, MS, 57; Univ Southern Calif, PhD(chem), 62. *Prof Exp:* Fel chem, Mellon Inst, 63-67; from asst prof to assoc prof, 67-73, PROF CHEM, FLA ATLANTIC UNIV, 73-, CHMN DEPT, 77- *Mem:* AAAS; Am Chem Soc; Royal Soc Chem; Chem Soc Japan; Am Phys Soc. *Res:* Transition-metal chemistry and physics, especially the electronic energy levels of transition-metal systems by electronic spectra; ligand field and molecular orbital theories; photochemistry; structural and magnetic properties. *Mailing Add:* Dept of Chem Fla Atlantic Univ Boca Raton FL 33431

PERUN, THOMAS JOHN, b Auburn, NY, Sept 28, 37; div; c 3. PHARMACEUTICAL CHEMISTRY. *Educ:* Rensselaer Polytech Inst, BS, 59; Univ Rochester, PhD(org chem), 63; Lake Forest Sch Mgt, MBA, 81. *Prof Exp:* Sr chemist, 63-71, assoc res fel, 71-75, MGR CHEM RES, ABBOTT LABS, 75- *Mem:* Am Chem Soc; Am Soc Microbiol. *Res:* Chemistry and structure-activity relationships of antibiotics; conformational analysis; enzyme inhibitors. *Mailing Add:* Abbott Labs North Chicago IL 60064

PERUZZOTTI, GEORGE PETER, b New York, NY, Jan 11, 35; m 61; c 4. MICROBIAL BIOCHEMISTRY. *Educ:* St John's Univ, NY, BS, 56, MS, 59; Univ Wis-Madison, PhD(microbiol), 73. *Prof Exp:* Asst res biologist biochem, Sterling-Winthrop Res Inst, 59-64; res scientist, 73-77, SR RES SCIENTIST CHEM, MILES LABS INC, 77- *Mem:* AAAS; Am Chem Soc; Soc Indust Microbiol; Am Soc Microbiol. *Res:* Research and development in microbial transformation of synthetic organic compounds; natural products and microbial enzymes. *Mailing Add:* Miles Labs Inc PO Box 40 Elkhart IN 46515

PERVIN, WILLIAM JOSEPH, b Pittsburgh, Pa, Oct 31, 30; m 81; c 3. MATHEMATICS, COMPUTER SCIENCE. *Educ:* Univ Mich, BS & MS, 52; Univ Pittsburgh, PhD(math), 57. *Prof Exp:* Sr scientist, Atomic Power Div, Westinghouse Elec Corp, 54-55; asst prof math, Univ Pittsburgh, 55-57; from asst prof to assoc prof, Pa State Univ, 57-64; prof math, Univ Wis-Milwaukee, 64-67, chmn dept, 65-66; prof math, Drexel Univ, 67-73, dir Comput Ctr, 71-73, dir regional comput ctr, 73-78, PROF MATH, UNIV TEX AT DALLAS, 73- *Concurrent Pos:* Vis prof, Univ Heidelberg, 63-64. *Mem:* AAAS; Am Math Soc; Asn Comput Mach; Soc Indust & Appl Math; Math Asn Am. *Res:* Topology. *Mailing Add:* Univ Tex at Dallas Box 688 Sta JO42 Richardson TX 75080

PERZ, JOHN MARK, b Paris, France, Mar 23, 40; Can citizen; m 66; c 2. METAL PHYSICS. *Educ:* Univ Toronto, BASc, 60, MASc, 61; Univ Cambridge, PhD(physics), 64. *Prof Exp:* From asst prof to assoc prof, 66-80, PROF PHYSICS, UNIV TORONTO, 80- *Mem:* Am Phys Soc; Can Asn Physicists. *Res:* Ultrasonics in metals; fermi surfaces. *Mailing Add:* Dept of Physics Univ of Toronto Toronto ON M5S 1A7 Can

PERZAK, FRANK JOHN, b Pittsburgh, Pa, July 27, 32. PHYSICAL CHEMISTRY, EXPLOSIVES. *Educ:* Carnegie Inst Technol, BSc, 54; Univ Pittsburgh, PhD, 79. *Prof Exp:* Chemist br health & safety, 57-62, chemist, Explosive Res Ctr, 62-64, res chemist explosives chem sect, 64-66, res chemist, Spec Res Group, Explosive Res Ctr, 66-72, RES CHEMIST, PITTSBURGH RES CTR, US BUR MINES, 72- *Mem:* AAAS; Am Phys Soc; Combustion Inst; Am Inst Chemists. *Mailing Add:* US Bur Mines Pittsburgh Res Ctr PO Box 18070 Pittsburgh PA 15236

PESCE, AMADEO J, b Everett, Mass, June 30, 38; m 64; c 3. CLINICAL CHEMISTRY. *Educ:* Mass Inst Technol, BS, 60; Brandeis Univ, PhD(biochem), 64; Am Bd Clin Chem, cert. *Prof Exp:* Dir biochem res, Renal Div, Michael Reese Hosp & Med Ctr, 67-73; assoc prof, 73-79, PROF EXP MED, PATH & LAB MED, UNIV CINCINNATI MED CTR, 79- *Concurrent Pos:* Adj asst & assoc prof, Dept Biol, Ill Inst Technol, 67-73. *Mem:* Am Asn Clin Chemists; Soc Exp Biol Med; Am Chem Soc; Nat Acad Clin Biochem. *Res:* Clinical chemistry toxicology; immunology of antigenic fragments; application of Elisa technology; urinary protein excretion. *Mailing Add:* Univ Cincinnati Med Ctr 3412 MSB 231 Bethesda Ave Cincinnati OH 45267

PESCH, LEROY ALLEN, b Mt Pleasant, Iowa, June 22, 31; c 3. MEDICINE. *Educ:* Washington Univ, MD, 56. *Prof Exp:* Res assoc biochem, Nat Inst Arthritis & Metab Dis, 57-59; clin fel med, Sch Med, Yale Univ, 60-61, from instr to asst prof med, 61-63; prof med & assoc dean sch med, Stanford Univ, 66-68; prof med, dean sch med & dir univ hosps, State Univ NY Buffalo, 68-71; prof biol sci & med, Univ Chicago, 72-76; pres, Michael Reese Hosp & Med Ctr, 72-76; PROF, DEPT PATH, NORTHWESTERN UNIV & PRES, THE CONCEPT GROUP, 76- *Concurrent Pos:* Mem gen med study sect, NIH, 65-70, chmn, 69-70; spec consult manpower, Off Secy, Dept Health, Educ & Welfare, 70-71. *Mem:* AAAS; Am Fedn Clin Res; Am Soc Biol Chemists. *Res:* Experimental cellular injury; liver disease. *Mailing Add:* L A Pesch Assoc 303 E Ohio St Suite 2106 Chicago IL 60611

PESCH, PETER, b Zurich, Switz, June 29, 34; US citizen; m 55; c 2. ASTRONOMY. *Educ:* Univ Chicago, BS, 55, MS, 56, PhD(astron), 60. *Prof Exp:* Res assoc, 60-61, from asst prof to assoc prof, 61-74, PROF ASTRON, CASE WESTERN RESERVE UNIV, 74-, CHMN DEPT & DIR WARNER & SWASEY OBSERV, 75- *Mem:* Am Astron Soc; AAAS. *Res:* Stellar photometry and spectroscopy. *Mailing Add:* Warner & Swasey Observ 1975 Taylor Rd East Cleveland OH 44112

PESCHKEN, DIETHER PAUL, b Cologne, Ger, Apr 3, 31; Can citizen; m 60; c 4. ENTOMOLOGY. *Educ:* Univ Man, BSA, 59, MSc, 60; Univ Gottingen, DScAgr, 64. *Prof Exp:* Res scientist I biol control, Can Dept Agr Res Inst, Belleville, Ont, 64-72; RES SCIENTIST II BIOL CONTROL WEEDS, RES STA AGR CAN, REGINA, 72- *Mem:* Entom Soc Can; Weed Sci Soc Am. *Res:* Investigations of insects for their suitability and safety as biological control agents against weeds; released several and studied their development and effect on the weed in the field. *Mailing Add:* Res Sta Agr Can Box 440 Regina SK S4P 3A2 Can

PESEK, JOHN THOMAS, JR, b Hallettsville, Tex, Nov 15, 21; m 52; c 3. SOIL FERTILITY, FERTILIZER USE. *Educ:* Tex Agr & Mech Col, BS, 43, MS, 47; NC State Col, PhD(agron), 50. *Prof Exp:* Asst agron, NC State Col, 47-50; res agronomist, 50-64, PROF AGRON & HEAD DEPT, IOWA STATE UNIV, 64- *Concurrent Pos:* Consult, Int Basic Econ Corp Res Inst, Brazil, 54 & Mid-Am State Univs, Colombia, 66; tech ed soils, Agron J, Am Soc Agron, 65-71; mem, Seventh Soil Sci Cong, Southern Africa. *Mem:* Fel AAAS; fel Am Soc Agron (pres, 79); fel Soil Sci Soc Am; Crop Sci Soc Am; Soil Conserv Soc Am. *Res:* Effect of edaphic and climatological factors on response of crops to fertilizer and the economics of fertilizer use. *Mailing Add:* 1304 Marston Ave Ames IA 50010

PESELNICK, LOUIS, b New York, NY, Mar 31, 24; m 61. SOLID STATE PHYSICS. *Educ:* Catholic Univ, BEE, 50, MS, 52, PhD(physics), 57. *Prof Exp:* Physicist, Power Condenser & Electronics Corp, 52-55; physicist, Catholic Univ, 55-57; physicist, 57-62, RES PHYSICIST, NAT CTR EARTHQUAKE RES, US GEOL SURV, 62- *Concurrent Pos:* Consult, Power Condenser & Electronics Corp, 55-57; lectr, Catholic Univ, 58-65. *Mem:* Am Phys Soc; Am Geophys Union; Soc Explor Geophys. *Res:* Ultrasonic relaxation in gases and liquids; elastic and anelastic properties of single crystals and condensed matter using infrasonic, sonic and ultrasonic techniques; pressure-temperature phase transitions in solids using ultrasonics; variational methods and average elastic constants. *Mailing Add:* Nat Ctr for Earthquake Res 345 Middlefield Rd Menlo Park CA 94025

PESETSKY, IRWIN, b New York, NY, Feb 17, 30; m 56; c 1. ANATOMY, NEUROEMBRYOLOGY. *Educ:* NY Univ, BA, 52; State Univ Iowa, MS, 54, PhD(zool), 59. *Prof Exp:* From instr to asst prof, 59-70, ASSOC PROF ANAT, ALBERT EINSTEIN COL MED, 70- *Concurrent Pos:* NIH res grants, Albert Einstein Col Med, 61-76, NIH fel behav & neurol sci, 62-64; vis asst prof biol, Yeshiva Col, Yeshiva Univ, 66-67. *Mem:* AAAS; Soc Develop Biol; Am Asn Anatomists; Am Soc Cell Biol; Am Soc Zoologists. *Res:* Developmental neurobiology; neuroendocrinology; histochemistry. *Mailing Add:* Dept of Anat Albert Einstein Col of Med Bronx NY 10461

PESHKIN, MURRAY, b Brooklyn, NY, May 17, 25; m 55; c 3. THEORETICAL PHYSICS. *Educ:* Cornell Univ, BS, 47, PhD(physics), 51. *Prof Exp:* From instr to asst prof, Northwestern Univ, 51-59; assoc physicist, 59-64, ARGONNE NAT LAB, 64- ASSOC DIR PHYSICS DIV, SR PHYSICIST, 67- *Concurrent Pos:* Weizmann fel, Weizmann Inst, Israel, 59-60, 68-69. *Mem:* AAAS; Sci Res Soc Am; Am Phys Soc. *Res:* Quantum theory. *Mailing Add:* Physics Div Argonne Nat Lab 9700 S Cass Ave Argonne IL 60439

PESKIN, ARNOLD MICHAEL, b Paterson, NJ, Mar 15, 44; m 65; c 2. ELECTRICAL ENGINEERING, COMPUTER SCIENCE. *Educ:* NJ Inst Technol, BS, 65; Polytech Inst NY, MS, 71. *Prof Exp:* Elec engr, Int Bus Mach, 65-67; digital systs engr, 67-69, group leader eng, 69-75, div head tech support, 75-78, actg chmn, 78-79, DEPUTY CHMN APPL MATH, BROOKHAVEN NAT LAB, 79- *Concurrent Pos:* Lectr math statist, Columbia Univ, 72; adj prof, State Univ NY, Stonybrook, 79 & 80. *Mem:* Inst Elec & Electronics Engrs. *Res:* Data communications; design automation of digital systems. *Mailing Add:* Dept Appl Math Brookhaven Nat Lab Upton NY 11973

PESKIN, EDWARD, b New York, NY, Oct 15, 13; m 42; c 1. ELECTRICAL ENGINEERING. *Educ:* Columbia Univ, BA, 35, MA, 37; Polytech Inst Brooklyn, DEE, 43. *Hon Degrees:* MEng, Stevens Inst Technol, 62. *Prof Exp:* Res worker, Proj Comput Math Tables, NY, 38; res assoc, Off Sci Res & Develop, Polytech Inst Brooklyn, 42-46, instr, 44-46; res engr, Radio Corp Am, NJ, 46-47; from asst prof to assoc prof elec eng, Stevens Inst Technol, 47-62, prof elec eng, 62-80; RETIRED. *Concurrent Pos:* Lectr, Columbia Univ, 45-48; adj prof elec eng, Stevens Inst Technol, 80- *Mem:* Sr mem Inst Elec & Electronics Engrs; AAUP; Sigma Xi. *Res:* Mathematical analysis in connection with heatflow and transmission line problems arising on microwave project; dielectrics; network analysis and synthesis. *Mailing Add:* Dept of Elec Eng Castle Pt Sta Stevens Inst of Technol Hoboken NJ 07030

PESKIN, GERALD WILLIAM, b Philadelphia, Pa, July 17, 25; m 49; c 3. MEDICINE. *Educ:* Univ Pa, BA, 47, MD, 51. *Prof Exp:* Assoc surg, Sch Med, Univ Pa, 57-61, from asst prof to assoc prof, 61-69, asst dir, Harrison dept surg res, 61-69; prof surg, Univ Chicago, 69-71; chief surg, Vet Admin Hosp, 71-78; PROF SURG, UNIV CALIF, SAN DIEGO, 71- *Concurrent Pos:* Consult, Vet Admin Hosp, Philadelphia, 57-69; chmn dept surg, Michael Reese Hosp, Chicago, 69-71. *Mem:* Am Surg Asn; Am Gastroenterol Asn; Am Asn Surg of Trauma; Am Soc Surg Alimentary Tract; Am Col Surg. *Res:* Gastrointestinal physiology; portal hypertension; endocrine diseases. *Mailing Add:* Dept of Surg Univ Calif Med Ctr San Diego CA 92103

PESKIN, RICHARD LEONARD, b Cambridge, Mass, May 31, 34; div; c 2. ENGINEERING. *Educ:* Mass Inst Technol, BS, 56; Princeton Univ, MS, 58, PhD(eng), 60. *Prof Exp:* Eng consult, Budd Co, 56-57; asst eng, Princeton Univ, 57-59, mem res staff plasma physics, 59-61; assoc prof mech & aerospace eng, 61-68, PROF MECH & AEROSPACE ENG, RUTGERS UNIV, NEW BRUNSWICK, 68- *Concurrent Pos:* Res engr, Budd Co, 55-57; consult, Macrosonics Corp & Inst Defense Anal, 64 & Esso Res & Eng Corp, 66. *Mem:* Am Phys Soc; AAAS; Aerospace Ground Unit; Am Meteorol Soc. *Res:* Fluid mechanics, turbulence, turbulent dispersion, gas-solid suspension flows and aerosol mechanics; geophysical fluid dynamics; ignition combustion theory; statistical thermodynamics; pollution dispersion. *Mailing Add:* Dept of Mech & Aerospace Eng Rutgers Univ New Brunswick NJ 08903

PESSEN, DAVID W, b Berlin, Ger, Nov 23, 25; US citizen; m 59; c 3. MECHANICAL ENGINEERING. *Educ:* Univ Pa, BS, 49, MS, 50; Israel Inst Technol, DSc(mech eng), 62. *Prof Exp:* Res asst thermodyn, Univ Pa, 49-50; res engr, Honeywell, Inc, 50-55; lectr mech eng, Israel Inst Technol, 55-62; eng analyst, Wiedemann Mach Co, Pa, 62-64; assoc prof mech eng, Israel Inst Technol, 64-69; sect supvr, Res & Develop Ctr, Gulf & West, 69-70; ASSOC PROF MECH ENG, ISRAEL INST TECHNOL, 70- *Concurrent Pos:* Consult, Twinworm Assocs, 60- *Honors & Awards:* Blackall Award, Am Soc Mech Engrs, 60. *Mem:* Am Soc Mech Engrs. *Res:* Machine dynamics; automatic control; automation. *Mailing Add:* Dept Mech Eng Israel Inst Technol Haifa Israel

PESSEN, HELMUT, b Berlin, Ger, Sept 6, 21; nat US; m 66. PHYSICAL CHEMISTRY, BIOCHEMISTRY. *Educ:* Drexel Inst Technol, BSChE, 49; Temple Univ, PhD(chem), 61. *Prof Exp:* Chemist, Fred Whitaker Co, 43 & 46; res asst, Am Viscose Corp, 48; inspector, US Food & Drug Admin, 50; res chemist, US Army Qm Pioneering Res Labs, 50-57; tech translator, 61-63; RES CHEMIST, EASTERN REGIONAL RES LAB, AGR RES SERV, USDA, 63- *Mem:* AAAS; Am Chem Soc; Am Crystallog Asn; Biophys Soc. *Res:* Fine structure of cellulose; microbial degradation of plasticizers; chemical kinetics; physical properties of enzymes; protein interactions; small-angle x-ray scattering; nuclear magnetic resonance; relaxation. *Mailing Add:* USDA Eastern Regional Res Ctr 600 E Mermaid Lane Philadelphia PA 19118

PESSL, FRED, JR, b Detroit, Mich, Nov 18, 32. GLACIAL GEOLOGY, ENVIRONMENTAL GEOLOGY. *Educ:* Dartmouth Col, AB, 55; Univ Mich, MS, 58. *Prof Exp:* Geologist, US Geol Surv, Conn, 63-71, proj geologist, Conn Valley Urban Pilot Proj, 71-76; CO-DIR, US GEOL SURV, PUGET SOUND EARTH SCI APPLN PROJ, SEATTLE, WASH, 76-; AFFIL PROF, DEPT GEOL SCI, UNIV WASH, 77- *Concurrent Pos:* Arctic Inst NAm res grants glacial geol, E Greenland, 59-61; vis prof, Wesleyan Univ, 71; proj chief, Conn Valley Urban Proj; vis prof geol, Wesleyan Univ, 73-74, Yale Univ, 75-76. *Mem:* Geol Soc Am; Glaciol Soc; Arctic Inst NAm. *Res:* Glacial chronology in East Greenland; distribution and stratigraphy of glacial deposits in New England; thermal expansion properties of lake ice; geology and hydrology for use in land-use planning and resource management. *Mailing Add:* US Geol Surv 1107 NE 45th St Suite 125 Seattle WA 98105

PESSON, LYNN L, b New Iberia, La, Oct 15, 27; m 50; c 3. AGRICULTURAL EDUCATION. *Educ:* La State Univ, BS, 48, PhD(agr educ), 60; Univ Md, MEd, 55. *Prof Exp:* Assoc county agent, 48-54, assoc state club agent, 54-60, prof exten educ & training specialist, 60-71, prof exten & int educ & head dept, 71-73, head dept exten educ & coordr int progs, 69-71, asst vchancellor, 73-74, vchancellor admin, 74-81, VCHANCELLOR STUDENT AFFAIRS, LA STATE UNIV, BATON ROUGE, 81- *Concurrent Pos:* Nat 4-H fel, USDA, DC, 53-54, specialist, Fed Exten Serv, USDA, 65; head dept exten, Col Agr, Malaya, 67-68. *Res:* Extension youth programs; effectiveness of extension teaching; diffusion of technology; international agriculture. *Mailing Add:* D Boyd Hall Rm 117 La State Univ Baton Rouge LA 70803

PESTANA, CARLOS, b Canary Islands, Spain, June 10, 36; m 66. SURGERY. *Educ:* Nat Univ Mex, BS, 52, MD, 59; Univ Minn, PhD(surg), 65. *Prof Exp:* From asst prof to assoc prof, 68-74, assoc dean acad develop, 71-73, PROF SURG, UNIV TEX MED SCH, SAN ANTONIO, 74-, ASSOC DEAN STUDENT AFFAIRS, 73- *Concurrent Pos:* Edward J Noble Found Award, 65; Piper Found Award, 72. *Mem:* Asn Acad Surgeons; Am Col Surgeons; NY Acad Sci; Soc Surg Alimentary Tract; Sigma Xi. *Mailing Add:* Dept of Surg Univ of Tex Med Sch San Antonio TX 78284

PESTANA, HAROLD RICHARD, b Honolulu, Hawaii, Dec 20, 31; m 53; c 2. PALEONTOLOGY. *Educ:* Univ Calif, Berkeley, BA, 57, MA, 59; Univ Iowa, PhD(geol), 65. *Prof Exp:* From instr to asst prof, 59-73, ASSOC PROF GEOL, COLBY COL, 73- *Mem:* AAAS; Paleont Soc; Geol Soc Am; Nat Asn Geol Teachers. *Res:* Morphology and ecology of Paleozoic corals and stromatoporoids; history of geology; origin of carbonate sediments. *Mailing Add:* Dept of Geol Colby Col Waterville ME 04901

PESTERFIELD, CHARLES HENRY, mechanical engineering, deceased

PESTKA, SIDNEY, b Drobnin, Poland, May 29, 36; US citizen; m 60; c 3. BIOCHEMISTRY, MEDICINE. *Educ:* Princeton Univ, AB, 57; Univ Pa, MD, 61. *Prof Exp:* Intern pediat & med, Baltimore City Hosps, Md, 61-62; med officer, Nat Heart Inst, 62-66 & Nat Cancer Inst, 66-69; head sect cell regulation, 69-80, HEAD LAB MOLECULAR GENETICS, ROCHE INST MOLECULAR BIOL, 80-, MEM, 69- *Concurrent Pos:* Adj prof path, Col Physicians & Surgeons, Columbia Univ, 73- *Mem:* NY Acad Sci; Am Soc Microbiol; Am Soc Biol Chemists. *Res:* Interferon synthesis, cloning, purification and action; biochemical genetics; genetic code; mechanism of protein biosynthesis; mode of action of antibiotics; cellular regulatory mechanisms; antibody synthesis; interferon synthesis. *Mailing Add:* Sect Cell Regulation Roche Inst Molecular Biol Nutley NJ 07110

PESTRONG, RAYMOND, b New York, NY, Apr 20, 37; m 62; c 2. ENVIRONMENTAL GEOLOGY, GEOMORPHOLOGY. *Educ:* City Col New York, BS, 59; Univ Mass, Amherst, MS, 61; Stanford Univ, PhD(geol), 65. *Prof Exp:* Asst eng geol, Linear Accelerator Ctr, Stanford Univ, 62-63; eng geologist, Soils Eng Firm, 65-66; dir, NSF Earth Sci Inst, 68-72 & 78-81, chmn dept geol, 69-73, PROF GEOL, SAN FRANCISCO STATE UNIV, 66- *Concurrent Pos:* Mem, Coun Educ Geol Sci; Off Naval Res res contractr, 64; dir earthquake educ, NSF Inst; mem, Calif Seismic Safety Educ Comt. *Mem:* Fel Geol Soc Am; Asn Eng Geol; Nat Asn Geol Teachers; Sigma Xi. *Res:* Processes and mechanisms of sedimentation within the tidal flat and tidal marsh environment; multi-media in education; engineering geologic studies of landslides and other slope stability problems; coastal geomorphic phenomena; alternative approaches to introductory geologic education. *Mailing Add:* Dept Geol San Francisco State Univ San Francisco CA 94132

PESTRONK, ALAN, b Cambridge, Mass, Jan 19, 46. NEUROMUSCULAR DISEASE. *Educ:* Princeton Univ, AB, 66; Johns Hopkins Sch Med, MD, 70. *Prof Exp:* Resident, 71-74, ASST PROF NEUROL, JOHNS HOPKINS SCH MED, 77- *Res:* Trophic interactions between nerve and muscle. *Mailing Add:* Dept Neurol Johns Hopkins Hosp 600 N Wolfe St Baltimore MD 21205

PESYNA, GAIL MARLANE, b Pittsburgh, Pa, June 16, 48. COMPUTER SCIENCES. *Educ:* Wells Col, AB, 70; Cornell Univ, MS, 73, PhD(anal chem), 75. *Prof Exp:* Sci consult, Comt Sci & Technol, US House Representatives, 75-78; oper res analyst, Off Mgt & Budget, Exec Off Pres, 78-80; prof staff, Pres Comn Nat Agenda Eighties, 80-81; PROG SPECIALIST, CENT RES & DEVELOP DEPT, E I DU PONT DE NEMOURS & CO, INC, 81- *Concurrent Pos:* Lectr, Grad Prog Sci Technol & Public Policy, George Washington Univ, 80; adv, Comt Sci Eng & Public Policy, AAAS, 81-84; appointee, Adv Coun, Nat Sci Found, 81-82. *Res:* Computer applications in analytical chemistry; science and technology policy. *Mailing Add:* Cent Res & Develop E I Du Pont de Nemours & Co Inc Wilmington DE 19898

PETAJAN, JACK HOUGEN, b Evanston, Ill, Apr 2, 30; m 52; c 3. NEUROLOGY, PHYSIOLOGY. *Educ:* Johns Hopkins Univ, BA, 53; Univ Wis, PhD(physiol) & MD, 59; Am Bd Psychiat & Neurol, dipl, 66. *Prof Exp:* Asst prof neurol & physiol, Univ Wis, 63-65; vis assoc prof physiol, Univ Alaska & chief physiol sect, Arctic Health Res Lab, Inst Arctic Biol, Univ Alaska, 65-69; assoc prof, 69-73, PROF NEUROL, MED SCH, UNIV UTAH, 73- *Concurrent Pos:* For exchange fel, 62-63; consult, Vet Admin, 63-65 & US Army, 66- *Mem:* Fel Am Acad Neurol; AMA; Int Soc Biometeorol; Am Phys Soc. *Res:* Study of motor unit control; neuromuscular disease; environmental health; toxicology. *Mailing Add:* Dept of Neurol Univ of Utah Med Sch Salt Lake City UT 84112

PETCH, HOWARD EARLE, b Agincourt, Can, May 12, 25; m 49, 76; c 3. NUCLEAR MAGNETIC RESONANCE. *Educ:* McMaster Univ, BSc, 49, MSc, 50; Univ BC, PhD(physics), 52. *Hon Degrees:* DSc, McMaster Univ, 74. *Prof Exp:* Fel, McMaster Univ, 52-53; Rutherford fel, Cavendish Lab, Cambridge Univ, 53-54; asst prof physics, McMaster Univ, 54-57, assoc prof physics & metall, 57-60, prof metall & metall eng, 60-67, chmn dept metall & metall eng, 58-62, dir res, 61-67, prin, Hamilton Col, 63-67, chmn interdisciplinary mat res unit, 64-67; prof physics & vpres acad, Univ Waterloo, 67-74, pres pro-tem, 69-70; prof physics, 75, PRES, UNIV VICTORIA, 75- *Concurrent Pos:* Mem Sci Coun Can, 66-72; asst secy, Ministry of State for Sci & Technol, 72; mem Defense Res Bd Can, 73-78 & Royal Comn Air Transp Needs of the Toronto Area, 73-74. *Honors & Awards:* Centennial Medal, 67. *Mem:* Fel Royal Soc Can; Can Asn Physicists (vpres, 66-67, pres, 67-68); Am Phys Soc; Int Union Crystallog. *Res:* Crystallography; solid state physics. *Mailing Add:* Off of the President PO Box 1700 Univ of Victoria Victoria BC V8W 2Y2 Can

PETER, ALBERT P, b Quincy, Ill, Sept 20, 42; m 68; c 3. RUMINANT NUTRITION. *Educ:* Univ Ill, BS, 65, MS, 68, PhD(ruminant nutrit), 71. *Prof Exp:* MGR BEEF RES, MOORMAN MFG CO, 70- *Mem:* Am Soc Animal Sci; Sigma Xi. *Res:* All phases of beef research; beef production. *Mailing Add:* RR 3 Box 68-B Quincy IL 62301

PETER, GEORGE, geophysics, marine geology, see previous edition

PETER, JAMES BERNARD, b Omaha, Nebr, June 27, 33; m 54; c 7. INTERNAL MEDICINE, BIOCHEMISTRY. *Educ:* Creighton Univ, BS, 54; St Louis Univ, MD, 58; Univ Minn, PhD(biochem), 63. *Prof Exp:* Lectr chem, 63, from asst prof to assoc prof, 65-72, PROF MED & RHEUMATOL, UNIV CALIF, LOS ANGELES, 72-; DIR, CLIN IMMUNOL LABS, INC, 72- *Concurrent Pos:* Fel med, Univ Minn Hosp, 59-60; attend specialist, Wadsworth Vet Hosp, Los Angeles, 65- *Mem:* Am Chem Soc; Am Soc Biol Chemists; Am Soc Clin Invest; Am Rheumatism Soc; Am Acad Neurol. *Res:* Immunology and biochemistry of human disease; clinical immunology of rheumatic diseases; biochemistry of muscle diseases; rheumatology; mycology; clinical immunology. *Mailing Add:* Clin Immunol Labs Inc 2216 Santa Monica Blvd Santa Monica CA 90404

PETER, RICHARD ECTOR, b Medicine Hat, Alta, Mar 7, 43; m 65; c 2. NEUROENDOCRINOLOGY, COMPARATIVE ENDOCRINOLOGY. *Educ:* Univ Alta, BSc, 65; Univ Wash, PhD(zool), 69. *Prof Exp:* Med Res Coun Can fel, Bristol Univ, 69-70; from asst prof to assoc prof, 71-79, PROF ZOOL, UNIV ALTA, 79- *Concurrent Pos:* vis scientist, Inst Nat Res Agron, France, 77, 78, 81 & Acad Agr, Poland, 81; Steacie fel, Nat Sci Eng Res Coun, Can, 80-82. *Mem:* Fel AAAS; Am Soc Zoologists; Can Soc Zoologists; Int Soc Neuroendocrinol; Soc Study Reproduction. *Res:* Neuroendocrine control of pituitary gland function in teleost fishes; effects of environmental factors on neuroendocrine function in teleost fishes; hypothalamic control and effects of hormones on spawning behavior and food intake. *Mailing Add:* Dept of Zool Univ of Alta Edmonton AB T6G 2E9 Can

PETERING, DAVID HAROLD, b Peoria, Ill, Sept 16, 42; m 66; c 2. BIOINORGANIC CHEMISTRY, BIOCHEMICAL PHARMACOLOGY. *Educ:* Wabash Col, BA, 64; Univ Mich, PhD(biochem), 69. *Prof Exp:* Fel, Northwestern Univ, Am Cancer Soc, 69-71; asst prof chem & biochem, 71-77, ASSOC PROF CHEM, UNIV WIS, 77- *Concurrent Pos:* Vis sr fel, Nat Inst Environ Health Sci, 81- *Mem:* Am Chem Soc; Int Asn Bioinorg Scientists; Sigma Xi. *Res:* Metabolism of essential transition metals, toxic metals and their complexes; role of zinc in cancer, of cadmium in biological toxicity and various metal complexes in cancer chemotherapy. *Mailing Add:* Booker Creek Apt 8D Chapel Hill NC 27514

PETERING, HAROLD GEORGE, b Laporte, Ind. BIOCHEMISTRY, BIOCHEMICAL PHARMACOLOGY. *Educ:* Univ Chicago, SB, 34; Univ Wis, PhD(chem, biochem), 38. *Prof Exp:* Asst prof biochem, Mich State Univ, 38-41; sr biochemist, E I du Pont de Nemours & Co, 41-45; sr scientist & group leader biochem pharmacol, Upjohn Co, 45-66; from assoc prof to prof, 66-78, EMER PROF ENVIRON HEALTH & BIOCHEM TOXICOL, COL MED, UNIV CINCINNATI, 78- *Mem:* AAAS; Am Soc Biol Chemists; Am Chem Soc; Am Asn Cancer Res; Am Inst Nutrit. *Res:* Biochemistry and toxicology of trace metals; chemotherapy of cancer; biological activity and metabolism of chelating agents; nutrition of zinc, copper and iron. *Mailing Add:* Kettering Lab Univ of Cincinnati Col of Med Eden & Bethesda Ave Cincinnati OH 45267

PETERJOHN, GLENN WILLIAM, b Cleveland, Ohio, June 30, 21; m 46; c 2. ZOOLOGY, PHYSIOLOGY. *Educ:* Univ Wis, BS, 47, MS, 49, PhD(zool), 56. *Prof Exp:* From instr to asst prof, 49-61, PROF BIOL, BALDWIN-WALLACE COL, 61- *Concurrent Pos:* Vis prof, Inst High Sch Sci Teachers, William Jewell Col, 59; NIH fel, 60; NSF res grant, 63. *Mem:* AAAS; Am Soc Parasitol; Am Inst Biol Sci; Nat Audubon Soc. *Res:* Physiology; parasitology; nucleic acids in migrating slime mold; fluke parasites of snails. *Mailing Add:* Dept of Biol Baldwin-Wallace Col Berea OH 44017

PETERKOFSKY, ALAN, b Mass, Aug 29, 30; m 56; c 2. BIOCHEMISTRY. *Educ:* City Col NY, BS, 53; Union Col NY, MS, 55; NY Univ, PhD(biochem), 60. *Prof Exp:* Asst scientist, State Dept Health, NY, 53-55; asst scientist, US Pub Health Serv Off, 59-61, CHEMIST, NIH, 61- *Mem:* AAAS; Am Soc Microbiol; Am Soc Biol Chem. *Res:* Enzymology; molecular biology; nucleic acids; neuropeptides. *Mailing Add:* Lab Biochem Genetics Nat Heart Lung & Blood Inst Bethesda MD 20014

PETERKOFSKY, BEVERLY, biochemistry, see previous edition

PETERLE, TONY J, b Cleveland, Ohio, July 7, 25; m 49; c 2. BIOLOGY, ECOLOGY. *Educ:* Utah State Univ, BS, 49; Univ Mich, MS, 50, PhD(wildlife ecol, zool), 54. *Prof Exp:* Res biologist, Dept Conserv, Mich, 51-54; Fulbright scholar natural history, Aberdeen Univ, 54-55; res biologist, Dept Conserv, Mich, 55-59; leader, Ohio Coop Wildlife Res Unit, 59-63; chmn fac pop & environ biol, Col Biol Sci, 68-70, chmn prog environ biol fac zool, 69-71, chmn dept, 71-81, PROF ZOOL, OHIO STATE UNIV, 62- *Concurrent Pos:* Mem panel, NSF, 65 & Adv Conf Pesticides, NATO, 65; ed, J Wildlife Mgt, 69-70; co-organizer, XIII Int Cong Game Biol, 77. *Mem:* Int Union Game Biol; Wildlife Soc (vpres, 70, pres-elect, 71, pres, 72); AAAS; Ecol Soc Am; Sigma Xi. *Res:* Ecology of wildlife, translocation and bioaccumulation of pesticides in natural environments; use of radioisotopes to study pesticides; natural regulation of animal populations; population dynamics and censusing; motivation in hunting. *Mailing Add:* Dept of Zool Ohio State Univ 1735 Neil Ave Columbus OH 43210

PETERLIN, ANTON, b Ljubljana, Yugoslavia, Sept 25, 08; m 41; c 2. POLYMER PHYSICS. *Educ:* Univ Ljubljana, MS, 30; Univ Berlin, DSc(physics), 38. *Hon Degrees:* DSc, Univ Mainz, 79. *Prof Exp:* Prof physics, Univ Ljubljana, 39-60, pres, J Stefan Inst, 49-59; prof physics, Munich Tech Univ, 60-61; dir Camille Dreyfus Lab, Res Triangle Inst, 61-73; adj prof polymer sci, Duke Univ, 61-73; ASST CHIEF POLYMERS DIV, NAT BUR STANDARDS, WASHINGTON DC, 73- *Concurrent Pos:* Vis prof, Case Western Reserve Univ, 73- *Honors & Awards:* Bingham Medal, Soc Rheol, 70; Ford High Polymer Physics Prize, Am Phys Soc, 72. *Mem:* Am Phys Soc; Am Chem Soc; Soc Rheol; NY Acad Sci; Austrian Acad Sci. *Res:* Solution properties; solid state of polymers; plastic deformation of crystalline polymers; acoustic emission; spin resonance; IR; neutron and x-ray scattering. *Mailing Add:* Polymers Div Nat Bur of Standards Washington DC 20234

PETERMAN, DAVID A, b Port Arthur, Tex, Sept 21, 35; m 59; c 5. MECHANICAL ENGINEERING. *Educ:* Lamar State Col, BS(mech eng) & BS(math), 56; Rice Univ, MS, 58, PhD(mech eng), 64. *Prof Exp:* Instr mech eng, Lamar State Col, 58-59; mem tech staff, 61-66, br mgr corp res & eng, 67-69, br mgr process technol res & develop, 69-76, mgr advan front end, 76-80, MGR ELECTRON BEAM SYSTS, TEX INSTRUMENTS, INC, 80- *Mem:* Am Soc Mech Engrs. *Res:* Semiconductor device manufacturing science and technology. *Mailing Add:* Tex Instruments Inc PO Box 225621 Mail Sta 3620 Dallas TX 75265

PETERMAN, KEITH EUGENE, b Elliottsburg, Pa, Dec 27, 47; m 71; c 4. INORGANIC CHEMISTRY, FLUORINE CHEMISTRY. *Educ:* Shippensburg State Col, BS, 69, MEd, 72; Univ Idaho, PhD(inorg chem), 75. *Prof Exp:* Teacher chem, S Middleton Sch Dist, 69-71; teaching asst chem, Shippensburg State Col, 71-72; res asst chem, Univ Idaho, 72-75; teaching fel chem, Millikin Univ, 75-76; asst prof, 76-80, ASSOC PROF CHEM, YORK COL PA, 80- *Mem:* Am Chem Soc; Sigma Xi. *Res:* Synthesis, reaction chemistry, photochemistry, mechanistic studies, and spectroscopic studies of fluorine containing compounds; model for enzyme assay utilizing nuclear magnetic resonance. *Mailing Add:* Dept of Phys Sci York Col of Pa York PA 17405

PETERMAN, ZELL EDWIN, b Cass County, Iowa, Nov 29, 34; m 60; c 2. GEOLOGY. *Educ:* Colo Sch Mines, GeolE, 57; Univ Minn, MS, 59; Univ Alta, PhD(geol), 62. *Prof Exp:* Geologist, Br Geochem Census, 62-64, geologist, Br Isotope Geol, 64-71, chief, Br Isotope Geol, 71-76, GEOLOGIST, BR ISOTOPE GEOL, US GEOL SURV, 76- *Mem:* Geol Soc Am; Mineral Soc Am; Soc Econ Geologists. *Res:* Geochronology; Precambrian geology; isotope tracer studies. *Mailing Add:* US Geol Surv Fed Ctr Lakewood CO 80226

PETERS, ALAN, b Nottingham, Eng, Dec 6, 29; m 55; c 3. ANATOMY. *Educ:* Bristol Univ, PhD(zool), 54. *Prof Exp:* Lectr anat, Univ Edinburgh, 58-66; PROF ANAT & CHMN DEPT, SCH MED, BOSTON UNIV, 66- *Concurrent Pos:* Res fel anat, Univ Edinburgh, 57-58; grants, Med Res Coun Gt Brit, 65-66, NIH & United Cerebral Palsy Found, 66-; vis lectr, Harvard Med Sch, 63-64; mem, Anat Test Comt, Nat Bd Med Examrs, 72-75; assoc ed, J Neurocytol, J Comp Neurol & Studies Brain Function; mem, Neurol B Study Sect, NIH. *Honors & Awards:* Symington Prize, Anat Soc Gt Brit & Ireland, 62. *Mem:* Am Soc Cell Biol; Soc Neurosci; Am Asn Anat; Anat Soc Gt Brit & Ireland. *Res:* Fine structure of the nervous system. *Mailing Add:* Dept of Anat Boston Univ Sch of Med Boston MA 02118

PETERS, ALEXANDER ROBERT, b Pender, Nebr, Nov 17, 36; m 59; c 2. MECHANICAL ENGINEERING. *Educ:* Univ Nebr, BS, 59, MS, 63; Okla State Univ, PhD(mech eng), 67. *Prof Exp:* Engr, Space & Info Div, N Am Aviation, Inc, 63-64; from instr to assoc prof mech eng, 66-75, PROF MECH ENG & CHMN DEPT, UNIV NEBR, LINCOLN, 75- *Concurrent Pos:* NSF res initiation grant, 68-69, instr sci equip grant, 68-70; Am Soc Eng Educ-

Ford Found residency fel, Ford Motor Co; prin investr, NIH Interdisciplinary res grant & NSF instrnl sci equip grant, 75-77. *Mem:* Am Soc Mech Engrs; Soc Automotive Engrs; Am Inst Aeronaut & Astronaut; Am Soc Eng Educ. *Res:* Boundary layer separation; aerodynamic heat transfer; automotive climate control; combustion; aerodynamics; energy. *Mailing Add:* Dept of Mech Eng Univ of Nebr Lincoln NE 68588

PETERS, B(RUNO) FRANK, b Drumheller, Alta, Jan 24, 33; m 57; c 5. METALLURGY. *Educ:* Univ BC, BASc, 55, MASc, 58; Univ Leeds, PhD(metall), 68. *Prof Exp:* Mem metall & nondestructive test group, Defence Res Estab Pac, 55-56 & 58-65; lectr metall, Univ Leeds, 65-68; HEAD METALL & NONDESTRUCTIVE TESTING GROUP, DEFENCE RES ESTAB PAC, 68- *Mem:* Am Soc Metals. *Res:* Metal failure analysis; electron fractography; recrystallization; engineering applications of nondestructive testing. *Mailing Add:* Defence Res Estab Pac Esquimalt Rd Victoria BC V0S 1B0 Can

PETERS, BRUCE C(HARLES), metallurgical engineering, physical metallurgy, see previous edition

PETERS, BRUCE HARRY, b Ft Dodge, Iowa, July 18, 37; m 64; c 3. NEUROLOGY. *Educ:* State Univ Iowa, BA, 59, MS & MD, 63. *Prof Exp:* Intern med, Univ Calif, San Francisco, 63-64; resident neurol, Univ Iowa, 66-69; ASSOC PROF NEUROL, UNIV TEX MED BR, GALVESTON & MARINE BIOMED INST, 69- *Concurrent Pos:* Consult, St Mary's Hosp, Galveston, USPHS Hosp & Glaveston County Mem Hosp, 69-; mem, Awards Comt, Am Acad Neurol, 70-72; examr, Am Bd Neurol & Psychiat, 74- *Mem:* Am Acad Neurol; Soc Neurosci; Am Fedn Clin Res. *Res:* Insulinogenesis in periodic paralysis, cellular immunity in myasthenia gravis and polymyositis, physiology of hyman pharyngeo-lingual reflexes, pain and depression in chronic headache treated with antidepressants. *Mailing Add:* Dept of Neurol Univ of Tex Med Br Galveston TX 77550

PETERS, CHARLES WILLIAM, b Pierceton, Ind, Dec 9, 27; c 5. NUCLEAR PHYSICS. *Educ:* Ind Univ, BA, 50. *Prof Exp:* Nuclear physicist, US Naval Res Lab, 50-71; physicist, Environ Protection Agency, 71-76; MGR ADVAN SYSTS, CONSOL CONTROLS CORP, 76- *Mem:* Am Phys Soc; Inst Elec & Electronics Eng. *Res:* Diagnostic measurements of nuclear weapons; experimental photodiodes and photomultipliers; nuclear radiation detectors; ultra-sensitive neutron detectors; radiation detection systems for military applications; applications of nuclear technology; neutron diagnostic probe. *Mailing Add:* 12323 Beechnut Ct Woodbridge VA 22192

PETERS, DALE THOMPSON, b Cincinnati, Ohio, Dec 5, 34; m 59; c 2. METALLOGRAPHY, BATTERIES. *Educ:* Univ Cincinnati, BS, 58; Ohio State Univ, PhD(metall), 62. *Prof Exp:* Res asst, Ohio State Univ, 58-62; res metallurgist, 62-67, sect supvr magnetic mat, 67-74, mgr phys/anal sect, 74-79, mgr secondary battery res sect, 80-81, RES FEL, ENERGY SYSTS DEPT, INCO RES & DEVELOP CTR, INT NICKEL CO, INC, 81- *Mem:* Am Inst Mining, Metall & Petrol Engrs; Am Soc Metals; The Electrochem Soc. *Res:* Internal friction, particularly grain boundary relaxation; mechanisms of strengthening of maraging steels; magnetic properties of nickel containing materials; metallography and electron beam analytical techniques; lead-acid and nickel alkaline battery research. *Mailing Add:* Inco Res & Develop Ctr Int Nickel Co Inc Sterling Forest Suffern NY 10901

PETERS, DAVID STEWART, b Danville, Pa, July 5, 41; m 59; c 4. FISH BIOLOGY, ECOLOGY. *Educ:* Utah State Univ, BS, 64; NC State Univ, MS, 68, PhD(zool), 71. *Prof Exp:* FISHERY BIOLOGIST, NAT MARINE FISHERIES SERV, 70- *Mem:* Am Fisheries Soc; AAAS; Ecol Soc; Sigma Xi. *Mailing Add:* Nat Marine Fisheries Serv Beaufort NC 28516

PETERS, DENNIS GAIL, b Los Angeles, Calif, Apr 17, 37. ANALYTICAL CHEMISTRY, ELECTROCHEMISTRY. *Educ:* Calif Inst Technol, BS, 58; Harvard Univ, PhD(anal chem), 62. *Prof Exp:* From instr to prof, 62-75, HERMAN T BRISCOE PROF CHEM, IND UNIV, BLOOMINGTON, 75- *Concurrent Pos:* NSF grant, 66-69, 73-75; Petrol Res Fund grants, 69-70, 78-81 & 81-84. *Mem:* Am Chem Soc. *Res:* Chronopotentiometry; polarography; coulometry; chemistry of noble metals; kinetics and mechanisms of electrode reactions; chemical instrumentation; organic electrochemistry. *Mailing Add:* Dept of Chem Ind Univ Bloomington IN 47401

PETERS, DON CLAYTON, b Corn, Okla, Sept 1, 31; m 53; c 3. ENTOMOLOGY. *Educ:* Tabor Col, AB, 53; Kans State Col, MS, 55, PhD, 57. *Prof Exp:* Asst prof biol, Tabor Col, 57; asst prof entom, Univ Mo, 57-59; asst prof zool & entom, Iowa State Univ, 59-70; HEAD DEPT ENTOM, OKLA STATE UNIV, 71-, PROF ENTOM, 77- *Concurrent Pos:* USAID consult, WAfrica, 79. *Mem:* Entom Soc Am. *Res:* Host plant resistance to insects; insect population management. *Mailing Add:* Dept of Entom Okla State Univ Stillwater OK 74074

PETERS, DOYLE BUREN, b Chester, Tex, Nov 23, 22; m 50; c 2. SOIL PHYSICS. *Educ:* Agr & Mech Col, Tex, BS, 49, MS, 51; Univ Calif, PhD(soil physics), 54. *Prof Exp:* Asst soils, Agr & Mech Col, Tex, 49-51 & Univ Calif, 51-54; agent, Soil & Water Mgt, USDA, Ill, 54-64; assoc prof agron, 64-70, prof agron & soil scientist, 70-77, PROF SOIL PHYSICS & RES LEADER, SCI & EDUC ADMIN-AGR RES, USDA, UNIV ILL, URBANA, 77-, PROF DEPT AGRON, 80- *Mem:* Am Soc Agron. *Res:* Soil physical conditions and plant growth; energy status of soil moisture during compression. *Mailing Add:* Dept of Agron Univ of Ill Urbana IL 61801

PETERS, E(RNEST), b Can, Jan 27, 26; m 49; c 2. EXTRACTIVE METALLURGY, ELECTROCHEMISTRY. *Educ:* Univ BC, BASc, 49, MASc, 51, PhD(metall), 56. *Prof Exp:* Metallurgist, Geneva Steel Co, Utah, 49-50; jr res engr, Consol Mining & Smelting Co, Can, 51-53; instr metall, Univ BC, 55-56; res engr, Metals Res Lab, Union Carbide Corp, 56-58; from asst prof to assoc prof metall, 58-67, PROF METALL, UNIV BC, 67- *Concurrent Pos:* Consult, Cominco, Ltd, Can, 58- & Kennecott Corp, 64-; Nat Res Coun Can travel award, Univ Gottingen, 65; vis prof, Univ Calif, Berkeley, 71. *Honors & Awards:* Authors Award, Chem Inst Can, 62; Extractive Metall Lectr, Am Inst Mining, Metall & Petrol Engrs, 76. *Mem:* Am Inst Mining, Metall & Petrol Engrs; fel Royal Soc Chem; Can Inst Mining & Metall; Chem Inst Can. *Res:* Corrosion and metal oxidation; extractive metallurgy; hydrometallurgy; pressure processes; electrochemistry of sulfide minerals; metallurgical thermodynamics and kinetics; reactor and plant design. *Mailing Add:* Dept Metall Univ BC Vancouver BC V6T 1W5 Can

PETERS, EARL, b Leipzig, Ger, Dec 28, 27; US citizen; m 57; c 3. CHEMISTRY, TEXTILES. *Educ:* Oberlin Col, AB, 47; Univ Buffalo, MA, 50, PhD(org chem), 58. *Prof Exp:* Chemist polymers, Sprague Elec Co, 52-54; guest worker, Nat Bur Standards, 54-56; sr res chemist textiles, Milliken Res Corp, 60-67; mgr tech liaison, Burlington Industs, 67-73; assoc prof textiles, 73-77, EXEC DIR DEPT CHEM, CORNELL UNIV, 78- *Mem:* AAAS; Am Chem Soc; Sigma Xi; Fiber Soc; Am Asn Textile Chemists & Colorists. *Res:* Textiles; fibers; educational administration. *Mailing Add:* Dept of Chem Baker Lab Cornell Univ Ithaca NY 14853

PETERS, EDWARD JAMES, b Milwaukee, Wis, Aug 5, 44; m 65; c 3. AQUATIC ECOLOGY, ICHTHYOLOGY. *Educ:* Wis State Univ, Stevens Point, BS, 67; Brigham Young Univ, MS, 69, PhD(zool), 74. *Prof Exp:* Instr biol, 72-74, asst prof, Mt Mercy Col, 74-75; asst prof fisheries, 75-80, ASSOC PROF, UNIV NEBR-LINCOLN, 80- *Mem:* Am Fisheries Soc; Am Soc Ichthyol & Herpetol; NAm Benthological Soc. *Res:* Effects of silt and sedimentation on fish growth and reproduction; ecology and distribution of freshwater fishes; trophic dynamics of freshwater communities. *Mailing Add:* Dept of Forestry Univ of Nebr Lincoln NE 68583

PETERS, EDWIN FRANCIS, b Rockford, Ill, Dec 31, 19; m 43; c 2. CHEMISTRY. *Educ:* Purdue Univ, BS, 42. *Prof Exp:* Chemist, Magnolia Petrol Co Div, Socony Mobil Oil Co, Inc, 43-46; sr res chemist, Standard Oil Co (Ind), 46-62; res assoc, Amoco Chem Corp, Ind, 62-72, res assoc, Ill, 72-74, sr res assoc to res consult, 74-82; RETIRED. *Honors & Awards:* Polyolefins Award, Soc Plastics Engrs, 75. *Mem:* Am Chem Soc. *Res:* Alkylation; polymerization; isomerization; hydrofluorination; catalysts, especially hydrocarbon conversion processes. *Mailing Add:* 155 Ethel St Winfield IL 60190

PETERS, ELROY JOHN, b Kaukauna, Wis, June 10, 22; m 53; c 4. AGRONOMY. *Educ:* Univ Wis, BS, 52, MS, 53, PhD(agron), 56. *Prof Exp:* Asst, Univ Wis, 53-56; from asst prof field crops to assoc prof, 66-71 to PROF AGRON, UNIV MO-COLUMBIA, 71-; AGRONOMIST, USDA, 56- *Mem:* Am Soc Agron. *Res:* Weed science, especially pastures and range land; pasture management. *Mailing Add:* 210 Waters Hall Univ of Mo Columbia MO 65201

PETERS, FRANK ALBERT, b Washington, DC, June 3, 31; m 55; c 4. CHEMICAL ENGINEERING. *Educ:* Univ Md, BS, 55. *Prof Exp:* Develop engr, Celanese Corp, 55-58; chem engr, College Park Metall Res Ctr, 58-66, prof leader process eval, 66-70, res supvr, 70-77, acting chief, Process Eval Off, 77-80, CHIEF, PROCESS EVAL STAFF, BUR MINES, 80- *Mem:* Am Inst Chem Engrs; Am Asn Cost Engrs. *Res:* Economic evaluation of research projects; cost engineering; development of techniques, including use of computers for making these evaluations; extractive metallurgical methods including production of alumina from non-bauxite resources. *Mailing Add:* Bur Mines Avondale Res Ctr 4900 La Salle Rd Avondale MD 20782

PETERS, GERALD ALAN, b Monroe, Mich, Mar 3, 43; m 65; c 2. PLANT PHYSIOLOGY. *Educ:* Eastern Mich Univ, BS, 66; Univ Mich, MS, 69, PhD(bot), 70. *Prof Exp:* Res asst, Univ Mich, 66-69; fel photosynthesis, 70-72, staff scientist, 72-76, investr, 76-80, SR INVESTR, C F KETTERING LAB, 80- *Mem:* Am Soc Plant Physiologists. *Res:* Symbiotic nitrogen fixation, particularly morphological and physiological investigations on the association which occurs between the water-fern, Azolla and the blue-green algal symbiont, Anabaena azollae. *Mailing Add:* C F Kettering Res Lab 150 S E College St Yellow Springs OH 45387

PETERS, GERALD JOSEPH, b Baltimore, Md, Sept 29, 41; m 67; c 2. PHYSICS. *Educ:* Loyola Col, BS, 63; Univ Toledo, MS, 65. *Prof Exp:* Res physicist nuclear radiation, White Oak Lab, Naval Surface Weapons Ctr, 65-80; PHYSICIST & SPEC ASST TO ASSOC DIR HIGH ENERGY & NUCLEAR PHYSICS, OFF ENERGY RES, US DEPT ENERGY, 80- *Concurrent Pos:* NASA trainee physics, Univ Toledo, 66-68. *Honors & Awards:* Outstanding Performance Award, Naval Surface Weapons Ctr, 78. *Mem:* AAAS; Inst Elec & Electronics Engrs; Am Nuclear Soc. *Res:* Accelerators; particle beam technology and applications; nuclear radiation instrumentation. *Mailing Add:* Off High Energy & Nuclear Physics US Dept Energy ER 20-1 Washington DC 20545

PETERS, GERALDINE JOAN, b San Diego, Calif; m 68. ASTRONOMY, ASTROPHYSICS. *Educ:* Calif State Univ, Long Beach, BS, 65; Univ Calif, Los Angeles, MA, 66, PhD(astron), 73. *Prof Exp:* Res assoc astron, Univ Calif, Los Angeles, 74-76; physicist, Div High Energy Astrophys, Ctr Astrophys, Smithsonian Astrophys Observ, Cambridge, Mass, 76-78; RES ASSOC/ADJ ASST PROF, DEPT ASTRON, UNIV SOUTHERN CALIF, LOS ANGELES, 78- *Concurrent Pos:* Prin investr grants, NASA. *Mem:* Am Astron Soc; Int Astron Union; Astron Soc Pac. *Res:* Observation and analysis of the spectra of B-type stars; studies of the spectral variations observed in Be stars; observational studies of binary mass transfer; ultraviolet astronomy. *Mailing Add:* Dept of Astron University Park Los Angeles CA 90007

PETERS, HENRY A, b Oconomowoc, Wis, Dec 31, 20; m 54; c 4. NEUROLOGY, PSYCHIATRY. *Educ:* Univ Wis, BA, 43, MD, 45; Am Bd Psychiat & Neurol, cert psychiat, 52, cert neurol, 55. *Prof Exp:* Intern, Germantown Hosp & Dispensary, Philadelphia, 45-46; resident neuropsychiat, 48-51, from instr to asst prof, 51-58, assoc prof neurol, 58-70, PROF NEUROL & REHAB MED, MED SCH, UNIV WIS-MADISON,

70- *Concurrent Pos:* Mem bd dirs, Dane County Res Prog & Comn Pub Policy, State Med-Soc; dir muscular dystrophy clin, Univ Hosps, 56-; mem adv comt, March Dimes; consult, Muscular Dystrophy Asn Am Inc, Cerebral Palsy Clin, Univ Hosps & Vet Admin Hosp, Tomah, Wis; examr neurol, Am Bd Neurol & Psychiat; mem tech adv comt drug abuse, Atty Gen; mem med adv bd, Nat Muscular Dystrophy Asn. *Honors & Awards:* Cert Merit, AMA, 68. *Mem:* AMA; fel Am Col physicians; fel Am Psychiat Asn; fel Am Acad Neurol; Soc Clin Neurol. *Mailing Add:* Dept Neurol Univ Wis Sch Med Madison WI 53706

PETERS, HENRY BUCKLAND, b Oakland, Calif, Nov 2, 16; c 5. OPTOMETRY. *Educ:* Univ Calif, AB, 38; Univ Nebr, MA, 39. *Hon Degrees:* DrOcularSci, Southern Col Optom, 71. *Prof Exp:* Lectr optom, Los Angeles Col Optom, 39-40; lectr, Sch Optom, Univ Calif, Berkeley, 47-48, from asst clin prof to assoc clin prof, 48-62, assoc prof & dir clins, 62-69, asst dean, 65-69; PROF OPTOM, DEAN SCH OPTOM & PROF PUB HEALTH, SCH MED, MED CTR, UNIV ALA, BIRMINGHAM, 69- *Concurrent Pos:* chmn optom adv comt, Vet Admin Dept Med & Surg; pres, Nat Health Coun. *Honors & Awards:* Carel C Koch Medal, 74. *Mem:* Am Optom Asn; fel Am Acad Optom. *Res:* Relation of vision to epidemiology of vision problems; vision performance. *Mailing Add:* Sch of Optom Univ of Ala Med Ctr Birmingham AL 35233

PETERS, HOWARD AUGUST, b Council Bluffs, Iowa, May 5, 26; m 48; c 3. ENVIRONMENTAL HEALTH. *Educ:* Univ Nebr, Omaha, BA, 51; Univ NC, Chapel Hill, MPH, 58, PhD(environmental health), 65. *Prof Exp:* Instr environ health, Univ NC, Chapel Hill, 61-62, res assoc, 62-64; asst prof pub health & dir environ health & safety, 64-71, ASSOC PROF PUB HEALTH, UNIV MASS, AMHERST, 71-, CHMN ENVIRON HEALTH PROG, 79- *Concurrent Pos:* NIH training grants air pollution & health & safety, 64-71. *Mem:* AAAS; Am Pub Health Asn; Air Pollution Control Asn; Am Indust Hyg Asn; Nat Environ Health Asn. *Res:* Urban environment; physical, chemical and biological contaminants in air, water and the industrial environment. *Mailing Add:* Div of Pub Health Univ of Mass Sch of Health Sci Amherst MA 01003

PETERS, HOWARD MCDOWELL, b Beech Creek, Pa, Oct 13, 40; m 64; c 2. ORGANIC CHEMISTRY. *Educ:* Geneva Col, BS, 62; Stanford Univ, PhD(org chem), 67. *Prof Exp:* Res chemist, Dow Chem Co, 66-69; res chemist, SRI Int, 69-75, asst dir chem lab, 75-77, indust economist, 77-78; attorney, Hexcel Corp, 78-80; PATENT ATTORNEY, SYNTEX CORP, 80- *Mem:* Am Chem Soc; Am Patent Law Asn. *Res:* Synthetic organic chemistry; organic fluorine chemistry; nitration chemistry. *Mailing Add:* 3469 Kenneth Dr Palo Alto CA 94303

PETERS, JACK WARREN, b Denver, Colo, Jan 7, 16; m 40; c 3. GEOPHYSICS. *Educ:* Colo Sch Mines, GeolE, 38. *Prof Exp:* Chief gravity interpreter, Magnolia Petrol Co, 38-53; regional geophysicist, Mobil Producing Co, 53-59, sr staff geophysicist, Mobil Oil Co, 60-66, div regional geophysicist, Mobil Oil Corp, 66-69, geophys adv, 69-80; GEOPHYS CONSULT, 80- *Mem:* Soc Explor Geophys; Europ Asn Explor Geophys. *Res:* Interpretation of gravity and magnetic data. *Mailing Add:* 13726 Peyton Dr Dallas TX 75240

PETERS, JAMES, b Mt Clemens, Mich, Aug 30, 34; m 56; c 1. COLLOID CHEMISTRY, POLYMER CHEMISTRY. *Educ:* Wayne State Univ, BS, 56, PhD(chem), 64. *Prof Exp:* Chemist, Ditzler Color Div, Pittsburgh Plate Glass Co, 56-57; RES CHEMIST, DOW CHEM CO, 64- *Mem:* Am Chem Soc; Sigma Xi. *Res:* Polymer characterization; water soluble polymers and polyelectrolytes; colloid coagulation; secondary oil recovery; flow through porous media; emulsion polymerization; cement reinforcement. *Mailing Add:* Dow Chem Co Cent Res Specialty Prod Res 1712 Bldg Midland MI 48640

PETERS, JAMES ALEXANDER, b Pensacola, Fla, Oct 7, 28; m 49; c 1. EPIDEMIOLOGY, SCIENTIFIC ADMINISTRATION. *Educ:* Auburn Univ, DVM, 54; Univ Mich, MPH, 68; Am Bd Vet Pub Health, dipl, 69; Am Bd Vet Prev Med, dipl, 80. *Prof Exp:* Pvt pract, 54-64; vet officer comp epidemiol, Nat Cancer Inst, 64-68, head prog anal unit carcinogenesis, 68-70, asst to dir etiology, Cancer Etiology, 70-71, dep sci dir, 71-72, actg sci dir, 72-73, dir, Div Cancer Cause & Prev, 73-78; med dir, Cystic Fibrosis Found, 78-80; ASSOC PROF & VCHMN, DEPT PREV MED & BIOMET, UNIFORMED SERV UNIV HEALTH SCI, 80- *Concurrent Pos:* Mem, Surg Gen Comt Eval Environ Carcinogenesis, 69, Adv Comt, Registry Exp Cancer, 70, President's Comt Environ Qual, 70 & Auth Toxicity Info Prog, Nat Libr Med, 70; consult, Am Asn Cancer Res, 72, mem, Asst Secy Health Toxicol Coord Comt, 73; corresp, Ctr Short Lived Phenomena, 71. *Mem:* AAAS; Am Pub Health Asn; Am Vet Med Asn; Am Soc Prev Oncol. *Res:* Epidemiology of low prevalence diseases; cancer program planning and management; experimental study design; scientific administration and program management. *Mailing Add:* Bldg 31 Rm 11A03 Nat Cancer Inst Bethesda MD 20014

PETERS, JAMES JOHN, b Ft Wayne, Ind, May 4, 41; m 64; c 2. METAL PHYSICS. *Educ:* Ind Inst Technol, BS, 63; Univ Detroit, MS, 65; Univ Ill, PhD(metall eng), 71. *Prof Exp:* Asst prof physics, Tri-State Col, 70-71; asst prof, 71-75, ASSOC PROF PHYSICS, HILLSDALE COL, 75- *Mem:* Sigma Xi; Am Asn Physics Teachers; Am Phys Soc. *Res:* Magnetic susceptibilities of transition metals in non-magnetic host liquid alloys. *Mailing Add:* Dept of Physics Hillsdale Col Hillsdale MI 49242

PETERS, JAMES MILTON, b Pomona, Calif, Nov 9, 26; m 50; c 4. BIOCHEMISTRY. *Educ:* Univ Calif, AB, 53, PhD, 57; Am Registry Med Technol, cert, 71. *Prof Exp:* Res biochemist, Univ Calif, 57-58; instr phys sci, Calif State Polytech Col, 58-60; biochemist, Geront Br, Nat Heart Inst, 60-61; assoc prof biochem, Sch Med, Univ Md, 61-63; assoc prof biochem, Calif State Polytech Univ, 63-71, prof, 71-80; MEM STAFF, CENT CALIF LAB INC, 80- *Concurrent Pos:* Med technol trainee, Children's Hosp, San Francisco, 69-70; consult, Cent Path Med Group, Inc, 71-; consult assoc, Cent Calif Lab, Inc. *Mem:* Am Soc Clin Pathologists; Am Asn Clin Chem; Am Chem Soc. *Res:* Intermediary metabolism. *Mailing Add:* 208 Casa St Cent Calif Lab Inc San Luis Obispo CA 93401

PETERS, JOHN BURL, animal husbandry, deceased

PETERS, JOHN HENRY, b Cincinnati, Ohio, May 31, 24; m 47; c 2. BIOCHEMISTRY, BIOCHEMICAL PHARMACOLOGY. *Educ:* Univ Cincinnati, BS, 49; Univ Fla, MS, 50; Univ Minn, PhD(physiol chem), 55. *Prof Exp:* Biochemist, Radioisotope Serv, Vet Admin Hosp, Minneapolis, 52-56; res assoc, Christ Hosp Inst Med Res, Cincinnati, 56-63; assoc res biol chemist, Nat Ctr Primate Biol, Univ Calif, Davis, 63-64; sr biochem pharmacologist, 65-68, mgr comp, 68-80, DIR, BIOCHEM PHARMACOL PROG, SRI INT, 80- *Concurrent Pos:* Asst prof, Sch Med, Univ Cincinnati, 60-63; mem, US Leprosy Panel, Nat Inst Allergy & Infectious Dis, 69-73. *Mem:* AAAS; Am Chem Soc; Am Asn Cancer Res; Soc Exp Biol & Med; NY Acad Sci. *Res:* Chemical mutagenesis and carcinogenesis; intermediary and drug metabolism; mechanism of vitamin and drug action; comparative biochemistry and pharmacology; pharmacogenetics; metabolism of amino acids in uremia of man; drug and amino acid metabolism in subhuman primates; metabolism of antileprotic and anticancer drugs in animals and man. *Mailing Add:* Life Sci Div SRI Int 333 Ravenswood Ave Menlo Park CA 94025

PETERS, JOSEPH EDWARD, b New Britain, Conn, Oct 12, 50. BIOCHEMICAL PHARMACOLOGY. *Educ:* Trinity Col, BS, 72; Univ Iowa, PhD(pharmacol), 79. *Prof Exp:* Res teaching fel pharmacol, Univ Iowa, 74-79; scholar, 80-81, PARDEE CANCER RES FEL HEMAT & ONCOL, SCH MED, UNIV MICH, 81- *Mem:* AAAS; NY Acad Sci. *Res:* Biochemical pharmacology of anticancer agents. *Mailing Add:* 8631 W Foster Chicago IL 60656

PETERS, JOSEPH JOHN, b Chicago, Ill, Aug 5, 07. BIOLOGY. *Educ:* St Louis Univ, MA, 34; Univ Detroit, MS, 36; Fordham Univ, PhD(zool), 46. *Prof Exp:* From asst prof to assoc prof, 45-57, PROF BIOL, XAVIER UNIV, OHIO, 57-, CHMN DEPT, 47- *Mem:* Am Physiol Soc; Soc Develop Biol; Am Soc Zool. *Res:* Electroencephalography and electrical activity of the nervous, sensory and muscular systems of the developing chick during various behavioral states such as sleep and attention and while under the influence of such environmental changes as temperature, anoxia and some drugs. *Mailing Add:* Dept of Biol Xavier Univ Cincinnati OH 45207

PETERS, KEVIN SCOTT, b Ponca City, Okla, May 5, 49; m 78. PHYSICAL ORGANIC CHEMISTRY. *Educ:* Univ Okla, BS, 71; Yale Univ, PhD(chem), 75. *Prof Exp:* ASST PROF CHEM, HARVARD UNIV, 78- *Mem:* Am Chem Soc. *Res:* Picosecond laser spectroscopy applied to organic photochemistry and protein dynamics. *Mailing Add:* Dept of Chem 12 Oxford St Cambridge MA 02138

PETERS, LEO CHARLES, b Smith Co, Kans, Sept 21, 31; m 57; c 8. MECHANICAL ENGINEERING. *Educ:* Kans State Univ, BS, 53; Iowa State Univ, MS, 63, PhD(mech eng & eng mech), 67. *Prof Exp:* Jr engr, John Deere Waterloo Tractor Works, Iowa, 57-59, engr, 59-61; from instr to asst prof, 61-68, ASSOC PROF MECH ENG, IOWA STATE UNIV, 68- *Concurrent Pos:* Eng consult, 62- *Mem:* Am Soc Mech Engrs; Am Soc Agr Engrs; Am Soc Eng Educ; Soc Automotive Engrs. *Res:* Design; products liability. *Mailing Add:* Dept of Mech Eng Iowa State Univ Ames IA 50011

PETERS, LEON, JR, b Columbus, Ohio, May 28, 23; m 53; c 7. ELECTRICAL ENGINEERING. *Educ:* Ohio State Univ, BEE, 50, MSc, 54, PhD(elec eng), 59. *Prof Exp:* Asst, Antenna Lab, 50-51, res assoc, 51-56, asst supvr, 56-59, from asst prof to assoc prof elec eng, 59-67, PROF ELEC ENG, OHIO STATE UNIV, 67-, ASSOC SUPVR, ANTENNA LAB, 59-, DIR TECH AREA, 69- *Mem:* Sigma Xi; fel Inst Elec & Electronics Engrs. *Res:* Properties of radar targets and the environment in which they may be observed; antennas. *Mailing Add:* 1320 Kinnear Rd Electrosci Lab Ohio State Univ Columbus OH 43212

PETERS, LEROY LYNN, b Deerfield, Mo, June 21, 31; m 54; c 3. ENTOMOLOGY. *Educ:* Kans State Univ, BS, 55, MS, 56; Univ Mo-Columbia, PhD(entom), 71; Am Registry Prof Entom, cert. *Prof Exp:* Admin asst agr chem, Indust Fumigant Co, 58; surv entomologist, Kans State Bd Agr, 59-64; exten entomologist, Univ Mo-Columbia, 64-72; ASSOC PROF ENTOM, UNIV NEBR, LINCOLN, 72- *Mem:* Entom Soc Am. *Res:* Control of corn and sorghum insects. *Mailing Add:* S Cent Sta Univ Nebr Box 66 Clay Center NE 68933

PETERS, LESTER JOHN, b Brisbane, Australia, Aug 23, 42; m 66. RADIOTHERAPY. *Educ:* Univ Queensland, MB, BS, 66; Royal Australasian Col Radiologists, MRACR, 71; FRCR, 75; MACR, 78. *Prof Exp:* Resident radiother, Queensland Radium Inst, 68-70, staff radiotherapist, 71; res fel radiobiol & oncol, Cancer Res Campaign, Eng, 72-74; res fel, Dimbleby Res Found, Eng, 74-75; asst prof, 75-78, assoc prof radiother, assoc radiotherapist, 75-79, PROF & HEAD, DIV RADIOTHER, UNIV TEX M D ANDERSON HOSP & TUMOR INST, HOUSTON, 81- *Concurrent Pos:* Sr radiol oncologist, Inst Oncol & Radiother, Prince of Wales Hosp, Sydney Australia, 79-81. *Mem:* Am Col Radiol; Am Asn Cancer Res; Am Soc Therapeut Radiologists; Brit Inst Radiol; Radiation Res Soc. *Res:* Mechanisms of metastasis and kinetics of transplantation of experimental animal tumors; response to radiation of normal and neoplastic tissues in mice; clinical neutron radiotherapy; bone marrow transplantation; hyperfractionated radiotherapy. *Mailing Add:* Div Exp Radiother M D Anderson Hosp & Tumor Inst Houston TX 77030

PETERS, LEWIS, b Evanston, Ill, Apr 10, 32; m 61, 80; c 6. PARASITOLOGY. *Educ:* DePauw Univ, AB, 54; Purdue Univ, MS, 56, PhD(zool), 60. *Prof Exp:* Instr zool, Univ Wis-La Crosse, 58-61; from asst prof to assoc prof, 61-70, dept head, 65-75, PROF BIOL, NORTHERN MICH UNIV, 70- *Mem:* Am Soc Parasitol; Am Micros Soc. *Res:* Parasitic helminths; echinococcus; allocreadium. *Mailing Add:* Dept Biol Northern Mich Univ Marquette MI 49855

PETERS, LYNN RANDOLPH, b Defiance, Ohio, Jan 25, 25. INDUSTRIAL ORGANIC CHEMISTRY. *Educ:* Oberlin Col, AB, 44; Univ Mich, MS, 49, PhD(chem), 52. *Prof Exp:* Asst, Univ Mich, 52; sr org chemist, 52-67, res scientist, 67-68, RES ASSOC, ELI LILLY & CO, 68- *Mem:* Am Chem Soc. *Res:* Process research; antibiotics; heterocyclic compounds. *Mailing Add:* Dept M-742 Eli Lilly & Co 307 E McCarty St Indianapolis IN 46285

PETERS, MARVIN ARTHUR, b Saginaw Co, Mich, June 23, 33; m 57; c 3. BIOCHEMICAL PHARMACOLOGY. *Educ:* Ferris State Col, BS, 57; Loma Linda Univ, MS, 65; Univ Iowa, PhD(pharmacol), 69. *Prof Exp:* Hosp pharmacist, Hinsdale Hosp, Ill, 57-63; from res asst to asst instr, 63-66, asst prof, 69-74, assoc prof, 74-79, PROF PHARMACOL, LOMA LINDA UNIV, 79- *Concurrent Pos:* NIMH grant, Div Narcotic Addiction & Drug Abuse, Loma Linda Univ, 72-78. *Mem:* Sigma Xi; Am Soc Pharmacol & Exp Therapeut. *Res:* Effect of methadone on perinatal development; effect of totigestational exposure to environmental chemicals on postnatal development; metabolism and distribution of drugs, and alterations in these processes which result in effects ranging from therapeutic ineffectiveness to extreme toxicity. *Mailing Add:* Dept of Pharmacol Loma Linda Univ Sch of Med Loma Linda CA 92354

PETERS, MAX S(TONE), b Delaware, Ohio, Aug 23, 20; m 47; c 2. CHEMICAL ENGINEERING. *Educ:* Pa State Univ, BS, 42, MS, 47, PhD(chem eng), 51. *Prof Exp:* Prod supvr, Nitric Acid Plant, Hercules Powder Co, 42-43; tech supvr, prod org chem, George I Treyz Chem Co, 47-49; from asst prof to prof chem eng & head dept, Univ Ill, 51-62; dean, Col Eng, 62-78, PROF CHEM ENG, UNIV COLO, 78- *Concurrent Pos:* Consult ed, McGraw-Hill ser chem eng, 60-; mem, President's Comt Nat Medal of Sci, 67-69, chmn, 69. *Honors & Awards:* Westinghouse Award, Am Soc Eng Educ, 59, Lamme Gold Medal, 73; Award of Merit, Am Asn Cost Engrs, 69; Founders Award, Am Inst Chem Engrs, 74. *Mem:* Nat Acad Eng; Am Soc Eng Educ; fel Am Inst Chem Engrs (pres, 68); Am Asn Cost Engrs; Am Chem Soc. *Res:* Reaction kinetics and catalysis; reduction reactions for nitrogen oxides; alternative energy sources. *Mailing Add:* Dept of Chem Eng OT 3-6 Eng Ctr Box 424 Univ of Colo Boulder CO 80309

PETERS, MICHAEL WOOD, b Midland, Tex, Mar 28, 38; m 59; c 1. PHYSICS. *Educ:* Calif Inst Technol, BS, 59; Univ Wis, PhD(physics), 64. *Prof Exp:* Proj assoc elem particle physics, Univ Wis, 64-66; asst prof, 66-73, ASSOC PROF PHYSICS, UNIV HAWAII, 73- *Mem:* Am Phys Soc. *Res:* High energy elementary particle phenomena; bubble chamber experimental techniques; data collection and processing for particle physics; numerical analysis. *Mailing Add:* Dept of Physics & Astron Univ of Hawaii Honolulu HI 96822

PETERS, PAUL CONRAD, b Kokomo, Ind, Dec 5, 28; m 55; c 4. SURGERY, UROLOGY. *Educ:* Ind Univ, AB, 50, MD, 53. *Prof Exp:* Intern med, Philadelphia Gen Hosp, 53-54; resident urol, Ind Univ, 54-57; from asst prof to assoc prof, 63-72, PROF UROL, UNIV TEX HEALTH SCI CTR DALLAS, 72-, CHMN DIV, 71- *Concurrent Pos:* Sr attend urologist, Parkland Mem Hosp, 63-; consult, Baylor Med Ctr Hosp, Dallas, 63-, Vet Admin Hosp, 64-, Children's Med Ctr, 64- & Presby Hosp, 66. *Mem:* AMA; Am Col Surg; Am Asn Genitourinary Surg; Am Soc Nephrology; Am Geriat Soc; Am Soc Transplant Surg. *Res:* Detection and management of genitourinary defects during intrauterine life and in newborn; renal failure and transplantation. *Mailing Add:* Univ of Tex Health Sci Ctr 5323 Harry Hines Blvd Dallas TX 75235

PETERS, PAUL JAMES, behavioral biology, see previous edition

PETERS, PHILIP BOARDMAN, b Baltimore, Md, May 17, 35; m 66; c 2. SOLID STATE PHYSICS. *Educ:* Va Mil Inst, BS, 57; Univ NC, Chapel Hill, PhD(physics), 68. *Prof Exp:* Instr physics, Va Mil Inst, 57-58; electronic engr, Bendix Corp, Md, 58-60; instr physics, Va Mil Inst, 60-62; asst, Univ NC, Chapel Hill, 62-67; from asst prof to assoc prof, 67-74, PROF PHYSICS, VA MIL INST, 74- *Mem:* Am Phys Soc; Am Asn Physics Teachers. *Res:* Point defects in metals, introduced by electron bombardment; defects in solids by internal friction measurements. *Mailing Add:* Dept of Physics Va Mil Inst Lexington VA 24450

PETERS, PHILIP CARL, b Berwyn, Ill, Apr 22, 38; div; c 4. GENERAL RELATIVITY, RELATIVISTIC ASTROPHYSICS. *Educ:* Purdue Univ, BS, 60; Calif Inst Technol, PhD(physics), 64. *Prof Exp:* Res asst prof, 64-66, from asst prof to assoc prof, 66-77, PROF PHYSICS, UNIV WASH, 77- *Mem:* Am Asn Physics Teachers; Am Phys Soc. *Res:* Gravitation; relativity; astrophysics. *Mailing Add:* Dept Physics Univ Wash Seattle WA 98195

PETERS, PHILIP H, b Cleveland, Ohio, Jan 19, 21; m 45; c 1. ELECTRICAL ENGINEERING, PHYSICS. *Educ:* Case Inst Technol, BS, 42; Union Col, NY, MS, 57; Rensselaer Polytech Inst, PhD, 62. *Prof Exp:* Engr, Advan Eng Prog, Gen Elec Co, 42-45, res assoc, Res Lab, 45-50, microwave engr, 50-59, res physicist, 59-61, consult engr, Light Mil Electronics Dept, 61-63, prog mgr process equip res & develop, Advan Technol Labs, 63-65, physicist microwave processes prog, Res & Develop Ctr, 66-68, mgr electrophys process equip, 68-69; sr scientist, Environ Technol Inc, 69-72; vpres & dir res, Environ/One Corp, 72-76; consult cool-top induction cooking, 76-77; ELEC ENGR, GEN ELEC CO CORP RES & DEVELOP, 77- *Concurrent Pos:* Lectr, Union Col, NY, 47-48, 50-51. *Mem:* Sr mem Inst Elec & Electronics Engrs; Sigma Xi. *Res:* Thermal mining technology; electron accelerators; magnetrons; microwave heating; high voltage direct current power line digital instrumentation; fiber-optic technology and applications; plasma torch; getter and ion vacuum pumps; submicron particle detection; land use planning and pollution control methods; solid state discharge lamp ballast circuits; pulse energization of electrostatic precipitators. *Mailing Add:* Corp Res & Develop PO Box 8 Schenectady NY 12301

PETERS, RALPH I, b Tulsa, Okla, June 30, 47. NEUROCHEMISTRY. *Educ:* Univ Tulsa, BS, 69; Wash State Univ, PhD(zoophysiol), 75. *Prof Exp:* Res assoc, Tex A&M Univ, 75-76; fel, Wash Col Vet Med, 76-77; asst prof, Bates Col, 77-80; ASST PROF, WICHITA STATE UNIV, 80- *Mem:* Am Soc Zoologists; AAAS; Sigma Xi; Soc Neurosci. *Res:* Tryptophan metabolism as it relatess to serotonergic neuronal function in the mammalian central nervous system, and the importance of these in locomotor control. *Mailing Add:* Dept Biol Sci Wichita State Univ Wichita KS 67208

PETERS, RANDALL DOUGLAS, b Big Stone Gap, Va, Feb 5, 42; m 65; c 3. ACOUSTICS, BIOPHYSICS. *Educ:* Univ Tenn, BS, 64, PhD(physics), 68. *Prof Exp:* ASST PROF PHYSICS, UNIV MISS, 68- *Mem:* Sigma Xi. *Res:* An attempt to determine relative changes, by non-invasive techniques, in cardiac output by measuring changes in the propagation time of the arterial pulse as a function of exercise and maneuvers such as Valsalva. *Mailing Add:* Dept of Physics Univ of Miss University MS 38677

PETERS, RICHARD MORSE, b New Haven, Conn, Feb 21, 22; m 46; c 4. SURGERY. *Educ:* Yale Univ, BS, 43, MD, 45; Am Bd Surg, dipl, Am Bd Thoracic Surg, dipl. *Prof Exp:* Asst, Washington Univ, 48-50; asst prof surg, Sch Med, Univ NC, 52-55, from assoc prof to prof surg in chg thoracic & cardiovasc surg, 55-65, thoracic & cardiovasc surg & biomath & bioeng, 65-69; head div thoracic surg, 69-77, PROF SURG & BIOENG, UNIV CALIF, SAN DIEGO, 69-, CO-HEAD DIV CARDIOTHORACIC SURG, 77- *Concurrent Pos:* Fel thoracic surg, Washington Univ, 50-52; head thoracic surg, Vet Admin Hosp, San Diego, mem surg, Merit Rev Bd; pres gov body, Health Systs Agency, San Diego & Imperial Counties, 76-78. *Mem:* Am Asn Thoracic Surg; fel Am Col Surgeons; Am Surg Asn; Am Asn Surg Trauma; Soc Univ Surgeons. *Res:* Cardiopulmonary pathophysiology; bioengineering; biomathematics; computers in patient care. *Mailing Add:* Div Thoracic Surg Univ Hosp San Diego CA 92103

PETERS, ROBERT EDWARD, b Jackson, Ohio, June 17, 40; m 64; c 2. ELECTROMAGNETICS. *Educ:* Miami Univ, BS, 62; Purdue Univ, MS, 65, PhD(high energy physics), 67. *Prof Exp:* Instr physics, Purdue Univ, 67-68; PHYSICIST, FERMI NAT ACCELERATOR LAB, 68- *Mem:* Am Phys Soc. *Res:* Particle accelerator design; superconducting magnet technology. *Mailing Add:* Fermi Lab PO Box 500 Batavia IL 60510

PETERS, ROBERT HENRY, b Toronto, Ont, Aug 2, 46; m 74; c 2. LIMNOLOGY, ALLOMETRY. *Educ:* Univ Toronto, BSc, 68, PhD(limnol), 72. *Prof Exp:* Fel hydrobiol, Italiano Inst Hydrobiol, 72-74; FEL ZOOL, UNIV MUNICH, 74-; asst prof, 74-79, ASSOC PROF BIOL, MCGILL UNIV, 79- *Concurrent Pos:* Vis scientist, Italian Inst Hydrobiol, 80-81. *Mem:* Int Asn Theoret & Appl Limnol; Am Soc Limnol & Oceanog; Can Soc Zool; Am Soc Naturalists. *Res:* Ecological implications of body size; cycling of phosphorus and polychlorobiephenyls; conceptual problems in ecology; philosophy of biology. *Mailing Add:* McGill Univ Dept of Biol 1205 Ave Docteur Penfield Montreal PQ H3A 1B1 Can

PETERS, ROGER PAUL, b Washington, DC, Oct 29, 43; m 74. ANIMAL BEHAVIOR. *Educ:* Univ Chicago, BA, 65; Univ Mich, Ann Arbor, PhD(psychol), 74. *Prof Exp:* Instr math, New Col, 66-69; lectr psychol, Univ Mich, Ann Arbor, 74-75; asst prof, 75-80, ASSOC PROF PSYCHOL, FT LEWIS COL, 80- *Concurrent Pos:* Res intern, US Forest Serv, 72-74. *Res:* Wildlife behavior; cognitive mapping; olfactory communication; evolution of cognition; mammalian communication; canine behavior. *Mailing Add:* Dept Psychol Ft Lewis Col Durango CO 81301

PETERS, STEFAN, b Posen, Poland, June 27, 09; US citizen; m 52; c 2. MATHEMATICS. *Educ:* Univ Erlangen, PhD(math), 31. *Prof Exp:* Asst actuary, NY Compensation Ins Rating Bd, 38-43; res mathematician, West Coast Life Ins Co, Calif, 46-48; assoc prof, Univ Calif, Berkeley, 49-51; actuary, Calif Inspection Rating Bur, 50-52; consult actuary, Morss & Seal, NY, 52-53 & Cornell & Price, Mass, 53-58; self employed, 58-60; opers res consult, Arthur D Little, Inc, Mass, 60-73; CHIEF ACTUARY, DIV INS, COMMONWEALTH OF MASS, 74- *Mem:* Fel Soc Actuaries; Opers Res Soc Am; Am math Soc; Int Math Statist; fel Casualty Actuarial Soc. *Res:* Operations research; numerical analysis. *Mailing Add:* Div of Ins Commonwealth of Mass 100 Cambridge St Boston MA 02202

PETERS, THEODORE, JR, b Chambersburg, Pa, May 12, 22; m 45; c 4. BIOCHEMISTRY. *Educ:* Lehigh Univ, BS, 43; Harvard Univ, PhD(biol chem), 50; Am Bd Clin Chem, dipl. *Prof Exp:* Asst chem eng, Mass Inst Technol, 43-44; instr physiol chem, Sch Med, Univ Pa, 50-51; assoc biol chem, Harvard Med Sch, 53-55; RES BIOCHEMIST, MARY IMOGENE BASSETT HOSP, 55- SURGEONS, COLUMBIA UNIV, 55- *Concurrent Pos:* Biochemist, Boston Vet Admin Hosp, 53-55; from adj asst prof to adj assoc prof biol chem, Col Physicians & Surgeons, Columbia Univ, 55-; Commonwealth Fund vis scientist, Carlsberg Lab, Copenhagen, 58-59; adj prof path, Albany Med Col, 69-; guest worker, NIH, 71-72. *Mem:* Am Chem Soc; Am Soc Biol Chemists; Am Asn Clin Chemists; Am Soc Cell Biol. *Res:* Protein synthesis in animal tissues; protein structure and function. *Mailing Add:* Mary Imogene Bassett Hosp Cooperstown NY 13326

PETERS, THOMAS MICHAEL, b Inglewood, Calif, Oct 7, 37; m 57. ENTOMOLOGY. *Educ:* Long Beach State Col, BS, 59; Univ Minn, MS, 61, PhD(entom), 64. *Prof Exp:* From instr to assoc prof, 64-75, head dept, 68-75, PROF ENTOM, UNIV MASS, AMHERST, 75- *Mem:* Entom Soc Am; Can Entom Soc; Soc Syst Zool. *Res:* Taxonomy of dixid flies; taxonomy of tropical crop pests, especially in Central America; insect fauna of North American crop ecosystems; associations between crop insects and weeds that occur in crops. *Mailing Add:* Dept of Entom Univ of Mass Amherst MA 01002

PETERS, TILL JUSTUS NATHAN, b Berlin, Ger, Jan 27, 34; US citizen; m 79; c 2. INORGANIC CHEMISTRY. *Educ:* Pa State Univ, BS, 57; Univ Wis, Madison, MS, 61; Western Reserve Univ, MS, 64, PhD, 66. *Prof Exp:* Teacher high sch, NJ, 57-63; res scientist, Sherwin-Williams Co, Ohio, 66-67;

advan develop engr, GTE Sylvania, Inc, 67-71; chmn bus & occup div, Berkshire Community Col, 72-74, chmn div occup studies, 74-75, asst dean fac, 75-77; DEAN OCCUP EDUC, GRAND RAPIDS JR COL, 77- *Mem:* Am Chem Soc; Am Voc Asn. *Res:* Coordination chemistry of high oxidation states of molybdenum and tungsten; synthesis of soluble tungstates; extractive metallurgy of heavy metals. *Mailing Add:* Dean Occup Educ 143 Bostwick Ave NE Grand Rapids MI 49503

PETERS, WALTER, b St Charles, Ill, July 17, 10. GENETICS. *Educ:* Xavier Univ, Ohio, LittB, 33; Yale Univ, MS, 51; Cambridge Univ, PhD(genetics), 54. *Prof Exp:* Instr genetics, Xavier Univ, Ohio, 51; asst Cambridge Univ, 51-54; instr, John Carroll Univ, 54-58; assoc prof biol, 58-70, head dept, 59-70, prof, 70-81, EMER PROF BIOL, LOYOLA UNIV, CHICAGO, 81- *Mem:* Genetics Soc Am. *Mailing Add:* Dept of Biol Loyola Univ Chicago 6525 N Sheridan Rd Chicago IL 60611

PETERS, WILLIAM CALLIER, b Oxford, Ohio, July 12, 20; m 42; c 1. GEOLOGY. *Educ:* Miami Univ, BA, 42; Univ Colo, MS, 48, PhD(geol), 57. *Prof Exp:* Engr, NJ Zinc Co, 42, geologist, Empire Zinc Div, 48-49; asst prof geol, Idaho State Col, 49-54; geologist, Mineral Develop Dept, FMC Corp, 54-60; div geologist, Utah Copper Div, Kennecott Copper Corp, Utah, 60-64; PROF MINING & GEOL ENG, UNIV ARIZ, 64- *Concurrent Pos:* Vis prof, Univ Geneva & Sch Mines, Leoben, Austria, 71. *Mem:* Soc Econ Geol; Geol Soc Am; Am Inst Mining, Metall & Petrol Eng; Can Inst Mining & Metall; Brit Inst Mining & Metall. *Res:* Exploration for mineral deposits; mining engineering and geology applied to industrial mineral resources; economics and conservation of natural resources. *Mailing Add:* 5702 E Seventh St Tucson AZ 85711

PETERS, WILLIAM LEE, b Leavenworth, Kans, June 27, 39; m 64; c 1. AQUATIC ENTOMOLOGY. *Educ:* Univ Kans, BA, 60; Univ Utah, MS, 62, PhD(entom), 66. *Prof Exp:* PROF ENTOM, FLA AGR & MECH UNIV, 66- *Concurrent Pos:* Prin investr, NSF grant & Coop State Res Serv, 66-; adj assoc prof, Fla State Univ, 67-; res assoc, Fla State Collection Arthropods, 67-; entomologist, Univ Fla, 67-; res dir agr sci, Fla Agr & Mech Univ, 70- *Mem:* AAAS; Entom Soc Am; Am Inst Biol Sci; fel Royal Entom Soc London. *Res:* Higher classification of Ephemeroptera, especially Leptophlebiidae. *Mailing Add:* Dept Entom Fla Agr & Mech Univ Tallahassee FL 32307

PETERSDORF, ROBERT GEORGE, b Berlin, Ger, Feb 14, 26; m 51; c 2. MEDICINE. *Educ:* Brown Univ, BA, 48; Yale Univ, MD, 52. *Hon Degrees:* DSc, Albany Med Col, 79; AM, Harvard Univ, 80. *Prof Exp:* Instr med, Sch Med, Yale Univ, 57-58; asst prof, Sch Med, Johns Hopkins Univ, 58-60; assoc prof, Sch Med, Univ Wash, 60-62, prof, 62-79, chmn dept, 64-79; prof med, Harvard Med Sch, 79-81; DEAN & VCHANCELLOR HEALTH SCI & PROF MED, UNIV CALIF, 81- *Concurrent Pos:* Physician, Johns Hopkins Hosp, 58-60; physician in chief, King County Hosp, 60-64; physician in chief, Univ Wash Hosp, 64-79; consult, USPHS Hosp, Madigan Army Hosp & US Vet Admin Hosp; mem, Training Grant Comt, Nat Inst Allergy & Infectious Dis, 65-69; mem, Am Bd Internal Med, 69-77, chmn-elect, 77-; mem, Adv Comt to Dir, NIH, 72-; physician, Brigham & Women's Hosp, 79-81, attending physician, Univ Calif Med Ctr, San Diego, 81. *Mem:* Fel Am Col Physicians (pres-elect, 74-75, pres, 75-76); Asn Am Physicians (vpres, 75-76); Nat Inst Med; Asn Am Med Cols; Asn Profs Med (pres, 70-71). *Res:* Infectious diseases. *Mailing Add:* Sch Med Univ Calif San Diego La Jolla CA 92093

PETERSEN, ARNOLD JEROME, b Racine, Wis, Jan 5, 21; m 45, 79; c 6. GENETICS, ORNITHOLOGY. *Educ:* St Olaf Col, BA, 47; Univ Wis, MA, 49, PhD(zool), 53. *Prof Exp:* Assoc prof biol, Concordia Col, 51-54; assoc prof, 54-68, chmn dept, 77-79, PROF BIOL, ST OLAF COL, 68- *Concurrent Pos:* Fel cytogenetics, Columbia Univ, 62-63; Fulbright lectr, Cuttington Col, Liberia, 65-66; vis prof, Assoc Col Midwest Prog Trop Biol, Costa Rica, 79-80 & Silliman Univ, Philippines, 81- *Mem:* Am Soc Zool; Am Ornith Union. *Res:* Avian reproductive physiology and behavior; tropical biology. *Mailing Add:* Dept of Biol St Olaf Col Northfield MN 55057

PETERSEN, BENT EDVARD, b Copenhagen, Denmark, July 31, 42; Can citizen; m 65; c 3. PARTIAL DIFFERENTIAL EQUATIONS, SEVERAL COMPLEX VARIABLES. *Educ:* Univ BC, BSc, 64; Mass Inst Technol, PhD(math), 68. *Prof Exp:* Asst prof, 68-74, assoc prof, 74-80, PROF MATH, ORE STATE UNIV, 80- *Concurrent Pos:* Mem, Inst Advan Study, Princeton, NJ, 73-74. *Mem:* Am Math Soc; Math Asn Am; Sigma Xi; Sci Res Soc. *Res:* Partial differential equations; pseudo-differential operators; cohomology with bounds. *Mailing Add:* Dept of Math Ore State Univ Corvallis OR 97331

PETERSEN, BRUCE WALLACE, b Minneapolis, Minn, Dec 2, 36; m 64; c 2. ZOOLOGY. *Educ:* Univ Nebr, Omaha, BA, 58, BS, 62; State Univ Iowa, MS, 60; Univ Colo, Boulder, PhD(zool), 68. *Prof Exp:* Sci teacher pub schs Nebr, 60-62; asst prof biol, Atlantic Christian Col, 65-66 & Meramec Community Col, St Louis, 67-68; ASST PROF ZOOL, SOUTHERN ILL UNIV, CARBONDALE, 68- *Res:* Human ecology, especially biological implication of the human population increase. *Mailing Add:* Dept of Zool Southern Ill Univ Carbondale IL 62901

PETERSEN, CARL FRANK, b Santa Rosa, Calif, Oct 24, 37; m 58; c 2. GEOPHYSICS. *Educ:* Stanford Univ, BS, 59, MS, 61, PhD(geophys), 69. *Prof Exp:* Peace Corps volunteer, 63-66; scientist, Dept Sci & Indust Res, NZ, 69-70; geophysicist shock studies, Stanford Res Inst, 62-63, 67-69 & 70-75; MGR SHOCK PHYSICS, SYSTS, SCI & SOFTWARE, 75- *Mem:* AAAS; Am Geophys Union; Soc Explor Geophysicists. *Res:* Dynamic properties of geologic materials; rock mechanics; geophysical exploration. *Mailing Add:* Systs Sci & Software PO Box 1620 La Jolla CA 92038

PETERSEN, CHARLIE FREDERICK, b Buhl, Idaho, Aug 5, 15; m 40; c 3. POULTRY NUTRITION. *Educ:* Univ Idaho, BSA, 40, MSA, 46. *Prof Exp:* Field serv agent, Albers Milling Co, Wash, 40-41; asst prof poultry nutrit & asst poultryman, 43-47, assoc prof & assoc poultryman, 47-57, PROF & POULTRYMAN, UNIV IDAHO, 57-, HEAD DEPT POULTRY SCI, 61-, HEAD DEPT ANIMAL SCI, 79- *Mem:* Am Poultry Sci Asn; Am Inst Nutrit; World Poultry Sci Asn. *Res:* Environmental factors related to energy requirements; protein biological value; vitamin requirements and unidentified growth factors. *Mailing Add:* Dept Animal Sci Univ of Idaho Moscow ID 83843

PETERSEN, DONALD FRANCIS, b Brookings, SDak, May 20, 26; m 49; c 4. PHARMACOLOGY. *Educ:* DePauw Univ, AB, 47; SDak State Col, MS, 50; Univ Chicago, PhD(pharmacol), 54. *Prof Exp:* Assoc chemist, Exp Sta, SDak State Col, 47-51; from asst to instr pharmacol, Univ Chicago, 51-56; mem staff, 56-77, ALTERNATE DIV LEADER, LOS ALAMOS SCI LAB, 77- *Mem:* AAAS; Am Chem Soc; Am Soc Pharmacol & Exp Therapeut; Am Indust Hyg Asn; NY Acad Sci. *Res:* Influence of ionizing radiations on enzymatic processes in mammalian cells; analytical biochemistry; metabolism of chemotherapeutic agents and isotopically labelled intermediates. *Mailing Add:* Biomed Res Br Los Alamos Sci Lab Univ Calif Los Alamos NM 87544

PETERSEN, DONALD H, b Hillsboro, Ore, Mar 17, 34; m 61; c 5. PHYSICAL CHEMISTRY, MATERIALS SCIENCE. *Educ:* Univ Portland, BS, 56; Univ Notre Dame, PhD(phys chem), 61. *Prof Exp:* Res scientist, Pioneering Res Lab, Weyerhaeuser Co, 61-63; res scientist, Ling-Temco-Vought, Inc, 63-65, sr scientist, 65-69, mgr pollution res prog, Advan Technol Ctr, 70-72, supvr, 72-74, MGR STRUCTURES & MATS RES, ADVAN TECHNOL CTR, INC, LTV CORP, 74- *Concurrent Pos:* Vchmn, Tech Comt Mat, Am Inst Aeronaut & Astronaut. *Mem:* Am Chem Soc; Am Inst Aeronaut & Astronaut. *Res:* Spectroscopy; chromatography; chemistry of high temperature materials including carbon composites and refractory alloys; graphite-epoxy composites; carbon fibers development; non-destructive testing; laminar structures; adhesive bonding. *Mailing Add:* 11628 Sonnet Dr Dallas TX 75229

PETERSEN, DONALD HARRY, b Ludington, Mich, Mar 21, 22; m 47; c 4. PLANT PATHOLOGY. *Educ:* Mich State Univ, BS, 48, MS, 49; Clemson Univ, PhD, 60. *Prof Exp:* Res plant pathologist, Agr Res Serv, USDA, 50-68; assoc prof plant path, Pa State Univ, 68-70, prof, 70-80; VPRES PROD, HILLTOP ORCHARDS & NURSERIES, INC, 80- *Mem:* Am Soc Hort Sci; Am Phytopath Soc. *Res:* Nature and control of fungal and bacterial diseases of peach, apple and pear; integrated pest management; plant disease detection. *Mailing Add:* Hilltop Orchards & Nurseries Inc Rte 2 Hartford MI 49057

PETERSEN, DONALD RALPH, b Wis, Apr 14, 29; m 52, 79; c 3. PHYSICAL CHEMISTRY, COMPUTER SCIENCE. *Educ:* Lawrence Col, BA, 51; Calif Inst Technol, PhD(phys chem), 55. *Prof Exp:* Res chemist, Chem Physics Res Lab, 55-65, group leader, 65-69, div leader, 69-70, res mgr, Comput Res Lab, 70-78, SR RES STAFF DOW CHEM CO, 78- *Mem:* Am Chem Soc; Asn Comput Mach; Am Crystallog Asn; Am Inst Chemists. *Res:* Molecular structures; properties of catalytic surfaces, x-ray and electron-beam techniques; computer applications to chemical information processing. *Mailing Add:* Chem Processes Res Bldg 1776 Dow Chem Co Midland MI 48640

PETERSEN, EDWARD LELAND, b Myrtle Point, Ore, Aug 12, 32; m 59; c 1. PHYSICS. *Educ:* Ore State Col, BS, 54, MS, 56; Univ Calif, Los Angeles, PhD(physics), 66. *Prof Exp:* Asst prof physics, San Fernando Valley State Col, 63-68 & Oberlin Col, 68-69; RES PHYSICIST, NAVAL RES LAB, 69- *Mem:* Am Phys Soc; AAAS. *Res:* Nuclear reactions; single event upset phenonema; single event upsets in computers in the space environment; satellite vulnerability and survivability. *Mailing Add:* Code 6611 Naval Res Lab Washington DC 20375

PETERSEN, EDWARD S, b Chicago, Ill, Nov 19, 21; m 44; c 2. INTERNAL MEDICINE. *Educ:* Harvard Med Sch, MD, 45. *Prof Exp:* Intern, St Lukes Hosp, Chicago, 45-46; resident med, Univ Chicago, 48-51; pvt practr, 51-53; asst dir prof serv, Vet Admin Res Hosp, 53-54; dir med clins & assoc prof med, Med Sch, Northwestern Univ, Chicago, 54-72; asst dir, 72-76, DIR DEPT UNDERGRAD MED EDUC, AMA, 76- *Concurrent Pos:* Med educ nat defense coordr, Northwestern Univ, 58-69, from asst dean to assoc dean, Med Sch, 60-72; pres, Inst Med Chicago, 75; co-secy, Liaison Comt Med Educ, 76- *Mem:* Fel Am Col Physicians; Asn Am Med Cols. *Res:* Diabetes; medical education and administration; community and social medicine. *Mailing Add:* Dept of Undergrad Med Educ AMA 535 N Dearborn St Chicago IL 60610

PETERSEN, EUGENE E(DWARD), b Tacoma, Wash, Mar 2, 24; m 48; c 2. CHEMICAL ENGINEERING. *Educ:* Univ Wash, BS, 49, MS, 50; Pa State Univ, PhD(fuel sci), 53. *Prof Exp:* Asst fuel technol, Pa State Univ, 50-52; from instr to assoc prof, 53-64, PROF FUEL TECHNOL, UNIV CALIF, BERKELEY, 64- *Concurrent Pos:* Consult, Chevron Res Corp, 61-66 & Stauffer Chem Co, 65-67. *Mem:* Am Chem Soc; Am Inst Chem Engrs. *Res:* Heterogeneous catalysis; chemical reaction engineering; combustion; crystallization. *Mailing Add:* Dept Chem Eng Univ Calif Berkeley CA 94720

PETERSEN, FREDERICK ADOLPH, b Chicago, Ill, Aug 19, 13; m 40; c 3. CERAMIC ENGINEERING. *Educ:* Univ Ill, BS, 37; Ohio State Univ, MSc, 39. *Prof Exp:* Eng trainee, Frigidaire Div, Gen Motors Corp, Ohio, 37-38; millroom operator, Rundle Mfg Co, Wis, 38; develop engr, Ingram-Richardson Mfg Co, Ind, 39-41; spec res prof, Univ Ill, 41-51; trade asn mgt, Thomas Assocs, Inc, 51-80, pres, 61-80; RETIRED. *Concurrent Pos:* Consult, 43-; chmn, Comt Safety Standards, Am Nat Standards Inst, 68- *Mem:* Fel Am Ceramic Soc; Nat Inst Ceramic Engrs; Sigma Xi. *Res:* Porcelain enamels development and research. *Mailing Add:* 3224 E Monmouth Rd Cleveland Heights OH 44118

PETERSEN, GARY WALTER, b Frederic, Wis, Aug 17, 39; m 64; c 3. SOIL MORPHOLOGY, REMOTE SENSING. *Educ:* Univ Wis-Madison, BS, 61, MS, 63, PhD(soil genesis, soil morphol), 65. *Prof Exp:* Res asst soils, Univ Wis-Madison, 61-64, teaching asst, 64-65; from asst prof to assoc prof, 65-76, PROF SOIL GENESIS & MORPHOL & CO-DIR REMOTE SENSING, PA STATE UNIV, 76- *Concurrent Pos:* Vis prof land use, Univ Wis, 74-75. *Mem:* Fel Am Soc Agron; fel Soil Sci Soc Am; Soil & Water Conserv Soc Am; Am Soc Photogram; Int Soc Soil Sci. *Res:* Soil interpretations for proper land use decisions; on site disposal of septic tank effluents; development and use of spatial data management systems; analysis and interpretation of remotely sensed data. *Mailing Add:* Dept of Agron 311 Tyson Bldg Pa State Univ University Park PA 16802

PETERSEN, HAROLD, JR, b Natick, Mass, Sept 18, 40; m 66; c 2. INFORMATION MANAGEMENT SYSTEMS, ENVIRONMENTAL STUDIES. *Educ:* Univ Mass, BS, 62; Univ Ill, PhD(chem), 66. *Prof Exp:* Teaching asst chem, Univ Ill, 62-66; fel, Univ Southern Calif, 66-67; asst prof, 67-73, assoc prof, 73-79, PROF CHEM, UNIV RI, 79- *Mem:* Sigma Xi; Am Chem Soc. *Res:* Data management and information system design; chemical oceanography; investigations of drug-receptor interactions by molecular orbital theory. *Mailing Add:* Dept of Chem 333 Pastore Lab Univ of RI Kingston RI 02881

PETERSEN, HAROLD E(MANUEL), b Chicago, Ill, Jan 12, 26; div; c 4. ELECTRICAL ENGINEERING. *Educ:* Univ Wis, BS, 46, MS, 51; Stanford Univ, PhD(elec eng), 57. *Prof Exp:* Engr, Zenith Radio Corp, Ill, 46-47 & Commonwealth Edison Co, 47-50; instr elec eng, Univ Wis, 50-51; engr, Naval Ord Test Sta, 51-53; asst, Stanford Univ, 53-57; sr engr, Int Bus Mach Corp, NY, 57-66; mem res staff, Rand Corp, 66-78; consult, Court Commun Corp, Santa Monica, Calif, 79-81. *Res:* Digital systems and techniques, primarily communications and information processing. *Mailing Add:* 1048 Seventh Santa Monica CA 90403

PETERSEN, INGO HANS, b Davenport, Iowa, July 27, 30; m 52; c 4. FLUORANTHENE CHEMISTRY. *Educ:* Iowa State Univ, BS, 52; Univ Iowa, MS & PhD(org chem), 61. *Prof Exp:* Res chemist, Union Carbide Corp, 60-64; from asst prof to assoc prof, 64-66, chmn dept, 66-70, PROF CHEM, STATE UNIV NY COL BROCKPORT, 66-, CHMN DEPT, 80- *Concurrent Pos:* Res assoc, Queen's Univ, Belfast, 70-71; vis prof, Duke Univ, 76-77. *Mem:* Am Chem Soc. *Res:* Synthesis of fluoranthene derivatives; substituent-orienting effects and products; synthesis and polymerization of thiiranes. *Mailing Add:* Dept of Chem State Univ NY Col Brockport Brockport NY 14420

PETERSEN, JAMES J, entomology, see previous edition

PETERSEN, JEFFREY LEE, b Racine, Wis, Nov 19, 47; m 73. PHYSICAL INORGANIC CHEMISTRY. *Educ:* Carthage Col, BA, 69; Univ Wis-Madison, MS, 71, PhD(chem), 74. *Prof Exp:* Res assoc chem, Argonne Nat Lab, 74; vis scholar, Northwestern Univ, Evanston, 74-75; asst prof, 75-81, ASSOC PROF CHEM, WEST VA UNIV, 81- *Mem:* Am Chem Soc; Sigma Xi; Am Crystallog Asn. *Res:* Systematic investigation by structural and spectroscopic techniques into the nature of the chemical bonding in transition metal complexes of current chemical interest. *Mailing Add:* Dept Chem WVa Univ Morgantown WV 26506

PETERSEN, JOHN DAVID, b Glendale, Calif, Nov 21, 47; m 70; c 2. INORGANIC CHEMISTRY. *Educ:* Calif State Univ, Los Angeles, BS, 70; Univ Calif, Santa Barbara, MA & PhD(chem), 75. *Prof Exp:* Asst prof chem, Kans State Univ, 75-80; asst prof, 80-81, ASSOC PROF CHEM, CLEMSON UNIV, 81- *Mem:* Am Chem Soc; InterAm Photochem Soc. *Res:* Photochemistry and electron transfer reactions of transition metal complexes to include synthetic techniques, ligand substituent effects and spectroscopic studies. *Mailing Add:* Dept Chem Clemson Univ Clemson SC 29631

PETERSEN, JOHN ROBERT, b LaCrosse, Wis, June 26, 29; m 52; c 5. MEDICAL ADMINISTRATION. *Educ:* Univ Wis-Madison, BMSc, 51, MD, 54. *Prof Exp:* From asst instr to asst prof, 57-68, asst dean, 65-67, ASSOC PROF MED, MED COL WIS, 68-; DIR MED SERV, MILWAUKEE COUNTY INSTS & DEPTS, 67-, ASSOC DEAN MILWAUKEE COUNTY MED COMPLEX, 80- *Concurrent Pos:* Fel internal med, Frank Bunts Educ Inst, 55; consult, Vet Admin Hosp, Wood, Wis, 61-; asst dir dept med, Milwaukee County Gen Hosp, 61-65. *Mem:* NY Acad Sci; Asn Am Med Cols; Am Fedn Clin Res. *Res:* Endocrinology wth emphasis on Diabetes Mellitus. *Mailing Add:* 8842 Watertown Plank Rd Wauwatosa WI 53226

PETERSEN, JOSEPH CLAINE, b Fielding, Utah, Feb 14, 25; m 49; c 4. ASPHALT CHEMISTRY, FOSSIL FUEL CHEMISTRY. *Educ:* Univ Utah, BS, 52, PhD(org chem), 56. *Prof Exp:* Res chemist, Am Gilsonite Co, Utah, 56-61; sr res chemist, New Prod Div, Textile Fibers Dept, Exp Sta, E I du Pont de Nemours, Del, 61-64; SECT SUPVR, ASPHALT RES & PROD UTILIZATION, LARAMIE ENERGY TECHNOL CTR, DEPT OF ENERGY, 64- *Concurrent Pos:* Chmn, Transp Res Bd Comt Characteristics Bituminous Mat, 74-80; mem adv panel, Nat Res Coun, 71- *Mem:* Am Chem Soc; Asn Asphalt Paving Tech. *Res:* Petroleum, asphalt and polymer chemistry; fossil fuel heavy liquids. *Mailing Add:* Laramie Energy Technol Ctr PO Box 3395 Univ Sta Laramie WY 82070

PETERSEN, KARL ENDEL, b Tallinn, Estonia, July 11, 43; US citizen; m 69; c 2. ERGODIC THEORY, DYNAMICAL SYSTEMS. *Educ:* Princeton Univ, AB, 65; Yale Univ, MA, 67, PhD(math), 69. *Prof Exp:* Asst prof, 69-75, assoc prof, 75-81, PROF MATH, UNIV NC, CHAPEL HILL, 81- *Concurrent Pos:* Vis assoc prof, Dept Math, Yale Univ, 79; prof assoc, Laboratoire de Calcul des Probabilities, Univ de Paris VI, 81. *Mem:* Am Math Soc. *Res:* Ergodic theory, probability and analysis, especially questions of mixing, almost everywhere convergence and maximal functions and information and coding. *Mailing Add:* Dept Math Phillips Hall 039A Univ NC Chapel Hill NC 27514

PETERSEN, KENNETH C, b Chicago, Ill, Mar 17, 36. ORGANIC POLYMER CHEMISTRY. *Educ:* Northwestern Univ, PhD, 60, MS, 63. *Prof Exp:* Sr chemist condensation polymers, Acme Resin Corp, 57-64; res mgr addn & condensation polymers, 64-76, mgr chem/tech develop & chem mfg, 77-78, mgr chem div, 78-79, mgr, mfg & chem develop, 79-80, vpres mfg, 80, exec vpres, 81, PRES, SCHENECTADY CHEM, INC, 81- *Mem:* Am Chem Soc. *Mailing Add:* 1301 Rosehill Blvd Schenectady NY 12309

PETERSEN, MORRIS SMITH, b West Jordan, Utah, Feb 21, 33; m 54; c 6. GEOLOGY. *Educ:* Brigham Young Univ, BS, 55, MS, 56; Univ Iowa, PhD(geol), 62. *Prof Exp:* Asst prof earth sci, Am Univ, 62-66; asst prof geol, 66-72, PROF GEOL, BRIGHAM YOUNG UNIV, 72-, CHMN DEPT, 75- *Mem:* Geol Soc Am; Paleont Soc. *Res:* Devonian stratigraphy and paleontology. *Mailing Add:* Dept of Geol Brigham Young Univ Provo UT 84601

PETERSEN, NANCY SUE, b Paris, Tex, Mar 11, 43; m 65; c 2. DEVELOPMENTAL BIOLOGY. *Educ:* Harvey Mudd Col, BS, 65; Brandeis Univ, MA, 68; Univ Calif, Irvine, PhD(biol), 72. *Prof Exp:* Fel bacteriol, Univ Calif, Los Angeles, 72-74; fel biol, City Hope Med Ctr, Duarte, 74-76; SR RES FEL BIOL, CALIF INST TECHNOL, 76- *Mem:* Genetics Soc; AAAS. *Res:* Gene expression in differentiating Drosophila tissues and the mechanisms by which heat shock interrupts normal gene expression and induces developmental defects. *Mailing Add:* Biol Div 156-29 Calif Inst Technol Pasadena CA 91125

PETERSEN, PHILIP RICHARD, organic polymer chemistry, see previous edition

PETERSEN, QUENTIN RICHARD, b Bridgeport, Conn, Mar 10, 24; m 46; c 2. ORGANIC CHEMISTRY. *Educ:* Antioch Col, BS, 48; Northwestern Univ, PhD(chem), 52. *Prof Exp:* Instr org chem, Northwestern Univ, 52; from instr to asst prof, Wesleyan Univ, 52-57; assoc prof, Wabash Col, 57-61, prof, 62-66; prof chem & chmn dept, Simmons Col, 66-69 & Monmouth Col, Ill, 69-73; PROF CHEM & CHMN DEPT, CENT MICH UNIV, 73- *Concurrent Pos:* Consult dir res & develop, Kelite Prod, Inc, 50-55; vis lectr, Trinity Col, Conn, 53-54; Fulbright lectr, Univ Valencia & Univ Barcelona, 61-62; vis scientist, Am Chem Soc, 62-; cor res fel, Inst Chem, Acad Sinica, Taiwan, 63-; corp dir, H-C Industs Inc, 65-; consult, NSF-USAID, Karnatak Univ, India, 69; vis prof, Tamkang Univ, Rep China, 79-80. *Mem:* AAAS; Am Chem Soc; The Chem Soc; Am Asn Univ Prof. *Res:* Stereochemistry of alicylic compounds; derived steroids; napthyridines; corrosion inhibition studies; molecular model design; reaction mechanism; stereochemistry of heterogenous catalysis; irreversible photochemical transformations; herbal medicine. *Mailing Add:* Dept Chem Cent Mich Univ Mt Pleasant MI 48858

PETERSEN, RAYMOND CARL, b Ware, Mass, July 24, 29; m 54; c 2. PHYSICAL CHEMISTRY, ANALYTICAL CHEMISTRY. *Educ:* Amherst Col, BA, 51; Brown Univ, PhD(chem), 56. *Prof Exp:* Chemist, Sprague Elec Co, 56-62, sr res scientist, 62-70, dept head phys chem, 66-69; res scientist, Res Inst Advan Studies, Martin Marietta Corp, 71-73, lab dir & toxicologist, Martin Marietta Labs, Baltimore, 73-79; MGR, MAT & CHEM, SOLAREX CORP, 79- *Concurrent Pos:* Ed, The Chesapeake Chemist, 79- *Mem:* Sigma Xi; Am Chem Soc; Electrochem Soc. *Res:* Electrochemistry; physical-organic and analytical chemistry; solar photovoltaics. *Mailing Add:* 9329 Joey Dr Ellicott City MD 21043

PETERSEN, RICHARD RANDOLPH, b Astoria, Ore, Mar 9, 40; m 64. LIMNOLOGY. *Educ:* Univ Wash, BS, 65; Duke Univ, PhD(zool), 70. *Prof Exp:* Res biologist, Rayonier Inc, 65-66; asst prof, 70-75, ASSOC PROF BIOL, PORTLAND STATE UNIV, 75- *Mem:* Am Soc Limnol & Oceanog; Am Soc Naturalists; AAAS. *Res:* Ecology of fresh water phytoplankton. *Mailing Add:* Dept of Biol PO Box 751 Portland State Univ Portland OR 97207

PETERSEN, ROBERT J, b Hillsboro, Ore, Sept 29, 37; m 65; c 2. ORGANIC CHEMISTRY. *Educ:* Univ Portland, BS, 59; Pa State Univ, PhD(chem), 65. *Prof Exp:* Sr res chemist, Tape Div, Minn Mining & Mfg Co, 64-66; res chemist, North Star Res & Develop Inst, 66-69, sr chemist, 69-74, assoc dir, Chem Div, 74-75, prin chemist, North Star Div, Midwest Res Inst, 75-77; DIR RES, FILMTEC CORP, 78- *Mem:* AAAS; Am Chem Soc; Filtration Soc. *Res:* Gas phase reactions of organic halides with potassium vapor; epoxy and polyester thermosetting adhesives; plating of plastics; development of new reverse osmosis, hemodialysis and blood oxygenator membranes. *Mailing Add:* 5936 Emerson Ave S Minneapolis MN 55419

PETERSEN, ROBERT VIRGIL, b South Jordan, Utah, Apr 21, 26; m 50; c 4. PHARMACEUTICAL CHEMISTRY. *Educ:* Univ Utah, BS, 50; Univ Minn, PhD(pharmaceut chem), 55. *Prof Exp:* Asst prof pharmaceut chem, Ore State Col, 55-57; from asst prof to assoc prof pharm, 57-66, chmn dept appl pharmaceut sci, 65-68, PROF PHARM, UNIV UTAH, 66-, CHMN DEPT PHARMACEUT, 78- *Mem:* Am Chem Soc; Am Pharmaceut Asn; Am Asn Cols Pharm (vpres, 71-72, pres, 72-73); Inst Hist Pharm. *Res:* Drug stability studies, especially of glycosides; biodegradable drug delivery systems; emulsion formation and stability, especially nonaqueous emulsions; toxicity of plastics. *Mailing Add:* Dept of Pharmaceut Col of Pharm Univ of Utah Salt Lake City UT 84112

PETERSEN, ROGER GENE, b Essington, Pa, July 22, 24; m 48; c 1. BIOMETRICS. *Educ:* Iowa State Col, MS, 50; NC State Col, PhD(soil fertil, statist), 54. *Prof Exp:* Asst soil fertil, Iowa State Col, 49-50; asst soil fertil, NC State Col, 50-53, asst statistician, 53-55; assoc prof statist, Ore State Col, 55-62, statistician, Exp Sta, 55-62; from assoc prof to prof statist, NC State Col, 62-65; PROF STATIST, ORE STATE UNIV, 65- *Concurrent Pos:* Biometrician, Int Ctr Agr Res Dry Areas, Syria, 78-80. *Mem:* Biomet Soc; Am Soc Agron. *Res:* Experimental designs for agricultural research. *Mailing Add:* Dept of Statist Ore State Univ Corvallis OR 97331

PETERSEN, ULRICH, b Zorritos, Peru, Dec 1, 27; m 52; c 3. ECONOMIC GEOLOGY. *Educ:* Nat Sch Eng, Lima, EM, 54; Harvard Univ, MA, 55, PhD(geol), 63. *Prof Exp:* Asst geologist, Geol Inst Peru, 49-50; geologist, Nat Inst Mining Res & Develop, 50-51; asst geologist, Cerro de Pasco Corp, 51, geologist, 51-54, asst chief geologist, 56-57, chief geologist, 58-63, consult geologist, 63; lectr geol, 63-66, assoc prof, 66-69, PROF MINING GEOL, HARVARD UNIV, 69- *Concurrent Pos:* Consult geologist. *Honors & Awards:* Order of Merit Distinguished Serv, Peruvian Govt, 68. *Mem:* AAAS; Geochem Soc; Mineral Soc Am; Am Inst Mining, Metall & Petrol Eng; Int Fedn Soc Econ Geol (pres, 75-79). *Res:* Ore deposition; phase equilibria and geochemistry applied to formation of ore deposits; exploration for economic mineral deposits; mineral economics and policies; zoning of hydothermal ore deposits. *Mailing Add:* Dept of Geol Sci 310 Hoffman Lab Harvard Univ 20 Oxford St Cambridge MA 02138

PETERSEN, WALLACE CHRISTIAN, b Kansas City, Mo, Feb 10, 43; m 67. CHEMISTRY. *Educ:* DePauw Univ, BA, 65; Northwestern Univ, Evanston, PhD(chem), 70. *Prof Exp:* res chemist, 69-80, SR RES CHEMIST, E I DU PONT DE NEMOURS & CO, INC, 80- *Mem:* Am Chem Soc; The Chem Soc. *Res:* Photochemistry; dye chemistry; organophosphorous chemistry; synthesis. *Mailing Add:* RD 6 Box 104 Hockessin DE 19707

PETERSEN-ADKISSON, KAREN, cytogenetics, see previous edition

PETERSON, ALAN HERBERT, b Moline, Ill, Aug 27, 32; m 55; c 2. PETROLEUM CHEMISTRY. *Educ:* Augustana Col, AB, 55; Univ Ill, PhD(org chem), 60. *Prof Exp:* Asst inorg chem, Univ Ill, 55-59; RES CHEMIST, MARATHON OIL CO, 59- *Mem:* Soc Automotive Eng; Am Chem Soc; Sigma Xi. *Res:* Petroleum refining and petrochemicals. *Mailing Add:* Petrol Chem Dept Marathon Oil Co PO Box 269 Littleton CO 80160

PETERSON, ALAN W, b Augusta, Ga, Sept 21, 26; m 56. PHYSICS, ASTRONOMY. *Educ:* Univ Calif, AB, 51; Univ NMex, MS, 57, PhD(physics), 60. *Prof Exp:* Res assoc astron, Univ NMex, 52-54 & 60-61; sr physicist, Gen Dynamics Ft Worth, 61-64, proj res scientist, 64-65; asst prof physics & astron, Univ Mo, 65-67; assoc prof astron, 67-75, PROF PHYSICS & ASTRON, UNIV NMEX, 75- *Mem:* Am Astron Soc; NY Acad Sci; Am Geophys Union. *Res:* Zodiacal light photometry; thermal emission from interplanetary dust; infrared photometry; infrared airglow. *Mailing Add:* Dept of Physics & Astron Univ of NMex Albuquerque NM 87131

PETERSON, ALLEN MONTGOMERY, b Santa Clara, Calif, May 22, 22; m 42; c 4. ELECTRICAL ENGINEERING. *Educ:* Stanford Univ, BS, 48, MS, 49, PhD(elec eng), 52. *Prof Exp:* Res assoc elec eng, 52-56, from asst prof to assoc prof, 56-61, PROF ELEC ENG, STANFORD UNIV, 61-, ASST DIR ELECTRONICS & RADIO DIV, SRI INT, 62- *Concurrent Pos:* Head spec tech group, SRI Int, 53-58, mgr, Commun & Propagation Lab, 59-62; mem bd dirs, Granger Assocs, Palo Alto, 54-; mem comn III & IV, US Comn Union Radio Sci Int, 56-; mem NSF panel, 57-60; consult, President's Sci Adv Comt, Washington, DC, 58-, Adv Res Proj Agency, 58-, Defense Atomic Support Agency, 58-, Inst Defense Anal, 60- & NAm Aviation, Inc, Calif, 62-63; tech adv, US Deleg to Geneva Conf on Discontinuation of Nuclear Tests, 59-; mem sci adv comt, Geophys Inst, Univ Alaska, 60-; mem panel adv group aeronaut res & develop, Avionics, 60-64. *Mem:* Sigma Xi; Inst Elec & Electronics Engrs; sr mem Am Astronaut Soc. *Res:* Radio propagation; communication; computer design; digital computer circuitry; ionospheric and space physics; radar astronomy; wave propagation and upper atmosphere research. *Mailing Add:* Dept of Elec Eng Stanford Univ Stanford CA 94305

PETERSON, ARNOLD (PER GUSTAF), b DeKalb, Ill, Aug 7, 14; m 43; c 3. ELECTRICAL ENGINEERING. *Educ:* Univ Toledo, BEng, 34; Mass Inst Technol, SM, 37, ScD(elec eng), 41. *Prof Exp:* Asst elec eng, Mass Inst Technol, 36-40; develop engr, 40-68, eng staff consult, 68-74, sr prin engr, 74-77, STAFF SCIENTIST, GEN RADIO, INC, 77- *Honors & Awards:* Potts Mem Award, Audio Eng Soc. *Mem:* AAAS; fel Acoust Soc Am (vpres, 58-59); Inst Elec & Electronics Engrs; Audio Eng Soc. *Res:* Acoustical instruments and measurements. *Mailing Add:* Gen Radio Inc AVA-E Div Rte 117 Bolton MA 01740

PETERSON, ARTHUR CARL, b Everett, Wash, Mar 30, 23; m 57; c 3. BACTERIOLOGY, IMMUNOLOGY. *Educ:* Univ Minn, BChE, 47, MS, 50, PhD(bact, immunol), 56. *Prof Exp:* Instr quant anal chem, Hamline Col, 49; asst dairy industs, Univ Minn, 50-51 & 55-56, Hormel Inst, 51-55; res technologist, Bact Res Dept, 56-62, sr res microbiologist, 62-66, div head, Microbiol Res Dept, 66-72, mgr qual control frozen food, 72-73, dir inspection serv, 73-76, DIR TECH ADMIN LABS, CAMPBELL SOUP CO, 77- *Mem:* Am Pub Health Asn; Am Chem Soc; Am Soc Microbiol; Inst Food Technologists. *Res:* Bacterial metabolism and physiology; psychrophilic bacteria and their enzymatic activities; lipid and protein metabolism; protein biochemistry and chromatography; Salmonella epidemiology; public health; food and public health microbiology. *Mailing Add:* Campbell Soup Co Campbell Pl Camden NJ 08101

PETERSON, ARTHUR EDWIN, b Curtiss, Wis, Mar 11, 23; m 44; c 3. SOILS. *Educ:* Univ Wis, BS, 47, MS, 48, PhD, 50. *Prof Exp:* Exten soils specialist, 50-64, PROF SOIL & WATER CONSERV, UNIV WIS-MADISON, 64- *Concurrent Pos:* Chief resident consult, Rockefeller-Ford Found Coop Maize Improv Prog, Egypt, 66-68. *Mem:* Fel AAAS; Am Soc Agron; Crop Sci Soc Am; Soil Sci Soc Am; fel Soil Conserv Soc Am. *Res:* Soil tillage and water movement; nutrient and sediment runoff; sludge and waste water renovation. *Mailing Add:* 509 Togstad Glenn Madison WI 53711

PETERSON, BARRY WAYNE, b Abington, Pa, June 25, 42; m 67. NEUROPHYSIOLOGY. *Educ:* Calif Inst Technol, BS, 64; Rockefeller Univ, PhD(neurophysiol), 69. *Prof Exp:* Res assoc neurophysiol, Rockefeller Univ, 69-71, asst prof, 71-75, assoc prof, 75-80; MEM FAC, DEPT PHYSIOL, MED SCH, NORTHWESTERN UNIV, 80- *Mem:* Soc Neurosci. *Res:* Study of central nervous structures involved in motor behavior. *Mailing Add:* Dept Physiol Med Sch Northwestern Univ Chicago IL 60611

PETERSON, BOBBIE VERN (ROBERT), b Price, Utah, Dec 16, 28; m 50; c 3. ENTOMOLOGY. *Educ:* Univ Utah, BS, 51, MS, 53, PhD(entom), 58. *Prof Exp:* Regist sanitarian, Salt Lake City Bd Health, 51-52; neuropsychiat aide, Vet Admin Hosp, 53-54; teaching asst, Univ Utah, 54-57, lectr, 57-58; entomologist, 58-63, RES SCIENTIST, BIOSYSTS RES INST, CENT EXP FARM, RES BR, CAN AGR, 63- *Mem:* Entom Soc Am; Am Mosquito Control Asn; Soc Syst Zool; Entom Soc Can; Can Soc Zool. *Res:* Systematic entomology; systematics of Diptera. *Mailing Add:* Head Diptera Sect Biosysts Res Inst Cent Exp Farm Can Agr Ottawa ON K2C 3N7 Can

PETERSON, BRUCE BIGELOW, b Boston, Mass, Mar 26, 35; m 56; c 3. MATHEMATICS. *Educ:* Middlebury Col, BA, 56; Syracuse Univ, MA, 58, PhD(math), 62. *Prof Exp:* Asst math, Syracuse Univ, 56-60, instr, 60-62; from instr to assoc prof, 63-72, prof, 72-80, CHARLES A DANA PROF MATH, MIDDLEBURY COL, 80-, CHMN DEPT, 68- *Concurrent Pos:* Vis scholar, Univ Wash, 70-71. *Mem:* Am Math Soc; Math Asn Am. *Res:* Convex figures; Euclidean topology and geometry. *Mailing Add:* Dept of Math Warner Sci Bldg Middlebury Col Middlebury VT 05753

PETERSON, BRUCE JON, b Chicago, Ill, Apr 9, 45; c 2. LIMNOLOGY, MARINE ECOLOGY. *Educ:* Bates Col, BS, 67; Cornell Univ, PhD(aquatic ecol), 71. *Prof Exp:* Res assoc limnol, Cornell Univ, 71-74; res asso marine ecol, NC State Univ, 75-76; asst scientist, 76-80, ASSOC SCIENTIST ECOL, MARINE BIOL LAB, 80- *Mem:* Am Soc Limnol & Oceanog; AAAS; Int Oceanog Found. *Res:* Aquatic primary productivity, nutrient cycling, phosphorus cycle, carbon cycle, nitrogen cycle and sulfur cycle. *Mailing Add:* Ecosysts Ctr Marine Biol Lab Woods Hole MA 02543

PETERSON, C DENIS, veterinary medicine, biochemistry, see previous edition

PETERSON, CHARLES FILLMORE, b Indianapolis, Ind, May 11, 20; m 44; c 4. PHARMACY. *Educ:* Univ Southern Calif, BS, 43; Purdue Univ, MS, 49, PhD(pharm), 52. *Prof Exp:* Asst prof pharm, Univ Kans, 50-56; assoc prof, 56-65, chmn dept, 59-70, PROF PHARM, SCH PHARM, TEMPLE UNIV, 65- *Concurrent Pos:* Vis prof, Univ Panama, 72. *Mem:* Fel Am Soc Consult Pharmacists; Am Pharmaceut Asn; Am Pub Health Asn; Am Soc Hosp Pharmacists; Am Asn Cols Pharm. *Res:* Effects of formulation on the biopharmaceutics of drugs; Latin American pharmacy practice; drug information in professional pharmacy practice. *Mailing Add:* Temple Univ Sch of Pharm 3307 N Broad St Philadelphia PA 19140

PETERSON, CHARLES HENRY, b Lawrenceville, NJ, Feb 18, 46; m 72. MARINE ECOLOGY, POPULATION BIOLOGY. *Educ:* Princeton Univ, AB, 68; Univ Calif, Santa Barbara, MA, 70, PhD(biol), 72. *Prof Exp:* Instr biol, Univ Calif Exten, 70-72; teaching assoc biol sci, Univ Calif, Santa Barbara, 71-72; asst prof biol sci, Univ Md, 72-76; ASSOC PROF MARINE SCI, UNIV NC, CHAPEL HILL, 76- *Concurrent Pos:* Fel, Ford Found grant, 72; biol oceanog panel, NSF, 80. *Mem:* Am Inst Biol Sci; Ecol Soc Am; Paleontol Soc Am; Paleontol Res Inst; Sigma Xi. *Res:* Population biology and community ecology, especially of marine benthic invertebrates and barrier island plants. *Mailing Add:* Inst Marine Sci Univ NC-Chapel Hill Morehead City NC 28557

PETERSON, CHARLES JOHN, b Seattle, Wash, Oct 13, 45; m 67. ASTRONOMY. *Educ:* Univ Wash, BS, 67; Univ Calif, Berkeley, MA, 68, PhD(astron), 75. *Prof Exp:* Carnegie fel astron, Carnegie Inst Wash, 74-76; res assoc, Cerro Tololo Inter-Am Observ, 76-78; ASST PROF ASTRON, DEPT PHYSICS, UNIV MO-COLUMBIA, 78- *Mem:* Am Astron Soc; Astron Soc Pac; Int Astron Union; Sigma Xi. *Res:* Globular clusters; structure and dynamics of galaxies. *Mailing Add:* Dept of Physics Univ of Mo Columbia MO 65211

PETERSON, CHARLES LESLIE, b Bradner, Ohio, Dec 23, 24; m 48; c 3. PHYSICAL CHEMISTRY, CORROSION. *Educ:* Bowling Green State Univ, BA, 48; Ohio State Univ, MSc, 50. *Prof Exp:* Res chemist, Diamond Alkali Co, 50-53; sr res chemist, Battelle Mem Inst, 53-63; proj mgr mat sci, 63-75, staff mem high temp chem, 75-81, STAFF MEM WEAPON SUB SYSTS, LOS ALAMOS SCI LAB, UNIV CALIF, 81- *Res:* Kinetics of metal-gas reactions; corrosion of metals and materials science; development of thermochemical processes for hydrogen production. *Mailing Add:* Group WX-5 MS-780 Los Alamos Nat Lab PO Box 1663 Los Alamos NM 87545

PETERSON, CHARLES MARQUIS, b New York, NY, Mar 8, 43; m 77. DIABETES, HEMOGLOBIN. *Educ:* Carleton Col, BA, 65; Columbia Univ Sch Physicians & Surgeons, MD, 69. *Prof Exp:* Intern, Harlem Hosp, 69-70, residency, 70-72, chief researcher, 72-73; guest invstr, biochem, 72-73, asst prof, 73-78, ASSOC PROF MED BIOCHEM, ROCKFELLER UNIV, 78- *Mem:* Am Soc Clin Invest; Am Soc Pharmacol; Am Soc Hematol; Soc Exp Biol & Med; Am Diabetic Asn. *Res:* Diabetic mellitas; sickle cell disease; nephrolithiasis; basic anac of metabolism. *Mailing Add:* Rockfeller Univ New York NY 10021

PETERSON, CLARE GRAY, b Scobey, Mont, Nov 24, 17; m 41; c 4. SURGERY, PHYSIOLOGY. *Educ:* Univ Ore, BA, 39, MD, 43, MS, 45; Am Bd Surg, dipl, 51. *Prof Exp:* Instr physiol, 44-45, from instr to asst prof, 48-49, from instr to assoc prof surg, 48-58, PROF SURG, MED SCH, UNIV ORE, 58-, CHIEF SURG SERV, UNIV HOSP, 65- *Concurrent Pos:* Sr surg consult, Vet Admin Hosp, 65- *Mem:* AAAS; fel Am Col Surgeons; NY Acad Sci. *Mailing Add:* Univ of Ore Health Sci Ctr 3181 SW Sam Jackson Park Rd Portland OR 97201

PETERSON, CLARENCE JAMES, JR, b Park City, Utah, Aug 23, 28; m 56; c 3. AGRONOMY. *Educ:* Univ Idaho, BS, 56, MS, 59; Ore State Univ, PhD(plant breeding), 70. *Prof Exp:* RES AGRONOMIST, WHEAT BREEDING & PROD UNIT, AGR RES SERV, USDA, 59- *Mem:* Am Soc Agron; Crop Sci Soc Am. *Res:* Wheat improvement; development of new winter wheat varieties for the Pacific Northwest. *Mailing Add:* Agr Res Serv USDA 209 Johnson Hall Wash State Univ Pullman WA 99163

PETERSON, CLINTON E, b Salt Lake City, Utah, July 2, 16; m 45; c 5. HORTICULTURE. *Educ:* Utah State Univ, BS, 38; Iowa State Univ, MS, 41, PhD(veg crops), 47. *Prof Exp:* Res assoc veg prod, Iowa State Univ, 45-47, from asst prof to assoc prof, 47-49; horticulturist, USDA, 49-54; from assoc prof to prof hort, Mich State Univ, 54-68; INVESTS LEADER CARROT & ONION INVESTS, SCI & EDUC ADMIN-AGR RES, USDA, UNIV WIS-MADISON, 68-, PROF HORT, 72- *Concurrent Pos:* Consult hort res, Ministry Agr, Greece, 64. *Honors & Awards:* Genetics & Plant Breeding Award, Nat Coun Com Plant Breeders, 64; Award Honor Hort, Am Seed Trade Asn, 81. *Mem:* Fel AAAS; Am Soc Hort Sci; Potato Asn Am. *Res:* Vegetable breeding and genetics; cucumbers; carrots; onions; disease resistant varieties. *Mailing Add:* Dept of Hort Univ of Wis Madison WI 53706

PETERSON, CURTIS MORRIS, b Fargo, NDak, Jan 16, 42; m 64; c 3. BOTANY. *Educ:* Moorhead State Univ, BS, 66; Univ Ore, PhD(biol), 70. *Prof Exp:* NDEA fel biol, Univ Ore, 66-69, teaching fel, 69-70; asst prof, 71-76, ASSOC PROF BOT, AUBURN UNIV, 76- *Concurrent Pos:* Plant physiologist, USDA Exp Sta, Pendleton, Ore, 79-80. *Mem:* Bot Soc Am; Am Soc Plant Physiologists; Agron Soc; Sigma Xi; Crop Sci Soc. *Res:* Environmental factors affecting vegetative reproductive development in soybeans of the genus Glycine max, particularly the factors causing abscission of flowers and pods. *Mailing Add:* Dept Bot Plant Path & Microbiol Auburn Univ Auburn AL 36849

PETERSON, CYNTHIA WYETH, b Philadelphia, Pa, Apr 28, 33; m 57; c 2. CONDENSED MATTER, ELECTRONIC PROPERTIES. *Educ:* Bryn Mawr Col, BA, 54; Cornell Univ, PhD(exp physics), 64. *Prof Exp:* Res asst atmospheric physics, Harvard Univ, 60-62; from instr to asst prof physics, Wesleyan Univ, 63-66; spec fel, Yale Univ, 66-68; asst prof, 68-73, ASSOC PROF PHYSICS, UNIV CONN, 73- *Concurrent Pos:* Vis assoc prof, Dept Molecular Biophysics, Yale Univ, 78-79; Am Asn Univ Women fel, Marie Curie Endowment. *Mem:* AAAS; Am Asn Physics Teachers; Am Astron Soc. *Res:* Optical and electrical properties of condenses matter: semiconductors, biomaterials and alloys; ultraviolet photoelectric emission; vacuum ultraviolet spectroscopy; metalloenzymes; spectroscopy of rare gas ion-atom collisions. *Mailing Add:* Dept Physics Univ Conn Storrs CT 06268

PETERSON, DALLAS ODELL, b Oakley, Idaho, Aug 17, 25; m 51; c 1. GEOLOGY. *Educ:* Brigham Young Univ, BS, 52, MS, 53; Wash State Univ, PhD, 59. *Prof Exp:* Asst geol, Wash State Univ, 54-57; asst prof, Chico State Col, 57-60; from asst prof to prof, Weber State Col, 60-69, chmn dept, 68, 69; dir acad prog develop & asst to vpres, 69-71, asst vpres acad affairs, 71-72, ASSOC VPRES ACAD AFFAIRS, SYST ADMIN, UNIV WIS-MADISON, 72- *Concurrent Pos:* Field geologist, Shell Oil Co, summers, 53, 56, 58-62; eng geologist, US Forest Serv, summers 66 & 67. *Mem:* Soc Econ Paleont & Mineral; Am Asn Petrol Geol. *Res:* Upper Paleozoic stratigraphy in the Rocky Mountain area. *Mailing Add:* Univ of Wis Syst Admin 1604 Van Hise Madison WI 53706

PETERSON, DANIEL WALTER, nutrition, biochemistry, deceased

PETERSON, DARWIN WILSON, b Redmond, Utah, Mar 23, 38; m 59; c 5. CARDIOVASCULAR PHYSIOLOGY. *Educ:* Univ Nev, BS, 66, MS, 67; Univ Ala, Birmingham, PhD(physiol), 72. *Prof Exp:* Fel physiol, Sch Med, Univ Ala, Birmingham, 72-73; ASST PROF PHYSIOL, BOWMAN GRAY SCH MED, WAKE FOREST UNIV, 73- *Concurrent Pos:* NIH trainee, Sch Med, Univ Ala, Birmingham, 68-72; NIH fel, Heart, Lung & Blood Inst, 72-73. *Mem:* Sigma Xi; Am Physiol Soc. *Res:* Pathophysiology; the pathophysiology of dietary lipids, diabetes and hypertension. *Mailing Add:* Bowman Gray Sch Med 300 S Hawthorne Rd Winston-Salem NC 27103

PETERSON, DAVID ALLAN, b Hayward, Wis, Nov 29, 38; m 64; c 2. VIROLOGY, MICROBIOLOGY. *Educ:* Wis State Univ-Stevens Point, BS, 66; St Joseph's Hosp, MT, 67; Ind Univ, MS, 70, PhD(microbiol), 71. *Prof Exp:* Asst prof microbiol, Rush Med Col, 72-81; asst scientist microbiol & chief diag virol, Rush-Presby-St Luke's Med Ctr, 72-81; CLIN PROJS MGR, ABBOTT LABS, INC, NORTH CHICAGO, ILL, 81- *Concurrent Pos:* Fel microbiol with Dr F Deinhard, Rush-Presby-St Luke's Med Ctr, 71-72, Nat Inst Allergy & Infectious Dis fel, 71-78; JJ Reingold Trust for congenital Rubella studies, 72-81. *Mem:* AAAS; Am Soc Microbiol; Soc Exp Biol Med; Sigma Xi. *Res:* Virologic aspects of hepatitis; congenital Rubella and slow degenerative diseases of the central nervous system; viral diagnostic systems. *Mailing Add:* Sci Affairs D-924 Abbott Labs Inc North Chicago IL 60064

PETERSON, DAVID K(AY), chemical engineering, see previous edition

PETERSON, DAVID MAURICE, b Woodward, Okla, July 3, 40; m 65; c 2. PLANT PHYSIOLOGY. *Educ:* Univ Calif, Davis, BS, 62; Univ Ill, Urbana, MS, 64; Harvard Univ, PhD(biol), 68. *Prof Exp:* Res biologist, Allied Chem Corp, 70-71; PLANT PHYSIOLOGIST, NAT OAT QUAL LAB, AGR RES SERV, USDA, 71- *Concurrent Pos:* Asst prof, Univ Wis-Madison, 71-75, assoc prof, 75-80, prof, 80-; assoc ed, Crop Sci, 75-78. *Mem:* AAAS; Am Soc Plant Physiol; Am Soc Agron; Crop Sci Soc Am; Am Asn Chemists. *Res:* Protein synthesis; nitrogen metabolism; plant physiology as related to quality improvement in oats; seed development. *Mailing Add:* Dept of Agron Univ of Wis Madison WI 53706

PETERSON, DAVID OSCAR, b Portland, Ore, June 22, 50. GENE EXPRESSION, MOLECULAR GENETICS. *Educ:* Pomona Col, BA, 72; Harvard Univ, PhD(chem), 78. *Prof Exp:* Fel, Dept Biochem & Biophysics, Univ Calif, San Francisco, 78-81; ASST PROF, DEPT BIOCHEM & BIOPHYSICS, TEX A&M UNIV, 81- *Res:* Transcriptional regulation of eukaryotic genes; glucocorticoid-mediated regulation of mouse mammary tumor virus gene expression. *Mailing Add:* Dept Biochem & Biophysics Tex A&M Univ College Station TX 77843

PETERSON, DAVID T, b Blue Earth, Minn, Nov 29, 22; m 45; c 2. METALLURGY. *Educ:* Iowa State Univ, BS, 47, PhD(phys chem), 50. *Prof Exp:* PROF METALL, IOWA STATE UNIV & SR METALLURGIST, AMES LAB, 50- *Mem:* Am Soc Metals; Am Inst Mining, Metall & Petrol Engrs. *Res:* Chemical metallurgy; kinetics and equilibria of metallic reactions. *Mailing Add:* 222 Metall Develop Bldg Iowa State Univ Ames IA 50011

PETERSON, DAVID WEST, b Schenectady, NY, Sept 3, 40; m 61; c 2. APPLIED MATHEMATICS. *Educ:* Univ Wis, BS, 62; Stanford Univ, MS, 63, PhD(elec eng), 65. *Prof Exp:* Mem tech staff, Ground Systs Group, Hughes Aircraft Co, 62-63; res asst systs group, Stanford Univ, 63-65; from asst prof to assoc prof quant methods, Grad Sch Mgt, Northwestern Univ, Evanston, 67-73; PROF BUS ADMIN, GRAD SCH BUS, DUKE UNIV, 73- *Concurrent Pos:* Consult, US Army Res Off, NC, 67-68 & USPHS, 70-71; res fel, Int Inst Mgt, Berlin, 71-72; vis lectr systs eng, Univ Ill, Chicago Circle, 73; statist consult, var corps & govt units, 74- *Mem:* Am Econ Asn; Economet Soc; Inst Elec & Electronics Eng; Ger Opers Res Soc; Int Asn Analog Comput. *Res:* Properties of multi-agent dynamic systems; applications of mathematical models to socio-economic systems; statistical frameworks for determining the fairness of employment practices. *Mailing Add:* 2738 Sevier St Durham NC 27705

PETERSON, DEAN EVERETT, b Aledo, Ill, Apr 14, 41; m 66; c 2. HIGH TEMPERATURE CHEMISTRY. *Educ:* Monmouth Col, BA, 64; Univ Kans, PhD(phys chem), 72. *Prof Exp:* Mem staff chem, Argonne Nat Lab, 63-64 & Savannah River Lab, 66-67; MEM STAFF CHEM, LOS ALAMOS SCI LAB, 72- *Honors & Awards:* Medal, Am Inst Chemists, 64. *Mem:* Am Chem Soc; Am Vacuum Soc; Sigma Xi; AAAS. *Res:* Thermodynamics, kinetics, vaporization processes, vapor pressures and mass spectrometry. *Mailing Add:* CMB-5 MS 730 Los Alamos Sci Lab Los Alamos NM 87545

PETERSON, DEAN F(REEMAN), JR, b Delta, Utah, June 3, 13; m 38; c 5. CIVIL & AGRICULTURAL ENGINEERING. *Educ:* Utah State Univ, BS, 34; Rensselaer Polytech Inst, MCE, 35, DCE, 39. *Hon Degrees:* DSc, Utah State Univ, 73. *Prof Exp:* Jr engr, Works Progress Admin, Utah, 35-36; road engr, Indian Serv, US Dept Interior, Wyo, 36-37; instr eng, Univ Wash, Seattle, 39-40; proj engr, Upper Potomac River Comn, 40-41; chief cost & progress engr, Pine Bluff Arsenal, 41-44; assoc prof civil eng, Utah State Univ, 46-49; prof & head dept, Colo State Univ, 49-57; prof eng & dean eng, Utah State Univ, 57-73, vpres res, 73-76; chief, Soil & Water Div, 76-78, DIR, OFF AGR, AID, 78- *Concurrent Pos:* Consult, Near East & South Asia, USAID, 59- & Tex, USAID, US Geol Surv, Dept of State; chmn panel weather modification, NSF, 63-65 & Univs Coun Water Resources, 64-65; tech asst water resources, Off Sci & Technol, Exec Off President & chmn comt water resources res, Fed Coun Sci & Technol, 65-66; vchmn, US Comt Int Hydrol Decade, Nat Acad Sci, 66-67, chmn, 67-70; dir off water for peace, US Dept State, 68-69. *Honors & Awards:* Royce Tipton Award, Am Soc Civil Engrs, 68. *Mem:* Nat Acad Eng; AAAS; Am Soc Eng Educ; hon mem Am Soc Civil Engrs; fel Am Acad Arts & Sci. *Res:* Stream hydraulics; environmental systems; water resources engineering and evaluation; irrigation. *Mailing Add:* Agency Int Develop New Delhi India

PETERSON, DENNIS RANDALL, biochemistry, see previous edition

PETERSON, DONALD BRUCE, b Erie, Pa, Dec 16, 31. PHYSICAL CHEMISTRY. *Educ:* Pa State Univ, BS, 54; Carnegie Inst Technol, MS, 57, PhD(chem), 58. *Prof Exp:* NSF fel radiation chem, Univ Leeds, 58-60; asst prof chem, McMaster Univ, 60-61; res scientist, Univ Notre Dame, 61-64; PROF CHEM, UNIV SAN DIEGO, 64- *Mem:* AAAS; Radiation Res Soc; Am Chem Soc. *Res:* Photochemistry and radiation chemistry. *Mailing Add:* Dept of Chem Univ of San Diego Alcala Park San Diego CA 92110

PETERSON, DONALD FREDERICK, b Great Bend, Kans, Aug 4, 41; m 67; c 2. PHYSIOLOGY. *Educ:* Kans State Univ, BS, 65, PhD(physiol), 70. *Prof Exp:* From instr to assoc prof pharmacol, Univ Tex Health Sci Ctr, San Antonio, 71-78; ASSOC PROF PHYSIOL, MED & DENT SCHS, ORAL ROBERTS UNIV, 78- *Concurrent Pos:* NIH trainee cardiol, Med Ctr, Univ Utah, 69-71. *Mem:* AAAS; Am Physiol Soc; Poultry Sci Asn; Am Heart Asn. *Res:* Neural control of circulation; peripheral sensory mechanisms. *Mailing Add:* Dept of Physiol Oral Roberts Univ Tulsa OK 74171

PETERSON, DONALD I, b Moscow, Idaho, July 26, 22; m 42; c 3. NEUROLOGY, PHARMACOLOGY. *Educ:* Walla Walla Col, BA, 44; Loma Linda Univ, MD, 47; FACP. *Prof Exp:* Med dir, Jengre Mission Hosp, 54-60; asst prof neurol, 69-74, ASSOC PROF PHARMACOL, LOMA LINDA UNIV HOSP, 60-, ASSOC PROF NEUROL, 74- *Mem:* Sigma Xi; Am Acad Neurol; Am Col Physicians. *Res:* Toxicity, muscle disease, metabolism. *Mailing Add:* Dept of Neurol Loma Linda Univ Med Ctr Loma Linda CA 92354

PETERSON, DONALD J, b Ladysmith, Wis, Nov 19, 35; m 57; c 2. ORGANIC CHEMISTRY. *Educ:* Wis State Univ, Superior, BS, 57; Iowa State Univ, PhD(org chem), 62. *Prof Exp:* RES CHEMIST, MIAMI VALLEY LABS, PROCTER & GAMBLE CO, 62- *Mem:* Am Chem Soc. *Res:* Organometallic chemistry, especially organolithium, organosilicon, organophosphorus and organotin chemistry. *Mailing Add:* Miami Valley Labs Procter & Gamble Co PO Box 175 Cincinnati OH 45239

PETERSON, DONALD LEE, b Reno, Nev, Apr 6, 30; m 52; c 3. PHYSICAL CHEMISTRY. *Educ:* Univ Nev, BS, 52; Univ Wash, PhD(chem), 56. *Prof Exp:* Chemist, Shell Develop Co, 56-62; NSF fel, Imp Col, Univ London, 62-63; chemist, Shell Develop Co, 63-66; assoc prof, 66-71, chmn dept, 76-82, PROF CHEM, CALIF STATE UNIV, HAYWARD, 71- *Concurrent Pos:* Vis prof chem, Univ Newcastle, NSW, 72-73. *Mem:* Am Chem Soc. *Res:* Adsorption and diffusion in zeolites; theory of gas chromatography; uses of molecular orbital theory. *Mailing Add:* Dept of Chem Calif State Univ 25800 Hillary St Hayward CA 94542

PETERSON, DONALD NEIL, b Detroit, Mich, Oct 14, 41; m 68. GEOPHYSICS. *Educ:* Wittenberg Univ, BS, 63; Ind Univ, Bloomington, MA, 65; Ohio State Univ, PhD(geol & geophys), 69. *Prof Exp:* Res assoc glaciol & geophys, Inst Polar Studies, Ohio State Univ, 64-68; res assoc geophys and paleomagnetism, Case Western Reserve Univ, 69-70; asst prof, 70-75, ASSOC PROF GEOPHYS, STATE UNIV NY COL FREDONIA, 75- *Concurrent Pos:* NSF grant, Case Western Reserve Univ, 69-70; vis assoc, Calif Inst Technol, 78. *Mem:* Am Geophys Union; Geol Soc Am; Soc Explor Geophysicists. *Res:* Paleomagnetism and continental drift; establishment of paleomagnetic stratigraphic sequence for Paleozoic time. *Mailing Add:* Dept of Geol State Univ NY Col Fredonia NY 14063

PETERSON, DONALD PALMER, b Bremerton, Wash, June 27, 29; m 52; c 4. MATHEMATICS. *Educ:* Wash State Univ, BA, 52, MA, 54; Univ Ore, PhD(math), 57. *Prof Exp:* Asst, Wash State Univ, 52-54; asst, Univ Ore, 54-55, instr, 56-57; mem staff, Sandia Corp, 57-61; eng specialist, Gen Tel & Electronics Labs, Inc, 62-63; mem staff, 63-68, supvr, 68-73, MEM TECH STAFF, SANDIA NAT LAB, 73- *Mem:* Soc Indust & Appl Math; Oper Res Soc Am; Asn Comput Mach. *Res:* Computer science; computer-aided design; pattern recognition. *Mailing Add:* Sandia Nat Lab PO Box 5800 Albuquerque NM 87116

PETERSON, DONALD RICHARD, b Portland, Ore, Jan 12, 21; m 45; c 4. EPIDEMIOLOGY. *Educ:* Ore State Univ, BA, 44; Univ Ore, MS, 46, MD, 47; Univ Calif, Berkeley, MPH, 57. *Prof Exp:* Dir adult health div, Dept Pub Health, Seattle, King County, Wash, 57-61; dir epidemiol div, 61-71, PROF EPIDEMIOL & CHMN DEPT, SCH PUB HEALTH & COMMUNITY MED, UNIV WASH, 71- *Concurrent Pos:* WHO traveling fel, 71. *Mem:* Int Epidemiol Asn; Soc Epidemiol Res; Am Epidemiol Soc. *Res:* Sudden infant death syndrome; disease seasonality. *Mailing Add:* Sch Pub Health & Community Med Univ of Wash Seattle WA 98195

PETERSON, DONALD WILLIAM, b San Francisco, Calif, Mar 3, 25; m 48; c 3. GEOLOGY. *Educ:* Calif Inst Technol, BS, 49; Wash State Univ, MS, 51; Stanford Univ, PhD, 61. *Prof Exp:* Asst, Wash State Univ, 49-51; GEOLOGIST, US GEOL SURV, 52- *Concurrent Pos:* Asst, Stanford Univ, 55-56; scientist-in-chg, Hawaiian Volcano Observ, US Geol Surv, 70-75. *Mem:* AAAS; fel Geol Soc Am; Soc Econ Geol; Am Geophys Union. *Res:* Geology and petrology of volcanic rocks; structural and economic geology; geology and volcanology of Hawaiian volcanoes. *Mailing Add:* US Geol Surv 345 Middlefield Rd Menlo Park CA 94025

PETERSON, EARL ANDREW, b Puyallup, Wash, Jan 8, 40. HIGH ENERGY PHYSICS. *Educ:* Univ Wash, BA, 62; Stanford Univ, MA, 67, PhD(physics), 68. *Prof Exp:* Res assoc, 67-73, asst prof, 73-78, ASSOC PROF PHYSICS, UNIV MINN, 78- *Res:* Experimental high energy physics. *Mailing Add:* Sch of Physics 116 Church St SE Minneapolis MN 55455

PETERSON, EDWARD CHARLES, b Duluth, Minn, Apr 12, 29; m 58; c 4. PHYSICS. *Educ:* Univ Minn, Duluth, BA, 51; Univ Wis, MS, 56; Mich State Univ, MA, 63. *Prof Exp:* From assoc physicist to physicist, 58-63, from assoc res physicist to res physicist, 63-74, SR RES PHYSICIST, WHIRLPOOL CORP, 74- *Mem:* Am Asn Physics Teachers; Am Vacuum Soc; Sigma Xi. *Res:* Electronics; mechanics; high vacuum techniques; instrumentation; particle accelerators; textile test work; development of test methods and instrumentation for evaluating home appliances. *Mailing Add:* Whirlpool Corp Res Lab Monte Rd Benton Harbor MI 49022

PETERSON, ELBERT AXEL, b Chicago, Ill, June 16, 18; m 43; c 2. BIOCHEMISTRY. *Educ:* Univ Chicago, BS, 41; Univ Calif, PhD(biochem), 51. *Prof Exp:* Chemist, Shell Develop Co, 41-46; fel, 50-52, CHEMIST, NAT CANCER INST, 52- *Mem:* Am Chem Soc; Am Soc Biol Chemists. *Res:* Biosynthesis of proteins; chromatography of proteins; maturation of leukocytes. *Mailing Add:* 4405 Cambria Ave Garrett Park MD 20766

PETERSON, ELLENGENE HODGES, b Abilene, Tex, Oct 20, 40. NEUROANATOMY, NEUROBIOLOGY. *Educ:* Radcliffe Col, BA, 62; Calif State Univ, Los Angeles, MA, 70; Univ Calif, Riverside, PhD(psychol), 76. *Prof Exp:* Fel neuroanat, Univ Calif, San Diego, 75-76 & Sch Med, Univ PR, 76-77; res assoc neuroanat, Univ Chicago, 77-80; MEM FAC, SCH ANAT, UNIV NEW SOUTH WALES, 80- *Concurrent Pos:* Fel, A P Sloan, 75-77. *Mem:* Soc Neurosci; Am Soc Zool; AAAS. *Res:* Functional morphology of retina and retino-tectal system. *Mailing Add:* PO Box 1 Sch Anat Univ New South Wales Kensington 60637 Australia

PETERSON, ELMOR LEE, b McKeesport, Pa, Dec 6, 38; m 66; c 2. MATHEMATICS, OPERATIONS RESEARCH. *Educ:* Carnegie Inst Technol, BS, 60, MS, 61, PhD(math), 64. *Prof Exp:* Sr mathematician, Westinghouse Res & Develop Ctr, 63-66; asst prof math, Univ Mich, 67-69; assoc prof math & indust eng/mgt sci, Northwestern Univ, 69-73, prof, 73-80; PROF MATH & INDUST ENG, NC STATE UNIV, 80- *Concurrent Pos:* Lectr, Carnegie Inst Technol, 63-66; Air Force Off Sci Res grants, 73-77; vis assoc prof math res ctr, Univ Wis, 68-69. *Mem:* Am Math Soc; Soc Indust & Appl Math; Math Asn Am; Opers Res Soc Am. *Res:* Geometric programming with applications to optimal engineering design, location and resource allocation; regression analysis; structural analysis and optimization; network analysis and design and variational analysis in the physical sciences and economics. *Mailing Add:* Williamsbourgh Ct NC State Univ Raleigh NC 27650

PETERSON, ERNEST A, b New York, NY, June 16, 31; m 52; c 2. ACOUSTICS. *Educ:* Rutgers Univ, BA, 59; Princeton Univ, MA, 61, PhD(psychol), 62. *Prof Exp:* Asst prof, 64-70, ASSOC PROF OTOLARYNGOL, SCH MED, UNIV MIAMI, 70- *Concurrent Pos:* NIH fel sensory psychol, Princeton Univ, 62-64. *Mem:* AAAS; Acoust Soc Am; Am Psychol Asn. *Res:* Non-auditory effects of noise; auditory evoked responses; electrophysiological responses of the ear. *Mailing Add:* Div Auditory Res D7-1 PO Box 016960 Miami FL 33101

PETERSON, ERNEST W, b Long Beach, Calif, Dec 10, 38; m 65; c 2. METEOROLOGY. *Educ:* Univ Calif, Los Angeles, BA, 62; Pa State Univ, PhD(meteorol), 69. *Prof Exp:* ASSOC PROF ATMOSPHERIC SCI, ORE STATE UNIV, 69- *Concurrent Pos:* Res assoc, Riso Nat Lab, Roskilde, Denmark, 73, adj scientist, 73-; res meteorologist, Corvallis Environ Res Lab, Environ Protection Agency, 75-81. *Mem:* Royal Meteorol Soc; AAAS; Am Meteorol Soc; Sigma Xi. *Res:* Flow over heterogeneous terrain; air pollution diffusion; boundary layer meteorology. *Mailing Add:* Dept Atmospheric Sci Ore State Univ Corvallis OR 97331

PETERSON, EUGENE JAMES, b Evergreen Park, Ill, Nov 18, 49; m 79. INORGANIC CHEMISTRY. *Educ:* St Procopius Col, BS, 71; Ariz State Univ, PhD(inorg chem), 76. *Prof Exp:* Staff mem, Los Alamos Sci Lab, 76-78; staff mem, Argonne Nat Lab, 78-79; STAFF MEM, LOS ALAMOS NAT LAB, 79- *Mem:* Am Chem Soc; AAAS. *Res:* Identification of water quality concerns associated with shale oil extraction and research of strategies for mitigation of health and environmental impacts. *Mailing Add:* Los Alamos Nat Lab CMB-8 MS-734 PO Box 1663 Los Alamos NM 87545

PETERSON, FRANCIS CARL, b Brooklyn, NY, Dec 13, 42; m 66; c 3. ELEMENTARY PARTICLE PHYSICS. *Educ:* Rensselaer Polytech Inst, BEE, 64; Cornell Univ, PhD(physics), 68. *Prof Exp:* Asst prof physics, Iowa State Univ, 68-72, assoc physicist, Ames Lab, 68-72, ASSOC PROF PHYSICS, IOWA STATE UNIV, 72-, PHYSICIST, AMES LAB, 72- *Mem:* Am Asn Physics Teachers. *Res:* Experimental high energy physics; educational development research. *Mailing Add:* Dept of Physics Iowa State Univ Ames IA 50010

PETERSON, FRANK LYNN, b Klamath Falls, Ore, May 8, 41; m 67. GROUNDWATER GEOLOGY, ENGINEERING GEOLOGY. *Educ:* Cornell Univ, BA, 63; Stanford Univ, MS, 65, PhD(geol), 67. *Prof Exp:* Asst prof geol & asst geologist, 67-71, assoc prof geol & assoc geologist, Water Resources Res Ctr, 71-76, PROF GEOL & HYDROL & HYDROLOGIST, RES CTR, UNIV HAWAII, 76- *Mem:* Am Water Resources Asn; Geol Soc Am; Am Geophys Union; Nat Water Well Asn; Asn Eng Geol. *Res:* Hydrologic cycle; occurrence of and exploration for groundwater; groundwater occurrence in volcanic rocks; salt water intrusion; fluid flow and groundwater storage; land subsidence; engineering geology problems. *Mailing Add:* Dept Geol & Geophys Univ Hawaii Honolulu HI 96822

PETERSON, FRANKLIN PAUL, b Aurora, Ill, Aug 27, 30; m 59. MATHEMATICS. *Educ:* Northwestern Univ, BS, 52; Princeton Univ, PhD, 55. *Prof Exp:* NSF fel, Univ Chicago, 55-56; Higgins lectr math, Princeton Univ, 56-58; from asst prof to assoc prof, 58-65, PROF MATH, MASS INST TECHNOL, 65- *Concurrent Pos:* Sloan fel, Oxford Univ, 60-61; Fulbright res grant, Kyoto Univ, 67. *Mem:* Am Math Soc (treas, 73-). *Res:* Algebraic topology, particularly homotopy and cohomology theory. *Mailing Add:* Dept of Math Mass Inst of Technol Cambridge MA 02139

PETERSON, FRED, b St Johns, Mich, June 29, 33. GEOLOGY. *Educ:* San Diego State Col, BS, 60; Stanford Univ, PhD(geol), 69. *Prof Exp:* GEOLOGIST, US GEOL SURV, 60- *Mem:* Am Asn Petrol Geol; Geol Soc Am; Soc Econ Paleont & Mineral; Int Asn Sedimentologists. *Res:* Stratigraphy. *Mailing Add:* US Geol Surv Mail Stop 916 Box 25046 Denver CO 80225

PETERSON, FREDERICK FORNEY, b Madison, Wis, Dec 21, 28; m 73; c 4. SOIL CLASSIFICATION, SOIL GENESIS. *Educ:* Univ Wis, BS, 50; Cornell Univ, MS, 53; Wash State Univ, PhD(soils), 61. *Prof Exp:* Res asst soil surv, Wis Natural Hist & Geol Surv & Univ Wis, 48-49; res asst, Cornell Univ, 50-52; soil genesis, Wash State Univ, 56-59; res soil scientist, Soil Conserv Serv, USDA, 59-62; asst prof soil morphol & classification & asst chemist, Univ Calif, Riverside, 62-67; assoc prof, 67-73, PROF, PLANT, SOIL & WATER SCI DIV, UNIV NEV, RENO, 73- *Mem:* Soil Sci Soc Am; Soc Range Mgt; Sigma Xi. *Res:* Soil classification and survey; geomorphology-soils interrelations. *Mailing Add:* Plant Soil & Water Sci Div Univ of Nev Reno NV 89557

PETERSON, GARY A, b Holdrege, Nebr, Apr 30, 40; m 65; c 2. SOIL SCIENCE, STATISTICS. *Educ:* Univ Nebr, BS, 63, MS, 65; Iowa State Univ, PhD(agron), 67. *Prof Exp:* Assoc prof, 67-74, PROF SOIL SCI, UNIV NEBR, LINCOLN, 67- *Concurrent Pos:* Vis prof, Colo State Univ, 80-81. *Mem:* Am Soc Agron; Soil Sci Soc Am; Am Soc Sugar Beet Technologists. *Res:* Soil-plant relationships and management of soils under semiarid dry land conditions, particularly effects of cultural practices on soil nitrogen and phosphorus chemistry and fertility; soil fertility of sugar beets. *Mailing Add:* 114 Keim Hall Univ of Nebr Lincoln NE 68583

PETERSON, GARY LEE, b Fargo, NDak, June 24, 36. GEOLOGY. *Educ:* Univ Colo, BA, 59; Univ Wash, MS, 61, PhD(geol), 63. *Prof Exp:* From asst prof to assoc prof, 63-69, chmn dept, 73-76, PROF GEOL, SAN DIEGO STATE UNIV, 69- *Concurrent Pos:* Vis prof geol, Univ Mont, 77. *Mem:* AAAS; Am Asn Petrol Geol; Geol Soc Am; Soc Econ Paleont & Mineral. *Res:* Cretaceous stratigraphy of the West Coast; late Mesozoic and Cenozoic stratigraphy of southwestern California and northwestern Baja California; Neogene stratigraphy of Imperial Valley, California; Mesozoic and Cenozoic paleoclimatology of the western United States. *Mailing Add:* Dept of Geol Sci San Diego State Univ San Diego CA 92182

PETERSON, GARY LEE, cell physiology, comparative biochemistry, see previous edition

PETERSON, GEORGE EARL, b Pittsburgh, Pa, June 7, 34. PHYSICS. *Educ:* Univ Pittsburgh, BS, 56, PhD(physics), 61. *Prof Exp:* Res asst physics, Univ Pittsburgh, 56-61; MEM STAFF CRYSTAL PHYSICS, BELL LABS, 61- *Mem:* Optical Soc Am; Am Phys Soc; Am Crystallog Asn; Am Asn Crystal Growth; Am Ceramic Soc. *Res:* Laser materials research; rare earth fluorescence; nuclear magnetic resonance and nuclear quadrupole resonance in ferroelectrics and other nonlinear dielectric materials. *Mailing Add:* Bell Labs Crystal Chem Res Dept Murray Hill NJ 07971

PETERSON, GEORGE HAROLD, b San Francisco, Calif, Apr 11, 31. MICROBIOLOGY. *Educ:* Univ Calif, BS, 53, PhD(soil microbiol), 57. *Prof Exp:* Asst prof bot & plant path, Purdue Univ, 57-63; asst prof, 63-66, assoc prof & assoc dean instr, 66-71, dean acad planning, 70-78, PROF BIOL SCI, CALIF STATE COL, HAYWARD, 71-, ASSOC VPRES ACAD RESOURCES, 78- *Mem:* Fel AAAS; Am Soc Microbiol; NY Acad Sci. *Res:* Physiology of soil microorganism; bacteriology; bacterial and cellular physiology. *Mailing Add:* Acad Resources Calif State Col Hayward CA 94542

PETERSON, GEORGE LAWRENCE, b Salt Lake City, Utah, June 3, 36; m 63; c 1. CIVIL ENGINEERING. *Educ:* Univ Utah, BSCE, 61; Northwestern Univ, MS, 62, PhD(urban & regional anal), 65. *Prof Exp:* Asst prof eng, Univ Calif, Los Angeles, 64-65; from asst prof to assoc prof civil eng, 65-74, PROF CIVIL ENG, NORTHWESTERN UNIV, EVANSTON, 74- *Concurrent Pos:* Res consult, US Dept HUD-NCA, 74; vis scientist, US Forest Serv, 77-78. *Res:* Urban and regional analysis; analysis and design of the quality of man's physical environment; social and environmental impact assessment; recreation research. *Mailing Add:* Dept of Civil Eng Technol Inst Northwestern Univ Evanston IL 60201

PETERSON, GERALD A, b Minneapolis, Minn, Jan 25, 32; m 57; c 2. THEORETICAL PHYSICS, SOLID STATE PHYSICS. *Educ:* Univ Minn, BA, 52; Cornell Univ, PhD(theoret physics), 59. *Prof Exp:* Res fel appl physics, Harvard Univ, 60-61, lectr, 62-64; consult, 62-64, sr theoret physicist, 64-67, PRIN SCIENTIST THEORET PHYSICS, RES CTR, UNITED TECHNOL CORP, 67- *Concurrent Pos:* Vis lectr, Wesleyan Univ, 64-65, vis assoc prof, 71- *Mem:* Am Phys Soc; Sci Res Soc Am. *Res:* Electronic and optical properties of solids; metals and semiconductors; band theory; impurity levels; current instabilities in semiconductors; nonlinear optics; laser physics. *Mailing Add:* Res Labs United Technol Corp Silver Lane East Hartford CT 06108

PETERSON, GERALD ALVIN, b Chesterton, Ind, Apr 12, 31; m 53; c 3. PHYSICS. *Educ:* Purdue Univ, BS, 53, MS, 55; Stanford Univ, PhD(physics), 62. *Prof Exp:* Physicist, Dept Defense, 57; res assoc physics, Yale Univ, 62-64, asst prof, 64-67; vis scientist, Amsterdam, Netherlands, 67; assoc prof, 68-73, PROF NUCLEAR PHYSICS, UNIV MASS, AMHERST, 73- *Concurrent Pos:* NATO fel, Scotland, 69-70; United Kingdom Res Coun sr fel, 70; Japan Soc for Promotion of Sci vis prof, Tohoku Univ, Japan, 72. *Mem:* Am Phys Soc. *Res:* Electron scattering; nuclear structure; instrumentation. *Mailing Add:* Dept of Physics & Astron Univ Mass Amherst MA 01002

PETERSON, GERALD E, b Ephraim, Utah, Aug 9, 38; m 62; c 7. INTELLIGENT SYSTEMS, MATHEMATICAL ANALYSIS. *Educ:* Univ Utah, BS, 61, MA, 63, PhD(math), 65. *Prof Exp:* Res engr, Jet Propulsion Lab, 63-64; asst prof math, Univ Utah, 65-66 & Brigham Young Univ, 66-68; asst prof, 68-71, ASSOC PROF MATH, UNIV MO, ST LOUIS, 71- *Concurrent Pos:* NSF res contract, 70-71; software eng, McDonnell Douglas Corp, 81- *Mem:* Am Math Soc; Math Asn Am; Asn Comput Mach; Am Asn Artificial Intel; Sigma Xi. *Res:* Automated mathematics; especially automatic theorem proving for first-order logic with equality. *Mailing Add:* Dept of Math Univ of Mo St Louis MO 63121

PETERSON, GLEN ERVIN, b Jackson, Minn, July 12, 26; m 49; c 5. BACTERIOLOGY, BIOCHEMISTRY. *Educ:* Luther Col, Iowa, BA, 49; Univ Minn, Minneapolis, MS, 52, PhD(bact), 54. *Prof Exp:* Asst prof biol, Univ Houston, 53-55; res assoc, Squibb Inst Med Res, 55-58; assoc prof, Univ Houston, 58-63, prof biol, 63-67; prof, Univ Colo, Boulder, 67-69; prof biol & dean arts & sci, Univ Nev, Reno, 69-70; actg assoc dean grad sch, 71-75, PROF BIOL & DIR GRAD STUDIES, MEMPHIS STATE UNIV, 70-, DEAN GRAD SCH, 75- *Concurrent Pos:* Am specialist to India, Inst Prog Biol Teachers, US Dept State, 63; vpres, Bio-Assay Labs, Inc, Tex, 63-67; consult, Lamar State Col, 64; NSF consult biol, Cent Am, 65-68; Educ Testing Serv writer, Grad Record Exam Microbiol, 66, Nat Teacher Exam, 67-69, col entrance exam bds, 68; consult biol, Asia Found, Southeast Asia, 66-; col biol, Inst Int Educ, Pakistan, 67-; UNESCO pilot proj biol English-speaking countries Africa, 67-68; bd dirs, Am Biomed Corp, Tex, 68-69; contrib ed, J Col Sci Teaching, 71-; dir, NSF Conf Sec Prin, 71, Elem Prin, 72; Capital Univ Assocs, 71-73. Mem NSF adv panels, 64, 66 & 71; rev comt, Educ Testing Serv, 69; ed comt, Nat Registry Microbiol, Am Acad Microbiol, 66-70; cor mem, Comn Biol Teaching Int Union Biol Sci, 68-; off rep of Am Soc Microbiol, Cent Am Cong Microbiol, Panama, 68; mem UN Adv Party, Improv Sci Educ Develop Countries, 69; mem UNESCO working party, Sci in Develop Countries, 69. *Honors & Awards:* Fulbright lectr, Uruguay, 66. *Mem:* AAAS; fel Am Acad Microbiol; Am Soc Microbiol; Nat Asn Biol Teachers; Am Inst Sci. *Res:* Mode of action of antibiotics; sterol and steroid utilization by microorganisms; international biological education; teacher training; academic administration. *Mailing Add:* 3098 Rising Sun Rd Memphis TN 38134

PETERSON, GLENN WALTER, b Shell Rock, Iowa, Oct 26, 22; m 57; c 3. PLANT PATHOLOGY. *Educ:* Iowa State Teachers Col, BA, 49; Iowa State Univ, MS, 51, PhD(plant path), 58. *Prof Exp:* Teacher high sch, Iowa, 49-56; PLANT PATHOLOGIST, US FOREST SERV, UNIV NEBR, LINCOLN, 58- *Mem:* Am Phytopath Soc. *Res:* Diseases of forest tree seedlings in great plains nurseries and diseases of trees in plains plantations. *Mailing Add:* Forestry Sci Lab East Campus Univ of Nebr Lincoln NE 68503

PETERSON, HAROLD A(LBERT), b Essex, Iowa, Dec 28, 08; m 34; c 2. ELECTRICAL ENGINEERING. *Educ:* Univ Iowa, BS, 32, MS, 33. *Prof Exp:* Elec engr, Works Lab, Gen Elec Co, Mass, 34-37, elec engr, Anal Div, 37-46; prof elec eng, 46-75, Wis Utilities Asn prof, 67-74, chmn dept, 47-67, Edward Bennett prof, 74-75, EMER EDWARD BENNETT PROF ELEC ENG, UNIV WIS-MADISON, 75- *Concurrent Pos:* Mem, Int Conf Large Elec Systs. *Honors & Awards:* Educ Medal, Inst Elec & Electronics Engrs, 78. *Mem:* Nat Acad Eng; Am Soc Eng Educ; Am Soc Mech Engrs; Nat Soc Prof Engrs; fel Inst Elec & Electronics Engrs. *Res:* Analysis of power system engineering problems; transients in power systems; applied superconductivity and energy storage in power systems; D-C power transmission. *Mailing Add:* 121 West Calle Green Valley AZ 85614

PETERSON, HAROLD ARTHUR, b St Paul, Minn, Sept 11, 26; m 50; c 4. SPEECH PATHOLOGY, PSYCHOLINGUISTICS. *Educ:* Minot State Col, BA, 50, BS, 58; State Univ Iowa, MA, 62; Univ Ill, PhD(speech path), 67. *Prof Exp:* Speech therapist, Ward County Pub Sch, 58-61; trainee speech path, Univ Iowa, 61-62; instr & speech clin coordr, Univ Ill, 62-67; assoc prof, dir speech practicum & admin asst to dept head speech path, 67-72, PROF DEPT AUDIOL & SPEECH PATH, UNIV TENN, 72-, DIR, HEARING & SPEECH CTR, 73- *Mem:* Am Speech & Hearing Asn; fel Am Speech, Lang & Hearing Asn. *Res:* Appraisal of speech and language disorders and psycholingustic variables in speech-language development and disorders. *Mailing Add:* Hearing & Speech Ctr Yale at Stadium Dr Knoxville TN 37996

PETERSON, HAROLD LEROY, b Mayville, NDak, Mar 24, 46; div; c 2. SOIL MICROBIOLOGY. *Educ:* Mayville State Col, BA, 68; Iowa State Univ, MS, 71, PhD(soil microbiol), 75. *Prof Exp:* Asst prof & asst agronomist, 75-80, ASSOC PROF AGRON & ASSOC AGRONOMIST, MISS AGR & FORESTRY EXP STA, MISS STATE UNIV, 80- *Concurrent Pos:* Vis prof agron & genetics, Iowa State Univ, 81. *Mem:* AAAS; Am Soc Microbiol; Am Soc Agron; Brit Soc Soil Sci; Soil Sci Soc Am. *Res:* Ecology of microorganisms in soil; dinitrogen fixation in plants and soil; relationships of soil microorganisms to food and fiber production; increased capture of solar energy; rhizobium DNA research. *Mailing Add:* Dept Agron Box 5248 Miss State Univ Mississippi State MS 39762

PETERSON, HAROLD LEROY, b Stromsburg, Nebr, Apr, 13, 38. MATHEMATICS. *Educ:* Stanford Univ, BS, 60; Univ Ore, MS, 63, PhD(math), 66. *Prof Exp:* Assoc engr, Lockheed Missiles & Space Co, 60-61; asst prof math, Univ Conn, 66-70; asst prof, 70-74, ASSOC PROF MATH, IND UNIV NORTHWEST, 74- *Mem:* Am Math Soc; Math Asn Am. *Res:* Topological groups; measure theory; general topology; subgroups of finite index, extensions of Haar measure. *Mailing Add:* Dept of Math Ind Univ Northwest Gary IN 46408

PETERSON, HAROLD OSCAR, b Dalbo, Minn, Apr 13, 09; m 34; c 4. MEDICINE, RADIOLOGY. *Educ:* Univ Minn, BS, 30, BM, 33, MD, 34; Am Bd Radiol, dipl, 38. *Prof Exp:* Intern, Kansas City Gen Hosp, Mo, 33-34; resident radiol, Mass Gen Hosp, Boston, 35-36; instr, 37-40, from clin instr to clin prof, 40-57, head dept, 57-70, prof, 57-74, PROF EMER, RADIOL, UNIV MINN, ST PAUL, 77- *Concurrent Pos:* Henry K Pancoast lectr, Philadelphia, 56; Freedman lectr, Univ Cincinnati, 59; Fred J Hodges lectr, Ann Arbor, Mich, 62; lectr, var univs & socs, 62-; radiologist, Interstate Clin, Red Wing, Minn, 40-57, St Joseph's Hosp, St Paul, 41-43 & Bethesda Hosp, 41-44; radiologist & head dept, Charles T Miller Hosp, 41-57 & Children's Hosp, 48-57; trustee, Am Bd Radiol, 58-71; mem neurol study sect, NIH, 68-72; vis prof radiol, Univ Tex Med Br, Galveston, 79, 80 & 81 & Univ Tex Health Sci Ctr, San Antonio, 80 & 81-82. *Honors & Awards:* Gold Medal, Am Roentgen Ray Soc, 61; Award, Am Acad Neurol, 63; Gold Medal, Am Col Radiol, 71. *Mem:* AAAS; Am Soc Neuroradiol (pres, 68); Am Roentgen Ray Soc (pres-elect, 63, pres, 64); fel Am Col Radiol (vpres, 63-64); fel Am Col Chest Physicians. *Res:* Neuroroentgenology. *Mailing Add:* 1995 W County Rd B St Paul MN 55113

PETERSON, HARRY C(LARENCE), b Greeley, Colo, Feb 23, 31; m 50; c 4. VIBRATION DYNAMICS, VEHICLE CRASHWORTHINESS. *Educ:* Colo State Univ, BSME, 53; Cornell Univ, MS, 56, PhD(eng mech), 59. *Prof Exp:* Instr eng mech, Cornell Univ, 53-55 & 57-59, asst prof, 59-60; asst res scientist, Martin Co, 60-62, chief aeroelasticity res sect, 62-66, mgr aeromech & mat dept, 66-67; prof eng mech, Univ Denver, 67-74; PROF BASIC ENG, COLO SCH MINES, 74- *Concurrent Pos:* Expert witness in motorcycle accident litigation, 72-; sr res engr, Res Inst, Univ Denver, 74-78. *Mem:* Am Inst Aeronaut & Astronaut; Am Soc Eng Educ; Sigma Xi; NY Acad Sci; AAAS. *Res:* Safety systems for mine conveyances; dynamics of motorcycle crashes, rider injuries and protection; nonstationary random vibrations; educational materials and apparatus for undergraduate education in engineering mechanics and mechanical design. *Mailing Add:* Dept of Basic Eng Colo Sch of Mines Golden CO 80401

PETERSON, HAZEL AGNES, b Houston, Tex, Apr 7, 16. GEOLOGY. *Educ:* NY Univ, BA, 39; Univ Tex, MA, 42. *Prof Exp:* Sr geologist, Tex Co, 42-44; subsurface geologist, Sun Oil Co, 44-52; supv geologist, Seaboard Oil Co, 52-54; instr, 58-67, asst prof geol, E Tex State Univ, 67-78; CONSULT GEOLOGIST, 78- *Concurrent Pos:* Consult geologist, 54-; grant, Nat Park Serv, 60-61; fac res grant, ETex State Univ, 65-66, & 68. *Mem:* Am Asn Petrol Geologists; Am Asn Petrol Geol; Sigma Xi. *Res:* Pleistocene vertebrates; stratigraphy of northeast Texas; geohydrology; water resources and environmental geology of Texas; petroleum geology of the Southwest; geoscience audio-visual education. *Mailing Add:* 1908 Walnut St Commerce TX 75428

PETERSON, HOWARD BOYD, b Redmond, Utah, Oct 10, 12; m 40; c 3. SOIL CHEMISTRY. *Educ:* Brigham Young Univ, BS, 35, AM, 37; Univ Nebr, PhD(soils), 40. *Prof Exp:* From instr to assoc prof agron, 40-50, chmn dept, 59-64, head dept agr & irrig eng, 71-73, prof agron, 50-80, EMER PROF AGR & IRREGATION ENG, UTAH STATE UNIV, 80- *Mem:* AAAS; Am Soc Agron; Soil Sci Soc Am. *Res:* Irrigation; water quality. *Mailing Add:* Dept of Agr & Irrig Eng Utah State Univ Logan UT 84321

PETERSON, HOWARD C(ARL), b Escanaba, Mich, Jan 13, 24; m 46; c 3. CHEMICAL ENGINEERING. *Educ:* Univ Mich, BSE, 49; Iowa State Univ, MS, 50, PhD(chem eng), 53. *Prof Exp:* Asst, Inst Atomic Res, Iowa State Univ, 49-50 & 51-53, res assoc, 50-51; res engr, M W Kellogg Co Div, Pullman, Inc, 53-59, supvr chem eng res, 59-63; eng assoc, Air Reduction Co, 63-64; tech asst to mgr res, NJ Zinc Co, 64-67, chief metall develop, 67-68, asst gen mgr develop, 68-70, mgr develop, 70-74; dir res & develop, 74-81, MGR SPECIAL PROJS, GULF & WESTERN NATURAL RESOURCES GROUP, 81- *Mem:* Am Chem Soc; Am Inst Chem Engrs; Am Inst Mining, Metall & Petrol Engrs; NY Acad Sci. *Res:* Process develop and analysis; pilot plant operations; computer applications; ferrous and non-ferrous metallurgy; petroleum, petrochemical and mineralogical processing. *Mailing Add:* Gulf & Western Nat Resources Br Foot of Water St Gloucester City NJ 08030

PETERSON, IDELLE M(ARIETTA), b Forest City, Iowa, Feb 25, 38; m 60; c 3. CHEMICAL ENGINEERING. *Educ:* Iowa State Univ, BS, 60, MS, 64, PhD(chem eng), 68. *Prof Exp:* Res scientist surface chem, McDonnell-Douglas Res, 68-69; engr aeronaut struct & mat, US Army Aviation Systs Command, 69-77, AEROSPACE ENGR, COMPUT AIDED DESIGN, US ARMY AVIATION RES & DEVELOP COMMAND, 77- *Mem:* Am Helicopter Soc. *Res:* Development of computer aided design software. *Mailing Add:* US Army Aviation Res & Develop Command 4300 Goodfellow Blvd St Louis MO 63120

PETERSON, IRVIN LESLIE, b Earlimart, Calif, Feb 25, 26; m 51; c 3. VETERINARY MEDICINE, POULTRY SCIENCE. *Educ:* Univ Calif, Davis, BS, 51, DVM, 63. *Prof Exp:* Partner, Kerners' Turkey Farms & Hatchery, Calif, 51-54; farm adv, Agr Exten Serv, Univ Calif, 54-59; poultry pathologist, Kimber Poultry Breeding Farm Inc, 63-68; mgr poultry & livestock serv, Western Farmers Asn, 68-71; vet coordr Nat Poultry Improv Plan, 71-77, Agr Res Serv, 71-77, CHIEF STAFF VET, ANIMAL & PLANT INSPECTION SERV, USDA, 77- *Mem:* Am Asn Avian Path; Am Vet Med Asn; Poultry Sci Asn; World Poultry Sci Asn; World Vet Poultry Asn. *Res:* Poultry egg transmitted and hatchery disseminated diseases; coordination of disease control measures through state agencies. *Mailing Add:* Fed Ctr Bldg Rm 712 Hyattsville MD 20782

PETERSON, JACK EDWIN, b Bremerton, Wash, Feb 7, 28; m 52; c 2. INDUSTRIAL HYGIENE. *Educ:* Wash State Univ, hons BS, 51; Univ Mich, MS, 52, PhD(indust health), 68. *Prof Exp:* Chem engr, Spec Assignments Prog, Dow Chem Co, Mich, 52-53, environ res engr, Biochem Res Lab, 53-65; asst prof civil eng, 68-73, ASSOC PROF CIVIL ENG, MARQUETTE UNIV, 73-; PROF OCCUP & ENVIRON MED, SCH PUB HEALTH, UNIV ILL, 77-; PROF PREVENTIVE MED, MED COL WIS, 80- *Concurrent Pos:* Asst prof environ health eng, Med Col Wis, 68-73; indust hyg consult, Peterson Assocs, 75- *Honors & Awards:* Authorship Award, Am Indust Hyg Asn, 62 & 70. *Mem:* Am Indust Hyg Asn; NY Acad Sci; Sigma Xi; Am Acad Indust Hyg. *Res:* Human biothermal stress-strain; inhalation exposure integration; effects of carbon monoxide on human performance; absorption-excretion of carbon monoxide and organic solvents by man; air pollution; industrial hygiene and toxicology. *Mailing Add:* Peterson Assocs 660 Forest Grove Circle Brookfield WI 53005

PETERSON, JACK KENNETH, b Chicago, Ill, Dec 3, 32; m 56; c 3. POLYMER CHEMISTRY, PHYSICAL CHEMISTRY. *Educ:* Purdue Univ, BS, 54; Ohio State Univ, PhD(phys chem), 61. *Prof Exp:* Sr res chemist, Mobil Chem Co, 61-63, sect leader, 63-68; mgr hot melts develop, Stein Hall & Co, Inc, 68-71; mgr tech corrd, USS Chem, 71-78; MGR ENVIRON CONTROL, US STEEL CORP, 78- *Concurrent Pos:* Res consult, USS Chem, 75-78. *Mem:* Am Chem Soc. *Res:* Solution, viscoelastic and solid state properties of polymers. *Mailing Add:* 600 Grant St Rm 1876 US Steel Corp Pittsburgh PA 15230

PETERSON, JACK MILTON, b Portland, Ore, Apr 25, 20; m 46; c 3. NUCLEAR PHYSICS. *Educ:* Harvard Univ, SB, 42; Univ Calif, PhD(physics), 50. *Prof Exp:* Res assoc & ed, Microwave Techniques, Radiation Lab, Mass Inst Technol, 42-45; from tech investr to asst dir vacuum tube develop comt, Columbia Univ, 43-46; physicist, 50-52, head nuclear physics div, Livermore, 52-61, physicist, B-div, 61-64, physicist, 64-80, SR SCIENTIST ADVAN ACCELERATOR DESIGN GROUP, LAWRENCE BERKELEY LAB, UNIV CALIF, BERKELEY, 80- *Concurrent Pos:* Lectr, Univ Calif, Berkeley, 50-53; Fulbright fel, Bohr Inst Theoret Physics, Copenhagen, 60-61; leader beam-transport & injection system Positron-Electron Proj, Stanford Linear Accelerator Ctr, 74-80. *Mem:* Am Phys Soc; mem, Nuclear Cross Sect Adv Group, AEC. *Res:* Design of microwave components; high energy neutron cross sections; excitation curves for high energy deuteron and alpha particle reactions; meson production by x-rays; x-ray fluorescence; design and operation of betatrons, cyclotrons, synchrotrons, storage rings and beam-transport systems; collective acceleration. *Mailing Add:* Lawrence Radiation Lab Univ of Calif Berkeley CA 94720

PETERSON, JAMES ALGERT, b Berrien Co, Mich, Apr 17, 15; m 44; c 3. GEOLOGY. *Educ:* St Louis Univ, BS, 48; Univ Minn, MS, 49, PhD(geol), 52. *Prof Exp:* Geologist paleont, US Geol Surv, 48-50, 75-78; instr geol, State Col Wash, 51; geologist, Shell Oil Co, 52-57, from div stratigrapher to sr geologist, 57-65; assoc prof, 65-67, PROF GEOL, UNIV MONT, 67-; GEOLOGIST, US GEOL SURV, 75- *Mem:* Fel AAAS; fel Geol Soc Am; fel Explorers Club; Soc Econ Paleont & Mineral; Am Asn Petrol Geol. *Res:* Jurassic, Cretaceous and upper Paleozoic stratigraphy; paleontology and geologic history; petroleum geology; ground water resources; carbonate petrology; world energy resources. *Mailing Add:* Dept of Geol Univ of Mont Missoula MT 59801

PETERSON, JAMES DOUGLAS, b St Louis, Mo, May 19, 48; m 74. ENGINEERING. *Educ:* Univ Chicago, BA, 71; PhD(biochem), 74. *Prof Exp:* Res biol chemist, Univ Calif, Los Angeles, 74-75; fel chem, Univ Del, 75-77; res assoc biochem, Univ Kans Med Ctr, Kansas City, 77-79; res chemist, Vet Admin Med Ctr, 78-79; MEM TECH STAFF, BELL LABS, NAPERVILLE, ILL, 79- *Concurrent Pos:* Adj asst prof, Univ Kans Med Ctr, 77-79; fel, Nat Inst Gen Med Sci, 76-77. *Mem:* Am Chem Soc. *Res:* Testing and validation of telephone switching software; planning of new network features. *Mailing Add:* Bell Labs Naperville-Wheaton Rd Naperville IL 60566

PETERSON, JAMES L, aquatic biology, limnology, see previous edition

PETERSON, JAMES LOWELL, b Weston, WVa, Feb 15, 42; m 64; c 2. INORGANIC CHEMISTRY. *Educ:* WVa Wesleyan Col, BA, 64; WVa Univ, MS, 66; Ohio State Univ, PhD(inorg chem), 73. *Prof Exp:* Instr chem, 66-70, from asst prof to assoc prof, 73-77, DEAN ACAD AFFAIRS, GLENVILLE STATE COL, 77- *Mem:* Am Chem Soc. *Mailing Add:* Off of Dean of Acad Affairs Glenville State Col Glenville WV 26351

PETERSON, JAMES MACON, b Elizabethtown, NC, Apr 8, 37; m 66; c 3. POLYMER SCIENCE, MATERIALS SCIENCE. *Educ:* Wake Forest Univ, BS, 58; Calif Inst Technol, PhD(chem), 63. *Prof Exp:* Res chemist, Chemstrand Res Ctr, 63-69; RES SCIENTIST, BOEING COMMERCIAL AIRPLANE CO, 69- *Mem:* Am Chem Soc; Am Phys Soc; Sigma Xi. *Res:* Polymer structure; materials flammability; chemical physics of fire. *Mailing Add:* Boeing Commercial Airplane Co Seattle WA 98124

PETERSON, JAMES OLIVER, b St Louis, Mo, Feb 26, 37; m 68; c 2. ORGANIC CHEMISTRY, CHEMISTRY OF SEMICONDUCTOR DEVICES. *Educ:* Northwestern Univ, BA, 59; State Univ NY Buffalo, PhD(org chem), 65. *Prof Exp:* Res Chemist, Gen Chem Div, Allied Chem Corp, 64-68, res chemist, Specialty Chem Div, 69-71, sr res chemist, Specialty Chem Div, 71-76, suprv, Prog Res, Thermoset Prods Lab, Specialty Chem Div, 76-79; MGR, PROD RES, PLASKON PROD, INC, 79- *Mem:* Am Chem Soc; Sigma Xi; Inst Elec & Electronics Engrs. *Res:* Development of encapsulation products for electronic semiconductor devices; development of epoxy, urea, melamine and phenolic molding compounds; synthesis of new and industrial organic compounds; fluorination of organic compounds; reaction of fluorinated compounds; preparation of fluorocarbon polymers. *Mailing Add:* Plaskon Prod Inc 2829 Glendale Ave Toledo OH 43614

PETERSON, JAMES RAY, b Hollywood, Calif, June 2, 24; m 52; c 4. ATOMIC PHYSICS. *Educ:* Univ Calif, Los Angeles, AB, 48; Univ Calif, PhD, 56. *Prof Exp:* Physicist, Radiation Lab, Univ Calif, 50-56; physicist, 56-75, ASSOC DIR MOLECULAR PHYSICS CTR, SRI INT, 75- *Concurrent Pos:* Vis assoc prof, Univ Wash, 66-67; vis fel, Joint Inst for Lab Astrophysics, Univ Colo, 74-75. *Mem:* Fel Am Phys Soc; Am Geophys Union; Am Asn Physics Teachers; AAAS. *Res:* Low energy atomic and molecular collisions and photon interactions. *Mailing Add:* Molecular Physics Ctr Stanford Res Inst Menlo Park CA 94025

PETERSON, JAMES ROBERT, b Chisago City, Minn, May 17, 34; m 60; c 3. SOIL FERTILITY. *Educ:* Calif State Polytech Col, BS, 61; Univ Minn, MS, 63, PhD(soil sci), 69. *Prof Exp:* Instr agron, Va Polytech Inst, 63-65; SOIL SCIENTIST III, METROP SANIT DIST GREATER CHICAGO, 69- *Concurrent Pos:* Mem Adv Comt, US Forest Serv, 71-76; Task Force on Strip Mine Reclamation, 72-73; EPA Task Force Agr Non-Point Source Pollution, 76-78. *Mem:* Am Soc Agron; Soil Sci Soc Am; Int Soc Soil Sci; Coun Agr Sci & Technol; Soc Environ Geochem & Health. *Res:* Wastewater sludge utilization for crop fertilization and land reclamation. *Mailing Add:* Res & Develop Dept Metro Sanit Dist Greater Chicago Cicero IL 60650

PETERSON, JANET BROOKS, b Brooklyn, NY, Mar 15, 24. ORGANIC CHEMISTRY. *Educ:* Univ Mich, BS, 45; Univ Ill, MA, 48, PhD(chem), 51. *Prof Exp:* Asst chem, Johns Hopkins Univ, 45-46 & Univ Ill, 46-49; admin & tech asst, Gen Aniline & Film Corp, 50-52; res chemist, Geigy Chem Corp, 52-70, sr res chemist, 70-79, STAFF SCIENTIST, CIBA-GEIGY CORP, 79- *Mem:* Am Chem Soc; fel Am Inst Chem. *Res:* Synthetic organic chemistry, especially heterocyclic nitrogen compounds; amino acids and derivatives; hindered phenol antioxidants. *Mailing Add:* Plastics & Additives Res Ciba-Geigy Corp Ardsley NY 10502

PETERSON, JANET SYLVIA, b McMinnville, Tenn. APPLIED MATHEMATICS. *Educ:* Calif State Univ, Los Angeles, BS, 73; Univ Tenn, MS, 77, PhD(math), 80. *Prof Exp:* Analyst, Jet Propulsion Lab, Calif Inst Technol, 73-75; ASST PROF MATH, UNIV PITTSBURGH, 81- *Concurrent Pos:* Vis scientist, Inst Comput Appln Sci & Eng, Langley Res Ctr, NASA, 81- *Mem:* Soc Indust & Appl Math; Asn Women Math. *Res:* Numerical solution of partial differential equations from both a theoretical and computational stand point; finite element and finite difference methods. *Mailing Add:* 215 MIB Univ Pittsburgh Pittsburgh PA 15261

PETERSON, JOHN BOOTH, b Salem, Ore, July 18, 05; m 30; c 2. AGRONOMY. *Educ:* Ore State Col, BS, 28; Iowa State Col, MS, 29, PhD(soil fertil), 36. *Prof Exp:* From instr to assoc prof agron, 29-46, prof soils, 46-48, head dept agron, 48-71, PROF AGRON, PURDUE UNIV, LAFAYETTE, 48-, ASSOC DIR, LAB APPLN REMOTE SENSING, PURDUE/NASA, 71- *Concurrent Pos:* Nat Res Coun fel, Univ Calif, 39-40; chmn, Nat Soil & Fertilizer Res Comt, 51-53; guest prof, Univ Ariz, 66. Consult, Latin Am Fel Prog, Rockefeller Found, 61-62, Orgn Nat Agr Res Prog, Greek Govt, 63, Ford Found Agr Prog for Arg, 65, consult soil erosion, Food & Agr Orgn, Arg, 70 & consult, Int Fertilizer Develop Ctr, 75- *Honors & Awards:* Stevenson Award, Am Soc Agron, 48; Agron Serv Award, Am Soc Agron, 78. *Mem:* Fel AAAS; fel Am Soc Agron (pres, 58-59); Soil Sci Soc Am; Latin Am Plant Sci Asn. *Res:* Soil microscopy, fertility, conservation, genesis, morphology, classification and chemistry; administration of research and teaching; remote sensing of natural resources; land use. *Mailing Add:* Lab Appln Remote Sensing Purdue Univ 1220 Potter Dr West Lafayette IN 47906

PETERSON, JOHN CARL, b US. FLORICULTURE, PLANT PHYSIOLOGY. *Educ:* Univ RI, BS, 74; Rutgers Univ, PhD(hort), 78. *Prof Exp:* Res asst hort, Rutgers Univ, 74-78; ASST PROF & EXTEN FLORICULTURIST, OHIO STATE UNIV, 78- *Mem:* Am Soc Hort Sci. *Res:* Applied physiology and production problems relating to growth and development of floral crops. *Mailing Add:* Dept of Hort 2001 Fyffe Ct Columbus OH 43210

PETERSON, JOHN CYRIL, pediatrics, deceased

PETERSON, JOHN EDWARD, JR, b Myrtle, Ill, June 19, 21; m 45; c 2. MYCOLOGY, MICROBIOLOGY. *Educ:* Northern Ill Univ, BEd, 42; Mich State Univ, MS, 52, PhD(bot), 57. *Prof Exp:* Instr biol, Jackson Jr Col, 46-50; from instr to prof bot, Univ Mo, Columbia, 53-71; DEAN SCH LIB ARTS & SCI, EMPORIA KANS STATE COL, 71- *Mem:* AAAS; Mycol Soc Am; Bot Soc Am; Soc Indust Microbiol; Am Soc Microbiol. *Res:* Myxobacteria; genera Fusarium and Micromonospora; microflora of the bark of living trees. *Mailing Add:* Off of the Dean Sch Lib Arts & Sci Emporia Kans State Col Emporia KS 66801

PETERSON, JOHN ERIC, b Norwalk, Ohio, Oct 26, 14; m 38; c 2. INTERNAL MEDICINE. *Educ:* Col Med Evangelists, MD, 39; Am Bd Internal Med, dipl, 47. *Prof Exp:* Resident med, Henry Ford Hosp, Detroit, Mich, 39-42; from instr to assoc prof, 42-54, PROF MED & CHMN DEPT & ASSOC DEAN, SCH MED, LOMA LINDA UNIV, 54- *Concurrent Pos:* Res assoc, Harvard Med Sch, 60-61. *Mem:* AMA; Am Col Physicians; Am Diabetes Asn. *Res:* Atheromatous disease; fat, lipoprotein metabolism. *Mailing Add:* Sch Med Loma Linda Univ Loma Linda CA 92354

PETERSON, JOHN IVAN, b Syracuse, NY, Mar 29, 28; m 50; c 5. ANALYTICAL CHEMISTRY. *Educ:* Syracuse Univ, BA, 50, PhD(anal chem), 54. *Prof Exp:* Sr scientist, Chem Div, Sylvania Elec Prod, Inc, 54-55; sr scientist, Res Div, Jones & Laughlin Steel Corp, 55-58; sr engr, Textile Fibers Div, E I du Pont de Nemours & Co, 58-59; group leader anal develop, Melpar, Inc, 59-60; supvr chem br, Chem Warfare Sect, 60, supvr anal br, Res Div, 60-62; mgr chem div, Woodard Res Corp, 62-64; mgr lab, Clin Serv Div, Bionctics Res Labs, Inc, 64-65; STAFF CHEMIST, BIOMED ENG BR, NIH, 65- *Mem:* Instr Soc Am; Am Chem Soc. *Res:* Instrumental methods of analysis and instrument development; chromatography; clinical chemistry; radiotracer analysis; electrochemistry; biochemical analysis. *Mailing Add:* Biomed Eng & Instrumentation Br NIH Rm 3W13 Bldg 13 Bethesda MD 20014

PETERSON, JOHN M, b Fillmore, Utah, Feb 14, 38; m 60; c 2. MATHEMATICS. *Educ:* Utah State Univ, BS, 62, MS, 64, EdD, 65. *Prof Exp:* Teacher pub schs, Utah, 61-63; from asst prof to assoc prof, 65-74, PROF MATH, BRIGHAM YOUNG UNIV, 74- *Res:* Efficiency of different methods of teaching mathematics at various academic levels. *Mailing Add:* Dept of Math Brigham Young Univ Provo UT 84601

PETERSON, JOHNNY WAYNE, b Gilmer, Tex, Aug 30, 46; m 65; c 2. MICROBIOLOGY. *Educ:* Univ Tex, Arlington, BS, 67; NTex State Univ, MS, 69; Univ Tex Southwestern Med Sch, PhD(microbiol), 72. *Prof Exp:* ASSOC PROF MICROBIOL, UNIV TEX MED BR GALVESTON, 77- *Concurrent Pos:* NIH contract, Univ Tex Med Br Galveston; Found for Microbiol lectr, 78-79. *Mem:* Am Soc Microbiol. *Res:* Pathogenic mechanisms of enteric infections and bacterial immunology; salmonellas; cholera. *Mailing Add:* Dept of Microbiol Univ of Tex Med Br Galveston TX 77550

PETERSON, JOSEPH LOUIS, b Pleasant Grove, Utah, May 16, 29; m 53; c 2. PLANT PATHOLOGY, MYCOLOGY. *Educ:* Utah State Univ, BS, 55, MS, 57; Univ Wis, PhD(plant path), 59. *Prof Exp:* Asst plant path, Utah State Univ, 53-56; agr aide hort crops res br, USDA, 56-57; asst prof plant path & res specialist, 59-63, assoc prof, 63-71, PROF PLANT PATH, RUTGERS UNIV, NEW BRUNSWICK, 71- *Mem:* Am Phytopath Soc; Mycol Soc Am. *Res:* Diseases of ornamental crops. *Mailing Add:* Dept of Plant Path Cook Col Rutgers Univ New Brunswick NJ 08903

PETERSON, JOSEPH RICHARD, b Wilmington, Del, Sept 16, 42; m 68; c 2. PHYSICAL INORGANIC CHEMISTRY, MICROCHEMISTRY. *Educ:* Swarthmore Col, AB, 64; Univ Calif, Berkeley, PhD(chem), 67. *Prof Exp:* Res asst, Lawrence Radiation Lab, Univ Calif, 64-67; asst prof, 67-73, assoc prof, 73-79, PROF CHEM, UNIV TENN, KNOXVILL3, 79- *Concurrent Pos:* Consult, Transuranium Res Lab, Oak Ridge Nat Lab, 67-; NATO fel nuclear chem, Univ Liege, 69-70; consult, Lawrence Livermore Lab, Univ Calif, 73-79; guest scientist, Inst Haisse Chemie, Kernforschgszentrum, Karlsruhe, 81-82. *Mem:* Am Chem Soc; Am Nuclear Soc; Sigma Xi. *Res:* Determination, correlation, and interpretation of the basic physical and chemical properties of the transuranium elements and their compounds. *Mailing Add:* Dept of Chem Univ of Tenn Knoxville TN 37996

PETERSON, JULIAN ARNOLD, b Detroit, Mich, Oct 3, 39; m 64. BIOCHEMISTRY. *Educ:* Wittenberg Univ, BS, 61; Univ Mich, Ann Arbor, MS, 65, PhD(biochem), 67. *Prof Exp:* Teaching asst org chem, Wittenberg Univ, 61-62; asst prof, 68-72, assoc prof biochem, 72-79, PROF BIOCHEM & MED COMPUT SCI, UNIV TEX HEALTH SCI CTR, DALLAS, 79- *Concurrent Pos:* NIH fel, Johnson Res Found, Univ Pa, 67-68; Nat Inst Arthritis & Metab Dis res grant, Univ Tex Health Sci Ctr, Dallas, 68-71; Robert A Welch Res Found res grant, 69- & Nat Inst Gen Med Sci res grant, 71-; mem, Phys Biochem Study Sect, NIH, 80- *Mem:* Am Soc Biol Chemists; AAAS; Am Chem Soc; Am Soc Pharmacol Exp Therapeut. *Res:* Electron transport and the biological activation of molecular oxygen for hydroxylation reactions; control of microbial reactions involving molecular oxygen; computer based education. *Mailing Add:* Dept of Biochem Univ of Tex Health Sci Ctr Dallas TX 75235

PETERSON, KENDALL ROBERT, b Quincy, Mass, Apr 23, 29; m 56; c 3. ATMOSPHERIC PHYSICS. *Educ:* Mass Inst Technol, BS, 51; Univ Chicago, MS, 54. *Prof Exp:* Res asst meteorol, Univ Chicago, 53-54; Mass Inst Technol, 55; res meteorologist, Air Resources Lab, Nat Oceanic & Atmospheric Admin, Md, 55-69, ATMOSPHERIC PHYSICIST, G-DIV, LAWRENCE LIVERMORE NAT LAB, 69- *Mem:* Am Geophys Union; Am Meteorol Soc; Royal Meteorol Soc. *Res:* Environmental assessments of dose to man from the atmospheric transport, diffusion, and deposition of radioactivity released by the nuclear industry. *Mailing Add:* G-Div Lawrence Livermore Nat Lab PO Box 808 Livermore CA 94550

PETERSON, KENNETH C(ARL), b Superior, Wis, Nov 2, 21; m 65; c 2. CHEMICAL ENGINEERING. *Educ:* Univ Wis, BS & MS, 47. *Prof Exp:* Chem engr, Res Dept, Standard Oil Co, Ind, 47-53, group leader, 53-59, sect leader, 59-65; div dir, Res & Develop Dept, Amoco Chem Corp, 65-69, mgr polymers & plastics res & develop, 69-76, mgr polymer properties & process design, 76-81; RETIRED. *Mem:* AAAS; Am Inst Chem Engrs; Am Chem Soc; Soc Plastics Engrs; Am Mgt Asn. *Res:* Petrochemicals. *Mailing Add:* 1033 Anne Rd Naperville IL 60540

PETERSON, LANCE GEORGE, b Duluth Minn, Jan 1, 40; m 63; c 3. INSECT PHYSIOLOGY, TOXICOLOGY. *Educ:* Univ Minn, BA, 62; Univ Ill, PhD(insect physiol & toxicol), 67. *Prof Exp:* sr entomologist, Eli Lilly & Co, 67-73, plant sci rep, 73-76, tech adv to agr mkt, 76-77; AREA RES ADMINR, LILLY INT, 77- *Mem:* Entom Soc Am; Am Soc Zool; Sigma Xi. *Res:* Mechanisms of control of insects that are economically important pests of agriculture; developing agricultural chemicals for international agricultural markets, including insecticides, herbicides and fungicides. *Mailing Add:* Eli Lilly & Co PO Box 708 Greenfield IN 46140

PETERSON, LARRY JAMES, b Winfield, Kans, Apr 23, 42; m 69; c 2. ORAL SURGERY. *Educ:* Univ Kans, BS, 64; Univ Mo-Kansas City, DDS, 68; Georgetown Univ, MS, 71. *Prof Exp:* From asst prof to assoc prof oral surg, Med Col Ga, 71-75; from assoc prof to prof oral surg, 75-81, PROF MAXILLOFACIAL SURG, HEALTH CTR, UNIV CONN, 81- *Concurrent Pos:* Adj prof, Col Eng, Clemson Univ, 74. *Mem:* Am Am Asn Oral & Maxillofacial Surgeons; Am Dent Asn; Int Asn Dent Res; Asn Acad Surgeons; Am Asn Dent Schs. *Res:* Use of alloplastic implant materials in dentistry and oral surgery; use of prophylactic antibiotics in major and surgical procedures; wound healing and revascularization following bone graft ridge augmentation. *Mailing Add:* Dept of Oral & Maxillofacial Surg Univ of Conn Health Ctr Farmington CT 06032

PETERSON, LAUREN MICHAEL, b Minneapolis, Minn, June 11, 43; m 68; c 3. OPTICAL PHYSICS, QUANTUM ELECTRONICS. *Educ:* Univ Minn, BPhys, 66; Pa State Univ, MS, 68, PhD(physics), 72. *Prof Exp:* RES PHYSICIST OPTICAL PHYSICS, ENVIRON RES INST MICH, 72- *Mem:* Optical Soc Am. *Res:* Nonlinear optics, especially stimulated light scattering, self induced transparency; electro- and acousto- optic modulation of infrared lasers; remote sensing; molecular spectroscopy. *Mailing Add:* 2160 Blaney Ann Arbor MI 48103

PETERSON, LAURENCE E, b Grantsburg, Wis, July 26, 31; m 56; c 4. HIGH ENERGY ASTROPHYSICS. *Educ:* Univ Minn, Minneapolis, BS, 54, PhD(physics), 60. *Prof Exp:* Res assoc physics, Univ Minn, Minneapolis, 60-62; res physicist, 62-63, from asst prof to assoc prof, 63-71, PROF PHYSICS, UNIV CALIF, SAN DIEGO, 71- *Concurrent Pos:* Mem physics subcomt, NASA Space Sci Steering Comt, 64-; NSF fel, 58-59; Guggenheim fel, 73-74. *Honors & Awards:* AIAA Space Sci Award & NASA Except Sci Achievement Award, 78. *Mem:* AAAS; Am Geophys Union; Am Phys Soc; Am Astron Soc. *Res:* Space astronomy; galactic and solar cosmic rays; solar gamma and x-rays; x-ray and gamma ray astronomy and high energy astrophysics; related balloon and satellite instrumentation. *Mailing Add:* Dept of Physics Univ of Calif at San Diego La Jolla CA 92093

PETERSON, LENNART RUDOLPH, b Kearny, NJ, Sept 27, 36; m 56; c 3. ATMOSPHERIC PHYSICS, ATOMIC PHYSICS. *Educ:* NC State Univ, BS, 58; Mass Inst Technol, SM, 63, PhD(theoret nuclear physics), 66. *Prof Exp:* Fel atmospheric physics, 66-67, interim asst prof physics & phys sci, 67-68, asst prof, 68-72, ASSOC PROF PHYSICS & PHYS SCI, UNIV FLA, 72- *Mem:* Am Phys Soc; Am Geophys Union. *Res:* Nuclear structure and reaction theory; electron impact cross sections and energy degradation as well as aurora and airglow. *Mailing Add:* Dept of Phys Sci Univ of Fla Gainesville FL 32611

PETERSON, LEROY ERIC, b Anaconda, Mont, July 22, 17; m 41; c 3. PHYSICS. *Educ:* Oberlin Col, AB, 38; Univ Notre Dame, MS, 40, PhD(physics), 42. *Prof Exp:* Instr physics, Univ Notre Dame, 42-45; physics sect leader, Am Viscose Corp, 46-55; res physicist, Polychem Dept, E I du Pont de Nemours & Co, 55-60, sr res physicist, Textile Fibers Dept, 60-61; assoc prof physics, Drexel Inst Technol, 61-67; ASSOC PROF PHYSICS, VILLANOVA UNIV, 67- *Concurrent Pos:* Res physicist, Manhattan Proj, Univ Notre Dame, 43-45; res physicist, SAM Labs, Carbide & Carbon Chem Corp, 45-46. *Mem:* AAAS; Am Phys Soc; Am Asn Physics Teachers. *Res:* Thermodynamics of natural and synthetic rubber; physical behavior of cellulosic and synthetic fibers; equation of state of some synthetic rubbers; optical and physical properties of cellulose and rayon; mechanical properties of thermoplastics; test development and physical testing of plastics; administration and teaching of physics. *Mailing Add:* Dept of Physics Villanova Univ Villanova PA 19085

PETERSON, LOUIS K, inorganic chemistry, see previous edition

PETERSON, LOWELL E, b Keokuk, Iowa, Apr 20, 26; m 48; c 5. PHYSICAL CHEMISTRY. *Educ:* Univ Minn, BS, 50, PhD, 54. *Prof Exp:* Proj leader, Cent Res Labs, Gen Mills, Inc, 54-60, res assoc, 60-64, head chem res dept, 64-68, mgr chem res, Chem Div, 68, dir appl res, Gen Mills Chem Inc, 68-74; DIR BASIC DEVELOP, HENKEL CORP, 75- *Mem:* Am Chem Soc. *Res:* Instrumental methods of organic analysis; resins; water soluble polymers. *Mailing Add:* Gen Mills Chem Inc 2010 E Hennepin Ave Minneapolis MN 55413

PETERSON, LYSLE HENRY, b Minneapolis, Minn, Jan 21, 21; m 43; c 4. PHYSIOLOGY, CARDIOVASCULAR REHABILITATION. *Educ:* Univ Minn, BA, 43; Univ Pa, MD, 50. *Prof Exp:* Asst physiol chem, Med Sch, Univ Minn, 42-43; from asst to instr physiol, Univ Pa, 46-51, intern, Hosp, 51-52, from asst prof to assoc prof physiol & surg res, 52-60, from vpres to pres, Univ City Sci Ctr, 65-71, prof physiol, 60-75, dir, Bockus Res Inst, 61-75, chmn med bd, Grad Hosp, 69-75; vpres acad affairs, 75-77, PROF PHYSIOL,

UNIV TEX HEALTH SCI CTR, HOUSTON, 75-; DIR HOUSTON CARDIOVASC REHAB CTR, 78- *Concurrent Pos:* Estab investr, Am Heart Asn, 52-56; mem sci adv bd, US Air Force, 61-77, chmn aerospace biosci panel, 70-77, consult, US Navy, NIH, Nat Acad Sci & Inst Defense Anal. *Honors & Awards:* Bordon Res Prize; Bell Res Prize; John Clark Res Award; Am Physiol Soc Award. *Mem:* Fel AAAS; Am Physiol Soc; Am Heart Asn (vpres, 65-68); fel Am Col Cardiol; Am Soc Clin Invest. *Res:* Control and regulation of circulatory system in health and disease; systems analysis and computer applications to biological systems. *Mailing Add:* 6418 Fannin Houston TX 77030

PETERSON, MALCOLM LEE, b Seattle, Wash, Nov 18, 27; c 1. COMMUNITY MEDICINE. *Educ:* Stanford Univ, BS, 50; Univ Wash, MD, 54; Rockefeller Inst, PhD, 60. *Prof Exp:* Intern, Philadelphia Gen Hosp, Pa, 54-55; asst resident, Barnes Hosp, 55-56; asst physician, Rockefeller Inst Hosp, 56-60; from asst prof to assoc prof med, Sch Med, Washington Univ, 61-69, dir div gastroenterol, 61-68; chief med serv, St Louis City Hosp, 68-69; assoc prof med & health care orgn, Johns Hopkins Univ, 69-78, Dean Sch Health Serv, 72-78; VIS RES SCIENTIST, HEALTH CARE STUDY CTR, BATTELLE HUMAN AFFAIRS RES CTR, 78-; ASSOC PROF MED & HEALTH SERV, UNIV WASH, 79-, DIR, DIV COMMUNITY MED, 80- *Concurrent Pos:* NIH trainee, NY Hosp, 60-61; vis fel gastroenterology, Cent Middlesex Hosp, London, 61; assoc, Div Health Care Res, Sch Med, Univ Wash, 68-69, sr fel, Ctr Study Natural Systs, Univ, 68-69; dir health serv res & develop ctr, Johns Hopkins Univ, 69-73; chmn, Joint Rev Comt Accreditation Progs Educ Assts Primary Care Physician, 72-75; vis scientist, Dept Med, Univ Wash, 78-; mem, Adv Comt, Robert Wood Johnson Found, 76- *Mem:* Am Col Physicians; Am Gastroenterol Soc; Am Pub Health Asn. *Res:* Health management; education for health professions; organization of health services; health care delivery. *Mailing Add:* 806 W Crockett St Seattle WA 98119

PETERSON, MAURICE LEWELLEN, b Lyons, Nebr, Dec 30, 13; m 38; c 3. AGRONOMY. *Educ:* Univ Nebr, BS, 38; Kans State Col, MS, 40; Iowa State Col, PhD(agron), 46. *Prof Exp:* Asst, Div Forage Crops & Dis, USDA, Kans State Col, 38-40; jr agronomist, S Great Plains Field Sta, USDA, Okla, 40-42, asst agronomist, 42-43; res assoc agron, Iowa State Col, 43-46, res asst prof, 46-48; from asst prof to assoc prof agron, 48-67, chmn dept, 52-59, dir agr exp sta, 62-65, dean col agr, 63-67, PROF AGRON, UNIV CALIF, DAVIS, 67- *Concurrent Pos:* Fulbright adv res scholar, Welsh Plant Breeding Sta, Aberystwyth, Wales, 56-57; consult, State Exp Stas Div, Agr Res Serv, USDA, 58- *Mem:* Crop Sci Soc Am (pres, 59); Am Soc Agron; Am Soc Plant Physiol. *Res:* Physiology of rice. *Mailing Add:* Dept of Agron Univ of Calif Davis CA 95616

PETERSON, MELBERT EUGENE, b Moline, Ill, July 30, 30. ORGANIC CHEMISTRY. *Educ:* Augustana Col, Ill, AB, 53; Univ Ill, MS, 55; Okla State Univ, PhD, 67. *Prof Exp:* Res chemist, Morton Chem Co, 56-58; from asst prof to assoc prof, 58-77, PROF CHEM, AUGUSTANA COL, ILL, 77- *Concurrent Pos:* Dir, Sky Ridge Observ, Ill, 58-64. *Mem:* Am Chem Soc. *Res:* Nucleophilic displacement reactions on organophosphorus compounds. *Mailing Add:* Dept of Chem Augustana Col Rock Island IL 61201

PETERSON, MELVIN NORMAN ADOLPH, b Evanston, Ill, May 27, 29; m 58; c 4. MARINE GEOLOGY. *Educ:* Northwestern Univ, BS, 51, MS, 56; Harvard Univ, PhD(geol), 60. *Prof Exp:* Asst res geologist, 60-62, asst prof oceanog, 63-67, chief scientist, 68-70, Drilling Proj, 68-70, prin investr & proj mgr, Deep Sea Drilling Proj, 70-75, prin investr & prog mgr, Int Phase of Ocean Drilling, Deep Sea Drilling Proj, 75-78, ASSOC PROF OCEANOG, SCRIPPS INST OCEANOG, UNIV CALIF, SAN DIEGO, 67- *Concurrent Pos:* NSF res grants, 62-66; Am Chem Soc grant, 64-66; mem adv comt to Secy Com, Marine Petrol & Minerals, 74- *Mem:* AAAS; fel Geol Soc Am. *Res:* Origin of minerals and mineral assemblages in sediments; kinetics of crystallization of low temperature phases; volcanism and hydrothermal emanations in ocean basins; deep sea sedimentary and tectonic processes; deep water drilling and scientific exploration technology; management of international phase of ocean drilling. *Mailing Add:* Deep Sea Drilling Proj Univ of Calif San Diego CA 92093

PETERSON, MILLER HARRELL, b Darlington, SC, Jan 3, 25; m 50; c 3. ELECTROCHEMISTRY, CORROSION. *Educ:* Clemson Univ, BS, 44; Univ NC, MA, 51. *Prof Exp:* Instr chem, Clemson Univ, 46-47; phys chemist, US Naval Ord Lab, 51-54, phys chemist, Naval Res Lab, 54-61, res chemist, 61-63, HEAD MARINE CORROSION SECT, US NAVAL RES LAB, 63- *Mem:* Am Chem Soc; Electrochem Soc; Nat Asn Corrosion Eng; AAAS; Sigma Xi. *Res:* Marine corrosion; stress corrosion cracking; corrosion fatigue; cathodic protection; corrosion in the deep ocean; materials for design of marine structures and ships. *Mailing Add:* Mat Sci & Tech Div (Code 6316) Naval Res Lab Washington DC 20375

PETERSON, NEAL ALFRED, b San Francisco, Calif, Sept 24, 29; m 58; c 2. BIOCHEMISTRY. *Educ:* Univ San Francisco, BA, 52, MA, 54; Stanford Univ, PhD(physiol), 59. *Prof Exp:* Res asst physiol, Stanford Univ, 59-61; USPHS res fel & res asst neurochem, Univ Calif, Berkeley, 61-66; res biochemist, Dept Ment Hyg, 66-73, assoc res biochemist, 73-78, RES BIOCHEMIST, LANGLEY PORTER NEUROPSYCHIAT INST, UNIV CALIF, SAN FRANCISCO, SONOMA STATE HOSP, 78- *Res:* Neurochemistry, including investigation of biochemical processes which take place in nerve endings isolated from the central nervous system. *Mailing Add:* Brain Behav Res Ctr Sonoma State Hosp Eldridge CA 95431

PETERSON, NORMAN CORNELIUS, b Joliet, Ill, May 3, 29; m 55; c 4. PHYSICAL CHEMISTRY. *Educ:* Mass Inst Technol, SB, 51; Iowa State Univ, PhD(chem), 56. *Prof Exp:* Assoc prof phys chem, NDak State Univ, 55-59; res assoc chem, 59-61, vis asst prof, 61-62, from asst prof to assoc prof, 62-72, PROF CHEM, POLYTECH INST NY, 72- *Concurrent Pos:* Vis scientist, US Nat Bur Stand, 70-71, consult, 71- *Mem:* Am Chem Soc; Am Phys Soc. *Res:* Kinetics of inorganic reactions; chemical instrumentation; molecular beam scattering. *Mailing Add:* Dept of Chem Polytech Inst of NY Brooklyn NY 11201

PETERSON, NORMAN L(EE), b Aurora, Ill, Jan 16, 35; m 63. PHYSICAL METALLURGY, CERAMICS SCIENCE & TECHNOLOGY. *Educ:* Mass Inst Technol, BS, 57, MS, 59, ScD(metall), 61. *Prof Exp:* Asst metallurgist, 61-64, assoc metallurgist, 64-66, group leader metal physics, 66-68, assoc dir metall div, 68-77, GROUP LEADER BASIC CERAMICS, ARGONNE NAT LAB, 77- *Concurrent Pos:* NSF fel, Solid State Physics Div, Atomic Energy Res Estab, Harwell, Eng, 64-65; Humboldt sr fel, Stuttgart, Germany, 73; guest prof, Julich, Germany, 77-81 & Tech Univ Denmark, 80. *Mem:* Am Ceramics Soc; fel Am Soc Metals; Am Inst Mining, Metall & Petrol Engrs; fel Am Phys Soc. *Res:* Atomic motion in solids; point defect interactions in solids; isotope effects in diffusion. *Mailing Add:* Mat Sci Div Bldg 212 C206 Argonne Nat Lab Argonne IL 60439

PETERSON, OTIS G, b Galesburg, Ill, Nov 17, 36; m 75; c 5. OPTICS, LASER PHOTOCHEMISTRY. *Educ:* Univ Ill, BS, 58, MS, 60, PhD(solid state physics), 65. *Prof Exp:* Staff mem thin films, Eastman Kodak Co, 65-68, sr staff mem org dye lasers, 69, group leader org dye lasers, 69-73; mem staff, Lawrence Livermore Lab, 73-75; res assoc, Allied Chem Corp, 75-78, mgr optical prod, 78-79; ASSOC GROUP LEADER, APPL PHOTOCHEM DIV, LOS ALAMOS NAT LAB, 79- *Honors & Awards:* Indust Res-100 Award, 71-80. *Mem:* Am Phys Soc; Inst Elec & Electronics Engrs; Optical Soc Am. *Res:* Thermodynamic properties of noble-gas solids; opto-electronic properties of evaporated thin films of II-IV compounds; tunable lasers, including organic dye lasers; laser isotope separation; laser induced chemistry; Alexandrite lasers. *Mailing Add:* Los Alamos Nat Lab MS J564 Los Alamos NM 87545

PETERSON, PAUL CONSTANT, b Kewanee, Ill, Mar 16, 40; m 61; c 2. ACAROLOGY, SYSTEMATICS. *Educ:* Gustavus Adolphus Col, BS, 68; Univ Nebr, PhD(entom), 68. *Prof Exp:* Instr & cur, Entom Div, Nebr State Mus, Univ Nebr, 67-68; from asst prof to assoc prof, 68-76, PROF BIOL, YOUNGSTOWN STATE UNIV, 76- *Mem:* AAAS; Entom Soc Am; Acarol Soc Am; Am Inst Biol Sci. *Res:* Biology, ecology and systematics of mites parasitic on birds; reproductive strategies among analgoid mites. *Mailing Add:* Dept Biol & Sci Youngstown State Univ Youngstown OH 44555

PETERSON, PAUL E, b Denison, Tex, Aug 27, 29. ORGANIC CHEMISTRY. *Educ:* NTex State Col, BS, 51, MS, 52. *Prof Exp:* NSF fel, Calif Inst Technol, 56-58; asst prof chem, Purdue Univ, 58-59; from asst prof to prof chem, St Louis Univ, 59-71; PROF CHEM, UNIV SC, 71- *Mem:* Am Chem Soc; Royal Soc Chem; Swiss Chem Soc. *Res:* Solvents of low nucleophilicity; cyclic halonium ions; kinetics in antimony pentafluoride sulfur dioxide solutions. *Mailing Add:* Dept Chem Univ SC Columbia SC 29208

PETERSON, PAUL W(EBER), b Sioux City, Iowa, Jan 3, 25; m 47; c 3. ENGINEERING MECHANICS. *Educ:* Iowa State Col, BS, 46, MS, 48, PhD(theoret & appl mech), 57. *Prof Exp:* Instr aeronaut eng, theoret & appl mech, Iowa State Col, 46-48, from instr to asst prof theoret & appl mech, 52-57; res engr, Well Survs, Inc, Okla, 48-50; self employed, 50-51; head exp structs, Lockheed Aircraft Corp, Calif, 57-59; sr res scientist, Aeronutronic Systs, Inc, 59-62; head, Solid Mech Dept, Aerospace Corp, 62-63, dir systs develop, 63-64, assoc group dir minuteman weapon syst, 64-65, dir Mark 17 prog, 65-66, sr staff engr, Tech Div, 66; sr staff engr, Sci & Tech Div, TRW Systs, San Bernardino, 66-72; PROF AEROSPACE ENG, ASSOC DEAN ENG & DIR ENG RES INST, IOWA STATE UNIV, 72- *Concurrent Pos:* Lectr, Eng Exten, Univ Calif, Berkeley, 57-59 & Univ Calif, Los Angeles, 60-63; consult, Meredith Pub Co, Rock Island Tool & Mach Co & Gen Filter Co. *Mem:* Am Soc Mech Engrs; Am Soc Eng Educ; Soc Exp Stress Anal; Sigma Xi; Am Inst Aeronaut & Astronaut. *Res:* Theoretical and experimental mechanics, primarily dynamic properties of materials, vibration, thermal stress, strain measurement, impact loading and photo-stress; weapon system development; system management. *Mailing Add:* Iowa State Univ 104 Marston Ames IA 50011

PETERSON, PETER ANDREW, b Bristol, Conn, Mar 17, 25; m 48; c 2. GENETICS. *Educ:* Tufts Col, BS, 47; Univ Ill, PhD(bot), 53. *Prof Exp:* Asst, Dept Genetics, Carnegie Inst, 47-48 & Univ Ill, 49-52; asst geneticist, Univ Calif, 53-56; assoc prof genetics, 56-68, PROF AGRON & GENETICS, IOWA STATE UNIV, 68- *Concurrent Pos:* NIH fel, 69; vis scientist, Univ Vienna, 73; Plant Breeding Inst, Cambridge, Eng, 73; co-ed, Maydica, 75-; vis prof, Max Planck Inst, Koln, WGer, 76- *Mem:* AAAS; Bot Soc Am; Genetics Soc Am. *Res:* Mutation; maize genetics; cytogenetics; linkage; male sterility; controlling regulatory elements; bacteria-insertion sequences. *Mailing Add:* Dept of Agron Iowa State Univ Ames IA 50010

PETERSON, RALPH EDWARD, b Paola, Kans, Aug 21, 18; m 44; c 6. ENDOCRINOLOGY. *Educ:* Kans State Col, BS, 40, MS, 41; Columbia Univ, MD, 46. *Prof Exp:* Dir biol lab, Standard Brands, Inc, 42-43; intern, Univ Minn, 46-47, instr med, 47-48; asst chief biochem, Army Med Serv Grad Sch, Walter Reed Army Med Ctr, 50-52; asst med, Peter Bent Brigham Hosp, 52-53; sr clin investr, Nat Inst Arthritis & Metab Dis, 53-58; assoc prof, 58-68, PROF MED, MED COL, CORNELL UNIV, 68-, DIR DIV ENDOCRINOL, 58- *Concurrent Pos:* Assoc attend physician, New York Hosp, 58-70, attend physician, 70- *Mem:* AAAS; Am Soc Clin Invest; Am Fedn Clin Res; Asn Am Physicians; Endocrine Soc. *Res:* Steroid metabolism. *Mailing Add:* Div of Endocrinol Cornell Univ Med Col New York NY 10021

PETERSON, RALPH W(ILBUR), electrical engineering, systems analysis, see previous edition

PETERSON, RANDOLPH LEE, b Roanoke, Tex, Feb 16, 20; m 42; c 1. MAMMALOGY. *Educ:* Agr & Mech Col, Tex, BS, 41; Univ Toronto, PhD(zool), 50. *Prof Exp:* Actg cur mammals, 46-50, CUR, DEPT MAMMAL, ROYAL ONT MUS, 50- *Concurrent Pos:* Spec lectr, Univ Toronto, 48-61, assoc prof, 62-68, prof, 68- *Mem:* Am Soc Mammal (secy, 52-62, vpres, 62-66, pres, 66-68); Soc Syst Zool; Can Soc Zool. *Res:* Taxonomy, ecology and life history of moose; mammals of Canada, British Guiana, Madagascar, Cameroun, Kenya, Rhodesia and British Honduras; taxonomy of bats. *Mailing Add:* Dept of Mammal Royal Ont Mus 100 Queen's Park Toronto ON M5S 2C6 Can

PETERSON, RAYMOND DALE AUGUST, b Minneapolis, Minn, Oct 5, 30; m 53; c 3. PEDIATRICS, IMMUNOLOGY. *Educ:* Univ Minn, BA, 52, BS, 53, MD, 55. *Prof Exp:* Pediatrician, Univ Minn Hosps, 58-60, Am Heart Asn estab investr, 63-65; Am Heart Asn estab investr, Univ Uppsala, 65-67; from assoc prof to prof pediat, Univ Chicago & La Rabida Inst, 67-73, from actg dir to dir, Inst, 68-73, dir, La Rabida Children's Hosp, 70-73; PROF PEDIAT, MED SCH, UNIV S ALA, 73- *Concurrent Pos:* Am Rheumatism Asn fel immunol, Univ Minn Hosps, 60-61, NIH fel, 61-63; Guggenheim fel, Univ Uppsala, 65-67. *Mem:* AAAS; Am Asn Immunologists; Am Soc Exp Path; Soc Pediat Res. *Res:* Development of the immune system; pathogenesis of malignancies of the lymphoid tissues; cellular differentiation. *Mailing Add:* Dept of Pediat Univ of SAla Med Sch Mobile AL 36617

PETERSON, RAYMOND GLEN, b Denver, Colo, Feb 12, 36; m 59; c 3. ANIMAL BREEDING, STATISTICS. *Educ:* Univ Wyo, BS, 62; Univ Ill, MSc, 65, PhD(animal breeding), 68. *Prof Exp:* Res asst animal breeding, Univ Ill, 62-68; ASST PROF ANIMAL BREEDING, UNIV BC, 68- *Res:* Estimation of environmental and genetic parameters of biological traits in cattle. *Mailing Add:* Dept of Animal Sci Univ of BC Vancouver BC V6T 1W5 Can

PETERSON, REIDER SVERRE, b Minot, NDak, May 17, 39; m 63; c 2. STATISTICS. *Educ:* Northern Ariz Univ, BS, 61; Univ Maine, MA, 65; Mont State Univ, PhD(statist), 74. *Prof Exp:* Teacher math, Idaho Falls High Sch, 61-62; instr math & statist, Northern Ariz Univ, 65-68; statistician, Union Carbide Corp, 74-75; ASST PROF MATH & STATIST, SOUTHERN ORE STATE COL, 75- *Mem:* Am Statist Asn. *Res:* Ratio extimation in randomized response designs. *Mailing Add:* Dept of Math Southern Ore State Col Ashland OR 97520

PETERSON, RICHARD BURNETT, b Omaha, Nebr, Apr 12, 49; m 81. PHOTORESPIRATION, PHOTOSYNTHESIS. *Educ:* Unvi Nebr, BA, 71; Univ Wis, Madison, PhD(biochem), 76. *Prof Exp:* Res assoc, Plant Res Lab, Mich State Univ, 76-78; res assoc, C F Kettering Res Lab, 78-79; ASST SCIENTIST, CONN AGR EXP STA, 79- *Mem:* Am Soc Plant Physiologists; AAAS. *Res:* Photosynthesis and nitrogen fixation by filamentous cyanobacteria; regulation of photorespiration in higher plants and relationship of photosynthesis to crop yield. *Mailing Add:* Dept Biochem & Genetics Conn Agr Exp Sta PO Box 1106 New Haven CT 06504

PETERSON, RICHARD CARL, b Duluth, Minn, Feb 10, 48; m 77. MECHANICAL ENGINEERING, INTERNAL COMBUSTION ENGINES. *Educ:* Univ Minn, Duluth, BA, 70; Purdue Univ, MS, 72, PhD(mech eng), 81. *Prof Exp:* Res asst, Purdue Univ, 74-81; assoc sr res engr, 79-81, SR RES ENGR, GEN MOTORS CORP, 81- *Mem:* Am Soc Mech Engrs; Combustion Inst; Soc Automotive Engrs. *Res:* Combustion and combustion diagnostics; chemical kinetics; heat transfer. *Mailing Add:* Eng Res Dept Gen Motors Res Labs Warren MI 48090

PETERSON, RICHARD CHARLES, b Los Angeles, Calif, Feb 25, 31; m 53; c 1. GEOLOGY, ENVIRONMENTAL SCIENCES. *Educ:* Univ Calif, Berkeley, AB, 53; Univ Ariz, MS, 63, PhD(geol), 68. *Prof Exp:* Geophysicist, Pan Am Petrol Corp, 53-60; instr geol, Univ Ariz, 63-68; assoc prof, 68-71, PROF GEOL & DIR ENVIRON SCI, ADAMS STATE COL, 71- *Mem:* AAAS; Geol Soc Am; Am Asn Petrol Geol; Nat Asn Geol Teachers; NY Acad Sci. *Res:* Structural geology of the Santa Catalina Mountains, Arizona; stratigraphy of the Sangre de Cristo Mountains, Colorado. *Mailing Add:* Dept of Geol Adams State Col Alamosa CO 81102

PETERSON, RICHARD ELSWORTH, b Seattle, Wash, Aug 27, 21; m 55; c 5. INTERNAL MEDICINE, NUCLEAR MEDICINE. *Educ:* Univ Wash, BS, 42; Northwestern Univ, MD, 46; Am Bd Internal Med, dipl; Am Bd Nuclear Med, dipl. *Prof Exp:* Clinician, Radioisotope Unit, Vet Admin Hosp, Long Beach, Calif, 50-52; chief radioisotope serv, Vet Admin Hosp, Iowa City, 52-70; from clin assoc to clin asst prof med, 53-60, clin assoc prof internal med, 60-63, assoc prof med & radiol, 63-66, PROF INTERNAL MED & RADIOL, UNIV IOWA, 66-; CHIEF NUCLEAR MED SERV, VET ADMIN HOSP, IOWA CITY, 70- *Mem:* Soc Nuclear Med (secy, 65-68, treas, 68-69); Am Bd Nuclear Med; Asn Am Med Cols; NY Acad Sci; Am Col Nuclear Physics. *Res:* Endocrinology; hematology; metabolism; genetics and human radiobiology; diagnostic applications of radioisotope techniques; body composition in health and disease; kinetics of radioactive metabolites as tracers of physiologic processes. *Mailing Add:* Dept of Radiol Univ of Iowa Hosp Iowa City IA 52240

PETERSON, RICHARD GEORGE, b Milwaukee, Wis, June 12, 41; m 64; c 2. NEUROBIOLOGY. *Educ:* Bethel Col, Minn, BA, 64; Univ NDak, MS, 67, PhD(anat), 69. *Prof Exp:* Asst res anatomist, Univ Calif, Los Angeles, 69-71; asst prof neurobiol, Med Sch, Univ Tex, Houston, 71-77; ASSOC PROF ANAT, SCH MED, IND UNIV, 77- *Mem:* Am Asn Anat; Electron Micros Soc Am; Am Soc Neurochem; Sigma Xi. *Res:* Neural ultrastructure; histochemistry of neural myelin; developmental neural structure. *Mailing Add:* Dept Anat Ind Univ Sch Med Indianapolis IN 46202

PETERSON, RICHARD WALTER, b Chewelah, Wash, Mar 6, 33; m 51; c 4. ENGINEERING, MATERIALS SCIENCE. *Educ:* Univ Idaho, BS, 57. *Prof Exp:* Process engr, Alcoa, Wenatchee, Wash, 57-64, Alcoa, Tenn, 64-65, STAFF ENGR RES & DEVELOP, ALCOA LABS, NEW KENSINGTON, PA, 65- *Mem:* Am Chem Soc. *Res:* Improvement in materials and processes for producing carbon electrodes for aluminum smelting by the Hall-Heroult process. *Mailing Add:* Alcoa Labs Box 772 New Kensington PA 15068

PETERSON, ROBERT C, b Suffern, NY, May 18, 36; m 63; c 2. PULP CHEMISTRY, PAPER CHEMISTRY. *Educ:* Mich Technol Univ, BS, 57; State Univ NY Col Forestry, BS, 60; NY Univ, MS, 67; State Univ NY Col Environ Sci & Forestry, PhD(paper sci), 71. *Prof Exp:* Res chemist, Eastern Res Div, ITT Rayonier, 60-62; tech serv engr, St Regis Tech Ctr, 62-65, res & develop engr wood chem, 65-67; asst prof, 71-74, ASSOC PROF PAPER TECHNOL, MIAMI UNIV, 74- *Honors & Awards:* Fulbright-Hays vis lectr, Coun Int Exchange Scholar, Malaysia, 74-75. *Mem:* Am Inst Chem Engrs; Tech Asn Pulp & Paper Indust. *Res:* Solid waste disposal, wastepaper recycling; water and air pollution abatement within the paper industry; sources of non-wood fibers for paper and the application of novel pulping methods to agricultural residues. *Mailing Add:* Dept of Paper Technol Miami Univ Oxford OH 45056

PETERSON, ROBERT H F, b Middletown, Pa, Dec 1, 35. MICROBIOLOGY. *Educ:* Elizabethtown Col, BS, 59; Univ Kans, PhD(microbiol), 70. *Prof Exp:* Res assoc cancer res, 72-74, 82, ASST MEM, SLOAN-KETTERING INST CANCER RES, 74-; ASST PROF CELL BIOL, SLOAN-KETTERING DIV, GRAD SCH MED SCI, CORNELL UNIV, 75- *Concurrent Pos:* Fel, Roche Inst Molecular Biol, 70-72; instr microbiol, Sloan-Kettering Div, Grad Sch Med Sci, Cornell Univ, 73-74. *Mem:* Am Soc Microbiol; Biochem Soc; Am Soc Cell Biol. *Res:* Biochemical changes of plasma membranes accompanying the malignant state. *Mailing Add:* Sloan-Kettering Inst for Cancer Res 145 Boston Post Rd Rye NY 10580

PETERSON, ROBERT HAMPTON, b Jamestown, NDak, Oct 29, 22; m 48; c 8. ORGANIC CHEMISTRY. *Educ:* St John's Univ, Minn, BA, 48; NDak State Univ, MS, 50; Univ Utah, PhD(chem), 62. *Prof Exp:* From instr to assoc prof chem, NDak State Univ, 50-68; PROF CHEM & CHMN DIV SCI & MATH, ST LEO COL, 68-, VPRES ACAD AFFAIRS, 72- *Mem:* Am Chem Soc. *Res:* Phenol-formaldehyde polymers; reaction mechanisms; correlation of properties with molecular structure; chemical modification of high polymers; aromatic azo compounds. *Mailing Add:* St Leo Col Box 2188 St Leo FL 33574

PETERSON, ROBERT LAWRENCE, b Strathmore, Alta, Jan 20, 39; m 63; c 2. BOTANY. *Educ:* Univ Alberta, BEd, 62, MSc, 64; Univ Calif, Davis, PhD(plant morphogenesis), 68. *Prof Exp:* assoc prof, 68-80, PROF BOT, UNIV GUELPH, 80- *Mem:* Bot Soc Am; Can Bot Asn; Int Soc Plant Morphol. *Res:* Experimental and anatomical studies on ferns and angiosperms. *Mailing Add:* Dept of Bot & Genetics Univ of Guelph Guelph ON N1G 2W1 Can

PETERSON, ROBERT LEE, b Brady, Nebr, May 21, 30; m 56; c 5. THEORETICAL SOLID STATE PHYSICS. *Educ:* Colo Sch Mines, MetE, 52; Lehigh Univ, MS, 54, PhD(physics), 59. *Prof Exp:* From instr to asst prof physics, Case Inst Technol, 59-63; PHYSICIST, NAT BUR STANDARDS, 63- *Mem:* AAAS; Am Phys Soc; Sigma Xi. *Res:* Semiconductor transport; solid state optics; statistical mechanics and transport theory; spin relaxation; magnetism; superconductivity. *Mailing Add:* Nat Bur of Standards Boulder CO 80302

PETERSON, ROBERT W, b Elizabeth, NJ, July 14, 25; m 65; c 1. NUCLEAR PHYSICS. *Educ:* Rutgers Univ, BS, 50; Calif Inst Technol, PhD(physics), 54. *Prof Exp:* Asst physics, Calif Inst Technol, 50-54; staff mem, 54-67, alt group leader, 67-71, group leader weapons test, 71-75, staff mem, 75-78, STAFF MEM THEORET DESIGN, LOS ALAMOS SCI LAB, UNIV CALIF, 78- *Mem:* Am Phys Soc; Am Geophys Union; Sigma Xi. *Res:* Low energy nuclear reactions; nuclear spectroscopy; nuclear weapons testing; cosmic ray physics; conjugacy of visual auroras. *Mailing Add:* Group TD-7 MS-231 Los Alamos Sci Lab Los Alamos NM 87544

PETERSON, ROGER SHIPP, b Ann Arbor, Mich, June 23, 31; m 53; c 3. BOTANY. *Educ:* Harvard Univ, AB, 53; Univ Mich, MA, 57, PhD(bot), 59. *Prof Exp:* Forest pathologist, US Forest Serv, 59-66 & Rocky Mt Forest & Range Exp Sta, Colo, 59-62, leader Native Rust Proj, Intermountain Forest & Range Exp Sta, Utah, 62-66; TUTOR, ST JOHN'S COL, NMEX, 66- *Mem:* AAAS; Ecol Soc Am; Int Asn Plant Taxonomists; Mycol Soc Am. *Res:* Ecology and taxonomy of rust fungi; forest tree diseases; ecology of New Mexico. *Mailing Add:* St John's Col Santa Fe NM 87501

PETERSON, ROGER TORY, b Jamestown, NY, Aug 28, 08; m 43; c 2. ORNITHOLOGY. *Hon Degrees:* DSc, Franklin & Marshall Col, 52, Ohio State Univ, 62, Fairfield Univ & Allegheny Col, 67, Wesleyan Univ, 70, Colby Col, 74 & Gustavus Adolphus Col, 78; DHL, Hamilton Col, 76 & Amherst Col, 77; Skidmore Col, 81; Univ Hartford, hon DFA, 81. *Prof Exp:* Instr sci & art, Rivers Sch, Brookline, Mass, 31-34; BIRD PAINTER & NATURE WRITER, 34- *Concurrent Pos:* Deleg, Int Ornith Cong, Uppsala, Sweden, 50, Basel, Switz, 54, Helsinki, Finland, 58, Ithaca, NY, 62, Oxford, Eng, 66 & Amsterdam, Netherlands, 70; art dir, Nat Wildlife Fedn, 51-; ed, Field Guide Ser & Am Naturalist Serv, Houghton Mifflin Co, 65-; spec consult, Nat Aududon Soc, 70-; roving reporter, Int Wildlife Mag, 70- *Honors & Awards:* Brewster Mem Medal, Am Ornithologists Union, 44; John Burroughs Medal, 50; Francis Hutchinson Gold Medal, Garden Clubs Am, 70; Audubon Conserv Medal, 71; Gold Medal, World Wildlife Fund, 72; Joseph Wood Krutch Medal, Humane Soc US, 73; Gold Key Award, Am Asn Sch Adminrs, 74; Explorers Club Medal, 74; Spec Conservationist Award, Nat Wildlife Fedn, 74; Green World Award, NY Bot Garden, 76; Linnaean Gold Medal, Swed Acad Sci, 76; Swedish American of 77, Vasa Order Am; Sarah Josepha Hale Award, Richards Library, 77; Horatio Alger Award, 77; Master Wildlife Artist Medal, 78. *Mem:* Fel Am Ornithologists Union; Nat Audubon Soc (secy, 60-64); Wilson Ornith Soc (pres, 64-65); Cooper Ornith Soc; hon mem Brit Ornithologists Union. *Res:* Natural history. *Mailing Add:* 125 Neck Rd Old Lyme CT 06371

PETERSON, ROLF EUGENE, b Minneapolis, Minn, Mar 10, 21; m 44; c 2. NUCLEAR PHYSICS. *Educ:* St Olaf Col, BS, 43; Univ Wis, PhD(physics), 50. *Prof Exp:* Asst, Univ Wis, 43-44; jr scientist, Metall Lab, Univ Chicago, 44; jr scientist, Manhattan Proj, Univ Calif, 44-46; asst, Univ Wis, 46-50; mem staff, 50-57, group leader, 58-64, ALT DIV LEADER, LOS ALAMOS SCI LAB, 64- *Mem:* Am Phys Soc; Am Nuclear Soc. *Res:* Neutron scattering; critical assemblies; development of homogeneous reactors and fast breeder power reactors. *Mailing Add:* Los Alamos Sci Lab PO Box 1663 Los Alamos NM 87544

PETERSON, ROLF OLIN, b Minneapolis, Minn, Apr 5, 49; m 70. WILDLIFE ECOLOGY. *Educ:* Univ Minn, Duluth, BA, 70; Purdue Univ, PhD(wildlife ecol), 74. *Prof Exp:* Fel wildlife ecol, Purdue Univ, 70-74, res assoc, 74-75; ASST PROF BIOL, MICH TECHNOL UNIV, 75- *Mem:* Wildlife Soc; Am Soc Mammal. *Res:* Population ecology of northern mammals; long-term study of wolves and moose in Isle Royale National Park, a Lake Superior island; variations in predator-prey relationships in response to environment and density. *Mailing Add:* Dept of Biol Sci Mich Technol Univ Houghton MI 49931

PETERSON, RONALD A, b Wayland, Mich, May 17, 37. AVIAN PHYSIOLOGY. *Educ:* Mich State Univ, BS, 60, MS, 62, PhD(avian physiol), 66. *Prof Exp:* Asst prof, 66-71, ASSOC PROF POULTRY PHYSIOL, W VA UNIV, 71- *Mem:* Poultry Sci Asn; World Poultry Sci Asn. *Res:* Physiology involved in feather release in birds; environmental physiology related to poultry. *Mailing Add:* Div of Animal & Vet Sci WVa Univ Morgantown WV 26506

PETERSON, RONALD M, b Parkers Prairie, Minn, Apr 8, 22; m 56; c 3. HORTICULTURE, PLANT BREEDING. *Educ:* Colo State Univ, BS, 47; Univ Calif, Davis, MS, 49; Univ Minn, PhD(plant breeding), 53. *Prof Exp:* From asst prof to assoc prof, 53-66, PROF HORT & HEAD DEPT, SDAK STATE UNIV, 66- *Mem:* Am Soc Hort Sci; Am Pomol Soc. *Res:* Breeding of improved varieties of fruit, especially apples, pears and grapes. *Mailing Add:* Dept of Hort SDak State Univ Brookings SD 57006

PETERSON, ROY JEROME, b Everett, Wash, Oct 18, 39; m 62; c 4. NUCLEAR PHYSICS. *Educ:* Univ Wash, BS, 61, PhD(physics), 66. *Prof Exp:* Instr physics, Princeton Univ, 66-68; res assoc, Yale Univ, 68-70; res assoc, 70-71, lectr, 71-74, from asst prof to assoc prof, 74-78, PROF PHYSICS & ASTROPHYS, UNIV COLO, BOULDER, 78- *Concurrent Pos:* Prog dir, Intermediate Energy Physics, NSF, 78-79. *Mem:* Am Phys Soc. *Res:* Direct nuclear reaction studies; medium energy physics. *Mailing Add:* Nuclear Physics Lab Univ of Colo Boulder CO 80309

PETERSON, ROY PHILLIP, b Alexandria, La, Nov 16, 34; m 66; c 4. ENDOCRINOLOGY, REPRODUCTIVE PHYSIOLOGY. *Educ:* Southern Univ, Baton Rouge, BS, 57; Univ Ore, MA, 61; Univ Iowa, PhD(endocrinol), 67. *Prof Exp:* Asst, Univ Ore, 59-61; instr biol, Southern Univ, New Orleans, 61-63; res asst, Univ Iowa, 63-64, US Pub Healths fel, 64-67; asst prof biol, Southern Univ, Baton Rouge, 67-69; from asst prof to assoc prof biol sci, Southern Ill Univ, Edwardsville, 69-78, asst dean grad sch, 71-76; assoc dir acad & health affairs, Ill Bd Higher Educ, 78-80; DEP EXEC DIR ACAD AFFAIRS, KY COUN HIGHER EDUC, 80- *Concurrent Pos:* Consult biol prog, Grambling Col, 61-63, undergrad biol, Fisk Univ, 71 & minorities program Univ Kans Med Sch, 71; assoc dir acad affairs, Ill Bd Higher Educ, 75-77; tech task force life-long learning, Educ Comn of the States, 79-80; fel, Am Coun Educ, 73-74; mem, Nat Comn Higher Educ Issues, 81-; vpres, Nat Bd Dir, Compassionate Friends, Inc, 80-, treas, 79. *Mem:* AAAS; Soc Study Reproduction; Am Soc Zool; Sigma Xi. *Res:* Uptake, distribution and utilization of serum proteins in the estrogen-stimulated uterus; fate of uterus during drug inhibition of metabolism. *Mailing Add:* Ky Coun Higher Educ US 127 S Frankfort KY 40601

PETERSON, ROY REED, b Kansas City, Mo, June 26, 24; m 46; c 4. ANATOMY. *Educ:* Univ Kans, AB, 48, PhD, 52. *Prof Exp:* From instr to assoc prof, 52-70, PROF ANAT, WASHINGTON UNIV, 70- *Concurrent Pos:* USPHS spec res fel, 60; vis prof anat, Stanford Univ, 75-76. *Mem:* Am Asn Anat. *Res:* Placental permeability; cross-sectional anatomy; thyroid and reproduction in guinea pigs; pituitary cytology. *Mailing Add:* Washington Univ Sch of Med St Louis MO 63110

PETERSON, RUDOLPH NICHOLAS, b New York, NY, June 6, 32. BIOCHEMISTRY, PHARMACOLOGY. *Educ:* St John's Univ, NY, BS, 57; Brooklyn Col, MA, 62; Univ Fla, PhD(biochem), 65. *Prof Exp:* Res assoc chem, Lever Bros Res Labs, 57-61; res asst biochem, Univ Fla, 65-66; from asst prof to assoc prof, pharmacol, New York Med Col, 66-76; assoc prof, 76-78, PROF PHARMACOL, SOUTHERN ILL UNIV, 78- *Concurrent Pos:* Prin investr, NIH, sperm-egg interaction, 79-, ion transport by sperm, 81-84, mapping of sperm surfaces, 81-84. *Mem:* Soc Exp Biol & Med; Am Soc Cell Biol; Am Soc Pharmacol & Exp Therapeut; Harvey Soc; Soc Develop Biol. *Res:* Energy metabolism in human spermatozoa; molecular mechanisms of fertilization. *Mailing Add:* Sch of Med Southern Ill Univ Carbondale IL 62901

PETERSON, RUDOLPH PRICE, biology, neurochemistry, see previous edition

PETERSON, SELMER WILFRED, b Owatonna, Minn, Sept 8, 17; m 41; c 4. PHYSICAL CHEMISTRY. *Educ:* St Olaf Col, BA, 38; Univ SDak, MA, 40; Univ Md, PhD(phys chem), 42. *Prof Exp:* Indust fel, Mellon Inst, 42-43; instr chem, La State Univ, 43-45, asst prof, 45-46; asst prof phys chem, Vanderbilt Univ, 46-49; prin chemist, Oak Ridge Nat Lab, 49-61; prof chem & chemist nuclear reactor, Wash State Univ, 61-67; SR SCIENTIST, CHEM DIV, ARGONNE NAT LAB, 67- *Concurrent Pos:* Fulbright advan res scholar, Netherlands, 54-55; res assoc, Atomic Energy Res Estab, Harwell, Eng, 66; consult, Pac Northwest Lab, Battelle Mem Inst. *Mem:* AAAS; Am Chem Soc; Am Phys Soc; Am Crystallog Asn; Royal Soc Chem. *Res:* Neutron diffraction; crystal structure; hydrogen bonding. *Mailing Add:* Chem Div Argonne Nat Lab Bldg 200 A-117 Argonne IL 60439

PETERSON, SHAILER ALVAREY, dentistry, deceased

PETERSON, SIGFRED, b San Francisco, Calif, July 14, 19; m 44, 57; c 8. CHEMISTRY. *Educ:* Univ Calif, BS, 40; Univ Minn, PhD(phys chem), 47. *Prof Exp:* Asst chem, Univ Minn, 40-44; res chemist, Metall Lab, Univ Chicago, 44-46; from asst prof to assoc prof chem, Univ Louisville, 47-52; CHEMIST, OAK RIDGE NAT LAB, 52- *Concurrent Pos:* Lectr, Oak Ridge Sch Reactor Technol, 52-55. *Mem:* Am Chem Soc; Soc Tech Commun. *Res:* Nuclear technology; technical writing and editing. *Mailing Add:* Oak Ridge Nat Lab PO Box X Oak Ridge TN 37830

PETERSON, SPENCER ALAN, b Sioux Falls, SDak, Jan 6, 40; m 61; c 2. LIMNOLOGY. *Educ:* Sioux Falls Col, BS, 65; Univ NDak, MS, 67, PhD(limnol), 71. *Prof Exp:* Res asst limnol, Univ NDak, 68-71; aquatic biologist water qual res, Mich Water Resources Comn, 71; RES AQUATIC BIOLOGIST EUTROPHICATION RES, NAT ENVIRON RES CTR, US ENVIRON PROTECTION AGENCY, 71-, SR STAFF ECOLOGIST, 74-, RES ECOLOGIST & COORDR NAT PROG TO EVAL LAKE RESTORATION TECHNIQUES, 75-, ACTG CHIEF, HAZARDOUS MAT ASSESSMENT TEAM, 81- *Mem:* Am Soc Limnol & Oceanog; Sigma Xi. *Res:* Eutrophication control methods; aquatic ecosystem nutrient budgets; algae macrophyte dynamics; lake restoration; ecological impacts of hazardous materials; plant and animal effects of hazardous materials. *Mailing Add:* Corvallis Environ Res Lab 200 SW 35th St Corvallis OR 97330

PETERSON, STEPHEN CRAIG, b Salt Lake City, Utah, Nov 19, 40; m 64; c 2. PHYSIOLOGY. *Educ:* Univ Calif, Berkeley, BA, 62; NMex Highlands Univ, MS, 64; Wash State Univ, PhD(physiol), 69. *Prof Exp:* Res assoc physiol, Yale Univ, 68-69; from asst prof to assoc prof biophys, Fac Med, Mem Univ Nfld, 69-76; SR SCIENTIST, FLUIDS, BIODYN & BIOMAT SECT, UBTL/DIV, UNIV UTAH RES INST, 76- *Mem:* Biol Photog Asn. *Res:* Mechanisms and modeling of cell movement. *Mailing Add:* UBTL/Div of Univ Utah Res Inst 520 Wakara Way Salt Lake City UT 84108

PETERSON, STEPHEN FRANK, b Lafayette, Ind, Mar 2, 42; m 68; c 1. ANALYTICAL CHEMISTRY. *Educ:* Ind Univ, Bloomington, BS, 64; Cornell Univ, PhD(anal chem), 69. *Prof Exp:* Res chemist, 68-73, res supvr, 73-80, RES STAFF CHEMIST, SAVANNAH RIVER LAB, E I DU PONT DE NEMOURS & CO, INC, 80- *Mem:* Am Chem Soc. *Res:* Neutron activation analysis; in-line radiochemical analysis; nuclear fuel cycle separations processes; application of small computers to analytical chemistry; automated control of nuclear fuel cycle separations processes. *Mailing Add:* Savannah River Lab E I du Pont de Nemours & Co Inc Aiken SC 29801

PETERSON, VERN LEROY, b Gothenburg, Nebr, Nov 8, 34; m 61; c 3. AERONOMY, METEOROLOGY. *Educ:* Univ Colo, BS, 56; Ind Univ, MA, 60, PhD(astrophys), 63. *Prof Exp:* Res physicist, Nat Oceanic & Atmospheric Admin, 63-69; assoc prof physics, Utah State Univ, 69-74; adj prof, Univ Sao Paulo, 74-77; sr scientist, Res Anal & Develop, Inc, 77-78; pres, Centennial Sci, Inc, 78-80; TECH DIR, OCEAN DATA SYSTS, INC, 80- *Mem:* Am Astron Soc; Am Meteorological Soc; Am Geophys Union; Int Union Radio Sci. *Res:* Synthesis of elements within stars, physics of the ionosphere and airglow; numerical modeling of upper atmosphere; nucleosynthesis; meteorology; digital signal processing; atmospheric radar; atmospheric turbulence; satellite image processing; ocean currents. *Mailing Add:* 22610 Murietta Rd Salinas CA 93908

PETERSON, VICTOR LOWELL, b Saskatoon, Sask, June 11, 34; US citizen; m 55; c 3. AERONAUTICS, ASTRONAUTICS. *Educ:* Ore State Univ, BS, 56; Stanford Univ, MS, 64; Mass Inst Technol, MS, 73. *Prof Exp:* Res scientist, 56-68, asst chief hypersonic aerodyn br, 68-69, dep chief spaceshuttle off, 69-71, chief aerodyn br, 71-74, CHIEF, THERMO & GAS DYNAMICS DIV, AMES RES CTR, NASA, 74- *Concurrent Pos:* Sloan fel, Mass Inst Technol, 72-73. *Honors & Awards:* Apollo Achievement Award, NASA, 69. *Mem:* Am Inst Aeronaut & Astronaut. *Res:* Direct research in fields of aero-acoustics, fluid mechanics, flight mechanics and internal and external aerodynamics; direct research in fields of computational fluid dynamics, entry technology, computational chemistry, surface physics and materials science. *Mailing Add:* NASA-Ames Res Ctr Moffett Field CA 94035

PETERSON, VINCENT ZETTERBERG, b Galesburg, Ill, June 18, 21; m 48; c 4. EXPERIMENTAL HIGH ENERGY PHYSICS. *Educ:* Pomona Col, BA, 43; Univ Calif, PhD(physics), 50. *Prof Exp:* Physicist, Naval Res Lab, 43-46 & Radiation Lab, Univ Calif, 47-50; res fel physics, Calif Inst Technol, 50-53, sr res fel, 53-58, asst prof, 58-62; PROF PHYSICS, UNIV HAWAII, 62- *Concurrent Pos:* Fulbright res scholar & Guggenheim travel grant, Italy, 59-60; prin investr high energy physics prog, Univ Hawaii; consult, AEC. *Mem:* AAAS; Am Phys Soc. *Res:* Elementary particle physics; multiwire proportional chambers and bubble chamber experiments; high energy neutrino interactions. *Mailing Add:* 311 Dune Circle Kailua Oahu HI 96734

PETERSON, WARD DAVIS, JR, b Ann Arbor, Mich, May 10, 27; m 50; c 5. MEDICAL MICROBIOLOGY. *Educ:* Univ Mich, Ann Arbor, BA, 47, MS, 51, PhD(epidemiol sci), 60. *Prof Exp:* Virologist, Mich State Dept Health, 51-55; res assoc, 59-62, SR RES ASSOC MICROBIOL, CHILD RES CTR MICH, 62- *Concurrent Pos:* Instr, Med Sch, 62-76, & assoc, Dept Immunol & Microbiol, Wayne State Univ, 73-76; assoc prof, Dept Pediat, Wayne State Univ, 79- *Mem:* Tissue Cult Asn; AAAS. *Res:* Development of mammalian cell lines in vitro; identification and characterization of cells in vitro; cytogenetics; cell transformation; tumor antigens. *Mailing Add:* Child Res Ctr Child Hosp Mich Detroit MI 48201

PETERSON, WESLEY JOHN, zoology, see previous edition

PETERSON, WILBUR CARROLL, b White Rock, SDak, Aug 20, 13; m 46. ELECTRICAL ENGINEERING. *Educ:* Univ Minn, BEE, 39; Mich State Univ, MS, 51; Northwestern Univ, PhD, 57. *Prof Exp:* Elec engr, Gen Elec Co, 39-48; from instr to asst prof elec eng, Mich State Univ, 48-58; ASSOC PROF ELEC ENG, NC STATE UNIV, 58- *Mem:* Inst Elec & Electronics Engrs. *Res:* Circuit theory and automatic control systems; automatic control and heat transfer. *Mailing Add:* Dept Elec Eng NC State Univ Raleigh NC 27650

PETERSON, WILLIAM ROGER, b Racine, Wis, May 22, 27; m 46; c 4. ORGANIC CHEMISTRY. *Educ:* Carroll Col, Wis, AB, 49; Univ Ill, PhD(org chem), 52. *Prof Exp:* Asst inorg chem, Univ Ill, 49-50; asst high polymers, Off Rubber Reserve, 50-52; res chemist polymer chem, E I du Pont de Nemours & Co, 52-57; sr chemist & div consult, Cent Res, Continental Can

Co, Ill, 57-59; supvr polymer res, United Carbon Co, Inc, 59-61, res div mgr, 61-63; res dir & exec vpres, Southeast Polymers Inc, Tenn, 63-69; tech dir, Chem Div, 69-74, mgr res & develop, 74-79, TECH DIR, TEXTILE RUBBER & CHEM, GAF CORP, 79- *Concurrent Pos:* Spec sci ed, McGraw-Hill Co, 59-62; adj prof & consult, Univ Tenn. *Mem:* Am Chem Soc; AAAS. *Res:* Polymer chemistry, including monomer synthesis; synthetic fibers; vinyl resins, elastomers and emulsion polymerization. *Mailing Add:* 1508 Dalewood Dr Chattanooga TN 37411

PETERSON, WILLIAM WESLEY, b Muskegon, Mich, Apr 22, 24; m 49; c 3. ELECTRICAL ENGINEERING. *Educ:* Univ Mich, AB, 48, BSE, 49, MSE, 50, PhD(elec eng), 54. *Prof Exp:* Assoc engr, Eng Lab, Int Bus Mach Corp, NY, 54-56; assoc prof elec eng, Univ Fla, 56-63; vis prof, Chiao Tung Univ, 63-64; PROF ELEC ENG, UNIV HAWAII, 64- *Concurrent Pos:* Vis assoc prof, Mass Inst Technol, 59-60; vis prof, Osaha Univ, 71 & 79. *Honors & Awards:* Shannon lectr, Int Symposium Instrumentation Theory, 81. *Mem:* Inst Elec & Electronics Engrs; fel Asn Comput Mach. *Res:* Information theory; reliability and error control; computers. *Mailing Add:* Dept of Info & Comput Sci Univ of Hawaii Honolulu HI 96822

PETERSON-FALZONE, SALLY JEAN, b Paxton, Ill, Feb 22, 42; m 75. SPEECH, HEARING SCIENCE. *Educ:* Univ Ill, BS, 64, MA, 65; Univ Iowa, PhD(speech path), 71. *Prof Exp:* Speech pathologist, Inst Phys Med & Rehab, Peoria, Ill, 70-71; res assoc audiol, Cleft Palate Clin, 65-67, ASSOC PROF SPEECH PATH, CTR CRANIOFACIAL ANOMALIES, UNIV ILL, 71- *Mem:* Am Speech & Hearing Asn; Am Cleft Palate Asn; Am Cleft Palate Educ Found; AAAS; Sigma Xi. *Res:* Craniofacial malformation syndromes; experimental phonetics; speech production in anomalous supralaryngeal vocal tracts. *Mailing Add:* Ctr Craniofacial Anomalies Box 6998 Chicago IL 60680

PETERSSON, GEORGE A, b New York, NY, July 6, 42; m 72; c 1. THEORETICAL CHEMISTRY. *Educ:* City Col New York, BS, 64; Calif Inst Technol, PhD(chem), 70. *Prof Exp:* Res fel chem, Harvard Univ, 70-71; J W Gibbs instr, Yale Univ, 71-73; asst prof, 73-78, ASSOC PROF CHEM, WESLEYAN UNIV, 78- *Mem:* Am Chem Soc; Am Phys Soc. *Res:* Theory of electron correlation in atoms, molecules and especially in transition states for chemical reactions; development of ab-initio and semiempirical methods for the calculation of pair correlation energies. *Mailing Add:* Hall-Atwater Labs of Chem Wesleyan Univ Middletown CT 06457

PETES, THOMAS DOUGLAS, b Washington, DC, Mar 27, 47; m 73; c 1. GENETICS, BIOCHEMISTRY. *Educ:* Brown Univ, ScB, 69; Univ Wash, PhD(genetics), 73. *Prof Exp:* Jane Coffin Childs fel, Div Microbiol, Nat Inst Med Res, 73-75; fel, Dept Biol, Mass Inst Technol, 75-77; ASST PROF, DEPT MICROBIOL, UNIV CHICAGO, 77- *Concurrent Pos:* Res grants, Jane Coffin Childs Mem Fund, 77-78, NIH, 77- & March of Dimes, 78-79. *Res:* Chromosome structure and replication in the yeast saccharomyces cerevisiae; genetic behavior of repeating DNA genes in eucaryotes. *Mailing Add:* Dept of Microbiol 920 E 58th St Chicago IL 60637

PETFIELD, ROBERT JOSEPH, b Bethlehem, Pa, Sept 26, 30; m 53; c 4. ORGANIC POLYMER CHEMISTRY. *Educ:* Moravian Col, BS, 52; Lehigh Univ, MS, 57, PhD(org chem), 59. *Prof Exp:* Res chemist, E I du Pont de Nemours & Co, Inc, 59-63, res & develop chemist, 64-71; res chemist, Chemetron, 71-73, res group leader, 73-75, sr res chemist, 75-76, technol info specialist, 76-78; RETIRED. *Mem:* Am Chem Soc; Sigma Xi. *Res:* Research and development of alkyd resins; general coatings research and development; research and development of vehicles for pigment dispersions used in inks and paints. *Mailing Add:* 1029 Central Ave Holland MI 49423

PETHICA, BRIAN ANTHONY, b London, Eng, July 9, 26; m 52, 78; c 5. SURFACE CHEMISTRY, COLLOID SCIENCE. *Educ:* London Univ, BSc, 46, PhD(phys chem), 50, DSc, 62; Cambridge Univ, PhD, 53, ScD, 71. *Hon Degrees:* DSc, Clarkson Col, 75. *Prof Exp:* Lectr pharmacol, Med Sch, Univ Birmingham, 49-53; sr res asst, Dept Colloid Sci, Univ Cambridge, 53-58; lectr phys chem, Inst Sci & Tech, Mannchester Univ, 58-61, sr lectr, 61-63 & hon reader, 63-71; dean arts & sci, 76-81, PROF BIOPHYS & CHEM, CLARKSON COL, 81- *Concurrent Pos:* Vis lectr, Columbia Univ, 58; div mgr chem physics, Unilever Res Lab, Port Sunlight, UK, 63-65, head lab, 65-75 & chmn, Technol Policy Study, 75-76; Chmn, Chem Interfaces, Gordon Conf, 79. *Mem:* Fel Royal Soc Chem; Am Chem Soc; Am PhysSoc; Faraday Soc (vpres, 74). *Res:* Surface chemistry; membrane biophysics; solution and surface thermodynamics; colloid science; biocolloids, including dietary fiber. *Mailing Add:* Dept Physics Clarkson Col Potsdam NY 13676

PETHICK, CHRISTOPHER JOHN, b Horsham, Eng, Feb 22, 42. THEORETICAL PHYSICS. *Educ:* Univ Oxford, BA, 62, DPhil(physics), 65. *Prof Exp:* Res assoc, 66-68, res asst prof, 68-69, assoc prof, 70-73, PROF PHYSICS, UNIV ILL, 73- *Concurrent Pos:* Fel physics, Magdalen Col, Oxford Univ, 65-70; Sloan res fel, 70-72; vis prof physics, Nordita, Copenhagen, Denmark, 75- *Res:* Theoretical low-temperature and solid state physics; theoretical astrophysics. *Mailing Add:* Dept of Physics Univ of Ill Urbana IL 61801

PETICOLAS, WARNER LELAND, b Lubbock, Tex, July 29, 29; m 55; c 5. PHYSICAL BIOCHEMISTRY. *Educ:* Tex Technol Col, BSc, 50; Northwestern Univ, PhD(phys chem), 54. *Prof Exp:* Res chemist, E I du Pont de Nemours & Co, 54-55, 57-59, res assoc, 59-60; sr asst scientist, NIH, 55-57; staff scientist, Res Lab, Int Bus Mach Corp, Calif, 60-65, mgr chem phys group, 66-67; vis assoc prof mat sci, Calif Inst Technol, 65-66; PROF CHEM, UNIV ORE, 67- *Concurrent Pos:* Guggenheim fel, Inst Laue-Langevin, Grenoble, France, 73-74; vis prof, Univ Paris, 80-81. *Mem:* Biophys Soc; Am Soc Biol Chemists; Am Chem Soc; The Chem Soc; Am Phys Soc. *Res:* Biomembranes; proteins; nucleic acids; Raman spectroscopy; inelastic laser light scattering. *Mailing Add:* Dept of Chem Univ of Ore Eugene OR 97403

PETIT, MICHAEL GEOFFREY, b Rockville Centre, NY, Oct 17, 38; m 69; c 2. PHYSICAL CHEMISTRY, ORGANIC GEOCHEMISTRY. *Educ:* San Diego State Univ, AB, 65; Univ Calif, PhD(chem), 69. *Prof Exp:* Res chemist, Beckman Instruments, Inc, 69-70; asst prof microbiol, Colo State Univ, 71-78; sci writer, 78-79; assoc prof chem eng, Colo State Univ, 79-80; PATENT ADV, UNIV CALIF, BERKELEY, 81- *Concurrent Pos:* Consult, Marathon Oil Co, 71-73. *Mem:* AAAS; Sigma Xi; Am Soc Mammalogists. *Res:* Biogeochemical cycling of elements during the last one hundred thousand years and the perturbation of naturally occurring cycles by man; racemization of amino acids in geochronology. *Mailing Add:* 238 Purdue Ave Berkeley CA 94708

PETITCLERC, CLAUDE JEAN, biochemistry, clinical biochemistry, see previous edition

PETITT, GUS A, b Birmingham, Ala, Apr 7, 37. PHYSICS. *Educ:* Mass Inst Technol, BS, 60; Duke Univ, PhD(physics), 65. *Prof Exp:* Mem tech staff, Northrop Space Labs, 64-65; ASSOC PROF PHYSICS, GA STATE UNIV, 65- *Concurrent Pos:* Consult, Northrop Space Labs, 65- *Mem:* Am Phys Soc. *Res:* Neutron scattering; Mossbauer effect; heavy ion nuclear reactions. *Mailing Add:* Dept Physics Univ Plaza Ga State Univ Atlanta GA 30303

PETKAU, ABRAM, b Lowe Farm, Man, Can, June 1, 30; m 59; c 4. MEDICAL BIOPHYSICS. *Educ:* Univ Man, BSc, 53, MSc, 56, MD, 60. *Prof Exp:* Intern, Winnipeg Gen Hosp, 61; HEAD MED BIOPHYS, WHITESHELL NUCLEAR RES ESTAB, ATOMIC ENERGY CAN, LTD, 62- *Concurrent Pos:* Fel, Yale Univ, 61-62; hon prof, Grad Studies, Univ Man, 66- *Mem:* Nuclear Med Soc; AAAS; Biophys Soc; Am Asn Photobiol. *Res:* Physical, chemical and biological properties of membranes; radio protection and internal dosimetry; membrane irradiation response; superoxide dismutase; activated oxygen. *Mailing Add:* Whiteshell Nuclear Res Estab Atomic Energy of Can Ltd Pinawa MB R0E 1L0 Can

PETKE, FREDERICK DAVID, b Cincinnati, Ohio, May 12, 42; m 67; c 2. SURFACE CHEMISTRY. *Educ:* Lehigh Univ, BA, 64; Wash State Univ, PhD(phys chem), 68. *Prof Exp:* Res chemist, 68-70, sr res chemist, Res Labs, 70-81, SR RES CHEMIST, EASTMAN CHEM DIV, RES LABS, TENN EASTMAN CO, 81- *Mem:* Am Chem Soc; Sigma Xi. *Res:* Surface chemistry of adhesion, polymers and fundamentals of hot melt adhesives. *Mailing Add:* Res Labs Tenn Eastman Co Box 511 Kingsport TN 37662

PETRACEK, FRANCIS JAMES, b Minn, Nov 30, 27; m 51; c 8. MEDICINAL CHEMISTRY. *Educ:* St John's Univ, Minn, BS, 49; Calif Inst Technol, MS, 51, PhD, 56. *Prof Exp:* Sr chemist, 56-65, sr res specialist, 65-71, mgr med chem, 71-75, MGR ADVAN PROJS, RIKER LABS, 75- *Mem:* AAAS; Am Chem Soc; NY Acad Sci. *Res:* Oxidation of carotenoids; alkaloids; structure determination; synthesis of medicinally active compounds. *Mailing Add:* Riker Labs Inc 19901 Nordhoff St Northridge CA 91324

PETRACK, BARBARA KEPES, b New York, NY, Aug 21, 27; m 49; c 2. BIOCHEMISTRY. *Educ:* Hunter Col, BA, 47; Polytech Inst Brooklyn, MS, 51; NY Univ, PhD(biochem), 57. *Prof Exp:* Guest investr biochem res, Rockefeller Inst, 58-61; biochemist, Geigy Res Labs, Geigy Chem Corp, 61-71, mgr basic biochem, 71-75, SR RES FEL, CIBA-GEIGY CORP, 75- *Concurrent Pos:* Dazian Found fel, 58; Runyon fel, 58-60; adj prof, Dept Biochem, New York Med Col. *Mem:* NY Acad Sci; Am Chem Soc; Am Soc Biol Chem; Sigma Xi. *Res:* Enzymes of catecholamine metabolism; nicotinamide-adenine dinucleotide and nicotinamide metabolism; photosynthetic phosphorylation; arginine metabolism; cyclic nucleotide metabolism; diabetes research; insulin and glucagon secretion; hormone receptors; benzodiazepine receptors. *Mailing Add:* Dept of Biochem Ciba-Geigy Corp Ardsley NY 10502

PETRAKIS, LEONIDAS, b Sparta, Greece, July 23, 35; US citizen; m 59; c 2. PHYSICAL CHEMISTRY. *Educ:* Northeastern Univ, 58; Univ Calif, Berkeley, PhD(phys chem), 61. *Prof Exp:* Nat Res Coun Can res fel, 61-62; asst prof phys chem, Univ Md, 62-63; res chemist, E I du Pont de Nemours & Co, 63-65; res chemist, 65-66, res assoc, 73-78, SUPVR MOLECULAR SPECTROS, GULF RES & DEVELOP CO, 66-, SR RES ASSOC, GULF SCI & TECHNOL CO, 78- *Concurrent Pos:* Sr lectr chem, Carnegie-Mellon Univ, 72-73; vis res prof, Univ Pittsburgh, 81- *Mem:* AAAS; Am Phys Soc; Am Chem Soc. *Res:* Magnetic resonance; surface chemistry and solid state; energy and the environment; strategic studies in fossil fuels and non-energy and energy minerals; analytical spectroscopy; characterization of materials; relaxation of nuclear spins and intermolecular forces; chemistry and physics of fossil fuels. *Mailing Add:* Gulf Sci & Technol Co PO Box 2038 Pittsburgh PA 15230

PETRAKIS, NICHOLAS LOUIS, b Bancroft, Iowa, Feb 6, 22; m 47; c 3. MEDICINE. *Educ:* Augustana Col, BA, 43; Univ SDak, BS, 44; Washington Univ, MD, 46. *Prof Exp:* Intern, Minneapolis Gen Hosp, 46-47; asst med officer, Naval Radiol Defense Lab, 47-49; sr asst surgeon, USPHS Lab Exp Oncol, Univ Calif, 50-54; from asst prof to assoc prof med & prev med, 54-66, from vchmn to actg chmn dept prev med, 60-66, vchmn dept epidemiol & int health, 66-69, assoc dir, G W Hooper Found, 70-74, actg dir, G W Hooper Found, 74-77, PROF PREV MED, DIV AMBULATORY & COMMUNITY MED, SCH MED, UNIV CALIF, SAN FRANCISCO, 66-, RES ASSOC, CANCER RES INST, 54-, CHMN DEPT EPIDEMIOL & INT HEALTH, 78- *Concurrent Pos:* Eleanor Roosevelt Int Cancer fel, Rome, 62-63; USPHS spec fel, Galton Lab, Dept Human Genetics & Biomet, Univ Col, Univ London, 69-70; consult, Vet Admin Hosps, Martinez, Calif; mem, Epidemiol Comt, Breast Cancer Task Force & consult, Nat Cancer Inst, 73-76, mem, Biometry & Epidemiol Contract Rev Comt, 78-81; consult, Calif State Dept Pub Health, 73- *Mem:* AAAS; Am Asn Cancer Res; Western Asn Physicians; Soc Epidemiol Res; Am Epidemiol Soc. *Res:* Genetic epidemiology of cancer; sickle cell disease; physical anthropology; hematology; oncology. *Mailing Add:* Sch of Med Univ of Calif San Francisco CA 94143

PETRALI, JOHN PATRICK, b Fairview, NJ, July 30, 33; m 63. ANATOMY, IMMUNOCYTOCHEMISTRY. *Educ:* Davis & Elkins Col, BS, 55; Univ Md, PhD(human anat), 69. *Prof Exp:* Biologist cytol, Med Res Lab, Edgewood Arsenal, 62-63, res biologist ultrastruct, Biomed Lab, 64-69, group leader, Electron Micros Sect, Biomed Lab, 69-79; RES ANATOMIST & TEAM LEADER, ELECTRON MICROS, COMP PATH, US AM MED RES INST CHEM DEFENSE, 79- *Concurrent Pos:* Adj asst prof anat, Sch Med, Univ Md, 69-75, adj asst prof, Univ Md, 75-79. *Mem:* Am Asn Anatomists; Electron Micros Soc Am. *Res:* Diagnostic pathology. *Mailing Add:* Comp Path & Surg Br US Am Med Res Inst Chem Defense Aberdeen Proving Ground MD 21010

PETRARCA, ANTHONY EDWARD, b Providence, RI, July 24, 29; m 55; c 6. ORGANIC CHEMISTRY, INFORMATION SCIENCE. *Educ:* RI Col, BEd, 53; Univ RI, MS, 55; Univ NH, PhD(org chem), 59. *Prof Exp:* Instr chem, Univ NH, 55-59; from instr to asst prof, Seton Hall Univ, 59-64; info scientist, Chem Abstr Serv, 64-68; asst prof, 68-71, ASSOC PROF COMPUT & INFO SCI, OHIO STATE UNIV, 71- *Mem:* AAAS; Am Chem Soc; Am Soc Info Sci; Asn Comput Mach. *Res:* Molecular rearrangements; oxime reductions; stereochemistry; automatic indexing; theory and design of automated search systems. *Mailing Add:* Dept of Comput & Info Sci Ohio State Univ Columbus OH 43210

PETRAS, JAMES MINAS, anatomy, neuroanatomy, see previous edition

PETRAS, MICHAEL LUKE, b Windsor, Ont, Aug 4, 32; m 56; c 4. ZOOLOGY, GENETICS. *Educ:* Assumption Col, BSc, 54; Univ Notre Dame, MS, 56; Univ Mich, PhD(zool), 65. *Prof Exp:* Lectr biol, Essex Col, Ont, 56-62; from asst prof to assoc prof, 62-70, PROF BIOL, UNIV WINDSOR, 70- *Concurrent Pos:* Genetics trainee, Univ Mich, 61-62; grants, Res Coun Can, 60-82; vis investr, Jackson Lab, 79. *Mem:* Genetics Soc Am; Am Soc Zool; Soc Study Evolution; Genetics Soc Can; Can Soc Zool. *Res:* Biochemical variants in mammals; the genetics of mammalian populations, especially mouse populations. *Mailing Add:* Dept Biol Univ Windsor Windsor ON N9B 3P4 Can

PETREE, MARCELLA COOPER, b Baltimore, Md, Nov 8, 11; m 48; c 3. SOLID STATE & RADIATION PHYSICS. *Educ:* Allegheny Col, BA, 43; Univ Wis, MA, 46, PhD(physics), 48. *Prof Exp:* PHYSICIST, NUCLEAR EFFECTS DIV, NAVAL SURFACE WEAPONS CTR, 53- *Res:* Radiation effects on solid state electronics; thermodynamic properties of polymers. *Mailing Add:* 13490 Old Columbia Pike Silver Spring MD 20904

PETRELLA, RONALD VINCENT, b Youngstown, Ohio, Feb 27, 35; m 57; c 3. PHYSICAL CHEMISTRY. *Educ:* Univ Youngstown, BS, 56; Western Reserve Univ, MS, 58, PhD(phys chem), 63. *Prof Exp:* Chemist, 61-65, res chemist, 65-68, sr res chemist, 68-73, RES SPECIALIST, DOW CHEM CO, 73- *Mem:* Combustion Inst; Am Chem Soc; Sigma Xi. *Res:* Thermodynamics; thermochemistry; molecular spectroscopy; flash pyrolysis; flash photolysis; kinetics; polymer combustion; flammability. *Mailing Add:* 3712 Hillgrove Ct Midland MI 48640

PETRELLA, VANCE JOHN, b Joliet, Ill, July 23, 47; m 72; c 1. TOXICOLOGY, BIOCHEMISTRY. *Educ:* Va Mil Inst, BS, 69; Va Polytech Inst & State Univ, PhD(biochem), 73; Am Bd Toxicol, cert, 80. *Prof Exp:* Res asst, 69-72, res fel biochem toxicol, Va Polytech Inst, 72-73; res biochemist toxicol natural toxins, US Army Med Res Inst Infectious Dis, 74-77, med review officer, 77-81, SR MED REVIEW OFFICER TOXICOL, GILLETTE MED EVAL LABS, 81- *Concurrent Pos:* Adj asst prof, Hood Col, 76. *Mem:* Am Col Toxicol; Soc Toxicol. *Res:* Biochemical toxicology of natural and synthetic toxins; industrial toxicology. *Mailing Add:* Gillette Med Eval Labs 1413 Research Blvd Rockville MD 20850

PETRI, LEO HENRY, b Garland, Nebr, Sept 24, 14; m 42; c 1. PARASITOLOGY. *Educ:* Nebr State Teachers Col, Peru, AB, 37; Univ Nebr, MA, 41; Kans State Col, PhD(parasitol), 51. *Prof Exp:* Prin pub sch, 37-39; asst, Univ Nebr, 39-41; instr & technician, Kans State Col, 41-42, 46-52; assoc prof, 52-57, prof, 57-79, EMER PROF BIOL, WARTBURG COL, 80- *Mem:* AAAS; Am Soc Parasitol; Am Micros Soc. *Res:* Trematodes and nematodes. *Mailing Add:* Dept Biol Wartburg Col Waverly IA 50677

PETRI, LESTER REINHOLD, b Garland, Nebr, Feb 18, 24; m 48; c 3. HYDROLOGY, WATER CHEMISTRY. *Educ:* Univ Nebr, BS, 49. *Prof Exp:* Chemist, 49-66, SUPVRY HYDROLOGIST, US GEOL SURV, 66- *Res:* Relations of water quality to quantity, availability, use and sources of pollution. *Mailing Add:* US Geol Surv 100 Centennial Mall N Lincoln NE 68508

PETRICCIANI, JOHN C, b Sacramento, Calif, Sept 4, 36. CLINICAL RESEARCH, TUMOR CELL BIOLOGY. *Educ:* Rensselaer Polytech Inst, BS, 58; Univ Nev, MS, 60; Stanford Univ, MD, 67. *Prof Exp:* House staff pediatrician, Buffalo Children's Hosp, NY, 67-68; NIH staff assoc, 68-72, chief, Exp Cytol Sect, Lab Path, 72-74; dep dir, Div Path, Bur Biologics, Food & Drug Admin, 74-78, asst dir, 78-81; ASST DIR, OFF PROTECTION FROM RES RISKS, NIH, 81- *Concurrent Pos:* Adj prof genetics & prof lectr biol sci, George Washington Univ, 78- *Mem:* AAAS; NY Acad Sci; Tissue Cult Asn; AMA. *Res:* cytogenetics. *Mailing Add:* Off Dir Nat Inst Health Bethesda MD 20205

PETRICH, ROBERT PAUL, b Barberton, Ohio, Jan 11, 41; m 64; c 3. POLYMER SCIENCE. *Educ:* Mass Inst Technol, BS, 63, MS, 64; Univ Akron, PhD(polymer sci), 68. *Prof Exp:* Chemist, Res Div, 64-66, group leader, 68-72, mgr, Int Mkt Area, 72-75, head, Europ Plastics Lab, 75-79, EUROP RES & DEVELOP MGR, INT DIV, ROHM & HAAS CO, 79- *Mem:* Am Chem Soc; Soc Plastics Engrs; Plastics & Rubber Inst. *Res:* Physical properties of polymers, especially multi-phase polymer systems. *Mailing Add:* Rohm & Haas Europ Labs Sophia Antipolis 06560 Valbonne France

PETRICK, ERNEST N(ICHOLAS), b Taylor, Pa, Apr 9, 22; m 46; c 4. MECHANICAL ENGINEERING. *Educ:* Carnegie Inst Technol, BS, 42; Univ Mich, cert, 45; Purdue Univ, MS, 48, PhD, 55. *Prof Exp:* Instr mech, Aeronaut, Chem & Metall Eng & co-supvr gas turbine lab, Purdue Univ, 46-53; head heat transfer sect, Wright Aeronaut Div, Curtiss-Wright Corp, 53-56, chief adv propulsion systs, Res Div, 55-60; chief res engr, Kelsey-Hayes Co, 60-65; chief scientist, Hq, US Army Mobility Command, 65-66; tech dir, 66-70, CHIEF SCIENTIST, HQ, US ARMY TANK-AUTOMOTIVE COMMAND, 70-, TECH DIR, 80- *Concurrent Pos:* Mem bd vis, Oakland Univ; mem adv bd eng, Univ Detroit; adj prof, Wayne State Univ; mem adv comt advan automotive power systs, Coun Environ Qual, Exec Off of Pres; eng consult; mem, NATO Panel combat vehicles. *Mem:* Sigma Xi; Soc Automotive Engrs. *Res:* Transportation systems; surface and flight propulsion; gas turbines; automotive and truck engines; commercial and military vehicles; engineering management. *Mailing Add:* 1540 Stonehaven Rd Ann Arbor MI 48104

PETRICK, L(EON) M(ICHAEL), b Little Falls, NY, Apr 23, 18; m 50; c 5. MATERIALS ENGINEERING. *Educ:* Rensselaer Polytech Inst, MetE, 53. *Prof Exp:* Welding engr, Carrier Corp, 53-55; metallurgist in charge welding sect, Res & Develop Div, Int Nickel Co, 55-63; chief welding engr, Res Div, Foster Wheeler Corp, 63-66 & Airco Welded Prod Div, Air Reduction Co, NJ, 66-68; supvr welding & joining, 68-71, chief welding engr, 71-73, CHIEF MAT ENGR, EBASCO SERV INC, 73- *Concurrent Pos:* Mem, Metal Properties Coun, Tech Adv Comt, Atomic Indust Forum, Welding Res Coun, Weldability Comt, Am Soc Mech Engrs & Comt Nuclear Power Mat. *Mem:* Am Soc Metals; Am Welding Soc; Am Soc Testing & Mat. *Res:* Materials selection, welding and failure causes for service conditions ranging from cryogenic to high temperatures. *Mailing Add:* Ebasco Serv Inc 2 World Trade Ctr New York NY 10048

PETRICK, STANLEY R, computer sciences, see previous edition

PETRIDES, GEORGE ATHAN, b New York, NY, Aug 1, 16; m 40; c 3. WILDLIFE MANAGEMENT, ECOLOGY. *Educ:* George Washington Univ, BS, 38; Cornell Univ, MS, 40; Ohio State Univ, PhD, 48. *Prof Exp:* Asst leader & instr zool, Wildlife Res Unit, Ohio State Univ, 46-48; unit leader, Tex Coop Wildlife Unit, 48-50; assoc prof, Agr & Mech Col, Tex, 48-50; assoc prof, 50-58, PROF FISHERIES & WILDLIFE, ZOOL, MICH STATE UNIV, 58- *Concurrent Pos:* Res fel, Inst Radiation Ecol, Univ Ga, 63; res prof, Univ Pretoria, 65; vis prof, Univ Kiel, 67; deleg, UNESCO, Paris, France, 68; World Wildlife Fund grant, WAfrica, 68; Smithsonian Inst grants, India & Nepal, 68, 69, 74, 75 & 77; chmn, Wildlife Comn, Rhodesia, 69; Mich State Univ studies grants, Africa, 69-73 & 77, Papua, New Guinea, 79; NSF antarctic exped, 72; Food Agr Orgn Mission Afghanistan, 72; NSF grants, Neth, 74, Maylasia, 79, Somali State Asn, Somalia, 80; World Bank Mission Malaysia, 75; Iran Dept Environ grants, 75 & 77; World Wilderness Soc grants, SAfrica, 77, Australia, 80; US Fish & Wildlife Serv grants, Pakistan, 80, India, 82; Man & Biosphere grant, Zaire, 81. *Mem:* Am Soc Mammal; Ecol Soc Am; Wildlife Soc (secy, 48-50, exec secy, 53); Wilderness Soc; Am Ornith Union. *Res:* Ecology of mammals and birds; international wildlife and wilderness resources. *Mailing Add:* Dept of Fisheries & Wildlife Mich State Univ East Lansing MI 48823

PETRIE, JOHN M(ATTHEW), b Phillipsdale, RI, Mar 17, 05; m 36; c 2. CHEMICAL ENGINEERING. *Educ:* Worcester Polytech Inst, BS, 29, MS, 31. *Prof Exp:* Asst chem, 29-31, instr chem & chem eng, 31-37, asst prof chem eng, 37-43 & chem, chem eng & math, 43, prof chem eng, 43-70, EMER PROF CHEM ENG, WORCESTER POLYTECH INST, 70- *Concurrent Pos:* NSF fels, Case Inst Technol, 59 & Washington Univ, 60; NSF-AM Inst Chem Eng Conf Optimization Theory, Stanford Univ, 65. *Mem:* Am Chem Soc; Am Inst Chem Engrs; Am Soc Eng Educ. *Res:* Mass, heat and momentum transfer; process control and dynamics; optimization; research. *Mailing Add:* Wellington Rd Box 171 Templeton MA 01468

PETRIE, WILLIAM LEO, b Assiut, Egypt, Jan 16, 23; US citizen; m 46; c 2. GEOLOGY. *Educ:* Monmouth Col, AB, 49; Univ Iowa, MS, 51. *Prof Exp:* Asst geol, Monmouth Col, 47-49 & Univ Iowa, 49-51; oceanogr, US Navy Hydrographic Off, 51-52, panel coordr geophys & geol, Res & Develop Bd, 52-54; analyst geophys, US Govt, 54-61; exec secy, Adv Comt Mohole Proj, 61-64 & Comt Alaska Earthquake, 64-73, EXEC SECY, US NAT COMT GEOCHEM, ASSEMBLY MATH & PHYS SCI, NAT ACAD SCI-NAT RES COUN, 72-, EXEC SECY, US NAT COMT INT GEOG UNION & US NAT COMT, INT UNION QUATERNARY RES, 74- *Mem:* Fel Geol Soc Am; Am Geophys Union; Soc Env Geochem & Health; Nat Speleol Soc. *Res:* Earth science administration; marine geology; solid-earth geophysics; deep drilling for scientific purposes; scientific and engineering studies of 1964 Alaska Earthquake; environmental geochemistry related to health and disease. *Mailing Add:* Nat Acad of Sci-Nat Res Coun 2101 Constitution Ave Washington DC 20418

PETRIELLO, RICHARD P, b Jersey City, NJ, July 6, 42; m 71. NEMATOLOGY. *Educ:* Iona Col, BS, 64; Seton Hall Univ, MS, 66; Rutgers Univ, PhD(nematol), 70. *Prof Exp:* Res asst nematol, Dept Entom & Econ Zool, Rutgers Univ, 66-68, res assoc, 68-69, asst prof biol, Livingston Col, 69-78; ASSOC PROF BIOL & CHMN DEPT, ST PETER'S COL, JERSEY CITY, NJ, 78- *Concurrent Pos:* NIH grant, 71-72. *Mem:* Am Pub Health Asn; Soc Nematol; Soc Parasitol. *Res:* Nematology, especially in relationship to parasites affecting man; parasitology and invertebrate zoology. *Mailing Add:* Dept of Biol St Peter's Col Jersey City NJ 07306

PETRILLO, EDWARD WILLIAM, b Neptune, NJ, Nov 4, 47; m 69. SYNTHETIC ORGANIC CHEMISTRY. *Educ:* Princeton Univ, AB, 69; Yale Univ, MPhil, 71, PhD(chem), 73. *Prof Exp:* Res fel chem, Calif Inst Technol, 73-74; res investr, 74-79, RES GROUP LEADER CHEM, E R SGUIBB & SONS INC, 79- *Mem:* Am Chem Soc. *Res:* Synthetic, organic and medicinal chemistry; cardiovascular drugs; enzyme inhibitors. *Mailing Add:* Squibb Inst Med Res PO Box 4000 Princeton NJ 08540

PETRO, ANTHONY JAMES, b Waterbury, Conn, Nov 28, 30; m 59; c 1. PHYSICAL CHEMISTRY. *Educ:* Trinity Col, Conn, BS, 52, MS, 54; Princeton Univ, PhD(phys chem), 57. *Prof Exp:* Chemist, Esso Res & Eng Co, 57-66; chemist, Mearl Corp, 66-78; CHEMIST, AVON PRODS, INC, 78- *Mem:* Am Chem Soc Colloid Sect; Soc Cosmetic Chemists. *Res:* Monodisperse sulfur hydrosols; microwave dielectric constant and loss; dipole moments; rubber latex; corrosion; nacreous pigments; particle size; surface area; porosity; thixotropic nail enamels; rheology; sunscreens; non-aqueous gels. *Mailing Add:* 3719 Briarhill St Mohegan Lake NY 10547

PETRO, JOHN WILLIAM, b Vinton, Iowa, Nov 5, 30; m 71; c 2. ALGEBRA. *Educ:* Univ Iowa, BA, 52, MS, 59, PhD(math), 61. *Prof Exp:* From asst prof to assoc prof, 61-71, PROF MATH, WESTERN MICH UNIV, 71- *Concurrent Pos:* Vis assoc prof, Ohio State Univ, 66-67; Vis prof, Univ Calif, Riverside, 79-80. *Mem:* Am Math Soc; Math Asn Am. *Res:* Theory of pseudovaluations in commutative algebra and number theory; theory of filtrations in commutative algebra; theory of boolean structures in commutative algebra. *Mailing Add:* Dept Math Western Mich Univ Kalamazoo MI 49008

PETRO, PETER PAUL, JR, b Mobile, Ala, Apr 13, 40; m 65; c 3. ANALYTICAL CHEMISTRY. *Educ:* Spring Hill Col, BS, 62; Univ Ala, MS, 64, PhD(chem), 66. *Prof Exp:* Res chemist, Res & Develop Lab, Lone Star Gas Co, 68-71, mgr chem & plastics sect, Corp Develop & Res Div, 71-75, dir plastics opers, Nipak, Inc, 75-77; dir tech serv, 78-79, VPRES TECH SERV & MAT, PLEXCO, 79- *Mem:* AAAS; Am Chem Soc; Soc Plastics Eng; The Chem Soc; Coblentz Soc. *Res:* Gas chromatography; infrared spectroscopy; thermal analysis; ultraviolet and visible spectrophotometry and polarography; plastics fabrication; chemical product development. *Mailing Add:* Plexco 3240 N Mannheim Rd Franklin Park IL 60131

PETROF, ROBERT CHARLES, b Beloit, Wis, June 7, 37; m 67; c 1. MECHANICAL ENGINEERING, APPLIED MECHANICS. *Educ:* Northwestern Univ, BSME, 60, MS, 62, PhD(mech eng, astronaut sci), 65. *Prof Exp:* Sr res engr, 65-68, PRIN RES ENGR, SCI RES STAFF, FORD MOTOR CO, 68- *Mem:* Am Inst Aeronaut & Astronaut; Am Soc Mech Engrs; Soc Automotive Engrs; Soc Mfg Engrs. *Res:* Heat transfer; thermal stress analysis; viscoelasticity; finite element structural analysis; mechanics of brakes; composite materials; machine design; vibration analysis; computer analysis methods. *Mailing Add:* Ford Motor Co Sci Res Staff 24500 Glendale Ave Detroit MI 48239

PETROFF, PIERRE MARC, b Paris, France, Apr 26, 40; m 64; c 4. MATERIALS SCIENCE, SOLID STATE ELECTRONICS. *Educ:* Sch Mines, France, BS, 63; Univ Calif, Berkeley, MS, 64, PhD(mat sci), 67. *Prof Exp:* Mil researcher mat sci, Physics Lab, Sci Fac, Orsay, France, 67-69; res fel, Dept Mat Sci, Cornell Univ, 69-71; MEM TECH STAFF, BELL TEL LABS, 71- *Concurrent Pos:* Int Atomic Energy Agency consult, Bhaba Atomic Res Ctr, Bombay, India, 73. *Mem:* Sigma Xi; Am Phys Soc; Am Soc Testing & Mat. *Res:* Crystallographic and electrical properties of defects in semiconductors and optoelectronics materials; study of radiation effects on semiconductors. *Mailing Add:* Bell Tel Labs 600 Mountain Ave Murray Hill NJ 07974

PETROFSKY, JERROLD SCOTT, physiology, bioengineering, see previous edition

PETRONIO, MARCO, b New York, NY, Aug 15, 12; m 41; c 1. CHEMICAL ENGINEERING. *Educ:* City Col New York, BChE, 37. *Hon Degrees:* Deutsch Mem Award, Am Soc Lubrication Engrs, 60. *Prof Exp:* Sales engr, Calo & Lydon, Inc, NY, 37-38; chem engr, Frankford Arsenal, US Dept Army, 40-47, chemist, 47-49, chem engr, 49-54, chemist, 54-59, chief fluids & lubricants br, 59-72; CONSULT, E M KIPP ASSOCS, 72- *Concurrent Pos:* Consult. *Mem:* Am Chem Soc; Am Soc Lubrication Engrs; Am Soc Testing & Mat; Sigma Xi; Am Ord Asn. *Res:* Lubricants research and development for the shaping and forming of metals; cleaners for the removal of lubricants; structural adhesives research for the bonding of metals, glass and plastics; hermetic sealing of instruments. *Mailing Add:* 2835 Winchester Ave Philadelphia PA 19136

PETROPOULOS, CONSTANTINE CHRIS, b South Norwalk, Conn, May 8, 31; m 56; c 4. ORGANIC POLYMER CHEMISTRY. *Educ:* Brown Univ, BS, 54; Fla State Univ, MS, 57. *Prof Exp:* Sr res chemist, Nat Cash Register Co, 59-65 & Loctite Corp, 65-67; sr res chemist, 67-77, res assoc, 77-79, TECH ASSOC, EASTMAN KODAK CO, 79- *Res:* Synthesis of photographic and photoimaging applications; photochemical rearrangement reactions, photoinitiator and sensitizers; organic reaction mechanisms. *Mailing Add:* 1229 Crown Point Webster NY 14580

PETROSKI, HENRY J, b New York, NY, Feb 6, 42; m 66; c 2. FRACTURE MECHANICS, NUCLEAR REACTOR SAFETY. *Educ:* Manhattan Col, BME, 63; Univ Ill, Urbana-Champaign, MS, 64, PhD(mech), 68. *Prof Exp:* Instr, Dept Theoret & Appl Mech, Univ Ill, Urbana, 66-68; asst prof mech, Dept Aerospace Eng & Eng Mech, Univ Tex, Austin, 68-74; mech engr, Reactor Anal & Safety Div, Argonne Nat Lab, 75-80; ASSOC PROF CIVIL ENG, DEPT CIVIL & ENVIRON ENG, DUKE UNIV, 80- *Concurrent Pos:* Prin investr, NSF grants appl mech, 73-73 & struct dynamics, 82- *Mem:* Am Soc Civil Engrs; Am Soc Mech Engrs; Soc Natural Philosophy; Am Acad Mechanics; Hist Sci Soc. *Res:* Dynamic response of cracked elastic bodies; structural dynamics of systems containing cracks, including large plastic deformations; simple mechanical models for predicting structural response of cracked bodies; articles and essays on technology and society. *Mailing Add:* Dept Civil & Environ Eng Duke Univ Durham NC 27706

PETROVIC, LOUIS JOHN, b Cleveland, Ohio, Oct 6, 40; m 67; c 2. CHEMICAL ENGINEERING. *Educ:* Case Inst Technol, BS, 62; Northwestern Univ, MS, 64, PhD(chem eng), 67; Boston Col, MBA, 73. *Prof Exp:* Group leader, Cabot Corp, 67-69; mgr coal prog, Ledgemont Lab, Kennecott Copper Corp, 69-78; PRES, RESOURCE ENG, INC, 78- *Mem:* Am Chem Soc; Am Inst Chem Engrs; Soc Mining Engrs; Am Asn Cost Engrs; Int Asn Energy Economists. *Res:* Flame technology; desulfurization of coal; new coal mining technologies; liquefaction and gasification of coal; hydrometallurgy of mineral ores. *Mailing Add:* Resource Eng Inc 80 Bacon St Waltham MA 02154

PETROVICH, FRED, b Binghamton, NY, July 16, 41; m 62; c 3. NUCLEAR PHYSICS. *Educ:* Clarkson Col Technol, BS, 63; Mich State Univ, MS, 66, PhD(nuclear physics), 71. *Prof Exp:* Instr physics, Mich State Univ, 69-71, res assoc, 71; res assoc physics, Lawrence Berkeley Lab, 71-73; from asst prof to assoc prof, 73-80, PROF PHYSICS, FLA STATE UNIV, 80- *Res:* Development of theoretical microscopic models for describing the inelastic scattering of protons and heavy-ions from nuclei. *Mailing Add:* Dept of Physics Fla State Univ Tallahassee FL 32306

PETROWSKI, GARY E, b LaCrosse, Wis, May 18, 41; m 67. FOOD CHEMISTRY, SURFACE CHEMISTRY. *Educ:* Loras Col, BS, 63; Univ Calif, Los Angeles, PhD(chem), 69. *Prof Exp:* Res assoc, Univ Colo, Boulder, 69-70; sr res scientist, Carnation Res Lab, 70-76; SECT HEAD FOOD DEVELOP, KELCO DIV, MERCK INC, 76- *Concurrent Pos:* Instr, Exten, Univ Calif, Los Angeles, 75-76. *Mem:* Am Chem Soc; Am Oil Chemists Soc; Inst Food Technologists. *Res:* Food emulsion stability; utilization of gums in foods. *Mailing Add:* Kelco Div 8225 Aero Dr San Diego CA 92123

PETRUCCI, RALPH HERBERT, b Saratoga, NY, Jan 21, 30; m 55; c 3. CHEMICAL EDUCATION, ACADEMIC ADMINISTRATION. *Educ:* Union Col, NY, BS, 50; Univ Wis, PhD(phys chem), 54. *Prof Exp:* Asst phys chem, Univ Wis, 50-54; from instr to assoc prof chem, Western Res Univ, 54-64; chmn div natural sci, 66-72, PROF CHEM, CALIF STATE COL, SAN BERNARDINO, 64-, DEAN ACAD PLANNING, 72- *Mem:* AAAS; Am Chem Soc; Sigma Xi. *Res:* Heterogeneous equilibrium; chemical education. *Mailing Add:* Dept of Chem Calif State Col San Bernardino CA 92407

PETRUCCI, SERGIO, b Rome, Italy, Feb 7, 32; m 57; c 1. PHYSICAL CHEMISTRY. *Educ:* Univ Rome, PhD(chem), 55, DrSci (phys chem), 66. *Prof Exp:* Instr phys chem, Univ Rome, 55-56; Fulbright fel, Yale Univ, 56-57; asst prof phys chem, Univ Rome, 57-61; NATO fel, Tech Univ Norway, 61-62; res assoc, Princeton Univ, 62-64; vis asst prof, Univ Md, College Park, 64-65; from asst prof to assoc prof, 65-70, PROF PHYS CHEM, POLYTECH INST NEW YORK, 70- *Mem:* Am Chem Soc; NY Acad Sci; Sigma Xi. *Res:* Ultrasonic and microwave dielectric relaxation in electrolytic solutions; containing macrocyclic ligands; electrical conductance of ionic solutions. *Mailing Add:* Dept Chem Polytech Inst New York 333 Jay St Brooklyn NY 11201

PETRUCELLI, LAWRENCE MICHAEL, b Bridgeport, Conn, July 25, 32; m 62; c 1. NEUROPHARMACOLOGY, NEUROANATOMY. *Educ:* Fordham Univ, BS, 54; Ohio State Univ, MS, 58; Georgetown Univ, PhD(pharmacol), 63. *Prof Exp:* Staff scientist, Litton Bionetics, 63-68; asst prof neuropharm, Sch Med, Univ Pittsburgh, 68-70; health scientist, Nat Inst Neurol & Commun Dis & Stroke, 70-71; exec secy, Pharmacol Study Sect, Div Res Grants, NIH, 71-74; PROG DIR, NAT INST ARTHRITIS, METAB & DIGESTIVE DIS, 74- *Concurrent Pos:* Res assoc, Sch Med, Univ Pittsburgh, 68-69; exec secy arthritis interagency coord comt, Nat Inst Arthritis, Metab & Digestive Dis, 77- *Mem:* Soc Neurosci. *Res:* Somatosensory physiology neuropharmacology; electrophysiology. *Mailing Add:* Westwood Bldg Rm 405 5333 Westbard Ave Bethesda MD 20205

PETRUK, WILLIAM, b Norquay, Sask, June 30, 30; m 59; c 2. GEOLOGY. *Educ:* Univ Saskatchewan, BEng, 54, MSc, 55; McGill Univ, PhD(geol), 59. *Prof Exp:* Sr geologist, Can Johns-Manville Co, 59-60; RES SCIENTIST, CAN DEPT ENERGY, MINES & RESOURCES, 60- *Mem:* Mineral Soc Am; Mineral Asn Can; fel Geol Asn Can; Can Inst Mining & Metall; Soc Econ Geol. *Res:* Ore microscopy, application of ore microscopy to mineral beneficiation and exploration; interpretation of textures and correlation of synthetic studies to naturally occurring minerals; semi-quantitative analysis by means of x-ray diffractometer. *Mailing Add:* Can Dept Energy Mines & Resources 555 Booth St Ottawa ON K1A 0G1 Can

PETRUSKA, JOHN ANDREW, b Winnipeg, Man, Feb 6, 33; m 58; c 1. CHEMICAL PHYSICS. *Educ:* Bishop's Univ, Can, BSc, 53; McMaster Univ, MSc, 54; Univ Chicago, PhD(chem physics), 60. *Prof Exp:* Asst molecular physics, Univ Chicago, 54-55, asst phys & anal chem, 56-58; from res fel to sr res fel biol, Calif Inst Technol, 60-68; ASSOC PROF BIOL, UNIV SOUTHERN CALIF, 68- *Res:* Theory and interpretation of molecular spectra; structure and interaction of biological molecules; properties of the chemical bond; molecular biology. *Mailing Add:* Dept of Biol Sci Univ of Southern Calif Los Angeles CA 90007

PETRY, ROBERT FRANKLIN, b Hebron, Ind, Sept 13, 36; m 59; c 2. NUCLEAR PHYSICS. *Educ:* Univ Ind, BS, 58, MS, 60, PhD(physics), 63. *Prof Exp:* Res assoc nuclear physics, Princeton Univ, 64-67; asst prof, 67-71, chmn dept physics & astron, 70-74, assoc prof, 71-80, PROF PHYSICS, UNIV OKLA, 80- *Mem:* Am Phys Soc. *Res:* Beta-ray and gamma-ray spectroscopy; production and study of nuclides far from stability. *Mailing Add:* Dept Physics & Astron Univ of Okla Norman OK 73019

PETRY, ROBERT KENDRICK, b Trenton, NJ, May 11, 12; m 34; c 4. BIOLOGY. *Educ:* Rutgers Univ, BS, 33. *Prof Exp:* Chemist, Sloane-Blabon Corp, 33-36; from chemist to chief chemist, Del Floor Prods, Inc, 36-45, dir res, 45-53; supvr res & develop, Congoleum Industs, Inc, 53-56, mgr res, 56-61, dir res & develop, 61-77; RETIRED. *Mem:* AAAS; Am Chem Soc. *Res:* Plastics applications in surface coverings. *Mailing Add:* 89 Powder Mill Rd Morris Plains NJ 07950

PETRYK, SYLVESTER, water resources, see previous edition

PETRYSHYN, WALTER A, b New York, NY, Feb 10, 22; m 46; c 4. OTOLARYNGOLOGY. *Educ:* Columbia Col, BA, 43; Long Island Col Med, MD, 45; Am Bd Otolaryngol, dipl. *Prof Exp:* Asst prof clin otolaryngol, Postgrad Med Sch, NY Univ, 53-63; CLIN PROF SURG, COL MED NJ, 63- *Concurrent Pos:* Chmn, Deafness Res Found; consult, East Orange Vet Hosp. *Honors & Awards:* Mosher Award, Am Laryngol, Rhinol & Otol Soc, 60. *Mem:* Am Laryngol, Rhinol & Otol Soc; fel Am Col Surgeons; Am Acad Ophthal & Otolaryngol. *Res:* Otology. *Mailing Add:* 349 Park St Upper Montclair NJ 07043

PETRYSHYN, WALTER VOLODYMYR, b Lviv, Ukraine, Jan 22, 29; US citizen; m 56. MATHEMATICS. *Educ:* Columbia Univ, BA, 53, MS, 54, PhD(appl math), 61. *Prof Exp:* Instr math, Notre Dame Col, NY, 54-56; lectr, City Col New York, 59-61; fel, Courant Inst Math Sci, NY Univ, 61-64; from asst prof to assoc prof math, Univ Chicago, 64-67; PROF MATH, RUTGERS UNIV, NEW BRUNSWICK, 67- *Mem:* Am Math Soc; Soc Indust & Appl Math. *Res:* Functional and numerical analysis, especially solution of linear and nonlinear operator equations. *Mailing Add:* Math Dept Rutgers Univ New Brunswick NJ 08903

PETSCHEK, ALBERT GEORGE, b Prague, Czech, Jan 31, 28; nat US; m 49; c 4. PHYSICS. *Educ:* Mass Inst Technol, BS, 47; Univ Mich, MS, 48; Univ Rochester, PhD(physics), 53. *Prof Exp:* Jr res physicist, Carter Oil Co, Okla, 48-49; mem staff, Los Alamos Sci Lab, 53-66; prof physics, NMex Inst Mining & Technol, 66-68; sr scientist, Systs Sci & Software, Calif, 68-71; PROF PHYSICS, NMEX INST MINING & TECHNOL, 71- *Concurrent Pos:* Vis asst prof, Cornell Univ, 60-61; consult, Los Alamos Sci Lab, 68-80 & Systs Sci & Software, 71-77; vis prof, Dept Geophys & Planetary Sci, Tel Aviv, 78; fel Los Alamos Nat Lab, 80- *Mem:* AAAS; Am Phys Soc; Am Astron Soc. *Res:* Mathematical physics; supernova theory; fracture; cloud physics. *Mailing Add:* MS 434 Box 1663 Los Alamos NM 87545

PETSCHEK, HARRY E, b Prague, Czech, Sept 12, 30; nat US; m; c 4. PHYSICS. *Educ:* Cornell Univ, BEngPhys, 52, PhD, 55. *Prof Exp:* Instr, Princeton Univ, 55-56; prin res scientist, 56-68, assoc dir, 68-73, chmn & chief exec officer, 78-81, PRES, AVCO-EVERETT RES LAB INC, 73- *Mem:* Am Geophys Union; Am Phys Soc; Am Inst Aeronaut & Astronaut; Am Soc Artificial Internal Organs. *Res:* High temperature gas dynamics; magnetohydrodynamics; plasma dynamics; space plasma; biomedical engineering. *Mailing Add:* 1314 Mass Ave 2385 Revere Beach Pkwy Lexington MA 02173

PETSCHEK, ROLFE GEORGE, b Los Alamos, NMex, Aug 25, 54; m 80. THERMAL PHYSICS. *Educ:* Mass Inst Technol, BS, 75, BS, 75; Harvard Univ, PhD(physics), 81. *Prof Exp:* FEL, UNIV CALIF, SANTA BARBARA, 80- *Concurrent Pos:* Vis lectr, Col Creative Studies, Univ Calif, Santa Barbara, 81- *Mem:* Am Phys Soc. *Res:* Behavior of materials near phase transitions, particularly dynamic behavior. *Mailing Add:* Dept Chem Univ Calif Santa Barbara CA 93106

PETSKO, GREGORY ANTHONY, b Washington, DC, Aug 7, 48; m 71. BIOPHYSICS, BIOCHEMISTRY. *Educ:* Princeton Univ, BA, 70; Oxford Univ, PhD(molecular biophys), 73. *Prof Exp:* Instr, Sch Med, Wayne State Univ, 73-76, asst prof biochem, 76-78; ASSOC PROF CHEM, MASS INST TECHNOL, 78- *Mem:* Am Crystallog Asn; Biophys Soc; Am Chem Soc. *Res:* Structure-function relations in biological macromolecules; protein structure determination by x-ray crystallography, enzyme crystallography at sub-zero temperatures, protein-drug interactions, and rational drug design; nervous system structure. *Mailing Add:* Dept Chem Mass Inst Technol Cambridge MA 02139

PETTEGREW, RALEIGH K, b July 7, 31; US citizen; m 58; c 2. MAMMALIAN PHYSIOLOGY. *Educ:* Baldwin-Wallace Col, BA, 53; Kent State Univ, PhD(physiol), 68. *Prof Exp:* Teacher pub sch, Ohio, 56-63; instr Eng, Kent State Univ, 58-62; asst prof, 63-74, ASSOC PROF BIOL, DENISON UNIV, 74- *Concurrent Pos:* Nat Defense Educ Act fel, 65-68. *Mem:* AAAS. *Res:* Mammalian temperature regulation. *Mailing Add:* Dept of Biol Denison Univ Granville OH 43023

PETTENGILL, GORDON HEMENWAY, b Providence, RI, Feb 10, 26; m 67; c 2. PHYSICS, ASTRONOMY. *Educ:* Mass Inst Technol, BS, 48; Univ Calif, Berkeley, PhD(physics), 55. *Prof Exp:* Res asst health physics, Los Alamos Sci Lab, 48-50; staff mem, Lincoln Lab, Mass Inst Technol, 54-58, assoc group leader, 58-62, group leader, 62-63; assoc dir, Arecibo Ionospheric Observ, Cornell Univ, 63-65, dir, 68-70; PROF PLANETARY PHYSICS, MASS INST TECHNOL, 70- *Concurrent Pos:* Pres comn 16, Int Astron Union, 70-73; mem, Comt Planetary & Lunar Explor, US Space Sci Bd, 74-77; Guggenheim fel, 80-81. *Mem:* Nat Acad Sci; Am Phys Soc; Int Union Radio Sci; fel Am Acad Arts & Sci; Am Astron Soc. *Res:* Nuclear and radio physics; planetary and radar astronomy. *Mailing Add:* Dept of Earth & Planetary Sci Mass Inst of Technol Cambridge MA 02139

PETTENGILL, OLIVE STANDISH, b Newport News, Va, Apr 27, 24. CELL CULTURE. *Educ:* Temple Univ, AB, 45; Brown Univ, MS, 48; Boston Univ, PhD(biol), 60. *Prof Exp:* Instr oncol, Mec Sch, Tufts Univ, 60-61; res assoc anat, Med Sch, Univ Pa, 61-63; res instr, Washington Univ, 63-67, asst prof pathol, 67-68; asst prof pathol, Med Sch, St Louis Univ, 68-71; asst prof, 72-77, RES ASSOC PROF PATHOL, DARTMOUTH MED SCH, 77- *Mem:* Am Soc Pathologists; Am Soc Cell Biol; Am Asn Cancer Res; Tissue Culture Asn. *Res:* Human lung cancer; biologic properties of tumor cells under in vitro conditions and in vivo in nude, athymic mice. *Mailing Add:* Dept Pathol Dartmouth Med Sch Hanover NH 03755

PETTERS, ROBERT MICHAEL, b Wilmington Del, June 8, 50. GENETICS, DEVELOPMENTAL BIOLOGY. *Educ:* Univ Del, BA, 72; NC State Univ, MS, 74, PhD(genetics), 76. *Prof Exp:* Res assoc genetics, NC State Univ, 76; assoc develop genetics, Yale Univ, 76-78; ASST PROF BIOL, PA STATE UNIV, 78- *Concurrent Pos:* USPHS trainee, Dept Biol, Yale Univ, 76-77. *Mem:* AAAS; Am Genetic Asn; Genetics Soc Am; Soc Develop Biol. *Res:* Insect and mammalian developmental genetics. *Mailing Add:* Dept of Biol Pa State Univ University Park PA 16802

PETTERSEN, HOWARD EUGENE, b Everett, Wash, Jan 8, 22; m 44; c 3. SOLID STATE PHYSICS. *Educ:* Whitman Col, AB, 43; Univ Minn, MA, 47; Mich State Univ, PhD(physics), 68. *Prof Exp:* Instr physics, Col Training Prog, Army Air Force, State Col Wash, 43-44; instr physics, Whitman Col, 44-45; asst, Univ Minn, 45-47; from asst prof to assoc prof, 47-69, PROF PHYSICS, ALBION COL, 69- *Concurrent Pos:* Fulbright res prof, Inst Crystallog, Univ Cologne, 72-73. *Mem:* Am Asn Physics Teachers. *Res:* Acousto-optics; strain-optical constants. *Mailing Add:* Dept Physics Albion Col Albion MI 49224

PETTERSEN, JAMES CLARK, b Winona, Minn, Aug 5, 32; m 57; c 3. ANATOMY. *Educ:* St Olaf Col, BA, 54; Univ NDak, MS, 61, PhD(anat), 63. *Prof Exp:* Instr anat, Univ NDak, 62-63; from instr to asst prof, 63-70, assoc prof, 70-80, PROF GROSS ANAT, MED SCH, UNIV WIS-MADISON, 80- *Mem:* AAAS; Am Asn Anat; Teratol Soc. *Res:* Spleen; cellular aspects of the immune response; gross anatomy; anatomical syndromes associated with trisomy. *Mailing Add:* 254 S Segoe Rd Madison WI 53705

PETTERSON, ROBERT CARLYLE, b Waterville, Maine, Jan 6, 23; m 51. ORGANIC CHEMISTRY. *Educ:* Univ Maine, BS, 47; Univ Southern Calif, PhD(org chem), 57. *Prof Exp:* Res chemist, Purex Corp, Ltd, Calif, 51-55, supvr basic res, 55-58, res coordr, 58-59; USPHS fel, Imp Col, London, 59-60 & Mass Inst Technol, 60-62, res assoc, 62; from asst res prof to assoc res prof, 62-68, RES PROF CHEM, LOYOLA UNIV, LA, 68- *Mem:* Am Chem Soc; Royal Soc Chem; Int Soc Heterocyclic Chem. *Res:* Photorearrangements of nitrogen haloimides, propenes and cyclopropanes; photolysis of aryl diazonium compounds; transannular radical reactions; singlet molecular oxygen; paint and oil removal; surface-active agents; photooxidation. *Mailing Add:* Dept of Chem Loyola Univ New Orleans LA 70118

PETTEY, DIX HAYES, b Salt Lake City, Utah, Mar 16, 41. TOPOLOGY, GRAPH THEORY. *Educ:* Univ Utah, BS, 65, PhD(math), 68. *Prof Exp:* Asst prof, 68-73, ASSOC PROF MATH, UNIV MO, 73- *Mem:* Am Math Soc; Soc Indust & Appl Math. *Res:* General topology; geometric topology. *Mailing Add:* Dept of Math Univ of Mo Columbia MO 65211

PETTI, RICHARD JAMES, geometry, numerical analysis, see previous edition

PETTIBONE, MARIAN HOPE, b Spokane, Wash, July, 08. ZOOLOGY. *Educ:* Linfield Col, BS, 30; Univ Ore, MS, 32, Univ Wash, PhD(zool), 47. *Prof Exp:* Asst zool, Univ Ore, 32-33; teacher high sch & jr col, 35-36; instr jr col, 36-42; actg assoc, Univ Wash, 45-46, assoc, Lab Embryol & Comp Anat, 46-47, instr marine plankton & comp anat, 47-49; res assoc, Johns Hopkins Univ, 49-53; from asst prof to assoc prof zool, Univ NH, 53-63; cur, 63-78, EMER CUR DIV WORMS, US NAT MUS, SMITHSONIAN INST, 78- *Mem:* AAAS; Soc Syst Zool; Am Soc Zool; Am Soc Limnol & Oceanog. *Res:* Nutrition; growth curves using planarian worms as test animals; taxonomy and ecology of polychaete worms. *Mailing Add:* Div Worms US Nat Mus Smithsonian Inst Washington DC 20560

PETTIGREW, JAMES EUGENE, JR, b Morris, Ill, Sept 17, 45. ANIMAL NUTRITION, SWINE. *Educ:* Southern Ill Univ, BS, 67; Iowa State Univ, MS, 69; Univ Ill, PhD(animal nutrit), 75. *Prof Exp:* Mgr swine res nutrit, Moorman Mfg Co, 74-80; ASSOC PROF, UNIV MINN, 80- *Mem:* Am Soc Animal Sci. *Res:* Effects of maternal nutrition on piglet energy nutrition and survival; protein, mineral, vitamin and energy nutrition of swine; evaluation of feedstuffs for swine. *Mailing Add:* Dept Animal Sci Univ Minn St Paul MN 55108

PETTIJOHN, DAVID E, b Cordova, Alaska, Dec 28, 34; m 64; c 1. CHROMOSOMIC STRUCTURE, GENETIC REGULATION. *Educ:* Wash State Univ, BS, 56, MS, 61; Stanford Univ, PhD(biophys), 64. *Prof Exp:* Res scientist human eng, Boeing Co, 59-61; USPHS fel molecular biol, Geneva, 64-66; asst prof, 66-71, assoc prof biophys, 71-77, PROF BIOCHEM, BIOPHYS & GENETICS, UNIV COLO MED CTR, DENVER, 78- *Mem:* AAAS; Am Soc Biol Chemists; Biophys Soc. *Res:* Nucleic acids; structure and synthesis; chromosomic structure with emphasis on DNA packosius, x-chromosomic reactiveatives; non-histone chromosomal proteins. *Mailing Add:* Dept Biochem Biophys Genetics Univ Colo Health Sci Ctr Denver CO 80262

PETTIJOHN, FRANCIS JOHN, b Waterford, Wis, June 20, 04; m; c 3. GEOLOGY. *Educ:* Univ Minn, BA, 24, MA, 25, PhD(geol), 30. *Hon Degrees:* LHD, Johns Hopkins Univ, 78. *Prof Exp:* Instr, Macalester Col, 24-25; instr geol, Oberlin Col, 25-29; from instr to prof geol, Univ Chicago, 29-52; prof, 52-73, chmn dept, 63-68, EMER PROF GEOL, JOHNS HOPKINS UNIV, 73- *Concurrent Pos:* Geologist, US Geol Surv, 43-53; ed, J Geol, 47-52. *Honors & Awards:* Twenhofel Medal, Soc Econ Paleont & Mineralogists, 74; Wollaston Medal, Geol Soc London, 74; Penrose Medal, Geol Soc Am, 75. *Mem:* Nat Acad Sci; fel Geol Soc Am; hon mem Soc Econ Paleont & Mineral (vpres, 54, pres, 55); Am Asn Petrol Geol; fel Am Acad Arts & Sci. *Res:* Precambrian geology; sedimentary petrology; sedimentation and geochronology. *Mailing Add:* Dept of Earth & Planetary Sci Johns Hopkins Univ Baltimore MD 21218

PETTIJOHN, RICHARD ROBERT, b San Francisco, Calif, Oct 29, 46; m 70. RADIOCHEMISTRY. *Educ:* Univ Calif, BS, 69; Univ Nebr, PhD(chem), 73. *Prof Exp:* Guest res assoc chem, Brookhaven Nat Lab, 72-73; res assoc, Univ Calif, Davis, 73-75; radiochemist, Stanford Res Inst, 76-77, MGR RADIATION PHYSICS, SRI INT, 77- *Mem:* Am Chem Soc. *Res:* Applications of fluorescence, phosphorescence and chemiluminescence to photography, electrophotography, electron multiplier array and glass capillary array applications, production and control of nonreflecting surfaces of silicon solar cells; night vision techniques; development of photographic image enhancement procedures. *Mailing Add:* Dept of Radiation Physics 333 Ravenswood Ave Menlo Park CA 94025

PETTIJOHN, TERRY FRANK, b Wyandotte, Mich, June 7, 48; m 70; c 3. ANIMAL BEHAVIOR, BIOPSYCHOLOGY. *Educ:* Mich State Univ, BS, 70; Bowling Green State Univ, MA, 72, PhD(psychol), 74. *Prof Exp:* ASST PROF PSYCHOL, OHIO STATE UNIV, MARION, 74- *Concurrent Pos:* Testing consult, Crawford County Coun on Alcohol & Drugs, 74- *Mem:* Animal Behav Soc; Psyconomic Soc; Int Soc Develop Psychobiol; Midwestern Psychol Asn; Am Psychol Asn. *Res:* Comparative development and organization of animal social systems, including study of genetic, chemical, and social and physical environmental influences on aggression, attachment, reproductive and learning behaviors in mammals. *Mailing Add:* Dept Psychol Ohio State Univ Marion OH 43302

PETTINATO, FRANK ANTHONY, b Whitefish, Mont, May 19, 21; m 46; c 2. PHARMACEUTICAL CHEMISTRY. *Educ:* Univ Mont, BS, 49, MS, 54; Univ Wash, PhD(pharmaceut chem), 58. *Prof Exp:* Asst pharmaceut chem, Univ Wash, 54-58; from asst prof to assoc prof, 58-70, PROF PHARMACEUT CHEM, SCH PHARM, UNIV MONT, 70- *Mem:* Fel Am Found Pharmaceut Ed. *Res:* Chemistry and medicinal applications of plant constituents. *Mailing Add:* Sch of Pharm Univ of Mont Missoula MT 59801

PETTINGA, CORNELIUS WESLEY, b Mille Lacs, Minn, Nov 10, 21; m 43; c 5. BIOCHEMISTRY. *Educ:* Hope Col, AB, 42; Iowa State Col, PhD(chem), 49. *Prof Exp:* Assoc biochemist, Argonne Nat Lab, 49-50; res biochemist, Eli Lilly & Co, 50-53, head biochem res 53-59, asst to vpres res, develop & control, 60-64, vpres, 64-71, pres, Elizabeth Arden, Inc, 71-72, EXEC VPRES, ELI LILLY & CO, 72- *Mem:* Am Chem Soc; NY Acad Sci. *Res:* Peptide synthesis; proteolytic enzymes; antibiotics. *Mailing Add:* Eli Lilly & Co 307 E McCarty St Indianapolis IN 46285

PETTINGILL, GENE M(EADER), b Grand Rapids, Mich, Feb 23, 29; m 53, 79; c 2. CHEMICAL ENGINEERING. *Educ:* Univ Colo, BS, 55. *Prof Exp:* Teaching asst gen chem, Univ Colo, 54-55; chem engr, Repauno Develop Lab, explosives dept, 55-60, exp sta lab, plastics dept, 60-63, res engr, Carney's Point Develop Lab, explosive dept, 63-64, sr asst admin, Res & Develop Div, 64-65, asst dir admin, Repauno Develop Lab, 66-68, res mgr, Eastern Lab, 68-69, DMT plant supt, 70-71, planning mgr, Polyester & Acrylic Intermediates Div, polymer intermediates dept, 72-73, plant mgr, Instrument Prod Div, Photo Prod Dept, 73-79, MFG MGR, ELECTRONIC MAT DIV, PHOTO PROD DEPT, E I DUPONT DE NEMOURS & CO, INC, 79- *Mem:* Am Inst Chem Engrs; AAAS. *Res:* Organic chemicals; polymer intermediates; process engineering; pilot plant design, construction and operation; polymer processing; plastics. *Mailing Add:* E I du Pont de Nemours & Co, Inc Electronic Mat Div, Photo Prod Dept Wilmington DE 19898

PETTINGILL, OLIN SEWALL, JR, b Belgrade, Maine, Oct 30, 07; m 32; c 2. ORNITHOLOGY. *Educ:* Bowdoin Col, AB, 30; Cornell Univ, PhD(ornith), 33. *Hon Degrees:* DSc, Bowdoin Col, 56, Colby Col, 79. *Prof Exp:* Teaching fel biol, Bowdoin Col, 33-34; instr, Westbrook Jr Col, Portland, Maine, 35-36; instr zool, Carleton Col, 36-41, from asst prof to assoc prof, 41-54; dir, Lab Ornith, Cornell Univ, 60-73. *Concurrent Pos:* Leader & co-leader expeds, Canada, Iceland, Antarctica, Argentina, New Zealand, Mexico and the Falkland Islands, 41-; res assoc, Cranbrook Inst Sci, 40-45; lectr, Audubon Screentours, 43-; trustee, Kents Hill Sch, 75-; vis prof biol, Va Polytech Inst & State Univ, 78. *Honors & Awards:* Arthur A Allen Award, Cornell Univ, 74. *Mem:* Wilson Ornith Soc (secy, 37-41, 42-47, pres, 48-50); Cooper Ornith Soc; Wildlife Soc; Nat Audubon Soc (secy, 57-59, 63-66); Am Ornith Union (secy, 46-51). *Res:* Life histories, behavior, distribution and ecology of birds in the United States, Canada, Mexico and the Falkland Islands; photography of wildlife. *Mailing Add:* Wayne ME 04284

PETTIT, BARBARA JANE, physiology, see previous edition

PETTIT, DAVID J, b Loma Linda, Calif, Sept 27, 36; m 56; c 3. CARBOHYDRATE CHEMISTRY. *Educ:* Univ Calif, Riverside, BA, 60, PhD(org chem), 64. *Prof Exp:* Res chemist, Textile Fibers Dept, Pioneering Res Div, E I du Pont de Nemours & Co, Inc, 64-66; sr res chemist, 66-67, sect head org res, 68-70, asst tech dir, 71-74, tech dir, 74-80, EXEC DIR, KELCO CO, 81- *Mem:* AAAS; Am Chem Soc; Sci Res Soc Am. *Res:* Chemistry of episulfides; stable episulfonium ions; new trialkyloxonium compounds; preparation, polymerization of small ring monomers for textile fibers; synthesis of polysaccharide derivatives; graft copolymers; fermentation biopolymers; polysaccharide structure and properties. *Mailing Add:* Res Dept Kelco Co 8225 Aero Dr San Diego CA 92123

PETTIT, FREDERICK S, b Wilkes-Barre, Pa, Mar 10, 30; m 58; c 4. METALLURGY, PHYSICAL CHEMISTRY. *Educ:* Yale Univ, BE, 52, MEng, 60, DEng(metall), 62. *Prof Exp:* Jr scientist, Westinghouse Atomic Power Div, Pa, 52-54 & Lycoming Div, Avco Mfg Corp, Conn, 57-58; res asst metall, Yale Univ, 58-62; NSF fel thermodyn & reaction kinetics, Max Planck Inst Phys Chem, Gottingen, WGer, 62-63; res assoc, Adv Mat Res & Develop Lab, United Aircraft Corp, North Haven, 63-64, sr res assoc, Middletown, 64-68 & East Hartford, 68-72, sr staff scientist, Pratt & Whitney Aircraft Div, 72-79; PROF & CHMN, METALL & MAT ENG DEPT, UNIV PITTSBURGH, 79- *Mem:* Am Inst Mining, Metall & Petrol Engrs. *Res:* Oxidation of metals and alloys; thermodynamics and kinetics of solid state reactions; electrochemical processes. *Mailing Add:* Univ Pittsburgh Pittsburgh PA 15261

PETTIT, GEORGE ROBERT, b Long Branch, NJ, June 8, 29; m 53; c 5. ORGANIC CHEMISTRY, CANCER. *Educ:* Wash State Univ, BS, 52; Wayne State Univ, MS, 54, PhD(org chem), 56. *Prof Exp:* Asst chem, Wash State Univ, 50-52, lect demonstr, 52; asst, Wayne State Univ, 52-53; sr res chemist, Morton-Norwich Co, 56-57; from asst prof to prof chem, Univ Maine, 57-65; vis prof, Stanford Univ, 65; chmn org div, 66-69, dir, Cancer Res Lab, 73-75, PROF CHEM, ARIZ STATE UNIV, 65-, DIR, CANCER RES INST, 75- *Concurrent Pos:* Consult, Nat Cancer Inst, 65-76, mem med chem fel panel, NIH, 68-70, Nat Cancer Inst, Div Cancer Treat Adv Bd, 71-74; mem, Special Study Sect, Nat Cancer Inst & NIH, 76-, Wash State Univ Found Bd, 81- *Mem:* Am Asn Cancer Res; Am Chem Soc; The Chem Soc; Am Soc Pharmacog. *Res:* Cancer chemotherapy; chemistry of natural products especially steroids, peptides, nucleotides, anticancer constituents, from marine animals, arthropods and plants; general organic synthesis. *Mailing Add:* Dept Chem & Cancer Res Inst Ariz State Univ Tempe AZ 85281

PETTIT, JOHN TANNER, b Salt Lake City, Utah, Aug 2, 23; m 46; c 4. THEORETICAL PHYSICS. *Educ:* Univ Calif, Los Angeles, BA, 47, MA, 49, PhD(theoret physics), 51. *Prof Exp:* Math reader, Univ Calif, Los Angeles, 46-47, res physicist, Eng Dept, 47-50, asst physics, 49-51, res assoc, Inst Geophys, 51-52; physicist, Admin Staff, Howard R Hughes, 52-58, dir indust dynamics, Hughes Aircraft Co, 58-61 & Hughes Tool Co, 61-62; TECHNOL & FINANCIAL CONSULT, DBA-IPL INFO PROCESSING LABS, 62- *Concurrent Pos:* Asst inst geophys, Univ Calif, Los Angeles, 50-51, asst res geophysicist, 52-54; pres, Faim Co, Burbank, 55-57, chmn bd, 57-; consult, 51- *Mem:* Seismol Soc Am; Am Geophys Union. *Res:* Theory of equations; electronic computers; mathematical theory of elasticity in isotropic and anisotropic media; earth tides; geophysics; econometrics; modeling economic systems; industrial management. *Mailing Add:* 1145 S El Molino Pasadena CA 91106

PETTIT, JOSEPH M(AYO), b Rochester, Minn, July 15, 16; m 40; c 3. ELECTRICAL ENGINEERING. *Educ:* Univ Calif, BS, 38; Stanford Univ, EE, 40, PhD(elec eng), 42. *Prof Exp:* Asst elec eng, Stanford Univ, 38-39; instr, Univ Calif, 40-42; spec res assoc, Radio Res Lab, Harvard Univ, 42-43, group leader, 43-45, asst exec engr, 45; supv engr, Airborne Instruments Lab, Inc, NY, 45-46; actg assoc prof elec eng, Stanford Univ, 47-48, from assoc prof to prof, 48-72, dean, Sch Eng, 58-72; PRES, GA INST TECHNOL, 72- *Concurrent Pos:* Assoc tech dir, Am-Brit Lab, Great Malvern, Eng, 54; mem sci adv panel, US Army, 57-67. *Honors & Awards:* Presidential Cert Merit, 49. *Mem:* Nat Acad Eng; fel AAAS; Soc Hist Technol; Am Soc Eng Educ; fel Inst Elec & Electronics Engrs. *Res:* Electronic measurements; circuit theory. *Mailing Add:* President's Off Ga Inst of Technol Atlanta GA 30332

PETTIT, MARY DEWITT, b Philadelphia, Pa, Jan 1, 08. GYNECOLOGY & OBSTETRICS. *Educ:* Bryn Mawr Col, AB, 28; Univ Pa, MD, 32, Med Col, DSc, 72. *Prof Exp:* Asst gynec & obstet, Albany Med Col, Union Univ (NY), 38-39, from instr to asst prof, 39-46; prof, 46-78, EMER PROF GYNEC & OBSTET, MED COL PA, 78- *Mem:* Fel AMA; fel Am Col Surg; fel Am Col Obstet & Gynec. *Mailing Add:* 606 Pembroke Rd Bryn Mawr PA 19010

PETTIT, PAUL HERSCHEL, JR, industrial chemistry, see previous edition

PETTIT, RAY HOWARD, b Canton, Ga, May 12, 33; m 58; c 3. ELECTRICAL ENGINEERING. *Educ:* Ga Inst Technol, 54, MSEE, 60; Univ Fla, PhD(elec eng), 64. *Prof Exp:* Appln engr, Westinghouse Elec Corp, 54-55, 57-58; sr engr, Orlando Div, Martin Co, 60-61, design specialist, 63; scientist, Lockheed-Ga Res Lab, 63-66; from assoc prof to prof elec eng, Ga Inst Technol, 66-78; PROF ELEC ENG, CALIF STATE UNIV, NORTHRIDGE, 78- *Concurrent Pos:* Lectr, Ga State Col, 64; consult, US Air Force, 75- *Mem:* Inst Elec & Electronics Engrs. *Res:* Communication theory; modulation theory; applied decision theory; information theory; adaptive systems; spread spectrum systems; communications electronic countermeasures and electronic counter-countermeasures. *Mailing Add:* 2124 Brentwood Ave Simi Valley CA 93063

PETTIT, RICHARD BOLTON, b Lockport, NY, Dec 4, 44; m 66; c 2. SOLID STATE PHYSICS. *Educ:* Univ Mich, BS, 66; Cornell Univ, PhD(appl physics), 72. *Prof Exp:* MEM TECH STAFF PHYSICS, SANDIA LABS, 71- *Concurrent Pos:* Ed mat, Solar Energy Eng. *Mem:* AAAS; Am Phys Soc; Int Solar Energy Soc. *Res:* Optical property measurement of solar energy materials including emittance and solar absorptance of solar selective coatings, specular reflectance properties of mirrors and solar transmittance of glazings. *Mailing Add:* Sandia Labs Div 5824 Albuquerque NM 87185

PETTIT, ROBERT EUGENE, b Edina, Mo, Dec 19, 28; m 56; c 4. PLANT PATHOLOGY & PHYSIOLOGY. *Educ:* Univ Mo-Columbia, BS, 55, MA, 60, PhD(plant path), 66. *Prof Exp:* Technician, Wolfe Elec Co, Kans, 51-52; technician, Cessna Aircraft Co, 52; technician, Beech Aircraft Corp, 52-53; teacher pub schs, Mo, 55-56; instr electronics, US Air Force, 56-58; res asst plant physiol, Univ Mo-Columbia, 58-60; teacher pub schs, Mo, 60-61; instr plant path, Univ Mo-Columbia, 61-66; asst prof, 66-72, ASSOC PROF PLANT PATH, TEX A&M UNIV, 72- *Mem:* Am Phytopath Soc; Am Soc Agron; Am Inst Biol Sci; Am Peanut Res & Educ Asn. *Res:* Biochemical factors within plants which impart frost hardiness; soil microbiology as related to plant root ecological balances; diseases of peanuts and their control; mycotoxins and the fungi which produce these metabolic compounds; correlation studies of biological sciences research and parapsychological sciences. *Mailing Add:* Dept of Plant Sci Tex A&M Univ College Station TX 77843

PETTIT, ROWLAND, organic chemistry, deceased

PETTIT, RUSSELL DEAN, b Burr Oak, Kans, Feb 17, 41; m 70. RANGE ECOLOGY. *Educ:* Ft Hays Kans State Col, BS, 63; Tex Tech Univ, MS, 65; Ore State Univ, PhD(range mgt), 68. *Prof Exp:* Asst prof range mgt, Tex A&I Univ, 68-69; asst prof, 69-74, ASSOC PROF RANGE MGT, TEX TECH UNIV, 74- *Mem:* Am Soc Agron; Soc Range Mgt; Soil Sci Soc Am. *Res:* Phytosociological relationships between plant communities; soil-plant-water relationships; grassland ecosystems. *Mailing Add:* Dept of Range & Wildlife Mgt Tex Tech Univ Lubbock TX 79409

PETTIT, THOMAS HENRY, b Salt Lake City, Utah, Jan 20, 29; m 53; c 6. OPHTHALMOLOGY. *Educ:* Univ Calif, Los Angeles, AB, 49; Univ Pa, MD, 55. *Prof Exp:* From asst prof to assoc prof ophthal, 63-69, PROF OPHTHAL, SCH MED, UNIV CALIF, LOS ANGELES, 69-, ASSOC DIR JULES STEIN EYE INST & CHIEF CORNEA EXTERNAL OCULAR

DIS DIV, HEALTH SCI CTR, 80- *Concurrent Pos:* NIH spec fel ophthal, Wash Univ, 61-62; NIH res fel, Proctor Found, San Francisco, 62-63; consult ophthal, Vet Admin Hosps, Long Beach, 63-70, Wadsworth, 63-70 & Sepulveda, 69-78; consult, Nat Eye Inst, NIH, 71-75. *Mem:* Asn Res Vision & Ophthal; Am Acad Ophthal (assoc secy, 78). *Res:* Herpes simplex infections in man; corneal and external ocular diseases. *Mailing Add:* Jules Stein Eye Inst Univ of Calif Sch of Med Los Angeles CA 90024

PETTOFREZZO, ANTHONY J, b Bayonne, NJ, Oct 12, 31; m 54; c 4. MATHEMATICS. *Educ:* Montclair State Col, BA, 53, MA, 57; NY Univ, PhD(math), 59. *Prof Exp:* Instr pub sch, NJ, 53 & 55-56; sr programmer comput math, Wright Aeronaut Corp, NJ, 56-57; asst prof math, Newark Col Eng, 57-60; assoc prof, Montclair State Col, 60-66; assoc prof math educ, Fla State Univ, 66-69; PROF MATH SCI, UNIV CENTRAL FLA, 69- *Mem:* Math Asn Am. *Res:* Linear algebra and its applications. *Mailing Add:* Dept Math Sci Univ Central Fla Alafaya Trail Orlando FL 32816

PETTRY, DAVID EMORY, b Beckley, WVa, Aug 1, 35; m 60; c 3. SOIL MORPHOLOGY. *Educ:* Univ Fla, BS, 62, MS, 65; Va Polytech Inst, PhD(soil sci), 69. *Prof Exp:* Soil scientist, Soil Conserv Serv, USDA, 60-69; from asst prof to assoc prof soil sci, Va Polytech Inst & State Univ, 69-75; PROF SOIL SCI, MISS STATE UNIV, 75- *Concurrent Pos:* NASA & Va State Health Dept grants, Va Polytech Inst & State Univ, 70-; consult, Va State Health Dept, 70-; res grants, Phillips Coal Co, 80-81. *Mem:* Soil Sci Soc Am; Clay Minerals Soc; Am Soc Photogram Eng; Am Soc Agron; Soil Conserv Soc Am. *Res:* Soil genesis, classification; urban soils; clay mineralogy; remote sensing of soils and plant species and conditions. *Mailing Add:* Agron Dept Miss State Univ Box 5248 Mississippi State MS 39762

PETTUS, DAVID, b Goliad, Tex, Nov 28, 25; m 47; c 5. VERTEBRATE ZOOLOGY, GENETICS. *Educ:* Ariz State Univ, BA, 51, MA, 52; Univ Tex, PhD, 56. *Prof Exp:* Assoc prof, 56-72, PROF ZOOL, COLO STATE UNIV, 72- *Mem:* Soc Study of Evolution; Am Soc Ichthyol & Herpet; Genetics Soc Am. *Res:* Ecology, genetics and evolution of fishes, amphibians and reptiles. *Mailing Add:* Dept of Zool & Entom Colo State Univ Ft Collins CO 80521

PETTUS, WILLIAM GOWER, b Lynchburg, Va, Aug 6, 25; m 47; c 1. FISSION, HYBRID POWER REACTORS. *Educ:* Lynchburg Col, BS, 49; Univ Va, MS, 53, PhD(physics), 56. *Prof Exp:* Instr physics, Lynchburg Col, 52-54; instr, Univ Va, 54-56; SR PHYSICIST, RES & DEVELOP DIV, BABCOCK & WILCOX CO, 56- *Concurrent Pos:* Vis res scientist, Plasma Physics Lab, Princeton Univ, 78; vis prof nuclear eng, Va Polytech Inst & State Univ, 81. *Mem:* Sigma Xi; Am Phys Soc; Am Nuclear Soc. *Res:* Neutron physics; nuclear reactor physics; fusion; systems analysis; advanced energy systems. *Mailing Add:* Nuclear Power Generation Div Babcock & Wilcox Co Box 1260 Lynchburg VA 24505

PETTY, CHARLES SUTHERLAND, b Lewistown, Mont, Apr 16, 20; m 57. MEDICINE. *Educ:* Univ Wash, BS, 41, MS, 46; Harvard Med Sch, MD, 50; Am Bd Path, dipl, 56. *Prof Exp:* From instr to asst prof path, Sch Med, La State Univ, 55-58; from asst prof to assoc prof forensic path, Sch Med, Univ Md, 58-67; prof, Med Ctr, Ind Univ, 67-69; PROF FORENSIC SCI, UNIV TEX HEALTH SCI CTR DALLAS, 69-, DIR SOUTHWESTERN INST FORENSIC SCI, 69- *Concurrent Pos:* Teaching fel path, Harvard Med Sch, 52-55; vis physician, Charity Hosp La, New Orleans, 55-58; clin pathologist, Md Gen Hosp, 58-61; lectr, Sch Hyg & Pub Health, Johns Hopkins Univ, 59-65, assoc, 65-67; asst state med examr, Md, 58-67; chief med examr, Dallas County, 69- *Mem:* Am Asn Pathologists & Bacteriologists; Am Col Physicians; Am Acad Forensic Sci. *Res:* Pathology; pathologic physiology. *Mailing Add:* PO Box 35728 Dallas TX 75235

PETTY, CLINTON MYERS, b Des Moines, Iowa, June 4, 23; m 57; c 4. GEOMETRY. *Educ:* Univ Southern Calif, AB, 48, MA, 49, PhD(math), 52. *Prof Exp:* Instr math, Princeton Univ, 52-53; res instr, Duke Univ, 53-54; instr, Purdue Univ, 54-55; consult scientist, Lockheed Missile & Space Co, 55-66; assoc prof, 66-74, PROF MATH, UNIV MO-COLUMBIA, 74- *Mem:* Am Math Soc; Math Asn Am. *Res:* Theory of convex sets; geometry of metric spaces. *Mailing Add:* Dept of Math Univ of Mo-Columbia Columbia MO 65211

PETTY, HOWARD RAYMOND, b Toledo, Ohio, Aug 1, 54; m 80; c 1. MEMBRANE BIOLOGY, COLLOID CHEMISTRY. *Educ:* Manchester Col, BS, 76; Harvard Univ, PhD(biophys), 79. *Prof Exp:* Fel, Stanford Univ, 79-81; ASST PROF BIOL, WAYNE STATE UNIV, 81- *Mem:* NY Acad Sci; Biophys Soc; Am Asn Immunologists; Am Soc Cell Biol; Reticuloendothelial Soc. *Res:* Role of the macrophage cell surface in phagocytosis and resistance to neoplasia. *Mailing Add:* Dept Biol Sci Wayne State Univ Col Liberal Arts Detroit MI 48202

PETTY, MILTON ANDREW, JR, b Bunkie, La, May 9, 15; m 40. MICROBIOLOGY, MYCOLOGY. *Educ:* Southwestern La Inst, BS, 35; La State Univ, MS, 37; Univ Minn, PhD(plant path), 40. *Prof Exp:* Asst plant path, Univ Minn, 37-39; asst prof biol, Southwestern La Inst, 39-42; instr biol & soc sci, Northern Mont Col, 42; from instr to asst prof plant path, Univ Md, 43-44; sr microbiol group leader, Lederle Labs Div, Am Cyanamid Co, NY, 44-62, tech consult, Law Div, 62-68; fel bot, Univ Calif, Los Angeles, 68-69; assoc prof, 69-78, EMER ASSOC PROF MICROBIOL, CALIF STATE UNIV, LONG BEACH, 78- *Mem:* Bot Soc Am; Mycol Soc Am; Soc Indust Microbiol. *Res:* Genetics and metabolism of bacteria and fungi; industrial fermentations; antibiotics and other bioactive materials; microbiology patents and their litigation. *Mailing Add:* 12528 Palero Rd San Diego CA 92128

PETTY, ROBERT OWEN, b Indianapolis, Ind, June 11, 33; m 59; c 3. ECOLOGY. *Educ:* Butler Univ, BS, 55; Purdue Univ, MS, 58, PhD(ecol), 66. *Prof Exp:* From instr to asst prof, 59-76, ASSOC PROF BIOL, WABASH COL, 76- *Concurrent Pos:* Vis lectr & vis prof biol sci, Purdue Univ, 70-75. *Mem:* Ecol Soc Am; AAAS. *Res:* Patterns and mechanisms of biotic succession; primary productivity; nutrient cycling. *Mailing Add:* Dept of Biol Wabash Col Crawfordsville IN 47933

PETTY, SCOTT, JR, b San Antonio, Tex, Apr 10, 37; m 59; c 3. GEOPHYSICS, PETROLEUM ENGINEERING. *Educ:* Univ Tex, BS, 60, MS, 61. *Prof Exp:* Asst to pres, Petty Geophys Eng Co, 61-63, vpres, 63-65, pres & exec officer, Petty Labs, 65-67, pres & dir, Co, 67-73; exec vpres, Petty-Ray Geophys, Inc, 73-75; CONSULT, 75- *Mem:* Soc Explor Geophys; Am Inst Mining, Metall & Petrol Engrs; assoc Am Asn Petrol Geologists; Soc Am Mil Engrs; Am Mgt Asn. *Res:* Exploration geophysics primarily related to oil, gas and mineral exploration. *Mailing Add:* 711 Navarro St San Antonio TX 78205

PETTY, THOMAS LEE, b Boulder, Colo, Dec 24, 32; m 54; c 3. PULMONARY DISEASES. *Educ:* Univ Colo, BA, 55, MD, 58. *Prof Exp:* Intern, Philadelphia Gen Hosp, 58-59; resident, Med Ctr, Univ Mich, 59-60; resident med, 60-62, fel pulmonary dis, 62-63, chief resident med, 63-64, from instr to assoc prof, 62-74, PROF MED, UNIV COLO MED CTR, 74- HEAD DIV PULMONARY MED, 71- *Mem:* Am Thoracic Soc; fel Am Col Chest Physicians (pres, 81-82); fel Am Col Physicians. *Res:* Basic and clinical research in pulmonary sciences; applied physiology. *Mailing Add:* Univ Colo Med Ctr 4200 E 9th Ave Denver CO 80220

PETTYJOHN, WAYNE A, b Portland, Ind, Aug 4, 33; m 56; c 2. HYDROLOGY. *Educ:* Univ SDak, BA & MA, 59; Boston Univ, PhD(geol), 64. *Prof Exp:* Instr geol, Bradford Jr Col, 60-63; hydrologist, US Geol Surv, 63-67; prof geol, Ohio State Univ, 67-80; PROF GEOL, OKLA STATE UNIV, 80- *Concurrent Pos:* Groundwater consult; attorney-at-law. *Mem:* Geol Soc Am; Am Bar Asn; Am Water Resources Asn; Am Inst Prof Geologists; Nat Water Well Asn. *Res:* Surface and ground-water relationships and quality of water, including natural quality and pollution; legal aspects of water law; mapping strip mines & detecting air pollution by satellite data. *Mailing Add:* Dept Geol Okla State Univ Stillwater OK 74078

PETURA, JOHN C, US citizen. WASTE TREATMENT & MANAGEMENT. *Educ:* Bucknell Univ, BS, 68; Drexel Univ, MS, 73; Am Acad Environ Engrs, dipl. *Prof Exp:* Chem & environ engr, Gulf Oil Corp, 68-73; sr proj engr & process mgr, Calgon Corp, 73-78; PROJ MGR & SR PROJ ENGR, ROY F WESTON, INC, 78- *Mem:* Am Inst Chem Engrs; Water Pollution Control Fedn; Am Water Works Asn; Am Inst Chem Engrs. *Res:* Water and wastewater treatment; industrial and solid and hazardous waste; sludge handling and disposal; sanitary landfill design and surveillance; control and removal of hazardous toxic substances; potable water supply and treatment; contaminated groundwater recovery. *Mailing Add:* Roy F Weston Inc Weston Way West Chester PA 19380

PETZOLD, EDGAR, b Grand Rapids, Mich, Oct 10, 30; m 52; c 4. BIOCHEMISTRY. *Educ:* Mich State Univ, BS, 52; Purdue Univ, MS, 55, PhD(biochem), 59. *Prof Exp:* Res chemist, Grain Processing Corp, 58-61; dept mgr, Salsbury Labs, 61-66; assoc scientist, Biochem Residue Anal Dept, 66-72, ASSOC SCIENTIST, PHYS & ANAL CHEM DEPT, METAB SECT, UPJOHN CO, 72- *Mem:* Am Chem Soc. *Res:* Drug absorption; bioavailability; distribution; metabolism excretion; mechanism of action; analytical methods for drugs in biological fluids; biochemistry of carotenoids; isolation and properties of peptide antibiotics; industrial enzymes; carbohydrate chemistry and production; metabolism and residue methods in animals; herbicide methods and metabolism; drug metabolism. *Mailing Add:* Unit 7256-136-2 Upjohn Co Kalmazoo MI 49001

PEURA, ROBERT ALLAN, b Worcester, Mass, Jan 26, 43; m 64; c 4. BIOMEDICAL ENGINEERING, ELECTRICAL ENGINEERING. *Educ:* Worcester Polytech Inst, BS, 64; Iowa State Univ, MS, 67, PhD(biomed & elec eng), 69. *Prof Exp:* Asst prof elec & biomed eng, 68-73, ASSOC PROF ELEC ENG & BIOMED ENG, WORCESTER POLYTECH INST, 73-, SITE DIR, WORCESTER POLYTECH INST-ST VINCENT HOSP INTERNSHIP CTR, 72- *Concurrent Pos:* Lectr biomed eng, Med Sch, Univ Mass, 74-; vis assoc prof, Health Sci & Technol Div, Mass Inst Technol, 81-82. *Mem:* Am Heart Asn; Int Elec & Electronics Engrs; Am Soc Eng Educ; Asn Advan Med Instrumentation. *Res:* Noninvasive measurement of circulation; impedance plethysmography; model of electrocardiogram conduction system; computers in biomedicine; models of biological systems; biomedical instrumentation systems; blood pressure measurements; engineering education. *Mailing Add:* Dept Elec Eng & Biomed Eng Worcester Polytech Inst Worcester MA 01609

PEURIFOY, PAUL VASTINE, b Wortham, Tex, June 10, 27; m 53; c 4. ANALYTICAL CHEMISTRY. *Educ:* Fla Southern Col, BS, 49; Univ Miami, MS, 51; Kans State Univ, PhD(chem), 56. *Prof Exp:* Instr chem, Kans State Univ, 54-56; res chemist, Houston Res Lab, Shell Oil Co, 56-66, sr res chemist, 67-72, SR RES CHEMIST, SHELL DEVELOP CO, 72- *Mem:* Am Chem Soc; fel Am Inst Chem. *Res:* Polarography; gas-liquid chromatography; spot tests; electrochemistry; high-pressure liquid chromatography; paper and thin layer chromatography; organic functional group analysis. *Mailing Add:* Westhollow Res Ctr Shell Develop Co PO Box 1380 Houston TX 77001

PEVEHOUSE, BYRON C, b Lubbock, Tex, Apr 5, 27; m 51; c 3. MEDICINE. *Educ:* Baylor Univ, BS, 49, MD, 52; McGill Univ, MSc, 60; Univ London, cert, 60. *Prof Exp:* From asst prof to assoc prof, 60-76, prof, 76-80, CLIN PROF NEUROL SURG, SCH MED, UNIV CALIF, SAN FRANCISCO, 80-, CHIEF DEPT, PAC MED CTR, 67- *Concurrent Pos:* NSF fel neuropath, 59; USPHS trainee neurophysiol, 59-60. *Mem:* Am Col Surgeons; Am Acad Neurol; Am Acad Neurol Surg; Am Asn Neurol Surg; fel Royal Soc Med. *Res:* Birth defects of the central nervous system; use of hypothermia in the treatment of injuries and diseases of the brain. *Mailing Add:* Dept of Neurol Surg Univ of Calif Med Ctr San Francisco CA 94143

PEVERLEY, J ROGER, physics, see previous edition

PEVERLY, JOHN HOWARD, b Danville, Ill, Oct 15, 44; m 66; c 4. PLANT BIOCHEMISTRY, SOIL CHEMISTRY. *Educ:* Purdue Univ, BS, 66; Univ Ill, MS, 68, PhD(plant physiol), 71. *Prof Exp:* Asst prof, 71-78, ASSOC PROF AGRON, CORNELL UNIV, 78- *Mem:* Am Asn Aquatic Plant Mgt; Int Asn Aquatic Vascular Plant Biol; AAAS; Am Soc Agron. *Res:* Influence of agricultural wastes on growth of aquatic plants; nutrient cycling in wetlands; control and biochemistry of aquatic plants. *Mailing Add:* Dept Agron Cornell Univ Ithaca NY 14850

PEVSNER, AIHUD, b Palestine, Dec 18, 25; nat US; m 49; c 2. PHYSICS. *Educ:* Columbia Univ, AB, 47, AM, 48, PhD(physics), 54. *Prof Exp:* Asst, Columbia Univ, 48-53; instr physics, Mass Inst Technol, 53-56; prof, 56-75, JACOB L HAIN PROF PHYSICS, JOHNS HOPKINS UNIV, 75- CHMN DEPT, 74- *Res:* High energy physics, properties of fundamental particles. *Mailing Add:* Dept of Physics Johns Hopkins Univ Baltimore MD 21218

PEW, WEYMOUTH D, b Gilbert, Ariz, Apr 9, 20; m 46; c 4. PHYSIOLOGY. *Educ:* Okla Agr & Mech Col, BSA, 42; Cornell Univ, PhD(veg crops), 49. *Prof Exp:* Asst, Div Veg Crops, NY Agr Exp Sta & Cornell Univ, 46-49; assoc horticulturist, 49-55, HORTICULTURIST, UNIV ARIZ, 55-, COORDR RES LAB, 53-, SUPT MESA BR STA, 58-, PROF PLANT SCI, 74- *Res:* Vegetable physiology, mineral nutriton, irrigation practices and methods; herbicide physiology, soil management. *Mailing Add:* Mesa Br Sta Univ Ariz PO Box 1308 Mesa AZ 85201

PEWE, TROY LEWIS, b Rock Island, Ill, June 28, 18; m 44; c 3. POLAR GEOMORPHOLOGY. *Educ:* Augustana Col, AB, 40; Univ Iowa, MS, 42; Stanford Univ, PhD(geol), 52. *Prof Exp:* Instr geol & head dept, Augustana Col, 42-46; instr geomorphol, Stanford Univ, 46; assoc prof, Univ Alaska, 54-58, prof & head dept, 58-65; chmn dept, 65-76, PROF GEOL, ARIZ STATE UNIV, 65-, DIR MUS GEOL, 76-; GEOLOGIST, US GEOL SURV, 46- *Concurrent Pos:* consult, Corps Eng, US Army, 45, geologist, 46; chief glacial geologist, US Nat Comt-Int Geophys Year, Antarctica, 57-58; US mem periglacial comt, Int Geog Comt; mem coun Alaska earthquake comt, Nat Acad Sci-Nat Res Coun, 65, glaciol panel on polar res, 71-73; chmn joint US planning comt, Sec Int Permafrost Conf, Nat Acad Sci-Nat Acad Eng-Nat Res Coun, 72-74; chmn, Permafrost Comn, Nat Acad Sci-Nat Res Coun, 75-81; leader US deleg, Third Int Permafrost Conf, 78, chmn US comt, Fourth Int Permafrost Conf, 80- *Honors & Awards:* US Cong Antarctic Medal, 66. *Mem:* Fel AAAS; fel Geol Soc Am; Am Asn Geol Teachers; Glaciol Soc; fel Arctic Inst NAm. *Res:* Geomorphology; permafrost; glaciation; Quaternary geology of Arctic, Subarctic and Antarctic areas. *Mailing Add:* Dept of Geol Ariz State Univ Tempe AZ 85281

PEWITT, EDWARD GALE, b Tenn, July 12, 32; m 56; c 4. EXPERIMENTAL HIGH ENERGY PHYSICS, ENGINEERING MANAGEMENT. *Educ:* Vanderbilt Univ, BEEE, 54; Carnegie Inst Technol, MS, 57, PhD, 61; Univ Chicago, MBA, 74. *Prof Exp:* Res physicist & lectr physics, Carnegie Inst Technol, 61-63, asst prof, 63-66; assoc physicist, 64-71, SR PHYSICIST & DIR HIGH ENERGY FACIL DIV, 71-, ASSOC LAB DIR ENERGY & ENVIRON TECHNOL, 73- *Honors & Awards:* Distinguished Performance Award, Univ Chicago, 75. *Mem:* Fel Am Phys Soc. *Res:* Particle detector development, particularly bubble chambers. *Mailing Add:* Bldg 205 Argonne Nat Lab Argonne IL 60439

PEWS, RICHARD GARTH, b Leamington, Ont, Mar 25, 38; m 60; c 2. ORGANIC CHEMISTRY. *Educ:* Univ Western Ont, BSc, 60, PhD(org chem), 63. *Prof Exp:* Fel with Prof R W Taft, Pa State Univ, 63-65; res chemist, Govt Res Labs, Esso Res & Eng Co, NJ, 65-66; res chemist, Polymer & Chem Labs, 66-67, proj leader, Hydrocarbons & Monomers Res Lab, 68-71, sr res chemist, Halogens Res Lab, 70-71, group leader, 71-75, sr res specialist, 76-77, assoc scientist, 77-81, SR ASSOC SCIENTIST, CENT PROCESS, DOW CHEM CO, 81- *Mem:* Am Chem Soc. *Res:* Organic reaction mechanisms; molecular rearrangements; reductions with complex metal hydrides; Hammett-Taft correlations; transmission of conjugation in three membered rings and biaryl systems; hexahalocyclopentadienes; propellant chemistry; nucleophilic aromatic substitution; synthesis of heterocycles; chemistry of sulfonyl cyanides. *Mailing Add:* 4403 Andre Midland MI 48640

PEYRONNIN, CHESTER A(RTHUR), JR, b New Orleans, La, July 26, 25; m 53; c 2. MECHANICAL ENGINEERING. *Educ:* Tulane Univ La, BE, 47; Ill Inst Technol, MS, 50. *Prof Exp:* From asst prof to assoc prof, 48-64, PROF MECH ENG, TULANE UNIV LA, 64- *Concurrent Pos:* Consult, Corps Engrs, US Army, Chrysler Corp & Gen Dynamics Corp. *Mem:* AAAS; Am Soc Mech Engrs; Nat Soc Prof Engrs; Am Inst Aeronaut & Astronaut. *Res:* Engineering medical research; tidal hydraulics; aerospace design; fire protection. *Mailing Add:* Dept of Eng Tulane Univ New Orleans LA 70118

PEYTON, LEONARD JAMES, b Compton, Calif, Feb 8, 24; m 60; c 2. ORNITHOLOGY. *Educ:* Utah State Univ, BS, 51. *Prof Exp:* Biologist, Arctic Health Res Ctr, USPHS, Anchorage, 55-62; asst zoophysiologist, 62-77, ZOOPHYSIOLOGIST, INST ARCTIC BIOL, UNIV ALASKA, FAIRBANKS, 77-, COORDR ENVIRON SERV, 62- *Mem:* AAAS; Am Ornith Union; Cooper Ornith Soc. *Res:* Geographic related song patterns of birds and their relationship within a given species; migration of birds and the use of song patterns in its study; distribution of birds in Alaska. *Mailing Add:* Inst of Arctic Biol Univ of Alaska Fairbanks AK 99701

PEZ, GUIDO PETER, b Fiume, Italy, Feb 10, 41; US citizen; m 66; c 3. CATALYSIS. *Educ:* Univ New South Wales, BSc, 62; Monash Univ, Australia, PhD(chem), 67. *Prof Exp:* Fel, McMaster Univ, 67-69; res chemist, Allied Chem Corp, 69-74, sr res chemist, 74-78, res assoc, 78-81; SR RES ASSOC, AIR PROD & CHEMICALS, INC, 81- *Mem:* Am Chem Soc. *Res:* Synthetic inorganic and organometallic chemistry applied to the development of new homogeneous and heteorgeneous catalysts and selective gas absorption and separation materials. *Mailing Add:* Air Prod & Chemicals Inc PO Box 538 Allentown PA 18105

PEZOLET, MICHEL, b Montreal, Que, Jan 30, 46; m 69; c 2. BIOPHYSICAL CHEMISTRY. *Educ:* Laval Univ, BS, 68, PhD(chem), 71. *Prof Exp:* Res assoc physics, Univ BC, 71-72; res assoc chem, Univ Ore, 72-73; asst prof, 73-77, ASSOC PROF CHEM, LAVAL UNIV, 77- *Concurrent Pos:* Fel, Nat Res Coun Can, 71-73; sabbatical leave, vis prof, Ctr Paul Pascal, Talence, France. *Mem:* Chem Inst Can. *Res:* Spectroscopic studies of molecules of biological interest; structure of proteins determined by Raman, infrared, optical rotatory dispersion and fluorescence spectroscopy. *Mailing Add:* Dept of Chem Laval Univ Quebec PQ G1K 7P4 Can

PFADT, ROBERT E, b Erie, Pa, May 22, 15; m 48; c 4. ENTOMOLOGY. *Educ:* Univ Wyo, BA, 38, MA, 40; Univ Minn, PhD(entom), 48. *Prof Exp:* Field asst, State Fish Comn, Wyo, 38; field supvr, Bur Entom & Plant Quarantine, USDA, 39; field asst, 40-42, from asst prof to assoc prof entom, 42-54, PROF ENTOM, UNIV WYO, 54- *Mem:* Entom Soc Am; Entom Soc Can; fel Royal Entom Soc London; Pan Am Acridol Soc; Asn d'Acridologie. *Res:* Ecology and control of insects. *Mailing Add:* Dept of Entom Box 3354 Univ of Wyo Laramie WY 82071

PFAENDER, FREDERIC KARL, b Long Beach, Calif, Aug 5, 43; m 72. MICROBIAL ECOLOGY. *Educ:* Calif State Col, Long Beach, BS, 66, MS, 68; Cornell Univ PhD(microbiol), 71. *Prof Exp:* Asst prof, 71-77, ASSOC PROF ENVIRON MICROBIOL, DEPT ENVIRON SCI & ENG, UNIV NC, CHAPEL HILL, 77- *Mem:* AAAS; Am Soc Microbiol; Am Soc Limnol & Oceanog; Asn Environ Eng Profs. *Res:* Environmental distribution and microbial degradation of organic compounds, especially molecules considered as pollutants; microbial activities in salt-marsh estuarine ecosystems. *Mailing Add:* Dept of Environ Sci Sch of Pub Health Univ of NC Chapel Hill NC 27514

PFAFF, DONALD CHESLEY, b Los Angeles, Calif, Nov 4, 36; m 64; c 2. MATHEMATICS. *Educ:* Univ Calif, Berkeley, AB, 57, MA, 59, PhD(math), 69. *Prof Exp:* From lectr to asst prof math, 61-72, ASSOC PROF MATH, UNIV NEV, RENO, 72- *Concurrent Pos:* Lectr, Math Asn Am, 70-75. *Mem:* Nat Coun Teachers Math; Math Asn Am. *Res:* Measure theory; discontinuous functions. *Mailing Add:* Dept of Math Univ of Nev Reno NV 89557

PFAFF, DONALD WELLS, b Rochester, NY, Dec 9, 39; m 63; c 3. NEUROPHYSIOLOGY, ANIMAL BEHAVIOR. *Educ:* Harvard Col, AB, 61; Mass Inst Technol, PhD(psychol), 65. *Prof Exp:* Res asst, Harvard Col, 59-61; asst, Mass Inst Technol, 62-65; res assoc, 65-66; NSF fel, 66-68, staff scientist, Pop Coun, 68-69, asst prof, 69-71, assoc prof physiol & psychol, 71-77, PROF NEUROBIOL & BEHAV, ROCKEFELLER UNIV, 77- *Mem:* AAAS; Am Asn Anat; Am Psychol Asn; Soc Neurosci; Am Physiol Soc. *Res:* Brain mechanisms of behavior; effects of hormones on brain electrical activity; brain chemistry and behavior. *Mailing Add:* Rockefeller Univ York Ave & 66th St New York NY 10021

PFAFF, WILLIAM WALLACE, b Rochester, NY, Aug 14, 30; m 60; c 4. SURGERY. *Educ:* Harvard Univ, AB, 52; Univ Buffalo, MD, 56. *Prof Exp:* Intern & jr resident surg, Univ Chicago, 56-58; clin assoc cardiac surg, NIH, 58-60; resident surg, Med Ctr, Stanford Univ, 60-64, instr & chief resident, 64-65; from asst prof to assoc prof, 65-71, PROF SURG, UNIV FLA, 71- *Concurrent Pos:* Consult, Vet Admin Hosps, Gainesville & Lake City & Univ Hosp, Jacksonville, 65-; pres, Southeastern Orgn Procurement Found. *Mem:* Am Col Surg; Asn Acad Surg; Soc Univ Surg; Transplantation Soc. *Res:* Organ transplantation, vascular physiology. *Mailing Add:* 1624 NW Seventh Pl Gainesville FL 32601

PFAFFENBERGER, CARL DALE, analytical biochemistry, cancer, see previous edition

PFAFFENBERGER, WILLIAM ELMER, b Cleveland, Ohio, Mar 16, 43; m 67; c 1. MATHEMATICS. *Educ:* Univ Ore, BA, 64, MA, 66, PhD(math), 69. *Prof Exp:* Asst prof, 69-80, ASSOC PROF MATH, UNIV VICTORIA, BC, 80- *Concurrent Pos:* Nat Res Coun Can res grant, 70-71. *Mem:* Am Math Soc; Can Math Cong. *Res:* Banach algebras and operator theory. *Mailing Add:* Dept of Math Univ of Victoria Victoria BC V8W 2Y2 Can

PFAFFMAN, MADGE ANNA, b Mobile, Ala, Feb 18, 39. PHARMACOLOGY. *Educ:* Judson Col, BA, 61; Univ Miss, MS, 63, PhD(pharmacol), 65. *Prof Exp:* ASST PROF PHARMACOL, MED SCH, UNIV MISS, 67- *Concurrent Pos:* NIH fel physiol, Med Sch, Duke Univ, 65-67; vis prof, Univ Southern Miss, 70- *Mem:* AAAS; Am Soc Pharmacol & Exp Therapeut; Biophys Soc. *Res:* Physiology and pharmacology of gastrointestinal and vascular smooth muscle involving the excitation-contraction (E-C) coupling and ionic basis of their function in the presence of drugs. *Mailing Add:* Dept of Pharmacol & Toxicol Univ of Miss Med Ctr Jackson MS 39216

PFAFFMANN, CARL, b New York, NY, May 27, 13; m 39; c 3. NEUROSCIENCES, PHYSIOLOGICAL PSYCHOLOGY. *Educ:* Oxford Univ, Eng, BA, 37; Brown Univ, PhB, 33, MSc, 35; Cambridge Univ, Eng, PhD(physiol), 39. *Prof Exp:* Res assoc biophysics, Johnson Found, Univ Pa, 39-40; instr psychol, Brown Univ, 40-42; from asst prof to prof psychol, Brown Univ, 45-60; vis prof, Yale Univ, 59 & Harvard Univ, 62-63; prof, Florence Pierce Grant Univ, Brown Univ, 60-65; vpres & prof, 65-78, VINCENT & BROOKE ASTOR PROF PHYSIOL PSYCHOL, ROCKEFELLER UNIV, 78- *Concurrent Pos:* Nat lectr, Sigma Xi, 63; chmn, Div Behav Sci, Nat Res Coun, 62-64; mem exec comt, Int Union Physiol Sci, 66-72; Kenneth Craik Res Award, St John's Col, Cambridge, Eng, 68-69; mem, Bd Fel, Brown Univ Corp, 69- *Honors & Awards:* Howard Crosby Warren Medal, Soc Exp Psychologists, 60. *Mem:* Nat Acad Sci; Soc Exp Psychol; Am Physiol Soc; Am Philos Soc; AAAS. *Res:* Neurophysiology and psychology of chemical senses, taste and smell; brain mechanisms and behavior. *Mailing Add:* Rockefeller Univ New York NY 10021

PFAHL, PETER BLAIR, b Pittsburgh, Pa, Apr 10, 19; m 51; c 2. HORTICULTURE. *Educ:* Pa State Univ, BS, 42, PhD(floricult), 58; Ohio State Univ, MS, 48. *Prof Exp:* From instr to prof floricult, 48-80, EMER PROF FLORICULT, PA STATE UNIV, 80- *Res:* Keeping quality of cut flowers; survey of florist industry; marketing and merchandising of cut flowers; time and motion study in retail flower shops. *Mailing Add:* 559 Easterly Parkway State Col University Park PA 16801

PFAHLER, PAUL LEIGHTON, b Essex Co, Ont, Nov 3, 30; nat US; m 67; c 2. GENETICS. *Educ:* Univ Mich, AB, 52; Mich State Univ, MS, 54; Purdue Univ, PhD(genetics, plant breeding), 57. *Prof Exp:* Asst, Mich State Univ, 53-54; fel, Carnegie Inst, Purdue Univ & Stanford Univ, 55-56; asst agron, Purdue Univ, 56-57, interim asst prof, 57, fel & interim asst prof hort, 57-58; from asst agronomist to assoc agronomist, 55-71, PROF & AGRONOMIST, UNIV FLA, 71- *Concurrent Pos:* Res prof, Univ Nijmegen, Netherlands, 69, vis prof, 77. *Mem:* AAAS; Am Soc Agron; Crop Sci Soc Am; Genetics Soc Am; Am Genetic Asn. *Res:* Population and physiological genetic studies involving small grains and maize. *Mailing Add:* Dept of Agron Univ of Fla 304 Newell Gainesville FL 32611

PFAHNL, ARNOLD, b Austria, June 25, 23. PHYSICS. *Educ:* Graz Univ, PhD(physics), 48; Univ Paris, ScDr, 56. *Prof Exp:* Asst, Graz Univ, 48; res engr, French X-ray Firm, 50-57; res asst, Stanford Univ, 57; mem tech staff, Bell Tel Labs, Inc, NJ, 57-69, supvr Film Technol Dept, 69-80, SUPVR, INTEGRATED CIRCUIT PACKAGING DEPT, BELL LABS INC, PA, 80- *Mem:* Int Soc Hybrid Microelectronics. *Res:* X-ray tubes; luminescent materials; light emitting diodes; GaAs lasers, photoconductors; image pick-up tubes; thin and thick film hybrid circuit development; integrated circuit packaging development. *Mailing Add:* Integrated Circuit Packaging Dept Bell Labs Inc 555 Union Blvd Allentown PA 18103

PFALTZGRAFF, JOHN ANDREW, b Huntingdon, Pa, Nov 1, 36; m 60; c 3. MATHEMATICS. *Educ:* Harvard Univ, AB, 58; Univ Ky, MS, 61, PhD(math), 63. *Prof Exp:* Asst prof math, Univ Kans, 63-65; vis asst prof, Ind Univ, Bloomington, 65-67; asst prof, 67-69, assoc prof, 69-76, PROF MATH, UNIV NC, CHAPEL HILL, 76- *Mem:* Am Math Soc; Math Asn Am. *Res:* Complex variables; conformal mapping and variational methods; spaces of analytic functions; potential theory; analytic functions in Banach spaces. *Mailing Add:* Dept of Math Univ of NC Chapel Hill NC 27515

PFALZNER, PAUL MICHAEL, b Vienna, Austria, Aug 18, 23; nat Can; m 50; c 1. MEDICAL PHYSICS. *Educ:* Univ Toronto, BA, 46; McGill Univ, MSc, 51. *Prof Exp:* Res officer, Nat Res Coun Can, 46-50; instr physics, McGill Univ, 50-51; physicist, Ont Cancer Found, 52-64; head dosimetry sect, Dept Res & Isotopes, Int Atomic Energy Agency, 67-68; SR PHYSICIST, ONT CANCER TREATMENT & RES FOUND, 68- *Concurrent Pos:* Ont Cancer Treatment & Res Found traveling fel, Eng & Scand, 55-56; lectr, Univ Western Ont, 51-66; Int Atomic Energy Agency tech assistance adv med physics, Govt Thailand, 64-65, first officer, Int Atomic Energy Agency, Vienna, 66-68; secy-gen, Fourth Int Conf Med Physics. *Mem:* Can Asn Physicists; Brit Hosp Physicists Asn; Brit Inst Radiol; Am Asn Physicists in Med; Ger Soc Med Physics. *Res:* Physical aspects of applications of radiation in biology and medicine; radioisotopes brachytherapy and teletherapy; use of computers in life sciences. *Mailing Add:* Ont Cancer Treat & Res Found Physics Dept 190 Melrose Ave Ottawa ON K1Y 4K7 Can

PFANDER, WILLIAM HARVEY, b Lamar, Mo, Aug 9, 23; m 53; c 3. INTERNATIONAL NUTRITION. *Educ:* Univ Mo, BS, 48; Univ Ill, MS, 49, PhD(nutrit), 51. *Prof Exp:* Asst, Univ Wis, 51; assoc prof, 52-54, chmn dept, 75-77, PROF ANIMAL SCI, UNIV MO-COLUMBIA, 54-, ASSOC DEAN & ASSOC DIR, AGR EXP STA, 77- *Concurrent Pos:* Fulbright res fel, Rowett Res Inst, Aberdeen Univ, 51-52; NSF sr fel, Clunies Ross Lab, Univ Sydney, 58-59; Fulbright fel, Univ Alexandria, 66-67; Moorman fel nutrit, 67; mem Nat Acad Sci-Nat Res Coun comt nitrate accumulation; US nat comt, Int Union Nutrit Sci; comt animal nutrit, Nat Res Coun, subcomt horse nutrit, subcomt nutrient & toxic properties water; mem Coun Agr Sci & Technol; nutrit res award, Am Soc Animal Sci. *Mem:* Fel AAAS; Am Dairy Sci Asn; Am Chem Soc; Am Inst Nutrit; Am Soc Animal Sci. *Res:* Experimental nutrition; ruminant metabolism and nutrition; carbohydrate utilization; metabolic disorders; appetite control; nutritional environmental interactions; mineral and amino acid requirements; comparative nutrition. *Mailing Add:* Box 170 RD2 Columbia MO 65201

PFANN, WILLIAM GARDNER, b Brooklyn, NY, Oct 25, 17. PHYSICAL METALLURGY. *Educ:* Cooper Union, BChE, 40. *Prof Exp:* MEM TECH STAFF, BELL TEL LABS, INC. *Honors & Awards:* Mathewson Gold Medal, Am Inst Mining, Metall & Petrol Engrs, 55; Clamer Medal, Franklin Inst, 57; Sauveur Award, Am Soc Metals, 58; Prof Progress Award, Am Inst Chem Engrs, 60; Moissan Medal, Paris, 62; Gano Dunn Medal, Cooper Union, 63; Creative Invention Award, Am Chem Soc, 68; Carborundum Co Award, 72; Solid State Sci & Technol Award, Electrochem Soc, 73; Indust Res Inst Achievement Award, 74; Int Prize New Mat, Am Phys Soc, 76. *Mem:* Nat Acad Sci; Am Phys Soc; fel Am Soc Metals; Am Inst Mining, Metall & Petrol Engrs; fel Metall Soc. *Res:* Crystal growth; zone melting; dislocations; separation processes; semiconducting devices. *Mailing Add:* Mat Sci Res Lab Bell Tel Labs Murray Hill NJ 07974

PFANNKUCH, HANS OLAF, b Berlin, Ger, Nov 23, 32; m 61; c 3. HYDROGEOLOGY. *Educ:* Aachen Tech Univ, MS, 59; Univ Paris, PhD(fluid mech), 62. *Prof Exp:* Res engr, French Petrol Inst, 61-65; res asst prof transport in porous media, Univ Ill, 65-66; asst prof technol, Southern Ill Univ, Carbondale, 66-68; ASSOC PROF HYDROGEOL, UNIV MINN, MINNEAPOLIS, 68- *Mem:* Am Inst Mining, Metall & Petrol Eng; Am Geophys Union; Geol Soc Am; Am Water Resources Asn. *Res:* Fluid mechanics and transport processes in porous media; ground water geology; analytical geohydrology; watershed modeling and analysis; analysis; surface water (lake)-groundwater interaction; subsurface propagation of oil spills; environmental geology; technical dictionaries. *Mailing Add:* Dept of Geol & Geophys Univ of Minn Pillsbury Hall Minneapolis MN 55455

PFAU, CHARLES JULIUS, b Troy, NY, Sept 29, 35; m 58; c 3. VIROLOGY, BIOCHEMISTRY. *Educ:* Rensselaer Polytech Inst, BS, 56; Ind Univ, MA, 58, PhD(bact), 60. *Prof Exp:* USPHS fel biophys, Yale Univ, 60-62 & Rickettsia & Virus Dept, State Serum Inst, Copenhagen, Denmark, 62-64; asst prof microbiol, Univ Mass, Amherst, 64-71; assoc prof, 71-76, PROF BIOL, RENSSELAER POLYTECH INST, 76- *Concurrent Pos:* Career develop award, USPHS, 65-70; chmn arenavirus study group, Int Comt Taxon Viruses, 74-80; intergovt fel, Nat Inst Neurol & Commun Disorders & Stroke, NIH, 79-80. *Mem:* Am Soc Microbiol; NY Acad Sci. *Res:* Biophysical and biochemical properties of arenaviruses; control mechanisms in animal virus-infected cells; antiviral chemotherapy. *Mailing Add:* Dept of Biol Rensselaer Polytech Inst Troy NY 12180

PFEFFER, JOHN T, b Ripley, Ohio, Oct 2, 35; m 58; c 2. SANITARY ENGINEERING. *Educ:* Univ Cincinnati, CE, 58, MS, 59; Univ Fla, PhD(sanit eng), 62. *Prof Exp:* Eng assoc, Univ Fla, 60-61; from asst prof to assoc prof sanit eng, Univ Kans, 62-67; assoc prof, 67-69, PROF SANIT ENG, UNIV ILL, URBANA, 69- *Mem:* Water Pollution Control Fedn; Am Soc Civil Engrs; Am Soc Microbiol; Am Soc Eng Educ. *Res:* Basic and applied research on biological processes for purification of wastewaters and for processing waste materials for energy recovery by methane fermentation. *Mailing Add:* 3230 Newmark Lab Univ Ill 208 N Romine St Urbana IL 61801

PFEFFER, PHILIP ELLIOT, b New York, NY, Apr 8, 41; m 62; c 3. PHYSICAL ORGANIC CHEMISTRY. *Educ:* Hunter Col in the Bronx, AB, 62; Rutgers Univ, MS, 64, PhD(chem), 66. *Prof Exp:* Res fel, Univ Chicago, 66-68; sr res chemist, Eastern Regional Res Ctr, 68-76, res leader milk components, 76-80, RES LEADER, SPECTROS LAB, USDA, 80- *Concurrent Pos:* Adj prof chem, Pa State Univ, Ogontz, 74-77; ed, J Carbohydrate Chem, 82- *Mem:* AAAS; Am Chem Soc; Sigma Xi; Soc Appl Spectros. *Res:* Nuclear magnetic resonance spectroscopy of lipids and lipid derivatives, polysaccharides and studies of molecular interactions; carbanion chemistry of carboxylic acids; 2H isotope effects in 13C nuclear magnetic resonance spectroscopy (deuterium induced differential isotope 13C nuclear magnetic resonance spectroscopy). *Mailing Add:* Phys Chem & Instrumentation Lab USDA Philadelphia PA 19118

PFEFFER, RICHARD LAWRENCE, b Brooklyn, NY, Nov 26, 30; m 53; c 4. DYNAMIC METEOROLOGY. *Educ:* City Col New York, BS, 52; Mass Inst Technol, MS, 54, PhD(meteorol), 57. *Prof Exp:* Res asst meteorol, Mass Inst Technol, 52-55; atmospheric physicist, Air Force Cambridge Res Ctr, 55-59; sr res scientist, Columbia Univ, 59-61, from lectr to asst prof geophys, 61-64; assoc prof, 64-67, PROF METEOROL & DIR GEOPHYS FLUID DYNAMICS INST, FLA STATE UNIV, 67- *Concurrent Pos:* Guest lectr, Mass Inst Technol, 54 & broadcast on tsunamis for The Voice of Am, 63; consult, N W Ayer Co, 62, Educ Testing Serv, Princeton, NJ, 63, Grolier Inc, 63 & Naval Res Lab, Washington, DC, 71-76; mem, Int Comn for Dynamical Meteorol, 72-76. *Mem:* Am Meteorol Soc. *Res:* Dynamics of atmospheric processes; momentum and energy exchanges in hurricanes, cyclones and the global atmospheric circulation; available potential energy; fluctuations of planetary atmospheric circulations; acoustic-gravity wave propagation; experimental and computer modeling of climatic variability. *Mailing Add:* Geophys Fluid Dynamics Inst Fla State Univ Tallahassee FL 32306

PFEFFER, ROBERT, b Vienna, Austria, Nov 26, 35; US citizen; m 60; c 2. CHEMICAL ENGINEERING. *Educ:* NY Univ, BChE, 56, MChE, 58, DEngSc(chem eng), 62. *Prof Exp:* From lectr to assoc prof, 57-67, prof, 73-80, HEBERT G KAYSER PROF CHEM ENG, CITY COL NEW YORK, 67-, CHMN DEPT, 73- *Concurrent Pos:* Res assoc, Brookhaven Nat Lab, 63; prin investr res grants, NSF, Environ Protection Agency, NIH, NASA, Office Naval Res, 63-; fac fel, NASA Lewis Res Ctr, 64 & Case Inst Technol, 65; consult, NASA Lewis Res Ctr-Cleveland, 65-68, US Army Res-Durham, 70-76 & various indust co, 77-; Nat Air Pollution Control Asn fel, 68-71; vis prof, Imp Col, Univ London, 69-70; vis prof technician, Israel Inst Technol, 76-77. *Mem:* Am Inst Chem Engrs; Am Soc Eng Educ. *Res:* Low Reynolds-number hydrodynamics; heat and mass transfer with applications to biomedical problems; flow of gas-particle suspensions; filtration of aerosols by granular beds. *Mailing Add:* Dept of Chem Eng City Col of New York New York NY 10031

PFEFFER, WASHEK F, b Prague, Czech, Nov 14, 36; m 59. MATHEMATICS. *Educ:* Charles Univ, Prague, RNDr, 60; Univ Md, PhD(math anal), 66. *Prof Exp:* Res assoc math, Charles Univ, Prague, 59-60; res asst, Inst of Heat Technique, Prague, 60-63; res asst, Czech Acad Sci, 63-64; vis res asst, Polish Acad Sci, spring, 64; res asst, Royal Inst Technol, Stockholm, Sweden, fall, 64; asst prof, George Washington Univ, 65-66; asst prof, Univ Calif, Davis, 66-68; vis assoc prof, Univ Calif, Berkeley, 68-69; assoc prof, Univ Calif, Davis, 69-71; vis prof, Univ Ghana & dir Ghana Ctr, Univ Calif Educ Abroad Prog, 71-73; PROF MATH, UNIV CALIF, DAVIS, 73- *Concurrent Pos:* Vis prof, Royal Inst Technol, Stockholm, Sweden, 75. *Mem:* Am Math Soc; Swedish Math Soc. *Res:* Non-absolute integration in topological spaces; topology and topological measure theory. *Mailing Add:* Dept of Math Univ of Calif Davis CA 95616

PFEFFERKORN, ELMER ROY, JR, b Manitowoc, Wis, Dec 13, 31; m 64; c 3. MICROBIOLOGY, PARASITOLOGY. *Educ:* Lawrence Col, BA, 54; Oxford Univ, BA & MA, 56; Harvard Univ, PhD(bact), 60. *Prof Exp:* Instr bact & immunol, Harvard Med Sch, 62-63, assoc, 63-65, asst prof, 65-67; assoc prof, 67-70, PROF & CHMN MICROBIOL, DARTMOUTH MED SCH, 70- *Concurrent Pos:* Res fel bact & immunol, Harvard Med Sch, 60-62; adj prof biol, Dartmouth Col, 70-; mem, virol study sect, 70-74 & trop med parasitol study sect, NIH, 80- *Mem:* Am Soc Microbiol; Am Soc Biol Chemists; Am Soc Parasitologists; Soc Protozoologists. *Res:* Genetics and biochemistry of animal viruses and intracellular parasites. *Mailing Add:* Dept of Microbiol Dartmouth Med Sch Hanover NH 03755

PFEFFERKORN, HERMANN WILHELM, b Muenster, Ger, Sept 25, 40; m 69; c 1. PALEOBOTANY, STRATIGRAPHY. *Educ:* Univ Muenster, WGer, Dipl, 66, Drrernat(geol), 68. *Prof Exp:* Fel paleobot, Univ Ill, Champaign-Urbana, 68-69; asst geologist paleobot, Ill State Geol Surv, 69-71; res assoc paleobot, Univ Muenster, WGer, 71-73; vis lectr, 73-74, asst prof, 74-79, ASSOC PROF GEOL, UNIV PA, 79- *Mem:* Geol Soc Am; Bot Soc Am; Paleont Soc; Int Orgn Paleobot. *Res:* Carboniferous (Pennsylvanian) floras of North America with special reference to biostratigraphy and paleoecology; stratigraphic correlation between different coal basins and between North America and Europe. *Mailing Add:* Dept Geol D4 Univ Pa 240 S 33rd St Philadelphia PA 19104

PFEIFER, GERARD DAVID, b Chicago, Ill, Sept 5, 37; m 64; c 2. OCCUPATIONAL HEALTH, BIOCHEMISTRY. *Educ:* Univ Tulsa, BS, 64; PhD(biochem), Univ Louisville, 71. *Prof Exp:* Chemist, Ozark-Mahoning Co, 64-65; Nat Res Coun Fel & res chemist, Human Nutrit Res Div, Agr Res Serv, USDA, 71-73; asst prof chem, Cent Mo State Univ, 73-77; mem staff res & technol, 77-81, SUPVR-CORP OCCUP HEALTH, ARMCO, INC, 81- *Mem:* Am Chem Soc; AAAS; Am Indust Hyg Asn. *Res:* Industrial toxicology. *Mailing Add:* Res & Technol Armco Inc Middletown OH 45043

PFEIFER, HOWARD WILLIAM, b Newark, NJ, Oct 2, 28; m 55; c 3. PLANT TAXONOMY. *Educ:* Univ Iowa, BA, 58; Wash Univ, AM, 60, PhD(plant taxon), 63. *Prof Exp:* Lectr bot, Southern Ill Univ, Edwardsville, 58-61; teaching asst, Wash Univ, 61, instr, eve sch, 62-63; asst prof, 63-66, ASSOC PROF BIOL, BOT SECT, BIOL SCI GROUP, 66-, CURATOR, HERBARIUM, 63- *Concurrent Pos:* Herbarium asst, Mo Bot Garden, 58-59; panel mem undergrad educ support, NSF, 65; sr Univ Conn rep adv coun, Orgn Trop Studies, Inc, 66-70, bd dirs, 70- mem terrestial biol fac exec comt, 68-71, mem-at-large exec comt, Bd Dirs, 71-73; mem bd adv, Amazon Exped & Res Ctr, 68-; educ rev panel, Memoirs NY Bot Garden, 72- *Mem:* AAAS; Am Soc Plant Taxon; Am Inst Biol Sci; Asn Trop Biol; Am Hort Soc. *Res:* Plant systematics; world Aristolochiaceae; Aristolochia of North America; floras of Mexico, Honduras, Panama and eastern United States; gymnosperms, wild populations and cultivars; taxonomy of cultivated plants. *Mailing Add:* Dept of Biol Univ of Conn Storrs CT 06268

PFEIFER, ROBERT PAUL, b Arcola, Ill, July 28, 20; m 42; c 2. PLANT BREEDING, GENETICS. *Educ:* Univ Ill, BS, 42, PhD(agr), 49. *Prof Exp:* Asst prof agron, Okla State Univ, 49-52; from asst prof to assoc prof, Univ Wyo, 52-57; assoc prof agron, 57-70, ASSOC PROF PLANT BREEDING, PA STATE UNIV, 70- *Concurrent Pos:* Fulbright-Hays lectr, Ataturk Univ, Turkey, 67. *Mem:* AAAS; Am Soc Agron; Am Genetic Asn. *Res:* Breeding of wheat, barley and oats. *Mailing Add:* Dept of Agron Pa State Univ Col of Agr University Park PA 16802

PFEIFFER, CARL CURT, b Peoria, Ill, May 19, 08; m 30; c 2. PHARMACOLOGY. *Educ:* Univ Wis, BA, 31, MA, 32, PhD(pharmacol), 35; Univ Chicago, MD, 37. *Prof Exp:* Asst instr pharmacol, Univ Wis, 30-35; instr, Univ Chicago, 36-37; intern, Wis Gen Hosp, 37-38; instr, Univ Chicago, 38-40; assoc prof, Col Med, Wayne Univ, 40-41; chief pharmacologist, Parke, Davis & Co, 41-43; prof pharmacol & head dept, Col Med, Univ Ill, 45-54; prof, Sch Med, Emory Univ, 54-60, dir div basic health sci, 57-60; head sect pharmacol, NJ Neuropsychiat Inst, 60-73; DIR, BRAIN BIO-CTR, 73- *Mem:* AAAS; Am Soc Pharmacol & Exp Therapeut; Soc Exp Biol & Med; NY Acad Sci; assoc AMA. *Res:* Chemotherapy; nature of pain; analgesic drugs; headache; neuropharmacology; biology of schizophrenia; clinical pharmacology. *Mailing Add:* Princeton Brain Bio-Ctr 862 Rte 518 Skillman NJ 08558

PFEIFFER, CARL GEORGE, b Rochester, NY, Apr 11, 31. APPLIED MATHEMATICS, COMPUTER SCIENCE. *Educ:* Cornell Univ, BME, 54. *Prof Exp:* Engr, Sperry Gyroscope Co, NY, 54; res engr, Jet Propulsion Lab, Pasadena, Calif, 57-59, supvr powered flight anal group, 59-61, supvr space guid theory group, 61-67; staff engr guid & anal dept, TRW Defense & Space Systs Group, 67-68, mgr mission anal dept, 68-70, sr staff engr, Syst Eng & Integration Div, 70-79; SR SCIENTIST, HUGHES AIRCRAFT CO, EL SEGUNDO, CALIF, 79- *Concurrent Pos:* Consult, NASA Jet Propulsion Lab, 70-78. *Res:* Statistical estimation and hypothesis testing and application to analysis of large, multi-state systems; design of data processing architecture; signal processing; microprocessor design. *Mailing Add:* 2800 Tennyson Pl Hermosa Beach CA 90254

PFEIFFER, CARL J, b Quincy, Ill, June 28, 37; m 62; c 2. PHYSIOLOGY, GASTROENTEROLOGY. *Educ:* Duke Univ, BA, 59; Southern Ill Univ, MA, 61, PhD(physiol), 64; Harvard Univ, MSHyg, 67. *Prof Exp:* Res asst cell physiol, Duke Univ, 58-59; res asst stress physiol, Ind Univ, 59-60; res asst pharmacol, Southern Ill Univ, 60-63; res scientist, Ames Res Ctr, NASA, Calif, 63-67; dir gastrointestinal res, Inst Gastroenterol, Presby-Univ Pa Med Ctr & asst prof pharmacol, Sch Med, Univ Pa, 67-71; assoc prof physiol, 71-75, PROF GASTROINTESTINAL PHYSIOL, FAC MED, MEM UNIV NFLD, 75- *Concurrent Pos:* Guest prof, Kyoto Univ Fac Med, 77-78. *Mem:* Am Gastroenterol Asn; Am Physiol Soc; Soc Toxicol; Electron Micros Soc Am. *Res:* Physiology; toxicology. *Mailing Add:* Dept of Physiol Fac of Med Mem Univ of Nfld St John's NF A1B 3V6 Can

PFEIFFER, CARROLL ATHEY, b Reno, Ohio, Apr 18, 06; m 37; c 1. ANATOMY. *Educ:* Marietta Col, AB, 29; Univ Iowa, MS, 31, PhD(zool), 35. *Hon Degrees:* ScD, Marietta Col, 57. *Prof Exp:* Asst zool, Univ Iowa, 29-35; res asst & instr primate biol, Sch Med, Yale Univ, 36-37, res asst & instr anat, 37-39, res asst & asst prof anat & endocrinol, 39-47, res assoc & asst prof histol, gross anat & endocrinol, 47-51; head dept, 54-66, prof, 51-75, EMER PROF ANAT, SCH MED, UNIV PR, SAN JUAN, 76- *Concurrent Pos:* Henry res fel med, New York Hosp & Med Col, Cornell Univ, 35-36. *Mem:* Am Soc Zoologists; Soc Exp Biol & Med; Endocrine Soc; Am Asn Cancer Res; Am Asn Anatomists. *Res:* Gonad-hypophyseal interrelationships; endocrine imbalance in relation to cancer; physiology of reproduction and of bone formation; relation of gonadotropin and sex hormones to cancer of the reproductive system. *Mailing Add:* 70 W Lucerne Circle Orlando FL 32801

PFEIFFER, DOUGLAS ROBERT, b Cedar Rapids, Iowa, June 3, 46; m 77. BIOCHEMISTRY, BIOPHYSICAL CHEMISTRY. *Educ:* Coe Col, BA, 68; Wayne State Univ, PhD(biochem), 73. *Prof Exp:* Asst, Wayne State Univ, 68-69, res asst biochem, 69-73, fel, 73; proj assoc, Enzyme Inst, Univ Wis, 73-76, asst scientist, 76-77; ASST PROF BIOCHEM, HORMEL INST, UNIV MINN, 77- *Concurrent Pos:* Noeller fel chem, 71-72. *Mem:* Am Chem Soc; AAAS; NY Acad Sci. *Res:* Ionophere transport mechanisms; mitochondrial calcium metabolism; mitochondrial phospholipid metabolism; ischemic tissue metabolism; bioenergetics; membrane permeability. *Mailing Add:* Hormel Inst Univ of Minn Austin MN 55912

PFEIFFER, EGBERT WHEELER, b New York, NY, May 23, 15; m 49; c 3. VERTEBRATE ZOOLOGY. *Educ:* Cornell Univ, BA, 37; Univ BC, MA, 48; Univ Calif, PhD(zool), 54. *Prof Exp:* Vis prof biol, Col Idaho, 54-55; asst prof zool, Utah State Univ, 55-57; asst prof anat, Univ NDak, 57-59; assoc prof zool, 59-70, PROF ZOOL, UNIV MONT, 70- *Concurrent Pos:* Prin investr, NIH & NSF grants, USPHS spec res fel, Western Reserve Univ, 65-66. *Mem:* AAAS; Am Soc Zool; Am Soc Mammal; Am Asn Anat. *Res:* Vertebrate reproduction; mammalian renal physiology and anatomy. *Mailing Add:* Dept of Zool Univ of Mont Missoula MT 59801

PFEIFFER, ERIC A, b Rauental, Ger, Sept 15, 35; US citizen; m 64; c 3. PSYCHIATRY, GERONTOLOGY. *Educ:* Washington Univ, AB, 56, MD, 60; Am Bd Psychiat & Neurol, dipl, 66. *Prof Exp:* Instr psychiat, Sch Med, Univ Rochester, 63-64; staff psychiatrist, USPHS Hosp, Lexington, Ky, 64-66; assoc, Med Ctr, Duke Univ, 66, asst prof, 67-69, assoc prof, 69-73, prof psychiat, 73-77, proj dir, Older Americans Resources & Serv Prog, 72-77, assoc dir, Ctr Study Aging & Human Develop, 74-77; dir, Davis Inst Care & Study Aging, Denver, 76-77; prof psychiat, Sch Med, Univ Colo, 76-78; PROF PSYCHIAT, COL MED, UNIV S FLA, 78-; CHIEF GERIAT PSYCHIAT, TAMPA VET ADMIN HOSP, 78- *Concurrent Pos:* Markle scholar acad med, 68-73; consult, Berea Col, 64-66; lectr, Law Sch, Duke Univ, 68-; dir, Suncoast Geront Ctr, Univ SFla, 70- *Mem:* Am Psychiat Asn; Geront Soc; Am Geriat Soc. *Res:* Psychiatric education; geriatric psychiatry; psychotherapy; behavior and adaptation in late life. *Mailing Add:* Dept Psychiat 12901 N 30th St Tampa FL 33612

PFEIFFER, FRANCIS RICHARD, organic chemistry, see previous edition

PFEIFFER, GERALD PETER, b Clifton, NJ, Feb 13, 43. TEXTILE CHEMISTRY. *Educ:* Univ Fla, BS, 64; Univ NC, Chapel Hill, PhD(org chem), 69. *Prof Exp:* MKT REP MENS WEAR, HOME FURNISHINGS & INTIMATE APPAREL, E I DU PONT DE NEMOURS & CO, INC, 69- *Res:* End use research of orlon products; includes preparation, finishing, styling and promoting. *Mailing Add:* PO Box 702 Wilmington DE 19899

PFEIFFER, HEINZ GERHARD, b Pforzheim, Ger, Mar 31, 20; US citizen; m 48; c 2. ENERGY CONVERSION. *Educ:* Drew Univ, AB, 41; Syracuse Univ, AM, 44; Calif Inst Technol, PhD(chem), 49. *Prof Exp:* Asst, Am Platinum Works, NJ, 39-41; asst, Syracuse Univ, 41-42, instr, 42-43; asst, Calif Inst Technol, 43-44, 47-48; res assoc, Gen Elec Co, 48-54, mgr dielectric studies, 54-64, div liaison scientist, 64-68, mgr educ technol, 68-71; dir, Ctr Study Sci & Soc, State Univ NY Albany, 71; MGR TECHNOL & ENERGY ASSESSMENT, PA POWER & LIGHT CO, 72- *Concurrent Pos:* Adj prof, Lehigh Univ, 73-77; chmn, Thermal & Mech Prog Comt, Elec Power Res Inst, 73-78; mem, Bd Dirs, Pa Sci & Eng Found, 75-79; chmn air & water qual tech adv comt, Pa Dept Environ Resources, 77-; mem energy storage comt, Nat Acad Sci, 76-81. *Mem:* AAAS; fel Am Inst Chemists; Am Chem Soc; sr mem Inst Elec & Electronics Engrs. *Res:* Diffraction; surface films; x-ray spectrography and electrochemistry, dielectrics; electronic properties of molecular compounds; educational technology; science and society; advanced energy systems; direct utilization of coal; use of reject heat. *Mailing Add:* Pa Power & Light Co 2N 9th St Allentown PA 18101

PFEIFFER, JOSEPH GEORGE, physical organic chemistry, see previous edition

PFEIFFER, LOREN NEIL, b Waukesha, Wis, Aug 21, 39; m 64. EXPERIMENTAL PHYSICS. *Educ:* Univ Mich, BS, 61; Johns Hopkins Univ, PhD(physics), 67. *Prof Exp:* Res assoc physics, Johns Hopkins Univ, 67-68; MEM TECH STAFF, BELL TEL LABS, 68- *Mem:* Am Phys Soc. *Res:* Mossbauer effect; nuclei in solids; hyperfine interactions; gamma ray optics. *Mailing Add:* Bell Tel Labs Inc Murray Hill NJ 07974

PFEIFFER, MILDRED CLARA JULIA, b Philadelphia, Pa, 10. MEDICINE. *Educ:* Univ Pa, BS, 33, MD, 36, MPH, 45; Am Bd Internal Med, dipl, 45; Indust Col Armed Forces, dipl, 71. *Prof Exp:* Intern & resident, Philadelphia Gen Hosp, 36-39; dir student health serv, Med Col Pa, 41-42, asst clin prof gastroenterol & proctol, 43-48, lectr med statist, 44-49, asst clin prof internal med, 44-51; dir adult health & heart prog, 52-53, dir, Bur Chronic Dis, 53-57, initiator & dir, Div Planning & Eval & Res, 57-61, dir div planning, 62-70, dir div chronic dis, Pa Dept Health, 70-77; CONSULT HEALTH & MED AFFAIRS, PROF STANDARDS REV ORGN, 77- *Concurrent Pos:* Intern & consult, Med Div, Dept Pub Safety, Philadelphia, 39-50; asst attend physician, Philadelphia Gen Hosp; chief med & gastroenterol, Woman's Hosp; proctologist, Doctor's Hosp; instr, Grad Sch, Univ Pa, 40-50, lectr, Sch Nursing, 54-57; asst dir, Dept Oncol, Med Col Pa, 48, dir, 49-52, vis prof pub health, 52-56; mem, Comn Community Serv & Clins, Am Heart Asn, 53-57; actg dir, Div Alcoholism, Drugs & Narcotics, Cancer, Heart & Metab, Addictive Dis, Home Safety, Aging, Arthritis & Diabetes, Pa Dept Health, 53-57, Div Chronic Renal Dis, 70-74; mem, Gov Bd, Arthritis Found, 58 & Bd Dirs, Pa Ctr Older Persons. *Mem:* Fel Am Col Prev Med; fel Am Col Physicians; fel Am Pub Health Asn; fel Am Col Chest Physicians; fel Am Geriatric Soc. *Res:* Health planning, evaluation, research and development; adminstrative medicine; public administration and health; internal and preventive medicine; chronic diseases; gastroenterology; proctology; biostatistics. *Mailing Add:* 358 Valley Rd Marion Station PA 19066

PFEIFFER, PAUL EDWIN, b Newark, Ohio, Sept 9, 17; m 43; c 4. MATHEMATICS. *Educ:* Rice Inst, BS, 38, MS, 48, PhD(math), 52; Southern Methodist Univ, BD, 43. *Prof Exp:* From instr to assoc prof elec eng, 47-59, chmn dept, 59-63, dean students, 65-69, chmn dept math sci, 74-75, PROF MATH SCI & ELEC ENG, RICE UNIV, 69- *Mem:* Am Math Soc; Math Asn Am; Inst Elec & Electronics Eng; Soc Indust & Appl Math; Inst Math Statist. *Res:* Applied probability and random processes. *Mailing Add:* Dept of Math Sci Rice Univ Houston TX 77001

PFEIFFER, RAYMOND JOHN, b Trenton, NJ, Apr 29, 37; m 74; c 1. ASTROPHYSICS, ASTRONOMY. *Educ:* Univ Mich, BSEd, 61; Temple Univ, MA, 68; Univ Pa, PhD(astron), 75. *Prof Exp:* Teacher phys sci, Hamilton Twp Bd Educ, 61-64; instr, 64-67, asst prof, 67-77, ASSOC PROF PHYSICS & ASTRON, TRENTON STATE COL, 77- *Concurrent Pos:* Res assoc, Univ Pa Observ, 75- *Mem:* Am Astron Soc. *Res:* Measurement and analysis of linear polarization in binary stars; spectrophotometry of peculiar stars. *Mailing Add:* Dept of Physics Trenton State Col Trenton NJ 08625

PFEIFFER, STEVEN EUGENE, b Watertown, Wis, Aug 13, 40; m 65; c 3. CELL BIOLOGY, NEUROSCIENCES. *Educ:* Carleton Col, BA, 62; Wash Univ, PhD(molecular biol), 67. *Prof Exp:* Nat Inst Neurol Dis & Stroke fel biochem, Brandeis Univ, 67-69; asst prof, 69-74, assoc prof, 74-81, PROF MICROBIOL, HEALTH CTR, UNIV CONN, 81- *Concurrent Pos:* Neurosci res prog, Intensive Study Prog fel, 69; Merck Found fac develop award, 70; Max Planck Soc fel, 72; Josiah Macy Jr fac scholar award, 76-77; vis scientist sabbatical leave, Pasteur Inst, 76-77. *Mem:* Am Asn Cell Biol; Soc Neurosci; Am Soc Neurochem; Int Soc Differentiation. *Res:* Use of cell culture to study biochemical development of myelination. *Mailing Add:* Dept of Microbiol Univ of Conn Health Ctr Farmington CT 06032

PFENDER, EMIL, b Germany, May 25, 25; US citizen; m 54; c 3. MECHANICAL ENGINEERING, PLASMA TECHNOLOGY. *Educ:* Univ Stuttgart, Dipl, 53, Dr Ing(elec eng), 59. *Prof Exp:* Res assoc gaseous elec, Univ Stuttgart, 53-55, asst, 55-61, first asst, Inst High Temperature Res, 62-64; vis scientist arc technol, Aerospace Res Labs, Wright-Patterson AFB, Ohio, 61-62; assoc prof, 64-67, PROF, DEPT MECH ENG, UNIV MINN, 67- *Concurrent Pos:* Mem adv panel, NSF, 74-76; dir, Minn Metric Ctr, 74- *Honors & Awards:* US Sr Scientist Award, Humboldt Found, Fed Repub Ger, 78. *Mem:* Am Phys Soc; fel Am Soc Mech Engrs; Inst Elec & Electronics Engrs. *Res:* Arc technology; plasma heat transfer; plasma chemistry and processing; energy conservation. *Mailing Add:* Dept Mech Eng Univ Minn Minneapolis MN 55455

PFENNIGWERTH, PAUL LEROY, b Ludlow, Ky, Apr 19, 29; m 55; c 3. MECHANICAL ENGINEERING. *Educ:* Univ Cincinnati, ME, 52; Univ Ky, MSME, 54; Univ Pittsburgh, PhD(mech eng), 63. *Prof Exp:* Instr mech eng, Univ Ky, 52-54; fel engr, Pa, 57-68, mgr eng mech, 68-71, tech consult to US Naval Nuclear Power Sch, Mare Island Naval Shipyard, Vallejo, 71-74, MGR FUEL SYSTEM PERFORMANCE, LWBR PROJ, BETTIS ATOMIC POWER LAB, WESTINGHOUSE ELEC CORP, 74- *Mem:* Am Soc Mech Engrs; Am Nuclear Soc. *Res:* Applied mechanics, including solid and structural mechanics, fluid flow and heat transfer; nuclear engineering including irradiation testing, radiation effects on materials and fuel element design. *Mailing Add:* Bettis Atomic Power Lab Box 79 Pittsburgh PA 15122

PFISTER, DONALD HENRY, b Kenton, Ohio, Feb 17, 45; m 71. MYCOLOGY. *Educ:* Miami Univ, AB, 67; Cornell Univ, PhD(mycol), 71. *Prof Exp:* Asst prof biol & mycol, Univ PR, Mayaguez, 71-74; asst prof biol & asst cur, 74-77, assoc prof & assoc cur, 77-80, PROF & CUR, FARLOW REF LIBR & HERBARIUM, HARVARD UNIV, 80- *Mem:* Mycol Soc Am; Sigma Xi. *Res:* Floristic and monographic studies of operculate Discomycetes; historical and bibliographical studies of mycological herbaria. *Mailing Add:* Farlow Herbarium Harvard Univ 20 Divinity Ave Cambridge MA 02138

PFISTER, PHILIP CARL, b New York, NY, Apr 12, 25; m 59; c 1. MECHANICAL ENGINEERING. *Educ:* City Col New York, BME, 47; Columbia Univ, MSME, 49; Ill Inst Technol, PhD(mech eng), 62. *Prof Exp:* Instr mech eng, City Col New York, 47-50 & WVa Univ, 50-52; asst prof, Univ Utah, 52-55; fel & asst prof, Ill Inst Technol, 55-67; head dept, 67-70, PROF MECH ENG, NDAK STATE UNIV, 67- *Concurrent Pos:* Vis prof, Kabul, Afghanistan, 64-66. *Mem:* Am Soc Mech Engr; Am Wind Energy Asn. *Res:* Vibrations; computer design; wind machines. *Mailing Add:* 30 Meadowlark Lane Fargo ND 58102

PFISTER, ROBERT DEAN, silviculture, plant ecology, see previous edition

PFISTER, ROBERT M, b New York, NY, Feb 25, 33; m 54; c 4. MICROBIOLOGY. *Educ:* Syracuse Univ, AB, 57, MS, 60, PhD(microbiol), 64. *Prof Exp:* Res assoc microbiol, Res Corp, Syracuse Univ, 57-62; res assoc, Lamont Geol Observ, Columbia Univ, 64-66; from asst prof to assoc prof, 66-72, PROF MICROBIOL & CHMN DEPT, OHIO STATE UNIV, 72- *Concurrent Pos:* NSF res grants, 65-67. *Mem:* Am Soc Microbiol; Electron Micros Soc Am. *Res:* Ultrastructure and function of bacterial organelles and microparticulate-microorganism interactions; microbial ecology. *Mailing Add:* Dept of Microbiol Ohio State Univ 484 W 12th St Columbus OH 43210

PFLANZER, RICHARD GARY, b Ashland, Wis, June 16, 40; m 64; c 2. MEDICAL PHYSIOLOGY. *Educ:* Ind Univ, Bloomington, AB, 64, PhD(physiol), 69. *Prof Exp:* From teaching asst to teaching assoc human physiol, Ind Univ, Bloomington, 63-69, asst prof physiol & anat, Ind Univ-Purdue Univ, Indianapolis, 69-75, ASSOC PROF PHYSIOL, SCH MED, IND UNIV, 75- *Concurrent Pos:* NASA-Univ Va fel biospace technol, Wallops Island, Va, 70; consult, John Wiley & Sons, Inc Publishers, 73- & Wm C Brown Co Publishers, 74- *Mem:* AAAS; Am Inst Biol Sci; Sigma Xi. *Res:* Comparative, environmental and adaptation physiology. *Mailing Add:* Dept Physiol Sch of Med Ind Univ 1100 W Michigan St Indianapolis IN 46202

PFLAUM, JOHN CHRISTIAN, b New York, NY, Aug 15, 51. CLOUD PRECIPITATION PHYSICS. *Educ:* NY Univ, BS, 72; Univ Calif, Los Angeles, MS, 74, PhD(atmospheric sci), 78. *Prof Exp:* Vis scientist, Nat Ctr Atmospheic Res, 78-80; ASST PROF CLOUD & PRECIPITATION PHYSICS, UNIV OKLA, 80- *Mem:* Am Meteorol Soc; AAAS; Sigma Xi. *Res:* Cloud formation and precipitation development process; improved weather modification techniques for the benefit of society. *Mailing Add:* Sch Meteorol Univ Okla Norman OK 73019

PFLAUM, RONALD TRENDA, b Webster, Minn, June 21, 22; m 48; c 3. ANALYTICAL CHEMISTRY. *Educ:* St Olaf Col, BA, 48; Purdue Univ, MS, 51, PhD(chem), 53. *Prof Exp:* Asst chem, St Olaf Col, 48-49; asst, Purdue Univ, 49-51; from instr to assoc prof, 53-63, PROF CHEM, UNIV IOWA, 63- *Mem:* Am Chem Soc. *Res:* Spectrophotometric methods of analysis; analytical chemistry of coordination compounds; organic reagents in inorganic analysis. *Mailing Add:* Dept Chem Univ Iowa Iowa City IA 52242

PFLEGER, RAYMOND C, biochemistry, see previous edition

PFLIEGER, WILLIAM LEO, b Columbus, Ohio, Oct 26, 32; m 53; c 2. ICHTHYOLOGY, FISHERIES. *Educ:* Ohio State Univ, BS, 58, MS, 60; Univ Kans, PhD(zool), 69. *Prof Exp:* SR FISHERIES BIOLOGIST, MO DEPT CONSERV, 61- *Concurrent Pos:* Res assoc, Univ Mo-Columbia, 73- *Mem:* Am Soc Ichthyol & Herpet; Am Fisheries Soc; Sigma Xi. *Res:* Systematics, distribution and life history of North American freshwater fishes; protection of endangered species; classification, inventory and evaluation of stream habitats in Missouri. *Mailing Add:* Fish & Wildlife Res Ctr Mo Dept Of Conserv 1110 College Columbia MO 65201

PFLUG, GERALD RALPH, b Philadelphia, Pa, July 30, 41; m 65; c 2. PHARMACEUTICS. *Educ:* Philadelphia Col Pharm, BSc, 63, MSc, 65; State Univ NY Buffalo, PhD(pharmaceut), 69. *Prof Exp:* Sect head develop, Vicks Div Res & Develop, 69-74; dir pharmaceut develop, USV Pharmaceut, NY, 74-75; dir, 75-80, VPRES PROPRIETARY DRUG RES & DEVELOP, CARTER PRODS DIV, CARTER-WALLACE INC, 80- *Mem:* Am Pharmaceut Asn; Acad Pharmaceut Sci; Am Chem Soc. *Res:* Catalytic reactions involving penicillins; biopharmaceutics; drug interactions; kinetics. *Mailing Add:* Carter-Wallace Inc Half-Acre Rd Cranbury NJ 08512

PFLUG, IRVING JOHN, b Gibson Co, Ind, Sept 17, 23; c 4. FOOD SCIENCE, MICROBIOLOGY. *Educ:* Purdue Univ, BSA, 46, BSAE, 48; Univ Mass, MS, 50, PhD, 53. *Prof Exp:* Asst instr agr eng, Purdue Univ, 46-48; from asst prof to assoc prof, Univ Mass, 48-54; from assoc prof to prof, Mich State Univ, 54-67; prof environ health, 67-77, PROF FOOD SCI & NUTRIT, SCH PUB HEALTH, UNIV MINN, MINNEAPOLIS, 77- *Concurrent Pos:* Indust consult. *Mem:* Am Soc Microbiol; fel Am Soc Heat, Refrig & Air Conditioning Engrs; fel Inst Food Technol; Soc Appl Bact; Int Inst Refrig. *Res:* Sterilization microbiology; sterilization of drugs; heating, cooling and thermal processing of food products; refrigerated storage of agricultural products; manufacture of pickle products; food engineering. *Mailing Add:* Environ Sterilization Lab Space Sci Ctr Univ of Minn Minneapolis MN 55455

PFLUGER, CLARENCE EUGENE, b Coupland, Tex, Sept 1, 30; m 61; c 3. ANALYTICAL CHEMISTRY, X-RAY CRYSTALLOGRAPHY. *Educ:* Univ Tex, BS, 51, PhD(anal chem), 58. *Prof Exp:* Shift chemist, Dana Plant, E I du Pont de Nemours Co, Ind, 51-52, shift supvr chem control, Savannah River Plant, SC, 52-54; from instr to asst prof anal chem, Univ Ill, Urbana, 59-66; asst prof, Univ Ga, 66-67; assoc prof, 67-76, PROF CHEM, SYRACUSE UNIV, 76- *Concurrent Pos:* Fulbright scholar, Darmstadt Tech Univ, 58-59; Fulbright lectr, Tech Univ Denmark, 65-66. *Mem:* AAAS; Am Chem Soc; Soc Appl Spectros; Am Crystallog Asn. *Res:* Crystal structure determinations, primarily of metal chelate complexes; analytical instrumentation and methods development in the trace and ultratrace region. *Mailing Add:* Dept of Chem Syracuse Univ Syracuse NY 13210

PFLUGFELDER, HALA, b Dec 3, 21; nat US; m 43; c 2. MATHEMATICS. *Educ:* Univ Gottingen, dipl, 47; Univ Freiburg, PhD, 49. *Prof Exp:* From instr to asst prof, 56-71, ASSOC PROF MATH, TEMPLE UNIV, 71- *Res:* Theory of loops. *Mailing Add:* Dept Math Temple Univ Philadelphia PA 19122

PFLUKE, JOHN H, b Peoria, Ill, June 17, 31; m 57; c 5. GEOPHYSICS, SEISMOLOGY. *Educ:* St Louis Univ, BS, 53, MS, 61; Pa State Univ, PhD(geophys), 63. *Prof Exp:* Geophysicist, US Coast & Geod Surv, 59-60; sr seismologist, Teledyne, Inc, 63-65; chief anal sect, Earthquake Mechanism Lab, Inst Earth Sci, Environ Sci Serv Admin, 65-70, sr res geophysicist, Nat Oceanic & Atmospheric Admin, 70-74; res geophysicist, 74-81, MGR, EXTERNAL RES PROG, US GEOL SURV, 81- *Mem:* Seismol Soc Am; Am Geophys Union; Soc Explor Geophysicists. *Res:* Seismic field and model studies; deep well and seismic instrumentation; geophysical inverse problems; model studies of earth strain data; statistics of earthquakes. *Mailing Add:* US Geol Surv 345 Middlefield Rd Menlo Park CA 94025

PFOHL, RONALD JOHN, b Baraboo, Wis, Aug 6, 37; m 67; c 1. DEVELOPMENTAL BIOLOGY. *Educ:* Wartburg Col, BA, 59; Mich State Univ, MS, 62, PhD(zool), 67. *Prof Exp:* USPHS-NIH fel, Res Unit Molecular Embryol, Univ Palermo, 67-69; asst prof, 69-76, ASSOC PROF ZOOL, MIAMI UNIV, 76- *Mem:* AAAS; Am Soc Zoologists; Soc Develop Biol; Am Chem Soc. *Res:* Determining the catalytic characteristics of membrane bound alkaline phosphatase and elucidating its role and the mechanisms which regulate its activity during the development of sea urchins and cellular slime molds. *Mailing Add:* Dept of Zool Miami Univ Oxford OH 45056

PFOST, HARRY B(ERNARD), b Cowgill, Mo, Mar 8, 19; m 37. AGRICULTURAL ENGINEERINGG. *Educ:* Univ Mo, BS, 40; Auburn Univ, MS, 48; Mich State Univ, PhD(agr eng), 59. *Prof Exp:* Jr engr rural electrification admin, US Dept Agr, 40-41; assoc prof agr eng, Auburn Univ, 41-49; self-employed, 49-53; eng mgr, Green Giant Co, 54-56; prod analyst,

Ford Motor Co, 56-57; prof feed processing, Kans State Univ, 59-78; SR ENGR, DEVELOP PLANNING & RES ASSOCS, INC, 78- *Mem:* AAAS; Am Soc Agr Engrs; Am Soc Animal Sci. *Res:* Processing and storage of agricultural products; grain drying; milling and processing of animal feeds; applications of statistics to problems of process and heat transfer engineering. *Mailing Add:* Shellenberger Hall Kans State Univ Manhattan KS 66506

PFRANG, EDWARD OSCAR, b New Haven, Conn, Aug 9, 29; m 58; c 3. CIVIL ENGINEERING, STRUCTURAL ENGINEERING. *Educ:* Univ Conn, BS, 51; Yale Univ, ME, 52; Univ Ill, Urbana, PhD(struct eng), 61. *Prof Exp:* Struct designer, Gibbs & Hill Inc, NY, 52 & Singmaster & Bryer, NY, 52-53; construct officer, US Naval Base, Cuba, 53-55; proj mgt officer, Dist Pub Work Off, Calif, 55-56; gen field supt, Major Concrete Co Inc, New York, 56-57; asst prof civil eng, Univ Nev, Reno, 57-59; univ & Ford Found fel, Univ Ill, Urbana, 59-61; asst prof civil eng, Univ Del, 61-66; chief supvry civil engr, 66-70, actg prog mgr off housing tech, 70-72, prog mgr, 72, chief, 72-73, CHIEF STRUCT DIV, NAT BUR STANDARDS, 73- *Concurrent Pos:* Chmn, US Panel Wind & Seismic Effect, 69-; chmn tech activ comt, Am Concrete Inst, 72- *Honors & Awards:* Raymond C Reese Struct Res Award, 71; ACI Wason Medal Award, Am Concrete Inst, 71; Spec Achievement Award, Dept Housing & Urban Develop, 72; Silver Medal, Dept Com, 81. *Mem:* Am Soc Civil Engrs; Am Soc Testing & Mat. *Mailing Add:* Struct & Mat Div Nat Bur of Standards Gaithersburg MD 20760

PFRIMMER, THEODORE ROSCOE, b Oklahoma City, Okla, Dec 11, 20; m 44; c 3. ENTOMOLOGY. *Educ:* Univ Ark, BS, 48; La State Univ, MS, 50; Agr & Mech Col, Tex, PhD(entom), 53. *Prof Exp:* From entomologist to invests leader, Agr Res Serv, 52-73, res leader, Bioenviron Insect Control Lab, 73-76, RES ENTOMOLOGIST, AGR RES SERV, USDA, 76- *Mem:* AAAS; Entom Soc Am; Am Registry Prof Entomologists. *Res:* Control of cotton insects; use of light traps for survey and detection; use of pheromone traps for survey. *Mailing Add:* PO Box 941 Leland MS 38756

PFROGNER, RAY LONG, b Meyersdale, Pa, Sept 30, 34; m 60; c 2. SOLID STATE PHYSICS, ENERGY CONVERSION. *Educ:* Juniata Col, BS, 60; Univ Del, MS, 64, PhD(physics), 71. *Prof Exp:* Geophysicist, Coast & Geod Surv, Dept Com, 61-62; ASSOC PROF PHYSICS, JUNIATA COL, 64- *Concurrent Pos:* Vis assoc prof, Inst Energy Conversion, Dept Eng, Univ Del, 75-76. *Mem:* Am Asn Physics Teachers. *Res:* Photovoltaic energy conversion; practical application of solar-thermal processes; deep-center luminescence. *Mailing Add:* Dept Physics Juniata Col Huntingdon PA 16652

PFUDERER, HELEN A, b Ames, Iowa, Mar 17, 39; m 59; c 2. ENVIRONMENTAL SCIENCE, NUTRITION. *Educ:* Iowa State Univ, BS, 61; Univ Tenn, MS, 69. *Prof Exp:* Dir environ info, Ecol Sci Info Ctr, 74-78; head, dept energy & environ info, 78-79, TECH ASST, ASSOC LAB DIR, BIOMED & ENVIRON SCI, INFO CTR COMPLEX, OAK RIDGE NAT LAB, 80- *Mem:* Am Nuclear Soc; Am Soc Info Sci; AAAS; Soc Risk Analysis. *Res:* Computerized information systems and newsletters on the environmental effects of energy technologies including the nuclear and fossil fuel cycles; emergency energy technologies; effects of electric power generation; research management and planning. *Mailing Add:* Info Ctr Complex PO Box X Oak Ridge TN 37830

PHADKE, MADHAV SHRIDHAR, b Bombay, India, Aug 28, 48; m 74; c 1. ENGINEERING, STATISTICS. *Educ:* Indian Inst Technol, Bombay, BTech, 69; Univ Rochester, MS, 71; Univ Wis-Madison, MS, 72, PhD(mech eng), 73. *Prof Exp:* Asst scientist eng statist, Math Res Ctr, 74-76, res assoc air pollution modeling & data anal, Dept of Statist, Univ Wis-Madison, 74-76; vis scientist, IBM T J Watson Res Ctr, 76-77; MEM TECH STAFF, BELL TEL LABS, 77- *Mem:* Am Statist Asn; Air Pollution Control Asn. *Res:* Time series analysis; system identification; process control; mathematical modeling; air quality data analysis; quality control. *Mailing Add:* Bell Tel Labs Holmdel NJ 07733

PHAFF, HERMAN JAN, b Winschoten, Netherlands, May 30, 13; nat US; m. FOOD TECHNOLOGY, MICROBIOLOGY. *Educ:* Delft Univ Technol, Chem Engr, 38; Univ Calif, PhD(pectin chem), 43. *Prof Exp:* Asst prof food technol & asst microbiologist, Exp Sta, Univ Calif, Berkeley, 46-52, assoc prof food technol & assoc microbiologist, 52-58; chmn dept, 70-75, PROF FOOD SCI & TECHNOL & MICROBIOLOGIST, UNIV CALIF, DAVIS, 58-, PROF BACTERIOL, 65- *Concurrent Pos:* Ed, Yeast Newslett, 55-; fac res lectr, Univ Calif, Davis, 68; grants, NIH, 68-82, NSF, 81-84; mem int comn yeast & yeast-like organisms, Int Asn Microbiol Socs. *Mem:* Am Chem Soc; Am Soc Microbiol; Mycol Soc Am; Inst Food Technol; Am Acad Microbiol. *Res:* Chemistry of pectins and pectic enzymes; biology, ecology and systematics of yeasts; prevention of microbiological spoilage of foods; hydrolytic enzymes; yeast cell walls. *Mailing Add:* Dept of Bact Univ of Calif Davis CA 95616

PHAIR, JOHN P, b Paris, France, July 17, 34; US citizen; m 58; c 2. MEDICINE. *Educ:* Yale Univ, BA, 56; Univ Cincinnati, MD, 60. *Prof Exp:* From intern to resident med, Yale New Haven Hosp, 60-65; from asst prof to prof med, Col Med, Univ Cincinnati, 67-76; CHIEF INFECTIOUS DIS, DEPT MED, NORTHWESTERN UNIV, 76- *Concurrent Pos:* USPHS trainee, Yale New Haven Hosp, 65-67. *Mem:* Am Soc Microbiol; Am Asn Immunologists; Am Fedn Clin Res. *Res:* Host defenses in infectious disease. *Mailing Add:* Dept Med Northwestern Univ Sch Med Chicago IL 60611

PHALEN, WILLIAM EDMUND, b Nebr, Dec 18, 16; m 42; c 3. BIOCHEMISTRY. *Educ:* Univ Omaha, BA, 41. *Prof Exp:* Chemist, Cudahy Packing Co, 41-42 & 45-46, supvr meat res, 47-63, lab dir, Cudahy Labs, 63-68; LAB DIR, AM LABS, INC, 68- *Concurrent Pos:* Mem comt food preserv, Am Meat Inst, 54-63, sci adv comt, 64- *Mem:* Am Oil Chem Soc; Inst Food Technol; Am Chem Soc. *Res:* Thermal processing of canned meats; curing and smoking of meat products; meat pigments; enzymology; conversion of animal tissues to pharmaceutical products. *Mailing Add:* 1339 S 93rd Ave Omaha NE 68124

PHAM, TUAN DUC, b Hanam, Vietnam, Dec 28, 38; US citizen; m 64; c 2. ANATOMY, PATHOLOGY. *Educ:* St Edward's Univ, BS, 63; Loyola Univ, MS, 67; Columbia Univ, PhD(anat), 75. *Prof Exp:* staff assoc path, 73-80, ASST PROF ANAT & PHARMACOL, COL PHYSICIANS & SURGEONS, COLUMBIA UNIV, 80- *Concurrent Pos:* Kevin Doyle fel, NY Heart Asn, 75-77; partic investr prog proj grant, 75-83; sr investr, NY Heart Asn, 80-84. *Mem:* Am Asn Anatomists; Sigma Xi. *Res:* Electron microscopy; immunoelectron microscopy; electrophysiology; heart disease. *Mailing Add:* Col of Physicians & Surgeons 630 W 168th St New York NY 10032

PHAN, CHON-TON, b Soctrang, S Viet-Nam, Apr 14, 30; m 57, 81; c 2. PLANT PHYSIOLOGY, BIOCHEMISTRY. *Educ:* Univ Paris, Lic es Sci, 53, Dipl d'Etudes Superieures, 56, Dr es Sci, 61. *Prof Exp:* From jr searcher to sr searcher plant biol, Nat Ctr Sci Res, France, 56-68, master in res, 68; from asst prof to assoc prof plant physiol & biochem, Univ Alta, 68-74; PROF PLANT PHYSIOL, UNIV MONTREAL, 74- *Mem:* Am Soc Plant Physiol; NY Acad Sci; Int Soc Hort Sci; Fr Soc Plant Physiol; Can Soc Hort Sci. *Res:* Plant metabolism as affected by the structure of the organ and by the physical and chemical changes in the environment; plant tissue culture. *Mailing Add:* Dept Biol Sci Univ Montreal CP 6128 Sta A Montreal PQ H3C 3J7 Can

PHAN, CONG LUAN, b Hue, Vietnam, Nov 22, 41; Can citizen; m 66; c 2. HIGH VOLTAGE ENGINEERING, ATMOSPHERIC GLACIOLOGY. *Educ:* Univ Laval, BSc, 64, MSc, 66, PhD(elec eng), 70. *Prof Exp:* From asst prof to assoc prof, 70-78, PROF ELEC, UNIV QUE, 78- *Concurrent Pos:* Vis researcher, Atmospheric Res Ctr, Lannemezan, France, 72-73; consult, Aluminium Co Can, 74-76; dir, Ctr Res Middle North, 79-81. *Mem:* Inst Elec & Electronics Engrs; Int Glaciol Soc; Electrostatic Soc Am. *Res:* Effect of atmospheric icing on power lines: accretion of ice in the presence of AC/DC electric field and flashover on iced insulators; corona discharge under fouth weather from power lines. *Mailing Add:* 735 Jacques-Cartier Chicoutimi PQ G7H 2B1 Can

PHAN, KOK-WEE, b Segamat, Johore, Malaysia, Nov 27, 39; m 62; c 3. ALGEBRA. *Educ:* Univ Melbourne, BE, 62, BSc, 64; Monash Univ, Australia, PhD(math), 69. *Prof Exp:* ASSOC PROF MATH, UNIV NOTRE DAME, 68- *Mem:* Am Math Soc. *Res:* Theory of finite groups. *Mailing Add:* Dept of Math Univ Notre Dame Notre Dame IN 46556

PHARES, CLEVELAND KIRK, b Many, La, Mar 7, 38; m 71; c 3. BIOCHEMISTRY, PARASITOLOGY. *Educ:* Univ SC, BS, 61, MS, 64; La State Univ, PhD(parasitol), 71. *Prof Exp:* Instr biol, Univ SC, 64-68; res assoc biochem, 71-72, asst prof, 72-77, ASSOC PROF BIOCHEM & MED MICROBIOL, COL MED, UNIV NEBR, 77- *Mem:* AAAS; Soc Exp Biol & Med; Am Soc Parasitologists; Sigma Xi. *Res:* Purification and characterization of the growth stimulating factor produced by the tapeworm, Spirometra mansonoides. *Mailing Add:* 5123 S 126th Plaza Omaha NE 68137

PHARES, ROBERT EUGENE, forest physiology, silviculture, see previous edition

PHARES, RUSSELL EUGENE, JR, b Richmond, Ind, May 9, 37; m 72. PHYSICAL PHARMACY. *Educ:* Purdue Univ, BS, 59, MS, 60, PhD(pharm), 62. *Prof Exp:* Asst prof, Col Pharm, Univ Fla, 62-66; tech dir, Barnes-Hind Pharmaceut, 66-73; proj leader bioerodible polymers, ALZA Res, 73-76; DIR BIOL RES, COOPER LABS, INC, 76- *Res:* Application of kinetics, mathematics, and statistics to drug delivery system design; ophthalmic and contact lens accessory solution development and contact lens design and fitting. *Mailing Add:* 115 Los Patios Los Gatos CA 95030

PHARIS, RICHARD PERSONS, b Indianapolis, Ind, Mar 19, 37. PLANT PHYSIOLOGY. *Educ:* Univ Wash, BS, 58; Duke Univ, MF, 59, DF(plant physiol), 61. *Prof Exp:* Plant physiologist, Forest Serv Exp Sta, USDA, Roseburg, Ore, 61-63; res fel plant physiol, Calif Inst Technol, 63-65; from asst prof to assoc prof, 65-72, PROF BOT, UNIV CALGARY, 72- *Concurrent Pos:* Natural Sci & Eng Res Coun oper & major equip grants, 65-; Can Dept Forestry res grant, 67-70 & 72; NATO grants, 70-72 & 79-82; Weyerhaeuser Found grant, 70-72, Natural Sci & Eng Res Coun strategic res grant, 79- & Agr Can extramural res grant, 79-81; assoc ed, Can J Bot. *Mem:* Fel AAAS; Am Soc Plant Physiol; Can Soc Plant Physiol (pres, 78); Can Inst Forestry; Scand Soc Plant Physiol. *Res:* Physiology of plant growth and development, especially gibbeallin physiology, flowering of woody perenmiol plants, including conifers and apical dominance. *Mailing Add:* Dept Biol Univ Calgary Calgary AB T2N 1N4 Can

PHARO, RICHARD LEVERS, b Allentown, Pa, Jan 15, 36; m 59; c 3. BIOCHEMISTRY. *Educ:* Pa State Univ, BS, 57, MS, 59; Johns Hopkins Univ, ScD(biochem), 62. *Prof Exp:* Res investr, Geront Br, Nat Inst Child Health & Human Develop, 62-67; asst to pres, 67-71, admin dir & assoc scientist, Retina Found, 71-76, ASST TO PRES SCI & SR SCIENTIST, EYE RES INST, 76- *Mem:* AAAS; Am Chem Soc; Friends of Eye Res Rehab & Treatment. *Res:* Enzymology, particularly enzyme mechanism in oxidative phosphorylation; biochemistry and physiology of the eye. *Mailing Add:* 6 Ivy Circle Winchester MA 01890

PHARRISS, BRUCE BAILEY, b Springfield, Mo, Dec 12, 37; m 60; c 1. BIOCHEMISTRY, PHARMACOLOGY. *Educ:* Univ Mo, BA, 60, MA, 62, PhD(physiol, pharmacol), 66. *Prof Exp:* Res scientist, Upjohn Co, 66-70; prin scientist, Alza Corp, 70-80; VPRES SCI AFFAIRS, COLLAGEN CORP, 80- *Concurrent Pos:* Tech adv coord off, Fam Planning Prog, Mex; mem adv panel device classification, Food & Drug Admin. *Mem:* AAAS; Am Soc Pharmacol & Exp Therapeut; Soc Study Reproduction; Am Fertil Soc; Int Family Planning Res Asn. *Res:* Role of prostaglandins in mediating responses of trophic hormones and steroid hormone research in development of new forms of contraception. *Mailing Add:* Collagen Corp 2455 Faber Place Palo Alto CA 94303

PHATAK, SHARAD CHINTAMAN, b Indore, India, Feb 28, 32; m 67; c 2. HORTICULTURE, PLANT PHYSIOLOGY. *Educ:* Agra Univ, BSc, 55; Indian Agr Res Inst, New Delhi, AIARI, 59; Mich State Univ, PhD(hort), 64. *Prof Exp:* Instr hort, Dept Agr, Madhya Pradesh, India, New Delhi, 59-60; regional agronomist, Indian Potash Supply Agency Ltd, 60-61; asst hort & veg crops, Mich State Univ, 61-64, fel & res assoc hort, 64-65; scientist div hort, Indian Agr Res Inst, New Delhi, 65-66; chief plant sci, Elanco Div, Eli Lilly & Co India Inc, 67-69; res scientist veg physiol & hort, Res Inst Ont, 69-75; ASSOC PROF HORT, COASTAL PLAIN EXP STA, COL AGR, UNIV GA, 75- *Mem:* Am Soc Hort Sci; Weed Sci Soc Am; Sigma Xi. *Res:* Use and physiology of herbicides and growth regulators; genetic basis for tolerance to herbicides; mechanism of herbicide action; physiology of flowering; precision seeding; plant population; vegetable production; chemigation. *Mailing Add:* Dept Hort Coastal Plain Exp Sta Col Agr Univ Ga Tifton GA 31793

PHEASANT, RICHARD, b Brookline, Mass, May 3, 20; m 45; c 1. ORGANIC CHEMISTRY, RESEARCH ADMINISTRATION. *Educ:* Harvard Univ, SB, 40. *Prof Exp:* Chemist, Schering Corp, 41-49, pharmaceut specifications, 49-53, new prod coordr, 53-57; adminr, Res Inst Med & Chem, 57-59; dir pharmaceut develop, Int Div, Schering Corp, 59-60; proj coordr, Aeroprojects, Inc, 61-63, prin scientist, 64-68, mgr, Technidyne, Inc, 69-70; TECH DATA MGR DRUG REGULATORY AFFAIRS, E R SQUIBB & SONS, INC, 70- *Mem:* AAAS; Am Chem Soc. *Res:* Steroids; organic proximate analysis; fine particle technology; colloid and surface chemistry; gelation; aerospace and military applications of chemistry; pharmaceutical chemistry. *Mailing Add:* E R Squibb & Sons Inc Georges Rd New Brunswick NJ 08903

PHEIFFER, CHESTER HARRY, b Louisville, Ky, Feb 10, 21; m 49; c 1. OPTOMETRY. *Educ:* Univ Louisville, AB, 43; Ohio State Univ, MA, 44, PhD(psychol), 49; Southern Col Optom, OD, 54. *Prof Exp:* Prof psychol, Southern Col Optom, 49-54; assoc prof optom, Univ Houston, 54-59, dean, Col Optom, 61-78, prof, 59-80; chmn, Div Optom, 79-81, PROF OPTOM, NORTHEASTERN STATE UNIV, 79-, DEAN, COL OPTOM, 81- *Concurrent Pos:* Consult, Nat Bd Exam Optom, 53-57 & 59 & Bur Health Manpower, Dept Health, Educ & Welfare, 74-75; mem, Bd Dirs, Southwest Contact Lens Soc, 60-64 & Adv Res Comt, Am Optom Found; consult study cost educ health profession, Nat Inst Med, 72-74; mem, Adv Res Coun, Am Optom Found, 68- & Optom Exten Prog Res Adv Coun, 72-; ed, 75-78, mem ed coun, J Optom Educ, 74-; trustee, Northeastern State Univ Educ Found Inc, 80. *Honors & Awards:* Leadership & Serv Award, Southwest Contact Lens Soc, 65; Gold Medal Award, Beta Sigma Kappa, 66. *Mem:* Asn Schs & Cols Optom (vpres, 69-71, pres, 71-73); AAAS; Am Acad Optom; Am Optom Asn; Sigma Xi. *Res:* Caecanometry, the detection and diagnosis of pathology by means of visual fields. *Mailing Add:* 508 Wheeler Tahlequah OK 74464

PHEIL, CHARLES GEORGE, b Detroit, Mich, Feb 6, 35; m 57; c 4. MICROBIOLOGY. *Educ:* Mich State Univ, BS, 57, MS, 62; Univ Ill, PhD(food microbiol), 66. *Prof Exp:* Res assoc microbiol, Mich State Univ, 58-62, res instr food sci & eng, 62-64; res asst food microbiol, Univ Ill, 64-66; chemist, Gen Mills, Inc, 66-67; chemist, R J Reynolds Tobacco Co, 67-69, head microbiol sect, 69-72, DIR PROD RES & DEVELOP, R J Reynolds FOODS, INC, 72- *Mem:* AAAS; Am Soc Microbiol; Soc Indust Microbiol. *Res:* Microbial physiology and nutrition; bacteriology of food products; industrial fermentations and waste disposal; yeast production; thermal processing of foods; thermophilic anaerobes. *Mailing Add:* Tech Servs Dept R J Reynolds Indust Inc 33rd St & Shorefair Dr Inc Winston-Salem NC 27105

PHELAN, EARL WALTER, b Rahway, NJ, Sept 24, 00; m 30; c 2. CHEMISTRY. *Educ:* Cornell Univ, BChem, 21, PhD(inorg chem), 28. *Hon Degrees:* LHD, Tusculum Col, 71. *Prof Exp:* Asst chem, Univ Wis, 21-23; instr, Ore State Col, 23-26; asst, Cornell Univ, 26-28; instr, Western Reserve Univ, 28-30; prof & head dept, Ga State Womans Col, 30-52; liaison asst, Argonne Nat Lab, 52-65; prof, 65-71, EMER PROF CHEM, TUSCULUM COL, 71- *Concurrent Pos:* Tech aide, Nat Defense Res Comt, 43-46. *Mem:* AAAS; Am Chem Soc. *Res:* Oxidation of hydroxylamine; tests in inorganic chemistry; minerals in foods; chemical education. *Mailing Add:* 1406 Woodmont Dr Greenville TN 37743

PHELAN, JAMES FREDERICK, b Sedalia, Mo, Jan 13, 17; m 46; c 2. MATHEMATICS, ELECTRICAL ENGINEERING. *Educ:* US Naval Acad, BS, 40; Univ Ill, MA, 50, PhD(math), 64. *Prof Exp:* Res asso elec eng, Univ Ill, 63-65; ASSOC PROF ELEC ENG TECHNOL, VA POLYTECH INST & STATE UNIV, 65- *Mem:* Inst Elec & Electronics Engrs. *Res:* Techniques for computer solutions of partial differential equations. *Mailing Add:* Dept of Elec Eng Technol Va Polytech Inst & State Univ Blacksburg VA 24061

PHELAN, JAMES JOSEPH, b San Francisco, Calif, Dec 28, 37; m 62; c 3. EXPERIMENTAL HIGH ENERGY PHYSICS. *Educ:* Univ San Francisco, BS, 59; St Louis Univ, PhD(physics), 68. *Prof Exp:* Fel, Argonne Nat Lab, 67-68; res assoc, Rutherford High Energy Lab, Eng, 68-72; ASST PHYSICIST, ARGONNE NAT LAB, 72- *Res:* Elementary particle research using bubble chamber and spark chamber techniques. *Mailing Add:* Argonne Nat Lab Bldg 362 9600 S Caso Ave Argonne IL 60439

PHELAN, NELSON FLAGGE, b Memphis, Tenn, Oct 27, 41; m 68; c 1. PHYSICAL INORGANIC CHEMISTRY. *Educ:* Occidental Col, BA, 64; Univ Cincinnati, PhD(chem), 69. *Prof Exp:* Teaching asst chem, Univ Cincinnati, 64-66, res fel, 65-69; asst prof chem, Ripon Col, 69-72, acting dean men, 72; vis asst prof chem, Pomona Col, 72-73; head dept environ & elemental anal, Shankman Labs, Inc, Los Angeles, 73-76, sr chemist & expert witness, Truesdail Labs, 76-78, chief chemist, Pomeroy, Johnston & Bailey, Environ Serv Div, Pasadena, 78-80; MEM STAFF ENVIRON SERV DIV, ACOB LABS, 80- *Mem:* Am Chem Soc; Sigma Xi. *Res:* Bonding and structure in transition metal complexes. *Mailing Add:* 1779 E Oakwood Pasadena CA 91104

PHELAN, R(ICHARD) M(AGRUDER), b Moberly, Mo, Sept 20, 21; m 51; c 2. MECHANICAL ENGINEERING. *Educ:* Univ Mo, BS, 43; Cornell Univ, MME, 50. *Prof Exp:* From instr to assoc prof, 47-62, PROF MECH ENG, CORNELL UNIV, 62- *Mem:* AAAS; Am Soc Mech Engrs; Am Soc Eng Educ; Soc Exp Stress Anal. *Res:* Experimental stress analysis, vibrations and dynamics of control systems. *Mailing Add:* Sibley Sch Mech & Aerospace Eng Cornell Univ Ithaca NY 14850

PHELAN, ROBERT J, JR, b Pasadena, Calif, Oct 18, 33; m 60; c 3. OPTICAL PHYSICS. *Educ:* Calif Inst Technol, BS, 58; Univ Colo, PhD(physics), 62. *Prof Exp:* Staff physicist solid state device res, Lincoln Lab, Mass Inst Technol, 62-69; PHYSICIST, NAT BUR STANDARDS, 69- *Mem:* Am Phys Soc; Optical Soc Am; Inst Elec & Electronic Engrs. *Res:* Semiconductor lasers; magneto resistance and superconductivity; optical measurement devices and systems. *Mailing Add:* 1780 Ithaca Dr Boulder CO 80303

PHELPS, ALLEN WARNER, b Washington, DC, Dec 1, 50. TOXICOLOGY, CELL CULTURE. *Educ:* Southwestern at Memphis, BS, 72; Univ Tenn, PhD(toxicol), 78. *Prof Exp:* Fel, Baylor Col Med, 77-80; res toxicologist, Shell Develop Co, 80-81; CELLULAR TOXICOLOGIST, STILLMEADOW, INC, 81- *Concurrent Pos:* Res assoc, Vet Admin, 77-; adj asst prof, Baylor Col Med, 80- *Mem:* Tissue Cult Asn; Environ Mutagen Soc; NY Acad Sci; AAAS; Sigma Xi. *Mailing Add:* 9525 Town Park Dr Houston TX 77036

PHELPS, ARTHUR VAN RENSSELAER, b Dover, NH, July 20, 23; m 56; c 2. ELECTRON COLLISIONS, GASEOUS ELECTRONICS. *Educ:* Mass Inst Technol, ScD(physics), 51. *Prof Exp:* Consult physicist, Res Labs, Westinghouse Elec Corp, 51-70; SR RES SCIENTIST, NAT BUR STANDARDS, 70-; fel, 70-79, CHMN, JOINT INST LAB ASTROPHYSICS, UNIV COLO, BOULDER, 79- *Mem:* Am Phys Soc. *Res:* Electron and atomic collision processes involving low energy electrons, molecules, ions, metastable atoms and resonance radiation; laser processes and modeling. *Mailing Add:* Joint Inst Lab Astrophys Univ Colo Boulder CO 80309

PHELPS, CHARLES DEXTER, b San Antonio, Tex, Sept 16, 37; m 64; c 4. OPHTHALMOLOGY. *Educ:* Univ Iowa, BA, 59, MD, 63. *Prof Exp:* From intern to resident internal med, Boston City Hosp, 63-65; NIH spec fel glaucoma, Dept Ophthal, Sch Med, Washington Univ, 71-72; resident, Hosps, 67-71, from asst prof to assoc prof ophthal, 72-80, PROF OPHTHAL, UNIV IOWA, 80- *Concurrent Pos:* NIH fel, Univ Iowa, 67-68. *Mem:* Am Acad Ophthal & Otolaryngol; Asn Res Vision & Ophthal; Int Perimetric Soc. *Res:* The pathogenesis of visual loss in glaucoma; the heredity of the primary glaucomas; the classification and treatment of secondary glaucomas; controlled therapeutic trials. *Mailing Add:* Dept of Ophthal Univ of Iowa Iowa City IA 52240

PHELPS, CHRISTOPHER PRINE, b Westfield, NJ, July 6, 43; m 69; c 1. NEUROENDOCRINOLOGY, NEUROSCIENCE. *Educ:* Lafayette Col, AB, 65; Rutgers Univ, PhD(endocrinol), 73. *Prof Exp:* Asst endocrinol, Grad Sch, Rutgers Univ, 65-72, fel, Bur Biol Res, 72-73; res anatomist, Sch Med, Univ Calif, Los Angeles, 73-75, fel neuroendocrinol, 75-76; asst prof, 76-81, ASSOC PROF ANAT, COL MED, UNIV SFLA, 81- *Concurrent Pos:* NIH proj dir, 78-81. *Mem:* Sigma Xi; Am Asn Anatomists; Soc Neurosci; Soc Study Reproduction; Endorine Soc. *Res:* Neuroendocrinology; limbic brain regulation of endocrine function; neuroplasticity; recovery of brain function after damage, endocrine and behavioral. *Mailing Add:* Dept Anat Box 6 Med Ctr Univ of SFla Tampa FL 33620

PHELPS, CREIGHTON HALSTEAD, b Logan, Ohio, Nov 12, 40. NEUROCYTOLOGY. *Educ:* Ohio Univ, BSc, 62; Univ Mich, Ann Arbor, MSc, 64, PhD(anat), 67. *Prof Exp:* Asst prof anat, Health Ctr, Univ Conn, 69-76; ASSOC PROF ANAT, SCH MED, WRIGHT STATE UNIV, 76- *Concurrent Pos:* USPHS fel, Univ Col, Univ London, 67-69. *Mem:* Am Asn Anatomists; Am Soc Cell Biol; Soc Neurosci. *Res:* Ultrastructure and cytochemistry of central nervous tissue under normal conditions and during development, degeneration and regeneration. *Mailing Add:* Dept of Anat Wright State Univ Dayton OH 45435

PHELPS, DANIEL JAMES, b Jackson, Mich, July 15, 47; m 71. SOLID STATE PHYSICS. *Educ:* Rose Polytech Inst, BS, 69; Univ Ill, MS, 70, PhD(physics), 74. *Prof Exp:* RES PHYSICIST, KODAK RES LABS, EASTMAN KODAK CO, 74- *Mem:* Am Phys Soc. *Res:* Design and use of solid state imaging and light emitting devices. *Mailing Add:* Eastman Kodak Co Bldg 81 Kodak Park Rochester NY 14650

PHELPS, DEAN G, b Grafton, NDak, Feb 7, 34; m 54; c 3. MATHEMATICS. *Educ:* Univ NDak, BS, 56; Univ Wis-Madison, MS, 59; Wash Univ, PhD(math), 68. *Prof Exp:* Proj engr, A C Spark Plug Div, Gen Motors Corp, 56-58; asst prof math, Univ NDak, 61-64; asst prof, Univ Fla, 68-71; PROF MATH, LOCK HAVEN STATE COL, 71-, CHMN DEPT MATH & COMPUT SCI, 75- *Mem:* Am Math Soc; Math Asn Am. *Res:* Complex analysis. *Mailing Add:* Dept of Math Lock Haven State Col Lock Haven PA 17745

PHELPS, DONALD KENNETH, biological oceanography, see previous edition

PHELPS, FREDERICK MARTIN, III, b Grand Rapids, Mich, June 11, 33; m 57; c 3. ATOMIC SPECTROSCOPY. *Educ:* Carleton Col, BA, 55; Univ Mich, MS, 58; Univ Alta, PhD(physics), 63. *Prof Exp:* Instr physics & math, Kalamazoo Col, 59-60; sessional lectr physics, Univ Alta, 62-64; res assoc, Univ Mich, 64-68, lectr, 66-68; assoc prof physics, Detroit Inst Technol, 67-69; head grating res lab, Bausch & Lomb Optical Co, 69-70; ASSOC PROF PHYSICS, CENT MICH UNIV, 70- *Concurrent Pos:* Assoc ed, J Optical Soc Am, 65-77; vis scientist, Am Inst Physics, 69, 70 & 72. *Mem:* Am Asn Physics Teachers; Optical Soc Am. *Res:* Precision spectroscopy, especially establishment of class A secondary standards of wavelength. *Mailing Add:* Dept of Physics Cent Mich Univ Mt Pleasant MI 48858

PHELPS, HARRIETTE LONGACRE, b Exeter, NH, Mar 15, 36; c 2. PHYSIOLOGICAL ECOLOGY. *Educ:* Carleton Col, BA, 56; Mt Holyoke Col, MA, 58; Ohio State Univ, PhD(zool), 64. *Prof Exp:* Staff fel virol, Nat Cancer Inst, 65-68; assoc prof biol, Fed City Col, 68-78; assoc prof, 78-80, PROF BIOL, UNIV DC, 80- *Mem:* AAAS; Atlantic Estuarine Res Soc; Am Chem Soc. *Res:* Estuarine research including biogeochemistry of metals in sediments and benthics and power plant effects. *Mailing Add:* Dept of Biol Univ DC 1321 H St NW Washington DC 20005

PHELPS, JACK, b Guymon, Okla, Feb 15, 26; m 46; c 4. MATHEMATICS. *Educ:* Panhandle Agr & Mech Col, BS, 48; West State Col Colo, MA, 54; Okla State Univ, EdD(math ed), 63. *Prof Exp:* Teacher pub sch, Okla, 48-58, supt & teacher, 58-61; asst prof math, Southwestern State Col, Okla, 63-66; chmn dept, 66-80, PROF MATH, NORTHWESTERN STATE COL, OKLA, 66- *Concurrent Pos:* Math consult, State Dept Educ, 63-64, Alaska, 66; consult, Concord Col. *Mem:* Math Asn Am. *Res:* Education in mathematics. *Mailing Add:* Dept of Math Northwestern State Col Alva OK 73717

PHELPS, JAMES PARKHURST, b Medford, Mass, Feb 13, 24. REACTOR PHYSICS. *Educ:* Univ Maine, BS, 51; Mich State Univ, PhD(exchange reactions kinetics), 56. *Prof Exp:* Asst chemist, coating develop group, Ansco, Gen Aniline & Film Corp, NY, 51-52; teaching asst, Mich State Univ, 52-54; sr engr, Nuclear Div, Martin Co, Md, 56-57; asst chemist, Reactor Physics Div, Nuclear Eng Dept, Brookhaven Nat Lab, 57-60, from assoc chemist to chemist, 60-70; prof chg nuclear reactor, 70-75, CHMN DEPT NUCLEAR ENG, UNIV LOWELL, 75- *Concurrent Pos:* Lectr, continuing educ prog, Martin Co, 57; mem staff atoms at work exhibit, Reactor Exp Prog, AEC, Bangkok, Thailand, 62. *Mem:* Am Phys Soc; Am Nuclear Soc. *Res:* Anisotropic neutron diffusion in graphite; buckling, prompt lifetime, disadvantage factor and spectral index measurements in graphite-uranium; fast critical experiments; time characteristics and spectra of delayed neutrons; radiographer safety. *Mailing Add:* Nuclear Ctr Univ of Lowell Lowell MA 01854

PHELPS, LEE BARRY, b Quirigua, Guatemala, May 14, 38; m 71; c 1. SURFACE MINING. *Educ:* Univ Idaho, BS, 66; Pa State Univ, MEng, 72, PhD(mining eng), 81. *Prof Exp:* Dredge supt, Int Mining Corp, 66-70; res asst, Pa State Univ, 70-72; mine supt, Aluminum Co Am, 72-76; proj entr, Dow Chem Co, 76-77; instr, 77-81, ASST PROF SURFACE MINING, PA STATE UNIV, 81- *Concurrent Pos:* Mem, Interstate Mining Compact Comn, 77-; consult, Dow Chem Co, 77- *Mem:* Soc Mining Eng; Inst Mining & Metall Engrs. *Res:* Surface mining systems and design to include reclamation and environmental controls. *Mailing Add:* 125 Mineral Sci Bldg Pa State Univ University Park PA 16802

PHELPS, LEROY NASH, b Logan, Ohio, Feb 19, 30; m 62; c 2. MICROBIOLOGY, IMMUNOLOGY. *Educ:* Ohio State Univ, BSc, 55; Univ Southern Calif, PhD(immunol, bacteriophages), 64. *Prof Exp:* Assoc biologist, Eli Lilly & Co, 55-59; lectr bact, Univ SC, 63-64; staff fel bact genetics lab, Venereal Dis Res Lab, Commun Dis Ctr, Atlanta, Ga, 64-66; asst prof, 66-71, ASSOC PROF MICROBIOL, SAN DIEGO STATE UNIV, 71- *Concurrent Pos:* Consult, San Diego Inst Path, 66- *Mem:* AAAS; Am Soc Microbiol; Brit Soc Gen Microbiol. *Res:* Antigens of bacteriophages and their hosts, including the effects of different hosts on specific bacteriophage antigens. *Mailing Add:* Dept of Microbiol San Diego State Univ San Diego CA 92182

PHELPS, MICHAEL EDWARD, b Cleveland, Ohio, Aug 24, 39; m 69; c 1. BIOPHYSICS, NEUROSCIENCES. *Educ:* Western Wash Univ, BA, 65; Wash Univ, PhD(nuclear chem), 70. *Prof Exp:* From asst prof to assoc prof radiation sci, Sch Med, Wash Univ, 71-75, from asst prof to assoc prof elec eng, 74-75; assoc prof radiol & biophysics, Med Sch, Univ Pa, 75-76; PROF RADIOL, BIOMATH & BIOPHYSICS, SCH MED, UNIV CALIF, LOS ANGELES, 76-, DIV CHIEF BIOPHYSICS, 80- *Concurrent Pos:* Mem, Comput & Biomath Study Sect, NIH, 74-78; prin investr, Dept Energy, 76-, adv, Lab Cerebral Metab, 77-; found mem, Int Soc Cerebral Blood Flow & Metab, 81-; mem, Am Heart Asn. *Mem:* Nuclear Med Soc; Neurosci Soc; NY Acad Sci; Radiol Soc NAm. *Res:* Development of timographic techniques for assaying local biochemical proceses in the human subject atramatically; approach uses tracer kinetic techniques with biologically active compounds labeled with radioactive isotopes of carbon, nitrogen, oxygen and fluorine primarily and an analytical imaging technique referred to as positron computed timography. *Mailing Add:* 13554 Valley Vista Blvd Sherman Oaks CA 91423

PHELPS, PAULDING, b Philadelphia, Pa, June 5, 33; c 2. RHEUMATOLOGY. *Educ:* Haverford Col, BA, 55, Col Physicians & Surgeons, MD, 60. *Prof Exp:* CHIEF RHEUMATOLOGY SECT, MAINE MED CTR, 78-, ATTEND PHYSICIAN, 71- *Concurrent Pos:* Attend physician, Mercy Hosp, 71- & Portland City Hosp, 72-; mem, Comt Rheumatology, Am Bd Internal Med, 76-; chmn, Med Sci Comt, Maine Arthritis Found, 72-77. *Mem:* Am Rheumatism Asn; fel Am Col Physicians; Am Bd Internal Med. *Mailing Add:* 180 Park Ave Portland ME 04102

PHELPS, PHARO A, b Biggs, Calif, Aug 24, 28; m 50; c 4. PHYSICS, CIVIL ENGINEERING. *Educ:* US Naval Acad, BS, 50; Rensselaer Polytech Inst, BCE, 53; US Naval Postgrad Sch, PhD(physics), 63. *Prof Exp:* Antisubmarine warfare officer, USS Brinkley Bass, US Navy Civil Eng Corps, 50-52, spec asst civil eng, Dist Pub Works Off, 11th Naval Dist, 53-55, housing officer, Pub Works Ctr, Guam, 55-57, training officer, Bur Yards & Docks, 57-59, instr physics, US Naval Acad, 63-66, cmndg officer, US Naval Mobile Construct Battalion 8, 65-67, exec officer, Europ Div, Naval Facil Eng Command, London, 67-69, officer in chg construct, Naval Facil Eng Command Contracts, Madrid, 69-70, asst comdr res & develop, Naval Facil Eng Command, Washington, DC, 70-71, asst comdr design & eng, 71-74, dep comdr facil acquisition, 73-74; applns eng group mgr, Bechtel Corp, 74-76, mgr eng res & eng oper, Bechtel Nat, Inc, 76-78, mgr eastern opers, Hydro & Community Facil Div, Kuwait, 78-80, MGR ENG & MAT, INT BECHTEL INC, SAN FRANCISCO, 80- *Concurrent Pos:* Vis lectr, Univ Md, 64; assoc prof, Anne Arundel Community Col, 64-65; mem, Interagency Comt Excavation Technol, 71-72. *Mem:* AAAS; Am Phys Soc; Am Asn Physics Teachers; Soc Am Mil Eng; Am Soc Civil Eng. *Res:* Low energy nuclear physics; nuclear spectroscopy and instrumentation; underground construction; advanced energy technologies. *Mailing Add:* 269 Birchwood Dr Moraga CA 94556

PHELPS, RICHARD A, b Pittsfield, Mass, Aug 5, 28; m 61; c 1. NUTRITION, BIOCHEMISTRY. *Educ:* Purdue Univ, BS, 51; Mich State Univ, MS, 56, PhD(dairy), 59. *Prof Exp:* Asst dir res & ed, Nat Cottonseed Prod Asn, 58-65; asst to tech dir, Oil & Feed Mills, 65-70, dir tech info serv, 70-80, DIR RES & DEVELOP, ANDERSON, CLAYTON & CO, 80- *Mem:* Am Chem Soc; Am Oil Chem Soc; Am Soc Animal Sci; Poultry Sci Asn; Am Dairy Sci Asn. *Res:* Oil seeds and by-products, especially cottonseed; ruminant nutrition with emphasis on bloat; remote sensing; eicosanoids-prostaglandins. *Mailing Add:* Dir Res & Develop Serv Anderson Clayton & Co Box 2538 Houston TX 77001

PHELPS, ROBERT RALPH, b San Bernardino, Calif, Mar 22, 26; m 55. MATHEMATICS. *Educ:* Univ Calif, Los Angeles, BA, 54; Univ Wash, PhD(math), 58. *Prof Exp:* Asst, Univ Calif, Los Angeles, 54-56; asst, Univ Wash, 56-57; mem, Inst Adv Study, 58-60, NSF fel, 59-60; lectr & asst res mathematician, Univ Calif, Berkeley, 60-62; from asst prof to assoc prof, 62-66, PROF MATH, UNIV WASH, 66- *Concurrent Pos:* Instr, Princeton Univ, 58-59. *Mem:* Am Math Soc; Math Asn Am. *Res:* Abstract functional analysis; convex sets in normed algebras, normed and topological vector spaces. *Mailing Add:* Dept of Math GN-50 Univ of Wash Seattle WA 98195

PHELPS, RONALD P, b Mobile, Ala, Oct 30, 47; m 75. FISHERIES. *Educ:* Auburn Univ, BS, 69, PhD(fisheries), 75. *Prof Exp:* Res asst, 70-75, ASST PROF FISHERIES, DEPT FISHERIES & ALLIED AQUACULT, AUBURN UNIV, 75- *Concurrent Pos:* Fel, Dept Fisheries & Allied Aquacult, Auburn Univ, 75. *Mem:* Am Fisheries Soc; Marine Technol Soc; Sigma Xi. *Res:* Chemical control if fish diseases and the related environmental effects; international aquaculture. *Mailing Add:* Dept of Fisheries & Allied Aquacult Auburn Univ Auburn AL 36830

PHELPS, WILLIAM ROBERT, b Baltimore, Md, Apr 30, 28; m 58; c 3. FOREST PATHOLOGY. *Educ:* NC State Univ, BS, 50; Duke Univ, MF, 51; PhD(plant path), Univ Wis, 58. *Prof Exp:* Res forester, US Rubber Co, 51-55; asst, Univ Wis, 55-58; plant pathologist, United Fruit Co, 58-62; PLANT PATHOLOGIST, US FOREST SERV, 62- *Honors & Awards:* Super Serv Award, USDA, 75. *Mem:* Am Phytopath Soc; Soc Am Foresters. *Res:* Forest pest management administration. *Mailing Add:* 988 Belle Glade Dr Stone Mountain GA 30083

PHEMISTER, ROBERT DAVID, b Framingham, Mass, July 15, 36; m 60; c 3. VETERINARY PATHOLOGY. *Educ:* Cornell Univ, DVM, 60; Colo State Univ, PhD(path), 67. *Prof Exp:* Assoc res vet, Univ Calif, Davis, 60-61; staff scientist, Armed Forces Inst Path, 62-64; leader path sect, Collab Radiol Health Lab, 64-68, dep dir, 68-72, assoc prof path, 68-73, sci dir, 72-73, dir collab radiol health lab, 73-76, assoc dean, 76-77, PROF PATH, 73-, DEAN COL VET MED & BIOMED SCI, COLO STATE UNIV, 77- *Concurrent Pos:* Vis res pathologist, Univ Calif, 74-75. *Mem:* AAAS; Am Vet Med Asn; Am Col Vet Path; Int Acad Path; Radiation Res Soc. *Res:* Diseases of pre- and postnatal development; canine nephropathology; radiation effects. *Mailing Add:* Off of the Dean Colo State Univ Ft Collins CO 80523

PHIBBS, MURRAY KENNETH, b Sarnia, Ont, Mar 19, 20; m 46; c 3. CHEMISTRY. *Educ:* Univ Western Ont, BA, 43; Univ Toronto, MA, 44; Laval Univ, DSc(chem), 50. *Prof Exp:* Res chemist polymers, E I du Pont de Nemours & Co, Inc, Del, 51-53; res chemist, 54-55, res supvr chem, 55-59, lab mgr, 59-69, RES FEL CHEM, DU PONT OF CAN, LTD, 69- *Mem:* Fel Chem Inst Can. *Res:* Synthesis of new polymers with unusual physical properties of practical value. *Mailing Add:* Res Centre du Pont of Can Ltd Kingston ON K7L 5A5 Can

PHIBBS, PAUL VESTER, JR, b Pulaski, Va, July 24, 42; m 68; c 2. MICROBIOLOGY. *Educ:* Bridgewater Col, BA, 64; Univ Ga, MS, 66, PhD(microbiol), 69. *Prof Exp:* Res fel microbial physiol, Univ Minn, Minneapolis, 69-70; asst prof, 70-75, ASSOC PROF MICROBIOL, MED COL VA, VA COMMONWEALTH UNIV, 75- *Concurrent Pos:* Dir microbiol grad prog, Va Commonwealth Univ, 75-76, leader microbiol, physiol-genetics cluster, 75- *Mem:* Am Soc Microbiol; Soc Exp Biol & Med. Res: Bacterial physiology and metabolism with emphasis on the regulation of metabolic pathways and membrane transport systems in Pseudomonas; genetics and mechanisms of exopolysaccharide synthesis by Pseudomonas. *Res:* NSF res grant, Va Commonwealth Univ, 71-, Nat Cystic Fibrosis Res Found res grant, 75-78; prog dir, NIH res training grant, 77-83; vis prof microbiol, Med Ctr, Univ Ala, 73, col med, Univ S Ala, 79; ed microbiol sect, Va Jour Sci, 77-79. *Mailing Add:* Va Commonwealth Univ PO Box 678 MCV Sta Richmond VA 23298

PHIBBS, RODERIC H, b Chicago, Ill, Nov 3, 30; m 52; c 4. PEDIATRICS, BIOPHYSICS. *Educ:* Syracuse Univ, AB, 54; State Univ NY, MD, 58. *Prof Exp:* Intern med, Med Ctr, 58-59, from asst resident to chief resident pediat, 59-62, asst clin prof pediat, Cardiovasc Res Inst, 64-65, asst prof peidat, 65-70, assoc prof pediat, 70-80, PROF PEDIAT, MED CTR, UNIV CALIF, SAN FRANCISCO, 80-, ASSOC STAFF, CARDIOVASC RES INST, 68- *Concurrent Pos:* USPHS fel biophys, Univ Western Ont, 62-64; res fel physiol, Cardiovasc Res Inst, Med Ctr, Univ Calif, San Francisco, 64-65. *Mem:* Biophys Soc; Int Soc Hemorheology; Soc Pediat Res. *Mailing Add:* Dept of Pediat Univ of Calif Med Ctr San Francisco CA 94143

PHIFER, HAROLD EDWIN, b Cincinnati, Ohio, Aug 13, 10; m 46; c 2. PHYSICAL CHEMISTRY. *Educ:* Univ Cincinnati, AB, 32, MA, 33, PhD(phys chem), 34. *Prof Exp:* Asst chem, Univ Cincinnati, 31-34; chief chemist, 34-54, res chemist, color & graphics div, Chicago Lab, Inmont Corp, 55-75; RETIRED. *Mem:* AAAS; Am Chem Soc. *Res:* Partial molal volumes of electrolytes; solute diffusion; rotogravure printing inks. *Mailing Add:* 4621 Stanley Ave Downers Grove IL 60515

PHIFER, KENNETH OSCAR, b Woodbury, NJ, June 7, 34; m 56; c 2. PARASITOLOGY. *Educ:* Rutgers Univ, BA, 56; Johns Hopkins Univ, ScD, 59. *Prof Exp:* Scientist, Lab Parasite Chemother, NIH, 59-68, prog officer, US-Japan Coop Med Sci Prog, 68-77; prog officer, Int Ctrs for Med Res Prog, 73-77; PARASITOLOGY PROG OFFICER, MICROBIOL & INFECTIOUS DIS PROG, NAT INST ALLERGY & INFECTIOUS DIS, NIH, 77- *Mem:* AAAS; Am Soc Parasitol; Am Soc Trop Med & Hygiene. *Res:* Tropical medicine and parasitology; science administration. *Mailing Add:* Room 737 Westwood Bldg Nat Inst of Health Washington DC 20014

PHIFER, LYLE HAMILTON, b Chester, SC, Nov 16, 27; m 51; c 4. ANALYTICAL CHEMISTRY. *Educ:* Wofford Col, BS, 48; Vanderbilt Univ, MS, 51, PhD(anal chem), 53. *Prof Exp:* Asst dept med, Med Sch, Vanderbilt Univ, 51-53; res assoc, FMC Corp, 53-76; VPRES & TECH DIR, CHEM SERV, INC, 76- *Mem:* Am Chem Soc; Am Soc Test & Mat. *Res:* Ultraviolet spectroscopy kinetics; gas and liquid chromatography; x-ray diffraction and fluorescence. *Mailing Add:* Chem Serv Inc PO Box 194 West Chester PA 19380

PHILANDER, SAMUEL GEORGE, physical oceanography, see previous edition

PHILBIN, DANIEL MICHAEL, b Dunmore, Pa, June 2, 35; m 64; c 2. ANESTHESIOLOGY. *Educ:* Duquesne Univ, BS, 57; St Louis Univ, MD, 61; Am Bd Anesthesiol, dipl, 69. *Prof Exp:* Resident anesthesia, Columbia-Presby Med Ctr, 65-68, NIH res fel, Dept Anesthesia, Columbia Univ, 67-68, assoc, Columbia-Presby Med Ctr, 68-70, asst prof, Columbia Univ, 70; asst prof, 71-79, ASSOC PROF ANESTHESIA, HARVARD MED SCH, MASS GEN HOSP, 79- *Honors & Awards:* Res Award Prize, Am Soc Anesthesiologists, 69. *Mem:* Am Physiol Soc; fel Am Col Cardiol; Am Soc Anesthesiologists; Asn Cardiac Anesthesiologists (secy-treas, 75-77, vpres, 77-78, pres, 78-79); Int Anesthesia Res Soc. *Res:* Cardiovascular effects of neuromuscular blocking agents; effect of anesthesia and open cardiac surgery on antidiurectic hormone and renal function; hormonal responses to anesthesia and surgery. *Mailing Add:* Dept of Anesthesia Mass Gen Hosp 32 Fruit St Boston MA 02114

PHILBIN, JEFFREY STEPHEN, b Orange, NJ, Feb 1, 42; m 69. NUCLEAR ENGINEERING. *Educ:* Univ Notre Dame, BSME, 64; Northwestern Univ, Ill, MS, 69; Univ Ill, Urbana, PhD(nuclear eng), 71. *Prof Exp:* NUCLEAR ENGR, SANDIA LABS, 70- *Mem:* Am Nuclear Soc (pres, 75-76). *Res:* Pulse reactor design and development; pulse reactor operations and experiments. *Mailing Add:* Div 4452 Sandia Labs Albuquerque NM 87185

PHILBRICK, CHARLES RUSSELL, b Jefferson City, Tenn, Sept 24, 40; m 60; c 2. ATMOSPHERIC & SOLID STATE PHYSICS. *Educ:* NC State Univ, BS, 62, MS, 64, PhD(physics), 66. *Prof Exp:* PROJ SCIENTIST, AIR FORCE CAMBRIDGE RES LAB, 66- *Concurrent Pos:* Mem working group II, Inter Union Comn on Solar-Terrestrial Physics; mem working group IV, panel IV A on struct of upper atmosphere, Comt on Space Res, Int Coun Sci Unions. *Honors & Awards:* Res & Develop Award, US Air Force. *Mem:* Am Phys Soc; Nat Asn Physics Teachers; Am Geophys Union; Sigma Xi. *Res:* Atmospheric composition studies in the mesosphere and thermosphere with rocket and satellite experiments; investigation of atmospheric structure, physical and chemical processes and models; ionospheric composition; mass spectrometry. *Mailing Add:* Air Force Geophys Lab Bedford MA 01731

PHILBRICK, RALPH NOWELL, b San Francisco, Calif, Jan 1, 34; m 55; c 3. BOTANY. *Educ:* Pomona Col, BA, 56; Univ Calif, Los Angeles, MA, 58; Cornell Univ, PhD(bot), 63. *Prof Exp:* Res assoc bot, Bailey Hortorium, Cornell Univ, 62-63; assoc, Univ Calif, Santa Barbara, 63-64; biosystematist, Santa Barbara Bot Garden, 64-73, cur Herbarium, 65-73, DIR, SANTA BARBARA BOT GARDEN, 74- *Concurrent Pos:* Lectr, Univ Calif, Santa Barbara, 64-65 & 72- *Mem:* Am Soc Plant Taxon; Bot Soc Am; Int Asn Plant Taxon; Soc Study Evolution. *Res:* Biosystematics of Pacific Coast cacti; taxonomy of Camellia cultivars; flora of the California Islands. *Mailing Add:* Santa Barbara Bot Garden Santa Barbara CA 93105

PHILBRICK, SHAILER SHAW, b Columbia, Mo, May 11, 08; m 36; c 3. GEOLOGY. *Educ:* DePauw Univ, AB, 30; Johns Hopkins Univ, PhD(geol), 33. *Prof Exp:* Jr topographic engr, US Geol Surv, 34; jr soil expert, Soil Conserv Serv, USDA, 35; from jr geologist to sr geologist, Corps Engrs, US Dept Army, 35-49, prin geologist & div geologist, Ohio River Div, 49-56, head geologist & div geologist, 56-66; vis prof geol sci, Cornell Univ, 63-64, prof, 66-72; CONSULT, 72- *Concurrent Pos:* Lectr, Northwestern Univ, 60; consult, Corps Engrs, US Army, US Nuclear Regulatory Comn & various indust concerns. *Honors & Awards:* Claire P Holdredge Award, Asn Eng Geologists, 77. *Mem:* Fel Geol Soc Am; Asn Eng Geol. *Res:* Engineering geology; geology of nuclear power plant sites. *Mailing Add:* 117 Texas Lane Ithaca NY 14850

PHILBROOK, WILLIAM OREN, b Chicago, Ill, Apr 25, 13; m 46. METALLURGICAL ENGINEERING, PHYSICAL CHEMISTRY. *Educ:* Univ Chicago, SB, 34. *Prof Exp:* Anal chemist, Wis Steel Works, Int Harvester Co, Ill, 34-36, res chemist, 36-43, foreman open hearth observers, 41-43 & metall div, 43-45; from asst prof to assoc prof metall eng, 45-55, prof & prin res metall engr, 55-65, prof, 65-81, EMER PROF METALL ENG & MAT SCI & PRIN RES METALLURGIST, CARNEGIE-MELLON UNIV, 81- *Concurrent Pos:* Consult, 47-; expert deleg, UN Conf Latin-Am Steel Indust, 52. *Honors & Awards:* Hunt Award, Am Inst Mining, Metall & Petrol Engrs, 52 & 69, Award, 71. *Mem:* Distinguished mem Iron & Steel Soc; fel Metallurgical Soc; AAAS; Am Soc Metals; Am Inst Mining, Metall & Petrol Engrs. *Res:* Kinetics of slag-metal reactions; physical chemistry and engineering analysis of smelting and refining processes, especially as related to iron and steel; iron ore reduction. *Mailing Add:* 2628 Orlando Dr Pittsburgh PA 15235

PHILIBERT, ROBERT LAWRENCE, b Sawyer, Kans, Apr 14, 22; m 42; c 3. PHYSIOLOGY, ENDOCRINOLOGY. *Educ:* Southwest Mo State Col, BS, 52; Univ Mo, MA, 61, PhD(zool), 64. *Prof Exp:* Teacher pub schs, Mo, 53-58; teaching asst zool, Univ Mo, 58-63; from asst prof to assoc prof biol, 63-70, PROF LIFE SCI, SOUTHWEST MO STATE COL, 70- *Concurrent Pos:* NSF student res partic grants, 65-67. *Mem:* Am Soc Zool. *Res:* Neurosecretion; hypothalamic-hypophyseal relationships. *Mailing Add:* Southwest Mo State Col Springfield MO 65802

PHILIP, A G DAVIS, b New York, NY, Jan 9, 29; m 64. ASTRONOMY. *Educ:* Union Col, BS, 51; NMex State Univ, MS, 59; Case Inst Technol, PhD(astron), 64. *Prof Exp:* Asst prof astron, Univ NMex, 64-66; from asst prof to assoc prof astron, State Univ NY, Albany, 66-76; RES PROF, UNION COL, 76- *Concurrent Pos:* Astronomer, Dudley Observ, 66-81 & Van Vleck Observ, 82-; secy & treas, New York Astron Corp, 68-; vis prof, 72-73, vis fel, Yale Univ, 76; vis prof, La State Univ, 73, 76 & Acad Sci, Lithuania USSR, 73 & 76; Harlow Shapley lectr, Am Astron Soc, 73-; secy comn 33, mem orgn comt & secy comn 30, Int Astronom Union, 73-; ed, Dudley Observ Report Series, 74. *Mem:* Am Phys Soc; Am Astron Soc; Royal Astron Soc; Sigma Xi; NY Acad Sci. *Res:* Photometry; spectroscopy; galactic structure. *Mailing Add:* Dudley Observ 69 Union Ave Schenectady NY 12308

PHILIP, ABRAHAM, medicinal chemistry, biochemistry, see previous edition

PHILIPP, HERBERT REYNOLD, b New York, NY, Nov 6, 28. EXPERIMENTAL SOLID STATE PHYSICS. *Educ:* Colgate Univ, AB, 50; Mass Inst Technol, SB, 50; Univ Mo, PhD(physics), 54. *Prof Exp:* PHYSICIST, RES & DEVELOP CTR, GEN ELEC CO, 54- *Mem:* Am Phys Soc. *Res:* Optical properties of crystalline and amorphous solids; physics of metal oxide varistor ceramic materials. *Mailing Add:* Res & Develop Ctr Gen Elec Co PO Box 8 Schenectady NY 12301

PHILIPP, MANFRED HANS, b Rostock, Ger, Sept 30, 45; US citizen; m 75; c 2. BIOCHEMISTRY. *Educ:* Mich Technol Univ, BS, 66; Northwestern Univ, PhD(biochem), 71. *Prof Exp:* Res assoc biochem, Inst Macromolecular Chem, Univ Freiburg, 71-75 & Sch of Hyg & Pub Health, Johns Hopkins Univ, 75-77; ASSOC PROF BIOCHEM, LEHMAN COL, 77- & CRAD CTR, CITY UNIV NY, 79- *Concurrent Pos:* Fels, Europ Molecular Biol Orgn, 72-75 & Ger Res Asn, 75; grant-in-aid, Sigma Xi, 78; res award, Prof Staff Cong-Bd Higher Educ, City Univ New York, 78-79; res grant, Muscular Dystrophy Asn, 80- *Mem:* Am Chem Soc; AAAS; Sigma Xi; NY Acad Sci. *Res:* Chemical mechanism of serine proteases; computer analysis of polynucleotide sequences. *Mailing Add:* Bedford Park Blvd W Dept Chem Lehman Col City Univ NY Bronx NY 10468

PHILIPP, RONALD E, b Easton, Pa, Sept 1, 32; m 55; c 2. MECHANICAL ENGINEERING. *Educ:* Lafayette Col, BS, 54; Lehigh Univ, MS, 56; Columbia Univ, PhD(mech eng), 64. *Prof Exp:* Instr mech & elec eng, Lafayette Col, 54-56; RES, DEVELOP & DESIGN, ORD CORPS, US ARMY, 56- *Concurrent Pos:* Instr, US Mil Acad, West Point. *Mem:* Am Soc Mech Engrs; NY Acad Sci; Sigma Xi. *Res:* Kinematics synthesis of two degree of freedom linkages for function generation. *Mailing Add:* Box 142 Phillipsburg NJ 08865

PHILIPP, WALTER V, b Vienna, Austria, Dec 14, 36; m 63; c 2. MATHEMATICS. *Educ:* Univ Vienna, MS & PhD(math), 60. *Prof Exp:* Asst math, Univ Vienna, 60-63; asst prof, Univ Mont, 63-64; Univ Ill, Urbana, 64-65; asst, Univ Vienna, 65-67, dozent, 67; from asst prof to assoc prof, Univ Ill, Urbana, 67-73, prof math, 73-80; MEM STAFF MATH, MASS INST TECHNOL, CAMBRIDGE, 80- *Concurrent Pos:* Vis prof, Univ NC, Chapel Hill, 72. *Mem:* Am Math Soc; Austrian Math Soc. *Res:* Metric problems in number theory; limit theorems in probability. *Mailing Add:* Dept of Math Mass Inst Technol Cambridge MA 02139

PHILIPPART, MICHEL PAUL, b Ixelles, Belgium, Aug 1, 35; m 58; c 2. NEUROLOGY, NEUROCHEMISTRY. *Educ:* Brussels Univ, BS, 56, MD, 60. *Prof Exp:* Head, Lab C, Inst Bunge, Belgium, 65, head lab neurol develop, 66-67; asst prof pediat & med, 67-69, assoc prof pediat, neurol & psychiat, 69-75, PROF PEDIAT, NEUROL & PSYCHIAT, UNIV CALIF, LOS ANGELES, 75- *Concurrent Pos:* Belg Am Educ Found fel, Johns Hopkins Univ, 62-64; Parkinson Dis Found sr fel, Inst Bunge, Belgium, 65-66; mem, Ment Retardation Ctr & Brain Res Inst, Los Angeles, 68- *Honors & Awards:* Travel award, Belg Govt, 63, Giannina Gaslini Award, 77. *Mem:* Soc Neurosci; Soc Pediat Res; Soc Exp Biol & Med; NY Acad Sci; Soc Neurochem. *Res:* Lipids, glycolipids; inborn errors of metabolism; hereditary degenerations of the nervous system; lysosomal functions; pediatric neurology. *Mailing Add:* Ment Retardation Inst 760 Westwood Plaza Los Angeles CA 90024

PHILIPPOU, ANDREAS NICOLAOU, b Nicosia, Cyprus, July 15, 44. ESTIMATION. *Educ:* Univ Athens, BSc, 67; Univ Wis, Madison, MSc, 70, PhD(statist), 72. *Prof Exp:* Teaching & res asst statist & probability, Univ Wis, Madison, 68-72; asst prof, Univ Tex at El Paso, 72-74; vis prof, Univ Patras, Greece, 74-78; asst prof, Am Univ Beirut, 78-79, assoc prof, 79-80; PROF STATIST PROBABILITY & BIOMATH, UNIV PATRAS, GREECE, 80- *Concurrent Pos:* Prof & consult, Beirut Univ Col, 79-80; dep chmn, Hellenic Aerospace Indust, 81- *Mem:* Am Statist Asn; Greek Math Soc; Inst Math Statist; Math Asn Am; Fibonaaci Asn. *Res:* Asymptotic properties of estimators of parameters, and optimal hypothesis testing; generalized fibonacci numbers and probability; odd-even games. *Mailing Add:* Dept Math Univ Patras Patras Greece

PHILIPS, BILLY ULYSES, b San Antonio, Tex, Oct 22, 46; m 75. PUBLIC HEALTH, SOCIAL EPIDEMIOLOGY. *Educ:* Oklahoma City Univ, BA, 69; Univ Okla, MPH, 71, PhD(public health), 74. *Prof Exp:* Asst dir prog eval, Nat Drug Educ Ctr, 72-73; eval specialist & instr, 73-74, assoc dir & asst prof continuing med educ, 74-76, dir, Off Spec Progs, 76-77, ASSOC PROF, UNIV TEX MED BR, GALVESTON, 78-, ASSOC DEAN ALLIED HEALTH SCI, 81- *Concurrent Pos:* fac consult, Am Med Student Asn, 74-; prin investr med component, Regional Resource Ctr Child Abuse & Neglect, 76-78; consult, Houston-Galveston Health Syst Agency, Area Health Comn, 77- & Univ Tex Med Br Nursing Serv, 77-; prin investr, Galveston Community Health Survey, Hall Found, 80-; prin investr, Cigarette Smoking & Hepatocollular Carcinoma, Nat Cancer Inst, 81- *Mem:* Sigma Xi; Am Pub Health Asn; Asn Teachers Prev Med; AAAS; Am Sociol Asn. *Res:* Community health; social epidemiology; health promotion and health behavior. *Mailing Add:* Univ Tex Med Br Sch Allied Health Sci Suite 3 A-45 Galveston TX 77550

PHILIPS, FREDERICK STANLEY, b Mt Vernon, NY, Sept 25, 16; m 40; c 3. PHARMACOLOGY. *Educ:* Columbia Univ, BA, 36; Univ Rochester, PhD(biol), 40. *Prof Exp:* Asst zool, Seth Low Jr Col, Columbia Univ, 36; asst biol, Univ Rochester, 36-40; assoc pharmacol, Sch Med, Yale Univ, 42-43; from instr to assoc prof, 46-57, assoc dir, Sloan-Kettering Div, 70-74, PROF PHARMACOL, GRAD SCH MED SCI, CORNELL UNIV, 57-; MEM, SLOAN-KETTERING INST CANCER RES, 56-, CHIEF PHARMACOL LAB, 67- *Concurrent Pos:* Sessell fel, Osborn Zool Lab, Yale Univ, 40-41, Nat Res Coun fel, Sch Med, 41-42; res fel, Mass Inst Technol; assoc, Sloan-Kettering Inst Cancer Res, 46-56, head pharmacol sect, 46-66; mem, Panel Bioassay, Comt Growth, Nat Res Coun, 47, Panel Chemother, 51-53; consult, USPHS, 54-56; mem, Pharmacol Study Sect, NIH, 54-56, Cancer Chemother Study Sect, 56-60, Res Career Award Comt, Inst Gen Med Sci, 62-65; mem, Panel Pharmacol, Cancer Chemother Nat Serv Ctr, 55-56; vis investr, Chester Beatty Res Inst, Inst Cancer Res, London, Eng, 65-66; mem, Ad Hoc Comt Biochem Studies Eval Toxicity, Drug Res Bd, Nat Res Coun, 65-66; mem, Cancer Spec Prog Adv Comt, Nat Cancer Inst, 75-77, secy-treas, Am Asn Cancer Res, 78- *Honors & Awards:* Alfred P Sloan Award, 64. *Mem:* AAAS; Am Soc Pharmacol & Exp Therapeut; Soc Exp Biol & Med; Am Asn Cancer Res. *Res:* Embryo respiration; cancer chemotherapy; chemical carcinogenesis. *Mailing Add:* Sloan Kettering Inst for Cancer Res 1275 York Ave New York NY 10021

PHILIPS, JUDSON CHRISTOPHER, b Glen Ridge, NJ, Nov 15, 42; m 64. ORGANIC CHEMISTRY. *Educ:* Pa State Univ, BS, 64; Ohio State Univ, PhD(chem), 69. *Prof Exp:* Fel, Ohio State Univ, 69; asst prof chem, Univ Detroit, 69-74, assoc prof, 74-78; RES SCIENTIST, PFIZER CENT RES, 78- *Mem:* Am Chem Soc. *Res:* Synthesis and characterization of polymers; structural modification of biopolymers. *Mailing Add:* Pfizer Cent Res Eastern Point Rd Groton CT 06340

PHILIPSON, JOSEPH, b Chicago, Ill, Aug 30, 18; m 42; c 4. POLYMER CHEMISTRY. *Educ:* Univ Wis, BS, 40; Univ Minn, MS, 41. *Prof Exp:* Process engr, NAm Aviation, Inc, Calif, 45-46; res chemist, Coast Paint & Chem Co, 46-47; develop chemist, Aerojet-Gen Corp, 47-52; chief chemist, Rocket Div, Grand Cent Rocket, 52-54; dir western div, Atlantic Res Corp, 55-61, dir European Opers, 61-63; CONSULT, 64- *Concurrent Pos:* Consult, US Navy, 68-, Am Hosp Supply, 74-, Hi-Shear Corp, 74-, Magic Mountain, 77-, Beckman Instruments, 78- & Bell Helmets, 81- *Mem:* Am Inst Aeronaut & Astronaut; Soc Plastics Eng; Soc Aerospace Mat & Process Eng; Asn Consult Chemists & Chem Engrs. *Res:* Propellants; plastics; rocketry; adhesives, polyurethane rubbers and sealants; new applications of polymers for coatings including corrosion resistant coatings and optical coating; applications of new polymers for optical use. *Mailing Add:* 1485 Old House Rd Pasadena CA 91107

PHILIPSON, LLOYD L, b Utica, NY, June 19, 28. ENERGY & TRANSPORTATION SYSTEMS, SAFETY ENGINEERING. *Educ:* Univ Calif, Los Angeles, BA, 50, MA, 51, PhD(math), 54, BS. *Prof Exp:* Staff mem indust math several co, 51-58; sr assoc opers anal, Planning Res Corp, 58-62; mgr opers anal dept, Hughes Aircraft Co, 62-66; mgr WCoast opers, Syst Sci Corp, Calif, 66-70; dir, Comput Sci Southeast Ctr, 70-72; PRIN, PLANNING RES CORP, 72-; SR SCI ADV, J H WIGGENS CO, 79- *Concurrent Pos:* Pvt consult, 60-; lectr & sr res assoc, Univ Southern Calif, 73-; fel, Nat Bur Standards. *Mem:* Nat Acad Sci; Systs Safety Soc; Opers Res Soc Am; Inst Elec & Electronics Engrs; Am Math Soc. *Res:* Systems engineering; operations analysis; applied mathematics; differential equations; statistics; risk analysis. *Mailing Add:* 924 Ninth St Santa Monica CA 90403

PHILLEO, ROBERT EUGENE, b Spokane, Wash, Aug 21, 23; m 48; c 4. MATERIALS SCIENCE, CIVIL ENGINEERING. *Educ:* Carnegie Inst Technol, BS, 46. *Prof Exp:* Res engr, Portland Cement Asn, 46-58; chief, Res Sect, 58-70, chief, Concrete Br, 70-77, CHIEF STRUCT BR, OFF CHIEF OF ENGRS, CORPS ENGRS, 77- *Concurrent Pos:* Ed, Cement & Concrete Res, 70; lectr mech, Northwestern Univ, 52-57. *Honors & Awards:* Anderson Award, Am Concrete Inst, 81. *Mem:* Am Concrete Inst (pres, 73-74); Am Soc Testing & Mat; Transp Res Bd; Concrete Soc London. *Res:* Rheological properties of concrete; response of concrete to high temperature; development of non-destructive test methods. *Mailing Add:* 7420 Annanwood Ct Annandale VA 22023

PHILLEY, JOHN CALVIN, b Indianola, Miss, Oct 17, 35; m 59; c 3. GEOLOGY. *Educ:* Millsaps Col, BS, 57; Univ Tenn, Knoxville, MS, 61; PhD(geol), 71. *Prof Exp:* From instr to assoc prof, 60-73, PROF GEOL, MOREHEAD STATE UNIV, 73-, HEAD DEPT PHYS SCI, 74- *Concurrent Pos:* Geologist, US Geol Surv, 67- *Mem:* Geol Soc Am; Am Asn Petrol Geol; Am Inst Prof Geologists. *Res:* Environmental carbonate stratigraphy; areal geologic mapping; paleozoic stratigraphy of southeastern United States. *Mailing Add:* 1001 Knapp Ave Morehead KY 40351

PHILLIES, GEORGE DAVID JOSEPH, b Buffalo, NY, July 23, 47. PHYSICAL CHEMISTRY, POLYMERS. *Educ:* Mass Inst Technol, SB(physics) & SB(biol), 69, SM, 71, DSc(physics), 73. *Prof Exp:* Res staff biophys, Harvard-Mass Inst Technol Health Sci & Technol Prog, 73-75; res chemist, Univ Calif, Los Angeles, 75-78; ASST PROF, DEPT CHEM, UNIV MICH, ANN ARBOR, 78- *Mem:* Am Phys Soc. *Res:* Experimental and theoretical statistical mechanics, quasi-elastic light scattering, diffusion in nonideal solutions, Raman and infrared spectroscopy and membrane-active antibiotics. *Mailing Add:* Dept of Chem Univ Mich Ann Arbor MI 48109

PHILLIP, MICHAEL J, b Port-of-Spain, Trinidad, W Indies, May 27, 29; m 56; c 2. GENETICS. *Educ:* Univ Toronto, BSA, 60, MSA, 62; Mich State Univ, PhD(genetics), 64. *Prof Exp:* From asst prof to assoc prof biol, John Carroll Univ, 64-72; assoc prof biol, 72-77, PROF BASIC SCI, UNIV DETROIT, 77- *Concurrent Pos:* Assoc dir NSF Inst Microbiol, NC Col, 66, vis prof, Inst Math & Sci, 67-68; consult, Rand Develop Corp, 67. *Mem:* Am Soc Microbiol; Genetics Soc Am. *Res:* Tumor immunology. *Mailing Add:* Dept of Basic Sci Univ of Detroit Dent Sch Detroit MI 48221

PHILLIPS, ALLAN ROBERT, b New York, NY, Oct 25, 14; m 64; c 3. ORNITHOLOGY. *Educ:* Cornell Univ, AB, 36, PhD(ornith), 46; Univ Ariz, MS, 39. *Prof Exp:* Cur ornith, Mus Northern Ariz, 39-57; guest researcher, Inst Biol, Nat Univ Mex, 57-69, tech counsr, 69-71, prof ornith, Ornith Lab, 72-74; GUEST RES ASSOC, SCH BIOL SCI, UNIV NUEVO LEON, 73- *Concurrent Pos:* Asst prof, Univ Ariz, 49 & 58; res assoc, Del Mus Nat Hist, 71-77; taxon consult & res assoc, Denver Mus Nat Hist, 77-, mem, Int Ornith Comt, 70-; res assoc, Smithsonian Inst, 79-, San Diego Natural Hist Mus, 79- & Can Mus Natural Hist, 80- *Mem:* Wilson Ornith Soc; Cooper Ornith Soc; Am Ornith Union; Brit Ornithologists Club. *Res:* Birds of Mexico, Arizona, Central America and adjacent regions; taxonomy and migration of North and Central American birds, Tyrannidae, Loxia. *Mailing Add:* Apartado Postal 370 San Nicolas de los Garza Nuevo Leon Mexico

PHILLIPS, ALLEN THURMAN, b Vicksburg, Miss, Oct 30, 38; m 61; c 2. BIOCHEMISTRY. *Educ:* La State Univ, BS, 60, MS, 61; Mich State Univ, PhD(biochem), 64. *Prof Exp:* Asst prof biochem, La State Univ, 64-66; assoc prof, 67-71, PROF DEPT BIOCHEM & BIOPHYSICS, PA STATE UNIV, UNIVERSITY PARK, 71- *Concurrent Pos:* Ed, J Bact, 75- *Honors & Awards:* Res Career Develop Award, NIH, 72-77. *Mem:* AAAS; Am Chem Soc; Am Soc Microbiol; Am Soc Biol Chem; Brit Biochem Soc. *Res:* Enzymology; chemistry and metabolism of amino acids; metabolic regulatory mechanisms; neurobiochemistry. *Mailing Add:* Dept of Biochem Althouse Lab Pa State Univ University Park PA 16802

PHILLIPS, ALVAH H, b Buffalo, NY, Aug 21, 28; m 49; c 2. PHYSIOLOGICAL CHEMISTRY. *Educ:* Allegheny Col, BA, 49; Univ Buffal Buffalo, MA, 52; Johns Hopkins Univ, PhD(physiol chem), 57. *Prof Exp:* Res fel chem, Harvard Univ, 57-59; from instr to asst prof physiol chem, Sch Med, Johns Hopkins Univ, 59-70; ASSOC PROF BIOL, UNIV CONN, 70- *Mem:* Am Chem Soc. *Res:* Mechanisms of enzyme action; hormonal control of metabolism; role of lipids in biological energy transfer. *Mailing Add:* Dept of Biol Univ of Conn Storrs CT 06268

PHILLIPS, ALVIN B(URT), b Milwaukee, Wis, July 25, 20; m 45; c 2. CHEMICAL ENGINEERING. *Educ:* Univ Mo, BS, 42. *Prof Exp:* Chem engr, 42-59, chief process eng br, 59-65, ASST MGR AGR & CHEM DEVELOP, NAT FERTILIZER DEVELOP CTR, TENN VALLEY AUTHORITY, 65- *Mem:* Am Chem Soc. *Res:* Phosphate fertilizers; nitrogen fixation; carbonization of coal; aluminum alloys; alumnia from clay; wood sugar by hydrolysis; fertilizer technology. *Mailing Add:* Nat Fertilizer Develop Ctr Tenn Valley Authority Muscle Shoals AL 35660

PHILLIPS, ANTHONY GEORGE, b Barrow, Eng, Jan 30, 43; Can citizen. BIOPSYCHOLOGY, NEUROSCIENCE. *Educ:* Univ Western Ont, BA, 66, MA, 67, PhD(biopsychol), 70. *Prof Exp:* Res assoc neurophysiol, Fels Res Inst, 69 & biol, Calif Inst Technol, 69-70; asst prof, 70-75, assoc prof, 75-80, PROF PSYCHOL, UNIV BC, 80- *Concurrent Pos:* Vis prof, Oxford Univ, 75-76; mem psychol comt, Natural Sci & Eng Res Coun Can, 76-79, chmn, 78-79, E W R Steacie fel, 79; mem behav sci comt, Med Res Coun Can, 78-81; Killam Sr Res Scholar, Can Coun, 78. *Mem:* Soc Neurosci. *Res:* Neural substrates of learning, memory and motivation; role of biogenic amines and neuropeptides in normal and pathological behavior. *Mailing Add:* Dept of Psychol Univ BC Vancouver BC V6T 1W5 Can

PHILLIPS, ARIS, b Smyrna, Asia Minor, Nov 30, 15; nat US; m 49; c 2. MECHANICS. *Educ:* Athens Tech Univ, dipl, 37; Tech Univ Berlin, DrIng, 39. *Hon Degrees:* MA, Yale Univ, 60. *Prof Exp:* Vis lectr eng mech, Calif Inst Technol, 47; res assoc & asst prof, Stanford Univ, 47-54; assoc prof civil eng, 54-60, dir grad studies, 63-70, prof eng & appl sci, 60-79, ROBERT HIGGIN PROF MECH ENG, YALE UNIV, 79- *Concurrent Pos:* Ed, Acta Mechanica, 65- *Mem:* Fel Am Soc Mech Engrs; Soc Eng Sci; fel Am Acad Mech; fel AAAS; Sigma Xi. *Res:* Applied mechanics; plasticity; rheology. *Mailing Add:* Becton Ctr Yale Univ New Haven CT 06520

PHILLIPS, ARTHUR PAGE, b Haverhill, Mass, Feb 14, 17; m 42, 50; c 2. ORGANIC CHEMISTRY. *Educ:* Tufts Col, BS, 38, MS, 39; NY Univ, PhD(org chem), 42. *Prof Exp:* Asst chem, NY Univ, 39-42; RES ORG CHEMIST, RES LABS, BURROUGHS WELLCOME & CO, INC, 42-, GROUP LEADER, 70- *Concurrent Pos:* Instr, Polytech Inst Brooklyn,

44-57. *Mem:* Am Chem Soc; The Chem Soc. *Res:* Synthetic and theoretical organic chemistry; medicinal chemistry; chemotherapy; heterocyclic compounds; mechanisms of reactions. *Mailing Add:* Burroughs Wellcome & Co Inc 3030 Cornwallis Rd Research Triangle Park NC 27709

PHILLIPS, ARTHUR WILLIAM, JR, b Claremont, NH, Sept 25, 15; m 50; c 2. MICROBIOLOGY, ENVIRONMENTAL SCIENCES. *Educ:* Univ Notre Dame, BS, 39, MS, 41; Mass Inst Technol, ScD, 47. *Prof Exp:* Asst, Univ Notre Dame, 36, asst bact, 39-41, res assoc, 43-45, prof bact & head bioeng, 49-53; PROF MICROBIOL, SYRACUSE UNIV, 54- *Concurrent Pos:* Res assoc, Mass Inst Technol, 47-49. *Mem:* Am Soc Microbiol; Soc Gen Microbiol; Asn Gnotobiotics. *Res:* Microbiol interactions with phagocytic cells. *Mailing Add:* Dept of Biol Syracuse Univ Syracuse NY 13210

PHILLIPS, BENJAMIN, b Galveston, Tex, Apr 1, 17; m 41; c 4. ORGANIC CHEMISTRY. *Educ:* Univ of the South, BS, 37; Johns Hopkins Univ, PhD(org chem), 41. *Prof Exp:* Res chemist, Chem Div, Union Carbide Corp, 41-55, asst dir res, 55-58, res consult, 58-60, assoc dir res, 60-61, dir res & develop, 61-64, mgr chem res develop dept, 64-65, mgr pharmaceut technol, 66-67, mgr corp res, 67-72, sr res fel, 72-78, CONSULT, UNION CARBIDE CORP, 78- *Concurrent Pos:* Collabr south chem utilization res & develop, USDA, 56-66, mem chem utilization res & develop adv comt, 66-69. *Honors & Awards:* Chem Pioneer Award, Am Inst Chem, 67. *Mem:* Am Chem Soc; fel Am Inst Chem; Asn Consult Chemists & Chem Engrs. *Res:* Industrial organic chemistry; polymers; peracids; epoxides; high performance materials; chemical systems; chemurgy. *Mailing Add:* 2 Wesskum Wood Rd Riverside CT 06878

PHILLIPS, BOBBY MAL, b Morris Chapel, Tenn, Apr 17, 41; 81. CHEMICAL ENGINEERING. *Educ:* Univ Tenn, BS, 62, MS, 63, PhD(chem eng), 68. *Prof Exp:* Res engr, 68-70, sr res chem engr, 70-77, RES ASSOC, TENN EASTMAN CO, 77- *Mem:* Am Inst Chem Engrs. *Res:* Rheology; fluid mechanics; fiber spinning and processing; futures. *Mailing Add:* Tenn Eastman Co Kingsport TN 37662

PHILLIPS, BRIAN ANTONY MORLEY, b Edinburgh, UK, Apr 10, 42; m 65; c 2. PHYSICAL GEOGRAPHY, CARTOGRAPHY. *Educ:* Univ Col Wales, BSc, 64, PhD(coastal geomorphol), 69. *Prof Exp:* ASSOC PROF GEOG & CHMN DEPT, LAKEHEAD UNIV, 67- *Concurrent Pos:* Nat Res Coun grant, Lakehead Univ, 69-72 & 78-81. *Mem:* Can Asn Geog; Am Asn Geog; Inst Brit Geog; fel Royal Geog Soc. *Res:* Present coastal processes and forms including beach stability and rock shore morphology; paleogeography of glacial lakes of Lake Superior basin; shoreline recreational potential and user perception. *Mailing Add:* Dept of Geog Lakehead Univ Thunder Bay ON P7B 5E1 Can

PHILLIPS, BRIAN ROSS, b Manchester, Eng, Oct 6, 35; m 67. PHYSICAL CHEMISTRY. *Educ:* Univ Edinburgh, BS, 58, PhD(phys chem), 61. *Prof Exp:* Res chemist, Calico Printers Assocs Ltd, 61-62; res chemist, Univ Copenhagen, 62-63; sr res chemist, 63-77, RES ASSOC, E I DU PONT DE NEMOURS & CO, INC, 77- *Mem:* Am Chem Soc; Royal Soc Chem. *Res:* Chemistry and kinetics of solid state reactions; low pressure oxidation of single copper crystals; textile fibers and fabrics; long range business planning. *Mailing Add:* Textile Fibers Dept Textile Res Lab E I du Pont de Nemours & Co Inc Wilmington DE 19898

PHILLIPS, BRUCE A, b Chicago, Ill, Aug 1, 38; m 63; c 1. MICROBIOLOGY, VIROLOGY. *Educ:* Univ Ill, BS, 60; Univ Mich, MS, 63, PhD(microbiol), 67. *Prof Exp:* Instr, 67-68, asst prof, 68-73, ASSOC PROF MICROBIOL, SCH MED, UNIV PITTSBURGH, 73- *Concurrent Pos:* Res fel virol, Albert Einstein Col Med, 65-67; NIH grants, 68-70, 71-73, 74-78 & 78-82; sabbatical leave, Univ Cambridge, Eng, 79-80. *Mem:* AAAS; Am Soc Microbiol; NY Acad Sci. *Res:* Morphogenesis of polio virus. *Mailing Add:* Dept of Microbiol Univ of Pittsburgh Sch of Med Pittsburgh PA 15261

PHILLIPS, BRUCE EDWIN, b Olivet, Ill, May 7, 34; m 55; c 2. ORGANIC CHEMISTRY. *Educ:* Olivet Nazarene Col, AB, 56; Wash Univ, PhD(org chem), 61. *Prof Exp:* Chemist, Res Ctr, Gen Foods Corp, 61-62; asst prof chem, Eastern Nazarene Col, 62-68; chemist, Agr Res Serv, USDA, 68-70; asst prof, 70-80, ASSOC PROF CHEM, ST LOUIS COL PHARM, 80- *Concurrent Pos:* Res Corp res grant, 64; NSF res participation prog grant, 65-67. *Mem:* Am Chem Soc. *Res:* Stereochemistry of acetal condensations and synthetic organic chemistry; analysis of lipids from botanical sources. *Mailing Add:* Dept of Chem 4588 Parkview Pl St Louis Col of Pharm St Louis MO 63110

PHILLIPS, CARLETON JAFFREY, b Muskegon, Mich, Nov 17, 42; m 65; c 2. MAMMALOGY, ORAL BIOLOGY. *Educ:* Mich State Univ, BS, 64; Univ Kans, MA, 67, PhD(zool), 69. *Prof Exp:* Res assoc zool, Bernice P Bishop Mus, Hawaii, 64-65; res asst, State Biol Surv Kans, Univ Kans, 65-66; res assoc, Sch Med, Univ Md, Baltimore City, 66-67; res asst, Univ Kans, 67-69; aerospace biologist, Grumman Aerospace Corp, NY, 69-70; asst prof, 70-74, ASSOC PROF BIOL, HOFSTRA UNIV, 74-, NAT INST DENT RES FEL, 72- DIR GRAD PROG BIOL & MEM UNIV RES COMT, 73- *Concurrent Pos:* Asst to pres, Synecology Corp, NY, 70-; chmn standing comt anat & physiol, Am Soc Mammal. *Mem:* AAAS; Am Soc Mammal; fel Explor Club. *Res:* Distribution, systematics and ecology of mammals; oral and dental biology of mammals; evolution and disease in mammals; environmental science and technology; aerospace biology. *Mailing Add:* Dept of Biol Hofstra Univ 1000 Fulton Ave Hempstead NY 11550

PHILLIPS, CHANDLER ALLEN, b Los Angeles, Calif, Dec 21, 42. BIOMEDICAL ENGINEERING. *Educ:* Stanford Univ, AB, 65; Univ Southern Calif, MD, 69. *Prof Exp:* Intern med, Good Samaritan Hosp, Los Angeles, 69-70; gen med officer, 8th US Air Force Dispensary, Thailand, 70-71, res med officer, 6570th Aerospace Med Res Lab, US Air Force, 71-72; res physician biomed eng, Univ Dayton Res Inst, 72-74; asst prof physiol & eng, 75-79, ASSOC PROF ENG & PHYSIOL, SCH MED, WRIGHT STATE UNIV, 79- *Concurrent Pos:* Consult biomed eng, 6570th Aerospace Med Res Lab, US Air Force, 80-; consult med, Stouder Mem Hosp, Troy, Ohio, 75-; Grantee, NIH, 78-; contractor, US Army, 80- *Mem:* Inst Elec & Electronics Engrs; Am Heart Asn; Biomed Eng Soc; Am Soc Eng Educ; Instrument Soc Am. *Res:* Muscle biomechanics, quantitative evaluation of cardiac and skeletal muscle; cardiovascular bioengineering, evaluation of ventricular function; rehabilitation engineering (neuromuscular prosthetics); biomedical engineering education. *Mailing Add:* Dept Eng Wright State Univ Dayton OH 45435

PHILLIPS, CHARLES ALAN, b New Haven, Conn, Jan 31, 33; m 56; c 4. VIROLOGY, INTERNAL MEDICINE. *Educ:* Yale Univ, BA, 54, MD, 59. *Prof Exp:* Intern, Mary Fletcher Hosp, Burlington, Vt, 59-60, resident internal med, 62-63; Nat Inst Allergy & Infectious Dis res training grant virol, Baylor Col Med, 63-64, asst prof virol & epidemiol, 64-66; asst prof med, Col Med, Univ Vt, 66-67, assoc prof med microbiol, 67-69, assoc prof med & med microbiol, 69-73, prof med, 73-81, prof med microbiol & dir Infectious Dis Unit, 76-81, EMER PROF MED & MED MIRCOBIOL, COL MED, UNIV VT, 81- *Concurrent Pos:* Career develop award, Univ Vt Col Med, 67-72. *Mem:* Am Soc Microbiol. *Res:* Upper respiratory infections, particularly rhinoviruses; rubella and congenital rubella syndrome; infantile diarrhea; St Louis encephalitis; epidemiology; chronic respiratory diseases. *Mailing Add:* 54 Bilodeau Ct Burlington VT 05401

PHILLIPS, CHARLES JOHN, physics, deceased

PHILLIPS, CHARLES W(ILLIAM), b Chicago, Ill, June 20, 20; m 46. METAL CUTTING. *Educ:* Univ Wis, BS, 42; Univ Mich, MS, 49, PhD(metall eng), 54. *Prof Exp:* Res metallurgist, Dept Chem & Metall Eng, Dow Chem Co, 42-45, 46-47; res asst, Univ Mich, 47-49, instr, asst prof & res supvr, 49-55; consult, Sci Lab, 55-56, supvr reactor mat sect, 56-57 & process, mech metall & reactor mat sects, 57-60, mgr res serv dept, 60-65, res planning assoc, Sci Res Staff, 65-67, mgr res & develop dept, Electrocure Opers, 67-72, prin staff engr, Alt Engines Dept, 72-76, PRIN STAFF ENGR, MACHINING & WEAR DEPT, RES STAFF, FORD MOTOR CO, 76- *Mem:* Am Soc Testing & Mat; Am Soc Metals; Am Inst Mining, Metall & Petrol Engrs. *Res:* Physical and mechanical metallurgy; machinability; physical and mechanical metallurgy. *Mailing Add:* 912 Aberdeen Dr Ann Arbor MI 48104

PHILLIPS, DAVID, b Marion, Ind, Oct 10, 36; m 58; c 3. PSYCHOPHYSIOLOGY. *Educ:* Wabash Col, BS, 58; Purdue Univ, MS, 60, PhD(olfaction), 62. *Prof Exp:* Cardiovasc grant, 62-63, from instr to asst prof, 63-67, assoc prof psychol, Med Sch, 67-78, PROF & CHIEF BIOSTATIST SECT, ORE HEALTH SCI UNIV, 78- *Concurrent Pos:* NIH fel, 63-65. *Mem:* Am Psychol Asn. *Mailing Add:* Dept Pub Health & Prev Med Univ Ore Health Sci Ctr Portland OR 97201

PHILLIPS, DAVID BERRY, b Highland Co, Ohio, May 30, 40. PHYSICAL CHEMISTRY. *Educ:* Miami Univ, Ohio, AB, 61; Univ Calif, Berkeley, PhD(phys chem), 65. *Prof Exp:* Asst prof, 65-75, ASSOC PROF CHEM, MIAMI UNIV, 75- *Mem:* Am Chem Soc; Am Phys Soc. *Res:* Electrical and magnetic properties of metals at high pressures. *Mailing Add:* Dept of Chem Miami Univ Oxford OH 45056

PHILLIPS, DAVID COLIN, b Rhosllanerchrugog, Wales, Sept 6, 40; m 68; c 2. CHEMISTRY. *Educ:* Univ Wales, BSc, 65, PhD(phys chem), 68. *Prof Exp:* sr scientist chem, 68-76, mgr chem reation dynamics, 76-80, MGR CHEMICAL PHYSICS, WESTINGHOUSE RES LABS, 80- *Concurrent Pos:* Mem fac, Univ Wales, Aberystwyth, 65-68. *Honors & Awards:* Indust Res -100 Award, Indust Res Mag, 76. *Mem:* Am Chem Soc; Electrochem Soc; Royal Inst Chem. *Res:* Physical chemistry; gas kinetics; polymer chemistry; laser chemistry; electropolymerization; photopolymerization, particulate chemistry. *Mailing Add:* Westinghouse Res Labs Pittsburgh PA 15235

PHILLIPS, DAVID LOWELL, b Rushville, Ind, May 21, 29; m 52; c 2. MATHEMATICS. *Educ:* Ball State Teachers Col, BS, 51; Purdue Univ, MS, 52, PhD(math), 57. *Prof Exp:* Asst math, Purdue Univ, 52-56; asst mathematician, 57-60, assoc mathematician, Argonne Nat Lab, 60-71; ASSOC PROF, UNIV SOUTHERN COLO, 71- *Mem:* Am Math Soc; Soc Indust & Appl Math; Math Asn Am. *Res:* Numerical analysis; matrix algebra; Hilbert space. *Mailing Add:* 4033 Hillside Dr Pueblo CO 81008

PHILLIPS, DAVID MANN, b Cincinnati, Ohio, Apr 25, 38; m 64; c 4. CELL BIOLOGY. *Educ:* Northeastern Univ, BS, 61; Univ Chicago, PhD(zool), 66. *Prof Exp:* NIH fel, Harvard Med Sch, 66-68; asst prof biol, Wash Univ, 68-73; STAFF SCIENTIST POP COUN, ROCKEFELLER UNIV, 73- *Mem:* AAAS; Am Soc Cell Biol; Soc Study Reproduction. *Res:* Sperm development, structure and motility. *Mailing Add:* Pop Coun Rockefeller Univ New York NY 10021

PHILLIPS, DAVID RICHARD, b Turlock, Calif, Feb 15, 42; m 61; c 2. BIOCHEMISTRY. *Educ:* Univ Calif, Los Angeles, BS, 64; Univ Southern Calif, PhD(biochem), 69. *Prof Exp:* Asst mem, St Jude Children's Res Hosp, 72-74; Roche Res Inst fel, Theodor Kocher Inst, Univ Bern, Switz, 74-75; assoc mem, St Jude Children's Res Hosp, Memphis, 75-80; MEM FAC, UNIV CALIF, SAN FRANCISCO, 80- *Concurrent Pos:* USPHS fel, St Jude Children's Res Hosp, 70-72; USPHS grant, 74-77, 77-80, 78-83; res career develop award, 75-80. *Mem:* Am Chem Soc; Am Soc Biol Chemists; Am Soc Hematol; Am Soc Cell Biol. *Res:* Membrane structure and function; mechanism of platelet aggregation. *Mailing Add:* Univ Calif PO Box 40608 San Francisco CA 94190

PHILLIPS, DAVID T, b Charles City, Iowa, Oct 9, 38; m 63; c 2. PHYSICS. *Educ:* Iowa State Univ, BS, 61; Univ Calif, SB, 66. *Prof Exp:* Physicist, Radiation Div, Naval Res Lab, DC, 60-61; asst prof physics, Univ Calif, Santa Barbara, 66-71, asst res scientist, 71-74; pres, Glendan Co, 71-76; chief scientist, Sci Spectrum, Inc, Santa Barbara, 75-76, vpres, 77-78; lectr parapsychol, Univ Calif, Santa Barbara, 78 & mech eng, Univ Calif, Santa Barbara, 79-80; PRES, THE INFO CONNECTION, 79-; SR STAFF ENG, RENCO CORP, GOLETA, CALIF, 80- *Concurrent Pos:* Dir exp physics, Sci Spectrum, Inc, Calif, 70-72; lectr parapsychol, Univ Calif Exten, Santa Barbara, 75. *Mem:* Am Phys Soc; Parapsychol Asn. *Res:* Lasers; quantum optics; electronics; light scattering; instrumentation; bacterial bio-assay; parapsychology. *Mailing Add:* 5107 Calle Asilo Santa Barbara CA 93111

PHILLIPS, DAVID WILLIAM, b Chicago, Ill, Aug 17, 46; m 67, 81. MARINE BIOLOGY. *Educ:* Univ Wash, BS, 68; Stanford Univ, PhD(biol sci), 74. *Prof Exp:* ASST PROF ZOOL, UNIV CALIF, DAVIS, 74- *Mem:* Am Soc Zoologists; AAAS; Western Soc Naturalists. *Res:* Behavioral, ecological and physiological aspects of marine invertebrate prey-predator interactions; interactions involving mollusks and chemoreception. *Mailing Add:* Dept of Zool Univ of Calif Davis CA 95616

PHILLIPS, DON IRWIN, b Kansas City, Mo, Nov 17, 45. SCIENCE POLICY, EDUCATION POLICY. *Educ:* Univ Mich, BS, 67; Harvard Univ, MA, 69, PhD(chem), 72. *Prof Exp:* Res fel chem, Harvard Univ, 73; staff assoc & proj dir sci educ, AAAS, 73-75; asst coordr aging & res admin, Ctr Aging, Univ Md, College Park, 74-75; educ policy prog fel & spec asst to assoc dir educ instnl res, Nat Inst Educ, 75-76; pub policy prog mgr, AAAS, 77-79; ASSOC DIR, SCI & PUB AFFAIRS, DUKE UNIV, DURHAM, 79- *Concurrent Pos:* Spec sci adv, Bd Sci & Technol, Off Gov,; consult, Off Environ Educ, 74, Fund for Improv PostSecondary Educ, 76-77, Nat Inst Educ, 78-80 & Nat Sci Found, 79-81; treas, Intersoc Liason Comt, Environ, State Legis, 79- *Mem:* Am Chem Soc; AAAS; NY Acad Sci. *Res:* Federal and private research and development budgets and policies; relationship between academic science policy studies and government science policy; science in state and local governments. *Mailing Add:* 410 Fairoaks Circle Chapel Hill NC 27514

PHILLIPS, DON T, b Bessemor, Ala, Feb 6, 42; m 66; c 1. OPERATIONS RESEARCH, INDUSTRIAL ENGINEERING. *Educ:* Lamar State Col Technol, BS, 65; Univ Ark, Fayetteville, MS, 67, PhD(opers res, indust eng), 69. *Prof Exp:* Instr, Univ Ark, Fayetteville, 65-69; asst prof opers res & indust eng, Univ Tex, Austin, 69-71; assoc prof indust & systs eng, Purdue Univ, West Lafayette, 71-75; PROF INDUST ENG, TEX A&M UNIV, COLLEGE STATION, 75- *Mem:* Opers Res Soc Am; Am Inst Indust Engrs. *Res:* Queueing theory; simulation analysis; nonlinear programming; applied stochastic processes; network flow theory. *Mailing Add:* Dept of Indust Eng Tex A&M Univ College Station TX 77843

PHILLIPS, DONALD ARTHUR, b Olean, NY, Apr 7, 45; m 68; c 1. PLANT PHYSIOLOGY. *Educ:* Duke Univ, BS, 67; Harvard Univ, PhD(biol), 71. *Prof Exp:* Asst prof life sci, Ind State Univ, 72-76; asst prof agron, 76-78, assoc prof, 78-81, PROF AGRON, UNIV CALIF, DAVIS, 81- *Concurrent Pos:* NSF fel, 71-72. *Mem:* Am Soc Plant Physiol; Am Soc Agron. *Res:* Symbiotic nitrogen fixation in legumes. *Mailing Add:* Dept of Agron & Range Sci Univ of Calif Davis CA 95616

PHILLIPS, DONALD DAVID, b Los Angeles, Calif, Apr 12, 26; m 50; c 4. ORGANIC CHEMISTRY. *Educ:* Univ Alta, BS, 49; Univ Calif, PhD(chem), 52. *Prof Exp:* Asst chem, Univ Calif, 49-51; from instr to asst prof chem, Cornell Univ, 52-58; chemist, Shell Develop Co, 58-62, supvr, 62-63; mgr cent res lab, Mobil Chem Co, 63-67, com develop, 67-71, mgr Edison Res & Develop Labs, 71-78, GEN MGR, RES & DEVELOP MOBIL CHEM CO, EDISON, 78- *Concurrent Pos:* Alfred P Sloan fel, 55-58. *Mem:* Am Chem Soc; Plastics Inst Am. *Res:* Petrochemicals; agricultural chemicals; chemistry of natural products and polynuclear aromatic hydrocarbons. *Mailing Add:* 294 Seneca Place Westfield NJ 07090

PHILLIPS, DONALD HERMAN, b Knoxville, Tenn, Mar 10, 41; m 59, 73; c 4. PHYSICS, PHYSICAL CHEMISTRY. *Educ:* Tenn Technol Univ, BS, 63; Va Polytech Inst, MS, 68, PhD(physics), 71. *Prof Exp:* STAFF SCIENTIST PHYSICS, NASA, 63- *Concurrent Pos:* Vis scholar, Appl Sci Div, Harvard Univ, 80-81; Floyd Thompson fel, 80-81. *Mem:* Am Phys Soc; Am Chem Soc. *Res:* Theoretical, atmospheric and surface chemistry; spectroscopy. *Mailing Add:* Langley Res Ctr NASA Hampton VA 23665

PHILLIPS, DONALD KENNEY, b Newark, Del, Apr 24, 31; m 71; c 2. ORGANIC CHEMISTRY. *Educ:* Univ Del, BS, 53; Ohio State Univ, PhD(org chem), 58. *Prof Exp:* Proj assoc chem, Univ Wis, 58-60; res chemist, 60-65, group leader, 65-68, sect head med chem, 68-79, MGR ANAL CHEM, CHEM PROG, STERLING-WINTHROP RES INST, 79- *Mem:* Am Chem Soc. *Res:* Medicinal chemistry; cardiovascular, lipid-lowering, anti-inflammatory and adrenergic agents. *Mailing Add:* Sterling-Winthrop Res Inst Rensselaer NY 12144

PHILLIPS, DONALD LUNDAHL, b Wilmington, Del, July 15, 52; m 78. PLANT ECOLOGY. *Educ:* Mich State Univ, BS, 74; Utah State Univ, MS, 77, PhD(biol & bot), 78. *Prof Exp:* ASST PROF BIOL, EMORY UNIV, 78- *Concurrent Pos:* Co-prin investr, NSF grant, 80- & US Forest Serv grant, 80- *Mem:* AAAS; Ecol Soc Am; Am Inst Biol Sci. *Res:* Plant community ecology and mathematical ecology; studies of southern Appalachian forest succession in response to chestnut blight and clearcuts of various sizes. *Mailing Add:* Dept Biol Emory Univ Atlanta GA 30322

PHILLIPS, DOUGLAS J, b Franklin Co, Iowa, Dec 11, 31; m 56; c 3. PLANT PATHOLOGY. *Educ:* Colo State Univ, BS, 58, MS, 60, PhD(bot sci), 68. *Prof Exp:* Jr plant pathologist, Dept of Bot, Colo State Univ, 60-68; asst res plant path, Univ Calif, Berkeley, 68-70; RES PLANT PATHOLOGIST, SCI & EDUC ADMIN, USDA, 70- *Mem:* Am Phytopath Soc; Sigma Xi. *Res:* Post-harvest diseases of fruits and vegetables. *Mailing Add:* USDA PO Box 8143 Fresno CA 93747

PHILLIPS, DWIGHT EDWARD, b Lewistown, Mont, Aug 16, 44; m 67; c 2. ANATOMY. *Educ:* Univ Mont, BA, 66; Tulane Univ, PhD(anat). *Prof Exp:* Asst prof anat, Sch Med, Univ SDak, 70-73; asst prof, 73-76; ASSOC PROF HUMAN ANAT, BIOL DEPT, MONT STATE UNIV, 76- *Mem:* Am Asn Anatomists; AAAS; Sigma Xi. *Res:* Development of the central nervous system; function of glial cells in mammalian central nervous system. *Mailing Add:* Dept of Biol Mont State Univ Bozeman MT 59715

PHILLIPS, E ALAN, b Boston, Mass, Oct 28, 37. OPTICS, NUCLEAR PHYSICS. *Educ:* Mass Inst Technol, BS, 57, PhD(physics), 61. *Prof Exp:* Instr physics, Mass Inst Technol, 61-62; from instr to asst prof, Princeton Univ, 62-69; physicist, Lawrence Berkeley Lab, 69-71; prin res scientist, Avco Everett Res Lab, Inc, 71-75; SCIENTIST, SCI APPLN, INC, 75- *Mem:* Am Phys Soc; Am Asn Physics Teachers; Sigma Xi; AAAS. *Res:* High energy lasers; diffraction; thermal blooming; atmospheric optics; nuclear moments. *Mailing Add:* Sci Appln Inc 1725 Jefferson Davis Hwy Arlington VA 22202

PHILLIPS, EDWARD, b Roselle, NJ, Aug 21, 26; m 49; c 4. MOLECULAR PHYSICS. *Educ:* US Naval Postgrad Sch, BS, 62; Univ RI, MS, 65; Univ Southern Calif, PhD(physics), 75. *Prof Exp:* Served US Navy, 44-70; res asst, 71-74, res staff physicist, 75-77, asst prof physics, 77-80, ASST CLIN PROF SURG, UNIV SOUTHERN CALIF, 80- *Res:* Study of the photodissociation process in simple atmospheric molecules through observation of fluorescence from photodissociation fragments. *Mailing Add:* Dept of Physics Univ of Southern Calif Los Angeles CA 90007

PHILLIPS, EDWIN ALLEN, b Lowell, Fla, Mar 18, 15; m 42; c 2. PLANT ECOLOGY. *Educ:* Colgate Univ, AB, 37; Univ Mich, MA, 41, PhD(bot), 48. *Prof Exp:* Teacher high sch, NY, 37-39; from instr to assoc prof bot, 46-57, chmn dept, 73-77, prof, 57-80, EMER PROF BOT, POMONA COL, 80- *Concurrent Pos:* Mem exped, Great Bear Lake, Northwest Territories, 48; vis prof ecol, Univ Mich Biol Sta, 55, 56, 58, 70 & 71; NSF sci fac fel, Oxford Univ, 61-62; consult, Agency Int Develop, India, 64-65, Indonesia, 72; consult, Biol Sci Curric Study, 61; NSF grant for physiol-ecol studies on Calif chaparral; AEC grant for tracer studies in mosses, 68-; Schenck res fund for bot, 68-80; consult fundamental approaches sci teaching study, Univ Hawaii, 68-, contextual approaches to secondary educ. *Honors & Awards:* Wig Distinguished Prof Award, 66. *Mem:* Fel AAAS; Am Soc Nat; Bot Soc Am; Sigma Xi; Ecol Soc Am. *Res:* Physiological ecology; desert and chaparral; bryophytes; ecological and general biology textbooks; succession studies on Michigan forests; factors influencing fall coloration in Liquidambar. *Mailing Add:* Dept of Biol Pomona Col Claremont CA 91711

PHILLIPS, ESTHER RODLITZ, b Brooklyn, NY, May 27, 33; m 67. MATHEMATICS, HISTORY OF SCIENCE. *Educ:* Brooklyn Col, BS, 55; NY Univ, MA, 56, PhD(math), 60. *Prof Exp:* Assoc prof math, NY Univ, 60-67; ASSOC PROF MATH, LEHMAN COL, 67- *Concurrent Pos:* Fulbright award, Rome, Italy, 59-60; managing ed, Historia Mathematica. *Mem:* Am Math Soc; Math Asn Am; Hist Sci Soc. *Res:* History of mathematics; modern theories of the integral; Russian mathematics; The Moscow School of the Theory of Functions. *Mailing Add:* Dept of Math Lehman Col Bedford Park Blvd W Bronx NY 10468

PHILLIPS, F(REDERICK) C, b Osceola Mills, Pa, Jan 18, 15; m 42; c 3. AERONAUTICAL ENGINEERING. *Educ:* NY Univ, BAeroEng, 38. *Prof Exp:* Aerodynamicist, Glenn L Martin Co, 39-47; prof, Tech Inst Aeronaut, Rio de Janeiro, Brazil, 47-51; test & design engr, McDonnell Aircraft Corp, Mo, 51-55; chief aerodyn & preliminary design, Canadair Ltd, 55-57, proj engr, 57-60, asst chief engr, 60-61, dir res & develop, 61-63, prog mgr, 63-75, chief develop engr, 75-80; AERONAUT CONSULT, 80- *Concurrent Pos:* Instr aerodyn, Johns Hopkins Univ, 42-44; consult, Brazilian Air Ministry, 47-51. *Honors & Awards:* McCurdy Award, Can Aeronaut & Space Inst, 69. *Mem:* Assoc fel Am Inst Aeronaut & Astronaut; Am Helicopter Soc; fel Can Aeronaut & Space Inst (pres, 66-67). *Res:* Development of fixed-wing land and sea planes, rotary-wing and vertical takeoff aircraft; administration of aerospace research and development. *Mailing Add:* RFD Box 201 Lyme NH 03768

PHILLIPS, GARY WILSON, b Golden City, Mo, June 11, 40; m 63; c 3. NUCLEAR SCIENCE, RADIATION PHYSICS. *Educ:* Mass Inst Technol, BS, 62; Univ Md, PhD(nuclear physics), 67. *Prof Exp:* Res assoc physics, Univ Wash, 66-69; res scientist assoc, Ctr Nuclear Studies, Univ Tex, Austin, 69-71; scientist, Geonuclear Dept, Teledyne Isotopes, Inc, 71-73; RES PHYSICIST, RADIATION SURVIVABILITY & DETECTION BR, CONDENSED MATTER & RADIATION SCI DIV, NAVAL RES LAB, 73- *Mem:* Am Phys Soc; Inst Elec & Electronics Engrs; Sigma Xi. *Res:* Nuclear radiation detection; nuclear materials; nuclear instrumentation and analysis; applied radiation physics. *Mailing Add:* Code 6613 Condensed Matter Radiation Sci Div Naval Res Lab Washington DC 20375

PHILLIPS, GEORGE DOUGLAS, b Stoke-on-Trent, Eng, Dec 3, 28; m 55; c 3. VETERINARY PHYSIOLOGY. *Educ:* Univ Liverpool, BVSc & MRCVS, 52, BSc, 54, PhD, 68. *Prof Exp:* Res student ruminant physiol, Univ Liverpool & Rowett Inst, Aberdeen, Scotland, 54-56; vet res off physiol, EAfrican Vet Res Orgn, 56-60; assoc prof, 60-70, PROF PHYSIOL, UNIV MAN, 70-, DEPT HEAD, 80- *Mem:* Brit Vet Asn; Can Vet Med Asn; Can Soc Animal Sci. *Res:* Physiology of digestion and acid-base control in cattle and sheep; electrolyte metabolism in ruminants, including intestinal absorption and renal excretion. *Mailing Add:* Dept of Animal Sci Univ of Man Winnipeg MB R3T 2N2 Can

PHILLIPS, GEORGE WYGANT, JR, b New York, NY, Aug 5, 29; m 58; c 2. PHYSICAL CHEMISTRY. *Educ:* Wesleyan Univ, BA, 51; Harvard Univ, PhD(chem), 57. *Prof Exp:* Asst, Ames Lab, AEC, 51-53; res chemist, Air Res & Develop Command, US Air Force, 53; res scientist, Union Carbide Plastics Co, 57-62, licensing mgr, Union Carbide Int Co, 62-65, mgr tech rels group, Union Carbide Europa SA, Switz, 65-68, acct mgr, Chem & Plastics Div, 68-72, prod mgr, Chem & Plastics Div, 72-76, COORDR INT TRADE

AFFAIRS, UNION CARBIDE CORP, 76- *Mem:* Sigma Xi; NY Acad Sci; Am Chem Soc. *Res:* Physical chemistry and structure of polymers; mechanism of polymerization; radiochemistry; patent licensing. *Mailing Add:* Union Carbide Corp Old Ridgebury Rd Danbury CT 06817

PHILLIPS, GERALD B, b Bethlehem, Pa, Mar 20, 25; m 70; c 2. MEDICINE. *Educ:* Princeton Univ, AB, 48; Harvard Med Sch, MD, 48; Am Bd Internal Med, dipl. *Prof Exp:* Intern med, Presby Hosp, New York, 48-50; res assoc, Harvard Med Sch, 52-53; from assoc to assoc prof, 56-73, PROF MED, COL PHYSICIANS & SURGEONS, COLUMBIA UNIV, 73- *Concurrent Pos:* Res fel, Harvard Med Sch, 50-52; vis fel biochem, Col Physicians & Surgeons, Columbia Univ, 54-56; Lederle med fac award, 63-66; sr asst surgeon, Nat Inst Arthritis & Metab Dis, 52-54. *Mem:* AAAS; Soc Exp Biol & Med; Am Fedn Clin Res; Am Soc Clin Invest; Am Soc Biol Chemists. *Res:* Aging; atherosclerosis; hormones; lipids; diabetes; liver disease; nutrition. *Mailing Add:* Dept of Med Roosevelt Hosp 428 W 59th St New York NY 10019

PHILLIPS, GERALD C, b Plainview, Tex, Feb 27, 22. PHYSICS. *Educ:* Rice Inst, AB, 44, AM, 46, PhD(physics), 49. *Prof Exp:* From instr to assoc prof, 49-58, chmn dept, 60-66, PROF PHYSICS, RICE UNIV, 58-, DIR BONNER NUCLEAR LABS, 60- *Concurrent Pos:* Fel, Carnegie Inst, 50-51; Guggenheim fel, 57-58; NSF sr fel, 66-67; mem earth sci div, Nat Res Coun, 58-61; mem coun, Oak Ridge Assoc Univs, 60-; mem nuclear cross sect adv group, AEC, 61-; mem subcomt nuclear struct, Nat Acad Sci-Nat Res Coun, 61-, nuclear sci, 68-; mem physics adv panel, NSF, 63-; mem comt physics fac in cols, Am Inst Physics, 63-; sr vpres, Columbia Sci Industs, 69-; mem bd trustees & exec comt, Univs Res Asn, 70-; chmn, Los Alamos Meson Physics Facil Users Group, 71. *Mem:* Fel Am Phys Soc; Am Geophys Union. *Res:* Nuclear and particle physics; geophysics. *Mailing Add:* Dept Physics Rice Univ Houston TX 77001

PHILLIPS, GRACE BRIGGS, b Mobile, Ala, Apr 15, 23; m 51; c 3. MICROBIOLOGY. *Educ:* Univ Md, BS, 54; NY Univ, PhD, 65; Nat Registry Microbiol, regist. *Prof Exp:* Bacteriologist, US Army Biol Labs, 44-63, asst dir indust health & safety, 63-66; microbiologist, Off of Chief, Commun Dis Ctr, USPHS, Tex, 66-69; dir, Becton-Dickinson Res Ctr, 69-76; V PRES FOR SCI & TECH AFFAIRS, HEALTH INDUST MFRS ASN, 76- *Concurrent Pos:* Secy of Army res & study fel, 59-60. *Mem:* Fel Am Pub Health Asn; Am Soc Microbiol; fel Am Acad Microbiologists; Am Asn Contamination Control (past pres); Sigma Xi. *Res:* Microbiological safety and contamination control; microbiological containment system technology; design of containment facilities; industrial sterilization; medical device research; planetary quarantine and protection; air filtration and sterilization; gaseous decontaminants; germicidal ultraviolet radiation; animal cross-infection; microbial sampling of air and surfaces. *Mailing Add:* Health Indust Mfrs Asn 1030-15th St NW Washington DC 20005

PHILLIPS, HANNAH MODELEVSKY, b Jonesboro, Ark, May 8, 40; m 64. BIOCHEMISTRY. *Educ:* Hendrix Col, BA, 62; La State Univ, MS, 64; Univ Ark, PhD(biochem), 74. *Prof Exp:* ASST PROF, UNIV ARK MED SCI, 76-; RES BIOCHEMIST, VET ADMIN HOSP, 75- *Concurrent Pos:* Stanley McCormack fel, Stanford Univ Med Ctr, 74-76; fel, Nat Cancer Inst, 76; prin investr, Royal Postgrad Med Sch, 80- *Mem:* AAAS; Am Chem Soc; Sigma Xi. *Res:* Structure-function studies of fibrinogen. *Mailing Add:* Med Res Vet Admin Hosp 300 E Roosevelt Little Rock AR 72206

PHILLIPS, HAROLD BRUCE, applied physics, see previous edition

PHILLIPS, HUGH JEFFERSON, b Augusta, Ga, July 12, 22; m 45; c 4. PHYSIOLOGY, PHARMACOLOGY. *Educ:* Univ Fla, BS, 47; Univ Nebr, MA, 48, PhD(physiol), 53. *Prof Exp:* Instr physiol & pharmacol, Sch Med, Creighton Univ, 52-54, asst prof, 54-59; assoc prof pharmacol, Sch Med, Univ Ark, 60; assoc prof, 60-66, PROF PHYSIOL, CREIGHTON UNIV, 66- *Concurrent Pos:* USPHS grants, 58-66; consult, Corvel, Inc & Eli Lilly & Co, 54-64, Cudahy Labs, 60-63, Dynion Water Systs, 61-64 & Armour Pharmaceut, 65-75. *Mem:* Am Physiol Soc; Am Soc Cell Biol; Soc Exp Biol & Med; Tissue Cult Asn. *Res:* Cell alteration; biological oxidation; fluids and electrolytes. *Mailing Add:* Med Res Bldg Creighton Univ Omaha NE 68178

PHILLIPS, JACOB ROBINSON, b Newport, Ark, June 24, 29; m 52; c 2. ENTOMOLOGY. *Educ:* Univ Ark, BSA, 52, MS, 61; La State Univ, PhD(entom), 65. *Prof Exp:* From asst prof to assoc prof, 64-73, PROF ENTOM, UNIV ARK, FAYETTEVILLE, 73- *Mem:* Entom Soc Am. *Res:* Insect biology and ecology; development of community-wide cotton insect management systems: an extension of integrated pest management to the inclusion of crop production systems that effect cotton insect population biology and dynamics. *Mailing Add:* Dept of Entom Univ of Ark Fayetteville AR 72701

PHILLIPS, JAMES A, b Johannesburg, SAfrica, May 17, 19; US citizen; m 48; c 3. PLASMA PHYSICS. *Educ:* Carleton Col, BA, 42; Univ Ill, MS, 43, PhD(physics), 49. *Prof Exp:* Tech asst, Tenn Eastman Corp, 44-45; asst, Univ Ill, 48-49; mem staff, 49-56, GROUP LEADER PHYSICS DIV, LOS ALAMOS NAT LAB, 56-, LAB FEL, 82- *Concurrent Pos:* Head physics sect, Int Atomic Energy Agency, Vienna, Austria, 75-79. *Mem:* Fel Am Phys Soc. *Mailing Add:* Los Alamos Nat Lab PO Box 1663 Los Alamos NM 87544

PHILLIPS, JAMES CHARLES, b New Orleans, La, Mar 9, 33; m 77. SOLID STATE PHYSICS. *Educ:* Univ Chicago, PhD(physics), 56. *Prof Exp:* Mem tech staff, Bell Tel Labs, Inc, 56-58; NSF fel physics, Univ Calif, 58-59 & Cambridge Univ, 59-60; from asst prof to prof physics, Univ Chicago, 60-68; MEM TECH STAFF, BELL LABS, INC, 68-; CONSULT, 60- *Concurrent Pos:* Guggenheim fel, 62-63; Sloan fel, 62-66. *Honors & Awards:* Buckley Prize, Am Phys Soc, 72. *Mem:* Nat Acad Sci; fel Am Phys Soc. *Res:* Electronic structure, optical spectra and chemical bonding in crystals and on crystal surfaces and in glasses. *Mailing Add:* Bell Labs Inc Murray Hill NJ 07974

PHILLIPS, JAMES M, b Fairfield, Ill, July 9, 34; m 54; c 2. PHYSICS. *Educ:* Cent Mo State Col, BS, 56; Univ Mo, Rolla, PhD(physics), 66. *Prof Exp:* Teacher high sch, Mo, 56-58; instr math, Univ Mo, Rolla, 58-61; asst prof, 65-69, assoc prof, 69-77, PROF PHYSICS, UNIV MO-KANSAS CITY, 77- *Mem:* Am Phys Soc; Am Asn Physics Teachers; Am Vacuum Soc. *Res:* Theory of liquids, especially structure of a cell-model liquid; surface physics, including theory of field ionization and binding energy of lamellar solids. *Mailing Add:* Dept of Physics Univ of Mo Kansas City MO 64110

PHILLIPS, JAMES WOODWARD, b Washington, DC, Mar 8, 43; m 65; c 3. ENGINEERING MECHANICS. *Educ:* Cath Univ Am, BME, 64; Brown Univ, ScM, 66, PhD(eng), 69. *Prof Exp:* Res asst eng, Brown Univ, 65-69, res assoc, 69; from asst prof to assoc prof, 69-81, PROF THEORET & APPL MECH, UNIV ILL, URBANA, 81- *Concurrent Pos:* Ed, Mechanics, Am Acad Mech, 75-78; vis assoc prof mech eng, Univ Md, 78-79. *Mem:* Soc Exp Stress Anal; Am Acad Mech. *Res:* Theoretical and experimental stress pulse propagation in solids; stress analysis; computer graphics. *Mailing Add:* 315 Talbot Lab Univ of Ill Urbana IL 61801

PHILLIPS, JEAN ALLEN, b Knoxville, Tenn, Dec 10, 18; m 43. FOOD SCIENCE, NUTRITION. *Educ:* Univ Tenn, BSHE, 40, MS, 55; Purdue Univ, PhD(food sci), 66. *Prof Exp:* Teacher high sch, WVa, 40-42; instr foods & inst mgt, Univ Tenn, 54-58; instr foods & nutrit, Purdue Univ, 58-63, asst prof, 65-66; assoc prof, Univ Tenn, Martin, 66-69; assoc prof, 69-75, PROF FOODS & NUTRIT, VA POLYTECH INST & STATE UNIV, 75- *Mem:* Am Home Econ Asn; Am Dietetic Asn; Inst Food Technol; Sigma Xi. *Res:* Cereal foods; lipids in flour products. *Mailing Add:* Dept of Human Nutrit & Foods Va Polytech Inst & State Univ Blacksburg VA 24061

PHILLIPS, JERRY CLYDE, b McKenzie, Tenn, Sept 23, 35; m 59; c 3. RADIOLOGY. *Educ:* Memphis State Univ, BA, 57; Univ Tenn, Memphis, MD, 60. *Prof Exp:* From instr to assoc prof, 65-72, PROF RADIOL, COL MED, UNIV TENN, MEMPHIS, 72- *Mem:* Radiol Soc NAm; Am Col Radiol; AMA; Am Roentgen Ray Soc; Soc Gastrointestinal Radiol. *Res:* Diagnostic radiology, especially gastrointestinal radiology. *Mailing Add:* 5725 Woodbriar Cove Memphis TN 38117

PHILLIPS, JERRY LEE, b Denver, Colo, Dec 10, 45; div; c 2. BIOCHEMISTRY. *Educ:* Univ Colo, BA, 67; Colo State Univ, PhD(biochem), 70. *Prof Exp:* Am Cancer Soc fel oncol, McArdle Lab, Univ Wis, 70-72; instr biochem, Colo State Univ, 73-75; asst prof, 75-78, ASSOC PROF BIOCHEM, UNIV TEX, 78- *Mem:* Am Chem Soc; Int Asn Bioinorgan Sci. *Res:* Role of zinc in human lymphocyte metabolism; role of zinc transferrin in lymphocyte transformation; zinc metabolism in leukemia. *Mailing Add:* Div of Allied Health & Life Sci Univ of Tex San Antonio TX 78285

PHILLIPS, JOHN EDWARD, b Montreal, Que, Dec 20, 34; m 56; c 5. COMPARATIVE PHYSIOLOGY. *Educ:* Dalhousie Univ, BSc, 56, MSc, 57; Cambridge Univ, PhD(zool), 61. *Prof Exp:* Asst prof zool, Dalhousie Univ, 60-64; from asst prof to assoc prof, 64-71, PROF ZOOL, UNIV BC, 71- *Concurrent Pos:* Chmn animal biol grant selection comt, Nat Res Coun Can, 69-71. *Mem:* Am Physiol Soc; fel Royal Soc Can; Am Soc Zool; Can Soc Zool (pres, 78-79). *Res:* Transport across biological membranes, particularly rectal absorption and renal function in insects; phosphorus cycle in lakes. *Mailing Add:* Dept of Zool Univ of BC Vancouver BC V6T 1W5 Can

PHILLIPS, JOHN HOWELL, JR, b Fresno, Calif, Dec 19, 25; wid; c 3. BIOCHEMISTRY, BACTERIOLOGY. *Educ:* Univ Calif, Berkeley, AB, 49, MA, 54, PhD(bact), 55. *Prof Exp:* Am Cancer Soc fel comp immunol, Hopkins Marine Sta, Stanford Univ, 55-56; Waksman Merch fel immunochem, Inst Microbiol, Rutgers Univ, 56-57; from instr to asst prof immunochem & microbiol, Univ Calif, Berkeley, 57-62; from asst prof to assoc prof comp biochem, Hopkins Marine Sta, 62-75, dir, 65-75, PROF COMP BIOCHEM, HOPKINS MARINE STA, STANFORD UNIV, 75- *Concurrent Pos:* Res grants, NSF, 57-59, USPHS, 57-66 & Environ Protection Agency, 72-; mem pesticide adv comt, Calif Dept Agr, 70-; consult aquaculture, Monterey Abalone Farms, 80- *Mem:* AAAS; Am Soc Immunol; NY Acad Sci. *Res:* Immunochemistry; comparative biochemistry; marine biology. *Mailing Add:* 2834 Treasure Rd Pebble Beach CA 93953

PHILLIPS, JOHN HUNTER, JR, b Houston, Tex, Nov 2, 30; m 54; c 3. INTERNAL MEDICINE, CARDIOLOGY. *Educ:* Tulane Univ, BS, 52, MD, 55; Am Bd Internal Med, dipl cardiovasc dis. *Prof Exp:* Intern, Charity Hosp, New Orleans, 55-56; asst instr med, 56-57, from instr to assoc prof, 57-70, PROF MED, SCH MED, TULANE UNIV, 70-, CHIEF CARDIOL SECT, 74- *Concurrent Pos:* Nat Heart Inst fel, 57-60; asst vis physician, Charity Hosp, New Orleans, 56-61, vis physician, 61-68, sr vis physician, 69-; consult, Lallie Kemp Charity Hosp, Independence, La, 56-63; clin asst, Vet Admin Hosp, New Orleans, 58-61, staff physician & chief cardiol sect, 61-; consult, Huey P Long Hosp, Alexandria, 60-62; fel, Coun Clin Cardiol, Am Heart Asn. *Honors & Awards:* Honor Achievement Award, Angiol Res Found, 68. *Mem:* AAAS; Am Fedn Clin Res; fel Am Col Physicians; fel Am Col Chest Physicians: fel Am Col Cardiol. *Res:* Peripheral vascular disease; geriatrics. *Mailing Add:* Dept of Med Tulane Univ Sch of Med New Orleans LA 70112

PHILLIPS, JOHN PERROW, b Lynchburg, Va, June 17, 25; m 53; c 2. ANALYTICAL CHEMISTRY. *Educ:* Univ Va, BS, 45; Univ Ind, MA, 47, PhD(chem), 49. *Prof Exp:* From asst prof to assoc prof, 49-56, PROF CHEM, UNIV LOUISVILLE, 56- *Concurrent Pos:* NSF sci fac fel, 63-64. *Mem:* Am Chem Soc. *Res:* Substituted 8-quinolinols. *Mailing Add:* Dept of Chem Univ of Louisville Louisville KY 40208

PHILLIPS, JOHN R, b Philadelphia, Pa, May 3, 35. INORGANIC CHEMISTRY. *Educ:* Dartmouth Col, AB, 57; Harvard Univ, MA, 59, PhD(chem), 62. *Prof Exp:* Asst prof chem, Univ Ottawa, 62-67; asst prof, 67-73, ASSOC PROF CHEM, PURDUE UNIV, CALUMET CAMPUS, 73- *Mem:* Am Chem Soc; Royal Soc Chem. *Res:* Organometallic and coordination chemistry; fluorocarbon compounds of metals. *Mailing Add:* Dept Chem Purdue Univ Calumet Campus Hammond IN 46323

PHILLIPS, JOHN RICHARD, b Portland, Ore, Feb 17, 34; m 53; c 5. COMPUTER SCIENCES, APPLIED MATHEMATICS. *Educ:* Lewis & Clark Col, BS, 59; Ore State Univ, PhD(math), 66. *Prof Exp:* Instr math, Ore State Univ, 62-66; fel, Lawrence Livermore Lab, Calif, 66-67; asst prof comput sci, Univ Ill, Urbana-Champaign, 67-74; prog dir software eng, Div Math & Comput Sci, NSF, 74-76; ASSOC PROF COMPUT SCI & CHMN DEPT, OKLA STATE UNIV, STILLWATER, 76- *Mem:* Asn Comput Mach. *Res:* Computer languages; design of array languages; information structures; data structures; microcomputers. *Mailing Add:* Dept of Comput Sci Okla State Univ Stillwater OK 74074

PHILLIPS, JOHN RICHARD, b Albany, Calif, Jan 30, 34; m 57; c 3. CHEMICAL ENGINEERING. *Educ:* Univ Calif, Berkeley, BS, 56; Yale Univ, MEng, 58, DEng, 60. *Prof Exp:* Chem engr, Stanford Res Inst, 60; res design & develop engr, Chevron Res Co, Calif, 62-66; from asst prof to assoc prof, 66-74, PROF ENG, HARVEY MUDD COL, 74-, DIR ENG CLIN, 77- *Concurrent Pos:* Pres, Claremont Eng Co, 73-; vis prof, Univ Edinburgh, 75; vis scientist, Southern Calif Edison Ctr, 80; vis scholar, Cambridge Univ, 81; vis prof, ESIEE Paris, 81. *Mem:* Am Inst Chem Engrs. *Res:* Permeation of gases through metals; thermodynamics and separations; desalination; research management; energy. *Mailing Add:* Dept of Eng Harvey Mudd Col Claremont CA 91711

PHILLIPS, JOHN SPENCER, b Baltimore, Md, May 22, 53; m 76. ELECTROANALYTICAL CHEMISTRY. *Educ:* Western Md Col, BA, 75; Purdue Univ, PhD(chem), 81. *Prof Exp:* Teaching asst chem, Purdue Univ, 75-78, res asst, 78-81; ASST PROF CHEM, JAMES MADISON UNIV, 81- *Mem:* Am Chem Soc; Electrochem Soc. *Res:* Development and application of electroanalytical methods; investigation of rapid photochemical processes via electrochemical probes; innovations in the teaching of undergraduate chemistry. *Mailing Add:* Dept Chem James Madison Univ Harrisonburg VA 22807

PHILLIPS, JOSEPH D, b Woodbury, NJ, Sept 11, 38; m 61; c 3. GEOPHYSICS. *Educ:* Rutgers Univ, BA, 61; Princeton Univ, MS, 63, MA, 64, PhD(geophys), 66. *Prof Exp:* Asst eng mgt, NJ Bell Tel Co, summer 61; res asst geol, Princeton Univ, 61-66; assoc scientist, Woods Hole Oceanog Inst, 66-77; prof, Mass Inst Technol, 77-78; RES SCI LECTR, UNIV TEX, 78- *Concurrent Pos:* Consult, Princeton Appl Res Corp, Mobil Corp, Exxon Corp & Bell Tel Labs, 65-; NSF & Off Naval Res oceanog & geophys res grants, 66-; vis prof, Cambridge Univ, 74-75. *Mem:* AAAS; Am Geophys Union; Soc Explor Geophys. *Res:* Paleomagnetism; geomagnetism; marine geophysics and geology; seismology. *Mailing Add:* Geol Sci Dept Geol Bldg 114 Inst Geophysics Austin TX 78712

PHILLIPS, JOY BURCHAM, b Decatur, Ill, Sept 7, 17; m 38. PHYSIOLOGY. *Educ:* Millikin Univ, AB, 39; Univ Ill, MA, 44; NY Univ, PhD(physiol), 54. *Prof Exp:* With biol dept, Queens Col, NY, 45-47; asst therapeut, NY Univ, 47-49; from asst prof to assoc prof, 52-63, chmn dept, 70-75, PROF ZOOL, DREW UNIV, 63- *Concurrent Pos:* NSF teaching fel, Columbia Univ, 59-60; Sigma Delta Epsilon grant, 61; Brown Hazen grant, Res Corp, 68-; mem res panel NSF Col Sci Improv Prog, 68 & 69. *Mem:* Sigma Xi; Am Soc Zool; Am Asn Anat; AAAS; NY Acad Sci. *Res:* Developmental endocrinology; histology. *Mailing Add:* Dept Zool Drew Univ Madison NJ 07940

PHILLIPS, KEITH L, b Broken Bow, Nebr, June 11, 37; m 60; c 2. MATHEMATICAL ANALYSIS. *Educ:* Univ Colo, BA, 59, MA, 61; Univ Wash, PhD(math), 64. *Prof Exp:* Instr math, Univ Wash, 64-65, NSF grant, 65; asst prof, Calif Inst Technol, 65-68; ASSOC PROF, NMEX STATE UNIV, 68- *Concurrent Pos:* NSF grant, Calif Inst Technol, 66-68; vis prof, Univ Colo, Boulder, 81- *Mem:* Am Math Soc; Math Asn Am. *Res:* Fourier analysis in locally compact groups, especially in locally compact fields. *Mailing Add:* Dept of Math NMex State Univ Las Cruces NM 88003

PHILLIPS, KENNETH LLOYD, b Moose Jaw, Sask, Nov 18, 18; m 40, 77; c 4. CHEMICAL ENGINEERING, BIOENGINEERING. *Educ:* Univ Sask, BE, 49, MSc, 56, PhD(chem eng), 66. *Prof Exp:* Asst to dir, 50-67, RES OFF CHEM ENG, PRAIRIE REGIONAL LAB, NAT RES COUN CAN, 49-, RES COUN OFF BIOENG, 67- *Concurrent Pos:* Coordr fermentation res & develop, Nat Res Coun Can, 78- *Mem:* Fel Chem Inst Can; Can Soc Chem Engrs; Am Chem Soc. *Res:* Gas-liquid mass transfer; combined absorption-adsorption mechanism for transfer of oxygen into aqueous solutions; industrial utilization of agricultural products. *Mailing Add:* Prairie Regional Lab Nat Res Coun of Can Saskatoon SK S7N 0W9 Can

PHILLIPS, LAWRENCE STONE, b Washington, DC, Sept 16, 41; m 71; c 2. ENDOCRINOLOGY, METABOLISM. *Educ:* Swarthmore Col, BA, 63; Harvard Univ, MD,67; Am Bd Internal Med, dipl, 72, cert endocrinol & metab, 73. *Prof Exp:* Intern & resident, Presby-St Luke's Hosp, Chicago, 67-69; staff assoc, Grady Mem Hosp, 69-71; fel metab, Sch Med, Wash Univ, 71-74; asst prof, 74-79, PROF MED, CTR ENDOCRINOL, METAB & NUTRIT, SCH MED, NORTHWESTERN UNIV, 79- *Concurrent Pos:* Mem lab prog, Ctr Dis Control, USPHS, 69-71; instr med, Sch Med, Emory Univ, 70-71; asst physician, Barnes Hosp, 72-74; adj attend physician, Northwestern Mem Hosp, 74-75, assoc attend physician, 75-81, attend physician, 81- *Honors & Awards:* Elliott P Joslin Res & Develop Award, Am Diabetes Asn, 77. *Mem:* Endocrine Soc; Am Diabetes Asn; Am Fedn Clin Res; Cent Soc Clin Res; Am Soc Clin Investr. *Res:* Somatomedin; nutrition; growth. *Mailing Add:* Ctr Endocrinol Metab & Nutrit 303 E Chicago Ave Chicago IL 60611

PHILLIPS, LEE REVELL, b Salt Lake City, Utah, Apr 7, 53; m 73; c 3. FORENSIC CHEMISTRY. *Educ:* Brigham Young Univ, BS, 76, MS, 79, JD, 81. *Prof Exp:* Researcher, Phillips Petrol Co, 73-74; geophysics interpreter, Cities Serv Co, 75-76; DIR, ALPINE WEST LABS, 79-; RES ASSOC, BRIGHAM YOUNG UNIV, 81- *Concurrent Pos:* Forensic chemist, Cent & Southern Utah Law Enforcement Agencies, 81- *Mem:* Am Chem Soc; Sigma Xi; Soc Environ Geochem & Health. *Mailing Add:* 1515 E 1575 N Provo UT 84604

PHILLIPS, LEE VERN, b Checotah, Okla, Feb 19, 30; m 54; c 2. ORGANIC CHEMISTRY. *Educ:* Univ Mo, PhD(chem), 57. *Prof Exp:* Mem staff, Res Ctr, Spencer Chem Co, 57-66, group leader pesticide synthesis & process develop, Gulf Res & Develop Co, 66-67, sect supvr, pesticide synthesis sect, 67-69, div dir agr chem, 69-75; MGR CHEM RES DEPT, RICHMOND RES CTR, STAUFFER CHEM CO, 75- *Mem:* Am Chem Soc. *Res:* Synthetic organic chemistry. *Mailing Add:* Stauffer Chem Co Richmond Res Ctr 1200 S 47th St Richmond CA 94804

PHILLIPS, LEO AUGUSTUS, b Nashville, Ark, Feb 21, 31; m 57; c 4. MOLECULAR BIOLOGY, BIOPHYSICAL CHEMISTRY. *Educ:* Univ Southern Calif, BA, 54; Ariz State Univ, MS, 63; Univ Kans, PhD(microbiol), 67. *Prof Exp:* Nat Cancer Inst-NIH fel molecular biophys, Pub Health Res Inst, City of New York, 67-69; Nat Cancer Inst-NIH staff fel, 69-71, sr staff fel, 71-73, SCIENTIST, NAT CANCER INST, NIH, 73- *Mem:* Fel Am Acad Microbiol; Am Soc Microbiol; Sigma Xi; Biophys Soc; Am Asn Cancer Res. *Res:* Biochemical and biophysical studies on the nucleic acids and polypeptides of mammalian and putative human leukemia and sarcoma viruses and studies on the nucleic acids of normal, benign, and malignant tissues. *Mailing Add:* Nat Cancer Inst NIH 9000 Rockville Pike Bethesda MD 20014

PHILLIPS, LEON A, b Mehoma, Ore, Sept 1, 23; m 48; c 2. MEDICINE, RADIOLOGY. *Educ:* Univ Wash, BS, 48; Yale Univ, MD, 52. *Prof Exp:* Instr radiol, Johns Hopkins Hosp, 56-59; asst prof, 60-64, ASSOC PROF RADIOL, SCH MED, UNIV WASH, 64- *Mem:* AMA; Am Col Radiol; Asn Univ Radiol. *Res:* Radiology utilization review. *Mailing Add:* Dept of Radiol Univ Hosp of Wash Sch Med Seattle WA 98195

PHILLIPS, LOU ELLEN, b Lexington, Ky, June 21, 43; c 1. MEDICAL MICROBIOLOGY, CLINICAL IMMUNOLOGY. *Educ:* Transylvania Col, AB, 65; Univ Ky, PhD(biol sci), 74. *Prof Exp:* Teacher sci, Fayette County Sch Syst, 65-68; res asst toxicol, Dept Agr Sci, Univ Ky, 74-75, fel med mycol, Med Ctr, 75-76; fel med microbiol, 76-77, ASST DIR MICROBIOL, IMMUNOL & SEROL, DEPT OF PATH, ST LUKE'S EPISCOPAL HOSP, 77- *Mem:* Am Soc Microbiol; Med Mycol Soc Am. *Res:* Developmental enzymology of fungi; serum aminoglycoside determinations; serum and CSF ratios of protein and albumin in multiple sclerosis. *Mailing Add:* 3821 Byron Houston TX 77005

PHILLIPS, LOUISE LANG, b Troy, Ohio, June 30, 13; m 37; c 2. HEMATOLOGY, ENZYMOLOGY. *Educ:* Col William & Mary, BS, 34; Columbia Univ, AM, 40, PhD(chem), 50. *Prof Exp:* Clin biochemist, Killian Res Lab, 34-38; lectr chem, Hunter Col, 50-52 & 60-62; res assoc chem, Columbia Univ, 50-52, res assoc obstet-gynec, Col Physicians & Surgeons, 53-66; pharmacologist, US Food & Drug Admin, 66-68; RES ASSOC & DIR COAGULATION LAB, DEPTS MED & OBSTET-GYNEC, ROOSEVELT HOSP, 68- *Concurrent Pos:* Assoc clin prof path, Columbia Univ, 73-; mem, Comt Blood Prod Obstet, Maternal Welfare Comn, New York, NY, 74- *Mem:* Am Soc Exp Path; Am Soc Hemat; Coun Thrombosis Am Heart Asn; Am Chem Soc. *Res:* Blood coagulation and the fibrinolytic enzyme system with particular attention to obstetrical and surgical patients. *Mailing Add:* 140 West End Ave New York NY 10023

PHILLIPS, LYLE LLEWELLYN, b Long Beach, Calif, June 14, 23; m 53; c 2. CYTOGENETICS. *Educ:* Univ Redlands, BA, 50; Claremont Cols, MA, 51; Univ Wash, PhD(bot), 54. *Prof Exp:* Asst bot, Pomona Col, 51; asst, Univ Wash, 51-54; fel genetics, State Col Wash, 54-56; from asst prof to assoc prof, 56-65, PROF CROP SCI, NC STATE UNIV, 65-, GENETICS, 70- *Mem:* Bot Soc Am; Genetics Soc Can. *Res:* Cytogenetics and evolution of Gossypium. *Mailing Add:* Dept of Crop Sci NC State Univ Raleigh NC 27607

PHILLIPS, LYLE WINSTON, physics, deceased

PHILLIPS, MARK MONROE, b San Diego, Calif, Mar 31, 51. ASTRONOMY. *Educ:* San Diego State Univ, AB, 73; Univ Calif, Santa Cruz, PhD(astron), 77. *Prof Exp:* res assoc astron, Cerro Tololo Interam Observ, 77-80; WITH ANGLO-AUSTRALIAN OBSERV, 80- *Mem:* Am Astron Soc; Astron Soc Pac. *Res:* Optical spectrophotometry of active nuclei galaxies and QSO's; chemical abundances in planetary nebulae and galactic and extragalactic H II regions. *Mailing Add:* Anglo Australian Observ Epping 2121 New South Wales Australia

PHILLIPS, MARSHALL, b Yankton, SDak, Dec 1, 32; m 57; c 2. BIOCHEMISTRY, ORGANIC CHEMISTRY. *Educ:* Yankton Col, AB, 56; Univ SDak, MA, 59; Univ Kans, PhD(biochem), 64. *Prof Exp:* Nat Res Coun res assoc southern regional lab, 63-65, RES CHEMIST, NAT ANIMAL DIS LAB, USDA, 65- *Mem:* AAAS; Am Chem Soc. *Res:* Complex macromolecules; ribosomal vaccines; animal body fluid protides. *Mailing Add:* Nat Animal Dis Lab PO Box 70 Ames IA 50010

PHILLIPS, MARVIN W, b Salem, Ind, Aug 9, 29; m 53; c 2. SOIL FERTILITY. *Educ:* Purdue Univ, BS, 53, MS, 58; Univ Minn, PhD(soil chem), 64. *Prof Exp:* From asst prof to assoc prof, 61-69, PROF AGRON, PURDUE UNIV, WEST LAFAYETTE, 69-, HEAD DEPT, 71- *Mem:* Soil Sci Soc Am; Crop Sci Soc Am; Int Soil Sci Soc; Am Soc Agron. *Res:* Soil fertility and management. *Mailing Add:* Dept of Agron Purdue Univ West Lafayette IN 47906

PHILLIPS, MELBA (NEWELL), b Hazleton, Ind, Feb 1, 1907. PHYSICS. *Educ:* Oakland City Col, Ind, AB, 26; Battle Creek Col, MA, 28; Univ Calif, Berkeley, PhD(physics), 33. *Hon Degrees:* DSc, Oakland City Col, Ind, 64. *Prof Exp:* Instr, Brooklyn Col, 34-44, asst prof physics, 44-52; assoc dir, Acad Year Inst, Washington Univ, St Louis, 57-62; prof physics, 62-72, EMER PROF PHYSICS, UNIV CHICAGO, 72- *Concurrent Pos:* Helen Huff res fel, Bryn Mawr Col, 35-36; Am Asn Univ Women fel, Inst Advan Study, 36-37; mem, Comn Col Physics, 62-68; mem gov bd, Am Inst Physics, 65-68 & 75-77; vis prof, State Univ NY Stony Brook, 72-75; actg exec officer, Am Asn

Physics Teachers, 75-77. *Honors & Awards:* Oerstad Medal, Am Asn Physics Teachers, 74; Karl Taylor Compton Award, Am Inst Physics, 81. *Mem:* Am Asn Physics Teachers (pres, 66-67); fel Am Phys Soc; AAAS. *Res:* Theory of complex spectra, theory of light nuclei; physics education. *Mailing Add:* 351 W 24th St New York NY 10011

PHILLIPS, MELVILLE JAMES, b Newport, Eng, Dec 9, 30; Can citizen; m 56; c 2. PATHOLOGY. *Educ:* McGill Univ, MD, 56. *Prof Exp:* Lectr path, Univ Toronto, 61-62, asst prof, 63-67; assoc prof, McGill Univ, 67-70; assoc prof, 70-74, PROF PATH, BANTING INST, UNIV TORONTO, 74- *Concurrent Pos:* Fel path, Royal Col Physicians & Surgeons Can, 61; Med Res Coun Can res grant, 62-; surg pathologist, Toronto Gen Hosp, 69- *Mem:* Am Soc Exp Path; Am Asn Path & Bact; Int Acad Path; fel Col Am Path; Can Asn Path. *Res:* Human and experimental liver disease, especially correlation of electron microscopic and biochemical changes in liver disease. *Mailing Add:* Dept of Path Banting Inst Univ of Toronto Toronto ON M5S 1A1 Can

PHILLIPS, MICHAEL CANAVAN, b London, Eng, Feb 23, 40; m 64; c 2. PHYSICAL BIOCHEMISTRY. *Educ:* Southampton Univ, BSc, 62, PhD(phys chem), 65, DSc, 76. *Prof Exp:* Fel theoret biol, State Univ NY Buffalo, 65-67; scientist & sect mgr biophys, Unilever Res Lab, Welwyn, Eng, 67-78; assoc prof, 78-80, PROF BIOCHEM, MED COL PA, 80- *Concurrent Pos:* Fel, Coun Arteriosclerosis, Am Heart Asn, 78- *Mem:* The Chem Soc; Am Chem Soc; fel Am Soc Biol Chemists. *Res:* Interactions of serum lipoproteins with cells; lipid and sterol metabolism and their influence on atherosclerosis; lipid-protein interaction; interfacial phenomena in biological systems. *Mailing Add:* Dept Physiol & Biochem Med Col Pa Philadelphia PA 19129

PHILLIPS, MICHAEL IAN, b London, Eng, July 30, 39; US citizen; m 65. NEUROPHYSIOLOGY, NEUROENDOCRINOLOGY. *Educ:* Univ Exeter, BSc, 62; Univ Birmingham, MSc, 65, PhD(neuropharmacol), 67. *Prof Exp:* Tutor psychol, Univ Birmingham, 66-67; vis asst prof, Univ Mich, 67-69; res fel biol, Calif Inst Technol, 69-70; asst prof physiol, Univ Iowa, 70-73, assoc prof, 73-76, prof physiol, 77-80, prof pharmacol, 78-80; PROF PHYSIOL, UNIV FLA, 80-, CHMN DEPT, 80- *Concurrent Pos:* NIMH career develop award, 73; vis scientist, Brain Res Inst, Zurich, 75 & 78; Humboldt Found scholar & fel, Pharmacol Inst Heidelberg, WGer, 76-77; mem neurobiol rev panel, NSF, 77-80; fel, Coun Circulation, Am Heart Asn, 78, Coun High Blood Pressure, 81; vis investr, NIH, 79-80; mem, Exp Cardiovasc Res, NIH, 80-84. *Mem:* Soc Neurosci; Am Physiol Soc; Endocrine Soc. *Res:* Neuroendocrinology; site and mode of peptide/angiotensin action in the brain; neurophysiology. *Mailing Add:* Dept Physiol Univ Fla Col Med Gainesville FL 32610

PHILLIPS, MILDRED E, b New York, NY, May 21, 28. PATHOLOGY. *Educ:* Hunter Col, BA, 46; Howard Univ, MD, 50. *Prof Exp:* Intern, King's County Hosp, Brooklyn, NY, 50-52; resident path, Mt Sinai Hosp, New York, 52-54; resident asst surg path, Presby Hosp, 54-55; instr path, State Univ NY Downstate Med Ctr, 55-56; from instr to asst prof, 57-65, ASSOC PROF PATH, MED CTR, NY UNIV, 65- *Concurrent Pos:* Fel surg path, Presby Hosp, New York, 54-55; fel, Postgrad Med Sch, Univ London & London Hosp, 56-57. *Mem:* AMA; Col Am Path; Transplantation Soc; NY Acad Sci; Int Acad Path. *Res:* Tumor specific antigenicity and serum protein production by experimental and human tumors. *Mailing Add:* Dept of Path NY Univ Med Ctr 550 First Ave New York NY 10016

PHILLIPS, NORMAN EDGAR, b Detroit, Mich, Dec 20, 28; m 51; c 2. PHYSICAL CHEMISTRY. *Educ:* Univ BC, BA, 49, MA, 50; Univ Chicago, PhD(chem), 54. *Prof Exp:* Nat Res Coun fel chem, 54-55, from instr to assoc prof, 55-66, dean, Col Chem, 78-80, PROF CHEM, UNIV CALIF, BERKELEY, 66- *Concurrent Pos:* Sloan Found fel, 62-64; Guggenheim fel, 63-64; NSF sr fel, Tech Univ, Helsinki, 70-71; prin investr inorg mat, Res Div, 73-77. *Mem:* Am Chem Soc; Am Phys Soc. *Res:* Cryogenics; low temperature calorimetry. *Mailing Add:* Dept of Chem Univ of Calif Berkeley CA 94720

PHILLIPS, NORMAN WILLIAM FREDERICK, b London, Eng, Mar 30, 13; m 38; c 4. PHYSICAL CHEMISTRY. *Educ:* Univ BC, BA, 33, MA, 35; McGill Univ, PhD(phys chem), 38. *Prof Exp:* Res chemist, Nat Res Labs, 38-41; head electrometall div, Alcan Res & Develop Ltd, 41-72, consult, Alcan Smelter Serv Ltd, 72-75, CONSULT, ALCAN INT LTD, 75- *Concurrent Pos:* Mem, Corp Prof Chem Quebec. *Mem:* Fel Chem Inst Can. *Res:* Atomic weights; photochemistry and kinetics of hydrocarbon reactions; electrochemistry of fused salts; labile molecules at high temperatures; carbon chemistry. *Mailing Add:* Alcan Int Ltd Box 6090 Montreal PQ H3C 3H2 Can

PHILLIPS, OWEN M, b Parramatta, Australia, Dec 30, 30; m 52; c 4. MECHANICS. *Educ:* Univ Sydney, BSc, 52; Cambridge Univ, PhD(appl math), 55. *Prof Exp:* Imp Chem Indust res fel theoret physics, Cambridge Univ, 55-57; from asst prof to assoc prof mech eng, 57-62, prof geophys mech, 62-68, chmn dept planetary sci, 68-77, PROF GEOPHYS JOHN'S HOPKINS UNIV, 78- *Concurrent Pos:* Fel, St John's Col, Cambridge Univ, 57-60, asst dir res appl math, univ, 61-64; consult, Martin Co, 58, Westinghouse Elec Corp, 58-59; Hydronautics, Inc, 61- & Phila Elec Co, 65-66; mem coun mem & rev & goals comt, Nat Ctr Atmospheric Res, 64-68, trustee, 65- *Honors & Awards:* Adams Prize, Cambridge Univ, 65. *Mem:* Geophys Union; fel Royal Soc. *Res:* Fluid mechanics, particularly turbulence and its applications to meteorology; oceanography; theory of surface waves on fluids. *Mailing Add:* Dept of Earth & Planetary Sci Johns Hopkins Univ Baltimore MD 21218

PHILLIPS, PAUL J, b Carlisle, Eng, Nov 26, 42; m 67; c 2. PHYSICAL CHEMISTRY. *Educ:* Univ Liverpool, BSc, 65, PhD(phys chem), 68. *Prof Exp:* Fel polymer sci, Univ Mass, 68-70; sr res assoc polymer sci, Queen Mary Col, Univ London, 70-71, lectr mat sci, 71-75; asst prof chem eng, State Univ NY, Buffalo, 75-77; assoc prof, 77-80, PROF MAT SCI, UNIV UTAH, 80- *Mem:* Am Chem Soc; Am Phys Soc; Soc Plastics Engrs; Sigma Xi. *Res:* Crystallization and morphology of polymers at atmospheric and elevated pressures; effects of morphology on the mechanical and electrical properties of polymers. *Mailing Add:* Dept Mat Sci & Eng Univ Utah Salt Lake City UT 84112

PHILLIPS, PERRY EDWARD, b Los Angeles, Calif, Sept 22, 44; m 66; c 1. PLASMA PHYSICS. *Educ:* Univ Calif, Santa Barbara, BA, 66; Univ Tex, Austin, PhD(physics), 71. *Prof Exp:* Nuclear physicist, Los Alamos Sci Lab, 67; RES SCIENTIST PLASMA PHYSICS, FUSION RES CTR, UNIV TEX, AUSTIN, 71- *Mem:* Am Phys Soc; Inst Elec & Electronics Engrs. *Res:* Experimental plasma devices including microwave and laser scattering on toroidal devices; strong magneto-hydrodynamic shock waves propagating in magnetized plasma. *Mailing Add:* Fusion Res Ctr Univ of Tex Austin TX 78712

PHILLIPS, RALPH SAUL, b Oakland, Calif, June 23, 13; m 42. PURE MATHEMATICS, APPLIED MATHEMATICS. *Educ:* Univ Calif, Los Angeles, AB, 35; Univ Mich, PhD(math), 39. *Prof Exp:* Rackham fel from Univ Mich, Inst Adv Study, 40; instr math, Univ Wash, 40-41; instr, Harvard Univ, 41-42; from staff mem to group leader, Radiation Lab, Mass Inst Technol, 42-46; asst prof math, NY Univ, 46-47; from assoc prof to prof, Univ Southern Calif, 47-58; prof, Univ Calif, Los Angeles, 58-60; PROF MATH, STANFORD UNIV, 60- *Concurrent Pos:* Mem, Inst Adv Study, 49-50; res assoc, Yale Univ, 53-54; Guggenheim fel, 54-55; mem inst math sci, NY Univ, 58; vis prof, Aarhus Univ, 68; Guggenheim fel, 75; Nat Acad Sci exchange vis to USSR, 75; Robert Grimmett prof math, Stanford Univ. *Mem:* Am Math Soc; Am Acad Arts & Sci. *Res:* Functional analysis; partial differential equations; mathematical physics; scattering theory. *Mailing Add:* Dept of Math Stanford Univ Stanford CA 94305

PHILLIPS, RALPH W, b Farmland, Ind, Jan 12, 18; m 43; c 1. DENTAL MATERIALS. *Educ:* Ind Univ, BS, 40, MS, 55; Univ Ala, DSc, 62. *Prof Exp:* Asst, 40-41, from instr to prof, 41-62, asst dean res, 69-74, RES PROF DENT MAT, SCH DENT, IND UNIV, INDIANAPOLIS, 62-, CHMN DEPT, 58-, DISTINGUISHED PROF, ASSOC DEAN RES & DIR, ORAL HEALTH RES INST, 74- *Concurrent Pos:* Hon vpres, Int Dent Cong, Rome, 57; chmn, Biomat Adv Comt, NIH; consult, NIH, US Army, Am Dent Asn, USPHS, US Air Force, & Vet Admin; lectr, US & abroad; mem dent panel, Food & Drug Admin. *Honors & Awards:* Souder Award, Int Asn Dent Res, 59; Callahan Award, Ohio State Dent Asn, 68; Gold Medal Res Award, Alumni Asn, Columbia Univ Dent Sch; distinguished citation, Washington Univ; Geiss Award, Am Col Dent; Mitch Nakayma Award, Mass Dent Soc; Int Award, Pierre Fauchard Acad. *Mem:* AAAS; Int Asn Dent Res (past pres); fel Int Col Dent; fel Am Col Dent; hon mem Am Acad Restorative Dent. *Res:* Application of fluorides in dentistry; physical properties of dental materials and tooth structure; clinical behavior of materials as related to their properties; author or coauthor of 14 publications. *Mailing Add:* Dept of Dent Mat Ind Univ Sch of Med Indianapolis IN 46202

PHILLIPS, RICHARD ARLAN, b Detroit, Mich, May 30, 33; m 56; c 2. OPTICS, APPLIED PHYSICS. *Educ:* Univ Mich, Ann Arbor, BS, 55, MS, 62, PhD(physics), 66. *Prof Exp:* Syst analyst petrol reservoirs, Exxon Corp, Venezuela, 55-60; asst prof elec eng & physics, Univ Minn, 66-71; sr optical engr, 71-72, MGR CONSUMER PROD RES & DEVELOP, FOSTER GRANT CO, INC, 72- *Concurrent Pos:* US del, Int Standards Orgn, 74- *Mem:* Optical Soc Am; Soc Cosmetic Chem. *Res:* Physical optics, lasers, nonlinear optics, color vision, thin films and coatings for plastics; ophthalmic lens design; translation of new products from research laboratory into mass production. *Mailing Add:* 3 Betsy Ross Circle Acton MA 01720

PHILLIPS, RICHARD DEAN, b Sacramento, Calif, Sept 17, 29; m 50. ENVIRONMENTAL PHYSIOLOGY, RADIATION BIOLOGY. *Educ:* Univ Calif, Berkeley, BA, 58, PhD(physiol), 66. *Prof Exp:* Res physiologist, US Naval Radiol Defense Lab, Calif, 58-69; RES & DEVELOP MGR, BIOELECTROMAGNETICS PROG, BIOL DEPT, PAC NORTHWEST LABS, BATTELLE MEM INST, 69- *Mem:* Int Microwave Power Inst; Am Physiol Soc; Radiation Res Soc; NY Acad Sci; Soc Exp Biol & Med. *Res:* Physiological responses of mammals to electromagnetic radiations, drugs and environmental stresses; cardiovascular physiology, metabolism and thermoregulation. *Mailing Add:* Biol Dept Pac Northwest Labs Battelle Mem Inst Richland WA 99352

PHILLIPS, RICHARD E, JR, b US, Dec 3, 36; m 63; c 1. MATHEMATICS. *Educ:* Otterbein Col, BS, 61; Univ Kans, MA, 62, PhD(math), 65. *Prof Exp:* Asst prof math, State Univ NY, 62-63; asst prof, Wis State Univ, 65-66; asst prof, Univ Kans, 66-69; assoc prof, 69-74, PROF MATH, MICH STATE UNIV, 74- *Mem:* Am Math Soc. *Res:* Group theory. *Mailing Add:* Dept of Math Mich State Univ East Lansing MI 48824

PHILLIPS, RICHARD EDWARD, b Hammond, Ind, Oct 31, 30; m 65; c 3. ANIMAL BEHAVIOR, AVIAN PHYSIOLOGY. *Educ:* Purdue Univ, BS, 52; Ore State Univ, MS, 54; Cornell Univ, PhD(physiol), 59. *Prof Exp:* Res assoc avian physiol, Cornell Univ, 59-62; asst prof zool, Va Polytech Inst, 62-64; from asst prof to assoc prof, 64-71, PROF ANIMAL SCI & ECOL & BEHAV BIOL, UNIV MINN, ST PAUL, 71- *Concurrent Pos:* NSF res grants, 59-62 & 63-66; NIH res grants, 66-69 & 72-74. *Mem:* AAAS; Am Physiol Soc; Am Ornith Union; Animal Behavior Soc; Am Soc Zool. *Res:* Neurophysiological mechanisms of animal behavior; physiological and behavioral mechanisms of reproduction and population regulation. *Mailing Add:* Dept of Animal Sci Inst of Agr Univ of Minn St Paul MN 55101

PHILLIPS, RICHARD FIFIELD, b Worcester, Mass, July 4, 17; m 42; c 3. ORGANIC CHEMISTRY. *Educ:* Amherst Col, AB, 39; Univ Ill, PhD(org chem), 42. *Prof Exp:* Chemist, Merck & Co, Inc, 42-65, treas, Merck Co Found, 72, ASST MGR CONTRIB, MERCK & CO, INC, 65- *Mem:* Am Chem Soc. *Res:* Administration of corporate support of education in sciences and related fields. *Mailing Add:* 909 Prospect St Westfield NJ 07090

PHILLIPS, RICHARD HART, b Atlanta, Ga, June 23, 22; m 45; c 5. PSYCHIATRY. *Educ:* Univ NC, BS, 44; NY Univ, MD, 45; Am Bd Psychiat & Neurol, dipl, 54. *Prof Exp:* Intern med, US Naval Hosp, Camp LeJuene, NC, 45-46; resident, Harrisburg Hosp, Pa, 48; psychiat, Duke Univ Hosp, 49-50, chief resident, 50-51; ward psychiatrist, Vet Admin Hosp, Wilmington,

Del, 52-53; asst prof, 53-57, ASSOC PROF PSYCHIAT, STATE UNIV NY UPSTATE MED CTR, 57- *Concurrent Pos:* Assoc psychiatrist, Syracuse Mem Hosp, 54-; attend psychiatrist, Vet Admin Hosp, Syracuse, 54-; consult psychiatrist, Syracuse Psychiat Hosp, 55-; Peace Corps, 62-; lectr, Postgrad Prog, NY State Dept Ment Hyg, 58-60. *Mem:* Fel Am Psychiat Asn; Acad Psychother. *Res:* Psychological aspects of environmental mastery, dreams and childrens games; creativity in art, music and literature. *Mailing Add:* Dept of Psychiat State Univ of NY Upstate Med Ctr Syracuse NY 13210

PHILLIPS, RICHARD LANG, b Saginaw, Mich, July 6, 34; m 56; c 3. COMPUTER GRAPHICS, AEROSPACE ENGINEERING. *Educ:* Univ Mich, BSE(aerospace eng) & BSE(math), 56, MSE, 57, PhD(elec arc behavior), 64. *Prof Exp:* Res engr, Space Technol Labs, Inc, 57-58 & Bendix Systs Div, Bendix Corp, 58-61; assoc res engr, 61-64, from asst prof to assoc prof aerospace eng, 65-74, PROF AEROSPACE ENG, UNIV MICH, ANN ARBOR, 74- *Concurrent Pos:* Consult, Clinton Motors Corp, 61-62; NSF scholar, Munich Tech Univ & Univ Liverpool, 64-65; vis staff mem, Los Alamos Sci Lab, 76-; consult, Tektronix, Inc, 78- *Mem:* Asn Comput Mach. *Res:* Data base management systems; computer aided design. *Mailing Add:* 3025 Hilltop Dr Ann Arbor MI 48103

PHILLIPS, RICHARD LEE, b Upland, Calif, Feb 14, 28; m 63; c 4. HORTICULTURE, PLANT PHYSIOLOGY. *Educ:* Calif State Polytech Col, BS, 58; Mich State Univ, MS, 62, PhD(hort), 64. *Prof Exp:* Lab technician hort, Citrus Res Ctr, Univ Calif, Riverside, 58-60; asst, Mich State Univ, 60-64; asst horticulturist, 64-73, asst prof hort, 69-73, assoc horticulturist, 73-74, ASSOC PROF HORT, 73-, EXTEN HORTICULTURIST, CITRUS EXP STA, INST FOOD & AGR SCI, UNIV FLA, 74- *Mem:* Am Soc Hort Sci; Am Inst Biol Sci. *Res:* Citrus pruning methods; growth regulators; foliar absorption of nutrients. *Mailing Add:* Inst of Food & Agr Sci Univ of Fla Gainesville FL 32601

PHILLIPS, RICHARD P, b Spokane, Wash, Mar 15, 28; m 49; c 6. EARTH SCIENCES. *Educ:* Stanford Univ, BS, 49, MS, 51 & 56; Univ Calif, San Diego, PhD(geophys), 64. *Prof Exp:* Explor geologist, Day Mines, Inc, Idaho, 50-54; chmn div math & natural sci, Univ San Diego, 58-61; res geophysicist marine phys lab, Scripps Inst, Univ Calif, 61-64; asst prof geol & geophys, San Diego State Col, 64-66; dir Natural Hist Mus, San Diego, Calif, 66-69; asst prof geol & geophys, San Diego State Col, 69-72; coordr environ studies, 72-80, ASST PROF PHYS SCI, UNIV SAN DIEGO, 80- *Concurrent Pos:* Mem working group 10 inter-union comn, Int Union Geodynamics & Geophys, 74-80. *Mem:* AAAS; Am Geophys Union; Geol Soc Am; Seismol Soc Am. *Res:* Geology and geophysics of continental margins; environmental geology of shallow marine and esturine environments. *Mailing Add:* Univ San Diego Alcala Park San Diego CA 92110

PHILLIPS, ROBERT ALLAN, b St Louis, Mo, July 2, 37; m 59; c 3. IMMUNOLOGY, CANCER. *Educ:* Carleton Col, BA, 59; Wash Univ, PhD(molecular biol), 65. *Prof Exp:* RES STAFF, BIOL DIV, ONT CANCER INST, 67-; PROF, DEPT MED BIOPHYS, UNIV TORONTO, 76- *Concurrent Pos:* Nat Cancer Inst Can grant, 67-, mem grant panel, 74-79, mem res adv group, 77-79; fel, Ont Cancer Inst, 65-67; grant, Med Res Coun Can, 70-; chmn immunol grant panel, Ont Cancer Treat & Res Found, 75-76. *Mem:* Transplantation Soc; Am Asn Immunol; Can Soc Immunol; Am Asn Cancer Res. *Res:* Regulation of early stages of lymphoid differentiation; molecular and cellular studies on the inherited form of retinoblastoma. *Mailing Add:* Ont Cancer Inst 500 Sherbourne St Toronto ON M4X 1K9 Can

PHILLIPS, ROBERT BASS, JR, b Campbell County, Va, Aug 26, 32. MATHEMATICS. *Educ:* Lynchburg Col, BS, 54; Univ Va, MEd, 60, DEd, 69. *Prof Exp:* Teacher math, Altavista High Sch, 57-60; assoc prof, 61-74, PROF MATH, LYNCHBURG COL, 74- *Mem:* Math Asn Am. *Res:* Mathematics education. *Mailing Add:* Dept of Math Lynchburg Col Lynchburg VA 24501

PHILLIPS, ROBERT EDWARD, b Evansville, Ind, Dec 30, 23; m 53; c 4. ORGANIC CHEMISTRY. *Educ:* Calif Inst Technol, BS; PhD(chem), 53. *Prof Exp:* Asst, Jr Org Chem Lab, Calif Inst Technol, 48-49, asst, Sr Org Chem Lab, 49-50, asst lectr, 51-52; chief chemist, Synthetic Lab, Calif Found Biochem Res, 52-56; res chemist, Aerojet-Gen Corp, Gen Tire & Rubber Co, Calif, 56-59; vpres, G K Turner Assocs, 59-71; consult, 72-74; V PRES TURNER DESIGNS, 74- *Mem:* Fel Am Inst Chem; Am Chem Soc; Asn Clin Sci. *Res:* Structure of alkaloids; synthesis of amino acids; polymers; solid propellants; analytical and clinical chemistry; application of fluorometry; analytical instrumentation. *Mailing Add:* Turner Designs 2247A Old Middlefield Way Mountain View CA 94043

PHILLIPS, ROBERT GIBSON, b Los Angeles, Calif, May 29, 36; m 59; c 3. MATHEMATICS. *Educ:* Univ Calif, BA, 60, MA, 61, PhD(math), 68. *Prof Exp:* Asst prof math, Calif State Col, Los Angeles, 63-67 & Univ SC, Columbia, 67-75; assoc prof, 75-80, PROF MATH, UNIV SC, AIKEN, 80- *Mem:* Am Math Soc; Asn Symbolic Logic. *Res:* Non-standard model theory. *Mailing Add:* Dept of Math Univ of SC 171 University Pkwy Aiken SC 29801

PHILLIPS, ROBERT RHODES, b Norfolk, Va. ETHOLOGY, ECOLOGY. *Educ:* Old Dominion Univ, BS, 63; Univ Md, MS, 68, PhD(zool), 71. *Prof Exp:* NIMH fel res assoc marine ethol, Hawaii Inst Marine Biol, 71-72; res assoc zool, Okla State Univ, 72-73; asst prof, 73-78, ASSOC PROF BIOL, STATE UNIV COL ONEONTA, NY, 78- *Mem:* Animal Behav Soc; Ecol Soc Am. *Res:* Relationships between social organization and environment; behavioral mechanisms of spacing; behavioral ecology; aquatic predation. *Mailing Add:* Dept of Biol State Univ Col Oneonta NY 13820

PHILLIPS, ROBERT WARD, b Peoria, Ill, Jan 21, 29; m 54; c 4. VETERINARY PHYSIOLOGY. *Educ:* Colo State Univ, BS, 59, DVM, 61; Univ Calif, PhD(physiol), 65. *Prof Exp:* NIH trainee, 61-64; from asst prof to assoc prof, 64-71, prof animal sci, 71-80, PROF DEPT PHYSIOL, COLO STATE UNIV, 71-, PROF DEPT BIOPHYSICS, 80- *Mem:* AAAS; Am Phys Soc; Am Inst Nutrit; Am Soc Vet Physiol & Pharmacol; Am Vet Med Asn. *Res:* General interest whole animal biochemistry, particularly the interactions of carbohydrate-lipid metabolism and their control; metabolic adaptations ot the environment; pathophysiology of diarrhea, altered transport and the individual's response to nutrient imbalance. *Mailing Add:* Dept of Physiol & Biophys Colo State Univ Ft Collins CO 80521

PHILLIPS, ROGER WINSTON, b Bristol, Eng, June 14, 42; US citizen; m 67; c 3. SURFACE CHEMISTRY. *Educ:* Univ of Calif, Berkeley, AB, 64; Univ Calif, Davis, PhD(phys chem), 68. *Prof Exp:* Res chemist phys res, E I du Pont de Nemours & Co, Inc, 68-74; mem tech staff res surface chem, The Aerospace Corp, 74-78; RES CHEMIST, CORP RES, OPTICAL COATING LABS, INC, 78- *Mem:* Am Chem Soc. *Res:* Characterization of surfaces by spectroscopic methods, particularly by auger and x-ray photoelectron spectroscopies, scanning electron spectroscopy and by infrared reflection spectroscopy; current emphasis is on surface contamination, surface reactions and thin film chemistry. *Mailing Add:* Optical Coating Lab Inc 2789 Giffen Ave Santa Rosa CA 95401

PHILLIPS, ROHAN HILARY, b Colombo, Sri Lanka. COMPUTER AIDED MANUFACTURING, ROBOTICS. *Educ:* Univ Sri Lanka, BSME, 70; Purdue Univ, MS, 75, PhD(indust eng), 78. *Prof Exp:* Mech engr, State Eng Corp, Sri Lanka, 70-71, Rice Mkt Bd, 71-73; instr indust eng, Purdue Univ, 75-78; ASST PROF MFG ENG, UNIV ILL, CHICAGO, 78- *Mem:* Am Inst Indust Engrs; Soc Mfg Engrs; Am Soc Eng Educ. *Res:* Group technology applications in computer aided manufacturing; flexible manufacturing technology; integration of robotics; computer integrated flexible manufacturing. *Mailing Add:* Dept Mat Eng Univ Ill Chicago IL 60680

PHILLIPS, RONALD CARL, b Carbondale, Ill, June 4, 32; m 54; c 3. MARINE BOTANY. *Educ:* Wheaton Col, BS, 54; Fla State Univ, MS, 56; Univ Wash, PhD, 72. *Prof Exp:* Biologist, Marine Lab, Fla State Bd Conserv, 57-61; from asst prof to assoc prof, 61-70, PROF BIOL, SEATTLE PAC COL, 70- *Concurrent Pos:* Sigma Xi-Sci Res Soc Am grant-in-aid, 62-63; NSF, Int Decade Ocean Exp, Seagrass Ecosyst Study Res Grants, 74-81; res consult, US Fish & Wildlife Serv, 63 & US Army Corps Engrs, 76-77. *Mem:* Am Inst Biol Sci; Ecol Soc Am. *Res:* Aquatic angiosperms; phycology. *Mailing Add:* Dept of Biol Seattle Pac Col Seattle WA 98119

PHILLIPS, RONALD EDWARD, b Williamstown, Ky, Nov 30, 29; m 50; c 3. SOIL PHYSICS, AGRONOMY. *Educ:* Univ Ky, BS, 54, MS, 55; Iowa State Univ, PhD(soil physics), 59. *Prof Exp:* From asst prof to assoc prof soil physics, Univ Ark, 59-66; assoc prof, 66-69, PROF SOIL PHYSICS, UNIV KY, 69- *Mem:* Fel Am Soc Agron; fel Soil Sci Soc Am. *Res:* Diffusion of plant nutrient ions and water in soil; relationships of soil physical properties and plant growth; effects of no-tillage on soil properties and plant growth. *Mailing Add:* Dept of Agron Univ of Ky Lexington KY 40506

PHILLIPS, RONALD LEWIS, b Huntington Co, Ind, Jan 1, 40; m 62; c 2. CYTOGENETICS, PLANT BREEDING. *Educ:* Purdue Univ, BS, 61, MS, 63; Univ Minn, PhD(genetics), 66. *Prof Exp:* NIH fel, Inst Gen Med Sci, Cornell Univ, 66-67; res assoc genetics, 67-68, asst prof, 68-72, assoc prof genetics, 72-76, PROF GENETICS & PLANT BREEDING, UNIV MINN, ST PAUL, 76- *Concurrent Pos:* Mem, Biol Stain Comn, 75-; assoc ed, Genetics, 78-81, ed bd, Maydica, 78-; NSF & USDA adv grants panels; prog dir, USDA Res Grants Off, Washington, DC, 79; vis prof, Exp Inst Cereal Crops, Italy, 81. *Mem:* Crop Sci Soc Am; AAAS; Genetics Soc Am; fel Am Soc Agron; Am Soc Advan Sci. *Res:* Chromosome function and behavior; nucleolus organizers and RNA genes; male sterility; amino acid mutants; tissue culture; recombination phenomena; applications of cytogenetics to plant breeding; plant genetic engineering. *Mailing Add:* Dept of Agron & Plant Genetics Univ of Minn St Paul MN 55108

PHILLIPS, RUSSELL ALLAN, b Lakewood, Ohio, Feb 19, 35; m 56; c 3. PHYSICS. *Educ:* Iowa State Univ, BS, 61, PhD(physics), 67. *Prof Exp:* Asst physics, Iowa State Univ, 62-67, assoc, 67-68, asst physicist, Inst Atomic Res, 68-71; asst prof, 71-75, assoc prof, 75-78, PROF PHYSICS, DIV ARTS & SCI, MO SOUTHERN STATE COL, 78- *Mem:* Am Asn Physics Teachers. *Res:* Experimental study of electronic structure of metals. *Mailing Add:* Dept of Physics Div of Arts & Sci Mo Southern State Col Joplin MO 64801

PHILLIPS, RUSSELL C(OLE), b Bad Axe, Mich, Apr 28, 23; m 46; c 2. CHEMICAL ENGINEERING. *Educ:* Mich State Univ, BS, 44; Polytech Inst Brooklyn, MChE, 48. *Prof Exp:* Asst chem engr, Gen Foods Corp, 45-47; res engr, Huron Milling Co, 47-49; chem engr, Blaw-Knox Co, 49-51; sr chem engr, 51-59, mgr res serv, Phys & Biol Sci Div, 59-61, mgr res & facil serv, 62-63, mgr chem eng, 64-76, DIR, CHEM ENG LAB, SRI INT, MENLO PARK, 76- *Mem:* Am Chem Soc; Am Inst Chem Engrs; Sigma Xi; Am Gas Asn. *Res:* Synthetic fuels; pollution control; high temperature research; mass transfer. *Mailing Add:* 861 Garland Dr Palo Alto CA 94303

PHILLIPS, RUTH BROSI, b Providence, RI, June 21, 40; m 66; c 2. GENETICS. *Educ:* Swarthmore Col, BA, 62; Ind Univ, Bloomington, MA, 64; Univ Ill, Urbana, PhD(genetics), 67. *Prof Exp:* Res assoc zool, Univ Ill, Urbana, 67, cell biol traineeship, 67-68, asst prof zool, 68-70; lectr, 70-71, asst prof, 71-75, ASSOC PROF ZOOL, UNIV WIS-MILWAUKEE, 75- *Concurrent Pos:* Clin consult, Milwaukee Childrens Hosp, 72- *Mem:* AAAS; Genetics Soc Am; Am Soc Human Genetics; NY Acad Sci. *Res:* Human and fish cytogenetics; frequency, inheritance and evolution of chromosomal polymorphisms in humans and fish and the use of these polymorphisms in linkage studies. *Mailing Add:* Dept of Zool Univ of Wis Milwaukee WI 53201

PHILLIPS, S MICHAEL, b San Francisco, Calif, Oct 9, 40. IMMUNOLOGY. *Educ:* Univ Wis, BS, 62, MD, 66; Am Bd Internal Med, dipl, 74. *Prof Exp:* Fel immunol, Harvard Univ, 69-71, instr, 71-72; sr res assoc, Walter Reed Army Inst Res, 72-75; intern med, Univ Hosp, 68-69, resident & fel, 67-69, asst prof, 75-80, ASSOC PROF DEPT MED

ALLERGY & IMMUNOL, UNIV PA, 80- *Mem:* Am Asn Immunologists; Transplantation Soc; Am Soc Trop Med & Hyg; Reticuloendothelial Soc. *Res:* Mechanisms of cellular immunity in diseases of human relevance. *Mailing Add:* Allergy & Immunol Sect Univ of Pa Sch of Med Philadelphia PA 19104

PHILLIPS, SAMUEL C, b 1921; US citizen. AERONAUTICAL & ASTRONAUTICAL ENGINEERING. *Educ:* Univ Wyo, BSEE, 42; Univ Mich, MSEE, 44. *Hon Degrees:* LLD, Univ Wyo. *Prof Exp:* Mem staff atomic exp & aircraft, space & missile progs, 50-59; dir, Minuteman Intercontinental Ballistic Missile Prog, 59-63; dir, Apollo Prog, NASA, 64-69; comdr space & missile orgn, US Air Force, 69-72; dir, Nat Security Agency, Dept Defense, 72-76; V PRES ENERGY SYSTS MGT DIV, TRW ENERGY PROD GROUP, 76- *Mem:* Nat Acad Eng. *Mailing Add:* Suite 1500 9841 Airport Blvd Los Angeles CA 90045

PHILLIPS, SHIRLEY ELIZABETH, microbiology, see previous edition

PHILLIPS, SIDNEY FREDERICK, b Melbourne, Australia, Sept 4, 33; m 57; c 3. GASTROENTEROLOGY. *Educ:* Univ Melbourne, MB, BS, 56, MD, 60; FRACP, 60. *Prof Exp:* Resident med officer internal med, Royal Melbourne Hosp, Univ Melbourne, 57-60, asst sub-dean clin teaching, Clin Sch, 61-62; res asst physiol, 63-64, gastroenterol, 64-66, instr & consult internal med & gastroenterol, 66-69, asst prof internal med, Mayo Clin & Grad Sch Med, 69-72, assoc prof, 72-76, PROF INTERNAL MED, MAYO MED SCH, UNIV MINN, 76- *Concurrent Pos:* Royal Australian Col Physicians traveling scholar gastroenterol, Cent Middlesex Hosp, London, Eng, 62-63. *Mem:* AAAS; Am Gastroenterol Asn; Brit Soc Gastroenterol; Am Soc Clin Invest. *Res:* Gastrointestinal absorption and secretion of water and electrolytes in man, in health and disease. *Mailing Add:* Dept of Internal Med Mayo Med Sch Univ of Minn Rochester MN 55901

PHILLIPS, STEPHANIE GORDON, cell biology, see previous edition

PHILLIPS, STEPHEN LEE, b Monte Vista, Colo, Apr 28, 40; m 60; c 2. MOLECULAR BIOLOGY. *Educ:* Adams State Col, BA, 63; Pa State Univ, MS, 65, PhD(biophys), 68. *Prof Exp:* USPHS fel, Wash Univ, 68-70; asst prof, 70-76, ASSOC PROF BIOCHEM, SCH MED, UNIV PITTSBURGH, 76- *Mem:* Am Soc Biol Chemists; AAAS; Am Soc Microbiol. *Res:* Biochemical genetics of ribosome function and synthesis; mechanisms of protein biosynthesis; messenger RNA synthesis and processing in eucaryotic cells; regulation of nitochandrial RNA synthesis during nitochandrial biogenesis; regulation of ribonucleic acid and protein synthesis in eucaryotic cells. *Mailing Add:* 206 Highland Terr Pittsburgh PA 15215

PHILLIPS, STEVEN J, b Alliance, Nebr, Feb 10, 48; m 69; c 2. SOIL PHYSICS, ENGINEERING GEOLOGY. *Educ:* Western Wash Univ, BS, 70; Mont State Univ, MS, 73. *Prof Exp:* Res asst soil sci, Mont State Univ, 71-73; SR RES SCIENTIST SOIL SCI, BATTELLE PAC NORTHWEST LAB, 73- *Concurrent Pos:* Mem, Nat Steering Comt, US Dept Energy, 76- *Mem:* Am Soc Agron; Soil Sci Soc Am; Int Soil Sci Soc. *Res:* Nuclear and hazardous waste management; soil chemistry. *Mailing Add:* Battelle Northwest Lab PO Box 999 Richland WA 99352

PHILLIPS, STEVEN JONES, b Atlantic City, NJ, Jan 2, 29; m 52; c 3. ANATOMY. *Educ:* Swarthmore Col, AB, 55; Hahnemann Med Col, MS, 58, MD, 60. *Prof Exp:* Intern, Philadelphia Gen Hosp, 60-61; instr, 63-64, asst prof, 64-69, assoc prof, 69-77, PROF ANAT, SCH MED, TEMPLE UNIV, 77- *Concurrent Pos:* USPHS trainee anat, Col Physicians & Surgeons, Columbia Univ, 61-63; NIH res grant, 67-69. *Mem:* AAAS; Am Asn Anatomists; Electron Micros Soc Am. *Res:* Fine structure of cardiovascular innervation, neuromuscular junctions and cardiac and skeletal muscle; metabolic growth disorders of cartilage. *Mailing Add:* Dept of Anat Temple Univ Sch of Med Philadelphia PA 19140

PHILLIPS, THEODORE LOCKE, b Philadelphia, Pa, June 4, 33; m 56; c 3. MEDICINE, RADIOBIOLOGY. *Educ:* Dickinson Col, BS, 55; Univ Pa, MD, 59. *Prof Exp:* Intern, Univ Hosps, Cleveland, Ohio, 59-60; resident therapeut radiol, 60-63, asst prof radiol, 65-68, assoc prof, 68-70, PROF RADIOL, MED CTR, UNIV CALIF, SAN FRANCISCO, 70-, CHMN, DIV RADIATION ONCOL, 73- *Concurrent Pos:* Consult, US Naval Radiol Defense Lab, 65-; head, Sect Radiation Oncol, Med Ctr, Univ Calif, San Francisco, 70-73. *Mem:* Radiation Res Soc; Radiol Soc NAm; Am Radium Soc; Am Soc Therapeut Radiol. *Res:* Radiation therapy; neutron radiobiology; normal tissue effects; experimental tumors; study of fractionation and pharmacologic effects on injury and recovery. *Mailing Add:* Dept of Radiation Oncol Univ of Calif Sch Med San Francisco CA 94143

PHILLIPS, THOMAS GOULD, b London, Eng. RADIOASTRONOMY. *Educ:* Oxford Univ, BA, 61, MA & DPhil, 64. *Prof Exp:* Jr res fel physics, Jesus Col, Oxford, 63-67; res assoc, Stanford Univ, 65-66; res officer, Clarendon Lab, Oxford, 66-68; mem tech staff, Bell Lab, Murray Hill, NJ, 68-80; PROF PHYSICS, CALIF INST TECHNOL, 80- *Concurrent Pos:* Lectr, Magdalen Col, 67-68; univ reader, Queen Mary Col, London Univ, 74-75; Consult, Bell Labs, 80-; Mem, Comt Space Astorn, Nat Acad Sci & Mgt Operations Working Group Space Astron, NASA, 81- *Mem:* Fel Am Phys Soc; Am Astron Soc; Int Astron Union. *Res:* Submillimeter-wave astronomy; development of heterodyne detection techniques including bolometer mixers and superconducting tunnel junctions; molecules (carbon monoxide) and atoms (carbon) in the interstellar medium to determine physical and chemical parameters of star forming clouds in the galaxy. *Mailing Add:* 320-47 Calif Inst Technol Pasadena CA 91125

PHILLIPS, THOMAS LEONARD, b US, May 2, 24. ENGINEERING. *Educ:* Va Polytech Inst, BS, 47, MS, 48. *Hon Degrees:* DCS, Stonehill Col, 68; DS, Northeastern Univ, 68 & Lowell Technol Inst, 70; LLD, Gordon Col, 70; DBA, Boston Col, 74. *Prof Exp:* Various eng & mgt positions, Raytheon Co, 48-61, exec vpres, 61-64, pres, 64-75, chief oper officer, 64-68, DIR, RAYTHEON CO, 62-, CHIEF EXEC OFFICER, 68-, CHMN BD, 75- *Mem:* Nat Acad Eng. *Mailing Add:* Raytheon Co 141 Spring St Lexington MA 02173

PHILLIPS, TIMOTHY DUKES, marine chemistry, see previous edition

PHILLIPS, TOM LEE, b Kingsport, Tenn, Dec 6, 31; m 67; c 4. PALEOBOTANY, PLANT MORPHOLOGY. *Educ:* Univ Tenn, BS, 53, BA, 57; Wash Univ, MA, 59, PhD(paleobot), 61. *Prof Exp:* From asst prof to assoc prof bot, 61-72, assoc head dept, 72-73, PROF BOT, UNIV ILL, URBANA, 72-; RES ASSOC, ILL GEOL SURV, 77- *Concurrent Pos:* Fel, John Simon Guggenheim Mem Found, 75-76; exchange scientist, Nat Acad Sci, USSR, 76. *Mem:* AAAS; Bot Soc Am; Torrey Bot Club; Brit Paleont Asn; Geol Soc Am. *Res:* Study of plant evolution and morphology based on Paleozoic age fossil plants and analyses of Pennsylvanian age coal swamp floras and vegetation based on petrified peat; paleoecology. *Mailing Add:* Dept of Bot Univ of Ill Urbana IL 61801

PHILLIPS, TRAVIS J, b Moline, Ill, Dec 13, 19; m 45; c 4. PHYSICAL CHEMISTRY. *Educ:* Iowa State Teachers Col, BA, 41; Univ Iowa, MS, 48; Ohio State Univ, PhD(chem), 58. *Prof Exp:* Instr physics, Iowa State Teachers Col, 46-47; instr chem, Evansville Col, 48-51; engr, Westinghouse Elec Corp, 57-64; chmn natural sci, Robert Morris Jr Col, 64-66; ASST PROF CHEM, PURDUE UNIV, CALUMET CAMPUS, 66- *Mem:* AAAS; Am Chem Soc; Am Crystallog Asn. *Res:* X-ray diffraction; solid state chemistry and physics. *Mailing Add:* Dept of Chem Purdue Univ Calumet Campus 2233 171st St Hammond IN 46323

PHILLIPS, V(ICTOR) A(RTHUR), metallurgy, see previous edition

PHILLIPS, VERIL LEROY, b Denison, Tex, July 15, 43; m 64; c 1. ALGEBRA, COMPUTER SCIENCE. *Educ:* Univ Tulsa, BS, 65; Mich State Univ, MA, 72, PhD(math), 75. *Prof Exp:* Programmer & analyst eng, Amerada Petrol Corp, 64-66; instr physics, US Naval Nuclear Power Sch, 67-70; math teaching & consult, 74-77; ASST PROF MATH, SAN JOSE STATE UNIV, 78- *Mem:* Math Asn Am; Am Math Soc; Asn Comput Math & Sci Teaching. *Res:* Theory of infinite groups, particularly the Cernikov p-groups. *Mailing Add:* 1962 Bowers Ave Santa Clara CA 95051

PHILLIPS, WALTER CHARLES, physics, see previous edition

PHILLIPS, WENDELL FRANCIS, b Revere, Mass, May 1, 21; m 49; c 3. ANALYTICAL CHEMISTRY. *Educ:* Colby Col, AB, 48. *Prof Exp:* Control chemist, Berke Bros, 48-49; res chemist, Beech-Nut Packing Co, 49-51, chief chemist, food lab, 51-56, mgr res & develop, 56-60; staff chemist, 60-71, mgr labs-tech admin, 71-75, dir tech resources, 76-78, sr scientist, 78-80, SR RES SCIENTIST, CAMPBELL SOUP CO, 80- *Mem:* Am Chem Soc; Inst Food Technol. *Res:* Analysis of agricultural chemicals; research and development of food products. *Mailing Add:* Campbell Soup Co Campbell Place Camden NJ 08101

PHILLIPS, WILLIAM, b Brooklyn, NY, Feb 21, 37; m 59; c 2. SOLID STATE PHYSICS, MATERIAL SCIENCE. *Educ:* Columbia Col, AB, 58; Carnegie Inst Technol, MS, 61, PhD(elec eng), 64. *Prof Exp:* MEM TECH STAFF, DAVID SARNOFF RES CTR, RCA LABS, 64- *Honors & Awards:* Outstanding Achievement Award, RCA Labs, 68, 70, 73 & 75; IR 100 Award, 68. *Mem:* Sr mem Inst Elec & Electronics Engrs; Am Phys Soc; Am Soc Crystal Growth; AAAS. *Res:* Applied solid state physics; single crystal growth and characterization, particularly electrooptic and semiconductor materials. *Mailing Add:* RCA Labs David Sarnoff Res Ctr Princeton NJ 08540

PHILLIPS, WILLIAM BAARS, b Nashville, Tenn, Oct 18, 34; m 72. SOLID STATE PHYSICS. *Educ:* David Lipscomb Col, BA, 56; Vanderbilt Univ, MS, 59; Fla State Univ, PhD(physics), 67. *Prof Exp:* Instr physics, Murray State Univ, 59-60, asst prof, 60-62; from asst prof to assoc prof, Univ WFla, 67-73; dir sci & eng, Bd Regents, State Univ Syst Fla, 73-77; acad planning coordr, 77-79, ASSOC DIR ACAD PROG, ARIZ BD REGENTS, 79- *Mem:* AAAS; Am Phys Soc; Am Asn Physics Teachers; Am Vacuum Soc. *Res:* Structure, surface morphology and electrical properties of very thin discontinuous vacuum-deposited metal films; high-vacuum techniques. *Mailing Add:* Ariz Bd of Regents 1535 W Jefferson St Phoenix AZ 85007

PHILLIPS, WILLIAM DALE, b Kansas City, Mo, Oct 10, 25; m 50; c 2. BIOPHYSICS, PHYSICAL CHEMISTRY. *Educ:* Univ Kans, AB, 48; Mass Inst Technol, PhD(phys chem), 51. *Prof Exp:* Assoc dir basic sci, Cent Res Dept, 51-74, tech mgr mycoprotein venture, The Lord Rank Res Ctr, Eng, 74-76, asst dir res & develop, Plastics Prod & Resins Dept, E I du Pont de Nemours & Co, Inc, 76-78; PROF & CHMN, DEPT CHEM, WASH UNIV, 78- *Mem:* Nat Acad Sci; AAAS; Am Chem Soc; Am Phys Soc; Am Acad Arts & Sci. *Res:* Molecular, electronic structure; proteins; magnetic resonance. *Mailing Add:* Dept Chem Wash Univ St Louis MO 63130

PHILLIPS, WILLIAM ERNEST JOHN, b Ottawa, Ont, July 31, 29. ANIMAL NUTRITION. *Educ:* McGill Univ, BSc, 51, MSc, 53; Univ Liverpool, PhD(biochem), 59. *Prof Exp:* Chemist, Sci Serv Div, Can Dept Agr, 53-59, res officer, Animal Res Inst, 59-64, chief biochem sect, 64-65; res scientist, 65-69, head pesticide sect, 69-73, RES SCIENTIST, NUTRIT RES DIV, HEALTH PROTECTION BR, DEPT NAT HEALTH & WELFARE, 73- *Concurrent Pos:* Mem subcomt, vitamin A, Nat Comt Animal Nutrit, 60. *Honors & Awards:* Borden Award Can, 71. *Mem:* Can Biochem Soc; Nutrit Soc Can; Prof Inst Pub Serv Can; Can Soc Animal Care; Am Inst Nutrit. *Res:* Vitamin metabolism; biochemical and nutritional aspects of the fat-soluble vitamins, particularly vitamin A; elucidating the ubiquinones; relationship of vitamin A to nonsaponifiable constituents; pesticide metabolism and toxicology. *Mailing Add:* 28 Gervin Crescent Ottawa ON K2G 0I8 Can

PHILLIPS, WILLIAM GEORGE, b Norristown, Pa, May 1, 29; m 55; c 1. ENTOMOLOGY. *Educ:* Pa State Univ, BA, 51; Univ Md, MS, 57, PhD(entom), 61. *Prof Exp:* Supvry entomologist, Insect Control & Res, Inc, 61-63; supvry entomologist, Dept Army, 63-67, entomologist, 67-70; entomologist, USDA, 70-72; supvry entomologist, 72-74, SUPVRY ECOLOGIST, ENVIRON PROTECTION AGENCY, 74- *Mem:* Entom Soc Am; Am Mosquito Control Asn; Sigma Xi. *Res:* Dietary and fecundity studies associated with insect rearing and colonization; effects of temperature and methods of feeding on the survival and life span of insects; federal regulation pesticides. *Mailing Add:* Environ Protection Agency 307 E McCarty St Frederick MD 21701

PHILLIPS, WILLIAM LEWIS, metallurgy, see previous edition

PHILLIPS, WILLIAM MAURICE, b Newton, Kans, Dec 4, 22; m 46; c 4. WEED CONTROL, CROP PRODUCTION. *Educ:* Kans State Univ, BS, 47, MS, 49. *Prof Exp:* Res agronomist weed control, US Dept Agr, 48-73; res agronomist, 73-76, HEAD, FT HAYS BR, KANS AGR EXP STA, KANS STATE UNIV, 76- *Mem:* Weed Sci Soc Am; Coun Agr Sci & Technol. *Res:* Weed control in reduced tillage systems, weed control in sorghum and winter wheat, control of field bindweed. *Mailing Add:* Ft Hays Exp Sta Kans State Univ Hays KS 67601

PHILLIPS, WILLIAM REVELL, b Salt Lake City, Utah, Jan 9, 29; m 50; c 4. MINERALOGY. *Educ:* Univ Utah, BS, 50, MS, 51, PhD(mineral), 54. *Prof Exp:* Teaching & res fels, Univ Utah, 49-50; res mineralogist & petrographer, Res Ctr, Kennecott Copper Corp, 54-56; asst prof geol, La Polytech Inst, 56-57; from asst prof to assoc prof, 57-66, PROF GEOL, BRIGHAM YOUNG UNIV, 66-, CHMN DEPT, 72- *Concurrent Pos:* Fulbright lectr, Univ Sind, Pakistan, 63-64 & Middle East Tech Univ, Ankara, 66-67; vis prof, Univ Waterloo, 71-72; vis res prof, Hacettepe Univ, Ankara, 75. *Mem:* Mineral Soc Am; Geol Soc Am. *Res:* Petrography; blueschist mineralogy of plate subduction zones. *Mailing Add:* 1839 N 1500 East Provo UT 84601

PHILLIPS, WILLIE EDWARD, b Clifton, Tenn, July 26, 23; m 49; c 3. APPLIED PHYSICS, ELECTRICAL ENGINEERING. *Educ:* Miss State Univ, BS, 49, MS, 55; Emory Univ, BD, 51; Vanderbilt Univ, PhD(physics), 59. *Prof Exp:* YMCA prog secy, Miss State Univ, 51-54, instr physics, 54-55; from asst prof to assoc prof, Tex Tech Univ, 58-67; PHYSICIST, SEMICONDUCTOR MAT DIV, NAT BUR STANDARDS, 67- *Concurrent Pos:* Lectr, Univ Md, 67-71 & Nat Bur Stand Grad Sch, 67-71. *Mem:* Inst Elec & Electronics Eng; Am Soc Test & Mat; Sigma Xi. *Res:* Field theory; solid state electronics; instrumentation; standards. *Mailing Add:* Semiconductor Mat Div Technol A331 Nat Bur Standards Washington DC 20234

PHILLIPS, WINFRED M(ARSHALL), b Richmond, Va, Oct 7, 40; m 60; c 2. FLUID MECHANICS, MECHANICAL ENGINEERING. *Educ:* VA Polytech Inst, BSME, 63; Univ Va, MAE, 66, DSc(aerospace eng), 68. *Prof Exp:* Res scientist, res labs, eng sci, Univ Va, 67-68; from asst prof to assoc prof, Pa State Univ, 68-78, prof aerospace eng, 78-80, assoc dean res, Col Eng, 79-80; PROF & HEAD, SCH MECH ENG, PURDUE UNIV, WEST LAFAYETTE, IND, 80- *Mem:* Am Soc Mech Engrs; Int Soc Biorheology; Am Soc Artificial Internal Organs; AAAS; Am Inst Aeronaut & Astronaut. *Res:* Fluid mechanics and gas dynamics; hemodynamics; blood rheology; cardiovascular dynamics; prosthetic devices; artificial heart and left ventricular assistance; bioengineering. *Mailing Add:* Sch Mech Eng Purdue Univ West Lafayette IN 47907

PHILLIPS, YORKE PETER, b Brooklyn, NY, Apr 1, 32; m 53; c 3. POLYMER CHEMISTRY. *Educ:* Polytech Inst Brooklyn, BChE, 53; Am Int Col, MBA, 59. *Prof Exp:* Res engr polymer processing, 56-60, res group leader polyvinyl chloride polymers, 60-68, mgr res polyvinyl chloride & polystyrene polymers, 68-77, MGR TECH ABS POLYMERS, MONSANTO CO, 78- *Mem:* Am Chem Soc; Soc Plastics Engrs. *Res:* Applications and processes for polystyrenes and polyvinyl chloride polymers. *Mailing Add:* 235 Ames Rd Hampden MA 01036

PHILLIPSON, PAUL EDGAR, b Newark, NJ, May 22, 33; m 65. CHEMICAL PHYSICS, BIOPHYSICS. *Educ:* Univ Chicago, BA, 53, MS, 56, PhD(physics), 62. *Prof Exp:* Res assoc physics, Univ Mich, 61-63; asst prof physics, 63-67, asst prof biophys, 65-71, assoc prof, 67-77, PROF PHYSICS, UNIV COLO, BOULDER, 77- *Concurrent Pos:* Alfred P Sloan Found fel, 65-67; Europ Molecular Biol Orgn res fel, Univ Rome, 72-74. *Mem:* Am Phys Soc. *Res:* Molecular quantum mechanics; electronic structure of molecules; theory of molecular force constants; molecular transition probabilities; mu-mesic molecules; macromolecular kinetics; statistical mechanics of liquids. *Mailing Add:* Dept of Physics & Astrophys Univ of Colo Boulder CO 80309

PHILLIPS-QUAGLIATA, JULIA MOLYNEUX, b London, Eng, July 22, 38; m 81. IMMUNOLOGY, ZOOLOGY. *Educ:* Univ London, BSc, 59; Univ Edinburgh, PhD(immunol), 63. *Prof Exp:* Sci officer, Med Res Coun Rheumatism Res Unit, Eng, 63-65; sci officer, Med Res Coun Nat Inst Med Res, Eng, 67-68; asst prof, 70-75, res assoc prof, 75-77, ASSOC PROF PATH, SCH MED, NY UNIV, 77- *Concurrent Pos:* Fel, Irvington House Inst, NY, 65-67; USPHS res grant, Sch Med, NY Univ, 69-, res career develop award, 73; Am Cancer Soc res grant, 77- *Mem:* Am Asn Immunologists; Am Soc Exp Path; Harvey Soc; Reticuloendothelial Soc; Brit Soc Immunol. *Res:* Cellular immunology; genetics of immune response. *Mailing Add:* Dept of Path NY Univ Med Ctr New York NY 10016

PHILLIS, JOHN WHITFIELD, b Trinidad, WI, Apr 1, 36; m 69. NEUROPHYSIOLOGY, NEUROPHARMACOLOGY. *Educ:* Univ Sydney, BVSc, 58, DVSc, 76; Australian Nat Univ, PhD(neurophysiol), 61; Monash Univ, Australia, DSc(neurophysiol), 70. *Prof Exp:* Wellcome res fel, Agr Res Coun Inst Animal Physiol, 61-62; lectr physiol, Monash Univ, Australia, 63-66, sr lectr, 67-69; prof physiol & assoc dean med, Univ Man, 71-73; prof physiol & head dept, Univ Sask, 43-81; PROF PHYSIOL & CHMN, WAYNE STATE UNIV, 81- *Concurrent Pos:* Vis prof, Ind Univ, 69. *Mem:* Brit Pharmacol Soc; Int Brain Res Orgn; Brit Physiol Soc; Can Physiol Soc; Soc Neurosci. *Res:* Pharmacology and identification of synaptic transmitters in the central nervous system; role of purines and sodium-potassium-adenosine triphosphatase in the modulation of removal exutability. *Mailing Add:* Dept Physiol Sch Med Wayne State Univ Detroit MI 78201

PHILLIS, WILLIAM AVERY, III, entomology, see previous edition

PHILLS, BOBBY RAY, b Shreveport, La, Sept 12, 45; m 68; c 2. HORTICULTURE, PLANT BREEDING. *Educ:* Southern Univ, Baton Rouge, La, BS, 68; La State Univ, MS, 72, PhD(hort), 75. *Prof Exp:* Res assoc veg crops, NY State Agr Exp Sta, Cornell Univ, 75-76; ASST PROF PLANT & SOIL SCI, TUSKEGEE INST, 76- *Concurrent Pos:* Rockefeller Found fel, Cornell Univ, 75-76. *Mem:* Am Genetics Asn; Am Soc Hort Sci; Sigma Xi. *Res:* Development and evaluation of tomatoes adapted to adverse environmental conditions coupled with pest resistance; development of sweet potato germplasm suitable for seedpiece propagation. *Mailing Add:* Dept of Plant & Soil Sci Tuskegee Inst Tuskegee AL 36088

PHILOON, WALLACE C, JR, b Peking, China, Mar 19, 23; US citizen; m 54; c 2. CHEMICAL ENGINEERING. *Educ:* Bowdoin Col, BS, 45; Mass Inst Technol, MS, 47, ScD(chem eng), 50. *Prof Exp:* Proj engr, Mallinckrodt Chem Works, Mo, 50-57, asst mgr process develop, Uranium Div, 57-61, proj engr, 61-64; ASSOC PROF CHEM ENG, UNIV TULSA, 64- *Mem:* Am Inst Chem Engrs; Nat Asn Corrosion Engrs. *Res:* Corrosion, especially stress corrosion cracking. *Mailing Add:* Dept of Chem Eng 600 S College Ave Tulsa OK 74104

PHILP, RICHARD BLAIN, b Guelph, Ont, Jan 19, 34; m 55; c 4. PHARMACOLOGY. *Educ:* Univ Toronto, DVM, 57; Univ Western Ont, PhD(pharmacol), 64. *Prof Exp:* Can Defence Res Bd fel aviation med, 64-65; from asst prof to assoc prof, 65-73, PROF PHARMACOL, FACULTIES MED, DENT & GRAD STUDIES, UNIV WESTERN ONT, 73- *Concurrent Pos:* Ont Heart Found res grant. *Mem:* Undersea Med Soc; Aerospace Med Asn; Pharmacol Soc Can; NY Acad Sci; AAAS. *Res:* Biological factors influencing susceptibility to decompression sickness; platelet aggregation and thrombus formation. *Mailing Add:* Dept of Pharmacol Med Sci Bldg Univ of Western Ont London ON N6A 5B8 Can

PHILP, RICHARD PAUL, b Plymouth, Eng, Aug 26, 47; m 75; c 2. ORGANIC GEOCHEMISTRY. *Educ:* Univ Aberdeen, Scotland, BSc, 68; Univ Sydney, PhD(org chem), 72. *Prof Exp:* Fel org geochem, Univ Bristol, Eng, 72-73; fel, Univ Calif, Berkeley, 74-75, asst res chemist org geochem, 76-78; RES SCIENTIST, COMMONWEALTH SCI & INDUST RES ORGN, SYDNEY, AUSTRALIA, 78- *Mem:* Royal Inst Chem London; AAAS. *Res:* Study of origin and method of formation of petroleum; crude oil correlation studies; coal and oil shale characterization and utilization. *Mailing Add:* PO Box 136 N Ryde 2113 Sydney Australia

PHILP, ROBERT HERRON, JR, b Demorest, Ga, Sept 10, 34; m 57; c 4. ANALYTICAL CHEMISTRY. *Educ:* Wheaton Col, Ill, BS, 56; Emory Univ, PhD(anal chem), 62. *Prof Exp:* Res assoc chem, Univ Kans, 62-63; asst prof, 63-73, ASSOC PROF CHEM, UNIV SC, 73- *Mem:* Am Chem Soc. *Res:* Mechanisms of polarographic reductions of carbonyl compounds; techniques related to square wave polarography. *Mailing Add:* Dept of Chem Univ of SC Columbia SC 29208

PHILPOT, CHARLES WALTER, forestry, see previous edition

PHILPOT, JOHN LEE, b Kansas City, Mo, May 7, 35; m 56; c 2. PHYSICS. *Educ:* William Jewell Col, AB, 57, Univ Ark, MS, 61, PhD(physics), 65. *Prof Exp:* From asst prof to assoc prof, 62-74, PROF PHYSICS, WILLIAM JEWELL COL, 74- *Concurrent Pos:* Consult, Thin Film Lab, Bendix Corp, 65-66. *Mem:* Am Asn Physics Teachers; Am Phys Soc. *Res:* Optics of thin films; solar heating; atomic and molecular collision phenomena. *Mailing Add:* Dept of Physics William Jewell Col Liberty MO 64068

PHILPOT, RICHARD MICHAEL, biochemistry, see previous edition

PHILPOTT, CHARLES WILLIAM, b Canadian, Tex, Jan 29, 32; m 60; c 2. CELL BIOLOGY. *Educ:* Tex Tech Col, BA, 57, MS, 58; Tulane Univ, PhD(zool), 62. *Prof Exp:* Fel cell biol, Harvard Univ, 62-64; from asst prof to prof, 64-69, PROF BIOL, RICE UNIV, 69- *Concurrent Pos:* Head master, Baker Residential Col, Rice Univ, 68- *Mem:* AAAS; Am Asn Anat; Am Soc Cell Biol; Am Soc Zool; Electron Micros Soc Am. *Res:* Comparative fine structure and cytochemistry of osmoregulatory tissues; ion transport and polyanions of the cell surface. *Mailing Add:* Dept of Biol Rice Univ Houston TX 77001

PHILPOTT, DELBERT E, b Loyal, Wis, Sept 24, 23; div. MOLECULAR BIOLOGY, MEDICAL RESEARCH. *Educ:* Ind Univ, BA, 46, MS, 49; Boston Univ, PhD(cytol), 63. *Prof Exp:* Res asst electron micros, Ind Univ, 47-49; res assoc, Ultrastruct Lab, Univ Ill Med Ctr, 49-52; head electron micros lab, Inst Muscle Res & Marine Biol Lab, Woods Hole, 52-63; prof biochem, Med Sch, Univ Colo, 63-65; head & co-dir, Electron Micros Lab, Ultrastruct Lab, Inst Biomed Res, Mercy Hosp, Denver, 65-66; HEAD ULTRASTRUCT LAB, AMES RES CTR, NASA, 66- *Concurrent Pos:* Res asst, Boston Univ, 60-63; mem bd dirs, Inst Biomed Res, Mercy Hosp, Denver, 71-75. *Mem:* AAAS; Am Soc Cell Biol; Electron Micros Soc Am; Biophys Soc. *Res:* Ultrastructure of retina; muscle and cartilage as changed by abnormal environments encountered in space. *Mailing Add:* Ultrastruct Lab NASA Ames Res Ctr Moffett Field CA 93045

PHILPOTT, JANE, b Kansas City, Mo, June 12, 18. BOTANY. *Educ:* Harris Teachers Col, AB, 40; Univ Iowa, MS, 41, PhD(plant anat), 47. *Prof Exp:* Teacher pub schs, Mo, 41-44; asst bot, Univ Iowa, 44-47; instr biol, Univ Chicago, 47-51; from asst prof to assoc prof bot, 51-68, dean instr, 61-72, PROF BOT, DUKE UNIV, 68- *Concurrent Pos:* Am Asn Univ Women fel, Duke Univ, 58; consult, Encycl Brittanica Films, Inc, 59-60. *Mem:* AAAS; Bot Soc Am. *Res:* Ecological anatomy of foliage leaves; ecological plant anatomy of woody plants. *Mailing Add:* Dept of Bot Duke Univ Durham NC 27706

PHILPOTT, MICHAEL RONALD, b Bristol, Eng, Jan 2, 40; div; c 2. CHEMICAL PHYSICS, ELECTROCHEMISTRY. *Educ:* Univ Col, London, BSc, 61, PhD(chem), 64, DSc, 74. *Prof Exp:* Res assoc theoret sci, 65-67, from asst prof to assoc prof chem, Univ Ore, 67-73; res staff mem, 73-75, RES MGR PHYS SCI, RES DIV, INT BUS MACH CORP, 75- *Concurrent Pos:* Ramsay fel, Univ Col, London, 64-65; Alfred P Sloan fel, 70-72, Camille & Henry Dreyfus Scholar, Univ Ore, 73; assoc ed, Advances Chem Physics, 75- *Mem:* Am Phys Soc; Am Chem Soc; Electrochem Soc. *Res:* Surface enhanced raman spectroscopy of metal electrodes; electronic processes in organic solids; surface polariton spectroscopy. *Mailing Add:* Dept K33/281 5600 Cottle Rd San Jose CA 95193

PHILPOTT, RICHARD JOHN, b London, Eng, Sept 4, 36; m 66. NUCLEAR PHYSICS. *Educ:* Oxford Univ, BA, 60, MA & DPhil(theoret physics), 63. *Prof Exp:* Res assoc nuclear theory, Univ Pittsburgh, 63-64, Univ Calif, Davis, 64-66 & Vanderbilt Univ, 66-68; asst prof, 68-74, assoc prof, 74-79, PROF PHYSICS, FLA STATE UNIV, 79- *Concurrent Pos:* Mellon fel, 63-64. *Mem:* Am Phys Soc; Sigma Xi. *Res:* Theory of nuclear structure and reactions; model calculations for nuclear continuum phenomena including many-body effects. *Mailing Add:* Dept of Physics Fla State Univ Tallahassee FL 32306

PHILPOTTS, ANTHONY ROBERT, b Bristol, Eng, July 27, 38; Can citizen; m 60; c 3. PETROLOGY, MINERALOGY. *Educ:* McGill Univ, BSc, 58, MSc, 60; Cambridge Univ, PhD(petrol), 63. *Prof Exp:* Asst prof petrol, McGill Univ, 63-70; assoc prof geol, 70-75, PROF GEOL, UNIV CONN, STORRS, 75-, HEAD DEPT GEOL & GEOPHYS, 78- *Mem:* Mineral Soc Am; Mineral Asn Can; Brit Mineral Soc; Geol Soc Can. *Res:* Liquid immiscibility in silicate melts. *Mailing Add:* Dept of Geol Univ of Conn Storrs CT 06268

PHILPOTTS, JOHN ALDWYN, b Bristol, Eng, May 22, 40; US citizen; m 63; c 2. GEOCHEMISTRY. *Educ:* McGill Univ, BSc, 59, MSc, 61; Mass Inst Technol, PhD(geochem), 65. *Prof Exp:* Aerospace technologist, Goddard Space Flight Ctr, NASA, 65-77; mem fac, 77-80, PROF, DEPT GEOL & GEOPHYSICS, HAWAII INST GEOPHYSICS, UNIV HAWAII, 80- *Mem:* AAAS; Meteoritical Soc; Geol Soc Am; Am Geophys Union; Int Asn Geochem & Cosmochem. *Res:* Geochemistry; petrology; trace element theory and analysis; extraterrestrial geochemistry. *Mailing Add:* Dept Geol & Geophysics Univ Hawaii Honolulu HI 96825

PHINNEY, BERNARD ORRIN, b Superior, Wis, July 29, 17; m 51, 65; c 4. BOTANY. *Educ:* Univ Minn, BS, 40, PhD(bot), 46. *Prof Exp:* Asst bot & plant physiol, Univ Minn, 40-46; inst fel, Calif Inst Technol, 46-48; from instr to assoc prof, 47-61, prof bot, 61-73, PROF BIOL, UNIV CALIF, LOS ANGELES, 73- *Concurrent Pos:* NSF sr fel, Genetics Inst, Copenhagen Univ, 59-60; US-Japan Coop Sci Prog NSF vis scientist, Int Christian Univ, Tokyo, 66-67; NSF vis prof, Dept Chem, Bristol Univ, UK, 74-75. *Mem:* AAAS; Bot Soc Am; Am Soc Plant Physiol; Genetics Soc Am; Scand Soc Plant Physiol. *Res:* Chemical genetics; gibberellins and plant growth. *Mailing Add:* Dept of Biol Univ of Calif Los Angeles CA 90024

PHINNEY, GEORGE JAY, b Columbus, Ohio, July 29, 30; m 53; c 1. VERTEBRATE ECOLOGY. *Educ:* Ohio State Univ, BSc, 53, MSc, 56, PhD(zool), 67. *Prof Exp:* Asst instr zool, Ohio State Univ, 57-59, instr, 59-62; from asst prof to assoc prof, 62-80, PROF BIOL, OTTERBEIN COL, 80- *Mem:* Ecol Soc Am; Am Soc Limnol & Oceanog; Am Fisheries Soc; Am Soc Ichthyologists & Herpetologists. *Res:* Freshwater ecology; lentic and lotic communities. *Mailing Add:* Dept Life Sci Otterbein Col Westerville OH 43081

PHINNEY, HARRY KENYON, b Grafton, WVa, May 19, 18; m 46; c 3. BOTANY. *Educ:* Univ Cincinnati, AB, 41; Albion Col, MA, 43; Northwestern Univ, PhD(bot), 45. *Prof Exp:* Seessel fel, Yale Univ, 45-46; asst cur cryptogams, Chicago Natural Hist Mus, 46-47; from asst prof to assoc prof, 47-62, PROF BOT, ORE STATE UNIV, 62- *Mem:* AAAS; Bot Soc Am; Phycol Soc Am; Am Micros Soc. *Res:* Taxonomy and ecology of fresh-water and marine algae; algal culture; stream ecology. *Mailing Add:* Dept of Bot Ore State Univ Corvallis OR 97331

PHINNEY, NANETTE, b Evanston, Ill, 1945. HIGH ENERGY PHYSICS. *Educ:* Mich State Univ, BS, 66; State Univ NY Stony Brook, MA, 69, PhD(physics), 72. *Prof Exp:* Charge res physics, Ecole Polytech Paris, 72-74; vis scientist, Europ Orgn Nuclear Res, 74-75; res officer physics, Nuclear Physics Lab, Oxford Univ, 75-80. *Concurrent Pos:* Vis scientist, Europ Orgn Nuclear Res, 81; vis mathematician, Stanford Linear Accelerator Ctr, 81- *Mem:* Am Phys Soc. *Res:* Accelerator control systems; lepton pair production; high transverse momentum phenomena; experimental high energy physics. *Mailing Add:* Stanford Linear Accelerator Ctr BIN 95 Stanford CA 94305

PHINNEY, RALPH E(DWARD), b Cleveland, Ohio, Mar 3, 28. AERODYNAMICS. *Educ:* Univ Mich, BS, 50, MS, 51, PhD(aerodyn), 53. *Prof Exp:* Asst, Univ Mich, 51-53; res assoc, Johns Hopkins Univ, 53-54; res & develop scientist, Martin Marietta Corp, Md, 59-68; RES & DEVELOP SCIENTIST, NAVAL ORD LAB, SILVER SPRING, 68- *Mem:* AAAS; Am Inst Aeronaut & Astronaut. *Res:* Theoretical and experimental aerodynamics; supersonic flow; boundary layer flow; liquid jet breakup. *Mailing Add:* 220 W Lanvale St Baltimore MD 21217

PHINNEY, ROBERT A, b Rochester, NY, Oct 7, 36; m 59; c 2. GEOPHYSICS. *Educ:* Mass Inst Technol, BS & MS, 59; Calif Inst Technol, PhD(geophys), 61. *Prof Exp:* Asst prof geophys, Calif Inst Technol, 61-63; assoc prof, 63-69, PROF GEOPHYS, PRINCETON UNIV, 69- *Mem:* AAAS; Am Geophys Union; Soc Explor Geophys; Seismol Soc Am; Geol Soc Am. *Res:* Seismology; solid earth geophysics; planetary physics; theoretical geophysics; wave propagation. *Mailing Add:* Dept of Geol & Geophys Sci Princeton Univ Princeton NJ 08540

PHINNEY, WILLIAM CHARLES, b South Portland, Maine, Nov 16, 30; m 53; c 4. GEOLOGY. *Educ:* Mass Inst Technol, SB, 53, SM, 56, PhD(geol), 59. *Prof Exp:* From asst prof to prof petrol, Univ Minn, Minneapolis, 59-71; GEOL BR CHIEF, JOHNSON SPACE CTR, NASA, 70- *Mem:* AAAS; Am Geophys Union. *Res:* Phase relations in igneous and metamorphic rocks; lunar geology. *Mailing Add:* Geol Br SN6 NASA Johnson Space Ctr Houston TX 77058

PHIPPS, JACK RALPH, b McCracken Co, Ky, Sept 27, 32; m 62; c 1. AUTOMOTIVE ENGINEERING. *Educ:* Wayne State Univ, BS, 66. *Prof Exp:* Physicist, Bendix Res Lab, 58-62, prin engr, Bendix Fuel Devices Div, 62-68, eng mgr fuel syst, Bendix Power & Engine Components Group, 68-74, prog mgr automotive eng controls, 74-77, EXEC CONSULT DIESEL ENGINES, BENDIX DIESEL EQUIP, BENDIX CTR, 77- *Concurrent Pos:* Gatekeeper-automotive engine controls, Bendix Corp, 76- *Mem:* Soc Automotive Engrs. *Res:* Automotive engine controls; gasoline and diesel; emphasis on electronic controls. *Mailing Add:* 21718 Tanglewood St Clair Shores MI 48082

PHIPPS, JAMES BIRD, b Birmingham, Eng, July 22, 34; m 67; c 3. SYSTEMATICS. *Educ:* Univ Birmingham, BSc, 56; Univ Western Ont, PhD(bot), 69. *Prof Exp:* Prof off, Br Bot & Plant Path, Ministry Agr, Govt Rhodesia & Nyasaland, Salisbury, Rhodesia & Nyasaland, 56-61; lectr bot, Dept Bot, 61-64, from asst prof to assoc prof, 64-77, PROF BOT, DEPT PLANT SCI, UNIV WESTERN ONT, 77-, CHMN DEPT, 80- *Concurrent Pos:* Mem panel plant systs, Study Fundamental Biol in Can-Privy Coun Sci Secretariat & Biol Coun Can, 68-70; mem, Pop Biol Grant Selection Comt, Nat Sci & Eng Res Coun Can, 79-81. *Mem:* Can Bot Asn (pres, 81-82); Soc Syst Zool; Int Asn Plant Taxon; Bot Soc Am; Brit Ecol Soc. *Res:* Plant systematics; numerical systematics; methods of comparing classifications; systematics and evolutionary biology of crataegus. *Mailing Add:* Dept of Plant Sci Univ of Western Ont London ON N6A 5B7 Can

PHIPPS, PATRICK MICHAEL, b New Martinsville, WVa, Oct 19, 45; m 67. PLANT PATHOLOGY, MYCOLOGY. *Educ:* Fairmont State Col, BS, 70; Va Polytech Inst & State Univ, MS, 72; WVa Univ, PhD(plant path), 74. *Prof Exp:* Res assoc plant path, NC State Univ, 74-76; ASST PROF PLANT PATH, TIDEWATER RES CTR, VA POLYTECH INST & STATE UNIV, 76- *Mem:* Am Phytopath Soc; Mycol Soc Am. *Res:* Plant diseases caused by soilborne microorganisms; mycoparasitism; physiology of fungi. *Mailing Add:* Tidewater Res Ctr Holland Sta Suffolk VA 23437

PHIPPS, PETER BEVERLEY POWELL, b London, Eng, Aug 5, 36; m 62; c 1. SOLID STATE CHEMISTRY, CORROSION. *Educ:* Oxford Univ, BA, 61, DPhil(chem), 63. *Prof Exp:* Res assoc mat sci, Stanford Univ, 63-65 & Univ Southern Calif, 65-67; MEM RES STAFF, IBM RES LABS, 67- *Res:* Redox reactions; nuclear resonance; semiconductivity; photoconductivity; luminescence; defect chemistry; corrosion. *Mailing Add:* IBM San Jose Res Lab 5600 Cattle Rd San Jose CA 95193

PHIPPS, RICHARD L, b Coles Co, Ill, Apr 5, 35; m 55; c 2. PLANT ECOLOGY. *Educ:* Eastern Ill Univ, BSc, 58; Ohio State Univ, MSc, 60, PhD(bot), 65. *Prof Exp:* Res asst plant ecol, Ohio Agr Exp Sta, 58-64; RES BOTANIST, WATER RESOURCES DIV, US GEOL SURV, 64- *Concurrent Pos:* Prof lectr, George Washington Univ. *Mem:* Ecol Soc Am; Am Inst Biol Sci; Tree-Ring Soc. *Res:* Tree growth physiology; reconstruction of climatic and hydrologic information from tree rings; ecology and physiology of tree growth in relation to microclimate; computer simulation of forest vegetation dynamics. *Mailing Add:* US Geol Surv Nat Ctr Reston VA 22092

PHIPPS, THOMAS ERWIN, JR, physics, see previous edition

PHISTER, MONTGOMERY, JR, b Calif, Feb 26, 26; m 49; c 3. COMPUTER PROGRAMMING. *Educ:* Stanford Univ, BS, 49, MS, 50; Cambridge Univ, PhD(physics, chem), 53. *Prof Exp:* Mem tech staff, Hughes Aircraft Co, 53-55 & Thompson-Ramo-Wooldridge, Inc, 55-60; vpres & dir, Scantlin Electronics, Inc, 60-66; vpres, Xerox Data Systs, 66-71; TECH & SCI RES & WRITING, 71- *Concurrent Pos:* Lectr, Univ Calif, Los Angeles, 54-65, Harvard Univ, 74-75 & Univ Sydney, Australia, 75; dir eng, Thompson-Ramo-Wooldridge Prod Co, 58-60. *Mem:* Asn Comput Mach; fel Inst Elec & Electronics Engrs. *Res:* Economics of computers and data processing; software engineering; management in the information industry. *Mailing Add:* 1210 Galisteo Parkway Santa Fe NM 87501

PHLEGER, FRED B, b Kansas City, Kans, July 31, 09; m 33; c 2. OCEANOGRAPHY. *Educ:* Univ Southern Calif, AB, 31; Calif Inst Technol, MS, 32; Harvard Univ, PhD(geol), 36. *Prof Exp:* Asst paleont, Harvard Univ, 34-36; Sheldon traveling fel geol, 36-37; instr paleont, Amherst Col, 37-40, from asst prof to assoc prof, 40-49; vis assoc prof, 49-51, assoc prof, 51-57, chmn geol res div, 70-74, prof, 57-77, EMER PROF OCEANOG, SCRIPPS INST OCEANOG, UNIV CALIF, SAN DIEGO, 77- DIR MARINE FORAMINIFERA LAB, 49- *Concurrent Pos:* Fel, Cushman Found Foraminiferal Res, dir, 50-, pres, 56-57, 63; hon & distinguished sci investr, Inst Geol, Nat Univ Mex, 60. *Honors & Awards:* Joseph A Cushman Award, Cushman Found Foraminiferal Res, 80. *Mem:* fel Geol Soc Am; Paleont Soc; Soc Econ Paleont & Mineral Mex Geol Soc. *Res:* Ecology of Recent Foraminifera; coastal lagoon sedimentology. *Mailing Add:* Geol Res Div Scripps Inst Oceanog Univ of Calif at San Diego La Jolla CA 92093

PHOENIX, CHARLES HENRY, b Webster, Mass, Aug 18, 22; m 51; c 2. BEHAVIORAL PHYSIOLOGY, REPRODUCTIVE BIOLOGY. *Educ:* Univ Conn, BA, 45; Boston Univ, MA, 50, PhD(psychol), 54. *Prof Exp:* Asst prof psychol, Univ Kans, 54-57, res assoc anat, 59-63; assoc scientist, Ore Regional Primate Res Ctr, 63-64; assoc prof, 64-65, PROF MED PSYCHOL, HEALTH SCI CTR, UNIV ORE, 66-, SCIENTIST & ASST DIR, ORE REGIONAL PRIMATE RES CTR, 65- *Concurrent Pos:* USPHS fel anat, Univ Kans, 57-59; vis prof, Sch Med, Univ Cincinnati, 61-62; vis scientist,

Christ Hosp Inst Med Res, Cincinnati, 61-62. *Mem:* AAAS; Am Asn Anatomists; Am Psychol Asn. *Res:* Reproductive physiology and behavior; neuroendocrinology. *Mailing Add:* Ore Regional Primate Res Ctr 505 NW 185th Ave Beaverton OR 97006

PHOENIX, DAVID A, b Lompoc, Calif, June 25, 16; m 38; c 2. GEOLOGY, HYDROLOGY. *Educ:* Univ Calif, Berkeley, AB, 41; Stanford Univ, MS, 54. *Prof Exp:* Geologist, US Geol Surv, 41-62, res hydrologist, 62-72; consult, Boyle Eng Corp, 73-79; CONSULT, INT EXEC SERV CORP, 76- *Concurrent Pos:* From teaching asst to instr, Stanford Univ, 51-53; vis lectr, Chapman Col, 73-74, Calif State Univ, Fullerton, 81. *Mem:* Fel Geol Soc Am; Asn Geol Teachers; Am Geophys Union; Soc Econ Geol; Sigma Xi. *Res:* Geology of chromite, quicksilver, lead-zinc and uranium ore deposits; field geology; geophysical investigations; geology and permeability of host rocks, geochemistry of ground water; remote sensing applications and research in hydrology; regional water resource appraisals. *Mailing Add:* 450 Ruby St Laguna Beach CA 92651

PHOENIX, DONALD R, US citizen. BIOLOGY, ECOLOGY. *Educ:* Univ Pa, BA, 68, PhD(biol & ecol), 76. *Prof Exp:* Mem staff, Acad Natural Sci, Pa, 68-76; PROJ MGR, WESTON, 76- *Concurrent Pos:* Lectr limnol & ecol communities. *Mem:* Am Fisheries Soc; Ecol Soc Am; Am Soc Limnol & Oceanog. *Res:* Ecological, hydrological, and large scale environmental impact assessment studies; impact of power-plant operations, acid mine drainage, toxin effluents, and thermal additions on rivers and other water bodies; fisheries population studies; trophic relationships between fish and their major food sources. *Mailing Add:* Weston Weston Way West Chester PA 19380

PHONG, DUONG HONG, b Nam-Dinh, Vietnam, Aug 30, 53; US citizen. ANALYSIS. *Educ:* Princeton Univ, BA, 73, MA, 74, PhD(math), 77. *Prof Exp:* Instr math, Univ Chicago, 75-77; mem, Inst Advan Study, 77-78; asst prof, 78-81, ASSOC PROF MATH, COLUMBIA UNIV, 81- *Mem:* Am Math Soc. *Res:* Theory of partial differential equations. *Mailing Add:* Dept Math Columbia Univ New York NY 10027

PHUNG, DOAN LIEN, b Battrang, Vietnam, Jan 1, 40; US citizen; m 70; c 2. NUCLEAR SAFETY, NUCLEAR ENERGY ECONOMICS. *Educ:* Fla State Univ, BA, 61; Mass Inst Technol, MS, 63, ScD, 72. *Prof Exp:* Engr nuclear eng, Vietnam Atomic Energy Off, 64-66; consult nuclear safety, US Atomic Energy Comn, 72-73; consult engr nuclear eng, United Engr & Construct, 66-75; SR SCIENTIST ENERGY, INST ENERGY ANAL, OAK RIDGE ASSOC UNIV, 75- *Concurrent Pos:* Lectr, Univ Pa, 74. *Mem:* Sigma Xi; AAAS; NY Acad Sci; Am Nuclear Soc. *Res:* Nuclear plant design and safety; nuclear energy and alternatives; energy economics; cost analysis; industrial energy conservation. *Mailing Add:* Inst Energy Anal Oak Ridge Assoc Univ PO Box 117 Oak Ridge TN 37830

PIACSEK, BELA EMERY, b Budapest, Hungary, Apr 17, 37; US citizen; m 62; c 4. PHYSIOLOGY, ENDOCRINOLOGY. *Educ:* Univ Notre Dame, BS, 59, MS, 61; Mich State Univ, PhD(physiol), 66. *Prof Exp:* Asst prof biol, 68-72, physiol, Med Sch, 69-72, assoc prof, 72-79, PROF BIOL, MARQUETTE UNIV, 79- *Concurrent Pos:* NIH res fel physiol, Med & Dent Sch, Harvard Univ, 66-68. *Mem:* Endocrine Soc; Am Physiol Soc; Soc Study Reproduction; Int Soc Neuroendocrinol. *Res:* Maturation and aging of the reproductive system; environmental influences in reproduction. *Mailing Add:* Dept Biol Marquette Univ Milwaukee WI 53233

PIALA, JOSEPH J, b Carrollville, Wis, Nov 1, 21; m 52; c 3. PHARMACOLOGY. *Educ:* Univ Wis, BS, 47; Univ Md, PhD(pharmacol), 51. *Prof Exp:* Sect head pharmacol, Squibb Inst Med Res, 50-59, sr res pharmacologist, 59-65, res assoc pharmacol, 65-67; dept head pharmacol, 67-77, SR RES INVESTR, BRISTOL-MYERS PROD, 77- *Mem:* AAAS; Am Soc Pharmacol & Exp Therapeut; NY Acad Sci; Am Pharmaceut Asn. *Res:* Central nervous system pharmacology; diuretics; cardiovascular drugs; tranquilizers; muscle relaxants; general anesthetics; tuberculostatic agents; trypanosomiasis; analgesics; anti-inflammatory agents; antacids; skin and hair products. *Mailing Add:* Bristol Myers Prod 1350 Liberty Ave Hillside NJ 07207

PIALET, JOSEPH WILLIAM, b Presto, Pa, June 6, 51. ORGANIC CHEMISTRY. *Educ:* Carnegie-Mellon Univ, BS, 73, MS, 74. *Prof Exp:* RES CHEMIST, LUBRIZOL CORP, 74- *Mem:* Am Chem Soc; Mensa. *Res:* Development of additives for lubricants and fuels to provide greater protection and fuel economy. *Mailing Add:* Lubrizol Corp 29400 Lakeland Blvd Wickliffe OH 44092

PIAN, CARLSON CHAO-PING, magnetofluid dynamics, energy conversion, see previous edition

PIAN, CHARLES HSUEH CHIEN, b Tientsin, China, June 21, 21; US citizen; m 45; c 3. ORGANIC CHEMISTRY. *Educ:* Fu Jen Univ, BS, 44; Northeastern Univ, MS, 64; State Univ NY, Albany, PhD(org chem), 69. *Prof Exp:* Asst engr, Ta-shin Paper & Pulp Factory, 45-46; chief engr & plant dir, Shinei Pharmaceut Factory, Taiwan Med & Supplies Co, 46-51; specialist, Bd Trustees Rehab Affairs, 51-52, Joint Comn Rural Reconstruct, 52-54, Joint Comt Med Supplies, 54-56 & Inst Nuclear Sci, Tsing Hua Univ, Taiwan, 56-58; chemist, Lexington Res Labs, Itek Corp, 59-62, sr chemist, 64-65, proj leader, 68-70; proj leader, 70-80, GROUP LEADER, NASHUA CORP, 81- *Mem:* Am Chem Soc; Soc Photog Sci & Eng. *Res:* Organic reaction mechanisms; organometallic chemistry; liquid transfer toner; photochemistry; organic photoconductors; image formation studies. *Mailing Add:* 64 Fifer Lane Lexington MA 02173

PIAN, RICHARD H(SUEH) J(UI), b Tientsin, China, Aug 30, 17; nat US; m 48; c 4. CIVIL ENGINEERING. *Educ:* Kung Shang Univ, China, BCE, 41; Cornell Univ, MS, 42, PhD(civil eng), 45. *Prof Exp:* Asst civil eng, Cornell Univ, 43; struct designer, H K Ferguson Co, Ohio, 45-46; struct engr, US Bur Reclamation, Colo, 46-47 & Smith, Hinchman & Grylls, Mich, 47-48; from asst prof to assoc prof civil eng, Mich State Univ, 48-59; PROF ENG, ARIZ STATE UNIV, 59- *Concurrent Pos:* Consult, State Hwy Dept, Mich, 50, 54 & 55, Cleverdon, Varney & Pikes, Mass, 53, Kenerson Engrs, Mich, 57-59 & Boeing Airplane Co, Wash, 58; independent struct eng consult, 59-; prof, Seato Grad Sch Eng, Bangkok, 61-63; vis prof & Fulbright lectr, Nat Taiwan Univ, 67-68; vis prof, Southwestern Jiao-Tong Univ, People's Repub China, 80. *Mem:* Am Soc Civil Engrs; Am Soc Eng Educ; Am Concrete Inst. *Res:* Structural engineering; concrete and steel structures; structural mechanics. *Mailing Add:* 619 E Loma Vista Dr Tempe AZ 85282

PIAN, THEODORE H(SUEH) H(UANG), b Shanghai, China, Jan 18, 19; nat US; m 45; c 1. STRUCTURAL MECHANICS, AERONAUTICS. *Educ:* Tsing Hua, China, BS, 40; Mass Inst Technol, MS, 44, ScD(aeronaut eng), 48. *Prof Exp:* Asst, 46-47, res assoc, 47-48, mem staff, Div Indust Coop, 48-52, from asst prof to assoc prof, 52-66, PROF AERONAUT ENG, MASS INST TECHNOL, 66- *Concurrent Pos:* Assoc ed, AIAA J, Am Inst Aeronaut & Astronaut, 73-75; vis prof, Univ Tokyo, 74 & Tech Univ Berlin, 75. *Honors & Awards:* Von Karman Mem Prize, TRE Corp, Beverly Hills, Calif, 74; Struct, Struct Dynamics & Mat Award, Am Inst Aeronaut & Astronaut, 75. *Mem:* Soc Exp Stress Anal; Am Soc Eng Educ; Am Inst Aeronaut & Astronaut; fel AAAS. *Res:* Finite element methods; structural mechanics. *Mailing Add:* Dept of Aeronaut & Astronaut Mass Inst of Technol Cambridge MA 02139

PIANFETTI, JOHN ANDREW, b Sawyerville, Ill, July 19, 07; m 40; c 2. ORGANIC CHEMISTRY. *Educ:* Univ Ill, BS, 30; Univ Wis, MA, 33; Purdue Univ, PhD(org chem), 41. *Prof Exp:* Asst phys chem, A O Smith Corp, Wis, 30-32; res chemist, Miner Labs, Chicago, 36-38; res chemist, Westvaco Chlorine Prod Corp, 40-48, Westvaco Chem Div, FMC Corp, 48-58, sr res chemist, FMC Corp, 59-68; CONSULT, 68- *Mem:* Am Chem Soc. *Res:* Diazonium salts; glycerol and its derivatives; chlorination and bromination of organic compounds; organic phosphates; resins and plasticizers; dichloro-diphenyl-trichloroethane; agricultural insecticides; war gases; nitrogen chemistry; high pressure synthesis; toxic agents; rocket fuels. *Mailing Add:* 5145 Russet Dr Charleston WV 25313

PIANKA, ERIC R, b Hilt, Calif, Jan 23, 39; div; c 2. ECOLOGY. *Educ:* Carleton Col, BA, 60; Univ Wash, PhD(ecol), 65. *Prof Exp:* NIH fel, Princeton Univ, 65-66, Univ Western Australia, 66-68 & Princeton Univ, 68; from asst prof to assoc prof, 68-76, PROF ZOOL, UNIV TEX, AUSTIN, 76- *Concurrent Pos:* Guggenheim fel, 78-79; vis prof, Univ Kansas, 78 & Univ Puerto Rico, 81; NSF grants & Nat Geog Soc grants. *Mem:* Am Soc Nat; Am Soc Ichthyol & Herpet; Soc Study Evolution; Ecol Soc Am; fel AAAS. *Res:* Reproductive tactics; foraging tactics; resource partitioning; species diversity and ecology of desert lizards; comparison of North American (Sonoran, Mojane & Great Basin), Western Australian (Great Victoria), and Southern African (Kalahari) deserts, especially environmental factors determining the number of coexisting species. *Mailing Add:* Dept of Zool Univ of Tex Austin TX 78712

PIANOTTI, ROLAND SALVATORE, b New York, NY, May 8, 30; m 58; c 1. MICROBIOLOGY, DENTAL RESEARCH. *Educ:* Iona Col, BS, 52; St Johns Univ, MS, 54. *Prof Exp:* Assoc scientist, Dept Microbiol, 57-66, scientist, 66-69, sr scientist, Dept Oral-Dent Sci, 69-73, SECT HEAD, DEPT ORAL-DENT SCI, WARNER-LAMBERT RES INST, 73- *Mem:* AAAS; Am Soc Microbiol; Int Asn Dent Res. *Res:* Chemistry of bacterial cell wall; antibiotics; enzymology; metabolism of dental plaque; microbiol biochemistry. *Mailing Add:* Dept Oral-Dent Sci Warner-Lambert Res Inst Morris Plains NJ 07950

PIANTADOSI, CLAUDE, b Naples, Italy, Jan 4, 23; nat US; m 45; c 3. MEDICINAL CHEMISTRY. *Educ:* Brooklyn Col, BS, 49; Columbia Univ, MS, 52; Univ NC, PhD(biochem, pharmaceut chem), 56. *Prof Exp:* Asst prof pharmaceut chem, Butler Univ, 55-56; asst prof pharmaceut chem & biochem, Fordham Univ, 56-57; from asst prof to assoc prof, 57-63, chmn, Med Chem Div & dir grad studies, Sch Pharm, 71-75, PROF MED CHEM, SCH PHARM & PROF BIOCHEM, SCH MED, UNIV NC, CHAPEL HILL, 63-, DIR GRAD STUDIES, 77- *Concurrent Pos:* Consult, Oak Ridge Inst Nuclear Studies, 63; vis scientist, Am Asn Cols Pharm, 66 & NC Acad Sci. *Mem:* AAAS; Am Chem Soc; Am Pharmaceut Asn; fel Am Inst Chemists; NY Acad Sci. *Res:* Lipid chemistry; chemistry of purine and pyrimidine; synthetic oriented medical chemistry and radioactive synthesis. *Mailing Add:* Dept Med Chem Sch Pharm Univ NC Chapel Hill NC 27514

PIASECKI, LEONARD R(ICHARD), b Michigan City, Ind, Nov 15, 23; m 54; c 5. CHEMICAL ENGINEERING. *Educ:* Purdue Univ, BS, 49. *Prof Exp:* Anal chemist, US Steel Corp, 49-50; res chemist, Reynolds Metals Corp, 51-53; res engr, 53-56, eng group supvr, 56-60, chief solid propellant rockets sect, 60-63, dep div chief, 63-64, chief propulsion sect & Voyager propulsion, 64-65, mgr Voyager capsule syst, 66-68, MGR LONG RANGE PLANNING, OFF PLANS & PROGS, JET PROPULSION LAB, CALIF INST TECHNOL, 68- *Mem:* Am Inst Aeronaut & Astronaut; Am Chem Soc. *Res:* Voyager capsule. *Mailing Add:* Mgr Spec Projs Jet Propulsion Lab 4800 Oak Grove Dr Pasadena CA 91103

PIATAK, DAVID MICHAEL, b Simpson, Pa, Jan 25, 36; m 60; c 3. ORGANIC CHEMISTRY. *Educ:* Pa State Univ, BS, 57; Univ Maine, MS, 59, PhD(org chem), 62. *Prof Exp:* Staff scientist, Worcester Found Exp Biol, 61-66; asst prof chem, 66-72, ASSOC PROF CHEM, NORTHERN ILL UNIV, 72- *Concurrent Pos:* Sr res award, Fulbright-Hays Comn, 74-75; vis assoc prof chem, Univ Belgrade, 74-75; US-Israel Fulbright-Hays Comn travel grantee, 75; exchange participant, Nat Acad Sci, 78. *Mem:* Phytochem Soc NAm; Am Chem Soc; Royal Soc Chem; Am Soc Pharmacog. *Res:* Isolation and identification of natural products; chemistry and biochemistry of steroids and related compounds; synthesis of potential antineoplastic agents; heterocyclic compounds; new organic synthetic methods. *Mailing Add:* Dept of Chem Northern Ill Univ De Kalb IL 60115

PIATIGORSKY, JORAM PAUL, b Elizabethtown, NY, Feb 4, 40. DEVELOPMENTAL BIOLOGY, BIOCHEMISTRY. *Educ:* Harvard Univ, AB, 62; Calif Inst Technol, PhD(develop biol), 67. *Prof Exp:* Sr staff fel develop biol, Nat Inst Child Health & Human Develop, 67-75, head, Sect Cellular Differentiation, Lab Molecular Genetics, 76-81; CHIEF, LAB MOLECULAR & DEVELOP BIOL, NAT EYE INST, 81- *Mem:* Am Soc Zool; Am Soc Cell Biol; Int Soc Embryol; Soc Develop Biol; NY Acad Sci. *Res:* Regulation of nucleic acid and protein synthesis in growing and differentiating cells, particularly in the ocular lens. *Mailing Add:* Nat Eye Inst Bethesda MD 20205

PIATKOWSKI, THOMAS FRANK, b Ann Arbor, Mich, Oct 24, 38; m 64; c 3. ELECTRICAL ENGINEERING. *Educ:* Univ Mich, BSE, 60, MSE, 61, PhD(elec eng), 63. *Prof Exp:* Asst res engr logic systs lab & asst lectr elec eng, Univ Mich, 62-63; asst prof & dir comput ctr, Tuskegee Inst, 64-66; res engr systs eng lab, Univ Mich, 66-67; assoc prof eng, Dartmouth Col, 67-72; staff systs analyst systs develop div, IBM Corp, 72-75; mgr commun archit, Burroughs Corp, 75-80; ASSOC PROF ELEC ENG, IOWA STATE UNIV, 80- *Mem:* Inst Elec & Electronics Engrs; Asn Comput Mach. *Res:* Computer applications; engineering and education. *Mailing Add:* Dept Elec Eng Iowa State Univ Ames IA 50011

PIAVIS, GEORGE WALTER, b Glen Lyon, Pa, May 4, 22; m 46; c 3. ZOOLOGY. *Educ:* Western Md Col, AB, 48, MEd, 52; Duke Univ, PhD(zool), 58. *Prof Exp:* Teacher high sch, Md, 50-53; asst instr comp anat embryol & zool, Duke Univ, 53-56; fisheries res biologist, Hammond Bay Lab, US Fish & Wildlife Serv, Mich, 55-58; from asst prof to assoc prof, 58-65, PROF ANAT, UNIV MD, BALTIMORE, 65- *Concurrent Pos:* Teacher high schs, Md, 56-58. *Honors & Awards:* Award, Bur Com Fisheries, US Fish & Wildlife Serv, 61. *Mem:* Fel AAAS; Am Soc Ichthyol & Herpet; Am Asn Anat; Am Soc Zool; NY Acad Sci. *Res:* Effects of antimetabolites on regeneration and embryological development in the sea lamprey. *Mailing Add:* Dept Anat Sch of Dent Univ of Md Baltimore MD 21201

PIBURN, MICHAEL D, geology, see previous edition

PICARD, GASTON ARTHUR, b Levis, Que, Aug 15, 43; m 67; c 3. FOOD CHAIN, ANALYTICAL CHEMISTRY. *Educ:* Univ Laval, BSc, 67, MSc, 69; City Univ New York, PhD(biol), 76. *Prof Exp:* PROF FOOD CHEM, UNIV LAVAL, 74- *Mem:* Can Inst Food Sci & Technol, AAAS. *Res:* Analytical and physical chemistry of food; enzymology involved with food degradation; recycling of waste water nutrient with unicellular algae; development of new method related to fish products, estimation of deterioration. *Mailing Add:* 1607 22e Rue Nord Charny PQ G6W 5J5 Can

PICARD, M DANE, b Washburn, Mo, Aug 7, 27; m 58; c 4. SEDIMENTARY PETROLOGY. *Educ:* Univ Wyoming, BS, 50; Princeton Univ, AM, 62, PhD(geol), 63. *Prof Exp:* Field asst, Texaco Inc, 50; from jr geologist to dist stratigrapher, Shell Oil Co, 50-56; geologist, St Helens Petrol Corp, 56-57; dist mgr & resident geologist, Am Stratig Co, 57-60; asst instr, Princeton Univ, 60-61; NSF fel, 61-63; from assoc prof to prof geol, Univ Nebr, Lincoln, 63-68; PROF GEOL, UNIV UTAH, 68- *Concurrent Pos:* Instr night sch, Ft Lewis Agr & Mech Col, 57-59; NIH grants, 62-72; sr geologist, Pan Am Petrol Corp, 64; consult, Utah Geol Surv, 69-74; deleg, House of Deleg, Am Asn Petrol Geologists, 71-77, mem adv coun, 73-76; sr consult, Mountain Fuel Supply Co, 72-75. *Mem:* Fel AAAS; fel Geol Soc Am; Soc Econ Paleont & Mineral; Am Asn Petrol Geologists; Int Asn Sedimentol. *Res:* Ephemeral streams; stratigraphy; petroleum geology; paleomagnetism. *Mailing Add:* Dept of Geol & Geophys Univ of Utah Salt Lake City UT 84112

PICARD, RICHARD HENRY, b Springfield, Mass, Aug 26, 38; m 67; c 2. ATMOSPHERIC OPTICS, LASER MATERIAL INTERACTIONS. *Educ:* Assumption Col, Mass, AB, 59; Boston Univ, MA, 62, PhD(physics), 68. *Prof Exp:* Res physicist, Air Force Cambridge Res Labs, 64-75; physicist, Rome Air Develop Ctr, 76-81, PHYSICIST, AIR FORCE GEOPHYSICS LAB, 81- *Mem:* Am Phys Soc; Sigma Xi; Optical Soc Am. *Res:* Atmospheric optics, infrared emission in the atmosphere; radiative transfer; statistical physics; atomic and molecular physics; laser spectroscopy and applications to frequency standards; nonlinear optics. *Mailing Add:* Air Force Geophysics Lab Optical Physics Div Optical Physic Res-1 Hanscom AFB Bedford MA 01731

PICARDI, ANTHONY CHARLES, b Boston, Mass, Apr 23, 48; m 70. SYSTEMS ANALYSIS, SIMULATION. *Educ:* Mass Inst Technol, BS, 71, MS, 72, ScD(social-environ syst), 75. *Prof Exp:* Res asst syst dynamics, 73-75, res assoc, Mass Inst Technol, 75; head syst anal group, Develop Anal Assocs, Inc, 75-80; sr res assoc, Charles River Assoc, Inc, 80-81; SR RES ASSOC, MGT TECHNOLOGIES, INC, 82- *Concurrent Pos:* Consult, Saline Water Conversion Corp, Saudi Arabia, 75-80, US Cong Off Technol Assessment, 80, US Dept Energy, 80 & US Dept Treas, 80; res assoc, Mass Inst Technol, 81. *Mem:* Soc Comput Simulation; Sigma Xi; Am Soc Civil Engrs. *Res:* Systems analysis with emphasis in system dynamic simulation of social-environmental-economic systems in developing countries, strategic planning models and macroeconomic simulation; projects include West African pastoralism, regional water and electricity demand in Saudi Arabia, agricultural technology assessment, oil export policy analysis, simulation of the US economy, oil price impacts on developing country economies. *Mailing Add:* Mgt Technologies Inc 1 Washington St Wellesley MA 02181

PICCHIONI, ALBERT LOUIS, b Klein, Mont, Aug 28, 21; m 53; c 4. PHARMACOLOGY. *Educ:* Univ Mont, BS, 43; Purdue Univ, MS, 50, PhD(pharmacol), 52. *Prof Exp:* Pharmacist supvr, Univ Mich Hosp, 46-48; res asst pharmacol, Purdue Univ, 48-52; actg dean, Col Pharm, 75-76, head dept, 70-81, PROF PHARMACOL, UNIV ARIZ, 52- *Concurrent Pos:* Exec dir, Ariz Regional Poison Control Ctr, 79- *Mem:* Am Soc Pharmacol & Exp Therapeut; Soc Toxicol; Acad Pharmaceut Sci; Sigma Xi. *Res:* Investigation of the role of the brain biogenic amines to susceptibility to seizures; application of pharmacokinetic principles in the management of acute poisoning. *Mailing Add:* Col of Pharm Univ of Ariz Tucson AZ 85721

PICCIANO, MARY FRANCES ANN, b Palmerton, Pa, Dec 19, 46. NUTRITION. *Educ:* St Francis Col, BS, 68; Pa State Univ, MS, 70, PhD(nutrit), 74. *Prof Exp:* Asst prof, 74-79, ASSOC PROF NUTRIT, UNIV ILL, URBANA, 79- *Concurrent Pos:* Fac res award, Ill Home Economics Asn, 79. *Mem:* Sigma Xi; AAAS; Am Inst Nutrit; Am Dietetic Asn; Am Soc Clin Nutrit. *Res:* Nutrition during growth and development; maternal nutrition; infant nutrition; nutritional status; iron metabolism; flate metabolism. *Mailing Add:* 905 S Goodwin Univ of Ill Urbana IL 61801

PICCIOLO, GRACE LEE, b Baltimore, Md, Feb 20, 34; div; c 2. CELL PHYSIOLOGY, SPACE BIOLOGY. *Educ:* Univ Md, PhD(cell physiol), 64. *Prof Exp:* Teacher, Convent of Sacred Heart Sch, 56-58; life scientist, NASA-Goddard Space Flight Ctr, 64-77; MEM STAFF REGULATORY CLIN MICROBIOL PROD, BUR MED DEVICES, FOOD & DRUG ADMIN, 77- *Res:* Determination of methods of life detection using bioluminescence for extraterrestrial analysis of atmospheric and planetary surface samples; analysis of mutant strain of Astasia, including growth and cellular organelle experimentation; development of microbial detection methods for automation in clinical laboratory; quantitation of immunofluorescent microscopy. *Mailing Add:* 13007 Renfrew Circle Ft Washington MD 20744

PICCIONI, ORESTE, b Siena, Italy, Oct 24, 15; nat US; m 45; c 5. NUCLEAR PHYSICS. *Educ:* Ginnaiso-Liceo, Italy, Dipl, 29; Univ Rome, Dr(physics), 38. *Prof Exp:* Instr, Univ Rome, 35-38, asst, 38-44, prof electromagnetism, 44-46; res assoc, Mass Inst Technol, 46-48; scientist, Brookhaven Nat Lab, 48-60; PROF PHYSICS, UNIV CALIF, SAN DIEGO, 60- *Res:* Cosmic rays; high energy physics; elementary particles; electronic circuits for nuclear researches; radiation. *Mailing Add:* Dept Physics B-019 Univ Calif at San Diego La Jolla CA 92093

PICCIOTTO, CHARLES EDWARD, b Buenos Aires, Arg, July 1, 42; US citizen; m 64; c 2. PARTICLE PHYSICS. *Educ:* Univ Calif, Berkeley, AB, 64; Univ Calif, Santa Barbara, MA, 66, PhD(physics), 68. *Prof Exp:* ASSOC PROF PHYSICS, UNIV VICTORIA, BC, 68- *Mem:* Am Phys Soc. *Res:* Quantum electrodynamics; intermediate energy physics. *Mailing Add:* Dept of Physics Univ of Victoria Victoria BC V8W 2Y2 Can

PICCIRELLI, ROBERT ANTHONY, b New York, NY, Dec 9, 30; m 59; c 6. STATISTICAL & ENGINEERING PHYSICS. *Educ:* Cath Univ Am, AB, 52, MS, 53, PhD(physics), 56. *Prof Exp:* Res physicist, Nat Bur Standards, 57-58; PROF MECH ENG SCI & MEM RES INST ENG SCI, WAYNE STATE UNIV, 68- *Concurrent Pos:* NSF-Nat Res Coun fel, Nat Bur Standards, 56-58; Dept Com sci & technol fel, 65-66; consult, Available Energy, Inc, Detroit, Mich. *Mem:* AAAS; Am Phys Soc. *Res:* Combustion engineering; performance of alternate fuels; nonequilibrium statistical mechanics; generalizations of classical fluid dynamics; relaxation phenomena; nonlocal and nonlinear effects; propagation and scattering of sound and light from fluids. *Mailing Add:* Res Inst for Eng Sci Wayne State Univ Detroit MI 48202

PICCOLINI, RICHARD JOHN, b Los Angeles, Calif, Mar 9, 33; m 59; c 2. PHYSICAL CHEMISTRY, ORGANIC CHEMISTRY. *Educ:* Calif Inst Technol, BS, 55; Univ of Calif, Los Angeles, PhD(org chem), 60. *Prof Exp:* Asst chem, Calif Inst Technol, 54-55 & Univ Calif, Los Angeles, 56-59; sr chemist, 59-70, sr chemist chem div, 70-73, SR RES ASSOC, ROHM & HAAS CO, 73- *Mem:* Am Chem Soc; Royal Soc Chem; AAAS. *Res:* Chemistry in bridged ring systems; metal carbonyl chemistry; photochemistry as applied to polymers; free radical reactions and solution properties of polymers; polymers as petroleum modifiers; chemical process research; organometallic chemistry; catalysis. *Mailing Add:* Rohm & Haas Co Independence Mall W Philadelphia PA 19105

PICHA, KENNETH G(EORGE), b Chicago, Ill, July 24, 25; m 48; c 3. MECHANICAL ENGINEERING. *Educ:* Ga Inst Technol, BME, 46, MS, 48; Univ Minn, PhD(mech eng), 57. *Prof Exp:* Aeronaut res scientist, Nat Adv Comt Aeronaut, Ohio, 48-49; prof mech eng, Ga Inst Technol, 49-58, from assoc dir to dir, Sch Mech Eng, 60-66; prog dir eng sci, NSF, 58-60; dean, Sch Eng, 66-76, dir, Off Coord Energy Res & Educ, 77-80, PROF MECH ENG, UNIV MASS, AMHERST, 80- *Concurrent Pos:* Consult, Orgn Europ Econ Coop, 60, NSF, 60-66 & Govt of Singapore, 70-72; chmn manpower develop comt, Environ Protection Agency, 71; chmn eng educ & accreditation comt, Eng Coun Prof Develop, 71-73; consult, Nat Acad Sci; dir, Off Univ Progs, US Energy Res & Develop Admin, 76-77. *Mem:* Fel AAAS; fel Am Soc Mech Engrs; Am Soc Eng Educ. *Res:* Thermal sciences. *Mailing Add:* 56 Oak Knoll Amherst MA 01002

PICHANICK, FRANCIS MARTIN, b Salisbury, Rhodesia, May 15, 36; div; c 1. ATOMIC PHYSICS. *Educ:* Univ Cape Town, MS, 58; Oxford Univ, PhD(physics), 61. *Prof Exp:* Instr physics, Yale Univ, 61-64, asst prof, 64-69; ASSOC PROF PHYSICS, UNIV MASS, AMHERST, 69- *Concurrent Pos:* Guest worker, Nat Bur Stand, 66-67; res collabr, Brookhaven Nat Lab, 69-; mem comt atoms & molecules, Nat Acad Sci, 71-; assoc ed, Phys Rev Lett, 74-; vis fel, Joint Inst Lab Astrophys, Boulder, Colo, 75-76. *Mem:* Fel Am Phys Soc. *Res:* Experimental investigations in basic atomic structure using radiofrequency spectroscopy and scattering techniques; electron-atom and electron-molecule scattering at low energies; nuclear moments; laser multiphoton excitation. *Mailing Add:* Hasbrouck Lab Univ of Mass Amherst MA 01002

PICHE, LUCIEN, b Montreal, Que, July 22, 15; m 45; c 2. ORGANIC CHEMISTRY. *Educ:* Univ Montreal, LSc, 35, PhD(chem), 40. *Prof Exp:* From asst prof to assoc prof Univ Montreal, 40-46; vpres & sci dir, Pharmed & Co, Ltd, Que, 46-51; prof & head dept, 52-59, vdean fac sci, 59-61, vrector univ, 61-71, PROF CHEM, UNIV MONTREAL, 71- *Honors & Awards:* David Prize, 42. *Mem:* Chem Inst Can. *Res:* Air and water pollution; environmental chemistry. *Mailing Add:* 520 Habitat Montreal PQ H3C 3R6 Can

PICK, GEORGE STEVEN, mechanical engineering, aerospace engineering, see previous edition

PICK, JAMES RAYMOND, b Baltimore, Md, Mar 6, 36; c 1. LABORATORY ANIMAL SCIENCE. *Educ:* Univ Ga, DVM, 61. *Prof Exp:* Fel lab animal med, Bowman Gray Sch Med, 61-63; prof assoc, Inst Lab Animal Resources, Nat Acad Sci-Nat Res Coun, 63-64; instr comp path, 65-66, asst prof, 66-70, ASSOC PROF COMP PATH, SCH MED, UNIV NC, CHAPEL HILL, 70-, DIR, DIV LAB ANIMAL MED, 65-, PROF PATH, 81- *Mem:* Am Vet Med Asn; Am Asn Lab Animal Sci. *Res:* Infectious and metabolic diseases of animals analagous to those in humans; alcohol dependence in animals; fetal alcohol syndrome. *Mailing Add:* Div of Lab Animal Med Univ of NC Sch of Med Chapel Hill NC 27514

PICK, ROBERT ORVILLE, b Madison, Wis, Apr 13, 40; m 65; c 2. MEDICINAL CHEMISTRY, CLINICAL CHEMISTRY. *Educ:* Univ Wis, Madison, BS, 62; Univ Calif, Los Angeles, PhD(org chem), 67. *Prof Exp:* Actg instr chem, Univ Calif, Los Angeles, 67-68; chemist, Div Med Chem, Walter Reed Army Med Ctr, 68-71; chief lab serv & asst chief dept med res & develop, William Beaumont Gen Hosp, 71-74; chief, Chem Br, Acad Health Sci, Ft Sam Houston, 75-78; chief, Chem Handling & Data Anal Br, 78-80, CHIEF, DEPT MED CHEM, DIV EXP THERAPEUT, WALTER REED ARMY INST RES, 80- *Mem:* Am Chem Soc. *Res:* Physical organic chemistry; mechanisms of reactions; structure-biological activity relationships; chemical information systems; drug development. *Mailing Add:* Chem Handling & Data Anal Br Walter Reed Army Inst of Res Washington DC 20012

PICK, ROY JAMES, b Vancouver, BC, Dec 28, 41; m 64; c 1. MECHANICAL ENGINEERING. *Educ:* Univ BC, BASc, 64; Univ London, MSc, 67, Imp Col, dipl, 67; Univ Waterloo, PhD(mech eng), 70. *Prof Exp:* Stress engr, Orenda Engines Ltd, 64-66; ASSOC PROF, UNIV WATERLOO, 68-, NAT RES COUN CAN FEL, 70- *Concurrent Pos:* Pres, R J Pick Ltd, 74-; consult, Conch Methane Servs Ltd. *Res:* Nuclear pressure vessels; fracture analysis; photoelasticity. *Mailing Add:* Dept of Mech Eng Univ of Waterloo Waterloo ON N2L 3G1 Can

PICKANDS, JAMES, III, b Cleveland, Ohio, Sept 4, 31; m 61; c 2. STATISTICS. *Educ:* Yale Univ, BA, 54; Columbia Univ, PhD(math, statist), 65. *Hon Degrees:* MA, Univ Pa, 73. *Prof Exp:* Mathematician-programmer, Ballistics Res Labs, Aberdeen Proving Ground, Md, 54-55; asst prof statist, Va Polytech Inst, 66-69; ASSOC PROF STATIST, UNIV PA, 69- *Concurrent Pos:* NSF grants, Va Polytech Inst, 68 & Univ Pa, 71. *Mem:* Am Statist Asn; Am Math Soc; Inst Math Statist; Sigma Xi. *Res:* Probability theory and stochastic processes; time series data analysis and interactive computing. *Mailing Add:* Dept of Statist Univ of Pa Philadelphia PA 19104

PICKARD, BARBARA GILLESPIE, b Charleston, WVa, Feb 24, 36; m 63; c 2. PLANT PHYSIOLOGY. *Educ:* Stanford Univ, BA, 58, MA, 59; Harvard Univ, PhD(biol), 63. *Prof Exp:* Fel biol, Harvard Univ, 63-64; NIH fel biol & res lab electronics, Mass Inst Technol, 64-66; with Wash Univ, 66-67, asst prof, 67-73, ASSOC PROF BIOL, WASH UNIV, 73- *Mem:* Am Soc Plant Physiol; Soc Gen Physiol; Am Chem Soc; Am Inst Biol Sci. *Res:* Plant development and physiology with emphasis on sensory systems and on wound responses. *Mailing Add:* Dept of Biol Wash Univ St Louis MO 63130

PICKARD, GEORGE LAWSON, b Cardiff, Wales, July 5, 13; m 36; c 2. OCEANOGRAPHY. *Educ:* Oxford Univ, BA, 35, DPhil(physics), 37, MA, 47. *Prof Exp:* Sci officer, Royal Aircraft Estab, 37-42; assoc prof, 47-54, PROF PHYSICS, UNIV BC, 54-, DIR INST OCEANOG, 58- *Honors & Awards:* Mem, Order of Brit Empire, 46. *Mem:* AAAS; Am Soc Limnol & Oceanog; Am Geophys Union; fel Royal Soc Can. *Res:* Physical oceanography of inlets and estuaries. *Mailing Add:* Inst of Oceanog Univ of BC Vancouver BC V6T 1W5 Can

PICKARD, PORTER LOUIS, JR, b Ft Worth, Tex, June 2, 22; m 44; c 4. ORGANIC CHEMISTRY, RESEARCH ADMINISTRATION. *Educ:* NTex State Teachers Col, BA, 43, MA, 44; Univ Tex, PhD(org chem), 47. *Prof Exp:* Lab instr chem, Lamar Jr Col, 40-41 & NTex State Teachers Col, 41-44; from asst prof to assoc prof, Univ Okla, 47-56; sr res chemist, Celanese Chem Co Tech Ctr, 56-60, group leader, 60-66, res assoc, 66-67; ASST TO VPRES RES & DEVELOP, UNION CAMP RES & DEVELOP DIV, 67- *Concurrent Pos:* Proj leader, Res Inst, Univ Okla, 51-56. *Mem:* Tech Asn Pulp & Paper Indust; Am Chem Soc. *Res:* Proof of structure by synthesis; reactions of hindered nitriles; reactions of aliphatic hydrocarbons; technical recruiting; administration of research in pulp, paper and natural products. *Mailing Add:* Union Camp Res & Develop Box 412 Princeton NJ 08540

PICKARD, WILLIAM FREEMAN, b Boston, Mass, Sept 16, 32; m 63; c 2. BIOPHYSICS, ELECTRICAL ENGINEERING. *Educ:* Boston Univ, AB, 54; Harvard Univ, AM, 55, PhD(appl physics), 62. *Prof Exp:* Assoc prof, 66-73, PROF ELEC ENG, WASHINGTON UNIV, 73- *Concurrent Pos:* Res fel electronics & lectr appl math, Harvard Univ, 62-63; res fel biol, Mass Inst Technol, 63-66. *Mem:* Am Phys Soc; Bioelectromagnetic Soc; Inst Elec & Electronics Engrs; Am Soc Plant Physiologists. *Res:* Energy and resource engineering; membrane electrobiology and the biological effects of electromagnetic waves; intracellular transport. *Mailing Add:* Dept of Elec Eng Washington Univ St Louis MO 63130

PICKART, DON EDWARD, organic chemistry, see previous edition

PICKART, STANLEY JOSEPH, b Norway, Iowa, May 12, 26; m 52; c 7. MAGNETISM, ADMINISTRATION. *Educ:* Univ Iowa, MA, 51; Univ Md, PhD(physics), 58. *Prof Exp:* Asst, Univ Iowa, 50-51; physicist, US Naval Ord Lab, 51-54, 56-74; CHMN DEPT PHYSICS, UNIV RI, 74- *Concurrent Pos:* Guest physicist, Brookhaven Nat Lab, 55-67; temp res assoc, Atomic Energy Res Estab, Harwell, Eng, 65; guest worker, Nat Bur Standards, 68-74; Nat Acad Sci foreign exchange scientist to Romania, 71; prog officer, NSF, 78-79. *Mem:* fel Am Phys Soc; Am Asn Physics Teachers; AAAS. *Res:* Ferromagnetism and antiferromagnetism; metals and alloys; amorphous magnetism; neutron scattering. *Mailing Add:* Dept of Physics Univ of RI Kingston RI 02881

PICKENS, CHARLES GLENN, b Clinton, Okla, Sept 15, 36; m 58; c 3. MATHEMATICS. *Educ:* Cent State Col, Okla, BS, 58; Okla State Univ, MS, 59, EdD, 67. *Prof Exp:* From asst prof to assoc prof, 60-72, PROF MATH, KEARNEY STATE COL, 72- *Mem:* Math Asn Am. *Res:* Number theory; analysis; linear algebra. *Mailing Add:* Dept of Math Kearney State Col Kearney NE 68847

PICKENS, PETER E, b Kuling, China, June 25, 28; US citizen; m 55; c 3. NEUROPHYSIOLOGY. *Educ:* Columbia Univ, AB, 53; Univ Calif, Los Angeles, PhD, 61. *Prof Exp:* Biologist, Lederle Labs, Am Cyanamid Co, 53-55; res scientist physiol, Inst Marine Sci, Univ Tex, 60-61; from asst prof to prof zool, 61-72, PROF ZOOL, UNIV ARIZ, 72- *Concurrent Pos:* NSF grant, 65-67. *Mem:* Fel AAAS; Am Soc Zool; Soc Neurosci. *Res:* Neurophysiology in invertebrates. *Mailing Add:* Dept of Cell & Develop Biol Univ of Ariz Tucson AZ 85721

PICKER, HARVEY SHALOM, b Manila, Philippines, Sept 3, 42; US citizen; m 70; c 2. THEORETICAL PHYSICS. *Educ:* Mass Inst Technol, BS, 63, PhD(physics), 66. *Prof Exp:* Res physicist, Carnegie Inst Technol, 66-67; NSF fel nuclear theory, Princeton Univ, 67-69; res assoc, Univ Md, College Park, 69-70, Ctr Theoret Physics fel, 70-71; asst prof, 71-75, ASSOC PROF PHYSICS, TRINITY COL, CONN, 75- *Mem:* Am Phys Soc; Soc Indust & Appl Math. *Res:* Nuclear astrophysics; applications of mathematical approximation theory to theoretical physics; two-nucleon interactions; scattering theory. *Mailing Add:* Dept of Physics Trinity Col Hartford CT 06106

PICKERING, ED RICHARD, b Cincinnati, Ohio, Dec 15, 34; m 62; c 2. PLANT PHYSIOLOGY. *Educ:* Ohio State Univ, BS, 56, MS, 58; Univ Calif, Davis, PhD(bot), 64. *Prof Exp:* Res asst bot, Ohio State Univ, 57-58; asst, Univ Calif, Davis, 58-62; instr, Univ SFla, 62-63; asst, Univ Calif, Davis, 64; asst prof, Rutgers Univ, 64-66; assoc prof biol, Adrian Col, 66-74; instr hort, Springfield-Clark Co Joint Voc Sch, 74-77; assoc prof biol, Central State Univ, Ohio, 77-78. *Concurrent Pos:* NSF fac partic grant, Adrian Col, 69-71. *Mem:* Am Soc Plant Physiol; Bot Soc Am; Am Inst Biol Sci; Sigma Xi. *Res:* Translocation; plant morphogenesis. *Mailing Add:* 2399 Versailles Ct Springfield OH 45505

PICKERING, HOWARD W, b Cleveland, Ohio, Dec 15, 35; m 63; c 4. METALLURGY, ELECTROCHEMISTRY. *Educ:* Univ Cincinnati, BMetEng, 58; Ohio State Univ, MS, 60, PhD(metall eng, stress corrosion), 61. *Prof Exp:* Res metallurgist, Res Lab, US Steel Corp, Pa, 62-72; assoc prof, 72-76, sect head, 75-80, PROF METALL, PA STATE UNIV, UNIVERSITY PARK, 76- *Concurrent Pos:* Guest scientist, Max Planck Inst Phys Chem, Gottingen, WGer, 64-65; consult, Gen Elec Co, 78-; Am ed, Corrosion Sci, 75- *Mem:* Electrochem Soc; Am Inst Mining, Metall & Petrol Engrs; Am Soc Metals; Nat Asn Corrosion Engrs. *Res:* Corrosion and oxidation of metals; electrode and electroplating reactions; hydrogen diffusion and surface and grain boundary segregation in metals; hydrometallurgy, atom probe field ion microscopy. *Mailing Add:* Metall Sect Pa State Univ University Park PA 16802

PICKERING, JERRY L, b Washington, Iowa, May 26, 42; m 63; c 3. SYSTEMATIC BOTANY. *Educ:* Iowa State Univ, BS, 64; Rutgers Univ, MS, 66, PhD(bot), 69. *Prof Exp:* Instr biol, Rutgers Univ, 69; asst prof, 69-74, assoc prof, 74-78, PROF BIOL, INDIANA UNIV, PA, 78- *Mem:* AAAS; Am Inst Biol Sci; Am Soc Plant Taxon; Int Asn Plant Taxon; Sigma Xi. *Res:* Comparative protein chemistry using plant materials and their value in systematics; seriological techniques; disc electrophoresis; chemotaxonomy. *Mailing Add:* Dept of Biol Ind Univ of Pa Indiana PA 15701

PICKERING, MILES GILBERT, b Beaconsfield, Eng, Apr 8, 43; US citizen. NUCLEAR CHEMISTRY. *Educ:* Yale Univ, BS, 65; Univ Wash, MS, 66; State Univ NY Stony Brook, PhD(chem), 70. *Prof Exp:* Vis asst prof chem, Reed Col, 70-71; Petrol Res Fund fel, State Univ NY Stony Brook, 71-72, lectr & res assoc nuclear chem, 72-73; lectr chem, Columbia Univ, 73-76; LECTR & DIR, UNDERGRAD LABS, PRINCETON UNIV, 76- *Concurrent Pos:* Consult, State Univ NY Stony Brook, 73-76, Yale Univ, 77-78, Columbia Univ, 78-79 & Harvard Univ, 80-81. *Mem:* Sigma Xi. *Res:* Nuclear reactions; nuclear magnetic resonance applied to inorganic systems and kinetics; computer control of instrumentation; innovative teaching in thermodynamics and physical chemistry. *Mailing Add:* Dept of Chem Princeton Univ Princeton NJ 08540

PICKERING, RANARD JACKSON, b Goshen, Ind, Mar 24, 29; m 50; c 3. HYDROLOGY, WATER QUALITY. *Educ:* Ind Univ, AB, 51, MA, 52; Stanford Univ, PhD(geol), 61. *Prof Exp:* Geologist, NJ Zinc Co, 52-55; raw mat engr, Columbia Iron Mining Co, 55-58; geologist, Water Resources Div, Tenn, 61-65, hydrologist, Ohio, 65-67, assoc dist chief, 67-70, asst chief, 70-72, CHIEF, QUAL OF WATER BR, US GEOL SURV, RESTON, VA, 72- *Concurrent Pos:* NSF fel, Stanford Univ, 58-61. *Mem:* AAAS; Geochem Soc; fel Geol Soc Am; Am Water Resources Asn. *Res:* Geochemistry of weathering processes; movement and fate of radionuclides in a fluvial environment; geochemistry and control of acid mine drainage; hydrologic processes affecting water quality. *Mailing Add:* 2321 N Richmond St Arlington VA 22207

PICKERING, RICHARD JOSEPH, b Medicine Hat, Alta, Aug 26, 34; m 59; c 2. PEDIATRICS, IMMUNOLOGY. *Educ:* Univ Sask, BA, 57, MD, 61; Am Acad Pediat, dipl, 74. *Prof Exp:* Asst prof pediat, Univ Minn, 69; assoc prof, Albany Med Col, 70-72; assoc prof microbiol & prof pediat, Dalhousie Univ, 72-73; res physician, NY State Kidney Dis Inst, 74-80; prof pediat & microbiol, 78-80, PROF MICROBIOL, IMMUNOL & PEDIAT, ALBANY COL, 80-; RES PHYSICIAN, NY STATE DEPT HEALTH, 80- *Concurrent Pos:* Queen Elizabeth II res fel, Univ Minn, 67-69; res physician, NY State Kidney Dis Inst, 70-72; prof pediat & microbiol, Albany Med Col, 74. *Mem:* AAAS; Am Soc Immunologists; Soc Exp Biol & Med; Soc Pediat Res. *Res:* Immunobiology of inflammation. *Mailing Add:* Dept of Microbiol Albany Med Col Albany NY 12208

PICKERING, W(ILLIAM) H(AYWARD), b Wellington, NZ, Dec 24, 10; nat US; m 32; c 2. ELECTRICAL ENGINEERING, PHYSICS. *Educ:* Calif Inst Technol, BS, 32, MS, 33, PhD(physics), 36. *Hon Degrees:* DSc, Clark Univ, 66 & Occidental Col, 66. *Prof Exp:* Asst physics, Calif Inst Technol, 32-36, from instr to prof elec eng, 36-76, dir, Jet Propulsion Lab, 54-76, div chief, 52-54; dir, Res Inst, Univ Petrol & Minerals, Saudi Arabia, 76-78; PRES, PICKERING RES CORP, 78- *Concurrent Pos:* Lectr, Univ Southern Calif, 38; mem sci adv bd, US Air Force, 45-48; mem, US Nat Comt Technol Panel Earth Satellite Prog, 56-59; mem, Army Sci Adv Panel, 63-65. *Honors & Awards:* Wyld Mem Award, Inst Aeronaut & Astronaut, 57, Louis W Hill Transp Award, 68; Space Flight Achievement Award, Nat Missile Indust Conf, 59; Distinguished Civilian Serv Medal, US Dept Army, 59; Columbus Gold Medal, 64; Crozier Gold Medal, 65; Distinguished Serv Medal, NASA, 65; Goddard Mem Trophy, 65; Spirit of St Louis Medal, 65; Procter Prize, 65; Magellanic Premium, 66; Italian Order of Merit; Edison Medal, Inst Elec & Electronics Engrs, 72; Hon Knight Commander, Order Brit Empire, 75; Nat Medal Sci, 76; Fahrney Medal, Franklin Inst, 76. *Mem:* Nat Acad Sci; Nat Acad Eng; hon fel Inst Aeronaut & Astronaut (pres, 63); fel Inst Elec & Electronics Engrs; fel Am Acad Arts & Sci. *Res:* Unmanned lunar and planetary exploration. *Mailing Add:* Pickering Res Corp 1401 S Oak Knoll Ave Pasadena CA 91109

PICKETT, ANDREW G(REER), b Ranger, Tex, Apr 19, 22; m 50; c 1. STRUCTURAL ENGINEERING. *Educ:* Univ Ariz, BS, 48. *Prof Exp:* Expressway engr, Killian-House Contractors, Tex, 49-51; construct mgt engr, Dept of Army, Austria, 51-53; assoc res engr, State Hwy Dept, Tex, 53-54; consult engr, Earl J Wentworth, 54-56; mgr strength anal sect, 56-67, sr res engr, Dept Mat Eng, 67-72, SR RES ENGR APPL MECH SECT, QUAL ASSURANCE SYSTS & ENG DIV, SOUTHWEST RES INST, 72- *Mem:* Am Soc Civil Engrs. *Res:* Engineering properties of high polymers; soils; concrete and metals; mathematical and experimental stress analysis; structural research and design; fatigue and fracture strength analysis; nuclear power plant coolant envelope safety. *Mailing Add:* Div Qual Assurance Systs & Eng PO Drawer 28510 San Antonio TX 78284

PICKETT, BILL WAYNE, b Cyril, Okla, Dec 14, 30; m 55; c 3. REPRODUCTIVE PHYSIOLOGY. *Educ:* Okla State Univ, BS, 52; Univ Mo, MS, 55, PhD(agr), 58. *Prof Exp:* Asst prof dairying, Univ Conn, 57-58, res asst, 58-59, from asst prof to assoc prof, 59-67; PROF PHYSIOL & BIOPHYS, COLO STATE UNIV, 67-, DIR ANIMAL REPROD LAB, COL VET MED & BIOMED SCI, 70- *Concurrent Pos:* Mem, Rockefeller Found Mex Agr Prog, 63. *Honors & Awards:* Physiol & Endocrinol Award, Am Soc Animal Sci, 78; Res Award, Nat Asn Animal Breeders, 80; L W Darrell Award, Colo State Univ, 81. *Mem:* Am Soc Animal Sci; AAAS; Soc Study Reprod; Soc Study Fertil; Am Dairy Sci Asn. *Res:* Reproductive physiology of the male with special emphasis on preservation of spermatozoa of the equine and bovine species. *Mailing Add:* Animal Reprod Lab Dept of Physiol Col of Vet Med Colo State Univ Ft Collins CO 80523

PICKETT, CECIL BRUCE, b Canton, Ill, Oct 5, 45; m 67; c 2. CELL & MOLECULAR BIOLOGY. *Educ:* Calif State Univ, Hayward, BS, 71; Univ Calif, Los Angeles, PhD(biol), 76. *Prof Exp:* Fel cell biol, Univ Calif, Los Angeles, 76-78; SR RES BIOCHEMIST, MERCK SHARP & DOHME RES LABS, 78- *Concurrent Pos:* NSF scholar, 76-77; scholar, Univ Calif, 77-78; Macy scholar, Marine Biol Lab, Woods Hole, 78; vis asst prof anat, Col Med, Howard Univ, 79- *Mem:* Am Soc Cell Biol; AAAS. *Res:* Molecular basis of induction of glutathione transferance and cytochrome P-450 by xenobiotics. *Mailing Add:* Merck Sharp & Dohme Res Labs 126 Lincoln Ave Rahway NJ 07065

PICKETT, DAVID FRANKLIN, JR, electrochemistry, electrochemical engineering, see previous edition

PICKETT, EDWARD ERNEST, b Greenfield, Ind, May 27, 20; m 50; c 3. ANALYTICAL CHEMISTRY. *Educ:* Purdue Univ, BS, 42; Ohio State Univ, PhD(org chem), 48. *Prof Exp:* Asst chem, Ohio State Univ, 42-44, Off Sci Res & Develop asst, Res Found, 44-48; from asst prof to assoc prof agr chem, 48-55, PROF AGR CHEM, UNIV MO-COLUMBIA, 55-, SUPVR SPECTROG LABS, 53- *Mem:* Am Chem Soc; Soc Appl Spectros. *Res:* Chemical spectroscopy; trace elements in biological materials; co-precipitation; atomic absorption analysis; role of lithium in living tissues. *Mailing Add:* Dept Biochem 31 Chem Bldg Univ Mo Columbia MO 65201

PICKETT, GEORGE R, b El Paso, Tex, Jan 13, 25; m 48; c 2. GEOPHYSICS, ENGINEERING. *Educ:* Univ Okla, BA, 51, MS, 52; Colo Sch Mines, DSc(geophys eng), 55. *Prof Exp:* Exploitation engr, Shell Develop Co, 55-63; sr petrophys entr, Shell Oil Co, 63-64, staff petrophys engr, 64-66; asst prof, 66-69, PROF GEOPHYS, COLO SCH MINES, 69- *Concurrent Pos:* Consult short course teaching, 66-; head, Dept Petrol Eng, Colo Sch Mines, 69-71; distinguished lectr, Soc Explor Geophys, 81. *Mem:* Soc Explor Geophys; Am Geophys Union; Soc Petrol Eng; Soc Prof Well Log Analysts. *Res:* Formation evaluation in hydrocarbon exploration, particularly well log interpretation; training methods. *Mailing Add:* 2554 Devinney Court Golden CO 80401

PICKETT, HERBERT MCWILLIAMS, b Baltimore, Md, Apr 2, 43; m 65; c 2. PHYSICAL CHEMISTRY. *Educ:* Williams Col, BA, 65; Univ Calif, Berkeley, PhD(chem), 70. *Prof Exp:* Fel chem, Harvard Univ, 70-72; Miller fel chem, Univ Calif, Berkeley, 72-73; asst prof chem, Univ Tex, Austin, 73-78; mem tech staff, 78-81, RES SCIENTIST, JET PROPULSION LAB, 81- *Concurrent Pos:* NIH fel, 70-71. *Mem:* Am Chem Soc; Am Phys Soc. *Res:* Microwave, millimeter wavelength and infrared spectroscopy; rotational energy transfer, molecular structure and conformational dynamics; astro-chemistry; millimeter and submillimeter wavelength radiometry. *Mailing Add:* Jet Propulsion Lab Pasadena CA 91103

PICKETT, JACKSON BRITTAIN, b San Antonio, Tex, Apr 30, 43; m 67. NEUROLOGY, PHYSIOLOGY. *Educ:* Occidental Col, BA, 64; Yale Univ, MD, 68. *Prof Exp:* Intern, Grady Mem Hosp, Atlanta, 68-69; resident neurol, Univ Calif, San Francisco, 69-72; neurologist, Regional Hosp, US Air Force, 72-74; fel clin neurophysiol, Mayo Clin, Minn, 74-75; ASST PROF NEUROL, UNIV CALIF, SAN FRANCISCO, 75- *Mem:* Am Acad Neurol; Am Asn Electromyography & Clin Neurophysiol. *Res:* Neuromuscular transmission. *Mailing Add:* Dept of Neurol Univ of Calif San Francisco CA 94143

PICKETT, JAMES EDWARD, b Plainwell, Mich, May 10, 54. ORGANIC PHOTOCHEMISTRY. *Educ:* Kalamazoo Col, BA, 76; Yale Univ, MPhil, 78, PhD(org chem), 80. *Prof Exp:* STAFF CHEMIST, GEN ELEC CORP RES & DEVELOP, 80- *Mem:* Am Chem Soc; AAAS. *Res:* Mechanisms of the photo-degradation of aromatic polymers; mechanisms by which anti-oxidants function. *Mailing Add:* Gen Elec Corp Res & Develp Bldg K-1 PO Box 8 Schenectady NY 12301

PICKETT, JAMES M, b Pampa, Tex, Jan 20, 37; m 60; c 2. PLANT PHYSIOLOGY. *Educ:* Rice Univ, BA, 60; Univ Tex, Austin, PhD(zool), 64. *Prof Exp:* Fel plant biol, Carnegie Inst Dept Plant Biol, 65-67; asst prof, 67-71, assoc prof, 71-78, PROF BOT, MONT STATE UNIV, 78- HEAD DEPT, 73- *Mem:* Am Soc Plant Physiol. *Res:* Light reactions, electron transport and oxygen evolution during photosynthesis. *Mailing Add:* Dept of Biol Mont State Univ Bozeman MT 59717

PICKETT, JOHN HAROLD, b Boston, Mass, June 21, 43. ANALYTICAL CHEMISTRY. *Educ:* Tufts Univ, BS, 65; Purdue Univ, PhD(chem), 70. *Prof Exp:* ANAL CHEMIST, FIBER INDUSTS, INC, 70- *Mem:* Am Chem Soc. *Res:* Infrared spectroscopy; nuclear magnetic resonance spectroscopy; mass spectroscopy. *Mailing Add:* Fiber Indust Inc Box 32414 Charlotte NC 28232

PICKETT, LAWRENCE KIMBALL, b Baltimore, Md, Nov 10, 19; m 43; c 4. SURGERY. *Educ:* Yale Univ, BA, 41, MD, 44. *Prof Exp:* Clin asst prof surg, State Univ NY Upstate Med Ctr, 50-54, clin assoc prof, 54-64; PROF SURG & PEDIAT, SCH MED, YALE UNIV, 64-, ASSOC DEAN CLIN AFFAIRS, 73- *Concurrent Pos:* Chief staff & chmn med bd, Yale-New Haven Hosp, 73- *Mem:* Fel Am Acad Pediat; fel Am Col Surgeons. *Mailing Add:* Yale-New Haven Hosp 789 Howard Ave New Haven CT 06504

PICKETT, LEROY KENNETH, b Clay Center, Kans, May 8, 37; m 63; c 2. AGRICULTURAL ENGINEERING. *Educ:* Kans State Univ, BS, 61; Univ Ill, Urbana, MS, 62; Purdue Univ, PhD(agr eng), 69. *Prof Exp:* Asst engr, Independence Works, Allis-Chalmers Mfg Co, 62-65; asst prof agr eng, Mich State Univ, 68-73; design engr, 73-75, proj engr, 75-81, PROD ENGR, EQUIP ENG CTR, INT HARVESTER, 81- *Mem:* Am Soc Agr Engrs; Soc Automotive Engrs. *Res:* Design and development of combine harvesters including mechanism and structures for cutting, threshing, separating and conveying grain; application of fluid power and mechanical power transmission systems; utilization of human factors engineering principles. *Mailing Add:* Int Harvester Equip Eng Ctr 7 South 600 County Line Rd Hinsdale IL 60521

PICKETT, MORRIS JOHN, b Beloit, Kans, Dec 3, 15; m 46; c 4. BACTERIOLOGY. *Educ:* Stanford Univ, BS, 38, PhD(bact), 42. *Prof Exp:* Asst bact, Harvard Med Sch, 42-45, instr, 45-46; asst prof, Sch Med, Univ Louisville, 46-47; from asst prof to assoc prof, 47-57, PROF BACT, UNIV CALIF, LOS ANGELES, 57- *Concurrent Pos:* Consult bacteriologist, New Eng Deaconess Hosp, 44-45, Olive View Hosp, 63-71 & Food & Drug Admin, 71-; USPHS spec res fel, Univ Queensland, 60; adv ed, Lab World, 61- & J Infectious Dis, 64-68. *Mem:* Am Soc Microbiol; fel Am Acad Microbiol; NY Acad Sci; Brit Soc Gen Microbiol. *Res:* Medical and diagnostic bacteriology; taxonomy; immunology. *Mailing Add:* Dept of Bact Univ of Calif Los Angeles CA 90024

PICKETT, PATRICIA BOOTH, b Anaheim, Calif, May 18, 31; m 53; c 3. CELL BIOLOGY. *Educ:* Univ Calif, Berkeley, BA, 53, MA, 68, PhD(zool), 71. *Prof Exp:* Teaching asst electron micros, Dept Bot, Univ Calif, Berkeley, 55-66, teaching asst biol, Dept Biol, 68; INSTR BIOL & ANAT, CHABOT COL, 71- *Res:* Tissue culture, especially the development of intercellular junctions and communication; normal and tumor cells; virology; electron microscopy. *Mailing Add:* Chabot Col 25555 Hesperian Blvd Hayward CA 94545

PICKETT, ROBERT COOPER, plant breeding, see previous edition

PICKETT, STEWARD T A, b Louisville, Ky, Nov 30, 50. ECOLOGY, BOTANY. *Educ:* Univ Ky, BS, 72; Univ Ill, PhD(bot), 77. *Prof Exp:* ASST PROF BOT & ECOL, RUTGERS UNIV, 77- *Concurrent Pos:* Vis fac, Orgn Trop Studies, 77. *Mem:* Ecol Soc Am; Soc Study Evolution; Sigma Xi; AAAS. *Res:* Plant population interaction and community organization; role of species adaptation in succession; successional theory. *Mailing Add:* Dept Biol Sci Nelson Labs Rutgers Univ PO Box 1059 Piscataway NJ 08854

PICKETT, THOMAS ERNEST, b Griffin, Ga, June 4, 37. GEOLOGY. *Educ:* Duke Univ, BS, 59; Univ NC, MS, 62, PhD(geol), 65. *Prof Exp:* Geol supvr, Smithsonian Inst, 65-66; geologist, 66-70, sr geologist, 70-78, ASSOC DIR, DEL GEOL SURV, 78- *Concurrent Pos:* Asst prof continuing educ div, Univ Del, 67-71, assoc prof, 71-; alt mem adv bd, Outer Continental Shelf Res Mgt, Dept Interior, 74-77. *Mem:* Soc Econ Paleontologists & Mineralogists. *Res:* Modern coastal sedimentary environments; sedimentary structures; coastal plain stratigraphy and sedimentation; trace fossils. *Mailing Add:* Del Geol Surv Univ of Del Newark DE 19711

PICKETT, WARREN EARL, solid state physics, see previous edition

PICKETT-HEAPS, JEREMY DAVID, b Bombay, India, June 5, 40; m 65; c 4. CELL BIOLOGY, PHYCOLOGY. *Educ:* Cambridge Univ, BS, 62, PhD(biochem), 65. *Prof Exp:* Res fel electron-micros, Australian Nat Univ, 65-69, fel, 69-70; asst prof, 70-71, assoc prof, 71-78, PROF PLANT CYTOL, UNIV COLO, BOULDER, 78- *Concurrent Pos:* NSF grant, 71-76; adv, NIH grant. *Honors & Awards:* Darbaker Prize, Am Bot Soc, 74. *Res:* Ultrastructure and function during cell division and differentiation in plant cells. *Mailing Add:* Dept Molecular & Cellular Biol Univ Colo Boulder CO 80302

PICKFORD, GRACE EVELYN, b Bournemouth, Eng, Mar 24, 02; nat US. ENDOCRINOLOGY, TAXONOMY. *Educ:* Yale Univ, PhD(zool), 31. *Prof Exp:* Res fel, Osborn Zool Lab, 31-33, from asst to res assoc, Bingham Lab, 35-70, from assoc prof to prof biol, 59-70, EMER PROF BIOL, YALE UNIV, 70-; SCIENTIST IN RESIDENCE, HIRAM COL, 70- *Concurrent Pos:* Instr, Albertus Magnus Col, 35-46. *Mem:* Am Soc Zool; Soc Study Evolution; Soc Syst Zool; Am Asn Anat. *Res:* Endocrinology of fishes; cephalopoda; oligochaeta. *Mailing Add:* Dept of Biol Hiram Col Hiram OH 44234

PICKHOLTZ, RAYMOND L, b New York, NY, Apr 12, 32; m 57; c 3. ELECTRONICS, COMMUNICATIONS. *Educ:* City Col New York, BS, 54, MS, 56; Polytech Inst Brooklyn, PhD(elec eng), 62. *Prof Exp:* Res engr, RCA Labs, 54-57; res specialist, ITT Labs, 57-61; from assoc prof to prof elec eng, Polytech Inst Brooklyn, 61-71; PROF & DEPT CHMN ELEC ENG & COMPUT SCI, GEORGE WASHINGTON UNIV, 72- *Concurrent Pos:* Adj assoc prof physics, Brooklyn Col, 63-71; prin investr, NASA space commun res grant, 65-; NSF res grant commun, 68-69; consult, IBM Corp, Fairchild Industs & Comput Sci Corp; vis prof, Inst Nat Reserches de la Sci, Que, 77-78. *Honors & Awards:* RCA Labs Res Award. *Mem:* Inst Elec & Electronics Engrs; Math Asn Am; Asn Comput Mach. *Res:* Communication theory, including data transmission, information theory, detection and estimation theory and coding. *Mailing Add:* Sch of Eng & Appl Sci George Washington Univ Washington DC 20006

PICKLESIMER, M(ARION) L(EWIS), b Thealka, Ky, Jan 27, 20; m 43; c 3. PHYSICAL METALLURGY. *Educ:* Univ Tenn, BS, 49, MS, 51, PhD(metall), 54. *Prof Exp:* Group leader zirconium metall group, Oak Ridge Nat Lab, 53-66, superconducting mat group, Metals & Ceramics Div, 61-66; head metall div, Southern Res Inst, Ala, 67-70; metallurgist, Nat Bur Standards, 70-72, sect chief mech properties, 72-73; nuclear metallurgist, US Atomic Energy Comn, 73-75; NUCLEAR METALLURGIST, US NUCLEAR REGULATORY COMN, 75- *Mem:* Am Inst Mining; Am Soc Testing & Mat. *Res:* Physical and mechanical metallurgy of zirconium alloys; physical metallurgy of superconducting materials; mechanical properties; failure analysis. *Mailing Add:* US Nuclear Regulatory Comn 7915 Eastern Ave Silver Spring MD 20910

PICKRAL, GEORGE MONROE, JR, b Gretna, Va, Jan 2, 22; m 45; c 5. INORGANIC CHEMISTRY, ANALYTICAL CHEMISTRY. *Educ:* Va Mil Inst, BS, 43; Miami Univ, MA, 50; Univ Cincinnati, PhD(inorg chem), 53. *Prof Exp:* Instr gen chem, 46-49, from asst prof to assoc prof, 52-60, PROF ANAL CHEM, VA MIL INST, 60-, HEAD DEPT CHEM, 68- *Mem:* Am Chem Soc. *Res:* Exchange reactions of rhenium; nitric oxide complexes of ruthenium; transition metal chemistry. *Mailing Add:* Dept Chem Va Mil Inst Lexington VA 24450

PICKRELL, JOHN A, b Decatur, Ill, May 8, 41; m 62; c 2. BIOCHEMISTRY, PHYSIOLOGY. *Educ:* Univ Ill, Urbana, BS, 63, DVM, 65, MS, 66, PhD(vet med sci), 68. *Prof Exp:* PHYSIOLOGIST, INHALATION TOXICOL RES INST, LOVELACE BIOMED & ENVIRON RES INC, 68- *Mem:* Am Vet Med Asn; Am Soc Vet Physiol & Pharmacol; Am Phys Soc; Fedn Am Soc Exp Biol; Soc Exp Biol & Med. *Res:* Veterinary clinical pathology; porcine edema disease; response of pulmonary connective tissue in health and disease; clinical pathology. *Mailing Add:* Inhalation Toxicol Res Inst PO Box 5890 Albuquerque NM 87116

PICKRELL, KENNETH LEROY, b Old Forge, Pa, June 6, 10; m 45; c 4. SURGERY. *Educ:* Franklin & Marshall Col, BS, 31; Johns Hopkins Univ, MD, 35; Am Bd Surg, dipl, 44; Am Bd Plastic Surg, dipl, 48. *Prof Exp:* Instr surg, Sch Med, Johns Hopkins Univ, 36-43; assoc prof surg & head dept plastic surg, 44-70, PROF SURG & CHMN DIV PLASTIC SURG, SCH MED, DUKE UNIV, 70- *Concurrent Pos:* Halsted fel surg, Sch Med, Johns Hopkins Univ, 36-37; chmn, Am Bd Plastic Surg, 61; consult, US Vet Admin. *Mem:* Fel Soc Univ Surgeons; fel Am Soc Plastic & Reconstruct Surg (pres, 59-60); fel AMA; fel Am Surg Asn; fel Am Asn Plastic Surgeons. *Res:* Plastic surgery; narcosis and intoxication as related to pneumonia and other infections; various suture materials; sub-total removal of the liver; principles and practice of surgery; plastic and reconstructive surgery; over 225 publications. *Mailing Add:* Central Med Park Suite 401 2609 N Duke St Durham NC 27704

PICKREN, JOHN WARREN, b Salem, Ark, Jan 29, 22; m 46; c 2. PATHOLOGY. *Educ:* Univ Ark, MD, 44; Am Bd Path, dipl, 51. *Prof Exp:* Intern, Gorgas Hosp, Ancon, CZ, 45; resident path, Sch Med, Univ Ark, 47-49; resident, Presby Hosp, New York, 49-51; instr & asst prof, Col Physicians & Surgeons, Columbia Univ, 51-54; CHIEF DEPT PATH, ROSWELL PARK MEM INST, 55- *Concurrent Pos:* Nat Cancer Inst trainee, 49-51; from asst chief to chief dept path, St Alban's Hosp, Albany, NY, 53-55. *Mem:* Am Soc Clin Path; AMA; fel Am Col Path; Am Asn Cancer Res. *Res:* Metastases in cancer. *Mailing Add:* Roswell Park Mem Inst 666 Elm St Buffalo NY 14203

PICKRUM, HARVEY MARVIN, microbiology, see previous edition

PICKWELL, GEORGE VINCENT, b San Jose, Calif, Oct 20, 33; m 60; c 2. PHYSIOLOGY, MARINE BIOLOGY. *Educ:* San Jose State Col, BA, 57; Univ Calif, San Diego, PhD(marine biol), 64. *Prof Exp:* Res biologist, Scripps Inst, Univ Calif, 60-61, res asst marine biol, 61-64; Nat Acad Sci-Nat Res Coun resident res assoc oceanog, Navy Electronics Lab, 64-66; OCEANOGR, NAVAL OCEAN SYST CTR, 66- *Mem:* AAAS; Am Soc Limnol & Oceanog; Am Inst Biol Sci; Am Soc Zoologists; Undersea Med Soc. *Res:* Biological oceanography; venomous marine animals; sea snakes and their venom; physiology and behavior of deep-sea animals; diving physiology; sound scattering and gas production by marine fishes and invertebrates. *Mailing Add:* Naval Ocean Syst Underseas Sci Dept Ctr Code 406 San Diego CA 92152

PICKWORTH, WALLACE BRUCE, b Rochester, NY, May 1, 46; m 74; c 1. PHARMACOLOGY. *Educ:* Albany Col Pharm, BS, 69; Univ Tenn, PhD(pharmacol), 74. *Prof Exp:* Staff fel, 74-78, PHARMACOLOGIST, ADDICTION RES CTR, NAT INST DRUG ABUSE, 78- *Mem:* Soc Neurosci; Sigma Xi. *Res:* Drug abuse; sleep; psychopharmacology; neuropharmacology. *Mailing Add:* Addiction Res Ctr PO Box 12390 Lexington KY 40583

PICO, GUILLERMO, b Coamo, PR, Dec 9, 15; m 40; c 3. OPHTHALMOLOGY. *Educ:* Univ PR, BS, 36; Univ Md, MD, 40. *Prof Exp:* Resident ophthal, St Luke's Hosp, New York, 45-46; prof, 52-77, EMER PROF OPHTHAL & HEAD DEPT, SCH MED, UNIV PR, SAN JUAN, 77- *Concurrent Pos:* Attend & chief dept ophthal, Univ Hosp, PR & San Juan City Hosp, PR, 52-77; consult & dir training prof, Vet Hosp, San Juan, 60-77; mem, Vision Res Training Comt, Nat Eye Inst, 67-71. *Honors & Awards:* Physician of the Year Award, President's Comt for Crippled, 66; PR Med Asn Award, 66; First Am J Ophthal Lectr Award, Cong Pan-Am Asn Ophthal, 71. *Mem:* Am Acad Ophthal & Otolaryngol (3rd vpres, 70); PR Med Asn (pres, 57); AMA; Am Acad Ophthal; Asn Res Vision & Ophthal. *Res:* Diseases and surgery of the lacrimal system, cornea and cataract; hereditary and congenital anomalies of the eyes; pathogenesis; clinical manifestation and treatment of Pterygium. *Mailing Add:* Dept of Ophthal Univ of PR San Juan PR 00905

PICOT, JULES JEAN CHARLES, b Edmundston, NB, July 23, 32; m 56; c 2. CHEMICAL ENGINEERING. *Educ:* NS Tech Col, BE, 55; Mass Inst Technol, SM, 57; Univ Minn, PhD(heat conduction), 66. *Prof Exp:* Control engr, Consol Bathurst Mills, 55-59; asst prof chem eng, Univ NB, 59-66; assoc prof, 66-70, chmn dept, 69-76, PROF CHEM ENG, UNIV NB, FREDERICTON, 70- *Concurrent Pos:* Mem grants selection comt, Nat Res Coun Can, 71-73 & 77-; dir, Can Soc Chem Engrs. *Mem:* Am Inst Chem Engrs; fel Can Inst Chem. *Res:* Transport phenomena, principally combined heat and momentum transfer; orientation effects in polymer liquids; atomization and dispersal of aerial sprays. *Mailing Add:* Dept Chem Eng Univ NB Fredericton NB E3B 5A3 Can

PICRAUX, SAMUEL THOMAS, b St Charles, Mo, Mar 3, 43; m 70; c 2. SOLID STATE PHYSICS, MATERIALS SCIENCE. *Educ:* Univ of Mo-Columbia, BS, 65; Calif Inst Technol, MS, 67, PhD(eng sci & physics), 69. *Prof Exp:* Tech staff mem, 69-72, SUPVR, ION SOLID INTERACTIONS RES, SANDIA LABS, 72- *Concurrent Pos:* Fulbright fel, physics, Cambridge Univ, 65-66; mem, Int Adv Comt Ion Beam Anal Conf, 73-, Appln of Ion Beams to Mat, 73-, Nat Res Coun Adv Comt, Ion Implantation Appln, 78. *Mem:* Fel Am Phys Soc; Int Elec & Electronics Engrs; Electrochem Soc; Mat Res Soc. *Res:* Ion-beam analysis techniques including ion backscattering, ion-induced nuclear reactions, ion channeling; ion implantation, surface modification, electron beam and laser pulsed annealing, hydrogen in solids, surface layer reactions, semiconductors, disorder studies, metals. *Mailing Add:* Sandia Labs Div 5111 Albuquerque NM 87185

PICTON, HAROLD D, b Bowman, NDak, Oct 6, 32; m 60; c 3. ZOOLOGY. *Educ:* Mont State Col, BS, 54, MS, 59; Northwestern Univ, PhD(biol), 64. *Prof Exp:* Jr biologist, Mont Fish & Game Dept, 54-55, biologist, 57-58, proj biologist, 59-63; asst prof comp physiol, 63-69, assoc prof environ physiol, 69-77, ASSOC PROF WILDLIFE MGT, MONT STATE UNIV, 77- *Mem:* AAAS; Ecol Soc Am; Am Soc Mammalogists; Wildlife Soc; Sigma Xi. *Res:* Ecology of large mammals; comparative physiology; environmental management. *Mailing Add:* Dept of Biol Mont State Univ Bozeman MT 59715

PICUS, GERALD SHERMAN, b Madison, Wis, Jan 9, 26; m 52; c 3. SOLID STATE SCIENCE. *Educ:* Univ Chicago, BS, 47, MS, 49, PhD, 54. *Prof Exp:* Physicist, US Naval Res Lab, 53-59; mem tech staff, Semiconductor Div, 59-62, sr staff physicist, Res Lab, 62-66, sr scientist, 66-68, MGR CHEM PHYSICS DEPT, HUGHES AIRCRAFT CO, 68- *Concurrent Pos:* Vis prof appl physics, Calif Inst Technol, 76-77. *Mem:* AAAS; fel Am Phys Soc; sr mem Inst Elec & Electronics Engrs; Sigma Xi. *Res:* Film flow in liquid helium; infrared properties of semi-conductors and other nonmetallic solids; infrared detectors; photoemission in tunnel structures. *Mailing Add:* 22545 Marylee St Woodland Hills CA 91364

PIDGEON, REZIN E, JR, US citizen. ELECTRICAL ENGINEERING. *Educ:* Ga Inst Technol, BEE, 49, MSEE, 61. *Prof Exp:* Field engr mil electronic equip, RCA Serv Co, 50-52, engr exp airborne radar, RCA Labs, 53-55; engr reactor instrumentation, Oak Ridge Lab, 56-57; asst res engr, Eng Exp Sta, Ga Inst Technol, 57-58, res engr, 58-62; sr engr, 62-68, staff engr instrumentation, 68-72, prin engr, Telecommun Prod Line, 72-79, PRIN ENGR, COMMUN GROUP, SCI-ATLANTA, INC, 79- *Res:* Antenna instrumentation; electronic circuitry; cable television systems and equipment design. *Mailing Add:* Sci-Atlanta Inc 3845 Pleasantdale Rd Atlanta GA 30340

PIE, RICHARD YU-SIEN, b Soochow, Kiangsu, China, July 24, 27; US citizen; m 51; c 3. ELECTRO-MECHANICAL ENGINEERING, APPLIED MATHEMATICS. *Educ:* Univ l'Aurore, BS, 47, MS, 48; Rensselaer Polytech Inst, PhD(mech), 64. *Prof Exp:* Apprentice engr, power, Taiwan Power Co, 48-49 & Shanghai Power Co, 49-50; lab supt, China Light & Power Co, 50-51; chief engr, United Prod Corp, 51-55; design engr, Copes-Vulcan Div, Blow-Know Co, 55-56; supvr eng serv, Gen Elec Co, 56-62; chief scientist instrumentation, Neptune Res Lab, 62-64; mem staff, Bellcomm, Inc,

64-67 & defense, Inst Defense Anal, 67-69; tech dir transp, TRW Syst Group, 69-71; PROJ LEADER DEFENSE, ENERGY, RAND CORP, 71- *Concurrent Pos:* Adj prof, Cath Univ Am, 64-69. *Mem:* Fel AAAS; Am Soc Mech Eng; Oper Res Soc AM. *Res:* Advanced weapon systems technologies; systems analysis; energy conversion technologies; mathematical analysis; applied mechanics; electromagnetics. *Mailing Add:* Rand Corp 2100 M St NW Washington DC 20037

PIECH, KENNETH ROBERT, b Buffalo, NY. OPTICAL PHYSICS. *Educ:* Canisius Col, BS, 62; Cornell Univ, PhD(physics), 67. *Prof Exp:* Staff scientist, Calspan Corp, 67-; VPRES, SCIPAR INC, 79- *Honors & Awards:* Autometric Award, Am Soc Photogram, 73. *Mem:* Am Soc Photogram; Sigma Xi. *Res:* Application of photometry to imaging systems; optical properties of surfaces; atmospheric propagation; optical meteorology; information systems and information extraction. *Mailing Add:* 51 Hetzel Rd Williamsville NY 14221

PIECH, MARGARET ANN, b Bridgewater, NS, Apr 6, 42; m 65; c 2. MATHEMATICS. *Educ:* Mt Allison Univ, BA, 62; Cornell Univ, PhD(math), 67. *Prof Exp:* Asst prof, 67-72, assoc prof, 72-78, PROF MATH, STATE UNIV NY BUFFALO, 78- *Concurrent Pos:* NSF res grants, 70-82; consult, NSF, 80-81. *Mem:* Am Math Soc. *Res:* Functional analysis; differential equations; probability theory. *Mailing Add:* Dept of Math State Univ NY Diefendorf Hall Buffalo NY 14214

PIECZENIK, GEORGE, b Cuba, Dec, 19, 44; US citizen. MOLECULAR BIOLOGY. *Educ:* Harvard Univ, AB, 65; Univ Miami, MS, 67; NY Univ, PhD(biol), 72. *Prof Exp:* Vis scientist, MRC Lab Molecular Biol, Cambridge, Eng, 71-72; res assoc microbial genetics, Rockefeller Univ, 72-75; ASST PROF BIOCHEM, RUTGERS UNIV, NEW BRUNSWICK, 75- *Concurrent Pos:* Vis scientist, MRC Lab Molecular Biol, Cambridge, Eng, 75- *Honors & Awards:* Claude Fuess Award, 80. *Mem:* AAAS; NY Acad Sci. *Res:* Investigation on the origin of nucleotide sequences; the theory of genotypic selection; the genotype as a phenotype for syntactical and structural selection. *Mailing Add:* 515 West End Ave New York NY 10024

PIEGARI, GEORGE, algebra, see previous edition

PIEHL, DONALD HERBERT, b Chicago, Ill, Jan 18, 39; m 65; c 2. TOBACCO & SMOKE CHEMISTRY. *Educ:* Carthage Col, BS, 61; Univ Iowa, MS, 64, PhD(inorg chem), 66. *Prof Exp:* Res chemist, 65-69, group leader res dept, 69-70, sect head phys chem res, 70-76, mgr, Chem Res Div, 76-80, DIR APPL RES & DEVELOP, R J REYNOLDS TOBACCO CO, 80- *Mem:* Am Chem Soc; Sigma Xi. *Res:* Tobacco and smoke chemistry; aerosol technology; heterogeneous catalysis; coordination chemistry; starch technology. *Mailing Add:* Res & Develop Ctr R J Reynolds Tobacco Co Winston-Salem NC 27102

PIEHL, FRANK JOHN, b Chicago, Ill, Oct 10, 26; m 55; c 1. ORGANIC CHEMISTRY. *Educ:* Univ Chicago, PhD(chem), 52. *Prof Exp:* dir anal res, 52-80, MGR ANAL SERV, STANDARDS OIL CO IND, NAPERVILLE, ILL, 80- *Mem:* Am Chem Soc; Am Soc Test & Mat. *Res:* Analytical chemistry. *Mailing Add:* 1129 Mary Lane Naperville IL 60540

PIEKARSKI, KONSTANTY, b Kiev, Ukraine, Mar 27, 15; Can citizen; m 40. MATERIAL SCIENCE, BIOENGINEERING. *Educ:* Univ London, DiplIng(mech eng) & DiplIng(metall), 50; Univ Cambridge, PhD(mat sci), 68. *Prof Exp:* Chief engr, M N Automation Ltd, Toronto, 53-58; from asst prof to assoc prof mat sci, 58-76, PROF MAT SCI, UNIV WATERLOO, 76- *Concurrent Pos:* Chmn bd, Biomed Eng Found, 75; dir bd, Can Fracture Corp, 77. *Mem:* Am Soc Metals; Am Soc Testing & Mat; Am Soc Mech Engrs; Soc Biomat. *Res:* Structure and properties of composite materials; structure and properties of bone; design of orthopaedic devices; effects of electrostatic and magnetic fields on tissue. *Mailing Add:* Dept of Mech Eng Univ of Waterloo Waterloo ON N2L 3G1 Can

PIEL, CAROLYN F, b Birmingham, Ala, Oct 18, 18; m 51; c 4. PEDIATRICS. *Educ:* Agnes Scott Col, AB, 40; Emory Univ, MS, 43; Washington Univ, MD, 46. *Prof Exp:* Instr pediat, Sch Med, Stanford Univ, 51-53, asst prof, 53-57; asst prof, 59-61, assoc prof, 61-76, PROF PEDIAT, SCH MED, UNIV CALIF, SAN FRANCISCO, 76- *Concurrent Pos:* USPHS fel, Med Col, Cornell Univ, 49-51. *Mem:* AAAS; Soc Pediat Res; Soc Exp Biol & Med; Am Pediat Soc; Am Soc Nephrology. *Res:* Electron microscopy of normal kidney; experimental and clinical renal diseases; metabolism of parathormone and vitamin D. *Mailing Add:* Dept of Pediat Univ of Calif Sch of Med San Francisco CA 91143

PIEL, GERARD, b Woodmere, NY, Mar 1, 15; m 38, 55; c 2. SCIENCE WRITING. *Educ:* Harvard Univ, AB, 37. *Hon Degrees:* DSc, Lawrence Col, 56, Colby Col, 60 & Univ BC & Brandeis Univ, 65; LittD, Rutgers Univ, 61 & Bates Col, 74; LHD, Columbia Univ, 62 & Williams Col, 66; LLD, Tuskegee Inst, 63, Univ Bridgeport, 64, Brooklyn Polytech Inst, 65 & Carnegie-Mellon Univ, 68. *Prof Exp:* Sci ed, Life Mag, 38-44; asst to pres, Henry J Kaiser Co, 45-46; PRES, SCI AM, INC, 46-; PUBL MAG, SCI AM, 47- *Concurrent Pos:* Trustee, Am Mus Natural Hist, Radcliffe Col, Phillips Acad, NY Bot Garden, NY Univ, Henry J Kaiser Family Found, Mayo Found & Found Child Develop; mem bd overseers, Harvard Univ, 66-68, 73- *Honors & Awards:* George K Polk Award, 61; Kalinga Prize, 62; Bradford Washburn Award, 66; Arches of Sci Award, 69. *Mem:* Inst of Med of Nat Acad Sci; fel Am Acad Arts & Sci; Am Philos Soc; Sigma Xi. *Mailing Add:* Sci Am 415 Madison Ave New York NY 10017

PIEL, KENNETH MARTIN, b Perry, Okla, Jan 19, 36; c 3. PALYNOLOGY. *Educ:* Univ Okla, BS, 57; Tulane Univ, MS, 65; Univ BC, PhD(bot), 69. *Prof Exp:* Asst palynologist, Shell Oil Co, 60-63; res palynologist, 67-73, sr res palynologist, 73-79, RES ASSOC, UNION OIL CO, CALIF, 79- *Mem:* Am Asn Stratig Palynologists (pres, 75-76; Brit Micropaleont Soc; Int Asn Angiosperm Paleobot; Soc Econ Paleontologists & Mineralogists; CIMP. *Res:* Dinoflagellate morphology and stratigraphy in the Jurassic and Cretaceous of Britain and the North Sea area. *Mailing Add:* Union Oil Co Calif Res Ctr PO Box 76 Brea CA 92621

PIEL, WILLIAM FREDERICK, b Indianapolis, Ind, Nov 14, 41. NUCLEAR PHYSICS. *Educ:* Ind Univ, BS, 64, MS & PhD(physics), 72. *Prof Exp:* Res assoc physics, Brookhaven Nat Lab, 72-75, asst physicist, 75-77; SR RES ASSOC, STATE UNIV NY, STONY BROOK, 77- *Mem:* Am Phys Soc. *Res:* Experimentation in the field of nuclear structure utilizing a tandem Van de Graaff; production of new nuclei far from beta stability; measurement of atomic masses utilizing a QDDD magnet facility; study of giant nuclear monopole resonances using a high-efficiency pair detector. *Mailing Add:* Dept of Physics State Univ NY Stony Brook NY 11794

PIELET, HOWARD M, b Chicago, Ill, Nov 13, 42; m 66; c 2. PROCESS METALLURGY. *Educ:* Mass Inst Technol, BS, 63, PhD(metall), 71; Columbia Univ, MS, 66. *Prof Exp:* res engr, 71-80, SR RES ENGR, STRAND CASTING, INLAND STEEL, 80- *Mem:* Am Inst Metall & Petrol Engrs; Sigma Xi. *Res:* Process metallurgy, solidification, casting processes, origin and elimination of nonmetallic defects and cracks in strand-cast slabs and billets, electric furnace steelmaking. *Mailing Add:* Inland Steel 3001 E Columbus Dr East Chicago IN 46312

PIELKE, ROGER ALVIN, b Baltimore, Md, Oct 22, 46. METEOROLOGY. *Educ:* Towson State Col, BA, 68; Pa State Univ, MS, 69, PhD(meteorol), 73. *Prof Exp:* Res meteorologist, Exp Meteorol Lab, Nat Oceanic & Atmospheric Admin, 71-74; asst prof, Univ Va, 74-78, assoc prof meteorol, 78-81; ASSOC PROF ATMOSPHERIC SCI, COLO STATE UNIV, 81- *Concurrent Pos:* Consulting meteorologist, 76-; prin investr grants & contracts, NSF, Environ Protection Agency & Dept Energy, 74- *Honors & Awards:* Spec Achievement Award, Nat Oceanic & Atmospheric Admin, 74; LeRoy Meisinger Award, Am Meteorol Soc, 77. *Mem:* Am Meteorol Soc. *Res:* Study of regional and local weather phenomena, including air quality, using sophisticated mathematical simulation models; air pollution meteorology; mesoscale meteorology. *Mailing Add:* Dept of Environ Sci Univ of Va Charlottesville VA 22903

PIELOU, DOUGLAS PATRICK, b Burton, Eng, Sept 1, 15; Can citizen; m 44; c 3. ENTOMOLOGY, ECOLOGY. *Educ:* Univ Birmingham, BSc, 36, PhD(entom), 39. *Prof Exp:* Beit Mem res fel, Imperial Col, Univ London, 39-40; entomologist, Colonial Serv, Northern Rhodesia, 45-47; asst prof entom, Ont Agr Col, Guelph, 47-49; res scientist, Entom Res Inst, Can Dept Agr, 49-71; Killam sr fel, 72-77, PROF BIOL, DALHOUSIE UNIV, 77- *Mem:* Entom Soc Can; fel Royal Entom Soc London. *Res:* Ecology of insects; host specificity of phytophagous invertebrates. *Mailing Add:* Dept of Biol Dalhousie Univ Halifax NS B3H 4H6 Can

PIELOU, EVELYN C, b Bognor, Eng, Feb 20, 24; Can citizen; m 44; c 3. ECOLOGY, BIOMETRICS. *Educ:* Univ London, BSc, 50, PhD(statist ecol), 62, DSc, 75. *Prof Exp:* Res off, Statist Res Serv, Can Dept Forestry, 63-65; res scientist, Can Dept Agr, 65-68; vis prof math ecol, NC State Univ, 68 & Yale Univ, 69 & Univ Sydney, Australia, 75; prof biol, Queen's Univ, Ont, 69-71; Killam res prof, 71-74, PROF BIOL, DALHOUSIE UNIV, 74- *Concurrent Pos:* Vis res prof, Oil Sands Environ, Univ Lethbridge, Alta, 81- *Mem:* AAAS; Ecol Soc Am; Biomet Soc; Am Statist Asn; Am Soc Naturalists. *Res:* Population and community ecology; statistical biogeography; statistical estimation and inference in ecology and biogeography. *Mailing Add:* Dept of Biol Dalhousie Univ Halifax NS B3H 3J5 Can

PIELOU, WILLIAM P, b Detroit, Mich, Mar 21, 22; m 46; c 2. NATURAL SCIENCE. *Educ:* Univ Mich, BS, 48, MS, 49, PhD(zool), 57. *Prof Exp:* Prof biol, Col Charleston, 49-50; asst prof, Alma Col, 51-53; instr zool, Mich State Univ, 53-54, from instr to asst prof, 54-63; asst prof, Ariz State Univ, 63-64; assoc prof, 64-80, PROF BIOL, FURMAN UNIV, 80- *Mem:* Am Ornith Union. *Res:* Ornithology; embryology; anatomy. *Mailing Add:* Dept Biol Furman Univ Greenville SC 29613

PIENAAR, LEON VISSER, b Cape Town, SAfrica, June 13, 36; US citizen; m 59; c 3. FOREST BIOMETRY, POPULATION DYNAMICS. *Educ:* Univ Stellenbosch, MSc, 60; Univ Wash, PhD(forest biomet), 65. *Prof Exp:* Res scientist, Dept Forestry, Pretoria SAfrica, 59-62 & 65-67; res scientist, Fisheries Res Bd Can, 67-69; from asst prof to assoc prof forestry, Wash State Univ, 69-73; asst prof, 73-75, ASSOC PROF FORESTRY, UNIV GA, 75- *Concurrent Pos:* Mem biomet sect, Int Union Forest Res Orgns, 65-; consult, Forest Serv, USDA, 74- *Res:* Growth, yield and management of plantations; fish population dynamics. *Mailing Add:* Sch Forest Resources Univ Ga Athens GA 30602

PIENE, HARALD, forest ecology, see previous edition

PIENKOWSKI, ROBERT LOUIS, b Cleveland, Ohio, Aug 22, 32; m 58; c 3. ENTOMOLOGY. *Educ:* Ohio State Univ, BS, 54; Univ Wis, MS, 58, PhD(entom), 62. *Prof Exp:* From asst prof to assoc prof, 61-72, PROF ENTOM, VA POLYTECH INST & STATE UNIV, 72- *Mem:* Weed Sci Soc Am; Int Orgn Biol Control; Entom Soc Am; Entom Soc Can; Brit Ecol Soc. *Res:* Ecology, behavior and biological control of forage crop insects; biological control of weeds. *Mailing Add:* Dept of Entom Va Polytech Inst & State Univ Blacksburg VA 24061

PIENTA, ROMAN JOSEPH, b Old Forge, Pa, Feb 28, 31; m 56; c 3. CARCINOGENESIS, TOXICOLOGY. *Educ:* Pa State Univ, BS, 54; Rutgers Univ, MS, 56, PhD(microbiol), 59. *Prof Exp:* Asst virol, Inst Microbiol, Rutgers Univ, 57-59, res assoc, 59-60, asst res specialist, 60-65; virologist, Univ Labs, Inc, NJ, 65; assoc prof microbiol & assoc microbiologist, Univ Tex M D Anderson Hosp & Tumor Inst, 65-69, actg chief microbiol unit, 67-69; sr scientist, Litton Bionetics, Inc, 69-70, actg dir dept exp oncol, 70-71, dir dept, 71-72, proj mgr in vitro carcinogenesis, 72-76, actg dir, 75-76, sect head & dep dir, Frederick Cancer Res Ctr, 76-81; SYSTS ANALYST & MEM TECH STAFF, DEPT ENVIRON CHEM & BIOL, METREK DIV, MITRE CORP, 81- *Concurrent Pos:* Res fel virol, Inst Microbiol, Rutgers Univ, 54-57, mem grad sch fac, 63-65. *Mem:* Am Soc

Microbiol; Am Asn Cancer Res; NY Acad Sci; Environ Mutagen Soc; Tissue Cult Asn. *Res:* Chemotherapy of viruses and tumors; virus-induced cancer; in vitro culture of human tumor and leukemia cells; in vitro chemcial carcinogenesis; in vitro carcinogenesis bioassay model systems; genomo rescue; primate tumor viruses. *Mailing Add:* Metrek Div Mitre Corp 1820 Dolly Madison Blvd McLean VA 22102

PIEPER, GEORGE FRANCIS, b Boston, Mass, Jan 1, 26; m 50; c 2. NUCLEAR PHYSICS, SPACE SCIENCES. *Educ:* Williams Col, BA, 46; Cornell Univ, MS, 49; Yale Univ, PhD(physics), 52. *Prof Exp:* Mem staff radiation lab, Mass Inst Technol, 44-45; instr physics, Williams Col, 46-47; assoc physicist, Tracerlab, Inc, 49-50; from instr to asst prof physics, Yale Univ, 52-60; sr physicist appl physics lab, Johns Hopkins Univ, 60-64; dep asst dir adv res, 64-65, DIR SCI, NASA GODDARD SPACE FLIGHT CTR, 65- *Concurrent Pos:* Fel dept terrestrial magnetism Carnegie Inst Technol, 56-57; consult to dir physics & astron prog, Off Space Sci, NASA Hq, 63-64; guest worker, Max Planck Inst Extraterrestrial Physics, 71-72. *Honors & Awards:* NASA Medal Outstanding Achievement, 69; NASA Medal Outstanding Leadership, 77. *Mem:* Fel Am Phys Soc; Am Geophys Union; Am Astron Soc. *Res:* Experimental nuclear physics; particle measurements from satellites; administration of space science program. *Mailing Add:* Code 600 NASA Goddard Space Flight Ctr Greenbelt MD 20771

PIEPER, GUSTAV RENE, b Bandung, Indonesia, Mar 28, 27; US citizen; m 66; c 2. ENTOMOLOGY, TOXICOLOGY. *Educ:* State Agr Univ, Wageningen, BS, 54, MS, 57; Univ Calif, Berkeley, PhD(entom), 65. *Prof Exp:* Lab technician, Univ Calif, Riverside, 57-59; res entomologist, 65-77, RES CHEMIST, FOREST SERV, USDA, 77- *Mem:* Entom Soc Am. *Res:* Ecology of cabbage fly; effects of fumigants on seed germination; control of stored product insects; insect toxicology and biochemistry; insecticide residue analysis; formulation of insecticides. *Mailing Add:* Forest Serv USDA 1960 Addison St Berkeley CA 94701

PIEPER, HEINZ PAUL, b Wuppertal-Barmen, Ger, Mar 24, 20; US citizen; m 45. CARDIOVASCULAR PHYSIOLOGY. *Educ:* Univ Munich, MD, 48. *Prof Exp:* Resident, Med Clin, Univ Munich, 49-50, res assoc & asst prof physiol, 50-57; from asst prof to assoc prof, 57-68, actg chmn dept, 73-74, PROF PHYSIOL, COL MED, OHIO STATE UNIV, 68-, CHMN DEPT, 74- *Concurrent Pos:* Res fel, Bremer Found, Youngstown, Ohio, 57-60; estab investr, Am Heart Asn, 62-67. *Mem:* Am Physiol Soc; Ger Physiol Soc. *Res:* Pressure flow relationships of the coronary system in intact anesthetized dogs; hemodynamic studies in intact dogs; aortic distensibility; instrumentation. *Mailing Add:* Dept Physiol Ohio State Univ Col Med Columbus OH 43210

PIEPER, REX DELANE, b Idaho Falls, Idaho, Jan 18, 34; m 65; c 3. RANGE SCIENCE, PLANT ECOLOGY. *Educ:* Univ Idaho, BS, 56; Utah State Univ, MS, 58; Univ Calif, Berkeley, PhD(bot), 63. *Prof Exp:* From asst prof to assoc prof, 63-75, PROF RANGE SCI, NMEX STATE UNIV, 75- *Mem:* Fel AAAS; Ecol Soc Am; Soc Range Mgt; Am Soc Animal Sci. *Res:* Nutrient cycles in Alaska; vegetation studies in New Mexico; nutrition studies on desert ranges in Utah; ecosystem analysis of desert grassland. *Mailing Add:* Dept Animal & Range Sci NMex State Univ Las Cruces NM 88003

PIEPER, RICHARD EDWARD, b Whittier, Calif, Mar 22, 41. BIOLOGICAL OCEANOGRAPHY. *Educ:* Univ Calif, Santa Barbara, BA, 64, MA, 67; Univ BC, PhD(zool & oceanog), 71. *Prof Exp:* Asst prof biol & biol oceanographer, Allan Hancock Found, 71-76, RES SCIENTIST, INST MARINE & COASTAL STUDIES, UNIV SOUTHERN CALIF, 76-, ASSOC RES PROF, DEPT BIOL & DIR RES, CATALINA MARINE SCI CTR, 80- *Concurrent Pos:* Assoc curator ichthyol, Los Angeles County Mus Natural Hist, 73-; consult marine ecol, Tracor, Inc, San Diego, 75-; res grants, Off Naval Res & NSF. *Mem:* Acoust Soc Am; Am Soc Limnol & Oceanog; Marine Biol Asn UK; Explorers Club; Sigma Xi. *Res:* Sound scattering by marine organisms; plankton and fish ecology; sampling gear evaluation and development. *Mailing Add:* Inst for Marine & Coastal Studies Univ of Southern Calif Los Angeles CA 90007

PIEPER, STEVEN CHARLES, b Oceanside, NY, Apr 25, 43; m 65; c 3. THEORETICAL NUCLEAR PHYSICS, SCATTERING CALCULATIONS. *Educ:* Univ Rochester, BS, 65; Univ Ill, Urbana, PhD(physics), 70. *Prof Exp:* Fel physics, Case Western Reserve Univ, 70-72; fel physics, 72-74, asst scientist physics, 74-77, SCIENTIST PHYSICS, ARGONNE NAT LAB, 77- *Mem:* Am Phys Soc. *Res:* The calculation of heavy-ion reactions by distorted-wave born approximation and coupled channel techniques; calculation of nuclear matter properties; computer techniques for physics research. *Mailing Add:* Physics Div Argonne Nat Lab Argonne IL 60439

PIEPHO, ROBERT WALTER, b Chicago, Ill, July 31, 42; m 65; c 3. PHARMACOLOGY, NEUROCHEMISTRY. *Prof Exp:* Registered pharmacist, South Park Pharm, Walther Mem Hosp, 65-70; asst prof pharm, Univ Nebr Med Ctr, 70-74, assoc prof, 74-80, coordr clin educ, 75-80; PROF PHARM & ASSOC DEAN CLIN PROG, UNIV COLO MED CTR, SCH PHARM, 80- *Concurrent Pos:* Fel pharmacol, Sch Med, Loyola Univ, Chicago, 65-70; mem, Nat Adv Comt, Student Am Pharmaceut Asn, 71- *Mem:* Am Asn Col Pharm; NY Acad Sci; Am Pharmaceut Asn. *Res:* Circadian rhythms; chronopharmacology and chronotherapeutics; investigation of central nervous system neurotransmitter candidates and their functional roles; neurochemical correlates of thermoregulation. *Mailing Add:* Sch Pharm Univ Colo Med Ctr Box C-238 Denver CO 80262

PIEPMEIER, EDWARD HARMAN, b St Louis, Mo, June 6, 37; m 61; c 3. ANALYTICAL CHEMISTRY. *Educ:* Northwestern Univ, BS, 60; Univ Ill, PhD(chem), 66. *Prof Exp:* Asst prof, 66-73, assoc prof, 73-79, PROF CHEM, ORE STATE UNIV, 79- *Concurrent Pos:* Res fel, Delft Univ Technol, 73-74; fac fel, NASA, 79. *Mem:* Am Chem Soc; Soc Appl Spectros; Am Asn Univ Prof. *Res:* Analytical applications of lasers; trace element analysis; instrumentation. *Mailing Add:* Dept Chem Ore State Univ Corvallis OR 97331

PIER, ALLAN CLARK, b Chicago, Ill, Jan 17, 28; m 50; c 3. VETERINARY MEDICINE. *Educ:* Univ Calif, Davis, BS, 51, DVM, 53, PhD(comp path), 60. *Prof Exp:* Vet, Arcata, Calif, 53-54; lectr & asst vet clin path, mastitis res & med mycol, Sch Vet Med, Univ Calif, Davis, 54-61; res vet & proj leader mycotic dis, Agr Res Serv, USDA, 61-64, chief, Bact & Mycol Res Lab, Nat Animal Dis Ctr, 64-81; HEAD DIV MICROBIOL & VET MED & DIR, WYO STATE DIAG LAB, UNIV WYO, 81- *Concurrent Pos:* Consult, Territory of Hawaii, 58, Univ Mont & US Dept Health, Educ & Welfare, 61 & Nat Acad Sci, 67-; collab prof, Iowa State Univ, 64- *Mem:* Am Vet Med Asn; Conf Res Workers Animal Dis; Am Col Vet Microbiologists; Int Soc Human & Animal Mycol. *Res:* Veterinary medical mycology; research administration; bacterial and mycotic diseases; medical mycology. *Mailing Add:* Microbiol & Vet Med Div Univ Wyo Laramie WY 82071

PIER, HAROLD WILLIAM, b Mt Jewett, Pa, Aug 9, 35; m 58; c 2. ORGANIC CHEMISTRY. *Educ:* Pa State Univ, BS, 57; Univ Del, MS, 59, PhD(org chem), 62. *Prof Exp:* Fel, Columbia Univ, 61-62; res assoc, Johns Hopkins Univ, 62-63; asst prof, 63-68, ASSOC PROF, ORG CHEM, UTICA COL, 68- *Concurrent Pos:* Res Corp grant, 63. *Mem:* Am Chem Soc. *Res:* Molecular rearrangements; reaction mechanisms; nature of dissolved organic matter in water. *Mailing Add:* Dept of Chem Utica Col Utica NY 13502

PIER, STANLEY MORTON, b Brooklyn, NY; m 55. ENVIRONMENTAL HEALTH. *Educ:* Brooklyn Col, BS, 48; Purdue Univ, MS, 49, PhD, 52. *Prof Exp:* Asst, Purdue Univ, 48-52; res chemist, Tex Co, 52-55, proj leader, 55-58; sect head, Cities Serv Res & Develop Co, 58-59, from div head to prof dir lab, 60-69; tech dir, Pace Co, 69-70, dir environ sci, 70-72; ASSOC PROF ENVIRON HEALTH, UNIV TEX SCH PUB HEALTH HOUSTON, 72- *Mem:* Am Chem Soc; Air Pollution Control Asn; Am Pub Health Asn. *Res:* Industrial hygiene; occupational health; water and air pollution; oil spills; petroleum products; organic chemistry. *Mailing Add:* Univ of Tex Sch of Pub Health PO Box 20186 Houston TX 77025

PIERARD, JEAN ARTHUR, b Liege, Belg, Jan 26, 34; Can citizen; m 58; c 5. VETERINARY ANATOMY, MAMMOLOGY. *Educ:* Univ Montreal, DVM, 57; Cornell Univ, MSc, 63. *Prof Exp:* Asst chief diag lab, Que Dept Agr, 57-58; inspector, Can Dept Agr, 58-59; instr micros & gross anat, Que Vet Col, 59-61; asst, State Univ NY Vet Col, Cornell Univ, 61-63; secy fac, 67-73 & 78-80, head dept animal anat & physiol, 73-78, PROF MICROS & GROSS ANAT, FAC VET MED, UNIV MONTREAL, 63- *Mem:* Am Asn Vet Anat; World Asn Vet Anatomists (secy gen, 75-); Can Asn Vet Anat (pres, 77-78); Am Soc Mammalogists; Can Vet Med Asn. *Res:* Pinnipeds and carnivores morphology; osteoarchaeology. *Mailing Add:* Dept Anat & Animal Physiol Fac Vet Med Univ Montreal Montreal Can

PIERCE, ALAN KRAFT, b Houston, Tex, Sept 3, 31; m 58; c 2. INTERNAL MEDICINE. *Educ:* Baylor Univ, MD, 55. *Prof Exp:* Resident internal med, Parkland Mem Hosp, 58-61; from instr to assoc prof, 62-69, PROF MED, UNIV TEX SOUTHWESTERN MED SCH DALLAS, 69- *Concurrent Pos:* Res fel pulmonary dis, Univ Tex Southwestern Med Sch Dallas, 61-62, NIH res fel, 61-64. *Mem:* Am Fedn Clin Res; Am Thoracic Soc; Am Col Chest Physicians; fel Am Col Physicians; Am Soc Clin Invest. *Res:* Exercise rehabilitation in patients with chronic lung disease; mechanics of breathing in patients with lung disease; nosocomial pulmonary infections; pathogenesis of pneumonia. *Mailing Add:* Dept Med Univ Tex Southwstern Med Sch Dallas TX 75235

PIERCE, ALEXANDER WEBSTER, JR, b Nashville, Tenn, Nov 13, 31; m 55; c 4. PEDIATRICS. *Educ:* Vanderbilt Univ, BA, 52, MD, 56; Am Bd Pediat, dipl, 62, recert, 81. *Prof Exp:* Instr pediat, Sch Med, Univ Okla, 61-63, from asst prof to assoc prof, 63-69; assoc prof, Univ Tex Med Sch, San Antonio, 69-75, prof pediat, dir pediat clin & dir ambulatory pediat, 75-78; PROF FAM PRACT, UNIV TEX HEALTH SCI CTR, 78- *Concurrent Pos:* Asst dir outpatient clins, Children's Mem Hosp-Univ Okla Hosps, 65-67, dir med serv, Out-Patient Dept, 67-69. *Mem:* Am Acad Pediat; Am Med Asn. *Res:* Ambulatory pediatrics. *Mailing Add:* Dept of Fam Pract 7703 Floyd Curl Dr San Antonio TX 78284

PIERCE, ARLEEN CECILIA, b New York, NY, Jan 29, 39. ORGANIC CHEMISTRY. *Educ:* Queens Col, NY, BS, 59; Univ Pa, PhD(chem), 62. *Prof Exp:* Sr res chemist, Cent Res Lab, Allied Chem Corp, 62-66; asst prof chem, Douglass Col, Rutgers Univ, 66-68; head dept, Unity Col, 68-72, dean fac, 70-72; head chemist, Northeast Labs, 72-74; CONSULT, 72- *Mem:* Sigma Xi; fel Am Inst Chemists. *Res:* Aminolysis of esters; animal feed from waste products; organic fertilizers and their effectiveness for salt water farming; effect of light on natural products. *Mailing Add:* RFD 2 Lubec ME 04652

PIERCE, AUSTIN KEITH, b Tacoma, Wash, Oct 2, 18; m 41; c 3. SOLAR PHYSICS. *Educ:* Univ Calif, AB, 40, PhD(astron), 47. *Prof Exp:* Physicist, radiation lab, Univ of Calif, 42-47; res assoc astron, Univ Mich, 47-48, instr McMath-Hulbert Observ, 48-50, asst prof, 50-54, assoc prof, 54-58; assoc dir solar astron, 58-75, ASTRONOMER, KITT PEAK NAT OBSERV, ASN UNIV RES ASTRON, INC, 75- *Concurrent Pos:* Physicist, Manhattan Proj, Tenn Eastman Co, Tenn, 44-45; mem comn 12, 36, Int Astron Union. *Mem:* Am Astron Soc; Int Astron Union. *Res:* Solar spectroscopy; infrared; design of solar telescopes and instrumentation. *Mailing Add:* Asn Univ Res Astron Inc Kitt Peak Nat Observ Box 26732 Tucson AZ 85726

PIERCE, CAMDEN BALLARD, b Shelbyville, Ky, July 17, 32; m 59; c 2. SOLID STATE PHYSICS. *Educ:* Univ Richmond, BS, 54; Univ Ill, MS, 56, PhD(exp physics), 60. *Prof Exp:* Staff mem, Sandia Lab, 60-66; coordr, Bronfman Sci Ctr, 74-77, acting chmn, dept physics & astron, 77-79, assoc prof, 66-79, PROF PHYSICS, WILLIAMS COL, 66-, CHMN, DEPT PHYS & ASTRON, 80- *Mem:* Am Phys Soc; Am Asn Physics Teachers. *Res:* Optical and electrical properties associated with point defects in crystalline solids; color centers; radiation damage; ionic conductivity; high pressure studies; diffusion. *Mailing Add:* Dept Physics & Astron Williams Col Williamstown MA 01267

PIERCE, CAROL S, b Lockport, NY, Mar 4, 38. SYPHILIS, PATHOGENIC MECHANISMS. *Educ:* Mt Union Col, BS, 60; Univ Chicago, MS, 63; State Univ NY, Buffalo, MS, 78, PHD(microbiol), 81. *Prof Exp:* Res assoc, Argonne Cancer Res Hosp, Chicago, 63-66, Nat Jewish Hosp, Colo, 66-67, Dairy Prod Lab, USDA, 67-70 & Vet Admin Hosp, Buffalo, NY, 72-74; fel, Erie Count Labs, Buffalo, 80-82; ASST PROF CLIN MICROBIOL, STATE UNIV NY, BUFFALO, 80- *Mem:* Am Soc Microbiol; AAAS. *Res:* Investigation of the cellular and humoral immune responses in guinea pigs infected with Treponema pallidum; evaluation of identification systems for the identification of anaerobic bacteria in the clinical laboratory. *Mailing Add:* Dept Med Technol State Univ NY 462 Grider St Buffalo NY 14215

PIERCE, CHESTER MIDDLEBROOK, b Glen Cove, NY, Mar 4, 27; m 49; c 2. PSYCHIATRY. *Educ:* Harvard Col, AB, 48; Harvard Med Sch, MD, 52; Am Bd Psychiat & Neurol, dipl, 58. *Hon Degrees:* ScD, Westfield Col, 77. *Prof Exp:* Instr psychiat, Univ Cincinnati, 57-60; from asst prof to prof, Univ Okla, 60-68; PROF PSYCHIAT, HARVARD UNIV, 68- *Concurrent Pos:* Sr consult, Peace Corps, 65-69; Alfred North Whitehead fel, Harvard Univ, 68-69; mem adv br, Children's TV Workshop, 68-; mem & pres, Am Bd Psychiat & Neurol, 70-78; nat consult Surgeon Gen, US Air Force, 76-; mem polar res bd, Nat Res Coun & mem working group human biol & med, Sci Comt Antarctic Res, 77- *Honors & Awards:* Pierce Peak Award, 68; Spec Recognition Award, Nat Med Asn, 71; Hon Fel Award, Australian & NZ Col Psychiatrists, 78. *Mem:* Inst of Med of Nat Acad Sci; Am Psychiat Asn; Am Octhopsychiat Asn (vpres, 76); Black Psychiatrists Am; Am Col Physicians. *Res:* Extreme environments; media; racism; sports medicine; education. *Mailing Add:* Nichols House Appian Way Cambridge MA 02138

PIERCE, CYRIL MARVIN, b Boston, Mass, Feb 15, 39; m 62; c 2. METALLURGY. *Educ:* Mass Inst Technol, BS, 60, MS, 61; Ohio State Univ, PhD(metall eng), 66. *Prof Exp:* Chief struct metals develop, Air Force Mat Lab, 73-74, asst chief mfg technol, 74-76, chief, 76; dir mfg, Air Force F16 Prog Off, 76-77; mgr mfg technol lab, 77-79, PLANT MGR, AIRCRAFT ENGINE GROUP, GEN ELEC CO, MADISONVILLE, KY, 79- *Concurrent Pos:* US Air Force rep, Mat Adv Bd Metalworking, 64, Int Tech Coop Prog, 73-76 & Mfg Tech Adv Group, Dept Defense, 74-76; adj prof, Eng & Sci Inst Dayton, 71 & Univ Dayton, 74. *Honors & Awards:* Sci Achievement Award, US Air Force, 73. *Mem:* Sigma Xi; fel Am Soc Metals; Am Inst Metall Engrs. *Res:* Titanium alloys; superalloys; manufacturing technology. *Mailing Add:* Hwy 41A N Gen Elec Co Madisonville KY 42431

PIERCE, DANIEL THORNTON, b Los Angeles, Calif, July 16, 40; m 70; c 2. PHYSICS, SURFACE SCIENCE. *Educ:* Stanford Univ, BS, 62, PhD(appl physics), 70; Wesleyan Univ, MA, 66. *Prof Exp:* Res assoc, Stanford Electronics Labs, Stanford Univ, 70-71; physicist, Swiss Fed Inst Technol, Zurich, 71-75; PHYSICIST, NAT BUR STANDARDS, 75- *Honors & Awards:* Indust Res 100 Award, 80. *Mem:* Am Phys Soc; Am Vacuum Soc; Swiss Phys Soc. *Res:* Physics of spin polarized electrons; scattering; emission; sources and detectors; structural, electronic and magnetic properties of surfaces; photoemission. *Mailing Add:* Rm B206 Bldg 220 Nat Bur Standards Washington DC 20234

PIERCE, DAVID ALAN, b Somerville, NJ, July 11, 42; m 67; c 2. MATHEMATICAL STATISTICS, APPLIED STATISTICS. *Educ:* Carleton Col, BA, 64; Univ Wis, MS, 66, PhD(statist), 68. *Prof Exp:* Res asst statist, Univ Wis, 67-68; asst prof, Univ Mo-Columbia, 68-70; statistician, Res Dept, Fed Reserve Bank Cleveland, 70-72; statistician, 72-80, SR STATISTICIAN, DIV RES & STATIST, FED RESERVE BD, 80- *Concurrent Pos:* Lectr, Opers Res Dept, George Washington Univ, 76- *Mem:* AAAS; Am Statist Asn; Inst Math Statist; Royal Statist Soc. *Res:* Statistical modelling, forecasting and seasonal adjustment of economic time series. *Mailing Add:* Div of Res & Statist Fed Reserve Bd Washington DC 20551

PIERCE, DONALD N(ORMAN), b Lincoln, Nebr, Oct 30, 21; m 43; c 2. SOLID MECHANICS, MATERIALS SCIENCE. *Educ:* Univ Nebr, BSc, 48, MSc, 54. *Prof Exp:* From instr to asst prof, 48-61, ASSOC PROF ENG MECH, UNIV NEBR, LINCOLN, 61- *Concurrent Pos:* Consult mech testing & stress anal. *Mem:* Am Soc Mech Engrs; Am Soc Eng Educ; Am Acad Mech; Soc Exp Stress Anal. *Res:* Dimensional analysis; solid mechanics; stresses in thin-wall shells; energy dissipation in concrete. *Mailing Add:* Dept of Eng Mech Univ of Nebr Lincoln NE 68588

PIERCE, EDWARD RONALD, b Chester, Pa, Mar 1, 37; m 63; c 2. HEALTH SCIENCES, MEDICAL GENETICS. *Educ:* Univ Louisville, BA, 62, PhD(zool), 68; Johns Hopkins Univ, MPH, 70. *Prof Exp:* Asst prof zool, Ohio Univ, 67-68; fel, Div Med Genetics, Johns Hopkins Univ Hosp, 68-70; asst prof biol, American Univ, 70-73, assoc prof, 73-74; asst dean & assoc prof health studies, Sch Health Studies, Univ NH, 74-78; PROF, DIR DIV ALLIED HEALTH SCI & DEAN SCH MED, IND UNIV, 78- *Concurrent Pos:* Asst in med, Div Med Genetics, Johns Hopkins Univ, 70-73. *Mem:* Am Soc Human Genetics; Genetics Soc Am; Am Pub Health Asn; Am Soc Allied Health Prof. *Res:* Cytogenetics, behavioral genetics; population genetics-human genetic counseling. *Mailing Add:* Div Allied Health Sci 1100 Michigan St Indianapolis IN 46223

PIERCE, EDWARD THOMAS, meteorology, physics, deceased

PIERCE, ELLIOT STEARNS, b Attleboro, Mass, Apr 30, 22; m 46; c 3. ENERGY-RELATED CHEMISTRY. *Educ:* Yale Univ, BS, 43, MS, 48, PhD(org chem), 51. *Prof Exp:* Res chemist, Socony-Vacuum Oil Co, 43-44; instr org & phys-org chem, Univ Mass, 50-51; res chemist, Am Cyanamid Co, 51-54, group leader, 54-55, univ recruiter, 55-56, govt res liaison, 56-59; res adminr, US Air Force Off Sci Res, 59-61; chemist, US AEC, 61-66, dep asst dir res, 66-67, dep dir div nuclear educ & training, 67-70, dir, 70-73, asst dir div phys res, 73-75, asst dir basic energy sci, Energy Res & Develop Admin, 75-77, DIR CHEM SCI DIV, DEPT ENERGY, 77- *Mem:* AAAS; Am Chem Soc; Am Phys Soc; Am Nuclear Soc; Sigma Xi. *Res:* Basic energy-related chemistry including coal chemistry, surface chemistry, photochemistry, combustion, photoelectron spectroscopy, molecular beam research, atomic physics, analytical chemistry, chemical and isotope separations, nuclear chemistry. *Mailing Add:* Div Chem Sci ER-14 Dept of Energy Washington DC 20545

PIERCE, EMMETT COIN, b Indianapolis, Ind, Aug 25, 22; m 54; c 8. PATHOLOGY. *Educ:* Butler Univ, BS, 49; Ind Univ, MD, 52. *Prof Exp:* Intern, St Elizabeth Hosp, Lafayette, Ind, 52-53; gen pract, Attica, 53-56; resident path, Marion County Gen Hosp, Indianapolis, 56-60, assoc pathologist, 60-61; sr pathologist, 61-64, head path, 64-74, RES ADV TOXICOL DIV, ELI LILLY & CO, 74- *Concurrent Pos:* Clin assoc prof, Sch Med, Ind Univ, 68- *Mem:* AAAS; AMA; Am Soc Clin Path; Col Am Path; Int Acad Path. *Res:* Mutagenesis; teratology; carcinogenesis. *Mailing Add:* Toxicol Div Eli Lilly & Co Box 708 Greenfield IN 46140

PIERCE, FELIX J(OHN), b Warren, RI, Nov 5, 32; m 55; c 3. FLUID MECHANICS. *Educ:* Univ RI, BS, 55; Cornell Univ, MS, 58, PhD(mech eng), 61. *Prof Exp:* From instr to asst prof mech eng, Cornell Univ, 58-66; assoc prof, 66-70, asst dean grad sch, 69-70, PROF MECH ENG, VA POLYTECH INST & STATE UNIV, 70- *Mem:* Am Soc Mech Engrs; Am Inst Aeronaut & Astronaut; Am Soc Eng Educ. *Res:* Three-dimensional turbulent flows; classical and statistical thermodynamics. *Mailing Add:* Dept of Mech Eng Col of Eng Va Polytech Inst & State Univ Blacksburg VA 24061

PIERCE, G(EORGE) ALVIN, b Philadelphia, Pa, Dec 22, 31; m 75; c 3. AEROSPACE ENGINEERING. *Educ:* Mass Inst Technol, BSc, 53; Ohio State Univ, PhD(aerospace eng), 66. *Prof Exp:* Jr engr, Nat Adv Comt Aeronaut, Langley Field, 51-52; mech engr, ADC Electronics Prod Corp, 53-54; dynamics engr, N Am Aviation, Inc, 56-58, sr engr, 58-61, res specialist aeroelasticity, 61-63; res assoc aerodyn, Ohio State Univ, 64-66; PROF AEROELASTICITY, GA INST TECHNOL, 66- *Concurrent Pos:* Consult various indust firms, 64-; Am Inst Aeronaut & Astronaut rep, Engr Coun Prof Develop, 70- *Mem:* Am Inst Aeronaut & Astronaut; Am Helicopter Soc; Sigma Xi. *Res:* Aeroelasticity and unsteady aerodynamics of fixed and rotary wing flight vehicles. *Mailing Add:* Sch of Aerospace Eng Ga Inst of Technol Atlanta GA 30332

PIERCE, GORDON BARRY, b Westlock, Alta, July 21, 25; m 52; c 5. PATHOLOGY. *Educ:* Univ Alta, BSc, 49, MSc, 50, MD, 52. *Prof Exp:* Intern, Univ Hosp, Univ Alta, 52-53, lectr path, Univ, 53-55; asst prof, Sch Med, Univ Pittsburgh, 59-61; assoc prof, Univ Mich, Ann Arbor, 61-65, prof, 65-68; PROF PATH & CHMN DEPT, MED CTR, UNIV COLO, DENVER, 68- *Concurrent Pos:* Scaife fel, Sch Med, Univ Pittsburgh, 55-59; Markle scholar med sci, 59-63; Am Cancer Soc career prof, 64-; mem med scientist training comt, Nat Inst Gen Med Sci, 63-67; mem cell biol study sect, NIH, 68-72 & path study sect, 72-77. *Mem:* AAAS; Am Asn Path (pres, 77); Fedn Am Socs Exp Biol (pres, 78); Am Soc Cell Biol; Am Asn Cancer Res. *Res:* Oncology; aspects of developmental carcinomas; teratocarcinoma; biology of basement membranes. *Mailing Add:* Dept Path Univ Colo Med Ctr Denver CO 80262

PIERCE, HARRY FREDERICK, b Baltimore, Md, Nov 29, 41; m 66; c 1. UNDERWATER ACOUSTICS, SONAR. *Educ:* Johns Hopkins Univ, BS, 67. *Prof Exp:* US Navy, 68-, officer acoustics, 68-72, physicist, 72-79, proj mgr, 79-82, SR PROJ MGR ACOUSTICS, DAVID W TAYLOR NAVAL SHIP RES & DEVELOP CTR, US NAVY, 82- *Concurrent Pos:* Physicist, David W Taylor Naval Ship Res & Develop Ctr, 72- *Mem:* Math Asn Am. *Res:* Underwater acoustics; sonar design and applications; signal processing. *Mailing Add:* Code 1932 David W Taylor Naval Ship Res & Develop Ctr Bethesda MD 20084

PIERCE, JACK ROBERT, b Sturgis, Mich, Mar 18, 39; m 71. ZOOLOGY. *Educ:* Western Mich Univ, BA, 61, MA, 63; Univ Tex, PhD(zool), 68. *Prof Exp:* Asst prof, 67-71, PROF BIOL, AUSTIN COL, 71-, CHMN DEPT, 76- *Concurrent Pos:* Dir, NSF student serv training prog environ qual. *Mem:* AAAS. *Res:* Anuran speciation and ecology, especially acoustic behavior. *Mailing Add:* Dept of Biol Austin Col Sherman TX 75090

PIERCE, JACK VINCENT, b Kalamazoo, Mich, Feb 2, 19. BIOCHEMISTRY. *Educ:* Kalamazoo Col, BA, 40; Univ Mich, MA, 41; Columbia Univ, MA, 50; Univ Ill, PhD(biochem), 56. *Prof Exp:* Res assoc, Lederle Labs, Am Cyanamid Co, 47-52; res assoc chem, Univ Ill, 55; res chemist, Lederle Labs, Am Cyanamid Co, 56-57; CHEMIST, NAT HEART, LUNG & BLOOD INST, 57- *Mem:* AAAS; Am Chem Soc; NY Acad Sci; Am Soc Biol Chemists. *Res:* Isolation and characterization of proteins, especially components of mammalian kinin system; methods for separating macromolecules. *Mailing Add:* 10508 Montrose Ave Bethesda MD 20814

PIERCE, JACK WARREN, b Springfield, Ill, Jan 23, 27; m 52; c 3. GEOLOGY. *Educ:* Univ Ill, BS, 49, MS, 50; Univ Kans, PhD(geol), 64. *Prof Exp:* Geologist, Pure Oil Co, 50-56, dist geologist, 56-60; assoc prof geol, George Washington Univ, 63-65; CUR SEDIMENTOLOGY, US NAT MUS, SMITHSONIAN INST, 65- *Concurrent Pos:* Adj prof, George Washington Univ, 65- *Mem:* Am Asn Petrol Geol; Soc Econ Paleont & Mineral; Int Asn Sedimentol; Geol Soc Am; Marine Technol Soc. *Res:* Sedimentology; stratigraphy; marine geology. *Mailing Add:* Div of Sedimentology US Nat Mus Smithsonian Inst Washington DC 20560

PIERCE, JAMES BENJAMIN, b St Catherines, Ont, Aug 11, 39; m 64; c 2. ORGANIC CHEMISTRY. *Educ:* Univ Toronto, BSc, 62, MSc, 64, PhD(chem), 66. *Prof Exp:* Res scientist chem, 67-81, SECT MGR ORG/ANAL, UNIROYAL LTD, 81- *Mem:* Chem Inst Can. *Res:* Organic chemistry particularly as applied to the synthesis of agricultural and rubber chemicals. *Mailing Add:* Uniroyal Res Labs 120 Huron St Guelph ON N1H 6N3 Can

PIERCE, JAMES BRUCE, b Edmon, Pa, Feb 15, 22; m 43. ELECTROCHEMISTRY. *Educ:* Thiel Col, BS, 50; Case Inst Technol, MS, 55, PhD(chem), 58. *Prof Exp:* Chemist, Jamestown Paint & Varnish Co, 50-52; asst petrol chem, Case Inst Technol, 52-54, instr gen & org chem, 54-58; prof, Lowell Technol Inst, 58-75, PROF ORG CHEM, UNIV LOWELL, 75- *Mem:* Am Chem Soc; Royal Soc Chem. *Res:* Organic semiconductors; heterogeneous and stereospecific catalysis; organic reaction mechanisms; selective ion electrodes; organic electrochemistry. *Mailing Add:* Dept of Chem Col Pure & Appl Sci Univ Lowell Lowell MA 01854

PIERCE, JAMES CLARENCE, surgery, immunology, see previous edition

PIERCE, JAMES KENNETH, b Kansas City, Mo, Aug 31, 44; m 66; c 2. CHEMISTRY. *Educ:* William Jewell Col, AB, 66; Univ Kans, PhD(chem), 70. *Prof Exp:* RES CHEMIST, DOW CHEM CO, 70- *Mem:* Am Chem Soc; Sigma Xi. *Res:* Synthetic organic chemistry; saran polymers. *Mailing Add:* Designed Latexes & Resins Res Dow Chem Co Midland MI 48640

PIERCE, JAMES OTTO, II, b Memphis, Tenn, May 15, 37; m 59; c 2. ENVIRONMENTAL HEALTH, INDUSTRIAL HEALTH. *Educ:* Univ Ala, BS, 58; Univ Cincinnati, MS, 63, ScD(indust health), 64. *Prof Exp:* Res asst indust hyg, Kettering Lab, Cincinnati, Ohio, 64, asst prof, 65; from asst prof to assoc prof environ health, Univ Cincinnati, 66-69; assoc prof bioeng & community Health & med pract & dir, Environ Trace Substances Ctr, Univ Mo-Columbia, 69-80; MEM FAC, DEPT BIOENG, UNIV SOUTHERN CALIF, 80- *Concurrent Pos:* Mem panel chromium, Nat Acad Sci-Nat Res Coun. *Mem:* Am Chem Soc; Am Indust Hyg Asn; Am Conf Govt Indust Hygienists; NY Acad Sci; fel Am Inst Chem. *Mailing Add:* Dept Bioeng Univ Southern Calif Los Angeles CA 90007

PIERCE, JOHN ALBERT, b Little Rock, Ark, Mar 10, 25; m 47; c 3. INTERNAL MEDICINE. *Educ:* Univ Ark, MD, 48. *Prof Exp:* Intern med, USPHS Hosp, Galveston, Tex, 48-49, resident internal med, New Orleans, La, 51-54; from instr to prof med, Med Ctr, Univ Ark, 54-67; assoc prof, 67-72, PROF MED, SCH MED, WASH UNIV, 72-; CHIEF DIV PULMONARY DIS, BARNES HOSP, 67- *Mem:* Am Fedn Clin Res; fel Am Col Physicians. *Res:* Mechanics of pulmonary ventilation; chemistry of sclero proteins. *Mailing Add:* Dept of Med Wash Univ Sch of Med St Louis MO 63111

PIERCE, JOHN FRANK, b Mountain City, Tenn, Dec 27, 20; m 40; c 2. ELECTRICAL ENGINEERING. *Educ:* Univ Tenn, BS, 43; Univ Pittsburgh, MS, 46, PhD(elec eng), 53. *Prof Exp:* Engr, Res Labs, Westinghouse Elec Corp, 43-46; asst prof elec eng, Univ Pittsburgh, 46-50, asst prof clin sci & head instrumentation group, Sch Med, 51-53; engr in chg res, Wright Mach Co, 53-54; from assoc prof to prof elec eng, 54-64, distinguished serv prof, 64-76, head dept, 68-76, PROF ELEC ENG, UNIV TENN, KNOXVILLE, 76- *Concurrent Pos:* Consult, Western State Psychiat Inst & Clin, 48-51, Am Inst Res, 52-53, Montefiore Inst Res, 53 & Instrumentation & Control Div, Oak Ridge Nat Lab, 59-69; chief engr, Pittsburgh Electronic Corp, 49-53; consult, ORTEC, Inc, 76- *Mem:* Sr mem Inst Elec & Electronics Engrs. *Res:* Design of radar equipment and electronic instruments; investigation of electro-shock; human engineering; automatic machinery; high-speed electonic circuits; nuclear electronics. *Mailing Add:* Dept Elec Eng Univ Tenn Knoxville TN 37916

PIERCE, JOHN GLYNN, physics, operations research, see previous edition

PIERCE, JOHN GREGORY, b Cleveland, Ohio, Jan 6, 42. APPLIED MATHEMATICS. *Educ:* Case Western Reserve Univ, BS, 63, MS, 67, PhD(math), 69. *Prof Exp:* Off Naval Res fel, Courant Inst Math Sci, NY Univ, 69-70; asst prof math, Univ Southern Calif, 70-76; assoc prof, 76-80, PROF MATH, CALIF STATE UNIV, FULLERTON, 80- *Mem:* Soc Indust & Appl Math; Asn Comput Mach. *Res:* Optimization and control theory applied to biological problems; spline functions and the finite element method. *Mailing Add:* Dept of Math Calif State Univ Fullerton CA 92634

PIERCE, JOHN GRISSIM, b San Jose, Calif, May 9, 20; m 49; c 4. BIOCHEMISTRY. *Educ:* Stanford Univ, AB, 41, AM, 42, PhD(biochem), 44. *Prof Exp:* Lab asst med biochem, Stanford Univ, 42, asst, Nutrit Proj, 44, actg instr biochem, 46-47; instr, Med Col, Cornell Univ, 48-49, asst prof, 49-52; asst prof, Sch Med, 52-55, assoc prof, Med Ctr, 55-61, vchmn, Dept Biol Chem, 63-79, PROF BIOL CHEM, MED CTR, UNIV CALIF, LOS ANGELES, 61-, CHMN DEPT, 79- *Concurrent Pos:* Fels, Am Chem Soc, Stanford Univ & Med Col, Cornell Univ, 46-47, Arthritis & Rheumatism Found, Cambridge Univ, 52-53 & Guggenheim Found, Mass Inst Technol, 60-61; Guggenheim Found fel, NIH, 76; Eli Lilly lectr award, Endocrine Soc Am, 71. *Mem:* AAAS; Am Chem Soc; Am Soc Biol Chem; Harvey Soc. *Res:* Pyrimidine requirements and inhibition of Neurospora; metabolism of biotin; pituitary hormones; chemistry of thyroid-stimulating hormone. *Mailing Add:* Dept of Biol Chem Univ of Calif Sch of Med Los Angeles CA 90024

PIERCE, JOHN ROBINSON, b Des Moines, Iowa, Mar 27, 10; m 64; c 2. ELECTRONICS, ELECTRICAL ENGINEERING. *Educ:* Calif Inst Technol, BS, 33, MS, 34, PhD(elec eng), 36. *Hon Degrees:* DEng, Newark Col Eng, 51, Carnegie Inst Technol, 64, Univ Bologna, 74; DSc, Northwestern Univ, 61, Yale Univ, 63, Polytech Inst Brooklyn, 63, Columbia Univ, 65, Univ Nev, 70; LLD, Univ Pa, 74. *Prof Exp:* Mem tech staff, Bell Tel Labs, Inc, 36-52, dir electronics res, 52-55, dir res elec commun, 55-58, dir res commun prin, 58-61, exec dir, 61-63, exec dir res commun prin & systs div, 62-65 & commun sci div, 65-71; prof eng, 71-80, EMER PROF ENG, CALIF INST TECHNOL, 80- *Concurrent Pos:* Ed, Inst Elec & Electronics Engrs, 54-55; coun, Nat Acad Sci, 71-74; chief technologist, Jet Propulsion Lab, 79-82; Marconi int fel, 79. *Honors & Awards:* Liebman Mem Prize, Inst Elec & Electronics Engrs, 47; Ballantine Medal, Franklin Inst, 60; H H Arnold Trophy, Air Force Asn, 62; Gen Hoyt St Vandenberg Trophy, Arnold Air Soc, 63; Edison Medal, 63; Valdemar Poulsen Medal, 63; Med of Sci, 63; H T Cedergren Medal, 64; John Scott Award, City of Philadelphia 74; Marconi Award, 74; Medal of Honor, Inst Elec & Electronics Engrs, 75; Founders Award, Nat Acad Eng, 77. *Mem:* Nat Acad Sci; Nat Acad Eng; fel Am Acad Arts & Sci; fel Am Phys Soc; fel Acoust Soc Am. *Res:* Vacuum tubes; microwave oscillators and amplifiers; low voltage microwave reflex oscillator; high current electron guns; traveling-wave amplifiers; satellites. *Mailing Add:* Calif Inst Technol Pasadena CA 91109

PIERCE, KEITH ROBERT, b Portland, Ore, Oct 15, 42; m 69. MATHEMATICS. *Educ:* Carnegie Inst Technol, BS, 65; Univ Wis-Madison, MA, 68, PhD(math), 70. *Prof Exp:* Instr math, Univ Wis-Rock County, 69-70; ASSOC PROF MATH, UNIV MO-COLUMBIA, 70- *Mem:* Am Math Soc; Math Asn Am. *Res:* Partially ordered groups. *Mailing Add:* Dept of Math Univ of Mo Columbia MO 65201

PIERCE, KENNETH LEE, b Washington, DC, Oct 21, 37; m 60; c 2. QUATERNARY GEOLOGY, GEOMORPHOLOGY. *Educ:* Stanford Univ, BS, 59; Yale Univ, PhD(geol), 64. *Prof Exp:* Geologist, 63-75, PROJ LEADER, QUATERNARY DATING & NEOTECTONICS, US GEOL SURV, 75- *Concurrent Pos:* Panel mem, Quaternary Geol & Geomorphol Div, Geol Soc Am, 74-76 & 78-80; comnr, Am Comn Stratig Nomenclature, 75-78. *Mem:* Geol Soc Am; Am Asn Quaternary Res. *Res:* Glacial geology and paleoglaciology of northern Yellowstone Park; Quaternary dating in western United States, especially combined relative-age and numerical methods; origin and chronology of loess and gravel of southern Idaho; Quaternary climate history. *Mailing Add:* US Geol Surv MS 913 Fed Ctr Denver CO 80225

PIERCE, KENNETH RAY, b Snyder, Tex, May 21, 34; m 56; c 2. VETERINARY PATHOLOGY, CLINICAL PATHOLOGY. *Educ:* Tex A&M Univ, DVM, 57, MS, 62, PhD(path), 65; Am Col Vet Path, Dipl, 64. *Prof Exp:* Instr vet anat, Tex A&M Univ, 57-59; practr vet med, San Angelo Vet Hosp, 59-61; from asst prof to assoc prof, 61-69, prof, 69-78, PROF & HEAD VET PATH, TEX A&M UNIV, 78- *Concurrent Pos:* NSF sci fac fel, 63-64; consult, Univ Tex M D Anderson Hosp & Tumor Inst, Houston; co-ed, J Vet Path; comparative pathologist, Inst Comparative Med, Baylor Col Med & Tex A&M Univ, 76-79. *Mem:* Int Acad Path; Am Vet Med Asn; Am Soc Vet Clin Path. *Res:* Pathology of metabolic diseases of animals; application of clinical pathology in the study and diagnosis of animal diseases; genetic influence on susceptibility to injury by exposure to low levels of toxins. *Mailing Add:* Dept of Vet Path Tex A&M Univ College Station TX 77843

PIERCE, LOUIS, b Ely, Minn, May 22, 29; m 54; c 5. PHYSICAL CHEMISTRY. *Educ:* Western Reserve Univ, BS, 51, MS, 52, PhD(phys chem), 54. *Prof Exp:* Res fel chem, Harvard Univ, 54-56; from asst prof to assoc prof, 56-63, PROF CHEM, UNIV NOTRE DAME, 63- *Concurrent Pos:* Sloan Found res fel, 61-65; NSF sr fel, 66-67; asst & actg dir comput ctr, Univ Notre Dame, 63-64. *Mem:* Am Chem Soc; Am Phys Soc; NY Acad Sci. *Res:* Molecular dynamics; microwave spectroscopy; molecular beams; low-temperature calorimetry. *Mailing Add:* Dept of Chem Univ of Notre Dame Notre Dame IN 46556

PIERCE, MADELENE EVANS, b Boston, Mass, Nov 7, 04. ECOLOGY. *Educ:* Radcliffe Col, AB, 26, AM, 27, PhD(zool), 33. *Prof Exp:* Instr zool, Smith Col, 27-29; instr, 31-38, from asst prof to prof, 38-70, EMER PROF ZOOL, VASSAR COL, 70- *Concurrent Pos:* Instr, Marine Biol Lab, Woods Hole, 43-52 & mem corp. *Mem:* Am Soc Zool; Am Soc Limnol & Oceanog; Weed Sci Soc Am; Am Inst Biol Sci. *Res:* Aquatic ecology; effect of weedicides on pond fauna and flora; effect of heated effluent on river fauna and flora. *Mailing Add:* Vassar Col Box 76 Poughkeepsie NY 12601

PIERCE, MARION ARMBRUSTER, b Folsomdale, NY, Mar 17, 10; m 47; c 2. PHYSICAL CHEMISTRY. *Educ:* Mt Holyoke Col, AB, 30; Bryn Mawr Col, AM, 32, PhD(chem), 34. *Prof Exp:* Asst chem, Barnard Col, Columbia Univ, 34-35, instr, 43-44, asst prof, 45-46; phys chemist, Res Lab, US Steel Corp, 35-43; SR RES ASSOC, E I DU PONT DE NEMOURS & CO, INC, ARLINGTON, NJ, 46- *Mem:* Am Chem Soc. *Res:* Chemical thermodynamics; electrochemistry; physico-chemical properties of metals; surface chemistry; high polymers. *Mailing Add:* 1706 N Bancroft Pkwy Wilmington DE 19806

PIERCE, MATTHEW LEE, b San Francisco, Calif, Nov 18, 52. ATOMIC SPECTROSCOPY. *Educ:* Univ San Francisco, BS, 74; Ariz State Univ, PhD(chem), 81. *Prof Exp:* Teaching assoc quantitative & instrumental anal, Ariz State Univ, 76-78, res assoc, 78-81; ENVIRON CHEMIST, ENVIRON SERV, TEX DIV, DOW CHEM, 81- *Concurrent Pos:* Consult, SEM/TEC Labs, 77-80. *Mem:* Am Chem Soc; Soc Appl Spectros. *Res:* Rates, extents and mechanisms of adsorption on oxide surfaces as well as oxidation kinetics of various arsenic species. *Mailing Add:* Environ Serv B-1226 Tex Div Dow Chem Freeport TX 77541

PIERCE, NATHANIEL FIELD, b Rudyard, Mich, July 27, 34; m 66; c 3. INFECTIOUS DISEASES. *Educ:* Univ Mich, MD, 58. *Prof Exp:* Instr med, Univ Louisville, 63-64 & Univ Southern Calif, 64-65; from instr to asst prof, 66-72, assoc prof, 72-79, PROF MED, SCH MED, JOHNS HOPKINS UNIV, 79- *Concurrent Pos:* Consult cholera, WHO, 71-74; mem, Cholera Adv Comt, Nat Inst Allergy & Infectious Dis, 71-73, Nat Inst Allergy & Infectious Dis res career develop award, 71; vis fel immunol, St Cross Col, Oxford Univ, 73-74; mem, Cholera Panel, US-Japan Coop Med Sci Prog, 72-76, chmn, 77-; mem adv comt health, biomed res & develop, Comn Int Rels, Nat Acad Sci. *Mem:* Infectious Dis Soc Am; Am Col Physicians; Am Soc Clin Invest; Am Fedn Clin Res; Am Soc Microbiol. *Res:* The mucosal immune system, especially that of the gut; improved means of immunizing against enteric infections. *Mailing Add:* Dept Med Baltimore City Hosps 4940 Eastern Ave Baltimore MD 21224

PIERCE, NORWIN C, b Ill, Dec 1, 21; m 42; c 4. CHEMICAL ENGINEERING. *Educ:* Univ Ill, BS, 42, MS, 47, PhD(chem eng), 49. *Prof Exp:* Asst chem & chem eng, Univ Ill, 46-49; res supvr, E I du Pont de Nemours & Co, Inc, 49-55, res assoc, 55-64, res fel, Textile Fibers Dept, 64-79; CONSULT TEXTILE FIBERS & ENG, 79- *Concurrent Pos:* vis prof math, East Carolina Univ, 81- *Mem:* Am Inst Chem Engrs. *Res:* Kinetics of nonuniform gas mixtures; thermal diffusion in the critical region; research and development of polymers and synthetic fibers. *Mailing Add:* 205 Pineview Dr Greenville NC 27834

PIERCE, OGDEN ROSS, chemistry, see previous edition

PIERCE, PERCY EVERETT, b Bayonne, NJ, Jan 16, 32; m 58; c 4. PHYSICAL CHEMISTRY. *Educ:* Case Western Univ, BS, 53; Yale Univ, MS, 56, PhD(chem), 58. *Prof Exp:* Asst chem, Case Western Reserve Univ, 53-55; asst chem, Yale Univ, 55-57; asst prof, Case Western Reserve Univ, 58-63; sect leader fundamental res, coatings & resins, Res Ctr, Glidden Co, 63-67, sr scientist, 67-69; scientist, 69-74, sr scientist, 74-78, MGR PHYS & ANAT RES, COATINGS & RESIN RES CTR, PPG INDUSTS, INC, 78- *Honors & Awards:* Mattiello lectr, Fedn Soc Coating Technol, 80. *Mem:* AAAS; Am Inst Chem; Am Chem Soc; Fedn Soc Coating Technol. *Res:* Rheology; physical chemistry of polymers and coatings. *Mailing Add:* Coatings & Resin Res Ctr PPG Indust Inc PO Box 9 Allison Park PA 15101

PIERCE, R(OBERT) DEAN, b Saginaw, Mich, Dec 7, 29; m 52; c 3. CHEMICAL ENGINEERING. *Educ:* Univ Mich, BS, 51, MS, 52, PhD(chem eng), 55. *Prof Exp:* Sr engr, Atomic Energy Div, Babcock & Wilcox Co, 54-58; CHEM ENGR, ARGONNE NAT LAB, 58- *Mem:* Am Inst Chem Engrs; Electrochem Soc; Catalysis Soc; Sigma Xi; Combustion Inst. *Res:* Liquid metal and liquid salt technology; molten-carbonate fuel cell technology; nuclear reactor fuel reprocessing, nuclear reactor safety; hydrocarbon combustion; hydrocarbon refining. *Mailing Add:* Argonne Nat Lab Chem Eng Div Bldg 205 9700 S Cass Ave Argonne IL 60439

PIERCE, RICHARD HARRY, JR, environmental chemistry, see previous edition

PIERCE, RICHARD SCOTT, b Calif, Feb 26, 27; m 71; c 2. ALGEBRA. *Educ:* Calif Inst Technol, BS, 50, PhD(math), 52. *Prof Exp:* Fel math, Off Naval Res, Yale Univ, 52-53; Jewett res fel, Harvard Univ, 53-55; from asst prof to prof, Univ Wash, 55-70; prof, Univ Hawaii, 70-75; PROF MATH, UNIV ARIZ, 75- *Concurrent Pos:* NSF sr fel, 61-62. *Mem:* Am Math Soc; Math Asn Am; Asn Symbolic Logic. *Res:* Lattice and ring theory; Boolean algebras; Abelian groups. *Mailing Add:* Dept of Math Univ of Ariz Tucson AZ 85721

PIERCE, ROBERT CHARLES, b Newark, NJ, Mar 2, 47; m 70; c 1. PHYSICAL CHEMISTRY. *Educ:* Rutgers Univ, BA, 69; Cornell Univ, MS, 72, PhD(phys chem), 74. *Prof Exp:* Res assoc biol mass spectrometry, Brookhaven Nat Lab, 74-75; res chemist, 75-78, sect head, 78-80, MGR CHEM RES, COLGATE-PALMOLIVE RES & DEVELOP, 80- *Mem:* Sigma Xi; Am Oil Chemists Soc; Am Chem Soc. *Res:* Gaseous ion chemistry; application of mass spectrometry to the structure elucidation of biologically important materials; physical chemistry of surface active agents. *Mailing Add:* Colgate-Palmolive Res & Develop 909 River Rd Piscataway NJ 08854

PIERCE, ROBERT HENRY HORACE, JR, b Pittsburgh, Pa, July 18, 10; m 47; c 2. PHYSICAL CHEMISTRY. *Educ:* Western Reserve Univ, BA, 31; Case Inst Technol, BS, 31; Ohio State Univ, MA, 37, PhD(phys chem), 40. *Prof Exp:* Phys chemist, Res Lab, US Steel Corp, NJ, 31-46; assoc dir, Cryogenic Lab, Res Found, Ohio State Univ, 46-49; res phys chemist, Ammonia Dept, 49-53, res supvr, Polychem Dept, 53-58, sr res chemist, 58-61, RES ASSOC, PLASTICS DEPT, E I DU PONT DE NEMOURS & CO, INC, 61- *Concurrent Pos:* Res engr, Eng Exp Sta, Ohio State Univ, 36-39. *Mem:* Am Chem Soc. *Res:* Physical properties of metals; refractories; thermal expansion; thermal conductivity; pyrometry; stress analysis; state of gases; cryogenics; x-ray diffraction; polymers. *Mailing Add:* 1706 N Bancroft Pkwy Wilmington DE 19806

PIERCE, ROBERT WESLEY, b Atlanta, Ga, Apr 4, 45; m 69; c 2. MICROPALEONTOLOGY, GEOLOGY. *Educ:* Univ Ala, BS, 67; La State Univ, MS, 69, PhD(paleont), 75. *Prof Exp:* Instr geol, La State Univ, 73-74; prof Auburn Univ, 74-77; RES SCIENTIST PALEONT, AMOCO PROD CO, STANDARD OIL IND, 77- *Concurrent Pos:* Res assoc, Cambridge Univ, 70-71. *Mem:* Soc Econ Paleontologists & Mineralogists; Sigma Xi. *Res:* Biostratigraphy of cenozoic calcareous nannoplankton; world-wide cenozoic stratigraphy; composite standard graphic correlations. *Mailing Add:* Amoco Prod Co Res Ctr PO Box 591 Tulsa OK 74102

PIERCE, ROBERT WILLIAM, b Des Moines, Iowa, Feb 26, 40; m 64. GEOLOGY. *Educ:* Monmouth Col, BA, 62; Univ Ill, MS, 67, PhD(geol), 69. *Prof Exp:* Instr geol, Univ Ill, 67-69; asst prof, 69-76, ASSOC PROF GEOL, UNIV FLA, 76- *Mem:* AAAS; Am Asn Petrol Geol; Geol Soc Am; Int Paleont Union; Soc Econ Paleont & Mineral. *Res:* Conodont biostratigraphy; electron microscopy; Paleozoic stratigraphy; field geology. *Mailing Add:* Dept of Geol Univ of Fla Gainesville FL 32601

PIERCE, RONALD CECIL, b Arnprior, Ont, Feb 25, 49; m 70; c 2. ENVIRONMENTAL SCIENCES. *Educ:* Univ Guelph, Ont, BSc, 70; York Univ, Downsview, Ont, PhD(chem), 75. *Prof Exp:* RES OFFICER ENVIRON SCI, NAT RES COUN CAN, 75- *Res:* Compilation and critical assessment of the scientific criteria required for the establishment of environmentally relevant standards pertaining to the aquatic and atmospheric environments. *Mailing Add:* Nat Res Coun Can 100 Sussex Dr Ottawa ON K1A 0R6 Can

PIERCE, RUSSELL DALE, b Iselin, Pa, July 17, 38; m 65. MAGNETISM. *Educ:* Carnegie Inst Technol, BS, 60, MS, 61, PhD(physics), 66. *Prof Exp:* Instr physics, Carnegie Inst Technol, 65-66; MEM TECH STAFF, BELL LABS, 66- *Mem:* Sigma Xi. *Res:* Low temperature calorimetry of dilute magnetic solids; magnetic properties of solids, especially materials applicable to memory devices; instrumentation for magnetic bubble materials preparation and characterization. *Mailing Add:* Bell Labs Murray Hill NJ 07974

PIERCE, SIDNEY KENDRICK, b Holyoke, Mass, Sept 19, 44; m 74; c 2. COMPARATIVE PHYSIOLOGY. *Educ:* Univ Miami, BEd, 66; Fla State Univ, PhD(physiol), 70. *Prof Exp:* Asst prof, 70-73, assoc prof, 73-78, PROF ZOOL, UNIV MD, COLLEGE PARK, 78- *Concurrent Pos:* NSF res grants, 73-75, 75-77; NIH grants, 77- mem corp, Marine Biol Lab, 73-; assoc ed, J Exp Zool, 80-; ed, Mach Biol, 81- *Mem:* AAAS; Am Soc Zool. *Res:* Physiological interactions of marine invertebrates with the environment and the control of cell membrane permeability. *Mailing Add:* Dept of Zool Univ of Md College Park MD 20742

PIERCE, TIMOTHY ELLIS, b York, Pa, Aug 6, 41; m 65; c 2. NUCLEAR CHEMISTRY, MEDICAL TECHNOLOGY. *Educ:* Kenyon Col, BA, 63; Univ Rochester, PhD(nuclear chem), 68. *Prof Exp:* Sr res chemist, Corning Glass Works, 68-75, mkt develop mgr, Med Prod Div, 75-76, tech mgr, 76-77, mkt mgr, Corning Int Serv SAm, 78-79, REGIONAL MGR, CORNING MED-JAPAN, 80- *Res:* Ranges of heavy ions in matter. *Mailing Add:* Corning Int Serv SA 1-9-20 Akasaka Minato-Ku Tokyo Japan

PIERCE, WAYNE STANLEY, b Atascadero, Calif, Mar 8, 42; m 64; c 1. PLANT PHYSIOLOGY. *Educ:* Humboldt State Col, AB, 64; Wash State Univ, MS, 67, PhD(bot), 71. *Prof Exp:* Asst prof, 71-74, assoc prof biol, 75-81, PROF BIOL, CALIF STATE COL, STANISLAUS, 81- *Concurrent Pos:* Fel, Univ Houston, 78. *Mem:* Am Soc Plant Physiol. *Res:* Mineral nutrition; cellular ion-transport mechanisms; electrophysiology. *Mailing Add:* Dept of Biol Sci Calif State Col Stanislaus Turlock CA 95380

PIERCE, WILLIAM ARTHUR, JR, b Dayton, Ohio, Apr 11, 18; m 46; c 2. MICROBIOLOGY. *Educ:* Ohio Wesleyan Univ, BA, 41; Univ Wis, MS, 47, PhD(med microbiol), 49. *Prof Exp:* Instr microbiol, 49, from asst prof to assoc prof, 50-60, PROF MICROBIOL & IMMUNOL, SCH MED, TULANE UNIV, 61- *Mem:* Am Soc Microbiol; Am Acad Microbiol. *Res:* In vitro phagocytosis studies; antigens of Neisseria Gonorrhoeae. *Mailing Add:* Dept of Microbiol Sch of Med Tulane Univ 1430 Tulane Ave New Orleans LA 70112

PIERCE, WILLIAM G, b Gettysburg, SDak, Sept 24, 04; m 30; c 3. STRUCTURAL GEOLOGY, EARTH SCIENCES, GENERAL. *Educ:* Univ SDak, AB, 27; Princeton Univ, MA, 29, PhD(geol), 31. *Prof Exp:* Field asst, SDak Geol Surv, 26; asst, Princeton Univ, 28-29; geologist, 29-46, staff geologist, Mo River Basin, 46-47, chief, Western Sect Fuels Br, 48-57 & Radioactive Waste Disposal & Salt Deposits, 57-60, RES GEOLOGIST, US GEOL SURV, 61- *Concurrent Pos:* NSF res grant tectonics of Italian Apennines & Swiss Jura, 63; adv lignite resources of Greece, Econ Coop Admin, 49; NSF & Nat Sci Coun Repub China res grant, Tectonics of Western Taiwan, 74-75. *Honors & Awards:* US Dept Interior Distinguished Serv Award, 65. *Mem:* AAAS; fel Geol Soc Am; Am Asn Petrol Geologists. *Res:* Oil, gas and coal resources; structural geology; stratigraphy; radioactive waste disposal. *Mailing Add:* 14380 Manuella Rd Los Altos Hills CA 94022

PIERCE, WILLIAM H, b Washington, DC, July 10, 33; m 56; c 2. ELECTRICAL ENGINEERING. *Educ:* Harvard Univ, AB, 55; Stanford Univ, MS, 59, PhD(elec eng), 61. *Prof Exp:* From asst prof to assoc prof elec eng, Carnegie Inst Technol, 61-69; PROF ELEC ENG, UNIV LOUISVILLE, 69- *Mem:* Inst Elec & Electronics Engrs. *Res:* Communications; biomedical engineering and medical science. *Mailing Add:* Dept of Elec Eng Univ of Louisville Louisville KY 40208

PIERCE, WILLIAM R, b Topeka, Kans, Aug 13, 15; m 42; c 2. FOREST MANAGEMENT. *Educ:* Wash Univ, BS, 40, PhD, 58; Yale Univ, MS, 47. *Prof Exp:* Dist ranger, US Forest Serv, 45-55; from assoc prof to prof forestry, Univ Mont, 55-81; RETIRED. *Mem:* AAAS; Soc Am Foresters; Int Union Forest Res Org; Sigma Xi; Am Forestry Asn. *Res:* Forest resource management planning and inventory; statistics, computer modeling and programming. *Mailing Add:* Sch of Forestry Univ of Mont Missoula MT 59812

PIERCE, WILLIAM SCHULER, b Wilkes Barre, Pa, Jan 12, 37; m 65; c 2. CARDIAC SURGERY. *Educ:* Lehigh Univ, BS, 58; Univ Pa, MD, 62. *Prof Exp:* Surg resident, Univ Pa Hosp, 62-69, sr cardiac surg resident, 69-70; from asst prof to assoc prof, 70-77, PROF THORACIC SURG, COL MED, PA STATE UNIV, 77- *Concurrent Pos:* USPHS grants, Nat Heart, Lung & Blood Inst, Bethesda, Md, 77-80 & 78-82. *Honors & Awards:* Becton-Dickinson Career Achievement Award, Asn Advan Med Instrumentation, 77. *Mem:* AMA; Am Col Surgeons; Soc Univ Surgeons; Am Surg Asn; Am Soc Artificial Internal Organs (secy-treas, 80-82). *Res:* Development of paracorporeal and implantable left ventricular assist devices and the artificial heart; mechanical cardiac valves. *Mailing Add:* Pa State Univ Col of Med 500 University Dr Hershey PA 17033

PIERCEY, MONTFORD F, b Meriden, Conn, July 25, 42; m 65; c 2. PHARMACOLOGY, NEUROBIOLOGY. *Educ:* Boston Univ, AB, 65, MS, 67; Yeshiva Univ, PhD(pharmacol), 72. *Prof Exp:* Fel, Albert Einstein Col Med, 72-74; res scientist, 74-82, SR RES SCIENTIST, THE UPJOHN CO, 82- *Mem:* Soc Neurosci; Am Soc Pharmacol & Exp Therapeut; Am Pain Soc; Int Narcotic Res Conf; AAAS. *Res:* Neurophysiology of motor control; neural control of respiration and circulation; analgesic drugs and their mechanism of action; neurotransmitter identification; anti-diarrheal mechanisms; pharmacological evaluation of central nervous system drugs and neuropeptides. *Mailing Add:* Upjohn Co Kalamazoo MI 49001

PIERCY, GEORGE ROBERT, b Vancouver, BC, May 27, 28; m 52; c 4. METALLURGY, SOLID STATE PHYSICS. *Educ:* Univ BC, BASc, 51, MASc, 52; Univ Birmingham, PhD(metall), 54. *Prof Exp:* Res scientist, Atomic Energy Can, 55-63; vis prof metall, Benares Hindu Univ, 64-65; res scientist, Atomic Energy Can, 65-69; PROF METALL & MAT SCI, MCMASTER UNIV, 69- *Res:* Deformation and irradiation damage in metals. *Mailing Add:* Dept of Metall McMaster Univ Hamilton ON L8S 4L8 Can

PIERINGER, ARTHUR PAUL, b Weehauken, NJ, Oct 30, 24; m 49; c 5. PLANT BREEDING. *Educ:* Univ Ky, BSAgr, 51; Cornell Univ, PhD, 56. *Prof Exp:* Asst, Cornell Univ, 51-56; asst horticulturist, 56-72, ASSOC HORTICULTURIST, CITRUS EXP STA, UNIV FLA, 72- *Mem:* Am Soc Hort Sci. *Res:* Citrus variety improvement. *Mailing Add:* Agr Res Educ Ctr Univ of Fla Lake Alfred FL 33850

PIERINGER, RONALD ARTHUR, b Jersey City, NJ, Nov 23, 35; m 57; c 2. BIOCHEMISTRY. *Educ:* Lebanon Valley Col, BS, 57; Univ Wis, MS, 59, PhD(physiol chem), 61. *Prof Exp:* Res assoc biochem of lipids, Harvard Med Sch, 61-63; from instr to assoc prof, 63-74, PROF BIOCHEM, SCH MED, TEMPLE UNIV, 74- *Concurrent Pos:* NIH fel, 61-63, Nat Inst Neurol Dis & Stroke res career develop award, 71-76; res grants, NSF & Nat Inst Neurol Dis & Stroke. *Mem:* Am Soc Biol Chem; Am Soc Neurochem; Am Oil Chem Soc; Am Chem Soc. *Res:* Metabolism and function of lipids in bacteria and animals. *Mailing Add:* Dept of Biochem Temple Univ Sch of Med Philadelphia PA 19140

PIERMARINI, GASPER J, b Leominster, Mass, Apr 26, 33; m 60; c 2. PHYSICAL CHEMISTRY, CRYSTALLOGRAPHY. *Educ:* Boston Univ, AB, 55; Am Univ, PhD(phys chem), 71. *Prof Exp:* PHYS CHEMIST, NAT BUR STAND, 58- *Concurrent Pos:* Adj prof chem, Am Univ, Washington, 76- *Honors & Awards:* Spec Achievement Award, US Dept Com, 73, 74, Gold Medal Award, 74. *Mem:* AAAS; Am Chem Soc; Am Crystallog Asn; Sigma Xi. *Res:* Crystal structures of inorganic compounds, especially determination of crystal structures of materials under high pressure; application of x-ray diffraction methods in solids under high pressure; high pressure measurement by ruby fluorescence method; diamond anvil cells. *Mailing Add:* Nat Bur of Standards Washington DC 20234

PIEROTTI, ROBERT AMADEO, b Newark, NJ, Nov 13, 31; m 59; c 2. PHYSICAL CHEMISTRY. *Educ:* Pomona Col, BA, 54; Univ Wash, PhD(chem), 58. *Prof Exp:* Asst chem, Pomona Col, 53-54 & Univ Wash, 54-58; instr, Univ Nev, 58-60; from asst prof to assoc prof, 60-68, PROF CHEM, GA INST TECHNOL, 68- *Concurrent Pos:* NATO sr fel, Univ Bristol, 68. *Mem:* AAAS; Am Chem Soc; Am Phys Soc; Royal Soc Chem. *Res:* Adsorption; interaction of gases with solids; solutions. *Mailing Add:* Sch of Chem Ga Inst of Technol Atlanta GA 30332

PIERPONT, CORTLANDT GODWIN, b New York, NY, Jan 26, 42; m 63; c 2. INORGANIC CHEMISTRY. *Educ:* Columbia Univ, BS, 67; Brown Univ, PhD(chem), 71. *Prof Exp:* Asst prof, WVa Univ, 71-75; ASSOC PROF CHEM, UNIV COLO, 75- *Mem:* Am Crystallog Asn; Am Chem Soc; Royal Soc Chem. *Res:* Organo-transition metal chemistry; coordination complexes of transition metals; x-ray crystallography. *Mailing Add:* Dept of Chem Univ of Colo Boulder CO 80302

PIERRARD, JOHN MARTIN, b Chicago, Ill, Mar 26, 28; m 64; c 5. AIR POLLUTION, ENVIRONMENTAL SCIENCES. *Educ:* Ill Inst Technol, BS, 52; Tex A&M Univ, MS, 58; Univ Wash, PhD, 69. *Prof Exp:* Res assoc atmospheric chem, Cloud Physics Proj, Univ Chicago, 52-53; res assoc micrometeorol, Res Found, Tex A&M Univ, 57-58, res scientist, 58-59; assoc meteorologist, Armour Res Found, 59-61, res meteorologist, 61-62; res scientist, Nat Ctr Atmospheric Res, 62-66; atmospheric chemist, 69-72, eng assoc, 72-78, ENG FEL, E I DU PONT DE NEMOURS & CO, INC, 79- *Honors & Awards:* Horning Mem Award, Soc Automotive Engrs. *Res:* Aerosol physics and chemistry; meteorological sensory systems; evaluation of social, econmic and environmental quality impacts of air pollution control strategies. *Mailing Add:* E I du Pont de Nemours & Co Inc Wilmington DE 19898

PIERRE, DONALD ARTHUR, b Bloomington, Wis, July 2, 36; m 59; c 3. CONTROL SYSTEMS, OPTIMIZATION TECHNIQUES. *Educ:* Univ Ill, Urbana, BS, 58; Univ Southern Calif, MS, 60; Univ Wis, PhD(elec eng), 62. *Prof Exp:* Res asst, Ill State Geol Surv, 55-58; mem tech staff, Hughes Aircraft Co, 58-60; asst prof elec eng, 62-65, assoc prof, 65-69, prof, 69-79, head elec eng, 79-80, HEAD ELEC ENG & COMPUT SCI, MONT STATE UNIV, 80- *Concurrent Pos:* Head syst group, Electronics Res Lab, Mont State Univ, 69-79; regist prof engr, State Mont, 75- *Mem:* Sr mem Inst Elec & Electronics Engrs; sr mem Instrument Soc Am; Sigma Xi; Am Soc Eng Educ. *Res:* Design of control systems and in the development of optimization algorithms; computer control; author of two books and numerous technical pulications. *Mailing Add:* Dept Elec Eng & Comput Sci Mont State Univ Bozeman MT 59717

PIERRE, LEON L, b Caracas, Venezuela, June 26, 22; m 65. BACTERIOLOGY, BIOCHEMISTRY. *Educ:* Dalhousie Univ, BS, 52; Fordham Univ, MS, 58, PhD(enzyme chem), 61. *Prof Exp:* Asst prof biol, Long Island Univ, 61-67; assoc prof, City Univ New York, 67-68; assoc prof biol, 68-69, ASSOC PROF LIFE SCI, NEW YORK INST TECHNOL, 69- *Mem:* Sigma Xi; Soc Exp Biol & Med; fel Royal Soc London. *Res:* Enzyme research into the function of the symbionts and fat bodies of the cockroach, Leucophaea maderae. *Mailing Add:* New York Inst of Technol 1855 Broadway New York NY 10023

PIERRE, ROBERT V, b Athens, Ohio, Aug 24, 28; m 55; c 2. INTERNAL MEDICINE. *Educ:* Univ Ohio, BS, 50; Northwestern Univ, MD, 54; Am Bd Internal Med, dipl, 63; cert hemat. *Prof Exp:* Intern, Chicago Wesley Mem Hosp, 54-55; resident internal med, Vet Admin Res Hosp, Chicago, 55-60, clin investr, 62-65, chief hemat sect, 65-67; asst prof med, 67-73, PROF LAB MED & INTERNAL MED, MAYO GRAD SCH MED, UNIV MINN, ROCHESTER, 73-, CONSULT LAB MED, MAYO CLIN, 67- *Concurrent Pos:* Fel hemat, Vet Admin Res Hosp, Chicago, 60-62; asst prof, Northwestern Univ, 65-67. *Mem:* Fel Am Col Physicians; Am Soc Hemat; Int Soc Hemat; Sigma Xi; Am Soc Clin Pathologists. *Res:* Cytogenetic studies in leukemia and preleukemia, automated hematology instruments. *Mailing Add:* 200 First St SW Rochester MN 55901

PIERRE, WILLIAM HENRY, b Brussels, Wis, Aug 2, 98; m 28; c 3. AGRONOMY, SOIL FERTILITY. *Educ:* Univ Wis, BS, 21, MS, 23, PhD(soil sci), 25. *Prof Exp:* Asst soil surveyor, SDak State Col, 21-22; assoc soil chemist, Exp Sta, Auburn Univ, 25-29; assoc prof agron & assoc agronomist, WVa Univ, 29-36, prof agron & head dept agron & genetics, 36-38; prof soils, 38-74, head dept agron, 38-64, EMER PROF, IOWA STATE UNIV, 74- *Concurrent Pos:* Deleg, Inter-Am Conf Agr, Mexico City, 42; mem, Food & Agr Orgn Mission, Uruguay, 50; mem agr bd, Nat Acad Sci-Nat Res Coun, 55-62; AID consult, Univ Rep Uruguay, 64-65. *Honors & Awards:* Nitrogen Res Award, Am Soc Agron, 31. *Mem:* Fel AAAS; hon mem & fel Am Soc Agron (vpres, 46, pres, 47); hon mem Soil Sci Soc Am (vpres, 39, pres, 40); Int Soc Soil Sci; Soil Conserv Soc Am. *Res:* Soil chemistry and fertility; soil acidity; base exchange; acidity and basicity of fertilizers; mineral nutrition and cation-anion balance of plants; aluminum and manganese toxicity to plants; corn yield-N nutrition relationship; phosphorous availability in soils. *Mailing Add:* Dept Agron Iowa State Univ Ames IA 50010

PIERRET, ROBERT FRANCIS, b East Cleveland, Ohio, Aug 20, 40; m 65; c 3. ELECTRICAL ENGINEERING, SOLID STATE PHYSICS. *Educ:* Case Inst Technol, BS, 62; Univ Ill, Urbana, MS, 63, PhD(physics), 66. *Prof Exp:* Res assoc elec eng, Univ Ill, Urbana, 66-67, asst prof, 67-70; assoc prof, 70-77, PROF ELEC ENG, PURDUE UNIV, 77- *Mem:* Inst Elec & Electronics Engrs. *Res:* Solid state devices and device physics, with special emphasis on metal-silicon dioxide-silicon devices and monolithic surface acoustic wave devices. *Mailing Add:* Sch of Elec Eng Purdue Univ West Lafayette IN 47907

PIERRO, LOUIS JOHN, b Bristol, Pa, Sept 5, 31; m 55; c 2. BIOLOGY. *Educ:* St Joseph's Col, BS, 52; Marquette Univ, MS, 54; Brown Univ, PhD(biol), 57. *Prof Exp:* USPHS res fel, Calif Inst Technol, 57-58; asst prof biol, Wheeling Col, 58-60; assoc prof animal genetics, 60-66, PROF ANIMAL GENETICS, UNIV CONN, 66-, HEAD DEPT, 65- *Mem:* AAAS; Genetics Soc Am; Am Genetic Asn; Am Soc Zoologists; Soc Develop Biol. *Res:* Developmental genetics; developmental abnormalities. *Mailing Add:* Dept of Animal Genetics Univ of Conn Storrs CT 06268

PIERSKALLA, WILLIAM P, b St Cloud, Minn, Oct 22, 34; m 53; c 3. OPERATIONS RESEARCH. *Educ:* Harvard Univ, AB, 56, MBA, 58; Univ Pittsburgh, MS, 62; Stanford Univ, MS & PhD(opers res), 65. *Prof Exp:* From asst prof to assoc prof opers res, Case Western Reserve, 65-68; assoc prof & actg dir comput sci opers res ctr, Southern Methodist Univ, 68-70; from assoc prof to prof indust eng & mgt sci, Northwestern Univ, 70-78; PROF DECISION SCI DEPT, WHARTON SCH, UNIV PA, 78-, EXEC DIR, LEONARD DAVIS INST HEALTH ECON & DIR, NAT HEALTH CARE MGT CTR, 78- *Concurrent Pos:* Ed, Opers Res J, 79-81. *Mem:* Soc Indust & Appl Math; Asn Comput Mach; Opers Res Soc Am (secy, 77-80, pres elect, 81-82, pres, 82-83); Inst Mgt Sci. *Res:* Inventory theory and mathematical programming; health care delivery. *Mailing Add:* Colonial Penn Ctr Univ Pa 3641 Locust Walk CE Philadelphia PA 19174

PIERSMA, BERNARD J, b Utica, NY, Mar 23, 38; m 66; c 2. PHYSICAL CHEMISTRY. *Educ:* Colgate Univ, BA, 59; St Lawrence Univ, MS, 61; Univ Pa, PhD(phys chem), 65. *Prof Exp:* Nat Acad Sci-Nat Res Coun res assoc electrochem, Naval Res Lab, 65-66; asst prof chem, Eastern Baptist Col, 66-70, assoc prof, 70-71; PROF PHYS CHEM, HOUGHTON COL, 71- *Concurrent Pos:* sabbatical leave, univ resident res prof, Frank J Seiler Res Lab, US Air Force Acad, 81-82. *Mem:* Am Chem Soc; Electrochem Soc; Am Sci Affiliation; Am Asn Univ Prof. *Res:* Kinetics and mechanisms of anodic organic oxidation reactions; hydrogen and oxygen electrodes; study of the electrical double layer; fundamental electrochemistry of physiological electrodes; electrocatalysis; electrochemistry of room temperature molten salts, espceially imidazolium chloride/aluminum chloride melts. *Mailing Add:* Dept Chem Houghton Col Houghton NY 14744

PIERSOL, ALLAN GERALD, b Pittsburgh, Pa, June 2, 30; m 58; c 3. MECHANICAL VIBRATIONS, STATISTICAL DATA ANALYSIS. *Educ:* Univ Ill, BS, 52; Univ Calif, Los Angeles, MS, 61. *Prof Exp:* Res engr, Douglas Aircraft Co, Inc, 52-59; tech staff, Ramo-Wooldridge Corp, 59-63; vpres, Measurement Analysis Corp, 63-71; PRIN SCIENTIST, BOLT BERANEK & NEWMAN INC, 71- *Concurrent Pos:* Lectr, Univ Calif, Los Angeles, 65-, Univ Southern Calif, 68- *Mem:* Am Soc Mech Engrs; Acoustical Soc Am. *Res:* Applications of random process theory to mechanical shock, vibration, and acoustic noise problems; author of three books on random data analysis and applications. *Mailing Add:* 23021 Brenford St Woodland Hills CA 91364

PIERSON, BERNICE FRANCES, b Auburn, Nebr, Aug 17, 06. PROTOZOOLOGY. *Educ:* Western Reserve Univ, AB, 28; Johns Hopkins Univ, AM, 37, PhD(protozool), 41. *Prof Exp:* Asst zool, Schs Dent & Pharm, Univ Md, 28-31, 36-38; instr biol, State Teachers Col, Towson, Md, 34-35 & Nat Park Col, 41-42; biologist, Off Sci Res & Develop & Nat Defense Res Coun, Johns Hopkins Univ, 42-45; instr anat & physiol, Dept Nursing Educ, Univ Baltimore, 45-46; from instr to prof, 46-73, chmn dept, 66-69, EMER PROF BIOL, MONTGOMERY COL, 73- *Mem:* AAAS; Soc Protozool; Am Soc Zool; Am Micros Soc; Sigma Xi. *Res:* Morphology and physiology of protozoa. *Mailing Add:* 19805 Bramble Bush Drive Gaithersburg MD 20879

PIERSON, BEVERLY KANDA, b Syracuse, NY, Jan 9, 44. MICROBIOLOGY. *Educ:* Oberlin Col, BA, 66; Univ Ore, MA, 69, PhD(biol), 73. *Prof Exp:* Asst prof biol, Oberlin Col, 74-75; ASST PROF BIOL, UNIV PUGET SOUND, 75- *Mem:* Am Soc Microbiol; Sigma Xi; AAAS. *Res:* Photosynthesis in green bacteria; photosynthetic reactions; organization and composition of the photosynthetic apparatus; pigments and their regulation; relations to oxygen. *Mailing Add:* Dept of Biol Univ of Puget Sound Tacoma WA 98416

PIERSON, DAVID W, b Ottumwa, Iowa, Jan 16, 26; m 57; c 2. SCIENCE EDUCATION, CONSERVATION. *Educ:* Colo State Col, AB, 51; State Col Iowa, MA, 57; Univ Mo, EdD, 62. *Prof Exp:* Teacher high sch, Colo, 52-55 & Iowa, 56-57; instr appl sci, Monticello Col, 57-58; teacher high sch, Iowa, 58-59; part-time instr educ, Univ Mo, 60-62; ASSOC PROF BIOL, FT HAYS KANS STATE COL, 62- *Concurrent Pos:* Dir, Kans Jr Acad Sci, 62-69; vis lectr, Scientist Prog, Jr Acad Sci Western Kans, 63-65. *Mem:* Fel AAAS; Am Asn Univ Professors; Am Nature Study Soc; Nat Sci Teachers Asn. *Res:* Development of teaching methods in soil and water conservation; mobility of Western Kansas science teachers and factors affecting movement; limnological study of bioenergetics in isolated farm pond; resource use education; wind erosion and soil bacteria dissemination; biological implications of energy production. *Mailing Add:* Dept of Biol Ft Hays State Univ Hays KS 67601

PIERSON, DOLORES LEHMANN, b Hamburg, Ger, Nov 3, 18; US citizen; m 49. ZOOLOGY, HUMAN ECOLOGY. *Educ:* Brooklyn Col, BA, 42; Columbia Univ, MA, 45; Duke Univ, PhD, 50. *Prof Exp:* Asst, Columbia Univ, 42-46; zoologist, Duke Univ, 46-48, 49; fel, Ohio State Univ, 50-52; instr biol, Montgomery Jr Col, 53; jr instr zool, Univ Md, 53-54, instr, 54-56; instr, Holton Arms Sch & Jr Col, 56-58; from instr to assoc prof, Prince George's Community Col, 58-70, chmn, Div Sci Math & Eng, 61-67, Div Sci, 67-68 & Dept Biol, 69-70, prof biol, 70-80; RETIRED. *Concurrent Pos:* Instr, DC Teachers Col, 57-60. *Mem:* AAAS. *Res:* Chromosome structure in insects; variations in wing patterns in moths; biological insect control in the home food garden. *Mailing Add:* 6209 Balfour Dr West Hyattsville MD 20782

PIERSON, EDGAR FRANKLIN, b Fairfield, Iowa, Aug 31, 09; m 42; c 2. BIOLOGY. *Educ:* Iowa Wesleyan Col, BS, 33; State Univ Iowa, MS, 36, PhD(bot), 38. *Prof Exp:* From instr to prof biol, 38-42, 46-63, head dept, 47-63, dean grad prog, 63-69, prof, 69-80, EMER PROF BIOL, UNIV WIS-STEVENS POINT, 80- *Mem:* AAAS. *Res:* Plant taxonomy; limnology; plankton development in Lake Macbride; botany; general zoology; freshwater biology. *Mailing Add:* Dept of Biol Univ of Wis Stevens Point WI 54481

PIERSON, EDWARD S(AMUEL), b Syracuse, NY, June 27, 37; m 71; c 1. ELECTRICAL ENGINEERING, MECHANICAL ENGINEERING. *Educ:* Syracuse Univ, BSEE, 58; Mass Inst Technol, SM, 60, ScD(elec eng), 64. *Prof Exp:* Teaching asst elec eng, Mass Inst Technol, 59-62, instr, 62-65, asst prof & fel, 65-66; from asst prof to assoc prof energy eng, Univ Ill, Chicago Circle, 66-75, assoc head dept, 71-74; PROG MGR LIQUID METAL MAGNETOHYDRODYNAMICS, ENG DIV, ARGONNE NAT LAB, 75- *Concurrent Pos:* Consult, Jet Propulsion Lab, 65-66, Thermo Electron Corp, 68 & Argonne Nat Lab, 69-75; adj assoc prof, Univ Ill, Chicago Circle, 75- *Mem:* AAAS; Inst Elec & Electronics Engrs. *Res:* Magnetohydrodynamic thermodynamic cycles as applied to practical liquid-metal and plasma magnetohydrodynamic power systems; liquid-metal induction and Faraday; plasma magnetohydrodynamic generators; energy conversion; electrical machinery; electromagnetic field theory. *Mailing Add:* Argonne Nat Lab Argonne IL 60439

PIERSON, ELLERY MERWIN, b Eugene, Ore, Mar 31, 35; m 58; c 2. STATISTICAL ANALYSIS. *Educ:* Portland State Col, BS, 57; Rutgers Univ, MEd, 65; Univ Pa, PhD(tech educ res), 75. *Prof Exp:* Res asst biochem, Col Physicians & Surgeons, Columbia Univ, 57-58; res asst physics, RCA Corp, Somerville, NJ, 58-60; welfare investr, Middlesex County, NJ, 60-61; res asst psychol, Educ Testing Serv, Princeton, NJ, 61-66; res psychologist, Franklin Inst Res Labs, Philadelphia, 66-67; res assoc educ, 67-70, res assoc design & anal, 70-75, MGR STATIST ANAL, SCH DIST PHILADELPHIA, 75- *Mem:* Psychomet Soc; Nat Coun Measurement Educ; Am Educ Res Asn. *Res:* Educational information management systems; semantic differential applications; optical mark scanning. *Mailing Add:* Off Res & Eval Rm 400 21st & The Parkway Philadelphia PA 19103

PIERSON, HUGH OTTHO, b Paris, France, Dec 21, 21; m 75; c 5. CHEMICAL METALLUGRY, HIGH TEMPERATURE CHEMISTRY. *Educ:* Univ Paris, BS, 39, MS, 41. *Prof Exp:* Staff engr appl chem, Metall Res & Develop Co, Washington, DC, 49-52; mem staff appl chem, Brunswick Corp, Marion, Va, 52-55; head polymer res, Goodyear Aerospace, Arkon, Ohio, 55-58; MEM SCI STAFF HIGH TEMPERATURE CHEM, SANDIA LABS, 58- *Mem:* Electrochem Soc. *Res:* Vapor deposition of metals and ceramic; high temperature composites, high temperature fibers; structure and properties of thin films. *Mailing Add:* Orgn 5834 Sandia Labs Albuquerque NM 87115

PIERSON, K KENDALL, b Idaho Falls, Idaho, Aug 11, 30; m 52; c 2. PATHOLOGY. *Educ:* Univ Utah, BS, 51; NY Univ, MD, 59. *Prof Exp:* Intern med, Bellevue Hosp, 59-60; resident path, Med Ctr, NY Univ, 60-63, asst prof, Col Med, 64-66, assoc prof, 66-68; from assoc prof to prof path, Col Med, Univ Fla, 68-77, assoc chemn, Dept Path, chief staff & asst dean, Clin Affairs, 77-79. *Concurrent Pos:* Consult pathologist, Gainesville Vet Hosp, 68- *Mem:* Am Col Path. *Res:* Tumor biology and dermatopathology. *Mailing Add:* J Hillis Miller Health Ctr Gainesville FL 32601

PIERSON, MERLE DEAN, b Mitchell, SDak, May 23, 42; m 62; c 3. FOOD MICROBIOLOGY, FOOD PROCESSING. *Educ:* Iowa State Univ, BS, 64; Univ Ill, MS, 69, PhD(food sci), 70. *Prof Exp:* Res chemist meat processing, George A Hormel & Co, 65-66; res asst food microbiol, Univ Ill, 66-68, Wright fel food sci, 68-70; asst prof, 70-79, ASSOC PROF FOOD SCI, VA POLYTECH INST & STATE UNIV, 79- *Mem:* Am Soc Microbiol; Soc Appl Bact; Inst Food Technologists; Int Asn Milk, Food & Environ Sanitarians. *Res:* Food microbiology; physiology of foodborne microorganisms; heat-injury of microorganisms; foodborne infections and intoxications; thermal processing of foods; antimicrobial food additives; food processing sanitation. *Mailing Add:* Dept of Food Sci & Technol Va Polytech Inst & State Univ Blacksburg VA 24061

PIERSON, WILLARD JAMES, JR, b New York, NY, July 7, 22; m 54; c 3. METEOROLOGY, OCEANOGRAPHY. *Educ:* Univ Chicago, BS, 44; NY Univ, PhD(meteorol), 49. *Prof Exp:* Prof oceanog, NY Univ, 49-73; PROF, OCEANOG INST MARINE & ATMOSPHERIC SCI, CITY COL NEW YORK, 73- *Concurrent Pos:* Chmn, SASS team, SEASAT; mem, Sci Adv Group, SEASAT. *Honors & Awards:* Mil oceanog award, Oceanogr of Navy, 69. *Mem:* Fel Am Meteorol Soc; Marine Technol Soc; Soc Naval Archit & Marine Eng; fel Am Geophys Univ (pres, sect oceanog, 68-69). *Res:* Ocean waves; ship motions; wave forecasting; satellite oceanography; study of SEASAT data that measures winds over the ocean. *Mailing Add:* 1641 Rosalind Ave Elmont NY 11003

PIERSON, WILLIAM GRANT, b Elizabeth, NJ, Jan 27, 33; m 58; c 2. ORGANIC CHEMISTRY, PHYSICAL CHEMISTRY. *Educ:* Seton Hall Univ, BA, 54, MS, 61, PhD(org chem), 68. *Prof Exp:* Res assoc, Ciba Pharmaceut Co, 58-67; res chemist, 68-70, sect head, oral prods, 70-78, mgr toiletries prod res, 78, dir res & develop, Far East Div, 78-81, DIR RES & DEVELOP, ORAL PLANNING & ADMIN, COLGATE-PALMOLIVE CO, 81- *Mem:* Am Chem Soc. *Res:* Exploration of electroorganic reaction mechanisms; organic synthesis; alkaloid structure elucidation; alkaloid synthesis and structural modification; pharmaceutical and oral health research. *Mailing Add:* Colgate-Palmolive Co 909 River Rd Piscataway NJ 08854

PIERSON, WILLIAM R, b Grand Rapids, Mich, Apr 3, 22; m 52; c 5. AEROSPACE MEDICINE. *Educ:* Mich State Univ, BS, 52, MA, 53, PhD(physiol psychol), 57. *Prof Exp:* From asst to assoc prof physiol, Calif Col Med, 58-63; chief physiologist, Lockheed-Calif Co, 63-71; ASSOC PROF PHYSIOL & HUMAN FACTORS, SCH MED & INST SAFETY & SYSTS MGT, UNIV SOUTHERN CALIF, 71- *Concurrent Pos:* Mem, Int Comt Sports & Phys Fitness, UNESCO, 62-; vpres & dean, Northridge Col Sci & Eng, 64-; ed, Sect XII, Index Medicus, 64-; assoc, US Govt Appeal Agent, 68-71; chief physiologist, Advan Designs, Lockheed-Calif Co, 68-71, consult, 71-; ed, Human Factors Bull, Flight Safety Found. *Mem:* Aerospace Med Asn; Am Psychol Asn; Am Astronaut Soc; fel Royal Aeronaut Soc. *Res:* Physiological psychology; psychopharmacology; aviation and environmental physiology; metabolic processes; work and applied physiology; fatigue; psychomoter skills. *Mailing Add:* Inst Safety & Systs Mgt Univ Southern Calif Los Angeles CA 90035

PIERSON, WILLIAM ROY, b Charleston, WVa, Oct 21, 30; m 61; c 2. AIR POLLUTION, ATMOSPHERIC CHEMISTRY. *Educ:* Princeton Univ, BSE, 52; Mass Inst Technol, PhD, 59. *Prof Exp:* Res assoc, Enrico Fermi Inst Nuclear Studies, Univ Chicago, 59-62; MEM SCI RES STAFF, CHEM DEPT, FORD MOTOR CO, 62- *Concurrent Pos:* Lectr chem, Univ Mich, 68. *Mem:* AAAS; Am Chem Soc; Am Phys Soc; Sigma Xi; Air Pollution Control Asn. *Res:* Nuclear level schemes and high-energy nuclear reactions; nuclear properties; atmospheric aerosols. *Mailing Add:* Res Staff Ford Motor Co PO Box 2053 Dearborn MI 48121

PIERUCCI, OLGA, b Crotone, Italy, Apr 17, 26. MOLECULAR BIOLOGY, PHYSICS. *Educ:* Univ Padua, Dipl, 43, DSc(physics), 48. *Prof Exp:* Fel physics, Univ Padua, 48-52; res asst, Indust Complex, Rome, 52-56; UNESCO vis prof, Gadjah Mada Univ, Jogjakarta, 56-58; Fulbright scholar; asst prof, Univ Buffalo, 59-60; radiation physicist, 60-63, sr cancer res scientist, 63-69, assoc cancer res scientist, 69-73, ASSOC RES PROF BIOL, GRAD SCH, ROSWELL PARK MEM INST, 73- *Mem:* AAAS; Radiation Res Soc; Am Soc Microbiol. *Res:* Control mechanisms in bacterial duplication; role of envelope in bacterial duplication. *Mailing Add:* Dept of Biol Grad Sch Roswell Park Mem Inst Buffalo NY 14203

PIESCO, NICHOLAS PETER, b Havre DeGrace, Md, Sept 15, 46; m 70; c 2. TISSUE CULTURE, ULTRASTRUCTURE. *Educ:* Univ SFla, BA, 69, MA, 72; Univ Fla, MSA, 75, PhD(poultry sci & anat), 79. *Prof Exp:* Res fel, Sch Dent, Univ Conn, 79-81; ASST PROF ANAT & HISTOL, SCH DENT, UNIV PITTSBURGH, 81- *Mem:* Tissue Cult Asn; Sigma Xi. *Res:* Developing dentition; evolution, embryology, ultrastructure and histochemistry of dental hard tissues. *Mailing Add:* Dept Anat & Histol Sch Dent Med Univ Pittsburgh Pittsburgh PA 15261

PIESKI, EDWIN THOMAS, b Dickson City, Pa, May 23, 24; m 60. POLYMER CHEMISTRY, PHYSICAL CHEMISTRY. *Educ:* Lehigh Univ, BS, 45, MS, 46, PhD(chem), 49. *Prof Exp:* Res chemist, Polychem Dept, 49-66, SR RES CHEMIST, PLASTICS DEPT, E I DU PONT DE NEMOURS & CO, 66- *Mem:* AAAS; Am Chem Soc; Sigma Xi; Soc Plastics Eng. *Res:* Physical chemistry of polymers; polyethylene; ethylene copolymers; polyvinyl alcohol. *Mailing Add:* Polymer Prod Dept Exp Sta E I du Pont de Nemours & Co Wilmington DE 19898

PIETERS, CARLE M, b Ft Sill, Okla, Nov 11, 43; m 78. PLANETARY SCIENCES. *Educ:* Antioch Col, BA, 66; Mass Inst Technol, BS, 71, MS, 72, PhD, 77. *Prof Exp:* Teacher math, Somerville High Sch, Mass, 66-67; teacher sci, Peace Corps, Sarawak, Malaysia, 67-69; staff scientist res, Planetary Astron Lab, Dept Earth & Planetary Sci, Mass Inst Technol, 72-75; space scientist, Johnson Space Ctr, NASA, 77-80; ASST PROF, DEPT GEOL SCI, BROWN UNIV, 80- *Mem:* Am Geophys Union; Am Astron Soc; AAAS. *Res:* Remote sensing of surface composition; planetary exploration; reflectance properties of rocks and minerals. *Mailing Add:* Dept Geol Sci Brown Univ Providence RI 02912

PIETRA, GIUSEPPE G, b Piacenza, Italy, Dec 30, 30; m 57; c 2. PATHOLOGY. *Educ:* Univ Milan, MD, 55. *Prof Exp:* Resident path, Mass Gen Hosp, 60-62; asst, Univ Zurich, 62-63, prosector, 63-64; asst prof oncol, Chicago Med Sch, 64-65; asst pathologist, Michael Reese Hosp, Chicago, 65-69; from asst prof to assoc prof, 69-77, PROF PATH, MED SCH, UNIV PA, 77- *Concurrent Pos:* Res fel oncol, Chicago Med Sch, 57-60; clin asst prof, Univ Ill Col Med, 66-69; res assoc, Cardiovasc Inst, Michael Reese Hosp, Chicago, 68-69. *Mem:* AAAS; Int Acad Pathologists; Am Thoracic Soc; Am Asn Pathologists; Am Physiol Soc. *Res:* Electron microscopy; developmental pathology; capillary permeability; cardiopulmonary pathology. *Mailing Add:* Dept Path Univ Pa Hosp Philadelphia PA 19104

PIETRAS, RICHARD JOSEPH, b Springfield, Mass, Sept 20, 47. ENDOCRINOLOGY, CANCER. *Educ:* Clark Univ, BA, 69; Univ Calif, Los Angeles, PhD(physiol), 74. *Prof Exp:* NAT CANCER INST FEL CANCER BIOL, UNIV CALIF, LOS ANGELES, 75- *Mem:* Endocrine Soc; Sigma Xi; AAAS; assoc Am Physiol Soc. *Res:* Cellular mechanisms of steroid and polypeptide hormone action; chemical carcinogenesis. *Mailing Add:* Dept of Biol Univ of Calif Los Angeles CA 90024

PIETREWICZ, ALEXANDRA THERESA, b Worcester, Mass, Aug 13, 49; m 81. PSYCHOLOGY, ANIMAL BEHAVIOR. *Educ:* Univ Mass, BS, 72, MS, 75, PhD(psychol), 77. *Prof Exp:* Vis lectr, Univ Mass, 76-77; ASST PROF PSYCHOL, EMORY UNIV, 77- *Concurrent Pos:* Co-prin investr, NSF res grant, 77-79; prin investr, Emory Univ res grant, 77-78 & 79-80. *Mem:* Animal Behav Soc; Am Psychol Asn; NY Acad Sci. *Res:* Predator-prey relationships; foraging strategies in birds; the role of discrimination learning in predation strategies; social mechanisms of population regulation. *Mailing Add:* Dept of Psychol Emory Univ Atlanta GA 30322

PIETRI, CHARLES EDWARD, b New York, NY, July 6, 30; c 3. ANALYTICAL CHEMISTRY, NUCLEAR CHEMISTRY. *Educ:* NY Univ, BA, 51. *Prof Exp:* Chemist, Oak Ridge Nat Lab, E I du Pont de Nemours & Co, 51-53 & Savannah River Lab, 53-56; res chemist, Curtiss-Wright Corp, 56-58; chief, Plutonium Chem Sect, USAEC, US Energy Res Develop Admin, 58-70, chief, Anal Chem Br, 70-75, asst dir oper, 75-77, ASST DIR OPER, US DEPT ENERGY, 77- *Mem:* Am Chem Soc; fel Am Inst Chem; Am Nuclear Soc; Health Physics Soc; fel Royal Soc Chem. *Res:* Chemistry of plutonium; chemical and radiochemical standards; corrosion of fuel elements; high radiation level chemical and radiochemical analyses; chemical separations; health physics; analytical methods development and evaluation; uranium chemistry; human resource management. *Mailing Add:* US Dept of Energy 9800 S Cass Ave Argonne IL 60439

PIETRUSEWSKY, MICHAEL, JR, b Boonville, NY, May 18, 44. PHYSICAL ANTHROPOLOGY. *Educ:* State Univ NY Buffalo, BA, 66; Univ Toronto, MA, 67, PhD(anthrop), 69. *Prof Exp:* From asst prof to assoc prof, 69-81, PROF ANTHROP, UNIV HAWAII, MANOA, 81- *Concurrent Pos:* Univ Hawaii grants, B P Bishop Mus, Honolulu, 69-70 & Marquesas Proj, Mus, 71-72; Wenner-Gren Found grants, Dept Anat, Siriraj Hosp, Bangkok, 70 & Mus, Univ Papua-New Guinea, 70-71; spec consult, Ford Found, 74, grant, 74; grant, Nat Ctr Sci Res, Paris, 75; grants, Ger Acad Exchange Serv, 75, Australian Inst Aboriginal Studies; vis prof, Univ Toronto, 80-81; res assoc anthrop, B P Bishop Mus, Hawaii, 78- *Mem:* Am Asn Phys Anthrop; Thailand Siam Soc; fel Am Asn Anthropologists. *Res:* Human biology of skeletal populations from the Pacific and southeast Asia, including paleodemography, skeletal and dental morphology, pathology, and the application of univariate and multivariate procedures to cranial variation. *Mailing Add:* Dept of Anthrop Univ of Hawaii 2424 Maile Way Honolulu HI 96822

PIETRUSZA, EDWARD WALTER, b Easthampton, Mass, Apr 21, 18; m 44; c 3. ORGANIC CHEMISTRY, POLYMER CHEMISTRY. *Educ:* Brown Univ, AB, 40; Pa State Univ, MS, 45, PhD(chem), 49. *Prof Exp:* Chemist, Gilbert & Barker Mfg Co, 40-42 & Merck & Co, 43-44; res chemist, Cent Res Lab, Allied Chem Corp, 48-52, proj leader, 53-58, sr scientist, 59-64, assoc dir res, 65-71; CONSULT, 71- *Mem:* AAAS; fel Am Inst Chem; Am Chem Soc. *Res:* Synthetic organic, organo-silicon, and polymer chemistry. *Mailing Add:* 36 Fairmount Ave Morristown NJ 07960

PIETRUSZKO, REGINA, b Hulicze, Poland, Feb 15, 29; UK citizen. BIOCHEMISTRY. *Educ:* Univ London, BS, 54, MS, 56, PhD(plant chem), 60. *Prof Exp:* Res asst lipid chem, Lister Inst Prev Med, London, 60-62; lectr enzymol, Royal Free Hosp Sch Med, London, 62-65; staff scientist biochem, Worcester Found Exp Biol, Mass, 65-67; docent, Nobel Inst, Karolinska Inst, Sweden, 67-70; asst prof, 70-74, assoc prof, 74-80, PROF BIOCHEM, RUTGERS UNIV, NEW BRUNSWICK, 80- *Concurrent Pos:* Res scientist develop award, Nat Inst Alcohol Abuse & Alcoholism, 78-83. *Mem:* Am Soc Biol Chemists; Res Soc Alcoholism; Brit Biochem Soc. *Res:* Structure and function relationships of isoenzymes of human aldehyde dehydrogenases; purification and characterization of these isoenzymes. *Mailing Add:* Ctr of Alcohol Studies Rutgers Univ New Brunswick NJ 08903

PIETRZYK, DONALD JOHN, analytical chemistry, see previous edition

PIETRZYKOWSKI, ANTHONY D, analytical chemistry, see previous edition

PIETRZYKOWSKI, TOMASZ, computer science, see previous edition

PIETSCH, GERHARD JOSEF, b Moravska Ostrava, Czech, June 7, 29; m 65. ORGANIC CHEMISTRY. *Educ:* Univ Bonn, BS, 53, MS, 56, PhD(org chem), 59; Univ Conn, MBA, 72. *Prof Exp:* Res assoc, Georgetown Univ, 59-61; res chemist, Esso Res & Eng Co, Standard Oil Co NJ, 61-64; res chemist, Stamford Res Labs, Am Cyanamid Co, 64-67, sr res chemist, 67-78; TECH MGR, HENKEL CORP, 79- *Mem:* Am Chem Soc; Soc Ger Chem. *Res:* Partial synthesis of cardiac glycosides; development of petroleum products; synthesis of polymers; radiation chemistry; development of new adhesive systems; electrodepositable primers for adhesives; polyester resins; surface active agents. *Mailing Add:* 156 Mill Rd Stamford CT 06903

PIETSCH, PAUL ANDREW, b New York, NY, Aug 8, 29; m 50; c 4. ANATOMY, MOLECULAR BIOLOGY. *Educ:* Syracuse Univ, AB, 54; Univ Pa, PhD(anat), 60. *Prof Exp:* Instr physiol, Sch Nursing, Univ Pa, 58; instr anat, Bowman Gray Sch Med, 59-61; asst prof, State Univ NY Buffalo, 61-64; sr res molecular biologist biochem, Dow Chem Co, 64-70; assoc prof anat, 70-78, PROF ANAT, SCH OPTOM, IND UNIV, BLOOMINGTON, 78-, CHMN DEPT BASIC HEALTH SCI, 77- *Concurrent Pos:* Adj prof anat, Sch Med, Med Sci Prog, Indiana Univ, Bloomington, 79- *Honors & Awards:* Med J Award, AMA, 72. *Mem:* Am Asn Anatomists; Biophys Soc; Pan-Am Asn Anatomists; Soc Develop Biol. *Res:* Regeneration; muscle differentiation; replication; biology of memory. *Mailing Add:* Sch of Optom Ind Univ Bloomington IN 47401

PIETSCH, THEODORE WELLS, b Royal Oak, Mich, Mar 6, 45; m 67; c 2. ICHTHYOLOGY, BIOSYSTEMATICS. *Educ:* Univ Mich, BA, 67; Univ Southern Calif, MS, 69, PhD(biol), 73. *Prof Exp:* Vis asst prof, Univ Southern Calif, 73; fel res, Mus Comparative Zool, Harvard Univ, 73-75; lectr, Dept Biol, Calif State Univ, Long Beach, 75-76, asst prof, 76-78; asst prof, 78-80, ASSOC PROF, SCH FISHERIES, UNIV WASH, 80- *Concurrent Pos:* Res assoc icthyol, Natural Hist Mus Los Angeles County, 73-, Mus Comparative Zool, Havard Univ, 75-; tutor biol, Havard Univ, 74-75; ed, Bulletin Southern Calif Acad Sci, 76-78. *Mem:* Am Soc Ichthyologists & Herpetologists; AAAS; Am Soc Zoologists; Sigma Xi. *Res:* Biosystematics, geographic distribution, and the behavior and functional morphology of feeding in marine fishes, particularly euteleostean fishes. *Mailing Add:* Sch Fisheries WH-10 Univ Wash Seattle WA 98195

PIETTE, LAWRENCE HECTOR, b Chicago, Ill, Jan 4, 32; m 57. BIOPHYSICS. *Educ:* Northwestern Univ, BS, 53, MS, 54; Stanford Univ, PhD, 57. *Prof Exp:* Res chemist, Varian Assocs, 56-65; PROF BIOPHYS, UNIV HAWAII, 65- *Concurrent Pos:* Guggenheim fel, Inst Biophys & Biochem, Paris & Grenoble Nuclear Res Ctr, Grenoble, France, 71-72; consult, Varian Assocs & NAm Aviation, Inc; Exec dir, Cancer Ctr Hawaii, 74- *Mem:* Am Chem Soc; NY Acad Sci; Biophys Soc; Am Asn Univ Prof. *Res:* Application of nuclear magnetic resonance and electron paramagnetic resonance to the study of chemical kinetics, photochemistry and rapid biological reactions; studies of chemical carcinogenesis. *Mailing Add:* Cancer Ctr of Hawaii Univ Hawaii 1236 Lauhala St Honolulu HI 96813

PIEZ, KARL ANTON, b Newton, Mass, Aug 30, 24; m 48; c 3. BIOCHEMISTRY. *Educ:* Yale Univ, BS, 47; Northwestern Univ, PhD(biochem), 52. *Prof Exp:* Biochemist, 52-61, chief sect protein chem, 61-66, CHIEF LAB BIOCHEM, NAT INST DENT RES, 66- *Honors & Awards:* T Duckett Jones Mem Award, Helen Hay Whitney Found, 70. *Mem:* Am Soc Biol Chemists; AAAS; Am Chem Soc; Biochem Soc. *Res:* Protein chemistry; biochemistry of connective tissues. *Mailing Add:* Lab Biochem Nat Inst Dent Res Bethesda MD 20205

PIFKO, ALLAN BERT, b Bronx, NY, Dec 12, 38; m 60; c 1. APPLIED MECHANICS. *Educ:* NY Univ, BAE, 60, MAE, 61; Polytech Inst Brooklyn, PhD(appl mech), 74. *Prof Exp:* Res engr, 61-74, res scientist, 74-79, staff scientist, 79-81, SR STAFF SCIENTIST, GRUMMAN AEROSPACE CORP, 81- *Mem:* Am Soc Mech Engrs; Sigma Xi. *Res:* Applied mechanics; computer software and numerical techniques for nonlinear analysis of complex structures; author or coauthor of more than 20 publications. *Mailing Add:* 2 George Ct Melville NY 11747

PIGAGE, LEO C(HARLES), b Rochester, NY, Nov 22, 13. INDUSTRIAL ENGINEERING. *Educ:* Cornell Univ, ME, 36, MME, 38. *Prof Exp:* Instr, Duke Univ, 38-41; asst prof, Purdue Univ, 41-47; assoc prof mech eng, 47-52, PROF INDUST ENG, UNIV ILL, URBANA, 52- *Mem:* Am Soc Mech Engrs; Am Soc Eng Educ; Am Inst Indust Engrs. *Res:* Industrial engineering, organization and management. *Mailing Add:* Dept Mech & Indust Eng Univ Ill Urbana IL 61801

PIGDEN, WALLACE JAMES, b Madoc, Ont, Jan 30, 20; m 49; c 3. RESEARCH MANAGEMENT. *Educ:* Ont Agr Col, Toronto, BSA, 48; Univ Alta, MSc, 50; Univ Sask, PhD(nutrit), 55. *Prof Exp:* Res officer, Exp Sta, Can Dept Agr, Sask, 50-53, Animal Husb Div, Exp Farms Serv, Ont, 53-59, chief, Nutrit Sect, Animal Res Inst, Res Br, 60-67, res coordr, Animal Sci Res Br, Ont, 67-78; PRES, FAW CONSULTS LTD, 79- *Concurrent Pos:* Secy, Nat Comt Animal Nutrit, Can, 58-64; Can Dept Agr fel, Nat Inst Res Dairying, Reading, Eng, 63-64; consult indust res assistance grant comt, Nat Res Coun Can, 63-66; res coordr, planning & evaluation, Agr Can, adv & consult, Can Govt res incentive & contract prog & Food & Agr Orgn United Nations, Can Int Develop Agency & Res Ctr, 67-78; pvt consult, 78-82. *Honors & Awards:* Borden Award, Nutrit Soc Can, 64; Cert Merit, Can Soc Animal Sci, 79; Queens Jubilee Medal, 77. *Mem:* Am Soc Animal Sci; Nutrit Soc Can; Agr Inst Can; Can Soc Animal Sci; Can Consult Agr Asn. *Res:* Forage utilization; methods of measuring herbage intake and animal production on pasture; in vivo, in vitro and chemical methods of evaluating forages; physical and chemical methods of increasing available energy content of forages. *Mailing Add:* FAW Consults Ltd 850 Norton Ave Ottawa ON K2B 5P6 Can

PIGFORD, ROBERT LAMAR, b Meridian, Miss, Apr 16, 17; m 39; c 2. CHEMICAL ENGINEERING. *Educ:* Miss State Col, BS, 38; Univ Ill, MS, 40, PhD(chem eng), 42. *Prof Exp:* Chem engr, Exp Sta, E I du Pont de Nemours & Co, 41-47; prof chem eng & chmn dept, Univ Del, 47-66; prof, Univ Calif, Berkeley, 66-75; UNIV PROF CHEM ENG, UNIV DEL, 75- *Concurrent Pos:* Vis prof, Univ Calif, 54, Cambridge Univ, 55 & 59 & Univ Wis, 57; indust consult; mem sci adv bd, US Air Force; ed, Fundamentals Quart, Indust & Eng Chem, 62- *Honors & Awards:* Walker Award, Am Inst Chem Engrs, 58, W K Lewis Award, 70. *Mem:* Nat Acad Sci; Nat Acad Eng; Am Chem Soc; Am Soc Eng Educ; Am Inst Chem Engrs. *Res:* Unit operations of chemical engineering; fluid mechanics; heat transfer; distillation; diffusion; applied mathematics; thermodynamics. *Mailing Add:* Dept of Chem Eng Colburn Lab Univ of Del Newark DE 19711

PIGFORD, THOMAS H(ARRINGTON), b Meridian, Miss, Apr 21, 22; m 48; c 2. CHEMICAL & NUCLEAR ENGINEERING. *Educ:* Ga Inst Technol, BS, 43; Mass Inst Technol, SM, 48, ScD(chem eng), 52. *Prof Exp:* Instr chem eng, Mass Inst Technol, 46-47, asst prof & dir sch eng pract, Oak Ridge, Tenn, 50-52, from asst prof to assoc prof nuclear & chem eng, 52-57; sr develop engr, Carbide & Carbon Chem Co, 52; chmn eng & asst dir lab, Gen Atomic Div, Gen Dynamics Corp, 57-59; PROF NUCLEAR ENG, UNIV CALIF, BERKELEY, 59-, CHMN DEPT, 59-64, 74- *Concurrent Pos:* Consult, govt & various industs, 53-; mem, Nat Panel Atomic Safety & Licensing Bds; consult, Union Carbide & Carbon, 67- & US Geol Surv, 68-; vis prof, Kyoto Univ, Japan, 75 & Kuwait Univ, 76; mem, Am Phys Soc Study Group on Nuclear Fuel Cycles & Waste Mgt, 76-77; mem, Presidents Comn Accident of Three Mile Island, 79; mem bd radioactive mgt, Nat Acad Sci & Eng, 78- *Honors & Awards:* Arthur H Compton Award, Am Nuclear Soc, 71; Robert E Wilson Award, Am Inst Chem Engrs, 80; John Wesley Powell Award, US Geol Surv, 81. *Mem:* Nat Acad Eng; AAAS; fel Am Nuclear Soc; Am Inst Chem Engrs; Am Inst Mech Engrs. *Res:* Design analysis of nuclear reactors; nuclear power economics; safety analysis of nuclear reactors; environmental transport of radionuclides; environmental effects of electric power production; radioactive waste management; nuclear fuel cycles. *Mailing Add:* 1 Garden Dr Kensington CA 94708

PIGGOTT, MICHAEL R(ANTELL), b Cheadle Hulme, Eng, Feb 13, 30; m 55; c 3. SURFACE CHEMISTRY, MATERIALS SCIENCE. *Educ:* Univ London, BSc, 51, MSc & dipl, Imp Col, 53, PhD(appl phys chem), 55. *Prof Exp:* Mem sci staff, Gen Elec Co, Eng, 55-56, proj engr, 56-58; res physicist, Bexford Ltd, 58-60 & Gillette Res Labs, 60-64; assoc res officer, Atomic Energy Can, Ltd, Ont, 64-68; assoc prof, 68-74, PROF CHEM ENG, UNIV TORONTO, 74-, CHMN, CTR STUDY MAT, 79- *Concurrent Pos:* UK Sci Res Coun sr traveling fel, 78-79. *Mem:* Asn Asphalt Paving Technologists; Asn Prof Engrs Ont; fel Brit Inst Physics. *Res:* Surface physical and chemical interactions; mechanical properties of materials, with special emphasis on load bearing fibre composites; properties of modified asphalts, especially for use on roads. *Mailing Add:* Dept of Chem Eng Univ of Toronto Toronto ON M5S 2R8 Can

PIGNATARO, AUGUSTUS, b Bronx, NY, Aug 12, 43; m 65; c 3. PHYSICS. *Educ:* Calif State Univ, Los Angeles, BS, 65; Calif Lutheran Col, MBA, 75. *Prof Exp:* Engr, Atlantic Res Corp, 65-67; SR PHYSICIST, NAVY PAC MISSILE TEST CTR, CALIF, 67- *Res:* Development, testing and evaluation of electro-optical systems for naval airborne applications; nonimaging infrared and ultraviolet sensors. *Mailing Add:* Pac Missile Test Ctr Code 1233 Point Mugu CA 93040

PIGNATARO, LOUIS J(AMES), b Brooklyn, NY, Nov 30, 23; m 54; c 1. CIVIL ENGINEERING. *Educ:* Polytech Inst Brooklyn, BCE, 51; Columbia Univ, MS, 54; Graz Tech Univ, Dr Techn Sc, 61. *Prof Exp:* Fac, 51-65, prof civil eng, 65-67, dir, Div Transp Planning, 67-70, head, Dept Transp, Planning & Eng, 70-75, DIR, TRANSP TRAINING & RES CTR, POLYTECH INST NEW YORK, 75- *Concurrent Pos:* Consult, var govt & pvt agencies. *Mem:* Fel Am Soc Civil Engrs; Am Rd & Transp Builders Asn; Am Rd Builders Asn; Inst Traffic Engrs; Transp Res Bd. *Res:* Transportation planning; traffic and highway engineering. *Mailing Add:* Dept Transp Planning & Eng Polytech Inst New York 333 Jay St Brooklyn NY 11201

PIGNOCCO, ARTHUR JOHN, b Jeanette, Pa, Apr 15, 29; m 59. PHYSICAL CHEMISTRY. *Educ:* Univ Pittsburgh, BS, 50; Carnegie Inst Technol, MS & PhD(chem), 54. *Prof Exp:* Chemist, Stand Oil Co, Ind, 54-56; sr technologist, 56-75, SECT SUPVR, US STEEL CORP, 75- *Mem:* Am Chem Soc. *Res:* Separations; mass spectroscopy; infrared and ultraviolet spectroscopy; auger and photoelectron spectroscopy; surface studies; low energy electron diffraction. *Mailing Add:* 3524 Mayer Dr Murrysville PA 15668

PIGNOLET, LOUIS H, b Orange, NJ, Mar 24, 43; m 69. INORGANIC CHEMISTRY, ORGANOMETALLIC CHEMISTRY. *Educ:* Lafayette Col, BS, 65; Princeton Univ, PhD(chem), 69. *Prof Exp:* Res assoc chem, Mass Inst Technol, 69-70; asst prof, 70-74, assoc prof, 74-81, PROF CHEM, UNIV MINN, MINNEAPOLIS, 81- *Concurrent Pos:* Res Corp grant, 71; NSF res grant, 73-84; consult, 3M Co. *Mem:* Am Chem Soc. *Res:* Synthesis, spectroscopy and photochemistry of transition metal and organometallic complexes, reaction mechanics; homogeneous catalysis and organometallic chemistry; x-ray crystallography. *Mailing Add:* Dept of Chem Univ of Minn Minneapolis MN 55455

PIGOTT, GEORGE M, b Vancouver, Wash, Oct 25, 28; m 48; c 5. FOOD SCIENCE. *Educ:* Univ Wash, Seattle, BS, 50, MS, 53, PhD(chem & food sci), 62. *Prof Exp:* Chem engr tech lab, US Fish & Wildlife Serv, 48-51, Continental Can Co, 53-55, Nat Canners Asn, 55-57 & Boeing Co, 57-59; lectr food sci, 63-65, from asst prof to assoc prof food eng, 65-72, PROF FISHERIES, UNIV WASH, 72- *Concurrent Pos:* Consult food engr, Sea Resources Eng, Inc 59- *Mem:* Inst Food Technol; Am Chem Soc; Am Soc Agr Engrs; Am Inst Chem Eng; Nat Soc Prof Eng. *Res:* Application of scientific and engineering principles as applied to processing of food products, especially sea foods. *Mailing Add:* Inst for Food Sci & Technol WH-10 Univ of Wash Seattle WA 98195

PIGOTT, MILES THOMAS, b Springfield, Ohio, Mar 23, 23; m 45; c 7. CRYOGENICS. *Educ:* Miami Univ, AB, 47; Univ Ill, MA, 48; Pa State Univ, PhD(physics), 55. *Prof Exp:* Res assoc, 51-55, from asst prof to assoc prof, 55-65, head, Acoust Unit, 70-74, PROF ENG RES, ORD RES LAB, PA STATE UNIV, 65-, ASST DIR, APPL RES LAB, 67- *Concurrent Pos:* Asst dir acad affairs, Pa State Univ, 74. *Mem:* Am Phys Soc; Acoust Soc Am; Am Asn Physics Teachers. *Res:* Ultrasonics; Navy ordnance development; cryophysics; general physics; vorticity and turbulence in liquid Helium II. *Mailing Add:* Appl Res Lab Pa State Univ University Park PA 16802

PIH, HUI, b Kunming, China, Feb 14, 22; US citizen; m 54; c 4. MECHANICAL ENGINEERING. *Educ:* Nat Inst Technol, China, BS, 45; Stanford Univ, MS, 49; Ill Inst Technol, PhD(mech), 53. *Prof Exp:* Supt, 53rd Arsenal, Kunming, China, 45-48; res asst, Ill Inst Technol, 51-53; proj engr, Res & Develop Lab, Int Harvester Co, 53-56; assoc engr, Int Bus Mach Corp, 56-57, staff engr, 57-59; assoc prof theoret & appl mech, Marquette Univ, 59-65; PROF ENG MECH, UNIV TENN, KNOXVILLE, 65- *Concurrent Pos:* Consult, Allis-Chalmers Mfg Corp, 61-62, A O Smith Corp, 62-65, Oak Ridge Nat Lab, 67-77 & ACF Industs Corp, 71- *Mem:* AAAS; Am Soc Mech Engrs; Am Acad Mech; Am Soc Eng Educ; Soc Exp Stress Anal. *Res:* Solid mechanics; experimental stress analysis; photoelasticity; fracture mechanics. *Mailing Add:* Dept Eng Sci & Mech Univ Tenn Knoxville TN 37996

PIIRMA, IRJA, b Tallinn, Estonia, Feb 4, 20; US citizen; m 43; c 2. POLYMER CHEMISTRY. *Educ:* Darmstadt Tech Univ, Dipl, 49; Univ Akron, MS, 57, PhD(polymer chem), 60. *Prof Exp:* Res chemist, Inst Polymer Sci, 52-60, from instr to asst prof chem, 63-76, assoc prof, 76-81, PROF POLYMER SCI, UNIV AKRON, 81-, RES ASSOC POLYMER CHEM, INST POLYMER SCI, 60- *Mem:* Am Chem Soc. *Res:* Polymerization kinetics in bulk as well as in emulsion. *Mailing Add:* Inst of Polymer Sci Univ of Akron 302 E Buchtel Ave Akron OH 44325

PIKAL, MICHAEL JON, b Henning, Minn, Aug 17, 39; m 63; c 5. PHYSICAL CHEMISTRY, PHARMACEUTICS. *Educ:* St John's Univ, Minn, BA, 61; Iowa State Univ, PhD(phys chem), 66. *Prof Exp:* Fel phys chem, Lawrence Radiation Lab, Univ Calif, 65-67; asst prof chem, Univ Tenn, Knoxville, 67-72; sr pharmaceut chemist, 72-76, RES SCIENTIST ELI LILLY & CO, 76- *Mem:* Acad Pharmaceut Sci; Am Chem Soc. *Res:* Thermodynamic properties of pharmaceuticals, characterization of amorphous materials, decomposition of solids; vacuum drying and freeze drying. *Mailing Add:* Pharmaceut Res Prod Develop Div Eli Lilly & Co Indianapolis IN 46206

PIKE, ARTHUR CLAUSEN, b Providence, RI, Aug 10, 39. METEOROLOGY. *Educ:* Univ Chicago, BS, 60, MS, 61; Univ Miami, PhD(atmospheric sci), 71. *Prof Exp:* Meteorologist, Nat Hurricane Res Lab, US Weather Bur, 58-62; meteorologist, Dept Civil Aviation, Bahamas, 63; fel advan study prog meteorol, Nat Ctr Atmospheric Res, 67; res scientist, Univ Miami, 67-71; meteorologist, Nat Oceanic & Atmospheric Admin, 71-81; PROF METEOROL, JACKSON STATE UNIV, 81- *Mem:* Am Meteorol Soc; Sigma Xi; Royal Meteorol Soc. *Res:* Education of minority college students in geophysical science. *Mailing Add:* Gen Sci Dept Jackson State Univ Jackson MS 39217

PIKE, CARL STEPHEN, b New York, NY, Apr 13, 45; m 69; c 2. PLANT PHYSIOLOGY. *Educ:* Yale Univ, BS, 66, MPhil, 67; Harvard Univ, PhD(biol), 72. *Prof Exp:* Asst prof, 71-77, ASSOC PROF BIOL, FRANKLIN & MARSHALL COL, 77- *Concurrent Pos:* NSF Sci Fac Prof Develop Grant, 78-79; sr fel, Dept Plant Biol, Carnegie Inst Wash, 78-79. *Mem:* AAAS; Am Soc Plant Physiol; Japanese Soc Plant Physiol. *Res:* Plant photomorphogenesis; physiological ecology; control of plant function and development by phytochrome; role of membrane lipids in plant responses to environmental stresses. *Mailing Add:* Dept Biol Franklin & Marshall Col Lancaster PA 17604

PIKE, CHARLES P, b Feb 21, 41; US citizen. GEOPHYSICS. *Educ:* Boston Col, BS, 63; Northeastern Univ, MS, 69. *Prof Exp:* PHYSICIST SPACE PHYSICS, AIR FORCE GEOPHYSICS LAB, 67- *Mem:* Am Inst Aeronaut & Astronaut. *Res:* Ionospheric physics; space physics. *Mailing Add:* Air Force Geophysics Lab Space Physics Div Hanscom AFB MA 01731

PIKE, EILEEN HALSEY, b London, Eng, Apr 18, 18; US citizen. MEDICAL PARASITOLOGY, MEDICAL MICROBIOLOGY. *Educ:* Hunter Col, BA, 56; Tulane Univ, MS, 58; Columbia Univ, PhD, 63. *Prof Exp:* Res asst parasitol, Med Sch, Tulane Univ, 58-59; lab instr, Col Physicians & Surgeons, Columbia Univ, 59-63; from asst prof to assoc prof, 64-76, prof, 76-81, EMER PROF PARASITOL, NY MED COL, 81- *Concurrent Pos:* Health Res Coun of City of New York grant, 65-68. NIH fel trop med, Caribbean Prog, La State Univ, 64; consult parsitologist, Hackensack Hosp, 67-69. *Mem:* AAAS; Am Soc Parasitol; Am Soc Trop Med & Hyg; Royal Soc Trop Med & Hyg; Int Col Trop Med. *Res:* Host-parasite realtionships; cellular and humoral responses of hosts to helminths and protozon. *Mailing Add:* Dept of Microbiol NY Med Col Valhalla NY 10595

PIKE, J(OHN) G(IBSON), b Hamilton, Ont, Apr 12, 30; m 59; c 2. MECHANICAL ENGINEERING, FLUID DYNAMICS. *Educ:* Queen's Univ, Ont, BSc, 53; Univ Birmingham, MSc, 56; McGill Univ, PhD(mech eng), 63. *Prof Exp:* Lectr mech eng, Royal Mil Col, Ont, 53-54; engr, Bristol Aeroplane Co, 54-55; res asst fluid dynamics, McGill Univ, 56-57, 58-60, lectr mech eng, 57-58; from asst prof to assoc prof, 60-70, PROF MECH ENG, ROYAL MIL COL CAN, 70- *Concurrent Pos:* Can Defence Res Bd grant, 64- *Mem:* Brit Inst Mech Engrs. *Res:* Thin liquid film flow; two-dimensional incompressible flow. *Mailing Add:* Dept of Mech Eng Royal Mil Col of Can Kingston ON K7L 2W3 Can

PIKE, JANE ELLEN NIELSON, geochemistry, petrology, see previous edition

PIKE, JOHN NAZARIAN, b Boston, Mass, Feb 13, 29; m 57; c 2. OPTICAL PHYSICS. *Educ:* Princeton Univ, AB, 51; Univ Rochester, PhD(physics, optics), 58. *Prof Exp:* PHYSICIST, TARRYTOWN TECH CTR, UNION CARBIDE CORP, 56- *Mem:* Optical Soc Am; Soc Photog Sci & Eng; AAAS; Soc Photo-optical Instrumentation Engrs. *Res:* Optical instrumentation; remote sensing methods; particulate scattering; radiative and conductive heat transfer in fibrous and porous materials at high temperatures; photosensitive materials systems; solar energy conversion; optical analytical methods. *Mailing Add:* Union Carbide Corp Tarrytown Tech Ctr Tarrytown NY 10591

PIKE, JULIAN M, b Eugene, Ore, Mar 14, 30; m 51; c 3. ATMOSPHERIC PHYSICS. *Educ:* Cascade Col, AB, 53; Oregon State Univ, MA, 56, PhD(physics), 58. *Prof Exp:* Res assoc meteorol, Ore State Univ, 57-58; prof physics, Ashbury Col, 58-66; scientist, 66-80, STAFF PHYSICIST, NAT CTR ATMOSPHERIC RES, 80- *Mem:* Am Meteorol Soc. *Res:* Meteorological instrumentation. *Mailing Add:* Nat Ctr for Atmospheric Res Box 3000 Boulder CO 80307

PIKE, KEITH SCHADE, b Ogden, Utah, Jan 20, 47; m 68; c 4. AGRICULTURAL ENTOMOLOGY. *Educ:* Utah State Univ, BS, 71; Univ Wyo, MS, 73, PhD(entom), 74. *Prof Exp:* Res assoc entom, Univ Nebr, 74-76; ASST ENTOMOLOGIST, WASH STATE UNIV, 76- *Concurrent Pos:* Asst entomologist, res grants, Wash Wheat Comn, 76-; Wash Mint Comn, 77-, Cent Wash Res Assoc, 77-, IR-4, USDA, 77- & var chem indust grants, 78- *Mem:* Entom Soc Am. *Res:* Resistance of plants to insects; insects affecting cereal grains, corn and mint. *Mailing Add:* Irrigated Agr Res & Exten Ctr Wash State Univ Prosser WA 99350

PIKE, LEROY, b Duncan, SC, Dec 25, 28; m 51; c 5. ANALYTICAL CHEMISTRY. *Educ:* Wofford Col, AB, 54; Clemson Univ, MS, 59; Univ Va, PhD(anal chem), 64. *Prof Exp:* Teacher high sch, SC, 54-56; lab asst, Clemson Univ, 55-58, assoc res chemist, 58-59; instr chem, Va Mil Inst, 59-61; asst prof, Appalachian State Univ, 63-65; sect head, Anal Serv, 65-73, MGR, RES ANAL SERV, CRYOVAC DIV, W R GRACE & CO, 73- *Mem:* Am Chem Soc; Am Soc Testing Mat; Int Standards Orgn. *Res:* Absorption and infrared spectroscopy, polymer properties, identification and characterization; analytical methods development; irradiation dosimetry. *Mailing Add:* Cryovac Div W R Grace & Co Duncan SC 29334

PIKE, LOY DEAN, b Howard Co, Tex, June 4, 40. MICROBIOLOGY. *Educ:* Univ Tex, BA, 67, MA, 70, PhD(microbiol), 73. *Prof Exp:* Lectr, Tex A&M Univ, 73-74; res assoc, Ind Univ, Bloomington, 74-76; ASST PROF MICROBIOL, IND UNIV, SOUTH BEND, 76- *Mem:* Am Soc Microbiol. *Res:* Control of glycerol catabolism in the purple nonsulfur bacteria. *Mailing Add:* Dept of Biol Sci 1825 Northside Blvd South Bend IN 46615

PIKE, RALPH EDWIN, b Rochester, NY, May 26, 15; m 41; c 2. CHEMICAL ENGINEERING, CORROSION. *Educ:* Univ Rochester, BS, 37, MS, 39. *Prof Exp:* Asst chem, Pa State Col, 37-38 & Univ Rochester, 38-39; chemist, E I du Pont de Nemours & Co, 39-42, chem engr, Wabash River Ord Works, 42-45, chemist, Pa, 45-48, res supvr, 48-52, sr develop supvr, Color Styling, Automotive Finishes & Develop, Data Processing, 52-64, from asst mgr to mgr, Marshall Develop Lab, Indust & Tech Serv, 64-69, mkt mgr wood finishes, Finishes Mkt Div, Fabrics & Finishes Dept, 69-70, mgr new prod develop & mkt, 70-76, res fel, 76-78; CONSULT, 78- *Mem:* Inter-Soc Color Coun (pres, 64-66); Am Chem Soc: Asn Finishing Processes (pres, 76-77); Soc Mfg Engrs. *Res:* Synthetic enamels; process engineering; automotive color styling; administration; color technology; organic finishes. *Mailing Add:* 280 Crum Creek Rd Media PA 19063

PIKE, RALPH W, b Tampa, Fla, Nov 10, 35; m 58; c 2. CHEMICAL ENGINEERING. *Educ:* Ga Inst Technol, BChE, 58, PhD(chem eng), 62. *Prof Exp:* Res engr, Swift & Co, Fla, 57-58 & Exxon Res & Eng Co, Tex, 62-64; from asst prof to assoc prof, 64-72, PROF CHEM ENG, LA STATE UNIV, BATON ROUGE, 72-, ASST VCHANCELLOR RES, 74-, DIR, LA MINERAL INST, 80- *Concurrent Pos:* Numerous res grants from fed, state and pvt orgn; vis scholar, Stanford Univ, 71. *Mem:* Am Inst Chem Engrs; Am Chem Soc; Am Soc Eng Educ; AAAS; Am Inst Aeronaut & Astronaut. *Res:* Reaction engineering; transport phenomena; systems engineering optimization; research management. *Mailing Add:* Off Res David Boyd Hall La State Univ Baton Rouge LA 70803

PIKE, RICHARD JOSEPH, JR, b Nantucket, Mass, June 28, 37; div; c 2. GEOLOGY, PHYSICAL GEOGRAPHY. *Educ:* Tufts Univ, BS, 59; Clark Univ, MA, 63; Univ Mich, Ann Arbor, PhD(geol), 68. *Prof Exp:* Geographer, US Army Natick Labs, Mass, 62; GEOLOGIST, BR ASTROGEOL STUDIES, US GEOL SURV, 68- *Concurrent Pos:* Assoc ed, Proc Lunar & Planet Sci Conf, 78 & 80. *Honors & Awards:* Apollo 11 Medallion, Marshall Space Flight Ctr, NASA, 71. *Mem:* AAAS; Geol Soc Am; Am Geophys Union. *Res:* Terrestrial and planetary geomorphology; quantitative physiography; numerical landform taxonomy; morphometry of craters; planetary geology. *Mailing Add:* Stop 46 US Geol Surv 345 Middlefield Rd Menlo Park CA 94025

PIKE, ROBERT MERRETT, b Hiram, Maine, Apr 5, 06; m 32; c 3. BACTERIOLOGY. *Educ:* Brown Univ, AB, 28, MA, 30, PhD(bact), 32; Am Bd Med Microbiol, dipl. *Prof Exp:* Asst biol, Brown Univ, 28-29, demonstr bact, 29-31; bacteriologist, Otsego County Lab & M I Bassett Hosp, NY, 32-43; from asst prof to prof, 43-74, EMER PROF BACT, UNIV TEX SOUTHWESTERN MED SCH DALLAS, 74- *Mem:* Am Soc Microbiol; assoc Soc Exp Biol & Med; Am Asn Immunol; fel Am Acad Microbiol. *Res:* Phagocytosis; virulence and antigenic structure; streptococci; laboratory infections; rheumatoid arthritis; leptospirosis; antibody activity. *Mailing Add:* Dept of Microbiol Univ of Tex Southwestern Med Sch Dallas TX 75235

PIKE, RONALD MARSTON, b Calais, Maine, Aug 16, 25; m 52; c 2. ORGANIC CHEMISTRY. *Educ:* Univ NH, BS, 49, MS, 50; Mass Inst Technol, PhD(org chem), 53. *Prof Exp:* Res chemist, Linde Air Prod Co Div, Union Carbide Corp, 53-57; prof chem, Lowell Tech Inst, 57-65; PROF CHEM, MERRIMACK COL, 65- *Concurrent Pos:* Vis Charles Weston Pichard prof chem, Bowdoin Col, Brunswick, Maine, 80-81. *Mem:* Am Chem Soc. *Res:* Rearrangement of benzyl phenyl and benzyl o-tolyl ethers; synthesis of cyclo-octatetraene derivatives; silicone polymers; organofunctional silanes; organogermanes; silicon and germanium coordination compounds. *Mailing Add:* Dept of Chem Merrimack Col North Andover MA 01845

PIKE, ROSCOE ADAMS, b Calais, Maine, Aug 16, 25; m 51; c 5. ORGANIC CHEMISTRY. *Educ:* Univ NH, BS, 49, MS, 50; Mass Inst Technol, PhD(chem), 53. *Prof Exp:* Res chemist, Silicones Div, Union Carbide Corp, 53-60, res supvr, 60-61; abrasives div, Norton Co, Mass, 61-64, sr res engr, 64-66, res assoc, 66-68; sr res scientist, 68-80, SR MAT SCIENTIST, UNITED AIRCRAFT RES LABS, 80- *Mem:* Am Chem Soc. *Res:* Rearrangement of triphenyl methyl o-cresol ethers; sterochemistry of Hofmann exhaustive methylation and amine oxide decomposition reactions; silicone monomers and polymers; aluminum oxide, silicon carbides and diamond resinoid abrasive products; grinding fluids and lubricants; high temperature organic resins and adhesives; structural composites. *Mailing Add:* United Technol Res Ctr Silver Lane East Hartford CT 06108

PIKE, RUTH LILLIAN, b New York, NY, Apr 5, 16. NUTRITION. *Educ:* Hunter Col, AB, 36; Columbia Univ, MA, 37; Univ Chicago, PhD(nutrit), 50. *Prof Exp:* From instr to prof nutrit sci, 43-77, EMER PROF PA STATE UNIV, UNIVERSITY PARK, 77- *Honors & Awards:* Borden Award, 67. *Mem:* Am Dietetic Asn; fel AAAS; Am Inst Nutrit; NY Acad Sci; Soc Exp Biol & Med. *Res:* Nutrition during pregnancy; sodium homeostasis and blood pressure. *Mailing Add:* 1275 Penfield Rd State Col PA 16801

PIKUS, IRWIN MARK, b Philadelphia, Pa, Apr 21, 36; m 59; c 1. PHYSICS, LAW. *Educ:* Drexel Univ, BS, 58; Univ Pa, MS, 60; Temple Univ, PhD(physics), 66, JD, 72. *Prof Exp:* Engr physics, Advan Airborn Systs Div, RCA Corp, 58-62; staff scientist, Phys Res Lab, Budd Co, 62-65; sr scientist environ, Space Sci Labs, Gen Elec Co, 66-73; atty & consult, pvt pract, 73-75; dep dir, Off Technol Policy, US Dept State, 75-79; DIR, DIV PLANNING & POLICY ANAL, NAT SCI FOUND, 79- *Concurrent Pos:* Vchmn, Philadelphia Air Pollution Control Bd, 73-75; mem, Mayor's Sci & Technol Adv Comt, 73-75. *Mem:* AAAS; Am Inst for Aeronaut & Astronaut; Am Bar Asn; Am Phys Soc; Int Inst Space Law. *Res:* Space sciences; science policy; US foreign policy; advanced technology; communications; materials; metals; re-entry physics; environmental science; nuclear effects; radio propagation. *Mailing Add:* Dir Div Planning & Policy Anal Nat Sci Found 1800 G St NW Washington DC 20550

PILACHOWSKI, CATHERINE ANDERSON, b Sacramento, Calif, Aug 20, 49. COMPOSITIONS OF STARS, GLOBULAR CLUSTERS. *Educ:* Harvey Mudd Col, BS, 71; Univ Hawaii, MS, 73, PhD(astron), 75. *Prof Exp:* res assoc astron, Univ Wash, 75-79; ASST SUPPORT SCIENTIST, KITT PEAK NAT OBSERV, 79- *Mem:* Am Astron Soc; AAAS; Astron Soc Pac; Int Astron Union. *Res:* Analysis of the composition of stellar atmospheres, with particular interest in stellar evolution and nucleosynthesis. *Mailing Add:* Kitt Peak Nat Observ 950 N Cherry Ave PO Box 26732 Tucson AZ 85726

PILANT, WALTER L, b Los Angeles, Calif, May 15, 31; m 54; c 5. GEOPHYSICS. *Educ:* Calif Inst Technol, BS, 53; Univ Calif, Los Angeles, MS, 56, PhD(physics), 60. *Prof Exp:* Asst res geophysicist, Univ Calif, Los Angeles, 55-62; res fel geol, Calif Inst Technol, 62-63; ASSOC PROF GEOPHYS, UNIV PITTSBURGH, 63- *Mem:* Inst Elec & Electronics Eng; Seismol Soc Am; Am Geophys Union; Soc Explor Geophysicists. *Res:* Elastic wave propagation; seismology; solid earth geophysics. *Mailing Add:* Dept of Earth & Planetary Sci Univ of Pittsburgh Pittsburgh PA 15260

PILAR, FRANK LOUIS, b Verdigre, Nebr, Aug 28, 27; m 54; c 5. PHYSICAL CHEMISTRY. *Educ:* Univ Nebr, BS, 51, MS, 53; Univ Cincinnati, PhD(chem), 57. *Prof Exp:* Jr chemist, Standard Oil Co(Ind), 52, asst chemist, 54-55; asst, Univ Wis, 53-54; from asst prof to assoc prof, 57-68, PROF CHEM, UNIV NH, 68- *Concurrent Pos:* Vis scientist, Math Inst, Oxford Univ, 63-64; vis prof, Univ Wis, 70-71. *Mem:* Am Chem Soc; Am Phys Soc; Sigma Xi. *Res:* Quantum chemistry. *Mailing Add:* Parsons Hall Univ of NH Durham NH 03824

PILAR, GUILLERMO ROMAN, b Buenos Aires, Arg, Oct 31, 30; m 58; c 2. NEUROPHYSIOLOGY. *Educ:* Univ Buenos Aires, MD, 54. *Prof Exp:* Teaching asst physiol, Univ Buenos Aires, 50-54, res assoc med, Inst Med Invest, 57-59; res assoc physiol, Univ Utah, 61-64; vis sr lectr, Monash Univ, Australia, 65; from asst res prof to assoc res prof, Univ Utah, 66-71; PROF BIOL SCI GROUP, UNIV CONN, 71-, HEAD PHYSIOL SECT, 73- *Concurrent Pos:* Squibb Found fel, 56-57; fel, Nat Coun Sci Invest Arg, 59-61; Guggenheim Found fel, 61-63; vis fel, Australian Nat Univ, 64-65; USPHS res career develop award, 67-71; vis assoc prof, Univ Calif, Los Angeles, 71, vis prof, 72. *Mem:* Soc Neurosci; NY Acad Sci; Am Physiol Soc. *Res:* Nerve cell interactions and communications, influences and changes during development, use and disuse; environment of the nerve cells. *Mailing Add:* Physiol Sect Sci Group Univ of Conn Storrs CT 06268

PILAT, MICHAEL JOSEPH, b Longview, Wash, Feb 19, 38. ENVIRONMENTAL ENGINEERING, CIVIL ENGINEERING. *Educ:* Univ Wash, BSChE, 60, MSChE, 63, PhD(civil eng), 67. *Prof Exp:* Engr, Boeing Co, 61-66; from asst prof to assoc prof civil eng, 67-78, PROF CIVIL ENG, UNIV WASH, 78- *Mem:* Air Pollution Control Asn; Am Inst Chem Engrs; Am Soc Civil Engrs; Am Chem Soc; AAAS. *Res:* Air pollution control technology; air pollutant source testing; aerosal behavior; plume opacity and atmospheric visibility; particulate control with wet scrubbers and electrostatic precipitations; particle sizing with cascade impactors. *Mailing Add:* Dept of Civil Eng Univ of Wash Seattle WA 98195

PILATI, CHARLES FRANCIS, b Wheeling, WVa, Aug 4, 45; m 82. CARDIOVASCULAR. *Educ:* Kent State Univ, BS, 69, PhD(physiol), 79. *Prof Exp:* Asst instr, Kent State Univ, 73-75, fel, 75-79; fel, 79-81, INSTR PHYSIOL, COL MED, NORTHEASTERN OHIO UNIV, 81- *Concurrent Pos:* Instr, Kent State Univ, 81- *Mem:* AAAS. *Res:* Cardiac research, including the effects of heavy metal, cardiac glycosides, and obesity on cardiac mechanical performance and ultrastructure. *Mailing Add:* Prog Physiol Col Med Northeastern Ohio Univ Rootstown OH 44272

PILATI, DAVID ALEXANDER, mechanical engineering, systems analysis, see previous edition

PILATO, JACK CARMEN, photographic chemistry, see previous edition

PILCHARD, EDWIN IVAN, b Urbana, Ill, Dec 14, 25; m 49; c 3. VETERINARY VIROLOGY, VETERINARY IMMUNOLOGY. *Educ:* Mich State Univ, DVM, 47; Univ Ill, MS, 59, PhD(immunol), 64. *Prof Exp:* Vet, 48-51, 53-57; pathologist, Ill Dept Agr, 57-58, dir vet path, Diag & Res Labs, 58-64; asst prof vet virol & immunol, Col Vet Med, Univ Ill, 64-69; prin vet, Coop State Res Serv, 69-77, PRIN STAFF OFF EMERGENCY PROG, USDA, 77- *Concurrent Pos:* Res asst, Col Vet Med, Univ Ill, 62-63; assoc mem, Ill Ctr Zoonoses Res, 66-69; NIH res grant, 66-69; prin investr proj livestock reproduction res, NSF Coop Prog Spain, 73-75; asst dir, Agr Exp Sta, Cornell Univ, 74-75. *Mem:* Am Vet Med Asn; Conf Res Workers Animal Dis; US Am Health Asn; Sigma Xi; Am Asn Vet Immunol. *Res:* Infectious diseases; immunology with emphasis in immunopathology and cellular immunity. *Mailing Add:* Emergency Prog Plant Health Insp Serv USDA Hyattsville MD 20782

PILCHER, BENJAMIN LEE, b Corpus Christi, Tex, Feb 25, 38; m 65; c 2. BOTANY. *Educ:* Tex Technol Col, BS, 61, MS, 63; Univ NMex, PhD(biol), 69. *Prof Exp:* Instr biol, Univ Tex, Arlington, 63-66; assoc prof, 69-79, head dept, 70-74, PROF, McMURRY COL, 69- *Mem:* Bot Soc Am; Cactus & Succulent Soc; Sigma Xi. *Res:* Developmental aspects of plants on both an anatomical and physiological basis; cactus seedling anatomy and development. *Mailing Add:* Rte 7 Box 186 Abilene TX 79605

PILCHER, CARL BERNARD, b Brooklyn, NY, Apr 7, 47. PLANETARY SCIENCES. *Educ:* Polytech Inst Brooklyn, BS, 68; Mass Inst Technol, PhD(chem), 73. *Prof Exp:* Asst astronomer, 73-77, asst prof, 77-79, ASSOC PROF, DEPT PHYSICS & ASTRON, INST ASTRON, UNIV HAWAII, HONOLULU, 79- *Mem:* Am Astron Soc; AAAS; Astron Soc Pac; Int Astron Union. *Res:* Study of atmospheres, surfaces and magnetospheres of solar system objects, particularly those in outer solar system. *Mailing Add:* Inst for Astron 2680 Woodlawn Dr Honolulu HI 96822

PILCHER, JAMES ERIC, b Toronto, Ont, Apr 23, 42; m 70. ELEMENTARY PARTICLE PHYSICS. *Educ:* Univ Toronto, BASc, 64, MSc, 66; Princeton Univ, PhD(physics), 68. *Prof Exp:* Res assoc, Princeton Univ, 68-69; vis scientist, Europ Orgn Nuclear Res, Geneva, Switz, 69-70; asst prof, Harvard Univ, 70-72; asst prof to assoc prof, 72-79, PROF ELEM PARTICLE PHYSICS, ENRICO FERMI INST, UNIV CHICAGO, 79- *Mem:* Am Phys Soc. *Res:* Experimental weak interactions including charge conjugation-parity violation and high energy neutrino scattering; proton-proton scattering at ultra-high energies; lepton pair production in strong interactions. *Mailing Add:* Enrico Fermi Inst Univ of Chicago Chicago IL 60637

PILCHER, VALTER ENNIS, b Savannah, Ga, Nov 7, 25; m 50; c 2. PHYSICS. *Educ:* Emory Univ, Ab, 48, MS, 49; NC State Col, PhD, 55. *Prof Exp:* Instr physics, Armstrong State Col, Ga, 49-50 & NC State Col, 50-53; jr res assoc, Brookhaven Nat Lab, 53, res assoc, 54-55; from asst prof to assoc prof, 56-72, PROF PHYSICS, UNION COL, NY, 72-, CHMN DEPT, 78- *Concurrent Pos:* Guest scientist, Swed Atomic Energy Co, 62-63; Fulbright lectr, Haile Selassie Univ, 68-69. *Mem:* Am Phys Soc; Am Asn Physics Teachers. *Res:* Neutron physics; nuclear spectroscopy. *Mailing Add:* Dept of Physics Union Col Schenectady NY 12308

PILEGGI, VINCENT JOSEPH, b Philadelphia, Pa, May 10, 28; m 57; c 3. CLINICAL CHEMISTRY. *Educ:* Drexel Inst, BS, 50; Univ Wis, MS, 53, PhD(biochem), 54. *Prof Exp:* Chief biochem, Letterman Army Hosp, San Francisco, Calif, 55-57; asst prof, Univ Pa, 57-59; chief, Iodine Div, Bio-Sci Labs, 59-65 & Spec Projs Prods, 65-66, dir res, 66-77; DIR SCI AFFAIRS, NAT HEALTH LABS, LA JOLLA, 77- *Mem:* Am Thyroid Asn; Am Asn Clin Chem. *Res:* Clinical biochemistry, especially thyroid; radioimmunoassay of hormones. *Mailing Add:* 1057 Via Mil Cumbres Solana Beach CA 92075

PILET, STANFORD CHRISTIAN, b Ft Benning, Ga, Nov 6, 31; m 57; c 2. OPERATIONS RESEARCH, ASTRODYNAMICS. *Educ:* US Mil Acad, BS, 54; Univ Cincinnati, MS, 60, PhD(dynamical astron), 63. *Prof Exp:* Res specialist, Orbital Flight Mech, Aero-Space Div, Boeing Co, Seattle, 63-65, RES SPECIALIST, MIL OPERS SYSTS ANAL, BOEING AEROSPACE CO, 65- *Mem:* Fel AAAS; Am Astron Soc; Sigma Xi. *Res:* Long term prediction of orbital motion; orbital motion of artificial satellites effected by various perturbations; analysis and evaluation of military systems and policies. *Mailing Add:* 7444 Mercer Terrace Dr Mercer Island WA 98040

PILETZ, JOHN EDWARD, b Rochester, NH, Mar 12, 52; m 78. BIOCHEMICAL GENETICS, DEVELOPMENTAL BIOLOGY. *Educ:* Univ NH, BA, 74; Univ Cincinnati, PhD(develop biol), 78. *Prof Exp:* RES ASST DEVELOP BIOL, UNIV CINCINNATI, 74- *Concurrent Pos:* Am Dental Asn grant, Univ Calif, Davis, 78- *Mem:* Am Dairy Sci Asn. *Res:* Control of gene expression in eukaryotes. *Mailing Add:* Dept of Fetal Pharmacol Children's Hosp Res Found Cincinnati OH 45229

PILGER, REX HERBERT, JR, b North Platte, Nebr, June 8, 48; m 73; c 3. TECTONOPHYSICS, GEOPHYSICS. *Educ:* Univ Nebr, BS, 70, MS, 72; Univ Southern Calif, PhD(geol), 76. *Prof Exp:* Geol field asst, US Geol Surv, 75-76; asst prof, 76-79, ASSOC PROF GEOL, LA STATE UNIV, 79- *Concurrent Pos:* Geophysicist, Naval Ocean Res & Develop Activ, 78- *Mem:* Geol Soc Am; Soc Explor Geophysicists; Am Geophys Union. *Res:* Plate tectonics of western United States, South America and Gulf of Mexico; hotspots; geophysics of sedimentary basins and continental margins; geophysics of goepressured-geothermal zones. *Mailing Add:* Dept of Geol La State Univ Baton Rouge LA 70803

PILGER, RICHARD CHRISTIAN, JR, b Hartford, Conn, June 13, 32; m 57; c 2. PHYSICAL CHEMISTRY, INORGANIC CHEMISTRY. *Educ:* Univ Notre Dame, BS, 54; Univ Calif, Berkeley, PhD(chem), 57. *Prof Exp:* Asst, Univ Calif, Berkeley, 55-56; asst prof chem, Univ Wash, 57-59; Univ Notre Dame, 59-64; assoc prof, 64-71, PROF CHEM & PHYSICS ST MARY'S COL, IND, 71- *Mem:* Am Chem Soc; Am Phys Soc. *Res:* Nuclear spectroscopy; coordination chemistry. *Mailing Add:* Dept Chem & Physics St Marys Col Notre Dame IN 46556

PILGERAM, LAURENCE OSCAR, b Great Falls, Mont, June 23, 24; m 51; c 2. BIOCHEMISTRY, PHYSIOLOGY. *Educ:* Univ Calif, BA, 49, PhD(biochem), 53. *Prof Exp:* Asst, Inst Exp Biol, Univ Calif, 45-47, asst, Div Biochem, 51-52; instr physiol, Col Med, Univ Ill, 54-55; asst prof biochem, Dept Chem, Stanford Univ, 55-57; dir arteriosclerosis res lab, Sch Med, Univ Minn & St Barnabas Hosp Res Found, 57-65; dir, Arteriosclerosis Res Lab, Calif, 65-71; dir, Coagulation Lab & assoc dir, Cerebrovascular Res Ctr, Baylor Col Med, 71-75; DIR CELL CULT LAB, CALIF, 75- *Concurrent Pos:* Life Insurance Med Res Fund fel physiol chem, Sch Med, Univ Calif, 52-54. *Honors & Awards:* Ciba Found Award, London, 58; Karl Thomae Award, Ger, 73. *Mem:* Am Soc Biol Chem. *Res:* Blood coagulation; cellular control mechanisms. *Mailing Add:* PO Box 1583 Goleta Sta Santa Barbara CA 93116

PILGRIM, DONALD, b Sioux City, Iowa, May 31, 29; m 56; c 5. MATHEMATICS. *Educ:* Morningside Col, AB, 51; Univ Iowa, MS, 52; Univ Wis, PhD(math), 63. *Prof Exp:* Mathematician, Gen Labs, US Rubber Co, 52-53; teacher high sch, Iowa, 54-55; instr math, Keokuk Community Col, 55-56; PROF MATH, LUTHER COL, IOWA, 56- *Concurrent Pos:* Treas, Iowa Acad Sci, 75- *Mem:* Am Math Soc. *Res:* Engel conditions on groups; groups of exponent four; additive theory of prime numbers. *Mailing Add:* 313 Ohio St Decorah IA 52101

PILGRIM, HYMAN IRA, b New York, NY, Feb 10, 25; m 47, 68; c 8. CANCER. *Educ:* Univ Calif, AB, 50, MA, 53, PhD, 56. *Prof Exp:* Asst zool, Univ Calif, 52-53; from instr to asst prof anat, Sch Med, Univ Buffalo, 56-61; asst res prof anat & surg, Col Med, Univ Utah, 61-68, assoc res prof anat, 68-72; vis reader & actg head dept anat, Univ Ibadan, 76-77. *Mem:* Am Asn Cancer Res; Am Asn Anatomists. *Res:* Experimental oncology; mouse genetics and pathology; genesis of adrenal and reticuloendothelial tumors; metastasis and kinetics of tumor growth; gnotobiotics. *Mailing Add:* 2251 Blackfield Dr Concord CA 94520

PILIERO, SAM JOSEPH, endocrinology, hematology, deceased

PILKERTON, A RAYMOND, b Washington, DC, Mar 27, 35; m 66. OPHTHALMOLOGY. *Educ:* Georgetown Univ, BS, 56, MD, 60. *Prof Exp:* Intern, Univ Pittsburgh, 60-61; resident ophthal, Med Ctr, Georgetown Univ, 61-64; from instr to asst prof, 65-73, assoc prof, 73-81, CLIN PROF OPHTHAL, MED CTR, GEORGETOWN UNIV, 81-, DIR RETINA SERV, 65- *Concurrent Pos:* Nat Inst Neurol Dis & Blindness spec fel retinal surg, Wills Eye Hosp, Philadelphia, 64-65; chief ophthal serv, Vet Admin Hosp, Washington, DC, 65- *Mem:* Am Col Surg; Am Acad Ophthal & Otolaryngol; Asn Res Vision & Ophthal. *Res:* Retina adhesion characteristics; vitreous fibraplasia. *Mailing Add:* Sibley Mem Hosp 5255 Loughboro Rd NW Washington DC 20016

PILKEY, ORRIN H, b New York, NY, Sept 19, 34; m 56; c 4. MARINE GEOLOGY. *Educ:* Wash State Univ, BS, 57; Mont State Univ, MS, 59; Fla State Univ, PhD(geol), 62. *Prof Exp:* Res assoc & asst prof, Marine Inst, Univ GA, 62-65; assoc prof, 65-71, PROF GEOL, DUKE UNIV, 71- *Concurrent Pos:* Vis prof, Univ PR, 71-72 & US Geol Surv, Woods Hole, Mass, 75-76; ed, J Sedimentary Petrol. *Mem:* Am Asn Petrol Geol; Geol Soc Am; Int Asn Sedimentol; Soc Econ Paleont & Mineral; AAAS. *Res:* Geological oceanography; continental rise and deep basin turbidite sedimentation; shoreline conservation. *Mailing Add:* Dept of Geol Duke Univ PO Box 6665 Col Sta Durham NC 27708

PILKEY, WALTER DAVID, b Chicago, Ill, Oct 28, 36; m 65; c 2. APPLIED MECHANICS, STRUCTURAL ENGINEERING. *Educ:* Wash State Univ, BA, 58; Purdue Univ, MS, 60; Pa State Univ, PhD(eng mech), 62. *Prof Exp:* Scientist mech, Ill Inst Technol Res Inst, 62-69; PROF MECH ENG, UNIV VA, 69- *Concurrent Pos:* Vis prof, Kabul Univ, Afghanistan, 63-64; adj assoc prof, Ill Inst Technol, 64-69; vis res scientist, Ruhr Univ, Ger, 75-76; sr lectr, Fulbright-Hays, Soviet Union, 78. *Mem:* Am Soc Mech Engrs; Am Soc Civil Engrs; Am Acad Mech; Am Soc Eng Educ. *Res:* Numerical methods of solid mechanics; optimization of mechanical systems; crashworthy vehicle design; balancing of rotating shafts; transient response of structural members. *Mailing Add:* Dept of Mech & Aerospace Eng Univ Va Charlottesville VA 22901

PILKIEWICZ, FRANK GEORGE, b Jersey City, NJ, June 21, 46; m 69; c 2. CHEMISTRY. *Educ:* St Peters Col, BS, 68; Rutgers Univ, MS, 73, PhD(chem), 74. *Prof Exp:* Teaching asst chem, Rutgers Univ, 69-71, res asst, 71-74; res assoc fel, Columbia Univ, 74-77; prod mgr, Waters Assoc, 77-79; SR RES INVESTR, SQUIBB INST MED RES, 79- *Mem:* Am Chem Soc. *Res:* High performance liquid chromatography: in identifying biologically active natural products and as an analytical method in pharmacokinetic studies; isolation and structural elucidation of biologically active natural products. *Mailing Add:* PO Box 4000 Princeton NJ 08540

PILKINGTON, DWAIN H, food science, see previous edition

PILKINGTON, HAROLD DEAN, b Laird, Colo, Dec 10, 20; m 54; c 4. GEOLOGY, PETROLOGY. *Educ:* Univ Colo, BA, 52, MS, 54; Univ Ariz, PhD(geol), 62. *Prof Exp:* Instr geol & petrol, Kans State Univ, 56-59; asst geol, Univ Ariz, 59-62; assoc geologist, Cyprus Mines Corp, 62-65; asst prof mineral & petrol, Univ Alaska, 65-66, assoc prof, 66-69; dist geologist, Int Chem & Minerals Corp, 69-72; consult, 72-73; DIST GEOLOGIST, AMAX EXPLOR, INC, 74- *Mem:* Fel Geol Soc Am; Soc Econ Geol; Can Inst Mining & Metall; Am Inst Mining, Metall & Petrol Engrs. *Res:* Structure, petrology and paragenesis of basic volcanic rocks and associated sulfide deposits. *Mailing Add:* 8428 Chase Dr Arvada CO 80003

PILKINGTON, LOU ANN, b Wichita, Kans, Apr 2, 24. PHYSIOLOGY. *Educ:* Univ Okla, BS, 48, MS, 59, PhD(physiol), 61. *Prof Exp:* NIH fel & instr physiol, Sch Med, Univ Okla, 62-63; fel, 63-65, from instr to asst prof physiol, Med Col, Cornell Univ, 66-72; DIR PULMONARY FUNCTION & WORK PHYSIOL LAB, GOLDWATER MEM HOSP, NEW YORK UNIV MED CTR, 72- *Concurrent Pos:* NIH career develop award, 65-70. *Mem:* AAAS; Am Physiol Soc; Harvey Soc; Sigma Xi. *Res:* Respiratory physiology; work physiology. intact functioning kidney; renal blood flow. *Mailing Add:* Pulmonary Lab Ward C-11 New York Univ Med Ctr New York NY 10044

PILKINGTON, THEO C(LYDE), b Durham, NC, June 23, 35; m 57; c 2. ELECTRICAL ENGINEERING. *Educ:* NC State Univ, BEE, 58; Duke Univ, MS, 60, PhD(elec eng), 63. *Prof Exp:* From instr to assoc prof elec eng, 61-69, chmn dept, biomed eng, 67-78, PROF BIOMED & ELEC ENG, DUKE UNIV, 69- *Concurrent Pos:* Ed, Transactions on Biomed Eng, Inst Elec & Electronics Engrs. *Mem:* Am Phys Soc; Inst Elec & Electronics Engrs; Biomed Eng Soc. *Res:* Biomedical engineering; field theory; numerical analysis. *Mailing Add:* Dept of Biomed Eng Duke Univ Durham NC 27706

PILLA, ARTHUR ANTHONY, b New York, NY, Aug 12, 36. BIOELECTROCHEMISTRY, BIOELECTRICITY. *Educ:* St Joseph's Col, BS, 56; Univ Pa, MS, 59; Univ Paris, PhD, 64. *Prof Exp:* Sr scientist, US Army Res Labs, Ft Monmouth, 66-69; dir, Bioelectrochem Lab, 69-75, PROF BIOELECTROCHEM, DEPT APPL CHEM, COLUMBIA UNIV, 72- *Concurrent Pos:* Ed, J Electrochem Soc, 74-80, Bioelectrochem & Bioenergetics, 75- & Electrochimica Acta, 75- *Mem:* Electrochem Soc; Int Bioelectrochem Soc; Am Chem Soc; AAAS. *Res:* Bioelectric phenomena in tissue growth and repair via electrochemical kinetics at cell surfaces; electrochemical relaxation techniques for cell membrane impedance; in vivo applications of electromagnetic modulation of bone and other tissue repair. *Mailing Add:* 133 Heights Rd Ridgewood NJ 07450

PILLAI, KRISHNA CHENNAKKADU SREEDHARAN, b Veliyanad, Kerala, India, Feb 24, 20; c 3. MATHEMATICAL STATISTICS. *Educ:* Univ Travancore, India, BSc, 41, MSc, 45. *Prof Exp:* Lectr, Univ Travancore, India, 45-51; res asst, Princeton Univ, 51-52; res assoc, Univ NC, 52-53; asst statistician, UN, 54-55, vis prof & UN sr statist adv, Univ Philippines, 56-59, statistician, UN, 60-62; PROF MATH & STATIST, PURDUE UNIV, LAFAYETTE, 62- *Mem:* Fel Am Statist Asn; Biomet Soc; fel Inst Math Statist; Philippine Statist Asn; Int Statist Inst. *Res:* Multivariate statistical analysis; order statistics; sampling theory. *Mailing Add:* Dept of Statist Purdue Univ West Lafayette IN 47907

PILLAI, PADMANABHA S, b Nov 13, 31; Indian citizen. SOLID STATE & POLYMER PHYSICS. *Educ:* Univ Kerala, BSc, 50; Banaras Hindu Univ, MSc, 53; WVa Univ, PhD(physics), 66. *Prof Exp:* lectr physics, Sree Narayan Col, India, 53-61 & Annamalai Univ, Madras, 59-61; prof, M D T Hindu Col, India, 61-63; NSF grant, Kans State Univ, 63-64; Atomic Energy Comn fel, WVa Univ, 65-66; SR RES PHYSICIST POLYMER PHYSICS, GOODYEAR TIRE & RUBBER CO, 66- *Mem:* Am Phys Soc; Am Chem Soc. *Mailing Add:* 509 Fairwood Dr Tallmadge OH 44278

PILLAR, WALTER OSCAR, b Philadelphia, Pa, Apr 14, 40; m 62; c 2. POLYMER CHEMISTRY, FOREST PRODUCTS. *Educ:* Pa State Univ, BS, 62; Univ Mich, PhD(wood technol), 68. *Prof Exp:* Lab chemist, Perkins Glue Co, 62-63; res scientist adhesives, Koppers Co, 66-70, res scientist expendable polystyrene, 70-72, sr res scientist, 72-74; sr res scientist, ARCO/Polymers, Inc, 74-77, prin scientist, Expandable Polystrene Thermoplastic Elastomers, 77-81; SR ENGR, ORG MAT DEVELOP & TROUBLESHOOTING, GEN ELEC AEROSPACE ELECTRONICS, 81- *Mem:* Am Chem Soc; Forest Prod Res Soc. *Res:* Plastic foams; wood products; adhesives; phenolic resins; flame retardance in plastics. *Mailing Add:* Gen Elec Aerospace Electronics Utica NY 13503

PILLARD, RICHARD COLESTOCK, b Springfield, Ohio, Oct 11, 33; c 3. PSYCHIATRY. *Educ:* Antioch Col, BA, 55; Univ Rochester, MD, 59. *Prof Exp:* Asst psychiatrist, Boston State Hosp, 63-67; from instr to asst prof, 66-70, head, basic studies unit, Psychopharmacol Lab, 68-78, ASSOC PROF PSYCHIAT, SCH MED, BOSTON UNIV, 70-, DIR, FAMILY STUDIES LAB, 78- *Concurrent Pos:* Pvt Pract, 63-; dir, Res Training Prog, Sch Med, Boston Univ, 70- *Mem:* Am Psychiat Asn; Soc Psychophysiol Res; Am Col Neuropsychopharmacol; Am Psychopathalogic Asn. *Res:* Psychopharmacology; homosexuality; drug abuse. *Mailing Add:* 80 East Concord St Boston MA 02118

PILLAY, DATHATHRY TRICHINOPOLY NATRAJ, b Hyderabad, India, Dec 16, 31; m 65; c 2. PLANT PHYSIOLOGY. *Educ:* Osmania Med Col, BScAg, 53; Cornell Univ MS, 59, PhD(pomol, plant physiol), 61. *Prof Exp:* Hort asst, Dept Agr, Hyderabad, India, 54-58; jr horticulturist tree fruit sta, Wash State Univ, 62-63; from asst prof to assoc prof, 63-72, PROF PLANT PHYSIOL, UNIV WINDSOR, 72- *Concurrent Pos:* Grants, Nat Res Coun Can, 63-72 & Ministry Univ Affairs Can, 66-67. *Mem:* AAAS; Am Soc Hort Sci; Am Soc Plant Physiol; Can Bot Soc; Can Soc Plant Physiol. *Res:* Physiological and biochemical effects of plant growth regulating chemicals, with special emphasis on nucleic acid metabolism during plant growth and development. *Mailing Add:* Dept of Biol Univ of Windsor Windsor ON N9B 3P4 Can

PILLAY, K K SIVASANKARA, b Puliyoor, India, Jan 28, 35; m 64; c 1. NUCLEAR CHEMISTRY, NUCLEAR ENGINEERING. *Educ:* Cent Col, Bangalore, India, BSc, 55; Univ Mysore, MSc, 56; Pa State Univ, PhD(chem), 65. *Prof Exp:* Lectr chem, Univ Mysore, 56-60; asst, Pa State Univ, 60-65; resident res assoc nuclear chem, Argonne Nat Lab, 65-66; res scientist, Western NY Nuclear Res Ctr, Inc, 66-67, sr res scientist, 67-71; res assoc nuclear eng, Pa State Univ, 71-74, asst prof, 75-77, assoc prof, 77-81; STAFF SCIENTIST, LOS ALAMOS NAT LAB, 81- *Concurrent Pos:* Consult radionuclear appln criminal invests, Pa State Police, 71-74, nuclear process chem & waste mgt, 76-81. *Mem:* AAAS; Am Chem Soc; Am Nuclear Soc; fel Am Inst Chem; NY Acad Sci. *Res:* Applications of neutron activation analysis in physical and life sciences; reactor fuel burn up analysis; industrial applications of nuclear analytical methods in process and quality control; environmental pollution studies and nuclear forensic applications; nuclear process chemistry; radioactive waste management. *Mailing Add:* Safeguards Systs Group Mail Stop 541 Los Alamos Nat Lab University Park PA 16802

PILLER, HERBERT, b Hartmanitz, Bohemia, May 18, 26; m 56; c 4. SOLID STATE PHYSICS. *Educ:* Univ Vienna, PhD(physics), 55. *Prof Exp:* Physicist, ZW Labor, Siemens AG, 55-60; SUPVRY RES PHYSICIST, NAVAL WEAPONS CTR LAB, CORONA & MICHELSON LAB, CHINA LAKE, CALIF, 60-; ASSOC PROF PHYSICS, LA STATE UNIV, BATON ROUGE, 69- *Mem:* Am Phys Soc; Am Asn Univ Prof. *Res:* Optical properties of solids; semiconductor physics. *Mailing Add:* 12467 Sherbrook Ave Baton Rouge LA 70815

PILLIAR, ROBERT MATHEWS, b Beamsville, Ont, Dec 14, 39. BIOMATERIALS, METALLURGY. *Educ:* Univ Toronto, BASc, 61; Univ Leeds, PhD(metall), 65. *Prof Exp:* Univ grant metall, McMaster Univ, 65-67; res engr, Int Nickel, Inc, 67-68; res scientist, Ont Res Found, 68-78; ASSOC PROF, FAC DENT, UNIV TORONTO, 78-, ASSOC PROF METALL & MAT SCI, 80- *Concurrent Pos:* Adj prof metall & mat sci, Univ Toronto, 77-, adj prof biomed eng, 78- *Mem:* Am Soc Testing & Mat; Biomat Soc Can (secy-treas, 77-78). *Res:* Powder metallurgy; interface studies; composite materials; mechanical properties. *Mailing Add:* Fac of Dent Univ of Toronto Toronto ON M5S 1A1 Can

PILLINGER, WILLIAM LEWIS, b Miami, Fla, Oct 7, 23; m 49; c 3. APPLIED PHYSICS. *Educ:* Ohio State Univ, BSc, 50, PhD(physics), 55. *Prof Exp:* RES PHYSICIST, SAVANNAH RIVER LAB, E I DU PONT DE NEMOURS & CO, 55- *Mem:* Am Phys Soc. *Res:* Low temperature physics; Mossbauer effect studies with actinide metals and compounds; materials science; effects of hydrogen in metals. *Mailing Add:* Savannah River Lab E I du Pont de Nemours & Co Aiken SC 29801

PILLION, DENNIS JOSEPH, b Hartford, Conn, Aug 15, 50; m 75. BIOCHEMISTRY, IMMUNOLOGY. *Educ:* Univ Hartford, BA, 72; Med Col Ga, PhD(cell & molecular biol), 76. *Prof Exp:* NIH fel insulin action, 76-79, ASST PROF PHARMACOL, BROWN UNIV, 79- *Honors & Awards:* Excellence in Res Award, Sigma Xi, 76; Baladimos Award, Am Diabetes Asn, 78; Louis N Katz award, Am Heart Asn. *Mem:* Sigma Xi; AAAS; NY Acad Sci; Immunopharmacol Soc; Am Diabetes Asn. *Res:* Insulin action; isolation of transport proteins; immunoregulation of membrane function; microvascular tissue response to insulin; renal response to insulin. *Mailing Add:* Dept Pharmacol Univ Ala Birmingham AL 35294

PILLMORE, CHARLES LEE, b Boulder, Colo, Apr 7, 30; m 54; c 3. COAL GEOLOGY, PHOTOGEOLOGY. *Educ:* Univ Colo, BA, 52, MS, 54. *Prof Exp:* Res geologist, 54-75, supvry geologist, 75-80, RES GEOLOGIST, US GEOL SURV, 80- *Mem:* Geol Soc Am; Am Soc Photogram. *Res:* Geology and coal resources of Raton coal field in New Mexico; iridium occurrenCes at the Tertiary/Cretaceous boundary; photogeology--application of photogrammetry to geology and development of a computer-supported photogrammetric mapping system for geologic studies. *Mailing Add:* US Geol Surv Fed Ctr Box 25046-MS 913 Denver CO 80225

PILLOFF, HERSCHEL SYDNEY, b Uhrichsville, Ohio, Aug 15, 40; m 68; c 3. MOLECULAR PHYSICS, LASERS. *Educ:* Mass Inst Technol, BS, 61; Cornell Univ, PhD(phys chem), 66. *Prof Exp:* USPHS fel molecular beams, Univ Toronto, 67-69; res chemist, Naval Res Lab, 69-74; PHYSICIST, OFF NAVAL RES, 74- *Mem:* Optic Soc Am. *Res:* Molecular physics, laser physics and radiation transport. *Mailing Add:* Code 412 Off of Naval Res 800 N Quincy St Arlington VA 22217

PILLSBURY, DALE RONALD, b Chico, Calif, Aug 10, 40; c 1. PHYSICAL OCEANOGRAPHY. *Educ:* Chico State Col, BS, 61; Univ Calif, Davis, MA, 64; Ore State Univ, PhD(oceanog), 71. *Prof Exp:* Asst, Univ Calif, Davis, 61-64; res asst oceanog, 64-67, RES ASSOC OCEANOG, ORE STATE UNIV, 67- *Mem:* Am Geophys Union. *Res:* Coastal upwelling; deep ocean current measurements. *Mailing Add:* Sch of Oceanog Ore State Univ Corvallis OR 97331

PILLSBURY, HAROLD C, b Baltimore, Md, Oct 18, 22; m 47; c 3. BIOCHEMISTRY. *Educ:* Loyola Col, Md, BS, 50. *Prof Exp:* Res chemist, Food & Drug Admin, 58-66; RES CHEMIST, FED TRADE COMN, 66- *Mem:* Fel Am Inst Chem. *Mailing Add:* Bur of Deceptive Practs Fed Trade Comn Sixth & Pa Ave NW Washington DC 20580

PILON, JEAN-GUY, b Ste Therese, Que, Can, Apr 7, 31; m 60; c 2. ENTOMOLOGY. *Educ:* Univ Montreal, BA, 53, BSc, 56; McGill Univ, MSc, 60; Yale Univ, PhD(bioclimat), 65. *Prof Exp:* Res officer entom, Can Dept Forestry, 56-65; asst prof, 65-67, assoc prof, 67-73, PROF ENTOM, UNIV MONTREAL, 73- *Mem:* AAAS; Entom Soc Can; Entom Soc Am. *Mailing Add:* Dept of Biol Sci Univ of Montreal CP 6128 Montreal PQ H3C 3J7 Can

PILSON, MICHAEL EDWARD QUINTON, b Ottawa, Ont, Oct 25, 33; m 57; c 2. MARINE BIOLOGY, CHEMISTRY. *Educ:* Bishop's Univ, BSc, 54; McGill Univ, MSc, 59; Univ Calif, PhD(marine biol), 64. *Prof Exp:* Asst res biologist, Inst Comp Biol, Zool Soc San Diego, 63-66; from asst prof to assoc prof, 67-78, PROF OCEANOG, GRAD SCH, UNIV RI, 78- *Concurrent Pos:* Dir, Marine Ecosysts Res Lab, 76- *Mem:* AAAS; Am Soc Mammal; Am Soc Limnol & Oceanog. *Res:* Marine chemistry; physiology of Mollusca; milk of marine mammals; chemical ecology of coral reefs; chemistry of marine sediments; ecology of marine microcosms. *Mailing Add:* Grad Sch of Oceanog Univ of RI Narragansett RI 02882

PILTCH, MARTIN STANLEY, b Brooklyn, NY, Aug 11, 39; m 69; c 2. LASERS. *Educ:* Columbia Univ, AB, 60; Polytech Inst Brooklyn, MS, 68, PhD(electrophys), 71. *Prof Exp:* Staff mem lasers, TRG Control Data Corp, 60-66; DEP GROUP LEADER LASERS, LOS ALAMOS SCI LAB, UNIV CALIF, 72- *Concurrent Pos:* NSF fel, 66-70; fel, Max-Planck Inst Biophys Chem, 71-72; adj asst prof physics, Univ NMex, 75-; guest scientist, Max Planck Inst, 81. *Mem:* Inst Elec & Electronics Engrs; Am Phys Soc. *Res:* Atomic and molecular physics as applied to high power ultraviolet and infrared lasers and to nonlinear optical processes. *Mailing Add:* Los Alamos Nat Lab Univ Calif Box 1663 Los Alamos NM 87545

PILZ, CLIFFORD G, b Chicago, Ill, Apr 20, 21; m 57; c 1. INTERNAL MEDICINE, CARDIOLOGY. *Educ:* Univ Ill, Chicago, BS, 44, MD, 45. *Prof Exp:* Intern med, Cook County Hosp, 45-46, resident, 49; resident, Hines Vet Admin Hosp, 49-52; physician, Vet Admin Hosp, Iowa, 52-53; asst to chief med serv, 53-58, asst chief med, 58-71, actg chief, 69-71, CHIEF MED, VET ADMIN W SIDE HOSP, 71- *Concurrent Pos:* Fel path, Cook County Hosp, 48; clin assoc prof, Chicago Med Sch, 55-60, assoc prof, 60-66; assoc prof, Univ Ill Col Med, 66-68, prof, 68- *Mem:* Fel Am Col Physicians; fel Am Col Cardiol; Am Rheumatism Asn. *Mailing Add:* Vet Admin W Side Hosp PO Box 8195 Chicago IL 60612

PIMBLEY, GEORGE HERBERT, JR, b Cleveland, Ohio, Mar 11, 22; m 51; c 3. MATHEMATICS. *Educ:* Western Reserve Univ, AB, 43; Univ Calif, Los Angeles, MA, 49; NY Univ, PhD(math), 57. *Prof Exp:* Mathematician, US Naval Electronics Lab, Calif, 47-50; MEM STAFF, LOS ALAMOS SCI LAB, 50- *Concurrent Pos:* Asst, Inst Math Sci, NY Univ, 53-55; Ger Res Asn travel grant; vis lectr, Cologne Univ, 74; prog dir, Appl Math & Statist, NSF, 77-78. *Mem:* Am Math Soc. *Res:* Differential, integral and nonlinear functional equations; nonlinear functional analysis; neutron transport theory; mathematical problems in physics; biophysical problems. *Mailing Add:* Los Alamos Sci Lab Univ of Calif PO Box 1663 Los Alamos NM 87545

PIMBLEY, WALTER THORNTON, b Cleveland Heights, Ohio, July 12, 30; m 56; c 2. PHYSICS. *Educ:* Kent State Univ, AB, 52; Pa State Univ, MS, 55, PhD(physics, math), 59. *Prof Exp:* Instr physics, Pa State Univ, 58-59; staff physicist, IBM Corp, 59-61, adv physicist, 61-67, SR PHYSICIST, IBM CORP, 67- *Mem:* Am Phys Soc; AAAS. *Res:* Surface studies, including emission of electrons and adsorption phenomena; propagation of electromagnetic waves; fluid dynamics. *Mailing Add:* 540 Torrance Vestal NY 13850

PIMENTEL, DAVID, b Fresno, Calif, May 24, 25; m 49; c 3. ECOLOGY, ENTOMOLOGY. *Educ:* Univ Mass, BS, 48; Cornell Univ, PhD(entom), 51. *Prof Exp:* Asst entom, Cornell Univ, 48-51; chief trop res lab, USPHS, San Juan, PR, 51-53, proj leader tech develop lab, Savannah, Ga, 54-55; from asst prof to prof insect ecol & head dept entom & limnol, State Univ NY Col Agr, Cornell Univ, 55-69, prof insect ecol, 69-76, PROF INSECT ECOL & AGR SCI, CORNELL UNIV, 76- *Concurrent Pos:* Fel, Univ Chicago, 54-55; Orgn Europ Econ Coop fel, Oxford Univ, 61; NSF comput scholar, Mass Inst Technol, 61; invited mem panel environ pollution, President's Sci Adv Coun, 64-66; chmn biol & renewable resources panel, Life Sci Comt, Nat Acad Sci, 66-67, mem ad hoc comt environ aspects foreign assistance progs, 70, mem panel on water in man's life in India, 70, mem comt agr & the environ, 70- & co-chmn panel innovative mosquito control, Off Foreign Secy, 72-; mem coun, Nat Inst Environ Health Sci, 67-68; chmn training comt, Int Biol Prog, 67-70; mem comt pesticides, Dept Health, Educ & Welfare, 69; US del, UNESCO Conf Univ Governance & Role of Stud, 69; ecol consult environ qual, Off Sci & Technol, Exec Off of the Pres, 69-70; chmn biol panel, Advan Training Proj, NSF, 70; chmn panel environ impact herbicides, Environ Protection Agency, 72-; chmn, Panel Econ & Environ Aspects Pest Mgt in Cent Am, Nat Acad Sci, 73-77, comt food & food prod, 74-76, comt world food health & pop, 74-75; consult, Food & Agr Org UN, 74; chmn, Bd Sci & Technol Int Develop, Off Foreign Secy, Nat Acad Sci, 75-79; chmn, Nat Adv Coun Environ Educ, Off Educ, HEW, 75-78; pesticide adv coun, Environ Protection Agency, 75-78; comn int rel, Nat Acad Sci, 75-79; chair biomass panel, Energy Res Adv Bd, US Dept Energy, 79-; mem genetics panel & chair land degradation panel, Off Technol Assessment, 80-; mem res adv comt, USAID, 79-; chair, Environ Studies Bd, Nat Acad Sci, 81-82. *Mem:* AAAS; Ecol Soc Am; Soc Study Evolution; Entom Soc Am; Am Soc Zool. *Res:* Ecology and genetics of insect-plant, parasite-host and predator-prey population systems; environmental resource management and pollution, energy and land resources in the food system; ecosystems management and pest control. *Mailing Add:* Dept of Entom Sect Ecol & Systs Cornell Univ Ithaca NY 14853

PIMENTEL, GEORGE CLAUDE, b Rolinda, Calif, May 2, 22; m 42; c 3. CHEMISTRY. *Educ:* Univ Calif, Los Angeles, AB, 43; Univ Calif, PhD(chem), 49. *Prof Exp:* From instr to assoc prof, 49-59, prof chem, Univ Calif, Berkeley, 59-77. *Concurrent Pos:* Guggenheim fel, 55; Humboldt Scholar, 74; ed, Chem Study; dep dir, NSF, 77-80. *Honors & Awards:* Joseph Priestly Award, Dickinson Col, 72; E K Plyler Prize, 79; Ellis R Lippincott Medal, 80. *Mem:* Nat Acad Sci; Am Chem Soc; Am Phys Soc; Am Acad Arts & Sci; Optical Soc Am. *Res:* Infrared spectroscopy and molecular structure; chemical lasers; hydrogen bonding; matrix isolation spectroscopy; infrared study of planetary atmospheres; rapid-scan infrared; thermodynamic properties of hydrocarbons. *Mailing Add:* Lab Chem Biodynamics Univ Calif Berkeley CA 94720

PIMENTEL, RICHARD A, b Campbell, Calif, June 7, 23; m 44; c 2. VERTEBRATE ZOOLOGY. *Educ:* San Jose State Col, BA, 47; Ore State Col, MS, 50, PhD(vert zool), 52. *Prof Exp:* Asst zool, Ore State Col, 48-50; from instr to assoc prof, 52-62, PROF ZOOL, CALIF POLYTECH STATE UNIV, SAN LUIS OBISPO, 62- *Mem:* Soc Syst Zool; Soc Study Evolution; Biomet Soc. *Res:* Multivariate data analysis applied to systematic and ecological problems. *Mailing Add:* Dept of Biol Sci Calif Polytech State Univ San Luis Obispo CA 93401

PIMLOTT, DOUGLAS HUMPHREYS, wildlife ecology, deceased

PINA, EDUARDO ISIDORIO, b New Bedford, Mass, Oct 2, 31; m 53; c 4. MATHEMATICAL STATISTICS, OPERATIONS RESEARCH. *Educ:* Univ Mass, BS, 53, MA, 54. *Prof Exp:* Instr math, Univ Mass, 53-54; mathematician, Boeing Co, 54-55, lead engr, Systs Criteria Group, 55-56, acting supvr, Appl Math Res Group, 56-58, supvr, 58-59, chief, Anal Unit, 59-63, mgr, Tech Support, 63-65, Prog Appln, 65-66 & Opers & Comput Tech Sect, 66-67, dir, Opers Res-Mgt Sci, Commercial Airplane Div, 67-71, dir sales technol, 71-78, dir sales strategy anal & comput, 78-81, DIR INT AIRLINE ANAL, BOEING COMMERCIAL AIRPLANE CO, 71- *Mem:* Opers Res Soc Am; Inst Mgt Sci; Sigma Xi. *Res:* Operations research; modeling; simulation; mathematical programming; airline passenger flight selector process considering departure/arrival time, airline cost, airplane services and preferences; aircraft routing and scheduling; competitive analysis of airlines and resulting market and profit impacts. *Mailing Add:* PO Box 98085 Zenith WA 98188

PINAJIAN, JOHN JOSEPH, b Clinton, NJ, Oct 31, 21; m 49; c 1. PHARMACEUTICAL CHEMISTRY, NUCLEAR PHYSICS. *Educ:* Rutgers Univ, BSc, 49; Purdue Univ, MSc, 54, PhD(pharmaceut chem), 55. *Prof Exp:* Res assoc radiochem, US AEC, Agr Res Prog, Univ Tenn, 55, prof & res scientist, 55-56; chemist 56-60, group leader appl physics, Electronuclear Res Div, 60-62, group leader neutron & cyclotron prod, Isotopes Div, 62-65, develop specialist, Isotopes Div, 65-75, RES STAFF MEM, EMPLOYEE RELATIONS DIV, OAK RIDGE NAT LAB, 75- *Concurrent Pos:* Sci expert, Off Atomic Energy for Peace, Thailand, 66-67; consult, Cyclotron & Isotopes Labs, N V Philips-Duphar, Petten, N Holland, 68-69, tech mgr, 69; USAEC sci rep, US Consulate, Bombay, India, 72-73; adj prof, Vanderbilt Univ, 70- *Mem:* Fel AAAS; Am Chem Soc; Am Nuclear Soc; Am Phys Soc. *Res:* Production of radioisotopes in nuclear reactors and cyclotrons; internal conversion coefficient measurements; nuclear decay schemes; nuclear chemistry. *Mailing Add:* Employee Relations Div Oak Ridge Nat Lab PO Box X Oak Ridge TN 37830

PINCH, HARRY LOUIS, b Toronto, Ont, July 7, 29; nat US; m 55; c 2. PHYSICAL INORGANIC CHEMISTRY. *Educ:* City Col New York, BS, 51; Pa State Univ, PhD(chem), 55. *Prof Exp:* Res chemist, Mineral Beneficiation Lab, Sch Mines, Columbia Univ, 55-57; RES CHEMIST, DAVID SARNOFF RES CTR, RCA CORP, 57- *Mem:* Am Chem Soc; Am Vacuum Soc, Sigma Xi. *Res:* Inorganic preparative chemistry; crystal growth; thin films; vacuum technics and sputtering. *Mailing Add:* David Sarnoff Res Ctr RCA Corp Princeton NJ 08540

PINCHAK, ALFRED CYRIL, b Cleveland, Ohio, Aug 5, 35; m 71; c 3. FLUID SCIENCES, ANESTHESIOLOGY. *Educ:* Case Inst Technol, BSEE, 57; Purdue Univ, MSE, 59; Calif Inst Technol, PhD(mech eng & physics), 63; Case Western Reserve Univ, MD, 73. *Prof Exp:* Res scientist thermomech, Aerospace Res Labs, Off Aerospace Res, 63-66; res assoc fluid sci, 66-68, sr res assoc, 68-76, ASST PROF ANESTHESIOL, CASE WESTERN RESERVE UNIV, CLEVELAND METROP GEN HOSP, 76- *Concurrent Pos:* Prin investr, Anal Res Assocs, Ohio, 67-; dir, Nat Avalanche Observ, Juneau Icefield, Alaska, 68-; consult, Forestry Sci Lab, US Forest Serv, 70-; sr res fel, Am Heart Asn, 72-73. *Mem:* Inst Elec & Electronics Engrs; Am Soc Anesthesiologists; Am Soc Mech Engrs. *Res:* Glaciology; supra-glacial meltwater streams; seismic detection of avalanches; two-phase flows; air-sea interaction; internal vortex flows; hydraulic transients; cardiovascular-pulmonary physiology; intragravel water flow; esophageal accelerometry; physiological measurements with accelerometers; flow measurement with self heated thermistors. *Mailing Add:* Anal Res Assocs 19750 Fairmount Blvd Shaker Heights OH 44118

PINCINCE, ALBERT B(ERNARD), environmental engineering, sanitary engineering, see previous edition

PINCK, ROBERT LLOYD, b Passaic, NJ, Aug 20, 20; m 49; c 3. RADIOLOGY. *Educ:* Washington & Lee Univ, AB, 42; Duke Univ, MD, 46; Am Bd Radiol, dipl, 53. *Prof Exp:* Clin assoc prof, 46-80, CLIN PROF RADIOL, STATE UNIV NY DOWNSTATE MED CTR, 80-; DIR DEPT RADIOL, LONG ISLAND COL HOSP, BROOKLYN, 46-, PRES MED BD, 72- *Concurrent Pos:* Asst attend radiologist, Roosevelt Hosp, New York, 53-54, assoc attend, 54-56. *Mem:* AMA; fel Am Col Radiol; fel Am Col Physicians; Am Roentgen Ray Soc; Radiol Soc NAm. *Res:* Diagnostic and therapeutic radiology. *Mailing Add:* Dept of Radiol State Univ of NY Downstate Med Ctr Brooklyn NY 11203

PINCKAERS, B(ALTHASAR) HUBERT, b Heerlen, Netherlands, Mar 21, 24; US citizen; m 47; c 4. ELECTRICAL ENGINEERING. *Educ:* HTS Eng Col, 44; Univ Minn, Minneapolis, MS, 60. *Prof Exp:* Civilian tech employee, US Army Signal Corps, Ger, 45-47; test engr, Honeywell Inc, 48-50, design engr, 50-57, prin develop engr, 57-66, staff engr, 66-71, design supvr, 71-77, mgr, Electronics Eng Residential Div, 77-78, chief engr advan technol residential group, 78-81; PRES, PINCKAERS ENG INC, 81- *Res:* Solid state electronics and control systems. *Mailing Add:* 6301 Ewing Ave S Edina MN 55410

PINCKARD, ROBERT NEAL, b Chicago, Ill, Apr 16, 41; c 2. IMMUNOPATHOLOGY, MICROBIOLOGY. *Educ:* Univ Kans, BA, 63; Univ Edinburgh, PhD(microbiol), 67. *Prof Exp:* From asst prof to assoc prof microbiol, Col Med, Univ Ariz, 68-76; PROF PATH, UNIV TEX HEALTH SCI CTR, 76-, PROF MED, 78- *Concurrent Pos:* Fel immunol, Scripps Clin & Res Found, 67-68; Nat Heart & Lung Inst grants, 81-86. *Mem:* Am Asn Path; Am Fedn Clin Res; Am Asn Immunol; Brit Soc Immunol. *Res:* Immunopathology of IgE induced acute allergic and inflammatory reactions; structure and function of platelet activating factor; mechanisms for complement activation during ischemia and its role in tissue injury. *Mailing Add:* Dept of Path Univ Tex Health Sci Ctr San Antonio TX 78284

PINCKNEY, DARRELL MAYNE, b Swift Current, Sask, Mar 16, 25; nat US; m 48; c 4. GEOLOGY. *Educ:* Univ NMex, AB, 51; Univ Colo, MS, 53; Princeton Univ, PhD, 65. *Prof Exp:* GEOLOGIST, US GEOL SURV, 52- *Mem:* Geol Soc Am. *Res:* Metamorphic structure; structure and petrology of the Boulder batholith, Montana; zoning; mesothermal and epithermal veins; wallrock alteration; Mississippi Valley deposits, especially the Illinois-Kentucky district; filling temperatures and composition of fluid inclusions. *Mailing Add:* 4571 S White Way Denver CO 80202

PINCOCK, RICHARD EARL, b Ogden, Utah, Sept 14, 35. ORGANIC CHEMISTRY. *Educ:* Univ Utah, BS, 56; Harvard Univ, AM, 57, PhD(chem), 59. *Prof Exp:* Res fel chem, Calif Inst Technol, 59-60; instr, 60-62, from asst prof to assoc prof, 62-70, PROF CHEM, UNIV BC, 70- *Res:* Organic reactions and stereochemistry. *Mailing Add:* Dept Chem Univ BC Vancouver BC V6T 1W5 Can

PINCUS, GEORGE, b Havana, Cuba, July 5, 35; US citizen; m 58; c 3. STRUCTURAL ENGINEERING. *Educ:* Ga Inst Technol, BCE, 59, MS, 60; Cornell Univ, PhD(struct), 63; Univ Houston, MBA, 74. *Prof Exp:* From res asst to res assoc struct eng, Cornell Univ, 61-63; from asst prof to assoc prof, Univ Ky, 63-67; chief-of-party, Grad Eng Prog, Brazil, 67-68, chmn dept, 75-79, PROF CIVIL ENG, UNIV HOUSTON, 69- *Concurrent Pos:* Consult, Architects Registr Bd, Ky, 63-64 & Engrs Registr Bd, 63-; fallout shelter instr & analyst, Off Civil Defense, 65-; consult, petrochem firms, 69-; syst design fel, NASA-AM Soc Eng Educ, 69, aeronaut & space res fel, 70; fel physiol with mod instrumentation, Baylor Col Med, 71. *Honors & Awards:* D V Terrel Award, Am Soc Civil Engrs, 65. *Mem:* Am Soc Civil Engrs; Am Soc Testing & Mat; Am Soc Eng Educ; Am Concrete Inst. *Res:* Structural performance of wood members; tension strength of concrete; wood-concrete beams; strength of pipeline joints; fatigue strength of thin shells; wind effects on structures; behavior of biomaterials. *Mailing Add:* Dept of Civil Eng Univ of Houston Houston TX 77004

PINCUS, HOWARD JONAH, b New York, NY, June 24, 22; m 53; c 2. ROCK MECHANICS, ENGINEERING GEOLOGY. *Educ:* City Col New York, BS, 42; Columbia Univ, AM, 48, PhD(geol), 49. *Prof Exp:* Instr geol, Ohio State Univ, 49-51, from asst prof to prof, 51-67, chmn dept, 60-65; res supvr & geologist, US Bur Mines, 67-68; dean, 69-72, PROF GEOL & CIVIL ENG, UNIV WIS-MILWAKEE, 68- *Concurrent Pos:* Res assoc, Columbia Univ, 49-52; consult, 56-; NSF sr fel, 62. *Mem:* AAAS; Geol Soc Am; Am Geophys Union; Soc Mining Engrs; Am Soc Test & Mat. *Res:* Rock mechanics; engineering geology; solid-earth geophysics; statistical analysis; optical data processing; fabric analysis as applied to deformation mechanics of rocks; tectonics. *Mailing Add:* Dept Geol Sci Univ Wis Milwaukee WI 53201

PINCUS, IRVING, b Brooklyn, NY, July 3, 18; m 43; c 4. MATERIALS ENGINEERING. *Educ:* City Col New York, BS, 38; George Washington Univ, MS, 47; Pa State Univ, PhD(fuel tech), 50; Rensselaer Polytech Univ, MS, 60. *Prof Exp:* Chemist, US Naval Powder Factory, 41-43, 45-48; res asst, Pa State Univ, 48-50; sect leader, Org By-prod, Great Lakes Carbon Corp, 50-56; coal chem, Curtiss-Wright Corp, 56-57; sr develop engr, Carbon Prod, Gen Elec Co, 57-60; prod mgr, Res Div, Raytheon Co, 60-63; chief mat eng & develop, Baltimore Div, Martin Co, 63-66; ASST TO PRES, IIT RES INST, 66- *Mem:* Am Chem Soc; Am Inst Aeronaut & Astronaut; Sigma Xi; Am Defense Prepardness Asn. *Res:* High temperature materials; graphites; carbons; cokes; advanced metals; composites; ceramics; plastics; fuels; tars; pitches; chemicals; management engineering. *Mailing Add:* 1099 Linda Lane Glencoe IL 60022

PINCUS, JACK HOWARD, b NeW York, NY, Jan 4, 39; m 66. BIOCHEMISTRY, IMMUNOCHEMISTRY. *Educ:* NY Univ, AB, 59; Columbia Univ, PhD(biochem), 66. *Prof Exp:* Res asst biochem, Res Found Ment Hyg, New York, 62-66; res fel med, Mass Gen Hosp, Boston, 66-69; spec fel, Lab Immunol, Nat Inst Allergy & Infectious Dis, Bethesda, Md, 69-70, sr staff fel, Lab Microbiol & Immunol, Nat Inst Dent Res, 70-73; res chemist, VA Res Hosp, Chicago Ill, 73-75; asst prof surgery & biochem, Med Sch, Northwestern Univ, Chicago, 73-75; sr immunochemist, 75-77; assoc dir, Biomed Res Dept, Stanford Res Inst Int, 77-81; DIR RES & DEVELOP, BECTON DICKINSON IMMUNODIAGNOSTICS, 81- *Mem:* AAAS; Am Chem Soc; Am Inst Chem; Am Asn Immunol; Fedn Am Sci. *Res:* Protein chemistry; immunochemistry; immunology; membrane biochemistry. *Mailing Add:* Becton Dickinson Immunodiagnostics Mountainview Ave Orangeburg NY 10962

PINCUS, JONATHAN HENRY, b Brooklyn, NY, May 4, 35; m 61; c 3. NEUROLOGY. *Educ:* Amherst Col, AB, 56; Columbia Univ, MD, 60. *Prof Exp:* From instr to assoc prof, 64-74, PROF NEUROL, YALE UNIV, 74- *Concurrent Pos:* Clin fel neurol, Yale Univ, 61-64; co-auth, Behav Neurol, 78. *Res:* Role of thiamine in nervous system; mechanism of action of diphenylhydantoin. *Mailing Add:* Dept of Neurol Yale Univ Med Sch New Haven CT 06510

PINCUS, JOSEPH B, biochemistry, deceased

PINCUS, PHILIP A, b New York, NY, May 4, 36; m 59; c 2. THEORETICAL SOLID STATE PHYSICS. *Educ:* Univ Calif, Berkeley, AB, 57, PhD(physics), 61. *Prof Exp:* NSF fel, Saclay Nuclear Res Ctr, France, 61-62; from asst prof to assoc prof, 62-68, PROF PHYSICS, UNIV CALIF, LOS ANGELES, 68- *Concurrent Pos:* Alfred P Sloan Found fel, 64-67; chmn dept physics, Univ Calif, Los Angeles, 71-74. *Mem:* Am Phys Soc. *Res:* Magnetic properties of solids; molecular crystals. *Mailing Add:* Dept of Physics Univ of Calif Los Angeles CA 90024

PINDER, ALBERT REGINALD, b Sheffield, Eng, June 10, 20; m 47; c 2. ORGANIC CHEMISTRY. *Educ:* Univ Sheffield, BSc, 41, PhD(chem), 48, DSc(chem), 63; Oxford Univ, DPhil(chem), 50. *Prof Exp:* Fel, Oxford Univ, 50-53; lectr org chem, Queen's Univ, Belfast, 53-56; sr lectr, Univ Wales, 56-65; PROF ORG CHEM, CLEMSON UNIV, 66- *Concurrent Pos:* Mem, Chem Defence Res Dept, Brit Govt, 41-45. *Mem:* Fel The Chem Soc; Am Chem Soc; fel Brit Chem Indust. *Res:* Natural product chemistry, including isolation, synthesis, stereochemistry, and application of modern physical methods. *Mailing Add:* Dept of Chem Clemson Univ Clemson SC 29631

PINDER, GEORGE FRANCIS, b Windsor, Ont, Feb 6, 42; m 63. GROUNDWATER HYDROLOGY. *Educ:* Univ Western Ont, BSc, 65; Univ Ill, PhD(geol), 68. *Prof Exp:* Geohydrologist, NS Dept Mines, 68; res hydrologist, US Geol Surv, 68-72; assoc prof, 72-77, PROF CIVIL ENG, PRINCETON UNIV, 77-, CHMN DEPT, 80- *Honors & Awards:* Robert E Horton Award, 68; O E Meinzer Award, Geol Soc Am, 75. *Mem:* Am Geophys Union; Am Soc Civil Engrs; Soc Petrol Engrs. *Res:* Theoretical and applied research concerning the mechanics of groundwater flow. *Mailing Add:* Dept Civil Eng Princeton Univ Princeton NJ 08540

PINDER, JOHN EDGAR, III, b Baltimore, MD, Oct 19, 44. ECOLOGY, BIOSTATISTICS. *Educ:* Towson State Univ, BS, 67; Univ Ga, MS, 71, PhD(zool), 77. *Prof Exp:* Res assoc, 77-81, ASST RES ECOL, SAVANNAH RIVER ECOL LAB, UNIV GA, 81- *Mem:* Ecol Soc Am; Am Statist Asn. *Res:* Structure and function of plant communities; succession; radioecology of transuranic elements; biogeochemical cycles; biostatistics. *Mailing Add:* Savannah River Ecol Lab Drawer E Aiken SC 29801

PINDER, KENNETH LYLE, b Chaplin, Sask, May 20, 29; m 54; c 3. CHEMICAL ENGINEERING. *Educ:* McGill Univ, BEng, 51, MEng, 52; Univ Birmingham, PhD(chem eng), 54. *Prof Exp:* Engr, Shell Oil Co, 55-56; res engr, Pulp & Paper Res Inst Can, 56-59 & Dow Chem Can Ltd, 59-63; assoc prof chem eng, 63-71, PROF CHEM ENG, UNIV BC, 71-, ASST TO HEAD DEPT, 78- *Concurrent Pos:* Nat Res Coun Can res grant, 63-; consult & dir, Multifibre Process Ltd, 76- *Mem:* Chem Inst Can. *Res:* Time dependent rheology; direct contact boiling and condensing; gas hydrate formation; desalination; pollution; biomedical engineering; computer simulation. *Mailing Add:* Dept of Chem Eng Univ of BC Vancouver BC V6T 1W5 Can

PINDERA, JERZY TADEUSZ, b Czchow, Poland, Dec 4, 14; m 49; c 2. EXPERIMENTAL MECHANICS. *Educ:* Lodz Tech Univ, MEng, 47; Polish Acad Sci, Dr Appl Sci(appl mech), 59; Cracow Tech Univ, Dr habil(appl mech), 62. *Prof Exp:* Asst tech serv, Polish Air Lines, Lot, 47; lab dir, Aeronaut Inst, Warsaw, 47-52; Inst Metallog, 52-54; asst prof exp mech, Inst Basic Probs, Polish Acad Sci, 54-56, dep prof & lab dir, Dept Civil Eng, 56-59; lab dir, Inst Bldg Technol, 59-62; vis prof exp mech, Mich State Univ, 63-65; PROF EXP MECH, UNIV WATERLOO, 65- *Concurrent Pos:* Vis Prof, Ruhr-Universität Bochum, 72-73, Univ Poitiers, 73 & Univ Braunschweig, 78. Nat Res Coun Can res grants, 65-, consult, 50- *Mem:* Soc Exp Stress Anal; Ger Soc Appl Math & Mech; NY Acad Sci; Am Soc Mech Eng; Soc Eng Sci. *Res:* Experimental mechanics; photoelasticity (spectral); coupled rheological responses of polymers; experimental stress and strength analysis; vibrations and shock problems; theory of modeling, observation and measurements; dynamic thermoelasticity; contact problems; nondestructive methods; behavior of structures; stress and flow birefringence. *Mailing Add:* Dept of Civil Eng Univ of Waterloo Waterloo ON N2L 3G1 Can

PINDOK, MARIE THERESA, b Chicago, Ill, Jan 20, 41. CARDIOVASCULAR PHYSIOLOGY. *Educ:* Loyola Univ, Chicago, BS, 63; Chicago Med Sch-Univ Health Sci, PhD(physiol), 78. *Prof Exp:* Res asst physiol, Stritch Sch Med, Loyola Univ, 63-70; res & teaching asst, 70-78, INSTR PHYSIOL, CHICAGO MED SCH-UNIV HEALTH SCI, 78- *Mem:* Am Physiol Soc; AAAS; Sigma Xi. *Res:* Hemodynamic and pharmacological intervention on cardiovascular dynamics with emphasis on changes in mycardial lipid metabolism. *Mailing Add:* Dept of Physiol & Biophys 2020 W Ogden Ave Chicago IL 60612

PINDZOLA, MICHAEL STUART, b Hartford, Conn, July 12, 48. THEORETICAL PHYSICS. *Educ:* Univ South, BA, 70; Univ Va, PhD(physics), 75. *Prof Exp:* Nat Acad Sci/Nat Res Coun res assoc, Theoret Div, Goddard Space Flight Ctr, NASA, 75-77; ASST PROF, PHYSICS DEPT, AUBURN UNIV, 77- *Concurrent Pos:* Consult, Physics Div, Oak Ridge Nat Lab, 80- *Mem:* Am Phys Soc; Brit Inst Physics. *Res:* Atomic and molecular physics for controlled fusion. *Mailing Add:* Physics Dept Auburn Univ Auburn AL 36849

PINE, ELLEN KANN, b Bingen, Ger, Apr 28, 25; nat US; m 54; c 3. BACTERIOLOGY, BIOCHEMISTRY. *Educ:* Hunter Col, BA, 47; Ind Univ, MA, 49; Univ Kans, PhD(biochem), 54. *Prof Exp:* Asst, Ind Univ, 47-49, Univ Kans, 50-53; NIH fel, Yale Univ, 54 & Roswell Park Mem Inst, 55; cancer res scientist, 55-57, part-time cancer res scientist, 60-68; res assoc & instr, State Univ NY Buffalo, 68-71; ASST PROF BIOL, ROSARY HILL COL, asst prof biol, Rosary Hill Col, 71-73; exec officer, div cell & molecular biol & dept biol sci, 74-78, DIR, LABS & TECH PERSONNEL, STATE UNIV NY, BUFFALO, 78-; DEPT BIOL SCI, STATE UNIV NY BUFFALO, 76- *Mem:* Am Soc Microbiol. *Res:* Microbial genetics; bacterial and tissue physiology. *Mailing Add:* 109 Cooke Hall State Univ NY Buffalo Amherst NY 14260

PINE, JEROME, b New York, NY, Apr 14, 28; m 51 & 67; c 2. PHYSICS. *Educ:* Princeton Univ, AB, 49, Cornell Univ, MS, 52, PhD, 56. *Prof Exp:* From instr to asst prof physics, Stanford Univ, 56-63; assoc prof, 63-67, PROF PHYSICS, CALIF INST TECHNOL, 67- *Res:* High energy experimental physics. *Mailing Add:* Dept of Physics Calif Inst of Technol Pasadena CA 91125

PINE, LEO, b Tucson, Ariz, Feb 13, 22; m 43; c 6. BIOCHEMISTRY, MICROBIOLOGY. *Educ:* Univ Ariz, BS, 43; Univ Wis, MS, 48; Univ Calif, Berkeley, PhD, 52. *Prof Exp:* Med bacteriologist, Nat Microbiol Inst, 52-56, biochemist, Nat Inst Allergy & Infectious Dis, 56-57; asst prof & sr res fel microbiol, Sch Med, Duke Univ, 57-62; res prof mycol lab, Pasteur Inst, Paris, 62-63; biochemist Mycol Unit, Nat Ctr Dis Control, 63-65, chief Res & Develop Unit, Biol Reagents Sect, 65-81, CHEMIST, BACTERIAL DIS DIV, USPHS, 81- *Concurrent Pos:* Mem, Int Comt Taxon & Anaerobic Actinomycetes, 62- *Mem:* Fel Am Acad Microbiol; Int Soc Human & Animal Mycol; fel AAAS; Am Soc Microbiol; Brit Soc Gen Microbiol. *Res:* Growth, physiology and metabolism of pathogenic bacteria and fungi. *Mailing Add:* 1302 Bernadette Lane Atlanta GA 30329

PINE, LLOYD A, b Emporia, Kans, June 5, 33; m 67; c 2. ORGANIC CHEMISTRY. *Educ:* Univ Kans, BA, 55, PhD(chem), 62. *Prof Exp:* Chemist, Esso Res Lab, La, 62-65, sr chemist, 65-67, group head, Enjay Chem Plant, 67-69; sr res chemist, 69-74, SR RES ASSOC EXXON RES LABS, 74- *Mem:* Fel Am Inst Chem. *Res:* Heterogeneous catalysis; petroleum resins; nitrogen heterocyclic compounds. *Mailing Add:* Exxon Res Lab PO Box 2226 Baton Rouge LA 70821

PINE, MARTIN J, b Forest Hills, NY, Nov 6, 27; m 54. BACTERIOLOGY, BIOCHEMISTRY. *Educ:* Cornell Univ, BS, 48; Univ Wis, MS, 50; Ind Univ, PhD(bact), 52. *Prof Exp:* Res assoc, 54-56, sr cancer res scientist, 56-67, ASSOC CANCER RES SCIENTIST, ROSWELL PARK MEM INST, 67- *Concurrent Pos:* NIH fel, Univ Calif, 52-53 & Yale Univ, 53-54. *Mem:* AAAS; Am Asn Cancer Res; Am Soc Biol Chem; Am Soc Microbiol. *Res:* Oncology; microbial physiology. *Mailing Add:* Dept Exp Therapeut Roswell Park Mem Inst Buffalo NY 14203

PINE, STANLEY H, b Los Angeles, Calif, June 27, 35; m 57; c 3. ORGANIC CHEMISTRY. *Educ:* Univ Calif, Los Angeles, BS, 57, PhD(carbanion stereochem), 63. *Prof Exp:* Fel, Harvard Univ, 63-64; PROF CHEM, CALIF STATE UNIV, LOS ANGELES, 64- *Mem:* Am Chem Soc. *Res:* Organic reaction mechanisms; synthesis. *Mailing Add:* Dept Chem Calif State Univ 5151 State Univ Dr Los Angeles CA 90032

PINEAULT, SERGE RENE, b Rimouski, Que, July 7, 47. ASTROPHYSICS, RADIO ASTRONOMY. *Educ:* Univ Laval, BSc, 70; Univ Toronto, MSc, 71, PhD(astron), 75. *Prof Exp:* Researcher astron, Inst Astron, Cambridge Univ, 76-77; lectr astron, Univ BC, 77-80; RES ASSOC, DOMINION RADIO ASTROPHYS OBSERV, BC, 80- *Concurrent Pos:* Nat Res Coun Can fel, 76-77. *Mem:* Can Astron Soc; Int Astron Union. *Res:* Theoretical astrophysics: compact objects, black holes, active galactic nuclei; plasma astrophysics; radio astronomy: radio source spectra, galactic recombination lines. *Mailing Add:* Dominion Radio Astrophys Observ PO Box 248 Penticton BC V2A 6K3 Can

PINERO, GERALD JOSEPH, b New Orleans, La, Feb 26, 43; m 69. HISTOLOGY, CYTOLOGY. *Educ:* La State Univ, New Orleans, BS, 64; La State Univ, Baton Rouge, PhD(zool), 70. *Prof Exp:* Asst prof, 71-75, assoc prof, 75-80, PROF HISTOL, DENT BR, HEALTH SCI CTR, UNIV TEX, HOUSTON, 80-, MEM FAC GRAD SCH BIOMED SCI, 81- *Concurrent Pos:* Rockefeller Pop Coun fel, La State Univ, 70-71. *Mem:* AAAS; Am Asn Univ Prof; Am Asn Anatomists; Tissue Cult Soc; Am Asn Dent Res. *Res:* Cytochemistry and fine structure of the male reproductive tubules; phagocytosis and intracellular digestion. *Mailing Add:* Dept Histol Dent Br Univ Tex PO Box 20068 Houston TX 77025

PINES, DAVID, b Kansas City, Mo, June 8, 24; m 48; c 2. THEORETICAL ASTROPHYSICS, THEORETICAL PHYSICS. *Educ:* Univ Calif, AB, 44; Princeton Univ, AM, 48, PhD(physics), 50. *Prof Exp:* Instr physics, Univ Pa, 50-52; res asst prof, Univ Ill, 52-55; asst prof, Princeton Univ, 55-58; mem, Inst Adv Study, NJ, 58-59; dir, Ctr Advan Study, 67-70, PROF PHYSICS & ELEC ENG, UNIV ILL, URBANA, 59- *Concurrent Pos:* NSF sr fel, Copenhagen Univ & Univ Paris, 57-58; ed, Frontiers in Physics, 61-; Guggenheim fel & prof, Univ Paris, 62-63; co-chmn, Joint Soviet-US Symp Condensed Matter Theory, 68-; vpres, Mem Exec Comt & Bd Trustees, Aspen Ctr Physics, 68-80; mem, Coun Biol Human Affairs, Salk Inst, 69-73; Guggenheim fel & Nordita prof, Copenhagen Univ, 70; Lorentz prof, Univ Leiden, 71; Fritz London Mem Lectr, Duke Univ, 72; ed, Rev Modern Physics, 73-; chmn, Bd Int Sci Exchange, Nat Res Coun, Nat Acad Sci, mem, Comt Int Rels, mem, Comt Scholarly Commun Peoples Repub China, 74-79; Guilio Racah Mem lectr, Hebrew Univ, Jerusalem, 74; mem, Bd Trustees, Univ Asn Res Astron, 75-; Sherman Fairchild distinguished scholar, Calif Inst Technol, 77-78; mem, Space Sci Bd, Nat Acad Sci, Nat Res Ctr, 78-81; mem, Ctr Adv Study, Univ Ill, Urbana, 79- *Honors & Awards:* Marchon lectr, Univ New Castle, Eng, 76. *Mem:* Nat Acad Sci; fel Am Astron Soc; fel Am Phys Soc; AAAS; fel Am Acad Arts & Sci. *Res:* Theoretical studies of neutron stars; compact x-ray sources; quantum liquids. *Mailing Add:* Dept Elec Eng Univ Ill 1110 W Green St Urbana IL 61801

PINES, HERMAN, b Lodz, Poland, Jan 17, 02; nat US; m 27; c 1. ORGANIC CHEMISTRY. *Educ:* Univ Lyon, ChEng, 27; Univ Chicago, PhD(org chem), 35. *Prof Exp:* From asst dir to assoc dir, Ipatieff Lab, 41-53; from asst prof to assoc prof, 41-53, Ipatieff res prof, 53-70, IPATIEFF EMER PROF CHEM, NORTHWESTERN UNIV, EVANSTON, 70-, DIR IPATIEFF LAB, 53- *Concurrent Pos:* Res chemist, Universal Oil Prods Co, 30-45, coord explor res, 45-53; chmn, Gordon Conf Catalysis, 60; co-ed, Advances in Catalysis, 62-; vis prof, Bar-Ilan Univ Israel, 71, 72-77, Weizmann Inst Sci, Israel, 72-77 & Fed Univ Rio de Janeiro, 73. *Honors & Awards:* Fritzsche Award, Am Chem Soc, 56 & Midwest Award, 63; Petrol Chem Award, Am Chem Soc, 81; Eugene J Houdry Award, Catalysis Soc, 81; Chem Pioneer Award, Am Inst Chemists, 82. *Mem:* Am Chem Soc. *Res:* Petroleum; catalysis; terpenes; isomerization; hydrogen transfer; hydrogenolysis; aromatization; dehydration; base-catalyzed reaction of hydrocarbons; study of intrinsic acidity and catalytic activity of transition metals. *Mailing Add:* Dept of Chem Northwestern Univ Evanston IL 60201

PINES, KERMIT L, b Brooklyn, NY, Oct 18, 16; m 40; c 3. INTERNAL MEDICINE. *Educ:* Columbia Univ, AB, 37, MD, 42, DMedSci, 47; Am Bd Internal Med, dipl, 50. *Prof Exp:* Intern internal med, Presby Hosp, New York, 42-43, asst resident, 46-47; from asst to assoc, 48-58, from asst prof to assoc prof clin med, 58-73, CLIN PROF MED, COL PHYSICIANS & SURGEONS, COLUMBIA UNIV, 73- *Concurrent Pos:* From asst physician to attend physician, Presby Hosp, New York, 47-; consult, Englewood Hosp, NJ, 58- *Mem:* Am Diabetes Asn; Harvey Soc; fel Am Col Physicians. *Res:* Metabolic diseases. *Mailing Add:* 161 Fort Washington Ave New York NY 10032

PINES, SEEMON H, b Portland, Maine, Jan 3, 26; m 49; c 2. ORGANIC CHEMISTRY. *Educ:* Lehigh Univ, BS, 48; Univ Ill, MS, 49, PhD(org chem), 51. *Prof Exp:* Sr chemist, Merck & Co, 51-58, sect leader, Merck Sharp & Dohme Res Labs, 58-69, sr res fel, 69-75, sr investr, 75-77, SR DIR, MERCK & CO, 77-, EXEC DIR, 79- *Mem:* Am Chem Soc. *Res:* Process research and development. *Mailing Add:* PO Box 2000 Merck & Co Rahway NJ 07065

PINGLETON, SUSAN KASPER, b Elsworth, Kans, Sept 27, 46; m 77; c 1. PULMONARY DISEASE. *Educ:* Univ Kans, BA, 68, Med Sch, MD, 72. *Prof Exp:* Asst prof, 77-79, ASSOC PROF MED, UNIV MO-KANSAS CITY MED SCH, 79-, HEAD, DIV PULMONARY MED, TRUMAN MED CTR, 77- *Concurrent Pos:* Prin investr, Pulmonary Academic Award, NIH, 77-82; Pulmonary Academic Award, NIH, 77-85; Res Day Award, Univ Kans, 67-68; NIH training grant, NIH, 75-77. *Mem:* Am Col Physicians; Am Col Chest Physicians; Am Thoracic Soc; Am Fedn Clin Res; Soc Critical Care Med. *Res:* Intensive care pulmonary disease; complications of respiratory failure, such as gastrointestinal hemorrhage and pulmonary emboli; effect of various treatment modalities on gastrointestinal hemorrhage in respiratory failure patients; complications of bronchodilators in respiratory failure secondary to spinal cord trauma. *Mailing Add:* 5720 State Line Shawnee Mission KS 66208

PINGS, C(ORNELIUS) J(OHN), b Conrad, Mont, Mar 15, 29; m 60; c 3. CHEMICAL ENGINEERING, CHEMISTRY. *Educ:* Calif Inst Technol, BS, 51, MS, 52, PhD(chem eng), 55. *Prof Exp:* Reservoir engr, Shell Oil Co, 52-54; from instr to asst prof chem eng, Stanford Univ, 55-59; assoc prof, Calif Inst Technol, 59-64, prof chem eng, 64-81, exec officer, 69-71, vprovost & dean grad studies, 70-81; VPRES ACAD AFFAIRS & PROF CHEM ENG, UNIV SOUTHERN CALIF, 81- *Concurrent Pos:* Co-ed, Phys & Chem Liquids, 67-78; ed, Chem Eng Commun, 72-77; consult, Adv Bd, US Naval Weapons Ctr & Bd Dirs, Asn Univs Res Astron, 72-81. *Honors & Awards:* Lectureship Award, Chem Eng Div, Am Soc Eng Educ, 69; Prof Progress Award, Am Inst Chem Engrs, 69, Tech Achievement Award, Univ Southern Calif, 72. *Mem:* Am Inst Chem Engrs; Am Chem Soc; Am Phys Soc; Am Soc Eng Educ. *Res:* Statistical mechanics; liquid state physics. *Mailing Add:* Div of Chem & Chem Eng Admin 101 Univ Southern Calif Los Angeles CA 90089

PINHEIRO, MARILYN LAYS, b Brockton, Mass, Apr 18, 24; m 46; c 2. NEUROSCIENCES, AUDIOLOGY. *Educ:* Boston Univ, BA, 45; Western Reserve Univ, MA, 57, Case Western Reserve Univ, PhD(exp audiol), 69. *Prof Exp:* Dir clin audiol, Rio de Janeiro, 58-65; asst prof, 71-73, ASSOC PROF NEUROSCI, MED COL OHIO, 73-, DIR HEARING & SPEECH SERV, 71-; RES ASST & INSTR, CASE WESTERN RESERVE UNIV, 69- *Concurrent Pos:* NIH fel, Case Western Reserve Univ, 69-71; NIH grant, 75-77; audiologist & speech therapist, Inst Neurol, Rio de Janeiro, 57-60; consult audiol, Cleveland Hearing & Speech Ctr, 70-71; adj prof, Grad Sch, Bowling Green State Univ, 71-73; adj asst prof commun, Univ Toledo, 73-, adj assoc prof, Grad Sch, 73-; consult, Family Learning Ctr, Toledo, 73-74. *Mem:* Am Speech & Hearing Asn; Soc Neurosci; Acoust Soc Am; Int Neuropsychology Soc. *Res:* Auditory perception and auditory dysfunction in central nervous system pathology. *Mailing Add:* Dept of Neurosci Med Col of Ohio Toledo OH 43614

PINK, DAVID ANTHONY HERBERT, b St Lucia, WI, Nov 1, 36; Brit & Can citizen. THEORETICAL SOLID STATE PHYSICS, BIOPHYSICS. *Educ:* St Francis Xavier Univ, BSc, 61; Univ BC, PhD(theoret physics), 64. *Prof Exp:* Nat Res Coun fel, Dept Theoret Physics, Oxford Univ, 65-67; asst prof physics, 67-70, from actg chmn to chmn dept, 70-74, assoc prof, 70-77, PROF PHYSICS, ST FRANCIS XAVIER UNIV, 77- *Concurrent Pos:* Vis fac mem physics, Univ Guelph, 74-75; vis researcher, Max Planck Inst Solid State Res, Stuttgart, Ger, 75; Humboldt Fel, Inst Neurolbiol Kernforchungsanlage, Julich, Ger, 77-78. *Mem:* Biophys Soc; Can Asn Physicists; Am Phys Soc. *Res:* Theoretical studies of magnetically ordered systems with emphasis on surface excitations and related phenomena; cooperative effects in model and bio-membranes. *Mailing Add:* Dept of Physics St Francis Xavier Univ Antigonish NS B0H 1C0 Can

PINKAVA, DONALD JOHN, b Cleveland, Ohio, Aug 29, 33; m 76; c 1. BOTANY. *Educ:* Ohio State Univ, BSc, 55, MS, 61, PhD(bot), 64. *Prof Exp:* Asst prof, 64-71, assoc prof, 71-78, PROF BOT, ARIZ STATE UNIV, 78-DIR, HERBARIUM, ARIZ STATE UNIV, 64- *Mem:* Am Soc Plant Taxon; Bot Soc Am; Int Asn Plant Taxon. *Res:* Biosystematic studies of Berlandiera and Opuntia; floristic studies in Arizona, Southwestern United States. *Mailing Add:* Dept of Bot & Microbiol Ariz State Univ Tempe AZ 85287

PINKEL, B(ENJAMIN), b Gloversville, NY, Mar 31, 09; m 40; c 2. ELECTRICAL ENGINEERING. *Educ:* Univ Pa, BS, 30. *Prof Exp:* Head engine anal sect, Nat Adv Comt Aeronaut, 38-42, chief, Thermodyn Res Div, 42-45, Fuels & Thermodyn Res Div, 45-50 & Mat & Thermodyn Res Div, 50-56; assoc head aero-astronaut dept, Rand Corp, 56-68, sr staff, 68-72; sr scientist, Bolt Beranek & Newman Inc, 72-74; CONSULT ENGR, 74- *Mem:* Am Soc Mech Engrs; Am Nuclear Soc; fel Am Inst Aeronaut & Astronaut. *Res:* Heat transfer; thermodynamics; propulsion systems; nuclear reactor analysis; author of 70 technical papers and one book. *Mailing Add:* 726 Adelaide Pl Santa Monica CA 90402

PINKEL, DONALD PAUL, b Buffalo, NY, Sept 7, 26; m 49; c 9. PEDIATRICS. *Educ:* Canisius Col, BS, 47; Univ Buffalo, MD, 51. *Prof Exp:* Intern pediat, Children's Hosp Buffalo, NY, 51-52, resident, 52-53, chief resident, 53-54; chief pediat, Roswell Park Mem Inst, 56-61; prof pediat & prev med, Univ Tenn, Memphis, 61-73; chmn dept, Med Col Wis, 74-78, prof pediat, 74-78, dir Midwest Children's Cancer Ctr, Milwaukee Children's Hosp, 78; CHMN PEDIAT, CITY OF HOPE NAT MED CTR, 78- *Concurrent Pos:* Mead Johnson resident fel, Children's Hosp Buffalo, NY, 53-54; res fel, Children's Cancer Res Found, Boston, 55-56; med dir, St Jude Children's Res Hosp, Memphis, 61-73; assoc dir, Wis Clin Cancer Ctr, Madison, 74-78; pediatrician-in-chief, Milwaukee Children's Hosp, 74-78.

Mem: Am Asn Cancer Res; Soc Pediat Res; Soc Exp Biol & Med; Am Pediat Soc. *Res:* Childhood cancer; leukemia virology; cancer chemotherapy; infectious diseases; child nutrition. *Mailing Add:* City of Hope Nat Med Ctr 1500 E Duarte Rd Duarte CA 91010

PINKEL, ROBERT, b Cleveland, Ohio, Mar 30, 46. PHYSICAL OCEANOGRAPHY. *Educ:* Univ Mich, BA, 68; Univ Calif, San Diego, MA, 69, PhD(phys oceanog), 74. *Prof Exp:* Fel phys oceanog, 74-75, ASST RES OCEANOGR, MARINE PHYS LAB, UNIV CALIF, SAN DIEGO, 75- *Mem:* Am Geophys Union; Acoust Soc Am; AAAS. *Res:* Upper ocean studies of internal waves, air-sea interactions and mixing processes. *Mailing Add:* Scripps Inst of Oceanog La Jolla CA 92093

PINKERTON, FRANK HENRY, b Nashville, Tenn, Sept 4, 45; m 67. CHEMISTRY. *Educ:* Vanderbilt Univ, BA, 67; Univ Southern Miss, PhD(chem), 71. *Prof Exp:* NASA fel, Univ Southern Miss, 71-72; asst prof chem, William Carey Col, 71-77; dept staff, 77-80, ASSOC PROF CHEM, CARSON-NEWMAN COL, 80- *Mem:* Am Chem Soc. *Res:* Organometallic chemistry; organosilicon chemistry; physiologically active organosilicon compounds; polymeric intermediates; thermally stable polymers; heterocyclic chemistry. *Mailing Add:* Dept of Chem Carson-Newman Col Jefferson City TN 37760

PINKERTON, JOHN EDWARD, b Cortland, NY, Mar 2, 39; m 61. EXPERIMENTAL NUCLEAR PHYSICS, ELECTRONIC ENGINEERING. *Educ:* Geneva Col, BS; Univ Wis-Milwaukee, MS, 65; Univ SC, PhD(nuclear spectroscopy), 73. *Prof Exp:* Teacher, Pine Richland Schs, 60-61 & Audubon High Sch, 61-65; from asst prof to assoc prof physics, 65-79, PROF ELEC ENG, GENEVA COL, 79- *Concurrent Pos:* Teaching asst, Univ SC, 69-71; pres, SPL Systems, 74-; fac physicist, US Bur Mines, Theoret Support Group, Bruceton Res Ctr, 76- *Mem:* Inst Elec & Electronics Engrs; Am Asn Physics Teachers; Optical Soc Am; Am Phys Soc. *Res:* Low energy nuclear physics, including associated solid state detectors and electronic instrumentation; design and development of digital systems for mini and micro computer experiment control and data acquisition. *Mailing Add:* 2002 13 and one half St Beaver Falls PA 15010

PINKERTON, PETER HARVEY, b Glasgow, Scotland, Feb 14, 34; m 66; c 2. HEMATOLOGY. *Educ:* Univ Glasgow, MB & ChB, 58, MD, 69; FRCP(E); FRCPath; FRCP(C). *Prof Exp:* Lectr haemat, Univ Glasgow, 63-65; asst res prof med, State Univ NY Buffalo, 65-67; PROF PATH, UNIV TORONTO, 67-; DIR LAB HAEMAT, SUNNYBROOK MED CTR, TORONTO, 67- *Concurrent Pos:* Med Res Coun Can grant, Univ Toronto, 68-75. *Honors & Awards:* Jr Sci Award, Can Asn Path, 69. *Mem:* Fel Am Col Physicians; Brit Soc Haemat; Am Soc Hemat; Can Hemat Soc. *Res:* Iron absorption; animal models of human blood diseases; application of research methods to laboratory haematology and hospital practice; proficiency testing in hematology and blood banking. *Mailing Add:* Sunnybrook Hosp Toronto ON M4N 3M5 Can

PINKERTON, ROBERT M(CLEAN), fluid mechanics, aerodynamics, deceased

PINKHAM, CHESTER ALLEN, III, b Ft Wayne, Ind, Aug 2, 36; m 59; c 2. PHYSICAL CHEMISTRY. *Educ:* Univ Ind, AB, 58; Purdue Univ, MS, 63; Rensselaer Polytech Inst, PhD(chem), 67. *Prof Exp:* Teacher high sch, 61-64; instr chem, Hudson Valley Community Col, 64-65; asst prof, 67-70, assoc prof, 70-77, PROF, TRI-STATE UNIV, 77- *Concurrent Pos:* abstractor, Chem Abstracts, 59-73. *Mem:* Fel Am Inst Chem; NY Acad Sci; Ind Acad Sci; Am Chem Soc; Nat Sci Teachers Asn. *Res:* asymmetric rotor theory and calculations; quantum chemistry; chemical education. *Mailing Add:* Dept of Chem Tri-State Univ Angola IN 46703

PINKHAM, HENRY CHARLES, b New York City, NY, Sept 26, 48; m; c 1. ALGEBRAIC GEOMETRY. *Educ:* Harvard Col, BA, 70; Univ Paris, DEA, 71; Harvard Univ, PhD(math), 74. *Prof Exp:* Asst prof, 74-79, ASSOC PROF MATH, COLUMBIA UNIV, 79- *Res:* Algebraic geometry: deformations of singularities, moduli problems. *Mailing Add:* Dept Math Columbia Univ New York NY 10027

PINKSTAFF, CARLIN ADAM, b Louisville, Ill, June 10, 34; m 58; c 1. HISTOLOGY, HISTOCHEMISTRY. *Educ:* Eastern Ill Univ, BS, 60; Emory Univ, PhD(anat), 64. *Prof Exp:* From instr to asst prof anat, Dent Sch, Univ Ore, 64-67; asst prof, 67-70, assoc prof, 70-81, PROF ANAT, MED SCH, WEST VA UNIV, 81- *Concurrent Pos:* External examr anat, Univ Ibadan, 73; vis scientist, Yerkes Regional Primate Res Ctr, 73. *Mem:* Am Asn Dent Res; NY Acad Sci; Int Asn Dent Res; Am Asn Anat; Histochem Soc. *Res:* Histochemistry of renal development; cytology, histology and histochemistry of salivary glands. *Mailing Add:* Dept of Anat WVa Univ Med Ctr Morgantown WV 26506

PINKSTON, EARL ROLAND, b Parrott, Ga, Jan 19, 10; m 35; c 2. PHYSICS. *Educ:* US Naval Acad, BS, 32; Catholic Univ, MS, 54. *Prof Exp:* Instr physics & eng, Bullis Sch, DC, 32-38; asst mat engr, Nat Bur Standards, 38-42; chmn physics comt, 58-67, from asst prof to assoc prof, 46-56, prof, 56-80, EMER PROF PHYSICS, US NAVAL ACAD, 80- *Mem:* Am Asn Physics Teachers; Southeastern Sect Am Phys Soc. *Mailing Add:* Dept of Physics US Naval Acad Annapolis MD 21402

PINKSTON, JOHN TURNER, b Meridan, Miss, Mar 5, 15; m 40; c 2. PHYSICAL CHEMISTRY. *Educ:* Miss State Col, BS, 36; Ind Univ, PhD(phys chem), 40. *Prof Exp:* Res chemist, Universal Oil Prod Co, Ill, 40-44; sr chemist, Manhattan Dist, NY, 44-45; chemist, Harshaw Chem Co, Ohio, 45-50, asst dir, Tech Develop, 50-52; process consult, Catalytic Construct Co, 52-55, mgr process, 55-59; vpres & process consult, United Engrs & Constructors, Inc, Philadelphia, 59-66, vpres chem, 66-81; RETIRED. *Concurrent Pos:* With AEC, 44-46, 50- *Mem:* Am Chem Soc; Am Inst Chem Eng. *Res:* Catalytic conversions of hydrocarbons; fuel gas technology; uranium technology; chemical process engineering. *Mailing Add:* 60 Forest Lane Swarthmore PA 19081

PINKSTON, JOHN TURNER, III, b Chicago, Ill, Nov 28, 42. ELECTRICAL ENGINEERING. *Educ:* Princeton Univ, BSE, 64; Mass Inst Technol, PhD(elec eng), 67. *Prof Exp:* Elec engr, Dept Defense, 67-69; asst prof elec eng, Univ Md, 69-70; mem res staff, Dept Defense, 70-75; MEM TECH STAFF CERAMIC RES, CORNING GLASS WORKS, 75- *Mem:* Inst Elec & Electronics Engrs. *Res:* Information and statistical communication theory; error correcting codes; signal processing by computer; architecture of computer systems. *Mailing Add:* Corning Glass Works Sullivan Park Corning NY 14830

PINKSTON, MARGARET FOUNTAIN, b Macon, Ga, Jan 27, 19; m 46; c 3. BIOCHEMISTRY. *Educ:* Brooklyn Col, BA, 71; City Univ NY, PhD(biochem), 76. *Prof Exp:* ASST PROF BIOCHEM, MARY BALDWIN COL, 76- *Mem:* Am Chem Soc; Biophys Soc; Am Oil Chemists Soc. *Res:* Study of possible relationship between plasma lipoproteins and delayed hypersensitivity reactions to certain foods characterized by a high percentage of saturated triglycerides; interaction between model proteins and deoxyribonucleic acids. *Mailing Add:* Dept of Biochem Mary Baldwin Col Staunton VA 24401

PINKSTON, WILLIAM THOMAS, b Albany, Ga, Jan 19, 31; m 57; c 5. NUCLEAR PHYSICS, THEORETICAL PHYSICS. *Educ:* Cath Univ, AB, 52, MS, 55, PhD, 57. *Prof Exp:* Physicist, US Naval Ord Lab, Md, 55-57; instr physics, Princeton Univ, 57-59; chmn dept physics, 69-76, from asst prof to assoc prof, 59-69, chmn dept, 70-76, PROF PHYSICS, VANDERBILT UNIV, 69- *Concurrent Pos:* Sr fel, Bartol Res Found, Pa, 63-64; consult, Oak Ridge Nat Lab; Sr US Scientist Award, Alexander von Humboldt Soc. *Mem:* AAAS; fel Am Phys Soc; Am Asn Physics Teachers; Fedn Am Sci. *Res:* Theory of nuclear structures and reactions. *Mailing Add:* Dept of Physics Vanderbilt Univ Nashville TN 37235

PINKUS, A(LBIN) G(EORGE), b Norwich, Conn, Jan 17, 22. PHYSICAL ORGANIC CHEMISTRY, STEREOCHEMISTRY. *Educ:* Columbia Univ, BS, 47; Univ Ill, MS, 49; Ohio State Univ, PhD(chem), 52. *Prof Exp:* Asst chem, Columbia Univ, 47; asst instr, Ohio State Univ, 49-52; from instr to assoc prof, 52-63, PROF CHEM, BAYLOR UNIV, 63- *Mem:* Fel AAAS; Am Chem Soc; Coblentz Soc; fel Am Inst Chem; Royal Soc Chem. *Res:* Stereochemistry; reaction mechanisms; absorption spectra; restricted rotation; organometallic chemistry and polymer chemistry; chemistry of phenols, organophosphorus compounds, Grignard reagents, sulfur and sulfur compounds, ketones, ethers, esters, peroxides, ammonium salts, carboxylic acids and oxidation; contact lens and synthetic biodegradable suture polymers. *Mailing Add:* Dept of Chem Baylor Univ Waco TX 76798

PINKUS, HERMANN (KARL BENNO), b Berlin, Ger, Nov 18, 05; nat US; m 35; c 1. DERMATOLOGY, ONCOLOGY. *Educ:* Univ Berlin, MD, 30; Univ Mich, MS, 35. *Prof Exp:* Asst dermat, Breslau Univ, 30-33; from instr to prof, 44-76, assoc path, 46-76, from actg chmn to chmn dept, 58-73, EMER PROF DERMAT, COL MED, WAYNE STATE UNIV, 76- *Concurrent Pos:* Res fel dermatopath, Wayne County Gen Hosp, Mich, 36-38; res assoc, Detroit Inst Cancer Res, 51-62. *Mem:* AAAS; Soc Invest Dermat (vpres, 57-58, pres, 58-59); Am Dermat Asn (vpres, 77-78); Am Asn Cancer Res; Am Acad Dermat (vpres, 71-72). *Res:* Anatomy and pathology of the skin, especially oncology. *Mailing Add:* Dept Dermat Detroit Gen Hosp Detroit MI 48226

PINKUS, JACK LEON, b Syracuse, NY, July 17, 30; m 61. ORGANIC CHEMISTRY. *Educ:* Syracuse Univ, BS, 52; Univ Southern Calif, PhD(chem), 56. *Prof Exp:* Fulbright scholar, Groningen, 56-58; res assoc biochem, Upstate Med Ctr, State Univ NY, 58; instr & res assoc chem, Univ Pittsburgh, 58-60, asst prof, 60-61; asst prof, Wheeling Col, 61-63; NASA fel, Univ Pittsburgh, 63-65, asst res prof obstet & gynec, Sch Med, Univ Pittsburgh, 65-67; asst res prof obstet & gynec, Sch Med, Boston Univ, 67-71, assoc res prof, 71-75; PRES, BOSTON BIOCHEM CORP, 76-; CLIN ASSOC, MASS REHAB HOSP, 79- *Concurrent Pos:* Vis assoc prof, Dept Chem, Clark Univ, 75-76. *Mem:* Am Chem Soc; Royal Soc Chem; Royal Neth Chem Soc. *Res:* Heterocyclic compounds; reaction mechanisms; organic synthesis; steroid hormones. *Mailing Add:* 75 Cleveland Rd Wellesley MA 02181

PINNAS, JACOB LOUIS, b Newark, NJ, Jan 31, 40; m 64; c 3. ALLERGY, IMMUNOLOGY. *Educ:* Rutgers Univ, AB, 61; Univ Chicago, MD & MS, 65. *Prof Exp:* Resident med, State Univ NY, Syracuse, 65-66 & 68-70; med epidemiologist, Ctr Dis Control, 66-68; fel allergy & immunol, Scripps Clin & Res Found, 70-73; DIR ALLERGY SERV, SCH MED, UNIV ARIZ, 73-, ASSOC PROF INTERNAL MED, 79- *Concurrent Pos:* Mem attend staff, Univ Hosp, Univ Ariz Health Sci Ctr, 73-, dir allergy serv, 73-79; consult & dir allergy clin, Vet Admin Hosp, Tucson, 73- *Mem:* Am Asn Immunologists; Am Fedn Clin Res; fel Am Acad Allergy; fel Am Col Physicians. *Res:* Hypersensitivity reactions in respiratory tissues and skin; insect allergens and aeroallergens. *Mailing Add:* Sect of Clin Immunol Univ of Ariz Health Sci Ctr Tucson AZ 85724

PINNAVAIA, THOMAS J, b Buffalo, NY, Feb 16, 38; m 59; c 2. INORGANIC CHEMISTRY. *Educ:* State Univ NY Buffalo, BA, 62; Cornell Univ, PhD(inorg chem), 67. *Prof Exp:* From asst prof to assoc prof, 66-76, PROF CHEM, MICH STATE UNIV, 76- *Mem:* Clay Mineral Soc; AAAS; Am Chem Soc. *Res:* Coordination chemistry; surface chemistry; intercalation reactions and catalytic properties of layered structures; metal ion-nucleic acid interactions. *Mailing Add:* Dept of Chem Mich State Univ East Lansing MI 48823

PINNELL, CHARLES, b Midland, Tex, Mar 16, 29; m 50; c 2. CIVIL ENGINEERING. *Educ:* Tex Tech Col, BS, 52; Purdue Univ, MS, 58; Tex A&M Univ, PhD, 64. *Prof Exp:* Asst prof civil eng, Tex Tech Col, 54-57; asst, Purdue Univ, 57-58; asst prof & asst res engr, 58-64, assoc prof, 64-70, PROF CIVIL ENG, TEX A&M UNIV, 70-, ASSOC DEAN ACAD AFFAIRS, 64-, ASST DIR, TEX TRANSP INST, 76-, ASSOC DEP CHANCELLOR ENG,

80- *Concurrent Pos:* Mem, Hwy Res Bd, Nat Acad Sci-Nat Res Coun, 58-; pres, PAWA Inc, 71-76. *Honors & Awards:* Award, Nat Acad Sci-Nat Res Coun, 59; Award, Inst Traffic Eng, 60. *Mem:* Am Soc Civil Engrs; Inst Traffic Eng. *Res:* Transportation; traffic control; freeway operations; administration; management science; computer utilization. *Mailing Add:* Tex Transp Inst Tex A&M Univ College Station TX 77843

PINNELL, ROBERT PEYTON, b Fresno, Calif, Dec 5, 38; m 62. ORGANIC CHEMISTRY. *Educ:* Fresno State Col, BS, 60; Univ Kans, PhD(chem), 64. *Prof Exp:* Robert A Welch Found fel, 64-66; from asst prof to assoc prof inorg chem, 66-78, PROF CHEM, CLAREMONT COLS, 78-, CHMN, JOINT SCI DEPT, 74- *Concurrent Pos:* Vis Assoc Prof, Calif Inst Technol, 73-74. *Mem:* Am Chem Soc; AAAS; Sigma Xi. *Res:* Chemistry of organometallic and organometalloidal compounds, phosphorus compounds. *Mailing Add:* Joint Sci Dept Claremont Cols Claremont CA 91711

PINNEY, EDMUND JOY, b Seattle, Wash, Aug 19, 17; m 45; c 2. MATHEMATICAL ANALYSIS. *Educ:* Calif Inst Technol, BS, 39, PhD(math), 42. *Prof Exp:* Res assoc, Mass Inst Technol, 42-43; res analyst, Consol Vultee Aircraft Co, Calif, 43-45; instr math, Ore State Col, 45-46; dir, Off Naval Res Contract, 53-70; lectr, 46-47, from asst prof to assoc prof, 47-59, PROF MATH, UNIV CALIF, BERKELEY, 59- *Concurrent Pos:* Civilian with Off Sci Res & Develop, 44. *Mem:* Fel AAAS; Am Phys Soc; Am Math Soc. *Res:* Electromagnetic theory; integral equations; hydrodynamics; mechanics; electricity; nonlinear mechanics; calculus of variations in abstract spaces; plasma theory. *Mailing Add:* Dept of Math Univ of Calif Berkeley CA 94720

PINNEY, JACK ERWIN, b Columbia, Mo, Sept 10, 24; m 49; c 3. APPLIED PHYSICS. *Educ:* Iowa State Univ, BS, 47. *Prof Exp:* Photog engr, Color Technol Div, 48-57, sr res physicist, Color Photog Div, Res Labs, 57-64, res assoc & head, Color Physics & Eng Lab, 64-67, head, Electro-Mech Lab, 67-69, SR LAB HEAD, ENG PHYSICS LAB, PHYSICS DIV, EASTMAN KODAK CO, 69- *Mem:* Optical Soc Am; Soc Photog Sci & Eng; Soc Motion Picture & TV Eng. *Res:* Engineering physics; scanning and printing applications of photographic materials; photographic equipment development. *Mailing Add:* Res Labs Eastman Kodak Co Rochester NY 14650

PINNICK, HARRY THOMAS, b Manhattan, Kans, Dec 18, 21; m 49; c 3. SOLID STATE PHYSICS. *Educ:* Southwestern Col, Kans, BA, 43; Univ Buffalo, PhD, 55. *Prof Exp:* Res physicist, Union Carbide Metals Co, 54-61; asst prof physics, Colo Sch Mines, 61-64; ASSOC PROF PHYSICS, UNIV AKRON, 64- *Concurrent Pos:* Vis staff mem, Los Alamos Sci Lab. *Mem:* Am Phys Soc. *Res:* Electron transport properties of metallic solid solutions; positron annihilation in transuranic elements; inelastic electron tunneling spectroscopy. *Mailing Add:* Dept of Physics Univ of Akron Akron OH 44325

PINNICK, HERBERT ROBERT, JR, physical organic chemistry, see previous edition

PINNINGTON, ERIC HENRY, b London, Eng, Aug 19, 38; m 68; c 3. ATOMIC SPECTROSCOPY, ASTROPHYSICS. *Educ:* Univ London, BSc, 59, PhD(physics), 62; Imp Col London, ARCS, 59, dipl, 62. *Prof Exp:* Nat Res Coun Can fel, McMaster Univ, 62-64; Alexander von Humboldt Stiftung res fel, Max Planck Inst Physics & Astrophys, Munich, Ger, 64-65; from asst prof to assoc prof, 65-75, PROF PHYSICS, UNIV ALTA, 75- *Concurrent Pos:* Alexander von Humboldt res fel, Nuclear Res Estab, Julich, Ger, 71-72 & Bielefeld Univ, 76; sr vis fel, Oxford Univ, 80. *Mem:* Optical Soc Am; Brit Inst Phys; Can Asn Physicists; NY Acad Sci. *Res:* Analysis of atomic spectra; measurement of atomic transition probabilities and fine structure effects using the beam-foil technique; investigations of new light sources for atomic spectra; laser excitation of fast ions. *Mailing Add:* Dept Physics Univ Alta Edmonton AB T6G 2G7 Can

PINNOW, KENNETH ELMER, b Villa Park, Ill, Nov 30, 28; m 58; c 3. METALLURGY. *Educ:* Mich Col Mining & Technol, BS, 51; Pa State Univ, MS, 55, PhD(metall), 61. *Prof Exp:* Jr metallurgist, Gen Motors Res, Mich, 51-53; instr metall, Pa State Univ, 58-60; sr res scientist, 61-78, mgr process res, 78-81, TECH DIR STAINLESS STEEL PROD & PROCESSING, CRUCIBLE RES CTR, COLT INDUSTS, 81- *Honors & Awards:* Mathews-Payson Award, Crucible Steel, Inc, 71. *Mem:* Nat Asn Corrosion Engrs; fel Am Soc Metals; Iron & Steel Soc. *Res:* Physical and process metallurgy of stainless steels and other high alloy steels, especially studies of product properties including mechanical properties, formability, corrosion, hot and cold working, new alloys; continuous casting. *Mailing Add:* Crucible Res Ctr Colt Industs PO Box 88 Pittsburgh PA 15230

PINO, JOHN ANTHONY, b Tyler, Pa, Jan 26, 23; m 44; c 4. ANIMAL SCIENCES. *Educ:* Rutgers Univ, BS, 44, PhD(zool), 51. *Prof Exp:* Instr poultry husb, Rutgers Univ, 47-51, from asst prof to assoc prof, 51-55; animal scientist, Rockefeller Found, 55-60, asst dir, Mex Agr Prog, 60-63, assoc dir, 63-65; assoc dir, 65-70, DIR, AGR SCI, NY, 70- *Concurrent Pos:* Mem expert panel animal breeding & climat, Food & Agr Orgn UN, 65-70; subpanel intensification animal prod, President's Sci Adv Comt, 67; comt animal health, Nat Acad Sci, 68-72, Agr Bd, 71-73 & Bd Agr & Renewable Res, 73-77; chmn bd trustees, Int Lab Res Animal Dis, 73-80; vchmn bd trustees, Int Ctr Trop Agr, 74-; vchmn bd dirs, Winrock Int Livestock Res & Training Ctr, 76-; mem bd trustees, Int Agr Develop Serv, 79-; mem, Nat Agr Res & Exten Users adv bd, 78-, chmn, 80-; mem, Comt Int de Liaison du Corps pour l'Alimentation, 79-; mem, Coun Foreign Relations, 80- *Mem:* Poultry Sci Asn; NY Acad Sci; Asn Advan Agr Sci Africa; World Poultry Sci Asn; Am Soc Animal Sci. *Mailing Add:* Rm 2300 Rockefeller Found 1133 Ave of the Am New York NY 10036

PINO, LEWIS NICHOLAS, b Niagara Falls, NY, June 1, 24; m 47; c 5. ORGANIC CHEMISTRY. *Educ:* Univ Buffalo, AB, 47, PhD(chem), 50. *Prof Exp:* Res assoc, Univ Buffalo, 49-50; instr org chem, Allegheny Col, 50-51, from asst prof to assoc prof chem, 51-56; asst dean, Colo Col, 56-57, assoc dean, 57-59; mem insts staff, NSF, 59-61, prog dir undergrad sci educ, 61-66; asst to chancellor, 66-67, dir res serv & dean spring & summer sessions, 67-71, PROF CHEM & DIR RES SERV, OAKLAND UNIV, 71-, ACTG DEAN, GRAD SCH, 81- *Concurrent Pos:* Mem nat comn undergrad educ & educ of teachers, US Off Educ, 71-74. *Mem:* AAAS; Am Chem Soc; Sigma Xi. *Res:* Heterocyclic chemistry; educational administration; higher education and public policy. *Mailing Add:* Res Serv Oakland Univ Rochester MI 48063

PINO, RICHARD M, b Brooklyn, NY, Mar 10, 50; m 77. CYTOCHEMISTRY, CELL BIOLOGY. *Educ:* Villanova Univ, BS, 72; Rutgers Univ, MS, 74; Hahnemann Med Col, PhD(anat), 78. *Prof Exp:* Fel cell biol, Sch Med, Wayne State Univ, 78-80; ASST PROF ANAT, LA STATE UNIV MED CTR, 80- *Mem:* Am Soc Cell Biol; Am Asn Anatomists; Histochem soc; Electron Micros Soc Am; Asn Res Vision & Opthal. *Res:* Structure and function of vascular endothelia in the eye, liver, and bone marrow; structure of Kupffer cells and retinal pigment epithelium; cell biology; cytochemistry; electron microscopy. *Mailing Add:* Dept Anat Med Educ Bldg La State Univ Med Ctr New Orleans LA 70112

PINSCHMIDT, MARY WARREN, b Washington, DC, Aug 10, 34; m 57; c 2. COMPARATIVE PHYSIOLOGY, EVOLUTION. *Educ:* Western Md Col, AB, 56; Duke Univ, MA, 61; Med Col Va, PhD(physiol), 73. *Prof Exp:* Instr, 61-67, asst prof,68-75, assoc prof biol, 75-80, PROF BIOL SCI, MARY WASHINGTON COL, 81- *Mem:* Am Soc Zool; Am Inst Biol Sci. *Res:* Biological clocks; history of biology. *Mailing Add:* Dept of Biol COMBS-108 Mary Washington Col Fredericksburg VA 22401

PINSCHMIDT, ROBERT KRANTZ, JR, b Los Angeles, Calif, July 25, 45; m 68; c 3. PHYSICAL ORGANIC CHEMISTRY, POLYMER CHEMISTRY. *Educ:* Wabash Col, BA, 67; Univ Ore, PhD(org chem), 71. *Prof Exp:* Vis asst prof phys org chem, Tech Univ Wroclaw, Poland, 71-73; independent fel, Dept Chem, Univ Ore, 73-74; sr res chemist ion exchange resins, Fluid Process Res, Rohm & Haas Co, Pa, 74-76; res chemist, environ & nitration chem, Indust Chem Res & Develop, 76-80, prin res chemist, polymer chem & technol, 80-81, SR PRIN RES CHEMIST & GROUP LEADER SCI CTR, AIR PROD & CHEM INC, 81- *Mem:* Am Chem Soc. *Res:* New monomer synthesis, emulsion and suspension synthesis, including absorbents and resin bound reagents; new reactions and molecular rearrangements; ion chromatography and nuclear magnetic resonance spectroscopy; waste abatement techniques. *Mailing Add:* Sci Ctr Air Prod & Chem Inc PO Box 538 Allentown PA 18105

PINSCHMIDT, WILLIAM CONRAD, JR, b Richmond, Va, Oct 30, 26; m 57; c 2. ZOOLOGY. *Educ:* Mt Union Col, BS, 50; Ohio State Univ, MS, 52; Duke Univ, PhD(zool), 63. *Prof Exp:* Asst zool, Ohio State Univ, 50-52, asst instr, 51-52; instr, 52-59, from asst prof to assoc prof, 59-68, chmn dept biol, 68-70, PROF BIOL, MARY WASHINGTON COL, 68- *Concurrent Pos:* Instr, Duke Univ, 56-57, asst to dir, Marine Lab, 59, investr, 64-; trustee, Va Chap Nature Conservancy, 71-75 & consult property acquisitions, 71-74. *Mem:* Ecol Soc Am; AAAS; Am Soc Zoologists; Atlantic Estuarine Res Soc. *Res:* Marine invertebrate zoology; crab larval development and ecological distribution; animal behavior and physiology; ecology. *Mailing Add:* Dept of Biol Sci Mary Washington Col Fredericksburg VA 22401

PINSKER, HAROLD M, b New York, NY, May 14, 37; m 67; c 1. PSYCHOPHYSIOLOGY, NEUROPHYSIOLOGY. *Educ:* Queens Col, NY, BA, 57; Univ Calif, Berkeley, PhD(physiol psychol), 66. *Prof Exp:* Instr physiol & biophys, Med Ctr, NY Univ, 68-72; asst prof, Dept Physiol & Biophys & Div Psychol, 72-77, ASSOC PROF, DEPT PHYSIOL & BIOPHYS & DIV PSYCHIAT & BEHAV SCI, UNIV TEX MED BR GALVESTON, 77- *Concurrent Pos:* Trainee psychiat & biol sci, Med Ctr, NY Univ, 66-68; neurobiol prog proj grant, Marine Biomed Inst, Univ Tex Med Br Galveston, 74-79; Nat Inst Neurol Dis & Shock neurobiol res grant, 75-78; asst, Dept Neurobiol & Behav, Pub Health Res Inst, City of New York, 69-72; mem, Marine Biomed Inst, Univ Tex Med Br Galveston. *Mem:* Soc Neurosci; Am Physiol Soc; Am Psychol Asn; Int Neuropsychol Soc. *Res:* Cellular analysis of behavior in simple systems; cellular mechanisms of learning; neuronal oscillators. *Mailing Add:* Univ of Tex Med Br Marine Biomed Inst 200 Univ Blvd Galveston TX 77550

PINSKI, GABRIEL, b New York, NY, Sept 9, 37; m 60; c 3. MATHEMATICAL STATISTICS, MEDICINE. *Educ:* Columbia Univ, AB, 57; Univ Rochester, PhD(physics), 64; Temple Univ, MS, 80; Univ Autonoma de Cd Juarez, MD, 82. *Prof Exp:* Instr physics, Syracuse Univ, 63-65; asst prof physics, Drexel Univ, 65-70; sr opers res analyst, Sun Oil Co, 70-73; res adv, Comput Horizons, Inc, 73-77; sr res scientist, Inst Sci Info, 77-80; CONSULT, 80- *Concurrent Pos:* Prin investr, NSF grant, 80-81. *Mem:* Sigma Xi; Opers Res Soc Am; Am Phys Soc. *Res:* Statistical applications to medical problems; developing indicators for influence of scientific journals and fields. *Mailing Add:* 411 Witley Rd Wynnewood PA 19096

PINSKY, CARL, b Montreal, Que, May 15, 28; m 55; c 2. NEUROPHARMACOLOGY, NEUROPHYSIOLOGY. *Educ:* Sir George Williams Univ, BSc, 55; McGill Univ, MSc, 57, PhD(neurophysiol), 61. *Prof Exp:* From lectr to assoc prof, 58-78, PROF PHARMACOL & THERAPEUT, UNIV MANITOBA, 78- *Concurrent Pos:* Operating & major equip grants, Med Res Coun Can, 62-79, Med Res Coun Can Scholar, 63-67; chmn, summer scholar comt, 74-75 & biomed grant rev comt, Non-Med Use of Drugs Directorate, Health & Welfare Can, 76-78. *Mem:* Pharmacol Soc Can; Am Soc for Pharmacol & Exp Therapeut. *Res:* Endogenous opiate-mimetic substances, their physiological mechanisms and role in opiate narcotic dependency; cholinergic mechanisms at the synaptic, membrane and molecular levels; cholinergic interactions with opiate narcotic drugs. *Mailing Add:* Dept of Pharmacol & Therapeut 770 Bannatyne Ave Winnipeg MB R3E 0W3 Can

PINSKY, CARL MUNI, b Philadelphia, Pa, May 7, 38; m 63. ONCOLOGY, IMMUNOLOGY. *Educ:* Univ Pa, AB, 60; Jefferson Med Col, MD, 64. *Prof Exp:* From intern to resident internal med, Med Ctr, Univ Ky, 64-66; resident med & Am Cancer Soc clin fel, Mem Hosp Cancer & Allied Dis, 66-67, USPHS clin res trainee, 67-70; instr, 70-75, asst prof med, 75-81, ASSOC PROF CLIN MED, CORNELL UNIV, 81-; ASST MEM, SLOAN-KETTERING INST CANCER RES, 74- *Concurrent Pos:* Res fel tumor immunol, Sloan-Kettering Inst Cancer Res, 67-70, res assoc, 70-74; fel med, Med Col, Cornell Univ, 67-70; clin asst physician med oncol, Mem Hosp Cancer & Allied Dis, 70-74, asst attend physician, 74- *Mem:* AAAS; Am Fedn Clin Res; Am Asn Cancer Res; Am Soc Clin Oncol. *Res:* Evaluation of immunocompetence; development of immunodiagnostic techniques and exploration of immunotherapy in patients with cancer. *Mailing Add:* Mem Sloan-Kettering Cancer Ctr 1275 York Ave New York NY 10021

PINSKY, LEONARD, b Montreal, Que, July 2, 35; m 60; c 3. GENETICS. *Educ:* McGill Univ, BSc, 56, MD, CM, 60; FRCPS(C), 67. *Prof Exp:* INVESTR SOMATIC CELL GENETICS, LADY DAVIS INST MED RES, JEWISH GEN HOSP, 67-, DIR DIV MED GENETICS, 67- *Concurrent Pos:* Med Res Coun Can operating grants, 67-; asst prof, McGill Univ, 68-, assoc prof, 73-; prof pediat, Ctr Human Genetics, 79- *Mem:* Am Soc Human Genetics; Soc Pediat Res; Can Col Med Scientists (pres, 78-80). *Res:* Experimental teratology; somatic cell genetics, particularly human gene mutations in monolayer cell culture. *Mailing Add:* Cell Genetics Lab Lady Davis Inst Jewish Gen Hosp Montreal PQ H3T 1E2 Can

PINSKY, MARK A, b Philadelphia, Pa, July 15, 40; m 63; c 2. MATHEMATICS. *Educ:* Antioch Col, BA, 62; Mass Inst Technol, PhD(math), 66. *Prof Exp:* Instr math, Stanford Univ, 66-68; asst prof, 68-72, assoc prof, 72-77, PROF, NORTHWESTERN UNIV, 77- *Concurrent Pos:* Vis prof, Univ Paris, 72-73. *Mem:* Am Math Soc; Inst Math Statist; Math Asn Am. *Res:* Stochastic differential equations; Markov processes; limit theorems in probability; asymptotic analysis of kinetic models. *Mailing Add:* Dept Math Northwestern Univ Evanston IL 60201

PINSLER, HEINZ WILLI, physics, physical chemistry, see previous edition

PINSLEY, EDWARD ALLAN, b New York, NY, June 18, 27; m 60; c 3. LASERS, ENGINEERING MANAGEMENT. *Educ:* City Col New York, BME, 49; Mass Inst Technol, MS, 50. *Prof Exp:* Res engr res labs, United Aircraft Corp, 50-55, supvr turbomach group, 55-59, supvr elec propulsion group, 59-64, chief advan technol, 64-67, prog mgr advan laser technol, 67-68, prog mgr lasers, 68-73, chief laser eng, 73-79, chief tech develop, 79-80, DEP DIR TECH & RES, GOVT PROD DIV, PRATT & WHITNEY AIRCRAFT GROUP, UNITED TECHNOL CORP, 81- *Honors & Awards:* George Mead Medal Eng Achievement, United Aircraft Corp, 67. *Mem:* Am Phys Soc; Am Inst Aeronaut & Astronaut; Inst Elec & Electronics Eng. *Res:* Laser systems and components. *Mailing Add:* Govt Prod Div United Technol Corp West Palm Beach FL 33402

PINSON, ELLIOT N, b New York, NY, Mar 18, 35; m 56; c 2. COMPUTER SCIENCE, ELECTRICAL ENGINEERING. *Educ:* Princeton Univ, BS, 56; Mass Inst Technol, SM, 57; Calif Inst Technol, PhD(elec eng), 61. *Prof Exp:* Mem tech staff, 61-65, supvr info processing res, 65-68, head, Comput Systs Res Dept, 68-77, dir, Bus Commun Systs Lab, 77-80, DIR, ADVAN SOFTWARE TECHNOL LAB, BELL LABS, 80- *Concurrent Pos:* Vis MacKay lectr, Univ Calif, Berkeley, 69-70. *Mem:* AAAS; Asn Comput Mach. *Res:* Computer science; graphical data processing; speech analysis and synthesis; operating systems design, modeling and evaluation; computer communications networks; private branch telephone exchange and office communications systems. *Mailing Add:* Advan Software Technol Lab Bell Tel Labs Murray Hill NJ 07974

PINSON, JAMES WESLEY, b Baton Rouge, La, Apr 10, 37; m 61; c 4. PHYSICAL CHEMISTRY & RADIATION CHEMISTRY. *Educ:* William Carey Col, BS, 59; Univ Miss, MSCS, 64, PhD(chem), 67. *Prof Exp:* Bookkeeper, W R Aldrich & Co, 59-60; head sci dept high sch, Miss, 60-63; from asst prof to assoc prof, 67-74, PROF CHEM, UNIV SOUTHERN MISS, 74-, ASST TO DEAN COL SCI, 71- *Concurrent Pos:* AEC-US Army mat loan grant, 68-70; Res Corp res grant, AEC nuclear educ & training grant & Miss State Bd Inst Higher Learning res grant, 69-70; Oak Ridge Assoc Univs-Atomic Energy Comn self-serv contract, Oak Ridge Nat Lab, 65-, consult, 67-; Sigma Xi grant, 70-71; Miss State Bd Inst Higher Learning grants, 70-72; NASA Earth Resources Lab grant, Air Pollution, Univ Miss, 71; mem, NASA Remote Sensing Study, Miss, 72- *Mem:* AAAS; Am Chem Soc; Am Phys Soc; Am Soc Mass Spectrometry; NAm Thermal Anal Soc. *Res:* Airborne radionuclides; remote sensing; air pollution; vibrational spectroscopy; cobalt 60 gamma ray radiolysis of boron, silicon, germanium and tin hydrides in the gas phase; characteriaztion of solid and liquid polymeric radiolytic products using mass spectrometric techniques. *Mailing Add:* Dept of Chem Box 8415 Univ of Southern Miss Hattiesburg MS 39401

PINSON, JOHN C(ARVER), b Lubbock, Tex, July 8, 31; m 52; c 1. SYSTEMS ENGINEERING, ELECTRICAL ENGINEERING. *Educ:* Tex Tech Col, BS, 52; Mass Inst Technol, SM, 54, ScD(elec eng), 57. *Prof Exp:* Sr res engr, 57-58, res specialist, 58-59, supvr systs eng, 59-60, group chief, 60-62, sect mgr, 62-63, asst chief engr, Systs Div, 63-65, CHIEF SCIENTIST, AUTONETICS STRATEGIC SYSTS DIV, ROCKWELL, INT, 65- *Res:* Systems engineering, mechanization and accuracy analysis on inertial guidance systems for marine, aircraft, missile and space vehicles. *Mailing Add:* 5069 Crescent Dr Anaheim CA 92807

PINSON, REX, JR, b Wichita, Kans, Oct 23, 25; m 54; c 3. BIOCHEMICAL PHARMACOLOGY. *Educ:* Univ of the South, BSc, 48; Univ Rochester, PhD(chem), 51. *Prof Exp:* Res chemist, Chas Pfizer & Co, Inc, 51-59, proj leader, 59-61, sect mgr, 61-65, asst dir pharmacol res, 65-67, dir, 67-71, dir res, 71-72, vpres med prod res & develop, 72-80, EXEC VPRES, PFIZER CENT RES, INC, 80- *Mem:* AAAS; Am Soc Pharmacol & Exp Therapeut; Am Chem Soc; fel NY Acad Sci; Int Soc Biochem Pharmacol. *Res:* Physiological disposition of drugs; lipid and carbohydrate metabolism; research administration; toxicology. *Mailing Add:* Pfizer Inc Cent Res Eastern Point Rd Groton CT 06340

PINSON, WILLIAM HAMET, JR, b Atlanta, Ga, Sept 6, 19; m 42; c 3. GEOLOGY. *Educ:* Emory Univ, BA, 48, MS, 49; Mass Inst Technol, PhD, 51. *Prof Exp:* Res fel geol & instr astron, Harvard Univ, 51-53; from res assoc to asst prof, 53-68, ASSOC PROF GEOL, MASS INST TECHNOL, 68- *Mem:* Geol Soc Am; Am Astron Soc; Mineral Soc Am; Meteoritical Soc. *Res:* Distribution and abundances of chemical elements; age determinations of rocks and meteorites; origin of meteorites, tektites; meteorite craters. *Mailing Add:* Dept of Geol & Geophys Mass Inst of Technol Cambridge MA 02139

PINTAR, MILAN MIK, b Celje, Yugoslavia, Jan 17, 34; m 74; c 3. NUCLEAR MAGNETIC RESONANCE. *Educ:* Univ Ljubljana, BS, 59, MS, 64, PhD(physics), 66. *Prof Exp:* Res fel physics, Jozef Stefan Inst, Ljubljana, 59-66; fel, McMaster Univ, 66-67; from asst prof to assoc prof, 67-75, PROF, UNIV WATERLOO, 75- *Concurrent Pos:* Chmn nuclear magnetic resonance, Waterloo Summer Sch, 69- *Honors & Awards:* B Kidric Nat Award, Slovenian Acad Sci & Arts, 61. *Mem:* Can Asn Physicists; Am Phys Soc; Ampere Soc; Int Soc Magnetic Resonances (secy gen, 78-). *Res:* Nuclear spin relaxation and thermodynamics in condensed matter; tunneling and time evolution spin torsional spectroscopy; nuclear magnetic resonance of dense solutions and lytropic liquid crystals. *Mailing Add:* 134 Dunbar Rd S Waterloo ON N2L 2E9 Can

PINTER, CHARLES CLAUDE, b Budapest, Hungary, Mar 5, 32; US citizen; m 64; c 3. MATHEMATICS. *Educ:* Columbia Univ, BSc, 56; Univ Paris, PhD(math), 64. *Prof Exp:* Lectr math, European Div, Univ Md, 61-64; assoc prof, Northern Mich, 64-65; assoc prof, 65-72, PROF MATH, BUCKNELL UNIV, 72- *Concurrent Pos:* Fulbright grants, 66-67 & 78; NSF res prog col teachers res grant, 69-70, fac fel, 71-72. *Res:* Algebraic logic; universal algebra. *Mailing Add:* Dept of Math Bucknell Univ Lewisburg PA 17837

PINTER, GABRIEL GEORGE, b Bekes, Hungary, June 23, 25; nat US; wid; c 2. MEDICINE, PHYSIOLOGY. *Educ:* Univ Budapest, MD, 51. *Prof Exp:* From asst to asst prof physiol, Med Univ Budapest, 47-56; res assoc, Inst Exp Med Res, Oslo, Norway, 57; res assoc, Univ Tenn, 57-58, asst prof, 59-61; from asst prof to assoc prof, 61-70, PROF PHYSIOL, SCH MED, UNIV MD, BALTIMORE CITY, 70- *Concurrent Pos:* Alexander von Humboldt Prize, WGer, 80. *Mem:* Am Physiol Soc; Scand Physiol Soc. *Res:* Renal physiology; hematology; capillary permeability. *Mailing Add:* Dept of Physiol Univ of Md Baltimore MD 21201

PINTER, PAUL JAMES, JR, b Abington, Pa, Oct 27, 46. ENTOMOLOGY, BIOMETEOROLOGY. *Educ:* Ariz State Univ, BS, 67, MS, 69, PhD(zool), 76. *Prof Exp:* Res assoc entom, Ariz State Univ, 72-75; RES ENTOMOLOGIST, US WATER CONSERV LAB, 77- *Concurrent Pos:* Africa travel grant, Sigma Xi, 74. *Mem:* Entom Soc Am; Sigma Xi. *Res:* Remote sensing applications to agricultural resource managemtn; microclimatic influences on insect development and survival. *Mailing Add:* 4386 E Alney Dr Phoenix AZ 85026

PINTO, FRANK G, b New York, NY, Jan 2, 34; m 59; c 2. ORGANIC CHEMISTRY. *Educ:* Fordham Univ, BS, 55; Seton Hall Univ, MS, 64, PhD(org chem), 66. *Prof Exp:* Chemist, Semet-Solvay Div, Allied Chem Corp, 55-57; chemist, Bound Brook, 59-64, res chemist, 64-68, group leader org pigments, 68-69, dyes mfg, chief chemist rubber chem & specialty elastomers mfg, 72-77, prod mgr rubber chem & chem intermediates mfg, Bound Brook, 77-79, MKT MGR ELASTOMERS, AM CYANAMID CO, WAYNE, 79- *Mem:* Am Chem Soc. *Res:* Synthesis of antioxidants, ultraviolet and infrared absorbers; process development of organic pigments; process and new product development of dyes; rubber chemicals and specialty elastomers; decomposition studies of mixed carboxylic and carbonic anhydrides. *Mailing Add:* 565 Emerald Trail Martinsville NJ 08836

PINTO, JOHN, biological chemistry, nutritional biochemistry, see previous edition

PINTO, JOHN DARWIN, b Chicago, Ill, Dec 10, 40; m 63; c 2. ENTOMOLOGY, SYSTEMATICS. *Educ:* Humboldt State Col, BA, 63; Univ Ill, Urbana, PhD(entom), 68. *Prof Exp:* Asst prof biol, Calif State Polytech Col, San Luis Obispo, 68-70; NSF grant, 72-74, asst prof entom, 70-77, ASST ENTOMOLOGIST, UNIV CALIF, RIVERISDE, 70-, ASSOC PROF ENTOM, 77- *Mem:* Am Entom Soc; Soc Syst Zool; Soc Study Evolution; Entom Soc Can. *Res:* Taxonomy, ethology and evolutionary studies of Meloidae. *Mailing Add:* Dept of Entom Univ of Calif Riverside CA 92502

PINTO, JOSEPH PETER, b New York, NY, Apr 3, 48. PLANETARY EVOLUTION, ATMOSPHERIC POLLUTION. *Educ:* New York Univ, PhD(atmospheric sci), 78. *Prof Exp:* Res assoc, Nat Res Coun, 79-81; RES ASSOC, CTR EARTH & PLANETARY PHYSICS, HARVARD UNIV, 81- *Res:* Physics and chemistry of the atmospheres of the earth and planets. *Mailing Add:* Ctr Earth & Planetary Physics Pierce Hall Harvard Univ Cambridge MA 02145

PINTO, LAWRENCE HENRY, b Paterson, NJ, Feb 9, 43. NEUROPHYSIOLOGY. *Educ:* Villanova Univ, BEE, 64; Northwestern Univ, Evanston, MS, 67, PhD(physiol), 70. *Prof Exp:* Asst prof, 70-75, assoc prof, 75-81, PROF BIOL, PURDUE UNIV, 81- *Mem:* AAAS; Asn Res Vision & Opthal; Biophys Soc; Soc Neurosci; Int Union Physiol Sci. *Res:* Genetics of visual system; mechanism for generation of potentials in vertebrate retinal neurons. *Mailing Add:* Dept Biol Sci Lilly Hall Purdue Univ Lafayette IN 47907

PINZKA, CHARLES FREDERICK, b New York, NY, Feb 5, 18; m 51; c 2. MATHEMATICS. *Educ:* Rutgers Univ, BS, 48; Univ Cincinnati, PhD(math), 62. *Prof Exp:* Res asst physics, Am Cyanamid Corp, 37-43; instr math, Xavier Univ, Ohio, 49-51; biometrician, E I du Pont de Nemours & Co, 51; math test specialist, Educ Testing Serv, 51-53, prog dir, 53-56; instr math, Xavier Univ, Ohio, 56-57; instr, 57-61, NSF sci fac fel, 61-62, asst prof, 62-70, ASSOC PROF MATH, UNIV CINCINNATI, 71- *Concurrent Pos:* Sr lectr, Univ Queensland, 68. *Mem:* Am Math Soc; Australian Math Soc; Math Asn Am. *Res:* Combinatorics; differential equations; probability; mathematics test construction; number theory. *Mailing Add:* Dept of Math Sci Univ of Cincinnati Cincinnati OH 45221

PIOCH, RICHARD PAUL, b South Haven, Mich, Sept 5, 22; m 51; c 5. MEDICINAL CHEMISTRY. *Educ:* Mich State Col, BS, 48; Pa State Col, MS, 50, PhD(org chem), 52. *Prof Exp:* Org chemist, 52-59, sr org chemist, 60-65, res scientist, 66-72, RES ASSOC, ELI LILLY & CO, 73- *Mem:* Am Chem Soc; Royal Soc Chem. *Res:* Synthesis of compounds affecting the human central nervous system or gastrointestinal system; structure activity relationships among compounds affecting the central nervous system or gastrointestinal system; synthesis of heterocyclic compounds. *Mailing Add:* 3750 Briarwood Dr Indianapolis IN 46240

PIOMELLI, SERGIO, b Naples, Italy, Mar 29, 31; m 56; c 2. HEMATOLOGY, PEDIATRICS. *Educ:* Univ Naples, MD, 54. *Prof Exp:* Asst med, Harvard Med Sch, 58-60; asst prof, Med Sch, Univ Naples, 60-61; investr, Ital Nat Res Coun, Univ Rome, 61-63; assoc hemat, Mt Sinai Hosp, New York, 63-64; from asst prof to assoc prof pediat, Sch Med, NY Univ, 64-71, dir pediat hemat, Med Ctr, 64-79, prof, 71-79; PROF PEDIAT & DIR PEDIAT HEMATOL, COL PHYSICIANS & SURGEONS, COLUMBIA UNIV, 79- *Concurrent Pos:* NIH grant & City of New York Health Res Coun career scientist, Bellevue Hosp, NY Univ, 64-; assoc attend physician, Univ & Bellevue Hosps, New York, 64-71, attend physician, 72-; vis prof, Med Fac, Rotterdam, Holland, 68-69. *Mem:* Am Soc Pediat Res; Am Soc Hemat; Am Soc Human Genetics; Am Soc Clin Invest; NY Acad Sci. *Res:* Red cell metabolism; lead poisoning; porphyrin metabolism; biochemical genetics; childhood cancer chemotherapy. *Mailing Add:* Pediat Hematol Div NY Univ Med Ctr New York NY 10016

PION, LAWRENCE V, b Providence, RI, July 11, 26; m 49; c 8. ANIMAL BEHAVIOR. *Educ:* Providence Col, BS, 50; Univ NH, MS, 52; Pa State Univ, PhD(animal behav), 70. *Prof Exp:* Instr, 51-64, actg head dept biol, 54-63, assoc prof, 64-71, chmn dept, 72-77, PROF BIOL, ST FRANCIS COL, PA, 71- *Mem:* Animal Behav Soc; AAAS. *Res:* Animal aggression. *Mailing Add:* Dept of Biol St Francis Col Loretto PA 15940

PION, RONALD JOSEPH, obstetrics & gynecology, see previous edition

PIONKE, HARRY BERNHARD, b Brooklyn, NY. SOIL CHEMISTRY. *Educ:* Univ Wis-Madison, BS, 63, MS, 66, PhD(soils), 67. *Prof Exp:* Asst prof soils, Univ Wis-Madison, 67-68; soil scientist, Agr Res Serv, 68-74, RES LEADER, NORTHEAST WATERSHED RES CTR, SCI & EDUC ADMIN, USDA, 74- *Mem:* Soil Sci Soc Am; Am Chem Soc. *Res:* Water chemistry of runoff and groundwaters related to geology and pollution potentials. *Mailing Add:* 111 Res Bldg A University Park PA 16802

PIORE, EMANUEL RUBEN, b Wilno, Russia, July 19, 08; US citizen; m 31; c 3. PHYSICS. *Educ:* Univ Wis, BA, 30, PhD(physics), 35. *Hon Degrees:* ScD, Union Col, 62, Univ Wis, 66. *Prof Exp:* Asst instr physics, Univ Wis, 30-35; physicist, Electronic Res Lab, Radio Corp Am Mfg co, 35-38; engr in charge TV lab, Columbia Broadcasting Syst, 38-42; sr physicist, Bur Ships, Dept Navy, 42-44, head, Electronics Br, Off Naval Res, 46-47, dir, Phys Sci Div, 47-48; dir, Res Lab Electronics, Mass Inst Tech, 48-49; dep nat sci, Off Naval Res, 49-51, chief scientist, 51-55; vpres res & dir, Avco Corp, 55-56; dir res, IBM Corp, 56-61, vpres res & eng, 60-63, vpres & group exec, 63-65, vpres & chief scientist, 65-72, mem bd dirs, 62-73. *Concurrent Pos:* Trustee, Woods Hole Oceanog Inst, 56-64, 65-; mem, Naval Res Adv Comt, 56-65; mem, President's Sci Adv Comt, 59-62, Nat Sci Bd, 61- & Bd Higher Educ, New York; mem bd dirs, Grad Res Ctr Southwest, 62-65; mem corp, Polytech Inst Brooklyn, 62-; trustee, Sloan-Kettering Inst Cancer Res, 64-; mem bd dirs, Sci Res Assocs; adj prof, Rockefeller Univ, 74- *Honors & Awards:* Gold Medal, Indust Res Inst; Kaplun Int Prize, Hebrew Univ, 75. *Mem:* Nat Acad Sci(treas, 66-); Nat Acad Eng; Am Philos Soc; fel Inst Elec & Electronics Engrs; Am Acad Arts & Sci. *Res:* Electronics; thermionic, photoelectric and secondary emission; composite surfaces; metallic and solid state. *Mailing Add:* 115 Central Park W New York NY 10023

PIORE, NORA, b New York, NY, Nov 28, 12; m 31; c 3. HEALTH ECONOMICS, HEALTH POLICY. *Educ:* Univ Wis, AB, 33, MA, 34. *Prof Exp:* Economist, Comt on Labor & Pub Welfare, US Senate, 50-53; prog analyst, Interdept Comt on Low Incomes, NY, 56-57; spec asst to comnr, Dept Health, New York, 62-68; vis scientist & dir, Hosp Out-Patient Studies Prog, Asn for Aid to Crippled Children NY, 68-71; ASSOC DIR CTR FOR COMMUNITY HEALTH SYSTS, COLUMBIA UNIV, 72- *Concurrent Pos:* Adj prof urban studies, Hunter Col, 62-71; consult, Cunegie Corp, R W Johnson Found, HEW, 65-; vis fel, Ctr for Health Care Studies, United Hosp Found, 78-; prog health admin & econ, Sch Pub Health, Columbia Univ, 72-; app mem, Nat Health Adv Coun, USPHS, HEW, 64-69, NY State Hosp Rev & Planning Coun, 75- & US Nat Comn Vital & Health Statist, 78-; mem, Nat Coun, Alan Guttmacher Inst, 74- & Tech Bd, Milbank Mem Fund, 76-78. *Mem:* Inst Med-Nat Acad Sci; assoc fel NY Acad Med; fel Am Pub Health Asn; Indust Relation Res Asn; Am Econ Asn. *Res:* Data systems and analytic tools for urban health planning, resource allocation and monitoring; health needs and services for urban children; changing role of hospitals in health delivery system. *Mailing Add:* United Hosp Fund 3 E 54th St New York NY 10022

PIOTROWICZ, STEPHEN R, b Cleveland, Ohio, Feb 20, 45; m 69. CHEMICAL OCEANOGRAPHY. *Educ:* Purdue Univ, BS, 67; Univ RI, MS, 72, PhD(oceanog), 77. *Prof Exp:* Res asst chem oceanog, Sch Oceanog, Univ RI, 70-72, teaching asst, 72-73; res assoc, Nat Acad Sci, 73; instr, Univ RI, 74-75 & res asst, Sch Oceanog, 75-76; prin scientist environ res, Energy Resources Co, Inc, Cambridge, 76-79; RES OCEANOGRAPHER CHEM, ATLANTIC OCEANOG & METEROL LABS & NAT OCEANIC & ATMOSPHERIC ADMIN, US DEPT COM, 79- *Concurrent Pos:* Adj asst prof oceanog, Rosenstiel Sch Marine Atmospheric Sci, Univ Miami, 82- *Mem:* Am Chem Soc; Am Geophys Union; Geochem Soc; Am Meteorol Soc; AAAS. *Res:* Marine chemistry, especially the biogeochemistry of trace elements in the marine environment; chemical fractionation at the air-sea interface; atmospheric chemistry primarily the cycles of trace elements and gases between the ocean, land and atmosphere. *Mailing Add:* Nat Oceanic & Atmospheric Admin 4301 Richenbacker Caseway Miami FL 33149

PIOTROWSKI, GEORGE, b Koenigsberg, Ger, Jan 4, 42; m. MECHANICAL ENGINEERING. *Educ:* Mass Inst Technol, BSME, 64, MSME, 65; Case Western Reserve Univ, PhD(biomed eng), 75. *Prof Exp:* Asst prof, 69-76, ASSOC PROF MECH ENG & ORTHOP SURG, UNIV FLA, 76- *Concurrent Pos:* Consult, Am Acad Orthop Surg, 72- & Food & Drug Admin, Dep Health & Human Serv, 76- *Mem:* Am Soc Mech Engrs; Am Soc Eng Educ; Am Soc Testing & Mat; Vet Orthop Soc. *Res:* Biomechanics and machine design. *Mailing Add:* 2011 NW 57th Terr Gainesville FL 32605

PIOTROWSKI, JOSEPH MARTIN, b New Haven, Conn, July 1, 36; m 61; c 2. PETROLOGY, MINERALOGY. *Educ:* Univ Conn, BA, 61; Univ Western Ont, PhD(igneous petrol), 66. *Prof Exp:* From asst prof to assoc prof petrol & mineral, 66-74, PROF BIOL, SOUTHERN CONN STATE COL, 74-, PROF GEOL, 80- *Concurrent Pos:* Res grants, Geol Soc Am & Sigma Xi, 65; Ont grad fel, 65-66. *Mem:* Mineral Soc Am. *Res:* Experimental studies pertinent to genesis of alkaline under saturated rocks and lithium bearing pegmatites; experimental igneous petrology. *Mailing Add:* Highland Dr Prospect CT 06702

PIOUS, DONALD A, b Bridgeport, Conn, Feb 12, 30; m 54; c 2. PEDIATRICS, GENETICS. *Educ:* Univ Pa, AB, 52, MD, 56; Am Bd Pediat, dipl, 61. *Prof Exp:* Intern, Cincinnati Gen Hosp, 56-57; intern pediat, Med Ctr, Yale Univ, 57-58, asst resident, 58-59; from asst prof to assoc prof, 64-76, PROF PEDIAT, SCH MED & ADJ PROF GENETICS, UNIV WASH, 76- *Concurrent Pos:* Fel biol, Univ Calif, San Diego, 61-64; NIH res career develop award, 66 & 71; mem attend staff, Univ Wash Hosp, 64- & Children's Orthopedic Hosp, 71; mem, Mammalian Genetics Study Sect, NIH, 77-81. *Mem:* Am Soc Human Genetics; Am Asn Immunol; Soc Pediat Res; Am Soc Cell Biol. *Res:* Somatic cell genetics; immunogenetics; regulation of gene expression. *Mailing Add:* Dept Pediat RD-20 Sch Med Univ Wash Seattle WA 98195

PIOVOSO, MICHAEL JOSEPH, electrical engineering, see previous edition

PIOWATY, JAMES MASON, b Sacramento, Calif, Apr 30, 37; m 71. NUCLEAR PHYSICS. *Educ:* Univ Notre Dame, BS, 59, PhD(physics), 70; NMex State Univ, MS, 61. *Prof Exp:* Physicist, Lawrence Radiation Lab, Livermore, Calif, 61-64; asst prof physics, DePaul Univ, 69-72; asst prof physics, Ind Univ, South Bend, 72-81; SR MEM TECH STAFFF, BALL AEROSPACE SYST DIV, 81- *Concurrent Pos:* Lectr, US Dept Energy, 78-80; vis asst prof physics, Univ Notre Dame, 79-80, energy consult, 78- *Mem:* Am Phys Soc; Sigma Xi; Am Asn Physics Teachers. *Res:* Aerospace sensor systems design; nuclear reaction physics; gamma ray interactions; reactor physics; accelerator design. *Mailing Add:* Ball Aerospace Syst Div PO Box 1062 Boulder IN 80306

PIPA, RUDOLPH LOUIS, b East Canaan, Conn, July 3, 30; m 53; c 2. ENTOMOLOGY. *Educ:* Cent Conn State Col, BS, 52; Univ Conn, MS, 55; Univ Minn, PhD(entom), 59. *Prof Exp:* NSF fel, Albert Einstein Col Med, 59-60; from asst prof to assoc prof, 60-72, PROF ENTOM, UNIV CALIF, BERKELEY, 72- *Concurrent Pos:* NIH postdoctoral fel, Cambridge Univ, Eng, 72-73. *Mem:* AAAS; Am Soc Zoologists. *Res:* Structure and histochemistry of the insect nervous system; endocrines and insect metamorphosis; hormones and insect neurometamorphosis; insect neurocytology. *Mailing Add:* Div of Entom Univ of Calif Berkeley CA 94720

PIPBERGER, HUBERT V, b Camberg, Ger, May 29, 20; m 55. MEDICINE. *Educ:* Bad Godesberg Col, Ger, BA, 38; Univ Bonn, MD, 51. *Prof Exp:* Chief lab clin electrophysiol, Univ Hosp, Univ Zurich, 53-55; from instr to assoc prof med, Sch Med, Georgetown Univ, 56-71; chief, cardiovasc data processing, Vet Admin Res Ctr, 57-81; PROF MED & CLIN ENG, SCH MED, GEORGE WASHINGTON UNIV, 71- *Concurrent Pos:* Res fel, Los Angeles County Heart Asn, Calif, 55-56; Life Ins Med Res Found res fel, 57-59. *Honors & Awards:* William S Middleton Award, 61; Einthoven Medal, 74. *Mem:* AAAS; Biophys Soc; Am Fedn Clin Res; Am Col Cardiol; Am Heart Asn. *Res:* Electrocardiography; vectorcardiography; electronic data processing. *Mailing Add:* Clin Eng George Washington Univ 901 23rd St Northwest Washington DC 20037

PIPENBERG, KENNETH JAMES, b Racine, Wis, Sept 20, 20; m 64; c 3. ANALYTICAL CHEMISTRY. *Educ:* Wheaton Col, Ill, BS, 43; Univ Ill, PhD(anal chem), 46. *Prof Exp:* Lab asst, Wheaton Col, 41-43; asst chem, Univ Ill, 43-45 & Penicillin Res Proj, Off Sci Res & Develop, 45-46; res assoc biol, Mass Inst Technol, 46-50; res chemist, Jackson Lab, 50-53, Petrol Lab, 53-58 & Eastern Lab, 58-61, sr res chemist, Repauno Develop Lab, 61-70 & Eastern Lab, 70-72, sr res chemist, Polymer Intermediates Dept, 72-77, SR RES CHEMIST, PETROCHEM DEPT, EXP STA, E I DU PONT DE NEMOURS & CO, 78- *Concurrent Pos:* Asst prof, King's Col, Del, 52-54, assoc prof, 54-55. *Mem:* AAAS; Am Chem Soc. *Res:* X-ray diffraction; starch; spectroscopy; combustion; air pollution; x-ray spectroscopy; trace element analysis. *Mailing Add:* 2037 Springhouse Rd Broomall PA 19008

PIPER, DAVID ZINK, b Lexington, Ky, Mar 12, 35; m 58; c 4. OCEANOGRAPHY. *Educ:* Univ Ky, BS, 60; Syracuse Univ, MS, 63; Scripps Inst, Calif, PhD(oceanog), 69. *Prof Exp:* Asst prof oceanog, Univ Wash, 68-75; OCEANOGR, US GEOL SURV, 75- *Mem:* AAAS; Am Geophys Union; Geochem Soc; Geol Soc Am. *Res:* Geochemical relationships between seawater and marine sediments, with particular interest in the transition elements and rare earth elements. *Mailing Add:* 3649 Ramona Circle Palo Alto CA 94306

PIPER, DOUGLAS EDWARD, b Cobourg, Ont, July 6, 23; nat US. ORGANIC CHEMISTRY. *Educ:* Univ Man, BSc, 46; Univ Toronto, PhD(chem), 49. *Prof Exp:* Res chemist, 50-58, asst div head, 58-61, assoc div head, 61-68, DIV HEAD RES LABS, EASTMAN KODAK CO, 68- *Mem:* Am Chem Soc; Soc Photog Sci & Eng. *Res:* Photographic chemistry. *Mailing Add:* 68 Great Wood Circle Fairport NY 14450

PIPER, EDGAR L, b Sacramento, Calif, Apr 23, 37; m 59; c 1. ANIMAL PHYSIOLOGY, REPRODUCTIVE PHYSIOLOGY. *Educ:* Univ Nev, Reno, BS, 60, MS, 61; Utah State Univ, PhD(animal physiol), 67. *Prof Exp:* Res asst animal sci, Utah State Univ, 64-67; asst prof, 67-72, ASSOC PROF ANIMAL SCI, UNIV ARK, FAYETTEVILLE, 72- *Mem:* Am Soc Animal Sci; Soc Study Reproduction. *Res:* Metabolic physiology of the fetus and neonate; endocrinology of lactation. *Mailing Add:* Animal Sci Ctr Univ of Ark Fayetteville AR 72701

PIPER, JAMES ROBERT, b Tallassee, Ala, Jan 14, 33; m 57; c 3. ORGANIC CHEMISTRY. *Educ:* Auburn Univ, BS, 55, PhD(org chem), 60. *Prof Exp:* SR CHEMIST, KETTERING-MEYER LAB, SOUTHERN RES INST, 59- *Mem:* Am Chem Soc. *Res:* Synthesis of organic compounds; indole derivatives; radioprotective agents; antimalarial agents; folate antagonists. *Mailing Add:* Kettering-Meyer Lab 2000 Ninth Ave S Birmingham AL 35205

PIPER, JAMES UNDERHILL, b Flint, Mich, July 30, 37; m 59; c 2. ORGANIC CHEMISTRY. *Educ:* Mass Inst Technol, BS, 59; Emory Univ, MS, 61, PhD(org chem), 63. *Prof Exp:* Asst prof chem, New Haven Col, 63-66; from asst prof to assoc prof, 66-78, chmn dept, 73-79, PROF CHEM, SIMMONS COL, 79- *Concurrent Pos:* Res staff chemist, Yale Univ, 63-66; res assoc, Mass Inst Technol, 66-67 & 72-73; vis fel, Worcester Found Exp Biol, 79-80. *Mem:* Am Chem Soc; AAAS; Royal Soc Chem. *Res:* Cycloaddition reactions; intramolecular interactions in heterocyclic compounds; chemistry of small ring compounds; penicillin chemistry. *Mailing Add:* Dept of Chem Simmons Col The Fenway Boston MA 02115

PIPER, JOHN, b London, Eng, Nov 25, 34; US citizen; m 58; c 3. PHYSICAL CHEMISTRY, METALLURGY. *Educ:* Trinity Col, BS, 56; Mass Inst Technol, PhD(phys chem), 60. *Prof Exp:* Phys chemist, Union Carbide Res Inst, 60-65, proj leader inorg mat, 65-67, MGR TECHNOL, COMPONENTS DEPT, ELECTRONICS DIV, UNION CARBIDE CORP, 67- *Mem:* Electrochem Soc; Inst Elec & Electronics Engrs. *Res:* Electronic components; high performance materials; thin metal films; inorganic fibers; superconductivity; transition metals, alloys and compounds; solid state diffusion; electronic band structure; physical measurements; far infrared spectrometry; ceramics; non-ferrous metallurgy. *Mailing Add:* Components Dept Electronics Div Union Carbide Corp PO Box 5928 Greenville SC 29606

PIPER, RICHARD CARL, b Cleveland, Ohio, Mar 10, 32; m 56; c 2. TOXICOLOGY, VETERINARY PATHOLOGY. *Educ:* Ohio State Univ, DVM, 56, MSc, 57, PhD(vet path), 60; Am Col Vet Path, dipl, 60; Am Bd Toxicol, cert, 80. *Prof Exp:* Instr vet path, Ohio State Univ, 56-57, res asst, 57-58, instr, 58-60; assoc prof, Kans State Univ, 61-64; prof vet path, Wash State Univ, 64-75; RES HEAD PATH & TOXICOL, UPJOHN CO, 75- *Mem:* AAAS; Am Vet Med Asn; Am Col Vet Path; Soc Toxicol; Int Acad Path. *Res:* Toxicology and pathology of drugs and chemicals; general comparative pathology; mercurialism. *Mailing Add:* Path & Toxicol Res Upjohn Co Kalamazoo MI 49001

PIPER, ROGER D, b Oberlin, Ohio, Apr 28, 28; m 56; c 2. PHYSICAL CHEMISTRY. *Educ:* Oberlin Col, BA, 49; Emory Univ, MS, 51. *Prof Exp:* Chemist, 51-62, proj supvr, 62-66, res chemist, 66-69, RES ASSOC, MALLINCKRODT CHEM WORKS, 69- *Mem:* Am Chem Soc. *Res:* Process development in uranium production technology; fused salt electrochemistry; inorganic precipitation processes. *Mailing Add:* Mallinckrodt Chem Works PO Box 5439 St Louis MO 63160

PIPER, WALTER NELSON, b Ravenna, Ohio, Dec 28, 40; m 65; c 3. BIOCHEMISTRY, PHARMACOLOGY. *Educ:* Kent State Univ, BS, 62; Ohio State Univ, MS, 64; Purdue Univ, PhD(pharmacol), 68. *Prof Exp:* Biochemist, Warren-Teed Pharmaceut, Ohio, 64-65; res biochemist, Dow Chem Co, Mich, 69-72; res assoc pharmacol, Col Med, Univ Iowa, 72-74; asst prof, Col Med, Univ Okla, 74-75; asst prof, 75-80, ASSOC PROF DEPT PHARMACOL, COL MED, UNIV CALIF, SAN FRANCISCO, 80- *Mem:* AAAS; Am Chem Soc; Sigma Xi; Soc Toxicol; Am Soc Pharmacol & Exp Therapeut. *Res:* Biochemical pharmacology; toxicology. *Mailing Add:* Dept of Pharmacol Univ of Calif Col of Med San Francisco CA 94143

PIPER, WILLIAM STEPHEN, mathematics, see previous edition

PIPER, WILLIAM WEIDMAN, b Columbus, Ohio, July 1, 25; m 50; c 2. SOLID STATE PHYSICS. *Educ:* Columbia Univ, BS, 46; Ohio State Univ, PhD(physics), 50. PHYSICIST, GEN ELEC RES & DEVELOP CTR, 50- *Mem:* Am Phys Soc; Inst Elec & Electronics Engrs; Electrochem Soc. *Res:* Luminescence; electrical and optical properties of semiconductors. *Mailing Add:* Gen Elec Res & Develop Ctr K-1 5C28 PO Box 8 Schenectady NY 12301

PIPERNO, ELLIOT, b New York, NY, Dec 30, 38; wid; c 2. VETERINARY MEDICINE, PHARMACOLOGY. *Educ:* Long Island Univ, BS, 61; Univ Mich, MS, 65; Mich State Univ, DVM, 68. *Prof Exp:* Instr pharmacol, Mich State Univ, 65-68; sr res toxicologist, Merck Inst Therapeut Res, 68-72; group leader, McNeil Labs, 72-78, prin scientist toxicol, 78-79, RES FEL, TOXICOL RES UNIT, MCNEIL PHARMACEUT INC, 79- *Concurrent Pos:* Wild game biologist, Mich Dept Conserv, 65-68; adj asst prof pharmacol & toxicol, Sch Vet Med, Univ Pa, 79- *Honors & Awards:* Philip B Hofman Award, 80. *Mem:* Am Vet Med Asn; Am Acad Clin Toxicol; Am Acad Vet Pharmacol & Therapeut; Europ Soc Toxicol; NY Acad Sci. *Res:* Comparative pharmacology; toxicology; mechanisms of drug-induced toxicity. *Mailing Add:* McNeil Pharmaceut Inc Spring House PA 19477

PIPES, CHARLES JEFFERSON, JR, b Terrell, Tex, Dec 24, 17; m 39; c 2. MATHEMATICAL ANALYSIS. *Educ:* Univ Okla, MA, 48, PhD(math), 50. *Prof Exp:* Instr math, Univ Okla, 46-50; from asst prof to assoc prof, 50-59, PROF MATH, SOUTHERN METHODIST UNIV, 59- *Mem:* Fel AAAS; Am Math Soc; Math Asn Am. *Res:* Point set topology; real function theory; functional analysis. *Mailing Add:* Dept of Math Southern Methodist Univ Dallas TX 75275

PIPES, GAYLE WOODY, b Butler, Mo, Feb 15, 21; m 52; c 2. BIONUCLEONICS, CHEMISTRY. *Educ:* Univ Mo, BS, 43, MS, 46, PhD, 55. *Prof Exp:* Chemist, Remington Arms Co, E I du Pont de Nemours & Co, 43-44; sr chemist, Coop Ref Asn, 44-45; dir res, Mo Farmers Asn, 47-55; asst prof dairy husb, Univ Mo, 56-64; sr scientist, Med Div, Lawrence Radiation Lab, Univ Calif, 64-69; consult, 69-73; nuclear med consult, 72-73, SR RES SCIENTIST BIOCHEM & HISTOCHEM, VA HOSP, LIVERMORE, 73- *Concurrent Pos:* Pres, Janewoody Enterprises. *Mem:* Sigma XI; Am Chem Soc; Soc Automotive Engrs; Soc Nuclear Med. *Res:* Biological application of radioisotopes; the use of radionuclides in biology, medicine, chemistry, histochemistry and environment studies; goitrogens, steroid and protein hormones, economic poisons and petroleum products. *Mailing Add:* 764 Jensen Livermore CA 94550

PIPES, PAUL BRUCE, b Ft Worth, Tex, July 22, 41; m 66; c 2. LOW TEMPERATURE PHYSICS. *Educ:* Rice Univ, BA, 63; Stanford Univ, MS, 64, PhD(physics), 70. *Prof Exp:* NATO fel, Kamerlingh Onnes Lab, Leiden, Holland, 69-70; res instr physics, La State Univ, 70-72; asst prof, 72-78, ASSOC PROF PHYSICS, DARTMOUTH COL, 78- *Concurrent Pos:* Alfred P Sloan res fel, 76-80. *Mem:* Am Phys Soc; AAAS: Sigma XI. *Res:* Low temperature physics; infrared technology. *Mailing Add:* Dept Physics Dartmouth Col Hanover NH 03755

PIPES, ROBERT BYRON, b Shreveport, La, Aug 14, 41; m 64; c 2. MECHANICAL ENGINEERING. *Educ:* La Tech Univ, BS, 64; Princeton Univ, MA & MSE, 69; Univ Tex, PhD(eng), 72. *Prof Exp:* Res engr composites, Gen Dynamics, 69-72; asst prof eng, Drexel Univ, 72-74; assoc prof, 74-78, PROF, UNIV DEL, 80-, DIR CTR COMPOSITE MAT, 78- *Concurrent Pos:* Auth; prin investr, 15 Grants from Nat Aeronaut & Space Admin, Air Force Mat Lab, Naval Air Systs, Air Force Off Sci Res, 74-; auth/consult, NASA/Dept Defense Composites Design Guide, 77-; mem Nat Mat Adv Bd, 78- *Mem:* Am Soc Testing Mat; Soc Exp Stress Anal; Am Soc Mech Engrs; Nat Res Coun. *Res:* Composite materials. *Mailing Add:* Mech Eng Dept Univ of Del Newark DE 19711

PIPES, WESLEY O, b Dallas, Tex, Jan 28, 32; m 70; c 4. ENVIRONMENTAL ENGINEERING, AQUATIC ECOLOGY. *Educ:* NTex State Univ, BS, 53, MS, 55; Northwestern Univ, Ill, PhD, 59. *Prof Exp:* Res engr, Univ Calif, 55-57; lectr civil eng, Northwestern Univ, Ill, 58-59, from asst prof to prof, 59-74, prof biol sci, 69-74; BETZ PROF ECOL, PROF BIOL SCI & PROF ENVIRON ENG & SCI, DREXEL UNIV, 75- *Mem:* Am Soc Microbiologists; Am Water Works Asn; Am Soc Civil Engrs; Ecol Soc Am. *Res:* Chemistry and biology of water and waste treatment; biology of polluted waters; aquatic and microbial ecology. *Mailing Add:* Dept of Biol Sci Drexel Univ Philadelphia PA 19104

PIPIRINGOS, GEORGE NICHOLAS, b Nashua, NH, Jan 21, 18; m 47; c 3. STRATIGRAPHY. *Educ:* Univ Wyo, AB, 47, MA, 48; Johns Hopkins Univ, PhD(geol), 56. *Prof Exp:* geologist, US Geol Surv, 51-79; CONSULT FUELS, 79- *Mem:* Am Asn Petrol Geol; Geol Soc Am; Soc Econ Paleontologists & Mineralogists; Am Inst Prof Geol. *Res:* Determination of the correlation, nomenclature, environment of deposition and geologic history of rocks of Triassic, Jurassic, Paleocene and Eocene ages in western interior of the United States; geologic mapping. *Mailing Add:* 1821 S Java Way Denver CO 80219

PIPKIN, ALLEN COMPERE, b Mena, Ark, May 21, 31; m 56; c 3. APPLIED MATHEMATICS. *Educ:* Mass Inst Technol, ScB, 52; Brown Univ, PhD(appl math), 59. *Prof Exp:* Res assoc fluid dynamics, Inst Fluid Dynamics & Appl Math, Univ Md, 58-60; from asst prof to assoc prof, 60-66, PROF APPL MATH, BROWN UNIV, 66- *Concurrent Pos:* Guggenheim fel, Univ Nottingham, 68; Sci Res Coun sr vis fel, Nottingham, 78. *Mem:* Soc Rheol; Soc Nat Philos. *Res:* Constitutive equations; viscoelastic fluids; fiber-reinforced composites. *Mailing Add:* Div of Appl Math Brown Univ Providence RI 02912

PIPKIN, BERNARD WALLACE, b Los Angeles, Calif, Dec 5, 27; m 57; c 3. ENVIRONMENTAL GEOLOGY. *Educ:* Univ Southern Calif, BA, 53, MA, 56; Univ Ariz, PhD(geol), 65. *Prof Exp:* Consult, Thomas Clements Assoc, 60-69; ADJ ASSOC PROF GEOL & ASST DEAN, COL LETT, ARTS & SCI, UNIV SOUTHERN CALIF, 69- *Concurrent Pos:* Consult, Los Angeles Sch Sci Adv Bd, 72- & Planning Comn, City Palos Verdes Estates, 75; panelist, Nat Res Coun Postdoctoral Assoc Prog, 74- *Mem:* Geol Soc Am; Am Asn Petrol Geologists; Asn Eng Geologists; Nat Asn Geol Teachers; Sigma Xi. *Res:* Geologic hazards in the urban environment, particularly landslides, seismic hazards and coastal erosion. *Mailing Add:* Dept of Geol Sci Univ of Southern Calif Los Angeles CA 90007

PIPKIN, FRANCIS MARION, b Marianna, Ark, Nov 27, 25; m 58; c 2. EXPERIMENTAL ATOMIC PHYSICS, EXPERIMENTAL HIGH ENERGY PHYSICS. *Educ:* Univ Iowa, BA, 50; Princeton Univ, MA, 53, PhD, 54. *Prof Exp:* Soc Fellows jr fel, 54-57, from asst prof to prof physics, 57-74, assoc dean, Fac Arts & Sci, 74-77, BAIRD PROF SCI, HARVARD UNIV, 76- *Concurrent Pos:* Sloan Found fel, 59-61. *Mem:* Fel Am Phys Soc; AAAS. Res Atomic beams; elementary particle physics. *Mailing Add:* 10 Kilburn Rd Belmont MA 02178

PIPPEN, RICHARD WAYNE, b Villa Grove, Ill, Sept 8, 35; m 61; c 1. SYSTEMATIC BOTANY, PLANT ECOLOGY. *Educ:* Eastern Ill Univ, BS, 57; Univ Mich, MA, 59, PhD(bot), 63. *Prof Exp:* From asst prof to assoc prof, 63-78, PROF BIOL, WESTERN MICH UNIV, 78- *Concurrent Pos:* Dir trop studies prog, Assoc Univs Int Educ, 74-76; actg chairperson biol dept, Western Mich Univ, 75-76, chairperson, 77- *Mem:* AAAS; Am Soc Plant Taxon; Int Asn Plant Taxon; Ecol Soc Am; Asn Tropical Biol. *Res:* Reproductive biology of flowering plants; ecology of rare and endangered plants; systematics and ecology of cacaliod complex of composites; ecology of wetlands in southern Michigan. *Mailing Add:* Dept of Biol Western Mich Univ Kalamazoo MI 49008

PIPPERT, GLEN FRANCIS, b Sheboygan, Wis, Mar 7, 20; m 41. OPTICS, MANAGEMENT. *Educ:* Boston Univ, AB & AM, 49, PhD(physics), 54. *Prof Exp:* Asst sci, Boston Univ, 49-51; asst prof physics, Wabash Col, 51-54; mem staff physics res, 54-63, assoc group leader reentry signature studies, 63-68, group leader radar signature studies, 68-74, mgr, Kiernan Reentry Measurement Site, 74-76, assoc head optics div, 76-80, HEAD OPTICS DIV, LINCOLN LAB, MASS INST TECHNOL, 80- *Mem:* AAAS; Am Inst Aeronaut & Astronaut. *Res:* Molecular vibrations and structures; high energy laser systems, laser radars, infrared search and track systems and adaptive optics. *Mailing Add:* Lincoln Lab PO Box 73 Lexington MA 02173

PIPPERT, RAYMOND ELMER, b Lawrence, Kans, May 18, 38; m 58; c 2. GRAPH THEORY. *Educ:* Univ Kans, BA, 59, PhD(math), 65. *Prof Exp:* From asst prof to assoc prof, 65-73, PROF MATH, PURDUE UNIV, FT WAYNE, 73- *Concurrent Pos:* Sabbatical, Western Mich Univ, 71-72. *Mem:* Am Math Soc; Math Asn Am; Sigma XI. *Res:* Graph theory and combinatorics, especially characterization and enumeration problems. *Mailing Add:* Dept of Math Purdue Univ 2101 Coliseum Blvd E Ft Wayne IN 46805

PIRANI, CONRAD LEVI, b Pisa, Italy, July 29, 14; nat US; m 48, 55; c 3. PATHOLOGY. *Educ:* Univ Milan, MD, 38. *Prof Exp:* Asst, Inst Path Anat, Univ Milan, 38-39; intern, Mother Cabrini Mem Hosp, Chicago, 40-41 & Columbus Mem Hosp, 41-42; resident, Michael Reese Hosp, 42-45; from instr to prof path, Univ Ill Col Med, 45-71; prof, Pritzker Sch Med, Univ Chicago, 71-72; PROF PATH, COL PHYSICIANS & SURGEONS, COLUMBIA UNIV, 72- *Concurrent Pos:* Chmn dept path, Michael Reese Hosp & Med Ctr, 65-72; consult, WSide & Hines Vet Hosps, 65-72; attend pathologist, Presby Hosp, 72- *Mem:* AAAS; Am Soc Clin Path; Am Soc Exp Path; Am Soc Nephrology; Int Soc Nephrology. *Res:* Pathology of renal diseases; rheumatic diseases. *Mailing Add:* Col of Physicians & Surgeons Columbia Univ New York NY 10032

PIRANIAN, GEORGE, b Thalwil, Switz, May 2, 14; nat US; m 41; c 5. MATHEMATICS, COMPLEX ANALYSIS. *Educ:* Utah State Univ, BS, 36, MS, 38; Rice Inst, MA, 41, PhD(math), 43. *Prof Exp:* Instr math, Rice Inst, 43; from instr to assoc prof, 45-58, PROF MATH, UNIV MICH, ANN ARBOR, 58- *Concurrent Pos:* Ed, Mich Math J, 54-75. *Mem:* Am Math Soc; Math Asn Am. *Res:* Functions of a complex variable; prime ends; power series; boundary behavior; conformal maps. *Mailing Add:* Dept Math Univ Mich Ann Arbor MI 48109

PIRCH, JAMES HERMAN, b Henrietta, Mo, July 10, 37; m 59; c 2. PHARMACOLOGY. *Educ:* William Jewell Col, AB, 59; Univ Kans, PhD(pharmacol), 66. *Prof Exp:* Asst prof pharmacol, Bowman Gray Sch Med, 67-69; asst prof, 69-72, assoc prof, Univ Tex Med Br Galveston, 72-76; assoc prof, 76-79, PROF PHARMACOL, SCH MED, TEX TECH UNIV, 79- *Concurrent Pos:* Fel pharmacol, Dartmouth Med Sch, 65-67; USPHS fel, 66-67. *Mem:* AAAS; Am Soc Pharmacol & Exp Therapeut; Soc Neurosci; Soc Exp Biol & Med. *Res:* Central mechanisms of drug induced behavioral changes; electrophysiological and biochemical correlates; pharmacology of marijuana; drug tolerance. *Mailing Add:* Dept of Pharmacol & Therapeut Tex Tech Univ Sch Med Lubbock TX 79430

PIRET, EDGAR L(AMBERT), b Winnipeg, Man, July 1, 10; nat US; m 45; c 6. CHEMICAL ENGINEERING, BIOCHEMICAL ENGINEERING. *Educ:* Univ Minn, BChE, 32, PhD(chem eng), 37, Univ Lyon, PhD(biochem, bact), 36. *Prof Exp:* Instr chem eng, Univ Minn, 37-41, asst prof, 41-43; chief chem engr, Minn Mining & Mfg Co, 43-45; prof chem eng, Univ Minn, Minneapolis, 45-65; sci attache, Am Embassy, Paris, 59-67, counr embassy for sci affairs, 67-75; asst exec dir, Am Chem Soc, 75-77; DIR EUROPEAN OPERS, ENERGY RESOURCES CORP, INC, 78- *Concurrent Pos:* Consult engr, Minn Mining & Mfg Co, 37-43 & 46-59; Fulbright res prof, Univs Nancy & Paris, 50-51; consult, Naval Res Lab, 51-57, dir chem peat proj, 54-59; mem int rels comt, Engrs Joint Coun, 53-; vis prof, Univs Gothenburg & Delft, 54 & Mass Inst Technol & Harvard Univ, 65-66; US State Dept tech mission, USSR, 57, 63; Hormel Co fel; pres, Edgar L Piret Assocs, 75-; consult energy & environ eng. *Honors & Awards:* Swed Asn Engrs Medal, 51; Off, Palmes d'Acad, France; Friedel-Craft Medal, Paris, 51; Medal Chem, Liege, 51; Walker Award, Am Inst Chem Engrs, 55; Croix de Chevalier, Legion d'honneur, 57. *Mem:* Fel AAAS; fel Am Inst Chem Engrs; Am Chem Soc; Am Geophys Union; fel NY Acad Sci. *Res:* Continuous reactor design; leaching; biochemical engineering; crushing; science and technology in international political, economic, and public affairs; industrial fluidized bed combustion and pyrolysis of biomass; enhanced oil recovery. *Mailing Add:* Energy Resources Co Inc 185 Alewife Brook Pkwy Cambridge MA 02138

PIRIE, ROBERT GORDON, b Dundas, Ont, June 19, 36. SEDIMENTOLOGY, PETROLEUM GEOLOGY. *Educ:* Indiana Univ, BS, 58, MS, 61, PhD(geol, sedimentology), 63. *Prof Exp:* From asst prof to assoc prof, 63-75, prof sedimentology, geol oceanog, Univ Wis, 75-78; RES GEOLOGIST, SCHLUMBERGER-DOLL RES, 78- *Concurrent Pos:* Grants, NSF, 64-66, Water Resources Ctr, 65-66, AEC, PR Nuclear Ctr, 66-70, Coastal Eng Res Ctr, 68-69, NDEA, 68, sea grant, 75 & US Corps Engrs, Dept Natural Resources Wis, 75. *Mem:* AAAS; Geol Soc Am; Am Soc Limnol & Oceanog; Soc Econ Paleont & Mineral; Int Asn Sedimentologists. *Res:* Marine and freshwater sedimentology; oceanography; analogs of modern and ancient depositional systems; dynamics of sediment-water interface phenomena, especially fine sediment-trace element chemistry and their variations in nearshore environments. *Mailing Add:* Schlumberger-Doll Res PO Box 307 Ridgefield CT 06877

PIRIE, WALTER RONALD, b Toronto, Ont, Dec 31, 34; US citizen; m 62; c 2. MATHEMATICAL STATISTICS, APPLIED STATISTICS. *Educ:* Temple Univ, BA, 61; Univ Toronto, MA, 64; Fla State Univ, NIH fel & PhD(math statist), 70. *Prof Exp:* Electronics engr, RCA Corp, 58-61, res scientist physics, 61; res assoc, Am Can Co, 64-65; res assoc physics & math, Univ Pa, 65-66; comput consult, Fla State Univ, 66-67; asst prof, 70-80, ASSOC PROF STATIST, VA POLYTECH INST & STATE UNIV, 80- *Concurrent Pos:* Instr electronics, Tech Inst, Temple Univ, 58-61. *Mem:* Am Statist Asn; Inst Math Statist; Statist Sci Asn Can; Nat Speleol Soc. *Res:* Nonparametric statistics, theory and applications; theory of statistical inference; limit theory of statistics. *Mailing Add:* Dept of Statist Va Polytech Inst & State Univ Blacksburg VA 24061

PIRIGYI, FRANCIS ELLSWORTH, b Elizabeth, NJ, Oct 6, 36. CERAMICS ENGINEERING. *Educ:* Rutgers Univ, BS, 58, MS, 61, PhD(ceramics), 66. *Prof Exp:* Res asst ceramics, Rutgers Univ, 58-61, res assoc, 63-66; ceramic engr, ITT Fed Labs, 61-63; res ceramist, Electrochem Dept, E I du Pont de Nemours & Co, Inc, 66-69; res ceramist, Alpha Metals, Inc, 69-71; res chemist, Ceramic Magnetics Inc, 71-80; MEM STAFF, ENGELHARD MINERALS & CHEM, 80- *Mem:* Am Ceramic Soc. *Res:* Ferroelectric ceramics; alumina ceramics; reactive sputtering; thick film techniques. *Mailing Add:* Engelhard Minerals & Chem Menlo Park Edison NJ 08818

PIRINGER, ALBERT ALOYSIUS, JR, b St Paul, Minn, Apr 24, 21; m 44; c 4. HORTICULTURE. *Educ:* Univ Minn, BS, 47, 48; Univ Md, PhD(hort), 53. *Prof Exp:* Asst hort, Univ Minn, 47-48, Univ Md, 48-52; asst horticulturist, Hort Crops Res Br, Plant Indust Sta, USDA, 52-53, assoc plant physiologist, 53-54; asst prof hort, Univ Minn, 54-56; plant physiologist, Crops Res Div, 56-62, asst chief, Fruit & Nut Crops Br, 62-68, asst dir, US Nat Arboretum, 68-72, asst area dir, Chesapeake-Potomac Area, Northeast Region, 72-79, SUPVRY HORTICULTURIST & CHMN, HORT SCI INST, AGR RES SERV, USDA, 79- *Honors & Awards:* Vaughn Award, Am Soc Hort Sci, 56. *Mem:* Am Soc Plant Physiol; Am Soc Hort Sci. *Res:* Photoperiodism and light effects on plant growth and development; physiology of horticultural plants; photoperiodism in tropical plants; fruit and nut crop culture; administration of varied agricultural research. *Mailing Add:* Hort Sci Inst Beltsville Agr Res Ctr Agr Res Serv USDA Beltsville MD 20705

PIRKLE, EARL C, b Morgan Co, Ga, Jan 8, 22; m 42; c 3. ECONOMIC GEOLOGY. *Educ:* Emory Univ, AB, 43, MS, 47; Univ Cincinnati, PhD(geol), 56. *Prof Exp:* Prod coordr & res crystallogr, Pan Electronics Labs, Inc, 42-45; instr geol, Univ Tenn, 47-50; asst prof phys sci & geol, 50-57, assoc prof, 57-63, chmn dept, 72-79, PROF PHYS SCI, UNIV FLA, 63-, DIR PHYS SCI, 79- *Concurrent Pos:* Vis instr, Univ Cincinnati, 55-56; consult geologist, 55- *Mem:* Geol Soc Am; Am Asn Petrol Geol; Soc Econ Geol; Am Inst Mining, Metall & Petrol Engrs, Inc. *Res:* Economic mineral deposits; physiography and sedimentation; origin of heavy mineral deposits and phosphate deposits. *Mailing Add:* Dept Geography & Phys Sci Univ of Fla Gainesville FL 32611

PIRKLE, HUBERT CHAILLE, b Indianapolis, Ind, Feb 18, 24; m 78; c 2. PATHOLOGY. *Educ:* Ind Univ, MD, 49. *Prof Exp:* Intern, Univ Chicago, 49-50, resident path, 52-54, asst, 54-55; asst prof, Sch Med, Univ Louisville, 55-61, assoc prof, 61-70; ASSOC PROF PATH, COL MED, UNIV CALIF, IRVINE, 70-, VCHMN, 78-, CHIEF, DIV CHEM PATH, 81- *Concurrent Pos:* Markle scholar, 60-65; NIH spec res fel, Karolinska Inst, Sweden, 64-65; vis investr, Karolinska Inst, Sweden, 64-65; mem path & anat fel rev comt, NIH; mem coun thrombosis, Am Heart Asn. *Mem:* Am Asn Path; Am Chem Soc; Am Soc Exp Path; Int Soc Thrombosis & Haemostasis. *Res:* Biochemistry of blood coagulation; cardiovascular disease. *Mailing Add:* Dept Path Univ Calif Col Med Irvine CA 92664

PIRKLE, JAMES CARL, JR, chemical engineering, see previous edition

PIRKLE, WILLIAM ARTHUR, b Atlanta, Ga, May 11, 45; m 68; c 2. GEOMORPHOLOGY. *Educ:* Emory Univ, BS, 67; Univ NC, Chapel Hill, MS, 70, PhD(geol), 72. *Prof Exp:* Asst prof, 72-75, ASSOC PROF GEOL, UNIV SC, AIKEN, 75- *Concurrent Pos:* Proj geologist, SC Geol Surv, 73- *Mem:* Geol Soc Am; Am Inst Mining Metall & Petrol Engrs; Sigma Xi. *Res:* Physiography and mineral resources, especially heavy mineral occurrences, of the Atlantic-Gulf Coastal Plain; physiography, sedimentation and structure of slate belt rocks of the Appalachian Piedmont. *Mailing Add:* 1767 Partridge Dr Aiken SC 29801

PIRKLE, WILLIAM H, b Shreveport, La, May 2, 34; m 56; c 4. ORGANIC CHEMISTRY. *Educ:* Univ Calif, Berkeley, BS, 59; Univ Rochester, PhD(chem), 63. *Prof Exp:* NSF fel, Harvard Univ, 63-64; asst prof, 64-69, ASSOC PROF CHEM, UNIV ILL, URBANA, 69- *Concurrent Pos:* Alfred P Sloan fel, 71-72. *Mem:* Am Chem Soc. *Mailing Add:* Dept of Chem Univ of Ill Urbana IL 61822

PIRLOT, PAUL, b Mettet, Belg, Mar 17, 20; m 47; c 3. ZOOLOGY. *Educ:* Cath Univ Louvain, dipl, 46; Univ London, PhD(zool), 49, DSc, 59. *Prof Exp:* Res assoc zool, Inst Sci Res Cent Africa, Belg Congo, 49-57; assoc prof, 58-63, PROF BIOL UNIV MONTREAL, 63- *Concurrent Pos:* Prof, Carroll Col, 55; Belg-Am Educ Found fel, 55-56; Nat Res Coun Can fel, 58. *Mem:* Can Soc Zoologists; Soc Study Evolution; NY Acad Sci; Can Soc Hist & Philos Sci; Am Soc Naturalists. *Res:* Comparative anatomy of vertebrates; neuroanatomy of sensory structures and adaptation of sense organs to environment and behavior. *Mailing Add:* Dept of Biol Univ of Montreal Montreal PQ H3C 3J7 Can

PIRNOT, THOMAS LEONARD, b Scranton, Pa, Sept 3, 43; m 68; c 3. ALGEBRA. *Educ:* Wilkes Col, BA, 65; Pa State Univ, Univ Park, PhD(math), 70. PROF MATH, KUTZTOWN STATE COL, 70- *Mem:* Math Asn Am; Am Math Soc; Asn Comp Mach. *Res:* Algebraic theory of semigroups, particularly congruences on semigroups. *Mailing Add:* Dept of Math Kutztown State Col Kutztown PA 19530

PIROFSKY, BERNARD, b New York, NY, Mar 27, 26; m 53; c 3. IMMUNOHEMATOLOGY, CLINICAL IMMUNOLOGY. *Educ:* NY Univ, AB, 46, MD, 50. *Prof Exp:* Intern med, Bellevue Hosp, New York, 50-51, resident, 51-52 & 54-55; dir, Pac Red Cross Blood Ctr, 56-58; from instr to assoc prof, 58-66, PROF MED & HEAD DIV IMMUNOL, ALLERGY & RHEUMATOLOGY, MED SCH, UNIV ORE, 66-, PROF MICROBIOL & IMMUNOL, 73-; CHIEF IMMUNOL, ALLERGY, RHEUMATOLOGY, PORTLAND VET ADMIN HOSP, 80- *Concurrent Pos:* Am Cancer Soc res fel hemat, Med Sch, Univ Ore, 55-56; Commonwealth fel, 66-67; consult immunohemat, Pac Red Cross Blood Ctr, 58-; mem med adv bd, Leukemia Soc, 65-70; vis prof immunol, Nat Inst Nutrit, Mexico City, 66-67; vis res prof, Nat Acad Sci, Hiroshima, Japan, 78-79. *Honors & Awards:* Emily Cooley Mem Award, Am Asn Blood Banks, 72. *Mem:* Fel Am Col Physicians; Am Soc Hemat; Int Soc Hemat; Int Soc Blood Transfusion; NY Acad Sci. *Res:* Influence of immunologic events in development of human disease; autoimmunity; homotransplantation; malignancies. *Mailing Add:* Div Immunol & Allergy Med Sch Univ Ore Portland OR 97201

PIRONE, THOMAS PASCAL, b Ithaca, NY, Jan 3, 36; m 61; c 2. PLANT PATHOLOGY. *Educ:* Cornell Univ, BS, 57; Univ Wis, PhD(plant path), 60. *Prof Exp:* Asst plant path, Univ Wis, 57-60; from asst prof to assoc prof, La State Univ, 60-67; assoc prof, 67-71, PROF PLANT PATH, UNIV KY, 71-, CHMN, 78- *Concurrent Pos:* Fulbright sr res fel, 74-75. *Mem:* AAAS; fel Am Phytopath Soc; Am Soc Virol. *Res:* Virology; insect transmission of plant viruses. *Mailing Add:* Dept of Plant Path Univ of Ky Lexington KY 40506

PIROOZ, PERRY PARVIZ, b Ahwaz, Iran, June 2, 28; US citizen; m 54; c 6. GLASS SCIENCE & TECHNOLOGY, INORGANIC CHEMISTRY. *Educ:* Univ Toledo, BS, 54, MS, 62. *Prof Exp:* Anal chemist, 55-59, glass res & develop engr, 59-69, PROJ MGR RES & DEVELOP, OWENS ILL, INC, 69- *Mem:* Am Chem Soc; Am Ceramic Soc; Brit Soc Glass Technol; Sigma Xi. *Res:* Compositions, physical and chemical properties, structure and manufacture of glass. *Mailing Add:* Owens Ill Inc PO Box 1035 1700 N Westwood Toledo OH 43607

PIROUE, PIERRE ADRIEN, b Switz, Sept 18, 31. PHYSICS. *Educ:* Univ Geneva, Lic es sc, 53, PhD(physics), 58. *Prof Exp:* Asst exp physics, Univ Geneva, 53-55, asst theoret physics, 55-56; asst physics physics, Princeton Univ, 57-60; res fel, European Orgn Nuclear Res, Geneva, Switz, 60-61; from instr to assoc prof, 61-70, PROF PHYSICS, PRINCETON UNIV, 70- *Mem:* Am Phys Soc. *Res:* High energy physics; electronics. *Mailing Add:* Dept of Physics Princeton Univ Princeton NJ 08540

PIRRAGLIA, JOSEPH A, b Providence, RI, July 15, 28; m 65; c 3. ATMOSPHERIC DYNAMICS. *Educ:* Univ RI, BS, 59; NY Univ, MS, 61; Polytech Inst Brooklyn, PhD(electrophysics), 71. *Prof Exp:* Mem tech staff, Bell Telephone Labs, Inc, 59-65; ASTROPHYSICIST, GODDARD SPACE FLIGHT CTR, NASA, 71- *Mem:* Am Meteorol Soc; Am Phys Soc; NY Acad Sci. *Res:* Theoretical studies of the dynamics and energy balance of planetary atmospheres. *Mailing Add:* Goddard Space Flight Ctr Code 6932 Greenbelt MD 20771

PIRRI, ANTHONY NICHOLAS, b Providence, RI, Apr 13, 43; m 68; c 2. APPLIED PHYSICS, ENGINEERING SCIENCE. *Educ:* Boston Univ, BS, 64; Mass Inst Technol, MS, 66; Brown Univ, PhD(eng), 70. *Prof Exp:* Res asst aeronaut & astronaut, Mass Inst Technol, 64-66; prin res scientist aerophysics, Avco Everett Res Lab, 69-73; mgr laser appln, 73-80, VPRES DEFENSE PROGS, PHYS SCI, INC, 80- *Mem:* Am Inst Aeronaut & Astronaut; Am Inst Physics. *Res:* High temperature gas dynamics and fluid mechanics; radiation gas dynamics and high power laser effects upon materials; laser produced plasmas; turbulent flows and classical fluid mechanics. *Mailing Add:* Phys Sci Inc 30 Commerce Way Woburn MA 01801

PIRSON, SYLVAIN J G, b Vogenee, Belg, June 28, 05; nat US; m 33; c 2. PETROLEUM ENGINEERING. *Educ:* Univ Louvain, MCE, 29; Univ Pittsburgh, MSc, 30; Colo Sch Mines, DSc(geophys), 31. *Prof Exp:* Instr geophys, Colo Sch Mines, 33-34; geophysicist, Seismog Serv Corp, Okla, 34-36 & Gulf Res & Develop Corp, Pa, 36; prof petrol eng & head petrol & natural gas eng, Pa State Univ, 36-46, prof geophys & geochem, 46-49; spec res assoc, Res Ctr, Amoco Prod Co, 49-56; prof petrol eng, 56-75, EMER PROF PETROL ENG, UNIV TEX, AUSTIN, 75- *Honors & Awards:* George Brown Gold Medal, Colo Sch Mines, 81. *Mem:* Soc Explor Geophysicists; Am Asn Petrol Geologists. *Res:* Oil reservoir engineering; electric logging of wells; geochemical and electrical prospecting; prospecting for hydrocarbon deposit by mangeto-electrotelluric techniques. *Mailing Add:* PEB 318 Univ of Tex Austin TX 78712

PIRTLE, EUGENE CLAUDE, b Wichita Falls, Tex, Nov 17, 21; m 44; c 5. VETERINARY MICROBIOLOGY. *Educ:* Univ Colo, BA, 47; Univ Iowa, MS, 50, PhD(bact), 52. *Prof Exp:* From asst prof to assoc prof microbiol, Med Sch, Univ SDak, 52-60; dir virus lab, Hawaii State Dept Health, 60-61; RES MICROBIOLOGIST, VIROL INVESTS NAT ANIMAL DIS CTR, 61- *Concurrent Pos:* Grants, USPHS, 54-56, AMA, 58 & SDak Game Dept, 58-60. *Mem:* Tissue Cult Asn; Am Soc Microbiol. *Res:* Virus replication; growth of cells in culture; metabolic alterations of virus infected cells, immune responses to viral diseases of animals; electron microscopy. *Mailing Add:* Nat Animal Dis Ctr PO Box 70 Ames IA 50010

PIRTLE, FRANCIS WILLIAM, III, mechanical engineering, see previous edition

PISACANE, VINCENT L, b Philadelphia, Pa, Apr 6, 33. ENGINEERING PHYSICS. *Educ:* Drexel Univ, BS, 55; Mich State Univ, MS, 57, PhD(appl mech), 62. *Prof Exp:* ASSOC HEAD, SPACE DEPT, APPL PHYS LAB, JOHNS HOPKINS UNIV, 62- *Concurrent Pos:* Instr, Johns Hopkins Univ, 68- *Mem:* Am Geophys Union; Am Inst Aeronaut & Astronaut; Am Astronaut Soc; Nat Space Coun. *Res:* Classical and celestral mechanics and geophysics; technical management of satellite borne instrumentation systems. *Mailing Add:* Appl Physics Lab Johns Hopkins Univ Johns Hopkins Rd Laurel MD 20707

PISANO, DANIEL JOSEPH, JR, b Mt Vernon, NY, Oct 30, 46; m 69; c 1. NUCLEAR PHYSICS. *Educ:* Columbia Univ, BA, 68; Yale Univ, MPhil, 73, PhD(physics), 73. *Prof Exp:* Res staff physicist, Wright Nuclear Struct Lab, Yale Univ, 73-74; res assoc nuclear physics, Brookhaven Nat Lab, 74-77, mem staff, FMI Med Inc, 77-80; MEM STAFF, AAKBROOK DIV, PERKIN ELMER CORP, 80- *Mem:* Am Phys Soc; Am Asn Physics Teachers. *Res:* A Study of heavy-ion induced nuclear reactions and the atomic physics of highly-stripped heavy ions. *Mailing Add:* Aakbrook Div 2000 York Rd Perkin Elmer Corp Aakbrook IL 60559

PISANO, FRANK D, physical pharmacy, see previous edition

PISANO, JOHN JOSEPH, b Norristown, Pa, Mar 14, 29; m 52; c 5. BIOCHEMISTRY. *Educ:* Pa State Univ, BS, 51; Rutgers Univ, MS, 53, PhD(biochem), 55. *Prof Exp:* Res fel biochem, Univ Wis, 55-56; biochemist lab clin biochem, 56-68, chemist, 68-72, head sect physiol chem, Exp Therapeut Br, 72-75, HEAD SECT PHYSIOL CHEM, LAB CHEM, NAT HEART LUNG & BLOOD INST, 75- *Concurrent Pos:* Nat Heart Inst res fel, 55-56; NIH advan trainee biol dept, Univ Calif, San Diego, 65-66. *Mem:* Am Chem Soc; Am Soc Biol Chemists; AAAS. *Res:* Metabolism of amino acids and related compounds; vasoactive peptides and amines; analytical biochemistry. *Mailing Add:* Lab of Chem Bldg 10 Rm 7N-260 Bethesda MD 20014

PISANO, JOSEPH CARMEN, b Wilkes-Barre, Pa, July 19, 41; m 63; c 3. CELL PHYSIOLOGY, IMMUNOBIOLOGY. *Educ:* King's Col (Pa), BS, 63; Univ Notre Dame, PhD(microbiol), 67. *Prof Exp:* Instr physiol, Med Units, Univ Tenn, Memphis, 67-68; asst prof, 68-72, ASSOC PROF PHYSIOL, SCH MED, TULANE UNIV, 72- *Mem:* AAAS; Am Soc Microbiol; Am Physiol Soc; Reticuloendothelial Soc. *Res:* Physiology of phagocytic cells; cellular involvement in the immune response. *Mailing Add:* Dept of Physiol Tulane Univ Sch of Med New Orleans LA 70112

PISANO, MICHAEL A, b Brooklyn, NY, Mar 31, 23; m 48; c 4. MICROBIOLOGY. *Educ:* Brooklyn Col, BA, 46; St John's Univ, NY, MS, 49; Mich State Col, PhD(bact, biochem), 53. *Prof Exp:* Bacteriologist, Mich State Dept Health, 51-53; microbiologist, Res Div, S B Penick & Co, 53-55; PROF MICROBIOL, GRAD SCH, ST JOHN'S UNIV NY, 55-, CHMN, DEPT BIOL, 81- *Concurrent Pos:* Res assoc, Mt Sinai Hosp, New York, 56-; consult, Merck & Co, Inc 57 & E R Squib & Sons, 60; res contract, US Naval Appl Sci Lab, 63-; consult, Miles Chem Co, 63-65 & Macrosonics Corp, 65-; fac res award, St John's Univ NY, 66; res fel, Dept Health, Educ & Welfare, 68-69; consult, Amstar Corp, 72-, Deltown Chemurgic, 79. *Mem:* Am Soc Microbiol; Soc Indust Microbiol (pres, 72-73); NY Acad Sci; Brit Soc Gen Microbiol. *Res:* Fermentation, antibiotics, vitamins; microbiological nutrition; cell morphology; sterilization procedures; microbial chemiluminescence; microbial lipids; microbial enzymes. *Mailing Add:* Dept Biol Sci St John's Univ Jamaica NY 11439

PISANO, ROCCI GEORGE, b San Jose, Calif, May 10, 11; m 52; c 2. BIOLOGY, AGRICULTURE. *Educ:* Univ Santa Clara, BS, 34; San Jose State Col, AB, 40; Univ Calif, BS, 41, MEd, 47; Stanford Univ, EdD, 54. *Prof Exp:* Dir agr dept high sch, Calif, 42-46; from asst prof to assoc prof biol & agr, 46-69, prof, 69-77, EMER PROF BIOL, SAN JOSE STATE UNIV, 77- *Concurrent Pos:* Mem, Parks & Recreation Comn, Bicentennial Comn, Conserv Element & Open Space Element of Master Plan & chmn, Alum Rock Park Restoration Adv Comn, City of San Jose; marine biol & conserv consult, R-3 Prog, San Jose Unified Sch Syst, Lockheed Corp & Rand Corp; consult, Environ Design & Planning, Inc. *Mem:* Int Soc Arborculture; AAAS. *Res:* Analysis of biological, physical and social needs in rural communities of California and the preparation of science teachers to meet these needs; burrows and feeding of the Norway rat; biotic study of waste disposal sites; improvements in methodology of environmental impact reports preparation, use and review; biotic survey of properties. *Mailing Add:* 671 S Clover Ave San Jose CA 95128

PISCIOTTA, ANTHONY VITO, b New York, NY, Mar 3, 21; m 51; c 3. INTERNAL MEDICINE. *Educ:* Fordham Univ, BS, 41; Marquette Univ, MD, 44, MS, 52; Am Bd Internal Med, dipl. *Prof Exp:* Intern, Med Ctr, Jersey City, NJ, 44-45; resident path, Fordham Hosp, New York, 47-48; resident internal med, Milwaukee County Gen Hosp, 48-51; instr internal med, Sch Med, Tufts Univ, 51-52; from instr to assoc prof, 52-66, PROF MED, MED COL WIS, 66- *Concurrent Pos:* Mem attend staff & dir blood res lab, Milwaukee County Gen Hosp, 52-; consult, St Mary's, St Joseph's,

Deaconess, Columbia, St Luke's & Lutheran Hosps; vchmn, Radiation Effects Res Found, Hiroshima, Japan, 81-83. *Honors & Awards:* Encaenia Award, Fordham Univ, 56. *Mem:* AAAS; AMA; Am Fedn Clin Res; fel Am Col Physicians; Am Soc Exp Path. *Res:* Mechanisms of autoimmunization; drug induced bone marrow damage; hematology. *Mailing Add:* 8700 W Wisconsin Ave Milwaukee WI 53226

PISCITELLI, JOSEPH, b Reading, Pa, June 28, 34; m; c 2. PHYSIOLOGY. *Educ:* Cath Univ Am, AB, 59, MS, 61, PhD(physiol), 68. *Prof Exp:* Instr biol, Allentown Col, 66-68; asst prof, Philadelphia Community Col, 68-69 & Philadelphia Col Osteop, 69-72; PROF BIOL, KUTZTOWN STATE COL, 72- *Mem:* Sigma Xi; Nat Asn Biol Teachers. *Res:* Effects of ultrasound and 6-chloropurine on the growth of Krebs-2 ascites cells; protein metabolism and amino-acid composition of regenerating Stentor coeruleus. *Mailing Add:* 435 W Main St Kutztown PA 19530

PISERCHIO, ROBERT J, b Pueblo, Colo, Feb 12, 34; m 63. PHYSICS. *Educ:* Univ Ariz, BS, 58, MS, 62, PhD(physics), 63. *Prof Exp:* Asst physics, Univ Ariz, 58-63; res asst prof & actg asst prof, Univ Wash, Seattle, 63-66, from asst prof to assoc prof, 66-74, PROF PHYSICS, SAN DIEGO STATE UNIV, 74- *Res:* High energy physics; cosmic rays. *Mailing Add:* Dept of Physics 5300 Campanile Dr San Diego CA 92182

PISH, GEORGE, b Chicago, Ill, Aug 2, 14; m 44; c 3. PHYSICAL CHEMISTRY. *Educ:* Cent Col, BS, 40; Univ Ill, PhD(chem), 43. *Prof Exp:* X-ray technician, Gen Elec Corp, Ill, 35-40; asst chem, Univ Ill, 40-43; engr mat div, Curtiss-Wright Airplane Res Lab, NY, 43-46; group leader res lab, Upjohn Co, Mich, 46-50; supvr res lab, Mound Lab, AEC, Monsanto Chem Co, 50-56; supvr mfg staff, Corning Glass Works, NY, 56-57; mgr chem physics, Southwest Res Inst, 57-59, dir mat res dept, 59-66; sr scientist & mgr, Owens-Ill Tech Ctr, 68-69; CONSULT, 69- *Mem:* Am Chem Soc; Am Phys Soc; Am Crystallog Asn. *Res:* Instrumental and optical methods of analysis; atomic and molecular structure; chemical physics and physical chemical research in solid state; radioactivity; electron microscopy; electron and x-ray diffraction. *Mailing Add:* 311 Gettysburg Rd San Antonio TX 78228

PISTER, KARL S(TARK), b Stockton, Calif, June 27, 25; m 50; c 6. APPLIED MECHANICS, SYSTEMS ENGINEERING. *Educ:* Univ Calif, BS, 45; MS, 48; Univ Ill, PhD(eng mech), 52. *Prof Exp:* Instr civil eng, Univ Calif, 47-49; instr theoret & appl mech, Univ Ill, 49-52; from asst prof to assoc prof civil eng, 52-62, PROF CIVIL ENG, UNIV CALIF, BERKELEY, 62-, DEAN, COL ENG, 81- *Concurrent Pos:* Fulbright lectr & researcher, Ireland, 65-66; sr Fulbright scholar, Univ Stuttgart, 73-74, Richard Merton vis prof, 78. *Honors & Awards:* Wason Medal Res, Concrete Inst, 60. *Mem:* Nat Acad Eng; Am Soc Mech Engrs; Concrete Inst; Soc Eng Sci; fel Am Acad Mechanics. *Res:* Structural and continuum mechanics; system science; optimal design; earthquake engineering. *Mailing Add:* Dept Civil Eng Univ Calif Berkeley CA 94720

PISTOLE, THOMAS GORDON, b Detroit, Mich, Sept 17, 42; m 65; c 1. MICROBIOLOGY, IMMUNOLOGY. *Educ:* Wayne State Univ, PhB, 64, MS, 66; Univ Utah, PhD(microbiol), 69. *Prof Exp:* Nat Res Coun res assoc microbiol, immunol br, US Army Biol Ctr, Ft Detrick, 69-70; res assoc dept microbiol, Univ Minn, Minneapolis, 70-71; asst prof, 71-77, ASSOC PROF MICROBIOL, UNIV NH, 77- *Concurrent Pos:* Vis scientist, Weizmann Inst Sci, Rehovot, Israel, 79. *Mem:* Am Asn Immunologists; Am Soc Zoologists; AAAS; Am Soc Microbiol; NY Acad Sci. *Res:* Lectins from marine invertebrates; comparative immunology; bacterial endotoxins. *Mailing Add:* Dept Microbiol Univ NH Durham NH 03824

PI-SUNYER, F XAVIER, b Barcelona, Spain, Dec 3, 33; US citizen; m 61; c 3. ENDOCRINOLOGY, NUTRITION. *Educ:* Oberlin Col, BA, 55; Columbia Univ, MD, 59; Harvard Univ, MPH, 63. *Prof Exp:* Intern & asst resident med, St Luke's Hosp, New York, 59-61; jr registr, St Bartholomew's Hosp & Med Sch, London, Eng, 61-62; from instr to asst prof, 65-78, ASSOC PROF MED, COL PHYSICIANS & SURGEONS, COLUMBIA UNIV, 78- *Concurrent Pos:* USPHS res fel, Sch Pub Health, Harvard Univ, 63-64, fel, Thorndike Mem Lab, 64-65; Norman Jolliffe fel nutrit, Inst Human Nutrit, Columbia Univ, 66-67; fel, NY Heart Asn, 67-68, sr investr, 68-72; dir, Div Endocrinol, St Luke's Roosevelt Hosp, 78-; Fogarty int fel, 79-80. *Mem:* AAAS; Am Diabetes Asn; Am Inst Nutrit; Am Soc Clin Nutrit; Am Fedn Clin Res. *Res:* Hormonal control of carbohydrate metabolism; obesity; trace metals. *Mailing Add:* Dept of Med St Luke's Hosp Ctr 114th & Amsterdam Ave New York NY 10025

PISZKIEWICZ, DENNIS, b Chicago, Ill, Dec 21, 41. BIOCHEMISTRY. *Educ:* Loyola Univ Chicago, BS, 63; San Diego State Col, MS, 65; Univ Calif, Santa Barbara, PhD(chem), 68. *Prof Exp:* Res assoc biol chem, Sch Med, Univ Calif, Los Angeles, 68-71; asst prof biol chem, Univ Calif, Irvine-Calif Col Med, 71-78; ASSOC PROF CHEM, DUQUESNE UNIV, 78- *Mem:* AAAS; Am Soc Biol Chem; Am Chem Soc. *Res:* Structure and function of proteins; protein chemistry; enzymology. *Mailing Add:* Dept of Chem Duquesne Univ Pittsburgh PA 15282

PITA, EDWARD GERALD, b New York, NY, Jan 22, 25; m 55; c 2. MECHANICAL ENGINEERING. *Educ:* Purdue Univ, BS, 44; Univ Mich, Ann Arbor, MA, 49; Columbia Univ, MS, 56; Univ Md, College Park, PhD(mech eng), 69. *Prof Exp:* Proj engr, Worthington Corp, 53-56; chief engr, Panero-Weidlinger-Salvadori, Engrs, 56-62; assoc prof mech eng, Manhattan Col, 63-71; ASSOC PROF ENVIRON TECHNOL, NEW YORK CITY TECH COL, 71- *Mem:* Am Soc Heating, Refrig & Air Conditioning Engrs; NY Acad Sci; Sigma Xi. *Res:* Heat transfer, thermal pollution, air conditioning and refrigeration. *Mailing Add:* Dept Environ Control Technol New York City Tech Col 450 W 41st St New York NY 10036

PITCAIRN, DONALD M, b Portland, Ore, Mar 23, 21; m 52; c 3. INTERNAL MEDICINE. *Educ:* Univ Ore, BA, 44, MD, 45. *Prof Exp:* Intern, Med Sch, Univ Ore, 45-46, resident thoracic surg, 48-49, instr physiol, 49-52, resident internal med, 52-53; asst med, Peter Bent Brigham Hosp, Boston, 53-55; from instr to prof, Med Sch, Univ Ore, 55-68, head div chest dis, 59-67; chief physician educ br, Div Physician Manpower, Bur Health Professions Educ & Manpower Training, 68-71, spec asst to dir, Fogarty Int Ctr Advan Study Health Sci, 71-80, ACTG CHIEF, CANCER CENTERS BR, NAT CANCER INST, NIH, 80- *Concurrent Pos:* Life Ins Med Res Fund fel med, Peter Bent Brigham Hosp, Boston, 54-55. *Res:* Bioassay of adrenal medullary hormones; oxyhemoglobin dissociation characteristics of old and young human erythrocytes and hemoglobin; pulmonary physiology and function; cardiopulmonary diseases; medical education. *Mailing Add:* 24 Orchard Way N Rockville MD 20854

PITCHER, ARTHUR EVERETT, b Hanover, NH, July 18, 12; m 73; c 2. MATHEMATICS. *Educ:* Case Western Reserve Univ, AB, 32; Harvard Univ, MA, 33, PhD(math), 35. *Hon Degrees:* DSc, Case Western Reserve Univ, 57. *Prof Exp:* Instr math, Harvard Univ, 34-35; asst, Inst Advan Study, 35-36; Benjamin Pierce instr, Harvard Univ, 36-38; from instr to assoc prof, 38-48, prof math, 48-78, chmn dept math & astron, 60-78, CONSULT TO PRES, LEHIGH UNIV, 78- *Concurrent Pos:* Mem Inst Advan Study, 45-46 & 47-50; consult, US Army & US Air Force, 47-54; Guggenheim Mem Found fel, 52-53. *Mem:* AAAS; Am Math Soc (assoc secy, 59-67, secy, 68-); Soc Indust & Appl Math; Math Asn Am. *Res:* Critical point theory; calculus of variations; exterior and terminal ballistics. *Mailing Add:* Dept Math Bldg 14 Lehigh Univ Bethlehem PA 18015

PITCHER, DEPUYSTER GILBERT, b Bay Shore, NY, Mar 2, 28; m 52; c 3. REACTOR INSTRUMENTATION. *Prof Exp:* Engr, 54-61, GROUP LEADER REACTOR INSTRUMENTATION NUCLEAR SCI, ASSOC UNIVS INC, 61- *Mem:* Inst Elec & Electronics Engrs; Am Nuclear Soc. *Res:* Safety and control instrumentation for research reactors. *Mailing Add:* HFBR Bldg 750 Brookhaven Nat Lab Upton NY 11973

PITCHER, ERIC JOHN, b St John's, Nfld, Aug 19, 46; US citizen; m 73; c 1. DYNAMIC METEOROLOGY. *Educ:* Mem Univ Nfld, BSc, 68; McGill Univ, MSc, 70; Univ Mich, PhD(atmospheric sci), 74. *Prof Exp:* Fel, Nat Ctr Atmospheric Res, 74-75; res assoc, Nat Res Coun, 75-76; ASST PROF METEOROL, UNIV MIAMI, 76- *Concurrent Pos:* Vis scientist, Nat Ctr Atmospheric Res, 79-80, 81 & 82. *Mem:* Am Meteorol Soc; Can Meteorol & Oceanog Soc; Sigma Xi. *Res:* Modeling of the general circulation of the atmosphere; climate dynamics; geophysical fluid dynamics. *Mailing Add:* Rosenstiel Sch Marine & Atmospheric Sci Univ Miami 4600 Rickenbacker Causeway Miami FL 33149

PITCHER, TOM STEPHEN, b Wenatchee, Wash, Apr 17, 26; m 50; c 3. MATHEMATICS. *Educ:* Univ Wash, BA, 49; Mass Inst Technol, PhD(math), 53. *Prof Exp:* Staff mem math, Lincoln Lab, Mass Inst Technol, 53-65; prof, Univ Southern Calif, 65-70; PROF MATH, UNIV HAWAII, 70- *Concurrent Pos:* Consult, Jet Propulsion Lab, 65-68, TRW Corp, 68-69 & Rand Corp, 69-70. *Mem:* Am Math Soc. *Res:* Probability theory and applications to engineering; statistics; number theory; complex variables. *Mailing Add:* Dept of Math Univ of Hawaii Honolulu HI 96822

PITCHER, WAYNE HAROLD, JR, b St Louis, Mo, Jan 5, 44; m 70; c 2. CHEMICAL ENGINEERING, BIOENGINEERING. *Educ:* Calif Inst Technol, BS, 66; Mass Inst Technol, SM, 68, ScD(chem eng), 72. *Prof Exp:* Sr chem engr bio-mat res & develop, 72-74, sr res chem engr, 74-76, eng supvr biotech develop, 80-81, MGR BIOTECH DEVELOP, CORNING GLASS WORKS, 81- *Mem:* Am Inst Chem Engrs; Am Chem Soc. *Res:* Development of immobilized biological systems for industrial applications. *Mailing Add:* Corning Glass Works Corning NY 14830

PITCHFORD, ARMIN CLOYST, b Mt Home, Ark, May 12, 22; m 44; c 2. PETROLEUM CHEMISTRY. *Educ:* Univ Ark, BS, 47. *Prof Exp:* Chemist, Phillips Petrol Co, 48-49; pvt consult, 49-50; chemist, Kans, 50-52, res chemist, Okla, 52-56, group leader, Rocket Fuels Div, Tex, 56-57, sr res chemist, Res Div Chem Labs, 57-69, PROJ MGR, PHILLIPS PETROL CO, PHILLIPS RES CTR, OKLA, 69- *Concurrent Pos:* Mem, Asphalt Inst Mat Comt & Int Tech Comt, Phillips Petrol Co. *Mem:* Am Chem Soc. *Res:* Emulsification, surfactants, rheology and composition of residual fractions and methods for enhancing durability, performance and ecological utilization of residual products as construction materials; processing, evaluation and analysis of foreign, domestic and synthetic crude oils derived from oil shale and coal; asphalt composition; demetalization processes. *Mailing Add:* 4912 SE Princeton Dr Bartlesville OK 74003

PITCHFORD, LEANNE CAROLYN, b Sedalia, Mo, Feb 9, 50. EXPERIMENTAL ATOMIC PHYSICS. *Educ:* ETex State Univ, BS, 70; Univ Tex, Dallas, MS, 73, PhD(physics), 76. *Prof Exp:* Physicist, Ctr Nuclear Res, France, 76-77; res assoc, Joint Inst Lab Astrophys, Univ Colo, 77-80; PHYSICIST, SANDIA NAT LAB, 80- *Mem:* Am Phys Soc. *Res:* Computer modeling of high pressure gas lasers including radiation fields and pumping chemistry; calculation of electron energy distribution; functions in gaseons electronics; stopping power and opaut; calculations in high temperature, high density plasmas. *Mailing Add:* Div 4211 Sandia Nat Labs Albuquerque NM 87185

PITELKA, DOROTHY RIGGS, b Marsovan, Turkey, Sept 13, 20; US citizen; m 43; c 3. ZOOLOGY. *Educ:* Univ Colo, BA, 41; Univ Calif, PhD(zool), 48. *Prof Exp:* Asst zool, 41-43 & 45-46, lectr, 49-52, from asst res zoologist to assoc res zoologist, 53-66, RES ZOOLOGIST, UNIV CALIF, BERKELEY, 66-, ADJ PROF ZOOL, 71- *Concurrent Pos:* USPHS fel, Paris, 57-58. *Mem:* AAAS; Am Soc Cell Biol; Soc Protozool (pres, 67-68); Am Asn Cancer Res; Tissue Cult Asn. *Res:* Tumor biology; cell junctions; ultrastructure, function and carcinogenesis in mammary gland; epithelial cell differentiation in cell culture; ultrastructure and morphogenesis of protozoa. *Mailing Add:* Cancer Res Lab Univ of Calif Berkeley CA 94720

PITELKA, FRANK ALOIS, b Chicago, Ill, Mar 27, 16; m 43; c 3. ZOOLOGY. *Educ:* Univ Ill AB, 39; Univ Calif, PhD(zool), 46. *Prof Exp:* Asst, 39-44, lectr, 44-46, from instr to assoc prof, 46-58, chmn dept, 63-66 & 69-71, PROF ZOOL, UNIV CALIF, BERKELEY, 58-; RES ECOLOGIST, MUS VERT ZOOL, 67- *Concurrent Pos:* Field researcher, Calif, Ore, Ariz & Nev, 40-51, Mex, 46-50, Alaska, 51-80; from asst cur to cur birds, Mus Vert Zool, 45-63; Guggenheim fel, 49-50; NSF sr fel, Oxford Univ & field researcher, England & Norway, 57-58; mem adv panel environ biol, NSF, 59-62; panel biol & med sci, Comt Polar Res, Nat Acad Sci, 60-65; ed, Ecol J, 62-64; res prof, Miller Inst, 65-66; panel biol & med sci, Int Biol Prog Subcomt Terrestrial Prod, Nat Acad Sci, 65-67, tundra biome dir, 67-69; chmn exec comt, Miller Inst, 67-70, mem, 67-71; mem US nat comm, UNESCO, 70-72; fel, Ctr Advan Study Behav Sci, Stanford Univ, 71; mem, Adv Panel Polar Progs, NSF, 78-80. *Honors & Awards:* Mercer Award, Ecol Soc Am, 53; Brewster Award, Am Ornith Union, 80. *Mem:* Fel AAAS; Ecol Soc Am; fel Am Ornith Union; hon mem Cooper Ornith Soc; Am Soc Mammal. *Res:* Animal ecology; population and behavior studies of birds and mammals; arctic biology. *Mailing Add:* Dept Zool Univ Calif Berkeley CA 94720

PITELKA, LOUIS FRANK, b Berkeley, Calif, Mar 28, 47; m 69; c 2. PLANT POPULATION BIOLOGY. *Educ:* Univ Calif, Davis, BS, 69; Stanford Univ, PhD(biol), 74. *Prof Exp:* Asst prof, 74-81, ASSOC PROF BIOL, BATES COL, 81- *Concurrent Pos:* Prin investr res grants, NSF, 80- *Mem:* Ecol Soc Am; Bot Soc Am; Am Inst Biol Sci; Int Soc Plant Pop Biologists; Torrey Bot Club. *Res:* Demography, life history strategies and physiological ecology of perennial forest understory herbs. *Mailing Add:* Dept Biol Bates Col Lewiston ME 04240

PITESKY, ISADORE, b Chicago, Ill, Apr 18, 18; m 69. BIOCHEMISTRY, IMMUNOLOGY. *Educ:* Univ Chicago, SB, 40; Univ Ill, BS, 48, MS & MD, 51. *Prof Exp:* Chemist, Univ Chicago, 40-42 & Northern Regional Res Lab, Bur Agr & Indust Chem, USDA, 42-46; asst pharmacol, Univ Ill Col Med, 48-51; intern, resident internal med & in chg renal clin, Vet Admin Hosp, Long Beach, Calif, 51-54; DIR, IMMUNO-CHEM LABS, 65-; PRES & CHMN BD, CREATIVE SCI EQUIP CORP, LONG BEACH, 71- *Concurrent Pos:* Chief allergy Mem Hosp, Long Beach, Calif; pres, Creative Sci Equip Corp, 71- *Mem:* AAAS; Am Acad Allergy; Am Chem Soc; Soc Exp Biol & Med; AMA. *Res:* Allergy; biochemistry of allergens. *Mailing Add:* Immuno-Chem Labs 3711 Long Beach Blvd Long Beach CA 90807

PITHA, JOHN JOSEPH, b New York, NY, Mar 19, 20; wid; c 4. INORGANIC CHEMISTRY. *Educ:* Polytech Inst Brooklyn, BS, 41, MS, 43, PhD(inorg chem), 46. *Prof Exp:* Asst anal chem, Polytech Inst Brooklyn, 41-43, res assoc inorg phosphors, 43-45; from instr to asst prof gen & inorg chem, Mich State Univ, 45-52; chemist, Gen Elec Co, Lennox, 52-66, mgr thyrite & ceramics res & develop, 66-75, sr ceramic engr, 75-81; SR CERAMIC ENGR, WESTINGHOUSE ELEC, 81- *Mem:* Am Chem Soc; Am Ceramic Soc; Sigma Xi. *Res:* Reactions at elevated temperatures; semiconductors; design of materials; non-linear resistors; ceramics; devices; metal oxide varistors. *Mailing Add:* Westinghouse Elec Co PO Box 344 Bloomington IN 47402

PITHA, JOSEF, b Tabor, Czech, Oct 28, 33; US citizen. POLYMER CHEMISTRY. *Educ:* Czech Acad Sci, PhD(chem), 60. *Prof Exp:* Res fel, Inst Org Chem & Biochem, Czech, 59-65; fel Nat Res Coun, Can, 65-66; res assoc, Johns Hopkins Univ, 66-68; RES CHEMIST, NIH GERONT RES CTR, BALTIMORE CITY HOSPS, 68-, CHIEF SECT MACROMOLECULAR CHEM, 80- *Mem:* Am Chem Soc. *Res:* Macromolecular drugs, aging; polymeric analogs of nucleic acids. *Mailing Add:* NIH Geront Res Ctr Baltimore City Hosps Baltimore MD 21224

PITHA-ROWE, PAULA MARIE, b Prague, Czech, Nov 7, 37; US citizen; m 61, 81; c 2. BIOCHEMISTRY, MOLECULAR BIOLOGY. *Educ:* Prague Tech Univ, BS & MS, 60; Czech Acad Sci, PhD(biochem), 64. *Prof Exp:* Instr radiol sci, Sch Hyg & Pub Health, Johns Hopkins Univ, 66-68; assoc res scientist, Dept Path, Sch Med, NY Univ, 68-69; asst researcher, Inst Phys-Chem Biol, Paris, 69; asst prof med, 71-75, asst prof microbiol, 72-80, asst prof oncol, 73-75, ASSOC PROF MED & ONCOL, JOHNS HOPKINS UNIV, 75-, ASSOC PROF MICROBIOL, 80- *Concurrent Pos:* Res fel, Inst Org Chem & Biochem, 64-65; jr res fel, Nat Res Coun Can, 65-66; fel, Nat Ctr Res, France, 69; Europ Molecular Biol Orgn travel award, 69; fel, Dept Med, Sch Med, Johns Hopkins Univ, 69-71; Eleanor Roosevelt cancer fel, 79. *Honors & Awards:* Prize, Czech Acad Sci, 65. *Mem:* Biophys Soc; Am Soc Microbiol; Am Asn Cancer Res; fel Leukemia Soc. *Res:* Physical, chemical and biological properties of synthetic analogues of nucleic acids; interferon-molecular mechanism of induction and action; regulation of gene expression; RNA tumor viruses. *Mailing Add:* 1214 Culvert Rd Baltimore MD 21204

PITKIN, EDWARD THADDEUS, b Putnam, Conn, Dec 14, 30; m 53; c 2. SOLAR ENERGY, SYSTEMS ANALYSIS. *Educ:* Univ Conn, BS, 52; Princeton Univ, MS, 53; Univ Calif, Los Angeles, PhD(astrodyn), 64. *Prof Exp:* Proj engr, Astro Div, Marquardt Corp, 56-58, mgr space propulsion dept, 58-61; consult astronaut, 61-64; assoc prof aerospace eng, 64-70, PROF AEROSPACE & MECH ENG, UNIV CONN, 70- *Concurrent Pos:* Vis prof eng, Univ Canterbury, 70-71 & 78. *Mem:* Assoc fel Am Inst Aeronaut & Astronaut; Solar Energy Soc. *Res:* Propulsion; fluid dynamics. *Mailing Add:* Dept of Mech Eng Univ of Conn Storrs CT 06268

PITKIN, ROY MACBETH, b Anthon, Iowa, May 24, 34; m 57; c 4. OBSTETRICS & GYNECOLOGY. *Educ:* Univ Iowa, BA, 56, MD, 59; Am Bd Obstet & Gynec, cert. *Prof Exp:* Intern, King County Hosp, Seattle, 59-60; resident obstet & gynec, Univ Iowa Hosps, 60-63; asst prof, Univ Ill, 65-68; assoc prof, 68-72, PROF OBSTET & GYNEC, UNIV IOWA, 72-, HEAD DEPT, 77- *Concurrent Pos:* Mem comt maternal nutrit, Nat Acad Sci. *Mem:* Am Gynec & Obstet Soc; Am Col Obstet & Gynec; Soc Gynec Invest; Perinatal Res Soc; Soc Exp Biol & Med. *Res:* Maternal and fetal physiology. *Mailing Add:* Dept of Obstet & Gynec Univ of Iowa Hosps Iowa City IA 52242

PITKOW, HOWARD SPENCER, b Philadelphia, Pa, May 21, 41; m 69; c 2. REPRODUCTIVE ENDOCRINOLOGY, ENVIRONMENTAL TOXICOLOGY. *Educ:* Univ Pa, BA, 62, MS, 63; Rutgers Univ, New Brunswick, PhD(reproductive physiol), 71. *Prof Exp:* instr histol & embryol, 65-66, asst prof anat, 67-68, asst prof physiol & biochem, 69-71, assoc prof physiol, 72-77, CHMN DEPT PHYSIOL SCI, PA COL PODIATRIC MED, 76-, PROF PHYSIOL, 78- *Concurrent Pos:* Actg chmn dept physiol sci, Pa Col Podiatric Med, 74-75; lectr, Dept Biol & guest lectr, Dept Allied Health Studies, Community Col Philadelphia, 72-75 & lectr, Dept Sci, Bucks County Community Col, 78, 79 & 81; vis assoc prof, Dept Obstet & Gynec, Hahnemann Med Col, Philadelphia, 80-; adj prof, Dept Biol, Drexel Univ, 80; res prof, Dept Physiol & Biophysics, Health Sci Ctr, Temple Univ, Philadelphia, 81-; travel grant, Argonne Nat Labs, 78 & 79. *Mem:* Fedn Am Soc Exp Biol; assoc Am Physiol Soc; Endocrine Soc; Soc Exp Biol & Med; Soc Study Reproduction. *Res:* Investigation of reproductive hormone mimiking effects of various amino acids and effects of dimethylbenzanthracene, a polycyclic parainogenic hydrocarbon, on pregnancy, lactation, and neonatal development; teratology. *Mailing Add:* Dept of Physiol Sci Eighth & Race Sts Philadelphia PA 19107

PITLICK, FRANCES ANN, b Pasadena, Calif, Feb 24, 40. BIOCHEMISTRY, CELL BIOLOGY. *Educ:* Univ Calif, Berkeley, AB, 61; Univ Wash, PhD(biochem), 68. *Prof Exp:* Instr, 70-71, asst prof med, Sch Med, Yale Univ, 71-77, sr res assoc, 77-78; HEALTH SCIENTIST ADMINR, DEVICES & TECHNOL BR, NAT HEART, LUNG & BLOOD INST, NIH, 78- *Concurrent Pos:* Conn Heart Asn fel, Sch Med, Yale Univ, 68-70. *Mem:* Am Soc Biol Chemists; Am Soc Hemat; Am Fedn Clin Res; AAAS. *Res:* Enzymology of blood coagulation, specifically mechanism of initiation by cell-surface tissue factor. *Mailing Add:* Fed Bldg Rm 310 7550 Wisconsin Ave Bethesda MD 20205

PITMAN, DUNCAN L, b Prince George, BC, June 26, 20; US citizen; m 43; c 5. ENGINEERING. *Educ:* Univ BC, BASc, 47; Purdue Univ, MS, 50. *Prof Exp:* Designer spectrog, Appl Physics Corp, 51; design engr, Benson Lehner Corp, 51-53; engr, Douglas Aircraft Co, Inc, Calif, 53-56, supvr guid & control, 56-61, chief, 61-64, mem sr tech staff, 64-71, mem sr tech staff, McDonnell Douglas Astronaut Co, Huntington Beach, 71-77; CONSULT, 77- *Concurrent Pos:* Lectr, Adv Group Aerospace Res & Develop Lect Series, NATO, 52-, Norway, Greece, Italy, 72; mem comt automatic controls, Nat Adv Comt Aeronaut, 58; lectr, Univ Calif, Los Angeles, 61- & NASA Space Tech Summer Inst, Calif Inst Technol, 64. *Mem:* Assoc fel Am Inst Aeronaut & Astronaut. *Res:* Guidance and control of missile and space boosters. *Mailing Add:* 3101 Tuna Canyon Topanga CA 90290

PITMAN, GARY BOYD, b Yreka, Calif, Aug 28, 34; c 4. ENTOMOLOGY. *Educ:* Univ Calif, Davis, BS, 60; Ore State Univ, MS, 62, PhD(entom), 64. *Prof Exp:* Res asst defoliatores, Ore State Syst Higher Educ, 60-62; res fel bark beetles, Boyce Thompson Inst Plant Res, 62-64, from asst entomologist to assoc entomologist, 64-73, entomologist, Forest Res Lab, 73-77; ASSOC PROF FOREST SCI, ORE STATE UNIV, 77- *Mem:* Entom Soc Am. *Res:* Behavior of Scolytids as mediated through chemical messengers, including population aggregating phenomena. *Mailing Add:* Dept of Forest Sci Ore State Univ Corvallis OR 97331

PITMAN, GEORGE RUBI, b Lakewood, Ohio, July 27, 27; m 56; c 2. OPERATIONS RESEARCH, SYSTEMS ANALYSIS. *Educ:* Univ Akron, BS, 50; Univ Cincinnati, MS, 51, PhD(physics), 55. *Prof Exp:* Res scientist, Autonetics Div, NAm Aviation, Inc, 55-57; mgr electronics dept, US Industs Tech Ctr, 57-58; staff engr, Hughes Aircraft Co, 58-61; dir arms control, Aerospace Corp, 61-65; sr staff scientist, TRW Systs, Inc, Calif, 65-68; br chief, Tactical Anal Br, 68-75, dep chief, Opers Anal Div, 77-79, ADV, US SALT DELEG, US ARMS CONTROL & DISARMAMENT AGENCY, 79- *Concurrent Pos:* Lectr, Eng Exten, Univ Calif, Los Angeles, 60-64. *Mem:* Fel AAAS; Opers Res Soc Am; Int Inst Strategic Studies. *Res:* International relations; arms control. *Mailing Add:* US Arms Control & Disarmament Agency Washington DC 20451

PITNER, SAMUEL ELLIS, b Knoxville, Tenn, Mar 8, 32; m 55; c 3. NEUROLOGY. *Educ:* Univ Tenn, Knoxville, AB, 53; Univ Tenn, Memphis, MD, 56. *Prof Exp:* From instr to assoc prof, 64-75, asst dir, Cerebral Vascular Clin Res Ctr, 68-72, prof neurol, Col Med, Univ Tenn, Memphis, 75-78; PROF & CHMN NEUROL, SCH MED, WRIGHT STATE UNIV, 78- *Concurrent Pos:* Fel clin neurol, Tulane Univ, 61-63; Nat Inst Neurol Dis & Blindness fel, Univ Tenn, Memphis, 63-64; consult, City of Memphis Hosps, Baptist Mem Hosp, Memphis, Memphis Vet Admin Hosp & St Jude Children's Res Hosp, 64-, dir clin for neuromuscular dis, 66-; mem staff, Miami Valley, Kettering, Good Samaritan, St Elizabeth's & Children's Hosp, Dayton, 78-; consult, US Air Force Wright Patterson Med Ctr & Dayton Vet Admin Ctr, 78- mem coun cerebrovascular dis, Am Heart Asn, 69- *Mem:* AAAS; fel Am Acad Neurol; fel Am Col Physicians. *Res:* Cerebrovascular diseases and neuromuscular disorders. *Mailing Add:* Dept of Neurol Box 927 Dayton OH 45401

PITOT, HENRY C, III, b New York, NY, May 12, 30; m 54; c 8. BIOCHEMISTRY, PATHOLOGY. *Educ:* Va Mil Inst, BS, 51; Tulane Univ, MD, 55, PhD, 59; Am Bd Path, dipl, 60. *Prof Exp:* Instr path, Tulane Univ, 55-59; from asst prof to assoc prof, 60-66, chmn dept path, 68-71, actg dean, 71-73, PROF ONCOL & PATH, SCH MED, UNIV WIS-MADISON, 66-, DIR McCARDLE LAB CANCER RES, 73- *Concurrent Pos:* Israel Mem fel, 57-60; fel oncol, Sch Med, Univ Wis-Madison, 59-60; Lederle med fac award, 63-65; Nat Cancer Inst res career develop award, 65-68; Lucy Wortham James res award, Soc Surg Oncol, 81. *Honors & Awards:* Borden Award, 55; Parke Davis Award Exp Path, 68. *Mem:* AAAS; Am Chem Soc; Am Asn Path; Am Soc Biol Chem; NY Acad Sci. *Res:* Biochemical mechanisms underlying the morphological changes in disease; biochemical and genetic pathology; oncology; regulatory mechanisms. *Mailing Add:* McArdle Lab Sch of Med Univ of Wis Madison WI 53706

PITRAT, CHARLES WILLIAM, b Kansas City, Mo, June 1, 28; m 63; c 3. PALEONTOLOGY, STRATIGRAPHY. *Educ:* Univ Kans, AB, 49; Univ Wis, MS, 51, PhD(geol), 53. *Prof Exp:* Asst, Univ Wis, 49-53, proj assoc, 53-55; asst prof geol, NMex Inst Mining & Technol, 55-56; from asst prof to assoc prof, Univ Kans, 56-64; assoc prof, 64-78, PROF GEOL, UNIV MASS, AMHERST, 78- *Concurrent Pos:* Co-ed, J Paleontol, 81- *Mem:* Geol Soc Am; Paleont Soc; Soc Econ Paleont & Mineral. *Res:* Devonian stratigraphy and paleontology, particularly brachiopods and corals; brachiopod systematics. *Mailing Add:* Dept Geol Univ Mass Amherst MA 01003

PITRE, HENRY NOLLE, JR, b Opelousas, La, Oct 23, 37; m 62; c 2. ENTOMOLOGY, PLANT PATHOLOGY. *Educ:* Univ Southwest La, BS, 60; La State Univ, MS, 62; Univ Wis, PhD(entom), 65. *Prof Exp:* PROF ENTOM, MISS STATE UNIV, 65- *Mem:* Entom Soc Am; Phytopath Soc Am. *Res:* Basic and applied aspects of field crop entomology, particularly dealing with insect biology, ecology and behavior related to pest management, and insect transmission of plant diseases. *Mailing Add:* PO Drawer EM Mississippi State MS 39762

PITT, CHARLES H, b Fremont, Wis, Aug 9, 29; m 56; c 5. METALLURGY, SURFACE CHEMISTRY. *Educ:* Univ Wis, BS, 51; Univ Utah, PhD(metall), 59. *Prof Exp:* Process engr, Gen Elec Co, 51-53; asst res prof metall, Univ Utah, 59-60; NSF fel, Cambridge Univ, 60-61; from asst prof to assoc prof, 61-71, PROF METALL & METALL ENG, UNIV UTAH, 71- *Mem:* Am Soc Metals; Am Inst Mining, Metall & Petrol Engrs; AAAS; Nat Asn Corrosion Engrs. *Res:* Corrosion; surface reactions. *Mailing Add:* 416 Browning Bldg Dept Metall Univ of Utah Salt Lake City UT 84112

PITT, COLIN GEOFFREY, b London, Eng, Sept 15, 35; m 60; c 2. ORGANOMETALLIC CHEMISTRY, POLYMER CHEMISTRY. *Educ:* Univ London, BSc, 56, PhD(silicon chem), 59. *Prof Exp:* Chemist, Midland Silicones, Eng, 59-60; fel, Fla State Univ, 60-62 & Mass Inst Technol, 62-63; chemist, asst dir, Chem & Life Sci Div, 71-75, DIR, PHYS SCI, CHEM & LIFE SCI DIV, RES TRIANGLE INST, 75- *Concurrent Pos:* Adj Duke Univ, 69- *Mem:* Am Chem Soc. *Res:* Synthetic and physical chemistry of polymers and organometallic compounds; medicinal chemistry. *Mailing Add:* Chem & Life Sci Div PO Box 12194 Res Triangle Park NC 27709

PITT, DONALD ALFRED, b Glen Ridge, NJ, June 19, 26; m 48; c 2. PHYSICAL CHEMISTRY. *Educ:* Princeton Univ, MA, 51, PhD(chem), 57. *Prof Exp:* Sr chemist, Cent Res Dept, 51-63, supvr chem physics res, 63-67, SR RES SPECIALIST, CENT RES LABS, MINN MINING & MFG CO, 67- *Mem:* Am Chem Soc; Am Phys Soc; Optical Soc Am; Soc Photog Scientists & Engrs; Fine Particle Soc. *Res:* Thermochemistry and thermodynamics; surface chemistry and adhesion; rheology; electrochemistry; dielectric relaxation phenomena; applied mathematics; optical scattering; submicron particle size distributions; physics of photographic emulsions. *Mailing Add:* Cent Res Labs 3M Cent St Paul MN 55144

PITT, JANE, b Frankfurt, Ger, Aug 25, 38; US citizen; m 62; c 2. MICROBIOLOGY, IMMUNOLOGY. *Educ:* Radcliffe Col, BA, 60; Harvard Univ, MD, 64. *Prof Exp:* From intern to resident pediat, Children's Hosp Med Ctr, 64-66; fel infectious dis, Med Sch, Tufts Univ, 66-67 & Harvard Med Sch, 67-70; asst prof pediat, State Univ NY Downstate Med Sch, 70-71; instr med, 71-73, asst prof, 73-77, ASSOC PROF PEDIAT, MED SCH, COLUMBIA UNIV, 77- *Concurrent Pos:* NIH spec fel, 71-73; prin investr, res grants, Food & Drug Admin, HEW, 75-77, NIH, HEW, 75-82 & Nat Found, 76-79. *Mem:* Soc Pediat Res; Am Fedn Clin Res; Harvey Soc; Infectious Dis Soc. *Res:* Bacterial virulence; development of host defense in the neonate; phagocytic function. *Mailing Add:* Dept of Pediat 630 168th St New York NY 10032

PITT, LOREN DALLAS, b Chewela, Wash, Sept 18, 39; m 61; c 2. MATHEMATICS. *Educ:* Univ Idaho, BS, 61; Cath Univ Am, MA, 64; Princeton Univ, MA, 66, PhD(math), 67. *Prof Exp:* Res assoc math, Rockefeller Univ, 67-68, asst prof, 68-70; from asst prof to assoc prof, 70-78, PROF MATH, UNIV VA, 78-, CHMN DEPT, 80- *Concurrent Pos:* Assoc ed, Multivariate Anal J. *Mem:* Am Math Soc; Inst Math Statist; Math Asn Am. *Res:* Probability; stochastic processes; prediction theory. *Mailing Add:* Dept Math Univ Va Charlottesville VA 22903

PITT, WILLIAM DANIEL, b Kansas City, Mo, Dec 19, 21; m 50; c 2. GEOLOGY. *Educ:* Northwestern Univ, Ill, BS, 46, MS, 50; Univ Wis, PhD(geol), 55. *Prof Exp:* Asst prof geol, Lamar State Col, 53-54 & Univ Okla, 54-63; assoc prof, 63-72, chmn dept, 63-76, PROF GEOL, EASTERN NMEX UNIV, 72- *Mem:* Fel Geol Soc Am; Am Asn Petrol Geologists. *Res:* Structural and petroleum geology; stratigraphy; geomorphology. *Mailing Add:* Dept of Geol Eastern NMex Univ Portales NM 88130

PITT, WOODROW WILSON, JR, b Rocky Mount, NC, Aug 14, 35; m 58; c 3. CHEMICAL ENGINEERING. *Educ:* Univ SC, BS, 57; Univ Tenn, Knoxville, MS, 66, PhD(chem eng), 69. *Prof Exp:* Develop engr, Union Carbide Nuclear Div, 60-70, group leader, 70-76, mgr biotechnol & environ progs, Advan Technol Sect, 76-81, HEAD, EXP ENG SECT, CHEM TECHNOL DIV, OAK RIDGE NAT LAB, 81- *Mem:* Am Inst Chem Engrs; Am Chem Soc; Nat Soc Prof Engrs. *Res:* Analytical liquid chromatography; analytical instrumentation for complex biochemical mixtures, such as physiological fluids and polluted waters; biochemical separations and processes; bioreactors; environmental control technology; nuclear fuel cycle; hazardous waste disposal. *Mailing Add:* Oak Ridge Nat Lab PO Box X Oak Ridge TN 37830

PITTEL, STUART, b New York, NY, Apr 13, 44; m 68; c 1. THEORETICAL NUCLEAR PHYSICS. *Educ:* Rensselaer Polytech Inst, BS, 64; Univ Minn, PhD(physics), 68. *Prof Exp:* Res assoc physics, Bartol Res Found, Franklin Inst, 68-70; vis asst prof physics, Univ Colo, 70-71; res assoc physics, Univ Pittsburgh, 71-73; asst prof physics, Bartol Res Found, Franklin Inst, 73-78, assoc prof, 78-; WITH BARTOL RES FOUND, 80- *Mem:* Am Phys Soc. *Res:* The microscopic shell-model theory of nuclear structure; the use of intermediate-energy nuclear reactions to probe nuclear structure. *Mailing Add:* 13 B Wharton Dr 1 Newark DE 19711

PITTENDRIGH, COLIN STEPHENSON, b Whitley Bay, Eng, Oct 13, 18; nat US; m 43; c 2. BIOLOGY. *Educ:* Univ Durham, BSc, 40; Imp Col, Trinidad, AICTA, 42; Columbia Univ, PhD(zool), 50. *Prof Exp:* Biologist int health div, Rockefeller Found, 42-45; adv malaria, Ministry Health & Educ, Brazil, 45; from asst prof to profbiol, Princeton Univ, 47-62, class of 1877 prof, 62-69, dean grad sch, 65-69; prof, 69-70, Bing prof human biol, 70-76, MILLER PROF BIOL & DIR HOPKINS MARINE STA, STANFORD UNIV, 76- *Concurrent Pos:* Phillipps lectr, Haverford Col, 57; Hopkins lectr, Stanford Univ, 57; Guggenheim fel, 59-60; Stearns lectr, Albert Einstein Col Med, Yeshiva Univ, 60; vis prof, Rockefeller Inst, 60; Van Uxem lectr, Princeton Univ, 67; adv malaria, Brit Colonial Off, 58; trustee, Rocky Mt Biol Lab, Colo; mem comt oceanog, Nat Acad Sci, 58-59, mem space sci bd, 60-; mem comt biotins & biol facil panel, NSF, 58-59; adv comt biol, NASA, 60- *Mem:* Nat Acad Sci; AAAS(vpres & chmn sect F); Am Soc Nat(pres, 67); Am Soc Zool; Soc Study Evolution. *Res:* Evolution; comparative and cellular physiology of daily rhythms. *Mailing Add:* Hopkins Marine Sta Stanford Univ Pacific Grove CA 93950

PITTENGER, ARTHUR O, b Indianapolis, Ind, Oct 24, 36; m 65; c 3. MATHEMATICS. *Educ:* Stanford Univ, BS, 58, MS, 60, PhD(math), 67. *Prof Exp:* Inter-Univ Comt Travel Grants grant, Moscow State Univ, 67-68; res assoc math, Rockefeller Univ, 68-70; asst prof, Univ Mich, Ann Arbor, 70-72; ASSOC PROF MATH, UNIV MD BALTIMORE COUNTY, 72- *Mem:* Am Math Soc; Inst Math Statist. *Res:* Probability theory. *Mailing Add:* Dept of Math Univ of Md Baltimore County Baltimore MD 21228

PITTENGER, ROBERT CARLTON, b Mincie, Ind, Feb 26, 20; m 45; c 5. MICROBIOLOGY. *Educ:* Butler Univ, BS, 42; Univ Wis, MS, 48, PhD(agr bact), 50. *Prof Exp:* Microbiologist, Res Labs, 50-56, mgr, Antibiotic Develop Dept, 56-66, mgr antibiotic prod, 66-69, DIR ANTIBIOTIC PROD, ELI LILLY & CO, 69- *Res:* Isolation of new antibiotic substances; mode of action of antimicrobial agents; action of mutagenic agents on microorganisms; taxonomy of actinomycetes. *Mailing Add:* Eli Lilly & Co PO Box 618 Indianapolis IN 46206

PITTENGER, THAD HECKLE, JR, b Omaha, Nebr, May 28, 21; m 43; c 3. GENETICS. *Educ:* Univ Nebr, BS, 47, PhD(genetics), 51. *Prof Exp:* AEC fel genetics, Calif Inst Technol, 51-53; geneticist, Biol Div, Oak Ridge Nat Lab, 53-57; asst prof biol, Marquette Univ, 57-59; PROF GENETICS, AGR EXP STA, KANS STATE UNIV, 59- *Mem:* AAAS; Genetics Soc Am; Am Soc Nat. *Res:* Genetics of Neurospora. *Mailing Add:* Div of Biol Kans State Univ Manhattan KS 66502

PITTER, RICHARD LEON, b Whittier, Calif, Apr 4, 47; m 71; c 2. CLOUD PHYSICS, AIR POLLUTION. *Educ:* Univ Calif, Los Angeles, AB, 69, MS, 70, PhD(meteorol), 73. *Prof Exp:* Instr, 73-74, asst prof environ technol, Ore Grad Ctr Study & Res, 74-77; asst prof meteorol, Univ Md, 77-81; ASSOC RES PROF, DESERT RES INST, UNIV NEV, 81- *Concurrent Pos:* Consult, Lawrence Livermore Lab, 74-, Comput Sci Corp, 78- & MITRE Corp, 78- *Mem:* Am Meteorol Soc; Am Geophys Union; Royal Meteorol Soc; AAAS; Air Pollution Control Asn. *Res:* Riming and scavenging by ice crystals; electrical nature of snowflakes; characterization of urban aerosols and their sources; interactions of cloud microphysics and dynamics. *Mailing Add:* Desert Res Inst PO Box 60220 Reno NV 89506

PITTILLO, JACK DANIEL, b Hendersonville, NC, Oct 25, 38; m 66. PLANT ECOLOGY. *Educ:* Berea Col, AB, 61; Univ Ky, MS, 63; Univ Ga, PhD(bot), 66. *Prof Exp:* From asst prof to assoc prof, 66-77, PROF BIOL, WESTERN CAROLINA UNIV, 77- *Concurrent Pos:* Consult, Natural Landmarks Prog, Nat Park Serv, 75. *Mem:* Ecol Soc Am; Am Inst Biol Sci; Bot Soc Am. *Res:* Cladrastis kentukea; fallout radionuclides; biogeochemical cycling; granitic outcrop studies; autecology; endangered and threatened plants; phytogeography of the Balsam and Craggy Mountains, North Carolina; vascular plants of Coweeta Ecological Reserve. *Mailing Add:* Dept of Biol Western Carolina Univ Cullowhee NC 28723

PITTILLO, ROBERT FRANCIS, bacteriology, see previous edition

PITTMAN, CHARLES U, JR, b Rahway, NJ, Oct 26, 39; m 65; c 2. ORGANIC CHEMISTRY. *Educ:* Lafayette Col, BS, 61; Pa State Univ, PhD(chem), 64. *Prof Exp:* Fel chem, Eastern Res Lab, Dow Chem Co, 64-65; fel, Case Western Reserve Univ, 65; from asst prof to prof, 67-77, RES PROF ORG CHEM, UNIV ALA, 77- *Concurrent Pos:* Vis lectr, Natick Army Lab, Lowell Tech Inst & Koppers Co Res Labs, Pa; mem vis fac, Oakwood Col 66. *Mem:* Am Chem Soc. *Res:* Carbonium ion chemistry; organic reactions in strong acids; organometallic polymers; propellant combustion mechanisms and catalysis; application of quantum mechanical calculations to organic structures; homogeneous catalysis and attatching homogeneous catalysts to polymers; polymer anchored photocatalysts and metal cluster catalysis. *Mailing Add:* Dept of Chem Box H Univ of Ala University AL 35486

PITTMAN, CHATTY ROGER, b Blakely, Ga; m 60; c 2. MATHEMATICS. *Educ:* N Ga Col, BS, 59; Univ Ga, MA, 62, PhD(math), 65. *Prof Exp:* From asst prof to assoc prof, 65-76, PROF MATH, WEST GA COL, 76-, CHMN DEPT, 70- *Concurrent Pos:* Actg head dept math, W Ga Col, 69-70. *Mem:* Am Math Soc. *Res:* Paracompact and ordered spaces; general and point-set topology. *Mailing Add:* Dept of Math West Ga Col Carrollton GA 30117

PITTMAN, EDWARD D, b Dublin, Tex, Feb 17, 30; m 55; c 2. PETROLOGY, SEDIMENTOLOGY. *Educ:* Univ Calif, Los Angeles, BA, 56, MA, 58, PhD(geol), 62. *Prof Exp:* Geologist, Pan Am Petrol Corp, 62-65; sr res scientist, 66-71, staff res scientist, 71-73, res group supvr, 73-79, SPECIAL RES ASSOC, AMOCO PROD CO, 79- *Concurrent Pos:* Chmn geol res comt, Am Petrol Inst, 73-77; distinguished lectr, Am Asn Petrol Geologists, 78-79; assoc ed, J Sedimentary Petrol, 77-79 & Am Asn Petrol Geologists, 77-; adj prof, Univ Tulsa, 79- *Mem:* Am Asn Petrol Geologists; Soc Econ Paleont & mineral. *Res:* Sedimentary petrology; carbonate petrology. *Mailing Add:* Res Ctr Amoco Prod Co Box 591 Tulsa OK 74102

PITTMAN, FRED ESTES, b Cleveland, Miss, June 29, 32; m 61; c 3. GASTROENTEROLOGY, MEDICAL RESEARCH. *Educ:* Yale Univ, BA, 55; Columbia Univ, MD, 59; Univ Birmingham, Eng, PhD(med sci), 66. *Prof Exp:* Asst med, Sch Med, Cornell Univ, 59-61; vis fel, Sch Med, Columbia Univ, 61-63; sr registr, Sch Med, Univ Birmingham, 63-66; asst prof, Sch Med, Tulane Univ, 66-69; ASSOC PROF MED, MED UNIV SC, 69- *Concurrent Pos:* Trainee, NIH, 61-63; fel, Helen Hay Whitney Found, 63-66; res fel, Cancer Res Inst, Nat Ctr Sci Res, France, 66; fel, Roche Found, Switz, 76. *Mem:* Am Fedn Clin Res; Am Gastroenterol Asn; Am Soc Cell Biol; Am Soc Trop Med & Hyg; AAAS. *Res:* Tissue toxicity of entamoeba histolytica using whole and cell fractions of axenically cultured organisms; mechanism of action of certain antibiotics in the production of colonic mucosal injury. *Mailing Add:* Dept Med Med Univ SC Charleston SC 29401

PITTMAN, G(EORGE) F(RANK), JR, b Pittsburgh, Pa, June 9, 27; m 49; c 2. ELECTRICAL ENGINEERING. *Educ:* Carnegie Inst Technol, BSEE, 49, MSEE, 50, DSc(elec eng), 52. *Prof Exp:* Lab asst elec eng, Carnegie Inst Technol, 49-50, res engr, 50-52; engr, Mat Eng Dept, 52-54, supv engr, 54-55, sect mgr, New Prod Labs, 55-59, mgr elec equip develop dept, 59-62, mgr power conversion eng, Indust Electronics Div, 62; mgr elec eng, Molecular Electronics Div, 63-66, mgr eng, 66-69, sr projs mgr, Prod Transition Lab, 69-76, mgr spec progs, Westinghouse Design & Develop Ctr, 77-79, MGR OPERS, WESTINGHOUSE PROD & QUALITY CTR, WESTINGHOUSE ELEC CORP, PITTSBURGH, 79- *Mem:* Inst Elec & Electronics Engrs. *Res:* Energy storage systems; power electronics; development and application of solid state devices. *Mailing Add:* Westinghouse Elec Prod Ctr PO Box 160 Pittsburgh PA 15230

PITTMAN, JAMES ALLEN, JR, b Orlando, Fla, Apr 12, 27; m 55; c 2. INTERNAL MEDICINE, ENDOCRINOLOGY. *Educ:* Davidson Col, BS, 48; Harvard Med Sch, MD, 52; Am Bd Internal Med, dipl, 59. *Hon Degrees:* DSc, Harvard Univ, 80. *Prof Exp:* Intern & resident med, Mass Gen Hosp, Boston, 52-54; clin assoc, Endocrinol Br, Nat Cancer Inst, 54-56; from instr to assoc prof med, Med Ctr, Univ Ala, Birmingham, 56-64, prof med & dir, Endocrinol & Metab Div, 64-71, co-chmn dept med, 69-71; prof med, Sch Med, Georgetown Univ, 71-73; EXEC DEAN, UNIV ALA SCH MED SYST, 73- *Concurrent Pos:* Fel, Harvard Med Sch, 53-54; instr, Sch Med, George Washington Univ, 55-56; chief radioisotope serv, Birmingham Vet Admin Hosp, 58-71; asst chief med dir res & educ in med, US Vet Admin, 71-73. *Mem:* Endocrine Soc; Soc Nuclear Med; Am Col Physicians; Am Thyroid Asn. *Res:* Control of thyroid function. *Mailing Add:* 5 Ridge Dr Birmingham AL 35213

PITTMAN, KENNETH ARTHUR, b Baltimore, Md, May 7, 37. DRUG METABOLISM, TOXICOLOGY. *Educ:* Univ Md, BS, 60, PhD(biochem), 66. *Prof Exp:* Res chemist, Dairy Cattle Res Br, Animal Health Res Div, USDA, 62-67; res biologist, Sterling-Winthrop Res Inst, 67-73; asst res prof environ toxicol, Inst Human & Comp Toxicol, Albany Med Col, 73-76; ASST DIR DRUG METAB, BRISTOL LABS, 76- *Mem:* Am Chem Soc; Am Soc Pharmacol & Exp Therapeut. *Res:* Metabolism, pharmacokinetics and mechanism of toxic action of drugs, pesticides and food additives. *Mailing Add:* 212 Hurlburt Rd Syracuse NY 13224

PITTMAN, MARGARET, b Prairie Grove, Ark, Jan 20, 01. BACTERIOLOGY. *Educ:* Hendrix Col, AB, 23; Univ Chicago, MS, 26, PhD(bact), 29; Dipl, Am Bd Microbiol, 62. *Hon Degrees:* LLD, Hendrix Col, 54. *Prof Exp:* Prin acad, Galloway Woman's Col, 23-25; asst scientist, Rockefeller Inst, 28-34; asst bacteriologist, NY State Dept Health, 34-36; bacteriologist, NIH, 36-71, chief lab bact prod, Div Biol Stand, 58-71, guest worker, 71-72; GUEST WORKER & CONSULT, BUR BIOLOGICS, FOOD & DRUG ADMIN, 72- *Concurrent Pos:* Consult at large, WHO, 58, 59, 62, 69, & 71-73; mem, US Pharmacopeia Panels, 66-75. *Honors & Awards:* Superior Serv Award, Dept Health, Educ & Welfare, 63 & Distinguished Serv Award, 68; Fed Woman's Award, 70. *Mem:* AAAS; hon mem Am Soc Microbiol; Am Acad Microbiol; Soc Exp Biol & Med; Int Asn Biol Standard. *Res:* Hemophilus, pneumococcus; meningococcus; respiratory infections, meningitis and conjuctivitis; standardization of biological products; pertussis, typhoid and cholera vaccines; tetanus toxoid. *Mailing Add:* 3133 Connecticut Ave NW Washington DC 20008

PITTMAN, MELVIN AMOS, b Chester, SC, Aug 4, 05; m 43; c 3. PHYSICS. *Educ:* The Citadel, BS, 25; Univ SC, MS, 29; Johns Hopkins Univ, PhD(physics), 36. *Prof Exp:* Instr physics, Univ Md, 29-36, asst prof & head dept, Baltimore br, 36-37; radar engr, Signal Corps, US Army, 42; prof physics & head dept, Madison Col, 46-55 & Col of William & Mary, 55-66, dir of insts, 66-67; dean, 67-74, EMER DEAN, SCH SCI, OLD DOMINION UNIV, 74- *Mem:* Am Phys Soc; assoc Optical Soc Am. *Res:* Infrared dispersion and absorption; polarization in infrared; effects of radiation. *Mailing Add:* 3449 Waverly Dock Rd Jacksonville FL 32217

PITTMAN, ROBERT PRESTON, b Lubbock, Tex, May 26, 40. CARDIOVASCULAR PHYSIOLOGY. *Educ:* Tex Tech Univ, BA, 63, MS, 66; Univ Houston, PhD(physiol), 70. *Prof Exp:* ASSOC PROF PHYSIOL, MICH STATE UNIV, 71- *Concurrent Pos:* NIH fel, Mich State Univ, 70-71. *Mem:* AAAS; Am Soc Zool; Sigma Xi. *Res:* Hemorrhagic shock; hepatic and gastrointestinal blood flow. *Mailing Add:* Dept of Physiol Mich State Univ East Lansing MI 48824

PITTMAN, ROLAND NATHAN, b Waco, Tex, Feb 13, 44; m 68; c 2. CARDIOVASCULAR PHYSIOLOGY. *Educ:* Mass Inst Technol, SB, 66; State Univ NY Stony Brook, MA, 68, PhD(physics), 71. *Prof Exp:* Fel physiol, Univ Va, 71-74; asst prof, 74-78, ASSOC PROF PHYSIOL, MED COL VA, 78- *Honors & Awards:* Louis N Katz Basic Sci Res Prize Young Investr, Am Heart Asn, 79. *Mem:* AAAS; Am Physiol Soc; Biophys Soc; Microcirculatory Soc; Sigma Xi. *Res:* The study of oxygen transport in the microcirculation and the role of oxygen on local regulation of blood flow. *Mailing Add:* Dept of Physiol Box 608 Med Col of Va MCV Sta Richmond VA 23298

PITTS, BARRY JAMES ROGER, b UK, Sept 27, 40. BIOCHEMISTRY, PHARMACOLOGY. *Educ:* Dublin Univ, BA, 64, PhD(biochem), 69. *Prof Exp:* Fel pharmacol, Med Col, Cornell Univ, 69-72; from instr to asst prof cell biophys, 72-77, ASST PROF MED & BIOCHEM, BAYLOR COL MED, 77- *Mem:* Am Heart Asn; Am Soc Biol Chem; Am Soc Pharmacol & Exp Therapeut; Biophys Soc; NY Acad Sci. *Res:* Ion transport systems in mammalian heart; role in excitation, contraction coupling and in myocardial ischemia; physiology. *Mailing Add:* Dept Med Baylor Col Med Houston TX 77030

PITTS, CHARLES W, b Corinth, Miss, Dec 11, 33; m 56; c 4. MEDICAL ENTOMOLOGY, INSECT PHYSIOLOGY. *Educ:* Miss State Univ, BS, 60; Kans State Univ, MS, 62, PhD(entom), 65. *Prof Exp:* From instr to prof entom, Kans State Univ, 62-78; PROF ENTOM & HEAD DEPT, PA STATE UNIV, 78- *Mem:* AAAS; Entom Soc Am. *Res:* Chemical control of insects attacking man and animal; insect attractants and sensory physiology and behavior; scanning electron microscopy. *Mailing Add:* Dept of Entom Pa State Univ University Park PA 16802

PITTS, DONALD GRAVES, b Perry Twp, Ark, Apr 11, 26; m 46; c 3. OPTOMETRY, PHYSIOLOGICAL OPTICS. *Educ:* Southern Col Optom, OD, 50; Ind Univ, MS, 59, PhD(physiol optics), 64. *Prof Exp:* Clin optometrist, Biomed Sci Corps, US Air Force, 51-57, mem vision res staff, Aerospace Med Res Lab, Wright-Patterson Air Force Base, Ohio, 59-62, mem fac, Sch Aerospace Med, 62-69, mem optics sect, 64-69; PROF OPTOM, COL OPTOM, UNIV HOUSTON, 69-, ASSOC DEAN, COL OPTOM, 73- *Concurrent Pos:* Mem Armed Forces vision comt, Nat Res Coun; mem panel ophthal devices, Food & Drug Admin, 74-77; mem adv coun, AAAS, 74-76. *Mem:* Fel AAAS; Am Asn Univ Prof; Optical Soc Am; Am Optom Asn; fel Am Acad Optom. *Res:* Visual neurophysiology; aerospace vision effects; effects of radiant energy on the visual system; color vision. *Mailing Add:* Col of Optom Univ of Houston Houston TX 77004

PITTS, DONALD ROSS, b Anniston, Ala, Sept 21, 29; m 51; c 3. MECHANICAL ENGINEERING. *Educ:* Auburn Univ, BME, 51; Ga Inst Technol, MSME, 60, PhD(mech eng), 68. *Prof Exp:* Develop engr, Goodyear Tire & Rubber Co, Ohio, 53-55; aircraft design engr, Lockheed Aircraft Corp, Ga, 55-58, sr aircraft res engr, Res & Develop Lab, 59-67; asst plant engr, H W Lay Co Div, Frito-Lay Corp, 58-59; assoc prof heat transfer & fluid mech, Tenn Technol Univ, 67-71, prof, 71-80; PROF MECH ENG, CLEMSON UNIV, 80- *Mem:* Am Soc Mech Engrs; Am Soc Eng Educ. *Res:* Transient film and nucleate boiling; free convection heat transfer; liquid droplet interaction with external boundary layer flow; fluidized bed heat transfer. *Mailing Add:* Clemson Univ Clemson SC 29631

PITTS, GERALD NELSON, b Brownwood, Tex, June 14, 43; m 64; c 1. COMPUTER SCIENCES. *Educ:* Tex A&M Univ, BA, 66, MS, 67, PhD(comput sci), 71. *Prof Exp:* Teaching asst math, Tex A&M Univ, 66-71; asst prof comput sci, Univ Southwestern La, 71-72; assoc prof & head dept, Central Tex Col, 72-74; assoc prof, Tex Tech Univ, 74-75; ASSOC PROF COMPUT SCI, MISS STATE UNIV, 75- *Concurrent Pos:* Adj prof comput sci, Fla Inst Technol, 72-73. *Mem:* Sigma Xi; Asn Comput Mach; Data Processing Mgt Asn. *Mailing Add:* Dept of Comput Sci Miss State Univ Starkville MS 39759

PITTS, GROVER CLEVELAND, b Richmond, Va, Apr 4, 18; m 47; c 3. PHYSIOLOGY. *Educ:* Univ Richmond, BA, 39; Harvard Univ, AM, 40, PhD(physiol), 43. *Prof Exp:* Lab asst anat, Harvard Univ, 40-41, asst invert physiol, 42-43, asst, Fatigue Lab, 42-44; investr physiol, Naval Med Res Inst, 44-49; asst prof, 50-58, assoc prof, 58-79, PROF PHYSIOL, SCH MED, UNIV VA, 79- *Mem:* AAAS; Am Physiol Soc; Am Soc Zool. *Res:* Physiologic effects of gravitation, exercise; regulation of body composition. *Mailing Add:* Dept Physiol Univ Va Sch Med Charlottesville VA 22903

PITTS, JAMES NINDE, JR, b Salt Lake City, Utah, Jan 10, 21; m 45; c 3. PHYSICAL CHEMISTRY, PHOTOCHEMISTRY. *Educ:* Univ Calif, Los Angeles, BS, 45, PhD(chem), 49. *Prof Exp:* Asst, Nat Defense Res Comt, Northwestern Univ, 42-45, res assoc spec projs div, US Army Serv Forces, 45-46, from instr to asst prof chem, 49-54; assoc prof phys chem, 54-59, PROF CHEM, UNIV CALIF, RIVERSIDE, 59-, DIR, STATEWIDE AIR POLLUTION RES CTR, 70-, PROJ CLEAN AIR, 71- *Concurrent Pos:* Guggenheim fel, 60-61; chmn dept chem, Univ Calif, Riverside, 61-63, fac res lectr, 65-66, dir dry lands res inst, 70-71; acad adv to chancellor, Univ Calif, Santa Cruz, 62-63; vis res fel, Merton Col, Oxford Univ, 65; mem Inst Geophys & Planetary Physics, 68-; Sigma Xi-Sci Res Soc Am lectr, 72-73; consult, USPHS & mem environ sci & eng study sect air pollution; mem adv coun protective comt, Chem Corps US Army; adv bd mil personnel supplies comt textile functional finishing, Nat Acad Sci-Nat Res Coun; co-chmn, 2nd Int Union Pure & Appl Chem Int Symp Photochem, Netherlands; adj fac mem, Off Manpower Develop, Environ Protection Agency, mem air pollution chem adv comt; tech & sci adv comt, Calif Air Resources Bd & Comt Biol Effects of Atmos Pollutants; chmn panel polycyclic org mat comt kinetics of chem reactions, Nat Acad Sci; consult. *Mem:* Am Chem Soc; Royal Soc Chem; Am Phys Soc. *Res:* Photochemical reactions in urban air and upper atmosphere; ozone chemiluminescent reactions; photochemical and thermal reactions of aromatic hydrocarbons, nitrogen dioxide and peroxyacetyl nitrate; singlet molecular oxygen; long path length spectroscopy; smog chamber studies; airborne monitoring. *Mailing Add:* Statewide Air Pollution Res Ctr Univ of Calif Riverside CA 92502

PITTS, ROBERT GARY, b Auburn, Ala, Aug 17, 45; div. DENTAL RESEARCH, MICROBIAL PHYSIOLOGY. *Educ:* Auburn Univ, BS, 67, MS, 69; La State Univ, Baton Rouge, PhD, 71; Rutgers Univ Law Sch, JD, 82. *Prof Exp:* Res assoc microbiol & NIH fel, Inst Dent Res, Univ Ala, Birmingham, 71-72; scientist, 72-76, sr scientist, 76-77, mgr chem & biol res, Personal Prod Div, 77-78, dir res serv, Personal Prod Div, 78-80, DIR BIOL RES, CONSUMER PROD GROUP, WARNER-LAMBERT CO, 80- *Mem:* Am Soc Microbiol; Am Chem Soc; Sigma Xi; Int Asn Dent Res. *Res:* Caries; gingivitis; periodontitis; oral malodor; acne; dandruff; dry skin. *Mailing Add:* Warner-Lambert Co Morris Plains NJ 07950

PITTS, THOMAS GRIFFIN, b Clinton, SC, Aug 19, 35; m 61; c 2. COMPUTER SOFTWARE, EXPERIMENTAL NUCLEAR PHYSICS. *Educ:* Presby Col SC, BS, 57. *Prof Exp:* Mathematician atomic energy div, 57-58, physicist, 59-76, SR RES ENGR, LYNCHBURG RES CTR, RES DEVELOP DIV, BABCOCK & WILCOX, CO, 77- *Mem:* Am Nuclear Soc; Asn Comput Mach. *Res:* Computer programming and evaluation; nuclear instrumentation design and testing; critical experiments; neutron noise measurements. *Mailing Add:* 1804 Parkland Dr Lynchburg VA 24503

PITTS, WANNA DENE, b Tonkawa, Okla, Jan 24, 32; m 47; c 2. POLLINATION ECOLOGY, FIRE ECOLOGY. *Educ:* San Jose State Col, BS, 70; San Jose State Univ, MS, 72; Univ Calif, Davis, PhD(ecol), 76. *Prof Exp:* Lectr, 72-76, asst prof, 76-80, ASSOC PROF BIOL SCI, SAN JOSE STATE UNIV, 80-, ASSOC DEAN, SCH SCI, 78- *Concurrent Pos:* Lectr biol sci, San Jose City Col, 71-73, Gavilan Commun Col, 72-73. *Mem:* AAAS; Am Bot Soc; Ecol Soc Am. *Res:* Biology of cupressus abramsiana; plant ecology. *Mailing Add:* Dept Biol Sci San Jose State Univ San Jose CA 95192

PITTZ, EUGENE P, b Albany, NY, Sept 17, 39; m 62; c 2. TOXICOLOGY, PHYSICAL BIOCHEMISTRY. *Educ:* Siena Col, BS, 62; State Univ NY, Buffalo, PhD(biophysics), 70. *Prof Exp:* Fel biochem, Brandeis Univ, 70-74; res asst prof toxicol, Albany Med Col, 74-78; SR RES SCIENTIST DERMATO-TOXICOL, LEVER BROTHERS CO, 78- *Mem:* AAAS; Am Chem Soc; Int Soc for Ecotoxicol & Environ Safety; Sigma Xi; Soc Cosmetic Chemists. *Res:* Safety evaluation of products; dermatoxicology; claim support research; carcinogenesis; systemic toxicology; physical biochemsitry. *Mailing Add:* Toxicol Sect Res Ctr 45 River Rd Edgewater NJ 07020

PITZER, KENNETH SANBORN, b Pomona, Calif, Jan 6, 14; m 35; c 3. PHYSICAL CHEMISTRY. *Educ:* Calif Inst Technol, BS, 35; Univ Calif, PhD(chem), 37. *Hon Degrees:* ScD, Wesleyan Col, 62; LLD, Univ Calif, 63, Mills Col, 69. *Prof Exp:* Asst chem, Univ Calif, Berkeley, 35-36, from instr to prof, 37-61, asst dean col letters & sci, 47-48, dean col chem, 51-60; prof chem & pres, Rice Univ, 61-68, Stanford Univ, 68-70; PROF CHEM, UNIV CALIF, BERKELEY, 71- *Concurrent Pos:* Tech dir, Md Res Lab, Off Sci Res & Develop, 43-44; assoc dir proj, Am Petrol Inst, 47-52, dir proj, 50, 52-58; dir div res, US AEC, DC, 49-51, mem gen adv comt, 58-65, chmn, 60-62; Guggenheim fel, 51; chmn sect chem, Nat Acad Sci, 59-62, coun, 64-68 & 73-76; trustee, Rand Corp, 62-72, Carnegie Found Advan Teaching, 66-70 & Pitzer Col, 66-; dir, Fed Reserve Bank Dallas, 65-68; mem, President's Sci Adv Comt, 65-68; chmn coun presidents, Univ Res Asn, 66-67, mem bd dirs, Owens-Ill, Inc, 66- *Honors & Awards:* Awards, Am Chem Soc, 43 & 50, G N Lewis Medal, 65, Priestly Medal, 69 & Gibbs Medal, 76; Clayton Prize, Brit Inst Mech Eng, 58; Priestley Mem Award, Dickinson Col, 63; Nat Medal of Sci, 75; Gold Medal, Am Inst Chem, 76. *Mem:* Nat Acad Sci; Am Chem Soc; Am Philos Soc; Am Nuclear Soc; fel Am Phys Soc; Faraday Soc; fel Am Inst Chem. *Res:* Chemical thermodynamics; quantum theory and statistical mechanics applied to chemistry; molecular spectroscopy. *Mailing Add:* Dept Chem Univ Calif Berkeley CA 94720

PITZER, RUSSELL MOSHER, b Berkeley, Calif, May 10, 38; m 59; c 3. THEORETICAL CHEMISTRY. *Educ:* Calif Inst Technol, BS, 59; Harvard Univ, AM, 61, PhD(chem, physics), 63. *Prof Exp:* Mem div sponsored res staff, Mass Inst Technol, 63; res instr chem, Calif Inst Technol, 63-66, asst prof, 66-68; assoc prof, 68-79, PROF, OHIO STATE UNIV, 79- *Concurrent Pos:* Consult, Battelle Mem Inst, 75-77, Lawrence Berkeley Lab, 78- & Lawrence Livermore Nat Lab, 80- *Mem:* Am Phys Soc; Am Chem Soc. *Res:* Treatment of small polyatomic molecules by quantum mechanics; use of symmetry in the computation of molecular electronic structure. *Mailing Add:* Dept of Chem Ohio State Univ Columbus OH 43210

PIVNICK, HILLIARD, b Toronto, Ont, Apr 26, 19; m 45; c 3. BACTERIOLOGY. *Educ:* Univ Toronto, BSA, 46; Dalhousie Univ, MSc, 49; Mich State Univ, PhD(bact), 52. *Prof Exp:* From asst prof to assoc prof bact, Univ Nebr, 52-58; res assoc, Connaught Lab, Toronto, 58-60, mem res staff, 60-66; mem res staff, Can Govt, 66-75, dir bur microbial hazards, 75-78, MEM RES STAFF, FOOD DIRECTORATE, HEALTH PROTECTION BR, HEALTH & WELFARE CAN, 78- *Mem:* Can Soc Microbiol; Can Pub Health Asn; Brit Soc Appl Bact; Can Inst Food Sci & Technol; Inst Food Technologists. *Res:* Microbial food-borne infections and toxemias; microbial quality of food; prevention of salmonella infection of young poultry by altering gut microflora. *Mailing Add:* Bur of Microbiol Hazards Health Protect Br Tunneys Pastr Ottawa ON K1A 0L2 Can

PIVONKA, WILLIAM, b Albert, Kans, Mar 31, 30; m 59; c 1. ORGANIC CHEMISTRY. *Educ:* St Benedict's Col, BS, 51, Dow Chem Co fel & PhD(chem), 59. *Prof Exp:* Shift chemist, Hercules Powder Co, 51-52; asst chem, Univ Kans, 54-59; asst prof org chem & chmn dept, 59-63, from assoc prof to prof, 63-72, DEAN SCH ARTS & SCI, PARKS COL, 72-, PROF CHEM, 76- *Mem:* Am Chem Soc; Am Inst Chem; Am Inst Chem Eng. *Res:* Organophosphorus and fluorocarbon chemistry; reaction mechanisms. *Mailing Add:* Dept of Chem Parks Col Kansas City MO 64152

PIVORUN, EDWARD BRONI, b Nashua, NH, Nov 5, 46; m 71. COMPARATIVE PHYSIOLOGY, ZOOLOGY. *Educ:* Tufts Univ, BS, 68; Univ Minn, PhD(zool), 74. *Prof Exp:* Asst prof, 74-80, ASSOC PROF ZOOL, CLEMSON UNIV, 80- *Mem:* Am Soc Zoologists; Ecol Soc Am; Sigma Xi; Int Hibernation Soc. *Res:* Physiology of hibernation; radiotelemetry of body temperature and heart rate patterns of mammals during hibernation; effects of blood-borne hibernation factors on homeothermic tissue; effects of opiods and peptides on daily torpor; influence of the pineal gland on hibernation and daily torpor. *Mailing Add:* Dept of Zool Clemson Univ Clemson SC 29631

PIWONI, MARVIN DENNIS, b Stanley, Wis, Mar 9, 47; m 74; c 1. WATER CHEMISTRY, ENVIRONMENTAL POLLUTANT TRANSPORT. *Educ:* Univ Wis, BS, 70, MS, 75; Univ Tex, Dallas, PhD(environ sci), 75. *Prof Exp:* Asst prof environ sci, Univ Tex, Dallas, 75-80; PHYS SCIENTIST, R S KERR ENVIRON RES LAB, US ENVIRON PROTECTION AGENCY, 80- *Concurrent Pos:* Chmn, Atomic Absorbtion Joint Task Standard Methods Comt, Water Pollution Control Fedn, 79- *Res:* Behavior of pollutants in aqueous systems including cyanide complexation studies; organic pollutant behavior previously on activated carbon, presently in the subsurface and in ground water. *Mailing Add:* R S Kerr Environ Res Lab PO Box 1198 Ada OK 74820

PIWONKA, THOMAS SQUIRE, b Cleveland, Ohio, Jan 8, 37; m 61; c 3. METALLURGY. *Educ:* Case Inst Technol, BS, 59; Mass Inst Technol, MS, 60, DSc, 63. *Prof Exp:* Sr engr, Gen Motors Corp, 63-66; sr metallurgist, TRW Metals Div, 66-70, prin engr, Mat Technol Lab, 70-73, tech dir, Kelsey-Hayes Invest Casting Orgn, 73-74, mgr casting res, TRW Mat Technol, 74-80, MGR, MAT RES DEPT, TRW INC, 80- *Concurrent Pos:* Mem comt high strength steel & titanium castings, Nat Mat Adv Bd, 72. *Mem:* Am Inst Mining, Metall & Petrol Engrs; Am Soc Metals; Am Foundrymen's Soc. *Res:* Solidification; titanium casting; directional solidification; microporosity in solidification; vacuum melting. *Mailing Add:* T/M 3201 23555 Euclid Ave Cleveland OH 44117

PIXLEY, ALDEN F, b Pasadena, Calif, Feb 27, 28; m 56; c 3. MATHEMATICS. *Educ:* Univ Calif, Berkeley, AB, 49, MA, 50, PhD(math), 61. *Prof Exp:* Spec rep to petrol indust, IBM Corp, 55-58; asst prof math, Col Notre Dame, 58-60 & San Francisco State Col, 60-62; from asst prof to assoc prof, 62-72, PROF MATH, HARVEY MUDD COL, 72- *Mem:* Am Math Soc; Math Asn Am. *Res:* Universal algebra and egualinal logic. *Mailing Add:* Dept of Math Harvey Mudd Col Claremont CA 91711

PIXLEY, CARL PRESTON, b Omaha, Nebr, Nov 3, 42; m 68. TOPOLOGY. *Educ:* Univ Omaha, BA, 66; Rutgers Univ, MS, 68; State Univ NY Binghampton, PhD(math), 73. *Prof Exp:* From instr to asst prof math, Univ Tex, Austin, 74-78; ASSOC PROF MATH, SOUTHWEST TEX STATE UNIV, 78- *Mem:* Am Math Soc; Asn Symbolic Logic. *Res:* Topological selection theory and geometrical topology. *Mailing Add:* Dept of Math Southwest Tex State Univ San Marcos TX 78666

PIXLEY, EMILY CHANDLER, b Knoxville, Tenn, Aug 19, 04; m 31; c 3. MATHEMATICS. *Educ:* Randolph-Macon Woman's Col, AB, 26; Univ Chicago, SM, 27, PhD, 31. *Prof Exp:* From instr to prof & head dept math, St Xavier Col, 27-36; res mathematician, US Govt, 34-35; from instr to asst prof math, Wayne State Univ, 36-48; from asst prof to prof, 48-73, EMER PROF MATH, UNIV DETROIT, 73- *Mem:* Am Math Soc; Math Asn Am. *Res:* Modern abstract algebra; theory numbers; analytical and additive number theory. *Mailing Add:* 20194 Briarcliff Rd Detroit MI 48221

PIZARRO, ENRIQUETA, b Mexico City, Mex, May 21, 18. VIROLOGY. *Educ:* Nat Univ Mex, BSc, 37; Univ Chicago, MSc, 47. *Prof Exp:* Prof chem & physics, Fitzgibbon Sch, 40-44; curator & lab asst bact & parasitol, Univ Chicago, 46-47; bacteriologist, Am-Mex Comt Aftosa Fever, 48; PROF VIRUSES, NAT SCH BIOL SCI, MEX, 49-; PROF MICROBIOL, NAT SCH DENT, NAT UNIV MEX, 61-; HEAD RESPIRATORY VIRSUSES LAB, INST HEALTH & TROP DIS, 72- *Concurrent Pos:* Nat Univ Mex fel, Harvard Univ, 52; lab asst, Manicomio Gen, 40-51; bacteriologist, Inst Health & Trop Dis, 48-51, head leprosy lab, 65-72; lectr, Nat Univ Mex, 51 & Nat Sch Health, 51-; head polio res lab, Virus Lab Palo Alto, 51-55; Mex deleg, Int Cong Microbiol, Italy, 53; head diag sect, Virus Lab, Huipulco, 55-57; head virol sect, Nat Inst Hyg, 57-60; head respiratory viruses lab, Nat Inst Virol, 61-65. *Honors & Awards:* Letter of Recognition, Pres of Mex Repub. *Mem:* Am Soc Microbiol; NY Acad Sci; Mex Asn Microbiol (pres, 63-65); Mex Asn Res Pharmacol & Therapeut; Latin Am Soc Microbiol (treas). *Res:* Viruses; respiratory viruses; inoculation of mice thymectomy and irradiation; diagnosis of leprosy; diagnosis and epidemiology of respiratory viral diseases; reference and control. *Mailing Add:* Moras 644 03100 Mexico City DF Mexico

PIZER, LEWIS IVAN, b New York, NY, Sept 14, 32; m 57; c 3. MICROBIOLOGY, BIOCHEMISTRY. *Educ:* Univ NZ, BS, 54; Univ Calif, Berkeley, PhD(biochem), 58. *Prof Exp:* Donner fel, 58-59; NIH fel, 59-60; from asst prof to assoc prof microbiol, Univ Pa, 61-77, prof, 77-80; PROF MICROBIOL & CHMN, DEPT MICROBIOL & IMMUNOL, SCH MED, UNIV COLO HEALTH SCI CTR, 80- *Mem:* Am Soc Biol Chem; Am Soc Microbiol. *Res:* Metabolic control mechanisms and the physiology of bacteriophage infected cells. *Mailing Add:* Unif Colo Health Sci Ctr Sch Med 4200 E Ninth Ave Denver CO 80262

PIZER, RICHARD DAVID, b Washington, DC, Mar 15, 44; c 2. INORGANIC CHEMISTRY. *Educ:* Johns Hopkins Univ, BA, 65, Brandeis Univ, PhD(chem), 69. *Prof Exp:* Asst prof chem, State Univ NY Col Potsdam, 69-71; asst prof, NY Univ, 71-73; ASSOC PROF CHEM, BROOKLYN COL, CITY UNIV NEW YORK, 73- *Concurrent Pos:* Vis fel, Res Sch Chem, Australian Nat Univ, 79-80. *Mem:* Sigma Xi; Am Chem Soc. *Res:* Study of fast reactions in aqueous solution studied by relaxation and stopped-flow methods; complexation reactions of boron acids; the dynamics of cryptate formation; metal ion inclusion complexes. *Mailing Add:* Dept Chem Brooklyn Col City Univ New York Brooklyn NY 11210

PIZIAK, ROBERT, b Hadley, Mass, Jan 17, 43; m 66. MATHEMATICS, QUANTUM MECHANICS. *Educ:* Amherst Col, BA, 64; Univ Mass, MA, 66, PhD(math), 69. *Prof Exp:* Asst prof math, Univ Mass, Amherst, 69-70 & Univ Fla, 70-73; asst prof math, Centre Col, KY, 73-77, assoc prof, 77-81; LECTR, BAYLOR UNIV, 81- *Mem:* Am Math Soc; Math Asn Am. *Res:* Hilbert space geometry; logic of quantum mechanics. *Mailing Add:* 113 Calvin Tenple TX 76501

PIZIAK, VERONICA KELLY, b Oak Bluffs, Mass, May 31, 42; m 66. ENDOCRINOLOGY, METABOLISM. *Educ:* Univ Mass, BS, 63, MS, 65, PhD(biochem), 70; Univ Ky, MD, 76; Am Bd Internal Med, cert, 79. *Prof Exp:* Fel biochem, Univ Fla, 70-73; resident internal med, Akron Gen Med Ctr, 76-79; fel endocrinol, Univ Cincinnati, 79-81; SR STAFF PHYSICIAN ENDOCRINOL, SCOTT & WHITE CLIN & HOSP, 81- *Mem:* Am Col Physicians; AMA. *Res:* Effect of acute and chronic disease and antineoplastic therapy on endocrine organ functions. *Mailing Add:* Scott & White Clin 2401 S 31st St Temple TX 76501

PIZZALATO, THOMPSON DEMETRIO, b New Orleans, La, Nov 8, 43; m 71; c 2. PLANT ANATOMY. *Educ:* La State Univ, BS, 65, MS, 68; Miami Univ, PhD(bot), 74. *Prof Exp:* Fel, Tex Tech Univ, 74-75, NC Cent Forest Exp Sta, 75-76 & Harvard Univ, 76-77; ASST PROF, UNIV DEL, 77- *Mem:* Bot Soc Am; Int Asn Wood Anatomists. *Res:* Anatomical studies on the vascular systems of the flowers of grasses; anatomical modifications of plants by herbicides. *Mailing Add:* Dept Plant Sci Univ Del Newark DE 19711

PIZZARELLO, DONALD JOSEPH, b Mt Vernon, NY, Aug 14, 33; m 61; c 4. RADIOBIOLOGY. *Educ:* Fordham Univ, AB, 55, MS, 57, PhD(exp embryol), 59. *Prof Exp:* AEC res assoc, Argonne Nat Lab, 59-60; from instr to assoc prof radiol, Bowman Gray Sch Med, 60-70; assoc prof, 70-73, PROF RADIOL, SCH MED, NY UNIV, 74- *Concurrent Pos:* Nat Cancer Inst res grants, Nat Ctr Radiation Health, 61 & 64; examr, Am Bd Radiol, 68-; lectr, Mt Sinai Sch Med, 72-; adj prof, Manhattan Col, 72- & Montefiore Hosp & Med Ctr, 72- *Mem:* AAAS; Radiation Res Soc; Int Chronobiol Soc. *Res:* Experimental embryology. *Mailing Add:* Dept of Radiol NY Univ Med Ctr New York NY 10016

PIZZARELLO, SANDRA, biochemistry, see previous edition

PIZZICA, PHILIP ANDREW, b Chicago, Ill, Sept 22, 45; m 75. NUCLEAR ENGINEERING. *Educ:* Univ Ill, BS, 68, MA, 73. *Prof Exp:* Nuclear engr, Argonne Nat Lab, 67-71; systs analyst math, United Aircraft Res Lab, 73-74; NUCLEAR ENGR, ARGONNE NAT LAB, 74- *Mem:* Am Nuclear Soc. *Res:* Fast breeder reactor safety research; building computer models to calculate accident conditions in a liquid metal fast breeder reactor; fuel cycle and core design studies. *Mailing Add:* 29W331 Staffeldt Dr Naperville IL 60540

PIZZINI, LOUIS CELESTE, b Black Eagle, Mont, June 7, 32; m 55. ORGANIC CHEMISTRY. *Educ:* Col Great Falls, BS, 54; Notre Dame, PhD(org chem), 59. *Prof Exp:* Res chemist, Wyandotte Chem Corp, 59-64 & Allied Chem Corp, 64; sr res chemist, 65-69, res assoc, 69-74, mgr, Urethane Applns Res & Develop, Tech Serv, 74-77, dir, Organic Res & Develop, 77-80, DIR, INDUST CHEM RES & DEVELOP, BASF WYANDOTTE CORP, 80- *Mem:* Am Chem Soc; Sci Res Soc Am; Soc Plastic Engrs. *Res:* Reactions of aromatic nitro compounds, surface active agents, detergents, alkylene oxides, polyalkylene oxides, polyols, polyethers and polyurethane polymers; polymer chemistry; microcellular, flexible and rigid polyurethane foams; automotive coolants; hydraulic fluids and plasticizers. *Mailing Add:* BASF Wyandotte Corp Wyandotte MI 48192

PIZZO, JOSEPH FRANCIS, b Houston, Tex; m 60; c 5. PHYSICS. *Educ:* Univ St Thomas, BA, 61; Univ Fla, PhD(physics), 64. *Prof Exp:* PROF PHYSICS, LAMAR UNIV, 64-, HEAD DEPT PHYSICS, 80- *Mem:* Am Asn Physics Teachers. *Res:* Electrophotography, including the study of the interaction of radiation, originating from human subjects exposed to high voltage, with photographic emulsions. *Mailing Add:* 965 Lockwood Beaumont TX 77706

PLAA, GABRIEL LEON, b San Francisco, Calif, May 15, 30; m 51; c 8. PHARMACOLOGY. *Educ:* Univ Calif, BS, 52, MS, 56, PhD(pharmacol), 58. *Prof Exp:* Asst pharmacol, Univ Calif, 54-58; from instr to asst prof, Tulane Univ, 58-62; from asst prof to assoc prof, Univ Iowa, 62-68; chmn dept, 68-80, PROF PHARMACOL, UNIV MONTREAL, 68-, VDEAN, FAC GRAD STUDIES, 79- *Concurrent Pos:* Asst toxicologist, San Francisco Coroner's Off, Calif, 54-58; mem toxicol study sect, NIH, 65-69, mem pharmacol-toxicol prog comt, 71-74; mem, Select Comt Generally Recognized As Safe Substances, Fedn Am Socs Exp Biol, 72-; mem comt scholars, Med Res Coun, 69-75; ed, Toxicol & Appl Pharmacol, 73-80. *Honors & Awards:* Thienes Mem Award, Am Acad Clin Toxicol, 77; Lehman Award, Soc Toxicol, 81. *Mem:* Am Soc Pharmacol & Exp Therapeut; Soc Toxicol; Soc Exp Biol & Med; Am Acad Forensic Sci; Soc Toxicol Can. *Res:* Forensic and clinical toxicology; liver injury; effects of drugs on liver function. *Mailing Add:* Dept of Pharmacol Univ of Montreal Fac of Med Montreal PQ H3C 3J7 Can

PLACE, JANET DOBBINS, b Decatur, Ill, Sept 14, 53; m 80. CLINICAL CHEMISTRY. *Educ:* Univ Mo, St Louis, BA, 74; Univ Kans, PhD(biochem), 79. *Prof Exp:* RES SCIENTIST, MILES LAB, AMES DIV, 79- *Mem:* Am Chem Soc; Am Asn Clin Chem. *Res:* Non-isotopic immunoassays for monitoring therapeutic drug levels in serum; monoclonal antibody characterization; Non-isotopic immunoassays for monitoring therapeutic drug levels in serum. *Mailing Add:* Miles Lab Ames Div PO Box 70 Elkhart IN 46515

PLACE, JOHN LOUIS, b Santa Monica, Calif, Sept 4, 25; m 52; c 3. PHYSICAL GEOGRAPHY. *Educ:* Univ Calif, Los Angeles, BA, 49, MA, 51; Univ Calif, Los Angeles, PhD(geog), 70. *Prof Exp:* Teaching asst geog, Univ Calif, Los Angeles, 49-51; cartog engr, Los Angeles Dist Off, US Army Corps Engrs, 51-52, geog analyst, Foreign Area Studies, Strategic Intel, DC, 52-54; geogr, Stanford Res Inst, 54-56, Rand Corp, Calif, 56-57, Syst Develop Corp, 57-63, Off Naval Res, DC, 63-66, US Geol Surv, 66-67; teaching assoc geog, Univ Calif, Los Angeles, 67-68; GEOGR, US GEOL SURV, 68- *Mem:* AAAS; Sigma Xi; Asn Am Geog; Am Soc Photogram. *Res:* Remote sensing; coastal environments; arid lands; terrain mapping. *Mailing Add:* 3418 Surry Lane Falls Church VA 22042

PLACE, RALPH L, b Chicago, Ill, 36; m 62; c 2. MICROCOMPUTER APPLICATIONS. *Educ:* Ball STate Univ, BS, 58; Univ Ky, MS, 62, PhD(physics), 69. *Prof Exp:* Instr physics, Northwest Ctr, Univ Ky, 61-63 & Ball State Univ, 63-65; res asst, Univ Ky, 65-68; from asst prof to assoc prof physics, 68-75, PROF PHYSICS & ASTRON, BALL STATE UNIV, 75-, ADMIN ASST TO HEAD DEPT PHYSICS, 72- *Concurrent Pos:* Cottrell res grant, Ball State Univ, 71-72; consult, Ball Res Corp, 71-72. *Mem:* Asn Comput Mach; Am Phys Soc; Inst Elec & Electronics Engrs. *Res:* Microcomputer applications in physics research and instruction. *Mailing Add:* Dept of Physics Ball State Univ Muncie IN 47306

PLACE, ROBERT DANIEL, b St Johns, Mich, May 10, 41; m 64; c 2. INORGANIC CHEMISTRY, PHYSICAL CHEMISTRY. *Educ:* Albion Col, AB, 63; Univ Calif, Berkeley, PhD(chem), 67. *Prof Exp:* asst prof, 67-80, ASSOC PROF CHEM, OTTERBEIN COL, 80- *Mem:* AAAS; Am Chem Soc. *Res:* Analysis of trace organic molecules in water and air. *Mailing Add:* Dept of Chem Otterbein Col Westerville OH 43081

PLACE, THOMAS ALAN, b Leeds, Eng, Apr 6, 38; Can citizen; m 64. METALLURGY, MATERIALS SCIENCE. *Educ:* Univ Nottingham, BSc, 61; McMaster Univ, MEng, 66; Univ BC, PhD(metall), 69. *Prof Exp:* Res metallurgist, Rolls-Royce Advan Mat Res Lab, Derby, Eng, 61-63; lectr phys metall, Teesside Polytech, Middlesbrough, 63-64; teaching fel mat sci, Univ BC, 69-70; assoc prof mech eng, 70-75, PROF MECH ENG, UNIV IDAHO, 75- *Concurrent Pos:* Vis prof, Univ Auckland, New Zealand, 76-77. *Mem:* Brit Inst Metall; Am Soc Metals; Am Soc Testing & Mat. *Res:* Mechanical properties and fracture mechanics of metals, particleboard and pesticide-damaged eggshells. *Mailing Add:* Dept of Mech Eng Univ of Idaho Moscow ID 83843

PLACE, VIRGIL ALAN, b Crown Point, Ind, Oct 24, 24; div; c 3. CLINICAL PHARMACOLOGY, INTERNAL MEDICINE. *Educ:* Ind Univ, AB, 44; Johns Hopkins Univ, MD, 48. *Prof Exp:* Intern med & biochem, Presby Hosp, Chicago, 48-51; asst to staff med, Mayo Clin, 55; pvt pract, Calif, 55-58; assoc dir clin pharmacol, Lederle Labs Div, Am Cyanamid Co, 58-59, dir, 59-66; assoc med dir, Syntex Res, 66-67, dir clin pharmacol, 67-68; pres & founder, Pharmaceut Res Int, 68-69; VPRES & MED DIR, ALZA CORP, 69- *Concurrent Pos:* Res fel, Presby Hosp, Chicago, 48-51; fel, Mayo Grad Sch Med, Univ Minn, 53-55; instr, Univ Ill, Chicago, 50; attend physician, City Hosp, County Hosp & Community Hosp, Modesto, Calif, 55-58, Bellevue Hosp, Cornell Div, New York, 59-61 & Bergen Pines Hosp, Paramus, NJ, 62-66. *Mem:* AAAS; Am Col Physicians; Am Diabetes Asn; Am Soc Clin Oncol; Am Thoracic Soc. *Res:* Human studies of therapeutic effects of drugs related to their chemical structure, physical form and methods of delivery. *Mailing Add:* 950 Page Mill Rd Palo Alto CA 94304

PLACIOUS, ROBERT CHARLES, b Rochester, NY, Jan 20, 23; m 54; c 5. RADIATION PHYSICS. *Educ:* Univ Rochester, BS, 50; Univ Iowa, MS, 53; Cath Univ, PhD(physics), 65. *Prof Exp:* Jr physicist, 53-56, physicist, 56-66, SR PHYSICIST, NAT BUR STAND, 67- *Mem:* Am Phys Soc; Am Asn Physics Teachers; NY Acad Sc; Am Soc Nondestructive Testing. *Res:* Electron physics; x-ray interactions; electron interactions using electron accelerators in the energy range of several kilo-electron volts to 4 mega-electron volts; radiation effects studies; Bremsstrahlung spectroscopy; optical spectroscopy of fluorescent materials; radiographic imaging and industrial radiographic standards. *Mailing Add:* Radiation Physics Div Ctr Radiation Res Nat Bur of Stand Washington DC 20234

PLAFKER, GEORGE, b Upland, Pa, Mar 6, 29; m 49; c 3. GEOLOGY. *Educ:* Brooklyn Col, BS, 49; Univ Calif, MS, 56; Stanford Univ, PhD(geol), 71. *Prof Exp:* Eng geologist, Sacramento Dist, US Corps Engrs, 49-50; geologist, Mil Geol Br, US Geol Surv, 51- 52, Alaskan Geol Br, 52-56, Guatemala Calif Petrol Co Ltd Div, Standard Oil Co Calif, 56-59 & Bolivia Calif Petrol Co Ltd Div, 59-62; RES GEOLOGIST, ALASKAN GEOL BR, US GEOL SURV, 62- *Honors & Awards:* Harry Oscar Wood Award Seismol, 67. *Mem:* AAAS; Geol Soc Am; Am Geophys Union; Asn Eng Geol. *Res:* Geologic earthquake hazards in Alaska; tectonic deformation and geologic effects related to major earthquakes; geology, geophysics and petroleum potential of the Gulf of Alaska margin and contiguous offshore areas. *Mailing Add:* US Geol Surv 345 Middlefield Rd Menlo Park CA 94025

PLAGEMANN, PETER GUENTER WILHELM, b Magdeburg, Ger, Oct 24, 28; US citizen; m 56; c 3. VIROLOGY, BIOCHEMISTRY. *Educ:* Univ Toronto, BSA, 59, MSA, 60; Case Western Reserve Univ, PhD(microbiol), 65. *Prof Exp:* From asst prof to assoc prof, 65-74, PROF MICROBIOL, MED SCH, UNIV MINN, MINNEAPOLIS, 74- *Mem:* AAAS; Am Soc Microbiol; Am Soc Biol Chem; Am Soc Cell Biol. *Res:* Biochemistry of virus replication and of cultured cells. *Mailing Add:* Dept of Microbiol Univ of Minn Med Sch Minneapolis MN 55455

PLAGER, JOHN EVERETT, b New York, NY, Mar 2, 27; m 50; c 3. BIOCHEMISTRY, INTERNAL MEDICINE. *Educ:* Tufts Univ, MS, 49; Univ Utah, PhD(biochem, physiol), 53, MD, 57. *Prof Exp:* Instr internal med, Univ Rochester, 59-60, sr instr, 60-61; res dir, Med Found Buffalo, NY, 61-66; ASSOC CHIEF MED, ROSWELL PARK MEM INST, 66- *Concurrent Pos:* USPHS fel, 59-60; assoc res prof med, State Univ NY Buffalo, 66- *Mem:* Am Soc Clin Oncol; Am Asn Cancer Res; fel Am Col Physicians; Endocrine Soc; Am Physiol Soc. *Res:* Pituitary-adrenal function; steroid biochemistry and enzymology; steroid-protein interactions; cancer medicine; endocrinology. *Mailing Add:* Dept of Med Roswell Park Mem Inst Buffalo NY 14203

PLAGGE, JAMES CLARENCE, b Barrington, Ill, Apr 5, 11; m 38, 72; m 3. ANATOMY. *Educ:* Univ Chicago, SB, 37, PhD(zool), 40. *Prof Exp:* Asst zool, Univ Chicago, 37-40; from instr to asst prof gross anat, Univ Md, 40-43; from assoc to prof anat, Col Med, Univ Ill Med Ctr, 43-80, asst dean int activities, 72-80, assoc dir, Off Spec Progs, 74-80. *Concurrent Pos:* Med ed adv, Int Coop Admin, Saigon, Vietnam, 58-60; coordr, Univ Ill-Chiang Mai Univ proj, 62, chief party, Thailand, 64-68; Univ Ill fac liaison officer, Med Opportunities Prog, 69-; mem, Int Health Survey Team, Nicaragua, 72; consult anat, Fac Med, Univ Azarabadegan, Tabriz, Iran, 77. *Mem:* Soc Exp Biol & Med; Am Asn Anat. *Res:* Physiology of the endocrines; sex organs; irradiation; liver diseases. *Mailing Add:* 2248 Kent St Okemos MI 48864

PLAINE, HENRY LEROY, genetics, deceased

PLAISTED, ROBERT LEROY, b Hornell, NY, Jan 1, 29; m 51; c 4. PLANT BREEDING. *Educ:* Cornell Univ, BS, 50; Iowa State Col, MS & PhD(hort), 56. *Prof Exp:* From asst prof to assoc prof, 56-65, head dept, 65-80, PROF PLANT BREEDING & BIOMETRY, CORNELL UNIV, 65- *Mem:* Potato Asn Am; Crop Sci Soc Am. *Res:* Methods of breeding potatoes and development of new varieties. *Mailing Add:* Dept of Plant Breeding & Biomet Cornell Univ Ithaca NY 14853

PLAIT, ALAN OSCAR, b Chicago, Ill, Aug 14, 26; m 53; c 4. ELECTRONICS ENGINEERING, MATHEMATICS. *Educ:* Ill Inst Technol, BS, 51 & 57; Va Polytech Inst & State Univ, MS, 76. *Prof Exp:* Engr electronics, Admiral Corp, 52-55; assoc engr, Armour Res Found, 55-59; sr engr, Magnavox Co, 59-62; mgr reliability eng, Melpar, Inc, 62-67, mgr reliability eng & opers res, Comput Sci Corp, 67-75, mgr reliability assurance, Amecom-Litton Systs, 75-77; TECH DIR, MANTECH INT CORP, 77- *Concurrent Pos:* Instr, Ill Inst Technol, 56-59, Grad Sch, USDA, 63- & Univ Conn, 73-75; adj prof, George Washington Univ, 70 & Va Polytech Inst & State Univ, 73-75, 81. *Mem:* Fel Am Soc for Qual Control; sr mem Inst Elec & Electronics Engrs; Nat Soc Prof Engrs. *Res:* Development of mathematical basis for reliability studies; application of reliability principles in the improvement of electronic systems; exploration of methods of failure recurrence control in minimizing system failures. *Mailing Add:* 5402 Yorkshire St Springfield VA 22151

PLAKKE, RONALD KEITH, b Holland, Mich, July 21, 35; m 58; c 2. VERTEBRATE ANATOMY, PHYSIOLOGY. *Educ:* Univ Northern Colo, AB, 62; Univ Mont, PhD(zool), 66. *Prof Exp:* From asst prof to assoc prof, 66-74, PROF ZOOL & WOMEN'S STUDIES, UNIV NORTHERN COLO, 74-, CHAIRPERSON, DEPT BIOL SCI, 80- *Mem:* AAAS; Am Soc Mammal; Am Soc Zool; Nat Asn Biol Teachers. *Res:* Mammalian renal anatomy and physiology; descriptive histology and histochemistry. *Mailing Add:* Dept of Biol Sci Univ of Northern Colo Greeley CO 80639

PLAMBECK, JAMES ALAN, b Chicago, Ill, Sept 16, 38; m 70; c 4. ANALYTICAL CHEMISTRY, ELECTROCHEMISTRY. *Educ:* Carleton Col, BS, 60; Univ Ill, Urbana, MSc, 62, PhD(chem), 65. *Prof Exp:* Res assoc chem eng, Argonne Nat Lab, 64-65; asst prof, 65-70, ASSOC PROF CHEM, UNIV ALTA, 70- *Concurrent Pos:* Assoc mem comn I.3 electrochem, Int Union Pure & Appl Chem, 71-76, 80- *Mem:* Am Chem Soc; Electrochem Soc; Chem Inst Can; AAAS. *Res:* Electroanalytical methods; electrochemistry of fused salts; electrochemical thermodynamics; environmental analytical chemistry; electrochemistry of antitumor antibiotics; computer interfacing of analytical instrumentation. *Mailing Add:* Dept of Chem Univ of Alta Edmonton AB T6G 2G7 Can

PLAMBECK, LOUIS, JR, b Moline, Ill, May 15, 12; m 40; c 1. ORGANIC CHEMISTRY. *Educ:* Univ Ill, BS, 35; Pa State Col, MS, 37, PhD(org chem), 39. *Prof Exp:* Asst chem, Pa State Col, 35-37; chemist, Chas Lennig & Co, 37; chemist, Exp Sta, E I du Pont de Nemours & Co, Inc, 39-77; CONSULT, 77- *Honors & Awards:* Kosar Mem Award, Soc Photog Sci & Eng, 70. *Mem:* Am Chem Soc. *Res:* Photopolymerization; photographic chemistry; coatings for plastics; biopolymers. *Mailing Add:* 107 Hoiland Dr Wilmington DE 19803

PLAMONDON, JOSEPH EDWARD, b Dubuque, Iowa, Mar 3, 41; m 66; c 1. ADHESIVES TECHNOLOGY. *Educ:* Loras Col, BS, 63; Univ Calif, Berkeley, MS, 65; Univ Calif, Davis, PhD(chem), 69. *Prof Exp:* RES CHEMIST SYNTHETIC FIBERS, ROHM AND HAAS CO, 69- *Mem:* AAAS; Am Chem Soc. *Res:* Hydorboration; organometallic chemistry; polymer synthesis and characterization; synthetic fibers; coated fabrics; pressure sensitive adhesives; textile chemistry; coated fabrics; automotive trim adhesives. *Mailing Add:* 55 Mill Creek Rd Holland PA 18966

PLAMONDON, MAYNARD ALFRED, b Hanover, NH, Dec 29, 40; m 61; c 2. STRUCTURAL ENGINEERING, ENGINEERING MECHANICS. *Educ:* Univ NH, BS, 62; Univ Ill, MS, 64, PhD(civil eng), 66. *Prof Exp:* Res asst struct dynamics, Univ Ill, 62-66; proj off protective struct technol, 66-69, res struct engr, 69-78; tech adv, 78-80, DIV CHIEF/NTE, AIR FORCE WEAPONS LAB, 80- *Honors & Awards:* Sci Achievement Award, Air Force Systems Command, US Air Force, 70. *Mem:* Am Soc Civil Engrs; Sigma Xi. *Res:* Structural dynamics; soil mechanics; nuclear weapons effects; structure-media interaction; vibrations; ground shock propagation. *Mailing Add:* Air Force Weapons Lab (NTE) Kirtland AFB NM 87117

PLAMTHOTTAM, SEBASTIAN S, b Kerala, India, Jan 22, 51. MATERIALS SCIENCE. *Educ:* Univ Kerala, India, BSc, 72; Univ Cochin, India, BTech, 75; Univ Akron, Ohio, PhD(polymer sci), 81. *Prof Exp:* RES CHEMIST, RES CTR, AVERY INT, PASADENA, CALIF, 80- *Mem:* Plastics & Rubber Inst; Am Chem Soc. *Res:* Laboratory synthesis and radiation (ultraviolet and electron beam); curing of novel hot melt adhesives and the evaluation of their melt rheology and adhesion properties. *Mailing Add:* 280 E Del Mar 223 Pasadena CA 91101

PLANCK, IVAN A(LBERT), b Warren, Ohio, Feb 7, 09; m 39; c 1. CHEMICAL & MECHANICAL ENGINEERING. *Educ:* Ohio State Univ, BChE, 31, MSc, 32, PhD(chem eng), 34, BS, 36. *Prof Exp:* Prof eng drawing, 39-42, prof mech eng & chmn dept, 42-71, EMER PROF MECH ENG, IND INST TECHNOL, 71- *Concurrent Pos:* Consult, Ft Wayne Air Conditioning Co, 45-47. *Mem:* Am Soc Mech Engrs. *Res:* Steam power plants and nuclear power; air conditioning and refrigeration. *Mailing Add:* 3902 E Shore Dr Helena MT 59601

PLANCK, ROY JONATHAN, physiology, ecology, see previous edition

PLANE, ROBERT ALLEN, b Evansville, Ind, Sept 30, 27; m 50; c 4. BIOINORGANIC CHEMISTRY, SPECTROSCOPY. *Educ:* Evansville Col, AB, 48; Univ Chicago, SM, 49, PhD(chem), 51. *Hon Degrees:* DSc, Univ Evansville, 68. *Prof Exp:* Chemist, Oak Ridge Nat Lab, 51-52; from instr to prof chem, Cornell Univ, 52-74, chmn dept, 67-70, provost, 69-73; PROF CHEM & PRES, CLARKSON COL TECHNOL, 74- *Concurrent Pos:* NIHspec fel, Nobel Inst, 60; Oxford Univ, 61; consult, Procter & Gamble Co, 65-; vis scientist, Univ Calif, 69. *Mem:* Am Chem Soc; Am Soc Enol & Viticulture; fel AAAS. *Res:* Metal ions in biological systems; fast reactions in solution; Raman spectroscopy. *Mailing Add:* Off of the Pres Clarkson Col Potsdam NY 13676

PLANJE, THEODORE JOHN, b St Louis, Mo, Mar 17, 19; m 42; c 2. CERAMICS ENGINEERING. *Educ:* Univ Mo, BS, 40, PhD(ceramic eng), 49. *Prof Exp:* Instr, 46-50, from asst prof to assoc prof, 50-55, chmn dept, 55-64, dir space sci res ctr, Univ, 68-80, PROF CERAMIC ENG, SCH MINES & METALL, UNIV MO-ROLLA, 55-, DEAN SCH, 64- *Mem:* Fel Am Ceramic Soc (pres, 71-72); Am Soc Eng Educ; Am Inst Mining, Metall & Petrol Engrs; Nat Inst Ceramic Engrs; Nat Soc Prof Engrs. *Res:* Physical and structural properties of crystalline and glassy ceramic systems; phase equilibria and thermodynamics of ceramics systems; natural and radiation induced defects in crystalline and glassy systems; nuclear properties of ceramic materials. *Mailing Add:* Sch of Mines & Metall Univ of Mo Rolla MO 65401

PLANK, CHARLES ANDREWS, b Charlotte, NC, Oct 12, 28; m 50; c 3. CHEMICAL ENGINEERING. *Educ:* NC State Univ, BChE, 49, MS, 51, PhD(chem eng), 57. *Prof Exp:* Res asst liquid extraction, NC State Univ, 51-52, instr chem eng, 52-57; assoc prof, Univ Louisville, 57-63; spec proj engr, Olin Mathieson Co, Ky, 63 & 66; assoc prof chem eng, 64-67, dir interdisciplinary prog eng, 71-73, chmn dept, 73-79, PROF CHEM ENG, UNIV LOUISVILLE, 67- . *Concurrent Pos:* Consult, Matt Corcoran, Inc, 58-, Tube Turns Plastics Co, 59-60, Am Air Filter Co, 64- & Raymond Meyer Corp, 77-; vis prof, Washington Univ, St Louis, 79. *Mem:* Am Inst Chem Engrs; Am Chem Soc; Am Soc Eng Educ. *Res:* Mass transfer and thermodynamics; distillation and absorption. *Mailing Add:* Dept of Chem Eng Univ of Louisville Speed Sci Sch Louisville KY 40208

PLANK, DON ALLEN, b Memphis, Tenn, Aug 8, 39. ORGANIC CHEMISTRY, PHOTOCHEMISTRY. *Educ:* Carleton Col, BA, 61; Purdue Univ, PhD(chem), 65. *Prof Exp:* NIH fel, Iowa State Univ, 65-67; res chemist, Esso Res & Eng Co, 67-74, staff chemist, Exxon Chem Co, 74-79, SR STAFF CHEMIST, EXXON CHEM AM, 79- *Mem:* Am Chem Soc. *Res:* Polymer stabilization. *Mailing Add:* Exxon Chem Am Baytown TX 77520

PLANK, DONALD LEROY, b Manchester, Conn, Aug 20, 37; m 61; c 3. MATHEMATICS. *Educ:* Trinity Col, Conn, BS, 60; Yale Univ, MA, 63; Univ Rochester, PhD(math), 67. *Prof Exp:* Asst prof math, Case Western Reserve Univ, 66-69, asst prof, Amherst Col, 69-71; assoc prof, 71-82, PROF MATH, STOCKTON STATE COL, 82- *Mem:* Am Math Soc; Math Asn Am. *Res:* Lattice-ordered rings; rings of functions; topology. *Mailing Add:* 9 Terry Lane Pomona NJ 08240

PLANK, STEPHEN J, b Rochester, NY, May 8, 27; m 56; c 3. PUBLIC HEALTH, POPULATION BIOLOGY. *Educ:* Univ Chicago, PhB, 48; Univ Calif, AB, 51, MD, 55; Harvard Univ, MPH, 61, DrPH, 64. *Prof Exp:* Intern, Gorgas Hosp, Balboa, CZ, 55-56; staff physician, Coco Solo Hosp, Cristobal, 56-60; asst prof pop studies, Sch Pub Health, Harvard Univ, 64-73, lectr, 69-73; mem staff health sci, Rockefeller Found, Bahia, Brazil, 73-78; mem staff Planning Off, 78-79, HEALTH OFFICER, EXEC OFF PRES, SHASTA COUNTY, CALIF, 80- *Concurrent Pos:* Asst surg, Peter Bent Brigham Hosp, Boston, 62-; temp adv, Pan-Am Health Orgn, 65-68; mem adv coun, Pathfinder Fund, 65-68; consult, Latin Am Prog, Ford Found, 66-67, WHO, 70 & World Bank, 77. *Mem:* Am Pub Health Asn. *Res:* Immunological control of fertility; relationships between health and population change; international health. *Mailing Add:* 2650 Hosp Lane Redding CA 96001

PLANKEY, FRANCIS WILLIAM, JR, b Malden, Mass, Feb 28, 45; m 68; c 2. ANALYTICAL CHEMISTRY. *Educ:* Univ Mass, BS, 71; Univ Fla, PhD(chem), 74. *Prof Exp:* ASST PROF CHEM, UNIV PITTSBURGH, 74- *Mem:* Am Chem Soc; Soc Appl Spectros; Optical Soc Am. *Res:* Analytical atomic spectroscopy; trace metal analysis; chemical instrumentation development and the application of computers to chemical instrumentation; forensic applications of analytical chemistry. *Mailing Add:* Dept of Chem Univ of Pittsburgh Pittsburgh PA 15260

PLANO, RICHARD JAMES, b Merrill, Wis, Apr 15, 29; m 56; c 2. PHYSICS. *Educ:* Univ Chicago, PhD(physics), 56. *Prof Exp:* From instr to asst prof physics, Columbia Univ, 56-60; assoc prof, 60-62, PROF PHYSICS, RUTGERS UNIV, NEW BRUNSWICK, 62- *Mem:* Am Phys Soc; Am Asn Physics Teachers. *Res:* Elementary particle physics. *Mailing Add:* Dept of Physics Rutgers Univ New Brunswick NJ 08903

PLANT, HOWARD LEON, b Burlington, Vt, Nov 20, 18; m 42; c 6. ORGANIC CHEMISTRY. *Educ:* Univ Vt, BS, 40, MS, 50. *Prof Exp:* Chemist, Metalectro Corp, 53-56 & Nat Distillers & Chem Corp, 56-60; res chemist, Olin Corp, 60-69; RES SCIENTIST, UNIROYAL CHEM, 69- *Res:* Synthesis of new biologically active compounds for use as agricultural chemicals. *Mailing Add:* Uniroyal Chem Elm St Naugatuck CT 06770

PLANT, J B, b Smith Falls, Ont, Aug 2, 33; m 56; c 4. ELECTRICAL ENGINEERING. *Educ:* Mass Inst Technol, PhD(elec eng), 65. *Prof Exp:* Lectr elec eng, 65-66, asst prof, 66-67, prof & head dept, 67-72, DEAN GRAD STUDIES & RES, ROYAL MIL COL CAN, 72-, CHMN GRAD STUDIES & RES DIV & PROF ELEC ENG, 80- *Concurrent Pos:* Defense Res Bd Can grant, 67- *Mem:* AAAS; Inst Elec & Electronics Engrs; Eng Inst Can. *Res:* Automatic control; optimization techniques and digital computer control. *Mailing Add:* Royal Mil Col of Can Kingston ON K7L 2W3 Can

PLANT, WILLIAM J, b Burlington, Vt, Mar 29, 26; m 55; c 7. ORGANIC POLYMER CHEMISTRY. *Educ:* Trinity Col, Conn, BS, 48; Univ Vt, MS, 50; Univ Tex, PhD(chem), 55. *Prof Exp:* Sr chemist, Gen Dynamics Corp, 55; res chemist, Celanese Corp Am , NJ, 55-59; ROBERTSON FEL, CARNEGIE-MELLON UNIV, 59- *Concurrent Pos:* Sr fel Carnegie-Mellon Inst Res, 59- *Mem:* Am Chem Soc; Soc Plastics Eng. *Res:* Organometallics; monomer synthesis; synthetic polymers, resins and coatings. *Mailing Add:* 1702 President Dr Glenshaw PA 15116

PLANT, WILLIAM JAMES, b Wichita, Kans, Sept 18, 44; m 64; c 2. PHYSICAL OCEANOGRAPHY. *Educ:* Kans State Univ, BS, 66; Purdue Univ, MS, 68, PhD(physics), 72. *Prof Exp:* NAT RES COUN ASSOC PHYSICS, NAVAL RES LAB, 71- *Mem:* Int Union Radio Sci; Am Geophy Union. *Res:* Electromagnetic scattering from water waves. *Mailing Add:* Ocean Sci Div Naval Res Lab Washington DC 20375

PLANTENBERG, GONZAGA, b Cold Spring, Minn, June 8, 13. PHYSICS. *Educ:* St Benedict Col, Minn, BA, 39; Univ St Louis, MS, 45, PhD(physics), 49. *Prof Exp:* Instr high sch, Minn & Wis, 35-42; instr physics & chem, St Benedict Col, Minn, 42-52, prof, 52-68; PROF PHYSICS, ST ANSELM'S COL, 68- *Mem:* Am Asn Physics Teachers. *Res:* Kinetic theory; vapor pressure; radioactivity. *Mailing Add:* Dept of Physics St Anselm's Col Manchester NH 03102

PLANTS, HELEN LESTER, b Desloge, Mo, Mar 9, 25; m 50; c 3. ENGINEERING EDUCATION. *Educ:* Univ Mo-Columbia, BSCE, 45; WVa Univ, MSCE, 53. *Prof Exp:* Jr engr reservoir develop, Atlantic Refining Co, 45; engr map drafting, Upham Eng Co, 45-46; struct consult, Harry E Graham, Consult Engr, 46-47; instr mech, 47-56, from asst prof to assoc prof, 56-72, PROF MECH, WVA UNIV, 72-, CURRICULUM & INSTR, 69- *Concurrent Pos:* US Off Educ res grant, WVa Univ, 67-68; mem acad adv bd, US Naval Acad, 76-80; adv, Nat Eng Ctr Phillipines, 80. *Honors & Awards:* Helen Plants Award, Inst Elec & Electronic Engrs & Am Soc Eng Educ, 79. *Mem:* Am Educ Res Asn; Nat Soc Prof Engrs; Am Soc Eng Educ (vpres, 75-76); Am Soc Mech Engrs; Am Soc Civil Engrs. *Res:* Development and evaluation of educational systems for teaching engineering subjects; programmed instruction applied to technical education; behavioral psychology in education. *Mailing Add:* Dept of Mech Eng & Eng Mech WVa Univ Morgantown WV 26506

PLANTZ, PHILIP EDWARD, food science, biochemistry, see previous edition

PLAPINGER, ROBERT EDWIN, b New York NY, Feb 23, 23; m 54; c 3. ORGANIC CHEMISTRY. *Educ:* City Col New York, BS, 44; Univ Md, PhD(chem), 51. *Prof Exp:* Org chemist, Montrose Chem Co, 43-44; asst, Univ Md, 46-49; res chemist, Chem Corps Med Labs, US Army Chem Ctr, 51-57; sr res chemist, Niagara Chem Div, Food Mach & Chem Corp, 57-58; sr res chemist, Chem Warfare Labs, US Army Chem Ctr, 58-62; res assoc Sinai Hosp Baltimore, 62-74, head div surg res, 70-72; res chemist, US Customs Lab, 74-75; RES CHEMIST, BUR MED DEVICES, FOOD & DRUG ADMIN, 75- *Concurrent Pos:* Consult, Biochem Res Div, Sinai Hosp Baltimore, 74- *Honors & Awards:* Dept of the Army Performance Award, 61. *Mem:* AAAS; Am Chem Soc; Royal Soc Chem; NY Acad Sci; Am Asn Clin Chemists. *Res:* Synthetic organic chemistry; chemistry of organic insecticides; organophosphorus compounds; peptides; chemical warfare agents; molecular rearrangements; cancer chemotherapy; enzyme histochemistry; clinical chemistry. *Mailing Add:* 3417 Merle Dr Baltimore MD 21207

PLAPP, BRYCE VERNON, b DeKalb, Ill, Sept 11, 39; m 62; c 2. BIOCHEMISTRY. *Educ:* Mich State Univ, BS, 61; Univ Calif, Berkeley, PhD(enzym), 66. *Prof Exp:* Am Cancer Soc fel, Inst Org Chem, Frankfurt, Ger, 66-68; res assoc, Rockefeller Univ, 68-70; asst prof, 70-74, assoc prof, 74-79, PROF BIOCHEM, UNIV IOWA, 79- *Concurrent Pos:* Merck Found grant fac develop, 70; res sci develop award, 75; vis scientist, Swed Univ Agr Sci, Uppsala, 76-77; mem, NIH Phys Study Sect, 81-82. *Mem:* Am Chem Soc; Am Soc Biol Chemists; Sigma Xi. *Res:* Protein chemistry, structure and function; active-site-directed reagents; bovine liver glucuronidase; amino groups and activators of liver alcohol dehydrogenase; pancreatic nucleases; alcohol metabolism. *Mailing Add:* Dept of Biochem Univ of Iowa Iowa City IA 52242

PLAPP, JOHN E(LMER), b El Paso, Tex, Feb 24, 29. MECHANICAL ENGINEERING. *Educ:* Rice Inst, BS, 50; Calif Inst Technol, MS, 51, PhD(mech eng), 57. *Prof Exp:* From asst prof to assoc prof mech eng, Rice Univ, 55-68; ASSOC PROF ENG SCI, TRINITY UNIV, TEX, 68- *Concurrent Pos:* USAID vis instr, Kabul Univ, Afghanistan, 63. *Mem:* Am Soc Mech Engrs; Am Inst Aeronaut & Astronaut. *Res:* Convective heat transfer; density currents; applied mathematics; fluid mechanics; thermodynamics. *Mailing Add:* Dept of Eng Sci Trinity Univ 715 Stadium Dr San Antonio TX 78284

PLASIL, FRANZ, b Progue, Czech, May 17, 39; m 64, 80; c 2. NUCLEAR PHYSICS, NUCLEAR CHEMISTRY. *Educ:* London Univ, BSc, 60; Univ Calif, Berkeley, PhD(chem), 64. *Prof Exp:* Chemist, Lawrence Radiation Lab, Calif, 64-65; res assoc nuclear chem, Brookhaven Nat Lab, 65-67; physicist, 67-79, MEM SR RES STAFF & GROUP LEADER, OAK RIDGE NAT LAB, 79- *Concurrent Pos:* Maitre de Recherche, Institut de Physique Nucleaire, Orsay, France, 74-75. *Mem:* Fel Am Phys Soc; Nuclear Div Am Chem Soc. *Res:* Nuclear fission; heavy ion reactions. *Mailing Add:* Oak Ridge Nat Lab PO Box X Oak Ridge TN 37830

PLASS, GILBERT NORMAN, b Toronto, Ont, Mar 22, 20; US citizen; m 62; c 2. PLANETARY ATMOSPHERES. *Educ:* Harvard Univ, BS, 41; Princeton Univ, PhD(physics), 47. *Prof Exp:* Assoc physicist metall lab, Univ Chicago, 42-45; from instr to assoc prof physics, Johns Hopkins Univ, 46-55; staff scientist, Lockheed Aircraft Corp, 55-56; adv res staff, Aeronutronic Div, Ford Motor Co, 56-60, mgr theoret physics dept res lab, 60-63; prof atmospheric & space sci, Southwestern Ctr Advan Studies, 63-68; head dept, 68-77, PROF PHYSICS, TEX A&M UNIV, 68- *Concurrent Pos:* Vis assoc prof, Northwestern Univ, 49 & Mich State Univ, 54-55, consult ed, Infared Physics, 60- *Mem:* Am Phys Soc; Optical Soc Am; Am Meteorol Soc; Am Asn Physics Teachers; AAAS. *Res:* Infrared absorption and emission; spectroscopy; electromagnetic and gravitational action at a distance; electrostatic electron lenses; fission and neutron physics; planetary atmospheres. *Mailing Add:* Dept of Physics Tex A&M Univ College Station TX 77843

PLASS, HAROLD J(OHN), JR, b Merrill, Wis, Dec 1, 22; m 46; c 5. ENGINEERING MECHANICS. *Educ:* Univ Wis, BS, 44, MS, 48; Stanford Univ, PhD(eng mech), 50. *Prof Exp:* From asst prof to prof eng mech, Univ Tex, Austin, 50-67; chmn dept mech eng, 67-76, PROF MECH ENG, UNIV MIAMI, 67- *Concurrent Pos:* Res engr, Defense Res Lab, Tex, 50-67. *Mem:* Am Soc Eng Educ; Am Soc Mech Engrs. *Res:* Structural dynamics. *Mailing Add:* Dept of Mech Eng Univ of Miami Coral Gables FL 33124

PLASSMANN, ELIZABETH HEBB, b Boston, Mass, Oct 4, 28; m 55; c 4. NUCLEAR PHYSICS. *Educ:* Bryn Mawr Col, AB, 50; Ind Univ, MS, 51, PhD, 55. *Prof Exp:* Asst prof physics, Bradley Univ, 55; mem staff, 55-60, asst group leader, 60-70, group leader, 70-81, ASST DIV LEADER, LOS ALAMOS NAT LAB, UNIV CALIF, 81- *Mem:* Am Phys Soc. *Res:* Nuclear components of atomic and thermonuclear weapons. *Mailing Add:* PO Box 1663 MS-945 Los Alamos Nat Lab Los Alamos NM 87545

PLASSMANN, EUGENE ADOLPH, b New York, NY, June 7, 21; m 55; c 4. NUCLEAR PHYSICS. *Educ:* Hastings Col, AB, 49; Ind Univ, MS, 52, PhD(physics), 55. *Prof Exp:* Instr, Univ Ky, 55; ASST GROUP LEADER, LOS ALAMOS SCI LAB, UNIV CALIF, 55- *Concurrent Pos:* Temp fac mem, Tex A&M Univ, 70-74. *Mem:* Am Nuclear Soc; Sigma Xi; Am Phys Soc. *Res:* Critical assemblies of fissionable materials; theoretical investigations of nuclear reactor systems; measurement and calculation of radiation effects; beta ray spectroscopy. *Mailing Add:* Group Q-14 MS560 Los Alamos Sci Lab PO Box 1663 Los Alamos NM 87545

PLATAU, GERARD OSCAR, b Potsdam, Ger, June 29, 26; nat US; m 61; c 1. ORGANIC CHEMISTRY. *Educ:* Brooklyn Col, BA, 46; Purdue Univ, MS, 48, PhD(org chem), 50. *Prof Exp:* Asst, Purdue Univ, 46-48; from asst ed to sr assoc ed, 50-61, head assignment & abstracting dept, 61-71, asst managing ed, 71-79, SR ASST ED OPERS, CHEM ABSTR SERV, 79- *Concurrent Pos:* Consult, NSF, 74-; dir, Am Soc Info Sci, 76- *Honors & Awards:* Watson Davis Award, Am Soc Info Sci, 80. *Mem:* Am Chem Soc; Am Soc Info Sci; Nat Fed Abstr & Indexing Serv. *Res:* Information storage and retrieval; abstracting and indexing; on-line data bases; synthesis of sympathomimetic drugs; synthetic sweetening agents. *Mailing Add:* Chem Abstr Serv PO Box 3012 Columbus OH 43210

PLATE, HENRY, b Jersey City, NJ, Oct 12, 25; m 58; c 2. AGRONOMY. *Educ:* Univ Maine, BS, 48, MS, 49. *Prof Exp:* Agronomist fertilizer res div, Eastern States Farmers' Exchange, Inc, 49-62, head, 62-64; mgr tech serv, 64-66, mgr blend plants, 66-67, MGR AGRON SERVS, FERTILIZER DIV, AGWAY, INC, 67- *Mem:* Am Soc Agron. *Res:* Plant nutrition; fertilizer technology and usage. *Mailing Add:* Fertilizer Div Agway Inc Box 4933 Syracuse NY 13221

PLATE, JANET MARGARET, b Minot, NDak, Nov 27, 43; m 64. IMMUNOLOGY, BIOCHEMISTRY. *Educ:* Jamestown Col, BA, 64; Duke Univ, PhD(immunol), 70. *Prof Exp:* Asst immunol, Mass Gen Hosp, 72-78, assoc, Harvard Med Sch, 70-77, asst prof immunol, Harvard Univ Sch Pub Health, 77-78; ASSOC PROF IMMUNOL, RUSH-PRESBY ST LUKE'S MED CTR, 78- *Concurrent Pos:* Am Cancer Soc fel, Mass Gen Hosp, Harvard Med Sch, 70-72, res fel transplantation immunol, 70-71; mem immunobiol study sect, Div Res Grants, NIH, 79-83. *Mem:* Transplantation Soc; Am Asn Immunol; Am Asn Clin Histocompatibility Testing. *Res:* Immunobiology; cell-cell interactions; differentiation; membrane function and biosynthesis; immunogenetics; control of the immune response. *Mailing Add:* Sect Med Oncol 1753 W Congress Pkwy Chicago IL 60612

PLATEK, RICHARD ALAN, b Brooklyn, NY, Sept 27, 40; m 60; c 2. MATHEMATICAL LOGIC. *Educ:* Mass Inst Technol, BS, 61; Stanford Univ, PhD(math, 65. *Prof Exp:* NATO fel, 65-66, C L E Moore instr math, Mass Inst Technol, 66-67; asst prof, 67-70, ASSOC PROF MATH, CORNELL UNIV, 70- *Res:* Axiomatic set theory; theory of recursive functions. *Mailing Add:* Dept of Math Cornell Univ Ithaca NY 14853

PLATFORD, ROBERT FREDERICK, b Unity, Sask, Can, June 29, 33; m 61; c 4. PHYSICAL CHEMISTRY. *Educ:* Univ BC, BA, 55, MSc, 56; PhD(radiation chem), Univ Sask, 58. *Prof Exp:* Sci officer, Suffield Exp Sta, Alta, 58-61; scientist, Atlantic Oceanog Group, Bedford Inst Oceanog, 61-67; RES SCIENTIST, CAN CTR INLAND WATERS, 67- *Res:* Electrochemistry; thermodynamics; surface chemistry. *Mailing Add:* Can Ctr for Inland Waters Box 5050 Burlington ON L7R 4A6 Can

PLATNER, EDWARD D, b Los Angeles, Calif, Apr 1, 34; c 2. PHYSICS. *Educ:* Walla Walla Col, BA, 56; Univ Wash, MS, 60, PhD(physics), 61. *Prof Exp:* PHYSICIST, BROOKHAVEN NAT LAB, 64- *Res:* High energy particle experimental physics. *Mailing Add:* Dept of Physics 510A Brookhaven Nat Lab Upton NY 11973

PLATNER, WESLEY STANLEY, b Newark, NJ, Sept 26, 15; m 42; c 1. PHYSIOLOGY, ENVIRONMENTAL PHYSIOLOGY. *Educ:* Philadelphia Col Pharm & Sci, BS, 39; Univ Pa, MS, 42; Univ Mo, PhD(mammalian physiol), 48. *Prof Exp:* Aquatic biologist, US Dept Interior, Washington, DC, 42-47; instr physiol & pharmacol, 46-48, from asst prof to prof physiol, 49-81, EMER PROF PHYSIOL, SCH MED, UNIV MO-COLUMBIA, 81-, CHMN DEPT, 77- *Concurrent Pos:* Res asst & fel dairy husb, Univ Mo, 48-55; NIH grant physiol, Univ Mo, 57-60, USPHS grant, 59-72; NSF travel fel, 21st Int Physiol Cong, Buenos Aires, Arg, 59; NIH fel, Univ Calif, Santa Barbara, 71-72; res investr, Space Sci Ctr, Univ Mo, 65-69; vis res physiologist, Univ Calif, Santa Barbara, 71-72; vchmn Mo sect, Soc Exp Biol & Med, 55- *Mem:* Fel AAAS; Am Physiol Soc; Soc Exp Biol & Med; Am Inst Biol Sci; Am Oil Chem Soc. *Res:* Adaptive mechanisms, especially hormonal, nutritional, and environmental stress factors which affect trace minerals, carbohydrates, and lipids at the tissue and cellular levels of physiology. *Mailing Add:* Dept of Physiol Univ of Mo Sch of Med Columbia MO 65201

PLATNICK, NORMAN I, b Bluefield, WVa, Dec 30, 51; m 70. ARACHNOLOGY, SYSTEMATIC BIOGEOGRAPHY. *Educ:* Concord Col, BS, 68; Mich State Univ, MS, 70; Harvard Univ, PhD(biol), 73. *Prof Exp:* Asst cur, 73-77, ASSOC CUR ENTOM, THE AM MUS NATURAL HIST, 77-; ADJ PROF, CITY UNIV New York, 78- *Concurrent Pos:* Trustee, NY Entom Soc, 75-76; rev ed, Syst Zool, 76- *Mem:* Am Arachnological Soc; AAAS; Philos Sci Asn; Soc Syst Zool; British Arachnological Soc. *Res:* Systematics and biogeography of spiders; theory of systematics and biogeography. *Mailing Add:* Dept Entom Am Museum Natural Hist New York NY 10024

PLATO, CHRIS C, b Nicosia, Cyprus, Oct 10, 31; US citizen; m 61; c 3. GERONTOLOGY, HUMAN GENETICS. *Educ:* Univ Ga, BSc, 55; Iowa State Univ, MSc, 56; Univ Mich, MSc, 60, PhD(growth & develop), 76. *Prof Exp:* Geneticist human, Nat Inst Neurol Dis & Stroke, 62-67 & Nat Inst Child Health & Human Develop, 67-72, GENETICIST AGING, NAT INST AGING, NIH, 72- *Concurrent Pos:* Vis lectr, Dept Med Genetics, Univ SAla Med Sch, 76-; consult, Ctr Human Growth & Develop, Univ Mich, 75- & Ctr Demog & Pop Genetics, Univ Tex, Houston, 78- *Mem:* Geront Soc; fel Int Soc Twin Studies; Am Dermatoglyphics Asn (pres, 75-78); Am Soc Human Genetics; NY Acad Sci. *Res:* Osteoarthritis, bone loss, amyotrophic lateral sclerosis, dermatoglyphics, genetics of aging, population genetics. *Mailing Add:* Geront Res Ctr Baltimore City Hosp Baltimore MD 21224

PLATO, PHILLIP ALEXANDER, b Nashville, Tenn, Nov 16, 43; m 64; c 2. RADIOLOGICAL HEALTH, PUBLIC HEALTH. *Educ:* Univ Miami, BS, 65, MS, 66; Iowa State Univ, PhD(sanitary eng), 68. *Prof Exp:* From asst prof to assoc prof, 69-78, PROF RADIOL HEALTH, UNIV MICH, 78- *Concurrent Pos:* Consult to various pvt & pub orgn, 69- *Mem:* Health Physics Soc; Am Pub Health Asn; Am Nat Standards Inst. *Res:* Radiation dosimetry, including calibration of radiation sources and movement of radionuclides from sources to people; design and operation of environmental monitoring programs around nuclear facilities. *Mailing Add:* Sch Pub Health Univ Mich Ann Arbor MI 48109

PLATT, ALAN EDWARD, b London, Eng, Dec 30, 36; m 65; c 2. PHYSICAL ORGANIC CHEMISTRY. *Educ:* Univ London, BSc, 58, PhD(chem), 61. *Prof Exp:* Res assoc chem, Univ Mich, 61-62; res fel, Calif Inst Technol, 62-63; res chemist, 63-38, group leader, 68-75, assoc scientist, 75-80, SR ASSOC SCIENTIST, DOW CHEM USA, 80- *Mem:* Sigma Xi. *Res:* Polymerization kinetics; polymer characterization and processes. *Mailing Add:* Dow Chemical USA 438 Bldg Midland MI 48640

PLATT, AUSTIN PICKARD, b Evanston, Ill, Oct 29, 37; m 63; c 1. ECOLOGY, POPULATION BIOLOGY. *Educ:* Williams Col, BA, 59; Univ Mass, MA, 63, PhD(zool), 65. *Prof Exp:* Instr zool, Univ RI, 65-66; asst prof biol, Wesleyan Univ, 66-69; asst prof, 69-71, ASSOC PROF BIOL SCI, UNIV MD BALTIMORE COUNTY, 71- *Concurrent Pos:* Univ RI grant, 65-66; NSF grant, 67-69; ed, J Lepid Soc, 78-80. *Mem:* Am Inst Biol Sci; Soc Study Evolution; Royal Entomol Soc London. *Res:* Calculation of small mammal home ranges; population fluctuations of small mammals; insect diapause; genetics of Nearatic Limenitis butterflies. *Mailing Add:* Dept Biol Sci Univ Md Baltimore County Catonsville MD 21228

PLATT, DAVID, b US, Sept 26, 23; m 58, 75; c 2. IMMUNOLOGY. *Educ:* Upper Iowa Univ, BS, 48; Univ Ala, MS, 52, PhD(biochem), 57. *Prof Exp:* From instr to asst prof biochem, 57-62, from asst prof to assoc prof microbiol, 62-67, PROF MICROBIOL, SCH DENT MED, UNIV PITTSBURGH, 68-, CHMN DEPT, 67- *Concurrent Pos:* Chmn microbiol & immunol res group, Int Asn Dent Res, 74-76. *Mem:* AAAS; Am Chem Soc; Am Soc Microbiol; Am Dent Asn; NY Acad Sci. *Mailing Add:* Sch Dent Med Dept Microbiol Univ of Pittsburgh Pittsburgh PA 15261

PLATT, DWIGHT RICH, b Chicago, Ill, Aug 4, 31; m 56; c 2. ZOOLOGY. *Educ:* Bethel Col, BS, 52; Univ Kans, MA, 54, PhD(zool), 66. *Prof Exp:* Asst instr zool, Univ Kans, 52-54; ed tech village develop, Am Friends Serv Comt, Barpali, India, 54-57; from instr to assoc prof, 57-69, PROF BIOL, BETHEL COL, 69- *Concurrent Pos:* Res asst, Univ Kans, 59-60; vis prof Sambalpur Univ, India, 70-71. *Mem:* Ecol Soc Am; Am Soc Ichthyol & Herpet; Am Ornith Union; Wilson Ornith Soc; Soc Study Amphibians & Reptiles. *Res:* Vertebrate population ecology; population dynamics of snakes as related to changes in their prey populations; prairie ecology. *Mailing Add:* Dept of Biol Bethel Col North Newton KS 67117

PLATT, JAMES EARL, b Greensburg, Ind, June 19, 44; m 65; c 1. COMPARATIVE ENDOCRINOLOGY. *Educ:* Ind Univ, BA, 66, MAT, 67; Univ Colo, PhD(biol), 74. *Prof Exp:* ASST PROF BIOL SCI, UNIV DENVER, 74- *Mem:* Am Soc Zoologists. *Res:* Role of prolactin in larval amphibian growth and development; prolactin-thyrozine interaction in amphibians and other lower vertebrates; amphibian metamorphosis. *Mailing Add:* Dept of Biol Sci Univ of Denver Denver CO 80210

PLATT, JOHN RADAR, b Jacksonville, Fla, June 29, 18; m 41, 79; c 2. ENVIRONMENTAL SCIENCES. *Educ:* Northwestern Univ, BS, 36, MS, 37; Univ Mich, PhD(physics), 41. *Hon Degrees:* Dr psychol, Utah State Univ, 74. *Prof Exp:* Rockefeller Found Proj fel & res assoc, Univ Minn, 41-43; instr physics, Northwestern Univ, 43-45, res assoc Nat Defense Res Comt Prog, 44-45; from asst prof to prof physics, Univ Chicago, 46-65; res scientist, Ment Health Res Inst, Univ Mich, Ann Arbor, 65-77; vis prof, Univ Calif, Santa Barbara, 77-79; lectr, Sch Med, Boston Univ, 79-81; vis lectr, Harvard Univ, 81-82. *Concurrent Pos:* Guggenheim fel, 51-52; fel, Ctr Adv Study, Stanford, 72-73. *Honors & Awards:* USPHS Career Award, 64; Regent's lectr, Univ Calif, Santa Barbara, 76. *Mem:* AAAS; Biophys Soc; Am Acad Polit & Soc Sci. *Res:* Theory of chemical spectra; interpretation of light absorption by biological systems; physics of perception; science and urgent research for future of man; social change and global problems; future global problems. *Mailing Add:* 14 Concord Ave Apt 624 Cambridge MA 02138

PLATT, JOSEPH BEAVEN, b Portland, Ore, Aug 12, 15; m 46; c 2. PHYSICS. *Educ:* Univ Rochester, BA, 37; Cornell Univ, PhD(exp physics), 42. *Prof Exp:* Asst physics, Cornell Univ, 37-41; instr, Univ Rochester, 41-43; staff mem & sect chief radiation lab, Mass Inst Technol, 43-46; from asst prof to assoc prof physics, Univ Rochester, 46-49; chief physics br, Res Div, AEC, 49-51; from assoc prof to prof physics & assoc chmn dept, Univ Rochester, 51-56; pres, Claremont Univ Ctr, Cambridge, 76-81; pres, 56-76, SR PROF, HARVEY MUDD COL, 81- *Concurrent Pos:* Consult, Nat Defense Res Comt, 41-45; adv comt sci educ, NSF, 65-70 & 73-74, vchmn, 67-68 & 73, chmn, 69-70 & 74; mem mine adv comt, Nat Acad Sci-Nat Res Coun, 55-61, mem comt sci in UNESCO, 60-62, comt int orgns & progs, 62-64, chmn, Subcomt Sino-Am Sci Coop; Gov comt study med aid & health, Calif, 59-60; trustee, Anal Serv, Inc, 59-, chmn, 62-; sci adv, US deleg, UNESCO Gen Conf, Paris, 60, alternate deleg, 62; mem panel int sci, President's Sci Adv Comt, 61-64, int tech coop & assistance panel, 66-67, comput in educ panel, 66-68; trustee, Thacher Sch, 62-74; chmn select comt on master plan for higher educ, Coord Coun Higher Educ, Calif, 71-73; study comt on NIH, 64-65; bd trustees, Carnegie Found Advan Teaching, 70-76; bd trustees, Aerospace Corp, 71-; trustee, China Found Prom Educ & Cult, 66-; mem, Carnegie Coun Policy Studies in Higher Educ, 75-80. *Mem:* Fel Am Phys Soc; sr mem Inst Elec & Electronics Engrs. *Res:* X-ray spectroscopy; radar systems engineering; nuclear and meson physics. *Mailing Add:* Dept Physics Harvey Mudd Col Claremont CA 91711

PLATT, KENNETH ALLAN, b Denver, Colo, Oct 14, 23; m 47; c 3. MEDICINE. *Educ:* Univ Colo, DrMed, 50. *Prof Exp:* Pres, 71-72, MED DIR, COLO FOUND MED CARE, 72-; CHMN BD, ST ANTHONYS HOSP, 81- *Concurrent Pos:* Mem, Nat Prof Standards Rev Orgn, 78-80. *Mem:* Inst Med-Nat Acad Sci; Am Acad Family Physicians; Am Med Soc. *Mailing Add:* 11435 Quivos Way Denver CO 80234

PLATT, LUCIAN B, b Syracuse, NY, Apr 9, 31; m 57; c 2. STRUCTURAL GEOLOGY. *Educ:* Yale Univ, BS, 53, MS, 57, PhD(geol), 60. *Prof Exp:* Fel, Princeton Univ, 60-61; asst prof geol, Villanova Univ, 61-64; assoc prof, George Washington Univ, 64-70; chmn dept, 71-75, assoc prof, 70-79, PROF GEOL, BRYN MAWR COL, 79- *Concurrent Pos:* Consult, Pa Geol Surv, 61-64; part time geologist, US Geol Surv, 65- *Mem:* AAAS; Geol Soc Am; Am Geophys Union; Am Asn Petrol Geol; Ger Geol Asn. *Res:* Structure and stratigraphy in complex shale areas. *Mailing Add:* Dept of Geol Bryn Mawr Col Bryn Mawr PA 19010

PLATT, MILTON M, b Bayonne, NJ, Mar 7, 21; m 43; c 3. MATERIALS ENGINEERING, TEXTILE MECHANICS. *Educ:* Mass Inst Technol, BS, 42, ScD(struct eng), 46. *Prof Exp:* Res technician, Mass Inst Technol, 42-46; sr res assoc, Fabric Res Labs, Inc, 46-47, asst dir res, 47-52, assoc dir res, 52-74, vpres, 53-74, treas, 70-74; dir, FRL Div, 74-78, SR DIR, ALBANY INT RES CO, ALBANY INT CORP, 78- *Concurrent Pos:* Lectr, Mass Inst Technol, 53-; consult, Off Qm Corps; mem comt textiles, Nat Acad Sci-Nat Res Coun; mem, Textile Res Inst. *Honors & Awards:* Space Shuttle Orbiter Award, Rockwell Int Corp, 78; Harold DeWitt Smith Mem Medal, Am Soc Testing & Mat, 67. *Mem:* Fiber Soc (vpres, 68-69, pres, 70-71); Soc Rheol; fel Brit Textile Inst. *Res:* Theory of structures; mechanics of textile materials; analysis of flat plates subject to transverse distributed loads; relation between mechanical properties and structural geometry of textile structures. *Mailing Add:* Albany Int Res Co Div Albany Int Corp 1000 Providence Hwy Dedham MA 02026

PLATT, ROBERT SWANTON, JR, b Chicago, Ill, Jan 2, 25; m 51; c 2. PLANT PHYSIOLOGY. *Educ:* Wash Univ, St Louis, AB, 49; Harvard Univ, AM, 51, PhD(biol), 54. *Prof Exp:* Fulbright fel, State Agr Univ, Wageningen, 54-55; instr, 56-57, asst dean col biol sci, 66-68, ASST PROF BOT, OHIO STATE UNIV, 57-66 & 68- *Concurrent Pos:* Danforth assoc, 70- *Mem:* AAAS; Am Soc Plant Physiol; Bot Soc Am. *Res:* Metabolism of plant growth substances and light-growth reactions. *Mailing Add:* Dept of Bot Ohio State Univ Columbus OH 43210

PLATT, RONALD DEAN, b Council Bluffs, Iowa, May 21, 42; m 63; c 2. MATHEMATICAL STATISTICS. *Educ:* Univ Northern Iowa, BA, 63; Univ Iowa, MS, 66, PhD(statist), 71. *Prof Exp:* Instr math, Univ Iowa, 65-66, programmer, Measurement Res Ctr, 66-67; instr math, Grinnell Col, 67-69; instr math & sr programmer, Measurement Res Ctr, Univ Iowa, 69-70, dir statist serv, 70-71; assoc prof statist, Northwest Mo State Univ, 71-74; biostatistician, Miles Labs Inc, 75-78; MGR PROD DEVELOP & PROG, CAP COMPUT CTR, 78- *Mem:* Am Statist Asn. *Res:* Probability theory; clinical studies and management of toxicity data. *Mailing Add:* 13616 Bayshore Dr Traverse City MI 49684

PLATT, THOMAS BOYNE, b Evanston, Ill, Sept 30, 27; m 54, 63; c 5. BACTERIOLOGY. *Educ:* Iowa State Col, BS, 50; NC State Col, MS, 52; Univ Wis, PhD(bact), 56. *Prof Exp:* SECT HEAD, SQUIBB INST MED RES, 56- *Mem:* Am Soc Microbiol; Brit Soc Gen Microbiol. *Res:* Analytical microbiology; chemotherapy; fermentation technology. *Mailing Add:* Squibb Inst for Med Res New Brunswick NJ 08903

PLATT, THOMAS REID, b Youngstown, Ohio, June 20, 49; m 73; c 1. PARASITOLOGY, SYSTEMATICS. *Educ:* Hiram Col, BA, 71; Bowling Green State Univ, MS, 73; Univ Alta, PhD(zool), 78. *Prof Exp:* ASST PROF BIOL, UNIV RICHMOND, 78- *Mem:* Am Soc Parasitologists; Soc Syst Zool; Can Soc Zoologists; Wildlife Dis Asn. *Res:* Systematics, evolution and zoogeography of parasitic helminths, particularly nematodes. *Mailing Add:* Dept Biol Univ Richmond Richmond VA 23173

PLATT, WILLIAM JOSHUA, III, b Gainesville, Fla, Nov 21, 42; m 68. ECOLOGY, VERTEBRATE BIOLOGY. *Educ:* Univ Fla, BS, 64; Cornell Univ, PhD(ecol), 71. *Prof Exp:* Asst prof zool, Univ Iowa, 69-77; ASST PROF BIOL SCI, UNIV ILL, 77- *Concurrent Pos:* Army Corps Engrs Environ Resources Study, Univ Iowa-Iowa State Univ, 72. *Mem:* AAAS; Am Inst Biol Sci; Ecol Soc Am; Am Soc Mammal. *Res:* Predator-prey relationships in prairie ecosystems; effects of predation upon ecosystems structure and dynamics; perturbations upon ecosystems stability; biology of shrews. *Mailing Add:* Dept of Zool Chicago Circle Chicago IL 60680

PLATTS, DENNIS ROBERT, b Kittaning, Pa, Mar 22, 33; m 54; c 4. GLASS TECHNOLOGY, CERAMICS. *Educ:* Alfred Univ, BS, 61, PhD(ceramic sci), 65. *Prof Exp:* Res engr, Glass & Chem Prod Div, Ford Motor Co, 64-66; res scientist, Linden Labs, Inc, 66-68 & Ceramic Finishing Co, 68-72; RES ENG ASSOC, FORD MOTOR CO, 72- *Mem:* Am Ceramic Soc. *Res:* Glass strength and defects; chemically strengthened glass. *Mailing Add:* 25500 W Outer Dr Lincoln Park MI 48146

PLATTS, WILLIAM SIDNEY, b Burley, Idaho, Apr 18, 28; m 51; c 2. FISHERIES. *Educ:* Idaho State Univ, BS, 55; Utah State Univ, MS, 57, PhD(fishery mgt), 74. *Prof Exp:* Regional biologist & enforcement supt, Idaho Fish & Game, 61-64; zone biologist, 67-74, RES BIOLOGIST, US FOREST SERV, 74- *Mem:* Am Fisheries Soc; Nature Conservancy; Nat Wildlife Fedn. *Res:* Aquatic documentation, methodology and classification; land use impacts. *Mailing Add:* 1603 Sunrise Rim Boise ID 83705

PLATUS, DANIEL HERSCHEL, b Los Angeles, Calif, Jan 19, 32; m 69; c 2. ENGINEERING. *Educ:* Univ Calif, Los Angeles, BS, 54, PhD(eng), 61. *Prof Exp:* Sr nuclear engr, Holmes & Narver, Inc, 58; sr res engr, Atomics Int Div, NAm Aviation, 61-62; proj scientist, ARA, Inc, 62-65; SR SCIENTIST, AEROPHYSICS RES LAB, AEROSPACE CORP, 65- *Mem:* Assoc fel Am Soc Aeronaut & Astronaut. *Res:* Applied mechanics; flight dynamics; solid mechanics; nuclear reactor technology. *Mailing Add:* Aerospace Corp PO Box 92957 Los Angeles CA 90009

PLATZ, JAMES ERNEST, b Bloomington, Ind, Sept 4, 43; m 69; c 1. EVOLUTIONARY BIOLOGY. *Educ:* Tex Tech Univ, BS, 67, MS, 70; Ariz State Univ, PhD(zool), 74. *Prof Exp:* asst prof, 74-78, ASSOC PROF BIOL, CREIGHTON UNIV, 79- *Mem:* AAAS; Am Soc Naturalists; Soc Study Evolution; Am Soc Zoologists; Am Soc Ichthyol & Herpetol. *Res:* Vertebrate evolutionary biology involving the study of the dynamics of the speciation process. *Mailing Add:* Dept of Biol Creighton Univ Omaha NE 68178

PLATZER, ANNA (COLVILLE), b Vancouver, BC, Feb 24, 32; m 62; c 1. DEVELOPMENTAL BIOLOGY. *Educ:* Univ BC, BSA, 54, MSc, 62; Univ Mass, PhD(zool), 71. *Prof Exp:* Res asst path, Univ BC, 62-64; res assoc genetics, Albert Einstein Col Med, 68-71; res assoc cancer res, Sch Med, Loma Linda Univ, 71-72; RES ASSOC DEVELOP BIOL, UNIV CALIF, RIVERSIDE, 72- *Res:* Developmental pathology of skeletal muscle; phylogeny of muscle development. *Mailing Add:* Dept of Biol Univ of Calif Riverside CA 92502

PLATZER, EDWARD GEORGE, b Vancouver, BC, Oct 3, 38; m 62; c 1. PARASITOLOGY, NUTRITION. *Educ:* Univ BC, BSc, 61, MSc, 64; Univ Mass, PhD(zool), 68. *Prof Exp:* Guest investr biochem malaria, Rockefeller Univ, 68-71; asst prof nematol, 71-77, ASSOC PROF NEMATOL BIOL, UNIV CALIF, RIVERSIDE, 77- *Concurrent Pos:* USPHS fel, 68-70. *Mem:* Am Soc Parasitol; AAAS; Soc Nematol. *Res:* Life history, biochemistry and physiology of nematodes; nematodes as agents for insect control. *Mailing Add:* Dept of Nematol Univ of Calif Riverside CA 92502

PLATZER, MAXIMILIAN FRANZ, b Vienna, Austria, June 26, 33; US citizen; m 58; c 3. FLUID MECHANICS, AEROSPACE ENGINEERING. *Educ:* Vienna Tech Univ, Dipl Ing, 57, Dr Tech Sci(appl mech), 64. *Prof Exp:* Aerospace engr, Marshall Space Flight Ctr, NASA, 60-66; aerospace scientist, Lockheed-Ga Co, 66-70; from assoc prof to prof aeronaut, 70-76, CHMN DEPT AERONAUT, NAVAL POSTGRAD SCH, 78- *Honors & Awards:* NASA Incentive Award, Marshall Space Flight Ctr, 65. *Mem:* Assoc fel Am Inst Aeronaut & Astronaut; Am Soc Mech Engrs. *Res:* Fluid and flight mechanics; propulsion aerodynamics. *Mailing Add:* Dept of Aeronaut Naval Postgrad Sch Monterey CA 93940

PLATZMAN, GEORGE WILLIAM, b Chicago, Ill, Apr 19, 20; m 45. METEOROLOGY, OCEANOGRAPHY. *Educ:* Univ Chicago, BS, 40, PhD, 48; Univ Ariz, MS, 41. *Prof Exp:* Instr eng, Sci & Mgt Defense Training Prog, Univ Chicago, 41, instr meteorol, 42-45; jr sci aide, USDA, Ill, 41-42; instr, Univ Ore, 45; engr hydrol, US Eng Dept, 45-46; res assoc, 46-49, from asst prof to assoc prof, 49-60, secy-counsr dept meteorol, 53-59, head phys sci sect, col, 59-60, chmn dept geophys sci, 71-74, PROF METEOROL, UNIV CHICAGO, 60- *Concurrent Pos:* Ed, J Meteorol, Am Meteorol Soc, 48-50; consult, Comput Proj, Inst Advan Study, 50-53; Guggenheim fel, Imp Col, Univ London, 67-68. *Honors & Awards:* Meisinger Award, Am Meteorol Soc, 66, Ed Award, 73. *Mem:* Fel Am Meteorol Soc; fel Am Geophys Union; fel AAAS. *Res:* Circulation and wave theory of atmosphere and ocean; dynamical prediction; storm surges; tides. *Mailing Add:* Dept of Geophys Sci 5734 S Ellis Ave Chicago IL 60637

PLATZMAN, PHILIP M, b Brooklyn, NY, May 1, 35; m 56; c 2. SOLID STATE PHYSICS. *Educ:* Mass Inst Technol, BS, 56; Calif Inst Technol, PhD(physics), 60. *Prof Exp:* Mem tech staff, Hughes Aircraft Co, 56-60; res physicist, 60-68, DEPT HEAD, BELL LABS, INC, 68- *Concurrent Pos:* Asst, Calif Inst Technol, 59-60; vis prof, Univ Calif, Berkeley, 68, ISSP Tokyo, 78, Hebrew Univ, 79 & KFA Julich, Ger, 80. *Mem:* Fel Am Phys Soc. *Res:* Nuclear structure corrections to the hyper-fine structure in hydrogen; mesonic origins of the two nucleon L-S potential; microwave breakdown of gases; polarons; wave propagation in plasmas; plasma effects in metals; light scattering in solids; inelastic x-ray scattering from electrons in solids, liquids and gases; properties of 2-d electron gas at the surface of liquid helium in metal oxide-silicon and in metal oxide-silicon structures. *Mailing Add:* Bell Labs Inc Mountain Ave Murray Hill NJ 07974

PLAUSH, ALBERT CHARLES, b Cleveland, Ohio. PHYSICAL CHEMISTRY. *Educ:* Adelbert Col, BA, 57; Case Western Reserve Univ, MS, 58, PhD(chem), 65. *Prof Exp:* NIH fel biochem, Case Western Reserve Univ, 65-67; asst prof, 67-71, ASSOC PROF CHEM, SAGINAW VALLEY STATE COL, 71- *Concurrent Pos:* Vis scholar, Univ Mich, 74-75. *Mem:* Sigma Xi; Am Chem Soc. *Res:* Nuclear magnetic studies of biological molecules. *Mailing Add:* Saginaw Valley State Col 2250 Pierce Rd University Center MI 48710

PLAUT, ANDREW GEORGE, b Leipzig, Ger, Feb 19, 37; US citizen; m 65; c 2. GASTROENTEROLOGY, IMMUNOLOGY. *Educ:* Ohio State Univ, BS, 58; Tufts Univ, MD, 62. *Prof Exp:* NIH res fel gastroenterol, Mem Hosp Cancer & Allied Dis & Second Med Div, Bellevue Hosp, 64-65; Buswell fel med, State Univ NY Buffalo, 68-73, asst prof med, 71-73; NIH spec fel infectious dis, 65-66, assoc prof, 73-77, PROF MED, SCH MED, TUFTS UNIV, 77- PHYSICIAN, TUFTS-NEW ENG MED CTR HOSP, 73- *Concurrent Pos:* Mem, Gen Med Study Sect, Div Res Grants, NIH, 73- & Sci Adv Bd, Ileitis & Colitis Found; Nat Inst Allergy & Infectious Dis res career develop award, 72; consult, Nat Inst Dent Res, Navy Med Res Lab & Walker Reed Army Inst Res. *Mem:* Am Asn Immunologists; Am Gastroenterol Asn; Am Soc Microbiol; AAAS; Royal Soc Trop Med. *Res:* Immunology of mucosal surfaces, mainly secretory immunoglobulin A; interactions of microbial proteolytic enzymes with mucosal immunoglobulin A antibody; pathogenesis of dental caries, gonorrhea, inflammatory bowel disease; intestinal microflora. *Mailing Add:* Tufts New Eng Med Ctr Hosp 171 Harrison Ave Boston MA 02111

PLAUT, GERHARD WOLFGANG EUGEN, b Frankfurt, Ger, Jan 9, 21; nat US; m 50; c 3. BIOCHEMISTRY. *Educ:* Iowa State Col, BS, 43; Univ Wis, MS, 49, PhD(biochem), 50. *Prof Exp:* Develop biochemist, E R Squibb & Sons, 43-47; asst biochem, Univ Wis, 47-49, asst prof, Inst Enzyme Res, 51-54; assoc prof biochem, NY Univ, 54-58; res prof med, Univ Utah, 58-66, assoc prof biol chem, 58-62, prof biol chem & head biochem lab study hereditary & metab disorders, 62-66; prof biochem & chmn dept, Rutgers Med Sch, 66-70; PROF BIOCHEM & CHMN DEPT, SCH MED, TEMPLE UNIV, 70- *Concurrent Pos:* Alumni Res Found fel, Univ Wis, 51; USPHS sr res fel, 59-62, res career award, 62-66; estab investr, Am Heart Asn, 53-58; consult to var nat orgns & asns, 60- *Mem:* Am Soc Biol Chemists; Am Inst Nutrit; Am Chem Soc; Brit Biochem Soc. *Res:* Intermediary metabolism; enzyme chemistry; vitamins. *Mailing Add:* Dept of Biochem Temple Univ Sch of Med Philadelphia PA 19140

PLAUT, WALTER (SIGMUND), b Darmstadt, Ger, Nov 21, 23; nat US; m 53; c 4. CELL BIOLOGY. *Educ:* Rutgers Univ, BSc, 49; Univ Wis, MS, 50, PhD(genetics), 52. *Prof Exp:* NIH fel, 52-54; asst res zoologist, Univ Calif, 54-56; asst prof bot, 56-60, assoc prof zool, 60-65, PROF ZOOL, UNIV WIS-MADISON, 65-, CHMN DEPT, 78- *Concurrent Pos:* Vis prof, Agrarian Univ, Lima, Peru, 70 & Fac Med, Ribeirao, Preto, Brazil, 74. *Mem:* Genetics Soc Am; Am Soc Cell Biol. *Res:* Chromosome structure and function. *Mailing Add:* Dept of Zool Univ of Wis Madison WI 53706

PLAUTZ, DONALD MELVIN, b Milwaukee, Wis, Dec 26, 42. FORENSIC SCIENCE. *Educ:* Elmhurst Col, BA, 65; SDak State Univ, PhD(chem), 71. *Prof Exp:* Asst prof chem, Madonna Col, 71-72; lab adv, Advan Med & Res Corp, 72; lab scientist forensic chem, Sci Lab, Mich Dept State Police, 72-78; ASST LAB DIR, BUR SCI SERV, ILL DEPT LAW ENFORCEMENT, 78- *Concurrent Pos:* Comnr, Community Comn on Drug Abuse, 75-78. *Mem:* Am Chem Soc; Int Asn Arson Investrs. *Res:* Forensic chemistry. *Mailing Add:* Ill Dept Law Enforcement 515 E Woodruff Rd Joliet IL 60432

PLAVEC, MIREK JOSEF, b Sedlcany, Czech, Oct 7, 25; US citizen; m 50; c 2. ASTROPHYSICS. *Educ:* Charles Univ, Prague, RNDr(astron), 49; Charles Univ, Prague & Czech Acad Sci, PhD(astron), 55, DSc(astron), 68. *Prof Exp:* Prin sci off astrophys, Astron Inst, Ondrejov, Czech, 54-67, chmn dept stellar astrophys, 68-70; vis prof astron, Ohio State Univ, 70; chmn dept, 75-77, PROF ASTRON, UNIV CALIF, LOS ANGELES, 71- *Concurrent Pos:* Int Astron Union grant, Dom Astrophys Observ, Victoria, BC, 61 & 65; assoc prof astron, Charles Univ, Prague, 68-70; pres comn eclipsing binaries, Int Astron Union, 7O-73; NSF res grant, Univ Calif, Los Angeles, 71- &

NASA res grants, Univ Calif, Los Angeles, 78- *Mem:* Int Astron Union; Am Astron Soc. *Res:* Evolution of close binary stars; mass transfer in binary stars; stars with extended atmospheres; physical characteristics of eclipsing binaries; circumstellar matter; satellite ultraviolet stellar spectra. *Mailing Add:* Dept of Astron Univ of Calif Los Angeles CA 90024

PLAXICO, JAMES SAMUEL, b Chester, SC, Oct 2, 24; m 45; c 4. AGRICULTURAL ECONOMICS. *Educ:* Clemson Col, BS, 45, MS, 48; Univ Minn, PhD(agr econ), 53. *Prof Exp:* From asst prof to prof agr econ, Va Polytech Inst, 47-55; head dept, 61-77, PROF AGR ECON, OKLA STATE UNIV, 55- *Concurrent Pos:* Ford Found prog adv, 68-69; state exec dir, Agr Stabilization & Conserv Serv, 79-81. *Mem:* Am Econ Asn; Am Agr Econ Asn. *Res:* Production economics. *Mailing Add:* Dept of Agr Econ Okla State Univ Stillwater OK 74074

PLAYER, MARY ANNE, b Oak Park, Ill, June 6, 20. PLANT PHYSIOLOGY. *Educ:* Northwestern Univ, BS, 43, MS, 45, PhD(plant physiol), 48. *Prof Exp:* Res asst, Surg Dept, Univ Chicago, 48-49; asst prof biol, Elmhurst Col, 54-56; fac mem, 56-64, assoc prof, 64-72, PROF BIOL, WRIGHT COL, 72- *Concurrent Pos:* Lectr, Roosevelt Univ, 56-80. *Mem:* Fel AAAS; Bot Soc Am; Am Soc Plant Physiol; Sigma Xi. *Res:* Effects of plant hormones on transpiration; plant metabolism and growth. *Mailing Add:* Wilbur Wright Col 3400 N Austin Ave Chicago IL 60634

PLAYTER, ROBERT FRANKLIN, b Perth, W Australia, Oct 2, 34; US citizen; m 55; c 3. VETERINARY SURGERY, VETERINARY OPHTHALMOLOGY. *Educ:* Kans State Univ, BS, 59, DVM, 61; Tex A&M Univ, MS, 74; Am Col Vet Ophthalmologists, dipl, 76. *Prof Exp:* Vet practr vet med & surg, Hays Vet Hosp, 61-70; from asst prof to assoc prof, 70-76, chief small animal clin, 76-77, PROF & HEAD DEPT SMALL ANIMAL MED & SURG, COL VET MED, TEX A&M UNIV, 77- *Mem:* Am Vet Med Asn; m Asn Vet Clinicians; Asn Am Vet Med Col; Am Soc Vet Ophthal; Am Col Vet Ophthal. *Mailing Add:* Dept Small Animal Med & Surg Tex A&M Univ College Station TX 77843

PLAZEK, DONALD JOHN, b Milwaukee, Wis, Jan 12, 31; m 55; c 7. PHYSICAL CHEMISTRY. *Educ:* Univ Wis, BS, 53, PhD, 57. *Prof Exp:* Res assoc phys chem, Univ Wis, 57-58; fel fundamental res, Mellon Inst, 58-67; assoc prof, 67-75, assoc chmn dept, 71-74, PROF METALL & MAT ENG, UNIV PITTSBURGH, 75- *Mem:* Am Chem Soc; Soc Rheol; fel Am Phys Soc. *Res:* Rheology; polymer chemistry and physics. *Mailing Add:* Dept of Metall & Mat Eng Univ of Pittsburgh Pittsburgh PA 15261

PLEASANT, JAMES CARROLL, b Greenville, NC, Jan 9, 36; m 57; c 3. MATHEMATICS. *Educ:* ECarolina Col, BS, 58, MA, 60; Univ SC, PhD(math), 65. *Prof Exp:* Teacher high sch, NC, 58-60; asst prof math, ECarolina Col, 60-61, assoc prof, 64-66; assoc prof, 66-69, PROF MATH, EAST TENN STATE UNIV, 69- *Mem:* Math Asn Am; Am Math Soc. *Res:* Ring and module theory; numerical analysis; applied mathematics. *Mailing Add:* Dept Math ETenn State Univ Johnson City TN 37601

PLEASANTS, ELSIE W, b Cincinnati, Ohio, Feb 10; m 47; c 3. INORGANIC CHEMISTRY, ORGANIC CHEMISTRY. *Educ:* Univ Cincinnati, ChE, 38; Columbia Univ, MA, 43, PhD(chem), 46. *Prof Exp:* Res worker biochem, Inst Divi Thomae, Cincinnati, 38-50; res worker skin cancer, NY Skin & Cancer Clin, 40-46; res worker enzymes, St Vincent Hosp, NY, 46-50; res scientist, St Anthony's Guild, 50-67; adj asst prof chem & lectr, Hunter Col, City Univ New York, 67-71; asst prof chem, Grad Sch Nursing, NY Med Col, 71-73; adj asst prof chem, Dent Sch, Farleigh Dickinson Univ, 73-74; adj asst prof chem, Queensborough Community Col, City Univ NY, 74-75, asst prof chem, 74-76; mem chem fac, Montclair State Col, 76-78; asst prof nutrit, Queens Col, City Univ NY, 78-79; asst prof chem, Seton Hall Univ, 79-80; ASST PROF NUTRIT, HUNTER COL, CITY UNIV NY, 80- *Mem:* AAAS; Sigma Xi; NY Acad Sci. *Mailing Add:* 27 Linden Terr Leonia NJ 07605

PLEASANTS, JULIAN RANDOLPH, b Palmetto, Fla, May 1, 18; m 48; c 7. ANIMAL NUTRITION, MICROBIAL ECOLOGY. *Educ:* Univ Notre Dame, BS, 39, MA, 50, PhD(microbiol), 66. *Prof Exp:* Asst biochemist, Lobund Lab, 46-53, chief mammal rearing, 53-60, res assoc biochem, 60-66, assoc res scientist, 66-68, asst prof microbiol, 68-73, ASSOC PROF MICROBIOL, LOBUND LAB, UNIV NOTRE DAME, 73- *Mem:* AAAS; Am Soc Microbiol; Am Asn Lab Animal Sci; Asn Gnotobiotics; Am Inst Nutrit. *Res:* Nutrition and physiology of germfree animals fed chemically defined diets from birth. *Mailing Add:* 52631 Gumwood Rd Granger IN 46530

PLEBUCH, RAYMOND OTTO, b St Paul, Minn, Jan 7, 24; m 70; c 4. HYDROLOGY. *Educ:* Macalester Col, BA, 55; Univ Ill, Urbana, MS, 57. *Prof Exp:* GEOLOGIST, WATER RESOURCES DIV, US GEOL SURV, 57- *Res:* Areal studies of groundwater resources. *Mailing Add:* Water Resources Div US Geol Surv PO Box 770 Paducah KY 42001

PLEBUCH, RICHARD KARL, b Longview, Wash, Sept 7, 35; m 56; c 4. NUCLEAR SCIENCE, NUCLEAR ENGINEERING. *Educ:* Univ Wash, BS, 57; Univ Mich, MS, 58; Mass Inst Technol, ScD(nuclear eng), 63. *Prof Exp:* Proj officer, US Army Chem Corps Bd, 59-60; sect head nuclear systs anal, 63-68, mgr nuclear anal dept, 68-70, MGR NUCLEAR SURVIVABILITY DEPT, TRW DEFENSE & SPACE SYSTS GROUP, REDONDO BEACH, 70- *Mem:* Am Nuclear Soc; Am Inst Aeronaut & Astronaut; Am Chem Soc. *Res:* Nuclear rocket engine system analysis; nuclear gauging systems; weapon environments and effects; weapon system survivability; nuclear safeguards; security systems analysis. *Mailing Add:* 28563 Blythewood Dr Rancho Palos Verdes CA 90274

PLEDGER, GORDON WAYNE, b Dallas, Tex, Dec 4, 42; m 68. MATHEMATICAL STATISTICS. *Educ:* Univ Tex, Austin, BA, 65, MA, 66; Univ Mo-Columbia, PhD(statist), 70. *Prof Exp:* Res assoc statist, Fla State Univ, 70-72; asst prof math & statist, Univ Nebr, Lincoln, 72-73; asst prof math & Statist, Univ Tex, Austin, 73-76; MEM STAFF MATH STATIST, BUR DRUGS, FOOD & DRUG ADMIN, 76- *Mem:* Inst Math Statist; Am Statist Asn. *Res:* Isotonic and other nonparametric regression; analysis of reliability of heterogeneous systems, and other topics in reliability theory. *Mailing Add:* 5600 Fishers Lane Rm 18B45 Rockville MD 20857

PLEDGER, HUEY, JR, organic chemistry, polymer chemistry, see previous edition

PLEDGER, RICHARD ALFRED, b Mineola, NY, July 3, 32; m 55; c 2. MICROBIOLOGY. *Educ:* Rensselaer Polytech Inst, BS, 54; Rutgers Univ, PhD(microbiol), 57. *Prof Exp:* Res biochemist, Plum Island Animal Dis Lab, USDA, 57-58, sr res biochemist, 58-63, prin res biochemist, 63-64; virologist, Hazleton Labs, Va, 64-66, head microbiol-virol sect, 66-69, dir biosci dept, 69-71; scientist-adminr, Nat Cancer Inst, 71-77; HEALTH SCIENTIST-ADMINR, NAT INST ARTHRITIS, DIABETES, DIGESTIVE & KIDNEY DIS, 77- *Res:* Mechanism of growth and reproduction of microbes, especially viral infection and replication within living tissue; chemical carcinogenesis; animal model development of major forms of human cancer. *Mailing Add:* Nat Inst Arthritis, Metab & Digestive Dis 5333 Westbard Ave Bethesda MD 20014

PLEIN, ELMER MICHAEL, b Dubuque, Iowa, Nov 21, 06; m 32, 52. PHARMACY. *Educ:* Univ Colo, BS & PhC, 29, MS, 31, PhD(chem), 36. *Prof Exp:* Instr pharm, Univ Colo, 29-38; from instr to prof pharm, Univ Wash, 38-77, coordr pharmaceut servs & dir drug serv dept, Hosp Pharm Educ, 58-77; RETIRED. *Mem:* Am Chem Soc; Am Soc Hosp Pharmacists; Am Pharmaceut Asn; Am Col Apothecaries. *Res:* Therapeutic efficiency of drug products; clinical and hospital pharmacy. *Mailing Add:* Sch of Pharm BG-20 Univ of Wash Seattle WA 98195

PLEIN, JOY BICKMORE, b Nov 10, 25; US citizen; m 52. PHARMACY. *Educ:* Idaho State Univ, BSPharm, 47; Univ Wash, MSPharm, 52, PhD(pharm), 56. *Prof Exp:* Pharmacist, Heinz Apothecary, Salt Lake City, Utah, 47-49; lectr pharm & pharmacol, Seattle Pac Col, 54-59 & 61-65; asst to chmn comt pharm & pharmaceut, Am Soc Hosp Pharmacists, 59-62, consult, Dept Sci Serv, 62-63, asst ed, Am Hosp Formulary Serv, 64-66; lectr, 66-72, assoc prof, 72-74, PROF PHARM, SCH PHARM, UNIV WASH, 74- *Concurrent Pos:* Mem continuing educ subcomt, Wash-Alaska Regional Med Prog, 69-71; mem ref panel, Am Hosp Formulary Serv, 69-76 & OTC Rev Panel Dentifrices & Dent Care Agents, Food & Drug Admin, 73-78; coordr, Interdisciplinary Nursing Home Prog, Univ Washington, Foss Home, Seattle. *Mem:* Am Soc Hosp Pharm; Am Pharmaceut Asn; Am Asn Cols Pharm; Geront Soc Am. *Res:* Clinical pharmacy; educational methods and materials; effects of aging on drug therapy; long term care. *Mailing Add:* Sch of Pharm SB-68 Univ of Wash Seattle WA 98195

PLEMMONS, ROBERT JAMES, b Old Fort, NC, Dec 18, 39; m 63; c 2. MATHEMATICS. COMPUTER SCIENCE. *Educ:* Wake Forest Univ, BS, 61; Auburn Univ, MS, 62, PhD(math), 65. *Prof Exp:* Res mathematician, Nat Security Agency, 65-66; assoc prof math, Univ Miss, 66-67; assoc prof math & comput sci, Univ Tenn, Knoxville, 67-74, prof, 67-81; PROF COMPUT SCI & MATH, NC STATE UNIV, RALEIGH, 81- *Concurrent Pos:* Consult, Oak Ridge Nat Lab. *Mem:* Soc Indust & Appl Math; Asn Comput Mach; Math Asn Am; Am Math Soc. *Res:* Numerical analysis; computer science. *Mailing Add:* Dept Math & Comput Sci NC State Univ Raleigh NC 27650

PLEMONS, TERRY DALE, b Seminole, Okla, Feb 19, 41; m 70; c 1. ACOUSTICS. *Educ:* Univ Tex, Austin, BS, 63, PhD(physics), 71. *Prof Exp:* Peace Corps vol teacher, Am Peace Corps, India, 64-66; res scientist, underwater acoust, Appl Res Lab, Univ Tex, Austin, 66-75; physicist, Appl Physics Lab & lectr elec eng, Univ Wash, Seattle, 75-78; ENGR SCIENTIST, TRACOR, INC, 78- *Mem:* Sigma Xi; Acoust Soc Am. *Res:* Underwater acoustics; signal processing; systems analysis; sonar development. *Mailing Add:* Tracor Inc 6500 Tracor Lane Austin TX 78712

PLENDL, HANS SIEGFRIED, b Berlin, Ger, June 12, 27; nat US; m 57; c 4. NUCLEAR PHYSICS. *Educ:* Harvard Univ, BA, 52; Yale Univ, MS, 54, PhD(physics), 58. *Prof Exp:* Asst physics, Yale Univ, 52-54, asst nuclear physics, 54-56; from asst prof to assoc prof, 56-77, PROF PHYSICS, FLA STATE UNIV, 77- *Concurrent Pos:* Res partic, Oak Ridge Nat Lab, 57-; vis scientist, Nuclear Res Ctr, Karlsruhe & Max Planck Inst Nuclear Physics, Heidelberg, 62-63; consult, Sch X-ray Technol, Tallahassee Mem Hosp, Fla, 64-72; mem bd dirs, Recon, Inc, 65-68; mem users adv comt, Space Radiation Effects Lab, Va, 69-; vis staff mem, Los Alamos Sci Lab, 69-81. *Mem:* Am Phys Soc; Europ Phys Soc; AAAS. *Res:* Nuclear structure; reactions of nucleons, heavy ions and pions with nuclei; applied nuclear physics. *Mailing Add:* Dept of Physics Fla State Univ Tallahassee FL 32306

PLESCIA, OTTO JOHN, b Utica, NY, Apr, 12, 21; m 49; c 4. IMMUNOCHEMISTRY, IMMUNOPHARMACOLOGY. *Educ:* Hamilton Col BS, 43; Cornell Univ, PhD(chem), 47. *Prof Exp:* Instr math, Hamilton Col, 43-44; res chemist, M W Kellogg Co, 47-49; res assoc chem, Univ Wis, 50-51; res assoc immunochem, Col Physicians & Surgeons, Columbia Univ, 51-55; assoc prof, 55-60, PROF IMMMUNOCHEM, WAKSMAN INST MICROBIOL, RUTGERS STATE UNIV NJ, 60- *Concurrent Pos:* Lectr, Brooklyn Col, 49; de pont fel, Univ Wis, 49-50; assoc mem, Comn Immunization, Dept Defense, 57-62; vis prof, Univ Puerto Rico, 65-68; vis investr, Salk Inst, 76-77. *Mem:* Am Asn Immunologists; AAAS; Am Soc Microbiol; Am Chem Soc. *Res:* Role of prostaglandins in the physiology and pathophysiology of immmune responses; host-tumor interactions; pathogenesis and regulation of antoimmune diseases. *Mailing Add:* Waksman Inst Microbiol Rutgers State Univ NJ PO Box 759 Piscataway NJ 08854

PLESS, IRWIN ABRAHAM, b New York, NY, Mar 11, 25; div; c 3. PHYSICS. *Educ:* Univ Chicago, SB, 50, SM, 51 & 53, PhD(physics), 55. *Prof Exp:* From instr to assoc prof, 56-64, PROF PHYSICS, MASS INST TECHNOL, 64- *Mem:* Sigma Xi; Am Phys Soc; Am Asn Physics Teachers. *Res:* Elementary particle physics. *Mailing Add:* APC Group Lab for Nuclear Sci 575 Technol Sq Rm 408 Cambridge MA 02139

PLESS, VERA STEPEN, b Chicago, Ill, Mar 5, 31; c 3. MATHEMATICS. *Educ:* Univ Chicago, PhB, 49, MS, 52; Northwestern Univ, PhD(math), 57. *Prof Exp:* Lectr, Boston Univ, 57-61; res mathematician, Air Force Cambridge Res Labs, 61-66; mathematician, Argonne Nat Lab, 67; res mathematician, Air Force Cambridge Res Labs, 68-72; res assoc elec eng, Mass Inst Technol, 72-75; PROF MATH & COMPUT SCI, UNIV ILL, CHICAGO CIRCLE, 75- *Honors & Awards:* Marcus O'Day Award, Air Force Cambridge Res Lab, 69; Patricia Keyes Glass Award, US Air Force, 71. *Mem:* AAAS; Am Math Soc; Math Asn Am. *Res:* Error correcting codes; combinatorial analysis; quadratic forms; representation of finite groups; computer strategies. *Mailing Add:* Dept of Math Col Lib Arts & Sci Univ Ill Chicago Circle Box 4348 Chicago IL 60680

PLESSET, MILTON SPINOZA, b Pittsburgh, Pa, Feb 7, 08; m 34; c 4. PHYSICS. *Educ:* Univ Pittsburgh, BS, 29, MS, 30; Yale Univ, PhD(physics), 32. *Prof Exp:* Nat Res Coun fel, Calif Inst Technol, 32-33, inst fel, 40-42; Nat Res Coun fel, Inst Theoret Physics, Copenhagen Univ, 33-34 & Belgium-Am Educ Found, 34-35; instr physics, Univ Rochester, 35-40; head anal group, Douglas Aircraft Co, Calif, 42-45; theoret physics consult, US Naval Ord Testing Sta, 46-47; assoc prof appl mech, 47-51, prof eng sci, 51-78, EMER PROF ENG SCI, CALIF INST TECHNOL, 78- *Concurrent Pos:* Mem, Sci Adv Bd, US Air Force, 51-53 & Maritime Res Adv Comt, 58-60; mem mech adv panel, Nat Bur Standards, 59-61, chmn exec comt, Fluid Eng Div, 70-72 & Fluid Dynamics Div, 72-74, mem, Adv Comt on Reactor Safeguards, 75-; consult, Rand Corp, 74-76. *Mem:* Fel Am Phys Soc; fel Am Soc Mech Eng; Am Nuclear Soc. *Res:* Theoretical physics; fluid dynamics; two-phase flow and cavitation; radiation effects; theory of two phase flow. *Mailing Add:* Dept of Eng Sci Calif Inst of Technol Pasadena CA 91125

PLESSY, BOAKE LUCIEN, b New Orleans, La, Sept 12, 38; m 59; c 3. PHYSICAL CHEMISTRY, POLYMER CHEMISTRY. *Educ:* Dillard Univ, BA, 59; Adelphi Univ, PhD(chem), 74. *Prof Exp:* Staff chemist, Pfizer Inc, 62-73; asst prof, 73-80, ASSOC PROF CHEM, DILLARD UNIV, 80- *Concurrent Pos:* Woodrow Wilson fel, 59. *Mem:* Soc Complex Carbohydrates. *Res:* Hydration of proteoglycans from bovine cornea; polymer dimensions in binary solvent systems. *Mailing Add:* Dept of Chem Dillard Univ 2601 Gentilly Blvd New Orleans LA 70122

PLETCHER, RICHARD H, b Elkhart, Ind, May 21, 35; m 57; c 3. MECHANICAL ENGINEERING. *Educ:* Purdue Univ, BSME, 57; Cornell Univ, MS, 62, PhD(mech eng), 66. *Prof Exp:* Instr mech eng, Cornell Univ, 61-64; sr res engr, Propulsion Sect, United Aircraft Res Labs, 66-67; assoc prof mech eng, 67-76, PROF MECH ENG, IOWA STATE UNIV, 76- *Mem:* Am Soc Mech Engrs; Am Inst Aeronaut & Astronaut. *Res:* Heat transfer and fluid mechanics of two-phase flows; analysis of turbulent flows; application of numerical methods of analysis to boundary layer phenomena, including turbulent flows with heat transfer. *Mailing Add:* Dept of Mech Eng Iowa State Univ Ames IA 50011

PLETCHER, WAYNE ALBERT, b Crooksville, Ohio, Aug 24, 42; m 68; c 2. ORGANIC & POLYMER CHEMISTRY. *Educ:* Ohio Univ, BS, 66; Univ Mich, MS, 67, PhD(chem), 71. *Prof Exp:* Teaching fel & lectr org chem, Univ Mich, 66-70, fel azide res, 71; fel natural prod res, Fla State Univ, 71; res specialist & proj coordr, 71-76, supvr, Adhesives, Coatings & Sealers Div, 76-78, mgr, Res Lab, 78-80, MGR, INDUST PROD LAB, ADHESIVES, COATINGS & SEALERS DIV, 3M CO, 80- *Mem:* Am Chem Soc. *Res:* Basic structure-property relationship in polymer chemistry, particularly the investigation of new adhesive systems, pressure sensitive, thermoplastic, reactive liquids and crosslinked, involving the synthesis of polymers having unique physical properties. *Mailing Add:* 2572 Irene St Roseville MN 55113

PLETSCH, DONALD JAMES, b Lake City, Minn, May 8, 12; m 34, 61; c 3. ENTOMOLOGY, MALARIOLOGY. *Educ:* Hamline Univ, BS, 32; Univ Minn, MS, 36, PhD(entom), 42. *Prof Exp:* Asst exp sta, Univ Minn, 33-37; asst state entomologist, Mont, 37; from asst prof to assoc prof entom, Mont State Col, 37-47, from asst entomologist to assoc entomologist, Exp Sta, 37-47; tech instr, Med Admin Corps, Officers Candidate Sch, 43-44; biologist sci & tech div, Econ & Sci Sect, Supreme Comdr Allied Powers, Japan, 47-50; biologist, Div Int Health, USPHS, 50-52; leader malaria team, WHO, Formosa, 52-55 & Pan Am Sanit Bur, Mex, 56-63; entomologist, AID, Addis Ababa, 64-66; dir, Cent Am Malaria Res Sta, USPHS, El Salvador, 67-69; MALARIA CONSULT, AID, 70- *Concurrent Pos:* Med entom consult, Dept Health, Govt Indonesia, 77-78; Consult, Pan-Am Health Orgn/WHO, Guyana, SAm, 81. *Mem:* AAAS; Am Soc Trop Med & Hyg; Soc Mexicana de Entomologia; Sigma Xi. Am Mosquito Control Asn; Am Pub Health Asn. *Res:* Insect ecology; medical entomology; research administration. *Mailing Add:* Apartado Postal 20-688 Mexico 20 DF Mexico

PLETT, EDELBERT GREGORY, b Bassano, Alta, Jan 17, 39; m 66; c 2. MECHANICAL ENGINEERING. *Educ:* Univ BC, BASc, 62; Mass Inst Technol, SM, 64, ScD(mech eng), 66. *Prof Exp:* Asst prof eng, Carleton Univ, 66-70, assoc prof, 70; mem res staff, Princeton Univ, 70-76, res engr, 76; assoc prof, 76-79, PROF, CARLETON UNIV, 79- *Concurrent Pos:* Consult, Comput Devices of Can, 69-70, Dashwood Indust Ltd & Energy North Int Ltd, 78-; pres, Asecor Ltd, 78- *Mem:* Combustion Inst; assoc fel Am Inst Aeronaut & Astronaut. *Res:* Combustion noise; coal gasification; coal gas combustion; solar energy; combustion. *Mailing Add:* South Sunset Dr Carleton Univ Manotick ON K0A 2N0 Can

PLETTA, DAN HENRY, b South Bend, Ind, Dec 31, 03; m 31; c 2. MECHANICS. *Educ:* Univ Ill, BS, 27, CE, 38; Univ Wis, MS, 31. *Prof Exp:* Instr mech, Univ Wis, 27-30; asst prof civil eng, Univ SDak, 30-32; from asst prof to prof appl mech, 32-70, univ prof eng mech, 69-72, head dept appl mech, 48-70, mem bd dirs, Res Found, 48-53, Univ distinguished prof, 70-72, EMER PROF ENG MECH, VA POLYTECH INST, 72- *Concurrent Pos:* Pvt engr, 22-30; consult engr, 45- *Honors & Awards:* Western Elec Fund Award Excellence in Teaching, Am Soc Eng Educ, 68. *Mem:* Am Soc Eng Educ; hon mem Am Soc Civil Engrs; Nat Soc Prof Engrs; Am Concrete Inst; fel Am Acad Mech. *Res:* Engineering materials; stress analysis. *Mailing Add:* 1414 Highland Circle SE Blacksburg VA 24060

PLEWA, MICHAEL JACOB, b Chicago, Ill, June 5, 47; m 78. GENETIC TOXICOLOGY. *Educ:* Loyola Univ, Chicago, BS, 69; Ill State Univ, MS, 71, PhD(genetics), 74. *Prof Exp:* Res assoc, 74-76, asst res geneticist, 76-78, asst prof, 78-82, ASSOC PROF GENETICS, UNIV ILL, 82- *Concurrent Pos:* Prin investr, US Environ Protection Agency, 76-82, Nat Inst Environ Health Sci, 78-83 & Joyce Found, 81-83; mem, Gene-Tox Prog, US Environ Protection Agency, 78-80. *Mem:* Environ Mutagen Soc; AAAS; Maize Genetics Coop; Sigma Xi. *Res:* Activiation of promutagens to mutagens by plant systems; comparison of the mutation induction kinetics between somatic and germinal cells after acute or chronic mutagen exposure regimens. *Mailing Add:* Environ Res Lab Inst Environ Studies Univ Ill 1005 W Western Ave Urbana IL 61801

PLIMMER, JACK REYNOLDS, b Liverpool, Eng, July 18, 27; m 49; c 2. ORGANIC CHEMISTRY. *Educ:* Trinity Col, Dublin, BA, 52; Univ Edinburgh, PhD(org chem), 55. *Prof Exp:* Asst chem, Univ Edinburgh, 52-55; Eli Lilly res fel, Univ WIndies, 55-56, res fel natural prod chem, 59-62, lectr, 62-64; scientist, Med Res Coun, Univ Exeter, 56-59; vis scientist, NIH, Md, 64-66; res chemist, Plant Sci Res Div, 66-75, CHIEF ORG CHEM SYNTHESIS LAB, AGR ENVIRON QUAL INST, AGR RES SERV, USDA, 75- *Concurrent Pos:* Hon res asst, Univ Col, London, 62. *Mem:* Am Chem Soc; Royal Soc Chem; Asn Off Anal Chemists. *Res:* Chemistry and synthesis of natural products; photochemistry of pesticides; pesticide degradation in soils; identification, synthesis and application of chemicals affecting insect behavior. *Mailing Add:* Rm 333 Bldg 007 BARC-East USDA Beltsville MD 20705

PLIMPTON, CALVIN HASTINGS, b Boston, Mass, Oct 7, 18; m 41; c 4. MEDICINE. *Educ:* Amherst Col, BA, 39; Harvard Univ, MD, 43, MA, 47; Columbia Univ, ScD(med), 51; Am Bd Internal Med, dipl, 51. *Hon Degrees:* Twelve from US & foreign cols & univs, 60-69. *Prof Exp:* Intern med, Columbia-Presby Med Ctr, 43, from asst resident to resident, 47-50; instr, Col Physicians & Surgeons, Columbia Univ, 50, assoc, 52-57, asst prof clin med & asst dean col, 59-60; prof med, chmn dept & assoc dean, Am Univ Beirut, 57-59; pres, Amherst Col, 60-71; dean med sch, 71-74 & 76-79, prof med & pres, 71-79, EMER PROF MED, STATE UNIV NY DOWNSTATE MED CTR, 79- *Concurrent Pos:* Trustee, Am Univ Beirut, 60-, Univ Mass, 62-70, Commonwealth Fund, 62-, World Peace Fund, 62-, Phillips Exeter Acad, 65-, Hampshire Col, 65-71 & Long Island Univ, 72-; mem bd overseers, Harvard Univ, 69-75. *Honors & Awards:* Comdr, Order Cedars Lebanon, 59. *Mem:* AMA; fel Am Col Physicians; Harvey Soc. *Res:* Calcium metabolism; diabetes; adrenal cortex. *Mailing Add:* Off of the Pres State Univ NY Downstate Med Ctr Brooklyn NY 11203

PLIMPTON, RODNEY F, JR, b Poughkeepsie, NY, May 16, 37; m 58; c 4. ANIMAL SCIENCE, MEAT SCIENCE. *Educ:* Rutgers Univ, BS, 59; Ohio State Univ, MS, 61, PhD(animal sci), 65. *Prof Exp:* From instr to assoc prof, 65-74, PROF ANIMAL SCI, OHIO STATE UNIV, 74- *Honors & Awards:* Nat Independent Meat Packers Asn-Wilbur LaRoe Mem Award Meat Res, 63. *Mem:* Am Soc Animal Sci; Am Meat Sci Asn; Inst Food Technol. *Res:* Hormone effect on carcass development and evaluation in swine; protein and fat studies in sausage processing; mechanical muscle treatment in cured meat processing. *Mailing Add:* Dept of Animal Sci Ohio State Univ 2029 Fyffe Rd Columbus OH 43210

PLINT, COLIN ARNOLD, b Liverpool, Eng, Jan 16, 26; m 47; c 5. PHYSICS. *Educ:* Oxford Univ, BA, 50; Univ Toronto, PhD(physics), 53. *Prof Exp:* From asst prof to prof, Univ Okla, 53-68, chmn dept, 59-63; prof physics & chmn dept, 68-69, dean fac arts & sci, 69-75, dean div math & sci, 75-76, PROF PHYSICS, BROCK UNIV, 68- *Mem:* Can Asn Physicists; Optical Soc Am. *Res:* Solid state physics--dislocations, ferrelectrics; optics--far infrared. *Mailing Add:* Brock Univ St Catharines ON L2S 3A1 Can

PLISKIN, WILLIAM AARON, b Akron, Ohio, Aug 9, 20; m 44; c 3. SEMICONDUCTORS, CHEMICAL PHYSICS. *Educ:* Kent State Univ, BSEd, 41; Univ Ohio, MS, 43; Ohio State Univ, PhD(physics), 49. *Prof Exp:* Asst, Ohio State Univ, 47-48; res physicist, Texaco Res Ctr, Texaco, Inc, 49-59; staff physicist, 59-60, adv physicist, 60-63, mgr spec studies oxides & insulators dept, 64-70, sr physicist, 63-79, mgr thin film insulators, IBM Components, Hopewell Junction, 70-79, SR TECH STAFF MEM, IBM CORP, 79- *Honors & Awards:* Corp Invention Award, IBM Corp, 66; Electronics Div Award, Electrochem Soc, 73. *Mem:* Am Phys Soc; Am Chem Soc; Electrochem Soc; fel Inst Elec & Electronics Engrs; AAAS. *Res:* Infrared spectroscopy; chemisorption; surface physics; semiconductor surfaces; passivation; oxidation; thin film measurements; thin insulating films; semiconductor device processing. *Mailing Add:* 31 Greenvale Farms Rd Poughkeepsie NY 12603

PLOC, ROBERT ALLEN, b Vancouver, BC, June 2, 39; m 65; c 3. METALLURGY. *Educ:* Univ BC, BApplSci, 62; Univ Cambridge, PhD(metall), 65. *Prof Exp:* ASSOC RES OFF MAT SCI, CHALK RIVER NUCLEAR LABS, ATOMIC ENERGY CAN LTD, 66- *Mem:* Electron Micros Soc Am; Microscopical Soc Can. *Res:* Physical formation of oxide films on zirconium and zirconium alloys; electron microscopy and electron diffraction. *Mailing Add:* Chalk River Nuclear Labs Atomic Energy Can Ltd Sta 82 Chalk River ON K0J 1J0 Can

PLOCK, RICHARD JAMES, b Mineola, NY, Apr 22, 31. CHEMICAL PHYSICS. *Educ:* Polytech Inst Brooklyn, BS, 52; Yale Univ, MS, 54, PhD(chem), 57. *Prof Exp:* Res physicist, Lawrence Radiation Lab, 56-62 & Goddard Space Flight Ctr, NASA, Md, 62-64; asst prof physics, Univ Redlands, 64-68; consult theoret chem, Lockheed Propulsion Co, 66-78; consult specialist, Systs Consults, Inc, 79-81; SCIENTIST, SCI APPLNS INC, 81- *Mem:* AAAS; Am Phys Soc; Am Inst Chem; Am Chem Soc. *Res:* Theoretical chemical physics. *Mailing Add:* PO Box 26876 San Diego CA 92126

PLOCKE, DONALD J, b Ansonia, Conn, May 5, 29. BIOPHYSICAL CHEMISTRY. *Educ:* Yale Univ, BS, 50; Boston Col, MA, 56; Mass Inst Technol, PhD(biophys), 61. *Prof Exp:* Res fel biol chem, Harvard Univ, 64; asst prof, 66-71, ASSOC PROF BIOPHYS & CHMN DEPT BIOL, BOSTON COL, 71- *Mem:* Am Chem Soc; Biophys Soc; Am Soc Microbiol; Am Soc Plant Physiol. *Res:* Role of metal ions in ribosomes; metalloenzymes; spectroscopy; chemistry of macromolecules. *Mailing Add:* Dept of Biol Boston Col Chestnut Hill MA 02167

PLODINEC, MATTHEW JOHN, b Kansas City, Mo, Mar 29, 46; m 68; c 2. PHYSICAL CHEMISTRY. *Educ:* Franklin & Marshall Col, BA, 68; Univ Fla, PhD(phys chem), 74. *Prof Exp:* Res chemist photochem, Wilmington, Del, 74-75, res chemist glass & cement, 75-80, RES SUPVR, GLASS TECHNOL GROUP, E I DU PONT DE NEMOURS & CO, INC, AIKEN, SC, 80- *Mem:* Am Chem Soc; Am Ceramic Soc; Mat Res Soc. *Res:* Encapsulation of nuclear waste in durable form; study of interactions of different waste components with encapsulating material. *Mailing Add:* Savannah River Lab E I du Pont de Nemours & Co Aiken SC 29801

PLONSEY, ROBERT, b New York, NY, July 17, 24; m 48; c 1. BIOMEDICAL ENGINEERING. *Educ:* Cooper Union, BEE, 43; NY Univ, MEE, 48; Univ Calif, PhD(elec eng), 56. *Prof Exp:* Asst antenna lab, Univ Calif, 53-55, actg asst prof elec eng, 55-57; prof, 57-68, chmn biomed engr, 76-80, dir bioeng group, 62-68, PROF BIOMED ENG, CASE WESTERN RESERVE UNIV, 68-, DIR BIOMED ENG TRAINING PROG, 70- *Concurrent Pos:* Mem biomed eng fel rev comt, NIH, 66-70, eng in med & biol training comt, 71-73; mem, Alliance Eng Med & Biol Coun, 72-74, treas, 76-78; from vpres to pres, Inst Elec & Electronics Engrs Group Eng in Med & Biol, 71-74 & chmn ad hoc comt cert, 75-77; pres, Am Bd Clin Eng, 75, mem comn trustees, 75-; vis prof & biomed engr, Duke Univ, 80-81; sr fel, NIH, 80-81. *Honors & Awards:* Morlock Award, Inst Elec & Electronics Engrs, 79. *Mem:* AAAS; fel Inst Elec & Electronics Engrs; Am Soc Eng Educ; Soc Neurosci; Biomed Eng Soc (from pres-elect to pres, 80-82). *Res:* Electrophysiology with special emphasis on electrocardiography and application of electromagnetic field theory to volume conductor problems. *Mailing Add:* Dept of Biomed Eng Wickenden Bldg Case Western Reserve Univ Cleveland OH 44106

PLONSKER, LARRY, b Brooklyn, NY, Aug 20, 34; m 62. ORGANIC CHEMISTRY, PETROLEUM PRODUCTS. *Educ:* City Col New York, BS, 52; Fla State Univ, PhD(org chem), 60. *Prof Exp:* Res chemist, 60-67, res supvr, 67-74, com develop assoc, Baton Rouge, 74-76, prod mgr, 76-77, dir com develop, Europe, 77-81, MGR PETROL CHEM COM DEVELOP, ETHYL CORP, 81- *Mem:* Am Chem Soc. *Res:* Small ring compounds; organo-metallics; phosphorus chemistry; agricultural chemicals; aromatic amines and phenols; fuels and lubricants. *Mailing Add:* 451 Florida St Ethyl Corp Baton Rouge LA 70801

PLONSKY, ANDREW WALTER, b Pa, Dec 19, 12; m 39; c 3. ELECTRICITY, PHYSICS. *Educ:* Univ Scranton, BS, 40; Mass Inst Technol, BS, 43, MS, 45. *Prof Exp:* Instr, Mass Inst Technol, 43-45; asst engr, New Haven RR, 45-47; PROF ENG, UNIV SCRANTON, 47- *Mem:* Math Asn Am; Inst Elec & Electronics Engrs; Asn Comput Mach. *Res:* Electric fields and circuits; electromagnetic fields; circuits and systems analysis; electrical controls and signal amplification; software systems; engineering mechanics. *Mailing Add:* Dept of Comput Sci Univ of Scranton Scranton PA 18510

PLONUS, MARTIN, b Trumpininken, Lithuania, Dec 21, 33; US citizen; m 65; c 2. ELECTRICAL ENGINEERING. *Educ:* Univ Ill, BS, 56, MS, 57; Univ Mich, PhD(elec eng), 61. *Prof Exp:* From asst prof to assoc prof elec eng, 61-69, PROF ELEC ENG, NORTHWESTERN UNIV, 69- *Concurrent Pos:* Mem bd dirs, Nat Electronics Conf, 63-; US Air Force contrOff Sci Res contract, 64-65; NSF grant, 66-67 & 75-76; assoc ed, Transactions on Antennas & Propagation, 68-72; mem US comn VI, Int Union Radio Sci. *Honors & Awards:* Best Paper Award, Transactions on Antennas & Propagation, 71. *Mem:* Sr mem Inst Elec & Electronics Engrs. *Res:* Electromagnetic theory; scattering and diffraction; antennas and propagation. *Mailing Add:* Dept of Elec Eng Northwestern Univ Evanston IL 60201

PLOOSTER, MYRON NIEVEEN, atmospheric physics, see previous edition

PLOTKA, EDWARD DENNIS, b Utica, NY, Oct 10, 38; m 66. ENDOCRINOLOGY, PHYSIOLOGY. *Educ:* Del Valley Col, BS, 60; Ore State Univ, MS, 63; Purdue Univ, PhD(physiol), 67. *Prof Exp:* Asst prof, Purdue Univ, 66-67; asst res prof, Univ Ga, 67-69; RES SCIENTIST, MARSHFIELD MED FOUND MED RES & EDUC, 69- *Mem:* Endocrine Soc; Am Soc Animal Sci; Brit Soc Study Fertil; Soc Exp Biol & Med; Am Physiol Soc. *Res:* Biochemical and physiological studies in the metabolism of reproductive hormones with special reference to steroids. *Mailing Add:* Marshfield Med Found 510 N St Joseph Ave Marshfield WI 54449

PLOTKE, FREDERICK, b Kattowitz, Ger, Nov 19, 09; nat US; m 39; c 1. MEDICINE. *Educ:* Univ Frankfurt, MD, 35; Vanderbilt Univ, MPH, 42; Am Bd Prev Med, dipl, 49. *Prof Exp:* Pub health physician, State Dept Pub Welfare, Ill, 39-43; venereal dis control officer, Chicago Bd Health, 47-50; chief, USPHS, State Dept Pub Welfare, Ill, 51-65; asst clin prof, 55-58, ASSOC CLIN PROF PREV MED, STRITCH SCH MED, LOYOLA UNIV CHICAGO, 58-; MED REP COMMUN DIS CTR, USPHS, STATE DEPT PUB WELFARE, ILL, 65- *Concurrent Pos:* Consult, State Civil Defense Agency, Ill, 55-; lectr, Sch Hosp Admin, Northwestern Univ, 58- *Mem:* AMA; fel Am Pub Health Asn; Asn Teachers Prev Med; Am Col Prev Med. *Res:* Communicable and venereal disease control; epidemiology and mental health. *Mailing Add:* 777 N Michigan Ave Chicago IL 60611

PLOTKIN, ALLEN, b New York, NY, May 4, 42; m 66. FLUID MECHANICS, AERODYNAMICS. *Educ:* Columbia Univ, BSc, 63, MSc, 64; Stanford Univ, PhD(mech), 68. *Prof Exp:* From asst prof to assoc prof, 68-77, PROF AEROSPACE ENG, UNIV MD, COLLEGE PARK, 77- *Concurrent Pos:* NASA res grant, Univ Md, 70-73 & 80-82, NSF res grant, 75-77; vis assoc, Calif Inst Technol, 75-76; consult, Naval Surface Weapons Ctr, White Oak, Md, 80- *Mem:* Am Inst Aeronaut & Astronaut; Am Soc Mech Engrs; Soc Naval Archit & Marine Eng. *Res:* Fluid mechanics; hydrodynamics; aerodynamics. *Mailing Add:* Dept of Aerospace Eng Univ of Md College Park MD 20742

PLOTKIN, DIANE JOYCE, b Brooklyn, NY, Oct 6, 48; m 72. GENETICS, CELL BIOLOGY. *Educ:* Wheaton Col, BA, 69; Univ Chicago, PhD(biol), 78. *Prof Exp:* FEL SOMATIC CELL GENETICS, DEPT BIOL, YALE UNIV, 78- *Concurrent Pos:* Fel, Damon Runyon-Walter Winchell Cancer Fund, 78-79; NIH fel, 79- *Mem:* Genetics Soc Am; AAAS. *Res:* Genetic control of meiosis; somatic cell genetics; transformation of mammaliam cells by exogenous DNA. *Mailing Add:* Dept of Biol PO Box 6666 Kline Biol Tower New Haven CT 06511

PLOTKIN, EUGENE ISAAK, b Leningrad, USSR, May 8, 32; m 56; c 2. SIGNAL PROCESSING. *Educ:* Inst Commun Eng, USSR, BSc & MSc, 55, PhD(signal processing), 63. *Prof Exp:* Assoc prof commun, Inst Commun Eng, 63-73; assoc prof commun networks, Ben Gurion Univ, Israel, 73-80; ASSOC PROF COMMUN SIGNAL PROCESSING, PA STATE UNIV, 80- *Concurrent Pos:* Assoc prof commun networks, Tel-Aviv Univ, 78-80. *Mem:* NY Acad Sci; Asn Engrs & Architects; sr mem Inst Elec & Electronic Engrs. *Res:* Problems of signal detection and parameter estimation; adaptive and non-linear filtering for suppression of non-gaussian interferences; phase space approach to speech signal recognition. *Mailing Add:* 121 Elec Eng East Bldg Pa State Univ University Park PA 16802

PLOTKIN, JACOB MANUEL, b Bloomfield, Conn, Mar 10, 41; m 66. MATHEMATICS. *Educ:* Yale Univ, BA, 63; Cornell Univ, PhD(math), 68. *Prof Exp:* assoc prof, 68-80, PROF MATH, MICH STATE UNIV, 80- *Mem:* Am Math Soc; Asn Symbolic Logic; Math Asn. *Res:* Mathematical logic and set theory. *Mailing Add:* Dept of Math Mich State Univ East Lansing MI 48823

PLOTKIN, KENNETH JAY, acoustics, aerodynamics, see previous edition

PLOTKIN, MARTIN, b Brooklyn, NY, July 22, 22; m 49; c 1. ELECTRONICS. *Educ:* City Col New York, BEE, 43; Polytech Inst Brooklyn, MEE, 51. *Prof Exp:* Electronic engr, Gunfire Control, Bendix Aviation Corp, 43-44; engr high energy accelerator electronics, 46-56, group leader, 56-65, chief elec engr, Accelerator Dept, 65-76, SR ENGR ISABELLE PROJ, BROOKHAVEN NAT LAB, 77- *Mem:* Inst Elec & Electronics Engrs; Nuclear & Plasma Sci Soc (pres, 77-78). *Res:* Radio frequency and electronics for alternating gradient synchrotron; high energy accelerator electronics; ferromagnetic ferrites. *Mailing Add:* 117 Clover Dr Massapequa Park NY 11762

PLOTKIN, STANLEY ALAN, b New York, NY, May 12, 32; m 56, 79; c 2. VIROLOGY, PEDIATRICS. *Educ:* NY Univ, BA, 52; State Univ NY Downstate Med Ctr, MD, 56; Am Bd Pediat, dipl, 65. *Prof Exp:* Intern med, Cleveland Metrop Gen Hosp, 56-57; from instr to assoc prof, 59-73, PROF PEDIAT, SCH MED, UNIV PA, 74- *Concurrent Pos:* Joseph P Kennedy Jr Found scholar, 64-; assoc mem, Wistar Inst Anat & Biol, 60-73, mem, 74-; resident, Children's Hosp Philadelphia, 61-63, assoc physician, 65-73, sr physician, 74-; registr, Hosp Sick Children, London, Eng, 62-63. *Mem:* AAAS; Am Asn Immunol; Soc Pediat Res; Infectious Dis Soc Am; Am Epidemiol Soc. *Res:* Rubella; poliomyelitis; cytomegalovirus; vaccination against viral diseases; infectious diseases; antibiotics. *Mailing Add:* Children's Hosp 34th St & Curie Ave Philadelphia PA 19104

PLOTNIKOFF, NICHOLAS PETER, b Aug 13, 27; m 59; c 2. PHARMACOLOGY. *Educ:* Univ Calif, AB, 49, MS, 51; Univ Tex, PhD(pharmacol), 56. *Prof Exp:* Pharmacologist, Merck Inst Therapeut Res, 57-59 & Stanford Res Inst, 59-62; group leader neuropharmacol, Abbott Labs, 62-68, sect head neuropharmacol, 68-76; staff mem, Trans-Neuro, Inc, 76-80; PROF PHARMACOL, DEPT PHARMACOL, ORAL ROBERTS MED SCH, TULSA, OKLA, 80- *Mem:* AAAS; Am Soc Pharmacol & Exp Therapeut; NY Acad Sci. *Res:* Neuropharmacology; psychopharmacology; pharmacodynamics; drug metabolism. *Mailing Add:* Dept Pharmacol Oral Roberts Med Sch 7777 S Lewis Tulsa OK 74171

PLOTZ, CHARLES M, b New York, NY, Dec 6, 21; m; c 3. INTERNAL MEDICINE, RHEUMATOLOGY. *Educ:* Columbia Col, BA, 41; Long Island Col Med, MD, 44; Columbia Univ, ScD(med), 51. *Prof Exp:* Intern internal med, New Haven Hosp, 44-45; resident, Kings County Hosp, 45-46 & Maimonides Hosp, 48-49; chief arthritis clin, Mt Sinai Hosp, 55-65; DIR CONTINUING EDUC, STATE UNIV NY DOWNSTATE MED CTR, 66-, PROF MED, 67-, CHMN DEPT FAMILY PRACT, 71- *Concurrent Pos:* USPHS res fel, Col Physicians & Surgeons, Columbia Univ, 49-50; attend physician, Kings County Hosp Ctr, Brooklyn, Long Island Col Hosp; asst attend physician, Mt Sinai Hosp; asst physician, Columbia-Presby Med Ctr; chief arthritis clin, Kings County Hosp, Brooklyn, 50, Long Island Col Hosp, 65- & State Univ Hosp, Brooklyn, 67-; attend physician, Brooklyn State Hosp; consult physician, Peninsula Gen Hosp; vis consult, Jewish Gen Hosp, Can & Avicenna Hosp & Wazir Akbar Hosp, Afghanistan, 65; consult, Bur Hearings & Appeals, Soc Security Admin, 67- & Bur Dis Prev & Environ

Control, Nat Ctr Chronic Dis Control, Diabetes & Arthritis Control Prog, USPHS, 67-; chief sci consult sect immunol, Vet Admin, 72-; mem bd gov, Arthritis Found, 64-, secy-treas & mem var comts, 66-; mem med adv coun, Iran Found, 65-; chmn comt educ, NY Acad Med, 76- *Mem:* Am Rheumatism Asn (secy-treas, 66-70); Am Acad Family Physicians. *Res:* Latex fixation reaction for rheumatoid arthritis. *Mailing Add:* Dept Med State Univ NY Downstate Med Ctr Brooklyn NY 11203

PLOTZ, PAUL HUNTER, b New York, NY, Oct 19, 37; m 63; c 2. IMMUNOLOGY, RHEUMATOLOGY. *Educ:* Harvard Univ, AB, 58, MD, 63. *Prof Exp:* From intern to resident, Beth Israel Hosp, Boston, 63-65; clin assoc arthritis, NIH, 65-68; Helen Hay Whitney fel immunol, Nat Inst for Med Res, London, 68-70; SR INVESTR IMMUNOL & RHEUMATOLOGY, NIH, 70- *Concurrent Pos:* Mem, Am Rheumatism Asn, Ctr Grants Comt, 76- *Mem:* Am Asn Immunologists; fel Am Col Physicians; Am Asn for Study Liver Dis; Am Rheumatism Asn; Am Soc Clin Invest. *Res:* Biology of immune complexes; pathogenesis and therapy of connective tissue diseases. *Mailing Add:* Arthritis & Rheumatism Br 9N 212 Bld 10 NIAMDD NIHRm Bethesda MD 20014

PLOUGHE, WILLIAM D, b Fort Wayne, Ind, Mar 30, 29; m 52; c 3. NUCLEAR PHYSICS, NUCLEAR SCATTERING. *Educ:* Ind Univ, BS, 51, MS, 53; Purdue Univ, PhD(physics), 61. *Prof Exp:* Instr physics, Univ Fla, 53-56; res assoc, 61-62, asst prof, 62-66, ASSOC PROF PHYSICS, OHIO STATE UNIV, 66- *Concurrent Pos:* Physicist, US AEC, 66-68. *Mem:* Am Phys Soc; Am Asn Physics Teachers; AAAS. *Res:* Experimental nuclear physics; nuclear reactions and spectroscopy; nuclear scattering of alpha particles and lithium ion at medium energies; optical model analysis. *Mailing Add:* Dept Physics Ohio State Univ 174 W 18th Ave Columbus OH 43210

PLOURDE, J ROSAIRE, b Cap-de-la-Madeleine, Que, July 20, 23; m 45; c 2. PHARMACY. *Educ:* Univ Montreal, BPharm, 47, MPharm, 53, DPharm, 60. *Prof Exp:* From asst prof to assoc prof chem anal, 48-74, PROF PHARMACEUT ANAL, UNIV MONTREAL, 74- *Concurrent Pos:* Res fel alkaloids, Univ RI, 60-61; co-ed, Int Pharmaceut Abstr. 14. *Mem:* Am Chem Soc; Am Soc Pharmacog; Can Pharmaceut Asn; Acad Pharmaceut Sci; Am Pharm Asn. *Res:* Phytochemical investigations on Xanthium strumarium, Arctium minus, Eupatorium purpureum and pleiocarpa mutica; analytical investigation on tranquilizers and anti-depressants; qualitative, quantitative and instrumental analysis of pharmaceuticals; quantitative methods of separation and determination of pharmaceuticals; biotransformation of steroids and antibiotics by the spores of microorganisms; ion pair extraction of alkaloids. *Mailing Add:* Fac of Pharm Univ of Montreal Montreal PQ H3C 3J7 Can

PLOVNICK, ROSS HARRIS, b Charlotte, NC, May 4, 42; m 65; c 2. CHEMISTRY. *Educ:* Northeastern Univ, BA, 64; Brown Univ, PhD(chem), 69. *Prof Exp:* Res mgr crystal growing facility, Mat Sci Ctr, Cornell Univ, 68-72; sr chemist, 72-75, res specialist, 75-79, supvr new prod, 79-81, PROG MGR, 3M CO, 81- *Mem:* Am Chem Soc. *Res:* Solid state inorganic chemistry; materials preparation, characterization, crystal growth. *Mailing Add:* Bldg 219-1-1 3M Co Technol Enterprises Div St Paul MN 55133

PLOWMAN, KENT MILTON, biochemistry, see previous edition

PLOWMAN, RONALD DEAN, b Smithfield, Utah, Aug 25, 28; m 51; c 5. DAIRY HUSBANDRY, RESEARCH ADMINISTRATION. *Educ:* Utah State Univ, BS, 51; Univ Minn, MS, 55, PhD(dairy cattle breeding), 56. *Prof Exp:* Herd mgr, Far Hills Farms, Ore, 52-53; county agr agent, Weber County, Utah, 53-54; asst, Univ Minn, 54-56; dairy res scientist, Dairy Cattle Res Br, Agr Res Serv, USDA, 57-63, leader genetics & mgt invests, 63-66, leader, dairy herd improv invests, 66-68, chief, 68-72, area dir, Idaho, Mont & Utah, 72-75; mem fac, Dept Dairy Sci, Univ Md, College Park, 75-77; MEM FAC, UTAH STATE UNIV, 77- *Mem:* Am Dairy Sci Asn. *Res:* Dairy cattle breeding, especially various types of mating systems; dairy cattle management; milk quality and influencing factors; nutrition; physiology. *Mailing Add:* Utah State Univ UMC 48 Logan UT 84322

PLOWMAN, TIMOTHY, b Harrisburg, Pa, Nov 17, 44. SYSTEMATIC BOTANY, ETHNOBOTANY. *Educ:* Cornell Univ, BA, 66; Harvard Univ, MA, 70, PhD(biol), 74. *Prof Exp:* Res assoc econ bot, Bot Mus, Harvard Univ, 73-76, Katharine Atkins res fel, 76-78, RES ASSOC ECON BOT, BOT MUS, HARVARD UNIV, 78-; ASST CUR SYST BOT, FIELD MUS NATURAL HIST, CHICAGO, 78- *Mem:* Int Asn Plant Taxon; Soc for Econ Bot; Sigma Xi; Linnean Soc London; Am Soc Plant Taxonomy. *Res:* Flora of tropical South America; ethnobotany of tropical America, especially the Amazon; systematics of Erythroxylum; systematics of Brunfelsia; botany and ethnobotany of Coca (the cocaine plant). *Mailing Add:* 801 W Cornelia Ave Chicago IL 60657

PLUCKNETT, WILLIAM KENNEDY, b De Witt, Nebr, Dec 20, 16; m 42; c 3. CHEMISTRY. *Educ:* Nebr State Col, Peru, AB, 37; Iowa State Univ, PhD(phys chem), 42. *Prof Exp:* Asst chem, Iowa State Col, 37-42, asst prof, 47-51; technologist, Shell Oil Co, Calif, 42-46; instr chem, Univ Calif, 47; assoc chemist, Ames Lab, AEC, 47-51; assoc prof & dir high temp lab, Fordham Univ, 51-53; ASSOC PROF CHEM, UNIV KY, 53-, DIR GEN CHEM, 75- *Mem:* AAAS; Am Chem Soc. *Res:* Inorganic hydrides; hafnium-zirconium; quantum chemistry; thermodynamics; polarizability of the halogen atoms in a series of organic halides; chemical kinetics; dielectric properties. *Mailing Add:* Dept of Chem Univ of Ky Lexington KY 40506

PLUE, ARNOLD FREDERICK, b Saugerties, NY, Mar 21, 17; m 38; c 3. ORGANIC CHEMISTRY. *Educ:* Siena Col, BS, 50; Rensselaer Polytech Inst, PhD(chem), 60. *Prof Exp:* Lab technician, GAF Corp, 34-42, prod supvr, 42-48, res & develop chemist, 48-55, sr develop chemist, 55-63, tech assoc, 63-74, mgr new prod introd, 74-75, mgr process develop, 75-78; RETIRED. *Mem:* AAAS; Am Chem Soc; fel Am Inst Chem. *Res:* Dyestuffs; intermediates; optical bleaches; ultraviolet absorbers; nitrogen heterocycles. *Mailing Add:* 9 Parkview Dr Woodland Park Rensselaer NY 12144

PLUHOWSKI, EDWARD JOHN, b Brooklyn, NY, June 20, 27; m 51; c 3. HYDROLOGY. *Educ:* City Col New York, BCE, 49; Johns Hopkins Univ, MS, 65, PhD(environ eng), 69. *Prof Exp:* Hydraulic engr, US Bur Reclamation, 49-50; hydraulic engr, 50-51, off engr, 51-58, proj chief hydrol, 58-62, RES HYDROLOGIST, US GEOL SURV, 62- *Res:* Remote sensing applied to detecting circulation patterns in lakes and estuaries; assessing man's impact on stream-temperature patterns by evaluating energy-budget changes. *Mailing Add:* 4903 Dowlais Ct Rockville MD 20853

PLUM, FRED, b Atlantic City, NJ, Jan 10, 24; c 3. NEUROLOGY. *Educ:* Dartmouth Col, BA, 44; Cornell Univ, MD, 47. *Prof Exp:* Instr med, Cornell Univ, 50-53; from asst prof to prof, Univ Wash, 53-63; TITZELL PROF NEUROL, CORNELL UNIV, 63-; NEUROLOGIST-IN-CHIEF, NEW YORK HOSP, 63- *Concurrent Pos:* Mem grad training comt, Nat Inst Neurol Dis & Stroke, 71-; chief ed, Arch Neurol, 72-76. *Mem:* Am Neurol Asn; Am Acad Neurol; Am Soc Clin Invest. *Res:* Cerebral energy metabolism and blood flow; experimental epilepsy. *Mailing Add:* NY Hosp-Cornell Med Ctr New York NY 10021

PLUMB, JOHN ALFRED, b Waynesboro, Va, Nov 29, 33; m 60; c 2. FISHERIES, MICROBIOLOGY. *Educ:* Bridgewater Col, BA, 60; Southern Ill Univ, MS, 63; Auburn Univ, PhD(fisheries), 72. *Prof Exp:* Hatchery mgr, US Fish & Wildlife Serv, 62-66, hatchery biologist, 66-69; res assoc fisheries, 69-72, asst prof, 72-78, ASSOC PROF FISHERIES, AUBURN UNIV, 78- *Concurrent Pos:* Pres, Fish Health Sect, Auburn Univ, 78. *Mem:* Am Fisheries Soc; Am Fisheries Asn; Sigma Xi. *Res:* Bacterial and viral diseases and immunology of fish; the effects of environmental stress on fish diseases; control of bacterial fish pathogens. *Mailing Add:* Dept of Fisheries & Allied Aquacult Auburn Univ Auburn AL 36830

PLUMB, JOHN LAVERNE, b Harlan, Iowa, Dec 24, 33; m 63; c 2. SOLID STATE DEVICES, MICROELECTRONICS. *Educ:* Iowa State Univ, BS, 55; Univ Minn, MS, 63; NY Univ, PhD(elec eng), 67. *Prof Exp:* Test engr, Honeywell, Inc, 55, eval engr, 57-60; teaching asst elec eng, Univ Minn, 61-62; res asst, NY Univ, 64-67; asst prof, Univ Conn, 67-73; design engr, Transitron Inc, 73-75; pvt consult, MCE Res, 75-78; ADV RES & DEVELOP ENGR, GTE SYLVANIA, INC, 78- *Mem:* Inst Elec & Electronics Engrs; Am Vacuum soc; Int Soc Hybrid Microelectronics. *Res:* High field effects in insulating thin films; thin film electroluminescent devices; electric breakdown in insulating thin films; dielectric films; electroluminescent displays; display drive circuits; digital circuits; digital integrated circuits. *Mailing Add:* GTE Sylvania Inc 60 Boston St Salem MA 01920

PLUMB, ROBERT CHARLES, b Springfield, Mass, Jan 24, 26; m 51; c 6. PHYSICAL CHEMISTRY. *Educ:* Clark Univ, AB, 49; Brown Univ, PhD(chem), 53. *Prof Exp:* Researcher chelation chem, Bersworth Chem Co, 47-49; asst chief phys chem, Aluminum Co Am, 52-58; from asst prof to assoc prof, 58-64, head dept, 64-76, PROF CHEM, WORCESTER POLYTECH INST, 64- *Concurrent Pos:* NSF fel, Cambridge Univ, 56-57. *Mem:* Am Chem Soc; Am Phys Soc. *Res:* Surface chemistry; metal oxidation; metal complex ions in solution; demonstrations for the teaching of statistical mechanics. *Mailing Add:* Dept of Chem Worcester Polytech Inst Worcester MA 01609

PLUMB, TIMOTHY ROY, JR, forest management, plant physiology, see previous edition

PLUMLEE, MILLARD P, JR, b Celina, Tenn, July 14, 21; m 49; c 5. NUTRITION. *Educ:* Tenn Tech Univ, BS, 44; Purdue Univ, MS, 48, PhD(nutrit), 53. *Prof Exp:* Asst nutrit, Univ Tenn, 48-51; res fel, 51-52, from instr to assoc prof, 52-62, PROF NUTRIT, PURDUE UNIV, LAFAYETTE, 62- *Mem:* Am Soc Animal Sci. *Res:* Mineral requirements and metabolism in farm animals. *Mailing Add:* Dept of Animal Sci Purdue Univ West Lafayette IN 47907

PLUMMER, ALBERT J, b Somerville, Mass, Apr 16, 08; m 40; c 2. PHARMACOLOGY. *Educ:* Boston Univ, AB, 29, AM, 30, PhD(biol chem), 35, MD, 49. *Prof Exp:* Asst, Mass Mem Hosp, 30-32; from instr to asst prof pharmacol, Sch Med, Boston Univ, 35-49; sr pharmacologist, Ciba Pharmaceut Co, 49-51, dir pharmacol res, 51-57, dir macrobiol res, 58-66, dir biol res, 66-67, exec dir biol res, 67-73, CONSULT BIOL RES, CIBA-GEIGY CORP, 73- *Concurrent Pos:* Lectr, Sch Med, Boston Univ, 49-; mem, Coun High Blood Pressure Res, Am Heart Asn. *Mem:* Soc Pharmacol & Exp Therapeut; Am Soc Clin Pharmacol & Therapeut; Am Col Neuropsychopharmacol. *Res:* Cardiovascular, gastrointestinal and central nervous system drugs; metabolism of drugs; diuretics. *Mailing Add:* Res Dept Ciba-Geigy Corp Summit NJ 07901

PLUMMER, BENJAMIN FRANK, b Burlington Junction, Mo, Feb 29, 36; m 62; c 4. ORGANIC CHEMISTRY. *Educ:* Iowa State Univ, BS, 58; Ohio State Univ, PhD(org chem), 62. *Prof Exp:* Res asst, Ga Inst Technol, 62-63; asst prof chem, SDak State Univ, 63-67; assoc prof, 67-74, chmn chem dept, 76-80, PROF CHEM, TRINITY UNIV, TEX, 74- *Concurrent Pos:* Robert A Welch Found grant; dir, NSF Undergrad Res Partic Proj, 72 & 75. *Mem:* AAAS; Am Chem Soc; NY Acad Sci; Sigma Xi; InterAm Photochem Soc. *Res:* Photochemistry and the heavy atom effect; molecular spectroscopy; liminescence. *Mailing Add:* Dept of Chem Trinity Univ 715 Stadium Dr San Antonio TX 78284

PLUMMER, CHARLES CARLTON, b Mexico City, Mex, Apr 21, 37; US citizen; m 72. PETROLOGY. *Educ:* Dartmouth Col, AB, 59; Univ Wash, MS, 64, PhD(geol), 69. *Prof Exp:* Glaciologist-geologist, Inst Polar Studies, Ohio State Univ, 64-66; instr geol, Olympic Col, 67-69; geologist, Antarctic Proj, US Geol Surv, 69-70; asst prof, 70-75, ASSOC PROF GEOL & CHMN DEPT, CALIF STATE UNIV, SACRAMENTO, 75- *Honors & Awards:* Antarctic Serv Medal, US Govt, 66 & 70. *Mem:* AAAS; Geol Soc Am; Nat Asn Geol Teachers. *Res:* Metamorphic petrology; geology of alpine and polar regions. *Mailing Add:* Dept of Geol Calif State Univ Sacramento CA 95819

PLUMMER, E WARD, b Astoria, Ore, Oct 30, 40; m 61; c 2. SOLID STATE PHYSICS. *Educ:* Lewis & Clark Col, BA, 62; Cornell Univ, PhD(physics), 67. *Prof Exp:* Nat Res Coun assoc, Nat Bur Standards, 67-69, physicist, 69-73; assoc prof, 73-77, PROF PHYSICS, UNIV PA, 77- *Honors & Awards:* Wayne Nottingham Prize, 68. *Mem:* Am Phys Soc. *Res:* Properties of solid surfaces; electron emission spectroscopies; atomic and molecular spectroscopy and electron optics. *Mailing Add:* Dept Physics David Rittenhouse Lab Univ of Pa Philadelphia PA 19174

PLUMMER, FRED L(EROY), b West Union, Ohio, Dec 30, 00; m 23; c 2. ENGINEERING. *Educ:* Ohio Univ, AB, 20; Case Inst Technol, BS, 22, MS, 24. *Prof Exp:* From instr to assoc prof struct eng, Case Inst Technol, 22-37; consult, Cuyahoga County, Ohio, 37-40; dir eng, Hammond Iron Works, Pa, 40-57; exec dir, Am Welding Soc, 57-70; EXEC CONSULT, 70- *Concurrent Pos:* Prof, Sch Archit, Case Inst Technol, 25-27; consult engr, 26-38; lectr, John Huntington Polytech Inst, 32-40; mem, Nat Res Coun, 35-59; gen mgr, Hammond Latin Am Construct Co, 48-57; mem, Welding Res Coun, 49- & Bailey Bridge Mission, Japan, 50; pres, Int Inst Welding, 66-69. *Mem:* Am Soc Civil Engrs; Am Soc Mech Engrs; Am Soc Eng Educ; Am Welding Soc (pres, 53-55); Am Soc Testing & Mat. *Res:* Photoelasticity model and structural analysis; soil mechanics; welding. *Mailing Add:* 2560 N Moreland Blvd Cleveland OH 44120

PLUMMER, GAYTHER LYNN, b Marion Co, Ind, Jan 27, 25; m 50. PLANT ECOLOGY. *Educ:* Butler Univ, BS, 48; Kans State Col, MS, 50; Purdue Univ, PhD(ecol), 54. *Prof Exp:* Asst, Kans State Col, 48-50; instr biol, Knox Col, 50-51; asst, Purdue Univ, 51-53; asst prof, Antioch Col, 54-55; from asst prof to assoc prof, 55-67, PROF BOT & ENVIRON DESIGN, UNIV GA, 67- *Concurrent Pos:* Naturalist, Ind State Parks, 50-51 & Oak Ridge Nat Lab, 58-60; ed Ga J Sci, 78- *Mem:* Fel AAAS; Ecol Soc Am; Am Soc Agron; Soil Sci Soc Am; Crop Sci Soc Am. *Res:* Bioclimatology; environmental biology; remote sensing. *Mailing Add:* Dept of Bot Univ of Ga Athens GA 30602

PLUMMER, JAMES WALTER, b Idaho Springs, Colo, Jan 29, 20; m 48; c 4. ELECTRONICS, ASTRONAUTICS. *Educ:* Univ Calif, Berkeley, BS, 42; Univ Md, MS, 53. *Prof Exp:* Vpres & asst gen mgr space syst, Lockheed Missiles & Space Co Inc, 65-68, vpres & asst gen mgr res & develop, 68-69, vpres & gen mgr space syst, 69-73; undersecy US Air Force, 73-76; EXEC V PRES, LOCKHEED MISSILES & SPACE CO INC, 76- *Concurrent Pos:* Mem, Space Appl Bd, Nat Acad Eng, 78- *Mem:* Fel Am Inst Aeronaut & Astronaut; fel Am Astronaut Soc; Nat Acad Eng. *Mailing Add:* Lockheed Missiles & Space Co Inc PO Box 504 Sunnyvale CA 94086

PLUMMER, MARK ALAN, b Wichita, Kans, July 30, 36; m 67; c 2. CHEMICAL ENGINEERING. *Educ:* Colo Sch Mines, BS, 58, MS, 63, PhD(chem eng), 72. *Prof Exp:* Process engr, Skelly Oil Co, 58-60; advan res engr, 62-80, SR RES ENGR, MARATHON OIL CO, 80- *Concurrent Pos:* mem hydrocarbon compressibility & thermal expansion comt, Am Petrol Inst. *Mem:* Am Inst Chem Engrs. *Res:* petrochemical manufacturing, separation techniques and heavy oils upgrading. *Mailing Add:* Marathon Oil Co 7400 S Broadway PO Box 269 Littleton CO 80160

PLUMMER, MICHAEL DAVID, b Akron, Ohio, Aug 31, 37; m 68; c 2. MATHEMATICS. *Educ:* Wabash Col, BA, 59; Univ Mich, MS, 61, PhD(math), 66. *Prof Exp:* Instr math, Yale Univ, 66-68; asst prof comput sci, City Col New York, 68-70; assoc prof, 70-78, PROF MATH, VANDERBILT UNIV, 78- *Mem:* AAAS; Am Math Soc; Math Asn Am. *Res:* Theory of graphs. *Mailing Add:* Dept of Math Vanderbilt Univ Nashville TN 37235

PLUMMER, MICHAEL VAN, b Tuscumbia, Ala, Mar 9, 45; m 67; c 2. HERPETOLOGY, ECOLOGY. *Educ:* Harding Col, BS, 67; Utah State Univ, MS, 69; Univ Kans, PhD(biol), 76. *Prof Exp:* Instr, 71-72, asst prof, Harding Col, 76-81, ASSOC PROF BIOL, HARDING UNIV, 81- *Concurrent Pos:* Index ed, Herpetologica, 80-; adj prof biol, Memphis State Univ, 81- *Mem:* Ecol Soc Am; Am Soc Ichthyologists & Herpetologists; Soc Study Amphibians & Reptiles; Sigma Xi; Herpetologists' League. *Res:* Reptilian ecology. *Mailing Add:* Dept Biol Harding Univ Searcy AR 72143

PLUMMER, OTHO RAYMOND, b Beaumont, Tex, Sept 27, 38; m 65. APPLIED MATHEMATICS, MATHEMATICAL PHYSICS. *Educ:* Univ Tex, BS, 61, MA, 63, PhD(physics), 66. *Prof Exp:* Res assoc physics & spec instr chem, Univ Tex, 66; asst prof physics, Univ Ark, Fayetteville, 66-68; asst prof, 68-71, ASSOC PROF MATH, UNIV MO-ROLLA, 71- *Concurrent Pos:* Actg chmn math, Univ Mo-Rolla, 78-79. *Mem:* Am Phys Soc; Soc Indust & Appl Math. *Res:* Group theory; operator theory; quantum theory; applications. *Mailing Add:* Dept of Math Univ of Mo Rolla MO 65401

PLUMMER, PATRICIA LYNNE MOORE, b Tyler, Tex; m 65. CLOUD PHYSICS, THEORETICAL CHEMISTRY. *Educ:* Tex Christian Univ, BA, 60; Univ Tex, PhD(theoret chem), 64. *Prof Exp:* Res assoc theoret chem, Univ Tex, 64-66, instr chem, 65-66; res assoc theoret chem, Univ Ark, Fayetteville, 66-68; res assoc grad ctr cloud physics res, 68-73, asst prof physics & sr investr, 73-77, ASSOC PROF PHYSICS & ASSOC DIR, CLOUD PHYS RES CTR, UNIV MO-ROLLA, 77- *Concurrent Pos:* Res grants water phenomena, Chem Div, Off Naval Res, 69-71 & molecular theory homogeneous nucleation of water, Atmospheric Sci Sect, NSF, 72-74, Molecular Models Applied to Heterogeneous Nucleation, Atmospheric Sci Sect, NSF, 74-80, Molecular Model for Ice Nucleation & Growth, NASA, 75-81, Theoretical Studies Sulfuioxidation Cycle, Atmospheric Chem, NSF, 81-84; adv bd, J Coloid & Interface Sci, 80-83; chmn, Int Symp Physics & Chem Ice, 82. *Honors & Awards:* Award Molecular Model Heterogeneous Nucleation, Atmospheric Sci Sect, NSF, 74; Award Molecular Model Formation & Growth Ice Crystals, NASA, 75. *Mem:* Am Chem Soc; Am Phys Soc; Am Geophys Union; Sigma Xi. *Res:* Ab initio calculations on small molecules; potential energy surfaces of triatomics; applications of group algebra to quantum mechanical systems; molecular theory for nucleation of water droplets and ices; calculated molecular properties of small ion clusters; stability and structure of atmospheric ions; molecular dynamic modeling of vapor clusters and processes on ice surfaces. *Mailing Add:* Cloud Physics Res Ctr Univ Mo Rolla MO 65401

PLUMMER, ROBERT PATRICK, b Beaumont, Tex, Oct 30, 41; m 66. DECISION SUPPORT SYSTEMS, TELECOMMUNICATIONS. *Educ:* Univ Tex, Austin, BA, 64, PhD(comput sci), 70; Stanford Univ, MS, 66. *Prof Exp:* From instr to asst prof comput sci, Univ Houston, 69-72; asst prof comput sci, Univ Utah, 72-78; RES FEL, INST FOR THE FUTURE, 78- *Concurrent Pos:* On leave, NASA-Ames Res Ctr, 77-78. *Mem:* Am Asn Artificial Intel. *Res:* Computer-based communications; social and organizational impacts of computers; man-computer interaction; computers and the handicapped; artificial intelligence. *Mailing Add:* Inst for the Future 2740 Sand Hill Rd Menlo Park CA 94025

PLUMMER, THOMAS H, JR, b Cleveland, Ohio, Aug 25, 33; m 60; c 4. BIOCHEMISTRY. *Educ:* Cornell Univ, BS, 55; Purdue Univ, MS, 57, PhD(plant physiol), 60. *Prof Exp:* Res assoc protein struct, Brookhaven Nat Lab, 60-63; ASSOC RES SCIENTIST, DIV LABS & RES, NY STATE HEALTH DEPT, 63- *Mem:* AAAS; Am Chem Soc; Am Soc Biol Chem. *Res:* Glycoprotein isolation and structure, particularly protein in pancreatic secretions and blood plasma. *Mailing Add:* Div of Labs & Res NY State Dept of Health Albany NY 12201

PLUMMER, WILLIAM ALLAN, b Wilkes-Barre, Pa, Jan 20, 27; m 57, 78; c 2. PHYSICAL CHEMISTRY. *Educ:* Wilkes Col, BS, 50; Univ Pittsburgh, PhD(chem), 56. *Prof Exp:* Sr chemist, 56-60, res chemist, 60-76, sr res scientist, 76-80, RES ASSOC, TECH STAFF DIV, CORNING GLASS WORKS, 80- *Mem:* AAAS; Am Chem Soc; Am Ceramic Soc. *Res:* Thermal expansion, specific heat, thermal diffusivity and conductivity; thermal properties of glasses and ceramics; glass viscosity. *Mailing Add:* 10 Fox Lane Rd Painted Post NY 14870

PLUMTREE, A(LAN), b Scunthorpe, Eng, Aug 1, 36; m 59; c 2. PHYSICAL METALLURGY, MECHANICAL METALLURGY. *Educ:* Univ Nottingham, BSc, 60, PhD(metall), 63. *Prof Exp:* Metallurgist, Appleby-Frodingham Steel Works Ltd, Eng, 54-57; lectr, Nottingham & Dist Tech Col, 60-63; fel, Univ Toronto, 63, asst prof phys metall, 63-65; asst prof mech eng, 65-68, assoc prof, 68-77, PROF MECH ENG, UNIV WATERLOO, 68-, ASSOC CHMN DEPT, 81- *Concurrent Pos:* Vis prof, Univ Paris, France, 79. *Mem:* Am Soc Metals; fel Brit Inst Metall. *Res:* Fatigue behaviour of metals; fracture mechanisms in metals; metal deformation and forgeability; solidification of metals. *Mailing Add:* 101 McDougall Waterloo ON N2L 2W4 Can

PLUNKETT, ROBERT, b New York, NY, Mar 15, 19; m 46; c 3. MECHANICS. *Educ:* Mass Inst Technol, SB, 39, ScD(mech eng), 48. *Hon Degrees:* DUniv, Nantes, 66. *Prof Exp:* Asst elec eng, Mass Inst Technol, 39-41, instr mech eng, 41, asst prof, 46-48; asst prof, Rice Inst, 48-51; vibration engr, Gen Elec Co, 51-56; consult engr, 56-60; PROF MECH, UNIV MINN, MINNEAPOLIS, 60- *Mem:* Nat Acad Eng; Am Soc Mech Engrs; Acoust Soc Am; Am Soc Eng Educ; Soc Exp Stress Analysts. *Res:* Vibration analysis; mechanics of materials; applied mechanics. *Mailing Add:* Dept of Aeronaut & Eng Mech Univ of Minn Minneapolis MN 55455

PLUNKETT, ROBERT LEE, b Lynchburg, Va, Mar 18, 22; m 43, 79; c 1. TOPOLOGY, MATHEMATICAL ANALYSIS. *Educ:* Randolph-Macon Col, BS, 43; Univ Chicago, MS, 49; Univ Va, PhD(math), 53. *Prof Exp:* Asst prof math, Vanderbilt Univ, 53-54; from asst prof to prof, Fla State Univ, 54-63; mem sr tech staff, Northrop Space Lab, Ala, 63-64; chmn dept, 66-73, PROF MATH, UNIV ALA, 63- *Mem:* Am Math Soc; Math Asn Am. *Mailing Add:* Dept of Math Box 1416 Univ of Ala University AL 35486

PLUNKETT, WILLIAM KINGSBURY, b Boston, Mass, May 4, 43; m 65; c 1. BIOCHEMISTRY, BIOCHEMICAL PHARMACOLOGY. *Educ:* Springfield Col, BS, 65; Univ Mass, PhD(biochem), 70. *Prof Exp:* Fel biochem, Univ Pa, 70-71; res assoc, Univ Colo Med Ctr, 71-75; asst prof, 75-80, ASSOC PROF BIOCHEM, UNIV TEX SYST CANCER CTR, 80- *Concurrent Pos:* Asst prof biochem, Grad Sch Biomed Sci, Univ Tex, Houston, 76-80, assoc prof, 80- *Mem:* Am Asn Cancer Res; Am Soc Cell Biol; AAAS; Am Soc Clin Oncologists; Am Soc Pharm Exp Therpeuts. *Res:* Biochemical basis for drug effectiveness and molecular basis of drug action. *Mailing Add:* Dept of Develop Therapeut Univ of Tex Syst Cancer Ctr Houston TX 77030

PLUSCEC, JOSIP, b Gornji Milanovac, Yugoslavia, June 6, 28; US citizen; m 61; c 2. ORGANIC CHEMISTRY. *Educ:* Univ Zagreb, BSc, 53, PhD(org chem), 60. *Prof Exp:* Chemist, Inst Invest Drugs, Zagreb, Yugoslavia, 55-57; asst prof org synthesis, Inst Org Chem, Sch Pharmacy, Univ Zagreb, 57-60 & Inst Chem, Sch Med, 60-64; res assoc biochem synthesis, Dept Bot, Univ Chicago, 65-66; sr res scientist, Dept Biochem Pharmacol, 66-67 & Dept Org Chem, 67-74, SR RES INVESTR, SQUIBB INST MED RES, 74- *Concurrent Pos:* Nat Res Coun Can Div Pure Chem fel, 62-64. *Mem:* AAAS; Am Chem Soc; Ger Chem Soc; Croatian Chem Soc. *Res:* Investigations in biochemistry of porphyrins; synthetic work in lipid, porphyrin, peptide chemistry and antibiotics; new antibiotics isolation. *Mailing Add:* Dept Org Chem Squibb Inst Med Res Princeton NJ 08540

PLUTH, DONALD JOHN, b Emmet Co, Iowa, Feb 5, 36; m 60; c 3. SOIL SCIENCE. *Educ:* Univ Minn, Minneapolis, BS, 58, MS, 62, PhD(soil sci), 65. *Prof Exp:* Res assoc soil sci, Univ Minn, 65-67; ASSOC PROF, UNIV ALTA, 67- *Mem:* Am Soc Agron. *Res:* Soil-vegetation relationships; site evaluation; nutrient cycling in forest ecosystems. *Mailing Add:* RR 1 Edmonton AB T6H 4N6 Can

PLUTH, JOSEPH JOHN, b Cook, Minn, Feb 18, 43; m 73. STRUCTURAL CHEMISTRY. *Educ:* Bemidji State Col, BA, 65; Univ Wash, PhD(chem), 71. *Prof Exp:* Res assoc chem, 71-72, res scientist chem, 71-80, SR RES ASSOC GEOPHYS SCI, UNIV CHICAGO, 81- *Mem:* Am Crystallog Asn; Sigma Xi. *Res:* Studies of the structural properties of zeolites and their relationship to observed physical and chemical properties. *Mailing Add:* Dept of Geophys Sci Univ Chicago 5734 S Ellis Ave Chicago IL 60637

PLUTZER, MARTIN DAVID, b New York, NY, Apr 27, 44; m 72; c 1. PSYCHIATRY. *Educ:* Alfred Univ, BA, 64; Univ Pittsburgh, MD, 68; Am Bd Psychiat & Neurol, dipl, 76. *Prof Exp:* asst prof, 74-80, ASSOC PROF PSYCHIAT, MED COL PA, 80- *Concurrent Pos:* Ward chief, inpatient psychiat unit, Eastern Pa Psychiat Inst, 74-; assoc dir undergrad educ psychiat, Med Col Pa, 77-80, dir, 80- *Mem:* Assoc mem Am Psychoanal Asn. *Mailing Add:* Dept of Psychiat 3300 Henry Ave Philadelphia PA 19129

PLYBON, BENJAMIN FRANCIS, b Huntington, WVa, Feb 12, 30; m 62; c 3. MATHEMATICAL PHYSICS. *Educ:* Marshall Univ, BS, 57; Carnegie-Mellon Univ, MS, 59; Ohio State Univ, PhD(math), 68. *Prof Exp:* Electronics technologist, Cubic Corp, 56; from instr to asst prof math, Marshall Univ, 59-64; instr, Ohio Wesleyan Univ, 64-66; asst prof, 66-74, ASSOC PROF MATH, MIAMI UNIV, 74- *Mem:* Soc Indust & Appl Math; Math Asn Am; Sigma Xi. *Res:* Variational principles and invariance groups for physical systems; conservation laws for physical systems. *Mailing Add:* Dept of Math Miami Univ Oxford OH 45056

PLYMALE, CHARLES E, b Gallipolis, Ohio, May 21, 35; m 56; c 3. PLASTICS ENGINEERING, CHEMICAL ENGINEERING. *Educ:* Marietta Col, BS, 58; Case Inst Technol, BSChE, 58; Princeton Univ, MSE, 59. *Prof Exp:* Proj engr, Owens-Ill Tech Ctr, 59-61, group leader plastics, 61-63, sect chief, 63-66, dir develop, Forest Prod Div, 66-73, vpres & tech dir, 73-75, VPRES & PROD MGR, BOX OPERS, OWENS-ILL TECH CTR, 75- *Mem:* Am Chem Soc; Am Inst Chem Engrs; Soc Plastics Engrs; Nat Soc Prof Engrs. *Res:* Diaelectrophoresis; plastics engineering and applications in packaging industry; blow molding; film extrusion; injection molding; rheology; corrugated box plant automation. *Mailing Add:* Owens-Ill Tech Ctr PO Box 1035 Toledo OH 43601

PLYMALE, DONALD LEE, b Huntington, WVa, June 12, 34; m 59; c 2. INORGANIC CHEMISTRY. *Educ:* Marshall Univ, BS, 57, MS, 62; Ga Inst Technol, PhD(inorg chem), 66. *Prof Exp:* Spectroscopist, Int Nickel Co, 59-62; sr res chemist, Monsanto Res Corp, 66-69; from asst prof to assoc prof chem, Roanoke Col, 71-75; PROG COORDR, US DEPT ENERGY, 76- *Mem:* AAAS; Am Chem Soc. *Res:* Transition metal complexes. *Mailing Add:* US Dept of Energy PO Box 5400 Albuquerque NM 87115

PLYMALE, EDWARD LEWIS, b Kenova, WVa, Sept 20, 14; m 48; c 2. BOTANY. *Educ:* Marshall Univ, AB, 35; Univ Ky, MS, 39; Univ Iowa, PhD(bot), 42. *Prof Exp:* Lab instr, 35-37, from asst prof to prof, 46-74, EMER PROF BOT, MARSHALL UNIV, 74- *Mem:* AAAS; Bot Soc Am. *Res:* Veins of mesomorphic leaves; taxonomy of vascular plants of Southern West Virginia; plant morphology and taxonomy. *Mailing Add:* 661 Buffalo Rd Huntington WV 25704

PLYMALE, HARRY HAMBLETON, b Huntington, WVa, July 13, 28; m 78; c 3. ZOOLOGY, VETERINARY MEDICINE. *Educ:* Mich State Univ, BS, 54, DVM, 56. *Prof Exp:* Instr vet sci, Calif Polytech Col, San Luis Obispo, 58-60; ASSOC PROF ZOOL, SAN DIEGO STATE UNIV, 62- *Mem:* Asn Mil Surgeons US. *Res:* Experimental animal surgery. *Mailing Add:* Dept of Zool San Diego State Univ San Diego CA 92182

PNEUMAN, GERALD W, b Gary, Ind, Aug 4, 31; m 57; c 3. ASTROPHYSICS. *Educ:* Purdue Univ, BS, 58, MS, 59, PhD(magnetohydrodyn), 63. *Prof Exp:* Instr aerodyn, Purdue Univ, 59-63; staff scientist, AC Electronics Defense Res Labs, 63-68; staff scientist, 68-81, SR SCIENTIST, HIGH ALTITUDE OBSERV, 81- *Concurrent Pos:* Lectr, Dept Astrophysics, Univ Colo, Boulder. *Honors & Awards:* Nat Ctr Atmospheric Res Pub Award, 68 & 75. *Mem:* Am Astron Soc; Am Phys Soc; Int Astron Union. *Res:* Influence of magnetic fields on phenomena occuring in the solar corona and interplanetary space; solar and interplanetary physics. *Mailing Add:* High Altitude Observ PO Box 5000 Boulder CO 80302

POË, ANTHONY JOHN, b Portsmouth, Eng, July 10, 29. INORGANIC CHEMISTRY. *Educ:* Oxford Univ, BA, 50, BSc, 51; Univ London, PhD(inorg chem) & DIC, 61, DSc(inorg chem), 71. *Prof Exp:* Sci officer, Atomic Energy Res Estab, Eng, 51-55; asst lectr inorg chem, Imp Col, Univ London, 55-57, lectr, 57-66, sr lectr, 66-70; PROF CHEM, ERINDALE COL, UNIV TORONTO, 70- *Concurrent Pos:* Vis lectr, Northwestern Univ, 61-62; vis prof, State Univ NY Buffalo, 68-69; fel, St John's Col, Cambridge Univ, Eng, 77-78. *Mem:* Am Chem Soc; fel Chem Inst Can; fel Royal Soc Chem. *Res:* Kinetics and mechanisms of reactions of inorganic complexes and metal carbonyls. *Mailing Add:* Dept Chem Erindale Col Univ Toronto Toronto ON M5S 2R8 Can

PO, HENRY NG, b San Fernando, Philippines, Oct 4, 37; m 66; c 2. PHYSICAL CHEMISTRY, INORGANIC CHEMISTRY. *Educ:* Mapua Inst Technol, BS, 60; Univ Wis-Madison, MS, 62; Univ Calif, Davis, PhD(phys chem), 67. *Prof Exp:* Res engr, Allis-Chalmers Mfg Co, 62-63; res fel chem, Brookhaven Nat Lab, 67-68; from asst prof, to assoc prof, 68-76, PROF CHEM, CALIF STATE UNIV, LONG BEACH, 76- *Mem:* Am Chem Soc. *Res:* Mechanism of hexa-aquometal ions redox reaction, ligand substitution and coordination chemistry; cryogenic electronic spectral of binuclear complexes of transition metal; electronic spectroscopy of inorganic complexes; energy conversion system; solar energy research; electrochemical inorganic system; bio-inorganic complexes. *Mailing Add:* Dept of Chem Calif State Univ Long Beach CA 90840

POAG, CLAUDE WYLIE, b Deland, Fla, Aug 12, 37; m 62; c 3. MICROPALEONTOLOGY, FORAMINIFERA. *Educ:* Fla State Univ, BS, 59; La State Univ, MS, 63; Tulane Univ, PhD(paleont), 71. *Prof Exp:* Micropaleontologist, Chevron Oil Co, 62-70; asst prof geol oceanog, Tex A&M Univ, 70-74; GEOLOGIST, US GEOL SURV, 74- *Concurrent Pos:* Asst field officer, Nat Sci Found, 73-74; co-chief scientist, Deep Sea Drilling Proj, 81- *Mem:* Am Asn Petrol Geologists; Soc Econ Paleontologists & Mineralogists; Paleont Soc; Paleont Res Inst; Am Quaternary Asn. *Res:* Microfossil analyses leading to intepretation of ecology, paleoecology, biostratigraphy, paleobiogeography, paleoceanography and depositional history of triassic to quaternary sodimentary rocks along the Atlantic and Gulf margins of the United States. *Mailing Add:* US Geol Surv Off Marine Geol Woods Hole MA 02543

POAGE, SCOTT T(ABOR), b Waco, Tex, Dec 5, 31. INDUSTRIAL ENGINEERING, OPERATIONS RESEARCH. *Educ:* Tex Tech Col, BS, 53; Agr & Mech Col, Tex, MS, 57; Okla State Univ, PhD(indust eng), 62. *Prof Exp:* Prod control engr, Phillips Petrol Co, 53; instr indust eng, Agr & Mech Col, Tex, 57-59; asst prof, Okla State Univ, 59-61; from assoc prof to prof, Arlington State Col, 61-68, head dept, 61-68; chmn dept, 68-77, PROF INDUST ENG, UNIV HOUSTON, 68- *Concurrent Pos:* Consult, Am Mfg Co, Tex & Tex Instruments, Inc, 59, Am Airlines, 60-62, Ling-Temco-Vought, 63, US Govt AID, India, 66 & Grocers' Supply Inc, 76. *Mem:* Fel Am Inst Indust Engrs (vpres, 65-67); Am Soc Eng Educ; Am Soc Qual Control; Opers Res Soc Am. *Res:* Operations research in production control, especially applications of queuing theory; statistical quality control; organizational and management theory. *Mailing Add:* Dept Indust Eng Univ Houston Houston TX 77004

POATE, JOHN MILO, b Devonport, Eng, Nov 12, 40; Australian citizen; m 65; c 2. PHYSICS, MATERIALS SCIENCE. *Educ:* Univ Melbourne, BSc, 62, MSc, 65; Australian Nat Univ, PhD(nuclear physics), 67. *Prof Exp:* Res fel nuclear physics, Atomic Energy Res Estab, Harwell, Eng, 67-71; MEM TECH STAFF PHYSICS, BELL LABS, 71- *Mem:* Am Phys Soc; Electrochemical Soc; Mat Res Soc. *Res:* Surface, near-surface and thin film properties of solids using energetic ion beams for analysis; material modification by implantation. *Mailing Add:* Bell Labs 600 Mountain Ave Murray Hill NJ 07974

POBER, KENNETH WILLIAM, b Chicago, Ill, Jan 3, 40; m 65; c 2. ORGANIC CHEMISTRY. *Educ:* Univ Colo, BS, 62; Univ Idaho, PhD(org chem), 67. *Prof Exp:* Fel, Boston Univ, 67-69; sr chemist process res & develop, Texaco Inc, 69-72; sr develop chemist systs develop, 3M Co, 72-75; sr res chemist fuels, Occidental Res Corp, 75-77; res scientist technol assessment, 77-80, GROUP LEADER, COMPLETION & DRILLING FLUIDS DEVELOP, NL BAROID PETROL SERV, 80- *Mem:* Am Chem Soc; Sigma Xi; Soc Petrol Engrs. *Res:* Completion/workover fluids; drilling fluids and oilfield chemicals; resource recovery; synthetic fuels; lignite and coal conversion; photopolymer systems development; homogeneous catalysis; organic photochemistry. *Mailing Add:* NL Baroid Petrol Serv PO Box 1675 Houston TX 77001

POBER, ZALMON, b Philadelphia, Pa, July 31, 39; m 69. MAMMALIAN PHYSIOLOGY. *Educ:* Drexel Inst Technol, BS, 62; Thomas Jefferson Univ, MS, 65, PhD(physiol), 69. *Prof Exp:* Instr physiol, Temple Univ, 66-67; physiologist, Food Labs, US Army Natick Labs, 68-76; asst prof, 77-81, ASSOC PROF, MASS COL PHARM, HAMPDEN, 81- *Mem:* Am Physiol Soc; NY Acad Sci; Am Pharmaceut Asn; Acad Pharmaceut Sci; Sigma Xi. *Res:* Mechanisms by which the intestine controls the body's response to food; intestinal regulation of food intake; stimulus and pathways for the intestinal phase of gastric secretion. *Mailing Add:* 5 Applewood Circle Easthampton MA 01027

POBERESKIN, MEYER, b Philadelphia, Pa, Sept 13, 16; m 46; c 2. PHYSICAL CHEMISTRY. *Educ:* City Col New York, BS, 37; Columbia Univ, MA, 39. *Prof Exp:* Chemist, Fales Chem Co, 39 & Mt Sinai Hosp, New York, 39-41; assoc chemist, Cent Concrete Lab, 41-42; chemist, Brush Develop Co Div, Clevite Corp, 46; assoc chemist, Argonne Nat Lab, 46-48; proj leader nuclear chem, Vitro Corp Am, 48-52; div consult, Battelle Mem Inst, 52-59; res assoc, M & C Nuclear, Inc, 59-61; sect mgr, Nuclear Div, Martin Co, 61-63; FEL, BATTELLE MEM INST, 63- *Mem:* Fel AAAS; Am Nuclear Soc; Am Chem Soc; fel Am Inst Chem. *Res:* Nuclear and radiochemistry; nuclear fuels; applications of radioisotopes; radiation processes; energy conversion devices; nuclear waste isolation. *Mailing Add:* Battelle Mem Inst 505 King Ave Columbus OH 43201

POBINER, HARVEY, b New York, NY, Mar 2, 27; m 54; c 2. ANALYTICAL CHEMISTRY, PHYSICAL CHEMISTRY. *Educ:* Brooklyn Col, BA, 48, MA, 56. *Prof Exp:* Chemist, Sperry Gyroscope Co, NY, 48-54; res chemist, Gen Aniline & Film Corp, NJ, 54-57 & Esso Res & Eng Co, 57-63; staff scientist, Gen Precision Aerospace Res Ctr, 63-64; supvr anal chem, 64-74, mgr org chem & anal chem, 74-77, MGR ANAL CHEM RES & SERV, PRINCETON RES CTR, AM CAN CO, 77- *Mem:* Am Chem Soc. *Res:* Instrumental methods of organic analysis; absorption and emission spectroscopy; chromatography; rare earth analysis; thin film characterizations; radiation-curable coatings; photochemistry; organic separations; lignin characterization. *Mailing Add:* Am Can Co Princeton Res Ctr Anal Res & Serv PO Box 50 Princeton NJ 08540

POCHAN, JOHN MICHAEL, b Kittanning, Pa, Apr 8, 42; m 76; c 4. POLYMER PHYSICS, PHYSICAL CHEMISTRY. *Educ:* Rensselaer Polytech Inst, BChE, 64; Univ Ill, Urbana, MS, 68, PhD(phys chem), 69. *Prof Exp:* Sr scientist polymer physics, Rochester Corp Res Ctr, Xerox Corp, 69-81; SCIENTIST ADHESION RES, CHEM RES LAB, EASTMAN KODAK, 81- *Concurrent Pos:* Vis prof, Chem Dept, Univ Ill, 78. *Mem:* NY Acad Sci; Am Chem Soc; Am Phys Soc. *Res:* Liquid crystals, physical and optical properties, rheooptic phenomena; polymers, dielectric, electrical and triboelectric properties, morphology, photoconduction and transport, oxidative stability; high resolution microwave spectroscopy; adhesion chemistry. *Mailing Add:* Rochester Corp Res Ctr W114 Xerox Corp Rochester NY 14650

POCHE, DAVID JOHN, quantitative stratigraphy, marine geology, see previous edition

POCHI, PETER E, b Boston, Mass, Mar 8, 29; m 55; c 2. MEDICINE, DERMATOLOGY. *Educ:* Harvard Univ, AB, 50; Boston Univ, MD, 55; Am Bd Dermat, dipl, 62. *Prof Exp:* Intern med, Boston City Hosp, Mass, 55-56; resident dermat, Boston Univ Hosp, 58-61, from asst to asst prof, Sch Med, 61-69, assoc prof, 69-76, PROF DERMAT, SCH MED, BOSTON UNIV, 76- *Concurrent Pos:* Consult, Lemuel Shattuck Hosp, Boston, 62-; asst vis dermatologist, Univ Hosp, Boston, 62-71, assoc vis dermatologist, 71-77, vis dermatologist, 77-; clin assoc, Boston City Hosp, 66-67, assoc vis physician, 67-78, vis physician dermat & assoc dir, 78-; consult, Boston Vet Admin Hosp, 78-; lectr dermat, Sch Med, Tufts Univ, 80- *Mem:* Soc Invest Dermat; fel Am Acad Dermat; Am Fedn Clin Res; Am Med Asn; Dermat Found. *Res:* Hormonal control of sebaceous gland function; evaluation of pathogenic factors in acne vulgaris. *Mailing Add:* Dept Dermat Sch Med Boston Univ Boston MA 02118

POCHOP, LARRY OTTO, b Winner, SDak, Sept 12, 40; m 65. AGRICULTURAL ENGINEERING. *Educ:* SDak State Univ, BS, 62; Univ Mo-Columbia, MS, 64, PhD(agr eng), 67. *Prof Exp:* Instr agr eng, Univ Mo-Columbia, 63-67; from asst prof to assoc prof, 67-77, PROF AGR ENG, UNIV WYO, 77- *Mem:* Am Soc Agr Engrs. *Res:* Agricultural animal and plant environment. *Mailing Add:* Agr Eng Div University Sta Box 3354 Laramie WY 82071

POCIUS, ALPHONSUS VYTAUTAS, b Emsdetten, Ger, May 20, 48; US citizen; m 70. PHYSICAL CHEMISTRY. *Educ:* Knox Col, BA, 70; Univ Ill, Urbana, PhD(phys chem), 74. *Prof Exp:* Sr res chemist, Chem Resources Div, 74-75, sr res chemist, Cent Res Div, 75-79, RES SPECIALIST, ADHESIVES, COATINGS & SEALERS DIV, 3M CO, 79- *Mem:* Soc Advan Mat & Process Eng. *Res:* Surface chemistry, corrosion and adhesion as well as adhesive polymer characterization and development. *Mailing Add:* Adhesives Coatings & Sealers Lab 3M Co 3M Ctr Bldg 209-1C-13 St Paul MN 55144

POCKER, YESHAYAU, b Kishineff, Romania, Oct 10, 28; m 50; c 2. PHYSICAL ORGANIC CHEMISTRY, BIOCHEMISTRY. *Educ:* Hebrew Univ, Israel, MSc, 49; Univ London, PhD(phys chem), 53, DSc(phys & org chem), 60. *Prof Exp:* Res assoc, Weizmann Inst, 49-50; from asst lectr to lectr chem, Univ Col London, 52-61, recognized teacher, Senate House, 59, exam sci Russian, 60; PROF CHEM, UNIV WASH, 61- *Concurrent Pos:* Vis assoc prof, Ind Univ, 60-61; Nat Speaker, Am Chem Soc, 70 & 74; bicentennial lectr, Mont State Univ, 76; horizons chem lectr, Univ NC, 77; chmn, Pauling Award Comt, 78. *Honors & Awards:* Plaque Award, Am Chem Soc, 70 & 74. *Mem:* Am Chem Soc; fel NY Acad Sci; Am Soc Biol Chem; The Chem Soc. *Res:* Kinetics and mechanisms of organic reactions; molecular rearrangements; mechanisms of chemical and enzymatic catalysis; metalloenzymes; respiration; inhibitory pollutants; hydration and hydrolysis; very fast reactions; high pressure effects; kinetic isotope effects; biophysical chemistry; storage and release of solar energy. *Mailing Add:* 3515 N E 42nd Seattle WA 98105

POCOCK, STANLEY ALBERT JOHN, b London, Eng, Dec 12, 28; Can citizen; m 55. GEOLOGY, PALYNOLOGY. *Educ:* Univ Col, Univ London, BSc, 50, PhD(palynol), 64. *Prof Exp:* Exp officer, Geol Surv & Mus, London, Eng, 52-56; res geologist, Imp Oil Ltd, 56-70, geol res specialist, 70-75, sr geol res specialist, res & tech serv dept, 75-80; RES ADVISOR, RES & TECH SERV DEPT, ESSO RESOURCES CAN, 81- *Mem:* Can Bot Asn; Int Asn Plant Taxon; Am Asn Stratig Palynologists; Can Asn Petrol Geol. *Res:* Palynology of Jurassic and Cretaceous sediments of Canada and worldwide; qualitative and quantitative aspects of the visual identification of the organic components of sediments. *Mailing Add:* Res & Tech Serv Dept Esso Resources Can 339-50th Ave SE Calgary AB T2G 2B3 Can

PODAS, WILLIAM M(ORRIS), b Minneapolis, Minn, June 15, 16; m 42; c 2. CHEMICAL ENGINEERING. *Educ:* Univ Minn, BChE, 38. *Prof Exp:* Chem engr, Econ Lab, Inc, 39-42, Chem Warfare Serv, Edgewood Arsenal, 42 & Rocky Mountain Arsenal, Colo, 42-43; ord engr, Ord Res Ctr, Aberdeen Proving Ground, Md, 43-45; chem engr, 45-47, asst dir res & develop div, 47-60, vpres & dir res & develop, 60-63, SR V PRES, ECON LAB, INC, 73- *Mem:* Am Chem Soc; Commercial Develop Asn; Am Inst Chem Engrs; AAAS; Am Pub Health Asn. *Res:* Detergents and sanitation; ecology; washing equipment and controls; chemical processing; water treatment. *Mailing Add:* Res & Develop Dept Osborn Bldg St Paul MN 55102

PODBIELNIAK, WALTER J(OSEPH), chemical engineering, deceased

PODGORSAK, ERVIN B, b Vienna, Austria, Sept 28, 43; Yugoslavian & Can citizen; m 65; c 2. MEDICAL PHYSICS, RADIATION PHYSICS. *Educ:* Univ Ljubljana, dipl ing, 68; Univ Wis-Madison, MS, 70, PhD(physics), 73. *Prof Exp:* Fel med biophys, Univ Toronto, 73-74; med physicist, Ont Cancer Inst, 74; sr physicist radiotherapy, 75-78, DIR RADIATION ONCOL PHYSICS, MONTREAL GEN HOSP, 78- *Concurrent Pos:* Asst prof, Fac Med, McGill Univ, 75-78, assoc prof, 78-; assoc scientist, Royal Victoria Hosp, 75- *Mem:* Am Asn Physicists Med; Can Asn Physicists; fel Can Col Physicists Med. *Res:* Solid state radiation dosimetry; high energy equipment used in cancer therapy. *Mailing Add:* Dept Radiation Oncol McGill Univ Mont Gen Hosp 1650 Ave des Cedres Montreal PQ H3G 1A4 Can

PODGWAITE, JOHN DAVID, microbiology, entomology, see previous edition

PODIO, AUGUSTO L, b Bogota, Colombia, Aug 14, 40; US citizen; m 65; c 1. PETROLEUM ENGINEERING. *Educ:* Univ Tex, Austin, BS, 63, MS, 65, PhD(petrol eng), 68; Univ of the Andes, Colombia, BS, 63. *Prof Exp:* Asst prof petrol eng, 68-69, res scientist petrol eng, 69-80, ASSOC PROF PETROL ENG, UNIV TEX, AUSTIN, 77- *Mem:* Am Inst Mining, Metall & Petrol Engrs; Soc Explor Geophys. *Res:* Drilling; exploration; rock mechanics; seismic exploration; wave propagation; well-logging; ultrasonics. *Mailing Add:* Dept of Petrol Eng Univ of Tex Austin TX 78712

PODLAS, THOMAS JOSEPH, b East Orange, NJ, Oct 15, 40; m 68; c 1. CHEMISTRY. *Educ:* Seton Hall Univ, BS, 62, MS, 64, PhD(phys chem), 68. *Prof Exp:* Res chemist, 68-74, SR RES CHEMIST, HERCULES INC, 74- *Mem:* Am Chem Soc. *Res:* Use of natural and synthetic polymers in foods, pharmaceutical and household products; use of cellulosic polymers for enhanced petroleum recovery. *Mailing Add:* 12 Spinet Rd Newark DE 19713

PODLESKI, THOMAS ROGER, b Bloomington, Ill, May 16, 34; m 65; c 2. PHYSIOLOGY, BIOCHEMISTRY. *Educ:* Univ NMex, BS, 56; Univ Rochester, MS, 60; Columbia Univ, PhD(physiol), 66. *Prof Exp:* Res assoc neurobiol, Columbia Univ, 66-68; USPHS fel, Pasteur Inst, Paris, 68, Gen Del Nat Ministry Educ fel, 69, NSF fel, 69-70, Nat Ctr Sci Res, France sr researcher, 70; ASSOC PROF NEUROBIOL & BEHAV, CORNELL UNIV, 70- *Res:* Molecular basis of excitability of nerve and muscle; regulatory properties of biological membranes. *Mailing Add:* Langmuir Lab Cornell Univ Ithaca NY 14850

PODOLSKY, RICHARD JAMES, b Chicago, Ill, Aug 20, 23; c 2. PHYSIOLOGY, BIOPHYSICS. *Educ:* Univ Chicago, BS, 46, PhD(biophys), 52. *Prof Exp:* Biophysicist, Naval Med Res Inst, 56-62, CHIEF SECT CELLULAR PHYSICS, LAB PHYS BIOL, NAT INST ARTHRITIS, DIABETES, DIGESTIVE & KIDNEY DIS, 62-, CHIEF LAB PHYS BIOL, 74- *Concurrent Pos:* Nat Found Infantile Paralysis res fel, Naval Med Res Inst, Md, 53-54; USPHS spec fel, Univ Col, Univ London, 55-56; mem physiol study sect, NIH, 65-69; vis prof, Univ Calif, Santa Cruz, 69; mem US nat comt, Int Union Pure & Appl Biophys, 75-81. *Mem:* Biophys Soc; Am Physiol Soc; Soc Gen Physiol. *Res:* Muscle physiology; membrane transport. *Mailing Add:* Lab Phys Biol Nat Inst Arthritis Diabetes Digestive & Kidney Dis Bldg 6 Rm 110 Bethesda MD 20014

PODOSEK, FRANK A, b Ludlow, Mass, Nov 26, 41. MASS SPECTROMETRY, METEORITICS. *Educ:* Harvard Univ, BA, 64; Univ Calif, Berkeley, PhD(physics), 69. *Prof Exp:* Asst physics, Univ Calif, Berkeley, 64-69; Kellogg Lab fel, Calif Inst Technol, 69-74; ASST PROF EARTH SCI, DEPT EARTH & PLANETARY SCI, WASH UNIV, ST LOUIS, 74- *Mem:* AAAS; Am Phys Soc; Am Geophys Union. *Res:* Rare gas mass spectroscopy of meteorites and lunar samples; extinct radioactivities. *Mailing Add:* Dept of Earth & Planetary Sci Wash Univ St Louis MO 63130

PODREBARAC, EUGENE GEORGE, b Kansas City, Kans, Nov 12, 29; m 60; c 2. MEDICINAL CHEMISTRY, QUALITY ASSURANCE. *Educ:* Rockhurst Col, BS, 52; Univ Kans, MS, 57, PhD(chem), 60. *Prof Exp:* Res chemist, US Army, 52-54; asst chem, Univ Kans, 55-56; assoc chemist, Midwest Res Inst, 56-57; asst chem, Univ Kans, 57-59; sr chemist, 60-80, MGR QUALITY ASSURANCE, MIDWEST RES INST, 80- *Mem:* Am Chem Soc; Sigma Xi; NY Acad Sci. *Res:* Synthetic organic chemistry; organometallics; pharmaceutical chemistry; design and synthesis of compounds for cancer chemotherapy; immobilized enzymes. *Mailing Add:* Midwest Res Inst 425 Volker Blvd Kansas City MO 64110

PODUSLO, SHIRLEY ELLEN, b Richeyville, Pa. NEUROCHEMISTRY. *Educ:* Ohio State Univ, BS; Johns Hopkins Univ, MA & PhD. *Prof Exp:* ASST PROF NEUROL & NEUROCHEM, SCH MED, JOHNS HOPKINS UNIV, 76- *Mem:* Am Soc Neurochem; Int Soc Neurochem; Soc Neurosci; Am Soc Cell Biol. *Res:* Characterization of purified oligodendroglia, their plasma membranes, and the whorls of membranes produced in culture; comparison of their properties to myelin and cells from normal human brain and from demyelinating brain, and to cell lines derived from glial tumors. *Mailing Add:* Dept Neurol Sch Med Johns Hopkins Univ 720 Rutland Ave Baltimore MD 21205

PODZIMEK, JOSEF, b Brandys NL, Czech, Mar 24, 23; m 50; c 2. CLOUD PHYSICS, METEOROLOGY. *Educ:* Charles Univ, Prague, BS & MS, 49, MS, 52, PhD(physics & meteorol), 59. *Prof Exp:* Res asst aerodyn, Flight Res Inst, Prague, 49-53; dir & head dept cloud physics, Inst Atmospheric Physics, Czech Acad Sci, 54-69; res assoc, Atmospheric Sci Res Ctr, State Univ NY, Albany, 69-71; SR INVESTR, GRAD CTR CLOUD PHYSICS RES & PROF MECH ENG, UNIV MO-ROLLA, 71- *Concurrent Pos:* From asst prof to assoc prof, Charles Univ, Prague, 62-69, lectr, 62-66, fel, 66-69. *Mem:* Am Geophys Union; Am Meteorol Soc; WGer Soc Aerosol Res. *Res:* Cloud and aerosol physics; aerodynamics of precipitation elements; tropospheric and stratospheric nuclei; formation of precipitation elements. *Mailing Add:* Grad Ctr for Cloud Physics Res Univ of Mo Rolla MO 65401

POE, DONALD PATRICK, b DuQuoin, Ill, Aug 19, 48. ANALYTICAL CHEMISTRY. *Educ:* Southern Ill Univ, BS, 70; Iowa State Univ, MS, 72, PhD(anal chem), 74. *Prof Exp:* asst prof, 74-80, ASSOC PROF ANAL CHEM, UNIV MINN, DULUTH, 80- *Mem:* Am Chem Soc; Sigma Xi. *Res:* Oxidation-reduction properties of metal complexes; spectrophotometric and electrochemical studies of mixed ligand complexes; liquid chromatography with electrochemical detection. *Mailing Add:* Dept of Chem Univ of Minn Duluth MN 55812

POE, MARTIN, b St Louis, Mo, Sept 26, 42; m 65; c 1. BIOPHYSICS, PHYSICAL BIOCHEMISTRY. *Educ:* Mass Inst Technol, BS, 64; Univ Pa, PhD(biophys), 69. *Prof Exp:* Fel biophys, E I du Pont de Nemours & Co, Inc, 69-70; sr res biophysicist, 70-74, res fel, 74-79, SR RES FEL BIOPHYSICS, MERCK INST THERAPEUT RES, 79- *Concurrent Pos:* Byron Riegel lectr, Northwestern Univ, 79. *Mem:* Biophys Soc; Am Soc Biol Chemists. *Res:* Physical chemistry of macromolecules, particularly dihydrofolate reductase and renin; biophysical chemistry, particularly rational design of drugs; high resolution nuclear magnetic resonance. *Mailing Add:* PO Box 2000 Merck Inst for Therapeut Res Rahway NJ 07065

POE, RICHARD D, b Commerce, Tex, Dec 13, 31; m 55; c 3. ANALYTICAL CHEMISTRY, ORGANIC CHEMISTRY. *Educ:* ETex State Col, BS, 57, MS, 58; Tex A&M Univ, PhD(anal chem), 64. *Prof Exp:* From instr to asst prof chem, Tarleton State Col, 58-61; head anal chem, 64-65, dir chem res,

65-68, head anal develop, Sci & Technol Div, 68-72, mgr chem serv, 72-74, mgr ophthalmic res, 74-78, assoc dir oththal res & develop, 78-80, DIR CHEM, ALCON LABS INC, 80- *Mem:* Am Chem Soc; Acad Pharmaceut Sci; fel Am Inst Chem. *Res:* Analytical chemistry, especially organic and pharmaceutical applications; organic chemistry, especially medicinal applications. *Mailing Add:* Sci & Technol Div Alcon Labs Inc 6201 S Freeway Ft Worth TX 76134

POE, SIDNEY LAMARR, b Leesville, La, Sept 29, 42; m 66; c 2. ENTOMOLOGY. *Educ:* Northwestern State Univ, BS, 64, MS, 66; Univ Mo-Columbia, PhD(entom), 70. *Prof Exp:* From asst prof to prof entom, Univ Fla, 69-79; PROF & HEAD, DEPT ENTOM, VA POLYTECH INST & STATE UNIV, 79- *Mem:* Entom Soc Am. *Res:* Acarology; biology and ecology of saprophytic and phytophagous mites; host plant resistance and integrated management of agronomic insect and mite pests; biological control of arthropods; zoology. *Mailing Add:* 216 Price Hall Va Polytech & State Univ Blacksburg VA 24060

POEHLEIN, GARY WAYNE, b Tell City, Ind, Oct 17, 36; m 58; c 4. CHEMICAL ENGINEERING, POLYMER CHEMISTRY. *Educ:* Purdue Univ, BS, 58, MS, 63, PhD(chem eng), 66. *Prof Exp:* Design engr, Procter & Gamble Co, 58-61; from asst prof to prof chem eng, Lehigh Univ, 65-78; PROF CHEM ENG & DIR SCH CHEM ENG, GA INST TECHNOL, 78- *Concurrent Pos:* Indust consult, 66- *Mem:* Am Inst Chem Engrs; Am Chem Soc; Soc Rheol; Am Soc Eng Educ. *Res:* Polymerization kinetics; latex technology; applied rheology. *Mailing Add:* Sch of Chem Eng Ga Inst of Technol Atlanta GA 30332

POEHLER, HORST ALBIN, b Gera, Ger, Oct 9, 17; nat US; m 42; c 1. ELECTRICAL ENGINEERING, PHYSICS. *Educ:* Polytech Inst Brooklyn, BEE, 39; Columbia Univ, MA, 42, PhD(pure sci), 48. *Prof Exp:* Res elec engr, Westinghouse Elec & Mfg Co, 42-44; proj engr, Int Electronic Labs, 44-46; sect head res dept, Gen Precision Labs, 48-58; mem tech staff, Space Tech Labs, Inc, 58-64; scientist, 64-72, SR SCIENTIST, GUIDED MISSILE RANGE DIV, PAN AM WORLD AIRWAYS, INC, 72- *Mem:* Sr mem Inst Elec & Electronics Engrs; Health Physics Soc; Ling Soc Am. *Res:* Vacuum tube technology; oxide cathodes; electron emission; electronic measuring and computing devices; industrial electronics; propagation; telemetry; missile-borne instrumentation; plasma physics; missile tracking. *Mailing Add:* 400 Third Ave Satellite Beach FL 32937

POEHLER, THEODORE O, b Baltimore, Md, Oct 20, 35; m 61; c 2. SOLID STATE PHYSICS, LASERS. *Educ:* Johns Hopkins Univ, BS, 56, MS, 58, DEng(solid state physics), 61. *Prof Exp:* Instr, 58-60, from res staff asst to res staff assoc, 59-62, consult, Appl Physics Lab, 62, solid state physicist, 63-69, prin staff physicist, 69-74, William S Parsons vis prof, 72-73, HEAD, QUANTUM ELECTRONICS GROUP, APPL PHYSICS LAB, JOHNS HOPKINS UNIV, 74-, LECTR, UNIV, 65- *Honors & Awards:* Nat Capital Award Eng, 71. *Mem:* AAAS; Am Phys Soc; Inst Elec & Electronics Engrs. *Res:* Semiconductors; thin films; optical masers; crystal growth techniques; solid state plasmas; millimeter waves; cyclotron resonance; band structure; quantum electronics; infrared and chemical lasers; organic conductors. *Mailing Add:* 8 Seminole Ave Baltimore MD 21228

POEHLMAN, JOHN MILTON, b Macon, Mo, May 9, 10; m 36; c 2. PLANT BREEDING, AGRICULTURE. *Educ:* Univ Mo, BS, 31, PhD(bot), 36. *Prof Exp:* From instr to assoc prof, 34-50, prof agron, 50-80, EMER PROF AGRON, UNIV MO-COLUMBIA, 80- *Concurrent Pos:* Res adv, Orissa Univ, India, 63-65. *Honors & Awards:* Thomas Jefferson Award, Univ Mo, 78. *Mem:* AAAS; fel Am Soc Agron; Crop Sci Soc Am; Europ Asn Plant Breeding; fel Indian Soc Genetics & Plant Breeding. *Res:* Breeding wheat, oats, barley, rice and pulses; international agricultural development. *Mailing Add:* Dept of Agron Univ of Mo Columbia MO 65211

POEL, ROBERT HERMAN, b Kalamazoo, Mich, Feb 10, 41; m 65; c 2. SCIENCE EDUCATION. *Educ:* Kalamazoo Col, BA, 62; Western Mich Univ, MA, 64, PhD(sci educ), 70. *Prof Exp:* Teacher pub sch, Mich, 63-66; asst prof, 70-74, ASSOC PROF NATURAL SCI, WESTERN MICH UNIV, 74-, COORDR GRAD SCI EDUC, 78- *Mem:* Nat Asn Res Sci Teaching; Am Asn Physics Teachers; Sch Sci & Math Asn. *Res:* Development of critical thinking skills within the context of science; problem solving and decision making. *Mailing Add:* Col Gen Studies Western Mich Univ Kalamazoo MI 49008

POEL, RUSSELL J, b Muskegon, Mich, July 24, 34; m 56; c 3. ORGANIC CHEMISTRY. *Educ:* Calvin Col, AB, 56; Mich State Univ, PhD(org chem), 65. *Prof Exp:* From instr to assoc prof, 62-77, chmn dept, 72-75 & 78-81, PROF CHEM, NORTH CENT COL, ILL, 77- *Mem:* Am Chem Soc; Royal Soc Chem. *Res:* Organic reaction mechanisms. *Mailing Add:* Dept Chem NCent Col Naperville IL 60540

POEL, WILLIAM ELIAS, b New York, NY, Feb 26, 16; m 39; c 2. PATHOLOGY. *Educ:* Brooklyn Col, BA, 37; George Washington Univ, PhD(physiol), 50. *Prof Exp:* Asst physiologist child hyg, NIH, 38-42, assoc physiologist, Lab Phys Biol, 46-48; res assoc physiol & anat, Sch Med, George Washington Univ, 48-50; physiologist, Lab Chem Pharmacol, Nat Cancer Inst, 50-52; res assoc & head lab exp carcinogenesis, Grad Sch Pub Health, 52-60, adj assoc prof histol, Sch Med, 60-66, ASSOC PROF CARCINOGENESIS, GRAD SCH PUB HEALTH, UNIV PITTSBURGH, 60- *Concurrent Pos:* Nat Cancer Inst spec fel path, Jackson Mem Lab, 58-59; Eleanor Roosevelt Int Cancer res fel, Weizmann Inst Sci, 62-63; lectr histopath & physiol, Dent Sch & Grad Sch Nursing, Univ Pittsburgh, 66-; vis assoc prof, Univ Tex M D Anderson Hosp & Tumor Inst, Houston, 69-70. *Mem:* Am Asn Cancer Res. *Res:* Experimental carcinogenesis and oncology; bioassays for experimental and environmental carcinogenesis; methodology in screen for carcinogens; histology and pathology of inbred mice; mammalian physiology. *Mailing Add:* Grad Sch of Pub Health Univ of Pittsburgh Pittsburgh PA 15213

POENITZ, WOFGANG P, b Erfurt, Ger, Apr 24, 38; m 64; c 1. PHYSICS. *Educ:* Univ Gottingen, vordiplon, 59; Karlsruhe Tech Univ, dipl, 62, Dr rer nat(physics), 66. *Prof Exp:* Physicist, Nuclear Res Ctr, Karlsruhe Tech Univ, 62-67; ASSOC PHYSICS, ARGONNE NAT LAB, 67- *Mem:* Am Phys Soc. *Res:* Neutron physics; nuclear structure. *Mailing Add:* Div Appl Physics 9700 S Case Argonne IL 60439

POEPPEL, ROGER BRIAN, b Staten Island, NY, July 6, 41; m 67; c 3. MATERIALS SCIENCE, CERAMICS. *Educ:* Cornell Univ, BEngPhys, 64, PhD(math sci), 69. *Prof Exp:* Instr mat sci, Cornell Univ, 68-69; asst metallurgist, 69-72, METALLURGIST, ARGONNE NAT LAB, 72-, GROUP LEADER CERAMICS, 76- *Concurrent Pos:* Instr dept gen surg, Rush Med Col, 71-78. *Mem:* Am Phys Soc; Nat Soc Prof Engrs. *Res:* Ceramic development and testing for new energy applications, including storage batteries, fuel cells, magnetohydrodynamic power generation; refractories for coal gasification; nuclear reactor fuel reprocessing, fabrication, testing and safety analysis. *Mailing Add:* Argonne Nat Labs 9700 S Cass Ave Argonne IL 60439

POESCHEL, GORDON PAUL, b Milwaukee, Wis, Nov 21, 42; m 66; c 2. PARASITOLOGY, BUSINESS MANAGEMENT. *Educ:* Univ Wis-Madison, BS, 65, MS, 66, PhD(vet sci), 68. *Prof Exp:* Res parasitologist, Walter Reed Army Inst Res, US Army, 68-69, clin lab off, 6th Convalescent Ctr, Vietnam, 69-70; group leader anthelmintic chemother, Am Cyanamid Co, Princeton, 70-73, group leader parasitol discovery, 74, mgr prod develop & agr, Cyanamid Latin Am-Asia, 74-76, mkt mgr animal prod, Cyanamid Americas Far East Div, Wayne, 76-78, mgr, Agr Div, Cyanamid Australia, Ltd, 79-80, MKT MGR, AMDRO FIRE ANT INSECTICIDE, AGR DIV, AM CYANAMID CO, WAYNE, 80- *Mem:* Am Soc Parasitol; Am Inst Biol Sci; Am Asn Vet Parasitol; World Asn Advan Vet Parasitol. *Res:* Parasites of domestic animals and man, their relationship with their host, and their potential control. *Mailing Add:* Agr Div Am Cyanamid Co Wayne NJ 07470

POESE, LESTER E, b St Charles, Mo, Apr 1, 13; m 37; c 2. CHEMICAL ENGINEERING, ENGINEERING. *Educ:* Mo Sch Mines & Metall, BS, 34. *Prof Exp:* Control chemist, Titanium Div, Nat Lead Co, Mo, 34-35 & NJ, 35-36, process foreman, 36-38, process engr, 38-42; area head, Merck & Co, Inc, 42-55; owner, Eastern Penn Oil Co, 55-65; GEN ENGR, US ARMY TECH DETACHMENT, US ARMY ARMAMENT RES & DEVELOP COMMAND, INDIAN HEAD, MD, 65- *Mem:* Am Chem Soc; Am Inst Chem Engrs; Nat Soc Prof Engrs. *Mailing Add:* RD No 4 Box 4164 La Plata MD 20646

POET, RAYMOND B, b Port Chester, NY, Feb 12, 20; m 43; c 2. BIOCHEMISTRY. *Educ:* City Col New York, BS, 42. *Prof Exp:* Jr chemist, NY Univ Res Div, Goldwater Mem Hosp, NY, 45-50; res asst anal chem, 50-57, sr res chemist, 58-68, res assoc, 68-69, res fel, 69-74, SECT HEAD, SQUIBB INST MED RES, 74- *Mem:* Soc Appl Spectros; Am Chem Soc; Am Pharmaceut Asn. *Res:* Development of analytical methods for synthetic and natural products. *Mailing Add:* Squibb Inst for Med Res Georges Rd New Brunswick NJ 08903

POETHIG, RICHARD SCOTT, b Buffalo, NY, July 17, 53. DEVELOPMENTAL GENETICS. *Educ:* Col Wooster, BA, 74; Yale Univ, MPhil, 81, PhD(biol), 81. *Prof Exp:* Fel, Stanford Univ, 81; FEL, UNIV MO-COLUMBIA, 81- *Mem:* Soc Develop Biol; Genetics Soc Am; Soc Econ Bot. *Res:* Clonal analysis of plant development; genetic and developmental analysis of homeotic mutations in plants. *Mailing Add:* Curtis Hall Univ Mo MO 65211

POETTMANN, FRED H(EINZ), b Moers, Ger, Dec 20, 19; US citizen; m 46; c 2. CHEMICAL ENGINEERING, PETROLEUM ENGINEERING. *Educ:* Case Inst Technol, BS, 42; Univ Mich, MS & ScD(chem eng), 46. *Prof Exp:* Chemist, Lubrizol Corp, Ohio, 42-43; mgr prod res sect, Phillips Petrol Co, 46-55; supvr engr, Res Dept, 55-61, mgr eng & chem dept, 61-63, assoc res dir, 63-72, RES ADV TO VPRES RES & CHEM, MARATHON OIL CO, 72-, MGR COM DEVELOP DIV, 72- *Concurrent Pos:* Spec lectr, Exten Div, Okla State Univ, 47-55; lectr, Ente Nazional Idrocarburi, Milan, Italy, 68; mem res comt, Interstate Oil Compact Comn, 67-; mem adv panel, US Off Technol Assessment, 76-77. *Honors & Awards:* Lester C Uren Award, Soc Petrol Engrs, 66, John Franklin Carll Award, 71. *Mem:* Nat Acad Eng; Am Chem Soc; Am Inst Chem Engrs; Am Inst Mining, Metall & Petrol Engrs; Soc Petrol Engrs. *Res:* Reservoir mechanics; natural gas engineering; phase behavior of hydrocarbons under pressure; multiphase-fluid flow; oil recovery processes. *Mailing Add:* Marathon Oil Co PO Box 269 Littleton CO 80123

POFFENBARGER, PHILLIP LYNN, b Lafayette, Ind, Oct 13, 37; m 57; c 6. INTERNAL MEDICINE, BIOCHEMISTRY. *Educ:* Ind Univ, Bloomington, AB, 59; Ind Univ, Indianapolis, MS & MD, 63. *Prof Exp:* Intern med, Univ Wash Hosp, 63-64, resident, Affiliated Hosps, 64-65; asst prof med, 70-73, asst prof biochem, 71-73, assoc prof, 73-76, PROF MED, HUMAN BIOL CHEM & GENETICS, UNIV TEX MED BR GALVESTON, 76-, DIR, CLIN RES CTR & DIV ENDOCRINOL & METAB, 75- *Concurrent Pos:* NIH fel, Univ Wash, 65-66; Am Diabetes Asn res & develop award, Harvard Med Sch, 68-69, NIH spec fel, 69-70. *Mem:* Am Soc Clin Investr; Am Fedn Clin Res; Endocrine Soc; Am Diabetes Asn. *Res:* Diabetes mellitus, insulin biosynthesis; insulin-like proteins in human blood. *Mailing Add:* Dept Med Univ of Tex Med Br Galveston TX 77550

POGANY, GILBERT CLAUDE, b Brussels, Belg, July 4, 32; US citizen; m 62; c 2. EXPERIMENTAL EMBRYOLOGY. *Educ:* Belmont Col, BS, 62; Tulane Univ La, MS, 64, PhD(biol), 66. *Prof Exp:* Res asst streptococci, Med Sch, Vanderbilt Univ, 61-62; asst prof embryol, Emory & Henry Col, 66-69; asst prof embryol, 69-74, asst prof biol, 74-80, ASSOC PROF BIOL, NORTHERN ARIZ UNIV, 80- *Concurrent Pos:* Biol Res Ctr fel, 67-68; Sigma Xi grant, 70. *Mem:* Am Soc Zool; Soc Develop Biol. *Res:* Effects of radiation on embryonic development. *Mailing Add:* Dept of Biol Sci Northern Ariz Univ Flagstaff AZ 86011

POGELL, BURTON M, b Baltimore, Md, Mar 3, 28; m 55; c 1. BIOCHEMISTRY, MICROBIOLOGY. *Educ:* Johns Hopkins Univ, BA, 48; Univ Wis, PhD(physiol chem), 52. *Prof Exp:* Asst prof biochem, Wilmer Ophthal Inst, Johns Hopkins Univ, 55-58; asst prof microbiol, Sch Med, Vanderbilt Univ, 60-64; assoc prof biochem, Albany Med Col, 64-69; prof microbiol, Sch Med, St Louis Univ, 69-80; PROF MED CHEM & PHARMACOG, SCH PHARM, UNIV MD, BALTIMORE, 80- *Concurrent Pos:* NIH spec trainee, Biochem Res Inst, Buenos Aires, 58-59, Carlsburg Lab, Copenhagen, 59-60 & career develop award, 60-69. *Mem:* Am Soc Biol Chem; Am Soc Microbiol. *Res:* Enzymology and intermediary metabolism; control and regulation of fructose-1, 6-diphosphatase activity and its role in glyconeogenesis; biosynthesis of puromycin; control of differentiation in actinomycetes and chick embryo liver. *Mailing Add:* Dept Med Chem & Pharmacognosy Sch Pharmacy Univ MD Baltimore MD 21201

POGGENBURG, JOHN KENNETH, JR, b New York, NY, Jan 18, 35; m 63; c 5. NUCLEAR CHEMISTRY, MICROBIOLOGY. *Educ:* Col Holy Cross, BS, 56; Univ Calif, Berkeley, PhD(chem), 66. *Prof Exp:* Res asst nuclear chem, Univ Calif, Berkeley, 59-65; res staff neutron prod, 65-73, group leader, Biomed Radioisotopes Group, Oak Ridge Nat Lab, 73-77, sect head biomed effects & instrumentation, 77-78; mgr nuclear prod res & develop, Med Prod Div, Union Carbide Corp, 78-81; DIR RES & DEVELOP, ANALYTAB PROD DIV, AYERST LABS, 81- *Concurrent Pos:* Exten instr, Univ Tenn, 67-70. *Mem:* Soc Nuclear Med; Am Chem Soc; AAAS; Sigma Xi; NY Acad Sci. *Res:* Nuclear spectroscopy; nuclear structure; theoretical alpha decay rates of heavy elements; radioisotope production, including nuclear reactions and chemical process development; radiopharmaceuticals; diagnostic applications of microbiology and immunology. *Mailing Add:* Dir Res & Develop 200 Express St Analytab Prod Inc Plainview NY 11803

POGGIO, ANDREW JOHN, b New York, NY, Nov 3, 41; div; c 1. ELECTRICAL ENGINEERING, RESEARCH ADMINISTRATION. *Educ:* Cooper Union Univ, BEE, 63; Univ Ill, MS, 64, PhD, 69. *Prof Exp:* Res specialist electrosci, MB Assocs, 69-71; res engr, Cornell Aeronaut Lab, 71-73; proj eng, 73-77, group leader, 77-79, NUCLEAR SAFEGUARD PROG LEADER, LAWRENCE LIVERMORE NAT LAB, UNIV CALIF, 79- *Concurrent Pos:* Assoc mem comn VI, Int Union Radio Sci. *Mem:* Inst Elec & Electronics Engrs; Sigma Xi. *Res:* Electromagnetic theory, antennas, scattering, propagation; acoustics; numerical analysis; systems analysis; systems research. *Mailing Add:* Lawrence Livermore Lab Univ of Calif Livermore CA 94550

POGGIO, GIAN FRANCO, b Genoa, Italy, Sept 21, 27. PHYSIOLOGY. *Educ:* Univ Genoa, MD, 51. *Prof Exp:* Asst neurol & psychiat, Univ Genoa, 52-54; from asst prof to assoc prof, 60-75, PROF PHYSIOL, SCH MED, JOHNS HOPKINS UNIV, 75- *Concurrent Pos:* Fel neurol surg, Sch Med, Johns Hopkins Univ, 54-56, fel physiol, 57-60. *Res:* Anatomy and physiology of the mammalian visual system; organization of the thalamus and cerebral cortex. *Mailing Add:* Dept of Physiol Johns Hopkins Sch of Med Baltimore MD 21205

POGO, A OSCAR, b Buenos Aires, Arg, Aug 28, 27; m 55; c 2. CELL BIOLOGY. *Educ:* Univ Buenos Aires, MD, DMSci, 59. *Prof Exp:* Res assoc, Inst Anat & Embryol, Fac Med Sci, Univ Buenos Aires, 55-59; asst prof, Inst Cell Biol, Fac Med Sci, Univ Cordoba, Arg, 61-64; res assoc, Rockefeller Univ, 64-66, asst prof, 66-67; investr, 67-74, HEAD, LAB CELL BIOL, NY BLOOD CTR, 67-, SR INVESTR, 74- *Concurrent Pos:* Fel, Guggenheim Found, 59-61; career develop award, NIH, 66; prin investr, NIH & NSF grants, 67- *Mem:* Am Soc Biol Chemists; Am Chem Soc; AAAS; Am Soc Cell Biol. *Res:* Biochemistry of the cell nucleus; nonhistone proteins and nuclear architecture; interacton of nucleosomes with nuclear matrix; transcription and processing of primary transcripts. *Mailing Add:* Lab Cell Biol Lindsley F Kimball Res Inst NY Blood Ctr 310 E 67th St New York NY 10021

POGORSKI, LOUIS AUGUST, b Lwow, Poland, Nov 7, 22; Can citizen; m 55; c 2. CHEMICAL ENGINEERING, EARTH SCIENCES. *Educ:* Polish Univ Col, London, dipl eng, 51; Univ Toronto, MASc, 53, PhD(chem eng), 58. *Prof Exp:* Chem engr, Barvue Mines, Que, 51-52; res chemist, Imp Oil Esso Res, Ont, 52; demonstr chem eng, Univ Toronto, 52-55; res engr, Air Prod, Inc, Pa, 55-57; sr process & proj engr, Chem Construct Corp, NY, 57-60; PRES & RES DIR, CHEM PROJS LTD, 60-; PRES & RES DIR, HELIUM SURVEYS INC, 75- *Concurrent Pos:* Consult, US & Can industs, 61- *Res:* Geochemical exploration for oil, natural gases, minerals; stable isotope ratio determination; sampling techniques; trace determination; pollution detection and control; cryogenic processes; chemical plant design methods; separation and ultrapurification of gases and liquids; plasma techniques. *Mailing Add:* 339 Maple Leaf Dr Toronto ON M6L 1P4 Can

POGORZELSKI, HENRY ANDREW, b Harrison, NJ, Sept 26, 22. MATHEMATICS. *Educ:* Princeton Univ, MA, 68; City Univ, New York, PhD(math), 69. *Prof Exp:* Sci ed, Math Rev, Am Math Soc, RI, 53-64; res asst math, Inst Advan Study, 64-65; lectr, City Col, New York, 65-66; res asst, Inst Advan Study, 66-67; lectr, Fordham Univ, 67-69; assoc prof, 69-74, PROF MATH, UNIV MAINE, ORONO, 74- *Res:* Recursive functions and number theory; mathematical logic. *Mailing Add:* Dept of Math Univ of Maine Orono ME 04473

POGORZELSKI, RONALD JAMES, b Detroit, Mich, Mar 25, 44; m 72. ELECTRICAL ENGINEERING, PHYSICS. *Educ:* Wayne State Univ, BS, 64, MS, 65; Calif Inst Technol, PhD(elec eng), 70. *Prof Exp:* Mem tech staff, Hughes Aircraft Co, 66; asst prof eng & appl sci, Univ Calif, Los Angeles, 69-73; assoc prof elec eng, Univ Miss, 73-77; SR STAFF ENG, TRW-DEFENSE & SPACE SYSTS GROUP, 77- *Concurrent Pos:* Consult, Sci & Technol Assocs, Inc, 70-71, Asn Sci Advisers, 72-73 & Univ Colo, 76. *Honors & Awards:* R W P King Award, Inst Elec & Electronics Engrs, 79. *Mem:* Inst Elec & Electronics Engrs; Am Phys Soc; Int Union Radio Sci; Optical Soc Am; NY Acad Sci. *Res:* Electromagnetic theory. *Mailing Add:* TRW-DSSG One Space Park Redondo Beach CA 90278

POGUE, JOHN PARKER, b Maysville, Ky, May 21, 25; m 50; c 6. VETERINARY MEDICINE. *Educ:* Miami Univ, AB, 49; Auburn Univ, DVM, 58. *Prof Exp:* Gen pract, 58-67; res vet, Commercial Solvents Corp, 68-73; clin vet, 74, MGR ANIMAL & LAB SERV, NORWICH EATON PHARMACEUT, 75- *Mem:* Am Vet Med Asn; Am Asn Swine Practrs; Indust Vet Asn; Am Asn Lab Animal Sci; Am Soc Lab Animal Practrs. *Res:* The effects of dantrolene sodium, a peripheral muscle relaxant, on muscle spasm resulting from trauma to the long bones. *Mailing Add:* Norwich Eaton Pharmaceut PO Box 191 Norwich NY 13815

POGUE, RICHARD EWERT, b Loma Linda, Calif, Jan 7, 30; m 53; c 3. MEDICAL STATISTICS, COMPUTER SCIENCE. *Educ:* Univ Minn, BA, 52, MS, 64, PhD(biostatist), 66. *Prof Exp:* Asst prof biomet, Col Med Sci, Univ Minn, 66-68; assoc prof community med, 68-73, assoc prof family pract & helth syst & info sci, 73-78, assoc dir syst & comput serv, 73-80, PROF HEALTH SYST & INFO SCI, MED COL GA, 78- *Mem:* Asn Comput Mach; Biomet Soc; Asn Develop Comput Based Instrnl Systs; Soc Comput Med. *Res:* Computers in medicine and education; education in computer medicine. *Mailing Add:* Systs & Comput Serv DSCS-RES (CI-21) Med Col of Ga Augusta GA 30902

POHL, HERBERT ACKLAND, b Lisbon, Portugal, Feb 17, 16; US citizen; m 41; c 5. BIOPHYSICS. *Educ:* Duke Univ, BS, 36, PhD(phys chem), 39. *Prof Exp:* Rockefeller fel anat, Johns Hopkins Univ, 39, Carnegie Inst fel, 40-41, Nat Defense res fel chem eng, 41-42; sr chemist, Naval Res Lab, 42-45; res assoc textile fibers dept, E I du Pont de Nemours & Co, 45-50, res assoc atomic energy div, 50-56, res assoc eng dept, 57; sr res assoc & lectr plastics, Sch Eng, Princeton Univ, 57-62; vis prof mat sci, Polytech Inst Brooklyn, 62-63; vis prof quantum chem group, Univ Uppsala, 63-64; PROF PHYSICS, OKLA STATE UNIV, 64- *Concurrent Pos:* Vpres, Sci-Tech Corp, NY; vis prof dept physics, Univ Calif, Riverside, 70; NATO sr sci fel, 71; vis prof, Cavendish Lab, Cambridge, 71-72; consult, WHO; ed, J Biol Physics. *Mem:* AAAS; Am Phys Soc; Am Asn Physics Teachers; Am Chem Soc; fel Am Inst Chem. *Res:* Biophysics; electronic behavior of molecular solids; dielectrics; nonuniform field effects; dielectrophoresis. *Mailing Add:* Dept of Physics Okla State Univ Stillwater OK 74074

POHL, RICHARD WALTER, b Milwaukee, Wis, May 21, 16; m 41; c 3. BOTANY. *Educ:* Marquette Univ, BS, 39; Univ Pa, PhD(bot), 47. *Prof Exp:* Asst instr bot, Univ Pa, 39-42; range conservationist, Soil Conserv Serv, USDA, Tex, 42 & 44-45; from asst prof to assoc prof bot, 47-55, PROF BOT, IOWA STATE UNIV, 56- *Concurrent Pos:* Ford Found fel, Univ Calif, 52-53; res assoc, Field Mus & Milwaukee Pub Mus; Hon Cur, Nat Mus Costa Rica. *Mem:* Bot Soc Am; Am Soc Plant Taxon (treas, 59-65, pres, 73). *Res:* Taxonomy of seed plants; Central American Gramineae, grassland vegetation. *Mailing Add:* Dept Bot Iowa State Univ Ames IA 50011

POHL, ROBERT O, b Goettingen, Ger, Dec 17, 29; nat US; m 61; c 3. SOLID STATE PHYSICS. *Educ:* Univ Erlangen, MS, 55, PhD(physics), 57. *Prof Exp:* Asst physics, Univ Erlangen, 57-58; res assoc, 58-60, from asst prof to assoc prof, 60-68, PROF PHYSICS, CORNELL UNIV, 68- *Concurrent Pos:* Vis prof, Aachen Tech Univ, 64 & Stuttgart Tech Univ, 66-67; Guggenheim fel, 73-74; Alexander von-Humboldt Sr Scientist fel, 80. *Mem:* Fel Am Phys Soc. *Res:* Low temperature solid state physics; lattice dynamics. *Mailing Add:* Dept of Physics Cornell Univ Ithaca NY 14853

POHL, VICTORIA MARY, b Haubstadt, Ind, Mar 29, 30. ALGEBRA. *Educ:* St Benedict Col, Ind, BS, 54; Univ Notre Dame, MS, 60, PhD(math), 69. *Prof Exp:* Teacher, St Theresa Elem Sch, 50-55; teacher math, Mater Dei High Sch, 55-59 & 60-62, chmn dept, 60-62; from instr to asst prof, St Benedict Col, Ind, 62-66 & 69-70, chmn dept, 65-66 & 69-70; asst prof, 70-73, ASSOC PROF MATH, IND STATE UNIV, EVANSVILLE, 73- *Concurrent Pos:* Consult math, Dubois County Sch Syst, 69-70. *Mem:* Math Asn Am; Nat Coun Teachers Math. *Mailing Add:* 615 Bellemeade Ave Evansville IN 47713

POHL, WILLIAM FRANCIS, b Clinton, Iowa, Sept 16, 37; m 81. MATHEMATICS. *Educ:* Univ Chicago, BS, 57, MS, 58; Univ Calif, Berkeley, PhD(math), 61. *Prof Exp:* NSF fel math, Mass Inst Technol, 61-62; instr, Stanford Univ, 62-63, actg asst prof, 63-64; from asst prof to assoc prof, 64-70, PROF MATH, UNIV MINN, MINNEAPOLIS, 70- *Concurrent Pos:* NSF res grant, 66- *Mem:* Am Math Soc. *Res:* Differential, integral and algebraic geometry. *Mailing Add:* Dept of Math 127 Vincent Hall Univ of Minn 206 Church St SE Minneapolis MN 55455

POHLAND, ALBERT, b Latrobe, Pa, Jan 23, 19; m 44; c 2. ORGANIC CHEMISTRY. *Educ:* St Vincent Col, BS, 40; Pa State Col, MS, 41, PhD(org chem), 44. *Prof Exp:* Asst war gases, Nat Defense Res Comt Proj, Univ Ill, 43-44; sr org chemist, Res Labs, 44-57, res assoc, 57-58, dept head, Div Org Chem, 58-64, res adv, 64-69, res consult, 69-80, FEL LILLY RES, ELI LILLY & CO, 80- *Mem:* Am Chem Soc. *Res:* War gases; structure-activity relationships of synthetic organic medicinals, especially analgesics; drug metabolism; structure of natural products. *Mailing Add:* Lilly Res Labs 307 E McCarty St Indianapolis IN 46206

POHLAND, FREDERICK G, b Oconomowoc, Wis, May 3, 31; m 66; c 1. SANITARY ENGINEERING, CIVIL ENGINEERING. *Educ:* Valparaiso Univ, BS, 53; Purdue Univ, MS, 58, PhD(sanit eng), 61. *Prof Exp:* From asst prof to assoc prof, 61-71, PROF CIVIL ENG, GA INST TECHNOL, 71- *Concurrent Pos:* Vis scholar, Univ Mich, 67-68; vis prof, Delft Univ Technol, Neth, 76-77. *Honors & Awards:* Harrison Prescott Eddy Award, Water Pollution Control Fedn, 65. *Mem:* AAAS; Am Water Works Asn; Am Chem Soc; Water Pollution Control Fed; Int Asn Water Pollution Res. *Res:* Environmental engineering operations and processes; water and waste chemistry and microbiology; solid and hazardous waste management; environmental impact monatoring and assessment. *Mailing Add:* Sch of Civil Eng Ga Inst of Technol Atlanta GA 30332

POHLAND, HERMANN W, b Karlsruhe, Ger, Nov 17, 34; m 62; c 2. ORGANIC CHEMISTRY. *Educ:* Univ Bonn, Vordiplom, 57, Hauptdiplom, 59, Dr rer nat(synthesis of isothiazoles), 61. *Prof Exp:* Lectr org anal, Univ Bonn, 60-61, Karl Duisberg fel, 61; fel, Univ Toronto, 61-62; res chemist, Jackson Lab, 62-68, sr res chemist, 68-69, res supvr, 69-71, sr supvr opers, dyes & chem, Org Chem Dept, 71-74, staff asst mfg dyes, 75-77, sr tech specialist, 77-79, TECH CONSULT PERMASEP REVERSE OSMOSIS SYSTS, E I DU PONT DE NEMOURS & CO, INC, 79- *Mem:* Am Chem Soc; Am Asn Textile Chem & Colorists; Soc Ger Chem; Int Desalination & Environ Asn; Nat Water Supply & Improvement Asn. *Res:* Synthesis of hetero-aromatic compounds and phospholipids; preparation and characterization of fluoropolymers; synthesis and application of dyes and textile chemicals; manufacture of dyes and intermediates; process for preventing biological fouling in membrane devices. *Mailing Add:* E I du Pont de Nemours & Co Inc Permasep Prods 104 Hitching Post Dr Wilmington DE 19803

POHLE, FREDERICK V, b Buena Vista, Va, Feb 21, 19; m 49; c 3. APPLIED MATHEMATICS. *Educ:* Cooper Union Inst Technol, BCE, 40; NY Univ, MS, 43, PhD(math), 50. *Prof Exp:* Instr mech, Eng Sch, NY Univ, 41-43, res asst math, Courant Inst, 46-48, instr, NY Univ, 48-50; asst prof mech, Polytech Inst Brooklyn, 50-53, from assoc prof to prof, 53-60; PROF MATH, ADELPHI UNIV, 60- *Concurrent Pos:* Consult, Knolls Atomic Power Lab, Gen Elec Co, 51-54; US Nat Bur Standards, 55; chmn dept math, Adelphi Univ, 62-72; US Air Force Off Sci Res grant, 64-66. *Mem:* Am Soc Eng Educ; Am Math Soc; Math Asn Am; Am Inst Aeronaut & Astronaut; Am Soc Mech Eng. *Res:* Theory of elasticity and of shells; vibration theory; non-linear mechanics; celestial mechanics. *Mailing Add:* Dept of Math Adelphi Univ Garden City NY 11530

POHLMANN, HANS PETER, b Waldenburg, Ger, Jan 30, 33; m 61; c 4. INORGANIC CHEMISTRY, PHYSICAL CHEMISTRY. *Educ:* Hanover Tech Univ, BS, 56, MS, 59, PhD(inorg chem), 61. *Prof Exp:* Asst prep inorg chem, Hanover Tech Univ, 62; asst proj chemist, Am Oil Co, Whiting, 62-63, proj chemist, 63-66; sr proj chemist, 67-69, group leader, 69-75, div dir, 75-79, MGR RES & DEVELOP, AMOCO CHEM CORP, 79- *Mem:* Am Chem Soc; Soc Ger Chem. *Res:* Liquid-liquid extraction for isolation and purification of rare earths, zirconium, hafnium; catalysis; high-pressure hydrogenations; liquid phase oxidations; reaction kinetics; petroleum technology; process development. *Mailing Add:* Res & Develop Dept Amoco Chem Corp PO Box 400 Naperville IL 60540

POHLMANN, JUERGEN LOTHAR WOLFGANG, b Berlin-Lichtenberg, Ger, Feb 2, 34; US citizen; m 61; c 3. SOLID STATE CHEMISTRY. *Educ:* Univ Tuebingen, BS, 56, MS, 59, PhD(org & phys chem), 61. *Prof Exp:* Res chemist, US Naval Propellant Plant, Indian Head, Md, 61-64; res chemist, US Army Engrs Res & Develop Labs, 64-66, RES CHEMIST, US ARMY NIGHT VISION & ELECTRO-OPTICS LAB, FT BELVOIR, VA, 66- *Mem:* Am Chem Soc; Soc Ger Chem. *Res:* Preparation of metalorganic compounds; synthesis of compounds exhibiting mesophases; liquid crystals; influence of impurities and molecular structure on mesomorphic behavior; preparation of solid state materials and infrared detector materials; anodization; surface passivation. *Mailing Add:* 8407 Camden St Alexandria VA 22308

POHLO, ROSS, b Chicago, Ill, Jan 31, 31; m 58; c 2. INVERTEBRATE ZOOLOGY. *Educ:* Univ Ill, BS, 54; Univ Ark, MS, 57; Univ Chicago, PhD(paleozool), 61. *Prof Exp:* Fel marine biol, Kristinebergs Zool Sta, Sweden, 61-62; Scripps Inst, Calif, 62-63; from asst prof to assoc prof, 63-74, PROF BIOL, CALIF STATE UNIV, NORTHRIDGE, 74- *Mem:* AAAS; Am Soc Limnol & Oceanog; Am Soc Zool. *Res:* Ecology and evolution of the bivalved mollusca. *Mailing Add:* Dept of Biol Calif State Univ Northridge CA 91330

POHM, A(RTHUR) V(INCENT), b Olmsted Falls, Ohio, Jan 11, 27; m 52; c 3. ELECTRICAL ENGINEERING. *Educ:* Fenn Col, BEE & BES, 50; Iowa State Col, MS, 53, PhD(physics), 54. *Prof Exp:* Lab instr, Fenn Col, 49-50; asst, Ames Lab, AEC, 50-54; res physicist, Remington Rand Univac Div, Sperry Rand Corp, 54-55, proj physicist, 55-56, res supvr, 57-58; assoc prof elec eng, 58-62, PROF ELEC ENG, IOWA STATE UNIV, 62- *Concurrent Pos:* Lectr, Univ Mich, 56. *Mem:* Fel Inst Elec & Electronics Engrs. *Res:* Thin films and solid electrical devices. *Mailing Add:* Dept of Elec Eng Iowa State Univ Ames IA 50010

POHORECKY, LARISSA ALEXANDRA, b Cholm, Ukraine, Jan 16, 42; US citizen. NEUROPHARMACOLOGY, ALCOHOLISM. *Educ:* Univ Ill, Chicago, BS, 63; Univ Chicago, PhD(pharmacol), 67. *Prof Exp:* Res assoc neuropharmacol, Mass Inst Technol, 67-71; asst prof neuropharmacol, Rockefeller Univ, 71-78; ASSOC PROF NEUROPHARMACOL, RUTGERS UNIV, 79- *Concurrent Pos:* USPHS fel, Mass Inst Technol, 67-71 & Rockefeller Univ, 71-78; mem alcohol res rev comt, Nat Inst Alcoholism & Alcohol Abuse, 77-79; adj assoc prof, Rockefeller Univ, 78- *Mem:* Endocrine Soc; Res Soc Alcoholism; Sigma Xi; Am Soc Pharmacol & Exp Therapeut; AAAS. *Res:* Influence of ethanol, hormonal and psychological factors on noradrenergic neurons and endocrine organs; psychopharmacology. *Mailing Add:* Ctr for Alcohol Studies Rutgers Univ New Brunswick NJ 08903

POIANI, EILEEN LOUISE, b Newark, NJ, Dec 17, 43. MATHEMATICS. *Educ:* Douglass Col, AB, 65; Rutgers Univ, MS, 67, PhD(math), 71. *Prof Exp:* Instr math, 67-70, asst prof, 70-74, assoc prof, 74-80, PROF MATH, ST PETER'S COL, NJ, 80-, ASST TO PRES PLANNING & RES, 76- *Concurrent Pos:* Residence counsr, Rutgers Univ, 66-67; Danforth Assoc; dir mid states self-study, St Peter's Col, 74-76 & 81-83; dir, Nat Prog Interest More Women in Math, Math Asn Am, 75-81, consult, 81-; speaker, Int Cong Math Educ, Berkeley, 80; consult sci related probs, minority cols & univs, AAAS, 81- *Mem:* Asn Women in Math; Math Asn Am. *Res:* Real analysis; special functions; Fourier analysis. *Mailing Add:* Dept Math St Peter's Col Jersey City NJ 07306

POINAR, GEORGE O, JR, b Spokane, Wash, Apr 25, 36; m 62. NEMATOLOGY. *Educ:* Cornell Univ, BS, 58, MS, 60, PhD(entom), 62. *Prof Exp:* Res asst entom, Cornell Univ, 58-62; asst entomologist, Univ Calif, Riverside, 62-63; nematologist, Rothamsted Exp Sta, 63-64; INSECT PATHOLOGIST & LECTR, DEPT ENTOM SCI, UNIV CALIF, BERKELEY, 77- *Concurrent Pos:* NIH fel, 63-64; consult, Nutrilite Corp, 67-68; mem, South Pac Comn, 68; Nat Acad Sci partic exchange prog, Soviet Union, 69; vis prof, Univ Amsterdam, 71- *Mem:* Soc Nematol; Entom Soc Am; Soc Invert Path; Soc European Nematol. *Res:* Biology and effect of light on the alfalfa weevil; biological control of nutgrass in California and Hawaii; taxonomy, morphology, biology and host-parasite relationship of entomophilic nematodes. *Mailing Add:* Div of Entom Univ of Calif Berkeley CA 94720

POINCELOT, RAYMOND PAUL, JR, b New Haven, Conn, June 10, 44; m 68; c 3. BIOCHEMISTRY. *Educ:* Southern Conn State Col, BA, 66; Case Western Reserve Univ, PhD(biochem), 70. *Prof Exp:* Asst agr scientist, 70-74, assoc agr scientist, Conn Agr Exp Sta, 74-77; asst prof, 77-80, ASSOC PROF BIOL, FAIRFIELD UNIV, 80-, CHMN DEPT, 79- *Concurrent Pos:* Plant sci writer, 74-; compos consult, 79- *Honors & Awards:* Cert of Achievement, Livestock Environ Sci Comt of Great Plains States, 74. *Mem:* Am Soc Hort Sci; Garden Writers Asn America; Nat Asn Sci Writers; Cactus & Succulent Soc America; Am Hort Soc. *Res:* Membranes, lipds and enzymes of photosynthetic systems; composting; membrane transport. *Mailing Add:* Dept of Biol Fairfield Univ Fairfield CT 06430

POINDEXTER, EDWARD HAVILAND, b Lansing, Mich, Dec 15, 30; m 59; c 2. CHEMICAL PHYSICS. *Educ:* Univ Mich, BS, 52, MS, 53, PhD(mineral), 55. *Prof Exp:* Asst mineral, Univ Mich, 50-55, res assoc, 55-57; res physicist, Calif Res Corp, Standard Oil Co Calif, 57-62; res phys scientist, 62-71, chief electronic mat res tech area, 71-73, supvry res phys scientist, 71-73, CHIEF DEVICE PHYS & ANALYSIS BR, US ARMY ELECTRONICS TECHNOL & DEVICES LAB, 73- *Mem:* Am Chem Soc; Am Phys Soc; Inst Elec & Electron Engrs; Mineral Soc Am. *Res:* Crystal optics; magnetic resonance; transient complexes; free radical solutions; asphaltene colloids; semiconductor oxide interface states; radiation damage in polymers. *Mailing Add:* 3 Rosedale Terr Holmdel NJ 07733

POINDEXTER, GRAHAM STUART, b Jeffersonville, Ind, Dec 18, 48; m 68; c 1. ORGANIC CHEMISTRY. *Educ:* Univ Louisville, BS, 71; Univ NC, PhD(org chem), 75. *Prof Exp:* Res assoc, Colo State Univ, 75-76, Nat Res Serv fel, 76-77; sr res chemist, Dow Chem USA, 77-80; MEM STAFF, CHEM RES DEPT, MEAD JOHNSON & CO, 80- *Mem:* Am Chem Soc. *Res:* Heterocyclic chemistry; synthetic methods; asymmetric synthesis; organic photochemistry. *Mailing Add:* Chem Res Dept Mead Johnson & Co Evansville IN 47721

POINDEXTER, JEANNE STOVE, b Lamoine Twp, Ill, Oct 5, 36; m 64; c 2. PROKARYOTE DEVELOPMENT, MICROBIAL ECOLOGY. *Educ:* Ind Univ, Bloomington, AB, 58; Univ Calif, Berkeley, MA, 61, PhD(bacteriol), 63. *Prof Exp:* Fel, Hopkins Marine Sta, Stanford Univ, 63; vis lectr bacteriol, Med Sch, Univ Edinburgh, 64; asst prof microbiol, Ind Univ, Bloomington, 64-67; assoc sci, Sch Med, NY Univ, 69-71; assoc prof biol, Medger Evers Col, City Univ New York, 71-75 & Marymount Manhattan Col, 75-76; ASSOC MICROBIOL, PUB HEALTH RES INST, NEW YORK CITY, 76- *Concurrent Pos:* Adj asst prof biol, Hunter Col, City Univ New York, 71; chmn, Nat Sci Math, Marymount Manhattan Col, 75-76; resident instr, Marine Biol Lab, 78-82; res assoc prof, Sch Med, NY Univ, 81- *Mem:* AAAS; Am Soc Microbiol; Am Inst Biol Sci. *Res:* Physiology, ultrastructure, cellular differentiation of stalked bacteria (Caulobacteraceae); bacterial anatomy; procaryote development; microbial ecology. *Mailing Add:* Pub Health Res Inst 455 First Ave New York NY 10016

POINTER, RICHARD HAMILTON, b Covington, Ga, June 4, 44; m 66; c 3. ENDOCRINOLOGY. *Educ:* Morehouse Col, BS, 68; Brown Univ, MS, 73, PhD(physiol chem), 75. *Prof Exp:* Res technician physiol, Emory Univ, 69-70; res assoc physiol, Sch Med, Vanderbilt Univ, 75-77; instr, Harvard Med Sch & Res Assoc, Howard Hughes Med Inst, 77-80; ASST PROF, DEPT BIOCHEM, COL MED, HOWARD UNIV, WASHINGTON, DC, 80- *Concurrent Pos:* Fel, Diabetes Prog, Nat Inst Arthritis Metab & Digestive Dis, NIH, 75-78. *Mem:* AAAS; Sigma Xi; Am Diabetes Asn; Am Physiol Soc; Orgn Black Scientists. *Res:* The mechanisms of hormone action at the cellular and molecular levels, specifically the mode of insulin action. *Mailing Add:* Diabetes Unit Mass Gen Hosp Boston MA 02114

POIRIER, CHARLES PHILIP, b Wyandotte, Mich, Feb 28, 37; m 63; c 4. NUCLEAR PHYSICS. *Educ:* Univ Detroit, BS, 59; Ind Univ, Bloomington, MS, 62, PhD(physics), 65. *Prof Exp:* res physicist, Aerospace Res Labs, US Air Force, 64-80; MEM STAFF, GEOPHYS TECH CORP, 80- *Mem:* Am Phys Soc. *Res:* Nuclear spectroscopy using charged particle, neutron and electromagnetic interactions; application of computers to problems in nuclear physics, both experimental and theoretical. *Mailing Add:* 1777 Conestoga St Graphics Tech Corp Boulder CO 80302

POIRIER, FRANK EUGENE, b Paterson, NJ, Aug 7, 40; m 63; c 2. BIOLOGICAL ANTHROPOLOGY, BEHAVIORAL ANTHROPOLOGY. *Educ:* Paterson State Col, BA, 62; Univ Ore, MA, 64, PhD(anthrop), 67. *Prof Exp:* Asst prof psychiat & anthrop, Univ Fla, 67-68; asst prof anthrop, Ohio State Univ, 68-70; assoc prof, 72-74, PROF ANTHROP, OHIO STATE UNIV, 74- *Concurrent Pos:* NSF, NIMH, Pacific Cultural Found grants, 65-82; res prof, Academia Seneca, 78. *Honors & Awards:* Outstanding Young Scientist, Sigma Xi, 74. *Mem:* AAAS; Int Primatol Soc; Am Asn Physical Anthrop; Am Anthrop Asn; Am Primatological Soc. *Res:* Primate ethology; paleoanthropology; primate socialization; ethnology of West Indies, India and Middle East. *Mailing Add:* Dept of Anthrop 65 S Oval Ohio State Univ Columbus OH 43210

POIRIER, GARY RAYMOND, b Bay City, Mich, Apr 10, 38; m 63; c 5. REPRODUCTIVE BIOLOGY. *Educ:* Mich State Univ, BS, 61, MS, 64, PhD(zool), 70. *Prof Exp:* Res asst chemother, Lederle Labs, 64-65; res asst immunochem, Hyland Labs, 65-67; asst prof biol, 70-74, ASSOC PROF BIOL, UNIV ALA, BIRMINGHAM, 74- *Mem:* AAAS; Am Soc Zool; Sigma Xi. *Res:* Gametogenesis, fertilization and early development. *Mailing Add:* Dept of Biol Univ of Ala Birmingham AL 35233

POIRIER, JACQUES CHARLES, b Mehun sur Yevre, France, Jan 3, 27; US citizen; m 51; c 3. THEORETICAL CHEMISTRY, PHYSICAL CHEMISTRY. *Educ:* Univ Chicago, PhB, 46, SB, 47, SM, 50, PhD, 52. *Prof Exp:* NSF fel, Yale Univ, 52-53; Corning Glass Works Found fel, Univ Calif, Berkeley, 53-55; from asst prof to assoc prof chem, 55-67, PROF CHEM, DUKE UNIV, 67- *Concurrent Pos:* Sloan fel, 59-63; vis assoc prof chem, Ind Univ, 61. *Mem:* Am Phys Soc; Am Chem Soc. *Res:* Statistical mechanical theory of fluids; liquid crystals. *Mailing Add:* Dept of Chem Duke Univ Durham NC 27706

POIRIER, JOHN ANTHONY, b Lewistown, Mont, May 15, 32; m 61; c 5. PHYSICS. *Educ:* Univ Notre Dame, BS, 54; Stanford Univ, MS, 57, PhD(physics), 59. *Prof Exp:* Mem staff, Lawrence Berkeley Lab & lectr, Univ Calif, Berkeley, 59-63, NSF fel, European Orgn Nuclear Res, Switz, 63-64; assoc prof physics, 64-72, PROF PHYSICS, UNIV NOTRE DAME, 72- *Concurrent Pos:* Consult, NASA, 62; prog assoc, Elementary Particle Physics, Nat Sci Found, 77-78. *Mem:* Am Phys Soc; Sigma Xi. *Res:* Experimental research in the field of elementary particle interactions. *Mailing Add:* Dept of Physics Univ of Notre Dame Notre Dame IN 46556

POIRIER, LIONEL ALBERT, b Providence, RI, Aug 4, 37; m 64; c 3. CANCER. *Educ:* Providence Col, BS, 59; Univ Wis-Madison, PhD(oncol), 65. *Prof Exp:* Fel oncol, McArdle Lab, Univ Wis-Madison, 65-67; investr cancer, Montreal Cancer Inst, Notre Dame Hosp, 67-71; chemist, Carcinogen Screening Sect, 71-73 & Carcinogen Metab & Toxicol Br, 73-76, HEAD NUTRIT & METAB SECT, NAT CANCER INST, 76- *Concurrent Pos:* Adj asst prof biochem, Univ Montreal, 68-71; consult, Health Protection Br, Can Govt, 72-75 & Food & Drug Admin, 73- *Mem:* Am Asn Cancer Res. *Res:* Chemical carcinogenesis; structure-activity correlations in chemical carcinogenesis and mutagenesis; one-carbon compounds in cancer. *Mailing Add:* 9515 Singleton Dr Bethesda MD 20034

POIRIER, LOUIS, b Montreal, Que, Dec 30, 18; m 47; c 4. NEUROBIOLOGY, EXPERIMENTAL NEUROLOGY. *Educ:* Col Jean-de-Brebeuf, BA, 41; Univ Montreal, MD; Univ Mich, MSc, 49, PhD(neuroanat), 50. *Prof Exp:* Asst prof histol, Univ Montreal, 50-55, assoc prof, 55-58, prof neurol, 58-65; chmn dept, 70-78, PROF EXP NEUROL, FAC MED, LAVAL UNIV, 65- *Concurrent Pos:* mem, Med Res Coun Can, 75-81. *Mem:* Am Asn Anat; AAAS; Can Asn Anatomists; Am Phys Soc; Soc Neurosci. *Res:* Neuroanatomy, neurochemistry, neuropharmacology, neurophysiology and histophathology of the brain; motor and psychomotor disorders. *Mailing Add:* Lab Neurobiol l'Hospital de l'Enfant-Jesus 1401 18e Rue Quebec PQ G1J 1Z4 Can

POIRIER, MIRIAM CHRISTINE MOHRHOFF, b Detroit, Mich, Apr 30, 40; m 64; c 3. ONCOLOGY, BIOCHEMISTRY. *Educ:* Marygrove Col, BSc, 62; Univ Wis-Madison, MSc, 64; Cath Univ Am, PhD(microbiol), 77. *Prof Exp:* Res asst oncol, Univ Wis, 62-64, lab asst biochem, 64-65, lab asst oncol, 65-67; lab asst, 71-78, RES CHEMIST ONCOL, NAT CANCER INST, NIH, 78- *Mem:* AAAS; Am Asn Cancer Res; Grad Women Sci; Environ Mutagen Soc. *Res:* Interactions of chemical carcinogens with DNA; developed radioimmunoassays to measure femtomole quantities of carcinogen bound to DNA; radioimmunoassay to quantitate epidermal keratins. *Mailing Add:* Rm 3A23 Bldg 37 Nat Insts of Health Bethesda MD 20205

POIRIER, ROBERT VICTOR, b San Francisco, Calif, Oct 27, 39; m 67; c 2. CHEMICAL ENGINEERING. *Educ:* Stanford Univ, BS, 65; Univ Minn, Minneapolis, PhD(chem eng), 70. *Prof Exp:* Res engr, Fluorocarbons Div, Plastics Dept, E I du Pont de Nemours & Co, Inc, 70-76; res supvr, 76-77, mgr finance & planning, 77-78, develop eng supvr, Plastics Div, 78-80, TECH SUPERINTENDENT, FILMS DIV, MOBIL CHEM CO, 80- *Mem:* Am Inst Chem Engrs; Soc Plastics Engrs. *Res:* Gas phase kinetics; film extrusion and materials development. *Mailing Add:* Mobil Chem Films Div 495 Landship Blvd Stratford CT 06497

POISNER, ALAN MARK, b Kansas City, Mo, Oct 15, 34; m 62; c 2. PHARMACOLOGY, CELL PHYSIOLOGY. *Educ:* Calif Inst Technol, BS, 56; Univ Kans, MD, 60. *Prof Exp:* Intern, Univ Ill Res Hosp, 60-61; asst prof pharmacol, Albert Einstein Col Med, 64-68; assoc prof, 68-73, PROF PHARMACOL, UNIV KANS MED CTR, KANSAS CITY, 73- *Concurrent Pos:* Fel pharmacol, Albert Einstein Col Med, 61-64; res career develop award, 65-68; vis scientist, Nat Inst Med Res, London, 63. *Mem:* Am Soc Pharmacol & Exp Therapeut; Endocrine Soc; Am Physiol Soc. *Res:* Physiology and pharmacology of secretory phenomena including release of hormones and neurotransmitters; renin and endocrinology of the placenta. *Mailing Add:* Dept of Pharmacol Univ of Kans Med Ctr Kansas City KS 66103

POIST, JOHN EDWARD, b Hanover, Pa, June 6, 41; m 65; c 3. ORGANOMETALLIC CHEMISTRY. *Educ:* King's Col, BS, 63; Lehigh Univ, MS, 65, PhD(inorg chem), 68. *Prof Exp:* Sr res chemist, Celanese Res Co, 68-77; MEM STAFF, PFIZER INC, 77- *Mem:* Am Chem Soc. *Res:* Catalysis; organic coatings; emulsion coagulation; reverse osmosis membranes. *Mailing Add:* Pfizer Inc 640 N 13th St Easton PA 18042

POITRAS, ADRIAN WILLIAM, b Rockford, Ill, June 12, 18; m 42; c 3. MYCOLOGY. *Educ:* Univ Ill, BS, 40, MS, 47, PhD(bot), 50. *Prof Exp:* From asst prof to assoc prof bot, Duquesne Univ, 50-55; from asst prof to assoc prof, Auburn Univ, 55-58; assoc prof, Fla State Univ, 58-61; dir div natural sci, 61-71, PROF BIOL, MIAMI-DADE COMMUNITY COL, 61- *Concurrent Pos:* Contrib ed, J Col Sci Teaching, 71- *Mem:* Soc Col Sci Teachers; Mycol Soc Am; Nat Sci Teachers Asn. *Res:* General biology. *Mailing Add:* Miami-Dade Community Col 11380 NW 27th Ave Miami FL 33167

POJASEK, ROBERT B, US citizen. HAZARDOUS MATERIALS MANAGEMENT, ENVIRONMENTAL MONITORING. *Educ:* Rutgers Univ, BS; Univ Mass, PhD(chem). *Prof Exp:* Consult, New Eng Res Inc, Worchester, Mass, 71-73; lab dir & sr staff chemist, Lawler, Matusky & Skelly Engrs, Pearl River, NY, 73-75; lab dir & sr environ chemist, JBF Sci Corp, Wilmington, Mass, 75-77; lab dir & hazardous waste consult, ERCO, Cambridge, Mass, 77-80; VPRES, WESTON, 80- *Concurrent Pos:* Consult, Exec Off Pres & Off Sci & Technol Policy; mem, Hazardous Waste Adv Comt; Consult, Regional Off Europe, WHO. *Mem:* Am Chem Soc; Sigma Xi; Am Soc Testing & Mat. *Mailing Add:* Roy F Weston Inc 111 S Bedford St Burlington MA 01803

POJETA, JOHN, JR, b New York, NY, Sept 9, 35; m 57; c 2. INVERTEBRATE PALEONTOLOGY, TAXONOMY. *Educ:* Capital Univ, BS, 57; Univ Cincinnati, MS, 61, PhD(paleont, zool), 63. *Prof Exp:* PALEONTOLOGIST, PALEONT & STRATIG BR, US GEOL SURV, 63- *Concurrent Pos:* Assoc prof lectr, George Washington Univ. *Mem:* Fel AAAS; Paleont Soc; fel Geol Soc Am. *Res:* Taxonomy, morphology, ontogeny, variation, phylogeny and ecology of early Paleozoic pelecypod faunas, especially comparison of these forms to recent pelecypod faunas and molluscan evolution. *Mailing Add:* US Geol Surv Washington DC 20244

POKORNY, ALEX DANIEL, b Taylor, Tex, Oct 18, 18; m 48; c 4. PSYCHIATRY. *Educ:* Univ Tex, BA, 39, MD, 42. *Prof Exp:* Intern, Hermann Hosp, Houston, Tex, 43; resident psychiat, McKinney Vet Admin Hosp, 46-47; resident, Topeka Vet Admin Hosp, 47-49; from instr to assoc prof, 49-63, clin prof, 63-67, PROF PSYCHIAT, BAYLOR COL MED, 67-, VCHMN DEPT, 72- *Concurrent Pos:* Menninger Found fel, Topeka Vet Admin Hosp, 47-49; asst chief psychiat & neurol serv, Vet Admin Hosp, Houston, 49-55, chief, 55-73; actg chmn dept psychiat, Baylor Col Med, 68-72. *Mem:* Fel AAAS; AMA; fel Am Psychiat Asn; fel Am Col Psychiat; Soc Biol Psychiat. *Res:* Suicidal behavior and violence; psychiatric classification; psychopharmacology; addictions and alcoholism. *Mailing Add:* Dept of Psychiat Baylor Col of Med Tex Med Ctr Houston TX 77030

POKORNY, FRANKLIN ALBERT, b Chicago, Ill, Feb 7, 30; m 57; c 2. HORTICULTURE. *Educ:* Univ Ill, BS, 53, MS, 56, PhD(hort), 59. *Prof Exp:* Asst prof, 59-66, ASSOC PROF HORT, UNIV GA, 66- *Mem:* Int Soc Hort Sci; Am Soc Hort Sci. *Res:* Plant nutrition; plant propagation; photoperiod; soils. *Mailing Add:* Dept of Hort Univ of Ga Athens GA 30602

POKORNY, GEROLD E(RWIN), b Czech, May 25, 28; US citizen; m 58; c 3. PHYSICS, ELECTRONICS. *Educ:* Vienna Tech Univ, MS, 51, PhD(tech sci), 53. *Prof Exp:* Physicist, US Army Signal Corps Labs, 53-56, sect chief microwave tubes, 56-60; sr scientist, 60-63, eng mgr display devices, 63-64, assoc dir res, 64-66, mgr res dept, 66-70, mgr electronics optics dept, 70-76, FACILITY MGR, ELECTRON TUBE DIV, LITTON INDUSTS, INC, TEMPE, 76-, DIV VPRES, 68- *Mem:* Sr mem Inst Elec & Electronics Engrs; Electron Devices Soc. *Res:* Electrooptics; night vision and infrared technology; solid state physics; electrooptic image detection and display; microwave physics and technology; solid state microwave devices; high power microwave generation; electron beam optics. *Mailing Add:* 1046 E Buena Vista Dr Tempe AZ 85284

POKORNY, JOEL, b Brooklyn, NY, July 29, 40; m 65; c 2. PSYCHOPHYSIOLOGY. *Educ:* Middlebury Col, AB, 62; Columbia Univ, PhD(psychol), 67. *Prof Exp:* Res assoc ophthal, 66-69, asst prof ophthal, 69-72, asst prof psychol, 71-72, assoc prof ophthal & psychol, 72-78, ASSOC PROF OPHTHAL & BEHAV SCI, PRITZKER SCH MED, UNIV CHICAGO, 78- *Concurrent Pos:* Mem, Int Res Group Colour Vision Deficiencies. *Mem:* Asn Res Vision & Ophthal; Optical Soc Am; Psychonomic Soc. *Res:* Mechanisms of normal and anomalous color vision in humans; theories of color vision; spatial and temporal factors in vision. *Mailing Add:* Dept Ophthal Div Biol Sci 950 E 59th St Chicago IL 60637

POKORNY, KATHRYN STEIN, b New York, NY, Mar 22, 44. PROTOZOOLOGY, CELL BIOLOGY. *Educ:* Hunter Col, BA, 63; Columbia Univ, MA, 69, PhD(biol), 71. *Prof Exp:* Electron microscopist, Osborn Labs Marine Sci, New York Aquarium, 72-80; MEM STAFF, DEPT OPHTHAL, MT SINAI SCH MED, NEW YORK, 80- *Concurrent Pos:* Biol consult, Columbia Univ Press, 71-74; adj asst prof biol, Baruch Col, City Univ NY, 75, 76. *Mem:* NY Acad Sci; Sigma Xi; Soc Protozool; Soc Cell Biol. *Res:* Ultrastructure and morphogenesis of cells and cellular organelles, particularly in marine parasitic protozoa, with emphasis on problems involved with host-parasite relationships and secretion of extracellular materials. *Mailing Add:* Dept Ophthal Mt Sinai Sch Med 5th Ave & 100th St New York NY 10029

POKOSKI, JOHN LEONARD, b St Louis, Mo, July 19, 37; m 62; c 4. ELECTRICAL ENGINEERING. *Educ:* St Louis Univ, BS, 59; Ariz State Univ, MSE, 65; Mont State Univ, PhD(elec eng), 67. *Prof Exp:* Assoc engr comput res & develop, Int Bus Mach Corp, 59-63; asst elec eng, Ariz State Univ, 63-65 & Mont State Univ, 65-67; assoc prof, 67-80, PROF ELEC ENG, UNIV NH, 80- *Mem:* Am Soc Eng Educ; Instrument Soc Am; Inst Elec & Electronics Engrs. *Res:* Digital computer design; switching theory and logic design; applications of control theory; sampled-data control systems. *Mailing Add:* Dept Elec Eng Univ NH Durham NH 03824

POKRANT, MARVIN ARTHUR, b Chicago, Ill, June 12, 43; m 67. STATISTICAL MECHANICS. *Educ:* Ill Inst Technol, BS, 65; Univ Fla, PhD(physics), 70. *Prof Exp:* Asst engr, Controls Co of Am, 65; postdoctoral assoc, Physics Dept, Univ Fla, 70-76; sr systs analyst, 76-78, PROJ MGR, MANTECH INT CORP, 78- *Mem:* Opers Res Soc Am; Am Phys Soc; Am Asn Physics Teachers. *Res:* Military operations research; many-body problem; structure of quantum fluids. *Mailing Add:* 5447 Harden Ave Orange Park FL 32073

POKRAS, HAROLD HERBERT, b Chicago, Ill, Sept 3, 18; m 43; c 2. CHEMISTRY. *Educ:* Univ Calif, BA, Los Angeles, 40, MA, 41; Ill Inst Technol, PhD(org chem), 44. *Prof Exp:* Jr instr chem, Ill Inst Technol, 41-43; res chemist, Emulsol Corp, 44 & Quincy Labs, 46; res assoc, Lever Bros, Co, 46-56; chemist, Louis Milani Foods, Inc, 56-65; assoc prof, 65-77, PROF CHEM, LOS ANGELES CITY COL, 65-, CHMN DEPT, 77- *Concurrent Pos:* Jr instr chem, Ill Inst Technol, 46. *Mem:* Am Chem Soc; Inst Food Technol. *Res:* Organic synthesis; surfactants; kinetic measurement; emulsion technology; products development of toilet goods; cosmetics; dentifrices and food products; food technology and heat processing; teaching of chemistry. *Mailing Add:* 15157 A Magnolia Blvd Sherman Oaks CA 91403

POLACK, JOSEPH A(LBERT), b New Orleans, La, Sept 11, 20; m 43; c 2. CHEMICAL ENGINEERING. *Educ:* Tulane Univ, BE, 41; Mass Inst Technol, MS, 43, ScD(chem eng), 48. *Prof Exp:* Res assoc, Chem Warfare Serv, Mass Inst Technol, 43-45, instr chem eng, 46, asst, 47-48; chem engr, Esso Res Labs, Humble Oil & Refining Co, 48-54, sect head, 54-57, asst dir, 57-61, asst to mgr res, Co, 61-63, admin asst, Esso Res Labs, 63-66, asst head tech div, Baton Rouge Refinery, 66, dir, Esso Res Labs, 66-70; prof chem eng & head dept, 70-76, DIR, AUDUBON SUGAR INST, LA STATE UNIV, BATON ROUGE, 76- *Mem:* Fel Am Inst Chem Engrs; Am Soc Sugar Cane Technologists. *Res:* Chemical process development; pilot plants; research and technical administration; cane sugar processing. *Mailing Add:* Audubon Sugar Inst La State Univ Baton Rouge LA 70803

POLAK, ARNOLD, b Michalovce, Czech, Aug 7, 27; US citizen. FLUID MECHANICS. *Educ:* Prague Tech Univ, Dipl Ing, 53; Univ Cincinnati, MS, 61, PhD(aerospace eng), 66. *Prof Exp:* Asst prof eng math, Col Transp, Prague, Czech, 53-57; asst prof prod planning, Am Ball Bearing Co, NY, 58; instr math & eng mech, Centralia Col, 58-59; instr math & mech, Univ Cincinnati, 59-62, res assoc gas dynamics, Dept Aerospace Eng, 62-66, asst prof fluid dynamics, 66-67; res aerospace engr appl aerodyn, US Naval Ord Lab, Md, 67-69; assoc prof, 69-76, PROF FLUID DYNAMICS, DEPT AEROSPACE ENG & APPL MECH, UNIV CINCINNATI, 76- *Concurrent Pos:* Fel, Nat Acad Sci, 67. *Mem:* Am Inst Aeronaut & Astronaut; Am Soc Eng Educ. *Res:* High speed gas dynamics; applied aerodynamics; separated flows. *Mailing Add:* Dept Aerospace Eng Univ Cincinnati Cincinnati OH 45221

POLAK, ELIJAH, b Bialystok, Poland, Aug 11, 31; m 61; c 2. ELECTRICAL ENGINEERING. *Educ:* Univ Melbourne, BEE, 57; Univ Calif, Berkeley, MSEE, 59, PhD(elec eng), 61. *Prof Exp:* Instrument engr, Imp Chem Industs, Ltd, 57-58; teaching asst elec eng, 58-59, teaching assoc, 59-61, from asst prof to assoc prof, 61-69, PROF ELEC ENG, UNIV CALIF, BERKELEY, 69- *Concurrent Pos:* Guggenheim fel, Inst Blaise Pascal, Paris, France, 68-69. *Mem:* Inst Elec & Electronics Engrs; Soc Indust & Appl Math. *Res:* Optimization theory and its applications to control systems and nonlinear programming; modern systems theory. *Mailing Add:* Dept of Elec Eng & Comput Sci Univ of Calif Berkeley CA 94720

POLAK, JOEL ALLAN, b New Haven, Conn, Sept 17, 37; m 60; c 2. PHYSICS, UNDERWATER ACOUSTICS. *Educ:* Yale Univ, BS, 59, MS, 60, PhD(theoret physics), 65. *Prof Exp:* Res assoc nuclear physics, Yale Univ, 65-67; mem tech staff, 67-71, SUPVR OCEAN ACOUST & SYSTS ANAL, BELL LABS, 71- *Mem:* Am Phys Soc; Am Math Soc; Math Asn Am. *Res:* Ocean acoustics; influence of rheological properties of bottom on sound propagation; undersea communications and sonar systems. *Mailing Add:* Bell Labs Whippany Rd Whippany NJ 07981

POLAKOSKI, KENNETH LEO, b Fond du Lac, Wis, Sept 6, 44. BIOCHEMISTRY, ANDROLOGY. *Educ:* Wis State Univ, BS, 66; Univ Ga, MS, 71, PhD(biochem), 72. *Prof Exp:* Res tech biochem, Marshfield Clin Found, 66-68; res assoc biochem, Univ Ga, 72-73; res asst prof, 73-77, ASST PROF OBSTET & GYNEC, WASHINGTON UNIV, 77- *Concurrent Pos:* Prin investr, NIH Biomed Res Grant, 77 & NIH Res Grant, 75-82. *Mem:* Am Chem Soc; AAAS; Am Fertil Soc; Soc Study Reproduction. *Res:* Biochemical mechanisms of sperm penetration of ovum; mechanisms of sperm motility. *Mailing Add:* Dept of Obstet & Gynec Washington Univ Sch of Med St Louis MO 63110

POLAN, CARL E, b Blandville, WVa, Sept 14, 31; m 56; c 4. DAIRY NUTRITION, BIOCHEMISTRY. *Educ:* Univ WVa, BS, 53, MS, 60; NC State Univ, PhD(animal nutrit), 64. *Prof Exp:* Farm supt, Potomac State Col, WVa, 56-58; res asst dairy sci & exten dairyman, Univ WVa, 58-60; res asst nutrit, NC State Univ, 60-63; res fel biochem, Univ Minn, St Paul, 63-65; from asst prof to assoc prof nutrit, 65-73, PROF NUTRIT, VA POLYTECH INST & STATE UNIV, 73- *Mem:* AAAS; Am Soc Animal Sci; Am Dairy Sci Asn; Am Inst Nutrit. *Res:* Nutrition and metabolism of amino acids and lipids; general nutritional considerations of large animals, particularly ruminants. *Mailing Add:* Dept of Dairy Sci Va Polytech Inst & State Univ Blacksburg VA 24061

POLAND, ALAN P, b Baltimore, Md, June 5, 40; m 75. PHARMACOLOGY, BIOCHEMISTRY. *Educ:* Univ Rochester, MS & MD, 66. *Prof Exp:* Fel drug metab, Rockefeller Univ, 69-71; asst prof pharmacol, Sch Med, Univ Rochester, 71-77; asst prof, 77-80, ASSOC PROF ONCOL, MCARDLE LAB CANCER RES, UNIV WIS-MADISON, 80- *Concurrent Pos:* NIH res career develop award, 75-; mem comt pentachlorophenol & its contaminants, Environ Protection Agency, 77-78; Burroughs-Wellcome scholar toxicol, 81-84. *Honors & Awards:* John Jacob Abel Award, Am Soc Pharmacol & Exp Therapeut, 76. *Mem:* Am Soc Pharmacol & Exp Therapeut; AAAS; Am Soc Cancer Res; Fedn Am Soc Exp Biol. *Res:* Toxicity of halogenated aromatic hydrocarbons; gene expression of aryl hydrocarbon hydroxylase activity by 2,3,7,8- tetrachlorodibenzo-p-dioxin. *Mailing Add:* McArdle Lab Cancer Res Univ of Wis Madison WI 53706

POLAND, ARTHUR I, b Asbury Park, NJ, Mar 30, 43; m 64. ASTROPHYSICS, SOLAR PHYSICS. *Educ:* Univ Mass, Amherst, BS, 64; Ind Univ, Bloomington, PhD(astrophys), 69. *Prof Exp:* Vis scientist, High Altitude Observ, Nat Ctr Atmospheric Res, 69-71, scientist, 71-; ASTROPHYSICIST, GODDARD SPACE FLIGHT CTR, NASA, 80- *Mem:* Am Astron Soc; Int Astron Union. *Res:* Solar research on the corona, solar prominences and flares. *Mailing Add:* Code 682 Goddard Space Flight Ctr NASA Greenbelt MD 20771

POLAND, JACK DEAN, b Isabel, Kans, Jan 30, 30; m 52; c 2. MEDICINE. *Educ:* Harding Col, BS, 52; Univ Kans, MD, 59; Univ Mich, MPH, 65; Am Bd Prev Med, cert. *Prof Exp:* Intern, USPHS Hosp, Norfolk, Va, 59-60; officer, Commun Dis Ctr, USPHS, 60-62, epidemiologist, Respiratory & Enteric Virus Dis Unit, 65, chief neurotropic virus dis unit, 65-67, actg chief virol, 65-68, chief virus dis sect, 67-68, chief zoonoses sect, Ecol Invest Prog, 68-72, asst chief, Ft Collins Br, 72-74, chief epidemiologist, 74-81, asst dir med sci, 59-80, DIR MED SCI, VECTOR BORNE DIV, BUR LABS, CTR DIS CONTROL, USPHS, 80- *Concurrent Pos:* Instr, Sch Med, Univ Kans, 66-68; affil prof microbiol, Colo State Univ, 68- *Mem:* AAAS; Am Epidemiol Soc; Am Soc Trop Med & Hyg. *Res:* Epidemiology of diseases of animals transmissible to man; primarily plaque and arthropod borne viral diseases. *Mailing Add:* Ctr for Dis Control USPHS PO Box 2087 Ft Collins CO 80522

POLAND, JAMES LEROY, b Washington, Pa, Nov 20, 40; m 66; c 2. PHYSIOLOGY. *Educ:* Waynesburg Col, BS, 62; WVa Univ, MS, 64, PhD(physiol), 67. *Prof Exp:* asst prof, 67-80, ASSOC PROF PHYSIOL, MED COL VA, 80- *Concurrent Pos:* Consult, Vet Admin Hosp, Richmond, Va. *Mem:* Am Physiol Soc; Soc Exp Biol & Med; Sigma Xi. *Res:* Myocardial changes accompanying repeated exercise. *Mailing Add:* Dept of Physiol Med Col of Va Richmond VA 23209

POLAND, JOHN C, b Toronto, Ont, Apr 25, 39; m 62; c 2. ALGEBRA. *Educ:* McGill Univ, BSc, 60, MSc, 63, PhD(group theory), 66. *Prof Exp:* Lectr math, McGill Univ, 61-66; Nat Res Coun Can fel, Australian Nat Univ, 66-67; asst prof, 67-74, ASSOC PROF MATH, CARLETON UNIV, 74- *Mem:* Am Math Soc; Can Math Cong. *Res:* Group theory. *Mailing Add:* Dept Math & Stats Carleton Univ Ottawa ON K1S 5B6 Can

POLAND, JOSEPH FAIRFIELD, b Boston, Mass, Mar 14, 08; m 35; c 5. HYDROGEOLOGY. *Educ:* Harvard Univ, AB, 29; Stanford Univ, AM, 35, PhD, 81. *Prof Exp:* Res geologist, Trop Oil Co, SAm, 29-31; asst, Stanford Univ, 34-36, instr geol, 36-39; from asst geologist to geologist, 40-46, dist geologist, 47-56, RES GEOLOGIST, US GEOL SURV, 56- *Concurrent Pos:* Consult groundwater geologist, Calif, 33-39. *Honors & Awards:* Distinguished Serv Award, Dept of Interior, 68; Claire P Holdredge Award, Asn Eng Geologists, 70; O E Meinzer Award, Geol Soc Am, 72. *Mem:* Fel Geol Soc Am; Am Asn Petrol Geol; Am Geophys Union; Asn Eng Geol (vpres, 59). *Res:* Groundwater geology; geology and mechanics of land subsidences; mechanics of deformation of aquifer systems due to changes of effective stress, both in the elastic and virgin range of stressing. *Mailing Add:* Water Resources Div US Geol Surv 2800 Cottage Way Sacramento CA 95825

POLANER, JEROME L(ESTER), b Newark, NJ, Sept 13, 15; m 53; c 3. MECHANICAL ENGINEERING. *Educ:* Newark Col Eng, BS, 38; Stevens Inst Technol, MS, 51. *Prof Exp:* Engr, Newark Gear Cutting Mach Co, 37-38; instr mech eng, Newark Col Eng, 38-42; engr, Robins Conveying Belt Co, 42; from asst prof to assoc prof mech eng, 42-58, PROF MECH ENG, NEWARK COL ENG, 58-, EXEC ASSOC, 52- *Concurrent Pos:* Consult, Am Leather Belting Assocs, 47-49; consult engr, 44-; lectr, Rutgers Univ, Newark, 52-67. *Mem:* AAAS; Am Soc Mech Engrs; Am Soc Eng Educ; NY Acad Sci; Nat Soc Prof Engrs. *Res:* Environmental control; industrial and automotive safety devices; accident reconstruction; product design. *Mailing Add:* 30 Tiffany Dr Livingston NJ 07039

POLANYI, JOHN CHARLES, b Berlin, Ger, Jan 23, 29; m 58; c 2. PHYSICAL CHEMISTRY. *Educ:* Univ Manchester, BSc, 49, MSc, 50, PhD(chem), 52, DSc, 65. *Hon Degrees:* DSc, Univ Waterloo, 70, Mem Univ Nfld, 76 & McMaster Univ, 77; LLD, Trent Univ, 77. *Prof Exp:* Res fel chem, Nat Res Coun Ottawa, 52-54; asst, Princeton Univ, 54-56; lectr, 56-57, from asst prof to assoc prof, 57-62, univ prof, 74, PROF CHEM, UNIV TORONTO, 62- *Concurrent Pos:* Sloan fel, 59-63; lectr numerous US & Can univs & insts, 65-; Guggenheim fel, 70; chmn, Can Pugwash Comt. *Honors & Awards:* Marlow Medal, Faraday Soc, 63; Steacie Prize Natural Sci, 65; Centennial Medal, The Chem Soc, 65, Award Kinetics, 71; Noranda Award, Chem Inst Can, 67, Medal, 76; Mack Award, Ohio State Univ, 69; Officer, Order of Can, 74; Henry Marshall Tory Medal, Royal Soc Can, 77; Remsen Award, Am Chem Soc, 78. *Mem:* Foreign assoc Nat Acad Sci; Fel Royal Soc Can; hon foreign mem Am Acad Arts & Sci; Royal Soc Chem; fel Royal Soc. *Res:* Reaction kinetics; photochemistry; chemiluminescence; energy exchange. *Mailing Add:* Dept of Chem Univ of Toronto Toronto ON M5S 1A1 Can

POLATNICK, JEROME, b New York, NY, Oct 4, 22; m 48; c 3. BIOCHEMISTRY. *Educ:* City Col New York, BS, 43; Columbia Univ, PhD(biochem), 54. *Prof Exp:* Res chemist, Schenley Res Inst, 43-47; res chemist, NY Bot Gardens, 48-50; asst biochem, Columbia Univ, 50-54; prin investr, Manhattan Eye & Ear Hosp, 54-57; RES BIOCHEMIST, PLUM ISLAND ANIMAL DIS LAB, USDA, 57- *Mem:* Am Chem Soc; Am Soc Microbiol. *Res:* Cell culture; virology; molecular biology of virus-host cell interactions; radioisotope safety programs. *Mailing Add:* 1310 Crittens Lane Southold NY 11971

POLCYN, DANIEL STEPHEN, b Montello, Wis, Sept 17, 33; m 69; c 2. ANALYTICAL CHEMISTRY. *Educ:* Wis State Col, Oshkosh, BS, 55; Univ Wis, PhD(chem), 65. *Prof Exp:* Teaching asst physics, Univ Wis, 55-57, res asst chem, 59-65, fel, 65; sr electrochemist, Gould, Inc, Minn, 65-70; res assoc, Univ Wis-Madison, 71-73, lectr, 73-75; asst prof chem, Univ Wis-

Oshkosh, 75-79, assoc prof, 79-80; RES DIR, POPE SCI, INC, 80- *Concurrent Pos:* Res assoc, Chem Dept, Univ Wis-Madison, 73-75, vis assoc prof, 79. *Mem:* AAAS; Am Chem Soc; Electrochem Soc; Int Electrochem Soc. *Res:* Electrode kinetics; electroanalytical chemistry; trace analysis; air pollution; environmental chemistry. *Mailing Add:* POPE Sci Inc PO Box 495 Menomonee Falls WI 53051

POLCYN, FABIAN CASIMIR, physics, oceanography, see previous edition

POLEJES, J(ACOB) D, b Ellenville, NY, June 5, 34; m 57. CHEMICAL ENGINEERING. *Educ:* Polytech Inst Brooklyn, BChE, 55; Univ Wis, MS, 56, PhD(chem eng), 59. *Prof Exp:* Res engr, Film Dept, NY, 59-69, SR RES ENGR, TEXTILE FIBERS DEPT, E I DU PONT DE NEMOURS & CO, INC, 69- *Mailing Add:* Textile Dept E I du Pont de Nemours & Co, Inc 1007 Market St Wilmington DE 19898

POLEN, PERCY B, b Chicago, Ill, Oct 13, 15; m 38; c 2. AGRICULTURAL CHEMISTRY. *Educ:* Lewis Inst, BS, 35; Univ Chicago, PhD(chem), 45. *Prof Exp:* Res chemist org synthesis dept med, Univ Chicago, 45; res chemist org chem res & develop, Visking Corp, 46-48; group leader, Velsicol Chem Corp, 48-53, sect leader agr, Develop & Appln Res, 53-56, mgr anal & control methods sect, 56-63, mgr anal res dept, 63-66, assoc dir phys chem & anal, 66-70, prin regulatory scientist, 70-77, sr scientist, 77-79; RETIRED. *Mem:* AAAS; Am Chem Soc; fel Am Inst Chem; Int Union Pure & Appl Chem. *Res:* Trace analysis of organic chemical residues in agriculture; instrumental and computer techniques; fate of pesticide residues in animals and environment. *Mailing Add:* 3906 Cleveland St Chicago IL 60076

POLESTAK, WALTER JOHN S, b New York, NY, Oct 27, 26; m 59; c 3. PHYSICAL CHEMISTRY. *Educ:* Manhattan Col, BS, 50; Tex A&M Univ, MS, 55; Univ Pa, PhD(phys chem), 60. *Prof Exp:* Chemist, Fisher Sci Co, 51-53; chemist, Fritzsche Bros, Inc, 54; asst instr chem, Tex A&M Univ, 54-55; asst instr, Univ Pa, 55-59; res chemist fibers, E I du Pont de Nemours & Co, 59-62; res chemist, Celanese Res Co, 62-68; sect leader basic group, ITT-Rayonier, Inc, 68-71; group leader resins & polymers, Nopco Chem Div, 71-75, group leader, Process Chem Div, 75-78, lab mgr resins & polymers, Process Chem Div, 78-80, GROUP LEADER, RESINS & POLYMERS, GEORGIA KAOLIN RES, DIAMOND SHAMROCK CHEM CO, 80- *Mem:* Am Inst Chem; NY Acad Sci; Am Chem Soc; Sigma Xi; Soc Plastics Engrs. *Res:* Kaolin and related minerals research for paint, plastics and rubber applications. *Mailing Add:* 36 Beekman Rd Summit NJ 07901

POLET, HERMAN, b Ghent, Belg, Aug 15, 30; m 65. PATHOLOGY, CELL BIOLOGY. *Educ:* Univ Ghent, MD, 56. *Prof Exp:* Part-time free collabr pharmacol, Univ Ghent, 54-58; asst resident path, Children's Med Ctr, 59-60; jr & sr asst resident, Peter Bent Brigham Hosp, 60-62; med officer, Walter Reed Army Inst Res, 64-68; asst prof path, Harvard Med Sch, 69-78; ASSOC PROF PATH, ABRAHAM LINCOLN SCH MED, 78- *Concurrent Pos:* Res fel cancer chemother, Children's Cancer Res Found, Boston, 58-59; res fel microbiol, Sch Pub Health, Harvard Univ, 62-64. *Mem:* Am Soc Cell Biol; Am Soc Exp Path; Am Soc Trop Med & Hyg; Soc Exp Biol Med; Tissue Cult Asn. *Res:* Cellular pharmacology and immunology; transplantation. *Mailing Add:* Abraham Lincoln Sch Med 1853 West Polk St Chicago IL 60612

POLGAR, GEORGE, b Gyongyos, Hungary, Apr 5, 19; US citizen; m 45; c 3. PEDIATRICS, PHYSIOLOGY. *Educ:* Univ Szeged, MD, 43. *Prof Exp:* Resident pediat, City Hosp, Szt Istvan, Budapest, 45-50; assoc pediat lung dis, State Sanitarium, 50-56; from asst prof to assoc prof pediat & physiol, Sch Med, Univ Pa, 67-74; chief div respiratory dis, Children's Hosp, Philadelphia, 71-74; PROF PEDIAT & ASSOC PHYSIOL, WAYNE STATE UNIV, 74-; CHIEF RESPIRATORY DIS DIV & DIR CYSTIC FIBROSIS CTR, CHILDREN'S HOSP MICH, 74- *Concurrent Pos:* Res fel pediat & physiol, Children's Hosp, Philadelphia, Univ Pa, 57-61; USPHS res fel, 59-60, spec res fel, 61, res career develop award, 62-; mem care-comt, Nat Cystic Fibrosis Res Found, 62-65; vis prof, Dept Pediat, Univ Geneva, 70-71; admin chmn, Philadelphia Pediat Pulmonary Prog, 72-74; mem exec comt, Assoc Pediat Pulmonary Centers, 73-; mem govt rels comt, Cystic Fibrosis Found, 74-75. *Mem:* Am Physiol Soc; Am Acad Pediat; Soc Pediat Res; Am Thoracic Soc; Royal Soc Med. *Res:* Respiratory diseases in children; pulmonary physiology in infants and children. *Mailing Add:* Children's Hosp Mich 3901 Beaubien Detroit MI 48201

POLGAR, TIBOR THOMAS, b Szolnok, Hungary, Feb 12, 43; US citizen. MARINE & ESTUARINE ECOLOGY. *Educ:* Amherst Col, AB, 65; Univ RI, MS, 70, PhD(oceanog), 73. *Prof Exp:* Res assoc oceanog, Grad Sch Oceanog, Univ RI, 70-73; res scientist estuarine ecol, Martin Marietta Lab, 73-75; tech dir aquatic ecol, 75-78, ASSOC DIR AQUATIC TECHNOL, ENVIRON CTR, MARTIN MARIETTA CORP, 78- *Concurrent Pos:* Consult, Md Dept Natural Resources, 75-, prin investr, grant, 75-; res assoc, Chesapeake Biol Lab, Univ Md, 76-; mem marine rev comn, Calif Coastal Comn, 77-; adj assoc prof biol sci, Univ Md, 79- *Mem:* Sigma Xi; Am Fisheries Soc; Estuarine Res Fedn; Atlantic Estuarine Res Soc. *Res:* Population dynamics; hydrography; population modeling; applied statistics; environmental impact assessment. *Mailing Add:* 8981 Footed Ridge Columbia MD 21045

POLGE, ROBERT J, b Anduze, France, Mar 11, 28; m 65; c 1. ELECTRICAL ENGINEERING. *Educ:* Montpellier Univ, Lic es sc, 50; Advan Sch Elec, Paris, EE, 52; Carnegie Inst Technol, MS, 61, PhD(elec eng, control), 63. *Prof Exp:* Engr, Andre Citroen Co, Paris, 53-56; head electronic lab, Sciaky Co, Paris, 56-59; head tech dept, Gen Wireless Tel Co, Paris, 59-60; asst elec eng, Carnegie Inst Technol, 60-63; assoc prof, 63-70, PROF ELEC ENG, UNIV ALA, 70-, ACTG CHMN DEPT, 80- *Mem:* Inst Elec & Electronics Engrs; French Soc Elec. *Res:* Communication theory. *Mailing Add:* Univ of Ala Dept of Elec Eng PO Box 1247 Huntsville AL 35807

POLGLASE, WILLIAM JAMES, b Vancouver, BC, May 31, 17; m 60; c 1. CHEMISTRY. *Educ:* Univ BC, BA, 43, MA, 44; Ohio State Univ, PhD(chem), 48. *Prof Exp:* Asst, Univ BC, 43-44; chemist, Imp Oil Co, Ont, 44-45; asst, Res Found, Ohio State Univ, 45-47; res instr, Sch Med, Univ Utah, 48-51; res chemist, Rayonier, Inc, Wash, 51-52; assoc prof, 52-62, actg head dept, 74-77, PROF BIOCHEM, FAC MED, UNIV BC, 62-, HEAD DEPT, 77- *Mem:* Am Chem Soc; Am Soc Microbiol; Am Soc Biol Chemists. *Res:* Microbial chemistry and metabolism; regulation; antibiotics. *Mailing Add:* Dept of Biochem Univ of BC Fac of Med Vancouver BC V6T 1W5 Can

POLHEMUS, JOHN THOMAS, b Ames, Iowa, Sept 11, 29; m 55; c 2. BIOENGINEERING, ENTOMOLOGY. *Educ:* Iowa State Univ, BSEE, 56; Univ Colo, PhD(syst biol), 77. *Prof Exp:* Res engr, Calif Res Corp, Standard Oil Calif, 56-60; sr staff engr, 60-80, SR STAFF SCIENTIST, MARTIN MARIETTA CORP, 80- *Concurrent Pos:* Assoc entom, Univ Colo Mus, 63- & Am Mus Natural Hist. *Mem:* Inst Elec & Electronic Engrs; Sigma Xi; Entom Soc Am; Soc Syst Zool. *Res:* Bioengineering research on non-invasive cardiovascular measurements; application of space technology to public needs; zoogeography; entomological research on aquatic Hemiptera, insect physiology. *Mailing Add:* 3115 S York Englewood CO 80110

POLHEMUS, NEIL W, b Fountain Hill, Pa, Apr 29, 51. STATISTICAL GRAPHICS, RISK ANALYSIS. *Educ:* Princeton Univ, BSE, 73, PhD(civil eng), 76. *Prof Exp:* Asst prof, Sch Bus Admin, Univ NC at Chapel Hill, 76-78; ASST PROF DEPT CIVIL ENG, PRINCETON UNIV, 78- *Concurrent Pos:* Mem, Trans Res Bd Quality Assurance, 81-; Consult, Statist Graphics Corp, 82-; vis scholar, Univ Calif, Berkeley, 82. *Mem:* Am Statist Asn; Inst Mgt Sci; Operations Res Soc Am. *Res:* Application of statistical methods to engineering systems, including stochastic modeling, time series analysis, collision risk estimation, and statistical graphics. *Mailing Add:* Sch Eng & Appl Sci Princeton Univ Princeton NJ 08544

POLI, CORRADO R(ALPH), b Troy, NY, Aug 9, 35; m 60; c 3. ENGINEERING MECHANICS. *Educ:* Rensselaer Polytech Inst, BS, 57, MS, 58; Ohio State Univ, PhD(eng mech), 65. *Prof Exp:* Aerospace eng, Air Force Res & Develop Command, Wright-Patterson AFB, 58-65, asst prof aeronaut eng, Air Force Inst Technol, 65-67; assoc prof mech eng, 67-71, PROF MECH ENG, UNIV MASS AMHERST, 72-, HEAD DEPT, 78- *Mem:* Soc Mfg Eng; Am Soc Eng Educ. *Res:* Dynamics; vibrations; manufacturing. *Mailing Add:* Dept of Mech Eng Univ of Mass Amherst MA 01002

POLIAK, AARON, b Buenos Aires, Arg, Apr 30, 25; m 51; c 3. OBSTETRICS & GYNECOLOGY. *Educ:* Univ Buenos Aires, MD, 49, PhD(med), 55; Am Bd Obstet & Gynec, dipl, 69. *Prof Exp:* Docente gynec, Med Sch, Univ Buenos Aires, 63-68; asst prof, 68-72, assoc prof obstet & gynec, 72-76, PROF OBSTET & GYNEC, ALBERT EINSTEIN COL MED, 76-; DIR GYNEC DIV, JACOBI HOSP, 78-; DIR OBSTES & GYNEC, DEPT BRONX MUNIC HOSP CTR, 80- *Concurrent Pos:* Fel obstet & gynec, Sch Med, Johns Hopkins Univ, 66-67; instr, Sch Med, Johns Hopkins Univ, 67-68; dir dept obstet & gynec, Lincoln Hosp, 72-77. *Mem:* Fel Am Col Surg; fel Am Col Obstet & Gynec; Am Fertil Soc. *Res:* Infertility, ovarian post-menopausal function; ovarian inervation; urinary stress incontinence. *Mailing Add:* Dept of Obstet & Gynec Albert Einstein Col of Med Bronx NY 10461

POLICOFF, LEONARD DAVID, b Wilmington, Del, Apr 22, 18; m 42; c 2. MEDICINE. *Educ:* Univ Richmond, BS, 38; Med Col Va, MD, 42; Am Bd Internal Med, dipl, 54; Am Bd Phys Med & Rehab, dipl, 56. *Prof Exp:* From instr med to asst prof phys med & rehab, Med Col Va, 47-55; prof phys med & rehab, head dept & med dir, Sch Phys Ther, Albany Med Col, 55-67; prof phys med & rehab & chmn dept, Sch Med, Temple Univ, 67-71; med dir, Merwick Rehab Ctr & chmn dept rehab med, Princeton Hosp, NJ, 71-75; prof clin phys med & rehab, Sch Med, Univ Pa, 71-78; chmn, Dept Rehab Med, Pac Med Ctr, 78-; CLIN PROF, PHYS, MED & REHAB MED SCH UNIV, CALIF, DAVIS, 81- *Concurrent Pos:* Consult, Vet Admin Hosp, 55; chief phys med & rehab serv, Albany Hosp, 55-67; med dir, Moss Rehab Hosp, Philadelphia, Pa, 67-70; dir phys med, Albert Einstein Med Ctr, 67-; chmn phys med & rehab, Hahnemann Med Col & Hosp, 70-71; clin prof phys med & rehab, Rutgers Med Sch, 73-78; dir rehab med, Somerset Hosp, Somerville, NJ, 75-78; actg chmn phys med & rehab, Med Sch, Rutgers Univ, 76-78. *Mem:* Am Rheumatism Asn; fel Am Col Physicians; Am Cong Rehab Med (vpres, 66-67, pres, 71-72); fel Am Acad Cerebral Palsy; fel Am Acad Phys Med & Rehab. *Res:* Chronic disease; neurologic rehabilitation. *Mailing Add:* Rehabilitation Med Serv Vet Admin Med Ctr 150 Muir Rd Martinez CA 94120

POLIFERNO, MARIO JOSEPH, b Derby, Conn, Feb 21, 30. MATHEMATICS. *Educ:* Yale Univ, BA, 52, MA, 54, PhD(math), 58. *Prof Exp:* Asst instr math, Yale Univ, 54-57; instr, Williams Col, 57-58; from instr to asst prof, 58-63, ASSOC PROF MATH, TRINITY COL, CONN, 63- *Mem:* Am Math Soc; Math Asn Am; Asn Symbolic Logic. *Res:* Symbolic logic; foundations of mathematics; set theory; point-set topology. *Mailing Add:* Dept of Math Trinity Col Hartford CT 06106

POLIMENI, ALBERT D, b Canandaigua, NY, Mar 14, 38. MATHEMATICS. *Educ:* Univ Buffalo, BA, 60, MA, 62; Mich State Univ, PhD(math), 65. *Prof Exp:* Lectr math, Univ Mich, Ann Arbor, 65-67; asst prof, Syracuse Univ, 67-70; assoc prof, 70-81, PROF MATH, STATE UNIV NY COL FREDONIA, 81- *Mem:* Am Math Soc; Math Asn Am. *Res:* Finite group theory. *Mailing Add:* Dept of Math State Univ of NY Col Fredonia NY 14063

POLIMENI, PHILIP INIZIATO, b New York, NY, May 23, 34; m 60; c 2. PHYSIOLOGY. *Educ:* City Col New York, BSc, 57; State Univ NY, PhD(physiol), 69. *Prof Exp:* Biochemist, State Univ NY, 59-64, teaching asst physiol, 66-68; instr, Pritzker Sch Med, Univ Chicago, 69-73, res assoc & asst prof, 73-78; ASSOC PROF FAC MED, UNIV MAN, 78- *Mem:* Int Soc Heart Res; Biophys Soc; Am Physiol Soc; Can Physiol Soc. *Res:* Cardiac cell physiology; transmembrane ionic fluxes. *Mailing Add:* Dept of Physiol Univ of Man Winnipeg MB R3E 0W3 Can

POLIN, DONALD, b Arlington, Mass, Dec 7, 25; m 54; c 3. AVIAN PHYSIOLOGY, AVIAN NUTRITION. *Educ:* US Merchant Marine Acad, BS, 50; Rutgers Univ, BS, 51, PhD(physiol), 55. *Prof Exp:* Asst avian physiol, Rutgers Univ, 51-55; res fel, Merck Inst Therapeut Res, NJ, 55-67; unit leader biochem, Norwich Pharmacal Co, NY, 67-69; assoc prof poultry sci, 69-73, PROF POULTRY SCI, MICH STATE UNIV, 73- *Concurrent Pos:* mem subcomt on effect of environ on nutrient requirements & subcomt on nutrient requirements of poultry, Nat Acad Sci-Nat Res Coun. *Mem:* Soc Exp Biol & Med; World's Poultry Sci Asn; NY Acad Sci; Am Inst Nutrit; Sigma Xi. *Res:* Avian biochemistry; nutritional physiology; tissue residues; energy utilization; metabolism and mode of action of drugs; regulation of feed intake; obesity and fatty liver-hemorrhagic syndrome; nutritional toxicology of farm animals. *Mailing Add:* 3865 Raleigh Dr Okemos MI 48864

POLING, BRUCE EARL, b Columbus, Ohio, Oct 8, 44; m 70; c 2. CHEMICAL ENGINEERING, CHEMISTRY. *Educ:* Ohio State Univ, BChE & MSc, 67; Univ Ill, PhD(chem eng), 71. *Prof Exp:* ASSOC PROF CHEM ENG, UNIV MO-ROLLA, 71- *Concurrent Pos:* Consult, Bartlesville Energy Res Ctr, 76; researcher, NSF, 76-78. *Mem:* Sigma Xi; Am Inst Chem Engrs. *Res:* Storage of thermal energy by means of reversible, liquid phase chemical reactions; kinetics of chemical reactions between diazo esters and olefins. *Mailing Add:* Dept of Chem Eng Univ of Mo Rolla MO 65401

POLING, CLYDE EDWARD, b Darke Co, Ohio, Dec 15, 14; m 40; c 4. NUTRITION. *Educ:* Ohio Wesleyan Univ, BA, 36; Syracuse Univ, MS, 39; Case Western Reserve Univ, PhD(biochem), 41. *Prof Exp:* Asst chem, Syracuse Univ, 37-39; jr chemist, City Dept Pub Health & Welfare, Cleveland, Ohio, 41-42; res chemist, Nutrit Div, Res & Develop Ctr, Swift & Co, 42-75, chief nutritionist & res biochemist, Biochem & Nutrit Div, 70-72, res nutritionist, Nutrit Div, Res & Develop Ctr, 72-80; RETIRED. *Concurrent Pos:* Exec secy, Comt Vet Serv Farm Animals, Nat Res Coun, 45-50. *Mem:* Am Chem Soc; Am Oil Chemists' Soc; Asn Vitamin Chemists; Am Inst Nutrit; Inst Food Technologists. *Res:* Nutritional values and interrelationships of proteins, fats, vitamins, and carbohydrates; physiological effects of insecticides; nutritional composition and labeling of food products. *Mailing Add:* 1903 Maple Ave Downers Grove IL 60515

POLING, GEORGE WESLEY, b Lloydminster, Alta, June 3, 35; m 58; c 5. METALLURGICAL ENGINEERING. *Educ:* Univ Alta, BS, 57, MSc, 61, PhD(metall eng), 63. *Prof Exp:* Trainee, Roan Antelope Copper Mines, North Rhodesia, 57-58; sr metall engr, Texaco Res Ctr, 63-68; from assoc prof to prof mineral eng, 68-78, PROF & HEAD, DEPT MINING & MINERAL PROCESS ENG, UNIV BC, 78- *Mem:* Can Inst Mining & Metall; fel Brit Inst Mining & Metall; Am Inst Mining, Metall & Petrol Engrs; Nat Asn Corrosion Engrs; Can Mineral Processors. *Res:* Flotation-mineral beneficiation; bulk materials transportation; recovery of placer gold; infrared spectroscopic study of adsorbed molecules and reactions at solid surfaces; surface chemistry of corrosion and corrosion inhibition processes. *Mailing Add:* Dept of Mineral Eng Univ of BC Vancouver BC V6T 1W5 Can

POLING, STEPHEN MICHAEL, b Long Beach, Calif, Sept 29, 46. PLANT BIOCHEMISTRY. *Educ:* Pomona Col, BA, 68; Univ Wash, MS, 70. *Prof Exp:* Res chemist citrus, 72-78, RES CHEMIST, FRUIT & VEGETABLE CHEM LAB, SCI EDUC ADMIN, USDA, 78- *Mem:* Am Chem Soc. *Res:* Use of bioregulators to improve citrus quality and to increase the rubber content of guayule. *Mailing Add:* Fruit & Vegetable Chem Lab 263 S Chester Ave Pasadena CA 91106

POLINSKI, LEON M, b Gary, Ind, Sept 3, 30; m 58; c 2. CHEMICAL ENGINEERING. *Educ:* Mass Inst Technol, SB, 52; Univ Cincinnati, MS, 55; Polytech Inst Brooklyn, PhD(chem eng), 61. *Prof Exp:* Jr chemist, Shell Develop Co, 55-56; res asst, Proj NAP, US Air Force Off Sci Res, Polytech Inst Brooklyn, 58-60; res engr, Org Chem Div, Am Cyanamid Co, 60-64; chief process engr, Givaudan Corp, 64-72, head process invest ctr, 71-72; sr res chem engr, Engelhard Industs, 72-78; SUPVY CHEM ENGR, PITTSBURGH ENERGY TECHNOL CTR, US DEPT ENERGY, 78- *Mem:* Am Inst Chem Engrs; Am Chem Soc; Catalysis Soc. *Res:* Heterogeneous catalysis, coal liquefaciton, catalytic deactivation rates, adsorption rate phenomena, reaction kinetics and diffusion; catalytic reactor design; frequency response techniques applied to kinetic rate measurements; batch reactor scale-up; economic evaluations. *Mailing Add:* US Dept of Energy PO Box 10940 Pittsburgh PA 15236

POLIS, DENNIS FRANCIS, b Los Angeles, Calif, July 28, 41; m 66; c 1. PHYSICS, SYSTEMS ANALYSIS. *Educ:* Loyola Univ Los Angeles, BS, 63; Univ Notre Dame, PhD(theoret physics), 70. *Prof Exp:* Assoc lab engr heat transfer, Garrett AiRes Corp, 63; opers res assoc, Lockheed Aircraft Corp, 69-70; ASST PROF ENVIRON SYSTS ANAL & OCEANOG, COL MARINE STUDIES, UNIV DEL, 70- *Mem:* Am Geophys Union. *Res:* Environmental systems analysis, especially estuarine oceanography, ecological modeling; theoretical physics, especially ocean waves, elementary particles; operations research, particularly technological forecasting, corporate planning, transportation studies. *Mailing Add:* Col Marine Studies Univ Del Newark DE 19711

POLIS, GARY ALLAN, b Los Angeles, Calif, Aug 28, 46. ECOLOGY, ZOOLOGY. *Educ:* Loyola Univ Los Angeles, BS, 69; Univ Calif, Riverside, MS, 75, PhD(biol), 77. *Prof Exp:* Asst prof ecol, Dept Zool, Ore State Univ, 77-79; ASST PROF ECOL, DEPT BIOL, VANDERBILT UNIV, 79- *Mem:* Ecol Soc Am; Am Soc Naturalists; Am Arachnological Asn; Sigma Xi; Brit Ecol Soc. *Res:* Evolution and dynamics of population self-regulatory systems; analysis of patterns and determinants of community structure; dynamics and patterns of predation; biology of Scorpionida, Araneae and predaceous insects. *Mailing Add:* Dept Zool Vanderbilt Univ Nashville TN 37285

POLITIS, DEMETRIOS JOHN, plant pathology, electron microscopy, see previous edition

POLITZER, HUGH DAVID, US citizen. PHYSICS. *Educ:* Univ Mich, BS, 69; Harvard Univ, PhD(physics), 74. *Prof Exp:* Jr fel, Harvard Soc Fels, 74-77; assoc prof physics, 77-79, PROF THEORETICAL PHYSICS, CALIF INST TECHNOL, 79- *Res:* High energy physics. *Mailing Add:* Dept of Physics 452-48 Calif Inst of Technol Pasadena CA 91125

POLITZER, PETER ANDREW, b Prague, Czech, Dec 12, 37; US citizen; m 68. THEORETICAL CHEMISTRY. *Educ:* Case Western Reserve Univ, BA, 60, MS, 61, PhD(chem), 64. *Prof Exp:* Lectr chem, Case Western Reserve Univ, 64; res assoc, Ind Univ, 64-66; from asst prof to assoc prof, 66-74, PROF CHEM, UNIV NEW ORLEANS, 74- *Concurrent Pos:* Vis fel, Johns Hopkins Univ, 73-74, res scientist, 74. *Mem:* Am Chem Soc; Royal Soc Chem; Int Soc Quantum Biol; Catalysis Soc; Am Phys Soc. *Res:* Distribution of electrons in molecules; properties of chemical bonds; chemisorption interactions; applications of theoretical chemistry to biological processes; molecular electrostatic potentials; relationship of energy to electronic density; chemical carcinogenesis. *Mailing Add:* Dept of Chem Univ of New Orleans New Orleans LA 70122

POLIVANOV, SERGEY, b Yaroslavl, Russia, Dec 15, 23; m 56; c 2. GENETICS. *Educ:* Columbia Univ, BS, 59, PhD(genetics), 64. *Prof Exp:* Res asst prof biol, 64-66, ASST PROF BIOL, CATH UNIV AM, 66- *Concurrent Pos:* USPHS trainee grant, 64. *Mem:* Fel AAAS; Genetics Soc Am; Soc Study Evolution; Am Genetic Asn; Behav Genetics Asn. *Res:* Effects of genetic loads on fitness of populations; genetics of photo and geotaxis of different Drosophila species. *Mailing Add:* Dept of Biol Cath Univ of Am Washington DC 20064

POLIVKA, RAYMOND PETER, b Chicago, Ill, July 18, 29; m 54; c 2. COMPUTER SCIENCES EDUCATORS. *Educ:* North Cent Col, Ill, BA, 51; Univ Ill, MS, 53, PhD(math), 58. *Prof Exp:* Asst math, Univ Ill, 52-53, asst comput lab, 53-55 & 57-58; eng programmer, Int Bus Mach Corp, 58-65; assoc prof math, North Cent Col, Ill, 65-66; programmer, Int Bus Mach Corp, 66-71, staff instr, 71-75, ADV INSTR, IBM CORP, 76- *Concurrent Pos:* Adj prof comput sci, Univ Md, College Park. *Mem:* Am Math Soc; Math Asn Am; Asn Comput Mach. *Res:* System programming; engineering analysis; programming educators and specializing in programming languages. *Mailing Add:* 60 Timberline Dr Poughkeepsie NY 12603

POLIZZOTTI, RICHARD SAMUEL, surface chemistry, see previous edition

POLK, ALBERT SIDNEY, JR, b Baltimore, Md, Dec 27, 13; m 37; c 2. AERONAUTICAL ENGINEERING, MECHANICAL ENGINEERING. *Educ:* Univ Ala, BS, 37. *Prof Exp:* Draftsman, Southern Alkali Corp, Tex, 37-38; airplane design, Glenn L Martin Co, 38, lofting supvr, 39-50, designer airplanes, 50-57, struct test designer, 57-59; sr staff engr, Appl Physics Lab, Johns Hopkins Univ, 59-81; CONSULT. *Res:* Aircraft, missiles and spacecraft test equipment; shapes and packaging of components in restricted volumes; evaluation of mass transit programs; plant-ship and machinery arrangement; ocean thermal energy conversion. *Mailing Add:* 118 Castlewood Rd Baltimore MD 21210

POLK, C(HARLES), b Vienna, Austria, Jan 15, 20; nat US; m 46; c 2. APPLIED ELECTROMAGNETICS, ENGINEERING EDUCATION. *Educ:* Washington Univ, BSEE, 48; Univ Pa, MS, 53, PhD(elec eng), 56. *Prof Exp:* Engr, Victor Div, Radio Corp Am, 48-52, mem tech staff, David Sarnoff Res Ctr Labs, 57-59; res assoc, Moore Sch Elec Eng, Univ Pa, 52-57; prof elec eng & chmn dept, Univ RI, 59-75; head elec sci & anal sect, Eng Div, NSF, 75-76, actg dir, Eng Div, 76-77; chmn dept, 77-79, PROF ELEC ENG, UNIV RI, 77- *Concurrent Pos:* Consult, Philco Corp & Am Electronics Labs, 55-56, Labs, Radio Corp Am, 59 & US Navy, 71-72; adj prof, Grad Div, Drexel Inst Technol, 57-59; vis prof, Stanford Univ, 68-69. *Mem:* AAAS; sr Inst Elec & Electronics Engrs; Am Geophys Union; Am Soc Eng Educ; Int Sci Radio Union. *Res:* Applied electromagnetic theory; antennas and radio propagation; geomagnetism and geoelectricity; upper atmosphere and ionospheric physics; extremely low frequency noise; biological effects of electromagnetic Fields. *Mailing Add:* Dept of Elec Eng Univ of RI Kingston RI 02881

POLK, CONRAD JOSEPH, b Chicago, Ill, Nov 9, 39; m 63. EQUIPMENT FAILURE ANALYSIS, MATERIALS ENGINEERING. *Educ:* Loyola Univ, BS, 61; Univ Toledo, MS, 63; Ill Inst Technol, PhD(mat eng), 68. *Prof Exp:* Instr metall eng, Ill Inst Technol, 66-68; res metallurgist, 68-71, sr res metallurgist, 71-72, assoc engr, 72-75, leader metall eng group, 73-77, SR ASSOC ENGR, MOBIL RES & DEVELOP CORP, 75-, LEADER FAILURE ANAL GROUP, 78- *Mem:* Am Soc Metals; Nat Asn Corrosion Engrs; Am Petrol Inst. *Res:* Mechanical behavior of materials for refinery and chemical processing equipment under various temperature, pressure and stream composition conditions. *Mailing Add:* Mobil Res & Develop Corp Box 1026 Princeton NJ 08540

POLK, DONALD EDWARD, materials science, see previous edition

POLK, HIRAM CAREY, b Jackson, Miss, Mar 23, 36; m 56; c 2. SURGERY. *Educ:* Millsaps Col, BS, 56; Harvard Med Sch, MD, 60. *Prof Exp:* Instr surg, Wash Univ, 64-65; from asst prof to assoc prof, Univ Miami, 65-71; PROF SURG & CHMN DEPT, UNIV LOUISVILLE, 71- *Concurrent Pos:* Clin trainee cancer control, USPHS, 64-65; dir tumor clin, Jackson Mem Hosp, Miami, Fla, 69-71; res assoc path, Lister Inst Prev Med, 69; mem consult staff, Vet Admin Hosp, 71-; mem attend staff, Louisville Gen & Norton-Children's Hosp, 71-; dir, Am Bd Surg. *Mem:* Asn Acad Surg; Soc Univ Surg; AMA; Am Surg Asn; Soc Surg Alimentary Tract. *Res:* Surgical infection; cancer; burns. *Mailing Add:* Dept of Surg Univ Louisville Louisville KY 40292

POLK, IRVING, b USA, Feb 1, 22; m 46; c 3. MECHANICAL ENGINEERING. *Educ:* Polytech Inst Brooklyn, BME, 43. *Prof Exp:* Mem staff gen eng, Radiation Lab, Mass Inst Technol, 43-45, mem staff, Instrumentation Lab, 45-46, engr, Res Lab Electron, 46-49; engr cosmotron,

49-52, engr alternating gradient synchrotron, 52-58, head mech eng div, 58-78, SR MECH ENGR, ISABELLE PROJ, BROOKHAVEN NAT LAB, 78- *Mem:* Am Soc Mech Engrs. *Res:* Vacuum chamber for cosmotron; linear accelerator injector for alternating gradient synchrotron; accelerator components. *Mailing Add:* Brookhaven Nat Lab Upton NY 11973

POLK, MALCOLM BENNY, b Chicago, Ill, Feb 2, 38. GAS CHROMATOGRAPHY, MASS SPECTROMETRY. *Educ:* Univ Ill, BS, 60; Univ Pa, PhD(chem), 64. *Prof Exp:* Asst instr chem, Univ Pa, 60-64; fel, Univ Calif, Davis, 64-65; res chemist, E I DuPont Co, 65-67 & 68-72; assoc prof chem, Prairie View Col, 67-68; res chemist, US Dept Interior, 72-73; PROF ORG & POLYMER CHEM, ATLANTA UNIV, 73- *Mem:* Am Chem Soc. *Res:* Synthesis and characterization of liquid crystalline block copolyesters and copolyamides. *Mailing Add:* Atlanta Univ Box 286 Atlanta GA 30314

POLKING, JOHN C, b Carroll, Iowa, June 6, 34. MATHEMATICS. *Educ:* Univ Notre Dame, BS, 56; Univ Chicago, SM, 61, PhD(math), 66. *Prof Exp:* Instr math, Univ Chicago, 65-66; Off Naval Res res assoc, Brandeis Univ, 66-67, lectr, 67-68; from asst prof to assoc prof math, 68-78, PROF MATH, RICE UNIV, 78-, CHMN DEPT, 79- *Concurrent Pos:* vis prof, Univ Utah, 78. *Mem:* Am Math Soc; Math Asn Am. *Res:* Partial differential equations; several complex variables. *Mailing Add:* Dept of Math Rice Univ Houston TX 77001

POLKOWSKI, LAWRENCE B(ENJAMIN), b Rockford, Ill, Feb 22, 29; m 51; c 3. SANITARY ENGINEERING. *Educ:* Univ Ill, BS, 50; Univ Wis, MS, 51, PhD(sanit eng), 58. *Prof Exp:* Asst, Univ Wis, 50-51, instr civil eng, 54-55, proj assoc, 55-57, from asst prof to assoc prof civil eng, 57-61; prof sanit eng, Univ Iowa, 61-64; fel, Ford Found, 60, assoc prof civil eng, 64, PROF CIVIL ENG, UNIV WIS-MADISON, 65- *Concurrent Pos:* Consult, Procter & Gamble, Co, 60-, S B Foot Tanning Co, 65-, Am Concrete Pipe Asn, 68-, Campbell Soup Co, 70, Libby, McNeil Libby, 71 & Lake to Lake Creameries, 72-; consult partner, Polkowski, Boyle & Assocs, 66-; comnr, Madison Metrop Sewerage Comn, 71- *Honors & Awards:* Harrison Prescott Eddy Medal, Water Pollution Control Fedn, 71. *Mem:* AAAS; Am Soc Eng Educ; Am Soc Civil Engrs; Am Water Works Asn; Water Pollution Control Fedn. *Res:* Biological treatment of wastes; design and development of waste treatment processes; combined treatment of industrial and municipal water treatment; solids-liquid separation; filtration wastewater effluents; farm waste disposal. *Mailing Add:* Dept of Civil Eng Univ of Wis Madison WI 53706

POLL, JACOBUS DANIEL, b Deventer, Neth, Mar 28, 30; m 58; c 4. THEORETICAL PHYSICS. *Educ:* Univ Leiden, Drs, 56; Univ Toronto, PhD(theoret physics), 60. *Prof Exp:* Lectr physics, Univ Toronto, 60-61, from asst prof to assoc prof, 61-70; PROF PHYSICS, UNIV GUELPH, 70- *Concurrent Pos:* Vis assoc prof, Univ Calif, Berkeley, 68-69. *Mem:* Am Phys Soc; Can Asn Physicists. *Res:* Theoretical molecular physics and statistical mechanics; infrared spectra; molecular distribution functions and interactions; molecular structure; astrophysics. *Mailing Add:* Dept Physics Univ Guelph Guelph ON N1G 2W1 Can

POLLACK, BERNARD LEONARD, b Detroit, Mich, Jan 18, 20; m 49; c 2. PLANT BREEDING. *Educ:* Pa State Univ, BS, 49, MS, 51, PhD(hort), 53. *Prof Exp:* Asst plant breeding, Pa State Univ, 49-52, from instr to asst prof, 52-60; VEG EXTEN SPECIALIST, RUTGERS UNIV, NEW BRUNSWICK, 60-, CHMN DEPT HORT & FORESTRY, COOK COL, 77- *Concurrent Pos:* consult, Int Agr, WAfrica, Peurto Rico & Jamaica. *Mem:* Am Soc Hort Sci. *Res:* Breeding early, disease resistant, fresh market tomatoes; disease resistance in eggplant; tomato genetics; plasticulture; degradable plastic mulches; eggplant and pepper genetics; trickle irrigation research. *Mailing Add:* 14 Watchung Rd East Brunswick NJ 08816

POLLACK, EDWARD, b New York, NY, Apr 28, 31; m 55; c 3. ATOMIC PHYSICS. *Educ:* City Col New York, BS, 52; NY Univ, MS, 54, PhD(physics), 63. *Prof Exp:* Asst physics, NY Univ, 52-54; lectr, City Col New York, 56-60; instr, NY Univ, 60-63; from asst prof to assoc prof, 63-74, PROF PHYSICS, UNIV CONN, 74- *Concurrent Pos:* Visiting physicist, Univ Paris, Orsay & NATO res grant, 74 & Service de Physique Atomique-Saclay, France, 81. *Mem:* Am Phys Soc. *Res:* Polarizabilities of the alkalis and metastable argon; differential cross sections for kilo electron volt region atom-atom scattering; thermal energy atom-atom collisions; inelastic ion-molecule collisions; energy loss scaling in atom-molecule collisions. *Mailing Add:* Dept of Physics Univ of Conn Storrs CT 06268

POLLACK, EMANUEL DAVIS, b Chicago, Ill, Mar 29, 42; m; c 2. ZOOLOGY, EMBRYOLOGY. *Educ:* Roosevelt Univ, BS, 64; Univ Iowa, MS, 67, PhD(zool), 70; Cell Sci Ctr, dipl, 74. *Prof Exp:* Teaching asst zool & embryol, res asst zool & instr embryol, Univ Iowa, 65-70; NIMH trainee & res fel, Albert Einstein Col Med, 70-72; res scientist neuroembryol, 72-79, ASSOC RES DIR, INST STUDY OF DEVELOP DISABILITIES, UNIV ILL, 79-, ASST PROF ANAT, COL MED & ASSOC PROF BIOL SCI, 75- *Concurrent Pos:* Consult, Ill Environ Protection Agency, 73- *Mem:* Am Soc Cell Biol; AAAS; Soc Neurosci; NY Acad Sci; Sigma Xi. *Res:* Developmental neurobiology and neurophysiology; development of neuro-neuronal and neuromuscular relationships; neural tissue culture; neural ontogeny in amphibian metamorphosis; behavioral ontogeny. *Mailing Add:* Ill Inst Develop Disabilities Chicago IL 60608

POLLACK, GERALD H, b New York, NY, May 20, 40; m 66; c 2. PHYSIOLOGY, BIOMEDICAL ENGINEERING. *Educ:* Polytech Inst Brooklyn, BS, 61; Univ Pa, PhD(biomed eng), 68. *Prof Exp:* From asst prof to assoc prof, 68-77, PROF ANESTHESIOL & BIOENG, UNIV WASH, 77- *Concurrent Pos:* Estab investr, Am Heart Asn, 74-79; mem bd dir, Biomed Eng Soc, 77-80; mem, Basic Sci Coun, Am Heart Asn, 79- *Mem:* Am Physiol Soc; Biophys Soc; Cardiac Muscle Soc; Inst Elec & Electronics Engrs; Biomed Eng Soc. *Res:* Molecular mechanisms of contraction in muscle; mechanisms of cardiac function. *Mailing Add:* Dept Anesthesiol RN-10 Univ Wash Seattle WA 98195

POLLACK, GERALD LESLIE, b Brooklyn, NY, July 8, 33; m 58; c 4. PHISICS LIQUIDS & SOLIDS, BIOPHYSICS. *Educ:* Brooklyn Col, BS, 54; Calif Inst Technol, MS, 57, PhD(physics), 62. *Prof Exp:* Asst math, Calif Inst Technol, 55-57, asst physics, 57-61; solid state physicist inorg mat div, Nat Bur Standards, 61-65; assoc prof physics, 65-69, PROF PHYSICS, MICH STATE UNIV, 69- *Concurrent Pos:* Consult, Nat Bur Standards, 65-71, Nuclear Regulatory Comn, 79- *Mem:* AAAS; fel Am Phys Soc; Am Asn Physics Teachers. *Res:* Liquid helium physics; rare-gas solids; molecular solids; crystal growth; surface physics; diffusion in biological systems; liquid helium films; solubility of gases in liquids. *Mailing Add:* Dept of Physics Mich State Univ East Lansing MI 48823

POLLACK, GORDON (PAUL), physical chemistry, see previous edition

POLLACK, HENRY NATHAN, b Omaha, Nebr, July 13, 36; m 63; c 2. GEOPHYSICS, GEOTHERMICS. *Educ:* Cornell Univ, AB, 58; Univ Nebr, MS, 60; Univ Mich, PhD(geophys), 63. *Prof Exp:* Res fel geophys, Harvard Univ, 63-64; from asst prof to assoc prof, 64-74, PROF GEOPHYS, UNIV MICH, ANN ARBOR, 74- *Concurrent Pos:* Sr lectr, Univ Zambia, 70-71; res scientist, Univ Durham & New Castle upon Tyne, UK, 77-78. *Mem:* AAAS; Am Geophys Union; Geol Soc Am; Seismol Soc Am. *Res:* State, composition, dynamics and evolution of the earth's interior; heat flow and geothermics. *Mailing Add:* Dept Geol Sci Univ of Mich Ann Arbor MI 48109

POLLACK, HERBERT, b New York, NY, June 29, 05; m 46; c 2. MEDICINE. *Educ:* Washington & Lee Univ, AB, 25; Cornell Univ, MD, 29; Univ Minn, PhD(physiol), 33. *Prof Exp:* Instr physiol med col, Cornell Univ, 28-29; asst med, Mayo Clin, 32-34; asst, Col Physicians & Surgeons, Columbia Univ, 34-48, lectr, 48-54; assoc prof clin med, Post-Grad Med Sch, NY Univ, 54-61; mem sr tech staff, Inst Defense Anal, 61-70; clin prof med, 62-71, EMER CLIN PROF MED, SCH MED, GEORGE WASHINGTON UNIV, 71-; EXPERT CONSULT, DEPT STATE, 76- *Concurrent Pos:* Instr med col, Cornell Univ, 34-40; from asst to assoc physician in charge metab clins, Mt Sinai Hosp, 34-61; vis physician, NY Univ & Bellevue Hosp, 54-61; consult, Secy War, interdept comn nutrit for nat defense, USPHS & Surgeon Gen, US Dept Army; panel consult food & nutrit bd, Nat Res Coun, 46, mem, 50-; mem adv panel med sci to dir res & eng, Dept Defense; mem & chmn med adv panel to the admin, Fed Aviation Agency; consult, Food & Drug Admin, 65- & Rand Corp, 70-; mem, Electromagnetic Radiation Mgt Adv Coun to Exec Off of President, 70-; chmn life sci adv comt, Fedn Am Socs Exp Biol, 72- *Honors & Awards:* Outstanding Civilian Serv Award, Dept of Army, 68 & 70. *Mem:* Am Physiol Soc; Am Soc Clin Invest; fel Am Med Asn; fel Am Pub Health Asn; fel Am Col Physicians. *Res:* Cellular physiology; carbohydrate metabolism; nutrition and vitamin functions; biomedical engineering; arteriosclerosis; convalescent nutrition. *Mailing Add:* 2700 Calvert St NW Washington DC 20008

POLLACK, IRWON W, b Philadelphia, Pa, Aug 14, 27; m 57; c 3. PSYCHIATRY. *Educ:* Temple Univ, BA, 50; Columbia Univ, MA, 51; Univ Vt, MD, 56. *Prof Exp:* Intern psychiat, Grad Hosp, Univ Pa, 56-57; res asst psychiat, Henry Phipps Psychiat Clin, Johns Hopkins Univ, 57-60, chief psychiat resident, 60-61, adminr, Clin & psychiatrist, Psychiat Liaison Serv, Univ, 61-64, asst prof psychiat, Univ, 64-68; assoc prof, Med Sch & dir, Ment Health Ctr, 68-70, chmn dept & exec dir, Rutgers Community Ment Health Ctr, 70-77, PROF PSYCHIAT, RUTGERS MED SCH, COL MED & DENT NJ, 70- *Concurrent Pos:* Psychiatrist-in-chief, Sinai Hosp, Baltimore, 64-68; consult, Lyons Vet Admin Hosp, NJ, Carrier Clin & Resident Training Prog, NJ State Hosp, Marlboro, 70-74 & Psychiat Educ Br, NIMH, 74-76; mem, Middlesex Ment Health Bd, 73-77. *Mem:* Fel Am Psychiat Asn; Am Psychosom Soc; fel Am Col Psychiatrists; fel Am Pub Health Asn. *Res:* Relationship of spatial and temporal orientation to personality and to psychopathology; muscle activity and emotions; rehabilitation of cognitive dys-function. *Mailing Add:* Dept of Psychiat PO Box 101 Rutgers Med Sch Col Med & Dent NJ Piscataway NJ 08854

POLLACK, J DENNIS, b Brooklyn, NY, Apr 3, 31; m 62. MICROBIOLOGY, MEDICAL MYCOLOGY. *Educ:* Univ Conn, BA, 58, MS, 64, PhD(bact), 66. *Prof Exp:* Res assoc microbiol, Hadassah Med Sch, Hebrew Univ Jerusalem, 66-67; from instr to assoc prof med microbiol, 66-77, from asst prof to assoc prof pediat, 68-78, from co-dir to dir phase III med curric, 76-80, PROF MED MICROBIOL, COL MED, OHIO STATE UNIV, 77-, PROF PEDIAT, 78- *Concurrent Pos:* NIH fel, Hadassah Med Sch, Hebrew Univ Jerusalem, 66-67; chmn sci adv bd, Nat Reyes Syndrome Found, 76-, ed-in-chief, J Nat Reyes Syndrome Found, 79- *Mem:* Am Soc Microbiol; Int Orgn Mycoplasmology; Med Mycol Soc Am; Int Soc Human & Animal Mycol; Sigma Xi. *Res:* Medical microbiology; biochemistry; Reye's Syndrome; medical administration. *Mailing Add:* Dept Med Microbiol & Immunol Ohio State Univ Col of Med Columbus OH 43210

POLLACK, JAMES BARNEY, b New York, NY, July 9, 38. PLANETARY SCIENCE, CLIMATOLOGY. *Educ:* Princeton Univ, AB, 60; Univ Calif, Berkeley, MA, 62; Harvard Univ, PhD(astron), 65. *Prof Exp:* Res physicist planets, Smithsonian Astrophys Observ, 65-68; sr res assoc, Cornell Univ, 68-70; RES SCIENTIST SPACE, NASA AMES RES CTR, 70- *Concurrent Pos:* Team mem, Mariner 9 Imaging Exp, 67-73 & Viking Lander Imaging Exp, 75-; inter-disciplinary scientist, Venus Pioneer Mission, 72- & Galileo Jupiter Mission, 78-, voyager imaging team, Saturn, 80-; mem exec coun, Div Planetary Sci, 76-78; chief scientist, Ames Climate Off, 78-; mem, Space Sci Adv Comt, NASA, 78- *Honors & Awards:* Medal for Exceptional Sci Achievement, NASA, 76 & 79; Space Sci Award, Am Inst Aeronaut & Astronaut. *Mem:* Div Planetary Sci; Am Astron Soc; Am Geophys Union; AAAS. *Res:* Planetary atmospheres; origin and evolution of the solar system; climate. *Mailing Add:* Space Sci Div NASA Ames Res Ctr Moffett Field CA 94035

POLLACK, JEROME MARVIN, b Chicago, Ill, Apr 16, 26; m 52; c 4. GEOLOGY. *Educ:* Univ Okla, BS, 49, MS, 51, PhD(geol), 59. *Prof Exp:* Asst geol, Univ Okla, 49-51; geologist, Humble Oil & Refining Co, 51-55; instr, Univ Okla, 55-58; asst prof, Okla City Univ, 59; asst prof, Harpur Col, 59-61; assoc prof & chmn dept, Univ NH, 61-65; prof, Univ RI, 65-71; prof, 71-74, vpres acad affairs, 71-74, PRES, FAIRLEIGH DICKINSON UNIV, 74- *Concurrent Pos:* Dean, Col Arts & Sci, Univ RI, 65-68 & 69-71, vpres acad affairs, 68-69; Am Asn Petrol Geol grant-in-aid, 58. *Mem:* Geol Soc Am; Soc Econ Paleont & Mineral; Am Asn Petrol Geol; Nat Asn Geol Teachers. *Res:* Sedimentology; statistical problems in geology; petroleum geology; science education; invertebrate paleontology. *Mailing Add:* Fairleigh Dickinson Univ Rutherford NJ 07070

POLLACK, LOUIS, b New York, NY, Nov 4, 20; m 45; c 3. COMMUNICATION ENGINEERING. *Educ:* City Col New York, BEE, 53. *Prof Exp:* Engr, ITT Fed Labs, 43-47, sr proj engr, 47-54, dept head commun, 54-55, exec engr, 55-60, assoc lab dir, 60-62, lab dir, 62-66, dir transmission systs oper, 66-67; mgr, Radio Frequency Transmission Lab, 67-73, dir, Technol Div, 73-74, asst tech dir, COMSAT Labs, 74-78, exec dir, 78-80, VPRES, COMSAT WORLD SYSTS DIV, COMMUN SATELLITE CORP, 80- *Concurrent Pos:* Nat Acad Sci deleg, XIIIth gen assembly, Int Union Radio Sci, 60; mem US deleg, Int Radio Consult Comt study group IV, Int Telecommun Union, 62, mem study group I & II. *Mem:* Fel Inst Elec & Electronics Engrs; assoc fel Am Inst Aeronaut & Astronaut; sr assoc mem Nat Soc Prof Engrs; Sigma Xi. *Res:* Communications processing; microwave; solid state devices; spacecraft structures and power; transmission system engineering. *Mailing Add:* COMSAT Labs 2230 Comsat Dr Clarksburg MD 20734

POLLACK, LOUIS RUBIN, b Chicago, Ill, Nov 3, 19; m 42. RADIOCHEMISTRY, POLYMER STABILITY. *Educ:* Univ Calif, Los Angeles, AB, 40. *Prof Exp:* Chemist, Mare Island Naval Shipyard, US Dept Navy, Vallejo, Calif, 41-49, supvry chemist, 49-61, chief chemist, 61-72; DIR, CHEM CONSULTS, 72-; CONSULT NUCLEAR ENGR, 76- *Mem:* AAAS; Am Chem Soc; Am Soc Metals; Fedn Am Scientists; fel Am Inst Chemists. *Res:* Nuclear reactor and analytical chemistry; radiochemistry; electrochemical power sources; materials compatability; marine corrosion; oxidative degradation of elastomens. *Mailing Add:* 425 Ocean View Ave Berkeley CA 94707

POLLACK, MAXWELL AARON, b New York, NY, June 11, 15; m 39; c 1. ORGANIC CHEMISTRY. *Educ:* City Col New York, BS, 34; Northwestern Univ, MS, 35, PhD(chem), 37. *Prof Exp:* Asst chem, Northwestern Univ, 34-37; res chemist & supvr org res, Pittsburgh Plate Glass Co, 37-40; asst prof chem & res chemist, Univ Tex, 40-42; chem dir, E F Drew & Co, Inc, NJ, 42-47; chem consult, 47-64; PRES & CHMN BD, VAN DYK RES CORP, 64- *Concurrent Pos:* Pres, Parco Chems, Inc & Garden State Chem Co, 60-64. *Mem:* AAAS; Am Chem Soc; Soc Plastics Eng; Soc Plastics Indust; fel Am Inst Chem. *Res:* Plastics and plasticizers; fats and oils; synthetic organic chemicals; cancer metabolism; B vitamins; allylic rearrangements; gerontology; photo-imaging processes; nutrition and aging. *Mailing Add:* 121 Glenbrook Rd Morris Plains NJ 07950

POLLACK, NORMAN MARK, bio-organic chemistry, chemical information, see previous edition

POLLACK, RALPH MARTIN, b Boston, Mass, May 25, 43; m 64; c 2. BIO-ORGANIC CHEMISTRY, ENZYMOLOGY. *Educ:* Brown Univ, ScBChem, 65; Univ Calif, Berkeley, PhD(chem), 68. *Prof Exp:* NIH fel chem, Northwestern Univ, 68-70; asst prof, 70-75, assoc prof, 75-81, PROF CHEM, UNIV MD, BALTIMORE COUNTY, 81- *Concurrent Pos:* Vis prof, Univ Montpellier, France, 78-79. *Mem:* AAAS; Am Chem Soc; Sigma Xi. *Res:* Mechanisms of organic reactions; mechanisms of enzyme reactions; amine catalysis; organic models for enzymes. *Mailing Add:* Dept of Chem Univ of Md Baltimore County Baltimore MD 21228

POLLACK, RICHARD M, b Brooklyn, NY, Jan 25, 35; m 57; c 2. MATHEMATICS. *Educ:* Brooklyn Col, BA, 56; NY Univ, PhD(math), 62. *Prof Exp:* Asst prof, 62-69, ASSOC PROF MATH, NY UNIV, 69- *Mem:* Am Math Soc; Math Asn Am. *Res:* Number theory. *Mailing Add:* Dept of Math NY Univ New York NY 10003

POLLACK, ROBERT ELLIOT, b Brooklyn, NY, Sept 2, 40; m 61; c 1. CELL BIOLOGY, ONCOLOGY. *Educ:* Columbia Univ, BA, 61; Brandeis Univ, PhD(biol), 66. *Prof Exp:* Asst prof path med ctr, NY Univ, 68-70; Nat Cancer Inst spec fel, Weizmann Inst Sci, 70-71; sr staff scientist, Cold Spring Harbor Lab Quant Biol, 71-75; from assoc prof to prof microbiol, Sch Basic Health Sci, State Univ NY Stony Brook, 75-78; PROF BIOL SCI, COLUMBIA UNIV, 78- *Concurrent Pos:* Nat Cancer Inst fel med ctr, NY Univ, 66-68, Nat Cancer Inst & Am Cancer Soc res grants, 68-75; NSF res grant, 75-78; NIH res grants, 78-; adj prof molecular pharmacol, Albert Einotein Col Med, 78-; McGregory lectr, Colgate Univ, 78. *Mem:* AAAS; Am Soc Microbiol; NY Acad Sci; Am Soc Cell Biol. *Res:* Engaged in a series of interlocking experiments in order to understand the separate growth controls of normal cells; linkages among them that give use to a healthy tissue; perturbations in such growth controls give use to cancer; muscle-proteins in non-muscle cells; nude mice; detection in vitro of pre-malignant phenotypes. *Mailing Add:* Dept of Biol Sci 813 Fairchild Ctr Columbia Univ New York NY 10027

POLLACK, ROBERT LEON, b Philadelphia, Pa, Apr 29, 26; m 52; c 2. BIOCHEMISTRY. *Educ:* Philadelphia Col Pharm, BS, 48 & 49, MS, 50; Univ Tenn, PhD(biochem), 54. *Prof Exp:* Instr chem, Philadelphia Col Pharm, 48-49, asst bact, 49-50; instr bact, Univ Tenn, 52-54, res assoc, Cancer Res Lab, 54; res scientist, Eastern Utilization Res Lab, USDA, 54-62; assoc prof, 61-69, PROF BIOCHEM, SCH DENT, TEMPLE UNIV, 69-, CHMN DEPT, 62-, DIR NUTRIT HEALTH CTR, 75- *Concurrent Pos:* Instr eve col, Drexel Inst, 57-62. *Mem:* AAAS; Am Chem Soc; Am Inst Chem; Int Asn Dent Res. *Res:* Human nutrition; cellular metabolism of normal and abnormal oral tissues. *Mailing Add:* Dept of Biochem & Nutrit Temple Univ Sch of Dent Philadelphia PA 19140

POLLACK, SIDNEY SOLOMON, b New York, NY, Sept 24, 29; wid; c 3. CRYSTALLOGRAPHY. *Educ:* Mich State Univ, BS, 51, MS, 53; Univ Wis, PhD(soil sci), 56. *Prof Exp:* Fel x-ray diffraction, Mellon Inst, 56-76; MEM STAFF, DEPT ENERGY, 76- *Mem:* Am Chem Soc; Mineral Soc Am; Am Crystallog Asn. *Res:* Clay mineralogy; catalysts; coal; low crystallinity carbons; small-angle x-ray scattering and crystallography; x-ray fluorescence; meteorites. *Mailing Add:* Pittsburgh Energy Technol Ctr Dept Energy 4800 Forbes Ave Pittsburgh PA 15213

POLLACK, SOLOMON R, b Philadelphia, Pa, May 7, 34; m 55; c 2. BIOENGINEERING, MATERIALS SCIENCE. *Educ:* Univ Pa, AB, 55, MS, 57, PhD(physics), 61. *Prof Exp:* Physicist, Univac Div, Sperry Rand Corp, 60-64; from asst prof to assoc prof metall, 64-77, PROF METALL, UNIV PA, 77-, ASSOC DEAN ENG, 80- *Concurrent Pos:* Consult, Univac Div, Sperry Rand Corp, 64-; vis scientist prog physics, Am Inst Physics, 64-; vpres, Cara Corp, 69-72, pres, 72- *Honors & Awards:* Lindback Award, Soc Biomat. *Mem:* Orthop Res Soc; Soc Biomat; Int Asn Dent Res; Bioelectric Repair & Growth Soc; AMA. *Res:* Electrical effects in bone; biomaterials. *Mailing Add:* Dept Bioeng Univ of Pa Philadelphia PA 19104

POLLACK, SYLVIA BYRNE, b Ithaca, NY, Oct 18, 40; c 2. IMMUNOLOGY. *Educ:* Syracuse Univ, BA, 62; Univ Pa, PhD(develop biol), 67. *Prof Exp:* Instr anat, Woman's Med Col Pa, 67-68; res assoc, 68-73, res asst prof microbiol, 73-77, res assoc prof microbiol & immunol, 77-81, RES ASSOC PROF BIOL STRUCTURE, UNIV WASH, 81- *Concurrent Pos:* Asst mem, Fred Hutchinson Cancer Res Ctr, 75- *Mem:* Am Asn Immunologists; Soc Develop Biol; Reticuloendothelial Soc; Am Asn Cancer Res. *Res:* Continued analysis of natural killer cells and antibody-dependent cell mediated cytoxicity to tumor cells both in vitro and in vivo. *Mailing Add:* Fred Hutchinson Cancer Res Ctr 1124 Columbia St Seattle WA 98104

POLLACK, WILLIAM, b London, Eng, Feb 26, 26; m 54; c 2. IMMUNOLOGY, IMMUNOCHEMISTRY. *Educ:* Univ London, BSc, 48, MSc, 50; Rutgers Univ, PhD(zool), 64. *Prof Exp:* Sci officer hemat & serol, St Georges Hosp Med Sch, London, Eng, 48-64; tech head clin lab, Royal Columbian Hosp, Vancouver, BC, 64-66; res fel immunol & immunochem, Ortho Res Found, 63-81, sr scientist, 66-69, vpres & dir res diag, 69-75, vpres & dir res diag, Ortho Res Inst Med Sci, 75-81; VPRES & DIR RES & DEVELOP, PURDUE FREDERICK CO, 81- *Concurrent Pos:* Assoc clin prof path, Col Physicians & Surgeons, Columbia Univ, 68; adj assoc prof immunol, Col Med & Dent NJ, Rutgers Med Sch, 74. *Honors & Awards:* Karl Landsteiner Award, 69. *Mem:* AAAS: fel NY Acad Sci; Inst Soc Blood Transfusion; Int Soc Hemat. *Res:* Physical chemistry of immune reactions; immunochemistry in diagnostic research; prevention of immune induction as applied to Rhesus disease; immunology of cancer and tissue transplantation. *Mailing Add:* 20 Buttonball Lane Weston CT 06883

POLLAINE, STEPHEN MILES, astrophysics, see previous edition

POLLAK, BARTH, b Chicago, Ill, Aug 14, 28; m 54; c 2. ALGEBRA. *Educ:* Ill Inst Technol, BS, 50, MS, 51; Princeton Univ, PhD(math), 57. *Prof Exp:* Instr math, Ill Inst Technol, 56-58; asst prof, Syracuse Univ, 58-63; assoc prof, 63-67, PROF MATH, UNIV NOTRE DAME, 67- *Concurrent Pos:* Tech staff mem, Inst Defense Anal, 60-62. *Mem:* Am Math Soc; Math Asn Am. *Res:* Algebra and the theory of numbers. *Mailing Add:* Dept of Math Univ of Notre Dame Notre Dame IN 46556

POLLAK, EDWARD, b New York, NY, June 29, 32. MATHEMATICAL STATISTICS. *Educ:* Cornell Univ, BS, 54; NC State Col, MS, 56; Columbia Univ, PhD(math statist), 64. *Prof Exp:* Instr math, Lehigh Univ, 63-64; from asst prof to assoc prof, 64-75, PROF STATIST & GENETICS, STATIST LAB, IOWA STATE UNIV, 75- *Mem:* AAAS; Am Statist Asn; Inst Math Statist; Biomet Soc; Am Inst Biol Sci. *Res:* Population genetics; theory of branching processes. *Mailing Add:* Statist Lab Iowa State Univ Ames IA 50010

POLLAK, EDWARD GEORGE, b Vienna, Austria, Feb 11, 19. MARINE ENGINEERING. *Educ:* Mass Inst Technol, BS, 40, MS, 41, ScD(naval archit, marine eng), 65. *Prof Exp:* Mgr systs eng, Fast Deployment Logistic Ship Proj, Lockheed Shipbldg & Construct Co, 65-66; STAFF MEM, A D LITTLE, INC, 66- *Concurrent Pos:* Asst US Naval Attache, London, Eng, 57-59. *Mem:* Soc Naval Archit & Marine Engrs; Am Soc Naval Engrs; Royal Inst Naval Architects. *Res:* Ship hydrodynamics; marine transportation; marine systems. *Mailing Add:* A D Little Inc 20 Acorn Park Cambridge MA 02140

POLLAK, EMIL JOHN, b Portland, Maine, June 17, 47; m 72. ANIMAL BREEDING. *Educ:* Cornell Univ, BS, 69; Iowa State Univ, MS, 74, PhD(animal breeding), 75. *Prof Exp:* Res asst animal breeding, Iowa State Univ, 69-75; ASST PROF ANIMAL SCI, UNIV CALIF, DAVIS, 75- *Mem:* Am Dairy Sci Asn; Am Soc Animal Sci. *Res:* Genetic improvement in beef cattle; estimation of genetic parameters and the application of selection techniques to the improvement in efficiency and production of beef cattle in the United States. *Mailing Add:* Dept of Animal Sci Univ of Calif Davis CA 95616

POLLAK, FRED HUGO, b Vienna, Austria, May 3, 35; US citizen; m 60; c 1. SOLID STATE PHYSICS. *Educ:* Franklin & Marshall Col, BS, 57; Univ Chicago, MS, 59, PhD(physics), 65. *Prof Exp:* From instr to assoc prof physics, Brown Univ, 64-72; prof physics, Belfor Grad Sch Sci, Yeshiva Univ, 72-80; MEM FAC DEPT PHYSICS, BROOKLYN COL, NEW YORK, 80- *Concurrent Pos:* Vis scientist & group proj leader, Francis Bitter Nat Magnet Lab, Mass Inst Technol, 69- *Mem:* Am Phys Soc; Am Asn Physics Teachers. *Res:* Optical and electronic properties of solids; modulation spectroscopy. *Mailing Add:* Dept Physics Brooklyn Col Bedford Ave & Ave H New York NY 11210

POLLAK, HENRY OTTO, b Vienna, Austria, Dec 13, 27; nat US; m 49; c 2. MATHEMATICS. *Educ:* Yale Univ, BA, 47; Harvard Univ, MA, 48, PhD(math), 51. *Hon Degrees:* DSc, Rose-Hulman Inst Technol, 64, Monmouth Col, NJ, 75 & Bowdoin Col, 77. *Prof Exp:* RES MATHEMATICIAN, BELL TEL LABS, INC, 51- *Mem:* Am Math Soc; Math Asn Am (pres, 75-76). *Res:* Function theory. *Mailing Add:* Math & Statist Res Ctr Bell Tel Labs Inc Murray Hill NJ 07974

POLLAK, KURT, b Vienna, Austria, Dec 27, 33; US citizen; m 61; c 2. ORGANIC CHEMISTRY. *Educ:* Harvard Univ, AB, 54; Mass Inst Technol, PhD(org chem), 60. *Prof Exp:* Chemist, Rayonier, Inc, 60-62; chemist, Collab Res Inc, 62-65; chemist, Esso Res & Eng Co, 65-73, chemist, Exxon Res & Eng Co, Linden, 73-80; CONSULT & EXEC RECRUITER, CHEM & PETROCHEM INDUST, 80- *Mem:* Soc Automotive Eng; Am Chem Soc. *Res:* Amino acid and peptide synthesis; cellulose modifications; cancer chemotherapy; heterocyclics; lubricant additives. *Mailing Add:* 622 Maye St Westfield NJ 07090

POLLAK, MICHAEL, b Ostrava, Czech, Sept 1, 26; m 64; c 2. SEMICONDUCTORS. *Educ:* Israel Inst Technol, BSc, 53, DiplIng, 54; Univ Pittsburgh, MS, 57, PhD(physics), 58. *Prof Exp:* Res engr electronics, Israeli Inst Defense, 53-54; asst physics & electronics, Israel Inst Technol, 54-55; physicist, Westinghouse Res Labs, Pa, 58-59; mem tech staff, Bell Tel Labs, 59-60; sr physicist, Westinghouse Res Labs, 60-66; assoc prof biophys, 66-69, PROF PHYSICS, UNIV CALIF, RIVERSIDE, 69- *Concurrent Pos:* Vis scientist quantum chem group, Univ Uppsala, 64-65; vis lectr physics, Okla State Univ, 66; vis prof, Israel Inst Technol, 70 & 77, Univ Wales, 72, Univ Calif, Los Angeles, 75 & Univ Cambridge, 77. *Mem:* AAAS. *Res:* Transport properties in disordered systems. *Mailing Add:* Dept of Physics Univ of Calif Riverside CA 92502

POLLAK, RICHARD D, molecular biology, health sciences, see previous edition

POLLAK, VICTOR EUGENE, b Johannesburg, SAfrica, Sept 7, 26; m 56; c 4. INTERNAL MEDICINE, NEPHROLOGY. *Educ:* Univ Witwatersrand, BA, 44, MB, BCh, 50; FRCP(E), 65. *Prof Exp:* Asst med, Univ Ill Col Med, 54-56, instr, 56-57, res assoc, 57-59, from res asst prof to res assoc prof, 59-65, clin assoc prof, 65-70; prof med, Pritzker Sch Med, Univ Chicago, 70-73; PROF MED & DIR DIV NEPHROL, COL MED, UNIV CINCINNATI, 73- *Concurrent Pos:* Attend physician, Res & Educ Hosp, Chicago, 56-73; res assoc, Hektoen Inst, Cook County Hosp, 59-65; asst attend physician, Presby-St Luke's Hosp, 59-65; estab investr, Am Heart Asn, 59-64; NIH grants, 60-81; USPHS res career develop award, 64-65; dir renal div, Michael Reese Hosp & Med Ctr, 65-72; attend physician, Univ Cincinnati & Vet Admin Hosps, 73- *Mem:* Am Soc Nephrology; Am Soc Clin Invest; Cent Soc Clin Res; Am Heart Asn; fel Am Col Physicians. *Res:* Renal disease-immunopathogenesis and role of coagulation; protein transport. *Mailing Add:* 5363 Med Sci Bldg 231 Bethesda Ace Cincinnati OH 45267

POLLAK, VICTOR LOUIS, b Vienna, Austria, Mar 25, 30; US citizen; m 57; c 1. PHYSICS. *Educ:* Case Western Reserve Univ, BSc, 52; Wash Univ, St Louis, PhD(physics), 60. *Prof Exp:* Sr physicist, Schlumberger Corp, 60-62; asst prof physics, Okla State Univ, 62-68; assoc prof, 68-73, chmn dept, 68-76, PROF PHYSICS, UNIV NC, CHARLOTTE, 73- *Concurrent Pos:* Lectr, Univ Houston, 61-62; vis asst prof, Case Western Reserve Univ, 67-68. *Mem:* Am Phys Soc; Am Asn Physics Teachers; Nat Sci Teachers Asn. *Res:* Magnetic resonance; liquid state; chemical physics. *Mailing Add:* Dept of Physics Univ of NC UNCC Sta Charlotte NC 28223

POLLAK, VIKTOR A, b Vienna, Austria, Mar 17, 17; m 66. BIOMEDICAL ENGINEERING, INFORMATION SCIENCE. *Educ:* Prague Tech Univ, Engr, 46, Dr Tech Sci(info theory), 53, CSc, 66; Univ Sask, PhD, 72. *Prof Exp:* Designer, Tesla Tel Works, Prague, 47-48; head dept indust commun, Res Inst Telecommun, Prague, 48-56; med electronics, Res Inst Med Eng, Prague, 56-58; res scientist, Inst Fuel Res, Prague, 58-66; vis assoc prof electronics, Tech Univ Denmark, 66-68; assoc prof elec eng & secy div biomed eng, 68-72, PROF ELEC ENG, UNIV SASK, 70-, CHMN BIOMED ENG DIV, 72- *Concurrent Pos:* Consult, var insts, Govt of China, 54-55; external lectr info theory, Prague Tech Univ, 55-65; independent res scientist, Czech Acad Sci, 56; vis prof biomed eng, Fed Univ Rio de Janeiro, 74-75, exchange prof, 75-76; exchange vis, Hokkaido Univ, 79 & Tokyo Univ, 81. *Mem:* Sr mem Inst Elec & Electronics Engrs; Can Med & Biol Eng Soc; NY Acad Sci. *Res:* Pattern recognition in medicine; medical communications; general systems theory applied to biological, social and economic problems; applied biophysics; optical quantitative assessment of thin media chromatograms. *Mailing Add:* Div Biomed Eng Univ Sask Saskatoon SK S7N 0W0 Can

POLLARA, BERNARD, b Chicago, Ill, July 28, 27; m 58; c 5. PEDIATRICS, IMMUNOLOGY. *Educ:* Northwestern Univ, PhB, 51, MS, 54; Univ Minn, MD, 60, PhD, 63. *Prof Exp:* Clin chemist, St Luke's Hosp, Chicago, 48; res technician, Argonne Nat Lab, 51-52; asst biochem, Northwestern Univ, 52-53; asst physiol chem, Univ Minn, 54-56, asst scientist pediat, 57-60; intern, USPHS, Seattle, Wash, 60-61; from asst prof to assoc prof pediat & biochem, Med Sch, Univ Minn, Minneapolis, 64-69; PROF PEDIAT, ALBANY MED COL, 69-, CHMN DEPT, 79- *Concurrent Pos:* Consult, St Mary's Hosp, 56-59; Arthritis & Rheumatism Found res fel, 61-65; dir, Kidney Dis Inst, NY State Dept Health, 69-79. *Mem:* AAAS; Am Pediat Soc; Am Asn Immunol; Am Soc Cell Biol; Soc Exp Biol & Med. *Res:* Immunoglobulin structure; clinical investigation of immunodeficiency disease; transplantation antigens; phylogenetic studies of immunity. *Mailing Add:* Dept Pediat Albany Med Col Albany NY 12208

POLLARD, ARTHUR JOSEPH, b San Francisco, Calif, Aug 14, 56; m 81. POPULATION BIOLOGY, ECOLOGICAL GENETICS. *Educ:* Duke Univ, BS, 77; Cambridge Univ, PhD(bot), 81. *Prof Exp:* ASST PROF BOT, OKLA STATE UNIV, 81- *Mem:* Ecol Soc Am; Brit Ecol Soc; AAAS. *Res:* Study of the nature of variation within plant species, and its ecological and evolutionary implications; variation in plant defense mechanisms, and the consequences for plant-herbivere interactions. *Mailing Add:* Dept Bot Okla State Univ Stillwater OK 74078

POLLARD, BARRY, b York, Eng, Dec 16, 39; m 70. METALLURGY. *Educ:* Univ London, BSc & ARSM, 62; Univ Birmingham, PhD(metall), 66. *Prof Exp:* Sci officer, Brit Iron & Steel Res Asn, Sheffield, Eng, 62-63; sr metallurgist, Rohr Corp, Calif, 66-68; STAFF METALLURGIST, GRAHAM RES LAB, JONES & LAUGHLIN STEEL CORP, 68- *Mem:* Am Soc Metals; Am Welding Soc. *Res:* Welding metallurgy; alloy development; stainless steels. *Mailing Add:* Graham Res Lab 900 Agnew Rd Pittsburgh PA 15230

POLLARD, CHARLES OSCAR, JR, b Henderson, Tex, Sept 6, 37; m 60; c 1. GEOCHEMISTRY, MINERALOGY. *Educ:* Rice Univ, BA, 60; Fla State Univ, PhD(geol), 67. *Prof Exp:* Asst prof phys geol, mineral & geochem, 67-72, ASSOC PROF GEOPHYS SCI, GA INST TECHNOL, 72- *Concurrent Pos:* Grants, Am Chem Soc-Petrol Res Fund, 68-72; grant, US Army Res Off-Durham, 69-72; grant, Off Water Resources & Technol, 74-76. *Mem:* Mineral Soc Am; Clay Minerals Soc; Am Geophys Union; Sigma Xi. *Res:* Correlation of physical properties with mineral structure and composition; growth mechanisms of natural crystals; geochemical classification of groundwaters; x-ray diffraction; scanning electron microscopy. *Mailing Add:* Sch Geophys Sci Ga Inst of Technol Atlanta GA 30332

POLLARD, DOUGLAS FREDERICK WILLIAM, b Morden, Eng, Feb 3, 40; m 78; c 3. PLANT PHYSIOLOGY. *Educ:* Univ Wales, BSc, 62, PhD(bot), 66. *Prof Exp:* Sci officer, Wildfowl Trust, Slimbridge, Eng, 65-67; RES SCIENTIST TREE PHYSIOL, DEPT ENVIRON, CAN FORESTRY SERV, 67- *Mem:* Can Inst Forestry. *Res:* Forest productivity; growth physiology of genetic variation of conifers; growth regulation; seed certification; ecological interpretation; global carbon dioxide issue. *Mailing Add:* Pac Forest Res Ctr Victoria BC V8Z 1M5 Can

POLLARD, HARRY, b Boston, Mass, Feb 28, 19; m 43; c 5. MATHEMATICS. *Educ:* Harvard Univ, AB, 39, AM, 40, PhD(math), 42. *Prof Exp:* Instr math, Harvard Univ, 42-43; asst prof, Kenyon Col, 43-44; asst res mathematician, Appl Math Group, Columbia Univ, 44-45; Jewett fel, Yale Univ, 45-46; from asst prof to prof math, Cornell Univ, 46-61; PROF MATH, PURDUE UNIV, LAFAYETTE, 61- *Concurrent Pos:* Vis prof math, Harvard Univ, 70-71 & Southern Methodist Univ, 78; consult. *Mem:* Am Math Soc; Math Asn Am. *Res:* Analysis; celestial mechanics. *Mailing Add:* Dept of Math Math Bldg Purdue Univ Lafayette IN 47907

POLLARD, HARVEY BRUCE, b San Antonio, Tex, May 26, 43; m 66; c 2. BIOCHEMISTRY, NEUROBIOLOGY. *Educ:* Rice Univ, BA, 64; Univ Chicago, MS & MD, 69, PhD(biochem), 73. *Prof Exp:* Res assoc, Lab Chem Biol, NIH, 69-71; med officer, Lab Molecular Biophys, Oxford Univ, 71-72; SR INVESTR NEUROBIOL, REPROD RES BR, NIH, 72-, SR INVESTR, NEUROENDOCRINOL-CLIN HEMAT BR, NIADDK, 76-, CHIEF, SECT CELL BIOL & BIOCHEM, 80-, CHIEF, LAB EXP PATH, 81- *Concurrent Pos:* Mem, Corp Marine Biol Lab, Woods Hole, Mass, 75- *Mem:* Biophys Soc; Soc Neurosci; Am Soc Pharmacol & Exp Therapeut; Soc Develop Biol. *Res:* Regulation of neurotransmitter and hormone release from cells and secretory vesicles; communication between cells; membrane structure and function; endocrinology; cell biology. *Mailing Add:* Bldg 10 Rm 9N250 NIH Bethesda MD 20014

POLLARD, JAMES EDWARD, b Little Rock, Ark, Apr 13, 43; m 67; c 1. PHYSIOLOGY, HORTICULTURE. *Educ:* Duke Univ, AB, 65; Univ Fla, PhD(hort), 69. *Prof Exp:* Res assoc plant physiol, Univ Fla, 69-70; asst prof, 70-77, ASSOC PROF PLANT SCI, AGR EXP STA, UNIV NH, 77- *Mem:* Am Soc Hort Sci; NY Acad Sci; Am Soc Plant Physiol. *Res:* Tree physiology including production of tree fruit crops, with emphasis on stress physiology; post-harvest physiology of fruit crops. *Mailing Add:* Dept of Plant Sci Agr Exp Sta Univ of NH Durham NH 03824

POLLARD, JEFFREY WILLIAM, b Rochford, Eng, Jan 23, 50. MOLECULAR GENETICS, REPRODUCTIVE ENDOCRINOLOGY. *Educ:* Sheffield Univ, BS, 71; London Univ, PhD(biochem), 75. *Prof Exp:* Nat Cancer Inst Can fel, Ont Cancer Inst & Dept Med Biophys, Univ Toronto, 71-79; LECTR DEPT BIOCHEM, QUEEN ELIZABETH COL, UNIV LONDON, ENGLAND, 79- *Mem:* Brit Biochem Soc; Brit Soc Res Aging. *Res:* Utilization of molecular genetic approaches to examine the control of ribosome production in eukaryotic cells; genetics and biochemistry of arginine metabolism in mammalian cells; regulation of protein synthesis by female sex steroids; evolutionary biology. *Mailing Add:* Ont Cancer Inst 500 Sherbourne St Toronto ON M4X 1K9 Can

POLLARD, JOHN HENRY, b Bristol, Eng, Nov 17, 33; m 66; c 4. SOLID STATE PHYSICS. *Educ:* Bristol Univ, Eng, BSc Hons, 57; Aberdeen Univ, Scotland, PhD(natural philos), 61. *Prof Exp:* Asst lectr natural philos, Aberdeen Univ, Scotland, 60-62; res fel physics, Bartol Res Found, Pa, 62-68; RES PHHYSICIST PHYSICS, VISION & ELECTRO-OPTICS LAB, US ARMY, VA, 68- *Concurrent Pos:* Assoc mem, Adv Group Electron Devices, 79- *Mem:* Sigma Xi. *Res:* Photoconductive and photovoltaic detectors; charge coupled devices; heterojuction devices for infrared sensors; photoemission from negative affinity surfaces; anger and angular photoemission spectroscopy. *Mailing Add:* 3610 Surrey Dr Alexandria VA 22309

POLLARD, LIN DAVIS, geochemistry, see previous edition

POLLARD, MORRIS, b Hartford, Conn, May 24, 16; m 38; c 3. MEDICAL MICROBIOLOGY. *Educ:* Ohio State Univ, DVM, 38; Va Polytech Inst, MSc, 39; Univ Calif, Berkeley, PhD, 50. *Prof Exp:* Prof prev med & dir virus lab, Med Br, Univ Tex, 46-61; prof biol, 61-66, chmn dept, 66-81, PROF MICROBIOL, UNIV NOTRE DAME, 66-, DIR LOBUND LAB, 61-

Concurrent Pos: Nat Found Infantile Paralysis fel, 49; McLaughlin fac fel, Cambridge Univ, 56; consult, Brooke Army Med Ctr, 46-50, M D Anderson Hosp, 54-61, US Dept Health, Educ & Welfare, 65-70 & Inst Lab Animal Resources, Nat Acad Sci, 65-69; mem microbiol adv panel, Off Naval Res, 66-70, chmn, 68-70; mem, Int Comt Lab Animals, 72-; mem colo-rectal cancer comt, Nat Cancer Inst, 73-79, chmn tumor immunol comt, 77-80; external examr, Med Res Coun, Australia, 75-; vis prof, Fed Univ Rio de Janeiro, Brazil, 76; corresp mem, Nat Acad Sci, Brazil; Raine Found Prof med microbiol, Univ Western Australia; consult, Chinese Acad Med Sci, 81-; mem prog rev panel, Argonne Nat Lab, 79-; guest prof, Katholicke Univ, Leuven, Belgium, 81; ed, Perspectives in Virol, 56- *Mem:* AAAS; Soc Bio & Med; Asn Pathologists; fel Am Acad Microbiol; Asn Gnotobiotics (pres, 77). *Res:* Virology; comparative pathology. *Mailing Add:* Lobund Lab Univ of Notre Dame Notre Dame IN 46556

POLLARD, ROBERT EUGENE, b Taunton, Mass, Nov 13, 24; m 47; c 4. POLYMER CHEMISTRY. *Educ:* Brown Univ, BS, 47. *Prof Exp:* Res chemist, vinyl chloride polymerization, 47-55, res group leader vinyl applns, 55-61, res specialist polyethylene applns, 62-67, res specialist vinyl applns, 67-70, res specialist reinforced thermoplastics, 70-77, SR RES SPECIALIST ENG THERMOPLASTICS, MONSANTO CO, 77- *Mem:* Soc Plastics Engrs; Am Chem Soc. *Res:* Polymer structure and properties; injection molding and extrusion; rheology of polymers; compounding, reinforcement of thermoplastics; testing of plastics. *Mailing Add:* 8031 Scenic Hills Dr Pensacola FL 32504

POLLARD, THOMAS DEAN, b Pasadena, Calif, July 7, 42. CELL BIOLOGY, MEDICINE. *Educ:* Pomona Col, BA, 64; Harvard Med Sch, MD, 68. *Prof Exp:* Intern med, Mass Gen Hosp, Boston, 68-69; staff assoc biochem, Nat Heart & Lung Inst, 69-72; from asst prof to assoc prof anat, Harvard Med Sch, 72-77; BAYARD HALSTED PROF ANAT & DIR DEPT CELL BIOL & ANAT, MED SCH, JOHNS HOPKINS UNIV, 77- *Mem:* Soc Gen Physiol; Am Soc Cell Biol; Biophys Soc. *Res:* Biochemical and ultrastructural investigation of the molecular mechanism of cell motility. *Mailing Add:* Dept of Cell Biol & Anat Johns Hopkins Univ Med Sch Baltimore MD 21205

POLLARD, WILLIAM BLAKE, b Tuskegee, Ala, Dec 4, 50. SEMICONDUCTOR PHYSICS. *Educ:* Fisk Univ, BA, 73; Mass Inst Technol, PhD(physics), 79. *Prof Exp:* Res assoc fel, Mass Inst Technol, 78-79; asst prof res & teaching, Atlanta Univ, 79-80; asst prof, NC State Univ, 80-81; DEP DIR ADMIN, INST RES, DEVELOP & ENG, AMAF IND, INC, 81-; ASST PROF, NC STATE UNIV, 81- *Concurrent Pos:* Adj asst prof, Atlanta Univ, 81- *Mem:* Am Phys Soc; Nat Soc Black Physicists. *Res:* Electronic and optical properties of bulk amorphous semiconductors and alloys; bonding structure and electronic properties of semiconductor-insulator interfaces. *Mailing Add:* E-31 1445 Monroe Dr NE Atlanta GA 30324

POLLART, DALE FLAVIAN, b Holly, Colo, Jan 7, 32; m 54; c 5. POLYMER CHEMISTRY. *Educ:* Regis Col, Colo, BS, 52; Northwestern Univ, PhD(chem), 56. *Prof Exp:* Res chemist plastics div, Union Carbide Corp, NJ, 56-60, proj scientist, 60-63, group leader, 63-67, group leader res & develop, Tech Ctr, WVa, 67-69, asst dir res & develop, 69-74, prod mgr urethane intermediates, 74-76, dir res & develop, NY, 76-79, bus mgr, 79-81; VPRES TECHNOL, HOOKER CHEM, 81- *Mem:* Am Chem Soc; Sigma Xi; AAAS. *Res:* Mechanism of organic reactions; organometallic catalysts; high temperature reactions; polymer synthesis; polyurethanes. *Mailing Add:* Hooker Chem Niagara Falls NY 14302

POLLATSEK, HARRIET SUZANNE, b Detroit, Mich, May 2, 42; m 64; c 2. MATHEMATICS, GROUP THEORY. *Educ:* Univ Mich, Ann Arbor, BA, 63, MA, 64, PhD(math), 67. *Prof Exp:* Instr math, Western Mich Univ, 67; asst prof, Univ Toledo, 68-69; asst prof, Univ Mass, 69-70; asst prof, 70-74, assoc prof math, 74-80, dean studies, 77-80, PROF MATH, MT HOLYOKE COL, 80- *Concurrent Pos:* NSF grantee, 70-71. *Mem:* Am Math Soc; Math Asn Am; Asn Women Mat; Fedn Am Scientists. *Res:* Finite groups, especially the classical linear groups. *Mailing Add:* Dept of Math Mt Holyoke Col South Hadley MA 01075

POLLAY, MICHAEL, b Boston, Mass, Mar 25, 31; m 57; c 3. NEUROSURGERY, NEUROPHYSIOLOGY. *Educ:* Univ Wis, BS, 52, MD, 55; Univ Colo, MS, 61; Am Bd Neurol Surg, dipl, 65. *Prof Exp:* Clin asst surg, Univ Colo, 62-63; from instr to asst prof neurosurg & neurobiol sci, Sch Med, Univ NMex, 63-68, assoc prof, 68-71, prof neurosurg & physiol, 71-76; chief neurosurg sect, neurol B study sect, 74-78, PROF NEUROSURG, SCH MED, UNIV OKLA, 76- *Concurrent Pos:* NIH spec fel physiol, Univ Col, Univ London, 61-62, res grants, Univ NMex, 64-68; consult, Albuquerque Vet Admin Hosp, 63-, Bernalillo County Med Ctr & Soc Security Comn. *Mem:* AAAS; Am Physiol Soc; Am Asn Neurol Surg; NY Acad Sci; Soc Neurosci. *Res:* Blood-brain barrier; central nervous system transport; blood-cerebrospinal fluid barrier and acid base balance. *Mailing Add:* Neurosurg Sect Okla Health Sci Ctr PO Box 26901 Oklahoma City OK 73190

POLLEY, EDWARD HERMAN, b Chicago, Ill, Sept 20, 23; m 53; c 2. NEUROSCIENCES. *Educ:* DePauw Univ, AB, 47; Univ St Louis, MS, 49, PhD(anat), 51. *Prof Exp:* USPHS fel, Lab Neurophysiol, Wash Univ, 51-53; instr anat, Hahnemann Med Col, 53-59; chief neurol br, Exp Med Dept, Med Res Lab, Army Edgewood Arsenal, 59-70; PROF ANAT & RES PROF OPHTHAL, UNIV ILL COL MED, 70- *Concurrent Pos:* From asst prof to assoc prof, Sch Med, Univ Md, 64-70; mem comns vision & bioacoust, Nat Res Coun. *Mem:* AAAS; Soc Neurosci; Am Asn Anatomists; Asn Res Vision & Ophthal. *Res:* Anatomy of autonomic nervous system; anatomy and physiology of visual system; plasticity in nervous system; retinal anatomy and organization; physiology. *Mailing Add:* Dept of Anat Univ of Ill Col of Med Chicago IL 60680

POLLEY, HOWARD FREEMAN, b Columbus, Ohio, Nov 12, 13; m 38; c 3. MEDICINE. *Educ:* Ohio Wesleyan Univ, BA, 34; Ohio State Univ, MD, 38; Univ Minn, MS, 45. *Hon Degrees:* DSc, Ohio Wesleyan Univ, 65. *Prof Exp:* Intern med, St Luke's Hosp, Chicago, Ill, 38-39, resident, 39-40; first asst med, Mayo Clin, 42-43, from instr to prof med, Mayo Grad Sch Med, 46-72, head sect rheumatol & internal med, 62-66, chmn div rheumatol, Dept Med, 66-76, PROF MED, MAYO MED SCH, 72- *Concurrent Pos:* Consult, Mayo Clin, 43-; mem exec comt, Arthritis Found, 64-68, vpres, 66-68; mem bd trustees & exec comt of bd, Ohio Wesleyan Univ, 67-; mem nat adv coun, Nat Inst Arthritis, Metab & Digestive Dis, 72-76. *Mem:* AMA; Am Rheumatism Asn (pres, 64-65); fel Am Col Physicians. *Res:* Internal medicine; rheumatology; clinical investigation of cortisone and ACTH in rheumatic diseases. *Mailing Add:* Mayo Clin 200 First St SW Rochester MN 55901

POLLEY, JOHN RICHARD, b Toronto, Ont, Dec 29, 17; m 45; c 2. BIOCHEMISTRY. *Educ:* Univ Western Ont, BA, 42, MA, 43; McGill Univ, PhD(chem), 46. *Prof Exp:* Fel, Life Ins Med Res Found, 47-49; biochemist, Lab Hyg, Can Dept Nat Health & Welfare, 49-74, dir, Bur Virol, Lab Ctr Dis Control, 74-80; REGISTR, CAN COL MICROBIOLOGISTS, 81- *Mem:* Am Chem Soc; Can Soc Microbiol; Can Physiol Soc; Am Nuclear Soc. *Res:* Virology; development of diagnostic antigens and vaccines. *Mailing Add:* 612 Highland Ave Ottawa ON K2A 2K3 Can

POLLEY, LOWELL DAVID, b Columbus, Ohio, Dec 31, 48; m 78. GENETICS, PLANT PHYSIOLOGY. *Educ:* Miami Univ, Ohio, BA, 70; Yale Univ, PhD(biol), 74. *Prof Exp:* Fel, Univ Utah, 75-76; res assoc, Wash Univ, 76-78; ASST PROF BIOL, WABASH COL, 78- *Concurrent Pos:* NSF res grant, 77-79. *Mem:* AAAS; Am Soc Plant Physiologists; Genetics Soc Am. *Res:* Genetic control of processes essential to plants; regulation of ion transport; isolation of mutants defective in ion transport. *Mailing Add:* Dept of Biol Wabash Col Crawfordsville IN 47933

POLLIKOFF, RALPH, virology, see previous edition

POLLIN, JACK MURPH, b Lawton, Okla, Apr 26, 22; m 44; c 2. MATHEMATICS, SYSTEMS ENGINEERING. *Educ:* US Mil Acad, BS, 44; Univ Pa, MS, 49; Rensselaer Polytech Inst, MS, 57; George Washington Univ, MA, 64; Univ Ariz, PhD(systs eng), 69. *Prof Exp:* US Army, 44-, instr math, US Mil Acad, 49-52, from asst prof to assoc prof, 57-60, dep dir commun & electronics, Artillery & Missile Ctr, 64-65, dep head dept, Acad, 68-74, PROF MATH, US MIL ACAD, 68-, HEAD DEPT, 74- *Mem:* Soc Indust & Appl Math; Math Asn Am. *Res:* General systems. *Mailing Add:* Dept of Math US Mil Acad West Point NY 10996

POLLIN, WILLIAM, b Philadelphia, Pa, May 13, 22; m 51; c 2. PSYCHIATRY, PSYCHOANALYSIS. *Educ:* Brooklyn Col, BA, 47; Columbia Univ, MD, 52. *Prof Exp:* Tutor & lectr biol, Brooklyn Col, 47-51; fel psychiat, Sch Med, Univ Pittsburgh, 53-56; res psychiatrist, NIMH, 56-68, chief, Sect Psychiat, Lab Clin Sci, 58-63, chief sect twin & sibling studies, Adult Psychiat Br, NIMH, 63-72, coordr res progs, Div Narcotic Addiction & Drug Abuse, 73-74, DIR, DIV RES, NAT INST DRUG ABUSE, 74- *Concurrent Pos:* Resident & teaching fel, Western Psychiat Inst & Clin Med Ctr, 53-56; mem, Int Post-Doct Fel Comt, 62-66; chmn, Surgeon Gen Med Rev Bd, 69-; temp adv, WHO Sci Group Biol Res Schizophrenia, 69; res consult, Thudicum Res Lab, Galesburg State Hosp, Ill State Dept Ment Health, 71-; res coordr, US-USSR Joint Schizophrenia Res Proj, 72; chief clin res, NIMH Task Force, 72-; res dir, White House Spec Action Off Drug Abuse Prevention, 74-75; mem adv comt res, Ill Dept Mental Health & Develop Disabilities, 73-; Alcohol, Drug Abuse & Mental Health Admin rep & Nat Inst Drug Abuse mem to NIH Clin Trials Discussion Group, 75-76; mem res & eval subcomt, Cabinet Comt Drug Abuse Prevention, Treatment & Rehab, 76. *Mem:* Soc Life Hist Res Psychpath; assoc mem Am Psychanal Asn; Soc Neurosci; Am Col Neuropsychopharmacol; Behav Genetics Asn. *Res:* Schizophrenia; psychotherapy; application of psychiatric knowledge to international relationships; monozygotic twins discordant for schizophrenia; conflict resolution; personality development; drug abuse. *Mailing Add:* 5600 Fishers Lane Nat Inst Drug Abuse Rockville MD 20852

POLLITZER, ERNEST LEO, b Harbin, China, Apr 14, 25; US citizen; m 52; c 4. PETROLEUM CHEMISTRY, SURFACE CHEMISTRY. *Educ:* St John's Univ, BS, 48; Ga Inst Technol, MS, 51, PhD(org chem), 53. *Prof Exp:* Res chemist, Universal Oil Prod Co, 53-56, res coord, 56-59, assoc dir process res, 59-63, assoc dir res, 63-73, DIR PROCESS RES & DEVELOP, UOP INC, 73- *Mem:* AAAS; Am Chem Soc. *Res:* Catalysis; petroleum refinery processes specifically heterogeneous catalysis; petroleum and petrochemicals. *Mailing Add:* Univ Oil Prod Inc 20 UOP Plaza Des Plaines IL 60016

POLLITZER, WILLIAM SPROTT, b Charleston, SC, May 6, 23; m 55; c 2. PHYSICAL ANTHROPOLOGY, GENETICS. *Educ:* Emory Univ, AB, 44, MA, 47; Columbia Univ, PhD(human variation), 57. *Prof Exp:* Instr biol, Armstrong Col, Ga, 47-49; instr anthrop, Hunter Col, 54 & 56; from instr to assoc prof, 57-73, PROF ANAT, UNIV NC, CHAPEL HILL, 73-, ADJ PROF ANTHROP, 76- *Concurrent Pos:* Ed, Am J Phys Anthrop, 70-77. *Mem:* Am Soc Human Genetics; Am Asn Phys Anthrop (vpres, 77-79); Genetics Soc Am. *Res:* Human evolution; populations serology; hemoglobin variants. *Mailing Add:* Dept of Anat Univ of NC Chapel Hill NC 27514

POLLMANN, D STEVEN, b Provo, Utah, May 12, 51; m 73; c 3. SWINE NUTRITION, SWINE MANAGEMENT. *Educ:* Utah State Univ, BS, 75; Univ Nebr, MS, 77, PhD(animal nutrit), 79. *Prof Exp:* Res assoc nutrit, Univ Nebr, 78-79; nutrit biochemist, US Army Med Serv Corp, 79-80. *Mem:* Am Soc Animal Sci; Sigma Xi; Coun Agr Sci & Technol. *Res:* Influence of the microflora of the young pig and influence of fiber utilization in gravid sows. *Mailing Add:* Dept Animal Sci & Indust Call Hall Kans State Univ Manhattan KS 66506

POLLNOW, GILBERT FREDERICK, b Oshkosh, Wis, Jan 17, 25; c 2. PHYSICAL CHEMISTRY. *Educ:* Wis State Univ, Oshkosh, BS, 50; Univ Iowa, MS, 51, PhD(phys chem), 54. *Prof Exp:* Res chemist, Dow-Corning Corp, 54-58; res scientist, Allis-Chalmers Mfg Co, 58-61; from asst prof to assoc prof chem, 61-66, chmn dept, 65-68, PROF CHEM, UNIV WIS-OSHKOSH, 66- *Mem:* AAAS; Am Chem Soc. *Res:* Macromolecular physical chemistry; computer automation of experiments and processes; application of energy conversion and cybernetic principles to social networks and deviant behavior. *Mailing Add:* Dept of Chem Univ of Wis Oshkosh WI 54901

POLLOCK, BRUCE MCFARLAND, b Rochester, NY, Mar 23, 26; m 47; c 2. PLANT PHYSIOLOGY. *Educ:* Cornell Univ, BS, 47; Univ Rochester, PhD(plant physiol), 50. *Prof Exp:* NIH res fel, Carlsberg Lab, Copenhagen, 50-51; res assoc, Conn Col, 51-53; from asst prof to assoc prof biol sci, Univ Del, 53-59; leader veg seed invests, Veg & Ornamentals Res Br, Crops Res Div, Agr Res Serv, USDA, Colo, 59-71; owner, Taylor Mt Enterprises, 71-76; attendant prof, 73-80, PROF ENVIRON POP & ORGANISMIC BIOL, UNIV COLO, BOULDER, 80-, DIR HEALTH SCI ADV, 73- *Concurrent Pos:* Res assoc, Mich State Univ-AEC Plant Res Lab, Mich State Univ, 69-70. *Honors & Awards:* Asgrow Award, Am Soc Hort Sci, 70. *Mem:* Am Soc Hort Sci; Am Inst Biol Sci; AAAS; Am Soc Plant Physiol; Soc Develop Biol. *Res:* Physiology of the rest period in buds and seeds; seed and germination physiology; seed production. *Mailing Add:* Room 303 Chem Univ of Colo Boulder CO 80309

POLLOCK, D(ANIEL) D(AVID), b Philadelphia, Pa, Mar 28, 18; m 42; c 1. SOLID STATE PHYSICS. *Educ:* Temple Univ, BS, 47; Lehigh Univ, MS, 48, PhD, 61. *Prof Exp:* Asst supt, Fogel Refrig Co, 36-39 & Metall Labs, Inc, 39-46; res metallurgist, Naval Air Mat Ctr, 46-47; res metallurgist, Leeds & Northrup Co, 48-62, chief alloy group res & develop dept, 57-62; chief metals-ceramics mat res, Douglas Aircraft Co, 62-66; PROF METALL ENG, STATE UNIV NY BUFFALO, 66- *Mem:* AAAS; Am Soc Metals; Am Soc Testing & Mat; Am Phys Soc; Am Inst Mining, Metall & Petrol Engrs. *Res:* Aqueous and high temperature corrosion of nonferrous alloys; electrical properties of alloys; thermoelectricity; electrical resistivity; temperature coefficient of resistance; Hall coefficient; semiconductors; insulators. *Mailing Add:* Dept of Mech Eng State Univ of NY Buffalo Amherst NY 14260

POLLOCK, DOROTHY JEAN, polymer physics, see previous edition

POLLOCK, EDWARD G, b Glen Lyon, Pa, July 9, 31; m 57; c 3. DEVELOPMENTAL BIOLOGY, CELL BIOLOGY. *Educ:* Wilkes Col, AB, 53; Univ Va, MS, 57; Univ Calif, Berkeley, PhD(bot), 62. *Prof Exp:* Chmn dept biol, 64-65, PROF BIOL, CALIF STATE UNIV, NORTHRIDGE, 61-, DIR LAB ELECTRON MICROS, 71- *Concurrent Pos:* NSF instnl awards, 63-67, in serv sch-col sci teaching grant, 63-64, sci fac fel, 68-69; consult, Los Angeles Sch Dist, 63 & 64; Lalor Found res fel reprod physiol, 66; Sigma Xi res award, 66; Calif Biochem Res Found award, 67 & 69; researcher, Ger Marine Biol Labs, Helgoland, Ger, 68; Swiss Fed Inst Technol, 68-70; Europ Molecular Biol Orgn fel, 69-70; researcher, Hopkins Marine Lab, Stanford Univ. *Mem:* AAAS; Soc Develop Biol; Am Soc Cell Biol; NY Acad Sci; Int Phycol Soc. *Res:* Biochemical and ultrastructural study of cell differentiation, with emphasis on membrane characteristics, in Fucus distichus; membrane studies on sarcoma 180 cells via biochemistry and freeze-fracture. *Mailing Add:* Dept of Biol Calif State Univ Northridge CA 91330

POLLOCK, F(RED) E(DWIN), b Hohenwald, Tenn, Sept 29, 25; m 45; c 3. CHEMICAL ENGINEERING. *Educ:* Vanderbilt Univ, BEChE, 47. *Prof Exp:* Chem engr mfg, Buckeye Cellulose Corp, 47-51, chem engr process develop, 51-57, assoc dir tech div, 57-64; assoc dir res & develop div, Procter & Gamble Co, 64-65, dir res & develop div, Procter & Gamble Co Can, 65-67, dir prod develop, 67-69, mgr prod res, Procter & Gamble Ltd, Eng, 69-71, ASSOC DIR RES & DEVELOP, PROCTER & GAMBLE CO, 71- *Mem:* Am Inst Chem Engrs. *Res:* Solvent extraction of edible oils; soya protein isolation and application; dissolving pulp processing and application; wood utilization; soaps and detergents; edible fats and oils; toiletries. *Mailing Add:* 10199 Winstead Lane Cincinnati OH 45231

POLLOCK, FRANKLIN, b New York, NY, Sept 1, 26; m 53; c 2. PHYSICS. *Educ:* Columbia Univ, AB, 47, AM, 49, PhD(physics), 52. *Prof Exp:* Res scientist, Hudson Labs, Columbia Univ, 51-54, Cyclotron Lab, 54-56; from asst prof to assoc prof, 56-67, PROF PHYSICS, STEVENS INST TECHNOL, 67- *Mem:* Am Phys Soc. *Res:* Low temperature physics. *Mailing Add:* Dept of Physics Stevens Inst of Technol Hoboken NJ 07030

POLLOCK, GEORGE HOWARD, b Chicago, Ill, June 19, 23; m 46; c 5. PSYCHIATRY. *Educ:* Univ Ill, BS, 44, MD, 45, MS, 48, PhD(physiol), 52. *Prof Exp:* Intern, Cook County Hosp, Chicago, 45-46; resident psychiat, Neuropsychiat Inst, Univ Ill, 48-50, from asst prof to assoc prof, Univ Ill Col Med, 52-62, clin prof, 62-72; PROF PSYCHIAT, NORTHWESTERN UNIV, CHICAGO, 72- *Concurrent Pos:* Mem attend staff, Ill Mason Hosp, 54-; res assoc, Inst Psychoanal, 53-56, mem staff, 56-60, asst dean & dir res, 60-71, dir, 71-; Found Fund Res Psychiat fel, 60-65; pres, Ctr Psychosocial Studies, 72-; chmn ed bd, Ann Psychoanal; pres, Ill Psychiat Asn, 73-74. *Mem:* Soc Exp Biol & Med; Am Electroencephalog Soc; Am Psychosom Soc; Soc Biol Psychiat; Am Psychoanal Asn (pres, 80-82). *Res:* Psychosomatic correlations; neuropharmacological and neurophysiological studies; psychoanalytic investigations; psychoanalysis; psychosomatic medicine. *Mailing Add:* 180 N Michigan Ave Chicago IL 60601

POLLOCK, HELEN MARY, microbiology, see previous edition

POLLOCK, HERBERT CHERMSIDE, b Staunton, Va, 1913; m 42, 80; c 4. PHYSICS. *Educ:* Univ Va, BA, 33; Oxford Univ, PhD(physics), 37. *Prof Exp:* Res assoc res lab, Gen Elec Co, 37-43; dir, Eglin Field Sta, Radio Res Lab, Harvard Univ, 43-44; physicist, Res & Develop Ctr, 44-78, CONSULT, GEN ELEC CO, 78- *Concurrent Pos:* Mem staff, Manhattan Proj, Radiation Lab, Univ Calif, 44-45; mem adv bd ctr advan studies, Univ Va, 70-76; pres bd trustees, Dudley Observ, 76-80; trustee, Alumni Patent Found, Univ Va, 78- *Mem:* Fel Am Phys Soc. *Res:* Electron physics; plasma physics. *Mailing Add:* 2147 Union St Schenectady NY 12309

POLLOCK, JOHN JOSEPH, b Kulpmont, Pa, Feb 6, 33; m 60; c 3. TOXICOLOGY, PHARMACOLOGY. *Educ:* Mt St Mary's Col, Md, BS, 54; Univ Man, MSc, 61, PhD(pharmacol), 65; Am Bd Toxicol, dipl. *Prof Exp:* Jr pharmacologist, Smith Kline & French Labs, 56-59, head toxicol unit, 65-68; sr toxicologist, Wyeth Labs, Pa, 68-72; DIR ANIMAL HEALTH DIV, AYERST RES LABS, 72- *Concurrent Pos:* Vis lectr, Univ Pa, 66-72; mem adv coun animal health sci, State Univ Canton, NY, 75-; mem adv coun regional continuing educ, State Univ Plattsburgh, NY, 75- *Mem:* AAAS; Soc Toxicol; Can Asn Res Toxicol; Soc Exp Biol & Med. *Res:* Safety evaluation in animals of drugs which have potential human clinical use; testing common household substances for hazard potential. *Mailing Add:* Animal Health Div Ayerst Res Labs Chazy NY 12921

POLLOCK, L(YLE) W(ILLIAM), b Bowman, NDak, June 14, 18; m 44; c 4. CHEMICAL ENGINEERING. *Educ:* Univ NDak, BS, 40; Univ Wash, MS, 42. *Prof Exp:* Process design engr, 43-45, design supvr, 48-56, mgr math eng, 56-58, mgr planning & correlation, 58-66, mgr advan eng sci, 66-69, staff engr, 69-74, ENVIRON ENGR, PHILLIPS PETROL CO, 74- *Mem:* Am Inst Chem Engrs. *Res:* Process development; environmental engineering. *Mailing Add:* 1416 Melmart Dr Bartlesville OK 74003

POLLOCK, LELAND WELLS, b Boston, Mass, Apr 3, 43; m 69. ECOLOGY, INVERTEBRATE ZOOLOGY. *Educ:* Bates Col, BS, 64; Univ NH, MS, 66, PhD(zool), 69. *Prof Exp:* Fed Water Qual Admin fel syst-ecol, Wellcome Marine Lab, Robin Hood's Bay, Yorkshire, Eng, 69-70; fel, Marine Biol Lab, Woods Hole, Mass, 70-72; asst prof, 72-79, ASSOC PROF ZOOL, DREW UNIV, 79- *Concurrent Pos:* Mem corp, Marine Biol Lab, Woods Hole, 71- *Mem:* AAAS; Am Soc Zool; Asn Meiobenthologists; Am Micros Soc. *Res:* Ecology of marine beaches and biology of Tardigrada; role of environmental variables in shaping meiofaunal distribution. *Mailing Add:* Dept of Zool Drew Univ Madison NJ 07940

POLLOCK, MICHAEL L, b Los Angeles, Calif, June 24, 36; m 63, 79. EXERCISE PHYSIOLOGY. *Educ:* Univ Ariz, BS, 58; Univ Ill, MS, 61, PhD(phys educ, physiol), 67. *Prof Exp:* Instr phys educ, Univ Ill, 61-67, asst supvr, Phys Fitness Res Lab, 64-67; dir, Phys Fitness Res Lab, Wake Forest Univ, 67-73, mem grad fac phys educ, 69-73, assoc prof, 71-73, assoc in med, Bowman Gray Sch Med, 71-73; dir res, Inst Aerobics Res, 73-77; DIR CARDIAC REHAB, MT SINAI MED CTR, 77-; assoc prof, 77-80, PROF MED, SCH MED, UNIV WIS-MILWAUKEE, 80- *Concurrent Pos:* Consult & symp staff mem, President's Coun Phys Fitness & Sport, 72-; mem, Am Heart Asn; fel, Epidemiol Coun, Am Heart Asn. *Mem:* Am Asn Health, Phys Educ & Recreation; fel Am Col Sports Med; fel Am Col Cardiol. *Res:* Sports medicine; adult fitness; cardiac rehabilitation. *Mailing Add:* Cardiac Rehab Mt Sinai Med Ctr Milwaukee WI 53201

POLLOCK, ROBERT ELWOOD, b Regina, Sask, Mar 2, 36; m 59; c 4. NUCLEAR PHYSICS. *Educ:* Univ Man, BSc, 57; Princeton Univ, MA, 59, PhD(physics), 63. *Prof Exp:* Instr physics, Princeton Univ, 61-63; Nat Res Coun Can fel nuclear physics, Atomic Energy Res Estab, Harwell, Eng, 63-64; asst prof physics, Princeton Univ, 64-69, res physicist, 69-70, assoc prof, 70-73, actg dir, Ind Univ Cyclotron Facil, 72-73, dir, 73-79, PROF PHYSICS, IND UNIV, BLOOMINGTON, 73- *Mem:* Fel Am Phys Soc; Can Asn Physicists. *Res:* Intermediate energy nuclear reactions; accelerator development. *Mailing Add:* Dept of Physics Ind Univ Swain Hall W Bloomington IN 47405

POLLOCK, ROBERT J, JR, b Oak Park, Ill, Apr 15, 33; m 56; c 2. ORAL BIOLOGY, HISTOLOGY. *Educ:* Northwestern Univ, DDS, 56; Loyola Univ Chicago, MS, 62, PhD(oral biol), 68. *Prof Exp:* Assoc prof, 68-77, PROF HISTOL, SCH DENT, LOYOLA UNIV CHICAGO, 77-, CHMN DEPT, 68-, ADMIN ASST, 80- *Mem:* AAAS; Am Dent Asn; Int Asn Dent Res; NY Acad Sci; Am Acad Periodont. *Res:* Integrated studies of structure and function of the feeding organ, especially in rodents; basic studies on the etiology of periodontal disease. *Mailing Add:* Dept of Histol Loyola Univ Sch of Dent Maywood IL 60153

POLLOCK, STEPHEN M, b New York, NY, Feb 15, 36; m 62; c 3. OPERATIONS RESEARCH. *Educ:* Cornell Univ, BEngPhys, 58; Mass Inst Technol, SM, 60, PhD(physics, opers res), 64. *Prof Exp:* Mem tech staff, Arthur D Little, Inc, 64-65; from asst prof to assoc prof opers res, US Naval Postgrad Sch, 65-69; assoc prof, 69-74, PROF INDUST & OPERS ENG & RES SCIENTIST, INST PUB POLICY STUDIES, UNIV MICH, ANN ARBOR, 74-, CHMN, 80- *Concurrent Pos:* Consult, Mellonics Systs Div, Litton Indust, 67-69, Vector Res Inc, 71-, US Law Enforcement Assistance Admin, 73-, PRC Pub Systs Mgt, Inc, 76- & Woodward Clyde Consults, 77-; NSF lectr & Opers Res Soc Am vis lectr, 68- *Mem:* AAAS; Sigma Xi; Opers Res Soc Am; Inst Mgt Sci. *Res:* Search and detection theory; sequential decision theory; social systems modeling. *Mailing Add:* Dept of Indust Eng Univ of Mich Ann Arbor MI 48104

POLLOK, NICHOLAS LEWIS, III, b Danville, Va, May 26, 26; m 51; c 3. MICROBIOLOGY. *Educ:* Univ Va, AB, 51; Univ Md, Baltimore, PhD(microbiol), 72. *Prof Exp:* Microbiologist, US Army Biol Labs, Ft Detrick, Md, 52-72; USPHS grant, Sch Dent, Univ Md, 72-73; MICROBIOLOGIST & RES PROGS MGT STAFF, BUR BIOLOGICS, FOOD & DRUG ADMIN, 73- *Mem:* AAAS; Am Soc Microbiol; Sigma Xi; Am Pub Health Asn. *Res:* Airborne mixed-infections; viral and rickettsial pathogenesis and immunology; airborne contamination in dentistry; nosocomial infections; airborne contamination control; aerogenic vaccination and respiratory diseases; aerobiology. *Mailing Add:* Bur Biologics FDA Bldg 29 NIH Bethesda MD 20205

POLLYCOVE, MYRON, b Nogales, Ariz; m 41; c 4. MEDICINE, BIOPHYSICS. *Educ:* Calif Inst Technol, BS, 42; Univ Calif, MD, 50; Am Bd Path, cert; Am Bd Nuclear Med, cert. *Prof Exp:* Intern, Harvard Med Serv, Boston City Hosp, 50-51; lectr, Med Sch, Tufts Univ, 53-55; res assoc & hematologist, Donner Lab, Univ Calif, Berkeley, 55-64, assoc prof, 61-68, vchmn dept, 68-76, prof clin path & lab med, 68-80, PROF LAB MED & RADIOL, SCH MED, UNIV CALIF, SAN FRANCISCO, 80- *Concurrent Pos:* Teaching fel, Med Sch, Tufts Univ, 53-55; from resident to sr resident, Med Serv, Boston Vet Admin Hosp, 53-55; dir, Donner-Highland Radioisotopes Unit, Highland Alameda County Hosp, 55-61; resident physician, Cowell Mem Hosp, 55-; attend physician, Vet Admin Hosp, San Francisco, 57-, Martinez Vets Admin Hosp, Oak Knoll US Naval Hosp, Oakland, Letterman Gen US Army Hosp, San Francisco, Travis AFB Hosp, Kaiser Found Hosp, Oakland & Univ Calif Cowell Mem Hosp, Berkeley; dir, Clin Labs & chief nuclear med div, San Francisco Gen Hosp, Calif, 64-81, chief, Nuclear Med Serv, 81-; mem, Nuclear Med Exam Comt, Bd Registry, Am Soc Clin Pathologists, 79- *Mem:* Am Soc Clin Pathologists; Acad Clin Lab Physicians & Sci; Nat Soc Nuclear Med; Am Soc Hemat; Am Fedn Clin Res. *Res:* Laboratory and nuclear medicine; iron kinetics and metabolism; functional kinetics in hematology; amino acid; vitamin B-12 and folic acid intermediary metabolism. *Mailing Add:* Dept of Lab Med Sch of Med San Francisco CA 94143

POLMANTEER, KEITH EARL, b Midland, Mich, Mar 19, 23; m 46; c 2. PHYSICS, CHEMISTRY. *Educ:* Cent Mich Univ, BS 48; Case Western Reserve Univ, MS, 50. *Prof Exp:* Technician, Dow Chem Co, 41-42; lectr & asst physics, Case Western Reserve Univ, 48-49; supvr res, 52-65, mgr elastomer develop, 65-66, mgr polymer physics, 66-69, scientist, 69-80, PHYSICIST SILICONE RUBBER, DOW CORNING CORP, 49-, RES SCIENTIST, 80- *Mem:* Am Chem Soc; Am Phys Soc. *Res:* Polymer chemistry; organo-silicon polymers as related to elastomers; physics and physical chemistry of polymers and elastomers; synthesis of new elastomeric polymers. *Mailing Add:* Res Dept Dow Corning Corp Midland MI 48640

POLNASZEK, CARL FRANCIS, b Nanticoke, Pa, Jan 6, 45. BIOPHYSICAL CHEMISTRY. *Educ:* Wilkes Col, BS, 66; Cornell Univ, PhD(phys chem), 76. *Prof Exp:* Nat Res Coun Can fel, 73-75; asst res officer, Nat Res Coun Can, 75-78; RES CHEMIST, VET ADMIN MED CTR, MINNEAPOLIS, 78- *Mem:* Am Chem Soc; Int Soc Magnetic Resonance. *Res:* Studies of free radical metabolites, drug molecular interactions and the molecular dynamics and organization of biological and model systems by means of electron spin resonance and nuclear magnetic resonance spectroscopies. *Mailing Add:* Vet Admin Med Ctr Clin Pharmacol 54th St & 48th Ave S Minneapolis MN 55417

POLO, SANTIAGO RAMOS, b Salamanca, Spain, Dec 15, 22; m 62; c 4. MOLECULAR PHYSICS, SOLID STATE PHYSICS. *Educ:* Univ Madrid, MS, 45, PhD, 49. *Prof Exp:* Res assoc phys chem, Higher Coun Sci Res, Spain, 49-50; res assoc, Ill Inst Technol, 50-51; res assoc, Harvard Univ, 51-55; res assoc physics, Nat Res Coun Can, 55-58; mem tech staff, RCA Labs, 58-65; PROF PHYSICS, PA STATE UNIV, 65- *Honors & Awards:* Award, Spanish Royal Acad Sci. *Mem:* Am Phys Soc. *Res:* Molecular structure and spectroscopy. *Mailing Add:* Davey Bldg Dept of Physics Pa State Univ University Park PA 16802

POLONIS, DOUGLAS HUGH, b North Vancouver, BC, Sept 2, 28; nat US; m 53; c 4. METALLURGY. *Educ:* Univ BC, BASc, 51, PhD(metall), 55; Univ Toronto, MASc, 53. *Prof Exp:* Metall engr, Steel Co Can, Ltd, 51-52; from asst prof to assoc prof, 55-62, chmn dept mining, metall & ceramic eng, 69-71, PROF METALL ENG, UNIV WASH, 62-, CHMN DEPT MINING, METALL & CERAMIC ENG, 73- *Mem:* Am Soc Metals; Am Inst Mining, Metall & Petrol Engrs. *Res:* Materials science; physical metallurgy; phase transformations in solids; reactive metal technology; mechanical behavior and microstructure of materials. *Mailing Add:* Div of Metall Eng FB-10 Univ of Wash Seattle WA 98195

POLONSKY, IVAN PAUL, b Brooklyn, NY, Aug 23, 29; m 53; c 3. MATHEMATICS, COMPUTER SCIENCE. *Educ:* NY Univ, BA, 49, MS, 52, PhD(math), 57. *Prof Exp:* Instr math, NY Univ, 51-53; instr, Queens Col, 53-60; MEM TECH STAFF COMPUT PROGRAMMING, BELL TEL LABS, INC, 60- *Concurrent Pos:* Assoc, Grad Fac, Rutgers Univ, 72- *Mem:* Am Math Soc; Math Asn Am; Asn Comput Mach. Res; Complex function theory; programming languages; applications of computers to nonnumeric problems. *Mailing Add:* Bell Tel Labs Inc Holmdel NJ 07733

POLOSA, CANIO, b Rome, Italy, Oct 17, 28; m 60; c 3. MEDICINE, PHYSIOLOGY. *Educ:* Univ Rome, MD, 53; McGill Univ, PhD(physiol), 66. *Prof Exp:* Asst med, Inst Med Path, Univ Rome, 55-57 & Inst Clin Med, 57-59; from lectr to asst prof, 63-74, ASSOC PROF PHYSIOL, McGILL UNIV, 74- *Concurrent Pos:* Nat Res Coun Italy fel, 57-58; USPHS trainee cardiovasc res, 59-62. *Mem:* Can Physiol Soc. *Res:* Cardiology-physiology of foetal circulation; cardio-pulmonary physio-pathology; physiology of nervous control of circulation; physiology of renal circulation; neurophysiology; physiology of sympathetic neurons. *Mailing Add:* Dept of Physiol McGill Univ 149 Cornwall Ave Montreal PQ H3P 1M9 Can

POLOWCZYK, CARL JOHN, b New York, NY, Oct 3, 33; m 53; c 3. PHOTOCHEMISTRY, ELECTROCHEMISTRY. *Educ:* City Col New York, BS, 58; NY Univ, MS, 64, PhD(chem), 65. *Prof Exp:* Chief chemist, NY Testing Lab, 51-55; chief chemist, Mich Res Div, Sun Chem, 55-58 & Faberge, Inc, 58-60; from instr to assoc prof, 60-74, head dept, 70-78, PROF CHEM, BRONX COMMUNITY COL, 74-, DEAN ACAD AFFAIRS, 78- *Concurrent Pos:* Adj asst prof, NY Univ, 65-; State Univ Res Found fel, 68-69 & grant, 69; chmn, Metrop Leadership Prog, NY Univ, 70- *Mem:* Am Chem Soc. *Res:* Photochemistry and electrochemistry of organic compounds; detection and estimation of trace organic and inorganic materials; environmental methods of analysis and monitoring. *Mailing Add:* 165 N Woods Rd Manhasset NY 11030

POLOWY, HENRY, b Elberfeld-Wuppertal, Ger, Mar 10, 18; nat US; m 55; c 6. APPLIED MATHEMATICS. *Educ:* NY Univ, AB, 48, MS, 49, PhD(math), 57. *Prof Exp:* Engr, Brewster Aeronaut Corp, 40-43; teacher high sch, NY, 50-51; engr, Gen Motors Corp, 51-52; teacher high sch, NJ, 52; asst prof math, Stevens Inst Technol, 52-67; head dept math, 67-75, PROF MATH, LINCOLN UNIV, 67- *Concurrent Pos:* Instr, Am Fedn Labor, 50-51; lectr, Int Tel & Tel, NJ, 57-58 & 63-64; lectr, NSF, 60-61, dir undergrad res math, 62-67. *Mem:* Math Asn Am; Am Math Soc; Inst Math Statist; Am Soc Qual Control; Sigma Xi. *Res:* Real and complex analysis; probability; game theory and decision theory; mathematical statistics; stability-catastrophe theory. *Mailing Add:* Dept of Math Lincoln Univ Jefferson City MO 65102

POLSON, CHARLES DAVID ALLEN, b Alpena, Mich, Dec 18, 47; m 70; c 1. MOLECULAR BIOLOGY. *Educ:* Cent Mich Univ, BS, 70, MS, 75; Fla Inst Technol, PhD(biol), 79. *Prof Exp:* Lectr, 75-78, instr, 78-81, ASST PROF BIOL, FLA INST TECHNOL, 81- *Mem:* Am Asn Univ Professors; Sigma Xi. *Res:* Effect of mutant genes on the life span of Drosophila and the effect of age on the DNA of mitochondria and chloroplasts. *Mailing Add:* Dept Biol Sci Fla Inst Technol Melbourne FL 32901

POLSON, JAMES BERNARD, b Kansas City, Mo, Apr 29, 38; m 59; c 2. PHARMACOLOGY. *Educ:* Univ Mo-Columbia, AB, 61, MS, 66, PhD(pharmacol), 68. *Prof Exp:* Fel pharmacol, Sch Med, Univ Mo-Columbia, 68-69; trainee pharmacol & toxicol, Med Sch, Univ Minn, Minneapolis, 69-71; asst prof, 71-75, ASSOC PROF PHARMACOL, COL MED, UNIV S FLA, 75- *Mem:* Am Soc Pharmacol & Exp Therapeut. *Res:* Biochemical mechanisms of drug action. *Mailing Add:* Dept of Pharmacol Univ of S Fla Col of Med Tampa FL 33612

POLSON, WILLIAM JERRY, b Sulphur Springs, Tex, July 14, 43; m 66; c 1. NUCLEAR PHYSICS. *Educ:* ETex State Univ, BS, 64; Stephen F Austin State Univ, MS, 66; Auburn Univ, PhD(physics), 69. *Prof Exp:* asst prof, 69-77, assoc prof, 77-80, PROF PHYSICS, SOUTHEASTERN OKLA STATE UNIV, 80- *Mem:* Am Phys Soc. *Res:* Theoretical nuclear physics; undergraduate programs in visual astronomy. *Mailing Add:* Dept of Physics Southeastern Okla State Univ Durant OK 74701

POLT, SARAH STEPHENS, b Leavittsburg, Ohio, Aug 22, 26; m 64; c 2. CLINICAL PATHOLOGY. *Educ:* Western Reserve Univ, BA, 48, MS, 50; Woman's Med Col Pa, MD, 57. *Prof Exp:* Assoc path, Duke Univ Med Ctr, 62-64; pathologist, Vet Admin Hosp, Birmingham, Ala, 65-67; asst prof clin path & dir serol clin labs, 67-71, ASSOC PROF CLIN PATH, HOSPS & CLINS, UNIV ALA, BIRMINGHAM, 71-, MED DIR CLIN MICROBIOL, 76- *Mem:* Am Soc Clin Path; Am Soc Microbiol. *Res:* Diagnosis of infectious disease by immunological techniques. *Mailing Add:* Dept of Path Univ of Ala Hosp & Clin Birmingham AL 35233

POLTORAK, ANDREW STEPHEN, b Somerville, NJ, Jan 11, 38; m 62; c 3. OPERATIONS RESEARCH, PHYSICS. *Educ:* Univ Notre Dame, BS, 60; Univ Mich, Ann Arbor, MS, 61, PhD(physics), 66. *Prof Exp:* Opers res analyst mil systs, Conductron Corp, 67-68; opers res analyst mil systs, Naval Ord Lab, Naval Surface Weapons Ctr, 68-73, br head syst anal, 74-76; analyst, Nuclear Regulatory Comn, 76-77; DIV MGR, SCI APPL, INC, 77- *Mem:* Inst Elec & Electronics Eng; Opers Res Soc Am. *Res:* Systems analysis of advanced military systems, determining feasibility, requirements and effectiveness of proposed systems with introductory dates of five to thirty years. *Mailing Add:* 2932 Beaverwood Ln Wheaton MD 20906

POLUHOWICH, JOHN JACOB, b Bridgeport, Conn, Mar 25, 39; m 62; c 4. PHYSIOLOGICAL ECOLOGY. *Educ:* Univ Bridgeport, BA, 62; Iowa State Univ, MS, 66; Univ Conn, PhD(zool), 69, MS, 82. *Prof Exp:* from asst prof to assoc prof, 69-77, PROF BIOL, UNIV BRIDGEPORT, 77-, DIR, INST ANGUILLIFORM RES & MARICULT, 74- *Concurrent Pos:* Mem, Conn Coastal Zone Mgt Comt, 71- *Mem:* Sigma Xi; World Maricult Soc; AAAS. *Res:* Physiology of catadromous and anadromous fishes; mariculture. *Mailing Add:* Dept Biol Univ Bridgeport Bridgeport CT 06602

POLVE, JAMES HERSCHAL, b Kenilworth, Utah, Feb 7, 21; m 48; c 3. AERONAUTICAL ENGINEERING. *Educ:* Univ Utah, BS, 48, ME, 54; Princeton Univ, MS, 51; Univ Ariz, PhD(aeronaut eng), 66. *Prof Exp:* Instr & chief opers, Exp Flight Test Pilot Sch, US Air Force, 51-55, from asst prof to assoc prof math, Air Force Acad, 55-58, assoc prof aeronaut, 58-60, dir flight test eng, Air Force Flight Test Ctr, Edwards AFB, 63-66, staff officer, Fed Aviation Admin, 66-67, chief Seattle Off at Boeing Co, 67-69; PROF MECH ENG, BRIGHAM YOUNG UNIV, 69- *Mem:* Am Soc Eng Educ; assoc fel, Am Inst Aeronaut & Astronaut; Am Soc Mech Eng. *Res:* Stability and control; flight testing; mechanical engineering. *Mailing Add:* Dept of Mech Eng Brigham Young Univ Provo UT 84601

POLYA, GEORGE, b Budapest, Hungary, Dec 13, 87; nat US; m 18. MATHEMATICS. *Educ:* Eotvos Lorand Univ, Budapest, PhD(math), 12. *Hon Degrees:* DSc, Polytech Inst, Zurich, 47, Univ Wis-Milwaukee, 69; LLD, Univ Alta, 61; DMath, Univ Waterloo, 71. *Prof Exp:* From asst prof to assoc prof math, Swiss Fed Inst Technol, Zurich, 14-28, prof, 28-40, dean & chmn dept, 38-40; vis prof, Brown Univ, 40-42; vis prof, Smith Col, 42; from assoc prof to prof, 42-53, EMER PROF MATH, STANFORD UNIV, 53- *Concurrent Pos:* Rockefeller traveling fel, Oxford Univ & Cambridge Univ, 24-25; vis lectr, Princeton Univ, 33; vis prof, Princeton Univ & Univ Geneva; vis lectr, Univ Paris, Univ Gottingen, Cambridge Univ, Eng, Univ Vancouver & Univ Toronto; vis lectr, Math Asn Am, 53-56. *Honors & Awards:* Distinguished Serv Award, Math Asn Am, 63; Top Honor Math & Physics, Educ Film Libr Asn, 68. *Mem:* Nat Acad Sci; Acad Sci, Paris; Hungarian Acad Sci; NY Acad Sci; Am Acad Arts & Sci. *Res:* Functions of complex variables; location of roots; probability; theory of numbers; applied mathematics; mathematical methods; problem-solving combinatorics. *Mailing Add:* Dept Math Stanford Univ Stanford CA 94305

POLYE, WILLIAM RONALD, b New York, NY, Dec 12, 14; m 41; c 3. PHYSICS. *Educ:* St Lawrence Univ, BS, 37; Univ Notre Dame, MS, 39. *Prof Exp:* Asst physics, Univ Notre Dame, 37-40; physicist, 40-65, SR SCIENTIST, BENDIX CORP, 65- *Concurrent Pos:* Consult applied physics, Bendix Corp, 77-; pvt tech consult. *Mem:* Am Phys Soc; Am Vacuum Soc. *Res:* Atmospheric physics; electro-optical and solid state devices; microelectronics; electron microscopy; vacuum deposition. *Mailing Add:* 144 Midland Ave River Edge NJ 07661

POLZER, WILFRED L, b Cameron, Tex, Apr 10, 31; m 58; c 6. GEOCHEMISTRY, ENVIRONMENTAL SCIENCES. *Educ:* Tex A&M Univ, BS, 53, MS, 56; Mich State Univ, PhD(soil sci), 60. *Prof Exp:* Res chemist, US Geol Surv, 60-67; geochemist, US AEC, US Energy Res & Develop Admin, 67-71, environ scientist, 71-76; SOIL CHEMIST, LOS ALAMOS NAT LAB, 76- *Mem:* Am Soc Agron. *Res:* Behavior of plutonium and americium in soil-water environments; radioactive waste and soil interactions; geochemical controls of water composition. *Mailing Add:* 7 La Rosa Court Los Alamos NM 87544

POMATO, NICHOLAS, molecular biology, see previous edition

POMERANCE, CARL, b Joplin, Mo, Nov 24, 44; m 71; c 2. MATHEMATICS. *Educ:* Brown Univ, BA, 66; Harvard Univ, MA, 70, PhD(math), 72. *Prof Exp:* asst prof, 72-77, ASSOC PROF MATH, UNIV GA, 77- *Concurrent Pos:* Vis assoc prof math, Univ Ill, 78-79. *Mem:* Am Math Soc; Math Asn Am. *Res:* Number theory including number theoretic algorithms. *Mailing Add:* Dept of Math Univ of Ga Athens GA 30602

POMERANCE, HERBERT (SOLOMON), b Chicago, Ill, July 24, 17; m 48; c 1. PHYSICS. *Educ:* Univ Chicago, SB, 37, PhD(physics), 50. *Prof Exp:* Asst chemist metall lab, Univ Chicago, 42-43; assoc chemist, Clinton Labs, Oak Ridge, 43-46; physicist, Oak Ridge Nat Lab, 46-64; ed, Int Atomic Energy Agency, 64-66; PHYSICIST, OAK RIDGE NAT LAB, 66- *Mem:* AAAS; Am Asn Physics Teachers; Am Nuclear Soc. *Res:* Molecular spectra; spectrochemistry; neutron absorption cross sections; nuclear physics; information services. *Mailing Add:* 104 Ulena Lane Oak Ridge TN 37830

POMERANTZ, DAVID KURT, reproductive physiology, see previous edition

POMERANTZ, IRWIN HERMAN, b Floral Park, NY, July 18, 34. ORGANIC CHEMISTRY, ENVIRONMENTAL CHEMISTRY. *Educ:* Antioch Col, BS, 57; Univ Colo, PhD(org chem), 62. *Prof Exp:* Steroid Biochem Training Prog fel, Worcester Found Exp Biol, 61-62; asst prof chem, Bethany Col, WVa, 62-64; res assoc, Antioch Col, 64-65, asst prof, 65-66; res chemist, 66-70, supvry res chemist, Food & Drug Admin, 70-77; ADMINR PHYS SCI, ENVIRON PROTECTION AGENCY, 77- *Concurrent Pos:* Adj prof chem, Am Univ, DC, 81- *Mem:* AAAS; Am Chem Soc; NY Acad Sci; Asn Off Anal Chemists. *Res:* Pesticide chemistry; industrial chemicals; analytical procedures for trace analysis; organic chemicals in drinking water; chemistry of chlorinated aromatic compounds. *Mailing Add:* Criteria & Standards Div WH-550 401 M St SW Washington DC 20460

POMERANTZ, MARTIN, b New York, NY, May 3, 39; m 61; c 3. ORGANIC CHEMISTRY. *Educ:* City Col New York, BS, 59; Yale Univ, MS, 61, PhD(chem), 64. *Prof Exp:* NSF fel chem, Univ Wis, 63-64; asst prof, Case Western Reserve Univ, 64-69; from assoc prof to prof, Belfer Grad Sch Sci, Yeshiva Univ, 69-76, chmn dept, 73-76; PROF, DEPT CHEM, UNIV TEX, ARLINGTON, 76- *Concurrent Pos:* Alfred P Sloan Found res fel, 71-76; vis assoc prof, Dept Chem, Univ Wis-Madison, 72-73; vis prof, Dept Chem, Columbia Univ, 70-75, Ben-Gurion Univ, Negev, Beer Sheva, Israel, 81; Alfred P Sloan Found res fel, 71-76. *Mem:* Am Chem Soc; Royal Soc Chem. *Res:* Organic chemical reaction mechanisms; free radical chemistry; thermal and photochemical reorganization reactions; reactive intermediates; synthesis and study of phosphorus-nitrogen compounds; nmr spectroscopy; new synthetic methods; study of microcyclic compounds. *Mailing Add:* Dept of Chem Univ of Tex Arlington TX 76019

POMERANTZ, MARTIN ARTHUR, b Brooklyn, NY, Dec 17, 16; m 41; c 2. PHYSICS. *Educ:* Syracuse Univ, AB, 37; Univ Pa, MS, 38; Temple Univ, PhD, 51. *Hon Degrees:* Fil Dr, Univ Uppsala, 67; ScD, Swarthmore Col, 73. *Prof Exp:* Asst, 38-41, res fel, 41-43, physicist, 43-59, DIR BARTOL RES FOUND, FRANKLIN INST, UNIV DEL, 59- *Concurrent Pos:* Fulbright scholar & vis prof, Aligarh Muslim Univ India, 52-53; vis prof, Swarthmore Col; ed, Jour & vpres, Franklin Inst; prof, Thomas Jefferson Univ, Bartol prof; mem comt polar res, Geophys Res Bd & Space Sci Bd, Nat Acad Sci; vpres comt & chmn US comt, Int Years of Quiet Sun & vpres int geophys comt, Int Coun Sci Unions; mem & leader numerous sci expeds; vis prof, Orgn Am States, 73. *Mem:* Fel AAAS; fel Am Phys Soc; fel Am Geophys Union. *Res:* Cosmic rays; secondary electron emission; semiconductors; electronic physics; solid state; radiation effects; geophysics; solar terrestrial physics; astrophysics; astronomy. *Mailing Add:* Bartol Res Found Univ of Del Newark DE 19711

POMERANTZ, MELVIN, b Brooklyn, NY, May 10, 32. PHYSICS. *Educ:* Polytech Inst Brooklyn, BS, 53; Univ Calif, Berkeley, MS, 55, PhD(physics), 59. *Prof Exp:* RES STAFF MEM, THOMAS J WATSON RES CTR, IBM CORP, 60- *Concurrent Pos:* Vis lectr, Univ Calif, Berkeley, 69-70. *Mem:* Am Phys Soc. *Res:* Microwave frequency ultrasonics; properties of semiconductors; phonons in solids; properties of organic film. *Mailing Add:* Thomas J Watson Res Ctr IBM Corp PO Box 218 Yorktown Heights NY 10598

POMERANTZ, SEYMOUR HERBERT, b Houston, Tex, Oct 4, 28; m 53; c 4. BIOCHEMISTRY. *Educ:* Rice Inst, BA, 48; Univ Tex, PhD(org chem), 52. *Prof Exp:* Asst chem, Univ Ill, 52-53; from sr instr to asst prof biochem, Western Reserve Univ, 53-61; asst prof pharmacol, St Louis Univ, 61-63; from asst prof to assoc prof, 63-69, PROF BIOCHEM, SCH MED, UNIV MD, BALTIMORE, 69- *Concurrent Pos:* Vis prof, Weizmann Inst Sci, 72 & 79. *Mem:* Am Soc Biol Chem; Am Chem Soc; Endocrine Soc. *Res:* Tyrosinase; oocyte maturation; hydroxylations. *Mailing Add:* Dept of Biochem Univ of Md Sch of Med Baltimore MD 21201

POMERANZ, BRUCE HERBERT, b Montreal, Que, July 24, 37; m 57; c 1. NEUROPHYSIOLOGY. *Educ:* McGill Univ, BSc, MD & CM, 61; Harvard Univ, PhD(physiol), 67. *Prof Exp:* NIH fel, Harvard Med Sch, 62-66; asst prof biol, Mass Inst Technol, 66-68; from asst prof to assoc prof, 68-80, PROF ZOOL, UNIV TORONTO, 80- *Mem:* AAAS; Am Physiol Soc; Soc Neurosci. *Res:* Physiology of endorphins such as, electrophysiology, biochemistry and behaviour; acupuncture and endorphins; nerve vegeneration. *Mailing Add:* Dept Zool Univ Toronto Toronto ON M5S 0R8 Can

POMERANZ, JANET BELLCOURT, b Albany, NY, Jan 15, 30. MATHEMATICS, STATISTICS. *Educ:* Col St Rose, BA, 56; Cath Univ, MS, 59, PhD(math), 62. *Prof Exp:* Teacher, St Patrick's High Sch, 53; teacher, Sacred Heart Sch, 53-54; teacher, St Vincent's Sch, 54-56; teacher, St Anthony's High Sch, 56-57; assoc prof math & chmn dept, Col St Rose, 62-68; assoc prof, State Univ NY Col Oneonta, 68-71; assoc prof, 71-78, PROF MATH, STATE UNIV NY MARITIME COL, FT SCHUYLER, 78- *Concurrent Pos:* NSF res participation for col teachers grant, Univ Okla, 64-65. *Mem:* Math Asn Am. *Res:* Functional analysis; abstract algebra; theory of linear operators on H-algebras; matrices over the quaternions; combinatorial problems in the theory of relations. *Mailing Add:* 23 Eastland Dr Glen Cove NY 11542

POMERANZ, YESHAJAHU, b Poland, Nov 28, 22; m 48; c 2. BIOCHEMISTRY, CEREAL CHEMISTRY. *Educ:* Israel Inst Technol, BSc, 48, Chem E, 49; Kans State Univ, PhD(cereal chem), 62. *Prof Exp:* Chief chemist, Israel Govt, 49-54, head cent food lab, 55-59; UN Food & Agr Orgn res fel cereal chem, Brit Milling Industs Res Asn, 54-55; res chemist, 62-69, chemist in charge barley & malt lab, 69-73, DIR, US GRAIN MKT RES CTR, USDA, 73- *Concurrent Pos:* ed, Adv Cereal Sci Technol; prof, Kans State Univ, 63-69; prof, Univ Wis-Madison. *Honors & Awards:* Osborne Medal, Am Asn Cereal Chem; Harvey W Wiley Award, Asn Off Anal Chemists. *Mem:* Fel AAAS; Am Chem Soc; Am Asn Cereal Chem; fel Inst Food Technol. *Res:* Chemical composition and functional properties of cereal grains; food analysis, nutritional value of cereals; high-protein foods; food rheology; microbiology of stored grain products. *Mailing Add:* US Grain Mkt Res Ctr Agr Res Serv USDA 1515 College Ave Manhattan KS 66502

POMERENE, JAMES HERBERT, b Yonkers, NY, June 22, 20; m 44; c 3. COMPUTER ARCHITECTURE. *Educ:* Northwestern Univ, BS, 42. *Prof Exp:* Design engr radar, Hazeltine Corp, Long Island, NY, 42-46; staff engr comput, Inst Advan Study, Princeton, NJ, 46-51, chief engr, 51-56; sr engr comput design, IBM Corp, Poughkeepsie, NY, 56-67, sr staff mem corp tech comt, Armonk, NY, 67-76, IBM FEL COMP ARCHIT, IBM TJ WATSON RES CTR, 76- *Mem:* AAAS; fel Inst Elec & Electronics Engrs; Sigma Xi. *Res:* High speed computer organizations, highly concurrent processors. *Mailing Add:* IBM TJ Watson Res Ctr PO Box 218 Yorktown Heights NY 10598

POMERENING, JAMES ALBERT, b New London, Wis, May 3, 29; m 58; c 2. SOIL CLASSIFICATION. *Educ:* Univ Wis, BS, 51; Cornell Univ, MS, 56; Ore State Univ, PhD(soil classification), 61. *Prof Exp:* Asst soils, Cornell Univ, 51-53 & 56; res fel soil classification, Ore State Univ, 56-60; asst prof, Univ Md, 60-65, from asst prof to assoc prof plant & soil sci, 65-73, assoc dean, Sch Agr, 74-75, PROF PLANT & SOIL SCI, CALIF STATE POLYTECH UNIV, POMONA, 73- *Concurrent Pos:* Soil scientist, US Dept Interior, Bur Land Mgt, 71- *Mem:* Soil Sci Soc Am; Am Soc Agron. *Res:* Soil genesis, morphology, classification and survey. *Mailing Add:* Calif State Polytech Univ 3801 W Temple Ave Pomona CA 91768

POMEROY, BENJAMIN SHERWOOD, b St Paul, Minn, Apr 24, 11; m 38; c 4. VETERINARY MICROBIOLOGY. *Educ:* Iowa State Univ, DVM, 33; Cornell Univ, MS, 34; Univ Minn, PhD(bact), 44. *Prof Exp:* From asst vet to vet, 34-38, instr, 38-41, from asst prof to assoc prof, 41-48, prof vet microbiol & pub health & head dept, 48-73, assoc dean col vet med, 70-74, prof vet microbiol, 73-81, actg dean, 79, EMER PROF, UNIV MINN, ST PAUL, 81- *Mem:* US Animal Health Asn; Am Vet Med Asn; Poultry Sci Asn; Conf Res Workers Animal Dis. *Res:* Salmonella infections and respiratory diseases of poultry; mycoplasma infections and enteric diseases of turkeys. *Mailing Add:* 1443 Raymond Ave St Paul MN 55108

POMEROY, JOHN HOWARD, b St Petersburg, Fla, Mar 5, 18; m 45; c 2. CHEMISTRY. *Educ:* Univ Fla, BS, 40, MS, 43; Mass Inst Technol, PhD(org chem), 49. *Prof Exp:* Chemist, Fla State Racing Comn, 40-41 & Tenn Eastman Co, 44-46; group leader org chem, Biol & Med Res Div, Argonne Nat Lab, 49-60; sr chemist & br chief, Div Res, US Atomic Energy Comn, 60-67; sr ed phys sci, Encycl Britannica, 67-69; asst dir lunar sample prog, HQ, NASA, 70-75; tech secy, Comt Radioactive Waste Mgt, Nat Acad Sci, 75-80; CONSULT, 80- *Concurrent Pos:* Deleg, UN Conf Peaceful Uses Atomic Energy, Geneva, 58; consult, Holt, Rinehart & Winston, Inc, 65, Div Tech Info, US Atomic Energy Comn, 67- & Compton's Encycl & Encycl Britannica, Jr, 70- *Mem:* AAAS; Am Chem Soc; Sigma Xi; Fedn Am Scientist. *Res:* Scientific education; radioactive waste management. *Mailing Add:* 5201 Fordyce Pl Bethesda MD 20814

POMEROY, JOHN S, b Bethlehem, Pa, May 7, 29; m 57; c 4. GEOLOGY. *Educ:* Lehigh Univ, BA, 51. *Prof Exp:* Geologist, NAm Geol Bibliog Unit, 53-55, geologist, Mineral Deposits Br, 55, geologist, Alaska Geol Br, Photogeol Sect, 56-64, geologist, Br Regional Geol Ky, 64-68, supvry geologist, Wash Tech Reports Unit, 68-70, geologist, Br Atlantic Environ Geol, Beltsville, Md, 70-75, GEOLOGIST, BR ATLANTIC ENVIRON GEOL, US GEOL SURV, RESTON, VA, 75- *Mem:* Fel Geol Soc Am. *Res:* Photogeologic reconnaissance of sedimentary, igneous and metamorphic terrains; reconnaissance geologic mapping of southeastern Alaska and the Colorado

Plateau; quadrangle geologic mapping in Kentucky and Massachusetts; applications of geology to environmental studies; landslide susceptibility studies in southwestern Pennsylvania. *Mailing Add:* 711 Fordham St Rockville MD 20850

POMEROY, LAWRENCE RICHARDS, b Sayre, Pa, June 2, 25; m 52; c 2. ECOLOGY. *Educ:* Univ Mich, BS, 47, MS, 48; Rutgers Univ, PhD(zool), 51. *Prof Exp:* Res assoc bur biol res, Rutgers Univ, 51-52, asst res specialist, NJ Oyster Res Lab, 52-54; from asst prof to assoc prof zool, Marine Inst, 54-60, assoc prof, Univ, 60-65, prof zool, 66-80, ALUMNI FOUND DISTINGUISHED PROF ZOOL, UNIV GA, 80- *Mem:* AAAS; Am Soc Limnol & Oceanog; Ecol Soc Am. *Res:* Energetics and cycles of elements in marine and aquatic ecosystems. *Mailing Add:* Inst of Ecol Univ of Ga Athens GA 30602

POMEROY, RICHARD DURANT, b Burbank, Calif, Dec 22, 04; m 35; c 4. CHEMISTRY. *Educ:* Calif Inst Technol, BS, 26, MS, 27, PhD(chem), 31. *Prof Exp:* Res chemist, Los Angeles County Sanit Dist, 32-40; consult, Chem Engr, 40-77; pres, Pomeroy, Johnston & Bailey Consults, 58-77; CONSULT, JAMES M MONTGOMERY CO, PASADENA, CALIF, 77- *Honors & Awards:* Eddy Award, Water Pollution Control Fedn, 47; Herring Medal, Am Water Works Asn, 73. *Mem:* Am Chem Soc; Am Soc Civil Eng; hon mem Water Pollution Control Fedn; Am Water Works Asn; Nat Asn Corrosion Eng. *Res:* Methods of water and waste water treatment; control of sulfide formation in sewers; methods of water and waste analysis; corrosion of metals by water. *Mailing Add:* 280 Malcolm Dr Pasadena CA 91105

POMEROY, ROLAND KENNETH, b London, Eng, Oct 20, 45; Can citizen. INORGANIC CHEMISTRY, ORGANOMETALLIC CHEMISTRY. *Educ:* Imperial Col Sci & Technol, London, Eng, BSc, 67; Univ Alta, PhD(chem), 71. *Prof Exp:* Fel chem, Univ BC, 72-74; res assoc, Univ Alta, 74-75; asst prof, Univ Sask, 75-76; ASST PROF CHEM, SIMON FRASER UNIV, 76- *Mem:* Fel Royal Soc Chem; Am Chem Soc; Can Inst Chem. *Res:* Synthesis and characterization of organometallic compounds, especially those involving derivatives of iron, ruthenium and osmium carbonyls. *Mailing Add:* Dept Chem Simon Fraser Univ Burnaby BC V5A 1S6 Can

POMES, ADRIAN FRANCIS, b Hattiesburg, Miss, Apr 18, 20; m 47; c 6. CHEMISTRY, CARBOHYDRATE. *Educ:* Loyola Univ, La, BS, 40; Tulane Univ, MS, 47. *Prof Exp:* Jr chemist, Breaux Bridge Sugar Coop, 40; jr chemist, Southern Regional Res Lab, USDA, 41-47; res chemist, Drackett Co, 47-49; fel, Mellon Inst, 49-57; chemist & zein specialist, Moffett Tech Ctr, CPC Int, 57-75, SR APPLN SPEC, MOFFETT TECH CTR, CORN PROD, DIV CPC NORTH AM, 75- *Concurrent Pos:* Mem bd dirs, Omni Res Found, 63-68, comdr reserve police, Downers Grove, Ill, 68-79, Red Cross First Aid Inst, 54- *Mem:* Am Soc Brewing Chemists; Sigma Xi; Master Brewers Asn Am. *Res:* Applications of vegetable proteins in paper and textiles; brewing and food applications of corn syrup, starch and dextrose; zein applications. *Mailing Add:* Tech Serv Dept CPC North Am PO Box 345 Argo IL 60501

POMILLA, FRANK R, b Brooklyn, NY, Oct 1, 26; m 53; c 4. ATOMIC PHYSICS. *Educ:* Fordham Univ, BS, 48, MS, 49, PhD(atomic scattering), 63. *Prof Exp:* Instr math, St John's Univ, NY, 49-51, instr physics, 51-53, from asst prof to assoc prof, 53-64, actg chmn dept, 51-52 & 70; res physicist res dept, Grumman Aircraft Eng Corp, 64-67; assoc prof physics, 67-70, chmn dept natural sci, 72-73, coordr physics & phys sci, 70-72, NSF-Alfred P Sloan Found dir educ res projs, 69-72, PROF PHYSICS, YORK COL, NY, 71-; PROF PHYSICS, DOCTORAL FAC, CITY UNIV NEW YORK, 71- *Concurrent Pos:* NSF fac fel, 60-61; assoc prof doctoral fac, City Univ New York, 68-71; proj dir SST progs, NSF, 73-76, 79 & 81, CCSS progs, 69-72 & CAUSE prog, 77-80, 81-84. *Mem:* Inst Elec & Electronics Eng; Am Phys Soc; Am Asn Physics Teachers; Sigma Xi. *Res:* Atomic scattering; lunar and planetary atmospheres. *Mailing Add:* Dept of Physics York Col Jamaica NY 11451

POMMERSHEIM, JAMES MARTIN, b Pittsburgh, Pa, Dec 5, 37; m 62; c 2. CHEMICAL ENGINEERING. *Educ:* Univ Pittsburgh, BS, 59, MS, 62, PhD(chem eng), 69. *Prof Exp:* From asst prof to assoc prof, 65-76, PROF CHEM ENG, BUCKNELL UNIV, 76- *Mem:* Am Inst Chem Engrs; Am Chem Soc. *Res:* Transport phenomena; modeling, evaporation; reaction analysis; thermodynamics of nonideal gases; quasi-steady-state processes; cement hydration. *Mailing Add:* Dept of Chem Eng Bucknell Univ Lewisburg PA 17837

POMONIS, JAMES GEORGE, b Santa Fe, NMex, Aug 11, 32; m 56; c 5. ORGANIC CHEMISTRY. *Educ:* Univ Denver, BS, 55, MS, 61. *Prof Exp:* Res asst chem, Denver Res Inst, 57-58; res chemist, Lasdon Found Res Inst Chemother, 59-63; res chemist, Geigy Chem Corp, 64-65; RES CHEMIST METAB & RADIATION RES LAB, USDA, 65- *Concurrent Pos:* Vis scientist & consult, Entomol Res Dept Biol, Demokritos, Nuclear Res Ctr, Athens, Greece, 81. *Mem:* Am Chem Soc; Sigma Xi. *Res:* Synthesis of steroids and heterocyclic compounds; isolation and identification of natural products from insects; synthesis and mass spectrometry of branched and straight chain hydrocarbons and thiophenes. *Mailing Add:* Metab & Radiation Res Lab Sci & Educ Admin-Fed Res Fargo ND 58105

POMPER, SEYMOUR, microbiology, see previous edition

POMRANING, GERALD C, b Oshkosh, Wis, Feb 23, 36; m 61; c 2. REACTOR PHYSICS, TRANSPORT THEORY. *Educ:* Univ Wis, BS, 57; Delft Technol Univ, cert, 58; Mass Inst Technol, PhD(nuclear eng), 62. *Prof Exp:* Physicist & group leader, Vallecitos Atomic Lab, Gen Elec Co, 62-64; physicist & group leader, Gen Atomic Div, Gen Dynamics Corp, 64-66, staff mem & physicist, 66-68, group leader, 68-69; staff scientist & asst to pres & vpres, Sci Applns, Inc, 69-76; PROF, SCH ENG & APPLIED SCI, UNIV CALIF, LOS ANGELES, 76- *Concurrent Pos:* Vis scientist, Brookhaven Nat Lab, 66; vis staff mem, Los Alamos Sci Lab, 68; vis lectr, Univ Calif, Los Angeles, 73-74. *Honors & Awards:* Mark Mills Award, Am Nuclear Soc, 63. *Mem:* AAAS; fel Am Nuclear Soc; fel Am Phys Soc; Soc Indust & Appl Math; Math Asn Am. *Res:* Transport phenomena; reactor physics; radiative transfer; radiation hydrodynamics; applied mathematics. *Mailing Add:* Univ Calif 6291 Boelter Hall Los Angeles CA 90024

PON, NING GIN, b Oakland, Calif, Dec 18, 25; m 64; c 1. BIOCHEMISTRY, PHOTOBIOLOGY. *Educ:* Univ Calif, Berkeley, BS, 50, PhD(chem), 60. *Prof Exp:* Lab technician hormone res lab, Univ Calif, Berkeley, 50-54, res chemist, Lawrence Radiation Lab, 60-63; asst prof enzyme, photosynthesis & phys biochem, 63-69, asst biochemist, 63-69, assoc prof enzyme & photosynthesis, 69-77, assoc biochemist, 69-77, ASSOC PROF PHYS BIOCHEM, UNIV CALIF, RIVERSIDE, 69- *Honors & Awards:* NY Bot Award, 62. *Mem:* Am Chem Soc. *Res:* Isolation and characterization of proteins, including mammalian pyruvate kinase and pentose phosphate cycle enzymes in photosynthesis; mechanism of action of enzymes; structure and function of chloroplast proteins. *Mailing Add:* Dept of Biochem Univ of Calif Riverside CA 92502

PONARAS, ANTHONY A, b New York, NY, May 12, 47. ORGANIC CHEMISTRY. *Educ:* Columbia Col, NY, AB, 67; Columbia Univ, PhD(chem), 72. *Prof Exp:* Fel chem, Swiss Fed Inst Technol, 73-75 & Univ Calif, Berkeley, 75-77; asst prof, Univ Md, 77-81; MEM FAC, CATH UNIV, 81- *Res:* Synthetic organic chemistry; stereospecific synthesis; pericyclic reactions. *Mailing Add:* Chem Dept Cath Univ Washington DC 20064

PONCELET, CLAUDE G(HISLAIN), b Brussels, Belg, June 20, 37; US citizen; m 60; c 4. ENERGY POLICY, ENVIRONMENTAL ISSUES. *Educ:* Manhattan Col, BEE, 58; NC State Univ, MS, 60, PhD(physics), 65. *Prof Exp:* From assoc scientist to sr scientist, Atomic Power Div, Westinghouse Elec Corp, 60-66, fel scientist, 66-67; from asst prof to prof nuclear eng, Carnegie-Mellon Univ, 67-77, chmn nuclear sci & eng div, 69-75; sci adv, 75-80, DIR ISSUE ANAL & MGT, POWER SYSTS CO, WESTINGHOUSE ELEC CORP, 81- *Concurrent Pos:* Instr, Carnegie Inst Technol, 66-77, lectr, 77-; consult nuclear energy systs, Westinghouse Elec Corp, 67-71, Gulf Gen Atomic, 69-70, Nuclear Fuel Serv, Inc, 72-73, Los Alamos Sci Lab & Westinghouse Elec Corp Advanced Reactors Div, 74-75. *Mem:* Am Nuclear Soc; AAAS. *Res:* Nuclear reactor physics; reactor kinetics and stability; reactor operations and safety; fuel and control management; energy conversion; energy generation systems; energy policy; communications theory. *Mailing Add:* 1117 S Negley Ave Pittsburgh PA 15217

PONCHA, RUSTOM PESTONJI, b Bombay, India; US citizen. INORGANIC CHEMISTRY, PHYSICAL CHEMISTRY. *Educ:* Univ Bombay, BSc, 47, MSc, 49; Northeastern Univ, PhD(chem), 68. *Prof Exp:* Res chemist, Amzel Ltd, Ind, 50-55; res chemist, Bhabha Atomic Res Ctr, 55-62; teaching asst chem, Northeastern Univ, 62-67; RES CHEMIST, CHEM CO, ALLIED CORP, 67- *Mem:* Am Chem Soc. *Res:* Nuclear chemistry; foam fractionation; separation of isotopes; ion exchange; development of new alkali products and processes; water treatment research; metallization of plastics. *Mailing Add:* Chem Co Allied Corp Solvay NY 13209

POND, DAVID MARTIN, b Washington, DC, Sept 14, 42; m 67; c 3. ORGANIC CHEMISTRY, PHOTOCHEMISTRY. *Educ:* Col William & Mary, BS, 64; Univ SC, PhD(org chem), 68. *Prof Exp:* Prof NJ Turro fel, Columbia Univ, 68-70; sr res chemist, 70-77, RES ASSOC TENN EASTMAN CO, 77- *Mem:* Am CHem Soc. *Res:* Organic synthesis; synthetic photochemistry; homogeneous catacysis. *Mailing Add:* Res Labs Tenn Eastman Co Kingsport TN 37660

POND, GEORGE STEPHEN, b Victoria, BC, Aug 16, 40; m 68. PHYSICAL OCEANOGRAPHY. *Educ:* Univ BC, BSc, 62, PhD(phys oceanog), 65. *Prof Exp:* Nat Res Coun Can res fel phys oceanog, Nat Inst Oceanog, Eng, 65-66 & exchange scientist, Inst Atmospheric Physics, Acad Sci, USSR, 67; from asst prof to assoc prof phys oceanog, Ore State Univ, 67-71; assoc prof, 71-77, PROF PHYSICS & OCEANOG, UNIV BC, 77- *Mem:* Am Meteorol Soc. *Res:* Air-sea interaction; coastal circulation; turbulence and turbulent fluxes in the air-sea boundary layer. *Mailing Add:* Inst of Oceanog Univ of BC Vancouver BC V6T 1W5 Can

POND, JUDSON SAMUEL, b Minneapolis, Minn, July 15, 22; m 59. INORGANIC CHEMISTRY. *Educ:* Univ Minn, BMechE, 43, BBA, 55, PhD(inorg chem), 64. *Prof Exp:* Asst, Univ Minn, 57-61, instr, 62-63; instr, Univ Mont, 63-64, asst prof, 64-66; res assoc inorg chem, Univ Chicago, 66-67; assoc prof, Lane Community Col, 67-68; sr instr inorg chem, Univ Ore, 68-77; EXEC ASST TO CHMN, DEPT BIOL SCI, UNIV PITTSBURGH, 77- *Mem:* Am Chem Soc. *Res:* Sulfur-amine chemistry; inorganic reaction mechanisms. *Mailing Add:* Dept Biol Sci Univ Pittsburgh Pittsburgh PA 15260

POND, THOMAS ALEXANDER, b Los Angeles, Calif, Dec 4, 24; m 58; c 2. NUCLEAR PHYSICS. *Educ:* Princeton Univ, AB, 47, AM, 49, PhD(physics), 53. *Prof Exp:* Instr physics, Princeton Univ, 51-53; from asst prof to assoc prof, Wash Univ, 53-62; chmn dept, 62-68, actg pres, 70, 75 & 78, prof physics, 62-82, exec vpres, 67-80, EMER PROF PHYSICS, STATE UNIV NY, STONY BROOK, 82-; PROF PHYSICS, EXEC VPRES & CHIEF ACADEMIC OFFICER, RUTGERS UNIV, NJ, 82- *Mem:* Am Phys Soc. *Res:* Positron processes; beta-decay. *Mailing Add:* State Univ NY Stony Brook NY 11794

POND, WILSON GIDEON, b Minneapolis, Minn, Feb 16, 30; m 53; c 1. ANIMAL NUTRITION. *Educ:* Univ Minn, BS, 52; Okla State Univ, MS, 54, PhD(animal nutrit), 57. *Prof Exp:* From asst prof animal husb to assoc prof animal sci, 57-70, prof animal sci, Grad Sch Nutrit, Cornell Univ, 70-78; RES LEADER NUTRIT, US MEAT ANIMAL RES CTR, AGR RES SERV, USDA, 78- *Mem:* AAAS; Am Soc Animal Sci; Am Inst Nutrit; Soc Exp Biol & Med. *Res:* Nutritional requirements of monogastric animals, especially swine; mineral, amino acid and energy relationships; swine management problems. *Mailing Add:* Res Leader Nutrit Box 166 Clay Center NE 68933

PONDER, BILLY WAYNE, b Chatham, La, Nov 4, 33; m 58; c 2. ORGANIC CHEMISTRY. *Educ:* La Polytech Inst, BS, 56; Iowa State Univ, MS, 59, PhD(org chem), 60. *Prof Exp:* Sr res chemist, Aerospace Res Labs, Wright-Patterson AFB, Ohio, 61-64; asst prof, 64-69, ASSOC PROF CHEM, UNIV ALA, 69- *Concurrent Pos:* Res chemist, Jefferson Chem Co, 60-61; US Army res grant, 65-69; NASA res grant, 67-71; chmn, Health Careers Off, 74-; Exxon Educ Found grant, 75. *Mem:* Am Chem Soc; Royal Soc Chem; Sigma Xi (pres, 73). *Res:* New synthetic methods; stereochemistry; organic reaction mechanisms. *Mailing Add:* Dept of Chem Univ of Ala Box H University AL 35486

PONDER, FELIX, JR, b Quitman, Ga, Oct 7, 46; m 69; c 2. PLANT SCIENCE, SOIL SCIENCE. *Educ:* Ft Valley State Col, BS, 69; Tuskegee Inst, MS, 71; Southern Ill Univ, PhD(bot), 78. *Prof Exp:* Soil conservationist agr, Soil Conserv Serv, USDA, 69; res asst soil sci, Tuskegee Inst, 69-71; soil scientist, Forest Serv, Nat Forest Syst, 71-75, RES SOIL SCIENTIST, N CENT FOREST EXP STA, USDA, 75- *Mem:* Am Soc Agron; Soil Sci Soc Am; Soc Am Foresters; Sigma Xi. *Res:* Growing black walnut faster on old field sites; assessing the contributions of mycorrhizal fungi; fertilization; physical and chemical soil properties. *Mailing Add:* NCent Forest Exp Sta Southern Ill Univ Carbondale IL 62901

PONDER, HERMAN, b Light, Ark, Jan 31, 28; m 47; c 2. MINERALOGY. *Educ:* Univ Mo, AB, 55, PhD(geol), 59. *Prof Exp:* Asst, Univ Mo, 55-56, asst instr, 56; geologist, A P Green Fire Brick Co, 57; geologist & mineralogist, Shell Develop Co, 58; res engr & mineralogist, A P Green Fire BRick Co, Mo, 59-61, group leader, 61-62, lab mgr, 62-63; sr proj engr, 63-66, mgr mining div, 66, dir res, 66-70, PRES, COLO SCH MINES RES INST, 70- *Concurrent Pos:* Geologist, US Geol Surv, 55-57; dir, La Land & Explor Co & Golden State Bank. *Mem:* Am Inst Mining, Metall & Petrol Eng; Am Inst Prof Geol. *Res:* Mineral exploration and beneficiation; mining engineering. *Mailing Add:* Box 112 Colo Sch of Mines Res Inst Golden CO 80401

PONDROM, LEE GIRARD, b Dallas, Tex, Dec 26, 33; m 61. EXPERIMENTAL PHYSICS. *Educ:* Southern Methodist Univ, BS, 53; Univ Chicago, MS, 56, PhD(physics), 58. *Prof Exp:* Instr physics, Columbia Univ, 60-63; assoc prof, 63-69, PROF PHYSICS, UNIV WIS-MADISON, 69- *Concurrent Pos:* Guggenheim fel, 71-72; secy, Users Exec Comt, Nat Accelerator Lab, Ill; mem, Bd Trustees, Univs Res Asn, 73-76; mem, High Energy Adv Comt, Brookhaven Nat Lab, 74-76; fel, Japan Soc Prom Sci, 81; mem, High Energy Phys Adv Panel, Us Dept Energy, 81 & Phys Adv Comt, Nat Sci Found, 81-; chmn, High Energy Phys Rev Comt, Argonne Univ Asn, 80-81 & Phys Adv Comt, Fermi Nat Accelerator Lab, 81-82. *Mem:* Fel Am Phys Soc. *Res:* Experimental studies in elementary particle physics using electronic techniques; general instrumentation problems in elementary particle physics. *Mailing Add:* Dept of Physics Univ of Wis Madison WI 53706

PONELEIT, CHARLES GUSTAV, b Collinsville, Ill, Oct 14, 40; m 63; c 2. PLANT GENETICS, PLANT BREEDING. *Educ:* Univ Ill, Champaign, BS, 62, MS, 64; Purdue Univ, Lafayette, PhD(plant genetics), 68. *Prof Exp:* Asst prof, 67-73, ASSOC PROF PLANT BREEDING & GENETICS, UNIV KY, 73- *Mem:* Am Soc Agron; Crop Sci Soc Am. *Res:* Biochemical and physiological genetics of corn; corn breeding. *Mailing Add:* Dept of Agron Univ of Ky Lexington KY 40546

PONESSA, JOSEPH THOMAS, b New York, NY, Sept 10, 41; m 65; c 3. ENERGY CONSERVATION, DESIGN CONSTRUCTION. *Educ:* St Francis Col, BS, 62; Univ NDak, MS, 65; Loyola Univ Chicago, PhD(physiol), 69. *Prof Exp:* NIH fel, Hahnemann Med Col, 69-71, asst prof physiol, 69-81; ASSOC PROF HOUSING & ENERGY CONSERVATION, COOP EXTEN, COOK COL RUTGERS UNIV, 81- *Concurrent Pos:* Foreign Exchange res fel, Semmelweis Med Univ, Budapest, 73. *Mem:* Sigma Xi; Asn Housing Educators. *Res:* Cardiovascular control; cerebral blood flow; autonomic nervous system control. *Mailing Add:* Coop Exten Serv Cook Col Rutgers Univ PO Box 231 New Brunswick NJ 08903

PONG, SCHWE FANG, b Hsin-Chu, Taiwan, June 4, 36; m 64; c 3. PHARMACOLOGY. *Educ:* Nat Taiwan Univ, BS, 62; Univ Tenn, MS, 66; Univ Miss, PhD(pharmacol), 70. *Prof Exp:* Res specialist neurochem & neuropharmacol, Tex Res Inst Ment Sci, 70-71; NIMH fel neurobiol, Inst Psychiat Res, Sch Med, Ind Univ, Indianapolis, 71-73, res assoc, 73-74; sr res pharmacologist, 74-76 & 76-78, RES ASSOC, NORWICH-EATON PHARMACEUT, 78- *Mem:* AAAS; Sigma Xi; Am Pharmaceut Asn; Am Soc Neurochem; Am Chem Soc. *Res:* Mechanisms of psychotropic and antihypertensive drug action; mechanism of drug induced hepatotoxicity; biochemical approach of psychotropic ankd antihypertensive drug evaluation; functional correlation of neurotransmitters in central nervous system; drug metabolism. *Mailing Add:* Res & Develop Dept Norwich-Eaton Pharmaceut Norwich NY 13815

PONG, WILLIAM, b Cincinnati, Ohio, Dec 26, 27. PHYSICS. *Educ:* Univ Cincinnati, PhD(physics), 54. *Prof Exp:* Res physicist, Electronics Div, Baldwin Co, 54-58; asst prof physics, Xavier Univ, Ohio, 58-60; assoc prof, 60-68, PROF PHYSICS, UNIV HAWAII, 68- *Res:* Nonlinear acoustics; UV photoemission from soilds. *Mailing Add:* Dept of Physics & Astron Univ of Hawaii Honolulu HI 96822

PONGRATZ, MORRIS BERNARD, b O'Neill, Nebr, Apr 10, 42; m 67; c 2. SPACE PHYSICS. *Educ:* Creighton Univ, BS, 64; Univ Md, College Park, PhD(space physics), 72. *Prof Exp:* Res assoc space physics, Inst Fluid Dynamics, Univ Md, 72-73; sci specialist neutron physics, Los Alamos Div, EG&G Co, 73-75; STAFF MEM SPACE PHYSICS, LOS ALAMOS NAT LAB, 75- *Mem:* Am Geophys Union; AAAS. *Res:* Active experiments in the magnetosphere and study of the magnetospheric electric and magnetic fields using high explosive shaped charge barium plasma injections; plasma physics associated with such injections. *Mailing Add:* MS 438 Los Alamos Nat Lab Los Alamos NM 87545

PONNAMPERUMA, CYRIL ANDREW, b Galle, Ceylon, Oct 16, 23; m 55; c 1. BIO-ORGANIC CHEMISTRY. *Educ:* Univ Madras, BA, 48; Univ London, BSc, 59; Univ Calif, Berkeley, PhD(chem), 62. *Hon Degrees:* DSc, Univ Sri Lanka, 78. *Prof Exp:* Res asst, Lawrence Radiation Lab, Univ Calif, Berkeley, 60-62; scientist, Ames Res Ctr, NASA, 63-65, chief chem evolution br, 65-71; PROF CHEM & DIR LAB CHEM EVOLUTION, UNIV MD, COLLEGE PARK, 71- *Concurrent Pos:* Prin investr org anal, Apollo Prog, 67; distinguished vis prof, Indian Atomic Energy Comn, 67; fac sci, Univ Sorbonne, 69; adj prof, Boston Col, 69; dir UNESCO Inst Early Evolution, Ceylon, 70; ed, J Molecular Evolution, 70-72; ed, Origins Life, 73-; distinguished prof, Univ Md, 78; Foreign mem, Indian Nat Sci Acad, 78. *Mem:* AAAS; Am Chem Soc; Royal Soc Chem; fel Royal Inst Chem; Int Soc Study Origin Life. *Res:* Chemical evolution exobiology; geochemistry; space sciences. *Mailing Add:* Lab of Chem Evolution Dept of Chem Univ of Md College Park MD 20742

PONNAPALLI, RAMACHANDRAMURTY, b Hyderabad, India, Mar 15, 33. MATHEMATICS, STATISTICS. *Educ:* Andhra Univ, India, BA, 53, MSc, 55; Univ Calif, Berkeley, PhD(statist), 64. *Prof Exp:* Lectr statist, Andhra Univ, India, 55-60; asst, Univ Calif, Berkeley, 60-64; asst prof, Case Inst Technol, 64-65; reader, Osmania Univ, India, 65-69, head dept, 66-69; asst prof math, Univ Alta, 69-76, Univ West Ont, 76-78; ASST PROF MATH, UNIV WINDSOR, 78- *Mem:* Inst Math Statist; Can Math Cong; Indian Statist Inst; Indian Sci Cong Asn. *Mailing Add:* 707 Sunset Windsor ON N9B 3B2 Can

PONOMAREV, PAUL, b Czestochowa, Poland, Oct 5, 44; US citizen; m 68; c 2. MATHEMATICS. *Educ:* Princeton Univ, AB, 66; Yale Univ, PhD(math), 70. *Prof Exp:* Asst prof math, Johns Hopkins Univ, 70-74; asst prof, 75-77, ASSOC PROF, OHIO STATE UNIV, 77- *Concurrent Pos:* Vis mem, Inst Advan Study, 74-75; vis prof, Gottingen Univ, 75. *Mem:* Am Math Soc. *Res:* Number theory; algebra. *Mailing Add:* Dept Math Ohio State Univ Columbus OH 43210

PONS, MARCEL WILLIAM, virology, see previous edition

PONS, STANLEY, US citizen. SPECTROELECTROCHEMISTRY, ELECTROCHEMICAL KINETICS. *Educ:* Wake Forest Univ, BS, 65; Univ Southampton, PhD(chem), 79. *Prof Exp:* Asst prof, Oakland Univ, 78-80; ASST PROF CHEM, UNIV ALBERTA, 80- *Mem:* Int Soc Electrochem; Electrochem Soc; Am Chem Soc; Can Inst Chem. *Res:* Spectroelectrochemistry; electrochemical kinetics; simulation of diffusion processes; electrochemistry of metallporphyrins; electroorganic synthesis; infrared structure of the electrode-electrolyte intertake. *Mailing Add:* Dept Chem Univ Alberta Edmonton AB T6G 2G2 Can

PONSETI, IGNACIO VIVES, b Balearic Islands, Spain, June 3, 14; nat; m 61; c 1. MEDICINE. *Educ:* Univ Barcelona, BA, 30, MD, 36. *Prof Exp:* Instr, 44-46. asst, 46-48, from asst prof to assoc prof, 48-57, PROF ORTHOP SURG, UNIV IOWA, 57- *Mem:* Am Acad Orthop Surgeons; Am Col Surgeons; Am Acad Cerebral Palsy; Am Orthop Asn; Orthop Res Soc (past pres). *Res:* Congenital and developmental skeletal deformities; factors influencing the growth of epiphyseal plates of bone; congenital anomalies of the skeleton. *Mailing Add:* Dept of Orthop Surg Univ Hosp Iowa City IA 52242

PONTARELLI, DOMENIC JOSEPH, b Philadelphia, Pa, May 26, 12; m 47; c 2. OBSTETRICS & GYNECOLOGY. *Educ:* Hahnemann Med Col, MD, 40. *Prof Exp:* From instr to assoc prof, 47-66, PROF OBSTET & GYNEC, HAHNEMANN MED COL & HOSP, 66- *Concurrent Pos:* Asst attend obstet & gynec, Philadelphia Gen Hosp, 53-64, chief serv, 64-66; chief obstet & gynec, Jeanes Hosp, Fox Chase. *Mem:* Fel Am Col Surgeons; fel Am Col Obstetricians & Gynecologists; Asn Profs Gynec & Obstet; AMA. *Mailing Add:* 1320 Race St Philadelphia PA 19107

PONTAU, ARTHUR E, b Philadelphia, Pa, July 27, 51. PLASMA MATERIALS INTERACTIONS, ION BEAM ANALYSIS. *Educ:* Univ Calif, San Diego, BA, 73; Univ Ill, MS, 75, PhD(physics), 78. *Prof Exp:* PHYSICIST, SANDIA NAT LABS, 78- *Mem:* Am Phys Soc; AAAS. *Res:* Analysis of materials appropriate for use in in-vessel components for magnetic confinement fusion reactors; characterization of plasma edge parameters. *Mailing Add:* Div 8347 Sandia Nat Labs Livermore CA 94550

PONTE, JOSEPH G, JR, b New Bedford, Mass, Aug 9, 25; m 56; c 3. FOOD SCIENCE. *Educ:* Northwestern Univ, BA, 56; Univ Minn, St Paul, MS, 58. *Prof Exp:* Baking technologist, Am Inst Baking, 54-56; res chemist, ITT Continental Baking Co, 58-65, sr res chemist, 65-70, res supvr, 70-74, mgr res serv, 74-75; PROF GRAIN SCI & INDUST, KANS STATE UNIV, 75- *Concurrent Pos:* Chmn comt on cereal products, Nat Res Coun, 74-78. *Mem:* Am Asn Cereal Chem (treas, 70-72, secy, 75-77); Sigma Xi; Am Soc Bakery Eng; Inst Food Technol. *Res:* Flour chemistry; lipids; carbohydrates; food technology; baking technology; nutrition food products. *Mailing Add:* Dept Grain Sci & Indust Kans State Univ Manhattan KS 66506

PONTER, ANTHONY BARRIE, b Staffordshire, Eng, Sept 27, 33; m 60; c 2. CHEMICAL ENGINEERING. *Educ:* Birmingham Univ, BSc hons, 56; Univ Manchester Inst Sci Technol, MSc, 62; Manchester Univ, PhD, 66. *Prof Exp:* Mem staff mech eng, Rubery Owens Orgn, 56-57; tech officer & plant mgr, Pilkington-Sullivan Works, 57-59; lectr, Inst Sci & Technol, Manchester Univ, 60-69; assoc prof, Univ NB, 69-72; prof & dir, Swiss Fed Inst Technol, 72-77; vis prof, Univ Aston, Eng, 77-78; DEPT HEAD & PROF, MICH TECHNOL UNIV, 78- *Mem:* fel Inst Chem Engrs UK; fel Chem Inst Can; Am Inst Chem Engrs; Ver Deut Ingenieure. *Res:* Distillation; absorption; condensation; wetting; surface phenomena; coalescence; nucleate boiling; diffusion; liquid flow in packed columns; boiling acoustics; liquid films; author of approximately 125 papers. *Mailing Add:* Dept Chem & Chem Eng Mich Technol Univ Houghton MI 49931

PONTICELLO, GERALD S, b Rochester, NY, Mar 31, 39; m 67; c 2. ORGANIC CHEMISTRY. *Educ:* Univ Toronto, BS, 61; Univ Rochester, PhD(org chem), 69. *Prof Exp:* Prod chemist, Eastman Kodak Co, 61-62; fel with Dr Henry Sobel, 69-70; SR RES CHEMIST, MERCK & CO, INC, WEST POINT, 70- *Mem:* Am Chem Soc. *Res:* Medicinal chemistry; testing of organic molecules in health related fields. *Mailing Add:* Merck Sharp & Dohme Res Lab West Point PA 19486

PONTICELLO, IGNAZIO SALVATORE, b Rochester, NY, Mar 31, 39; m 67; c 2. ORGANIC CHEMISTRY. *Educ:* Univ Toronto, BSc, 61; Univ Rochester, PhD(org chem), 69. *Prof Exp:* SR RES CHEMIST, RES LABS, CHEM DIV, EASTMAN KODAK CO, 69- *Mem:* Am Chem Soc. *Res:* Synthesis and polymerization of new monomers for evaluation in photographic processes. *Mailing Add:* Kodak Res Labs Eastman Kodak Co 1669 Lake Ave Rochester NY 14650

PONTINEN, RICHARD ERNEST, b Eveleth, Minn, Sept 21, 33; m 56; c 2. PHYSICS. *Educ:* Hamline Univ, BS, 55; Univ Minn, Minneapolis, PhD(solid state physics), 62. *Prof Exp:* From asst prof to assoc prof, 61-68, PROF PHYSICS, HAMLINE UNIV, 68-, CHMN DEPT, 71- *Mem:* Am Phys Soc; Am Asn Physics Teachers. *Res:* Liquids using lasers; low temperature solid state physics. *Mailing Add:* Dept of Physics Hamline Univ St Paul MN 55104

PONTIUS, DIETER J J, b Zurich, Switz, July 31, 14; US citizen; m 51. ORGANIC CHEMISTRY, ANALYTICAL CHEMISTRY. *Educ:* Univ Frankfurt, MSc, 47, PhD(chem physics & physiol chem), 50. *Prof Exp:* German Scientist's Res Asn scholar, Steroid Res, Endocrine Res Unit, Trier, Ger, 51-54; univ hosp, Hamburg, 54-55; Montreal Gen Hosp, Que, 56; asst chem, Clark Univ, 57-59; res scientist, Neuro-Endocrine Res Unit, Willowbrook State Sch, NY, 59-60; res chemist, Fairmount Chem Co, 60-69; PVT RES, 69- *Mem:* Am Chem Soc; NY Acad Sci. *Res:* Organic synthesis; steroid biochemistry; absorption spectroscopy; development of new color reactions; quantum chemistry. *Mailing Add:* 165 E 60th St New York NY 10022

PONTIUS, DUANE HENRY, b Urbana, Ill, Feb 16, 39; m 60; c 2. SOLID STATE PHYSICS. *Educ:* Auburn Univ, BS, 62, MS, 69, PhD(physics), 72. *Prof Exp:* Fel, Auburn Univ, 72-73; asst prof physics, Univ WFla, 73-75; RES PHYSICIST, SOUTHERN RES INST, 75- *Mem:* Am Asn Physics Teachers. *Res:* Electrical charging of fine particles in aerosol suspension. *Mailing Add:* 5342 Dixie Land Rd Birmingham AL 35210

PONTIUS, E(UGENE) C(AMERON), b Napoleon, Ohio, Mar 18, 15; m 41; c 2. CHEMICAL ENGINEERING, MATERIALS & SCIENCE ENGINEERING. *Educ:* Ohio State Univ, BChE, 39, MS, 49, PhD(chem eng), 50. *Prof Exp:* Chem engr res & develop, Va Smelting Co, 39-42; asst chem eng, Ohio State Univ, 46-50; res engr, Textile Fibers Dept, E I Du Pont De Nemours & Co, Inc, 50-56, process design engr, Eng Dept, 56-69, sr process engr, Design Div, 69-70, sr design consult, Eng Dept, Design Div, 70-80; RETIRED. *Mem:* Am Chem Soc; Instrument Soc Am; fel Am Inst Chemists; Am Inst Chem Engrs; NY Acad Sci. *Res:* Process design and development; plant design. *Mailing Add:* 29 Possum Hollow Rd Newark DE 19711

PONTOPPIDAN, HENNING, b Copenhagen, Denmark, July 24, 25; US citizen; m 49; c 3. ANESTHESIOLOGY, RESPIRATORY PHYSIOLOGY. *Educ:* Copenhagen Univ, MD, 52. *Prof Exp:* From instr to asst prof, 59-70, assoc prof, 70-75, PROF ANESTHESIA, HARVARD MED SCH, 75-; CHIEF RESPIRATORY UNIT, MASS GEN HOSP, 61-, ANESTHETIST, 67- *Mem:* Am Soc Anesthesiol; Am Thoracic Soc; Soc Critical Care Med; Am Col Chest Physicians. *Res:* Acute respiratory failure; physiology of artificial ventilation. *Mailing Add:* Dept Anesthesia Mass Gen Hosp Boston MA 02114

PONTRELLI, GENE J, b Bronx, NY, Dec 25, 33; m 56; c 3. TEXTILE PHYSICS. *Educ:* City Col New York, BS, 58; Univ Wis, PhD(chem), 63. *Prof Exp:* Teaching asst chem, Univ Wis, 59-60; res phys chemist, Eng Physics Lab, E I du Pont de Nemours & Co, 62-65; res chemist, Textile Res Lab, 65-66, sr res chemist, 66, res supvr, 66-69; tech mgr, Fibers Div, Allied Chem Corp, 70-73; res assoc, 76-81, RES FEL, TEXTILE FIBERS DEPT, E I DU PONT DE NEMOURS & CO, INC, 81- *Concurrent Pos:* Woodrow Wilson fel. *Honors & Awards:* Medal, Am Inst Chemists. *Mem:* Am Chem Soc; Am Phys Soc. *Res:* Mechanism of moisture transport in clothing as a function of fiber, yarn and fabric construction; technology forecasting for synthetic fibers; advanced composites. *Mailing Add:* Chestnut Run Lab E I Du Pont de Nemours & Co Inc Wilmington DE 19898

PONZIO, NICHOLAS MICHAEL, US citizen. IMMUNOLOGY. *Educ:* Seton Hall Univ, BA, 68, MS, 70; State Univ NY Brooklyn, PhD(immunol), 73. *Prof Exp:* Fel, Albert Einstein Col Med, 73-74; fel, Sch Med, NY Univ, 74-76; asst prof, Med Sch, Northwestern Univ, 76-80, assoc prof, 80-81; ASSOC PROF, SCH MED, UNIV MED & DENT NJ, 81- *Concurrent Pos:* Res career develop award, 79-84. *Mem:* AAAS; Sigma Xi; Am Asn Immunologists; Am Asn Pathologists; Am Asn Cancer Res. *Res:* In vivo and in vitro analysis of lymphocyte responses to mitogens, alloantigens, tumor antigens and hapten-carrier conjugates. *Mailing Add:* Dept Path Univ Med & Dent NJ 100 Bergen St Newark NJ 07103

PONZO, PETER JAMES, b Toronto, Ont, Nov 6, 34; m 60; c 1. APPLIED MATHEMATICS. *Educ:* Univ Toronto, BASc, 57, MA, 59; Univ Ill, PhD(elec eng), 64. *Prof Exp:* Lectr math, Univ Waterloo, 57-58 & 59-60; res assoc elec eng, Univ Ill, 63-64; asst prof, 64-66, assoc prof, 66-76, PROF MATH, UNIV WATERLOO, 76- *Res:* Nonlinear differential equations. *Mailing Add:* Dept of Appl Math Univ of Waterloo Waterloo ON N2J 2C8 Can

POOCH, UDO WALTER, b Berlin, WGer, Apr 20, 43; m 62; c 2. THEORETICAL PHYSICS, COMPUTER SCIENCE. *Educ:* Univ Calif, Los Angeles, BS, 65; Univ Notre Dame, PhD(theoret physics), 69. *Prof Exp:* Asst physics, Univ Notre Dame, 66-69; assoc prof, 69-80, PROF COMPUT SCI & MEM GRAD FAC, TEX A&M UNIV, 80- *Concurrent Pos:* Consult, Decision Systs Assoc, 63-; Comput Graphics Int, 69-70; Quest Res Corp-US Air Force, 71-; Tex Transp Inst, Tex A&M Univ, 71-; registered prof engr, 75; nat lectr, Asn Comput Mach, 75 & IBM, 81. *Mem:* Am Phys Soc; Asn Comput Mach; Simulation Coun; Soc Indust & Appl Math; Opers Res Soc Am. *Res:* Softwave systems for mini-maxi computers; interactive computer graphics; information storage-retrieval systems; natural language query systems; artificial intelligence; teleprocessing applications; data structures; pattern recognition; mathematical linguistic; time sharing. *Mailing Add:* Dept Comput Sci Tex A&M Univ College Station TX 77843

POOCHIKIAN, GUIRAGOS K, b Beirut, Lebanon, 45; US citizen; m 75; c 2. PHARMACEUTICAL CHEMISTRY, MEDICINAL CHEMISTRY. *Educ:* Am Univ Beirut, BS, 70; Ohio State Univ, PhD(pharmaceut & med chem), 74. *Prof Exp:* Dir qual control lab, Scierlabs, Sci & Pharmaceut Res Labs, 74-76; formulation chemist, Anal & Prod Develop Sect, Pharmaceut Resources Br, Nat Cancer Inst, NIH, 76-80; CHEMIST, BUR DRUGS, FOOD & DRUG ADMIN, 80- *Concurrent Pos:* Res asst, Col Pharmacy, Ohio State Univ, 70-71, res assoc, 71-74. *Mem:* Am Chem Soc; AAAS. *Res:* Product development of delivery systems; study of new formulation approaches, evaluation of dosage form problems, and development of new analytical methods pertaining to the formulation studies. *Mailing Add:* 536 W Deer Park Rd Gaithersburg MD 20877

POODRY, CLIFTON ARTHUR, b Buffalo, NY, July 31, 43; m 74; c 1. DEVELOPMENTAL BIOLOGY. *Educ:* State Univ NY, Buffalo, BA, 65, MA, 68; Western Reserve Univ, PhD(biol), 71. *Prof Exp:* Res assoc genetics, Univ BC, 71-72; asst prof, 72-77, ASSOC PROF BIOL, UNIV CALIF, SANTA CRUZ, 77- *Concurrent Pos:* Mem, Gen Res Adv Comt, NIH, 77-81; adv mem & fac, Headlands Indian Health Careers Prog, Univ Okla, 77-; adv mem, NSF Develop Biol Prog, 80-, adv coun mem, 81- *Mem:* Genetics Soc Am; Am Soc Zoologists; Sigma Xi; Soc Develop Biol; Am Indian Sci & Eng Soc. *Res:* Developmental genetics; cell surface proteins and morphogenesis. *Mailing Add:* Thimann Labs Univ of Calif Santa Cruz CA 95064

POOL, EDWIN LEWIS, b Eagle Grove, Iowa, Mar 2, 21; m 49; c 3. ANALYTICAL CHEMISTRY, ENVIRONMENTAL CHEMISTRY. *Educ:* Iowa State Univ, BS, 43, MS, 49, PhD(biophys chem), 52. *Prof Exp:* Asst prof chem, DePauw Univ, 53-54; from instr to assoc prof, 54-70, PROF CHEM, MIDDLEBURY COL, 71- *Mem:* Am Chem Soc; Sigma Xi. *Res:* Environmental analyses; analytical chemistry; colorimetric analysis; enzyme production by microorganisms. *Mailing Add:* Dept of Chem Middlebury Col Middlebury VT 05753

POOL, JAMES C T, b Wellsville, Kans, Feb 27, 37; m 56; c 2. MATHEMATICAL ANALYSIS. *Educ:* Univ Kans, AB, 59; Univ Iowa, PhD(physics), 63. *Prof Exp:* Res scientist, Sci Lab, Ford Motor Co, 63-65; NSF fel, Brandeis Univ, 64-65; asst mathematician, Appl Math Div, Argonne Nat Lab, 66-68; asst prof math, Univ Mass, 68-69; asst div dir, Argonne Nat Lab, 69-70, actg div dir, 70-71, assoc div dir res, Appl Math Div, 71-78; PROG DIR APPL MATH SCI, BASIC ENERGY SCI, DEPT ENERGY, WASHINGTON, DC, 78- *Concurrent Pos:* Fel, Inst Theoret Physics, Univ Hamburg, Ger, 66-67; Swiss Nat Fund fel, Inst Theoret Physics, Univ Geneva, 67; chmn working group numerical software, Int Fed Info Processing, 74-78. *Mem:* AAAS; Soc Indust & Appl Math; Inst Math & its Appln; Asn Comput Mach. *Res:* Software for numerical computation; functional analysis algebras of operators on Hilbert space; lattice theory. *Mailing Add:* Basic Energy Sci Dept of Energy Washington DC 20545

POOL, KARL, b Norristown, Pa, Aug 3, 39; m 61; c 2 2. ANALYTICAL CHEMISTRY. *Educ:* Calif Inst Tech, BS, 61; Univ Wash, PhD(anal chem), 65. *Prof Exp:* From instr to asst prof, 55-73, ASSOC PROF ANAL CHEM, WASH STATE UNIV, 73- *Mem:* Am Chem Soc; Sigma Xi. *Res:* Design and characterization of new ion selective electrodes. *Mailing Add:* Dept of Chem Wash State Univ Pullman WA 99163

POOL, MONTE J, b Toledo, Ohio, Nov 18, 34; m 52; c 3. METALLURGY, THERMODYNAMICS. *Educ:* Univ Cincinnati, BMetE, 58; Ohio State Univ, MS, 59, PhD(metall), 61. *Prof Exp:* From asst prof to assoc prof metall, Univ Denver, 61-68, res metallurgist, Denver Res Inst, 61-68; assoc prof mat sci & metall eng, 68-72, PROF METALL ENG, UNIV CINCINNATI, 72- *Concurrent Pos:* Vis sr scientist, Max Planck Inst Metall-forsch, Stuttgart, 76-77. *Mem:* AAAS; Am Soc Metals; Am Inst Mining, Metall & Petrol Engrs; Am Soc Eng Educ. *Res:* Alloy thermochemistry, especially binary systems; dilute metallic liquid solutions using solution calorimetry. *Mailing Add:* Dept of Mat Sci & Metall Eng Univ of Cincinnati Cincinnati OH 45221

POOL, ROBERT ALFRED FRANK, plant pathology, plant physiology, see previous edition

POOL, ROBERT MORRIS, b Sacramento, Calif, Feb 22, 40. VITICULTURE, PLANT PHYSIOLOGY. *Educ:* Univ Calif, Davis, BS, 62, MS, 69; Cornell Univ, PhD(pomol), 74. *Prof Exp:* Staff res assoc viticult, Univ Calif, Davis, 62-71; res asst pomol, Cornell Univ, 71-74; ASST PROF VITICULT, NY STATE AGR EXP STA, 74- *Concurrent Pos:* Chmn, Nat Grape Germplasm Comt, 74-; assoc ed, Am Soc Hort Sci, 76- *Mem:* Am Soc Hort Sci; Am Soc Enology; Sigma Xi. *Res:* Grape breeding; cultural practices in vineyards in relation to wine quality; growth regulators; grapevine growth and development. *Mailing Add:* Dept of Pomol & Viticult NY State Agr Exp Sta Geneva NY 14456

POOL, ROY RANSOM, b Raleigh, NC, Oct 8, 34; m 67; c 1. VETERINARY PATHOLOGY, RADIOBIOLOGY. *Educ:* Duke Univ, BS, 57; Okla State Univ, BS, 62, DVM, 64; Univ Calif, Davis, PhD(comp path), 67. *Prof Exp:* Asst prof vet anat, Okla State Univ, 67-69; asst prof & asst res pathologist, 69-75, ASSOC PROF VET PATH & ASSOC RES PATHOLOGIST, SCH VET MED, UNIV CALIF, DAVIS, 75- *Mem:* Am Vet Med Asn; Vet Cancer Soc. *Res:* Bone pathology; radionuclide toxicity. *Mailing Add:* Dept of Path Univ of Calif Sch of Vet Med Davis CA 95616

POOL, THOMAS BURGESS, b Houston, Tex, Oct 10, 48; m 81. CELL BIOLOGY, DEVELOPMENTAL BIOLOGY. *Educ:* Sam Houston Univ, BS, 70, MA, 73; Univ Va, PhD(biol), 76. *Prof Exp:* Res assoc, 76-78, ASST PROF ANAT, UNIV TEX HEALTH SCI CTR, SAN ANTONIO, 78- *Honors & Awards:* Outstanding Res Award, Sigma Xi, 73. *Mem:* Am Soc Cell Biol; Am Asn Anatom. *Res:* Ionic regulation of mitosis in cancer and development; hormone-directed cell differentiation; cell cycle regulation. *Mailing Add:* Dept of Anat 7703 Floyd Curl Dr San Antonio TX 78284

POOL, WILLIAM ROBERT, b Ft Lauderdale, Fla, May 14, 37; m 58; c 4. TOXICOLOGY, PHARMACOLOGY. *Educ:* Fla State Univ, BS, 60, MS, 63, PhD(physiol), 66, Am Bd Toxicol, dipl. *Prof Exp:* Teacher, high sch, Fla, 60-63; res assoc, Inst Molecular Biol, Fla State Univ, 66-67; sr pharmacologist, 67-70, res group chief, 71-73, sect head, 73-75, assoc dir toxicol, Hoffmann-La Roche, Inc, 75-76; DIR TOXICOL, G D SEARLE & CO, 76- *Mem:* AAAS; NY Acad Sci; Am Soc Pharmacol & Exp Therapeut; Am Col Toxicol; Soc Toxicol. *Res:* Drug safety evaluation. *Mailing Add:* G D Searle & Co Skokie IL 60076

POOL, WINFORD H, (JR), b Atlanta, Ga, Oct 2, 26; m 50; c 5. RADIOLOGY. *Educ:* Mercer Univ, BS, 49; Med Col Ga, MD, 52. *Prof Exp:* Assoc prof, 64-68, PROF RADIOL, MED COL GA, 68-, CHMN DEPT, 74-, CHIEF DIAG RADIOL, 70- *Mem:* Fel Am Col Radiol; Radiol Soc NAm; AMA; Am Roentgen Ray Soc; Asn Univ Radiologists. *Mailing Add:* Dept of Radiol Med Col of Ga Augusta GA 30902

POOLE, ANDREW E, b Eng, Aug 4, 35; m 62; c 2. HUMAN GENETICS, PEDODONTICS. *Educ:* London Hosp, BDS, 60; Royal Col Surgeons, LDS, 60; Univ Rochester, MS, 67, PhD(genetics, anat), 71. *Prof Exp:* Instr pedodont, London Hosp Med Sch, 61-62; asst prof, 70-74, ASSOC PROF PEDIAT DENT, HEALTH CTR, UNIV CONN, 75- *Mem:* Am Soc Human Genetics; Int Asn Dent Res; AAAS; Sigma Xi. *Res:* Biochemical human genetics; genetic polymorphisms; inborn error of metabolism; birth defects; dental caries prevention; anthropology and dental health of the Aleuts. *Mailing Add:* Dept of Pediat Dent Univ of Conn Health Ctr Farmington CT 06032

POOLE, ANTHONY ROBIN, b Southend-on-sea, Eng, Oct 1, 39; m 64; c 3. CELL BIOLOGY, IMMUNOLOGY. *Educ:* Reading Univ, BSc, 61, PhD(biochem, physiol), 69. *Prof Exp:* Res scientist microbiol, Unigate, 61-63; res scientist biochem, Marie Curie Mem Found, 63-69 & Royal Free Hosp Med Sch, London, 69-70; res scientist cell biol, Strangeways Res Lab, Cambridge Univ, 70-77; DIR BIOCHEM & IMMUNOCHEM, JOINT DIS LAB, SHRINERS HOSP CRIPPLED CHILDREN, 77-; PROF EXP SURG & ASSOC MEM IMMUNOL, MICROBIOL & MED, MCGILL UNIV, 81- *Concurrent Pos:* Res scientist immunol, Cambridge Univ, 74-77; consult, Med Ctr, Univ Tex, Dallas, 74-; res assoc ed, J Bone Foot Surg Am. *Mem:* Am Soc Cell Biol; Biochem Soc; Orthopaedic Res Soc; Am Soc Immunol; Am Rheumatism Asn. *Res:* Immunology and biochemistry of arthritic diseases; proteinases and autoimmunity; tumor proteirases and invasiveness; structure of proteoglycans and their degradation. *Mailing Add:* Joint Dis Lab 1529 Cedar Ave Montreal PQ H3G 1A6 Can

POOLE, BRIAN HOWARD, cell biology, biochemistry, deceased

POOLE, CHARLES PATTON, JR, b Panama City, Panama, June 7, 27; US citizen; m 53; c 5. PHYSICS. *Educ:* Fordham Univ, BS, 50, MS, 52; Univ Md, PhD(physics), 58. *Prof Exp:* Physicist, Westinghouse Elec Corp, 52-53; physicist, Gulf Res & Develop Co, Pa, 58-64; assoc prof, 64-66, prof astron, 77-80, PROF PHYSICS, UNIV SC, 66- *Concurrent Pos:* Ed, J Magnetic Resonance Rev. *Honors & Awards:* Jesse Beams Award, Am Phys Soc, 80. *Mem:* Fel Am Phys Soc; Philos Sci Asn. *Res:* Solid state physics; magnetic resonance; spectroscopy; chemical physics. *Mailing Add:* Dept of Physics Univ of SC Columbia SC 29208

POOLE, DONALD RAY, b Pontiac, Mich, Jan 8, 32; m 54. PHYSICAL CHEMISTRY. *Educ:* Cent Mich Col Educ, BS, 54; Univ Maine, MS, 56; Univ Ore, PhD, 61. *Prof Exp:* Asst chem, Univ Maine, 54-56; asst anal chem, Univ Ore, 56-57; chemist, US Naval Ord Test Sta, 60-66; sr res chemist, 66-71, dir chem technol, 71-76, SR STAFF SCIENTIST, ROCKET RES CORP, 76- *Mem:* Am Chem Soc. *Res:* Combustion and chemistry of rocket propellants; catalysts; hydrazine chemistry; chemical processing. *Mailing Add:* Rocket Res Corp 11441 Willows Rd Redmond WA 98052

POOLE, DORIS THEODORE, b Greenville, SC, Mar 9, 23; m 47; c 2. BIOCHEMISTRY, PHARMACOLOGY. *Educ:* Winthrop Col, BS, 44; Univ NC, PhD(biochem), 62. *Prof Exp:* Chem analyst, Standard Oil Development Co, 44-46; asst prof zool, Madison Col, 58-59; from instr to asst prof, 62-71, ASSOC PROF PHARMACOL, SCH MED, UNIV NC, CHAPEL HILL, 71- *Mem:* Am Soc Pharmacol & Exp Therapeut. *Res:* Determination of intracellular pH of various tissues from the distribution of the weak acid 5, 5-dimethyl-2, 4-oxazolidinedione; effects produced by various metabolic inhibitors and environmental changes on intracellular pH; ion transport. *Mailing Add:* Dept of Pharmacol Univ of NC Sch of Med Chapel Hill NC 27514

POOLE, GEORGE DOUGLAS, b Miami, Fla, Nov 30, 42; m 63. MATHEMATICS. *Educ:* Kans State Teachers Col, BSEduc, 64; Colo State Univ, MS, 66; Tex Tech Univ, PhD(math), 72. *Prof Exp:* Instr math, Washburn Univ, Topeka, 66-67 & Tex Tech Univ, 67-68; asst prof, 71-76, ASSOC PROF MATH, EMPORIA STATE UNIV, 76- *Mem:* Math Asn Am; Am Math Soc. *Res:* Abelian group theory; numerical linear algebra; matrix theory. *Mailing Add:* Dept of Math Emporia State Univ Emporia KS 66801

POOLE, H K, b Hagerstown, Md, Apr 16, 31; m 57; c 2. AIR POLLUTION, ENVIRONMENTAL BIOLOGY. *Educ:* Gettysburg Col, AB, 53; Univ Md, MS, 57. *Prof Exp:* Asst zool, Univ Md, 53-56; agr res scientist & geneticist, Agr Res Serv, USDA, 56-67, res zoologist, Bee Res Lab, 67-74; dep air qual control officer, Pima County Air Qual Control Dist, Pima County Health Dept, 74-80; ENVIRON PROTECTION SPECIALIST, DAVIS-MONTHAN AFB, ARIZ, 80- *Mem:* Air Pollution Control Asn; Am Inst Biol Sci. *Res:* Parthenogenesis; cytology and cytogenetics of birds and honey bees; reproductive biology of honey bees; biological effects of air pollution; environmental compliance and planning. *Mailing Add:* 4942 E Alta Vista Tucson AZ 85712

POOLE, JAMES P(URVIS), b Butler, Pa, Apr 19, 17; m 40; c 3. CERAMICS. *Educ:* Pa State Col, BS, 40, PhD(glass technol), 47. *Prof Exp:* Prod engr, Sylvania Elec Prod, Inc, 40-42; asst, Pa State Col, 42-48; dir res, Brockway Glass Co, Inc, 48-72, vpres & develop, 72-73, vpres, Int Brockway Glass Co, Inc, 73-82; RETIRED. *Honors & Awards:* Forrest Award, Am Ceramic Soc, 50; Chesterman Award, 58. *Mem:* Am Chem Soc; Am Ceramic Soc; Brit Soc Glass Technol. *Res:* Low temperature glazes; raw material beneficiation; kinetics studies of glass melting; viscosity of glasses; development of low alkali glasses; equipment design; instrumentation; quality control; glass technology. *Mailing Add:* E & R Ctr Brockway Glass Co Inc Brockway PA 15824

POOLE, JAMES PLUMMER, b Gloucester, Mass, May 6, 89; m 13, 73; c 3. BOTANY. *Educ:* Univ Maine, BS, 12; Harvard Univ, AM, 18, PhD(bot), 21. *Hon Degrees:* AM, Dartmouth Col, 27. *Prof Exp:* Instr bot, Washburn Col, 12-13; asst, Kans State Col, 13-16; asst bot, Bussey Inst, Harvard Univ, 21-22; asst prof, Univ Wyo, 18-20; from instr to prof evolution, 22-36, prof, 36-57, EMER PROF BOT, DARTMOUTH COL, 57-; CURATOR, JESUP HERBARIUM, 65- *Mailing Add:* Dept of Biol Sci Dartmouth Col Hanover NH 03755

POOLE, JOHN ANTHONY, b New York, NY, Apr 19, 32; m 60; c 2. PHYSICAL CHEMISTRY. *Educ:* St John's Univ, NY, BS, 54; Univ Alta, PhD(chem), 62. *Prof Exp:* Fel chem, Univ Alta, 62 & Univ Rochester, 63-64; asst prof, 64-69, ASSOC PROF CHEM, TEMPLE UNIV, 69- *Mem:* Am Asn Univ Prof; Inter-Am Photochem Soc. *Res:* Photochemistry; spectroscopy. *Mailing Add:* Dept of Chem Temple Univ Philadelphia PA 19122

POOLE, JOHN TERRY, b Washington, DC, Oct 4, 37; m 60; c 2. MATHEMATICS. *Educ:* Univ NC, BS, 59; Univ Md, MA, 62, PhD(math), 65. *Prof Exp:* Asst prof math, Fla State Univ, 64-68; assoc prof, Clemson Univ, 68-69; ASSOC PROF MATH, FURMAN UNIV, 69- *Mem:* Math Asn Am. *Res:* Complex analysis; geometric function theory. *Mailing Add:* Dept of Math Furman Univ Greenville SC 29613

POOLE, JOHN WILLIAM, b Nanticoke, Pa, Nov 28, 31; m 54; c 1. PHARMACEUTICAL CHEMISTRY. *Educ:* Philadelphia Col Pharm, BS, 54; Temple Univ, MS, 56; Univ Wis, PhD(phys pharm), 59. *Prof Exp:* Instr chem, Temple Univ, 54-56; res pharmaceut chemist, McNeil Labs, Inc, 59-65, MGR EXPLOR PHARM SECT, WYETH LABS, INC, 65- *Mem:* Am Chem Soc; Am Pharmaceut Asn; NY Acad Sci. *Res:* Physiochemical studies of drug substances as a means of developing efficient dosage forms; biopharmaceutics. *Mailing Add:* Wyeth Labs Inc PO Box 8299 Philadelphia PA 19101

POOLE, RICHARD TURK, JR, b Memphis, Tenn, June 16, 31; m 55; c 4. ORNAMENTAL HORTICULTURE. *Educ:* Principia Col, BS, 53; Southwestern La Inst, BS, 59; Univ Fla, MSA, 61, PhD(bot), 65. *Prof Exp:* Res assoc ornamental hort, Univ Fla, 61-65, asst prof, 65-66; asst prof, Univ Hawaii, 66-68; from asst prof to assoc prof, 68-75, PROF ORNAMENTAL HORT, UNIV FLA, 75-, PLANT PHYSIOLOGIST, AGR RES CTR, APOPKA, FLA, 68- *Mem:* Am Soc Hort Sci. *Res:* Production of tropical indoor foliage plants. *Mailing Add:* Agr Res Ctr Univ of Fla Route 3 Box 580 Apopka FL 32703

POOLE, ROBERT WAYNE, b Oakland, Calif, Nov 11, 44; m 69. ECOLOGY, STATISTICS. *Educ:* Cornell Univ, BS, 66, PhD, 69. *Prof Exp:* ASST PROF, DIV BIOMED SCI, BROWN UNIV, 74- *Mem:* Ecol Soc Am; Biomet Soc. *Res:* Statistical and mathematical problems in population ecology. *Mailing Add:* Div of Biomed Sci Brown Univ Providence RI 02912

POOLE, RONALD JOHN, b Leicester, Eng, Mar 16, 36; div; c 1. PLANT PHYSIOLOGY, BIOPHYSICS. *Educ:* Univ Birmingham, BSc, 57, PhD(plant physiol), 60. *Prof Exp:* Cabot fel, 60-62; NATO fel, 62-63; asst lectr biophys, Univ Edinburgh, 63-64, lectr, 64-65; asst prof bot, 65-71, ASSOC PROF BIOL, MCGILL UNIV, 71- *Mem:* Am Soc Plant Physiol; Brit Soc Exp Biol. *Res:* Biophysical aspects of ion transport in plant cells. *Mailing Add:* Dept Biol McGill Univ 1205 Docteur Penfield Ave Montreal PQ H3A 1B1 Can

POOLE, WILLIAM GEORGE, JR, b Houston, Tex, Apr 24, 41; m 65; c 2. NUMERICAL ANALYSIS. *Educ:* Univ Tex, Austin, BA, 63, MA, 65; Univ Calif, Berkeley, PhD(appl math), 70. *Prof Exp:* Asst prof, math & comput sci, Col William & Mary, 70-76, assoc prof, 76-79; SR MATHEMATICIAN, BOEING COMPUT SERV, 79- *Concurrent Pos:* Vis scientist, Inst Comput Appl Sci & Eng, 73-76. *Mem:* AAAS; Am Math Soc; Soc Indust & Appl Math; Asn Comput Mach. *Res:* Numerical algorithms with emphasis on linear algebra, scientific computing, and parallel and vector computers. *Mailing Add:* Boeing Comput Serv 565 Andover Pk West Tukwila WA 98188

POOLE, WILLIAM HOPE, b Kimberly, BC, Feb 20, 27; m 54; c 2. REGIONAL GEOLOGY, RESEARCH MANAGEMENT. *Educ:* Univ BC, BASc, 49; Princeton Univ, PhD(geol), 56. *Prof Exp:* head, Appalachian Sect, 67-79, head, Correlation & Standards Subdiv, 74-79, FIELD GEOLOGIST, GEOL SURV CAN, 52-, SPEC PROJ, 79- *Honors & Awards:* Medal of Merit, Alta Soc Petrol Geologists, 68. *Mem:* Fel Geol Soc Am; fel Geol Asn Can. *Res:* Field geology; structure; igneous and metamorphic petrology; stratigraphy. *Mailing Add:* Geol Surv Can 601 Booth St Ottawa ON K1A 0E8 Can

POOLE, WILLIAM KENNETH, b Cheatham Co, Tenn, Apr 9, 39; c 3. STATISTICS. *Educ:* Austin Peay State Univ, BS, 61; Univ NC, MPH, 63, PhD(statist), 68. *Prof Exp:* Statistician, 67-75, DIR, STATIST METHODOLOGY & ANAL CTR, RESEARCH TRIANGLE INST, 76- *Concurrent Pos:* Mem, Am Heart Asn. *Mem:* Am Statist Asn; Soc Clin Trials. *Res:* Statistical methodology and applications; multivariate analysis; stochastic processes. *Mailing Add:* Research Triangle Inst PO Box 12194 Research Triangle Park NC 27709

POOLER, FRANCIS, JR, b Waltham, Mass, Mar 30, 26; m 52; c 4. METEOROLOGY. *Educ:* Mass Inst Technol, BS, 49; Pa State Univ, PhD, 72. *Prof Exp:* Meteorologist, US Weather Bur, 50-52 & Wallace E Howell Assocs, 52; meteorologist, US Weather Bur, 53-55, Robert A Taft Sanit Eng Ctr, 55-69; RES METEOROLOGIST, NAT ENVIRON RES CTR, ENVIRON PROTECTION AGENCY, 69- *Mem:* Am Meteorol Soc; Geophys Union. *Res:* Atmospheric turbulence and diffusion; transport of pollutants in the atmosphere; micrometeorology. *Mailing Add:* Div of Meteorol Nat Env Res Ctr EPA Research Triangle Park NC 27711

POOLER, JOHN PRESTON, b Waltham, Mass, June 10, 35; m 65; c 2. BIOPHYSICS, PHOTOBIOLOGY. *Educ:* Brown Univ, AB, 62; Duke Univ, PhD(physiol), 67. *Prof Exp:* Training prog, Duke Univ, 67-69; asst prof, 69-74, ASSOC PROF PHYSIOL, EMORY UNIV, 74- *Mem:* Soc Photobiol; Biophys Soc; Am Asn Univ Profs; AAAS. *Res:* Photosensitization; excitable membrane biophysics. *Mailing Add:* Dept of Physiol Emory Univ Atlanta GA 30322

POOLEY, ALAN SETZLER, b Madison, Wis, Dec 1, 38; m 65; c 3. SCANNING ELECTRON MICROSCOPY. *Educ:* Univ Wis-Madison, BS, 61, MS, 64, PhD(zool), 68. *Prof Exp:* Fel, Imp Cancer Res Fund, London, 68-70; scientist, Searle Res Labs, 70-72; res assoc, Univ Conn, 72-74; ASSOC MICROSCOPIST, PEABODY MUS, YALE UNIV, 74- *Mem:* Electron Micros Soc Am. *Res:* Scanning electron microscopy; energy dispersive x-ray analysis; mineralized biological structures. *Mailing Add:* Peabody Mus Yale Univ Box 6666 New Haven CT 06511

POON, BING TOY, b San Francisco, Calif, Feb 26, 24. ORGANIC CHEMISTRY. *Educ:* Univ Calif, BS, 48; Univ Colo, MS, 50, PhD(org chem), 51. *Prof Exp:* Res asst, Univ Colo, 48-51; res chemist, Solvay Process Div, Allied Chem & Dye Corp, 51-52, Nitrogen Div, 52-55, sr res chemist, Allied Chem Corp, 55-65; ORG CHEMIST, DIV EXP THERAPEUT, WALTER REED ARMY INST RES, 65- *Mem:* AAAS; Am Soc Mass Spectrometry; Am Chem Soc; Sigma Xi. *Res:* Diene synthesis; chlorinations; industrial organic chemicals and nitrogen derivatives. *Mailing Add:* Div of Exp Therapeut Walter Reed Army Inst of Res Washington DC 20012

POON, CALVIN P C, b China, Nov 8, 35; US citizen; m 63; c 2. WATER POLLUTION CONTROL. *Educ:* Nat Taiwan Univ, BS, 58; Univ Mo, MS, 60; Univ Ill, PhD(sanit eng), 64. *Prof Exp:* Design engr wastewater treatment, J Stephen Watkins Consult Eng, 60; proj engr water treatment, Gannet Fleming Corddry & Carpenter Eng Inc, Pa, 63-65; from asst prof to assoc prof, 65-75, PROF POLLUTION CONTROL, UNIV RI, 75- *Concurrent Pos:* Mem, Nat Sci Adv Comt, US Coast Guard, 72-74; consult, US Environ Protection Agency & var other co; UN adv & consult, Pollution Mgt Prog, Nat Taiwan Univ & Rep China govt; vis prof, Univ Edinburgh, Scotland. *Mem:* Water Pollution Control Fedn; Am Soc Civil Engrs; Am Asn Environ Eng Prof; Inst Chinese-Am Engrs. *Res:* Industrial wastewater treatment processes; biological treatment, water quality control and advanced treatment technology. *Mailing Add:* Dept Civil & Environ Eng Univ RI Kingston RI 02881

POOR, HAROLD VINCENT, b Columbus, Ga, Oct 2, 51; m 73. ELECTRICAL ENGINEERING. *Educ:* Auburn Univ, BEE, 72, MS, 74; Princeton Univ, MA, 76, PhD(elec eng), 77. *Prof Exp:* Asst prof & res asst prof, Coord Sci Lab, 77-81, ASSOC PROF ELEC ENG & RES ASSOC PROF, COORD SCI LAB, UNIV ILL, URBANA-CHAMPAIGN, 81- *Concurrent Pos:* consult, M & S Comput, Inc, Huntsville, Ala, 77- & Columbus Labs, Battelle Mem Inst, Durham, NC, 80; assoc ed, Trans Automatic Control, Inst Elec & Electronics Engrs, 81-82. *Mem:* Inst Elec & Electronics Engrs; Sigma Xi. *Res:* Statistical communication theory; signal detection and estimation. *Mailing Add:* Coord Sci Lab Univ Ill 1101 W Springfield Ave Urbana IL 61801

POORE, AUBREY BONNER, b LaGrange, Ga, Feb 4, 45; m 66; c 2. APPLIED MATHEMATICS, OPTIMIZATION. *Educ:* Ga Inst Technol, BS, 67, MS, 69; Calif Inst Technol, PhD(appl math), 73. *Prof Exp:* Asst prof math, State Univ NY, Buffalo, 72-74; asst prof, 74-77, assoc prof, 77-82, PROF MATH, COLO STATE UNIV, 82- *Concurrent Pos:* Assoc prof math, Math Res Ctr, Univ Wisc, 79-80. *Mem:* Soc Indust & Appl Math; Soc Natural Philos. *Res:* Differential equations; applied mathematics, physical mathematics, numerical analysis; chemical reactor dynamics; water resource management. *Mailing Add:* Dept Math Colo State Univ Ft Collins CO 80523

POORE, EMERY RAY VAUGHN, b Mumfordville, Ky, July 30, 37; m 59; c 1. NUCLEAR PHYSICS. *Educ:* Duke Univ, BS, 59; Univ NC, PhD(physics), 66. *Prof Exp:* From res assoc to asst prof nuclear physics, Duke Univ, 66-70; asst dir, Comput Res Ctr, Univ SFla, 70-72; MEM STAFF, LOS ALAMOS SCI LAB, 72- *Mem:* Am Phys Soc; Am Asn Physics Teachers. *Res:* Nuclear spectroscopy with direct reactions. *Mailing Add:* P-9 MS-480 Los Alamos Sci Lab Los Alamos NM 87545

POORE, JESSE H, JR, b Louisville, Ky. COMPUTER SCIENCE. *Educ:* Ga Inst Technol, PhD(comput sci), 70. *Prof Exp:* ASSOC PROF MATH & DIR COMPUT CTR, FLA STATE UNIV, 71-, ASSOC DEAN GRAD STUDIES & RES, 80- *Concurrent Pos:* Proj mgr comput-based educ, NSF, 74-75; vis prof, Univ Simon Bolivar; pres, Exec Loan Prog, President's Reorgn Prog. *Mem:* Asn Comput Mach. *Mailing Add:* 110 Love Bldg Fla State Univ Tallahassee FL 32306

POORMAN, DOUGLAS HAROLD, b Palmyra, Pa, Apr 11, 45. ANATOMY. *Educ:* Elizabethtown Col, BS, 66; Univ Fla, PhD(anat), 70. *Prof Exp:* Asst prof anat, Med Ctr, Univ Kans, Kansas City, 70-77, asst dean admis, 74-77; ASSOC PROF & DEAN ACAD AFFAIRS, SOUTHERN CALIF COL OPTOM, FULLERTON, 77- *Mem:* AAAS; Am Soc Zoologists; Asn Am Med Cols. *Res:* Calcium homeostasis as regulated by parathormone and calcitonin. *Mailing Add:* Southern Calif Col of Optom 2001 Associated Rd Fullerton CA 92631

POORMAN, LAWRENCE EUGENE, b Ft Wayne, Ind, July 27, 26; m 51; c 2. PHYSICS. *Educ:* Ball State Univ, BS, 50; Ind Univ, MS, 53, EdD(sci educ), 67; Purdue Univ, MS, 64. *Prof Exp:* Teacher, Salem Pub Schs, Ind, 50-51, Jamestown Schs, 51-52, Edinburg Schs, 52-54, Columbus Schs, 54-60; instr physics, Lab Sch, Ind Univ, Bloomington, 60-66; res assoc proj physics, Harvard Univ, 66-67; from asst prof to assoc prof, 67-75, PROF PHYSICS, IND STATE UNIV, 75- *Concurrent Pos:* Field consult, Proj Physics, Harvard Univ, 64-66, 67- *Res:* Computer assisted instruction in physics; multi-media systems approach in physics teaching; programmed instruction used in physics; curricular development in physical science courses. *Mailing Add:* Dept of Physics Ind State Univ Terre Haute IN 47809

POOROOSHASB, HORMOZD BAHMAN, b Tehran, Feb 23, 36; m 55; c 2. FOUNDATION ENGINEERING. *Educ:* Univ Manchester, BSc, 58; Cambridge Univ, PhD(soil sci), 61. *Prof Exp:* Fel soil mech, Emmanuel Col, 61-63; from asst prof civil eng to prof, Univ Waterloo, 63-69; dir, Iranian Geotech Inst, 69-71; consult engr geotech eng, Kantab Consult Engrs, 71-79; PROF CIVIL ENG, CONCORDIA UNIV, 79- *Concurrent Pos:* Vis prof, Danish Geotech Inst, 69-70; pres, Iranian Geotech Soc, 71-73; sr vis scientist, McGill Univ, 81- *Res:* Constitutive relationships of granular media soil structure interaction; numerical techniques applied to geotechnical engineering; tailings deposits. *Mailing Add:* 7570 Milan Blvd Brossard PQ J4Y 1H5 Can

POORT, JON MICHAEL, geology, see previous edition

POORVIN, DAVID WALTER, b Brooklyn, NY, Aug 25, 46; m 70; c 2. CLINICAL RESEARCH. *Educ:* Hunter Col, BA, 67; Rutgers Univ, PhD(physiol), 72. *Prof Exp:* From res asst to res assoc physiol, Rutgers Univ, 67-73; res physiologist, 73-75, group leader pharmacol, Lederle Labs, 75-77; asst dir new drug develop, Pfizer Pharmaceut, 77-79, assoc dir, 79-81; ASSOC MED DIR, SCHERING-PLOUGH, 81- *Mem:* NY Acad Sci; Am Heart Asn; Sigma Xi. *Res:* Clinical research management of cardiovascular drugs. *Mailing Add:* Schering-Plough Galloping Hill Rd Kenilworth NJ 07033

POOS, GEORGE IRELAND, b Sandusky, Ohio, Apr 15, 23; m 76; c 3. ORGANIC CHEMISTRY. *Educ:* Va Mil Inst, BS, 47; George Wash Univ, BS, 47; Univ Ill, PhD(chem), 50. *Prof Exp:* Res chemist, Merck & Co, Inc, 50-56; sr chemist, 56-57, asst dir chem res, 57-65, assoc dir chem res, 65-66, dir chem res, 66-67, exec dir res, 67-71, vpres sci affairs, 71-79, VPRES PLANNING & CORP DEVELOP, MCNEIL PHARMACEUT, 79- *Mem:* Am Chem Soc; AAAS; Sigma Xi; NAm Soc Corp Planning. *Res:* Total synthesis of adrenal steroids; steroid chemistry; heterocycles; bicyclic compounds; stereochemistry; medicinal chemistry. *Mailing Add:* McNeil Pharmaceut Welsh & McKean Rd Spring House PA 19422

POOTJES, CHRISTINE FREDRICKA, b Montclair, NJ, Sept 19, 27. MICROBIOLOGY. *Educ:* Rutgers Univ, BS, 49, PhD(microbiol), 64; Purdue Univ, MS, 55. *Prof Exp:* Lab asst microbiol, Wallace & Tiernan, Inc, NJ, 49-52; lab asst, Schering Corp, 52-53; res asst biochem, Fels Res Inst, Antioch Col, 54-55; res assoc microbiol, Rutgers Univ, 55-62; asst prof, 63-68, ASSOC PROF MICROBIOL, COL SCI, PA STATE UNIV, UNIVERSITY PARK, 68- *Mem:* Am Soc Microbiol. *Res:* Bacterial viruses, especially those associated with the facultative autotroph Hydrogenomonas facilis; lysogeny in Agrobacterium tumefaciens. *Mailing Add:* Dept of Microbiol Frear-5 Pa State Univ University Park PA 16802

POOVAIAH, BACHETTIRA WTHAPPA, b Coorg, India, May 10, 43; m 70. PLANT PHYSIOLOGY. *Educ:* Karnataka Univ, India, BS, 64; Utah State Univ, MS, 68, PhD(plant physiol), 70. *Prof Exp:* Lectr agr chem, Agr Col, Dharwar, 64-65; fel, Mich State Univ, 70-71 & Purdue Univ, 71-75; asst prof & asst horticulturist, 75-78, ASSOC PROF HORT & ASSOC HORTICULTURIST, WASH STATE UNIV, 78- *Mem:* Am Soc Plant Physiol; Am Soc Hort Sci; Sigma Xi; AAAS; Bot Soc Am. *Res:* Plant hormones and growth regulators; vegetable and fruit physiology, including post-harvest physiology; abscission, senescence and stress physiology. *Mailing Add:* Dept of Hort Wash State Univ Pullman WA 99163

POPE, ALFRED, b Cleveland, Ohio, Jan 23, 15; m 50. NEUROPATHOLOGY. *Educ:* Harvard Univ, AB, 37, MD, 41. *Prof Exp:* House officer path, Children's Hosp, Boston, 41-42; res asst med, Mass Gen Hosp, 43; teaching fel biol chem, Harvard Med Sch, 44-45; Nat Res Coun fel, Montreal Neurol Inst, 45-46; asst neuropath, 46-49, instr, 49-51, assoc, 51-52, from asst prof to assoc prof, 53-64, PROF NEUROPATH, HARVARD MED SCH, 64- *Concurrent Pos:* Tutor, Harvard Univ, 47-49; res assoc, McLean Hosp, 46-52, assoc 55-56, neuropathologist, 56-; mem ed bd, J Neurochem, 55-69 & Arch Neurol, 61-66; mem neurol field invests comt & study sect, USPHS, 66-69, mem neurol study sect, 61-65, mem adv comt epilepsies, 66-69, mem neurol dis prog proj comt, 69-73; mem res adv comt, United Cerebral Palsy Res & Educ Found, 63-69; mem adv comt fundamental res, Nat Multiple Sclerosis Soc, 68-74. *Mem:* Asn Res Nerv & Ment Dis; Am

Asn Neuropath; Am Acad Neurol; Am Neurol Asn; Int Brain Res Orgn. *Res:* Quantitative histochemistry of the nervous system; experimental neuropathology. *Mailing Add:* Res Lab McLean Hosp 115 Mill St Belmont MA 02178

POPE, BILL JORDAN, b Salt Lake City, Utah, Sept 12, 22; m 43; c 4. CHEMICAL ENGINEERING, MATERIAL SCIENCE ENGINEERING. *Educ:* Univ Utah, BA, 47; Univ Wash, MS, 49, PhD, 59. *Prof Exp:* Proj chem engr, Utah Oil Refining Co, 51-58; assoc prof chem eng, 58-63, chmn dept, 66-70, prof, 63-78, EMER PROF CHEM ENG, BRIGHAM YOUNG UNIV, 78- *Concurrent Pos:* Lectr grad sch, Univ Utah, 53-54; prof, Abadan Inst Technol, Iran, 59-62; consult, Hercules Powder Co, 63-66 & Keysor Chem Co, 64-66; vpres, Megadiamond Corp, 66-69, exec vpres, 70-73, pres & chmn bd, 73-; pres, US Synthetic Corp, 79- *Mem:* Am Inst Chem Engrs; Am Chem Soc; Nat Soc Prof Engrs; Am Soc Eng Educ. *Res:* Chemical kinetics; heat transfer; process design; ultra high pressure synthesis of diamond and cubic boron nitride; sintering of diamond and other materials. *Mailing Add:* 1886 N 1450 E Provo UT 84601

POPE, C LORENZO, genetics, plant breeding, see previous edition

POPE, CHARLES EDWARD, II, b Cleveland, Ohio, Sept 18, 31; m 58; c 2. GASTROENTEROLOGY. *Educ:* Cornell Univ, BA, 53; Western Reserve Univ, MD, 57. *Prof Exp:* Trainee gastroenterol, Royal Free Hosp, London, 61-62; res fel, Mass Mem Hosp & Boston Hosp, 61-64; clin investr, Vet Admin Hosp, 64-67; asst prof, 66-70, ASSOC PROF MED, UNIV WASH, 70-; CHIEF GASTROENTEROL, VET ADMIN HOSP, 66- *Mem:* AMA; Am Fedn Clin Res; Am Gastroenterol Asn. *Mailing Add:* Dept of Med Univ of Wash Seattle WA 98105

POPE, DANIEL LORING, b Buffalo, NY, Mar 4, 31; m 52; c 3. ENGINEERING MECHANICS. *Educ:* Cornell Univ, BCE, 53, PhD(mech), 61. *Prof Exp:* Struct engr, Pittsburgh-Des Moines Steel Co, 53; instr eng mech, Cornell Univ, 56-59; mem tech staff, Continuum Mech Group, 60-63, supvr, 63-69, supvr phys design group, 69-72, SUPVR BELOW GROUND INSTALLATION GROUP, BELL TEL LABS, INC, 72- *Mem:* Am Pub Works Asn; Soc Indust & Appl Math. *Res:* Nonlinear problems; soil mechanics; dynamics of machines. *Mailing Add:* Below Ground Installation Group Bell Tel Labs Inc Rm 2E-352 Whippany NJ 07981

POPE, DANIEL TOWNSEND, b Edisto Island, SC, Dec 24, 13; m 39; c 1. HORTICULTURE. *Educ:* Clemson Univ, BS, 35; La State Univ, MS, 37; Cornell Univ, PhD, 52. *Prof Exp:* Asst prof agr, Berry Col, 37-40; asst, Cornell Univ, 40-42; res assoc prof hort, NC State Col, 47-50; asst agr, Cornell Univ, 50-52; res assoc prof, 52-62, prof hort sci, NC State Univ, 62-76; RETIRED. *Mem:* Fel Am Soc Hort Sci. *Res:* Breeding new varieties of sweet potatoes. *Mailing Add:* Box 126 Edisto Island SC 29438

POPE, DAVID PETER, b Waukesha, Wis, July 31, 39; m 65. METALLURGY, MATERIALS SCIENCE. *Educ:* Univ Wis, BS, 61; Calif Inst Technol, MS, 62, PhD(mat sci), 67. *Prof Exp:* Res fel mat sci, Calif Inst Technol, 67-68; asst prof, 68-73, ASSOC PROF METALL & MAT SCI, UNIV PA, 73- *Mem:* Am Inst Mining, Metall & Petrol Engrs; Am Soc Metals. *Res:* Plastic deformation of metals; mechanical properties of ordered alloys; high temperature deformation and fracture of metals. *Mailing Add:* Sch Metall & Mat Sci 3231 Walnut St Philadelphia PA 19104

POPE, JOHN KEYLER, b Cincinnati, Ohio, July 27, 31; m 54; c 2. PALEONTOLOGY, GEOLOGY. *Educ:* Harvard Univ, AB, 53; Univ Mich, MS, 56; Univ Cincinnati, PhD(geol), 66. *Prof Exp:* From instr to assoc prof, 60-76, PROF GEOL, MIAMI UNIV, 76- *Concurrent Pos:* Vis asst prof, Univ Cincinnati, 65; mem, Paleont Res Inst. *Mem:* Paleont Soc; Brit Paleont Asn. *Res:* Ordovician brachiopods, faunas and stratigraphy; Cambrian and Ordovician echinoderms; Cretaceous mollusks and stratigraphy; zoological nomenclature; techniques of paleontological preparation. *Mailing Add:* Dept of Geol Miami Univ Oxford OH 45056

POPE, JOSEPH, US citizen. NOISE CONTROL, DIGITAL SIGNAL ANALYSIS. *Educ:* Mass Inst Technol, SB, 72; Stanford Univ, MS, 73, PhD(mech eng), 78. *Prof Exp:* Res asst, Dept Mech Eng, Stanford Univ, 73-77; sr res engr, Res Labs, Gen Motors, 77-81, staff res engr, 81-82; APPLN ENGR, BRUEL & KJAER INSTRUMENTS, INC, 82- *Mem:* Acoust Soc Am. *Res:* Digital signal analysis; measurement techniques in acoustics; noise control. *Mailing Add:* Bruel & Kjaer Instruments Inc 185 Forest St Marlborough MA 01752

POPE, JOSEPH HORACE, b Salem, Mass, Mar 29, 28; m 50, 71; c 1. ATMOSPHERIC PHYSICS, INSTRUMENTATION. *Educ:* Univ Alaska, BS, 53; Ore State Col, MS, 55. *Prof Exp:* Physicist, Geophys Inst, Univ Alaska, 53-54, whistlers & very low frequency emissions, 55-61; physicist, Environ Res Labs, Nat Oceanic & Atmospheric Admin, 61-75, physicist, Nat Environ Satellite Serv, 75-78; RETIRED. *Res:* Natural electromagnetic phenomena occurring in the exosphere such as whistlers, very low frequency emissions and micropulsations in the ultra low and very low frequency ranges; charged particle density in the magnetosphere; small scale ionospheric irregularities producing scintillation on trans-ionospheric signals, polar cap absorption events, ionospheric modeling; solar energy consulting. *Mailing Add:* 7328 Mt Sherman Rd Longmont CO 80501

POPE, LARRY DEBBS, b Corpus Christi, Tex, Dec 22, 40; m 63; c 3. ENGINEERING ACOUSTICS. *Educ:* Tex Tech Col, BSME, 63; Southern Methodist Univ, MSME, 66; Univ Houston, PhD, 70. *Prof Exp:* Design engr, Collins Radio Co, Tex, 63-66; prin engr, Houston Aerospace Systs Div, Lockheed Electronics Co, 66-68; sr scientist, 70-77, SR SCIENTIST, BOLT BERANEK & NEWMAN, INC, 78- *Concurrent Pos:* Assoc prof mech eng, Tex A&M Univ, 77-78. *Mem:* Acoust Soc Am; Am Soc Mech Engrs. *Res:* Theoretical acoustics; sound transmission and radiation; random vibration; turbulent boundary layers; statistical energy methods; underwater acoustics. *Mailing Add:* Bolt Beranek & Newman Inc Canoga Park CA 91303

POPE, LARRY ELMER, b Vernal, Utah, Jan 6, 41; m 63; c 5. METALLURGY, MATERIALS SCIENCE. *Educ:* Univ Utah, BA, 65, PhD(metall), 69. *Prof Exp:* Vis asst prof metall, Univ Utah, 69-70; mem tech staff, Sandia Labs, 70-73; mgr res projs, Fansteel, Inc, 73-74, mgr grad res, 74-79; MEM TECH STAFF PROCESS METALL, SANDIA NAT LABS, 79- *Mem:* Am Soc for Metals; Sigma Xi; Am Welding Soc; Laser Inst Am. *Res:* Effect of surface preparation, ion implantation, laser glazing and surface alloying on friction coefficients and wear of unlubricated material couples; solid film lubrication; laser welding; laser beam characterization; carbide cermets. *Mailing Add:* 9000 Galaxia Way NE Albuquerque NM 87185

POPE, MARTIN, b New York, NY, Aug 22, 18; m 46; c 2. SOLID STATE PHYSICS. *Educ:* City Col New York, BS, 39; Polytech Inst Brooklyn, PhD(chem), 51. *Prof Exp:* Res chemist, Balco Res Lab, 46-47, asst tech dir, 51-56; res assoc prof physics, 56-66, assoc prof chem, 66-68, PROF CHEM & ASSOC DIR SOLID STATE & RADIATION LAB, NY UNIV, 68- *Mem:* Fel AAAS; fel Am Phys Soc; Am Chem Soc; fel NY Acad Sci. *Res:* Photoconductivity and semiconductivity in organic materials; electrical properties of thin metallic films; ion exchange kinetics; exciton dynamics in organic crystals. *Mailing Add:* NY Univ 4 Washington Pl New York NY 10003

POPE, MICHAEL THOR, b Exeter, Eng, Apr 14, 33; m 57; c 2. INORGANIC CHEMISTRY. *Educ:* Oxford Univ, BA, 54, DPhil(chem), 57, MA, 58. *Prof Exp:* Monsanto fel inorg chem, Boston Univ, 57-58, AEC fel, 58-59; res chemist, Laporte Chem Ltd, Eng, 59-61, jr sect leader inorg chem, 61-62; from asst prof to assoc prof, 62-73, PROF INORG CHEM, GEORGETOWN UNIV, 73- *Concurrent Pos:* Petrol Res Fund int award fel & vis prof, Tech Univ Vienna, 70-71; vis scientist, Oxford Univ, 78; assoc prof, Univ Pierre et Marie Currie, Paris & guest prof, Free Univ Berlin, 79. *Mem:* Am Chem Soc; Royal Soc Chem. *Res:* Structures and reactions of transition metal oxide complexes, heteropoly anions and their organic derivatives; mixed-valence chemistry; catalysis; electron and nuclear magnetic resonance; electrochemistry; crystallography. *Mailing Add:* Dept Chem Georgetown Univ Washington DC 20057

POPE, NOEL KYNASTON, b Christchurch, NZ, July 31, 18. KINETIC EQUATIONS. *Educ:* Univ NZ, BSc, 40, MSc, 42; Univ Edinburgh, PhD(theoret physics), 48. *Prof Exp:* Lectr demonstr physics, Univ Victroia Wellington, 43-45; fel, Nat Res Coun Can, 59-50; asst res officer theoret physics, Chalk River Labs, Atomic Energy Can, Ltd, 56-61; head dept, 67-82, PROF MATH, ROYAL MIL COL CAN, 61- *Concurrent Pos:* Consult, Solid State Div, Harshaw Chem Co, 63-67; vis prof, Mass Inst Technol, 80-81. *Mem:* Am Phys Soc; Can Asn Physicists. *Res:* Theory of kinetic equations; correlation functions in fluids; elastic scattering of thermal neutrons by fluids and solids; lattice dynamics; positron annihilation in solids. *Mailing Add:* 295 Alfred St Kingston ON K7L 3S3 Can

POPE, PAUL TERRELL, b Ft Worth, Tex, Mar 28, 42; m 64; c 3. STATISTICS, MATHEMATICS. *Educ:* Abilene Christian Col, BA, 64; Univ Tex, MA, 66; Southern Methodist Univ, PhD(statist), 69. *Prof Exp:* Asst prof math, Univ Tulsa, 69-74; RES MATHEMATICIAN, CITIES SERV OIL CO, 74- *Mem:* Am Statist Asn. *Res:* Linear models; simulation. *Mailing Add:* Cities Serv Oil Co Box 300 Tulsa OK 74102

POPE, ROBERT EUGENE, b Bolivar, Mo, Oct 21, 27; m 54; c 3. VETERINARY PUBLIC HEALTH. *Educ:* Univ Mo, BS & DVM, 55; Univ Calif, Berkeley, MPH, 63. *Prof Exp:* Vet officer, US Air Force, Lackland AFB, Tex, 55-59, Yokota Air Base, Japan, 59-62 & Monthan AFB, Ariz, 63-65, instr vet med & pub health, Med Serv Sch, Gunter AFB, Ala, 65-66 & Sheppard AFB, Tex, 66-68, staff vet, Hq, 17th Air Force, Ramstein AFB, Ger, 68-70, Air Force rep to Dept Defense Food Res, Develop, Technol & Eng Prog, Natick Labs, 70-74, chief vet serv, US Air Force Hosp, Barksdale AFB, La, 74-77; DIR, ZOONOSIS CONTROL, TEX DEPT HEALTH, PUB HEALTH REGION 11, 77- *Mem:* Am Vet Med Asn; Am Pub Health Asn; Asn Mil Surg US. *Res:* Epidemiology. *Mailing Add:* 1701 Mulberry Dr Richmond TX 77469

POPE, WENDELL LAVON, b Arco, Idaho, Jan 16, 28; m 50; c 9. COMPUTER ANALYSIS. *Educ:* Utah State Univ, BS, 56; Stanford Univ, MS, 58; Univ Wis, MS, 68. *Prof Exp:* Math analyst, Missiles & Space Div, Lockheed Aircraft Corp, 56-59; from asst to assoc prof math, 59-77, dir comput ctr, 69-77, PROF COMPUT SCI, UTAH STATE UNIV, 77- *Mem:* Asn Comput Mach. *Mailing Add:* Dept of Comput Sci UMC37 Utah State Univ Logan UT 84322

POPEJOY, WILLIAM DEAN, b Norfolk, Va, Feb 22, 25; m 57; c 1. MATHEMATICS. *Educ:* Ill State Univ, BS, 49, MS, 50; Colo State Col, EdD, 59. *Prof Exp:* Teacher high schs, Ill, 50-53; instr math, Ill State Univ, 53-58; from instr to assoc prof, 58-67, PROF MATH, UNIV NORTHERN COLO, 67- *Concurrent Pos:* Consult, 58-; fel, NY Univ, 70-71. *Res:* Mathematical education. *Mailing Add:* Dept of Math Univ of Northern Colo Greeley CO 80639

POPEL, ALEKSANDER S, b Moscow, USSR, Oct 8, 45; citizen US; m 66; c 1. FLUID MECHANICS, MATHEMATICAL MODELING. *Educ:* Moscow Univ, USSR, MS, 67, PhD(fluid mech), 72. *Prof Exp:* Res scientist fluid mech, Inst Mech, Moscow State Univ, 70-75; asst prof mech eng, Tulane Univ, 76; res assoc prof fluid mech, Depts Chem Eng, Aerospace & Mech Eng & Physiol, Univ Ariz, 76-80; ASSOC PROF FLUID MECHANICS, UNIV HOUSTON, 80- *Mem:* Am Soc Mech Engrs. *Res:* Mechanics of blood flow in small vessels and in vascular networks; oxygen transport to tissue; mathematical modeling of physiological processes. *Mailing Add:* Mech Eng Dept Univ Houston Houston TX 77004

POPELAR, CARL H(ARRY), b Dundee, Mich, Feb 5, 38; m 61; c 3. ENGINEERING MECHANICS. *Educ:* Mich State Univ, BS, 60, MS, 61; Univ Mich, PhD(eng mech), 65. *Prof Exp:* Engr, Martin Col, 61-62; instr eng mech, Univ Mich, 64-66; from asst prof to assoc prof, 66-72, PROF ENG MECH, OHIO STATE UNIV, 72- *Mem:* Am Acad Mech; Am Soc Civil Engrs. *Res:* Dynamic stability of thin-walled members and shells; elastic stability; structural optimization; fracture mechanics. *Mailing Add:* 314 Boyd Lab Ohio State Univ Columbus OH 43210

POPENOE, EDWIN ALONZO, b Topeka, Kans, Aug 3, 22; m 50; c 2. BIOCHEMISTRY. *Educ:* Pomona Col, BA, 47; Univ Wis, MS, 48, PhD(biochem), 50. *Prof Exp:* Res assoc biochem, Med Col, Cornell Univ, 50-54; head, Biochem Div, 70-78, RES BIOCHEMIST, MED DEPT, BROOKHAVEN NAT LAB, 54- *Concurrent Pos:* NIH res fel, Med Col, Cornell Univ, 50-52; consult, Off Sci & Technol, 64. *Mem:* Am Chem Soc; Am Soc Biol Chem. *Res:* Chemistry of proteins, peptides and mucoproteins; biosynthesis of DNA. *Mailing Add:* Biochem Div Med Dept Brookhaven Nat Lab Upton NY 11973

POPENOE, HUGH, b Tela, Honduras, Aug 28, 29; US citizen. SOIL SCIENCE. *Educ:* Univ Calif, BS, 51; Univ Fla, PhD(soils), 60. *Prof Exp:* Asst soil scientist, Econ Coop Admin, Thailand, 51-52; res assoc, 54-59, interim instr, 59-60, from asst prof to assoc prof soils, 60-71, asst to provost, Inst Food & Agr Sci, 65-66, actg dir, Ctr Aquatic Sci, 69-81, dir, State Univ Syst Fla Sea Grant Prog, 71-81, PROF SOILS, UNIV FLA, 71-, DIR CTR TROP AGR, 65-, DIR INT PROG AGR, 66- *Concurrent Pos:* Consult, USDA, Nicaragua; Soc Sci Res Coun, Latin Am; Rockefeller Found, Columbia Univ; US Agency Int Develop, Panama, El Salvador, Honduras, Costa Rica, Jamaica & Vietnam; Univ Hawaii; For Area Fel Prog, 69-72; mem bd dirs, Orgn Trop Studies, 64-67; vchmn, Gulf Univ Res; mem bd trustees, Pan Am Sch Agr, Honduras, 70, chmn, 71-80; Latin Am Scholar Prog, Am Univ, 71-74; vis lectr trop pub health, Harvard Univ, 75-; mem int sci & educ coun, Nat Asn State Univ & Land-Grant Cols & USDA, 74-81 & int affairs comt, Nat Asn State Univs & Land-Grant Cols, 74-; chmn, Sea Grant Asn, 76-77; mem bd dirs, League Int Food Educ, 76-; mem, Joint Res Comt, Bd Int Food & Agr Develop, Title XII, 77- & chmn, Adv Comt Technol Innovations, Nat Acad Sci, 77-; mem bd, Sci Technol Int Develop, Nat Acad Sci, 79- *Mem:* Fel AAAS; fel Am Geog Soc; fel Int Soc Soil Sci; Soil Sci Soc Am; Int Soc Trop Ecol. *Res:* Development of tropical agriculture; tropical ecology. *Mailing Add:* Int Prog Agr 3028 McCarty Hall Univ of Fla Gainesville FL 32611

POPENOE, JOHN, b Los Angeles, Calif, Jan 24, 29; m 52; c 4. HORTICULTURE. *Educ:* Univ Calif, Los Angeles, BS, 50; Univ Md, MS, 52, PhD(hort), 55. *Prof Exp:* Horticulturist, USDA, 55-58; assoc prof & assoc horticulturist, Exp Sta, Ala Polytech Inst, 58-59; assoc horticulturist, Subtrop Exp Sta, Fla, 59-63; DIR, FAIRCHILD TROP GARDEN, 63- *Mem:* Am Soc Hort Sci. *Res:* Breeding, cultivars and uses of tropical ornamentals and fruit plants. *Mailing Add:* Fairchild Trop Garden 10901 Old Cutler Rd Miami FL 33156

POPHAM, RICHARD ALLEN, b Charleston, Ill, Sept 29, 13. BOTANY. *Educ:* Eastern Ill Univ, BEd, 36; Ohio State Univ, MSc, 37, PhD(bot), 40. *Prof Exp:* Asst bot, Ohio State Univ, 37-40, instr, 40-42; chief ballistician, Scioto Ord Plant, 42-43; plant supt, Atomic Bomb Prod Unit, Los Alamos Sci Lab, 43-46; from asst prof to assoc prof, 46-68, PROF BOT, OHIO STATE UNIV, 68- *Concurrent Pos:* Bus mgr, Am J Bot, 72- *Mem:* Bot Soc Am; Sigma Xi; Soc Econ Bot; Torrey Bot Club; Int Soc Plant Morphol. *Res:* Developmental and physiological plant anatomy; morphology of embryo sacs of angiosperms; taxonomy of composites; plant microtechnique; zonation in shoot apices; floral histogenesis; tissue differentiation in root tips; primary thickening meristems. *Mailing Add:* Dept of Bot Ohio State Univ Columbus OH 43210

POPJAK, GEORGE JOSEPH, b Kiskundorozsma, Hungary, May 5, 14; m 41. BIOCHEMISTRY. *Educ:* Univ Szeged, MD, 38; Univ London, FRIC, 55, DSc(biochem), 61. *Prof Exp:* Demonstr path, St Thomas' Hosp Med Sch, Univ London, 41-47; res scientist, Nat Inst Med Res, London, 47-53; dir exp radiopath res unit, Med Res Coun, Hammersmith Hosp, 53-62; co-dir chem enzymol lab, Shell Res Ltd, Sittingbourne, 62-68; PROF BIOCHEM, UNIV CALIF, LOS ANGELES, 68- *Honors & Awards:* Stouffer Found Prize, 67; Ciba Medal, Brit Biochem Soc, 66; Davy Medal, Royal Soc, 68; Lipid Chem Award, Am Oil Chemists Soc, 77. *Mem:* AAAS; fel Royal Soc; Brit Biochem Soc; Am Acad Arts & Sci; hon mem Am Soc Biol Chemists. *Res:* Biosynthesis of lipids, particularly that of cholesterol; enzyme stereochemistry and regulation. *Mailing Add:* 511 Cashmere Terrace Los Angeles CA 90049

POPKIN, A(LEXANDER) H, b New York, NY, Nov 7, 13; m; c 2. ORGANIC CHEMISTRY. *Educ:* Brooklyn Col, BS, 34; Pa State Univ, MS, 35, PhD(org chem), 39. *Prof Exp:* Asst chem, Pa State Univ, 35-36, asst org chem, 37-38, instr, 38-39; res chemist, Sun Chem Corp, NY, 39-42, group leader, 42-45; dir res, Maltbie Chem Co, NJ, 45-46; res chemist, 46-58, res assoc, 58-68, CONSULT, EXXON RES & ENG CO, 69- *Concurrent Pos:* Pres, A H Popkin Assocs, 78- *Mem:* Am Chem Soc; Sigma Xi; Soc Automotive Engrs. *Res:* Chemical market studies, petroleum additives; gasolines; automotive and aviation lubricants; improved uses of petroleum products; petrochemicals; new energy sources; patent searches and analyses. *Mailing Add:* 534 Academy St Maplewood NJ 07040

POPKIN, GEORGE LIONEL, b Brockton, Mass, Jan 3, 21; m 42; c 4. DERMATOLOGY. *Educ:* Tufts Col, BS, 42, MD, 45. *Prof Exp:* Chief Dermat Serv, 69-77, DIR, POST-GRAD DERMAT SURG FEL PROG, NY SKIN & CANCER UNIT, 77- *Concurrent Pos:* Attend, Univ Hosp, Sch Med, New York Univ, clin prof dermat, 66- *Mem:* Am Acad Dermat; Int Soc Dermat Surg; Am Soc Dermat Surg. *Mailing Add:* NY Skin & Cancer Unit 4277 Hempstead Turnpike Bethpage NY 11714

POPKIN, MICHAEL KENNETH, b Trenton, NJ, Dec 31, 43; m 71; c 2. CONSULTATION-LIAISON PSYCHIATRY, PSYCHOSOMATIC MEDICINE. *Educ:* Princeton Univ, BA, 65; Univ Chicago Med Sch, MD, 69. *Prof Exp:* Intern, NY Univ-Bellevue Hosp, 69-70; resident, Mass Gen Hosp, 70-73; asst prof, 75-78, ASSOC PROF PSYCHIAT MED, UNIV MINN MED SCH, 78- *Concurrent Pos:* Consult, Brevard County Mental Health Ctr, 73-75; prin investr, NIMH Training Prog Consultation Liaison Psychiat grant, 77-82; dir, Consultation Psychiat Serv, Univ Minn Hosps, 75-; reviewer, Archives Gen Psychiat, Am J Psychiat, J Nervous Mental Dis & Gen Hosp Psychiat, 79- *Mem:* Am Psychopathol Asn; Am Psychosomatic Soc; Am Psychiat Asn; Am Col Sports Med; Asn Acad Psychiat. *Res:* Studies in consultation psychiatry directed at increasing clinical effectiveness and revising practices; psychiatric features and presentations of medical illness; stress response. *Mailing Add:* Box 345 Mayo Bldg Univ Hosps Minneapolis MN 55455

POPLAWSKY, ALEX JAMES, b Scranton, Pa, July 12, 48; m 72. PHYSIOLOGICAL PSYCHOLOGY. *Educ:* Univ Scranton, BS, 70; Ohio Univ, MS, 72, PhD(exp psychol), 74. *Prof Exp:* asst prof, 74-78, ASSOC PROF PSYCHOL, BLOOMSBURG STATE COL, 79- *Concurrent Pos:* Vis assoc prof, State Univ NY, Binghamton, 81-82. *Mem:* Am Psychol Asn; Sigma Xi; Psychonomic Soc. *Res:* Effects of brain lesions on learning and motivation; septal lesions; aversive conditioning. *Mailing Add:* Dept Psychol Bloomsburg State Col Bloomsburg PA 17815

POPLAWSKY, ROBERT P, physics, see previous edition

POPLE, JOHN ANTHONY, b Somerset, Eng, Oct 31, 25; m 52; c 4. THEORETICAL CHEMISTRY. *Educ:* Cambridge Univ, BA, 46, MA, 50, PhD(math), 51. *Prof Exp:* Res fel math, Trinity Col, Cambridge Univ, 51-54, lectr, 54-58; supt basic Physics Div, Mat Phys Lab, Teddington, Eng, 58-61, 62-64; Ford vis prof chem, Carnegie Inst Technol, 61-62, Carnegie Prof chem physics, 64-74, adj fel chem, Mellon Inst, 64-76, JOHN CHRISTIAN WARNER PROF NATURAL SCI, CARNEGIE-MELLON UNIV, 74- *Honors & Awards:* Irving Langmuir Award, Am Chem Soc, 70, Harrison Howe Award, 71; Marlow Medal, Faraday Soc, 58; Gilbert Newton Lewis Award, 72; Morley Award, 76; Pittsburgh Award, 75; Pauling Award, 77. *Mem:* Foreign assoc Nat Acad Sci; Am Phys Soc; fel Am Acad Arts & Sci; Royal Soc Chem; fel Royal Soc. *Res:* Application of quantum mechanics to the structure of molecules and theories of physical properties. *Mailing Add:* Carnegie-Mellon Univ Mellon Inst 4400 5th Ave Pittsburgh PA 15213

POPLI, SHANKAR D, b Panjab, India, Aug 4, 41; m 63; c 3. PHARMACEUTICS. *Educ:* Panjab Univ, India, BPharm, 63, MPharm, 65; Univ Alta, PhD(pharmaceut), 72. *Prof Exp:* Pharmacist, Panjab Health Serv, India, 59-60; tech asst pharm, Pharm Coun India, 65; teaching asst, Univ Alta, 67-71; res assoc, Col Pharm, Univ Mich, Ann Arbor, 71-72; res asst II, Sch Pharm, Univ Conn, Storrs, 72-73; sr res pharmacist, 73-79, GROUP MGR BIOPHARMACEUTICS, A H ROBINS CO, 79- *Mem:* Am Pharmaceut Asn; Sigma Xi. *Res:* Applications of physico-chemical principles in designing solid dosage forms. *Mailing Add:* A H Robins Co 1211 Sherwood Ave Richmond VA 23220

POPOFF, IVAN CHRISTOFF, organic chemistry, see previous edition

POPOV, ALEXANDER IVAN, b Vladivostok, Russia, Mar 22, 21; nat US; m 50; c 1. ANALYTICAL CHEMISTRY, INORGANIC CHEMISTRY. *Educ:* Aurora Univ, China, BS, 44; Univ Iowa, MS, 48, PhD(phys chem), 50. *Prof Exp:* Instr chem, Aurora Univ, 44-46; res assoc, Iowa Univ, 49-50, instr, 50-52, from asst prof to assoc prof anal chem, 52-60; prof chem & dean col lib arts & sci, Northern Ill Univ, 60-62; chmn dept, 62-69, PROF CHEM, MICH STATE UNIV, 62- *Mem:* AAAS; Am Chem Soc. *Res:* Spectroscopic studies; structure of electrolyte solvents; non-aqueous solvents; chemistry of neurological drugs; complex compounds of alkali metal ions. *Mailing Add:* Dept of Chem Mich State Univ East Lansing MI 48824

POPOV, E(GOR) P(AUL), b Kiev, Russia, Feb 19, 13; nat US; m 39; c 2. STRUCTURAL ENGINEERING. *Educ:* Univ Calif, BS, 33; Mass Inst Technol, MS, 34; Stanford Univ, PhD(civil eng), 46. *Prof Exp:* Struct designer, Calif, 35-39; asst prod engr, Southwestern Portland Cement Co, 39-42; mach designer, Goodyear Tire & Rubber Co, 42-43; design engr, Aerojet Corp, 43-45; from asst prof to assoc prof, 46-53; chmn div struct eng & mech & dir struct eng lab, 57-60, Miller res prof, Miller Inst Basic Res Sci, 67-68, PROF CIVIL ENG, UNIV CALIF, BERKELEY, 53- *Honors & Awards:* Hetenyi Award, Soc Exp Stress Anal, 69; T R Higgins Award, Am Inst Steel Construct, 71; Am Soc Civil Engrs, E E Howard Award, 76, J James R Croes Medal, 79, Nathan M Newmark Medal, 81. *Mem:* Nat Acad Eng; Int Asn Shell Struct (vpres, 70-); Am Concrete Inst; Am Soc Eng Sci; Am Soc Eng Educ. *Res:* Structural mechanics; limit design; shell theory; earthquake-resistant design. *Mailing Add:* Davis Hall Univ of Calif Berkeley CA 94720

POPOVIC, VOJIN, b Belgrade, Yugoslavia, Sept 18, 22; m 53; c 1. PHYSIOLOGY. *Educ:* Univ Belgrade, dipl, 49, PhD, 51. *Prof Exp:* Asst prof physiol, Univ Belgrade, 49-53, prof, 53-56, chmn dept, 54-56; res fel, Nat Ctr Sci Res, France, 56-57; res assoc, Univ Rochester, 57-58; Nat Res Coun Can fel, 58-60; assoc prof physiol, Univ Houston, 60-61; assoc prof, 61-66, PROF PHYSIOL, SCH MED, EMORY UNIV, 66- *Mem:* Am Physiol Soc; Soc Exp Biol & Med; Int Soc Chronobiol; Aerospace Med Asn; fel Royal Soc Health. *Res:* Thermoregulation; hypothermia; cardiovascular cancer research. *Mailing Add:* Dept of Physiol Emory Univ Sch of Med Atlanta GA 30322

POPOVIC, ZORAN, b Belgrade, Yugoslavia, Dec 7, 41; m 71; c 2. SOLID STATE PHYSICS, SEMICONDUCTORS. *Educ:* Univ Belgrade, dipl eng, 65, MSc, 69; McMaster Univ, PhD(mat sci), 74. *Prof Exp:* Asst, Fac Elec Eng, Univ Belgrade, 66-71; mem sci staff, 74-80, SR SCIENTIST ORG SEMICONDUCTORS, XEROX RES CTR CAN LTD, 80- *Mem:* Am Phys Soc; Asn Prof Engrs, Ont. *Res:* Photovoltaic energy conversion; photovoltaic phenomena in organic semiconductors. *Mailing Add:* Xerox Res Ctr of Can Ltd 2480 Dunwin Dr Mississauga ON L5L 1J9 Can

POPOVICH, FRANK, b Czech, Nov 2, 23; Can citizen; m 53; c 4. DENTISTRY. *Educ:* Univ Toronto, DDS, 51, MScD, 53; FRCD(C), 67. *Prof Exp:* Orthodontist, 53, dir, 55-60, co-dir, 62-65, assoc prof orthod, 69-74, PROF ORTHOD, FAC DENT, UNIV TORONTO, 74-, DIR & CUR, BURLINGTON GROWTH STUDY, 65- *Mem:* Can Dent Asn; Can Asn Orthod; Int Asn Dent Res; Human Biol Coun. *Res:* Facial growth and development; orthodontic treatment. *Mailing Add:* Div of Clin Sci 1244 Edward St Univ of Toronto Fac of Dent Toronto ON M5G 1G6 Can

POPOVICH, M(ILOSH), b Pittsburg, Calif, Sept 3, 17; m 39; c 2. MECHANICAL ENGINEERING. *Educ:* Ore State Col, BS, 39, MS, 41. *Prof Exp:* Asst prof mech eng, Ore State Col, 45-46; engr, Union Oil Co, Calif, 46-47; from asst prof to assoc prof mech eng, 47-50, chmn dept mech eng, 50-54, asst dean eng, 54-59, dean admin, 59-76, PROF, ORE STATE UNIV, 50-, VPRES ADMIN, 76- *Mem:* Fel Am Soc Mech Engrs. *Res:* Fuels and lubricants. *Mailing Add:* 1390 NW 14 St Corvallis OR 97330

POPOVICH, ROBERT PETER, b Sheboygan, Wis, Jan 9, 39; div; c 4. BIOMEDICAL ENGINEERING, CHEMICAL ENGINEERING. *Educ:* Univ Wis, BS, 63; Univ Wash, MS, 68, PhD(chem eng), 70. *Prof Exp:* Chem engr, Pac Northwest Labs, Battelle Mem Inst, 63-65; teaching asst chem eng, Univ Wash, 65-70, asst prof, 70-72; asst prof chem & biomed eng, 72-74, ASSOC PROF CHEM & BIOMED ENG, UNIV TEX, 74- *Concurrent Pos:* Biomed & chem eng consult to var pvt, pub & govt agencies, 72-; pres, Hemotherapy Instruments Inc, 74-; co-dir, Moncriet-Popovich Res Inst Inc, 77-; biomed eng consult, Boxter-Travenal Labs Inc, 77- *Mem:* Am Soc Artificial Internal Organs; Am Inst Chem Engrs; Nat Soc Prof Engrs; Am Soc Nephrol; Europ Dialysis & Transplant Asn. *Res:* Industrial and biomedical applications of membrane systems; development of artificial internal organs; transport phenomena and biomedical instrumentation; continuous ambulatory peritoneal dialysis. *Mailing Add:* ENS-617 Dept of Chem Eng Univ of Tex Austin TX 78712

POPOVICS, SANDOR, b Budapest, Hungary, Dec 24, 21; US citizen; m 61; c 2. CONCRETE TECHNOLOGY, OPTIMIZATION TECHNIQUES. *Educ:* Polytech Univ Budapest, BS, 44; Hungarian Acad Sci, MS, 56; Purdue Univ, PhD(civil eng), 61. *Prof Exp:* Res engr mat, Metrop Lab, 44-48; mgr mat, Inst Bldg Sci, 49-56; prof civil eng, Auburn Univ, 59-67; prof civil eng, Northern Ariz Univ, 67-76; prof civil eng, King Abdul Azziz Univ, Saudi Arabia, 77-78; PROF CIVIL ENG, DEPT CIVIL ENG, DREXEL UNIV, 78- *Concurrent Pos:* Consult, Hungarian Bur Standards, 48-56 & NASA, 69; mem, Nat Highway Safety Adv Comn, 72-73; prin investr, Ala Dept Transp, 60-67 & Ariz Dept Transp, 72-76. *Mem:* Fel Am Concrete Inst; fel Am Soc Civil Engrs; Transp Res Bd; Am Soc Testing & Mat. *Res:* Mathematical modeling of materials properties; mechanical properties of concrete and concrete making materials; deformability and fracture of composite materials; linear and non-linear optimization; applied mathematics and statistics. *Mailing Add:* Dept Civil Eng Drexel Univ Philadelphia PA 19104

POPP, CARL JOHN, b Chicago, Ill, Apr 3, 41; m 65; c 3. INORGANIC CHEMISTRY. *Educ:* Colo State Univ, BS, 62; Southern Ill Univ, Carbondale, MA, 65; Univ Utah, PhD(inorg chem), 68. *Prof Exp:* Instr chem, Southern Ill Univ, 65; fel, Univ Utah, 68-69; asst prof, 69-74, ASSOC PROF CHEM, N MEX INST MINING & TECHNOL, 74- *Mem:* AAAS; Am Chem Soc. *Res:* Preparation and characterization of coordination compounds; calorimetric studies of Lewis acid-base reactions; geochemistry of ore leaching; inorganic aspects of water chemistry. *Mailing Add:* Dept of Chem NMex Inst of Mining & Technol Socorro NM 87801

POPP, FRANK DONALD, b New York, NY, Dec 25, 32; m 55, 77; c 2. ORGANIC CHEMISTRY. *Educ:* Rensselaer Polytech Inst, BS, 54; Univ Kans, PhD(chem), 57. *Prof Exp:* Asst, Univ Kans, 54-57; jr res chemist, Univ Calif, 57-58; res assoc, Univ Mich, 58-59, USPHS fel, 59; asst prof chem, Univ Miami, 59-62; from asst prof to prof chem, Clarkson Col Technol, 62-76; PROF CHEM & MED, CHMN DEPT CHEM, UNIV MO-KANSAS CITY, 76- *Concurrent Pos:* USPHS fel, Univ East Anglia, 64-65. *Mem:* AAAS; Am Chem Soc; Am Asn Cancer Res; NY Acad Sci; Royal Soc Chem. *Res:* Synthesis and reactions of nitrogen heterocyclic compounds; medicinal chemistry; synthesis of alkaloids. *Mailing Add:* Dept of Chem Univ of Mo Kansas City MO 64110

POPP, GERHARD, b Obernzenn, Ger, Apr 10, 40. INORGANIC CHEMISTRY. *Educ:* Univ Würzburg, MS, 65, PhD(chem), 67. *Prof Exp:* Res asst chem, Phys Chem Inst, Univ Würzburg, 65-67; fel inorg chem, Univ Calif, Riverside, 67-69; SR RES CHEMIST, RES LABS, EASTMAN KODAK CO, 69- *Res:* Electroorganic chemistry, particularly electro-organic synthesis; transition metal chemistry. *Mailing Add:* Res Labs Eastman Kodak Co 343 State St Rochester NY 14650

POPP, RAYMOND ARTHUR, b Northport, Mich, Nov 23, 30; m 54; c 4. EMBRYOLOGY, GENETICS. *Educ:* Univ Mich, BS, 52, MA, 54, PhD PhD(zool), 57. *Prof Exp:* Res assoc, Biol Div, 57-58, biologist, 58-65, SR STAFF BIOLOGIST, OAK RIDGE NAT LAB, 65- *Concurrent Pos:* Mem fac, Univ Tenn Biomed Grad Sch, 66-; prin investr, Genetics Training Grant, 77- *Mem:* AAAS; Sigma Xi; Am Genetics Asn; Genetics Soc Am; Environ Mutagen Soc. *Res:* Experimental embryology; metabolism of embryonic tissues in vitro; transplantation and cellular differentiation of hematopoietic tissues in mice; genetics of mouse hemoglobins. *Mailing Add:* Biol Div Oak Ridge Nat Lab Box Y Oak Ridge TN 37830

POPPE, CARL HUGO, b Chicago, Ill, Nov 23, 36; m 57; c 4. NUCLEAR REACTIONS, NUCLEAR SCATTERING. *Educ:* DePauw Univ, BA, 57; Univ Wis, MS, 59, PhD(physics), 62. *Prof Exp:* From asst prof to assoc prof physics, Univ Minn, Minneapolis, 62-76; MEM STAFF, LAWRENCE LIVERMORE NAT LAB, UNIV CALIF, 76-, ASSOC DIV LEADER, EXP PHYSICS DIV, 79- *Mem:* Fel Am Phys Soc; Am Asn Physics Teachers. *Res:* Nuclear physics. *Mailing Add:* Lawrence Livermore Lab Univ of Calif PO Box 808 Livermore CA 94550

POPPE, WASSILY, b Riga, Latvia, Nov 10, 18; US citizen; m 42; c 1. PHYSICAL CHEMISTRY. *Educ:* Univ Tübingen, BS, 47; Univ Stuttgart, MS, 49; Univ Pittsburgh, PhD(phys chem), 66. *Prof Exp:* Chemist, Dr Hans Kittel Chem Lab, Ger, 49-50; develop chemist, Karl Worwag Lack & Farbenfabrik, 50-51; prod mgr paint, Pinturas Iris, Venezuela, 51-53; lab supvr paint chem, Pinturas Tucan affiliated PPG Industs, Inc, Venezuela, 53-54, tech dir, 54-57, plant mgr paint prod, 57-59; res chemist, Springfield Res Ctr, PPG Industs, Inc, 59-64, res asst phys chem, Univ Pittsburgh, 64-66; group leader surface chem, Avicun Corp, 66-68; group leader polypropylene prod res, 68-76, res supvr, Plastic Prod Div, 76-78, RES ASSOC, AMOCO CHEM, NAPERVILLE, 78- *Mem:* Am Chem Soc; fel Am Inst Chemists. *Res:* Surface chemistry; nonequilibrium thermodynamics; color research of plastic products; adhesion of coatings and metals to plastic surfaces. *Mailing Add:* 105 N Main St Lombard IL 60148

POPPELBAUM, WOLFGANG JOHANNES, b Frankfurt, Ger, Aug 28, 24. ELECTRICAL ENGINEERING, COMPUTER SCIENCE. *Educ:* Univ Lausanne, MS, 52, PhD(physics), 54. *Prof Exp:* Swiss fel, Univ Lausanne, 54-55; res assoc elec eng, 55-56, from asst prof to assoc prof, 56-63, PROF ELEC ENG & COCOMPUT SCI, UNIV ILL, URBANA-CHAMPAIGN, 63- *Concurrent Pos:* Consult, Elliott Automation, 60- & Los Alamos Sci Lab, 71- *Mem:* Fel Inst Elec & Electronics Engrs; Swiss Phys Soc; Am Phys Soc; Soc Info Display. *Res:* Semiconductor physics; circuit design and research; electro optics and hybrid digital-analog circuitry; display devices with bandwidth compression; probabilistic and deterministic averaging processors. *Mailing Add:* 230 Digital Comput Lab Univ of Ill Urbana IL 61801

POPPELE, RICHARD E, b Irvington, NJ, Mar 6, 36; m 59; c 4. NEUROPHYSIOLOGY. *Educ:* Tufts Univ, BSEE, 58; Univ Minn, PhD(physiol), 65. *Prof Exp:* Res assoc neurophysiol, Univ Minn, 65; Nat Inst Neurol Dis & Stroke fel, Univ Pisa, 65-67; from asst prof to assoc prof, 67-75, PROF PHYSIOL, UNIV MINN, MINNEAPOLIS, 75- *Concurrent Pos:* Dir Neurophysiol Lab, 68- *Mem:* Int Brain Res Orgn; Soc Neurosci; NY Acad Sci; Biophys Soc: Am Physiol Soc. *Res:* Behavior of muscle receptors, especially systems analysis approach to the behavior of receptors and the reflex activity evoked by receptors. *Mailing Add:* Dept of Physiol 424 Millard Hall Univ of Minn Minneapolis MN 55455

POPPENDIEK, HEINZ FRANK, b Altona, Ger, Nov 8, 19; nat US; m 43; c 3. PHYSICS. *Educ:* Univ Calif, BS, 42, MS, 44, PhD(mech eng), 49. *Prof Exp:* Res engr, Univ Calif, 42-46, lectr & res engr, Univ Calif, Los Angeles, 46-49, asst prof & res engr, 49-50; group leader, Oak Ridge Nat Lab, 50-52, sect chief, 52-56; mem staff, Gen Atomic Div, Gen Dynamics Corp, 56-58, staff specialist, Convair Div, 58-60; dir appl res, Geophys Corp, Am, 60-61; PRES, GEOSCI LTD, 61- *Concurrent Pos:* Lectr, Univ Mich, 53 & Oak Ridge Sch Reactor Tech, 52-56; consult, Los Alamos Sci Lab, 56- *Honors & Awards:* Award, Am Geophys Union, 53. *Mem:* Am Nuclear Soc. *Res:* Applied physics and mathematics; heat, mass and momentum transfer; nuclear reactor physics; elasticity; micro-meteorology and atmospheric turbulence; selenography; physical properties; sea water conversion; electromagnetic pumping of blood. *Mailing Add:* 7834 Esterel Dr La Jolla CA 92037

POPPENSIEK, GEORGE CHARLES, b New York, NY, June 18, 18; m 43; c 2. VETERINARY MEDICINE. *Educ:* Univ Pa, VMD, 42; Cornell Univ, MS, 51; Am Bd Microbiol, dipl; Am Col Vet Microbiol, dipl. *Prof Exp:* Asst instr med, Sch Vet Med, Univ Pa, 42-43; asst prof vet sci, Univ Md, 43-44; dept head, Lederle Labs Div, Am Cyanamid Co, 44-49; dir diag lab, State Univ NY Vet Col, Cornell Univ, 49-51, res assoc vet virus res inst, 51-55, actg prof bact, 53-54; vet, Plum Island Dis Lab, Animal Dis & Parasite Res Div, Agr Res Serv, USDA, 55-56, supvry vet, Immunol Invests, 56-59; prof microbiol & dean, 59-74, prof comp path, Med Col, 74-76, JAMES LAW PROF COMP MED, NY STATE COL VET MED, CORNELL UNIV, 74-; RES PROF DEPT PREV MED, MED COL, UPSTATE MED CTR, STATE UNIV NY SYRACUSE, 74- *Concurrent Pos:* Chmn bd dirs, Cornell Vet, Inc, 76-; external examr, Col Vet Med, Miss State Univ, 78-; external adv vet med, Mount Hope Med Complex, Univ West Indies, Trinidad/Tobago, 78- *Honors & Awards:* XII Int Vet Cong Prize, Am Vet Med Asn, 77. *Mem:* Fel AAAS; US Animal Health Asn; Am Vet Med Asn; Am Col Vet Microbiol; fel Am Acad Microbiol. *Res:* Virus diseases of domestic animals. *Mailing Add:* 122 E Remington Rd Ithaca NY 14850

POPPER, ARTHUR N, b New York, NY, May 9, 43; m 68; c 1. ZOOLOGY, NEUROSCIENCES. *Educ:* NY Univ, BA, 64; City Univ NY, PhD(biol), 69. *Prof Exp:* From asst prof to assoc prof zool, Univ Hawaii, 69-78; ASSOC PROF ANAT, SCH MED & DENT, GEORGETOWN UNIV, 78- *Concurrent Pos:* Assoc zoologist, Lab Sensory Sci, Univ of Hawaii, 73-78; adj sr scientist, Mote Marine Lab, Sarasota, Fla, 79-; res career develop arard, NIH, 78-83. *Mem:* AAAS; Acoust Soc Am; Animal Behav Soc; Soc Neurosci; Sigma Xi. *Res:* Mechanisms of sound detection and processing in aquatic vertebrates; animal communications and behavior. *Mailing Add:* Dept of Anat Sch Med & Dent Georgetown Univ Washington DC 20007

POPPER, DANIEL MAGNES, b Oakland, Calif, Aug 11, 13; m 40; c 1. ASTRONOMY. *Educ:* Univ Calif, AB, 34, PhD(astron), 38. *Prof Exp:* Kellogg fel, Lick Observ, Univ Calif, 38-39; asst astron, McDonald Observ, Chicago-Tex, 39-40, instr, 40-42; instr, Yerkes Observ, Univ Chicago, 42-43; physicist, Radiation Lab, Univ Calif, 43-45; instr astron, Yerkes Observ, Univ Chicago, 45-46, asst prof, 46-47; from asst prof to assoc prof, 47-55, chmn dept, 51-57, 59-63, prof astron, 55-78, PROF EMER & RES ASTRON, UNIV CALIF, LOS ANGELES, 78-; guest investr, Mt Wilson & Palomar Observs, 49-; NSF sr fel, 64-65. *Mem:* Am Astron Soc. *Res:* Stellar spectroscopy; radial velocities of stars; spectroscopic and eclipsing binaries. *Mailing Add:* Dept of Astron Univ of Calif Los Angeles CA 90024

POPPER, HANS, b Vienna, Austria, Nov 24, 03; nat; m 42; c 2. PATHOLOGY. *Educ:* Univ Vienna, MD, 28; Univ Ill, MS, 42, PhD(path), 44; Am Bd Path, dipl. *Hon Degrees:* MD, Cath Univ Louvain, 65, Univ Bologna, 65, Univ Hannover, 74, Univ Turin, 75, Univ Tüebingen, 77, Cath Univ Seoul, 78, Univ Lisbon, 81, Univ Münster, 81 & Col Med Dent, NJ, 81; PhD, Univ Vienna, 65; DSc, Mt Sinai Sch Med, 79. *Prof Exp:* Demonstr, Dept Path, Univ Vienna, 27-28, asst, 28-33, asst dept internal med, 33-38; prof path, Cook County Grad Sch Med, 43-44, prof & head div, 46-56; prof path, Columbia Univ, 57-65; prof path, chmn dept & dean acad affairs, 65-72, pres & dean, 72-73, DISTINGUISHED SERV PROF, MT SINAI SCH MED, 72- *Concurrent Pos:* Instr, Univ Ill, 39-46; dir clin labs, Cook County Hosp, 42-44, dir labs, 44-46, dir dept path, 46-56; sci dir & mem bd trustees, Hektoen Inst Med Res, 43-56; from asst prof to prof, Northwestern Univ, 46-57; pathologist-in-chief, Mt Sinai Hosp, 57-72; consult, NIH; mem adv coun, Nat Inst Arthritis, Metab & Digestive Dis, 73-75, mem nat comt digestive dis, 77-79. *Honors & Awards:* Friedenwald Medal, Am Gastroenterol Asn, 71; Fogarty Scholar, NIH, 74; John Phillips Mem Award, Am Col Physicians, 81. *Mem:* Nat Acad Sci; fel Am Soc Clin Path; Am Asn Study Liver Dis (secy, 49-58, pres, 63); fel Col Am Pathologists; Int Asn Study Liver (pres, 62-66). *Res:* Anatomical, experimental and clinical pathology of liver diseases. *Mailing Add:* Mt Sinai Sch of Med One Gustave L Leevy Pl New York NY 10029

POPPER, THOMAS LESLIE, b Budapest, Hungary, May 5, 33; US citizen; m 62; c 2. ORGANIC CHEMISTRY. *Educ:* Eotvos Lorand Univ, Budapest, dipl chem, 56; Mass Inst Technol, PhD(org chem), 61. *Prof Exp:* Res chemist, Wander Pharmaceut Co, Budapest, 56; asst chemist, Schering Corp, NJ, 57-58; Nat Inst Gen Med Sci fel, Biochem Inst, Med Sch, Vienna Univ, 62-63; sr chemist, Rohm & Haas Co, Pa, 63-65; sr res scientist, 65-69, sect head, 69-70, mgr natural prod res, 70-74, ASSOC DIR CHEM RES, NATURAL PROD, SCHERING CORP, 74- *Mem:* AAAS; Am Chem Soc; Royal Soc Chem; NY Acad Sci. *Res:* Isolation, characterization and synthesis of natural products; compounds of biological activity for pharmaceutical uses, particularly on steroidal field; radiochemistry; medicinal chemistry (allergy and inflammation). *Mailing Add:* Natural Prod Res Schering Corp 60 Orange St Bloomfield NJ 07003

POPPERS, PAUL JULES, anesthesiology, see previous edition

POPPLEWELL, JAMES MALCOLM, b UK, June 2, 42; US citizen; m 66; c 2. METALLURGY, CORROSION. *Educ:* Univ Leeds, BSc, 64, PhD(metall), 68. *Prof Exp:* Eng specialist metall, 68-69, supvr corrosion group, 69-74, cheif chem metallurgist, 74-76, assoc dir chem metall & eng, 76-81, DIR PROD RES, OLIN CORP, 81- *Mem:* Nat Asn Corrosion Engrs; Electrochem Soc; Am Soc Testing & Mat. *Res:* Corrosion and surface studies; physical and chemical metallurgy; electron optics; glass sealing; materials useage in solar energy, chemical plants and power generation. *Mailing Add:* Olin Metals Res Labs 91 Shelton Ave New Haven CT 06504

POPPOFF, ILIA GEORGE, b San Diego, Calif, Apr 9, 24; m 44; c 3. AERONOMY. *Educ:* Whittier Col, BA, 47. *Prof Exp:* Physicist, US Naval Radiol Defense Lab, 43-53; assoc physicist, Stanford Res Inst, 53-56, sr physicist, 56-63, chmn dept atmospheric sci, 63-67; chief atmospheres & astrophysics br, Space Sci Div, NASA Ames Res Ctr, 67-70, actg chief space sci div, 68-69, chief earth sci applns off, 71-74, asst chief space div, 70-79, chief stratospheric proj off, 74-79; PRES, FLICK POINT ASSOCS, INC, 79- *Concurrent Pos:* Ed adv bd, Geophys Surv, 72- *Mem:* AAAS; Am Meteorol Soc; Am Geophys Union; assoc fel Am Inst Aeronaut & Astronaut. *Res:* Chemistry and physics of the stratosphere. *Mailing Add:* Flick Point Assocs Inc PO Box 35 Carnelian Bay CA 95711

POPPY, WILLARD JOSEPH, b New London, Wis, June 23, 07; m 34; c 2. PHYSICS. *Educ:* Univ Wis, Oshkosh, EdB, 30; Univ Iowa, MS, 33, PhD(physics), 34. *Prof Exp:* Assoc prof physics & head dept, Cleveland State Univ, 34-42, prof & head dept, 43-49; lectr, Univ Iowa, 42-43; from assoc prof to prof, 49-75, EMER PROF PHYSICS, UNIV NORTHERN IOWA, 75- *Mem:* AAAS; Am Asn Physics Teachers. *Res:* Zinc crystals; electrical resistivity of zinc crystals. *Mailing Add:* Dept of Physics Univ of Northern Iowa Cedar Falls IA 50613

POPS, HORACE, b Queens, NY, July 20, 36; m 58; c 3. METALLURGY. *Educ:* Rensselaer Polytech Inst, BMetE, 57; Lehigh Univ, MMetE, 58; Univ Pittsburgh, DSc(metall), 62. *Prof Exp:* Jr fel ferrous alloys, Mellon Inst, 58-63, fel & head ferrous alloy group, 62-63, fel metal physics, 63-65, sr fel & head copper alloys, 65-67; head res & develop metall, 67-72, DIR METALS LAB, ESSEX INT, 72- *Concurrent Pos:* Mem adj staff, Univ Pittsburgh, 67-69. *Honors & Awards:* Medal Award, Wire Asn, 76 & 80. *Mem:* Am Soc Metals; Am Inst Mining, Metall & Petrol Engrs. *Res:* Physical metallurgy; phase transformations; cryogenics; x-ray diffraction; dispersion hardening; copper alloys; martensite. *Mailing Add:* Essex Int 1550 Wall St Ft Wayne IN 46804

POP-STOJANOVIC, ZORAN RISTA, b Belgrade, Yugoslavia, May 30, 35; US citizen; m 66. MATHEMATICS. *Educ:* Univ Belgrade, BS, 58, PhD(math), 64. *Prof Exp:* Instr math, Univ Belgrade, 59-64, asst prof, 64-65; from asst prof to assoc prof, 65-72, PROF MATH, UNIV FLA, 72- *Concurrent Pos:* Army Res Off-Durham fel, Univ Fla, 68-70. *Mem:* Am Math Soc. *Res:* Probability theory; random processes; laws of large numbers; Martingales; stochastic integration; spectral theory of random fields. *Mailing Add:* Dept of Math Univ of Fla Gainesville FL 32601

PORANSKI, CHESTER F, JR, b Brooklyn, NY, Mar 13, 37; m 59; c 4. PHYSICAL CHEMISTRY, SPECTROSCOPY. *Educ:* Univ San Francisco, BS, 59; St Joseph's Col, Pa, MS, 61; Univ Md, PhD(phys chem), 73. *Prof Exp:* Qual control & applns chemist, Prod Res & Chem Corp, 59-61; RES CHEMIST, NAVAL RES LAB, 63- *Mem:* Am Chem Soc; Sigma Xi. *Res:* Basic and applied research for the characterization of the processes occuring during thermal and radiation induced degradation of materials; characterization of polymers by spectroscopic and other techniques. *Mailing Add:* 6480 Gainer St Annandale VA 22003

PORCELLA, DONALD BURKE, b Modesto, Calif, Oct 2, 37; m 61; c 3. ENVIRONMENTAL SCIENCE. *Educ:* Univ Calif, Berkeley, AB, 59, MA, 61, PhD(environ health sci), 67. *Prof Exp:* Asst specialist, USPHS, 61-63; asst specialist, Univ Calif, Berkeley, 63-65; Fulbright fel, Norweg Inst Water Res, 67-68; asst res zool, Univ Calif, Berkeley & Lake Tahoe Area Coun, 68-70; asst prof, Utah State Univ, 70-72, assoc prof biol, 72-78, prof, Civil Environ Eng, 78-79, assoc dir, Utah Water Res Lab, 77-79; PRIN SCIENTIST, TETRA TECH INC, 79- *Concurrent Pos:* Consult, Bechtel Corp, 70-71, Procter & Gamble, 71-72, Intermountain Consults & Planners, 75-79, Kennecott Copper Corp, 76-80 & PUD, South Lake Tahoe, 77-81; head div environ eng, IPA, US Environ Protect Agency, 76-77. *Mem:* AAAS; Am Soc Limnol & Oceanog; Water Pollution Control Fedn; Sigma Xi; Int Asn Water Pollution Res. *Res:* Eutrophication; nutrients and productivity; radiological health and radioecology; resource utilization and environmental management; water quality and pollution control; minimum flow requirements in streams; stream productivity; ecosystem modeling; hazardous wastes and toxicity; bioassay-soils, fresh and salt water. *Mailing Add:* Tetra Tech Inc 3746 Mt Diablo Blvd Lafayette CA 94549

PORCELLO, LEONARD J(OSEPH), b New York, NY, Mar 1, 34; m 62; c 2. ELECTRICAL ENGINEERING, PHYSICS. *Educ:* Cornell Univ, BA, 55; Univ Mich, MS, 57, MSE, 59, PhD(elec eng), 63. *Prof Exp:* Res asst radar & optics, Inst Sci & Technol, Univ Mich, Ann Arbor, 55-57, res asst, 57-58, instr elec eng, Univ, 58-61, res engr, Inst, 61-69, asst head radar & optics lab, 63-68, head, 68-70, from assoc prof to prof elec eng, Univ, 69-72, assoc dir, Willow Run Labs, 70-72; dir radar & optics div, Environ Res Inst Mich, 73-76; asst vpres & div mgr, 76-79, VPRES, SCI APPLNS, INC, 79- *Concurrent Pos:* Consult, Radar & Optics Lab, Inst Sci & Technol, Univ Mich, 58-61; lectr, Eng Summer Conf Prog, Univ Mich, 63-70, course co-chmn, 66-70; adj prof elec eng, Univ Mich, 73-76; spec adv, Div Adv Group, Aeronaut Systs Div, US Air Force, 75-76. *Mem:* Fel Inst Elec & Electronics Engrs; Optical Soc Am; AAAS. *Res:* Radar technology and applications; synthetic aperture radar; coherent optics technology; optical data processing; radio wave propagation through the atmosphere; remote sensing. *Mailing Add:* Sci Applns Inc 5055 E Broadway Suite A-214 Tucson AZ 85711

PORCH, WILLIAM MORGAN, b Athens, Ohio, Nov 8, 44; m 78. ATMOSPHERIC PHYSICS, GEOPHYSICS. *Educ:* Univ Utah, BA, 66; Univ Wash, MS, 68, PhD(geophys), 71. *Prof Exp:* Optical engr, Boeing Aircraft Co, 66-68; res assoc geophys, Univ Wash, 68-72; PHYSICIST ATMOSPHERIC SCI, LAWRENCE LIVERMORE LAB, 72- *Concurrent Pos:* Fel, Univ Wash, 71-72; lectr atmospheric sci, Univ Calif, Davis, 73. *Mem:* Am Meteorol Soc; Am Geophys Union; Optical Soc Am. *Res:* Physical and chemical properties of atmospheric aerosols; remote sensing of transport and diffusion of atmospheric pollutants in complex terrain and wind energy prospecting. *Mailing Add:* L-262 Lawrence Livermore Lab Livermore CA 94550

PORCHER, RICHARD DWIGHT, b Charleston, SC, Jan 1, 39; m 69; c 2. BOTANY, TAXONOMY. *Educ:* Col Charleston, BS, 62; Univ SC, MS, 66, PhD(biol), 74. *Prof Exp:* Teacher sci, N Charleston High Sch, 62-63; lab asst, Univ SC, 64-67; from instr to asst prof, Voorhees Col, 69-70; asst prof, 70-78, ASSOC PROF BIOL, THE CITADEL, 78- *Concurrent Pos:* Dir & cur, The Citadel Herbarium, 71-; contractor, Belle W Baruch Found grant, 76-80, Nat Audubon Soc grant, 77-80 & US Forest Serv grant, 78-80. *Mem:* Sigma Xi; Bot Soc Am. *Res:* Taxonomy and ecology of vascular flora of Coastal Plain of South Carolina; endangered and threatened species. *Mailing Add:* Dept of Biol The Citadel Charleston SC 29409

PORE, NORMAN ARTHUR, b Connellsville, Pa, Feb 25, 28; m 50; c 2. METEOROLOGY. *Educ:* Pa State Univ, BS, 53, MS, 54. *Prof Exp:* Oceanogr, US Navy Hydrographic Off, 54-55; res meteorologist, Off Meteorol Res, 55-65, RES METEOROLOGIST, TECH DEVELOP LAB, NAT WEATHER SERV, 65- *Mem:* Am Meteorol Soc; Int Asn Great Lakes Res. *Res:* Marine meteorology; ocean waves; tides; storm surges; development of techniques for forecasting state of the marine environment such as wave conditions and storm surges. *Mailing Add:* Nat Weather Serv NOAA 8060 13th St Silver Spring MD 20910

PORE, ROBERT SCOTT, b Toledo, Ohio, Feb 26, 38; m 65; c 1. MEDICAL MYCOLOGY, MICROBIOLOGY. *Educ:* Univ Tex, Austin, BA, 60; Tex A&M Univ, MS, 62; Univ Calif, Los Angeles, PhD(plant sci), 65. *Prof Exp:* NIH fel med mycol, Univ Okla, 65-67, asst prof microbiol, 67-68; asst prof, 68-74, ASSOC PROF MICROBIOL, MED SCH, W VA UNIV, 74- *Mem:* Med Mycol Soc of the Americas; Int Soc Human & Animal Mycol; Am Soc Microbiol; Mycol Soc Am. *Res:* Pathobiology and systematics of fungi and algae; phylogeny of Prototheca species; mucor dimorphism; mycotoxicoses. *Mailing Add:* 1286 Braewick Dr Morgantown WV 26506

PORETZ, RONALD DAVID, b New York, NY. BIOCHEMISTRY, IMMUNOCHEMISTRY. *Educ:* Hartwick Col, BA, 61; Long Island Univ, MS, 63; State Univ NY Buffalo, PhD(biochem), 68. *Prof Exp:* Nat Heart Inst fel, Lister Inst Prev Med, London, 68-70; asst prof biochem, Med Ctr, UniV Kans, 70-73; asst prof, 73-75, ASSOC PROF DEPT BIOCHEM, NELSON BIOL LAB, RUTGERS UNIV, NEW BRUNSWICK, 75- *Mem:* AAAS; Sigma Xi; Am Soc Biol Chemists; Am Chem Soc; Royal Soc Chem. *Res:* Characterization of lectins and the properties and characteristics of cell surface glycoronjugates. *Mailing Add:* Dept of Biochem Rutgers Univ New Brunswick NJ 08903

PORGES, KARL G, nuclear physics, see previous edition

PORIES, WALTER J, b Munich, Ger, Jan 18, 30; US citizen; m 51; c 6. SURGERY, NUTRITION. *Educ:* Univ Rochester, MD, 55; Wesleyan Univ, BA, 73; Am Bd Surg & Bd Thoracic Surg, dipl, 63. *Prof Exp:* Chief surg & obstet, Rosieres AFB Hosp, US Air Force, Toul, France, 56-58, resident gen & thoracic surg, Strong Mem Hosp, Rochester, NY, 58-62, instr, 60-62; surgeon, Wright-Patterson AFB Hosp, 62-64, chief gen & thoracic surg,

64-67; asst prof surg & assoc surgeon, Sch Med & Dent, Univ Rochester, 67-69; prof surg & assoc dir dept, Sch Med, Case Western Reserve Univ, 69-77; chief dept surg, Cleveland Metrop Gen Hosp, 69-77; PROF & CHMN DEPT SURG, SCH MED, EAST CAROLINA UNIV, 77-; CHIEF SURG, PITT CO MEM HOSP, 77- *Concurrent Pos:* Atomic Energy Comn fel radiation biol, Univ Rochester, 58-59; dir intern & residency training prog, Wright-Patterson AFB Hosp, 65-67; dir, Cancer Ctr, Northeast Ohio, 72-74; chief of staff, Cuyahoga County Hosp, 72-74. *Mem:* Am Surg Asn; Soc Univ Surgeons; Vascular Soc; Am Col Surgeons; Am Col Cardiol. *Res:* Metabolism of trace metals; wound healing; problems in pulmonary embolism and vascular surgery; effects of diet on arteriosclerosis; cancer. *Mailing Add:* Dept of Surg East Carolina Univ Sch Med Greenville NC 27834

PORILE, NORBERT THOMAS, b Vienna, Austria, May 18, 32; nat US; m 57; c 1. NUCLEAR CHEMISTRY. *Educ:* Univ Chicago, AB, 52, PhD(chem), 57. *Prof Exp:* Res assoc chem, Brookhaven Nat Lab, 57-59, from assoc chemist to chemist, 59-64; assoc prof, 65-69, PROF CHEM, PURDUE UNIV, LAFAYETTE, 69- *Concurrent Pos:* Vis scientist, Univ Tokyo Inst Nuclear Study & Kyoto, 61; vis prof, McGill Univ, 63-65; Guggenheim Mem fel, Inst Nuclear Physics, France, 71-72; Alexander von Humboldt award, Marburg, 82; fel Soc Prom Sci Japan. *Mem:* AAAS: Am Chem Soc; Am Phys Soc. *Res:* Nuclear reactions and fission; high and intermediate energy nuclear reactions. *Mailing Add:* Dept of Chem Purdue Univ Lafayette IN 47907

PORKOLAB, MIKLOS, b Budapest, Hungary, Mar 24, 39; US citizen. PLASMA PHYSICS. *Educ:* Univ BC, BASc, 63; Stanford Univ, MS, 64, PhD(appl physics), 67. *Prof Exp:* Res asst, Plasma Physics, Microwave Lab, Stanford Univ, 64-67; res assoc, Princeton Univ, 67-68, mem res staff, 68-71, res physicist, 71-75, sr res physicist, Plasma Physics Labs, 75-77, from assoc prof to prof astrophys sci, 73-77; PROF PHYSICS, MASS INST TECHNOL, 77- *Concurrent Pos:* Consult, Bell Labs, 70-77, Plasma Physics Labs, Princeton Univ, 77-81, Lawrence Livermore Nat Lab, 78- & United Technol, 78-80; vis prof, Univ Colo, Boulder, 75; vis scientist, Max Planck Inst, WGer, 75-76; Alexander von Humboldt US sr scientist award, 75. *Mem:* Fel Am phys Soc. *Res:* Experimental and theoretical plasma physics; plasma waves; instabilities; nonlinear phenomena; radio frequency heating of thermonuclear plasmas. *Mailing Add:* Mass Inst of Technol Dept of Physics 36-213 Cambridge MA 02139

PORSCHE, JULES D(OWNES), b London, Eng, July 7, 09; US citizen; m 35; c 3. CHEMISTRY. *Educ:* Univ Chicago, BS, 30, PhD(org chem), 33. *Prof Exp:* Res chemist, Munic Tuberc Sanit, Chicago, 33-35; res chemist, Armour & Co, 35-40, head biol sect, 40-44, asst dir chem res & develop dept, 44-50, dir res & develop chem & by-prod dept, 50-52, mgr cent res dept, 52-56, staff asst to vpres, 58-61; PRES, JULES D PORSCHE & ASSOCS, 61- *Mem:* AAAS; Am Chem Soc; fel Am Inst Chem; Am Oil Chem Soc; Inst Food Technologists. *Res:* Hydrolytic instability of carbon to carbon and carbon to nitrogen bonds; silicosis chemistry; fractionation of plasma and plasma proteins; chemistry of fatty and amino acids; chemical market research; research administration. *Mailing Add:* Jules D Porsche & Assocs 2 S 680 Normandy W Oak Brook IL 60521

PORSCHING, THOMAS AUGUST, b Pittsburgh, Pa, Jan 25, 36; div; c 1. MATHEMATICS. *Educ:* Carnegie Inst Technol, BS, 57, MS, 58, PhD(math), 64. *Prof Exp:* Staff mathematician, Bettis Atomic Power Lab, Westinghouse Elec Corp, 60-68, fel mathematician, 68-71, adv mathematician, 71-73; assoc prof, 73-79, PROF MATH, UNIV PITTSBURGH, 79- *Concurrent Pos:* Lectr, Carnegie Inst Technol, 65-71; consult, Westinghouse Elec Corp, 73- *Mem:* Math Asn Am; Soc Indust & Appl Math. *Res:* Numerical analysis; differential equations; computational fluid dynamics. *Mailing Add:* Dept Math Univ Pittsburgh Pittsburgh PA 15260

PORT, CURTIS DEWITT, b Cheyenne, Wyo, Aug 25, 30; m 57; c 2. LABORATORY ANIMAL MEDICINE, VETERINARY PATHOLOGY. *Educ:* Univ Calif, Davis, BS, 54, DVM, 56; Northwestern Univ, MS, 67; Univ Chicago, PhD(pathol), 72. *Prof Exp:* Dir, animal care, Northwestern Univ, 64-67; vet med res investr, Hines Vets Hosp, 67-70; sr veterinary pathologist, Ill Inst Technol Res Inst, 70-74, sci adv, 74-77; actg dir, Lab Animal Med, 78-80, ASSOC PROF & ASSOC DIR, PATHOL & ANIMAL RESOURCES, NORTHWESTERN UNIV, 77- *Concurrent Pos:* Instr pathol, Ill Col Podiat Med, 75-77; consult pathologist, Tvavenol Labs, 76-, Lincoln Park Zoo, Chicago, 78-, Standard Oil Corp, 78-; lectr, Safety Carcinogenesis Lab, Nat Cancer Inst, 77-81. *Mem:* AAAS; Soc Toxicol Pathologists; Am Asn Lab Animal Sci. *Res:* Lung pathology; lung cancer. *Mailing Add:* 1448 Lois Ave Park Ridge IL 60068

PORT, SIDNEY C, b Chicago, Ill, Nov 27, 35; m 57; c 3. MATHEMATICS. *Educ:* Northwestern Univ, AB, 57, MS, 58, PhD(math), 62. *Prof Exp:* Mathematician, Rand Corp, 62-66; lectr, 65-66, assoc prof, 66-69, PROF MATH, UNIV CALIF, LOS ANGELES, 69- *Mem:* Am Math Soc; fel Inst Math Statist. *Res:* Mathematical probability theory. *Mailing Add:* Dept Math Univ Calif Los Angeles CA 90024

PORTA, EDUARDO ANGEL, b Buenos Aires, Arg, Dec 12, 24; nat; m 55; c 3. EXPERIMENTAL PATHOLOGY. *Educ:* Univ Buenos Aires, BSc, 43, MD, 52. *Prof Exp:* Asst pathologist, Children Hosp, Buenos Aires, Arg, 52-57; asst resident, Sch Med, Wash Univ, 57-58, lectr, 57-60, instr path & Life Ins Found Res fel, 58-60; chmn dept path, Inst Biol & Exp Med, Buenos Aires, 60-61; res assoc path, Albany Med Col, 61-63; res assoc, Res Inst, Hosp Sick Children, 63-65, asst scientist, 65-68, assoc scientist, 68-70; prof path & chmn dept, Univ Buenos Aires, 70-71; PROF PATH, UNIV HAWAII, MANOA, 71- *Honors & Awards:* Price Award, Arg Soc Pediat, 56-57. *Mem:* Am Soc Exp Path; Am Asn Path & Bact; Am Inst Nutrit; Nutrit Soc Can; Int Acad Path. *Res:* Nutritional hepatic injuries; electron microscopy of hepatic diseases; ceroid pigment formation; acute and chronic alcoholism. *Mailing Add:* Dept of Path Univ of Hawaii at Manoa Honolulu HI 96822

PORTE, DANIEL, JR, b New York, NY, Aug 13, 31; m 51; c 3. MEDICINE, METABOLISM. *Educ:* Brown Univ, AB, 53; Univ Chicago, MD, 57; Am Bd Internal Med, dipl, 64. *Prof Exp:* Asst prof med & clin investr, 65-70, assoc prof, 70-73, PROF MED, UNIV WASH, 73- *Concurrent Pos:* Assoc chief of staff, Vet Admin Hosp, Seattle, 65- *Mem:* Am Fedn Clin Res; Am Diabetes Asn; Am Soc Clin Invest; Asn Am Physicians; fel Am Col Physicians. *Res:* Endocrinology; mechanism of insulin secretion in man; effects of catecholamines; mechanism for lipemia in man; effects of diet on serum lipid levels; relation between adipose tissue enzymes and triglyceride turnover in man. *Mailing Add:* Vet Admin Hosp (151) 4435 Beacon Ave S Seattle WA 98108

PORTELANCE, VINCENT DAMIEN, b Woonsocket, RI, June 5, 23; Can citizen. MICROBIOLOGY. *Educ:* Univ Montreal, BSc, 46, MSc, 47, PhD(org chem), 50. *Prof Exp:* Govt France fel, 50-51; asst prof org chem, Univ Montreal, 51-52, res assoc, Microbial Biochem, Inst Microbiol & Hyg, 52-55, res officer, 55-57, head lab & exec res secy, 57-75, lectr bact physiol, Fac Med, 57-69; DIR BACT, INST ARMAND-FRAPPIER, 75- *Concurrent Pos:* Res prof fac med, Univ Montreal, 69-; prof, Univ Quebec, 74- *Mem:* Am Soc Microbiol; Am Chem Soc; Soc Nuclear Med; sr mem Chem Inst Can; Soc Can Microbiol (secy-treas, 61-64, 2nd vpres, 68, pres, 75-76). *Res:* Chemistry of natural products; structure determination and synthesis of alkaloids; chemistry and biochemistry of mycobacteria. *Mailing Add:* 130 Clermont L Rap PO Box 100 Laval PQ H7N 2Z7 Can

PORTER, A DUANE, b Detroit, Mich, Dec 31, 36; m. MATHEMATICS. *Educ:* Mich State Univ, BS, 60, MS, 61; Univ Colo, Boulder, PhD(math), 64. *Prof Exp:* From asst prof to assoc prof, 64-69, actg head, Math Dept, 78-79, PROF MATH, UNIV WYO, 69-, DIR, SCI/MATH TEACHING CTR, 79- *Concurrent Pos:* Vis prof, Clemson Univ & Humboldt State Univ, 78. *Mem:* Am Math Soc; Math Asn Am; Nat Coun Teachers Math; Nat Sci Teachers Asn. *Res:* Matrix theory; combinatorial problems; finite fields. *Mailing Add:* Dept of Math Univ of Wyo Laramie WY 82070

PORTER, ALAN LESLIE, b Jersey City, NJ, June 22, 45; m 68; c 3. TECHNOLOGY ASSESSMENT, INDUSTRIAL ENGINEERING. *Educ:* Calif Inst Technol, BS, 67; Univ Calif, Los Angeles, MA, 68, PhD(eng psychol), 72. *Prof Exp:* Res assoc, Prog in Social Mgt Technol, Univ Wash, 72-74; asst prof, 75-78, ASSOC PROF INDUST & SYSTS ENG, GA INST TECHNOL, 78- *Concurrent Pos:* Mem Comn on Orgn & Admin, Transp Res Bd, 74-76; co-prin investr, NSF grant, 74-75 & Fund for Improvement Post Secondary Educ grant, 77-78; prin investr, Dept Transp grant, 77-79 & NSF grant, 78-80. *Mem:* AAAS; Am Psychol Asn; Am Soc Eng Educ; Inst Asn Impact Assessment (secy, 81-84). *Res:* Public policy analysis for technology intensive issues; quasi-experimental statistical designs; social studies of science. *Mailing Add:* Sch of Indust & Systs Eng Ga Inst of Technol Atlanta GA 30332

PORTER, CHARLES WARREN, b Patterson, La, Aug 16, 25; m 49; c 4. ZOOLOGY, PHYSIOLOGY. *Educ:* Fisk Univ, AB, 49; Univ Mich, AM, 51, PhD, 70. *Prof Exp:* Prof biol, Miss Indust Col, 50-51; asst prof, San Antonio Jr Col, 51-52; asst prof, Southern Univ, 52-55; res asst genetics, Univ Mich, 56-57, res assoc surg, 57-60; chief technician, Mich Sci Co, 60-62; asst prof, 62-70, ASSOC PROF BIOL, SAN JOSE STATE COL, 70- *Concurrent Pos:* Nat Found fel, 56-57; Ford Found fel, Univ Mich, 69-70, NSF fel, 70. *Res:* Steroid hormones and their effects on metabolism in certain target organs, particularly the estrogens and adrenal cortical hormones. *Mailing Add:* Dept of Biol Sci San Jose State Col San Jose CA 95114

PORTER, CHASTAIN KENDALL, b Kansas City, Mo, Oct 6, 32; m 63; c 5. DENTISTRY, ORAL PATHOLOGY. *Educ:* Univ Mo-Kansas City, BA, 54, DDS, 57; Ohio State Univ, MSc, 59. *Prof Exp:* From instr to asst prof oral path, 59-62, asst prof dent, 63-69, assoc prof, 69-77, PROF DENT, SCH DENT, UNIV MO-KANSAS CITY, 77-, COORDR RES & EDUC GRANTS & CONTRACTS, 76- *Concurrent Pos:* Consult, Leavenworth Vet Admin Ctr, Kans, 67- *Mem:* Int Asn Dent Res; Am Asn Dent Res. *Res:* Bone formation and resorption in vitro; development of oral mucosa in vitro; histochemistry of oral lesions and oral tissues; clinical dental trial studies. *Mailing Add:* Sch Dent Dept Path Univ Mo Kansas City MO 64108

PORTER, CLARENCE A, b McAlester, Okla, Mar 19, 39; div; c 2. PARASITOLOGY. *Educ:* Portland State Col, BS, 62; Ore State Univ, MS, 64, PhD(parasitol), 66. *Prof Exp:* Asst prof biol, Portland State Univ, 66-71, assoc prof biol & exec asst to pres, 71-72; asst v-provost acad affairs & adj assoc prof zool, Univ NH, 72-76; assoc vchancellor acad affairs, State Univ Minn, 77-79; EXEC DIR, PHYLLIS WHEATLEY COMMUNITY CTR, MINNEAPOLIS, 79- *Mem:* AAAS; Am Soc Parasitol; Sigma Xi. *Res:* Molluscan taxonomy of Northwest pulmonates; parasite-host relationships. *Mailing Add:* Phyllis Wheatley Community Ctr 919 Fremont Ave N Minneapolis MN 55411

PORTER, CLARK ALFRED, b Chico, Calif, Apr 3, 25; m 50; c 2. PLANT GROWTH REGULATORS, HERBICIDES. *Educ:* Chico State Col, AB, 48; Ore State Col, PhD(plant path), 53. *Prof Exp:* Assoc plant pathologist, Boyce Thompson Inst Plant Res, 52-59, plant pathologist, 59-62; scientist, 62-70, sci fel, 70-79, SR SCI FEL, MONSANTO CO, 79- *Mem:* Am Soc Plant Physiol; Am Phytopath Soc; Am Chem Soc. *Res:* Biochemistry and physiology of virus-diseased plants; chemotherapy and its biochemical basis; metabolism of pesticidal chemicals; plant growth regulators; crop yield physiology: photosynthesis, transport, nitrogen, metabolism and drought; physiology/biochemistry of herbicidal action. *Mailing Add:* Monsanto Co 800 N Lindbergh Blvd St Louis MO 63167

PORTER, CLYDE L, JR, b Williston, SC, Sept 24, 32; m 57; c 2. ECOLOGY. *Educ:* Univ SC, BS, 57, MS, 59; Univ Okla, PhD(bot), 63. *Prof Exp:* Instr, Univ Okla, 62; asst prof biol, Univ Miami, 63-68; assoc prof, 68-80, PROF BIOL, PURDUE UNIV, NORTH CENT CAMPUS, 80- *Concurrent Pos:* NSF grant, Univ Miami, 64-66. *Mem:* Ecol Soc Am. *Res:* Methods in determining trophic relationships; effects of various pollutants on community structure and metabolism. *Mailing Add:* Dept of Biol NCent Campus Purdue Univ Westville IN 46391

PORTER, CURT CULWELL, b Weatherford, Tex, Sept 14, 14; m 37; c 1. BIOCHEMISTRY. *Educ:* Agr & Mech Col, Tex, BS, 36; Johns Hopkins Univ, PhD(biochem), 41. *Prof Exp:* Asst org chem, Johns Hopkins Univ, 41-45; res chemist, Merck Inst Therapeut Res, Merck & Co Inc, 45-58, dir physiol chem, 58-71, sr scientist, 71-81; RETIRED. *Mem:* Am Soc Biol Chem; Am Soc Pharmacol. *Res:* Biochemical pharmacology. *Mailing Add:* 711 Fitzwatertown Rd Glenside PA 19038

PORTER, DANIEL MORRIS, b Newton Grove, NC, July 6, 36; m 59; c 2. PHYTOPATHOLOGY. *Educ:* Atlantic Christian Col, BS, 60; NC State Univ, MS, 63, PhD(plant path), 66. *Prof Exp:* PLANT PATHOLOGIST, SOUTHERN REGION, TIDEWATER RES CTR, AGR RES SERV, USDA, 66- *Mem:* Am Phytopath Soc; Am Peanut Res & Educ Soc. *Res:* Soil-borne diseases of the peanut; ecology of soil-borne peanut diseases; peanut pod mycoflora. *Mailing Add:* Southern Region Tidewater Res Ctr Holland Sta Suffolk VA 23437

PORTER, DARRELL DEAN, b Fennimore, Wis, May 21, 38; m 64; c 3. MINING ENGINEERING. *Educ:* Wis State Col & Inst Technol, BS, 60; Colo Sch Mines, MS, 62; Univ Minn, PhD(mining eng), 71. *Prof Exp:* Res engr, 62-76, TECH SPECIALIST, EXPLOSIVES PROD DIV, E I DU PONT DE NEMOURS & CO, INC, 76- *Mem:* Am Inst Mining, Metall & Petrol Engrs. *Res:* Rock mechanics pertaining mainly to science of rock fragmentation and blasting mechanics; design and application of commercial explosives. *Mailing Add:* 5438 S Iola Way Englewood CO 80111

PORTER, DAVID, b Bronxville, NY, Oct 20, 41; m 65; c 2. BOTANY. *Educ:* Yale Univ, BS, 63; Univ Wash, 66-67, PhD(bot), 67. *Prof Exp:* Fel, Woods Hole Oceanog Inst, 67-68; NIH fel, Harvard Univ, 68-69; asst prof, 69-74, ASSOC PROF BOT, UNIV GA, 74- *Concurrent Pos:* NIH grant, 72-74. *Mem:* Mycol Soc Am; Soc Protozool; Bot Soc Am; Am Soc Cell Biol; Sigma Xi. *Res:* Marine mycology; ultrastructural cytology and cell motility. *Mailing Add:* Dept of Bot Univ of Ga Athens GA 30601

PORTER, DAVID BRUCE, b Mount Morris, NY, July 28, 22; m 49; c 5. VETERINARY MEDICINE. *Educ:* Cornell Univ, DVM, 44. *Prof Exp:* Pvt practice, 47-48; vet, Panama Canal Co, 48-51; vet adv, Int Coop Admin, US Dept State, 51-60; int dir vet clin res, Norwich Pharmacal Co, 60-66, actg head vet sci, 66-68, dir avian clin sect, 68-72, dir, Div Vet Res, 72-77; MGR CLIN RES, PITMAN-MOORE, INC, 77- *Concurrent Pos:* Mem adv comt foot & mouth dis, Nat Acad Sci, 63-66. *Mem:* Am Vet Med Asn; Indust Vet Asn; Am Asn Swine Practioners; Nat Mastitis Coun. *Res:* Pharmaceutical product development; veterinary antimicrobials; food animal anabolics. *Mailing Add:* Pitman-Moore Inc Washington Crossing NJ 08560

PORTER, DAVID DIXON, b Columbus, Ohio, Apr 21, 35; m 66; c 1. VIROLOGY, PATHOLOGY. *Educ:* Univ Pittsburgh, BS, 57, MD, 61. *Prof Exp:* Intern, Med Ctr, Duke Univ, 61-62; NIH & San Diego County United Fund fel, Scripps Clin & Res Found, Calif, 62-65; NIH fel Wistar Inst Anat & Biol, 65-67; asst prof virol, Baylor Col Med, 67-69; from asst prof to assoc prof, 69-75, PROF PATH, SCH MED, UNIV CALIF, LOS ANGELES, 75- *Mem:* NY Acad Sci; Am Asn Immunol; Am Soc Microbiol; Reticuloendothelial Soc; Am Asn Pathologists. *Res:* Slow virus infections; viral immunology and pathology. *Mailing Add:* Dept of Path Univ of Calif Sch of Med Los Angeles CA 90024

PORTER, DONALD HENRY, b Medina Co, Ohio, Nov 29, 07; m 30; c 2. MATHEMATICS. *Educ:* Marion Col, AB & BS, 29; Ind Univ, AM, 30, PhD(math), 50. *Prof Exp:* Asst prof math, Marion Col, Ind, 30-38, registr, 32-35, assoc prof math & physics, 38-48, prof, 52-59; instr, Ind Univ, 50-52; prof math & physics, Taylor Univ, 59-68, chmn div natural sci, 62-68; prof & chmn div natural sci & math, 68-74, EMER PROF MATH & PHYSICS, MARION COL, IND, 74- *Mem:* Nat Coun Teachers of Math; Sigma Xi; Am Sci Affil. *Res:* Contact transformations; two-dimensional bounded variation and absolute continuity. *Mailing Add:* 4105 S Wigger St Marion IN 46952

PORTER, DUNCAN MACNAIR, b Kelseyville, Calif, Apr 20, 37; m 66; c 4. SYSTEMATIC BOTANY, PHYTOGEOGRAPHY. *Educ:* Stanford Univ, AB, 59, AM, 61; Harvard Univ, PhD(biol), 67. *Prof Exp:* Asst, Calif Acad Sci, San Francisco, 66-67; asst prof biol, Univ San Francisco, 67-68; asst botanist & cur flora panama, Mo Bot Garden, 68-72; ed-in-chief, Flora NAm Prog, Smithsonian Inst, 72-73; assoc prog dir syst biol, NSF, 73-75; ASSOC PROF BOT, VA POLYTECH INST & STATE UNIV, 75- *Concurrent Pos:* Asst prof, Washington Univ, 68-73; res assoc, Smithsonian Inst, 75- *Mem:* AAAS; Am Soc Plant Taxonomists (secy, 72-73); Asn Trop Biol; fel Linnean Soc London. *Res:* Systematics of the families Burseraceae, Rutaceae, and Zygophyllaceae; phytogeography of tropical America, especially the Galapagos Islands; Charles Darwin's botanical work. *Mailing Add:* Dept of Biol Va Polytech Inst & State Univ Blacksburg VA 24061

PORTER, FREDERIC EDWIN, b Cleveland, Ohio, Dec 9, 22; m 47; c 4. BACTERIOLOGY. *Educ:* Ohio State Univ, BSc, 48, MSc, 50, PhD(bact), 52. *Prof Exp:* Asst instr bact, Ohio State Univ, 51-52; proj leader, Battelle Mem Inst, 52-59; res bacteriologist, 59-77, PROJ MGR, NORTHRUP KING & CO, 77- *Res:* Seed processing technology; control seed germination; microbial interactions; legume inoculation. *Mailing Add:* 9255 W 23rd St Minneapolis MN 55426

PORTER, FREDERICK STANLEY, JR, b Baltimore, Md, Sept 18, 26; m 51; c 1. PEDIATRICS. *Educ:* Princeton Univ, BSE, 48; Johns Hopkins Univ, MD, 52. *Prof Exp:* Intern pediat, Johns Hopkins Hosp, 52-54, asst resident, 54-55; fel pediat hemat, Children's Med Ctr, Boston, 55-58; asst prof, Sch Med, Univ Ark, 58-64; from assoc prof to prof pediat hemat, Med Ctr, Duke Univ, 64-75; PROF & CHMN, DEPT PEDIAT, EASTERN VA MED SCH & PHYSICIAN-IN-CHIEF, CHILDREN'S HOSP OF THE KING'S DAUGHTERS, NORFOLK, 75- *Res:* Pediatric hematology. *Mailing Add:* Children's Hosp of the King's Daughters 800 West Olney Rd Norfolk VA 23507

PORTER, GARY DEAN, b Alliance, Nebr, June 3, 42; m 64; c 2. MIRROR CONFINEMENT PHYSICS, NEUTRAL BEAM HEATING. *Educ:* Pa State Univ, MS, 66, PhD(nuclear eng), 68. *Prof Exp:* PHYSICIST, LAWRENCE LIVERMORE LAB, 68- *Mem:* Am Physics Soc. *Res:* Magnetic confinement of controlled fusion plasmas. *Mailing Add:* L-441 Lawrence Livermore Lab PO Box 808 Livermore CA 94550

PORTER, GEORGE A, b Medford, Ore, Dec 22, 31; c 4. MEDICINE. *Educ:* Ore State Univ, BS, 53; Univ Ore, MS & MD, 57. *Prof Exp:* Instr med, Univ Ore, 61-62; res assoc, Cardiovasc Res Inst, San Francisco, 62-64; from asst prof to assoc prof, 64-73, chief nephrology sect, 70-73, head div nephrology, 73-77, PROF MED, MED SCH, UNIV ORE, 73-, CHMN MED, UNIV ORE HEALTH SCI CTR, 77- *Concurrent Pos:* Ore Heart Asn Howard Irwin fel cardiol, Med Sch, Univ Ore, 60-62; NIH career develop award, 65-70; mem exec comt, Coun Kidney in Cardiovasc Dis, Am Heart Asn, 71-, chmn coun kidney in cardiovasc dis, 77-79, pres sci councils, 80-; ed-in-chief, Am J Kidney Disease, 80- *Mem:* Endocrine Soc; Am Fedn Clin Res; Am Heart Asn; Am Physiol Soc; Am Soc Nephrology. *Res:* Regulation of sodium transport; drug induced nephrotoxicity. *Mailing Add:* Dept Med Univ Ore Health Sci Ctr Portland OR 97201

PORTER, GERALD BASSETT, b Eng, Apr 5, 26; Can citizen; m 50; c 2. PHYSICAL CHEMISTRY, INORGANIC CHEMISTRY. *Educ:* Univ Calif, BS, 50; Univ Southern Calif, PhD(chem), 55. *Prof Exp:* Res chemist, Calif Res Corp, Standard Oil Co Calif, 50-51; Shell fel, Univ Rochester, 54-56; from instr to assoc prof, 56-66, prof, 66-81, HON PROF CHEM, UNIV BC, 81-; PRES, ENCHEM DEVELOP CO, 81- *Concurrent Pos:* Vis prof, Univ Frankfurt, 62-63, Univ Bologna, 70-71 & Univ Victoria, 77-78. *Mem:* Am Chem Soc; Int-Am Photochem Soc; fel Chem Inst Can; Solar Energy Soc Can. *Res:* Photochemistry; inorganic complexes; coordination compounds; solar energy conversion; emission spectroscopy; energy conversion; energy conservation. *Mailing Add:* Enchem Develop Co 509-2024 Fullerton Ave North Vancouver BC V7P 3G4 Can

PORTER, GERALD JOSEPH, b Elizabeth, NJ, Feb 27, 37; m 60; c 3. MATHEMATICS. *Educ:* Princeton Univ, AB, 58; Cornell Univ, PhD(math), 63. *Hon Degrees:* MA, Univ Pa, 71. *Prof Exp:* Instr math, Mass Inst Technol, 63-65; from asst prof to assoc prof, 65-75, undergrad chmn dept, 71-73, PROF MATH, UNIV PA, 75-, MEM FAC ARTS & SCI & ASSOC DEAN COMPUT, 81- *Concurrent Pos:* Off Naval Res res grant, Brandeis Univ, 65-66; vis, Inst Adv Studies, 69-70. *Mem:* Am Math Soc; Asn Comput Mach; Math Asn Am (gov, 79-). *Res:* Algebraic topology; homotopy theory, especially homotopy operations, higher order Whitehead products; computer graphics; use of computers in undergraduate mathematics instruction. *Mailing Add:* Dept of Math E1 Univ of Pa Philadelphia PA 19104

PORTER, GILBERT HARRIS, b Northampton, Mass, Nov 25, 25; m 50; c 2. ANIMAL NUTRITION. *Educ:* Univ Mass, BS, 49; Univ Conn, MS, 51; Pa State Univ, PhD(dairy prod, biochem), 56. *Prof Exp:* Asst dairy husb, Univ Conn, 49-51; asst prof, Univ Mass, 51-52; instr, Pa State Univ, 54-56; dairy & livestock specialist, Beacon Milling Co, 56-61, dir dairy & livestock res, 61-63, dir res & develop, 64; dir nutrit & tech sales, Specialty Div, Albers Milling Co, 64-65; dir animal nutrit & health dept, Div, Allied Chem Corp, 65-69; dir dairy & livestock mgt, 69-70, dir res, 70-72, VPRES RES & DEVELOP, AGWAY INC, 72- *Mem:* Am Soc Animal Sci; Am Dairy Sci Asn; Agr Res Inst (treas, 76). *Res:* Utilization of alfalfa hay and alfalfa silage by the mature dairy cow and the dairy calf; feeding high-producing cows to obtain maximum net profits; intensive, semi-environmentally controlled veal production; ruminant utilization of non-protein nitrogen. *Mailing Add:* Agway Inc PO Box 4933 Syracuse NY 13221

PORTER, HARDIN KIBBE, b Kingsville, Tex, Aug 19, 17; m 45; c 4. ORGANIC CHEMISTRY. *Educ:* Univ Tex, BS, 40; Ga Inst Technol, MS, 42; Duke Univ, PhD(chem), 52. *Prof Exp:* Chemist, Merck & Co, Inc, 46-48; asst, Duke Univ, 50-51; chemist, 51-58, PROCESS SUPVR, E I DU PONT DE NEMOURS & CO, 58- *Mem:* Fel Am Inst Chem; Am Chem Soc. *Res:* Antimalarial quinoline compounds; fungicidal phenolic compounds and effect of structure; amino acids; development and organic research; synthetic chemistry. *Mailing Add:* 2005 Kynwyd Rd Wilmington DE 19803

PORTER, HAYDEN SAMUEL, JR, b Cincinnati, Ohio, June 2, 45; m 67; c 2. APPLIED PHYSICS, AERONOMY. *Educ:* Univ Cincinnati, BS, 67, PhD(physics), 73. *Prof Exp:* Instr & res assoc, Univ Fla, 73-75, asst res scientist physics, 75-76; sr mem tech staff, Comput Sci Corp, 76-79; ASST PROF, FURMAN UNIV, 79- *Concurrent Pos:* Consult, Comput Sci Corp, 79-80; prin investr, NASA, 80- *Mem:* Am Phys Soc; Am Geophys Union; Sigma Xi; Asn Comput Mach. *Res:* Computer simulation, real-time computation, fluid dynamics and the interaction of photons and electrons with matter. *Mailing Add:* Dept Comput Sci Furman Univ Greenville SC 29613

PORTER, HERSCHEL DONOVAN, b Silverton, Ohio, Aug 9, 24; m 64; c 1. ORGANIC CHEMISTRY. *Educ:* Wilmington Col, BS, 44; Univ Ill, PhD(org chem), 47. *Prof Exp:* Asst chem, Univ Ill, 44-47; res chemist, 47-70, RES SCIENTIST, ELI LILLY & CO, 70- *Concurrent Pos:* Res chemist, Monsanto Chem Co, Ala, 46. *Mem:* Am Chem Soc. *Res:* Steric hindrance; addition of Grignard reagents to an olefinic hydrocarbon; Willgerodt reaction; esters of geometrically isomeric vinyl alcohols; herbicides; anthelmintics. *Mailing Add:* 150 S Meridan Rd Rte 4 Box 14 Greenfield IN 46140

PORTER, JACK R, b Oklahoma City, Okla, Mar 31, 38; m 59; c 2. TOPOLOGY. *Educ:* Univ Okla, BS, 60; NMex State Univ, MS, 64, PhD(math), 66. *Prof Exp:* Asst prof, 66-70, assoc prof, 70-77, PROF MATH, UNIV KANS, 77- *Mem:* Am Math Soc; Math Asn Am. *Res:* Topological extensions (especially H-closed extensions) and absolutes of Hausdorff spaces; minimal topological spaces. *Mailing Add:* Dept Math Univ Kans Lawrence KS 66044

PORTER, JAMES ARMER, JR, b Fredonia, Kans, Oct 8, 22; m 43; c 3. PRIMATOLOGY, VETERINARY PARASITOLOGY. *Educ:* Kans State Univ, DVM, 44; Tulane Univ, MPH, 61; Univ Ill, Urbana, PhD(parasitol), 65. *Prof Exp:* Vet, US War Food Admin, 44; pvt practice, 45-47, 49-60; vet, Foot & Mouth Dis Eradication, Bur Animal Industs, 47-49; parasitologist, Univ Miami, 62; vet ext serv, Univ Ill, Urbana, 62-63; vet parasitologist, Gorgas Mem Lab, 65-68; vet lab animal med, Vet Admin, 68-70; VET PRIMATOLOGIST & DIR S AM PRIMATES, 70- *Mem:* Am Soc Lab Animal Pract; Am Soc Parasitol; Am Col Lab Animal Med; Am Vet Med Asn; Am Asn Lab Animal Sci. *Mailing Add:* SAm Primates PO Box 970768 Miami FL 33157

PORTER, JAMES COLEGROVE, b Nov 5, 37; m 66. PLASMA PHYSICS, STATISTICAL MECHANICS. *Educ:* Purdue Univ, BS, 59, PhD(physics), 64. *Prof Exp:* Res assoc physics, Univ Mich, 64, instr, 64-67; asst prof, 67-70, ASSOC PROF PHYSICS, EASTERN MICH UNIV, 70- *Mem:* Am Phys Soc. *Res:* Quantum and classical theory of pair correlations in many-body systems. *Mailing Add:* Dept of Physics Eastern Mich Univ Ypsilanti MI 48197

PORTER, JAMES FRANKLIN, b Coshocton, Ohio; m 63; c 1. MATHEMATICS, TOPOLOGY. *Educ:* Ohio State Univ, BS, 57, MS, 62; Syracuse Univ, PhD(math), 71. *Prof Exp:* From instr to asst prof math, Hiram Col, 63-66; asst prof, 71-76, ASSOC PROF MATH, UNIV ARK, FAYETTEVILLE, 76- *Concurrent Pos:* Sr vis res assoc, Calif Inst Technol, 81. *Mem:* Am Math Soc; Math Asn Am. *Res:* Riesz spaces and representations; analysis of positive operations. *Mailing Add:* Dept of Math Univ of Ark Fayetteville AR 72701

PORTER, JAMES WINSTON, chemical engineering, see previous edition

PORTER, JOHN CHARLES, b Paducah, Tex, Mar 1, 25; m 52. PHYSIOLOGY. *Educ:* Baylor Univ, BA, 49; Tex Technol Col, MA, 50; Iowa State Col, PhD(zool, physiol), 52. *Prof Exp:* Asst physiol, Iowa State Col, 50-52; res instr endocrinol, Duke Univ, 52-53; from instr to assoc prof, 53-63, PROF PHYSIOL, UNIV TEX HEALTH SCI CTR DALLAS, 63- *Mem:* AAAS; Endocrine Soc. *Res:* Metabolic function of androgens; functional relationship of the hypothalamus and the pituitary. *Mailing Add:* Div Reprod Biol Dept OB/GYN 5323 Harry Hines Blvd Dallas TX 75235

PORTER, JOHN E(DWARD), b Charleston, WVa, July 6, 21. ELECTRONIC ENGINEERING, ASTRONOMY. *Educ:* Ore State Col, BS, 46. *Prof Exp:* Instr physics, Northrop Aeronaut Inst, 47-55, PROF ELECTRONIC ENG & TECHNOL, NORTHROP UNIV, 55- *Res:* Atomic physics; celestial mechanics; circuit theory; field theory. *Mailing Add:* Dept of Electronic Eng 1155 Arbor Vitae St Inglewood CA 90301

PORTER, JOHN G(LEAVES), JR, b Wytheville, Va, July 7, 22; m 50; c 2. CHEMICAL ENGINEERING. *Educ:* Va Polytech Inst, BS, 43; Univ Mich, MS, 48. *Prof Exp:* Technologist, Socony Mobil Oil Co, 48-53, sr technologist, 54-60, analyst com opportunities, 61, MGR RES PLANNING, MOBIL OIL CORP, 62- *Mem:* Am Chem Soc. *Res:* Development of new lubricating processes for petroleum refining; identifying and analyzing commerical opportunities; evaluation of potential and existing research programs. *Mailing Add:* 545 Grant Ave Pitman NJ 08071

PORTER, JOHN J, b East Orange, NJ, Feb 15, 32; m 59; c 3. PHYSICAL ORGANIC CHEMISTRY. *Educ:* Ga Inst Technol, BS, 56, PhD(org chem), 61. *Prof Exp:* Res chemist, Am Cyanamid Corp, 60-62; asst prof, 62-67, assoc prof, 67-76, PROF TEXTILE CHEM, CLEMSON UNIV, 76- *Concurrent Pos:* Mem, Nat Comt Textile Educ, Am Asn Textile Chemists & Colorists, 67-; consult, Fed Water Pollution Control Admin, US Dept Interior, 68-, US Dept Interior grant, 69-70. *Mem:* Am Chem Soc; Am Inst Chem Engrs; Am Asn Textile Chemists & Colorists. *Res:* Water pollution and waste treatment; membrane recovery of chemicals, water and energy from wastewater; photochemistry of dye degradation; organometallic polymers, dyeing thermodynamics; cellulose chemistry. *Mailing Add:* Dept of Textiles Clemson Univ Clemson SC 29631

PORTER, JOHN ROBERT, b Conroe, Tex, May 25, 40; m 62. MATHEMATICS, MATHEMATICAL PHYSICS. *Educ:* Univ Tex, BS, 62, PhD(physics), 64. *Prof Exp:* Res assoc low energy nuclear physics, Tex Nuclear Corp, 59-62; res assoc gen relativity, Southwest Inst Adv Studies, 63-64; vis lectr, King's Col, Univ London, 65-67; vis prof, Free Univ Brussels, 66; asst prof, 67-74, ASSOC PROF MATH, UNIV PITTSBURGH & RES ASSOC, CTR PHILOS SCI, 74- *Mem:* AAAS; Am Math Soc; Sigma Xi. *Res:* Application of modern methods of mathematics to the problems of mathematical physics, particularly to the general theory of relativity; differential topology. *Mailing Add:* Dept of Math & Statist Univ of Pittsburgh Pittsburgh PA 15260

PORTER, JOHN T, b Douglas, Wyo, Aug 1, 30; m 50; c 3. PHYSICAL CHEMISTRY. *Educ:* Univ Chicago, BA, 49, BS, 51; Cornell Univ, PhD(anal chem), 55. *Prof Exp:* Staff assoc, Knolls Atomic Power Lab, Gen Elec Co, 54-57; staff mem, Res Lab, Corning Glass Co, 57-60; STAFF MEM, GEN ATOMIC CO, 60- *Mem:* AAAS; Am Chem Soc. *Res:* Electrochemistry; photochemistry; nuclear fuel and processing; isotope separations; environmental impact; thermochemical processes. *Mailing Add:* Gen Atomic Co PO Box 81608 San Diego CA 92121

PORTER, JOHN WILLARD, b Mukwonago, Wis, June 12, 15; m 41; c 4. BIOCHEMISTRY, GENETICS. *Educ:* Univ Wis, BS, 38, PhD(biochem), 42. *Prof Exp:* Fel, Dept Agr Chem, Purdue Univ, 42-44; asst chemist nutrit, Med Nutrit Lab, Chicago, 45; assoc chemist & asst prof agr chem, Purdue Univ, 45-49; sr scientist biol sect, Hanford Atomic Works, Gen Elec Co, Richland, Wash, 49-54; Nat Heart Inst fel, Enzyme Inst, Univ Wis, 54-56; asst chief, Radioisotope Serv, 56-64, CHIEF, LIPID METAB LAB, VET ADMIN HOSP, MADISON, 64-; PROF PHYSIOL CHEM, UNIV WIS-MADISON, 64- *Concurrent Pos:* From asst prof to assoc prof, Univ Wis-Madison, 56-64. *Mem:* AAAS; Am Inst Chem; Am Chem Soc; Am Soc Biol Chem; Am Inst Biol Sci. *Res:* Enzymatic synthesis of fatty acids, cholesterol and carotenoids; isolation and identification of intermediates; purification of enzymes; study of control mechanisms, synthesis of enzymes; mechanism of plaque formation in atherosclerosis. *Mailing Add:* Vet Admin Hosp 2500 Overlook Terr Madison WI 53705

PORTER, JOHN WILLIAM, b Longview, Tex, Aug 24, 37. FLUID MECHANICS. *Educ:* Rice Univ, BA, 59; Calif Inst Technol, MS, 60, PhD(eng sci), 63. *Prof Exp:* Asst prof aerospace eng, WVa Univ, 63-64; asst prof, 64-69, ASSOC PROF AEROSPACE ENG & ENG MECH, UNIV TEX, AUSTIN, 69- *Concurrent Pos:* Consult, Res & Eng Support Div, Inst Defense Anal, 64- *Mem:* Am Inst Aeronaut & Astronaut. *Res:* High-temperature gas dynamics; jet propulsion; combustion; solid-gas interface interactions. *Mailing Add:* Dept of Aerospace Eng & Eng Mech Univ of Tex Austin TX 78712

PORTER, JOHNNY RAY, b Bernice, La, Sept 18, 44; m 68; c 1. PHYSIOLOGY, ENDOCRINOLOGY. *Educ:* Western Ky Univ, BS, 66; Northeast La Univ, MS, 68; La State Univ, PhD(physiol), 73. *Prof Exp:* Asst biol, Northeast La Univ, 66-68; grad asst physiol, 70-73, instr, 73-77, ASST PROF PHYSIOL, LA STATE UNIV MED CTR, 77- *Mem:* Am Physiol Soc; Soc Exp Biol Med. *Res:* Hypothalamic-pituitary adrenalaxis; pituitary biosynthesis of rat ACTH; pineal interaction with hypothalamic-pituitary-adrenal axis; brain uptake of melanin; brain gut peptides: possible interaction with hypothalamic-pituitary-adrenal axis. *Mailing Add:* Dept Physiol La State Univ Med Ctr New Orleans LA 70119

PORTER, KEITH ROBERTS, b Yarmouth, NS, June 11, 12; nat US; m 38. ZOOLOGY, CELL BIOLOGY. *Educ:* Acadia Univ, BSc, 34; Harvard Univ, AM, 35, PhD(biol), 38. *Hon Degrees:* DSc, Acadia Univ, 64; LLD, Queen's Univ, Ont, 66; DSc, Med Col Ohio, Toledo & Univ Toronto, 78. *Prof Exp:* Nat Res Coun fel zool, Princeton Univ, 38-39; asst, Rockefeller Univ, 39-45, assoc, 45-50, assoc mem, 50-56, mem & prof, 56-61; prof biol, Harvard Univ, 61-70, chmn dept, 65-67; prof molecular, cellular & develop biol & chmn dept, 68-74, distinguished prof, 78, PROF, UNIV COLO, BOULDER, 74- *Concurrent Pos:* Co-ed, Protoplasma, 64-; ed, J Biophys & Biochem Cytol; dir, Marine Biol Lab, Woods Hole, Mass, 75-76; organizer, First Int Cong Cell Biol. *Honors & Awards:* Warren Triennial Award, 62; Passano & Gardner Found Awards, 64; co-recipient, Louisa Gross Horwitz Prize, 70; co-recipient, Paul-Ehrlich-Ludwig-Darmstaedter Prize, 71; co-recipient, Dickson Prize, 71; EMSA Award, Electron Micros Soc, 75; Nat Medal Sci, 77; Waterford Biomedical Award, Scripps Clinic, 79; Henry Gray Award, Am Asn Anat, 81; E B Wilson Award, Am Soc Cell Biol, 81. *Mem:* Nat Acad Sci; Am Soc Zool; Tissue Cult Asn (pres, 78-80); Am Soc Cell Biol (first pres, 61, pres, 78); Electron Micros Soc Am (pres, 62). *Res:* Experimental embryology; tissue culture; electron microscopy; cell fine structure. *Mailing Add:* Dept of Molecular Cellular & Develop Biol Univ of Colo Boulder CO 80302

PORTER, KENNETH BOYD, b Stafford, Kans, Apr 10, 18; m 51. PLANT BREEDING. *Educ:* Kans State Univ, BS, 40; Iowa State Univ, MS, 47; Tex A&M Univ, PhD(agron), 57. *Prof Exp:* County agent, Kans Agr Exten Serv, 40-41; agronomist wheat breeding, 47-65, PROF IN CHG ADMIN & WHEAT BREEDING, TEX AGR EXP STA, USDA, BUSHLAND, TEX, 65- *Concurrent Pos:* Chmn, Hard Red Winter Wheat Improv Comt, 68-74; chmn, Nat Wheat Improv Comt, 69-74. *Mem:* Am Soc Agron; Crop Sci Soc; Am Genetics Asn; AAAS. *Res:* Improvement of wheat varieties for the high plains of Texas; production of wheat hybrids. *Mailing Add:* Tex Agr Exp Sta USDA Southwestern Great Plains Res Ctr Bushland TX 79012

PORTER, KENNETH RAYMOND, b Laramie, Wyo, Oct 20, 31; m 60; c 3. VERTEBRATE ECOLOGY, SPECIATION & EVOLUTION. *Educ:* Univ Wyo, BS, 53; Ore State Col, MS, 59; Univ Tex, PhD(zool), 62. *Prof Exp:* From asst prof to assoc prof ecol, Univ Denver, 62-74; sr ecologist & proj mgr, 74-80, PARTNER & PROJ DIR, DAMES & MOORE ENVIRON CONSULT, 80- *Concurrent Pos:* NSF res grants, 62-64 & 65-66; adj assoc prof zool, Univ Denver, 73- *Mem:* AAAS; Soc Study Evolution; Am Soc Naturalists; Ecol Soc Am. *Res:* Vertebrate evolution and speciation; ecology and biogeography; interdisciplinary environmental impact assessments; ecology and systematics of Eutamias; physiological ecology of amphibians. *Mailing Add:* 53 Village Rd RFD #1 Parker CO 80134

PORTER, LAWRENCE DELPINO, b Los Angeles, Calif, Oct 5, 32; m 64; c 2. GEOPHYSICS, APPLIED MATHEMATICS. *Educ:* Stanford Univ, BS, 55; Univ Calif, Los Angeles, MS, 57, PhD(physics), 62. *Prof Exp:* Res geophysicist, Univ Calif, Los Angeles, 55-61; Alexander von Humboldt Found res fel theoret physics, Aachen Tech Univ, 61-63; res assoc, Courant Inst Math Sci, NY Univ, 63-64; asst prof aerospace eng, Polytech Inst Brooklyn, 64-68; physicist, Lawrence Radiation Lab, 68-71; sci specialist, EG&G, Inc, 71-72; vis assoc prof geol, Northern Ill Univ, 72-73; Nat Res Coun-NASA sr resident res assoc, Jet Propulsion Lab, 73-75, mem tech staff, 75-76; seismologist, Calif Div Mines & Geol, 76-80; LEAD ANALYST, SOHIO PETROL CO, 81- *Concurrent Pos:* Lectr geol, Calif State Univ, Los Angeles, 75-76 & Calif State Univ, Northridge, 76. *Mem:* Am Geophys Union; Royal Astron Soc; Soc Indust & Appl Math; Am Phys Soc; Seismol Soc Am. *Res:* Geophysics, geodesy and seismology; use of applied mathematics in data analysis; statistics; engineering studies of earthquakes and explosions; wave propagation; diffraction theory. *Mailing Add:* PO Box 915 Danville CA 94526

PORTER, LEE ALBERT, b Cleveland, Ohio, July 24, 34; m 68; c 2. NATURAL PRODUCTS CHEMISTRY. *Educ:* Univ Calif, Los Angeles, BSc, 57, PhD(org chem), 64. *Prof Exp:* Instr chem, Univ Calif, Los Angeles, 63; res assoc med chem, Sch Med, Univ Louisville, 64-65; Nat Inst Arthritis & Metab Dis fel chem inst, Univ Vienna, 65-66; res assoc org chem, Univ Minn, Minneapolis, 66-67; career res chemist, Lab Exp Metab Dis, Vet Admin Hosp, Long Beach, Calif, 67-71; asst prof, 71-78, ASSOC PROF

CHEM, JACKSONVILLE UNIV, 78-, DIR MILLAR WILSON LAB CHEM RES, 71- *Mem:* Am Chem Soc. *Res:* Isolation, structure, chemistry, biosynthesis and biological action of substances of plant and marine origin; structure-activity relations; organometallic chemistry; chemical taxonomy. *Mailing Add:* Millar Wilson Lab Chem Res Jacksonville Univ Jacksonville FL 32211

PORTER, LEO EARLE, b Pueblo, Colo, Feb 3, 39; m 59; c 2. CHEMICAL MICROSCOPY, MATERIALS SCIENCE. *Educ:* Univ Colo, BA, 63. *Prof Exp:* SR RES MICROSCOPIST, THE GOODYEAR TIRE & RUBBER CO, 63- *Honors & Awards:* Best Paper Award, Am Chem Soc, 69. *Mem:* Am Chem Soc. *Res:* The microscopy of rubber chemicals, their identification and characterization in trace amounts; failure analysis; modes and interactions of components in composite structures. *Mailing Add:* Dept 455B Res Div 142 Goodyear Blvd Akron OH 44316

PORTER, LEONARD EDGAR, b New Limerick, Maine, Nov 19, 34; m 58; c 2. NUCLEAR PHYSICS. *Educ:* Miami Univ, AB, 56; Univ Wis-Madison, MS, 61, PhD(physics), 65. *Prof Exp:* Res assoc res in particle physics, Univ Calif, Riverside, 65-66, lectr physics & asst res physicist, 66-67; asst prof, 67-73, assoc prof, 73-77, PROF PHYSICS & ASTRON, UNIV MONT, 77-, CHMN DEPT, 76- *Concurrent Pos:* Mem adj fac, Marine Corps Command & Staff Col, 74-80. *Mem:* Am Phys Soc; Am Asn Physics Teachers; Sigma Xi. *Res:* Nucleon polarization in reactions and scatterings; hypernuclei; stopping power of matter for charged projectiles. *Mailing Add:* Dept of Physics & Astron Univ of Mont Missoula MT 59812

PORTER, LEW F(ORSTER), b Madison, Wis, July 18, 18; m 52; c 3. PHYSICAL METALLURGY. *Educ:* Univ Wis, BS, 40, MS, 50, PhD(metall eng), 55. *Prof Exp:* Chief chemist, Ind Harbor Works, Am Steel Foundries, 40-44; res metallurgist, Chain Belt Co, Wis, 46-49; instr metall eng & proj asst, Univ Wis, 49-54; res technologist, Res Lab, 55-62, sect supvr, 62-74, res consult phys metall, 74-76, SR RES CONSULT PHYS METALL, RES LAB, US STEEL CORP, 76- *Honors & Awards:* Howe Medal, Am Soc Metals, 53 & 66. *Mem:* Am Soc Testing & Mat; fel Am Soc Metals; Am Inst Mining, Metall & Petrol Engrs; The Metals Soc. *Res:* Basic research in physical metallurgy of steel; vitreous enameling of gray cast iron; effect of stress on transformations in steel; radiation effects in steel; alloy-steel development. *Mailing Add:* 1234 Northwestern Dr Monroeville PA 15146

PORTER, LYNN K, b Helper, Utah, June 26, 29; m 54; c 4. SOIL CHEMISTRY. *Educ:* Utah State Univ, BS, 53, MS, 54; NC State Col, PhD(soil chem), 57. *Prof Exp:* Asst agron, Utah State Univ, 53-54 & NC State Col, 54-56; soil scientist, 57-74, SUPVRY SOIL SCIENTIST, SOIL & WATER CONSERV RES DIV, AGR RES SERV, USDA, 74- *Mem:* Am Soc Agron; Soil Sci Soc Am. *Res:* Chemistry and biochemistry and the efficiency of nitrogen in the soil-water-plant system; investigations of nitrogen pollution and mechanisms of nitrogen loss from soils. *Mailing Add:* USDA Agr Res Serv PO Box E Ft Collins CO 80521

PORTER, MARCELLUS CLAY, b Louisville, Ky, May 14, 38; m 62; c 2. CHEMICAL ENGINEERING. *Educ:* Mass Inst Technol, BS, 60, MS, 62, ScD(chem eng), 64. *Prof Exp:* Group leader mat sci, Avco Space Systs Div, 64-69; prod develop mgr, Amicon Corp, Lexington, Mass, 69-70, mgr indust separations div, 70-72; VPRES RES & DEVELOP & FOUNDER, NUCLEPORE CORP, 72- *Concurrent Pos:* Tech consult, Indust Membrane Technol, Ctr Prof Advan. *Mem:* Am Inst Chem Engrs; Am Chem Soc. *Res:* Membrane separations, particularly microfiltration, ultrafiltration and reverse osmosis. *Mailing Add:* 3449 Byron Ct Pleasanton CA 94566

PORTER, NED ALLEN, b Marion, Ohio, May 10, 43; m 64; c 2. ORGANIC CHEMISTRY. *Educ:* Princeton Univ, BSChE, 65; Harvard Univ, PhD(chem), 70. *Prof Exp:* Asst prof, 69-74, assoc prof, 74-79, PROF CHEM, DUKE UNIV, 79- *Mem:* Royal Soc Chem; Am Chem Soc. *Res:* Physical organic chemistry; mechanisms of photochemical and free radical reactions; concerted reactions. *Mailing Add:* Dept of Chem Duke Univ Durham NC 27706

PORTER, OWEN ARCHUEL, b Tuckerman, Ark, Dec 21, 43. AGRONOMY. *Educ:* Agr, Mech & Norm Col, Ark, BS, 66; NDak State Univ, MS, 70, PhD(soils), 75. *Prof Exp:* RES AGRONOMIST, UNIV ARK, PINE BLUFF, 72- *Mem:* Am Soc Agron; Sigma Xi; Am Soybean Asn. *Res:* Soybean production, fertility and nutrition. *Mailing Add:* 3115 Old Warren Rd Apt 10 Pine Bluff AR 71603

PORTER, RAYMOND P, b Worcester, Mass, Nov 1, 30; m 57; c 3. PHYSICAL CHEMISTRY. *Educ:* Worcester Polytech Inst, BS, 53; Univ Rochester, PhD(phys chem), 58. *Prof Exp:* Res chemist, E I du Pont de Nemours & Co, 58-61; fel, Mellon Inst, 61-65; chemist, Space & Missile Div, Gen Elec Co, Pa, 65-68, res chemist, Res & Develop Ctr, NY, 68-72; RES CHEMIST, ACUSHNET CO, 72- *Res:* Photochemistry of gases; mechanical behavior of polymers; heterogeneous catalysis; high temperature kinetics; friction, lubrication and wear of rubber. *Mailing Add:* Acushnet Co 686 Belleville Ave New Bedford MA 02742

PORTER, RICHARD A, b Edwardsville, Ill, Feb 25, 33; m 63; c 1. PHYSICAL CHEMISTRY. *Educ:* Northwestern Univ, BS, 54; Univ Calif, Los Angeles, PhD(chem), 59. *Prof Exp:* Physicist, Lawrence Radiation Lab, Univ Calif, Berkeley, 58-61; vis res chemist, Univ Calif, San Diego, 61-62; asst prof chem, Univ Idaho, 62-70, assoc prof, 70-80; MEM FAC, DEPT CHEM, UNIV WIS, 80- *Concurrent Pos:* Consult, Rand Corp, 63- *Mem:* Am Chem Soc. *Res:* Quantum chemistry; Mossbauer effect; surface adsorption. *Mailing Add:* Dept Chem Univ Wis Madison WI 53706

PORTER, RICHARD DEE, b Harrisville, Utah, July 11, 23; m 52; c 2. WILDLIFE ECOLOGY. *Educ:* Univ Utah, BS, 50, MS, 52; Tex A&M Univ, PhD(wildlife mgt), 62. *Prof Exp:* Assoc ecologist & chief ornith sect, Dugway Ecol Res Proj, Univ Utah, 52-55; asst prof biol, Tex Western Col, 59-60; from asst prof to assoc prof, Wis State Univ-Whitewater, 61-65; asst prof, NMex Inst Mining & Technol, 65-67; pollution biologist, Patuxent Wildlife Res Ctr, US Fish & Wildlife Serv, 67-73, res biologist, Denver Wildlife Res Ctr, 73-80; RETIRED. *Mem:* Am Ornith Union; Cooper Ornith Soc; Wilson Ornith Soc; Raptor Res Found. *Res:* Ecology, taxonomy and distribution of birds and mammals, especially habitat requirements and study of population; reproduction and ecology of raptors; effects of environmental pollutants on wildlife. *Mailing Add:* US Fish & Wildlife Serv PO Box 388 325 N 300 West Mapleton VT 84663

PORTER, RICHARD FRANCIS, b Fargo, NDak, Feb 8, 28; m 55; c 2. PHYSICAL INORGANIC CHEMISTRY. *Educ:* Marquette Univ, BS, 51; Univ Calif, PhD(chem), 54. *Prof Exp:* Res assoc physics, Univ Chicago, 54-55; from instr to asst prof chem, 55-59, assoc prof, 60-64, PROF CHEM, CORNELL UNIV, 64- *Concurrent Pos:* Sloan fel, 60-64; Guggenheim fel, Nat Res Coun Can, 64; vis prof, Univ Fla, 64; NATO sr fel, Univ Freiburg, 70-71; vis collabr, Brookhaven Nat Lab, 78-79. *Mem:* Am Chem Soc; Am Soc Mass Spectrometry. *Res:* Mass spectrometric, spectroscopic and electron diffraction studies of gaseous systems at high temperatures; thermodynamic studies of vaporization reactions; high temperature boron chemistry; photochemistry of boron compounds; chemical ionization studies of inorganic compounds. *Mailing Add:* Dept of Chem Cornell Univ Ithaca NY 14850

PORTER, RICHARD NEEDHAM, b Texarkana, Ark, Oct 22, 32; m 60; c 2. PHYSICAL CHEMISTRY, THEORETICAL CHEMISTRY. *Educ:* Tex A&M Univ, BS, 54; Univ Ill, PhD(phys chem), 60. *Prof Exp:* Instr & res assoc, Univ Ill, 60-61; mem theoret chem staff, IBM Watson Lab, Columbia Univ, 61-62; from asst prof to prof chem, Univ Ark, 62-69; assoc prof, 69-70, PROF CHEM, STATE UNIV NY STONY BROOK, 70- *Concurrent Pos:* Vis fel, Joint Inst Lab Astrophys, Univ Colo, 68-69; Alfred P Sloan fel, 68-70; consult, Los Alamos Sci Lab, 72-; vis prof chem, Harvard Univ, 73 & 80. *Honors & Awards:* Alexander von Humboldt Sr US Scientist Award, 78. *Mem:* AAAS; fel Am Inst Chemists; Am Chem Soc; Am Phys Soc. *Res:* Chemical dynamics; theoretical studies of reactive collisions; hot atom chemistry; potential energy surfaces for collision complexes; quantum theory of molecules; nonadiabatic molecular dynamics. *Mailing Add:* Dept of Chem State Univ of NY Stony Brook NY 11794

PORTER, RICHARD W(ILLIAM), b Salina, Kans, Mar 24, 13; m 46; c 3. SYSTEMS ENGINEERING, AEROSPACE ENGINEERING. *Educ:* Univ Kans, BS, 34; Yale Univ, PhD(elec eng), 37. *Hon Degrees:* ScD, Yale Univ, 47. *Prof Exp:* Assoc prof elec eng, New Haven Jr Col, 36-37; engr, Gen Elec Co, 37-50, mgr guided missiles dept, 50-55, consult corp eng staff, 55-70, mgr sci & tech affairs, Aerospace Group, 70-76; CONSULT. *Concurrent Pos:* Mem tech eval group, Guided Missiles Comt Res & Develop Bd, US Dept Defense, 47-50, adv comt spec capabilities, 55-56; mem sci adv bd, US Air Force, 48-51 & 60-78; chmn panel earth satellites, US Comt for Int Geophys Year, Nat Acad Sci, 56-58, mem, Space Sci Bd, 58 & chmn int rels comt, 59-70; sci adv, Geophys Inst, Univ Alaska, 61-69; mem planetary quarantine adv panel, NASA-Am Inst Biol Sci, 70-75; aerospace, energy & environ consult, 76- *Honors & Awards:* Except Civilian Serv Award, US Air Force, 75. *Mem:* Fel Am Inst Aeronaut & Astronaut (pres, Am Rocket Soc, 55); sr mem Inst Elec & Electronics Engrs; Am Geophys Union; NY Acad Sci; Am Soc Eng Educ. *Res:* Industrial and military control equipment; servomechanisms; radar; aircraft and space technology; space research; meteorology; environmental pollution monitoring and control. *Mailing Add:* 164 Cat Rock Rd Cos Cob CT 06807

PORTER, ROBERT WILLIAM, b Pontiac, Mich, Jan 19, 38. MECHANICAL & AEROSPACE ENGINEERING. *Educ:* Univ Ill, BSME, 61; Northwestern Univ, MS, 63, PhD(mech eng), 66. *Prof Exp:* Res asst plasma physics, Northwestern Univ, 62; engr missiles div, Bendix Corp, 62-63; res asst magnetogasdynamics, Northwestern Univ, 64-65 & 66; assoc prof, 66-80, PROF MECH ENG, ILL INST TECHNOL, 80- *Honors & Awards:* Chanute Medal, Western Soc Engrs, 76. *Mem:* Am Soc Mech Engrs; Am Inst Aeronaut & Astronaut. *Res:* Heat transfer; electrical power generation; cogeneration; engineering economics. *Mailing Add:* Dept Mech & Aerospace Eng Ill Inst Technol Chicago IL 60616

PORTER, ROBERT WILLIS, b San Diego, Calif, Dec 18, 26; m 68; c 1. NEUROSURGERY, NEUROPHYSIOLOGY. *Educ:* Northwestern Univ, BS, 47, MS, 48, MB, 50, MD, 51, PhD(anat), 52; Am Bd Neurol Surg, dipl, 58. *Prof Exp:* Asst anat, Northwestern Univ, 49-50; intern, Los Angeles County Hosp, 50-51; from lectr anat to assoc clin prof surg, Univ Calif, Los Angeles, 51-69; PROF NEUROSURG, UNIV CALIF, IRVINE, 69- *Concurrent Pos:* USPHS fel, Univ Calif, Los Angeles, 51-52; from resident to staff neurosurgeon, Vet Admin Hosp, 52-55, chief neurosurgeon, 58-, assoc chief staff res, 59-; NIH spec fel surg neurol, Univ Edinburgh, 63-64. *Mem:* Am Asn Neurol Surgeons; Am Physiol Soc; Am Asn Anatomists; Am Col Surgeons; Am Acad Neurol Surg. *Res:* Experimental neurosurgery; neuroendocrinology; psychosomatic interrelationships. *Mailing Add:* Dept of Neurosurg Univ of Calif Irvine CA 92664

PORTER, ROGER J, b Pittsburgh, Pa, April 4, 42; m 68; c 2. EPILEPSY, PHARMACOLOGY. *Educ:* Eckerd Col, BS, 64; Duke Univ, MD, 68. *Prof Exp:* Med intern, Univ Calif, San Diego, 68-69; staff assoc, Epilepsy Br, NIH, 69-71; resident neurol, Univ Calif, San Francisco, 71-74; sr staff assoc, Epilepsy Br, 74-78, asst chief, 78-79, actg chief, 79-80, CHIEF, NEUROL & COMMMUN DISORDERS & STROKE, NIH, 80- *Concurrent Pos:* Consult & lectr, Nat Naval Med Ctr, Bethesda, Md, 79-; clin prof neurol & adj assoc prof pharmacol, Uniform Serv Univ Health Sci, 80- *Mem:* Am Acad Neurol; Am Epilepsy Soc; Soc Neurosci; Am Soc Clin Pharmacol & Therapeut. *Res:* Epilepsy and the development of new antiepileptic drugs. *Mailing Add:* Fed Bldg Rm 114 Nat Inst Health Bethesda MD 20205

PORTER, ROGER STEPHEN, b Windom, Minn, June 2, 28; m 53, 68; c 4. POLYMER CHEMISTRY. *Educ:* Univ Calif, Los Angeles, BS, 50; Univ Wash, PhD(chem), 56. *Prof Exp:* From res chemist to sr res assoc, Chevron Res Co, Stand Oil Co, Calif, 56-66; assoc prof, 66-70, head dept, 66-76, PROF POLYMER SCI & ENG, UNIV MASS, AMHERST, 70-, CODIR, MAT RES LAB, 73- *Concurrent Pos:* Ed, Polymer Eng & Sci; lectr, USSR, Brazil, & Rumanian Acad Sci; mem comt, Nat Acad Sci; mem adv panels chem & mat res, NSF. *Mem:* Am Chem Soc; Soc Rheol; fel Am Phys Soc; Brit Soc Rheol; Plastics Inst Am. *Res:* Thermodynamic measurements; polymer physics; rheology; liquid crystals. *Mailing Add:* 220 Rolling Ridge Rd Amherst MA 01003

PORTER, RONALD DEAN, b Elmira, NY, Dec 20, 45. MOLECULAR GENETICS. *Educ:* Cornell Univ, BS, 67; Duke Univ, MA, 69, PhD(biochem & genetics), 76. *Prof Exp:* Fel assoc, Radiobiol Lab, Yale Univ, 76-78; ASST PROF MICROBIOL & GENETICS, PA STATE UNIV, 78- *Concurrent Pos:* Prin investr, Pub Health Serv, 79-81. *Mem:* Am Soc Microbiol; Biophhys Soc. *Res:* Studies of recombination mechanism and kinetics in E coli and the development of genetic systems in blue-green algae; genetic regulation of photosynthetic pigments. *Mailing Add:* Microbiol Prog Pa State Univ 5101 Frear Bldg University Park PA 16802

PORTER, SPENCER KELLOGG, b Hartford, Conn, Aug 7, 37; m 64; c 1. PHYSICAL CHEMISTRY, INORGANIC CHEMISTRY. *Educ:* Grinnell Col, AB, 59; DePauw Univ, MA, 64; Iowa State Univ, PhD(phys chem), 68. *Prof Exp:* Asst prof phys chem, Concordia Col, 68-71; fel, Ames Lab, Iowa State Univ, 71-72; asst prof chem, physics & math, St Meinrad Col, 72-74; fel phys chem, Ames Lab, Iowa State Univ, 74-75; asst prof, 75-79, chmn dept chmn, 78-81, ASSOC PROF INORG CHEM, CAPITAL UNIV, 79- *Concurrent Pos:* Northwest Col & Univ Asn for Sci fel, Pac Northwest Div, Battelle Mem Inst, 77-79; NASA-Am Soc Elec Engrs fel, Stanford Univ, 81; sabbatical leave, chem dept, Ariz State Univ, 81-82. *Mem:* Am Chem Soc; Royal Soc Chem. *Res:* Heterogeneous catalysis especially with the rare earths; surface science especially surface composition of alloys; single crystal x-ray crystallography. *Mailing Add:* Dept Chem Capital Univ Columbus OH 43209

PORTER, STEPHEN CUMMINGS, b Santa Barbara, Calif, Apr 18, 34; m 59; c 3. QUATERNARY GEOLOGY. *Educ:* Yale Univ, BS, 55, MS, 58, PhD(geol), 62. *Prof Exp:* From asst prof to assoc prof geol, 62-71, assoc dir, Quaternary Res Ctr, 67-72, 80-82, PROF GEOL, UNIV WASH, 71- *Concurrent Pos:* NSF res grants, 64-81; Fulbright-Hays sr res fel, NZ, 73-74; ed, Quaternary Res, 76-; assoc ed, Radiocarbon, 77-; vis fel, Clare Hall, Univ Cambridge, 80-81. *Mem:* AAAS; fel Geol Soc Am; Int Glaciol Soc; fel Arctic Inst NAm; Int Union Quaternary Res. *Res:* Stratigraphy and chronology of glaciated alpine regions; volcanic stratigraphy and tephrochronology; Quaternary snowlines. *Mailing Add:* Dept of Geol Sci Univ of Wash Seattle WA 98195

PORTER, SYDNEY W, JR, b Baltimore, Md, June 27, 32; m 61; c 1. HEALTH PHYSICS, PHYSICAL CHEMISTRY. *Educ:* St John's Col, Md, BA, 54; Am Bd Health Physics, cert, 66. *Prof Exp:* Health physics coordr power reactors, Elec Boat Div, Gen Dynamics Corp, 58-63; head radiol safety dept health physics, Armed Forces Radiobiol Res Inst, 63-69; vpres, Radiation Mgt Corp, 69-74; PRES HEALTH PHYSICS, PORTER-GERTZ CONSULT INC, 74- *Concurrent Pos:* Consult, Univ Pa, Dept of the Navy & Tellurometer Inc; mem, Army Inspector General's Reactor Inspection Team; health physics consult, Philadelphia Elec Co, 68. *Mem:* Am Asn Physicists in Med; Am Chem Soc; Am Indust Hyg Asn; Am Nuclear Soc; Health Physics Soc. *Res:* Radiological environmental monitoring; emergency planning. *Mailing Add:* Porter-Gertz Consult Inc 76 Rittenhouse Pl Ardmore PA 19003

PORTER, TERENCE LEE, b New Britain, Conn, Aug 31, 35; m 64; c 2. OPTICAL PHYSICS. *Educ:* Mass Inst Technol, SB, 57; Univ Calif, Berkeley, PhD(physics), 61. *Prof Exp:* Assoc, Nat Bur Stand, 61-63, physicist, 63-65; from asst prog dir to assoc prog dir, Div Grad Educ Sci, 65-73, prog mgr, Div Higher Educ Sci, 73-76, prog dir, Div Sci Manpower Improvement, 76-77, dep div dir, 77-78, actg div dir, 78-79, dep div dir, 79-81, ACTING DIV DIR, DIV SCI EDUC RESOURCES IMPROV, NSF, 81- *Mem:* Optical Soc Am. *Res:* Atomic and molecular physics; optical spectroscopy; science education. *Mailing Add:* Div Sci Educ Resources Improv Nat Sci Found Washington DC 20550

PORTER, THOMAS WAYNE, b Bowling Green, Ohio, Aug 8, 11; m 35; c 2. INVERTEBRATE ZOOLOGY. *Educ:* Bowling Green State Univ, AB, 35, BS, 36; Univ Mich, MA, 40; Univ Kans, PhD(entom), 50. *Prof Exp:* Teacher high sch, Ohio, 36-42 & Mich, 42-44; instr biol, Univ Kans, 46-48; asst prof entom & biol, Iowa State Col, 48-50; asst prof invert zool, 50-59, PROF ZOOL & ASST DIR KELLOGG GULL LAKE BIOL STA, MICH STATE UNIV, 59- *Mem:* AAAS; Am Inst Biol Sci; Am Micros Soc (treas, 56-74, pres elect, 75, pres, 76); Entom Soc Am; Wilson Ornith Soc. *Res:* Taxonomy, life cycles and ecology of arthropods, aquatic and semiaquatic Hemiptera; Hebridae of the world. *Mailing Add:* Dept of Zool Mich State Univ East Lansing MI 48824

PORTER, VERNON RAY, b Huntington Park, Calif, Sept 9, 35; m 59; c 2. INORGANIC CHEMISTRY. *Educ:* NTex State Univ, BS, 58; Ga Inst Technol, MS, 61; Pa State Univ, PhD(solid state sci), 65. *Prof Exp:* Mem tech staff, 65-79, SR MEM TECH STAFF SEMICONDUCTOR PROCESS RES, TEX INSTRUMENTS INC, 80- *Mem:* Am Ceramic Soc; Am Chem Soc; Electrochem Soc. *Res:* Chemical reactions in cool plasmas; electrochemistry of group IV elements. *Mailing Add:* 450 N Maxwell Creek Rd Plano TX 75074

PORTER, WALTER KENNETH, JR, b Long Beach, Miss, Dec 23, 23; m 45; c 2. PLANT PHYSIOLOGY. *Educ:* Miss State Col, BS, 49; Univ Wis, PhD(bot), 53. *Prof Exp:* Asst plant pathologist, Exp Sta, Miss State Col, 49-50; asst plant pathologist, Exp Sta, La State Univ, 53-56, assoc prof plant path, 56-60; supt, Delta Exp Sta, 61-69, asst dir, Miss Agr & Forest Exp Sta, 69-70, ASSOC DIR, MISS AGR & FOREST EXP STA, MISS STATE UNIV, 70- *Mem:* Am Soc Plant Physiol. *Res:* Growth regulation; basic metabolism; weed control. *Mailing Add:* Miss Agr & Forest Exp Sta Miss State Univ Mississippi State MS 39762

PORTER, WARREN PAUL, b Madison, Wis, Jan 26, 39; m 61; c 2. ECOLOGY. *Educ:* Univ Wis-Madison, BS, 61; Univ Calif, Los Angeles, MA, 63, PhD(physiol ecol), 66. *Prof Exp:* NIH res assoc, Wash Univ & Mo Bot Garden, 66-68; from asst prof to assoc prof, 68-74, PROF ZOOL, UNIV WIS-MADISON, 74- *Mem:* AAAS; Ecol Soc Am; Am Soc Ichthyologists & Herpetologists. *Res:* Animal-physical environment interactions; system modeling of large and small ecosystems. *Mailing Add:* Dept of Zool Univ of Wis Madison WI 53706

PORTER, WAYNE MELVIN, b Chase, Md, Jan 4, 44; m 72; c 2. PLANT BREEDING. *Educ:* Western Md Col, BA, 66; Purdue Univ, MS, 69, PhD(plant breeding), 72. *Prof Exp:* Res asst germplasm, Int Inst Trop Agr, 72-74; coordr bean prog, Inst Agr Sci & Technol, 74-76; RES AGRONOMIST, GERMPLASM RESOURCES LAB, AGR RES SERV, USDA, 77- *Concurrent Pos:* Rockefeller Found fel, 72-74. *Mem:* Agron Soc Am; Crop Sci Soc Am. *Res:* Computer facilitated utilization of information from evaluations to select materials having a greater probability of serving as useful breeding lines. *Mailing Add:* Germplasm Resources Lab B-001 Rm 330 BARC-W Beltsville MD 20705

PORTER, WILBUR ARTHUR, b Dallas, Tex, Mar 29, 41; m 63; c 2. MATERIALS SCIENCE. *Educ:* NTex State Univ, BS, 63, MS, 64; Tex A&M Univ, PhD(interdisciplinary eng), 70. *Prof Exp:* Mem tech staff, Semiconductor Res & Develop Labs, Tex Instruments Inc, 66-68; from asst prof to assoc prof, Tex A&M Univ, 68-76, dir, Inst Solid State Electronics, 72-79, asst dir, Tex Eng Exp Sta, Tex A&M Univ Syst, 79-80, PROF ELEC ENG, TEX A&M UNIV, 76-, DIR, TEX ENG EXP STA, 80- *Concurrent Pos:* Consult, Electro Sci Industs, 75- & Tex Instruments Inc, 76. *Mem:* Am Phys Soc; sr mem Inst Elec & Electronics Engrs (pres, 81-); Electro-Chem Soc. *Res:* Solid state device development; integrated circuit fabrication and materials processing; manufacturing systems development. *Mailing Add:* 1815 Bee Creek Dr College Station TX 77840

PORTER, WILLIAM A, b South Haven, Mich; m; c 3. ELECTRICAL ENGINEERING. *Educ:* Mich Tech, 57; Univ Mich, MS, 58, PhD(elec eng), 61. *Prof Exp:* Res asst elec eng, Univ Mich, Ann Arbor, 59-61, assoc res engr, 61-62, from asst prof to prof elec eng, 61-77, res engr, 64-77; PROF ELEC ENG & CHMN DEPT, LA STATE UNIV, BATON ROUGE, 77- *Mem:* Soc Indust & Appl Math; Inst Elec & Electronics Engrs. *Res:* Automatic control and system theory; pattern recognition; applications of functional analysis to system engineering problems. *Mailing Add:* Dept of Elec Eng La State Univ Baton Rouge LA 70803

PORTER, WILLIAM L, b Philadelphia, Pa, Nov 3, 17. BIOCHEMISTRY. *Educ:* Oberlin Col, AB, 38; Univ Chicago, MS, 52; Harvard Univ, PhD, 64. *Prof Exp:* Meteorologist, 52-64, RES CHEMIST, SCI & ADVAN TECHNOL LAB, US ARMY NATICK RES & DEVELOP LABS, 64- *Mem:* AAAS; Sigma Xi; Am Oil Chem Soc. *Res:* Autoxidative degradation of membrane lipids; structural requirements for action of plant auxins; mechanism of action of plant auxins; effect of storage temperature on food degradation; oxidation products of lipids and alpha-tocopherol in membranes; relative effectiveness of antioxidants on membranes of freeze-dried and whole tissue foods; flourescence detection of autoxidation. *Mailing Add:* Food Sci Lab US Army Natick Develop Ctr Natick MA 01760

PORTER, WILLIAM SAMUEL, b Niagra Falls, NY, May 5, 30; m 55; c 1. THEORETICAL PHYSICS. *Educ:* Univ Buffalo, BA, 52; Yale Univ, MS, 53, PhD(physics), 58. *Prof Exp:* Mem staff physics, Los Alamos Sci Lab, Univ Calif, 57-59; from asst prof to assoc prof, Bucknell Univ, 59-66; assoc prof, 66-69, PROF PHYSICS, SOUTHERN CONN STATE COL, 69- *Concurrent Pos:* NSF grant, 61-66. *Mem:* AAAS; Am Asn Physics Teachers; Am Phys Soc. *Res:* Nuclear reaction theory; plasma physics; planetary constitutions. *Mailing Add:* Dept of Physics Southern Conn State Col New Haven CT 06515

PORTERFIELD, IRA DEWARD, b Greenville, WVa, July 8, 20; c 4. DAIRY HUSBANDRY. *Educ:* Univ Md, BS, 44; WVa Univ, MS, 50; Univ Minn, PhD, 56. *Prof Exp:* Asst exten dairyman, WVa Univ, 46-51, assoc prof dairy husb, 51-54; asst, Univ Minn, 54-55; prof dairy sci & head dept, WVa Univ, 56-62; head dept, 62-76, PROF ANIMAL SCI, NC STATE UNIV, 76- *Mem:* Fel AAAS; Am Soc Animal Sci; Am Dairy Sci Asn. *Res:* Breeding and physiology of dairy cattle. *Mailing Add:* 123 Polk Hall NC State Univ Raleigh NC 27607

PORTERFIELD, JAY G, b Holton, Kans, July 1, 21; m 57; c 1. AGRICULTURAL ENGINEERING. *Educ:* Iowa State Univ, BS, 47, MS, 50. *Prof Exp:* From instr to asst prof agr eng, Iowa State Univ, 47-51; assoc prof, 52-56, head dept agr eng, 74-78, PROF AGR ENG, OKLA STATE UNIV, 56- *Concurrent Pos:* Serv engr, Iowa Ford Tractor Co, 49; consult, Brazil, 58; res reviewer, USDA SEA-CR, Washington, DC, 78-79. *Mem:* Am Soc Eng Educ; Am Soc Agr Engrs. *Res:* Agricultural power and field machinery. *Mailing Add:* Dept of Agr Eng Okla State Univ Stillwater OK 74078

PORTERFIELD, RICHARD LEE, forestry, see previous edition

PORTERFIELD, SUSAN PAYNE, b Plainfield, NJ, Sept 6, 43; m 64; c 2. ENDOCRINOLOGY, PERINATAL PHYSIOLOGY. *Educ:* Ohio State Univ, BS, 65, MS, 67, PhD(physiol), 73. *Prof Exp:* Instr biol, Ohio Northern Univ, 69-73; asst prof, Ga Inst Technol, 73-76; asst prof, 76-79, ASSOC PROF PHYSIOL, MED COL GA, 79- *Mem:* Am Physiol Soc; Soc Exp Biol & Med; Endocrine Soc; AAAS. *Res:* Perinatal endocrinology; perinatal metabolism; effects of maternal endocrine disturbances on fetal development. *Mailing Add:* Dept of Physiol Med Col of Ga Augusta GA 30902

PORTERFIELD, WILLIAM WENDELL, b Winchester, Va, Aug 24, 36; m 57; c 2. INORGANIC CHEMISTRY. *Educ:* Univ NC, BS, 57, PhD(inorg chem), 62; Calif Inst Technol, MS, 60. *Prof Exp:* Sr res chemist, Allegany Ballistics Lab, 62-64; from asst prof to assoc prof, 64-68, PROF CHEM, HAMPDEN-SYDNEY COL, 68- *Mem:* Am Chem Soc; Royal Soc Chem. *Res:* Metal halide synthesis; coordination chemistry; molten salt coordination studies. *Mailing Add:* Dept of Chem Hampden-Sydney Col Hampden-Sydney VA 23943

PORTEUS, JAMES OLIVER, b Wilmington, Del, Oct 25, 29; m 53; c 3. SURFACE PHYSICS. *Educ:* Univ Del, BS, 51; Cornell Univ, PhD(physics), 58. *Prof Exp:* Asst x-ray spectros, Cornell Univ, 52-58, res assoc, 58-59; res physicist, 59-69, HEAD QUANTUM SURFACE DYNAMICS BR, NAVAL WEAPONS CTR, 69- *Mem:* Am Phys Soc; Am Vacuum Soc; Sigma Xi. *Res:* Low energy electron diffraction and spectroscopy; physical optics; laser damage. *Mailing Add:* Code 3817 Naval Weapons Ctr China Lake CA 93555

PORTIS, ALAN MARK, b Chicago, Ill, July 17, 26; m 48; c 4. SOLID STATE PHYSICS. *Educ:* Univ Chicago, PhB, 48; Univ Calif, AB, 49, PhD(physics), 53. *Prof Exp:* Asst physics, Univ Calif, 49-51; asst prof, Univ Pittsburgh, 53-56; From asst prof to assoc prof physics, 56-63, dir, Lawrence Hall Sci, 69-72, PROF PHYSICS, UNIV CALIF, BERKELEY, 63-, UNIV OMBUDSMAN, 81- *Honors & Awards:* Millikan Award, Am Asn Physics Teachers, 66. *Mem:* Fel Am Phys Soc; fel AAAS; Am Asn Physics Teachers. *Res:* Nuclear and electron spin resonace; solar energy; microwave magnetoconductivity; physics of low dimensional materials. *Mailing Add:* Dept Physics Univ Calif Berkeley CA 94720

PORTLOCK, DAVID EDWARD, b Fall River, Mass, Dec 5, 44. MEDICINAL CHEMISTRY, PHARMACEUTICAL CHEMISTRY. *Educ:* Southeastern Mass Univ, BS, 66; Cent Mich Univ, MS, 68; Va Polytech Inst & State Univ, PhD(chem), 72. *Prof Exp:* Fel alkaloids, Univ NH, 71-72 & Sheehan Inst Res, 72-74; proj dir narcotics, Sharps Assocs, 74-77; MEM STAFF, AMINO ACID SECT, NORWICH PHARMACEUT CO, 77- *Mem:* Sigma Xi. *Res:* Alkaloids, especially the synthesis of narcotic analgesics and antagonists; design and synthesis of peptide related drugs. *Mailing Add:* Amino Acid Sect Norwich Phamaceut Co Woods Corners Norwich NY 13815

PORTMAN, DONALD JAMES, b Amherst, Ohio, Apr 25, 22; div; c 3. MICROMETEOROLOGY. *Educ:* Univ Mich, BS, 46; Johns Hopkins Univ, PhD(phys sci), 55. *Prof Exp:* Meteorologist, Univ Akron, 47-49; res staff asst, Johns Hopkins Univ, 49-54; physicist, Beckman & Whitley, Inc, 54-56; assoc res meteorologist, Res Inst, 56-62, lectr meteorol, 57-62, PROF METEOROL, UNIV MICH, ANN ARBOR, 62- *Concurrent Pos:* Consult, Durant Insulated Pipe Co, 55-56, qm res & eng comn, US Dept Army, 58-59, Bendix Aviation Corp, 59, Inst Defense Anal, 65-66, Detroit Edison Co, 70-, Consumers Power Co, 71- & Murray & Trettel, Inc, 72-; Am Meteorol Soc vis scientist, NSF, 59-60; vis res prof, Univ Calif, 60. *Mem:* AAAS; Am Meteorol Soc; Am Geophys Union; Royal Meteorol Soc. *Res:* Turbulent trasfer of heat, mass and momentum; optical propagation in turbulence; air-sea interaction; turbulent diffusion of air pollutants; formation and dissipation of steam fogs. *Mailing Add:* 4041 Thornoaks Ann Arbor MI 48104

PORTMAN, OSCAR WILLIAM, b Denison, Tex, July 20, 24; m 48; c 3. MEDICINE. *Educ:* US Mil Acad, BS, 45; Harvard Med Sch, MD, 54. *Prof Exp:* Life Ins Med Res Fund fel nutrit, Sch Pub Health, Harvard Univ, 54-56, from assoc to asst prof nutrit, 56-64; SR SCIENTIST, ORE REGIONAL PRIMATE RES CTR, 64-; PROF BIOCHEM, MED SCH, UNIV ORE, 65- *Concurrent Pos:* Estab investr, Am Heart Asn, 59-64, mem coun atherosclerosis. *Mem:* Am Soc Clin Nutrit; Am Inst Nutrit. *Res:* Nutritional factors; cardiovascular disease; gallstone disease; metabolism of phospholipids and lipoproteins. *Mailing Add:* Ore Regional Primate Res Ctr 505 N W 185th Ave Beaverton OR 97006

PORTMANN, GLENN ARTHUR, b Canton, Ohio, Aug 13, 31; m 60; c 4. PHARMACEUTICS. *Educ:* Ohio State Univ, BS, 54, MS, 55, PhD(pharmaceut chem), 57. *Prof Exp:* Res pharmacist, Chas Pfizer & Co, 57-60 & White Labs, 60-63; RES PHARMACIST, STERLING-WINTHROP RES INST, 63- *Mem:* AAAS; Am Pharmaceut Asn; Am Chem Soc. *Res:* Mechanism and rates of drug decomposition and interaction; dissolution, bioavailability and disposition of drugs; preformulation physical and chemical studies; analytical method development. *Mailing Add:* Sterling-Winthrop Res Inst Rensselaer NY 12144

PORTMANN, WALTER ODDO, b Canton, Ohio, Oct 5, 29; m 56; c 3. MATHEMATICS. *Educ:* Kent State Univ, BS, 52; Case Inst Technol, MS, 54, PhD(math), 57. *Prof Exp:* Instr math, Case Inst Technol, 56-57, asst prof, 58-59; aeronaut res scientist, NASA, 57-58; assoc prof math, Ariz State Univ, 59-65; PROF MATH & CHMN DEPT, WILSON COL, 65- *Mem:* Sigma Xi; Math Asn Am. *Res:* Matrix theory; analytic functions of matrices or hyper-complex variables. *Mailing Add:* 146 Harvest Lane Chambersburg PA 17201

PORTNER, ALLEN, b Brooklyn, NY, Jan 19, 34; m 63; c 1. VIROLOGY, BIOCHEMISTRY. *Educ:* Brooklyn Col, BA, 57; Long Island Univ, MS, 64; Univ Kans, PhD(microbiol), 68. *Prof Exp:* Sr res aide, Sloan-Kettering Inst Cancer Res, 59-63; fel virol, St Jude's Children's Res Hosp, 68-70; ASSOC PROF MICROBIOL, MED UNIV TENN CTR HEALTH SCI, MEMPHIS, 70-, ASSOC MEM LABS VIROL & IMMUNOL, ST JUDE'S CHILDREN'S RES HOSP, 70- *Mem:* Am Soc Microbiol. *Res:* Biochemistry of virus replication. *Mailing Add:* St Jude's Children's Res Hosp 332 N Lauderdale Memphis TN 38101

PORTNOFF, MICHAEL RODNEY, b Newark, NJ, July 1, 49. SIGNAL PROCESSING. *Educ:* Mass Inst Technol, SB, 73, SM, 73, EE, 73, ScD, 78. *Prof Exp:* Coop student, Bell Tel Labs, 69-71; res asst, Res Lab Electronics, Mass Inst Technol, 71-78, teaching asst, Dept Elec Eng & Comput Sci, 71-78, res assoc, Res Lab Electronics, 78-79; PROJ ENGR, ENG RES DIV, LAWRENCE LIVERMORE NAT LAB, 79- *Honors & Awards:* Browder J Thompson Mem Prize, Inst Elec & Electronics Engrs, 77, Acoust, Speech & Signal Processing Soc Award, 80. *Mem:* Inst Elec & Electronics Engrs. *Res:* Theory of digital signal processing and its application to speech, image, and seismic signal processing. *Mailing Add:* L-156 Lawrence Livermore Nat Lab Livermore CA 94550

PORTNOY, BERNARD, b Brooklyn, NY, Jan 20, 29; m 50; c 2. EPIDEMIOLOGY, PEDIATRICS. *Educ:* Syracuse Univ, BA, 50, MA, 51; State Univ NY, MD, 55. *Prof Exp:* From asst to instr psychol, Grad Sch, Syracuse Univ, 50-51; from instr to asst prof pediat, State Univ NY Upstate Med Ctr, 60-61; from asst prof pediat to assoc prof pediat & community med & pub health, 61-72, PROF PEDIAT & COMMUNITY & FAMILY MED, SCH MED, UNIV SOUTHERN CALIF, 72-; DEP REGIONAL DIR, CENT HEALTH SERV REGION, LOS ANGELES COUNTY DEPT HEALTH SERV, 74- *Concurrent Pos:* Dep dir infectious dis lab, Los Angeles County-Univ Southern Calif Med Ctr, 61-64, dir lab, 64-70, asst med dir, 70-74; USPHS res career develop award, 64; Nat Inst Allergy & Infectious Dis res grants. *Mem:* Am Epidemiol Asn; fel Am Pub Health Asn; Infectious Dis Soc Am; NY Acad Sci. *Res:* Psychology; infectious diseases; clinical virology; environmental studies. *Mailing Add:* Los Angeles County Univ of Southern Calif Med Ctr Los Angeles CA 90033

PORTNOY, ESTHER, b Dearborn, Mich, Jan 4, 45. GEOMETRY. *Educ:* Stanford Univ, BS, 66, MS, 68, PhD(math), 69. *Prof Exp:* Instr math, Lowell State Col, 70-73; VIS LECTR MATH, UNIV ILL, URBANA-CHAMPAIGN, 74-, ASST PROF, 81- *Mem:* Am Math Soc; Asn Women in Math. *Res:* Hyperbolic geometry, especially global analysis of hypersurfaces; Gauss-Bonnet theory. *Mailing Add:* Dept of Math Univ of Ill Urbana IL 61801

PORTNOY, JOSEPH, b Russia, Nov 14, 15; nat; m 39; c 2. IMMUNOLOGY. *Educ:* City Col New York, BS, 36; NY Univ, MS, 37; Columbia Univ, PhD(microbiol), 54. *Prof Exp:* Lab technician serol, NY State Dept Health, 39-42; bacteriologist, Venereal Dis Res Lab, USPHS, 42-54, immunologist, Venereal Dis Exp Lab, 54-60, asst dir, Venereal Dis Res Lab, Commun Dis Ctr, Ga, 60-62; dir res & develop, Hynson, Westcott, & Dunning, Inc, 62-76; CONSULT IMMUNOLOGIST-SEROLOGIST, 76- *Honors & Awards:* Award, Am Acad Dermat & Syphil, 55: Hektoen Bronze Medal, AMA, 56; Distinguished Serv Award, US Dept Health, Educ & Welfare, 59. *Mem:* Am Soc Clin Path; Am Pub Health Asn; Am Soc Microbiol. *Res:* Serology and microbiology. *Mailing Add:* 3900 Oaks Clubhouse Dr Pompano Beach FL 33060

PORTNOY, NORMAN ABBYE, b New Orleans, La, Oct 26, 44; m 66; c 2. ORGANIC CHEMISTRY, CELLULOSE CHEMISTRY. *Educ:* La State Univ, New Orleans, BS, 66; NDak State Univ, PhD(chem), 70. *Prof Exp:* Fel organophosphorus chem, Newcomb Col, Tulane Univ, 70-71; Nat Res Coun res assoc cellulose chem, Southern Regional Res Ctr, USDA, 71-73; res chemist, Eastern Res Div, ITT Rayonier, Inc, 73-77, group leader, 78-81; SR RES CHEMIST, GAF CORP, 81- *Mem:* Am Chem Soc. *Res:* Novel methods of cellulosic fiber and film production; chemical modifications of cellulose for end product improvement; photochemically initiated processes for cellulose modification; flame retardance of cellulosic fibers and textiles. *Mailing Add:* GAF Corp 114 Canal Rd South Bound Brook NJ 08880

PORTNOY, STEPHEN LANE, b Kankakee, Ill, Dec 2, 42; m 65; c 2. MATHEMATICAL STATISTICS, APPLIED STATISTICS. *Educ:* Mass Inst Technol, BS, 64; Stanford Univ, MS, 66, PhD(statist), 69. *Prof Exp:* Asst prof statist, Harvard Univ, 69-74; assoc prof, 74-81, PROF MATH, UNIV ILL, URBANA-CHAMPAIGN, 81- *Mem:* Inst Math Statist; Am Statist Asn. *Res:* Mathemtical statistics and probability, especially decision theory and robust estimation. *Mailing Add:* Dept of Math Univ of Ill at Urbana-Champaign Urbana IL 61801

PORTNOY, WILLIAM M, b Chicago, Ill, Oct 28, 30; m 56; c 2. ELECTRICAL ENGINEERING, PHYSICS. *Educ:* Univ Ill, BSc & MSc, 52, PhD(physics), 59. *Prof Exp:* Mem tech staff, Semiconductor Div, Hughes Aircraft Co, 59-61; mem tech staff, Semiconductor-components Div, Tex Instruments, Inc, 61-67; from assoc prof to prof elec eng, 67-73, PROF BIOMED ENG, SCH MED, TEX TECH UNIV, 73-; CONSULT, LOS ALAMOS NAT LAB. *Concurrent Pos:* Resident res associateship, NASA Manned Spacecraft Ctr, 68; Nat Heart Inst trainee, Baylor Col Med, 69, adj assoc prof, 69-73; Fulbright prof elec eng, Univ Warwick, Coventry, UK, 75-76; ed newsletter, Inst Elec & Electronics Engrs. *Mem:* Int Soc Hybrid Microelectronics; Sigma Xi; sr mem Inst Elec & Electronics Engrs; Am Phys Soc; Am Soc Eng Educ. *Res:* Semiconductor device and integrated circuit physics and technology; biomedical instrumentation; power semiconductor switches. *Mailing Add:* Dept of Elec Eng Tex Tech Univ Lubbock TX 79409

PORTOGHESE, PHILIP S, b Brooklyn, NY, June 4, 31; m 60; c 3. MEDICINAL CHEMISTRY. *Educ:* Columbia Univ, BS, 53, MS, 58; Univ Wis, PhD(pharmaceut chem), 61. *Prof Exp:* From asst prof to assoc prof med chem, 61-69, PROF MED CHEM, COL PHARM, UNIV MINN, MINNEAPOLIS, 69-, HEAD DEPT, 75- *Concurrent Pos:* NIH res grants, 62-; Lederle Pharm award, 63-65; consult, NIMH, 71-72; ed, J Med Chem, Am Chem Soc, 72-; consult, Med Chem B Study Sect, NIH, 72-; Gustavus Pfeiffer fel, 73-74. *Honors & Awards:* Res Award, Acad Pharmeceut, 80. *Mem:* Fel Acad Pharmaceut Sci; AAAS; Am Chem Soc; Am Pharmaceut Asn; Am Soc Pharmacol & Exp Therapeut. *Res:* Sterochemical factors in drug action, including design and synthesis of drugs and configurational and conformational analysis of medicinal agents; distribution and metabolism of drugs. *Mailing Add:* Col of Pharm Univ of Minn Minneapolis MN 55455

PORTWOOD, LUCILE MITCHELL, b Ft Worth, Tex, Apr 8, 13. BACTERIOLOGY. *Educ:* Mary Hardin-Baylor Col, BA, 33; Okla State Univ, MS, 34; Mich State Univ, PhD(bact), 44. *Prof Exp:* Sr bacteriologist, Globe Labs, Tex, 36-40; asst, Bur Animal Indust, USDA, Mich State Col, 41-42; bacteriologist, Mich Dept Pub Health, 42-47, biochemist, 47-80; RETIRED. *Mem:* Am Chem Soc; Am Soc Microbiol; Am Pub Health Asn. *Res:* Antibiotics; vaccines; antitoxin and antiserum production; purification and testing. *Mailing Add:* PO Box 76 Okemos MI 48864

PORTZ, HERBERT LESTER, b Waukesha, Wis, July 8, 21; m 44; c 3. PLANT PHYSIOLOGY. *Educ:* Univ Wis, BS, 48, MS, 52; Univ Ill, PhD(agron), 54. *Prof Exp:* Instr high sch, Wis, 48-52; asst crop prod, Univ Ill, 52-54; from asst prof to assoc prof, 54-67, PROF FARM CROPS, SOUTHERN ILL UNIV, CARBONDALE, 67- *Concurrent Pos:* Asst dean, Sch Agr, Southern Ill Univ, 57-67; int agriculturalist, US AID, Nepal, 67-69 & Food & Agr Orgn, UN, Brazil, 72-74. *Mem:* Am Soc Agron; Am Forage & Grassland Coun. *Res:* Forage crop production; turfgrass mgt; international agricultural development. *Mailing Add:* Dept of Plant & Soil Sci Southern Ill Univ Carbondale IL 62901

PORVAZNIK, MARTIN, b Hammond, Ind, Oct 30, 47; m 71; c 3. EXPERIMENTAL HEMATOLOGY, PERIODONTICS. *Educ:* St John's Univ, Collegeville, Minn, BA, 69; Univ Minn, Minneapolis, MS, 75, PhD(biol), 76. *Prof Exp:* Fel, Univ Calif, Irvine, 76; prin investr, Armed Forces Radiobiol Res Inst, Bethesda, Md, 76-80; PRIN INVESTR, NAVAL DENT RES INST, GREAT LAKES, ILL, 80- *Mem:* Am Soc Cell Biol. *Res:* Ultrastructural aspects of cell culture model systems in experimental hematology and dental research. *Mailing Add:* Naval Dent Res Inst Bldg 1-H Great Lakes IL 60088

PORZEL, FRANCIS BERNARD, b Chicago, Ill, July 28, 13; m 40; c 7. EXPLOSION SAFETY, UNIFIED DYNAMICS. *Educ:* Univ Idaho, BS, 40; Princeton Univ, MS, 48. *Prof Exp:* Chemist, Bunker Hill & Sullivan Smetting, 40-41; Lt Colonel, US Army, 41-48; group leader, Los Alamos Nat Lab, 48-54; sr sci adv, Armour Res Found, Ill Inst Technol, 54-61; sr staff, Inst Defense Anal, 61-68; SR SCIENTIST, NAVAL SURFACE WEAPONS CTR, 68- *Concurrent Pos:* Prog & proj dir, Nuclear Tests, US Atomic Energy, 51-58; official dele, UN Conf Peaceful Uses Atomic Energy, 58; mem, Panel Ocean Eng, Nat Acad Sci, 64-65; consult, US Atomic Energy Agencies, 54-59. *Honors & Awards:* Legion Merit, US Army, 48; Air Power Award, US Air Force Asn, 59. *Res:* Definitive theory and tests on nuclear blast and thermal phenomena; reactor containment techniques against internal explosion; comprehensive technology base for improved safety in handling-storage of explosives; unified dynamics model for physical and social behavior. *Mailing Add:* 500 Hillwood Ave Falls Church VA 22042

PORZIO, MICHAEL ANTHONY, b East Orange, NJ, Apr 5, 42; m 71. FOOD CHEMISTRY. *Educ:* Rutgers Univ, BS, 64; Univ Hawaii, PhD(chem), 69. *Prof Exp:* Mem staff fish protein, Dept Food Sci & Human Nutrit, Univ Hawaii, 68-70; consult oil pollution, Dept Trans, State Hawaii, 71-72; res assoc muscle chem, Dept Food Sci, Mich State Univ, 73-75; SR RES CHEMIST, GEN MILLS INC, 76- *Mem:* Am Chem Soc; AAAS; NATA; Inst Food Technologists. *Res:* Thermoanalysis of carbohydrates; food carbohydrates and fibres; new techniques of protein analyses; structure and composition of contractile proteins; hydrolyses mechanisms of 3- and 4-member substituted ring ethers. *Mailing Add:* c/o Gen Mills Inc 9000 Plymouth Ave N Minneapolis MN 55427

POSCHEL, BRUNO PAUL HENRY, b Brooklyn, NY, June 6, 29; m 56; c 2. PSYCHOPHARMACOLOGY. *Educ:* Roosevelt Univ, BS, 51; Univ Ill, PhD(psychol), 56. *Prof Exp:* NIMH res fel, Univ Ill, 56-57; asst prof psychol, Wayne State Univ, 57-59; assoc res pharmacologist, 59, SECT DIR PSYCHOPHARMACOL, PARKE, DAVIS & CO, 59- *Mem:* Am Col Neuropsychol-Pharmacol; Am Soc Pharmacol & Exp Therapeut; Am Psychol Asn. *Res:* Brain-behavior relations; psychopathology. *Mailing Add:* Res Div Parke Davis & Co Ann Arbor MI 48106

POSEN, GERALD, b Toronto, Ont, Sept 23, 35; m 63; c 2. INTERNAL MEDICINE, NEPHROLOGY. *Educ:* Univ Western Ont, MD, 61; FRCP(C), 67. *Prof Exp:* Fel med, Sch Med, Johns Hopkins Univ, 65-66; res asst nephrology, Montreal Gen Hosp, 66-67; lectr, 67-70, asst prof, 70-77, ASSOC PROF MED, UNIV OTTAWA, 77- CHIEF, DIV NEPHROLOGY, OTTAWA CIVIC HOSP, 74- *Mem:* Am Soc Nephrology; Am Soc Artificial Internal Organs; Can Soc Nephrology; Int Soc Nephrology. *Res:* Fluoride metabolism and bone disease in renal failure and hemodialysis; immunological integrity in renal failure; dialysis and transplantation. *Mailing Add:* RR 1 Stittsville ON K0A 3G0 Can

POSEN, HAROLD, solid state physics, metallurgy, see previous edition

POSEY, C(HESLEY) J(OHNSTON), b Mankato, Minn, June 12, 06; m 40; c 2. HYDRAULICS, STRUCTURAL ENGINEERING. *Educ:* Univ Kans, BS & BSCE, 26, CE, 33; Univ Ill, MS, 27. *Prof Exp:* Struct draftsman, Am Bridge Co & Modjeski & Chase, Pa, 28-29; from instr to asst prof mech & hydraul, Univ Iowa, 29-39, asst prof struct eng, 37-39, in-chg mat test lab, 37-50, assoc prof hydraul & struct eng, 40-46, res engr, 42-50, prof civil eng & head dept, 50-62, consult engr, Inst Hydraul Res, 50-62; prof civil eng, 62-76, EMER PROF CIVIL ENG, UNIV CONN, STORRS, 76- *Concurrent Pos:* Dir, Rocky Mountain Hydraul Lab, 45-; vol teaching & res. *Mem:* Am Soc Civil Engrs; Am Geophys Union. *Res:* Open channel flow; reinforced concrete structures; engineering education. *Mailing Add:* Dept of Civil Eng Univ of Conn Storrs CT 06268

POSEY, ELDON EUGENE, b Oneida, Tenn; m 43; c 2. MATHEMATICS. *Educ:* Eastern Tenn State Col, BS, 47; Univ Tenn, MA, 49, PhD(math), 54. *Prof Exp:* Instr math, Univ Tenn, 52-54; asst prof, WVa Univ, 54-59; from assoc prof to prof, Va Polytech Inst & State Univ, 59-64; PROF MATH & HEAD DEPT, UNIV NC, GREENSBORO, 64- *Mem:* Am Math Soc; Math Asn Am. *Res:* Theory of Knotts; free groups; fixed point theory; imbedding of cells in space. *Mailing Add:* Dept of Math Univ of NC Greensboro NC 27412

POSEY, FRANZ ADRIAN, b Jackson, Miss, Jan 10, 30; m 52; c 3. ELECTROCHEMISTRY, PHYSICAL CHEMISTRY. *Educ:* Millsaps Col, BS, 51; Univ Chicago, MS, 52, PhD(chem), 55. *Prof Exp:* Chemist, 54-61, GROUP LEADER CHEM DIV, OAK RIDGE NAT LAB, 61- *Mem:* AAAS; fel Am Inst Chemists; Am Chem Soc; Electrochem Soc; Sigma Xi. *Res:* Theoretical electrochemistry and electrochemical kinetics; electrochemistry of corrosion and porous electrodes; electroanalysis. *Mailing Add:* Chem Div Oak Ridge Nat Lab PO Box X Oak Ridge TN 37830

POSEY, JOE WESLEY, b Jackson, Miss, Dec 21, 44; m 72; c 2. ACOUSTICS. *Educ:* Ga Inst Technol, BS, 67; Mass Inst Technol, SM, 68, PhD(mech eng), 72. *Prof Exp:* Res engr acoust, GM Res Lab, 71-73; res scientist duct acoust, Langley Res Ctr, NASA, 73-79; RES PHYSICIST UNDERWATER ACOUST, NAVAL OCEAN RES & DEVELOP ACTIV, DEPT NAVY, 79- *Mem:* Acoust Soc Am. *Res:* High-frequency underwater acoustics; dynamic signal analysis; duct acoustics. *Mailing Add:* Naval Ocean Res & Develop Activ Nat Space Technol Labs Sta Bay St Louis MS 39529

POSEY, ROBERT GILES, b Plainfield, NJ, Sep 18, 47; m 69; c 2. POLYMER CHEMISTRY. *Educ:* Furman Univ, BS, 79, MS, 71; Univ Fla, PhD(chem), 75. *Prof Exp:* Fel chem, Univ Maine, Orono, 75-76; res chemist, Celanese Plastics Co, 76-79; SR RES CHEMIST, AM HOECHST CORP, 79- *Concurrent Pos:* Instr polymer chem, Greenville Tech Col, 80- *Mem:* Am Chem Soc. *Res:* Synthetic routes to methal enecyclopropene and spiropentene; diels-alder reactions of halocyclopropenes; organometallic complexes of cyclopropenes; polyester chemistry. *Mailing Add:* PO Box 1400 Greer SC 29652

POSHUSTA, RONALD D, b Calmar, Iowa, June 28, 35; m 70; c 4. CHEMICAL PHYSICS. *Educ:* Iowa State Univ, BS, 57; Univ Tex, PhD(chem), 63. *Prof Exp:* Instr physics, Univ Tex, 63-65; NSF fel, Univ Keele, 65-66; from asst prof to assoc prof, 66-76, PROF CHEM & PHYSICS, WASH STATE UNIV, 76- *Mem:* Am Phys Soc; Am Chem Soc. *Res:* Energy and properties of small molecules such as H-3 positive, H-5 positive; permutation group theory; evaluation of matrix elements; lower bounds; properties of solids. *Mailing Add:* Dept of Chem Wash State Univ Pullman WA 99163

POSIN, DANIEL Q, b Turkestan, Russia, Aug 13, 09; nat US; m 33; c 2. PHYSICS. *Educ:* Univ Calif, BS, 32, MS, 34, PhD(physics), 35. *Prof Exp:* Instr physics, Univ Calif, 35-37; prof & chmn dept, Univ Panama, 37-41; asst prof, Univ Mont, 41-42; prof & chmn dept, Mont Sch Mines, 42-44; mem staff, Radiation Lab, Mass Inst Technol, 44-46; prof physics & chmn dept, NDak State Col, 46-55; prof, DePaul Univ, 56-67; PROF PHYS SCI & PHYSICS, CALIF STATE UNIV, SAN FRANCISCO, 67-, CHMN DEPT INTERDISCIPLINARY SCI, 69- *Concurrent Pos:* Consult, NSF, 54-56, Columbia Broadcasting Syst, 57-59, World Bk Encycl, 59-, Borg-Warner Corp for Hall of Sci, Chicago, 63-65, Allied Chem Corp for Sci Tower, New York, 64-65 & Encycl Britannica, 64-; Schwab Found lectr, Mus Sci & Indust, Chicago, 62-64. *Honors & Awards:* James T Grady Award, Am Chem Soc, 72. *Mem:* AAAS; Am Phys Soc; Am Asn Physics Teachers; Fedn Am Scientists; Am Inst Physics. *Res:* Gas discharge; microwaves; radioactivity. *Mailing Add:* Dept of Interdisciplinary Sci Calif State Univ San Francisco CA 94132

POSKA, F(ORREST) L(YNN), b Lincoln, Nebr, July 11, 35; m 58; c 2. CHEMICAL ENGINEERING. *Educ:* Univ Nebr, BSChE, 58; Univ Fla, MSE, 59, PhD(liquid-liquid extraction), 61. *Prof Exp:* Chem eng specialist, Phillips Petrol Co, 61, sr process design engr, 63-66, proj leader kinetics, 66, sect mgr kinetics & mas transfer, 66-71, sect mgr process fundamentals, 71-72, sect mgr light hydrocarbons processing, 72-74, sect mgr alternate fuels, 74-77, br mgr, Planning & Budgeting, 77-79, VPRES COAL SYNFUELS DEVELOP, PHILLIPS COAL CO, 79- *Mem:* Am Inst Chem Engrs; Am Mgt Asn. *Res:* Process development and process improvements; automation of pilot plants; application of mathematic techniques. *Mailing Add:* Phillips Coal Co 2929 North Central Expressway Richardson TX 75080

POSKANZER, ARTHUR M, b New York, NY, June 28, 31; m 54; c 3. NUCLEAR STRUCTURE. *Educ:* Harvard Col, AB, 53; Columbia Univ, MA, 54; Mass Inst Technol, PhD(phys chem), 57. *Prof Exp:* Chemist, Brookhaven Nat Lab, 57-66; staff sr chemist, 66-80, STAFF SR SCIENTIST, LAWRENCE BERKELEY LAB, 80- *Concurrent Pos:* Chmn Gordon Conf Nuclear Chem, 70; John Simon Guggenheim Mem fel, Orsay, France, 70-71; NATO sr fel, 75; mem, Panel Future Nuclear Sci, Nat Res Coun, 76; sci dir of Bevalac, 78-79; sci assoc, Europ Orgn Nuclear Res, Geneva, Switz, 79-80. *Mem:* Fel Am Phys Soc. *Res:* High enregy nuclear reactions; isotopes far from stability. *Mailing Add:* Lawrence Berkeley Lab Berkeley CA 94720

POSKANZER, DAVID CHARLES, b Albany, NY, Mar 5, 29; m 57; c 1. NEUROLOGY, PREVENTIVE MEDICINE. *Educ:* Harvard Univ, AB, 50, MD, 54, MPH, 62; Am Bd Psychiat & Neurol & Am Bd Prev Med, dipl, 63. *Prof Exp:* Res physician, Mass Gen Hosp, 57-59, clin asst, 61, asst, 62; res assoc epidemiol, Sch Pub Health, Harvard Univ, 62-64, asst prof prev med, 64-69, ASSOC PROF NEUROL, HARVARD MED SCH, 69- *Concurrent Pos:* Jr assoc, Peter Bent Brigham Hosp, 62-; Med Found res fel, Harvard Med Sch, 62-65, Milbank fac fel, 65-; asst neurologist, Mass Gen Hosp, 63-; assoc dir res, Walter E Fernald State Sch, 65-; mem coun epidemiol, Am Heart Asn. *Mem:* Am Fedn Clin Res; Am Acad Neurol. *Res:* Epidemiology and prevention of diseases of the nervous system. *Mailing Add:* Dept of Neurol Mass Gen Hosp Boston MA 02114

POSKOZIM, PAUL STANLEY, b Chicago, Ill, Dec 15, 40. INORGANIC CHEMISTRY. *Educ:* Loyola Univ, Ill, BS, 61; Northwestern Univ, PhD(chem), 67. *Prof Exp:* Asst prof chem, Sam Houston State Col, 66-68; from asst prof to assoc prof, 68-74, PROF CHEM, NORTHEASTERN ILL UNIV, 74- *Concurrent Pos:* Fel, Univ Calif, Berkeley, 74. *Mem:* Am Chem Soc; Royal Soc Chem. *Res:* Organogermanium chemistry; divalent germanium chemistry; germanium-cobalt, metal-metal bonds; cobalt-cyanide complex chemistry. *Mailing Add:* Dept of Chem Northeastern Ill Univ Chicago IL 60625

POSLER, GERRY LYNN, b Cainesville, Mo, July 24, 42; m 63; c 3. AGRONOMY, FORAGE UTILIZATION. *Educ:* Univ Mo, BS, 64, MS, 66; Iowa State Univ, PhD(crop breeding), 69. *Prof Exp:* Asst agron, Univ Mo, 64-66; res assoc, Iowa State Univ, 66-69; asst prof agr, Western Ill Univ, 69-74; assoc prof, 74-80, PROF AGRON, KANS STATE UNIV, 80- *Mem:* Am Forage & Grassland Coun; Am Soc Agron; Crop Sci Soc Am; Nat Asn Col & Teachers Agr. *Res:* Hail damage on corn; breeding legume crops; forage utilization; forage systems planning. *Mailing Add:* Dept of Agron Kans State Univ Manhattan KS 66506

POSLUSNY, JERROLD NEAL, b Chicago, Ill, Oct 19, 44; m 67; c 2. SYNTHETIC ORGANIC CHEMISTRY, ELECTROCHEMISTRY. *Educ:* Stevens Inst Technol, BS, 66, MS, 68, PhD(org chem), 72. *Prof Exp:* Fel synthetic org chem, Natural Prod Res Ctr, Univ NB, 71-73; SR RES CHEMIST, EASTMAN KODAK CO, 73- *Mem:* Am Chem Soc. *Res:* Electroorganic chemistry, particularly electroorganic synthesis. *Mailing Add:* 118 Burrows Hills Dr Rochester NY 14625

POSLUSZNY, USHER, b Hof, WGer, July 20, 47; Can citizen. PLANT MORPHOLOGY. *Educ:* McGill Univ, BSc, 69, PhD(bot), 75. *Prof Exp:* Fel bot, Cabot Found, Harvard Univ, 75-77; ASST PROF BOT, UNIV GUELPH, ONT, 77- *Mem:* Can Bot Asn; Bot Soc Am; Sigma Xi; Am Inst Biol Sci. *Res:* Floral developmental study of freshwater and marine monocotyledons using both organographic and histological data. *Mailing Add:* Dept of Bot & Genetics Univ of Guelph Guelph ON N1G 2W1 Can

POSNER, AARON SIDNEY, b Newark, NJ, Nov 10, 20; m 44; c 2. PHYSICAL CHEMISTRY, BIOCHEMISTRY. *Educ:* Rutgers Univ, BS, 41; Polytech Inst Brooklyn, MS, 49; Univ Liege, PhD(chem), 54. *Prof Exp:* Res chemist, P J Schweitzer, Inc, 41-42; res chemist, Johnson & Johnson, 46-47; chem crystallogr, Squier Signal Lab, 47-50; res assoc, Am Dent Asn Res Div, Nat Bur Standards, 50-61; chem crystallogr, NIH, 61-63; assoc prof ultrastruct biochem, 63-69, PROF BIOCHEM, MED COL, CORNELL UNIV, 69-, ASSOC DIR RES, HOSP SPEC SURG, 63- *Concurrent Pos:* Chem crystallogr, Inst Exp Therapeut, Univ Liege, 53-54; Claude Bernard guest prof, Univ Montreal, 62. *Honors & Awards:* Kappa Delta Award, Am Acad Orthop Surgeons, 77; Award for Basic Res in Biol Mineralization, Int Asn Dent Res, 78. *Mem:* AAAS; Am Chem Soc; Am Crystallog Asn; Biophys Soc; Am Dent Asn. *Res:* Crystal chemistry of bone and tooth mineral and allied phosphates; crystal chemistry of biological materials; ultrastructural biochemistry. *Mailing Add:* Hosp for Spec Surg 535 E 70th St New York NY 10021

POSNER, EDWARD CHARLES, b Brooklyn, NY, Aug 10, 33; m 56; c 2. COMMUNICATIONS, COMPUTER SCIENCES. *Educ:* Univ Chicago, BA, 52, MS, 53, PhD(math), 57. *Prof Exp:* Res asst, Univ Chicago, 56; mem tech staff, Bell Tel Labs, NY, 56-57; instr math, Univ Wis, 57-60, Wis Alumni Res Found fel, 58-60; asst prof, Harvey Mudd Col, 60-62; res group supvr info processing group, 61-67, dep sect mgr commun systs res sect, 67-69, res & develop mgr telecommun div, 69-73, mgr data processing & mgt sci, 73-78, MGR TELECOMMUNICATION PLANNINGS & DATA ACQUISITION OFF, JET PROPULSION LAB, CALIF INST TECHNOL, 78- *Concurrent Pos:* vis prof elec eng, Calif Inst Technol, 78- *Mem:* Math Asn Am; Soc Indust & Appl Math; Am Math Soc; fel Inst Elec & Electronics Engrs; Soc Explor Geophysicists. *Res:* Digital networks; space communication systems; information theory; seismic signal processing; acoustic signal processing. *Mailing Add:* Jet Propulsion Lab 4800 Oak Grove Dr Pasadena CA 91109

POSNER, GARY HERBERT, b New York, NY, June 2, 43; m 65. ORGANIC CHEMISTRY. *Educ:* Brandeis Univ, BA, 65; Harvard Univ, MA, 65, PhD(org chem), 68. *Prof Exp:* Res asst, Univ Calif, Berkeley, 68-69; asst prof, 69-74, ASSOC PROF CHEM, JOHNS HOPKINS UNIV, 74- *Concurrent Pos:* Johns Hopkins Univ fac res grant, 69-70; Res Corp grant, 70-71; NIH res grant, 71-74, 75-79; NSF res grant, 72-74, 75-78; Petrol Res Fund res grant, 79-81; res grant, US Army contract, 80-81 & 81-84. *Mem:* AAAS; Am Chem Soc; The Chem Soc. *Res:* New synthetic methods; synthesis of natural products; organic reactions at solid surfaces; organometallic chemistry. *Mailing Add:* Dept of Chem Johns Hopkins Univ Baltimore MD 21218

POSNER, GERALD SEYMOUR, b New York, NY, Sept 30, 27; m 51; c 1. OCEANOGRAPHY. *Educ:* City Col New York, BS, 49; Univ Miami, MS, 51; Yale Univ, PhD(zool), 56. *Prof Exp:* Tissue technician, Col Dent, NY Univ, 48-49; asst, Univ Miami, 49-51 & Yale Univ, 51-53 & 53-54; oceanogr, Yale exped, SAm, 53; instr biol, Wesleyan Univ, 54-55; instr & investr marine biol, Inst Fisheries Res, Univ NC, 55-56, from asst prof to assoc prof, 56-61; from asst prof to assoc prof, 61-70, actg dir, Inst 71-75, PROF BIOL, CITY COL NEW YORK, 71- *Concurrent Pos:* Vis sr res assoc, Lamont-Doherty Geol Observ, Columbia Univ; mem, Mayor's Oceanog Adv Comt, 69-75; intern & consult to Nat Oceanic & Atmospheric Admin, Dept Com, 77-79. *Mem:* Am Soc Limnol & Oceanog; Am Soc Zoologists; Marine Biol Asn UK. *Res:* Plankton dynamics and hydrography of estuarine and near shore waters. *Mailing Add:* Dept of Biol City Col of New York New York NY 10031

POSNER, HERBERT BERNARD, b Brooklyn, NY, Apr 16, 30; m 58; c 2. PLANT PHYSIOLOGY. *Educ:* Brooklyn Col, BS, 53, MA, 58; Yale Univ, PhD(bot), 62. *Prof Exp:* Res assoc radiobot, Brookhaven Nat Lab, 62-64; asst prof biol, 64-67, ASSOC PROF BIOL, STATE UNIV NY BINGHAMTON, 67- *Concurrent Pos:* NSF grants, 65-73. *Mem:* Am Soc Plant Physiol; Japanese Soc Plant Physiol; Bot Soc Am. *Res:* Physiology of plant growth and development. *Mailing Add:* Dept of Biol Sci State Univ of NY Binghamton NY 13901

POSNER, HERBERT S, b New York, NY, Aug 30, 31; m 53; c 3. BIOCHEMISTRY, PHARMACOLOGY. *Educ:* City Col New York, BS, 53; Purdue Univ, MS, 55; George Washington Univ, PhD(biochem), 58. *Prof Exp:* Biochemist, Nat Heart Inst, 54-58, biochemist, Clin Neuropharmacol Res Ctr, NIMH, 58-65, biochemist, lab biochem, Nat Inst Dent Res, 65-67, head sect growth & develop, 67-71, PHARMACOLOGIST, NAT INST ENVIRON HEALTH SCI, 71- *Concurrent Pos:* Fel genetics, Sch Med, Stanford Univ, 63-64; assoc clin prof, Duke Univ, 68- *Mem:* AAAS; Am Chem Soc; Am Soc Pharmacol & Exp Therapeut; NY Acad Sci; Teratology Soc. *Res:* Chemical metabolism; pharmacologic effects of chemicals and metabolites; mechanisms of action; causes of individual differences; abnormal growth and development; chemical and physical environmental health interactions. *Mailing Add:* Nat Inst Environ Health Sci PO Box 12233 Research Triangle Park NC 27709

POSNER, JEROME B, b Cincinnati, Ohio, Mar 20, 32; m 54; c 3. NEUROLOGY. *Educ:* Univ Wash, BS, 51, MD, 55; Am Bd Psychiat & Neurol, dipl, 62. *Prof Exp:* Intern med, King County Hosp, Seattle, 55-56; asst resident neurol, affiliated hosps, Univ Wash, 56-59; instr med, Sch Med, Univ Louisville, 59-61; res instr biochem & neurol, Univ Wash, 61-63; from asst prof to assoc prof, 63-70, PROF NEUROL, MED COL, CORNELL UNIV, 70-, CHMN DEPT NEUROL, MEM HOSP CANCER & ALLIED DIS, 75- *Concurrent Pos:* Fel neurol, Univ Wash, 58-59, NIH spec fel biochem, 61-63; attend neurologist, King County Hosp, Seattle, 62-63; from asst attend neurologist to assoc attend neurologist, Mem Hosp Cancer & Allied Dis, 63-70, attend neurologist, 70-, chief neurol serv, 67-75; assoc, Sloan-Kettering Inst Cancer Res, 67-76; mem, Cotzias Lab Neuro-Oncol Sloan Kettering Inst Cancer Res, 77- & mem Neurol B Study Sect, NIH, 72-76; mem med adv bd, Burke Rehab Ctr, 73-; adj prof & vis physician, Rockefeller Univ & Hosp, 73-75; mem med adv bd, Asn Brain Tumor Res. *Mem:* AAAS; Am Acad Neurol; Am Fedn Clin Res; Am Electroencephalog Soc; Am Neurol Asn. *Res:* Neuro-oncology. *Mailing Add:* Mem Sloan-Kettering Cancer Ctr 1275 York Ave New York NY 10021

POSNER, MARTIN, b Pasadena, Calif, Jan 26, 35. NUCLEAR PHYSICS, ATOMIC PHYSICS. *Educ:* Univ Calif, Los Angeles, BA, 56; Princeton Univ, PhD(physics), 61. *Prof Exp:* NSF fel nuclear physics, Weizmann Inst, 61-62, NATO fel, 62-63; res assoc & lectr physics, Yale Univ, 63-67; ASST PROF PHYSICS, UNIV MASS, BOSTON, 67- *Concurrent Pos:* Am Cancer Soc scholar's grant, 69-71. *Mem:* Am Phys Soc. *Res:* Experimental nuclear and atomic physics; radioactive atomic beams; nuclear reactions and spectroscopy; production of high intensity polarized electron source; cancer research and endocrinology using hormone dependent cell lines in tissue culture. *Mailing Add:* Dept of Physics Univ of Mass Harbor Campus Boston MA 02125

POSNER, MORTON JACOB, b Toronto, Ont, Jan 9, 42; m 65; c 5. OPERATIONS RESEARCH. *Educ:* Univ Toronto, BASc, 63, PhD(indust eng), 67. *Prof Exp:* Asst prof indust eng, 67-73, ASSOC PROF INDUST ENG, UNIV TORONTO, 73-, NAT RES COUN CAN FEL, 67- *Concurrent Pos:* Consult, Bur Mgt Consult, Govt Can, 72-73; Ford Found & Am Soc Eng Educ fel, 72-73. *Mem:* Opers Res Soc Am; Can Opers Res Soc. *Res:* Stochastic models in operations research, primarily queueing theory with applications in networks and communications systems. *Mailing Add:* Dept of Indust Eng Univ of Toronto Toronto ON M5S 2R8 Can

POSNER, PHILIP, b Brooklyn, NY, Nov 14, 44. PHYSIOLOGY. *Educ:* Wagner Col, BS, 60; State Univ NY Downstate, PhD, 72. *Prof Exp:* Instr surg, State Univ NY, 64-67; NIH fel, 67-70; asst prof physiol, 72-76, ASSOC PROF PHYSIOL, UNIV FLA, 76- *Mem:* Am Physiol Soc; Soc Gen Physiologists. *Res:* cardiac cell physiology; pharmacology. *Mailing Add:* Dept of Physiol Col of Med Gainesville FL 32610

POSS, HOWARD LIONEL, b Brooklyn, NY, Oct 25, 25; m 63; c 1. ASTRONOMY, PLASMA PHYSICS. *Educ:* Harvard Univ, BS, 44; Yale Univ, MS, 45; Mass Inst Technol, PhD(physics), 48. *Prof Exp:* Staff mem radiation lab, Mass Inst Technol, 45, res asst physics, 45-48; assoc scientist, Brookhaven Nat Lab, 48-51; res physicist, Hudson Labs, Columbia Univ, 51-53, asst dir, 53-56; sr physicist, Res & Adv Develop Div, Avco Corp, 56-59; mem tech staff, RCA Labs, 59-61; ASSOC PROF PHYSICS & ASTRON, TEMPLE UNIV, 61- *Concurrent Pos:* Vis scientist, Am Asn Physics Teachers & Am Inst Physics, 71-72; lectr, Mid-Atlantic Region, Sigma Xi, 79- *Mem:* Am Phys Soc; Am Astron Soc; Sigma Xi. *Res:* Photoelectric astronomy; microwave propagation in plasmas; nuclear physics; underwater acoustics. *Mailing Add:* Dept of Physics Temple Univ Philadelphia PA 19122

POSS, RICHARD LEON, b Aurora, Ill, Aug 21, 44; m 67; c 2. MATHEMATICS. *Educ:* St Procopius Col, BS, 66; Univ Notre Dame, MS, 69, PhD(math), 70. *Prof Exp:* Asst prof, 70-77, ASSOC PROF MATH, ST NORBERT COL, 77- *Mem:* Math Asn Am. *Res:* Set theory-strong axiom systems, general principles of induction. *Mailing Add:* Dept of Math St Norbert Col De Pere WI 54115

POSSANZA, GENUS JOHN, b Jessup, Pa, Dec 21, 37; m 70. PHARMACOLOGY. *Educ:* Univ Scranton, BS, 59; Univ Tenn, Memphis, MS, 62, PhD(pharmacol), 64. *Prof Exp:* Fel, Worcester Found Exp Biol, 64-66; pharmacologist, Ayerst Labs, Am Home Prod, 66-67; pharmacologist, Pharma-Res Can, Ltd, 67-78; PHARMACOLOGIST, BOEHRINGER INGELHEIM LTD, 78- *Mem:* Pharmacol Soc Can. *Res:* Effects of nonsteroidal and immunosuppressant agents on inflammatory reactions. *Mailing Add:* Boehringer Ingelheim Ltd Ridgefield CT 06877

POSSIN, GEORGE EDWARD, b Fond du Lac, Wis, Oct 23, 41. EXPERIMENTAL SOLID STATE PHYSICS. *Educ:* Univ Wis-Madison, BS, 63; Stanford Univ, MS, 65, PhD(physics), 69. *Prof Exp:* PHYSICIST, GEN ELEC CORP RES & DEVELOP, 70- *Mem:* Am Phys Soc. *Res:* Solid state physics; semiconductors, radiation effects in solids, information recording. *Mailing Add:* 2361 Algonquin Rd Schenectady NY 12309

POSSLEY, LEROY HENRY, b St Anna, Wis, May 22, 28; m 57; c 3. PHARMACEUTICAL CHEMISTRY. *Educ:* St Ambrose Col, BS, 50; Univ Ill, MS, 54. *Prof Exp:* Biochemist, Vet Admin, 55-60; sr biochemist, Anar-Stone Lab, Inc, 60-64, chief chemist, 64-69, dir qual control, 69-75, dir drug regulatory affairs, 75-80; DIR REGULATORY AFFAIRS, AM CRITICAL CARE, AM HOSP SUPPLY CORP, 80- *Mem:* Am Chem Soc; Am Pharmaceut Asn; Pharmaceut Mfrs Asn. *Res:* Pharmaceutical analysis; neurochemistry; new drug evaluation; drug stability. *Mailing Add:* Am Critical Care 1600 Waukegan Rd McGaw Park IL 60085

POSSMAYER, FRED, b Montreal, Que, Apr 24, 39; m 69; c 2. BIOCHEMISTRY, NEUROBIOLOGY. *Educ:* Univ Toronto, BSc, 61; Univ Western Ont, PhD(biochem), 65. *Prof Exp:* Med Res Coun Can fels, Physiol Chem Inst, Univ Cologne, 66-67 & Biochem Lab, State Univ Utrecht, 67-68; res assoc, Air Pollution Res Ctr, Univ Calif, Riverside, 68-71; asst prof, 71-78, ASSOC PROF BIOCHEM, OBSTET & GYNEC, UNIV WESTERN ONT, 78- *Concurrent Pos:* Med Res Coun Can scholar, Univ Western Ont, 72-78. *Honors & Awards:* Soc Obstetricians & Cynaecologists Award, 73. *Mem:* Am Soc Biol Chemists; Biochem Soc; Can Biochem Soc. *Res:* Control of lipid metabolism; pulmonary surfactant production. *Mailing Add:* Dept of Obstet & Gynec Univ of Western Ont London ON N6A 5B8 Can

POST, BENJAMIN, b New York, NY, July 23, 11; m 39; c 3. CRYSTALLOGRAPHY. *Educ:* City Col New York, BS, 30; Polytech Inst Brooklyn, MS, 46, PhD(chem), 49. *Prof Exp:* Res assoc, 47-54, from asst prof to assoc prof, 54-60, PROF PHYSICS & CHEM, POLYTECH INST NEW YORK, 60- *Mem:* Am Chem Soc; fel Am Phys Soc; Am Crystallog Asn (treas, 62-65, pres, 66); Ital Asn Crystallog. *Res:* Crystal structure analysis; dynamical diffraction effects; x-ray instrumentation; powder methods. *Mailing Add:* Dept of Physics Polytech Inst of New York Brooklyn NY 11201

POST, BOYD WALLACE, b Glouster, Ohio, Oct 5, 28; m 52; c 4. FORESTRY. *Educ:* Ohio Univ, BS, 50; Duke Univ, MF, 58, DF, 62. *Prof Exp:* Asst ranger, Ohio Div Forestry, 53-55; from asst prof forestry & asst forester to assoc prof forestry & assoc forester, Univ Vt, 59-69; FOREST BIOLOGIST, SCI & EDUC ADMIN-COOP RES, USDA, 69-, ASST DEP ADMINR, 81- *Mem:* Fel AAAS; Soc Am Foresters; Am Soc Agron; Soil Sci Soc Am. *Res:* Forest ecology, physiology and genetics; administration of forestry; remote sensing; agricultural meteorology; wildlife research. *Mailing Add:* Coop State Res Serv US Dept Agr Washington DC 20250

POST, DANIEL, b Brooklyn, NY, Apr 5, 29; m 48; c 3. ENGINEERING MECHANICS. *Educ:* Univ Ill, BS, 50, MS, 51, PhD(theoret & appl mech), 57. *Prof Exp:* Physicist, US Naval Res Lab, 51-55; instr appl mech, Univ Ill, 55-57; sr res engr, Res Labs, United Aircraft Corp, 57-60; assoc prof, Rensselaer Polytech Inst, 60-63; staff consult, Vishay Intertech, Inc, 62-78; PROF ENG SCI & MECH, VA POLYTECH INST & STATE UNIV, 78- *Concurrent Pos:* Adj prof, Rensselaer Polytech Inst, 64-78; vis assoc prof, Col Physicians & Surgeons, Columbia Univ, 65; vis sr res fel, Univ Sheffield, 65-66; mem, US-India Exchange Prog, NSF, 75. *Honors & Awards:* W M Murray lectr, 71. *Mem:* Fel Soc Exp Stress Anal; Am Soc Mech Engrs; Sigma Xi. *Res:* Experimental mechanics, particularly by photoelastic and optical methods; optical interferometry; instrument design. *Mailing Add:* Dept Eng Sci & Mech Va Polytech Inst & State Univ Blacksburg VA 24061

POST, DOUGLAS MANNERS, b Elko, Nev, May 31, 20; m 50; c 3. BOTANY. *Educ:* Univ Wash, BS, 48, MA, 50; Univ Calif, PhD(bot), 56. *Prof Exp:* Instr bot, Univ Ill, 55-57, asst prof, 57-61; assoc prof, 61-68, PROF BIOL, SAN FRANCISCO STATE UNIV, 68- *Mem:* Am Soc Plant Taxon; Bot Soc Am; Int Soc Plant Morphol. *Res:* Plant anatomy; systematics of Gentianaceae; cytology. *Mailing Add:* Dept of Biol 1600 Holloway Ave San Francisco State Univ San Francisco CA 94132

POST, DOUGLASS EDMUND, JR, b Gulfport, Miss, Mar 16, 45; m 69; c 2. PLASMA PHYSICS. *Educ:* Southwestern at Memphis, BS, 67; Stanford Univ, MS, 68, PhD(physics), 75. *Prof Exp:* Physicist, Lawrence Livermore Lab, 68-71; res assoc plasma physics, 74-80, PHYSICIST PLASMA PHYSICS LAB, PRINCETON UNIV, 80- *Concurrent Pos:* Consult, Lawrence Livermore Lab, 71-72 & 74-; actg instr physics, Stanford Univ, 74. *Mem:* Am Phys Soc; Am Vacuum Soc; Am Nuclear Soc. *Res:* Computational modeling of plasma physics experiments, with emphasis on plasma physics, atomic physics and numerical techniques; plasma diagnostics. *Mailing Add:* Plasma Physics Lab Princeton Univ PO Box 451 Princeton NJ 08540

POST, EDWIN VAN HORN, b Decatur, Ill, Aug 31, 28; m 51; c 3. ECONOMIC GEOLOGY, GEOCHEMISTRY. *Educ:* Dartmouth Col, AB, 51; State Col Wash, MS, 53. *Prof Exp:* Geologist, US Geol Surv, 53-67; PRES & CHIEF GEOLOGIST, SKYLINE LABS, INC, 67- *Mem:* Am Inst Mining, Metall & Petrol Engrs; Asn Explor Geochemists (secy, 75-76). *Res:* Geochemical exploration for mineral deposits. *Mailing Add:* Skyline Labs Inc 12090 W 50th Pl Wheat Ridge CO 80033

POST, ELROY WAYNE, b Raymond, Minn, July 18, 43; m 67. INORGANIC CHEMISTRY, ORGANOMETALLIC CHEMISTRY. *Educ:* Dordt Col, AB, 65; Kans State Univ, PhD(inorg chem), 69. *Prof Exp:* Asst prof, 69-77, ASSOC PROF CHEM, UNIV WIS-OSHKOSH, 77- *Concurrent Pos:* NSF res grant, Univ Wis-Oshkosh, 70-72. *Mem:* Am Chem Soc; Am Sci Affiliation. *Res:* Synthesis of organometallic compounds; transition metal carbonyl carbenes; amine activated metalation of ferrocene; boron halide reactions with organometallic compounds; photo chemistry of metal carbonyls. *Mailing Add:* Dept of Chem Univ of Wis Oshkosh WI 54901

POST, FREDERICK JUST, b Berkeley, Calif, Feb 20, 29; m 58; c 3. MICROBIAL ECOLOGY, POLLUTION BIOLOGY. *Educ:* Univ Calif, BS, 52; Mich State Univ, MS, 53, PhD(microbiol), 58. *Prof Exp:* Asst, Mich State Univ, 53, 55-58; from instr to asst prof pub health microbiol, Univ Calif, Los Angeles, 58-65; assoc prof pub health microbiol, 65-76, PROF BIOL, UTAH STATE UNIV, 76- *Mem:* AAAS; Am Soc Microbiol; Am Pub Health Asn; Sigma Xi; Soc Oceanog & Limnol. *Res:* Water and sewage microbiology; food poisoning organisms; dairy microbiology; ecology of microorganisms in natural environments; halophilic microorganisms. *Mailing Add:* Dept of Biol UMC55 Utah State Univ Logan UT 84322

POST, GEORGE, b Rapid City, SDak, May 12, 18; m 43; c 2. FISH PATHOLOGY, WILDLIFE PATHOLOGY. *Educ:* Univ Wyo, BS, 47, MS, 48; Utah State Univ, PhD(fish path), 63. *Prof Exp:* Parasitologist, Wyo State Vet Lab, Laramie, 47-48; biologist, Wyo Game & Fish Res Lab, 48-52, lab dir, 56-60; fish pathologist & nutritionist, Utah Dept Fish & Game, 60-64; asst leader, Colo Coop Fishery Unit, 64-66; assoc prof fishery & wildlife biol, 66-76, assoc prof microbiol, 69-76, PROF FISHERY & WILDLIFE BIOL & MICROBIOL, COLO STATE UNIV, 76- *Mem:* Wildlife Dis Asn; Am Fisheries Soc; Sigma Xi. *Res:* Diseases, parasites and nutrition of fishes and wildlife; effects of energy development on fish and wildlife. *Mailing Add:* A103 Dept of Microbiol Colo State Univ Ft Collins CO 80523

POST, IRVING GILBERT, b New York, NY, Feb 11, 37; m 65; c 3. SOLID STATE ELECTRONICS. *Educ:* Lafayette Col, BS(elec eng) & BS(physics), 58; Ohio State Univ, MS, 59, PhD(physics), 62. *Prof Exp:* Res asst, Ohio State Univ, 58-62; MEM TECH STAFF, READING LABS, BELL LABS, 63- *Mem:* AAAS; Inst Elec & Electronics Engrs. *Res:* Integrated circuit design; semiconductor device development and applications; electron spin resonance in solids. *Mailing Add:* Div 21 Bell Labs Box 241 Reading PA 19604

POST, J(AMES) L(EWIS), b South Bend, Ind, Sept 25, 29; m 67. CIVIL & MINING ENGINEERING. *Educ:* NMex Inst Mining & Technol, BS, 51; Univ Ariz, MS, 63, PhD(civil eng), 66. *Prof Exp:* Mining engr, United Park City Mines Co, 54-56; mining engr, US Bur Mines, 57-58; civil engr asst, County of Los Angeles Rd Dept, 59-61; teaching assistantships, Univ Ariz, 63-66; assoc res engr, E H Wang Civil Eng Res Facility, Univ NMex, 66-68; assoc prof, 68-77, PROF CIVIL ENG, CALIF STATE UNIV, SACRAMENTO, 77- *Mem:* Fel AAAS; Am Soc Civil Engrs; Am Inst Mining, Metall, & Petrol Engrs; Clay Minerals Soc. *Res:* Physical-chemical nature of soils including mineralogy and soil stabilization for construction purposes; applied x-ray diffraction procedures; microstructure investigations; geological engineering. *Mailing Add:* Dept of Civil Eng Calif State Univ Sacramento CA 95819

POST, JOHN E, b Sussex, NJ, Mar 2, 26; m 52; c 4. VETERINARY PATHOLOGY, VETERINARY ONCOLOGY. *Educ:* Rutgers Univ, BS, 51; Cornell Univ, DVM, 58, PhD(vet path), 68. *Prof Exp:* Vet, Middlebury, VT, 58-61; res oncologist, 62-67, assoc prof vet path, 67-74, SR RES ASSOC VET PATH, CORNELL UNIV, 74- *Mem:* Am Vet Med Asn; NY Acad Sci. *Res:* Tumor virology. *Mailing Add:* 5 Knoll Tree Rd Ithaca NY 14850

POST, JOSEPH, b New York, NY, Mar 6, 13; m 42; c 2. MEDICINE. *Educ:* City Col New York, BS, 32; Univ Chicago, MD, 36; Columbia Univ, MedScD, 41. *Prof Exp:* Asst liver physiol, Dept Surg, Univ Chicago, 36-37; intern, Michael Reese Hosp, Chicago, 37-38; from asst to instr med, Col Physicians & Surgeons, Columbia Univ, 38-47, resident, Res Div Chronic Dis, Univ, 38-42; from asst prof to assoc prof, 46-71, PROF CLIN MED, SCH MED, NY UNIV, 71- *Concurrent Pos:* Attend consult, Vet Admin Hosp, New York, 46-; consult gastroenterologist, US Naval Hosp, NY, 47-; res fel, Goldwater Mem Hosp, 48, attend physician, 80-; assoc physician, Lenox Hill Hosp, New York, 47-64, attend physician, 64-; assoc attend physician, Hosp, NY Univ, 52-71, attend physician, 71- *Mem:* Am Gastroenterol Asn; Radiation Res Soc; Am Asn Cancer Res; fel Am Col Physicians; fel NY Acad Sci. *Res:* Physiology and pathology of liver; nutrition and metabolism; cell replication kinetics; tumor cell replication; radiation biology. *Mailing Add:* 29 Washington Square W New York NY 10011

POST, M(AURICE) DEAN, b Topeka, Kans, Sept 16, 16; m 47; c 3. ELECTRONICS. *Educ:* Univ Colo, BSEE, 38. *Prof Exp:* Radio engr, Sta KOBH, SDak, 38-39; audio engr, Shirley Savoy Hotel, 39-40; instr commun & radar, Army Air Force Tech Training Command, 40-44; tech aide, Off Sci Res & Develop, Eng, 44-45; chief electronics intel, Asst Chief of Staff, Pentagon, 46-51; staff asst res & develop, Asst Secy Defense, 51-56; spec asst to dept dir, Nat Security Agency, DC, 56-58; planning adminr defense electronics prod, Radio Corp Am, NJ, 58-60, adminr electronic data processing custom appln, 60-61; Washington mgr, Emerson Elec Mfg Co, Mo, 61-62; mkt mgr, Babcock Electronics Corp, 62-63; consult, US Off Emergency Planning, 63-64; vpres, Computronics E, Washington, 64-65; mem staff, US Army Automatic Data Field Systs Command, Ft Belvoir, 65-67; mem staff, Dept Defense, Pentagon, 67-77; RETIRED. *Concurrent Pos:* Adv, Nat Security Agency, 60-61. *Mem:* Sr mem Inst Elec & Electronics Engrs. *Res:* Radio-frequency oscillation; class C and high fidelity amplifiers. *Mailing Add:* 704 Cedar Ave Fairhope AL 36532

POST, MADISON JOHN, b Detroit, Mich, Oct 4, 46. ATMOSPHERIC PHYSICS, OPTICS. *Educ:* Univ Ill, Champaign, BS(elec eng) & BS(math), 69; Univ Colo, Boulder, MS, 75. *Prof Exp:* Elec engr, Environ Sci Serv Admin, 69-71, elec engr, Wave Propagation Lab, 71-75, PHYSICIST, WAVE PROPAGATION LAB, US DEPT COM, 75- *Mem:* Optical Soc Am; Sigma Xi. *Res:* Atmospheric propagation and scattering of electromagnetic energy, with application to remote sensing by laser probing; development of pulsed, coherent transverse electric atmospheric carbon monoxide doppler lidar for remote sensing of atmospheric winds. *Mailing Add:* Nat Oceanic & Atmospheric Admin Wave Propagation Lab R45-9 Boulder CO 80302

POST, RICHARD FREEMAN, b Pomona, Calif, Nov 14, 18; m 46; c 3. PHYSICS. *Educ:* Pomona Col, BA, 40; Stanford Univ, PhD(physics), 50. *Hon Degrees:* ScD, Pomona Col, 59. *Prof Exp:* From asst to instr physics, Pomona Col, 40-42; physicist underwater sound, Naval Res Lab, 42-46; res assoc physics, Stanford Univ, 47-51; res group leader controlled thermonuclear res, 51-74, DEP ASSOC DIR, MAGNETIC FUSION PHYSICS, LAWRENCE LIVERMORE LAB, UNIV CALIF, 74- PROF IN RESIDENCE ENG &

APPL SCI, UNIV CALIF, DAVIS, 63- *Concurrent Pos:* Mem, NASA Adv Comt, Nuclear Energy Systs, 60-62; Physics Surv Comt, Nat Acad Sci, 64-65; vis comt, Dept Nuclear Eng, Mass Inst Technol, 65-71; mem, adv comt to Air Force Systs Command, 66. *Honors & Awards:* Robert Henry Thurston Award, Am Soc Mech Engr, 63; Am Acad Achievement Golden Plate Award, Dallas, 67; Distinguished Assoc Award, US Energy Res & Develop Admin, 77; Outstanding Achievement Award, Am Nuclear Soc, 78; James Clark Maxwell Prize Award, Am Phys Soc, 78. *Mem:* Nat Acad Sci; fel Am Phys Soc; fel Am Nuclear Soc. *Res:* Electron physics; traveling wave electron linear accelerators; controlled fusion; scintillation counter resolving time; high temperature plasmas. *Mailing Add:* Lawrence Livermore Lab Livermore CA 94550

POST, ROBERT ELLIOTT, b Paterson, NJ, Mar 17, 24; m 53; c 2. ELECTROCHEMISTRY. *Educ:* Yale Univ, BE, 44; Univ Wis, MS, 48; Univ Ill, PhD(phys chem), 57; Cleveland State Univ, JD, 66. *Prof Exp:* Engr indust rayon div, Midland-Ross Corp, 49-51, chemist, 55-61; sr res chemist, Tee-Pak, Inc, 61-62; chemist, 62-81, ENGR, LEWIS RES CTR, NASA, CLEVELAND, 81- *Res:* Electrochemically related aspects of catalysis; mass transport and analytical techniques. *Mailing Add:* Lewis Res Ctr NASA 21000 Brookpark Rd Bay Village OH 44140

POST, ROBERT LICKELY, b Philadelphia, Pa, Nov 4, 20; m 47. PHYSIOLOGY. *Educ:* Harvard Univ, AB, 42, MD, 45. *Prof Exp:* Instr physiol, Sch Med, Univ Pa, 46-48; from instr to assoc prof, 48-66, PROF PHYSIOL, SCH MED, VANDERBILT UNIV, 66- *Mem:* Am Physiol Soc; Biophys Soc; Soc Gen Physiol; Am Soc Biol Chem; Am Chem Soc. *Res:* Adenosine triphosphate dependent transport of sodium and potassium ions across cell membranes. *Mailing Add:* Vanderbilt Univ Sch of Med Nashville TN 37232

POST, ROBERT M, b New Haven, Conn, Sept 16, 42; m 66; c 2. PSYCHOPHARMACOLOGY. *Educ:* Yale Univ, BA, 64; Univ Pa, MD, 68. *Prof Exp:* Clin assoc, Lab Clin Sci, Sect Psychiat, 70-72, res fel, 72-73, chief, 3-West Clin Res Unit, 73-77, Sect Psychobiol, 77-82, ACTG CHIEF, BIOL PSYCHIAT BR, NAT INST MENTAL HEALTH, 82- *Concurrent Pos:* Intern neurol & pediat, Albert Einstein Sch Med, Jacobi Hosp, New York, 68-69; resident psychiat, Mass Gen Hosp, 69-70; A E Bennett Neuropsychiat Res Awarc, Soc Biol Psychiat, 73; psychiat residency, Dept Psychiat & Behav Sci Prog, George Washington Univ, 73-75. *Mem:* Am Col Neuropsychopharmacol; Am Psychiat Asn; Soc Biol Psychiat; Soc Neurosci. *Res:* Interactions between psychological and biological phenomena in patients with manic-depressive and anxiety disorders and in laboratory animal models of psychopathology. *Mailing Add:* Rm 3N212 Bldg 10 9000 Rockville Pike Bethesda MD 20205

POST, ROY G, b Asherton, Tex, June 24, 23; m 46; c 4. PHYSICAL INORGANIC CHEMISTRY. *Educ:* Univ Tex, BS, 44, PhD(chem), 52. *Prof Exp:* Assoc engr, Argonne Nat Lab, 44-49; chemist, Magnolia Petrol Co, 51-52; sr engr, Gen Elec Co, 52-58; sect head, Tex Instruments, Inc, 58-61; dir spec prof educ, Col Eng, 74-76, PROF NUCLEAR ENG, UNIV ARIZ, 61- *Concurrent Pos:* Ed, Nuclear Technol, 69- *Mem:* Am Nuclear Soc; AAAS; Sigma Xi. *Res:* Solvent extraction; surface chemistry; nucleonics; water desalting; nuclear fuel cycles; nuclear wastes. *Mailing Add:* Dept of Nuclear Eng Univ of Ariz Tucson AZ 85721

POST, THEODORE B, endocrine physiology, see previous edition

POSTE, GEORGE HENRY, b Polegate, Eng, Apr 30, 44; m 68; c 1. CANCER RESEARCH, CELL BIOLOGY. *Educ:* Univ Bristol, DVM, 66, PhD(virol), 69; FRCVS, 66; MRC(path), 76. *Prof Exp:* Lectr virol, Univ London, Eng, 69-72; assoc prof path, Roswell Park Mem Inst & State Univ NY, Buffalo, 72-75, prof, 75-80; PROF PATH, DEPT PATH, MED SCH, UNIV PA, PHILADELPHIA, 80-; VPRES PHARMACEUT RES, SMITHKLINE CORP, PHILADELPHIA, 80- *Concurrent Pos:* Res fel virol, Univ Bristol, 66-69; sr lectr, Univ London, 75; mem, Path B Study Sect, NIH, 79-; PROF PATH, DEPT CELL & MOLECULAR BIOL, STATE UNIV NY, BUFFALO, 76- *Mem:* Path Soc Gt Brit & Ireland; Brit Soc Gen Microbiol; Am Soc Microbiol; Am Soc Cell Biol; Brit Inst Biol. *Res:* Mechanisms of cancer metastasis; regulation of the metastatic phenotype in tumor cells; uses of liposomes as drug carriers; cell surface organization. *Mailing Add:* SmithKline & French Labs 1500 Spring Garden St POB 7929 Philadelphia PA 19101

POSTELNEK, WILLIAM, b Peoria, Ill, Jan 22, 18; m 45; c 3. ORGANIC CHEMISTRY, MATERIALS SCIENCE. *Educ:* Ill Inst Technol, BS, 42; Ohio State Univ, MSc, 54; Univ Chicago, MBA, 59. *Prof Exp:* Res chemist, L R Kerns Co, 46-48 & Dawe's Mfg Co, 48-50; proj officer polymer res sect, Air Force Mat Lab, US Air Force, 51-53, chief polymer res sect, 54-58, chief mat div, Europ Off, Off Aerospace Res, 59-62, chief mat appln div, Air Force Mat Lab, 62-67; consult, Gen Elec Co, Pa, 67-70; dir mat & processes lab, Kearfott Div, Singer Co, 70-80; CONSULT, MAT & PROCESS ENG, 80- *Honors & Awards:* Legion of Merit, 59. *Mem:* Am Chem Soc; Am Inst Chem; Am Soc Test & Mat; Soc Advan Mat & Process Eng. *Res:* Organic fluorine and organometallic compounds; polymer and high temperature chemistry; combustion; propulsion; aerospace materials. *Mailing Add:* 4725 Cove Circle 907 St Petersburg FL 33708

POSTEN, HARRY OWEN, b Middletown, NY, Feb 6, 28; m 57; c 3. MATHEMATICAL STATISTICS. *Educ:* Cent Conn State Col, BS, 56; Kans State Univ, MS, 58; Va Polytech Inst, PhD, 60. *Prof Exp:* Mem res staff, IBM Res Ctr, 60-62; asst prof math, Univ RI, 62-63; ASSOC PROF MATH STATIST, UNIV CONN, 63- *Mem:* Am Statist Asn; Inst Math Statist. *Res:* Statistical robustness; multivariate statistical analysis. *Mailing Add:* Dept Statist Univ Conn Storrs CT 06268

POSTIC, BOSKO, b Novi Sad, Yugoslavia, Feb 9, 31; m 67; c 2. MEDICINE, INFECTIOUS DISEASES. *Educ:* Univ Zagreb, MD, 55; Harvard Univ, MPH, 62; Univ Pittsburgh, DSc(microbiol), 65; Am Bd Internal Med, cert, 74 & 80, cert infectious disease, 76. *Prof Exp:* Intern med, Mt Auburn Hosp, Cambridge, Mass, 57-58; asst resident, Lemuel Shattuck Hosp, Boston, 58-59; resident med bact, Boston City Hosp, 59-60, res fel, Thorndike Mem Lab, 60-61; trainee microbiol, Sch Pub Health, Harvard Univ, 61-62; trainee, Grad Sch Pub Health, Univ Pittsburgh, 62-65, from asst prof to assoc prof epidemiol, Grad Sch Pub Health, 66-78, assoc prof med, Sch Med, 72-78; chief infectious dis sect, Vet Admin Hosp, Pittsburgh, 75-78, chief med serv, 76-78; PROF MED, SCH MED, UNIV SC, COLUMBIA, SC, 78-, CHIEF MED SERV, VET ADMIN HOSP, 78- *Concurrent Pos:* Am Cancer Soc fel, Sch Med, Univ Pittsburgh, 70-71, WHO fel, 70-, asst prof med, 71-72, Health Res & Serv Found fel, 72-; fel, Res Dept, Vet Admin, 76-78. *Mem:* Am Soc Microbiol; fel Am Col Physicians; fel Infectious Dis Soc Am. *Res:* Medical virology; interferon; epidemiology. *Mailing Add:* Vet Admin Hosp Columbia SC 29201

POSTL, ANTON, b Graz, Austria, June 16, 16; nat US; m 42; c 3. ORGANIC CHEMISTRY. *Educ:* Univ Hawaii, BS, 40, MS, 42; Ore State Col, PhD(gen sci), 55. *Prof Exp:* Asst chem, Univ Hawaii, 40-41; instr sci, Mid-Pac Inst, 41-43; instr chem, Univ Hawaii, 43-45; instr, Schs, Ore, 46-47; from instr to assoc prof chem & physics, 47-58, chmn dept natural sci & math, 58-72, prof chem, Western Oregon State Col, 58-81. *Mem:* Fel AAAS; Am Chem Soc; Nat Sci Teachers Asn; Hist Sci Soc. *Res:* Colloid chemistry of soils; geology; history of science. *Mailing Add:* 916 E Jackson Monmouth OR 97361

POSTLE, DONALD SLOAN, b Columbus, Ohio, July 18, 22; m 47; c 4. VETERINARY SCIENCE. *Educ:* Ohio State Univ, DVM, 50; Univ Wis-Madison, MS, 67. *Prof Exp:* Pvt pract, 50-62; from instr to asst prof vet sci, Univ Wis-Madison, 62-69, proj assoc mastitis res & prin investr, USPHS res grant, 62-67; ASSOC PROF VET SCI, NY STATE COL VET MED, 69- *Concurrent Pos:* Dir, NY State Mastitis Control Prog, 72. *Mem:* Am Vet Med Asn; US Animal Health Asn. *Res:* Mastitis research and control; bovine mastitis. *Mailing Add:* NY State Col of Vet Med Cornell Univ Ithaca NY 14853

POSTLETHWAIT, JOHN HARVEY, b Kittery, Maine, July 15, 44; m 64; c 2. DEVELOPMENTAL BIOLOGY, GENETICS. *Educ:* Purdue Univ, BA, 66; Case Western Reserve Univ, PhD(biol), 70. *Prof Exp:* Fel, Harvard Univ, 70-71; asst prof, 71-77, assoc prof, 77-81, PROF BIOL, UNIV ORE, 81- *Concurrent Pos:* Fulbright fel, Inst Molecular Biol, Austria, 77-78. *Mem:* AAAS; Genetics Soc Am; Soc Develop Biol. *Res:* Hormonal and genetic control of development in Drosophila melanogaster; pattern formation during regeneration; determination in homoeotic mutants; mechanism of action of ecdysterone and juvenile hormone on yolk polypeptide synthesis in Drosophila using cloned copies of genes to assay gene activity and mutants disrupting gene action. *Mailing Add:* Dept of Biol Univ of Ore Eugene OR 97403

POSTLETHWAIT, RAYMOND WOODROW, b New Martinsville, WVa, Oct 9, 13; m 37; c 4. SURGERY. *Educ:* WVa Univ, BS, 35; Duke Univ, MD, 37; Am Bd Surg, dipl. *Prof Exp:* Intern, Duke Hosp, NC, 37-39; house officer surg, Henry Ford Hosp, Mich, 39-40, Palmerton Hosp, Pa, 40-41 & Duke Hosp, NC, 45-47; instr, Bowman Gray Sch Med, 48-49; asst prof, Med Col SC, 49-55; assoc prof, 55-57, PROF SURG, SCH MED, DUKE UNIV, 57- *Concurrent Pos:* Chief surg serv, Vet Admin Hosp, Durham, 55-65, chief of surg, 65- *Mem:* Soc Univ Surgeons; AMA; Am Col Surgeons. *Res:* Surgery of the esophagus. *Mailing Add:* Vet Admin Hosp Durham NC 27705

POSTLETHWAIT, SAMUEL NOEL, b Wileysville, WVa, Apr 16, 18; m 41; c 2. BOTANY. *Educ:* Fairmont State Col, AB, 40; WVa Univ, MS, 47; State Univ Iowa, PhD, 49. *Prof Exp:* Teacher pub schs, WVa, 40-41; instr bot & biol, Univ Iowa, 48-49; from asst prof to assoc prof, 49-63, PROF BOT & BIOL, PURDUE UNIV, WEST LAFAYETTE, 63- *Concurrent Pos:* Nat Sci Found fac fel, Manchester Univ, 57-58; Fulbright fel, Macquarie Univ, Australia, 68; Lilly Endowment fac open fel award, 79. *Honors & Awards:* AV Instr Dir Award, 65; Eastman Kodak Gold Medal Award, 67; Postlethwait award, Int Cong Individualized Instr, 80. *Mem:* Bot Soc Am; Am Inst Biol Sci; AAAS; Sigma Xi; Am Genetic Asn. *Res:* Plant morphology; science education. *Mailing Add:* Dept of Biol Sci Purdue Univ West Lafayette IN 47907

POSTMA, HERMAN, b Wilmington, NC, Mar 29, 33; m 60; c 2. PHYSICS. *Educ:* Duke Univ, BS, 55; Harvard Univ, MA, 58, PhD(physics), 59. *Prof Exp:* Physicist, Oak Ridge Nat Lab, 59-63 & Inst Plasma Physics, Neth, 63-64; physicist, 64-67, dir thermonuclear div, 67-73, DIR, OAK RIDGE NAT LAB, 74- *Concurrent Pos:* Consult, Lab Laser Energetics, Rochester Univ, 74-; bd adv, Univ Tenn Bus Sch; bd adv, NC Energy Inst. *Mem:* Fel AAAS; fel Am Phys Soc; Am Nuclear Soc. *Res:* Nuclear, atomic and plasma physics; controlled fusion feasibility. *Mailing Add:* Oak Ridge Nat Lab PO Box X Oak Ridge TN 37830

POSTMAN, ROBERT DEREK, b Jersey City, NJ, July 13, 41; m 65; c 3. MATHEMATICS, COMPUTER EDUCATION. *Educ:* Kean Col, NJ, BA, 66; Columbia Univ, MA, 67, EdD(math), 71. *Prof Exp:* Asst prof math, Hunter Col, City Univ New York, 71-76; ASSOC PROF MATH & EDUC, MERCY COL, DOBBS FERRY, NY, 76-, DIR, INST GIFTED CHILDREN, 79- *Concurrent Pos:* Math consult, Columbia Univ-Royal Afghan Univ Coop Proj Math, 72-73 & Harcourt, Brace & Jovanovich Inc, 75-; fac mem, Dept Math, Statist & Comput, Educ Teachers Col, Columbia Univ, 76-; dir, Teachers Col, Columbia Univ Exten Ctr, Mercy Col, 77- *Mem:* Am Math Soc; Math Asn Am. *Res:* microcomputers and microcomputers in education. *Mailing Add:* Dept of Math Mercy Col Dobbs Ferry NY 10522

POSTMUS, CLARENCE, JR, b Grand Rapids, Mich, Dec 12, 27; m 52; c 3. INORGANIC CHEMISTRY. *Educ:* Calvin Col, AB, 50; Univ Wis, PhD(chem), 54. *Prof Exp:* Assoc chemist, Argonne Nat Lab, 54-69; from asst prof to assoc prof, 69-78, PROF CHEM, NORTH PARK COL, 73- *Mem:* Soc Appl Spectros; Am Chem Soc. *Res:* Solution chemistry; far infrared. *Mailing Add:* Dept of Chem North Park Col 5125 N Spaulding Ave Chicago IL 60625

POSTON, FREDDIE LEE, JR, b Jacksonville, Fla, Nov 19, 46; m 67; c 2. ENTOMOLOGY. *Educ:* WTex State Univ, BS, 71; Iowa State Univ, MS, 73, PhD(entom), 75. *Prof Exp:* Res assoc entom, Iowa State Univ, 73-75; asst prof, 75-80, ASSOC PROF ENTOM, KANS STATE UNIV, 80- *Mem:* Entom Soc Am. *Res:* Crop management and insect damage/crop loss relationship. *Mailing Add:* Dept of Entom Kans State Univ Manhattan KS 66502

POSTON, HUGH ARTHUR, b Canton, NC, May 5, 29; m 54; c 3. REPRODUCTIVE PHYSIOLOGY, ANIMAL NUTRITION. *Educ:* Berea Col, BS, 51; NC State Univ, MS, 54, PhD(reproductive physiol), 62. *Prof Exp:* Mgr dairy animal res, NC State Cent Dairy Res Sta, 56-58; RES PHYSIOLOGIST, TUNISON LAB FISH NUTRIT, FISH & WILDLIFE SERV, US DEPT INTERIOR, 61-; ADJ ASSOC PROF, COL VET MED, CORNELL UNIV, 78- *Mem:* AAAS; Am Fisheries Soc; Am Inst Nutrit; Am Inst Fishery Res Biologists; World Maricult Soc. *Res:* Mammalian nutrition and physiology; fish nutrition, physiology and endocrinology. *Mailing Add:* Tunison Lab of Fish Nutrit 28 Gracie Rd Cortland NY 13045

POSTON, JOHN WARE, b Sparta, Tenn, July 8, 37; m 58; c 3. HEALTH PHYSICS, NUCLEAR ENGINEERING. *Educ:* Lynchburg Col, BS, 58; Ga Inst Technol, MS, 69, PhD(nuclear eng), 71. *Prof Exp:* Exp reactor physicist, Critical Exp Lab, Babcock & Wilcox Co, 57-64; health physicist, Oak Ridge Nat Lab, 64-74, chief, Med Physics Internal Dosimetry Sect, Health Physics Div, 74-77; ASSOC PROF, SCH NUCLEAR ENG, GA INST TECHNOL, ATLANTA, 77- *Concurrent Pos:* Consult, Int Atomic Energy Agency, Austria, 65-70; lectr & consult, Inst Atomic Energy, Brazil, 71. *Mem:* AAAS; Soc Nuclear Med; Int Radiation Protection Asn; Health Physics Soc (secy, 74-76); Am Nuclear Soc. *Res:* Neutron and gamma ray dosimetry; nuclear accident dosimetry; internal dosimetry; dosimetry for medical physics purposes. *Mailing Add:* Sch of Nuclear Eng Ga Inst of Technol Atlanta GA 30332

POSTOW, ELLIOT, b New York, NY, June 21, 40; m 70; c 2. BIOPHYSICS. *Educ:* City Col New York, BS, 61; Mich State Univ, PhD(biophys), 68. *Prof Exp:* Biophysicist, Off Naval Res, Navy Dept, 68-72 & Bur Med & Surg, 72-74, BIOPHYSICIST, NAVAL MED RES & DEVELOP COMMAND, 74- *Concurrent Pos:* Ed, Bioelectromagnetics, 78- *Mem:* AAAS; Biophys Soc; Bioelectromagnetics Soc; NY Acad Sci; Int Microwave Power Inst. *Res:* Biological effects and medical uses of electromagnetic radiation; bioenergetics; radiation; research administration. *Mailing Add:* Naval Med Res & Develop Command Nat Naval Med Ctr Bethesda MD 20814

POSVIC, HARVEY WALTER, b Cicero, Ill, Apr 22, 21. ORGANIC CHEMISTRY. *Educ:* Univ Chicago, BS, 40; Carleton Col, MA, 42; Univ Wis, PhD(org chem), 46. *Prof Exp:* Asst chem, Carleton Col, 40-42; asst, Univ Wis, 42-44, instr, 44-45; du Pont fel, Cornell Univ, 46-47, instr chem, 47-52; asst prof, 52-58, ASSOC PROF CHEM, LOYOLA UNIV CHICAGO, 58- *Mem:* Am Chem Soc. *Res:* Stereochemistry; physical organic chemistry; reaction mechanisms; natural products; drugs. *Mailing Add:* Dept Chem Loyola Univ Chicago IL 60626

POTASH, LOUIS, medical microbiology, see previous edition

POTASH, MILTON, b New York, NY, Nov 23, 24; m 49; c 3. ECOLOGY, LIMNOLOGY. *Educ:* Univ Louisville, AB, 47; Ind Univ, MA, 50; Cornell Univ, PhD(zool), 53. *Prof Exp:* Asst zool, Cornell Univ, 49-51; instr, 51-54, from asst prof to assoc prof, 54-67, PROF ZOOL, UNIV VT, 67- *Mem:* Ecol Soc Am; Am Soc Limnol & Oceanog; Am Water Resources Asn. *Res:* Wetlands ecology; water quality; limnology of Lake Champlain. *Mailing Add:* Dept of Zool Univ of Vt Burlington VT 05401

POTASHNER, STEVEN JAY, b Lowell, Mass, July 29, 45; m 66; c 2. NEUROCHEMISTRY. *Educ:* McGill Univ, BSc, 66, PhD(biochem), 71. *Prof Exp:* Fel, Physiol Lab, Univ Cambridge, 70-73; res assoc, Dept Res Anesthesia, McGill Univ, 73-78; asst prof neurochem, Dept Physiol, McGill Univ, 75-78; ASST PROF NEUROANAT, DEPT ANAT, UNIV CONN HEALTH CTR, 78- *Mem:* Int Soc Neurochem; Soc Neurosci. *Res:* Chemical basis of information processing in the normal and diseased nervous system. *Mailing Add:* Dept Anat Univ Conn Health Ctr Farmington CT 06032

POTCHEN, E JAMES, b Queens Co, NY, Dec 2, 32; m; c 4. RADIOLOGY, NUCLEAR MEDICINE. *Educ:* Mich State Univ, BS, 54; Wayne State Univ, MD, 58; Am Bd Radiol, dipl, 65; Am Bd Nuclear Med, dipl, 72. *Prof Exp:* Chief res radiologist, Peter Bent Brigham Hosp, 64, jr assoc, 65; asst radiol, Harvard Med Sch, 65; dir nuclear med, Mallinckrodt Inst, Wash Univ, 66-73, from asst prof to prof, Sch Med, 70-73; prof radiol & dean mgt resources, Sch Med, Johns Hopkins Univ, 73-75; PROF RADIOL & CHMN DEPT & PROF HEALTH CARE SYSTS, MICH STATE UNIV, 75- *Concurrent Pos:* Teaching fel radiol, Harvard Med Sch, 64-66; Nat Acad Sci-Nat Res Coun advan fel acad radiol, James Picker Found, 65-66 & scholar radiol res, 67-68; radiologist, Barnes Hosp, St Louis, 66-71 & Johns Hopkins Hosp, 73-75; consult, Nat Heart Inst, 67-73, Nat Inst Gen Med Sci, 68-, Nat Heart & Lung Inst, 71-, Vet Admin Cent Off Prof Serv Div, 71-73, Bur Drugs, Food & Drug Admin, 72-, Health Systs Group, Westinghouse Corp, 74- & Gen Bus Develop, IBM Corp, 74-; examr, Am Bd Radiol, 68-; mem comt radiol, Nat Acad Sci-Nat Res Coun, 71-75; mem coun stroke & thrombosis, Am Heart Asn, 71-; Sloan fel, Mass Inst Technol, 72-73, vis lectr, 73-74. *Mem:* Am Soc Clin Invest; Am Fedn Clin Res; Soc Nuclear Med (pres, 75-76); fel Am Col Chest Physicians; fel Am Col Radiol. *Res:* Social and economic implications of transfer technology in medicine; diagnostic decision making; efficacy of diagnostic procedure; reconstructive imaging using transmitted photons, emitted protons and ultrasound. *Mailing Add:* Dept Radiol B220 Clin Ctr Mich State Univ East Lansing MI 48824

POTEAT, WILLIAM LOUIS, b Brooklyn, NY, May 14, 44; m 68; c 1. ANATOMY. *Educ:* Wake Forest Univ, BS, 66, PhD(anat), 71. *Prof Exp:* From instr to asst prof anat, Med Col Va, 71-75; assoc prof anat, Sch Med, Univ SC, 75-80; MEM FAC, ANAT DEPT, VA MED COL, 80- *Res:* Uterine glycogen metabolism; blastocyst implantation; pertussis vaccine and experimental allergic encephalomyelitis; uterotrophic action of clomiphene citrate. *Mailing Add:* 1200 E Broad St Dept Anat Va Med Col Richmond VA 23298

POTEMRA, THOMAS ANDREW, b Cleveland, Ohio. Oct 23, 38; m 62; c 3. PHYSICS. *Educ:* Case Inst Technol, BS, 60; NY Univ, MEE, 62; Stanford Univ, PhD(elec eng), 66. *Prof Exp:* Mem tech staff, Bell Tel Labs, 60-62; res asst, Radiosci Lab, Stanford Univ, 62-65; SUPVR SPACE PHYSICS & INSTRUMENTATION GROUP, APPL PHYSICS LAB, JOHNS HOPKINS UNIV, 65-, FAC MEM, EVE COL, 68- *Concurrent Pos:* Mem, Int Sci Radio Union, 66-; mem working group 11, Inter-Union Comn Solar-Terrestrial Physics, Int Coun Sci Unions; mem Comn V, Int Asn Geomagnetism & Aeronomy; assoc ed, J Geophys Res, 77-81. *Mem:* Am Geophys Union. *Res:* Auroral and magnetospheric phenomena; ionospheric dynamics; solar-terrestrial relationships. *Mailing Add:* Appl Physics Lab Johns Hopkins Univ Laurel MD 20707

POTENZA, JOSEPH ANTHONY, b New York, NY, Nov 13, 41; m 64; c 2. PHYSICAL CHEMISTRY, INORGANIC CHEMISTRY. *Educ:* Polytech Inst Brooklyn, BS, 62; Harvard Univ, PhD(chem), 67. *Prof Exp:* From asst prof to assoc prof, 68-77, dir, Sch Chem, 77-80, PROF CHEM, RUTGERS UNIV, NEW BRUNSWICK, 77-, CHMN, DEPT CHEM & DIR, GRAD PROG CHEM, 80- *Concurrent Pos:* Alfred P Sloan Found fel, 71-73; Alexander von Humboldt Found sr US scientist award for res & teaching, 74; guest prof, Univ Münster, WGer, 74-75. *Mem:* Am Chem Soc; Am Crystallog Asn; Am Phys Soc. *Res:* Molecular structure and dynamics; magnetic resonance; x-ray crystallography. *Mailing Add:* Dept Chem Rutgers Univ New Brunswick NJ 08903

POTH, EDGAR J, b Seguin, Tex, Feb 1, 99; m 28. SURGERY. *Educ:* Univ Tex, BA, 22, MA, 23; Univ Calif, PhD(phys chem), 25; Johns Hopkins Univ, MD, 31; Am Bd Surg, dipl, 49. *Prof Exp:* Instr pharmacol, Sch Med, Johns Hopkins Univ, 27, asst, 27-30, substitute intern, 30-31; surg house officer, Lane Hosp, San Francisco, 31-32; asst surg, Stanford Univ, 32-36, from instr to asst prof, 36-39; prof surg & head dept, Sch Med & surgeon in chief, Hosp, Univ Ark, 39-40; instr surg, Johns Hopkins Univ, 40-41, assoc, 41-42; from assoc prof to prof, 42-64, dir surg res lab, 43-61, chief div gen surg, 61-64, ASHBEL SMITH PROF SURG, UNIV TEX MED BR, GALVESTON, 64- *Concurrent Pos:* Nat Res Coun fel, Stanford Univ, 32-34, res fel, Univ Hosp, 35-36; chief surgeon, Bahrein Petrol Co, 36-37; surgeon, Standard Oil Co Calif, 37-39; attend vis surgeon, San Francisco Hosp, 37-39; asst vis surgeon, City Hosp, Baltimore, 42; dir tumor clin, John Sealy Hosp, Tex, 43-55, surgeon, 44-; consult to Surgeon Gen, US Air Force, 57-63. *Mem:* Soc Exp Biol & Med; Soc Univ Surgeons; Am Physiol Soc; Am Surg Asn; Am Col Surgeons. *Res:* Gastric physiology; bowel healing, especially the importance of mucosa, submucosa and serosa; the influence of the partial pressure of carbon dioxide and oxygen on the bacterial flora of the colon. *Mailing Add:* Dept of Surg Univ of Tex Med Br Galveston TX 77550

POTH, JAMES EDWARD, b Galion, Ohio, May 19, 33; m 60; c 3. NUCLEAR PHYSICS, ENVIRONMENTAL PHYSICS. *Educ:* Miami Univ, BS, 55, MA, 60; Yale Univ, MS, 62, PhD(nuclear physics), 66. *Prof Exp:* Res physicist, Yale Univ, 66; from asst prof to assoc prof, 66-70, PROF PHYSICS, MIAMI UNIV, 76- *Concurrent Pos:* NASA-Am Soc Eng Educ fel, 67-68. *Mem:* Am Phys Soc; Am Asn Physics Teachers; Sigma Xi. *Res:* Low energy nuclear physics; environmental physics; neutron activation analysis. *Mailing Add:* Dept of Physics Miami Univ Oxford OH 45056

POTHOVEN, MARVIN ARLO, b Pella, Iowa, Apr 15, 46; m 69; c 2. ANIMAL NUTRITION. *Educ:* Cent Col, Iowa, BA, 68; Iowa State Univ, MS, 72, PhD(animal nutrit), 74. *Prof Exp:* Researcher qual control, 74-78, COORDR, LAB SERV & QUAL ASSURANCE, MOORMAN MFG CO, 78- *Mem:* Sigma Xi; Am Soc Animal Sci; Am Dairy Sci Asn. *Res:* Maintaining and improving the product quality of livestock feed through testing and revising present and future manufacturing techniques and developing new quality tests. *Mailing Add:* Moorman Mfg Co 1000 N 39th St Quincy IL 62301

POTKAY, STEPHEN, b New Bedford, Mass, July 15, 37; m 71; c 2. LABORATORY ANIMAL MEDICINE. *Educ:* Univ Pa, VMD, 62. *Prof Exp:* Assoc vet, Salem Vet Hosp, Mass, 62-63; vet officer lab animal prod, med & surg, 63-78, asst chief, 78-80, DEPT CHIEF, VET RESOURCES BR, DIV RES SERV, NIH, 80- *Concurrent Pos:* Assoc ed, Lab Animal Sci, 75- *Mem:* Wildlife Dis Asn; Am Col Lab Animal Med; AAAS; Am Asn Lab Animal Sci; Am Soc Vet Ethology. *Res:* Diseases of laboratory and exotic animals; experimental surgery; management of laboratory animal resources. *Mailing Add:* Vet Resources Br Div of Res Serv NIH Bethesda MD 20014

POTMESIL, MILAN, b Prague, Czech, Sept 22, 26; US citizen; m 51, 74; c 3. ONCOLOGY, HEMATOLOGY. *Educ:* Charles Univ, Prague, MD, 51, PhD(exp hematol), 67. *Prof Exp:* Clin hematologist, Cent Mil Hosp, Prague, 60-68; vis scientist, Wash Sq Col, 68-70, res scientist, 70-75, sr res scientist, 75-77, adj assoc prof biol, Fac Arts & Sci, 77-78, ASSOC PROF RADIOL, MED SCH & DIR EXP THER RADIOBIOL UNIT, CANCER CTR, NY UNIV, 78- *Concurrent Pos:* Co-prin investr, Nat Cancer Inst, NIH res grants, 71-75, 75-78 & 78-81; prin investr, Am Cancer Soc res grant, 79-82 & Inst res grant, NY Univ, 78. *Mem:* Am Soc Hematol; Am Soc Cell Biol; Cell Kinetic Soc; Radiation Res Soc; Soc Exp Biol & Med. *Res:* Clinical and experimental hematology; experimental oncology; cell and tissue kinetics; drug and radiation effects; predictive and screening systems for therapy of neoplasias. *Mailing Add:* Dept of Biol NY Univ Washington Square New York NY 10003

POTNIS, VASANT RAGHUNATH, b Lashkar, India, Mar 10, 28; m 57. PHYSICS. *Educ:* Agra Univ, BSc, 48, MSc, 52, PhD(nuclear physics), 59. *Prof Exp:* Teacher high sch, Lashkar, India, 49-50; sci asst, Phys Res Lab, Ahmedabad, 52-54; physicist, Bartol Res Found, Pa, 57-60; sci pool officer, Aligarh Muslim Univ, India, 61-62; asst prof physics, Kans State Univ, 63-68; assoc prof, 68-72, PROF PHYSICS, MICH TECHNOL UNIV, 72- *Mem:* AAAS; fel Am Phys Soc; Am Asn Physics Teachers; Sigma Xi. *Res:* Cosmic ray time variations and their relation with solar activity; nuclear physics; radioactivity; energies and intensities of gamma and beta rays; study of nuclear energy levels and their properties. *Mailing Add:* Dept of Physics Mich Technol Univ Houghton MI 49931

POTOCKI, KENNETH ANTHONY, b Chicago, Ill, Oct 8, 40. APPLIED PHYSICS, TECHNICAL MANAGEMENT. *Educ:* Loyola Univ Chicago, BS, 62; Ind Univ, Bloomington, MS, 65, PhD(physics), 68. *Prof Exp:* Physicist anal, US Army Missile Command, 68-70; sr staff physicist, 70-77, nagiv group supvr systs anal, 77-81, SATELLITE PROG MGR, APPL PHYSICS LAB, JOHNS HOPKINS UNIV, 81- *Concurrent Pos:* Instr appl physics, Johns Hopkins Univ, 74- *Mem:* Am Phys Soc; Inst Navig; Am Geophys Union. *Res:* Ocean acoustics; navigation; nuclear physics; missile systems analysis. *Mailing Add:* Appl Physics Lab Johns Hopkins Rd Laurel MD 20707

POTOCZNY, HENRY BASIL, b Philadelphia, Pa, Mar 18, 44. MATHEMATICS. *Educ:* La Salle Col, BA, 65; Univ Ky, MA, 67, PhD(math), 69. *Prof Exp:* Asst prof, 69-75, ASSOC PROF MATH, UNIV DAYTON, 75- *Mem:* Am Math Soc; Math Asn Am; Asn Comput Mach. *Res:* Point set topology. *Mailing Add:* Comput Sci Dept Univ of Dayton Dayton OH 45469

POTRAFKE, EARL MARK, b Wellsville, NY, Oct 25, 30. ENVIRONMENTAL CHEMISTRY. *Educ:* Alfred Univ, BA, 52; Pa State Univ, MS, 56; Univ Tex, PhD(inorg chem), 60. *Prof Exp:* Res chemist, Res & Develop Div, Pioneering Res Sect, 60-64, Petrol Chem Res Sect, 64-65 & Freon Prod Div, 65-69, proj leader, Permasep Prod Div, 69-75, ENVIRON CONTROL COORDR, DEPT CHEM, DYES & PIGMENTS, E I DU PONT DE NEMOURS & CO, INC, 75- *Mem:* Am Chem Soc; Sigma Xi. *Res:* Reactions in liquid ammonia; coordination chemistry of transitional metal complexes; phosphine-metal salt complexes; inorganic photochemistry; ceramics; fluorocarbon chemistry; chemistry of water and waste water. *Mailing Add:* Dept of Chem Dyes & Pigments E I du Pont de Nemours & Co Inc Wilmington DE 19898

POTSWALD, HERBERT EUGENE, b Duluth, Minn, July 23, 37; m 60; c 2. INVERTEBRATE EMBRYOLOGY, CYTOLOGY. *Educ:* Univ Minn, Duluth, BA, 59; Univ Wash, PhD(zool), 65. *Prof Exp:* NSF fel anat, Sch Med, Univ Wash, 65-66; asst prof zool, 66-72, ASSOC PROF ZOOL, UNIV MASS, AMHERST, 72- *Mem:* AAAS; Am Soc Zool. *Res:* Gametogenesis, reproductive biology and development of Spirorbis; fine structural analysis of asexual reproduction and reparative regeneration in annelids. *Mailing Add:* Dept of Zool Univ of Mass Amherst MA 01003

POTTASCH, STUART ROBERT, b New York, NY, Jan 16, 32; m 56; c 3. ASTROPHYSICS. *Educ:* Cornell Univ, BEngPhys, 54; Harvard Univ, MA, 57; Univ Colo, PhD(astrophys), 58. *Prof Exp:* Astrophysicist, Nat Bur Stand, Colo, 57-59, Observ of Paris & Inst Astrophys, 59-60, Princeton Univ & Inst Advan Study, 60-62 & Ind Univ, 62-63; PROF ASTROPHYS, KAPTEYN ASTRON INST 63- *Concurrent Pos:* Ed-in-chief, Astron & Astrophys, 69-76, Lett ed, 76- *Mem:* Int Astron Union. *Res:* Theory of stellar atmospheres; solar physics; interstellar medium; novae outburst; infrared astronomy; planetary nebulae. *Mailing Add:* Kapteyn Astron Inst PO Box 800 Groningen 9700 AV Netherlands

POTTER, ALLAN G, b Frankfort, Kans, May 9, 30; m 52; c 3. ELECTRICAL & BIOMEDICAL ENGINEERING. *Educ:* Kans State Univ, BSEE, 55; Iowa State Univ, MSEE, 59, PhD(elec eng), 66. *Prof Exp:* Elec engr, Minneapolis-Honeywell Regulator Co, 52-53; assoc elec engr, Magnavox Corp, 55-56; from instr to assoc prof, 56-76, PROF ELEC ENG, IOWA STATE UNIV, 77- *Concurrent Pos:* Co-prin investr, HEW res grant, 60-63; consult, Bendix Corp, 66-68; prin investr, Voc Rehab Admin res grant, 68- *Mem:* Assoc Inst Elec & Electronics Engrs; Am Soc Eng Educ. *Res:* Application of engineering principles in the development of myoelectric control systems for upper extremity braces used by quadraplegic patients. *Mailing Add:* Dept of Elec Eng Iowa State Univ Ames IA 50011

POTTER, ANDREW ELWIN, JR, b St Petersburg, Fla, Nov 29, 26; m 51; c 3. ENVIRONMENTAL EFFECTS, REMOTE SENSING. *Educ:* Univ Fla, BS, 48; Univ Wis, PhD(chem), 53. *Prof Exp:* Aeronaut res scientist, Lewis Res Ctr, NASA, Ohio, 53-56, head combustion fundamentals sect, 56-58, head reaction kinetics sect, 58-62, chief elec energy sources br, 62-68, staff scientist, Space Physics Div, Johnson Space Ctr, 68-71, chief, Appl Physics Br, 71-76, MGR, ENVIRON EFFECTS OFF, NASA, JOHNSON SPACE CTR, NASA, 76- *Concurrent Pos:* Mem planetary atmospheres subcomt, Space Sci Steering Comt, NASA, 61-70 & Photovoltaic Specialists Comt, 64-68; mission scientist, Shuttle Orbital Flight 2, 78- *Mem:* Am Astron Soc; Combustion Inst. *Res:* Chemical kinetics of radical reactions in flames and upper atmosphere; infrared spectroscopy of lunar and planetary surfaces; environmental effects of space shuttle; remote sensing of earth resources; research administration. *Mailing Add:* NASA Johnson Space Ctr Houston TX 77058

POTTER, BRIAN, b Manchester, Eng; US citizen; c 4. DERMATOLOGY. *Educ:* Univ Educ: McGill Univ, MD, CM, 50. *Prof Exp:* From res assoc to asst prof dermat, Univ Chicago, 58-61; clin asst prof, Univ Colo, 61-62; assoc prof, 62-74, CLIN PROF DERMAT, UNIV ILL COL MED, 75- *Mem:* Soc Invest Dermat; fel Am Acad Dermat; fel Royal Col Physicians Can; fel Royal Soc Med; Am Soc Dermatopath. *Res:* Histopathology. *Mailing Add:* Med Group of Michigan City Michigan City IN 46360

POTTER, CARLA JEAN, b Mt Morris, Ill, July 10, 50. GEOLOGY, MARINE GEOLOGY. *Educ:* Univ Mo-Columbia, BS, 72, MA, 75. *Prof Exp:* Geol technician basin anal, US Geol Surv, Denver, 75-76; GEOLOGIST MARINE GEOL, ENVIRON DATA INFO SERV, NAT GEOPHYS & SOLAR-TERRESTRIAL DATA CTR, NAT OCEANIC & ATMOSPHERIC ADMIN, 76- *Mem:* Geol Soc Am; Sigma Xi. *Mailing Add:* Environ Data Info Serv/NGSDC Code D621 Boulder CO 80303

POTTER, DAVID DICKINSON, b Chicago, Ill, Dec 22, 30; m 52; c 4. NEUROPHYSIOLOGY. *Educ:* Swarthmore Col, BA, 52; Harvard Univ, PhD, 56. *Prof Exp:* Hon res asst biophys, Univ Col, Univ London, 56-58; fel neurophysiol, Med Sch, Johns Hopkins Univ, 58-59; from instr to assoc prof, 59-69, PROF NEUROBIOL, HARVARD MED SCH, 69- *Res:* Development, physiology and chemistry of synaptic transmission. *Mailing Add:* 132 Brattle Cambridge MA 02138

POTTER, DAVID EDWARD, b Tyler, Tex, June 30, 37; m 59; c 3. PHARMACOLOGY. *Educ:* Tex Tech Univ, AB, 60; Univ Kans, PhD(pharmacol), 69. *Prof Exp:* Res asst neuropharmacol, Parke, Davis & Co, 60-64; jr scientist, Alcon Labs, Inc, 64-65; from instr to assoc prof pharmacol, Univ Tex Med Br, Galveston, 69-77; PROF PHARMACOL, SCH MED, TEX TECHNOL UNIV, LUBBOCK, 77- *Mem:* Am Soc Pharmacol & Exp Therapeut; Soc Exp Biol & Med; Endocrine Soc; Sigma Xi; Asn Res Vision & Ophthalmol. *Res:* Autonomic pharmacology; polypeptides; drug-receptor interaction; metabolic effects of catecholamines and alcohol. *Mailing Add:* Dept of Pharmacol & Therapeut Tex Technol Univ Sch of Med Lubbock TX 79430

POTTER, DAVID SAMUEL, b Seattle, Wash, Jan 16, 25. ACOUSTICS. *Educ:* Yale Univ, BS, 45; Univ Wash, PhD(physics), 51. *Prof Exp:* Asst dir, Appl Physics Lab, Univ Wash, 55-60; head, Sea Opers, Defense Res Lab, Gen Motors, 60-66, dir, Santa Barbara Opers, 66-69, dir res & develop, Delco Electronics Div, 69-70, chief engr, 70-73, dir res, Detroit Diesel Allison Div, 73; asst secy res & develop, Navy, Dept Defense, US Govt, 73-74, under secy Navy, 74-76; vpres, environ actg staff, 76-78, VPRES PUB AFFAIRS GROUP, GEN MOTORS CORP, 78- *Honors & Awards:* Special Commendation, Marine Technol Soc, 76. *Mem:* Nat Acad Eng; Soc Automotive Engrs; Am Phys Soc; Acoust Soc Am; Am Inst Aeronaut & Astronaut. *Res:* Underwater acoustics with primary emphasis on absorption and scattering phenomenon. *Mailing Add:* 14-154 Gen Motors Bldg 3044 W Grand Blvd Detroit MI 48202

POTTER, DAVID W, b Passaic, NJ, May 11, 35; m 58; c 3. PHYSICS, ELECTRICAL ENGINEERING. *Educ:* Rensselaer Polytech Inst, BS, 57. *Prof Exp:* asst physicist, 57-80, PHYSICIST, BROOKHAVEN NAT LAB, 80- *Res:* Electronic nuclear instrumentation. *Mailing Add:* Brookhaven Nat Lab Bldg 535 Upton NY 11973

POTTER, DONALD IRWIN, b Detroit, Mich, May 28, 41; m 61; c 1. METALLURGY, MATERIALS SCIENCE. *Educ:* Wayne State Univ, BPh, 64, BS, 66; Univ Ill, Urbana, MS, 67, PhD(metall eng), 70. *Prof Exp:* Asst prof mat sci, Union Col, NY, 71-74; metallurgist, Mat Sci Div, Argonne Nat Lab, 74-79; ASSOC PROF METALL, UNIV CONN, 79- *Concurrent Pos:* NSF initiation and continuing grants & Res Corp Frederick Cottrell award. *Mem:* Am Inst Mining, Metall & Petrol Engrs. *Res:* Phase transformations in metals, especially interstitial elements in refractory metals; gas-metal equilibria; internal friction; electron microscopy; ion irradiation damage and implantation; phase stability and precipitate growth and dissolution during irradiation. *Mailing Add:* Inst Mat Sci U-136 Univ Conn Storrs CT 06268

POTTER, DONALD N, b Utica, NY, June 4, 23; m 45; c 6. GEOLOGY. *Educ:* Williams Col, AB, 47; Brown Univ, MS, 49; Calif Inst Technol, PhD, 54. *Prof Exp:* Asst, Brown Univ, 47-49; asst, Calif Inst Technol, 49-50 & 52-54; geologist, US Geol Surv, 50-52; from asst prof to assoc prof, 54-67, PROF GEOL, HAMILTON COL, 67- *Concurrent Pos:* Vis scientist, Los Alamos Nat Lab, 81-82. *Res:* High alumina metamorphic rocks; stratigraphy and structure of central Taconic region; seismic refraction studies of drumlin cores; photo interpretation of Martian surface; flow direction indicators in ash flows. *Mailing Add:* Dept of Geol Hamilton Col Clinton NY 13323

POTTER, DOUGLAS MARION, b Mineola, NY, Feb 22, 45. ELEMENTARY PARTICLE PHYSICS, DETECTOR DEVELOPMENT. *Educ:* Mass Inst Technol, BS, 67, MS, 69, PhD(physics), 72. *Prof Exp:* Fel physics, Northeastern Univ, 72-77; ASST PROF, PHYSICS DEPT, RUTGERS UNIV, 77- *Mem:* Am Phys Soc. *Res:* Polarization phenomena in high energy photon physics; large momentum transfer elastic scattering. *Mailing Add:* Physics Dept Busch Campus Rutgers Univ Piscataway NJ 08854

POTTER, ELIZABETH VAUGHAN, b Detroit, Mich, Jan 27, 14; m 37; c 3. MEDICINE. *Educ:* Univ Chicago, BS, 35, MD, 39. *Prof Exp:* Intern, Swed Covenant Hosp, Chicago, 39-40; resident, Chicago Contagious Dis Hosp, 40-41; Am Heart Asn fel, 60-61, from instr to assoc, 61-68, asst prof, 68-73, ASSOC PROF MED, NORTHWESTERN UNIV, CHICAGO, 73- *Concurrent Pos:* Mem coun cardiovasc-renal dis & coun thrombosis, Am Heart Asn; mem expert adv panel bact dis, WHO. *Mem:* Int Soc Nephrology; Am Soc Nephrology; Infectious Dis Soc Am. *Res:* Immunological and coagulation associated aspects of renal disease, particularly of post streptococcal glomerulonephritis and acute rheumatic fever. *Mailing Add:* 303 E Chicago Ave Chicago IL 60611

POTTER, EMERSON LUCINE, animal nutrition, see previous edition

POTTER, FRANK ELWOOD, b Webster, Maine, Apr 18, 21; m 47; c 2. FOOD SCIENCE, DAIRY CHEMISTRY. *Educ:* Univ Maine, BS, 42; Univ Md, MS, 48; Pa State Univ, PhD(dairy sci), 55. *Prof Exp:* Asst dairy technol, Univ Md, 42-43, 46-48; res technologist, Bur Dairy Indust, USDA, 48-50; instr, Agr & Mech Col, Tex, 50-53; asst, Pa State Univ, 53-55; asst prof, 55-61, assoc prof dairy technol, 61-81, PROF FOOD SCI & NUTRIT DEPT, UNIV MASS, AMHERST, 81- *Mem:* Am Dairy Sci Asn. *Mailing Add:* Dept of Food Sci & Nutrit Univ of Mass Amherst MA 01002

POTTER, FRANK WALTER, JR, b Worcester, Mass, June 27, 42; m 68; c 2. PALEOBOTANY, PALEOECOLOGY. *Educ:* Pa State Univ, BS, 65, MS, 70; Ind Univ, PhD(paleobot), 75. *Prof Exp:* Instr biol, Pa State Univ, Beaver Campus, 66-67 & Ball State Univ, 74-75; res assoc paleobot, Ind Univ, 75-76; ASST PROF BIOL, FT HAYS STATE UNIV, 76- *Mem:* Bot Soc Am; Ecol Soc Am; Sigma Xi; Int Asn Angiosperm Paleobotanists; Am Asn Stratig Palynologists. *Res:* Evolution and phylogeny of early Angiosperms; paleoecology and terrestrial ecosystem evolution during the Cretaceous and early Tertiary. *Mailing Add:* Dept Biol Sci Ft Hays State Univ Hays KS 67601

POTTER, GERALD LEE, b Klamath Falls, Ore, Jan 24, 45. CLIMATOLOGY. *Educ:* Univ Calif, Los Angeles, BA, 67, MA, 70, PhD(geog), 75. *Prof Exp:* Teaching & res asst geog, Univ Calif, Los Angeles, 66-71; instr, Calif State Univ, Hayward, 71-72; GEOGR & CLIMATOLOGIST, LAWRENCE LIVERMORE LAB, UNIV CALIF, 72- *Mem:* Am Geophys Union. *Res:* Investigation of anthropogenic induced and natural climate variations using numerical modeling techniques; comparison of various models sensitivities. *Mailing Add:* Lawrence Livermore Lab PO Box 808 Livermore CA 94550

POTTER, GILBERT DAVID, b Calgary, Alta, May 23, 24; m 55; c 3. PHYSIOLOGY. *Educ:* Univ BC, MA, 50, PhD(physiol), 56. *Prof Exp:* From jr res physiologist to asst res physiologist, Univ Calif, Berkeley, 56-59; res pharmacologist & asst lab dir, Miles Labs, Inc, 59-63; res physiologist & group leader biomed div, Lawrence Livermore Lab, Univ Calif, 63-73; BIOLOGIST & BR CHIEF, ENVIRON MONITORING & SUPPORT LAB, 73- *Concurrent Pos:* Adj prof biol, Univ Nev, Las Vegas, 76- *Mem:* AAAS; Am Physiol Soc. *Res:* Endocrinology; trace element metabolism; radiobiology. *Mailing Add:* Environ Monitoring & Support Lab Environ Protection Agency Las Vegas NV 89114

POTTER, HENSON DAVID, b Albion, Ill, Apr 6, 34. NEUROANATOMY, NEUROPHYSIOLOGY. *Educ:* Univ Ill, Urbana, BS, 58, MS, 59; Univ Wis, PhD(physiol), 64. *Prof Exp:* Asst prof biol, Lawrence Univ, 63-65; Nat Inst Neurol Dis & Blindness fel anat & zool, Univ Wis, 65-68; asst prof anat, Wash Univ, 68-69; assoc prof anat, 69-74, ASSOC PROF NEURAL SCI, IND UNIV, BLOOMINGTON, 74- *Mem:* Soc Neurosci; Am Physiol Soc; Am Asn Anat. *Res:* Neurocytology; cytoplasmic and synaptic organization in neurons. *Mailing Add:* Dept of Neurol Sci Chem Bldg Ind Univ Bloomington IN 47401

POTTER, HOWARD A, b Ithaca, Mich, Apr 26, 11; m 34; c 4. ORGANIC CHEMISTRY. *Educ:* Alma Col, Mich, BS, 32; Harvard Univ, MA, 34, PhD(org chem), 36. *Prof Exp:* Res asst, Harvard Univ, 36-39, lab instr, 37-39; inspector, Bur Foods & Stand, Mich State Dept Agr, 40-41; instr chem, Swarthmore Col, 42-45; prof & head dept, 46-75, EMER PROF CHEM, ALMA COL, MICH, 75- *Mem:* Am Chem Soc. *Res:* Comparison of chemistry of certain sulfur compounds to analogous ketones; chemistry of large ring compounds; reactions of Grignard reagents with sulfoxides. *Mailing Add:* Dept of Chem Alma Col Alma MI 48801

POTTER, HOWARD SPENCER, b Philadelphia, Pa, Apr 22, 15; m 50; c 4. PLANT PATHOLOGY, ENTOMOLOGY. *Educ:* Pa State Univ, BS, 38; Cornell Univ, MS, 40; Univ Md, PhD(plant path, bot), 56. *Prof Exp:* Res biologist, State Fish Comn Pa, 39-41; economist fisheries, Food & Agr Orgn, UN, 45-46; economist agr, US Dept State, 46; forest ecologist, US Forest Serv, 46-52; asst plant pathologist, Univ Md, 52-54, instr plant path, 54-56; PROF PLANT PATH & EXTEN SPECIALIST, MICH STATE UNIV, 56- *Mem:* AAAS; Soc Am Foresters; Am Phytopath Soc; Bot Soc Am. *Res:* Soil inhabiting pathogens affecting economic plants; ecological factors determining their population and pathogenicity and cultural and chemical methods for their control. *Mailing Add:* Dept of Bot & Plant Path Mich State Univ East Lansing MI 48823

POTTER, JAMES GREGOR, b Manhattan, Kans, Apr 2, 07; m 41; c 2. PHYSICS. *Educ:* Princeton Univ, BS, 28; NY Univ, MS, 31; Yale Univ, PhD(physics), 39. *Prof Exp:* Jr physicist, US Naval Res Lab, 30-31; asst physics, Mass Inst Technol, 31-32; instr math, Armour Inst Technol, 35-36, physics, 36-39, asst prof, 39-40; prof physics & head dept & adminr gen eng, SDak Sch Mines & Technol, 40-44; mem tech staff, Bell Tel Labs, Inc, NY, 44-45; prof physics & head dept, Tex A&M Univ, 45-66, prof & asst dean student resources, 66-67; head dept, 67-74, PROF PHYSICS, FLA INST TECHNOL, 67- *Concurrent Pos:* Assoc prog dir advan sci educ, NSF, 59-60. *Honors & Awards:* Distinguished Achievement Award, Am Asn Physics Teachers, 57. *Mem:* AAAS; Am Phys Soc; Am Soc Eng Educ; Am Asn Physics Teachers. *Res:* Electronic work functions and emission; cathode sputtering; education in physics. *Mailing Add:* Dept of Physics & Space Sci Fla Inst of Technol Melbourne FL 32901

POTTER, JAMES MARTIN, b Peoria, Ill, Aug 15, 41; m 64; c 5. PHYSICS, ELECTRONICS. *Educ:* Univ Ill, Urbana, BS, 64, MS, 70, PhD(physics), 75. *Prof Exp:* Staff mem physics, 64-68 & 70-80, SECT LEADER ACCELERATOR STRUCTURE DEVELOP, LOS ALAMOS NAT LAB, 80- *Concurrent Pos:* Consult accelerator structures. *Mem:* Sigma Xi. *Res:* Accelerator structures; parity violation in p-nucleon scattering; radio frequency quadruple accelerator; analysis of periodic systems. *Mailing Add:* 2245 47th Los Alamos NM 87544

POTTER, JANE HUNTINGTON, b Chicago, Ill, Feb 21, 21; m 42; c 3. ZOOLOGY. *Educ:* Univ Chicago, SB, 42, MS, 48, PhD(zool), 49. *Prof Exp:* Asst prof zool, Am Univ Beirut, 49-52; from instr to asst prof, 62-70, ASSOC PROF ZOOL, UNIV MD, COLLEGE PARK, 70- *Res:* Factors affecting sexual isolation in sympatic species of Drosophila. *Mailing Add:* Dept of Zool Univ of Md College Park MD 20742

POTTER, JOHN CLARKSON, b Chicago, Ill, May 15, 21; m 46; c 2. RADIOCHEMISTRY, ANALYTICAL CHEMISTRY. *Educ:* Univ Wash, BS, 43; Duke Univ, PhD(chem), 50. *Prof Exp:* Asst prof chem, NC State Col, 50-51; fel, Mellon Inst, 51-52; res chemist, Koppers Co, Inc, 52-54; RES CHEMIST, SHELL DEVELOP CO DIV, SHELL OIL CO, 54- *Mem:* Am Chem Soc; Sigma Xi. *Res:* Chemical analysis; radioactive tracers; metabolic fate of pesticides in biological systems; mathematical models in biology. *Mailing Add:* 649 Geer Ct Modesto CA 95354

POTTER, JOHN F, b New York, NY, July 26, 25; m 56; c 3. SURGERY, ONCOLOGY. *Educ:* Georgetown Univ, MD, 49; Am Bd Surg, dipl, 58. *Prof Exp:* Resident surg, Hosp, Georgetown Univ, 50-56; sr investr, Nat Cancer Inst, 57-60; from asst prof to assoc prof, 59-72, PROF SURG, MED SCH & DIR VINCENT T LOMBARDI CANCER RES CTR, GEORGETOWN UNIV, 72-, HEAD DIV ONCOL SURG, 60- *Concurrent Pos:* Mem cancer clin invest res comt, Nat Cancer Inst, 69; consult, Clin Ctr, NIH & Vet Admin Hosp, Washington, DC; hon prof, Universidad Gayetawo Heredia Pervana, Lima, Peru. *Mem:* Fel Am Col Surgeons; AMA. *Res:* Cancer surgery and cancer biology. *Mailing Add:* Div of Oncol Surg Georgetown Univ Med Sch Washington DC 20007

POTTER, JOHN FRED, b Toronto, Ont. ATMOSPHERIC SCIENCE. *Educ:* McMaster Univ, BSc, 56; Univ Paris, PhD(theoret physics), 63. *Prof Exp:* NY Univ fel, Inst Space Studies, Goddard Space Flight Ctr, 64-65, Nat Acad Sci-Nat Res Coun res assoc, 65-68; STAFF ENGR, LOCKHEED ENERGY MGT & SERV CO, 68- *Res:* Atmospheric effects in remote sensing of the environment; planetary photometry and spectroscopy; radiative transfer; automatic pattern recognition and machine classification of remotely sensed data. *Mailing Add:* PO Box 15027 Lockheed Energy Mgt & Serv Co Las Vegas NV 89114

POTTER, JOHN LEITH, b Metz, Mo, Feb 5, 23; m 57; c 3. AEROSPACE ENGINEERING, MECHANICAL ENGINEERING. *Educ:* Univ Ala, BS, 44, MS, 49; Vanderbilt Univ, PhD(mech eng), 74, MS, 76. *Prof Exp:* Engr, Curtis-Wright Corp, 44-47; from instr to asst prof aeronaut eng, Univ Ala, 47-51; res engr, Naval Ord Lab, 51-52; chief flight & aerodynamics lab, Ord Missile Labs, 52-56; mgr res & aerophysics brs, ARO, Inc, 56-71, chief aerospace div, 71-73, dep dir, von Karman Facil, 73-77, dep tech dir, 77-81; SR STAFF SCIENTIST, SVERDRUP TECHNOL, INC, 81- *Concurrent Pos:* Aerodynamicist, NAm Aviation, Inc, 49; prof, Univ Tenn, 56-; consult, US Air Force, 63; hon adj prof, Univ Ala, 65-; USSR Acad lectr, Russia, 67; assoc ed, Am Inst Aeronaut & Astronaut J, 70-73, mem publ comt, 70-, assoc ed, Am Inst Aeronaut & Astronaut Progress Series, 81-; adj prof, Vanderbilt Univ, 81-; consult to indust. *Honors & Awards:* Gen H H Arnold Award, Am Inst Aeronaut & Astronaut, 64. *Mem:* Sigma Xi; Am Inst Aeronaut & Astronaut; fel Am Asn Eng Mgt; Nat Asn Mgt. *Res:* Aerodynamics and gas dynamics; stressing boundary layers; rarefied flows; development of experimental facilities and simulation; engineering management. *Mailing Add:* Sverdrup Technol Inc AEDC Group Arnold Air Force Station TN 37398

POTTER, JOHN WOODALL, nematology, plant pathology, see previous edition

POTTER, LAWRENCE MERLE, b Sabattus, Maine, Dec 28, 24; m 50; c 4. POULTRY NUTRITION. *Educ:* Univ Maine, BS, 51; Univ NH, MS, 53; Univ Conn, PhD(animal nutrit), 58. *Prof Exp:* Asst, Univ NH, 51-53; res asst, Univ Conn, 53-55, asst instr, 55-58, res assoc, 58-60; assoc prof, 60-72, PROF POULTRY SCI, VA POLYTECH INST & STATE UNIV, 72- *Honors & Awards:* Res award, Nat Turkey Fedn, 80. *Mem:* Poultry Sci Asn; Animal Nutrit Res Coun. *Res:* Determination of metabolizable energy values of feed ingredients for poultry; statistical analysis of experimental data; turkey nutrition. *Mailing Add:* Dept of Poultry Sci Va Polytech Inst & State Univ Blacksburg VA 24061

POTTER, LINCOLN TRUSLOW, b Chicago, Ill, Mar 26, 33; m 56; c 4. NEUROBIOLOGY. *Educ:* Swarthmore Col, AB, 55; Yale Univ, MD, 59. *Prof Exp:* From intern to resident med, Peter Bent Brigham Hosp, Boston, 59-61; res assoc, NIMH, 61-63; from instr to asst prof pharmacol, Harvard Med Sch, 63-70; sr res assoc biophys, Univ Col, Univ London, 66-72; PROF PHARMACOL, PHYSIOL & BIOPHYS, MED SCH, UNIV MIAMI, 72- *Concurrent Pos:* USPHS spec fel, Harvard Med Sch, 63-66, Markle Found scholar, 65-70. *Mem:* Am Soc Pharmacol & Exp Therapeut; Brit Physiol Soc; Neurosci Soc. *Res:* Neurobiology of synaptic transmission; receptor mechanisms. *Mailing Add:* Dept Pharmacol Univ Miami Med Sch Miami FL 33101

POTTER, LOREN DAVID, b Fargo, NDak, June 23, 18; m 41; c 4. BOTANY. *Educ:* NDak Col, BS, 40; Oberlin Col, MA, 46; Univ Minn, PhD(bot), 48. *Prof Exp:* Field asst, NDak State Game & Fish Dept, 41-42; mem staff fiber & textile res, Goodyear Tire & Rubber Co, Ohio, 43-45; from asst prof to assoc prof bot, NDak Agr Col, 48-58; chmn dept biol, 58-72, PROF BIOL, UNIV NMEX, 58- *Mem:* AAAS; Ecol Soc Am; Soc Range Mgt. *Res:* Postglacial forest vegetation by pollen analysis; life history of grasses; thermosetting resin for strengthening cord; ecological plant geography. *Mailing Add:* Dept of Biol Univ of NMex Albuquerque NM 87131

POTTER, LOUISE FRANCES, b Ware, Mass, Oct 10, 20. MICROBIOLOGY. *Educ:* Univ Mass, BS, 42; Smith Col, MA, 44; Univ Wis, PhD(bact, biochem), 47. *Prof Exp:* Instr bact, Univ Wis, 46-47 & Smith Col, 47-49; from instr to assoc prof plant sci, Vassar Col, 49-60; prof biol, Windham Col, 62-63; assoc prof, 63-65, PROF BIOL, ELMIRA COL, 65- *Concurrent Pos:* Sigma Xi-Sci Res Soc Am res grant, 51; Ford Found fel, Hopkins Marine Sta, Stanford Univ, 53-54; grants, NSF, 54-56 & 59-62, sci fac fel, 59-60, proj dir basic limnol, Col Ctr Finger Lakes, 67-68 & ecol sch coop prog, 69-71; Schering Corp consult grant, 65. *Mem:* Fel AAAS; Am Pub Health Asn; Am Soc Microbiol; Am Chem Soc; Am Inst Biol Sci. *Res:* Fermentation; aquatic and soil microbiology; microbial ecology; Micromonospora. *Mailing Add:* Div of Natural Sci Elmira Col Elmira NY 14901

POTTER, MEREDITH WOODS, b Chicago, Ill, Aug 10, 34; div; c 4. MATHEMATICS, COMPUTER SCIENCE. *Educ:* San Jose State Col, BA, 55; Western Mich Univ, MA, 67, SpA, 68. *Prof Exp:* Vis instr, Kalamazoo Col, 68-69; from asst prof to assoc prof math, 69-78, prof, 78-80, PROF & CHMN, DEPT COMPUT SCI, ROCKFORD COL, 80- *Concurrent Pos:* Mary Ashby Cheek grants, Rockford Col, 70-71 & 76-78; Rockford Med Clin res grant, 75-77; consult, Gifted Math Prog & Educ Res, Rockford Pub Sch Dist 205, 69-76 & fire ecol & fire mgt, modelling, Northern Forest Res Ctr, Can Forest Serv, 78-; assoc ed, Ill Math Teacher, 74-77; systs analyst, Gradient Modeling, Inc, 76-78, vpres, 78-80, actg pres, 80-; mem invited fac, USDA Forest Serv, Nat Interagency Training Ctr, Ariz, 78; vpres, Alberta Ecosystem Consults, 80- *Mem:* Am Math Soc; Math Asn Am; Nat Coun Teachers Math; Sigma Xi. *Res:* Mathematical simulation and computer modelling of synecological and land management problems; carcinoma of the breast; achievement of disadvantaged and gifted children. *Mailing Add:* Dept Math 5050 E State St Rockford IL 61101

POTTER, MERLE C(LARENCE), b Grand Rapids, Mich, Oct 13, 36; m 57; c 2. MECHANICAL ENGINEERING, FLUID MECHANICS. *Educ:* Mich Tech, BS, 58, MS, 61; Univ Mich, MS, 64, PhD(eng mech), 65. *Prof Exp:* Instr eng mech, Mich Tech, 58-61 & Univ Mich, 63-65; from asst prof to assoc prof, 65-74, PROF MECH ENG, MICH STATE UNIV, 74- *Mem:* Am Soc Mech Engrs; Am Soc Eng Educ. *Res:* Linear and nonlinear stability of fluid flow; experimental transition studies in channel flow. *Mailing Add:* Dept of Mech Eng Mich State Univ East Lansing MI 48824

POTTER, NEIL H, b Lancaster, Pa, Oct 14, 38; m 62; c 4. ORGANIC CHEMISTRY. *Educ:* Franklin & Marshall Col, BS, 60; Middlebury Col, MS, 62; Pa State Univ, PhD, 66. *Prof Exp:* From asst prof to assoc prof, 66-81, PROF CHEM, SUSQUEHANNA UNIV, 81- *Concurrent Pos:* Consult, Pa Dept Hwy, 67- *Mem:* Am Chem Soc. *Res:* Oxidation of organic compounds by bromine and chromic acid; effect of paraffin wax on bituminous concrete. *Mailing Add:* Dept of Chem Susquehanna Univ Selinsgrove PA 17870

POTTER, NOEL, JR, b Burlington, Vt, Jan 24, 40. GEOLOGY. *Educ:* Franklin & Marshall Col, AB, 61; Darmouth Col, MA, 63; Univ Minn, Minneapolis, PhD(geol), 69. *Prof Exp:* From teaching asst to teaching assoc geol, Univ Minn, 63-68, instr, 68-69; asst prof, 69-73, chmn, 77-81, ASSOC PROF GEOL, DICKINSON COL, 73- *Concurrent Pos:* Instr, Col St Thomas, 67-68. *Mem:* AAAS; Geol Soc Am; Glaciol Soc; Am Geophys Union; Am Quaternary Asn. *Res:* Geomorphology; glacial geology; structural geology; rock glaciers; effects of snow avalanches; periglacial features. *Mailing Add:* Dept Geol Dickinson Col Carlisle PA 17013

POTTER, NOEL MARSHALL, b Machias, Maine, May 11, 45; m 69; c 2. CLASSICAL INORGANIC ANALYSIS, LIQUID CHROMATOGRAPHY. *Educ:* Worcester Polytech Inst, BS, 67; Cornell Univ, MS, 69, PhD(anal chem), 71. *Prof Exp:* STAFF RES SCIENTIST, GEN MOTORS RES LABS, 71- *Mem:* Am Chem Soc. *Res:* Classical inorganic analytical chemistry, including geological materials, catalyst materials and noble metals; liquid chromatography; atomic absorption spectroscopy; optical emission. *Mailing Add:* 7007 Grenadier Ct Utica MI 48087

POTTER, NORMAN D, b Portland, Ore, Sept 22, 28; m 57; c 2. PHYSICAL CHEMISTRY, POLYMER CHEMISTRY. *Educ:* Willamette Univ, BS, 52; Ore State Univ, MS, 55, PhD(phys chem), 62. *Prof Exp:* Res engr, Atomics Int Div, NAm Aviation, Inc, 54-57; teaching fel, Ore State Univ, 57-60; res asst, Ore State Univ, 60-62; RES SCIENTIST, AERONUTRONIC DIV, FORD AEROSPACE & COMMUN CORP, NEWPORT BEACH, 62- *Mem:* AAAS; Sigma Xi; Am Chem Soc. *Res:* Determination of thermodynamic properties using recoil and mass spectrometric techniques; physical chemistry of membrane processes; air pollution monitoring instrumentation research; ceramics development. *Mailing Add:* Ford Aerospace Commun Corp Aeonutronic Div Newport Beach CA 92663

POTTER, NORMAN N, b New York, NY, Oct 10, 26; m 50; c 2. FOOD SCIENCE, NUTRITION. *Educ:* Cornell Univ, BS, 50; Iowa State Col, MS, 51, PhD(dairy bact), 53. *Prof Exp:* Asst bact viruses, Iowa State Col, 50-53; asst head cereal chem div, Fleischmann Labs, Stand Brands, Inc, 53-60; mgr food tech, Am Mach & Foundry Co, 60-66; assoc prof food sci, 66-73, PROF FOOD SCI, CORNELL UNIV, 73- *Concurrent Pos:* Consult to food indust, 66- & US Food & Drug Admin, 81-; chmn, Gordon Res Conf Food & Nutrit, 80. *Mem:* Inst Food Technol; Int Asn Milk Food & Environ Sanitarians; AAAS; Am Asn Cereal Chem. *Res:* Food processing; nutrition, food safety; food microbiology. *Mailing Add:* Dept of Food Sci Stocking Hall Cornell Univ Ithaca NY 14853

POTTER, PAUL EDWIN, b Springfield, Ohio, Aug 30, 25. GEOLOGY. *Educ:* Univ Chicago, PhB, 49, MS, 50, PhD(geol), 52; Univ Ill, MS, 59. *Prof Exp:* From asst geologist to assoc geologist, Ill State Geol Surv, 52-61; Guggenheim fel, Johns Hopkins Univ, 61-62; from assoc prof to prof geol, Ind Univ, Bloomington, 63-71; MEM FAC GEOL, UNIV CINCINNATI, 71- *Concurrent Pos:* NSF sr fel, Univ Ill, 57-58. *Res:* Sedimentary petrology; sedimentation; directional structures; applications of statistics to geological problems; mega sedimentology, big rivers and geological history; South America. *Mailing Add:* Dept of Geol Univ of Cincinnati Cincinnati OH 45221

POTTER, RALPH MILES, b Mt Vernon, Wash, Aug 21, 27; m 57; c 1. PHYSICAL CHEMISTRY. *Educ:* State Col Wash, BS, 48; Purdue Univ, MS, 50, PhD(phys chem), 53. *Prof Exp:* RES PHYS CHEMIST, LAMP DIV, GEN ELEC CO, 52- *Mem:* Am Chem Soc. *Res:* Physical chemistry of phosphor preparation; nature of luminescent centers in sulfide type phosphors; optical and electrical properties of wide band gap semiconductors as related to injection electroluminescence; tin oxide thin films; chemical photoflash lamps. *Mailing Add:* Gen Elec Co Lamp Div 1310 Nela Park Cleveland OH 44112

POTTER, RICHARD C(ARTER), b Ekalaka, Mont, May 19, 19; m 48; c 6. MECHANICAL ENGINEERING. *Educ:* Purdue Univ, BS, 40, MS, 47, PhD(eng), 50. *Prof Exp:* Test engr, Crane Co, Ill, 40-41, asst res engr, 46; instr mech eng, Purdue Univ, 47-48; prof mech & assoc dean, Kansas State Univ, 49-59; mem res staff, Gen Atomic Div, Gen Dynamics Corp, 59-60; head tech staff develop, Ramo Wooldridge Div, Thompson Ramo Wooldridge, Inc, 60, mgr prof placement & develop, Space Tech Labs, Inc, 60-63; prof & dir res, Inst Indust Res, Univ Louisville, 63-65; pres, Northrop Inst Technol, 66-67; dir educ serv, 67-69, PROF MECH ENG & DEAN, SCH ENG, CALIF STATE UNIV, 69- *Mem:* Am Soc Mech Engrs; Am Soc Eng Educ. *Res:* Heat transfer; fluid flow; thermodynamics; power. *Mailing Add:* Sch Eng Calif State Univ 1250 Bellflower Blvd Long Beach CA 90840

POTTER, RICHARD LYLE, b Regina, Sask, June 5, 26; nat US; m 65. BIOCHEMISTRY. *Educ:* Reed Col, BA, 50; Wash State Univ, MS, 52; Univ Rochester, PhD(biochem), 57. *Prof Exp:* Instr gen biol, State Univ NY Teachers Col, Geneseo, 56-58; res fel neurochem, Biol Div, Calif Inst Technol, 58-61; from asst prof to assoc prof, 61-78, PROF BIOL, CALIF STATE UNIV, NORTHRIDGE, 78- *Mem:* Sigma Xi; Am Soc Zoologists. *Res:* Amino acids, respiration and cell counts of bullfrog brain regions. *Mailing Add:* Dept of Biol Calif State Univ Northridge CA 91330

POTTER, RICHARD R(ALPH), b Lawrence, Kans, May 9, 26; m 50; c 1. ELECTRONIC ENGINEERING. *Educ:* Univ Kans, MS, 50. *Prof Exp:* Jr electronic engr, Proving Ground, US Dept Navy, 50-51, electronic engr, 52, electronic scientist, 53-54, supvry gen engr, 55, head ballistic measurement div, 56-58, head eval br, Electromagnetic Hazards Div, 59-64, asst dir weapons develop & eval lab, Naval Weapons Lab, 64-68, asst head advan systs dept, 68-74; RETIRED. *Concurrent Pos:* Instr exten serv, Univ Va, 53; assoc, George Washington Univ, 59. *Mem:* Inst Elec & Electronics Engrs. *Res:* Hazards of electromagnetic radiation to ordnance; range instrumentation for ordnance tests; electronic countermeasures. *Mailing Add:* Rte 2 Box 371-J King George VA 22485

POTTER, ROBERT JOSEPH, b New York, NY, Oct 29, 32; m 56; c 3. OPTICS. *Educ:* Lafayette Col, BS, 54; Univ Rochester, MA, 57, PhD(optics), 60. *Prof Exp:* Asst, Univ Rochester, 54-60; optical sci & pattern recognition mgr, T J Watson Res Ctr, Int Bus Mach Corp, 60-65; info tech mgr, Res Labs, Xerox Corp, 65-66, vpres & mgr, Advan Eng Dept, 67-68, Develop Eng, 68-69, vpres & gen mgr, New Ventures Div, 69-70, Spec Prod & Systs Div, Calif, 70-71, vpres, Info Technol Group, NY, 71-75, pres, Off Systs Div, 75-78; SR VPRES & CHIEF TECH OFFICER, INT HARVESTER CO, 78- *Concurrent Pos:* Mem, US Nat Comn on Optics, 65-68; mem, Nat Acad Sci-Int Comn on Optics, Paris, 66; mem bd dirs, Xerox Ctr Health Care Res, Baylor Sch Med; mem comt telecommun, Nat Acad Eng; mem, President's Task Force, 67; mem bd dirs, Inst Technol, Southern Methodist Univ, 73-, Molex, Inc, 81, First City Bank of Dallas, 80; trustee, Ill Inst Technol, 78. *Honors & Awards:* Outstanding Tech Contrib Award, IBM Corp, 64; Soc Mfg Engrs Distinguished Engrs Award, 81. *Mem:* Fel Optical Soc Am; Am Phys Soc. *Res:* Information processing, optical and electronic image and character processing; technologies for image reproduction, particularly xerography, electrography, and photoelectrophoresis; optical pattern recognition; fiber optics; radiometry; optical instrumentation and scanning techniques; word processing; communications; technologies for transportation; agricultural equipment. *Mailing Add:* Int Harvester Co 401 N Michigan Ave Chicago IL 60611

POTTER, ROSARIO H YAP, b Manila, Philippines, Aug 21, 28; m 64; c 1. GENETICS, DENTAL RESEARCH. *Educ:* Univ of the East, Manila, DMD, 52; Univ Ore, MSD, 63; Ind Univ, MS, 67. *Prof Exp:* Clin fel, Eastman Dent Dispensary, NY, 59-60, res asst dent, 60-61; USPHS training grant med genetics, Sch Med, 63-66, from asst prof to assoc prof, 67-80, PROF DENT RES, SCH DENT, IND UNIV, INDIANAPOLIS, 80- *Concurrent Pos:* USPHS res grant awards, 80- *Honors & Awards:* First Place Award, Philippine Nat Dent Bd Exam, 55. *Mem:* AAAS; Am Soc Human Genetics; Int Soc Cranio-Facial Biol; Int Asn Dent Res. *Res:* Biometrical genetics of dento-facial variables; experimental designs in dental research. *Mailing Add:* Ind Univ Sch of Dent 1121 W Michigan St Indianapolis IN 46202

POTTER, THOMAS FRANKLIN, b New York, NY, July 1, 41. MATHEMATICS. *Educ:* Yale Univ, BA, 62; Univ Calif, Berkeley, MA, 64, PhD(math), 70. *Prof Exp:* Asst prof, 68-77, ASSOC PROF MATH, FISK UNIV, 77- *Mem:* Am Math Soc. *Res:* Algebraic groups; group representations; functional analysis. *Mailing Add:* Dept of Math Fisk Univ Nashville TN 37203

POTTER, VAN RENSSELAER, b Day Co, SDak, Aug 27, 11; m 35; c 3. BIOCHEMISTRY. *Educ:* SDak State Col, BS, 33; Univ Wis, MS, 36, PhD(biochem), 38. *Hon Degrees:* ScD, SDak State Col, 59. *Prof Exp:* Asst chem, Exp Sta, SDak State Col, 30-35; asst biochem, Univ Wis, 36-38; Nat Res Coun fel, Stockholm, Sweden, 38-39; Rockefeller traveling fel, Sheffield, Eng & Chicago, 39-40; Bowman res fel cancer res, 40-42, from asst prof to assoc prof, 42-47, prof, 47-80, HILLDALE PROF ONCOL, UNIV WIS-MADISON, 80- *Concurrent Pos:* Vis prof, Lima, 52-53; mem comt environ physiol, Nat Res Coun, 65-67. *Honors & Awards:* Paul-Lewis Award, Am Chem Soc, 47; Award, Bertner Found, 61; Clowes Medal, Am Asn Cancer Res, 64. *Mem:* Nat Acad Sci; Am Soc Biol Chem; Am Asn Cancer Res (pres, 74-75); Am Soc Cell Biol (pres, 64-65); Am Acad Arts & Sci. *Res:* Enzymes of normal and cancer tissue; control mechanisms in intermediary metabolism. *Mailing Add:* McArdle Lab Univ of Wis Madison WI 53706

POTTHOFF, RICHARD FREDERICK, b Champaign, Ill, Mar 17, 32; m 63; c 2. MATHEMATICAL STATISTICS, OPERATIONS RESEARCH. *Educ:* Swarthmore Col, BA, 53; Univ NC, Chapel Hill, PhD(math statist), 59. *Prof Exp:* Mem staff, Blue Bell, Inc, 58-61; res assoc statist, Univ NC, Chapel Hill, 61-65; OPERS RES ANALYST, BURLINGTON INDUSTS, INC, 65- *Mem:* Am Statist Asn; Inst Math Statist; Biomet Soc. *Res:* Various uses of theoretical and applied statistics in business, economics, and other areas; operations research, including especially forecasting, inventory control, and production planning. *Mailing Add:* 803 Winview Dr Greensboro NC 27410

POTTLE, CHRISTOPHER, b New Haven, Conn, Feb 14, 32; m 61; c 3. ELECTRICAL ENGINEERING, COMPUTER SCIENCE. *Educ:* Yale Univ, BE, 53; Univ Ill, MS, 58, PhD(elec eng), 62. *Prof Exp:* Asst proj engr, Sperry Gyroscope Co, 53-54; instr elec eng, Univ Ill, 59-60, res assoc, 60-62, asst prof, 62; asst prof elec eng & comput sci, 62-66, assoc prof, 66-80, PROF ELEC ENG, CORNELL UNIV, 66- *Concurrent Pos:* Fulbright lectr, Univ Erlangen, 66-67; consult math sci dept, IBM Corp, 70-71; resident prog prof, EUSED, Gen Elec Co, 77-78. *Mem:* Asn Comput Mach; Inst Elec & Electronics Engrs. *Res:* Application of digital computers to electrical system theory and design. *Mailing Add:* 410 Phillips Hall Sch Elec Eng Cornell Univ Ithaca NY 14853

POTTS, ALBERT MINTZ, b Baltimore, Md, June 8, 14; m 38; c 3. BIOCHEMISTRY. *Educ:* Johns Hopkins Univ, AB, 34; Univ Chicago, PhD(biochem), 38; Western Reserve Univ, MD, 48. *Prof Exp:* Asst, Univ Chicago, 38-42, res assoc & instr biochem, Nat Defense Res Coun Proj, 42-44, biochemist, Metall Lab, 44-45; sr instr biochem in ophthal, Sch Med, Western Reserve Univ, 48-50, from asst prof to assoc prof ophthal res, 51-59; prof ophthal & dir res ophthal, Sch Med, Univ Chicago, 59-75; PROF OPHTHAL & CHMN DEPT, UNIV LOUISVILLE, 75- *Mem:* AAAS; Am Chem Soc; Asn Res Vision & Ophthal. *Res:* Ocular physiology and pharmacology; chromatographic adsorption; chemical endocrinology; poisons and cellular metabolism; radiobiology; chemical ophthalmology. *Mailing Add:* Dept of Ophthal Univ of Louisville Louisville KY 40202

POTTS, BYRON C, b Springfield, Ohio, Oct 2, 30; m 76; c 4. ELECTRICAL ENGINEERING. *Educ:* Ohio State Univ, BEE & MS, 59, PhD(elec eng), 63. *Prof Exp:* Tech asst, Ohio State Univ, 55-59, res assoc, Antenna Lab, 59-63, assoc supvr lab & asst prof elec eng, 63-64; mem tech staff, Rand Corp, Santa Monica, 64-72; mem tech staff, Marina Del Rey, Calif, 72-76 & Munich, WGer, 76-79, MEM TECH STAFF, R&D ASSOCS, MARINA DEL REY, 79- *Concurrent Pos:* Instr, Eng Exten, Univ Calif, Los Angeles, 65-66. *Mem:* Inst Elec & Electronics Engrs; Prof Soc Antenna & Propagation; Prof Soc Aerospace Electronics. *Res:* Military electronics including such specialties as command and control, communications, electronic warfare, radar and effects of nuclear bursts. *Mailing Add:* R&D Assocs PO Box 9695 Marina Del Rey CA 90291

POTTS, DONALD HARRY, b Seattle, Wash, Dec 15, 21; m 62; c 4. MATHEMATICS. *Educ:* Calif Inst Technol, BS, 43, PhD(math), 47. *Prof Exp:* Asst math, Calif Inst Technol, 43-46; from instr to asst prof, Northwestern Univ, 46-51; mathematician, US Navy Electronics Lab, 51-58; assoc prof math, Long Beach State Col, 58-61; lectr, Univ Calif, Santa Barbara, 61-64; res assoc, Univ Calif, Berkeley, 64-65; PROF MATH, CALIF STATE UNIV, NORTHRIDGE, 65- *Concurrent Pos:* NSF sci fac fel, 64-65. *Mem:* AAAS; Am Math Soc; Math Asn Am; Asn Symbolic Logic. *Res:* Diophantine equations; real variables; wave propagation; mathematical logic; foundations of mathematics; universal algebra. *Mailing Add:* Dept of Math Calif State Univ Northridge CA 91330

POTTS, GORDON OLIVER, b Wheeling, WVa, Oct 10, 24; m 43; c 2. ENDOCRINOLOGY. *Educ:* Bethany Col, WVa, BS, 48; WVa Univ, MS, 49; Univ Cincinnati, PhD(zool), 52. *Prof Exp:* Asst zool, Univ Cincinnati, 48-51; res chemist, Hilton Davis Chem Co, Sterling Drug, Inc, 51-55, sect head endocrinol, Sterling-Winthrop Res Inst, 55-73, dir endocrinol, 73-76, VPRES RES, STERLING-WINTHROP RES INST, 76- *Mem:* AAAS; Endocrine Soc; NY Acad Sci; Soc Study Reproduction; Sigma Xi. *Res:* Pituitary, gonodal and adrenal hormones; physiology of reproduction, anti-hormones; hormonal control of metabolism. *Mailing Add:* Box 602 Main St Greentrees North Chatham NY 12132

POTTS, HOWARD CALVIN, b Stillwater, Okla, Oct 18, 28; m 50; c 3. PLANT BREEDING. *Educ:* Okla State Univ, BS, 50; Miss State Univ, MS, 56; Tex A&M Univ, PhD(plant breeding), 66. *Prof Exp:* Technician, Tex A&M Univ, 52-54; com prod mgr, Harpool Seed's Inc, 55-59; assoc prof seed technol, Va Polytech Inst & State Univ, 59-63; assoc prof, Miss State Univ, 66-68, chief party, Miss State Univ-AID contract, Rio de Janeiro, 68-70, assoc prof & assoc agronomist, Seed Technol Lab, 70-73, PROF AGRON, MISS STATE UNIV, 73- Mem; Am Soc Agron; Am Genetic Asn. Res; Genetics, breeding and seed production of native and introduced grasses. *Mailing Add:* Dept of Agron Miss State Univ Mississippi State MS 39762

POTTS, JAMES EDWARD, b Alexandria, La, Oct 28, 18; m 44; c 2. POLYMER CHEMISTRY, RADIATION CHEMISTRY. *Educ:* La Col, BS, 39; La State Univ, MS, 41, PhD(phys chem), 48. *Prof Exp:* Res chemist, Dept Chem Eng, Tenn Valley Authority, 42-46; res chemist, Bakelite Co Div, Union Carbide Corp, NJ, 47-52, group leader, 52-58 & Union Carbide Plastics Co, 58-70, sr res scientist chem & plastics, Res & Develop Lab, 70-80, SR RES SCIENTIST, COATINGS MATS DIV, UNION CARBIDE CORP, 80- *Mem:* Am Chem Soc; Sigma Xi; Soc Mach Engrs. *Res:* Radiation chemistry of polymers; photodegradable plastics; biodegradable plastics; polymer synthesis; biomedical and agricultural plastics; polymeric coatings for concrete. *Mailing Add:* Union Carbide Corp Res & Develop Lab River Rd Bound Brook NJ 08805

POTTS, JOHN CALVIN, b St Louis, Mo, June 23, 06; m 41. INORGANIC CHEMISTRY, PHYSICAL CHEMISTRY. *Educ:* Univ Calif, BS, 30, MS, 32, PhD(phys chem), 35. *Prof Exp:* With Food & Drug Admin, USDA, 36-37; res engr, Owens-Ill Glass Co, 37-42; phys chemist, Res Div, Int Minerals & Chem Corp, NMex, 42-44, Calif Res Corp, 45-48 & Los Alamos Sci Lab, 48-56; asst to Comnr W F Libby, Atomic Energy Comn, 56-59; asst to assoc dir, Lawrence Radiation Lab, Univ Calif, 59-61; mem staff, Aerojet-Gen Corp Div, Gen Tire & Rubber Co, 61-64; from asst prof to prof chem, Univ of the Pac, 65-75; RETIRED. *Mem:* AAAS; Am Chem Soc; Am Phys Soc. *Res:* Kinetics of gaseous reactions; glass melting process; phase equilibria in salt solutions; atomic energy; chemical education. *Mailing Add:* 324 Indio Dr Pismo Beach CA 93449

POTTS, JOHN EARL, b Lake City, Minn, Nov 25, 44; m 71. SOLID STATE PHYSICS. *Educ:* Marquette Univ, BS, 66; Northwestern Univ, Evanston, PhD(physics), 72. *Prof Exp:* Lectr physics, Ariz State Univ, 71-73; asst prof, 73-77, ASSOC PROF PHYSICS, UNIV MICH-DEARBORN, 77- *Concurrent Pos:* Vis scientist, Argonne Nat Lab, 80-81. *Mem:* Am Phys Soc; Am Asn Physics Teachers. *Res:* Experimental solid state physics; studies of elementary excitations in solids using laser light scattering techniques. *Mailing Add:* Dept Natural Sci Univ Mich Dearborn MI 48128

POTTS, JOHN THOMAS, JR, b Philadelphia, Pa, Jan 19, 32; m 61; c 3. ENDOCRINOLOGY, INTERNAL MEDICINE. *Educ:* La Salle Col, BA, 53; Univ Pa, MD, 57. *Prof Exp:* From intern to asst resident med, Mass Gen Hosp, Boston, 57-59; resident, Nat Heart Inst, 59-60, res fel med, 60-63, sr res staff, 63-66, head sect polypeptide hormones, 66-68; from asst prof to assoc prof med, 68-75, prof, 75-81, JACKSON PROF CLIN MED, HARVARD MED SCH, 81-; CHIEF GEN MED SERV, MASS GEN HOSP, 81- *Concurrent Pos:* Chief endocrine unit, Mass Gen Hosp, 68-81. *Honors & Awards:* Ernest Oppenheimer Award & Andre Lichwitz Prize, Endocrine Soc, 68. *Mem:* Am Soc Biol Chem; Endocrine Soc; Asn Am Physicians; Am Fedn Clin Res; Am Soc Clin Invest. *Res:* Polypeptide hormones; parathroid hormone; calcitonin; polypeptide structure and synthesis; hormone radioimmunoassay; vitamin D; biosynthesis, secretion and metabolism of hormones; mode of action of hormones; structure and function of genes for peptide hormones. *Mailing Add:* Mass Gen Hosp Endocrine Unit Fruit St Boston MA 02114

POTTS, KEVIN T, b Sydney, Australia, Oct 26, 28; m 59; c 4. ORGANIC CHEMISTRY. *Educ:* Univ Sydney, BSc, 50, MSc, 51; Oxford Univ, DPhil(org chem), 54, DSc(org chem), 73. *Prof Exp:* Demonstr chem, Univ Sydney, 50; res asst org chem, Oxford Univ, 51-54; scientist, Med Res Coun, Eng, 54-56; res asst org chem, Harvard Univ, 56-58; lectr, Univ Adelaide, 58-61; assoc prof chem, Univ Louisville, 61-65; assoc prof, 65-66, chmn dept, 73-80, PROF CHEM, RENSSELAER POLYTECH INST, 66- *Concurrent Pos:* Res grants, Nat Cancer Inst, Nat Heart & Lung Inst, NSF, US Army Med Res & Develop Command & Dept Energy. *Mem:* Am Chem Soc; Royal Soc Chem; Royal Inst Chem; Int Soc Heterocyclic Chem. *Res:* Synthetic organic chemistry. *Mailing Add:* Dept of Chem Cogswell Lab Rensselaer Polytech Inst Troy NY 12181

POTTS, LAWRENCE WALTER, b Buffalo, NY, Sept 22, 45; m 70; c 3. ELECTROANALYTICAL CHEMISTRY, TRACE METALS ANALYSIS. *Educ:* Oberlin Col, AB, 67; Univ Minn, PhD(chem), 72. *Prof Exp:* ASSOC PROF ANAL & INORG CHEM, GUSTAVUS ADOLPHUS COL, 72- *Concurrent Pos:* Vis assoc prof, Oberlin Col, 81-82. *Mem:* Am Chem Soc; Sigma Xi; AAAS. *Res:* Application of tetrazolium compounds as colorimetric oxidizing reagents; Synthesis and electrochemical properties of formazan-metal ion complexes. *Mailing Add:* Dept Chem Gustavus Adolphus Col St Peter MN 56082

POTTS, MARK JOHN, b St Louis, Mo. GEOPHYSICS, GEOCHEMISTRY. *Educ:* Wash Univ, BS, 66, PhD(geochem), 71. *Prof Exp:* Res radiochemist uranium purification, Mallinckrodt Chem Corp, 66; asst prof neutron activation anal, Geochem Inst, Univ Gottingen, 71-72; asst prof geochem, Dept Earth Sci, Wash Univ, 72-73, res assoc environ geochem, Ctr Biol of Natural Systs, 73; staff geoscientist uranium explor, Airborne Geophys Serv, 73-79, STAFF SCIENTIST, SEISMIC RES DEPT, TEX INSTRUMENTS INC, 79- *Mem:* Asn Explor Geochemists; Geol Soc Am. *Res:* Application of geochemistry, statistics and data processing techniques to the analysis of geophysical and geochemical data; hardware and software development for geophysical systems; software systems; technical management. *Mailing Add:* 13707 Spring Grove Dallas TX 75240

POTTS, MELVIN LESTER, b Lewellen, Nebr, July 19, 21; m 46; c 2. PHYSICAL INORGANIC CHEMISTRY. *Educ:* Kans State Col, Pittsburg, BSc, 54, MSc, 57; Colo State Univ, PhD(phys chem), 63. *Prof Exp:* Teacher high sch, Kans, 55-56; instr chem & physics, Chanute Jr Col, 56-57; instr physics, Kans State Col Pittsburg, 57-59; instr chem, Colo State Univ, 62-63; PROF CHEM, KANS STATE COL PITTSBURG, 63-, CHMN DEPT, 76- *Mem:* Am Chem Soc. *Res:* Surface chemistry. *Mailing Add:* Dept of Chem Pittsburg State UniV Pittsburg KS 66762

POTTS, RICHARD ALLEN, b Massillon, Ohio, Jan 2, 40; m 66; c 1. INORGANIC CHEMISTRY. *Educ:* Hiram Col, BA, 62; Northwestern Univ, PhD(inorg chem), 66. *Prof Exp:* AEC res assoc, Ames Lab, Iowa State Univ, 65-66; from asst prof to assoc prof chem, 66-73, PROF CHEM, UNIV MICH-DEARBORN, 73- *Mem:* Am Chem Soc; AAAS. *Res:* Compounds containing metal-to-metal bonds; coordination chemistry of mercury and gold. *Mailing Add:* Dept of Chem Univ of Mich Dearborn MI 48128

POTTS, RICHARD CARMECHIAL, b Headrick, Okla, Feb 7, 12; m 36; c 4. AGRONOMY. *Educ:* Okla Agr & Mech Col, BS, 35; Agr & Mech Col Tex, MS, 45; Univ Nebr, PhD, 50. *Prof Exp:* Instr agron, Okla Agr & Mech Col, 36; agronomist asst cotton invest, Agr Exp Sta, Univ Ga, 36; from asst prof to prof agron, 36-77, asst dean, 56-68, EMER PROF AGRON, TEX A&M UNIV, 77- ASSOC DEAN, 68- *Mem:* Am Soc Agron. *Res:* Pasture management and forage production; plant ecology; turf. *Mailing Add:* Dept of Agron Tex A&M Univ College Station TX 77843

POTTSEPP, L(EMBIT), b Tartu, Estonia, Feb 24, 29; nat US; m 66. AERONAUTICAL ENGINEERING. *Educ:* Univ Ill, BS, 53, MS, 54, PhD(aeronaut eng), 59. *Prof Exp:* Design specialist, Douglas Aircraft Co, 59-62, chief, Flight Mech Res Sect, McDonnell Douglas Astronaut Co, 62-65, chief, Appl Math Br, 65-76; PRES, ENG RES ASSOCS, 77- *Concurrent Pos:* Res fel appl math, Harvard Univ, 63-64. *Mem:* Am Inst Aeronaut & Astronaut. *Res:* Optimal control theory; fluid mechanics; analytical mechanics. *Mailing Add:* Eng Res Assocs 5642 Highgate Irvine CA 92715

POTVIN, ALFRED RAOUL, b Worcester, Mass, Feb 5, 42; m 65. BIOMEDICAL ENGINEERING. *Educ:* Worcester Polytech Inst, BS, 64; Stanford Univ, MS, 65; Univ Mich, MS(bioeng) & MS(psychol), 70, PhD(bioeng), 71. *Prof Exp:* Asst prof elec eng, Univ Tex, Arlington, 66-68; clin asst prof biophys, Univ Tex Southwestern Med Sch, Dallas, 67-70; assoc prof biomed eng, 71-76, PROF ELEC ENG & PROF BIOMED ENG & CHMN DEPT, UNIV TEX, ARLINGTON, 76- *Concurrent Pos:* NSF res grant, 72-74; consult, Merck, Sharpe & Dohme & NASA, 72-77; NASA life scientist, 74-75; consult, US Food & Drug Admin, 77-, Vet Admin Rehab Eng Res & Develop Serv, 79-; mem bd dir, Rocky Mountain Bioeng Symp Inc, 80- *Mem:* Soc Neurosci; AAAS; sr mem Inst Elec & Electronics Engrs; Am Soc Eng Educ; Biomed Eng Soc. *Res:* Neuro-bioengineering; application of clinical quantitative testing techniques for evaluating neuropharmacological drug trials. *Mailing Add:* Bioeng Prog Univ of Tex Arlington TX 76019

POTVIN, PIERRE, b Quebec, Que, Jan 5, 32; m 63. PHYSIOLOGY. *Educ:* Laval Univ, BA, 50, MD, 55; Univ Toronto, PhD(physiol), 62. *Prof Exp:* From asst prof to assoc prof, 60-69, univ exec coun, 76-80, PROF PHYSIOL, FAC MED, LAVAL UNIV, 69-, SECY, 75-, ASSOC DEAN, 77- *Mem:* Can Physiol Soc. *Res:* Hepatic physiology, especially hepatic circulation. *Mailing Add:* Dept of Physiol Laval Univ Fac of Med Quebec G1K 7P4 PQ G1K 7P4 Can

POTWOROWSKI, EDWARD FRANCIS, b Lyon, France, May 15, 40; Can citizen; m 69; c 2. IMMUNOLOGY. *Educ:* Loyola Col Montreal, BA, 62; Univ Montreal, MSc, 64; Monash Univ, Australia, PhD(immunol), 67. *Prof Exp:* Sr res asst, 67 70, head tissue antigens lab, Inst Microbiol & Hyg, 70-75; mem res staff, 75-80, PROF, IMMUNOL RES CTR, INST ARMAND-FRAPPIER, 80- *Concurrent Pos:* Med Res Coun Can & Nat Cancer Inst Can grants, 67-79; assoc, Dept Med, McGill Univ & McGill Cancer Ctr. *Mem:* Can Soc Immunol; Transplantation Soc; Sigma Xi; Brazilian Soc Immunol; Am Asn Immunologists. *Res:* Role of thymic microenvironmental fractions in T cell maturation and in leukemogenesis. *Mailing Add:* Immunol Res Ctr Inst Armand-Frappier Laval PQ H7N 4Z3 Can

POTZICK, JAMES EDWARD, b Cincinnati, Ohio, Apr 20, 41. PHYSICS, PHYSICAL INSTRUMENTATION. *Educ:* Xavier Univ, BS, 63, MS, 65. *Prof Exp:* Physicist, Eng Mech Sect, 66-70, PHYSICIST, FLUID ENG DIV, NAT BUR STANDARDS, 70- *Mem:* Am Phys Soc. *Res:* Mechanical and electronic instrumentation for fluid dynamics; acoustic flowmeter for dynamic measurement of mass flowrate of hot gases such as automotive exhaust. *Mailing Add:* FM 105 Nat Bur Standards Washington DC 20234

POU, JACK WENDELL, b Shereveport, La, Sept 30, 23. OTOLARYNGOLOGY. *Educ:* Tulane Univ, BS, 43, MD, 46; Am Bd Otolaryngol, dipl. *Prof Exp:* Ear, nose & throat consult, Schumpert Hosp, Physicians & Surgeons Hosp & Doctors Hosp, 51; CHIEF EAR, NOSE & THROAT SERV, CONFEDERATE MEM MED CTR, 62-; PROF OTOLARYNGOL & CHMN DEPT, SCH MED, LA STATE UNIV, SHREVEPORT, 70- *Concurrent Pos:* Chief med adv, Deaf Oral Dept, Caddo Parish, La, 52-; mem bd dirs, Caddo Found Except Children, 52-; ear, nose & throat consult, Barksdale AFB Hosp, 62 & Vet Admin Hosp, Shreveport, 68; mem adv admis bd, Speech Correction Ctr, 62-; chief otolaryngol, Confederate Mem Med Ctr, 63. *Mem:* AMA; Am Acad Ophthal & Otolaryngol; Am Laryngol, Rhinol & Otol Soc. *Res:* Feasibility of decompression of the facial nerve. *Mailing Add:* 2121 Line Ave Shreveport LA 71104

POU, WENDELL MORSE, b Laurel, Miss, Oct 11, 37. PHYSICS. *Educ:* Millsaps Col, BS, 59; Vanderbilt Univ, MS, 62, PhD(physics), 69. *Prof Exp:* Asst prof, 66-74, ASSOC PROF PHYSICS & ASTRON, ST CLOUD STATE COL, 74- *Mem:* Am Phys Soc; Am Asn Physics Teachers. *Res:* Radiation chemistry; electron spectroscopy. *Mailing Add:* Dept of Physics St Cloud State Col St Cloud MN 56301

POUCHER, JOHN SCOTT, b Evanston, Ill, Apr 10, 45; m 69. SYSTEMS DESIGN. *Educ:* Mass Inst Technol, BS, 67, PhD(physics), 71. *Prof Exp:* Instr, Mass Inst Technol, 71-74; asst prof physics, Vanderbilt Univ, 74-80; MEM TECH STAFF, BELL LABS, 81- *Concurrent Pos:* Vis fel, Lab Nuclear Studies, Cornell Univ, 77 & 78-; Univ Res Coun fel, Vanderbilt Univ, 79. *Mem:* Am Phys Soc; AAAS; Fedn Am Scientists; NY Acad Sci; Sigma Xi. *Res:* Experimental high energy physics; study of hadron structure and interactions, especially quark-parton models, using deep inelastic electron scattering and electron-positron collisions at high energies; operations systems planning and design. *Mailing Add:* 1 Pheasant Run Freehold NJ 07728

POUCHER, MELLOR PROCTOR, b London, Eng, Jan 14, 29; m 57; c 3. CIVIL ENGINEERING. *Educ:* Univ London, BSc, 49, MSc, 51. *Prof Exp:* Assoc prof eng sci, 54-67, PROF ENG SCI, UNIV WESTERN ONT, 67-, CHMN CIVIL ENG GROUP, 60- *Mem:* Fel Royal Soc; Can Soc Civil Engrs; Am Soc Civil Engrs; Am Concrete Inst. *Res:* Concrete technology; structural analysis and design. *Mailing Add:* Fac of Eng Sci Univ of Western Ont London ON N6G 1P4 Can

POUGH, FREDERICK HARVEY, b Brooklyn, NY, June 26, 06; m 38; c 2. MINERALOGY. *Educ:* Harvard Univ, SB, 28, PhD(mineral), 35; Wash Univ, MS, 32. *Prof Exp:* Instr crystallog, Harvard Univ, 32-34; asst cur mineral, Am Mus Natural Hist, 35-41, actg cur, 41-43, cur phys geol & mineral, 43-52; consult mineralogist, 53-64; dir, Santa Barbara Mus Natural Hist, 65-66; CONSULT MINERALOGIST, 66- *Concurrent Pos:* Am Fedn Mineral Socs scholar, 66. *Mem:* Fel Mineral Soc Am; fel Geol Soc Am; Mineral Soc Gt Brit & Ireland; Gemmol Asn Gt Brit. *Res:* Morphological crystallography; mineral paragenesis; gemmology; vulcanism; synthetic crystal growth. *Mailing Add:* PO Box 7004 Reno NV 89510

POUGH, FREDERICK HARVEY, b New York, NY, Jan 13, 42; m 67; c 1. ENVIRONMENTAL PHYSIOLOGY, HERPETOLOGY. *Educ:* Amherst Col, BA, 64; Univ Calif, Los Angeles, MA, 66, PhD(zool), 68. *Prof Exp:* Asst prof, 69-74, ASSOC PROF HERPET, NY STATE COL AGR & LIFE SCI, CORNELL UNIV, 75- *Concurrent Pos:* Cur, Herpet Collection, 69- *Mem:* Soc Study Evolution; Ecol Soc Am; Am Soc Ichthyologists & Herpetologists. *Res:* Biology of amphibians and reptiles. *Mailing Add:* Sect of Ecol & Systs Langmuir Lab Cornell Univ Ithaca NY 14853

POUGH, RICHARD HOOPER, b New York, NY, Apr 19, 04; m 37; c 2. ORNITHOLOGY, ECOLOGY. *Educ:* Mass Inst Technol, SB, 26. *Hon Degrees:* LLD, Haverford Col, 70. *Prof Exp:* Chem engr, Southern Acid & Sulphur Co, Tex, 27-28; mech engr, Fulton Iron Works, Mo, 29-31; retail exec, MacCallam, Inc, Pa, 31-36; res assoc & mem tech staff, Nat Audubon Soc, NY, 36-48; cur & chmn dept conserv & gen ecol, Am Mus Natural Hist, 48-56; PRES, NATURAL AREA COUN, INC, 57- *Concurrent Pos:* Gov & past pres, Nature Conserv; trustee, Nat Parks & Conserv Asn; Natural Sci Youth Found, Thorne Ecol Inst & Sapelo Island Res Found; dir, Scenic Hudson Preservation Conf; dir & past pres, Open Space Inst; adv coun, Trust for Pub Lands; dir & past pres, Defenders of Wildlife; chmn, Am The Beautiful Fund. *Mem:* Fel AAAS. *Res:* Conservation; plant-animal distribution; preservation of biotic communities in a natural condition. *Mailing Add:* 33 Highbrook Ave Pelham NY 10803

POULARIKAS, ALEXANDER D, b Desylla, Greece, Sept 1, 33; m 62. PLASMA PHYSICS, ELECTROMAGNETICS. *Educ:* Univ Ark, BS, 60, MS, 63, PhD(plasmas), 66. *Prof Exp:* From asst prof to assoc prof, 65-76, PROF ELEC ENG, UNIV RI, 76- *Concurrent Pos:* NASA Fac fel, 68 & 71; vis scientist, Mass Inst Technol, 71-72; consult, Naval Underwater Systs Ctr, Newport, RI, 71-73. *Mem:* Optical Soc Am; Soc Photo-Optical Instrumentation Engrs; Inst Elec & Electronics Engrs. *Res:* Nuclear reactions; magnetohydrodynamics power generation; plasma interactions with magnetic fields; plasma waves; optics. *Mailing Add:* Dept of Elec Eng Univ of RI Kingston RI 02881

POULIK, DAVE, b Brno, Czech, June 6, 23; US citizen; m 50; c 2. IMMUNOLOGY, IMMUNOCHEMISTRY. *Educ:* I Real Gym, Brno, BA, 42; Univ Toronto, MD, 60. *Prof Exp:* Res asst hyg & prev med, Univ Toronto, 51-56; res assoc, Child Res Ctr, Children's Hosp, Detroit, 56-60; guest investr, Rockefeller Inst, 60-61; asst dir res, Am Red Cross, Washington, DC, 61-62; from asst prof to prof pediat, 62-72, coordr med genetics, Sch Med, 65-68, PROF IMMUNOL MICROBIOL, WAYNE STATE UNIV, 72-, CHIEF IMMUNOL, WILLIAM BEAUMONT HOSP, 71- *Concurrent Pos:* Sr res assoc, Child Res Ctr, Children's Hosp, Detroit, 62-71; temp adv, Immunol Lab, WHO, Lausanne, 65-68, mem expert adv comt & mem WHO, 68-73; consult, Vet Admin Hosp, Dearborn, 69- *Mem:* Am Asn Immunol; Am Soc Human Genetics; NY Acad Sci; Soc Exp Biol & Med; Can Soc Immunol. *Res:* Structure and function of antibodies; deficiency diseases; serum and urinary proteins in health and disease; cancer cell immunology. *Mailing Add:* William Beaumont Hosp Royal Oak MI 48072

POULOS, DENNIS A, b Brooklyn, NY, Jan 18, 32. NEUROPHYSIOLOGY. *Educ:* Univ Wis, BS, 60, MS, 63, PhD(physiol), 66. *Prof Exp:* Nat Inst Neurol Dis & Blindness fel, Univ Wis, 66-67; from asst res prof to assoc res prof neurosurg & from asst prof to assoc prof physiol, 67-74, res prof neurosurg & prof physiol, 74-78, PROF ANAT, ALBANY MED COL, 78- *Mem:* AAAS; Am Physiol Soc; Int Brain Res Orgn; Sigma Xi; Soc Neurosci. *Res:* Sensory physiology, especially peripheral and central neural mechanisms of thermal sensation; physiological psychology. *Mailing Add:* Dept of Anat Div of Neurosurg Albany Med Col Albany NY 12208

POULOS, NICHOLAS A, b Maywood, Ill, Dec 20, 26. ORGANIC CHEMISTRY. *Educ:* Univ Ill, BS, 48; Northwestern Univ, PhD(org chem), 57. *Prof Exp:* Lab asst, Northwestern Univ, 49, 51, asst, 50, 52; mem staff, Olin Mathieson Chem Corp, 53-61; task engr, Wright-Patterson AFB, 62-64; proj supvr, Aeroproj, Inc, 64; assoc prof chem, Union Col, Ky, 65-70; INSTR ORG CHEM, TRITON COL, 70- *Res:* Chemistry. *Mailing Add:* 800 Sherman St Melrose Park IL 60160

POULOSE, PATHICKAL K, b Kerala, India, Jan 22, 39; m 71; c 2. MATERIALS SCIENCE ENGINEERING. *Educ:* Indian Inst Sci, BS, 65, MS, 67; Univ Conn, PhD(mat sci), 73. *Prof Exp:* Res assoc, 73-74, res scientist mat eng, 74-77, ASST RES PROF MAT SCI & ENG, GEORGE WASHINGTON UNIV, 77- *Mem:* Am Soc Metals. *Res:* Determination of fracture characteristics of brittle and semibrittle materials; fatigue crack growth and life studies in structural alloys; effect of microstructure on mechanical properties of titanium alloys. *Mailing Add:* 9415 Woodberry St Lanham MD 20706

POULSEN, BOYD JOSEPH, b Tetonia, Idaho, Aug 30, 33; m 53; c 2. PHARMACY. *Educ:* Idaho State Col, BS, 56; Univ Wis, PhD(pharm), 63. *Prof Exp:* Sr chemist, Pharmaceut Prod Develop, Ayerst Labs, Inc, 63-65; staff researcher, Syntex Corp, 65-69, assoc dir, 69-77, dir, Inst Pharmaceut Sci, 77-79, VPRES, SYNTEX RES DIV, 79- *Concurrent Pos:* Adj prof, Univ of Pac, 74- *Mem:* Fel Acad Pharmaceut Sci; Am Pharmaceut Asn; NY Acad Sci; AAAS; Sigma Xi. *Res:* Pharmaceutics; surface chemistry; percutaneous absorption of drugs. *Mailing Add:* Syntex Res Div 3401 Hillview Ave Palo Alto CA 94304

POULSEN, LAWRENCE LEROY, b Salmon, Idaho, Nov 27, 33; m 57; c 6. BIOCHEMISTRY, BIOCHEMICAL PHARMACOLOGY. *Educ:* Univ Calif, Riverside, BA, 65, PhD(biochem), 69. *Prof Exp:* Phys sci technician chem, USDA, 57-65; fel biol, Tex A&M Univ, 69-70; res assoc, Univ Tex, Austin, 71-72, USPHS fel, 72-74, res scientist assoc, Clayton Found Biochem Inst, 75-81. *Concurrent Pos:* Consult, Alcon Labs, Inc, 81. *Res:* Enzymology and control of drug metabolism; interactions of enzymes and environmental contaminants and carcinogens in the control of growth and metabolism; mechanism of plant and mammalian growth control. *Mailing Add:* Clayton Found Biochem Inst Univ of Tex Austin TX 78712

POULSEN, NIEL BOWMAN, b Lethbridge, Alta, Dec 20, 35; m 79; c 4. NUCLEAR ENGINEERING. *Educ:* Univ Alta, BSc, 60; Tex A&M Univ, MSc, 63, PhD(nuclear eng), 70. *Prof Exp:* Instr nuclear eng, Tex A&M Univ, 63-65, res asst reactor design, Nuclear Sci Ctr, 67-68, res engr, Variable Energy Cyclotron, 68-70; NUCLEAR ENGR, CHALK RIVER NUCLEAR LABS, ATOMIC ENERGY CAN LTD, 70- *Res:* Computer code development; thermal hydraulics; applied mathematics; heterogeneous reactor core physics. *Mailing Add:* Chalk River Nuclear Labs Atomic Energy Can Ltd Chalk River ON K1A 0S4 Can

POULSON, DONALD FREDERICK, b Idaho Falls, Idaho, Oct 5, 10; m 34; c 2. GENETICS. *Educ:* Calif Inst Technol, BS, 33, PhD(genetics), 36. *Hon Degrees:* MA, Yale Univ, 55. *Prof Exp:* Res asst embryol, Carnegie Inst, 36-37; from instr to assoc prof biol, 37-55, prof, 56-81, chmn dept, 62-65, fel, Calhoun Col, 54-81, EMER PROF BIOL & EMER FEL, CALHOUN COL, YALE UNIV, 81- *Concurrent Pos:* Gosney fel, Calif Inst Technol, 49; res collabr, dept biol, Brookhaven Nat Lab, 51-55; Fulbright sr res scholar, Commonwealth Sci & Indust Res Orgn, Canberra, Australia, 57-58, 66-67; Guggenheim Mem Found fel, 57-58; Japan Soc Promotion Sci fel, 79. *Mem:* AAAS; Am Soc Naturalists (treas, 51-53); Am Soc Zoologists; Genetics Soc Am; Soc Develop Biol. *Res:* Cytology; genetics of Drosophila; embryology of insects; physiology of development; hereditary infections. *Mailing Add:* Dept Biol 201 Osborn Mem Lab Yale Univ PO Box 6666 New Haven CT 06511

POULSON, RICHARD EDWIN, b Detroit, Mich, Sept 26, 28; m 54; c 4. PHYSICAL CHEMISTRY. *Educ:* Mich State Univ, BS, 53, PhD(phys chem), 59; Univ Calif, Berkeley, MS, 57. *Prof Exp:* Chemist, Mich Dept Agr, 54-55; res asst, Lawrence Radiation Lab, Univ Calif, 56; res chemist, Beckman Instruments Inc, 59-63; res chemist, 63-74, proj leader, 74-76, MGR, DIV ENVIRON SCI, LARAMIE ENERGY TECHNOL CTR, US Dept Energy, 76- *Mem:* Am Chem Soc. *Res:* Design and implementation of a multidisciplinary research program in environmental monitoring and control technology for determination and mitigation of potential effects from fossil-fuel recovery and utilization processes. *Mailing Add:* Laramie Energy Technol Ctr US DOE PO Box 3395 Univ Sta Laramie WY 82071

POULTER, CHARLES DALE, b Monroe, La, Aug 29, 42; m 64; c 1. CHEMISTRY. *Educ:* La State Univ, Baton Rouge, BS, 64; Univ Calif, Berkeley, PhD(org chem), 67. *Prof Exp:* NIH fel, Univ Calif, Los Angeles, from asst prof to assoc prof, 69-78, PROF CHEM, UNIV UTAH, 78- *Concurrent Pos:* Alfred P Sloan Found fel & NIH res develop award, 75. *Mem:* AAAS; Am Chem Soc; Royal Soc Chem; Am Asn Biol Chemists. *Res:* Bioorganic chemistry; biosynthesis of terpenes; applications of nuclear magnetic resonance techniques to polynucleotides. *Mailing Add:* Dept of Chem Univ of Utah Salt Lake City UT 84112

POULTER, HOWARD C, b Chicago, Ill, Mar 16, 25; m 49, 69; c 6. ELECTRICAL ENGINEERING. *Educ:* Ill Inst Technol, BS, 46, MS, 47; Stanford Univ, PhD(elec eng), 55. *Prof Exp:* Res assoc microwave tubes, Stanford Univ, 52-54; engr, Hewlett-Packard Co, 54-56, proj supvr instrumentation, 56-58, engr mgr, Microwave Div, 59-64, sr staff engr, 65-66, sect mgr anal instruments, 66-70; INSTR ELECTRONICS, MATH & PHYSICS, PERALTA JR COL DIST, 70- *Concurrent Pos:* Sci fac professional develop grant, NSF, 81-82. *Res:* Electrical measurement techniques to the development of instrumentation for chemical and biological areas; microwave instrumentation. *Mailing Add:* Merritt Col 12500 Campus Dr Oakland CA 94602

POULTNEY, SHERMAN KING, b Leominster, Mass, Mar 18, 37. APPLIED PHYSICS, OPTICAL PHYSICS. *Educ:* Worcester Polytech Inst, BS, 58; Princeton Univ, MA, 60, PhD(physics), 62. *Prof Exp:* Res assoc physics, Univ Md, College Park, 64-66, asst prof, 66-73; res assoc prof, Old Dominion Univ, 73-75; SR STAFF SCIENTIST, PERKIN-ELMER CORP, 75- *Concurrent Pos:* Consult, Naval Ord Sta, Indian Head, Md, 71-73. *Honors & Awards:* Apollo Achievement Award, NASA, 70. *Mem:* Am Phys Soc; Am Geophys Union; Optical Soc Am. *Res:* Active and passive remote sensing of atmosphere and earth resources; upper atmosphere physics; molecular infrared spectroscopy, imaging interferometers; satellite and lunar laser ranging; single photon detection, timing and imaging; electro-optical system design and engineering. *Mailing Add:* 279 Cheese Spring Rd Wilten CT 06897

POULTON, BRUCE R, b Yonkers, NY, Mar 7, 27; m 50; c 4. ANIMAL SCIENCE. *Educ:* Rutgers Univ, BS, 50, MS, 52, PhD, 56. *Prof Exp:* Asst animal sci, Rutgers Univ, 50-51, from instr to asst prof, 51-56; from assoc prof to prof, Univ Maine, Orono, 56-75, chmn dept, 58-66, dean, Col Life Sci & Agr, 68-71, dir, Life Sci Exp Sta, 68-72, vpres, Res & Pub Serv, 72-75; CHANCELLOR, UNIV SYST NH, 75-, DEAN, SCH LIFELONG LEARNING, 77- *Concurrent Pos:* Am Coun Educ fel acad admin & vis prof, Mich State Univ, 66-67; dir, Univ Maine, Bangor, 67-68. *Mem:* Am Soc Animal Sci; Am Dairy Sci Asn; Am Inst Nutrit; Brit Nutrit Soc. *Res:* Rumen nutrition; role of the endocrine system in certain physiological disorders; parathyroid physiology and effect of soil fertility on nutritive value of forages; author and co-author of over 32 publications. *Mailing Add:* Chancellor's Off Univ Syst NH Dunlap Ctr Durham NH 03824

POULTON, CHARLES EDGAR, b Oakley, Idaho, Aug 2, 17; m 39; c 4. ECOLOGY, RANGE SCIENCE & MANAGEMENT. *Educ:* Univ Idaho, BS, 39, MS, 48; Wash State Univ, PhD(ecol), 55. *Prof Exp:* Forest adminr & dist forest ranger, US Forest Serv, 37-39, 40-47, field asst, Inter-Mt Forest & Range Exp Sta, 39-40; instr range mgt, Univ Idaho, 47-49; assoc prof & organizer, Range Mgt Prog, Ore State Univ, 49-59, prof range ecol, 59-74, dir, Environ Remote Sensing Appln Lab, 72-74, head range mgt, Agr Exp Sta, 59-70; dir, Rangeland & Resource Ecol Div, Earth Satellite Corp, 74-75; sr officer range & pastures, Food & Agr Orgn UN, Rome, Italy, 76-78; training officer remote sensing applns, Ames Res Ctr, NASA, 79-81; CONSULT, 81- *Concurrent Pos:* Asst prof, Mont State Col, 46-47; consult, Southern Forest Exp Sta, US Forest Serv, 58-59 & Ore State Land Bd, 65-70; remote sensing & resource analyst, 71-; consult range sci & mgt, remote sensing appl renewable natural resources mgt & bus develop, 78- *Honors & Awards:* Merit Cert, Am Grassland Coun, 63. *Mem:* Fel Soc Range Mgt; Soc Am Foresters; Soil Sci Soc Am; Ecol Soc Am. *Res:* Rangeland resources improvement and management planning; plant ecology-soils; environmental impact analysis; application of remote sensing technology in solving renewable natural resource problems. *Mailing Add:* 121 Muir Ave Santa Clara CA 95051

POUND, G(UY) M(ARSHALL), b Portland, Ore, Apr 2, 20; m 44; c 5. PHYSICAL METALLURGY. *Educ:* Reed Col, BA, 41; Mass Inst Technol, MS, 44; Columbia Univ, PhD(phys chem), 51. *Prof Exp:* Chem engr, Standard Oil Co, Calif, 44-46; from asst prof to prof metall eng, Carnegie Inst Technol, 49-66; PROF MAT SCI, STANFORD UNIV, 66- *Concurrent Pos:* Fulbright sr res scholar, Guggenheim fel & vis prof, Univ Sheffield, 59-60; Alcoa prof, Carnegie Inst Technol, 61-66, dir metal res lab, 63-66; vis prof, Tech Univ, Berlin, 64-65 & Univ Vienna, 72-73. *Mem:* Am Soc Metals; Am Chem Soc; Am Inst Mining, Metall & Petrol Engrs. *Res:* Phase transformation kinetics; properties of solid surfaces. *Mailing Add:* Dept of Mat Sci Stanford Univ Stanford CA 94035

POUND, ROBERT VIVIAN, b Ridgeway, Ont, May 16, 19; nat US; m 41; c 1. PHYSICS. *Educ:* Univ Buffalo, BA, 41. *Hon Degrees:* AM, Harvard Univ, 50. *Prof Exp:* Res physicist, Submarine Signal Co, Mass, 41-42; mem staff, Radiation Lab, Mass Inst Technol, 42-46; Soc of Fels jr fel, 45-48, from asst prof to prof physics, 48-68, chmn dept, 68-72, MALLINCKRODT PROF PHYSICS, HARVARD UNIV, 68-, DIR PHYSICS LABS, 75- *Concurrent Pos:* Fulbright scholar, Clarendon Lab, Oxford Univ, 51; Guggenheim fel, 57-58 & 72-73; Fulbright lectr, Univ Paris, 58; vis prof, Col de France, 73-; assoc etranger, Acad Sci, 78-; vis fel, Joint Inst Lab Astrophys, Univ Colo, 79-80 & Merton Col, Oxford, 80. *Honors & Awards:* Thompson Mem Award, Inst Elec & Electronics Eng, 48; Eddington Medal, Royal Astron Soc, 65. *Mem:* Nat Acad Sci; fel Am Phys Soc; Soc Physics France; fel Am Acad Arts & Sci; assoc etranger, Acad Sci, Paris. *Res:* Nuclear moments by radio-frequency spectroscopy; nuclear physics; microwaves and radar; experimental relativity. *Mailing Add:* Lyman Lab of Physics Harvard Univ Cambridge MA 02138

POUNDER, ELTON ROY, b Montreal, Que, Jan 10, 16; wid; c 2. ICE PHYSICS, PHYSICAL OCEANOGRAPHY. *Educ:* McGill Univ, BSc, 34, PhD(physics), 37. *Prof Exp:* Engr, Can Bell Tel Co, 37-39; from asst prof to assoc prof, 45-58, PROF PHYSICS, McGILL UNIV, 59- *Mem:* Am Phys Soc; Am Geophys Union; Can Asn Physicists (secy, 56-59, pres, 61-62); fel Royal Soc Can. *Mailing Add:* Dept of Physics 3600 University St Montreal PQ H3A 2T8 Can

POURCHO, ROBERTA GRACE, b Toledo, Ohio, Mar 6, 34; m 55; c 3. ANATOMY, CELL BIOLOGY. *Educ:* Univ Mich, BS, 54; Wayne State Univ, PhD(anat), 72. *Prof Exp:* asst prof, 73-79, ASSOC PROF ANAT, SCH MED, WAYNE STATE UNIV, 79- *Mem:* AAAS; Asn Res Vision & Ophthal; Am Soc Cell Biol; Soc Neurosci; Am Asn Anatomists. *Res:* Identification of neuronal subpopulations in the mammalian retina which employ specfic neurotransmitters with elucidation of their synaptic relationships and the stimulus conditions to which they respond; electron cytochemistry. *Mailing Add:* Dept of Anat Sch of Med Wayne State Univ Detroit MI 48201

POUR-EL, AKIVA, b Tel Aviv, Israel, Sept 26, 25; US citizen; m 55; c 1. RENEWABLE RESOURCE UTILIZAITON, FUNCTIONALITY OF BIOLOGICAL PRODUCTS. *Educ:* Phila Col Pharm, BS, 52; Univ Calif, Berkeley, PhD(biochem), 60. *Prof Exp:* Anal chemist, US Vitamin Corp, 55-56; anal develop chemist, Calif Spray Chem Corp, 56-57; NIH fel, Pa State Univ, 60-61, fel biophys, 61-62; biochemist, Vet Admin Hosp, Phila, 63-64; biochemist, T L Daniels Res Ctr, Minn, 64-69, mgr biochem sect, Res Dept, Archer Daniels Midland Co, Decatur, Ill, 69-75, consult, 75-77; DIR, PEACO, 78- *Mem:* Am Chem Soc (secy-treas, 77-78); Inst Food Technol; Am Asn Cereal Chemists; fel Am Inst Chem; NY Acad Sci. *Res:* Physical chemistry of nucleic acids; rotatory dispersion of macromolecules; protein modifications by chemical and biological means; functional properties of foods and ingredients; analytical chemistry of natural products. *Mailing Add:* 1389 Keston St St Paul MN 55108

POUR-EL, MARIAN BOYKAN, b New York, NY; m; c 1. MATHEMATICS. *Educ:* Hunter Col, AB, 49; Harvard Univ, AM, 51, PhD(math), 58. *Prof Exp:* From asst prof to assoc prof math, Pa State Univ, 58-64; assoc prof, 64-68, PROF MATH, UNIV MINN, MINNEAPOLIS, 68- *Concurrent Pos:* Mem, Inst Advan Study, 62-64; Nat Acad Sci grant, Int Cong Mathematicians, Moscow, USSR, 66; vis prof, Univ Bristol, England, 69-70. *Mem:* Am Math Soc; Math Asn Am; Asn Symbolic Logic; AAAS. *Res:* Computable and noncomputable aspects of the mathematical and physical universes; ideas from mathematical logic (recursion theory), mathematical analysis (both classical and functional analyses) and physical theory are used in the work. *Mailing Add:* Dept Math Univ Minn Minneapolis MN 55455

POURING, ANDREW A, b New York, NY, Feb 12, 32; m 57; c 4. PHYSICS, GAS DYNAMICS. *Educ:* Rensselaer Polytech Inst, BME, 54, MME, 59; Yale Univ, PhD, 63. *Prof Exp:* Instr mech eng, Rensselaer Polytech Inst, 56-59; lectr, Yale Univ, 62-63, res fel, 63-64; assoc prof, 64-70, PROF AEROSPACE ENG, US NAVAL ACAD, 70- *Concurrent Pos:* Consult, Trident Eng Assocs. *Mem:* Am Phys Soc; Am Soc Mech Engrs. *Res:* Steady and non-steady fluid dynamics phenomena, especially thermal choking; nucleation and phase change; relaxation effects; multi-phase flows; simulation of gas kinetic systems. *Mailing Add:* Dept of Eng US Naval Acad Annapolis MD 21402

POUSSAINT, ALVIN FRANCIS, b East Harlem, NY, May 15, 34; m 73. PSYCHIATRY. *Educ:* Columbia Col, BA, 56; Cornell Univ, MD, 60; Univ Calif, Los Angeles, MS, 64; Am Bd Psychiat & Neurol, cert, 70. *Prof Exp:* Intern, Ctr for Health Sci, 60-61, resident, 61-64, chief resident psychiat, Neuropsychiat Inst, Univ Calif, Los Angeles, 64-65; sr clin instr psychiat,

Tufts Univ, 65-66, asst prof prev med & psychiat, 67-69; dean students, 75-78, ASSOC DEAN STUDENTS & ASSOC PROF PSYCHIAT, HARVARD MED SCH, 69- *Concurrent Pos:* Southern field dir, Med Comt for Human Rights, Miss, 65-66; dir psychiat, Columbia Point Health Ctr, Boston, 68-69; mem bd trustees, Nat Asn Afro-Am Artists, 68-, Wesleyan Col, 68-69 & Oper People United To Save Humanity, 71-; assoc psychiatrist, Mass Mental Health Ctr, 69-; fac sponsor, Student Health Orgn, 69 & Student Health League, Boston, 69-73; consult & adv, Dept HEW, 69-73; co-dir, Behav Sci Course, Harvard Med Sch, 69-; chmn of bd, Solomon Fuller Inst, 72-; deleg, Official Med Deleg to People's Repub China, 75; health consult, Cong Black Caucus, 76- *Mem:* Nat Med Asn; fel Am Psychiat Asn; Med Comt for Human Rights (treas, 68-69). *Mailing Add:* Judge Baker Guid Ctr 295 Longwood Ave Boston MA 02115

POUSSART, DENIS, b France, Oct 3, 40; Can citizen; m 64; c 3. BIOELECTRIC SIGNAL PROCESSING. *Educ:* Laval Univ, BSc, 63; Mass Inst Technol, MSc, 65, PhD(elec eng), 68. *Prof Exp:* PROF ELEC ENG, LAVAL UNIV, 68- *Mem:* Inst Elec & Electronics Engrs. *Res:* Bioelectric signals; membrane biophysics; processing in nervous system; biomedical instrumentation; computer vision; imaging; 3-dimensional shape analysis. *Mailing Add:* Dept Elec Eng Laval Univ Quebec City PQ G1V 7P4 Can

POUST, ROLLAND IRVIN, b Warren, Pa, June 19, 43; m 66; c 2. PHARMACEUTICS. *Educ:* Univ Pittsburgh, BS, 66, MS, 68; Purdue Univ, PhD(pharm), 71. *Prof Exp:* Asst prof pharmaceut, Sch Pharm, Univ Pittsburgh, 71-73, assoc prof, 73-79; SECT HEAD, PHARMACEUT RES & DEVELOP LABS, BURROUGHS WELLCOME CO, 79- *Mem:* Acad Pharmaceut Sci; NY Acad of Sci; Am Pharmaceut Asn. *Res:* Nonlinear pharmacokinetics; pharmacokinetics of lithium in humans; pharmacokinetics of diazoxide. *Mailing Add:* Burroughs Wellcome Co PO Box 1887 Greenville NC 27834

POUTSIAKA, JOHN WILLIAM, b Newark, NJ, Feb 6, 25; m 47; c 2. PHYSIOLOGY. *Educ:* Seton Hall Univ, BS, 48; Fordham Univ, MS, 49, PhD(physiol), 54. *Prof Exp:* Lab instr biol, Fordham Univ, 48-50; sr res scientist, 50-60, head dept toxicol, 60-68, dir toxicol dept, 68-72, assoc dir res, 72-76, V PRES DRUG REGULATION & CONTROL, SQUIBB INST MED RES, 76- *Mem:* Am Soc Pharmacol & Exp Therapeut; Soc Toxicol; NY Acad Sci. *Res:* Pharmacology and toxicology of new drugs; renal physiology; body fluids and electrolytes. *Mailing Add:* 179 North Woods Dr South Orange NJ 07079

POVAR, MORRIS LEON, b New York, NY, Feb 19, 20; m 45; c 2. VETERINARY MEDICINE, PRIMATOLOGY. *Educ:* State Univ NY Col Agr, BS, 41; Cornell Univ, DVM, 44; Brown Univ, MA, 69. *Prof Exp:* Assoc pathologist, Rutgers Univ, 44-45; pathologist, Kimber Farms, 45-46; veterinarian, 46-52, 54-67; assoc prof, 68-73, PROF PSYCHOL & MED SCI, BROWN UNIV, 73-, DIR ANIMAL CARE FACILITY & DIR ANIMAL HEALTH, 68- *Concurrent Pos:* Consult ed, Lab Primate Newsletter, Brown Univ, 62-; lectr, Sch Dent Med, Harvard Univ, 71-; consult, Northeastern Univ, 71- & Health Ctr, Univ Conn, 72- *Mem:* AAAS; Am Soc Lab Animal Practitioners (vpres, 74-75, pres, 75-76); Am Vet Med Asn; Am Asn Lab Animal Sci. *Res:* Nonhuman primate husbandry and behavior; dental implants in experimental animals. *Mailing Add:* Animal Care Facil Brown Univ Providence RI 02912

POVICH, MICHAEL JEAN, b Chicago, Ill, Apr 19, 41; div; c 2. COLLOID CHEMISTRY, CORROSION. *Educ:* Southern Ill Univ, BS, 65; Univ Hawaii, PhD(phys chem), 71. *Prof Exp:* Staff mem, Res & Develop, US Gypsum Co, 65-66; researcher biophys, Univ Hawaii, 71-72; sales engr, Brewer Chem Corp, 72-73; STAFF MEM CORROSION, RES & DEVELOP, GEN ELEC CO, 73- *Res:* Interdisciplined research in surface and colloid chemistry, corrosion, metallurgy and industrial water treatment. *Mailing Add:* Silicone Prod Div Gen Elec Co Waterford NY 12188

POVINELLI, LOUIS A, b New York, NY, June 10, 31; m 58; c 7. MECHANICAL ENGINEERING. *Educ:* Univ Detroit, BME, 54; Univ Ky, MSME, 56; Northwestern Univ, PhD(mech eng), 59. *Prof Exp:* Rocket design engr, Bell Aircraft Corp, 51-56; asst, Northwestern Univ, 56-58; abstractor, Comt Fire Res, Nat Acad Sci-Nat Res Coun, 57-76; aeronaut res scientist, 60-81, SECT HEAD TURBINE AERODYNAMICS, LEWIS RES CTR, NASA, 81- *Concurrent Pos:* Instr, Univ Ky, 55-56 & Siebel Inst Technol, 56-57; res engr, Armour Res Found, Ill Inst Technol, 57-59; Fiat fel & Fulbright grant, Turin Polytech Inst, 59-60; consult, Off Sci & Technol, Exec Off of the President, 63 & Dept of Defense Working Group, 65-72; lectr, Lewis Advan Study Prog, NASA, 66-72; consult NASA study team, 72. *Mem:* Am Inst Aeronaut & Astronaut; Am Soc Metal Engrs. *Res:* Turbine aerodynamics; fluid mechanics; jet propulsion; gas dynamics; turbulence; solid propellants; supersonic combustion. *Mailing Add:* NASA Lewis Res Ctr 21000 Brookpark Rd Cleveland OH 44135

POWANDA, MICHAEL CHRISTOPHER, b Jersey City, NJ, Jan 15, 42. INFECTIOUS DISEASES, TRAUMA. *Educ:* St Peter's Col, BS, 63; Univ Miami, PhD(biochem), 68. *Prof Exp:* Biochemist, US Army Med Res Inst Infectious Dis, 68-77; CHIEF, BIOCHEM BR, US ARMY INST SURG RES, 78- *Mem:* Am Inst Nutrit; Am Soc Cell Biol; Am Fedn Clin Res; NY Acad Sci; Sigma Xi. *Res:* Alterations in metabolism and physiology during injury, inflammation and infection; mode of induction and regulation and role in host defense against infection and repair of injury; nutritional management of injured and infected individuals. *Mailing Add:* Biochem Br US Army Inst of Surg Res Ft Sam Houston TX 78234

POWDERS, VERNON NEIL, b Woodward, Okla, June 14, 41; m 67. PARASITOLOGY. *Educ:* Northwestern State Col, BS, 63; Okla State Univ, MS, 64; Univ Tenn, Knoxville, PhD(parasitol), 67. *Prof Exp:* Asst prof biol, Ga Southwestern Col, 67-73, assoc prof, 73-80; MEM FAC, DEPT ENTOMOL, UNIV TENN, 80- *Mem:* Am Soc Parasitol; Am Soc Ichthyol & Herpet; Soc Study Amphibia & Reptiles. *Res:* Systematics of Orthoptera and parasitism in salamanders; reptilian and avian parasites; biology of amphibians. *Mailing Add:* Dept Entomol Univ Tenn Knoxville TN 37916

POWE, RALPH ELWARD, b Tylertown, Miss, July 27, 44; m 62; c 3. MECHANICAL ENGINEERING, APPLIED PHYSICS. *Educ:* Miss State Univ, BS, 67, MS, 68; Mont State Univ, PhD(mech eng), 70. *Prof Exp:* Trainee mech eng, NASA, 62-65; res asst, Miss State Univ, 65-68, lab instr physics, 66-67, instr mech eng, 68; res asst, Mont State Univ, 68-70, teaching asst civil eng, 69-70, asst prof mech eng, 70-74; assoc prof, 74-78, PROF MECH ENG, MISS STATE UNIV, 78-, ASSOC DEAN ENG, 81- *Concurrent Pos:* AEC contract, Mont State Univ, 71-72, NSF grant, 72-74; US Dept Energy contract, 76-79. *Honors & Awards:* Ralph R Teetor Award, Soc Automotive Engrs, 71. *Mem:* AAAS; Am Soc Mech Engrs; Soc Automotive Engrs; Nat Soc Prof Engrs; Am Soc Eng Educ. *Res:* Heat transfer; natural convection; fluid mechanics; magnetohydrodynamics power generation. *Mailing Add:* Dept of Mech Eng Miss State Univ Mississippi State MS 39762

POWELL, ALAN, b Buxton, Eng, Feb 17, 28; US citizen; m 56. ENGINEERING, PHYSICS. *Educ:* Loughborough Col, DLC, 48 & Hons, 49; Univ London, BSc Hons, 49; Univ Southampton, PhD(eng), 53. *Hon Degrees:* DTech, Loughborough Univ Technol, 80. *Prof Exp:* Tech asst aeronaut eng, Percival Aircraft Co, Eng, 49-51; asst aeronaut, Univ Southampton, 51-53, lectr, 53-56; res fel aeronaut, Calif Inst Technol, 56-57; from assoc prof to prof eng, Univ Calif, Los Angeles, 57-64, head aerosonics lab, 57-64; assoc tech dir & head acoust & vibration lab, David W Taylor Model Basin, 64-65, tech dir, 66-67; TECH DIR, DAVID W TAYLOR NAVAL SHIP RES & DEVELOP CTR, 67- *Concurrent Pos:* Consult, Gen Elec Co, 56, Douglas Aircraft Co, 56-64, Ramo-Wooldridge Corp, 57, Indust Acoust, Inc, 58 & Rocketdyne Div, NAm Aircraft Co, 60; mem noise suppression comt, Brit Ministry of Supply, 52-56, mem exec comt, 54-56; mem, Aeronaut Res Coun, London, 53-56; mem comt hearing, bioacoust & biomech, Nat Acad Sci-Nat Res Coun, 62-, mem exec coun, 63-65, chmn exec coun, 65-66, mem comt undersea warfare panel on submarine noise measurement, 65-; mem comt shock & vibration, Am Standards Asn; initial mem & dir, Inst Noise Control Engrs, 74-77. *Honors & Awards:* Baden-Powell Prize, 48 & Wright Prize, 53, Royal Aeronaut Soc; Navy Meritorious Civilian Serv Award, 70; Aeroacoustics Award, Am Inst Aeronaut & Astronaut, 80. *Mem:* Sr mem Inst Elec & Electronics Engrs (Acoust, Speech & Signal Processing Soc); fel Royal Aeronaut Soc; fel Brit Inst Mech Engrs; fel Am Inst Aeronaut & Astronaut; fel Acoust Soc Am (pres-elect, 80-81). *Res:* Basic and applied research in applied mechanics, especially acoustics, fluid mechanics and structures; noise control in aircraft and ships; engineering design, especially aircraft; research direction; engineering and science education. *Mailing Add:* Taylor Naval Ship Res & Dev Ctr Bethesda MD 20084

POWELL, ALBERT E, b Larimer, Pa, Nov 8, 19; m 43; c 4. AGRICULTURAL ENGINEERING. *Educ:* Pa State Univ, BSc, 41; Purdue Univ, MSc, 43; Iowa State Univ, PhD(agr & mech eng), 60. *Prof Exp:* Prof consult engr, 48-49; agr engr, Midwest Plan Serv, 49-50; agr engr, Douglas Fir Plywood Asn, 50-56, regional mgr, 56-57, agr engr, 57-58, sr agr engr, 58-59; from asst prof to assoc prof, 60-75, PROF AGR ENG, WASH STATE UNIV, 75- *Mem:* Am Soc Agr Engrs; Nat Soc Prof Engrs; Am Soc Eng Educ; Am Acad Environ Engrs. *Res:* Connections between wood members; adhesives; structural analysis; grain storage; solar energy applications. *Mailing Add:* Dept of Agr Eng Wash State Univ Pullman WA 99163

POWELL, ALBERT MICHAEL, b Coleman, Tex, Aug 26, 37; m 56; c 1. BOTANY. *Educ:* Sul Ross State Col, BS & MA, 60; Univ Tex, PhD(bot), 63. *Prof Exp:* Assoc prof, 63-68, PROF BIOL, SUL ROSS STATE UNIV, 68- *Concurrent Pos:* Sigma Xi res grant, 64; NSF res grants, 64-78. *Mem:* AAAS; Am Soc Plant Taxon. *Res:* Botanical systematics; cytotaxonomy of Compositae. *Mailing Add:* Dept Biol Sul Ross State Univ Alpine TX 79830

POWELL, ALFRED R(ICHARD), chemical engineering, deceased

POWELL, ARNET L, b Worcester, Mass, Feb 4, 15; m 48; c 2. PHYSICAL CHEMISTRY. *Educ:* Worcester Polytech Inst, BS, 38, MS, 40; Clark Univ, PhD(chem), 56. *Prof Exp:* Asst physics, Worcester Polytech Inst, 38-40; phys chemist, Dow Chem Co, 40-44; sr res engr, Sylvania Elec Co, 44-47; chemist, US Off Naval Res, Boston Br, 47-54, asst chief scientist, 54-59, dep dir sci, 67-77, chief scientist, 59-79, dir sci, 77-79; CONSULT, 79- *Concurrent Pos:* Guest researcher, Mass Inst Technol, 56- & Oxford Univ, 64. *Mem:* AAAS; Am Chem Soc; NY Acad Sci. *Res:* Determination of halogens in organic compounds; indicators; electroanalytical methods; corrosion; Friedel-Crafts reactions; fluorescence; glow discharge; electrical conductivity in nonaqueous solvents; mechanism of Cannizzaro reaction; halogenation kinetics; correlation of solvent effects. *Mailing Add:* 65 Woodridge Rd Wayland MA 01778

POWELL, BENJAMIN NEFF, b Montclair, NJ, Oct 28, 41; m 64; c 1. PETROLOGY, GEOLOGY. *Educ:* Amherst Col, BA, 64; Columbia Univ, MA, 66, PhD(geol), 69. *Prof Exp:* Res assoc geol, Smithsonian Astrophys Observ & Harvard Col Observ, 69-70; asst prof, Rice Univ, 70-76, lectr geol, 76-80; SR RES GEOLOGIST RES & DEVELOP, PHILLIPS PETROL CO, 80- *Concurrent Pos:* Prin investr, NASA, 71-76 & NSF, 73 & 76-79. *Honors & Awards:* Nininger Meteorite Prize, Ariz State Univ, 68. *Mem:* AAAS; Geol Soc Am; Geochem Soc; Mineral Soc Am. *Res:* Mineralogy and petrology of lunar samples and meteorites; igneous petrology; geochemistry; terrestrial igneous petrology; ore deposits. *Mailing Add:* 237 GB Phillips Petrol Co Bartlesville OK 74004

POWELL, BERNARD LAWRENCE, b Kansas City, Kans, June 7, 45; m 67; c 3. STEROID HORMONE ENDOCRINOLOGY, RADIOISOTOPE TECHNOLOGY. *Educ:* Rockhurst Col, BA, 67; Univ Okla, PhD(biochem), 75. *Prof Exp:* NIH trainee, Res Inst Hosp Joint Dis, Mt Sinai Sch Med, 75-77; res assoc, Dept Med & Oncol, Univ Tex Health Sci Ctr, 77-81; SR RES ASSOC, DEPT MED & INFECTIOUS DIS, AUDIE MURPHY VET ADMIN HOSP & UNIV TEX HEALTH SCI CTR, 81- *Mem:* AAAS. *Res:* Steroid and polypeptide hormone receptor in cancer and fungal diseases, in particular the isolation and physicochemical charecterrization of such receptors. *Mailing Add:* 9418 Cliff Way Dr San Antonio TX 78250

POWELL, BOBBY EARL, b Moultrie, Ga, Jan 15, 41; m 65; c 2. SOLID STATE PHYSICS. *Educ:* Ga Inst Technol, BS, 63; Clemson Univ, MS, 65, PhD(physics), 67. *Prof Exp:* From asst prof to assoc prof, 67-75, PROF PHYSICS, WEST GA COL, 75-, DIR, COL OBSERV, 79- *Mem:* Am Phys Soc; Am Asn Physics Teachers; Sigma Xi. *Res:* Measurement of elastic constants of crystals from finite deformations; growth of crystals; x-ray diffraction studies. *Mailing Add:* Dept of Physics West Ga Col Carrollton GA 30118

POWELL, BRUCE ALLAN, b Waterbury, Conn, Aug 12, 41; m 64; c 3. OPERATIONS RESEARCH. *Educ:* Denison Univ, BS, 63; Case Western Reserve Univ, MS, 65, PhD(opers res), 67. *Prof Exp:* Sr mathematician, 67-73, fel mathematician, 73-77, ADV MATHEMATICIAN, WESTINGHOUSE RES LABS, 77- *Mem:* Opers Res Soc Am; Inst Mgt Sci. *Res:* Inventory systems; queuing theory; practical application of mathematical models; optimization; development of elevator control strategies; computer simulation of manufacturing plants. *Mailing Add:* Dept of Math Westinghouse Res Labs Pittsburgh PA 15235

POWELL, BURWELL FREDERICK, b Washington, DC, June 9, 33; m 54; c 2. ORGANIC CHEMISTRY. *Educ:* Univ Md, BS, 56; Polytech Inst Brooklyn, MS, 66, PhD(chem), 70. *Prof Exp:* CHEMIST, MERCK SHARP & DOHME RES LABS, MERCK & CO, 56- *Mem:* Am Chem Soc; The Chem Soc; AAAS; Sigma Xi. *Res:* Synthetic organic chemistry. *Mailing Add:* RD 1 Box 42 Neshanic Station NJ 08853

POWELL, CEDRIC JOHN, b Australia, Feb 19, 35; US citizen; m 58; c 3. PHYSICS, SURFACE SCIENCE. *Educ:* Univ Western Australia, BSc Hons, 56, PhD(physics), 62. *Prof Exp:* Res physicist, Imp Col, London, 60-62; physicist, 62-78, CHIEF SURFACE SCI DIV, NAT BUR STANDARDS, 78- *Concurrent Pos:* Course dir instrumental surface anal, Ctr Prof Advan, 77 & 78 & Soc Appl Spectros, 79; co-chmn, Phys Electronics Conf, 79; vchmn, Gordon Res Conf Electron Spectros, 80. *Mem:* AAAS; fel Am Phys Soc; Am Chem Soc; fel Brit Inst Physics; Am Vacuum Soc. *Res:* Solid-state, atomic and molecular science; thin-film, liquid-state, alloy, radiation and electron physics; surface characterization; small-particle science; environmental science. *Mailing Add:* Chem B-248 Nat Bur of Standards Washington DC 20234

POWELL, CHARLES CARLETON, JR, b Massillon, Ohio, May 11, 42; m 64; c 2. PLANT PATHOLOGY. *Educ:* Ohio State Univ, BSc, 64; Univ Calif, Berkeley, PhD(plant path), 69. *Prof Exp:* Res scientist, Agr Res Serv, US Dept Agr, 69-70; asst prof, 70-77, ASSOC PROF PLANT PATH, OHIO STATE UNIV, 77- *Mem:* Am Phytopath Soc. *Res:* Diseases of ornamental plants; flower crops; woody ornamentals; landscape plantings; research and extension appointment. *Mailing Add:* Dept of Plant Path Ohio State Univ Columbus OH 43210

POWELL, CHARLES HERBERT, b Alton, Ill, July 19, 26; m 48; c 2. INDUSTRIAL HYGIENE. *Educ:* Shurtleff Col, BS, 49; Univ Cincinnati, MS, 59, ScD(indust health), 60; Bd Cert Safety Prof, cert. *Prof Exp:* Chemist, Superior Lab, Ill, 49-52, 54-55; res indust hygienist, Eng Sect, Div Occup Health, USPHS, 62-63, asst chief training opers sect, Occup Health Res & Training Facil, 63-64, chief, 64-66, chief, State Serv Br, Ohio, 67-68; assoc prof bioeng, Col Eng, assoc prof community health & med pract, Med Sch & dir Environ Health Ctr, Univ Mo-Columbia, 68-70; asst dir div criteria & stand develop, Bur Occup Safety & Health, 70-71, dir off res & stand develop & asst dir, Nat Inst Occup Safety & Health, 71-73, asst dir spec prog, Nat Inst Occup Safety & Health, USPHS, 73-75; CORP MGR INDUST HYG, MARTIN MARIETTA CORP, 75-77; CORP MGR HEALTH SERVS, PPG INDUSTS, 77- *Concurrent Pos:* Adj asst prof, Univ Cincinnati, 65- *Mem:* Am Conf Govt Indust Hygienists; Am Indust Hyg Asn; Am Acad Indust Hyg. *Res:* Environmental and occupational health aspects of rocket and missile propellants; non-ionizing radiation; particulates; education in occupational health. *Mailing Add:* PPG Industs 1 Gateway Ctr Pittsburgh PA 15222

POWELL, CLINTON COBB, b Hartford, Conn, Mar 9, 18; m 44; c 3. RADIOLOGY. *Educ:* Mass Inst Technol, SB, 40; Boston Univ, MD, 44; Am Bd Radiol, dipl, 54. *Prof Exp:* Intern, US Marine Hosp, Boston, 44-45; asst surgeon, NIH, 46-47, from sr asst surgeon to sr surgeon, 47-56, med dir, 56-64, exec secy radiation & surg study sect, 58-59, asst chief res grants rev br, 59-60, dep dir div res grants, 60-61, assoc dir extramural progs, Nat Inst Allergy & Infectious Dis, 61-62, dir, Nat Inst Gen Med Sci, 62-64; assoc coord & actg coordr, Med & Health Sci, 64-66, coordr, 66-70, spec asst to pres health affairs, Systwide Admin, 70-79, EMER SPEC ASST TO PRES HEALTH AFFAIRS, UNIV CALIF, 79- *Concurrent Pos:* Instr, Univ Pa, 52-54; chief radiol health med prog, USPHS, 56-58; mem comn Radiol units, Standards & Protection, Am Col Radiol, 57-, chmn comt radiation exposure of women, 65-72. *Mem:* Radiation Res Soc; Am Col Radiol. *Res:* Radiotherapy; radiation protection; medical administration. *Mailing Add:* 542 Tahos Rd Orinda CA 94563

POWELL, DAVID LEE, b Bucyrus, Ohio, July 27, 36; m 59; c 2. PHYSICAL CHEMISTRY. *Educ:* Oberlin Col, AB, 58; Univ Wis, PhD(phys chem), 62. *Prof Exp:* Fel molecular spectros, Univ Minn, 62-64; from asst prof to assoc prof, 64-73, chmn dept, 77-81, PROF CHEM, COL WOOSTER, 73- *Concurrent Pos:* Res leave, Univ Oslo, 71-72, 76-77 & 81-82. *Mem:* Am Chem Soc; Sigma Xi. *Res:* Vibrational spectroscopy; conformational behavior of organic compound as studied by infrared and Raman spectroscopy. *Mailing Add:* Dept of Chem Col of Wooster Wooster OH 44691

POWELL, DON WATSON, b Gadsden, Ala, Aug 29, 38; m 60; c 3. GASTROENTEROLOGY. *Educ:* Auburn Univ, BS, 60; Med Col Ala, MD, 63; Am Bd Internal Med, dipl, 72, dipl gastroenterol, 79. *Prof Exp:* From intern to jr asst resident med, Peter Bent Brigham Hosp, Boston, 63-65; assoc investr gastroenterol, Walter Reed Army Inst Res, 65-68; asst resident & teaching asst internal med, Yale-New Haven Hosp, 68-69, USPHS spec fel, Yale Univ, 69-71; asst prof, 71-74, assoc prof med, 74-78, PROF MED & CHIEF DIV DIGESTIVE DIS & NUTRIT, SCH MED, UNIV NC, CHAPEL HILL, 78- *Concurrent Pos:* USPHS res grants, 71-81, Nat Inst Arthritis, Metab & Digestive Dis res career develop award, 73-78; mem, Vet Admin Merit Rev Bd Gastroenterol, 78-81. *Mem:* AAAS; Am Fedn Clin Res; Am Gastroentrol Asn; Biophys Soc; Am Physiol Soc. *Res:* Transport of water and electrolytes by gastrointestinal epithelia; intestinal absorption and secretion; pathophysiology of diarrheal diseases; ion transport by esophageal epithelium; pathophysiology of esophagitis. *Mailing Add:* Dept Med Univ NC Sch Med Chapel Hill NC 27514

POWELL, EDWARD GORDON, b Washington, DC, Apr 5, 46. ROBOTICS, EXPERT SYSTEMS. *Educ:* Univ Md, BS, 68, MS, 72. *Prof Exp:* Res physicist, US Naval Ordnance Sta, 68-73, US Naval Ordnance Lab, 73-74, US Naval Surface Weapons Ctr, 74-81, PROJ MGR, ARTIFICIAL INTELLIGENCE, US NAVAL SURFACE WEAPONS CTR, 81- *Concurrent Pos:* Guest worker, Nat Bur Standards, 76-79. *Mem:* Am Astron Soc. *Res:* Autonomous naval defense systems; plausible inference; missile control and propulsion. *Mailing Add:* 1126 Apple Valley Rd Accokeek MD 20607

POWELL, ERVIN WILLIAM, b Niles, Ohio, Nov 8, 22; m 45; c 3. NEUROANATOMY. *Educ:* Youngstown Univ, AB, 48; Western Reserve Univ, MS, 50, PhD(zool), 53. *Prof Exp:* Lectr anat & physiol, Western Reserve Univ, 51-53; from instr to asst prof anat, Sch Med, Creighton Univ, 54-60; assoc prof, Med Ctr, Univ Miss, 60-66; PROF ANAT, SCH MED, UNIV ARK, LITTLE ROCK, 66- *Mem:* AAAS; Am Asn Anatomists; Soc Neurosci; Soc Chronobiol; Sigma Xi. *Res:* Neurophysiology; limbic system; neuropathology. *Mailing Add:* Dept of Anat Univ of Ark Col of Med Little Rock AR 72201

POWELL, FRANCIS X, b Hoxie, Ark, Sept 23, 29; m 53; c 1. CHEMISTRY. *Educ:* Univ Calif, Berkeley, BS, 56; Univ Md, PhD(chem), 62. *Prof Exp:* Res engr, Jet Propulsion Lab, Calif Inst Technol, 56-57; fel chem, Univ Md, 62; asst prof, 62-68, ASSOC PROF CHEM, CATH UNIV AM, 68- *Concurrent Pos:* Consult, Nat Bur Standards, 63-70, Am Instrument Co, 64-70, Naval Res Lab, 70- & Goddard Space Flight Ctr, 71- *Mem:* Am Phys Soc; Am Chem Soc. *Res:* Spectrscopy of free radicals; electrical discharges through gases. *Mailing Add:* Dept of Chem Cath Univ of Am Washington DC 20017

POWELL, FRANK LUDWIG, JR, b Pasadena, Calif, Aug 10, 52; m 81. RESPIRATORY PHYSIOLOGY, NEUROPHYSIOLOGY. *Educ:* Univ Calif, Irvine, BS, 74, Davis, MS, 78, PhD(systs physiol), 78. *Prof Exp:* Res asst, Univ Calif, Davis, 74-75, asst instr, 75-76; DAAD fel, Max-Planck Inst Exp Med, WGer, 76-77; assoc, systs physiol, Univ Calif, Davis, 77-78; res fel, 78-80, ASST PROF MED, UNIV CALIF, SAN DIEGO, 80- *Concurrent Pos:* Prin investr, Function & Structure of the Avian Lung, NIH grant, 82-85. *Mem:* Am Physiol Soc; Am Thoracic Soc; AAAS; Audobon Soc. *Res:* Structure-function relationships of avian lungs, especially inert and physiological gas exchange and electron microscopy; control of breathing, especially intrapulmonary carbon dioxide sensitivity and role of vagal afferents and high altitude acclimatization. *Mailing Add:* Sect Physiol M-023 Dept Med Univ Calif Sch Med La Jolla CA 92093

POWELL, G(EORGE) M(ATTHEWS), III, b Montgomery, Ala, Mar 29, 10; m 37; c 2. CHEMICAL ENGINEERING. *Educ:* Columbia Univ, AB, 31, BS, 32, ChE, 33. *Prof Exp:* Researcher, Carbide & Carbon Chem Co, 33-44, tech head res div, 44-55, asst dir res, Union Carbide Chem Co, 55-60, res supt plastics, 60-61, supt polymer chem div, 61-64, assoc dir res & develop dept, Chem Div, Union Carbide Corp, 64-69, res consult coatings mat, 69; consult coatings technol, 69-77. *Honors & Awards:* Hyatt Award, 50. *Mem:* Am Chem Soc; Soc Rheology; Am Inst Chem Engrs. *Res:* Vinyl resin technology; surface coatings; organosols; plastisols; water-soluble polymers, paper chemicals and resins; solvents, intermediates and polymer latexes for industrial and trade paints. *Mailing Add:* 2114 Glenfield Terr South Charleston WV 25303

POWELL, GARY LEE, b Fullerton, Calif, Jan 24, 41; m 65; c 2. BIOCHEMISTRY. *Educ:* Univ Calif, Los Angeles, BS, 62; Purdue Univ, PhD(chem), 67. *Prof Exp:* From asst prof to assoc prof, 67-79, PROF BIOCHEM, CLEMSON UNIV, 79- *Concurrent Pos:* NIH trainee biol chem, Sch Med, Wash Univ, 67-69. *Mem:* Am Chem Soc; Am Soc Biol Chemists; AAAS. *Res:* Control of lipid metabolism; lipid-protein interactions in biological membranes. *Mailing Add:* Dept of Biochem Clemson Univ Clemson SC 29631

POWELL, GEORGE LOUIS, b Wilmington, NC, Oct 17, 40; m 64; c 1. PHYSICAL CHEMISTRY. *Educ:* Presby Col, BS, 63; Univ NC, Chapel Hill, PhD(phys chem), 67. *Prof Exp:* Chemist, 67-78, SECT LEADER PHYS CHEM, OAK RIDGE Y-12 PLANT, NUCLEAR DIV, UNION CARBIDE CORP, 69- *Mem:* Sigma Xi; Am Chem Soc. *Res:* Gas phase kinetics, including gas-solid interactions and energy transfer reactions; metal-hydrogen phase relationships; hydrogen embrittlement; trace analysis of gases in solids; mass- and optical-kinetic spectroscopy; surface chemistry of lithium compounds. *Mailing Add:* Bldg 9202 Y-12 Plant Nuclear Div Union Carbide Corp Oak Ridge TN 37830

POWELL, GEORGE WYTHE, b Aiken, SC, Oct 26, 36; m 58; c 1. ANIMAL NUTRITION. *Educ:* Clemson Univ, BS, 58; Univ Ga, MS, 64, PhD(animal nutrit), 67. *Prof Exp:* Res assoc dairy sci, Univ Fla, 67-68; PROF BIOL, ABRAHAM BALDWIN AGR COL, 68-, CHMN SCI & MATH DIV, 74- *Mem:* Sigma Xi. *Res:* Trace mineral metabolism in ruminants. *Mailing Add:* Div of Sci & Math Abraham Baldwin Agr Col Tifton GA 31794

POWELL, GORDON W, b Providence, RI, Mar, 10, 28; m 55; c 4. PHYSICAL METALLURGY. *Educ:* Mass Inst Technol, BS, 51, MS, 52, ScD(phys metall), 55. *Prof Exp:* Sr metallurgist, Nuclear Metals, Inc, 55-57; asst prof, Univ Wis, 57-58; PROF METALL ENG, OHIO STATE UNIV, 58- *Concurrent Pos:* Consult, Monsanto Res Corp, 66-; consult to various law & ins firms. *Mem:* Am Inst Mining, Metall & Petrol Engrs; Am Soc Metals. *Res:* Diffusion; phase transformations; failure analysis. *Mailing Add:* Dept of Metall Eng Ohio State Univ Columbus OH 43210

POWELL, GRAHAM REGINALD, b Hampton, Eng, Mar 19, 35; Can citizen; m 60; c 2. TREE DEVELOPMENT, TREE REPRODUCTION. *Educ:* Univ Edinburgh, BSc, 56, Hons, 57, PhD(tree develop), 71; Univ NB, Fredericton, MSc, 61. *Prof Exp:* Lectr, 61-64, asst prof, 64-71, assoc prof, 71-77, PROF FORESTRY, UNIV NB, FREDERICTON, 77- *Mem:* Can Inst Forestry; Can Bot Asn; Can Tree Improv Asn. *Res:* Tree development; interrelations between reproductive and vegetative forms of growth in tree species; seed production; seed germination; seedling development; litter fall in forest stands. *Mailing Add:* Dept Forest Resources Bag #44555 Fredericton NB E3B 6C2 Can

POWELL, HAROLD, b Jacksonboro, SC, Dec 17, 32. SPEECH PATHOLOGY, AUDIOLOGY. *Educ:* SC State Col, BA, 61; Pa State Univ, MS, 63, PhD(speech path), 66. *Prof Exp:* Assoc prof speech correction, 65-69, PROF SPEECH PATH, SC STATE COL, 69-, KIRKLAND W GREEN PROF, 68- *Concurrent Pos:* Mem, SC State Bd Examrs in Speech Path & Audiol, 73-78, chmn, 77-78; mem adv comt, Deaf-Blind in SC, 74-79; mem, Am Bd Examrs in Speech Path & Audiol, 75-78, secy, 76-78; mem adv comt, Off Progs for Handicapped, SC Dept Educ, 75-78; mem, SC Gov's Comt Employment of Handicapped, 77-78; mem bd dirs, Nat Black Asn Speech, Lang & Hearing, 78-81. *Mem:* Am Speech & Hearing Asn. *Res:* Communicative problems of the rural disadvantaged child. *Mailing Add:* Dept Speech Path SC State Col Orangeburg SC 29115

POWELL, HARRY DOUGLAS, b Wallace, NC, Oct 14, 37; m 63; c 1. SOLID STATE PHYSICS. *Educ:* Davidson Col, BS, 60; Clemson Univ, MS, 62, PhD(physics), 65. *Prof Exp:* Assoc prof, 65-70, PROF PHYSICS, E TENN STATE UNIV, 70- *Mem:* Am Phys Soc; Am Asn Physics Teachers. *Res:* Methods of crystal growth; electron spin resonance of impurities in crystalline solids. *Mailing Add:* Dept of Physics E Tenn State Univ Johnson City TN 37601

POWELL, HOWARD B, b Benton, Ky, May 2, 33; m 52; c 3. INORGANIC CHEMISTRY. *Educ:* Murray State Col, BS, 55; Univ Tex, MA, 61, PhD(inorg chem), 63. *Prof Exp:* Control chemist, Nat Carbide Co, Ky, 53-57; teacher, Benton Independent Schs, 57-59; asst, Univ Tex, 60-61; asst prof chem, Univ Miami, 63-69; assoc prof, 69-74, PROF CHEM, EASTERN KY UNIV, 74- *Mem:* Am Chem Soc. *Res:* Investigation of the structure and reactivity of coordination compounds containing the ligand pyridine 1-oxide, particularly the thermal behavior of these compounds. *Mailing Add:* Dept of Chem Eastern Ky Univ Richmond KY 40475

POWELL, HUGH N, b Birmingham, Ala, June 16, 22; m 50; c 3. CHEMICAL ENGINEERING. *Educ:* Ga Inst Technol, BS, 43; Univ Del, PhD(chem eng), 50. *Prof Exp:* Res engr combustion and thermodynamics, Aircraft Gas Turbine Div, Gen Elec Co, Ohio, 51-57; assoc prof, Cornell, 57-61; PROF MECH ENG, UNIV WIS-MADISON, 61- *Concurrent Pos:* Consult, Gen Elec Co, 57-61. *Mem:* Am Inst Aeronaut & Astronaut. *Res:* Properties of high temperature gases; shock tube technique; plasma dynamics; spectroscopy. *Mailing Add:* Dept of Mech Eng Univ of Wis Madison WI 53706

POWELL, JACK EDWARD, b Avon, Ill, June 11, 21; m 44; c 4. PHYSICAL CHEMISTRY, INORGANIC CHEMISTRY. *Educ:* Monmouth Col, BS, 43; Iowa State Univ, PhD(chem), 52. *Prof Exp:* Asst, 43-46, jr scientist, 46-52, from asst prof to assoc prof, 52-63, PROF CHEM, AMES LAB, IOWA STATE UNIV, 63- *Mem:* Am Chem Soc. *Res:* Ion exchange; rare earth chemistry; chelate formation constants; chelate structures; synthesis; isotope separations; ion exclusion techniques. *Mailing Add:* Ames Lab Iowa State Univ Ames IA 50010

POWELL, JAMES DANIEL, b Paducah, Tex, Sept 13, 34; m 58; c 3. GEOLOGY. *Educ:* Tex Tech Col, BS, 56, MS, 58; Univ Tex, PhD(geol), 61. *Prof Exp:* Res geologist, Res Div, Continental Oil Co, 61-63; asst prof geol, WTex State Univ, 63-64 & Univ Tex, Arlington, 64-70; asst prof, Univ Idaho, 70-74, affil prof geol, US Geol Surv, 74-76; chief res geologist, Union Carbide Corp, 76-79; CONSULT GEOLOGIST, POWELL & ASSOCS, 79- *Mem:* Am Asn Petrol Geologists; Paleont Soc; Soc Econ Paleont & Mineral. *Res:* Mesozoic Ammonoidea; stratigraphy in North and Central America. *Mailing Add:* Powell & Assocs 2697 Continental Dr Grand Junction CO 81501

POWELL, JAMES EDWARD, nuclear engineering, physics, see previous edition

POWELL, JAMES HENRY, b Columbus, Ohio, May 21, 26. MATHEMATICAL STATISTICS. *Educ:* Mich State Univ, BA, 49, MA, 51, PhD(math statist), 54. *Prof Exp:* Instr math, Univ Detroit, 54-55; from asst prof to assoc prof, 55-60, head dept, 60-66, assoc dean sci & arts, 66-69, assoc chmn dept, 73-77, PROF MATH, WESTERN MICH UNIV, 60-, CHMN DEPT, 77- *Mem:* Inst Math Statist; Am Statist Asn; Am Math Soc; Math Asn Am. *Res:* Probability sociometric investigations. *Mailing Add:* Dept of Math Western Mich Univ Kalamazoo MI 49008

POWELL, JAMES LAWRENCE, b Berea, Ky, July 17, 36; m 59; c 2. GEOCHEMISTRY, PETROLOGY. *Educ:* Berea Col, AB, 58; Mass Inst Technol, PhD(geochem), 62. *Prof Exp:* Asst prof, 62-71, chmn dept, 65-74, PROF GEOL, OBERLIN COL, 71-, PROVOST COL, 74-, ACTG PRES, 81- *Mem:* AAAS; fel Geol Soc Am. *Res:* Application of isotope geochemistry to problems of petrology; use of radiogenic isotopes as natural tracers. *Mailing Add:* Dept of Geol Oberlin Col Oberlin OH 44074

POWELL, JAMES R, JR, b Rochester, Pa, June 3, 32; m 65. NUCLEAR ENGINEERING. *Educ:* Carnegie Inst Technol, BS, 53; Mass Inst Technol, ScD(nuclear eng), 57. *Prof Exp:* HEAD, FUSION TECHNOL GROUP, BROOKHAVEN NAT LAB, 56- *Mem:* AAAS; Am Phys Soc; Am Geophys Union; Am Inst Aeronaut & Astronaut; Am Nuclear Soc. *Res:* Fusion and fission technology and cryogenic applications. *Mailing Add:* T-318 Brookhaven Nat Lab Upton NY 11973

POWELL, JEANNE ADELE, b Los Angeles, Calif, Jan 18, 33. DEVELOPMENTAL BIOLOGY. *Educ:* Brown Univ, AB, 54; Bryn Mawr Col, MA, 59, PhD(develop biol), 67. *Prof Exp:* Res asst biol, Brown Univ, 54-55; teacher, Baldwin Sch, 55-64; instr biol, Bryn Mawr Col, 66-67; from asst prof to assoc prof biol, 67-79, PROF BIOL, SMITH COL, 79- *Concurrent Pos:* Assoc investr, NIH fel, Smith Col, 68-73; res fel, Carnegie Inst Wash, 72; vis scientist, Inst Nat de la Sante et de la Recherche Medicale, Paris, 79. *Mem:* AAAS; Soc Develop Biol; Am Soc Cell Biologists. *Res:* Tissue and organ culture of muscle and nerves. *Mailing Add:* Dept of Biol Sci Smith Col Northampton MA 01060

POWELL, JEFF, b Syracuse, NY, Nov 16, 39; m 63; c 1. RANGE SCIENCE. *Educ:* Southeastern La Col, BS, 61; Ore State Univ, BS, 64; Tex Tech Col, MS, 66; Colo State Univ, PhD(range sci), 68. *Prof Exp:* Asst prof range mgt, Humboldt State Col, 68-70; from asst prof to assoc prof, 70-81, PROF RANGE MGT, OKLA STATE UNIV, 81- *Mem:* Fel Soc Range Mgt; Am Soc Animal Sci; Wildlife Soc; Am Soc Agron; Weed Sci Soc Am. *Res:* Range nutrition; management and nutritive value of range plants. *Mailing Add:* Dept of Agron Okla State Univ Stillwater OK 74074

POWELL, JERREL B, b Knowles, Okla, Aug 15, 30; m 52; c 4. GENETICS, AGRONOMY. *Educ:* Okla State Univ, BS, 53, MS, 58; Wash State Univ, PhD(agron), 63. *Prof Exp:* Chief, Field Crops Lab, 77-80, RES GENETICIST, AGR RES SERV, USDA, 63-, ASST DIR, BELTSVILLE AGR RES CTR, 80- *Mem:* AAAS; Am Soc Agron; Crop Sci Soc Am; Am Genetic Asn. *Res:* Breeding and cytogenetics of annual and perennial grasses; mutation breeding of turf grasses. *Mailing Add:* Agr Res Serv USDA Beltsville Agr Res Ctr Beltsville MD 20705

POWELL, JERRY ALAN, b Glendale, Calif, May 23, 33; m 56, 77; c 3. ENTOMOLOGY. *Educ:* Univ Calif, Berkeley, BS, 55, PhD(entom), 61. *Prof Exp:* From jr entomologist to asst entomologist, 61-67, assoc prof entom, Univ, 69-73, assoc entomologist, 67-73, ENTOMOLOGIST, EXP STA, UNIV CALIF, BERKELEY, 73-, PROF ENTOM, UNIV, 73- *Concurrent Pos:* Ed, J Lepidop Soc, 64-69; chief investr, NSF grant, 65-70; vis res fel, Smithsonian Inst, 70-71. *Mem:* Entom Soc Am; Entom Soc Can; Lepidop Soc. *Res:* Comparative biology; systematics and phylogeny of Lepidoptera, particularly the Tortricoidea; behavior of solitary wasps; behavior of predacious Diptera. *Mailing Add:* Dept of Entom & Parasitol Univ of Calif Berkeley CA 94720

POWELL, JOHN DAVID, b Cordele, Ga, Jan 26, 45. ELECTROMAGNETIC PROPULSION. *Educ:* Univ Fla, BS, 67, PhD(physics), 72. *Prof Exp:* Fel, Univ Fla, 72-75; RES PHYSICIST, BALLISTIC RES LAB, 75- *Mem:* Am Phys Soc. *Res:* Electromagnetic propulsion phenomena, plasma dynamics and the molecular dynamic simulation of shock propagation on crystal lattices. *Mailing Add:* 143 Farm Rd Aberdeen MD 21001

POWELL, JOHN EDWARD, b Galesville, Wis, Dec 2, 18; m 43; c 2. HYDROLOGY. *Educ:* Marquette Univ, PhB, 40; Univ NDak, BS, 50. *Prof Exp:* Geologist, US Geol Surv, 45-51, hydraul engr, 51-58, dist engr, 58-66, dist chief water resources div, 66-78; CONSULT HYDROLOGIST, 78- *Mem:* Nat Soc Prof Eng; fel Geol Soc Am; Nat Water Well Asn. *Res:* Civil engineering; movement of water through igneous and/or metamorphic host rocks, especially in the vicinities of intrusives; design of ground-water quality monitoring systems. *Mailing Add:* 1831 McClellan Dr Huron SD 57350

POWELL, JOHN LEONARD, b Portland, Ore, May 12, 19; m 43; c 2. PHYSICS. *Educ:* Reed Col, BA, 43; Univ Wis, PhD(physics), 48. *Prof Exp:* Res assoc, Radiation Lab, Mass Inst Technol, 43-45; asst physics, Univ Wis, 45-48, from asst prof to assoc prof, 49-54; res assoc, Inst Nuclear Studies, Univ Chicago, 48-49; lab dir, Theoret Group, Missile Systs Div, Lockheed Aircraft Corp, 54-55; assoc prof, 55-57, head dept, 60-66, PROF PHYSICS, UNIV ORE, 57- *Mem:* Fel Am Phys Soc; Am Asn Physics Teachers. *Res:* Quantum electrodynamics; nuclear scattering; particle accelerators; neutron transport theory. *Mailing Add:* Dept of Physics Univ of Ore Eugene OR 97403

POWELL, JUSTIN CHRISTOPHER, physical organic chemistry, see previous edition

POWELL, LESLIE CHARLES, b Beaumont, Tex, Dec 13, 27; m 52; c 4. OBSTETRICS & GYNECOLOGY. *Educ:* Southern Methodist Univ, BS, 48; Johns Hopkins Univ, MD, 52; Am Bd Obstet & Gynec, dipl, 61. *Prof Exp:* Rotating intern, 52-53, resident, 53-55, from instr to assoc prof, 57-68, PROF OBSTET & GYNEC, UNIV TEX MED BR, GALVESTON, 68- *Concurrent Pos:* Ed consult, Tex State J Med, 64-; USPHS grant cancer screening, 67-71; consult, Tex State Dept Ment Health & Retardation, 70-; Fulbright-Hayes lectr & vis prof obstet & gynec, Union of Burma, 75-76. *Mem:* Fel Am Col Obstetricians & Gynecologists; AMA. *Res:* Isoimmunization in pregnancy; hormones, effects and side effects; gynecological malignancy; treatment of sexual dysfunction; fertility control. *Mailing Add:* Dept of Obstet & Gynec Univ of Tex Med Br Galveston TX 77550

POWELL, LOYD EARL, JR, b Ravenwood, Mo, Oct 17, 28; m 56; c 3. POMOLOGY, PLANT PHYSIOLOGY. *Educ:* Univ Mo, BS, 51; Ohio State Univ, MS, 52; Cornell Univ, PhD, 55. *Prof Exp:* Asst prof, NY State Agr Exp Sta, Geneva, 55-61; assoc prof, 61-74, PROF POMOL, NY STATE COL AGR & LIFE SCI, CORNELL UNIV, 74- *Concurrent Pos:* Res assoc, Yale Univ, 62-63; NATO vis prof, Univ Pisa, Italy, 75. *Honors & Awards:* J H Gourley Award, Am Soc Hort Sci, 75. *Mem:* fel Am Soc Hort Sci; Am Soc Plant Physiol; Scandinavian Soc Plant Physiol. *Res:* Plant hormones; dormancy; fruit development. *Mailing Add:* Dept of Pomol Cornell Univ Ithaca NY 14850

POWELL, MICHAEL ROBERT, b Detroit, Mich, Nov 23, 41; m 64; c 4. HYPERBARIC PHYSIOLOGY, HYPERBARIC MEDICINE. *Educ:* Mich State Univ, BS, 63, MS, 67, PhD(biophys), 69. *Prof Exp:* Res biophysicist, Res Inst, Union Carbide Corp, 69-75; dir hyperbaric lab, Inst Appl Physiol & Med, 75-77; mem staff, Inst Flugmedizin, 77-80; PRES & DIR, HYPERBARIC LAB, INST APPL PHYSIOL & MED, 80- *Mem:* Am Physiol Soc; Am Chem Soc; Biophys Soc; Undersea Med Soc; Aerospace Med Asn. *Res:* Inert gas narcosis; hyperbaric physiology; gas transport; in vivo bubble formation; pathophysiology of decompression sideness; oxygen toxicity; hyperbaric medicine. *Mailing Add:* Inst Appl Physiol & Med 701 16th Ave Seattle WA 98122

POWELL, NATHANIEL THOMAS, b Halifax, Va, July 7, 28; m 51; c 3. PLANT PATHOLOGY. *Educ:* Va Polytech Inst & State Univ, BS, 50; NC State Univ, MSc, 56, PhD(plant path), 58. *Prof Exp:* Res asst prof plant path, 58-62, assoc prof, 62-67, PROF PLANT PATH & GENETICS, NC STATE UNIV, 67- *Mem:* Am Phytopath Soc. *Res:* Disease complexes in plants; genetics and nature of disease resistance in plants; host-parasite relationships; physiology of parasitism. *Mailing Add:* NC State Univ PO Box 5397 State Univ Sta Raleigh NC 27607

POWELL, NOBLE R, b New Kensington, Pa, Apr 19, 30; m 53; c 3. ELECTRIAL ENGINEERING. *Educ:* Columbia Univ, BSEE, 58; Syracuse Univ, PhD(elec eng), 68. *Prof Exp:* Consult engr, Signal Processing, Instrumentation, 76, mgr, Integrated Functional Processors, 76-79, mgr, Architecture & Processor Devint, 79-81, PRIN STAFF ENGR, ELECTRONICS LAB, GEN ELEC, 81- *Concurrent Pos:* Adj prof very-large-scale integration, Syracuse Univ, 79 & Cornell Univ, 80- *Honors & Awards:* Indust Res-100 Award, Indust Res Corp, 75. *Mem:* Sigma Xi. *Res:* Critical issues pertaining to large scale electronic integration of modular functions; digital filters; graphics functional generators; matrix array processors. *Mailing Add:* Bldg 3 Electronics Park Gen Elec Co Syracuse NY 13221

POWELL, NORBORNE BERKELEY, b Montgomery, Ala, July 24, 14; m 39; c 2. UROLOGY. *Educ:* Baylor Univ, MD, 38. *Prof Exp:* Asst urol, Sch Med, Tulane Univ, 40-42; assoc prof, 43-65, PROF CLIN UROL, BAYLOR COL MED, 65-; CHIEF UROL, TWELVE OAKS HOSP, HOUSTON, 66- *Concurrent Pos:* Trustee, Baylor Med Found, 49-; chief of staff, Twelve Oaks Hosp, 74; pvt pract. *Honors & Awards:* Prize, Am Urol Asn, 51. *Mem:* Am Urol Asn; Am Fertil Soc; Biol Photog Asn; fel Am Col Surgeons; fel Int Col Surgeons. *Res:* Clinical research on urological problems. *Mailing Add:* 1726 Twelve Oaks Tower 4126 Southwest Freeway Houston TX 77027

POWELL, R(AY) B(EDENKAPP), b Buffalo, NY, June 13, 20; m 48; c 3. MECHANICAL ENGINEERING. *Educ:* Univ Mich, BSME, 43. *Prof Exp:* Tech asst to supt area plant, Manhattan Eng Dist, Res Labs, Union Carbide Carbon Corp, 43-44; mech engr & leader design & maintenance group, Los Alamos Sci Lab, 44-45, admin asst leader chem & metall div, 45-46, asst to personnel dir, 47; personnel mgr, 47-49, mgr, Employ & Personnel Dept, 49-54, supt personnel & pub rels, 54-59, asst vpres admin, 59, VPRES, SANDIA NAT LABS, 59- *Mailing Add:* Sandia Nat Labs Albuquerque NM 87185

POWELL, RALPH ROBERT, b Beech Grove, Ind, June 23, 36; m 65; c 4. PHYSICAL CHEMISTRY. *Educ:* Marian Col, Ind, BS, 58; Purdue Univ, PhD(chem), 65. *Prof Exp:* Instr chem, Purdue Univ, 64-65, asst prof, 65-66; asst prof, 66-76, ASSOC PROF CHEM, EASTERN MICH UNIV, 76- *Mem:* AAAS; Am Chem Soc. *Res:* Application of quantum theory to chemical systems using computer programs; development of the use of computers for instructional purposes both in the laboratory and in the classroom. *Mailing Add:* Dept of Chem Eastern Mich Univ Ypsilanti MI 48197

POWELL, REX LYNN, b Lansing, Mich, Nov 19, 42; m 64; c 2. ANIMAL BREEDING. *Educ:* Mich State Univ, BS, 64, MS, 69; Iowa State Univ, PhD(animal breeding), 72. *Prof Exp:* RES GENETICIST, ANIMAL IMPROV PROG LAB, ANIMAL SCI INST, SCI & EDUC ADMIN-AGR RES, USDA, 72- *Concurrent Pos:* Mem comt standards for estimating yield and other performance traits, Coord Group Nat Coop Dairy Herd Improv Prog, 75-80, Res Comt Policy Bd, 80- *Mem:* Am Dairy Sci Asn; Dairy Shrine; Sigma Xi. *Res:* Developing and analyzing methods for genetic evaluation of dairy cattle and inclusion of non-yield traits in the national program; examination of genotype-environment interaction and estimation of genetic trends. *Mailing Add:* Bldg 263 Agr Res Ctr Sci & Educ Admin-Agr Res USDA Beltsville MD 20705

POWELL, RICHARD ANTHONY, b Buffalo, NY, Apr 11, 17; m 43; c 5. DENTISTRY. *Educ:* Syracuse Univ, AB, 39; Univ Buffalo, DDS, 49. *Prof Exp:* Clin instr oper dent, 49-53, from asst prof to assoc prof oper dent & endodontics, 53-61, asst dean clin opers & student affairs, 65-68, PROF OPER DENT & ENDODONTICS, STATE UNIV NY BUFFALO, 61-, ASSOC DEAN CLIN OPERS & STUDENT AFFAIRS, 68, DIR CLINS, 71- *Concurrent Pos:* Consult, Vet Admin Hosp, Buffalo, NY, 65-; chmn coun sects, Am Asn Dent Schs. *Mem:* Am Dent Asn; fel Am Col Dent; fel Int Col Dentists. Res; Operative dentistry; endodontics; silver amalgam restorations. *Mailing Add:* 194 Farber Hall State Univ NY Buffalo NY 14214

POWELL, RICHARD CINCLAIR, b South Bend, Ind, July 28, 29; m 54; c 2. INTERNAL MEDICINE, ENDOCRINOLOGY. *Educ:* DePauw Univ, AB, 51; Northwestern Univ, MD, 55; Am Bd Internal Med, dipl, 63. *Prof Exp:* From instr to assoc prof, 61-72, PROF MED, SCH MED, IND UNIV, INDIANAPOLIS, 72- *Concurrent Pos:* Attend physician, Vet Admin Hosp, Indianapolis, 63-; assoc staff, med sect, Marion County Gen Hosp, Ind, 65- *Mem:* AMA; fel Am Col Physicians; Endocrine Soc; Am Diabetes Asn; Am Heart Asn. *Res:* Thyroid physiology; lipid metabolism. *Mailing Add:* Dept of Med Ind Univ Med Ctr Indianapolis IN 46202

POWELL, RICHARD CONGER, b Lincoln, Nebr, Dec 20, 39; m 62; c 2. SOLID STATE PHYSICS. *Educ:* US Naval Acad, BS, 62; Ariz State Univ, MS, 64, PhD(physics), 67. *Prof Exp:* Res scientist, Air Force Cambridge Res Labs, 64-68; res scientist, Sandia Labs, NMex, 68-71; assoc prof, 71-73, PROF PHYSICS, OKLA STATE UNIV, 73- *Mem:* Am Phys Soc. *Res:* Optical spectra of solids; energy transfer in solids. *Mailing Add:* 1324 N Washington St Stillwater OK 74074

POWELL, RICHARD GRANT, b Avon, Ill, Oct 29, 38; m 60; c 2. NATURAL PRODUCTS CHEMISTRY. *Educ:* Western Ill Univ, BS, 61, MSEd, 63. *Prof Exp:* RES CHEMIST, NORTHERN REGIONAL RES CTR, AGR RES SERV, USDA, 63- *Concurrent Pos:* Res fel, Univ St Andrews, 66-67. *Mem:* Am Chem Soc; Phytochem Soc NAm; Soc Econ Bot; Am Soc Pharmacog. *Res:* Alkaloids; lipids; antitumor compounds; natural products. *Mailing Add:* Northern Regional Res Ctr USDA 1815 N University St Peoria IL 61604

POWELL, RICHARD JAMES, b Muskogee, Okla, Mar 15, 31; m 54; c 5. POLYMER CHEMISTRY. *Educ:* Okla State Univ, BS, 53. *Prof Exp:* Chem engr, 53-65, sr res engr, 65-72, res assoc, 72-78, RES FEL, E I DU PONT DE NEMOURS & CO, INC, 78- *Mem:* Am Chem Soc. *Res:* Product and process development on Surlyn ionomer resins; all product end uses, including molding, film, sheeting and extrusion coating. *Mailing Add:* E I Du Pont de Nemours & Co, Inc Sabine River Lab Orange TX 77630

POWELL, RICHARD JAMES, b Detroit, Mich, May 21, 35; c 3. SOLID STATE PHYSICS. *Educ:* San Jose State Col, BS, 59; Stanford Univ, MS, 61, PhD(elec eng), 67. *Prof Exp:* Eng specialist microwave device develop, Sylvania Electronic Systs, 59-68; mem tech staff device physics res, Bell Tel Labs, 68-73; MEM TECH STAFF, RCA LABS/DAVID SARNOFF RES CTR, 73- *Concurrent Pos:* Instr, Electronic Physics Dept, LaSalle Col Philadelphia, 74- *Honors & Awards:* Outstanding Paper Award, Inst Elec & Electronics Engrs Conf Nuclear & Space Radiation Effects, 71 & 74. *Mem:* sr mem Inst Elec & Electronics Engrs. *Res:* Electronic structure of solids; photoinjection into insulators; radiation effects, particularly charge accumulation in metal oxide semiconductor devices; interface devices; semiconductor device processing and development; device engineering. *Mailing Add:* David Sarnoff Res Ctr RCA Labs Princeton NJ 08540

POWELL, RICHARD L, b Toledo, Ohio, Jan 31, 28; m 51; c 3. SPEECH PATHOLOGY, AUDIOLOGY. *Educ:* Cent Mich Univ, BS, 53; Univ Mich, MA, 58; Mich State Univ, PhD(audiol, speech sci), 67. *Prof Exp:* Speech therapist, Beecher Pub Sch, 53-58 & Albion Pub Schs, 58-61; PROF SPEECH PATH & AUDIOL, CENT MICH UNIV, 61- *Concurrent Pos:* Area coordr commun dis, 68-72. *Mem:* Am Speech & Hearing Asn. *Res:* Speech and hearing science; communication disabilities. *Mailing Add:* Dept of Speech 416 Moore Hall Cent Mich Univ Mt Pleasant MI 48859

POWELL, ROBERT DELAFIELD, b St Paul, Minn, Aug 14, 19; m 46; c 4. PLANT PHYSIOLOGY. *Educ:* Univ Minn, BS, 43; Iowa State Univ, PhD(plant physiol), 50. *Prof Exp:* Instr bot, Iowa State Col, 48-49; asst prof, Univ Fla, 49-56, assoc prof, 56-63; assoc prof, 63-72, PROF PLANT PHYSIOL, TEX A&M UNIV, 72- *Mem:* Am Soc Plant Physiol. *Res:* Effect of environmental factors on growth and development. *Mailing Add:* Dept Plant Sci Tex A&M Univ College Station TX 77843

POWELL, ROBERT ELLIS, b Lansing, Mich, Mar 16, 36; m 58; c 3. MATHEMATICS. *Educ:* Mich State Univ, BA, 58, MA, 59; Lehigh Univ, PhD(math), 66. *Prof Exp:* Assoc res engr, Boeing Co, Wash, 59-61; instr math, Highline Col, 61-63; instr, Lehigh Univ, 64-66; asst prof, Univ Kans, 66-69; assoc prof, 69-74, assoc dean, 74-75, dean, Grad Col, 75-76, PROF MATH, KENT STATE UNIV, 74-, DEAN, GRAD COL, 80- *Concurrent Pos:* Vis res asst prof, Univ Ky, 67-68. *Mem:* Math Asn Am. *Res:* Examination of summability and related approximation procedures in complex analysis. *Mailing Add:* Dept of Math Kent State Univ Kent OH 44242

POWELL, ROBERT LEE, b Chicago, Ill, Mar 11, 28; div; c 4. ORTHOPEDIC RES, THERMOMETRY. *Educ:* Univ Colo, BS, 50, MA, 51; Cambridge Univ, PhD, 66. *Prof Exp:* proj leader, sect chief & consult, Cryogenics Div, Nat Bur Standards, 51-61, 63-76; CONSULT, 76-; ORTHOP PHYSICIANS ASST, UNIV COLO HEALTH SCI CTR, 81- *Honors & Awards:* Exceptional Serv Award, US Dept Com, 53; Award of Merit, Am Soc Test & Mat, 72. *Mem:* Am Phys Soc; Am Soc Test & Mat; fel Brit Inst Physics; Am Soc Orthop Phys Asst. *Res:* Low temperature transport properties of solids; thermal and electrical conductivity of pure metals and dilute alloys; thermometry; applications of superconductivity; basic science of orthopedics. *Mailing Add:* 2795 Stanford Ave Boulder CO 80303

POWELL, ROBERT W, JR, b Mobile, Ala, Nov 11, 29; m 58; c 4. BOTANY. *Educ:* Memphis State Univ, BS, 51; Univ Houston, MS, 53; Duke Univ, PhD(bot), 60. *Prof Exp:* Asst prof biol, Memphis State Univ, 59-61; asst prof bot, Humboldt State Col, 61-63; PROF BIOL & CHMN DEPT, CONVERSE COL, 63- *Mem:* Sigma Xi; Am Inst Biol Sci. *Res:* Plant taxonomy; ecology; local flora; horticulture; plant propagation. *Mailing Add:* Dept Biol Converse Col Spartanburg SC 29301

POWELL, ROBIN DALE, b Indianapolis, Ind, Apr 19, 34; m 57; c 3. MEDICINE. *Educ:* Univ Chicago, MD, 57. *Prof Exp:* Intern med, Minneapolis Gen Hosp, 57-58; resident internal med, Univ Chicago, 58-61, from instr to asst prof med, 63-69; assoc prof, Col Med, Univ Iowa, 69-72, prof internal med, 72-78; PROF INTERNAL MED, SCH MED & ASSOC DEAN ACAD AFFAIRS, NORTHWESTERN UNIV, 78- *Concurrent Pos:* Mem comn malaria, Armed Forces Epidemiol Bd, 64-72; consult, Surgeon Gen, US Dept Army, 64-; mem expert adv panel malaria, WHO, 65-; assoc chief of staff res & educ, Iowa City Vet Admin Hosp, 70- *Mem:* AAAS; Am Heart Asn; AMA; Am Fedn Clin Res; Am Soc Trop Med & Hyg. *Res:* Internal medicine; human malaria; erythrocyte biochemistry. *Mailing Add:* Med Sch Northestern Univ 303 E Chicago Ave Chicago IL 60611

POWELL, ROGER ALLEN, b Joliet, Ill, Jan 24, 49; m 72; c 1. BEHAVIORAL ECOLOGY, MAMMALOGY. *Educ:* Carleton Col, BA, 71; Univ Chicago, PhD(biol), 77. *Prof Exp:* Lectr natural resources, Univ Mich, 77; lectr biol, Univ Chicago, 78; ASST PROF BEHAV ECOL, MAMMAL & WILDLIFE, DEPT ZOOL & FORESTRY, NC STATE UNIV, 79- *Concurrent Pos:* Coop res asst, US Forest Serv, 73-76; vis asst prof behav ecol, Dept Ecol, Ethol & Evolution, Univ Ill, 78-79. *Mem:* Am Soc Mammalogists; Animal Behav Soc; British Ecol Soc; Ecol Soc Am; Wildlife Soc. *Res:* Ecology with special interests in theory, predation, vertebrate predators and mammals; broad experience with carnivora, especially Mustelidae. *Mailing Add:* Dept Zool & Forestry PO Box 5577 NC State Univ Raleigh NC 27650

POWELL, RONALD ALLAN, b Brooklyn, NY, Oct 18, 46; m 75. SOLID STATE PHYSICS. *Educ:* Union Col, BS, 67; Stanford Univ, MS, 69, PhD(physics), 73. *Prof Exp:* Teaching & res asst physics, Stanford Univ, 68-73, res assoc physics, 74-76, sr res assoc elec eng, 76-78; SR STAFF SCIENTIST, VARIAN ASSOC, 78- *Mem:* Am Phys Soc; Am Vacuum Soc; Am Asn Physics Teachers. *Res:* Advanced processing techniques for integrated circuit technology of silicon and III-V compound semiconductors; plasma etching; ion implantation; photon and electron beam processing of semiconductors. *Mailing Add:* 427 Crest Dr Redwood City CA 94062

POWELL, S(HANNON) CURTIS, engineering, deceased

POWELL, SMITH THOMPSON, III, b Kirksville, Mo, Jan 8, 40; m 78; c 7. PHYSICS. *Educ:* Berea Col, BA, 61; Univ Mich, Ann Arbor, MS, 63, PhD(physics), 70. *Prof Exp:* Asst prof, 70-78, ASSOC PROF PHYSICS, BEREA COL, 78- *Mem:* AAAS; Am Asn Physics Teachers; Am Phys Soc. *Res:* Elementary particle physics; astronomy; optics; demography; computer sciences. *Mailing Add:* CPO 1630 Berea KY 40404

POWELL, STEPHEN EDWARD, b Peru, Ind, Oct 22, 48; m 75; c 2. MEAT SCIENTIST. *Educ:* Purdue Univ, BS, 70, MS, 72, PhD(meat sci), 78. *Prof Exp:* Instr animal sci, WVa Univ, 72-75 & Purdue Univ, 75-78; ASST PROF ANIMAL INDUST, SOUTHERN ILL UNIV, 78- *Mem:* Am Soc Animal Sci; Am Meat Sci Asn. *Res:* Meat animal growth and composition; grade standards; swine nutrition and production. *Mailing Add:* Dept Animal Indust Agr Bldg Southern Ill Univ Carbondale IL 62901

POWELL, THOMAS EDWARD, b Warrenton, NC, July 6, 99; m 22, 45; c 4. BIOLOGY. *Educ:* Elon Col, AB, 19; Univ NC, MA, 24; Duke Univ, PhD(biol), 30. *Hon Degrees:* DSc, Elon Col, 68. *Prof Exp:* From instr to prof biol & geol, Elon Col, 19-36; PRES, CAROLINA BIOL SUPPLY CO, 36-, WAUBUN LABS, LA, 45- & POWELL LABS, ORE, 60- *Mem:* AAAS; Am Soc Limnol & Oceanog; Soc Protozool; Am Micros Soc; Nat Asn Biol Teachers. *Res:* Microbiology; ecology; life history and control of Lasioderma serricorne. *Mailing Add:* Carolina Biol Supply Co Burlington NC 27215

POWELL, THOMAS SHAW, b Hahira, Ga, Aug 28, 46; m 72; c 1. POULTRY NUTRITION, MANAGEMENT. *Educ:* Univ Fla, BS, 68, MS, 71; NC State Univ, PhD(animal Sci), 74. *Prof Exp:* Poultry nutritionist, Cent Soya Res, 74-79; nutritionist, Crystal Farms, Inc, 79-80; NUTRITIONIST, CARNATION CO, 80- *Mem:* Poultry Sci Asn. *Res:* Nutritional requirements of broiler breeders and turkeys; nutritional requirements of broilers and management factors affecting leghorn pullets. *Mailing Add:* 2830 Cascade Dr Gainesville GA 30501

POWELL, WARREN HOWARD, b North Collins, NY, Jan 1, 34; m 55; c 3. ORGANIC CHEMISTRY. *Educ:* Antioch Col, BS, 55; Ohio State Univ, PhD(chem), 59. *Prof Exp:* Asst, Kettering Found, Antioch Col, 52-53; jr technician, Battelle Mem Inst, 53-54; asst, Kettering Found, Antioch Col, 54-55; asst, Ohio State Univ, 55-57, asst instr, 57-58, instr, 58; res chemist org chem dept, E I du Pont de Nemours & Co, 59-64; asst ed, 64-67, assoc ed, 67-69, sr assoc ed, 69-73, SR ED, CHEM ABSTRACTS SERV, 73- *Concurrent Pos:* Mem comt nomenclature inorg chem div chem & chem technol, Nat Acad Sci-Nat Res Coun, 68-72; assoc mem comn nomenclature inorg chem, Int Union Pure & Appl Chem, 69-75, Titular mem, 75- & assoc mem comn nomenclature org chem, 75- *Mem:* Am Chem Soc. *Res:* Heterocyclic compounds, especially acridines and benzothiazoles; aromatic fluorine compounds; biphenyl derivatives; chemical nomenclature, especially organic. *Mailing Add:* Chem Abstracts Serv PO Box 3012 Columbus OH 43210

POWELL, WILLIAM ALLAN, b Wallace, NC, May 28, 21; m 41; c 3. ANALYTICAL CHEMISTRY. *Educ:* Wake Forest Col, BS, 42; Duke Univ, PhD(chem), 53. *Prof Exp:* Asst chief chemist, Carolina Aluminum Co, 42-46; indust hyg chemist, Aluminum Co Am, 46-48; instr chem, Wake Forest Col, 48-49 & Duke Univ, 49-51; from asst prof to assoc prof, 52-66, PROF CHEM, UNIV RICHMOND, 66-, CHMN DEPT, 59- *Concurrent Pos:* Consult, Philip Morris, 57- *Mem:* AAAS; Am Chem Soc. *Res:* Instrumental methods of analysis. *Mailing Add:* Dept of Chem Univ of Richmond Richmond VA 23173

POWELL, WILLIAM EDWARD, III, b Jackson, Ala, Mar 29, 44; m 67. FOOD SCIENCE. *Educ:* Auburn Univ, BS, 66, PhD(meat sci), 70. *Prof Exp:* Asst prof animal sci, Auburn Univ, 69-70, specialist in food sci, Coop Exten Serv, 70-76; MEM STAFF, LAPEYROUSE GAIN CORP, 76- *Mem:* Am Meat Sci Asn; Am Soc Animal Sci; Inst Food Technol. *Res:* Carcass compositon of beef and swine; sanitation and quality control of food processing firms. *Mailing Add:* Lapeyrouse Gain Corp PO Box 926 Mobile AL 36601

POWELL, WILLIAM MORTON, b Halifax, Va, May 12, 30; m 53; c 4. PLANT PATHOLOGY. *Educ:* Va Polytech, BS, 53; NC State Univ, MS, 57, PhD(plant path), 60. *Prof Exp:* From asst prof to assoc prof, 60-73, PROF PLANT PATH, UNIV GA, 73- *Mem:* Am Phytopath Soc; Soc Nematol. *Res:* Host-parasite relations of plant parasitic nematodes; nematode-fungus interactions in plant disease. *Mailing Add:* Dept of Plant Path & Genetics Univ of Ga Athens GA 30601

POWELSON, ELIZABETH EUGENIE, b New York, NY, Jan 30, 24. GENETICS. *Educ:* Oberlin Col, AB, 46; Wellesley Col, MA, 48; Ind Univ, PhD(zool), 57. *Prof Exp:* Instr biol, Hood Col, 48-52; from instr to assoc prof, 57-71, chmn dept, 64-73, prof, 71-73, GREENAWALT PROF BIOL, WITTENBERG UNIV, 73- *Concurrent Pos:* Fel, Johns Hopkins Med Sch, 73-75. *Mem:* AAAS; Am Soc Human Genetics; Sigma Xi; Am Dermat Asn. *Res:* The relationship of chromosomal translocations to birth defects in humans and its implication for genetic counseling. *Mailing Add:* Dept of Biol Wittenberg Univ Springfield OH 45501

POWELSON, ROBERT LORAN, b Salt Lake City, Utah, Sept 23, 29; m 48, 73; c 4. PLANT PATHOLOGY. *Educ:* Utah State Univ, BS, 51, MS, 56; Ore State Col, PhD(plant path), 59. *Prof Exp:* From asst plant pathologist to assoc plant pathologist, 59-74, PROF PLANT PATHOL, ORE STATE UNIV, 74- *Mem:* Am Phytopath Soc. *Res:* Ecology of soil-borne plant pathogens; epidemiology of plant diseases. *Mailing Add:* Dept Bot & Plant Path Ore State Univ Corvallis OR 97331

POWER, DENNIS MICHAEL, b Pasadena, Calif, Feb 18, 41; m 65; c 2. EVOLUTIONARY BIOLOGY, ZOOGEOGRAPHY. *Educ:* Occidental Col, BA, 62, MA, 64; Univ Kans, PhD(zool), 67. *Prof Exp:* From asst cur to assoc cur ornith, Royal Ont Mus, 67-72; DIR, SANTA BARBARA MUS NATURAL HIST, 72- *Concurrent Pos:* Nat Res Coun Can res grant, 68-; Dept Univ Affairs Ont res grant, 68-72 & NSF grants, 73-74; asst prof, Univ Toronto, 68-72; assoc res zoologist, Univ Calif, Santa Barbara, 72- *Mem:* AAAS; Soc Syst Zool; Soc Study Evolution; Am Ornith Union; Cooper Ornith Soc. *Res:* Statistical analysis in systematic and evolutionary biology; evolutionary and ecological studies of birds and bird communities. *Mailing Add:* Santa Barbara Mus Natural Hist 2559 Puesta del Sol Rd Santa Barbara CA 93105

POWER, GEOFFREY, b Accrington, Eng, Sept 21, 33; Can citizen; m 56; c 2. FISH BIOLOGY. *Educ:* Univ Durham, BSc, 54; McGill Univ, PhD(zool), 59. *Prof Exp:* From asst prof to assoc prof, 57-71, PROF BIOL, UNIV WATERLOO, 71- *Concurrent Pos:* Assoc marine biol, Woods Hole Oceanog Inst; res prof, Univ Laval, 74-78. *Mem:* Am Fisheries Soc; Can Soc Zoologists; Brit Freshwater Biol Asn; fel Arctic Inst NAm. *Res:* Arctic and subarctic freshwater fisheries. *Mailing Add:* Dept of Biol Univ of Waterloo Waterloo ON N2L 3G1 Can

POWER, GORDON G, b Baltimore, Md, July 12, 35; m 60; c 3. PHYSIOLOGY, INTERNAL MEDICINE. *Educ:* Swarthmore Col, BA, 57; Univ Pa, MD, 61. *Prof Exp:* Intern, Philadelphia Gen Hosp, 61-62; resident internal med, Hosp, Univ Va, 62-63; Nat Heart Inst fel pulmonary physiol, Univ Pa, 63-65; resident, Philadelphia Gen Hosp, 65-66; from asst prof to assoc prof, 69-75, PROF OBSTET & GYNEC, SCH MED, LOMA LINDA UNIV, 75- *Concurrent Pos:* Nat Inst Child Health career develop award, NIH, 69-74. *Mem:* Am Fedn Clin Res; Am Physiol Soc; Soc Gynec Invest; Perinatal Res Soc. *Res:* Pulmonary physiology; gas exchanges; diffusion, fetal and placental physiology; blood flow regulation; blood gases; control of circulation. *Mailing Add:* Dept of Obstet & Gynec Loma Linda Univ Sch of Med Loma Linda CA 92354

POWER, HARRY WALDO, III, b Conrad, Mont, Jan 24, 45. EVOLUTIONARY BIOLOGY. *Educ:* Univ Mont, BA, 67; Univ Mich, MA, 69, PhD(zool), 74. *Prof Exp:* Vis asst prof, Syracuse Univ, 74-76; asst prof, 76-81, ASSOC PROF BIOL, LIVINGSTON COL, RUTGERS UNIV, 81- *Concurrent Pos:* NSF grant, 76-79. *Mem:* Ecol Soc Am; Am Ornithologists Union; Cooper Ornith Soc; Animal Behav Soc; AAAS. *Res:* Evolution of social behavior and clutch sizes. *Mailing Add:* Dept of Biol Rutgers Univ New Brunswick NJ 08903

POWER, JAMES FRANCIS, b Saybrook, Ill, Sept 18, 29; m 58; c 9. SOIL SCIENCE. *Educ:* Univ Ill, BS, 51, MS, 52; Mich State Univ, PhD, 54. *Prof Exp:* RES SOIL SCIENTIST, USDA, 55- *Concurrent Pos:* Vis staff mem, Cornell Univ, 66-67; fel, Grad Facil, Univ Nebr. *Mem:* Soc Range Mgt; fel Am Inst Chemists; Soil Sci Soc Am; Am Soc Agron; Soil Conserv Soc Am. *Res:* Chemistry and biochemistry of soil nitrogen and phosphorus as affected by soil management and environment; reclamation of land disturbed by surface mining; nutrient cycling in rangeland soils. *Mailing Add:* USDA Agr Res Serv 122 Keim Hall, UNL Lincoln NE 68583

POWER, RICHARD B, b Aug 23, 18; US citizen. BIOLOGY. *Educ:* Fordham Univ, BS, 43, MS, 46, PhD(biol), 55, LHD, 65; Manhattan Col, PdD, 64. *Prof Exp:* Teacher, Power Mem Acad, NY, 37-47; instr biol, Iona Col, 47-54; prin, All Hallows Inst, NY, 54-59; pres, Iona Col, 59-65; teacher, Essex Cath High Sch, NJ, 65-67; PROF BIOL, IONA COL, 67- *Mem:* Nat Wildlife Fedn; Electron Micros Inst. *Mailing Add:* Dept Biol Iona Col 715 North Ave New Rochelle NY 10801

POWER, WALTER ROBERT, b Seattle, Wash, Nov 7, 24; m 60; c 2. GEOLOGY. *Educ:* Univ Wash, BS, 50; Johns Hopkins Univ, PhD, 59. *Prof Exp:* Geologist, US Geol Surv, 50-54; asst prof geol, Univ Ga, 57-61; chief geologist, Ga Marble Co, 61-67; PROF GEOL, GA STATE UNIV, 67- *Concurrent Pos:* Consult geologist indust minerals. *Mem:* AAAS; Geol Soc Am; Am Inst Mining, Metall & Petrol Engrs; Soc Econ Geol. *Res:* Geology of industrial minerals; economic geology. *Mailing Add:* Dept of Geol Ga State Univ Atlanta GA 30303

POWERS, CHARLES F, b Romney, WVa, Nov 5, 25; m 55; c 2. LIMNOLOGY. *Educ:* Univ NC, AB, 50; Cornell Univ, PhD(oceanog), 55. *Prof Exp:* Res assoc oceanog, Cornell Univ, 51-53; instr zool, Univ & res assoc, Great Lakes Res Inst, Univ Mich, Ann Arbor, 55-58, asst prof, Inst & Univ, 58-62, assoc res oceanogr, Great Lakes Res Div, Inst Sci & Technol, 60-68; res aquatic biologist, Marine & Freshwater Ecol Br, 68-80, RES BIOLOGIST, CORVALLIS ENVIRON RES LAB, ENVIRON PROTECTION AGENCY, 80- *Concurrent Pos:* Investr, US Bur Commercial Fisheries, 59- *Mem:* AAAS; Sigma Xi; Int Asn Theoret & Appl

Limnol. *Res:* Eutrophication of fresh waters; pollution of coastal waters; bioenergetics of aquatic environments; restoration of eutrophic lakes; environmental effects of acid precipitation. *Mailing Add:* Corvallis Environ Res Lab 200 SW 35th St Corvallis OR 97331

POWERS, DALE ROBERT, b Yankton, SDak, Mar 13, 49; m 74; c 1. PHYSICAL CHEMISTRY, CHEMICAL ENGINEERING. *Educ:* Iowa State Univ, BS, 70; Calif Inst Technol, PhD(phys chem), 75. *Prof Exp:* Consult chem anal, Jet Propulsion Labs, 73-74; SR CHEMIST, CORNING GLASS WORKS, 74- *Mem:* Am Chem Soc. *Res:* Process research on optical waveguide preparation; kinetics of hydrocarbon reactions; kinetics of organometalic compounds. *Mailing Add:* 582 Victory Hwy Painted Post NY 14870

POWERS, DANA AUBURN, b Ironton, Mo, July 16, 48; m 74. INORGANIC CHEMISTRY, HIGH TEMPERATURE CHEMISTRY. *Educ:* Calif Inst Technol, BS, 70, PhD(inorg chem), 74. *Prof Exp:* MEM TECH STAFF MAT SCI, SANDIA LABS, 75- *Mem:* Am Chem Soc. *Res:* Experimental investigations with the consequences of nuclear reactor core-meltdown accidents; kinetics of metallothermic reactions. *Mailing Add:* Div 5831 Sandia Labs Albuquerque NM 87115

POWERS, DANIEL D, b Wichita, Kans, Jan 23, 35; m 60; c 2. ORGANIC CHEMISTRY. *Educ:* Univ Wichita, BS, 56, MS, 58; Univ Kans, PhD(chem), 66. *Prof Exp:* From asst prof to assoc prof, 63-70, PROF CHEM, STERLING COL, 70-, CHMN DEPT, 71- *Concurrent Pos:* Vis prof, Biochem Dept, Kans State Univ, 78-79. *Mem:* Am Chem Soc. *Res:* Chemical education; protein chemistry. *Mailing Add:* Dept Chem Sterling Col Sterling KS 67579

POWERS, DARDEN, b Holly Springs, Miss, Nov 15, 32; m 57; c 4. ATOMIC & MOLECULAR PHYSICS. *Educ:* Univ Okla, BS, 55; Calif Inst Technol, MS, 57, PhD(physics), 61. *Prof Exp:* From asst prof to assoc prof, 61-68, PROF PHYSICS, BAYLOR UNIV, 68- *Concurrent Pos:* Head, Van de Graaff Accelerator Lab, Baylor Univ; NSF res grants 64-74 & Robert A Welch Found, 68-82; mem, Int Comn on Radiation Units Stopping Power Comt. *Res:* Atomic & molecular structure effects on energy loss of alpha particles in matter; author of 32 publications. *Mailing Add:* Dept Physics Baylor Univ Waco TX 76703

POWERS, DAVID LEUSCH, b Abington, Pa, Feb 17, 39; m 66; c 3. GRAPH THEORY, MATRIX THEORY. *Educ:* Carnegie Inst Technol, BS, 60, MS, 61; Univ Pittsburgh, PhD(math), 66. *Prof Exp:* Prof math, Tech Univ Santa Maria, Chile, 65-67; asst prof, 67-71, ASSOC PROF MATH, CLARKSON COL TECHNOL, 71- *Concurrent Pos:* Fulbright lectr, State Tech Univ, Chile, 71-72; Off Advan Studies res fel, Tech Univ Santa Maria, Chile, 79-80. *Mem:* Soc Indust & Appl Math. *Mailing Add:* Dept Math Clarkson Col Technol Potsdam NY 13676

POWERS, DENNIS A, b Detroit, Mich, May 4, 38; m 63; c 3. MOLECULAR ECOLOGY, PHYSIOLOGICAL ECOLOGY. *Educ:* Ottawa Univ, BA, 63; Univ Kans, PhD(biol), 70. *Prof Exp:* NIH trainee biol, Univ Kans, 67-70; AEC fel biochem, Argonne Nat Labs, 70-71; NSF fel biol, Woods Hole Marine Biol Labs & State Univ NY, Stony Brook, 71-72; asst prof, 72-79, assoc prof, 79-82, PROF BIOL, JOHNS HOPKINS UNIV, 82- *Concurrent Pos:* NSF fel, Univ Hawaii, 67; physiol teaching staff, Woods Hole Marine Biol Labs, 72-76; consult, UN Food & Agr Orgn Comt Fish Genetics, 80; ed, Physiol Zool & Biol Oceanog, 82-; consult marine biotechnol. *Mem:* Am Soc Biophysics; Sigma Xi; NY Acad Sci; Genetics Soc Am; Am Soc Zoologists. *Res:* Multivariant-interdisciplinary approach to resolve the molecular mechanisms that marine animals use to adapt to environmental stress. *Mailing Add:* Dept Biol Johns Hopkins Univ 3400 N Charles Baltimore MD 21218

POWERS, DONALD HOWARD, JR, b Providence, RI, Feb 23, 30; m 50; c 3. INORGANIC CHEMISTRY. *Educ:* Amherst Col, Mass, AB, 51; Brown Univ, Providence, RI, PhD(org chem), 55. *Prof Exp:* Fel, Univ Rochester, 54-55; chemist, Owens-Corning Fiberglas Corp, 55-59; sr res assoc, Fabric Res Labs, Inc, 59-71; consult, Fram Corp, 72-77; SR RES CHEMIST, CHOMERICS, INC, 77- *Mem:* Am Chem Soc; Am Electroplaters Soc; Sigma Xi. *Res:* Mechanism of organic reactions; adhesion to glass fibers; wool processing; cotton finishing, fiber spinning; glass fiber manufacuture; crosslinking of thermoplastic resins; electroless plating of fine particles. *Mailing Add:* 776 Webster St Needham MA 02192

POWERS, EDMUND MAURICE, b Tarrytown, NY; m 62; c 2. FOOD MICROBIOLOGY. *Educ:* Univ NH, BA, 59; Univ Md, MS, 64. *Prof Exp:* Bacteriologist, Norwich Pharmacal Co, 59-62; life scientist space biol, Goddard Space Flight Ctr, NASA, 64-68; RES FOOD MICROBIOLOGIST, US ARMY NATICK DEVELOP CTR, 68- *Concurrent Pos:* Mem intersoc, Agency Comt Compendium Methods Microbiol Exam Foods, 70-74. *Mem:* Am Soc Microbiol; Int Asn Milk Food & Environ Sanitarians; Acad Microbiol. *Res:* Recovery of microbes from food; rapid methods for microbiological analysis of foods; sanitation. *Mailing Add:* Food Sci Lab US Army Natick Develop Ctr Natick MA 01760

POWERS, EDWARD JAMES, b Pittsfield, Mass, Nov 27, 36; m 67; c 1. ORGANIC CHEMISTRY, MATERIALS SCIENCE. *Educ:* Siena Col, BS, 61; Fla State Univ, PhD(org chem), 69. *Prof Exp:* Res chemist, 69-72, proj leader polybenzimidazole stabilization & dyeing techniques, 72-74, sr res chemist, Summit, NJ, 74-76, sr develop engr, Fiber Industs Inc, Celanese Res Co, Charlotte, NC, 76-80, DEVELOP ASSOC, CELANESE PLASTICS & SPECIALTIES CO, LOUISVILLE, 80- *Mem:* Am Chem Soc; Am Asn Textile Chem & Colorists. *Res:* Water borne coatings for paper, foil and film; fiber process finishes; textile dyeing and finishing; tire cord hysteresis; tire cord adhesion. *Mailing Add:* Tech Ctr Celanese Plastics & Specialties Co Bluegrass Pkwy Louisville KY 40299

POWERS, EDWARD JOSEPH, JR, b Winchester, Mass, Nov 29, 35; m 59; c 4. ELECTRICAL ENGINEERING, PHYSICS. *Educ:* Tufts Univ, BS, 57; Mass Inst Technol, MS, 59; Stanford Univ, PhD(elec eng), 65. *Prof Exp:* Res asst microwave circuits & antennas, Mass Inst Technol, 57-59; scientist, Lockheed Missiles & Space Co, 59-65; res asst plasmas, Stanford Univ, 65; from asst prof to assoc prof, 65-73, prof elec eng, 73-81, N GAFFORD PROF ELEC ENG, UNIV TEX, AUSTIN, 81-, DIR ELECTRONICS RES CTR, 77, CHMN DEPT ELEC ENG, 81- *Concurrent Pos:* Mem honor coop prog, Lockheed Aircraft Corp, Stanford Univ, 59-65. *Mem:* Am Phys Soc; Inst Elec & Electronics Engrs; Int Sci Radio Union. *Res:* Digital time series analysis; plasma diagnostics; laser applications; electromagnetics. *Mailing Add:* 8703 Mountainwood Circle Austin TX 78759

POWERS, EDWARD LAWRENCE, b Columbia, SC, Dec 30, 15; m 39; c 7. RADIATION BIOLOGY. *Educ:* Col Charleston, BSc, 38; Johns Hopkins Univ, PhD(zool), 41. *Prof Exp:* From instr to asst prof biol, Univ Notre Dame, 41-46; from assoc biologist to sr biologist, Argonne Nat Lab, 46-65, assoc dir div biol & med res, 49-62; PROF ZOOL & DIR LAB RADIATION BIOL, UNIV TEX, AUSTIN, 65- *Concurrent Pos:* Guggenheim fel, Eng, 58-59; Douglas Lea mem lectr, Univ Leeds, 61; mem, Radiation Study Sect, NIH, 70-74; dir, Ctr Fast Kinetics Res, 74- *Mem:* Fel AAAS; Genetics Soc Am; Am Soc Microbiol; Soc Protozool. *Res:* Action of genetic determiners in cells; ultrastructure of cell inclusions; genetic effects of atomic transmutations in cells; fast kinetic techniques applied to biology; roles of water in radiation damage in living cells; general radiation biophysics. *Mailing Add:* Dept of Zool Univ of Tex Austin TX 78712

POWERS, GARY JAMES, b Highland Park, Mich, Sept 18, 45; m 66; c 3. CHEMICAL ENGINEERING. *Educ:* Univ Mich, BSChE, 67; Univ Wis, PhD(chem eng), 71. *Prof Exp:* Engr, Dow Chem Co, 68-70; asst prof chem eng, Mass Inst Technol, 71-74; assoc prof, 74-75, PROF CHEM ENG, CARNEGIE-MELLON UNIV, 75- *Concurrent Pos:* Dir, Design Res Ctr; pres, Design Sci, Inc, 77- *Mem:* AAAS; Am Inst Chem Engrs; Am Chem Soc. *Res:* Computer-aided synthesis of chemical processing systems; separation science; risk assessment and fault free analysis. *Mailing Add:* Dept of Chem Eng 5000 Forbes Ave Pittsburgh PA 15213

POWERS, HAROLD O, b Girard, Pa, July 14, 20; m 62; c 4. HUMAN GENETICS, CYTOGENETICS. *Educ:* Pa State Teachers Col, Edinboro, BS, 42; Syracuse Univ, MS, 49, PhD(bot), 60. *Prof Exp:* Instr, Rochester City Schs, 46-48; asst prof physics, 48-50, from asst prof to assoc prof biol, 53-60, chmn dept, 60-68, prof, 60-80, EMER PROF ZOOL, STATE UNIV NY COL OSWEGO, 80- *Concurrent Pos:* Consult, 65-; Nat Inst Arthritis & Metab Dis res fel, Genetics & Endocrine Unit, State Univ NY Upstate Med Ctr. *Mem:* Fel AAAS; NY Acad Sci; Am Genetic Asn; Genetics Soc Am; Am Soc Human Genetics. *Res:* Human chromosomes and related abnormalities. *Mailing Add:* Dept of Zool State Univ of NY Col Oswego NY 13126

POWERS, HARRY ROBERT, JR, b Suffolk, Va, July 25, 23; m 47; c 2. PLANT PATHOLOGY. *Educ:* NC State Col, BS, 49, PhD(plant path), 53; Duke Univ, MF, 50. *Prof Exp:* Pathologist, Agr Res Serv, 53-59, Southeastern Forest Exp Sta, 59-68, prin plant pathologist, 68-80, CHIEF PLANT PATHOLOGIST, FORESTRY SCI LAB, US DEPT AGR, 80- *Mem:* Am Phytopath Soc; Soc Am Foresters. *Res:* Tree diseases; wheat mildew and rust; genetics. *Mailing Add:* Forestry Sci Lab Carlton St Athens GA 30601

POWERS, J BRADLEY, b Framingham, Mass, Dec 16, 37; m 66; c 1. BEHAVIORAL NEUROSCIENCE. *Educ:* Harvard Col, AB, 59; Brown Univ, MA, 63; Univ Calif, Berkeley, PhD(physiol psychol), 70. *Prof Exp:* Asst res scientist, Univ Mich, 74-77; sr fel, Univ Wash, 78-79; RES ASSOC PROF, VANDERBILT UNIV, 80- *Mem:* Soc Neurosci; Animal Behav Soc; Sigma Xi. *Res:* Elucidating neuroendocrine and enviornmental mechanisms regulating mammalian social behavior, especially reproduction. *Mailing Add:* Dept Psychol Vanderbilt Univ Nashville TN 37240

POWERS, JAMES ALLEN, nuclear chemistry, physical chemistry, see previous edition

POWERS, JAMES CECIL, b Highland Park, Mich, Dec 13, 37. ORGANIC BIOCHEMISTRY. *Educ:* Wayne State Univ, BS, 59; Mass Inst Technol, PhD(chem), 63. *Prof Exp:* Asst prof chem, Univ Calif, Los Angeles, 63-67; NIH spec fel, Univ Wash, 67-69, actg asst prof chem, 69-70; asst prof, 70-74, assoc prof, 74-78, PROF CHEM, GA INST TECHNOL, 78- *Concurrent Pos:* Consult, Merck, Inc, 75- *Mem:* Am Chem Soc; AAAS; Am Soc Biol Chemists. *Res:* Enzyme inhibitors; enzyme mechanism; active site modification of enzymes; proteases. *Mailing Add:* Dept of Chem Ga Inst of Technol Atlanta GA 30332

POWERS, JAMES MATTHEW, b Cleveland, Ohio, Sept 15, 43; c 2. NEUROPATHOLOGY, APTHOLOGY. *Educ:* Manhattan Col, BS, 65; Med Univ SC, MD, 69. *Prof Exp:* Asst prof, 73-76, assoc prof path, 76-80, PROF PATH, MED UNIV SC, 80- *Concurrent Pos:* Dir electron micros, Vet Admin Hosp, SC, 73-76. *Honors & Awards:* Moore Award, Am Asn Neuropathologists, 75, 76, & 77. *Mem:* Am Asn Neuropathologists (asst secy-treas, 76-81); Am Asn Pathologists; Int Acad Path; AAAS. *Res:* Adreno-leukodystrophy; diseases of myelin; dementia, especially Alzheimer's senile and presenile. *Mailing Add:* Dept of Path 171 Ashley Ave Charleston SC 29403

POWERS, JEAN D, b Hamilton, Ohio, Dec 24, 30; m 75; c 2. BIOMETRICS, BIOSTATISTICS. *Educ:* Ohio State Univ, BS, 50, MS, 51, PhD(biostatist), 68. *Prof Exp:* Statistician, Ohio Dept Health, 51-52; instr, St Mary's High Sch, 63-64; assoc prof math, Capital Univ, 68-73; asst prof, 73-80, ASSOC PROF BIOSTATIST, OHIO STATE UNIV, 80- *Concurrent Pos:* Vis asst prof, Ohio State Univ, 68-73; statistician res found cancer grant, Ohio State Univ, 78-80; consult, Abbott Labs, Am Hoechst, Burroughs Wellcome & Schering Corp, 82- *Mem:* Am Statist Asn; Am Acad Pharmacologists & Therapeut; Am Soc Vet Physicians & Pharmacists; Sigma Xi. *Res:* Estimating pharmacokinetic parameters. *Mailing Add:* Vet Physiol & Pharmacol Ohio State Univ 1900 Coffey Rd Columbus OH 43210

POWERS, JEAN HENSEL, b Hamilton, Ohio, Dec 24, 30; m. BIOSTATISTICS. *Educ:* Ohio State Univ, BSc, 50, MSc, 51, PhD(biostatist), 68. *Prof Exp:* Statistician biomet, Ohio Dept Health, 51-52; teacher high sch, 63-64; from asst prof to assoc prof math, Capital Univ, 68-73; ASST PROF MATH, OHIO STATE UNIV, 73- *Concurrent Pos:* Vis prof, Ohio State Univ, 68-73. *Mem:* Biomet Soc; Inst Math Statist; Sigma Xi. *Res:* Genetic mechanisms of collie eye anomaly; mathematical characterization of electrocardiogram; mathematics of drug actions; pharmacokinetics. *Mailing Add:* Dept of Math Ohio State Univ 1900 Coffey Rd Columbus OH 43210

POWERS, JOHN CLANCEY, JR, b Billings, Mont, Dec 27, 31; m 64; c 2. ORGANIC CHEMISTRY, BIOCHEMISTRY. *Educ:* Yale Univ, BS, 53; Harvard Univ, AM, 54, PhD(chem), 58. *Prof Exp:* Fel chem, Bryn Mawr Col, 58-59; chemist, Metal Hydrides, Inc, 59-61; res chemist, Int Bus Mach Corp, 61-67; asst prof chem, Hunter Col, 67-70; assoc prof, 70-80, PROF CHEM, PACE UNIV, 81- *Mem:* Am Chem Soc; Sigma Xi. *Res:* Reaction mechanisms; photochemistry; electrooptic effects in dyes and polymers; chemistry of biologically important macromolecules. *Mailing Add:* Dept of Chem Pace Univ New York NY 10038

POWERS, JOHN E(DWARD), b Wilkensburg, Pa, Oct 12, 27; m 51; c 3. CHEMICAL ENGINEERING. *Educ:* Univ Mich, BS, 51; Univ Calif, Berkeley, PhD(chem eng), 54. *Prof Exp:* Assoc chem eng, Univ Calif, Berkeley, 53-54; res engr, Shell Develop Co, 54-56; asst prof chem eng, Univ Okla, 56-58, assoc prof & chmn dept, 58-61, prof, 61-63; PROF CHEM METALL ENG, UNIV MICH, ANN ARBOR, 63- *Concurrent Pos:* Mem at large, Gordon Res Confs Coun, 59-62, chmn conf & purification, 60; NSF sr fel, Univ Erlangen, 62-63. *Mem:* AAAS; Am Inst Chem Engrs; Inst Chem Eng, PR. *Res:* Separation processes; crystallization; thermodynamics; biomedical applications of chemical engineering. *Mailing Add:* Dept of Chem Eng Univ of Mich Ann Arbor MI 48109

POWERS, JOHN JOSEPH, b Pittsfield, Mass, Feb 3, 18; m 45; c 3. FOOD TECHNOLOGY. *Educ:* Univ Mass, BS, 40, PhD(food technol), 45. *Prof Exp:* Instr food technol, Univ Mass, 42-46; asst prof, Exp Sta, Ohio State Univ, 46-47; assoc prof, 47-52, head dept, 52-67, prof food technol, 52-79, WILLIAM JENILL DISTINGUISHED PROF AGR, UNIV GA, 79- *Concurrent Pos:* Mem, Toxicol Study Sect, USPHS, 64-67, Environ Biol & Chem Study Sect, 67-70; sr Fulbright-Hays fel, 72; mem, Nat Acad Sci Exchange Visit, Bulgaria, 72, Yugoslavia & Hungary, 74 & Poland, 77. *Honors & Awards:* Res Award, Soc Med Friends Wine, 72. *Mem:* Am Chem Soc; Am Soc Testing & Mat; fel Inst Food Technol. *Res:* Flavor chemistry; plant compounds; food industries methods; acidification of foods. *Mailing Add:* Dept of Food Sci Univ of Ga Athens GA 30602

POWERS, JOHN MICHAEL, b Ft Wayne, Ind, Apr 16, 46; m 68; c 2. DENTAL MATERIALS. *Educ:* Univ Mich, Ann Arbor, BSCh, 67, PhD(dent mat, mech eng), 72. *Prof Exp:* Res asst, Sch Dent, Univ Mich, Ann Arbor, 65-67; instr health sci, Washtenaw Community Col, 68-69; teaching fel, 69-72, asst prof, 72-74, assoc prof, 74-79, PROF DENT MAT, SCH DENT, UNIV MICH, ANN ARBOR, 79- *Mem:* Int Asn Dent Res; Soc Biomat. *Res:* Physical and mechanical properties of materials as applied to dentistry; thermal analysis of waxes; friction and wear of dental materials; color and optical properties of dental materials. *Mailing Add:* Sch of Dent Univ of Mich Ann Arbor MI 48109

POWERS, JOHN ORIN, b Mt Olive, Ill, Mar 6, 22; m 48; c 2. AERODYNAMICS. *Educ:* Univ Mich, BS(aeronaut eng) & BS(mech eng), 43; Cath Univ, MS, 51; Univ Md, PhD(aeronaut eng), 65. *Prof Exp:* Aeronaut engr, David Taylor Model Basin, Dept Navy, 48-50, aeronaut engr, Bur of Aeronaut, 50-51; aeronaut engr, Proj Hermes, Gen Elec Co, 51-53, Guided Missiles Dept, 53-55 & Missile & Ord Dept, 55-57; aeronaut engr, US Naval Ord Lab, 57-66; chief tech support staff, Off Noise Abatement, 66-69, actg dir, 69-71, CHIEF ENVIRON SCIENTIST, OFF ENVIRON & ENERGY, FED AVIATION ADMIN, 71- *Concurrent Pos:* Mem sonic boom res panel, Interagency Noise Prog, 68- *Mem:* Am Soc Mech Engrs; Am Inst Aeronaut & Astronaut. *Res:* Boundary layer stability; stability and control characteristics of aircraft and missiles; aircraft noise emissions; sonic boom. *Mailing Add:* 13700 Carlisle Silver Spring MD 20904

POWERS, JOHN PATRICK, b Winchester, Mass, Dec 28, 43; m 67; c 2. ELECTRICAL ENGINEERING. *Educ:* Tufts Univ, BS, 65; Stanford Univ, MS, 66; Univ Calif, Santa Barbara, PhD(elec eng), 70. *Prof Exp:* Res asst elec eng, Univ Calif, Santa Barbara, 67-70; asst prof, 70-76, ASSOC PROF ELEC ENG, NAVAL POSTGRAD SCH, 76- *Concurrent Pos:* Vis exchange scientist, Univ Paris VI, 74-75. *Mem:* Inst Elec & Electronics Engrs; Acoust Soc Am; Optical Soc Am; Sigma Xi. *Res:* Acoustic imaging systems; electro optics. *Mailing Add:* Dept of Elec Eng Naval Postgrad Sch Monterey CA 93940

POWERS, JOSEPH, b Fall River, Mass, June 4, 31; m 57; c 2. MATERIALS SCIENCE, POLYMER SCIENCE. *Educ:* Univ Mass, BS, 53, MS, 59, PhD(phys chem), 61. *Prof Exp:* Off Naval Res fel, 61; proj leader polymer physics, Nat Bur Standards, 61-65; proj leader phys chem, Am Cyanamid Co, Stamford, 65-69, group leader, 69-72; Instr, Univ Bridgeport, 72-73; sr anal engr, 73-77, RES ENGR, UNITED TECHNOLOGIES CORP, 77- *Concurrent Pos:* Nat Acad Sci-Nat Res Coun fel, 61-62. *Mem:* Am Phys Soc; Am Chem Soc. *Res:* Physical properties of polymers, polymer stability in severe environments, thermal, chemical and electrical; use of polymers in fuel cell applications; states of aggregation in polymeric systems. *Mailing Add:* 26 Spring St Riverside CT 06878

POWERS, JOSEPH EDWARD, b Gustine, Calif, Feb 19, 49; m 73. FISHERIES MANAGEMENT, OPERATIONS RESEARCH. *Educ:* Univ Calif, Davis, AB, 71; Calif State Univ, Humboldt, MS, 73; Va Polytech Inst & State Univ, PhD(fish & wildlife), 75. *Prof Exp:* Systs analyst fisheries, Dept Fisheries & Wildlife Sci, Va Polytech Inst & State Univ, 75; opers res analyst fisheries, Southwest Fisheries Ctr, Nat Marine Fisheries serv, 75-80; MEM STAFF, NAT MARINE FISHERIES SERV, SOUTHEAST FISHERIES CTR, 80- *Mem:* Am Fisheries Soc; Soc Comput Simulation; Opers Res Soc. *Res:* Application of operations research technology to the management and planning of environmental and ecological systems. *Mailing Add:* 75 Va Beach Dr SE Fisheries Ctr Miama FL 33149

POWERS, JOSEPH ROBERT, b Tillamook, Ore, July 3, 48; m 75; c 1. BIOCHEMISTRY OF FOODS PROTEINS, ENZYMOLOGY. *Educ:* Ore State Univ, BS, 70; Wash State Univ, MS, 73; Univ Calif, Davis, PhD(biochem), 77. *Prof Exp:* Asst food scientist, Irrigated Agr Res Ext Ctr, 76-80, ASST PROF FOOD SCI, DEPT FOOD SCI & TECHNOL, WASH STATE UNIV, 80- *Concurrent Pos:* Prin investr, Pac NW Regional Comn, 77-80. *Mem:* Inst Food Technologists; Am Soc Enologists; Am Asn Cereal Chemists; Sigma Xi. *Res:* Biochemistry of food proteins including structure, function relations, biological activity; enzymes of foods especially plant products in relation to food quality specifically related to fiber (lignin) biosynthesis. *Mailing Add:* Dept Food Sci & Technol Wash State Univ Pullman WA 99164

POWERS, K(ERNS) H(ARRINGTON), b Waco, Tex, Apr 15, 25; m 52; c 2. COMMUNICATIONS. *Educ:* Univ Tex, BS & MS, 51; Mass Inst Technol, ScD(elec eng), 56. *Prof Exp:* Chief engr, Radio Sta KTXN, Tex, 49-51; mem tech staff, RCA Labs, 51-53; res asst, Mass Inst Technol, 55-56; mem tech staff, RCA Labs, 56-60, tech dir new systs & spec projs, 60-66, dir commun res lab, 66-77, STAFF V PRES COMMUN RES, RCA CORP, 77- *Concurrent Pos:* Adj prof elec eng, Newark Col Eng, 57-60. *Mem:* Inst Elec & Electronics Engrs; fel Soc Motion Picture & Television Engrs. *Mailing Add:* David Sarnoff Res Ctr RCA Corp Princeton NJ 08540

POWERS, KENDALL GARDNER, b Rockland, Maine, May 15, 30; m 60; c 1. VETERINARY PARASITOLOGY. *Educ:* Univ Wis, BS, 56, MS, 58, PhD(vet parasitol-bacteriol), 61. *Prof Exp:* Instr vet sci, Univ Wis, 60-61; head parasitol res, Schering Corp, 61-63; res parasitologist, Nat Inst Allergy & Infectious Dis, NIH, 63-75; HEAD PARASITOL RES, BUR VET MED, FDA, 75- *Mem:* Am Soc Trop Med & Hyg; Am Soc Parasitol; Royal Soc Trop Med & Hyg. *Res:* Chemotherapy and immunology of parasitic diseases. *Mailing Add:* Div Vet Med Res BARC-East Beltsville MD 20705

POWERS, LARRY JAMES, b Dillsboro, Ind, July 11, 44; m 68; c 2. MEDICINAL CHEMISTRY. *Educ:* Purdue Univ, Lafayette, BS, 66; Univ Kans, PhD(med chem), 69. *Prof Exp:* Asst prof, Med Units, Univ Tenn, Memphis, 69-73, assoc prof, 73-75; sr res chemist, 75-77, res assoc, 77-79, RES SUPVR, DIAMOND SHAMROCK CORP, 80- *Mem:* Am Chem Soc; AAAS; NY Acad Sci. *Res:* Herbicide and fungicide synthesis; synthesis of antibacterial, antihypertensive and antiinflamatory agents. *Mailing Add:* 149 Square Dr Madison OH 44057

POWERS, LINDA SUE, b Pittsburgh, Pa, Feb 8, 48. BIOPHYSICS, SYNCHROTRON RADIATION. *Educ:* Va Polytech Inst & State Univ, BS, 70; Harvard Univ, MS, 72, PhD(biophysics), 76. *Prof Exp:* MEM TECH STAFF BIOPHYSICS & PHYSICS, BELL LABS, 76- *Concurrent Pos:* Adj prof biophys, Univ Pa, 78-; vis fel, Princeton Univ, 81. *Mem:* Am Phys Soc; Biophys Soc; NY Acad Sci. *Res:* Physical studies of biological molecules to investigate structure-function relationship; development and application of synchrotron radiation and optical spectroscopy to metalloenzymes and proteins; structural kinetics; enzyme mechanics. *Mailing Add:* 600 Mountain Ave Murray Hill NJ 07974

POWERS, LOUIS JOHN, b St Louis, Mo, Oct 8, 12; m 35; c 3. MECHANICAL ENGINEERING. *Educ:* Tex Tech Col, BS, 39; Univ Tex, MS, 50. *Prof Exp:* Mech engr, Gen Petrol Corp, 39-42; assoc prof mech eng, 42-52, PROF MECH ENG, TEX TECH UNIV, 52- *Mem:* Am Soc Eng Educ; Am Soc Mech Engrs; Nat Soc Prof Engrs. *Res:* Structural vibrations. *Mailing Add:* Dept Mech Eng Tex Tech Univ Lubbock TX 79409

POWERS, MARCELINA VENUS, b Abra, Philippines, Mar 22, 27; m 60; c 1. TOXICOLOGY. *Educ:* Univ Philippines, DVM, 51; Univ Wis, MS, 57. *Prof Exp:* Instr biol sci, Araneta Univ, Philippines, 51-55; res asst vet sci, Univ Wis, 55-57, staff vet & toxicologist, Wis Alumni Res Found, 57-59, head dept biol, 59-63; res coordr, Hazelton Labs, 63-69, asst dir drugs & indust chem dept, 69-70, dir dept, 70-72, proj mgr, 72-78; STAFF TOXICOLOGIST, NAT TOXICOL PROG, NIH, 78- *Mem:* Am Vet Med Asn; Am Soc Trop Med & Hyg; Soc Toxicol; Am Col Vet Parasitol. *Res:* Toxicology of drugs, industrial and agricultural chemicals, chemical carcinogenesis. *Mailing Add:* 6311 Alcott Rd Bethesda MD 20817

POWERS, MICHAEL JEROME, b Freeport, Ill, May 5, 41; m 64; c 3. SYSTEMS ANALYSIS & DESIGN. *Educ:* Carthage Col, BA, 63; Ind Univ, Bloomington, MA, 65, PhD(math), 68. *Prof Exp:* Asst prof math, Ind State Univ, 67-68 & Northern Ill Univ, 68-74; mem staff, De Kalb Agresearch, 74-76; ASSOC PROF & CHMN APPL COMPUT SCI DEPT, ILL STATE UNIV, 76- *Mem:* Asn Comput Mach; Data Processing Mgt Asn; Asn Educ Data Systs; Inst Elec & Electronic Engrs; Sigma Xi. *Res:* System development and design; database processing. *Mailing Add:* Appl Comput Sci Ill State Univ Normal IL 61761

POWERS, RICHARD JAMES, b Chicago, Ill, Jan 20, 40. PHYSICS. *Educ:* Ill Inst Technol, BS, 61; Univ Chicago, MS, 62, PhD(physics), 67. *Prof Exp:* Res assoc physics, Univ Chicago, 67-68; asst prof, Va Polytech Inst & State Univ, 68-72; sr res fel physics, 73-76, res assoc, 76-81, SR RES ASSOC PHYSICS, CALIF INST TECHNOL, 81- *Concurrent Pos:* Vis scientist, CEN-Saclay, 72-73, Swiss Fed Inst Technol, 79-81, Univ Zürich, 80. *Mem:* Am Phys Soc. *Res:* Nuclear charge and matter distribution using x-rays from exotic atoms; weak interactions of leptons. *Mailing Add:* Calif Inst Technol 1201 E California Blvd Pasadena CA 91109

POWERS, ROBERT D, b Scotts Hill, Tenn, Sept 19, 33; m 62; c 1. PATHOLOGY, LABORATORY ANIMAL MEDICINE. *Educ:* Univ Tenn, BS, 57, PhD(exp path), 67; Auburn Univ, DVM, 62. *Prof Exp:* NIH training fel, 63-67; asst prof path & assoc dir, Vivarium, Med Units, Univ Tenn, 67-70; ASSOC PROF PATH & PARASITOL, AUBURN UNIV, 70- *Concurrent Pos:* Am Cancer Soc study grant, 64-65. *Mem:* AAAS; Am Vet Med Asn; Am Asn Zool Vets; Am Asn Lab Animal Sci; Am Soc Lab Animal Practrs. *Res:* Veterinary pathology; experimental and comparative pathology; zoo animal pathology. *Mailing Add:* Dept of Path Auburn Univ Auburn AL 36830

POWERS, ROBERT FIELD, b Los Angeles, Calif. FOREST SOILS, PLANT NUTRITION. *Educ:* Humboldt State Univ, BS, 63; Univ Calif, Berkeley, PhD, 81. *Prof Exp:* Res asst forest ecol, Humboldt State Univ, 64-65; RES SCIENTIST FOREST MGT, PAC SOUTHWEST FOREST & RANGE EXP STA, FOREST SERV, USDA, 66-, CHMN, 80- *Concurrent Pos:* Vchmn, Calif Forest Fertil Coun, 74-81, chmn, 81-; mem, Regionwide Forest Soil Fertil Steering Comt, Forest Serv, USDA, 76- & 9 Comt Scientists, Pac Southwest Exp Sta, mem working group soil & site factors, Int Union Forest Res Orgn, 76- *Mem:* AAAS; Ecol Soc Am; Int Union Forest Res Orgn; Soc Am Foresters; Soil Sci Soc Am. *Res:* Nutrient requirements of forest trees; properties of forest ecosystems affecting productivity; effects of forest practices on soil fertility and forest productivity. *Mailing Add:* Pac Southwest Exp Sta 2400 Washington Ave Redding CA 96001

POWERS, ROBERT S(INCLAIR), JR, b Dallas, Tex, Apr 7, 34; m 62; c 2. PHYSICAL CHEMISTRY, ELECTRICAL ENGINEERING. *Educ:* Southern Methodist Univ, BS, 55; Univ Wis, PhD(phys chem), 60. *Prof Exp:* Nat Bur Standards-Nat Res Coun fel plasma physics, Boulder Labs, Nat Bur Standards, 60-61, chemist, 61-65, gen phys scientist, 65-70; spec asst urban telecommun, Off Telecommun, US Dept Commerce, 70-75; sr engr, Cable TV Bur, 75-79, ACTG DEP CHIEF SCIENTIST, OFF SCI & TECHNOL, FED COMMUN COMN, 79- *Mem:* AAAS; Am Phys Soc; Inst Elec & Electronics Engrs. *Res:* Urban communications systems analysis; communications technology and standards. *Mailing Add:* Fed Commun Comn 1919 M St NW Washington DC 20554

POWERS, ROBERT WILLIAM, b Peoria, Ill, Feb 3, 22; m 50; c 1. PHYSICAL CHEMISTRY. *Educ:* Bradley Univ, BS, 43; Univ Ill, PhD(phys chem), 46. *Prof Exp:* Chemist, Exp Sta, E I du Pont de Nemours & Co, 46-47; res assoc, Res Found, Ohio State Univ, 47-51; PHYS CHEMIST, RES & DEVELOP, GEN ELEC CORP, 51- *Mem:* Am Ceramic Soc; Am Chem Soc; Electrochem Soc; Am Phys Soc. *Res:* Polymerization kinetics; thermal conductivity measurements at low temperatures; mechanical relaxation in metals; anodic film formation; alkaline zinc electrochemistry; fabrication and properties of beta-alumina. *Mailing Add:* Gen Elec Res & Develop Ctr PO Box 8 Schenectady NY 12301

POWERS, SAMUEL RALPH, JR, b Minneapolis, Minn, Sept 25, 19; m 42; c 4. SURGERY. *Educ:* Swarthmore Col, BS, 41; Columbia Univ, MD, 45, DSc, 54. *Prof Exp:* Res asst phys chem, Manhattan Proj, Columbia Univ, 41-42; intern surg, Presby Hosp, 45-46; Nat Res Coun fel, Johns Hopkins Hosp, Md, 48-49; resident, Presby Hosp, 49-54; from asst prof to assoc prof, 54-56, PROF EXP SURG, ALBANY MED COL, 56-, CHMN DEPT SURG, 74- *Res:* Cardiorespiratory physiology. *Mailing Add:* Dept of Surg Albany Med Col Albany NY 12208

POWERS, THOMAS E, b Cedarville, Ohio, Dec 29, 25; m 48; c 3. VETERINARY PHARMACOLOGY. *Educ:* Ohio State Univ, DVM, 53, MSc, 54, PhD(physiol, pharmacol), 60. *Prof Exp:* Instr bact, 54-55, from instr to assoc prof, 55-66, PROF VET PHYSIOL & PHARMACOL, OHIO STATE UNIV, 66-, MEM GRAD FAC, 60-, CHMN DEPT, 70- *Mem:* Am Col Vet Pharmacol & Therapeut; AAAS; Am Vet Med Asn; Am Asn Vet Physiologists & Pharmacologists (pres, 75). *Res:* Veterinary pharmacodynamics; renal physiology; comparative pharmacology and physiology; antimicrobial therapy; animal disease modeling. *Mailing Add:* Dept of Vet Pharmacol Ohio State Univ 1900 Coffey Rd Columbus OH 43210

POWERS, WENDELL HOLMES, b Richford, Vt, Mar 30, 15; m 42; c 2. BIOCHEMISTRY. *Educ:* Middlebury Col, BS, 37; Univ NH, MS, 39; Columbia Univ, PhD, 43. *Prof Exp:* Instr chem, Univ NH, 38-39; asst, Columbia Univ, 39-42; from instr to assoc prof, 42-58, prof, 58-81, EMER PROF CHEM, WAYNE STATE UNIV, 81- *Concurrent Pos:* Asst dir, Kresge-Hooker Sci Libr Assocs, 43-49, actg dir, 49-50, assoc dir, 50-56, exec secy, 56-69; ed, Record Chem Prog, 52-71. *Mem:* Sigma Xi; AAAS; Am Chem Soc. *Res:* Synthetic organic chemistry involving preparation of various aromatic ethers; respiratory enzymes and biological oxidations. *Mailing Add:* 16556 Greenlawn Detroit MI 48221

POWERS, WILLIAM ALLEN, III, b Baltimore, Md. STATISTICS. *Educ:* Univ Richmond, BS, 66; Univ Conn, MS, 70, PhD(statist), 72. *Prof Exp:* lectr math, Univ Bridgeport, 70-71; lectr, 71-72, asst prof, 72-77, ASSOC PROF MATH, UNIV NC GREENSBORO, 77- *Mem:* Am Statist Asn; Math Asn Am. *Res:* Applied statistical methods; unbalanced A nova; robustness of statistical procedures. *Mailing Add:* Dept Math Univ NC PO Box 5036 Tate St Sta Greensboro NC 27403

POWERS, WILLIAM FRANCIS, b Philadelphia, Pa, Dec 11, 40; m 63; c 2. ENGINEERING. *Educ:* Univ Fla, BS, 63; Univ Tex, Austin, MS, 66, PhD(eng mech), 68. *Prof Exp:* Mathematician, Marshall Space Flight Ctr, NASA, 63-64; from asst prof to assoc prof aerospace eng, Univ Mich, Ann Arbor, 68-75, prof aerospace eng, 76-80; MGR, CONTROL SYSTS DEPT, FORD RES, DEARBORN, MICH, 80- *Concurrent Pos:* Consult, Johnson Space Ctr, NASA, 71-79. *Mem:* Am Inst Aeronaut & Astronaut; Am Astronaut Soc; Math Asn Am; Soc Indust & Appl Math; Inst Elec & Electronics Engrs. *Res:* Optimization of dynamic systems; guidance and control; automotive control systems. *Mailing Add:* 2032 Greenview Ann Arbor MI 48103

POWERS, WILLIAM L, soil physics, water resources, see previous edition

POWIS, GARTH, b West Bromwich, Eng, June 12, 46; m 67; c 2. PHARMACOLOGY, BIOCHEMISTRY. *Educ:* Univ Birmingham, BSc, 67; Oxford Univ, DPhil(biochem, physiol), 70. *Prof Exp:* Univ lectr pharmacol, Glasgow Univ, 70-77; CONSULT ONCOL & ASSOC PROF PHARMACOL, MAYO CLIN, 77- *Mem:* Brit Physiol Soc; Brit Pharmacol Soc; Am Asn Cancer Res; Am Soc Pharmacol & Exp Therapeut. *Res:* Drug metabolism; pharmacology of anticancer agents. *Mailing Add:* Mayo Clin 200 First St SW Rochester MN 55901

POWLES, PERCIVAL MOUNT, b Takada, Japan, Jan 16, 30; Can citizen; m 60; c 3. MARINE ECOLOGY. *Educ:* McGill Univ, BA, 51; Univ Western Ont, BSc, 55, MSc, 57; McGill Univ, PhD(marine zool), 64. *Prof Exp:* Scientist pleuronectid res, Fisheries Res Bd, Can, NB, 57-68; assoc prof, 68-74, PROF BIOL, TRENT UNIV, 74-, CHMN DEPT, 75- *Mem:* AAAS; Am Soc Ichthyol & Herpet; Am Fisheries Soc; Can Soc Zoologists; Can Comt Fisheries Res. *Res:* Fish biology; pleuronectid growth; feeding and population dynamics; larval fish ecology; thermal ecology. *Mailing Add:* Dept Biol Trent Univ Peterborough ON K9J 6S7 Can

POWLES, WILLIAM EARNEST, b Matsumoto, Japan, Sept 6, 19; Can citizen; m 43; c 2. PSYCHIATRY. *Educ:* McGill Univ, BA, 40, MD, CM, 43, dipl, 52. *Prof Exp:* Clin instr psychiat, Univ BC, 52-58; asst prof psychiat & indust med, Univ Cincinnati, 58-66; assoc prof, 66-72, PROF PSYCHIAT, QUEEN'S UNIV, ONT, 72- *Concurrent Pos:* Asst clin dir, Prov Ment Health Serv, BC, 52-56; sr specialist, Ment Health Ctr, 57-58; attend psychiatrist, Kingston Gen Hosp, 66-; consult, Ont Hosp, 66- *Mem:* Fel Am Group Psychother Asn; fel Royal Col Physicians & Surgeons Can; fel Am Psychiat Asn; Can Psychiat Asn; Can Med Asn. *Res:* Clinical psychiatry; group psychotherapy and milieu therapy; medical education; health manpower studies; psychosomatic medicine. *Mailing Add:* Dept of Psychiat Queen's Univ Kingston ON K7L 3N6 Can

POWLEY, GEORGE R(EINHOLD), b New London, Ohio, Mar 7, 16; m 40; c 4. ELECTRICAL ENGINEERING. *Educ:* Va Polytech Inst, BS, 38, MS, 39. *Prof Exp:* Induction motor design engr, Electrodyn Works, Elec Boat Co, 39; test & control engr, Gen Elec Co, 39-41, control engr, 45-49; from assoc prof to prof elec eng, Va Polytech Inst & State Univ, 49-64, head dept, 58-64, Westinghouse prof, 64-68, prof, 68-81, chmn elec eng technol, 74-81. *Concurrent Pos:* Vis prof elec eng, Va Mil Inst, 81. *Honors & Awards:* Wine Award, Va Polytech Inst, 57. *Mem:* Inst Elec & Electronics Engrs. *Res:* Automatic controls; rotating machinery; transformers. *Mailing Add:* 1401 Hillcrest Dr Blacksburg VA 24060

POWNALL, HENRY JOSEPH, b Lancaster, Pa, Dec 9, 42; m 71. BIOCHEMISTRY. *Educ:* Elizabethtown Col, BS, 65; Wilkes Col, MS, 67; Northeastern Univ, PhD(chem), 70. *Prof Exp:* NSF grant, Univ Houston, 71; NIH grant, 72-73, asst prof, 73-79, ASSOC PROF EXP MED, BAYLOR COL MED, 79- *Concurrent Pos:* Estab investr, Am Heart Asn. *Mem:* Am Chem Soc. *Res:* Investigation of biological systems by physical chemical methods; principally molecular spectroscopy; model aromatic hydrocarbons. *Mailing Add:* Div Atherosclerosis & Lipoprot Baylor Col Med Houston TX 77025

POWNALL, MALCOLM WILMOR, b Coatesville, Pa, Jan 6, 33; m 61; c 4. MATHEMATICS. *Educ:* Princeton Univ, AB, 54; Univ Pa, AM, 57, PhD(math), 60. *Prof Exp:* Instr, 59-61, from asst prof to assoc prof, 61-71, PROF MATH, COLGATE UNIV, 71- *Concurrent Pos:* Assoc dir comn undergrad prog, Math Asn Am, 66-67, dir, 67-68. *Mem:* Am Math Soc. *Res:* Graph theory; mathematical education. *Mailing Add:* Dept of Math Colgate Univ Hamilton NY 13346

POWRIE, WILLIAM DUNCAN, b Toronto, Ont, Nov 1, 26; m 55; c 4. FOOD SCIENCE. *Educ:* Univ Toronto, BA, 49, MA, 51; Univ Mass, PhD(food tech), 55. *Prof Exp:* Sr food technologist, Can Dept Agr, 55-56; asst prof food technol, Mich State Univ, 56-59; from asst prof to assoc prof, Univ Wis-Madison, 59-69; PROF FOOD SCI & CHMN DEPT, UNIV BC, 69- *Honors & Awards:* William J Eva Award, Can Inst Food Sci & Technol. *Mem:* Chem Inst Can; Inst Food Technol; Can Inst Food Sci & Technol; Can Soc Nutrit Sci. *Res:* Denaturation of proteins; egg yolk proteins; steroids; freezing of foods; mutagens in food. *Mailing Add:* Dept Food Sci Univ BC Vancouver BC V6T 1W5 Can

POWSNER, EDWARD R, b New York, NY, Mar 17, 26; c 4. PATHOLOGY, NUCLEAR MEDICINE. *Educ:* Mass Inst Technol, SB, 48, SM, 49; Yale Univ, MD, 53; Wayne State Univ, MS, 57; Am Bd Internal Med, dipl, 60; Am Bd Path, dipl & cert clin path, 63, cert anat path, 78; Am Bd Nuclear Med, 72. *Prof Exp:* Asst instr med, Sch Med, Wayne State Univ, 54-56, fels hemat, Sch Med & Detroit Receiving Hosp, 56-58, from instr med to prof path, Sch Med, 59-78; PROF PATH, SCH MED, MICH STATE UNIV, 78- *Mem:* Am Soc Clin Path; Am Soc Hemat; Soc Nuclear Med; Int Acad Path; Col Am Path. *Mailing Add:* Dept of Path Mich State Univ East Lansing MI 48824

POYDOCK, MARY EYMARD, b Skyesville, Pa, Dec 3, 10. EXPERIMENTAL MEDICINE. *Educ:* Mercyhurst Col, BA, 43; Univ Pittsburgh, MA, 46; St Thomas Inst, PhD(biol & exp med), 65. *Prof Exp:* Elem sch teacher, Erie Diocese, Pa, 35-41; high sch teacher, Pittsburgh Diocese, 41-47; from asst prof to prof biol, 47-75, EMER PROF BIOL & DIR RES, MERCYHURST COL, 75- *Mem:* AAAS. *Res:* Preparation and synthesis of the compound Mercytamin; study of the effect of Mercytamin on normal and neoplastic tissues in vitro and in vivo, especially on the mitotic activity. *Mailing Add:* 501 E 38th St Erie PA 16501

POYER, JOE LEE, b Tulsa, Okla, Dec 29, 31. BIOCHEMISTRY. *Educ:* Univ Okla, BS, 54, PhD(biochem), 69. *Prof Exp:* Res assoc, 59-64, fel, 69-72, staff scientist, 72-75, ASST MEM BIOCHEM, OKLA MED RES FOUND, 75- *Res:* The mechanism of enzymic formation of activated oxygen species and free radicals and the effects on biological systems. *Mailing Add:* Okla Med Res Found 825 NE 13th St Oklahoma City OK 73104

POYNTER, JAMES WILLIAM, b Winchester, Ky, Mar 30, 09; m 38; c 1. PHYSICAL CHEMISTRY. *Educ:* Univ Ky, BS, 30; Mass Inst Technol, MS, 32. *Prof Exp:* Lab asst, Res Labs, Armco Steel Corp, 33-36; metallurgist, Mat Lab, US Air Force, 37-52, asst chief, Metall & Ceramics Br, Aeronaut Res Lab, 53-61, phys metallurgist, Metals & Ceramics Div, Air Force Mat Lab, 61-72; RETIRED. *Concurrent Pos:* Abstr, Chem Abstracts Serv, 36-80. *Mem:* Am Soc Metals. *Res:* Alloy development; kinetics of heat treatment of alloys; research administration. *Mailing Add:* 4279 Catalpa Dr Dayton OH 45405

POYNTER, ROBERT LOUIS, b St Louis, Mo, Feb 25, 26; m 60; c 5. MOLECULAR SPECTROSCOPY. *Educ:* Univ Ill, Urbana, BSc, 50; Univ Iowa, MS, 52, PhD(chem), 54. *Prof Exp:* Res assoc physics, Ohio State Univ, 53-54; res assoc chem, Columbia Univ, 54-56; res engr, 56-60, from scientist to sr scientist, 60-69, MEM TECH STAFF, JET PROPULSION LAB, CALIF INST TECHNOL, 69- *Mem:* AAAS; Am Phys Soc; Am Chem Soc; Am Inst Chemists. *Res:* Microwave spectroscopy; earth and planetary spectra; interstellar microwave spectra. *Mailing Add:* 2541 N Marengo Altadena CA 91001

POYTON, HERBERT GUY, b London, Eng, Nov 24, 11; m 38. RADIOLOGY. *Educ:* Univ London, LDS, 34, HDD(Edin), 49, FDS(Eng), 51, FDS(Edin), 72; FRCD(C), 69. *Prof Exp:* Lectr dent radiol, Inst Dent Surg, Univ Loncon, 54-59; prof, 59-80, EMER PROF RADIOL, FAC DENT, UNIV TORONTO, 80- *Concurrent Pos:* Consult, Hosp Sick Children, Toronto & Ont Crippled Children's Ctr; dent radiologist, Toronto Gen Hosp. *Mem:* Am Acad Dent Radiol; Int Asn Dent Res; Can Acad Oral Radiol (founding pres); Brit Soc Dent Radiol. *Res:* Dental radiology. *Mailing Add:* Fac of Dent Univ of Toronto Toronto ON M5G 1G6 Can

POYTON, ROBERT OLIVER, b Providence, RI, Sept 3, 44; m; c 2. MOLECULAR BIOLOGY, MICROBIOLOGY. *Educ:* Brown Univ, AB, 66; Univ Calif, Berkeley, PhD(microbiol), 71. *Prof Exp:* NIH fel molecular biol, Cornell Univ, 71-73; asst prof, 73-76, ASSOC PROF MICROBIOL, HEALTH CTR, UNIV CONN, 76- *Mem:* Am Soc Microbiol; Am Soc Cell Biol; AAAS. *Res:* Membrane biochemistry; mitochondrial biogenesis. *Mailing Add:* Dept of Microbiol Univ of Conn Health Ctr Farmington CT 06032

POZIOMEK, EDWARD JOHN, b Albany, NY, June 15, 33; m 54; c 4. ORGANIC CHEMISTRY, RFSEARCH ADMINISTRATION. *Educ:* Rensselaer Polytech Inst, BS, 54; Univ Del, MS, 60, PhD(chem), 61. *Prof Exp:* Chemist, Durez Plastics Div, Hooker Electrochem Co, NY, 54-55; asst chem, Rensselaer Polytech, 55-56; chemist, Protective Develop Div, Army Chem Ctr, Md, 58-62, res chemist, Res Labs, 62-71, chief mat & eval sect, Develop & Eng Directorate, 71-74, physical scientist, 74-75, dep dir chem lab, Edgewood Arsenal, 75-77, asst chief, 77-79, chief scientist, 79-80, CHIEF, RES DIV, CHEM SYSTS LAB, 81- *Concurrent Pos:* Secy Army res & study fel, State Univ NY Stony Brook, 62-63; Fulbright res scholar, Univ Leiden, 65-66; instr, Div Univ Exten, Univ Del, 66-67; fel, Educ Pub Mgt, Mass Inst Technol, 75-76 & Ctr Advan Study, 75-76; Fed Exec Inst fel, 77. *Mem:* AAAS; Am Chem Soc; Am Microchem Soc; Sigma Xi. *Res:* Heterocyclic chemistry; chemotherapy; olfaction; microchemistry; free radicals; organonitrogen compounds; photochemistry; detection; pollution control; air filtration; gas chromatography; charcoal; sorption; fluorescence. *Mailing Add:* Res Div Chem Systs Lab Aberdeen Proving Ground MD 21010

POZNANSKI, ANDREW K, b Czestochowa, Poland, Oct 11, 31; US citizen; m 57; c 2. RADIOLOGY. *Educ:* McGill Univ, BSc, 52, MD, CM, 56. *Prof Exp:* Intern, Montreal Gen Hosp, 56-57; from resident radiol to radiologist, Henry Ford Hosp, 57-68; from assoc prof to prof radiol, Med Sch, Univ Mich, Ann Arbor, 68-79; RADIOLOGIST IN CHIEF, CHILDREN'S MEM HOSP, 79-; PROF RADIOL, NORTHWESTERN UNIV, 79- *Concurrent Pos:* Mem, Nat Coun Radiation Protection; co-dir, Div Pediat Radiol, C S Mott Children's Hosp, 71-79. *Mem:* Radiol Soc NAm; Am Col Radiol; Soc Pediat Radiol (past pres); Am Roentgen Ray Soc; Asn Univ Radiologists. *Res:* Congenital abnormalities of hands and feet; skeletal maturation; radiation protection; growth and development; physical foundation of radiology. *Mailing Add:* Children's Mem Hosp Dept of Radiol 2300 Children's Plaza Chicago IL 60611

POZNANSKY, MARK JOAB, b Montreal, Que, Apr 25, 46. PHYSIOLOGY, BIOPHYSICS. *Educ:* McGill Univ, BSc, 67, PhD(physiol), 70. *Prof Exp:* Fel biophys, Harvard Med Sch, 70-71, instr, 71-73; sr researcher physiol, Col France, 73-74; lectr biophys, Harvard Med Sch, 74-75; ASSOC PROF PHYSIOL, UNIV ALTA, 75- *Res:* Structure and function studies on biological and model membrane systems; enzyme replacement therapy for treatment of genetic and metabolic diseases. *Mailing Add:* Dept of Physiol Univ of Alta Edmonton Can

POZOS, ROBERT STEVEN, b Ventura, Calif, Dec 28, 42; m 66; c 3. NEUROPHYSIOLOGY, BIOPHYSICS. *Educ:* St Southern Ill Univ, MA, 67, PhD(physiol, biophys), 69. *Prof Exp:* Fel clin physiol & instr physiol & biophys, Univ Tenn, Memphis, 69-71; asst prof physiol, 71-75, ASSOC PROF PHYSIOL, SCH MED, UNIV MINN, DULUTH, 75- *Mem:* AAAS; Am Inst Biol Sci; Inst Elec & Electronics Eng; Am Acad Neurol; NY Acad Sci. *Res:* Tremor, shivering, electromyogram, rigidity, Parkinson's disease and computer application to these problems; catecholamine levels of central nervous system; motor control diseases; nerve tissue culture and electrical recordings. *Mailing Add:* Dept of Physiol Univ of Minn Duluth MN 55812

PRABHAKAR, JAGDISH CHANDRA, b Malikwal, Pakistan, Sept 14, 25; US citizen; m 50; c 2. ELECTRICAL ENGINEERING & EDUCATION. *Educ:* Panjab Univ, India, BS, 46, MS, 48; Ill Inst Technol, MS, 64; Southern Methodist Univ, PhD(elec eng), 69. *Prof Exp:* Sr engr, All India Radio, New Delhi, 49-62; design engr, Oak Mfg Co, Ill, 64-66; sr engr, Tex Instruments Inc, 66-69; asst prof elec eng, Tex Tech Univ, 70-72, assoc prof, 72-77; PROF, CALIF STATE UNIV, NORTHRIDGE, 78- *Concurrent Pos:* Tex State grant, 71-72. *Honors & Awards:* Res Award, US Air Force, 69. *Mem:* Sr mem Inst Elec & Electronics Engrs; Int Soc Hybrid Microelectronics. *Res:* Stochastic processes and optional control; homomorphic filters for communication systems; information and coding theories. *Mailing Add:* Elec Eng Dept Calif State Univ Northridge CA 91330

PRABHAKARA, CUDDAPAH, b India, Feb 8, 34; US citizen; m 62; c 3. ATMOSPHERIC SCIENCES, PHYSICS. *Educ:* Univ Madras, BSc, 54; Andhra Univ, India, MSc, 57; NY Univ, PhD(meteorol), 64. *Prof Exp:* Res asst, Tata Inst Fundamental Res, Bombay, India, 57-58; res asst, NY Univ, 58-62; res assoc, Nat Acad Sci-Nat Res Coun, 63-66; aerospace technologist, 66-77, SR RES METEOROLOGIST, GODDARD SPACE FLIGHT CTR, NASA, 77- *Honors & Awards:* Except Performance Award, Goddard Space Flight Ctr, NASA, 77. *Mem:* Am Meteorol Soc; Am Geophys Union. *Res:* Satellite meteorology; remote sensing; climate modelling; radiative transfer; stratospheric ozone; stratospheric climatology. *Mailing Add:* Lab Atmospheric Sci Code 915 NASA Goddard Space Fl Ctr Greenbelt MD 20771

PRABHU, NARAHARI UMANATH, b Calicut, India, Apr 25, 24; m 51; c 2. MATHEMATICS, STATISTICS. *Educ:* Univ Madras, BA, 46; Univ Bombay, MA, 50; Univ Manchester, MSc, 57. *Prof Exp:* Lectr math, Baroda Col, Bombay, 46-47 & Victoria Jubilee Tech Inst, 47-48; lectr math & statist, Gauhati Univ, India, 50-52; reader statist, Karnatak Univ, India, 52-61 & Univ Western Australia, 61-64; assoc prof, Mich State Univ, 64-65; assoc prof, 65-67, PROF OPERS RES, CORNELL UNIV, 67- *Concurrent Pos:* Chief ed, Stochastic Process Appln, Amsterdam, 80-, prin ed, 73-79. *Mem:* Inst Math Statist; Am Math Soc; Opers Res Soc Am; Opers Res Soc India; Int Statist Inst. *Res:* Probability and stochastic processes with special reference to applications. *Mailing Add:* Dept of Opers Res Cornell Univ Ithaca NY 14850

PRABHU, VENKATRAY G, b Shirali, India, Mar 15, 30; m 57; c 2. PHARMACOLOGY. *Educ:* Univ Bombay, BS, 53 & 55, MS, 58; Loyola Univ, Ill, PhD(pharmacol), 62. *Prof Exp:* Sr pharmacologist, Arnar-Stone Labs, Ill, 62-63; assoc dir pharmacol, Sarabhai Chem Res Inst, India, 64-67; from instr to assoc prof, 67-74, actg chmn dept, 71-74, PROF PHARMACOL & CHMN DEPT, CHICAGO COL OSTEOP MED, 74- *Mem:* Am Soc Pharmacol & Exp Therapeut. *Mailing Add:* Dept of Pharmacol 1122 E 53rd St Chicago IL 60615

PRABULOS, JOSEPH J, JR, b Cincinnati, Ohio, Nov 21, 38; m 63; c 2. NUCLEAR & CHEMICAL ENGINEERING. *Educ:* Purdue Univ, BS, MS, 64, PhD(nuclear eng), 66. *Prof Exp:* Staff mem nuclear eng, Los Alamos Sci Lab, Univ 66-67; staff physicist, Fast Breeder Reactor Group, Utility Div, 67-75, NUCLEAR ENGR, ADVAN DEVELOP DEPT, COMBUSTION ENG, INC, 75- *Mem:* Am Nuclear Soc. *Res:* Development of fast reactor nuclear design computing programs; nuclear design of fast breeder reactors. *Mailing Add:* Combustion Eng Inc 1000 Prospect Hill Rd Windsor CT 06095

PRADDAUDE, HERNAN CAMILO, b Rosario, Arg, Oct 18, 32; m 57; c 3. SOLID STATE PHYSICS. *Educ:* Nat Univ Litoral, CEng, 57; Mass Inst Technol, PhD(physics), 64. *Prof Exp:* Instr physics, Fac Math, Nat Univ Litoral, 54-59; res collabr accelerator dept, Brookhaven Nat Lab, 59-60; sr scientist, 63-77, ASST LEADER, NAT MAGNET LAB, MASS INST TECHNOL, 77- *Mem:* Fel Am Phys Soc; sr mem Inst Elec & Electronics Engrs. *Res:* Theory of magnetism; magnetic measurements; resonance and transport phenomena in solid state. *Mailing Add:* Nat Magnet Lab Mass Inst of Technol Cambridge MA 02139

PRADOS, JOHN W(ILLIAM), b Spring Hill, Tenn, Oct 12, 29; m 51; c 3. CHEMICAL ENGINEERING. *Educ:* Univ Miss, BS, 51; Univ Tenn, MS, 54, PhD(chem eng), 57. *Prof Exp:* Asst, 53-55, from instr to assoc prof chem eng, 55-64, assoc dean eng, 69-71, dean admis & rec, 71-73, actg chancellor, Knoxville Campus, 73, Martin Campus, 79, vpres acad affairs, 73-81, PROF CHEM ENG, UNIV TENN, KNOXVILLE, 64-, VPRES ACAD AFFAIRS & RES, 73-81. *Concurrent Pos:* Consult, Oak Ridge Nat Lab, 57-73 & Ford Found Res, 65-66. *Honors & Awards:* Eng of the Year Award, Knoxville-Oak Ridge Sect, Am Inst Chem Engrs, 77. *Mem:* Am Chem Soc; Am Soc Eng Educ; fel Am Inst Chem Engrs; Sigma Xi. *Res:* Transfer and rate processes; chemical reactor design; mathematical analysis of chemical and nuclear systems. *Mailing Add:* 731 Andy Holt Tower Univ of Tenn Knoxville TN 37996

PRADOS, RONALD ANTHONY, b New Orleans, La, July 9, 46; m 71; c 2. PHYSICAL CHEMISTRY, INORGANIC CHEMISTRY. *Educ:* Univ New Orleans, BS, 68, PhD(chem), 71. *Prof Exp:* Teacher chem, Univ Va, 71-72; res, Georgetown Univ, 72-74; res chemist, 74-77, sr res chemist, 77, res supvr chem, 77-79, mgr process eng, 79-80, SITE TECH SUPT, E I DU PONT DE NEMOURS & CO, INC, 80- *Mem:* Sigma Xi; Am Chem Soc. *Res:* Silver halide and photo polymer photographic systems; electroplating theory and processes; oxidation-reduction mechanisms. *Mailing Add:* Berg Electronics Div E I du Pont de Nemours & Co Inc Emig & Busser Rds Emigsville PA 17318

PRAG, ARTHUR BARRY, b Portland, Ore, Apr 14, 38; m 70; c 1. ATMOSPHERIC PHYSICS, IONOSPHERIC PHYSICS. *Educ:* Univ Portland, BS, 59; Univ Wash, MS, 62, PhD(physics), 64. *Prof Exp:* Mem tech staff, 64-72, STAFF SCIENTIST, AEROSPACE CORP, 72- *Mem:* NY Acad Sci; AAAS; Am Phys Soc; Am Geophys Union. *Res:* Aeronomy; upper atmospheric composition; particle precipitation; satellite instrumentation; upper atmospheric density; ionospheric structure. *Mailing Add:* Space Sci Lab The Aerospace Corp PO Box 92957 Los Angeles CA 90009

PRAGAY, DESIDER ALEXANDER, b Clausenburg, Hungary, Aug 12, 21; US citizen; m 56. CLINICAL BIOCHEMISTRY, CLINICAL CHEMISTRY. *Educ:* Agr Col, Clausenburg, BS, 45; Eotvos Lorand Univ, Budapest, MS, 50, PhD(biochem), 56. *Prof Exp:* Instr chem, Med Chem Inst,

Eotvos Lorand Univ, Budapest, 50-53, assoc chem & biochem, Biochem Inst, 53-55, asst prof biochem, 55-56; asst prof, Biochem Inst, Univ Utrecht, 56-60; res assoc, Univ Buffalo, 60-64; adv res fel, Mass Gen Hosp & Retina Found, 64-66; asst prof biochem, State Univ NY Buffalo, 66-70; asst dir, Clin Chem Lab, 66-70, DIR, ERIE COUNTY LABS, ERIE COUNTY MED CTR, 70-; CLIN ASSOC PROF BIOCHEM, STATE UNIV NY BUFFALO, 70-, CLIN ASSOC PROF PATH, 77-; DIR CHEM LAB, CMX LABS, 79- *Concurrent Pos:* Grant-in-aid, Erie County Heart Asn, 62-64; NIH fel, 62-63, asst dir gen med sci training grant clin chem, NIH, 69-78; consult, Buffalo Columbus Hosp, 68, Jamestown Gen Hosp, 78, Colombia's Nat Clin Chem Orgn & Harbin Health Dept, People's Repub China; advan res fel, Am Heart Asn, 64-66; assoc dir postdoctoral training prog, Erie Co Med Ctr, 78-; vis prof, People's Repub China, 81. *Honors & Awards:* Fisher Sci Award, 81. *Mem:* Am Chem Soc; fel Nat Acad Clin Chemists; fel Am Inst Chem; Int Soc Clin Enzym; Am Soc Clin Pathologists. *Res:* Diagnostic enzymology; analysis of microelements; muscular proteins; Bence-Jones proteins; laboratory pollution control and safety; ion selective electrodes; chemical tests used in rape cases. *Mailing Add:* Chem Dept Erie County Med Ctr 462 Grider St Buffalo NY 14215

PRAGER, DENIS JULES, b Dayton, Ohio, Nov 7, 38. SCIENCE POLICY. *Educ:* Univ Cincinnati, BEE, 62; Stanford Univ, PhD(physiol), 68. *Prof Exp:* Investr med instrumentation, Lab Tech Develop, Nat Heart Inst, Md, 62-69; chief contraceptive develop br, Ctr Pop Res, Nat Inst Child Health & Human Develop, 69-71; dir pop study ctr, Battelle Mem Inst, 71-77; sr policy analyst, 77-79, ASSOC DIR, OFF SCI & TECHNOL POLICY, EXEC OFF PRES, WHITE HOUSE, 79- *Concurrent Pos:* Affil assoc prof, Sch Pub Health, Ctr Bioeng, Univ Wash, 72- *Mem:* AAAS. *Res:* Science policy, science administration, program planning; biomedical and health sciences. *Mailing Add:* 6015 Namakagan Rd Bethesda MD 20816

PRAGER, GERALD DAVID, economic geology, see previous edition

PRAGER, JAN CLEMENT, b Cincinnati, Ohio, Mar 17, 34; m 59; c 2. MARINE MICROBIOLOGY. *Educ:* Univ Cincinnati, BS, 54, MSc, 56; NY Univ, PhD(microbiol), 61. *Prof Exp:* Res assoc biol, Hasksins Labs, Inc, NY, 58-61; chief microbiologist, Sandy Hook Marine Lab, US Fish & Wildlife Serv, 61-66; unit leader, Fed Water Pollution Control Admin, 66-69, prof coordr plankton environ studies, Nat Marine Water Qual Lab, 69-77; CHIEF TECH ASSISTANCE BR, ENVIRON RES LAB, US ENVIRON PROTECTION AGENCY, 77- *Concurrent Pos:* Lectr, Queens Col, NY, 60-61; adv, Philipp Co, NJ, 65-66. *Honors & Awards:* Founders Day Award, NY Univ, 61. *Mem:* AAAS; Soc Protozool; Am Soc Microbiol; Am Soc Limnol & Oceanog; Phycol Soc Am. *Res:* Nutrition, physiology, biochemistry and morphology of marine phytoplankton species; man's effects on growth of phytoplankton species in the coastal marine environment. *Mailing Add:* Environ Res Lab S Ferry Rd Narragansett RI 02882

PRAGER, JULIANNE HELLER, b Boston, Mass, June 5, 24; m 48. ORGANIC CHEMISTRY. *Educ:* Brown Univ, ScB, 46; Cornell Univ, PhD(org chem), 53. *Prof Exp:* Res assoc biochem, Univ Utah, 51-52; mem staff cent res, 52-73, EXEC DIR TECH INFO & TECHNOL ANAL, MINN MINING & MFG CO, 73- *Concurrent Pos:* Trustee, Brown Univ, 78. *Honors & Awards:* Spurgeon Award, 80. *Mem:* Am Chem Soc. *Res:* Information handling; polymer chemistry; fluorine chemistry. *Mailing Add:* 3320 N Dunlap St St Paul MN 55112

PRAGER, MARTIN, b Brooklyn, May 23, 39; div; c 2. PHYSICAL METALLURGY, MATERIALS SCIENCE. *Educ:* Cornell Univ, BChE, 61, 62; Univ Calif, Los Angeles, PhD(mat eng), 69. *Prof Exp:* Sr res engr, Rocketdyne Div, NAm Rockwell Corp, 61-68; supvr metall develop, Copper Develop Asn, 69-72, supvr tech serv, 72-76; CONSULT, 76- *Concurrent Pos:* Assoc dir, Metal Properties Coun, 78- *Mem:* Am Soc Testing & Mat; Am Soc Metals; Am Welding Soc; Mining, Metall & Petrol Engrs; Nat Asn Corrosion Engrs. *Res:* Environmental embrittlement; fracture; welding; weld cracking; precipitation hardenable nickel base alloys; high pressure technology; thermodynamics; magnetic properties of materials; corrosion resistance; fractography; adhesive bonding; copper and copper alloys. *Mailing Add:* 125 E 87th St New York NY 10028

PRAGER, MORTON DAVID, b Dallas, Tex, Dec 12, 27; m 51; c 4. BIOCHEMISTRY. *Educ:* Univ Tex, BA, 47; Purdue Univ, MS, 49, PhD(chem), 51. *Prof Exp:* Res chemist, Org Chem Res Div, B F Goodrich Co, 51-53; consult chemist, Dallas Labs, 53-54; res chemist, Wadley Res Inst & Blood Bank, 54-67, asst dir res, 63-67; assoc prof, 67-72, PROF BIOCHEM, UNIV TEX HEALTH SCI CTR DALLAS, 72-, PROF SURG, 67- *Concurrent Pos:* From asst prof to prof chem, Grad Res Inst, Baylor Univ, 54-68, prof microbiol, 64-68; consult, Vet Admin Hosp, Temple, 60-68; assoc ed, Cancer Res, 79- *Mem:* Am Chem Soc; Am Soc Hemat; Am Asn Immunol; Int Soc Hemat; Am Asn Cancer Res. *Res:* Biochemistry and immunology of cancer; biochemical studies of the traumatized patient. *Mailing Add:* Dept Surg Univ Tex Health Sci Ctr Dallas TX 75235

PRAGER, STEPHEN, b Darmstadt, Ger, July 20, 28; nat US; m 48. PHYSICAL CHEMISTRY. *Educ:* Brown Univ, BSc, 47; Cornell Univ, PhD(phys chem), 51. *Prof Exp:* Res assoc phys chem, Cornell Univ, 50-51; Jewett fel, Univ Utah, 51-52; from asst prof to assoc prof, 52-62, PROF PHYS CHEM, UNIV MINN, MINNEAPOLIS, 62- *Concurrent Pos:* Consult, Union Carbide Corp, Tenn, 54-; Fulbright grant & Guggenheim fel, Univ Brussels, 58-59; Fulbright lectr & Guggenheim fel, Univ Erlangen, 66-67. *Mem:* Am Chem Soc; fel Am Phys Soc; Soc Rheol. *Res:* Diffusion; rheology; statistical and quantum mechanics; hydrodynamics; polymers. *Mailing Add:* Dept of Chem Univ of Minn Minneapolis MN 55455

PRAGER, STEWART CHARLES, b New York, NY, Oct 21, 48; m 72; c 2. PLASMA STABILITY. *Educ:* Queens Col, BA, 70; Columbia Univ, BS, 70, PhD(plasma physics), 75. *Prof Exp:* Sr scientist, Gen Atomic Co, 75-77; asst prof, 77-81, ASSOC PROF PHYSICS, UNIV WIS, MADISON, 81- *Mem:* Am Phys Soc. *Res:* Physics of magnetically confined plasmas; micro and macrostability of plasmas using the tokamak and octopoh as experimental devices. *Mailing Add:* Physics Dept Univ Wis Madison WI 53706

PRAGER, WILLIAM, applied mechanics, deceased

PRAHL, HELMUT FERDINAND, b Ludwigshafen, Ger, Oct 16, 33; div; c 3. ORGANIC CHEMISTRY, CHEMICAL ENGINEERING. *Educ:* Univ Rochester, BS, 54; Univ Wis, MS & PhD(chem), 58. *Prof Exp:* Chemist, Chemstrand Res Ctr, Inc, 58-60; proj leader, Stand Oil Co, Ohio, 60-62; actg dir org & polymer div, Bjorksten Res Labs, 62-63, dir, 63-65, asst to pres, 65-66; exec vpres, 64-72, PRES, Pb SCI CORP, 72-; PRES, DYNATRON RES CORP, 66-, EXEC DIR, DYNATRON RES FOUND, 67- *Mem:* Fiber Soc. *Res:* Synthetic, natural fibers; modification of cotton; polyolefins; polyamides; acrylics; polyureas; polyurethanes; polyesters; epoxies; films; molding resins; adhesives; plasticizers; detergents; monomers; fine chemicals; sugar derivatives; enzymes; process engineering; long chain alcohols as therapy in neuropathies. *Mailing Add:* PO Box 4098 Madison WI 53711

PRAHL, JAMES WILLIAM, biochemistry, medicine, deceased

PRAHLAD, KADABA V, b Tumkure, India, Oct 18, 26; US citizen; c 3. DEVELOPMENTAL BIOLOGY. *Educ:* Univ Mysore, BSc, 48, MSc, 49; Univ Mo, PhD(zool), 59. *Prof Exp:* Fel reprod physiol, Univ Wis, 59-60; guest investr, Cent Drug Res Inst, India, 60-62; res assoc biol, Wabash Col, 63-65, vis asst prof, 65-66; assoc prof, 66-70, PROF DEVELOP BIOL, NORTHERN ILL UNIV, 70- *Mem:* AAAS; Soc Develop Biol; Am Soc Zool. *Res:* Influence of endocrines on developmental processes; influence of pesticides on development. *Mailing Add:* Dept of Biol Sci Northern Ill Univ De Kalb IL 60115

PRAIRIE, RICHARD LANE, b Chicago, Ill, Apr 25, 34; m 63; c 2. BIOCHEMISTRY. *Educ:* Univ Chicago, BA, 56, BS, 57, PhD(biochem), 61. *Prof Exp:* Res assoc biochem, Pub Health Res Inst New York, 61-63; from instr to asst prof, Univ Ill, Urbana, 63-67; asst prof, 67-80, ADJ ASST PROF BIOCHEM, COL MED, UNIV CINCINNATI, 80- *Concurrent Pos:* NSF fel, 61-63. *Res:* Mechanism and specificity of mammalian dehydrogenases; application of computer techniques to biochemistry. *Mailing Add:* Dept of Biol Chem Univ of Cincinnati Col Med Cincinnati OH 45267

PRAISSMAN, MELVIN, b Philadelphia, Pa, Aug 23, 40; m 63; c 1. BIOCHEMISTRY, PHYSICAL CHEMISTRY. *Educ:* Univ Pittsburgh, BS, 62; Univ Ariz, PhD(chem), 67. *Prof Exp:* Res assoc biochem, Purdue Univ, 67-68; RES BIOCHEMIST, DEPT MED, MEADOWBROOK HOSP, 68-; ASST PROF MED, MED SCH, STATE UNIV NY STONY BROOK, 72- *Concurrent Pos:* NIH fel, 67-; assoc, Dept Physiol, Mt Sinai Sch Med, 72- *Mem:* AAAS; Am Chem Soc. *Res:* Membrane phenomena with emphasis on ion and water movement across biologic membranes; molecular factors in gastrin release and action; gastric physiology. *Mailing Add:* Dept Med Meadowbrook Hosp 2201 Hempstead Turnpike East Meadow NY 11554

PRAKASH, ANAND, b India, Jan 1, 15; m 56; c 2. GROUNDWATER, HYDRAULIC STRUCTURES. *Educ:* Univ Roorkee, India, BS, 57, MS, 69; Colo State Univ, PhD(civil eng), 74. *Prof Exp:* Asst engr, Irrigation Dept, Univ Roorkee, India, 58-69; res asst civil eng, Colo State Univ, 72-74; eng supvr water resources, Sargent & Lundy Engrs, Chicago, 74-77, hydrol, Bechtel Inc, San Francisco, 77-79; CHIEF WATER RESOURCES ENG, DAMES & MOORE, DENVER, 79- *Concurrent Pos:* Lectr civil eng, Univ Roorkee, India, 66-69, exec engr, 66-71. *Mem:* Am Soc Chem Engrs; Am Water Resources Asn; Asn Hydraulic Res; Am Geophys Union; Am Nuclear Soc. *Res:* Hydrology; groundwater; hydraulic structures; hydraulics; water resources engineering. *Mailing Add:* 8892 W Progress Pl Littleton CO 80123

PRAKASH, LOUISE, b Lyon, France, Apr 11, 43; US citizen; m 65. MOLECULAR GENETICS. *Educ:* Bryn Mawr Col, BA, 63; Wash Univ, MA, 65; Univ Chicago, PhD(microbiol), 70. *Prof Exp:* Fel, 70-72, asst prof, 72-78, ASSOC PROF RADIATION BIOL & BIOPHYS, UNIV ROCHESTER, 78- *Mem:* Biophys Soc; Environ Mutagen Soc; Genetics Soc Am. *Res:* Repair of damaged DNA; mechanisms of mutagenesis and recombination in yeast. *Mailing Add:* Dept of Radiation Biol & Biophys Univ of Rochester Sch of Med Rochester NY 14642

PRAKASH, SATYA, b Pilkhuwa, India, July 8, 38; m 65. GENETICS. *Educ:* Meerut Col Agra Univ, BSc, 56; Vet Col, Mhow, BVScAH, 60; Indian Vet Res Inst, Izatnagar, MVSc, 62; Wash Univ, PhD(zool), 66. *Prof Exp:* NIH trainee, Univ Chicago, 66-67, res assoc zool, 68-69; asst prof, 69-74, assoc prof, 74-80, PROF BIOL, UNIV ROCHESTER, 80- *Mem:* AAAS; Am Soc Nat; Genetics Soc Am. *Res:* Gene polymorphisms; mechanisms of DNA repair and recombination in eukaryotes. *Mailing Add:* Dept of Biol Univ of Rochester Rochester NY 14627

PRAKASH, SHAMSHER, b Mansa Mandi, India, Jan 3, 33. GEOTECHNICAL ENGINEERING, EARTHQUAKE ENGINEERING. *Educ:* Univ Roorkee, BE, 54; Univ Ill, Urbana, MS, 61, PhD(civil eng), 62. *Prof Exp:* Asst engr civil eng, Punjab Pub Works Dept, India, 55-57; lectr, Univ Roorkee, 57-62, reader, 62-66, prof civil eng & earthquake eng, 66-78; assoc prof, 78-80, PROF CIVIL ENG, UNIV MO, ROLLA, 80- *Honors & Awards:* Invention Promotion Bd Prize, Govt India, 73; Khosla Res Award & Gold Medal, Univ Roorkee, 78. *Mem:* Fel Am Soc Civil Engrs; fel Brit Inst Civil Engrs; fel Indian Inst Engrs; Indian Geotech Soc (pres, 71-75); Indian Soc Earthquake Technol (secy, 69-71). *Res:* Effect of earthquakes on pile foundations; seismic stability of retaining walls; liquefaction of soils; machine foundation design and analysis and dynamic soil contents. *Mailing Add:* 308 Dept of Civil Eng Univ of Mo Rolla MO 65401

PRAMER, DAVID, b Mt Vernon, NY, Mar 25, 23; m 50; c 2. MICROBIAL ECOLOGY. *Educ:* Rutgers Univ, BSc, 48, PhD(microbiol), 52. *Prof Exp:* Vis investr, Imp Chem Indust, Ltd, Eng, 52-54; from asst prof to assoc prof, 54-61, chmn dept biochem & microbiol, 65-69, dir biol sci, 69-73, assoc vpres res, 75-81, dir univ res, 73-75, PROF MICROBIOL, RUTGERS UNIV, NEW BRUNSWICK, 61-, DIR, WAKSMAN INST MICROBIOL, 81- *Concurrent Pos:* Fulbright-Hays res scholar & lectr; mem, Int Comn Microbial Ecol, 71-

Mem: AAAS; Am Soc Microbiol; Brit Soc Gen Microbiol. *Res:* Microbial ecology; nature and activity of microorganisms in aquatic and terrestrial environments; biological control; biochemical bases of microbial interrelationships; chemical transformations mediated by microorganisms. *Mailing Add:* Waksman Inst Microbiol Rutgers Univ New Brunswick NJ 08903

PRANCE, GHILLEAN T, b Brandeston, Eng, July 13, 37; m 61; c 2. BOTANY. *Educ:* Oxford Univ, BA, 60, DPhil(bot), 63, MA, 65. *Prof Exp:* Res fel trop bot, 63-66, assoc cur, 66-68, B A Krukoff Cur Amazonian Bot, 68-75, vpres bot res, 77-81, DIR BOT, NEW YORK BOT GARDEN, 75-, SR VPRES RES, 81- *Concurrent Pos:* NSF study grants, 66-67, 68-70, 72-75, 75-76, 76-78, 79-80 & 81-; adj prof, Herbert H Lehman Col, City Univ New York, 69-; ed adv, Torrey Bot Club, 70-; dir grad prog, Instituto Nacional de Pesquisas da Amazonia, Brazil, 73-75. *Mem:* Am Soc Plant Taxon; Asn Trop Biol; Am Inst Biol Sci; Acad Brasileira de Ciencias. *Res:* Taxonomy of tropical plant families, especially Chrysobalanaceae, Dichapetalaceae, Caryocaraceae and Lecythidaceae; floristic studies of the Amazon basin; ethnobotany. *Mailing Add:* New York Bot Garden Bronx NY 10458

PRANE, JOSEPH W(ILLIAM), b New York, NY, June 18, 23; m 45; c 2. COATINGS, ADHESIVES. *Educ:* City Col New York, BChE, 43; Columbia Univ, MS, 48. *Prof Exp:* Metallurgist, Bendix Aviation Corp, 43; asst, SAM Labs, Columbia Univ, 43-44; head oil & resin develop labs, Nat Lead Co, 46-61, tech dir, Pecora, 61-64; tech serv & develop mgr specialty chem div, Celanese Corp Am, 64-65; consult, Skeist Labs, Pa, 65-68; INDUST CONSULT, 69- *Concurrent Pos:* Adj prof, Dept Chem Eng, Polytech Inst New York. *Mem:* Am Chem Soc; Am Soc Testing & Mat; Am Inst Chem; Asn Consult Chemists & Chem Engrs; Soc Mfg Engrs. *Res:* Organic coatings; synthetic resins; emulsion polymers; adhesives; sealants; statistical methods. *Mailing Add:* 213 Church Rd Elkins Park PA 19117

PRANGE, ARTHUR JERGEN, JR, b Grand Rapids, Mich, Sept 19, 26; c 4. PSYCHIATRY. *Educ:* Univ Mich, BS, 47, MD, 50. *Prof Exp:* Intern, Wayne County Gen Hosp, Eloise, Mich, 50-51; resident anesthesiol, Detroit Receiving Hosp, 51-52; resident, Mem Hosp, 54-57, from instr to assoc prof, 57-68, PROF PSYCHIAT, SCH MED, UNIV NC, CHAPEL HILL, 68- *Concurrent Pos:* Consult, Vet Admin Hosp, Fayetteville, NC, 60-74; NIH grant, 61-64, NIMH career develop awards, 61-69 & career scientist award, 69-; consult, Dorothea Dix Hosp, Raleigh, 63- & Cherry State Hosp, Goldsboro, 68-70; mem med adv coun, NC State Bd Ment Health, 70- *Mem:* Fel Am Psychiat Asn; Psychosom Soc; Am Psychiat Asn; Am Col Neuropsychopharmacol; Int Col Neuropsychopharmacol. *Res:* Biological apsects of mental depression and its nosology; relationship of hormones to catecholamine metabolism in depression; role of thyroid status in drug response and in psychological processes. *Mailing Add:* Dept of Psychiat Univ of NC Sch of Med Chapel Hill NC 27514

PRANGE, HENRY DAVIES, b Chicago, Ill, Oct 28, 42; c 2. ANIMAL PHYSIOLOGY. *Educ:* Duke Univ, BA, 64, MA, 67, PhD, 70. *Prof Exp:* Asst prof zool, Univ Fla, 70-75; asst prof, 76-79, ASSOC PROF PHYSIOL, SCH MED, IND UNIV, 79- *Mem:* Am Physiol Soc; AAAS. *Res:* Energetics of animal locomotion; comparative respiratory physiology; skeletal allometry; temperature regulation. *Mailing Add:* Physiol Sect Med Sci Prog Ind Univ Sch of Med Bloomington IN 47405

PRANGE, RICHARD E, b Ohio, Sept 23, 32; m. PHYSICS. *Educ:* Univ Chicago, MS, 55, PhD(physics), 57. *Prof Exp:* Instr physics, Univ Pa, 57-59; fel, Inst Theoret Physics, Copenhagen, Denmark, 59-60; staff mem, Inst Advan Study, 60-61; from asst prof to assoc prof, 61-68, PROF PHYSICS & ASTRON, UNIV MD, COLLEGE PARK, 68- *Concurrent Pos:* NSF fel, 59-61. *Mem:* Am Phys Soc. *Res:* Theoretical, many-particle, and solid state physics. *Mailing Add:* Dept of Physics & Astron Univ of Md College Park MD 20742

PRAPAS, ARISTOTLE G, b Athens, Greece, Feb 21, 22; US citizen. ORGANIC POLYMER CHEMISTRY, PETROLEUM CHEMISTRY. *Educ:* Athens Tech Univ, ChemE, 45; Northwestern Univ, PhD(chem), 56. *Prof Exp:* Sr res chemist, Davison Div, W R Grace & Co, 55-57, Res Div, 57-59; sr res chemist, Mobil Oil Corp, 59-60, SR RES CHEMIST, MOBIL CHEM CO, 61- *Mem:* AAAS; Am Chem Soc. *Res:* Product and process research and development; development of polymerization processes, and of styrenic, acrylic, polyester and polyolefin resins; synthesis of specialty chemicals, and additives for plastics and petroleum; fast curing protective coatings. *Mailing Add:* 26 Winthrop Rd Edison NJ 08817

PRASAD, ANANDA S, b Buxar, India, Jan 1, 28; m 52; c 4. INTERNAL MEDICINE, HEMATOLOGY. *Educ:* Patna Univ, BSc, 46, MB, BS, 51; Univ Minn, Minneapolis, PhD(internal med), 57. *Prof Exp:* Instr med, Hosp, Univ Minn, 57-58; vis assoc prof, Fac Med, Univ Shiraz, 58-60, vis prof & chmn dept, 60; asst prof med & nutrit, Vanderbilt Univ, 61-63; assoc prof, 63-68, PROF MED, SCH MED, WAYNE STATE UNIV, 68-, CHIEF HEMAT, 63- *Concurrent Pos:* Assoc, Nemazee Hosp, Shiraz, Iran, 58-60; hon prof, Univ Shiraz, 60-; head nutrit proj, US Naval Med Res Unit 3, Cairo, UAR, 61-63; mem subcomt trace elements, food & nutrit bd, Nat Acad Sci-Nat Res Coun, 65. *Mem:* Am Physiol Soc; Am Fedn Clin Res; Am Soc Hemat; Am Inst Nutrit; fel Am Col Physicians. *Res:* Trace metal metabolism; dysproteinemias and various hematological disorders; author of numerous articles and books. *Mailing Add:* Dept of Med Wayne State Univ Sch Med Detroit MI 48201

PRASAD, CHANDAN, b Chain Patti, India, Jan 1, 41; m 74; c 3. NEUROPEPTIDES, ENDOCRINOLOGY. *Educ:* Andhra Pradesh Agr Univ, India, BSc, 64, MSc, 66; La State Univ, PhD(microbiol biochem), 70. *Prof Exp:* Sr staff fel, NIH, 74-78; asst prof, 78-82, ASSOC PROF MED & BIOCHEM, LA STATE UNIV MED CTR, 82- *Mem:* Soc Neurosci; Brit Brain Res Asn; European Brain & Behav Soc; Am Soc Biol Chemists. *Res:* Biochemistry, pharmacology and endocrinology of brain peptides; biochemistry of stimulus-secretion coupling. *Mailing Add:* 69 Marywood Ct New Orleans LA 70128

PRASAD, KAILASH, b Peshaur, India, Apr 2, 30; m 44, 78; c 1. PHARMACOLOGY, PHYSIOLOGY. *Educ:* Patna Univ, BSc, 52; Univ Bihar, MB, BS, 57; Univ Delhi, MD, 61; Univ Alta, PhD(pharmacol), 67. *Prof Exp:* Surgeon obstet & gynec, Darbhanga Med Col & Hosp, India, 57; demonstr pharmacol, Gandhi Med Col & Hosp, 58; from demonstr to lectr, Lady Hardinge Med Col & Hosp, 58-64; teaching asst, Univ Alta, 64-65, from asst prof to assoc prof pharmacol, 67-73; assoc prof, 73-77, PROF PHYSIOL, COL MED, UNIV SASK, 77- *Concurrent Pos:* Can Heart Found fel, 65-69; Alta Heart Found & Med Res Coun Can res grants, 68- *Mem:* Can Cardiovasc Soc; Int Col Angiol; Pharmacol Soc Can; Am Soc Clin Pharmacol & Therapeut; NY Acad Sci. *Res:* Neuropharmacology; mechanism of cardiac arrhythmias and congestive heart failure; cardiovascular pharmacology; electrophysiology of guinea pig and human heart in relation to the mechanism of drug action; cardiac arrhythmias, adenosinetriphosphatase and ions in drug action; development of noninvasive diagnostic techniques. *Mailing Add:* Dept of Physiol Univ of Sask Col of Med Saskatoon SK S7H 0W0 Can

PRASAD, KEDAR N, b Barhiya, India, Jan 8, 35. RADIOBIOLOGY, ONCOLOGY. *Educ:* Univ Bihar, BSc, 55, MSc, 57; Univ Iowa, PhD(radiation biol), 63. *Prof Exp:* Asst scientist radiation biol, Brookhaven Nat Lab, 63-66; instr, Univ Rochester, 66-67; asst prof, 68-73, assoc prof, 74-79, PROF RADIATION BIOL, COL MED, UNIV COLO HEALTH SCI CTR, DENVER, 80- *Mem:* Radiation Res Soc; Soc Exp Biol & Med; Am Asn Cancer Res; Am Soc Neurochem; Am Soc Pharmacol & Exp Therapeut. *Res:* Differentiation of neuroblastoma cells in culture and cyclic nucleotides; vitamins and cancers. *Mailing Add:* Dept Radiol #A031 Univ Colo Health Sci Ctr Denver CO 80262

PRASAD, MAHENDRA, b Majagawan, India, Oct 13, 48; m 69; c 2. TRANSPORT THEORY, COLLISION THEORY. *Educ:* Banaras Hendu Univ, BSe, 68, MSe, 72; Univ Rochester, MA, 74; State Univ NY Buffalo, PhD(physics), 78. *Prof Exp:* Fel res asst physics, Oxford Univ, 77-79; res assoc, McGill Univ, 79-80; fel, Univ New Brunswick, Fredericton, 80-81; PROF PHYSICS, DAWSON COL, 81- *Concurrent Pos:* Lectr, McGill Univ, 80. *Mem:* Inst Physics. *Res:* Quantum statistical theories of transport mechanisms in semiconductors and metal-oxide semiconductor layers; cyclotron resonance in inversion layers; collisional effects on the spectra of high density gases in interaction with lasers. *Mailing Add:* Physics Dept Dawson Col 1001 Sherbrooke St E Montreal PQ H2L 1L3 Can

PRASAD, NARESH, b Auria, Bihar, India, Dec 11, 39; m 65; c 3. RADIOBIOLOGY, CYTOGENETICS. *Educ:* Patna Univ, BSc, 59, MSc, 61; NDak State Univ, PhD(bot), 67. *Prof Exp:* Lectr bot, Ranchi Univ, India, 61-63; USPHS fel, Baylor Col Med, 67-69; asst prof radiobiol, 69-74; assoc dir & consult, Vet Admin Hosp, Houston, 74-78; ASSOC PROF RADIOBIOL, BAYLOR COL MED, 74-; DIR RADIOBIOL RES, VET ADMIN HOSP, HOUSTON, 78- *Concurrent Pos:* Asst dir radiobiol res & consult, Vet Admin Hosp, Houston, 69-74; ed-in-chief, Radiation & Immunol Series, CRC Pres, Inc, Boca Raton, Fla. *Mem:* AAAS; Radiation Res Soc; Am Asn Cancer Res; Am Inst Ultrasound Med; Sigma Xi. *Res:* Chromosomes; radiation effects; lymphocytes; lung cancer; ultrasound; nuclear magnetic resonance. *Mailing Add:* Dept of Radiol Baylor Col of Med Houston TX 77030

PRASAD, RAGHUBIR (RAJ), b Allahabad, India, July 5, 36; m 66; c 3. PLANT PHYSIOLOGY. *Educ:* Univ Allahabad, BSA, 54, MS, 56; Oxford Univ, PhD(plant physiol), 61. *Prof Exp:* AEC fel, Univ Calif, Davis, 61-63; res biochemist, Univ Calif, Berkeley, 63-65; assoc prof agron, Univ Ibadan, 65-67; professional assoc bot, Univ Man, 67-68; RES SCIENTIST, FED DEPT ENVIRON, 68- *Concurrent Pos:* Consult, Food & Agr Orgn, Kenya, 68-72. *Honors & Awards:* Weed Sci Soc Am Excellence Award, 67. *Mem:* Am Soc Plant Physiol; Weed Sci Soc Am; Am Chem Soc; Can Soc Plant Physiol; Soc Environ Toxicol Chem. *Res:* Pesticide physiology and biochemistry; fate of pesticides in aquatic and forest environment; pesticide pollution; systemic pesticides in forests. *Mailing Add:* Forest Pest Mgt Inst PO Box 490 Sault Ste Marie ON P6A 5M7 Can

PRASAD, RAJ NANDAN, organic chemistry, see previous edition

PRASAD, RAMESHWAR, b Sayadpur, India, July 3, 36; m 61; c 3. IMMUNOLOGY, IMMUNOCHEMISTRY. *Educ:* Allahabad Univ, India, PhD(chem), 59, DSc, 67. *Prof Exp:* Reader chem, Patna Univ, 68-70; head res & develop immunol, 72-79, CHIEF RADIOIMMUNOASSAY, UNIV ILL MED CTR, 79- *Honors & Awards:* Hill Mem Prize, Allahabad Univ, 61. *Mem:* Fel Indian Nat Acad Sci. *Res:* Study of immunoglobulin levels in cerebrospinal fluid of patients with central nervous system diseases; purification, characterization and clinical evaluation of organ specific antigens. *Mailing Add:* Dept Path Univ Ill Med Ctr Chicago IL 60612

PRASAD, RUPI, b Ranchi, India. MEDICAL GENETICS, ENZYMOLOGY. *Educ:* Ranchi Univ, BS, 62, MS, 64; NDak State Univ, PhD(bot), 68. *Prof Exp:* Fel med genetics, Univ Tex M D Anderson Hosp & Tumor Inst, 69-71; asst prof genetics, Dept Obstet & Gynec, Baylor Col Med, 72-79; RES CHEMIST, CHAMPION CHEM, INC, 80- *Concurrent Pos:* Biochem geneticist, Vet Admin Hosp, Houston, 74- *Mem:* Sigma Xi; Am Chem Soc; Nat Asn Corrosion Eng. *Mailing Add:* Champion Chem Inc PO Box 45509 Houston TX 77045

PRASAD, SHEO SHANKER, b Bihar, India, Feb 18, 32; m 54; c 1. PHYSICS. *Educ:* Univ Patna, BSc, 50, MSc, 52; Queen's Univ Belfast, PhD(appl math), 64. *Prof Exp:* Lectr physics, Sci Col, Univ Patna, 52-54 & L S Col, Muzaffarpur, India, 52-62; res assoc appl math, Queen's Univ Belfast, 62-65; res assoc, Arecibo Ionospheric Observ, Cornell Univ, PR, 65-68; assoc prof physics, Univ Fla, 68-75; MEM STAFF, JET PROPULSION LAB, CALIF INST TECHNOL, 75- *Mem:* Am Geophys Union; Brit Inst Physics & Phys Soc. *Res:* Physics of the ionosphere; atomic collision; molecular spectroscopy. *Mailing Add:* Jet Propulsion Lab 4800 Oak Grove Dr Pasadena CA 91103

PRASAD, SURESH, b Chapra, India, Jan 26, 37; m 60; c 3. POULTRY SCIENCE, LABORATORY ANIMAL SCIENCE. *Educ:* Bihar Vet Col, India, DVM, 59, Univ Mo-Columbia, MS, 64, PhD(poultry sci), 67. *Prof Exp:* Animal husb exten supvr, Animal Husb Dept, Govt Bihar, India, 59-60, key village inspector, 60-63; dir res & qual control, Mountaire Poultry, Mountaire Corp, 66-68, dir res & diag serv, 68-72; vet, Biol Vet Serv, 73-75, MGR BIOL VET SERV, MERCK, SHARP & DOHME, MERCK & CO, INC, 75- *Mem:* Am Vet Med Asn; Am Asn Avian Path; Poultry Sci Asn. *Res:* Poultry and laboratory animal care administration. *Mailing Add:* 1520 Tennis Circle Lansdale PA 19446

PRASHAR, PAUL D, b Lahore, India, Sept 10, 30; US citizen; m 66. HORTICULTURE, PLANT BREEDING. *Educ:* Punjab Univ, BSc, 52; Univ Minn, MS, 55; Univ Mo, PhD(hort), 60. *Prof Exp:* Asst hort, Univ Mo, 57-60; from instr to assoc prof, 60-77, PROF HORT, SDAK STATE UNIV, 78- *Mem:* Am Soc Hort Sci; Int Soc Hort Sci. *Res:* Tomato breeding for early maturity; Septoria resistance; pepper breeding to develop early red pepper for home gardeners. *Mailing Add:* Dept of Hort SDak State Univ Brookings SD 57007

PRASK, HENRY JOSEPH, b Detroit, Mich, Sept 26, 36. SOLID STATE PHYSICS. *Educ:* Univ Notre Dame, BS, 58, PhD(nuclear physics), 63. *Prof Exp:* Consult, Feltman Res Lab, 64-65, solid state physicist, Explosives Div, Feltman Res Lab, Picatinny Arsenal, 65-80, SOLID STATE PHYSICIST, ENERGETIC MATS DIV, LARGE CALIBER WEAPONS SYSTS LAB, ARRADCOM, DOVER, NJ, 80- *Concurrent Pos:* Guest scientist, Reactor Radiation Div, Nat Bur Standards, Washington, DC, 71- *Mem:* Am Phys Soc. *Res:* Lattice dynamics and crystallographic studies by means of thermal neutron scattering with particular emphasis on energetic materials and metallurgical samples. *Mailing Add:* Reactor Radiation Div Nat Bur of Standards Washington DC 20234

PRASTEIN, SOLOMON MATTHEW, b New York, NY, June 17, 29; m 58; c 3. ENVIRONMENTAL LAW, PATENT LAW. *Educ:* Columbia Univ, AB, 49; Univ Chicago, MS, 50; Ill Inst Technol, PhD(physics), 66; JD, Loyola Univ Chicago, 77. *Prof Exp:* Res asst radiochem, Enrico Fermo Inst, 51-54; resident res assoc solid state physics, Argonne Nat Lab, 56; assoc chemist, Armour Res Found, 56-57; res scientist, Bell & Howell Co, 57-58; assoc prof physics, Ill Wesleyan Univ, 58-65, actg head dept, 60-65; vis asst prof, Ill Inst Technol, 65-66; asst mathematician, 66-74, comput scientist, 74-79, ENVIRON SCIENTIST, ARGONNE NAT LAB, 80- *Concurrent Pos:* Lectr Ill Inst Technol, 66-74. *Mem:* Am Bar Asn; AAAS; Inst Elec & Electronics Engrs. *Res:* Electromagnetic field theory; wave propagation; statistical properties of radiation fields. *Mailing Add:* Argonne Nat Lab 9700 S Cass Ave Argonne IL 60439

PRASUHN, ALAN LEE, b Columbus, Ohio, Feb 19, 38; m 59; c 3. FLUID MECHANICS, HYDRAULICS. *Educ:* Ohio State Univ, BCE, 61; State Univ Iowa, MS, 63; Univ Conn, PhD(fluid mech), 68. *Prof Exp:* Res specialist mixing stratified flows, Univ Conn, 65-68; from asst prof to prof civil eng, Calif State Univ, Sacramento, 68-78; PROF CIVIL ENG, SDAK STATE UNIV, 78- *Concurrent Pos:* Hon res fel, Birmingham Univ, 77; Nat Sci Found travel grant, 77. *Mem:* Am Soc Civil Engrs; Am Soc Eng Educ; Int Asn Hydraul Res. *Res:* Sediment transport, determination of turbulence field flows over sand beds using hot film anemometers; various model studies; scour at bridges. *Mailing Add:* Dept of Civil Eng SDak State Univ Brookings SD 57007

PRATER, ARTHUR NICKOLAUS, b Driscoll, NDak, Oct 22, 09; m 36; c 1. NUTRITION, FOOD SCIENCE. *Educ:* Univ Calif, Los Angeles, AB, 32; Calif Inst Technol, MS, 33, PhD(chem), 35. *Prof Exp:* Asst org chem, Calif Inst Technol, 33-35, res asst & res fel bio-org chem, 38-41; res chemist, Continental Oil Co, Okla, 35-36; refining technologist, Shell Oil Co, Calif, 36-38; assoc chemist, Western Regional Res Lab, Bur Agr & Indust Chem, USDA, 41-45; dir, Gentry Div Consol Foods Corp, 45-54, vpres, tech dir & prod mgr, 54-55, exec vpres, 55-56, pres, 56-64; CONSULT, 64- *Concurrent Pos:* Past pres, Res & Develop Assocs Food & Container Inst; mem, Assocs Calif Inst Technol. *Mem:* Fel AAAS; Am Chem Soc; fel Inst Food Technologists (treas, 58-70); fel Am Inst Chemists. *Res:* Bio-organic chemistry; technical assistance to legal counsel; food development and processing; food dehydration. *Mailing Add:* 17400 Weddington St Encino CA 91316

PRATER, C(HARLES) D(WIGHT), b Sylacauga, Ala, Jan 2, 17; m 38; c 2. PHYSICS, CHEMICAL ENGINEERING. *Educ:* Auburn Univ, BS, 40; Univ Pa, PhD(biophys), 51. *Prof Exp:* Physicist, Bartol Res Found, 42-46; res asst biophys, Johnson Found, Pa, 46-51; sr res physicist, Res Dept, Paulsboro Lab, Cent Res Div, Socony Mobil Oil Co, Inc, 51-55, group leader, 55-57, res assoc, 57-62, sr res assoc, Res Dept, Princeton Lab, Mobil Oil Corp, 62-67, mgr process res & develop, Process Res & Tech Serv Div, Res Dept, Mobil Res & Develop Corp, 67-77, sr scientist, 77-80; CONSULT, 82- *Mem:* Nat Acad Eng; AAAS; Am Chem Soc; Am Inst Chem Engrs. *Res:* Thermionic emission; magnetron; bacteriophage; catalysis; solid state physics; chemical kinetics; heat and mass transport; coal conversion and gasification. *Mailing Add:* Res Dept Mobil Res & Develop Corp Paulsboro NJ 08066

PRATER, JOHN D, b Dalroy, Alta, June 24, 17; US citizen; m 41; c 4. METALLURGY. *Educ:* Mont Sch Mines, BS, 39; Univ Idaho, MS, 40. *Prof Exp:* Chemist, Anaconda Co, 40-42; metallurgist, US Bur Mines, 42-52; sr scientist, 52-65, sect head hydrometall, Western Mining Div, Kennecott Copper Co, 65-77, MGR SPEC PROJ, KENNECOTT MINERALS CO, 77- *Res:* Chemical metallurgy; extraction and purification of nonferrous metals. *Mailing Add:* Metal Mines Div Kennecott Minerals Co 1515 Mineral Sq Salt Lake City UT 84147

PRATER, KEITH BURNS, chemistry, see previous edition

PRATER, T(HOMAS) A(LLEN), b Can, Mar 5, 20; nat US; m 48; c 3. PHYSICAL METALLURGY. *Educ:* Mont Sch Mines, BS, 41; Pa State Col, MS, 42, PhD(metall), 50. *Prof Exp:* Asst metall, Pa State Col, 43-44, 45-48, from instr to asst prof, 48-51; asst, Carnegie Inst Technol, 44-45; metall engr, Carboloy Dept, 51-52, res assoc metall, Res Lab, 52-60, mat engr, 60-61, mgr metals processing, Res & Develop Ctr, 61-69, METALLURGIST, RES & DEVELOP CTR, GEN ELEC CO, 69- *Mem:* Am Soc Metals; Am Inst Mining, Metall & Petrol Engrs. *Res:* High temperature materials development. *Mailing Add:* 2120 Morrow Ave Schenectady NY 12309

PRATHER, CHARLES WAYNE, b Union, SC, Feb 10, 41; m 69; c 2. BIOCHEMISTRY. *Educ:* Belmont Abbey Col, BS, 63; NC State Univ, MS, 65, PhD(biochem), 71. *Prof Exp:* From chemist to res chemist nonwovens, 65-73, sr res chemist textile fibers, 73, SUPVR RES & DEVELOP TEXTILE FIBERS, E I DU PONT DE NEMOURS & CO, 73- *Mem:* Am Chem Soc. *Res:* Management of research and development of synthetic textile fibers. *Mailing Add:* PO Box 800 E I du Pont de Nemours & Co Kinston NC 28501

PRATHER, ELBERT CHARLTON, b Jasper, Fla, Mar 13, 30; m 54; c 2. PREVENTIVE MEDICINE, PUBLIC HEALTH. *Educ:* Univ Fla, BS, 52, MS, 54; Bowman Gray Med Sch, MD, 59; Univ NC, MPH, 63. *Prof Exp:* Mem staff, Fla State Div Health, Jacksonville, 52-62; mem staff, Div Health, Hillsborough County Health Dept, Tampa, Fla, 62-63; state epidemiologist, 64-70, chief, Bur Prev Dis, 70-74, dir, 74-79, SUPVR, DIV HEALTH, FLA DEPT HEALTH & REHAB SERV, 80- *Res:* Epidemiology of disease and health. *Mailing Add:* 1323 Winewood Blvd Tallahassee FL 32301

PRATHER, MARY ELIZABETH STURKIE, b Auburn, Ala, Dec 2, 29; m 51; c 1. NUTRITION. *Educ:* Auburn Univ, BS, 51, MS, 55; Iowa State Univ, PhD(body composition), 63. *Prof Exp:* Res asst human nutrit, Ala Agr Exp Sta, Auburn Univ, 52-55, from instr to asst prof foods & nutrit, Univ, 55-63, assoc prof nutrit, 63-67; PROF FOOD, NUTRIT & INST ADMIN & HEAD DEPT, COL HUMAN ECOL, UNIV MD, COLLEGE PARK, 67- *Mem:* AAAS; Am Dietetic Asn; Am Home Econ Asn; Am Inst Nutrit; Soc Nutrit Educ. *Res:* Dietary factors affecting blood lipids; body composition and obesity. *Mailing Add:* Dept of Food Nutrit & Inst Admin Univ of Md College Park MD 20742

PRATHER, MICHAEL JOHN, b Pittsburgh, Pa, Aug 31, 47; m 74; c 2. ATMOSPHERIC SCIENCES, PLANETARY ATMOSPHERES. *Educ:* Yale Univ, BS, 69 & PhD(astron), 76; Oxford Univ, BA, 71. *Prof Exp:* RES FEL ATMOSPHERIC CHEM, HARVARD UNIV, 75- *Mailing Add:* Ctr for Earth & Planetary Physics Harvard Univ Pierce Hall Cambridge MA 02138

PRATHER, THOMAS LEIGH, b Hastings, Nebr, Sept 12, 36. GEOLOGY. *Educ:* Carleton Col, BA, 59; Univ Colo, MS, 61, PhD(geol), 64. *Prof Exp:* Geologist, US Geol Surv, 64-65; from asst prof to assoc prof, 65-75, PROF GEOL, WESTERN STATE COL COLO, 75- *Mem:* Geol Soc Am. *Res:* Structural geology and stratigraphy of the Elk Mountains of Colorado. *Mailing Add:* Dept of Geol Western State Col of Colo Gunnison CO 81230

PRATLEY, JAMES NICHOLAS, b Eastland, Tex, Sept 20, 28. PHYSIOLOGY. *Educ:* Oberlin Col, AB, 49; Univ Tex, MA, 51, PhD(physiol), 57. *Prof Exp:* From asst prof to assoc prof, 57-66, PROF BIOL SCI SAN JOSE STATE UNIV, 66- *Mem:* AAAS; Am Soc Cell Biol; Am Soc Zoologists. *Res:* Cell physiology; bioelectric phenomena and permeability properties of plant and animal tissue; cellular correlation and biological oxidation. *Mailing Add:* Dept of Biol Sci San Jose State Univ San Jose CA 95192

PRATS, FRANCISCO, b Guadalajara, Spain, June 3, 22; m 60; c 2. THEORETICAL PHYSICS. *Educ:* Univ Madrid, BS, 46; Univ Md, PhD(physics), 58. *Prof Exp:* Res fel physics, Univ Birmingham, 58-60; res assoc, Univ Md, 60-61; physicist, Nat Bur Standards, 61-65; from asst prof to assoc prof, 65-70, PROF PHYSICS, GEORGE WASHINGTON UNIV, 70-, CHMN DEPT, 80- *Mem:* Am Phys Soc; Sigma Xi. *Res:* Theoretical nuclear physics; photonuclear processes on light nuclei at intermediate energy. *Mailing Add:* Dept of Physics George Washington Univ Washington DC 20052

PRATT, ARNOLD WARBURTON, b Binghamton, NY, Nov 24, 20; m. BIOPHYSICS. *Educ:* Univ Rochester, MD, 46. *Prof Exp:* Intern & fel, New York Hosp, 46-47; assoc pub health & prev med, Med Col, Cornell Univ, 47-48; officer, USPHS, 48-66, DIR DIV COMPUT RES & TECHNOL, NIH, 66- *Res:* Biomedical applications of computers. *Mailing Add:* Nat Inst Health Bethesda MD 20014

PRATT, ARTHUR JOHN, b Norwich, NY, May 3, 05; m 31; c 3. VEGETABLE CROPS. *Educ:* Cornell Univ, BS, 26, PhD(veg crops), 33. *Prof Exp:* Asst veg crops, Cornell Univ, 29-32, from exten instr to exten assoc prof, 32-48, prof, 48-62; consult, Tasmania & Victoria Depts Agr, 63-64; prof veg crops, Univ Liberia, 64-65; USAID contracting veg specialist, Jamaica Sch Agr, 65-67; secy-treas & gen mgr, Perry City Farms, Inc, 68-74; CONSULT, 74- *Concurrent Pos:* Vchmn, Nat Jr Veg Growers Found, 35-58; dir, Eastern Coop League, 40-42; asst horticulturist, Veg Crops Lab, Fla, 45-46; vpres, Consumers Coop, NY, 46-47, pres, 47-49, 54-57, 73-74 & 77-78; researcher, Maple Leaf Farms, Calif, 53; consult, Exp Sta, Alaska, 59; mem adv comt, Nat Jr Veg Growers; vis scholar irrigation res, Univ Ariz, 79-80; vis prof, Dept Veg Crops, Cornell Univ, 80- *Mem:* Potato Asn Am; Am Soc Hort Sci. *Res:* Irrigation of vegetable crops; vegetable production; potato breeding; practical farm management. *Mailing Add:* Maple Grove Place Ithaca NY 14850

PRATT, CHARLES BENTON, b Madison, NC, Aug 7, 30; m 58; c 5. PEDIATRICS, CANCER. *Educ:* Univ NC, Chapel Hill, BA, 51; Univ Md, Baltimore City, MD, 55. *Prof Exp:* Intern, Hosps, Med Col Va, 55-56; resident pediat, Babies Hosp, Columbia-Presby Med Ctr, 58-60, fel cancer chemother, 60-61; Nat Cancer Inst spec fel, 65-66, asst mem, 67-69, assoc mem, 69-75, MEM, ST JUDE CHILDREN'S RES HOSP, 75- *Mem:* Am

Acad Pediat; Am Asn Cancer Res; Am Soc Clin Oncol; Am Pediat Soc. *Res:* Clinical pediatric cancer chemotherapy; pharmacology of oncolytic agents. *Mailing Add:* St Jude Children's Res Hosp 332 N Lauderdale Memphis TN 38101

PRATT, DAN EDWIN, b High Point, NC, Feb 7, 24; m 59; c 1. FOOD CHEMISTRY, NUTRITION. *Educ:* Univ Ga, BSA, 50, MS, 52; Fla State Univ, PhD(food sci), 63. *Prof Exp:* Teaching fel food technol, Univ Ga, 50-52, from instr to asst prof, 52-61; Nuclear Sci fel food sci, Fla State Univ, 61-62, res asst, 62-63; from asst prof to assoc prof foods & nutrit, Univ Wis-Madison, 63-69; assoc prof, 69-79, PROF FOODS & NUTRIT, PURDUE UNIV, WEST LAFAYETTE, 78- *Mem:* Inst Food Technologists. *Res:* Thermal processing; food color stability; lipid oxidation; pesticides; fruit and vegetable processing; methods of food analyses; enzymatic and non-enzymatic browning of fruits and vegetables. *Mailing Add:* Dept of Foods & Nutrit Purdue Univ West Lafayette IN 47907

PRATT, DARRELL BRADFORD, b Millinocket, Maine, Oct 22, 20; m 43; c 1. BACTERIOLOGY. *Educ:* Univ Maine, BS, 42; Purdue Univ, MS, 45; Harvard Med Sch, PhD, 51. *Prof Exp:* Instr bact & immunol, Harvard Med Sch, 51-52; Hite fel, Univ Tex, 52-53; from asst prof to prof bact, Univ Fla, 53-66; prof biol, Univ Houston, 66-67; chmn dept, 67-79, PROF MICROBIOL & ZOOL, UNIV MAINE, ORONO, 67- *Concurrent Pos:* Vis prof, Univ Leeds, 56-57. *Mem:* Sigma Xi; Am Acad Microbiologists; Am Soc Microbiologists; Soc Gen Microbiol; Can Soc Microbiologists. *Res:* Bacterial nutrition; marine microbiology. *Mailing Add:* Dept Microbiol Univ Maine Orono ME 04473

PRATT, DAVID, b Ithaca, NY, June 7, 32; m 54; c 4. GENETICS, VIROLOGY. *Educ:* Cornell Univ, BS, 54; Univ Calif, Davis, PhD(genetics), 58. *Prof Exp:* Virol trainee, Virus Lab, Univ Calif, Berkeley, 59-60; NIH fel microbiol, Univ Copenhagen, 60-61; Helen Hay Whitney fel biophys, Univ Geneva, 61-62; from asst prof to assoc prof bact, Univ Wis-Madison, 62-70; assoc prof, 70-74, PROF BACT, UNIV CALIF, DAVIS, 74- *Res:* Plant cell genetics. *Mailing Add:* Dept of Bact Univ of Calif Davis CA 95616

PRATT, DAVID MARIOTTI, b Williamstown, Mass, Feb 18, 18; m 41; c 2. BIOLOGICAL OCEANOGRAPHY. *Educ:* Williams Col, BA, 39; Harvard Univ, MA, 41, PhD(biol), 43. *Prof Exp:* Instr biol, Harvard Univ, 46-49; from asst prof to assoc prof marine biol, 49-60, prof, 60-80, EMER PROF OCEANOG, UNIV RI, 80- *Concurrent Pos:* Res assoc, Oceanog Inst, Woods Hole, 46-48, instr, Comn Exten Courses, 48-49. *Res:* Animal behavior, especially predator-prey relationships and chemoreception in mollusks; social development and relationships in giraffe. *Mailing Add:* Grad Sch of Oceanog Univ of RI Kingston RI 02881

PRATT, DAVID R, b Dallas, Tex, Oct 20, 29; m 51; c 4. PHYSIOLOGY, GENETICS. *Educ:* Southwest Tex State Col, BS, 51, MEd, 54; Mich State Univ, PhD(animal breeding), 60. *Prof Exp:* Assoc prof animal husb, Panhandle Agr & Mech Col, 58-60; assoc prof, 61-72, PROF BIOL, TEX A&I UNIV, 72- *Mem:* Am Soc Animal Sci. *Res:* Animal nutrition; reproductive physiology of Whitetail deer; population dynamics in kangaroo rats; inbreeding in laboratory rats. *Mailing Add:* Dept of Biol Tex A&I Univ Kingsville TX 78363

PRATT, DAVID TERRY, b Shelley, Idaho, Sept 14, 34; m 56; c 3. MECHANICAL ENGINEERING. *Educ:* Univ Wash, BSc, 56; Univ Calif, Berkeley, MSc, 62, PhD(mech eng), 68. *Prof Exp:* Instr eng, US Naval Acad, 57-60, asst prof, 61-64; lectr mech eng, Univ Calif, Berkeley, 64-65, asst res engr, 66-68; from asst prof to prof, Wash State Univ, 68-76, asst dean col eng, 70-73; prof mech eng & adj prof chem eng, Univ Utah, 76-78; PROF MECH ENG & CHMN DEPT, UNIV MICH, ANN ARBOR, 78- *Concurrent Pos:* Fulbright-Hays sr res fel, Imp Col, Univ London, 74-75. *Mem:* Combustion Inst; Am Inst Aeronaut & Astronaut; Am Soc Mech Engrs; Am Soc Eng Educ. *Res:* Aerothermochemistry; prediction and measurement of emissions from steady-flow combustion; mathematical modelling of combustion phenomena. *Mailing Add:* 225 W Eng Bldg Univ of Mich Ann Arbor MI 48104

PRATT, DAVID W, b Providence, RI, Sept 14, 37; m 61; c 2. CHEMICAL PHYSICS, PHYSICAL CHEMISTRY. *Educ:* Princeton Univ, AB, 59; Univ Calif, Berkeley, PhD(chem), 67. *Prof Exp:* Teaching asst chem, Univ Calif, Berkeley, 62-63, res asst, Lawrence Radiation Lab, 63-67; NIH fel chem physics, Univ Calif, Santa Barbara, 67-68; NIH fel, 68, from asst prof to assoc prof, 68-78, PROF CHEM, UNIV PITTSBURGH, 78- *Concurrent Pos:* Merck Found fac develop award, 69; vis prof, Univ Leiden, 79. *Mem:* AAAS; Am Phys Soc; Am Chem Soc. *Res:* Molecular spectroscopy; magnetic resonance and optical spectroscopy; applications of magnetic resonance and optical spectroscopy to problems in molecular and electronic structure; multiple resonance studies of excited states; dynamics of energy transfer in molecular crystals. *Mailing Add:* Dept of Chem Univ of Pittsburgh Pittsburgh PA 15260

PRATT, DOUGLAS CHARLES, b Minneapolis, Minn, Mar 31, 31; m 51; c 7. PLANT PHYSIOLOGY. *Educ:* Univ Minn, BS, 52, MA, 59, PhD, 60. *Prof Exp:* Asst natural sci, Univ Minn, 55-56, res assoc photosynthesis & nitrogen fixation, 59-60, res fel phys chem, 60-62; asst prof, Carleton Col, 62-66; assoc prof, 66-70, PROF BOT, UNIV MINN, ST PAUL, 70-, HEAD DEPT, 74- *Mem:* AAAS; Am Soc Plant Physiologists; Am Soc Photobiol. *Res:* Photophysiology; photochemistry of phytochrome; bioenergy. *Mailing Add:* Dept of Bot Univ of Minn St Paul MN 55108

PRATT, EDWARD LOWELL, b Great Barrington, Mass, Dec 19, 13; m 40; c 1. PEDIATRICS. *Educ:* Mass Inst Technol, BS, 36; Harvard Med Sch, MD, 40. *Prof Exp:* Intern bact & path, Infants & Children's Hosp, 40-41, from asst resident to sr resident pediat, 42-44; instr, Harvard Med Sch, 44-46; Nat Found sr fel, Sch Med, Yale Univ, 46-48; fel exp med, Cambridge Univ, 48-49; assoc prof pediat, Col Med, NY Univ, 49-54; prof & chmn dept, Univ Tex Southwestern Med Sch Dallas, 54-63; B K Rackford prof pediat & chmn dept, 63-79, PROF PEDIAT, COL MED UNIV CINCINNATI, 79-; CHIEF STAFF & DIR RES FOUND, CHILDREN'S HOSP, 63- *Concurrent Pos:* Asst, Harvard Med Sch, 42-44; assoc physician, Infants & Children's Hosp, 45-46; mem, Unitarian Serv Comt Med Exchange Team to Greece & Italy, 47 & MidE, 58; vis physician, Bellevue Hosp, 49-54; attend physician, Univ Hosp, NY Univ, 49-54; chief staff, Children's Med Ctr & Parkland Mem Hosp, 54-63; med dir, Pediat Serv, Cincinnati Gen Hosp, 63-; chief staff & dir, Res Found, Children's Hosp, 63-79. *Mem:* AAAS; Am Pediat Soc; Am Soc Clin Invest; Soc Pediat Res. *Res:* Child health services; metabolic disorders. *Mailing Add:* Children's Hosp Cincinnati OH 45229

PRATT, ELIZABETH ANN, b Orange, NJ, Jan 2, 33; m 58; c 4. MEMBRANE PROTEINS. *Educ:* Oberlin Col, BA, 54; Univ Chicago, MS, 57, PhD(microbiol), 61. *Prof Exp:* Res asst, Biochem Dept, Stanford Univ, 59-61, fel, 61-63; asst prof biol sci, Univ Pittsburgh, 66-73, res assoc, 73-80; RES ASSOC BIOL SCI, CARNEGIE MELLON UNIV, 80- *Mem:* Am Soc Microbiol; Am Inst Biol Sci. *Res:* Membrane proteins and their interaction with lipids; labeling with 19 fluorine for nuclear magnetic resonance spectroscopy. *Mailing Add:* Biol Sci Dept Carnegie-Mellon Univ Pittsburgh PA 15213

PRATT, GEORGE L(EWIS), b Fargo, NDak, Jan 31, 26; m 55; c 2. AGRICULTURAL ENGINEERING. *Educ:* NDak State Univ, BS, 50; Kans State Univ, MS, 51; Okla State Univ, PhD, 67. *Prof Exp:* Asst prof agr eng, NDak State Univ, 51; salesman, 52; from asst prof to assoc prof, 53-67, PROF AGR ENG, NDAK STATE UNIV, 67-, DEPT CHMN, 77- *Mem:* Am Soc Agr Engrs; Sigma Xi. *Res:* Agricultural buildings design; control of pollution from agricultural sources; nonpetroleum fuels for tractors. *Mailing Add:* Dept of Agr Eng NDak State Univ Fargo ND 58102

PRATT, GEORGE WOODMAN, JR, b Boston, Mass, Aug 13, 27; m 48; c 2. THEORETICAL PHYSICS. *Educ:* Mass Inst Technol, BS, 49, PhD(physics), 52. *Prof Exp:* Instr physics, Boston Univ, 51-52; mem staff, Lincoln Lab, 52-60, vis lectr, Inst, 60, assoc prof elec eng, 60-65, consult, Lincoln Lab, 61-77, PROF ELEC ENG, MASS INST TECHNOL, 65- *Concurrent Pos:* Vis asst prof, Brandeis Univ, 57-58; vis prof, Dartmouth Col, 68; consult, Monsanto Co, Kennecott Copper Corp & Ford Motor Co; adj prof vet med, Tufts Univ, 79- *Mem:* Fel Am Phys Soc; fel Phys Soc Japan. *Res:* Solid state physics; quantum electronics; magnetism; optoelectronic devices; biological effects of laser radiation; biomedical engineering; gait analysis. *Mailing Add:* Dept of Elec Eng Rm 13-3057 Mass Inst of Technol Cambridge MA 02139

PRATT, HARLAN KELLEY, b Berkeley, Calif, Mar 18, 14; m 39; c 2. PLANT PHYSIOLOGY, HORTICULTURE. *Educ:* Univ Calif, Los Angeles, BS, 39, PhD(plant physiol), 44. *Prof Exp:* Res fel biol, Calif Inst Technol, 44-46; from instr veg crops & jr plant physiologist to assoc prof & assoc plant physiologist, 46-63, prof, 63-81, EMER PROF VEG CROPS & EMER PLANT PHYSIOLOGIST, AGR EXP STA, UNIV CALIF, DAVIS, 81-; CONSULT, 81- *Concurrent Pos:* Fulbright res scholar food res, Australia, 56; USPHS spec fel, UK, 63-64; scientist, Plant Dis Div, Dept Sci & Indust Res, NZ, 70-71; vis prof & NSF-SEED grant, Dept Hort, Univ Philippines, Los Banos, 77-78. *Honors & Awards:* Campbell Award for Outstanding Veg Res, Am Inst Biol Sci, 69. *Mem:* Bot Soc Am; Am Soc Hort Sci; Am Soc Plant Physiologists. *Res:* Postharvest physiology of fruits and vegetables; handling, transportation and storage; senescence; role of ethylene in plant physiology. *Mailing Add:* Dept of Veg Crops Univ of Calif Davis CA 95616

PRATT, HARRY DAVIS, b North Adams, Mass, Apr 13, 15; m 44, 52; c 3. ENTOMOLOGY. *Educ:* Mass State Col, BS, 36, MS, 38; Univ Minn, PhD(entom, zool), 41. *Prof Exp:* Asst entom, Mass State Col, 36-38; jr biologist, Upper Miss River Malaria Surv, 40-41; asst entomologist & dist entomologist, Malaria Control, USPHS, PR, 41-42, assoc entomologist, 42-43, asst sanitarian, 43-46, chief med entom lab, Communicable Dis Ctr, Ga, 46-53, chief insect & rodent control training sect, 53-64, chief training sect, Aedes Aegypti Eradication Br, 64-68, chief insect & rodent control br, Environ Control Admin, 69-72; RETIRED. *Concurrent Pos:* Spec consult, Econ Coop Admin, Vietnam, 50, Pan Am Health Orgn Guatemala, 57 & Jamaica, 58, WHO, Switz, 66 & SPac Comn, 65; dir training, Stephenson Chem Co, College Park, Ga, 74- *Honors & Awards:* Gorgas Medal, Asn Mil Surgeons US, 64; Distinguished Serv Medal, US Dept Health, Educ & Welfare, 71; Commendation Medal, USPHS. *Mem:* Entom Soc Am; Am Mosquito Control Asn (pres, 67); Sigma Xi; hon mem Nat Pest Control Asn. *Res:* Medical entomology; vector control; mosquito taxonomy and control. *Mailing Add:* 879 Glen Arden Way NE Atlanta GA 30306

PRATT, JUDITH DUNLAP, b Waltham, Mass, Mar 10, 19. PHYSIOLOGY. *Educ:* Univ NH, BS, 44, MS, 51; Duke Univ, PhD(zool, cytol), 58. *Prof Exp:* Asst instr sci, Lawrence & Mem Assoc Hosps, New London, Conn, 43-45; head nurse, Waltham Hosp, Mass, 46-47, instr sci, 47-49; instr physiol, Goucher Col, 54-58; asst prof biol, Berea Col, 58-60; asst prof physiol & nursing & coordr phys & biol sci, 60-65, ASSOC PROF PHYSIOL & BIOPHYS, MED CTR, UNIV KY, 65- *Mem:* NY Acad Sci. *Res:* Morphology of mitochondria and metabolic activity of the cell. *Mailing Add:* Dept of Physiol & Biophys Univ of Ky Med Ctr Lexington KY 40506

PRATT, LEE HERBERT, b Oakland, Calif, Dec 3, 42; m 63; c 2. PLANT PHYSIOLOGY. *Educ:* Stanford Univ, BA, 63, MA, 64; Ore State Univ, PhD(bot), 67. *Prof Exp:* NSF fel, Univ Calif, San Diego, 67-68, USPHS fel, 68; from asst prof to assoc prof biol, Vanderbilt Univ, 69-74, prof, 74-79; PROF BOT, UNIV GA, 79- *Concurrent Pos:* NSF res grants, Vanderbilt Univ, 70-81; res assoc, Inst Molecular Genetics, Univ Freiburg, WGermany, 75-76; counr, Am Soc Photobiol, 78-81; assoc ed, J Photochem & Photobiol, 78-81. *Honors & Awards:* Charles Albert Shull Award, Am Soc Plant Physiologists, 81. *Mem:* AAAS; Am Soc Plant Physiologists; Bot Soc Am; Am Soc Photobiol. *Res:* Photobiology; plant photomorphogenesis; photochemistry, biochemistry and immunochemistry of phytochrome; immunocytochemistry. *Mailing Add:* Dept Bot Univ Ga Athens GA 30602

PRATT, NEAL EDWIN, b Cincinnati, Ohio, July 19, 37; m 60; c 1. ANATOMY. *Educ:* Wheaton Col, BS, 59; Univ Pa, cert phys therapy, 60; Temple Univ, PhD(anat), 67. *Prof Exp:* Assoc prof, 67-80, PROF ANAT, SCH MED, TEMPLE UNIV, 80- *Concurrent Pos:* Pa Heart Asn res grant-in-aid, Sch Med, Temple Univ, 68-69. *Res:* Ultrastructure of irradiated rat parotid gland; mitochondrial evaluation in the hypertrophied and failing mammalian heart. *Mailing Add:* Dept Anat Temple Univ Sch Med Philadelphia PA 19122

PRATT, PARKER FROST, b Virden, NMex, Nov 21, 18; m 45; c 4. SOIL CHEMISTRY, WATER CHEMISTRY. *Educ:* Utah State Univ, BS, 47, MS, 48; Iowa State Univ, PhD, 50. *Prof Exp:* Asst, Utah State Univ, 47-48; from asst to instr, Iowa State Univ, 48-50; asst prof agron, Ohio State Univ, 50-55; asst chemist, Dept Soils & Plant Nutrit, 55-58, assoc chemist, 58-64, assoc prof, 60-64, chmn dept soil sci & agr eng, 65-75, CHEMIST, DEPT SOIL SCI & AGR ENG, UNIV CALIF, RIVERSIDE, 64-, PROF, 65-, CHMN DEPT, 80- *Honors & Awards:* Agron Serv Award, Am Soc Agron, 75. *Mem:* Soil Sci Soc Am (pres, 78). *Res:* Criteria for water quality for use in agriculture; effect of agricultural production on water quality; crop production and animal waste disposal in relation to nitrates in drainage waters. *Mailing Add:* Dept of Soil & Environ Sci Univ of Calif Riverside CA 92522

PRATT, PERRY W(ALTER), mechanical engineering, deceased

PRATT, PHILIP CHASE, b Livermore Falls, Maine, Oct 19, 20; m 45; c 2. PATHOLOGY. *Educ:* Bowdoin Col, AB, 41; Johns Hopkins Univ, MD, 44; Am Bd Path, dipl, 58. *Prof Exp:* Instr path, Johns Hopkins Hosp, 44-46; pathologist, Saranac Lab, NY, 46-52, asst dir, 52-55; chief lab, Ohio Tuberc Hosp, Columbus, 55-66; assoc prof, 66-71, PROF PATH, MED CTR, DUKE UNIV, 71- *Concurrent Pos:* Consult, Raybrook State Tuberc Hosp, NY, 52-54, Nat Inst Occup Safety & Health, 70- & Nat Inst Environ Health Sci, 71-; from clin instr to assoc prof path, Col Med, Ohio State Univ, 55-66; chief lab serv, Vet Admin Hosp, Durham, 71- *Mem:* AAAS; Int Acad Path; Am Thoracic Soc; Am Col Chest Physicians; Am Asn Pathologists. *Res:* Pulmonary pathology, especially pneumoconiosis, tuberculosis and emphysema in man and experimental animals; pathology of acute respiratory distress. *Mailing Add:* Dept of Path Duke Univ Med Ctr Durham NC 27710

PRATT, RICHARD HOUGHTON, b New York, NY, May 5, 34; m 58; c 4. THEORETICAL PHYSICS. *Educ:* Univ Chicago, AB, 52, SM, 55, PhD(physics), 59. *Prof Exp:* Res assoc physics, Stanford Univ, 59-61, asst prof, 61-64; assoc prof, 64-69, PROF PHYSICS, UNIV PITTSBURGH, 69- *Concurrent Pos:* Consult, Lawrence Livermore Lab & mem adv comt, Gov's Energy Coun, Pa; prin investr, Nat Sci Found. *Mem:* Fel Am Phys Soc; AAAS. *Res:* Electron-photon interactions in atomic and nuclear fields, bremsstrahlung, photoeffect, photon and electron scattering, quantum electrodynamics; atomic processes at high temperature and pressure. *Mailing Add:* Dept of Physics Univ of Pittsburgh Pittsburgh PA 15260

PRATT, RICHARD J, b Chicago, Ill, May 17, 27; m 55; c 2. ORGANIC CHEMISTRY. *Educ:* Univ Ill, BS, 49; Wayne State Univ, MS, 52, PhD(chem), 54. *Prof Exp:* Res assoc, Ben May Lab Cancer Res, Chicago, 54-56; asst prof chem, Colo Sch Mines, 56-58; res chemist, A E Staley Mfg Co, 58-62; proj leader new prod, Allis Chalmers Mfg Co, 62-63; head resins modifications lab, Sinclair Res Inc, 63-69; res assoc, Charles Bruning Div, Addressograph-Multigraph Corp, 69-71, sr res chemist, Graphics Res & Develop Ctr, 71-75; supplies develop mgr, Multigraphics Develop Ctr, 75-77; GROUP LEADER PAPER PIGMENTS RES, ENGELHARD MINERALS & CHEM DIV, 77- *Mem:* Am Chem Soc. *Res:* Polymer modification; paper and textile chemistry; coatings; water soluble films and paints; enamels; flocculants; dielectrics; dispersants; photoconductors; polymeric corrosion inhibitors, lubricants, antiwear and antiscalants; electrographics; product development and applications. *Mailing Add:* Engelhard Minerals & Chem Div Menlo Park Edison NJ 08817

PRATT, TERRENCE WENDALL, b Minneapolis, Minn, Mar 9, 40; div; c 3. PROGRAMMING LANGUAGES. *Educ:* Univ Tex, BA, 61, MA, 63, PhD(math), 65. *Prof Exp:* Asst prof math & eng, Mich State Univ, 65-66; asst prof comput sci, Univ Tex, Austin, 66-72, assoc prof, 72-77; assoc prof, 77-81, PROF COMPUT SCI, UNIV VA, CHARLOTTESVILLE, 81- *Concurrent Pos:* Vis assoc prof appl math & comput sci, Univ Va, 75-76. *Mem:* Asn Comput Mach; Math Asn Am; Inst Elec & Electronics Engrs; Comput Soc. *Res:* Programming languages; formal models of syntax and semantics; software engineering. *Mailing Add:* Univ Va Thornton Hall Dept Appl Math & Comput Sci Charlottesville VA 22901

PRATT, THOMAS HERRING, JR, b Kingsport, Tenn, May 15, 28; m 55. PHYSICAL CHEMISTRY. *Educ:* ETenn State Col, BS, 55; Yale Univ, MS, 59, PhD, 60. *Prof Exp:* Res chemist, Rohm and Haas Co, Redstone Arsenal, 59-71; staff engr, 71-79, SR RES SCIENTIST, HERCULES INC, 80- *Mem:* Am Chem Soc; Am Soc Testing & Mat. *Res:* Systems safety analysis testing; combustion; explosives. *Mailing Add:* Hercules Inc Allegany Ballistics Lab Cumberland MD 21502

PRATT, WALDEN PENFIELD, b Columbus, Ohio, Mar 22, 28; m 57; c 3. GEOLOGY. *Educ:* Univ Rochester, AB, 48; Yale Univ, 49; Stanford Univ, MS, 56, PhD(geol), 64. *Prof Exp:* Geologist, US Geol Surv, 49-55; explor geologist, Pac Coast Borax Co, Arg, 55; RES GEOLOGIST, US GEOL SURV, 55- *Mem:* Fel Geol Soc Am; Soc Econ Geol; Am Inst Mining Engrs; Am Asn Petrol Geologists. *Res:* Geology of borate deposits; areal geology of northwestern California, southwestern New Mexico, southwestern Colorado and southeast Missouri; mineral-resource appraisal; geology for the layman; exploration models for Mississippi Valley-type deposits. *Mailing Add:* US Geol Surv Fed Ctr Denver CO 80225

PRATT, WILLIAM EDMUND, b Asheville, NC, Sept 28, 52. PHYSICAL ORGANIC CHEMISTRY, SYNTHETIC CHEMISTRY. *Educ:* Pfeiffer Col, BA, 73; Yale Univ, MS, 77, MPhil & PhD(chem), 78. *Prof Exp:* res chemist, Shell Develop Co, 78-80; MEM STAFF, WESTVACO CUSTOM CHEM, 80- *Mem:* Am Chem Soc. *Res:* Synthesis and reactions of highly strained compounds; C-13 magnetic resonance; applications of heterogeneous and homogeneous catalysis. *Mailing Add:* Westvaco Custom Chem PO Box 237 Mulberry FL 33860

PRATT, WILLIAM WINSTON, b Columbus, Ohio, Aug 9, 21; m 47; c 4. NUCLEAR PHYSICS. *Educ:* Univ Rochester, BS, 43; Iowa State Univ, PhD, 50. *Prof Exp:* Assoc physicist, Brookhaven Nat Lab, 50-52; res assoc, Univ Iowa, 52-54; from asst prof to assoc prof, 54-63, PROF PHYSICS, PA STATE UNIV, UNIVERSITY PARK, 63- *Mem:* Am Phys Soc. *Res:* Nuclear decay schemes. *Mailing Add:* Dept of Physics Pa State Univ University Park PA 16802

PRATT-THOMAS, HAROLD RAWLING, b Barnsley, Eng, June 9, 13; US Citizen; m 41; c 4. PATHOLOGY. *Educ:* Davidson Col, AB, 34; Med Col SC, MD, 38. *Hon Degrees:* LLD, Col Charleston, 64; DSc, Davidson Col, 71. *Prof Exp:* From instr to assoc prof path, 40-51, chmn dept path & dean sch med, 60-62, pres, 62, PROF PATH, MED UNIV SC, 52- *Concurrent Pos:* Consult, Charleston Naval Hosp, 54 & Charleston Vet Admin Hosp. *Honors & Awards:* Am Cancer Soc Award, 58. *Mem:* Am Asn Path & Bact; Am Col Physicians. *Res:* General anatomic and surgical pathology with emphasis on cancer; etiologic and environmental factors in carcinoma of cervix, lung and stomach; toxoplasmosis; ovarian tumors. *Mailing Add:* Dept of Path Med Univ of SC Charleston SC 29401

PRAUSNITZ, JOHN MICHAEL, b Berlin, Ger, Jan 7, 28; nat US; m 56; c 2. CHEMICAL ENGINEERING. *Educ:* Cornell Univ, BChE, 50; Univ Rochester, MS, 51; Princeton Univ, PhD(chem eng), 55. *Prof Exp:* Instr chem eng, Princeton Univ, 53-55; from asst prof to assoc prof, 55-63, PROF CHEM ENG, UNIV CALIF, BERKELEY, 63- *Concurrent Pos:* Guggenheim fels, 62 & 73; res prof, Miller Inst Basic Sci, Univ Calif, Berkeley, 65-66 & 78-79; Am Chem Soc petrol res fund res grant, 66-; Lacey lectr, Calif Inst Technol, 69; Kelly lectr, Purdue Univ, 69; consult cryogenic petrol & petrochem industs; vis prof, Univ Karlsruhe, 73 & Tech Univ, Berlin, 81. *Honors & Awards:* Honor Scroll, Am Chem Soc, 60, E V Murphree Award, 79; Colburn Award, Am Inst Chem Engrs, 62, Walker Award, 67; Alexander von Humboldt Sr Scientist Award, Tech Univ Berlin, 76; Wohl lectr, Univ Del, 73; Centennial lectr, La State Univ, 80; Wilhelm lectr, Princeton Univ, 80. *Mem:* Nat Acad Sci; Nat Acad Eng; Am Inst Chem Engrs; Am Chem Soc; AAAS. *Res:* Thermodynamic properties and intermolecular forces in fluid mixtures; applications of molecular physics to fluid-phase equilibria as required for chemical engineering design. *Mailing Add:* Dept of Chem Eng Univ of Calif Berkeley CA 94720

PRAWEL, SHERWOOD PETER, JR, b Buffalo, NY, Jan 17, 32; m 54; c 5. CIVIL ENGINEERING. *Educ:* Ga Inst Technol, BCE, 53, MSCE, 59; Univ Waterloo, PhD(civil eng), 71. *Prof Exp:* Asst prof, 58-62, ASSOC PROF CIVIL ENG, STATE UNIV NY, BUFFALO, 62- *Concurrent Pos:* Spec lectr, Am Inst Steel Construct, 71. *Mem:* Am Soc Civil Engrs; Am Concrete Inst. *Res:* Structural mechanics; numerical analysis; machine computation; applied mathematics. *Mailing Add:* Dept of Civil Eng State Univ of NY Buffalo NY 14214

PRAY, DONALD GEORGE, b Troy, NY, Jan 19, 28; m 50; c 4. FRACTURE MECHANICS, SERVICE LIFE ASSESSMENT. *Educ:* Tex Christian Univ, BA, 55; Southern Methodist Univ, MSME, 79. *Prof Exp:* Jr engr, Radio Sonic Corp, NY, 48-49; sr engr, Gen Dynamics/Ft Worth, 53-62; eng specialist, Astronaut Div, Ling-Temco-Vought Aerospace Corp, 62-65; group supvr aerospace physics, Space Div, Chrysler Corp, La, 65-67; sr engr aerospace technol, 67-74, SR STRUCT ENGR, FATIGUE & FRACTURE ANAL GROUP, GEN DYNAMICS CORP, 74- *Concurrent Pos:* US deleg, 2nd Cong, Int Comn Acoust, 56; instr, Tex Christian Univ, 58-59; consult, Ft Worth, Tex, 61-62. *Mem:* Acoust Soc Am; Inst Noise Control Eng. *Res:* Jet noise; random vibration; aeroelasticity; noise control; low-frequency acoustic emission of proof-loaded structure; structural service-life assessment. *Mailing Add:* 3628 Wedgway Dr Ft Worth TX 76133

PRAY, FRANCIS ADAMS, zoology, see previous edition

PRAY, LLOYD CHARLES, b Chicago, Ill, June 25, 19; m 46; c 4. GEOLOGY. *Educ:* Carleton Col, BA, 41; Calif Inst Technol, MS, 43, PhD(geol), 52. *Prof Exp:* From asst to assoc prof geol, Calif Inst Technol, 41-56; sr res geologist, Marathon Oil Co, 56-62, res assoc, 62-68; PROF GEOL, UNIV WIS-MADISON, 68- *Concurrent Pos:* Geologist, Magnolia Petrol Co, 42 & Mineral Deposits Br, US Geol Surv, 43-44 & 46-56; vis prof, Univ Tex, 64; mem coun educ, Am Geol Inst, 64-66, mem comt educ, 66-68, house delegs, 71-72; vis prof, Univ Colo, 67 & Univ Miami, 71; mem adv panel earth sci, NSF, 73-76. *Honors & Awards:* George C Matson Trophy, Am Asn Petrol Geologists, 67; Am Diabetes Soc Award, 68. *Mem:* Fel AAAS; Am Inst Prof Geologists; Geol Soc Am; Soc Econ Paleontologists & Mineralogists (secy-treas, 61-63, vpres, 66, pres, 69); Am Asn Petrol Geologists. *Res:* Geology of sedimentary carbonates; classification; diagenesis; facies relationships; porosity; petroleum reservoirs; reef facies; allochthonous basin carbonates; stratigraphy of New Mexico and West Texas; rare earth deposits in California; geological education. *Mailing Add:* Dept of Geol & Geophys Univ of Wis Madison WI 53706

PRAY, RALPH EMERSON, b Troy, NY, May 12, 26; m 59; c 4. METALLURGICAL ENGINEERING, EARTH SCIENCE. *Educ:* Univ Alaska, BS, 61; Colo Sch Mines, DSc(metall eng), 66. *Prof Exp:* Partner, Santa Fe Lead & Zinc Co, NMex, 47-53; owner, Socorro Assay Lab, NMex, 55-57; assayer & engr-in-chg, Alaska Div Mines & Minerals, 57-61; asst mgr res, Universal Atlas Cement Div, US Steel, 65-66; res metallurgist, Inland Steel Co, 66-67; proj mgr, Jacobs Eng Co, 67-68; PRES, MINERAL RES

LABS, 68- *Concurrent Pos:* Instr, Ketchikan Community Col, Univ Alaska, 58-60; lectr, Calumet Campus, Purdue Univ, 66-67; vpres, Wilbur Foote Plastics, Pasadena, 68-72; panelist, Nat Mining Seminar, Barstow Col, Calif, 69-70; dir, Bagdad-Chase Inc, Pasadena-Los Angeles, 69-72; pres, Keystone Canyon Mining Co, Inc, Pasadena, 72-76; pres, US Western Mines, Pasadena, 73-; guest lectr, Calif State Tech Univ, Pomona, 77-80; guest ed, Calif Mining J, 78-80. *Mem:* Can Inst Mining & Metall Engrs; Am Inst Mining, Metall & Petrol Engrs; fel Geol Mining & Metall Soc India. *Res:* Hydrometallurgy of gold and silver ores; heap leach rate of gold in cyanide as function of particle size; detection of chromium mineralization in northern California peridotite and donite; detection of chromium mineralization in Northern California peridotite and donite; rapid determination of tungsten in diamond drill core by x-ray fluorescence; exploration for company and detection of cobalt, in zones of copper mineralization. *Mailing Add:* 212 W Sierra Madre Blvd Arcadia CA 91006

PRAY, THOMAS RICHARD, b Modesto, Calif, May 5, 23. BOTANY. *Educ:* Univ Calif, BA, 47, PhD(bot), 53. *Prof Exp:* Asst bot, Univ Calif, 50-53; from instr to assoc prof, 53-71, PROF BOT, UNIV SOUTHERN CALIF, 71- *Concurrent Pos:* Res assoc, Dept Plant Biol, Carnegie Inst, 60-61; vis assoc prof, Univ Calif, 64 & Calif State Col, Palos Verdes, 66. *Mem:* Am Fern Soc; Bot Soc Am; Int Soc Plant Morphologists. *Res:* Anatomy and organogenesis of seed plants and ferns; comparative anatomy and ontogeny of foliar venation. *Mailing Add:* Dept of Biol Univ of Southern Calif Los Angeles CA 90007

PREAS, BRYAN THOMAS, electrical engineering, see previous edition

PREBLE, OLIVIA TOBY, b Oak Park, Ill, June 3, 47; m 67; c 1. VIROLOGY. *Educ:* Univ Ill, Urbana, BS, 68; Univ Pittsburgh, PhD(virol), 73. *Prof Exp:* Res assoc, 73-74, instr virol, 74-80, RES INSTR, DEPT MICROBIOL, SCH MED, UNIV PITTSBURGH, 80- *Mem:* Am Soc Microbiol; AAAS. *Res:* In vitro models of the regulation and maintenance of persistent virus infections. *Mailing Add:* Dept of Microbiol Univ of Pittsburgh Sch of Med Pittsburgh PA 15261

PREBLUDA, HARRY JACOB, b Fall River, Mass, May 19, 11; m 46; c 2. BIOCHEMISTRY, ORGANIC CHEMISTRY. *Educ:* RI State Col, BS, 32, MS, 33; Johns Hopkins Univ, PhD(biochem), 37. *Prof Exp:* Asst instr chem, RI State Col, 32-33, instr, 33-35; Res Corp fel, Johns Hopkins Univ, 37-38; develop biochemist, US Indust Chem, Inc, NY, 38-44, mgr spec prod, 44-52; mgr spec prod sales, US Indust Chem Co Div, Nat Distillers Prod Corp, 52-59; mgr spec prod, Nat Distillers & Chem Corp, 59-61; consult chemist, 61-73; assoc, 73-75, CONSULT CHEM & PROJ LEADER, ROGER WILLIAMS TECH & ECON SERV, INC, PRINCETON, NJ, 75-, DIR, 79- *Concurrent Pos:* Consult, US Indust Alcohol Co, Md, 37-38; ed, Chemurgic Digest, 63-; Roger Williams group proj leader, 75-; mem, Dr E V McCollum commemorative comt, 79- *Mem:* AAAS; Am Chem Soc; World Poultry Sci Asn; fel Am Inst Chemists; Coun Agr & Chemurgic Res (secy, 65-). *Res:* Inorganic and organic compounds of vanadium; diazo compounds; chemical and microbiological tests for vitamins; feeding and agronomic value of fermentation products; insect repellents; marketing amino acids; physiology of egg production; industrial wastes; petroculture crops; nutritional value of ethanol; oxidation-reduction potential in the rumen. *Mailing Add:* 4101 Pine Tree Dr Miami Beach FL 33140

PRECKSHOT, G(EORGE) W(ILLIAM), b Collinsville, Ill, Nov 18, 18; m 42; c 4. CHEMICAL ENGINEERING, FLUID DYNAMICS. *Educ:* Univ Ill, BS, 40; Univ Mich, MS, 41, PhD(chem eng), 51. *Prof Exp:* Res assoc, Univ Mich, 46-48; from asst prof to assoc prof chem eng, Univ Minn, Minneapolis, 48-64; PROF CHEM ENG & CHMN DEPT, UNIV MO-COLUMBIA, 64- *Concurrent Pos:* Consult, Minneapolis-Honeywell Regulator Co, 52, Gen Mills, 55-56, Minn Mining & Mfg Co, 59 & Mo Rolling Mills Corp, 69-; Guggenheim fel, Univ Edinburgh, 57-58. *Mem:* AAAS; Am Chem Soc; Am Soc Eng Educ; Am Inst Chem Engrs. *Res:* Thermodynamics; diffusion; heat transfer; mass transfer. *Mailing Add:* 1101 Parkridge Dr Columbia MO 65201

PRECOPIO, FRANK MARIO, b Providence, RI, Mar 12, 25; m 56; c 3. ORGANIC CHEMISTRY. *Educ:* Brown Univ, ScB, 48; Yale Univ, PhD(chem), 52. *Prof Exp:* Res assoc, Res Lab, Gen Elec Co, 51-55, mgr chem & insulation, Direct Current Motor & Generator Dept, 55-61, mgr res, Develop & Eng, Wire & Cable Dept, 61-66; corp tech dir, 66-68, VPRES, AMCHEM PROD, INC, AMBLER, 68- *Mem:* Am Chem Soc; Inst Elec & Electronics Engrs; fel Am Inst Chemists. *Res:* High temperature polymers; plastics; elastomers; electrical insulation; wire and cable; chemical conversion coatings for metals; herbicides; plant growth regulators. *Mailing Add:* 310 Powder Horn Rd Ft Washington PA 19034

PREDECKI, PAUL K, b Warsaw, Poland, May 29, 38; US citizen; m 69. MATERIALS SCIENCE. *Educ:* Univ Witwatersrand, BSc, 58; Mass Inst Technol, MS, 61, PhD(metall), 64. *Prof Exp:* Res metallurgist, E I du Pont de Nemours & Co, Inc, 64-66; asst prof mat sci, 66-69, ASSOC PROF METALL & MAT SCI, UNIV DENVER, 69- *Concurrent Pos:* Consult, Coors Porcelain Co, Colo. *Mem:* Am Phys Soc; Am Chem Soc; Am Inst Mining, Metall & Petrol Engrs. *Res:* Application of x-ray diffraction to materials problems: x-ray stress measurement and thermal expansion studies; mechanical behavior of polymers and biomaterials. *Mailing Add:* 4830 E Harvard Lane Denver CO 80222

PREECE, CAROLYN M, b Hazel Grove, Eng. PHYSICAL METALLURGY. *Educ:* Imp Col, Univ London, BSc & ARSM, 62, DIC & PhD(metall), 66. *Prof Exp:* Res scientist, Res Inst for Advan Studies, Martin Marietta Corp, 66-70; asst prof mat sci, Columbia Univ, 70-71; from asst prof to assoc prof, State Univ NY Stony Brook, 71-76; mem tech staff, Bell Tel Labs, 76-80; RES SCIENTIST, KORROSIONSCENTRALEN ATV, DENMARK, 80- *Concurrent Pos:* Guggenheim fel & Churchill overseas fel, Cambridge Univ, 77-78. *Honors & Awards:* Hardy Gold Medal, Am Inst Mining, Metall & Petrol Engrs, 70. *Mem:* Am Soc Metals; Am Inst Mining, Metall & Petrol Engrs; Brit Inst Metallurgists; Am Soc Testing & Mat. *Res:* Environment sensitive mechanical behavior of materials, including embrittlement and erosion of metals and ceramics; physical and mechanical properties of materials at cryogenic temperatures. *Mailing Add:* Korrosionscentralen Atv Park Alle 345 Glostrup DK-2600 Denmark

PREECE, SHERMAN JOY, JR, b Salt Lake City, Utah, May 2, 23. PLANT TAXONOMY. *Educ:* Univ Utah, BA, 45, MS, 50; Wash State Univ, PhD(bot), 56. *Prof Exp:* Asst, Univ Utah, 47-50; asst, Wash State Univ, 50-54, actg instr bot, 54-56; from instr to assoc prof, 56-68, PROF BOT, UNIV MONT, 68-, CHMN DEPT, 66-, CUR HERBARIUM, 77- *Concurrent Pos:* Actg cur herbarium, Wash State Univ, 54-55. *Mem:* Bot Soc Am; Am Soc Plant Taxonomists; Int Asn Plant Taxonomists. *Res:* Botany; cytotaxonomy. *Mailing Add:* Dept of Bot Univ of Mont Missoula MT 59812

PREEDOM, BARRY MASON, b Stamford, Conn, Dec 31, 40; m 63; c 2. NUCLEAR PHYSICS. *Educ:* Spring Hill Col, BS, 62; Univ Tenn, MS, 64, PhD(nuclear physics), 67. *Prof Exp:* Res assoc nuclear physics, Cyclotron Lab, Mich State Univ, 67-70; asst prof, 70-73, assoc prof, 73-76, PROF PHYSICS, UNIV SC, 76- *Mem:* Am Phys Soc. *Res:* Pion-nucleus reactions; including elastic and inelastic scattering and pion absorption and production; nuclear structure. *Mailing Add:* Dept of Physics Univ of SC Columbia SC 29208

PREEDY, JOHN ROBERT KNOWLTON, b Leeds, Eng, Feb 20, 18; nat US; m 66. MEDICINE. *Educ:* Cambridge Univ, MB, BCh, 42, MA, 45, MD, 56; FRCP. *Prof Exp:* House surgeon, Postgrad Med Sch, London, 42, jr med registr, 46; from med registr to sr med registr, London Hosp, Univ London, 46-52, from instr to sr lectr, 52-57; assoc prof, 57-67, PROF MED, SCH MED, EMORY UNIV, 67- *Concurrent Pos:* Vis fel, Col Physicians & Surgeons, Columbia Univ, 53-54. *Mem:* Am Soc Clin Invest; Endocrine Soc; Am Fedn Clin Res. *Res:* Clinical endocrinology; methods for chemical estimation of estrogens in body fluids; estrogen metabolism in the human in normal and disease states. *Mailing Add:* 1670 Clairmont Rd Decator GA 30033

PREER, JAMES RANDOLPH, b Monahans, Tex, May 22, 44; m 67; c 2. ENVIRONMENTAL CHEMISTRY. *Educ:* Swarthmore Col, AB, 65; Calif Inst Technol, PhD(chem), 70. *Prof Exp:* Woodrow Wilson teaching intern & asst prof chem, Fed City Col, 69-72, assoc prof chem, 72-73, assoc prof interdisciplinary sci, 73-78; prof interdisciplinary sci, 78-79, PROF ENVIRON SCI, UNIV DC, 79- *Concurrent Pos:* Fel, Mass Inst Technol, 76-77. *Mem:* AAAS; Am Chem Soc. *Res:* Environmental contamination of urban gardens, soil and vegetables with heavy metals; electronic spectra and electronic structures of coordination compounds. *Mailing Add:* 2005 Klingle Rd NW Washington DC 20010

PREER, JOHN RANDOLPH, JR, b Ocala, Fla, Apr 4, 18; m 41; c 2. ZOOLOGY, MOLECULAR BIOLOGY. *Educ:* Univ Fla, BS, 39; Ind Univ, PhD(zool), 47. *Prof Exp:* Assoc zool, Univ Pa, 47-50, from assoc prof to prof, 50-68, chmn grad group, 58-62, admis officer, Grad Sch Arts & Sci, 61-62; chmn dept biol, 77-79, PROF ZOOL, IND UNIV, BLOOMINGTON, 68- *Concurrent Pos:* Guggenheim fel, 76-77. *Mem:* Nat Acad Sci; Genetics Soc Am; Am Soc Naturalists; Am Soc Zoologists; Soc Protozool. *Res:* Genetics of microorganisms; cytoplasmic inheritance in paramecium; genetics of proteins. *Mailing Add:* Dept of Biol Ind Univ Bloomington IN 47401

PREGGER, FRED TITUS, b Paterson, NJ, May 14, 24; m 53; c 2. PHYSICS, SCIENCE EDUCATION. *Educ:* Montclair State Col, BA, 48, MA, 50; Columbia Univ, EdD(sci educ), 56. *Prof Exp:* High sch teacher, NJ, 48-55; asst prof sci, 55-57, assoc prof physics, 57-62, chmn dept, 68-80, PROF PHYSICS, TRENTON STATE COL, 62- *Concurrent Pos:* Dir, NSF Inst Physics, Elem Sch Sci, Radioisotope Tech Energy, 70-73 & 75-81. *Mem:* Am Asn Physics Teachers; Nat Sci Teachers Asn; Nat Asn Res Sci Teaching; Asn Educ Teachers in Sci. *Res:* Teaching of science at the secondary school and college levels; finding and updating physics lecture demonstrations which have been lost. *Mailing Add:* Dept of Physics Hillwood Lakes CN550 Trenton NJ 08625

PREHN, RICHMOND TALBOT, b New York, NY, Dec 8, 22; m 46; c 3. EXPERIMENTAL PATHOLOGY. *Educ:* Long Island Col Med, MD, 47. *Prof Exp:* Intern, Philadelphia Naval Hosp, 47-48; fel, Nat Cancer Inst, 48-50, mem staff, 50-56, res physician, USPHS Hosp, Seattle, 56-58; from asst prof to prof path, Sch Med, Univ Wash, 58-66; prof path, Sch Med, Univ Pa & sr mem, Inst Cancer Res, 66-76; dir, Jackson Lab, 76-81; SCI DIR, INST MED RES, SAN JOSE, 81- *Mem:* Am Soc Cancer Res; Am Soc Exp Path. *Res:* Tissue transplantation; immunopathology; oncology. *Mailing Add:* Inst Med Res 751 S Bascom Ave San Jose CA 95128

PREIKSCHAT, EKKEHARD, b Insterburg, Ger, Apr 25, 43; US citizen; m 68; c 3. ELECTRICAL ENGINEERING, PHYSICS. *Educ:* Univ Wash, BS, 64, MS, 65; Univ Birmingham, PhD(physics), 68. *Prof Exp:* Res asst nuclear physics, Univ Wash, 64-65; res assoc physics, Univ Birmingham, 65-68, fel, 68-69; vpres eng, F P Res Lab, Inc, 70-79, VPRES ENG, EUR-CONTROL M&D USA, INC, 79- *Concurrent Pos:* Res assoc, Univ Wash, 69-72. *Mem:* Tech Asn of Pulp & Paper Indust; Inst Elec & Electronics Engrs; Am Phys Soc. *Res:* Development of instrumentation for pulp and paper industry; development and optimization of moisture measurement in various mineral and organic materials. *Mailing Add:* Eur-Control M&D USA Inc PO Box 1442 Bellevue WA 98009

PREIKSCHAT, F(RITZ) K(ARL), b Finkengrund, Ger, Sept 11, 10; m 37; c 2. ELECTRICAL ENGINEERING. *Educ:* Sch Eng, Oldenburg, BSEE, 34, PE, 72. *Prof Exp:* Develop engr, Siemens, Berlin, Ger, 36-39; dir lab group radar & infrared develop, Gema, Berlin, 40-45; dir lab radar & radio guid systs, NII 88, Moscow, Russia, 46-52; dir lab teletypewriter develop, Telefon Bau und Normal Zeit Co, Frankfurt, 53-57; sr staff mem, Appl Physics Lab, Johns Hopkins Univ, 57-59; res specialist radio guid commun, Boeing Co,

59-62; prin engr, Seattle Develop Lab, Honeywell Inc, 62-64; develop engr, Laucks Labs, 64-66; res specialist, Space Div, Boeing Co, 66-71; dir res & develop, F P Res Lab, 71-79; DIR RES & DEVELOP, APPA-SYSTS INC, 80- *Mem:* Sr mem Inst Elec & Electronics Engrs; Am Ord Asn. *Res:* Radar equipment research and development; infrared target seekers; missile guidance systems; teletypewriter equipment; blind landing systems; industrial control equipment. *Mailing Add:* 16020 Lake Hills Blvd Bellevue WA 98008

PREISENDORFER, RUDOLPH W, b New York, NY, Dec 30, 27; m 52; c 2. PHYSICAL CLIMATOLOGY. *Educ:* Mass Inst Technol, BS, 52; Univ Calif, PhD(math), 56. *Prof Exp:* From asst res mathematician to res mathematician, Scripps Inst Oceanog, Univ Calif, 53-70; prof math, Naval Postgrad Sch, 70-71; res mathematician, Joint Tsunami Res Effort, Pac Marine Environ Lab, Environ Res Labs, Nat Oceanic & Atmospheric Admin, Honolulu, Hawaii, 71-77; mem climate res group, Scripps Inst Oceanog, 77-79; RES MATHEMATICIAN, PAC MARINE ENVIRON LAB, SEATTLE, WASH, 79- *Mem:* Soc Indust & Appl Math; Am Geophys Union. *Res:* Mathematical foundations of radiative transfer theory with applications to atmospheric and hydrologic optics and visibility calculations in the atmosphere and sea; wave propagation in random media; geophysical random processes; fluid mechanics; diagnosis and prediction of short term climate changes. *Mailing Add:* Pac Marine Environ Lab 3711 15th Ave NE Seattle WA 98105

PREISER, STANLEY, b New York, NY, Nov 25, 27; m 51; c 1. NUMERICAL ANALYSIS, COMPUTATION. *Educ:* City Col New York, BS, 49; NY Univ, MS, 50, PhD, 58. *Prof Exp:* Mathematician, Nuclear Develop Corp Am, 50-60, mgr math sect, United Nuclear Corp, 60-65; from asst prof to assoc prof, 65-69, dir comput sci div, 75-76, PROF MATH & COMPUT SCI, POLYTECH INST NEW YORK, 69-, DEAN, WESTCHESTER CTR, 80- *Concurrent Pos:* Consult scientist, United Nuclear Corp, 65-66; consult, Radioptics, Inc, 66-69, IBM, Inc, 67-68, State Univ NY Downstate Med Ctr, 70 & Bridgeport Eng Inst, 71- *Mem:* AAAS; Am Math Soc; Soc Indust & Appl Math; Math Asn Am; Asn Comput Mach. *Res:* Numerical analysis; theory of computation; mathematics of computation; computer sciences. *Mailing Add:* Dept of Math Polytech Inst New York New York NY 11201

PREISLER, HARVEY D, b Brooklyn, NY, Feb 5, 41; m 63; c 3. ONCOLOGY, CELL BIOLOGY. *Educ:* Brooklyn Col, BA, 61; Univ Rochester, MD, 65. *Prof Exp:* Res assoc, Leukemia Serv, Nat Cancer Inst Med Br, 67-69; fel med, Columbia Presby Hosp, 69-71; asst prof med, Mt Sinai Sch Med, 71-74; clinician II, 74-75, ASSOC CHIEF DEPT MED A, ROSWELL PARK MEM INST, 75- *Mem:* Am Asn Cancer Res; Am Soc Clin Oncol. *Res:* Regulation of cell proliferation and differentiation; anti-cancer chemotherapy. *Mailing Add:* Dept Med A Roswell Pk Mem Inst 666 Elm St Buffalo NY 14263

PREISLER, JOSEPH J(OHN), b New York, NY, May 17, 19; m 42; c 2. METALLURGY, CHEMICAL ENGINEERING. *Educ:* City Col New York, BChE, 40. *Prof Exp:* Metallurgist, 40-43, sr methods engr, 43-44, methods eng supvr, 44-45, standards mat engr, 45-51, sr mat engr, 52-53, head sect mat & processes, 53-59, dept head, Mat Labs, 59-70, MGR ENG DEPT, SPERRY GYROSOCPE CO DIV, SPERRY RAND CORP, 70- *Concurrent Pos:* Instr, Polytech Inst Brooklyn, 44; mem conf elec insulation, Nat Acad Sci-Nat Res Coun, 56-60. *Mem:* Fel Am Inst Chemists; Am Soc Metals; Am Soc Testing & Mat; Soc Automotive Engrs; Am Foundrymen's Soc. *Res:* Materials engineering; electric and magnetic alloys; ferrous and nonferrous alloys; electrochemical and organic finishes; microelectronic device processing; environmental testings; electrical testing. *Mailing Add:* Sperry Gyroscope Co Div Sperry Rand Corp Great Neck NY 11020

PREISS, BENJAMIN, b Hamburg, Ger, Sept 16, 33; Israeli citizen. BIOLOGICAL CHEMISTRY. *Educ:* Hebrew Univ Jerusalem, MSc, 57, PhD(biochem), 62. *Prof Exp:* Fel biochem, Harvard Univ, 62-64; res assoc, Yale Univ, 64-66; vis prof, Nat Univ Mex, 67-69; res fel, McGill Univ, 69-70; asst prof, 70-77, ASSOC PROF BIOCHEM, UNIV SHERBROOKE, 78- *Mem:* AAAS; Can Biochem Soc; Brit Biochem Soc; NY Acad Sci. *Res:* Regulation of cholesterol biosynthesis in vitro studies of nerve cell differentiation. *Mailing Add:* Dept of Biochem Univ of Sherbrooke Sherbrooke PQ J1K 2R1 Can

PREISS, DONALD MERLE, b Minn, Jan 5, 27; m 49; c 2. ORGANIC CHEMISTRY. *Educ:* Willamette Univ, BS, 49; Univ Del, MS, 50, PhD(org chem), 52. *Prof Exp:* Asst, Univ Del, 49-51; res technologist, Shell Oil Co, 52-59, res chemist, Shell Develop Co, 59-62; MGR MAT LAB, IBM CORP, 62- *Concurrent Pos:* Adj prof, NC State Univ. *Mem:* Am Chem Soc; Soc Plastics Eng. *Res:* Elastomers, plastics, high temperature greases, lubricating oil additives, synthetic rubber; extending oils and plasticizers for synthetic rubber; reaction mechanisms; engineering uses of materials. *Mailing Add:* IBM Corp PO Box 12275 Research Triangle Park NC 27709

PREISS, IVOR LOUIS, b New York, NY, Mar 24, 33; m 56; c 3. NUCLEAR CHEMISTRY. *Educ:* Rensselaer Polytech Inst, BS, 55; Univ Ark, MS, 57, PhD(chem), 60. *Prof Exp:* Res asst nuclear chem, Univ Ark, 56-58; res assoc physics, Yale Univ, 60-65, res assoc chem, 65-66, lectr, 60-65, lectr, Foreign Students' Inst, 63-65, asst dir, Heavy Ion Accelerator Labs, 64-66; assoc prof chem, 66-73, PROF PHYS CHEM, RENSSELAER POLYTECH INST, 73- *Concurrent Pos:* Mem comt nuclear educ & employment, Nat Res Coun-Nat Acad Sci, 69-71; chmn, Interdisciplinary Ctr Nuclear Studies, Rensselaer Polytech Inst, 70-; vis prof, State Univ NY Albany, 70-; resident staff nuclear med, Albany Med Ctr Hosp, 73- *Mem:* AAAS; Am Chem Soc; Am Phys Soc; Sigma Xi; NY Acad Sci. *Res:* Nuclear and atomic spectroscopy; trace element analysis; heavy ion and neutron reactions; new isotopes. *Mailing Add:* Cogswel Lab Rensselaer Polytech Inst Troy NY 12181

PREISS, JACK, b Brooklyn, NY, June 2, 32; m 59; c 3. BIOCHEMISTRY. *Educ:* City Col New York, BS, 53; Duke Univ, PhD(biochem), 57. *Prof Exp:* Asst, Duke Univ, 53-56; Am Cancer Soc fel microbiol, Washington Univ, 58-59; Am Cancer Soc fel biochem, Stanford Univ, 59-60; biochemist, Nat Inst Arthritis & Metab Dis, 60-62; from asst prof to assoc prof, 62-68, chmn dept, 71-74 & 77-81, PROF BIOCHEM & BIOPHYS, UNIV CALIF, DAVIS, 68- *Concurrent Pos:* Consult, Physiol Chem Study Sect, NIH, 67-72 & Metab Biol Study Sect, NSF, 72-75. *Honors & Awards:* Pfizer Prize, Am Chem Soc, 71. *Mem:* Am Soc Biol Chem; Am Soc Plant Physiologists; Am Soc Microbiol; NY Acad Sci; Brit Biochem Soc. *Res:* Carbohydrate metabolism; regulation of glycogen and starch synthesis; enzymology; molecular biology. *Mailing Add:* Dept of Biochem & Biophys Univ of Calif Davis CA 95616

PREISS, JOHN WILLIAM, b West Haven, Conn, Jan 1, 23; m 58; c 2. PHYSICS. *Educ:* Yale Univ, BS, 51, MS, 53, PhD(physics), 55. *Prof Exp:* Instr physics, Univ Conn, 54-55; res assoc biophys, Yale Univ, 55-58; physicist, Nat Cancer Inst, 58-60 & Nat Inst Arthritis & Metab Dis, 60-61; assoc prof, 61-70, PROF PHYSICS, UNIV DEL, 70- *Mem:* AAAS; Radiation Res Soc; Am Phys Soc; Biophys Soc. *Res:* Molecular biophysics; spectroscopy. *Mailing Add:* Dept of Physics Univ of Del Newark DE 19711

PREJEAN, JOE DAVID, b Pampa, Tex, Feb 9, 40; m 78; c 2. PHYSIOLOGY, BIOCHEMISTRY. *Educ:* Stephen F Austin State Col, BS, 63; E Tex State Univ, MA, 65; Tex A&M Univ, PhD(physiol), 69. *Prof Exp:* Sr biologist, 69-72, HEAD CHEM CARCINOGENESIS DIV, SOUTHERN RES INST, 72- *Concurrent Pos:* Fel, Tex A&M Univ, 69. *Mem:* NY Acad Sci; Am Col Toxicol. *Res:* Effects of intra-arterial hydrogen peroxide on isotope localization and wound healing; effects of chronic cobalt 60 irradiation on longevity and fertility; cancer chemotherapy; carcinogenesis; toxicology. *Mailing Add:* Southern Res Inst 2000 Ninth Ave S PO Box 3307-A Birmingham AL 35205

PRELAS, MARK ANTONIO, b Pueblo, Colo, July 2, 53; m 79. LASERS, FUSION ENGINEERING. *Educ:* Colo State Univ, BS, 75; Univ Ill, MS, 76, PhD(nuclear eng), 79. *Prof Exp:* PROF NUCLEAR ENG, UNIV MO, 79-, RES SCIENTIST, 80-, DIR FUSION ENGR LAB, 80- *Concurrent Pos:* Prin investr, NSF res initiation grant, 80; fel, Workshop Fuels Inorg Resources, Gas Res Inst, 81. *Mem:* AAAS; Am Nuclear Soc; Am Phys Soc; Inst Elec & Electronics Engrs; Am Soc Eng Educ. *Res:* Nuclear-pumped lasers; chemical synthesis; plasma chemistry; plasma engineering; gaseous electronics; direct energy conversion; cryogenics. *Mailing Add:* Nuclear Eng Dept Univ Mo Columbia MO 65211

PRELL, WARREN LEE, b Oakpark, Ill, June 18, 43; m 67; c 2. MARINE GEOLOGY, PALEOCEANOGRAPHY. *Educ:* Hanover Col, BA, 66; Columbia Univ, PhD(marine geol), 74. *Prof Exp:* Dir geol & oceanog projs, NY State Energy & Res Develop Authority, 73-75; asst prof oceanog & paleoceanog, 75-80, ASSOC PROF MARINE GEOL, BROWN UNIV, 80- *Concurrent Pos:* Actg dir, Climate: Long-range Invest, Mapping & Prediction Proj, 78-81; consult, Ocean Sci Div, NSF, 80-82; cochief scientist, Leg 68, Deep Sea Drilling Proj, 79. *Mem:* AAAS; Am Geophys Union; Geol Soc Am; Soc Econ Paleontologists & Mineralogists. *Res:* Evolution of climate as recorded in deep-sea sediments; history of monsoonal variations in the Indian Ocean; marine geology of the Caribbean; reconstruction of past oceanic circulation. *Mailing Add:* Dept Geol Sci Brown Univ Providence RI 02912

PREM, KONALD ARTHUR, b St Cloud, Minn, Nov 6, 20; m 47; c 3. GYNECOLOGIC ONCOLOGY. *Educ:* Univ Minn, BS, 47, MB, 50, MD, 51; Am Bd Obstet & Gynec, dipl, 58, cert gynec oncol, 74. *Prof Exp:* Med fel, 51-54, Am Cancer Soc clin fel, 53-54, from instr to assoc prof, 55-70, PROF OBSTET & GYNEC, SCH MED, UNIV MINN, MINNEAPOLIS, 70-, DIR GYNEC ONCOL, 70-, HEAD OBSTET & GYNEC, 76- *Concurrent Pos:* Mem bd dirs, Nat Comn Human Life, Reproduction & Rhythm, 66-; mem sci adv bd, Human Life Found, 70- *Mem:* Am Col Obstet & Gynec; Soc Gynec Oncol; Soc Pelvic Surg. *Res:* Natural family planning; gynecologic oncology; stress incontinence. *Mailing Add:* Box 395 Univ Hosps Minneapolis MN 55455

PREMACHANDRA, BHARTUR N, b Bangalore, India, May 17, 30; US citizen; m 63; c 2. ENDOCRINOLOGY, IMMUNOLOGY. *Educ:* Univ Mysore, BSc, 50; Univ Bombay, MSc, 55; Univ Mo-Columbia, PhD(endocrinol), 58; FRIC. *Hon Degrees:* DSc, Univ Bombay, 81. *Prof Exp:* Res assoc & asst prof endocrinol, Univ Mo-Columbia, 58-60; res assoc, Jewish Hosp, St Louis, 60-62; ENDOCRINOLOGIST, VET ADMIN HOSP, ST LOUIS, 62- *Concurrent Pos:* Fel endocrinol, Univ Mo-Columbia, 58-59; res prof, Wash Univ, 67; consult, Nat Sci Found, 67. *Mem:* Royal Soc Health; Endocrine Soc; Am Physiol Soc; Am Thyroid Asn; Soc Exp Biol & Med. *Res:* Autoimmune diseases, diabetes, thyroid physiology and thyroid hormone-protein interaction; immunoendocrinology; author and coauthor of over 100 publications. *Mailing Add:* 5 Blaytonn Lane Ladue MO 63124

PREMANAND, VISVANATHA, b Cannanore, India, Oct 2, 29; US citizen; m 63. MICROELECTRONICS. *Educ:* Univ Madras, MA, 50; Univ Paris, PhD(physics), 62. *Prof Exp:* Res asst microwaves, Tata Inst Fundamental Res, India, 51-57; sci officer electron micros, Bhabha Atomic Res Ctr, 62-67; prin scientist, Appl Sci Div, Litton Indust, 67-68; res assoc electron micros, Sch Metall, Univ Minn, 68-69; mgr process develop, Control Data Corp, 69-74; sr engr spec solid state sensor develop, Emerson Elec, 75-76; consult microelectronics, 76-80; eng mgr, Dahlberg Electronics, 80-81; PROJ ENGR, RESISTANCE TECHNOL INC, 81- *Mem:* Int Soc Hybrid Microelectronics. *Res:* Electron microscopy; physical metallurgy. *Mailing Add:* 10 W 107th St Minneapolis MN 55420

PREMUZIC, EUGENE T, b Zagreb, Yugoslavia, Feb 2, 29; Can citizen; m 52; c 1. SYNTHETIC ORGANIC CHEMISTRY. *Educ:* Univ Birmingham, BSc, 54, MSc, 55; Univ BC, PhD(biochem), 57; Univ Sussex Sch Molecular Sci, D Phil(chem natural prod), 67. *Prof Exp:* Sr res scientist, NY Ocean Sci Lab,

72-76; consult, 76-77, sr res assoc, 77-81, SR CHEM ASSOC, BROOKHAVEN NAT LAB, 81-; PROF CHEM, LONG ISLAND UNIV, 75- *Concurrent Pos:* Sr scientist, World Life Res Inst, 71-72; adj prof, Fordham Univ, 73-74. *Mem:* Am Chem Soc; sr mem Can Inst Chem; fel Chem Soc UK. *Res:* Chemistry of primitive organisms: the role of primitive organisms in the process of chemical transformation, chemical communication and transport; organic geochemistry: biological markers in organic geochemistry; distribution of organic matter in sediments. *Mailing Add:* Dept Energy & Environ Brookhaven Nat Lab Upton NY 11973

PREND, JOSEPH, b Slawkow, Poland, Apr 18, 20; nat US; m 49; c 3. HORTICULTURE. *Educ:* Munich Tech Univ, MS, 48, ScD, 50. *Prof Exp:* Plant breeder, F H Woodruff & Sons, Inc, 52-58; sr res horticulturist, Crops Res Dept, 58-67, chief res horticulturist, Agr Res Dept, 67-75, ASSOC MGR AGR RES, H J HEINZ CO, 75- *Mem:* AAAS; Am Soc Hort Sci. *Res:* Breeding and development of tomatoes and cucumber varieties; introducing disease resistance; laboratory and processing evaluation of varieties. *Mailing Add:* 2531 Sheridan Way Stockton CA 95207

PRENDERGAST, KEVIN HENRY, b Brooklyn, NY, July 9, 29; m 65; c 1. ASTRONOMY. *Educ:* Columbia Univ, AB, 50, PhD, 54. *Prof Exp:* Asst astron, Columbia Univ, 50-54, Adams res fel, 54-56; asst prof astrophys, Yerkes Observ, Univ Chicago, 56-66; PROF ASTRON, COLUMBIA UNIV, 66- *Mem:* Am Astron Soc; Am Phys Soc. *Res:* Hydromagnetics; theoretical astrophysics. *Mailing Add:* Dept of Astron Columbia Univ New York NY 10027

PRENDERGAST, ROBERT ANTHONY, b Brooklyn, NY, Nov 6, 31. IMMUNOLOGY, PATHOLOGY. *Educ:* Columbia Univ, BA, 53; Boston Univ, MD, 57. *Prof Exp:* Intern med, Cornell Div, Bellevue Hosp, 57-58; resident path, Mallory Inst, Boston City Hosp, 58-59; resident, Mem-Sloan Kettering Hosp, 59-61; vis physician, Rockefeller Univ, 63-65; asst prof, 65-70, ASSOC PROF OPHTHAL & PATH, SCH MED, JOHNS HOPKINS UNIV, 70- *Concurrent Pos:* USPHS fel, Rockefeller Univ, 63-65; prof, Res Prev Blindness, Inc, 71- *Mem:* Am Asn Immunol; Am Soc Exp Path; Transplantation Soc; Reticuloendothelial Soc. *Res:* Delayed hypersensitivity and cellular immunology; ontogeny of the immune response; transplantation immunology; immunology of neoplasia; viral immunopathology; immunopathology of ocular inflammatory diseases. *Mailing Add:* Johns Hopkins Univ Sch of Med Baltimore MD 21205

PRENER, ROBERT, b Brooklyn, NY, Feb 27, 39; m 58. MATHEMATICS EDUCATION. *Educ:* Cornell Univ, AB, 60; Columbia Univ, MA, 63; Polytech Inst Brooklyn, PhD(math), 69. *Prof Exp:* Lectr math, Cornell Univ, 59-60; asst, Columbia Univ, 60-61; instr, 61-64, asst prof, 61-69, ASSOC PROF MATH, LONG ISLAND UNIV, 69- *Concurrent Pos:* Math adv, Rockland Proj Sch, 69-70 & Skunk Hollow High Sch, NY, 70- *Mem:* Math Asn Am. *Res:* Group theory; secondary mathematics and science teaching methods; elementary arithmetic and mathematics learning. *Mailing Add:* Dept of Math Long Island Univ Brooklyn NY 11201

PRENGLE, H(ERMAN) WILLIAM, JR, b Connelsville, Pa, Nov 6, 19; m 41; c 3. CHEMICAL ENGINEERING. *Educ:* Carnegie Inst Technol, BS, 41, MS, 47, DSc(chem eng), 49. *Prof Exp:* Jr res engr, Linde Air Prod Co, NY, 41; from sr engr to sr technologist, Shell Oil Co, Tex, 49-52; assoc prof, 52-59, PROF CHEM ENG, UNIV HOUSTON, 59- *Concurrent Pos:* Consult, Houston Res Inst, Inc, 52-, mem bd dirs, 63-; res grants, NSF, 56-59 & 62-66, Dept Interior Off Saline Water, 64-66 & Environ Protection Agency, 68-71; vis scholar, Cambridge Univ, 71-72. *Mem:* AAAS; Am Inst Chem Engrs; Am Chem Soc; Royal Soc Chem. *Res:* Thermodynamics and structure of liquids and solutions; molecular spectroscopy; kinetics of chemical reactions in liquid and vapor phases; remote of pollutants; environmental science. *Mailing Add:* Dept of Chem Eng Univ of Houston Houston TX 77004

PRENSKY, WOLF, b Koenigsberg, Ger, Dec 26, 30; US citizen; m 66. GENETICS, CELL BIOLOGY. *Educ:* Cornell Univ, BS, 53; Univ Ill, MS, 57, PhD(genetics, plant breeding), 61. *Prof Exp:* NIH fel biol, Brookhaven Nat Lab, 61-63, res assoc biol, 63-64; from instr to asst prof physiol & genetics, Sch Med, Tufts Univ, 65-73; WITH SLOAN-KETTERING INST CANCER RES, 73- *Mem:* AAAS; Genetics Soc Am; Am Soc Cell Biol; Biomet Soc. *Mailing Add:* Sloan-Kettering Inst Cancer Res 424 E 68th St New York NY 10021

PRENTICE, GEOFFREY ALLAN, b Cleveland, Ohio, Oct 15, 46; m 68; c 2. ELECTROCHEMICAL ENGINEERING. *Educ:* Ohio State Univ, BS & MS, 69; Univ Calif, Berkeley, PhD(chem eng), 81. *Prof Exp:* Engr, Goodyear Tire & Rubber Co, 69-71, Sweden, 71-73, chief chemist, Zaire, 73-75; ASST PROF CHEM ENG, JOHNS HOPKINS UNIV, 81- *Mem:* Electrochem Soc; Am Inst Chem Engrs. *Res:* Modeling electrochemical cells and calculating current distributions especially when the electrode shape changes with time; passivation inhibition in the zinc/alkaline electrolyte system. *Mailing Add:* Dept Chem Eng Johns Hopkins Univ Baltimore MD 21218

PRENTICE, JACK L, b Santa Barbara, Calif, Sept 25, 31; m 51; c 3. PHYSICAL CHEMISTRY, HIGH TEMPERATURE CHEMISTRY. *Educ:* Calif State Polytech Col, BS, 59. *Prof Exp:* RES CHEMIST, NAVAL WEAPONS CTR, 59- *Res:* Metal combustion. *Mailing Add:* PO Box 659 Enterprise OR 97828

PRENTICE, JAMES DOUGLAS, b Auckland, NZ, Oct 31, 30; Can citizen; m 60; c 2. PHYSICS. *Educ:* McGill Univ, BSc, 51, MSc, 53; Univ Glasgow, PhD(physics), 59. *Prof Exp:* Lectr, 58-59, from asst prof to assoc prof, 59-70, PROF PHYSICS, UNIV TORONTO, 70- *Concurrent Pos:* Sr sci officer, Rutherford High Energy Lab, 63-64. *Mem:* Can Asn Physicists. *Res:* High energy particle physics; high energy Hadron interactions and Hadron spectroscopy. *Mailing Add:* Dept of Physics Univ of Toronto Toronto ON M5S 1A1 Can

PRENTICE, NEVILLE, b Longbenton, Eng, Feb 10, 20; US citizen; m 59; c 2. AGRICULTURAL BIOCHEMISTRY. *Educ:* Univ Man, BSc, 50; Univ Minn, MS, 55, PhD(biochem), 56. *Prof Exp:* RES CHEMIST, BARLEY LAB, USDA, 56- *Concurrent Pos:* Assoc ed, J Am Asn Cereal Chemists, 73-76. *Mem:* Am Asn Cereal Chemists; Sigma Xi. *Res:* Microbiological metabolites toxic to animals or plants; enzyme systems involved in germination of cereals. *Mailing Add:* Barley Lab USDA 501 N Walnut St Madison WI 53705

PRENTICE, WILBERT NEIL, b Nagpur, India, Nov 19, 23; nat US; m 55; c 2. NUMERICAL ANALYSIS. *Educ:* Middlebury Col, AB, 44; Brown Univ, AM, 50; Syracuse Univ, PhD(math), 59. *Prof Exp:* Instr math, Clarkson Tech Univ, 49-51; asst instr, Syracuse Univ, 52-57; from instr to assoc prof, 57-74, dir, Denison Comput Ctr, 64-71, PROF MATH, DENISON UNIV, 74- *Concurrent Pos:* Vis fel, Ohio State Univ, 72. *Mem:* Math Asn Am; Asn Comput Mach. *Res:* Computer programming and its use in liberal arts education. *Mailing Add:* Dept of Math Denison Univ Granville OH 43023

PRENTISS, WILLIAM CASE, b Baltimore, Md, Sept 5, 24; m 45; c 2. LEATHER CHEMISTRY. *Educ:* Amherst Col, AB, 47; Brown Univ, PhD(phys chem), 51. *Prof Exp:* Chemist, Res & Develop, 50-57, head lab, 57-62, sales develop rep, 62-64, sr res chemist, 64-66, head lab, 66-70, leader tech serv group, Leather Chem & Finishes, 70-76, PROJ LEADER, LEATHER & COATED FABRICS CHEM RES, 76- ROHM AND HAAS CO, 76- *Mem:* Am Chem Soc; Am Leather Chemists Asn; Am Soc Testing & Mat. *Res:* Waterborn polymers; surfactants; acrylic monomers and polymers; leather chemicals. *Mailing Add:* Rohm and Haas Co Norristown Rd Spring House PA 19477

PRENZLOW, CARL FREDERICK, b Long Beach, Calif, Apr 11, 30; m 67; c 2. PHYSICAL CHEMISTRY. *Educ:* Univ Colo, BA, 51; Univ Wash, PhD(phys chem), 57. *Prof Exp:* Res chemist, Dow Chem Co, 56-58; asst adminr chem sci div, Off Ord Res, US Dept Army, 58-60; res chemist, Nat Bur Standards, 60-64; chemist, Allied Chem Co, 64-65; PROF CHEM, CALIF STATE UNIV, FULLERTON, 65-, CHMN DEPT, 71- *Mem:* Am Chem Soc. *Res:* Physical adsorption; organic reaction mechanisms and synthesis; surface chemistry and related fields. *Mailing Add:* Dept of Chem Calif State Univ Fullerton CA 92634

PREPARATA, FRANCO PAOLO, b Reggio Emilia, Italy, Dec 29, 35; m 64; c 2. COMPUTER SCIENCE, ENGINEERING. *Educ:* Univ Rome, Dr Ing, 59, Libera docenza, 69. *Prof Exp:* Fel, Nat Inst Appl Calculation, Rome, 59-60; tech mgr comput, Univac Italia, Rome, 60-63; sr engr, Selenia, SpA, Rome, 63-65; res assoc elec eng, 65-66, from asst prof to assoc prof, 66-70, PROF ELEC ENG, UNIV ILL, URBANA, 70- *Mem:* Fel Inst Elec & Electronics Engrs; Asn Comput Mach; AAAS; Europ Asn Theoret Comput Sci. *Res:* Theory of computation, design and analysis of algorithms, digital systems, information and coding theory. *Mailing Add:* Coord Sci Lab Univ of Ill Urbana IL 61801

PREPOST, RICHARD, b New York, NY, Mar 20, 35. ELEMENTARY PARTICLE PHYSICS. *Educ:* Rensselaer Polytech Inst, BS, 56; Columbia Univ, PhD(physics), 61. *Prof Exp:* Res assoc physics, Yale Univ, 61-63; asst prof, Stanford Univ, 63-67; assoc prof, 67-73, PROF PHYSICS, UNIV WIS-MADISON, 73- *Mem:* Am Phys Soc. *Res:* Particle and muon physics; electron-positron colliding beams; strong and electromagnetic interactions. *Mailing Add:* Dept Physics Physics Astron Bldg Univ Wis 1150 Univ Ave Madison WI 53706

PRESBY, HERMAN M, b Jersey City, NJ, Sept 25, 41; m; c 4. PHYSICS. *Educ:* Yeshiva Univ, BA, 62, PhD(physics), 66. *Prof Exp:* Res scientist plasma physics, Columbia Univ, 66-67; asst prof physics, Belfer Grad Sch, Yeshiva Univ, 67-72; MEM TECH STAFF OPTICAL FIBERS, BELL LABS, 72- *Mem:* Optical Soc Am. *Res:* Optical fiber waveguides. *Mailing Add:* Bell Labs Crawford Hill Holmdel NJ 07733

PRESCH, WILLIAM FREDERICK, b Columbus, Ohio, Aug 27, 42; m 63; c 2. HERPETOLOGY. *Educ:* San Diego State Univ, BS, 65, MA, 67; Univ Southern Calif, PhD(biol), 70. *Prof Exp:* Asst prof biol, Univ Southern Calif & marine biol, Santa Catalina Marine Sta, 70-71; asst prof zool, Univ Calif, Berkeley, 71-73; asst prof, 73-76, ASSOC PROF ZOOL, CALIF STATE UNIV, FULLERTON, 76- *Concurrent Pos:* Orgn Trop Studies fel, Univ Costa Rica, 67. *Mem:* AAAS; Am Soc Ichthyol & Herpet; Am Soc Zoologists; Soc Study Amphibians & Reptiles; Am Soc Naturalists. *Res:* Comparative osteology; systematics and evolution of lizards; functional anatomy and mechanics in lower vertebrates; biogeography of reptiles. *Mailing Add:* Dept of Zool Calif State Univ 800 N State College Blvd Fullerton CA 92634

PRESCOTT, BASIL OSBORNE, b Matehuala, Mex, Nov 23, 11; US citizen; m 41; c 2. GEOLOGY. *Educ:* Colo Sch Mines, GE, 35. *Prof Exp:* Seismol computer, Shell Oil Co, 35-36, asst seismologist, 36-41, seismologist, 41-47, geologist, 47-49, spec probs geologist, 49-52, sr geologist, 52-56, explor petrophysicist, 51-56; explor geologist & physicist, Shell Develop Co, 56-71, res assoc instrumentation, 57-71; CONSULT INSTRUMENTATION, 71- *Res:* Macropaleontology; structural geology; petroleum hydrodynamics; inorganic and organic geochemistry; analog computator design; chromatography of hydrocarbon gases; special instrument design. *Mailing Add:* 3618 Elmridge Houston TX 77025

PRESCOTT, BENJAMIN, b Fall River, Mass, Feb 7, 07; m 32; c 2. BIOCHEMISTRY. *Educ:* Univ Chicago, BS, 30; Georgetown Univ, PhD(biochem), 41. *Prof Exp:* Asst metab in Bright's dis, Peter Bent Brigham Hosp, Boston, 33-34; asst chem, Franklin Union, 34-35; immunochemist, Johns Hopkins Hosp, 35-38; immunochemist, NIH, 38-79; RETIRED. *Mem:* Hon mem Am Soc Microbiol; emer mem Am Chem Soc; NY Acad Sci. *Res:* Biochemical and serological studies of bacterial products; chemistry of antigenic and immunogenic fractions from mycoplasma, pneumococcal and Streptococci. *Mailing Add:* 12000 Old Georgetown Rd Apt N 801 Rockville MD 20852

PRESCOTT, CHARLES YOUNG, b Ponca City, Okla, Dec 14, 38; m 64; c 1. ELEMENTARY PARTICLE PHYSICS. *Educ:* Rice Univ, BA, 61; Calif Inst Technol, PhD(physics), 66. *Prof Exp:* Res assoc physics, Calif Inst Technol, 66-70; asst prof, Univ Calif, Santa Cruz, 70-71; mem staff, 71-80, ASSOC PROF PHYSICS, STANFORD LINEAR ACCELERATOR CTR, 80- *Res:* Photoproduction; electroproduction reactions; weak interactions; electron-positron annihilation. *Mailing Add:* Stanford Linear Accelerator Ctr PO Box 4349 Stanford CA 94305

PRESCOTT, DAVID JULIUS, b Philadelphia, Pa, Oct 8, 39; m 64; c 3. PROTEIN CHEMISTRY, NEUROCHEMISTRY. *Educ:* Univ Pa, BA, 61, PhD(biochem), 67. *Prof Exp:* Instr biochem, Univ Pa, 67-68; asst chief radioisotopes res, Vet Admin, 67-69; fel biol chem, Sch Med, Washington Univ, 68-70; asst prof, 70-77, ASSOC PROF BIOL, BRYN MAWR COL, 77- *Concurrent Pos:* Vis asst prof neurobiol, Harvard Sch Med, 74-75. *Honors & Awards:* Dreyfus Found Award, 74. *Mem:* AAAS; Am Chem Soc; Soc Neurosci; Sigma Xi. *Res:* Enzymology of fatty acid biosynthesis; chemical synthesis of proteins; structure and function of acyl carrier protein; lepidopteran cholinergic development. *Mailing Add:* Dept of Biol Bryn Mawr Col Bryn Mawr PA 19010

PRESCOTT, DAVID MARSHALL, b Clearwater, Fla, Aug 3, 26; m 69; c 3. CELL BIOLOGY, GENETICS. *Educ:* Wesleyan Univ, BA, 50; Univ Calif, Berkeley, PhD(zool), 54. *Prof Exp:* Res assoc biol, Univ Copenhagen, 51-52; Am Cancer Soc fel, Carlsberg Lab, Copenhagen, 54-55; asst prof anat, Univ Calif, Los Angeles, 55-59; biologist, Oak Ridge Nat Lab, 59-63; prof & chmn, Dept Anat, Med Sch, 63-66, prof, Inst for Develop Biol, 66-68, chmn, 74-75, prof, 68-80, DISTINGUISHED PROF, DEPT MOLECULAR, CELLULAR & DEVELOP BIOL, UNIV COLO, 80- *Concurrent Pos:* Humboldt Found Sr US Scientist Award, 79-80. *Mem:* Nat Acad Sci; fel Am Acad Arts & Sci; Am Soc Cell Biol (pres, 65-66). *Res:* Factors regulating initiation of synthesis of DNA during cellular reproduction; mechanisms of chromosome replication and function; structure of the chromosome; biology of cancer. *Mailing Add:* Dept of Molecular Cellular & Develop Biol Univ of Colo Boulder CO 80309

PRESCOTT, GERALD H, b Wendell, Idaho, June 16, 37; div; c 3. MEDICAL GENETICS, ORAL MEDICINE. *Educ:* Col Idaho, BS, 59; Wash Univ, DMD, 64; Ind Univ, Indianapolis, MS, 66. *Prof Exp:* Fel med genetics, Ind Univ, Indianapolis, 66-68; assoc prof med genetics & perinatal med, Dir Antenatal Diag Clin, Med Ctr, Univ Ore, 68-81; DIR PRENATAL DIAG PROG, EMANUEL HOSP, 82-, ASSOC DIR, ORE MED GENETICS & BIRTH DEFECTS CTR, 82- *Concurrent Pos:* Consult, Good Samaritan Hosp & St Vincents Hosp. *Mem:* AAAS; Genetics Soc Am; Am Acad Oral Path; Sigma Xi; Am Soc Human Genetics. *Res:* Bioethics of genetic counseling; amniotic fluid studies; craniofacial anomalies; prenatal diagnosis. *Mailing Add:* 2801 N Ganthenbein Ave Portland OR 97227

PRESCOTT, GLENN CARLETON, JR, b Northampton, Mass, Feb 23, 23; m 50; c 6. HYDROLOGY. *Educ:* Brown Univ, AB, 44, MS, 50; Harvard Univ, MPA, 54. *Prof Exp:* Geologist, State Geol Surv, Kans, 47-48; geologist, 48-57, geologist in chg, 57-66, HYDROLOGIST, GROUND WATER BR, US GEOL SURV, 66- *Mem:* Geol Soc Am; Am Geophys Union. *Res:* Glacial geology; ground-water hydrology. *Mailing Add:* US Geol Surv Ganneston Dr Augusta ME 04330

PRESCOTT, HENRY EMIL, JR, b Philadelphia, Pa, July 1, 36; m 65; c 1. FOOD SCIENCE, BOTANY. *Educ:* Drexel Inst Technol, BS, 59; Univ Pa, PhD(bot), 66. *Prof Exp:* Asst instr biol, Rutgers Univ, 65-66; chemist, 66-67, sr chemist, 67-75, proj specialist, 75-78, RES SPECIALIST, TECH CTR, GEN FOODS CORP, 78- *Mem:* Bot Soc Am; Mycol Soc Am; Sigma Xi; Am Micros Soc; Microbeam Anal Soc. *Res:* Preservation methods; freezing phenomena; techniques for microscopy. *Mailing Add:* Tech Ctr Gen Foods Corp Tarrytown NY 10591

PRESCOTT, JOHN MACK, b San Marcos, Tex, Jan 22, 21; m 46; c 2. BIOCHEMISTRY. *Educ:* Southwest Tex State Col, BS, 41; Tex A&M Univ, MS, 49; Univ Wis, PhD(biochem), 52. *Prof Exp:* Instr chem, Tex A&M Univ, 46-48, asst biochem, 48-49; asst, Univ Wis, 49-51; asst, Biochem Inst, Univ Tex, 51-52; from asst prof to assoc prof, 52-59, head dept, 69, dean col sci, 70-77, prof biochem & biophys, 59-81, vpres acad affairs, 77-81, PROF MED BIOCHEM, TEX A&M UNIV, 81-, DIR INST OCCUP & ENVIRON MED, 81- *Mem:* Am Chem Soc; Am Inst Nutrit; Am Soc Biol Chemists; Soc Exp Biol & Med. *Res:* Proteolytic enzymes; microbial metabolism. *Mailing Add:* 31 Forest Dr College Station TX 77840

PRESCOTT, JON MICHAEL, b Amarillo, Tex, June 17, 39; m 73; c 3. PLANT PATHOLOGY, PLANT BREEDING. *Educ:* Okla State Univ, BS, 65, MS, 67; Univ Minn, PhD(plant path), 70. *Prof Exp:* Res asst plant path, Okla State Univ, 65-67; res fel, Univ Minn, 67-70; asst plant pathologist, Rockefeller Found, 70-71; cereal pathologist, 71-75, REGIONAL CEREAL PATHOLOGIST, INT CTR IMPROV WHEAT & MAIZE, CIMMYT, 72- *Mem:* Am Phytopath Soc; Am Soc Agron; Crop Sci Soc Am; Indian Phytopath Soc; Turkish Phytopath Soc. *Res:* Surveillance, epidemiology, virulence analysis, host-pathogen interactions of cereal diseases, especially of wheat and barley; disease resistance breeding. *Mailing Add:* Wheat Res & Training Ctr CIMMYT PK 120 Yenimahalle Ankara Turkey

PRESCOTT, LANSING M, b Tulsa, Okla, Sept 29, 41; m 64; c 2. MICROBIOLOGY, BIOCHEMISTRY. *Educ:* Rice Univ, BA, 63, MA, 64; Brandeis Univ, PhD(biochem), 69. *Prof Exp:* Asst prof, 69-74, ASSOC PROF BIOL, AUGUSTANA COL, 74- *Mem:* Am Chem Soc; Soc Protozoologists; Am Soc Microbiol; Sigma Xi; Electron Micros Soc Am. *Res:* toxicology and microbial ecology; morphology of bacteria and diatoms; microbial physiology. *Mailing Add:* Dept Biol Augustana Col Sioux Falls SD 57102

PRESCOTT, PAUL ITHEL, b Sanford, Maine, Dec 7, 31; m 55; c 2. RESEARCH ADMINISTRATION, CLAY MINERALOGY. *Educ:* Univ Maine, BS, 58, MS, 60. *Prof Exp:* Chemist silicones, Res & Develop Ctr, Gen Elec Co, 60-62, develop chemist, Insulating Mat Dept, 62-65, mgr mat anal & testing, Wire & Cable Dept, 65-69; supvr plastics res, 69-74, asst res dir clay, 74-79, MGR MKT DEVELOP, FREEPORT KAOLIN, FREEPORT MINERALS CO, 79- *Mem:* Sigma Xi; Am Chem Soc; Soc Plastics Engrs; Fedn Socs Coating Technol. *Res:* Surface modification of pigments and fillers to improve their compatability on polymeric systems; development of kaolin clays for paint, rubber, plastics, and paper industries. *Mailing Add:* Freeport Kaolin Res Lab Gordon GA 31031

PRESENT, RICHARD DAVID, b New York, NY, Feb 5, 13; m 43; c 2. CHEMICAL PHYSICS. *Educ:* City Col New York, BS, 31; Harvard Univ, AM, 32, PhD(physics), 35. *Prof Exp:* Instr physics, Purdue Univ, 35-40; asst prof, NY Univ, 41-43; res physicist, Manhattan Proj, SAM Labs, Columbia Univ, 43-46; assoc prof, 46-48, prof, 48-69, DISTINGUISHED PROF PHYSICS, UNIV TENN, KNOXVILLE, 69- *Concurrent Pos:* Fr Govt sci fel, 37-38; NSF vis scientist, 58-71, grantee, 63-71. *Mem:* Fel Am Phys Soc. *Res:* Molecular quantum theory; nuclear theory; kinetic theory of gases; intermolecular forces; liquid state. *Mailing Add:* Dept Physics Univ Tenn Knoxville TN 37916

PRESES, JACK MICHAEL, b Amityville, NY, Oct 11, 47. PHYSICAL CHEMISTRY. *Educ:* Hofstra Univ, BS, 69; Columbia Univ, PhD(chem), 75. *Prof Exp:* Res asst chem, Columbia Univ, 69-75; res assoc, 75-78, ASSOC CHEMIST, BROOKHAVEN NAT LAB, 78- *Concurrent Pos:* Mem staff, Div Chem Sci, US Dept Energy, 78-80. *Mem:* Am Chem Soc; Am Phys Soc. *Res:* Gas-phase energy transfer in polyatomic molecules; infrared laser induced chemistry; applications of synchrotron radiation to photochemistry and photophysics. *Mailing Add:* Dept of Chem 555A Brookhaven Nat Lab Upton NY 11973

PRESKILL, JOHN P, b Highland Park, Ill, Jan 19, 53; m 75. THEORETICAL PHYSICS. *Educ:* Princeton Univ, AB, 75; Harvard Univ, AM, 76, PhD(physics), 80. *Prof Exp:* Jr fel, Harvard Soc Fels, 80-81; ASST PROF PHYSICS, HARVARD UNIV, 81- *Mem:* Am Phys Soc. *Res:* Theory of elementary particles; cosmology. *Mailing Add:* Dept Physics Harvard Univ Cambridge MA 02138

PRESLEY, BOBBY JOE, b Poplar Bluffs, Mo, July 27, 35; m 67; c 2. CHEMICAL OCEANOGRAPHY. *Educ:* Okla State Univ, BS, 57; WVa Univ, MA, 65; Univ Calif, Los Angeles, PhD(geol), 69. *Prof Exp:* Computer, Geophys Serv, Inc, 57-59; teacher, Sacramento City Unified Schs, 60-61, Marysville Union High Sch, 61-63 & Sacramento City Unified Schs, 63-64; fel, Univ Calif, Los Angeles, 69-70; asst prof, 70-74, ASSOC PROF OCEANOG, TEX A&M UNIV, 74- *Concurrent Pos:* Prog mgr, NSF, 74-75. *Res:* Pore water chemistry; diagenesis of sediments; stable isotope geochemistry; trace elements; heavy metal pollution. *Mailing Add:* Dept of Oceanog Tex A&M Univ College Station TX 77843

PRESLEY, CECIL TRAVIS, b Marshall, Ark, Nov 3, 41. PHYSICAL CHEMISTRY. *Educ:* Ark Polytech Col, BS, 63; Rice Univ, PhD(chem), 68; Univ Denver, JD, 78. *Prof Exp:* RES SCIENTIST, DENVER RES CTR, MARATHON OIL CO, 67- *Mem:* AAAS; Am Chem Soc; Sigma Xi; Soc Petrol Engrs. *Res:* Areas of x-ray crystallography; light scattering, small angle x-ray scattering; ultracentrifugation; micro-emulsions; water-soluble polymers. *Mailing Add:* Denver Res Ctr Marathon Oil Co PO Box 269 Littleton CO 80160

PRESLOCK, JAMES PETER, b Newark, NJ. ENDOCRINOLOGY, REPRODUCTIVE PHYSIOLOGY. *Educ:* Univ Scranton, BS, 64; Univ Md, College Park, PhD(endocrinol), 69. *Prof Exp:* Fel steroid biochem, Worcester Found, 69-70; asst prof physiol, 70-80, ASSOC PROF REPRODUCTIVE MED & BIOL, UNIV TEX GRAD SCH BIOMED SCI, 80- *Mem:* AAAS; Soc Study Reproduction; Endocrine Soc. *Res:* Enzymatic control mechanisms in the molecular actions of steroid hormones in pineal glands of Coturnia quail; metabolic pathways in the biosynthesis of testicular steroids. *Mailing Add:* Prog Reprod Biol & Endocrinol Univ Tex Grad Sch Biomed Sci Houston TX 77025

PRESNALL, DEAN C, b Cedar City, Utah, Nov 6, 35; m 64; c 1. GEOCHEMISTRY, PETROLOGY. *Educ:* Pa State Univ, BS, 57, PhD(geochem), 63; Calif Inst Technol, MS, 59. *Prof Exp:* Fel, Carnegie Inst Geophys Lab, 63-67; asst prof geosci, Southwest Ctr Advan Studies, 67-69; from asst prof to assoc prof, 69-78, PROF GEOSCI, UNIV TEX, DALLAS, 78- *Mem:* Fel Geol Soc Am; Am Geophys Union; fel Mineral Soc Am; Geochem Soc. *Res:* Experimental and theoretical igneous petrology; phase equilibrium studies of silicate systems at high temperatures and pressures; petrogenesis of granites and oceanic volcanic rocks; chemical evolution of the earth's mantle and crust. *Mailing Add:* Prog in Geosci PO Box 688 Richardson TX 75080

PRESNELL, ALEXANDER KOEHNE, b Torreon, Mex, Dec 29, 09; US citizen; m 35; c 1. BIOCHEMISTRY. *Educ:* Miami Univ, AB, 32; Univ Cincinnati, MS, 33, PhD(biochem), 35. *Prof Exp:* Jergens fel biochem, Univ Cincinnati, 35-40, asst prof pharm, 35-38; res biochemist, Andrew Jergens Co, 40-43 & 46-66, assoc dir res, 66-69; CONSULT, 69- *Mem:* AAAS; Am Chem Soc; Am Soc Microbiol; Am Oil Chemists Soc. *Res:* Vitamins; blood clotting; tissue respiration; antiseptics; spectrophotometry. *Mailing Add:* 1412 Paseo Del Ocaso Santa Barbara CA 93105

PRESNELL, RONALD I, b Boulder, Colo, Feb 12, 33; m 57; c 2. ELECTRONIC ENGINEERING. *Educ:* Stanford Univ, BS, 54, MS, 55, Engr, 59. *Prof Exp:* Jr res engr, 54-56, res engr, 56-64, SR RES ENGR ELECTRONICS, SRI INT, 64- *Mem:* Inst Elec & Electronics Engrs. *Res:* Radar systems; upper atmospheric physics; nuclear detonation effects on radar systems. *Mailing Add:* Radio Physics Lab SRI Int 333 Ravenswood Menlo Park CA 94025

PRESS, FRANK, b Brooklyn, NY, Dec 4, 24; m 46; c 2. GEOPHYSICS. *Educ:* City Col New York, BS, 44; Columbia Univ, MA, 46, PhD(geophys), 49. *Hon Degrees:* LLD, Univ Notre Dame, 73; DSc, City Univ New York, 74. *Prof Exp:* From asst to assoc prof physics, Columbia Univ, 45-55; prof geophys, Calif Inst Technol, 55-65, dir seismol lab, 57-65; dir, Off Sci & Technol Policy, Exec Off Pres, Washington, DC, 77-81; inst prof, Mass Inst Technol, 81; PRES, NAT ACAD SCI, 81- *Concurrent Pos:* Consult, US Navy, 56-57, US Geol Surv, 57-59, Dept State & Dept Defense, 58-62, President's Asst for Sci & Technol, 59-60 & 64-, NASA, 60-62 & 65-, AID, 62-63 & Arms Control & Disarmament Agency, 62-; mem, Gov Adv Coun Atomic Activities, Calif, 59; mem, President's Sci Adv Comt, 61-64; mem bd adv, Nat Ctr Earthquake Res, US Geol Surv, 66- Mem glaciol & seismol panel, Int Geophys Year, 55-59, comt polar res, 57-, interdisciplinary res panel, 58-, seismol working group, Upper Mantle Proj, 64-, int geophys comt, Int Coun Sci Unions, 59-, panel solid earth probs, Geophys Res Bd, Nat Acad Sci, 61 & mem coun, 75-78; chmn earthquake prediction panel, Off Sci & Technol, 65-; mem planetology subcomt, NASA, 66- & Nat Sci Bd, NSF, 71- Mem, UNESCO Tech Assistance Mission, 53; US deleg, Nuclear Test Ban Conf, Geneva, 59-61, Moscow, 63 & UN Conf Sci & Technol Underdeveloped Nations, 63; prof geophys & head dept earth & planetary sci, Mass Inst Technol, 65- *Honors & Awards:* Distinguished Serv Award, Dept of Interior, 71; Gold Medal, Royal Astron Soc, 71; Distinguished Pub Serv Medal, NASA, 73. *Mem:* Nat Acad Sci; Am Acad Arts & Sci; Geol Soc Am; Seismol Soc Am (secy, 57-58, vpres, 59-61, pres, 62); Am Geophys Union (pres, 74-76). *Res:* Planetary interiors; crustal and mantle structure; regional and submarine geophysics; seismology, including earthquake mechanism and elastic wave propagation. *Mailing Add:* Pres Nat Acad Sci 2101 Constitution Ave NW Washington DC 20418

PRESS, JEFFERY BRUCE, b Rochester, NY, May 24, 47. ORGANIC CHEMISTRY, MEDICINAL CHEMISTRY. *Educ:* Bucknell Univ, BS, 69; Ohio State Univ, PhD(org chem), 73. *Prof Exp:* Fel org chem, Harvard Univ, 73-74, NIH fel, 74-75; sr res chemist, 77, mem res staff, 75-81, GROUP LEADER, LEDERLE LABS, 81- *Mem:* Am Chem Soc; AAAS. *Res:* Heterocyclic chemistry, natural products, reactive intermediates and chemistry of strained polycyclic ring systems; organo sulfur chemistry; synthetic methods; central nervous system and cardiovascular agents. *Mailing Add:* Lederle Labs Pearl River NY 10965

PRESS, LINDA SEGHERS, b Jacksonville, Fla, Dec 2, 50; m 76. ORGANIC CHEMISTRY. *Educ:* Ohio State Univ, BSc, 72, PhD(org chem), 77. *Prof Exp:* Res assoc org chem, 77-81, MGR BIOCHEM RES, INT PAPER CO, 81- *Mem:* Am Chem Soc. *Res:* Biochemical processes in plants; isolation and characterization of phytochemicals; transport and metabolism of plant growth regulators; lignin biochemistry; organic reaction mechanisms. *Mailing Add:* Int Paper Co PO Box 797 Tuxedo Park NY 10987

PRESS, M(EYER), b Poland, May 2, 26; nat US; m 53; c 3. ELECTRICAL ENGINEERING. *Educ:* Northeastern Univ, BS, 48, MS, 55. *Prof Exp:* Jr engr, Hazeltine Electronics Corp, 48-50; from jr engr to eng specialist, Sylvania Elec Prod, Inc, Gen Tel & Electronics Corp, 50-70, MGR INDEPENDENT RES & DEVELOP, ELECTRONIC SYSTS GROUP, GTE SYLVANIA, 70- *Res:* Applied research in system analysis and circuit design. *Mailing Add:* Electronic Systs Group GTE Sylvania 77 A St Needham MA 02194

PRESS, NEWTOL, b New York, NY, Nov 27, 30; m 51; c 3. CELL BIOLOGY. *Educ:* NY Univ, BA, 51; Univ Iowa, MS, 55, PhD(zool), 56. *Prof Exp:* Asst zool, Univ Iowa, 52-56; from instr to assoc prof, 56-60, chmn dept, 64-66, PROF ZOOL, UNIV WIS-MILWAUKEE, 77- *Res:* Histology; photoreception; embryology; history of science; theoretical biology; aging. *Mailing Add:* Dept of Zool Univ of Wis Milwaukee WI 53201

PRESS, S JAMES, b New York, NY, Feb 4, 31; m 51; c 3. MATHEMATICAL STATISTICS. *Educ:* NY Univ, BA, 50; Univ Southern Calif, MS, 55; Stanford Univ, PhD(statist), 64. *Prof Exp:* Physicist, Brookhaven Nat Lab, 49-50; res analyst, Northrop Aircraft Corp, 51-54; res engr, Douglas Aircraft Co, Inc, Long Beach, Calif, 54-57, design specialist, Santa Monica, 58-61; lectr statist, Univ Calif, Los Angeles, 64-66, assoc prof, Grad Sch Bus, Univ Chicago, 66-74; prof statist, Univ BC, 74-77; PROF & CHMN DEPT STATIST, UNIV CALIF, RIVERSIDE, 77- *Concurrent Pos:* Res statistician, Rand Corp, 64-66, consult, 66-; consult, Real Estate Res Corp, Ill, 66, probs mgr educ in India, AID, 67, John Wiley & Sons & McGraw-Hill Bk Co; vis prof, Univ Col, Univ London, 70-71, London Sch Econ & Polit Sci, 70-71 & Yale Univ, 72-73; assoc ed, J Am Statist Asn & J Economet; prin investr, Biometric Proj, Citrus Res Ctr & Agr Exp Sta. *Mem:* fel Inst Math Statist; fel Am Statist Asn; Economet Soc; Inst Mgt Sci; fel Royal Statist Soc. *Res:* Multivariate statistical analysis; Bayesian statistics; econometrics; probability distribution theory; operations research. *Mailing Add:* Dept Statist Univ Calif Riverside CA 92521

PRESS, WILLIAM HENRY, b New York, NY, May 23, 48; m 69; c 1. ASTROPHYSICS, GENERAL RELATIVITY. *Educ:* Harvard Univ, AB, 69; Calif Inst Technol, MS, 71, PhD(physics), 72. *Prof Exp:* Richard Chace Tolman res fel theoret physics, Calif Inst Technol, 72-73, asst prof, 73-74; asst prof physics, Princeton Univ, 74-76; PROF ASTRON & PHYSICS, HARVARD UNIV, 76-, CHMN, DEPT ASTRON, 82- *Concurrent Pos:* Consult, Lawrence Livermore Lab, 73- & SRI Int, 77-; Alfred P Sloan Found res fel, 74-78; mem adv comt on physics, NSF, 78-81; mem ad hoc comt innovation, NASA, 79 & comt on role of theory in space sci, 80; mem, Astron Surv Comt Panel on Theoret Astrophys, Nat Acad Sci/Nat Res Coun, 79-80 & mem, Advocacy Panel on Physics of the Sun, 80-81; chmn, Subcomt Comput Facil for Theoret Physics, NSF, 80-81. *Honors & Awards:* Warner Prize, Am Astron Soc, 81. *Mem:* Am Phys Soc; Am Astron Soc; Int Soc on Gen Relativity & Gravitation; Int Astron Union. *Res:* Relativistic astrophysics; theoretical astrophysics; cosmology; galaxy formation; general relativity; numerical methods. *Mailing Add:* Harvard Col Observ 60 Garden St Cambridge MA 02138

PRESSBURG, BERNARD S(AMUEL), b Alexandria, La, Jan 23, 18; m 47; c 2. CHEMICAL ENGINEERING. *Educ:* La State Univ, BS, 37, MS, 39, PhD(chem eng), 41. *Prof Exp:* Asst prof, 41-42, from asst prof to assoc prof, 46-55, actg dean, 64-65, PROF CHEM ENG, LA STATE UNIV, BATON ROUGE, 55-, ASSOC DEAN, 65- *Concurrent Pos:* Consult, 46- *Mem:* Am Chem Soc; Am Soc Eng Educ; Am Inst Chem Engrs. *Res:* Unit operations; fluid flow; heat and mass transfer. *Mailing Add:* Col of Eng La State Univ Baton Rouge LA 70803

PRESSER, BRUCE DOUGLAS, b Bellmawr, NJ; m 59. ENTOMOLOGY. *Educ:* Temple Univ, BA, 49, MA, 51; Pa State Univ, PhD(entom), 55. *Prof Exp:* Prof biol, Belmont Col, 57-61; ASSOC PROF BIOL, SUSQUEHANNA UNIV, 61- *Mem:* Entom Soc Am; Am Soc Zoologists. *Res:* Insect embryology and morphology. *Mailing Add:* Dept of Biol Susquehanna Univ Selinsgrove PA 17870

PRESSER, LEON, b Matanzas, Cuba, Jan 23, 40; US citizen; m 69; c 2. COMPUTER SCIENCE. *Educ:* Univ Ill, Champaign, BS, 61; Univ Southern Calif, MS, 64; Univ Calif, Los Angeles, PhD(eng, comput sci), 68. *Prof Exp:* Design engr, Comput Measurements Co, 61-62; mem tech staff, Comput Div, Bendix Corp, 62-63; systs engr, Gen Instrument Corp, 63-64; asst comput, Univ Calif, Los Angeles, 64-68, asst prof comput sci, 68-69; asst prof elec eng & comput sci, Univ Calif, Santa Barbara, 69-77; PRES, SOFTOOL CORP, 77- *Concurrent Pos:* Grant, Univ Calif, Santa Barbara, 69-76, NSF grant, 72-74. *Mem:* Asn Comput Mach; Inst Elec & Electronics Engrs. *Res:* Software development and management. *Mailing Add:* Softool Corp 340 S Kellogg Ave Goleta CA 93017

PRESSEY, RUSSELL, b Man, Can, Sept 5, 35; US citizen; m 62; c 4. BIOCHEMISTRY, PLANT PHYSIOLOGY. *Educ:* Univ Man, BSc, 58, MSc, 59; Iowa State Univ, PhD(biochem), 62. *Prof Exp:* Res chemist, Gen Mills, Inc, Minn, 62-64 & USDA, Minn, 64-69; RES CHEMIST, RICHARD B RUSSELL AGR RES CTR, 69- *Mem:* Am Chem Soc; Am Soc Plant Physiologists. *Res:* Plant biochemistry; cell wall polysaccharides and the enzymes involved in their changes; regulation of plant metabolism by natural enzyme inhibitors. *Mailing Add:* 410 Greencrest Dr Athens GA 30605

PRESSMAN, ADA IRENE, b Shelby Co, Ohio, March 3, 27; m 69. TECHNICAL MANAGEMENT. *Educ:* Ohio State Univ, BME, 50; Golden Gate Univ, MBA, 74. *Prof Exp:* Engr, Bailey Meter Co, Cleveland, Ohio, 50-55; engr, 55-74, chief engr, 74-79, ENG MGR, BECHTEL POWER CORP, LOS ANGELES, 79- *Mem:* Am Nuclear Soc; Instr Soc Am (vpres 73-78); Soc Women Engrs (pres 79-80). *Mailing Add:* 1301 S Alantic Blvd Monterey Park CA 91754

PRESSMAN, BERTON CHARLES, b Brooklyn, NY, Sept 25, 26; m 56; c 3. BIOCHEMISTRY, BIOPHYSICS. *Educ:* Univ Wis, BS, 48, MS, 50, PhD(biochem), 53. *Prof Exp:* USPHS fel, Cath Univ Louvain, 53 & Wenner-Gren Inst, Sweden, 54; proj assoc, Enzyme Inst, Univ Wis, 55-58; biochemist, Radioisotope Serv, Vet Admin Hosp, Kansas City, Mo, 59-61; from asst prof to assoc prof phys biochem, Univ Pa, 61-69; PROF PHARMACOL, PHYSIOL & BIOPHYS, MED SCH, UNIV MIAMI, 70- *Concurrent Pos:* Asst prof, Univ Kans, 59-61; USPHS career develop award, 64-71. *Mem:* Am Soc Biol Chemists; Biophys Soc; Am Soc Pharmacol & Exp Therapeut. *Res:* Molecular basis of action and biological effects of transport-inducing antibiotics, known as ionophores; mechanism of ion transport in mitochondria and other membrane systems; cardiovascular effects of ionophores. *Mailing Add:* Dept of Pharmacol Univ of Miami Med Sch Miami FL 33152

PRESSMAN, DAVID, immunochemistry, deceased

PRESSMAN, IRWIN SAMUEL, b Port Arthur, Ont, Aug 17, 39; m 66; c 3. MATHEMATICS. *Educ:* Univ Man, BSc, 60; Cornell Univ, PhD(math), 65. *Prof Exp:* Res asst math, Swiss Fed Inst Technol, 65-67; asst prof, Ohio State Univ, 67-71; ASSOC PROF MATH, CARLETON UNIV, 71- *Concurrent Pos:* Consult, Dept Finance, Health & Welfare, Govt Can; Woodrow Wilson fel; Nat Res Coun fel. *Mem:* Opers Res Soc Am; Am Math Soc. *Res:* Operations Res; K-theory; computer aided learning systems; adaptation of psycholgical tests to microcomputers and intelligent terminals; linear programming. *Mailing Add:* 290 Acacia Ave Village Rockcliffe Park Ottawa ON K1M 0L7 Can

PRESSMAN, NORMAN JULES, b New York, NY, Sept 30, 48; m 71. BIOMEDICAL ENGINEERING. *Educ:* Columbia Univ, BS, 70; Univ Pa, MS, 72, PhD(biomed eng), 76. *Prof Exp:* Biomed engr, Lawrence Livermore Lab, Univ Calif, 73-76; HEAD, QUANT CYTOPATH LABS, JOHNS HOPKINS MED INSTS & ASST PROF PATH, MED SCH, UNIV, 76- *Concurrent Pos:* Consult, NIH, 77-78 & US Food & Drug Admin, 78-; chmn, Int Coun on Automated & Quant Cytol, Int Acad Cytol, 77- *Mem:* Inst Elec & Electronics Engrs; Biomed Eng Soc; Int Acad Cytol; Am Soc Cytol; Asn for Advan Med Instrumentation. *Res:* Quantitative and automated cytopathology; medical image processing and analysis; flow system analysis and sorting of biological cells; clinical laboratory computerized information systems. *Mailing Add:* Dept of Path Johns Hopkins Hosp Baltimore MD 21205

PRESSMAN, RALPH, b Philadelphia, Pa, May 1, 01; m 27. BACTERIOLOGY. *Educ:* Philadelphia Col Pharm & Sci, BS, 29, PhG, 30, MSc, 31; Univ Pa, MA, 34, PhD(med sci), 36. *Prof Exp:* From instr to asst prof bact, Philadelphia Col Pharm & Sci, 30-48; tech dir, Scudder Food Prod, Inc, Calif, 48-52; res biochemist, Vet Admin Ctr, Los Angeles, 52-54; dir res, Dartell Labs, 54-55; dir res, Truesdail Labs, 56-57; USPHS grant, Shankman Labs, 58-59; res bacteriologist, Calif Inst Technol, 59-64; res bacteriologist, Space Gen Corp, 64-66; PROF PATH & PARASITOL & CHMN DEPT PATH, LOS ANGELES COL CHIROPRACTIC, 66- *Concurrent Pos:* Dir bact, Dean Lab, Pa, 30-34; consult, Zeller Labs, 33-35; researcher, Henry Phipps Inst, Univ Pa, 36-38; researcher, Chem Warfare Serv, US Dept Army, 40-41; bacteriologist, Nat Drug Co, Pa, 44-45; tech dir, Golden Brand Food

Co, 45-48. *Mem:* Am Pharmaceut Asn; Inst Food Technol. *Res:* Isolation, purification and solubilization of the antibiotic Prodigiosin, for use in the treatment of coccidiomycosis. *Mailing Add:* 350 Acacia St Sierra Madre CA 91024

PREST, DOROTHY B, b Manchester, Mass, July 25, 20. MICROBIOLOGY. *Educ:* Mass State Col, BS, 42; Boston Univ, MA, 57; Univ Ariz, PhD(microbiol), 66. *Prof Exp:* Med technologist, Salem Hosp, 42-46; med technologist, New Eng Baptist Hosp, Boston, 46-47; chief med technologist, Salem Hosp, 47-49; microbiologist, Tucson Med Ctr, Ariz, 59-65; teaching asst, Univ Ariz, 63-65, res asst, 65-66; proj assoc, Univ Wis, 66-68; asst prof, 68-72, assoc prof, 72-78, PROF MICROBIOL, KEUKA COL, 78- *Mem:* NY Acad Sci; Am Soc Microbiol; Mycol Soc Am. *Res:* Yeasts and molds. *Mailing Add:* Dept of Biol Keuka Col Keuka Park NY 14478

PREST, VICTOR KENT, b Edmonton, Alta, Apr 2, 12; m 42; c 2. GEOLOGY. *Educ:* Univ Man, BSc, 35, MSc, 36; Univ Toronto, PhD(geol), 41. *Prof Exp:* Asst geol, Univ Toronto, 36-39, lectr, 39-40; geologist, Res Lab, Int Nickel Co, 42 & Ont Dept Mines, 45-50; geologist, Geol Surv Can, 50-78; CONSULT, 78- *Concurrent Pos:* Mus asst, Royal Ont Mus, 37-39; geologist, Ont Dept Mines, 37-41. *Mem:* Royal Soc Can; Geol Asn Can. *Res:* Quaternary geology. *Mailing Add:* 405-1465 Base Line Rd Ottawa ON K2C 3L9 Can

PREST, WILLIAM MARCHANT, JR, b Boston, Mass, Nov 4, 41; m 69; c 2. POLYMER PHYSICS. *Educ:* Union Col, BS, 63; Univ Pa, MS, 65; Univ Mass, MS, 69, PhD(polymer physics), 72. *Prof Exp:* Physicist polymer rheol, Gen Elec Res & Develop Ctr, 65-68; scientist polymer physics, 71-77, PRIN SCIENTIST, WEBSTER RES CTR, XEROX CORP RES LAB, 77- *Mem:* Fel Am Phys Soc; Soc Rheol; Am Chem Soc; NAm Thermal Anal Soc; Soc Plastics Engrs. *Res:* Thermodynamic and spectroscopic properties of single and multi component glasses; compatibility of polymer blends; orientation processes in amorphous polymers; polymorphin of semi-crystalline polymers; rehology of polymer melts. *Mailing Add:* Xerox Corp W-114 Xerox Sq Rochester NY 14644

PRESTAYKO, ARCHIE WILLIAM, b Dauphin, Man, July 27, 41; m 69; c 2. BIOCHEMISTRY. *Educ:* Colo Col, BA, 62; Univ Tenn, Knoxville, PhD(radiation biol), 66. *Prof Exp:* Am Cancer Soc fel, Baylor Col Med, 67-68, from instr to asst prof pharmacol, 68-75; asst dir med res, 75-76, ASST DIR RES & DEVELOP, BRISTOL LABS, 76- *Mem:* Am Asn Cancer Res. *Res:* Molecular and clinical pharmacology of anticancer drugs. *Mailing Add:* Bristol Labs BOX 657 Syracuse NY 13201

PRESTEMON, DEAN R, b Waukon, Iowa, Oct 4, 34; m 56; c 6. FOREST PRODUCTS. *Educ:* Iowa State Univ, BS, 56; Univ Minn, St Paul, MS, 57; Univ Calif, Berkeley, PhD(forestry), 66. *Prof Exp:* Res technician wood technol, Douglas Fir Plywood Asn, Wash, 58; tech rep, Nat Lumber Mfrs Asn, Calif, 58-62; asst specialist, Forest Prod Lab, Univ Calif, 62-65; from asst to assoc prof, 65-76, PROF WOOD TECHNOL, IOWA STATE UNIV, 76- *Mem:* Forest Prod Res Soc. *Res:* Glues and gluing; log grade-lumber yield; wood quality-growth relations; use and marketing of forest products in residential construction; mechanical processing; wood mechanics; wood quality evaluation. *Mailing Add:* Dept of Forestry Iowa State Univ Ames IA 50011

PRESTON, DUDLEY A, b Spokane, Wash, Jan 6, 10; m 41. BOTANY. *Educ:* State Col Wash, BS, 33; Univ Minn, MS, 40, PhD(plant path), 47. *Prof Exp:* Asst bot, Univ Minn, 38-42; instr, Ala Polytech Inst, 42-43; assoc mycologist bur plant indust, USDA, Okla, 43-45; asst prof bot, Okla Agr & Mech Col, 45-48; asst prof, 48-59, actg chmn dept, 59-60, chmn dept, 64-67, ASSOC PROF BOT, SAN DIEGO STATE UNIV, 59- *Mem:* AAAS; Am Phytopath Soc; Mycol Soc Am; Asn Study Evolution; Air Pollution Control Asn. *Res:* Aerobiology; host indexes of plant diseases; plant pathology; mycology; myxomycetes of Minnesota; rusts of Malvaceae; air pollution damage to crops; palynology. *Mailing Add:* Dept of Bot San Diego State Univ San Diego CA 92182

PRESTON, ERIC MILES, b Cortland, NY. ECOLOGY. *Educ:* State Univ NY Binghamton, BA, 66; Univ Hawaii, MS, 68, PhD(zool), 71. *Prof Exp:* NIH trainee, Univ Minn, 71-72; asst prof marine ecol, Univ PR, Rio Piedras, 72-75; proj leader, Mont Coal-Fired Power Plant Proj, 75-80, PROJ LEADER, NAT CROP LOSS ASSESSMENT NETWORK, US ENVIRON PROTECTION AGENCY, 81- *Mem:* Ecol Soc Am; Sigma Xi. *Res:* Population and community dynamics; ecological and agronomic effects of air pollution. *Mailing Add:* Corvallis Environ Res Lab US Environ Protection Agency Corvallis OR 97333

PRESTON, FLOYD W, b Albuquerque, NMex, Feb 11, 23; m 45; c 4. PETROLEUM ENGINEERING. *Educ:* Calif Inst Technol, BS, 44; Univ Mich, MS, 48; Pa State Univ, PhD(petrol eng), 57. *Prof Exp:* Res chemist, Nat Defense Res Comt Proj, Calif Inst Technol, 44-45; res engr, Eng Exp Sta, Univ Mich, 45-46; res engr, Calif Res Corp, Standard Oil Co Calif, 48-50; res assoc, Pa State Univ, 50-55; from asst prof to assoc prof, 57-65, asst chmn, Dept Chem & Petrol Eng, 66-76, PROF PETROL ENG, UNIV KANS, 65-, CHMN, DEPT CHEM & PETROL ENG, 76- *Concurrent Pos:* Consult, Ministry Mines & Hydrol, Venezuela, 59-61. *Mem:* AAAS; Chem Soc; Am Inst Chem Engrs; Am Inst Mining, Metall & Petrol. *Res:* Petroleum production; digital computers. *Mailing Add:* Dept of Chem & Petrol Eng Univ of Kans Lawrence KS 66045

PRESTON, FREDERICK WILLARD, b Chicago, Ill, June 27, 12; m 61; c 3. SURGERY. *Educ:* Yale Univ, BA, 35; Northwestern Univ, MD, 40, MS, 42; Univ Minn, MS, 47. *Prof Exp:* Fel surg, Mayo Clin, 42-48; clin asst, Col Med, Univ Ill, 48-49; from instr to prof surg, Med Sch, Northwestern Univ, Chicago, 60-78; DIR SURG EDUC, SANTA BARBARA COTTAGE HOSP, 78- *Concurrent Pos:* Assoc surgeon, Cook County Hosp, Chicago, Ill, 48-49; attend surgeon, Vet Admin Hosp, Hines, 50-53; assoc attend surgeon, Chicago Wesley Mem Hosp, 50-; chief surg serv, Vet Admin Res Hosp, Chicago, 53-68; sr attend surgeon, Henrotin Hosp, Chicago & Skokie Valley Community Hosp, Skokie, 64-75. *Mem:* Am Asn Cancer Res; Am Surg Asn; fel Am Col Surgeons; Int Soc Surg; Soc Surg Alimentary Tract. *Res:* Cancer; antibiotics; cirrhosis of liver; trauma; abdominal surgery. *Mailing Add:* Cottage Hosp Bath & Pueblo Streets Santa Barbara CA 93102

PRESTON, GERALD COWLES, b Minneapolis, Minn, Aug 24, 28; m 50; c 3. MATHEMATICS. *Educ:* Univ Minn, BA, 50, MA, 51, PhD, 54. *Prof Exp:* Asst math, Univ Minn, 50-52; asst prof, Macalester Col, 52-54; instr, Purdue Univ, 54-55; chmn dept, 70-74, PROF MATH, SAN JOSE STATE UNIV, 55- *Concurrent Pos:* Consult, IBM Corp, 56-58; NSF sci fac fel, 64-65. *Mem:* Am Math Soc; Math Asn Am. *Res:* Topological algebra; theory of numbers. *Mailing Add:* Dept of Math San Jose State Univ San Jose CA 95192

PRESTON, GLENN WETHERBY, b Welch, WVa, Mar 30, 22; m 44; c 3. COMPUTER SCIENCES, ELECTRONICS. *Educ:* Trinity Col, BS, 47; Yale Univ, MS, 48. *Prof Exp:* Mathematician systs anal, Goodyear Aircraft Corp, 50-51; math consult electronic physics, Philco Corp, 51-56; vpres eng, Gen Atronics Corp, 56-62; pres, Preston Assocs Inc, 62-66; MEM TECH STAFF MICROELECTRONICS, INST DEFENSE ANAL, 66- *Concurrent Pos:* Noyes-Clark Fel, Yale Univ, 48; consult, Rand Corp, 60-62, Nat Acad Sci, 67-68 & Air Traffic Control Adv Comt, 69. *Mem:* Inst Elec & Electronics Engrs. *Res:* Integrated circuit architecture; algorithmic analysis; logic synthesis. *Mailing Add:* Inst for Defense Anal 400 Army Naval Dr Arlington VA 22202

PRESTON, J(ACK), b Newcastle-on-Tyne, Eng, Aug 30, 24; nat US; m 53; c 1. METALLURGY. *Educ:* Durham Univ, BSc, 45. *Prof Exp:* Res investr, Brit Non-Ferrous Metals Res Asn, Eng, 45-52, Nickel fel, 52-53 & Metals Div, Imp Chem Industs, 53-55; with prod develop dept, Titanium Metals Corp Am, NY, 55-56; chief metallurgist, Spec Metals Sect, Res Dept, Allegheny Ludlum Steel Co, 56-61, supv metallurgist, 61-69, chief metallurgist process develop, Bar Div, 69-76, SR DEVELOP ENGR, AL TECH SPECIALTY STEEL CORP, 76- *Mem:* Am Soc Metals; Am Inst Mining, Metall & Petrol Engrs. *Res:* Alloy steel and processing development; vacuum melting; metal powder production. *Mailing Add:* Prod Appln Develop Al Tech Specialty Steel Corp Spring St Watervliet NY 12189

PRESTON, JACK, b Birmingham, Ala, Aug 7, 31; m 60; c 2. ORGANIC CHEMISTRY, POLYMER CHEMISTRY. *Educ:* Howard Col, BS, 52; Univ Ala, MS, 54, PhD, 57. *Prof Exp:* Res chemist, Chemstrand Res Ctr, Inc, Durham, 57-63, sr res chemist, 63-65, assoc scientist, 65-66, scientist, 66-70, sci fel, 70-74, sr sci fel, 74-81; SR MONSANTO FEL, MONSANTO TEXTILES CO, PENSACOLA, FLA, 81- *Mem:* AAAS; Am Chem Soc; NY Acad Sci; fel Am Inst Chemists; Fiber Soc. *Res:* Preparation and characterization of linear condensation polymers, including polyaromatic heterocycles, amides, amide-hydrazides and amide-heterocycles; thermally stable fibers and films; high strength and high modulus fibers from organic polymers; evaluation of fibers, especially under extreme environments; specialty acrylic fibers. *Mailing Add:* Monsanto Textiles Co Pensacola FL 32560

PRESTON, JAMES BENSON, b Nelsonville, Ohio, Feb 4, 26; m 47; c 3. PHYSIOLOGY. *Educ:* Univ Cincinnati, MD, 52. *Prof Exp:* Intern, Res & Educ Hosps & instr pharmacol, Col Med, Univ Ill, 52-54; from instr to assoc prof, 54-60, PROF PHYSIOL & CHMN DEPT, STATE UNIV NY UPSTATE MED CTR, 60- *Concurrent Pos:* USPHS sr res fel, 58-60; mem physiol training comt, Nat Inst Gen Med Sci, 71-73; mem physiol test comt, Nat Bd Med Exam, 72-76. *Mem:* Soc Gen Physiol; Am Physiol Soc; Asn Chmn Depts Physiol; Soc Neurosci. *Res:* Physiology of the nervous system; primate motor control systems with emphasis on cerebral cortex influences on spinal motor systems. *Mailing Add:* Dept of Physiol State Univ NY Upstate Med Ctr Syracuse NY 13210

PRESTON, JAMES FAULKNER, III, b Boston, Mass, July 4, 39; m 66; c 2. BIOCHEMISTRY, MICROBIOLOGY. *Educ:* Colgate Univ, BA, 61; Ohio State Univ, MS, 64; Univ Minn, PhD(biochem), 67. *Prof Exp:* NIH fel microbiol, Yale Univ, 67, Am Cancer Soc fel, 67-69; asst prof, 69-75, ASSOC PROF MICROBIOL, UNIV FLA, 75- *Mem:* AAAS; Am Chem Soc. *Res:* Biosynthesis and function of peptides of fungi; organelle development, especially DNA, RNA and protein synthesis in chloroplasts; antibody and lectin medrated drug targeting; somatu cell hybridization and plant development. *Mailing Add:* Dept of Microbiol Univ of Fla Gainesville FL 32601

PRESTON, JANATH LYNN, biology, ethology, see previous edition

PRESTON, KEITH FONCELL, b Chase Terrace, Eng, Apr 3, 38; Can citizen; m 62; c 3. CHEMICAL PHYSICS, PHYSICAL CHEMISTRY. *Educ:* Univ Cambridge, BA, 59, MA, 62, PhD(chem), 63. *Prof Exp:* Fel photochem, 63-65, SR RES OFFICER KINETICS, NAT RES COUN CAN, 65- *Res:* Electron spin resonance of inorganic free radicals; kinetics of gas-phase reactions; photochemistry; combustion. *Mailing Add:* Div of Chem Montreal Rd Ottawa ON K1A 0R9 Can

PRESTON, KENDALL, JR, b Boston, Mass, Oct 22, 27; m 52; c 1. COMPUTER ENGINEERING, HEALTH SCIENCE. *Educ:* Harvard Col, AB, 50; Harvard Univ, SM, 52. *Prof Exp:* Engr hydraul, United Shoe Mach Corp, 51; mem tech staff electronics, Bell Tel Labs, 52-60; mem sci staff electro-optics, Perkin-Elmer Corp, 60-74; PROF ELEC ENG, CARNEGIE-MELLON UNIV, 74-; PROF RADIATION HEALTH, GRAD SCH PUB HEALTH, UNIV PITTSBURGH, 77- *Concurrent Pos:* Ed adv, Biocharacterist, 70-73; consult, Perkin-Elmer Corp, 74- & Bausch & Lomb Ind, 76-77; assoc ed, Pattern Recognition, 75-; mem, Tech Audit Bd, 76- *Mem:* Inst Elec & Electronics Engrs; NY Acad Sci; Biomed Eng Soc. *Res:* Computer science and engineering with application to coherent radiation systems, health science and pattern recognition. *Mailing Add:* Dept of Elec Eng Carnegie-Mellon Univ Pittsburgh PA 15215

PRESTON, MELVIN ALEXANDER, b Toronto, Ont, May 28, 21; m 47, 66; c 2. THEORETICAL PHYSICS, NUCLEAR PHYSICS. *Educ:* Univ Toronto, BA, 42, MA, 46; Univ Birmingham, PhD, 49. *Prof Exp:* Asst lectr math physics, Univ Birmingham, 47-49; asst prof physics, Univ Toronto, 49-53; assoc prof physics, McMaster Univ, 53-59, dean grad studies, 65-71, prof physics, 59-77, prof appl math, 67-77, chmn dept appl math, 75-77; acad vpres, 77-82, PROF PHYSICS, UNIV SASK, 77- *Concurrent Pos:* Nuffield fel, 57; Nat Res Coun Can sr fel, 63-64; chmn, Ont Coun Grad Studies, 70-71; pres, Can Asn Grad Schs, 71; exec vchmn adv comt acad planning, Coun Ont Univs, 71-75. *Honors & Awards:* Centennial Medal of Can, 67. *Mem:* Fel AAAS; fel Am Phys Soc; Can Asn Physicists (treas, 52-58); fel Royal Soc Can; Brit Inst Physics. *Res:* Theoretical nuclear physics, especially nuclear structure and nuclear forces. *Mailing Add:* Acad V Pres Univ of Sask Saskatoon SK S7N 0W0 Can

PRESTON, RICHARD SWAIN, b Natick, Mass, Feb 4, 25; m 54; c 2. PHYSICS. *Educ:* Wesleyan Univ, BA, 49, MA, 50; Yale Univ, MS, 52, PhD(physics), 54. *Prof Exp:* Assoc dir, Geochronometric Lab, Yale Univ, 54-55; physicist, Argonne Nat Lab, Ill, 55-72; PROF PHYSICS, NORTHERN ILL UNIV, 70- *Concurrent Pos:* Vis scientist, UK Atomic Energy Res Estab, Harwell, Eng, 65-66; vis prof, Univ Saarlandes, WGer, 77-78 & 81. *Mem:* Am Phys Soc. *Res:* Nuclear resonant fluorescence and solid-state physics. *Mailing Add:* Dept Physics Northern Ill Univ De Kalb IL 60115

PRESTON, ROBERT ARTHUR, b New York, NY, June 29, 44; m 70; c 1. RADIO ASTRONOMY. *Educ:* Cornell Univ, BS, 66, MS, 67; Mass Inst Technol, PhD(astronaut), 72. *Prof Exp:* Sr scientist, Lockheed Res Lab, 72-73; scientist, 73-76, SUPVR, ASTRON MEASUREMENTS GROUP, JET PROPULSION LAB, 76- *Mem:* Am Astron Soc; Int Union Radio Sci. *Res:* Investigations of quasars and galaxies; tracking of interplanetary spacecraft. *Mailing Add:* 264-781 Jet Propulsion Lab 4800 Oak Grove Dr Pasadena CA 91109

PRESTON, ROBERT JULIAN, b London, Eng, June 5, 42; m 64, 80; c 5. CYTOGENETICS. *Educ:* Cambridge Univ, BA, 63, MA, 66; Reading Univ, PhD(radiation biol), 70. *Prof Exp:* Staff mem biophys, Radiol Unit, Med Res Coun, Harwell, Eng, 63-70; STAFF MEM CYTOGENETICS, BIOL DIV, OAK RIDGE NAT LAB, 70- *Concurrent Pos:* Assoc dir, Biomed Grad Sch, Univ Tenn, Knoxville, 70-; ed, Mutation Res Letters, 80- *Mem:* Radiation Res Soc; Environ Mutagen Soc. *Res:* Assessment of radiation and chemical genetic hazards to man by extrapolation from cytogenetic data obtained in laboratory animals; mechanisms of chromosome aberration induction by radiation and chemicals. *Mailing Add:* Biol Div Oak Ridge Nat Lab Oak Ridge TN 37830

PRESTON, ROBERT KREIG, b Saskatoon, Sask, Sept 29, 19; US citizen; m 49; c 7. ORGANIC CHEMISTRY. *Educ:* Cath Univ Am, BS, 42; Univ Md, PhD(chem), 48. *Prof Exp:* Res chemist, E I du Pont de Nemours & Co, 48-50 & Nat Drug Co, 50-56; ASST MEM, INST CANCER RES, 56- *Concurrent Pos:* Chmn, Chem Dept, Eve Div, La Salle Col, 56- *Mem:* Am Chem Soc. *Res:* Medicinal chemistry; chemotherapy of cancer. *Mailing Add:* 29 Holyoke Rd Richboro PA 18954

PRESTON, ROBERT LESLIE, b Stevens Point, Wis, Apr 24, 42; m 65; c 4. CELL PHYSIOLOGY. *Educ:* Univ Minn, BA, 66; Univ Calif, Irvine, PhD(biol), 70. *Prof Exp:* Res asst, Dept Develop & Cell Biol, Univ Calif, Irvine, 66-70; NIH fel membrane physiol, Med Sch, Yale Univ, 70-73, res assoc, 73-74; ASST PROF PHYSIOL, ILL STATE UNIV, 74- *Concurrent Pos:* Lectr gastrointestinal physiol, Physicians Asn Prog, Med Sch, Yale Univ, 72; vis prof, Univ of Ill, Urbana, 78. *Mem:* Am Soc Zoologists; AAAS; Inst for Biol Sci. *Res:* Membrane transport of nonelectrolytes; comparative physiology and transport in marine organisms. *Mailing Add:* Dept of Biol Ill State Univ Normal IL 61761

PRESTON, RODNEY LEROY, b Denver, Colo, Jan 11, 31; m 50; c 3. ANIMAL NUTRITION, ANIMAL PHYSIOLOGY. *Educ:* Colo State Univ, BS, 53; Iowa State Univ, MS, 55, PhD(animal nutrit), 57. *Prof Exp:* From asst prof to prof animal husb, Univ Mo-Columbia, 57-69; prof animal sci, Ohio Agr Res & Develop Ctr, 69-75; prof animal sci & chmn dept, Wash State Univ, 75-81; THORNTON DISTINGUISHED PROF, DEPT ANIMAL SCI, TEX TECH UNIV, 82- *Concurrent Pos:* NIH spec fel, Lab Vet Biochem, State Univ Utrecht, 64-65. *Mem:* Am Soc Animal Sci; Am Inst Nutrit; Soc Exp Biol & Med. *Res:* Nutrition, biochemistry and physiology of animals, especially ruminants. *Mailing Add:* Dept Animal Sci Tex Tech Univ Lubbock TX 79409

PRESTON, STEPHEN BOYLAN, b Burnwell, WVa, May 5, 19; m 43. FOREST PRODUCTS. *Educ:* Colo Agr & Mech Col, BS, 46, MF, 47; Yale Univ, MF, 48, DF, 51. *Prof Exp:* Forester, Tex Longleaf Lumber Co, 47; res asst & asst instr wood technol, Yale Univ, 49-50; from instr to assoc prof wood technol, 50-55, res consult & wood technologist, Res Inst, 51-65, chmn dept wood technol, 54-65, actg dean sch natural resources, 69-70, chmn dept resource planning & conserv, 70-71, prof wood technol, 55-59, PROF NATURAL RESOURCES, UNIV MICH, ANN ARBOR, 59-, ASSOC DEAN SCH NATURAL RESOURCES, 71- *Concurrent Pos:* Exec dir, Orgn Trop Studies, Costa Rica, 65-69, vpres, 70-72, pres, 72-74. *Honors & Awards:* Wood Mag Award, 50. *Mem:* Soc Am Foresters; Forest Prod Res Soc; Soc Wood Sci & Technol (pres, 61-62 & 63-64); Int Soc Trop Foresters. *Res:* Physical and mechanical properties of veneer laminates drying of wood; tropical wood; tropical forestry. *Mailing Add:* 3012C Sch Natural Resources Univ Mich Ann Arbor MI 48104

PRESTON, THOMAS ALEXANDER, b Hampton-on-Thames, Eng, Aug 13, 27; UK & Can citizen; m 54, 72; c 5. AGRICULTURAL ENGINEERING, PRODUCTION ENGINEERING. *Educ:* Univ Cambridge, BA, 51, MA, 56. *Prof Exp:* Mgr feeds div, UNGA Nairobi, Kenya, 53-57; mgr agr div, Prod Eng Ltd, London, 57-63; mem efficiency surv, Sierra Leone govt, 60-61; assoc prof, 63-72, PROF AGR ENG, UNIV ALTA, 72- *Concurrent Pos:* Consult orgn & methods, Univ Alta & Royal Alexander Hosps, 64-69; fel, Nat Col Agr Eng, UK, 70-71; coordr, Fac Agr, Univ Nigeria, 72-74; ed, Rural Work Sci Abstr, Commonwealth Agr Bur, 78; mem, Irish Geneal Res Soc Coun. *Mem:* Fel Brit Inst Mgt Services; Am Soc Agr Engrs; Agr Inst Can. *Res:* Ergonomics; work design; productivity methods; chronocyclegraphy; work study; network analysis and operations research; rural medicine. *Mailing Add:* Dept of Agr Eng Univ of Alta Edmonton AB T6G 2G7 Can

PRESTON, WILLIAM BURTON, b Penticton, BC, Mar 6, 37; m 63; c 3. HERPETOLOGY, ECOLOGY. *Educ:* Univ BC, BSc, 61, MSc, 64; Univ Okla, PhD(zool), 70. *Prof Exp:* Cur lower vert & invert, 70-76, CUR LOWER VERT, MAN MUS MAN & NATURE, 76- *Mem:* Am Soc Ichthyologists & Herpetologists; Soc Study Amphibians & Reptiles; Lepidopterists Soc; Entom Soc Can; Herpetologists League. *Res:* Ethoecology; ecology, behavior and distribution of amphibians and reptiles in Manitoba; ecology and distribution of insects and arachnids. *Mailing Add:* Man Mus Man & Nature 190 Rupert Ave Winnipeg MB R3B 0N2 Can

PRESTON-THOMAS, HUGH, b Eng, Dec 26, 23. EXPERIMENTAL PHYSICS. *Educ:* Bristol Univ, BSc, 45, PhD(physics), 50. *Prof Exp:* RES PHYSICIST, DIV PHYSICS, NAT RES COUN CAN, 51- *Res:* Advances in both fundamental and practical metrology of the basic units of measurement. *Mailing Add:* Div of Physics Nat Res Coun Can Ottawa ON K1A 0R6 Can

PRESTWICH, GLENN DOWNES, b Canal Zone, Panama, Nov 29, 48; US citizen. ORGANIC CHEMISTRY, ENTOMOLOGY. *Educ:* Calif Inst Technol, BS, 70; Stanford Univ, PhD(chem), 74. *Prof Exp:* Res scientist, Int Ctr Insect Physiol & Ecol, Kenya, 74-75; NIH fel, Cornell Univ, 76-77; asst prof, 77-82, ASSOC PROF CHEM, STATE UNIV NY STONY BROOK, 82- *Concurrent Pos:* Alfred P Sloan res fel, 81-83; Camille & Henry Dreyfus teacher scholar grant, 81- *Mem:* Am Chem Soc; AAAS; Am Entom Soc; Int Union Study Social Insects. *Res:* Termite chemical defense, specifically evolution, natural products and chemosystematics; termite lipid metabolism; chemical ecology; organic synthesis; insect juvenile hormone and steroid metabolism; new termiticides; synthetic organic and natural products chemistry; chemical ecology. *Mailing Add:* Dept Chem State Univ NY Stony Brook NY 11794

PRESTWIDGE, KATHLEEN JOYCE, b New York, NY, Jan 7, 27. BIOLOGY. *Educ:* Hunter Col, BA, 49; Brooklyn Col, MA, 57; St John's Univ, NY, PhD(biol), 70. *Prof Exp:* Teacher, Bd Educ, City of New York, 56-59; PROF BIOL & MED LAB TECHNOL, BRONX COMMUNITY COL, CITY UNIV NEW YORK, 59- *Mem:* AAAS; Am Inst Biol Sci; NY Acad Sci; Royal Soc Trop Med & Hyg. *Res:* Medical laboratory technology; human physiology, health; delivery of community health services; career training, curriculum development and biological education. *Mailing Add:* Bronx Community Col University Ave & West 181st St Bronx NY 10453

PRESTWOOD, ANNIE KATHERINE, b Lenoir, NC, July 4, 35. VETERINARY PARASITOLOGY, WILDLIFE DISEASES. *Educ:* NC State Univ, BS, 60; Univ Ga, DVM, 62, MS, 64, PhD(parasitol), 68. *Prof Exp:* Fel, Southeastern Coop Wildlife Dis Study, 64-66, res assoc, 66-76, assoc prof parasitol, 76-81, PROF PARASITOL, COL VET MED, UNIV GA, 81- *Mem:* Wildlife Dis Asn (secy, 77-80); Am Soc Parasitologists; Am Vet Med Asn; Wildlife Soc; Can Soc Zoologists. *Res:* Helminth and Protozoan diseases of domestic and wild animals, particularly the lungworm fauna of these animals. *Mailing Add:* Dept of Parasitol Univ of Ga Col of Vet Med Athens GA 30602

PRESTWOOD, RENE JESSE, b San Rafael, Calif, Oct 18, 20; m 44; c 3. RADIOCHEMISTRY. *Educ:* Univ Calif, BS, 42; Washington Univ, PhD(radiochem), 48. *Prof Exp:* Jr scientist, Manhattan Proj & Off Sci Res & Develop contracts, Los Alamos Sci Lab, Univ Calif, 42-46; asst, Washington Univ, 46-48; MEM STAFF, LOS ALAMOS SCI LAB, UNIV CALIF, 48- *Res:* Radiochemical separations and purifications; neutron excitation functions of many elements; absolute beta counting; symmetry of resonance fission; heavy element chemistry. *Mailing Add:* 683 47th St Los Alamos NM 87544

PRESZLER, ALAN MELVIN, b Missoula, Mont, July 11, 39; m 66; c 1. SPACE PHYSICS. *Educ:* Univ Wash, BA, 63; Univ Calif, Riverside, MS, 72, PhD(physics), 73. *Prof Exp:* Res assoc physics, Univ Calif, Riverside, 69-73; res assoc, Univ NH, 73-75; res physicist, Univ Calif, Riverside, 75-77; asst prof, Loma Linda Univ, 77-80; PHYSICIST, APPL AUTOMATION, INC, 80- *Concurrent Pos:* Instr, Riverside City Col, 75- & Med Ctr, Loma Linda Univ. *Mem:* Am Asn Advan Med Instr. *Res:* Interpretation of atmospheric neutron data obtained from a large area double-scattering detector and from neutron spectrometers flown on Skylab and the Apollo-Soyuz test project; pulmonary system data interpretation through measurements of gas composition, airway flow, pressure and temperature; development of elemental analyses for process control. *Mailing Add:* Appl Automation, Inc 125 ARB Pawhuska Rd Bartlesville GA 74004

PRETI, GEORGE, b Brooklyn, NY, Oct 7, 44; m 73. ORGANIC CHEMISTRY, MASS SPECTROMETRY. *Educ:* Polytech Inst Brooklyn, BS, 66; Mass Inst Technol, PhD(org chem), 71. *Prof Exp:* Res assoc, 71-73, ASSOC MEM, MONELL CHEM SENSES CTR, UNIV PA, 73- *Mem:* Am Chem Soc. *Res:* Use of gas chromatography and mass spectrometry to profile the small, organic constituents of human female reproductive tract secretions for metabolites diagnostic of the fertile period and/or pathological conditions. *Mailing Add:* Monell Chem Senses Ctr Univ Pa 3500 Market St Philadelphia PA 19104

PRETKA, JOHN E, b Lawrence, Mass, May 21, 19; m 43; c 2. TEXTILE FIBERS, ORGANIC CHEMISTRY. *Educ:* Tufts Col, BS, 42; Columbia Univ, MA, 47; NY Univ, PhD(chem), 50. *Prof Exp:* Org res chemist, Evans Assocs, 42-44, Stauffer Chem Co, 46 & Calco Div, Am Cyanamid Co, 50-55;

org res chemist, Textile Fibers Dept, 55-60, SR RES CHEMIST, TEXTILE FIBERS DEPT, E I DU PONT DE NEMOURS & CO, INC, 60- *Mem:* Am Chem Soc; Am Asn Textile Chemists & Colorists. *Res:* Applied textile end use research; textile fibers; new product development; static electricity; finishing; fabric uniformity; physical tests; organic synthesis; optical bleaches; dyes; pigments; heterocycles; organic intermediates; agricultural chemicals; resin finishes. *Mailing Add:* 2617 Turnstone Dr Wilmington DE 19808

PRETLOW, THOMAS GARRETT, II, b Warrenton, Va, Dec 11, 39; m 63; c 3. PATHOLOGY. *Educ:* Oberlin Col, AB, 60; Univ Rochester, MD, 65. *Prof Exp:* From intern internal med to resident path, Univ Hosps, Univ Wis, 65-67; res assoc cell biol sect, Viral Etiol Br, Nat Cancer Inst, 67-69; asst prof path, Rutgers Med Sch, 69-71; assoc prof path, 71-74, asst prof biophys, 71-76, dir, Div Cancer Res, 76-78, PROF PATH, MED CTR, UNIV ALA, BIRMINGHAM, 74-, ASSOC PROF BIOCHEM, 76-, DIR DIV RES, 78- *Concurrent Pos:* USPHS res career develop award, 73-78; mem path B study sect, NIH, 76-80; ed, Cell Biophys. *Mem:* Am Asn Cancer Res; Am Soc Biol Chem; Am Asn Path; Int Acad Path; Am Asn Immunol. *Res:* Neoplastic diseases; cellular physiology; mechanism of drug action; isolation of cell types in vitro. *Mailing Add:* Dept of Path Univ of Ala Med Ctr Birmingham AL 35294

PRETO, RAYMOND JOSEPH, physical organic chemistry, polymer science, see previous edition

PRETTY, KENNETH MCALPINE, b Wilkesport, Ont, June 19, 29. SOIL SCIENCE, CROP SCIENCE. *Educ:* Univ Toronto, BSA, 51; Mich State Univ, MS, 55, PhD(soil sci), 58. *Prof Exp:* Soils fieldman, Soil & Crop Improv Asn, 54; from instr to asst prof soil sci, Mich State Univ, 57-59; Can dir indust agron, 59-67, VPRES INDUST AGRON & COORDR FOREIGN PROGS, AM POTASH INST, 67-; PRES, POTASH & PHOSPHATE INST CAN, 71- *Mem:* AAAS; Am Soc Agron; Soil Sci Soc Am; Crop Sci Soc Am; Am Chem Soc. *Res:* Nutrient availability in soils; factors affecting plant uptake; components of yield; sources of plant nutrients; distribution and function of nutrients in plants. *Mailing Add:* Potash/Phosphate Inst of Can Suite 507 555 Burnhamthorpe Rd Etobicoke ON M9C 2Y3 Can

PRETTYMAN, CLINTON ELMER, computer sciences, see previous edition

PRETZER, C ANDREW, b Scranton, Pa, Sept 10, 28; c 8. STRUCTURAL ENGINEERING, CIVIL ENGINEERING. *Educ:* Univ Mich, BSE, 50, MS, 51; Mass Inst Technol, PhD(civil eng), 63. *Prof Exp:* Instr civil eng, Mass Inst Technol, 60-63; engr struct eng, Le Messurier Assoc, Inc, 63-66; assoc prof civil eng, Northeastern Univ, 66-72; PRES STRUCT ENG, C A PRETZER ASSOCS INC, 72- *Concurrent Pos:* Consult civil eng, Douglas G Peterson & Assoc Inc, 72- *Mem:* Am Concrete Inst; Am Soc Civil Engrs; Prestressed Concrete Inst. *Mailing Add:* C A Pretzer Assocs Inc PO Box 248 North Scituate RI 02857

PRETZER, DONAVON DONALD, b Fresno, Calif, June 12, 31; m 57; c 2. IMAGING PROCESSING. *Educ:* Fresno State Col, BS, 57; Wash Univ, MS, 60, PhD(atomic physics), 63. *Prof Exp:* Mem tech staff, Bel Tel Res Labs, 63-65; scientist, Nortronics Appl Res Labs, Northrup Res & Technol Ctr, 65-66, chief radiation effects, 66, shock physics, 66-67, sr mem tech staff, 67-70, dir technol anal, 70-74, mgr advan prog & plans, 74-76, mgr elec & electrical optical devices, 76-77; mgr image sensor systs, Hughes Res Labs, 77-79, asst lab mgr, Adv Prog Lab, Tactical Systs Div, 79-80, MGR, IMAGE PROCESSING LAB, ELECTRO-OPTICAL ENG DIV, HUGHES AIRCRAFT CO, CULVER CITY, CALIF, 80- *Res:* Image processing; fire control; electro-optical imaging systems; data compression, command and control systems; charge transfer cross sections in atomic and molecular gases; Lyman alpha emission from hydrogen ion-noble gas collisions; auger effect-noble gas ion neutralization at a semiconductor surface; radiation effects to electronics; research planning; technological forecasting. *Mailing Add:* 1307 Valley High Ave Thousand Oaks CA 91360

PREUL, HERBERT C, b Berger, Mo, Jan 11, 26; m 50; c 1. CIVIL & ENVIRONMENTAL ENGINEERING. *Educ:* Univ Iowa, BS, 50; Univ Minn, Minneapolis, MS, 55, PhD(civil eng), 64. *Prof Exp:* Civil engr, US Bur Reclamation, Colo & Calif, 50-52; supvry civil engr, US Corps Engrs, Minn & Nebr, 52-60; teaching asst civil eng, Univ Minn, Minneapolis, 60-64; assoc prof, 64-75, PROF CIVIL & ENVIRON ENG, COL ENG, UNIV CINCINNATI, 75- *Concurrent Pos:* Consult sanit & hydraul eng for var orgn, 55-; res grants, Off Water Resources Res, Univ Cincinnati, 65-67, USPHS, 68-70 & Environ Protection Agency, 69-82; eng educ consult, USAID & NSF for water resources & sanit eng in India, 66, 68 & 70; int consult sanit eng for WHO, World Bank & var foreign govt. *Mem:* Am Soc Civil Engrs; Am Soc Eng Educ; Water Pollution Control Fedn; Am Water Works Asn; Am Water Resources Asn. *Res:* Water resources and sanitary engineering; water pollution control; waste water treatment; groundwater contamination. *Mailing Add:* Dept Civil & Environ Eng Col Eng Univ Cincinnati Cincinnati OH 45221

PREUS, MARILYN IONE, b Edmonton, Alta, Oct 20, 44; m 73. HUMAN GENETICS. *Educ:* Univ Alta, BS, 67; McGill Univ, MS, 71, PhD(biol), 75. *Prof Exp:* RES SCIENTIST, MCGILL UNIV-MONT CHILDREN'S HOSP, RES INST, 75-, FULL MEM, 78-, ASST PROF, DEPT PEDIAT & CTR HUMAN GENETICS, 80-, AFFIL PROF BIOL, 80- *Concurrent Pos:* Fac lectr, Dept of Pediat, McGill Res Inst, 78-81. *Mem:* Teratology Soc; Am Soc Human Genetics. *Res:* Numerical classification of dysmorphic syndromes by phenotypic resemblance. *Mailing Add:* Dept Med Genetics 2300 Tupper St Montreal PQ H3H 1P3 Can

PREUS, MARTIN WILLIAM, b Chicago, Ill, Feb 26, 54; m 76. OIL FIELD CHEMICALS. *Educ:* Calif State Polytech Univ, BS, 75; Univ Calif, San Diego, MS, 78, PhD(org chem), 79. *Prof Exp:* Res chemist, Rohm and Haas Co, 80-81; RES CHEMIST, MAGNA CORP, 81- *Mem:* Am Chem Soc. *Res:* Biocides, sulfide scavengers, corrosion inhibitors and emulsion breakers; herbicides for aquatic weed control; abrasion resistant coated transparent plastic sheet; synthesis of biologically active natural products. *Mailing Add:* Magna Corp 11808 S Bloomfield Ave Santa Fe Springs CA 90670

PREUSCH, CHARLES D, b Elmhurst, NY, June 19, 17; m 42; c 3. METALLURGICAL ENGINEERING. *Educ:* Columbia Univ, BS, 39, MS, 40. *Prof Exp:* Chief metallurgist, Crucible Steel Co, 55-60, asst dir res & develop, 60-64, dir planning & develop, 64-69, dir advan planning & magnetics, 69-72, sr consult engr, 72-81, CONSULT PRIN ENGR, CRUCIBLE, INC/COLT INDUSTS, 81- *Honors & Awards:* Gary Medal, Am Iron & Steel Inst, 61. *Mem:* Am Inst Mining, Metall & Petrol Engrs; Am Soc Metals; Asn Iron & Steel Engrs. *Res:* Specialty steels melting; steel processing; casting; vacuum metallurgy; materials systems; product design; manufacturing technology; powder metallurgy. *Mailing Add:* Colt Industs Crucible Res Ctr PO Box 88 Pittsburgh PA 15230

PREUSS, ALBERT F, b Gleason, Wis, Sept 17, 26; m 49; c 2. CHEMISTRY. *Educ:* Univ Wis, BS, 49, PhD(chem), 53. *Prof Exp:* Asst anal chem, Univ Wis, 47-52; res chemist, Rohm and Haas Co, Pa, 52-63, lab head, 63-68; assoc dir res, Ionac Chem Co, NJ, 68-69, dir res, 69-71, vpres res & develop, 71-72; pres, Aldex Co, Inc, 72-75, PRES, ALDEX CHEM CO, LTD, 75- *Mem:* Am Chem Soc; Soc Automotive Engrs; Soc Plastics Engrs. *Res:* Ion exchange technology; chemistry of rhenium; hydrometallurgy of uranium; solvent extraction; nonaqueous chemistry; oil additives. *Mailing Add:* 2439 Martindale Rd Shelburne VT 05482

PREVATT, RUBERT WALDEMAR, b Seville, Fla, May 15, 25; m 53; c 2. SOIL CHEMISTRY, HORTICULTURE. *Educ:* Univ Fla, BSA, 48, MSA, 51, PhD, 59. *Prof Exp:* Lab asst in charge soil testing, Univ Fla, 48-51; soil chemist, Dr P Phillips Co, 51-54; asst, Cornell Univ, 54-56; asst, Univ Fla, 56-59; sr res agronomist, Int Minerals & Chem Corp, Ill, 59-64, supvr Fla Agr Res, 64-70; PROF CITRUS & SOILS, FLA SOUTHERN COL, 71-, DIR 80-, JOHN V & RUTH A TYNDALL CITRUS CHAIR, 81- *Concurrent Pos:* Consult hort, 71- *Mem:* Am Soc Agron; Soil Sci Soc Am; Am Hort Soc. *Res:* Soil fertility; citrus; vegetables and ornamentals; roses; chrysanthemums; agronomic crops; fertilizers; growth regulators. *Mailing Add:* PO Box 426 Lakeland FL 33802

PREVEC, LUDVIK ANTHONY, b Kirkland Lake, Ont, Aug 19, 36; m 62; c 3. BIOLOGY. *Educ:* Univ Toronto, BA, 59, MA, 62, PhD(biophys), 65. *Prof Exp:* Res assoc virol, Wistar Inst Anat & Biol, 65-67; asst prof, 67-71, assoc prof, 71-79, PROF BIOL, MCMASTER UNIV, 79- *Concurrent Pos:* Res fel, Inst Virol, Glasgow, Scotland, 73-74; assoc ed, J Can Soc Cell Biol, 71-73 & J Virol, 76-78. *Mem:* Can Soc Cell Biol; Can Soc Biochem; Am Soc Microbiol. *Res:* Biological and biochemical aspects of virus replication. *Mailing Add:* Dept of Biol McMaster Univ Hamilton ON L8S 4L8 Can

PREVIC, EDWARD PAUL, b Export, Pa, June 29, 31; m 81; c 2. MICROBIAL PHYSIOLOGY. *Educ:* Carnegie Inst Technol, BS, 53; Univ Ill, PhD(biochem), 63. *Prof Exp:* Exp coatings formulator, Thompson & Co, 54-55; org res chemist, Res & Develop Div, Consol Coal Co, 55-60; fel microbiol, Col Med, Tufts Univ, 63-64; Nat Inst Allergy & Infectious Dis fel, Inst Microbiol, Copenhagen, Denmark, 64-65; from instr to asst prof, Col Med, 65-70, ASSOC PROF MICROBIOL, COL ARTS & SCI, UNIV FLA, 71- *Mem:* Am Soc Microbiol; Am Inst Chemists. *Res:* Microbial biochemistry and physiology; mechanisms and control of cell division processes in bacteria and other microorganisms; biochemistry and enzymology of cell division and other growth related phenomena. *Mailing Add:* Dept Microbiol & Cell Sci Univ Fla Gainesville FL 32601

PREVITE, JOSEPH JAMES, b Lawrence, Mass, Jan 25, 36. PHYSIOLOGY, MICROBIOLOGY. *Educ:* Merrimack Col, AB, 56; Boston Col, MS, 59; Bryn Mawr Col, PhD(physiol), 62. *Prof Exp:* Instr biol, Villanova Univ, 58-62; asst prof zool, Smith Col, 62-63; res physiologist-microbiologist, US Army Navy Natick Labs, 63-68 & Exp Path Lab, US Army Res Inst Environ Med, 68-70; PROF PHYSIOL & IMMUNOL, FRAMINGHAM STATE COL, 70- *Concurrent Pos:* Consult, Div Allied Health Manpower, USPHS. *Mem:* AAAS; Am Physiol Soc; Am Soc Microbiol; Soc Exp Biol & Med. *Res:* Host-parasite relations; endotoxins; environmental physiology and disease; food microbiology; radiation microbiology; salmonellae; Cl botulinum toxins; staphylococci; food borne infections and intoxications. *Mailing Add:* Dept of Biol Framingham State Col Framingham MA 01701

PREVORSEK, DUSAN CIRIL, b Ljubljana, Yugoslavia, Feb 14, 22; US citizen; m 63; c 1. POLYMER PHYSICS, POLYMER CHEMISTRY. *Educ:* Univ Ljubljana, BS, 50, PhD(chem), 56. *Prof Exp:* Fel physics, Univ Paris, 56-57, res assoc, 57-58; proj leader polymer physics, Goodyear Tire & Rubber Co, 58-61; fel, Textile Res Inst, 61-62, prin scientist, 62-65; sr res assoc, 65-77, sr res scientist, Chem Res Ctr, Allied Chem Corp, 77-80, MGR POLYMER SCI, CORP TECHNOL, ALLIED CORP, 80- *Concurrent Pos:* Lectr, Fiber Soc, 70; chmn, Gordon Conf Fiber Sci, 76. *Honors & Awards:* Harold DeWitt Smith Award, Am Soc Testing & Mat, 75. *Mem:* Am Chem Soc; Am Phys Soc; Soc Rheol; Fiber Soc; NY Acad Sci. *Res:* Structure of complex organic molecules; theoretical and experimental viscoelasticity, diffusion and fracture; textile and tire mechanics; synthesis and properties of ordered copolymers; polymer compatibility; interpenetrating networks; composites; adhesion. *Mailing Add:* Chem Res Ctr Allied Chem Morristown NJ 07960

PREVOST, JEAN HERVE, b Fez, Morocco, Sept 10, 47; French citizen; m 75; c 1. GEOTECHNICAL ENGINEERING, NUMERICAL METHODS. *Educ:* ETP, France, 71; Stanford Univ, MS, 72, PhD(soil mech), 74. *Prof Exp:* Teaching asst civil eng, Stanford Univ, 72-74; res fel soil mech, Norwegian Geotech Inst, Oslo, 74-76; lectr civil eng, Calif Inst Technol, 76-78; asst prof, 78-82, ASSOC PROF CIVIL ENG, PRINCETON UNIV, 82- *Concurrent Pos:* Fulbright fel, 71-74; Royal Norwegian Coun Sci & Indust Res fel, 74-76. *Mem:* Am Soc Civil Engrs; Soc Eng Sci; Int Soc Soil Mech. *Res:* Dynamics;

nonlinear continuum mechanics; mixture theories; finite element methods; constitutive theories; soil mechanics; centrifuge soil testing; author or coauthor of over 40 publications. *Mailing Add:* Dept Civil Eng Princeton Univ Princeton NJ 08544

PREVOST, MARCEL R, industrial engineering, see previous edition

PREWITT, CHARLES THOMPSON, b Lexington, Ky, Mar 3, 33; m 58; c 1. EARTH SCIENCE. *Educ:* Mass Inst Technol, SB, 55, SM, 60, PhD(crystallog), 62. *Prof Exp:* Crystallogr, Cent Res Dept, E I du Pont de Nemours & Co, Inc, 62-69; from assoc prof to prof crystallog, 69-75, chmn dept, 77-80, PROF EARTH SCI & MAT SCI, STATE UNIV NY STONY BROOK, 75- *Concurrent Pos:* Churchill Found fel, 75; vis prof, Monash Univ, Australia, 76; ed, Physics & Chem of Minerals, 77- *Mem:* Am Crystallog Asn; Mineral Soc Am; Am Geophys Union; Geol Soc Am. *Res:* Solid state geochemistry and geophysics; mineralogy, crystallography and chemistry of silicates and sulfides. *Mailing Add:* Dept of Earth & Space Sci State Univ of NY Stony Brook NY 11794

PREWITT, JUDITH MARTHA SHIMANSKY, b Brooklyn, NY, Oct 16, 35; m 56; c 1. MATHEMATICS, COMPUTER SCIENCE. *Educ:* Swarthmore Col, BA, 57; Univ Pa, MA, 59; Univ Uppsala, PhD(comput sci & numerical anal), 78. *Prof Exp:* Mathematician, Burroughs Corp, 56-58, Auerbach Corp, 61-62; instr math & radiol, Grad Sch Med, Univ Pa, 62-71; mathematician, 71-74, RES MATHEMATICIAN, NIH, 74- *Concurrent Pos:* Instr math, Univ Pa, 60-63; mem comt cytol automation, Nat Cancer Inst, 72-77, diag radiol adv comt, 73-77 & diag res adv comt, 77-; consult & vis scientist, Uppsala Univ & Hosp, 73-; assoc ed, Comput Graphics & Image Processing, 74-; co-chmn, NSF Proj Ultrasonic Tissue Characterization, 76- *Honors & Awards:* Sustained High Performance Qual Award, NIH, 73. *Mem:* Soc Indust & Appl Math; Biomed Eng Soc; Inst Elec & Electronics Engrs; Math Sci Asn; Asn Comput Mach. *Res:* Machine intelligence (sensors, pattern recognition and decision-making) applied to quantitative characterization of biological images; use of computers in cancer detection, diagnosis and therapy optimization. *Mailing Add:* NIH Div of Comput Res & Technol Bldg 12A Rm 2053 Bethesda MD 20205

PREWITT, RUSSELL LAWRENCE, JR, b St Louis, Mo, June 19, 43; m 67; c 1. CARDIOVASCULAR PHYSIOLOGY. *Educ:* St Louis Univ, AB, 65; Univ Mo, PhD(physiol), 71. *Prof Exp:* Res assoc physiol, Col Med, Univ Ariz, 71-74; asst prof physiol, Ctr Health Sci, Univ Tenn, 74-81; ASSOC PROF PHYSIOL, LA STATE UNIV MED CTR, 81- *Concurrent Pos:* Res grants, Tenn Heart Asn, 75 & NIH, 76. *Mem:* Microcirculatory Soc; Am Physiol Soc. *Res:* Autoregulation of blood flow in the microcirculation and hemodynamic alterations in spontaneous hypertension. *Mailing Add:* Dept Physiol La State Univ Med Ctr 1501 Kings Hwy Shreveport LA 71130

PREZBINDOWSKI, DAVID LEON, nuclear engineering, see previous edition

PREZELIN, BARBARA BERNTSEN, b Portland, Ore, Apr 13, 48; m 72. MARINE PHYCOLOGY, PHOTOSYNTHESIS. *Educ:* Univ Ore, BS, 70; Scripps Inst Oceanog, Univ Calif, San Diego, PhD(marine biol), 75. *Prof Exp:* NSF res partic phycol, Univ Ore, 69, teaching asst biol, 68-70; NIH trainee marine bot, Marine Biol Lab, Woods Hole, 70; NIH trainee marine biol, Scripps Inst Oceanog, Univ Calif, San Diego, 70-75, res asst, 75; NSF res assoc, 75-77, ASST PROF, DEPT BIOL SCI, MARINE SCI INST, UNIV CALIF, SANTA BARBARA, 77- *Concurrent Pos:* Lectr, NATO, 80. *Mem:* Am Inst Biol Sci; Am Soc Photobiol; Phycol Soc Am; Am Soc Limnol & Oceanog; AAAS. *Res:* Studies of mechanisms regulating algal photosynthesis, primary productivity and growth with special interest in light-regulation, diel periodicity and biological clocks and photonutritive interactions of the photosynthetic apparatus of red tide species of dinoflagellates; study of mechanism of circadian rhythmicity in photosynthetic capacity. *Mailing Add:* Dept of Biol Sci Univ of Calif Santa Barbara CA 93106

PRIAN, V(ASILY) D(IMITRY), mechanical engineering, deceased

PRIBBLE, MARY JO, b Macfarlan, WVa, Jan 20, 30. INORGANIC CHEMISTRY. *Educ:* Maryville Col, BA, 52; Duke Univ, MA, 57; La State Univ, Baton Rouge, PhD(chem), 70. *Prof Exp:* Instr chem, Davis & Elkins Col, 54-55 & Marietta Col, 57-59; documentation chemist, Ethyl Corp, 59-61; instr, Marshall Univ, 61-63; from asst prof to assoc prof chem, Limestone Col, 63-70, prof & chmn, Div Sci & Math, 70-77, chmn dept, 69-70; ASSOC PROF CHEM, GLENVILLE STATE COL, 77- *Concurrent Pos:* NSF sci fac fel, La State Univ, Baton Rouge, 68-69. *Mem:* AAAS; Am Chem Soc. *Res:* Coordination compounds; preparation, interpretation of electronic and vibrational spectra, magnetic properties, unusual oxidation states; chemical education. *Mailing Add:* Dept Chem Glenville State Col Glenville WV 26351

PRIBIL, STEPHEN, b Pressbourg, Czech, Oct 27, 19; US citizen; m 59; c 2. THERMODYNAMICS, LOW TEMPERATURE PHYSICS. *Educ:* Slovak Tech Univ, DiplIng, 45, DrIngSc(appl physics), 50. *Prof Exp:* Scientist, SKODA, Czech, 45-48; sr scientist, A G Dynamit Nobel, 48-51; prof mech eng, Sch Eng, Pressbourg, 52-58; scientist, Div Natural Sci, Inst Appl Physics, Czech Acad Sci, 58-62; res consult thermodyn & heat transfer, Worthington Corp, NY, 62-63; PROF PHYSICS, STATE UNIV NY COL BROCKPORT, 64- *Concurrent Pos:* Sci adv, Czech Govt, Ministry Health, Mining Indust & Heavy Indust, 54-62. *Mem:* Am Asn Physics Teachers; Am Phys Soc; Am Soc Heat, Refrig & Air-Conditioning; Royal Soc Health; Int Inst Refrig. *Res:* Phase-equilibria of cryogens; solidification of gases and mixtures of gases; cryoacoustics; dielectric properties of cryogens; solid state biophysics. *Mailing Add:* Dept of Physics Smith Bldg State Univ of NY Col Brockport NY 14420

PRIBOR, DONALD B, b Detroit, Mich, Dec 4, 32; m 61; c 4. CELL PHYSIOLOGY, CRYOBIOLOGY. *Educ:* St Louis Univ, BS, 54; Cath Univ Am, MS, 61, PhD(physiol), 64. *Prof Exp:* Consult, Inst Lab Med, Perth Amboy Gen Hosp, 68- *Concurrent Pos:* Res assoc, Inst Med Res, Toledo Hosp, Ohio, 68- Concurrent. *Mem:* Soc Gen Physiol; Biophys Soc; Soc Cryobiol. *Res:* Integration of science and human values; prevention of psychosomatic illness; psychobiology; human sexuality; development of human personality. *Mailing Add:* Dept Biol Univ Toledo Toledo OH 43606

PRIBRAM, JOHN KARL, b Chicago, Ill, Feb 1, 41; m 63; c 2. OPTICAL PROPERRTIES. *Educ:* Middlebury Col, AB, 62; Wesleyan Univ, MA, 65; Univ Mass, Amherst, PhD(physics), 73. *Prof Exp:* Instr, 70-73, asst prof physics, 73-80, ASSOC PROF PHYSICS, BATES COL, 80- *Concurrent Pos:* Mellon fel, 77-78; vis asst prof physics, Univ Ill, Urbana, 79-80. *Mem:* Am Phys Soc; Am Asn Physics Teachers; History Sci Soc. *Res:* Optical properties of semiconductors and insulators. *Mailing Add:* Dept of Physics Bates Col Lewiston ME 04240

PRIBRAM, KARL HARRY, b Vienna, Austria, Feb 25, 19; nat US; m 40, 60; c 5. NEUROPSYCHOLOGY. *Educ:* Univ Chicago, SB, 39, MD, 41; Am Bd Neurol Surg, dipl, 48. *Prof Exp:* Asst resident neurol surg, Chicago Mem Hosp, 42-43; resident, St Luke's Hosp, Chicago, 43-45; instr neurol surg, Univ Tenn, 45-46; neurosurgeon & neurophysiologist, Yerkes Labs Primate Biol, Fla, 46-48; res asst prof physiol & psychol, Sch Med, Yale Univ, 48-51, lectr, 51-58; fel, Ctr Advan Study Behav Sci, 58-59; assoc prof, 59-62, PROF PSYCHIAT & PSYCHOL & NIMH RES PROF, STANFORD UNIV, 62- *Concurrent Pos:* Asst, Univ Ill, 43-45; vis lectr, Mass Inst Technol, 54, Clark Univ, 56 & Harvard Univ, 56, vis prof, Trinity Col, Conn, 57 & Menninger Found, 73-75. *Honors & Awards:* Phillips Lectr, Haverford Col, 61; Spencer Lectr, Univ Chicago, 73. *Mem:* Am Psychol Asn; Psychonom Soc; Soc Exp Psychologists; Int Soc Res on Agression; Sigma Xi. *Res:* Neurophysiology. *Mailing Add:* Dept Psychol Bldg 420 Stanford Univ Stanford CA 94305

PRIBULA, ALAN JOSEPH, b Irvington, NJ, Jan 18, 48. INORGANIC CHEMISTRY. *Educ:* Bucknell Univ, BS, 69; Univ Ill, Urbana, PhD(inorg chem), 74. *Prof Exp:* Res assoc, Princeton Univ, 74-75, instr, 75-76; instr 76-80, ASST PROF CHEM, TOWSON STATE UNIV, 80- *Mem:* Am Chem Soc; Sigma Xi; Am Asn Univ Prof. *Res:* Transition-metal compounds; complexes of unusual sulfur and phosphorus ligands; complexes of disulfur and related ligands; thermodynamics and mechanism of metal-bound bond formation and cleavage. *Mailing Add:* Dept of Chem Towson State Univ Baltimore MD 21204

PRICE, ALAN ROGER, b Pontiac, Mich, Jan 15, 42; m 62; c 4. BIOCHEMISTRY. *Educ:* Fla State Univ, BS, 64; Univ Minn, PhD(biochem), 68. *Prof Exp:* NIH fel, 68-69, asst prof, 70-75, ASSOC PROF BIOL CHEM, MED SCH, UNIV MICH, ANN ARBOR, 75- *Honors & Awards:* Rumsey Mem Res Award, Fla State Univ, 68; Sigma Xi Meritorious Res Award, Mich State Univ, 69; Distinguished Serv Award, Univ Mich, 73; Josiah Macy jr fac scholar award, 77. *Mem:* AAAS; Am Soc Microbiol; Am Soc Biol Chemists; fel Am Coun Educ. *Res:* Enzymology of nucleotide and nucleic acid biosynthesis; biochemistry of bacterial virus infections; biosynthesis and function of unusual nucleosides in deoxyribonucleic acids. *Mailing Add:* Dept of Biol Chem Univ of Mich Med Sch Ann Arbor MI 48109

PRICE, ALSON K, b Putney, WVa, Feb 14, 38. ORGANIC CHEMISTRY, CATALYSIS. *Educ:* Morris Harvey Col, BS, 60; Yale Univ, PhD(org chem), 64. *Prof Exp:* Res chemist polymers, Chem Div, Union Carbide Corp, 60; res chemist org fluorine chem, Div Gen Chem, 63-70, res corrdr, 70-71, mgr nutrit res, 71-72, mgr spec projs, 72-74, mgr catalysis, 74-79, mgr org chem, 79-80, MGR CATALYST & PROCESS RES, CORP RES CTR, ALLIED CORP, 80- *Mem:* Am Chem Soc. *Res:* Inorganic chemistry; homogeneous and heterogeneous catalysis; coal chemistry. *Mailing Add:* Allied Corp PO Box 1021 R Morristown NJ 07960

PRICE, ALVIN AUDIS, b Lingleville, Tex, Oct 8, 17; m 43; c 2. VETERINARY MEDICINE. *Educ:* Tex A&M Univ, BS, 40, DVM, 49, MS, 56. *Prof Exp:* Prod mgr, Lockhart Creamery, Tex, 40-42; from instr to asst prof vet anat, 49-57, dean, Col Vet Med, 57-73, adminr biomed sci, 73-80, PROF PHYSIOL, TEX A&M UNIV, 73-, DIR BIOMED SCI, 80- *Concurrent Pos:* Consult, Intercol Exchange Prog, Int Coop Admin, 59, Univ Puerto Rico & Miss State Univ; nat civilian consult, Surgeon Gen, US Air Force, 66; mem adv comt, Nat Health Resources & Selective Serv Syst. *Mem:* Am Vet Med Asn; Am Asn Vet Anat (pres, 57); Asn Am Vet Med Cols (secy, 63-66, pres, 67); Am Asn Vet Clinicians; US Animal Health Asn. *Res:* Reproductive physiology; embryology. *Mailing Add:* Col of Vet Med Tex A&M Univ College Station TX 77843

PRICE, B(ILLY) G(LENN), chemical engineering, see previous edition

PRICE, BOBBY EARL, b Henderson, Tex, Nov 21, 37; m 58; c 2. CIVIL ENGINEERING. *Educ:* Arlington State Col, BS, 62; Okla State Univ, MS, 63; Univ Tex, Austin, PhD(civil eng, water resources), 67. *Prof Exp:* Civil engr aide, Drainage Div, City of Dallas, Tex Pub Works Dept, 57-60, civil engr, 60-62, civil engr, City of Austin, 64; grad asst water resources, Okla State Univ, 62-64; res engr, Univ Tex, Austin, 66-67; PROF CIVIL ENG, DIR ENG GRAD STUDIES & DIR WATER RESOURCES CTR, LA TECH UNIV, 67- *Mem:* Am Soc Civil Engrs; Am Water Works Asn; Am Soc Eng Educ. *Res:* Water resources; culverts set on steep grades; urban hydrology and design methods. *Mailing Add:* Water Resources Ctr La Tech Univ Ruston LA 71272

PRICE, BRANDON JAY, b Detroit, Mich, Aug 21, 48. AUTOMATED CYTOLOGY, COMPUTER SCIENCE. *Educ:* Univ Mich, Ann Arbor, BS, 70, PhD(biophysics), 75. *Prof Exp:* Staff mem biophysics & instrumentation, Los Alamos Sci Lab, 75-77; res asst prof biomed eng, 77-80, ASST DIR, INST FOR CELL ANAL, UNIV MIAMI, 77-, ASST PROF ONCOL & BIOMED ENG, 80- *Concurrent Pos:* Eng consult, Coulter Electronics, Inc, 77-; mem,

Comt on Cytol Automation, Nat Cancer Inst, HEW, 78-80; comput asst, Vet Admin, 78- *Mem:* Biophys Soc; Soc for Anal Cytol; Cell Kinetics Soc; AAAS. *Res:* Development and application of flow systems technology for the rapid and accurate detection, identification and sorting of biological cells; water pollution; exfoliative cytology; development of computer based systems for storage and retrieval of patient information in hospital intensive care units. *Mailing Add:* Inst for Cell Anal NCCH 1475 NW 12th Ave Miami FL 33101

PRICE, BYRON FREDERICK, b Pittsburgh, Pa, May 13, 36; m 63; c 1. ANALYTICAL BIOCHEMISTRY. *Educ:* Pa State Univ, BS, 58; Univ Mo, MS, 64. *Prof Exp:* Res asst anal chem, Chem Lab, Mo Exp Sta, 61-64, res instr anal biochem, 64-65; jr res assoc, New Prod Div, 65-66, res assoc, 66-68, asst mgr anal res div, 68-71, asst mgr res, New Prod Div, 71-81, RES MGR, DEPT RES & DEVELOP, AM TOBACCO CO, 81- *Mem:* AAAS. *Res:* Development of analytical methods for biological materials and chemical compounds associated with tobacco and tobacco smoke using wet-chemistry combined with instrumental techniques such as gas chromatography, spectroscopy and ion-selective electrodes. *Mailing Add:* Am Tobacco Co PO Box 899 Hopewell VA 23860

PRICE, CHARLES COALE, b Passaic, NJ, July 13, 13; m 36; c 5. ORGANIC CHEMISTRY. *Educ:* Swarthmore Col, BA, 34; Harvard Univ, MA, 35, PhD(chem), 36. *Hon Degrees:* DSc, Swarthmore Col, 50, Case Inst Technol, 65, La Salle Col, 75 & Rensselaer Polytech Inst, 77; DHL, Wilkes Col, 64; LLD, Haverford Col, 66. *Prof Exp:* From asst to assoc prof chem, Univ Ill, 36-46; prof & head dept, Univ Notre Dame, 46-54; Blanchard prof, 54-66, dept dir, 54-65, univ prof, 66-78, EMER PROF CHEM, UNIV PA, 78- *Concurrent Pos:* Vis lectr, Polytech Inst Brooklyn, 45; mem qm corps subcomt plastics, Nat Res Coun, 47-51; mem div comt math, phys & eng sci, NSF, 51-55, chmn, 53-55. *Honors & Awards:* Award, Am Chem Soc, 46. *Mem:* AAAS (vpres chem div, 71); Am Chem Soc (pres, 65). *Res:* Epoxide polymerization; thiabenzenes; sulfur chemistry; nucleic acid and protein alkylation. *Mailing Add:* Dept of Chem Univ of Pa Philadelphia PA 19104

PRICE, CHARLES MORTON, b Chicago, Ill, Apr 12, 26; m 51; c 3. MATHEMATICS. *Educ:* Univ Chicago, BPh & BS, 44, MS, 47, PhD(math), 50. *Prof Exp:* Instr math, Ill Inst Technol, 46-53; supvr design anal, NAm Aviation, Inc, 53-61; HEAD SATELLITE NAVIG DEPT, AEROSPACE CORP, 61- *Concurrent Pos:* Sr mathematician, Inst Air Weapons Res, 47-53. *Mem:* Am Math Soc; Soc Indust & Appl Math; Am Inst Aeronaut & Astronaut. *Res:* Orbit determination and prediction; atmosphere and gravitational potential of the earth; optimal filtering theory; matrix theory; numerical and operations analysis; technical management. *Mailing Add:* Satellite Navig Dept Aerospace Corp PO Box 95085 Los Angeles CA 90045

PRICE, CHARLES R(ONALD), b Wolfe, WVa, Sept 17, 32; m 61; c 2. CHEMICAL ENGINEERING. *Educ:* Va Polytech Inst, BS, 53, MS, 56, PhD(chem eng), 58. *Prof Exp:* Asst plant mgr, Southern Cotton Oil Co, Ga, 53-56; design engr, Union Carbide Chem Co Div, Union Carbide Corp, 56-58; res engr, E I du Pont de Nemours & Co, 58-62, tech investr econ eval, 62-63; sr res engr, 63-71, TECH DIR CLAY DIV, RES DEPT, J M HUBER CORP, 71- *Mem:* Am Chem Soc; Am Inst Chem Engrs; Can Pulp & Paper Asn; Am Ceramic Soc; Tech Asn Pulp & Paper Indust. *Res:* Characterization of molecular sieves; processing of highly viscous liquids; cellulosic and plastic films development; economic evaluations; carbon black process and product development; research and development activity with clay products and processes. *Mailing Add:* J M Huber Corp Rte 4 Huber Macon GA 31201

PRICE, DAVID ALAN, b New York, NY, July 16, 48; m 74; c 2. PHYSIOLOGY. *Educ:* Cooper Union, BS, 70; Fla State Univ, PhD(molecular biophys), 77. *Prof Exp:* Res assoc, Fla State Univ, 75-81; RES ASSOC, C V WHITNEY LAB, UNIV FLA, 81- *Mem:* Am Soc Zoologists; Soc Neurosci; Sigma Xi. *Res:* Neuropeptides; neural communication. *Mailing Add:* C V Whitney Lab Univ Fla Rte 1 Box 121 St Augustine FL 32084

PRICE, DAVID C, b Toronto, Ont, July 3, 34; m 59; c 2. NUCLEAR MEDICINE, HEMATOLOGY. *Educ:* Univ Toronto, MD, 58; FRCP(C), 64. *Prof Exp:* Res assoc, Med Res Ctr, Brookhaven Nat Lab, 60-62; Med Res Coun Can fel, Donner Lab, Univ Calif, Berkeley, 65-66; scientist, Lawrence Radiation Lab, 67; asst prof, 68-74, ASSOC PROF RADIOL & MED, SCH MED, UNIV CALIF, SAN FRANCISCO, 75- *Mem:* AAAS; Am Soc Hemat; Soc Nuclear Med. *Res:* Hematologic applications of radioisotopes; iron kinetics; vitamin B-12 metabolism; isotopic imaging devices; whole body counting; experimental hematology, particularly radiation effects on bone marrow. *Mailing Add:* Nuclear Med Lab 4555 Univ of Calif Hosps & Clins San Francisco CA 94143

PRICE, DAVID EDGAR, b San Diego, Calif, July 5, 14; m 36; c 2. PUBLIC HEALTH ADMINISTRATION. *Educ:* Univ Calif, AB, 36, MA, 37, MD, 40; Johns Hopkins Univ, MPH, 45, DrPH, 46; Am Bd Prev Med, dipl, 50. *Prof Exp:* Med intern, USPHS, DC, 40-41, epidemiologist, San Diego City & County Health Dept, 41-42, staff physician, Venereal Dis Ctr, Ark, 42-44, fever therapy trainee & clin dir, 44; Rockefeller Found fel, Johns Hopkins Univ, 44-46; asst to chief, Res Grants Div, NIH, 46-47, chief cancer res grants br, Nat Cancer Inst, 47-48, chief div res grants & fels, NIH, 48-50, assoc dir, 50-52, asst surgeon gen, 52-57, dep chief bur med serv, 57, chief bur state serv, 57-60, dep dir, NIH, 60-62, dep surgeon gen, USPHS, 62-65; consult, Ford Found, India, 65-67; dir planning, Med Insts, 67-75, prof pub health admin, 67-80, dir res progs, 75-80, EMER PROF HEALTH SERV ADMIN & DIV PUB HEALTH ADMIN, JOHNS HOPKINS UNIV, 80- *Res:* Experimental and pituitary endocrinology; population; family planning. *Mailing Add:* Johns Hopkins Univ 720 Rutland Ave Baltimore MD 21205

PRICE, DAVID LONG, b London, Eng, Jan 17, 40; m 66; c 2. SOLID STATE PHYSICS. *Educ:* Cambridge Univ, BA, 61, PhD(physics), 66. *Prof Exp:* Res assoc physics, Brookhaven Nat Lab, 66-68; asst physicist, 68-71, assoc physicist, 71-74, dir, Solid State Sci Div, 74-79, dir, Intense Pulsed Neutron Source Prog, 79-81, SR PHYSICIST, ARGONNE NAT LAB, 74- *Mem:* Am Phys Soc. *Res:* Solid and liquid state physics; neutron scattering. *Mailing Add:* Solid State Sci Div Argonne Nat Lab Argonne IL 60439

PRICE, DAVID THOMAS, b Chicago, Ill, Nov 21, 43; m 69. ALGEBRA. *Educ:* Calif Inst Technol, BS, 65; Univ Chicago, MS, 67, PhD(math), 71. *Prof Exp:* Asst prof, 69-74, assoc prof, 74-80, PROF MATH, WHEATON COL, 80- *Concurrent Pos:* Consult software, Western Elec Corp, 80- *Mem:* Math Asn Am; Am Math Soc; Asn Comput Mach. *Res:* Nilpotent rings, finite groups. *Mailing Add:* Dept Math Wheaton Col Wheaton IL 60187

PRICE, DON, b Salt Lake City, Utah, May 12, 29. HYDROLOGY, GEOLOGY. *Educ:* Univ Utah, BS, 56. *Prof Exp:* Geologist hydrol, 56-67, HYDROLOGIST, US GEOL SURV, 67- *Honors & Awards:* Spec Achievement Award, US Bur Land Mgt, 76. *Mem:* Geol Soc Am; Asn Eng Geologists. *Res:* Areal water resources appraisals; sources, occurrence, uses, quality, development options and impacts from energy development. *Mailing Add:* US Geol Surv 1740 W 1700 So Salt Lake City UT 84104

PRICE, DONALD ALBERT, b Bridgeport, Ohio, Dec 25, 19; m 52; c 3. VETERINARY MEDICINE. *Educ:* Ohio State Univ, DVM, 50. *Prof Exp:* Assoc vet, Agr Exp Sta, Agr & Mech Col Tex, 50-55; co-owner, San Angelo Vet Hosp, Tex, 55-58; assoc ed, 58-59, ed-in-chief jours, 59-72, EXEC VPRES, AM VET MED ASN, 72- *Mem:* Am Vet Med Asn; Am Soc Asn Execs; Am Med Writers Asn; Am Asn Equine Practitioners; Am Animal Hosp Asn. *Res:* Animal disease investigation, with emphasis on diseases of sheep and Angora goats in southwestern United States. *Mailing Add:* Am Vet Med Asn 930 N Meacham Rd Schaumburg IL 60196

PRICE, DONALD RAY, b Rockville, Ind, July 20, 39; m 63; c 3. ENGINEERING, AGRICULTURE. *Educ:* Purdue Univ, BS, 61, PhD(agr eng), 71; Cornell Univ, MS, 63. *Prof Exp:* Test engr hydraul, Int Harvester Co, 60-61; exten specialist agr eng, Cornell Univ, 62-63, asst prof, 63-69, assoc prof, 69-77, prof & dir energy progs, 77-80; PROF & ASST DEAN, UNIV FLA, 80- *Concurrent Pos:* NY Farm Electrification res grant, Cornell Univ, 64-72; proj leader, NY Farm Electrification Coun, 64-72; owner, Price Assocs Consult, 68-72; Northeast rep, Nat Food & Energy Coun, 75-; prog mgr, US Dept of Energy, 77-78; consult, President Carter's Reorgn Proj, 78- *Mem:* Am Soc Agr Engrs; Illum Eng Soc. *Res:* Systems engineering; environmental quality; electric power and processing; environmental control; thermal pollution. *Mailing Add:* McCarth Hall West Univ Fla Gainesville FL 32611

PRICE, DONNA, b Baltimore, Md, Oct 23, 13. PHYSICAL CHEMISTRY, EXPLOSIVES. *Educ:* Goucher Col, AB, 34; Cornell Univ, PhD(phys chem), 37. *Hon Degrees:* DSc, Goucher Col, 74. *Prof Exp:* Instr chem, Rockford Col, 38-40; Berliner fel, Radcliffe Col, 40-41; fel, Univ Chicago, 42; res chemist, Hercules Powder Co, Del, 42-48; sr scientist, 49-71, actg chief phys chem div, 61-62, SR RES SCIENTIST, EXPLOSIVES DIV, NAVAL SURFACE WEAPONS CTR, WHITE OAK LAB, 71- *Concurrent Pos:* Consult, Am Marietta Co, 55 & Spec Proj Off & Armed Serv Explosives Safety Bd, 61-; lectr explosives, Brit Ministry of Supply, 59; mem ad hoc comts on safety, US Air Force; mem, Fourth Detonation Symp Comn, 65, Fifth, 70; mem propellant hazard assessment panel, Strategic Systs Proj Off, Navy, Dept of Defense, 72- *Honors & Awards:* Fliedner Trophy Award, US Bur Naval Weapons, 62. *Mem:* Am Chem Soc; Combustion Inst; Am Phys Soc. *Res:* Characterization of explosives; thermodynamics of dense gases and of explosives; sensitivity of explosives and propellants. *Mailing Add:* 3706 Manor Rd Chevy Chase MD 20815

PRICE, EDWARD HECTOR, b Baltimore, Md, Nov 25, 20; m 45; c 3. ORGANIC CHEMISTRY. *Educ:* Univ Md, BS, 42, PhD(org chem), 49. *Prof Exp:* Res chemist, 49-57, supvr plants technol, 57-59, sr supvr res & develop, 59-66, lab mgr, 66-70, res mgr, 70-77, RES MFG MGR, PLASTICS PROD DIV, PLASTICS DEPT, E I DU PONT DE NEMOURS & CO, INC, 78- *Mem:* Electrochem Soc; Am Chem Soc; Sigma Xi. *Res:* Podophyllotoxin; polymer and fluorochemical chemistry and electrochemical membranes; process product development; research management. *Mailing Add:* Polymer Prod Dept Exp Sta E I du Pont de Nemours & Co Inc Wilmington DE 19898

PRICE, EDWARD WARREN, b Detroit, Mich, Dec 6, 20; m 51; c 3. COMBUSTION, ROCKET PROPULSION. *Educ:* Univ Calif, Los Angeles, BA, 48. *Prof Exp:* Ord engr rocket propulsion, Calif Inst Technol, 41-44 & US Naval Ord Test Sta, 44-46, physicist gas dynamics, 48-56, head gas dynamics br, 56-57, head aerothermochem group, 57-60, head, Aerothermochem Div, 60-74; PROF AEROSPACE ENG, GA INST TECHNOL, 74- *Concurrent Pos:* Lectr, Univ Conn, 58-64; prof aerospace eng, Ga Inst Technol, 67-68. *Honors & Awards:* L T E Thompson Award, US Navy, 60, Super Civilian Serv Award, 74; Dryden Res Award, Am Inst Aeronaut & Astronaut, 67, G Edward Pendray Award, 71, R H Goddard Award, 76. *Mem:* Fel Am Inst Aeronaut & Astronaut; Int Combustion Inst; AAAS. *Res:* High temperature gas dynamics; combustion and rocket propulsion; solid rocket propellant combustion; combustor instability. *Mailing Add:* Sch Aerospace Eng Ga Inst Technol Atlanta GA 30332

PRICE, ELTON, b Pitt Co, NC, Feb 5, 33; m 55; c 3. PHYSICAL CHEMISTRY. *Educ:* Howard Univ, BS, 54; Yale Univ, MS, 56; Boston Univ, PhD(chem), 61. *Prof Exp:* Lab asst chem, Yale Univ, 54-56; fel, Pa State Univ, 60-62; mem tech staff, Bell Tel Labs, 62-64; from asst prof to assoc prof, 64-71, PROF CHEM, HOWARD UNIV, 71- *Mem:* Am Chem Soc. *Res:* Chemical kinetics; application of nuclear magnetic resonance techniques to study relaxation phenomena of molecules in the liquid and solid states. *Mailing Add:* Dept of Chem Howard Univ Washington DC 20001

PRICE, FRANK DUBOIS, b Peterborough, NH, May 16, 40; m 63; c 2. DIELECTRIC MATERIALS, ELECTRICAL ENGINEERING. *Educ:* Bucknell Univ, BS, 62; Utah State Univ, MS, 66. *Prof Exp:* Instr electronics, Rangely Jr Col, 64-65; advan prod engr, 66-73, mgr design & prod engr, 73-74, mgr eng, 74-77, MGR CAPACITATOR TECHNOL CTR, GEN ELEC CO, 77- *Mem:* Electronics Industs Asn. *Res:* Solid and liquid dielectric behavior; chemical and physical dielectric breakdown mechanisms; materials development; product reliability analysis relating to capacitators and their applications. *Mailing Add:* Capacitator Technol Ctr John St Hudson Falls NY 12839

PRICE, FREDERICK WILLIAM, b London, Eng, Mar 4, 32. MOLECULAR BIOLOGY, BIOCHEMISTRY. *Educ:* Univ Bristol, BSc, 53; Univ London, PhD(biochem), 63. *Prof Exp:* Chemist, Int Chem Co, Eng, 56-57; res assoc enzyme assay, Brit Empire Cancer Campaign Unit, Dept Zool, King's Col, Univ London, 57-62; res assoc, Dept Biochem Pharmacol, State Univ NY Buffalo, 63-64; cancer res scientist, Viral Oncol Dept, Roswell Park Mem Inst, 64-67; assoc prof biol, 67-74, NSF grant, 72-73, PROF BIOL, STATE UNIV NY COL BUFFALO, 74- *Mem:* AAAS; Brit Astron Asn; Nat Asn Biol Teachers. *Res:* Reactions of carbohydrates with cuprammonium compounds; spectrophotometric methods of enzyme assay; toxohormone; precipitation reactions in biocolloids; methods of biochemical analysis. *Mailing Add:* Dept of Biol 1300 Elmwood Ave Buffalo NY 14222

PRICE, GLENN ALBERT, b Minn, Feb 9, 23; m 50; c 4. ACADEMIC ADMINISTRATION, REACTOR PHYSICS. *Educ:* Univ Ky, BS, 46; Univ Ill, MS, 48, PhD(physics), 52. *Prof Exp:* Assoc physicist, 52-58, PHYSICIST, BROOKHAVEN NAT LAB, 58-, HEAD, OFF ACAD RELS, 73- *Concurrent Pos:* Vis scientist, Atomic Energy Res Estab-Harwell, 58-59; consult, India AEC, 67. *Mem:* Am Phys Soc; Am Nuclear Soc. *Res:* Photoneutrons; reactor physics. *Mailing Add:* Brookhaven Nat Lab Upton NY 11973

PRICE, GRIFFITH BALEY, b Brookhaven, Miss, Mar 14, 05; m 40; c 6. MATHEMATICS. *Educ:* Miss Col, AB, 25; Harvard Univ, MA, 28, PhD(math), 32. *Hon Degrees:* LLD, Miss Col, 62. *Prof Exp:* Instr math, Miss Col, 25-26 & 29-30, Union Univ, NY, 32-33, Univ Rochester, 33-36 & Brown Univ, 36-37; from asst prof to prof, 37-75, chmn dept, 51-70, EMER PROF MATH, UNIV KANS, 75- *Concurrent Pos:* Guggenheim fel, 46-47; ed bull, Am Math Soc, 50-57; chmn comt regional develop math, Nat Res Coun, 52-54; vis prof, Calif Inst Technol, 59-60; exec secy, Conf Bd Math Sci, Washington, DC, 60-62; mem, US Nat Comn, UNESCO, 61-66; trustee, Argonne Univs Asn, 65-69; vis prof, Univ Western Australia, Perth, 75; consult, Orgn Am States, 78. *Honors & Awards:* Math Asn Am Award, 70. *Mem:* Am Math Soc (assoc secy, 44 & 46-49); Nat Coun Teachers Math; Math Asn Am (vpres, 55-56, pres, 57-58); Inst Math Statist; NY Acad Sci. *Res:* Analysis. *Mailing Add:* Dept Math Univ Kans Lawrence KS 66045

PRICE, HAROLD ANTHONY, b Glenwood, Minn, May 27, 19; m 52. ANALYTICAL CHEMISTRY. *Educ:* Univ Ill, BS, 45; Ind Univ, AM, 46; Purdue Univ, PhD(chem), 50. *Prof Exp:* Asst prof res, Mich State Univ, 50-57; res chemist, Dow Chem Co, 57-63; lab mgr, Allied Paper Corp, 64-65; CHIEF, ENVIRON EPIDEMIOL LAB, MICH DEPT PUB HEALTH, 65- *Mem:* Am Chem Soc. *Res:* Polyolefins; pesticide residue analysis and industrial chemical residue analysis in biological systems. *Mailing Add:* PO Box 30035 Mich Dept Pub Health Lansing MI 48909

PRICE, HAROLD JAMES, b Bremerton, Wash, Oct 7, 43; m 66; c 2. PLANT EVOLUTION, PLANT CYTOGENETICS. *Educ:* Western Wash State Col, BA, 65; Brigham Young Univ, MS, 67; Univ Calif, Davis, PhD(genetics), 70. *Prof Exp:* Res assoc, Brookhaven Nat Lab, 70-72; asst prof biol, Fla Technol Univ, 72-74; ASSOC PROF GENETICS, TEX A&M UNIV, 75- *Mem:* Genetics Soc Am; Bot Soc Am; Soc Study Evolution; Sigma Xi. *Res:* Plant evolution and cytogenetics, with emphasis on the interactions of DNA content and genotype on plant development and evolution. *Mailing Add:* Dept Plant Sci Tex A&M Univ College Station TX 77843

PRICE, HAROLD M, b Chicago, Ill, Aug 24, 31; m 54; c 4. PATHOLOGY. *Educ:* Univ Southern Calif, BA, 53, MD, 57; Am Bd Path, dipl; Univ Pittsburgh, MPH, 73. *Prof Exp:* Intern, Univ Hosps, Cleveland, 57-58; resident path, Western Reserve Univ, 58-61; USPHS fel, Brain Res Inst, Univ Calif, Los Angeles, 61-62; pathologist, Armed Forces Inst Path, 62-64; resident clin path, Walter Reed Hosp, 64-65; pathologist, Armed Forces Inst Path, 65-67; assoc prof path, Sch Med, Univ Pittsburgh, 67-78; pathologist, Magee-Womens Hosp, 67-78; DIR ANATOMIC PATH, VALLEY MED CTR, FRESNO, 78-; ASSOC CLIN PROF PATH, SCH MED, UNIV CALIF, SAN FRANCISCO, 78- *Mem:* AAAS; fel Soc Clin Path; Am Asn Pathologists; fel Col Am Pathologists; NY Acad Sci. *Res:* Disorders affecting skeletal, cardiac and smooth muscle; electron microscopy. *Mailing Add:* Dept of Path Valley Med Ctr Fresno CA 93702

PRICE, HARRY JAMES, b Reading, Pa, June 1, 41; m 64; c 4. INORGANIC CHEMISTRY. *Educ:* Univ Rochester, BS, 63; Stanford Univ, PhD(inorg chem), 67. *Prof Exp:* RES ASSOC, RES LABS, EASTMAN KODAK CO, 66- *Mem:* Am Chem Soc; Soc Photog Sci & Eng. *Res:* Mechanisms of inorganic electron transfer reactions; photographic processing chemistry; silver halide surface chemistry. *Mailing Add:* Res Labs Eastman Kodak Co Rochester NY 14650

PRICE, HARVEY SIMON, b Pittsburgh, Pa, Aug 17, 35; m 56; c 3. APPLIED MATHEMATICS. *Educ:* Cornell Univ, BS, 58; Case Western Reserve Univ, PhD(math), 65. *Prof Exp:* Res mathematician, Gulf Res & Develop Co, 58-61; res asst math, Case Western Reserve Univ, 62-63; res mathematician, Gulf Res & Develop Co, 63-65, sr res mathematician, 65, sect supvr reservoir eng, 65-68, mgr systs develop & appln, Comput & Commun Serv Dept, Gulf Oil Corp, Pa, 68-70; vpres, 70-78, exec vpres, 78-80, pres, Enhanced Energy Resources, 80-82, EXEC VPRES & CORP DIR, INTERCOMP RESOURCE DEVELOP & ENG INC, 82- *Mem:* Am Math Soc; Asn Comput Mach; Am Inst Mining, Metall & Petrol Eng; Soc Indust & Appl Math. *Res:* Reservoir engineering; numerical solution of partial differential equations arising from the simulation of fluid flow in porous media; development of mathematical models simulating all phases of oil recovery. *Mailing Add:* Intercomp 1201 Dairy Ashford Rd Houston TX 77079

PRICE, HENRY LOCHER, b Philadelphia, Pa, Oct 21, 22; m 53; c 2. PHARMACOLOGY, ANESTHESIOLOGY. *Educ:* Swarthmore Col, AB, 45; Univ Pa, MD, 46; Am Bd Anesthesiol, dipl, 53. *Prof Exp:* Chief oper room sect, Tripler Gen Hosp, 49-50; from instr to res assoc anesthesiol, Sch Med, Univ Pa, 50-52; Nat Res Coun fel med sci, Harvard Med Sch, 52-53; from asst prof to prof anesthesiol, Sch Med, Univ Pa, 53-70; prof, Sch Med, Temple Univ, 70-71; chmn dept, 71-78, PROF ANESTHESIOL, HAHNEMANN MED COL, 71- *Concurrent Pos:* Mem comt anesthesia, Nat Res Coun, 59-66; NIH fel, Univ Calif, San Francisco, 60-61; prin investr, USPHS Grants; mem clin res training comn, Nat Inst Gen Med Sci, 63-65 & 66-67, mem nat anesthesiol training comn, 66-67; consult, US Naval & Vet Admin Hosps, Philadelphia. *Mem:* Am Soc Clin Invest; Sigma Xi; Am Physiol Soc; Am Soc Pharmacol; Am Soc Anesthesiol. *Res:* Applied physiology; pharmacology of anesthetic agents. *Mailing Add:* Dept of Anesthesiol Hahnemann Med Col Philadelphia PA 19102

PRICE, HOWARD CHARLES, b South Gibson, Pa, Feb 26, 42; m 67; c 2. BIOCHEMISTRY, ORGANIC CHEMISTRY. *Educ:* Dickinson Col, BS, 63; State Univ NY Binghamton, PhD(org chem), 71. *Prof Exp:* NIH fel, Dept Neurol, Albert Einstein Col Med, Yeshiva Univ, 70-71; from asst prof to assoc prof chem, Marshall Univ, 71-81; MEM STAFF ADVAN TECHNOL, ZIMMER, INC, 81- *Mem:* Am Chem Soc; AAAS; Sigma Xi; Soc Plastic Engrs. *Res:* Synthesis, chiroptical phenomena and biochemistry of aromatic amino acid analogues; isolation and structure determination of gangliosides; neurochemistry; medical polymers. *Mailing Add:* Advan Technol Zimmer Inc PO Box 708 Warsaw IN 46580

PRICE, HUGH CRISWELL, b Newark, Ohio, Nov 1, 39; m 65; c 2. HORTICULTURE. *Educ:* Ohio State Univ, BS, 61; Univ Del, MS, 66; Mich State Univ, PhD(hort), 69. *Prof Exp:* Biologist herbicide res, Am Cyanamid Co, 69-71; asst prof, 71-74, assoc prof, 74-80, PROF HORT, MICH STATE UNIV, 80- *Mem:* Am Soc Hort Sci; Sigma Xi. *Res:* Growth and development of vegetable crops. *Mailing Add:* Dept of Hort Mich State Univ East Lansing MI 48824

PRICE, JACK D, biochemistry, nutrition, see previous edition

PRICE, JAMES CLARENCE, b London, Ark, Nov 20, 32; m 61; c 4. PHARMACY. *Educ:* Univ Ark, BS, 53; Univ Utah, MS, 57; Univ RI, PhD(pharm), 63. *Prof Exp:* From instr to assoc prof pharm, Univ RI, 61-68; ASSOC PROF PHARM, UNIV GA, 68- *Mem:* Am Pharmaceut Asn; Acad Pharmaceut Sci. *Res:* Microencapsulation; tablet technology; suspension-emulsion stability. *Mailing Add:* Sch of Pharm Univ of Ga Athens GA 30602

PRICE, JAMES F, b Columbia, Tenn, Apr 13, 32; m 59; c 2. FOOD SCIENCE. *Educ:* Univ Tenn, BS, 54; Mich State Univ, MS, 56, PhD(animal sci), 60. *Prof Exp:* Specialist livestock & meat mkt, USDA, 56; asst prof animal sci, Auburn Univ, 60-62; asst prof food sci, 63-77, PROF FOOD SCI & HUMAN NUTRIT, MICH STATE UNIV, 77- *Mem:* Am Soc Animal Sci; Am Meat Sci Asn; Inst Food Technol. *Res:* Body composition of meat animals; post mortem changes in muscle; meat processing, preservation and microbiology-technologies; improve utilization and value of undesirable fish. *Mailing Add:* Dept of Food Sci & Human Nutrit Mich State Univ East Lansing MI 48823

PRICE, JAMES FELIX, b Hartselle, Ala, June 17, 47; m 68; c 2. ENTOMOLOGY. *Educ:* Univ Fla, BS, 72, MS, 74; Clemson Univ, PhD(entom), 77. *Prof Exp:* ASST PROF ENTOM, UNIV FLA, 78- *Mem:* Entom Soc Am; Sigma Xi. *Res:* Biological, cultural and chemical control of insects and mites; ecology of arthropod populations; ornamental entomology; apiculture. *Mailing Add:* Agr Res & Educ Ctr 5007 60th St E Bradenton FL 33508

PRICE, JAMES FRANKLIN, physical oceanography, see previous edition

PRICE, JAMES GORDON, b Brush, Colo, June 20, 26; m 49; c 4. MEDICINE. *Educ:* Univ Colo, BA, 47, MD, 51; Am Bd Family Med, dipl. *Prof Exp:* Intern, Denver Gen Hosp, 51-52; assoc clin instr med, Sch Med, Univ Colo, 67-79; ASSOC PROF FAMILY PRACT, UNIV KANS MED CTR, 80- *Concurrent Pos:* Pvt pract gen med, Brush, Colo, 52-78; trustee, Family Health Found & Univ Colo Med Develop Fund. *Mem:* Inst of Med of Nat Acad Sci; fel Am Acad Family Physicians (pres-elect, 72, pres, 73). *Mailing Add:* Univ Kans Med Ctr 39th & Rainbow Blvd Kansas City KS 66103

PRICE, JERRY L(OYD), b Dallas, Tex, Jan 12, 27; m 49; c 4. CHEMICAL ENGINEERING. *Educ:* Okla Agr & Mech Col, BSCE, 50, MSCE, 57. *Prof Exp:* Res engr, Monsanto Chem Co, 51-58, res group leader bench unit chem eng, 58-61, res group leader tech serv, Vinyl Chloride Plant, 61-66, group supvr styrene process eng, 66-68, group supvr pilot plant acetic acid process develop, 68-70, group supvr acetic acid process improv, Tech Serv, 70-77, group supvr process develop bench unit cumeme, 78-79, group supvr process develop styrene, 80-81, TECHNOL CONSULT, PROCESS TECHNOL DEPT, MONSANTO CO, 81- *Mem:* Am Inst Chem Engrs. *Res:* Process development on bench scale and pilot plant level; fluidization; oxidative chlorination of ethylene; purification techniques; operation and automation of small equipment; computer applications; statistical design of experiments. *Mailing Add:* 122 22nd Ave N Texas City TX 77590

PRICE, JESSIE ISABEL, veterinary microbiology, see previous edition

PRICE, JOHN AVNER, b Ogdensburg, NY, July 13, 32; m 53; c 3. ORGANIC CHEMISTRY, CHEMICAL ENGINEERING. *Educ:* St Lawrence Univ, BS, 53; Univ Rochester, PhD(org chem), 57. *Prof Exp:* Res chemist elastomers, E I du Pont de Nemours & Co, Inc, 56-58; res chemist, 58-70, res assoc & group head new prod, 70-76, SECT HEAD INFO TECHNOL, EXXON RES & ENG CO, 76- *Concurrent Pos:* NSF grant, 77-78. *Mem:* Am Chem Soc; Am Inst Chem Engrs; Am Petrol Inst. *Res:* Management, administration and the innovation of information technology; mini-computers, distributed processing, micrographics, information networking. *Mailing Add:* Exxon Res & Eng Co PO Box 101 Florham Park NJ 07932

PRICE, JOHN CHARLES, b Chicago, Ill, Feb 9, 37; m 62; c 2. REMOTE SENSING, METEOROLOGY. *Educ:* Calif Inst Technol, BS, 59; Univ Calif, Berkeley, PhD(plasma physics), 66. *Prof Exp:* Aerospace scientist, Theoret Studies Br, NASA Goddard Space Flight Ctr, 66-71, Aerospace scientist, Lab Meteorol & Earth Sci, 71-80; PHYSICIST, HYDROL LAB, BELTSVILLE AGR RES CTR, USDA, 80- *Concurrent Pos:* Proj scientist, Heat Capacity Mapping Mission, 76-80. *Mem:* Am Phys Soc; Am Geophys Union; Am Soc Photo Eng. *Res:* Plasma kinetic theory; fluid mechanics; atmospheric radiative transfer; remote sensing. *Mailing Add:* 707 Orchard Way Silver Springs MD 20904

PRICE, JOHN DAVID EWART, b Kingswood, Eng, Apr 26, 27; Can citizen; m 58; c 5. INTERNAL MEDICINE. *Educ:* McGill Univ, BSc, 50, MD, CM, 54; FRCPS(C), 61. *Prof Exp:* Can Life Ins fel, 57-58, from instr to assoc prof, 61-73, PROF MED, UNIV BC, 73- *Concurrent Pos:* Mem attend staff internal med, Vancouver Gen Hosp, 61- *Mem:* Fel Am Col Physicians; Am Soc Artificial Internal Organs; Can Soc Clin Invest; Can Soc Nephrology (pres); Am Soc Nephrology. *Res:* Renal disease; physiology, natural history and the treatment of medical diseases of the kidney; design, application and biochemistry of artificial kidneys. *Mailing Add:* 10th & Health Univ of BC Vancouver BC V6T 1W5 Can

PRICE, JOSEPH EARL, b Denver, Colo, Sept 23, 30; m 63; c 2. PHYSICS, MICROCOMPUTER USAGE. *Educ:* Colo Col, BS, 52; Rice Univ, MS, 54, PhD(physics), 56. *Prof Exp:* Asst prof physics, Lamar State Col, 56-59; from asst prof to assoc prof, 59-67, chmn dept, 66-72, PROF PHYSICS, IDAHO STATE UNIV, 67-, CHMN DEPT, 77- *Honors & Awards:* Perkins Prize, Colo Col. *Mem:* Am Phys Soc; Sigma Xi; Am Asn Physics Teachers. *Res:* Use of computers in teaching situations; nuclear physics; programming microcomputers in assembler language for teaching and interfacing situations. *Mailing Add:* Dept of Physics Idaho State Univ Pocatello ID 83201

PRICE, JOSEPH LEVERING, b Ala, Oct 17, 42; m 67; c 3. ANATOMY, NEUROSCIENCE. *Educ:* Univ of the South, BA, 63; Oxford Univ, BA, 66, DPhil(anat), 69. *Prof Exp:* From instr to asst prof anat, 69-76, ASSOC PROF ANAT & NEUROBIOL, SCH MED, WASHINGTON UNIV, 76- *Concurrent Pos:* USPHS res grant, 70- *Honors & Awards:* C J Herrick Award Neuroanatomy, 73. *Mem:* Am Asn Anat; Soc Neurosci. *Res:* Neuroanatomy; structure, organization and development of the cerebral cortex, with special reference to the olfactory system. *Mailing Add:* Dept Anat & Neurobiol Wash Univ Sch Med 660 S Euclid Ave St Louis MO 63110

PRICE, KEITH ROBINSON, b Oxnard, Calif, Nov 24, 30; m 58; c 4. PLANT ECOLOGY, RADIOECOLOGY. *Educ:* Univ Calif, Davis, BS, 58; Wash State Univ, PhD(bot), 65. *Prof Exp:* Asst prof bot, Univ Nev, Reno, 64-68; mgr soil relationships sect, Pac Northwest Labs, Battelle Mem Inst, 68-71, sr res scientist, 71-74; staff environ scientist, Atlantic Richfield Hanford Co, 74-78; SR RES SCIENTIST, PAC NORTHWEST LAB, BATTELLE MEM INST, 78- *Mem:* AAAS; Am Inst Biol Sci; Ecol Soc Am; Health Physics Soc; Sigma Xi. *Res:* Behavior of radionuclides important to radioactive waste management in plants and soils; environmental management; environmental surveillance of radioactive and nonradioactive waste materials. *Mailing Add:* Battelle Northwest PO Box 999 Richland WA 99352

PRICE, KENNETH ELBERT, b Cumberland, Md, Aug 12, 26; c 2. CHEMOTHERAPY. *Educ:* Univ Md, BS, 50, MS, 52, PhD(bact), 54. *Prof Exp:* Head dept bact, Agr Res & Develop Ctr, Chas Pfizer & Co, Inc, Ind, 54-60; coordr cancer res prog, 60-65, asst dir microbiol res, 65-70, dir microbiol res, 70-76, ASSOC DIR RES & DEVELOP, BRISTOL LABS, 76- *Concurrent Pos:* Chmn, Gordon Res Conf Med Chem, 77. *Mem:* AAAS; Am Soc Microbiol; NY Acad Sci; Infectious Dis Soc Am. *Res:* Discovery and characterization of antibiotics and other chemotherapeutic and chemoprophylactic agents to be utilized in malignant, immunological and infectious diseases of both animals and man; mode of action of chemotherapeutic agents. *Mailing Add:* Bristol Labs Thompson Rd Syracuse NY 13201

PRICE, KENNETH HUGH, b Greenville, Tex. MATHEMATICS. *Educ:* Univ Tex, Austin, BA, 63, PhD(math), 70. *Prof Exp:* Asst prof, 70-77, ASSOC PROF MATH, STEPHEN F AUSTIN STATE UNIV, 77- *Concurrent Pos:* Software engr, 80-81. *Mem:* AAAS; Am Math Soc; Math Asn Am; Sigma Xi. *Res:* Approximation theory; functional analysis. *Mailing Add:* Dept of Math Stephen F Austin State Univ Nacogdoches TX 75962

PRICE, KENT SPARKS, JR, b Trenton, NJ, Oct 2, 36; m 58; c 2. MARINE BIOLOGY. *Educ:* Univ Md, BS, 59; Univ Del, MS, 61, PhD(zool), 64. *Prof Exp:* Biol aid insecticide toxicity, Patuxent Refuge, US Dept Interior, Md, 59; asst prof biol, Old Dom Col, 64-67; asst prof biol sci & dir field sta, Marine Labs, 67-70, dir, Lewes Field Sta, 67-72, asst dean, Col Marine Studies, 70-72, assoc prof biol sci, 70-80, dir marine adv serv, 71-75, assoc dean, Col Marine Studies & dir, Lewes Marine Studies Ctr, 72-79, ASSOC PROF MARINE STUDIES, UNIV DEL, 80- *Concurrent Pos:* Assoc prog dir fisheries & aquaculture, Off Sea Grant, 79-81. *Res:* Ecology of estuaries; fisheries; water regulation and reproduction in Elasmobrachs; mariculture. *Mailing Add:* Col of Marine Studies Univ Del Box 286 Lewes DE 19958

PRICE, LEONARD, b New Orleans, La, Nov 3, 33. ORGANIC CHEMISTRY. *Educ:* Xavier Univ, La, BS, 57; Univ Notre Dame, PhD(chem), 62. *Prof Exp:* From asst prof to assoc prof, 61-63, PROF CHEM, XAVIER UNIV, LA, 63-, CHMN DEPT, 70- *Concurrent Pos:* Am Chem Soc-Petrol Res Fund fel fundamental res undergrad level, 64-66; NSF fel undergrad res participation proj, 64-65. *Res:* Synthesis of acetylenic amino alcohols and amino ethers. *Mailing Add:* Dept of Chem Xavier Univ New Orleans LA 70125

PRICE, MARTIN BURTON, b New York, NY, June 6, 28; m 48; c 3. ORGANIC CHEMISTRY. *Educ:* Syracuse Univ, BA, 48, MS, 50; Univ Del, PhD, 56. *Prof Exp:* Res chemist, Pa Indust Chem Co, 50-57, group leader, 57-60; res assoc, Celanese Res Co, Celanese Corp, 60, group leader, 60-63, sect head, 63-71, mgr phys chem & prod technol, 71-73; DIR RES & DEVELOP, RELIANCE UNIVERSAL INC, 73- *Mem:* AAAS; Am Chem Soc; Sigma Xi. *Res:* Polymers, preparation and characterization; polyacetals; polyolefins; chemical coatings for wood and metal industries; gas chromatography; ultraviolet light reactions. *Mailing Add:* Reliance Universal Inc 4730 Crittenden Dr Louisville KY 40233

PRICE, MICHAEL GLENDON, b Washington, DC, July 27, 47. ELECTRICAL ENGINEERING. *Educ:* Univ Va, BS & ME, 75, PhD(elec eng), 78. *Prof Exp:* Res engr, Res Labs for Eng Sci, Univ Va, 72-77; anal engr controls & dynamic systs, United Technol Res Ctr, 77-78; SR SCIENTIST, AMECOM DIV, LITTON SYSTS, INC, 78- *Concurrent Pos:* Design engr, Dept Pharmacol, Univ Va, 75-77. *Mem:* Inst Elec & Electronics Engrs; Sigma Xi. *Res:* Modelling and simulation of dynamic physical systems; analysis and synthesis of automatic control systems; acousto/optic wideband receiver development; optical signal processing. *Mailing Add:* 9525 Worrell Ave Seabrook MD 20706

PRICE, PAUL ARMS, b Inglewood, Calif, Apr 17, 42; m 78; c 2. BIOCHEMISTRY. *Educ:* Pomona Col, BA, 64; Rockefeller Univ, PhD(biochem), 68. *Prof Exp:* Asst prof, 68-74, ASSOC PROF BIOL, UNIV CALIF, SAN DIEGO, 75- *Mem:* AAAS; Am Soc Biol Chem; Am Chem Soc; Am Soc Bone & Mineral Res. *Res:* Protein structure and function; chemical modification of proteins; biochemistry of the gamma carboxyglutamic acid containing bone protein and of other mineralized tissue proteins; biochemical and physiological mechanisms of action for vitamin K and vitamin D. *Mailing Add:* Dept Biol Univ Calif at San Diego La Jolla CA 92037

PRICE, PAUL BUFORD, JR, b Memphis, Tenn, Nov 8, 32; m 58; c 4. EXPERIMENTAL PHYSICS. *Educ:* Davidson Col, BS, 54; Univ Va, MS, 56, PhD(physics), 58. *Hon Degrees:* ScD, Davidson Col, 73. *Prof Exp:* Fulbright fel, H H Wills Physics Lab, Bristol Univ, 58-59; NSF fel, Cavendish Lab, Cambridge Univ, 59-60; physicist, Res Lab, Gen Elec Co, 60-65, physicist, Res & Develop Ctr, 65-69; PROF PHYSICS, UNIV CALIF, BERKELEY, 69-, DIR, SPACE SCI LAB, 79- *Concurrent Pos:* Adj prof metall dept, Rensselaer Polytech Inst, 61; vis scientist, Lawrence Radiation Lab, 63; Fulbright sr vis prof, Tata Inst Fundamental Res, India, 65-66; consult, NASA, Lunar Sample Anal Planning Team, 71-72; mem space sci bd, Nat Acad Sci & mem comt space astron & astrophys, 73-76; Guggenheim fel, 76-77. *Honors & Awards:* Co-recipient, Am Nuclear Soc Award, 64 & Ernest O Lawrence Award, AEC, 71; Exceptional Sci Achievement Medal, Nat Aeronaut & Space Admin, 73. *Mem:* Nat Acad Sci; fel Am Phys Soc; fel Am Geophys Union; Am Astron Soc. *Res:* Cosmic rays; solar system physics; nuclear tracks and radiation effects in solids; relativistic heavy ion physics; high energy interactions. *Mailing Add:* Dept Physics Univ Calif Berkeley CA 94720

PRICE, PAUL JAY, b Washington, DC, June 28, 37; m 59; c 3. CELL BIOLOGY. *Educ:* Univ Md, BS, 59; George Washington Univ, MS, 61, PhD(cell biol), 63. *Prof Exp:* Technician, 58-59, supvr tissue cult dept, 59-61, sr investr virus res, 61-65, dir cell & media prod & cell res & develop, 65-69, co-dir & dir, NIH contract, Microbiol Assocs, Inc, 69-78, assoc dir res oncol, 76-78; CO-DIR, HYBRIDOMA LAB, CHIEF CELL CULTURE LAB, CTR INFECTIOUS DIS, CTR DIS CONTROL, 78- *Mem:* AAAS; Tissue Cult Asn; Soc Cryobiol; Am Soc Cell Biol; Am Soc Cancer Res. *Res:* Tumor viruses; tumor cell metabolism; tissue cell physiology; viral-chemical co-carcinogenesis; hybridoma technology. *Mailing Add:* Ctr for Dis Control 1600 Clifton Rd NE Atlanta GA 30333

PRICE, PETER J, b London, Eng, July 29, 24; m 56; c 2. THEORETICAL SOLID STATE PHYSICS. *Educ:* Oxford Univ, BA, 46; Cambridge Univ, PhD, 51. *Prof Exp:* Asst lectr, Univ Southampton, 46-47; Off Naval Res, res asst, Duke Univ, 51-52; mem, Inst Advan Study, 52-53; MEM RES STAFF, IBM CORP, 53- *Mem:* Fel Am Phys Soc. *Res:* Statistical mechanics; solid state physics; computational physics. *Mailing Add:* Watson Res Ctr IBM Corp Yorktown Heights NY 10598

PRICE, PETER WILFRID, b London, Eng, Apr 17, 38; m 68; c 2. ECOLOGY, ENTOMOLOGY. *Educ:* Univ Wales, BSc, 62; Univ NB, MSc, 64; Cornell Univ, PhD(ecol), 70. *Prof Exp:* Res officer entom, Can Dept Fisheries & Forestry, 64-70, res scientist, 70-71; asst prof entom, Univ Ill, Urbana, 71-75, assoc prof, 75-79; ASSOC PROF BIOL, NORTHERN ARIZ UNIV, 80- *Concurrent Pos:* Asst prof, Ill Agr Exp Sta, 74-79; asst entomologist, Ill Natural Hist Surv, 74-79; Guggenheim fel, 77-78. *Mem:* Ecol Soc Am; Brit Ecol Soc; Entom Soc Am; Entom Soc Can; Soc Study Evolution. *Res:* General concepts on the evolutionary biology of parasites, parasite ecology, reproductive strategies of plants and insects, community organization of insects. *Mailing Add:* Dept Biol Sci Box 5640 Northern Ariz Univ Flagstaff AZ 86011

PRICE, PHILIP B, agronomy, horticulture, see previous edition

PRICE, R(OBERT) J(OHN), b Birmingham, Eng, June 10, 36. MATERIALS SCIENCE. *Educ:* Cambridge Univ, BA, 59, PhD(metall), 63. *Prof Exp:* Vis metallurgist, Gen Atomic Div, Gen Dynamics Corp, 62-65; staff mem mat sci, 65-75, SR STAFF SCIENTIST, GEN ATOMIC CO, 75- *Mem:* Am Carbon Soc. *Res:* Structure and properties of carbons, graphites and silicon carbide; neutron irradiation effects in solids; carbonization. *Mailing Add:* Gen Atomic Co Box 81608 San Diego CA 92138

PRICE, RALPH LORIN, b Arco, Idaho, Sept 8, 39; m 64; c 6. FOOD SCIENCE, BIOCHEMISTRY. *Educ:* Brigham Young Univ, BA, 65; Purdue Univ, PhD(food sci), 69. *Prof Exp:* Asst prof food sci, 69-74, ASSOC PROF FOOD SCI, UNIV ARIZ, 74- *Concurrent Pos:* Int adv food technol, Univ

Ariz-Fed Univ Ceara, Brazil, 70-74. *Mem:* Inst Food Technol. *Res:* detoxification and utilization of jojoba seed meal; dehydration of foods using greenhouse-like structures as solar heat collectors; use and technology of the cashew fruit and nut; aflatoxins; mycotoxins. *Mailing Add:* Dept Nutrit & Food Sci Univ Ariz Tucson AZ 85721

PRICE, RAYMOND ALEX, b Winnipeg, Man, Mar 25, 33; m 56; c 3. STRUCTURAL GEOLOGY, TECTONICS. *Educ:* Univ Man, BSc, 55; Princeton Univ, AM, 57, PhD(geol), 58. *Prof Exp:* Geologist, Geol Surv Can, 58-68; assoc prof geol, Queen's Univ, Ont, 68-70, head, Dept Geol Sci, 72-77, prof geol, 70-81; DIR, GEN GEOL SURV, CAN, 81- *Concurrent Pos:* Pres, Inter-Union Comn Lithosphere, Int Coun Sci-Unions; assoc ed, Can Bull Petrol Geol & Geol Soc Am; mem, Can Nat Comt Int Geol Correlation Prog & Int Union Geol Sci; foreign secy, Can Geosci Coun; Killam sr res fel, 78-80. *Mem:* Fel Geol Soc Am; fel Geol Asn Can; Am Asn Petrol Geologists; fel Royal Soc Can; Am Geophys Union. *Res:* Regional geology of southern Canadian Rockies; tectonic evolution of North American Cordillera; nature and significance of variations in tectonic style; mechanics of large-scale thrust faulting. *Mailing Add:* Geol Surv Can 601 Booth St Ottawa ON K1A 0E8 Can

PRICE, RICHARD GRAYDON, b Bartlesville, Okla, Nov 8, 33; m 61; c 2. ENTOMOLOGY. *Educ:* Okla State Univ, BS, 55, MS, 59, PhD(entom), 63. *Prof Exp:* Technologist, Shell Chem Co, NY, 63-64 & SC, 64-65; asst prof, 65-69, assoc prof, 69-78, PROF ENTOM, OKLA STATE UNIV, 78- *Mem:* Entom Soc Am. *Res:* Evaluation of insecticidal, ecological and cultural controls of cotton insects; biology and control of arthropod pests of the home. *Mailing Add:* Dept of Entom Okla State Univ Stillwater OK 74074

PRICE, RICHARD HENRY, b New York, NY, Mar 1, 43. THEORETICAL PHYSICS, ASTROPHYSICS. *Educ:* Cornell Univ, BEng, 65; Calif Inst Technol, PhD(physics), 71. *Prof Exp:* Fel, Calif Inst Technol, 71; asst prof, 71-75, ASSOC PROF PHYSICS, UNIV UTAH, 75- *Concurrent Pos:* Lectr, Fulbright Comn, Nat Seminar Physics, 70 & Inst Cultural Integration, Colombia, 70. *Mem:* AAAS; Am Phys Soc. *Res:* Relativistic astrophysics; black holes; gravitational waves; cosmology; x-ray astronomy. *Mailing Add:* 201 N Physics Bldg Univ of Utah Salt Lake City UT 84112

PRICE, RICHARD MARCUS, b Colorado Springs, Colo, Jan 18, 40; m 68; c 2. ASTRONOMY, PHYSICS EDUCATION. *Educ:* Colo State Univ, BS, 61; Australian Nat Univ, PhD(astron), 66. *Prof Exp:* Vis res officer radiophysics, Radiophysics Lab, Commonwealth Sci & Indust Res Orgn, 61-65; from asst prof to assoc prof physics, Mass Inst Technol, 67-75, staff mem, Res Lab Electronics, 67-75, staff mem, Educ Res Ctr, 69-73; radio spectrum mgr, NSF, 75-77, head, Astron Res Sect, 76-79; PROF & CHMN PHYSICS & ASTRON, UNIV NMEX, 79- *Concurrent Pos:* Vis scientist, Max Planck Inst Radioastron, 70-71; consult, Off Int Progs, NSF, 72-73 & Mass Inst Technol-Del Inst Technol Educ Asn, 72-75; fel, Res Lab Electronics, Mass Inst Technol, 70-71; assoc scientist, Nat Radio Astron Observ, 74-75; Harlow Shapley vis lectr, Am Astron Soc, 74-; NSF rep, Interdept Radio Adv Comt, Off Telecommun, 75-77; mem, Comt on Radio Frequences, Nat Acad Sci, 75-77; mem, US Nat Comt, Union Radio Sci Int, 75-77. *Mem:* Inst Astron Union; Am Astron Soc; NY Acad Sci; Am Asn Physics Teachers; Int Union Radio Sci. *Res:* Galactic structure; radiometer systems; development of undergraduate physics laboratory programs; radio galaxies; nuclei of galaxies; galactic structure; develop of physics and astronomy programs; research administration. *Mailing Add:* Dept Physics & Astron Univ NMex Albuquerque NM 87131

PRICE, ROBERT, b West Chester, Pa, July 7, 29; m 58; c 3. HARDWARE SYSTEMS, COMPUTER SCIENCES. *Educ:* Princeton Univ, AB, 50; Mass Inst Technol, ScD(elec eng), 53. *Prof Exp:* Asst, Res Lab Electronics, Mass Inst Technol, 51-53; Fulbright fel radio astron, Commonwealth Sci & Indust Res Orgn, Sydney, Australia, 53-54; staff mem, Lincoln Lab, Mass Inst Technol, 54-62, 63-65; lectr elec eng, Univ Calif, Berkeley, 62-63; head radar res, 65-67, head systs studies, 67-70, mgr data transmission dept, 70-77, STAFF CONSULT COMMUN SCI, SPERRY RES CTR, 77- *Concurrent Pos:* Dir, Northeast Electronics Res & Eng Meeting, 68-70; mem adv coun, Dept Elec Eng & Comput Sci, Princeton Univ, 71-77 & Franklin Inst. *Mem:* Fel Inst Elec & Electronics Engrs; Sigma Xi. *Res:* Statistical communication and noise theory; signal design and processing with data, sensor and magnetic recording applications; techniques innovation, systems engineering and project consultations in advanced electronics, including spread spectrum communications. *Mailing Add:* Comput Res Lab Sperry Res Ctr North Rd Sudbury MA 01776

PRICE, ROBERT ALLEN, b Chicago, Ill, Sept 4, 34. PEDIATRICS, PATHOLOGY. *Educ:* Univ Ill, Urbana, BS, 57, DVM, 59; Univ Tenn, Memphis, MD, 65. *Prof Exp:* Resident path, Univ Tenn & John Gaston Hosp, Memphis, 66-67; resident, Baptist Mem Hosp, Memphis, 68-69; chief resident, Children's Hosp Med Ctr, Boston, 69-70; asst mem, 71-74, ASSOC MEM PATH, ST JUDE CHILDREN'S RES HOSP, 74- *Concurrent Pos:* Res fel path, Harvard Med Sch, Children's Hosp Med Ctr, Boston & New Eng Regional Primate Res Ctr, Boston, 70; asst clin prof path, Ctr Health Sci, Univ Tenn, 73- *Mem:* Am Asn Cancer Res. *Res:* Pathology of childhood cancer; central nervous system diseases in children with cancer; comparative pathology. *Mailing Add:* Path Lab St Jude Children's Res Hosp Memphis TN 38101

PRICE, ROBERT HAROLD, b Lansing, Mich, Apr 9, 49. PLASMA PHYSICS. *Educ:* Mass Inst Technol, BS, 71, PhD(physics), 77. *Prof Exp:* Res asst high energy particle physics, Univ Md, 66, phys chem, 67, atomic & low temperature physics, Res Lab Electronics, Mass Inst technol, 68, plasma physics, 69-71; res asst physicist, Lawrence Livermore Nat Lab, 71; mem staff laser plasma, Res Lab Electronics, Mass Inst Technol, 71-76; STAFF PHYSICIST PLASMA PHYSICS & X-RAY OPTICS, LAWRENCE LIVERMORE NAT LAB, 76- *Concurrent Pos:* Hertz fel, Fannie & John Hertz Found, Mass Inst Technol, 71-75. *Mem:* Am Phys Soc. *Res:* Development of high resolution x-ray optics and high speed imaging devices to study the dynamics of laser fusion targets using the images produced to study plasma physics under ICF conditions. *Mailing Add:* PO Box 2045 Livermore CA 94550

PRICE, ROGER DEFORREST, b Lawrence, Kans, Aug 4, 29; m 52; c 3. ENTOMOLOGY. *Educ:* Univ Kans, AB, 51, MA, 53, PhD(entom), 55. *Prof Exp:* From instr to assoc prof, 55-70, PROF ENTOM, UNIV MINN, ST PAUL, 70- *Mem:* Entom Soc Am. *Res:* Insect taxonomy, especially chewing lice. *Mailing Add:* Dept Entom Fisheries & Wildlife Univ of Minn St Paul MN 55108

PRICE, SAMUEL, b Burley, Idaho, May 14, 23; m 53; c 3. GENETICS. *Educ:* Utah State Agr Col, BS, 49; Univ Calif, PhD(genetics), 52. *Prof Exp:* Asst bot, Utah State Agr Col, 47-49; asst genetics, Univ Calif, 49-52; asst prof agron, Univ Hawaii, 52-53; geneticist, Crops Res Div, Agr Res Serv, USDA, Md, 53-67; grants assoc, Div Res Grants, NIH, 67-68, health sci adminr, Nat Inst Environ Health Sci, NIH, 68-69, health sci adminr, Nat Eye Inst, 69-70, chief, Sci Progs Br, Nat Eye Inst, 70-71, health sci adminr, Nat Cancer Inst, 71-72, chief Nat Organ Site Progs Br, Nat Cancer Inst, 72-80; RES COORDR, UNIV MD, 80- *Mem:* Am Genetic Asn (treas, 63, pres, 72); Am Soc Human Genetics; Genetics Soc Am. *Res:* Cytogenetics. *Mailing Add:* Univ Md Cent Admin Adelph MD 20783

PRICE, STANLEY JAMES WHITWORTH, physical chemistry, see previous edition

PRICE, STEVEN, b New York, NY, May 13, 37; m 58; c 2. CELL PHYSIOLOGY, SENSORY PHYSIOLOGY. *Educ:* Adelphi Col, AB, 58; Princeton Univ, MA, 60, PhD(biol), 61. *Prof Exp:* Nat Cancer Inst fel chem, Fla State Univ, 61-63; from sr res biologist to res group leader biochem, Boston Lab, Monsanto Res Corp, 63-66; from asst prof to assoc prof, 66-75, PROF PHYSIOL, MED COL VA, 75- *Concurrent Pos:* Nat Inst Dent Res res career develop award, 72-76. *Mem:* Am Physiol Soc; Asn Chemoreception Sci; Europ Chemoreception Res Orgn; Soc Gen Physiologists. *Res:* Receptor mechanisms in taste and smell, including stimulus recognition and transduction; insulin secretion. *Mailing Add:* Dept of Physiol Med Col of Va Richmond VA 23298

PRICE, THOMAS MUNRO, b Madison, Wis, Oct 2, 37; m 59; c 2. COMPUTER PROGRAMMING, TOPOLOGY OF MANIFOLDS. *Educ:* Carroll Col, BS, 59; Univ Wis, MS, 61, PhD(math), 64. *Prof Exp:* From asst prof to prof math, Univ Iowa, 64-77; vis prof, Univ Auckland, 77; vis prof, 78-79, COMPUT USER CONSULT, UNIV WYO, 79- *Concurrent Pos:* Vis prof, Univ Melbourne, 74 & 78 & Univ Adelaide, 75. *Mem:* Am Math Soc; Math Asn Am. *Res:* Topology of manifolds. *Mailing Add:* Div Comput Serv Univ of Wyo Laramie WY 82070

PRICE, THORNTON WALTON, b Summit, NJ, Aug 22, 19; m 43; c 3. MECHANICAL ENGINEERING. *Educ:* Univ Ill, BS, 42, PhD, 52; Lehigh Univ, MS, 50. *Prof Exp:* Asst mech eng, Lehigh Univ, 50; res assoc, Univ Ill, 52, from instr to assoc prof, 52-61; PROF MECH ENG, ARIZ STATE UNIV, 61- *Mem:* Am Soc Mech Engrs; Am Soc Eng Combustion Inst. *Res:* Thermodynamics and power conversion; combustion; design. *Mailing Add:* 336 E Concorda Dr Tempe AZ 85281

PRICE, VANEATON, JR, geology, see previous edition

PRICE, WALTER H(UGH), b Schriever, La, May 10, 07; m 36; c 2. CIVIL ENGINEERING. *Educ:* Tulane Univ, BE, 30. *Prof Exp:* Engr hydraul model studies, US Bur Reclamation, 30-32, struct design, 32-34, concrete invests, 34-51, head concrete lab, 42-51, chief eng labs, 51, chief res engr, 51-62; dir tech serv, Am Cement Corp, 62-64, tech dir, 64-69, vpres, 69-72; CONSULT ENG, 72- *Concurrent Pos:* Chmn concrete comt, US Comt Large Dams, 61-70, mem building res adv bd, 68-70. *Honors & Awards:* Distinguished Serv Award, US Dept Interior, 59; Wason Medal Res, Am Concrete Inst, 50, Henry L Kennedy Award, 64; award merit, Am Soc Testing & Mat, 66; Henry C Turner Award, 81. *Mem:* Hon mem Am Concrete Inst; fel Am Soc Civil Eng; fel Am Soc Testing & Mat. *Res:* Portland cement and concrete; author or coauthor of over 35 publications. *Mailing Add:* 3035-0 Via Vista Laguna Hills CA 92653

PRICE, WILLIAM ALRICH, JR, b Chester, Pa, Jan 5, 24; m 47; c 2. PHARMACOLOGY. *Educ:* Pa State Col, BS, 48, MS, 50; Rutgers Univ, PhD(biochem), 51. *Prof Exp:* Res chemist, 51-62, SR RES BIOCHEMIST, E I DU PONT DE NEMOURS & CO, INC, 62- *Mem:* Am Chem Soc; NY Acad Sci. *Res:* Animal nutrition; chemistry of natural products; neuropharmacology; cardiovascular pharmacology. *Mailing Add:* Stine Lab Biochem Dept E I du Pont de Nemours & Co Newark DE 19711

PRICE, WILLIAM ARMSTRONG, b Richmond, Va, Mar 27, 89; m 21, 64; c 2. GEOLOGY, OCEANOGRAPHY. *Educ:* Davidson Col, AB, 09; Johns Hopkins Univ, PhD(geol), 13. *Prof Exp:* From instr to asst prof geol, WVa Univ, 13-19; CONSULT GEOLOGIST, 20- *Concurrent Pos:* Paleontologist, State Geol Surv, WVa, 13-19; prof, Agr & Mech Col, Tex, 50-54, res geologist, 54-55; mem, Shoreline Comt, Int Asn Quaternary Res, 53-61; hon mem, Italian Inst Human Paleont, Rome; US del cong, Rome & Pisa, 53; collabr, Quaternaria, Rome; adj prof marine geol, Tex A&I Univ, Corpus Christi, 76- *Honors & Awards:* Francis P Shepard Medal Excellence Marine Geol, Soc Econ Paleontologists & Mineralogists, 73. *Mem:* Fel AAAS; fel Geol Soc Am; fel Am Geog Soc; Am Asn Petrol Geol; Soc Econ Paleontologists & Mineralogists. *Res:* Stratigraphy; geology, geomorphology, oceanography and petroleum resources of Gulf of Mexico coastal plain and continental shelf; geomorphology and Quaternary geology of the nonglaciated regions of North America; shoreline development and classification. *Mailing Add:* 428 Ohio St Corpus Christi TX 78404

PRICHARD, BENJAMIN ARNOLD, JR, b Bozeman, Mont, Nov 12, 45; m 66; c 3. PLASMA PHYSICS. *Educ:* Colo State Univ, BS, 67; Univ Wis-Madison, MS, 69, PhD(physics), 72. *Prof Exp:* Physicist, Fermi Nat Accelerator Lab, 72-75; RES STAFF MEM, PLASMA PHYSICS LAB, PRINCETON UNIV, 75- *Res:* Development of high-current high- energy neutral deuterium atom ion sources and beam lines to be used for plasma heating in the Princeton large torus and Tokamak fusion test reactor toka maks. *Mailing Add:* 7 Sutton Pl East Windsor NJ 08520

PRICHARD, GEORGE EDWARDS, b Corbin, Ky, July 29, 16; m 42; c 2. GEOLOGY. *Educ:* Univ Ky, BS, 40. *Prof Exp:* Asst geol, Univ Denver, 40-41; asst comput, Seismog Serv Corp, Okla, 46-47; geologist, Org Fuels Br, US Geol Surv, 48-66, Br Regional Geol Southern Rocky Mt, 66-69 & Br Rocky Mt Environ Geol, 69-72, Br Cent Environ Geol, 72-81, Br Cent Regional Geol, 81; RETIRED. *Mem:* Geol Soc Am; Am Asn Petrol Geologists. *Res:* Mineral fuels; sedimentology; stratigraphy; structure. *Mailing Add:* 3665 W Floyd Ave Fed Ctr Box 25046 Denver CO 80236

PRICHARD, ROBERT WILLIAMS, b Jersey City, NJ, May 30, 23; m 46; c 2. PATHOLOGY. *Educ:* George Washington Univ, MD, 47. *Prof Exp:* Asst instr path, Univ Pa, 50-51; from instr to assoc prof, 51-55, PROF PATH, BOWMAN GRAY SCH MED, 55-, CHMN DEPT, 73- *Concurrent Pos:* Adv med educ, US Opers Mission, Thailand, 55-57. *Mem:* Am Soc Clin Path; Am Soc Exp Path; Am Asn Hist Med; Am Asn Path & Bact; AMA. *Res:* Atherosclerosis; diseases of the hematopoietolytic organs; medical history. *Mailing Add:* Dept of Path Bowman Gray Sch of Med Winston-Salem NC 27103

PRIDDY, RALPH BANTA, b Los Angeles, Calif, Mar 14, 17; m 42; c 1. VERTEBRATE ZOOLOGY, INSECT TAXONOMY. *Educ:* Pomona Col, BA, 37; Claremont Grad Sch, MA, 39; Cornell Univ, PhD(vert zool), 42. *Prof Exp:* Instr biol, St Lawrence Univ, 42-43 & Adelphi Col, 43-45; from instr to asst prof, Boston Univ, 45-49; teacher, Reedley Col, 50-51; prof biol & chmn div sci, Union Col, Ky, 51-52; asst prof zool, Univ Pittsburgh, 52-57; assoc prof biol, Carthage Col, 57-61; ASSOC PROF BIOL, WAGNER COL, 64- *Concurrent Pos:* Sigma Xi res grant, 55; Am Philos Soc grant, 57. *Mem:* AAAS; Sigma Xi. *Res:* Revision of the genera Conophorus and Sparnopolius in North America; facial musculature, nerves and blood vessels of the hamster in relation to the cheek pouch. *Mailing Add:* Dept of Biol Wagner Col Staten Island NY 10301

PRIDDY, STEWART BEAUREGARD, b Lumberton, NC, Mar 31, 40; m 63; c 2. MATHEMATICS. *Educ:* Univ NC, BS, 61, MA, 63; Mass Inst Technol, PhD(math), 68. *Prof Exp:* From asst prof to assoc prof, 68-78, PROF MATH, NORTHWESTERN UNIV, EVANSTON, 78- *Mem:* Am Math Soc. *Res:* Algebraic topology; homotopy theory; infinite loop space theory; simplicial homotopy theory; homological algebra. *Mailing Add:* Dept of Math Northwestern Univ Evanston IL 60201

PRIDE, DOUGLAS ELBRIDGE, b Eau Claire, Wis, July 18, 42; m 66; c 2. ECONOMIC GEOLOGY, EXPLORATION GEOCHEMISTRY. *Educ:* Univ Wis-Madison, BS, 64, MS, 66; Univ Ill, Urbana, PhD(geol), 69. *Prof Exp:* Asst prof geol, Univ Ill, Urbana, 69-73; ASST PROF GEOL, OHIO STATE UNIV, 73- *Mem:* Geol Soc Am; Am Inst Mining, Metall & Petrol Engrs; Sigma Xi. *Res:* Geologic field mapping, microscopic studies and researches in exploration geochemistry, coordinated to locate metallic mineral deposits, in particular those associated with deep-seated and near-surface intrusive igneous activity. *Mailing Add:* Dept of Geol & Mineral Ohio State Univ Columbus OH 43210

PRIDMORE-BROWN, DAVID CLIFFORD, b Mexico City, Mex, Sept 1, 28; m 58; c 2. PHYSICS, COMPUTER SIMULATION. *Educ:* Principia Col, BS, 49; Mass Inst Technol, SM, 51, PhD(physics), 54. *Prof Exp:* Researcher acoustics, Mass Inst Technol, 54-56; Imp Chem Industs fel, Univ Manchester, 56-57; asst prof mech eng, Mass Inst Technol, 57-62; STAFF SCIENTIST, AEROSPACE CORP, 62- *Mem:* Am Phys Soc. *Res:* Acoustic, magnetohydrodynamic and plasma wave motion; radiation problems; computational physics. *Mailing Add:* Space Physics Lab Aerospace Corp Box 92957 Los Angeles CA 90009

PRIELIPP, ROBERT WALTER, b Wausau, Wis, Mar 11, 36. MATHEMATICS. *Educ:* Wis State Univ, Stevens Point, BS, 58; Univ Ill, Urbana, MS, 60; Univ Wis-Madison, PhD(math, math educ), 67. *Prof Exp:* Teacher high sch, Wis, 58-59; instr math, Wis State Univ, Stevens Point, 60-62; proj asst math educ, Univ Wis-Madison, 62-63 & Res & Develop Ctr, 66-67; asst prof, 67-69, assoc prof, 69-79, PROF MATH, UNIV WIS-OSHKOSH, 79- *Concurrent Pos:* Co-ed, Prob Dept, Sch Sci & Math, 76- *Mem:* Math Asn Am; Sch Sci & Math Asn; Nat Coun Teachers Math. *Res:* Algebra; elementary number theory; mathematics education. *Mailing Add:* Dept of Math Univ of Wis Oshkosh WI 54901

PRIEMER, ROLAND, b Oct 28, 43. ELECTRICAL ENGINEERING. *Educ:* Ill Inst Technol, BS, 65, PhD(elec eng). *Prof Exp:* Engr, Zenith Radio Corp, 65-69; asst prof, 69-77, ASSOC PROF INFO ENG, UNIV ILL, CHICAGO CIRCLE, 77- *Mem:* Inst Elec & Electronics Engrs. *Res:* Estimation theory; network topology; use of computer in instruction; educational technology. *Mailing Add:* Dept of Info Eng PO Box 4348 Chicago IL 60680

PRIEN, CHARLES H(ENRY), chemical engineering, deceased

PRIER, JAMES EDDY, b Richmond Co, NY, July 20, 24; m 46; c 4. PUBLIC HEALTH. *Educ:* Cornell Univ, DVM, 46; Univ Ill, MS, 49, PhD(path), 53. *Prof Exp:* Bacteriologist, Lederle Labs, Am Cyanamid Co, NY, 46-47; exten vet, Univ Ill, 47, res instr path, 47-50; head dept bact & vet sci, Univ Wyo, 50-53; asst prof microbiol, Col Med, State Univ NY Upstate Med Ctr, 53-56; dir biol develop labs, Merck Sharpe & Dohme, Inc, 56-60; assoc prof microbiol, Sch Vet Med, Univ Pa, 60-64; from asst dir to dir div labs, Pa Dept Health, 64-72, dir bur labs, 72-76; DIR, CENTRE SQ VET CLIN, ARDMORE ANIMAL HOSP & FELINE MED CTR, JENKINTOWN, 78-; DIR, COMP MED LAB, PHILADELPHIA COL OSTEOPATH MED, 78- *Concurrent Pos:* Vis assoc, Sch Vet Med, Univ Pa, 57-60; prof microbiol, Sch Med, Temple Univ, 64-76; dir labs, Henry R Landis State Hosp, 71-73; co-dir, Penndel Med Lab, Ardmore, 76- *Mem:* Am Soc Microbiol; fel Am Pub Health Asn; Am Vet Med Asn; US Animal Health Asn; Royal Soc Health. *Res:* Virology, especially host-parasite relationships; epidemiology; infectious diseases of domestic animals; viruses of man and animals. *Mailing Add:* 103 DeKalb Pike Centre Square PA 19422

PRIESING, CHARLES PAUL, b Boston, Mass, June 26, 29; m 55; c 6. ORGANIC CHEMISTRY. *Educ:* Merrimack Col, BS, 52; Mass Inst Technol, PhD(org chem), 57. *Prof Exp:* Res chemist, Dow Chem Co, Mich, 57-64, proj leader, 64-65; chief treatment & control res progs, Robert S Kerr Water Res Ctr, Fed Water Pollution Control Admin, 65-68; from supvr environ eng to mgr environ eng, 68-74, DIR, ENVIRON PROTECTION DEPT, AM CYANAMID CO, 74- *Mem:* Am Chem Soc; Water Pollution Control Fedn; Am Water Works Asn. *Res:* Vitamin syntheses; functional monomers and polymers; polymer association; flocculation and solid-liquid separations; polyelectrolytes; water and waste treatment; product and process technology; water quality and pollution control; corporate environmental programs management and administration. *Mailing Add:* Am Cyanamid Co Berdan Ave Wayne NJ 07470

PRIEST, DAVID GERARD, b Tampa, Fla, Oct 16, 38; m 57; c 2. BIOCHEMISTRY, ENZYMOLOGY. *Educ:* Univ S Fla, BA, 64; Fla State Univ, PhD(chem), 69. *Prof Exp:* Chemist, Eastman Kodak, 69-70; assoc, 70-72, asst prof, 72-75, assoc prof, 75-81, PROF BIOCHEM, MED UNIV SC, 81- *Mem:* Am Chem Soc; Am Soc Biol Chemists. *Res:* Studies of the regulation of folate metabolism in eucaryotic cells. *Mailing Add:* Dept of Biochem Med Univ SC 171 Ashley Ave Charleston SC 29403

PRIEST, HOMER FARNUM, b Nelson, NH, June 14, 16; m 41. CHEMISTRY. *Educ:* Univ NH, BS, 38; Williams Col, MA, 40; Mass Inst Technol, PhD(chem), 48. *Prof Exp:* Asst instr & stock clerk, Univ NH, 34-37; asst chem, Williams Col, 38-40; instr, Columbia Univ, 40-41, div & sect head, Manhattan Proj, Div War Res, 41-44; works chemist, Carbide & Carbon Chem Corp, Tenn, 44-46, dir chem res, 46; tech adv to chief tech command, Decontamination Br, Radiol Warfare Div, US Army Chem Ctr, 48-50, consult, 51; asst group leader, Solid State Transistor Group, Lincoln Lab, Mass Inst Technol, 51-54; solid state res group, Baird Assocs, 54-57; supvry phys chemist, Mat Res Lab, Ord Mat Res Off, Watertown Arsenal, US Army, 57-63, dir mat res lab, Mat Res Agency, Watertown, 63-72, chief mat sci div, Army Mat & Mech Res Ctr, 72-80; RETIRED. *Concurrent Pos:* Exec asst to pres, High Voltage Eng Corp, 50-51. *Mem:* Am Chem Soc. *Res:* Uranium chemistry; solid state semiconductors; pure materials; fluorides; fluorine. *Mailing Add:* PO Box 406 Manchester MA 01944

PRIEST, JEAN LANE HIRSCH, b Chicago, Ill, Apr 5, 28; m 58; c 3. PEDIATRICS, MEDICAL GENETICS. *Educ:* Univ Chicago, PhB, 47, BS, 50, MD, 53; Am Bd Pediat, dipl, 58. *Prof Exp:* Intern, King County Hosp Syst, Seattle, Wash, 53-54; resident pediat, Univ Chicago Clins, 54-57; clin instr pediat, Univ Ill, 57-58; staff pediatrician & res cytogeneticist, Ranier Sch, Buckley, Wash, 58-62; instr pediat, Med Ctr, Univ Colo, 63-65, asst prof pediat & path, 65-71; assoc prof pediat & asst prof path, 71-78, PROF PEDIAT, SCH MED, EMORY UNIV, 71- *Concurrent Pos:* Fel, Nat Found for Infantile Paralysis, 57 & Chicago Heart Asn, 57-58; physician, Infant Welfare Soc, Chicago, 57-58 & Seattle-King County Dept Pub Health, 58-61; fel genetics, Univ Wash, 58-62, clin instr pediat, 60-62; vis mem staff, Dept Zool, Univ St Andrews, Scotland, 69-70. *Mem:* Am Soc Cell Biol; Am Asn Pathologists; Am Soc Human Genetics; Am Acad Pediat; Tissue Cult Asn. *Res:* Cytogenetics of human chromosome abnormalities; differentiated function in cultured cells. *Mailing Add:* Med Genetics PO Drawer AM Emory Univ Sch Med Atlanta GA 30322

PRIEST, JOSEPH ROGER, b Highland, Ohio, Oct 14, 29; m 59; c 4. NUCLEAR PHYSICS. *Educ:* Wilmington Col, BS, 51; Miami Univ, MS, 56; Purdue Univ, PhD(physics), 60. *Prof Exp:* Asst, Purdue Univ, 56-60; physicist, Int Bus Mach Res Lab, 60-62; from asst prof to assoc prof, 62-70, PROF PHYSICS, MIAMI UNIV, 70- *Mem:* Am Phys Soc. *Res:* Low energy nuclear reactions; radioisotope techniques. *Mailing Add:* 402 Maxine Dr Oxford OH 45056

PRIEST, MELVILLE S(TANTON), b Cassvile, Mo, Oct 16, 12; m 41. HYDRAULICS. *Educ:* Univ Mo, BS, 35; Univ Colo, MS, 43; Univ Mich, PhD(civil eng), 54. *Prof Exp:* Jr engr, US Corps Eng, Ill, 37-39; jr engr, US Bur Reclamation, Colo, 39-40, asst engr, 40-41; from instr to assoc prof mech, Cornell Univ, 41-55; prof hydraul, Auburn Univ, 55-65, head dept civil eng, 58-65; exec dir, Water Resources Res Inst, Miss State Univ, 65-77; CONSULT, 77- *Concurrent Pos:* Adv, UN Tech Asst Admin to Egypt, 56, 57, 60. *Mem:* Am Soc Civil Engrs; Int Asn Hydraul Res; Am Water Resources Asn. *Res:* Hydraulic engineering. *Mailing Add:* PO Box 541 Starkville MS 39759

PRIEST, ROBERT EUGENE, b Anacortes, Wash, Jan 6, 26; m 58; c 3. EXPERIMENTAL PATHOLOGY, CELL BIOLOGY. *Educ:* Reed Col, BA, 50; Univ Chicago, MD, 54. *Prof Exp:* From instr to res asst prof path, Univ Wash, 57-62; from asst prof to prof, Univ Colo, 62-72; PROF PATH, EMORY UNIV, 71- *Concurrent Pos:* Clin investr, Vet Admin Hosp, Seattle, 60-62; vis scientist, Univ St Andrews, Scotland, 69-70; fel coun arteriosclerosis, Am Heart Asn; Fogarty sr int fel, Univ Auckland, New Zealand, 80-81. *Mem:* AAAS; Am Asn Pathologists; Am Soc Cell Biol; Int Acad Path. *Res:* Connective tissue biochemistry and disease; cell culture; differentiation. *Mailing Add:* Dept of Path Emory Univ Atlanta GA 30322

PRIESTER, WILLIAM ALFRED, veterinary medicine, epidemiology, see previous edition

PRIESTLEY, JAMES TAGGART, surgery, deceased

PRIEVE, DENNIS CHARLES, b Portage, Wis, Sept 1, 47. CHEMICAL ENGINEERING, COLLOID CHEMISTRY. *Educ:* Univ Fla, BSChE, 70; Univ Del, MChE, 73, PhD(chem eng), 75. *Prof Exp:* Res engr chem eng, Westvaco Corp, 70; res fel, Univ Del, 70-73, teaching assoc, 73-74; asst prof, 75-80, ASSOC PROF CHEM ENG, CARNEGIE-MELLON UNIV, 80- *Concurrent Pos:* Consult, Kopper's Co, Inc, 76- *Honors & Awards:* George Tallman Ladd Award, Carnegie-Mellon Univ, 77. *Mem:* Assoc mem Am Inst Chem Engrs; Am Chem Soc; Sigma Xi; Am Soc Eng Educ; AAAS. *Res:* Transport of hydrosols as particulate solutes with applications to deep-bed filtration; deposition of films of water-based paints; flocculation. *Mailing Add:* Dept of Chem Eng Carnegie-Mellon Univ Pittsburgh PA 15213

PRIGOT, MELVIN, b Boston, Mass, Nov 16, 20; m 43; c 2. ORGANIC CHEMISTRY, ANALYTICAL CHEMISTRY. *Educ:* Boston Univ, AB, 43; Univ Fla, MS, 48, PhD(org chem), 51. *Prof Exp:* Chemist, Monsanto Chem Co, 51-52, Pennwalt Corp, 52-54, ICI-Am, 55-60 & Gen Aniline & Film Corp, 60-61; CHEMIST, H KOHNSTAMM & CO, INC, 61- *Mem:* Am Chem Soc; AAAS. *Res:* Process development; food, drug and cosmetic dyes; textile dyes. *Mailing Add:* 438 Clifton St Westfield NJ 07090

PRIKRY, KAREL LIBOR, b Chvalkovice, Czech, Apr 28, 44; m. MATHEMATICS. *Educ:* Univ Warsaw, Magister of Math, 65; Univ Calif, Berkeley, PhD(math), 68. *Prof Exp:* Res asst math, Univ Calif, Berkeley, 65-68; asst prof, Univ Wis-Madison, 68-72; assoc prof, 72-80, PROF, UNIV MINN, MINNEAPOLIS, 80- *Concurrent Pos:* Vis asst prof, Univ Calif, Los Angeles, 71-72. *Mem:* Asn Symbolic Logic. *Res:* Theory of sets; combinatorial properties of families of sets; ultrafilters; consistence and independence proofs. *Mailing Add:* Sch of Math 127 Vincent Hall Univ of Minn Minneapolis MN 55455

PRILL, ARNOLD L, b New York, NY. METALLURGY. *Educ:* Mass Inst Technol, BS, 62, MS, 63; Lehigh Univ, PhD(metall), 66. *Prof Exp:* Res metallurgist, Int Nickel Co, 63-66; chief metallurgist, Sintercast Div, 66-68, sect mgr, Res & Develop Div, 68-69, dir eng, Chromalloy Div, 69-70, vpres eng & opers, 70-77, EXEC VPRES ENG & OPERS, CHROMALLOY DIV, CHROMALLOY AM CORP, 77- *Mem:* Mfg Engrs; Am Powder Metall Inst. *Res:* Powder metallurgy, particularly cermets; superalloy joining and forming; ternary diffusion. *Mailing Add:* Chromalloy Div National Blvd Midwest City OK 73110

PRIM, ROBERT CLAY, b Sweetwater, Tex, Sept 25, 21; m 42; c 3. MATHEMATICS. *Educ:* Univ Tex, BSEE, 41; Princeton Univ, PhD(math), 49. *Prof Exp:* Asst appl math, Univ Tex, 40-41; engr, Gen Elec Co, NY, 41-44; engr & mathematician, US Naval Ordn Lab, 44-49; res assoc dynamics, Princeton Univ, 48-49; res mathematician, Bell Tel Labs, Inc, 49-58, dir math & mech res, 58-61; spec asst to Dir Defense Res & Eng, 61-63; vpres res, Sandia Corp, 63-64; vpres, Data Systs Div, Litton Industs, Inc, Calif, 64-66 & defense systs group, 66-69; exec res assoc, Bell Labs, Inc, 69-71, exec dir res, 71-80; PVT CONSULT, 80- *Concurrent Pos:* Mem adv comt eng, NSF, 72, mem adv comt res, 73-74; mem vis comt eng & appl physics, Harvard Univ, 73-78. *Mem:* Am Math Soc; Math Asn Am; Asn Comput Mach; Am Asn Adv Sci. *Res:* Research and development management; management science; systems analysis; systems engineering. *Mailing Add:* 17361 Plaza Maria San Diego CA 92128

PRIMACK, JOEL ROBERT, b Santa Barbara, Calif, July 14, 45; m 77; c 1. THEORETICAL PHYSICS, ELEMENTARY PARTICLE PHYSICS. *Educ:* Princeton Univ, AB, 66; Stanford Univ, PhD(physics), 70. *Prof Exp:* Harvard Soc Fellows jr fel physics, Harvard Univ, 70-73; asst prof, 73-77, ASSOC PROF PHYSICS, UNIV CALIF, SANTA CRUZ, 77- *Concurrent Pos:* Sloan Found res fel, 74-78; vis prof, Ecole Normale Superieure, Paris, 78. *Mem:* AAAS; Am Phys Soc. *Res:* High energy theoretical physics, especially gauge theory of electroweak and strong interactions, monopoles, lattice gauge theory and supersymmetry; national science and technology policy, especially nuclear power, energy conservation and other energy issues; public interest science. *Mailing Add:* Physics Dept Univ of Calif Santa Cruz CA 95064

PRIMACK, MARSHALL PHILIP, b Louisville, Ky, Aug 30, 41; m 67; c 2. ENDOCRINOLOGY. *Educ:* Univ Louisville, BA, 61; Johns Hopkins Univ, MD, 65. *Prof Exp:* From intern to resident internal med, Bellevue Hosp, New York, 65-68; fel endocrinol, 68-71, assoc, 71-72, instr, 72-73, ASST PROF MED, COL PHYSICIANS & SURGEONS, COLUMBIA UNIV, 73- *Mem:* Endocrine Soc; Am Thyroid Asn. *Res:* The mechanism of action of thyroid hormones; emphasis on the way these hormones increase the rate of metabolism. *Mailing Add:* Col of Physicians & Surgeons Columbia Univ 630 W 168th St New York NY 10032

PRIMAINI, MICHAEL M, b Norwich, Conn, Sept 7, 50; m 79. CHEMICAL COMMUNICATION. *Educ:* Univ Conn, BA, 72, MS, 74; Univ Md, PhD(entom, 79. *Prof Exp:* Res asst, Agr Exp Sta, Puerto Rico, 74-75; RES BIOLOGIST ENTOM RES, E I DUPONT DE NEMOURS & CO, INC, 79- *Res:* Identifying chemical control agents of agricultural insect pest. *Mailing Add:* E335 Biochem Dept DuPont Exp Sta Wilmington DE 19898

PRIMAK, WILLIAM LEO, b New York, NY, June 4, 17; wid; c 3. CHEMISTRY, PHYSICS. *Educ:* City Col New York, BS, 37; Polytech Inst Brooklyn, MS, 43, PhD(phys chem), 46. *Prof Exp:* Jr physicist, Queens Col NY, 38-42; res assoc, Polytech Inst Brooklyn, 43-46; assoc chemist, 46-60, SR CHEMIST, ARGONNE NAT LAB, 60- *Mem:* Am Chem Soc; Am Phys Soc. *Res:* Radiation effects in solids. *Mailing Add:* Argonne Nat Lab Bldg 223 9700 S Cass Ave Argonne IL 60439

PRIMAKOFF, HENRY, b Odessa, Russia, Feb 12, 14; nat US; m 38; c 3. THEORETICAL PHYSICS. *Educ:* Columbia Univ, AB & AM, 35; NY Univ, PhD(physics), 38. *Prof Exp:* Instr physics, Polytech Inst Brooklyn, 38-40 & Queens Col NY, 40-42; physicist, Div War Res, Columbia Univ, 42-45; asst prof physics, NY Univ, 45-46; from asst prof to prof, Wash Univ, 46-60; PROF PHYSICS, UNIV PA, 60- *Mem:* Nat Acad Sci; Am Acad Arts & Sci; fel Am Phys Soc. *Res:* Theory of elementary particles; theory of weak interactions in nuclei. *Mailing Add:* Dept of Physics Univ of Pa Philadelphia PA 19104

PRIMAKOFF, PAUL, b New York, NY, March 14, 44. BIOCHEMISTRY. *Educ:* Haverford Col, BA, 66; Stanford Univ, PhD(biochem), 73. *Prof Exp:* Res assoc physiol, Harvard Med Sch, 77-81; ASST PROF PHYSIOL, MED SCH, UNIV CONNN, 81- *Mem:* Am Soc Cell Biol; AAAS. *Res:* Localization of molecules in domains in membranes; localized surface antigens of the sperm cell; immunological approaches to contraception. *Mailing Add:* Dept Physiol Univ Conn Farmington CT 06032

PRIMIANO, FRANK PAUL, JR, b Cleveland, Ohio, July 5, 39. BIOMEDICAL ENGINEERING. *Educ:* Drexel Univ, BSME, 62, MSBME, 63; Case Western Reserve Univ, PhD(biomed eng), 71. *Prof Exp:* Engr, Gen Elec Co, 63-64; res engr, Technol, Inc, 64-65; ASST PROF BIOMED ENG, CASE WESTERN RESERVE UNIV, 71- *Concurrent Pos:* Pulmonary consult, Cleveland Vet Admin Hosp. *Mem:* AAAS; Am Soc Mech Eng; Soc Automotive Eng; Inst Elec & Electronics Eng. *Res:* Biomedical engineering, modeling and control of physiological systems; respiratory physiology; biomechanics. *Mailing Add:* Dept Pediat Univ Hosps Case Western Reserve Univ Cleveland OH 44106

PRINCE, ALAN THEODORE, b Toronto, Ont, Feb 15, 15; m 42; c 2. CHEMISTRY, GEOLOGY. *Educ:* Univ Toronto, BA, 37, MA, 38; Univ Chicago, PhD(physico-chem petrol), 41. *Prof Exp:* Jr res chemist, Div Chem, Nat Res Coun Can, 40-42; res chemist & petrogr, Can Refractories Ltd, Que, 43-45; lectr petrol, Univ Man, 45-46; head, Ceramic Chem Sect, Mines Br, Dept Mines & Tech Surv, Can, 46-50, head, Phys & Crystal Chem Sect, 50-55, sr res officer, Mineral Dressing & Process Metall Div, 55-59, chief, Mineral Sci Div, 59-65, dir, Water Res Br, 65-67, dir, Inland Waters Br, 67-70, Dept Energy, Mines & Resources, dir gen, Inland Waters Br, Environ Can, 70-72, asst dep minister planning & eval, Dept Energy, Mines & Resources, 72-75, pres, Atomic Energy Control Bd, 75-78; RETIRED. *Concurrent Pos:* Mem, Can Nat Comt for Int Hydrol Decade. *Mem:* Fel Am Ceramic Soc; Mineral Soc Am; Nat Inst Ceramic Engrs; Mineral Asn Can; Can Inst Mining & Metall. *Res:* Science and technology of earth-forming materials, minerals, rocks, water and technological materials, metals and ceramics. *Mailing Add:* Atomic Energy Control Bd Box 1046 Ottawa ON K1P 5S9 Can

PRINCE, ALFRED M, b Berlin, Ger, Dec 16, 28; US citizen; m 62; c 2. VIROLOGY, PATHOLOGY. *Educ:* Yale Univ, BA, 49; Columbia Univ, MA, 51; Western Reserve Univ, MD, 55. *Prof Exp:* Intern path, Sch Med, Yale Univ, 55-56, res fel virol, 56-59; assoc mem virol, Wistar Inst Anat & Biol, 62-63; asst prof path, Sch Med, Yale Univ, 63-65; SR INVESTR VIROL, NEW YORK BLOOD CTR, 65- *Concurrent Pos:* NIH res grant, 62-; clin assoc prof path, Sch Med, Cornell Univ, 65-; career investr, New York City Res Coun, 66-74. *Honors & Awards:* Landsteiner Award, Am Asn Blood Banks, 75. *Mem:* Am Asn Immunologists; Am Soc Exp Pathologists; Am Asn Pathologists. *Res:* Hepatitis viruses; chronic liver disease. *Mailing Add:* New York Blood Ctr 310 E 67th St New York NY 10021

PRINCE, ALLAN BIXBY, soil chemistry, see previous edition

PRINCE, DAVID ALLAN, b Newark, NJ, July 14, 32; m 56; c 3. NEUROLOGY, NEUROPHYSIOLOGY. *Educ:* Univ Vt, BS, 52; Univ Pa, MD, 56. *Prof Exp:* From asst prof to assoc prof med, 63-71, actg chmn dept neurol, 70-71, PROF MED & CHMN DEPT NEUROL, SCH MED, STANFORD UNIV, 71- *Concurrent Pos:* NIH spec fel neurophysiol, Sch Med, Stanford Univ, 62-63, Nat Inst Neurol Dis & Stroke res & training grant neurol, 69-73, Epilepsy Found Am grant, 71-72; Guggenheim fel, 71-72. *Mem:* Am Neurol Asn; Am Acad Neurol; Asn Res Nerv & Ment Dis; Am Epilepsy Soc (secy, 70-72, pres 73-74); Soc Neurosci. *Res:* Neurophysiology-synaptic potentials and impulse generation in experimental epilepsy; effects of convulsant agents on electrical activity of the brain. *Mailing Add:* Dept of Neurol Stanford Univ Med Ctr Stanford CA 94305

PRINCE, DENVER LEE, b Beaton, Ark, Oct 16, 32; m 51; c 3. PHYSICS. *Educ:* Henderson State Col, BS, 54; Univ Utah, MScEd, 58; Okla State Univ, EdD(higher educ in physics), 65. *Prof Exp:* Teacher high sch, Ark, 54-59; asst prof, 59-65, PROF PHYSICS & CHMN DEPT, UNIV CENT ARK, 65- *Concurrent Pos:* NSF res grant, 66-; consult pub schs, Ark, 67-; Intermediate Sci Curric Study; teacher, Phys Sci for Nonsci Student Trial Ctr. *Mem:* Am Asn Physics Teachers; Nat Sci Teachers Asn. *Res:* Science education. *Mailing Add:* Dept of Physics Univ of Cent Ark Conway AR 72032

PRINCE, EDWARD, b Schenectady, NY, Nov 29, 28; m 54; c 3. SOLID STATE PHYSICS. *Educ:* Harvard Univ, AB, 49; Cambridge Univ, PhD(physics), 52. *Prof Exp:* Mem tech staff, Bell Tel Labs, Inc, 52-58; physicist, US Naval Res Lab, Washington, DC, 58-68; RES PHYSICIST, NAT BUR STANDARDS, 68- *Mem:* AAAS; Am Phys Soc; Am Crystallog Asn. *Res:* Structure of crystals; thermal motion; experimental automation. *Mailing Add:* Reactor Radiation Div Nat Bur Standards Washington DC 20234

PRINCE, ERIC D, b New York, NY, Oct 10, 46. FISHERIERS. *Educ:* Univ Pac, BS, 69; Humboldt State Univ, MS, 72; Va Polytech Inst & State Univ, PhD(fish & wildlife sci), 77. *Prof Exp:* Fishery biologist, US Fish & Wildlife Serv, Southeast Reservoir Inst, 77-80; FISHERY BIOLOGIST, NAT MARINE FISHERIES SERV, SOUTHEAST FISHERIES CTR, MIAMI LAB, 80- *Concurrent Pos:* Adj asst prof, Rosenstiel Sch Marine & Atmospheric Sci, Univ Miami, 81-; assoc ed, NAm J Fisheries Mgt, 81- *Mem:* Am Fisheries Soc; Am Inst Fishery Res Biologists. *Res:* Biological effects of artificial reefs in aquatic environments; tracking movements of fishes using ultrasonic telemetry; trophic dynamics of marine and freshwater habitats; determining entrainment mortality of ichthyoplankton passing through power plants; age and growth of oceanic pelagic fishes. *Mailing Add:* Miami Lab Nat Marine Fisheries 75 Virginia Beach Rd Miami FL 33148

PRINCE, HAROLD HOOPES, b Keokuk, Iowa, Mar 29, 41; m 62; c 3. BEHAVIORAL ECOLOGY. *Educ:* Iowa State Univ, BSc, 62; Univ NB, MSc, 65; Va Polytech Inst, PhD(wildlife biol), 69. *Prof Exp:* Asst prof, 68-72, assoc prof, 72-78, PROF & ASST CHMN FISHERIES & WILDLIFE, MICH STATE UNIV, 78- *Concurrent Pos:* Vis Scholar, Delta Waterfowl Res Sta, Delta, Man, 75; Dansforth Assoc, 75. *Mem:* Wilson Ornith Soc; Wildlife Soc; Am Ornith Union; Cooper Ornith Soc. *Res:* Effects of genetic and environmental parameters on reproduction, survival and behavior of game birds, especially waterfowl; interaction of biocides with avian populations. *Mailing Add:* Dept Fisheries & Wildlife Mich State Univ East Lansing MI 48824

PRINCE, HERBERT N, b New York, NY, Aug 8, 29; m 55; c 3. MICROBIOLOGY, TOXICOLOGY. *Educ:* NY Univ, AB, 50; Univ Conn, PhD(bact), 56. *Prof Exp:* Bacteriologist, New York City Health Dept, 50; head microbiol res & qual control, Wallace & Tiernan, Inc, NJ, 56-60; sr virologist, Hoffmann-La Roche, Inc, 60-63, asst to dir, 63-66, asst dir chemother, 67-70; PRES, GIBRALTAR BIOL LABS, INC, 70- *Concurrent Pos:* Adj prof, Fairleigh Dickinson Univ, 57-72; vis prof, Seton Hall Univ, 70; adj prof, Rutgers Col, 79- *Mem:* Am Soc Microbiol; Soc Exp Biol & Med; Soc Indust Microbiol; fel Am Acad Microbiol; NY Acad Sci. *Res:* Industrial and public health microbiology; chemotherapy and experimental toxicology. *Mailing Add:* Gibraltar Biol Labs Inc 23 Just Rd Fairfield NJ 07006

PRINCE, JACK, b Bronx, NY, Feb 12, 38; m 57; c 4. PHYSICS. *Educ:* Yeshiva Univ, BA, 59; NY Univ, MS, 63, PhD(physics), 67. *Prof Exp:* NY State Regents teaching fel physics, NY Univ, 59-61; instr, Bronx Community Col, 60-63 & NY Univ, 63-64; from asst prof to assoc prof, 64-71, PROF & CHMN PHYSICS, BRONX COMMUNITY COL, 71- *Mem:* Am Asn Physics Teachers. *Res:* Theoretical solid state physics; many-body problem; differential and integral variational methods. *Mailing Add:* Dept of Physics Bronx Commun Col Bronx NY 10453

PRINCE, JAMES T, b Winchester, Tenn, June 29, 20; m 47; c 2. VIROLOGY, MEDICAL MICROBIOLOGY. *Educ:* Univ Minn, Minneapolis, BS, 53, MS, 61. *Prof Exp:* From instr to asst prof, 58-68, ASSOC PROF MICROBIOL, MED SCH, UNIV MINN, MINNEAPOLIS, 68-, DIR, MS DEGREE PROG IN MED MICROBIOL, 74- *Mem:* Am Soc Microbiol. *Res:* Virology, including Shope papilloma to carcinoma sequence; medical diagnostic microbiology. *Mailing Add:* Dept of Microbiol Univ of Minn Med Sch Minneapolis MN 55455

PRINCE, JOHN L(UTHER), III, b Austin, Tex, Nov 13, 41; m 60; c 4. ELECTRICAL ENGINEERING, SOLID STATE PHYSICS. *Educ:* Southern Methodist Univ, BSEE, 65; NC State Univ, MEE, 68, PhD(elec eng), 69. *Prof Exp:* Res assoc elec eng, NC State Univ, 65-68; res engr, Res Triangle Inst, 68-70; mem tech staff, Semiconductor Res & Develop Lab, Tex Instruments, Inc, Dallas, 70-75; prof elec & comput eng, Clemson Univ, 75-80; DIR RELIABILITY ASSURANCE, INTERMEDICS, INC, 80- *Concurrent Pos:* Consult, Dept Defense, 76-, mem adv group electron devices, 79- *Mem:* Sr mem Inst Elec & Electronics Engrs; Am Soc Qual Control; Electrochem Soc. *Res:* Semiconductor device performance at high temperatures; solar cell reliability; integrated circuit reliability and technology projection; medical systems reliability and performance. *Mailing Add:* Intermedics Inc Box 617 Freeport TX 77541

PRINCE, M(ORRIS) DAVID, b Greensboro, NC; m 47; c 4. COMPUTER GRAPHICS, COMPUTER AIDED DESIGN. *Educ:* Ga Inst Technol, BS, 46, MS, 49. *Prof Exp:* Instr math, Ga Inst Technol, 47-51, res engr, Eng Exp Sta, 51-56; sr staff mem, ITT Labs, 56-59; res & develop engr, 59-64, assoc dir res, 64-68, res lab dir, 68-70, dir res progs, 70-71, sr res & develop engr, 71-75, STAFF SPECIALIST, LOCKHEED-GA CO, 75- *Concurrent Pos:* Consult, NSF, 72-73; pres, First Am Systs, Inc, 72-75; adj prof, Sch Info & Comput Sci, Ga Inst Technol; vis lectr, Inst Elec & Electronics Engrs Comput Soc, 73. *Mem:* Fel Inst Elec & Electronics Engrs. *Res:* Computer graphics for aircraft cockpit displays using full-color high resolution raster graphics; graphics for the engineer's work station and for management information systems; research and engineering management technology transfer and utilization; audiovisual education aids; computer aided instruction. *Mailing Add:* 3132 Frontenac Ct Atlanta GA 30319

PRINCE, MACK J(AMES), b Vienna, Austria, Sept 28, 19; nat US; m 54; c 3. ELECTRICAL ENGINEERING. *Educ:* Worcester Polytech Inst, BS, 49; Univ RI, MS, 54. *Prof Exp:* Asst physics, 49-54, from instr to asst prof elec eng, 55-61, ASSOC PROF ELEC ENG, UNIV RI, 61- *Res:* Circuit theory; instrumentation. *Mailing Add:* Dept of Elec Eng 116 Kelley Hall Univ of RI Kingston RI 02881

PRINCE, MARTIN IRWIN, b New York, NY, Sept 19, 37; m 60; c 3. ORGANOMETALLIC CHEMISTRY. *Educ:* NY Univ, BA, 58, MS & PhD(org chem), 62. *Prof Exp:* Assoc res scientist, Res Div, NY Univ, 62-64, res scientist, 64-67; PRES, SYNTHATRON CORP, 67- *Mem:* Am Inst Chemists; Am Chem Soc; NY Acad Sci; AAAS; Sigma Xi. *Res:* Organic synthesis; high pressure reactions; radiation chemistry; organometallic synthesis; preparation of new polymer systems; polymer coatings; metal hydrides; fiber optic chemicals gases. *Mailing Add:* Synthatron Corp 50 Intervale Rd Parsippany NJ 07054

PRINCE, MORTON BRONENBERG, b Philadelphia, Pa, Apr 1, 24; m 47; c 1. SEMICONDUCTORS. *Educ:* Temple Univ, AB, 47; Mass Inst Technol, PhD, 51. *Prof Exp:* Mem tech staff, Bell Tel Labs, 51-56; dir res & develop, Semiconductor Div, Hoffman Electronics Corp, 56-59, vpres & gen mgr, 60-61, Electro-Optical Systs, Inc, Calif, 61-69; pres, SSR Instruments Co, 70-74; gen mgr & vpres, Meret, Inc, 74-75; br chief, Energy Res & Develop Admin, 75-77, BR CHIEF, DEPT OF ENERGY, 77- *Honors & Awards:* Marconi Premium, Inst Radio Engrs, Gt Brit, 59. *Mem:* Am Phys Soc; Inst Elec & Electronics Engrs; Int Solar Energy Soc. *Res:* Semiconductor device development; semiconductor materials; photovoltaic devices; solar energy; scientific instrumentation. *Mailing Add:* 2700 Virginia Ave NW Washington DC 20037

PRINCE, ROBERT HARRY, b Slough, Eng, Jan 26, 42; m 64; c 2. SURFACE PHYSICS. *Educ:* Univ Toronto, BASc, 63, MASc, 64, PhD(aerophysics), 68. *Prof Exp:* Nat Res Coun Can fel, Univ Col, London, 68-69; res assoc aerophysics, Inst Aerospace Studies, Univ Toronto, 69-70; from asst prof to assoc prof physics, 70-81, PROF PHYSICS, YORK UNIV, 81- *Concurrent Pos:* Consult, Ont Res Found, 66-67, Martin Marietta Inc, 70- & Commun Res Ctr, Ottawa, 71-73, Nuffield fel, Univ Cambridge, 78. *Mem:* Can Asn Physicists. *Res:* Particle-surface interactions; surface science. *Mailing Add:* Dept of Physics York Univ Downsview ON M3J 1P3 Can

PRINCE, TERRY JAMISON, b Elwood, Ind, Mar 18, 49; m 78. ANIMAL NUTRITION. *Educ:* Purdue Univ, BSc, 71; Univ Ky, PhD(monogastric nutrit), 76. *Prof Exp:* ASST PROF SWINE NUTRIT & PROD, AUBURN UNIV, 76- *Mem:* Am Soc Animal Sci; Animal Nutrit Res Coun. *Res:* Swine nutrition and production. *Mailing Add:* Dept of Animal & Dairy Sci Auburn Univ Auburn AL 36830

PRINCE, WALTER RAY, b Carbon Glow, Ky, May 2, 27; m 45. PHYSIOLOGY. *Educ:* Univ Ky, BS, 58, MS, 59; NC State Univ, PhD(physiol), 65. *Prof Exp:* Res assoc poultry sci, 63-64, from instr to asst prof, 64-75, ASSOC PROF POULTRY SCI, NC STATE UNIV, 75- *Mem:* Poultry Sci Asn; World Poultry Sci Asn. NY Acad Sci. *Res:* Physiological bases for natural resistance to diseases of poultry; hormones and hormonal relationships. *Mailing Add:* Dept of Poultry Sci NC State Univ Raleigh NC 27607

PRINCEN, HENRICUS MATTHEUS, b Eindhoven, Neth, Apr 15, 37; m 60; c 2. SURFACE CHEMISTRY, COLLOID CHEMISTRY. *Educ:* State Univ Utrecht, BSc, 56, Drs, 60, PhD(colloid chem), 65. *Prof Exp:* Res assoc, Res Lab, N V Philips' Glocilampenfabrieken, Eindhoven, 60; res scientist detergency, Foam Stability & Wetting Phenomena, Lever Bros Co, Edgewater, mgr phys chem, 73-80; RES ASSOC, EXXON RES & ENG CO, 80- *Mem:* Am Chem Soc; Sigma Xi. *Res:* Surface chemistry, especially detergency, capillarity, wetting and thin liquid films. *Mailing Add:* Exxon Res & Eng Co Corp Res Lab PO Box 45 Linden NJ 07036

PRINCEN, LAMBERTUS HENRICUS, b Eindhoven, Neth, Aug 31, 30; US citizen; m 55; c 1. CHEMISTRY, AGRICULTURE. *Educ:* State Univ Utrecht, BS, 52, Drs, 55, DSc(colloid chem), 59. *Prof Exp:* Res assoc, Univ Southern Calif, 55-58; res scientist, Nat Defense Res Coun, Neth, 58-60 & Nat Flaxseed Processors Asn, 60-62; proj leader linseed oil paints, 62-75, CHIEF, HORT & SPEC CROPS LAB, NORTHERN REGIONAL RES CTR, USDA, 75- *Concurrent Pos:* Lectr, Univ Southern Calif, 56-58; lectr, Bradley Univ, 63- *Honors & Awards:* Superior Serv Award, USDA, 69. *Mem:* Am Chem Soc; Am Oil Chemists Soc; Sigma Xi; Soc Econ Bot. *Res:* Colloid chemistry; light scattering of detergent solutions, aerosols and aerosol filtration; pigment interactions in emulsion paint systems; emulsion technology; paint degradation; particle size distributions in colloidal systems; electron microscopy; agricultural chemistry; synthetic modification of natural products; new crops development; natural toxicants; renewable resources. *Mailing Add:* 677 E High Point Terr Peoria IL 61614

PRINDLE, BRYCE, b Brule, Wis, Oct 23, 09; m 33; c 4. MICROBIOLOGY. *Educ:* Mass Inst Technol, SB, 31, PhD(microbiol), 35. *Prof Exp:* Textile Found sr res fel, Mass Inst Technol, 35-37; from instr to asst prof bact, Iowa State Col, 37-43; field supvr dehydration, Qm Corp, US Dept Army, 43-45; biologist, Plymouth Cordage Co, 45-60; instr, 60-76, prof sci, Babson Col, 63-76; vis investr, Woods Hole Oceanog Inst & instr biol, Bridgewater State Col, 76-78. *Mem:* AAAS; Am Soc Microbiol; Soc Indust Microbiol; Inst Food Technol. *Res:* Biological oceanography; marine deterioration; preservation of materials. *Mailing Add:* 15 Flintlock Way Yarmouth Port MA 02675

PRINDLE, RICHARD ALAN, b Mansfield, Ohio, Dec 28, 25; wid; c 6. MEDICINE. *Educ:* Harvard Univ, MD, 48, MPH, 54; Am Bd Prev Med & Pub Health, dipl. *Prof Exp:* Intern, Columbia-Presby Med Ctr, 49-50; asst chief poliomyelitis invests sect, USPHS, 51-53, tech consult, US Opers Mission to Haiti, 54-57, epidemiologist, Air Pollution Med Prog, 57-58, chief, 58-60, dep chief div air pollution, 60-63, chief div pub health methods, 63-66, chief bur state serv, 66, dir bur dis prev & environ control, 67-68; fed exec fel, Brookings Inst, 68-69; chief div family health, Pan-Am Health Orgn, 70-77; DIR THOMAS JEFFERSON HEALTH DIST, 77- *Concurrent Pos:* Res assoc, Harvard Univ, 54-56, vis lectr, 56-60 & 63-65; vis lectr, Univ Pa, 60-65; adj prof pop sci & int health, Sch Pub Health, Univ Ill, 72-78-, clin prof med, Univ Va, 78-, prof epidemiol, 81- *Mem:* Fel AAAS; fel Am Col Prev Med; fel Am Pub Health Asn; Asn Teachers Prev Med; Am Mgt Asn. *Res:* Epidemiology; demography; public health administration; population dynamics and family planning; demography. *Mailing Add:* Thomas Jefferson Health Dist PO Box 7546 Charlottesville VA 22906

PRINE, GORDON MADISON, b Valdosta, Ga, Feb 16, 28; m 57; c 2. AGRONOMY. *Educ:* Univ Ga, BSA, 52, MS, 54; Ohio State Univ, PhD, 57. *Prof Exp:* Asst agronomist, Ga Coastal Exp Sta, 54-55; asst agronomist, 58-65, assoc agronomist, 65-77, AGRONOMIST, AGR EXP STA, UNIV FLA, 77- *Mem:* Am Soc Agron. *Res:* Field crop ecology, with emphasis on new crops and plant introductions; low light intensities on crop production; multiple cropping; selection of superior reseeding annual rye grasses, perennial peanuts, late-maturing soybeans and pigeon peas. *Mailing Add:* Dept of Agron Univ of Fla Gainesville FL 32611

PRINEAS, JOHN WILLIAM, b Junee, Australia, May 30, 35; m 60; c 3. NEUROLOGY, NEUROPATHOLOGY. *Educ:* Univ Sydney, MB & BS, 58; MRCP & MRCPEd, 61. *Prof Exp:* House physician, Royal Prince Alfred Hosp, Sydney, 58; sr house physician cardiol, Glasgow Royal Infirmary, Scotland, 60-61; house physician neurol, Nat Hosps Nervous Dis, London, 61-62, sr registr, 63-64; first asst neurol, Royal Victoria Infirmary, Eng, 65-67; res fel, Albert Einstein Col Med, 67-69; sr res fel, Univ Sydney, 69-72, sr lectr med, 72-74; PROF NEUROSCI, COL MED & DENT NJ, 74- *Concurrent Pos:* Hon neurologist, Royal Prince Alfred Hosp, Sydney, 69-74; attending neurologist, Vet Admin Hosp, East Orange, 76-; vis prof path, Albert Einstein Col Med, 77- *Honors & Awards:* Weil Award, Am Asn Neuropathologists, 69 & 75, Moore Award, 76. *Mem:* Am Asn Neuropathologists; Brit Med Asn; Australian Asn Neurologists. *Res:* Myelin pathology; multiple sclerosis. *Mailing Add:* Dept of Neurol Vet Admin Hosp Tremont Ave East Orange NJ 07019

PRINEAS, RONALD JAMES, b NSW, Australia, Sept 19, 37; m 61; c 4. CARDIOVASCULAR DISEASES. *Educ:* Univ Sydney, MB & BS, 61; Univ London, PhD(epidemiol), 69. *Prof Exp:* Jr resident med, Prince Henry Hosp, Australia, 61; sr resident, Royal Perth Hosp, 62; sr house officer cardiol, Glasgow Royal Infirmary, 63, registr, 64; res fel epidemiol, Sch Hyg & Trop Med, London, 65-67, lectr, 68; from second asst to third asst, Dept Med, Royal Melbourne Hosp, Univ Melbourne, 69-72; assoc prof, Sch Pub Health, 73-78, assoc prof, Sch Med, 74-80, PROF, SCH PUB HEALTH, UNIV MINN, 79-, PROF, SCH MED, 81- *Concurrent Pos:* Fel, Coun Epidemiol, Am Heart Asn, 73- *Honors & Awards:* Shared Spec Lasker Award, 80. *Mem:* Am Col Cardiol; Royal Col Physicians Edinburgh; Royal Col Physicians London; Am Heart Asn. *Res:* Epidemiology of cardiovascular diseases; hypertension; sudden death; population electrocardiography; preventive cardiology; methodology of cardiovascular epidemiology. *Mailing Add:* Lab Physiol Hyg Sch Pub Health Univ of Minn Minneapolis MN 55455

PRING, DARYL ROGER, b Morris, Minn, June 6, 42; m 63; c 3. PLANT PATHOLOGY. *Educ:* NDak State Univ, BS, 64, MS, 66, PhD(plant path), 67. *Prof Exp:* Fel plant path, Univ Nebr, Lincoln, 68-71; res plant pathologist, 71-77, ASSOC PLANT PATHOLOGIST, PLANT VIRUS LAB, AGR RES SERV, USDA, FLA, 77- & ASSOC PROF PLANT PATH, UNIV FLA, 78- *Mem:* Am Phytopath Soc. *Res:* Plant virology; nucleic acid replication; nature of cytoplasmic inheritance; gene-cytoplasm interactions. *Mailing Add:* Plant Virus Lab Univ of Fla Gainesville FL 32611

PRINGLE, DOROTHY JUTTON, b Evanston, Ill, Feb 20, 19; m 61. NUTRITION. *Educ:* Univ Ill, BS, 40; Univ Wis, MS, 51, PhD(nutrit biochem), 56. *Prof Exp:* Dietetic intern, Univ Hosp, Univ Mich, 40-41; staff & consult dietitian, St Luke's Hosp, Chicago, Ill, 42-49; asst prof foods & nutrit, 51-53, PROF NUTRIT SCI, UNIV WIS-MADISON, 56- *Mem:* Am Dietetic Asn. *Res:* Socioeconomic influences on food habits and nutritional adequacy of minority families; evaluation of nutrition education methods. *Mailing Add:* Dept of Nutrit Sci Univ of Wis Madison WI 53706

PRINGLE, JAMES SCOTT, b Danvers, Mass, Aug 14, 37. BOTANY. *Educ:* Dartmouth Col, AB, 58; Univ NH, MS, 60; Univ Tenn, PhD(bot), 63. *Prof Exp:* Asst, Univ Tenn, 60-62; TAXONOMIST, ROYAL BOT GARDENS, 63- *Concurrent Pos:* Spec lectr biol, McMaster Univ, 74- *Mem:* Am Soc Plant Taxon; Soc Study Evolution; Bot Soc Am; Can Bot Asn; Int Asn Plant Taxon. *Res:* Taxonomy and evolutionary biology of vascular plants, especially Gentianaceae; taxonomy and breeding of Syringa; history of Canadian floristics. *Mailing Add:* Royal Bot Gardens Box 399 Hamilton ON L8N 3H8 Can

PRINGLE, JOHN W(ATSON), b La Junta, Colo, Oct 9, 23; m 45; c 3. CHEMICAL ENGINEERING. *Educ:* Univ Calif, Los Angeles, BA, 47; Univ Colo, BS, 48, MS, 49, PhD(chem eng), 51. *Prof Exp:* Instr math, Univ Colo, 48-51; dept supt, Rocky Flats Plant, Dow Chem Co, 51-60; plant supt, 60-66, gen supt prod, 66-67, TECH DIR MFG, ARAPAHOE CHEM, INC, 67- *Mem:* Am Inst Chem Engrs (pres, 47). *Res:* Resources in Colorado for pulp and paper industry; high pressure hydrogenation of Colorado oil shale; vacuum retorting of oil shale in a fluidized bed; detection and tracking of hurricanes by microseismic activity; isolation of americum 241 from plutonium processing wastes. *Mailing Add:* Arapahoe Chem Inc 2075 N 55th St Boulder CO 80301

PRINGLE, ORAN A(LLAN), b Lawrence, Kans, Sept 14, 23; m 47; c 4. MECHANICAL ENGINEERING. *Educ:* Univ Kans, BS, 47; Univ Wis, MS, 48, PhD(mech eng), 67. *Prof Exp:* Design engr, Black & Veatch, Consult Engrs, 48-50; from asst prof to assoc prof mech eng, 50-68, PROF MECH & AEROSPACE ENG, UNIV MO-COLUMBIA, 68- *Mem:* Am Soc Mech Engrs; Am Soc Eng Educ. *Res:* Dynamics of machinery; nonlinear vibrations; fatigue of metals and polymers; automatic control; machine elements. *Mailing Add:* Dept of Mech & Aerospace Eng Univ of Mo Columbia MO 65201

PRINGLE, ROSS BARTON, biochemistry, see previous edition

PRINGLE, WALLACE C, JR, b Hartford, Conn, Oct 23, 41; m 63; c 3. PHYSICAL CHEMISTRY. *Educ:* Middlebury Col, AB, 63; Mass Inst Technol, PhD(chem), 66. *Prof Exp:* Res assoc atomic physics, Nat Bur Stand, 66-67; asst prof, 68-74, ASSOC PROF CHEM, WESLEYAN UNIV, 74- *Concurrent Pos:* Nat Res Coun fel, 66-67. *Res:* Molecular spectroscopy and structure of small molecules, especially microwave and far infrared spectra of ring molecules. *Mailing Add:* Dept of Chem Wesleyan Univ Middletown CT 06457

PRINS, RUDOLPH, b Grand Rapids, Mich, Dec 21, 35; m 58; c 4. AQUATIC ECOLOGY, ZOOLOGY. *Educ:* Calvin Col, BA, 58; Western Mich Univ, MA, 62; Univ Louisville, PhD(zool), 65. *Prof Exp:* Teacher high sch, Mich, 58-60 & 61-62; asst zool, Univ Louisville, 62-65; asst prof entom & zool, Clemson Univ, 65-68; assoc prof, 68-74, PROF BIOL, WESTERN KY UNIV, 74- *Mem:* Am Soc Limnol & Oceanog. *Res:* Ecology and taxonomy of freshwater invertebrates; aquatic biology. *Mailing Add:* Dept Biol Western Ky Univ Bowling Green KY 42101

PRINTZ, MORTON PHILIP, b Portsmouth, Va, Sept 24, 36; m 59; c 2. PHARMACOLOGY. *Educ:* Univ Pittsburgh, BS, 58, PhD(biophys), 63. *Prof Exp:* USPHS fel, 62-64; res assoc biochem, Dartmouth Med Sch, 64-65; asst prof, Rockefeller Univ, 65-72; asst prof med, 72-77, ASSOC PROF MED, UNIV CALIF, SAN DIEGO, 78- *Mem:* Am Soc Biol Chemists; Am Soc Pharmacol & Exp Therapeut. *Res:* Endocrine and neuroendocrine mechanisms of blood pressure regulation; reninangiotensin system; protaglandin biosynthesis in blood vessels and relation to cardiocirculatory diseases. *Mailing Add:* Sch of Med Univ of Calif at San Diego La Jolla CA 92093

PRINZ, DIANNE KASNIC, b Conway, Pa, Sept 29, 38; m 60. PHYSICS. *Educ:* Univ Pittsburgh, BS, 60; Johns Hopkins Univ, PhD(physics), 67. *Prof Exp:* Res scientist, Space Sci Div, Naval Res Lab, 67-68; E O Hulburt fel physics & astron, Univ Md, College Park, 68-71; RES SCIENTIST, SPACE SCI DIV, NAVAL RES LAB, 71- *Concurrent Pos:* NSF grants, 68-71. *Mem:* Am Geophys Union. *Res:* Infrared spectroscopy of atmospheric gases; ultraviolet spectroscopy of solar and atmospheric gases. *Mailing Add:* Naval Res Lab Washington DC 20375

PRINZ, GARY A, b Cleveland, Ohio, Oct 2, 38; m 60. SOLID STATE PHYSICS. *Educ:* Univ Pittsburgh, BS, 60; Johns Hopkins Univ, PhD(physics), 66. *Prof Exp:* Res asst, Johns Hopkins Univ, 66-67; RES PHYSICIST, US NAVAL RES LAB, 67- *Mem:* Am Phys Soc; Sigma Xi. *Res:* Magnetism of rare earth ions in insulators. *Mailing Add:* 1704 Mason Hill Dr Alexandria VA 22307

PRINZ, MARTIN, b New York, NY, Sept 5, 31; m 61; c 3. PETROLOGY, MINERALOGY. *Educ:* City Col New York, BS, 53; Ind Univ, MA, 57; Columbia Univ, PhD(geol), 61. *Prof Exp:* Lectr geol, Brooklyn Col, 60-61; from instr to assoc prof, Tufts Univ, 61-69; sr res scientist, Inst Meteoritics, Univ NMex, 69-76, CHMN & CUR DEPT OF MINERAL SCI, AM MUS NAT HIST, 76- *Mem:* Fel Geol Soc Am; fel Mineral Soc Am; Int Asn Geochem & Cosmochem (asst secy, 73-76); Meteoritical Soc; AAAS. *Res:* Igneous petrology; lunar petrology; mafic and ultramafic rocks; oceanic rocks; meteorites; volcanology; minerals and medicine; rock forming minerals; electron microprobe analysis. *Mailing Add:* Dept Mineral Sci Am Mus Nat Hist New York NY 10024

PRINZ, PATRICIA N, b Huntington, WVa, July 17, 42; m 63; c 1. NEUROSCIENCES, GERONTOLOGY. *Educ:* Duke Univ, BS, 63; Stanford Univ, PhD(pharmacol), 69. *Prof Exp:* Fel neurosci, Med Ctr, Duke Univ, 69-71 & Ctr for Aging, 71-74, asst prof, Dept Physiol, 74-76; asst prof, 76-81, ASSOC PROF, DEPT PSYCHIAT, UNIV WASH, 81- *Concurrent Pos:* Preceptor, NIH Res Training Prog & sr fel sleep res, Ctr for Study Aging, Duke Univ, 74-76; Dir sleep & aging prog, Seattle-Tacoma Vet Admin Hosp & Univ Wash, 76-; res grants, NIMH, 71-73, NC Alcoholism Res Authority, 74-76, Univ Wash, 76-78, Nat Inst Aging, 76-80 & Vet Admin Merit Rev, 78- *Mem:* Geront Soc; Neurosci Soc; Asn for Psychophysiol Study Sleep; AAAS. *Res:* Neurobiology of aging, including sleep/wakefulness patterns, neuroendocrine rhythms, electroencephalographic signal analysis by computer; correlation of neurobiological changes with neuroanatomical change in normal aging and in Alzheimer's disease. *Mailing Add:* Dept Psychiat Univ Wash Seattle WA 98195

PRINZ, WILLIAM CHARLES, b Dayton, Ohio, Oct 11, 28; m 52; c 2. ECONOMIC GEOLOGY. *Educ:* Ohio State Univ, BSc, 50, MSc, 52; Yale Univ, PhD(geol), 59. *Prof Exp:* GEOLOGIST, US GEOL SURV, 53- *Mem:* Geol Soc Am; Soc Econ Geologists; Am Inst Mining, Metall & Petrol Engrs. *Res:* Metallic mineral deposits and resources. *Mailing Add:* US Geol Surv Nat Ctr Stop 913 Reston VA 22092

PRIOLA, DONALD VICTOR, b Chicago, Ill, Sept 8, 38; m 60; c 4. PHYSIOLOGY, PHARMACOLOGY. *Educ:* Loyola Univ Chicago, BS, 60, PhD(physiol), 66. *Prof Exp:* Res assoc physiol, Stritch Sch Med, Loyola Univ Chicago, 65-66; from instr to assoc prof pharmacol, 66-70, assoc prof physiol, 70-75, asst chmn dept, 71-78, PROF PHYSIOL, SCH MED, UNIV NMEX, 75-, CHMN DEPT, 79- *Concurrent Pos:* NIH res grant, 66-, NIH career develop award, 70-75; prin investr, USPHS Grant, 67-; responsible investr, Life Ins Med Res Fund grant, 68-71; NMex Heart Asn grant, 70-71; mem cardiovasc/pulmonary study sect, Nat Heart, Lung & Blood Inst, 80-84; ed, J Pharmacol & Exp Therapeut, 80- *Mem:* Am Physiol Soc; Am Heart Asn; Fedn Am Socs Exp Biol; Am Soc Pharmacol & Exp Therapeut; Soc Exp Biol & Med. *Res:* Nervous control of the heart and vascular system; autonomic nervous system especially related to the pharmacology of drugs affecting the cardiovascular system. *Mailing Add:* Dept of Physiol Univ of NMex Sch of Med Albuquerque NM 87131

PRIOR, DAVID JAMES, US citizen. NEUROBIOLOGY. *Educ:* Olivet Col, AB, 65; Cent Mich Univ, MS, 68; Univ Va, PhD(physiol), 72. *Prof Exp:* Fel neurobiol & behav, Princeton Univ, 72-73; asst prof, 73-78, ASSOC PROF BIOL SCI, UNIV KY, 78- *Mem:* Soc Neurosci; Am Soc Zool; Sigma Xi; Am Soc Physiol; AAAS. *Res:* Use of certain molluscan nervous systems to study aspects of cyclical motor output, including initiation, maintenance, modulation, and termination of the rhythm. *Mailing Add:* Sch of Biol Sci Univ Ky Lexington KY 40506

PRIOR, JEAN CUTLER, b Akron, Ohio, Nov 5, 40; m 64. GEOLOGY, GEOMORPHOLOGY. *Educ:* Purdue Univ, BA, 62; Univ Ill, MS, 64. *Prof Exp:* RES GEOLOGIST, IOWA GEOL SURV, 65- *Mem:* Geol Soc Am; Asn Am Geogr. *Res:* Quaternary geology; environmental geology; history of geology; water resources. *Mailing Add:* Iowa Geol Surv 123 N Capitol Iowa City IA 52242

PRIOR, JOHN ALAN, b Columbus, Ohio, Apr 17, 13; m 36; c 3. MEDICINE. *Educ:* Ohio State Univ, BS, 35, MD, 38. *Prof Exp:* Instr med, Univ Cincinnati, 43-44; from instr to assoc prof, 44-51, from assoc dean to dean col med, 63-72, PROF MED, OHIO STATE UNIV, 51- *Concurrent Pos:* Consult, USPHS, 46-51, Ohio State Dept Health, 48-51, Vet Admin Hosp & US Air Force Hosp, Dayton, 60-; mem bd dirs, Ohio State Univ Res Found & Willson Children's Ctr. *Mem:* Am Col Chest Physicians; Am Thoracic Soc; fel Am Col Physicians. *Res:* Pulmonary and fungus diseases; physical diagnosis. *Mailing Add:* Ohio State Univ Hosp Rm 340 466 W Tenth Ave Columbus OH 43210

PRIOR, JOHN THOMPSON, b St Albans, Vt, Oct 8, 17; m; c 6. PATHOLOGY. *Educ:* Univ Vt, BS, 39, MD, 43. *Prof Exp:* Lab dir, Crouse Irving Hosp, 50-71; PROF PATH, COL MED, STATE UNIV NY UPSTATE MED CTR, 54-, ASSOC LAB DIR, UNIV HOSP, 50- *Concurrent Pos:* Attend pathologist, Vet Admin Hosp, 53- *Mem:* Am Asn Path & Bact; Am Fedn Clin Res. *Res:* Pathologic anatomy; cardiovascular and pulmonary disease. *Mailing Add:* Community Gen Hosp Syracuse NY 13215

PRIOR, MICHAEL HERBERT, b Riverside, Calif, July 14, 39; m 63; c 2. PHYSICS. *Educ:* Pomona Col, BA, 61; Univ Calif, Berkeley, PhD(physics), 67. *Prof Exp:* Res physicist, Lawrence Berkeley Lab, Univ Calif, 67-68 & Roman Cath Univ Nijmegen, 68-69; RES PHYSICIST, LAWRENCE BERKELEY LAB, UNIV CALIF, 69- *Mem:* Am Phys Soc. *Res:* Atomic beam magnetic resonance; atomic hyperfine structure; lifetimes of metastable ions; magnetic resonance spectroscopy of stored ions; optical pumping; laser fluorescence spectroscopy; ion-neutral collision studies. *Mailing Add:* Lawrence Berkeley Lab Univ of Calif Berkeley CA 94720

PRIOR, PAUL VERDAYNE, b Cedar Rapids, Iowa, July 2, 21; m 43; c 2. PLANT MORPHOLOGY, PLANT PHYSIOLOGY. *Educ:* Univ Iowa, BA, 46, MS, 47, PhD, 54. *Prof Exp:* Instr biol, Bethany Col Kans, 47-48; assoc prof, Northern Ill Univ, 48-56; prof, Tex Tech Univ, 56-70; PROF BIOL & CHMN DEPT, UNIV NEBR, OMAHA, 70- *Mem:* AAAS; Am Inst Biol Sci; Bot Soc Am; Am Bryol & Lichenological Soc. *Res:* Stem apex; bryophyte ecology and physiology. *Mailing Add:* Dept of Biol Univ of Nebr Omaha NE 68132

PRIOR, RICHARD MARION, b Dunedin, Fla, July 17, 42; m 64; c 2. NUCLEAR MEDICINE. *Educ:* Univ Fla, BS, 64, MS, 65, PhD(physics), 68. *Prof Exp:* Res assoc physics, Univ Notre Dame, 68-70; asst prof physics, 70-74, asst prof nuclear med, Sch Med, 72-74, assoc prof physics & assoc prof nuclear med, 74-81, PROF PHYSICS, SCH MED, UNIV ARK, LITTLE ROCK, 79- *Mem:* Am Phys Soc; Am Asn Physics Teachers. *Res:* Effects of fast neutrons on mammalian cells; neutron dosimetry; nuclear reactions and scattering using polarized beams. *Mailing Add:* Dept of Physics Univ of Ark Little Rock AR 72204

PRIOR, RONALD LEON, b McCook, Nebr, Mar 9, 45; m 67; c 1. ANIMAL NUTRITION, BIOCHEMISTRY. *Educ:* Univ Nebr-Lincoln, BS, 67; Cornell Univ, PhD(nutrit), 71. *Prof Exp:* Trainee, NY State Vet Col, Cornell Univ, 71-73; RES CHEMIST, US MEAT ANIMAL RES CTR, 73- *Concurrent Pos:* Fac mem, Univ Nebr-Lincoln, 73- *Mem:* Am Soc Animal Sci; Am Inst Nutrit. *Res:* Nutritional influences in fetal development; gluconeogenesis in the mature and fetal ruminant animal; lactic acid metabolism and lipid biosynthesis in the ruminant. *Mailing Add:* US Meat Animal Res Ctr PO Box 166 Clay Center NE 68933

PRIORESCHI, PLINIO, b Florence, Italy, May 20, 30; US citizen; m 67; c 2. PHARMACOLOGY, MEDICINE. *Educ:* Univ Pavia, MD, 54; Univ Montreal, PhD(exp med), 61. *Prof Exp:* Res assoc exp med, Univ Montreal, 61-63; asst prof pharmacol, Queen's Univ, Ont, 63-67; assoc prof, 67-73, PROF PHARMACOL, CREIGHTON UNIV, 73-, ASST PROF MED, 67- *Concurrent Pos:* Chief, Creighton Geriat Serv, Douglas County Hosp, Omaha, Nebr, 71-78; attend physician, Vet Admin Hosp, Omaha. *Mem:* Am Soc Pharmacol & Exp Therapeut; Can Physiol Soc; Pharmacol Soc Can. *Res:* Experimental cardiac necroses. *Mailing Add:* 1315 S 79th St Omaha NE 68124

PRIPSTEIN, MORRIS, b Montreal, Que, Nov 24, 35; m 58; c 2. PHYSICS. *Educ:* McGill Univ, BEng, 57; Univ Calif, Berkeley, PhD(physics), 62. *Prof Exp:* Asst physics, Univ Calif, Berkeley, 57-62; res physicist, Col France, 62-63; res asst prof elem particle physics, Univ Ill, 63-65; res physicist, 65-73, GROUP LEADER, LAWRENCE BERKELEY LAB, UNIV CALIF, 73- *Concurrent Pos:* Atomic Energy Commissariat France Louis de Broglie fel, 62-63. *Mem:* Am Phys Soc. *Res:* Experimental elementary particle physics. *Mailing Add:* Dept of Physics Lawrence Berkeley Lab Berkeley CA 94720

PRISBREY, KEITH A, b St George, Utah, June 23, 45; m 69; c 4. METALLURGY, MINERAL PROCESSING. *Educ:* Univ Utah, BS, 69, PhD(metall), 76; Stanford Univ, MS, 71. *Prof Exp:* Res officer minerals process, Julius Kruttschwitt Res Ctr, Univ Queensland, 72-73; res engr, Amax Res, 75-76; ASST PROF METALL, UNIV IDAHO, 76- *Concurrent Pos:* Res grants, Univ Idaho, 77-78, NSF, 78-80. *Mem:* Am Inst Metall Eng; Sigma Xi. *Res:* Comminution; control of mineral processing plants; surface chemistry of minerals; hydrometallurgy. *Mailing Add:* Dept of Mining & Univ of Idaho Moscow ID 83843

PRISTOU, ROBERT, b Fiume, Italy, May 18, 20; nat US; c 5. PLANT PATHOLOGY. *Educ:* Waynesburg Col, BS, 49; WVa Univ, MS & PhD(plant path), 58. *Prof Exp:* Staff mycologist, C A Swanson's & Sons & Campbell Soup Co, Nebr, 55-57; sanitarian, Omaha Douglas County Health Dept, 57-58; plant pathologist, Exp Sta, 69-74, ASSOC PROF PLANT PATH & PHYSIOL, VA POLYTECH INST & STATE UNIV, 58- *Concurrent Pos:* Exten specialist plant path, Exp Sta, 58-78. *Mem:* Mycol Soc Am; Am Phytopath Soc. *Res:* Extension pathology; vegetable crops; soybean, small grains, corn and peanut diseases; plant disease diagnosis. *Mailing Add:* Dept of Plant Path & Physiol Va Polytech Inst & State Univ Blacksburg VA 24061

PRITCHARD, ALAN BRYAN, b New York, NY, Aug 13, 43. MEDICAL & HEALTH SCIENCES. *Educ:* Middlebury Col, AB, 65; Cornell Univ MNS, 67, PhD(nutrit), 77; Am Bd Toxicol, dipl. *Prof Exp:* Sr toxicologist, 70-77, res scientist, 77-82, MGR TOXICOL, GEN FOODS CORP, 82- *Mem:* NY Acad Sci; AAAS. *Res:* Metabolism and metabolite formation; pharmacokinetics as it relates to risk evaluation and the interaction of toxicity on experimental carcinogenesis. *Mailing Add:* 555 S Broadway Tarrytown NY 10591

PRITCHARD, AUSTIN WYATT, b Loma Linda, Calif, Mar 8, 29; m 49 & 72; c 5. COMPARATIVE PHYSIOLOGY. *Educ:* Stanford Univ, AB, 48, MA, 49; Univ Hawaii, PhD(zool), 53. *Prof Exp:* From instr to assoc prof, 53-63, PROF ZOOL, ORE STATE UNIV, 63- *Mem:* Fel AAAS; Am Soc Zoologists; Soc Gen Physiol; Marine Biol Asn UK. *Res:* Body fluid regulation in aquatic animals; metabolism of fish; metabolism of marine intertidal organisms. *Mailing Add:* Dept of Zool Ore State Univ Corvallis OR 97331

PRITCHARD, DAVID EDWARD, b New York, NY, Oct 15, 41; m 67; c 2. ATOMIC PHYSICS, MOLECULAR PHYSICS. *Educ:* Calif Inst Technol, BS, 62; Harvard Univ, PhD(physics), 68. *Prof Exp:* Mem staff, Div Sponsored Res, 68, from instr to asst prof, 68-75, assoc prof, 75-80, PROF PHYSICS, MASS INST TECHNOL, 80- *Concurrent Pos:* Dir, Interbuild Corp, 69-73. *Mem:* Am Phys Soc. *Res:* Atomic collisions; inter-atomic forces; van der Waals molecules; dye laser spectroscopy. *Mailing Add:* 88 Washington Ave Cambridge MA 02140

PRITCHARD, DAVID GRAHAM, b Montreal, Que, Oct 2, 45; m 75. CARBOHYDRATE CHEMISTRY, PROTEIN CHEMISTRY. *Educ:* Univ Sask, BA, 66, Hons, 67; Univ Calif, Los Angeles, PhD(biochem), 75. *Prof Exp:* Jr res scientist biochem, Dept Immunol, Nat Med Ctr, City of Hope, 73-75, asst res scientist, 75-80; MEM FAC, DEPT MICROBIOL, UNIV ALA, BIRMINGHAM, 80- *Mem:* Sigma Xi. *Res:* Glycoprotein structure determination. *Mailing Add:* Dept Microbiol Univ Ala Univ Sta Birmingham AL 35299

PRITCHARD, DAVID LEE, b Mountain View, Okla, Apr 15, 39; m 61; c 2. FISHERIES MANAGEMENT. *Prof Exp:* Dist biologist fishery mgt, Tex Parks & Wildlife Dept, 68-70, res proj leader, 70-72, dir, Inland Fisheries Mgt, 72-76, chief, Inland Fisheries, 76-77; ASST CHIEF GRANT PROG BR, NAT MARINE FISHERIES SERV, 77- Tex Fisheries Worker Award, Am Fisheries Soc, 77. *Mem:* Am Fisheries Soc; Inland Com Fisheries Asn. *Res:* Reservoir fisheries management; fish marking techniques; hooking mortality of recreational fishes. *Mailing Add:* Nat Marine Fisheries Serv 9450 Koger Blvd St Petersburg FL 33702

PRITCHARD, DONALD WILLIAM, b Santa Ana, Calif, Oct 20, 22; m 43; c 5. OCEANOGRAPHY. *Educ:* Univ Calif, Los Angeles, AB, 46; Scripps Inst, Univ Calif, San Diego, MS, 48, PhD(oceanog), 51. *Prof Exp:* Chg current anal sect, Scripps Inst, Univ Calif, 46-47; oceanogr, Navy Electronics Lab, Calif, 47-49; from assoc dir to dir, Chesapeake Bay Inst, 49-74, prof oceanog, 58-77, PROF EARTH & PLANETARY SCI, CHESAPEAKE BAY INST, JOHNS HOPKINS UNIV, 78- *Concurrent Pos:* Consult, Comt Hydraul & Waterways Exp Sta, Corps Engrs, US Dept Army, 54-; mem, Bd Rev Dept Natural Resources, Md, 59-; mem radiation adv bd, Health Dept, 60-; mem comt oceanog, Nat Acad Sci, 61-, chmn panel radioactivity in ocean, 62-66; mem, Air Pollution Control Coun, Md, 66-; mem adv comt isotopes & radiation develop, AEC, 66-; mem steering comt & environ qual comt, Gov Sci Adv Coun, State of Md, 71. *Mem:* AAAS; Am Meteorol Soc; Am Soc Limnol & Oceanog (vpres, 55-56); Am Geophys Union. *Res:* Dynamics of estuarine circulation and mixing; inshore and coastal oceanography; turbulent diffusion of natural waters. *Mailing Add:* Chesapeake Bay Inst Johns Hopkins Univ Baltimore MD 21218

PRITCHARD, ERNEST THACKERAY, b Ottawa, Ont, Mar 29, 28. BIOCHEMISTRY. *Educ:* Carleton Univ, BSc, 52; McGill Univ, MSc, 54; Univ Western Ont, PhD(biochem), 57. *Prof Exp:* Asst prof biochem, Univ Alta, 57-61; Nat Multiple Schlerosis Soc fel, McLean Hosp, Harvard Univ, 61-62; assoc prof, 62-70, PROF BIOCHEM & ORAL BIOL, UNIV MAN, 70- *Mem:* Am Soc Neurochem; Int Soc Neurochem; Can Biochem Soc; Nutrit Soc Can; Brit Biochem Soc. *Res:* Lipid metabolism of the nervous tissue during growth and development; secretion mechanisms of salivary glands and placental tissues. *Mailing Add:* Dept of Oral Biol Univ of Man Winnipeg MB R3E 0W3 Can

PRITCHARD, G IAN, b Alcove, Que, Nov 28, 29; m 56; c 4. FISHERIES. *Educ:* McGill Univ, BSc, 52; Univ Vt, MS, 54; NC State Univ, PhD(nutrit), 59. *Prof Exp:* Res scientist, Animal Res Inst, Can Dept Agr, 58-64; assoc ed & sci adv to chmn, Fisheries Res Bd, Can, 65-71; aquacult coordr, Fisheries Serv, Environ Can, 71-76, assoc dir fisheries res, 76-80, DIR AQUACULT & RESOURCE DEVELOP, FISHERIES & OCEANS, CAN, 80- *Concurrent Pos:* Consult int develop, Turkey, 75, Latin Am, 77 & Philippines, 81. *Mem:* Am Fisheries Soc; Nutrit Soc Can; Agr Inst Can. *Res:* Aquaculture; applied nutrition, fish health strategic planning. *Mailing Add:* 520 Denbury Ave Ottawa ON K2A 2N7 Can

PRITCHARD, GLYN O, b Bangor, Wales, Sept 26, 31; m 60; c 3. PHYSICAL CHEMISTRY. *Educ:* Univ Manchester, BSc, 52, PhD, 55. *Prof Exp:* Nat Res Coun Can fel phys chem, 55-57; phys chemist, Defence Res Bd Can, Royal Mil Col Can, 57-58; from asst prof to assoc prof, 58-69, PROF CHEM, UNIV CALIF, SANTA BARBARA, 69- *Mem:* Am Chem Soc. *Res:* Fluorine chemistry; kinetics; photochemistry. *Mailing Add:* Dept of Chem Univ of Calif Santa Barbara CA 93106

PRITCHARD, GORDON, b Burton-on-Trent, Eng, Feb 9, 39; m 63; c 2. ENTOMOLOGY. *Educ:* Univ London, BSc, 60; Univ Alta, PhD(entom), 63. *Prof Exp:* Res scientist, Commonwealth Sci & Indust Res Orgn, Australia, 63-66; sessional instr entom, Univ Alta, 66-67; from spec instr to assoc prof, 67-70, PROF BIOL, UNIV CALGARY, 76- *Mem:* Can Soc Zoologists; Entom Soc Can; Royal Entom Soc London; Sigma Xi; Int Soc Odontol. *Res:* Structure, behavior and population ecology of insects. *Mailing Add:* Dept of Biol Univ of Calgary Calgary AB T2N 1N4 Can

PRITCHARD, HAYDEN N, b Bangor, Pa, Feb 13, 33; m 62; c 2. BOTANY, HISTOCHEMISTRY. *Educ:* Princeton Univ, AB, 55; Lehigh Univ, MS, 60, PhD(biol), 63. *Prof Exp:* Instr biol, Cedar Crest Col, 59-60; res asst, Lehigh Univ, 59-62; res fel path, Univ Fla, 62-63, asst prof biol, 63-64; asst prof, 64-70, ASSOC PROF BIOL, LEHIGH UNIV, 70- *Concurrent Pos:* Co-investr, Am Cancer Soc res grant, 66-67. *Res:* Botanical histochemistry and botanical growth and development, especially botanical embryology. *Mailing Add:* Dept of Biol Lehigh Univ Bethlehem PA 18015

PRITCHARD, HUW OWEN, b Bangor, Wales, July 23, 28; m 56; c 2. PHYSICAL CHEMISTRY, THEORETICAL CHEMISTRY. *Educ:* Univ Manchester, BSc, 48, MSc, 49, PhD(chem), 51, DSc, 64. *Prof Exp:* From asst lectr to lectr chem, Univ Manchester, 51-65; PROF CHEM, YORK UNIV, 65- *Concurrent Pos:* Vis res fel, Calif Inst Technol, 57-58. *Mem:* Royal Soc Chem; fel Royal Soc Can. *Res:* Thermochemistry; kinetics, photochemistry and thermodynamics of simple systems; theory of unimolecular reactions and of relaxation processes in gaseous systems. *Mailing Add:* Dept of Chem York Univ Downsview ON M3J 1P3 Can

PRITCHARD, JACK ARTHUR, b Painesville, Ohio, July 25, 21; m 45; c 3. OBSTETRICS & GYNECOLOGY. *Educ:* Ohio Northern Univ, BS, 42; Western Reserve Univ, MD, 46. *Prof Exp:* Intern, Univ Hosps, Western Reserve Univ, 46-47, fel pharmacol, Univ, 47-48, resident obstet & gynec, Hosps, 50-54, Oglebay fel, Univ, 52-54, asst prof, 54-55; PROF OBSTET & GYNEC & CHMN DEPT, UNIV TEX HEALTH SCI CTR DALLAS, 55- *Concurrent Pos:* Chief obstet & gynec serv, Parkland Mem Hosp, Dallas, 55-; consult, Vet Admin Hosp, St Paul Hosp, Baylor Hosp & Methodist Hosp, Dallas, William Beaumont Army Hosp, El Paso, Brooke Army Hosp, Ft Sam Houston, US Air Force Hosp, Lackland AFB & Carswell AFB, Ft Worth; mem obstet & gynec test comt, Nat Bd Med Examr, 56-60; mem human embryol & develop study sect, NIH, 60-64. *Mem:* Soc Gynec Invest; Am Asn Obstet & Gynec; Am Col Obstet & Gynec. *Res:* Res blood cell production and destruction; blood coagulation. *Mailing Add:* 5323 Harry Hines Blvd Dallas TX 75235

PRITCHARD, JAMES EDWARD, b Swaledale, Iowa, Jan 28, 22; m 42; c 3. CHEMISTRY. *Educ:* Univ Iowa, BA, 42, MS, 43; Purdue Univ, PhD(pharmaceut chem), 48. *Prof Exp:* Asst chem, Univ Iowa, 42-43; res chemist, Phillips Petrol Co, Okla, 43-46; asst chem, Purdue Univ, 46-47; res chemist, 48-59, mgr polyolefins br, Res Div, 59-74, consult, Mgt Serv, 73-74, DIR DEVELOP PLANNING, PHILLIPS PETROL CO, 74- *Mem:* Am Chem Soc; Am Mgt Asn. *Res:* Surface chemistry; halogenation of organic compounds; synthetic rubber emulsion polymers; study of surface lipids of skin; polyolefins. *Mailing Add:* 2219 Skyline Dr Bartlesville OK 74003

PRITCHARD, JOHN B, b Buffalo, NY, July 31, 43; m 67; c 1. RENAL PHYSIOLOGY, TRANSPORT. *Educ:* Oberlin Col, AB, 65; Harvard Univ, PhD(physiol), 70. *Prof Exp:* NSF fel, State Univ NY Upstate Med Ctr, 70-71; NIH fel, Mt Desert Island Biol Lab, 71-72; asst prof, 72-76, ASSOC PROF PHYSIOL, MED UNIV SC, 76-; RES PHYSIOLOGIST, NAT INST ENVIRON HEALTH SCI, 76-, HEAD, MARINE LAB, 79- *Concurrent Pos:* Adj assoc prof pharmacol, Sch Med, Univ Fla, 79- *Mem:* Am Physiol Soc; Am Soc Zoologists; Am Soc Pharmacol & Exp Therapeut. *Res:* Interaction of environmental contaminants with physiological systems, particularly renal function and transport. *Mailing Add:* Lab Pharmacol Nat Inst Environ Health Sci c/o C V Whitney Lab Rte 1 Box 121 St Augustine FL 32084

PRITCHARD, JOHN PAUL, JR, b Washington, Pa, June 23, 29; m 57; c 2. ELECTRICAL ENGINEERING, MATHEMATICS. *Educ:* Univ Okla, BA, 50, MS, 55; Iowa State Univ, PhD(elec eng), 60; Univ Dallas, MBA, 78. *Prof Exp:* Comput programmer, Boeing Airplane Co, Kans, 55-56, group head appl math serv group, 57-60; mem tech staff, Corp Res & Eng Div, Tex Instruments, Inc, 60, sect head adv systs res, 61-64, br mgr info components res, 65-71; div staff engr, Electronic Eng Div, Martin Marietta Corp, 71-74; proj engr, 75-80, SR SPECIALIST, AIRCRAFT SYSTS GROUP, E-SYSTS INC, 80- *Mem:* Inst Elec & Electronics Engrs. *Res:* intrusion detection systems and devices; electronic warfare systems; optical counter-measures; digital computer design; thin film technology; data processing theory. *Mailing Add:* 5404 Stonewall St Greenville TX 75401

PRITCHARD, MARY (LOUISE) HANSON, b Lincoln, Nebr, July 16, 24; m 56. PARASITOLOGY. *Educ:* Univ Nebr, BS, 46, MA, 49. *Prof Exp:* Assoc cur, State Mus, 48-57, res assoc parasitol, 59-68, asst prof zool, 68-74, assoc cur, 68-72, assoc prof, 74-80, PROF ZOOL, UNIV NEBR, LINCOLN, 80-; CUR PARASITOL, HAROLD W MANTER LAB, NEBR STATE MUS, 72- *Concurrent Pos:* Mem, Coun on Standards, Asn Systs Collections, 73-79, Coun on Biol Nomenclature, 81- & ecol adv comt, Sci Adv Bd, US Environ Protection Agency, 74-78. *Mem:* Fel AAAS; Soc Syst Zool; Am Soc Parasitol; Am Micros Soc; Sigma Xi. *Res:* Taxonomy, geographical distribution and host-parasite relationships of digenetic trematodes. *Mailing Add:* Div of Parasitol Univ of Nebr State Mus Lincoln NE 68588

PRITCHARD, PARMELY HERBERT, b Evanston, Ill, Aug 25, 41; m 64; c 2. MICROBIAL ECOLOGY. *Educ:* Univ RI, BS, 63; Cornell Univ, MS, 66, PhD(microbiol), 69. *Prof Exp:* Fel, Woods Hole Oceanog Inst, 69-71; assoc prof microbiol, State Univ NY Col Brockport, 71-78; ENVIRON SCIENTIST, US ENVIRON PROTECTION AGENCY, 78- *Mem:* Soc Indust Microbiol; Am Soc Microbiol. *Res:* Microbial degradation of organic pollutants; oil degradation; physiology of autochthonous bacterial populations in aquatic environments; continuous culture in microbial ecology; fate and transport of toxic organic pollutants in estuarine environments. *Mailing Add:* US Environ Protection Agency Environ Res Lab Gulf Breeze FL 32561

PRITCHARD, ROBERT LESLIE, b Irvington, NJ, Sept 8, 24; m 48. APPLIED PHYSICS. *Educ:* Brown Univ, BSc, 46; Harvard Univ, MSc, 47, PhD(acoust), 50. *Prof Exp:* Tech asst, Bell Tel Labs, Inc, 42-43; res asst, Acoust Res Lab, Harvard Univ, 47-50; res assoc, Res Lab, Gen Elec Co, 50-57; from develop engr to staff dir eng, Semiconductor Div, Tex Instruments, Inc, 57-63; dir eng, Motorola, Inc, 63-64; prof elec eng, Stanford Univ, 64-70; MEM RES & DEVELOP STAFF, GEN ELEC CO, 70- *Concurrent Pos:* Tech adv, US Nat Comt, Int Electrotech Comn Semiconductor Devices. *Mem:* Acoust Soc Am; fel Inst Elec & Electronics Engrs. *Res:* Acoustics, sound radiation and reception problems in technical acoustics; transistor, from electric-circuit point of view; integrated circuits. *Mailing Add:* Res & Develop Gen Elec Co 3135 Easton Turnpike Fairfield CT 06431

PRITCHARD, WALTER HERBERT, b Hancock, NY, 1910; m 39; c 6. MEDICINE. *Educ:* Hamilton Col, AB, 32; Harvard Univ, MD, 36. *Prof Exp:* Rees fel med, 39-40, teaching fel, 40-42, from instr to prof, 42-65; chief of staff, Univ Hosps, Cleveland, 71-78; Argyl J Beams prof, 65-78, EMER ARGYL J BEAMS PROF MED, SCH MED, CASE WESTERN RESERVE UNIV, 78- *Mem:* Am Soc Clin Invest; Soc Exp Biol & Med; Asn Am Physicians; Am Col Physicians. *Res:* Clinical cardiology and use of isotopes in determining total and regional blood flows, for example cardiac output and renal and myocardial flow. *Mailing Add:* Univ Hosps Cleveland 2065 Adelbert Rd Cleveland OH 44106

PRITCHARD, WENTON MAURICE, b Wilson, NC, Nov 8, 31. SOLID STATE PHYSICS. *Educ:* NC State Univ, BNE, 54, MSNE, 55; Ga Inst Technol, PhD(physics), 60. *Prof Exp:* Nuclear engr, Newport News Shipbuilding & Dry Dock Co, 55-57, sr lab analyst, 60-62; PROF PHYSICS, OLD DOMINION UNIV, 62-, PROF GEOPHYS SCI, 78- *Concurrent Pos:* Tech asst expert, Int Atomic Energy Agency, 62-63; NASA grant, Old Dominion Univ, 65-68; tech asst expert, UNESCO, 68-69. *Mem:* AAAS; Am Phys Soc; Am Nuclear Soc. *Res:* Radiation effects on solids; physical properties of metals; nuclear reactor theory. *Mailing Add:* Dept of Physics Old Dominion Univ Norfolk VA 23508

PRITCHARD, WILBUR L(OUIS), b New York, NY, May 31, 23; m 49; c 3. ELECTRICAL ENGINEERING. *Educ:* City Col New York, BSEE, 43. *Prof Exp:* Jr engr, Philco Corp, Pa, 42-46; sr commun engr, Raytheon Co, Mass, 46-49, engr, Microwave Sect, 49-54, mgr microwave-transmitter br, 54-57, dept mgr surface radar, 58-59, mgr eng, surface radar & navig opers, 59-60, dir eng, Europe, 60-62; group dir, Commun Satellite Systs, Aerospace Corp, 62-67; asst vpres & dir, Comsat Labs, Commun Satellite Corp, 67-72, vpres & dir, 72-73; pres, Fairchild Space & Electronics Co, 73-74; PRES, SATELLITE SYSTS ENG, INC, 74-; PRES, DIRECT BROADCAST SATELLITE CORP, 80- *Concurrent Pos:* Chmn panel broadcast satellites, Nat Acad Sci, 67-68. *Honors & Awards:* Aerospace Commun Award, Am Inst Aeronaut & Astronaut, 72. *Mem:* Fel Am Inst Aeronaut & Astronaut; fel Inst Elec & Electronics Engrs; NY Acad Sci. *Res:* Communications satellites; microwave systems. *Mailing Add:* 7315 Wisconsin Ave Bethesda MD 20814

PRITCHARD, WILLIAM ROY, b Portage, Wis, Nov 15, 24; c 4. VETERINARY MEDICINE. *Educ:* Kans State Univ, DVM, 46; Univ Minn, PhD, 53; Univ Ind, JD, 57. *Hon Degrees:* DSc, Kans State Univ, 70, Purdue Univ, 77. *Prof Exp:* Asst prof vet sci, Univ Wis, 46-49; assoc prof vet med & head div, Univ Minn, 49-53; prof & dir cattle dis res, Purdue Univ, 53-57; prof vet sci & head dept, Univ Fla, 57-61; prof & assoc dir, Vet Med Res Inst, Iowa State Univ, 61-62; assoc dir, Agr Exp Sta, 62-72, PROF VET MED & DEAN SCH VET MED, UNIV CALIF, DAVIS, 62- *Concurrent Pos:* Mem bd consults agr sci, Rockefeller Found, 62-66; med consult, US Air Force, 63-64; mem panel world food supply, President's Sci Adv Comt, 66-67, panel biol & med, 69-71, construct sch vet med comt, USPHS, 67-70, comt vet med res & educ, Nat Acad Sci, 68-72 & adv comt res to USDA, 68-71; mem int task force, African Livestock Ctr, 71; chmn, Int Exec Comt Estab Int Lab Res Animal Dis, 72-73; mem, Joint Res Comt, Bd Int Food & Agr Develop, USAID, 77- *Mem:* Am Vet Med Asn; Am Pub Health Asn; US Animal Health Asn. *Res:* International development; veterinary medical law. *Mailing Add:* Sch of Vet Med Univ of Calif Davis CA 95616

PRITCHETT, ERVIN GARRISON, b Hamlet, NC, Mar 6, 20; m 42; c 1. ORGANIC CHEMISTRY. *Educ:* The Citadel, BS, 41; Johns Hopkins Univ, MA, 48, PhD(chem), 51. *Prof Exp:* Asst prof chem, Washington & Jefferson Col, 50-51; res assoc, 51-74, SR RES ASSOC, US INDUST CHEM CO, 74- *Mem:* Am Chem Soc. *Res:* Organic synthesis; organometallics; polyolefins; vinyl polymers; polyblends. *Mailing Add:* 10597 Swindon Ct Cincinnati OH 45241

PRITCHETT, JOHN FRANKLYN, b Evanston, Ill, June 30, 42; m 64; c 2. ENDOCRINOLOGY. *Educ:* Auburn Univ, BS, 65, MS, 68; Iowa State Univ, PhD(physiol), 73. *Prof Exp:* Asst prof biol, Lambuth Col, 67-70; instr physiol, Iowa State Univ, 71-72; ASSOC PROF PHYSIOL, AUBURN UNIV, 73- *Mem:* Sigma Xi. *Res:* Interaction of aging and/or environmental stressors with mammalian endocrine systems. *Mailing Add:* Dept of Zool & Entom Auburn Univ Auburn AL 36830

PRITCHETT, P(HILIP) W(ALTER), b Austin, Tex, July 31, 28; m 54; c 4. CHEMICAL ENGINEERING. *Educ:* Univ Tex, BS, 49, MS, 51; Univ Del, PhD(chem eng), 60. *Prof Exp:* Process engr, Ethyl Corp, 50-55; sr engr, Esso Res Labs, 58-66, res specialist, Esso Res & Eng Co, 66-70, ENG ASSOC, PLASTICS TECHNOL DIV, EXXON CHEM CO, 70- *Mem:* Am Inst Chem Engrs. *Res:* Process development and design in polymerization of olefins, polymer extrusion, flow of granular solids, conveying, reaction kinetics, absorption with reaction, phase equilibrium and petrochemical processes. *Mailing Add:* 317 S Burnett Baytown TX 77520

PRITCHETT, RANDALL FLOYD, b Oakland, Calif, Sept 28, 45; m 63; c 2. ANIMAL VIROLOGY. *Educ:* Univ Calif, Davis, AB, 69, PhD(microbiol), 73. *Prof Exp:* Res assoc virol, Sch Vet Med, Univ Calif, 71-73 & Univ Chicago, 73-76, res assoc & instr, 76-77; ASST PROF MICROBIOL, UNIV ARIZ, 77- *Concurrent Pos:* NIH fel, Dept Med & Comt on Virol, Univ Chicago, 74-76. *Mem:* Am Soc Microbiol. *Res:* Molecular events regulating virus expressions. *Mailing Add:* Dept of Microbiol Univ of Ariz Tucson AZ 85721

PRITCHETT, THOMAS RONALD, b Colorado City, Tex, Sept 2, 25; m 48; c 3. METALLURGY, PHYSICAL CHEMISTRY. *Educ:* Univ Tex, BS, 48, MA, 49, PhD(chem & chem eng), 51. *Prof Exp:* Res scientist corrosion, Defense Res Lab, US Navy, 48-51; res chemist, Monsanto Chem Co, 51-52; res engr & head corrosion, 52-60, tech mgr & lab mgr, 60-68, VPRES RES & DEVELOP, KAISER ALUMINUM & CHEM CORP, 68- *Concurrent Pos:* Instr chem, Univ Tex, 48-50; dir, Metal Properties Coun, 75-; chmn,

Aluminum Asn Tech Comt, 81- *Mem:* Fel Am Soc Metals; Am Inst Mining, Metall & Petrol Engrs; Nat Asn Corrosion Engrs; Am Chem Soc; Sigma Xi. *Res:* Solidification phenomena of molten aluminum; corrosion and inhibition of metals; surface chemistry and physics of metals; aluminum metallurgy. *Mailing Add:* Ctr for Technol PO Box 877 Pleasanton CA 94566

PRITCHETT, WILLIAM HENRY, b Davidson, NC, Jan 16, 30; m 53; c 2. DEVELOPMENTAL BIOLOGY. *Educ:* Davidson Col, BS, 51; Univ Va, PhD, 67. *Prof Exp:* From jr buyer to supvr, Vick Chem Co, 54-57; instr biol, Augusta Mil Acad, 57-58 & Woodberry Forest Sch, 58-63; asst prof, 67-70, assoc prof, 70-73, PROF BIOL, FAIRMONT COL, 73- *Concurrent Pos:* Pres fac Senate, Fairmont Col, 72-74. *Mem:* AAAS. *Res:* Regeneration in vertebrates; factors affecting the rate of regeneration. *Mailing Add:* Dept of Biol Fairmont State Col Fairmont WV 26554

PRITCHETT, WILLIAM LAWRENCE, b Lavaca, Ark, Sept 17, 18; m 49; c 4. FOREST SOILS. *Educ:* Univ Ark, BSA, 41; Iowa State Col, MS, 47, PhD(soils), 50. *Prof Exp:* Agriculturist, United Fruit Co, Guatemala, 41; res assoc, Iowa State Col, 46-48 & 49-50; asst soil chemist, 48-49, PROF SOIL SCI & FOREST SOIL SCIENTIST, UNIV FLA, 53- *Concurrent Pos:* Res agronomist, USDA & dir agr exp sta, Serv Agr Interam, Bolivia, 50-53; Fulbright lectr, Univ WI, Trinidad, 64; consult, Costa Rican Ministry of Agr, 66 & coordr coop res, Forest Fertilization Proj, 67- ; Bullard fel, Harvard Univ, 73-74; consult pulp & paper co, Fla, 55, Bahamas, 62, Venezuela, 75, French Guiana 76, Ala, 77 & UN Develop Prog/Food & Agr Orgn, 81. *Mem:* AAAS; fel Am Soc Agron; fel Soil Sci Soc Am; Sigma Xi. *Res:* Soil management of forests; improvement of methods and interpretation of results of soil tests; fertilizer evaluation; forest fertilization and tree nutrition. *Mailing Add:* Soil Sci Dept G171 Fla Gainesville FL 32611

PRITHAM, GORDON HERMAN, b Freeport, Maine, Apr 7, 07; m 32; c 4. PHYSIOLOGICAL CHEMISTRY. *Educ:* Pa State Col, BS, 30, MS, 31, PhD(physiol chem), 36; Nat Registry Clin Chem, cert. *Prof Exp:* From assoc prof to prof chem, Univ Scranton, 33-47; from assoc prof to prof physiol chem, Pa State Univ, 47-67; prof biochem, 67-75, assoc dean basic sci, 71-73, EMER PROF OSTEOP MED, KANSAS CITY COL, 73- *Concurrent Pos:* Consult, Mo State Dept Mental Health, 73-74; affil fac, Univ Mo, Kans City, 80-81. *Mem:* AAAS; Am Chem Soc; Am Asn Clin Chem; Am Asn Ment Deficiency; NY Acad Sci. *Res:* Metabolism of fungi; methods of blood analysis; biosynthesis of cholesterol; biochemistry of mental retardation; blood chemistry in relation to disease; survey of college courses in biochemistry. *Mailing Add:* 8415 Spring Valley Rd Raytown MO 64138

PRITSKER, A(DRIAN) ALAN B(ERYL), b Philadelphia, Pa, Feb 5, 33; m 56; c 4. INDUSTRIAL ENGINEERING. *Educ:* Columbia Univ, BSEE, 55, MSIE, 56; Ohio State Univ, PhD(stochastic processes), 61. *Prof Exp:* Dir systs anal, Battelle Mem Inst, 56-62; prof indust eng, Ariz State Univ, 62-69 & Va Polytech Inst, 69-70; prof indust eng & dir, Ctr Large-Scale Systs, Purdue Univ, West Lafayette, 70-81; PRES, PRITSKER & ASSOCS, INC, 73- *Concurrent Pos:* Consult, Battelle Mem Inst, 62-63, Rand Corp, 63- & Motorola, Inc, 65-68. *Honors & Awards:* H B Maynard Innovation Award, Am Inst Indust Engrs, 78. *Mem:* Fel Am Inst Indust Engrs; Opers Res Soc Am; Inst Mgt Sci; Am Soc Eng Educ. *Res:* Simulation; large-scale systems; developer of GASP and SLAM simulation languages; developer of Q-Gert network language. *Mailing Add:* Pritsker & Assocs PO Box 2413 West Lafayette IN 47906

PRITZLAFF, AUGUST H(ENRY), JR, b Culver, Ind, Aug 25, 24; m 52; c 2. CHEMICAL ENGINEERING. *Educ:* Northwestern Univ, PhD(chem eng), 52. *Prof Exp:* Chem engr res dept, Standard Oil Co Ind, 51-60; eng res dept, Swift & Co, 60-67; Commonwealth Assocs, 67-70; RES ENGR, BEATRICE FOODS RES CTR, CHICAGO, 70- *Mem:* Am Soc Naval Engrs; Am Inst Chem Engrs; Inst Food Technol. *Res:* Fluidization; unit operations; food processing mechanization. *Mailing Add:* Beatrice Foods Res Ctr 1526 S State St Chicago IL 60605

PRIVAL, MICHAEL JOSEPH, b New York, NY, Aug 22, 45. MUTAGENESIS. *Educ:* Columbia Col, BA, 66; Mass Inst Technol, PhD(microbiol), 72. *Prof Exp:* Proj dir, Ctr Sci Pub Interest, 72; microbiologist, US Environ Protection Agency, 73-76; RES MICROBIOLOGIST, US FOOD & DRUG ADMIN, 76- *Concurrent Pos:* Mem, Comt Diet, Nutrit & Cancer, Nat Acad Sci, 80-83. *Mem:* Environ Mutagen Soc; Am Soc Microbiol; Sigma Xi; AAAS. *Res:* Methodologies used for testing chemicals for mutagenicity in bacteria, particularly chemicals that are false negatives in standard test procedures, such as nitrosamines and azo dyes. *Mailing Add:* Genetic Toxicol Br Food & Drug Admin Washington DC 20204

PRIVETT, ORVILLE SAMUEL, b London, Ont, June 6, 19; nat US; m 49. AGRICULTURAL BIOCHEMISTRY. *Educ:* Univ Toronto, BSA, 42; McGill Univ, MSc, 44, PhD(agr biochem), 47. *Prof Exp:* Res fel agr biochem, Purdue Univ, 46-48; res fel, 49-52, asst prof biochem, 52-55, assoc prof agr biochem, 55-60, PROF AGR BIOCHEM, HORMEL INST, UNIV MINN, 60- *Honors & Awards:* Sci Award, Glycerol Producers Asn, 61; Stefano Fachini Medal, Italy, 68; Alton E Bailey Award, Am Oil Chemists' Soc, 78. *Mem:* Am Chem Soc; Sigma Xi; Am Oil Chemists' Soc; Am Soc Biol Chemists; NY Acad Sci. *Res:* Lipid biochemistry; nutrition; metabolism; preparation, fractionation and analysis of fatty acids and complex lipids; liquid chromatography-mass spectrometry of liquids; kinetics and mechanism of fatty peroxide decomposition; polymerization of fatty acids; rancidity and preservation of fatty foods. *Mailing Add:* Hormel Inst Univ of Minn 801 16th Ave NE Austin MN 55912

PRIVITERA, CARMELO ANTHONY, b Buffalo, NY, May 12, 23; m 48; c 6. BIOLOGY. *Educ:* Canisius Col, BS, 47; Univ Notre Dame, MS, 49; St Louis Univ, PhD(biol), 57. *Prof Exp:* Instr zool, Col St Thomas, 48-54, asst prof, 56-59; from asst prof to assoc prof biol, St Louis Univ, 59-65; assoc prof, 65-72, vchmn dept, 65-68, PROF BIOL, STATE UNIV NY BUFFALO, 73- *Mem:* Sigma Xi; Am Soc Zoologists; Am Physiol Soc; Am Soc Cryobiol; Ecol Soc Am. *Res:* Comparative physiology; depressed metabolism; temperature adaptation; environmental physiology; physiological adaptation of cells and organisms to cold, metals and aging. *Mailing Add:* Dept of Biol State Univ NY Buffalo NY 14260

PRIVITERA, PHILIP JOSEPH, b New York, NY, Aug 29, 38; m 61; c 3. PHARMACOLOGY. *Educ:* St John's Univ, NY, BS, 59; Albany Med Col, PhD(pharmacol), 66. *Prof Exp:* Fel pharmacol, Col Med, Univ Cincinnati, 66-68, from instr pharmacol to asst prof exp med & pharmacol, 68-72; ASSOC PROF PHARMACOL, COL MED, MED UNIV SC, 72- *Mem:* Sigma Xi; Am Soc Pharmacol & Exp Therapeut; NY Acad Sci; Am Fedn Clin Res. *Res:* Cardiovascular pharmacology; reinin-angiotensin system; central nervous system control of blood pressure and renin release. *Mailing Add:* Dept of Pharmacol Med Univ of SC Charleston SC 29403

PRIVOTT, WILBUR JOSEPH, JR, b Chowan County, NC, Oct 8, 38; m 60. TECHNICAL MANAGEMENT, COMMERCIAL DEVELOPMENT. *Educ:* NC State Univ, BS, 61, PhD(chem eng), 65. *Prof Exp:* Res chem engr, Chemstrand Res Ctr, Inc Div, 64-68, group leader, New Enterprise Div, 68-71, prod develop mgr, 71-73, dir commercial prods div, 73-78, DIR PROD MGT, MONSANTO CO, 78- *Mem:* Am Inst Chem Engrs. *Res:* Basic chemical engineering phenomena of heat transfer, momentum transfer, mass transfer, process control and reaction kinetics with analog and digital computer applications. *Mailing Add:* Monsanto Co 800 N Lindbergh Ave St Louis MO 63156

PRIZER, CHARLES J(OHN), b Lake Forest, Ill, Apr 24, 24; m 44; c 4. CHEMICAL ENGINEERING. *Educ:* Univ Ill, BS, 44; Drexel Inst, MS, 56. *Prof Exp:* Chem engr, Tenn Eastman Corp, Div, 44-45, co, 45-46; chem engr, Brooklyn Naval Shipyard, 46-47 & Edwal Labs, Inc, 47-51; chem engr, 51-54, group leader process develop, 54-57, head, Petrol Chem Res Lab, 57-63, supvr petrol chem res, 63-65, asst dir res, 65-68, mgr petrol chem dept, 68-70, PROD MGR, CHEM DIV, ROHM & HAAS CO, 70-, V PRES & GEN MGR ENG & ENVIRON CONTROL, 72-, ASST GEN MGR, INT DIV, 74-, CORP BUS GROUP DIR, INDUST CHEM, POLYMERS, RESINS & MONOMERS, 75-, REGIONAL DIR N AM, 78- *Concurrent Pos:* Lectr, Drexel Inst, 56-59. *Mem:* Am Inst Chem Engrs; Am Chem Soc. *Res:* Process research and development; pilot plant design and operation; process economics. *Mailing Add:* Rohm & Haas Co Independence Mall W Philadelphia PA 19105

PROAKIS, ANTHONY GEORGE, b Chios, Greece, May 26, 40; US citizen; m 63; c 3. PHARMACOLOGY. *Educ:* WVa Univ, BS, 62; Purdue Univ, PhD(pharmacol), 72. *Prof Exp:* Mgr, Medco Pharm Inc, 62-66, vpres, 66-67; mgr, Guardian Pharm Inc, 67-69; sr res pharmacologist, 72-77, res assoc, 77-80, MGR CARDIOVASC PHARMACOL, A H ROBINS CO, 80- *Mem:* AAAS; Sigma Xi; Soc Exp Biol Med. *Res:* Cardiovascular and autonomic pharmacology; mechanism of action of antihypertensive and cardiac antiarrhythmic agents. *Mailing Add:* A H Robins Res Labs 1211 Sherwood Ave Richmond VA 23220

PROAKIS, JOHN GEORGE, b Chios, Greece, June 10, 35; US citizen; m 68. ELECTRICAL ENGINEERING. *Educ:* Univ Cincinnati, BS, 59; Mass Inst Technol, MS, 61; Harvard Univ, PhD(eng), 67. *Prof Exp:* Staff mem elec eng, Mass Inst Technol, 59-63; res asst, Harvard Univ, 63-66; staff mem, Gen Tel & Electronics, 67-69; PROF ELEC ENG, NORTHEASTERN UNIV, 69- *Concurrent Pos:* Consult, Gen Tel & Electronics, 69-71 & 74-, Arthur D Little, Inc, 70-71, Stein Assocs, Inc, 70-74, EG&G, Inc, 71-72 & Digital Equip Corp, 77-78; NSF grant, Northeastern Univ, 71-78. *Mem:* Inst Elec & Electronics Engrs. *Res:* Communication systems; adaptive filtering and equalization; digital signal processing; data transmission; computer optimization techniques; radar detection and estimation. *Mailing Add:* Dept of Elec Eng Northeastern Univ 360 Huntington Ave Boston MA 02115

PROBER, DANIEL ETHAN, b Schenectady, NY, Oct 16, 48; m 70. LOW TEMPERATURE PHYSICS, SOLID STATE PHYSICS. *Educ:* Brandeis Univ, AB, 70; Harvard Univ, MA, 71, PhD(physics), 75. *Prof Exp:* asst prof eng & appl sci, 75-80, ASSOC PROF, APPL PHYSICS, YALE UNIV, 80- *Mem:* Am Phys Soc; Inst Elec & Electronics Engrs. *Res:* Superconductivity, especially research on superconducting quantum devices and materials; microstructure science and microlithography. *Mailing Add:* Appl Physics Yale Univ PO Box 2157 New Haven CT 06520

PROBER, MAURICE, b New York, NY, Dec 30, 18; m 42; c 3. ORGANIC CHEMISTRY, POLYMER CHEMISTRY. *Educ:* City Col New York, BS, 39; Cornell Univ, MS, 43, PhD(org chem), 46. *Prof Exp:* Res chemist, Commonwealth Fund for Study Respiratory Physiol, 39-40; asst org chem, Cornell Univ, 40-42; res chemist, Manhattan Proj, Cornell Univ, SAM Labs, Columbia Univ & Union Carbide Chem Corp, 42-46; res chemist, Gen Elec Co, 46-58, liaison scientist chem, Res & Develop Ctr, 58-61, mgr insulation develop, Wire & Cable Dept, 61-74, consult engr, 74-81. *Honors & Awards:* Student Medal, Am Inst Chemists. *Mem:* Am Chem Soc; Am Inst Chemists; Soc Plastics Eng; Inst Elec & Electronic Engrs. *Res:* Fluorinated organic compounds; high polymers; silicones; radiation chemistry; elastomers; dielectrics; corona; crosslinked polyolefins; polymer processing; patent evaluation; technology licensing; technology evaluation. *Mailing Add:* 116 Deep Wood Rd Fairfield CT 06430

PROBER, RICHARD, b Chicago, Ill, May 30, 37; m 59; c 3. ENVIRONMENTAL ENGINEERING, CHEMICAL ENGINEERING. *Educ:* Ill Inst Technol, BS, 57; Univ Wis, MS, 58, PhD(chem eng), 62. *Prof Exp:* Engr, Shell Develop Co, 61-65; chem engr, Aerochem Res Labs, Inc, NJ, 65-68; sr res scientist, Permutit Res Labs, NJ, 68-70; from asst prof to assoc prof chem eng, Case Western Reserve Univ, 70-77; sr engr & secy-treas, GMP Assoc Inc, 77-81; ENVIRON/CHEM ENGR, HAVENS & EMERSON INC, CLEVELAND, 81- *Concurrent Pos:* Adj prof chem eng, Case Western Reserve Univ, 77-79. *Honors & Awards:* EPRI Award, Int Ozone Inst, 77.

Mem: Water Pollution Control Fedn; Am Inst Chem Engrs; Am Chem Soc. *Res:* Water resources; water pollution control; membrane technology; ion exchange; industrial waste treatment. *Mailing Add:* Havens & Emerson Inc Bond Ct Bldg Cleveland OH 44113

PROBST, ALBERT HENRY, b Lawrenceburg, Ind, Jan 25, 12; m 39; c 2. AGRONOMY. *Educ:* Purdue Univ, BSA, 36, MS, 38, PhD(plant breeding, genetics), 48. *Prof Exp:* From jr agronomist to assoc agronomist in chg soybean invests in Ind, Bur Plant Indust, Soils & Agr Eng, USDA, Exp Sta, 36-50, res agronomist, Crops Res Div & prof agron, Univ, 50-70, EMER PROF AGRON, PURDUE UNIV, LAFAYETTE, 70- *Mem:* Fel Am Soc Agron; Am Soybean Asn. *Res:* Breeding new soybean varieties; genetics of soybeans; cultural studies; inheritance of leaf abscission and other characters in soybeans. *Mailing Add:* 418 Evergreen West Lafayette IN 47906

PROBST, GERALD WILLIAM, b Morris, Minn, May 4, 22; m 46; c 4. BIOCHEMISTRY. *Educ:* Col St Thomas, BS, 43; Univ Minn, MS, 49, PhD, 50. *Prof Exp:* Asst biochem, Univ Minn, 46-50; biochemist, 50-59, sr biochemist, 59-61, res scientist, 61-63, dept head insulin testing, 63-65, asst head agr anal develop, 65-67, head agr biochem, 67-69, DIR REGULATORY SERV, ELI LILLY & CO, 69- *Concurrent Pos:* Dir serving as liaison with state and fed regulatory agencies, Food & Drug Admin & Environ Protection Agency, Elanco Regulatory Serv. *Mem:* AAAS; Am Chem Soc. *Res:* Antibiotics; cancer; immunochemistry; pesticides; analytical biochemistry. *Mailing Add:* Eli Lilly & Co Elanco Regulatory Serv 740 S Ala St Indianapolis IN 46285

PROBSTEIN, RONALD F(ILMORE), b Bronx, NY, Mar 11, 28; m 50; c 1. MECHANICAL ENGINEERING. *Educ:* NY Univ, BME, 48; Princeton Univ, MSE, 50, AM, 51, PhD(aeronaut eng), 52. *Prof Exp:* Asst, Eng Res Div, NY Univ, 46-48, instr eng mech, 47-48; asst aeronaut eng, Princeton Univ, 48-52, res assoc, 52-53, asst prof, 53-54; from asst prof to prof eng, Brown Univ, 54-62; guest & Guggenheim fel, 60-61, PROF MECH ENG, MASS INST TECHNOL, 62- *Concurrent Pos:* Consult ed, Plenum Pub Corp, 67-; sr partner, Water Purification Assocs, 74-; mem, Assembly of Eng, Nat Res Coun, 80- *Honors & Awards:* Freeman award, Am Soc Mech Engrs, 71. *Mem:* Nat Acad Eng; fel Am Acad Arts & Sci; AAAS; fel Am Phys Soc; Am Soc Mech Engrs. *Res:* Water purification, desalination and synthetic fuel production. *Mailing Add:* Dept of Mech Eng Rm 3-246 Mass Inst of Technol Cambridge MA 02139

PROCACCINI, DONALD J, b Providence, RI, Oct 19, 39. DEVELOPMENTAL PHYSIOLOGY, SYSTEMATICS. *Educ:* Providence Col, AB, 61; Fordham Univ, MS, 63, PhD(biol), 66. *Prof Exp:* Adj instr biol, St Peter's Col, 64-65; instr, Pace Col, 65-66; from asst prof to assoc prof, 66-74, chmn dept, 72-75, prof biol, 74-77, vpres acad planning & develop, 75-80, PROF BIOL & ART, EMMANUEL COL, 80- *Mem:* Soc Study Evolution; Soc Develop Biol; Soc Syst Zool; Am Soc Zoologists; Sigma Xi. *Res:* Genetics; numerical taxonomy, evolution, zoogeography and systematics of Lepidoptera; developmental physiology; histochemistry, enzymology and histology of amphibian embryology, regeneration and teratogenesis; theoretical and computer models of development. *Mailing Add:* Dept Biol Emmanuel Col Boston MA 02115

PROCCI, WARREN R, b Staten Island, NY, Jan 19, 47; m 72. PSYCHIATRY. *Educ:* Wagner Col, BS, 68; Univ Wis, MD, 72. *Prof Exp:* Asst prof, 75-81, ASSOC PROF PSYCHIAT, SCH MED, UNIV SOUTHERN CALIF, 81-, DIR, DIV GEN HOSP PSYCHIAT, 80- *Concurrent Pos:* Fel, Sch Med, Univ Southern Calif, 74-75; NIH fel, Nat Inst Arthritis Metab & Digestive Dis, Los Angeles County/Southern Calif Med Ctr, 77-81. *Mem:* Am Psychiat Asn; Am Psychoanal Asn; Am Psychosom Soc; Asn Acad Psychiat; Am Asn Dirs Psychiat Residency Training. *Res:* Sexual dysfunction in end stage renal disease; residency education and medical student education in psychiatry; psychological problems in end stage renal disease. *Mailing Add:* Dept Psychiat 1934 Hospital Pl Los Angeles CA 90033

PROCHAZKA, SVANTE, b Prague, Czech, May 19, 28; m 51; c 2. CERAMICS. *Educ:* Prague Tech Univ, EngChem, 51, PhD(chem), 55; Mass Inst Technol, SM, 68. *Prof Exp:* Asst prof ceramics, Prague Tech Univ, 54-58; head res & develop ceramics, PAL, Tabor, Czech, 58-65; sr res chemist, VUEK, Czech, 69-70; STAFF SCIENTIST CERAMICS, CORP RES & DEVELOP, GEN ELEC CO, 71- *Mem:* Am Ceramic Soc. *Res:* Sintering covalent solids; silicon carbide ceramics; high temperature structural materials. *Mailing Add:* Corp Res & Develop Gen Elec Co Box 8 Schenectady NY 12301

PROCITA, LEONARD, b Gloversville, NY, May 24, 21. PHARMACOLOGY. *Educ:* Univ Mich, AB, 48, MS, 51, PhD(pharmacol), 54. *Prof Exp:* Asst pharmacol, Univ Mich, 50-51 & 52-53; instr, Sch Med, St Louis Univ, 54-56; asst prof, Col Med, State Univ NY Downstate Med Ctr, 57-63; assoc prof, 63-73, prof pharmacol, 73-81, PROF ANAT & PHARMACOL, ALBANY MED COL, 81- *Concurrent Pos:* Actg chmn dept, 73-76. *Mem:* Am Soc Pharmacol & Exp Therapeut; Optical Soc Am; Soc Rheol; Am Math Soc; Biophys Soc. *Res:* Cardiovascular action of polyglycols and ryanodine; action of antihypertensive drugs on isolated brain; action of constituents of tobacco smoke on isolated brain and heart; cardiovascular phenomena; action of ryanodine on skeletal muscle and muscle proteins; contractures; muscle contractility; action of drugs on retina. *Mailing Add:* Dept Anat Albany Med Col Albany NY 12208

PROCK, ALFRED, b Baltimore, Md, Aug 11, 30; m 53; c 1. PHYSICAL CHEMISTRY. *Educ:* Johns Hopkins Univ, BE, 51, MA, 53, PhD(chem), 55. *Prof Exp:* NSF fel chem, Harvard Univ, 55-56; res assoc, Cornell Univ, 56-61; from asst prof to assoc prof, 61-72, PROF CHEM, BOSTON UNIV, 72- *Mem:* Am Chem Soc; Am Phys Soc. *Res:* Electronic energy migration and photoconductivity in fluid aromatic hydrocarbons; atomic and molecular electronic energy transfer to surfaces. *Mailing Add:* Dept of Chem Boston Univ Boston MA 02215

PROCKOP, DARWIN J, b Palmerton, Pa, Aug 31, 29; m 61; c 2. BIOCHEMISTRY, MEDICINE. *Educ:* Haverford Col, BA, 51; Oxford Univ, MA, 53; Univ Pa, MD, 56; George Washington Univ, PhD(biochem), 61. *Prof Exp:* Intern med, New York Hosp-Cornell Med Ctr, 56-57; res fel pharmacol, Nat Heart Inst, 57-58, res investr biochem, 58-61; from assoc biochem to prof biochem & med, Univ Pa, 61-72; PROF BIOCHEM & CHMN DEPT, RUTGERS MED SCH, 72- *Mem:* Am Chem Soc; Am Soc Biol Chemists; Am Soc Clin Invest; Asn Am Physicians. *Res:* Synthesis, catabolism and gene expression of collagen and other components of connective tissue. *Mailing Add:* Col Med & Dent of NJ Rutgers Med Sch Piscataway NJ 08540

PROCKOP, LEON D, b Palmerton, Pa, Mar 28, 34; div; c 2. NEUROLOGY. *Educ:* Princeton Univ, AB, 55; Univ Pa, MD, 59. *Prof Exp:* Intern, Lenox Hill Hosp & Hunterdon Med Ctr, 59-60; res asst, NIH, 60-62; assoc physiol, George Washington Univ, 62; from resident to chief resident neurol, Columbia-Presby Med Ctr, 62-65, asst neurologist & independent investr, 65-67; from asst prof to assoc prof neurol, Univ Pa, 67-73, assoc in neurol, Univ Hosp, 67-73; PROF MED & CHIEF NEUROL SECT, COL MED, UNIV S FLA, 73- *Concurrent Pos:* Asst, NY Neurol Inst, 62-64; from asst to instr neurol, Columbia Univ, 65-67; Nat Inst Neurol Dis & Blindness fels, 65-67; chief, Penn Neurol Serv, Philadelphia Gen Hosp, 67-73; neurol consult, Tampa Vet Admin Hosp, Tampa Gen Hosp & St Joseph Hosp, Tampa, Fla, 73-; mem coun stroke, Am Heart Asn. *Mem:* AAAS; AMA; Am Neurol Asn; Am Soc Pharmacol & Exp Therapeut; Am Acad Neurol. *Res:* Rate and mechanisms of transfer of various substances between blood and cerebrospinal fluid; pathophysiology of hypoglycorrhachia in meningitis; pathology of cerebral edema following sustained hyperglycemia; biochemical correlates of spinal cord injury; peripheral neuropathy secondary to organic solvents. *Mailing Add:* Col of Med Univ of SFla Tampa FL 33620

PROCTER, ALAN ROBERT, b London, Eng, Nov 13, 39; m 65; c 2. PULP CHEMISTRY, PAPER CHEMISTRY. *Educ:* Univ Edinburgh, BSc, 62, PhD(chem), 65. *Prof Exp:* Otto Maass fel, McGill Univ, 65-66; sr res chemist, 66-73, sect head, 71-78, MGR PULP & PAPER RES, MACMILLAN BLOEDEL RES LTD, 78- *Mem:* Tech Asn Pulp & Paper Indust; Can Pulp & Paper Asn; Royal Soc Chem; Royal Inst Chem; assoc mem Am Chem Soc. *Res:* Wood chemistry, chemical pulping, wood fiber properties, pulp and paper technology; carbohydrates, lignin, cellulose chemistry; polymers. *Mailing Add:* MacMillan Bloedel Res Ltd 3350 E Broadway Vancouver BC V5M 4E6 Can

PROCTOR, ALAN RAY, b Edgecombe Co, NC, June 22, 45; m 64; c 2. GENE EXPRESSION, FERMENTATION. *Educ:* Univ NC, Chapel Hill, AB, 67; NC State Univ, MS, 69, PhD(genetics), 71. *Prof Exp:* Am Cancer Soc fel microbiol, Scripps Clin & Res Found, 71-73; res staff scientist, Fermentation Res & Develop Dept, 73-80, DIR, MOLECULAR GENETICS DEPT, PFIZER CENT RES DIV, PFIZER, INC, 80- *Mem:* Am Soc Microbiol; AAAS; Sigma Xi. *Res:* Technical management of DNA research; cloning and in vitro alteration of gene structure and expression; organization and regulation of genetic loci for biosynthetic pathways. *Mailing Add:* Dept Molecular Genetics Pfizer Cent Res Div Pfizer Inc Groton CT 06340

PROCTOR, CHARLES DARNELL, b St Louis, Mo, Sept 10, 22; m 50; c 4. NEUROPHARMACOLOGY, TOXICOLOGY. *Educ:* Fisk Univ, BA, 43, MA, 46; Loyola Univ, Chicago, PhD(pharmacol & toxicol), 50. *Prof Exp:* Sr toxicologist, Cook County, Ill, 46-50; from instr to assoc prof pharmacol, Med Sch, Loyola Univ, Chicago, 50-62; dir, Lab for Chem Pharmacol, McCrone Res Inst, Chicago, 62-64; prof neuropharmacol, 64-68, PROF & CHMN DEPT PHARMACOL, MEHARRY MED COL, 68- *Concurrent Pos:* Sr toxicol consult, Bd Health, Chicago, 62-64; spec consult, Presidential Asst for HEW, 67-68; mem comt on new drug probs, Clin Pharmacol Assocs, HEW, 72-73; dir, Gillette Mem Lab, Meharry Med Col, 64-; mem res comt, Tenn Dept Pub Health, 68-; Michael J Bent Mem Scholar, Meharry Med Col, 78- *Honors & Awards:* Frontiers of Am Award, Frontiers Int, 59. *Mem:* Am Soc for Pharmacol & Exp Therapeut; Soc Toxicol; Am Chem Soc; fel Inst Chemists; fel AAAS. *Res:* Biochemistry of schizophrenia; tranquilizer drug actions; actions of addictive and abused drugs. *Mailing Add:* Dept of Pharmacol 1005 18th Ave N Nashville TN 37208

PROCTOR, CHARLES LAFAYETTE, b Collinsville, Okla, Feb 28, 23. INDUSTRIAL & SYSTEMS ENGINEERING. *Educ:* Okla State Univ, BSME, 51, PhD(indust & systs eng), 63; Purdue Univ, MSME, 55. *Prof Exp:* Engr, Tinker AFB, 46-49; asst mech eng, Okla State Univ, 49-51; aeronaut design engr, Beech Aircraft Corp, Kans, 51-53; instr gen & mech eng, Purdue Univ, 53-55; missile thermodynamicist, McDonnell Aircraft Corp, Mo, 55-56; asst prof mech eng, Univ Toronto, 56-63; dir indust eng, Univ Okla, 64-66; resident dir grad eng educ syst & prof indust & systs eng, Univ Fla, 66-72; prof & head dept, Univ Windsor, 72-75; chmn dept indust eng, Western Mich Univ, 75-77, prof, 75-80; PROF & HEAD DEPT ENG & SCI MGT, UNIV ALASKA, 80- *Concurrent Pos:* Ford grant, Mass Inst Technol, 65; NASA fac fel, Jet Propulsion Lab, Calif Inst Technol, 69; mem bd trustees, Embry Riddle Aeronaut Univ, 68-; res grants, NASA, 70 & Nat Res Coun Can, 74; prof, Univ Windsor, 75-76; mem grants & award selection comt, Nat Res Coun Can, 75-78; fac fel, US Air Force, Wright-Patterson AFB, 77. *Mem:* Am Soc Mech Engrs; Am Soc Qual Control; Am Inst Indust Engrs; Opers Res Soc Am; Inst Elec & Electronics Engrs. *Res:* The study of operating systems, including mathematical modeling of system reliablity, risk assessment and production research; construction management. *Mailing Add:* Dept Eng & Sci Mgt Univ Alaska Fairbanks AK 99701

PROCTOR, CHARLES MAHAN, b Belva, WVa, Oct 4, 17; m 41& 51; c 1. BIOSCIENCES. *Educ:* Berea Col, AB, 39; Univ Utah, MS, 49; Tex A&M Univ, PhD(oceanog), 58. *Prof Exp:* Asst chem, Univ Ky, 40-41; chemist, Test Plant, Pa RR, 41-42; res assoc, Manhattan Proj, Univ Rochester, 46-47; asst & biochemist, Univ Utah, 47-51; in chg chem test sect, Dugway Proving Ground, Dept Army, 51-52; asst & actg asst prof oceanog, Tex A&M Univ,

52-57; in chg chem studies germicides for water treatment, Robert A Taft Sanit Eng Ctr, USPHS, 57-59; sr res specialist, 59-61, Boeing Aerospace Co, 59-61, sr bioscientist, 61-76; sr assoc, Envirodyne Engrs, Inc, 77-78; CONSULT, 79- *Mem:* Fel AAAS; Am Inst Biol Sci; fel Am Inst Chemists. *Res:* Biological systems; marine resources; human engineering; environmental science. *Mailing Add:* 2540 122nd Ave SE Bellevue WA 98005

PROCTOR, CLARKE WAYNE, b Houston, Tex, Feb 27, 42. MATHEMATICS. *Educ:* Univ Houston, BS, 65, MS, 66, PhD(math), 69. *Prof Exp:* Instr math, Univ Houston, 68-69; asst prof, Memphis State Univ, 69-70; asst prof, 70-80, ASSOC PROF MATH, STEPHEN F AUSTIN STATE UNIV, 80- *Mem:* Am Math Soc; Math Asn Am. *Res:* Topology. *Mailing Add:* Box 13040 Dept of Math Stephen F Austin State Univ Nacogdoches TX 75961

PROCTOR, DAVID GEORGE, b Youngstown, Ohio, Jan 20, 28; m 49; c 6. PHYSICS EDUCATION, AUTOMATIC TESTING OF MATERIALS. *Educ:* Case Inst Technol, BS, 52, MS, 55, PhD(physics), 58. *Prof Exp:* Asst physics, Case Inst Technol, 52-57; physicist, Phillips Petrol Co, 57-60; assoc prof physics & chmn dept, 60-66, PROF PHYSICS & CHMN SCI DIV, BALDWIN-WALLACE COL, 66- *Concurrent Pos:* Consult, Union Carbide Corp, 61- & USAID, India, 66. *Mem:* Am Asn Physics Teachers; Acoust Soc Am; Am Phys Soc. *Res:* Reactor physics; nuclear spectroscopy; photonuclear reactions; mechanical properties of solids; high current arc physics. *Mailing Add:* 485 Wyleswood Dr Berea OH 44017

PROCTOR, DONALD FREDERICK, b Red Bank, NJ, Apr 19, 13; m 37; c 2. OTOLARYNGOLOGY, ENVIRONMENTAL MEDICINE. *Educ:* Johns Hopkins Univ, AB, 33, MD, 37; Am Bd Otolaryngol, dipl. *Prof Exp:* Assoc prof laryngol & otol, 46-51, prof anesthesiol, 51-55, asst prof physiol, 55-65, assoc prof laryngol & otol, 58-74, PROF LARYNGOL & OTOL, SCH MED, JOHNS HOPKINS UNIV, 74-, PROF ANESTHESIOL, SCH HYG & PUB HEALTH, 77- *Concurrent Pos:* Prof environ health sci, Sch Hyg & Pub Health, 65-77. *Mem:* Am Physiol Soc; Am Thoracic Soc; fel Am Col Surg; Am Acad Ophthal & Otolaryngol; Am Broncho-Esophagol Asn. *Res:* Conservation of hearing in children; pathogenesis of the common cold; significance of the pneumotachogram; mechanics of breathing; measurement of intrapleural pressure; anesthesia and otolaryngology; the pulmonary circulation; airborne disease, air pollution and air hygiene; physiology of singing. *Mailing Add:* Sch Hyg & Pub Health Johns Hopkins Univ Baltimore MD 21205

PROCTOR, EDWARD K(NOX), JR, b Lumberton, NC, July 11, 22; m 49. ELECTRICAL ENGINEERING. *Educ:* NC State Univ, BEE, 43; Harvard Univ, SM, 47; NY Univ, 47-52; Stanford Univ, EE, 60. *Prof Exp:* Test engr, Gen Elec Co, 43-44, consult engr, microwave lab, 55-59; engr, Tenn Eastman Co, 44-45; proj engr, Sperry Gyroscope Co, 47-50, sr proj engr, 50-52, eng sect head, 52-54; SR RES ENGR, STANFORD RES INST INT, 59- *Mem:* Inst Elec & Electronics Engrs. *Res:* Microwave antennas; weapons systems analysis; electromagnetic theory; lidar applications; remote sensing of atmospheric constituents. *Mailing Add:* Stanford Res Inst Int Menlo Park CA 94025

PROCTOR, IVAN D, b Bloomfield, Iowa, Nov 15, 39; m 66; c 2. NUCLEAR PHYSICS. *Educ:* Iowa State Univ, BS, 66; Mich State Univ, MS, 69, PhD(physics), 72. *Prof Exp:* PHYSICIST NUCLEAR PHYSICS, LAWRENCE LIVERMORE LAB, 72- *Mem:* Am Phys Soc. *Res:* Charged particle spectroscopy; accelerator technology. *Mailing Add:* Lawrence Livermore Lab Univ of Calif Livermore CA 94550

PROCTOR, J(OHN) F(RANCIS), b Newark, NJ, Oct 21, 28; m 54; c 4. CHEMICAL ENGINEERING. *Educ:* Cooper Union, BChE, 51. *Prof Exp:* Engr, Dana Plant, Atomic Energy Div, 51-54, supvr tech studies group, 54-57, engr, Savannah River Lab, SC, 57-64, sr engr, 64-68, sr res supvr, 68-70, process supt separations areas, Atomic Energy Div, 70-73, process mgr, 73-81, SR TECH CONSULT, ATOMIC ENERGY DIV, PETROL CHEM DEPT, E I DU PONT DE NEMOURS & CO, INC, 81- *Mem:* Am Inst Chem Engrs. *Res:* Administrator and manager of process design for nuclear reactor, fuel fabrication, fuel reprocessing, radioactive waste storage, and heavy water facilities of the Atomic Energy Division. *Mailing Add:* Atomic Energy Div 6600 Montchanin Bldg Wilmington DE 19898

PROCTOR, JAMES SIMPSON, b Wrentham, Mass, Nov 5, 21; m 50; c 3. CHEMISTRY. *Educ:* Boston Univ, AB, 47; Iowa State Col, MS, 49; Univ Rome, Drchem, 52. *Prof Exp:* Instr chem, Franklin & Marshall Col, 49-51; res chemist, E I du Pont de Nemours & Co, 52-58; asst prof chem, Univ Mass, 58-62; CHEMIST, JACKSON LAB, E I DU PONT DE NEMOURS & CO, INC, WILMINGTON, DEL, 62- *Res:* Instrumental analysis. *Mailing Add:* 204 Howard Ave Woodstown NJ 08098

PROCTOR, JAMES THORNTON, b Blytheville, Ark, Nov 20, 22; m 54; c 2. PSYCHIATRY. *Educ:* Univ Kans, AB, 43, MD, 46. *Prof Exp:* Assoc prof psychiat, Sch Med, Univ NC, 54-62; clin prof psychiat, Sch Med, Univ Okla, 62-73; CLIN PROF PSYCHIAT, BOWMAN GRAY SCH MED, WAKE FOREST UNIV, 73- *Concurrent Pos:* Med & training dir, Children's Med Ctr, Tulsa, 62-73; med dir, Child Guid Clin, Winston-Salem, NC, 73- *Mem:* AMA; fel Am Psychiat Asn; fel Am Orthopsychiat Asn; fel Am Acad Child Psychiat; fel Am Asn Ment Deficiency. *Res:* Child psychiatry; treatment of delinquency; children's dreams; childhood hysteria. *Mailing Add:* 1200 Glade St Winston-Salem NC 27101

PROCTOR, JERRY FRANKLIN, b Westminster, Tex, Jan 4, 32; m 71; c 4. NUTRITION. *Educ:* Tex A&M Univ, BS, 55; Cornell Univ, MS, 58, PhD(animal nutrit), 60. *Prof Exp:* Lab analyst, Nat Lead Co, Tex, 53-54; asst nutrit, Cornell Univ, 55-60; res nutritionist, Res & Develop Div, Nat Dairy Prod Corp, 60-68, mgr, Nutrit Res Lab, Kraft Inc, 68-80, DEP MANAGING DIR, TINAMENOR, SUBSID KRAFT INC, 80- *Concurrent Pos:* Mem res comt, Nat Asn Margarine Mfrs, 61-; mem sci adv comt, Spec Dairy Indust Bd, 62-; mem food additives comt, Fatty Acid Producers' Coun, 64- *Mem:* AAAS; Am Nutrit Soc; Animal Nutrit Res Coun; Am Soc Animal Sci; Inst Food Technologists. *Res:* Nutritional muscular dystrophy; antibiotic response in animals; nutrition deficiency diseases; toxicity testing; bio-assay. *Mailing Add:* Res & Develop Div Kraft Inc 801 Waukegan Rd Glenview IL 60025

PROCTOR, JOHN THOMAS ARTHUR, b Armagh, Ireland, Dec 19, 40; m 68. HORTICULTURE, PLANT PHYSIOLOGY. *Educ:* Univ Reading, BSc, 64; Cornell Univ, MS, 67, PhD(pomol), 70; Inst Biol, Eng, MIBiol, 69. *Prof Exp:* Res scientist, 69-71, actg chief res scientist, 71-72, actg dir, 74-75, res scientist, Simcoe Sta, Hort Res Inst Ont, 72-78; ASSOC PROF, UNIV GUELPH, 78- *Concurrent Pos:* Vis res fel, Long Ashton Res Sta, Univ Bristol, Eng, 75. *Mem:* Am Soc Hort Sci; Hort Educ Asn; Brit Inst Biol. *Res:* Plant growth and development; microclimatology of crop production; air pollution damage to horticultural crops. *Mailing Add:* Dept of Hort Sci Univ Guelph Guelph ON N1G 2W1 Can

PROCTOR, JULIAN WARRILOW, b Cheltenham, UK, Mar 20, 42. CANCER, IMMUNOLOGY. *Educ:* Univ London, MBBS, 67, PhD(cancer), 73. *Prof Exp:* Res assoc path, Med Sch, Mem Univ Nfld, 72-73; lectr, McGill Univ, 73-77, sr scientist cancer res, 73-76; assoc biologist cancer res, 76-79, SR BIOLOGIST, ALLEGHENY GEN HOSP, 76-79. *Concurrent Pos:* Adj asst prof, Univ Pittsburgh, 76-; sr fel radiother radiation oncol, Allegheny Gen Hosp, 76-78, assoc staff radiation therapist, 79-; NIH fel, 78. *Mem:* Can Cancer Soc; Can Soc Oncol; Reticuloendothelial Soc. *Res:* Tumor immunology; biology and immunology of metastatic cancer; function of macrophages; immunotherapy of metastatic animal tumors; human melanoma; epidemiology endocrinology of malignant melanoma. *Mailing Add:* Clin Radiation Ther Res Ctr 320 E North Ave Pittsburgh PA 15212

PROCTOR, PAUL DEAN, b Salt Lake City, Utah, Nov 24, 18; m 45; c 4. ECONOMIC GEOLOGY, STRUCTURAL GEOLOGY. *Educ:* Univ Utah, BA, 42; Cornell Univ, MA, 43; Ind Univ, PhD(geol), 49. *Prof Exp:* From jr geologist to geologist, US Geol Surv, 43-53; from asst prof to assoc prof geol, Brigham Young Univ, 47-50; assoc prof, Ind Univ, 50-52; assoc prof, Brigham Young Univ, 52-53; asst supvr raw mat explor, US Steel Western States, 53-57; prof & chmn dept, Mo Sch Mines, 57-64, dean, Sch Sci, 64-70, PROF GEOL, UNIV MO-ROLLA, 64- *Concurrent Pos:* Deleg, Int Geol Cong, 56, 60 & 68; mem, Int Geol Field Inst, Italy, 64; UNESCO geol specialist, Middle Eastern Tech Univ, Ankara, 66-67; consult, McDonnell Aircraft, Miss River Fuel, US Steel, Rohm & Haas & USAID, Vietnam; scientist econ develop, Turkey, NSF, 73-74 & 75; spec lectr, Belem, Para, Brazil, 73-75; consult, Phillips Petrol Co, 74-; consult Egypt, Smithsonian Inst, 80. *Mem:* AAAS; Fel Geol Soc Am; Am Inst Mining, Metall & Petrol Eng; Soc Econ Geologists. *Res:* Ore genesis, localization and evaluation; trace elements; water supplies. *Mailing Add:* Dept of Geol & Geophys Univ of Mo Rolla MO 65401

PROCTOR, THOMAS GILMER, b Winston-Salem, NC, Oct 4, 33; m 57. MATHEMATICS. *Educ:* NC State Univ, BNE, 56, MS, 62, PhD(math), 64. *Prof Exp:* Nuclear engr, Ingalls Shipbldg Corp, Miss, 56-60; instr math, NC State Univ, 64-65; from asst prof to assoc prof, 65-74, PROF MATH, CLEMSON UNIV, 74- *Mem:* Am Math Soc; Math Asn Am; Soc Indust & Appl Math. *Res:* Linear and nonlinear ordinary differential equations; functional differential equations. *Mailing Add:* Dept of Math Sci Clemson Univ Clemson SC 29631

PROCTOR, VERNON WILLARD, b Valentine, Nebr, Apr 25, 27; m 64; c 2. PHYCOLOGY. *Educ:* Univ Mo, AB, 50, AM, 51, PhD(bot), 55. *Prof Exp:* From asst prof to assoc prof, 56-63, PROF BIOL, TEX TECH UNIV, 63- *Mem:* Bot Soc Am; Phycol Soc Am. *Res:* Systematics, phylogeny and biogeography of Charophytes. *Mailing Add:* Dept of Biol Tex Tech Univ Lubbock TX 79409

PROCTOR, W(ILLIAM) J(EFFERSON), JR, b Dublin, Ga, Sept 21, 25. CERAMICS, KAOLIN PROCESSING. *Educ:* Univ Ala, BS, 49. *Prof Exp:* Chemist, Southern Clays Inc, 49-56, ceramist, 57-63; ceramist, 63-76, RES CHEMIST, FREEPORT KAOLIN CO, INC, 76- *Mem:* Am Ceramic Soc; Nat Inst Ceramic Eng. *Res:* Minerals processing; paper. *Mailing Add:* Freeport Kaolin Co Inc Div Freeport-McMoran Inc Gordon GA 31031

PRODANY, NICHOLAS WALTER, chemical engineering, bioengineering, see previous edition

PRODELL, ALBERT GERALD, b Newark, NJ, Feb 28, 25; m 58; c 2. PHYSICS. *Educ:* Columbia Univ, AB, 47, MA, 48, PhD(physics), 54. *Prof Exp:* Asst physics, Columbia Univ, 47-50, lectr, 50-51, lectr, Barnard Col, 51-52, from instr to asst prof, 52-56, res assoc, 56-59; PHYSICIST, BROOKHAVEN NAT LAB, 59- *Mem:* Am Phys Soc. *Res:* Atomic and molecular beams; high energy nuclear physics. *Mailing Add:* Brookhaven Nat Lab 911B Upton NY 11973

PROEBSTING, EDWARD LOUIS, JR, b Calif, Mar 2, 26; m 47; c 3. HORTICULTURE. *Educ:* Univ Calif, BS, 48; Mich State Col, PhD(hort), 51. *Prof Exp:* Asst horticulturist, Irrig Exp Sta, 51-59, assoc horticulturist, 59-63, HORTICULTURIST, IRRIG AGR RES & EXTEN CTR, WASH STATE UNIV, 63- *Concurrent Pos:* Vis prof, Cornell Univ, 66, Hokkaido Univ, 78. *Honors & Awards:* Joseph Gourley Award, 55 & Charles Woodbury Award, 58, Soc Hort Sci. *Mem:* AAAS; fel Soc Hort Sci. *Res:* Pomology; orchard management; cold hardiness; fruit tree water relations; sweet cherry culture including growth regulators and fruit quality. *Mailing Add:* Irrigated Agr Res & Exten Ctr Wash State Univ Prosser WA 99350

PROEBSTING, WILLIAM MARTIN, b Lansing, Mich, Feb 4, 51. PLANT PHYSIOLOGY. *Educ:* Univ Wash, BS, 73; Cornell Univ, PhD(plant physiol), 78. *Prof Exp:* PLANT PATHOLOGIST, SCI & EDUC ADMIN, USDA, 77- *Mem:* Am Soc Plant Physiologists; AAAS. *Res:* Regulation of plant growth and development by environmental factors which are mediated by gibberellins; genetic control of gibberellin metabolism. *Mailing Add:* Western Regional Res Ctr 800 Buchanan St Berkeley CA 94710

PROFFIT, WILLIAM R, b Erwin, NC, Apr 19, 36; m; c 3. ORTHODONTICS, PHYSIOLOGY. *Educ:* Univ NC, BS, 56, DDS, 59; Med Col Va, PhD(physiol), 62; Univ Wash, MSD, 63. *Prof Exp:* Nat Inst Dent Res clin investr, 63-65; from asst prof to prof orthod, Univ Ky, 65-73, chmn dept, 65-73; prof orthod & chmn dept pediat dent, Univ Fla, 73-75; PROF ORTHOD & CHMN DEPT, SCH DENT, UNIV NC, CHAPEL HILL, 75- *Mem:* Am Dent Asn; Am Asn Orthod; Am Speech & Hearing Asn; Int Asn Dent Res; Int Soc Cranio-Facial Biol. *Res:* Functional influences on facial growth; bone growth in vivo; physiology of swallowing. *Mailing Add:* Dept of Orthod Univ of NC Sch of Dent Chapel Hill NC 27514

PROFFITT, MAX ROWLAND, b Knoxville, Tenn, Oct 27, 40. VIROLOGY, IMMUNOLOGY. *Educ:* Univ Tenn, Knoxville, BS, 64, MS, 66, PhD(exp path), 70. *Prof Exp:* Res fel med, Mass Gen Hosp, 70-73; res assoc, Harvard Med Sch, 73-74, instr med, 74-76; STAFF SCIENTIST, CLEVELAND CLIN FOUND, 76-; ADJ ASSOC PROF BIOL, CASE WESTERN RESERVE UNIV, 76- *Concurrent Pos:* Gen res support grant, Mass Gen Hosp, 70-71, Damon Runyon Mem Fund fel, 71-73; asst microbiol, Mass Gen Hosp, 73-76; Charles A King Trust fel, 73-74; Leukemia Soc Am spec fel, 74-76; NIH res grant, 74-; scholar, Leukemia Soc Am, 77- *Res:* Viral and tumor immunology; effects of oncogenic and non-oncogenic viruses on immunological functions of the host; host-virus relationships in oncogenesis and in other diseases. *Mailing Add:* Cleveland Clin Found Dept Immunol Res Div 9500 Euclid Ave Cleveland OH 44106

PROFFITT, THOMAS JEFFERSON, JR, b Columbia, Va, Dec 23, 32; m 56; c 3. ORGANIC CHEMISTRY. *Educ:* Va Polytech Inst, BS, 55. *Prof Exp:* Chemist, 55-56 & 58-62, res chemist, 62-72, SR RES CHEMIST, E I DU PONT DE NEMOURS & CO, INC, 72- *Mem:* Am Chem Soc. *Res:* Formulation of synthetic textile fiber lubricating and antistatic compositions; surface chemistry and emulsion technology. *Mailing Add:* E I du Pont de Nemours & Co Inc PO Box 800 Kinston NC 28501

PROFIO, A(MEDEUS) EDWARD, b New Castle, Pa, Apr 18, 31; m 54; c 3. NUCLEAR ENGINEERING. *Educ:* Mass Inst Technol, SB, 53, PhD(nuclear eng), 63. *Prof Exp:* Scientist, Westinghouse Bettis Atomic Power Lab, 53-55; res assoc nuclear eng, Mass Inst Technol, 57-63, asst prof, 63-64; mem res & develop staff, Gen Atomic Div, Gen Dynamics Corp, 64-69; assoc prof nuclear eng, 69-74, PROF NUCLEAR ENG, UNIV CALIF, SANTA BARBARA, 74- *Concurrent Pos:* Fel eng, 63-64. *Mem:* Am Nuclear Soc. *Res:* Radiation technology, including applications to medicine and environmental monitoring; nuclear reactor physics and shielding. *Mailing Add:* Dept of Chem & Nuclear Eng Univ of Calif Santa Barbara CA 93106

PROGELHOF, RICHARD CARL, b Orange, NJ, Aug 13, 36; m 63; c 2. MECHANICAL ENGINEERING. *Educ:* Newark Col Eng, BSME, 58; Stanford Univ, MS, 59; Lehigh Univ, PhD(mech eng), 62. *Prof Exp:* Asst prof mech eng, Lehigh Univ, 62-64; res scientist heat transfer, Am Standard Res, 64-67; from assoc prof to prof, Newark Col Eng, 67-72; PROF MECH ENG, NJ INST TECHNOL, 72- *Mem:* Am Soc Mech Engrs; Soc Plastics Engrs; Am Optical Soc; Am Soc Eng Educ. *Res:* Heat transfer, fluid mechanics, plastics processing and plastic properties. *Mailing Add:* Dept Mech Eng 323 High St Newark NJ 08854

PROGER, SAMUEL, b US, Jan 21, 06; m 29; c 2. INTERNAL MEDICINE. *Educ:* Emory Univ, BS, 25, MD, 28. *Hon Degrees:* DSc, Tufts Univ, 52 & Emory Univ, 75. *Prof Exp:* Prof med & chmn dept, Sch Med, 48-71, pres, Tufts-New Eng Med Ctr, 71-80, EMER PROF & CHMN, DEPT MED, SCH MED, TUFTS UNIV, 80- *Concurrent Pos:* Physician-in-chief, New Eng Med Ctr, 48-71, vpres bd govs, 71-80, chmn bd trustees, 80-, emer physician-in-chief, 80- *Honors & Awards:* Am Design Award, 51; Robert Williams Chariman Med Award, 80. *Mem:* Am Soc Clin Invest; Am Col Physicians; Asn Am Physicians; Am Acad Arts & Sci. *Res:* Cardiovascular disease, including atherosclerosis and hypertension; medical education. *Mailing Add:* Tufts-New Eng Med Ctr 171 Harrison Ave Boston MA 02111

PROHAMMER, FREDERICK GEORGE, b New York, NY, Mar 26, 22; m 51; c 3. PHYSICS. *Educ:* City Col New York, BME, 43. *Prof Exp:* Mem staff mech eng, Radiation Lab, Mass Inst Technol. 43-46; asst instr physics, Univ Pa, 46-50; physicist, Oak Ridge Nat Lab, 50-55; assoc physicist, 55-80, PHYSICIST, ARGONNE NAT LAB, 80- *Concurrent Pos:* Vis prof, Northwestern Univ, 58-59; Kans State, 64, Ill Benedictine Col, 70. *Mem:* Am Phys Soc; Am Nuclear Soc; AAAS. *Res:* Low energy nuclear physics; reactor physics; reactor safety computer analysis. *Mailing Add:* Argonne Nat Lab 9700 S Cass Ave Argonne IL 60439

PROHASKA, CHARLES ANTON, b Oak Park, Ill, Mar 21, 20. NUCLEAR CHEMISTRY. *Educ:* Mass Inst Technol, BS, 42; Wesleyan Univ, MA, 49; Univ Calif, PhD(chem), 51. *Prof Exp:* Asst, Univ Calif, 48-49, chemist radiation lab, 49-51; sr chemist, E I du Pont de Nemours & Co, Inc, 51-78; RETIRED. *Mem:* Am Chem Soc; Sigma Xi. *Res:* Computer programming for chemical analyses; analytical research. *Mailing Add:* RD 1 Box 234 Dingman's Ferry PA 18328

PROHASKA, JOSEPH ROBERT, b Chicago, Ill, June 5, 45; m 68; c 2. BIOCHEMISTRY, NUTRITION. *Educ:* Univ Wis-Oshkosh, BS, 68; Mich State Univ, PhD(biochem), 74. *Prof Exp:* Res assoc nutrit sci, Univ Wis-Madison, 74-77; ASST PROF BIOCHEM, UNIV MINN, DULUTH, 77- *Mem:* Am Inst Nutrit; Soc Environ Geochem & Health; Sigma Xi. *Res:* Trace element metabolism. *Mailing Add:* Dept Biochem Univ Minn Sch Med Duluth MN 55812

PROHOFSKY, EARL WILLIAM, b St Paul, Minn, Feb 8, 35; m 60. SOLID STATE PHYSICS. *Educ:* Univ Minn, BS, 57; Cornell Univ, PhD(physics), 63. *Prof Exp:* Asst physics, Cornell Univ, 57-62, res assoc, 62-63; mem staff, Sperry Rand Res Ctr, Mass, 63-66; assoc prof physics, 66-73, PROF PHYSICS, PURDUE UNIV, 73- *Mem:* Fel Am Phys Soc. *Res:* Collective effects; second sound; ultrasonics; thermal conductivity; magnetism; fluorescence; lattice dynamics of nucleic acids. *Mailing Add:* Dept of Physics Purdue Univ West Lafayette IN 47907

PROKAI, BELA, b Eger, Hungary, Feb 19, 37; m 62; c 2. ORGANOMETALLIC CHEMISTRY. *Educ:* Univ Leicester, BSc, 60; Univ Manchester, MSc, 62, PhD(chem), 64. *Prof Exp:* Res fel chem, Mass Inst Technol, 64-66; proj scientist, 66-73, res scientist, 73-75, group leader, 75-79, ASSOC DIR RES & DEVELOP, UNION CARBIDE CORP, 79- *Mem:* Am Chem Soc; NY Acad Sci; The Chem Soc. *Res:* Investigation of the preparation, mechanism and properties of organometallic derivatives. *Mailing Add:* Union Carbide Corp Old Saw Mill River Rd Tarrytown NY 10591

PROKIPCAK, JOSEPH MICHAEL, b Niagara Falls, Ont, Oct 22, 37; m 60; c 3. ORGANIC CHEMISTRY. *Educ:* Univ Windsor, BSc, 59, PhD(chem), 64. *Prof Exp:* Vis res assoc org chem, Ohio State Univ, 64-66; asst prof, 66-71, ASSOC PROF ORG CHEM, UNIV GUELPH, 71- *Mem:* Am Chem Soc; Chem Inst Can. *Res:* Physical organic-mechanisms. *Mailing Add:* Dept of Chem Col of Phys Sci Univ of Guelph Guelph ON N1G 2W1 Can

PROKOP, JAN STUART, b Cleveland, Ohio, June 23, 34; m 57; c 3. COMPUTER SCIENCE. *Educ:* US Naval Acad, BS, 56; Naval Postgrad Sch, MS, 64; Univ NC, PhD(comput sci). *Prof Exp:* US Navy, 56-76, instr marine eng, US Naval Acad, 58-60, logistical adv to Venezuelan Navy, US Military Group Venezuela, 60-63, fel, Naval Postgrad Sch, 63-64, chief, Data Systs Support Off, US Navy, 64-69, asst dep comptroller, Dept Defense, Off Secy Defense, 69-72, dir, US Navy Comput Selection Off, 72-76; dir, Automatic Data Processing Mgt, US Dept Com, 76-79; assoc commr, US Social Security Admin, 79-80; SR VPRES, DATA RESOURCES INC, 80- *Concurrent Pos:* Fel, Univ NC, 66-69. *Mem:* Asn Comput Mach. *Res:* Graphical displays; statistical inventory control; simulation; natural and languages. *Mailing Add:* 104 Chandler St Unit #2 Boston MA 02116

PROKOP, MICHAEL JOSEPH, b Leigh, Nebr, May 6, 44; m 66; c 3. RUMINANT NUTRITION, ANIMAL SCIENCE. *Educ:* Univ Nebr, BS, 66, MS, 71, PhD(nutrit), 76. *Prof Exp:* Lab supvr nutrit, Univ Nebr, 67-73, dir nutrit lab, 73-74, staff res assoc animal sci, 74-76, asst prof, 76-77; ASST PROF ANIMAL SCI, IMPERIAL VALLEY FIELD STA, UNIV CALIF, 77- *Mem:* Am Soc Animal Sci; Am Inst Biol Scientists; Coun Agr Sci & Technol; Sigma Xi. *Res:* Improvement of beef cattle production with emphasis on feedlot nutrition; increased utilization of by-product feeds; reduced stress in management systems; relationship of environment and animal performance. *Mailing Add:* Imperial Valley Field Sta 1004 E Holton Rd El Centro CA 92243

PROKOP, ROBERT A, fluorine chemistry, electrochemistry, see previous edition

PROKSCH, GARY J, b La Crosse, Wis, May 25, 44; m 64; c 2. BIOCHEMISTRY, CLINICAL CHEMISTRY. *Educ:* Univ Ariz, BS, 65; Univ Iowa, MS, 68, PhD(biochem), 70; Nat Registry Clin Chem, cert. *Prof Exp:* asst prof clin path, 70-80, ASSOC PROF PATH, MED CTR, IND UNIV, INDIANAPOLIS, 80- *Mem:* Am Chem Soc; Am Asn Clin Chemists. *Res:* Metabolism and regulatory role of human protease inhibitors; clinical chemistry methodolgy; development of optically clear lyophilized human serum base standards for clinical laboratory. *Mailing Add:* Dept of Clin Path Ind Univ Med Ctr Indianapolis IN 46202

PROMERSBERGER, WILLIAM J, b Littlefork, Minn, May 28, 12; m 38; c2. AGRICULTURAL ENGINEERING. *Educ:* Univ Minn, BS, 35; Kans State Univ, MS, 41. *Prof Exp:* Instr agr eng, Univ Minn, 35-38; asst prof, NDak Col, 38-40; asst, Kans State Univ, 40-41; asst prof agr eng, 41-45, prof, 46-77, chmn dept, 41-77, EMER PROF AGR ENG, N DAK STATE UNIV, 77- *Concurrent Pos:* Vis prof, Univ Col, Dublin, 65-66. *Honors & Awards:* Massey-Ferguson Gold Medal, Am Soc Agr Engrs, 79. *Mem:* Fel Am Soc Agr Engrs; Am Soc Eng Educ. *Res:* Farm power and machinery; farm buildings. *Mailing Add:* 55-18th Ave N Fargo ND 58102

PROMISEL, NATHAN E, b Malden, Mass, June 20, 08; m 31; c 2. METALLURGICAL ENGINEERING, ELECTROCHEMISTRY. *Educ:* Mass Inst Technol, BS, 29, MS, 30. *Hon Degrees:* DE, Mich Technol Univ, 78. *Prof Exp:* Res electrochemist & asst tech dir, Int Silver Co, 30-40; consult, 40-41; chief mat scientist, Bur Aeronaut, US Dept Navy, 41-59, chief mat scientist & dir mat div, Bur Naval Weapons, 59-66, mat adminr, US Dept Navy & chief mat engr, Naval Air Systs Command, 66; exec dir nat mat adv bd, 66-74, EMER EXEC DIR, NAT MAT ADV BD, NAT ACAD SCI, 74- *Concurrent Pos:* Carnegie lectr, 59; Sauveur lectr, 60; Gillett lectr, 64; Burgess lectr, 67; mem & chmn struct & mat panel, NATO Adv Group, 59-71; US mem mat adv group, Orgn Econ Coop & Develop, 67-70; mem adv bds, Navy Labs, Univs, Govt & Nat Labs; chmn, US Working Group on Electromet in US/USSR Sci Exchange Prog, 73-77; mem, Cong Off Technol Assessment, Mat Adv Comn, 74- & Nat Mat Adv Bd, Nat Acad Sci, 77-80; consult, Oak Ridge Nat Lab, 75-78. *Honors & Awards:* Burgess Award, 61; Nat Capital Engr of the Year Award, Coun Eng & Archit Socs, 74. *Mem:* Nat Acad Eng; hon mem Am Inst Mining, Metall & Petrol Engrs; fel & hon mem Am Soc Metals; Fedn Mat Socs (pres, 72-73); hon mem Am Soc Testing & Mat. *Res:* Aeronautical, space, missile and underwater vehicle materials sciences and processes, including disciplines of chemistry, electrochemistry, metallurgy; behavioristic phenomena of materials in earth, space and ocean environments. *Mailing Add:* 12519 Davan Dr Silver Spring MD 20904

PROMNITZ, LAWRENCE CHARLES, b Berwyn, Ill, Nov 21, 44; m 78. FORESTRY, STATISTICS. *Educ:* Southern Ill Univ, BS, 67; Iowa State Univ, MS, 70, PhD(forest biomet), 72. *Prof Exp:* Assoc prof forestry & statist, Iowa State Univ, 71-77; RES FORESTER BIOMET, CROWN ZELLERBACH CAN LTD, 77- *Mem:* Am Statist Asn. *Res:* Forest biometry; quantitative biology; dynamics of forest populations. *Mailing Add:* Forestry Res Div Crown Zellerbach Can Ltd New Westminster BC V3L 5A4 Can

PRONI, JOHN ROBERTO, b Hempstead, NY, June 5, 42; m 65; c 3. UNDERWATER ACOUSTICS, OCEANOGRAPHY. *Educ:* Univ Miami, BS, 63, MS, 65; NC State Univ, PhD(physics), 70. *Prof Exp:* Mem tech staff underwater acoust, Bell Tel Labs, 69-72; PHYSICIST & OCEANOGR, ATLANTIC OCEANOG & METEOROL LABS, NAT OCEANIC & ATMOSPHERIC ADMIN, 72- *Concurrent Pos:* Tech adv, Off Naval Res, 72- *Mem:* Am Geophys Union. *Res:* Environmental acoustics; acoustical studies of internal waves, sewage dumping, dredging operations, sewage outfalls and oceanic microstructure; artificial seawater. *Mailing Add:* Nat Oceanic & Atmospheric Admin 4301 Rickenbacker Causeway Miami FL 33176

PRONKO, PETER PAUL, b Peckville, Pa, Mar 29, 38; m 67; c 2. PHYSICS, MATERIALS SCIENCE. *Educ:* Univ Scranton, BS, 60; Univ Pittsburgh, MS, 62; Univ Alta, PhD(physics), 66. *Prof Exp:* Asst prof physics, Univ Scranton, 66-68; res assoc mat res, McMaster Univ, 68-72; res assoc physics, Argonne Nat Lab, 72-74, asst metallurgist physics, 74-75, physicist solid state physics, 75-80; SR SCIENTIST, UNIVERSAL ENERGY SYSTS, 80- *Mem:* Am Phys Soc; Mat Res Soc; Inst Elec & Electronics Engrs; Am Soc Metals. *Res:* Ion beam interactions in solids; laser solid interactions; ion implantation of solids; metallurgy and materials science of implanted solids. *Mailing Add:* Universal Energy Systs 3195 Plainfield Rd Dayton OH 45432

PRONOVE, PACITA, b Magdalena, Laguna, Philippines, Oct 12, 19; US citizen; m 50. PEDIATRICS. *Educ:* Univ Philippines, MD, 44; Am Bd Pediat, dipl. *Prof Exp:* Mem med staff maternal & child health, Pasay City Health Dept, Philippines, 46-52; resident pediat, Children's Hosp, DC, 52-54; vis scientist endocrinol, Nat Heart Inst, 56-59, instr pediat, Sch Med, Georgetown Univ, 59-66; exec secy neurol study sect, NIH, 61-64, exec secy child health & human develop prog proj comt, 64-65, exec secy gen med B study sect, Div Res Grants, NIH, 65-72, scientist adminr, 61-73; RETIRED. *Concurrent Pos:* Mem courtesy staff, Children's Hosp, DC, 56-73; pediatrician & res assoc, Children's Convalescent Hosp, 59-60; attend staff, Nat Heart Inst, 60-73. *Mem:* Am Acad Pediat; Endocrine Soc; Am Soc Nephrology. *Res:* Research grants administration; endocrinology and metabolism; adrenal and parathyroid physiology; renin-angiotensin-aldosterone; calcium, phosphorus and bone metabolism; maternal and child health; co-discoverer, syndrome of juxtaglomerular hyperplasia with aldosteronism, hypokalemic alkalosis and normal blood pressure, known as Bartter's syndrome. *Mailing Add:* Lomas del Marbella Club Pueblo Marbella Spain

PROOPS, WILLIAM ROBERT, b Brooklyn, NY, Dec 5, 29; m 52, 75; c 4. ORGANIC CHEMISTRY. *Educ:* Polytech Inst Brooklyn, BS, 49; Columbia Univ, AM, 51, PhD(chem), 53. *Prof Exp:* Res chemist, Union Carbide Chem Co, 52-71; res & develop mgr, 71-77, VPRES RES & DEVELOP, ISOCYANATE PROD DIV, WITCO CHEM CORP, 77- *Mem:* Am Chem Soc. *Res:* Synthetic organic and polymer chemistry. *Mailing Add:* Isocyanate Prod Div Witco Chem Corp 900 Wilmington Rd New Castle DE 19720

PROPES, ERNEST (A), b Jacksonville, Ala, Feb 5, 09; m 33; c 4. ALGEBRA. *Educ:* Univ Ala, BS, 37, MA, 39. *Prof Exp:* Instr high sch, Ala, 36-37; instr math, Univ Ala, 39-42; asst prof, Birmingham-Southern Col, 43-44; instr, Univ Ill, 45-48; assoc prof, 48-74, prof math, 74-80, RES PROF MATH, LLANO ESTACADO CTR ADVAN PROF STUDIES & RES, EASTERN NMEX UNIV, 80-, MEM RES INST, 48- *Concurrent Pos:* Consult, Sandia Corp. *Mem:* Am Math Soc; Math Asn Am. *Res:* Groups, rings, fields in modern algebra. *Mailing Add:* 1325 W 17th Lane Portales NM 88130

PROPHET, CARL WRIGHT, b Anthony, Kans, Sept 20, 29; m 51; c 3. AQUATIC ECOLOGY. *Educ:* Kans State Teachers Col, BS, 55, MS, 57; Univ Okla, PhD(zool), 62. *Prof Exp:* Jr high sch teacher, 49-51; from instr to assoc prof, 56-58, PROF BIOL, EMPORIA STATE UNIV, 68- *Mem:* Am Soc Limnol & Oceanog. *Res:* Limnology of artificial impoundments; invertebrate ecology. *Mailing Add:* Div of Biol Sci Emporia State Univ Emporia KS 66801

PROPP, JACOB HENRY, b Ft Morgan, Colo, Nov 28, 41; m 63; c 1. ANALYTICAL CHEMISTRY. *Educ:* Univ Colo, BA, 63; Univ Minn, MS, 65; Univ Ill, PhD, 68. *Prof Exp:* asst prof, 68-77, ASSOC PROF ANAL CHEM, UNIV WIS-OSHKOSH, 77- *Concurrent Pos:* Dir, Med Technol Prog, Univ Wis, Oshkosh, 75- *Mem:* Sigma Xi; Am Soc Med Technol; Am Chem Soc. *Res:* Electrochemical methods of trace analysis; environmental analysis of pollutants. *Mailing Add:* Dept of Chem Univ of Wis Oshkosh WI 54901

PROPST, CATHERINE LAMB, b Charlotte, NC, Mar 10, 46. MOLECULAR BIOLOGY. *Educ:* Vanderbilt Univ, BA, 67; Yale Univ, MPhil, 70, PhD(microbiology), 73. *Prof Exp:* Instr genetics & microbiol, Miss State Col Women, 67-68; microbiologist, Dome Div, Miles Labs, 72-73; asst prof chem, Quinnipiac Col, 73-74; head microbiol, GTE, Inc, 74-77; mgr microbiol & IQA, Abbott Labs, 77-78, mgr biol develop & advan technol, 78-80; VPRES RES & DEVELOP, API-AYERST LABS, 80- *Mem:* Am Soc Microbiol; Soc Indust Microbiol; Nat Wildlife Fedn; Sigma Xi. *Res:* Research and development of new diagnostic products; applied research in recombinant DNA, interferon, cell growth and aging. *Mailing Add:* API-Ayerst Labs 200 Express St Plainview NY 11803

PROPST, FRANKLIN MOORE, b Ohatchee, Ala, Mar 30, 35; m 60; c 1. PHYSICS. *Educ:* Ala Polytech Inst, BS, 57; Univ Ill, Urbana, MS, 59, PhD(physics), 62. *Prof Exp:* Res assoc, 62-63, asst prof, 63-70, assoc prof physics, coordr sci lab, 70-77, PROF COMPUT BASED EDUC RES LAB & ASSOC PLANNING UNIV ILL, URBANA, 78- *Concurrent Pos:* Ed, J Vacuum Sci & Technol, 66- *Mem:* Am Phys Soc; Am Vacuum Soc. *Res:* Surface physics measurements, specifically studies of interactions of electrons, ions and neutral particles with solid surfaces; vacuum technology; solid state. *Mailing Add:* Coord Sci Lab Univ of Ill Urbana IL 61801

PROSCHAN, FRANK, b New York, Apr 7, 21; m 52; c 2. STATISTICS. *Educ:* City Col New York, BS, 41; George Washington Univ, MA, 48; Stanford Univ, PhD, 59. *Prof Exp:* Lab asst cement testing, Nat Bur Standards, 41-42, mathematician, 51-52; geod computer, US Geol Surv, 42-46; res analyst, US Army Security Agency, 46-49; statistician, AEC, 49-51 & Sylvania Elec Prod Inc, 52-60; mem staff, Sci Res Lab, Boeing Co, 60-70; PROF STATIST, FLA STATE UNIV, 70- *Concurrent Pos:* Consult, US Army Materiel Command, 70- & Aberdeen Proving Ground, 72-73. *Mem:* Int Statist Inst; Am Statist Asn; Soc Indust & Appl Math; Inst Math Statist. *Res:* Statistical quality control; industrial statistics; reliability theory using probability and statistics. *Mailing Add:* Dept of Statist Fla State Univ Tallahassee FL 32306

PROSE, PHILIP H, b New York, NY, Nov 20, 16; m 42; c 2. PATHOLOGY. *Educ:* City Col New York, BS, 36; Univ Lausanne, MD, 41; Am Bd Dermat, dipl, 50; Am Bd Path, dipl, 55. *Prof Exp:* Fel dermat, Postgrad Med Sch, NY Univ, 47-52; from instr to asst prof path, State Univ NY, 53-56; from asst prof to assoc prof, 56-66, PROF PATH, SCH MED, NY UNIV, 66-; DIR LABS, BELLEVUE HOSP, 80- *Concurrent Pos:* Consult, Manhattan Vet Admin Hosp. *Mem:* AAAS; fel Soc Invest Dermat; fel Am Asn Path & Bact; fel Harvey Soc; fel NY Acad Sci. *Res:* Electron microscopy. *Mailing Add:* Dept of Path NY Univ Sch of Med New York NY 10016

PROSEN, HARRY, b Saskatoon, Sask, June 27, 30; m 54; c 4. PSYCHIATRY. *Educ:* Univ Man, MD, 55, MSc, 57; FRCP(C). *Prof Exp:* Am Fund Psychiat bursary, 58-60; assoc prof psychiat, 65-71, co-dir grad training prog, 65-70, chmn postgrad educ comt psychiat, 70-75, actg head dept psychiat, 71-72, PROF PSYCHIAT, UNIV MAN, 71- HEAD DEPT PSYCHIAT, 75-; CHIEF PSYCHIAT, HEALTH SCI CTR, WINNIPEG, 75- *Concurrent Pos:* Consult, Deer Lodge Vet Hosp, Winnipeg, 59-66; dir psychiat out-patient dept, Winnipeg Gen Hosp, 59-68. *Mem:* Fel AAAS; fel Am Psychiat Asn; Can Psychiat Asn. *Res:* Life cycle; psychotherapy. *Mailing Add:* Dept of Psychiat Univ of Man 770 Rannatyne Ave Winnipeg MB R3E 0W3 Can

PROSHOLD, FREDRICK IRVING, entomology, radiation biology, see previous edition

PROSKAUER, ERIC S, b Frankfurt, Ger, Mar 19, 03; US citizen; m 31. PHYSICAL CHEMISTRY. *Educ:* Univ Leipzig, PhD(phys chem), 33. *Prof Exp:* Ed, Akademische Verlagsgesellschaft, Ger, 25-37; secy-treas, Nordeman Publ Co, NY, 37-40; chmn, Intersci Publ, Inc, 40-61; vpres & mgr, Wiley-Intersci Div, 61-70, sr vpres, 70-73, DIR, JOHN WILEY & SONS, INC, 70- *Concurrent Pos:* Consult, 73- *Mem:* AAAS; Am Chem Soc; Am Phys Soc; fel NY Acad Sci. *Res:* Publishing. *Mailing Add:* 220 Central Park S New York NY 10019

PROSKE, JOSEPH WALTER, b DuBois, Pa, Oct 11, 36; m 66; c 2. CERAMICS, METALLURGY. *Educ:* Pa State Univ, BS, 58, MS, 60, PhD(metall), 64. *Prof Exp:* Res engr, Carbon Co, 64-68, asst dir magnetic res, 68-69, dir, 69-71, sr res engr, Magnet Div, 71-73, SR RES ENGR, ELECTRONIC DIV, STACKPOLE CORP, 73- *Mem:* Am Ceramic Soc; Am Soc Metals; Am Inst Mining, Metall & Petrol Engrs; Inst Elec & Electronics Engrs. *Res:* Infiltration in metal-ceramic systems; properties and microstructure of magnetic ceramics; hard and soft ferrite materials development and characterization. *Mailing Add:* Electronic Div Stackpole Corp 201 Stackpole St St Mary's PA 15857

PROSKUROWSKI, WLODZIMIERZ, b Warsaw, Poland, Jan 19, 36; Swed citizen; m 74; c 1. NUMERICAL ANALYSIS. *Educ:* Warsaw Univ, MSc, 69; Royal Inst Technol, Stockholm, Sweden, PhD(numerical anal), 76. *Prof Exp:* Res assoc appl math, Lawrence Berkeley Lab, 76-78; ASST PROF MATH, UNIV SOUTHERN CALIF, LOS ANGELES, 78- *Mailing Add:* Math Dept Univ Southern Calif Los Angeles CA 90007

PROSKY, LEON, b New York, NY, Aug 2, 33. NUTRITIONAL BIOCHEMISTRY. *Educ:* Brooklyn Col, BS, 54; Rutgers Univ, MS, 55, PhD(biochem), 58. *Prof Exp:* Fel pharmacol, Sch Med, Washington Univ, 60-62; res assoc biochem, Albert Einstein Med Col, 63-65; sect chief biosynthesis, 65-67, asst br chief div nutrit, 67-74, prog mgr nutrit, 74-79, chief, proteins, amino acids & carbohydrates sect, 71-79, DEP CHIEF, EXP NUTRIT BR, BUR FOODS & DRUG ADMIN, 79- *Concurrent Pos:* Adj prof biochem, George Washington Univ Med Ctr, 80- *Mem:* Am Inst Nutrit; Fel AAAS; Am Chem Soc; fel Am Inst Chemists; Soc Exp Biol & Med. *Res:* Carbohydrate metabolism; protein synthesis and metabolism; vitamin-enzyme interactions; nutritional status and drug efficacy; nucleic acids; nutrition and development; brain biochemistry. *Mailing Add:* Div of Nutrit Food & Drug Admin 200 C St SW Washington DC 20204

PROSNITZ, DONALD, US citizen. PHYSICS. *Educ:* Yale Univ, BSc, 70; Mass Inst Technol, PhD(physics), 75. *Prof Exp:* Asst prof eng, Yale Univ, 75-77; PHYSICIST, LAWRENCE LIVERMORE LAB, 77- *Mailing Add:* Lawrence Livermore Lab Univ Calif PO Box 804 Livermore CA 94550

PROSS, HUGH FREDERICK, b Wales, UK, Nov 8, 42; m 65; c 3. TUMOR BIOLOGY. *Educ:* Queen's Univ, BA, 63, MSc & MD, 68, PhD(microbiol & immunol), 72. *Prof Exp:* Intern med, Med Ctr, Duke Univ, 68-69; fel tumor biol, Karolinska Inst Stockholm, 72-74; asst prof path & radiation oncol, 74-77, ASSOC PROF RADIATION ONCOL, QUEEN'S UNIV, 77-, MICROBIOL & IMMUNOL, 79- *Concurrent Pos:* Res assoc, Ont Cancer Treatment & Res Found, 74- *Mem:* Can Soc Immunol; Reticuluendothelial Soc; Am Asn Immunologists; Am Asn Cell Biol. *Res:* Immunology and tumor biology; human natural killer cells. *Mailing Add:* Ont Cancer Found Kingston Clinic King St W Kingston ON K7L 2V7 Can

PROSSER, CLIFFORD LADD, b Avon, NY, May 12, 07; m 34; c 3. COMPARATIVE PHYSIOLOGY. *Educ:* Univ Rochester, AB, 29; Johns Hopkins Univ, PhD(zool), 32. *Hon Degrees:* DSc, Clark Univ, 75. *Prof Exp:* Asst zool, Johns Hopkins Univ, 29-32; Parker fel physiol, Harvard Med Sch

& Cambridge Univ, 32-34; res assoc, Clark Univ, 34-35, from asst prof to assoc prof physiol, 35-39; from asst prof to assoc prof zool, 39-49, prof physiol, 49-75, head dept, 60-70, EMER PROF PHYSIOL, UNIV ILL, URBANA, 75- *Concurrent Pos:* Mem physiol staff, Marine Biol Lab, Woods Hole, 35-41, trustee, 50-; biologist & assoc sect chief metall lab, Univ Chicago, 43-46; Hopkins lectr, Stanford Univ, 54; Carnegie prof, Univ Hawaii, 57; Guggenheim fel, 63-64; vis prof, Monash Univ Australia, 71-72. Consult, Nat Defense Res Comt Proj, 42-43 & NSF, 51-; mem, Macy Conf Nerve Impulse; Maytag prof zool, Ariz State Univ, 78. *Mem:* Nat Acad Sci; fel Am Acad Arts & Sci; AAAS (pres zool sci sect, 65); Am Soc Zoologists (pres, 61); Am Physiol Soc (pres, 69-70). *Res:* Nerve and muscle physiology; comparative animal physiology; physiological adaptation; smooth muscle. *Mailing Add:* Dept of Physiol Univ of Ill Urbana IL 61801

PROSSER, FRANCIS WARE, JR, b Wichita, Kans, June 30, 27; m 52; c 3. NUCLEAR PHYSICS. *Educ:* Univ Kans, BS, 50, MS, 54, PhD(physics), 55. *Prof Exp:* Res assoc physics, Rice Inst, 55-57; from asst prof to assoc prof, 57-67, PROF PHYSICS, UNIV KANS, 67- *Concurrent Pos:* Nat Res Coun-Off Aerospace Res sr assoc, Aerospace Res Labs, Wright-Patterson AFB, 69-70; fac res partic, Argonne Nat Lab, 75-76, vis scientist, 77 & 78. *Mem:* fel Am Phys Soc; Am Asn Physics Teachers. *Res:* Nuclear structure; heavy-ion reactions; gamma ray spectroscopy; angular correlations. *Mailing Add:* Dept of Physics Univ of Kans Lawrence KS 66045

PROSSER, FRANKLIN PIERCE, b Atlanta, Ga, July 4, 35; m 60; c 2. COMPUTER SCIENCE. *Educ:* Ga Inst Technol, BS, 56, MS, 58; Pa State Univ, PhD(chem), 61. *Prof Exp:* NSF fel, 61-63, lectr, Comput Ctr, 63-67, asst dir, 67-71, assoc prof, 69-77, chmn dept, 71-77, assoc dir, Ctr, 71-80, PROF COMPUT SCI, IND UNIV, BLOOMINGTON, 77- *Mem:* Asn Comput Mach; Inst Elec & Electronics Engrs. *Res:* Digital hardware design; programming systems and languages; operating systems; computer science education. *Mailing Add:* Dept of Comput Sci Ind Univ Bloomington IN 47401

PROSSER, REESE TREGO, b Minneapolis, Minn, May 18, 27; m 52; c 4. MATHEMATICS. *Educ:* Harvard Univ, AB, 49; Univ Calif, PhD(math), 55. *Prof Exp:* Mathematician, Lawrence Radiation Lab, Univ Calif, 54-55; res instr math, Duke Univ, 55-56; Moore instr, Mass Inst Technol, 56-58, mem staff, Lincoln Lab, 58-62, group leader, 62-66; assoc prof math, 66-68, vchmn dept, 67-70, chmn sci div, 71-72, PROF MATH, DARTMOUTH COL, 68- *Concurrent Pos:* Ed, Duke Math J, 64-72. *Mem:* Am Math Soc; Am Phys Soc; Asn Comput Mach; Soc Indust & Appl Math; sr mem Inst Elec & Electronics Engrs. *Res:* Functional analysis. *Mailing Add:* Dept of Math Dartmouth Col Hanover NH 03755

PROSSER, ROBERT M, b Philadelphia, Pa, Apr 3, 23. ORGANIC CHEMISTRY. *Educ:* Yale Univ, BS, 43. *Prof Exp:* Supvr prod, E I Du Pont De Nemours & Co, Inc, 47-49, engr, 49-52, sr supvr develop, 52-55, supt prod, 55-58, supt develop, 58-65, gen supt, 65-67, mgr res & develop, 67-70, mgr new ventures, 70-72, prod mgr neoprene res & develop, 72-81; RETIRED. *Mem:* Am Chem Soc; AAAS. *Res:* Product and process development on dyes and intermediates; neoprene, isocyanates; urethanes; fluoroelastomers; rubber chemicals. *Mailing Add:* 2205 W 11th St Wilmington DE 19805

PROSSER, THOMAS JOHN, b Chicago, Ill, Feb 17, 31; m 56; c 2. ORGANIC CHEMISTRY. *Educ:* Ill Inst Technol, BS, 53; Univ Notre Dame, PhD(org chem), 57. *Prof Exp:* Res chemist, 56-73, SR RES CHEMIST, HERCULES INC, 73- *Mem:* Am Chem Soc. *Res:* Synthetic organic chemistry; chemistry of rosin and rosin derivatives; synthetic resins; polymerization, copolymerization, polymer modification and characterization; cycloaddition reactions. *Mailing Add:* Hercules Res Ctr Wilmington DE 19899

PROSTAK, ARNOLD S, b Brooklyn, NY, Apr 8, 29; m 71; c 2. CHEMICAL INSTRUMENTATION. *Educ:* Col William & Mary, BS, 50; Johns Hopkins Univ, MA, 55; Univ Mich, Ann Arbor, MS, 60, PhD(chem), 69. *Prof Exp:* Chemist, Edgewood Arsenal, US Army, 50-58; res assoc infrared technol, Willow Run Labs, Univ Mich 58-60; sr res & develop engr, Aerospace Systs Div, Bendix Corp, 60-66 & 68-71; develop engr, 72-80, STAFF PROJ ENGR, VEHICLE EMISSION LAB, GEN MOTORS PROVING GROUND, MILFORD, 80- *Mem:* AAAS; Am Chem Soc; Soc Automotive Engrs. *Res:* Detection and measurement of trace materials in air using chemical and infrared techniques; infrared technology; gas chromatography; electrochemical and optical instrumentation. *Mailing Add:* 1707 Harding Rd Ann Arbor MI 48104

PROSTKA, HAROLD J, geology, see previous edition

PROTHERO, JOHN W, b Toronto, Ont, Feb 5, 32; m 55; c 3. BIOPHYSICS, BIOLOGICAL STRUCTURE. *Educ:* Univ Western Ont, BSc, 56, PhD(biophys), 60. *Prof Exp:* Med Res Coun Can fel molecular biol, Royal Inst, London, Eng, 61-62 & Lab Molecular Biol, Cambridge Univ, 62-64; res assoc biophys, Mass Inst Technol, 65; asst prof, 65-69, ASSOC PROF BIOL STRUCT, UNIV WASH, 70- *Mem:* Biophys Soc; Can Asn Physicists. *Res:* Quantitative morphology; growth; models. *Mailing Add:* Dept Biol Struct SM-20 Univ of Wash Seattle WA 98105

PROTHEROE, WILLIAM MANSEL, b Wales, UK, Oct 16, 25; nat US; m 49; c 4. ASTRONOMY. *Educ:* Ohio State Univ, BSc, 50, PhD(astron), 55. *Prof Exp:* Res assoc astron, Ohio State Univ, 53-55; from asst prof to assoc prof, Univ Pa, 55-67, vdean grad sch, 60-66; assoc dean grad sch, 67-70, PROF ASTRON, OHIO STATE UNIV, 67- *Concurrent Pos:* Consult, Franklin Inst, 58-66; Guggenheim fel, 66-67. *Mem:* AAAS; Am Astron Soc; Int Astron Union; Royal Astron Soc. *Res:* Photoelectric photometry; eclipsing binary stars. *Mailing Add:* Dept of Astron Ohio State Univ Columbus OH 43210

PROTHRO, JOHNNIE W, b Atlanta, Ga, Feb 26, 22; m 49, 64; c 1. FOODS, NUTRITION. *Educ:* Spelman Col, BS, 41; Columbia Univ, MS, 46; Univ Chicago, PhD, 52. *Prof Exp:* High sch instr, 41-45; instr chem, Southern Univ, 47-48; from asst prof to prof, Tuskegee Inst & res assoc, Carver Found, 52-63; assoc prof, Univ Conn, 63-68; prof nutrit & res, Tuskegee Inst, 68-72; nutrit adv, Cent Dis Control, Dept Health, Educ & Welfare, Ga, 72-73; prof nutrit, Tuskegee Inst, 73-75; prof nutrit, Emory Univ, 75-79; PROF COMMUNITY HEALTH NUTRIT, GA STATE UNIV, 79- *Concurrent Pos:* NIH spec fel, Univ Calif, Los Angeles, 58-59. *Mem:* Am Dietetic Asn; Am Inst Nutrit; Inst Food Technologists. *Res:* Physiological availability and patterns of amino acids; presence of nonantiscorbutic reducing substances in baked foods; protein utilization in adolescent male. *Mailing Add:* 919 Falcon Dr SW Atlanta GA 30311

PROTOPOPESCU, SERBAN DAN, b Yacuma-Beni, Bolivia, Oct 25, 45; m 72. EXPERIMENTAL HIGH ENERGY PHYSICS. *Educ:* Princeton Univ, BA, 68; Univ Calif, Berkeley, PhD(physics), 72. *Prof Exp:* Res asst high energy physics, Lawrence Berkeley Lab, 69-72; asst physicist, 72-74, assoc physicist, 74-76, PHYSICIST, BROOKHAVEN NAT LAB, 77- *Concurrent Pos:* Vis scientist, Lab de l'Accelerator Lineaire, Univ Paris-Sud, Orsay, 76-77. *Mem:* Am Phys Soc. *Res:* Study of production and decay of meson resonances; partial wave analysis. *Mailing Add:* Dept Physics Bldg 510A Brookhaven Nat Lab Upton NY 11973

PROTSCH, REINER ROBERT RUDOLF, b Berlin, Ger, Jan 14, 39; US citizen; m 75. PHYSICAL ANTHROPOLOGY, MEDICAL ANTHROPOLOGY. *Educ:* Univ Calif, Los Angeles, BA, 68, MA & MS, 70, PhD(anthrop), 73. *Prof Exp:* Res asst chem & geophys, Inst Geophys, Univ Calif, Los Angeles, 67-70, res geophysicist, 70-72, asst res geophysicist & anthropologist, 73; res chemist, geophysicist & oceanogr, Univ Calif, San Diego & Los Angeles, 73-74; prof anthrop, J W Goethe Univ, Frankfurt, 74-80; dir, Inst Anthrop, 78-80; MEM FAC, DEPT GEOPHYS, UNIV CALIF, LOS ANGELES, 80- *Concurrent Pos:* Prof anthrop, Occidental Col, 70-73; Ger Res Asn Award, 74. *Mem:* Am Anthrop Asn; AAAS; Am Quaternary Asn; Ger Soc Anthrop & Human Genetics; Ger Soc Natural Sci & Med. *Res:* Chemical and physical absolute dating techniques, like radiocarbon and amino-acid dating; paleoanthropology, morphology and chronology of fossil man; paleopathology of fossil man; all chronometric dating techniques; prehistoric archaeology. *Mailing Add:* 405 Hilgard Dept Geophys Univ Calif Los Angeles CA 90024

PROTTER, MURRAY HAROLD, b New York, NY, Feb 13, 18; m 45; c 2. MATHEMATICS. *Educ:* Univ Mich, AB, 37, AM, 38; Brown Univ, PhD(math), 46. *Prof Exp:* Instr math, Ore State Col, 38-40; appl mathematician, David Taylor Model Basin, US Dept Navy, Washington, DC, 42-43 & Chance Vought Aircraft, Conn, 43-45; instr math, Brown Univ, 45-47; asst prof, Syracuse Univ, 47-51; mem, Inst Advan Study, Princeton, 51-53; assoc prof, 53-58, chmn dept, 62-65, PROF MATH, UNIV CALIF, BERKELEY, 58- *Mem:* Am Math Soc; Math Asn Am; Soc Indust & Appl Math. *Res:* Partial differential equations; fluid dynamics. *Mailing Add:* Dept of Math Univ of Calif Berkeley CA 94720

PROTTER, PHILIP ELLIOTT, b Syracuse, NY, Aug 19, 49. PURE MATHEMATICS. *Educ:* Yale Univ, BA, 71; Univ Calif, San Diego, MA, 73, PhD(math), 75. *Prof Exp:* Asst prof math, Duke Univ, 75-78; ASST PROF MATH & STATIST, PURDUE UNIV, 78- *Concurrent Pos:* NSF fel, Nat Ctr Sci Res, France, 79-80; mem, Inst Advan Study, 77-78; assoc prof, Univ Rennes, France, 81-82. *Mem:* Am Math Soc; Inst Math Statist; AAAS. *Res:* Probability theory, in particular stochastic integration and stochastic differential equations. *Mailing Add:* Dept of Math Purdue Univ West Lafayette IN 47906

PROTZ, RICHARD, b Willowbrook, Sask, Aug 8, 34; m 59; c 4. SOIL SCIENCE. *Educ:* Univ Sask, BSA, 56, MSc, 60; Iowa State Univ, PhD(soils), 65. *Prof Exp:* Soil surveyor, Univ Sask, 56-60; res assoc soils, Iowa State Univ, 60-65; res officer, Can Dept Agr, Guelph, 65-66; asst prof, 66-69, assoc prof, 69-77, PROF SOIL SCI, UNIV GUELPH, 78- *Concurrent Pos:* Consult soil sci, Malaysia, Egypt, Saudi Arabia, Nigeria & Indonesia. *Mem:* Soil Sci Soc Am; Am Soc Agr Sci; Can Soc Soil Sci; Agr Inst Can; Int Soil Sci Soc. *Res:* Soil genesis; morphology and classification; remote sensing. *Mailing Add:* Land Resource Sci Univ of Guelph Guelph ON N1G 2W1 Can

PROUD, G O'NEIL, b Oregon, Mo, Aug 6, 13; m 37; c 2. OTOLARYNGOLOGY. *Educ:* Univ Mo, AB, 35; Wash Univ, MD, 39. *Prof Exp:* Asst prof otolaryngol, Sch Med, Wash Univ, 46-50; chmn dept, 50-80, PROF OTOLARYNGOL, SCH MED, UNIV KANS MED CTR, KANSAS CITY, 50- *Mem:* Am Otol Soc; Am Laryngol, Rhinol & Otol Soc; Am Acad Ophthal & Otolaryngol. *Res:* Otology. *Mailing Add:* Dept Otorhinolaryngol Univ of Kans Med Ctr Kansas City KS 66103

PROUDFIT, CAROL MARIE, b Cincinnati, Ohio, Nov 22, 37; div; c 1. PHARMACOLOGY, REPRODUCTIVE PHYSIOLOGY. *Educ:* Univ Cincinnati, BS, 59; Univ Kans, Kansas City, PhD(med physiol), 71. *Prof Exp:* Trainee reprod physiol, Univ Ill, 71-74; SR SCIENTIST ENDOCRINE PHARMACOL, AMA, 76- *Concurrent Pos:* Lectr physiol, Triton Col, 74 & Northwestern Univ, 75; lectr pharmacol, Med Ctr, Univ Ill, 74- *Mem:* Am Fertil Soc; Am Women Sci; Am Soc Clin Pharmacol & Therapeut. *Res:* Endocrine pharmacology. *Mailing Add:* Dept of Drugs 535 N Dearborn St Chicago IL 60610

PROUDFOOT, BERNADETTE AGNES, b Jersey City, NJ, June 22, 21. BIOLOGY. *Educ:* Caldwell Col Women, BA, 52; St Thomas Inst, MS, 59, PhD(biol, exp med), 72. *Prof Exp:* Lectr, 55-56, from instr to assoc prof, 56-72, PROF BIOL & CHMN DEPT, CALDWELL COL, 72- *Mem:* AAAS; Nat Asn Biol Teachers; Nat Sci Teachers Asn. *Res:* Microrespiration studies on neoplasms and normal tissues. *Mailing Add:* Dept of Biol Caldwell Col Caldwell NJ 07006

PROUDFOOT, F G, b Salt Springs, NS, Mar 9, 21; m 47; c 4. POULTRY GENETICS, POULTRY PHYSIOLOGY. *Educ:* McGill Univ, BSc, Cornell Univ, MSc, 47. *Prof Exp:* Poultry fieldman, Govt NS, 45-46, poultry husbandman, 47-55; poultry geneticist, 55-61, HEAD POULTRY SECT, RES STA, CAN DEPT AGR, 62- *Concurrent Pos:* Mem, NS Poultry Adv Comt, 47-, Poultry Res Comt, NS Res Found, 50-61 & Nat Poultry Genetics Comt, 52-55. *Honors & Awards:* Can Silver Jubilee Medal, 77. *Mem:* Poultry Sci Asn; World Poultry Sci Asn; Agr Inst Can. *Res:* Genetics in genotype-environmental studies; physiology in the avian embryo and spermatozoa. *Mailing Add:* Res Sta Can Dept Agr Kentville NS B4N 1J5 Can

PROUGH, RUSSELL ALLEN, b Twin Falls, Idaho, Nov 5, 43; m 65; c 2. BIOCHEMISTRY. *Educ:* Col Idaho, BSc, 65; Ore State Univ, PhD(biochem), 69. *Prof Exp:* Vet Admin fel, Vet Admin Hosp, Kansas City, Mo, 69-72; instr, 72-73, asst prof, 73-77, ASSOC PROF BIOCHEM, UNIV TEX HEALTH SCI CTR DALLAS, 77- *Mem:* Am Soc Biol Chemists; Am Soc Pharmacol & Exp Therapeut; Am Asn Cancer Res. *Res:* Pyridine nucleotide-dependent flavoproteins, hydrazine and azo metabolism. *Mailing Add:* Dept of Biochem Univ of Tex Health Sci Ctr Dallas TX 75235

PROULX, PIERRE R, b Montreal, Que, June 27, 38; m 61; c 3. BIOCHEMISTRY. *Educ:* McGill Univ, BSc, 59, MSc, 60, PhD(biochem), 62. *Prof Exp:* Lectr biochem, McGill Univ, 62-63; from lectr to assoc prof, 63-73, PROF BIOCHEM, UNIV OTTAWA, 73- *Concurrent Pos:* Med Res Coun Can fel, 66-67 & scholar, 67-72. *Mem:* Can Biochem Soc; Chem Inst Can; AAAS. *Res:* Metabolism of phospholipids in bacteria and cell membrane-lipid vesicle interactions. *Mailing Add:* Dept of Biochem Univ of Ottawa Ottawa ON K1N 6N5 Can

PROUT, FRANKLIN SINCLAIR, b Washington, DC, Jan 10, 20; m 55; c 7. ORGANIC CHEMISTRY. *Educ:* Univ Colo, AB, 41; Vanderbilt Univ, BS, 43, PhD(chem), 47. *Prof Exp:* Asst, Off Sci Res & Develop, Vanderbilt Univ, 43-45; res assoc, Northwestern Univ, 47-48; from instr to assoc prof, 48-80, PROF CHEM, DEPAUL UNIV, 80- *Mem:* Am Chem Soc. *Res:* Organic syntheses of aliphatic, optically active compounds. *Mailing Add:* Dept of Chem DePaul Univ Chicago IL 60614

PROUT, GEORGE RUSSELL, JR, b Boston, Mass, July 23, 24; m 50; c 2. UROLOGY. *Educ:* Albany Med Col, MD, 47. *Hon Degrees:* MA, Harvard Univ, 70. *Prof Exp:* Instr surg, New York Hosp, 52-54; asst clinician urol, Sloan-Kettering Inst, 54-58; asst prof urol & chmn dept, Sch Med, Univ Miami, 57-60; from assoc prof to prof, Med Col, Va, 60-69, chmn dept, 60-69; PROF SURG, HARVARD MED SCH, 69-; CHIEF UROL SERV, MASS GEN HOSP, 69- *Concurrent Pos:* Spec fel, Mem Ctr Cancer & Allied Dis, 54-55, asst attend, 56-57; asst clinician, James Ewing Hosp, 56-57; consult, McGuire Vet Admin Hosp, Richmond, Va, 61-69 & Crippled Children's Hosp, 63-69; chmn study group adjuvants in surg treatment bladder cancer, Nat Cancer Inst, 65-; chmn, Nat Bladder Cancer Collab Group A, NIH, 73- *Mem:* Am Urol Asn; fel Am Col Surg; Soc Pelvic Surg; Am Asn Genitourinary Surg; Soc Peidat Urol. *Res:* Urological neoplasms. *Mailing Add:* Mass Gen Hosp Boston MA 02114

PROUT, JAMES HAROLD, b Oak Park, Ill, Dec 23, 27; m 54; c 1. APPLIED PHYSICS, ACOUSTICS. *Educ:* Purdue Univ, BS, 52; Univ Mich, MS, 58. *Prof Exp:* Res asst physics, Willow Run Labs, Univ Mich, 53-57, res assoc, 57-61; asst prof, 61-67, ASSOC PROF ENG RES, PA STATE UNIV, UNIVERSITY PARK, 67- *Mem:* Acoust Soc Am; Am Auditory Soc. *Res:* Air and waterborne acoustic signal analysis and data acquisition systems; design and testing of ear protectors, noise monitoring systems and speech communication systems; audiological electronics; ultrasonic characterization of materials. *Mailing Add:* Appl Res Lab Pa State Univ PO Box 30 State College PA 16801

PROUT, THADDEUS EDMUND, b Owings, Md, Dec 8, 23; m 50; c 3. MEDICINE. *Educ:* Harvard Med Sch, MD, 48; Am Bd Internal Med, dipl, 56. *Prof Exp:* Asst med, Harvard Med Sch, 49-50; asst, Sch Med, Boston Univ, 53-54; sr fel, 55-58, asst prof, 58-64, ASSOC PROF MED, SCH MED, JOHNS HOPKINS UNIV, 64-; CHIEF MED, GREATER BALTIMORE MED CTR, 64- *Concurrent Pos:* Resident, Boston Vet Admin Hosp, 53-54; dir diabetes training prog & assoc physician in chg, Endocrine Diabetes Clin, Johns Hopkins Hosp, 58-66, physician, 58-; consult, Food & Drug Admin & Fed Trade Comn. *Mem:* Endocrine Soc; assoc Royal Soc Med; Am Diabetes Asn; fel Am Col Physicians; Am Thyroid Asn. *Res:* Clincal trials on therapeutic agents. *Mailing Add:* 6701 N Charles St Baltimore MD 21204

PROUT, TIMOTHY, b Watertown, Conn, June 14, 23; m 50; c 2. GENETICS. *Educ:* Hobart Col, BA, 48; Columbia Univ, MA & PhD, 54. *Prof Exp:* From asst prof to prof zool, Univ Calif, Riverside, 54-74, PROF GENETICS, UNIV CALIF, DAVIS, 74- *Concurrent Pos:* Guest prof, Genetics Inst, Aarhus Univ, 67-68 & 74-75. *Mem:* AAAS; Soc Study Evolution; Am Soc Human Genetics; Genetics Soc Am; Am Soc Naturalists. *Res:* Population genetics in Drosophila. *Mailing Add:* Dept of Genetics Univ of Calif Davis CA 95616

PROUTY, RICHARD METCALF, b Milford, Mass, May 20, 24; m 51; c 3. ANALYTICAL CHEMISTRY. *Educ:* Univ Mass, BS, 51; Univ Conn, MS, 57; Univ Minn, PhD(animal husb), 63. *Prof Exp:* Res fel, Sch Pub Health, Univ Minn, 61-63; RES CHEMIST, ENVIRON CHEM SECT, PATUXENT WILDLIFE RES CTR, US DEPT INTERIOR, 63- *Mem:* Am Chem Soc. *Res:* Identification and measurement of organochlorine compounds accumulating in the tissues of wild birds. *Mailing Add:* Environ Chem Sect Patuxent Wildlife Res Ctr Laurel MD 20708

PROVASOLI, LUIGI, b Busto Arsizio, Italy, Feb 13, 08; nat US; m 38. MICROBIOLOGY. *Educ:* Univ Milan, BS, 31, PhD(zool), 39. *Prof Exp:* Asst prof entom, Univ Milan, 33-42; prof zool, Univ Camerino, 43-46; instr biol, St Francis Col, NY, 47, prof & chmn dept, 48-51; mem staff, Haskins Labs, 51-81, secy, 69-81; SR RES BIOLOGIST, YALE UNIV, 76- *Concurrent Pos:* Lectr, Brooklyn Col, 49, 51-52; ed jour, Phycol Soc Am, 65-75; adj prof, Yale Univ, 70-76; mem corp, Marine Biol Lab, Woods Hole, Mass. *Mem:* Phycol Soc Am; Am Soc Limnol & Oceanog; Soc Protozool; NY Acad Sci; French Soc Microbiol. *Res:* Nutrition and vitamin requirements of fresh water and marine algae; morphogenetic factors for seaweed; nutrition of crustacea. *Mailing Add:* Biol Dept Yale Univ New Haven CT 06520

PROVDER, THEODORE, b Brooklyn, NY, Dec 26, 39; m 61; c 3. PHYSICAL CHEMISTRY. *Educ:* Univ Miami, BS, 61; Univ Wis-Madison, PhD(phys chem), 66. *Prof Exp:* Sr res chemist, Monsanto Co, Mo, 65-70; tech mgr fundamental & comput sci dept coatings res, 70-77; SR SCIENTIST POLYMER RES & COMPUT SCI GROUP, POLYMER & COATINGS RES DEPT, GLIDDEN COATINGS & RESINS DIV, SCM CORP, STRONGSVILLE, 79- *Concurrent Pos:* Mem exec comt, Div Org Coatings & Plastics, 81-82, adv bd, Advan in Chem & Symp series, Am Chem Soc, 81-84. *Honors & Awards:* SCM Corp Sci & Tech Award, 77; ACM Glidden Coatings & Resins Div Award for Tech Excellence, 81. *Mem:* Am Soc Testing & Mat; fel Am Inst Chemists; Am Chem Soc; Sigma Xi. *Res:* Research in solution property and solid state characterization; mechanical properties and rheological studies of polymer, colloids and coatings, and new coatings concepts; use of computerization in polymer science and laboratory automation and instrument and process control. *Mailing Add:* 26320 Hickory Lane Olmsted Falls OH 44138

PROVENCIO, JESUS ROBERTO, b Juarez, Mex, Feb 24, 25; US citizen; m 49; c 6. COMMUNICATIONS, PHYSICS. *Educ:* Tex Col Mines, BS, 48; Tex Western Col, MS, 65; Univ Chihuahua, DUniv, 72. *Prof Exp:* Instr physics, Univ Denver, 48-51; asst prof math & elec eng, Fed Schs, Mex, 51-53; systs scientist commun, Motorola, Inc, 53-63; asst prof math & physics, 63-73, ASST PROF MATH, UNIV TEX, EL PASO, 73- *Concurrent Pos:* Consult, Dept Health, Educ & Welfare, 70-, mem, Nat Adv Comt Educ, 70-72, Nat Task Force Res Phys Sci, 72-73; consult, US Off Educ, 70- & Nat Ctr Vol Action; systs analyst, Dept Housing & Urban Develop; mem, Nat Ctr Latin Am Studies Asn. *Mem:* Soc Advan Educ (pres, 69-70); Mex Phys Soc; Am Inst Physics. *Res:* Information-communications theory, especially communications among persons of different cultural backgrounds; propagation and decay of shocks in air. *Mailing Add:* Dept of Math Univ of Tex El Paso TX 79668

PROVENZA, DOMINIC VINCENT, b Baltimore, Md, Nov 27, 17; m 64. ZOOLOGY. *Educ:* Univ Md, BS, 39, MS, 41, PhD(zool), 52. *Prof Exp:* From instr to assoc prof biol, Loyola Col, Md, 47-55; assoc prof anat, Univ Col, 55-56, assoc prof, Dent Sch, 55-57, actg head dept, 57-61, PROF ANAT, DENT SCH, UNIV MD, BALTIMORE, 57-, HEAD DEPT, 61- *Concurrent Pos:* Prof biol & chmn dept sci, Eve Sch, Loyola Col Md, 47-55; NIH spec fel, 62-63; ed, J Baltimore Col Dent Surg, 65- *Mem:* Am Asn Anatomists; NY Acad Sci; Int Asn Dent Res. *Res:* Histophysiology of mammalian microcirculation; intercellular substances of periodontium; physiology of spermatozoa; feeding mechanisms of Coccidae; physical-chemical ecology; electron microscopy dentino-genesis; adhesive restorative materials; ultrastructure of accessory boring organ of gastropods; formed intercellular components of oral mucosa; histo-cytochemistry of odentogenesis. *Mailing Add:* Dept of Anat Univ of Md Sch of Dent Baltimore MD 21201

PROVER, CORINNE BEA, b New York, NY, May 2, 28; m 46; c 2. PLANT MORPHOGENESIS, PLANT PHYSIOLOGY. *Educ:* Hofstra Univ, BA, 62, MA, 63; NY Univ, PhD(biol), 71. *Prof Exp:* Instr, 63-69, asst prof, 70-80, ASSOC PROF BIOL, HOFSTRA UNIV, 80- *Concurrent Pos:* NSF lectr, Hofstra Univ, 66-73; consult, Eyegate House, 67-69. *Mem:* Sigma Xi; Bot Soc Am; Am Soc Plant Physiologists; AAAS. *Res:* Effects of red light, growth hormones and media additives on the growth of fern gametophytes; effects of autoclaving media that contain sucrose. *Mailing Add:* Dept of Biol Hofstra Univ Hempstead NY 11550

PROVERB, ROBERT JOSEPH, b Chelsea, Mass, Dec 20, 46; m 68; c 1. ORGANIC CHEMISTRY. *Educ:* Northeastern Univ, BA, 69, PhD(org chem), 73. *Prof Exp:* Fel org chem, Univ Alta, 73-75, Rice Univ, 75-76 & Univ Calif, Los Angeles, 77; SR RES CHEMIST, AM CYANAMID CO, 77- *Mem:* Am Chem Soc; Royal Soc Chem; Sigma Xi; NY Acad Sci. *Res:* Synthetic organic chemistry; organic reaction mechanisms; natural product chemistry; biological chemistry. *Mailing Add:* Am Cyanamid Co 1937 W Main St Stamford CT 06904

PROVERBS, MAURICE DESMOND, economic entomology, see previous edition

PROVOST, ERNEST EDMUND, b Needham Heights, Mass, June 19, 21; m 47; c 2. ZOOLOGY. *Educ:* Purdue Univ, BS, 50; Wash State Univ, MS, 53, PhD(zool), 58. *Prof Exp:* From asst to instr zool, Wash State Univ, 50-58; asst prof, Univ Ill, 58-60; assoc prof wildlife mgr & zool, 60-74, MEM STAFF, EXP STA, UNIV GA, 60-, PROF WILDLIFE & ZOOL, 74- *Mem:* AAAS; Wildlife Soc; Am Soc Mammalogists. *Res:* Wildlife biology; vertebrate zoology; mammalian reproduction and ecology of feral populations. *Mailing Add:* Sch of Forest Resources Univ of Ga Athens GA 30602

PROVOST, PHILIP JOSEPH, b Bristol, Conn, May 28, 35; m 62; c 2. MICROBIOLOGY, VIROLOGY. *Educ:* Univ Conn, AB, 57; Univ Md, MS, 59, PhD(microbiol), 61. *Prof Exp:* Res fel microbiol, Sch Med, Univ Md, 61-63 & McCollum-Pratt Inst, Johns Hopkins Univ, 63-64; asst prof microbiol, Fac Med, Dalhousie Univ, 64-66; res virologist, Lederle Labs, Am Cyanamid Co, 66-69, head dept biol res & develop, 69-70; res fel virus & cell biol res, 70-76, sr res fel, 76-80, SR INVESTR, MERCK INST THERAPEUT RES, MERCK & CO, INC, 80- *Mem:* AAAS; Am Soc Microbiol; NY Acad Sci; Can Soc Microbiologists; Sigma Xi. *Res:* Viral hepatitis; mechanisms of microbial pathogenesis; immunity to infectious diseases. *Mailing Add:* Merck Inst for Therapeut Res Merck & Co Inc West Point PA 19486

PROVOST, RONALD HAROLD, b Burlington, Vt, May 25, 42; m 68. PHYSICAL CHEMISTRY. *Educ:* St Michael's Col, Vt, AB, 64; Univ Vt, PhD(phys chem), 68. *Prof Exp:* ASSOC PROF CHEM & CHMN DEPT, ST MICHAEL'S COL, 68-, ACAD VPRES, 80- *Mem:* Am Chem Soc; Sigma Xi. *Res:* Thermodynamics characterization of transition metal systems. *Mailing Add:* Dept of Chem St Michael's Col Winooski VT 05404

PROWSE, GERALD ALBERT, marine phycology, deceased

PRUCHA, JOHN JAMES, b River Falls, Wis, Sept 22, 24; m 48; c 10. STRUCTURAL GEOLOGY. *Educ:* Univ Wis, PhB, 45, MPh, 46; Princeton Univ, MA, 48, PhD(geol), 49. *Prof Exp:* From instr to asst prof geol, Rutgers Univ, 48-51; sr geologist, NY State Geol Surv, 51-56; res geologist, Shell Develop Co, 56-63; chmn dept geol, 63-70, dean col arts & sci, 70-72, PROF GEOL, SYRACUSE UNIV, 63-, VCHANCELLOR ACAD AFFAIRS, 72- *Mem:* Fel AAAS; fel Geol Soc Am; Am Asn Petrol Geologists. *Res:* Precambrian geology; structural geology; regional tectonics; salt deformation in folding. *Mailing Add:* 300 Admin Bldg Syracuse Univ Syracuse NY 13210

PRUCKMAYR, GERFRIED, b Vienna, Austria, Feb 1, 33; m 63. ORGANIC CHEMISTRY. *Educ:* Univ Vienna, PhD(org chem), 61. *Prof Exp:* Res assoc, Case Inst Technol, 61-62; res chemist, 62-71, staff scientist, 71-76, RES ASSOC, E I DU PONT DE NEMOURS & CO, INC, 76- *Mem:* Am Chem Soc. *Res:* Synthesis of pharmacologically active heterocyclic compounds; heterocyclic polymers; reaction mechanisms; ring-opening polymerizations. *Mailing Add:* Indust Chem Dept E I du Pont de Nemours & Co Inc Wilmington DE 19898

PRUDEN, BARRY BLYTHE, chemical engineering, see previous edition

PRUDENCE, ROBERT THOMAS, b San Francisco, Calif, Nov 19, 44; m 68; c 1. ORGANIC POLYMER CHEMISTRY. *Educ:* John Carroll Univ, BS, 66; Purdue Univ, PhD(org chem), 71. *Prof Exp:* SR RES CHEMIST, GOODYEAR RES LABS, GOODYEAR TIRE & RUBBER CO, 70- *Mem:* Am Chem Soc. *Res:* Anionic polymerization techniques used to develop thermoplastic block polymers and diene homopolymers. *Mailing Add:* Goodyear Tire & Rubber Co Res Lab 142 Goodyear Blvd Akron OH 44316

PRUDER, GARY DAVID, b Detroit, Mich, June 23, 32; m 57; c 2. BIOENGINEERING, AQUACULTURE. *Educ:* Gen Motors Inst, BME, 56; Univ Del, MBA, 67, PhD PhD(marine studies), 78. *Prof Exp:* Sr exp engr, Hydra-matic Div, Gen Motors Corp, 52-62; head applns res, Elkton Div, Thiokol Chem Corp, 62-66; gen mgr, Technidyne Div, Aeroprojs Inc, 66-69; dir eng & mfg, Chem Data Systs, 69-71; PRIN INVESTR CONTROLLED ENVIRON SYST DEVELOP, UNIV DEL, 71- *Concurrent Pos:* Consult maricult, Kahuku Seafood Plantation, Hawaii, 77-78. *Mem:* World Maricult Soc; AAAS. *Res:* Intensive controlled mariculture; mass production of algae; solar ponds; waste treatment and recycle; rearing bivalve molluscs. *Mailing Add:* Ctr for Maricult Res Univ of Del Lewes DE 19958

PRUD HOMME, JACQUES, b Montreal, July 15, 40; m 63; c 3. POLYMER SCIENCE. *Educ:* Univ Montreal, PhD, 67. *Prof Exp:* Nat Res Coun Can fel, 67-69, asst prof, 69-74, assoc prof, 74-80, PROF CHEM, UNIV MONTREAL, 80- *Mem:* Chem Inst Can. *Res:* Polymer chemistry; synthesis, characterization and properties of block copolymers. *Mailing Add:* Dept Chem Univ Montreal PO Box 6128 Montreal PQ H3C 3U1 Can

PRUD'HOMME, ROBERT EMERY, b Ste-Martine, Que, July 12, 46. POLYMER CHEMISTRY. *Educ:* Univ Montreal, BSc, 69, MSc, 70; Univ Mass, Amherst, PhD(chem), 73. *Prof Exp:* Res scientist pulp & paper, Pulp & Paper Res Inst Can, 73-75; asst prof, 75-80, ASSOC PROF CHEM, LAVAL UNIV, 80- *Mem:* Am Chem Soc; Am Phys Soc; Inst Chem Can; Can Asn Advan Sci. *Res:* The solid state of polymers, including crystallization, morphology and mechanical properties. *Mailing Add:* Dept of Chem Laval Univ Quebec City PQ G1K 7P4 Can

PRUD'HOMME, ROBERT KRAFFT, b Sacramento, Calif, Jan 28, 48; m 73; c 2. CHEMICAL ENGINEERING, RHEOLOGY. *Educ:* Stanford Univ, BS, 69; Univ Wis, PhD(chem eng), 78. *Prof Exp:* Environ engr, US Army Armaments Command, 71-72; res asst, Dept Chem Eng, Univ Wis, 73-78; ASST PROF CHEM ENG, PRINCETON UNIV, 78- *Concurrent Pos:* Mem comt on undergrad educ, Univ Wis, 75-77; consult, Mobil Oil Co, 78- *Mem:* Sigma Xi; Am Inst Chem Engrs; Am Soc Rheol. *Res:* Transport processes; fluid mechanics of polymeric materials; polymerization reactions; environmental science. *Mailing Add:* Dept of Chem Eng Princeton Univ Princeton NJ 08540

PRUDHON, ROLLAND A, JR, b Princeton, NJ, June 16, 42; m 65; c 3. PARASITOLOGY. *Educ:* Maryville Col, BS, 65; Univ Tenn, Knoxville, MS, 68, PhD(zool), 72. *Prof Exp:* Asst prof natural sci, 72-80, chmn dept, 73-80, ASSOC PROF BIOL & HEAD DEPT NATURAL SCI, SHELBY STATE COMMUNITY COL, 80- *Concurrent Pos:* Mem, Audio-tutorial Cong. *Mem:* Am Soc Parasitologists. *Mailing Add:* Shelby State Community Col PO Box 4568 Memphis TN 38104

PRUESS, KENNETH PAUL, b Troy, Ind, June 21, 32; m 64; c 2. ENTOMOLOGY. *Educ:* Purdue Univ, BS, 54; Ohio State Univ, MS, 55, PhD(entom), 57. *Prof Exp:* Asst prof, 57-63, assoc prof, 63-75, PROF ENTOM, UNIV NEBR-LINCOLN, 75- *Mem:* Entom Soc Am. *Res:* Economic entomology; applied ecology crop and rangeland insects. *Mailing Add:* Dept of Entom Univ of Nebr Lincoln NE 68583

PRUESS, STEVEN ARTHUR, b Cedar Rapids, Iowa, June 8, 44. NUMERICAL ANALYSIS. *Educ:* Iowa State Univ, BS, 66; Purdue Univ, MS, 68, PhD(comput sci), 70. *Prof Exp:* Asst prof, 70-75, ASSOC PROF MATH, UNIV NMEX, 75- *Concurrent Pos:* Sabbatical leave, Univ BC, 80-81. *Mem:* Soc Indust & Appl Math. *Res:* Solutions of differential equations; eigenvalue problems; approximation theory. *Mailing Add:* Dept Math & Statist Univ NMex Albuquerque NM 87131

PRUETT, JACK KENNETH, b Kinston, Ala, Sept 22, 32; m 56; c 3. PHARMACOLOGY. *Educ:* Auburn Univ, BS, 60, MS, 63; Med Col SC, PhD(pharmacol), 67. *Prof Exp:* From instr to assoc prof pharmacol, Med Univ SC, 66-77; ASSOC PROF ANESTHESIOL, MED COL GA, 77-, ASSOC PROF PHARMACOL, 80- *Mem:* Am Soc Pharmacol & Exp Therapeut; Am Soc Anesthesiologists; Am Heart Asn; Soc Cardiovasc Anesthesiologists; Int Anesthesia Res Soc. *Res:* Cardiovascular pharmacology and cardiac electrophysiology. *Mailing Add:* Dept Anesthesiol Med Col Ga Augusta GA 30912

PRUETT, JOHN ROBERT, b Plankinton, SDak, Mar 8, 23; m 60; c 1. PHYSICS, COMPUTER SCIENCE. *Educ:* Ind Univ, PhD(physics), 49. *Prof Exp:* Asst physics, Ind Univ, 42, asst, Manhattan Proj, 42-44; jr physicist, Appl Physics Lab, Johns Hopkins Univ, 44 & Naval Res Lab, 45; asst physics, Ind Univ, 45-49; from asst prof to assoc prof, 49-64, PROF PHYSICS, BRYN MAWR COL, 64- & CHMN DEPT, 78- *Concurrent Pos:* US State Dept rep, Int Conf Orgn Econ Coop & Develop, Milan, Italy, 63 & Uppsala, Sweden, 64. *Mem:* Am Phys Soc; Am Asn Physics Teachers. *Res:* Beta and gamma ray spectroscopy; beta decay theory; nuclear resonance fluorescence; nuclear structure; hardware and software design for direct computer controlled experimentation in the sciences. *Mailing Add:* Dept of Physics Bryn Mawr Col Bryn Mawr PA 19010

PRUETT, PATRICIA ONDERDONK, b Chicago, Ill, June 11, 30; m 60; c 1. CELL PHYSIOLOGY, BIOCHEMISTRY. *Educ:* Bryn Mawr Col, AB, 52, MA, 61, PhD(biol), 65. *Prof Exp:* Teaching asst biol, 58-60, asst dean, 60-67, actg dean, 68-69, 76-77 & 77-78, ASSOC DEAN & LECTR BIOL, BRYN MAWR COL, 70- *Mem:* AAAS; Am Soc Cell Biologists; Soc Protozoologists. *Res:* Computer applications in the biological sciences, molecular modeling of phospholipids; membrane transport; anion accumulation; transport mechanisms; ortho-phosphate fluxes across the membrane of a ciliated protozoan. *Mailing Add:* 823 Old Gulph Rd Bryn Mawr PA 19010

PRUETT, ROY L, b Union City, Tenn, Nov 26, 24; m 61; c 2. TRANSITION METAL CHEMISTRY. *Educ:* Murray State Univ, BS, 44; Univ Tenn, MS, 48, PhD(org chem), 51. *Prof Exp:* Corp res fel, Union Carbide Corp, 48-79; sr res assoc, 79-81, SCI ADV, EXXON RES & ENG CO, 81- *Mem:* Am Chem Soc. *Res:* Homogeneous catalysis with transition metal complexes; rhodium-catalyzed hydroformylation reaction; synthesis and reaction of metal cluster compounds. *Mailing Add:* Exxon Res & Eng Co PO Box 45 Linden NJ 07036

PRUGH, JOHN DREW, b Greybull, Wyo, Dec 18, 32; m 54; c 3. MEDICINAL CHEMISTRY. *Educ:* Univ Wyo, BS, 58; Univ Wash, PhD, 64. *Prof Exp:* NIH fel chem, Yale Univ, 64-66; sr res chemist, 66-80, RES FEL, MERCK SHARP & DOHME RES LABS, 80- *Mem:* Am Chem Soc. *Res:* Furan chemistry; mechanism of acetal oxidation; dibenzocycloheptene chemistry; heterocycles; carbohydrates. *Mailing Add:* Dept of Med Chem Merck Sharp & Dohme Res Labs West Point PA 19486

PRUGOVECKI, EDUARD, b Craiova, Rumania, Mar 19, 37; Can citizen. MATHEMATICAL PHYSICS. *Educ:* Univ Zagreb, dipl physics, 59; Princeton Univ, PhD(theoret physics), 64. *Prof Exp:* Prof assoc theoret physics, Princeton Univ, 64-65; lectr, Univ Alta, 66-67; from asst prof to assoc prof, 67-74, FULL PROF APPL MATH, UNIV TORONTO, 75- *Concurrent Pos:* Fel, Theoret Physics Inst, Univ Alta, 65-67; Nat Res Coun Can grant, Univ Toronto, 68- *Res:* Scattering theory; foundations of quantum mechanics; quantum field theory; functional analysis; group theory. *Mailing Add:* Dept Math Univ Toronto Toronto ON M5S 1A1 Can

PRUITT, ALBERT WESLEY, b Anderson, SC, Jan 1, 40; m 61; c 1. PHARMACOLOGY. *Educ:* Emory Univ, BA, 61, MD, 65. *Prof Exp:* Resident pediat, Grady Mem Hosp, 65-68; fel, 70-72, asst prof, 72-77, assoc prof pediat, 75-81, ASSOC PROF PHARMACOL, EMORY UNIV, 77-, PROF PEDIAT, 81-; CHIEF PEDIAT, GRADY MEM HOSP, 81- *Mem:* Soc Pediat Res; Am Soc Pharmacol & Exp Therapeut; Am Soc Clin Pharmacol & Therapeut; Am Acad Pediat; Am Fedn Clin Res. *Res:* Age-related changes in metabolism of drugs and responses to drugs. *Mailing Add:* Glenn Mem Bldg Emory Univ Atlanta GA 30335

PRUITT, KENNETH M, b Winston-Salem, NC, Oct 3, 33; m 56; c 4. BIOCHEMISTRY. *Educ:* Univ NC, BS, 56; Pa State Univ, BS, 57; Brown Univ, PhD(phys chem), 65. *Prof Exp:* Chief chemist, Diabetic Res Lab, Birmingham Vet Admin Hosp, 64-65; investr, Lab Molecular Biol, 65-68, scientist, Inst Dent Res, 67-77, from asst prof to assoc prof biochem, 64-78, assoc prof biomath, 78-80, dir, Div Molecular Biol, 80-81, PROF BIOCHEM, LAB MOLECULAR BIOL, SCH MED, UNIV ALA, BIRMINGHAM, 78-, PROF, DEPT BIOMATH, 79-, ASST VPRES RES, 79-, SR SCIENTIST, CYSTIC FIBROSIS RES CTR, 81- *Concurrent Pos:* Assoc prof chem, Univ Col, Birmingham, Ala, 68-71, 73-77; vis scientist pharmacol, Hershey Med Ctr, Pa State Univ, 70-71; vis scientist, Fac Odontol, 71-72, 73, Gothenburg vis prof, Lab Oral Biochem, 76; vis prof, fac Odontol, Univ Umea, Umea, Sweden, 77. 71-72. Am Soc Biol Chemists; Am Chem Soc; Am Phys Soc; Am Meteorol Soc; vis prof, Lab Oral Biochem, Univ Umea, 78 & 79, Dept Physics, Univ Linkoping, Sweden, 79; chmn, Saliva Res Physiol Session, Int Asn Dent Res, Japan, 80; ad hoc mem, Oral Biol & Med Study Sect, NIH, 78-79; external rev, NSF, 80-81, exten rev, Cell & Physiol Biosci Sect, 81; invited lectr, Int Res Course, Univ Umea, Sweden, 81. *Mem:* AAAS; Am Soc Biol Chem; Int Asn Dent Res; Am Asn Dent Res; NY Acad Sci. *Res:* The peroxidase system and other non-immunoglobulin defense mechanisms; defense mechanisms on mucosal surfaces. *Mailing Add:* Lab of Molecular Biol Univ of Ala Med Ctr Birmingham AL 35294

PRUITT, RAYMOND DONALD, b Wheaton, Minn, Feb 6, 12; m 42; c 4. MEDICINE. *Educ:* Baker Univ, BS, 33; Oxford Univ, BA, 36; Univ Kans, MD, 39; Univ Minn, MS, 44; Am Bd Internal Med, dipl. *Prof Exp:* Intern, Hosps, Univ Kans, 39-40; fellow, Mayo Grad Sch Med, 40-43; from instr to prof med, Mayo Found, Univ Minn, 45-59; prof internal med & chmn dept,

Baylor Col Med, 59-68, vpres med affairs & chief exec officer, 66-68; dir, Mayo Grad Sch Med, Univ Minn, 68-75, dean, Mayo Med Sch, 71-77, dir educ, Mayo Found, 68-77, PROF MED, MAYO MED SCH, MAYO FOUND, 68- *Concurrent Pos:* Mem div med & consult cardiovasc dis, Mayo Clin, 43-59, 78-; mem adv coun, Div Res Resources, NIH, 70-73; mem, Nat Adv Heart Coun & President's Adv Panel Heart Dis. *Mem:* AMA; Asn Am Physicians. *Res:* Cardiovascular disease. *Mailing Add:* Mayo Found Rochester MN 55901

PRUITT, ROGER ARTHUR, b Kansas City, Mo, July 10, 36; m 60; c 2. PHYSICS. *Educ:* Univ Kans, BS, 59; Colo State Univ, MS, 67, PhD(physics), 69. *Prof Exp:* High sch teacher, Kans, 59-62; pub sch teacher, Colo, 62-64; instr physics, Colo State Univ, 69-70; from asst prof to assoc prof, 70-76, PROF PHYSICS, FT HAYS KANS STATE COL, 76- *Mem:* Am Asn Physics Teachers; Am Phys Soc; Sigma Xi. *Res:* Mossbauer spectroscopy in intermallic compounds. *Mailing Add:* Dept Physics Ft Hays Kans State Col Hays KS 67601

PRUITT, WILLIAM EDWIN, b Oklahoma City, Okla, May 11, 34; m 56; c 3. PROBABILITY. *Educ:* Okla State Univ, BS, 55, MS, 56; Stanford Univ, PhD(statist), 60. *Prof Exp:* From asst prof to assoc prof, 60-70, PROF MATH, UNIV MINN, MINNEAPOLIS, 70- *Concurrent Pos:* Vis prof, Cornell Univ, 77-78; assoc ed, Annals Probability, 72-78. *Mem:* Am Math Soc; Inst Math Statist; Math Asn Am. *Res:* Probability theory. *Mailing Add:* Sch of Math Univ of Minn Minneapolis MN 55455

PRUNIER, VIVIAN JOYCE, physiology, see previous edition

PRUNTY, LYLE DELMAR, b Charles City, Iowa, Oct 8, 45; m 75; c 1. SOIL PHYSICS. *Educ:* Iowa State Univ, BS, 67, MS, 69, PhD(soil physics), 78. *Prof Exp:* Develop engr, Western Elec Co, 70-75; res assoc, Dept Agron, Iowa State Univ, 76-78; ASST PROF SOILS SCI, NDAK STATE UNIV, 78- *Mem:* Am Soc Agron. *Res:* Coal surface mine reclamation; soil crusting; water use by sunflowers. *Mailing Add:* Dept of Soils NDak State Univ Fargo ND 58102

PRUSACZYK, JOSEPH EDWARD, b Cleveland, Ohio, 1944; m 67; c 1. PHYSICAL CHEMISTRY. *Educ:* Univ Dayton, BS, 66; Case Western Reserve Univ, PhD(phys chem), 71. *Prof Exp:* Interim asst prof chem, Univ Fla, 70-71, fel radiation chem, 71-72; res assoc chem, Univ Md, College Park, 72-73 & Fla State Univ, 73-74; SUPVR, OWENS CORNING FIBERGLAS CORP, 74- *Mem:* Am Chem Soc; Am Soc Mass Spectrometry. *Res:* Mass spectrometry; high temperature chemistry; thermodynamics; radiation chemistry; gas chromatography-mass spectrometry; ion-molecule reactions; fire research; instrumentation; analytical chemistry; polymer characterization. *Mailing Add:* Owens Corning Fiberglas Corp Tech Ctr Granville OH 43023

PRUSAS, ZENON C, b Butenal, Lithuania, June 5, 21; US citizen; m 52; c 1. PULP & PAPER TECHNOLOGY. *Educ:* Univ Vilnius, Luthuania, MF, 43; Univ Munich, PhD(econ), 48; Syracuse Univ, MS, 55. *Prof Exp:* Res scientist pulp & paper, 55-63, sr res engr, 63-66, sr consult, 67-78, RES FEL PULP & PAPER, MEAD CORP, 79- *Mem:* Sigma Xi; Tech Asn Pulp & Paper Indust. *Res:* Solving of technical problems in pulp and paper mills. *Mailing Add:* Mead Corp Cent Res Eight & Hickory Chillicothe OH 45601

PRUSCH, ROBERT DANIEL, b Lackawanna, NY, July 13, 39; m 69. INVERTEBRATE PHYSIOLOGY. *Educ:* Univ Portland, BSc, 64; Syracuse Univ, PhD(physiol), 69. *Prof Exp:* USPHS fel, Case Western Reserve Univ, 69-71; asst prof physiol, Brown Univ, 71-78; ASSOC PROF BIOL, RI COL, 78- *Mem:* Am Physiol Soc; Soc Exp Biol; Soc Gen Physiologists; Am Soc Zoologists. *Res:* Physiology of inorganic ion and water relationships in invertebrate cellular and epithelial systems. *Mailing Add:* Dept of Biol RI Col Providence RI 02908

PRUSINER, STANLEY BEN, b Des Moines, Iowa, May 28, 42; m 70; c 1. NEUROLOGY. *Educ:* Univ Pa, AB, 64, MD, 68. *Prof Exp:* Asst prof neurol, Univ Calif, San Francisco, 74-80; ASST PROF VIROL, UNIV CALIF, BERKELEY, 79-; ASSOC PROF NEUROL, UNIV CALIF, SAN FRANCISCO, 80-, LECTR, BIOCHEM & BIOPHYS, 76- *Concurrent Pos:* Investr, Howard Hughes Med Inst, Univ Calif, San Francisco, 76-81; Res Career Develop Award, NIH, 75-76. *Mem:* Am Soc Biol Chemists; Am Soc Clin Invest; Am Asn Immunologists; Am Chem Soc; Am Acad Neurol. *Res:* Molecular structure of unusual slow infectious agents (prions) that cause degenerative diseases in humans and animals. *Mailing Add:* Dept Neurol M-794 Univ Calif Sch Med San Francisco CA 94143

PRUSOFF, WILLIAM HERMAN, b New York, NY, June 25, 20; m 48; c 2. BIOCHEMISTRY, PHARMACOLOGY. *Educ:* Univ Miami, BS, 41; Columbia Univ, MS, 47, PhD(chem), 49. *Prof Exp:* From res assoc to sr instr pharmacol res, Western Reserve Univ, 49-53; from res assoc to assoc prof, 53-66, PROF PHARMACOL, SCH MED, YALE UNIV, 66- *Mem:* Am Chem Soc; Am Soc Biol Chemists; Am Asn Cancer Res; Am Soc Pharmacol & Exp Therapeut; Am Soc Microbiol. *Res:* Nucleic acids; protein isolation; cancer chemotherapy; biopharmacology; viral chemotherapy; radiation; Design aglsynthesis of compounds for antiviral and anticancer activity and elucidation of the molecular basis for the biological activity for those compounds that are active. *Mailing Add:* Dept of Pharmacol Yale Univ Sch of Med New Haven CT 06510

PRUSS, STANLEY MCQUAIDE, b Detroit, Mich, Sept 24, 43; div. EXPERIMENTAL HIGH ENERGY PHYSICS, ACCELERATOR TECHNOLOGY. *Educ:* Univ Mich, Ann Arbor, BS, 65, MS, 66, PhD(physics), 69. *Prof Exp:* Assoc physicist, Nat Accelerator Lab, 69-72, assoc physicist, 72-81, APPL SCIENTIST, FERMI NAT LAB, 81- *Mem:* Am Phys Soc. *Res:* Experimental particle physics-strong interactions. *Mailing Add:* Cross-Gallery Fermi Nat Lab PO Box 500 Batavia IL 60510

PRUSS, THADDEUS P, b Baltimore, Md, Jan 13, 34; m 63; c 2. PHARMACOLOGY. *Educ:* Univ Md, BS, 56, MS, 59; Georgetown Univ, PhD(pharmacol), 62. *Prof Exp:* Sect head cardiovasc pharmacol, Cutter Labs, Inc, 62-66; from sect head cardiovasc pharmacol to actg dir pharmacol, McNeil Labs, Inc, 66-69, dir pharmacol res, 69-80; DIR BIOL RES & DEVELOP, REVLON HEALTH CARE GROUP, 80- *Mem:* Am Soc Pharmacol & Exp Therapeut; Am Soc Biochem Pharmacol; NY Acad Sci; Soc Exp Biol & Med; Am Heart Asn. *Res:* Cardiovascular research in development of drugs for treatment of hypertension, arrhythmias of the heart, coronary artery disease and pulmonary vascular disease. *Mailing Add:* Revlon Health Care Group 1 Scarsdale Rd Tuckahoe NY 10707

PRUSSIN, STANLEY GERALD, b Bridgeport, Conn, Nov 20, 39. NUCLEAR CHEMISTRY, RADIOCHEMISTRY. *Educ:* Mass Inst Technol, BS, 60; Univ Mich, MS, 62, PhD(chem), 64. *Prof Exp:* Nuclear chemist, Lawrence Radiation Lab, 64-66, from asst prof to assoc prof nuclear eng, 66-77, PROF NUCLEAR ENG, UNIV CALIF, BERKELEY, 77- *Concurrent Pos:* NSF fel, 64-65; Lawrence Radiation Lab fel, 65-66; consult, Lawrence Radiation Lab, 68-; NATO fel, 72. *Mem:* Am Chem Soc; Am Phys Soc; NY Acad Sci. *Res:* Nuclear spectroscopy; activation analysis. *Mailing Add:* Dept of Nuclear Eng 4113 Etcheverry Hall Univ of Calif Berkeley CA 94720

PRUSSING, JOHN E(DWARD), b Oak Park, Ill, Aug 19, 40; m 65; c 3. ASTRONAUTICS, CONTROL ENGINEERING. *Educ:* Mass Inst Technol, SB, 62, SM, 63, ScD(aeronaut & astronaut), 67. *Prof Exp:* Res asst aeronaut & astronaut, Mass Inst Technol, 63-67; res engr aerospace eng, Univ Calif, San Diego, 67-69; asst prof aeronaut eng, 69-72, asst dean, 76-77, assoc prof, 72-81, PROF AERONAUT ENG, UNIV ILL, URBANA-CHAMPAIGN, 81- *Concurrent Pos:* Chmn, Astrodynamics Tech Comt, Am Inst Aeronaut & Astronaut, 82. *Mem:* Assoc fel Am Inst Aeronaut & Astronaut; sr mem Am Astronaut Soc. *Res:* Orbital mechanics; dynamics, control theory; stochastic stability; helicopter rotor dynamics. *Mailing Add:* Dept of Aeronaut & Astronaut Eng Univ of Ill Urbana IL 61801

PRUTKIN, LAWRENCE, b Brooklyn, NY, Dec 6, 35; m 70; c 2. ANATOMY. *Educ:* Brooklyn Col, BS, 57, MA, 60; NY Univ, PhD(basic med sci), 64. *Prof Exp:* From instr to asst prof, 64-70, ASSOC PROF ANAT, MED CTR, NY UNIV, 70- *Concurrent Pos:* USPHS fel, 64-65; vis scientist, Mass Inst Technol, 78-79. *Mem:* Fel NY Acad Sci; Am Asn Anatomists; Am Asn Cancer Res; Am Inst Nutrit; AAAS. *Res:* Electron microscopy of skin tumors; electron microscopic autoradiography; cancer chemotherapy; evaluation of new dermatologic drugs. *Mailing Add:* Dept of Cell Biol NY Univ Med Ctr New York NY 10016

PRUZANSKI, WALDEMAR, b Warsaw, Poland, Oct 23, 28; Can citizen; m 63; c 2. MEDICINE, IMMUNOLOGY. *Educ:* Hebrew Univ, Israel, MD, 56; FRCP(C), 68. *Prof Exp:* Chief physician, Asaf Harofe Hosp, Tel Aviv Univ, 64-65; res assoc immunol, Inst Cancer Res, Columbia Univ, 65-66; asst prof, 68-72, assoc prof, 72-77, PROF MED, UNIV TORONTO, 77- DIR IMMUNOL, DIAG & RES CTR, 68-, SR STAFF MED, WELLESLEY HOSP, 68-, HEAD DIV IMMUNOL, 75- *Concurrent Pos:* Mem, Inst Med Sci, Univ Toronto, 72-, mem Inst Immunol, 75- *Mem:* Am Asn Immunol; Am Rheumatism Asn; Am Fedn Clin Res; Can Soc Immunol; fel Am Col Physicians. *Res:* Immunoglobulins in human diseases; metabolism and biological function of lysozyme; humoral and cellular defense mechanisms; rheumatology. *Mailing Add:* Wellesley Hosp Toronto ON M4Y 1J3 Can

PRUZANSKY, JACOB JULIUS, b Brooklyn, NY, June 20, 21; m 51; c 3. BIOCHEMISTRY. *Educ:* Brooklyn Col, BA, 41; Iowa State Univ, PhD(chem), 49. *Prof Exp:* Dir biochem res lab, Red Star Yeast Co, 49-51; instr biochem, Western Reserve Univ, 51-54; res assoc, Univ Pittsburgh, 54-56; from asst prof to assoc prof, 56-74, PROF MICROBIOL, MED SCH, NORTHWESTERN UNIV, CHICAGO, 74-, ASSOC DIR ALLERGY RES LAB, 56- *Res:* Immunochemistry. *Mailing Add:* Dept of Microbiol 303 E Chicago Ave Chicago IL 60611

PRUZANSKY, SAMUEL, b New York, NY, Sept 10, 20; m 52; c 2. TERATOLOGY, ORTHODONTICS. *Educ:* Univ Md, DDS, 45; City Col New York, BS, 47; Tufts Col, MS, 49; Am Bd Orthod, dipl. *Prof Exp:* Asst, Tufts Col, 45, instr, 46-47; res assoc, Univ Ill, 47-50, USPHS spec res fel physiol, 50-53; clin investr & actg chief clin invest br, Nat Inst Dent Res, 53-55; assoc prof orthod, 55-61, dir Ctr Craniofaci L Anomalies, Abraham Lincoln Sch Med, Abraham Lincoln Sch Med, 68-80, PROF ORTHOD, UNIV ILL MED CTR, 61-, PROF, DEPT PEDIAT, 72- *Concurrent Pos:* Intern, New Eng Med Ctr, 45-46, asst dent surgeon, 46-47; consult, Crippled Children's Progs, Maine, 55, NMex, 56, Fla, 57, Mont, 57, Calif, 58, Minn, 68, Pa, 73 & Idaho, 74; assoc dir cleft palate clin, Ctr Handicapped Children, Univ Ill, Chicago, 55-; consult, Clin Ctr, NIH, 56-, mem, Dent Study Sect, 58-62; mem fac, Inst Advan Educ Dent Res, 63-65; mem bd sci counr, Nat Inst Dent Res, 63-67; mem joint comt, Am Speech & Hearing Asn & Am Asn Dent Schs; vis biologist, Am Inst Biol Sci; mem panel handicapping malocclusion, Nat Acad Sci-Nat Res Coun; assoc ed, Teratology, Int J Abnormal Develop; Sheldon Friel mem lectr, Europe Orthod Soc, 77. *Honors & Awards:* Res Awards, Am Asn Orthod, 57 & 60; Commemorative Medal, Univ Bratislava 65; William John Gies Award, Am Col Dent, 68; Honors Award, Am Cleft Palate Asn, 76. *Mem:* Fel Am Pub Health Asn; fel Am Col Dent; Am Cleft Palate Asn (pres, 60-61); Int Soc Cranio-Facial Biol (pres, 67-68); Teratology Soc (pres, 71-72). *Res:* Electromyography; growth and development; congenital malformations. *Mailing Add:* 525 Longwood Ave Glencoe IL 60022

PRY, ROBERT HENRY, b Dormont, Pa, Dec 28, 23; m 49; c 5. MATERIALS SCIENCE, RESEARCH ADMINISTRATION. *Educ:* Tex Col Arts & Indust, BA, 47; Rice Inst, MA, 49, PhD(physics), 51. *Prof Exp:* Res assoc solid state physics, Gen Elec Co, Res & Develop Ctr, 51-60, mgr alloy & properties studies, 60-65, liaison & transition, 65-68, metall & ceramics lab, 68-73, mat sci & eng, 73-74, elec sci & eng, 74-76; vpres res &

develop, Combustion Eng, Inc, 76-77; VPRES RES & DEVELOP, GOULD INC, 77- *Mem:* Fel AAAS; fel Am Soc Metals; Am Phys Soc; Am Inst Mining Metall & Petrol Engrs; Inst Elec & Electronics Engrs. *Res:* Electrical, magnetic and structural properties of solids; physical metallurgy; technological forecasting and assessment; research application processes. *Mailing Add:* 900 Long Ridge Rd Stamford CT 06902

PRYCHODKO, WILLIAM WASYL, b Mlyny, Ukraine, Feb 21, 22; nat US; m 49; c 1. ECOLOGY. *Educ:* Univ Munich, PhD(zool), 49. *Prof Exp:* Sr res asst, 51-56, res assoc, 56-63, ASSOC INVESTR, DETROIT INST CANCER RES, 63-; PROF BIOL, WAYNE STATE UNIV, 74- *Concurrent Pos:* Assoc investr, Inst Human Biol, Ann Arbor, 51-55; res assoc biol, Wayne State Univ, 58-60, from asst prof to assoc prof, 60-74. *Mem:* Am Soc Mammalogists; Am Asn Lab Animal Sci; Asn Trop Biol; Ecol Soc Am; Soc Study Evolution. *Res:* Geographic variations of morphological and physiological features in small mammals; responses of small mammals to isolation and aggregation; environmental physiology; biogeography. *Mailing Add:* Dept of Biol Wayne State Univ Detroit MI 48202

PRYDE, EVERETT HILTON, b Chicago, Ill, Feb 18, 18; m 59; c 2. LIPID CHEMISTRY, INDUSTRIAL ORGANIC CHEMISTRY. *Educ:* Amherst Col, AB, 39; Univ Mich, AM, 40; Univ Wis, PhD(chem), 48. *Prof Exp:* Res chemist synthetic resin & adhesives, Chem Div, Borden Co, 41-42; sr chemist, Control Lab, Butadiene Div, Koppers Co, 43-45; chemist, Res Div, Electrochem Dept, E I du Pont de Nemours & Co, Inc, 48-57; prin chemist, Northern Regional Res Ctr, 57-61, leader explor org reactions res, 62-76, res coordr, Oilseed Crops Lab, 77-79, LEADER EXPLOR ORG REACTIONS RES, REGIONAL RES CTR, 79- *Mem:* AAAS; Am Chem Soc; Am Oil Chemists Soc; Inst Food Technologists; Am Soc Agr Engrs. *Res:* Polymers; aliphatic acids; aldehydes, amines; ozonization; plasticizers; utilization of lipids and fatty acids; hybrid fuels. *Mailing Add:* 234 Tower Lane Peoria IL 61614

PRYOR, C(ABELL) NICHOLAS, JR, b Washington, DC, Feb 26, 38; m 57; c 2. ELECTRICAL ENGINEERING. *Educ:* Mass Inst Technol, BS & MS, 60; Univ Md, PhD(elec eng), 66. *Prof Exp:* Chief signal processing div, US Naval Ord Lab, 60-76; TECH DIR HQ, NEWPORT LAB, NAVAL UNDERWATER SYSTS CTR, 77- *Concurrent Pos:* Instr, Mass Inst Technol, 60-; lectr, Catholic Univ, 62-; Univ Md, 66- *Mem:* Inst Elec & Electronics Engrs. *Res:* Development of digital signal processing techniques; digital computers; communication theory. *Mailing Add:* Newport Lab Naval Underwater Systs Ctr Newport RI 02840

PRYOR, JOSEPH EHRMAN, b Melber, Ky, Mar 19, 18; m 46; c 3. PHYSICAL CHEMISTRY. *Educ:* Harding Col, BA & BS, 37; La State Univ, MA, 39, PhD(phys chem), 43. *Prof Exp:* Instr math, La State Univ, 42-44; PROF CHEM & PHYSICS & DEAN, HARDING COL, 44-, VPRES ACAD AFFAIRS, 74- *Mem:* AAAS; Am Chem Soc; Am Asn Physics Teachers; Am Sci Affil. *Res:* Electrokinetics; zeta potentials; polygons of maximum area inscribed in an ellipse. *Mailing Add:* Dept of Phys Sci Harding Univ Searcy AR 72143

PRYOR, MARILYN ANN ZIRK, b Harrisonburg, Va, Mar 9, 36. CELL PHYSIOLOGY, COMPARATIVE PHYSIOLOGY. *Educ:* Madison Col, Va, BS, 56; Univ Tenn, MS, 58, PhD(physiol), 61. *Prof Exp:* Instr cell physiol & biochem, Bryn Mawr Col, 61-62; res assoc renal physiol, 62-64, dean studies, 74-77, from asst prof to assoc prof, 70-77, PROF BIOL SCI, MT HOLYOKE COL, 77- *Concurrent Pos:* NSF fac fel, Inst Arctic & Alpine Res, Univ Colo, 70-71. *Mem:* Am Soc Zoologists. *Res:* Comparative physiology and biochemistry of amphibian liver tissue; biochemical mechanisms of environmental adaptation. *Mailing Add:* Dept of Biol Sci Mt Holyoke Col South Hadley MA 01075

PRYOR, MICHAEL J, b Leek, Eng, Mar 31, 25; nat US; m; c 3. METALLURGY. *Educ:* Cambridge Univ, BA, 46, MA & PhD(metallic corrosion), 49. *Prof Exp:* Fel phys chem, Nat Res Coun Can, 49-51, asst res officer, 51-53; head, Basic Physics Br, Kaiser Aluminum & Chem Corp, 53-57; chief, Metall Sect, 57-63, assoc dir, 63-71, DIR, METALS RES LABS, OLIN CORP, 71- *Honors & Awards:* Young Author's Award, Electrochem Soc, 54. *Mem:* Hon mem Electrochem Soc; Am Inst Mining, Metall & Petrol Engrs. *Res:* Chemistry and physics of metals. *Mailing Add:* Metals Res Labs Olin Corp 91 Shelton Ave New Haven CT 06504

PRYOR, RICHARD J, b Pittsburgh, Pa, Aug 25, 40; m 65; c 1. NUCLEAR PHYSICS. *Educ:* Pa State Univ, BS, 65; Univ Pittsburgh, PhD(nuclear physics), 70. *Prof Exp:* Res physicist, Savannah River Lab, E I Du Pont de Nemours & Co, Inc, 70-72, sr res supvr, 72-76; MEM STAFF, LOS ALAMOS SCI LAB, 76- *Concurrent Pos:* Lectr, Univ SC, 71- *Mem:* Am Phys Soc; Am Nuclear Soc. *Res:* Direct transport solutions of reactor problems, numerical methods and analysis. *Mailing Add:* Los Alamos Sci Lab Ms 616 PO Box 1663 Los Alamos NM 87544

PRYOR, WAYNE ARTHUR, b Bellvue, Pa, May 6, 28; m 48. GEOLOGY. *Educ:* Centenary Col, BS, 52; Univ Ill, MS, 54; Rutgers Univ, PhD(geol), 59. *Prof Exp:* Sr asst geol, Centenary Col, 50-52; asst, Univ Ill, 52-53; asst groundwater, Ill Geol Surv, 53-56; asst geol, Rutgers Univ, 56-57; asst groundwater, Ill Geol Surv, 57-59; geologist, Gulf Res & Develop Co, 59-66; assoc prof geol, 66-71, PROF GEOL & FEL, GRAD SCH, UNIV CINCINNATI, 71- *Mem:* Geol Soc Am; Am Asn Petrol Geologists. *Res:* Sedimentary petrology and environmental stratigraphy; groundwater geology and micropaleontology. *Mailing Add:* Dept of Geol Univ of Cincinnati Cincinnati OH 45221

PRYOR, WILLIAM AUSTIN, b St Louis, Mo, Mar 10, 29; m 62. ORGANIC CHEMISTRY, BIOLOGICAL CHEMISTRY. *Educ:* Univ Chicago, PhB, 48, BS, 51; Univ Calif, PhD(chem), 54. *Prof Exp:* Res chemist, Calif Res Corp, 54-60; asst prof chem, Purdue Univ, 60-63; from assoc prof to prof, 63-72, BOYD PROF CHEM, LA STATE UNIV, BATON ROUGE, 72- *Concurrent Pos:* Spec lectr, Univ Calif, Berkeley, 55-60; lectr, Fla State Univ, 67; DuPont lectr, Univ SC, 68; instr, Off Continuing Educ, Washington Univ, 68, San Francisco State Univ, 68, Wright State Univ, 68 & Eastman Kodak Labs, NY, 70; Guggenheim fel, Univ Calif, Los Angeles, 70-71; La State Univ Found distinguished fac fel, 70-71; NIH spec fel, Berkeley, 71; vis scientist, Lab Chem Biodyn, Calif, 71; indust consult; vis prof, Univ Calif, Davis, 78, Univ Calif, San Diego, 78 & Duke Univ, 79. *Honors & Awards:* Am Chem Soc Award, 75; Petroleum Chemistry Award, Am Chem Soc, 80. *Mem:* Am Chem Soc; Royal Soc Chem; fel Geront Soc; Radiation Res Soc; Pan-Am Med Asn. *Res:* Kinetics and mechanisms of organic reactions; free radical chemistry; vinyl polymerization; sulfur chemistry; chemistry of aging; chemistry of smog; destructive reactions of free radicals in biological systems. *Mailing Add:* Dept of Chem La State Univ Baton Rouge LA 70803

PRYSE-PHILLIPS, WILLIAM EDWARD MAIBEN, b London, Eng, Dec 13, 37; Brit & Can citizen; m 77; c 2. MEDICINE, NEUROLOGY. *Educ:* Univ London, MD, 68; MRCP, 68; FRCP(C), MRCPsychiat, 72, FRCP, 81. *Prof Exp:* Cullip sr res fel psychiat, Univ Birmingham, 64-66; Med Res Coun fel biochem, 68; assoc prof, 72-80, PROF NEUROL, MEM UNIV NFLD, 80- *Concurrent Pos:* Attend mem staff, Gen Hosp, St John's, Nfld, 72-; ed, Nfld Med Asn J, 76-81; univ orator, Mem Univ. *Mem:* Am Epilepsy Soc; Can Epilepsy Asn; Multiple Sclerosis Soc Can; Can Neurol Soc. *Res:* Research of migraine, multiplesclerosis and myotomic dystrophy. *Mailing Add:* Health Sci Complex St John's NF A1B 3V6 Can

PRYSTOWSKY, HARRY, b Charleston, SC, May 18, 25; m 51; c 3. MEDICINE. *Educ:* The Citadel, BS, 44; Med Col SC, MD, 48; Am Bd Obstet & Gynec, dipl, 59. *Prof Exp:* Intern, Johns Hopkins Hosp, 48-49; res fel, Cincinnati Gen Hosp, 49-50; asst resident, Johns Hopkins Hosp, 50-51 & 53-54, resident & instr, 54-55; res fel, Yale Univ, 55-56; asst prof obstet & gynec, Sch Med, Johns Hopkins Univ, 56-58; prof obstet & gynec & head dept, Col Med, Univ Fla, 58-73; PROF OBSTET & GYNEC, DEAN & PROVOST, COL MED, M S HERSHEY MED CTR, PA STATE UNIV, 73- *Concurrent Pos:* Consult, Jacksonville Naval Hosp; nat consult, US Air Force; mem bd dirs, Am Bd Obstet & Gynec. *Mem:* Am Fertil Soc; Am Col Surg; Am Gynec Soc; Am Col Obstet & Gynec; Am Fedn Clin Res. *Res:* Delivery of female health care. *Mailing Add:* Pa State Univ Col Med M S Hershey Med Ctr Hershey PA 17033

PRYWES, NOAH S(HMARYA), b Warsaw, Poland, Nov 28, 25; nat US; m 53; c 3. COMPUTER SCIENCE, ENGINEERING. *Educ:* Israel Inst Technol, BSc, 49; Carnegie Inst Technol, MSc, 51; Harvard Univ, PhD(appl physics), 54. *Prof Exp:* Asst, Carnegie Inst Technol, 50-52; develop engr, Radio Corp Am, 54-55; dept mgr, Univac Div, Sperry Rand Corp, 56-58; from asst prof to assoc prof elec eng, 58-68, PROF COMPUT SCI, UNIV PA, 68- *Concurrent Pos:* Consult, Industry & US Gov; pres, Comput Command & Control Co, 63-; adj prof, Shanghai Jiao Teng Univ. *Mem:* Fel Inst Elec & Electronics Engrs; Sigma Xi. *Res:* Design and application of computers, computing devices; automatic programming; information retrieval. *Mailing Add:* 122 Moore Sch of Elec Eng Univ of Pa Philadelphia PA 19104

PRZIREMBEL, CHRISTIAN E G, b Brunn, Ger, Mar 30, 42; US citizen; m 63; c 2. SEPARATED FLOWS, GAS DYNAMICS. *Educ:* Rutgers Univ, BS, 63, MS, 64, PhD(mech eng), 67. *Prof Exp:* From asst prof to prof mech eng, Rutgers Univ, 67-81, assoc dean, Eng Acad Affairs, 77-81; PROF MECH ENG & HEAD DEPT, CLEMSON UNIV, 81- *Concurrent Pos:* Consult, Singer-Gen Precision, Kearfolt Div, 71-72, L B Foster Co, 75, Flo-Tron Inc, 77-80 & Porzio & Bromberg, 79-80; fac fel, US Air Force & Am Soc Eng Educ fac res prog, 76. *Mem:* Am Soc Mech Engrs; assoc fel Am Inst Aeronaut & Astronaut; Am Soc Eng Educ; Sigma Xi. *Res:* Primary research and teaching interests are in the general area of fluid mechanics and gas dynamics; subsonic and supersonic near-wakes; vehicle aerodynamics; aerothermodynamics; slender body aerodynamics. *Mailing Add:* Dept Mech Eng Clemson Univ Clemson SC 29631

PRZYBYLOWICZ, EDWIN P, b Detroit, Mich, June 29, 33; m 54; c 11. ANALYTICAL CHEMISTRY. *Educ:* Univ Mich, BS, 53; Mass Inst Technol, PhD(chem), 56. *Prof Exp:* Res chemist, Dow Chem Co, 54; res chemist, 56-69, head gen anal lab, 59, sr staff res labs, 60-68, asst div head, Methods Res & Tech Div, 69-72, asst head emulsion res div, 72-74, tech asst to dir res labs, 74, dir photog prog develop, 75-77, ASST DIR RES LABS, RES LABS, EASTMAN KODAK CO, 77- *Concurrent Pos:* Acad assignment, Nat Bur Standards & Mass Inst Technol, 68-69; mem, Nat Res Coun Eval Panel Anal Chem, 74-77, chmn, 78-81; cor assoc rep, Am Chem Soc. *Res:* Electroanalytical methods of analysis; trace analysis; chromatography; photographic chemistry; neutron activation analysis. *Mailing Add:* 1219 Crown Point Dr Webster NY 14580

PRZYBYLSKA, MARIA, b Warsaw, Poland, Mar 2, 23; nat Can; m 47; c 2. X-RAY CRYSTALLOGRAPHY. *Educ:* Univ Glasgow, BSc, 46, PhD(x-ray crystallog), 49. *Prof Exp:* Fel, Div Physics, 50-52, asst res officer, Div Appl Chem, 52-54 & Div Pure Chem, 54-56, assoc res officer, 56-60; sr res officer, 60-69, sr res officer, Biochem Lab, 69-72, SR RES OFFICER, DIV BIOL SCI, NAT RES COUN CAN, 72- *Mem:* Am Crystallog Asn. *Res:* Determination of molecular and crystal structures of organic compounds and proteins. *Mailing Add:* Div of Biol Sci Nat Res Coun Can 100 Sussex Dr Ottawa ON K1A 0R6 Can

PRZYBYLSKI, RONALD J, b Chicago, Ill, Jan 5, 36; m 59; c 3. ZOOLOGY, CYTOLOGY. *Educ:* DePaul Univ, BS, 57, MS, 59; Univ Chicago, PhD(zool), 63. *Prof Exp:* From sr instr to asst prof, 65-72, ASSOC PROF ANAT, SCH MED, CASE WESTERN RESERVE UNIV, 72- *Concurrent Pos:* Estab investr, Am Heart Asn, 72-77. *Mem:* Am Soc Cell Biol; Am Soc Zool; Soc Develop Biol; Am Asn Anatomists; Int Soc Develop Biol. *Res:* Cell surface proteins and glycoproteins, nucleic acid and protein synthesis correlated with ultrastructural morphology and cell physiology of developing cardiac and skeletal muscle cells; experimental cardiac hypertrophy; autoradiography techniques; insulin receptors and action in developing skeletal muscle. *Mailing Add:* Dept of Anat Sch of Med Case Western Reserve Univ Cleveland OH 44106

PRZYBYSZ, JOHN XAVIER, b Steubenville, Ohio, July 22, 50; m 73; c 4. POWER ELECTRONICS. *Educ:* Mich State Univ, BS, 71; Univ Ill, Urbana, 74, PhD(physics), 76. *Prof Exp:* Instr physics, Wayne State Univ, 76-78; SR ENGR SOLID STATE RES, WESTINGHOUSE RES CTR, 78- *Mem:* Am Phys Soc. *Res:* Power electronics; new device designs and improved fabrication techniques; self-protected, light-triggered thyristors. *Mailing Add:* Westinghouse Res Ctr 501-2Y58 Pittsburgh PA 15235

PRZYBYTEK, JAMES THEODORE, b Chicago, Ill, July 27, 45; m 70; c 2. ANALYTICAL CHEMISTRY, ORGANIC CHEMISTRY. *Educ:* Univ Ill, Chicago Circle, BS, 67, MS, 69, PhD(chem), 72. *Prof Exp:* Chemist, Nalco Chem Co, 72-73, sr chemist, 73-75, group leader, 75-77; qual control mgr org chem, 77-78, LAB DIR, BURDICK & JACKSON LABS, 79- *Mem:* Am Chem Soc; Soc Appl Spectros. *Res:* Chromatography; spectroscopy; photochemistry. *Mailing Add:* Burdick & Jackson Labs 1953 S Harvey St Muskegon MI 49442

PSAROUTHAKIS, JOHN, b Canea, Greece, June 29, 32; US citizen; m 59; c 2. MECHANICAL ENGINEERING. *Educ:* Mass Inst Technol, BSc, 57, MSc, 62; Univ Md, PhD(eng), 65; Carnegie-Mellon Univ, cert exec mgt, 68. *Prof Exp:* Engr, Boston Edison Co, 57-58; tech, Mgr Isotope Dept, Thermo Electron Corp, 58-62; sr staff scientist & mgr thermionic res, Martin-Marietta Co, 62-66; dir physics, controls & elec res, Allis-Chalmers Co, 66-68, dir, Technol Ctr, 68-70; vpres corp planning & technol, Masco Co, 70-73; group vpres, Int Opers, 73-77; pres, 77-81, CHMN & PRES, J P INDUSTS, INC, ANN ARBOR, MICH, 81- *Concurrent Pos:* Consult, Lab Electronics, Inc, 62; lectr, Chalmers Tech Univ, Sweden, 63 & 65 & Grad Sch Indust Admin, Carnegie-Mellon Univ, 69-71. *Mem:* Am Mgt Asn; Am Soc Metals. *Res:* Energy conversion; surface phenomena; controls; metal forming; thermionic energy conversion, adsorption and emission phenomena of alkaline, and alkaline earths on high temperature metal surfaces, high temperature heat transfer, and hydroextrusion of metals and plastics. *Mailing Add:* 2119 Melrose Ann Arbor MI 48104

PSCHEIDT, GORDON ROBERT, b Madison, Wis, Nov 4, 28; div; c 4. BIOCHEMISTRY. *Educ:* Univ Wis, BS, 50, MS, 53, PhD(physiol chem), 57. *Prof Exp:* Res assoc, Sch Med, Univ Wash, 57-58; med res assoc, Galesburg State Hosp, 58-68; counr chem & eng, Personnel Inc, 68-74; res assoc psychiat, Univ Chicago, 74-81. *Rcs:* Intermediary metabolism of the brain; enzyme inhibitor-neurohormone relationships; relationship of blood enzymes to mental illness. *Mailing Add:* 527 N Barstow St Eau Claire WI 54701

PSCHUNDER, RALPH J(OSEF), b Marburg, Austria, June 20, 20; US citizen; m 43; c 4. MECHANICAL ENGINEERING. *Educ:* Vienna Tech Univ, MME, 41, PhD(mech eng), 65. *Prof Exp:* Res engr, Viennese Locomotive Works, Austria, 41-47; lectr mech eng, Inst Technol, Vienna, 48-54, consult, Fed Testing Lab, 51-54; res engr, NY Air Brake Co, 54-59; PRIN DESIGN ENGR, RCA CORP, 59- *Honors & Awards:* David Sarnoff Award, RCA Corp, 74. *Res:* Structural dynamics of radars; stress analysis of antennas and radomes; cable structures; guyed towers; radar foundations; structural dynamics finite element analysis. *Mailing Add:* RCA-108-203 Moorestown NJ 08057

PSIODA, JOSEPH ADAM, b Pittsburgh, Pa, Apr 22, 49; m 71. MATERIALS SCIENCE. *Educ:* Carnegie-Mellon Univ, BS, 71, MS, 73, PhD(mat sci), 77. *Prof Exp:* Mfg mgt enr, Gen Elec Co, 71-72; asst instr mat sci, Carnegie-Mellon Univ, 74-75; sr res metallurgist, Linde Div, Union Carbide Corp, 76-77, St Joe Minerals Corp, 77-78; proj scientist, 78-79, RES SCIENTIST, UNION CARBIDE CORP, 81- *Mem:* Am Soc Metals; Am Inst Mining, Metall & Petrol Engrs Metall Soc; Am Soc Testing & Mat; Electrochem Soc; Nat Asn Corrosion Engrs. *Res:* Effects of microstructure on the properties of structural alloys and materials; role of microstructure in the corrosion resistance of alloys with particular emphasis of applying a multidisciplinary approach; electrochemical and surface science techniques. *Mailing Add:* Cent Sci Lab Union Carbide Corp Tarrytown Tech Ctr Tarrytown NY 10591

PSUTY, NORBERT PHILLIP, b Hamtramck, Mich, June 13, 37; m 59; c 3. COASTAL GEOMORPHHOLOGY, COASTAL ECOLOGY. *Educ:* Wayne State Univ, BS, 59; Miami Univ, Ohio, MS, 60; La State Univ, PhD(geog), 66. *Prof Exp:* Instr geol & geog, Univ Miami, Fla, 64-65; asst prof, Univ Wis, Madison, 65-69; assoc prof, 69-73, PROF GEOG & GEOL, RUTGERS UNIV, 73-, DIR, 76- *Concurrent Pos:* Mem, Comn Coastal Environ Int Geog Union, 77-, US mem, Pan Am Inst Geog & Hist Orgn Am States, 78- & Mid NAtlantic Outer Continental Shelf Tech Working Group, Bur Land Mgt, 79-; chair, Marine Geog Spec Group, Asn Am Geog, 76-78 & 81- *Mem:* Coastal Soc; AAAS. *Res:* Coastal geomorphology, incorporating both the natural processes and coastal management based on scientific data and theory; barrier island and coastal dune systems. *Mailing Add:* Ctr Coastal Environ Studies Rutgers Univ Busch Campus New Brunswick NJ 08903

PSYCHOYOS, STACY, b Brooklyn, NY, Nov 20, 25; m 51; c 5. BIOCHEMISTRY. *Educ:* NY Univ, BA, 48, MA, 50, MS, 54, PhD(biol), 67. *Prof Exp:* Phys therapist, Bellevue Hosps, 49-51; res asst biochem, Sch Med, NY Univ, 52-55; res biochemist, US Vitamin & Pharmaceut Corp, 55-62; SR STAFF SCIENTIST, DEPT BIOCHEM, CIBA-GEIGY CORP, 62- *Mem:* Sigma Xi; NY Acad Sci. *Res:* Intracellular location, metabolic pathway and biochemistry of aldosterone biosynthesis; biochemistry and physiology of standard and novel thyroid hormone analogs; lipolysis and protein kinase of fat cells; Helium-1 and Helium-2 histamine receptors linked to adenylate cyclase in brain; adenosine receptor linked adenylate cyclase. *Mailing Add:* Dept of Biochem Ciba-Geigy Corp Ardsley NY 10502

PTACEK, ANTON D, b Chicago, Ill, Nov 17, 33; m 60; c 2. GEOLOGY. *Educ:* Univ Wis, BS, 59; Univ Wash, MS, 62, PhD(geol), 65. *Prof Exp:* Instr geol, Olympic Col, 64-65; asst prof, 65-70, ASSOC PROF GEOL, SAN DIEGO STATE UNIV, 70- *Mem:* AAAS; Geol Soc Am; Geochem Soc. *Res:* Volcanology and the distribution of trace elements in various volcanic tectonic settings. *Mailing Add:* Dept of Geol San Diego State Univ San Diego CA 92182

PTAK, ROGER LEON, b Wyandotte, Mich, Sept 17, 38; m 63; c 3. ASTROPHYSICS. *Educ:* Univ Detroit, BS, 60; Cornell Univ, MS, 64, PhD(physics), 66. *Prof Exp:* Asst prof physics, De Pauw Univ, 66-68; asst prof, 68-72, ASSOC PROF PHYSICS, BOWLING GREEN STATE UNIV, 72- *Mem:* Am Asn Physics Teachers; Am Astron Soc; Sigma Xi. *Res:* The role of atomic collisions in astrophysical systems, particularly the understanding of the broad emission lines observed in Seyfert galaxies and quasars and the nature of these objects. *Mailing Add:* Dept of Physics Bowling Green State Univ Bowling Green OH 43403

PTASHNE, MARK, b Chicago, Ill, June 5, 40. MOLECULAR BIOLOGY. *Educ:* Reed Col, BA, 61; Harvard Univ, PhD(molecular biol), 65. *Prof Exp:* Soc Fels jr fel, 65-68, lectr, 68-71, PROF BIOCHEM & MOLECULAR BIOL, HARVARD UNIV, 71-, CHMN DEPT, 80- *Honors & Awards:* Eli Lilly Award Biol Chem, 75; Charles-Leopold Mayer Prize, Acad Sci, Inst France, 77. *Mem:* Nat Acad Sci; Am Acad Arts & Sci; NY Acad Sci; Fedn Am Scientists. *Res:* Gene control by repressors. *Mailing Add:* Dept of Biochem & Molecular Biol Harvard Univ 7 Divinity Ave Cambridge MA 02138

PUAR, MOHINDAR S, b Ghurial, India, Jan 3, 35; m 66; c 1. PHYSICAL ORGANIC CHEMISTRY, ANALYTICAL CHEMISTRY. *Educ:* Punjab Univ, India, BSc, 56, MSc, 58; Boston Univ, PhD(phys org chem), 66. *Prof Exp:* Fel, Brandeis Univ, 65-67; sr res chemist, Olin Mathieson Chem Corp, 67-69; sr res investr anal res & develop, Squibb Inst Med Res, 69-78; RES GROUP LEADER NMR PHYS ORG CHEM, SCHERING CORP, 78- *Mem:* Am Chem Soc. *Res:* Equilibrium and kinetics; reaction mechanisms; spectroscopic methods; nuclear magnetic resonance spectroscopy; drugs. *Mailing Add:* Schering Corp 60 Orange St Bloomfield NJ 07003

PUBOLS, BENJAMIN HENRY, JR, b Washington, DC, Sept 1, 31; m 64; c 1. NEUROPHYSIOLOGY. *Educ:* Univ Va, BA, 53; Univ Wis, MS, 55, PhD(psychol), 57. *Prof Exp:* Asst prof psychol, Utah State Univ, 57-58; asst prof, Univ Miami, 58-61; Nat Inst Neurol Dis & Blindness fel neurophysiol, Univ Wis, 61-64; res assoc animal behav, 64-67, from assoc prof zool to asst prof anat, 66-70, ASSOC PROF ANAT, HERSHEY MED CTR, PA STATE UNIV, 70- *Mem:* Am Asn Anatomists; Neurosci Soc. *Res:* Neural electrophysiology and functional neuroanatomy of mammalian somatic sensory systems. *Mailing Add:* Milton S Hershey Med Ctr Pa State Univ Hershey PA 17033

PUBOLS, LILLIAN MENGES, b Columbus, Ohio, Oct 13, 39; m 64; c 1. NEUROPHYSIOLOGY. *Educ:* Rutgers Univ, AB, 61; Univ Wis, MA, 64, PhD(psychol), 66. *Prof Exp:* Proj assoc, Animal Behav Res Lab, Pa State Univ, 66-67, res assoc, Hershey Med Ctr, 67-71, asst prof anat, 71-74; asst prof, 74-77, ASSOC PROF ANAT, MED COL PA, 77- *Concurrent Pos:* Prin investr, NIH grant, 80-83; Fogarty Sr Int fel, 80-81; mem bd sci counsrs, Nat Inst Dent Res, 80-84. *Mem:* Am Asn Anat; Neurosci Soc. *Res:* Anatomy and physiology of the mammalian somatic sensory nervous system. *Mailing Add:* Dept of Anat Med Col of Pa Philadelphia PA 19129

PUBOLS, MERTON HAROLD, b Portland, Ore, Sept 2, 31; m 53; c 4. NUTRITIONAL BIOCHEMISTRY. *Educ:* Lewis & Clark Col, BA, 53; Purdue Univ, MS, 60, PhD(biochem), 62. *Prof Exp:* Chemist, Ore State Bd Health, 53-55; analyst, State Chemist, Purdue Univ, 55-61, res asst biochem, 61-62; asst prof, 66-70, ASST SCIENTIST, DEPT ANIMAL SCI, WASH STATE UNIV, 62-, ASSOC PROF, 70- *Concurrent Pos:* NIH spec fel; guest assoc scientist, Brookhaven Nat Lab, 68-69. *Mem:* Am Chem Soc. *Res:* Naturally occuring toxicants and enzyme inhibitors; polypeptide hormones. *Mailing Add:* Dept of Animal Sci Clark Hall Wash State Univ Pullman WA 99163

PUCCI, PAUL F(RANCIS), b Haledon, NJ, Dec 16, 23; m 47; c 2. MECHANICAL ENGINEERING. *Educ:* Purdue Univ, BSME, 49, MSME, 50; Stanford Univ, PhD(mech eng), 55. *Prof Exp:* Sr res engr, Ford Motor Co, 53-55; sr thermodyn engr, Convair Div, Gen Corp, 55-56; assoc prof, 56-66, PROF MECH ENG, NAVAL POSTGRAD SCH, 66- *Mem:* Am Soc Mech Engrs. *Res:* Fluid mechanics; heat transfer; gas turbines. *Mailing Add:* Dept of Mech Eng Naval Postgrad Sch Monterey CA 93940

PUCCIA, CHARLES JOSEPH, population biology, see previous edition

PUCEL, ROBERT A(LBIN), b Ely, Minn, Dec 27, 26; m 52; c 5. ELECTRICAL ENGINEERING. *Educ:* Mass Inst Technol, MS, 51, DSc(elec eng, network synthesis), 55. *Prof Exp:* Staff mem, Microwave Tube Noise Group, 55-65, staff mem, Solid State Physics Group & proj mgr, Microwave Semiconductor Prog, 65-70, consult microwave solid state devices, 70-74, CONSULT SCIENTIST, RES DIV, RAYTHEON CO, WALTHAM, 74- *Concurrent Pos:* Nat lectr, Microwave Theory & Technol Soc, 80- *Honors & Awards:* Microwave Prize, Microwave Theory & Tech Soc, 77. *Mem:* Fel Inst Elec & Electronics Engrs; Microwave Theory & Technol Soc; Electron Devices Soc. *Res:* Novel semiconductor concepts for microwave applications; feasibility studies of integrated microwave circuits using novel materials and device designs; network synthesis theory; solid state devices and microwave devices research; gallium arsenic monolithic microwave circuits. *Mailing Add:* 427 South St Needham MA 02192

PUCHTLER, HOLDE, b Kleinlosnitz, Ger, Jan 1, 20; nat US. HISTOCHEMISTRY, PATHOLOGY. *Educ:* Univ Cologne, MD, 51. *Prof Exp:* Res assoc path, Univ Cologne, 51-55; Damon Runyon Mem Fund res fel, 55-58; Nat Cancer Inst Can res fel, 58-59; from res assoc to assoc res prof, 59-68, PROF PATH & DIR, HISTOCHEM RES UNIT, MED COL GA, 68- *Mem:* Fel Am Inst Chem; fel Royal Micros Soc; Anatomische Gesellschaft; Histochem Soc; Ger Histochem Soc. *Res:* Chemical basis of staining technics; application of principles of textile and leather dyeing to histology; development of staining, polarization and fluorescence microscopic methods; histochemistry of arteriosclerosis. *Mailing Add:* Dept of Path Med Col of Ga Augusta GA 30902

PUCK, MARY HILL, b Takoma Park, Md, Oct 29, 19; m 46; c 3. HUMAN GENETICS. *Educ:* Judson Col, BA, 40; Univ Chicago, MA, 46. *Prof Exp:* Psychiat social worker child welfare, NMex State Dept, Sante Fe, 45-47; psychiat social worker adolescents, Scholar & Guid Asn, Chicago, 47-48; psychiat social worker diag, 63-75, RES ASSOC CHROMOSOME ABNORMALITIES, DEPT BIOCHEM, BIOPHYS, GENETICS & PSYCHIAT, MED CTR, UNIV COLO, 75- *Concurrent Pos:* Sr res fel, Eleanor Roosevelt Inst Cancer Res, Denver, 76- *Mem:* Am Soc Human Genetics; AAAS; Nat Asn Social Workers. *Res:* Application of genetic and cell biology concepts to study of human developmental diseases; assessment of biological and cultural needs in specific populations; study of child and adolescent development. *Mailing Add:* Dept of Psychiat Box A-004 4200 E Ninth Ave Denver CO 80262

PUCK, THEODORE THOMAS, b Chicago, Ill, Sept 24, 16; m 46; c 3. BIOPHYSICS, GENETICS. *Educ:* Univ Chicago, BS, 37, PhD(phys chem), 40. *Prof Exp:* Res assoc med, Univ Chicago, 41-44, asst prof med & biochem, 45-47; Am Cancer Soc sr fel, Calif Inst Technol, 47-48; prof biophys & chmn dept, 48-67, RES PROF BIOCHEM, BIOPHYS & GENETICS, UNIV COLO MED CTR, DENVER, 67-, DIR, ELEANOR ROOSEVELT INST CANCER RES, 62- *Concurrent Pos:* Mem, Comn Airborne Infections, Army Epidemiol Bd, Off Surgeon Gen, 44-46; mem, Comn Physicians for Future, Macy Found. *Honors & Awards:* Lasker Award, Am Pub Health Asn, 58; Borden Award, Asn Am Med Cols, 59; Louisa Gross Horwitz Award, 73; Gordon Wilson Medal, Am Clin & Climat Asn, 77. *Mem:* Nat Acad Sci; Inst Med-Nat Acad Sci; Am Soc Cell Biol; Am Soc Human Genetics. *Res:* Somatic cell genetics and genetic biochemistry; mammalian development; cancer. *Mailing Add:* E Roosevelt Inst Cancer Res Med Ctr Univ Colo 4200 Ninth Ave Box B-129 Denver CO 80262

PUCKETT, ALLEN EMERSON, b Springfield, Ohio, July 25, 19; m 40, 63; c 5. AERONAUTICAL ENGINEERING. *Educ:* Harvard Univ, BS, 39, MS, 41; Calif Inst Technol, PhD(aeronaut eng), 49. *Prof Exp:* Consult aerodyn, Calif Inst Technol, 41-45, lectr aeronaut & chief wind tunnel sect, Jet Propulsion Lab, 45-49; from dept head to exec vpres & asst gen mgr, 49-76, pres, 77-78, CHMN & CHIEF EXEC OFFICER, HUGHES AIRCRAFT CO, 78- *Concurrent Pos:* Consult various indust & govt; mem, US Mil Tech Mission, 45, US Mil Intel Mission, 47 & guided missile comt, Res & Develop Bd, past chmn subcomt high speed aerodyn & mem comt aerodyn, Nat Adv Comt Aeronaut, 53-55, mem subcomt automatic stabilization & control, NASA, 56-59, chmn res adv comt on control guid & navig, 59-64; mem group, Adv Panel Aeronaut, Off Asst Secy Defense, Res & Eng, chmn mutual weapons develop prog, 56-61; mem exec comt & full bd, Defense Sci Bd, 62-64, vchmn, 62-64; mem army sci adv panel, Dept Army, 65-69. *Honors & Awards:* Sperry Award, Inst Aeronaut Sci, 49; Berkner Award, Am Astron Soc, 74. *Mem:* Nat Acad Eng; fel Am Inst Aeronaut & Astronaut. *Res:* Supersonic aerodynamics; supersonic airfoil theory; guided missiles. *Mailing Add:* Hughes Aircraft Co Centinela at Teale Culver City CA 90230

PUCKETT, HOYLE BROOKS, b Jesup, Ga, Oct 15, 25; m 45; c 3. AGRICULTURAL ENGINEERING. *Educ:* Univ Ga, BS, 48; Mich State Univ, MS, 49. *Prof Exp:* Res agr engr, 49-59, invest leader, 59-72, RES LEADER, AGR RES SERV, USDA, 72- *Mem:* Inst Elec & Electronics Engrs; Am Soc Agr Engrs. *Res:* Development of controls and equipment for farmstead materials handling and processing operations. *Mailing Add:* AGr Res Serv USDA Rm 226 Agr Eng Bldg Univ of Ill Urbana IL 61801

PUCKETT, HUGH, b Louisville, Ky, Aug 9, 29; m 55; c 1. INVERTEBRATE ENDOCRINOLOGY. *Educ:* Western Ky State Col, BS, 54; Univ Va, MA, 59, PhD(biol), 64. *Prof Exp:* Asst prof biol, Norfolk Div, Col William & Mary, 59-61 & Univ Tenn, 62-64; asst prof, 64-69, PROF BIOL, WESTERN KY UNIV, 69- *Mem:* Sigma Xi. *Res:* Sexual endocrinology of the crustaceans; function and development of the androgenic gland of the crayfish; vertebrate developmental endocrinology. *Mailing Add:* Dept of Biol Western Ky Univ Bowling Green KY 42101

PUCKETT, LAWRENCE JACKSON, physics, physical chemistry, see previous edition

PUCKETT, RUSSELL ELWOOD, b Ewing, Ky, Mar 28, 29; m 49; c 5. ELECTRICAL ENGINEERING. *Educ:* Univ Ky, BS, 56, MS, 59. *Prof Exp:* Engr, Dept of Defense, 56-57; asst prof elec eng, Col Eng, Univ Ky, 57-66, res engr, Dept Physics, 67-68, assoc dir eng res, 68-80; ASST PROF ENG TECHNOL, TEX A&M UNIV, 80- *Concurrent Pos:* Mem spec comt electronic res, Hwy Res Bd, Nat Acad Sci-Nat Res Coun, 64-69 & comt traffic control devices, 69-70; assoc prof, Lexington Tech Inst, Univ Ky, 71-80. *Mem:* AAAS; Inst Elec & Electronics Engrs. *Res:* Administration and management of engineering research; electronic instrumentation with emphasis on development and design utilizing components in novel applications. *Mailing Add:* Eng Technol Dept Texas A&M Univ Col Sta TX 77843

PUCKETT, WILLIAM THOMAS, JR, b Radford, Va, Nov 21, 05; m 34; c 2. TOPOLOGY. *Educ:* Roanoke Col, BS, 27; Univ Va, MS, 31, PhD(math), 37. *Prof Exp:* Instr math, Roanoke Col, 29-30; student instr, Univ Va, 30-37, instr, 37-39; from instr to assoc prof math, 39-73, registr, 58-73, EMER PROF MATH, UNIV CALIF, LOS ANGELES, 73- *Mem:* Am Math Soc. *Res:* Topology, especially of transformations. *Mailing Add:* 11361 Homedale St Los Angeles CA 90049

PUCKETTE, STEPHEN ELLIOTT, b Ridgewood, NJ, Oct 18, 27; m 57; c 5. MATHEMATICS. *Educ:* Univ of the South, BS, 49; Yale Univ, MS, 50, MA, 51, PhD(math), 57. *Prof Exp:* Asst, Yale Univ, 53-56; asst prof math, Univ of the South, 56-62, assoc prof, 62-66; assoc prof, Univ Ky, 66-69; dean col arts & sci, 69-79, PROF, UNIV OF THE SOUTH, 79- *Concurrent Pos:* NSF fac fel, 64-65; Fulbright-Hays prof, Univ Abidjan, Ivory Coast, 79-80. *Mem:* Am Math Soc; Math Soc France; Ger Math Soc. *Res:* Functional analysis. *Mailing Add:* Univ of the South Sewanee TN 37375

PUCKNAT, JOHN GODFREY, b New York, NY, Feb 22, 31; m 60; c 1. ORGANIC CHEMISTRY. *Educ:* City Col New York, BS, 57; NY Univ, MS, 65, PhD(org chem), 66. *Prof Exp:* Res chemist, Cent Res Labs, Interchem Corp, 57-63; fel, Israel Inst Technol, 66-67; fel, Org Chem Inst, Zurich, 67-68; sr res chemist, Argus Chem Corp, Brooklyn, 69-70; RES ASSOC, INMONT CORP, NJ, 70- *Mem:* AAAS; Am Chem Soc; Am Inst Chemists. *Res:* Organic synthesis and reaction mechanisms; thiophene and natural product chemistry; dyes and pigments; polymer research and development. *Mailing Add:* 565 West End Ave New York NY 10024

PUDDEPHATT, RICHARD JOHN, b Aylesbury, Eng, Oct 12, 43; m 69; c 2. ORGANOMETALLIC CHEMISTRY, INORGANIC CHEMISTRY. *Educ:* Univ London, BSc, 65, PhD(chem), 68. *Prof Exp:* Teaching fel, Univ Western Ont, 68-70; lectr, Univ Liverpool, 70-77, sr lectr, 77-78; PROF CHEM, UNIV WESTERN ONT, 78- *Mem:* The Chem Soc; Can Inst Chem. *Res:* Reactivity and mechanism in organometallic chemistry, particularly of the elements platinum, gold and lead. *Mailing Add:* Dept of Chem Univ of Western Ont London ON N6A 5B8 Can

PUDELKIEWICZ, WALTER JOSEPH, b Oil City, Pa, Feb 3, 23; m 60; c 2. BIOCHEMISTRY. *Educ:* Pa State Univ, BS, 51, MS, 53, PhD, 55. *Prof Exp:* ASSOC PROF NUTRIT SCI, UNIV CONN, 55- *Mem:* AAAS; Am Chem Soc; Am Inst Nutrit. *Res:* Fat soluble vitamins; chlorinated hydrocarbon toxicants. *Mailing Add:* Dept of Nutrit Sci Univ of Conn Storrs CT 06268

PUECHL, KARL HEINZ, physics, nuclear engineering, see previous edition

PUEPPKE, STEVEN GLENN, b Fargo, NDak, Aug 1, 50. PHYTOPATHOLOGY, PLANT BIOCHEMISTRY. *Educ:* Mich State Univ, BSc, 71; Cornell Univ, PhD(phytopath), 75. *Prof Exp:* Sr res assoc, C F Kettering Res Lab, 75-76; asst prof biol, Univ Mo-St Louis, 76-79; ASST PROF PLANT PATH, UNIV FLA, 79- *Mem:* Am Phytopath Soc; Am Soc Plant Physiologists; Bot Soc Am; Am Soc Microbiol. *Res:* Biochemistry of plant-microorganism interactions; recognition of bacteria by plants; phytoalexins; lectins. *Mailing Add:* Dept Plant Path Univ Fla Gainesville FL 32611

PUERCKHAUER, GERHARD WILHELM RICHARD, b Regensburg, Ger, Apr 28, 30. ORGANIC CHEMISTRY. *Educ:* Purdue Univ, PhD, 56; Univ Minn, MBA, 64. *Prof Exp:* Fel org fluorine compounds, Purdue Univ, 56; sr res chemist, 57-64, group leader, 64-65, develop specialist, 66, int tech mgr, 66-70, DEVELOP MGR, MINN MINING & MFG CO, 70- *Mem:* Am Chem Soc. *Res:* Research, development and production of organic and organometallic compounds; copying products; non-impact printing papers; data base management and systems analysis. *Mailing Add:* 1929 Stanford Ave St Paul MN 55105

PUESCHEL, RUDOLF FRANZ, b Tetschen, Czech, Apr 9, 34; US citizen; m 63; c 3. ATMOSPHERIC PHYSICS, ATMOSPHERIC CHEMISTRY. *Educ:* Univ Frankfurt, BS, 58; Univ Giessen, MS, 62; Univ Wash, PhD(civil eng), 69. *Prof Exp:* Assoc res physicist, Calif Inst Technol, 62-64; res physicist, Univ Wash, 64-66; Nat Res Coun res assoc aerosol sci, Environ Res Labs, 69-70, dir, Mauna Loa Observ, 70-72, SUPV PHYSICIST, ENVIRON RES LABS, NAT OCEANIC & ATMOSPHERIC ADMIN, 72- *Concurrent Pos:* Consult, Spec Meteorol Appln Dept, World Meteorol Orgn, Geneva, Switz, 74-; adj prof physics, Denver Univ, 77- *Mem:* Ger Phys Soc; Am Geophys Union; AAAS; Am Meteorol Soc; Sigma Xi. *Res:* Effects of aerosols on cloud nucleation and on radiative transfer. *Mailing Add:* 4610 Greylock St Boulder CO 80301

PUESCHEL, SIEGFRIED M, b Waldenburg, Ger, July 28, 31; US citizen; m 62; c 4. PEDIATRICS. *Educ:* Braunschweig Col, BS, 55; Univ Düsseldorf, MD, 60; Harvard Univ, MPH, 67. *Prof Exp:* Instr pediat, Harvard Med Sch, 67-74, asst prof, 74-75; asst prof, 75-77, ASSOC PROF PEDIAT, PROG MED, BROWN UNIV, 77- DIR CHILD DEVELOP CTR, RI HOSP, 75- *Concurrent Pos:* Dir Down's syndrome prog, Children's Hosp Med Ctr, 70-75 & PKU Clin, 72-75. *Mem:* Am Acad Pediat. *Res:* Phenylketonuria, particularly maternal phenylketonuria and amino acid transfer across placenta; amino acid metabolism, Down's syndrome, etiology, epidemiology and counseling. *Mailing Add:* Child Develop Ctr RI Hosp 593 Eddy St Providence RI 02902

PUETT, JOHN DAVID, b Morganton, NC, Mar 23, 39; m 61; c 2. BIOCHEMISTRY, ENDOCRINOLOGY. *Educ:* NC State Univ, BS, 61; Univ NC, Chapel Hill, MS, 65, PhD(biochem), 69. *Prof Exp:* Scientist biopolymers, Chemstrand Res Ctr Inc, Monsanto Co, 62-67; asst prof, 69-74, ASSOC PROF BIOCHEM, VANDERBILT UNIV, 74- *Concurrent Pos:* USPHS res grant, Vanderbilt Univ, 72- *Honors & Awards:* Camille & Henry Dreyfus Found Award, 71. *Mem:* Biophys Soc; Am Chem Soc; Am Soc Biol Chemists; Endocrine Soc; Soc Complex Carbohydrates. *Res:* Protein structure-function; polypeptide and glycoprotein hormone structure, mechanism-of-action and metabolism; physical biochemistry. *Mailing Add:* Dept of Biochem Sch of Med Vanderbilt Univ Nashville TN 37232

PUFF, ROBERT DAVID, b St Louis, Mo, Sept 30, 33; m 54; c 3. THEORETICAL PHYSICS. *Educ:* Washington Univ, BS, 54; Harvard Univ, PhD(physics), 60. *Prof Exp:* Asst physics res, Lincoln Lab, Mass Inst Technol, 59-60; res assoc, Univ Ill, Urbana, 60-62; from asst to assoc prof, 62-74, PROF PHYSICS, UNIV WASH, 74- *Mem:* Am Phys Soc. *Res:* Nuclear and solid state many-body theory. *Mailing Add:* Dept of Physics Univ of Wash Seattle WA 98195

PUFFER, JOHN H, b Buffalo, NY, July 4, 41; m 61; c 3. PETROLOGY, GEOCHEMISTRY. *Educ:* Mich State Univ, BS, 63, MS, 65; Stanford Univ, PhD(geol), 69. *Prof Exp:* Asst prof geol, Eastern NMex Univ, 68-70; asst prof, 70-80, ASSOC PROF GEOL, RUTGERS UNIV, NEWARK, 80- *Concurrent Pos:* Consult, Mid States Asn Cols & Sec Schs, 72- *Mem:* Geol Soc Am. *Res:* Granite petrology; geochemistry of ferrum, magnesium and titanium silicates and oxides. *Mailing Add:* Dept of Geol Rutgers Univ Newark NJ 07102

PUGH, CLAUD ERVIN, b Asheboro, NC, Oct 6, 39; m 67; c 2. INELASTIC SOLID MECHANICS. *Educ:* NC State Univ, BS, 61, MS, 64, PhD(eng mech), 68. *Prof Exp:* Instr eng mech, NC State Univ, 65-68; researcher, 68-79, PROG MGR DESIGN TECHCNOL, OAK RIDGE NAT LAB, 79- *Concurrent Pos:* Instr mech eng, Univ Tenn, 69. *Mem:* Am Soc Mech Engrs; Soc Exp Stress Analysis; Sigma Xi. *Res:* Structural design technology for high temperature components; emphasis on elastic-plastic and creep behavior of alloys and structures; constitutive equation development; creep-fatigue failure criteria; confirmatory structural testing. *Mailing Add:* Oak Ridge Nat Lab PO Box Y Oak Ridge TN 37830

PUGH, DAVID GRAHAM, b Rushville, Ind, Sept 12, 09; m 35; c 3. RADIOLOGY. *Educ:* Ind Univ, BS, 30, MD, 32; Am Bd Radiol, dipl. *Prof Exp:* Intern, Indianapolis City Hosp, Ind, 32-33; Mayo Found fel radiol, Mayo Clin, 38-41, from asst to assoc roentgenol, 42-74, prof radiol, 61-74, MEM EMER STAFF, MAYO GRAD SCH MED, UNIV MINN, 74- *Concurrent Pos:* Mem, Mayo Grad Sch Med, Univ Minn, 49-; secy to staff, Mayo Clin, 54-56. *Mem:* Radiol Soc NAm; Am Roentgen Ray Soc (past 2nd vpres); fel Am Col Radiol. *Res:* Diagnostic roentgenology; diseases of bones and joints. *Mailing Add:* 10034 Lancaster Dr Sun City AZ 85351

PUGH, DAVID MILTON, b Philadelphia, Pa, July 13, 29; m 55; c 3. INTERNAL MEDICINE, CARDIOLOGY. *Educ:* Univ Rochester, BA, 51; Yale Univ, MD, 58. *Prof Exp:* Intern, US Naval Hosp, 58-59; resident, Univ Wash, 59-61, NIH fel, 61-64; from instr to assoc prof, 64-76, PROF CARDIOL, SCH MED, UNIV KANS MED CTR, KANSAS CITY, 76- *Concurrent Pos:* Consult, Vet Admin Hosp, Kansas City, 64-, St Margaret's Hosp & Providence Hosp, Kansas City, 70- *Mem:* Am Soc Clin Res; AMA; fel Am Col Physicians; fel Am Col Cardiol. *Res:* Cardiovascular physiology with particular reference to left ventricular function. *Mailing Add:* Cardiovasc Sect Univ of Kans Sch of Med Kansas City KS 66103

PUGH, E(DISON) NEVILLE, b Glamorgan, Gt Brit, May 5, 35; m 56; c 2. METALLURGY. *Educ:* Univ Wales, BSc, 56, PhD(metall), 59. *Prof Exp:* Sci officer, Defence Standards Labs, NSWBr, Australian Dept Supply, 59-63; scientist, Res Inst Advan Studies, Martin Marietta Corp, Md, 63-65, staff scientist, 65-66, sr res scientist, 66-69; assoc prof eng & appl sci, George Washington Univ, 69-70; assoc prof metall & mining eng, Univ Ill, Urbana, 70-73, prof metall & mining eng, 73-80; MEM STAFF, NAT BUR STANDARDS, 80- *Mem:* Metall Soc; Am Inst Mining, Metall & Petrol Engrs; Am Soc Metals; Nat Asn Corrosion Engrs. *Res:* Fracture of crystalline solids, principally the influence of environments on fracture. *Mailing Add:* Nat Bur Standards Washington DC 20234

PUGH, EMERSON WILLIAM, b Pasadena, Calif, May 1, 29; m 58; c 3. SOLID STATE ELECTRONICS. *Educ:* Carnegie Inst Technol, BSc, 51, PhD(physics), 56. *Prof Exp:* Asst prof physics, Carnegie Inst Technol, 56-57; staff physicist, Res Lab, 57-61, mgr metals physics group, 58-61, vis scientist, Zurich Lab, 61-62, sr engr components div, 62-65, dir oper memory, 65-66, dir tech planning, Res Div, 66-68, spec asst to vpres & chief scientist, 68-71, consult to dir res, 71-75, mgr explor magnetics, Res Div, 75-80, MEM RES REV BD, RES DIV, IBM CORP, 81- *Mem:* Fel AAAS; fel Am Phys Soc; fel Inst Elec & Electronics Eng. *Res:* Data processing devices and systems; magnetic materials and device physics. *Mailing Add:* IBM Res Lab Yorktown Heights NY 10598

PUGH, GEORGE EDGIN, b Pittsburgh, Pa, Jan 16, 26; m 52; c 3. OPERATIONS RESEARCH, NUCLEAR PHYSICS. *Educ:* Carnegie Inst Technol, 50; Mass Inst Technol, PhD(physics), 54. *Prof Exp:* Mem staff, Lab Nuclear Sci, Mass Inst Technol, 54-55, asst prof physics, 55-56; mem staff, Weapon Systs Eval Div, Inst Defense Anal, 56-62, head nucleonics sect, 58-62; dep asst dir, US Arms Control & Disarmament Agency, 62-64; mem founding staff, Lambda Corp, 64-66, vpres, 66-74; SR SCIENTIST, GEN RES CORP, 75- *Mem:* Am Phys Soc; Opers Res Soc Am; Inst Mgt Sci. *Res:* Optimization mathematics; decision science; value theory; human values. *Mailing Add:* 6509 Waterway Dr Falls Church VA 22044

PUGH, HOWEL GRIFFITH, b Abercarn, Eng, Oct 13, 33; m 60; c 2. NUCLEAR PHYSICS, HIGH ENERGY PHYSICS. *Educ:* Cambridge Univ, BA, 55, PhD(nuclear physics), 61. *Prof Exp:* Fel nuclear physics, Atomic Energy Res Estab, Eng, 59-62; physicist, Lawrence Radiation Lab, Univ Calif, 62-65; assoc prof, Univ Md, College Park, 65-70, prof physics & astron, 70-77; head, Nuclear Sci Sect, NSF, 77-79; SCI DIR, BEVALAC, LAWRENCE BERKELEY LAB, UNIV CALIF, 79- *Concurrent Pos:* Prog dir intermediate energy physics, NSF, Washington, DC, 75-77. *Mem:* Fel Am Phys Soc. *Res:* Nuclear spectroscopy; quasi-free scattering; nuclear reactions at medium energies; ultra-relativistic proton-proton and nucleus-nucleus interactions; relativistic heavy ion collisions. *Mailing Add:* Nuclear Sci Div Lawrence Berkeley Lab Univ Calif Berkeley CA 94720

PUGH, JEAN ELIZABETH, b Newport News, Va, Apr 25, 28. INVERTEBRATE ZOOLOGY. *Educ:* Madison Col, BS, 50; Univ Va, MA, 54, PhD(invert histol), 61. *Prof Exp:* From instr to assoc prof biol, Old Dominion Col, 54-65; assoc prof, 65-66, chmn dept, 66-74, PROF BIOL, CHRISTOPHER NEWPORT COL, 66- *Mem:* AAAS; Am Micros Soc. *Res:* Invertebrate histology; hindgut of the decapod crustaceans. *Mailing Add:* Dept of Biol Christopher Newport Col Newport News VA 23606

PUGH, JOHN W(ILLIAM), b Pekin, Ill, July 4, 23; m 56; c 1. METALLURGY, REFRACTORY METALS. *Educ:* Univ Ill, BS, 48; Rensselaer Polytech Inst, MMetE, 54. *Prof Exp:* Student engr, 48-49, metallurgist, Res Lab, 49-56, assoc in metall, Lamp Div, 56-59, mgr metall studies & alloy develop, Lamp Metals & Components Dept, 59-63, mgr metall res, 63-68, mgr res & develop, 68-70, RES ADV, GEN ELEC LIGHTING RES & TECHNOL SERV OPER, GEN ELEC CO, 70- *Mem:* Am Soc Metals; Am Inst Mining, Metall & Petrol Engrs. *Res:* High temperature alloys; refractory metals; arc melting; powder metallurgy; mechanical properties; lighting systems development; lamp engineering. *Mailing Add:* Gen Elec Lighting Res & Tech Serv Oper Nela Park Cleveland OH 44112

PUGH, MILTON EARL, b Mt Rainier, Md, Apr 8, 21. THEORETICAL PHYSICS. *Educ:* Mass Inst Technol, SB, 47. *Prof Exp:* Physicist, Jacobs Instrument Co, Md, 51-53, head electronic digital comput group, 53-58; PRES & TECH DIR, ARTRONIC INSTRUMENT CO, 59- *Concurrent Pos:* Consult, 56-59. *Mem:* Am Phys Soc; Inst Elec & Electonics Eng. *Res:* Quantum field theory; electronic digital computers; military instrumentation; network theory; controlled thermonuclear reactions; earth satellite components. *Mailing Add:* 2110 Arcola Ave Silver Spring MD 20902

PUGH, ROBERT E, b Kelowna, BC, Apr 29, 33; m 61, 68; c 1. THEORETICAL PHYSICS. *Educ:* Univ BC, BA, 54, MA, 55; Univ Iowa, PhD(physics), 63. *Prof Exp:* Sci officer, Defense Res Bd, 58-59; lectr math, Queen's Univ, Ont, 59-60; instr physics, Univ Iowa, 60-62, res assoc, 62-63; from asst prof to assoc prof, 63-72, assoc dean arts & sci, 78-81, PROF PHYSICS, UNIV TORONTO, 72- *Concurrent Pos:* Secy-treas, Inst Particle Physics, 73- *Mem:* Am Phys Soc; Can Asn Physicists. *Res:* Quantum field theory; elementary particle physics. *Mailing Add:* Dept of Physics Univ of Toronto Toronto ON M5S 2R8 Can

PUGH, THOMAS L, b Windsor, Ont, Dec 13, 29; nat US; m 53; c 4. ANALYTICAL CHEMISTRY. *Educ:* Wayne State Univ, BS, 52, MS, 54, PhD(chem), 56. *Prof Exp:* SR RES CHEMIST ELASTOMERS, E I DU PONT DE NEMOURS & CO, INC, 56- *Res:* Elastomers; colloids; polymers; analysis of elastomers and elastomer chemicals; artificial latexes; textile-rubber adhesion; urethanes. *Mailing Add:* Chestnut Run E I du Pont de Nemours & Co Inc Wilmington DE 19898

PUGLIA, CHARLES DAVID, b Paterson, NJ, Sept 5, 41; m 67; c 1. PHARMACOLOGY, ENVIRONMENTAL PHYSIOLOGY. *Educ:* St Johns Univ, NY, BS, 63; Rutgers Univ, MS, 65; Temple Univ, PhD(pharmacol), 71. *Prof Exp:* Res assoc environ physiol, Inst Environ Med, Univ Pa, 71-73, assoc pharmacol, Sch Med, 73-77; ASST PROF PHARMACOL, MED COL PA, 77- *Mem:* AAAS; Undersea Med Soc. *Res:* Mechanisms of oxygen and oxidant toxicity; endogenous antioxidants; thermal homeostasis in extreme environments. *Mailing Add:* Dept Pharmacol 3300 Henry Ave Philadelphia PA 19129

PUGLIA, CHARLES RAYMOND, b Oak Park, Ill, Aug 3, 27; m 54; c 3. INVERTEBRATE ZOOLOGY. *Educ:* Elmhurst Col, BS, 52; Univ Ill, MS, 53, PhD(zool), 59. *Prof Exp:* Instr biol, Elmhurst Col, 53-54; from assoc prof to prof, Wells Col, 59-70; dean div natural sci, 70-74, dean admin, 74-76, PROF BIOL, NEW ENG COL, 76- *Concurrent Pos:* NSF sci fac fel, 64-65. *Mem:* Am Inst Biol Sci; Am Micros Soc; Soc Syst Zool. *Res:* Tardigrade taxonomy and ecology. *Mailing Add:* New Eng Col Henniker NH 03242

PUGLIELLI, VINCENT GEORGE, b Newton, Mass, Feb 12, 43; m 68; c 2. SOLID STATE PHYSICS, ELECTRICAL ENGINEERING. *Educ:* Boston Col, BS, 64; Univ Mass, Amherst, MS, 66, PhD(physics), 70. *Prof Exp:* Res asst high energy physics, Brookhaven Nat Lab, 65; res asst physics, Univ Mass, Amherst, 68-70; SR SCIENTIST PROG MGR ELECTROMAGNETICS, NAVAL SURFACE WEAPONS CTR, 70- *Concurrent Pos:* Vis prof physics, US Naval Acad, 80-81. *Mem:* Inst Elec & Electronics Engrs (pres, 77). *Res:* Semiconductor devices; electromagnetic compatibility; microwaves and radar systems. *Mailing Add:* Naval Surface Weapons Ctr Dept F56 Dahlgren VA 22448

PUGLIESE, MICHAEL, b Jan 10, 27; US citizen; m 54; c 4. ORGANIC CHEMISTRY. *Educ:* Univ Bologna, PhD(org chem), 51. *Prof Exp:* Develop chemist, Interchem Corp, 55-57; res org chemist, S B Penick & Co, 57-59; res org chemist, 59-72, MGR RES & DEVELOP PRINTING INK VEHICLES, RES DEPT, J M HUBER CORP, EDISON, 72- *Mem:* Am Chem Soc. *Res:* Development of printing ink vehicles with particular interest in letterpress, lithographic, and flexographic inks. *Mailing Add:* J M Huber Corp Thornall St Edison NJ 08837

PUGMIRE, RONALD J, b Shelley, Idaho, Jan 6, 37; m 65; c 2. PHYSICAL CHEMISTRY. *Educ:* Idaho State Univ, BS, 59; Univ Utah, PhD(phys chem), 66. *Prof Exp:* Fel, 66-68, asst to vpres res, 70-73, asst vpres res, 73-78, sr res chemist, 68-80, PROF FUELS ENG, UNIV UTAH, 80-, ASSOC VPRES RES, 78- *Mem:* Am Chem Soc. *Res:* Nuclear magnetic resonance. *Mailing Add:* Dept Chem Univ Utah Salt Lake City UT 84121

PUGSLEY, JAMES H(ARWOOD), b Berea, Ky, Mar 28, 36; m 57; c 2. ELECTRICAL ENGINEERING. *Educ:* Oberlin Col, AB, 56; Univ Ill, MS, 58, PhD(elec eng), 63. *Prof Exp:* ASSOC PROF ELEC ENG, UNIV MD, COLLEGE PARK, 63- *Mem:* Inst Elec & Electronics Engrs; Asn Comput Mach; Am Soc Eng Educ. *Res:* Switching circuit theory and digital computer design; use of computers in electrical engineering problems. *Mailing Add:* Dept of Elec Eng Univ of Md College Park MD 20740

PUHALLA, JOHN EDWARD, b Scranton, Pa, Mar 30, 39. MICROBIAL GENETICS. *Educ:* Pa State Univ, BS, 61; Cornell Univ, PhD(genetics), 66. *Prof Exp:* Asst geneticist, Conn Agr Exp Sta, 65-70; res geneticist, Nat Cotton Path Lab, USDA, 71-80; MEM FAC, DEPT PLANT PATH, UNIV CALIF, 80- *Concurrent Pos:* Fac mem, Grad Sch, Tex A&M Univ, 75- *Mem:* Am Phytopath Soc; Genetics Soc Am. *Res:* Inheritance of mating type in fungi; genetics of pathogenicity in plant parasitic fungi; parasexual recombination. *Mailing Add:* Nat Cotton Path Lab Box JF College Station TX 77840

PUHL, RICHARD JAMES, b Eau Claire, Wis, Oct 12, 44; m 67; c 1. PESTICIDE CHEMISTRY. *Educ:* Univ Wis-Eau Claire, BS, 66; Univ Minn, Minneapolis, PhD(org chem), 71. *Prof Exp:* Res chemist, Uniroyal Chem Div, Uniroyal, Inc, 71-74; res chemist, Chemagro Agr Div, 74-81, SR RES CHEMIST, MOBAY CHEM CORP, 81- *Mem:* Am Chem Soc. *Res:* Metabolic and environmental fate of agricultural chemicals. *Mailing Add:* Agr Chem Div Mobay Chem Corp Hawthorn Rd Kansas City MO 64120

PUHVEL, SIRJE MADLI, b Tallinn, Estonia, July 26, 39; US citizen; m 60; c 3. MEDICAL MICROBIOLOGY. *Educ:* Univ Calif, Los Angeles, BA, 61, PhD(med microbiol, immunol), 63. *Prof Exp:* NIH fel dermat, 63-65, asst res immunologist, 65-72, assoc res immunologist, 72-73, adj assoc prof, 73-78, ADJ PROF, DEPT MED, UNIV CALIF, LOS ANGELES, 78- *Mem:* Am Soc Microbiol; Soc Invest Dermat; Am Acad Dermat. *Res:* Microbiology and immunology of skin diseases, particularly acne vulgaris; microbiology of normal skin; biochemistry of keratinization. *Mailing Add:* Dept Med Univ Calif Ctr Health Sci Los Angeles CA 90024

PULESTON, HARRY SAMUEL, b Wellington, Colo, July 6, 17; m 41; c 3. CHEMISTRY. *Educ:* Colo State Univ, BS, 41; Iowa State Col, MS, 42; Univ Colo, PhD(pharmaceut chem), 50. *Prof Exp:* Asst state chemist, State Dept Agr, Iowa, 42; asst res fel, Mellon Inst, 42-43; res chemist, Wander Co, 43-46; asst instr chem, Univ Colo, 46-47, asst, Atomic Energy Proj, 49-50; asst prof chem, Colo State Univ, 50-55; assoc prof, Univ Wyo, 55-56; from asst prof to assoc prof, 56-64, PROF CHEM, COLO STATE UNIV, 64- *Mem:* Am Chem Soc. *Res:* Bacterial and plant irradiation and its counteraction; radiochemistry; biochemistry. *Mailing Add:* Dept of Chem Colo State Univ Ft Collins CO 80521

PULFORD, CARL TREVOR, polymer physics, see previous edition

PULIDO, MIGUEL L, b Havana, Cuba, Dec 17, 34; m 80; c 3. WEED SCIENCE, PLANT PATHOLOGY. *Educ:* Univ Havana, BS, 56; La State Univ, MS, 61, PhD(plant path), 65. *Prof Exp:* Agron engr, Agr Div, Agr & Indust Develop Bank Cuba, 56-58, Eastern regional supvr, 58-59; agron engr, Tech Serv Dept, Productora Superfosfatos, 59-60; res asst plant path, La State Univ, 62-65; res agronomist, Agr Div, Velsicol Chem Corp, 65-66, asst mgr tech serv, Int Div, 66-67; sr agr specialist, 67-71, mgr agr mkt, 71-77, V PRES AGR MKT, BUCKMAN LABS, INC, 76-, MGR INDUST & AGR MKT, 77- *Concurrent Pos:* Ed, Fitopatologia, 76. *Mem:* AAAS; Weed Sci Soc Am; Am Soc Plant Physiologists; Am Phytopath Soc; Am Inst Biol Sci. *Res:* Weed control; agricultural chemicals and plant disease control. *Mailing Add:* Buckman Labs Inc 1256 N McLean Blvd Memphis TN 38108

PULIGANDLA, VISWANADHAM, b Vijayawada, Andhra, India, Jan 12, 38; m 62; c 2. PHYSICAL CHEMISTRY, INORGANIC CHEMISTRY. *Educ:* Sri Venkateswara Univ, India, BSc, 57; Univ Saugor, MSc, 59; Univ Toledo, PhD(chem), 74. *Prof Exp:* Sr teacher chem, Andhra Educ Soc Higher Secondary Sch, New Delhi, 60-61; sr res asst, Indian Inst Astrophys & Indian Meteorol Dept, 61-68; asst prof chem, Ohio Dominican Col, 74-78; asst res chemist magnetohydrodyn & energy, Dept Chem, Mont State Univ, 78-79; STAFF ENGR MATS & PROCESS ENG, IBM CORP, 79- *Mem:* Am Chem Soc; Astron Soc India; fel Indian Chem Soc; Sigma Xi; NY Acad Sci. *Res:* Corrosion research; analytical chemistry; high temperature chemistry of inorganic materials, specifically synthesis, characterization, vaporization, thermodynamics and phase studies; stellar physics, specifically studies of eclipsing and intrinsic variable stars. *Mailing Add:* Mats & Process Eng Dept 577 IBM Corp Hwy 52 NW 37th St Rochester MN 55901

PULITO, ALDO MARTIN, b West Cromwell, Conn, Aug 5, 20; m 48; c 3. CHEMISTRY. *Educ:* Trinity Col, Conn, BS, 42; Va Polytech Inst, BS, 44; Univ Conn, PhD(chem), 50. *Prof Exp:* Pilot plant operator, Columbia Univ, 44-45; plant operator, Fercleve Corp, Tenn, 45; scientist, Los Alamos Sci Lab, 45-46; asst chem, Univ Conn, 47-50; chemist & treas, Ames Labs, 50-70; ASST PROF CHEM, FAIRFIELD UNIV, 70- *Concurrent Pos:* Lectr, Fairfield Univ, 53-70. *Mem:* Am Chem Soc. *Res:* Preparation of amines and diamines; organic chemistry; oximes and antioxidants. *Mailing Add:* 502 Ferry Rd Orange CT 06477

PULLAN, GEORGE THOMAS, b Tadcaster, Eng, Feb 1, 29; m 53; c 5. RESEARCH ADMINISTRATION. *Educ:* Cambridge Univ, BA, 49, MA, 53, PhD(physics), 52. *Prof Exp:* Fel physics, Nat Res Coun Can, Toronto, 52-54; sr sci officer, Nat Phys Lab, Dept Sci & Indust Res, Eng, 54-56; defence sci serv officer, Can Armament Res & Develop Estab, 56-69; planning staff, Defence Res Bd Can, 69-74; dir gen res & develop, Plans & Prog, 74-76, DIR TECHNOL APPLN LAND, DEPT NAT DEFENCE, CAN, 76- *Mailing Add:* 1693 Featherston Dr Ottawa ON K1H 6P3 Can

PULLAN, HARRY, b Shipley, Eng, Nov 12, 28; Can citizen; m 53; c 4. PHYSICS. *Educ:* Oxford Univ, BA, 50, MA & DPhil(physics), 53. *Prof Exp:* Fel physics, Nat Res Coun Can, 54-56; group head infrared physics, Res Labs, RCA Victor Co Ltd, 56-64, dir solid state physics, 64-66; dept dir physics, 66-77, DIR DEPT APPL PHYSICS, ONT RES FOUND, 77- *Mem:* Can Asn Physicists; sr men Inst Elec & Electronics Engrs. *Res:* Properties of semiconductor materials and their application in cooled infrared detectors and detector systems for specific applications requiring the highest achievable performance. *Mailing Add:* Ont Res Found Sheridan Park Mississauga ON Can

PULLARKAT, RAJU KRISHNAN, b North Parur, India, Aug 13, 39; m 69; c 1. BIOCHEMISTRY. *Educ:* Univ Kerala, BS, 58, MS, 60; Tex A&M Univ, PhD(biochem), 66. *Prof Exp:* Asst oils & fats, Regional Res Labs, Hyderabad, India, 60-62; asst biochem, Tex A&M Univ, 62-65, technician II, 65-66, res assoc, 66-68, res scientist, 68-73; sr res scientist, 73-74, assoc res scientist, 74-75, HEAD, LIPID STORAGE DIS LAB, INST BASIC RES MENT RETARDATION, 75- *Mem:* AAAS; Am Soc Neurochem; Int Soc Neurochem; Asn Res Nervous & Ment Dis. *Res:* Lipid metabolism in mental retardation. *Mailing Add:* Inst Basic Res Ment Retardation Dp Neurochem 1050 Forest Hill Rd Staten Island NY 10314

PULLEN, BAILEY PRICE, b Town Creek, Ala, June 21, 40; m 67; c 2. CHEMICAL PHYSICS. *Educ:* Univ Tenn, BS, 63, MS, 67, PhD(chem), 70. *Prof Exp:* Chemist, Spec Training Div, Oak Ridge Inst Nuclear Studies, 63-66; radiation safety off, Univ Tenn, 67-68; AEC fel, Oak Ridge Nat Lab, 68-70; PROF CHEM, SOUTHEASTERN LA UNIV, 70- *Concurrent Pos:* Vis prof, Oak Ridge Nat Lab, 70-74, consult, Health Physics Div, 75-76; consult, Gamma Indust, 78- *Res:* Ion and electron collision spectroscopy. *Mailing Add:* Southeastern La Univ Box 842 Col Sta Hammond LA 70401

PULLEN, DAVID JOHN, b London, Eng, June 28, 36; m 60; c 4. NUCLEAR PHYSICS. *Educ:* Univ London, BSc, 58; Oxford Univ, DPhil(nuclear physics), 63. *Prof Exp:* Res assoc nuclear physics, Mass Inst Technol, 63-64, instr, 64-65; asst prof, Univ Pa, 65-70; assoc prof, 70-74, PROF PHYSICS & APPL PHYSICS, UNIV LOWELL, 74- *Concurrent Pos:* Royal Comn Exhibition of 1851 sr studentship, Oxford Univ, 63-65. *Mem:* Am Phys Soc. *Res:* Low energy nuclear physics, espcially reaction mechanisms and nuclear structure employing high resolution experimental techniques. *Mailing Add:* Dept of Physics & Appl Physics Univ of Lowell Lowell MA 01854

PULLEN, EDWIN WESLEY, b Flushing, NY, June 2, 23; m 46; c 4. ANATOMY. *Educ:* Colgate Univ, AB, 43; Univ Mass, MS, 48; Univ Va, PhD(biol), 53. *Prof Exp:* Instr biol, Univ Va, 50-51, from instr to assoc prof anat, 51-73, PROF ANAT, SCH MED, UNIV VA, 73-, ASSOC DEAN, 74- *Mem:* AAAS; Am Soc Zool; Am Asn Anat. *Res:* Invertebrate histology; mesenchyme of rhabdocoels; microscopy of circulation in the amphibian kidney; human surgical anatomy. *Mailing Add:* Dept of Anat Univ of Va Sch of Med Charlottesville VA 22908

PULLEN, KEATS A(BBOTT), JR, b Onawa, Iowa, Nov 12, 16; m 45; c 5. ELECTRICAL ENGINEERING, CIRCUITS ANALYSIS. *Educ:* Calif Inst Technol, BS, 39; Johns Hopkins Univ, EngD(elec eng), 46. *Prof Exp:* Teacher eng sci & mgt, War Training Prog, Johns Hopkins Univ, 41-44; electronic engr, Liberty Motors & Eng Corp, Md, 43-45; res engr, Columbia Mach Works, NY, 45-46; instr elec eng, Pratt Inst, 46-47; ELECTRONIC RES ENGR, ARMY MAT SYSTS ANAL ACTIVITY, ABERDEEN PROVING GROUND, 46- *Concurrent Pos:* Adj prof, Drexel Inst Technol; mem exten fac, Univ Del. *Mem:* Fel Inst Elec & Electronics Engrs. *Res:* Tube and transistor circuits; circuit theory; information theory and engineering; electron devices, antennas and propagation; communication systems. *Mailing Add:* 2817 Jerusalem Rd Kingsville MD 21087

PULLEN, MILTON WILLIAM, JR, b Waterville, NY, Nov 5, 14; m 40; c 2. GEOLOGY. *Educ:* Colgate Univ, BA, 38; Syracuse Univ, MS, 40; Univ Ill, PhD(geol), 50. *Prof Exp:* Instr gen geol, Syracuse Univ, 38-40 & Univ Ill, 40-42; asst geologist, Coal Div, State Geol Surv, Ill, 42-46, geologist, Div Ground Water Geol & Geophys Explor, 46-50, geologist & head, Div Geophys Res, 50-53; geologist & geophysicist, C A Bays & Assocs, Inc, 53-57; assoc prof, 57-79, EMER ASSOC PROF GEOSCI, PURDUE UNIV, WEST LAFAYETTE, 79- *Concurrent Pos:* Consult, C A Bays & Assocs, Inc, 47-53. *Mem:* Geol Soc Am; Am Asn Petrol Geologists; Am Inst Mining, Metall & Petrol Engrs. *Res:* Solution mining; subsurface geology; waste disposal. *Mailing Add:* 618 Eastview Rd Largo FL 33540

PULLEN, THOMAS MARION, b Elmodel, Ga, June 17, 19; m 40; c 1. BOTANY. *Educ:* Univ Ga, BSA, 40, MEd, 58, PhD(bot), 63. *Prof Exp:* Pub sch teacher, Ga, 40-44; teacher, Mt Berry Sch Boys, 46-47; high sch teacher, Ga, 50-57, chmn sci dept, 58-59; teaching asst bot, Univ Ga, 60-63; from asst prof to assoc prof, 63-66, PROF BIOL, UNIV MISS, 66- *Mem:* AAAS; Am Soc Plant Taxon; Int Asn Plant Taxon; Am Inst Biol Sci. *Res:* Taxonomy and biosystematics of the vascular flora of the southeastern United States. *Mailing Add:* Dept of Biol Univ of Miss University MS 38677

PULLIAM, H RONALD, b Miami Beach, Fla, Sept 7, 45; m 69; c 1. BEHAVIORAL ECOLOGY. *Educ:* Univ Georgia, BS, 68; Duke Univ, PhD(biol), 70. *Prof Exp:* Res fel, Univ Chicago, 70-71; asst prof biol, Univ Ariz, 71-75, assoc prof, 75-78; biologist, Mus Northern Ariz, 78-80; ASSOC PROF BIOL, STATE UNIV NY, ALBANY, 80- *Concurrent Pos:* Vis scientist, Sch Biol Sci, Sussex Univ, 77-78; ed, Ecology, Ecol Soc Am, 81-; prin investr, NSF grant, 74- *Mem:* Ecol Soc Am; Animal Behav Soc. *Res:* Ecology and behavior of vertebrates including social behavior and feeding behavior of birds; theoretical projects concerning the evolution of learning and cultural evolution. *Mailing Add:* Dept Biol Sci State Univ NY Albany NY 12222

PULLING, NATHANIEL H(OSLER), b Boston, Mass, Jan 10, 20; m 55. PHYSIOLOGY, MECHANICAL ENGINEERING. *Educ:* Brown Univ, AB, 42; Harvard Univ, PhD, 51. *Prof Exp:* Res fel, Harvard Univ, 51-53; develop engr, Gen Elec Co, 53-61, develop engr bus & prod planning, 61-67; PROJ DIR AUTOMOTIVE SAFETY, LIBERTY MUTUAL INS CO, 67- *Concurrent Pos:* Adj prof mech eng, Worcester Polytech Inst, 73-; mem, Transp Res Bd, Nat Acad Sci-Nat Res Coun. *Mem:* Soc Automotive Engrs; Am Soc Mech Engrs; Human Factors Soc; Am Asn Automotive Med. *Res:* Directing automotive safety research in physiological driving impairments; driving performance measurement; accident avoidance techniques; crash injury protection of vehicles and car occupants. *Mailing Add:* Manito Rd PO Box 335 East Orleans MA 02643

PULLMAN, IRA, b New York, NY, May 31, 21; m 44, 56; c 3. PHYSICS. *Educ:* Columbia Univ, BS, 41, ChE, 42; Univ Ill, MS, 49, PhD(physics), 53. *Prof Exp:* Jr engr, Tenn Valley Authority, 42-44; engr, Publicker Com Alcohol Co, 44-45; asst, SAM Lab, Columbia Univ, 45-46 & Argonne Nat Lab, 46; asst physics, Univ Ill, 46-50; scientist, Nuclear Develop Assoc, 52-55; asst prof biophys, Sloan-Kettering Div, Cornell Univ, 55-72; asst prof radiol & biochem, NY Med Col, 72-78; RES ASSOC PROF, NY UNIV DENT CTR, 78- *Concurrent Pos:* Consult, Genetics Comt, Nat Acad Sci, 55; from asst to assoc, Sloan-Kettering Inst Cancer Res, 55-72. *Mem:* AAAS; Am Phys Soc; Radiation Res Soc; Inst Elec & Electronics Engrs; fel NY Acad Sci. *Res:* Electron spin resonance spectroscopy of free radicals; radiation physics. *Mailing Add:* 140 Grand Blvd Scarsdale NY 10583

PULLMAN, MAYNARD EDWARD, b Chicago, Ill, Oct 26, 27; m 48; c 3. BIOCHEMISTRY. *Educ:* Univ Ill, BS, 48, MS, 50; Johns Hopkins Univ, PhD(biochem), 53. *Prof Exp:* Res assoc pediat, Hopkins Hosp, 53-54 53-54; from asst to assoc mem, 54-65, mem dept biochem, 65-76, CHIEF DEPT BIOCHEM, PUB HEALTH RES INST OF CITY OF NEW YORK, INC, 76-; RES PROF, NY UNIV SCH MED, 76- *Concurrent Pos:* mem biochem study sect, NIH, 69-73. *Mem:* AAAS; Am Soc Biol Chemists; Am Chem Soc. *Res:* Oxidative phosphorylation; biosynthetic processes in mitochondria. *Mailing Add:* Pub Health Res Inst of City of New York Inc 455 First Ave New York NY 10016

PULLMAN, NORMAN J, b New York, NY, Mar 31, 31; m 53; c 2. MATHEMATICS. *Educ:* NY Univ, BA, 56; Harvard Univ, MA, 57; Syracuse Univ, PhD(math), 62. *Prof Exp:* Instr math, Syracuse Univ, 60-62; lectr, McGill Univ, 62-63, asst prof, 63-66; assoc prof, 66-71, PROF MATH, QUEEN'S UNIV, ONT, 71- *Concurrent Pos:* Nat Res Coun Can fel, 65-66; Nat Res Coun Can operating grant, 67-; NY Acad Sci acad scholar, 71. *Mem:* Am Math Soc; Can Math Cong; Soc Indust & Appl Math; Sigma Xi. *Res:* Matrix theory; combinatorics. *Mailing Add:* Dept of Math Queen's Univ Kingston ON K7L 3N6 Can

PULLMAN, THEODORE NEIL, b New York, NY, Sept 30, 18; m 48. INTERNAL MEDICINE, NEPHROLOGY. *Educ:* Harvard Univ, BS, 38; Columbia Univ, MD, 43. *Prof Exp:* Intern med, New Haven Hosp, Conn, 43-44; asst resident med, Sch Med, Univ Chicago, 47-49, from instr to prof, 50-73; PROF MED, SCH MED, NORTHWESTERN UNIV, CHICAGO, 73-; ASSOC CHIEF STAFF, VET ADMIN LAKESIDE HOSP, 73- *Concurrent Pos:* Asst, Yale Univ, 43-44; attend physician, Albert Merritt Billings Mem Hosp, 51-73 & Northwestern Mem Hosp, 73- *Mem:* Soc Exp Biol & Med; Am Soc Clin Invest; Am Physiol Soc; Am Heart Asn; Am Col Physicians. *Res:* Renal physiology; fluid and electrolyte metabolism; cardiovascular and endocrine physiology. *Mailing Add:* Dept of Med Northwestern Univ Sch of Med Chicago IL 60611

PULLON, PETER AKINS, b Kalamazoo, Mich, Dec 6, 38; m 62; c 2. ORAL PATHOLOGY. *Educ:* Albion Col, BA, 60; Univ Mich, DDS, 65, MS, 68; Am Bd Oral Path, dipl. *Prof Exp:* NIH training grant, Univ Mich, 65-67, Nat Cancer Inst fel, 67-68; from asst prof to assoc prof path, Sch Dent, Temple Univ, 68-72; ASSOC PROF PATH & CHMN DEPT, WASH UNIV, 72- *Mem:* Am Dent Asn; fel Am Acad Oral Path. *Res:* Electron microscopy of mucocutaneous lesions; dental education. *Mailing Add:* Dept of Path Wash Univ St Louis MO 63110

PULLUKAT, THOMAS JOSEPH, b India, Apr 28, 41; m 70; c 1. CHEMISTRY. *Educ:* Univ Kerala, BSc, 61; Purdue Univ, Lafayette, PhD(inorg chem), 68. *Prof Exp:* Res scientist, 67-71, group leader anal group, 71-78, SR RES SCIENTIST, CHEMPLEX CO, 71-, ASST MGR, 78- *Mem:* Am Chem Soc. *Res:* Heterogeneous catalyst; olefin polymerization; organosilicon chemistry; general organometallic chemistry. *Mailing Add:* Res & Develop Dept Chemplex Co 3100 Golf Rd Rolling Meadows IL 60008

PULSIFER, ALLEN HUNTINGTON, b Johnstown, NY, Sept 18, 37; m 62; c 4. CHEMICAL ENGINEERING. *Educ:* Dartmouth Col, BA, 58; Mass Inst Technol, MS, 60, ChE, 61; Syracuse Univ, PhD(chem eng), 65. *Prof Exp:* From asst prof to assoc prof, 65-75, PROF CHEM ENG, IOWA STATE UNIV, 75- *Concurrent Pos:* Vis prof, Prairie View Agr & Mech Col, 70-71; Fulbright travel grant, 75; Humboldt Found res fel, 75-76; vis scientist, Bergbau-Forshung, W Ger, 75-76. *Mem:* Am Inst Chem Engrs; Am Chem Soc; Am Soc Eng Educ. *Res:* Fluidized bed reactors; coal gasification; solid-gas reactions. *Mailing Add:* 231 Sweeney Hall Iowa State Univ Ames IA 50011

PULVARI, CHARLES F, b Karlsbad, Austria-Hungary, July 19, 07; nat US; m 37; c 3. ELECTRICAL ENGINEERING. *Educ:* Royal Hungarian Univ Tech Sci, DrEng, 29. *Prof Exp:* Res engr lab, Tel Factory Co, Ltd, Hungary, 29-33; tech adv, Hungarian Radio & Commun Co, 33-35; chief engr, Hungarian Film Co, 35-41, tech mgr, 41-45; owner, Pulvari Electrophys Lab, 43-49; prof elec eng, George Washington Univ, 49-51; mem staff, 51-53, res prof, 53-56, prof elec eng & head solid state physics lab, 56-72, EMER PROF ELEC ENG, CATH UNIV AM, 72- *Concurrent Pos:* Prin investr, Mil Res & Instrumentation Projs, Hungary; consult, various insts, Hungary, 33-43; consult engr, Scophony, Ltd, London, 37; lectr, Hungarian Univ Tech Sci, 43 & Wayne State Univ, 53; pres, Electrocristal Corp, DC. *Honors & Awards:* IR 100 Award, 63. *Mem:* Fel Inst Elec & Electronics Engrs; fel NY Acad Sci; Sigma Xi (pres, 66); fel Am Ceramic Soc. *Res:* Electrostatic recording and reproducing; electric switch; electrical condensers; cathode ray tube; transpolarizer; ferrielectricity in crystals; solid state engineering; crystal growth; solar to electrical energy conversion research. *Mailing Add:* 2014 Taylor St NE Washington DC 20018

PUMMER, WALTER JOHN, b Allentown, Pa, Dec 3, 25; m 50; c 5. ORGANIC CHEMISTRY. *Educ:* Mt St Mary's Col, Md, BS, 50; Wayne State Univ, MS, 53. *Prof Exp:* Org chemist, Schering Corp, 52-53; ORG CHEMIST, POLYMER SCI & STANDARDS DIV, NAT BUR STANDARDS, 53- *Honors & Awards:* Dept Com Silver Medal Award, 66. *Mem:* Am Chem Soc. *Res:* Organic systhesis; polymers derived from these fluorocarbons; kinetics and mechanisms of the thermal decomposition of aromatic heat transfer fluids; combustion and thermal properties of v-irradiated polymers; syntheses and hydrolytic stability studies of polyurethane elastomers; study of additional migrations from polyolefins using radioactive traces; analyses of unified chloride monomer in pvc. *Mailing Add:* Polymer Sci & Standards Div Nat Bur of Standards Washington DC 20234

PUMO, DOROTHY ELLEN, b Charleston, WVa, Oct 27, 51. CELL BIOLOGY. *Educ:* Univ Mich, Ann Arbor, BS, 73, MS, 74, PhD(biol), 76. *Prof Exp:* Teaching asst biol & cell biol, Univ Mich, Ann Arbor, 74-75, res asst, 75-76; res assoc, Univ Colo, Boulder, 76-78, Univ Vt, Burlington, 78-79; res assoc, Univ Vt, Burlington, 81; ASST PROF CELL BIOL, HOFSTRA UNIV, 81- *Concurrent Pos:* Trainee, NIH Training Grant, Univ Vt, 81. *Mem:* AAAS; Am Soc Cell Biol. *Res:* Molecular interactions involved in the regulation of genetic transcriptive activity (chromosomal proteins and nucleic acids). *Mailing Add:* Biol Dept Hofstra Univ Hempstead NY 11550

PUMPER, ROBERT WILLIAM, b Clinton, Iowa, Sept 12, 21; m 51; c 1. VIROLOGY, MEDICAL MICROBIOLOGY. *Educ:* Univ Iowa, BA, 51, MSc, 53, PhD, 55; Am Bd Med Microbiol, dipl & cert pub health & med lab virol. *Prof Exp:* Mem staff, Virus & Rickettsial Div, US Army Chem Res & Develop Labs, Ft Detrick, Md, 55-56; asst prof microbiol, Hahnemann Med Col, 56-57; from asst prof to assoc prof, 57-61, PROF MICROBIOL, UNIV ILL COL MED, 61- *Concurrent Pos:* Consult, St James Hosp. *Honors & Awards:* Raymond B Allen, Med Lectr Award, 70, 74, 76 & 79. *Mem:* AAAS; Sigma Xi; Tissue Cult Asn. *Res:* Effect of viruses on in vitro tissue cell growth; growth of tissue in defined media and its use for disease diagnosis. *Mailing Add:* Dept of Microbiol Univ of Ill Col Med Chicago IL 60612

PUNCH, JAMES DARRELL, b Conover, NC, Dec 31, 36; m 59; c 2. MICROBIOLOGY, BIOCHEMISTRY. *Educ:* NC State Univ, BS, 59; Univ Minn, MS, 63, PhD(microbiol), 65. *Prof Exp:* Asst prof microbiol, Med Col Va, 67-73; HEAD CULT DEVELOP & GENETICS, UPJOHN CO, 73- *Concurrent Pos:* Consult, A H Robins Pharmaceut Co, Richmond, Va, 68-73. *Mem:* Am Soc Microbiol; Am Inst Biol Sci; NY Acad Sci. *Res:* R factors, bacterial plasmids and molecular genetics; molecular biology; DNA and RNA replication; protein synthesis; cell permeability. *Mailing Add:* Dept of Cult Develop Upjohn Co Kalamazoo MI 49001

PUNCH, JERRY LEROY, b Newton, NC. AUDIOLOGY. *Educ:* Wake Forest Univ, BA, 65; Vanderbilt Univ, MS, 67; Northwestern Univ, PhD(audiol), 72. *Prof Exp:* Asst prof commun disorders, Univ Miss, 71-73; asst prof, Memphis State Univ, 73-75; res assoc audiol, Univ Md, 75-80; DIR RES DIV, AM SPEECH-LANG-HEARING ASN, 80- *Concurrent Pos:* Proj dir, Vet Admin Contract, Univ Md, 76-; instr audiol, Towson State Univ, 77- *Mem:* Am Speech-Lang-Hearing Asn; Acoust Soc Am; Am Auditory Soc. *Res:* Psychoacoustics; diagnostic and rehabilitative aspects of hearing disorders; hearing aid electroacoustic measurements and hearing aid elvaluation methods. *Mailing Add:* Am Speech-Lang-Hearing Asn 10801 Rockville Pike Rockville MD 20852

PUNDERSON, JOHN OLIVER, b Northfield, Minn, Oct 28, 18; m 47; c 3. ORGANIC CHEMISTRY, POLYMER SCIENCE. *Educ:* Univ Chicago, BS, 40; Univ Minn, PhD(chem), 50. *Prof Exp:* Res chemist, Columbia Chem Div, Pittsburgh Plate Glass Co, 41-44; res chemist, Plastics Dept, 50-56, res supvr, 56-61, sr res chemist, 61-67, res assoc, Plastics Prods & Resins Dept, 67-80, RES ASSOC, POLYMER PRODS DEPT, E I DU PONT DE NEMOURS & CO, INC, WASHINGTON WORKS, WEST VA, 80- *Concurrent Pos:* Mem, Int Standards Orgn comts on fire standards, Int Electrotech Comn. *Mem:* Am Soc Testing & Mat; Inst Elec & Electronics Engrs; Am Chem Soc. *Res:* Polymer chemistry; fluoropolymer resins-properties and applications; electrical insulations science and dielectric phenomena; polymer flammability, combustion toxicology and fire safety test methods. *Mailing Add:* 108 Alden Ave Marietta OH 45750

PUNDSACK, ARNOLD L, b Albany, Minn, Apr 9, 38. PHYSICS, MATHEMATICS. *Educ:* St John's Univ, Minn, BS, 60. *Prof Exp:* Physicist, Nat Security Agency, 60-63; assoc scientist, Xerox Corp, 63-74, SCIENTIST MAT SCI, XEROX RES CTR CAN, 74- *Mem:* Soc Photog Scientists & Engrs. *Res:* Thin films, including nucleation and growth; electron microscopy and materials science; electrography and novel imaging systems. *Mailing Add:* Xerox Res Ctr Can Ltd 2480 Dunwin Dr Mississauga ON L5L 1J9 Can

PUNDSACK, FREDERICK LEIGH, b Pinckneyville, Ill, Sept 14, 25; m 48; c 5. INORGANIC CHEMISTRY. *Educ:* Univ Ill, BS, 49, PhD(chem), 52. *Prof Exp:* Sr res chemist, Johns-Manville Res Ctr, 52-60, sect chief, 60-61, mgr cent res, 62-63, dir res, 63-69, vpres res & develop, 69-71, sr vpres res, Technol & Corp Bus Develop, Johns-Manville Corp, 75-76, sr vpres res & develop group, 76-78, exec vpres-opers, 78-79, PRES & CHIEF OPER OFFICER, JOHNS-MANVILLE CORP, 79- *Concurrent Pos:* Mem bd dirs, Indust Res Inst, 76-79. *Mem:* AAAS; Am Chem Soc; Sigma Xi. *Res:* Chemistry of asbestos, silicates; surface chemistry; reinforced plastics. *Mailing Add:* Johns-Manville Corp PO Box 5108 Denver CO 80217

PUNNETT, HOPE HANDLER, b New York, NY, Jan 24, 27; m 50; c 3. GENETICS. *Educ:* Smith Col, AB, 48; Yale Univ, MS, 49, PhD(bot), 55. *Prof Exp:* Asst bot, Univ Ill, 50-52; asst lectr genetics, Univ Rochester, 59-63, res instr obstet & gynec, Sch Med, 62-63; from asst prof to assoc prof, 63-74, PROF PEDIAT, SCH MED, TEMPLE UNIV, 74-; DIR GENETICS LAB, ST CHRISTOPHER'S HOSP FOR CHILDREN, 63-; ASSOC-BIOSCI STAFF PEDIAT, ALBERT EINSTEIN MED CTR, 79- *Concurrent Pos:* NIH fel, Johns Hopkins Hosp, 61; NIH grant meiotic & mitotic chromosomes in man, 63-68 & NIH grant cystic fibrosis & other inherited disorders, 70-72; study leave, Univ Col, Univ London, 69; bd dirs, Planned Parenthood Southeastern Pa, 72-78; NIH grant genetic constitutions predispose cancer, 76-78; cystic fibrosis fedn grant, carrier detection, NIH. *Mem:* Soc Pediat Res; AAAS; Genetics Soc Am; Am Soc Human Genetics (secy, 77-). *Res:* Human genetics; cytogenetics. *Mailing Add:* St Christopher's Hosp Children 2600 N Lawrence St Philadelphia PA 19133

PUNNETT, THOMAS R, b Buffalo, NY, May 25, 26; m 50; c 3. PLANT BIOCHEMISTRY. *Educ:* Yale Univ, BS, 50; Univ Ill, PhD(physico-chem biol), 54. *Prof Exp:* Nat Found Infantile Paralysis fel, Sch Biochem, Cambridge Univ, 54-56; from instr to asst prof biol, Univ Rochester, 56-63; from asst prof to assoc prof, 63-69, PROF BIOL, TEMPLE UNIV, 69- *Mem:* Am Soc Plant Physiologists; Bot Soc Am; Am Soc Cell Biologists; Am Soc Biol Chemists; Am Soc Photobiol. *Res:* Photosynthesis; control of chloroplast biochemistry and fine structure. *Mailing Add:* Dept of Biol Temple Univ Philadelphia PA 19122

PUNTENNEY, DEE GREGORY, b Muncie, Ind, Feb 21, 48; m 71. PHYSICS, RADIOLOGICAL HEALTH. *Educ:* Taylor Univ, BA, 70; Purdue Univ, MS, 72, PhD(health physics), 73. *Prof Exp:* Asst prof, 73-79, ASSOC PROF PHYSICS, ASBURY COL, 79- *Mem:* Am Phys Soc; Am Asn Physics Teachers; Sigma Xi. *Res:* Microwave dosimetry; microwave bio-effects in amphibians and reptiles. *Mailing Add:* Dept Sci & Math Asbury Col Wilmore KY 40390

PUNWANI, DHARAM VIR, b Multan, India, Aug 23, 42; US citizen; m 70; c 2. CHEMICAL ENGINEERING. *Educ:* Indian Inst Technol, Bombay, BS, 65; Ill Inst Technol, MS, 67; Loyola Univ, Chicago, MBA, 74. *Prof Exp:* Chem engr, 67-74, supvr, 74-76, mgr, 76-77, asst dir, 77-78, ASSOC DIR CHEM PROCESSING RES, INST GAS TECHNOL, 78- *Mem:* Am Inst Chem Engrs. *Res:* Coal gasification; peat gasification; oil shale processing; high-temperature and high-pressure fluidization; high pressure solids transport. *Mailing Add:* Process Res Div 3424 S State St Chicago IL 60616

PUNWAR, JALAMSINH K, b Santrampur, India, Mar 25, 23; US citizen; m 58; c 2. CHEMISTRY. *Educ:* Univ Bombay, BSc, 48; Mich State Univ, MS, 50; Univ Wis, PhD(soil chem), 54. *Prof Exp:* Chemist, Pennsalt Int Corp, 53-54; anal res chemist, Wis Alumni Res Found, 55-69; anal res chemist & group leader, Warf Inst, Inc, 69-74, asst head, Food & Drug Dept, 74-77, RES SCIENTIST, RES & DEVELOP DEPT, RALTECH SCI SERV, INC, 77- *Mem:* Am Chem Soc; Am Oil Chemists Soc; Sigma Xi. *Res:* Analytical method research in fats and oils; gas chromatography of fats, oils and pesticides; polarography and chemical analysis; analytical method development for determination of total cholesterol in multicomponent foods; nitrosation reaction rates inhibition and determination of N-nitrosomines. *Mailing Add:* 614 Orchard Dr Madison WI 53711

PURBRICK, ROBERT LAMBURN, b Salem, Ore, Dec 5, 19; m 53; c 3. PHYSICS. *Educ:* Willamette Univ, AB, 42; Univ Wis, MA, 44, PhD(physics), 47. *Prof Exp:* Asst physics, Univ Wis, 42-44; jr physicist, Argonne Nat Lab, Ill, 44-46; asst physics, Alumni Res Found, 46-47; from asst prof to assoc prof, 47-55, PROF PHYSICS, WILLAMETTE UNIV, 55- *Mem:* AAAS; Am Phys Soc; Am Asn Physics Teachers; Inst Elec & Electronics Engrs; Optical Soc Am. *Res:* Molecular spectroscopy; nuclear physics; electronics and nuclear counter work. *Mailing Add:* Dept of Physics Willamette Univ Salem OR 97301

PURCELL, ALEXANDER HOLMES, III, b Summit, Miss, Oct 12, 42; m 70; c 2. ENTOMOLOGY, PLANT PATHOLOGY. *Educ:* US Air Force Acad, BS, 64; Univ Calif, Davis, PhD(entom), 74. *Prof Exp:* Asst prof, 74-81, ASSOC PROF ENTOM, UNIV CALIF, BERKELEY, 81- *Concurrent Pos:* Consult, UN Food & Agr Orgn, 81. *Mem:* Entom Soc Am; Am Phytopath Soc. *Res:* Insect transmission of plant pathogens, expecially Pierce's disease of grapevines, X-disease and aster yellows and the role of insects in the epidemiology of plant diseases. *Mailing Add:* Dept Entom Sci Univ of Calif Berkeley CA 94720

PURCELL, EDWARD MILLS, b Taylorville, Ill, Aug 30, 12; m 37; c 2. PHYSICS. *Educ:* Purdue Univ, BSEE, 33; Harvard Univ, AM, 35, PhD(physics), 38. *Hon Degrees:* DEng, Purdue Univ, 53. *Prof Exp:* From instr to assoc prof, 38-49, Soc of Fels sr fel, 50-71, prof, 49-80, Gerhard Gade Univ Prof, 60-80, EMER PROF PHYSICS, HARVARD UNIV, 80- *Concurrent Pos:* Mem staff, Radiation Lab, Mass Inst Technol, 41-46; mem sci adv bd, US Air Force, 53-57 & President's Sci Adv Comt, 57-60 & 62-66. *Honors & Awards:* Nobel Prize in Physics, 52; Oersted Medal, Am Asn Physics Teachers, 68. *Mem:* Nat Acad Sci; Am Acad Arts & Sci; fel Am Phys Soc; Am Philos Soc. *Res:* Nuclear magnetism; radio astronomy; biophysics; astrophysics. *Mailing Add:* Lyman Lab Harvard Univ Cambridge MA 02138

PURCELL, EVERETT WAYNE, b Omaha, Nebr, May 18, 24; m 47; c 3. MATHEMATICS, AEROSPACE ENGINEERING. *Educ:* Univ Nebr, BS, 47, MS, 49; Univ Southern Calif, MS, 60. *Prof Exp:* Instr math & physics, Univ Wyo, 49-50; prog analyst, Douglas Aircraft Co, Inc, 55-59; res engr, 59-62, sect supvr, 62-64, PRIN ENGR, FORD AEROSPACE & COMMUN CORP, FORD MOTOR CO, 65- *Concurrent Pos:* Instr, Biola Col, 61-64; mem, Creation-Sci Res Ctr. *Mem:* Am Inst Aeronaut & Astronaut; Simulation Coun; Am Sci Affiliation. *Res:* Digital and analog computing; numerical analysis and methods; redundant structural analysis; aircraft stability and dynamics; missile trajectory calculations and missile dynamics and stability; Kalman filters; statistical studies. *Mailing Add:* 18451 Saugus Ave Santa Ana CA 92705

PURCELL, JAMES EUGENE, b Henry Co, Va, Sept 25, 36; div; c 3. PHYSICS. *Educ:* Berea Col, BA, 59; Case Inst Technol, PhD(physics), 66. *Prof Exp:* Res assoc nuclear theory, Fla State Univ, 66-68; asst prof physics, Univ Fla, 68-70; asst prof, 70-74, ASSOC PROF PHYSICS, GA STATE UNIV, 74- *Mem:* Am Phys Soc; Am Asn Physics Teachers; AAAS. *Res:* Theory of nuclear structure and nuclear reactions; scattering of electrons by atoms. *Mailing Add:* Dept of Physics Ga State Univ Atlanta GA 30303

PURCELL, JOSEPH CARROLL, b Cleveland, Va, Feb 5, 21; m 55. AGRICULTURAL ECONOMICS. *Educ:* Va Polytech Inst, BA, 48, MS, 51; Iowa State Univ, PhD(agr econ), 56. *Prof Exp:* Agr economist, USDA, 51-52; from asst prof to assoc prof, 53-60, PROF AGR ECON, UNIV GA, 60-, HEAD DEPT, 71- *Concurrent Pos:* Econ adv panelist, Milk Indust Found, 68; prin agr economist, Coop State Res Serv, USDA, 75-76; mem, Econ Adv Bd, Dairyman, Inc, 70-; assoc dir, Agr Res Planning & Eval, Sci & Educ Admin, USDA, 79-81. *Honors & Awards:* Res Award, Sears Found, 62. *Mem:* Am Agr Econ Asn. *Res:* Planning and execution of research in the economics of commercial agriculture production and marketing; monitoring of the domestic market by product, space and time detail. *Mailing Add:* Dept of Agr Econ Univ of Ga Ga Sta Experiment GA 30212

PURCELL, KEITH FREDERICK, b St Louis, Mo, Sept 12, 39; m 62; c 2. INORGANIC CHEMISTRY. *Educ:* Cent Col, AB, 61; Univ Ill, PhD(chem), 65. *Prof Exp:* Asst prof chem, Wake Forest Col, 65-67; asst prof, 67-70, assoc prof, 70-78, PROF CHEM, KANS STATE UNIV, 78- *Mem:* AAAS; Am Chem Soc; Royal Soc Chem; Am Phys Soc. *Res:* Synthesis of and electronic structures of transition metal and non-metal adducts; vibrational analyses and electronic structure calculations. *Mailing Add:* Dept of Chem Kans State Univ Manhattan KS 66506

PURCELL, KENNETH, b New York, NY, Oct 21, 28; m 49; c 2. CLINICAL PSYCHOLOGY. *Educ:* Univ Nebr, BA, 49, PhD, 53. *Prof Exp:* Asst prof psychol, Univ Ky, 56-58; dir state training prog clin psychol, Commonwealth of Ky, 56-58; dir behav sci div, Children's Asthma Res Inst & Hosp, 59-68; prof psychol & dir grad training prog clin psychol, Univ Mass, Amherst, 68-70, chmn dept psychol, 69-70; chmn dept, 70-76, PROF PSYCHOL, UNIV DENVER, 70-, DEAN COL ARTS & SCI, 76- *Mem:* Fel AAAS; fel Soc Res Child Develop; fel Am Psychol Asn. *Res:* Personality theory and function; child development; psychosomatic research. *Mailing Add:* Dept of Psychol Univ of Denver Denver CO 80208

PURCELL, ROBERT HARRY, virology, epidemiology, see previous edition

PURCELL, TERRY, solid state physics, see previous edition

PURCELL, WILLIAM PAUL, b Tulsa, Okla, Dec 11, 35; m 57; c 3. MOLECULAR BIOLOGY. *Educ:* Ind Univ, AB, 57; Princeton Univ, AM, 59, PhD(phys chem), 60. *Prof Exp:* Chief inorg res chemist, Buckman Labs, 60-63; instr physics & chem, Christian Bros Col, Tenn, 61-63; from assoc prof to prof med chem, Col Pharm, 63-69, chmn dept molecular & quantum biol, 69-74, PROF MOLECULAR & QUANTUM BIOL, COL PHARM, CTR HEALTH SCI, UNIV TENN, MEMPHIS, 69-, DIR DIV DRUG DESIGN, 74-, PROF, DEPT PHARMACOL & COL COMMUNITY & ALLIED HEALTH PROFS, 75- *Concurrent Pos:* Co-prin investr, NSF grant, 64-67; prin investr, US Army Med Res & Develop Command res contract, 65-71, Cotton Prod Inst contract, 69-, FMC Corp, 71- & Diamond Shamrock Corp, 72-; grants, Eli Lilly & Co, 68- & Smith, Kline & French Found, 69-; co-prin investr, Nat Inst Dent Res grant, 69-; vis prof, Univ Lausanne, Lausanne, Switz, 75- *Mem:* Int Soc Quantum Biol (secy, 71-); Am Chem Soc; Royal Soc Chem; Acad Pharmaceut Sci; Sigma Xi. *Res:* Dipole moments; molecular orbital calculations; partition chromatography of molecules of biological and biochemical interest; application of regression analyses to structure-activity data; quantitative structure-activity relationships. *Mailing Add:* Univ Tenn PO Box 41151 Memphis TN 38104

PURCHASE, EARL RALPH, b Oceana Co, Mich, July 2, 19; m 41; c 2. POLLUTION CHEMISTRY. *Educ:* Hope Col, AB, 40; Univ Vt, MS, 43; Ohio State Univ, PhD(org chem), 48. *Prof Exp:* Instr chem, Univ Vt, 40-41; assoc chemist, Clinton Labs, Tenn, 44-45; res chemist, 48-50, group supvr, 50-62, sr supvr int dept, 62-67, lycra prod supt, 67-70, Netherlands, PROCESS SPECIALIST, E I DU PONT DE NEMOURS & CO, INC, 71- *Mem:* Am Chem Soc. *Res:* Halogenated hydrocarbons; cellulose and polymer chemistry; wastewater treatment and air pollution control; hazardous material control and disposal. *Mailing Add:* EI du Pont de Nemours & Co Inc PO Box 27001 Richmond VA 23261

PURCHASE, HARVEY GRAHAM, b Livingstone, NRhodesia, Aug 8, 36; US citizen; m 63; c 2. PATHOLOGY, VIROLOGY. *Educ:* Univ Witwatersrand, BSc, 55; Univ Pretoria, BVSc, 59; Univ London, MRCVS, 61; Mich State Univ, MS, 65, PhD, 70; dipl, Am Col Vet Microbiol, 67. *Prof Exp:* Pvt pract, SAfrica, 60-61 & Eng, 61; vet med off, Regional Poultry Res Lab, USDA, Mich, 61-74; staff scientist, 74-78, ACTG CHIEF LIVESTOCK & VET SCI, NAT PROG STAFF, AGR RES SERV, USDA, 78- *Concurrent Pos:* Res exchange, Leukosis Unit, Houghton Poultry Res Sta, Eng, 65-66; asst prof microbiol, Mich State Univ, 70-74. *Honors & Awards:* Sir Arnold Theiler Medal, Agricura Prize & Imp Chem Ltd Prize, 59; CPC Int Award, Poultry Sci Asn, 71; Arthur S Flemming Award, 72; Tom Newman Mem Award, Poultry Stock Asn Gt Brit, 73. *Mem:* Am Vet Med Asn; Poultry Sci Asn; Am Asn Avian Path; Brit Vet Asn; US Animal Health Asn. *Res:* Immunology, virology and pathology of oncogenic viruses, mainly of the lymphoid leukosis-sarcoma group and Marek's disease of poultry and all diseases of poultry. *Mailing Add:* Rm 207 N Bldg BARC-West Nat Prog Staff USDA Beltsville MD 20705

PURCIFULL, DAN ELWOOD, b Woodland, Calif, July 1, 35; m 66; c 2. PLANT VIROLOGY. *Educ:* Univ Calif, Davis, BS, 57, MS, 59, PhD(plant path), 64. *Prof Exp:* Res asst plant path, Univ Calif, Davis, 59-64; from asst prof to assoc prof, 64-75, PROF PLANT PATH, UNIV FLA, 75- *Honors & Awards:* Lee M Hutchins Award, Am Phytopath Soc, 81. *Mem:* AAAS; Am Phytopath Soc; Sigma Xi. *Res:* Biological and serological and physicochemical properties of plant viruses; etiology and control of plant virus diseases. *Mailing Add:* Dept Plant Path Univ Fla Gainesville FL 32611

PURCUPILE, JOHN CHARLES, b Los Angeles, Calif, Oct 3, 30; m 53; c 3. MECHANICAL ENGINEERING. *Educ:* Univ Calif, Los Angeles, BS, 53; Carnegie Inst Technol, MS, 66; Carnegie-Mellon Univ, PhD(mech eng), 71. *Prof Exp:* Design engr, Borg Warner Corp, 53-57, proj engr, 57-61; chief engr, Time-O-Matic Inc, 61-63; sr engr, Atomic Power Div, Westinghouse Elec Corp, 63-68; ASSOC PROF MECH ENG, CARNEGIE-MELLON UNIV, 68- *Concurrent Pos:* Consult, Am Shear Knife, 70-, Westinghouse Elec Corp, 71- & Lear Siegler, 72- *Mem:* Am Soc Mech Engrs. *Res:* Critical heat flux: two phase flow; design coal conversion. *Mailing Add:* Mech Eng Dept Carnegie-Mellon Univ Pittsburgh PA 15213

PURDIE, NEIL, b Castle Douglas, Scotland, Sept 16, 35; wid; c 3. INORGANIC CHEMISTRY, PHYSICAL CHEMISTRY. *Educ:* Univ Glasgow, BSc, 58, PhD(chem), 61. *Prof Exp:* Asst lectr chem, Univ Glasgow, 60-62; res assoc, Brookhaven Nat Lab, 62-63; Turner & Newall res fel inorg chem, Univ Glasgow, 63-65; from asst prof to assoc prof, 65-75, PROF CHEM, OKLA STATE UNIV, 75- *Concurrent Pos:* Vis assoc prof chem, Univ Utah, 73-74. *Mem:* Am Chem Soc; The Chem Soc. *Res:* Chemical reaction kinetics using relaxation methods; analysis of complex mixtures for dangerous drugs using circular dichroism; thermodynamics of metal complexes and polybasic acids in solution by potentiometry, calorimetry, spectroscopy and conductance. *Mailing Add:* Dept of Chem Okla State Univ Stillwater OK 74074

PURDOM, PAUL W, JR, b Atlanta, Ga, Apr 5, 40; m 65; c 2. ANALYSIS OF ALGORITHMS, COMPILER DESIGN. *Educ:* Calif Inst Technol, BS, 61, MS, 62, PhD(physics), 66. *Prof Exp:* From asst prof to assoc prof comput sci, Univ Wis-Madison, 65-71; ASSOC PROF COMPUT SCI, IND UNIV, BLOOMINGTON, 72-, CHMN DEPT, 78- *Concurrent Pos:* Mem tech staff, Bell Tel Labs, 70-71. *Mem:* Asn Comput Mach; AAAS; Soc Indust & Appl Math. *Res:* Analysis of alforithms with an emphasis on the average time required for the satisfiability problem. *Mailing Add:* Dept of Comput Sci Ind Univ Bloomington IN 47401

PURDOM, PAUL WALTON, SR, b Sparta, Ga, July 23, 17; m 39; c 3. ENVIRONMENTAL ENGINEERING. *Educ:* Ga Inst Technol, BS, 37; Univ Mich, MSE, 51; Univ Pa, MGovtAdmin, 58, PhD(polit sci), 63. *Prof Exp:* Sr sanit engr, Tenn Dept Pub Health, 43-47; dir sanit, Knoxville Bur Health, 47-52; dir environ health, Philadelphia Dept Pub Health, 53-63; assoc prof civil eng, 63-64, prof environ eng & sci & dir prog, 64-70, dir, Ctr Urban Res & Environ Studies, 70-73, chmn civil eng, 73-75, DIR, ENVIRON STUDIES INST, DREXEL UNIV, 75- *Concurrent Pos:* Lectr, Sch Dent, Temple Univ, 54-62; lectr, Sch Med, Univ Pa, 54-63, Sch Nursing, 58-63; mem subcomt training & utilization sanit engrs, Nat Res Coun, 57; mem study group community solid waste disposal, USPHS, 57, consult & mem subcomt environ eng, 61; mem steering comt, Nat Conf Air Pollution, 58; mem task force environ health, Nat Comn Community Health Serv, 63-65; staff dir comt state health rels, Secy Health, Educ & Welfare, 66; consult subcomt, Hazardous Prod Comt, Environ Protection Agency, 71; mem sci adv bd, US Environ Protection Agency, 74-81; consult mem, Atomic Safety & Licensing Bd Panel, US Nuclear Regulatory Comn, 72-, admin judge, 81- *Honors & Awards:* Crumbine Award, 61. *Mem:* Am Acad Environ Engrs; fel Am Pub Health Asn (pres, 71); hon fel Royal Soc Health; Conf Local Environ Health Adminr. *Res:* Solid wastes; water supply; water pollution control; air pollution; public administration; environmental health. *Mailing Add:* Environ Studies Inst 32nd & Chestnut St Philadelphia PA 19104

PURDOM, RAY CALDWELL, b Lebanon, Ky, Sept 8, 43; m 65; c 3. PHYSICS. *Educ:* Duke Univ, BS, 65; Purdue Univ, MS, 67, PhD(physics), 70. *Prof Exp:* asst prof, 70-75, assoc prof, 75-80, PROF PHYSICS, KY WESLEYAN COL, 80- *Concurrent Pos:* Res assoc, Dept Radiol, Col Med, Univ Cincinnati, 77-78. *Mem:* Am Phys Soc; Am Asn Physics Teachers. *Res:* Phonon-phonon interactions in solids; ultrasonic attenuation in solids at low temperatures; medical physics. *Mailing Add:* Dept of Physics & Math Ky Wesleyan Col Owensboro KY 42301

PURDOM, WILLIAM BERLIN, b De Kalb, Ill, Apr 6, 34; m 60. ECONOMIC GEOLOGY. *Educ:* Univ Ky, BS, 56; Univ Ariz, PhD(econ geol), 60. *Prof Exp:* Asst prof geol, Univ Ore, 60-62, mineral examr, US Bur Land Mgt, 62-63; asst prof geol, Univ Ore, 63-64; from asst prof to assoc prof geol, 64-74, PROF GEOL & GEN SCI, SOUTHERN ORE COL, 74-, CHMN DEPT GEOL, 77- *Mem:* AAAS; Mineral Soc Am; Geol Soc Am; Nat Asn Geol Teachers; Am Inst Prof Geologists. *Res:* Mineralogy. *Mailing Add:* Dept of Geol Southern Ore Col Ashland OR 97520

PURDON, JAMES RALPH, JR, b Akron, Ohio, Feb 9, 33; m 54; c 5. POLYMER CHEMISTRY. *Educ:* Univ Akron, BS & MS, 55, PhD(polymer chem), 61. *Prof Exp:* Chemist colloid appln, 57-63, sect head phys & chem anal, 63-66, mgr prod develop rubbers & chem, 66-74, mgr chem develop serv, 74-75, mgr chem mat & processes develop, 75-79, MGR LATEX & COATINGS DEVELOP, GOODYEAR TIRE & RUBBER CO, 79- *Honors & Awards:* Rubber Age Award for Rubber Technol, Palmerton Publ Co, 61. *Mem:* Am Chem Soc. *Res:* Development of products and processes in the fields of elastomers, latices, reinforcing resins, polymer coatings and rubber chemicals. *Mailing Add:* Goodyear Tire & Rubber Co Dept 480D 1485 Archwood Ave Akron OH 44306

PURDUE, JACK OLEN, b McLoud, Okla, Mar 2, 13; m 41:; c 3. CHEMISTRY. *Educ:* Okla Baptist Univ, BS, 34; Univ Okla, MS, 39, PhD(chem), 48. *Prof Exp:* Instr physics, Okla Baptist Univ, 38-43; dir ground sch, Regional Sch, Civil Aeronaut Admin, 43-44; from assoc prof to prof, 46-64, distinguished serv prof, 64-80, EMER DISTINGUISHED SERV PROF CHEM, OKLA BAPTIST UNIV, 80- *Mem:* Am Chem Soc; Math Asn Am. *Res:* Colloids; some factors in the stability of emulsions; preparation and properties of clay systems; modification of carbon surfaces to enhance anion adsorption. *Mailing Add:* 2000 N Market Shawnee OK 74801

PURDUE, PETER, b Dublin, Ireland, Sept 18, 43; m 71. MATHEMATICS, STATISTICS. *Educ:* Univ London, BS, 67; Purdue Univ, Lafayette, MS, 69, PhD(statist), 72. *Prof Exp:* Asst prof, 71-76, ASSOC PROF STATIST, UNIV KY, 76- *Concurrent Pos:* Consult, Oak Ridge Nat Lab. *Mem:* Inst Math Statist; Am Statist Asn; Opers Res Soc Am; AAAS. *Res:* Queueing theory; stochastic processes; stochastic models in biology. *Mailing Add:* Dept Statist Univ Ky Lexington KY 40506

PURDY, ALAN HARRIS, b Mt Clemens, Mich, Dec 13, 23. BIOMEDICAL ENGINEERING, OCCUPATIONAL HEALTH. *Educ:* Univ Miami, BS, 54; Univ Calif, Los Angeles, MS, 67; Univ Mo-Columbia, PhD(biomed eng), 70. *Prof Exp:* Proj engr acoust, Arvin Industs, 54-56 & AC Spark Plug Co, Mich, 56-61; asst prof eng, Calif State Polytech Univ, 61-67; assoc dir biomed eng, Univ Mo, 67-71; dep assoc dir, Nat Inst Occup Safety & Health, 71-76, biomed engr, 76-80; ASST DIR, FLA INST OCEANOG, 81- *Concurrent Pos:* Consult acoust, Smithy Muffler Co, 61-63; Nat Heart Inst spec fel, 63-67; consult biomed, Statham Instruments, Inc, 66-67; consult fac, Sch Med, Tex Tech Univ, 71-74; mem adv bd, Fla Inst Technol, 76- *Mem:* Asn Advan Med Instrumentation; Biomed Eng Soc; Oceanic Soc; Undersea Med Soc. *Res:* Occupational safety and health; man-machine interface; man undersea; solar power. *Mailing Add:* 3901 14th Lane NE St Petersburg FL 33703

PURDY, D(AVID) C(ARL), b Bethlehem, Pa, Jan 17, 29; m 52; c 4. MECHANICAL & NUCLEAR ENGINEERING. *Educ:* Webb Inst, BS, 50. *Prof Exp:* Naval archit, Preliminary Design Div, Bur Ships, Navy Dept, 50-51, marine engr, 51-55; proj engr, Reactor Develop Dept, Chrysler Corp, 56-57; sr engr, Atomic Energy Div, Babcock & Wilcox Co, 57-59, eng supvr, 59-61, prof engr, 61-66; supvry engr, 66-72, asst chief nuclear engr, 72-73, chief mech engr, 73-79, chief nuclear engr, 79-80, MGR ADVAN TECHNOL, GIBBS & HILL, INC, 80- *Concurrent Pos:* Adj prof nuclear & mech eng, Polytech Inst NY, 78- *Mem:* Am Soc Mech Engrs; Int Solar Energy Soc. *Res:* Design and construction of nuclear power plants and alternate energy systems. *Mailing Add:* Gibbs & Hill Inc 393 Seventh Ave New York NY 10001

PURDY, DAVID LAWRENCE, b New York, NY, Sept 18, 28; m 51; c 4. BIOMEDICAL ENGINEERING. *Educ:* Cornell Univ, Mech Engr, 51. *Prof Exp:* Prof engr, Gen Elec Co, 53-55, mgr eng prog, Eng Serv Div, 55-57, space propulsion engr, Space Power Oper, 57-60, systs engr, Missile & Space Div, 60-64; mgr, Nuclear Mat & Equip Corp, 64-72; PRES, CORATOMIC, INC, 72- *Concurrent Pos:* Dir radioisotope powered artificial heart contract, Nat Heart & Lung Inst; mgr radioisotope powered cardiac pacemaker contract, AEC. *Mem:* Fel Am Soc Mech Engr; Am Inst Aeronaut & Astronaut; Asn Advan Med Instrumentation. *Res:* Application of atomic energy, mechanical and electrical engineering and electronics to implantable prosthetics such as the artificial heart; radioisotope powered cardiac pacemaker. *Mailing Add:* Coratomic Inc Box 434 Indiana PA 15701

PURDY, EDWARD GEORGE, b New Rochelle, NY, Dec 4, 31. GEOLOGY. *Educ:* Rutgers Univ, BS, 56; Columbia Univ, PhD(geol), 60. *Prof Exp:* From asst prof to assoc prof geol, Rice Univ, 59-65; sr geologist, 65-72, sr prof geologist, Europe-Africa Div, 74-79, sr explor geologist, 77-79, GEOL MGR, EUROPE-AFRICA DIV, ESSO EXPLOR INC, 79- *Honors & Awards:* Award, Soc Econ Paleont & Mineral, 64. *Mem:* AAAS; Paleont Soc; Soc Econ Paleont & Mineral; Int Asn Sedimentologists; Geol Soc London. *Res:* Sedimentation; recent and ancient environments of calcium carbonate deposition; tectonics; time dependent patterns in earth history. *Mailing Add:* Europe-Africa Div Esso Explor Inc 89-93 New Zealand Ave Walton-on-Thames England

PURDY, GARY RUSH, b Edmonton, Alta, Oct 8, 36; m 61; c 4. PHYSICAL METALLURGY. *Educ:* Univ Alta, BS, 57, MS, 59; McMaster Univ, PhD(metall), 62. *Prof Exp:* Res assoc metall, Univ Alta, 59-60; fel, 62-63, from asst prof to assoc prof metall & metall eng, 63-71, assoc dean grad studies, 71-74, chmn, Metall & Mat Sci Dept, 78-81, PROF METALL & METALL ENG, MCMASTER UNIV, 71- *Concurrent Pos:* Vis prof, Cent Elec Res Labs, Eng, 69-70 & Royal Inst Technol, Stockholm, 76-77. *Honors & Awards:* C D Howe Mem Found Fel, 69. *Mem:* Can Inst Mining & Metall; Am Inst Mining, Metall & Petrol Engrs; Am Soc Metals. *Res:* Thermodynamic properties of alloys; diffusion; phase transformations in solids; solidification of alloys. *Mailing Add:* Dept Metall & Mat Sci McMaster Univ Hamilton ON L8S 4L8 Can

PURDY, JAMES LEALON, plant genetics, see previous edition

PURDY, KENNETH RODMAN, mechanical engineering, see previous edition

PURDY, LAURENCE HENRY, b Miami, Ariz, Sept 28, 26; m 48; c 4. PLANT PATHOLOGY. *Educ:* San Diego State Col, BS, 49; Univ Calif, PhD(plant path), 54. *Prof Exp:* Res asst, Univ Calif, 52-53; pathologist, Agr Res Serv, USDA, 53-67; chmn dept, 67-79, PROF PLANT PATH, INST FOOD & AGR SCI, UNIV FLA, 67- *Mem:* Am Phytopath Soc (treas, 70-76, vpres, 78, pres elect, 79, pres, 80). *Res:* Biology of rust and smut of sugar cane and other diseases of sugar cane; epidemiology and control of diseases of cocoa (Theobroma cacao); tropical agriculture and international cooperative research programs. *Mailing Add:* Dept Plant Path Univ Fla Gainesville FL 32611

PURDY, ROBERT H, b Bloomfield, NJ, Feb 26, 30. BIOCHEMISTRY. *Educ:* Yale Univ, BS, 51; Harvard Univ, PhD(biochem), 60. *Prof Exp:* USPHS fel, 59-61; Milton Found fel, 61-62; Lalor Found fel, 62-63; res assoc biol chem, Harvard Med Sch & Boston City Hosp, 62-64; FOUND SCIENTIST, SOUTHWEST FOUND RES & EDUC, 65- *Mem:* Am Chem Soc; Endocrine Soc; Am Soc Neurochem. *Res:* Mutagenic and carcinogenic potential of estrogens; drug metabolism. *Mailing Add:* Southwest Found Res & Educ PO Box 28147 San Antonio TX 78284

PURDY, WILLIAM CROSSLEY, b Brooklyn, NY, Sept 14, 30; m 53; c 3. ANALYTICAL CHEMISTRY. *Educ:* Amherst Col, BA, 51; Mass Inst Technol, PhD(chem), 55. *Prof Exp:* Instr chem, Univ Conn, 55-58; from asst prof to prof, Univ Md, College Park, 58-76, head Anal Chem Div, 68-76; PROF CHEM & ASSOC IN MED, MCGILL UNIV, MONTREAL, QUE, 76- *Concurrent Pos:* Consult, US Dept Army, 58-; vis prof inst nutrit sci, Univ Giessen, Ger, 65-66. *Mem:* Am Chem Soc; fel Nat Acad Clin Biochem; Am Asn Clin Chem; Chem Inst Can; fel Royal Soc Chem UK. *Res:* Electroanalytical chemistry; electrode studies in aqueous and nonaqueous media; complexes of transition elements; separation of stereoisomers; clinical analyses; application of electroanalytical techniques to biochemistry; clinical chemistry; lipid analyses. *Mailing Add:* Dept Chem McGill Univ Montreal PQ H3A 2K6 Can

PURI, KEWAL KRISHAN, b Sialkot, India, Oct 1, 33; m 67; c 1. MATHEMATICS, FLUID DYNAMICS. *Educ:* Delhi Univ, BA, 53, MA, 55; NY Univ, MS, 65, PhD(math), 67. *Prof Exp:* Sci asst, Defense Sci & Res Orgn, Delhi, India, 57-63; asst prof appl math, NY Univ, 67-70; assoc prof, Ala State Univ, 70-76; ASSOC PROF MATH, UNIV MAINE, 77- *Mem:* Am Math Soc. *Res:* Viscous and inviscid flows in channels. *Mailing Add:* Dept of Math & Astron Stubles Hall Orono ME 04473

PURI, NARINDRA NATH, b New Delhi, India, Nov 30, 33; US citizen; m 62; c 1. ENGINEERING, MATHEMATICS. *Educ:* Indian Inst Tech, Kharagpur, BSEE, 55; Univ Wis, MS, 58; Univ Pa, PhD(elec eng), 60. *Prof Exp:* From asst prof to assoc prof elec eng, Drexel Inst, 60-63; assoc prof, Univ Pa, 63-64; mgr guid & control systs, Missile & Space Div, Gen Elec Co, 64-68; PROF ELEC ENG, RUTGERS UNIV, NEW BRUNSWICK, 68- *Concurrent Pos:* Consult, Honeywell Spec Syst Div, Pa, 62-63, Gen Elec Co, 63-64 & Astro Div, RCA, 69- *Mem:* Inst Elec & Electronics Engrs. *Res:* Optimal and adaptive control systems; design of control systems for artificial heart including computer simulation; research in guidance and control of aerospace vehicles; communication satellites; mathematical modeling of multi-element antennas. *Mailing Add:* Dept of Elec Eng Rutgers Univ New Brunswick NJ 08903

PURI, OM PARKASH, b Sialkot, India, Apr 27, 35; m 63; c 1. SOLID STATE PHYSICS. *Educ:* Punjab Univ, India, BA, 55; Univ Saugar, MS, 58, PhD(physics), 61. *Prof Exp:* Assoc prof, 61-64, PROF PHYSICS, CLARK COL, 64-, CHMN DEPT, 61-, CHMN, DIV NAT SCI & MATH, 77- *Concurrent Pos:* Assoc prof physics, State Univ NY, 63-64; dir, Coop Gen Sci Proj, Clark Col & NSF Prog, 66-; consult, US Off Educ; dir, Nigerian Manpower Proj, Clark Col, 78- *Mem:* Am Phys Soc; Am Soc Metals; Am Inst Mining, Metall & Petrol Engrs; Am Asn Physics Teachers. *Res:* X-ray diffraction; dielectrics; fiber glass; wax electrets; stresses in metals; magnetic materials; polarization; energy storage. *Mailing Add:* Dept of Physics Clark Col Atlanta GA 30314

PURI, PRATAP, b Lahore, India, Mar 15, 38; m 68; c 1. APPLIED MATHEMATICS, CONTINUUM MECHANICS. *Educ:* Panjab Univ, India, BA Hons, 57; Delhi Univ, MA, 59; Indian Inst Technol, Kharagpur, MTech, 60, PhD(appl math), 65. *Prof Exp:* Assoc lectr math, Indian Inst Technol, Bombay, 62-63, lectr, 63-68; from asst prof to assoc prof, 68-76, PROF MATH, UNIV NEW ORLEANS, 76- *Mem:* Am Acad Mech; Calcutta Math Soc; Soc Indust & Appl Math. *Res:* Fluid mechanics, solid mechanics. *Mailing Add:* Dept of Math Univ of New Orleans New Orleans LA 70122

PURI, PREM SINGH, b Montgomery, Pakistan, Apr 15, 36. STATISTICS, OPERATIONS RESEARCH. *Educ:* Agra Univ, BSc, 53, MSc, 56; Inst Agr Res Statist, India, dipl, 58; Univ Calif, Berkeley, MA, 63, PhD(biostatist), 64. *Prof Exp:* Sr statist investr, Inst Agr Res Statist, India, 58-59; asst res statistician, Univ Calif, Berkeley, 63-65, actg asst prof statist, 65-66; from asst prof to assoc prof, 66-74, PROF STATIST, PURDUE UNIV, LAFAYETTE, 74- *Concurrent Pos:* Consult, Forest Serv, USDA, 71-73; vis res statistician, Univ Calif, Berkeley, 75-76. *Mem:* Biomet Soc; fel Am Statist Asn; Int Statist Inst; fel Inst Math Statist; fel Royal Statist Soc; Bernoulli Soc Math Statist & Probability. *Res:* Theory of statistical inference; applied probability theory as applied to biological sciences. *Mailing Add:* Dept of Statist Purdue Univ Lafayette IN 47907

PURI, SURENDRA KUMAR, b New Delhi, India, Oct 26, 40; m 68; c 4. PHARMACOLOGY, PHARMACEUTICAL SCIENCES. *Educ:* Univ Saugar, BPharm, 66; Univ RI, MS, 71, PhD(pharmacol), 74. *Prof Exp:* Teaching asst biochem pharm, Col Pharm, Univ RI, 70-73; res pharmacologist, Sch Med, Boston Univ, 73-74, asst prof pharm, 74-76; sr res biochemist, 76-78, asst dir, 78-81, ASSOC DIR CLIN PHARM, HOECHST-ROUSSEL PHARMACEUTS INC, 81- *Concurrent Pos:* Adj asst prof pharmacol, Sch Med, Boston Univ, 76- *Mem:* Am Soc Pharmacol & Exp Therapeut; Soc Neurosci; Am Pharmaceut Asn; AAAS; Brit Brain Res Asn. *Res:* Behavioral and biochemical approaches to study drug action and disease states; pharmacokinetic, metabolism and toxicological aspects of drugs; neuropharmacological aspects of aging. *Mailing Add:* Hoechst-Roussel Pharmaceuts Inc Rte 202-206 N Somerville NJ 08876

PURI, YESH PAUL, b Sangrur, India, Sept 20, 29; m 71; c 3. PLANT BREEDING, GENETICS. *Educ:* Punjab Univ, India, BSc, 49; Benares Hindu Univ, BSc, 54; Ore State Univ, MS, 58, PhD(plant breeding, genetics), 60. *Prof Exp:* Asst farm crops, Ore State Univ, 55-56, fiber crops, 56-59, jr agronomist, 59-61; asst prof agron, Univ Baghdad, 61; sr res technician, 62-65, SPECIALIST & SUPT RES & ADMIN, TULELAKE FIELD STA, UNIV CALIF, 65- *Mem:* AAAS; Am Soc Agron; Crop Sci Soc Am; Soil Sci Soc Am; Am Genetic Asn. *Res:* Breeding, genetics, pollen physiology and other physiological aspects of cereal, oil and forage crops. *Mailing Add:* Tulelake Field Sta Univ of Calif Tulelake CA 96134

PURIFOY, DOROTHY JANE MARTIN, virology, molecular biology, see previous edition

PURISCH, STEVEN DONALD, b New York, NY, Mar 25, 45; div; c 1. TOPOLOGY. *Educ:* Carnegie-Mellon Univ, BS, 67, PhD(math), 73; Univ Wis-Madison, MA, 69. *Prof Exp:* Asst prof math, Rust Col, 73-74; lectr, Univ Ibadan, Nigeria, 74-78; vis asst prof, State Univ NY, Oswego, 78-79, Lehigh Univ, 79-81; ASST PROF MATH, LAFAYETTE COL, 81- *Concurrent Pos:* Vis lectr, Univ Toronto, 78. *Mem:* Am Math Soc. *Res:* General topology particularly total orderabiltiy and suborderability; categorical topology. *Mailing Add:* Dept Math Lafayette Col Easton PA 18042

PURKERSON, MABEL LOUISE, b Goldville, SC, Apr 3, 31. MEDICAL SCIENCE, NEPHROLOGY. *Educ:* Erskine Col, AB, 51; Med Univ SC, MD, 56. *Prof Exp:* Intern, St Louis City Hosp, Mo, 56-57; resident pediat, St Louis Children's Hosp, 57-60, fel pediat metab, 60-62; instr pediat, 62-67, from instr to asst prof med, 66-76, ASSOC PROF MED & ASSOC DEAN CURRIC, SCH MED, WASH UNIV, 76-, ASST PROF PEDIAT, 67- *Concurrent Pos:* Vis asst prof anat & spec fel, Dept Anat, Col Physicians & Surgeons, Columbia Univ, 71-72; asst physician, Barnes Hosp, St Louis; chief nephrol, Med Serv, Wash Univ, John Cochran Vet Admin Med Ctr, 73-76, res grantee, 73-78; mem merit rev bd, Nephrol, Vet Admin Cent Off, 77-80. *Mem:* Sigma Xi; Am Soc Nephrol; Int Soc Nephrol; Am Soc Pediat Nephrol; Am Fedn Clin Res. *Res:* Renal physiology, notably pathophysiology of kidney. *Mailing Add:* Renal Div Dept Internal Med Box 8126 Wash Univ Sch Med 660 Euclid Ave St Louis MO 63110

PURKETT, CHARLES A, JR, b Havre, Mont, May 23, 25; m 46; c 5. FISH BIOLOGY. *Educ:* Mont State Col, BS, 49, MS, 50. *Prof Exp:* Fishery biologist, 50-61, asst supt fisheries, 61-64, chief div fisheries, 64-78, ASST DIR, MO DEPT CONSERV, 78- *Concurrent Pos:* Mem, Upper Miss River Conserv Comt, 59-63, Univ Mo Coop Fishery Unit, 64-, Coop Fish Dis Study Steering Comt, Auburn Univ, 73-75, & Sch Forestry, Fisheries and Wildlife Adv Coun, Univ Mo, 75- *Mem:* Am Fisheries Soc; Int Asn Game, Fish & Conserv Comnrs. *Res:* Life history of paddlefish; fish growth and populations, photography; fishery administration. *Mailing Add:* Mo Dept of Conserv PO Box 180 Jefferson City MO 65101

PURKHISER, E DALE, b Reynolds, Ind, Aug 8, 31; m 60; c 3. ANIMAL NUTRITION, BIOCHEMISTRY. *Educ:* Purdue Univ, Lafayette, BS, 57, PhD(animal nutrit), 62; Mich State Univ, MS, 58. *Prof Exp:* Asst prof animal sci, Rutgers Univ, 61-63 & Univ Ky, 63-67; SWINE SPECIALIST, AGR EXTEN OFF, MICH STATE UNIV, 67- *Concurrent Pos:* Mem, Swine Exten Adv Comt, USDA & Southern Regional Swine Exten Comt, USDA, 63-67. *Mem:* Am Soc Animal Sci; Am Chem Soc. *Res:* Swine nutrition; monogastric nutrition; physiology; reproductive physiology; animal breeding. *Mailing Add:* Agr Exten Off Mich State Univ Cassopolis MI 49031

PURKIS, IAN EDWARD, b London, Eng, July 22, 25; m 47; c 2. ANESTHESIOLOGY. *Educ:* Univ London, MB, BS, 53. *Prof Exp:* Registr anesthesia, St Thomas Hosp, London, Eng, 55-57; from asst prof to assoc prof, 58-74, PROF ANESTHESIA, DALHOUSIE UNIV,74- *Concurrent Pos:* Clin fel, Royal Victoria Hosp, Montreal, Que, 57-58; chmn, Respiratory Curric Comt, 75-, Dalhousie Univ, asst dir, Continuing Med Educ, 76- *Mem:* Can Anesthetists Soc (pres, 66-67); Acad Anesthesiol. *Res:* Pharmacological action of drugs in anesthesia; medical education. *Mailing Add:* Dept of Anesthesia Dalhousie Univ Halifax NS B3H 3J5 Can

PURKO, JOHN, b Telacze, Ukraine, Feb 29, 29; Can citizen; m 52; c 4. DEVELOPMENTAL BIOLOGY. *Educ:* Univ Western Ont, BA, 52, MSc, 58, PhD(biochem), 63. *Prof Exp:* Instr biol, St Francis Xavier Univ, 53-56; res asst med res, Univ Western Ont, 58-59; Nat Cancer Inst Can fels, Chester Beatty Res Inst, Univ London, 63-65 & Cancer Res Lab, Univ Western Ont, 65-66; from asst prof to assoc prof develop biol, 66-77, ASSOC PROF ZOOL, UNIV WESTERN ONT, 68- *Mem:* Can Biochem Soc; Can Soc Cell Biologists. *Res:* Regulation and role of macromolecular, nucleic acid and protein synthesis in early teleost development; integrity and role of chorion in teleost development; biological action of alkylating agents in embryogenesis. *Mailing Add:* Dept of Zool Fac of Sci Univ of Western Ont London ON N6A 5B8 Can

PURL, O(LIVER) THOMAS, b East St Louis, Ill, June 5, 24; m 48; c 2. ELECTRICAL ENGINEERING. *Educ:* Univ Ill, BS, 48 & 51, MS, 52, PhD(elec eng), 55. *Prof Exp:* Res engr, Collins Radio Co, Iowa, 48-49; asst phys electronics, Univ Ill, 50-54, res assoc, 54-55; mem tech staff, Res Labs, Hughes Aircraft Co, 55-57, sr mem tech staff & head power tube sect, Microwave Tube Dept, 57-58; mem tech staff, 58-66, vpres & mgr electron devices group, 67-78, vpres & mgr systs group, 78-81, VPRES SHAREOWNER RELS & PLANNING COORD, WATKINS-JOHNSON CO, 81- *Mem:* Am Meteorol Soc; Sigma Xi; sr mem Inst Elec & Electronics Engrs. *Res:* Microwave electron devices, particularly microwave tubes. *Mailing Add:* 466 La Mesa Court Menlo Park CA 94025

PURNELL, DALLAS MICHAEL, b Tacoma, Wash, July 9, 39; m 72; c 2. EXPERIMENTAL PATHOLOGY, CANCER. *Educ:* Univ Puget Sound, BS, 63; Idaho State Univ, MS, 65; Univ Wash, PhD(exp path), 71. *Prof Exp:* Res asst, Pa State Univ, 72-73, instr, 73-75, asst prof path, Hershey Med Ctr, 75-77; ASSOC PROF PATH, SCH MED, UNIV MD, BALTIMORE, 77- *Concurrent Pos:* Fel path, Hershey Med Ctr, Pa State Univ, 71-72. *Mem:* Am Asn Pathologists Am Asn Cancer Res; AAAS; Int Soc Human & Animal Mycol; Nat Acad Sci. *Res:* Mammary gland biology; mammary neoplasia and preneoplasia; fungal pathogenicity and genetics; cancer biology. *Mailing Add:* Dept of Path 660 W Redwood St Baltimore MD 21201

PURO, DONALD GEORGE, b Elmira, NY, Nov 2, 47; m 75; c 2. OPHTHALMOLOGY, NEUROBIOLOGY. *Educ:* Univ Pa, BA, 69; Univ Rochester, MD, 74, PhD(physiol), 75; Am Bd Opthal, Dipl, 81. *Prof Exp:* Intern path, Univ Rochester, 74-75; res assoc pharmacol, NIH, 75-77; resident ophthal, Bascom Palmer Eye Inst, Univ Miami, 77-80; MED OFF OPTHAL, NAT EYE INST, NIH, 80- *Mem:* Soc Neurosci; Asn Res Vision & Opthal. *Res:* Informaton basic to understanding retinal disorders at a cellular level; technologies of neuropharmacology; intracellular electrophysiology; cell biology and culture. *Mailing Add:* Bldg 6 Rm 210 Nat Eye Inst NIH Bethesda MD 20205

PUROHIT, SURENDRA NATH, reactor physics, nuclear physics, see previous edition

PURPLE, RICHARD L, b Cooperstown, NY, Oct 1, 36; m 60; c 4. PHYSIOLOGY, NEUROPHYSIOLOGY. *Educ:* Hamilton Col, AB, 58; Rockefeller Univ, PhD(life sci), 64. *Prof Exp:* From instr to assoc prof, 64-76, PROF PHYSIOL, SCH MED, UNIV MINN, MINNEAPOLIS, 76-, JOINT PROF PHYSIOL & OPHTHAL, 78-, DIR ELECTRORETINOGRAPHY LAB, DEPT OPHTHAL, 75- *Concurrent Pos:* Lectr, Gen Exten Div, Univ Calif, Berkeley, 67; consult, reading comt screening grad applns fel support, Danforth Found, 67-68. *Mem:* AAAS; Am Physiol Soc; Soc Neurosci. *Res:* Neurophysiology of sensory systems; integrative mechanisms of single cells in the visual system; systems analysis of sensory pathways. *Mailing Add:* 424 Millard Hall Univ of Minn Minneapolis MN 55455

PURPURA, DOMINICK PAUL, b New York, NY, Apr 2, 27; m 48; c 4. NEUROPHYSIOLOGY. *Educ:* Columbia Univ, AB, 49; Harvard Med Sch, MD, 53. *Prof Exp:* Assoc prof neurosurg res, Col Physicians & Surgeons, Columbia Univ, 58-66; prof anat & chmn dept, 66-76, PROF & CHMN NEUROSCI DEPT, ALBERT EINSTEIN COL MED, 76-, DIR

KENNEDY CTR RES MENT RETARDATION, 72- *Mem:* Am Physiol Soc; Am Acad Neurol; Am Asn Anat. *Res:* Neuroanatomy; neuropharmacology; functions of cerebral cortex and related structures. *Mailing Add:* Dept of Neurosci Albert Einstein Col of Med Bronx NY 10461

PURPURA, JAMES A(RTHUR), civil engineering, see previous edition

PURRINGTON, ROBERT DANIEL, b Alamosa, Colo, Apr 11, 36; m 59; c 4. THEORETICAL NUCLEAR PHYSICS. *Educ:* Tex A&M Univ, BS, 58, MS, 63, PhD(physics), 66. *Prof Exp:* From asst prof to assoc prof, 66-74, PROF PHYSICS, TULANE UNIV LA, 75- *Mem:* Sigma Xi; Am Phys Soc. *Res:* Study of few-nucleon systems; three-body theory of direct reactions; coupled-channel treatment of few nucleon reactions and of nuclear inelastic scattering; excitations of vibrational nuclei. *Mailing Add:* Dept of Physics Tulane Univ New Orleans LA 70118

PURRINGTON, SUZANNE T, b New York, NY, Apr 30, 38; m 63; c 3. ORGANIC CHEMISTRY. *Educ:* Wheaton Col, Mass, AB, 60; Radcliffe Col, AM, 62; Harvard Univ, PhD(chem), 63. *Prof Exp:* Fel & instr chem, Duke Univ, 63-65; from asst prof to assoc prof chem, Shaw Univ, 65-68; assoc prof chem, NY Inst Technol, 68-70; chmn chem, Peace Col, 72-77; ASST PROF CHEM, NC STATE UNIV, 78-; CONSULT, 69- *Concurrent Pos:* Petrol Res Fund grant, 65-67. *Mem:* Am Chem Soc. *Res:* Free radicals and fluorine chemistry. *Mailing Add:* Dept of Chem NC State Univ Raleigh NC 27650

PURSEL, VERNON GEORGE, b Yerington, Nev, Nov 11, 36; m 76; c 2. PHYSIOLOGY, ANIMAL SCIENCE. *Educ:* Univ Nev, BS, 58; Univ Minn, MS, 61, PhD(dairy husb), 65. *Prof Exp:* Instr dairy sci, Univ Minn, 64-65, asst prof, 65-67; RES PHYSIOLOGIST, REPRODUCTION LAB, AGR RES, USDA, 67- *Mem:* Soc Study Reproduction; Am Soc Animal Sci. *Res:* Control of estrus and ovulation; freezing of porcine spermatozoa; phospholipids and fatty acids of bovine and porcine spermatozoa. *Mailing Add:* Reproduction Lab Agr Res USDA Beltsville MD 20705

PURSELL, LYLE EUGENE, b Paola, Kans, Apr 23, 26; m 50; c 4. MATHEMATICAL ANALYSIS. *Educ:* Purdue Univ, BS, 49, MS, 50, PhD(math), 52. *Prof Exp:* Instr math, Ohio State Univ, 52-55; from asst prof to assoc prof math, Grinnell Col, 55-67; assoc prof, 67-68, PROF MATH, UNIV MO-ROLLA, 68- *Concurrent Pos:* Vis asst prof math, Purdue Univ, 58-59; vis fel, Dartmouth Col, 64. *Mem:* Am Math Soc; Math Asn Am. *Res:* Rings of real functions and their transformation groups; non-Archimedean ordered fields. *Mailing Add:* Dept of Math Univ of Mo Rolla MO 65401

PURSELL, MARY HELEN, b Philadelphia, Pa, July 5, 39; m 71. GENETICS. *Educ:* Glassboro State Col, BA, 63, MA, 66; Pa State Univ, PhD(genetics), 75. *Prof Exp:* Teacher high sch, NJ, 63-65; asst prof biol, Glassboro State Col, 66-68; ASSOC PROF BIOL, LOCK HAVEN STATE COL, 75- *Mem:* Genetics Soc Am; AAAS. *Res:* DNA evolution in lower vascular plants. *Mailing Add:* Dept Biol Lock Haven State Col Lock Haven PA 17745

PURSELL, RONALD A, b Pa, Dec 7, 30; m 71. BOTANY. *Educ:* Pa State Univ, BS, 52, MS, 54; Fla State Univ, PhD, 57. *Prof Exp:* Actg asst prof biol, Univ Colo, 57-58; instr bot, Univ Tenn, 58-59; instr bot, sch forestry, 59-63, from asst prof to assoc prof, 63-77, PROF BOT, PA STATE UNIV, 77- *Mem:* Am Bryol & Lichenological Soc (vpres, 73-75, pres, 75-77); Am Soc Plant Taxon; Int Asn Plant Taxon; Bot Soc Am. *Res:* Taxonomy and geography of bryophytes. *Mailing Add:* Dept of Biol Buckhout Lab Pa State Univ University Park PA 16802

PURSER, FRED O, b Greenville, NC, June 6, 31; m 55; c 4. NUCLEAR PHYSICS, PARTICLE PHYSICS. *Educ:* US Naval Acad, BS, 53; Duke Univ, PhD(nuclear physics), 66. *Prof Exp:* RES ASSOC, DUKE UNIV, 66-, ASST TO DIR, TRIANGLE UNIVS NUCLEAR LAB & PROJ ENGR, CYCLO-GRAAFF PROJ, 68- *Mem:* Am Phys Soc. *Res:* Nuclear structure; nuclear fission; particle accelerator development. *Mailing Add:* Dept of Physics 3425 Cromwell Rd Durham NC 27705

PURSGLOVE, LAURENCE ALBERT, b Pa, July 29, 24; m 44; c 5. SCIENCE WRITING, COMPUTER SCIENCE. *Educ:* Carnegie Inst Technol, BS, 44, MS, 47, ScD(org chem), 49. *Prof Exp:* Jr chem engr, Minn Mining & Mfg Co, 44-46; consult, Food Mach Corp, 47-48; asst prof chem, WVa Univ, 49-53; chemist, Dow Chem Co, 53-59; instr chem, Bay City Jr Col, 59-61; asst prof chem, Delta Col, 61-63; SCI WRITING, COMPUT PROG, TRANSLATING & CONSULT, 64- *Concurrent Pos:* Chemist, US Bur Mines, 51-53. *Mem:* Am Chem Soc. *Res:* Heterocyclic synthesis; metabolite antagonists; programed self-instruction; educational technology; computer programing. *Mailing Add:* R R 1 Laingsburg MI 48848

PURSLEY, MICHAEL BADER, b Winchester, Ind, Aug 10, 45; m 68; c 1. COMMUNICATIONS SYSTEMS, INFORMATION THEORY. *Educ:* Purdue Univ, BS, 67, MS, 68; Univ Southern Calif, PhD(elec eng), 74. *Prof Exp:* Engr, Northrop Corp, 68; staff engr commun, Hughes Aircraft Co, 68-74; asst prof, 74-77, assoc prof elec eng, 77-80, PROF ELEC ENG, UNIV ILL, URBANA, 80- *Concurrent Pos:* Actg asst prof syst sci, Univ Calif, Los Angeles, 74; prin investr, NSF grants, 76-80, 76-78 & 78-80 & Army Res Off grant; consult, Army Res Off, 77-78 & Int Tel & Tel, 78-; assoc mem, Ctr Advan Study, Univ Ill, 80-81. *Mem:* Sr mem Inst Elec & Electronics Engrs; Inst Math Statist. *Res:* Communications systems, information theory and error-control coding with emphasis on spread spectrum communications, universal data compression and rate distortion theory. *Mailing Add:* Coord Sci Lab Univ of Ill 1101 W Springfield Ave Urbana IL 61801

PURTON, CHRISTOPHER ROGER, b Toronto, Ont, Sept 10, 38; m 61, 69; c 3. ASTRONOMY. *Educ:* Univ Toronto, BA, 60, MA, 62; Cambridge Univ, PhD(astron), 66. *Prof Exp:* Asst res officer astron, Nat Res Coun Can, 66-68; asst prof, 68-72, ASSOC PROF PHYSICS, YORK UNIV, 72- *Mem:* Royal Astron Soc Can; Royal Astron Soc; Am Astron Soc. *Res:* Radio astronomy. *Mailing Add:* Div of Physics/CRESS York Univ Toronto ON M3J 1P3 Can

PURUSHOTHAMAN, KRISHNIER, civil & environmental health engineering, see previous edition

PURVES, DALE, b Philadelphia, Pa, Mar 11, 38; m 68; c 2. NEUROBIOLOGY. *Educ:* Yale Univ, BA, 60; Harvard Univ, MD, 64. *Prof Exp:* From asst prof to assoc prof, 73-79, PROF PHYSIOL & NEUROBIOL, MED SCH, WASHINGTON UNIV, 79- *Res:* Formation and maintenance of synaptic connections. *Mailing Add:* Dept Physiol & Biophysics Sch Med Washington Univ St Louis MO 63110

PURVES, ROBERT BYRON, acoustics, see previous edition

PURVES, WILLIAM KIRKWOOD, b Sacramento, Calif, Oct 28, 34; m 59; c 1. PLANT PHYSIOLOGY. *Educ:* Calif Inst Technol, BS, 56; Yale Univ, MS, 57, PhD(bot), 59. *Prof Exp:* NSF fel, Univ Tübingen, Ger, 59-60; Nat Cancer Inst fel, Univ Calif, Los Angeles, 60-61; asst prof bot, Univ Calif, Santa Barbara, 61-65, assoc prof biochem, 65-70, prof biol, 70-73, chmn dept biol sci, 72-73; prof biol & head Biol Sci Group, Univ Conn, 73-77; STUART MUDD PROF BIOL, HARVEY MUDD COL, 77- *Concurrent Pos:* Res collabr, Brookhaven Nat Lab, 65, 66; NSF sr fel, Univ London, 67, Harvard Univ, 68; adj prof plant physiol, Univ Calif, Riverside, 79- *Mem:* Fel AAAS; Sigma Xi; Am Soc Plant Physiol; Am Inst Biol Sci. *Res:* Chemical and physical regulation of plant cell expansion; enzymology. *Mailing Add:* Dept Biol Harvey Mudd Col Claremont CA 91711

PURVIS, COLBERT THAXTON, b Odum, Ga, May 31, 20; m 41; c 2. MATHEMATICS. *Educ:* Ga Teachers Col, BS, 41; ETex State Teachers Col, MS, 48; Peabody Col, PhD(math), 57. *Prof Exp:* From instr to asst prof math, Ga Inst Technol, 46-60; PROF MATH, CALIF STATE UNIV, HAYWARD, 60- *Concurrent Pos:* Dir & teacher, NSF Insts Teachers Math. *Mem:* Nat Coun Teachers Math. *Mailing Add:* Dept of Math Calif State Univ Hayward CA 94542

PURVIS, GEORGE ALLEN, b Las Animas, Colo, Mar 30, 33; m 59; c 4. FOOD SCIENCE, NUTRITION. *Educ:* Colo State Univ, BS, 54, MS, 62; Mich State Univ, East Lansing, PhD(food sci, nutrit), 69. *Prof Exp:* Mgt trainee, Safeway Stores, Inc, 54-58; state chemist, Colo Dept Agr, 58-60; res assoc, Colo Exp Sta, Ft Collins, 60-62 & Ohio Exp Sta, Columbus, 62-63; lab mgr, 63-69, res mgr nutrit, 69-71, dir nutrit, 77-80, VPRES NUTRIT SCI, GERBER PROD CO, 80- *Mem:* Inst Food Technologists; NY Acad Sci; Am Inst Nutrit; Soc Nutrit Educ; Sigma Xi. *Res:* Research management in food and nutrition related to infants; evaluation of infant nutrition status in the United States; evaluation and design of foods for infants. *Mailing Add:* Gerber Prod Co 445 State St Fremont MI 49412

PURVIS, JOHN C, b Ruby, SC, Sept 26, 19. METEOROLOGY, HYDROLOGY. *Educ:* Wake Forest Univ, BS, 40; Univ SC, MS, 66. *Prof Exp:* Asst meteorologist, US Weather Bur, 40-47; METEOROLOGIST-IN-CHG, NAT WEATHER SERV, 47- *Concurrent Pos:* Teacher, Dept Geog, Univ SC, 68- *Honors & Awards:* Bronze Medal Award, Nat Weather Serv, 68. *Mem:* Am Meteorol Soc. *Mailing Add:* 701 Naples Ave Cayce SC 29033

PURVIS, JOHN L, b Montclair, NJ, Mar 3, 26; m 64; BIOCHEMISTRY. BIOCHEMISTRY. *Educ:* McGill Univ, BSc, 52, MSc, 54, PhD, 56. *Prof Exp:* Res fel, Univ Amsterdam, 56-58 & Brandeis Univ, 59-61; assoc prof, 61-69, chmn dept, 66-77, PROF BIOCHEM, UNIV RI, 69- *Mem:* Am Chem Soc. *Res:* Pyridine nucleotides; oxidative phosphorylation; steroid biochemistry. *Mailing Add:* Dept of Biochem Univ of RI Kingston RI 02879

PURVIS, MERTON BROWN, b Dubuque, Iowa, Feb 16, 23; m 44; c 7. MECHANICAL ENGINEERING, APPLIED PHYSICS. *Educ:* Iowa State Univ, BS, 44, MS, 49; Pa State Univ, PhD(mech eng), 54. *Prof Exp:* Engr, Hardsocg Pneumatic Tool Co, Iowa, 46-48; instr mech eng, Iowa State Univ, 48-49; from instr to asst prof, Pa State Univ, 49-55; mem tech staff appl optics, 55-58, supvr appl optics & magnetics, 58-69, HEAD, DEPT ELECTROMECH COMPONENTS, BELL TEL LABS, INC, 69- *Concurrent Pos:* Chmn comt C83.1, Am Nat Standards Inst. *Mem:* AAAS; Am Soc Mech Engrs. *Res:* Design and development on optical and photographic systems for computer memory, on switching matrices for both voice and radio frequencies, on relays, switches and manual apparatus for the Bell System. *Mailing Add:* Bell Tel Labs Inc 6200 E Broad Columbus OH 43213

PUSCH, ALLEN LEWIS, b Richmond, Va, July 4, 34; m 55; c 3. CLINICAL PATHOLOGY. *Educ:* Johns Hopkins Univ, BA, 56, MD, 60; Am Bd Path, dipl & cert anat & clin path, 68. *Prof Exp:* From intern to asst resident path, Johns Hopkins Hosp, 60-64; resident clin path, 64-65, asst prof path, 67-71, ASSOC PROF PATH, STATE UNIV NY UPSTATE MED CTR, 71-, DIR MED TECH PROGS, 78- *Concurrent Pos:* Fel path, Johns Hopkins Univ, 60-64. *Mem:* AAAS; Am Soc Clin Path; Am Soc Microbiol; Am Soc Cytol. *Res:* Congenital heart disease; diseases of skeletal muscle with emphasis on muscular dystrophy; infectious diseases; resistant transfer factor in bacteria; immunoglobulins in man. *Mailing Add:* Dept of Med Tech Upstate Med Ctr Syracuse NY 13210

PUSHKAR, PAUL, b Winnipeg, Man, Dec 14, 36; m 60. GEOLOGY, GEOCHEMISTRY. *Educ:* Univ Man, BSc, 59; Univ Calif, San Diego, PhD(earth sci), 66. *Prof Exp:* Asst prof geol, Algoma Col, 67-68; asst prof to assoc prof, 68-78, PROF GEOL, WRIGHT STATE UNIV, 78- *Mem:* Geol Soc Am; AAAS; Geochem Soc; Sigma Xi; Tobacco Root Geol Asn. *Res:* Geochemistry of strontium isotopes; petrology of igneous rocks. *Mailing Add:* Dept Geol Wright State Univ Dayton OH 45431

PUSKI, GABOR, b Budapest, Hungary, Jan 2, 38; US citizen; m 62; c 3. FOOD SCIENCE, BIOCHEMISTRY. *Educ:* Univ Toronto, BA, 63; Univ Mass, Amherst, PhD(food sci & technol), 66. *Prof Exp:* Chemist, Food & Drug Directorate, Can, 63; res scientist, Carnation Res Labs, Calif, 66-70; sr res scientist-group leader food sci res, Food Res Lab, Cent Soya, 70-74, group leader explor protein res, 74-78; GROUP LEADER PROTEIN LAB, KRAFT, INC, 78- *Mem:* Am Chem Soc; Inst Food Technol; Am Asn Cereal Chem. *Res:* Process development for vegetable protein products. *Mailing Add:* Kraft Inc 801 Waukegan Rd Glenview IL 60025

PUSKIN, JEROME SANFORD, b Akron, Ohio, Oct 15, 42; m 69. BIOPHYSICS. *Educ:* Johns Hopkins Univ, BA, 64; Harvard Univ, MA, 66, PhD(physics), 70. *Prof Exp:* NIH fel, 70-74, ASST PROF BIOPHYS, UNIV ROCHESTER, 74- *Mem:* Biophys Soc. *Res:* Mitochondrial ion transport; ion binding to membranes; electron paramagnetic resonance. *Mailing Add:* Dept of Radiation Biol & Biophys Univ of Rochester Sch Med & Dent Rochester NY 14620

PUSZKIN, SAUL, b Tucuman, Arg, Feb 3, 38; US citizen; m 62; c 2. CELL BIOLOGY, NEUROBIOLOGY. *Educ:* Univ Tucuman, BS, 60, MS, 63, PhD(biochem), 68. *Prof Exp:* Asst neurol, Col Physicians & Surgeons, Columbia Univ, 68-70, res assoc neurochem & neurol, 70-72; res asst prof, 72-77, res assoc prof, 77-80, PROF PATH, MT SINAI SCH MED, 80- *Concurrent Pos:* Estab investr path, Am Heart Asn, 74- *Mem:* Am Soc Biol Chemists; Am Soc Neurochem; Am Heart Asn; Biophys Soc. *Res:* Protein chemistry and function of contractile systems from muscle and nonmuscle tissues. *Mailing Add:* Mt Sinai Sch of Med Dept of Path 100th St & Fifth Ave New York NY 10029

PUTALA, EUGENE CHARLES, b Turnersfalls, Mass, Oct 7, 22; m 61; c 2. BOTANY. *Educ:* Univ Mass, BS, 50, MS, 52; Univ Calif, PhD, 67. *Prof Exp:* From instr to asst prof bot, Univ Mass, 50-68; prof bot, Kirkland Col, 68-78, chmn div sci, 68-70; PROF BOT, HAMILTON COL, 78- *Res:* Plant morphology and anatomy; plant microtechnique and ultrastructure. *Mailing Add:* Biol Dept Hamilton Col Clinton NY 13323

PUTERBAUGH, WALTER HENRY, organic chemistry, deceased

PUTHOFF, HAROLD EDWARD, b Chicago, Ill, June 20, 36; m 74; c 3. QUANTUM PHYSICS. *Educ:* Univ Fla, BEE, 58, MSE, 60; Stanford Univ, PhD(elec eng), 67. *Prof Exp:* Res engr comput design, Gen Eng Lab, Gen Elec Co, Schenectady, NY, 58; Sperry res fel microwave eng, Univ Fla, 58-59; res engr microwave tube eng, Sperry Electronic Tube Div, Gainesville, Fla, 59-60; res engr comput, Nat Security Agency, Ft Meade, Md, 60-63; res assoc quantum electronics & lasers, Hansen Labs, Stanford Univ, 63-71; SR RES ENGR EXTRASENSORY PERCEPTION, SRI INT, 71- *Concurrent Pos:* Lectr elec eng, Stanford Univ, 69-70. *Mem:* AAAS; Inst Elec & Electronics Engrs; Am Phys Soc; Sigma Xi; fel Am Soc Psychical Res. *Res:* Laser research and development; quantum electronics; electron beam and microwave tube research; parapsychological phenomena; investigation of paranormal perceptual abilities. *Mailing Add:* SRI Int 333 Ravenswood Ave Menlo Park CA 94025

PUTMAN, DONALD LEE, b Cuero, Tex, Apr 26, 44; m 69; c 3. MICROBIOLOGY. *Educ:* Lamar Univ, BS, 66; George Washington Univ, PhD(microbiol), 76. *Prof Exp:* Teaching fel microbiol, George Washington Univ, 71-74; sr lab technician immunol, 74-76, investr immunol, 76-79, GENETIC TOXICOLOGIST, MICROBIOL ASSOC, 79- *Mem:* Am Soc Microbiol; Environ Mutagen Soc. *Res:* Chemical mutagenesis; chemical carcinogenesis; immunology; cellular biology. *Mailing Add:* Microbial Assoc 5221 River Rd Bethesda MD 20016

PUTMAN, EDISON WALKER, b Omaha, Nebr, Oct 31, 16; m 44; c 2. PLANT BIOCHEMISTRY. *Educ:* Univ Calif, Berkeley, AB, 42, PhD(plant physiol), 52. *Prof Exp:* From jr res biochemist to asst res biochemist, Univ Calif, Berkeley, 52-59; ASSOC PLANT PHYSIOLOGIST, EXP STA, UNIV HAWAII, 59- *Mem:* Am Chem Soc; Am Soc Biol Chem. *Res:* Carbohydrate metabolism in plants; structural analysis of carbohydrates; biochemical preparations of C-14 labeled compounds; intermediary metabolism in mineral deficient plant tissue. *Mailing Add:* Dept Bot Univ Hawaii 3190 Maile Way Honolulu HI 96822

PUTMAN, GEORGE WENDELL, b Schenectady, NY, Dec 11, 29; m 57; c 2. GEOLOGY, GEOCHEMISTRY. *Educ:* Union Col, NY, BS, 51; Pa State Univ, MS, 58, PhD(geol, geochem), 61. *Prof Exp:* Assoc geochemist, Calif Div Mines & Geol, 61-66; chmn dept geol sci, 72-73, ASSOC PROF GEOL & GEOCHEM, STATE UNIV NY ALBANY, 66- *Mem:* Geol Soc Am; Am Geophys Union. *Res:* Igneous and metamorphic petrology and geochemistry. *Mailing Add:* Dept of Geol Sci State Univ of NY Albany NY 12222

PUTMAN, THOMAS HAROLD, b Pittsburgh, Pa, Nov 22, 30; m 56; c 3. CONTROL SYSTEMS DESIGN, POWER ELECTRONICS. *Educ:* Union Col, BS, 52; Mass Inst Technol, SM, 54, ScD(elec eng), 58. *Prof Exp:* MGR ELECTROMECH TECHNOL & CONSULT ENGR, RES & DEVELOP CTR, RES LABS, WESTINGHOUSE ELEC CORP, 58- *Mem:* Inst Elec & Electronics Engrs; Soc Naval Archit & Marine Engrs. *Res:* Application of disciplines of field theory, circuit theory, mechanics, hydraulics, heat transfer to design and development of all types of electromechanical equipment, control systems, electric drives, static var generators, power systems, magnetic circuits and transformers. *Mailing Add:* 354 Stoneledge Dr Pittsburgh PA 15235

PUTNAM, ABBOTT (ALLEN), b Wellsboro, Pa, Nov 24, 20; m 42; c 2. ENGINEERING. *Educ:* Cornell Univ, BME, 42. *Prof Exp:* Jr engr, Dravo Corp, Pa, 42-43; instr, Cornell Univ, 43-44; res engr, 46-52, asst div chief, 53-58, div consult, 59-60, staff mech engr, 60-65, FEL, BATTELLE MEM INST, 65- *Concurrent Pos:* Mech engr, Nat Adv Comt Aeronaut, Langley Field, Va. *Mem:* Am Soc Mech Engrs; Am Inst Aeronaut & Astronaut; Combustion Inst; Brit Inst Energy. *Res:* Gas dynamics of combustion systems, including flame holding, spreading and turbulence; flame driven oscillations; impaction and diffusion of particles; fluid flow modeling; combustion roar; pulse combustion. *Mailing Add:* Battelle Columbus Labs 505 King Ave Columbus OH 43201

PUTNAM, ALAN R, b Keene, NH, Apr 3, 39; m 70; c 3. WEED SCIENCE, HORTICULTURE. *Educ:* Univ NH, BS, 61; Mich State Univ, MS, 63, PhD(plant physiol), 66. *Prof Exp:* Res asst hort, 61-66, asst prof, 66-70, assoc prof, 70-74, PROF WEED SCI, MICH STATE UNIV, 74- *Mem:* Weed Sci Soc Am; Ctr Appl Sci & Technol; Soc Am Hort Sci; Sigma Xi. *Res:* Weed biology, ecology and weed crop interaction; allelopathy and plant competition; herbicide action and fate in agroecosystems. *Mailing Add:* 105 Pesticide Res Ctr Mich State Univ East Lansing MI 48824

PUTNAM, ALFRED LUNT, b Dunkirk, NY, Mar 10, 16; m 66. MATHEMATICS. *Educ:* Hamilton Col, BS, 38; Harvard Univ, AM, 39, PhD(math), 42. *Prof Exp:* Instr math, Yale Univ, 42-45; from asst prof to assoc prof, 45-63, PROF MATH, UNIV CHICAGO, 63- *Concurrent Pos:* Fulbright fel, Western Australia, 60; NSF sci faculty fel, 66-67. *Mem:* AAAS; Am Math Soc; Math Asn Am. *Res:* Origins and development of abstract algebra. *Mailing Add:* Dept of Math Univ of Chicago Chicago IL 60637

PUTNAM, CALVIN RICHARD, b Baltimore, Md, May 25, 24; m 52; c 3. MATHEMATICS. *Educ:* Johns Hopkins Univ, AB, 44, MA, 46, PhD(math), 48. *Prof Exp:* Instr math, Johns Hopkins Univ, 48-50; mem, Inst Adv Study, NJ, 50-51; from asst prof to assoc prof, 51-59, PROF MATH, PURDUE UNIV, W LAFAYETTE, 59- *Mem:* Am Math Soc; Math Asn Am. *Res:* Singular boundary value problems; differential equations; operator theory; hyponormal operators. *Mailing Add:* Dept of Math Purdue Univ West Lafayette IN 47907

PUTNAM, FRANK WILLIAM, b New Britain, Conn, Aug 3, 17; m 42; c 2. BIOCHEMISTRY, IMMUNOLOGY. *Educ:* Wesleyan Univ, BA, 39, MA, 40; Univ Minn, PhD(biochem), 42. *Hon Degrees:* MA, Cambridge Univ, 73. *Prof Exp:* Instr & res assoc biochem, Sch Med, Duke Univ, 42-46; biochemist, Res & Develop Dept, US Chem Corps, Md, 46; asst prof biochem, Sch Med, Univ Chicago, 47-52, assoc prof, 52-55; prof & head dept, Col Med, Univ Fla, 55-65; prof biol & dir div biol sci, 65-69, prof molecular biol & biochem, 69-74, DISTINGUISHED PROF MOLECULAR BIOL & BIOCHEM, IND UNIV, BLOOMINGTON, 74- *Concurrent Pos:* Markle scholar; Lasdon fel, Cambridge Univ, 52-53; Guggenheim overseas fel, Churchill Col, 70; specialist educr, US Dept State, 56; ed, Arch Biochem & Biophys, 54-59; mem comt med biol, NSF, chmn adv comn instnl rels, Nat Adv Gen Med Sci Coun; chmn biophys study sect, NIH; chmn, Assembly of Life Sci, Nat Res Coun-Nat Acad Sci, 77-81; bd visitors, Duke Med Ctr, 70-75; Guggenheim fel, 70; ed, Proc Fedn Am Socs Exp Biol, 58-63, ed sci, 68-80, Immunochem, 72-75 & Biomed News, 69-73; overseas fel, Churchill Col, Cambridge Univ, 72-; mem bd trustees, Argonne Univ Asn, 81- *Honors & Awards:* Distinguished Serv Award, Univ Chicago Med Sch, Univ Minn & Wesleyan Univ. *Mem:* Nat Acad Sci; Am Asn Immunologists; fel Am Soc Biol Chemists (secy, 58-63); Fedn Am Socs Exp Biol. *Res:* Denaturation of proteins; isolation, physical chemistry and structure of plasma proteins, enzymes, toxins and viruses; isotopic study of protein synthesis and virus reproduction; immunoglobulins. *Mailing Add:* 206 Jordan Hall Dept Biol Ind Univ Bloomington IN 47405

PUTNAM, G(ARTH) L(OUIS), b Reardan, Wash, June 11, 13; m 38; c 3. CHEMICAL ENGINEERING. *Educ:* Univ Wash, Seattle, BS, 35, MS, 37; Columbia Univ, PhD(chem eng), 42. *Prof Exp:* Asst to Dr C G Fink, electrochem develop, Columbia Univ, 38-42; res engr, Carborundum Co, 42-46; assoc prof chem eng, Ore State Col, 46-47; res assoc, Univ Wash, Seattle, 47-51; CONSULT ENGR, 51- *Mem:* AAAS; Am Chem Soc. *Res:* Industrial and applied electrochemistry; prevention of scale and corrosion in heating systems; chemistry of gold; occupational health hazards. *Mailing Add:* 1628 N 167th St Seattle WA 98133

PUTNAM, HUGH D, b Carrington, NDak, Feb 12, 28; m 50; c 3. MICROBIOLOGY. *Educ:* Univ Minn, BA, 53, MS, 56, PhD(pub health, biol), 63. *Prof Exp:* Asst soil microbiol, Univ Minn, 52-54, asst microbiol, 54-55, instr sanit biol, 56-60, res fel microbiol, 60-63; from asst prof to prof microbiol, Univ Fla, 63-74; VPRES, WATER & AIR RES, INC, 74- *Concurrent Pos:* USPHS res grants, 64-68; comt mem, Assembly Life Sci, Nat Res Coun. *Mem:* Am Soc Testing & Mat; Am Soc Limnol & Oceanog; Water Pollution Control Fedn; Am Soc Microbiol; Ecol Soc Am. *Res:* Aquatic microbiolosgy, especially marine and fresh water phytoplankton and transformations of organic matter in sediments; lake eutrophication. *Mailing Add:* Water & Air Res Inc Gainesville FL 32602

PUTNAM, JERRY L, b Ft Worth, Tex, Dec 29, 39; m 59; c 2. COMPARATIVE ANATOMY, HISTOLOGY. *Educ:* Tex A&M Univ, BS, 65, MS, 67, PhD(zool), 70. *Prof Exp:* Asst prof biol, Holyoke Community Col, 70-73; asst prof, 73-80, ASSOC PROF BIOL, DAVIDSON COL, 80- *Mem:* Am Soc Zoologists; Am Soc Ichthyologists & Herpetologists. *Res:* Comparative anatomy and histology of the vertebrate heart with emphasis on the amphibians. *Mailing Add:* Dept of Biol Davidson Col Davidson NC 28036

PUTNAM, LOREN SMITH, b Morrison, Ill, Oct 24, 13; m 40; c 1. ORNITHOLOGY. *Educ:* Murray State Col, BS, 35; Ohio State Univ, MS, 41, PhD(zool), 47. *Prof Exp:* Asst ornith, F T Stone Lab, 41-42; civilian instr, US Dept Navy, 43-45; assoc prof zool & entom, 45-61, dir F T Stone Lab, 56-73, PROF ZOOL, OHIO STATE UNIV, 61- *Mem:* Wilson Ornith Soc; Am Ornith Union. *Res:* Biology of birds; bird behavior. *Mailing Add:* Dept of Zool Ohio State Univ 1735 Neil Ave Columbus OH 43210

PUTNAM, PAUL A, b Springfield, Vt, July 12, 30; m 56; c 4. ANIMAL NUTRITION, PHYSIOLOGY. *Educ:* Univ Vt, BS, 52; Wash State Univ, MS, 54; Cornell Univ, PhD(animal nutrit), 57. *Prof Exp:* Res animal husbandman, Animal Sci Res Div, 57-64, leader nutrit & mgt invest, 64-68, chief beef cattle res br, 68-72, asst dir, 72-80, DIR, BELTSVILLE AGR RES CTR, USDA, 80- *Mem:* Am Dairy Sci Asn; AAAS; Coun Agr Sci & Technol; Am Soc Animal Sci. *Res:* Ruminant nutrition, specifically feeding, management and physiology including physical form salivary secretion, feeding behavior, digestibility, digestibility indicators and noncompetitive feedstuffs. *Mailing Add:* Beltsville Agr Res Ctr USDA Agr Res Serv Beltsville MD 20705

PUTNAM, ROBERT CONRAD, b Boston, Mass, June 12, 14; m 44; c 2. ORGANIC CHEMISTRY. *Educ:* Harvard Univ, SB, 36, AM, 45; Boston Univ, PhD(chem), 51. *Prof Exp:* Res chemist, Rohm and Haas Co, 36-40; proj engr, United Shoe Mach Corp, 40-54; chief chemist, US Testing Co, 54-56; chief chemist, E F Drew Co, 57-60; chief chemist, US Testing Co, 60-61; anal supvr, M & T Chem, Inc, 62-67; anal supvr, Arkansas Co, 67-69; anal supvr, Foster D Snell, 69-71; pres, Polaris Chem Corp, 71-73; SR SCIENTIST, HAZARDS RES CORP, 74- *Mem:* Am Chem Soc. *Res:* Organic and inorganic synthesis and analysis; instrumentation; corrosion; waste treatment; organometallics; processing hazards research; tannins; textiles. *Mailing Add:* 147 Boulevard Mountain Lakes NJ 07046

PUTNAM, STEARNS TYLER, b Springfield, Vt, July 30, 17; m 40; c 3. PAPER CHEMISTRY, POLYMER CHEMISTRY. *Educ:* Brown Univ, ScB, 38; Harvard Univ, AM, 40, PhD(org chem), 42. *Prof Exp:* Asst org chem, Harvard Univ, 38-41, Nat Defense Res Comt, 41-42; res chemist, 42-46, res supvr, 46-71, res assoc, 71-79, SR RES ASSOC,, HERCULES INC, 79- *Mem:* Am Chem Soc; assoc Tech Asn Pulp & Paper Indust. *Res:* Carcinogenic hydrocarbons; terpenes and derivatives; rosin derivatives; fatty acid derivatives; paper chemicals; adhesives; polymers. *Mailing Add:* Apt 2 C4 400 Foulk Rd Wilmington DE 19803

PUTNAM, THOMAS MILTON, b Oakland, Calif, Jan 3, 45; m 70. COMPUTER SCIENCES. *Educ:* Univ Colo, BA, 66; Univ Wis-Madison, MS, 68. *Prof Exp:* Syst programmer time-sharing, Honeywell Inc, 68-72, supvr fed syst, Med Syst Ctr, 73-74, mgr res & develop, 74-77; assoc sr analyst info retrieval syst, Cindas, Purdue Univ, 77-79; MGR, USER SERV, PURDUE UNIV COMPUT CTR, 79- *Mem:* Asn Comput Mach. *Res:* Operating systems design; computer user education; computer networks. *Mailing Add:* Math Sci Bldg Purdue Univ Comput Ctr West Lafayette IN 47907

PUTNAM, THOMAS MILTON, JR, b Oakland, Calif, Feb 26, 22; m 43; c 2. SYSTEM SAFETY & SAFETY PROGRAM MANAGEMENT, EXPERIMENTAL NUCLEAR PHYSICS. *Educ:* Univ Calif, PhD(physics), 51. *Prof Exp:* Supvr 60 inch cyclotron, Radiation Lab, Univ Calif, Berkeley, 44-52; mem staff, Physics Div, 52-58, group leader, Sherwood Eng Group, 59-64, group leader, Accelerator Controls & Instrumentation Group, Los Alamos Meson Physics Facil, 65-72, ASST DIV LEADER, MEDIUM ENERGY PHYSICS DIV & LAMPF SAFETY OFFICER, LOS ALAMOS NAT LAB, 72- *Mem:* Am Phys Soc; Health Physics Soc; Systs Safety Soc. *Res:* Accelerator development and operational safety; nuclear physics. *Mailing Add:* 3197 Woodland Rd Los Alamos NM 87544

PUTNEY, BLAKE FUQUA, b Farmville, Va, July 16, 23; m 50; c 3. PHARMACY. *Educ:* Med Col Va, BS, 47; Univ Minn, PhD(pharmaceut chem), 52. *Prof Exp:* Asst pharm, Med Col Va, 47-48; asst pharm, Univ Minn, 48-50; from asst prof to assoc prof, Rutgers Univ, 52-67; asst dean, 70-80, PROF PHARM & CHMN DEPT, COL PHARM, MED UNIV SC, 67-, ASSOC DEAN, 81- *Concurrent Pos:* Consult pharm, Prof Exam Serv, Am Pub Health Asn, 60-67. *Mem:* Am Pharmaceut Asn. *Res:* Synthesis of plant alkaloids; steroid analysis. *Mailing Add:* 479 Wade Hampton Dr Charleston SC 29412

PUTNEY, FLOYD JOHNSON, b Easton, Md, Jan 30, 10; m 41, 57; c 5. MEDICINE, SURGERY. *Educ:* Furman Univ, BS, 30; Jefferson Med Col, MD, 34. *Prof Exp:* PROF OTOLARYNGOL, MED UNIV SC, 67- *Concurrent Pos:* Ed, Am Laryngol Asn, 64-71. *Honors & Awards:* Newcomb Award, Am Laryngol Asn. *Mem:* Am Laryngol Asn (pres, 72); Am Laryngol, Rhinol & Otol Soc (vpres, 60); Am Broncho-Esophagol Asn (secy, 53-60, pres, 60); Am Col Surg; Am Acad Ophthal & Otolaryngol. *Res:* Diseases of the larynx, bronchi and esophagus. *Mailing Add:* Dept of Otorhinolaryngology Med Univ of SC Charleston SC 29425

PUTNEY, JAMES WILEY, JR, b Farmville, Va, Mar 8, 46. PHARMACOLOGY. *Educ:* Univ Va, BA, 68; Med Col Va, PhD(pharmacol), 72. *Prof Exp:* asst prof pharmacol, Sch Med, Wayne State Univ, 74-78, assoc prof, 78-80; ASSOC PROF PHARMACOL, MED COL VA, VA COMMONWEALTH UNIV, 80- *Mem:* AAAS; Biophys Soc. *Res:* Calcium, cyclic nucleotides and coupling mechanisms, specifically excitation-contraction and stimulus-secretion coupling. *Mailing Add:* Dept Pharmacol Med Col Va Va Commonwealth Univ Richmond VA 23298

PUTT, ERIC DOUGLAS, b Sask, Can, Aug 27, 15; m 57; c 5. PLANT BREEDING. *Educ:* Univ Sask, BSA, 38, MSc, 40; Univ Minn, PhD(genetics), 50. *Prof Exp:* Agronomist, Co-op Veg Oil Ltd, 47-52; res officer plant breeding, 52-65, res scientist, plant breeding, 65-66, DIR RES MGT, CAN DEPT AGR, 66- *Concurrent Pos:* Plant breeder, FAO, Chile, 59-60 & Can Int Develop Agency, 74-75. *Honors & Awards:* V S Pustovoit Award, Int Sunflower Asn, 80. *Mem:* Am Soc Agron; Crop Sci Soc Am; Agr Inst Can. *Res:* Breeding, genetics and pathology of sunflowers; management of research in oil crops and horticultural crops. *Mailing Add:* Box 544 Creston BC V0B 1G0 Can

PUTT, JOHN WARD, b Huntingdon, Pa, Feb 11, 24; m 67; c 1. SPACE PROPULSION. *Educ:* Juniata Col, BS, 45. *Prof Exp:* Res chemist fuels, Tide Water Assoc Oil Co, 45-52; chief chemist mat & processes, Walter Kidde & Co Inc, 52-63; mem tech staff, 63-66, head satellite propulsion, 66-74, mgr propulsion proj, 74-77, MGR PROPULSION DEPT, HUGHES AIRCRAFT CO, 77- *Mem:* Assoc fel Am Inst Aeronaut & Astronaut. *Mailing Add:* Propulsion Dept PO Box 92919 MS S12/V329 Los Angeles CA 90009

PUTTASWAMAIAH, BANNIKUPPE M, b Bannikuppe, India, June 24, 32; m 58; c 2. PURE MATHEMATICS. *Educ:* Univ Mysore, BSc, 55, MSc, 57; Univ Toronto, MA, 61, PhD(algebra), 63. *Prof Exp:* Lectr math, Univ Mysore, 56-63; asst prof, 63-67, ASSOC PROF MATH, CARLETON UNIV, 67- *Mem:* Am Math Soc; Math Asn Am; Can Math Cong; Indian Math Soc. *Res:* Representation theory of finite groups; group theory; application of modular representation theory. *Mailing Add:* Dept of Math Carleton Univ Ottawa ON K1S 5B6 Can

PUTTER, IRVING, b New York, NY, Dec 27, 23; m 47; c 2. NATURAL PRODUCTS CHEMISTRY. *Educ:* City Col New York, BS, 45. *Prof Exp:* Sr chemist, 45-67, head sect biophys & pharmacol, 67-69, sr res fel, Basic Res Dept, 69-75, dir natural prod isolation dept, 80-82, SR TECH ADV, EXPLOR BIOL RES, MERCK SHARPE & DOHME RES LABS, 82- *Mem:* Am Chem Soc; NY Acad Sci; AAAS; Am Soc Microbiol. *Res:* Isolation of natural products; ion exchange purifications; chromatography; antibiotics; steroids; vitamins; amino acid process development and factory break in of new processes; counter current extraction; insecticides; pesticides; agricultural chemicals. *Mailing Add:* Merck Sharpe & Dohme Res Labs Rahway NJ 07065

PUTTERMAN, GERALD JOSEPH, b Norwalk, Conn, July 2, 37; m 66; c 2. BIOCHEMISTRY, PROTEIN CHEMISTRY. *Educ:* Johns Hopkins Univ, AB, 59; Yale Univ, PhD(biochem), 65. *Prof Exp:* Fel biochem, Yale Univ, 65-66; biochemist, Abbott Labs, 66-69; assoc scientist, Papanicolaou Cancer Res Inst, 69-71; res supvr biochem, Gillette Res Inst, 71-73, sr res assoc, 73-76; scientist, Frederick Cancer Res Ctr, 76-82; SR RES ASSOC OPHTHAL & VISUAL SCI, MED SCH, YALE UNIV, 82- *Concurrent Pos:* Adj asst prof, Sch Med, Univ Miami, 69-71. *Mem:* Am Chem Soc. *Res:* Isolation and purification of proteins and peptides; amino acid sequencing and chemical modification of peptides and proteins; peptide synthesis; biochemistry of proteases. *Mailing Add:* Dept Ophthal & Visual Sci Sch Med Yale Univ New Haven CT 06510

PUTTERMAN, SETH JAY, b Brooklyn, NY. FLUID MECHANICS. *Educ:* Calif Inst Technol, BS, 66; Rockefeller Univ, PhD(physics), 70. *Prof Exp:* Asst prof, 70-75, assoc prof, 75-81, PROF PHYSICS, UNIV CALIF, LOS ANGELES, 81- *Concurrent Pos:* Lectr, Cent Invest, Mexico, 72 & Scottish Univ, 74; Researcher, Philips Res Lab, 69-74, Ultrasonics Lab, Univv Paris, 74, Cent Nat Res Sci, Grenoble, 74 & Inst Lorentz, 78; sr fel, Univ Newcastle upon Tyne, 81. *Res:* Non-linear fluid mechanics, in and out of equilibrium in the presence of thermal and quantum fluctuations with applications to superfluids and mode coupling. *Mailing Add:* Dept Physics Univ Calif Los Angeles CA 90024

PUTTLER, BENJAMIN, b Bronx, NY, Dec 21, 30; m 61; c 2. ENTOMOLOGY. *Educ:* Univ Calif, Berkeley, BS, 55. *Prof Exp:* Sr lab technician, Citrus Exp Sta, Univ Calif, Riverside, 54-55; ENTOMOLOGIST, N CENT REGION, SCI & EDUC ADMIN-AGR RES, USDA, 55- *Mem:* AAAS; Entom Soc Am; Am Entom Soc; Int Orgn Biol Control. *Res:* Biological control of insects; insect parasite biology; host-parasite interactions, particularly on encapsulation. *Mailing Add:* Biol Control of Insect Res Lab USDA Sci & Educ Agr Res PO Box A Columbia MO 65205

PUTTLITZ, DONALD HERBERT, b Kingston, NY, Apr 21, 38; m 69; c 3. MEDICAL MICROBIOLOGY. *Educ:* State Univ NY Col New Paltz, BS, 59; State Univ NY Albany, MS, 61; Cornell Univ, PhD(bact), 65; Am Bd Med Microbiol, dipl, 72. *Prof Exp:* ASSOC MICROBIOLOGIST, BETH ISRAEL MED CTR, 67-; INSTR PATH, MT SINAI SCH MED, 68- *Concurrent Pos:* USPHS trainee clin microbiol, Col Physicians & Surgeons, Columbia Univ, 65-67. *Mem:* Am Soc Microbiol; Am Pub Health Asn. *Res:* Clinical microbiology; microbial nutrition. *Mailing Add:* Dept Microbiol Beth Israel Med Ctr New York NY 10003

PUTTLITZ, KARL JOSEPH, b Kingston, NY, Aug 4, 41; m 67; c 4. HARDWARE SYSTEMS. *Educ:* Mich State Univ, BS, 65, MS, 67, PhD(metall & mat sci), 71. *Prof Exp:* Chem technician, 61-65, assoc engr, 65-67, sr assoc engr, 67-71, staff engr, 71-72, ADV ENGR, IBM CORP, 72- *Concurrent Pos:* Consult, 74- *Mem:* Am Soc Metals; Int Soc Hybrid Microelectronics; Sigma Xi; NY Acad Sci. *Res:* Develop new methods and materials for computer interconnections, primarily device-to-substrate, to increase the reliability of cost-performance and high-end technology machines. *Mailing Add:* B-330-75A E Fishkill Facil IBM Corp Hopewell Jct NY 12533

PUTZ, GERARD JOSEPH, b Philadelphia, Pa, May 23, 43; div; c 1. SCIENCE ADMINISTRATION. *Educ:* St Norbert Col, Wis, BS, 67; Northwestern Univ, MS, 70 PhD(chem), 73. *Prof Exp:* Instr physics, Bishop Newmann High Sch, Philadelphia, 67-68; fel chem, Univ Minn, Duluth, 72-73; lectr, Univ Colo, Denver, 73-74; asst prof, Barat Col, 74-79; mgr, Anal Lab Serv, Northview Labs, Ill, 79-81; MGR QUAL DEPT, IN VITRO DIAG, NEW ENGLAND NUCLEAR CORP, 81- *Mem:* Am Chem Soc; Am Soc Qual Control. *Res:* Stereochemistry and mechanistic partitioning during solvolytic reactions; quality control and assurance of in vitro diagnostic products. *Mailing Add:* 744 Princeton Blvd Lowell MA 01851

PUTZIER, EDWARD ANTHONY, b Litchfield, Minn, Nov 4, 24; m 52; c 2. HEALTH PHYSICS. *Educ:* Mankato State Col, BA, 50. *Prof Exp:* Mgr health physics opers, Rocky Flats Div, Dow Chem Co, 52-75, mgr health sci, 75-77, MGR HEALTH SCI & SAFETY, ATOMICS INT DIV, ROCKY FLATS PLANT, ROCKWELL INT, 78- *Mem:* Health Physics Soc; Am Indust Hyg Asn; Am Mgt Asn. *Res:* Health physics instrumentation and administration; radiation dosimetry; industrial hygiene; industrial safety. *Mailing Add:* 4630 Ricara Dr Boulder CO 80303

PUTZIG, DONALD EDWARD, b Rochester, NY, Mar 10, 43; m 65; c 1. ORGANIC CHEMISTRY. *Educ:* Univ Rochester, BS, 65; Cornell Univ, PhD(org chem), 69. *Prof Exp:* Res chemist, 69-72, RES SUPVR, E I DU PONT DE NEMOURS & CO, INC, DEEPWATER, NJ, 73- *Mem:* Am Chem Soc. *Res:* Synthesis and finishing of dyestuffs. *Mailing Add:* 11 Forge Rd Drummond Hill Newark DE 19711

PUYAU, FRANCIS A, b New Orleans, La, Dec 1, 28; m 51; c 5. MEDICINE. *Educ:* Univ Notre Dame, BS, 48; La State Univ, New Orleans, MD, 52. *Prof Exp:* From instr to asst prof pediat, Sch Med, La State Univ, 57-61; asst prof, Vanderbilt Univ, 61-68; clin assoc prof, La State Univ Med Ctr, 68-71, prof radiol & pediat & head dept radiol, 71-74; PROF PEDIAT & RADIOL &

MED, SCH MED, TULANE UNIV, 74- *Concurrent Pos:* NIH fel, Charity Hosp New Orleans, 69-70; asst radiologist, Charity Hosp, New Orleans, 69-, vis physician peidat & sr vis physician radiol, 71. *Mem:* Am Col Cardiol; Am Col Radiol. *Res:* Cardiac radiology; heat metabolism; angiography; interventional radiology. *Mailing Add:* Sch of Med Tulane Univ New Orleans LA 70118

PUYEAR, DONALD E(MPSON), b Cape Girardeau, Mo, Aug 21, 32; m 57; c 4. CHEMICAL ENGINEERING. *Educ:* Univ Mo, BS, 54; MS, 48; Va Polytech Inst, PhD(chem eng), 65. *Prof Exp:* Jr engr, E I du Pont de Nemours & Co, 54-55; asst prof chem eng, Va Polytech Inst, 58-64, prof eng & dir, Clifton Forge-Covington Div, 64-67; pres, Dabney S Lancaster Community Col, 67-69; pres, Va Highlands Community Col, 69-74; PRES, CENT VA COMMUNITY COL, 74- *Res:* Mass transfer; extraction; college administration. *Mailing Add:* Cent Va Community Col PO Box 4098 Lynchburg VA 24502

PUYEAR, ROBERT LOUIS, comparative physiology, see previous edition

PUZANTIAN, VAHE ROPEN, b Beirut, Lebanon, June 21, 29; m 63; c 2. PSYCHIATRY. *Educ:* Am Univ Beirut, BA, 50, MD, 54; Royal Col Physicians, dipl psychiat med, 59; Am Bd Psychiat & Neurol, dipl, 80. *Prof Exp:* From instr to asst prof psychiat, Am Univ Beirut, 62-75; asst prof, 76-77, ASSOC PROF PSYCHIAT, UNIV TENN, 77- *Concurrent Pos:* Clin asst, Royal Edinburgh Hosp, 59; consult psychiatrist, Lebanon Hosp, 59-75, govt prisons, Lebanon, 60-61, US & Can embassies, Lebanon, 71-75 & Vet Admin Hosp, Memphis, 77-; dir psychiat serv, City Memphis Hosp, 76-79; dir med educ psychiat, Univ Tenn, 78-79; asst chief psychiat, Vet Admin Hosp, Memphis, 79- *Mem:* Am Psychiat Asn; AAAS; Royal Col Psychiatrists; Lebanese Soc Psychiat, Neurol & Neurosurg (pres, 74-75). *Res:* Nosological status of neurotic depression; retrospective chart review study of the phenomenologic and bleulerian approaches to the diagnosis of major psychotic disorders and their variants. *Mailing Add:* Gailor Clin 42 N Dunlap 4th Floor Memphis TN 38103

PUZISS, MILTON, b Philadelphia, Pa, Feb 17, 20; m 51; c 3. MICROBIOLOGY. *Educ:* Kans State Col, BS, 48; Univ Wis, MS, 49; Univ Southern Calif, PhD(bact), 56. *Prof Exp:* Asst, Univ Wis, 48-49; res bacteriologist, Biol Labs, US Dept Army, Ft Detrick, Md, 51-53; asst, Univ Southern Calif, 53-55; med res bacteriologist, Chem Res & Develop Labs, US Dept Army, Ft Detrick, 55-62, microbiologist, Biol Labs, 62-68; asst chief, Virol & Rickettsial Br, 68, actg chief, 68-70, CHIEF, BACT & VIROL BR, EXTRAMURAL PROGS, NAT INST ALLERGY & INFECTIOUS DIS, NIH, 73- *Concurrent Pos:* Secy Army Res & Study Fel, Karolinska Inst, Stockholm, Sweden, 63-64; sr asst scientist, USPHSR, 56- *Honors & Awards:* US Army Res & Develop Award, 62; NIH Dirs Award, 76. *Mem:* AAAS; Am Soc Microbiol; Sigma Xi. *Res:* Microbial physiology; toxin formation; biphasic culture techniques; vaccine development; fermentation and mass culture methods; infectious diseases and immunology; health administration. *Mailing Add:* 5 Watchwater Ct Rockville MD 20850

PYATT, EDWIN E, b Bloomington, Ill, May 13, 29. ENVIRONMENTAL ENGINEERING. *Educ:* Calif Inst Technol, BS, 51; Univ Calif, MS, 53; Johns Hopkins Univ, DrEng, 59. *Prof Exp:* Instr sanit eng, Johns Hopkins Univ, 56-59; asst prof civil eng, Northwestern Univ, 59-62; sr res engr, Travelers Res Ctr, Inc, Conn, 62-65; chmn dept, 77-81, PROF ENVIRON ENG, UNIV FLA, 65- *Concurrent Pos:* Lectr, Univ Conn, 63; consult, US Geol Surv, Travelers Res Ctr, City of Jacksonville & Environ Protection Agency; mem, Nat Acad Sci-Nat Res Coun panel on flood studies in riverine areas, 73-75; mem, Gov's adv coun waste recycling, 74-79. *Mem:* AAAS; Am Soc Civil Engrs; Am Soc Eng Educ; Nat Soc Prof Engrs; Am Water Works Asn. *Res:* Water resources management; water quality control. *Mailing Add:* Dept of Environ Eng Sci Univ of Fla Gainesville FL 32611

PYBURN, WILLIAM F, b Corsicana, Tex, Mar 22, 27; m 49; c 1. VERTEBRATE ZOOLOGY. *Educ:* Univ Tex, BA, 51, MA, 53, PhD, 56. *Prof Exp:* From asst prof to assoc prof, 56-70, PROF BIOL, UNIV TEX, ARLINGTON, 70- *Mem:* Am Soc Ichthyologists & Herpetologists; Soc Study Evolution; Soc Study Amphibians & Reptiles. *Res:* Amphibian behavior, ecology. *Mailing Add:* Dept of Biol Univ of Tex Arlington TX 76010

PYE, EARL LOUIS, b Merino, Colo, Aug 18, 26; m 49; c 6. ELECTROCHEMISTRY, CORROSION ENGINEERING. *Educ:* Chico State Col, AB, 58; Univ Calif, Davis, MS, 61; La State Univ, PhD(physical chem), 66. *Prof Exp:* Asst prof chem, Calif State Polytech Univ, 61-65; assoc prof, Parsons Col, 66-67; assoc prof, 67-68, chmn dept, 67-69, PROF CHEM, CALIF STATE POLYTECH UNIV, 68-, DEAN GRAD STUDIES & RES, 78- *Concurrent Pos:* Eng & corrosion consult. *Mem:* Am Chem Soc; Nat Asn Corrosion Eng; Sigma Xi. *Res:* Electrode kinetics; electrochemical techniques of corrosion rate determinations and control; surface and corrosion chemistry; underground corrosion problems; infrared spectroscopy; nuclear chemistry. *Mailing Add:* PO Box 811 Pomona CA 91769

PYE, EDGAR GEORGE, b Toronto, Ont, May 18, 25; m 53; c 2. ECONOMIC GEOLOGY. *Educ:* Univ Toronto, BASc, 47, MASc, 49, PhD(geol), 54. *Prof Exp:* Field geologist, 48-52, from resident geologist to chief geologist, 52-72, DIR GEOL BR, ONT DIV MINES, MINISTRY NATURAL RESOURCES, 72- *Mem:* Geol Asn Can; Geol Soc Can; Am Inst Mining Engrs; Can Inst Mining & Metall. *Res:* Stratigraphic, petrologic and tectonic evolution of the Canadian Shield and the temporal and spatial association of mineral deposits with rock units and structures; Phanerozoic stratigraphy and syngenetic mineral deposits of Ontario. *Mailing Add:* Ministry Natural Resources-Geol Br 77 Grenville St Rm 914 Toronto ON M5S 1B3 Can

PYE, EDWARD KENDALL, b Bexleyheath, Eng, Jan 16, 38; m 61; c 2. BIOCHEMISTRY. *Educ:* Univ Manchester, BSc, 61, PhD(biochem), 64. *Prof Exp:* Assoc, 67-68, asst prof, 68-73, ASSOC PROF BIOCHEM & BIOPHYS, SCH MED, UNIV PA, 73- *Concurrent Pos:* NIH fel biophys, Johnson Res Found, Univ Pa, 65-67, NIH res career develop award, 70-75. *Mem:* AAAS; Am Chem Soc. *Res:* Metabolic control, particularly carbohydrate metabolism; oscillating biochemical reactions; fuels from biomass; affinity chromatography; biological rhythms and timing mechanisms; enzyme technology; use of immobilized enzymes; fermentation. *Mailing Add:* Dept of Biochem & Biophys Univ of Pa Sch of Med Philadelphia PA 19104

PYE, LENWOOD D(AVID), b Little Falls, NY, May 16, 37; m 58; c 4. CERAMICS, CHEMISTRY. *Educ:* Alfred Univ, BS, 59, PhD(ceramics), 68. *Prof Exp:* Proj leader, Pittsburgh Plate Glass Industs, Inc, 59-60 & Bausch & Lomb Inc, 60-64; assoc prof, 68-80, PROF GLASS SCI, NY STATE COL CERAMICS, ALFRED UNIV, 80- *Concurrent Pos:* Vis prof, Univ Erlangen-Nurnberg, 75 & 80. *Mem:* Am Ceramic Soc; Nat Inst Ceramic Engrs; Sigma Xi; Am Soc Eng Educ. *Res:* Radiation damage in glasses; nuclear waste disposal; physical optics; crystallization phenomena. *Mailing Add:* NY State Col of Ceramics Alfred Univ Alfred NY 14802

PYKE, RONALD, b Hamilton, Ont, Nov 24, 31; m 53; c 4. MATHEMATICAL STATISTICS. *Educ:* McMaster Univ, BA, 53; Univ Wash, Seattle, MS, 55, PhD(math), 56. *Prof Exp:* Res assoc, Stanford Univ, 56-57, vis asst prof math, 57-58; asst prof, Columbia Univ, 58-60; from asst prof to assoc prof, 60-66, PROF MATH, UNIV WASH, 66- *Mem:* Am Math Soc; Math Asn Am; fel Am Statist Asn; fel Inst Math Statist. *Res:* Theory of distribution free statistics; Markov processes; Markov Renewal processes; limit theorems and weak convergence; multiparameter processes. *Mailing Add:* Dept of Math Univ of Wash Seattle WA 98195

PYKE, THOMAS NICHOLAS, JR, b Washington, DC, July 16, 42; m 68; c 2. HARDWARE SYSTEMS, SOFTWARE SYSTEMS. *Educ:* Carnegie Inst Technol, BS, 64; Univ Pa, MSE, 65. *Prof Exp:* Electronic engr res & develop, 64-69, chief, Comput Systs Sect, 69-73, chief, Comput Networking Sect & actg div chief Standards-Res, 73-75, chief, Comput Systs Eng Div Standards-Res, 75-79, dir, Ctr Comput Systs, 79-81, DIR, CTR PROG SCI & TECHNOL, NAT BUR STANDARDS, 81- *Mem:* Inst Elec & Electronics Engrs; Asn Comput Mach; AAAS. *Res:* Computer networking, computer system architecture and data communications, distributed systems; computer network protocols, performance measurement and network access techniques. *Mailing Add:* Ctr Prog Sci & Technol Nat Bur Standards Washington DC 20234

PYKE, THOMAS RICHARD, b Center, Ind, Jan 8, 32; m 51; c 3. MICROBIOLOGY, BIOCHEMISTRY. *Educ:* Purdue Univ, BS, 54, MS, 58, PhD, 61. *Prof Exp:* Sr res microbiologist, Squibb Inst Med Res, 60-62; res assoc infectious dis, 62-72, res head, Anal Methods Res & Develop & Microbiol Testing, 72-75, res assoc, Fermentation Res & Develop, 75-81, RES MGR, CULTURE IMPROV & FERMENTATION PREP, UPJOHN CO, 81- *Mem:* AAAS; Am Soc Microbiol. *Res:* Physiology of microsclerotia of verticillium albo-atrum; antibiotics and pharmacologically active compounds produced by fungi and actinomycetes; diseases caused by Streptococcus and Neisseria; microbial genetics. *Mailing Add:* Fermentation Res & Develop Upjohn Co Kalamazoo MI 49001

PYLE, JAMES JOHNSTON, b Calgary, Alta, Apr 26, 14; nat US; m; c 3. PLASTICS CHEMISTRY. *Educ:* Univ BC, BA, 35, MA, 37; McGill Univ, PhD(org chem), 39. *Prof Exp:* Asst chem, Univ BC, 35-37 & McGill Univ, 37-39; develop chemist, Gen Elec Co, Mass, 39, res chemist, 39-40, group leader laminated plastics, 40-41, res group leader, 41-43, dir plastics lab, 43-49, mgr new prod develop lab, 49, mgr eng, laminated prod dept, Chem & Metall Div, 49-66, mgr overseas bus, 66-68; CONSULT PLASTICS TECHNOL, 68- *Concurrent Pos:* Res chemist, Can Fishing Co, BC, 36-37; civilian with AEC, 46-47. *Mem:* AAAS; Am Chem Soc. *Res:* Organic, lignin and cellulose biochemistry; flotation of ores; plastics; rubber; ion exchange; fibers. *Mailing Add:* 1677 Bayberry Lane Coshocton OH 43812

PYLE, JAMES L, b Wilmington, Ohio, Aug 5, 38; m 60; c 5. ORGANIC CHEMISTRY, ENVIRONMENTAL CHEMISTRY. *Educ:* Univ Ohio, BS, 60; Brown Univ, PhD(chem), 67. *Prof Exp:* Res assoc chem, Univ Calif, Davis, 65-66; asst prof, 66-75, ASSOC PROF CHEM & DIR RES, MIAMI UNIV, 75- *Mem:* Am Chem Soc; AAAS; NY Acad Sci. *Res:* Steroids; university research administration; oxidations in organic systems; synthesis of chlorinated aromatic compounds. *Mailing Add:* Dept of Chem Miami Univ Oxford OH 45056

PYLE, JOHN TILLMAN, b Atlanta, Ga, May 3, 35; m 71. ANALYTICAL CHEMISTRY. *Educ:* Ga State Col, BS, 59; Univ Ga, PhD(chem), 64. *Prof Exp:* Assoc prof chem, Mars Hill Col, 64-69; assoc prof, 69-75, PROF CHEM, COLUMBUS COL, 75- *Mem:* Am Chem Soc. *Res:* spectrophotometric determinations of trace quantities of platinum group metals using various derivatives of dithio-oxamide as color producing reagents. *Mailing Add:* Sci-Math Div Columbus Col Columbus GA 31993

PYLE, KENNETH ROGER, b Shanghai, China, Nov 5, 41; m 65; c 2. COSMIC RAY PARTICLE PHYSICS. *Educ:* Mass Inst Technol, SB, 63; Univ Chicago, MS, 65, PhD(physics), 72. *Prof Exp:* PHYSICIST, ENRICO FERMI INST, UNIV CHICAGO, 72- *Mem:* Am Geophys Union; Sigma Xi. *Res:* Space physics, primarily interplanetary, focussing on cosmic ray and solar energetic charged particles, their origin and propagation. *Mailing Add:* 933 E 56th St Chicago IL 60637

PYLE, LEONARD DUANE, b Crawfordsville, Ind, July 13, 30; m 54; c 4. COMPUTER SCIENCE, MATHEMATICS. *Educ:* Rose Polytech Inst, BS, 52; Purdue Univ, MS, 54, PhD(math), 60. *Prof Exp:* Res asst, Statist & Comput Lab, Purdue Univ, Lafayette, 54-58, actg head comput div, 58-60, head, 60-61, from asst prof to assoc prof math & comput sci, 60-71, asst dir, Comput Sci Ctr, 61-65, asst head dept comput sci, 65-69; chmn dept, 71-74, PROF COMPUT SCI UNIV HOUSTON, 71- *Concurrent Pos:* Consult, Ind State Dept Data Processing, 61 & Stewart Warner Corp, 62; hon fel, Math Res Ctr, Univ Wis, 65; vis prof, Univ Tex, Austin, 69-70; vis scholar, Univ Tex, Austin, 79. *Mem:* Asn Comput Mach; Soc Indust & Appl Math. *Res:* Linear and nonlinear programming; acceleration of vector sequences; theory and applications involving the generalized inverse of a matrix; numerical analysis; applications of vector computers. *Mailing Add:* Dept of Comput Sci Univ of Houston Houston TX 77004

PYLE, ROBERT LAWRENCE, b Wilmington, Del, Aug 27, 23; m 54; c 4. METEOROLOGY, ENVIRONMENTAL SATELLITES. *Educ:* NY Univ, BS, 43; Univ Calif, Los Angeles, MA, 51; Univ Wash, PhD, 58. *Prof Exp:* Asst res geophysicist, Inst Geophys, Univ Calif, Los Angeles, 53-56; meteorologist Bur Commercial Fisheries, US Fish & Wildlife Serv, 58-60 & res & develop, Meteorol Satellite Lab, US Weather Bur, 60-64; tech asst to dir, Nat Environ Satellite Ctr, Environ Sci Serv Admin, 64-66; field dir, Pac Prog, Div Birds, Smithsonian Inst, 66-69; tech asst to dir, Washington, DC, 69-75, MGR SATELLITE FIELD SERV STA, HONOLULU, NAT ENVIRON SATELLITE SERV, NAT OCEANIC & ATMOSPHERIC ADMIN, US DEPT COM, 75- *Mem:* Am Meteorol Soc. *Res:* Interpretation and application of environmental satellite data. *Mailing Add:* Satellite Field Serv Sta Tower Bldg Rm 514 Int Airport Honolulu HI 96819

PYLE, ROBERT V, b Washington, DC, Oct 4, 23; m 50. PLASMA PHYSICS. *Educ:* Univ Calif, Berkeley, AB, 44; Univ Calif, Berkeley, MA & PhD(physics), 51. *Prof Exp:* PHYSICIST, LAWRENCE BERKELEY LAB, UNIV CALIF, 51-, SR LECTR, BERKELEY NUCLEAR ENG DEPT, 65- *Mem:* Fel Am Phys Soc; Am Vacuum Soc. *Res:* Controlled thermonuclear energy physics. *Mailing Add:* 3023 Benvenue Ave Berkeley CA 94705

PYLE, ROBERT WENDELL, b Phoenixville, Pa, Mar 3, 08; m 33; c 2. ZOOLOGY. *Educ:* Univ Pa, BS, 33, MA, 39; Harvard Univ, PhD(biol), 41. *Prof Exp:* Mem fac, Georgetown Spec Sch, Del, 34-37 & Caesar Rodney Spec Sch, 37-38; zool librn, Univ Pa, 38-39; teaching fel, Radcliffe Col, 41; fel & asst, Nat Defense Res Comt Proj, Oceanog Inst, Woods Hole, Mass, 41-42; instr biol, Rensselaer Polytech Inst, 42-44; assoc prof biol, Mary Washington Col, 44-50; from asst prof to prof biol, 50-73, dean col, 59-65, EMER PROF BIOL, STATE UNIV NY COL NEW PALTZ, 73- *Concurrent Pos:* Vis prof educ, Teachers Col, Columbia Univ & specialist teacher educ, Univ Team, India, 65-67. *Res:* Histology and cytology of invertebrates, primarily Arthropods. *Mailing Add:* 150 Susan Lane RD 1 Brewster MA 02631

PYLE, ROBERT WENDELL, JR, b Lewes, Del, Mar 11, 36; m 63; c 4. PHYSICS. *Educ:* Harvard Univ, AB, 57, AM, 58, PhD(appl physics), 63. *Prof Exp:* Res fel acoust, Harvard Univ, 63-65; consult archit acoust, 65-66, SR SCIENTIST, BOLT BERANEK & NEWMAN, INC, 66- *Mem:* AAAS; Acoust Soc Am; Audio Eng Soc; Inst Elec & Electronics Engrs. *Res:* Physical acoustics, including underwater sound, noise and vibration and ultrasonics; musical and architectural acoustics. *Mailing Add:* Bolt Beranek & Newman Inc 50 Moulton St Cambridge MA 02138

PYLE, THOMAS EDWARD, b New York, NY, Oct 31, 41; m 63; c 2. MARINE GEOLOGY. *Educ:* Columbia Col, BA, 63; Tex A&M Univ, MS, 66, PhD(oceanog), 72. *Prof Exp:* From asst prof to assoc prof marine sci, Univ S Fla, 69-76; PROG DIR, MARINE GEOL & GEOPHYS, OFF NAVAL RES, 76- *Concurrent Pos:* Geologist, US Geol Surv, 70-72; grants, Off Naval Res, NSF, Dept of Interior & Fla Dept Natural Resources; mem geodynamics comn, Working Group 2, Int Coun Sci Unions, 74-76. *Mem:* Am Geophys Union; Soc Explor Geophysicists; Europ Asn Explor Geophysicists; Geol Soc Am. *Res:* Structural aspects of marine geology and geophysics; suspended sediments and light transmission. *Mailing Add:* Off of Naval Res Code 483 800 N Quincy St Arlington VA 22217

PYLER, RICHARD ERNST, b Chicago, Ill, May 26, 41; m 71; c 2. CEREAL CHEMISTRY, BREWING CHEMISTRY. *Educ:* Univ Chicago, BS, 63; Kans State Univ, MS, 65; Purdue Univ, PhD(biochem), 69. *Prof Exp:* Sr res chemist, Anheuser-Busch, Inc, Mo, 69-72; asst prof cereal chem, NDak State Univ, 72-73; ed, Baker's Digest & tech ed, Brewer's Digest, 73-77; ASSOC PROF CEREAL CHEM, NDAK STATE UNIV, 77- *Mem:* Am Asn Cereal Chemists; Am Soc Brewing Chemists; Master Brewers Asn Am; Am Soc Bakery Engrs. *Res:* Synthesis of monosaccharide derivatives; biochemical constituents of cereal grains, especially polysaccharides; malting and brewing science. *Mailing Add:* Dept of Cereal Chem & Technol NDak State Univ Fargo ND 58102

PYNADATH, THOMAS I, b Karukutty, India, Apr 24, 29; m 55; c 4. BIOCHEMISTRY, ORGANIC CHEMISTRY. *Educ:* Madras Univ, BS, 49, MS, 53; Georgetown Univ, PhD(biochem), 63. *Prof Exp:* Lectr chem, Madras Univ, 52-56; sr lectr, Kerala Univ, 56-59; res fel biol chem, Univ Calif, Los Angeles, 63-65; asst prof chem, Georgetown Univ, 65-66; asst prof, 66-70, ASSOC PROF CHEM, KENT STATE UNIV, 70- *Mem:* AAAS; Am Chem Soc. *Res:* Metabolism of lipids; biosynthesis of glycerides and fatty acids; metabolism of nucleic acids in Neurospora crassa; lipid metabolism in obese and atherosclerotic animals. *Mailing Add:* Dept of Chem Kent State Univ Kent OH 44242

PYNES, GENE DALE, b Zwolle, La, Dec 25, 33; m 58; c 3. BIOCHEMISTRY, MICROBIOLOGY. *Educ:* Hendrix Col, BA, 56; Univ Ark, Little Rock, MS, 59, PhD(biochem), 67; Univ Ark Med Sci, Col Pharm, BS, 78. *Prof Exp:* Asst prof, 67-71, ASSOC PROF MED CHEM, COL PHARM, UNIV ARK MED SCI, LITTLE ROCK, 71- *Mem:* Sigma Xi; Am Asn Col Pharm. *Res:* Inorganic pyrophosphatase; kinetic properties of the enzyme from erythrocytes, pancreas and yeast; pharmacy. *Mailing Add:* 7008 Morgan Dr Little Rock AR 72209

PYOTT, WILLIAM TUCKER, range ecology, systems analysis, see previous edition

PYPER, DIANE MARIE, astronomy, see previous edition

PYPER, GORDON R(ICHARDSON), b Cedar Falls, Iowa, Sept 1, 24; m 46; c 3. ENVIRONMENTAL ENGINEERING, WATER RESOURCES. *Educ:* Brown Univ, ScB, 48; Univ Mich, MSE, 49, PhD, 70. *Prof Exp:* Sanit engr, Ill State Dept Pub Health, 49-53; from instr to prof sanit & civil eng, Norwich Univ, 53-73, head dept, 65-73; comnr water resources, State of Vt Dept Water Resources, 73-77; head res & develop & sr environ engr, 77-78, head, Water Resources Dept & Res & Develop sr engr, 78-80, MANAGING DIR, RES & SPEC PROJ, BUFRESNE-HENRY INC, 80- *Concurrent Pos:* Comnr, NE Interstate Water Pollution Cent Comn, 73-77. *Mem:* Water Pollution Control Fedn; Am Soc Civil Engrs; Am Soc Eng Educ; Nat Soc Prof Engrs. *Res:* Civil engineering; environmental engineering; Ability of fresh water mussels to remove solids from and improve the quality of aerated lagoon waste treatment effluent. *Mailing Add:* Dufresne-Henry Inc North Springfield VT 05150

PYPER, JAMES WILLIAM, b Wells, Nev, Sept 5, 34; m 57; c 9. PHYSICAL CHEMISTRY, MASS SPECTROMETRY. *Educ:* Brigham Young Univ, BS, 58, MS, 60; Cornell Univ, PhD(phys chem), 64. *Prof Exp:* Group leader mass spectros, 73-75, group leader appl phys chem group, 79-80, RES CHEMIST, LAWRENCE LIVERMORE NAT LAB, UNIV CALIF, 63-, SECT LEADER, ANAL CHEM SECT, 80- *Mem:* Am Soc Mass Spectrometry; Sigma Xi. *Res:* Isotopic exchange reactions; mass spectroscopy; physical chemistry of the hydrogen isotopes at low temperatures. *Mailing Add:* Lawrence Livermore Nat Lab Univ of Calif Box 808 Livermore CA 94550

PYRCIOCH, EUGENE JOSEPH, b Chicago, Ill, Aug 10, 20. CHEMICAL ENGINEERING. *Educ:* Northwestern Univ, BSChE, 48; Ill Inst Technol, MS, 58. *Prof Exp:* Chem engr, 48-53, supvr, 53-62, SCIENTIST, INST GAS TECHNOL, ILL INST TECHNOL, 62- *Mem:* Am Chem Soc; Am Inst Chem Engrs; Am Meteorol Soc; fel Am Inst Chem; Sigma Xi. *Res:* Process design and development of synthetic gas processes; pilot plant design and operation; fossil fuel gasification and processing; solids fluidization; high pressure technology; particulate solids feeding, grinding and drying. *Mailing Add:* Inst of Gas Technol 3424 S State St Chicago IL 60616

PYRON, RAYMOND SCOTT, b Moncks Corner, SC, Apr 13, 38; m 58; c 2. GRANTS ADMINISTRATION, CONSULTATION. *Educ:* Furman Univ, BS, 60; Univ Fla, PhD(org chem), 65. *Prof Exp:* Welsh fel org chem, Univ Tex, Austin, 65-66; from asst prof to assoc prof chem, Furman Univ, 66-75, chmn dept, 72-75; EASTERN REGIONAL DIR, RES CORP, 75- *Mem:* AAAS; Am Chem Soc. *Res:* Synthesis and investigations of strained hydrocarbon rings; carbene chemistry, nuclear magnetic resonance in conformational analysis. *Mailing Add:* Res Corp 6075 Roswell Rd NE Atlanta GA 30328

PYSH, EUGENE STEPHEN, physical chemistry, see previous edition

PYSH, JOSEPH JOHN, b Olyphant, Pa, Nov 14, 35; m 69. NEUROCYTOLOGY, ELECTRON MICROSCOPY. *Educ:* Chicago Col Osteopath Med, DO, 62, Wayne State Univ, BA, 63; Northwestern Univ, PhD(anat), 67. *Prof Exp:* From instr to asst prof, 66-73, actg chmn dept, 78-81, ASSOC PROF ANAT, MED & DENT SCHS, NORTHWESTERN UNIV, CHICAGO, 73- *Concurrent Pos:* NSF grant reviewer, 74-; mem, NIH Neurol Study Sect, 76-77; manuscript referree, J Cell Biol Sci, Am J Anat, Exp Neurol & Brain Res Bull. *Mem:* AAAS; Am Asn Anat; Am Soc Cell Biol; Electron Micros Soc Am; Soc Neurosci. *Res:* Developmental neurobiology; morphology and physiology of synaptic transmission. *Mailing Add:* Dept Cell Biol & Anat McGaw Med Ctr Northwestern Univ Chicago IL 60611

PYTKOWICZ, RICARDO MARCOS, b Sao Paulo, Brazil, Jan 31, 29; US citizen; m 62. PHYSICAL CHEMISTRY, OCEANOGRAPHY. *Educ:* La State Univ, BS, 53; Univ Calif, Berkeley, PhD(phys chem), 57. *Prof Exp:* Res chemist, Arthur D Little, Inc, 57-58; res assoc phys chem, Mass Inst Technol, 58-60; res chemist, Calif Res Corp, Standard Oil Co, 60-61; from res instr to res asst prof chem oceanog, Univ Wash, 61-63; from asst prof to assoc prof, 63-70, PROF OCEANOG, ORE STATE UNIV, 70- *Concurrent Pos:* NSF grants, 64-72. *Mem:* AAAS; Am Soc Limnol & Oceanog; Am Geophys Union. *Res:* Physical chemistry of electrolytes in seawater; distribution of chemical species in the oceans. *Mailing Add:* Dept of Oceanog Ore State Univ Corvallis OR 97331

PYTLEWSKI, LOUIS LAWRENCE, b Philadelphia, Pa, May 11, 32; m 57; c 3. INORGANIC CHEMISTRY. *Educ:* Univ Pa, BA, 54, MS, 56, PhD(inorg chem), 60. *Prof Exp:* Instr chem, St Joseph's Col, Pa, 58-59; res chemist, Res & Develop Lab, Armstrong Cork Co, 59-62; asst prof, 62-67, ASSOC PROF INORG CHEM, DREXEL UNIV, 67- *Concurrent Pos:* Consult, Astromech Div, Giannini Controls Corp, 65-68 & Edgewood Arsenal, US Army, 71-; prin scientist, Franklin Res Ctr, Philadelphia, 77-78. *Mem:* AAAS; Am Chem Soc. *Res:* Synthesis and characterization of metal salt organophosphorus and organonitrogen complexes and polymers; thermal and hydrolytic decomposition of metalammine complexes. *Mailing Add:* Dept of Chem Drexel Univ Philadelphia PA 19104

PYTTE, AGNAR, b Norway, Dec 23, 32; nat US; m 55; c 3. THEORETICAL PHYSICS. *Educ:* Princeton Univ, AB, 53; Harvard Univ, PhD(physics), 58. *Prof Exp:* From instr to assoc prof, 57-67, chmn dept, 71-75, PROF PHYSICS, DARTMOUTH COL, 67-, DEAN GRAD STUDY & ASSOC DEAN FAC SCI, 75- *Concurrent Pos:* Proj Matterhorn, Princeton Univ, 59-60; NSF sci fac fel, Univ Brussels, 66-67; mem staff, Princeton Plasma Physics Lab, 78-79. *Mem:* Am Phys Soc; Europ Phys Soc. *Res:* Plasma physics. *Mailing Add:* Dept of Physics Dartmouth Col Hanover NH 03755

PYTTE, ERLING, b Hvittingfoss, Norway, July 29, 37; m 63; c 3. SOLID STATE PHYSICS. *Educ:* Princeton Univ, AB, 59; Harvard Univ, MA, 61, PhD(physics), 64. *Prof Exp:* Res assoc physics, Univ Calif, Berkeley, 63-64; asst prof, Univ Oslo, 64-65; res physicist, IBM Res Lab, Zurich, Switz, 65-69, MGR THEORET PHYSICS, T J WATSON RES CTR, IBM CORP, 69- *Mem:* Fel Am Phys Soc. *Res:* Theoretical solid state physics. *Mailing Add:* T J Watson Res Ctr IBM Corp PO Box 218 Yorktown Heights NY 10598

PYUN, CHONG WHA, b Korea, May 11, 30; m 57; c 2. PHYSICAL CHEMISTRY, POLYMER CHEMISTRY. *Educ:* Seoul Nat Univ, BS, 55, MS, 58; Brown Univ, PhD(chem), 64. *Prof Exp:* Instr chem, Seoul Nat Univ, 58-60; res assoc, Inst Theoret Sci, Univ Ore, 63-65; res fel, Univ Minn, 65-66; fel, Mellon Inst, Carnegie-Mellon Univ, 66-70; from asst prof to assoc prof, 70-78, PROF CHEM, UNIV LOWELL, 78- *Concurrent Pos:* Lectr, Dept Chem, Carnegie-Mellon Univ, 67-70; vis prof, Dept Chem, Seoul Nat Univ, 77-78. *Mem:* Am Chem Soc; Am Phys Soc; Korean Chem Soc; Sigma Xi; Korean Scientists & Engrs Asn Am (pres, 76-77). *Res:* Physical chemistry of high polymers and chemical kinetics; polymer chain dynamics; comonomer sequence and sterosequence distribution statistics; polymerization kinetics; gas-phase reactions and multistate kinetics. *Mailing Add:* Dept of Chem Univ of Lowell Lowell MA 01854